**Who's Who
Among American
High School Students®**
Honoring Tomorrow's Leaders Today®

1986-87
Twenty-first Annual Edition
Volume II

WHO'S WHO AMONG AMERICAN HIGH SCHOOL STUDENTS® is a publication of Educational Communications, Inc. of Lake Forest, Illinois and has no connection with "Who's Who In America" and its publisher, Marquis — Who's Who, Inc. Students featured in this volume attended school in the following states: Pennsylvania and New Jersey.

Compilation of the copyright matter published in this volume has required considerable time, and has been carried out only at great expense. The copyright matter contained herein is intended for the exclusive use of our subscribers. No information contained in this volume may be key-punched, entered into a computer, or photocopied in any manner for any purpose whatsoever. The use of any such information as a mailing list, either in whole or in part, is strictly forbidden unless authorized in writing by the publishers. The contents have been coded, and cannot be copied without detection. Infringements will be prosecuted.

©Copyright 1987
Educational Communications, Inc.
721 N. McKinley Road
Lake Forest, Illinois 60045
Printed in U.S.A.
ISBN 0-930315-29-4
ISBN 0-930315-27-8 (12 Volume Set)
Library of Congress Catalog Card Number 68-43796

WHO'S WHO AMONG AMERICAN HIGH SCHOOL STUDENTS® is a registered trademark owned by Educational Communications, Inc.

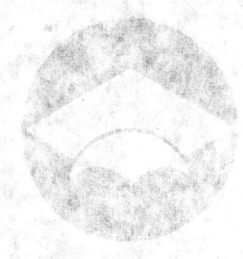

Who's Who
Among American
High School Students
Honoring Tomorrow's Leaders Today

1986-87
Twenty-first Annual Edition
Volume II

WHO'S WHO AMONG AMERICAN HIGH SCHOOL STUDENTS is published by Educational Communications, Inc., of Lake Forest, Illinois and is an outgrowth of the Who's Who in America" and its publisher. Marquis Who's Who, Inc. Students featured in this volume attend school in the states of Pennsylvania and New Jersey.

© Copyright 1987
Educational Communications, Inc.
721 N. McKinley Road
Lake Forest, Illinois 60045
Printed in U.S.A.
Book ... P ...
ISBN 0-930315-29-9 (Volume II)
Library of Congress Catalog Card Number: ...

TABLE OF CONTENTS

*Wherever students attend school out of state they will be listed in
the state where they attend school.

III

PUBLISHER'S CORNER:

Who's Who turns 21 and we're still growing and more committed than ever ... to you

Pardon my lack of humility, a little chest puffing and strutting as I indulge myself a bit and reflect on this momentous birthday. After all, you only turn 21 once and that is a milestone.

Twenty-one years ago my wife and I determined that teenagers were getting a bad rap. At the height of the Vietnam War, high school and college students were all being characterized in the press as flag-burning, pill-popping, anti-establishment radicals. We believed that was an unfair and misleading representation and decided to do something to provide a more balanced perspective. That something became WHO'S WHO AMONG AMERICAN HIGH SCHOOL STUDENTS and a few years later, THE NATIONAL DEAN'S LIST for college students.

From our cozy apartment on the north side of Chicago we labored at the kitchen table and checked files in our guest closet as we developed our plan to celebrate the positive achievements of outstanding high school students. During the day I worked a "regular job" while my wife was busy nurturing our two young daughters. (A son and another daughter have since joined us.) Somehow, in our "spare time," we managed to publish our first edition which honored 13,500 students from approximately 4,000 high schools throughout the country. The current 21st annual edition, published in twelve regional volumes, honors 539,000 outstanding students representing almost 20,000 high schools nationwide. Since 1967 over 5,500,000 high achieving students have been recognized in WHO'S WHO.

Along the way the publication became an entire program and expanded in scope as well as size. In 1968, our second year, our Scholarship Foundation was established. Initially $5,000 in scholarships were awarded. Today, through three separate programs, our Scholarship Committee awards over $100,000 annually to academically qualified students. Here it is important to emphasize the enormous commitment of our Scholarship Committee, a group of professional educators who individually and collectively spend over 100 hours each year as they carefully evaluate several thousand student applications. It is not easy to pick "winners" from a pool of students who are all winners and high achievers.

In 1970 we began polling the attitudes and opinions of WHO'S WHO students in a survey which has become "The Annual Survey of High Achievers." The results of this study are released to government and educational leaders and are widely reported in the press each year.

In 1975 we began our Free Book Program in which we distribute complimentary copies of the book to all participating high schools and interested colleges and libraries. By circulating over 15,000 free books each year, we are assuring listed students of the national recognition they deserve and providing them with the opportunity to view their published data conveniently and at no cost. After all, legitimate honors should not cost the recipient money and meaningful recognition can only be accomplished if circulation goes well beyond listed subscribers.

Also, in 1975 we began funding grants to youth and educational organizations as an extension of our commitment to assist those groups which are providing services and benefits to the youth of our nation. To date, over $400,000 has been distributed to these organizations, much of it through special scholarship programs sponsored by these organizations.

Other student services implemented and refined in the mid-70's include the College Referral Service (CRS) which links college-bound students with the colleges and universities they wish us to notify about their WHO'S WHO recognition. This reference service on behalf of listed students has been widely acclaimed by hundreds of colleges who use these referrals in their recruitment programs. The newspaper publicity program for listed students was greatly enhanced when our own data processing procedures provided sophisticated and state-of-the-art capabilities for routing student listings to over 2,000 local newspapers which were interested in honoring their local WHO'S WHO students.

Throughout the years of growth and expansion, one problem kept reoccuring with ever-increasing negative results. As WHO'S WHO became more well known, the fly-by-nighters jumped aboard with imitation publications, most of which were never published. Some of these charlatans copied our name, some copied our literature and some did both. Although most of these organizations disappeared through their own ineptitude or the efforts of diligent consumer protection agencies, they left in their wake a large group of exploited students, disillusioned parents, skeptical educators and an army of investigative reporters who tended to paint all recognition publications and programs with the same brush.

The WHO'S WHO response to this dilemma was to involve the educational community in the solution. In 1979 we assembled a group of distinguished educators who thoroughly reviewed our programs, procedures and policies and studied the problems created by imitators. This group became our Committee on Ethics, Standards and Practices. Their first major objective was to create clearly defined standards for our program which could be used by all high school administrators for evaluating the merits of all student recognition programs and publications.

The standards developed by our Committee have been distributed each year to principals and counselors at more than 20,000 high schools nationally. In addition, between 1980 and 1983 we hosted over 100 seminars with key executives representing most major educational associations to promote the need for uniform standards for all student recognition programs. As a result of these meetings, our standards have been used as a model for guidelines adopted by the National Association of College Admissions Counselors, the American School Counselors Association and the state principals associations from Wisconsin, Iowa and Colorado. The WHO'S WHO standards have also been cited by the American Association of Attorneys General and the Parent Teacher Association ("PTA Today," Dec. 86/Jan. 87).

WHO'S WHO AMONG AMERICAN HIGH SCHOOL STUDENTS is the only student recognition program/ publication to be favorably reviewed by the prestigious American Library Association (Booklist, 3/1/82).

In reflecting on the history, growth and prominence of the WHO'S WHO program it is important to emphasize the ongoing role of our Committee on Ethics, Standards and Practices. Initially, the Committee's major objective was the creation and acceptance of standards. Since 1979, however, this group of prominent and respected educators meets with us each year for two evenings and one day to review all programs, policies and procedures. They discuss new objectives, overall educational concerns and opportunities for providing better services for students. The involvement and dedication of these professional, dedicated educators assures all schools, students and parents that the goals and objectives of our program and publication are consistent and compatible with the high standards of the educational community.

Now that we have reached our 21st birthday, we are renewing our commitment to providing meaningful recognition for meritorious students in a professional and dignified manner. With the experience and wisdom of our staff and the members of our educational committees, we will continuously strive to seek more and improved services for the students we are privileged to honor. We are all very proud of the publication and programs we have developed. Most of all, we are all very proud of the students we continue to recognize.

Who's Who Review

A Summary of the Objectives, Programs, Policies for
WHO'S WHO AMONG AMERICAN HIGH SCHOOL STUDENTS®

Since 1967, WHO'S WHO AMONG AMERICAN HIGH SCHOOL STUDENTS® has been committed to celebrating outstanding students for their positive achievements in academics, athletics, school and community service. Our first edition recognized 13,500 students from 4,000 high schools; the current, 21st edition, published in twelve regional volumes, honors over 539,000 high school students representing 20,000 public, private, and parochial high schools nationwide.

As our publication has grown and matured over the years, we have expanded the scope and depth of the services and benefits provided for listed students and refined our policies and procedures in response to the needs of the schools and youth organizations who share our objectives.

Commencing with the 1986-87 academic year, we have expanded eligibility for recognition in WHO'S WHO to freshman and sophomore class students. This policy change was in direct response to educators who requested the opportunity to nominate younger students at a crucial point in their academic careers and reward those who excel through listing in the publication.

In our view, the growth, acceptance, and preeminence of WHO'S WHO AMONG AMERICAN HIGH SCHOOL STUDENTS as the leading student recognition publication in the nation, can be attributed to the involvement of educators in the policy-making areas of our programs.

During the past several years, we have hosted over 90 day-long reviews with key educational association executives to exchange ideas and perspectives regarding our standards, criteria, and services.

Most importantly, we must acknowledge the contributions of our Committee on Ethics, Standards and Practices, a group of distinguished educators representing relevant areas in secondary and post-secondary education. The committee was created in 1979 in order to formalize appropriate standards for our program which could be used as a guide for all student recognition programs. These standards are distributed to 80,000 high school principals, guidance counselors, and other faculty members each year.

It is a tribute to the committee that the standards they developed have been used as a model by several educational associations who have created their own guidelines for evaluating student recognition programs on a uniform basis. WHO'S WHO is proud of its well documented leadership role in promoting standards and ethics for all student recognition programs.

The committee meets each year and reviews literature, policies, programs, and services. They bring a perspective to the company which assures students and school administrators that WHO'S WHO policies and programs are in compliance and compatible with the standards and objectives of the educational community.

Major Policies and Procedures

Free Book Program—*Guarantees extensive recognition through wide circulation*

WHO'S WHO sponsors the largest Free Book Program of any publisher in any field. The book is automatically sent free to all participating high schools and youth organizations and offered free to all 7,500 libraries and 3,000 colleges and universities. Up to 15,000 complimentary copies are distributed each year.

The major purposes of this extensive free distribution system are to provide meaningful, national recognition for listed students among institutions traditionally concerned with student achievement, and to make it convenient and easy for these students to view their published biography without purchasing the book.

For students who cannot locate an inspection copy of the book in their community, a listing of libraries within their state which received the most current edition is available upon request.

The recognition and reference purpose(s) of WHO'S WHO AMONG AMERICAN HIGH SCHOOL STUDENTS® have been acknowledged in the favorable review of the publication by the Reference and Subscription Books Reviews Committee of the American Library Association (*Booklist*, 3/1/82).

Financial Policies—*Legitimate honors do not cost the recipient money*

There are no financial requirements whatsoever contingent upon recognition in WHO'S WHO AMONG AMERICAN HIGH SCHOOL STUDENTS. The vast majority of students featured in all past editions have not purchased the book, but have received the recognition they have earned and deserve.

For those students who do purchase the publication or any related award insignia, satisfaction is guaranteed. Refunds are always issued on request.

Nominating Procedures—*Representation from all areas of student achievement*

Each year all 22,000 public, private, and parochial high schools are invited to nominate students who have achieved a "B" grade point average or better and demonstrated leadership in academics, athletics, or extracurricular activities. On rare occasions, students with slightly under a "B" average have been included when their achievements in non-academic areas were extraordinary. Nominators are requested to limit selections to 15 percent of their eligible students. Most nominate less.

Approximately 14,500 high schools participate in our program by nominating students. An additional 5,000-7,500 schools are represented by their outstanding students as a result of nominations received from bona fide youth organizations, churches with organized youth activities, scholarship agencies, civic and service groups. Most of our nation's major youth groups participate in our program by nominating their meritorious student leaders.

Editing—*Maintains the integrity of the honor*

Occasionally, nominators recommend students who are not qualified for recognition. When these students receive our literature and forms, there may be confusion concerning our standards and criteria. When biography forms are submitted for publication, they are all reviewed and edited to monitor compliance with our high standards. In the past 11 years, approximately 211,662 students were disqualified by our editors because they did not meet our standards, including several thousand who ordered the publication. More than $1,298,021 in orders were returned to these students. Our standards are never compromised by the profit motive. (Auditor's verification available upon request.)

Verification of Data—*A continuous safety check on the effectiveness of our procedures*

To monitor the accuracy and integrity of data submitted by students, a nationally respected accounting firm conducts annual, independent audits of published biographical data. Previous audits reveal that up to 97.2 percent of the data published was substantially accurate. (Complete studies available upon request.)

Educational Communications Scholarship Foundation Committee members meet to select 50 scholarship winners for the 1983-84 academic year. Each winner receives a $1,000 award. Left: Dr. Norman Feingold, President, National Career & Counseling Services; Morton Temsky, Educator; Lester Benz, Executive Secretary Emeritus, Quill & Scroll Society; Wally Wikoff, Former Director, National Scholastic Press Association; Lily Rose, Scholarship Committee Chairperson and Director of Admissions, Roosevelt University; Fred Brooks, Asst. VP for Enrollment Services & Management, SUNY at Binghamton; Aline Rivers, 1979-80 Executive Board, National Association of College Admissions Counselors; Robert MacVicar, President Emeritus. Oregon State University; and Dr. James Schelhammer, Dean of Admissions, Austin Peay State University. Committee member not shown: Neill Sanders, Director of Admissions, Wichita State University.

Programs, Services and Benefits for Students

Scholarship Awards—From $4,000 in 1968 to $100,000 annually since 1982

The Educational Communications Scholarship Foundation®, a not-for-profit organization which is funded by the publishing company, now sponsors three separate scholarship award programs, which award over $100,000 in college scholarships each year. Over $900,000 has been funded to date.

Through the general high school program, 65 awards of $1,000 each are awarded to students by a committee of knowledgeable educators on the basis of grade point average, class rank, test scores, activities, an essay and financial need. An additional $15,000 in scholarships is funded through grants to youth organizations where we sponsor awards for their officers or contest winners. For students already in college, $25,000 in scholarships is awarded through THE NATIONAL DEAN'S LIST® Program.

Our research indicates that the Educational Communications Scholarship Foundation's programs represent one of the 10 largest scholarship programs in the nation funded by a single private sector organization. The Foundation is listed in numerous government and commercial directories on financial aid and scholarships.

Grants-In-Aid—Financial support for organizations who work with or for students

Since 1975, we have funded grants to youth and educational organizations to support their programs and/or services on behalf of high school students. The stipends fund scholarships or subsidize research, educational publications or competitive events, and programs. A brief summary of grants issued or committed to date, totaling approximately $346,000 appears in this review.

The College Referral Service (CRS)® — Links students with colleges

WHO'S WHO students receive a catalog listing all 3,000 colleges and universities. They complete a form indicating which institutions they wish us to notify of their honorary award. This service links interested students with colleges and universities and serves as a "third party" reference.

Certainly, listing in WHO'S WHO will not assure a student of admission into the college of his or her choice any more than any other award or honor society. Most selective colleges rely almost exclusively on grade point average, class rank, and test scores. Nevertheless, several hundred colleges have indicated that the CRS and/or the publication is a valuable reference source in their recruitment programs. (Letters from colleges available for inspection.)

18th Annual Survey of High Achievers™ —The views of student leaders are as important as their achievements

Since 1969, we have polled the attitudes and opinions of WHO'S WHO students on timely issues of interest. This study provides students with a collective voice otherwise not available to them. As young voters and future leaders, their views are important. Therefore, survey results are sent to the President, all members of Congress, state Governors, educational agencies, high school administrators, and the press.

Each year, survey results are widely reported in the press and have been utilized in academic studies and research indicating the educational value of this program.

WHO'S WHO Spokesteen Panel™— Another voice for student leaders and a service for media

Because WHO'S WHO has become an authoritative source on high school students, we receive frequent inquiries from reporters when they are preparing special features on teen views, lifestyles, etc. To assist reporters and to assure teens of appropriate representation of their views, we have created a network of articulate and well-informed students, nationwide, who are made available to the press for interviews of local and national coverage. WHO'S WHO Spokesteens have appeared on the "CBS Morning News," NBC "Today Show," "Merv Griffin Show," "Hour Magazine," and numerous other broadcasts, newspaper and magazine stories.

College-Bound Digest®—What students need to know

A compilation of articles written by prominent educators covering the various opportunities available to college-bound students, i.e., financial aid opportunities, the advantages of large schools, small schools, research universities, achievement test usage, and preparation and numerous other topics of similar relevancy. The Digest appears in the introductory section of this publication and is offered as a separate publication, free of charge, to 20,000 high school guidance offices, 20,000 principals, and 3,000 college admissions offices.

Local Newspaper Publicity—Additional recognition for honored students

Consistent with our primary purpose of providing recognition for meritorious students, we routinely provide over 2,000 newspapers nationwide with rosters of their local students featured in the publication with appropriate background information. (Students must authorize this release.)

Other Publications

Who's Who Among Black Americans®

This publication has been extremely well received by librarians, government agencies, educational institutions, and major corporations. All four major library trade journals reviewed and recommended earlier editions for their subscribers. The book was selected by the American Library Association as one of the "Outstanding Reference Books of the Year" and by *Black Scholar* as "A Notable Book," one of only 19 publications to receive this distinction.

WHO'S WHO AMONG BLACK AMERICANS was one of 380 titles chosen by the Library of Congress to be exhibited at The White House Conference on Library & Information Services held in November, 1979 and was selected for inclusion in the Presidential Library at Camp David.

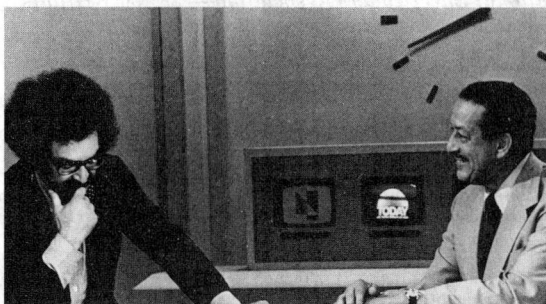

William C. Matney, of WHO'S WHO AMONG BLACK AMERICANS, was introduced on the "Today Show" by book and theatre critic Gene Shalit. The publication has received numerous awards and honors.

The National Dean's List®

The tenth edition of THE NATIONAL DEAN'S LIST® recognizes 91,000 outstanding students representing 2,500 colleges and universities. All students were selected by their respective deans or registrars because of their academic achievements. This year, $25,000 in scholarships were distributed to twenty-five students. For 1987-88, a minimum of $25,000 in scholarships will again be awarded.

Memberships

Educational Communications, Inc. or its publisher is a member of the following organizations:
  American Association of Higher Education
  American Association of School Administrators
  Chicago Metropolitan Better Business Bureau
  Distributive Education Clubs of America,
    National Advisory Board
  Educational Press Association
  Future Farmers of America, Executive Sponsor
  National Association of Financial Aid Administrators
  National School Public Relations Association
  Office Education Association,
    National Business Advisory Council

Profile of Who's Who Student

(Statistics From 1987 Edition)

General Listing
Total Number of Students 539,001
WHO'S WHO Students as Percentage of 12,000,000
  High School Students Enrolled Nationwide....... 4½%
Females (%) 62%
Males (%)... 38%

Academics
Grade Point Average (%)
  "A" 72%
  "B" 27%
  "C" .... less than 1%
Local Honor Roll 250,798
National Honor Society 145,672
Valedictorian/Salutatorian 10,463

Leadership Activities/Clubs
Student Council 91,586
Boys State/Girls State 35,572
Senior Class Officers 29,236
Junior Class Officers 48,896
Sophomore Class Officers........................ 47,082
Freshman Class Officers 44,198
Key Club 32,275

Major Vocational Organizations
4-H 38,732
Future Farmers of America 24,882
Junior Achievement 24,433
Distributive Education Clubs of America 10,203
Office Education Association 8,120

Varsity Athletics
Basketball 100,232
Track 80,551
Cheerleading/Pom Pon 60,642
Football... 57,011
Volleyball 44,785
Baseball 34,545
Tennis 32,893
Soccer... 30,972
Cross Country 26,184
Wrestling 15,205

Music/Performing Arts
Orchestra/Band................................... 110,150
Chorus 80,406
Drama 52,334

Miscellaneous
Church/Temple Activities 200,846
Yearbook... 97,310
School Paper 73,944
Students Against Driving Drunk 61,931
Community Worker................................. 38,649
Fellowship of Christian Athletes 34,762

Grants to Youth and Educational Organizations

American Association for Gifted Children — $2,000, 1 Grant
To sponsor a conference for educators concerning "The Gifted Child, the Family and the Community."

American Children's Television Festival — $2,000, 1 Grant
To promote excellence in television programming for our nation's youth. Founded by the Central Educational Network.

American Council on the Teaching of Foreign Language
$500, 1 Grant
To support the general goals and objectives in the field of foreign language.

American Legion Auxiliary Girls Nation — $22,000, 9 Grants
Scholarships for Vice President and Outstanding Senator of program where students participate in mock government structure.

American Legion Boys Nation — $24,000, 10 Grants
Scholarships for President and Vice President of program where students learn about government through participation.

Animal Welfare Institute — $1,582, 2 Grants
For biology textbook on experiments which do not involve cruelty towards animals. Second grant to fund convention booth equipment.

Black United Fund — $5,000, 1 Grant
Scholarships for Black students selected by BUF Committee.

Colorado Forum of Educational Leaders — $1,000, 1 Grant
To fund a series of quarterly activities regarding the educational successes of Colorado Schools.

Contemporary-Family Life Curriculum — $1,500, 1 Grant
Funded formal grant request, resulting in $100,000 grant from government to test this contemporary curriculum.

Distributive Education Clubs of America (DECA)
$49,800, 13 Grants
ECI serves on the National Advisory Board for this major vocational/educational organization and sponsors scholarships for officers.

Earthwatch — $3,000, 3 Grants
Scholarships for students conducting scientific expeditions with scientists, researchers.

Education Roundtable — $5,000, 1 Grant
To fund the creation of a committee of representatives from government, education, private industry, and the general public to support and improve education in America.

Fellowship of Christian Athletes — $12,800, 5 Grants
Original stipend funded seminar of athletic directors. Subsequent grants for scholarships for coaches' conferences concerning spiritual, professional and family growth.

Joint Council on Economic Education — $11,000, 4 Grants
Funds ongoing economic education program for students and educators from elementary school to college level.

Junior Achievement — $14,000, 7 Grants
Scholarship for the winner of the WHO'S WHO Essay Contest.

Junior Classical League — $6,000, 6 Grants
Funds a scholarship to the outstanding member selected by an educational committee for this organization whose members study the civilizations of Greece and Rome to provide a better understanding of our culture, literature, language and arts.

Junior Engineering Technical Society — $6,000, 2 Grants
Stipends were used to help revise the National Engineering Aptitude Search Test.

Key Club International — $2,000, 2 Grant
For two scholarships of $500 each for two outstanding Key Clubbers.

Law & Economic Center, University of Miami Law School
$4,500, 1 Grant
Funded study on use of media to effectively communicate economic issues and policies to general public.

Miss Teenage America Scholarship Program
$33,000, 8 Grants
Currently funds a $5,000 scholarship for student selected as Miss Teenage America; previously funded four $1,000 awards for each of the semifinalists.

Modern Miss — $1,000, 2 Grants
Scholarship for the National Academic Winner.

Modern Music Masters — $4,500, 2 Grants
For chapter expansion program of this national music honor society, high school level.

Mr. U.S.A. Teen Program — $5,500, 4 Grants
Scholarships for outstanding student selected on basis of leadership, citizenship, academics, and community involvement.

Mu Alpha Theta — $3,000, 1 Grant
Grant to be used for scholarships for outstanding Mu Alpha Theta students.

National Cheerleaders Association — $8,100, 8 Grants
Scholarships for winners of state drill team contests.

National Exchange Club — $1,000, 1 Grant
Grant to fund a scholarship for the Student of the Year.

National Federation for Catholic Youth Ministry
$3,000, 2 Grants
Funds a scholarship of $1,000 for the student elected President of the National Youth Council and a $500 scholarship for another Catholic Teen Leader selected by the National organization.

National Forensic League — $11,000, 6 Grants
For two scholarships of $1,000 each to the members of the first place National Debate Team.

National Foundation for Advancement in the Arts
$4,000, 4 Grants
For general support for the Arts, Recognition, and Talent Search Program of this Foundation.

National 4-H Council — $22,500, 9 Grants
Grants are used for scholarships for outstanding 4-H students.

National Future Farmers of America (FFA)
$30,000, 11 Grants
Grants are used for scholarships for outstanding FFA students.

National Society of Professional Engineers — $1,000, 1 Grant
Grant to be used for scholarships for outstanding NSPE students.

Office Education Association (OEA) — $46,000, 12 Grants
ECI serves on the National Business Advisory Council and sponsors scholarship program for national officers.

Performing & Visual Arts Society (PAVAS)
$4,000, 2 Grants
To conduct expansion program for high school chapters.

The President's Committee on the Employment
of the Handicapped — $5,000, 5 Grants
Scholarship for the winner of the President's Committee National Poster contest, high school division.

Quill & Scroll Society — $11,000, 6 Grants
For two scholarships of $1,000 each to students who apply as contestants in Quill & Scroll's Current Events Quiz and National Writing/Photography Contest.

Soroptimist International of the Americas, Inc.
$4,000, 4 Grants
Scholarship for organization's Youth Citizenship Award Winner.

Special Olympics, Inc. — $1,000, 1 Grant
Scholarship for outstanding student volunteer and direct mail promotion to high school athletic directors requesting volunteers to work with handicapped children.

Standards for
Who's Who Among American High School Students and Other Recognition Programs and Societies

1. Nominations will be from established organizations that work with and for the benefit of high school aged youth. Under no circumstances will recommendations be accepted from students, their parents or solicited from standard commercial lists.

2. Criteria for students to be selected will be clearly defined and reflect high personal achievement.

3. Listing in "Who's Who" will not require purchase of any items or payments of any fees.

4. Additional programs and services which are available to those listed in "Who's Who" at cost to the students, will be clearly described in the literature provided.

5. A refund policy will be clearly stated in all literature.

6. Nominators will be able to recommend students without releasing confidential data or fear of having confidential data released by program sponsors.

7. Student information will be confidential and will not be released except where authorized by the student.

8. Home addresses will not be published in the book or made public in any way.

9. Under no circumstances will "Who's Who" sell student information or lists.

10. The publisher will describe, disseminate and verify the methods employed to assure national/regional recognition to students listed.

11. The publisher will respond to all inquiries, complaints and requests for relevant background information.

12. The basis for the scholarship program competition will be defined. Number and amount of awards will be stated, lists of previous winners will be available. Finalist selection process and funding method will be clearly defined. Employees or their relatives will not be eligible for scholarships.

13. There will be an advisory council (external to the organization) to review and make recommendations regarding the policies, procedures, and evaluation process of the "Who's Who" programs.

14. The publisher will set forth in writing and make publicly known the policies and procedures it follows in the implementation of these standards.

Our company's adherence to the above standards has been attested to by an independent public accounting firm. A copy of their report is available upon request.

Members of the Committee on Ethics, Standards and Practices:

Dr. Wesley Apker
Executive Director
Association of California
School Administrators
Sacramento, CA

James T. Barry
Assoc. Vice President
for University Relations
St. Ambrose University
Davenport, IA

Phyllis Blaunstein
Executive Director
National Association of State
Boards of Education
Alexandria, VA

Dr. Harold Crosby
Regents Professor
University of West Florida
Pensacola, FL

Dr. S. Norman Feingold
President
National Career &
Counseling Services
Washington, DC

Charles R. Hilston
Executive Director
Association of Wisconsin
School Administrators
Madison, WI

Dr. Betty James
Assoc. Dean for
Academic Affairs
Livingstone College
Salisbury, NC

Dr. John Lucy
Asst. Superintendent for
Curriculum & Instruction
Downers Grove Public School
District 58
Downers Grove, IL

Dr. Paul Masem
Superintendent of Schools
Alexandria City Public
Schools
Alexandria, VA

Dr. Edward J. Rachford
Superintendent
Homewood-Flossmoor
Community High School
Flossmoor, IL

Dr. Vincent Reed
Vice President for
Communications
The Washington Post
Washington, DC

David Hartman, host of ABC's "Good Morning America" (right), interviewed WHO'S WHO Spokesteen Shannin Mealiffe from LaCanada High School, LaCanada, CA (second from left) with two authorities on teen suicide.

On the NBC "Today Show," host Tom Brokow (center) interviews WHO'S WHO Spokesteens (left) Burnell Newsome, Hazelhurst, Mississippi, Amy Krentzman, Deerfield Beach, Florida, Tari Marshall, ECI Representative, and Mike McGriff, Chicago, Illinois.

Merv Griffin interviews WHO'S WHO Spokesteen Steven Silver from South Shore High School, Brooklyn, New York on the nationally televised talk show.

WHO'S WHO Spokesteens are interviewed by Gary Collins, host of the popular, nationally syndicated TV talk show, "Hour Magazine."

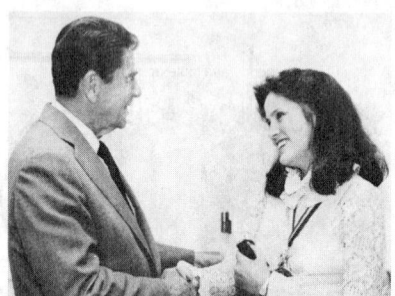

President Reagan greets Miss Teenage America, Amy Sue Brenkacz in the Oval Office. WHO'S WHO sponsors a $5,000 scholarship for Miss Teenage America and listed Amy Sue in the publication.

Bill Kurtis, host of the "CBS Morning News," interviews WHO'S WHO Spokesteens Stephanie Woolwich, Long Beach, New Jersey and Alex Tachmes, Miami Beach, Florida.

A group of 12 WHO'S WHO Spokesteens appear with host Pat Robertson (center) on the popular TV magazine program, "700 Club" (CBN) to present teen leaders' views on America's future in a special 7 part, 8 hour debate.

WHO'S WHO sponsors $1,500 and $1,000 scholarships for the president and vice-president of the American Legion Boy's Nation program. (Left to right) Marcus R. Dilworth, Jr., 1985 Boy's Nation President; Mike Ayers, Director, Americanism and Children & Youth Division; and Daniel Bricken, 1985 Boy's Nation Vice-President.

Penni Ann McClean, right, Congress delegate advisor from North Carolina, presents a citation to Mrs. Jackie McGuinn, assistant to the publisher of WHO'S WHO, for five years support of the 4-H Citizenship-Washington Focus program.

Right to left: Debbie Moyer from Allentown, PA pointing to her prize winning poster in the high school category with Harold Russell, Chairman, President's Committee on Employment of the Handicapped. WHO'S WHO sponsors a $1,000 college scholarship for this annual contest.

College-Bound Digest®

As a public service to the 96% of WHO'S WHO students who will continue their education after graduation from high school, we have invited a group of distinguished educators to use our publication as a forum to inform and assist students through the articles in this section.

While we do not presume that these articles contain "everything you need to know" about preparing for college, we believe you will find they will be helpful in learning "some of the things you need to know."

We wish to acknowledge the special contribution of Robert McLendon, Executive Director, Brookstone College of Business, High Point, North Carolina, who was instrumental in selecting appropriate topics and authors for this section.

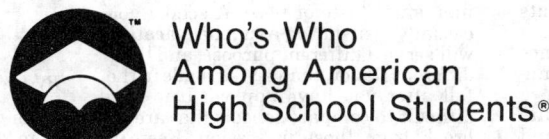

Who's Who
Among American
High School Students®

Getting the most from your high school counselor

By James Warfield

A high school counselor, helping you apply to college, is able to provide a wide variety of services tailored to your needs. The nature of this assistance will depend upon your abilities and achievement as well as the nature and quality of the colleges to which you apply. Effective use of the counselor's services will require you to have frequent discussions. Although your ideas about which colleges to apply to will change often, the more closely you work with your counselor the more valuable he/she will be to you.

Finding, selecting and applying to the colleges that are right for you is a long and studied process. It involves a lot of letter-writing, telephoning, research, weighing alternatives, and just plain old thinking. It's a decision-making process.

Your counselor makes recommendations as to which courses you should be taking in high school. These recommendations should be based upon your academic abilities and goals. This is a critical issue because the appropriateness of this advice is determined by the consistency between your aspirations and aptitudes. Verifying the accuracy of your self-perceptions is important in order to avoid sudden surprises caused by false hopes or unrealistic expectations. The reason why your counselor exists, is to help you become everything you are capable of within a realistic framework.

For many students, the college selection process begins with the PSAT, taken in the fall of the junior year. Your counselor should advise you which of the college entrace tests to take, SAT, ACT, ACH and AP, and when to take them. The type of college you apply to will determine which tests to take. The quality of the college, or the quality of your own academic program, and whether or not you plan to apply Early Decision, will determine when you should take such tests. Many students don't know in their junior year to which schools they'd like to apply, so advance planning is necessary in order to maintain open options.

Finding the right college will require you to know yourself, your likes and dislikes. In what kind of environment do you see yourself being most comfortable? Can you picture yourself at a small college or a mid-size or large university setting? Do you want a school to be in a rural community, a suburb or to be in an urban environment? Do you want to be in a different geographic part of the country or is being close to home important to you? What are some of your academic areas of interest? What kind of extra curricular offering do you want to participate in? As you answer these questions the attributes of your ideal college will become more clear. Through discussion with your counselor you'll be able to assess your needs, and more clearly focus your perceptions of yourself and of the schools you will be researching.

Your counselor should help generate a list of colleges that meet your requirements by drawing upon his/her own wealth of knowledge or utilizing the many reference materials available.

Many counselors have access to computers that will provide a list of colleges for you to investigate, once you have determined the characteristics you are looking for. If the guidance office does not have a computer, the same information can be obtained, with a little effort, from the commercially published reference books that are available through your counselor. After generating a list of perhaps twelve to twenty schools, your research really begins.

Resource books provide a wealth of statistical and narrative descriptions on virtually every college. The counseling office is likely to have college catalogs as well as files on each college containing brochures, view books and leaflets of the various academic and extracurricular offerings available at that particular school. Although college catalogs are boring reading material, information relating to admission procedures and requirements, course offerings and requirements for each of the academic majors are outlined. In addition, course prerequisites and methods of exempting yourself from some prerequisites are also indicated. As your research continues, you'll be able to eliminate schools and determine some colleges in which you are seriously interested.

Many high schools set up procedures whereby students may meet with representatives from colleges to obtain more information or answer individual questions. These representatives may be the Director of Admission, Admissions officers, or personnel hired to represent the college. Of course, the more you know about the college, before talking with the college representative, the more value they will be to you. Some colleges require an interview either by the representative, an alumni, or by an admissions officer. Your counselor should help you determine if an interview is necessary in your situation.

Campus visits are the most effective means to determine if the college is right for you. When to visit is a matter of individual taste or need. A school you casually visit during a summer vacation will serve a different purpose, and have different flavor, than a visit made in the fall after you have applied. It is also difficult to compare schools that are on break from those in session. Keep in mind that as you visit more schools your observational skills will become more sophisticated and your reflections of each will be altered. It may be more prudent to visit only those schools to which you have been accepted, after you have received all your admissions decisions.

As you narrow your choice of colleges, your counselor should review with you the possibilities of acceptance or rejection at each. At least one of your choices should be a safety choice, one in which you are almost guaranteed of being admitted.

After the list of colleges to which you are going to apply has been determined, it is your responsibility to obtain the application and meet deadline dates. Many colleges require a counselor's recommendation or a Secondary School Reference. Some require additional recommendations from specific teachers. Establish application procedures with your counselor so that he/she, the teacher, and school have adequate time to do their part in order to meet your deadline dates. If you are required to write an essay, or personal statement, discuss this with your counselor. These discussions serve several purposes: help you generate ideas and narrow topics that you wish to write about; provide you with suggestions that will enhance your applications; and provide the counselor with insights that will compliment your application.

It is your responsibility to file your applications on time, see that your test scores are sent to the admissions office, and file the financial aid applications. Your counselor will help you determine which scores to send, which financial aid form is required and how to fulfill these requirements.

Selecting and applying to a college is a decision-making process. The truly wise decision maker knows that he must clarify questions, obtain the most information possible, and probe until no new information becomes evident. Generally, the more information obtained, the better the decision, and the happier the college experience.

Jim Warfield is Director of Guidance at Lake Forest High School, Lake Forest, Illinois. Jim is currently involved and active in a number of professional organizations, and presently serving on the National Advisory Council for The Educational Records Bureau, Wellesley, Massachusetts.

The use of the SAT at selective colleges

By Dr. Judith Gatlin

For many students the numbers — from 200 to 800 on the verbal and on the quantitative sections of the College Board examination — seem to be the voice of doom; for others, they announce the possibility of admission into the nation's most selective colleges. But just how important, really, are those scores, and how will college admissions committees interpret them?

It is important to remember that the SAT (or ACT) is only one part of your total record. Your rank in your high school class, your grades, extracurricular activities which show leadership potential, and your recommendations are all extremely important. In addition, some colleges will consider your geographic location (it may be easier for the valedictorian of a South Dakota high school to enter Harvard than for the top student in a Connecticut prep school), your relationship with alumni, your religious preference at some denominational colleges, and the success of other graduates from your school at the institution.

Colleges treat scores, grades, rank, activities and recommendations in a variety of ways, but very few use arbitrary cut-off scores to determine acceptance. Every selective college or university attempts to select a class which will be successful (they don't want you to flunk out after your first year). Students who are admitted are those who they can predict will do well; and admissions staff experience with standardized tests suggests that certain levels of achievement, can be predicted with a fair degree of accuracy when used in conjunction with the high school record.

Often the total score on the SAT is less important than the individual score on either the verbal or the quantitative aptitude section. While colleges and universities may publish their average SAT as a combination, many liberal arts colleges believe that the verbal score is a particularly good indicator of ability, and many technically oriented engineering programs will be impressed with a very good quantitative score. A pre-engineering student with an 1150 SAT may be a very good candidate if his scores are 450 on the verbal section and 700 in the quantitative area; he might be substantially less impressive with 650/500.

One of the problems that many students confront when they first look at their scores is a sinking feeling that their numbers do not match their high school achievement level. The 'A' student who is third in her class and barely makes a 450/450 on the SAT is disappointed for days afterwards. It is important, however, to understand what your scores mean. The national average on the verbal section of the SAT is 427; on the mathematics section it is 467. Clearly, many college bound students will have a total score under 900. Many colleges and most state universities have average scores at this level or below it; more selective institutions will generally have average scores that are substantially higher, but even among these colleges there will be a number of students whose scores are at this level if their grades and rank indicate a strong chance of success.

But how can you explain or understand an average score when you have been an excellent student? It may be that you had a bad day (or a bad night before); a headache, too little sleep, a testing environment that is too hot or too cold may cause your scores to be less than your best. It may be that the scores are an accurate indicator of your aptitude and that you are a high achiever. Or it may mean that your grades have

been inflated and that you have not been challenged by teachers or peers. One way that you can determine if it was just the specific test day is to compare your scores on the SAT with your PSAT. If you scored, for example, 48/50 on the PSAT and have a combined total on the SAT of from 970 to 1020 your test is probably valid. If, on the other hand, your PSAT was 55/58 and you scored 1020 on the SAT, you probably should plan to retake the examination to see if the second time might show real improvement.

In addition to the "bad day" low score there are other reasons that good students do not do well on standardized tests. It may be that they panic under time pressure, that they are unfamiliar with national tests and the testing environment, or that their skills and abilities cannot be shown on such tests. Really creative students, those with talents in the arts, and those who work very slowly through a problem, analyzing as they go, are sometimes at a disadvantage. If you fall in one of these categories, it is especially useful for a teacher whose recommendation you have requested be asked to discuss your other strengths in an admissions letter.

Some students retake the SAT two or three times to see if they can improve their overall scores, and it is important to realize that scores will vary slightly every time you take a Scholastic Aptitude Test. A variation of 30 points in either direction is normal; more than 50 points, unusual. How worthwhile is it to retake the SAT if your scores are under the average published by the college of your choice? Some schools, like Furman, accept your best scores from each test. Others may average your test results. It is probably true that you can improve your quantitative score with tutoring over several months; improving verbal scores is far more difficult. You should remember, however, that while selective colleges have many high-scoring students, their *average* SAT is just that: there have been many others whose scores are under the average but who have the proven achievement to be admitted.

Suppose, however, that you are very interested in an institution which indicates an average SAT of 1275; your score is 1050, but your parents are alumni, you graduated in the top 20% of your class, and you have been an outstanding high school leader. Academically you would be in the bottom quarter of your class, yet you may well be admitted because of your parents and your activities. Should you attend such a college? Will you be able to compete at a level comfortable for you with students whose high school backgrounds may be substantially superior? Are you ready to make a number of "C's" or to study harder and longer than your roommates?

You should consider, too, that very high scores do not necessarily mean admission to the college of your choice. Several years ago a young man with an SAT score of 1440 applied to a selective Southeastern liberal arts college. He had graduated in the lower half of his high school class and although he had been involved in some extracurricular activities, he also had been a discipline problem in high school. After substan-

tial discussion, he was not admitted, but the college admissions office was interested enough to trace his career several years later. He had flunked out of two other colleges. SAT scores indicate aptitude — the ability to learn — not achievement. They do not show the desire to learn, the ambition to succeed or the perserverance necessary for academic excellence. College admissions officers are aware of these facts and they will read your entire application with an awareness that you are more than a score on a computer printout.

Dr. Judith Gatlin is the Director of Educational Services and Assistant Professor of English at Furman University, Greenville, South Carolina. She has authored various articles for the *Journal of College Placement* and is a former columnist for the *Charlotte Observer*.

Tips on taking the SAT

By Dr. Ernest W. Beals

If you are college-bound or plan to be, chances are that you will be required to take a college admissions test such as the Scholastic Aptitude Test (SAT) of The College Board or the American College Testing Program's assessment test (ACT).

The SAT's format and content have changed enormously over its 55 years of existence, and is now designed to measure the extent to which your reasoning abilities, that is skill with verbal expressions and mathematical concepts, have been developed up to the time you take the test.

It is important to realize that students are neither accepted nor denied admission to an institution solely on the basis of SAT or other test scores. When looking at prospective students, institutions of higher learning also stress to varying degrees such factors as your high school record (including courses taken, grade patterns, and class rank or high school average) and extracurricular activities. Other factors may be the outcome of personal interviews and teacher or counselor recommendations, as well as the student body needs of the college or university itself.

Students frequently ask: What can I do about raising my SAT scores or about making them better than they would be otherwise? The answer is: Quickly and immediately, probably not much. Over longer periods it depends on how much time, effort and concentration goes into the preparation. The abilities measured by the test are related to academic success in college. These abilities grow over a period of time through learning experiences such as those encountered in the family, in the classroom, with your friends and associates, and in reading and independent study.

The best preparation for the SAT is to have had varied opportunities of this kind and to have made the most of them. The contents of the tests cover such a broad area that trying to "cram" for it has never been found to yield validly measurable results. You may, however, find it useful to review some of the fundamental principles of algebra and geometry in order to refresh your memory for the mathematical section of the test.

In order to reduce anxiety and increase confidence when test time arrives, here are some valuable tips: First, become familiar with the format of the test. Obtain a copy of the informative booklet, *Taking the SAT,* from your guidance counselor. This free booklet describes the nature and components of the SAT and, provides a full sample SAT which you can administer and score yourself. By taking this sample test, you will familiarize yourself with the directions and the format of the questions. You will also gain valuable practice in allocating your time to each item.

You will also learn that, as a rule, the easier questions of each section come at the beginning of that section, with the questions growing progressively more difficult to the end of the section. Use your time wisely. If you find the individual items of a particular section are extremely difficult for you, read quickly through the remaining questions in the group, answering only those that you feel you know. You should then begin work on the next set of questions, returning to the omitted questions in that section if you have time. You receive as much credit for answering correctly the questions you find easy as you get for answering the hard ones. Above all, don't panic. You receive one point for each question correctly answered; you lose a fraction of a point for each item incorrectly answered. You neither gain nor lose points for omitted questions. Therefore, keep in mind that random guessing on questions will rarely increase your scores, and might even have the effect of reducing your raw score. However, some selective guessing can pay off for you: If you can confidently eliminate as incorrect at least two of the possible four or five answers to a question, then it would be to your advantage to take a stab at one of the remaining answers to that question.

Your raw score on the SAT is determined by adding up all correct answers and subtracting from that total the sum of the fractions for all incorrect answers. The raw score is then converted to the College Board scale ranging from a low of 200 to a high of 800 on the verbal and mathematics sections of the SAT.

The Test of Standard Written English (TSWE) is a 30-minute multiple-choice test administered with the SAT. The questions evaluate your ability to recognize standard written English, the language of most college textbooks and the English you will be expected to use in the papers you write for college courses. The scores may be used to place you in a freshman English course that is appropriate for you.

Contrary to the anxiety-ridden expectations of students taking the SAT and TSWE for the first time, these tests do not require specialized knowledge in science, social sciences, literature, or any other field.

In brief summary, the best strategies to follow in order to prepare yourself for taking the SAT include: enroll in college preparatory courses that your school offers, maintain good solid and consistent effort in your everyday classroom work and classroom tests, force yourself to read as many and varied outside readings as possible, brush up on your algebra and geometry lessons, become familiar with the SAT format, content, directions, etc. (obtain a copy of *Taking the SAT* booklet from your counselor and take the sample SAT test, score it yourself, and read the suggestions and explanations included with it), get a good night's sleep the night before the examination and take a positive attitude with you to the test center. If you do all of the above, you will be putting your best foot forward and enhancing your chances of obtaining good test scores. Good luck to you.

Dr. Ernest W. Beals is Association Director of the Southern Regional Office of The College Board. Dr. Beals has worked in the field of education for the past 26 years at the high school and college level including 13 years in college admissions.

Can you prepare for the SAT?

By Stanley H. Kaplan

The discussion of the issue of preparation for the SAT has come full circle since the 1950's. In the 1957 Bulletin, issued to the students, the College Board stated, "Coaching may be a sound and rewarding method. If coaching means an honest effort, under the guidance of a good teacher, over an extended period of time, to improve those skills in which you are weak, then it can be recommended as effective study." In the 1960's, the statement about the possible positive effects of coaching was withdrawn. The reason, I was told, was the proliferation of cram schools that preyed on students' (and parents') anxieties and offered little of educational value and little possibility of an improvement on the SAT. And now in the 1980's, the College Board and ETS which constructs the SAT, once again are distinguishing between cramming and long-term coaching which is now looked upon as "supplementary education."

Can one be prepared for the SAT? My answer is an emphatic yes. Some students can prepare by self-study. There are many materials, including tests released by the College Board and SAT review books available at bookstores.

My organization has been preparing students for the SAT for more than thirty years. Actually — and this is important — we are not preparing for the SAT per se. Rather, we are working to improve a student's basic math, verbal, and reasoning skills. The SAT does not measure a scholastic aptitude — if by aptitude we mean an innate, unchangeable indication of academic potential. The SAT measures the level of verbal and mathematical achievement, including the ability to handle innovative, non-routine approaches in these areas. The SAT evaluates the learning experiences of students in and out of school. The more the experience, the higher the level of achievement and therefore the higher the SAT score. Only an improved student can achieve an improved score. It seems that many students and parents still believe that all a test preparation program has to do is teach a few test techniques and strategies, wave a magic wand, and presto — a higher score. The goal of an SAT preparation program should go beyond that of improved SAT scores. It should provide improved skills to insure better performance at the college level. In fact, parents are beginning to realize the valuable long-range effects of SAT preparation. When reports of declining SAT scores made a big splash in the press, several years ago, the enrollments in our programs increased dramatically, despite the decreasing importance of SAT scores in the college admissions process. Declining SAT scores indicate a deficiency in basic skills which in turn could mean a poorer performance at the college level. Years of experience have convinced me that the "specter" of the SAT is an excellent device in motivating students toward working and improving these skills necessary for success at the college level.

Unfortunately, too many students memorize facts that teachers and textbooks provide, regurgitate this information on a test, and then promptly proceed to forget. A review can be of immense value in "bringing it all back," in making what one has learned more meaningful, and in giving the student an opportunity to think more creatively. This does not mean that every student should enroll in an SAT preparation program. Certainly, you should take at least one of the released exams to become familiar with the instructions, format, content, and time pressures of the test. If you feel, however, that you would like to enroll in a structured program of preparation, here are some tips you might follow in choosing a legitimate program that could give you the maximum benefit:

1) The program should be a long-range one — extending over a period of at least several months. Cram courses are of little value. The lessons should be held weekly with home-study assignments in between to reinforce what has been taught in class.

2) The classes should be small — not seminars of 100 or so. A class size should not exceed 25.

3) There should be an opportunity to make up missed lessons. Very frequently, you might miss a lesson because of illness or other commitments. Certainly,

you should not give up studying for an important school exam in order to attend a class session.

4) The program should offer you the option of continuing your study for the SAT if you choose to take the exam for a second time.

5) Most important, the school should have a *permanent* location where you might look at the materials and be able to talk in depth with a person in charge. Beware of fly-by-night programs that advertise by box numbers, have telephone answering services, hold classes in hotels or other meeting rooms, and silently steal away when the course is over.

6) The better programs offer scholarship assistance if you cannot afford to pay for the program.

7) You should check a program out with others who have taken it previously. Their experiences as to the quality of the teaching, the adequacy of the materials, and most important, the improvement they have achieved, can be most helpful in making your decision.

Be suspicious of high pressure tactics designed to corral you as a student — such as statements that the SAT is the most important exam you will ever take, claims of fantastic improvements, and guarantees of improved scores. Avoid correspondence courses. They are often expensive — almost as much as a course with live class programs. Usually the purchase of an SAT review book and use of materials supplied by the College Board itself is just as helpful.

Remember, the SAT is *not* the most important exam you'll ever be taking. It is only one of many criteria used by admissions officers to make a decision. Certainly your high school record is more important than the SAT score you will get.

Perhaps one of the best reasons for some kind of preparation is to make sure that the SAT score evaluates your achievement as reliably as possible. After all, you wouldn't enter a tennis tournament cold. I've seen hundreds of cases of underachievers or poor "test-takers" whose self-images have been enhanced by improved scores that more accurately evaluated this academic achievement.

Remember, there is much you can do on your own long before you take a preparation course or even decide to do so. You can start reading — newspapers, magazines, best-sellers, — read something that interests you, but read! At the same time, you'll be improving your vocabulary and the ability to integrate ideas. In math, as well as in science, don't just memorize rules and standard ways of attacking problems. Try to reason things through and find out the why as well as the how as well as the what. Then, when the time comes to review for the SAT, you will have done most of your preparation already. Good luck!

Stanley H. Kaplan is Executive Director of the Stanley H. Kaplan Educational Center, Ltd., New York, New York with offices nationwide and abroad. Kaplan has been featured in numerous articles including *Time*, *Newsweek*, and the *New York Times*. He has also appeared on numerous public radio and television programs as an authority on test preparation.

Searching for student financial aids

By S. Norman Feingold and Marie Feingold

The purpose of this article is to suggest practical techniques and pathways for gathering accurate information about financial aids that are available and to indicate time frames within which it is advisable to initiate financial aid seeking efforts.

1. Start Early

The high school student should begin not later than the beginning of the junior year of high school. Many scholarships require that the student have taken the Scholastic Aptitude Test or the Preliminary SAT. The National Merit Scholarship competitions start the beginning of the junior year in high school. Many organizations use the results of this exam for the selection of their recipients; and this includes some companies which provide scholarships for the children of its employees. Some colleges select student aid recipients from National Merit competitors. Some competitions for research fellowships, overseas grants may close a year before recipients are announced.

2. Federal Publications

A. The U.S. Department of Education publishes two helpful pamphlets, that are revised annually. They are *Five Federal Financial Aid Programs: A Student Consumer's Guide* and *Federal Financial Aid for Men and Women Resuming Their Education or Training*. They are both available without cost from Federal Financial Aid, Box 84, Washington, DC 20044.

B. Veterans Administration each January publishes *Federal Benefits for Veterans and Dependents*. It contains details of educational assistance and is available from the Superintendent of Documents, U.S. Printing Office, Washington, DC 20402. Cost $1.50.

C. The Department of Defense. Each of the armed forces has ROTC programs and annually revises its pamphlets about programs.

Achievement through Education, Air Force ROTC is obtained from the Department of the Air Force, Air Force Reserve Officers Training Corps, Maxwell Air Force Base, AL 36112.

Navy-Marine Corps Scholarship Programs. U.S. Department of the Navy, Navy Recruiting Command, 4015 Wilson Boulevard, Arlington, VA 22203.

Information about Army ROTC scholarships can be obtained by writing to:

Army ROTC, P.O. Box 7000
Larchmont, NY 10538.

D. The U.S. Department of Health and Human Services, Washington, DC 20201 maintains up-to-date publications about social security benefits. Details should be obtained from the local Social Security office. Generally dependents of deceased or disabled contributors to Social Security are eligible for benefits while they are full-time elementary or high school students under the age of 19. Until April, 1985, there is a phasing out of the benefits as they existed until August, 1981.

Information about financial aid for students in the health and allied health professions is available from the U.S. Public Health Service, Bureau of Health Manpower, Student Assistance Branch, Center Building, Room G-23, 3700 East-West Highway, Hyattsville, MD 20782.

E. The U.S. Department of the Interior, Bureau of Indian Affairs, Washington, DC 20245 publishes pamphlets about educational assistance for native Americans.

If you are having difficulty locating information about Federal financial assistance for training and education, write to your Congressman or Senator at either his local office or at his Washington, DC office in the House of Representatives of the Senate.

3. State Publications

Most if not all states publish booklets or flyers about the student financial aid programs they administer. *Five Federal Financial Aid Programs: A Student Consumer's Guide* lists the names, addresses and telephone numbers of every state agency that provides information on the Guaranteed Student Loan Program and *Federal Financial Aid for Men and Women Resuming Their Education or Training* lists the names and addresses of each state scholarship agency. For details write to the state scholarship agency of the state in which you are a resident.

States also publish material on scholarships for special groups within the state such as veterans and their dependents, policemen, prison guards and firemen. It is likely that the state scholarship agency can give you the name and address you need.

Your state Senator can help you locate state aids.

4. Local Publications
(City and County)

Many communities have a printed or typed listing of student aids available to their residents. Your counselor may be helpful in directing you to these sources.

5. Know the ethnic, religious, and place origins of your family.

A fairly large amount of student financial aid is awarded by private organizations to persons of specific origin. Consult *Scholarships, Fellowships and Loans, Volumes VI and VII*, by S. Norman Feingold and Marie Feingold, and the *Scholarships, Fellowships, and Loans News Service and Counselors Information Services*, Bellman Publishing Company, P.O. Box 164, Arlington, MA 02174-0164.

6. Know for whom your parents or guardian work.

Some corporations and labor unions provide awards for their employees and members respectively. Have your parents speak to the personnel department of the company and the steward of the labor union for details. Company and union newspapers/magazines are good sources of keeping abreast of these financial aids.

7. As soon as practical for you, try to determine a **field of interest and hobby.** Some aids are given for majoring or studying certain subjects or having engaged in specific activities.

8. Enter Contests.

There are many different kinds of contests. The National Federation of Music Clubs, 310 South Michigan Ave., Suite 1936, Chicago, IL 60604 publishes scholarships and awards charts for two-year periods.

9. Get your own work experience.

Students who have been caddies or delivered newspapers or worked in other capacities are often eligible for scholarship competitions. Tuition refunds from the company for which you work cover a part or all of the fees for courses. Generally, the course must be related to your work and permission must be obtained.

10. Attend free post-secondary institutions of education and training.

The military academies and the Webb Institute of Naval Architecture are schools for which there are no tuition or room and board fees.

11. Consider scholarship loans.

In areas of work in which there are manpower shortages, it is possible to convert a loan to a scholarship by working in a given geographical area or in a specific subject matter field. Teaching the handicapped and working in rural poverty areas where there are shortages of specific personnel are two ways. Generally these programs are federally or state sponsored.

12. Loans to parents, to children of employees, to residents of service areas.

Such loans may be administered and awarded by business, foundations, banks, non-profit corporations. Two programs for which you should write for information are those of the United Student Aid Funds, Inc., 200 East 42nd St., New York, NY 10017 and Richard C. Knight Insurance Agency, Inc., 53 Beacon St., Boston, MA 02108.

13. Attend Cooperative or Work-Study Schools.

Your earnings will cover much if not all of your tuition and living expenses. More than 200,000 college students are enrolled in cooperative education programs. In the "typical" co-op program, students alternate semesters of study and supervised paid work. More than 1,000 colleges now offer co-op programs. Request *Undergraduate Programs of Cooperative Programs in the United States and Canada* which is available at no cost from the National Commission for Cooperative Education, 360 Huntington Ave., Boston, MA 02115.

14. Apprenticeship Training.

In the skilled trades this is a way to learn and earn. Details are available from the following four sources: State Bureau of Apprenticeship and Training (one office is located in each state capital); a network of approximately 2,300 local and state employment offices; in a number of states there is a state apprenticeship council; U.S. Department of Labor, Bureau of Apprenticeship and Training, 601 D St., N.W., Washington, DC 20213.

15. Teachers, principals, ministers, lawyers, bankers, business people, counselors may know of individuals who anonymously assist deserving individuals to obtain the training and education they are seeking.

16. How do you locate the donors and administrators of financial aid programs?

There are a number of publications that should either be in the public library, school library, or college library. If not, request the library to order them. Some are:

Need a Lift, American Legion, P.O. Box 1055, Indianapolis, IN 46206. Revised every fall.

Scholarships, Fellowships and Loans, Volumes VI and VII, S. Norman Feingold and Marie Feingold. Bellman Publishing Company, P.O. Box 164, Arlington, MA 02174-0164, 1977 and 1982 respectively.

Scholarships, Fellowships and Loans News Service and Counselors Information Services, quarterly newsletter. Bellman Publishing Company, P.O. Box 164, Arlington, MA 02174-0164.

Don't Miss Out. The Ambitious Student's Guide to Scholarships and Loans, 5th ed., 1980/82, Robert Leider, Octameron Associates, Alexandria, VA. Published biennially.

Financial Aids for Higher Education 1980-81 Catalog, 9th ed., 1980, Wm. Brown Publisher, Dubuque, IA.

AFL-CIO Guide to Union Sponsored Scholarships, Awards, and Student Financial Aid, 1981. AFL-CIO Department of Education, 815 16th St., N.W., Washington, DC 20006.

Additionally, there are local newspapers, particularly suburban ones. They generally announce who won what and provide a name or address you can contact.

Local banks, community foundations, and social service agencies are aware of funds about which there is little or no publicity.

Usually there is less competition for local student aid funds in comparison with those available to candidates on a national level.

Many states publish directories of local aids. Your guidance counselor or public librarian will know how to obtain a copy or will have a copy for you to read.

17. The financial aid office of the institution you wish to attend or are attending.

Many funds are administered by the schools themselves, and you must let the financial aids officer know of your need for assistance. Many schools and colleges and universities publish a directory of their aids; they are usually free.

18. Answer all letters and application forms with great care.

Be certain that you have answered *every* question; for those not applicable, write N/A. If at all possible, type; be certain of accuracy and neatness. Meet all deadline dates. Deadline dates may change from those listed in directories. You need enough time to edit your answers several times. The quality of essays when they are required with the application blank is an important screening device. Be certain you remind your references and schools you've attended to submit requested material on time.

19. If you try each one of the methods described above and have ability and potential, you have a good chance of getting student aid. A study by the authors showed that with students of equal ability, the ones who applied to more resources were more successful in obtaining assistance. You may get a scholarship on your second try from the same fund.

Good luck. Don't let the lack of money deter you from seeking further education and training. Your post-secondary education can open up rewarding careers to which you otherwise would not have access.

Dr. S. Norman Feingold is President, National Career and Counseling Services, Washington, DC; Honorary National Director of B'nai B'rith Career and Conseling Services; Past-President of the American Personnel and Guidance Association and the author of several publications including seven volumes of *Scholarships, Fellowships and Loans.* Marie Feingold is a Rehabilitation Counselor, Washington, DC and co-author of volumes six and seven of *Scholarships, Fellowships and Loans.*

Tough questions to ask any admissions officer

By Robert G. McLendon

As a college admissions officer for the past fouteen years, it is clear to me that today's prospective students are carefully comparing colleges and striving to learn all they can about the colleges to which they apply. The age group of 18 to 24 year olds is declining in the United States, and this is creating a type of "buyer's market" in the market place of higher education.

In order to assure yourself that your expectations of a college are met, you, the student consumer, need not hesitate to ask admissions officers some "tough questions." This article will offer you a few suggestions of some tough questions that I hope will help you make the right choice when selecting a college.

Academic Questions

1. How many students in last year's

freshman class returned for their sophomore year?

2. What percent of the freshman class obtained a 2.00 (C) average or above last year?

3. If accepted, will you tell me my predicted freshman grade-point average?

Many colleges use a mathematical formula based on studies of currently enrolled students to predict an applicant's freshman grade average.

4. What is the college's procedure for class placement?

This is especially important in the areas of English and mathematics because freshmen often vary significantly in their ability to handle these important academic skills.

5. What procedure is used to assign a faculty advisor when the student is undecided as to the major area of study?

6. What type of additional academic services does your college offer at no additional cost to the student (e.g., tutoring, career or personal counseling, study-skills workshops, improving reading speed, etc.)?

7. How effective is your college's honor code? What is the penalty for cheating?

Social Questions

1. What is the average age of your student body and what percent resides on campus?

Many colleges today have a large and increasing population of commuting part-time adult students and a dwindling enrollment of 17 to 18 year old full-time, degree-seeking students residing on campus.

2. Is your college a "suitcase college" on the weekends? If not, what are some typical weekend activities for students on your campus?

3. What procedure is used to select roommates if no preference is listed?

4. What are some of the causes of students being suspended or dismissed from your college? Is there a system of appeal for those who have been dismissed?

5. How can a prospective student arrange a campus visit?

Clearly the best possible way to evaluate a college socially is to plan a visit to the campus. When you visit, try not to be shy. After your talk and tour with the admissions officer, walk around by yourself and informally ask students their opinions. A good place to chat with students is in the college's student center or at the dining hall.

6. What are some of the rules and regulations that govern residence hall life? Are there coeducational residence halls?

Financial Questions

1. What percent of your students received financial aid based on financial need?

2. What percent of your students received scholarships based on academic ability?

3. What percent of a typical financial aid offer is in the form of a loan?

4. How much did your college increase cost (room, board, tuition, and fees) from last year to current year?

5. If an accepted student must submit a room deposit, when is the deposit due, and when is it refundable?

The deposit should be refundable in full up to May 1, if the college or university is a member of the National Association of College Admissions Counselors.

6. If my family demonstrates a financial need on the FAF or FFS forms; what percent of the established need will typically be awarded? When can I expect to receive an official financial aid award letter?

The distinguishing quality of any person is the quality of the mind, and the college you select will have a long-lasting impact on your career and life. I realize that you are painfully aware of the need to make the right college choice because most high school students realize that the college years are often the most productive stage of life. Knowing what questions to ask an admissions officer is an important part of this decision-making process. Most admissions officers want you to ask "tough questions" because if you make the wrong choice we, too, have failed in our job.

Bob McLendon is Executive Director, Brookstone College of Business, High Point, North Carolina. He served on the Admissions Practices Committee of the National Association of College Admissions Counselors and has been Chairman of the Admissions Practices Committee of the Southern Association of College Admissions Counselors. He is a member of the Executive Board of SACAC and President-Elect of the Carolinas Association of Collegiate Registrars and Admissions Officers.

Common mistakes students make in selecting a college

By William B. Stephens, Jr.

The process of choosing a college can be a rewarding, worthwhile experience or it can be an endless, frustrating series of mistakes. Those mistakes are common and are usually the result of inadequate research and preparation — both characteristics you will need as a successful college student. The selection of a college is a good place to begin developing those virtues.

Begin the process with a series of questions. Am I most interested in a small, medium, or large college? Do I want to stay close to home or go away? What will be my major? Does the college have a broad curriculum if my major is undecided? How academically competi-

tive do I want my college to be? What are the costs? Is financial aid available? Which extracurricular activities are the most important to me? When these questions are satisfactorily answered, it is time to begin the next stage.

Research is of primary importance in selecting a college. Do not make the mistake of choosing a college simply because your friends go there. List priorities. Be willing to invest time and effort in investigating colleges which share these priorities.

In writing to colleges for information, be neat, concise, and accurate in providing information about yourself. Many students forget to include the address to which the college should send material. Also include your high school graduation date, the high school you attend, your anticipated major (if that has been decided), and any pertinent information regarding grades and test scores. Decisions are made about students on the basis of their initial contact with the college. Do not be careless in this important decision.

There are numerous publications which are helpful in gathering information. These publications may be located in school and public libraries, bookstores, and guidance offices. Many are cross-referenced according to majors offered, geographic locations, costs, and sizes. Once familiar with college publications, the task of choosing a college becomes an easier one. Do not make the mistake of floundering with too many college options.

Your school guidance office can offer an abundance of information. Among the many contributions of guidance counselors is the provision of data concerning financial aid, college representatives scheduled to visit the school and/or vicinity, College Fairs, and testing for college entrance. In addition, most schools provide counseling to help students choose colleges compatible with their scholastic aptitudes, personality, financial means, and extracurricular interests. Often these guidance resources are not tapped, yet they can be among the most beneficial that you could explore.

Do not neglect the value of contacting alumni, college representatives, and currently enrolled students. Alumni can provide firsthand accounts of life at college while representatives will have the current facts about admissions requirements, new majors offered, scholarships, sports, and campus activities. Students who are currently enrolled in a particular college can provide additional insight into the actual experiences you can expect at the institution.

It is important that you visit the colleges which are your first preferences. Never will catalogs, counseling, or recommendations from alumni replace an actual visit to the campus. Much can be learned from sitting in on a few classes, walking through dormitories, and talking to faculty and staff. It is extremely risky to choose a college without personal observation.

Many colleges have orientation programs to acquaint students and their parents with the facilities and various aspects of student and faculty involvement. Investigate the colleges being considered to discover their plans for orientation programs. Do not fail to be present at the programs in which you are most interested.

Since the cost of attending college can be one of the greatest factors determining your choice, the possibility of obtaining financial aid is to be taken into careful consideration. Watch for the deadlines in applying for financial assistance, and have the appropriate forms completed well in advance. If financial aid is offered, be certain to compare the amount of aid offered and the total cost of attending that particular college. Remember that the matter of final importance is in determining the amount which has to be paid by you and your family.

College preparations should begin in the ninth grade. Solid academic courses (usually beyond the minimum required for high school graduation) should be completed each year. Four years of English is normally expected. Most colleges expect a student to complete at least three years of math, including two years of algebra and one of geometry. Although requirements vary from college to college, it is generally advantageous to have a sound background in biology, chemistry, physics, history, and a foreign language.

High schools administer PSAT, SAT, and ACT exams to juniors and seniors. It is wise to plan to take a College Board exam more than once. As these exams take four to six weeks to be graded, you should allow plenty of time so as not to delay the application process. Your score on a college board exam will further indicate the type of college to attend. Colleges vary considerably in their College Board score requirements.

By October of your senior year, choices should be narrowed to two or three prospective colleges. You should be aware of all admission requirements for each institution considered. Do not delay the application process until after Christmas. Many colleges begin waiting lists very soon after the beginning of each new year. Your application and all required documents should be on file by November 1 at each college considered. Do not expect high schools to send transcripts or teachers to send recommendations the day the request is made. Allow a couple of weeks for these items to be completed and mailed to the college.

Incomplete or illegible applications will greatly diminish the opportunity for rapid processing. These types of delays can mean the difference between being able to attend your first choice of colleges and having to wait another full academic year to enroll.

College-bound students should never hesitate to ask questions. Begin early and be organized. Parental involvement is essential in choosing a college that will meet the need of you and your family. Diligent research and careful planning are the keys to the prevention of the most common mistakes made by college applicants today.

Bill Stephens is Director of Admissions at Florida Southern College, Lakeland, Florida and has worked in the Admissions field for ten years. Stephens is a member of the National Association of Admissions Counselors, the Southern Association of Admissions Counselors, the American Association of Collegiate Admissions and Registrar Officers, and the Southern and Florida Associations of Collegiate Admissions and Registrars Officers.

The advantages and pitfalls of advanced placement and credit by examination for the freshman year of college

By Carl D. Lockman

I think we all agree that gifted young people need help in order to recognize their potential role in society. Through advanced placement and credit by examination programs, secondary school systems and universities alike are making a bona fide effort to encourage the development of academic talent, thus helping students to better understand their contributions to society and self.

Perhaps an explanation of the main difference between advanced placement and credit by examination is appropriate at this point. Both programs serve the purpose of awarding the student college course credit for acceptable scores on examinations. However, the Advanced Placement Program is a function of the College Entrance Examination Board. It is a formally structured program of instruction culminating with an examination. Institutions also may give departmental examinations which may be referred to as advanced placement. Credit by examination may or may not be a formally structured program. The College Level Examination Program (CLEP) is an example of the former, through which a student can receive credit for non-traditional (learning outside the classroom) educational experiences by presenting satisfactory scores on examinations.

All programs designed to award credit at the university level have advantages that are worth the student's consideration. Credit programs complement conventional instruction by allowing students to begin academic study at a level appropriate to their experience. They require students to demonstrate that they have achieved at a level equal to college experience. By being given this opportunity, the student can save both time and money.

A second advantage is that studies indicate that advanced placement continues throughout the undergraduate years. Quantitatively and qualitatively the student benefits. Course credit granted through advanced placement generally allows for increased hours to be completed in a four-year program, much of which may be completed at the junior level and above. This certainly allows for greater flexibility and versatility in designing one's curriculum. Somewhat the opposite has shown up in early studies of CLEP credit. Students with CLEP credit tend to graduate earlier. However, this still permits the student the advantages of having saved money and time and allows the opportunity to move into graduate studies at an earlier date. The challenge for the student is brought to the front when he/she is placed into courses recognizing achievement when his/her ability surpasses basic proficiency level courses.

Another advantage to the participation in and the receiving of credit through these programs is the quality of instruction associated with advanced placement. Generally speaking, it is safe to say that some of the best secondary instructors are asked to conduct the advanced courses. These instructors will stretch to stay ahead of these bright students who comprise the classes. Also, students in these programs not only benefit from the quality of instruction, but from the fact that most schools set up programs by drawing on the experiences of other school systems. In effect, students are being exposed to highly researched programs that have been trial tested for years by many systems.

A closer look at these programs reveals additional advantages. Many advanced placement programs borrow lectures, lab facilities, and equipment from local businesses and universities to accelerate their programs. Schools sometimes pool courses to give a wider curriculum offering. Credit programs allow secondary schools and colleges to articulate their programs, thus helping to bridge the curriculum gap that has been prevalent for years. In bridging this gap the student with an outstanding background can be recognized.

The advantages far outweigh the disadvantages when studying advanced placement and credit by examination programs. Two negative comments might be made at this point. There is always the possibility that students entering these programs do not have a thorough understanding of the extra demands that will be placed on them. Remember that the courses offered in the secondary schools are rigorous college-level courses. College credit granted may result in the student being placed in upper-level courses, which in turn will demand more effort on the student's part. It is not a bad idea either that parents be made aware of what is to be expected of students involved in advanced placement programs and of those having received credit by examination.

Secondly, uninformed secondary and college personnel cause very definite problems. After a student has participated in an advanced placement program or has the experience to achieve credit through examination, it is imperative that the secondary counselors advise students and their parents of colleges that have established policies that would meet the needs of the student. I can think of few things more disappointing than for a student to miss the opportunity to have more flexibility in his courses and to avoid repetition. The other fears are that the college officials may not have required faculty members in the subject areas covered by the tests to review the examinations and that the procedures and practices of the college regarding credit have not been carefully studied. As you can see, such omissions by the institution in establishing policies could lead to improper credit and, even worse, improper placement in courses "over the head" of the student.

In conclusion, whether a student goes through the CEEB Advanced Placement Program, participates in the institution's own advanced placement program by taking departmental examinations, or receives credit for life experiences, the importance of the programs is that they are attempts to equate classroom and/or non-classroom experience to college-level learning. The programs are models of learning closely conforming with college courses. Placement and credit programs are relatively new opportunities which each year seem to become more and more accepted by the academic communities. These are ways to recognize the individual differences in students, an attempt to confront the age-long problems of recognizing the variety of experiences students bring to college, and a breaking from the tradition that all students need to enroll in core curricula.

For students with exceptional learning experiences and/or intellectual talents, advanced placement and credit by examination programs are recommended. The rewards for such accomplishments are great.

Carl D. Lockman is Assistant Director of Admissions at Georgia Institute of Technology, Atlanta, Georgia. Lockman serves on the Admissions Practices Committee of the Southern Association for College Admissions Counselors and is a member of the American and Georgia Associations of Collegiate Registrars and Admissions Officers. He was appointed to the Governor's Committee to study recruitment techniques and is a board member of the Middle Georgia Drug Council.

The academic and social benefits of large American universities

By James C. Blackburn

There is no type of collegiate experience which is most appropriate for all students. The purpose(s) of this essay are to identify and discuss the academic and social benefits of large universities.

In almost every state in the union, there is at least one large university whose enrollment exceeds 10,000 persons. More than a score of states have within their borders, universities enrolling more than 30,000 students. There are several community colleges whose enrollments meet the criterion of having 10,000+ enrollments. Those institutions are not included within the scope of this essay.

A substantial number of large universities are state-supported. However, more than a few large universities are private institutions of higher education. Such universities are more common in the more populous regions of the nation, e.g. the East Coast and upper Midwest. The tuition prices of large universities vary from nominal charges to $10,000 per year. It is, therefore, possible to select a large university from any price range. Some of America's most expensive and least costly institutions can be classified as large universities.

Large universities are located in large cities such as New York, Boston, and Los Angeles, as well as in small towns, e.g. Bloomington, Indiana and Tuscaloosa, Alabama. The selectivity of admission to large universities is also quite varied. Some universities admit as few as one in five of its applicants. Other moderately large institutions offer admission to more than 90% of their applicant pools.

In short, the diversity between and among large universities makes it possible for almost every student who desires to attend such an institution. Enrollment at a large university is not the private privilege of any socio-economic or intellectual sub-segment of American society. That being the case, there must be some good reasons for matriculation at and graduation from a large university.

There are academic benefits which apply to each size and type of college or university. The academic benefits of enrolling at a large university are especially striking.

Few freshmen actually complete the academic major which they begin. At a large university, the available academic majors often number in the hundreds, not dozens. If a student changes his or her major or career choice, the large university is most likely to be able to accommodate that change.

As a result of the "knowledge explosion," many undergraduate *curricula* now require extensive equipment and large library resources. Because of their graduate and professional schools, large universities tend to offer more sophisticated laboratory equipment and libraries of considerable size. So called "economies of scale" seem likely to perpetuate this circumstance. At a large university, undergraduates often compete with others for these resources. The point is that the equipment and libraries are available.

For most students, post-graduate employment is a major reason for college enrollment. Large universities typically offer a multiplicity of services designed to help students in the identification and pursuit of career options. Selecting a career and finding a job are not often easy; it may be well to get as much help as possible.

There is an additional "job search" benefit to holding a degree from a large university. Most such institutions are well known on at least a regional basis. Assuming the reputation of a given institution is good, the employer or graduate school may be more impressed if they are familiar with an applicant's university.

Each type and size of college and university has academic benefits to offer. Ony a few of the academic benefits of the large university have been addressed here. There are other benefits related to the academic learning environment of each large university. Academic learning is clearly the primary reason for the existence of colleges and universities. It would be foolish to suggest that all of the benefits of college attendance happen inside the classroom, laboratory, and library. Many of the non-academic benefits of college attendance are social in nature. It is well that those benefits be discussed.

The typical ages of college attendance (18-22) constitute an important period of intellectual and social development. It is important that these changes take place in the most nearly appropriate environment possible. Intellectual development is obviously an academic enterprise. Social development, which means more than just dating, parties, and football games, happens throughout the campus environment. As with the academic areas, each type of college or university has social benefits to offer prospective students. The social benefits of large universities are significant; those benefits should be considered carefully by aspiring freshmen.

It is reasonable to state that larger universities offer more student activities and more varied opportunities to associate with other students. In fact, many freshmen who enroll at the largest university find themselves inundated with opportunities for social involvement, community service, etc. It may be difficult to select the activities, clubs, and personal associations which are most appropriate for individual students.

The variety of opportunities for student involvement at a large university are often more impressive than the sheer number of such involvements, activities, clubs, etc. Many larger universities offer organizations which cater to a plethora of interests ranging from handicrafts to hang gliding. There are often religious organizations for many faiths and denominations. The opportunities for political involvement are often wide ranging. From the most serious of religious or political convictions to the desire for big or small parties, large universities can frequently provide activities which meet the needs of all their students.

As universities grow, the size of the student services staffs also grow. With regard to academics, this growth in student services results in improved opportunities for career identification and job seeking. In the arena of social development, this growth means more opportunities for personal counseling and other activities which are designed to help a person to improve their social awareness and skills.

A final social benefit of large universities has to do with one's classmates.

Because of their size, large universities often enroll students whose backgrounds present a wide variety of experiences, values, and perspectives. Exceptions to this rule do exist, but is is generally true that one's classmates at a large university will be less homogeneous than might be the case at smaller colleges and universities.

There is an important social benefit in this lack of sameness among a student's classmates. Most students will study, work, and live out their lives in a world composed of a huge variety of persons. Our society has become more pluralistic in recent years. It seems, therefore, likely that there is a good in being able to live and work with a wide variety of persons. College is an excellent place to gain experience in dealing with people whose backgrounds and perspectives may be different from your own. Large universities offer many opportunities for such experiences.

By way of the above, it is hoped the nature(s) and benefits of large universities may be better understood by qualified prospective students. The more important points of this essay are that American higher education is quite varied and that no type of colleges or universities is inherently superior to any other type or types. Each student must make his or her own decisions about the appropriateness of small colleges, community colleges, church affiliated colleges, and large universities.

This writer's bias for large universities should be obvious. Huge varieties of academic and social opportunities are available at large universities. Those varieties serve to make such institutions an excellent choice for many aspiring freshmen. Large universities, although varied themselves, are not for everyone. They do present very appropriate choices for many prospective students.

Jim Blackburn is Director of Admissions at the University of Northern Colorado, Greeley, Colorado and has been involved in the college admissions process for over ten years. He has conducted a number of conference presentations for admissions personnel at various association meetings.

The academic and social advantages of a private church-related college or university

By A. Mitchell Faulkner

Many educators in recent days are concerned that moral and ethical matters have been so largely excluded from the educational experience. Under the influence of a technology expanding beyond all expectations, the demands placed upon most professions, including the social and natural sciences, have worked to exclude serious consideration of moral and ethical concerns inseparably bound up in that expanding technology.

But the assumption that our complex society can be safely led by technicians untrained in the making of serious ethical decisions affecting our corporate well being is totally unacceptable to any thinking person.

As Bruce Haywood has written in *The Chronicle of Higher Education,* "too many of our colleges and universities have become vocational schools... Whereas once they offered our children avenues to a larger sense of their humanity, they now direct them to the market place. Instead of seeing themselves enlarged under the influence of great minds and grand ideas, students find themselves shrunken to fit the narrowing door of the graduate school or tailored to a job description. It is time for our colleges and universities to talk again about the worth of a free life, time while we are still able to distinguish between the *training* of young people and their *education.*" (1/8/79)

Young people are not born with moral and ethical convictions. They are learned in the educational process, if learned at all, by precept and by example, by being in the presence of people with convictions. Healthy self identity, says Lloyd Averill, emerges out of an environment which has convictional distinctiveness, in which the maturing self has access to a range of clear and competing values where the competition serves to sharpen and enliven the options rather than to subjugate or obliterate them.

A subtle but pervasive element emerging in our day is what Archibald MacLeish has called the diminution of man, the "long diminishment of value put upon the idea of man" in our society. Why has this happened now at the moment of our greatest intellectual triumphs, our never equalled technological mastery, our electronic miracles? "Man was a wonder to Sophocles when he could only sail and ride horseback and plow; now that he knows the whole of modern science he is a wonder to no one," says MacLeish.

At least part of this loss of the humane is caused by the knowledge explosion, the sheer weight of information in the print and electronic media, so that man despairs of any cognitive wholeness and surrenders ever increasing areas of knowledge to a vast array of experts.

Earl McGrath, former Commissioner of Education, says on the other hand, that this vast array of facts and theories needs to be collated and evaluated within the framework of philosophic convictions and religious beliefs in order for the wisdom of the ages to again invest dehumanizing facts with meaning for man.

One further point of definition needs stating. Our sense of community has well nigh been lost, and every social philosopher recognizes the need to restore it. What is at stake here, says John Gardner, is the individual's sense of responsibility for something beyond the self. The "me" generation threatens the cohesiveness of our social fabric, and a spirit of concern and caring is virtually impossible to sustain in a vast, impersonal society.

All of the above points directly to the purpose of the church-related liberal arts college. The essence of the liberal arts is the passion for man, the development of the humane values in literature, philosophy, history, and religion; and the great ideas of the race, such as truth, justice, love, beauty, honor, and wisdom are precisely the vehicles through which the deepest purposes of religion are served. Religion is only secondarily a matter of creeds and rituals. At its heart it is a matter of meaning, and this meaning is conveyed most effectively through the wisdom of the ages, the liberal arts.

Education is more than a learned set of mental exercises, the ability to respond properly to fixed mental inquiries. A computer does this admirably. To be fully human is to add to this a capacity for imagination, the ability to feel reverence and awe in the presence of mystery, a capacity for caring and compassion, and appreciation for the mixed grandeur and misery of the human experience. These represent the uniquely human accomplishment and point the direction for the church-related liberal arts college.

Further, the church-related college, usually smaller, offers a community in which students have more opportunity to learn through experience the interpersonal skills so necessary to effective participation in today's society. The development of the whole person involves taking responsibility for the care of the community, its governance, its social life, its ethical and moral tone, its operative effectiveness. A broad participation in all aspects of the campus community should mark the church-related college.

Students are not uniformly at the same place in their development, and ought not to be coerced to march lock step through some standardized program. The undergraduate program, through flexibility made possible by forms of governance and individual care, ought to allow as much as possible for diversity of interest and differences in development as the student progresses. A college ought to find ways to encourage each student to develop to the fullest potential his individual gifts and educational aspirations. A student's goals ought to be headed by the desire not only to master the curriculum but to develop himself. The church-related college will seek to aid this through the total experience, intellectual, social, cultural and religious.

The church-related college, if dedicated to the fully human development of its students, will retain a healthy respect for the vocational skills. In order to fully *be,* a person must be able to *do.* Life cannot be divorced from work, and a healthy self identity depends in part upon the ability to make some significant contribution to society. Thus the great truths of the liberal arts must be brought to focus and a point of service through competency in a chosen area of the world's work, where one may serve and fully live.

After all, as Montaigne said a long time ago, the purpose of education is not to make a scholar but a man.

A. Mitchell Faulkner is the former Executive Director, Council for Higher Education, Western North Carolina Conference, The United Methodist Church. He is on the Board of Trustees for Pfeiffer, Greensboro, High Point and Brevard Colleges, and is a member of many educational associations including the North Carolina Association of Independent Colleges and Universities, Secretary, S.E. Jurisdictional Commission on Higher Education.

Advantage of attending a state university

By Stanley Z. Koplik

For most students and their families, the cost of a four-year college education is an important consideration, and for this reason alone, many choose state colleges and universities. These institutions are usually considerably less expensive than private institutions and in many cases provide students with the option of living at home while pursuing a degree.

State scholarship programs are frequently available providing monetary incentives even to those who attend state institutions. Some families appreciate the opportunity of utilizing a system they continue to support with their tax dollars. But state universities are a wise choice for the college bound for many reasons other than simply economics. For young people growing toward independence, the proximity of the state college or university to parents, friends and home communty can provide the firm base of support students need as they adjust to the academic, social and emotional pressures of a more demanding way of life.

High school graduates seeking to continue their education in an atmosphere of intellectual challenge and academic diversity should also look to the state universities and colleges. With a wide range of courses and curricula from which to choose, state institutions of higher education provide a solid grounding in most fields from vocational and technical training to liberal arts education. No longer stereotyped as teacher training schools, state colleges and universities now emphasize engineering, computer technology, business, and science as well as teacher education and the humanities.

As a first step for those seeking professional careers, state institutions offer programs in such fields as medicine, dentistry, law and architecture. Virtually, any area of academic interest can be satisfied through state college programs. At the University of Kansas, for example, there are 112 degree programs offered; the University of Missouri offers approximately 125. Other states offer an equally broad array of programs. With outstanding faculties in many disciplines, and national reputations in many areas, state institutions have developed into comprehensive universities where intellectual inquiry and academic excellence flourish.

A large number of state colleges and universities are equipped with fine research facilities and outstanding libraries providing unlimited opportunities for questioning and stimulating creative minds. In some areas the most complete and comprehensive library in the state thrives on the campus of the state university, while inter-library loan systems enhance access of all state residents to study and research materials.

For those who are concerned about "being lost in the crowd," state higher education systems usually provide a variety of campus sizes ranging from the very small school with 1-2,000 students to the "mega-campus" with a student population of 25,000 or more. Attendance at a smaller campus does not imply inferior educational quality or diminished services. Excellent instruction, stimulating classroom discussion and challenging extracurricular activities can be found on all state college campuses regardless of size.

Providing an integrated educational program with a maximum of flexibility is the goal of many state systems. To facilitate student choice, states such as Kansas and Missouri have developed clear articulation or transfer agreements with junior college for a senior institution. Many junior college graduates enter four-year institutions as juniors with legitimate standing.

Continuous attendance at college or university is ideal for those pursuing a degree but it is not always possible. When attendance must be interrupted, many state universities provide cooperative extension programs and programs of continuing education for those who cannot attend classes full-time on campus. State higher education institutions also use sophisticated telecommunications systems to bring the university and its courses to the most outlying areas of the state.

The college years are, for many, a time to develop relationships which will provide a source of friendships and professional contacts for a lifetime. Attending college in one's home state increases opportunities to establish such long-lasting relationships and to be woven more fully into the fabric of state life.

Young people are increasingly aware of significant roles they will play in the social, political and economic life of this country. A college education in the state in which they are most likely to live can provide students with early involvement in the complexities of state activity. Increasingly, states are encouraging participation by student government groups in legislative activities. Some states, including Kansas, have authorized the appointment of a Student Advisory Committee to the Board of Regents, thus ensuring direct student participation in the decision making process.

State universities have long been known for athletic as well as academic excellence, and this continues to be true. On many campuses, intramural sports along with intercollegiate sports, enable large numbers of students to develop athletic prowess. As early responders to the growing need for quality in women's athletics, state universities provide equal opportunity in such sports as basketball, volleyball, swimming and tennis. Large multipurpose buildings springing up on many campuses indicate a dedication of state institutions to physical development and the cultural development of both campus and community. In some areas, the state college campus is the site of important cultural events, bringing lecturers, exhibits and the performing arts to an entire region. Attention must be given to the academic interest, the scholastic ability and the social and emotional maturity of the student as well as to the range of curricula, quality of instruction and extracurricular activities of the institution. A close examination of state university systems in the United States will indicate that there is virtually around every corner a quality institution of higher education solidly grounded in academics and attuned to the social and cultural needs of both students and community. State colleges and universities are a vital link in the network of public educational services and as such, merit serious consideration by the college bound.

Stanley Z. Koplik is Executive Officer of the Kansas Board of Regents, the governing body of public higher education in Kansas. Prior to assuming his current duties, Koplik served as Commissioner of Higher Education for the State of Missouri, where he directed activities of the Coordinating Board for Higher Education.

Advantages of a women's college

By Dr. Julia McNamara

Women's colleges are alive and well, even in 1982's all-too-realistic environment which predicts financial aid cuts, decreasing numbers of traditional college-age students, and a tight job market. Today, the mission and goals of 117 women's colleges in the United States matches neatly and clearly those of thousands of young women precisely because of these realities which they must face.

Women's colleges affirm and strengthen a woman's talent and ability; they exist specifically to develop the potential of their students; they demand and expect student participation and involvement. Women's colleges implant in women an attitude that is invaluable for success and achievement: "I can accomplish this task *and* I am a woman," not "even though" or "because" one is a woman. Rather the emphasis is on the fact that being a woman *and* accomplishing the task are quite compatible. Women's colleges instill in students the attitude that there is no sex-based limit to their potential for success. "I've lost that 'If-you're-a-woman-maybe-you-can't' attitude," said a 1982 women's college graduate who was also a student governor.

At a women's college, women learn that they can handle things because they have to handle them. They run the show; they exert influence; they wield power in student organizations which are exclusively their own. No one ever tells them that a particular leadership role is inappropriate for a woman. They can become properly aggressive and assertive without fear of seeming unattractive to men.

They learn to compete intellectually in an environment that consciously prepares them to realize that, if they seek it, the opportunity is there to excel. Their femininity will not be a deterrent at a women's college. Thus, women in leadership roles are not conspicuous at a women's college. Theirs is the only leadership that will occur, and they become comfortable with it. Women have to be in front of and behind all campus activities and events through which they learn to expect the best of themselves and of one another.

One woman, slightly overwhelmed by the extent of her responsibilities as student government treasurer, a task which involved budgets and planning, told me that she learned more from that experience than from some of her accounting classes, because she had final responsibility, and she had to make hard and unpopular decisions. She also said that her shyness and timidity would, in another setting, have prevented her from running for that office. "I would have thought some sharp guy could do it better."

When considering a women's college, it is important to understand several facts: First, women's colleges are not havens for people who could not survive elsewhere. Challenges and difficulties are just as much a part of this educational scene as any other, but there is emphasis on assisting women to meet the challenges which are special to them. Second, traditional views of women's colleges as protective shelters for innocent girls just do not pertain in 1982. Women's colleges are usually exciting places where learning and living mesh to create a viable educational and human experience. Third, women's colleges are not islands or ivory towers which exist by themselves, tiny spheres of influence which no other form of life can touch. Today, women's colleges often share facilities, faculty, and activities with neighboring schools so that students do participate in other educational environments. Thus, women's colleges can and do enjoy the benefits of co-education while maintaining their basic identity. This identity distinguishes her college and gives the young woman a chance to

become a competitor, an achiever, a doer in an environment that is specifically concerned with her own development as a woman.

If women's colleges do not apologize for their *raison d'etre* of being for and about women's education, neither do they ignore men. Quite the contrary: women at a college for women, know well that this environment is only a temporary one, a step on the way to fuller participation in the human, common endeavor. If the college does its job well, the woman will realize that this environment prepares her for the next move and, indeed, sets the pace for it.

"You probably won't find your husband at a women's college," said one admissions counselor to a roomful of high school juniors, "but you will find out a lot about yourself, and about the kind of man you may want to marry." In considering a college, a woman needs to be clear about the reason for attendance at *any* college. Social life and experience are part of the rationale, but her intellectual development, the best and most comprehensive of which she is capable, is the key factor. To honor a woman's desire for quality education and self-development is the mission of a college which proclaims that it is *for* women.

Both academic and student services programs at women's colleges are consciously designed to achieve this mission. The opportunity to be leaders increases a student's self-awareness and inculcates a sense of feminine identity, preparing women for participation in every area of endeavor. No matter how secure or talented they are, young women do need affirmation and assistance in developing self-confidence. For example, two young women on my campus participated recently in the management of a political campaign. They were hired as business manager and associate to the candidate who was a woman. Because of specific communication skills that they had learned while working in a college office where the woman supervisor constantly exemplified a serious professional relationship with them, they succeeded admirably in a tough task. Of course, such training could occur on any college campus, but the point is that on a women's college campus specific efforts to develop a young woman's potential are a priority in all aspects of campus life from residence hall to classroom.

At women's colleges, career development offices train women for the competitive environment of the job market. Internship programs established in cooperation with local business and professional offices give students initial experience in administration or management or one of the professions, and provides a bridge between the world of academe and the business scene. When academic credit is linked with direct work experience a student's incentive increases; so does her personal satisfaction. And before she started out for the office, the student learned in a seminar room or through directed role-play what would be expected of her as a woman in the internship environment.

Faculties and administrative staffs at women's colleges are aware of their

responsibility to develop young women's awareness of problems which she may face because she is a woman in a particular environment. The realities of discrimination and sexual harassment, can be a shock for the individual who needs to learn to deal with them effectively and, above all, to move beyond them.

When considering a women's college, these are questions which an applicant may want to ask during interviews:

1. Do the college's representatives seem to value their institution's specific identity as a women's college?

2. Does the college offer career guidance and advice for women?

3. Does the college have an internship program for its women?

4. What rapport has this institution established with neighboring universities and colleges?

5. What do students there say about their experience at a women's college?

6. Does the social life there give them a chance to meet men?

Responses to such questions give the prospective student a clear picture of the institution's commitment to the specific and unique character of a women's college. Certainly, a women's college is not for every woman. But equally as certain is the fact that these colleges continue to be extremely advantageous to the women who choose them.

Note: For more information on women's colleges, see: "A Profile of Women's Colleges" Women's College Coalition, Suite 1003, 1725 K St. N.W. Washington, DC 20006.

Dr. Julia McNamara is President of Albertus Magnus College in New Haven, Connecticut where she is also adjunct assistant professor of French literature. Dr. McNamara has also served as Dean of Students at this women's college. As an undergraduate she attended two women's colleges, Marymount Manhattan in New York City and St. Mary of the Springs, now Ohio Dominican, Columbus, Ohio and holds a Master's degree from Middlebury College and a Ph.D. from Yale University. She has been a Fulbright scholar and has studied for two years in Paris.

Opportunities at independent research universities

By F. Gregory Campbell

The diversity in American higher education is one of the greatest glories of our culture. No where else in the world does a prospective student enjoy such a wide range of choice. Public or private, large or small, urban or rural, secular or religiously oriented — American universities and colleges vary so greatly that any student should be able to find an institution seemingly tailor-made for that individual.

The major independent research universities constitute an important segment of American higher education. Frequently, they are considered primarily graduate or professional centers, and it is true that many students would be well advised to spend their undergraduate years elsewhere. But those universities typically possess vital undergraduate colleges offering a highly stimulating intellectual and extracurricular environment. For the right kind of student there is no better place.

In academic circles, the independent research universities enjoy an extraordinary reputation. That image depends on the quality of the faculty, and research is normally the means by which a scholar is evaluated. No one has yet devised a reliable method of measuring, comparing, and publicizing good teachers across the country. Good researchers are easy to spot, however, for they publish their discoveries for their colleagues around the world to evaluate. The research universities boast outstanding faculties containing highly innovative scholars with world-wide reputations.

But do they — or can they — teach? In ideal circumstances, the answer is yes. A standard view is that teachers are best when they continue to discover knowledge in their respective fields of scholarship. Conversely, the challenge of sharing their discoveries with critical young minds makes researchers better as a result of their also being teachers. Clearly, this ideal is not always realized. No university can guarantee that its most recent Nobel-prize winner will be teaching freshman chemistry, but such does happen.

The hope of learning from such scholars lures top-notch students to the research universities. Indeed, those institutions would have to do very little in order to produce outstanding graduates. Most college students quickly discover that they learn as much, or more, from their fellow students as from their professors. In as much as the research universities serve as a meeting point for many bright young people, much of the intellectual stimulation on the campuses is provided by the students themselves. Compatibility with others who take their studies seriously is an essential prerequisite for prospective students.

But college life cannot be all work and pressure. There have been persistent efforts over the past fifteen years or so to reduce intellectual competition among students. Professorial complaints about "grade inflation" reflect the fact that it is much easier for a student to stay in the universities than to get into them to begin with. The dropout rate is low, the failure rate even lower.

The learning experience extends beyond classrooms, libraries, and laboratories, and cannot be measured by grades alone. Extracurricular opportunities for learning and growth are central to a college experience. Most of the independent research universities seek to encourage informal association between professors and students. Professors may be encouraged to eat meals regularly with students in the dining halls. Leaders in public affairs or the arts and sciences may be invited to the campuses in order to engage in informal meetings with students. How does one measure the worth to a pre-law student of a breakfast conversation with a Supreme Court justice?

The independent research universities almost never appear on the list of major NCAA powers in football or basketball. Their teams normally compete at a lower level. But their programs do offer opportunities to participate in intercollegiate athletics to many young men and women who could not make the teams of the major powers. In addition, the intramural programs typically attract the vast majority of students on campus. The schools do not figure prominently in the sports pages, but the student communities are active and vigorous.

The undergraduate colleges within the independent research universities are normally quite small. Whereas they enroll more students than a typical liberal arts college, they have many fewer students than the state universities. That size both provides a critical mass for a wide variety of activities and allows for a sense of community and personal identity in a manageable environment.

The student bodies themselves are quite diverse. Admissions officers try hard to insure a nationally representative student body — including students from various regions of the country, diverse ethnic groups, and economic levels. There is also a significant number of foreign students. This intimate exposure to differences among people is a key element in the growth to adulthood.

The kind of education that is offered in the independent research universities is expensive, and tuition levels are high. Yet, since the 1960's, those institutions have tried to provide sufficient amounts of aid to enable students to matriculate regardless of financial need. It is an open question whether that policy can be maintained, even formally, in a more difficult economic environment.

The concept of a "University College" is the most apt way of thinking about undergraduate programs in an independent research university. Students find a relatively small college with a distinct identity of its own. Yet that college lives within a much larger institution possessing resources available for undergraduates to exploit. Those "University Colleges" are not appropriate for everyone, and there are many other excellent institutions from which to choose. But, when the match is right, a "University College" can offer gifted and serious young people opportunities seldom found elsewhere.

F. Gregory Campbell is Secretary of the Board of Trustees and Special Assistant to the President at The University of Chicago. He is a historian specializing in the history of international relations and Central and Eastern European history. In addition to administrative duties, he teaches in the college and the Graduate Divisions at Chicago.

Choosing the right college major

By James E. Moore

Implicit in this analysis is the assumption that there are some important decisions to make before choosing a major. A brief look at these is in order. First is the decision to enroll in a college or university. There is much rewarding and lucrative work in the world which does not require a college education. Furthermore, a wealth of adult programs have sprung up in the last decade, making the college education readily available later on to those who for a variety of reasons do not attend on a full-time basis immediately after high school. While there is immense peer and parental pressure in favor of college directly after grade twelve, there are many fascinating people who can attest to the value of travel or work after twelve years of formal schooling; these experiences shape and enrich the college experience when it is finally pursued.

Once the decision to go to college is made, one must choose the right college in order to be able to choose the right major. Not all schools teach everything, nor do they all teach as well as one another in a particular area. Obviously, the school should offer a program in what is the applicant's current major interest. Then, with some agressive questioning of students, faculty, and admissions personnel, the applicant can get a sense of how well the school does in that area and what, if any, particular perspective on the discipline is represented by that department.

The choosing of the major — in educational parlance, it is called "declaring the major" — is something which usually occurs toward the end of the sophomore year. While colleges and universities are interested in knowing what a prospective student intends to study and generally solicit that information on the application, that designation is neither binding nor necessary. Admissions officers and academic advisors are understanding of the many freshmen who simply do not know in what field they will concentrate, and it is not uncommon for a person to change directions a number of times during the first two years of college. It is, however, difficult to change majors as a junior or senior and still complete degree requirements in four years.

How does one determine what should be the major area of interest? A critical look at the high school record and aptitude and preference tests is a good way to start. What were the courses that proved exciting? In what did the student excel? Are the verbal or the quantitative skills more highly developed? The Kuder Preference Test asks the taker to respond to a variety of hypothetical situations and, by patterns that emerge from the responses, is a decent indicator of the general kind of work that will be congruent with the sense of self and others that is reflected in a person's answers.

Most colleges and universities require all students to complete course work in a variety of broad areas regardless of the intended major. This work commences during the freshman year and can be a useful way to further define the primary interest. Colleges offer courses in subjects that most high schools cannot or do not. In the process of meeting course requirements in the humanities, social sciences, and natural sciences or math, students expose themselves to new disciplines, one of which might well become the major.

In recent years, along with curricular development, there has been much interest and innovation in the issue of modes of learning. While the conventional classroom-lecture-textbook-test method of teaching and learning remains prevalent, the opportunity of "learning by doing" has become a widespread option. Some high schools offer their seniors the opportunity to do volunteer work for a variety of agencies, businesses, and charities. This work often evolves into summer employment for high school students. At the college level, the programs are more comprehensive, often involving both college credit and remuneration. Internships and cooperative education placements are an excellent way for students to discover exactly what a particular workplace is like and to determine just how suitable their preparation for that career is.

In addition to faculty, libraries, and laboratories, one of the most important resources for the undergraduate is the student who lives two doors down the hall. He or she probably studies in an area far removed from one's own or comes to the same interests for entirely different reasons. That person has parents who may well have had professional experiences and can share a sense of that professionalism from a perspective more personal than one that is offered in the classroom. The "bull session" is both misnamed and underestimated; these hours of informal exchange are often fundamental in shaping the direction and quality of life for many college students.

These are times when choosing the right major entails a gamble, regardless of how one sees it. The numbers of options are mind-boggling. The lack of certainty about the usefulness of a particular degree is a reality which should not be ignored, given rapid and constant change in the nature and needs of the workplace. Perhaps more than ever there is a case to be made for seeing the undergraduate years as ones for refining skills in reading, writing, and reasoning well, whichever department serves as the context for such endeavors. The risks are substantially reduced if the student is realistic about his or her capabilities and commitments, and thorough in exposure to the wealth of opportunity and resources colleges and universities offer. Above all, choosing the right major is cast in an appropriate light when seen as but one milestone of many in the process of learning, a venture which lasts a lifetime.

Jim Moore is an Admissions Officer at The American University in Washington, DC and previously worked in admissions at Aurora College, Aurora, Illinois; Goddard College, Plainfield, Vermont; and The New England Graduate Center of Antioch College, Keene, New Hampshire.

A yearn to earn

By Lawrence B. Durham

Throughout the 1970's much was made over the fact that the earnings differential between those with college degrees and those with only high school diplomas had shrunk. Many sought to interpret this statistical fact as evidence of the lessened worth of a college education. In the latter part of the decade, spiraling inflation and unemployment rates combined to produce a generation of college-bound young people more dedicated than ever to securing degrees which would assure them of employment upon graduation.

High school graduates of the early 1980's have thus been conditioned towards a very pragmatic view of the value of a college education. Yet, while post-college employment should be enhanced by this credentialing process, there is a real danger of overlooking the far more important and life-spanning aspects of the collegiate experience.

Indeed, many college faculties have contributed to this trend since the Russians launched their first Sputnik in 1957. Now, increasing numbers of these unwitting advocates of vocationalism are breathing fresh life into time-proven concepts such as core curricula and general education programs. Thus, the student entering college in the early 1980's faces the perplexing efforts of college faculties and our national economy as both seek to regain lost equilibrium through seemingly contradictory means.

In order to plot a realistic and rewarding course through the uncharted waters of higher education in this decade, students should be careful to expect neither too much nor too little from their collegiate experience. In an era where many college graduates may have to accept employment in jobs which had typically been filled by persons without degrees, certainly one would be unwise to expect a guaranteed position upon graduation. On the other hand, the rate of change in our society and in technological development is so rapid that a significant portion of the jobs in the next decade are non-existent at the present time. Consequently, one must seek to attain preparation for the unknown.

Education at its best results in the participant learning *how to learn* and *how to cope with change*. Given these two skills, the future can be faced with confidence. "Educational experiences" not producing these skills would better be labeled "training." And, it is crucial to note that such skills cannot be *taught*, they must be *learned*. As a result, the burden is on the student, not the teacher!

How then should one pursue such lofty goals? First, and foremost, there should be a commitment made to be an active participant in the educational process rather than to be satisfied as a passive subject. Then, a process of exploration should ensue during which the fear of the unknown is overcome by the excitement of discovery. In short, courage will lead to adventure!

Perhaps it would be useful at this point to emphasize the scope of these considerations. During the course of a life's work, a person may well change jobs eight to ten times. While several jobs may be in the same field, such as engineering, others may be in another field altogether, such as education. Generally, the different jobs are referred to as vocations, while the different fields are spoken of as careers. Thus an engineer might have several jobs within the field of engineering and then change careers to education where his vocation might be teaching in a particular college. In today's world and even more so in the future, students can ill afford to prepare for only a single career, let alone for a single vocation!

In this context, this author submits that the academic debate between specialized curricula and liberal arts programs is little more than a semantic exercise if the importance of developing both useful skills and broad perspectives is recognized. Just as an engineering program can include courses in the humanities, so can a liberal arts program include basic business courses. Studies continue to show that those who communicate effectively (orally as well as in writing), reason analytically, work well with others, and understand basic business principles find their respective pursuits far more rewarding.

A word of caution is in order, too, lest the reader fail to acknowledge consciously that the most important "rewards" are not financial. Over the years, studies of worker attitudes and values have increasingly revealed that pay ranks below other aspects of work such as the nature of the job environment the degree of individual autonomy, and the self-esteem derived from performing the work. Therefore, students should be careful not to choose a career path for purely financial reasons.

The process of choosing a course of study is no mean feat! Unless one has a burning desire to qualify for a particular profession, it is quite likely that several fields are of interest. Naturally, in the former case, the student would follow that academic track leading to certification in the chosen field. However, even in such cases, sampling courses in other fields and apprenticeships in the field of primary interest will often pay unexpected dividends. A person who is undecided should not develop an inferiority complex and go through senior high school and college apologizing! Rather, that individual should seek counsel and work experiences in areas of interest and engage in a sound, broadly-based course of study up to the point where declaration of a major field is required.

As of this writing, energy and computer science head the list of promising fields with other engineering and business areas and health services close behind. As we become more and more dependent on information exchange, related vocations in that field will increase in their attractiveness. And who knows where we are headed in the fields of microelectronics and genetic engineering. Yet, the reader who selected a course of collegiate study based solely on this or any similar listing would have missed the real point of this article. The true value of a college education cannot be quantified. To the contrary, its qualitative dimensions transcend the relatively narrow considerations of vocation and career to affect our entire lives.

Yearn to learn and you will learn to live. Live to learn and you will learn to earn.

Dr. Lawrence B. Durham is Dean of Admission Services, The University of Alabama. He holds memberships in many associations including the American, Southeastern and Alabama Associations of Collegiate Registrars and Admissions Officers. He has published numerous articles in the field of education.

The two-year experience

By Dr. Jacob C. Martinson, Jr.

It is a difficult adjustment for a student to go from a high school, sometimes a small high school at that, directly into a multi-complex university often with thousands and thousands of other students. Are the majority of high school graduates equipped for this kind of transition? The answer, of course, is that some are, and some are not. There is an alternative approach.

There is a wide range of academic programs available among two-year colleges today. There are many accredited institutions which offer outstanding two-year terminal programs in areas such as business arts, computer science, and medical arts. This article, however, will focus on the two-year colleges that are designed to prepare the students for continuation at a four-year college or university. It will address the belief that, in many cases, the pursuit of the baccalaureate degree is greatly enhanced by "The Two-Year Experience."

When it comes to the role of a college

education in career performance, an academically recognized two-year college can provide the essential foundations of undergraduate training often better than the best universities. After all, it doesn't take an expert to see that faculty qualifications are not that different from one center of learning to another. For example, a survey of the educational credentials of faculty members at good two-year colleges reveals that they have received their graduate training at the finest colleges and universities in the country.

The advantages of getting a good start at a two-year college are numerous. I will cite some reasons why a two-year college program should be considered.

1. Access to the Faculty

A faculty member ordinarily does not choose to teach at a two-year college unless he/she is specifically dedicated to teaching. Those faculty members who are interested in publishing or research usually go to the multi-complex universities where much of their undergraduate teaching responsibilities are delegated to graduate assistants. Classes in two-year colleges are generally taught by first-line faculty members.

Students have a right to expect some time with their professors who have spent many hours embodying much of the knowledge in which the students are interested. In the smaller two-year colleges, the opportunity is provided to know professors on a one-to-one basis. It is not uncommon to observe ballgames between faculty and students, or for faculty to invite students to their homes for refreshments.

2. A Good Beginning

The first two years of college are probably the most important of a student's college career. With the exception of kindergarten and first grade, they are all-important to the pursuance of formal education. Statistics show that when a student does well in an academically sound two-year college, he/she seldom does poorly academically anywhere else. A good start can make the difference.

3. Budget Appropriations

Many multi-complex universities give the "lion's share" of the funds to the upper-level undergraduate courses and to the graduate programs. Two-year colleges, on the other hand, give their entire budget to those critical first two undergraduate years.

4. Less Expense to the Student

One can attend a fine two-year college with a superb academic reputation for less than one can attend most universities. The community colleges are less expensive to the student, but even the private residential two-year colleges are relatively inexpensive. Of course, if commuting is possible, the expense is even less. Since the private college also wants to serve the surrounding community, special scholarships to commuting area residents are offered by some colleges.

5. Opportunities for Leadership and Participation

The freshmen and sophomores at a two-year college will have no juniors and seniors to compete with in extra-

curricular activites for campus leadership roles, team sport participation, and faculty time. The individual has an opportunity to become involved more quickly and more deeply in the total life of the college. Where else could a student be a representative to the college committees and the Board of Trustees at the age of 18? In short, there is no "sophomore slump" in the two-year college.

6. Vocational Future

The two-year college can enrich one's vocational future. The fact is that too many college graduates today are ignorant of the English language, history, science, and math. Many are deficient in their ability to get along with others and in that all-important skill of communication. One need only watch a nationally televised athletic event to observe the inability of some students from the so-called "prestigious" centers of learning to speak proper English. This is not to imply that the two-year college student will consistently perform any better; however, at good two-year colleges, there is a concerted effort to start wherever a student is academically and teach him/her to read and write effectively. For example, some of the better two-year colleges have three or four different levels of beginning English. The same is true of math. These schools place great emphasis on English and math with the conviction that if one can read and write and add and subtract, one has the educational foundation to function in the world. The hallmark of the best two-year colleges is that of toughness with caring. Such colleges encourage the formulation of long-range educational goals and positive views on how education can assist one in meeting vocational objectives. Obviously, there are some limitations to the depth to which one can pursue objectives in a two-year setting, but the seeds are planted and the incentives aroused.

7. The Best of Both Worlds

A student can have the best of the two-year and the four-year educational systems. During those critical first two years of college, a fine two-year school can provide an excellent academic program and curriculum, caring faculty members, and a concerned college community, all of which prepare the student to transfer to the larger college or university.

There are those in educational circles who would have one believe that transferring is dangerous to one's educational future. In most cases this belief is unfounded. On the contrary, it is sometimes easier to get into the best four-year schools after a two-year Associate of Arts/Science/Fine Arts degree than to apply right out of high school. Academic credits from a good, academically sound, two-year college are accepted by most of the finest universities. In fact, transfer students are not only accepted, they are actively recruited because of the natural attrition in the senior colleges and universities after the first and second years. Also, some students perform better in a two-year college than they did in high school; therefore, these students are more likely to have their application accepted when they leave the two-year college than when they graduated from high school. Further, there are certain rights and responsibilities which are uniquely applicable to the transferring student. A statement of these rights and responsibilities has been approved by the NACAC (National Association of College Admissions Counselors) in 1980 and revised in 1982.

In conclusion, today's two-year college generally offers a university-parallel curriculum. It is nearly always designed for the brilliant as well as the average student. The task is to successfully meet and challenge each student where he/she is academically despite varying aptitudes, dispositions, and outlooks.

The two-year college experience is not for everyone, but it certainly fills a need. It is a good place to start in higher educational pursuits — a good place to begin on the way toward the baccalaureate degree.

Jake Martinson is President of Brevard College, Brevard, North Carolina. Before going to Brevard in 1976, he was President of Andrew College in Cuthbert, Georgia. Dr. Martinson holds degrees from Huntingdon College, Duke University, and Vanderbilt University. Beyond serving Brevard College, he has been President of the Brevard Chamber of Commerce and Secretary of the Independent College Fund of North Carolina and is an elected Board member of the National Association of Schools and Colleges of the United Methodist Church. Born of Norwegian-American lineage, he is an honorary member of the American-Scandinavian Foundation.

The value of a liberal arts education

By Dr. David Maxwell

We are in the midst of a crisis that threatens the very fabric of higher education in America today, and that endangers the quality of education that we all desire for our children. The crisis centers on the relationship between undergraduate education and the so-called "real world": What are we preparing our students for? The resolution of this crisis has serious implications for the undergraduate curriculum, for the nature of the demands placed on our students by the institutions, by their parents and by themselves — and profound consequences for the continuing health and vitality of our nation.

A liberal education has always been measured in terms of its relevance to society's needs, and there is no reason that it should not continue to be; the notion of utility is firmly ingrained in our national character. The crisis to which I refer lies in the determination of precisely what those needs are, for it is in those "needs" that we express the relationship between education and the "real world."

I have witnessed a trend in American

College students that I find particularly disturbing. An increasingly large number of students are demanding what they term "relevance" in their studies. Clearly, I feel that liberal education has profound relevance to the "real world," but these students have a definition of that term that is different from mine. By "relevance," they often mean professional training; training not for the future, but for jobs. With an entirely justifiable concern for their future economic well-being, they are making — I am afraid — a terrible and potentially devastating error of logic.

Although few of our students would accept the state of our "reality" as ideal, many are allowing the priorities of that reality — as expressed in economic terms — to dictate the priorities of their education. They are mistaking financial reward, prestige, and excitement for genuine intellectual interest. Many, I fear, view the undergraduate experience as a "credentialling" process, rather than as an education that will make them productive, fulfilled adults. I am not suggesting that our students do have neither genuine intellectual curiosity nor the thirst for pure knowledge, for they have ample supplies of both. But they are subjected to enormous pressures from the outside: the fear that the field in which they are truly interested will not provide them with a comfortable income; the fear that their parents (often professionals themselves) will not approve of their interests; the fear that their ambitions are not sufficiently "prestigious" in the eyes of their peers. These are all very real fears and pressures that must be recognized as valid, but they have two important — and destructive — consequences. It is my sense that many of our students go on to careers in the so-called "professions" with very little idea of what these professions entail and, what is worse, they have tailored their entire undergraduate education to fit what they feel is appropriate preparation for those professions.

We are engaging in the process of creating many unhappy adults as such students grow up to find that they have no real intellectual investment in the occupation toward which they have aspired since they were teenagers. Having focused their education at an early stage, with the mistaken impression that you have to major in economics to go into business, in political science to enter law school, or in biology to be a physician, they will be plagued with the gnawing feeling that they have missed something — but without knowing quite what it was that they have missed.

Furthermore, the misplaced emphasis on grades caused by the intense competition for professional schools discourages many students from their natural inclination to question, to challenge, to experiment, to take risks. Rather than risk the uncharted waters of their own ideas and their own imagination, many students choose the safe route of repeating what they've heard and read as they write their examinations and papers.

Clearly, it is our responsibility to find ways to encourage our students to follow their natural inclinations, to resist the pressures — we must make it clear to them that, as teachers, we will reward initiative, originality, and risk-taking. Perhaps most important is that we must convince them that it is precisely these skills that are the most "pre-professional," that no business ever grew without developing original ideas, that every physician must take calculated risks daily, and that the practice of law rests on the principle of challenge to ideas.

Most people with professional aspirations hope to advance beyond entry-level positions into managerial or executive roles; positions in which they can assume responsibility, control, and authority and positions in which they can implement their own visions. It is precisely these roles that demand breadth of education — not only in subject matter, but breadth in the range of personal and intellectual skills that the student acquires in his/her studies.

There is growing evidence that the "real world" is taking notice of the correlation between liberal arts skills at the professions. For the past twenty-nine years, AT&T has been conducting longitudinal studies of its managers, correlating field of undergraduate major to career advancement and managerial skills. The AT&T study showed clearly that those with non-technical majors (humanities and the social sciences) were "clearly superior in administrative and interpersonal skills." (Robert E. Beck, *The Liberal Arts Major in Bell System Management*, [Washington, D.C.: 1981], pp. 6, 8). Significantly, "Nearly half of the humanities and social science majors were considered to have potential for middle management, compared to only thirty-one percent of the business majors ..." (p. 12) Within eight years of employment, the average management level of humanities and social science majors was significantly higher than that of other groups. As the author of the Bell report states: "One overall conclusion from these data is that there is no need for liberal arts majors to lack confidence in approaching business careers." (p. 13) It is interesting to note that this affirmation of the professional value of a liberal education comes from the experience of one of the world's largest high-tech corporations!

I am not presenting this evidence to argue that those who genuinely love engineering and the sciences should not pursue them, for their love is the best reason to enter those fields. Rather, the evidence presents a powerful argument for those whose interests lie elsewhere to *follow* their interests without fearing that their skills and knowledge will not be needed.

Not long ago, I had a meeting with several people who work in admissions at the Harvard Business School. We discussed the criteria for evaluating applicants, and they stressed that the single most important criterion was academic excellence at a respected, selective institution. Certainly, a few courses in economics and a familiarity with mathematics were an advantage, but the field of undergraduate major was not significant. As do the law and medical schools, they stress breadth of excellence and potential ability as reflected in the quality of the student's educational experience. It is significant that at Harvard, like many of the nation's best business schools, ninety-seven percent of their admitted applicants have had at least one year of full-time work experience before applying.

It should be clear from what I've said that liberal education *is* valued in certain segments of the "real world," and that there is often no correlation between choice of major and choice of career. Therefore we must encourage our students to spend their first year or more exploring, taking courses in a broad range of fields; courses in which they suspect they might be interested because of previous experience, courses in which they might be interested because they sound fascinating, courses in subjects that they know nothing about.

They should talk with their teachers, their advisors, their deans, their fellow students, with their parents, with other adults. In this process of exploration —if they are allowed to explore without pressure — they will find something in which they are genuinely fascinated. Pursuit of that fascination will lead them not only to sophisticated knowledge of a particular field, but to the development of intellectual and personal skills that will enable them to survive, happily and productively, as adults. The fascination will lead them to accept challenges, exercise their creativity, to take risks in the name of learning, to find out what they are good at and what to avoid, to be critical rather than accepting, and to be pathfinders rather than followers. It will also lead them, the evidence suggests, to a career that will allow them to use what they've learned in the broadest sense; one which they will find rewarding, interesting and challenging. To put it simply, they should decide *who* they want to be when they grow up, not just *what* they want to be.

David Maxwell has been the Dean of Undergraduate Studies at Tufts University since 1981. Formerly the Director of the Program in Russian at Tufts, he has been teaching Russian language and literature nearly fifteen years, and in 1979 was the recipient of the Lillian Leibner Award for Distinguished Teaching and Advising. A Fulbright Fellow in Moscow in 1970-71, Dean Maxwell is the author of numerous scholarly articles on Russian literature. He is active in a number of organizations concerned with liberal arts education, and is a charter member of the Council on Liberal Learning.

Preparing for a career in the arts

By Dr. William Banchs

Although the notion that there is no future in a career in the arts is still espoused by many, the number and quality of opportunities in the arts has dramatically increased in the past ten years. Many colleges and universities are responding to this trend, by greatly expanding their programs in the arts (dance, music, theater, visual arts and writing) for developing performers, creative artists, arts educators and arts administrators. In addition, there are many course offerings in the arts for those students less determined to pursue a career in the arts, but who also desire further training and experience.

Many young people are able to combine their artistic and academic skills in preparation for the demands of being an artist. A combination of skills is also necessary for careers in the management of artists or arts organizations.

If you are seriously considering further training and education in dance, music, theater, visual arts or writing, you should be aware of a program designed to assist young artists. The *Arts Recognition and Talent Search (ARTS)* program of the National Foundation for Advancement in the Arts is a national program to recognize and support excellence in the arts. Over 5,000 high school seniors from every state participate in ARTS every year.

Miami Dade Community College, Miami, Florida administers the selection process of ARTS for the Foundation. Applications received from aspiring young artists include a video tape of performances in dance and theater, an audio tape of solo music performance, a slide portfolio for visual artists and a portfolio of manuscripts by writers.

Each year, high school seniors with ability in the arts register for the ARTS program by these two dates: the regular registration deadline on May 15 (as a junior), and the late registration deadline on October 1 (as a senior).

The decisions of a panel of expert judges in each art field are made solely on the basis of the artistic content of the student's application packets. No other criteria, such as grades or academic standing, have any bearing on their decisions.

As a result of these evaluations, applicants are granted one of four award levels: Level I consisting of $3,000 Level II consisting of $1,500, Level III consisting of $500 and Honorable Mention which carries no cash award. In addition, through NFAA's Scholarship List Service, all applicants and award winners are recruited by leading colleges, universities and professional arts organizations and offered in excess of three million dollars in scholarships and internships.

The Foundation recommends their top artistic talent to the Presidential Scholars Commission each year and twenty are selected as Presidential Scholars in the Arts. These young artists are presented in concert at the John F. Kennedy Center for the Performing Arts and at an exhibit in a prominent art gallery in Washington, DC. In addition, all the Presidential Scholars are honored by the President of the United States at a ceremony in the White House. These events are all part of National Recognition Week which takes place in Washington, DC in June of every year.

If you aspire to a creative career, you need to be realistic about your talent, for that is what is most important in getting a job in the arts or establishing a reputation. Practical experience outside of the school environment — with local theaters, music and dance groups, galleries and community newspapers — can give you an extra edge. Even the most talented artists must be willing to spend years of their lives mastering their skills. It is never too early to develop that necessary dedication and commitment to your art.

Dr. William Banchs is the Programs Officer for the National Foundation for Advancement in the Arts.

Guide to guides for high-school students

Reprinted with permission from the "Chronicle of Higher Education."

The Best Buys in College Education, by Edward B. Fiske (Times Books; 393 pages). Mr. Fiske, the education editor of the New York *Times*, has published his *Selective Guide to Colleges* since 1982. This fall he released *Best Buys*, which lists 200 colleges — both public and private — that are identified as particularly good values. The institutions range from Pratt Institute ($10,088 tuition) to Cooper Union ($300).

Included are statistics (including admissions and financial-aid figures), and essays describing what Mr. Fiske calls "the academic and social climate" of the institutions.

The Insider's Guide to the Colleges, by the staff of the Yale *Daily News* (St. Martin's Press; 568 pages). "Obviously," the editors say in their preface, "it's impossible to capture the full scope and breadth of any institution in two or three pages of text." The editors of the Yale *Daily News* — and student correspondents on more than 150 campuses — offer readers, according to the book's cover, an account of "what . . . colleges are really like."

The brief descriptive sections tend to give colleges labels, provide a sweeping sense of the atmosphere, and describe campus social life. The book also provides an introduction to college "trends in the Eighties" and includes lists of colleges in categories such as "liberal arts colleges with an emphasis on pre-professionalism," and "colleges de-emphasizing varsity sports."

100 Top Colleges, by John McClintock (John Wiley & Sons, Inc.; 225 pages). In addition to its statistical descriptions of what it calls "America's best" institutions, *100 Top Colleges* suggests a systematic method for selecting a college. By answering a series of multiple-choice questions and plugging the answers into boxes, students may narrow their choice of institutions to conform to the qualities they value. "Choosing a college may never become a strictly scientific process," writes Mr. McClintock, "but it can be rational." The profiles of institutions rely heavily on statistics of all kinds, including ratings for "personal life," "mix of students," and "student motivation."

Rugg's Recommendations on the Colleges, by Frederick E. Rugg (Whitebrook Books; 65 pages). Mr. Rugg, a high-school guidance counselor, organizes his book by academic majors, from agriculture to zoology. In each section, the book recommends several colleges whose departments are felt to be among the best in the country. Within majors, the lists are divided into three categories: "most selective," "very selective," and "selective." Information about the colleges was obtained primarily through random interviews with students and others affiliated with institutions, according to the book.

"I even did weird things like interview the scorer and timer at the halftime of a basketball game at Williams College," Mr. Rugg writes. "We ended up discussing the classics department there (small, but good)." Mr. Rugg rates William's classics department among the best in the nation.

Lisa Birnbach's College Book, by Lisa Birnbach (Ballantine Books; 515 pages). Lake Forest College has the best salad bar of any College. The most promiscuous students are at Boston University. Connoisseurs of such information will find plenty of it in Ms. Birnbach's book, which describes student life at 186 colleges. "This is the inside scoop," writes Ms. Birnbach, "the juicy stuff you can only learn by visiting the campuses, by going to school there. This is the real thing." Entries place little emphasis on statistics and list such categories as "best professors," "gay situation," and "best thing about school."

The Public Ivys: A Guide to America's Best Public Undergraduate Colleges and Universities, by

Richard Moll (Viking; 289 pages) "Even the parents with ready cash are wondering if Olde Ivy is worth two or three times the price of a thoroughly respectable public institution," Mr. Moll writes. His book contains lengthy narrative and statistical descriptions of 17 public institutions he says are comparable to Ivy League universities. Mr. Moll chose the 17 based on admissions selectivity, "quality" of "undergraduate experience," institutions' financial resources, and prestige.

America's Lowest Cost Colleges, by Nicholas A. Ross (Freundlich Books; 253 pages). North Carolina residents will be delighted to learn that, according to Mr. Ross's book, 13 institutions in their state charge $150 or less for one year's tuition. Californians have more reason to celebrate: 36 colleges are identified here as charging $100.

"This book was written," Mr. Ross writes, "because too many parents have been forced to sacrifice for their children's education. . . . Worst of all, too many young people have decided not to go to college, because they think they can't afford it." The book includes brief descriptions of more than 700 colleges with annual tuitions of less than $1,500.

The College Handbook, 1985-86 (College Entrance Examination Board; 1,900 pages). The College Board's guide is filled with facts and figures that answer any basic question a prospective student might have about more than 3,000 institutions: number of students, a description of the location ("city," "small town," etc.), major fields of study, and special programs. It also gives a brief "class profile" and statistics on the number of applicants admitted from the most recent pool. The introduction offers students advice on how to choose a college.

Selective Guide to Colleges, by Edward B. Fiske (Times Books; 482 pages). "If you are wondering whether to consider a particular college," Mr. Fiske writes, "it is logical to seek out friends or acquaintances who go there and ask what it's like. What we have done is exactly this. . . ." Mr. Fiske has written brief, general descriptions of what the book calls "the 275 colleges you are most likely to consider." The descriptions tend to emphasize various components of student life, as well as the academic reputations of institutions. In addition to the narrative descriptions, Mr. Fiske rates three qualities — "Academics," "Social Life," and "Quality of Life," on a subjective one-to-five scale.

GENERAL CATALOGUES

Barron's Guide to the Two-Year Colleges (Barron's Educational Series, Inc.; volume one: 319 pages; volume two: 282 pages). The first volume of this two-volume set lists facilities, costs, programs and admissions requirements of more than 1,500 two-year institutions. Using charts, the second volume identifies institutions offering programs in five general categories: business and commerce; communications, media, and public services; health services; agricultural and environmental management; engineering and technologies. It also provides a separate list of institutions offering liberal-arts programs.

Barron's Profiles of American Colleges (Barron's Educational Series, Inc.; 1,151 pages). In addition to providing statistical information — including median S.A.T. scores, student-faculty ratio, and tuition costs — *Barron's* ranks each college on a scale from "most competitive" to "non-competitive." The book's introduction says the rankings are determined by a combination of the institution's rate of acceptance and the average high-school grade-point average and median S.A.T. scores of students who are accepted.

Comparative Guide to American Colleges, by James Cass and Max Birnbaum (Harper & Row; 706 pages). While it includes many of the statistical laundry lists of other fact-filled guides, Cass and Birnbaum's book also throws in an introductory paragraph giving a general description of each institution. Each entry also includes sections on "academic environment," "religious orientation," and "campus life" and information on the proportion of degrees conferred in various departments. Like *Barron's*, the book uses what it calls a "selectivity index," rating institutions with competitive admissions from "selective" to "among the most selective in the country."

Lovejoy's College Guide, edited by Charles Straughn and Barbarasue Lovejoy Straughn (Monarch Press; 604 pages). Listing more than 2,500 colleges and universities, *Lovejoy's* is concise and informative but offers less statistical material than do some of the other catalogues. Its decriptions are much briefer than those in most of the other guides, such as *Barron's* and Cass and Birnbaum.

Peterson's Competitive Colleges, Karen C. Hegener, editor (Peterson's Guides; 358 pages). In its fourth edition, it includes one-page profiles of 301 "selective" institutions — those whose students do well on standardized tests and which consistently have more applicants who meet entrance standards than are admitted. The book contains lists of the colleges and universities by cost, size, religious affiliation, and other factors. It also includes one-paragraph profiles of selective arts colleges and conservatories.

Peterson's Four-Year Colleges 1986, Andrea E. Lehman, editor (Peterson's Guides; 2,237 pages). In a volume larger than the Manhattan telephone directory, *Peterson's*, which is updated annually, provides general information about more than 3,000 institutions. It also includes a section of two-page "messages from the colleges," profiles provided by institutions that each pay $895 for the space. In addition, the book provides a chart with a state-by-state breakdown of colleges, listings of institutions organized by majors offered, difficulty of admission, and costs.

Lovejoy's Concise College Guide, edited by Charles Straughn and Barbarasue Lovejoy Straughn (Monarch Press; 375 pages). "The criteria used for the selection of the 370 institutions are varied to include the most diverse selection of schools for you to choose from," says the introduction. The book never explains those criteria, but the editors seem to have included the most selective institutions. The descriptions of the colleges are slightly abbreviated selections from the larger *Lovejoy's*, including information on enrollment, cost, academic majors, and student life.

SPECIALIZED GUIDES

Who Offers Part-Time Degree Programs? edited by Karen C. Hegener (Peterson's Guides; 417 pages). The listings include more than 2,500 institutions offering part-time undergraduate and graduate degree programs. The guide also includes separate directories of colleges with evening, summer, and weekend programs.

The Black Student's Guide to Colleges, edited by Barry Beckham (Beckham House Publishers; 495 pages). Mr. Beckham, a professor of English at Brown University, writes in his introduction that he wishes to provide information "in both objective and subjective terms" to help black students choose among colleges. Each campus profile is based on information supplied by the institution and by five of its students, whose individual statements are often noted. In narrative form, the book provides details on topics including race relations, support services, cultural opportunities, and black organizations.

Everywoman's Guide to Colleges and Universities, edited by Florence Howe, Suzanne Howard, and Mary Jo Boehm Strauss (Feminist Press; 512 pages). For each of the 600 colleges it evaluates, *Everywoman's Guide* provides a ranking — on a three-star scale — for each of several categories: "students," "faculty," "administrators," "women and the curriculum," and "women and athletics." An introduction notes that those are areas of "special importance." In narrative form, each entry provides additional material under such headings as "policies to ensure fairness to women," "women in leadership positions," and "special services and programs for women."

A Guide to Colleges for Learning Disabled Students, edited by Mary Ann Liscio (Academic Press, Inc.; 490 pages). In addition to some basic information about admissions requirements and tuition, each entry lists services for learning disabled students, "modifications to the traditional learning environment" (including such details as tape recorders provided to tape lectures, and "longer time to complete exams"), and a person on campus for learning-disabled students to contact.

Learning a new role

By Paul and Ann Krouse

Most literature directed to parents of college-bound students focuses on financial matters, an area of great interest and concern to most of us. Yet there are other roles besides bankrolls which require attention and involvement. Some are obvious and others more subtle. Having just completed the college admissions process with our

(Continued next column)

eldest daughter, my wife and I would like to share our experiences and views.

Be involved.

Selecting a college is just one more experience in the parenting process with the usual mixture of risks, rewards, joys, and uncertainties. You will find yourself pouring over directories, college catalogs, counselor recommendations, applications, and financial aid forms. The more you do together, the less tedious the tasks and the more enlightening the process becomes. We found ourselves engaged in a very productive cycle which started with counselor/student meetings. From this counselor-to-parent shuttle which was repeated several times over a period of a few weeks, our daughter developed a list of six or seven college choices. We visited several of her college choices on a 4-day car trip and ultimately she selected a college which happily accepted her. Waiting for the acceptance letter was agonizing, receiving it was joyous. The family celebration which followed was memorable.

Our experiences were undoubtedly quite common. The subtleties merit equal awareness.

Listen to your child.

Most of us have our own preferences of where we would like our children to go to school, but we've had our chance(s) and now it's their turn. Certainly your guidance, opinions, and views are important. You may have some inflexible requirements which your child must be responsive to such as financial limitations. Nevertheless, it is imperative that you listen to your child's preferences and to the best of your ability and with your best judgement encourage your child to fulfill his or her dreams, not yours.

Be patient and "tune-in."

The separation between child and family is beginning and it impacts on everyone involved in different ways and at different times. So much of the college admissions process requires that the children initiate action which will cause separation that there is frequently a reluctance to complete a task which can easily be misinterpreted as laziness or irresponsibility. An application may remain untouched, an essay delayed, a conference postponed. You must "tune-in" to your child's emotions and try to determine when he or she is being lax and when normal anxieties are rising to the surface, slowing down progress. Try to be patient, guide instead of push and acknowledge your mutual feelings instead of hiding them. The closer the family is, the more pronounced these experiences may be.

Respect your child's privacy.

Social gatherings will undoubtedly bring you into contact with other parents of college-bound students and the plans and experiences of your children will become timely topics of conversation. Sharing experiences with other parents can be mutually beneficial. But, revealing your child's exact SAT scores, GPA, class rank and similar information is an invasion of privacy. If your child wants to announce this information to friends, relatives or other parents, that's his or her business

and choice — not yours. Certainly you wouldn't want your child publicizing your income or other personal information to outsiders. Similarly, your child probably would prefer that some aspects of this process remain within the family. You will be amazed at what remarkably bad taste some parents exhibit in discussing their children's experiences.

Shop carefully.

As adults, you are undoubtedly a more experienced and sophisticated shopper than your child and your experience can be significant as your child shops for a college. Most colleges are very ethical and professional in their recruitment practices, but remember they are "selling." At college fairs, admissions officers can be persuasive which is not to their discredit. College catalogs can be slick and attractive which is also understandable and acceptable. But remember, most colleges are selling a package that can cost $5,000 to $15,000 per year or $20,000 to $60,000 over four years. They need from 100 to 10,000 new students each year to keep their doors open. That's not an indictment of their motives, but simply a representation of their realities. Read between the lines and beyond the pretty pictures. Don't hesitate to confer with your child's counselors about the choices and options available — counselors are generally objective and committed to serving the student, not a particular institution. When you visit campuses allow enough time to wander on your own *after* your formal tour, usually conducted by the admissions office. Walk into the library, dormitories, student union and even classrooms, if possible. Talk to students around the campus and observe as much as you can. Virtually all college admissions officials will encourage such "investigations" on your part since they don't want your child to make a mistake and stay for one year or less anymore than you do.

Naturally, each family's experiences will be a little different. The process is not very scientific yet, inspite of computerbanks, search services, video presentations, etc. Like looking for a house, there is more emotion in the process than some are ready to acknowledge. Nevertheless, as we look back, it was another enjoyable family experience where the rewards far outweigh the risks.

Paul and Ann Krouse are the publishers of WHO'S WHO AMONG AMERICAN HIGH SCHOOL STUDENTS and the parents of four delightful children. This article was written shortly after they completed the college selection/admissions process for the first time with their eldest daughter Amy who entered the freshman class at Tufts University, Medford, Massachusetts in the fall of 1983. WHEW!

THE EDUCATIONAL COMMUNICATIONS SCHOLARSHIP FOUNDATION®

During the 1986-87 academic year, approximately 20,000 students competed for scholarship awards sponsored by the Educational Communications Scholarship Foundation® which is funded by the publishing company. Students competed by completing an application which requested data regarding aptitude test scores, grade point average, extracurricular activities, work experience and general background information. Semifinalists were selected based on careful examination of all this information and were then requested to provide information regarding financial need. In addition, semifinalists were asked to write an essay from which the Scholarship Awards Committee attempted to evaluate the overall maturity of the students.

Sixty-six winners were selected and a total of $66,000 was awarded. Over $900,000 has been distributed through the Scholarship Foundation to date.

1986-87 SCHOLARSHIP WINNERS

Jennifer L. Anastasoff
Cape Elizabeth High School
Cape Elizabeth, ME
Georgetown University
Washington, DC

Robert S. Booker, III
Engineering & Science
Philadelphia, PA
M.I.T.
Cambridge, MA

Matthew E. Cunningham
Red Bank Catholic High School
West Allenhurst, NJ
Johns Hopkins University
Baltimore, MD

Jim Donahue
Marian High School
Osceola, IN
M.I.T.
Cambridge, MA

Miriam Aukerman
Westminster Senior High
Union Bridge, MD
Cornell University
Ithaca, NY

Cynthia F. Burnham
Incarnate Word High School
San Antonio, TX
Trinity University
San Antonio, TX

Robert L. Deal
Portal High School
Statesboro, GA
Georgia Institute of Technology
Atlanta, GA

Carrie Lyn Donigan
Iolani School
Makakilo, HI
Yale University
New Haven, CT

Kevin Berger
Adlai E. Stevenson
Livonia, MI
University of Michigan
Ann Arbor, MI

Eric G. Clary
Indian Springs High School
Tuscaloosa, AL
Vanderbilt University
Nashville, TN

Thomas Dinsenbacher
Saugus High School
Saugus, CA
Pomona College
Claremont, CA

David A. Edwards
Moreno Valley High School
Moreno Valley, CA
California Institute of Technology
Pasadena, CA

Rebecca Berkau
Texarkana High School
Texarkana, AR
David Lipscomb College
Nashville, TN

Heather A. Crum
John F. Kennedy High School
Richmond, CA
M.I.T.
Cambridge, MA

Laura M. Dobeck
Medford Senior High School
Medford, WI
Univ. of Wisconsin-Madison
Madison, WI

Michael Patrick Frank
Tyner High School
Chattanooga, TN
Stanford University
Stanford, CA

1986-87 SCHOLARSHIP WINNERS

Colleen Ann Fretz
Penn Yan Academy
Penn Yan, NY
State Univ. of NY at Buffalo
Buffalo, NY

Nicholas B. Harding
South Lakes High School
Reston, VA
Yale University
New Haven, CT

Kimberly L. Joyce
Granite City Senior High
Granite City, IL
Western Illinois University
Macomb, IL

David J. Levy
Baldwin Senior High School
Baldwin, NY
Brown University
Providence, RI

Derek L. Lundberg
Comm. H.S. District 99 South
Downers Grove, IL
University of Chicago
Chicago, IL

Alexia Leontyne Gordon
Oxon Hill High School
Clinton, MD
Vassar College
Poughkeepsie, NY

Dierk Hofreiter
Charles City High School
Charles City, IA
Iowa State University
Ames, IA

Theresa Klosterman
Clackamas High School
Milwaukie, OR
Stanford University
Stanford, CA

Ivy J. Livingston
The Episcopal Academy
Philadelphia, PA
Brown University
Providence, RI

Michael B. McFarland
Middleburg High
Middleburg, FL
University of Florida
Gainesville, FL

Tiffany A. Grine
Christiana High School
New Castle, DE
University of Delaware
Newark, DE

Nathaniel F. Hudson
John F. Kennedy Senior H.S.
Bloomington, MN
Yale University
New Haven, CT

Brian L. Kosobud
Red River High School
Grand Forks, ND
University of North Dakota
Grand Forks, ND

William F. Lombard, III
Rockdale County H.S.
Conyers, GA
Tulane University
New Orleans, LA

Gregory J. Mills
Borah High School
Boise, ID
College of Idaho
Caldwell, ID

Samer Hamadeh
Bullard High School
Fresno, CA
Stanford University
Stanford, CA

Suzanne C. Isham
Parkway Central H.S.
Oldsman, FL
University of Virginia
Charlottesville, VA

Michele La Fountain
Academia Perpetuo Socorro
Miramar, PR
Harvard University
Cambridge, MA

Jason S. Love
Taft High School
Lincoln City, OR
Oregon State University
Corvallis, OR

Kris J. Mitchener
South Salem High School
Salem, OR
Univ. of California-Berkeley
Berkeley, CA

Willis E. Hansen
Gladys Porter High School
Brownsville, TX
Princeton University
Princeton, NJ

Jennifer A. Jackson
Renaissance High School
Detroit, MI
M.I.T.
Cambridge, MA

Houghton Lee
George Washington H.S.
San Francisco, CA
Univ. of California-Berkeley
Berkeley, CA

Kristen L. Lukitsch
Franklin Regional H.S.
Murrysville, PA
Princeton University
Princeton, NJ

Vincent M. Monical
Pontiac Township High
Pontiac, IL
University of Illinois
Champaign, IL

1986-87 SCHOLARSHIP WINNERS

Kendra Nave
Maranacook Comm. School
Winthrop, ME
University of Pennsylvania
Philadelphia, PA

Christina O'Brien
Wayne Valley Senior H.S.
Wayne, NJ
University of Virginia
Charlottesville, VA

David H. Reiley, Jr.
Somerset Area High School
Somerset, PA
Princeton University
Princeton, NJ

Cynthia Spencer
Duchesne High School
Duchesne, UT
Brigham Young University
Provo, UT

Binh Truong
LA Schl for Math, Science, Arts
Shreveport, LA
LA State Univ.-Shreveport
Shreveport, LA

Jennifer Marie Neidenback
Thousand Oaks High School
Thousand Oaks, CA
University of Notre Dame
Notre Dame, IN

Tonia C. Poteat
N.C. Schl of Science & Math
Graham, NC
Yale University
New Haven, CT

Todd Renger
St. John High School
Swea City, IA
Yale University
New Haven, CT

Michael A. Stone
Burlington High School
Burlington, IA
Harvard University
Cambridge, MA

Jeffrey J. Watts
Fred J. Page High School
College Grove, TN
Auburn University
Auburn, AL

Deborah Newquist
St. Johnsbury Academy
St. Johnsbury, VT
Brown University
Providence, RI

Pratik Pradhan
George W. Hewlett High
Lynbrook, NY
Harvard University
Cambridge, MA

Stephanie C. Robinson
Steubenville High School
Steubenville, OH
University of Maryland
College Park, MD

Tracy Stone
Webster High School
Webster, NY
University of Rochester
Rochester, NY

Lee W. Webb IV
Central High School
Carrollton, GA
University of Georgia
Athens, GA

Ann Kim Ngo
Bellaire High
Houston, TX
Trinity College
Washington, DC

Keith E. Ramsdell
Galion High School
Galion, OH
University of Toledo
Toledo, OH

David C. Roper
Cascade High School
Everett, WA
University of Washington
Seattle, WA

Susan Marie Sunkin
St. Vincent-St. Mary
Akron, OH
Miami University
Oxford, OH

Albert J. Wong
Oak Ridge High School
Oak Ridge, TN
Princeton University
Princeton, NJ

Maithao T. Nguyen
Sharpstown Senior H.S.
Houston, TX
Univ. of Houston-Univ. Park
Houston, TX

Natalie J. Reed
Santa Ana High School
Santa Ana, CA
Univ. of California-Berkeley
Berkeley, CA

Paul K. Saint-Amour
The York School
Pacific Grove, CA
Yale University
New Haven, CT

Cuong-Dung Trong Do
Fountain Valley H.S.
Fountain Valley, CA
University of Miami
Coral Cables, FL

Christopher B. Yohn
Hannibal Senior High
Hannibal, MO
Northwestern University
Evanston, IL

GLOSSARY OF ABBREVIATIONS

Acpl Chr ....Acappella Choir
AFS ....American Field Service
Am Leg Boys St........ American Legion Boys State
Am Leg Aux Girls St ....American Legion
                            Auxiliary Girls State
Aud/Vis ....Audio-Visual
Awd...Award

Badmtn .... Badminton
Bsbl .... Baseball
Basktbl .... Basketball
Btty Crckr Awd .... Betty Crocker Award
Bus .... Business
Bwlng.................................. Bowling

C of C Awd........... Chamber of Commerce Award
Camp Fr Inc .... Camp Fire, Inc.
CAP................................ Civil Air Patrol
Capt.......................................Captain
Cit Awd .... Citizenship Award
Clb .... Club
Cmnty Wkr .... Community Worker
Coach Actv .... Coaching Activities
Crs Cntry .... Cross Country

DAR Awd................ Daughters of the American
                           Revolution Award
DECA ....Distributive Education Clubs of America
Dnfth Awd............Danforth (I Dare You) Award
Drm & Bgl .... Drum & Bugle Corps
Drm Mjr(t) ....Drum Major(ette)

Ed-Chief ....Editor-In-Chief

FBLA .... Future Business Leaders of America
FCA ....Fellowship of Christian Athletes
FFA ....Future Farmers of America
FHA.............. Future Homemakers of America
Fld Hcky ....Field Hockey
FNA .... Future Nurses of America
FTA .... Future Teachers of America
Ftbl .... Football

GAA...................... Girls Athletic Association
Gov Hon Prg Awd ....Governors Honor
                           Program Award
Gym.................................. Gymnastics

Hist .... Historian
Hon .... Honor
Hosp Aide........................... Hospital Aide

Ice Hcky .... Ice Hockey
Intnl Clb .... International Club

JA..............................Junior Achievement
JC Awd ....Jaycees Award
JCL .... Junior Classical League
JETS Awd .... Junior Engineering Technical
                           Society Award
JP Sousa Awd .... John Philip Sousa Award
Jr NHS.............. Junior National Honor Society
JV.................................. Junior Varsity

L ....Letter
Lcrss .... Lacross
Lion Award...................Lions Club Award
Lit Mag .... Literary Magazine

Mgr(s) .... Manager(s)
MMM .... Modern Music Masters
Mrchg Band....................... Marching Band

NCTE Awd .... National Council of Teachers
                          of English Award
NEDT Awd ...... National Educational Development
                          Test Award
NFL.................. National Forensic League
NHS...................... National Honor Society
Ntl ....National
Nwsp.....................................Newspaper

OEA .... Office Education Association
Opt Clb Awd .... Optimist Club Award
Orch .... Orchestra

PAVAS........Performing & Visual Arts Society
Phtg................................. Photographer
Pres .... President
Prfct Atten Awd ....Perfect Attendance Award

Rep.. Representative
Rptr .... Reporter
ROTC .... Reserve Officer Training Corps

S.A.D.D.	Students Against Driving Drunk	Trea	Treasurer
Sal	Salutatorian	Trk	Track
SAR Awd	Sons of the American Revolution Award	Twrlr	Twirler
Schol	Scholarship		
Sec	Secretary	V	Varsity
SF	Semifinalist	Val	Valedictorian
Sftbl	Softball	VICA	Vocational Industrial Clubs of America
Socr	Soccer	Vllybl	Volleyball
Sprt Ed	Sports Editor	Voice Dem Awd	Voice of Democracy Award
St Schlr	State Scholar	VP	Vice President
Stf	Staff		
Stu Cncl	Student Council		
Swmmng	Swimming	Wrstlng	Wrestling
Symp Band	Symphonic Band	Wt Lftg	Weight Lifting
Tm	Team		
Thesps	Thespians	Yrbk	Yearbook

Sample Biography

This sample is presented to familiarize the reader with the format of the biographical listings. Students are identified by name, school, home, city and state. In order to protect the privacy and integrity of all students, home addresses are not published.

KEY

1 Name
2 High School
3 Home, City and State
4 Year in School*
5 Class Rank (when given)
6 Accomplishments
7 Future Plans

* 1 = Freshman
   2 = Sophomore
   3 = Junior
   4 = Senior

1 Wolk, Sheffield L.; **2** Normandy Isle H.S.; **3** Miami, FL; **4** (4); **5** 10-350; **6** Pres Stu Cncl; VP Sr Cls; Ftbl; 4-H; NHS; Cit Awd; Am Leg Awd; **7** Harvard University; Biochemist

STUDENT BIOGRAPHIES

NEW JERSEY

AAGAARD, PATRICIA; Cranford HS; Cranford, NJ; (4); 30/267; Church Yth Grp; French Clb; Science Clb; Yrbk Stf; Hon Roll; Crnfrd-Prnt Tchr Cncl Schlrshp 87; Scl Stds Awd 87; FL Inst Tchnlgy; Blgly.

ABARAY, CHERYL; John F Kennedy Memorial HS; Avenel, NJ; (3); 16/249; Dance Clb; Girl Scts; Band; Concert Band; Mrchg Band; Pep Band; Rep Frsh Cls; VP Soph Cls; Rep Trs Jr Cls; Rep Stu Cncl; Vc Chrmn Woodbridge Bus Wmns Debtnt Ball 87; 4th Pl Cnty NJ ST Bar Assn Mock Trail Compttn 86; Music.

ABATE, HOLLY; Holmdel HS; Holmdel, NJ; (3); 3/209; Chess Clb; Trs Church Yth Grp; NFL; Acpl Chr; Band; Lit Mag; Var Capt Crs Cntry; Gov Hon Prg Awd; NHS; Spanish NHS; Hnr Rll, Hnrs Distctn; Gldn Poet Awd; ST Wnnr Miss Amercn Co Ed Pgnt; Princeton U; Elec Engrng.

ABBATE, LORRAINE; Paramus HS; Paramus, NJ; (2); Chorus; Italn Hnr Socty 87; Monclair ST Coll; Acctg.

ABBATTISTA, STEVEN; Paramus HS; Paramus, NJ; (3); Am Leg Boys St; Orch; Yrbk Sprt Ed; Var Capt Ftbl; Var Trk; Var Wrstlng; Hon Roll; NHS; Italian Ntl Hon Soc; Engr.

ABBEY, JASON; Sacred Heart HS; Davis, CA; (3); Aud/Vis; Cmnty Wkr; Science Clb; Ski Clb; Spanish Clb; Varsity Clb; Var L Bsbl; Var L Socr; Hon Roll; U Of CA; Vet Med.

ABBOTT, CINDY; Millville SR HS; Millville, NJ; (4); Aud/Vis; Camera Clb; Dance Clb; Latin Clb; Yrbk Stf; Pres Stu Cncl; Var Cheerleading; Gym; Tennis; High Hon Roll; SR Pres Pin Outstndng Pres Awd; Stu Cncl Clete Cannone Mem Schlrshp; Womns Clb Lit Schlrshp; Montclair ST Coll; Chorgrphr.

ABBOTT, EMILY; Holy Spirit HS; Ventnor, NJ; (4); 18/363; Pep Clb; SADD; Chorus; School Musical; Nwsp Rptr; JV Var Tennis; NHS; Garden ST Dist Schlr 86-87; Bus.

ABDELAL, MOHAMED Y; Marist HS; Jersey City, NJ; (3); Boy Scts; Chess Clb; Key Clb; Yrbk Stf; American U-Cairo; Arch.

ABDOU, TOMMY; Manalapan HS; Manalapan, NJ; (3); Computer Clb; NHS; Hnr Awd Acdmc Excllnc Socl Sci, Alg II 87.

ABEL, TODD; Lakewood HS; Lakewood, NJ; (3); 41/330; Boy Scts; Church Yth Grp; French Clb; Band; Tennis; French Hon Soc; Rutgers Schl Of Engrng.

ABELLO, ROSANNA; Hunterdon Central HS; Lebanon, NJ; (3); 240/543; Church Yth Grp; Dance Clb; Spanish Clb; Chorus; Concert Band; Orch; Swmmng; Trk; Hon Roll; NHS.

ABERE, DOUG; Montville HS; Montville, NJ; (2); FBLA; Var Bsktbl; Var Lcrss; Var Socr; Hon Roll; Rogate Tooh SAT 83; Lbrl Arts.

ABIKO, MEGUMI; Hillsborough HS; Belle Mead, NJ; (3); 90/328; Art Clb; Drama Clb; Service Clb; SADD; School Musical; School Play; Variety Show; JV Cheerleading; Hon Roll; Pervntn Using Stu Help Awd 86-87; Orthodntcs.

ABOULHOSN, NADA; Lenape Valley Regional HS; Netcong, NJ; (3); Key Clb; SADD; Nwsp Rptr; Ed Yrbk Stf; Lit Mag; Trs Soph Cls; Rep Jr Cls; Rep Sr Cls; Rep Stu Cncl; Hon Roll.

ABOYOUN, CHRISTINA; Wayne Valley HS; Wayne, NJ; (3); 68/285; FBLA; Ski Clb; Variety Show; Lit Mag; Rep Frsh Cls; Pres Soph Cls; Pres Jr Cls; Pres Sr Cls; Coach Actv; Mgr(s); Sccr Coachs Awd 84 86; Med.

ABRAHAM, JULIE M; Pascack Hills HS; Woodcliff Lake, NJ; (4); 2/240; Debate Tm; Hosp Aide; Nwsp Stf; Lit Mag; Rep Soph Cls; Rep Jr Cls; Var JV Cheerleading; NHS; Ntl Merit SF; SADD.

ABRAMO, TEDDY; Hudson Catholic HS; Hoboken, NJ; (4); 21/180; Am Leg Boys St; Dance Clb; Pres SADD; Var JV Bsktbl; Capt Var Bsktbl; Coach Actv; Vllybl; Hon Roll; Pres Schlr; Schlr Athlt Awd 87fde La Salle Svc Awd 87; Seton Hall U; Bus.

ABRAMS, HEATHER; Florence Twp Memorial HS; Roebling, NJ; (3); FBLA; Yrbk Ed-Chief; Stat Mgr(s); Accntng.

ABRAMS, JASON; Wood-Ridge HS; Wood Ridge, NJ; (3); 8/90; Art Clb; Church Yth Grp; Spanish Clb; Var Bsktbl; Var Socr; High Hon Roll; Hon Roll.

ABREU, MARITZA; Trenton Central HS; Trenton, NJ; (4); 8/500; Dance Clb; Hon Roll; Alumni Assoc Schlrshp Awd 87; Anonymous Schlrshp Awd 87; Latinos Unidos Club Bk Awd 87; Rutgers U; Bus Admin.

ABREU, ROSEMARY; South River HS; S River, NJ; (2); #1 In Class; Church Yth Grp; French Clb; Library Aide; Spanish Clb; High Hon Roll; Hon Roll.

ABREU, SANDRA; Hosoken HS; Hoboken, NJ; (3); French Clb; Library Aide; Office Aide; Spanish Clb; Teachers Aide; Yrbk Phtg; Yrbk Stf; Tennis; High Hon Roll; Hon Roll; High Aver Awd 84; Splng Bee 3rd Pl 84; Rutgers Coll; Psych.

ABRILLA, MELODY; Cedar Ridge HS; Matawan, NJ; (3); Church Yth Grp; Hosp Aide; Math Clb; Teachers Aide; Yrbk Stf; Lit Mag; Var Cheerleading; Hon Roll; Frnch Natl Compttn Awd 84; Golden Poet Awd 86; Psych.

ABRUTYN, ELISE; Montville Twp HS; Pine Brook, NJ; (3); 14/280; FBLA; Ski Clb; Varsity Clb; VP Frsh Cls; Rep Soph Cls; VP Jr Cls; JV Lcrss; Var Tennis; High Hon Roll; NHS; Gftd Tlntd.

ABRUZESE, JOSEPH; St Joseph Regional HS; Valley Cottage, NY; (3); 4/225; Aud/Vis; Boy Scts; Camera Clb; Math Tm; SADD; Rep Stu Cncl; Tennis; Hon Roll; NHS; Spanish NHS; MVP Frshmn Tennis 85; Bus.

ACACIA, JOE; Manalapan HS; Manalapan, NJ; (3); 29/429; JCL; Var Bsbl; NHS; Phys Thrpy.

ACCATATTA, ANNETTE; Hillsborough HS; Neshanic Station, NJ; (4); CAP; Drama Clb; Pep Clb; Ski Clb; Band; Concert Band; School Play; Stage Crew; Lit Mag; Powder Puff Ftbl; Miss Teen Am Cont 86; Kutztown U; Crmnl Jstc.

ACCILIEN, OLGA; Vailsburg HS; Newark, NJ; (3); Church Yth Grp; English Clb; French Clb; Intnl Clb; Variety Show; Sr Cls; Stu Cncl; Prfct Atten Awd; Boston U; Law.

ACEMYAN, ALICE; St Josephs Of The Palisades HS; Weehawken, NJ; (2); 1/125; DECA; Nwsp Rptr; Nwsp Stf; Pres Frsh Cls; Pres Soph Cls; Var Sftbl; Var Tennis; High Hon Roll; Modeling Clb 86-87; Princeton; Jrnlst.

ACKERMAN, JAN; Dover HS; Dover, NJ; (2); Cheerleading; Gym; Hon Roll; Concert Band; Yrbk Stf; Rep Soph Cls; High Hon Roll; Bio Awd 87; Vet.

ACKERMAN, MARC; Indian Hills HS; Oakland, NJ; (4); 60/280; Drama Clb; Jazz Band; Symp Band; Ed Nwsp Phtg; Nwsp Stf; Trs Soph Cls; Trs Jr Cls; Trs Sr Cls; Var Socr; NHS; WA & Lee U.

ACKERMAN, MICHAEL; Indian Hills HS; Franklin Lks, NJ; (4); #28 In Class; Temple Yth Grp; Yrbk Stf; Lit Mag; Off Frsh Cls; Off Soph Cls; Off Jr Cls; Off Sr Cls; Stu Cncl; Var Bsbl; High Hon Roll; U Of MD; Pre-Med.

ACKERMANN, ANDREA; Palisadea Park JR-SR HS; Palisades Pk, NJ; (3); JCL; Band; Nwsp Stf; Yrbk Stf; Rep Stu Cncl; Capt Crs Cntry; Capt Trk; Hon Roll; Jr NHS; NHS; Indoor Winter Trck Capt 86-88; Art.

ACKERMANN, ROLF; Hunterdon Central HS; Whitehouse Sta, NJ; (3); 118/552; Hon Roll; Intl Stds.

ACKERS, JARED; Southern Regional HS; N Beach, NJ; (3); 1/435; Aud/Vis; Camera Clb; Nwsp Phtg; Ed Yrbk Phtg; Socr; High Hon Roll; NHS; 3rd Pl Chem Stu-Monmouth Jr Sci Sympsm 86; Schlr-Athlt 85; Med.

ACOCELLA, MARY ANNE; Bloomfield SR HS; Bloomfield, NJ; (3); Church Yth Grp; Cmnty Wkr; Library Aide; Teachers Aide; Yrbk Stf; Rep Jr Cls; Stu Cncl; Hon Roll; Emplyd Library Pg Blmfld Publc Library 85; Educ.

ACOSTA, ALEC; Immaculate Conception HS; Orange, NJ; (4); 11/77; Art Clb; Chorus; Pres Soph Cls; Rep Stu Cncl; JV Var Bsktbl; Var L Ftbl; Var Trk; French Hon Soc; Hon Roll; NHS; Natl Hispanic Schlrs Awd Pgm Semi-Fnlst 86-87.

ACOSTA, ANNYA; Memorial HS; W New York, NJ; (4); 57/358; Church Choir; Color Guard; Rep Frsh Cls; Rep Soph Cls; Rep Jr Cls; Rep Sr Cls; Sftbl; Hon Roll; Bus.

ACOSTA, IRIS; Vineland HS; Vineland, NJ; (2); 270/838; Church Yth Grp; Cmnty Wkr; DECA; Spanish Clb; Nwsp Stf; Hon Roll; 7 Merit Rolls 85-87; Entrd Miss Amer Co-Ed Pgnt 86.

ACOSTA, MARLON; Essex Catholic Boys HS; North Newark, NJ; (3); Var Bsbl; Var Crs Cntry; Var Socr; Hon Roll; NYU; Pre-Dntstry.

ACTON, MARY; Salem HS; Salem, NJ; (3); Church Yth Grp; SADD; Teachers Aide; Band; Concert Band; Mrchg Band.

ADAJAR, GAY; Immaculate Conception HS; Secaucus, NJ; (2); 8/89; Civic Clb; Hosp Aide; Ski Clb; SADD; Stage Crew; Yrbk Stf; Rep Frsh Cls; Tennis; Hon Roll; Spanish NHS.

ADAM, RAYMOND; Wood-Ridge HS; Wood Ridge, NJ; (3); 20/90; Science Clb; JV Bsbl; Capt Bowling; Cit Awd; Hon Roll; Hgh Awds Bwlg Prfct Game HS Comp 87; Mech Engrng.

ADAMCHAK, SUE; Wayne Hills HS; Wayne, NJ; (4); 76/300; Church Yth Grp; Dance Clb; FBLA; GAA; Spanish Clb; Varsity Clb; Yrbk Stf; JV Socr; Var Vllybl; Hon Roll; Stu Athletic Assn Awd 87; Wilkes Coll; Sci.

ADAMCZYK, DIANE; Lyndhurst HS; Lyndhurst, NJ; (3); 26/174; Key Clb; Office Aide; Ski Clb; Trk; Vllybl; Frsh Numbrs Trk & Fld 84-85; JV Awd Vllybl 85-86; Vrsty Awd & Vrsty Jckt Vllybl 86-87; Acctg.

ADAMEC, JAMES; St John Vianney HS; Aberdeen, NJ; (3); 32/287; FBLA; Math Tm; SADD; Capt Ice Hcky; High Hon Roll; Hon Roll; Ntl Merit Ltr; Trenton ST; Elec Engrng.

ADAMES, ROCIO; New Brunswick HS; New Brunswick, NJ; (1); Church Yth Grp; Y-Teens; Band; Chorus; Hon Roll; Prfct Atten Awd; Pres Schlr; Achvt Awd 86-87; Pedtrcn.

ADAMS, DANINE; Vineland HS; Vineland, NJ; (3); 39/600; Sec Art Clb; French Clb; Color Guard; Drill Tm; Mrchg Band; Nwsp Phtg; Nwsp Sprt Ed; Nwsp Stf; Stat Bsktbl; Score Keeper.

ADAMS, DEBBIE; Rancocas Valley HS; Mt Holly, NJ; (2); Ski Clb; Sftbl; Twrlr; High Hon Roll.

ADAMS, DWAYNE; Lincoln HS; Jersey City, NJ; (2); DECA; FBLA; NAACP; JV Ftbl; Tennis; Natl Engl Merit Awd 85-87; Morehouse Coll; Bnkng.

ADAMS, JACKIE; Holy Spirit HS; Ocean City, NJ; (2); Church Yth Grp; Drama Clb; Hosp Aide; School Play; VP Frsh Cls; High Hon Roll; Hon Roll; 3 Schlrshps Theactrcl Art Schl 85-8; ST Fnlst Miss Amrcn Co Ed Pgnt 87; JR Miss Ocean Cty Brdwlk Qn; La Salle U; Bus Admin.

ADAMS, KATHLEEN JANE; Pennsgrove HS; Bridgeton, NJ; (4); 4/153; VP German Clb; Band; Concert Band; Yrbk Stf; VP Sr Cls; Var Tennis; Hon Roll; Sec NHS; Hugh O Brian Yth Ldrshp Ambsdr 85; Elzbth Coll; Ocptnl Thrpy.

ADAMS, LAUREN; Vernon Township HS; Glenwood, NJ; (3); Scholastic Bowl; Rep Frsh Cls; Rep Soph Cls; Sec Jr Cls; Cheerleading; Crs Cntry; Trk; Cit Awd; DAR Awd; NHS; Phys Ed.

ADAMS, LESLEY; Queen Of Peace HS; Lyndhurst, NJ; (3); 38/279; Art Clb; Church Yth Grp; Debate Tm; Ski Clb; Spanish Clb; SADD; Stage Crew; Stu Cncl; Bowling; Vllybl; U S Phy Fit Awd Signd By Reagan 86.

ADAMS, RACHEL; The Kings Christian HS; Pennsauken, NJ; (3); 1/41; Church Yth Grp; Ski Clb; Band; Sec Stu Cncl; Stat Bsbl; Var L Bsktbl; Var L Fld Hcky; Cit Awd; High Hon Roll; NHS; Amer Biogrphcl Inst; Wheaton Coll.

ADAMS, SUSAN; The Kings Christian HS; Pennsauken, NJ; (4); 1/23; Church Yth Grp; FCA; French Clb; GAA; Latin Clb; Letterman Clb; Ski Clb; Varsity Clb; Sec Soph Cls; Sec Jr Cls; All Strs Awd Fld Hcky & Bsktbll 84-86; ST NJ Schlrshp 86; Amrcn Biogrphcl Inst 86; Wheaton Coll; Acctg.

ADAMS, TOM; Toms River HS South; Beachwood, NJ; (2); Var Bsbl; JV Bsktbl; High Hon Roll; Hon Roll; CIBA-GEIGY Sci Awd 87; Amer Chem Soc Chem Awd 87; Acdmc Ltr 86.

ADAMSON, KRISTINE; St Rose HS; Pt Pleasant, NJ; (3); 13/226; Key Clb; Yrbk Rptr; Yrbk Stf; Mgr(s); Hon Roll; NEDT Awd.

ADDARI, LARRY; Burlington Township HS; Burlington, NJ; (4); 3/110; Am Leg Boys St; Pres Frsh Cls; Rep Soph Cls; Var Capt Bsbl; Var Capt Ftbl; Cit Awd; High Hon Roll; JETS Awd; Pres NHS; Pres Schlr; Lafayette Coll; Engrng.

ADDUCI, FABIO; Waldwick HS; Waldwick, NJ; (3); Boy Scts; Church Yth Grp; Office Aide; Varsity Clb; Rep Frsh Cls; Rep Soph Cls; Rep Jr Cls; Stu Cncl; JV Bsbl; Var Capt Socr; Bus Mngmnt.

ADELMAN, DOUG; Columbia HS; South Orange, NJ; (4); Model UN; Spanish Clb; Yrbk Phtg; JV Crs Cntry; Im Sftbl; Ntl Merit SF; St Schlr; Engrng.

ADINOLFE, BRIAN; Monsignor Donovan HS; Jackson, NJ; (3); Computer Clb; Spanish Clb; School Play; Score Keeper.

ADJOGA-OTU, NAA-MOMO; Weequahic HS; Newark, NJ; (4); 15/346; Debate Tm; Exploring; Quiz Bowl; Color Guard; Nwsp Ed-Chief; Nwsp Phtg; Nwsp Rptr; Nwsp Stf; Yrbk Ed-Chief; Yrbk Phtg; Dstnghsd Scty Of Amer Stu 86; Thms Edsn & Max Mcgraw Sci Cert 84; Rutgers U; Pre-Med.

ADJOGA-OTU, NII-ABLADEY; Arts HS; Newark, NJ; (3); Am Leg Boys St; Art Clb; Aud/Vis; Church Yth Grp; Exploring; Church Choir; Yrbk Sprt Ed; Yrbk Stf; Bsktbl; Trk; STEP Pre-Coll Dir Awd 87; STEP Pre-Coll Art Lab Awd 86; Fine Art.

ADLER, AMY; Buena Regional HS; Newfield, NJ; (4); 7/171; Tennis; Hon Roll; Jr NHS; NHS; Sec Church Yth Grp; Cmnty Wkr; Math Clb; Office Aide; Ski Clb; Spprtv Stf Schlrshp Awd 87; Pres Acadmc Ftns Awd 86-87; Phila Coll Txtls Sci; Chem.

ADLER, JENNIFER; Lakewood HS; Lakewood, NJ; (3); 110/360; Cmnty Wkr; Drama Clb; FBLA; Spanish Clb; School Musical; School Play; Stage Crew; Variety Show; Comm.

ADLER, SANDY; Manalapan HS; Manalapan, NJ; (3); Science Clb; Drill Tm; NHS.

ADLER, SCOTT; Westwood Regional HS; Washington Twp, NJ; (2); Art Clb; Boy Scts; French Clb; Varsity Clb; Var L Bsktbl; Ftbl; Var Trk; French Hon Soc; High Hon Roll; Jr NHS; Natl Art Hnr Scty 87.

ADRIANCE, LAURA A; Westfield HS; Westfield, NJ; (4); 9/484; Intnl Clb; Model UN; Latin Clb; Cit Awd; High Hon Roll; Hon Roll; NHS; Ntl Merit SF; Gov Schlr 86; Garden ST Distngshd Schlr 86; Pol Sci.

ADRIANZEN, CHARLES; Orange HS; Orange, NJ; (3); Boy Scts; Computer Clb; Rep Jr Cls; Rep Stu Cncl; High Hon Roll; Hon Roll; Urban Educ Project Basic Cert 84; NJ Inst Of Tech Comp Olympics 86; Engr.

ADRIANZEN, MARIO MARTIN; St Mary HS; Jersey City, NJ; (3); Art Clb; Yrbk Stf; Socr; Vllybl; Prfct Atten Awd; 1st & 2nd Hnr Stu 84-87; NY Inst Of Tech; Mech Engrng.

AFFSA, JENNIFER; Hillside HS; Hillside, NJ; (3); 2/233; Leo Clb; Math Tm; Sec Service Clb; Sec Spanish Clb; Off Sr Cls; Gov Hon Prg Awd; High Hon Roll; Jr NHS; Church Yth Grp; Computer Clb; Govnrs Schl Pub Issues 87; Fut NJ Monmouth Coll 87; Girls Ctznshp Inst Douglass Coll 87; CPA.

AGAMAN, ALLISON; Shore Regional HS; Oceanport, NJ; (3); Band; Concert Band; Mrchg Band; Stage Crew; Symp Band; Bus.

AGANS, KENNETH; Hillsborough HS; Somerville, NJ; (3); 123/328; JV Wrstlng; Montclair ST Coll; Bus.

AGAR, TYRONE P; Moorestown Friends Schl; Camden, NJ; (4); Chess Clb; Pres Spanish Clb; School Play; Off Jr Cls; Rep Stu Cncl; Var L Bsktbl; Var L Trk; Hon Roll; Rotary Awd; ABC Schlrshp Moorestown Friends Schl 83-87; Natl Achvt Schlrshp Outstndg Negro Stu 86-87; 3rd Pl Trk; Yale U; Economics.

AGOES, STEPHANIE; Bordentown Regional HS; Bordentown, NJ; (3); 8/141; Art Clb; SADD; Yrbk Stf; Rep Soph Cls; Rep Jr Cls; Var Bsktbl; Var JV Socr; Var JV Sftbl; Hon Roll; NHS; MVP-BSKTBLL 85-86; 2nd Tm All Frdm Dvsn Sccr 86; Drftng.

AGUIAR, BEATRIZ; Paul VI Regional HS; Passaic, NJ; (3); Yrbk Stf; JV Sftbl; JV Trk; Hon Roll; Spanish NHS.

AGUILAR, ANITA; Immaculate Heart Acad; Paramus, NJ; (4); 6/171; Pres Model UN; Ed Lit Mag; Rep Stu Cncl; Var Tennis; Hon Roll; NHS; Spanish NHS; Capt Quiz Bowl; Science Clb; Prfct Atten Awd; NJ Acad Decthln ST Comp Gold Mdl 87; Congressnl Schlr 87; HOBY Ldrshp Sem Amb 85; Barnard Coll; Intl Rel.

AGUILAR, SILVIA A; Our Lady Of Good Counsel HS; Newark, NJ; (3); Pep Clb; Chorus; Cheerleading; Natl Sci Olympd 86-87; Pre-Med.

AGUILERA, FRANCIE; Union Hill HS; Union City, NJ; (4); 2/250; Sec Mu Alpha Theta; Science Clb; Trs Ski Clb; Drill Tm; High Hon Roll; Hon Roll; Sec NHS; Spanish NHS; Computer Clb; Math Clb; Stevens Inst Of Tech; Cvl Eng.

AGUILERA, RALPH; Wayne Hills HS; Wayne, NJ; (3); 33/320; Ftbl; High Hon Roll; Accntnt.

AHMED, KHURRAM; Ridgefield Park HS; Ridgefield Pk, NJ; (2); 10/204; Chess Clb; Computer Clb; Debate Tm; Math Tm; Spanish Clb; Nwsp Rptr; Crs Cntry; Trk; Natl Sci Olympiad Awd 87; Schl Svc Awd 87; Rutgers U; Medicine.

AHMED, RIAZ M; Paramus HS; Paramus, NJ; (4); 14/330; Quiz Bowl; Nwsp Sprt Ed; Ed Yrbk Stf; Ed Lit Mag; VP Stu Cncl; Capt Tennis; VP NHS; Ntl Merit SF; Spanish NHS; St Schlr.

AHN, CAROL; Paramus Catholic Girls HS; Fort Lee, NJ; (4); Pres Church Yth Grp; Hosp Aide; Nwsp Ed-Chief; Yrbk Ed-Chief; Rep Soph Cls; Sec Rep Jr Cls; Sec Stu Cncl; Cheerleading; High Hon Roll; Hon Roll; NY U; Accntng.

AHN, ELLEN; Palisades Park HS; Palisades Pk, NJ; (3); Church Yth Grp; Speech Tm; Nwsp Stf; Yrbk Stf; Lit Mag; Hon Roll; Jr NHS; NHS; VFW Speech Finalist 86-87; Rutgers; Comm.

AHRENDITS, LESLIE; Lower Cape May Regional HS; N Cape May, NJ; (3); 25/238; Church Yth Grp; 4-H; Spanish Clb; SADD; Chorus; Church Choir; Orch; Lit Mag; Cit Awd; Hon Roll; Engl Tchr.

AIBEL, JONATHAN R; Northern Valley Regional HS; Demarest, NJ; (4); 1/228; Pres Drama Clb; Chorus; Madrigals; School Musical; School Play; Rep Stu Cncl; VP NHS; Ntl Merit SF; Rnsslr Sci Awd 86.

AIDALA, JENNIFER; Sparta HS; Sparta, NJ; (4); Key Clb; Var JV Bsktbl; JV Var Cheerleading; PDP Ldr; Hmcmg Ct.

AIRES, CECILIA; St Marys Of The Assumption HS; Linden, NJ; (4); 5/59; Art Clb; Chess Clb; Yrbk Stf; Pres Jr Cls; Hon Roll; Seton Hall U.

AKER, GREGORY; Linden HS; Linden, NJ; (4); 3/345; Quiz Bowl; Science Clb; School Play; High Hon Roll; Hon Roll; NHS; Prfct Atten Awd; NJ Distngshd Schlr 86-87; German Hnr Soc Delta Epsilon Phi 84-87; Math Exam Achvt Pin 86 & 87; NJIT; Elec Engrng.

AKKAWAY, ALAN; Clifton SR HS; Clifton, NJ; (4); 120/589; Computer Clb; Drama Clb; Science Clb; Ski Clb; Spanish Clb; Swmmng; Wt Lftg; Jr NHS; NHS; Rotary Awd; Rutgers U.

ALA, VALERIE; Parsippany HS; Parsippany, NJ; (2); Church Yth Grp; Spanish Clb; SADD; Varsity Clb; Band; JV Cheerleading; JV Var Fld Hcky; JV Sftbl; Hon Roll; Prfct Atten Awd.

ALAIE, PARIZATIS; Washington Township HS; Sewell, NJ; (2); Drama Clb; French Clb; School Play; Stage Crew; Nwsp Rptr; JV Bsktbl; Hon Roll; Jr NHS; 2nd Pl Thomas Edison Sci Fair 86; Med.

ALBA, CHRISTINE M; Dumont HS; Dumont, NJ; (4); 5/217; Am Leg Aux Girls St; Mu Alpha Theta; School Musical; School Play; Variety Show; Lit Mag; JV Var Crs Cntry; High Hon Roll; NHS; Ntl Art Hnr Soc Treas; Comms.

ALBAN, THERESE M; Somerville HS; Somerville, NJ; (4); 2/239; Pres French Clb; Model UN; Thesps; Stu Cncl; NHS; Sal; Church Yth Grp; Cmnty Wkr; Drama Clb; Math Tm; Grls Ctznshp Inst 86; Jostens Fndtn Recog Awd 87; Rutgers U Women Worth Essy Cntst Hnbl Mntn 87; Drew U; Pre-Med.

ALBANESE, TRACY; Nutley HS; Nutley, NJ; (4); Debate Tm; Office Aide; Color Guard; Nwsp Rptr; Sec Frsh Cls; Sec Soph Cls; Sec Jr Cls; Sec Sr Cls; Var Cheerleading; Hon Roll; Stu Apprctn Day 87; Montclair ST Coll; Chld Ed.

ALBANKIS, ELIZABETH A; Abraham Clark HS; Roselle, NJ; (4); 17/120; Hosp Aide; Office Aide; Spanish Clb; Teachers Aide; Yrbk Stf; High Hon Roll; Hon Roll; NHS; 2 Letter R Acad Excllnce 84 & 86; Kean Coll; Phys Ther.

ALBANO, GERALD; Delran HS; Delran, NJ; (4); Im Bsktbl; Pres Acad Ftns Awd 87; U Of DE; Accntng.

ALBANO, PETER; Verona HS; Verona, NJ; (4); 34/185; Church Yth Grp; Nwsp Rptr; Nwsp Stf; Yrbk Rptr; Yrbk Stf; Im Tennis; French Hon Soc; Hon Roll; Pres Schlr; Anthony Iuso Scholar Awd 87; Drew U; Orthodntst.

ALBER, JULIE; Middletown HS; Middletown, NJ; (2); Church Yth Grp; Cmnty Wkr; Dance Clb; German Clb; Chorus; Swmmng; Hon Roll; Prfct Atten Awd; Civic Clb; FCA; Secy St Agnes CYO 87; Piano Tchrs Forum Fstvl Awd 85; St Alexander Nevsky Russn Schl Diplma 87; Intl Bus Admin.

ALBERQUE, WILLIAM; Christian Brothers Acad; Freehold, NJ; (3); Church Yth Grp; German Clb; Yrbk Stf; JV Crs Cntry; Im Ftbl; Ntl Merit SF; Washington & Lee U; Artfcl Inte.

ALBERS, JENNIFER; Parsippany Hills HS; Morris Plains, NJ; (2); Key Clb; Spanish Clb; Var Fld Hcky; Var Stat Trk; High Hon Roll; Hon Roll; Inst Women Schlrs 87; Spn Day Comptn Drew U 87; Steering Committee 87; Chem.

ALBERT, NICOLE; John P Stevens HS; Edison, NJ; (3); 31/451; Dance Clb; Hosp Aide; Office Aide; Capt Pep Clb; Mrchg Band; Mgr(s); Capt Pom Pon; French Hon Soc; Hon Roll; NHS; Acceptance To Middlesex Arts HS For Modern Dance 87; Engnrg.

ALBERT, PAUL; Seton Hall Prep; Irvington, NJ; (4); 40/200; Art Clb; Church Yth Grp; French Clb; Key Clb; Capt Bsktbl; Hon Roll; NEDT Awd; Martin Luther King Jr Schlrshp 87; Holy Cross Coll; Econ.

ALBERTO, NORAH; Holy Rosary Acad; Jacksonergn, NJ; (3); Drama Clb; Math Tm; Spanish Clb; Variety Show; Nwsp Stf; Yrbk Stf; Sec Frsh Cls; Sec Jr Cls; Twrlr; Hon Roll; CMNCTNS.

ALBERTSON, CHRISTOPHER E; Millville HS; Mauricetown, NJ; (4); 3/460; Am Leg Boys St; Cmnty Wkr; Latin Clb; Var Capt Bsktbl; Var Crs Cntry; Var Capt Tennis; Im Wt Lftg; High Hon Roll; Kiwanis Awd; NHS; Natl Schlr-Athlt Awd U S Army Rsrv 87; VP Ldrs Club 87; Jewish War Vets Schlr Athlt Awd 87; Montclair ST; Physcl Ed.

ALBIN, GEORGE; Monsignor Donovan HS; Howell, NJ; (3); Boy Scts; Church Yth Grp; Ski Clb; SADD; Church Choir; JV Var Ftbl; Chef.

ALBINO, ROSELLE RAE; Jackson Memorial HS; Jackson, NJ; (4); 126/403; FBLA; FNA; Ski Clb; SADD; Chorus; Chrmn Yrbk Stf; Rep Frsh Cls; Rep Soph Cls; Stat Fld Hcky; Stat Socr; Robert Dale Trust Moose Schlrshp 86; Ocean Cnty Assoc Off Persnl Schlrshp 87; Katherine Gibbs Schl; Sec.

ALBINSON, LAUREL; Paul VI HS; Runnemede, NJ; (4); 20/503; Spanish Clb; Var Cheerleading; Coach Actv; Hon Roll; Spanish NHS; Amer Dstngshd HS Stu 86; Poli Sci.

ALBRECHT, ANNE; Middletown HS South; Middletown, NJ; (4); 31/452; Church Yth Grp; Pres VP Girl Scts; Hosp Aide; Ski Clb; Church Choir; Flag Corp; Yrbk Stf; JV Trk; Hon Roll.

ALBRECHT, GLENN; West Milford HS; West Milford, NJ; (3); 12/465; Cmnty Wkr; German Clb; Varsity Clb; Var Socr; JV Sftbl; Gov Hon Prg Awd; High Hon Roll; Hon Roll; NHS; Ntl Merit Ltr; Grmn Hnr Soc, Delta Epsln Phi 87; Yng Artsts Expo-Rngwd Mnr NJ-1ST 86 & 2nd 87; Arch.

ALBRECHT, STEPHANIE L; Ocean City HS; Ocean City, NJ; (2); 56/340; Church Yth Grp; Dance Clb; Exploring; Band; Church Choir; Concert Band; Mrchg Band; Orch; Symp Band; Hon Roll; Law Enfrcmnt.

ALBRECHT, TRACY A; A L Johnson Regional HS; Clark, NJ; (4); 1/197; Science Clb; Spanish Clb; Band; Jazz Band; Stu Cncl; Bausch & Lomb Sci Awd; Pres NHS; Ntl Merit SF; Spanish NHS; Val; Rensselaer Polytechnic Inst Mdl.

ALCANTARA, SHERRY; Indian Hills HS; Franklin Lakes, NJ; (3); 22/306; AFS; Science Clb; Spanish Clb; Concert Band; Jazz Band; Mrchg Band; High Hon Roll; Hon Roll; NHS.

ALCID, MARK G; St Joseph Regional HS; Paramus, NJ; (3); Camera Clb; Math Tm; L Trk; High Hon Roll; NHS; Spanish NHS; Schlrshp Deans Smmr Schlr Pgm Rutgers 87; Pre-Med.

ALDERFER, SUSAN E; Toms River HS East; Seaside Hts, NJ; (4); 15/565; Church Yth Grp; Math Tm; Church Choir; Orch; Var L Fld Hcky; High Hon Roll; NHS; Ntl Merit SF; St Schlr; Key Clb; NJ All-St Orchestra 85-86; Commendations Schl Brd Music/Schlrshp 84-86.

ALEJANDRO, DORIS; Hoboren HS; Hoboken, NJ; (4); 63/263; Cmnty Wkr; Key Clb; Latin Clb; Teachers Aide; Nwsp Stf; Rep Sr Cls; Rep Stu Cncl; Marine Midland Atlntc Awd 87; Pace U; Acctg.

ALEJANDRO, JESSICA; Saint Marys HS; Jersey City, NJ; (3); Service Clb; Yrbk Stf; Hon Roll; Comptr Engnr.

ALESANDRO, STACY; Bridgewater Raritan HS East; Bridgewater, NJ; (3); Cmnty Wkr; Rep Frsh Cls; Var JV Cheerleading; JV Fld Hcky; Var Pom Pon; Var Powder Puff Ftbl; Hon Roll; Miss JR NJ Semifnlst 86; Villanova; Fin.

ALESSANDRINI, PATRICIA; Paramus Catholic Girls HS; Wallington, NJ; (2); Art Clb; Band; Church Choir; Im Gym; Im Sftbl; Im Tennis; Im Vllybl; Hon Roll; Engl Awd 87; MEDT Perf Engl 87; Music Perf.

ALESSI, KELLY; Hamilton High West; Trenton, NJ; (4); 31/344; VP SADD; VP Band; Concert Band; Drm Mjr(t); School Musical; School Play; Symp Band; Sec Stu Cncl; Instrmntlst Mag Musicnshp Awd 87; $500 Schlrshp Form MCCC For High Achvt 87; MCCC; Music Tchr.

ALESSI, MARK; Ocean Twp HS; Ocean, NJ; (3); 150/353; Computer Clb; French Clb; Stage Crew; Var L Golf; Socr; Im Vllybl; Arch.

ALEXANDER, ALPHONSE; C J Scott HS; Newark, NJ; (3); 2/300; Aud/Vis; Math Tm; Varsity Clb; Socr; Capt Tennis; Bausch & Lomb Sci Awd; Hon Roll; NHS; Rensselaer Math Mdl 87.

ALEXANDER, AMY; Hawthorne HS; Hawthorne, NJ; (3); Church Yth Grp; 4-H; Service Clb; Chorus; Church Choir; Capt Flag Corp; Mrchg Band; Masonic Awd; Outstndng Svc Bus Clb VP 86-87; Katherine Gibbs; Exec Sec.

ALEXANDER, DAWN; Jackson Memorial HS; Jackson, NJ; (4); 60/412; Ski Clb; Varsity Clb; Var Capt Socr; High Hon Roll; Art Clb; GAA; Library Aide; Band; Nwsp Sprt Ed; Yrbk Sprt Ed; Soccer Schlrshp 87; LIU; Bus.

ALEXANDER, JEFFREY M; Solomon Schechter Day Schl; Maplewood, NJ; (3); Nwsp Rptr; Nwsp Stf; Var Bsbl; JV Bsktbl; Var Socr; NEDT Comm For Standardized Test Scores 85-86; 1st Early Adm Male To Attend Goudner Coll; Gouder Coll; Ec.

ALEXANDER, KAKIVA; Lincln HS; Jersy City, NJ; (4); 23/211; Drama Clb; FBLA; Nwsp Sprt Ed; Yrbk Stf; Lit Mag; Crs Cntry; Sftbl; Prfct Atten Awd; Cert-Acadmc Excllnc 86; Rutgers U; Crmnl Jstc.

ALEXANDER, MARY JO; Red Bank Catholic HS; Rumson, NJ; (4); Pep Clb; Ski Clb; Variety Show; Rep Frsh Cls; Rep Soph Cls; Rep Jr Cls; L Cheerleading; Golf; Twrlr; Rosemont; Law.

ALEXANDER, RICHARD; Brick Township HS; Brick Town, NJ; (3); 36/408; Spanish Clb; Rep Jr Cls; Rep Stu Cncl; Var Tennis; High Hon Roll; Hon Roll; Spanish.

ALEXANDER, SUSAN; Montville HS; Montville, NJ; (4); 111/268; Church Yth Grp; Pres Sec Civic Clb; DECA; Hosp Aide; Pep Clb; Trs SADD; Varsity Clb; Nwsp Stf; Capt Var Fld Hcky; Gym; Saferiders Acad 86-87; Field Hockey All Conf All Cnty; Rider Coll; Phy Educ.

ALEXANDRE, RAEANNE; Paul VI HS; Glendora, NJ; (4); 85/500; Var Pom Pon; Hon Roll; NHS; Atten Awd 84-85; Rutgers; Hotel Mtmg.

ALFE, KAREN; Highland Regional HS; Blackwood, NJ; (4); #19 In Class; French Clb; Sec Nwsp Stf; Yrbk Stf; Hon Roll; NHS; Ntl Merit Ltr; St Schlr; Am Leg Essay Cntst 86; Trenton ST Coll; Nrsng.

ALFIERI, JENNIFER; Morristown-Beard HS; Basking Ridge, NJ; (2); 7/73; AFS; Art Clb; Church Yth Grp; French Clb; Varsity Clb; Yrbk Stf; Var Fld Hcky; Var Lcrss; Hon Roll; NHS; Hnr Roll 85-87; Natl Art Hrnr Scty 87; Arch.

ALFONSO, LUIS; Memorial HS; West New York, NJ; (3); Intnl Clb; Spanish Clb; Katharine Gibbs Schl; Comps.

ALFORD, MELISSA ANN; Sparta HS; Sparta, NJ; (3); Drama Clb; French Clb; Key Clb; Keywanettes; Nwsp Sprt Ed; Nwsp Stf; Rep Stu Cncl; Var Crs Cntry; JV Trk; Law.

ALGAYER, ALEXANDER; Burlington County Vo-Tech; Cinnaminson, NJ; (3); Church Yth Grp; VICA; Hon Roll; NHS; Atlantic Co CC; Culinary Arts.

ALI, KAREN; St Rose HS; Belmar, NJ; (4); 26/217; Am Leg Aux Girls St; Ski Clb; Rep Jr Cls; Trs Stu Cncl; JV Var Cheerleading; Mgr(s); Hon Roll; NHS; NEDT Awd; Spanish NHS; Prsnl Typng Awd 86.

ALI, ROSEMARIE; St John Vianney Regional HS; Hazlet, NJ; (2); 23/270; SADD; Chorus; Mrchg Band; Off Lit Mag; Mgr(s); Hon Roll; NHS; Cmnty Wkr; Intnl Clb; Concert Band; Omicron Gamma Drew U Cert Merit Spn Lang Day 86 & 87; Cert Merit Spn 87; Cert Merit Religion 87; USAF Acad; Aerospc Engrng.

ALIA, JOSEPH; Saddle Brook HS; Saddle Brook, NJ; (3); 7/120; Latin Clb; Nwsp Ed-Chief; Nwsp Sprt Ed; Bsktbl; Ftbl; Trk; Wrstlng; High Hon Roll; Rcvd Several Acdmcs Awds 84-87; Prtcptd NJ Boys ST & Stu Of Natl Hon Soc 86-87; Biology.

ALICEA, SARA; Hoboken HS; Hoboken, NJ; (3); Chorus; Exec Sec.

ALICEA, VICTORIA; Holy Rosary Acad; Jersey City, NJ; (3); Drama Clb; Math Tm; Chorus; Sec Frsh Cls; Sec Soph Cls; Twrlr; Bio Sci Awd 84; Intl Rltns.

ALISE, VINCENZA; New Milford HS; New Milford, NJ; (2); Office Aide; Chorus; Color Guard; Yrbk Stf; Cheerleading; Prfct Atten Awd; Am Leg Awd 85; Comp Prgmr.

ALIZIERI, LORI ANN; Memorial HS; Cedar Grove, NJ; (4); 10/123; Sec Key Clb; Ski Clb; JV Sftbl; Swmmng; Var Tennis; Hon Roll; Lion Awd; NHS; Pres Schlr; St Schlr; Mem HS APT Schlrshp 87; Fairfield U; Bus.

ALLAWAY, RICHARD D; West Orange HS; West Orange, NJ; (3); Am Leg Boys St; Church Yth Grp; Math Tm; Ski Clb; Chorus; Pres Jr Cls; VP Stu Cncl; Var Ftbl; Jr NHS; Rotary Awd; Stu Mngmt Cmtte 86-87; Spnsh Clb 84-87; Vrsty Trk 85-87; Bus Mngmt.

ALLEGRETTO, CINDI NOELLE; Egg Harbor Township HS; Mays Landing, NJ; (4); 35/289; Church Yth Grp; Girl Scts; Office Aide; Ski Clb; Yrbk Stf; Stu Cncl; Swmmng; High Hon Roll; Natl Engl Mrt Awd 86; Ldrshp/Svc Awd 87; Westchester U; Elem Educ.

ALLEN, ANGELICA; Irvington HS; Irvington, NJ; (4); 5/462; VP Key Clb; Pres Latin Clb; Scholastic Bowl; Church Choir; Yrbk Ed-Chief; Trs Jr Cls; Tennis; High Hon Roll; Hon Roll; Pres NHS; Indstrl Engr.

ALLEN, BECKY; Hunterdon Central HS; Flemington, NJ; (2); 22/481; German Clb; Ski Clb; Sftbl; Hon Roll; Grmn Natl Hnr Soc 87; Interact 87; Hunterdon Athlts Making A Postv Stand 87; Commercial Art.

ALLEN, CHERYL; Watchung Hills Regional HS; Gillette, NJ; (3); 174/321; Cmnty Wkr; Drama Clb; PAVAS; Ski Clb; Band; Concert Band; Mrchg Band; Orch; School Musical; Stage Crew; Schlrshp Awd-Gardn St Ballet Schl 84-87; Apprntc-Gdn St Ballet Co 85-86; U Of Cincinnati; Prfrmg Arts.

ALLEN, CHRISTINE; Hawthorne HS; Hawthorne, NJ; (3); Cmnty Wkr; L Band; L Chorus; Mrchg Band; JV L Bsktbl; L Var Sftbl; High Hon Roll; Hon Roll; NHS; Church Yth Grp; Tri Cnty Band & Clarinet Bagpipes 84-87; Vet Med.

ALLEN, DAWN; Salem HS; Salem, NJ; (3); Math Clb; Spanish Clb; SADD; Teachers Aide; Rep Stu Cncl; Psycht.

ALLEN, EARNEST CHRIS; Marist HS; Bayonne, NJ; (3); 46/106; Aud/Vis; Camera Clb; Computer Clb; Office Aide; Rep Frsh Cls; Rep Stu Cncl; Mgr Bsbl; Mgr Bsktbl; Mgr Ftbl; JV Var Mgr(s); Real Estate Develpmnt.

ALLEN, ERIK; Phillipsburg HS; Bloomsbury, NJ; (4); 2/292; Boy Scts; Church Yth Grp; Scholastic Bowl; Band; Mrchg Band; Var Capt Crs Cntry; Var Capt Trk; High Hon Roll; NHS; Ntl Merit Ltr; Yth Of The Yr Phillipsbrg Exchng Clb 87; Dpt Hnrs Engl Phy Sci & Soc Stud 87; Grdn ST Dstngd Schlr 87; US Military Acad; Elec Engrng.

ALLEN, KATHLEEN; Mc Corristin Catholic HS; Trenton, NJ; (3); Art Clb; GAA; Off Pep Clb; Yrbk Stf; Hon Roll.

ALLEN, KRISTIN; Baptist HS; Cherry Hill, NJ; (3); Drama Clb; Chorus; Church Choir; School Play; Yrbk Phtg; Yrbk Stf; Trs Stu Cncl; High Hon Roll; Prfct Atten Awd; Bob Jones U; Math.

ALLEN, LINDA; Ridge HS; Basking Ridge, NJ; (2); 4/169; Church Yth Grp; Girl Scts; Ski Clb; Chorus; Church Choir; Concert Band; Var Socr; Var Trk; Hon Roll; Spanish NHS.

ALLEN, LISA; Hamilton HS East; Trenton, NJ; (3); Aud/Vis; Church Yth Grp; French Clb; Office Aide; Church Choir; Drill Tm; Nwsp Phtg; Lit Mag; Sftbl; Sftbl Ltr 85; 2nd Pl Sftbl Troph & 2nd Pl Bwlg Troph 84; Lib Arts.

ALLEN, MELISSA; Morristown HS; Morristown, NJ; (4); Cmnty Wkr; JCL; Latin Clb; Pres NAACP; Spanish Clb; SADD; Chorus; Church Choir; Hon Roll; Campus Minstry Awd Treas 85-86; St Elizabeth; Bio.

ALLEN, PAUL D; John F Kennedy Memorial HS; Metuchen, NJ; (4); 36/274; Cmnty Wkr; Math Clb; School Play; Trk; Cit Awd; NHS; Pres Schlr; Middlesex Cnty Schl Boards Assoc Stu Rcgntn Awd 87; OH St U; Physcl Thrpy.

ALLEN III, PAYTON EDWARD; Linden HS; Linden, NJ; (4); Church Yth Grp; Drama Clb; FHA; SADD; Chorus; Church Choir; Mrchg Band; School Play; JV Bsktbl; Trk; FHA 2nd Pl 87; St Johns Coll; Music.

ALLEN, PHILLIP; Cresskill HS; Cresskill, NJ; (3); Pres Church Yth Grp; Debate Tm; Drama Clb; Q&S; Ski Clb; Band; Chorus; School Musical; Ed Nwsp Stf; Yrbk Stf; Hugh O Brian Yth Fndtn Ldrshp Conf, Marge Roukema S Odel Congress Rep, St Sci Fair Day Exam Rep 86.

ALLEN, SAMUEL; Millville SR HS; Millville, NJ; (3); 24/524; Am Le[g] Boys St; Nwsp Stf; Pres Jr Cls; Pres Sr Cls; Pres Stu Cncl; Var Bsktbl; Va[r] Ftbl; Var Trk; NHS; Acad Achvmt Awd 84; Ldrshp Awd 86; Natl Yt[h] Physc Ftns Pgm 87; U Of PA; Pol Sci.

ALLEN, TALLEY J; Woodbury HS; Woodbury, NJ; (4); 7/120; Boy Scts; Church Yth Grp; JA; Math Tm; Scholastic Bowl; Varsity Clb; Wt Lftg; Wrstlng; Elks Awd; Alpha Kappa Beta Schlrshp; Mothers Club Schlrshp; Awd; Drexel U; Elec Engrng.

ALLEN, TERRY; Millville SR HS; Millville, NJ; (2); Dance Clb; Math Tm; SADD; Y-Teens; Variety Show; Off Soph Cls; Bsktbl; Ftbl; Trk; Hon Roll.

ALLERTON, CARRIE L; South Plainfield HS; South Plainfield, NJ; (4) 7/190; Art Clb; Drama Clb; SADD; Capt Flag Corp; Nwsp Stf; Yrbk Stf; Rep Stu Cncl; NHS; Spanish NHS; S Plnfld Subrbn Wmns Clb Schlrshp 87; Outstndng Drftng Stu 87; Fulvio D Alessio Awd 87; Tyler Schl Art; Visual Art.

ALLEY, BETSY; New Providence HS; New Providence, NJ; (4); 14/167; Scholastic Bowl; Flag Corp; School Musical; School Play; Var Sftbl; Var Swmmng; French Hon Soc; NHS; St Schlr; Debate Tm; JETS Tm 4th P[l] 87; Cornell U; Intl Law.

ALLIEGRO III, JOSEPH A; Pennsville Memorial HS; Salem, NJ; (3) 22/230; Am Leg Boys St; Ski Clb; Yrbk Phtg; Im Bsktbl; High Hon Roll; Rcvd Svngs Bond In Am Legion Oratorical Cont 87; Schlstc Achvt Awd 8[6] & 87; 3rd Pl Comp Prog Cont 87; VA Tech; Elec Engrng.

ALLRICH JR, JACQUES; Irvington HS; Irvington, NJ; (4); 7/375; Pre[s] Church Yth Grp; French Clb; FBLA; Key Clb; Quiz Bowl; Church Choir; Pres Stu Cncl; Trk; Hon Roll; Lion Awd; Rutgers HS Schvt Awd, Cer[t] Elect Boy & Grls Wk 87; NJIT; Engrng.

ALLSHOUSE, DAVID; Phillipsburg HS; Bloomsbury, NJ; (3); Church Yth Grp; FFA; Concert Band; Musicians Inst; Music.

ALLSPACH, ERIKA; Watchung Hills Regional HS; Warren, NJ; (3) Church Yth Grp; VP Girl Scts; Band; Concert Band; Mrchg Band; Schoo[l] Musical; School Play; Fld Hcky; Hon Roll; Bst Def Plyr Fld Hcky 84-85 MVP Fld Hcky 86-87; Gold Ldrshp Girl Scts 86-87.

ALMARIO, FELICIA; Mary Help Of Christians Acad; Paterson, NJ; (3) 2/82; Church Yth Grp; Service Clb; SADD; Drill Tm; Nwsp Rptr; Rep Stu Cncl; Score Keeper; Hon Roll; NHS.

ALMAZAN, ASHLEY; Ridgefield Park HS; Ridgefield Park, NJ; (2); 38/183; Var Bsbl; Natl Sci Olympd 87; 4 Cmmndtns Comp Pgmmg 87; Elec Engr.

ALMEIDA, FRANK G; Union HS; Union, NJ; (3); Am Leg Boys St; Boy Scts; Chess Clb; Spanish Clb; High Hon Roll; Hon Roll; NHS; Eagle Scout 86; Vet.

ALMEIDA, JANICE P; Union Catholic Regional HS; Union, NJ; (4); 81/316; Church Yth Grp; Pep Clb; PAVAS; Service Clb; Ski Clb; School Play Yrbk Ed-Chief; Yrbk Stf; Var Capt Cheerleading; Var Capt Pom Pon; Va[r] Ltrs Socr Chrldng 85-86; Var Ltrs Bsktbl Chrldng 86-87; Yrbk Edtr Ch[...] Plg 87; NCAS; Bus.

ALMEN, FRED; Clifton HS; Clifton, NJ; (3); Math Clb; Science Clb; Va[r] L Socr; Var L Vllybl; High Hon Roll; JETS Awd; Merck ST Sci Day Awd 3rd Pl 87; Gehin NJ ST Sci Leag Chem 87; Engrng.

ALOI, PETER; Marist HS; Bayonne, NJ; (4); 4/98; Am Leg Boys St; Key Clb; Scholastic Bowl; Nwsp Rptr; Stu Cncl; Var Capt Bsbl; Ice Hcky; Hon Roll; NHS; Spanish NHS; Natl Ldrshp & Svc Awd 85; Bro Leo Sylviu[s] Awd 83-86.

ALONSO, ADAMARYS; Memorial HS; West New York, NJ; (3) Computer Clb; FTA; Intnl Clb; Math Clb; Teachers Aide; Off Soph Cls Off Jr Cls; Stevens Inst Of Tech; Comp Engr.

ALONZO, JOANN; Bridgewater-Raritan High Schl West; Bridgewater NJ; (4); Am Leg Aux Girls St; Cmnty Wkr; School Play; Yrbk Ed-Chief Var Capt Fld Hcky; Im Powder Puff Ftbl; Var Sftbl; Cit Awd; Hon Roll NHS; Mid-St Conf 2nd Tm Fld Hcky 86; Telecasting.

ALPAUGH, BECKY; Delaware Valley Reg HS; Bloomsbury, NJ; (4); 10/170; Church Yth Grp; Pres VP 4-H; Hosp Aide; Key Clb; Chorus; Cit Awd 4-H Awd; High Hon Roll; Hon Roll; VP NHS; Hugh O Brian NJ ST Ldrshp Smnr Rep 85; Natl 4-H Cngrss/Ctznshp-WA Fows 85-86; Cnty 4-H Mdls 85-86; Trenton ST Coll; Nrsng.

ALSDORF, KARIN; Wayne Hills HS; Wayne, NJ; (3); 8/334; Model UN Science Clb; Ski Clb; Sec Frsh Cls; Sec Soph Cls; Sec Stu Cncl; Socr; Sftbl High Hon Roll; NHS; Psych.

ALSTON, DAWN; John F Kennedy HS; Willingboro, NJ; (3); Am Le[g] Aux Girls St; Mrchg Band; Trs Stu Cncl; Mgr(s); Capt Pom Pon; Hon Roll Hampton U; CPA.

ALSTON, MONIQUE; Plainfield HS; Plainfield, NJ; (4); 23/408; DECA Pep Clb; Band; Drm Mjr(t); Mrchg Band; Yrbk Stf; Rep Stu Cncl; Hon Roll; Vllybl; Jr NHS; Ankolowitz-Bradshaw Awd 83; Hnr Rl Hnrs 85; Mis[s] Plainfield HS 86; Spelman Coll; Psych.

ALTENAU, LISA; St Pius X Reginal HS; S Plainfield, NJ; (3); 23/90 Church Yth Grp; Computer Clb; Dance Clb; Teachers Aide; Stage Crew Variety Show; Co-Capt Cheerleading; Var Pom Pon; Hon Roll; NHS; Mis[s] Talent Unlmtd Mdlng Title 85; Miss MBC Teen Model 87; Numerou[s] Awds For Dncng; Bio.

ALTILIO, MICHAEL; Secaucus HS; Secaucus, NJ; (3); 16/170; Am Le[g] Boys St; Key Clb; Mu Alpha Theta; VP Ski Clb; Varsity Clb; Chorus; Rep Frsh Cls; Trs Sr Cls; Var Bsbl; Var Ftbl; Engrng.

ALTMAN, HEATHER; Deptford HS; Deptford, NJ; (3); Science Clb Capt Flag Corp; School Musical; Nwsp Rptr; Rep Stu Cncl; Bsktbl; Pres J[r] NHS; South Jrsy Sci Fair 1st Plc Best Of Ctgry 87; DE Vly Sci Fair 2nd Plc 87; DE Vly Sci Fair Nvl Awd 87; Med.

ALTMAN, JOHN S; Princeton HS; Princeton, NJ; (4); Nwsp Stf; Lit Mag; Gov Hon Prg Awd; Harvard Coll; Crtv Wrtng.

ALTMAN, MEREDITH; Manalapan HS; Manalapan, NJ; (4); Thesps Acpl Chr; Chorus; Madrigals; School Play; Stage Crew; Variety Show; S[...] Editor Yrbk 87; All Shore Chorus 86; Johnson & Wales Coll; Cul Arts.

ALTMAN, SYLVIA; Toms River High School North; Toms River, NJ (3); 64/448; Church Yth Grp; Ski Clb; Band; Concert Band; Mrchg Band Orch; Yrbk Stf; Elctrnc Engrng.

ALTOBELLO, KEN; Paramus HS; Paramus, NJ; (3); Aud/Vis; Boy Scts Sec Church Yth Grp; Library Aide; Church Choir; Ed Yrbk Phtg; Cit Awd God Cntry Awd; VFW Awd; Fin Yth Speaks Out 87; Eagle Scout 86 Partcle Physcs Rsrch.

ALTOM, JOHN; Wardlaw-Hartridge HS; Plainfield, NJ; (4); 5/48 SADD; School Musical; School Play; Sec Frsh Cls; Sec Jr Cls; Sec Sr Cls Capt L Bsktbl; Capt L Ftbl; Capt L Trk; High Hon Roll; Garden S[T] Dstngshd Schlr 87; Swarthmore Coll; Engrng.

ALTON, KATHERINE; Kent Place HS; Chatham Twp, NJ; (2); Cmnty Wkr; French Clb; Scholastic Bowl; Teachers Aide; School Musical; Schoo[l] Play; NJ Acad Of Sci Grant 86; NJ Sci League 86-8; Arch.

ALVARADO, LOUIS; Passaic Valley HS; West Paterson, NJ; (4); 32/346; Am Leg Boys St; Boy Scts; Chess Clb; Civic Clb; Cmnty Wkr; Debate Tm; Political Wkr; Quiz Bowl; Scholastic Bowl; Science Clb; Cornell U; Biochem.

ALVAREZ, BEGONIA; Queen Of Peace HS; Newark, NJ; (2); French Clb; Pyschlgy.

ALVAREZ, BENITA G; Weehawken HS; Weehawken, NJ; (3); 3/103; Pres Intnl Clb; Color Guard; Yrbk Stf; Stu Cncl; Trk; Twrlr; High Hon Roll; Hon Roll; NHS; Brown Bk Awd 87; Med.

ALVAREZ, CARLOTA; Memorial HS; West New York, NJ; (3); Spanish Clb; Varsity Clb; Rep Frsh Cls; Rep Soph Cls; Rep Jr Cls; Rep Sr Cls; Rep Stu Cncl; Var Cheerleading; Var Pom Pon; Hon Roll.

ALVAREZ, EDWARD; Essex Catholic Boys HS; Newark, NJ; (2); Math Tm; Nwsp Rptr; Im Fld Hcky; High Hon Roll; Ntl Merit Ltr; Natl Ldrshp & Svc Awd 87; Acad All Amer Awd 86; Computers.

ALVAREZ, HUBERT; Memorial HS; West New York, NJ; (3); Computer Clb; Math Clb; Science Clb; JV Var Bsbl; Hon Roll; MJIT; Comp Engr.

ALVAREZ, JUAN; Memorial HS; West New York, NJ; (3); Church Yth Grp; Computer Clb; French Clb; Intnl Clb; Math Clb; Varsity Clb; Stage Crew; JV Ftbl; Var Socr; Comp Prgr.

ALVAREZ, LIZETTE V; Monsignor Donovan HS; Beachwood, NJ; (4); 62/243; Am Leg Aux Girls St; Sec Church Yth Grp; Hosp Aide; Ski Clb; Yrbk Stf; VP Soph Cls; VP Jr Cls; VP Stu Cncl; Stat Bsktbl; JV Sftbl; A J Gordon Schlrshp 87; Chllng Schlrshp 87; Stu Ldr Schlrshp 87; Gordon Coll; Bus.

ALVAREZ, PEDRO; North Bergen HS; N Bergen, NJ; (3); Farleigh Dickinson U; Bus Admin.

ALVAREZ, SANDRA; Passaic County Tech; Paterson, NJ; (4); 47/366; Spanish Clb; Nwsp Stf; Yrbk Stf; Rep Stu Cncl; Hon Roll; Fshn Inst Of Tech; Tshn Merch.

ALVEAR, ANTOINETTE; Southern Regional HS; Barnegat, NJ; (3); Hon Roll; Prfct Atten Awd; Monmouth Coll; Vet Med.

ALVERIO, CLARIBEL; Trenton Central HS; Trenton, NJ; (3); Church Yth Grp; Dance Clb; Hon Roll; Prfct Atten Awd; Drama Clb; JA; Mgr Bsbl; Var Mgr(s); Var Score Keeper; Cert Of Achvt For Prfrmng Arts Clb 84-85; Cert Of Rcgntn For Red Crss Clb Actvts 84-85; Comp Pgmnr.

ALVES, ALBERTINA; Our Lady Of Good Counsel HS; Kearny, NJ; (3); 8/123; Camera Clb; Hon Roll; NHS; Chorus; School Play; Acadmc All Amer 86-87; Hi Cum Avg 85-86.

ALVEZ, DEBBIE; Dwight Morrow HS; Englewood, NJ; (4); 30/229; Drama Clb; Hosp Aide; VP Spanish Clb; School Musical; Sec Stu Cncl; Hon Roll; Lion Awd; NHS; Katherine Gardner Human Rltns Awd 87; Stu Org Svc Awd Gold E 87; York Coll Of PA; Chld Psych.

AMABILE, MICHAEL; Toms River HS South; Toms River, NJ; (4); 1/324; Boy Scts; Capt Math Tm; Pres Mrchg Band; VP Soph Cls; Bausch & Lomb Sci Awd; High Hon Roll; Pres NHS; Pres Schlr; St Schlr; Val; Princeton U; Astrphyscs.

AMANN, WILLIAM JAMES; Red Bank Regional HS; Little Silver, NJ; (3); Debate Tm; English Clb; Letterman Clb; Science Clb; Ski Clb; Yrbk Stf; Bsktbl; Var Ftbl; Var Trk; Wt Lftg; Wake Forest U; Pol Sci.

AMATELLI, SALLY; Neptune HS; Neptune, NJ; (4); 35/355; GAA; Science Clb; Teachers Aide; Sec Frsh Cls; Rep Soph Cls; Rep Jr Cls; Rep Sr Cls; Sec Stu Cncl; Jr NHS; Sec NHS; Lcl Sci Fair 2 1st Pls; ST Lvl Sci Fair 2nd Pl, 1st Pl; Rgnl Lvl Sci Fair 2 Hnrb Mntns; Cabrini Coll; Elem Ed.

AMATO, KATHLEEN; Hackensack HS; Rochelle Park, NJ; (3); 10/410; Am Leg Aux Girls St; Church Yth Grp; Exploring; Variety Show; Yrbk Rptr; Score Keeper; Btty Crckr Awd; God Cntry Awd; NCTE Awd; SAR Awd; Seton Hall; Polit Sci.

AMATUCCI, GLENN; Immaculata HS; Raritan, NJ; (3); Band; Concert Band; Drm & Bgl; Jazz Band; VP Mrchg Band; School Musical; Symp Band; Gov Hon Prg Awd; NHS; Church Yth Grp; The Govr Schl Of Arts Schlrshp 87; Wind Ensmbl & Symphnc Band 86-87; All Cnty Symphnc Band 86-87; Elec Engr.

AMBLE, ERIKA; Bloomfield HS; Mt Sinai, NY; (3); Am Leg Aux Girls St; Church Yth Grp; GAA; Hosp Aide; Key Clb; Trs Latin Clb; Ski Clb; Var L Tennis; Hon Roll; NCTE Awd; Recog Essy Wrld Peace Sprtl Assmbly Bahais 87.

AMBRICO, SHERRY; Kingsway Regional HS; Mullica Hl, NJ; (2); Art Clb; Cmnty Wkr; Computer Clb; 4-H; FBLA; JA; Library Aide; Model UN; Office Aide; PAVAS; Chrs 86; Miss Hmsphr Beauty Pgnt 86.

AMBROSI, JENNIFER L; Morris Knolls HS; Denville, NJ; (4); 18/384; Am Leg Aux Girls St; Band; Capt Cheerleading; High Hon Roll; Hon Roll; NHS; Summa Awd; Accntng.

AMBROSINI, DENISE; Holy Cross HS; Mt Laurel, NJ; (3); Church Yth Grp; Cmnty Wkr; Ski Clb; Teachers Aide; Lit Mag; Off Frsh Cls; Crs Cntry; Trk; Varsity Clb; Yrbk Stf; Comm.

AMBRUSTER, MARK; Union Catholic Regional HS; Union, NJ; (3); #60 In Class; Church Yth Grp; Ski Clb; SADD; Bsktbl; Hon Roll; Bus.

AMERY, JANE; St John Vianney HS; Holmdel, NJ; (3); Service Clb; SADD; School Musical; School Play; Rep Frsh Cls; Mgr Ftbl; Mgr Wrstlng; Hon Roll; Church Yth Grp; NFL; Outstndng Achvt World Cultures; Gold & White Outstndng Invlmnt Activities Awd; Cmmnctns.

AMES, ADELA; Junior HS No 1; Trenton, NJ; (1); VP Stu Cncl; Cheerleading; Cit Awd; French Hon Soc; High Hon Roll; NCTE Awd; NHS; Prfct Atten Awd; Myrs Achvt Awd 87; Ms Am Coed Pgnt 86; Collbnd Pgm Trenton ST Coll 87; Law.

AMET, CHRIS D; Collingswood HS; Collingswood, NJ; (3); 11/255; Am Leg Boys St; Boy Scts; Computer Clb; French Clb; JA; Quiz Bowl; Ski Clb; SADD; Yrbk Stf; Var Im Ftbl; Comp Sci.

AMEY, KEVIN; West Deptford HS; Woodbury, NJ; (3); 10/260; Am Leg Boys St; Model UN; SADD; Varsity Clb; Pres Stu Cncl; Var L Socr; Var L Trk; Hon Roll; NHS; 4th Pl Natl Math Exam 87; HOBY Ldrshp Smnr Rep 886; Hstry.

AMICO, DENISE; Vineland HS; Vineland, NJ; (2); Color Guard; Drill Tm; Indoor Grd Ltnt 87; Flag Ltnt Of Mrchng Band 87.

AMMAN, TIMOTHY R; Holy Cross HS; Mt Laurel, NJ; (3); 18/407; Am Leg Boys St; Church Yth Grp; Ski Clb; Spanish Clb; Nwsp Ed-Chief; Yrbk Stf; Rep Jr Cls; Var Ftbl; JV Tennis; High Hon Roll.

AMMERMAN, KERI A; Secaucus HS; Secaucus, NJ; (2); 14/130; Dance Clb; Mu Alpha Theta; Spanish Clb; Color Guard; Mrchg Band; Yrbk Stf; Lit Mag; High Hon Roll; Hon Roll; Wrtng.

AMMERMAN, SHARI; Wayne Hills HS; Wayne, NJ; (4); 22/320; Church Yth Grp; FBLA; Spanish Clb; Varsity Clb; Capt Var Swmmng; Capt Var Tennis; Capt Var Trk; High Hon Roll; NHS; Pres Stu Athltc Assoc Svc Schlrshp 87; Phys Ed Awd 87; Douglass; Bus.

AMOROSO, PAUL; Union HS; Union, NJ; (2); Aud/Vis; Key Clb; Rep Stu Cncl; Var L Bsbl; JV Ftbl; JV L Wrstlng; Hon Roll; Prfct Atten Awd; Law.

AMOS, KECIA; University High 081987 HS; Newark, NJ; (3); Drama Clb; Spanish Clb; Chorus; Lit Mag; High Hon Roll; Hon Roll; NHS; Pre-Med.

AMPUERO, MANUELA; St Aloysius HS; Jersey City, NJ; (3); Exploring; Bowling; Awd Merit Typing 87; Rutgers; Bus Admin.

AMRICH, DANIEL; Notre Dame HS; Trenton, NJ; (2); Church Yth Grp; Cmnty Wkr; Computer Clb; Drama Clb; 4-H; FBLA; Office Aide; PAVAS; Teachers Aide; Chorus; Outstndng Male Religion Svc 85; Perfrmng Arts.

ANAGNOSTACHE, LINIC; West Windsor-Plainsboro HS; Princeton Junct, NJ; (3); 24/744; Church Yth Grp; Spanish Clb; Drill Tm; Variety Show; Yrbk Sprt Ed; Tennis; High Hon Roll; Hon Roll; Jr NHS; NHS; Rdlgy.

ANANTHARAMAN, KRISHNAN; South Brunswick HS; Kendall Park, NJ; (4); #13 In Class; Trs Debate Tm; Math Tm; Capt Scholastic Bowl; Trs Spanish Clb; Trs Mrchg Band; Nwsp Ed-Chief; Rep Stu Cncl; JV L Tennis; VP NHS; Pres Spanish NHS; Grdn St Dstngshd Schlr 87; Excel Jrnslm & Frgn Lang Awd 87; Northwestern U; Jrnlsm.

ANASTASIO, CHRISTINE; Madison Central HS; Old Bridge, NJ; (3); FBLA; SADD; Varsity Clb; Rep Civic Clb; Rep Soph Cls; Rep Jr Cls; Rep Jr Cls; VP Stu Cncl; Capt Gym; Hon Roll; Italian Club Secy 86-87; Italian Honor Scty 86-87; Nrsng.

ANASTASIOU, MARTHA; Mother Seton Regional HS; Irvington, NJ; (4); 2/96; Drama Clb; Math Tm; Drill Tm; School Play; Stage Crew; Nwsp Ed-Chief; Nwsp Rptr; Yrbk Stf; Lit Mag; Rep Frsh Cls; NJ Dstngshd Schlr 86-87; Rutgers Coll Of Pharmacy; Phrmc.

ANATOL, GISELLE; Scotch Plains Fanwood HS; Fanwood, NJ; (3); Church Yth Grp; Key Clb; VP Spanish Clb; SADD; Chorus; Mrchg Band; Symp Band; JV Capt Vllybl; High Hon Roll; Spanish NHS; Med.

ANCONA, ROBIN; Matawan Regional HS; Matawan, NJ; (3); 27/800; Church Yth Grp; Concert Band; Jazz Band; Mrchg Band; School Musical; Stu Cncl; Hon Roll; NHS; Peer Ldrshp 84-86; Bnd Pres 87-88; Physcl Therpy.

ANDERSEN, ELAINE; Hightstown HS; East Windsor, NJ; (2); Church Yth Grp; Spanish Clb; SADD; Var Swmmng; High Hon Roll; Hon Roll; Pres Schlr; U Of NC Chapel Hill; Acct.

ANDERSEN, KATIE; Morris Catholic HS; Rockaway, NJ; (1); 53/157; Church Yth Grp; Score Keeper; Trk; Amer Lgn Awd 86; Lawyer.

ANDERSEN, KIMBERLY; Mater Dei HS; Middletown, NJ; (4); 15/165; Rep Latin Clb; Model UN; Rep Pep Clb; Spanish Clb; Varsity Clb; Capt Powder Puff Ftbl; Var Capt Socr; Hon Roll; NHS; Latin Awd-Cum Laude 85; Spanish Awd 87; Loyola Coll; Pre-Law.

ANDERSEN, KORY A; Morris Knolls HS; Denville, NJ; (4); 39/382; Pres Chorus; School Musical; Pres Jr Cls; Pres Sr Cls; Var Capt Cheerleading; Var L Swmmng; High Hon Roll; Hon Roll; NJ Grls ST Rep 86; Elem Ed.

ANDERSON, ADRIENNE; Mount Saint Mary Acad; S River, NJ; (4); Pres Art Clb; German Clb; Nwsp Phtg; Nwsp Rptr; Yrbk Ed-Chief; Yrbk Stf; High Hon Roll; Hon Roll; Natl Art Hnr Scty Pres; Hampshire Coll; Art.

ANDERSON, ANGEL; Clifford J Scott HS; East Orange, NJ; (2); 7/382; Trs Intnl Clb; Math Clb; Math Tm; Varsity Clb; Mrchg Band; Trk; High Hon Roll; Hon Roll; Trs Jr NHS; NHS; Comp Sci.

ANDERSON, BARBARA; Green Brook HS; Green Brook, NJ; (4); 1/49; Pres AFS; Pres Church Yth Grp; Sec Thesps; School Musical; Lit Mag; Var L Tennis; NHS; Val; Girl Scts; Chorus; Frank Gannett Nwps Carrier Schlrshp 87; Jostens Fndtn Schlrshp 87; Alleghny Schlr 87; Allegheny Coll; Math.

ANDERSON, BRIAN; Paramus HS; Paramus, NJ; (2); Ski Clb; Im Bsbl; L Bowling; Trk.

ANDERSON, CRYSTAL; Edgewood Regional HS; Berlin, NJ; (2); Dance Clb; Latin Clb; Yrbk Stf; Hon Roll; Prfct Atten Awd; Dstngshd Prsn Awd 87; Cabrini Coll; Comm.

ANDERSON, DAVID; De Paul HS; Ringwood, NJ; (4); 30/170; Ski Clb; Capt Socr; Hon Roll; Soccer 2nd Tm All Cnty, 2nd Tm All Conf,1st Tm All Parachl ST 86-87; Engrng.

ANDERSON, ELIZABETH; Hunterdon Central HS; Flemington, NJ; (3); 60/543; AFS; VP Church Yth Grp; SADD; Concert Band; Drm Mjr(t); Mrchg Band; School Musical; Stu Cncl; High Hon Roll; Hon Roll; Grmn Hnrs Scty; Amer Lgn Awd; Phrmcy.

ANDERSON, J CHRISTOPHER; Tom River HS East; Toms River, NJ; (4); 26/585; Am Leg Boys St; Church Yth Grp; Chorus; Orch; Capt L Swmmng; Gov Hon Prg Awd; JETS Awd; NHS; Ntl Merit SF; St Schlr; NROTC Full Schlrshp 87; Georga A Reister Schlrshp 87; Swim Tm MVP 86; U Of VA; Sci.

ANDERSON, JACQUITA K; Morris Knolls HS; Denville, NJ; (2); Church Yth Grp; NAACP; Sftbl; Frshmn Awrnss Pgm Ldr 86; NJ ST NAACP Yth & Coll Div 3rd VP 85-87; Mrrs Cnty Yth Cncl NAACP Treas; Comp Sci.

ANDERSON, JANE; Lyndhurst HS; Lyndhurst, NJ; (2); German Clb; Chorus; Drill Tm; Drl Tm 87; Chef.

ANDERSON, JOAN; Holy Spirit HS; Absecon, NJ; (4); 10/363; 4-H; Spanish Clb; High Hon Roll; Hon Roll; NHS; NJ ST Distngshd Schlr Schlrhshp 86; Stockton NJ ST Coll.

ANDERSON, LESLIE C; Rahway HS; Rahway, NJ; (4); 1/231; French Clb; Science Clb; Teachers Aide; School Musical; High Hon Roll; Jr NHS; NHS; St Schlr; Val; Rutgers ST U; Chem.

ANDERSON, LISA; West Milford Twp HS; West Milford, NJ; (3); 57/405; Spanish Clb; SADD; Varsity Clb; Yrbk Bus Mgr; Var Stat Crs Cntry; Var Stat Sftbl; High Hon Roll; Hon Roll; Jr NHS; NHS; Ft Lauderdale; Fash Merch.

ANDERSON, MEGAN; Chatham HS; Chatham, NJ; (4); 29/94; Church Yth Grp; French Clb; Key Clb; Acpl Chr; Chorus; Yrbk Stf; Bsktbl; Tennis; Trk; Hon Roll; St Lawrence U.

ANDERSON, PETER; Columbia HS; Maplewood, NJ; (3); Church Yth Grp; Drama Clb; Rep Jr Cls; Ltry Awds 85-87; UCLA Bus Pgm Cmpltn Awd 87; Ivy League Schl.

ANDERSON, SARAH H; Lawrence HS; Cranbury, NJ; (4); French Clb; Library Aide; Chorus; Madrigals; School Musical; Yrbk Stf; Hon Roll; Schlrs Fr Dllrs, Ladies Aux Cranbury Fire Co Awd Outstndng Acdmc Achvt 87; U Of VT; Elem Educ.

ANDERSON, SUZANNE; Toms River HS North; Toms River, NJ; (3); 26/459; Spanish Clb; Yrbk Stf; Trk; High Hon Roll; Hon Roll; Voice Dem Awd; Math.

ANDERSON, WILLARD; Blair Acad; Loudonville, NY; (3); 2/100; JV Bsktbl; Var Ftbl; Var Lcrss; Var Socr; JV Trk; JV Wrstlng; Actvties Cmte 87; Bus.

ANDL, EVELYN; New Milford HS; New Milford, NJ; (4); 20/136; Pres Church Yth Grp; Library Aide; Mgr Concert Band; Mgr Jazz Band; Mgr Mrchg Band; Rptr Nwsp Stf; Cit Awd; High Hon Roll; Jr NHS; Pres Acad Fit Awd 87; Philip Nicholas Mem Scholar 87; Trenton ST Coll.

ANDRADE, CLAUDIA; Holy Rosary Academy HS; Union City, NJ; (3); Art Clb; Math Tm; Nwsp Stf; Trs Soph Cls; High Hon Roll; NHS; Ntl Merit Ltr; Computer Clb; Intnl Clb; Natl Sci Olympiad Mdl 87.

ANDRADE, MARY; Mount St Mary Acad; Bound Brook, NJ; (3); Church Yth Grp; Drama Clb; French Clb; Latin Clb; Library Aide; Service Clb; Chorus; Nwsp Rptr; Lit Mag; Hon Roll; Acad Exclnce Awd 86-87; Awd Hnr Outstndng Achvt Mus, Hnr Roll Awd 86-87; Spec Educ.

ANDRADE, MONICA; Dickinson HS; Jersey City, NJ; (3); Math Clb; Hon Roll; Med.

ANDRANOWSKI, YOLANTA; Mother Seton Regional HS; Linden, NJ; (2); Art Clb; Church Yth Grp; Computer Clb; Hosp Aide; Latin Clb; Science Clb; Spanish Clb; Chorus; Church Choir; School Play; Geom Awd Grt Imprvmnt 86-87; Awd Recrtng Schls 86-87; Union Cnty Coll; Nrsng.

ANDREADIS, TINA; Cresskill HS; Cresskill, NJ; (3); 10/104; Church Yth Grp; Drama Clb; French Clb; Girl Scts; Library Aide; Office Aide; Ski Clb; Teachers Aide; Band; Concert Band; Alpha Omega Awd 85; Ahepa Mdl Of Hnr 83; Jrnlsm.

ANDREEKO, ANDREW A; Warren Hills Regional HS; Hackettstown, NJ; (4); 24/226; Am Leg Boys St; Boy Scts; Var L Chess Clb; Concert Band; Var L Bsbl; Var L Golf; Cit Awd; Pres Schlr; All Cnty Band 85-87; Natl BS Jamboree Band 85; Army ROTC Schlrshp 4 Yr 87; Clemson U; Civil Engrng.

ANDREJCO, PAUL; North Hunterdon R HS; Clinton, NJ; (4); 99/346; Civic Clb; Computer Clb; Drama Clb; Q&S; School Play; Stage Crew; Nwsp Stf; Lit Mag; Hon Roll; Quill & Scroll Best Newspaper Cartoon 87; Comp Sci Awd 85; RI Schl Of Design; Illstrtn.

ANDREJEWSKI, KEITH; St Marys HS; Spotswood, NJ; (4); Am Leg Boys St; Scholastic Bowl; Ski Clb; School Play; Off Lit Mag; Socr; Tennis; High Hon Roll; NHS; St Schlr; Grdn ST Schlrshp, Trenton ST Alumni Schlrshp, Naval ROTC Schlrshp Fnlst 87-88; Trenton ST Coll-NJ.

ANDREOLI, JEANNE; Toms River HS North; Toms River, NJ; (3); 42/456; CAP; Drill Tm; High Hon Roll; Hon Roll; NHS; Billy Mitchell Awd 87; Acad Lttr 87; Cadet Advsry Cncl Scrtry 87; Nvgtr In US Air Force.

ANDREU, MARIA; Holy Rosary Acad; North Bergen, NJ; (3); Math Tm; Science Clb; Nwsp Ed-Chief; Yrbk Stf; VP Frsh Cls; Pres Jr Cls; JV Bsktbl; Hon Roll; NHS; Natl Sci Olympd Acad Advncd Biol & Distinction Chem 86-87; Lbrl Arts.

ANDREWS, DAWN; Paramus Catholic HS; Maywood, NJ; (3); Hosp Aide; Spanish Clb; School Play; Var Cheerleading; Hon Roll; Nrsng.

ANDREWS, DEBBIE; Orange HS; Orange, NJ; (4); 9/159; Cmnty Wkr; FBLA; Hosp Aide; SADD; Lit Mag; Crs Cntry; Trk; Hon Roll; NHS; Spanish NHS; Rutgers; Engnrng.

ANDREWS, FREDERICK; Pitman HS; Pitman, NJ; (3); Art Clb; Pres Church Yth Grp; Ski Clb; Spanish Clb; Varsity Clb; School Play; Stage Crew; Rep Frsh Cls; Rep Soph Cls; Rep Jr Cls; Comm Arts.

ANDREWS, JEFFREY A; Moorestown HS; Moorestown, NJ; (3); Am Leg Boys St; Boy Scts; Trs Service Clb; Jazz Band; Mrchg Band; School Musical; Crs Cntry; Rotary Awd; Church Yth Grp; Exploring; S Jersey Symphnc Bnd Wnd Ensmble 85-87; New Jersey All ST Bnd & All ST Orchstra 87; Bio Sci.

ANDREWS, OMEGA; Burlington City HS; Edgewater Pk, NJ; (2); Cmnty Wkr; Drill Tm; Nwsp Stf; Soph Cls; Gym; Hon Roll; RCA Engrng Prgm 86; Acad Achvmnt 86; Sttlmnt Music Schl 86; Wharton.

ANDREZO, ANA; Perth Amboy HS; Perth Amboy, NJ; (4); Key Clb; Office Aide; Ski Clb; Chorus; Church Choir; Hon Roll; Accntng.

ANDRIEUX, NAROLD; Dwight Morrow HS; Englewood, NJ; (3); 45/312; Aud/Vis; Exploring; Hosp Aide; School Play; Stage Crew; Nwsp Stf; Yrbk Stf; Lit Mag; High Hon Roll; Prfct Atten Awd; Psych.

ANDRIUOLO, FRANK; Hudson Catholic HS; Hoboken, NJ; (3); 10/200; Computer Clb; Nwsp Rptr; Nwsp Stf; Yrbk Stf; High Hon Roll; Hon Roll; Jr NHS; NHS; Bus.

ANDROS, JOSEPH; Holy Spirit HS; Brigantine, NJ; (2); 50/397; Rep Soph Cls; Hon Roll.

ANDROS, MARIE; Holy Spirit HS; Brigantone, NJ; (4); 48/363; Art Clb; Girl Scts; Crs Cntry; Fld Hcky; Physcl Ftns Awd 86; Rutgers U.

ANDRUS, JULIA; Pitman HS; Pitman, NJ; (3); Pres Church Yth Grp; Acpl Chr; Chorus; Church Choir; JV Fld Hcky; JV Capt Socr; Hon Roll; Modern Music Mstrs 87; Prvte Voice Lssns.

ANDRUS, SARAH; Baptist HS; Haddon Twp, NJ; (2); 4/30; Church Yth Grp; Hosp Aide; Band; Chorus; Yrbk Stf; Rep Stu Cncl; JV Var Fld Hcky; Hon Roll; TSAC Acad 86; Wheaton Coll; Mdcl Fld.

ANDZESKI, MARILYN R; Central Regional HS; Bayville, NJ; (4); Art Clb; Exploring; French Clb; Ski Clb; Nwsp Rptr; Stu Cncl; Hon Roll; Douglass Coll; Bus Admin.

ANEIROS, ROSANA; Linden HS; Linden, NJ; (3); Church Yth Grp; Key Clb; Library Aide; Office Aide; Yrbk Bus Mgr; Lit Mag; Hon Roll; NHS; Law.

ANGAROLA, CARLA; Hunterdon Central HS; Flemington, NJ; (4); Church Yth Grp; Hosp Aide; Latin Clb; Ski Clb; Varsity Clb; Soph Cls; Jr Cls; JV Fld Hcky; Stat Lcrss; JV Trk; West Chester U; Ed.

ANGELINI, LISA; Paulsboro HS; Gibbstown, NJ; (4); 40/155; JA; VP Sec VICA; Lit Mag; JV Bsktbl; Cheerleading; Var Fld Hcky; Sftbl; High Hon Roll; Hon Roll; Rcgntn Awd VICA Skll Olympcs 86-87; Cert Prtcptng Teen Arts Fstvl 85-86; Glou Co Vo-Tech Csmtlgy 87; Burlington Police Acad; Law.

ANGELL, DAVID; Bayonne HS; Bayonne, NJ; (4); 88/350; Rep Frsh Cls; Rep Soph Cls; Rep Jr Cls; Rep Sr Cls; Rep Stu Cncl; Wm Paterson Coll; Envrnmntl Sci.

ANGELLO, PHILIP; Monmouth Regional HS; Eatontown, NJ; (3); JCL; Latin Clb; Hon Roll; Bio.

ANGELO, LISA; Monsignor Donovan HS; Toms River, NJ; (3); Dance Clb; Girl Scts; Service Clb; Ski Clb; SADD; Sec Rep Stu Cncl; Cheerleading; Tennis; Hon Roll.

ANGELO, TABITHA DELL; Paul VI HS; Blenheim, NJ; (3); 149/518; SADD; School Musical; School Play; Yrbk Stf; Lit Mag; Var Fld Hcky; Var Sftbl; Itln Clb; Prfrmng Arts.

ANGELOTTI, PHILIP; Parsippany HS; Parsippany, NJ; (3); Pres VP FBLA; Spanish Clb; Pres Frsh Cls; Rep Soph Cls; Rep Jr Cls; Rep Sr Cls; Rep Stu Cncl; Var Bsbl; JV Bsktbl; Var Socr; Bus.

ANGELOZZI, GINA; Phillipsburg HS; Phillipsburg, NJ; (3); 69/315; Key Clb; Office Aide; Ski Clb; SADD; Bsktbl; Var L Sftbl; Var L Tennis; Hon Roll; Prfct Atten Awd; Elem Tchr.

ANGKUSTSIRI, KESINEE; West Orange HS; West Orange, NJ; (4); 1/372; Jazz Band; Mrchg Band; Orch; School Play; Lit Mag; Trs Soph Cls; Cit Awd; Pres Jr NHS; NHS; Voice Dem Awd; Gov Schl Of Public Issues At Monmouth Schlrshp 86; NJ Girls Citznshp Inst Schlrshp 86; Stanford U; Marine Biology.

ANGLIM, ALEXANDER; Point Pleasant Boro HS; Pt Pleasant, NJ; (2); Key Clb; JV Bsbl; JV Socr; Lawyer.

ANGSTER, SCOTT; Wall HS; Manasquan, NJ; (3); 6/300; Camera Clb; German Clb; Ski Clb; Yrbk Phtg; Rep Jr Cls; Socr; Tennis; High Hon Roll; Kiwanis Awd; NHS; Engrng.

ANGUS IV, WILLIAM A; Lenape HS; Medford, NJ; (3); 16/531; Am Leg Boys St; Cmnty Wkr; Varsity Clb; Var Socr; L Var Trk; Pres NHS; Pres Lenapes Rtry Interact Clb 87-88; Wshngtn Wrkshp Cngrssnl Smnr, & Rtry Yth Ldrshp Awds Conf 87; Pol Sci.

ANKIEL, CYNTHIA; Ridge HS; Basking Ridge, NJ; (3); 35/192; Church Yth Grp; Key Clb; Spanish Clb; Chorus; Concert Band; Mrchg Band; Stat Bsbl; Stat Bsktbl; Hon Roll; Music Eductrs Assn Piano Audtn 85; Hstry Educ.

ANKINS, BERNIE; Buena HS; E Vineland, NJ; (4); 31/172; FFA; Ski Clb; Capt Var Crs Cntry; Var Capt Trk; Pres Acdmc Fit Awds 87; Wood Tlnt Awd 87; Gloucester Cnty Coll.

ANNASENZ, MARIE; Mc Corristin Catholic HS; Trenton, NJ; (3); 1/268; Am Leg Aux Girls St; GAA; Pep Clb; Sec Service Clb; Nwsp Stf; Yrbk Stf; Rep Stu Cncl; High Hon Roll; NHS; Art Clb; 1st Pl Schl Sci Fair 86 & 87; Air Frc Outstndng Awd Sci & Engrng Fair, Rutgers Schlr-Rutgers ST 87.

ANNESE, ANNA; Secaucus HS; Secaucus, NJ; (3); Computer Clb; Mu Alpha Theta; Hon Roll; Mu Alpha Theta Awd; NHS; Itln Frgn Lang Awd 87; Berkley,Fshn Mrchdsng.

ANNESE, PAIGE; Paramus Catholic Girls HS; Mahwah, NJ; (3); Intnl Clb; Teachers Aide; Lit Mag; Stat Timer; Hon Roll; NHS; Rep Frsh Cls; Stat Score Keeper; Poltcl Sci.

ANNUNZIATA, THEA; Bayonne HS; Bayonne, NJ; (3); Art Clb; Church Yth Grp; Library Aide; Acpl Chr; Chorus; Mrchg Band; Swing Chorus; Lit Mag; Hon Roll; Engl Hnrs; Wrld Cltrs Hnrs; Saint Peters Coll; Poet.

ANOUGE II, CHRISTIAN; Morris Catholic HS; Landing, NJ; (3); 26/135; Natl Beta Clb; Var Bsbl; High Hon Roll; Princeton; Ophthlmlgy.

ANOUNA, LARRY; Columbia HS; South Orange, NJ; (4); 91/430; Math Tm; Science Clb; Stage Crew; Hon Roll; Ntl Merit Ltr; St Schlr; Deans Smmr Schlrs Prg Rutgers Coll 86; NJ Dstngshd Schlr 86; Rutgers U; Bio Sci.

ANSBRO, KEVIN; Toms River HS South; Toms River, NJ; (4); 27/365; Ski Clb; Variety Show; Crs Cntry; Ftbl; Var L Swmmng; Hon Roll; NHS; 3rd ST 100 Yd Bckstrk 87; Swm Tm MVP & Capt 87; All S Jersey Swim Tm 86-87; US Naval Acad; Engrng.

ANSBRO, KIM; Toms River South HS; Toms River, NJ; (3); 9/405; Ski Clb; Color Guard; Variety Show; Socr; Var Capt Swmmng; High Hon Roll; Hon Roll; NHS.

ANSTEY, CYNTHIA; Pinelands Regional HS; Tuckerton, NJ; (3); French Clb; Science Clb; Spanish Clb; Band; JV Sftbl; DAR Awd; French Hon Soc; Hon Roll; Intl Bus.

ANTAO, EDITH; Kearny HS; Kearny, NJ; (3); Am Leg Aux Girls St; French Clb; Science Clb; Yrbk Stf; French Hon Soc; High Hon Roll; Hon Roll; NHS; German Hnr Scty 87; Govr Schl Of NJ Fnlst At Cnty Level 87; Embry; Aviation Mngmnt.

ANTERAMION, VICTOR; Waldwick HS; Waldwick, NJ; (3); 5/140; Var JV Ftbl; JV Wrstlng; High Hon Roll; Hon Roll; Ntl Merit SF; Engr.

ANTHONY, DARRAN; Phillipsburg HS; Phillipsburg, NJ; (4); 51/350; Letterman Clb; Pep Clb; Varsity Clb; Rep Soph Cls; Stu Cncl; Trk; Wt Lftg; Var Capt Wrstlng; Hon Roll; NJSIAA Dist 16 Wrstlng Chmpn 85-86; Psychlgy.

ANTHONY, MICHELLE; Holy Cross HS; Maple Shade, NJ; (3); Band; Concert Band; Mrchg Band; Orch; Pep Band; School Musical; Hon Roll; Ntl Merit Ltr; Prfct Atten Awd.

ANTICO, KIMBERLY; Red Bank Catholic HS; Freehold, NJ; (3); VP French Clb; School Play; Yrbk Stf; Pres Frsh Cls; Pres Soph Cls; Rep Jr Cls; Var JV Cheerleading; Var L Trk; Hon Roll; Church Yth Grp; Exctv Brd Pres-Red Bnk Cthlc 87-88; Educ.

ANTOLINI, LEA; Vineland HS; Vineland, NJ; (3); 41/850; Sec Church Yth Grp; Dance Clb; Drama Clb; Key Clb; Pep Clb; Band; Chorus; School Musical; Rep Sr Cls; Hon Roll; Voice Prfrmnc.

ANTONAZ, ISABEL; Highland HS; Somerdale, NJ; (4); GAA; Latin Clb; Science Clb; Stu Cncl; Socr; Var Sftbl; Var Tennis; Hon Roll; NHS; Med.

ANTONELLE, GREGORY; Watchung Hills HS; Watchung, NJ; (4); 107/311; Cmnty Wkr; SADD; Variety Show; Nwsp Stf; JV Bsktbl; Var Capt Crs Cntry; Var Trk; Hon Roll; Coaches Awd Crs Cntry; Yth Mnstry Day Grpldr; Muhlenberg Coll; Bus.

ANTONOVA, PAVLINA; Lawrence HS; Lawrenceville, NJ; (3); 42/250; Dstnqshd Ldrshp Awd 87; Awd Plcd In Top 10 In JR Ntls Of Czech 83; Rutgers; Tchng.

ANTONUCCI, STEVEN F; Keyport HS; Keyport, NJ; (3); #5 In Class; Am Leg Boys St; Spanish Clb; Var Capt Bsbl; Var Capt Bsktbl; Var Capt Ftbl; Wt Lftg; Hon Roll; NHS; All Div & All Mnmth Hnrb Mntn.

ANZALDO, MARIAH; Woodstown HS; Woodstown, NJ; (3); Drama Clb; Chorus; Drm Mjr(t); School Musical; Cit Awd; Hon Roll; NHS; Rotary Awd; Church Yth Grp; English Clb; Philadelphia Colonial Hstrcl Soc Essay Contest 2nd Pl 86; NJ Schl Of Arts Winter Session 84-85; Engl.

APGAR, CHRIS; Cranford HS; Cranford, NJ; (2); JV Bsbl; MVP Ramapo Bantam Major Hockey Tm 85; Phil Little Flyers Bantam Natl Fnlsts 4th Pl 87.

APGAR, KARIN; Hunterdon Central HS; Whitehouse St, NJ; (2); 92/478; Varsity Clb; Var Bsktbl; Var L Sftbl; Hon Roll; Prfct Atten Awd.

APPARICIO, SEAN R; Piscataway HS; Piscataway, NJ; (3); Am Leg Boys St; Boy Scts; Hosp Aide; Intnl Clb; Key Clb; Math Tm; Science Clb; Spanish Clb; Varsity Clb; Rep Frsh Cls; Med.

APPEL, COURTNEY; Vernon Twsp HS; Sussex, NJ; (3); School Musical; School Play; Stage Crew; Lit Mag; Stat Fld Hcky; High Hon Roll; Hon Roll; NHS; Ntl Art Hon Society 87; Art Museum Curator.

APPEL, SCOTT; Bricktown HS; Bricktown, NJ; (3); 90/430; Hst Drama Clb; Key Clb; Service Clb; VP Temple Yth Grp; Hst Thesps; School Musical; School Play; Stage Crew; Nwsp Phtg; Hon Roll; Photo.

APPIO, JIM; Red Dank Regional HS; Little Silver, NJ; (3); Mgr Stu Cncl; Var Ftbl; High Hon Roll; Hon Roll; NHS; Ntl Merit SF; Advrtsng.

APPIO, ROCCO; Don Bosco Technical HS; W Paterson, NJ; (3); 9/93; Boys Clb Am; Boy Scts; Church Choir; School Play; Variety Show; Nwsp Sprt Ed; Nwsp Stf; JV Socr; JV Trk; Hon Roll; Military.

APPLEGATE, DARLENE; Steinert HS; Hamilton Square, NJ; (3); Hon Roll; Anml Tech.

APPLETON, SCOTT; Kinnelon HS; Kinnelon, NJ; (4); Clemson; Chem Engrng.

APPLING, EUJEANIA; Frank H Morrell HS; Irvington, NJ; (2); Church Yth Grp; Cmnty Wkr; Red Cross Aide; Church Choir; Hon Roll; Honor Rl Recogntn Awd Cert 87; Yth Chr Spiritual Grwth Cert 86; Bus Exec Secy.

AQUILINO, LORI; Paul VI HS; Somerdale, NJ; (3); 140/418; FBLA; GAA; Office Aide; Teachers Aide; Yrbk Stf; Lit Mag; Im Bowling; Pom Pon; Hon Roll; Katherine Gibbs Schl; Exec Sec.

AQUINO, ALAN; Union Hill HS; Union City, NJ; (4); Math Clb; Mu Alpha Theta; Var Bowling; Var Tennis; Hon Roll; NHS; Rutgers U; Engnrng.

ARACENA, GIANILDA; Dickinson HS; Jersey City, NJ; (4); French Clb; Swmmng; Vllybl; NHS; Rutgers Coll; Comp Sci.

ARAGON, CHRISTOPHER; Monsighnor Donovan HS; Toms River, NJ; (3); Church Yth Grp; Computer Clb; Chorus; Mrchg Band; JV Trk; Hon Roll; PA ST; Aerospc Engrng.

ARAHILL, JACQUELINE; Ramapa HS; Wyckoff, NJ; (3); 29/322; Nwsp Rptr; Yrbk Ed-Chief; Trk; High Hon Roll; Hon Roll; NHS; Girls Ctznshp Inst 87; Law Explorers 86-87; IBM Ldrshp Smnr 86; Law.

ARANETA, RUBEN; Dickinson HS; Jersey City, NJ; (4); 40/450; Computer Clb; French Clb; Q&S; Nwsp Ed-Chief; Yrbk Ed-Chief; Lit Mag; NHS; NYU; Comp Pgmmr.

ARANGIO, LUANNE; St James HS; Mullica Hill, NJ; (3); 11/88; Drama Clb; French Clb; VP SADD; School Play; Yrbk Stf; Rep Soph Cls; Rep Jr Cls; Hon Roll; NHS; Ntl Merit Ltr; Htl Mng.

ARANOW, ANDREW; Northern Valley Regional HS; Haworth, NJ; (4); 8/235; Am Leg Boys St; Chess Clb; Cmnty Wkr; Drama Clb; Intnl Clb; Political Wkr; Temple Yth Grp; School Musical; Yrbk Stf; Rep Frsh Cls; Tufts U; Polit Sci.

ARASIN, JO ANNE; St James HS; Carneys Point, NJ; (4); 8/69; Sec Hosp Aide; Service Clb; Pres SADD; School Musical; Yrbk Stf; Hon Roll; Sec NHS; Rotary Awd.

ARASZ, JAMIE; Brick Township HS; Brick, NJ; (3); 50/410; SADD; Concert Band; Jazz Band; Trs Mrchg Band; Hon Roll; Voice Dem Awd; Mst Outstndng Muscn 85-86; Music.

ARBESFELD, GLENN; Manalapan HS; Englishtown, NJ; (4); 30/417; Stage Crew; NHS; Pres Schlr; Scott Rice Fndtn Memrl Schlrshp Fnd, Qulfd Grdn ST Dstngshd Schlr Awd 86-87; NJ Inst Tech; Arch.

ARCABOS, LYNNETTE; Memorial HS; West New York, NJ; (4); 16/364; Key Clb; Office Aide; Stu Cncl; High Hon Roll; Jr NHS; NHS; PTA Schlrshp Awd; Rider Coll; Accntng.

ARCHER, DAVID E; Bordentown Regional HS; Bordentown, NJ; (4); 3/114; Sec Computer Clb; Drama Clb; Math Tm; VP Mu Alpha Theta; Capt Var Ftbl; VP NHS; Ntl Merit SF; Math Clb; Q&S; School Play; Nvl Acad Smmr Smnr 86; Olympcs Of Mind-T Fnlst 86; NROTC Schlrshp Pgm Wnr 86-87; Duke U; Cvl Engrng.

ARCHIBALD, PETRA; Weequahic HS; Newark, NJ; (4); 4/390; Computer Clb; Science Clb; Church Choir; Nwsp Stf; Lit Mag; Rep Sr Cls; Bausch & Lomb Sci Awd; High Hon Roll; NHS; Ntl Merit Ltr; Stu Of The Mnth Sep 86; Minoity HS Stu Achvmnt Awds 87; MA Inst Of Tech; Chem Engrng.

ARCHIE, DESIREE DENISE; Immaculate Conception HS; Irvington, NJ; (4); Yrbk Stf; Hon Roll; Berkeley Schl Annual Awd 87; Cert Outstndng Achvmt Bus 87; Katharine Gibbs Schl.

ARCURI, DEBRA; Parsippany HS; Parsippany, NJ; (3); Girl Scts; Band; Concert Band; Symp Band; Yrbk Stf; Lit Mag; Montclair ST Coll; Diagn Ultra.

ARELLANO, E ROBERT; Summit HS; Summit, NJ; (4); 27/271; Church Yth Grp; Red Cross Aide; Spanish Clb; Nwsp Stf; Yrbk Ed-Chief; Ftbl; NHS; Hst Ntl Merit SF; St Schlr; Stdnt Mnth 86; Centry III Ldrshp SF 87; Vet.

ARENA, JACQUELYN; Manchester Regional HS; N Haledon, NJ; (1); Art Clb; Cheerleading; Hon Roll; Spn Cmmndtn 86.

ARENA, NANCY; Holy Spirit HS; Smithville, NJ; (3); 23/332; JV Cheerleading; NHS; Nrs.

ARENCIBIA, MARILYN; St Josephs Of The Palisade; Union City, NJ; (3); VP Spanish Clb; Capt Vllybl; Hon Roll; Bus Mgnt.

ARENCIBIA, MARK; Maple Shade HS; Maple Shade, NJ; (3); Am Leg Boys St; Pres Sec DECA; FBLA; Spanish Clb; Rep Frsh Cls; Var Bsbl; Var Bsktbl; High Hon Roll; Hon Roll; Stockton.

ARENDT, EILEEN; Toms River HS North; Toms River, NJ; (4); 5/388; FBLA; High Hon Roll; NHS; 1st Pl Ocean Cnty Soil Cnsrvtn Dist Bmpr Stckr Cont 84; Cert Amer Assn U Wmn 85; 1st Pl FBLA Comp 87; Trenton ST Coll; Math.

ARENT, NANCY; Brick Township HS; Brick Town, NJ; (3); 3/410; DECA; Intnl Clb; Cit Awd; High Hon Roll; Prfct Atten Awd; Delg Girls Ctznshp Inst NJ 87; Pres Frgn Lang Clb 87-88; Hlth Occptnl Stu Am 87; Intntl Trade.

ARETZ, STEPHANIE; Buena Reg HS; Landisville, NJ; (4); 13/180; Varsity Clb; Nwsp Stf; VP Jr Cls; Stu Cncl; Var Capt Crs Cntry; Var Trk; Stat Wrstlng; Hon Roll; Jr NHS; NHS; Mst Vlbl Crss Cntry Rnnr 86; Mst Dedctd Crss Cntry Rnnr 85.

AREY, HOWARD J; The Bergen Schl; Jersey City, NJ; (4); 1/10; Art Clb; Debate Tm; French Clb; Model UN; Quiz Bowl; Spanish Clb; School Play; Yrbk Ed-Chief; Pres Stu Cncl; Stat Score Keeper; Yale Cornell; Fine Arts.

ARGESON, ALYSIA; Wayne Hills HS; Wayne, NJ; (3); #5 In Class; Am Leg Aux Girls St; Exploring; Math Clb; Sec Science Clb; Nwsp Sprt Ed; Var Capt Crs Cntry; Var Trk; High Hon Roll; VP NHS; French Clb; Girls Citznshp Inst Alg 87.

ARIA, LALENA; Long Branch HS; Long Br, NJ; (3); Dance Clb; Drama Clb; Pep Clb; School Musical; Twrlr; New England Coll; Bio Med Engrn.

ARIANI, CLAUDIA; Paul VI HS; Cherry Hill, NJ; (2); Church Yth Grp; Library Aide; Sec Frsh Cls; JV Cheerleading; JV Pom Pon; Vllybl; Hon Roll; JC Awd; Law.

ARKLISS, NADLINE; Lincoln HS; Jersy City, NJ; (4); 3/213; Hst Stu Cncl; Mgr Cheerleading; Var Crs Cntry; Capt Trk; Dnfth Awd; Hon Roll; VP Jr NHS; VP NHS; Ntl Merit Ltr; Rutgers Coll; Pre-Med.

ARMSTRONG, JANE; Kent Place Schl; Bernardsvle, NJ; (3); Debate Tm; VP GAA; Hosp Aide; VP Ski Clb; Rep Soph Cls; Pres Jr Cls; Pres Stu Cncl; Var Bsktbl; Var Fld Hcky; Var Lcrss; All Str Tmm Fld Hcky Trenton ST Coll Sprts Cmp 87.

ARMSTRONG, JODY; Ranney Schl; Middletown, NJ; (3); Latin Clb; Ski Clb; Spanish Clb; Nwsp Rptr; Nwsp Stf; Yrbk Phtg; Yrbk Stf; Capt JV Cheerleading; Var Socr; Var Capt Swmmng; Hnrb Mntn Photo Awd, MV Swmmng HS 86; Comms.

ARMSTRONG, MARCELLINE; Pemberton Township HS; Browns Mills, NJ; (2); Church Yth Grp; Math Clb; Math Tm; Band; Concert Band; Mrchg Band; Hon Roll; Church Folk Grp 85-86; 1st Yr Hnr Band Patch 86; Vet.

ARNDT, CHERYL; Boonton HS; Boonton, NJ; (3); 11/227; Church Yth Grp; Dance Clb; French Clb; GAA; Capt Crs Cntry; Var Trk; High Hon Roll; NHS; Art Awd 87.

ARNDT, JOHN P; Raritan HS; Hazlet, NJ; (3); Am Leg Boys St; Boy Scts; Church Yth Grp; Teachers Aide; Rep Frsh Cls; Rep Soph Cls; Rep Jr Cls; Var Ftbl; Var Trk; Var Wrstlng; Eagle Sct 87.

ARNEDT, JOSHUA J; Blair Acad; Branchville, NJ; (2); Capt Scholastic Bowl; Chorus; School Musical; Symp Band; Nwsp Stf; Lit Mag; Lcrss; Hon Roll; Hamilton Coll.

ARNELLA JR, BENEDICT; Christian Brothers Acad; Colts Neck, NJ; (4); Drama Clb; School Play; Stage Crew; Nwsp Stf; Yrbk Stf; Mgr(s); JV Wrstlng; Hon Roll; 2nd Hnrs; Drama Awd 87; Stu Dir 2 Prod; U Of MD; Engrng.

ARNOLD, CHRISTINE M; Notre Dame HS; Trenton, NJ; (4); 52/380; Hosp Aide; Drill Tm; Mrchg Band; Pom Pon; High Hon Roll; Hon Roll; NHS; Natl Bus Hnr Scty 85-87; E Rakers Mem Schlrshp 87; J K Riskamm Yng Ldrshp Awd 86; Mrcr Cnty CC; Scrtrl Sci.

ARNOLD, CYNTHIA; North Hunterdon HS; Clinton, NJ; (3); 21/328; Church Choir; Bsktbl; Coach Actv; Var Fld Hcky; Sftbl; High Hon Roll; Acdmc Achvt Soc 85-87; Spnsh Schvt Awd 86-87; Scl Wrk.

ARNOLD, DIAL; Woodrow Wilson HS; Camden, NJ; (3); Sec Church Yth Grp; Drama Clb; Sec FBLA; Varsity Clb; Mgr Chorus; Church Choir; School Musical; School Play; Rep Jr Cls; Capt Socr; Schlrshp Essy 87; Psych.

ARNOLD, MARGARET E; Summit HS; Morristown, NJ; (4); 20/274; Chorus; Nwsp Stf; Lit Mag; Var Capt Crs Cntry; Var Capt Trk; High Hon Roll; Hon Roll; NHS; Ntl Merit SF; Govrnr Schl SF Creatv Wrtg 85-86; Engl.

ARNOLD, MARK; De Paul Diocesan HS; Lincoln Pk, NJ; (3); 45/150; Am Leg Boys St; Church Yth Grp; Cmnty Wkr; Var Capt Bowling; Var Hon Roll; All Leag Allcnty Bwlg 87; Advrtsg.

ARNOLD, NELLY; Pennsauken HS; Pennsauken, NJ; (3); Cmnty Wkr; DECA; Political Wkr; Chorus; Swing Chorus; Yrbk Stf; JV Sftbl; Hon Roll; Jr NHS; Semi-Fnlst Walt Whitman Poetry Cntst 87; AZ ST U; Finnc.

ARNOLD, SONIA; Colonia HS; Colonia, NJ; (4); 36/250; Church Yth Grp; DECA; Drill Tm; Rep Stu Cncl; High Hon Roll; Hon Roll; Pres Cncl Schlrshp, Career Schl Schlrshp & TCI Awd 87; The Cittone Inst; Crt Reporting.

ARNOWITZ, SANDI; Morris Hills HS; Rockaway, NJ; (2); FBLA; Hosp Aide; Temple Yth Grp; School Musical; School Play; Yrbk Stf; Sftbl; Brandeis; Law.

AROCHO, BRENDA; Mary Help Of Christians Acad; Paterson, NJ; (1); Hosp Aide; Spanish Clb; SADD; Drm Mjr(t); Pep Band; School Play; Nwsp Stf; Yrbk Stf; Hon Roll; PA ST U; Med.

AROCHO, TAMMY LEE; Emerson HS; Union City, NJ; (4); 59/281; Hosp Aide; Letterman Clb; Library Aide; Color Guard; School Play; Nwsp Stf; Yrbk Stf; Sec Frsh Cls; Rep Soph Cls; Rep Jr Cls; DECA Gld Metl 85; Decthln Cert 87; Seton Hall U; Psych.

ARONSON, TRACY; Wayne Hills HS; Wayne, NJ; (2); 6/340; Math Clb; Spanish Clb; Varsity Clb; Concert Band; VP Stu Cncl; Var Bsktbl; Var Socr; JV Capt Sftbl; High Hon Roll; Mrchg Band; Hnrb Mntn Passaic Cnty Soccr 86.

ARROW, JULIE; Wayne Hills HS; Wayne, NJ; (3); 87/360; FBLA; GAA; Pep Clb; Ski Clb; Spanish Clb; Y-Teens; Rep Jr Cls; Stu Cncl; Hon Roll.

ARROYO, CHRISTOFER; Bergen Catholic HS; Hasbrouck Hts, NJ; (4); 121/261; Church Yth Grp; Computer Clb; Hosp Aide; Capt Im Bowling; Capt Im Fld Hcky; Im Vllybl; JV Wrstlng; Hon Roll; Spanish NHS; Ntl Hspnc Schlr Awds Pgm Semi Fnlst 86-87; Inroads Intnshp Pgm 86-87; UCLA; Aerospc Engnrng.

ARROYO, EVELYN; Middletown North HS; Belford, NJ; (4); 39/420; SADD; Varsity Clb; Nwsp Stf; Yrbk Phtg; Yrbk Stf; Bsktbl; Cheerleading; Hon Roll; Nwsp Rptr; Natl Hispanic Schlr Awds Pgm SF 87; FL Intl U; Crimnl Justc.

ARSI, MELANIE; Cliffside Park HS; Cliffside Park, NJ; (1); GAA; Off Frsh Cls; Sftbl; Hon Roll; Intl Frgn Lagn Awd 86; Boston.

ARTALE, JOSEPH; West Windsor-Plainsboro HS; Hightstown, NJ; (3); Spanish Clb; SADD; Stage Crew; Yrbk Stf; Var L Trk; Surgeon.

ARTEAGE, MADELYNE; Saint Patrick HS; Elizabeth, NJ; (4); Church Yth Grp; Spanish Clb; Chorus; School Play; Vllybl; Hon Roll; NHS; Rlgn Awds; FL Intl U; Accntng.

ARTHUR, SHANNON; Middletown HS South; Middletown, NJ; (4); 101/450; Pres Church Yth Grp; Dance Clb; Pres French Clb; Hosp Aide; Natl Beta Clb; Pep Clb; Ski Clb; Varsity Clb; Church Choir; School Play; Osbourne Schlrshp 87; All-Arnd Chrldr Awd 87; FL ST U; Indstrl Psychlgy.

ARTIGLIERE, DIANE G; Allentown HS; New Egypt, NJ; (3); Am Leg Aux Girls St; Drama Clb; Trs FBLA; JCL; Office Aide; Ski Clb; Chorus; Orch; Pep Band; Var Ice Hcky; Bus.

ARTIN, KEITH; Toms River HS East; Toms River, NJ; (3); 1/550; French Clb; Math Tm; Science Clb; Stu Cncl; JV Tennis; High Hon Roll; NHS; Ntl Merit Ltr; SADD; Frsh Cls; Amer Chem Soc Awd 85-86; 3rd Pl Chem 85-86; Mem Teens Eductng On Alcohol Missuse.

ARTURI, JOSEPH; St Joseph Of The Palasides HS; Jersey City, NJ; (3).

ARZT, RONALD; Brick Memorial HS; Brick, NJ; (4); 9/290; 4-H; Spanish Clb; Var Wrstlng; 4-H Awd; High Hon Roll; Hon Roll; NHS; Brick Comp Sci Inst; Comp Tech.

ASACK, ALAN; Highland Park HS; Highland Park, NJ; (4); 56/148; Radio Clb; Ftbl; Hon Roll; Ntl Merit Ltr; U Of FL; Advrtsng.

ASH, WENDY; Franklin HS; Somerset, NJ; (3); Office Aide; Var Sftbl; Hon Roll.

ASHE, PORTIA; Trenton Central HS; Trenton, NJ; (4); 27/500; Church Yth Grp; Cmnty Wkr; Church Choir; Cit Awd; High Hon Roll; Hon Roll; Myrs Acadc Excel Awd 84; Hnr Awd 84; Trenton ST; Elec Engr.

ASHER, ELANA; Bruriah HS; Allentown, PA; (3); Pres VP Temple Yth Grp; Lit Mag; Awd Judaic Stds 86; Stern Coll; Judaic Stds.

ASHTON, JENNIE ANN; Pemberton Twnshp HS; Browns Mills, NJ; (2); Cmnty Wkr; Teachers Aide; Acpl Chr; Chorus; Rep Stu Cncl; Hon Roll; Mrn Bio.

ASHTON, STACEY; Parsippany Hills HS; Parsippany, NJ; (4); 16/304; Pres Sec AFS; Hosp Aide; Sec NFL; Political Wkr; Sec Temple Yth Grp; Concert Band; Rep Stu Cncl; Stat Tennis; High Hon Roll; NHS; Inst Of Wmn Schlrs; Intl Rltns.

ASIE, ANNA; Linden HS; Linden, NJ; (3); Hosp Aide; Band; Chorus; Church Choir; Madrigals; Mrchg Band; School Musical; Stat Bsktbl; Var Cheerleading; Stat Crs Cntry; Westminister Vcl Cmp Schlrshp-Choir Booster Clb 87; Nrsg.

ASKIN, DAVINA; Lakewood Prep; Brick, NJ; (4); Scholastic Bowl; VP Sec Temple Yth Grp; Nwsp Ed-Chief; Yrbk Ed-Chief; Pres Rep Frsh Cls; Pres Rep Soph Cls; Rep Sec Stu Cncl; Var L Crs Cntry; Rgnl Exctv Brd Pres-Untd Syngog Yth NJ 86-87; Gvrnrs Schl-Pblc Issues & Ftur Of NJ 86; Comm.

ASKIN, MATTHEW; Lakewood Prep; Brick, NJ; (3); Cmnty Wkr; Math Clb; Science Clb; Temple Yth Grp; Nwsp Stf; VP Jr Cls; VP Stu Cncl; Var Tennis; NJ Region United Synagogue Yth Exec Religious Study VP 86-87; Yth Schlr Chem Pgm 86; Medicine.

ASSON, KAREN; Raritan HS; Hazlet, NJ; (3); Church Yth Grp; Band; Church Choir; Mrchg Band; Nwsp Stf; Yrbk Stf; Hon Roll; Nrsng.

ASTLE, PATRICIA C; Ocean City HS; Ocean City, NJ; (3); 92/341; Church Yth Grp; Drama Clb; SADD; Band; Church Choir; Crs Cntry; Var Swmmng; Var Trk; Hon Roll; Smwng Trphy Mst Imprvd 86-87.

ASTOR, TARA; Rancocas Valley Regional HS; Mt Holly, NJ; (3); French Clb; Quiz Bowl; Spanish Clb; Orch; School Musical; JV Fld Hcky; JV Lcrss; Rotary Club Exch Stu In Italy 87-88; Acad Achvmnt Awd 86-87; Gifted & Talented Indpndnt Mntrshp 85-87; NYCU; Interpreter.

ASTRELLA, LAURA; Pascack Hills HS; Woocliff Lk, NJ; (3); Cmnty Wkr; SADD; Lit Mag; Rep Soph Cls; Rep Jr Cls; Trs Stu Cncl; Var Capt Cheerleading; High Hon Roll; NHS; Ntl Merit Ltr; Coachs Chrldng Awd 86-87; Typng, US Hstry & Shrthnd I & II Awds 84-87; Boston Coll; Acctng.

ATHERTON, HEATHER; Highland Regional HS; Clementon, NJ; (2); VP JA; Hosp Aide; Chorus; Concert Band; Mrchg Band; Stage Crew; Nwsp Rptr; Sec Nwsp Stf; JV Fld Hcky; Trk; Rgstrd Thrpst.

ATKINS, TIFFANY; Mendham HS; Chester, NJ; (2); Church Yth Grp; Ski Clb; Im Cheerleading; Stat Socr; Hon Roll; Counseler For Transfer Stu Orentn Prog 87-88; Genesis Singers 87; Chapel Hill NC; Photogrphr.

ATKINS, VICTORIA; Deptford HS; Wenonah, NJ; (2); Church Yth Grp; Girl Scts; JV Bsktbl; Var Trk; Hon Roll; Comp.

ATKINSON, DESMOND; Holy Cross HS; Burlington, NJ; (3); German Clb; Latin Clb; Var Capt Golf; High Hon Roll; Hon Roll; Dstngshd Hnrs All Str-Glf 85; MVP-GLF 86; Hnrb Mntn-Glf-Brlngtn Cnty Opn 87; Wake Forest; Pro Glfr.

ATKINSON, MICHELLE; Salem HS; Salem, NJ; (4); Computer Clb; Hosp Aide; Math Clb; Office Aide; Ski Clb; Spanish Clb; Hon Roll; NHS; NJ Leag Nrsng Schlrshp 87; Rutgers U Camden; Nrsng.

ATKINSON, STEPHANIE; Vineland HS; Vineland, NJ; (3); 54/770; French Clb; Key Clb; Pep Clb; Band; Color Guard; Mrchg Band; Jr Cls; Bsktbl; Hon Roll; Phrmcy.

ATTANASIO, ROBERT; Freehold Twp HS; Freehold, NJ; (3); 38/385; Var Bsbl; JV Socr; FTHS Drnkng & Drvng Pstr Cntst Wnnr 86; Rutgers; Engnrng.

ATTERBURY, PATRICIA; Columbia HS; South Orange, NJ; (4); Church Yth Grp; Stafford Hall.

ATWAN, CHRISTOPHER; Don Bosco Technical HS; Wayne, NJ; (3); Computer Clb; SADD; JV Crs Cntry; JV Trk; Air Force Acad; Comp Sci.

ATWELL, DEBORAH; Cumberland Regional HS; Bridgeton, NJ; (3); 20/386; Sec Church Yth Grp; Drama Clb; Sec Exploring; JCL; Chorus; Church Choir; School Musical; Stage Crew; Im Bsktbl; Var Fld Hcky; Chem.

ATWOOD, TANYA M; Bloomfield HS; Bloomfield, NJ; (4); 6/442; Am Leg Aux Girls St; VP French Clb; Ed Key Clb; Capt Math Tm; Yrbk Stf; Stu Cncl; French Hon Soc; High Hon Roll; NHS; Pres Schlr; Natl Mrt Commended Stu 86; Hmcmng Awd 87; Blmfld Tchrs Assoc Awd 87; Lehigh U; Bus Mrktng.

AUER, DAVID; Middletown HS South; Middletown, NJ; (4); 20/456; Capt Chess Clb; Math Tm; Science Clb; Temple Yth Grp; Bausch & Lomb Sci Awd; Gov Hon Prg Awd; High Hon Roll; NHS; Ntl Merit SF; St Schlr; George Washington U Awd Math & Sci 86; Partcpnt AIME 86; Research Math.

AUER, JEFF; Monsignor Donovan HS; Island Heights, NJ; (3); Church Yth Grp; Political Wkr; Nwsp Stf; Yrbk Stf; Pres Frsh Cls; Pres Stu Cncl; Var Ftbl; Hon Roll; NHS; Im Bsktbl; Cum Laude Latin Exam 86; Brdcstng.

AUERBACH, GLENN; Morris Hills HS; Rockaway, NJ; (3); 3/265; French Clb; Math Tm; Science Clb; Off Stu Cncl; JV Bsbl; JV Bsktbl; JV Capt Socr; French Hon Soc; NHS; Ntl Merit Ltr; Math.

AUFFORT, NANCY; Baptist HS; Cherry Hill, NJ; (4); 1/45; Pres Drama Clb; Band; Chorus; School Play; Stage Crew; Trs Frsh Cls; Rep Stu Cncl; High Hon Roll; Baptist Hgh Hnr Soc 85-87; Baptist Bible Coll; Sec Ed Engl.

AUGUSTINE, AIMEE; Mary Help Of Christians Acad; Paterson, NJ; (2); Church Yth Grp; Computer Clb; Drama Clb; Quiz Bowl; School Musical; Variety Show; Im Bsktbl; Hon Roll; NEDT Awd; Law.

AUGUSTINE, STACEY; Queen Of Peace HS; Belleville, NJ; (3); 30/288; Church Yth Grp; GAA; Speech Tm; Varsity Clb; Im Bsktbl; Im Bowling; Capt Vllybl; High Hon Roll; Jr NHS; Tchg CCD Awd 85-87; Relig Ed.

AUGUSTO, ANDY; Kearny HS; Kearny, NJ; (2); Band; Concert Band; Jazz Band; Mrchg Band; School Musical; Stage Crew; Rep Soph Cls; French Hon Soc; Hon Roll.

AULETTO, LISA MARIE; Secaucus HS; Secaucus, NJ; (4); Drama Clb; Ed Key Clb; Math Clb; Mu Alpha Theta; Varsity Clb; School Play; Rep Sr Cls; Var Capt Cheerleading; Hon Roll; Mu Alpha Theta Awd; Flnst Mss Natl Teenager Pgnt 87; Montclair ST; Bus Mgmt.

AUSTIN, ALISA; Spotswood HS; Milltown, NJ; (4); Am Leg Aux Girls St; Cmnty Wkr; Girl Scts; VP Intnl Clb; Model UN; Pres Temple Yth Grp; Trs Jr Cls; Pres Sr Cls; Mgr(s); High Hon Roll; Rutgers U; Psych.

AUSTIN, FRANK; Ranney HS; Atlantic Highland, NJ; (3); 9/46; VP Spanish Clb; Nwsp Sprt Ed; Yrbk Bus Mgr; Rep Frsh Cls; Rep Soph Cls; Rep Jr Cls; Pres Stu Cncl; Var Capt Bsbl; Var Capt Bsktbl; Math Clb; In Search Of Exclince Scholar 85-88.

AUSTIN, KIMBERLY; Bridgeton HS; Bridgeton, NJ; (3); Latin Clb; Var JV Mgr(s); High Hon Roll; Hon Roll; Latin.

AUSTIN JR, WILLIAM J; St Augustine Prep HS; Franklinville, NJ; (3); 47/55; Pres Church Yth Grp; Red Cross Aide; Yrbk Stf; Lit Mag; Rep Sr Cls; L Var Wrstlng; Hon Roll; Poltcl Sci.

AUSTRIA, HAZEL G; Mt St Dominic Acad; Newark, NJ; (3); 10/53; Library Aide; Yrbk Ed-Chief; High Hon Roll; NHS; Natl SRA Cert 85; Outstndng Svc Library Cncl Cert 86-87; Comp Sci.

AUTENRIETH, DANIELLE; Pt Pleasant Beach HS; Pt Plsnt Bch, NJ; (2); Spanish Clb; Varsity Clb; Rep Stu Cncl; Var L Socr; Var L Trk; High Hon Roll; Hon Roll; Teachers Aide; Chorus; Stage Crew; Grl Grp I Rlys ST Chmpns 1st Pl 85-86, 3rd Pl 86-87; Off Awd Grl Scer 86-87; Chld Thrpy.

AUTENRIETH, STEPHANIE; Point Pleasant Beach HS; Po Pleasant Bch, NJ; (3); 6/109; Drama Clb; French Clb; Varsity Clb; School Play; Var L Mgr(s); Var L Tennis; High Hon Roll; Hon Roll; NHS; Pres Schlr; Poli Sci.

AVALA, JOHNNY; Trenton Central HS; Trenton, NJ; (3); Art Clb; Aud/Vis; Stage Crew; Variety Show; Nwsp Rptr; Off Lit Mag; Pres Frsh Cls; CC Awd; Cit Awd; Hon Roll; NY U; Flmmkng.

AVALLONE, CHARLIE; Maple Shade HS; Maple Shade, NJ; (2); Computer Clb; Spanish Clb; Rep Soph Cls; JV Crs Cntry; JV Trk; High Hon Roll; Hon Roll.

AVEDISSIAN, MONIQUE; Cherry Hill E HS; Cherry Hill, NJ; (3); French Clb; Latin Clb; School Play; Im Mgr Bsbl; Im Mgr Fld Hcky; Im Mgr Lcrss; Im Tennis; Im Vllybl; Hon Roll; Frtrnl Ordr Of Polc 85.

AVERILL, JASON; Lower Cape May Regional HS; W Cape May, NJ; (3); 8/192; Band; Concert Band; Drm Mjr(t); Jazz Band; Mrchg Band; Orch; School Musical; Var Trk; Hon Roll; NHS; Engrng.

AVERILL, LAURIE; Palmyra HS; Riverton, NJ; (4); 11/117; French Clb; Yrbk Stf; Rep Stu Cncl; Var Capt Socr; Var Capt Trk; Hon Roll; NHS; SADD; Varsity Clb; Nwsp Stf; 1st Team Frdm Div Scer Mdfld 86; Elizabeth Mc Donald Schlrshp 87; Hmcmng Rep 84-86; Cook Coll; Bio.

AVERSA, FRANCES; Highland Regional HS; Erial, NJ; (2); Cum Laude Awd 85-86; MD.

AVERSANO, SCOTT P; The Lawrenceville Schl; Yardley, PA; (4); Drama Clb; School Musical; School Play; Nwsp Rptr; Nwsp Stf; Lit Mag; Var Ftbl; Hon Roll; Ntl Merit SF; Dramatic Arts Prize 86; French Prize 84; Engl Prize 84; Yale.

AYALA, IVETTE; Dover HS; Dover, NJ; (2); Art Clb; Camera Clb; Computer Clb; Math Clb; Science Clb; Spanish Clb; SADD; Tennis; Vllybl; Hon Roll; Comp Sci.

AYALA, JOANNE; Hoboken HS; Hoboken, NJ; (3); Spanish Clb; Chorus; Trs Frsh Cls; Trs Soph Cls; Trs Jr Cls; Var Cheerleading; Hon Roll; Peer Ldrshp Pgm 87; Aspira Clb 84-86.

AYALA, MAYRA; Our Lady Of Good Counsel HS; Newark, NJ; (3); 50/121; Teachers Aide; Chorus; Church Choir; School Musical; School Play; CCD Volunteer Awd 86-87; Criminal Law.

AYAYO, CHRIS; Emerson HS; Emerson, NJ; (4); 2/97; French Clb; Math Tm; School Play; Stage Crew; Nwsp Phtg; Yrbk Phtg; Stu Cncl; Coach Actv; Capt Ftbl; Capt Trk; Garden ST Dist Schlr, Pres Acad Ftns Awd, Ltr Cmndtn Natl Merit 87; Rutgers Coll; Pol Sci.

AYRES, KIMBERLY; Gateway Regional HS; Wenonah, NJ; (2); French Clb; FHA; SADD; Stat Bsbl; Var Diving; JV Fld Hcky; Var Swmmng; Hon Roll; Gateway HS Gator Mnth 86.

AZARCON, VINCENT; Holy Spirit HS; Linwood, NJ; (2); 37/397; Boy Scts; Nwsp Ed-Chief; Elks Awd; High Hon Roll; Hon Roll; Kiwanis Awd; Ntl Merit Ltr; Prfct Atten Awd; Plstc Srgry.

AZIZ, ABID; West Windsor Plainsboro HS; Princeton Jct, NJ; (3); 1/320; Am Leg Boys St; Capt Debate Tm; Hosp Aide; Math Tm; Orch; Nwsp Bus Mgr; High Hon Roll; NHS; St Schlr; Voice Dem Awd; Lawrencevlle Schl Summr Sci Inst Scholar 86; Black Hstry Mnth Awd 86-87; Islamic Schl Essay Wnnr 85; Biochem.

AZMY, BAHER; Princeton HS; Princeton, NJ; (3); Chess Clb; Debate Tm; Math Tm; Model UN; Nwsp Stf; Ntl Merit SF; Bus.

AZZARANO, ANTHONY; Washington Township HS; Sewell, NJ; (3); 80/500; German Clb; Nwsp Ed-Chief; Nwsp Rptr; Nwsp Stf; Im Vllybl; Hon Roll; Delta Epsilon Phi Ntl German Hon Soc 87; Law.

AZZARITI, JENNIFER A; Dwight Morrow HS; Englewood, NJ; (4); 6/229; Math Tm; School Play; Stage Crew; Yrbk Ed-Chief; Sec Soph Cls; JV Vllybl; High Hon Roll; Hon Roll; NHS; Congress Schlr 87; 1st Pl Leonardo Davinci Art Soc Cntst 85; Smith Coll; Poltcl Sci.

AZZINNARI, GINA; Franklin HS; Somerset, NJ; (3); Art Clb; SADD; Band; Im Gym; Art Awds 85-86; Beauty Culture.

AZZOLINA, ANDREA; North Hunterdon HS; Clinton, NJ; (4); Church Yth Grp; Dance Clb; Drama Clb; French Clb; FBLA; Girl Scts; Yrbk Stf; Stu Cncl; Trk; Our Lady Lourdes Knghts Columbus Hmntrn Awd 87; American U; Jrnlsm.

BABCOCK, JOE; Raritan HS; Hazlet, NJ; (3); 75/300; Band; Ftbl; Music.

BABCOCK, MAUREEN; Barnstable Acad; Mahwah, NJ; (4); Church Yth Grp; SADD; School Musical; School Play; Variety Show; Nwsp Rptr; Yrbk Stf; Pres Sr Cls; Hon Roll; Stage Crew; Mst Imprvd Prfrmer Act II 84-85; Wright ST; Mscl Thtrtr.

BABER, SHARON; South River HS; South River, NJ; (3); 14/130; German Clb; Spanish Clb; Rep Stu Cncl; JV Var Cheerleading; JV Var Sftbl; Jr NHS; NHS; 1st Tm Al-Cnty Sftbl, 2nd Tm Al-St 87; Grap I Sftbl 1st Tm; Al Grap Sftbl 2nd Tm 87; Psych.

BABEY, MARK; Hillsborough HS; Somerville, NJ; (3); 20/340; French Clb; Latin Clb; Off Stu Cncl; Trk; Hon Roll; Jrnlsm.

BABILINO, GINA; Our Lady Of Mercy Acad; Turnersvile, NJ; (4); Dance Clb; Soroptimist; Nwsp Rptr; Pres Soph Cls; Pres Jr Cls; Pres Stu Cncl; Dnfth Awd; Hon Roll; NHS; Ntl Merit SF; Srptmst Intl Vnlnd Schlrshp 86-87; GFWC JR Wmns Clb WA Twp Schlrshp 86-87; Amer Lgn Awd 86-87; La Salle U; Bio.

BABINSKI, CARL; Kearny HS; Kearny, NJ; (3); 18/383; Am Leg Boys St; German Clb; Band; Chorus; Concert Band; Jazz Band; Mrchg Band; School Musical; Yrbk Stf; High Hon Roll; Ger Natl Hnr Soc 87.

BABOLA, KIM; Notre Dame HS; Mercerville, NJ; (3); 43/270; Drama Clb; Ski Clb; SADD; School Play; Variety Show; Yrbk Stf; Rep Stu Cncl; Stat Bsktbl; High Hon Roll; Hon Roll; Bus.

BABULSKI, LISA K; Linden HS; Linden, NJ; (3); 2/350; French Clb; Key Clb; Science Clb; Nwsp Stf; VP Soph Cls; Rep Stu Cncl; Var Capt Sftbl; Var Tennis; High Hon Roll; NHS.

BABUSCHAK, GRETCHEN; Monsignor Donovan HS; Toms River, NJ; (3); Art Clb; Church Yth Grp; Drama Clb; Ski Clb; Thesps; School Musical; School Play; Stage Crew; Hon Roll; 3rd Pl Over All Window Painting Cont 86; Schl Muscl Publcty Photogrphy 87, Schls 25th Anniv 86-87; Theatrcl Arts.

BABUSCHAK, TORI; Nottingham HS; Mercervill%, NJ; (3); Varsity Clb; Chorus; Cheerleading; Sftbl; Hon Roll; Principals List 85-86; Fashn Merch.

BABYAK, KARLEEN; Linden HS; Linden, NJ; (3); French Clb; Key Clb; Pres Chorus; Stage Crew; Rep Soph Cls; Rep Stu Cncl; Hon Roll; NHS.

BACCARELLA, MICHELE; Holy Family Acad; Bayonne, NJ; (4); 3/130; Church Yth Grp; NFL; Chorus; Nwsp Rptr; Lit Mag; Bowling; CC Awd; Elks Awd; High Hon Roll; Sec NHS; Alumnae Awd, Hist Mdl 87; Roger Williams Coll; Jrnlsm.

BACCELLIERI, CARL R; Lenape HS; Mt Laurel, NJ; (3); Am Leg Boys St; Boy Scts; Chess Clb; German Clb; High Hon Roll; Hon Roll; NHS; Rep Jr Cls; JV Gym; German Natl Hnr Soc 86-87; Cornell.

BACH, TAMI L; Paul VI HS; Blackwood, NJ; (4); 2/511; Cmnty Wkr; Hosp Aide; SADD; Concert Band; Capt Cheerleading; Hon Roll; Sec NHS; Sal; Trs Spanish NHS; Hmcmg Qn 86-87; 1st Rnnr Up Camden Co JR Miss Prgm 86-87; Accompianist-Choirs, Sngrs & Plays 83-87; Med.

BACHI, MARYLYN; Holy Spirit HS; Margate, NJ; (2); 11/397; Var Trk; Im Vllybl; Hon Roll.

BACHMAN, CHRISTINA; Toms River H S East; Toms River, NJ; (3); Dance Clb; Key Clb; Drill Tm; Mrchg Band; Variety Show; Co-Capt Pom Pon; High Hon Roll; Hon Roll; Acad Lttr 85; Accntng Awd 86; Law.

BACHMURA, DEBRA; Morristown-Beard HS; Randolph, NJ; (3); AFS; Church Yth Grp; Drama Clb; Hosp Aide; Service Clb; School Musical; School Play; Var Cheerleading; JV Vllybl; Hon Roll; Natl Art Hnr Scty 87; Public Svc Electric & Gas Co Art Cont 86; Psychobiology.

BACHO, BRETT; Phillipsburg HS; Phillipsburg, NJ; (4); 4/315; VP Exploring; Capt Scholastic Bowl; Ski Clb; Band; Bsktbl; L Var Tennis; High Hon Roll; Trs NHS; VFW Awd; Exch Clb Yth Of Mnth 87; Bst All Arnd 87; Lafayette Coll Grnt 87; Lafayette Coll; Rbtcs Engr.

BACKER, SAMANTHA; Vernon Township HS; Highland Lks, NJ; (3); Dance Clb; SADD; School Musical; Rep Stu Cncl; Var Swmmng; Hon Roll; NHS; Drama Clb; Temple Yth Grp; Varsity Clb; GATE; SR Advsr Incoming Frshmn; Eng.

BACON, ANNETTE; Hopewell Valley Central HS; Pennington, NJ; (4); 25/200; AFS; Church Yth Grp; Service Clb; Nwsp Rptr; Nwsp Sprt Ed; Rep Stu Cncl; Capt L Bsktbl; Capt L Sftbl; High Hon Roll; NHS; Hi-Profcncy Arch Drwng Awd 87; All-Mercer All Cnty All CVC Sftbl Tm 87; PA ST U; Arch Engrng.

BACON, BRUCE H; Salem HS; Salem, NJ; (3); 33/170; Am Leg Boys St; Computer Clb; Math Tm; Ski Clb; Spanish Clb; SADD; Rep Frsh Cls; Rep Soph Cls; Rep Stu Cncl; Var Bsbl; Stu Of Mnth 84-85; Capt Ftbl Team 84-85; Capt JV Ftbl Team 85-86.

BADALMENTI, TERESA; Morristown HS; Morristown, NJ; (3); Church Yth Grp; Red Cross Aide; Band; Church Choir; Concert Band; School Musical; Variety Show.

BADHEKA, PRANAV; Dickinson HS; Jersey City, NJ; (3); Camera Clb; Cmnty Wkr; Computer Clb; Exploring; Math Clb; Math Tm; Scholastic Bowl; Science Clb; Rep Jr Cls; Hon Roll; Mech Engrng.

BADUKLU, ARZU; Mary Help Of Christians Acad; Paterson, NJ; (2); Computer Clb; Drama Clb; English Clb; SADD; Chorus; School Musical; Trs Soph Cls; Bsktbl; Hon Roll; Natl Ed Dev Test Awd 86; NJIT Stu Sci Training Pgm Awd 85; Montclair ST Coll Prep Awd 85; Med.

BAE, SANG; Northern Valley Regional HS; Harrington Pk, NJ; (3); Church Yth Grp; Hosp Aide; Ski Clb; Spanish Clb; Band; Concert Band; Orch; Symp Band; JV Bsbl; JV Ftbl; U MA; Bus.

BAER, JAMES; Burlington City HS; Edgewater Pk, NJ; (3); Am Leg Boys St; Var Wrstlng; Pharm.

BAETIONG, CECILIA; Lakewood HS; Lakewood, NJ; (3); 67/330; Drama Clb; FBLA; Spanish Clb; Hon Roll; U Philippines; Dentstry.

BAGATELLE, ADRIEN; Wayne Hills HS; Wayne, NJ; (3); 93/320; Pres Cmnty Wkr; Library Aide; Model UN; Office Aide; Ski Clb; Spanish Clb; Temple Yth Grp; JV Socr; Stat Trk; Hon Roll; Pre-Med.

BAGDI, WENDY; Toms River HS East; Toms River, NJ; (4); 2/560; Hosp Aide; Spanish Clb; SADD; Capt Bsktbl; Mgr(s); Pom Pon; Powder Puff Ftbl; Pres NHS; Sal; St Schlr; Boston Coll; Bus.

BAGLIO, MICHAEL; Millville SR HS; Haleyville, NJ; (3); 70/545; Pres Church Yth Grp; VP 4-H; Var Bsbl; JV Ftbl; Var Trk; 4-H Awd; Hon Roll; Navy; Engrng.

BAGNOLE, WENDY; Immaculate Conception HS; Bloomfield, NJ; (2); Camera Clb; Science Clb; Chorus; Variety Show; Nwsp Rptr; Tennis.

BAGTAS, RUBY; Mary Help Of Christians Acad; Paterson, NJ; (3); 6/83; Hosp Aide; Letterman Clb; SADD; Drill Tm; Nwsp Rptr; Pres Soph Cls; Score Keeper; Sftbl; Hon Roll; NHS; William Paterson; Elem Ed.

BAGUER, EDWARD; Esses Catholic Boys HS; N Newark, NJ; (3); 3/150; Nwsp Stf; VP Sr Cls; Rep Stu Cncl; Var L Ftbl; CC Awd; Cit Awd; High Hon Roll; NHS; Ntl Merit Schol; US JR Olympc Natl Cadt Fencg Champ 87; Mst Outstndng Fencr 87; MIP Ftbl 86-87; Comp Sci.

BAHR, GINNY; Middletown HS South; Lincroft, NJ; (2); Cmnty Wkr; Teachers Aide; L Var Gym; Var Trk; Grls Gymnstcs MVP & Coachs Awd 85-86.

BAHRKE, PATRICIA; Livingston HS; Livingston, NJ; (3); 84/470; JA; Nwsp Rptr; Rep Frsh Cls; Rep Soph Cls; Stat Bsktbl; Mgr(s); Powder Puff Ftbl; Trk; Hon Roll; Jr NHS; U Of WI; Chld Psychlgy.

BAHTIARIAN, DONNA V; Northern Valley Regional HS; Closter, NJ; (4); 15/238; Trs Frsh Cls; Trs Jr Cls; Pres Sr Cls; Var Bsktbl; Var Capt Trk; Hon Roll; NHS; Model UN; Ski Clb; Sr Athlete Of Yr 87; U S Army Reserve Schlr Athl Awd 87; Armenian Stu Assoc-Silver Medal Awd 87; Boston Coll; Business.

BAI, MARIO; St Peters Prep; Lodi, NJ; (4); 19/207; Pres Camera Clb; Sec Computer Clb; Dance Clb; Drama Clb; French Clb; Math Clb; Math Tm; Pres Radio Clb; Stage Crew; Ed Nwsp Phtg; US Naval Acad Smmr Schlr, Rutgers Deans Smmr Schlr 86; Garden State Dstngshd Schlr 87; Carnegie-Mellon U; Comp Prgmmr.

BAILEY, JENNIFER; Collingswood HS; Collingswood, NJ; (3); Church Yth Grp; Library Aide; Office Aide; Yrbk Bus Mgr; Yrbk Stf; JV Fld Hcky; Var Gym; JV Lcrss; Hon Roll; Sprts Awd Sftbll & Field Hockey 86-87; Phys Thrpst.

BAILEY, JENNIFER; Haddonfield Memorial HS; Haddonfield, NJ; (4); Church Yth Grp; Intnl Clb; Spanish Clb; Capt Flag Corp; Stat JV Bsktbl; Mgr(s); Var L Trk; High Hon Roll; NHS; Spanish NHS; Ursinus Coll; Intl Bus.

BAILEY, JOSEPH; Wayne Hills SR HS; Wayne, NJ; (3); 6/306; Boy Scts; Math Clb; Sec Nwsp Phtg; Yrbk Phtg; Var Socr; Var Trk; CC Awd; Cit Awd; High Hon Roll; NHS; Engrng.

BAILEY, LISA D; Vineland HS; Vineland, NJ; (4); French Clb; Key Clb; Office Aide; Pep Clb; Spanish Clb; Nwsp Bus Mgr; Nwsp Rptr; Nwsp Stf; Lit Mag; Rep Sr Cls; Commended Stu Natl Achvt Scholar Pgm; Hugh N Boyd Urban Jrnlsm Wrkshp Rider Coll 86; Hofstra U; Mass Cmmnctns.

BAILEY, SHAWNELLE; Snyder HS; Jersey City, NJ; (4); 2/197; Cmnty Wkr; JA; Letterman Clb; Scholastic Bowl; L Sftbl; CC Awd; Hon Roll; NHS; Prfct Atten Awd; Sal; Stockton ST Coll; Bus Mngmt.

BAIN, EMILY; Bridgeton HS; Bridgeton, NJ; (2); Art Clb; GAA; Math Tm; Office Aide; Varsity Clb; Crs Cntry; Trk; Ntl Merit Ltr; Prfct Atten Awd; Med.

BAIN, MICHAEL; Wayne Valley HS; Wayne, NJ; (3); Computer Clb; Math Tm; Model UN; Mrchg Band; Nwsp Rptr; Lit Mag; Var Swmmng; High Hon Roll; NHS; All-Conf Swim Tm 86; Fnlst-NJ Gvrnrs Schl Of Sci 87; Bio Sci.

BAINE, JULIE; Brick Memorial HS; Point Pleasant, NJ; (4); 8/290; Cmnty Wkr; VP Key Clb; Math Tm; Ski Clb; Yrbk Phtg; Im Socr; Var Tennis; High Hon Roll; Trs NHS; Schl Exchng Stu To Greece 87; Just Say No To Drugs Schl Rep 87; Archoelgy.

BAIRD, AIMEE ANNE; Northern Valley Regional HS; Norwood, NJ; (4); 28/283; Pres AFS; Drama Clb; Hosp Aide; Band; Concert Band; Mrchg Band; School Musical; School Play; Symp Band; JP Sousa Awd; U Of VA; Psychology.

BAJGER, JACQUELINE; Roselle Catholic HS; Linden, NJ; (3); 15/213; French Clb; SADD; Church Choir; Variety Show; Rep Frsh Cls; Rep Stu Cncl; French Hon Soc; Hon Roll; NHS; High Hon Roll; NJIT; Chem Engrng.

BAKER, ANDREW S; Spotswood HS; Milltown, NJ; (2); 1/127; Intnl Clb; Model UN; Science Clb; School Play; Yrbk Stf; Rep Stu Cncl; Var Crs Cntry; Var Trk; High Hon Roll; Hon Roll; Cross Cntry All Div 1st Tm 86.

BAKER, BRIAN; Wayne Valley HS; Wayne, NJ; (3); Church Yth Grp; FBLA; Var Golf; Hon Roll; Prfct Atten Awd; Sking JV & Vrsty 85-87; Bus.

BAKER, DONYALE; Cherry Hill High Schl West; Cherry Hill, NJ; (4); Church Yth Grp; Boys Clb Am; Teachers Aide; Stu Cncl; Var Mgr(s); Var Swmmng; Var Trk; Hmcmg Qn 86; Hall Fm 87; Millersville U.

BAKER, JAMI; Eastern Christian HS; Newark, NJ; (3); 7/88; Off Church Yth Grp; Chorus; Church Choir; School Play; Nwsp Rptr; Sec Stu Cncl; Bsktbl; Socr; Cit Awd; High Hon Roll; Psychology.

BAKER, JODI M; Spotswood HS; Milltown, NJ; (4); 15/186; Am Leg Aux Girls St; Intnl Clb; Spanish Clb; Color Guard; Yrbk Sprt Ed; Sec Stu Cncl; Stat Crs Cntry; Mgr(s); Score Keeper; Timer; Garden ST Dist Schlr.

BAKER, LALENA; Highland Regional HS; Blackwood, NJ; (2); Drama Clb; GAA; Trs Spanish Clb; School Musical; School Play; Nwsp Rptr; Cheerleading; Hon Roll; Coach Twnshp Chrldrs 86-87; Princeton Coll; Actrs.

BAKER, RICHARD; Toms River South HS; Beachwood, NJ; (3); 32/405; Ftbl; High Hon Roll; Hon Roll; Rutgers; Dentistry.

BAKER, TYRONE; Essex Catholic Boys HS; Irvington, NJ; (3); Church Yth Grp; Var Crs Cntry; Var Trk; Hon Roll; Howard U; Elec Engr.

BAKHSH, SHAMEELA; Academic HS; Jersey City, NJ; (3); Boy Scts; Spanish Clb; Tennis; High Hon Roll; Hon Roll; NHS; Psych.

BAKIA, MARIANNE; Manalapan HS; Englishtown, NJ; (4); 70/437; Aud/Vis; Church Yth Grp; Ed Nwsp Stf; Yrbk Stf; Rep Frsh Cls; Rep Sr Cls; JV Var Mgr(s); Trk; Lwyr.

BAKMAN, LANA; Bloomfield HS; Bloomfield, NJ; (3); Aud/Vis; Computer Clb; Hon Roll; Teachers Aide; Aud/Vis Stff Awd 86-87; Svc Cls Of 88 86-87; Engrng.

BAKOS, DENNIS; Hunterdon Central HS; Flemington, NJ; (4); 46/560; French Clb; SADD; Band; Chorus; Jazz Band; School Musical; Variety Show; Pres Frsh Cls; Pres Soph Cls; Pres Jr Cls; Century III Schlrshp 87; Dartmouth Bk Awd 86; Schlr/Athlt Awd MVP Awd 84 & 85; Engrng.

BAKOS, GWEN; Red Bank Catholic HS; Atlantic Highland, NJ; (3); Church Yth Grp; Exploring; Science Clb; Ski Clb; VP SADD; Chorus; Powder Puff Ftbl.

BAKOS, JENNIFER; Linden HS; Linden, NJ; (2); Church Yth Grp; Computer Clb; FHA; Key Clb; Office Aide; Pep Clb; Pom Pon; High Hon Roll; Hon Roll; NHS; Fashn Inst Tech; Fshn.

BAL, KEITH M; St Joseph Of The Palisades HS; Union City, NJ; (3); #2 In Class; Hon Roll; Comp Sci.

BALABIS, CHRIS; Cherry Hill West HS; Cherry Hill, NJ; (3); Latin Clb; Library Aide; Im Socr; Hon Roll; Engrng.

BALDERSTONE, THOMAS C; Cherry Hill HS East; Cherry Hill, NJ; (4); FCA; Model UN; SADD; Thesps; Acpl Chr; School Play; Variety Show; Pres Frsh Cls; Pres Soph Cls; Rep Sr Cls; Boys ST 86; Drexel U; Math.

BALDES, CHRISTINE; Manalapan HS; Englishtown, NJ; (3); Var L Crs Cntry; JV Var Socr; Var L Trk; NHS; Natl Hon Soc 86-87; Capt & Let Wnnr Crss Cntry 84-87; Track 2 Time Letter Wnnr; Chld Psychlgy.

BALDINO, CHRISTINE; Audubon HS; Audubon, NJ; (3); Office Aide; Teachers Aide; Mrchg Band; Yrbk Phtg; Var Capt Tennis; Hon Roll; Civic Clb; German Clb; Band; Concert Band; Govt Day Rep 86-87; Chld Psych.

BALDO, CARA; Manchester Regional HS; N Haledon, NJ; (1); Spanish Clb; Pres Frsh Cls; JV Cheerleading; Spnsh Awd Hghn Avg 86; Comp Eng.

BALDWIN, CHARLONDA A; Malcolm X Shabazz HS; Newark, NJ; (4); 52/265; Boys Clb Am; Church Yth Grp; Cmnty Wkr; Computer Clb; Chorus; Mrchg Band; Rep Stu Cncl; JV Badmtn; Capt Cheerleading; Swmmng; Awd Gov Leon Refer Pollution 85; Stockton ST Coll; Nrsng.

BALDWIN, JENNIFER; Middletown HS South; Ft Monmouth, NJ; (3); Church Yth Grp; Thesps; Acpl Chr; School Musical; School Play; Variety Show; Hon Roll; NHS; Drama Clb; German Clb; All Shore Chorus 87; German Hon Soc 86-87; Bio.

BALE, ASHA; John P Stevens HS; Edison, NJ; (3); 11/457; Cmnty Wkr; Debate Tm; Model UN; Science Clb; Mrchg Band; Nwsp Stf; Yrbk Ed-Chief; French Hon Soc; Hon Roll; NHS; Lebanon Vly Coll Hnrs Pgm Sci 87; 100 Hr, 250 Hr Srvc Awd Hosp 86-87; Med.

BALES, DOMINIQUE; Morristown-Beard HS; Mt Tabor, NJ; (3); AFS; Concert Band; Yrbk Stf; Sec Jr Cls; Var Capt Cheerleading; Var Lcrss; Hon Roll; Socl Wrk.

BALF, DEBORAH A; Toms River HS South; Beachwood, NJ; (4); 14/329; Mrchg Band; Symp Band; Powder Puff Ftbl; Capt Sftbl; Swmmng; High Hon Roll; Hon Roll; NHS; Pres Schlr; Acdmc Lets 84-87; Ithaca Coll; Spch Pthlgy.

BALICA, ANA; Kearny HS; Belleville, NJ; (4); 16/380; German Clb; Science Clb; Ski Clb; Chorus; JV Crs Cntry; JV Trk; High Hon Roll; Hon Roll; NHS; Chrch Yth Grp; VP Grmn Clb; Dela-Epsilon-Phi Grmn Hnr; Soc 85; JV Awd 85; Ntl Sci Olympd 86; NY U; Bio,Dntstry.

BALIS, ERIC; Morris Knolls HS; Rockaway, NJ; (2); Computer Clb; Service Clb; Temple Yth Grp; Varsity Clb; Pres Soph Cls; Rep Stu Cncl; JV Socr; Var L Tennis; High Hon Roll; Hon Roll; Law.

BALISTA, TONI; Manchester Twp HS; Lakehurst, NJ; (4); 25/165; Dance Clb; French Clb; Girl Scts; Stage Crew; Var Capt Crs Cntry; Var Capt Trk; God Cntry Awd; Hon Roll; Prfct Atten Awd; JV Bsktbl; Girls State Delegate 86; Rutgers U; Chld Psych.

BALL, CHRISTOPHER; Union Catholic Regional HS; N Plainfield, NJ; (4); 4/293; Am Leg Boys St; Debate Tm; Quiz Bowl; Science Clb; Service Clb; Nwsp Ed-Chief; JV Swmmng; High Hon Roll; NHS; Ntl Merit Ltr; Law Day Essay Cont 86; Pol Sci.

BALLARD, CASIE; Bricktown HS; Brick Town, NJ; (3); Band; Mrchg Band; Rep Stu Cncl; Capt Var Gym; High Hon Roll; FL Inst Of Tech; Marine Bio.

BALLAS, ANGELA; Camden Catholic HS; Pennsauken, NJ; (3); Church Yth Grp; Dance Clb; FBLA; Pep Clb; Spanish Clb; Variety Show; Nwsp Stf; Cheerleading; Tennis; Cit Awd; Johnson & Wales Coll; Fshn Mrch.

BALLASTY, ROBERT M; Mater Dei HS; Middletown, NJ; (4); 10/147; Model UN; Mrchg Band; School Musical; Ed Nwsp Ed-Chief; Ed Yrbk Ed-Chief; Yrbk Phtg; Ed Yrbk Sprt Ed; Mgr(s); NHS; Ntl Merit SF; Garden ST Distngshd Schlr 86; Msgr Robert T Bulman Scholar 83; Aerontcl Engrng.

BALLAUER, CANDY; Washington Twp HS; Sewell, NJ; (3); French Clb; SADD; Rep Stu Cncl; Var L Gym; U Of MI; Aerodynmcs.

BALLINA, MICHAEL; Toms River HS South; Toms River, NJ; (4); 38/328; Church Yth Grp; Cmnty Wkr; Red Cross Aide; Teachers Aide; Band; Chorus; Church Choir; Concert Band; Jazz Band; Mrchg Band; Emergency Med Tech 87; 1st Aid Sqd 85-87; Natl Piano Plyg Gld & Top Tlnt 85-86; Ocean County Coll; Med Tech.

BALLINA, STEPHEN; Toms River HS South; Toms River, NJ; (2); Teachers Aide; Band; Mrchg Band; Orch; School Musical; Symp Band; High Hon Roll; Hon Roll; All South Jrsy Band 86-87; Grdn St Phlhrmnc Yth Orchstra 86-87; Music Educ.

BALLON, LUISITO; Essex Catholic Boys HS; East Orange, NJ; (3); 6/31; Aud/Vis; Church Yth Grp; Rep Frsh Cls; Rep Soph Cls; Rep Jr Cls; Rep Stu Cncl; JV Var Crs Cntry; High Hon Roll; Hon Roll; NHS; PA ST U; Engrng.

BALLOTTA, ANGELA; Monroe Twp HS; Spotswood, NJ; (4); 30/193; Ski Clb; Chorus; VP Soph Cls; VP Jr Cls; Trs Sr Cls; Stu Cncl; JV Var Cheerleading; High Hon Roll; Hon Roll; NHS; U Of Dayton; Psychlgy.

BALOG, JAMES; Woodbridge SR HS; Woodbridge, NJ; (2); 15/350; Cmnty Wkr; Computer Clb; Hosp Aide; Quiz Bowl; Scholastic Bowl; Band; Concert Band; School Musical; Pre-Med.

BALOT, DAVID; Manchester Twp HS; Toms River, NJ; (2); Drama Clb; Science Clb; Spanish Clb; Tennis; Rutgers; Bus.

BALOT, LINDA; Manchester Twp HS; Toms River, NJ; (2); Math Tm; Science Clb; SADD; Bsktbl; Tennis; Trk; High Hon Roll; Kiwanis Awd; Spanish Clb; Temple Yth Grp; Stu Of Mnth Math 85, Scl Stud 85, Spnsh 87; U Of PA; Vet Med.

BALSLEY, ELIZABETH; North Hunterdon HS; Lebanon, NJ; (4); Church Yth Grp; JCL; Latin Clb; Band; Mrchg Band; Stu Cncl; JV Var Ftbl; Stat Lcrss; Im Wt Lftg; Hon Roll; Albright Coll; Pltcl Sci.

BALTIMAE, JOY; Orange HS; Orange, NJ; (3); 3/180; Church Yth Grp; Cmnty Wkr; Capt Color Guard; Yrbk Stf; Pres Frsh Cls; Pres Soph Cls; Pres Stu Cncl; Gov Hon Prg Awd; Hon Roll; Trs NHS; Rutgers U; Sci.

BALTOZER, ROSE; Sacred Heart HS; Glassboro, NJ; (4); 7/63; Church Yth Grp; French Clb; School Play; Yrbk Rptr; Yrbk Stf; Var JV Bsktbl; Var JV Sftbl; High Hon Roll; Hon Roll; NHS; Ntl Hist Gov Awd 86-87; Ntl Math Awd 86; Ldrshp Clb 86-87; Rutgers; Biochem.

BALZANO, ANDREA; Paul VI HS; Audubon, NJ; (3); 18/540; Church Yth Grp; Math Clb; Spanish Clb; Lit Mag; Capt Pom Pon; Powder Puff Ftbl; Hon Roll; NHS; Spanish NHS.

BANAS, ROBERT; Jackson Memorial HS; Jackson, NJ; (3); 26/416; Band; Concert Band; Mrchg Band; JV Im Ftbl; High Hon Roll; Hon Roll; NHS.

BANASIAK, MICHELLE A; Rahway HS; Rahway, NJ; (3); Church Yth Grp; Girl Scts; Hosp Aide; JA; Service Clb; Ski Clb; Band; Yrbk Stf; Sec Soph Cls; Cheerleading; Chrldg Awd 86; Tchr.

BANDOLA, GOEFFREY; De Paul HS; Pompton Lakes, NJ; (4); 14/165; Var L Ftbl; Var L Trk; High Hon Roll; NHS; Acadmc All Amer Ftbl 86-87; Natl Awd Ftbl 86-87; All Cnty Trck Javelin 87; Union Coll.

BANDOLA, LIZABETH; De Paul HS; Pompton Lakes, NJ; (3); 48/150; Ski Clb; Stage Crew; Stat Ftbl; Score Keeper; Trk; Hon Roll.

BANFE, MICHELLE; Bishop Eustace Prep Schl; Medford, NJ; (3); Dance Clb; Drama Clb; Pep Clb; Spanish Clb; SADD; School Play; Lit Mag; Rep Frsh Cls; Var Cheerleading; Bus.

BANGASH, HILARY; Saddle River Day Schl; Ridgewood, NJ; (3); Art Clb; Math Tm; Varsity Clb; Stage Crew; Trs Jr Cls; Stu Cncl; Bsktbl; Cheerleading; Socr; Hon Roll.

BANGHART, KYLE; Belvidere HS; Belvidere, NJ; (3); 15/135; Cmnty Wkr; Varsity Clb; Rep Soph Cls; Rep Jr Cls; Rep Stu Cncl; JV Bsbl; Bsktbl; L Ftbl; Im Wt Lftg; Hon Roll; Ed.

BANK, MICHAEL; Roselle Park HS; Roselle Park, NJ; (3); 37/141; Am Leg Boys St; Bsktbl; Drew U; Comp Sci.

BANKO, MATTHEW; Freehold Township HS; Freehold, NJ; (3); Varsity Clb; Var Bsbl; Bnkng.

BANKOWSKI, BRENDA; Manchester Regional HS; Haledon, NJ; (3); Church Yth Grp; Library Aide; Chorus; Church Choir; Madrigals; Yrbk Stf; Var Socr; Cit Awd; Hon Roll; NHS; Mst Imprvd Sccr Plyr Plaq 85-86; Hnr Grd Grad 87; Rcgnzd Nwsp Peer Cnslng 87; Bus.

BANKS, MELISSA ANN; Paulsboro HS; Paulsboro, NJ; (3); Church Yth Grp; Cmnty Wkr; Drama Clb; FBLA; Girl Scts; JA; Church Choir; Flag Corp; Mrchg Band; School Play; Word Processng.

BANKS, NOEL; Marist HS; Jersey City, NJ; (4); Im Bsktbl; Var Mgr(s); Im Vllybl; Hon Roll; U MD Coll Pk; Marketing.

BANKS, STACIE; Cinnaminson HS; Cinnaminson, NJ; (3); Sec Church Yth Grp; Debate Tm; JA; Color Guard; Stage Crew; Rep Frsh Cls; Bowling; Tennis; Trk; Hon Roll; Bus.

BANNISTER, ROBERT P; Cherokee HS; Atco, NJ; (4); 5/401; Am Leg Boys St; Art Clb; Pres Church Yth Grp; Nwsp Stf; Stu Cncl; JV Bowling; Hon Roll; NHS; Ntl Merit Ltr; Pres Spanish NHS; Pres Schlrshp Amer U 87; NOPA Schlrshp 87; American U; Intl Rltns.

BANNON, BONNIE ANN; West Morris Central HS; Long Valley, NJ; (1); Church Yth Grp; Dance Clb; Teachers Aide; Band; Concert Band; Mrchg Band; Cit Awd; 1st Pl Dnc Cmptns In NY, NJ & PA 86-87; Frnsc Crmnlst.

BANNON, DENISE; Monongahela HS; Sewell, NJ; (1); Library Aide; Yrbk Stf; Hon Roll; Acad Awd 87; Dietary Tech.

BANTA, KATHLEEN; Mary Help Of Christians Acad; Ramsey, NJ; (3); Drama Clb; Library Aide; Model UN; NFL; Spanish Clb; SADD; School Play; Variety Show; Prfct Atten Awd; Bus Mth 87; Mt St Marys Coll; Bus Cmmnctns.

BANUA, MARIA; Mt Olive HS; Budd Lake, NJ; (3); 145/318; FBLA; Science Clb; Ski Clb; SADD; Varsity Clb; School Musical; Sci Teachers Recogntn Awd Earth Sci; Natl Art Hnr Scty; Boston U; Arch.

BANUA JR, WILLIAM L; Seton Hall Prep; Livingston, NJ; (3); Church Yth Grp; French Clb; Hosp Aide; High Hon Roll; Hon Roll; Med.

BARAGONA, STEVE; Morristown HS; Morristown, NJ; (3); Church Yth Grp; Cmnty Wkr; Radio Clb; Ski Clb; Swmmng; High Hon Roll; Hon Roll; NHS; Bio.

BARAN, CAYSEL; North Bergen HS; Guttenberg, NJ; (3); 100/480; Cmnty Wkr; Latin Clb; Nwsp Stf; Rep Stu Cncl; JV Crs Cntry; Var Sftbl; JV Trk; Var Vllybl; Hon Roll; Med Sci.

BARANELLO, JOSEPH; Union HS; Union, NJ; (3); Am Leg Boys St; VP Spanish Clb; Ed Nwsp Rptr; Off Soph Cls; Off Stu Cncl; Hon Roll; NHS; Outstndng Charctr & Schlrshp 85; Intl Rltns.

BARANIK, KATHY; West Milford Twp HS; West Milford, NJ; (4); 22/375; Sec Latin Clb; SADD; Varsity Clb; Nwsp Stf; Yrbk Ed-Chief; Yrbk Stf; Var Bsktbl; Var Trk; Hon Roll.

BARANOFF, JOSHUA; Cherry Hill HS West; Cherry Hill, NJ; (4); Aud/Vis; Computer Clb; Drama Clb; SADD; Temple Yth Grp; Stage Crew; Hon Roll; Untd Synagogue Yth DE Vly Regnl Dir Awd 87; Ithaca Coll; Comm

BARANOWSKI, FAITH; Hackettstown HS; Hackettstown, NJ; (4); Rep Am Leg Aux Girls St; Pep Clb; Q&S; Yrbk Ed-Chief; Rep Stu Cncl; Var Cheerleading; Gym; Stat Wrstlng; Hon Roll; NHS; Acad Awd Excel 84-87; All DRC 1st Strng Crldr 86-87; Pol Sci.

BARATTA, DAVID; Passiac County Tech; Paterson, NJ; (4); NHS; Aca All Amer 86; Comp Pgmmg.

BARBAGIANNIS, MARINA; Immaculate Conception HS; Rochelle Pk, NJ; (3); Church Yth Grp; Spanish Clb; SADD; Stage Crew; Bsktbl; Hon Roll; NEDT Awd; Spanish NHS; Lbrl Arts.

BARBAGIANNIS, OLGA; Immaculate Conception HS; Rochelle Park, NJ; (4); 5/92; Church Yth Grp; SADD; Yrbk Stf; Var Co-Capt Bsktbl; In Swmmng; High Hon Roll; Pres NHS; Ntl Merit Ltr; NEDT Awd; NY U; Intl Bus.

BARBAGLI, JILL; Vineland HS; Vineland, NJ; (3); 9/900; Church Yth Grp; French Clb; Key Clb; Pep Clb; Drill Tm; Orch; Sec Frsh Cls; Var Swmmng; Hon Roll; NHS; Psych.

BARBARA, CHRISTINE; Salem HS; Woodstown, NJ; (3); Spanish Clb; SADD.

BARBARA, DAN; Washington Twnshp HS; Turnersville, NJ; (4); 87/480; VP Sr Cls; Var Capt Bsbl; Var Capt Bsktbl; Var L Ftbl; Var L Socr; Hon Roll; Bsbl Schlrshp 87; All Conf, Carpntr Cup Plyr Bsbl 87; 1st Tm Glcstr Cnty Times All Stars 87; Old Dominion U; Bus.

BARBELLA, MARC; Audubon HS; Audubon, NJ; (3); 15/120; French Clb; Letterman Clb; Office Aide; Quiz Bowl; Varsity Clb; Nwsp Stf; Yrbk Stf; Sec Frsh Cls; Off Stu Cncl; Bsbl; Mt Ephraim SR Little Leag All Sta 86; Temple U; Pre Med.

BARBER, JAY; Belvidere HS; Phillipsburg, NJ; (3); 2/130; Scholastic Bowl; School Musical; Rep Frsh Cls; Trs Jr Cls; Hon Roll; NHS; Cmnty Wkr; School Play; Acad Achvt Awd Hstry, Spn & Bio 87; Physcn.

BARBER, LINDA; Vineland HS; Millville, NJ; (2); 42/770; Church Yth Grp; Drama Clb; Key Clb; Spanish Clb; Mrchg Band; Stage Crew; Nwsp Rptr; Nwsp Stf; Yrbk Stf; Hon Roll.

BARBER, SHERRY; Red Bank Regional HS; Red Bank, NJ; (3); Hosp Aide; Political Wkr; Teachers Aide; Yrbk Phtg; Var L Trk; High Hon Roll; NHS; VP Girl Scts; Red Cross Aide; Science Clb; Girls Scouts Silver Aw 85; Bronze Cngrssnl Awd 85; NJ St Fed Womens Clbs Girls Ctznshp Ins 87; Poltcl Sci.

BARBERA, JEN; Hunterdon Central HS; Flemington, NJ; (3); FBLA; Girl Scts; Intnl Clb; Key Clb; Ski Clb; Nwsp Phtg; Yrbk Stf; Rep Soph Cls; Im JV Cheerleading; Im JV Fld Hcky; Glassboro ST Coll; Accntnt.

BARBERA, JOHN; Mammonton HS; Hammonton, NJ; (4); Church Yth Grp; Chorus; Church Choir; Concert Band; Jazz Band; Mrchg Band; Pep Band; Hon Roll; NHS; Prfct Atten Awd; Hnrs Englsh II, III, IV 84-87; Atlantic Chrstn Coll; Modelng.

BARBIER, JOSEPH; Don Bosco Tech; Haledon, NJ; (3); Boy Scts; Church Yth Grp; Computer Clb; Drama Clb; ROTC; SADD; Band; Chorus; Stage Crew; Var Capt Crs Cntry; Most Imrpoved Person YMCA Camp 86; Navy; Naval Officer.

BARBIERI, JANE; Paramus HS; Paramus, NJ; (3); Art Clb; Political Wkr; Yrbk Phtg; Yrbk Stf; Lit Mag; Locl Art Recog 86-87; Jrnlsm.

BARBOSA, MARIE; East Side HS; Newark, NJ; (3); Exploring; JA; Math Clb; Chorus; School Musical; Yrbk Rptr; Rep Jr Cls; Var Cheerleading; Hon Roll; Opt Clb Awd; Upward Bound Pgm-Seton Hall 86 & 87; Tchr.

BARCELLONA, KATRINA T; Mount Saint Mary Acad; Cape Coral, FL; (3); Art Clb; German Clb; Nwsp Stf; Yrbk Stf; Lit Mag; N J St Ba Assoc Mock Trl Cert Of Achvmnt 86; German Club Svc Awd 86; Natl Ar Hnr Scty 87; Hospitality Mgmnt.

BARCKLEY, MICHAEL; Florence Twp Mem HS; Florence, NJ; (3); FBLA; Varsity Clb; L Var Bsbl; Natl Bus Hnr Soc JR; NJ Grp I St Chmps S Jersey Grp I, Freedom Div Bsbl Soph; Accntng.

BARCOMB, GERALDINE; Immaculate Conception HS; Secaucus, NJ; (3); 1/70; Church Yth Grp; Quiz Bowl; Chorus; School Musical; Yrbk St; High Hon Roll; NHS; Spanish NHS; English Clb; Intl Rel.

BARCZYK, DAVID; Franklin HS; Somerset, NJ; (4); 66/327; JV Var Ftbl; Im Ice Hcky; Im Wt Lftg; Hon Roll; Damski Mem Awd For Math 87; Somerset Cnty Coll; Chrprctcs.

BARD, MELINDA; Northern Valley Regional HS; Norwood, NJ; (3); 273; AFS; Drama Clb; Hosp Aide; Math Tm; Science Clb; School Musica; Stu Cncl; NHS; Ntl Merit SF; Computer Clb; NJ St Champ Aca Decathlon Tm 86-87.

BARD, SCOTT; Riverside HS; Riverside, NJ; (3); 39/101; Drama Clb; FTA; Varsity Clb; Band; Jazz Band; School Musical; School Play; Var Ftbl; Var L Trk; Var L Wrstlng; Outstndng Trombone; 5th Frdm Div Tr & Wrstlng; 4th Shtpt Grdn St Gms; Math.

BARDOWSKI, DENISE; South River HS; South River, NJ; (3); Cmnt Wkr; Pres Sec FNA; Office Aide; Pres Spanish Clb; Color Guard; Nws Stf; Yrbk Stf; Rep Stu Cncl; Hon Roll; NHS; Rutgers; Pediatrcn.

BAREIS, MICHELLE; Manasquan HS; Manasquan, NJ; (3); 17/250; Drama Clb; French Clb; Band; Concert Band; Mrchg Band; Stage Crew; Lit Mag; High Hon Roll; Hon Roll; SOAR 87; Law.

BARGER, MICHELLE; Red Bank Regional HS; Shrewsbury, NJ; (3); Dance Clb; Key Clb; Office Aide; Political Wkr; Spanish Clb; Varsity Clb; Yrbk Stf; Trs Frsh Cls; Trs Soph Cls; Rep Jr Cls; Ldrshp Trning Camp; Outstndng Wrld Hstry Stu 85; Focus At Tufts 86; NJ Grls Ctznshp Inst 87

BARILE, NICOLE; Ocean City HS; Marmora, NJ; (4); 4/291; Science Clb; Spanish Clb; Band; Hst Frsh Cls; Stu Cncl; Var Fld Hcky; Var Capt Sftb; Var Swmmng; High Hon Roll; VP NHS; Pre-Med.

BARILLA, DENISE; Roselle Catholic HS; Union, NJ; (4); 14/200; French Clb; Ski Clb; Score Keeper; VP Tennis; Var Trk; French Hon Soc; High Hon Roll; Hon Roll; Jr NHS; NHS; George Washington U; Bio.

BARK, JENNIFER; Paul VI HS; Haddonfield, NJ; (4); 4/511; Church Yth Grp; Math Clb; Spanish Clb; High Hon Roll; Hon Roll; Jr NHS; NHS; Spanish NHS; Accntnt.

BARKER, CHRIS; Mount Olive HS; Flanders, NJ; (3); 22/365; Tr Church Yth Grp; Science Clb; Varsity Clb; JV Bsktbl; JV Capt Socr; Hon Roll; Trs NHS; Ntl Merit Ltr; Mst Imprvd Var Soccr 86; Treas Yth Gr 85-87; UC Coast Guard Acad.

BARKLEY, MONE; Washington Township HS; Sewell, NJ; (4); Church Yth Grp; Intnl Clb; Math Tm; Spanish Clb; SADD; School Musical; Nwsp Rptr; Rep Sr Cls; High Hon Roll; Hon Roll; Rutgers U; Bio.

BARKOW, DEBORAH; Montclair HS; U Montclair, NJ; (4); 63/409; PAVAS; Yrbk Stf; Off Lit Mag; Sec Frsh Cls; Sec Soph Cls; Pres Jr Cls; Pres Sr Cls; Rep Stu Cncl; JV Lcrss; Hon Roll; Syracuse U; Cmrcl Art.

BARLATIER, HENRY; Franklin Morrel HS; Irvington, NJ; (4); 152/460; Drama Clb; French Clb; Quiz Bowl; Scholastic Bowl; Lit Mag; Arts.

BARLOTTA, AUDRA; Morris Catholic HS; Morris Plains, NJ; (3); 70/135; Hosp Aide; Pep Clb; Ski Clb; JV Cheerleading; Im Powder Puff Ftbl; JV Var Sftbl; Im Vllybl; Psychlgy.

BARLOW, DEIDRA; Lakewood HS; Lakewood, NJ; (4); FBLA; Chorus; Church Choir; Trk; High Hon Roll; Hon Roll; Upwrd Bnd Awd-Acadc Achvt 87; Upwrd Bnd Vldctrn 87; Miss Upwrd Bnd 86-87; Seton Hall U.

BARNES, APRIL; Union Catholic Regional HS; Plainfield, NJ; (4); 142/293; Church Yth Grp; Cmnty Wkr; Intnl Clb; JV Bsktbl; JV Lcrss; JV Sftbl; JV Vllybl; Commended Stu Ntl Achvt Schrlshp Outstndng Negro Stu 87; Pres Eminent Schlr Awd 87; Hampton U; Soclgy.

BARNES, BEVERLY; John F Kennedy HS; Willingboro, NJ; (3); JV Trk; Hon Roll; NJ Tech Inst; Elec Engr.

BARNES, CYNTHIA; Hunterdon Central HS; Flemington, NJ; (2); 10/485; Intnl Clb; Model UN; Band; Concert Band; Mrchg Band; Pep Band; Stage Crew; Rep Stu Cncl; Hon Roll; Spanish NHS; Intrprtr.

BARNES, DOLORES; Orange HS; Orange, NJ; (3); Cmnty Wkr; Cheerleading; Trk; Katherine Gibbs Awd 87; Comp Tech.

BARNES, JOY; West Side HS; Newark, NJ; (3); Boys Clb Am; Dance Clb; School Musical; Capt Cheerleading; Hon Roll; Pres NHS; Prfct Atten Awd; Bsbl; Bsktbl; Sftbl; Pre Med.

BARNES, MORIA; Egg Harbor Township HS; Pleasantville, NJ; (3); 26/329; Pres Cmnty Wkr; Dance Clb; Spanish Clb; Hon Roll; NHS; Cmptr Mgmnt.

BARNES, TRACIE; Shore Regional HS; Oceanport, NJ; (3); Church Yth Grp; Drama Clb; Girl Scts; NAACP; SADD; Band; Chorus; Flag Corp; Mrchg Band; School Play.

BARNETT, AUDRA; Toms River HS South; Beachwood, NJ; (3); 6/405; Am Leg Aux Girls St; Math Tm; Concert Band; Orch; Sec Stu Cncl; High Hon Roll; Hon Roll; NHS; Acad Ltr Awd 85.

BARNETT, EVA; Freehold Township HS; Freehold, NJ; (3); 16/380; Pep Clb; Temple Yth Grp; Mgr Varsity Clb; Yrbk Stf; Lit Mag; Rep Stu Cncl; Bsktbl; Powder Puff Ftbl; Trk; High Hon Roll; Summer Arts Inst At Rutgers U 85.

BARNETT, STACEY; Eastside HS; Paterson, NJ; (3); 19/450; GAA; Mrchg Band; Variety Show; Off Frsh Cls; Crs Cntry; Trk; Twrlr; Hon Roll; Prfct Atten Awd; NHS 85; Villinova U; Chem.

BARNEY, LINDA; Gloucester Catholic HS; Gloucester, NJ; (3); Cmnty Wkr; Nwsp Stf; Yrbk Stf; Rep Stu Cncl; Im Bsktbl.

BARNHARDT, S TROY; Clifford J Scott HS; East Orange, NJ; (3); FBLA; Intnl Clb; Letterman Clb; Math Clb; Ski Clb; Spanish Clb; SADD; Varsity Clb; Nwsp Rptr; Nwsp Stf; Harvard Bk Awd 87; U Of MD; Bus.

BARNOCK, BRIAN; Notre Dame HS; Hamilton Sq, NJ; (3); 14/371; Math Tm; Ski Clb; Spanish Clb; Varsity Clb; Nwsp Stf; JV Socr; Var Tennis; JV Wrstlng; High Hon Roll; Hon Roll; Homeroom Rep 84-87; MIP Vrsty Ten 86-87; Elect Engrng.

BARNUM, MARCY; Mahwah HS; Mahwah, NJ; (4); 25/175; Church Yth Grp; Nwsp Ed-Chief; Sec NHS; Pres Schlr; Rotary Awd; Pres Spanish NHS; Cmnty Wkr; Drama Clb; Pres Spanish Clb; Teen Tlnt Dist Wnnr 85; Miss NJ Teen ST Fnlst 86; Thundrbrd Schlrshp 87; Messiah Coll; Elem Educ.

BARON, JEFFREY; E P Memorial HS; Elmwood Park, NJ; (3); Band; Concert Band; Drm & Bgl; Jazz Band; Mrchg Band; Orch; Pep Band; School Musical; Berkly Schl Of Music; Music.

BARON, MARIA; Franklin HS; Somerset, NJ; (3); Capt Color Guard; Mrchg Band; Orch; Mgr(s); Swmmng; Hon Roll; NHS; Church Yth Grp; Cmnty Wkr; Ski Clb; Cert Mrt-Rdr Coll Frgn Lang Frnsc Trnmnt-Spnsh 85.

BARON, MELISSA; Princeton Day School; Whitehouse, NJ; (3); AFS; Spanish Clb; Orch; Nwsp Phtg; Nwsp Stf; Yrbk Phtg; Lcrss; JV Mgr Tennis; Wellngtn Coll England; Intl Bus.

BARONE, ANGELA; Bishop Eustace Prep Schl; Haddonfield, NJ; (4); 11/175; Math Clb; Pep Clb; VP Spanish Clb; Var L Bowling; Var L Trk; High Hon Roll; NHS; Pres Schlr; Spanish NHS; JR Miss 87; Diplma-Ntl Gld Piano Tchrs-Ntl Audtns 87; Temple U.

BARR, DEBBIE; Gloucester City JR-SR HS; Gloucester, NJ; (3); SADD; FBLA; Office Aide; Pep Clb; Spanish Clb; Stage Crew; Yrbk Stf; Rep Frsh Cls; Rep Soph Cls; Score Keeper; Gregg-Shrthnd Awds For Typng & Shrthnd 87; Camden Cnty Coll; Sec.

BARR, JON-HENRY; Arthur L Johnson Regional HS; Clark, NJ; (3); 26/189; Spanish Clb; Nwsp Rptr; Lit Mag; Rep Jr Cls; VP Stu Cncl; Var Stat Ftbl; Gov Hon Prg Awd; Hon Roll; Spanish NHS; Rep Soph Cls; Video Tpng Clb 86-87; Law.

BARR, JUDI; Middlesex HS; Middlesex, NJ; (2); Girl Scts; SADD; Sftbl; Hon Roll; Bus.

BARR, PENNI; West Windsor Plainsboro HS; Princeton Junct, NJ; (3); AFS; Cmnty Wkr; Model UN; VP Spanish Clb; Cheerleading; Hon Roll.

BARR, TIMOTHY; Edgewood Regional HS; Elm, NJ; (3); 36/390; Latin Clb; Gftd & Tlntd Clss; Vet Med.

BARRA, MARISA; The Hun Schl Of Princeto; Lawrenceville, NJ; (3); 8/123; French Clb; Math Tm; Nwsp Stf; JV Var Bsktbl; JV Var Fld Hcky; Var L Lcrss; High Hon Roll; Wlsly Bk Awd For Exc Schlrshp & Ldrshp 87; Ntl Hnr Roll 87; Yale U; Law & Ecnmcs.

BARRALE, BILL; Buena Regional HS; Landisvlle, NJ; (2); Letterman Clb; Ski Clb; Varsity Clb; Rep Stu Cncl; Var Bsbl; Var Ftbl; Var Wt Lftg; U Of MD; Bus Admin.

BARRE, LYNNE; Ridge HS; Basking Ridge, NJ; (3); 5/192; Trs Pres Drama Clb; School Musical; School Play; Nwsp Rptr; Rep Sr Cls; JV Var Cheerleading; Church Yth Grp; Girl Scts; Scholastic Bowl; Ski Clb; Ambssdr HOBY 86; Hme/Schl Assn Smmr Prgm Schlrshp 87; Marine Bio.

BARRESI, PAUL RYAN; North Bergen HS; North Bergen, NJ; (3); Off ROTC; Hon Roll; Bio.

BARRETT, AMY; Morris Catholic HS; Dover, NJ; (3); Church Yth Grp; German Clb; Pep Clb; Yrbk Stf; Bsktbl; Sftbl; Hon Roll; Religious Awd 85; Jrnlsm.

BARRETT, JASON; St John Vianney HS; Freehold, NJ; (2); Stage Crew; Crs Cntry; Princeton U Sci Lectures 87; Astrophy.

BARRETT, KELLY; Holy Family Acad; Bayonne, NJ; (2); 36/89; Bsktbl; Var Cheerleading; Coach Actv; Var Pom Pon; Sftbl; Vllybl; Hon Roll; Montclair ST Coll; Nrs.

BARRETT, KIM; Sussex County Vo Tech; Hopatcong, NJ; (3); Nwsp Rptr; Sec Soph Cls; Sec Jr Cls; Hon Roll; Fshn Merch.

BARRETT, MICHELLE; Highland Regional HS; Erial, NJ; (4); FTA; Nwsp Rptr; Yrbk Bus Mgr; Yrbk Stf; Rep Sr Cls; Stat Var Sftbl; Glassboro ST; Elem Ed.

BARRETT, TRACY; Scotch Plains-Fanwood HS; Fanwood, NJ; (4); 20/300; Drama Clb; French Clb; Chorus; Rep Sr Cls; High Hon Roll; Hon Roll; Spanish NHS; Presdntl Acadc Ftnss Awd 87; Boston U; Pol Sci.

BARRETT, WILLIAM; Holy Spirit HS; Margate, NJ; (4); 20/363; Church Yth Grp; Im Crs Cntry; NHS; Vrsty Ltr In Crew 84-87; Med.

BARRON, PETER; Toms River H S East; Toms River, NJ; (3); 29/520; Am Leg Boys St; Key Clb; SADD; Stage Crew; JV Ftbl; Wt Lftg; High Hon Roll; Hon Roll; NHS; Ntl Merit Ltr; 3rd Pl Kata East Coast JR Cls Karate Champshps 86; 1st Pl East Coast JR Cls Karate Champshps 86; Aero Engrng.

BARROS, RUI; Perth Amboy HS; Perth Amboy, NJ; (3); Am Leg Boys St; French Clb; Letterman Clb; Varsity Clb; Chorus; Madrigals; School Play; L Capt Socr; Var Trk; Dance Clb; FIT; Flight Tech.

BARROW, NICOLE; Essex Catholic Girls HS; E Orange, NJ; (3); Sec Church Yth Grp; Dance Clb; Drama Clb; Girl Scts; Model UN; Pep Clb; Chorus; Church Choir; Drill Tm; School Musical; 1st Rnnr-Up Miss Black Pgnt Teenage Wrld Of NJ 87; Manhattan Schl Of Music; Voice.

BARRY, KRISTEN; Paramus Catholic G HS; Woodcliff Lake, NJ; (3); Service Clb; Ski Clb; Spanish Clb; Varsity Clb; Var Socr; Var Sftbl; Var Soccr & Sftbl Ltr; Phys Thrpy.

BARRY, STEVEN; Lenape Valley HS; Andover, NJ; (2); 12/210; Boy Scts; 4-H; SADD; Jazz Band; Mrchg Band; Yrbk Stf; Stu Cncl; Bsktbl; Socr; High Hon Roll; Lenape Scholar 87.

BARRY, SUZANNE; Newton HS; Andover, NJ; (3); French Clb; Trs Latin Clb; Math Tm; Science Clb; Varsity Clb; Bsktbl; Fld Hcky; Sftbl; Hon Roll; NHS; Math.

BARSCZEWSKI, LISA; Notre Dame HS; Hamilton Sq, NJ; (2); 37/400; JV Cheerleading; JV Sftbl; High Hon Roll; Hon Roll; Cert Of Awd Of Excllnc In Spnsh I 86; Cert Of Awd For Excllnc In Spnsh II 87; Princeton U; Arch.

BARSKY, CRAIG W; Wayne Hills HS; Wayne, NJ; (3); Ski Clb; Spanish Clb; JV Im Bsbl; Im Bowling; JV Ftbl; Var Swmmng; Hon Roll.

BARSKY, DEANA; Camden Catholic HS; Atco, NJ; (3); 171/243; Drama Clb; French Clb; Chorus; School Play; Lit Mag; Rutgers; Law.

BARSKY, DENNIS; Cliffside Park HS; Fort Lee, NJ; (4); 43/240; Am Leg Boys St; Pres Chess Clb; Drama Clb; School Play; Stage Crew; Nwsp Rptr; Lit Mag; JV Ftbl; Var Golf; Var Wrstlng; Acdmc Dcthln 86 & 87; STAIRS Frgn Rltns Smnr 86; The American U; Intl Affrs.

BARSOOM, PETER N; East Brunswick HS; East Brunswick, NJ; (3); Pres Am Leg Boys St; Pres Church Yth Grp; Debate Tm; Intnl Clb; Model UN; Pres Spanish Clb; Ed Nwsp Phtg; Yrbk Phtg; JV Tennis; Georgetown U; Diplomat.

BARTEK, PAULA; Middlesex HS; Middlesex, NJ; (3); 9/171; French Clb; Ski Clb; Band; Mrchg Band; Var Bsktbl; Bowling; Var Fld Hcky; JV Sftbl; Hon Roll; NHS.

BARTELLI, MARINA; Mt St Dominic Acad; Lake Hiawatha, NJ; (3); 1/55; Church Yth Grp; Nwsp Rptr; Nwsp Stf; Lit Mag; Bausch & Lomb Sci Awd; High Hon Roll; NHS; Ntl Merit Ltr; JCL; NFL; Rutgrs Schlrs; St Peters Coll Smmr Schlr Pgm; George Wshngtn U Engrn Mdl.

BARTLESON, RACHEAL LYNN; Highland HS; Erial, NJ; (3); FHA; Hon Roll.

BARTLETT, ELIZABETH; Collingswood SR HS; Collingswood, NJ; (2); Latin Clb; Ski Clb; Chorus; Rep Stu Cncl; Gym; Lcrss; Swmmng; High Hon Roll; Jr NHS; NHS; 2nd Pl Essay Cntst; Marine Bio.

BARTLETT, LYNN ANN; Rutherford HS; Rutherford, NJ; (4); 24/168; Pep Clb; SADD; Varsity Clb; Yrbk Stf; Rep Soph Cls; Rep Jr Cls; Rep Sr Cls; Stat Bsktbl; VP Stat Ftbl; Sftbl; Brd Educ Brnz Awd 84-85; U Of PA; Bio.

BARTLEY, ROSLYN E; Cumberland Regional HS; Bridgeton, NJ; (3); Mgr(s); Bus.

BARTOLINO, JODI; Notre Dame HS; Lawrenceville, NJ; (4); 60/323; Key Clb; VP Latin Clb; Pres Ski Clb; JV Capt Fld Hcky; Hon Roll; Lawrence Italian Civic Assoc Schlrshp Awd 87; Syracuse Univ; Lbrl Arts.

BARTOLO, JENNIFER; West Orange HS; W Orange, NJ; (3); Church Yth Grp; Cmnty Wkr; Girl Scts; Hosp Aide; Office Aide; Service Clb; Spanish Clb; Band; Chorus; Mrchg Band; Bus.

BARTOLOMEI, MARC J; Hamilton HS West; Trenton, NJ; (3); Am Leg Boys St; Sec Trs Science Clb; SADD; Concert Band; Mrchg Band; Symp Band; Amer Musical Fndtn Band Hnrs 87; Engrng.

BARTON, EMILY L; Kent Place Schl; Summit, NJ; (4); Chorus; Madrigals; School Musical; School Play; Lit Mag; Ntl Merit SF; NJ Ptry Cont 86-87; Am Jwsh Cmmtte Essy Cont 86; AFL-CIO Essy Cont 86; Harvard U; Eng Lit.

BARTOSIK, SHERRY; Red Bank Regional HS; Red Bank, NJ; (3); Science Clb; Varsity Clb; Mrchg Band; Orch; School Musical; Var Crs Cntry; Var Gym; Hon Roll; NHS; Spanish NHS; Air Force Acad.

BASAK, SANDIP; Elmwood Park Memorial HS; Elmwood Park, NJ; (3); Math Clb; Spanish Clb; Band; Concert Band; Mrchg Band; Var Tennis; Hon Roll; NHS; Spanish NHS; Acad All Amer; Natl Ledrshp & Svc Awd.

BASAMAN, MARY; Lakewood HS; Lakewood, NJ; (3); 5/353; FBLA; English Clb; French Clb; Intnl Clb; Latin Clb; Mrchg Band; Symp Band; Yrbk Rptr; Yrbk Stf; Stat Bsbl; Jrnlsm.

BASICH, MICHELE; Delsea Regional HS; Vineland, NJ; (4); Key Clb; Var Im Tennis; Hon Roll; Jr NHS; NHS; Delsea Educ Assoc Schlrshp & Pres Acdmc Fitness Awd 87; Outstndng Frnch Awd 85; Cumberand Cnty Coll; Accntng.

BASIL, ROBERT; Dumont HS; Dumont, NJ; (4); 11/217; Church Yth Grp; Mu Alpha Theta; Im Swmmng; Capt Var Wrstlng; Hon Roll; Italian Hnr Soc Treas 84-87; Hi Hnr Acadmc Achvt Awd.

BASKERVILLE, JUNE; Lincoln HS; Jersey City, NJ; (4); 12/208; Art Clb; Trs JA; Key Clb; Yrbk Stf; Rep Stu Cncl; Jr NHS; NHS; Art Awd 86; Prfct Attndnc 84-86; William Paterson; Acct Exec.

BASS, DEREK; West Morris Mendham HS; Chester, NJ; (2); Church Yth Grp; JV Bsktbl; Hon Roll; Ecmncs.

BASSANO, ANN; Vineland HS; Vineland, NJ; (3); 41/800; VP Art Clb; English Clb; French Clb; Nwsp Stf; Lit Mag; French Hon Soc; NHS; Ntl Merit Ltr; Cosmetology.

BASSANO, DAVID; Ridgefield Park HS; Ridgefield Pk, NJ; (3); 14/203; Letterman Clb; Varsity Clb; Var JV Ftbl; Wt Lftg; Var Wrstlng; High Hon Roll; Hon Roll; Schlr Athl Awd Outstndng Schlrshp, Wrstlng Awds 86-87; Gld Mdl Dist 5 Champ Wrstlng 87; Bus.

BASSETT, RICHARD; Holy Cross HS; Florence, NJ; (4); 121/362; JV Tennis; Hon Roll; Burlington Cnty Coll; Chem Engr.

BASSI, ANN MARIE; Keansburg HS; Keansburg, NJ; (4); 4/100; FBLA; German Clb; Teachers Aide; Lit Mag; Trs Sr Cls; Sec Stu Cncl; High Hon Roll; Hon Roll; Trs NHS; Acdmc Awd Bus Engl, Home Econ 87; Pres Acdmc Ftns Awd 87; Fashn Merchdsng.

BASSILLO, TRACY H; Brick Memorial HS; Brick, NJ; (3); 52/350; Sec Church Yth Grp; Drama Clb; NFL; School Musical; School Play; Sec Frsh Cls; Pres Soph Cls; Socr; High Hon Roll; Hon Roll.

BASTARDI III, ANTHONY V; Delbarton Schl; Boonton, NJ; (4); 2/109; Church Yth Grp; Cmnty Wkr; Model UN; Science Clb; Service Clb; Ski Clb; Yrbk Phtg; Rep Stu Cncl; Im Bsktbl; JV Crs Cntry; Delbarton Spn Achvt Awd 87; Delbarton Math Achvt Awd 87; Morris Cnty Prtnrshp Acad Achvt 87; Princeton U; Physics.

BASZKIEWICZ, NADIA; Steinert HS; Allentown, NJ; (3); AFS; Capt Color Guard; Ed.

BATCHELOR, KAREN; Vernon Township HS; Sussex, NJ; (3); Concert Band; Jazz Band; Mrchg Band; JV Var Fld Hcky; Var Trk; High Hon Roll; NHS; Prfct Atten Awd; Acadc Dcthln Tm Hnrs Div 86-87; Math Ed.

BATE, LINDA; Fair Lawn HS; Fair Lawn, NJ; (4); 2/329; Science Clb; Sec Band; Rep Sr Cls; Stu Cncl; Var Crs Cntry; Capt Swmmng; Var Trk; Chrmn NHS; Sal; St Schlr; Air Force ROTC; Cngrssnl Yth Schlr; Tufts U; Sci.

BATELLI, GIUSEPPINA; Mary Help Of Christians HS; Paterson, NJ; (3); 8/84; SADD; Acpl Chr; Band; Chorus; Church Choir; Variety Show; Nwsp Stf; Hon Roll.

BATEMAN, DAWN; Warren County Vo-Tech Schl; Phillipsburg, NJ; (2); Key Clb; VICA; Hon Roll; Graphics.

BATES, BARBARA; Central Jersey Christian HS; Neptune, NJ; (4); 5/17; Church Yth Grp; French Clb; Chorus; Yrbk Ed-Chief; High Hon Roll; Hon Roll; Testmny Awd 87; Kngsmn Awd 87; Columbia Bible Coll; Cnslg.

BATES, DEBBIE; North Warren Regional HS; Columbia, NJ; (4); Color Guard; Mrchg Band; Stage Crew; Voice Dem Awd; 2 Yr Schlrshp & N Warrens Educ Assoc Schlrshp 87; Warren Cnty CC; Hstry Teacher.

BATES, LIISA; Northwest Christian Schl; Sussex, NJ; (2); 1/10; Church Yth Grp; Office Aide; Teachers Aide; Orch; Stage Crew; Score Keeper; High Hon Roll; Hon Roll; Sussex Cnty Music Fndtn 86.

BATES, RICHARD; Woodbury HS; Woodbury, NJ; (3); Art Clb; Quiz Bowl; Teachers Aide; Pres VICA; Variety Show; Nwsp Stf; JV Bsbl; JV Bsktbl; Im Ftbl; Score Keeper; Pres Of Voc Indstrl Cbs Of Amer 86-88; Prfssnl Cmmrcl Artst.

BATH, DENA; St Pius X Regional HS; Perth Amboy, NJ; (3); Debate Tm; Drama Clb; JA; Office Aide; Speech Tm; Pres SADD; Stage Crew; Tennis; Hon Roll; Accntng.

BATIATO, MAUREEN ANN; Brick Town HS; Brick Town, NJ; (3); 10/400; SADD; Yrbk Stf; Trs Frsh Cls; Trs Soph Cls; Trs Jr Cls; Trs Sr Cls; Rep Stu Cncl; Var Capt Crs Cntry; Var Capt Trk; High Hon Roll; MVP Crss Cntry 85; Al-Cnty Crss Cntry Tm 85-86; MVP Trk 87; Rutgers.

BATIATO, MICHELLE; Brick Town HS; Brick Town, NJ; (3); 15/400; SADD; Yrbk Stf; Sec Frsh Cls; Sec Soph Cls; Sec Jr Cls; Sec Sr Cls; Stu Cncl; Var Capt Crs Cntry; Var Capt Trk; High Hon Roll; MVP Crs Cntry 85; All Cnty Crs Cntry Tm 85-86; All Cnty Wntr Trk Tm 85; Rutgers.

BATISTA, EDDIE; Queen Of Peace HS; North Arlington, NJ; (3); Bsktbl; Ftbl; Socr; Trk; Vllybl; Wt Lftg.

BATOR, RICHARD; St Joseph Regional HS; Norwood, NJ; (3); Church Yth Grp; Cmnty Wkr; Office Aide; Yrbk Stf; Im Bsbl; Im Ftbl; JV Swmmng; Im Trk; Hon Roll; VFW Awd; Oratorcl Cont Awd 86; Staff Achvt Yrbk Awd 87; Spn Hnr Soc Awd 86; U DE; Bus.

BATRA, MONTY S; Pennsville Memorial HS; Pennsville, NJ; (4); 18/201; Am Leg Boys St; French Clb; Ski Clb; Nwsp Ed-Chief; Lit Mag; Off Stu Cncl; Capt Tennis; High Hon Roll; NHS; Prfct Atten Awd; Suprntndt Schlr Awd Recpt; JR Rotatn Mnth April; Todays Sun Lean Plyr Yr Boys Tennis; Rutgers Coll; Intl Finc.

BATTAGLIA, DONNA ANN; Brick Memorial HS; Brick, NJ; (3); 43/280; VP Church Yth Grp; Drama Clb; Chorus; Church Choir; Mrchg Band; School Musical; School Play; High Hon Roll; Hon Roll; NHS; Bst Supprtng Actress-Musical 86-87; Rutgers; Theatre.

BATTEN, DANIELLE; Edgewood SR HS; Cedar Brook, NJ; (2); 1/280; Pres Latin Clb; JV Socr; Im JV Sftbl; Stat Wrstlng; High Hon Roll; Pres Jr NHS; Prfct Atten Awd; Engl Schlr 85-86; Ltn Schlr 85-86; Bus.

BATTIPAGLIA, JOSEPH; St Josephs HS; Edison, NJ; (4); 112/208; Church Yth Grp; Service Clb; Ski Clb; Spanish Clb; JV Bsbl; Capt Wrstlng; Hon Roll; Yth Grp Awd 86; Vrsty Lttrmmn 85-86; Blgy.

BATTISTA, JULIANNE; Mount Olive HS; Flanders, NJ; (3); Drama Clb; Teachers Aide; School Play; Hon Roll.

BATTISTA, KRISTA; Paul VI HS; Marlton, NJ; (4); 129/511; Spanish Clb; Bowling; Math.

BATTISTA, PAUL; Christian Brothers Acad; Colts Neck, NJ; (3); Chess Clb; Trk; High Hon Roll; Hon Roll; VA Poly Tech; Bus.

BATTISTE, CATHLEEN; Paul VI HS; Bellmawr, NJ; (4); 35/503; Drama Clb; Hosp Aide; Math Clb; Math Tm; Chrmn SADD; School Musical; Stage Crew; High Hon Roll; Pres NHS; Math.

BATTISTUZ, ELLEN; Clifton HS; Clifton, NJ; (3); Art Clb; Drama Clb; French Clb; Office Aide; Spanish Clb; Nwsp Stf; Yrbk Stf; Hon Roll; Jr NHS; Spanish NHS; Arch.

BAUAH, ANA; Essex Catholic Girls HS; E Orange, NJ; (4); 12/55; Debate Tm; Am Leg Boys St; Pep Clb; Pres Service Clb; Sec Church Choir; Yrbk Stf; Hon Roll; Rutgers; Bio.

BAUBLES, JEANETTE; Manasquan HS; Spring Lake, NJ; (2); 9/200; Key Clb; Bsktbl; Fld Hcky; Socr; Hon Roll; NHS.

BAUER, KIMBERLY; Paul VI HS; Waterford, NJ; (3); 2/420; Camera Clb; Math Clb; Math Tm; Nwsp Phtg; Rep Jr Cls; Stat Bsktbl; Score Keeper; High Hon Roll; Hon Roll.

BAUER, NANCY; Lakeland Regional HS; Ringwood, NJ; (3); 6/340; Library Aide; Math Clb; Science Clb; Chorus; High Hon Roll; NHS; NEDT Awd; Natl Sci Awd 86; All Amer Schlr Awd 85; Accntng.

BAUER, STEPHEN; Madison HS; Madison, NJ; (3); 5/220; AFS; Boy Scts; French Clb; Science Clb; Chorus; Lit Mag; JV Golf; Var L Tennis; French Hon Soc; High Hon Roll; Bridge Club Pres.

BAULIG, DANIEL; Egg Harbor Township HS; Pleasantville, NJ; (3); 21/370; Church Yth Grp; Model UN; Ftbl; Trk; Wt Lftg; Wrstlng; USNA; Engrng.

BAUMAN, DAVID ALAN; Parsippany HS; Parsippany, NJ; (4); 33/330; Civic Clb; Intnl Clb; Model UN; Political Wkr; VP Spanish Clb; Sr Cls; Stu Cncl; Socr; NHS; Ski Clb; Sccr Schlrshp, Pres Ftns Awd, Outstndng Statsmn Mdl Congrss 87; Emory U; Law.

BAUMANN, JAMES; Wildwood Catholic HS; Stone Harbor, NJ; (3); Var L Bsbl; JV Bsktbl; L Crs Cntry; Hon Roll; NHS.

BAUMANN, LORRAINE; Hackensack HS; Maywood, NJ; (4); 125/402; Dance Clb; School Play; Off Jr Cls; Rep Stu Cncl; Var Capt Cheerleading; Var Capt Gym; Hon Roll; Gymnstcs 2 Yrs All Leag Hnr Mntn, Coachs Awd, Mst Dedctn Awd 86-87; Chrldng Untd Chrng Compttn 87; Rutgers Coll; Phys Ed.

BAUTISTA, LALAINE L; Dumont HS; Dumont, NJ; (4); 4/217; French Clb; Mu Alpha Theta; Science Clb; Jazz Band; Chorus; High Hon Roll; Hon Roll; Dentistry.

BAUTZ, JENNIFER; Bloomfield HS; Bloomfield, NJ; (4); 60/470; Church Yth Grp; Cmnty Wkr; Key Clb; Spanish Clb; Rep Frsh Cls; Rep Soph Cls; Rep Jr Cls; L Crs Cntry; L Gym; Capt Trk; 5th ST Sctnl Trk 87; John I Crecco Humanitrn Awd Schlrshp 87; Outstndng Tm Prsn Awd Schlrshp 87; Daemen Coll; Phys Ther.

BAUZON, BENJAMIN; Passaic HS; Passaic, NJ; (3); Am Leg Boys St; Debate Tm; Pres French Clb; Band; Jazz Band; School Play; Yrbk Stf; Hon Roll; VP NHS; Rotary Awd; Awd Recog Teen Arts Fstvl 86; Mock Trial 86-87; Mod Congress 86-87; Rutgers U Coll Engrng; Mech Eng.

BAVA, MICHELLE; Our Lady Of Good Counsel HS; Newark, NJ; (4); 2/102; Cmnty Wkr; Debate Tm; Scholastic Bowl; Chorus; School Play; Gov Hon Prg Awd; Hon Roll; NHS; St Schlr; UNICO Schlrshp Awd 87-88; Garden ST Dstngshd Schlrs Awd 87-88; Garden ST Schlrshp 87-88; Rutgers Coll; Neuroscience.

BAXT, REBECCA; Dwight-Englewood Schl; Saddle River, NJ; (4); Orch; Yrbk Stf; Capt Tennis; Hon Roll; NHS; Ntl Merit Ltr; Garden ST Schlr 86-87; Frnch Awd 86-87; Short Stry Awd 86-87.

BAXTER, RUTH; West Milford HS; Oak Ridge, NJ; (3); 45/391; Church Yth Grp; Spanish Clb; Varsity Clb; Band; Rptr Yrbk Stf; JV Cheerleading; Sftbl; Hon Roll; NHS; Spanish NHS; Bio Sci.

BAYER, DEBBIE; Wayne Valley HS; Wayne, NJ; (3); 84/286; Dance Clb; FBLA; JV Var Gym; Hon Roll.

BAYERS, JEANNE; Saint Mary HS; W Keansburg, NJ; (4); 25/127; Church Yth Grp; French Clb; Stage Crew; Lit Mag; Cheerleading; Crs Cntry; High Hon Roll; Hon Roll; NHS; Christian Brothers Schlrshp 87; Anthony Di Marzio Meml Schlrshp Fund 87; La Salle U; Cmmnctns.

BAYKOWSKI, LORI BETH; Linden HS; Linden, NJ; (2); Church Yth Grp; FHA; Key Clb; Ski Clb; Color Guard; Rep Soph Cls; Var Sftbl; Var Swmmng; Hon Roll; Band; Ntl Bnd Awd 86-87.

BAYKOWSKI, SUSAN; Linden HS; Linden, NJ; (3); Cmnty Wkr; Hosp Aide; Rep Stu Cncl; Hon Roll; Church Yth Grp; FHA; Office Aide; Ski Clb; Stat Score Keeper; Var Swmmng; Bill Bradley Outstndng Yth Ctzn Awd 86.

BAYLIS, MARYANN; Jackson Memorial HS; Jackson, NJ; (3); Art Clb; Varsity Clb; VP Trk; Im Vllybl; Hon Roll; Stockton ST Coll.

BAYOFSKI, ANNA; Perty Amboy HS; Perth Amboy, NJ; (4); Church Yth Grp; Chorus; Church Choir; School Play; High Hon Roll; Hon Roll; Ntl Mgmt Awd; Schlr Awd; Middlesex Cnty Coll; Lawyer.

BAYRON, CARLOS; Hoboken HS; Hoboken, NJ; (3); Aud/Vis; Tennis; Hon Roll; Drftsmn.

BAZAAR, ALAN; West Essex SR HS; No Caldwell, NJ; (3); High Hon Roll; Hon Roll; NHS; Equestrian Show Jumping Events.

BEABER, TRACY; Washington Twp HS; Turnersville, NJ; (4); 60/480; Am Leg Aux Girls St; Church Yth Grp; Model UN; Pres Ski Clb; SADD; Stage Crew; Yrbk Stf; JV Fld Hcky; Score Keeper; Sprntndnts Awd 86-87; JR Wmns Clb Schlrshp & Awd 86-87; Hall Of Fame 86-87; Northeastern U; Bus.

BEAM, LAURA; Warren Cnty Vo-Tech; Washington, NJ; (4); 2/47; Sec Key Clb; Pres Sec VICA; Nwsp Stf; Yrbk Stf; Rep Frsh Cls; Pres Soph Cls; Sec Jr Cls; Rep Sr Cls; Rep Stu Cncl; NHS; Trenton ST Coll; Comp Pgrmr.

BEAMER, CURTIS; Pinelands Regional HS; Tuckerton, NJ; (3); 8/190; Socr; Trk; High Hon Roll; Hon Roll; NHS; Spanish NHS; Soccer Sportsmanshp Awd 85; Stu Of The Month Awd 87; Bus Mgmnt.

BEANEY, JAMES; Cherry Hill High School East; Cherry Hill, NJ; (3); Church Yth Grp; JA; JV Socr; Hon Roll; Engnrng.

BEARD, ELISSA-LYNN; St John Vianney HS; Colts Neck, NJ; (3); 10/260; Intnl Clb; Math Tm; Ski Clb; Concert Band; Mrchg Band; High Hon Roll; Hon Roll; NHS; Prfct Atten Awd; Church Yth Grp; Amer Chem Scty Chem Test 86-87; Genetics.

BEASLEY, KIP L; Hackensack HS; Hackensack, NJ; (4); Pres Am Leg Boys St; Aud/Vis; Pres Church Yth Grp; Computer Clb; Pres FBLA; OEA; Stu Cncl; CC Awd; Cit Awd; Teachers Aide; INROADS 87; Mary Mc Leod Bethune Schlrshp 87; Bus Ldrshp Awd 87; Boston U; Comp Sci.

BECK, KARINA; John F Kennedy HS; Willingboro, NJ; (2); Church Yth Grp; Intnl Clb; Latin Clb; SADD; Yrbk Phtg; Yrbk Stf; Var Capt Fld Hcky; Var Lcrss; Hon Roll; Med.

BECKER, CYNTHIA; Asbury Park HS; Bradley Beach, NJ; (3); Var Mgr(s); Hon Roll; Kybrdg Achvt Awd 86-87; Acctg.

BECKER, JOANNA; Kingsway Regional HS; Mullica Hl, NJ; (2); 32/190; Office Aide; Concert Band; Mrchg Band; School Musical; Bsktbl; Var Trk; Hon Roll; All S Jersey Symph Band 86-87; Glassboro Yth Orch 86-87; Bus.

BECKER, JOANNE; Delaware Valley Regional HS; Bloomsbury, NJ; (4); 9/167; Church Yth Grp; Hosp Aide; Key Clb; Var Sr Cls; Elks Awd; High Hon Roll; Hon Roll; NHS; Moravian Coll; Physcl Thrpy.

BECKER, MARY; Delaware Valley Reg HS; Bloomsbury, NJ; (3); 6/235; Trs Art Clb; Church Yth Grp; Hosp Aide; Key Clb; Office Aide; Teachers Aide; High Hon Roll; Hon Roll; Sec NHS; Walk Amer Rep No 1 In Cnty & Raised The Most Money 87; Chld Psych.

BECKER, STACEY; Secaucus HS; Secaucus, NJ; (3); 1/166; Mu Alpha Theta; Trs Spanish Clb; Drm Mjr(t); Mrchg Band; Trs Frsh Cls; VP Soph Cls; High Hon Roll; Hon Roll; NHS; Spanish NHS; Best Spnsh I Hnrs Stu 85 & Bst Spnsh II 86; Alternate For Congress 86; Bio Engr.

BECKERMAN, J ZOE; Columbia HS; Maplewood, NJ; (3); Drama Clb; Thesps; Concert Band; School Musical; School Play; Variety Show; Rep Soph Cls; Rep Stu Cncl; Library Aide; Band.

BECKERT, AMY; Cinnaminson HS; Cinnaminson, NJ; (3); Church Yth Grp; JV Bsktbl; Var JV Sftbl; Hon Roll; Prfct Atten Awd; Bio Weekend 87; Frnch Awd 86; Kutztown-PA; Grphc Arts.

BECKETT, KARA; Paul VI HS; Haddon Hts, NJ; (3); 29/419; Church Yth Grp; Cmnty Wkr; French Clb; SADD; Ed Yrbk Stf; Ed Lit Mag; Off Pom Pon; Hon Roll; NHS; Camera Clb.

BECKETT, ROBERT A; West Morris Central HS; Long Valley, NJ; (3); 5/340; Am Leg Boys St; Math Tm; Science Clb; Band; Chorus; Concert Band; Var L Socr; Var Capt Tennis; High Hon Roll; NHS; Mddl STS Tnns Assn Rnk 27, NJ Tnns Assn Rnk 7 86; Med.

BECKLER, MONIKA; Pennsauken HS; Merchantville, NJ; (2); 15/420; Girl Scts; Leo Clb; JV Fld Hcky; Var Lcrss; Var Swmmng; Hon Roll; Lion Awd; Rotary Awd; Phys Ther.

BECKMAN, JENNIFER; Clearview HS; Sewell, NJ; (1); Art Clb; Church Yth Grp; Dance Clb; Band; Concert Band; Mrchg Band; Variety Show; Var Cheerleading; JV Gym; Var Tennis; Acad All Amer 87; Brown Belt Karate 87; Secy & Princess NJ Jr Grange 87; Phila Coll Of Art; Art.

BECKWITH, ALISYN; Pitman HS; Pitman, NJ; (4); Key Clb; Var L Crs Cntry; Var L Socr; Var L Trk; Outstndng Trk Evnt Mst Vlbl Rnnr 86-87; Sccr Awd 85; Advrtsng.

BEDELL, BARRY; West Essex Regional HS; Fairfield, NJ; (4); French Clb; Math Tm; Science Clb; Temple Yth Grp; High Hon Roll; Hon Roll; NHS; Med.

BEDNARCZYK, BARBARA; Immaculate Conception HS; Clifton, NJ; (3); Art Clb; Church Yth Grp; Q&S; SADD; School Play; Stage Crew; Lit Mag; Bsktbl; Prfct Atten Awd; Natl Art Hnr Soc 86-87; Cmrcl Art.

BEDNARCZYK, LISA MARIE; Bayonne HS; Bayonne, NJ; (3); Church Yth Grp; Drama Clb; Hosp Aide; Intnl Clb; Teachers Aide; Band; VP Chorus; Church Choir; Jazz Band; School Musical; Frdrck Chpn Awd 88; Rutgers; Music.

BEDNAROVSKY, JESSICA; Lakeland Regional HS; Wanaque, NJ; (4); JV Bsktbl; JV Vllybl; Hon Roll; Hofstra U; Bus.

BEDNARSKI, DENISE; S Marys Of The Assumption HS; Elizabeth, NJ; (2); Chess Clb; Service Clb; Spanish Clb; Speech Tm; Sftbl; Hon Roll; Svc Awd 86-87; Athltc Awd 85-86; Advrtsng.

BEDNARZ, IRENA; Wallington HS; Wallington, NJ; (4); 12/87; Cmnty Wkr; Office Aide; Service Clb; Hon Roll; NHS; Intrnl Foreign Language Awd 84; Lab Tech.

BEEBE, ELAINE; Hopewell Valley Central HS; Pennington, NJ; (2); AFS; Pres Latin Clb; Math Tm; Service Clb; Chorus; School Play; Nwsp Sprt Ed; Jr Cls; Stu Cncl; JV Fld Hcky.

BEER, AMY; Trenton HS; Trenton, NJ; (3); Hosp Aide; JA; Red Cross Aide; Mercer Cnty CC; Phys Thrpy.

BEER, CAROLYN M; Toms River HS North; Toms River, NJ; (4); 29/405; Church Choir; Orch; School Musical; Var Diving; Var Mgr(s); Var Swmmng; Var Tennis; Var Trk; 4-H Awd; High Hon Roll; All Sth Jrsy Rgn III Orchstr 86-87; Grdn ST Phlhrmnc Yth Orchstr 85-87; Sr Mnstr-Yth Wk 87; U Of AZ; Engrng.

BEERES, KELLY A; Wood-Ridge HS; Wood Ridge, NJ; (3); 15/90; Art Clb; Girl Scts; Spanish Clb; Sec Jr Cls; Var Cheerleading; High Hon Roll; Hon Roll; NHS.

BEERS, BONNIE; Phillipsburg HS; Phillipsburg, NJ; (4); 1/315; Nwsp Stf; Stu Cncl; L Var Bsktbl; L Var Fld Hcky; Var Capt Trk; High Hon Roll; NHS; Val; Grdn ST Dstngshd Schlr 87; Rtgrs Schlr 86-87; Lptng Educ Assc Schlrshp 87; U Of DE; Bus.

BEERS, ROBERT; Sayreville War Memorial HS; Parlin, NJ; (4); 60/350; Math Clb; Nwsp Rptr; Rep Stu Cncl; Capt Crs Cntry; Capt Trk; NHS; Middlesex Cnty Crss Cntry Champ 87; Rutgers U; Med.

BEFUMO, CHRISTOPHER J; Hanover Park Regional HS; E Hanover, NJ; (3); 67/277; Var Trk; Hon Roll; Bus.

BEGARNEY, LAURA A; Linden HS; Linden, NJ; (3); VP French Clb; Key Clb; Science Clb; Swmmng; High Hon Roll; NHS; Art Clb; SADD; Most Outstndng Awd Art 85-86; Rutgers Schlr 87; ST Gov Schl 87; Chem Engr.

BEGLEY, MAUREEN; West Milford Township HS; West Milford, NJ; (3); 27/402; Spanish Clb; SADD; Varsity Clb; Band; Ed Lit Mag; Var Stat Bsktbl; JV Cheerleading; Hon Roll; Jr NHS; Spanish NHS; Mrchndsng.

BEGTRUP, KRISTEN; De Paul HS; Wayne, NJ; (3); Pep Clb; Stage Crew; JV Capt Cheerleading; Hon Roll; Hnrbl Mntn Schl Art Shw 86; Hnrs Art IV Crs 87-88; Montclair ST Coll; Art.

BEHM, HEATHER; Clearview Regional HS; Glassboro, NJ; (4); 6/150; Am Leg Aux Girls St; Band; Drm Mjr(t); Mrchg Band; School Musical; VP Stu Cncl; High Hon Roll; VP NHS; St Schlr; Debate Tm; Hgh O Brn Awd 85; Douglass Coll.

BEHSON, NOELLE; Wall Township HS; Manasquan, NJ; (4); 9/269; Sec German Clb; Ski Clb; Rep Jr Cls; L Gym; Var Trk; Stat Wrstlng; NHS; Garden ST Schlr Awd; Comp Scie.

BEILIS, MARC; Lakewood HS; Lakewood, NJ; (4); Ocean County Coll; Comps.

BEJARANO, ERIC; Rutherford HS; Rutherford, NJ; (3); Art Clb; Pep Clb; Rep Soph Cls; Rep Jr Cls; Rep Sr Cls; Rep Stu Cncl; JV Bsbl; JV Bsktbl; JV Cheerleading; JV Trk; Aero Engr.

BEKESI, ZOLTAN; Ocean Township HS; Ocean, NJ; (3); Chess Clb; Hon Roll; Boston U; Bus.

BELBY, KATERI; Manasquan HS; Manasquan, NJ; (3); Church Yth Grp; FBLA; Key Clb; Pres Latin Clb; Stage Crew; Pres Frsh Cls; Var Crs Cntry; Var Fld Hcky; JV Socr; High Hon Roll; Bll Brdly NJ Yng Ctzns Awd 87; JR Statesmn Smmr Schl 86; Hood Coll; Ecnmcs.

BELCEA, DAN; Notre Dame HS; Princeton, NJ; (3); 2/370; Boy Scts; Church Yth Grp; Computer Clb; German Clb; Math Clb; Math Tm; Ski Clb; Nwsp Rptr; Lit Mag; L Var Tennis; Boy Sct Eagle Awd 87; Hnr Rl Distnctn 85-87; Sci.

BELCHER, SUE; Hunterdon Central HS; White House Stati, NJ; (4); Church Yth Grp; Band; Concert Band; Mrchg Band; Cmnty Wkr; Somerst County Coll; Bus.

BELFIGLIO-WILLIAMS, TANIA; Haddonfield Memorial HS; Haddonfield, NJ; (2); Church Yth Grp; Girl Scts; Mrchg Band; Stage Crew; Nwsp Rptr; Yrbk Rptr; Yrbk Stf; JV Cheerleading; Socr; Trk; Pilot.

BELL, BRIAN; Cumberland Regional HS; Bridgeton, NJ; (3); 25/384; Ski Clb; Yrbk Phtg; Yrbk Sprt Ed; Yrbk Stf; Var Socr; Var Tennis; Hon Roll; Jr NHS; NHS; Rotary Yth Ldrshp Alt 87; Med Prof.

BELL, CAROLE V; Newark Acad; Livingston, NJ; (4); Cmnty Wkr; Key Clb; Math Clb; School Musical; School Play; Stage Crew; Nwsp Stf; Yrbk Rptr; Lit Mag; Score Keeper; Natl Achvt Outstndg Negro Stu 86; NJ Schlr 86; Editor In Chf Lit Mag; Engl.

BELL, CHARLES; Salem HS; Salem, NJ; (3); Chess Clb; Spanish Clb; Hon Roll; Auto Tech.

BELL, CHARLOTTE; Ridge HS; Basking Ridge, NJ; (2); Church Yth Grp; French Clb; Library Aide; Stage Crew; Yrbk Stf; Sec Soph Cls; Var Tennis; Hon Roll; All Mountain Vly Conf Tm V Tennis 85 & 86.

BELL, DEBRA; Mainland Regional HS; Northfield, NJ; (4); 18/255; Church Yth Grp; Intnl Clb; Chorus; High Hon Roll; Pres Schlr; 4.0 Or Better GPA 4 Yrs 87; Dstngshd Schlr 86-87; Stockton ST Coll.

BELL, FELICIA; South River HS; South River, NJ; (3); 9/145; Am Leg Aux Girls St; German Clb; Chorus; Symp Band; Nwsp Rptr; VP Jr Cls; VP Sr Cls; Stat Bsktbl; L Var Cheerleading; NHS; Stu Recogntn Prog 87; Rutgers U; Bus Admin.

BELL JR, FLOYD TRAVIS; Passaic HS; Passaic, NJ; (4); Camera Clb; NAACP; Speech Tm; Church Choir; Nwsp Sprt Ed; Rep Stu Cncl; Stat Bsktbl; Var Ftbl; Var Mgr(s); Var Score Keeper; Outstndng Dedication To Passaic Indns; Prfct Atndnc; Cmnctns.

BELL III, FRANK C; North Hunterdon HS; Lebanon, NJ; (4); Boy Scts; Latin Clb; Ski Clb; Ftbl; Lcrss; Wt Lftg; Hon Roll; Pres Schlr; St Schlr; A... Force ROTC Schlrshp 87; Stevens Inst Of Tech; Elec Engr.

BELL, JASON; Edison HS; Edison, NJ; (4); 19/402; Math Tm; Qui... Bowl; Science Clb; Band; Concert Band; Drm Mjr(t); Jazz Band; Mrch... Band; Hon Roll; NHS; Rensselaer Polytech Inst 87; PTSA Outstndng S... To Schl 87; Rensselaer Polytech Inst; Mech.

BELL, JEFFREY; Sayreville War Memorial HS; Sayreville, NJ; (2); Bo... Scts; German Clb; JV Bsktbl; Hon Roll; Pres Schlr; U S Air Force Acad... Aerontcs.

BELL, JENNIFER; Bloomfield HS; Bloomfield, NJ; (4); 25/442; Art Clb... Pres Drama Clb; Pres French Clb; Key Clb; Ski Clb; VP Temple Yth Grp... Chorus; Color Guard; School Play; Yrbk Stf; Govnrs Dstngshd Schlr 86-8... GWFC JR Wmns Clb Bloomfield Excllnce Comm 87; Syracuse U; Comm...

BELL, KAHDIJAH; Benedictine Acad; Hillside, NJ; (3); Drama Clb; Sk... Clb; Spanish Clb; School Play; Variety Show; Sec Soph Cls; Cheerleading... Trk; Typng Effcncy 87; Chrldng Co Capt 87; Ski Clb 87; Mgmt.

BELL, KATHLEEN; Mainland Regional HS; Northfield, NJ; (3); 19/265... Church Yth Grp; JV Bsktbl; JV Sftbl; Var Tennis; Hon Roll.

BELL, MARPESSA; Long Branch HS; Asbury Park, NJ; (4); 5/269; Pre... Key Clb; Band; Nwsp Rptr; Pres Soph Cls; Pres Jr Cls; VP Stu Cncl; Va... Crs Cntry; JV Sftbl; Hon Roll; NHS; USAF ROTC, Carr & Douglass Co... Hnrs Schlrshps 87; Douglass Coll; Elec Engrng.

BELL, RONNI; Palmyra HS; Palmyra, NJ; (3); 2/120; Service Clb; V... Frsh Cls; VP Soph Cls; VP Jr Cls; VP Sr Cls; Var Fld Hcky; JV Sftbl; Hig... Hon Roll; Hon Roll; Drama Clb.

BELL, TOM; Paul VI HS; Turnersville, NJ; (4); Ski Clb; Im Bsbl; Im Ftb... JV Trk; JV Wrstlng; 2nd Hnrs-All A S & B S-Fnl Grds; Philly Co... Phrmcy/Sci; Bio.

BELLAMENTE, JENNIFER; West Deptford HS; West Deptford, N... (3); 1/260; Am Leg Aux Girls St; Varsity Clb; Yrbk Stf; VP Jr Cls; Var ... Swmmng; Var L Tennis; NHS; Ntl Merit Ltr; St Schlr; Key Clb; Ge... Washington U Math & Sci Awd 87.

BELLIA, CHRISTINE; Bayonne HS; Bayonne, NJ; (4); 23/350; Intr... Clb; Math Tm; JV Bsktbl; High Hon Roll; Hon Roll; Jr NHS; NHS... Semi-Fnlst In Garden St Tlnt Cont 84; Cmptr Sci.

BELLO, CRAIG; Paul VI HS; Somerdale, NJ; (3); Math Clb; Math Tm... Lit Mag; Rep Jr Cls; L Var Tennis; High Hon Roll; NHS; Ntl Merit SF; Iv... League U; Sci.

BELLO, LAUREN; Paul VI HS; Turnersville, NJ; (3); 11/418; Math Cl... Var Crs Cntry; Var Trk; Hon Roll; All Cnfrnc Crs Cntry 85 & 86; All St... Jrsy Crs Cntry 86.

BELLO, TINA; Manchester Regional HS; Haledon, NJ; (3); Church Yt... Grp; Dance Clb; Drama Clb; Cheerleading; Powder Puff Ftbl; Hon Rol... Trs Frsh Cls; VP Soph Cls; VP Jr Cls; Rep Stu Cncl; Mst Actv Of Yr 85-8...

BELLUSCIO, KIM; John P Stevens HS; Edison, NJ; (3); Acpl Ch... Chorus; Hon Roll; Elem Ed.

BELO, HERMINIA; Benedictine Acad; Newark, NJ; (3); French Cl... Hosp Aide; JCL; Sec Math Clb; Science Clb; Service Clb; Nwsp Ed-Chie... Sftbl; Hon Roll; NHS; Frnch & Latin Achvt Awds 84-86; Chem Achvt Aw... 86-87; Pre-Med.

BELTON, MONICA-ANDREA; Newton HS; Andover, NJ; (2); 6/25... Sec Church Yth Grp; Latin Clb; Church Choir; Yrbk Stf; Rep Soph Cl... Rep Stu Cncl; Var Cheerleading; Hon Roll; Jr NHS; Howard U; Bio Sci.

BELTRAN, SUSAN; Mother Seton Regional HS; Mountainside, NJ; (2... 17/128; Math Tm; School Musical; JV Vllybl; Hon Roll; NEDT Aw... Drama Clb; Chorus; Church Choir; Rep Frsh Cls.

BELVEDERE, FRANCESCO; Jackson Memorial HS; Jackson, NJ; (3... 26/416; Art Clb; Band; Concert Band; Jazz Band; Mrchg Band; High Ho... Roll; Art.

BENDER, KYLE; Cresshill HS; Cresskill, NJ; (3); 36/105; Cmnty Wk... Letterman Clb; Ski Clb; Varsity Clb; Rep Stu Cncl; Var Bsbl; Var Soc... Var Wrstlng; Hon Roll; All-League Wrstlng 2nd Tm; Bus.

BENDINGER, JEAN MARIE; Bishop Eustace Prep; Haddonfield, N... (4); Drama Clb; French Clb; Pep Clb; SADD; School Play; Rep Frsh Cl... Var Trk; French Hon Soc; Hon Roll; NHS; Loyola Coll; Mktng.

BENECKI, MICHELLE; Lyndhurst HS; Lyndhurst, NJ; (3); 65/174; Ke... Clb; Ski Clb; JV Vllybl.

BENEDETTI, DEBRA; Rancocas Valley Regional HS; Mt Holly, NJ; (2... Church Yth Grp; Pep Clb; SADD; Acpl Chr; Chorus; Lit Mag; Gym; Lcrs... Sftbl; High Hon Roll; Socl Wrkr.

BENEDICT, LEAH; Point Pleasant Beach HS; Pt Pleasant Beach, N... (4); 2/96; Am Leg Aux Girls St; Drama Clb; French Clb; Key Clb; Mat... Clb; Varsity Clb; VP Band; Chorus; Concert Band; Mrchg Band; Ky Cl... Outstndng Dist Brd Indvdl Awd, Jostens Ldrshp Schlrshp & ADK Zet... Chapter Schlrshp 87; Amer U; Jrnlsm.

BENEDICT, WILLIAM F; Wayne Hills HS; Wayne, NJ; (3); 25/350; Ar... Leg Boys St; VP Stu Cncl; Capt Crs Cntry; Cit Awd; Dnfth Awd; 4-H Aw... Hon Roll; NHS; Rotary Awd; Church Yth Grp; All ST Chorus 85-87; N... Governors Schl For Voice 87; Hugh O Brien Yth Fndntn Ldrshp Semin... 86; Sci.

BENEDIK, BETTY; North Hunterdon Regional HS; Lebanon, NJ; (4... 33/365; Pres 4-H; FBLA; OEA; Teachers Aide; Cit Awd; 4-H Awd; NH... Cmnty Wkr; Hon Roll; 1st & 3rd Hnrb Mntn Natl Grange Swng Co... 84-86; 1st Pl Natl Level Grange Pblc Spkng Cont 85; Trenton ST Co... Acctng.

BENESH, SANDRA; Washington Twp HS; Sewell, NJ; (4); 86/47... French Clb; Pres Girl Scts; Hosp Aide; Concert Band; Mrchg Band; Yrb... Stf; Off Stu Cncl; Var JV Mgr(s); JV Swmmng; Hon Roll; Gloucester Cnt... Coll; Nrsng.

BENEVENTANO, JOHN A; Westwood HS; Washington Twp, NJ; (4... 3/221; Boy Scts; Stu Cncl; Capt JV Socr; JV L Wrstlng; French Hon So... High Hon Roll; Trs NHS; Ntl Merit SF; Pres Schlr; St Schlr; Eagle Scou... 86; Engrng.

BENIGNO, JOHN; Jonathan Dayton Regional HS; Springfield, NJ; (4... 14/232; Church Yth Grp; French Clb; School Musical; Ed Lit Mag; Frenc... Hon Soc; High Hon Roll; NCTE Awd; NHS; NHS; St Schlr; U Of P... Philosophy.

BENITEZ, JOSE L; Bergen Catholic HS; Paramus, NJ; (4); 11/261; Hos... Aide; Lit Mag; Im Bowling; JV Trk; Im Vllybl; NHS; Ntl Merit Lt... Spanish NHS; Amercn Assoc Tchrs Spnsh & Portgse Tst 2nd Pl 86; Io... Coll Frgn Lang Cont Spnsh 3rd Pl 85.

BENJAMIN, MICHELLE A; Jonathan Dayton Regional HS; Springfield, NJ; (4); 76/232; Off Church Yth Grp; Cmnty Wkr; Drama Cl... Key Clb; Library Aide; Q&S; Spanish Clb; Varsity Clb; Nwsp Bus Mg... Nwsp Stf; Natl Achvmnt Commnd Stu 86; Quill & Scroll 86; Nestr... Summer Inst What Is Engrng 86; Duke U; PHD.

BENJAMIN, VAUGHN; Lincoln HS; Jersey City, NJ; (3); Church Yth Grp; JA; Chorus; Church Choir; School Musical; Variety Show; VP Jr Cls; NHS; Ntl Merit Ltr.

BENKO, COLEEN; Highland Regional HS; Erial, NJ; (3); 56/285; GAA; Spanish Clb; Pres Jr Cls; Stu Cncl; Var Socr; JV Sftbl; Var Swmmng; Hon Roll; Scr Player Of Week 86; Accntng.

BENNETT, DAVID; Holdy Spirit HS; N Field, NJ; (3); Var Bsbl; Var Ftbl; Hon Roll; Awd Bsbl-Cal Div All-Star Tm 86-87; Sprts Med.

BENNETT, DAVID; Middletown HS South; Leonard, NJ; (4); 74/444; Variety Show; Golf; Socr; Hon Roll; Osborn Schlrshp 87; Silver Cngrssnl Awd 86; Susquehanna U; Accntng.

BENNETT, JESSICA; Vineland HS; Vineland, NJ; (3); 35/800; French Clb; Key Clb; Latin Clb; Red Cross Aide; VP SADD; Mrchg Band; Stu Cncl; Crs Cntry; Sftbl; NHS; Commctns.

BENNETT, LORNE; Irvington HS; Irvington, NJ; (4); 40/600; Chorus; Capt Bsktbl; Var Ftbl; Hon Roll; Comp.

BENNETT, SHIRNET A; Dwight Morrow HS; Englewood, NJ; (3); Art Clb; Church Yth Grp; Debate Tm; Math Tm; Band; Chorus; Concert Band; Mrchg Band; Nwsp Rptr; High Hon Roll.

BENNETT, STEPHANIE; Pennsauken HS; Pennsauken, NJ; (2); 7/346; Aud/Vis; GAA; Spanish Clb; Varsity Clb; Chorus; School Musical; School Play; Variety Show; Rep Frsh Cls; Rep Soph Cls; Prfrmng Arts.

BENNETT, TIMOTHY; Notre Dame HS; E Windsor, NJ; (2); 17/410; Art Clb; Rep Frsh Cls; Var Tennis; Hon Roll; NHS; Excllnc Spnsh, Art II & 1st Pl Awds 86-87; Ballboy Wmns Virginia Slims Tnns Tournmnt 86; Bus.

BENNETT RAGLAND, CHERYL; Madison HS; Madison, NJ; (3); French Clb; Pep Clb; Teachers Aide; Chorus; Yrbk Stf; Cit Awd; Hon Roll; Bus.

BENNINGTON, TODD; North Hunterdon HS; Asbury, NJ; (2); 97/355; Bsbl; Hon Roll.

BENNIS, EILEEN; Hunterdon Central HS; Flemington, NJ; (3); Church Yth Grp; Fld Hcky; Var Trk; Hon Roll; Physcl Thrpy.

BENOIT, ARTIE; St Joseph Regional HS; New City, NY; (3); Church Yth Grp; Latin Clb; Ski Clb; Spanish Clb; Var Capt Bsktbl; Crs Cntry; Trk; NHS; Spanish NHS; Engr.

BENOIT, DUDLEY; Essex Catholic Boys HS; Irvington, NJ; (2); Chess Clb; Variety Show; Yrbk Stf; Rep Frsh Cls; Rep Soph Cls; JV Bsbl; Im Bsktbl; JV Crs Cntry; Im Sftbl; JV Trk; Law.

BENOR, REBECCA; Mt Olive HS; Flanders, NJ; (4); 4/280; AFS; Drama Clb; French Clb; SADD; Sec Temple Yth Grp; Yrbk Stf; French Hon Soc; High Hon Roll; Hon Roll; NHS; Georgetown U; Frnch.

BENSCOTER, KIMBERLY; West Windsor-Plainsboro HS; Lawrenceville, NJ; (3); Church Yth Grp; Spanish Clb; Nwsp Rptr; Nwsp Stf; JV Fld Hcky; JV Sftbl; Var Swmmng; Pres Schlr.

BENSHOFF, KIM A; Spotswood HS; Spotswood, NJ; (4); 26/179; FBLA; Var Capt Bsktbl; Var Capt Sftbl; High Hon Roll; Hon Roll; Douglass; Bus Adm.

BENSON, ERICA; Trenton Central HS; Trenton, NJ; (3); AFS; Church Yth Grp; Dance Clb; Drama Clb; ROTC; Scholastic Bowl; Chorus; Church Choir; School Musical; School Play; Cert Of Achvt In Data Prcsng 87; 3rd Pl Schlr Bwl 87; 1st Pl Drama 87; Intl Bus Mngmnt.

BENSON, KIRSTEN; Woodbridge HS; Woodbridge, NJ; (4); 4/386; Sec French Clb; Trs SADD; Acpl Chr; Chorus; School Musical; Swing Chorus; Ed Yrbk Stf; French Hon Soc; NHS; St Schlr; OH Nrthrn U Hnr Schlrshp 87-88; Vcl Music Awd 87; NJ Dstngshd Schlr 87; OH Northern U; Phrmcy.

BENSON, VALERIE; Parsippany Hills HS; Parsippany, NJ; (3); Hosp Aide; Trs Key Clb; NFL; Concert Band; Mrchg Band; School Musical; Lit Mag; Tennis; Poems Publshd-Merlins Pen & Schl Lit Mag 85-86; Rcvd Golden Poet Awd Frm Wrld Of Poetry 86; Brown U; Sci.

BENTLEY, MARCUS; Marist HS; Jersey City, NJ; (3); 10/95; High Hon Roll; NHS; Spanish NHS; Acdmc Schlrshp Grant 86-88; Engrng.

BENTLEY, PATRICIA; Freehold Township HS; Freehold, NJ; (3); 3/350; Yrbk Bus Mgr; VP Frsh Cls; Rep Soph Cls; Pres Stu Cncl; Var Bsktbl; Stat Ftbl; Im Powder Puff Ftbl; Var Socr; NHS.

BENTROVATO, GIORGIO; Boonton HS; Boonton, NJ; (2); Concert Band; Var Stat Bsktbl; Var Mgr(s); Var Stat Sftbl; Hon Roll; Mgmt.

BENTZ, DAVE; Mc Corristin Catholic HS; Trenton, NJ; (4); 42/264; Am Leg Boys St; Boy Scts; Im Badmtn; JV Bsbl; Var Bsktbl; Im Bowling; Ftbl; Im Wt Lftg; Hon Roll; U Central FL; Comp Engrng.

BENTZ, ELLEN; Notre Dame HS; Morris, PA; (4); Drama Clb; French Clb; School Play; Lit Mag; Rep Frsh Cls; Rep Soph Cls; Fld Hcky; French Hon Soc; NHS; Parsons Schl Of Design; Fshn.

BENZLER, FREDRIC; Mahwah HS; Mahwah, NJ; (4); High Hon Roll; Hon Roll; U Of Pittsburg; Bus.

BERBERICH, PAMELA; Chatham Twp HS; Chatham Twp, NJ; (4); 63/140; Church Yth Grp; Drama Clb; Chorus; Church Choir; Pep Band; School Musical; Swing Chorus; Nwsp Stf; Var Cheerleading; Var Lcrss.

BERCAW, LISA; Westfield SR HS; Westfield, NJ; (3); Pres Church Yth Grp; Intnl Clb; Natl Beta Clb; Chorus; Church Choir; NHS; Prfct Atten Awd; Bus.

BERCHTOLD, KATHRYN; Vineland HS North; Vineland, NJ; (1); German Clb; Chorus; Madrigals; Var Socr; Var Swmmng; Hon Roll.

BERENYI, NORBERT; Northern Valley Regional HS; Northvale, NJ; (4); 19/271; Capt Crs Cntry; Capt Trk; Hon Roll; NHS; Ntl Merit SF; St Schlr; 1st Tm All Cnty Crss Cntry 86; 2nd Tm All Cnty 1 Mile Sprg Trck 86; 1st Tm All Leal Mile Wntr Trck 86; Bucknell U; Comp Sci.

BERG, DEBRA; Highstown HS; East Windsor, NJ; (4); 31/449; Drama Clb; French Clb; Service Clb; Ski Clb; SADD; Stage Crew; Yrbk Stf; High Hon Roll; Hon Roll; NHS; Pro Marksman Riflrey 84; American U.

BERG, GLEN; Franklin HS; Franklin Pk, NJ; (3); Boy Scts; Church Yth Grp; Ski Clb; Varsity Clb; Var Golf; Var L Socr; High Hon Roll; Hon Roll; Bus.

BERGAMO, PAUL R; Saint Augustine Prep; Vineland, NJ; (3); 13/53; Pres Civic Clb; Pep Clb; JV Bsbl; Var L Crs Cntry; Stat Mgr(s); JV Stat Timer; Var L Wrstlng; Hon Roll; NEDT Awd; Prfct Atten Awd; Villanova U; Accntg.

BERGE, JENNIFER; Immaculate Conception HS; Garfield, NJ; (4); Hosp Aide; Q&S; Sec Spanish Clb; SADD; Nwsp Ed-Chief; Nwsp Phtg; Nwsp Rptr; Nwsp Stf; Sec Frsh Cls; VP Soph Cls; Cert Awd March Of Dimes 86; Fordham U; Jrnlsm.

BERGEN, JASON; West Milford Twp HS; W Milford, NJ; (2); Boy Scts; Church Yth Grp; Cmnty Wkr; Hon Roll; Var JV Bsbl; Pres Ftnss Awd 85-87; Rutgers; Engrng.

BERGENTY, LISA; Delaware Valley Regional HS; Little York, NJ; (3); Chorus; Concert Band; School Musical; School Play; Rep Stu Cncl; Gov Hon Prg Awd; High Hon Roll; Hon Roll; Governors Schl Arts 87; Musical Theatre.

BERGER, MICHELLE; Barnstable Acad; Orangeburg, NY; (4); 3/29; Camera Clb; Hosp Aide; Ski Clb; Temple Yth Grp; Bowling; Tennis; High Hon Roll; Hon Roll; Math Awd 86; Nurse.

BERGER, WILLIAM; Matawan Regional HS; Aberdeen, NJ; (4); 9/325; Computer Clb; Math Tm; Q&S; Ski Clb; Nwsp Bus Mgr; Nwsp Phtg; Yrbk Ed-Chief; Var L Tennis; Hon Roll; Trs NHS; Grdn ST Schlr 87; Genetics.

BERGERON, JENNIFER; Middletown H S South; Red Bank, NJ; (3); Capt GAA; Var L Bsktbl; Var L Socr; Hon Roll; NHS; Ntl Merit Ltr; Ski Clb; Variety Show; JV L Fld Hcky; Im Powder Puff Ftbl; Acad Achvmnt 85; MVP Soccer Var 87; Frgn Rltns.

BERGHAHN, KRISTIN; Paramus Catholic Girls HS; Saddle Brook, NJ; (2); 20/175; Church Yth Grp; Sec 4-H; Ski Clb; Rep Stu Cncl; Im Sftbl; JV Var Vllybl; Hon Roll; NEDT Awd; STEED Pgm; Lthrn Chrch MO Synod Delegt WA DC; AHA.

BERGHAUS, JEAN; Columbia HS; Maplewood, NJ; (3); Church Yth Grp; Latin Clb; Service Clb; Varsity Clb; Nwsp Stf; Rep Soph Cls; L Var Fld Hcky; Ntl Merit Ltr; Bio.

BERGMAN, KRISTINE; Howell HS; Howell, NJ; (4); 4-H; French Clb; Color Guard; Flag Corp; 4-H Awd; Hon Roll; Monmouth 4-H Ambsdr Proj Awd 84; Monmouth 4-H Queen & Ntl Cong Chicago 86; Georgian Ct Coll; Bus Admn.

BERGMAN, TIMOTHY P; Belvidere HS; Belvidere, NJ; (4); 7/142; Am Leg Boys St; Madrigals; Yrbk Stf; Pres Frsh Cls; VP Soph Cls; Pres Jr Cls; VP Stu Cncl; Var Capt Wrstlng; Trs NHS; Hoffman La Roche Schlr WA Wrkshps 86; Indstrl Arts Clb Off 86; Hugh O Brien Awd Fnlst 84; US Air Force Acad; Aero Engrng.

BERISH, LORI; Notre Dame HS; Trenton, NJ; (3); 86/387; Church Yth Grp; FBLA; Trs Red Cross Aide; Sec Service Clb; Off Soph Cls; Off Jr Cls; Off Sr Cls; Sec Stu Cncl; Crs Cntry; Mgr(s); Vrsty Ltr 86; Finance.

BERK, NATHAN A; Holy Spirit HS; Linwood, NJ; (4); NHS; Drexel U; Elec Engrng.

BERK, SCOTT; Ocean Township HS; Oakhurst, NJ; (4); 32/327; Computer Clb; Science Clb; Spanish Clb; High Hon Roll; Hon Roll; JETS Awd; Ntl Merit Ltr; Aud/Vis; Band; Stage Crew; Spartan Schlr Awd 85-87; Natl Sci Olymp Awd 83; Trustee Schlrshp 87; Rider Coll; Biochem.

BERKLEY, ERIK; Morris Knolls HS; Boonton, NJ; (2); Ski Clb; SADD; Socr; JV Wrstlng; Hon Roll.

BERKOWITZ, DANIEL; Parsippany HS; Lake Hiawatha, NJ; (3); Chess Clb; Computer Clb; Band; Chorus; Concert Band; School Musical; Symp Band; Capt Crs Cntry; Trk; Hon Roll; Elec Engrng.

BERKOWITZ, PAUL; Union HS; Union, NJ; (4); 52/550; Science Clb; Temple Yth Grp; Bowling; Sftbl; Cit Awd; Hon Roll; Pres Acdmc Ftnss Awd 87; Rebel League All Star Tm-Pitcher 83-85; Rutgers-Cook Coll; Comp Sci.

BERLIN, RITA; Fair Lawn HS; Fair Lawn, NJ; (3); 25/340; Math Clb; Math Tm; Science Clb; Service Clb; Temple Yth Grp; Hon Roll; NHS; Natl Vlntry Exmntn Hebrew Cltr & Knwldg 85-87; Intl Law.

BERLIN, STEPHEN; Toms River East HS; Toms River, NJ; (4); 108/569; Q&S; Ski Clb; Nwsp Ed-Chief; Nwsp Rptr; Nwsp Sprt Ed; Var Ftbl; JV Trk; Im Wt Lftg; Jrnlsm.

BERLINER, ROBERTA; W Morris Mendham HS; Brookside, NJ; (4); FTA; Hosp Aide; Intnl Clb; Chorus; Yrbk Stf; Hon Roll; NHS; 200 Clb Schlrshp & NJ Teachers Assn Medal 87; Vet Admin Medical Ctr Volunteer Awd 85-86; Miami U; Spcl Educ.

BERLINGERI, LINDA; Washington Twp HS; Sewell, NJ; (2); Art Clb; Church Yth Grp; Chorus; Church Choir; Color Guard; Mrchg Band; School Musical; 1987 Annual Art Shw & Adjudication-Hon Men 87.

BERLINGHIERI, SARAH L; Academy Of The Holy Angels; River Vale, NJ; (3); French Clb; Math Tm; Mu Alpha Theta; Chorus; Nwsp Rptr; Nwsp Stf; High Hon Roll; Hon Roll; NHS; Pblc Rltns Ofcr Schl Scl Actn Clb 86-87; Natnl Latn Cont 85 & 86; Interntnl Law.

BERLOWITZ, ARINA; St Pius X Regional HS; Somerset, NJ; (3); 3/88; JA; Library Aide; ROTC; School Play; VP Jr Cls; High Hon Roll; Hon Roll; NHS; Kean Coll; Hndcppd Tchr.

BERMUDEZ, BETSY; Memorial HS; West New York, NJ; (4); 45/356; VP Math Clb; Spanish Clb; Hon Roll; PTA Schl Schlrshp 87; Montclair ST Coll; Math Tchr.

BERMUDEZ, PABLO A; Millville SR HS; Millville, NJ; (3).

BERNARD, KATHY LYNN; Mt St Mary Acad; Cranford, NJ; (3); Drama Clb; GAA; Latin Clb; Library Aide; School Play; Rep Jr Cls; Var Capt Cheerleading; Fld Hcky; Score Keeper; Hon Roll; Comm.

BERNARDI, PATRICIA; Vineland HS; Vineland, NJ; (3); 365/869; Pep Clb; SADD; Bsktbl; Cheerleading; Cit Awd; Hon Roll; Church Yth Grp; Letterman Clb; Socr; Glassboro; Phys Educ.

BERNATH, BRIAN; Marine Acad Of Science & Technlgy; Matawan, NJ; (4); 9/32; Boy Scts; Computer Clb; ROTC; Ski Clb; Spanish Clb; Drill Tm; Nwsp Ed-Chief; Nwsp Rptr; Nwsp Stf; Yrbk Ed-Chief; Daedillion Awd 86; Cadet Of The Mnth 86fcade Of The Annual Inspctn 85; US Naval Acad; Engr.

BERNIER-LEARN, CHRISTOPHER; Holy Spirit HS; Brigantine, NJ; (2); 50/397; Boy Scts; JV Ftbl; High Hon Roll; Hon Roll; Penn ST U; Engr.

BERNSTEIN, BONNIE; Howell HS; Howell, NJ; (3); 4/350; Trs Latin Clb; Jazz Band; Mrchg Band; VP Stu Cncl; Var Gym; Var Trk; High Hon Roll; NHS; School Musical; Symp Band; JR All Amercn Hall Of Fame Music; MVP Gymnstc Capt; 1ST Chair Tenor Saxo Wind Ens; Journlsm.

BERNSTEIN, DREW; Middleton South HS; Leonardo, NJ; (4); 65/450; Am Leg Boys St; Band; School Musical; Trs Soph Cls; Off Jr Cls; Off Stu Cncl; Hon Roll; Hugh O Brien Yth Fndtn NJ Ldrshp Smnr 85; Cnvntn II-CHRMN Admnstrtv Cmmtte 86; Natl Yng Ldrs Confrnc.

BERNSTEIN, SCOTT; Madison Central HS; Old Bridge, NJ; (3); 39/360; VP Latin Clb; Spanish Clb; Temple Yth Grp; Varsity Clb; Im Bowling; Var Crs Cntry; Stat Swmmng; Var Trk; NHS; Ntl Merit Ltr; Grtr Middlesex Conf All Acad Hnr Rl Boys Trk, Crss Cntry 87; Comp Prgrmmng.

BERRINGTON, KIMBERLY; Highland Regional HS; Erial, NJ; (2); Art Clb; Camera Clb; Var Crs Cntry; Var Trk; High Hon Roll; Drexel U; Comp Engrng.

BERRIOS, CARMEN; Our Lady Of Good Counsel HS; Newark, NJ; (3); Church Yth Grp; Letterman Clb; Library Aide; Pep Clb; JV Cheerleading; JV Sftbl; JV Wt Lftg; NHS; Chorus; MVP In Sftbl 87; All Star Sftbl 86-87.

BERRIOS, THERESA; Cedar Ridge HS; Laurence Harbor, NJ; (3); 64/344; Church Yth Grp; Trs Intnl Clb; Pep Clb; Color Guard; Var L Trk; Hon Roll; Spanish NHS; Child Psych.

BERRY, DONALD; Edgewood Regional SR HS; Braddock, NJ; (2); JV Bsbl; JV Bsktbl; Var Ftbl; Hon Roll; Pres Acdmc Ftnss Awd 85-86.

BERRY, GWEN; Lakeland Regional HS; Ringwood, NJ; (4); 75/340; Girl Scts; Varsity Clb; Lit Mag; JV Bsktbl; Im Diving; Capt Powder Puff Ftbl; Var Sftbl; Im Swmmng; Im Tennis; High Hon Roll; Glassboro ST Coll; Crmnl Law.

BERRY, JENNIFER; Nutley HS; Nutley, NJ; (4); 70/304; AFS; Camera Clb; Church Yth Grp; Hosp Aide; Key Clb; Library Aide; Red Cross Aide; Church Choir; Rep Stu Cncl; Trk; Red Cross Yth Cncl Staff Aide Yr 86; Hunting Awd 84; Lib Arts.

BERRY, MICHAEL; Don Bosco Prep HS; Thiells, NY; (3); 3/200; Science Clb; Ski Clb; Mgr(s); Im Socr; Var Trk; High Hon Roll; NHS; Pep Clb; Gen Excllnc Awd; Trck Vrsty Ltr.

BERRY, STEPHANIE MICHELE; Holy Cross HS; Mount Laurel, NJ; (4); 24/365; Church Yth Grp; Cmnty Wkr; Girl Scts; JA; Service Clb; Spanish Clb; Teachers Aide; Stage Crew; Yrbk Stf; Vllybl; Cookie Cert Merit; WDAS FM 3rd Pl Essay Cont; Ladies Aux Awd; Adam Scholar; United Way Campgn Awd; Drexel U; Bus Adm.

BERRY, STEVEN; Highland HS; Somerdale, NJ; (2); JV Crs Cntry; JV Trk; JV Wrstlng; Hon Roll.

BERSALONA, LOUIS; Highland Regional HS; Laurel Springs, NJ; (3); 1/350; Chess Clb; German Clb; Science Clb; NHS; Rotary Awd; Val; High Hon Roll.

BERSANI, DEAN; Highland Regional HS; Laurel Springs, NJ; (2); Hon Roll; JV Bsktbl; JV Golf; Temple:Mech Engr.

BERSHTEIN, KAREN; John P Stevens HS; Edison, NJ; (3); 70/450; Cmnty Wkr; Office Aide; Red Cross Aide; Science Clb; SADD; Temple Yth Grp; Y-Teens; Nwsp Bus Mgr; Nwsp Stf; Stu Cncl; Mrktng.

BERTH, DEBORA; Paulsboro JR SR HS; Paulsboro, NJ; (3); 11/150; Sec Church Yth Grp; Library Aide; Acpl Chr; Chorus; Church Choir; Nwsp Stf; Stu Cncl; High Hon Roll; Hon Roll; Sec NHS; Nrsg.

BERTINO, CATHY A; Egg Harbor Township HS; Pleasantville, NJ; (3); 15/329; Ski Clb; Spanish Clb; Drill Tm; Mrchg Band; Yrbk Stf; VP Jr Cls; Sftbl; Jr NHS; Acdmc All Am Schlr Pgm 84; Temple; Communications.

BERTOLDO, JONATHAN; Delaware Valley Regional HS; Milford, NJ; (3); Am Leg Boys St; Cmnty Wkr; Exploring; Off Jr Cls; Swmmng; Trk; Wrstlng; Hon Roll; Bloomsburg Coll; Pre Med.

BERTOLINI, ANGELA; St Mary HS; Jersey City, NJ; (3); Church Yth Grp; Computer Clb; FBLA; Girl Scts; JA; Yrbk Stf; Hon Roll; Chrstn Svc Awd, JR Ring Ceremony Hnr 86-87; Rutgers Coll; Cmptr Sci.

BERTRAND, MARK; The Vail-Deane Schl; Westfield, NJ; (3); Church Yth Grp; Ski Clb; Spanish Clb; Chorus; Stage Crew; Pres Jr Cls; Pres Sr Cls; Rep Stu Cncl; Var L Bsbl; Var L Socr; Acctng.

BESHAR, ROBERT; W Morris Mendham HS; Mendham, NJ; (4); 56/318; FBLA; Radio Clb; Stu Cncl; Im Bsktbl; Im Golf; JV Socr; Im Tennis; Im Wrstlng; High Hon Roll; Hon Roll; Fairfield U; Bus.

BESKE, BARBARA; Buena Regional HS; Newfield, NJ; (3); 3/218; Trs Church Yth Grp; Ski Clb; SADD; Varsity Clb; Trs Jr Cls; Var L Tennis; Var L Trk; Hon Roll; NHS; Tnns MVP 84-86; Acad Vrsty Ltr 86; Tchr.

BESSIN, JAMES; Madison HS; Madison, NJ; (3); 13/200; Boy Scts; Church Yth Grp; Dance Clb; Chorus; School Musical; Var L Crs Cntry; High Hon Roll; NHS; JR Statesman Diploma 87; Natl Outdoor Ldrshp Schl Dipolam 86; Soc Sci.

BEST, TANYA E; Dwight Morrow HS; Englewood, NJ; (4); Dance Clb; Teachers Aide; Color Guard; Flag Corp; Yrbk Phtg; Off Frsh Cls; Var Bsktbl; Var Trk; Twrlr; Vrsty Ltr Awd/Track 85-86; NC Cntrl U; Bus.

BETHEA, BRANDON; Trenton Central HS; Trenton, NJ; (3); NAACP; Pep Clb; Capt Golf; Im Wt Lftg; NEDT Awd; Rutgers; Engr.

BETHEA, DEIDRA; Eastside HS; Paterson, NJ; (3); 5/450; Trs Leo Clb; Sec Science Clb; Chorus; Church Choir; Rep Soph Cls; Trs Jr Cls; JV Sftbl; Hon Roll; NHS; Prfct Atten Awd; Spcl Incentive Science Awd Prog 87; Montclair ST Coll Prog Acad Tlntd Stu 86; Chem.

BETHEA, KEISHA; St Anthony HS; Jersey Cty, NJ; (3); Cheerleading; Sftbl; Hon Roll; Nrsng.

BETHEA, LISA; Lincoln HS; Jersy City, NJ; (3); JA; Rep Stu Cncl; Hon Roll; NHS; Prfct Atten Awd; Bus Adm.

BETHEL, KAMA LYNN; Rutgers Prep Schl; Plainfield, NJ; (4); Church Yth Grp; Hosp Aide; Key Clb; Letterman Clb; Model UN; Science Clb; Varsity Clb; Chorus; Nwsp Rptr; Pres Frsh Cls; Parents Assc Schlrfshp Awd 85-86; Liberty Loan Awd 86; Schlr Athlete 87; Princeton U; Law.

BETZ, COLLEEN; De Paul HS; Wayne, NJ; (3); 29/165; Latin Clb; Yrbk Phtg; Yrbk Rptr; Trs Frsh Cls; Sec Soph Cls; Sec Pres Stu Cncl; Var Bsktbl; Var Capt Socr; Var Trk; High Hon Roll; Bst Def Plyr Scr Awd 86; 2nd Tm Conf Javln 87; Ldrshp Conf 86-87; Bus Exec.

BETZ, ERIC; Toms River North HS; Toms River, NJ; (3); 32/459; Ski Clb; Band; Jazz Band; Mrchg Band; L Var Bsbl; Ftbl; Wt Lftg; Hon Roll; Acad Ltr 85; Band Ltr/Pin 85-86&86-87; Natl Hnr Rl 86-87; Engrng.

BETZ, JAMES P; Northern Valley-Old Tappan HS; Harrington Park, NJ; (4); Aud/Vis; Nwsp Phtg; Nwsp Stf; Hon Roll; Acdmc Decthln Tm No 9 Natn 2 Glds, 3 Slvr, 5 Brnz 86-87; Long Island U; Photo.

BEVAN, MARNIE; Gloucester JR-SR HS; Gloucester, NJ; (3); Am Leg Aux Girls St; Q&S; Spanish Clb; Chorus; Church Choir; School Musical; School Play; Yrbk Stf; Pres Frsh Cls; Rep Soph Cls.

BEVANS, LORI; Kittatinny Regional HS; Layton, NJ; (4); 55/224; Church Yth Grp; Pres Spanish Clb; Teachers Aide; Chorus; Church Choir; Stage Crew; Yrbk Stf; JV Bsktbl; Var Swmmng; Spnsh Stu Mnth 86; Wilson Coll; Vet Med Tech.

BEVERIDGE, DAVID A; Hamilton High West; Trenton, NJ; (3); Am Leg Boys St; Cmnty Wkr; Hosp Aide; Jr Civitan Int; Key Clb; Band; Concert Band; Mrchg Band; Pep Band; Symp Band; Kent ST; Pilot.

BEVERSLUIS, JANET; Highland HS; Clementon, NJ; (3); 20/285; Church Yth Grp; Spanish Clb; School Play; Swmmng; Hon Roll; NHS; English.

BEVILACQUA, PHIL; Gloucester Catholic HS; Deptford, NJ; (3); 5/175; Var Bowling; Var Tennis; High Hon Roll; Hon Roll; NHS; Mst Imprvd Plyr Tens 86-87; Intl Sonatina Awd 87.

BEVILAQUA, GINA; Highland Regional HS; Blackwood, NJ; (2); La Salle Coll; Radlgy.

BEVIS, BLAINE R; The Pennington Schl; Princeton Jct, NJ; (4); 11/77; Am Leg Boys St; Ski Clb; Nwsp Rptr; Var Ftbl; Richmond U; Bus.

BEY, FATIMAH; Plainfield HS; Plainfield, NJ; (3); 22/400; VP Debate Tm; Drama Clb; School Musical; School Play; Hon Roll; NHS; Notre Dame For Engrng 87; Jr Statesmns Summer Schl 87; UCLA; Law.

BEYERS, JOANN; Matawan Regional HS; Cliffwood Bch, NJ; (4); 76/403; French Clb; Var Capt Bsktbl; Var L Sftbl; Kean Coll; Elem Educ.

BEZNER, MICHAEL; Manalapan HS; Englishtown, NJ; (2); 17/425; Computer Clb; Math Tm; Temple Yth Grp; Stage Crew; Var Tennis; Comp.

BHATT, KIRIT; Rutherford HS; Rutherford, NJ; (3); Chess Clb; Key Clb; Math Tm; Pres NFL; Stage Crew; JV Socr; JV Trk; High Hon Roll; NHS; St Schlr; Future Problem Solving 3rd In St Awd 86-87; Boston U; Pre-Med.

BHATTACHARYA, SASWATI; Princeton HS; Princeton, NJ; (2); Cmnty Wkr; Debate Tm; French Clb; Hosp Aide; Orch; Mgr(s); Biolgy.

BIAGI, SUSAN; Our Lady Of Mercy Acad; Vineland, NJ; (4); Dance Clb; Library Aide; Teachers Aide; Trs Frsh Cls; VP Soph Cls; Var Cheerleading; Swmmng; Hon Roll; Miss Amer Coed Fnlst 87; Cabrini Coll; Erly Chldhd Ed.

BIALOUS, KIM; Manalapan HS; Manalapan, NJ; (3); Yrbk Stf; Psych.

BIANCAMANO, JOHN; Hudson Catholic HS; Clifton, NJ; (3); 19/196; Pep Clb; SADD; Yrbk Rptr; Capt Bsbl; Im Bsktbl; Capt Ftbl; High Hon Roll; Hon Roll; NHS; All Cnty Ftbl 86; All Cnty Bsbl 85-86; Pre-Med.

BIANCHERI, MARIA F; De Paul Diocesan HS; Wayne, NJ; (3); 15/150; Church Yth Grp; Quiz Bowl; Nwsp Stf; JV Socr; Var Twrlr; Hon Roll; NHS; Ntl Merit Ltr; Poem Pblshd-Cthlc Tn Mag 87; Nwspr Asst Sprts Edtr 86-87; Nwspr Edtrls Edtr 87-88; Lbrl Arts.

BIANCHINI, MIRELLA; Columbia HS; South Orange, NJ; (4); Dance Clb; Spanish Clb; Chorus; Church Choir; Variety Show; Lit Mag; Vllybl; Hon Mntn Frgn Lang Comptns 86-87; Seton Hall U; Engl.

BIANCULLI, ERIN; Lenape Valley Regional HS; Stanhope, NJ; (3); 27/224; Hon Roll; USGF Natl Elite Cmptr 87; USGF Cls I Zone Chmpn; Cert Of Merit In Frnch; Med.

BIANK, LISA; Randolph HS; Randolph, NJ; (3); Key Clb; Natl Sci Olympd 86; Berkeley Bus Schl; Mrktng.

BIAZZO, DAWN; Collegiate Schl; Garfield, NJ; (3); JCL; Key Clb; Teachers Aide; Nwsp Ed-Chief; Tennis; Vllybl; Hon Roll; NHS; Ntl Merit Schol; Neurosurgn.

BIDIC, SEAN; Cumberland Regional HS; Bridgeton, NJ; (3); 1/400; Am Leg Boys St; Debate Tm; German Clb; Model UN; Science Clb; Varsity Clb; Var Sr Cls; Var Ftbl; Capt Wrstlng; High Hon Roll; Rotry Yth Ldrshp Awd 87; Schlrshp Awd Wrstlg 87; Legsltv Excllnc Model Congrss 87; Med.

BIEBER, KELLEY; Kinnelon HS; Kinnelon, NJ; (2); Church Yth Grp; French Clb; Hosp Aide; Ski Clb; School Play; Yrbk Phtg; Rep Stu Cncl; Var JV Cheerleading; JV Socr; French Hon Soc; PA ST; Accntnt.

BIEDERMANN, RICHARD; Woodstown HS; Woodstown, NJ; (4); Am Leg Boys St; Church Yth Grp; English Clb; German Clb; Key Clb; Yrbk Stf; Trs Frsh Cls; Trs Soph Cls; Bsktbl; Var Ftbl; Hugh Obrian Yth Ldrshp Semnr 86; Bus.

BIEGEL, BRIAN; St Joseph Regional HS; Old Tappan, NJ; (3); 31/256; Church Yth Grp; Cmnty Wkr; JV Crs Cntry; JV Trk; Hon Roll; NHS; Spanish NHS; Vet.

BIEL, CINDY; Union HS; Union, NJ; (3); Key Clb; Pres Temple Yth Grp; Yrbk Phtg; Ed Yrbk Stf; Var Crs Cntry; L Mgr(s); Var Trk; Phrmcy.

BIELEN, LISA; Mt Olive HS; Flanders, NJ; (3); 13/318; AFS; Church Yth Grp; Dance Clb; FBLA; SADD; Rep Jr Cls; Stat Crs Cntry; High Hon Roll; VP NHS; Voice Dem Awd; Spec Ed CCD Tchr 86-87; Lib Arts.

BIELEN, RACHEL; John F Kennedy HS; Willingboro, NJ; (3); Computer Clb; Boy Scts; Intnl Clb; Latin Clb; Math Tm; Spanish Clb; Chorus; School Musical; Hon Roll; Jr NHS; NJ Garden ST Schlrshp Fnlst, Spllng Chmpn, Bst Typng Stu 86-87; Bus.

BIELING, KYRA; Florence Twp Mem HS; Burlington, NJ; (4); 7/80; Am Leg Aux Girls St; Rep Stu Cncl; Cit Awd; Hon Roll; Voice Dem Awd; Sen Bradleys Yng Ctznshp Awd 87; 1st Pl Enrgy Mgmt Compttn Tm Entry 87; Vol Wrk Masonic Hm 86; Rutgers U.

BIELSKI, THERESE; Hackettstown HS; Hackettstown, NJ; (3); 11/200; Church Yth Grp; Sec Key Clb; Q&S; Nwsp Rptr; Ed Nwsp Stf; Off Stu Cncl; High Hon Roll; Hon Roll; NHS; Ntl Merit Ltr; Elem Educ.

BIENKOWSKI, KEITH; Marist HS; Bayonne, NJ; (3); Ski Clb; Var Socr; Var Tennis; Seton Hall U.

BIER, SETH; Ocean Twsp HS; Wayside, NJ; (3); 33/342; Hosp Aide; Ski Clb; Temple Yth Grp; Nwsp Rptr; Var L Bsktbl; High Hon Roll; Im Wt Lftg; Med.

BIESE, CHRISTINA; St Rose HS; Spring Lk Heights, NJ; (4); Key Clb; Ski Clb; Var Capt Cheerleading; Socr; Hon Roll; CPA.

BIGGAR, DAPHNE; Rartian HS; Hazlet, NJ; (3); Var Bsktbl; Var Sftbl; Hotel Mgmt.

BIGIONI, NADINE; Burlington Township HS; Burlington, NJ; (3); 4/136; Hosp Aide; Varsity Clb; Pres Band; Chorus; Concert Band; Jazz Band; Yrbk Stf; JV Sftbl; High Hon Roll; NHS.

BIGIONI, NICOLE; Burlington Township HS; Burlington, NJ; (3); 3/136; Hosp Aide; Varsity Clb; VP Band; Chorus; Concert Band; Jazz Band; Yrbk Stf; Sftbl; High Hon Roll; NHS.

BIHLMIER, JOSEPH M; Southern Regional HS; Ship Bottom, NJ; (4); 24/381; Church Yth Grp; Model UN; Yrbk Stf; VP Jr Cls; VP Sr Cls; Rep Stu Cncl; Var Tennis; DAR Awd; Hon Roll; NHS; Pres Acdmc Ftnss Awd 87; Berry Coll.

BILIK, JENNIFER; Newton HS; Andover, NJ; (3); French Clb; Latin Clb; Varsity Clb; Yrbk Stf; Var Fld Hcky; Mgr(s); JV Sftbl; Hon Roll; Nrth Jrsy Fld Hcky All Star Tm-Hnrb Mntn 87.

BILL, JENNIFER; Woodstown HS; Monroeville, NJ; (4); 30/215; Cmnty Wkr; English Clb; Hosp Aide; Spanish Clb; Flag Corp; Im Vllybl; Hon Roll; Exploring; Ski Clb; Nwsp Stf; Gov Tchng Schlrs Pgm 87; SICO Fndtn Schlrshp 87; Fennie B Miller Schlrshp 87; West Chester U; Erly Chldh Ed.

BILLEK, CARL; Bayonne HS; Bayonne, NJ; (4); 128/350; Rutgers Coll; Pres Of US.

BILODEAU, LAURA A; Westfield SR HS; Westfield, NJ; (4); 1/484; Scholastic Bowl; Yrbk Stf; Var Trk; French Hon Soc; Gov Hon Prg Awd; NHS; Ntl Merit Schol; St Schlr; French Clb; George Washington U Medal For Math & Sci 86; Astrophysics.

BILOTTA, JODIE; North Hunterdon HS; Stanton, NJ; (3); 15/350; Church Yth Grp; L Crs Cntry; L Trk; French Hon Soc; Acad Achvmnt Scty; Crss Cnty ST Chmpn 85-86; Track ST Chmpn 85-87.

BILOW, KATHY; Mount Olive HS; Budd Lake, NJ; (3); Dance Clb; Ski Clb; Chorus; JV Bsktbl; JV Capt Cheerleading; JV Sftbl; Hon Roll; Lib Art.

BINDAS, PAMELA; Manalapan HS; Manalapan, NJ; (4); 44/417; Nwsp Rptr; Yrbk Stf; Rep Soph Cls; Pres Jr Cls; Pres Sr Cls; Mgr Tennis; NHS; Hmcmng Queen 86; Presdntl Acad Fitnss Awd 87; Jr Prom Ct 86; Sr Ball Ct 87; U CT.

BINGLER, AIMEE; St John Vianney HS; Colts Neck, NJ; (3); Art Clb; Church Yth Grp; Cmnty Wkr; Drama Clb; Sec Intnl Clb; Key Clb; Band; Chorus; Church Choir; Concert Band; Fnlst Chnnl 13 Welcme Art Fstvl Drwng, Pblshd Fmly Cir 85; Wnnr Chnnl 13 Draw Me Stry Art Fstvl 86; Write.

BINNS JR, RUSSELL WM; Brick Township HS; Mantoloking, NJ; (4); 9/314; Debate Tm; Key Clb; Crs Cntry; Ftbl; Trk; Vllybl; Wrstlng; High Hon Roll; NHS; Pres Schlr; Clarkson U; Elec Engrng.

BIRCH, CINDY M; St Pius X HS; Piscataway, NJ; (4); 11/107; Church Choir; School Musical; Ed Yrbk Stf; Pres Stu Cncl; Hon Roll; Pres NHS; NEDT Awd; Var Bowling; Var Trk; Natl Achvt Scholar Pgm Outstndng Negro Stu 86-87; Hnrb Mntn Grdn ST Schlrs Pgm 86-87; Rutgers Scholar; Douglass Coll Rutgers; Bus Adm.

BIRD, CHRISTINE; Phillipsburg HS; Phillipsburg, NJ; (3); Key Clb; Ski Clb; Drill Tm; Hon Roll; Early Chldhd Educ.

BIRD, GEOFFREY; Clifton HS; Clifton, NJ; (4); 139/589; Am Leg Boys St; French Clb; Pres Temple Yth Grp; JV Trk; NHS; Wellesly Coll Summer Session 85; Boston Coll Summer Session 86; Cnty Champ Mock Trial Tm 86-87; Boston U; History.

BIRD, PATRICK; Hunterdon Central HS; Stockton, NJ; (3); 112/557; Boy Scts; Pres Church Yth Grp; Cmnty Wkr; 4-H; Band; Church Choir; Mrchg Band; Off Sr Cls; Sftbl; Im Vllybl; Eagle Sct Awd 87; 4-H Awds; 4-H Camp Counselor; Trenton ST; Electrncs.

BIRD, ROBERT E; Pennington HS; Hamilton Square, NJ; (2); 1/58; Quiz Bowl; Var Crs Cntry; Var Trk; NHS; 1st In Class 86-87; Chmstry.

BIRDSONG, VICKI; Hillside HS; Hillside, NJ; (4); Aud/Vis; Church Yth Grp; Cmnty Wkr; Debate Tm; Leo Clb; Band; Church Choir; Concert Band; Mrchg Band; Pep Band; Yrbk Stff Awd 87; PA ST U; Accntng.

BIRIBIN, THEODORE; South Plainfield HS; S Plainfield, NJ; (3); 2/265; Am Leg Boys St; Trs SADD; Mrchg Band; Pres Frsh Cls; Pres Soph Cls; Pres Jr Cls; Pres Sr Cls; Pres Stu Cncl; Crs Cntry; Var Trk; Natl Hnr Soc 87; Spnsh Natl Hnr Soc 85; Salutatorian 88; Pol Sci.

BIRKNER, SHARON; Wayne Hills HS; Wayne, NJ; (3); 157/320; Church Yth Grp; Cmnty Wkr; GAA; Office Aide; Spanish Clb; Capt Flag Corp; Mgr School Play; Cheerleading; Hon Roll; Peer Helper 86-87; Kean Coll; Occuptnl Thrpy.

BIRNIE, CHRISTINE; Toms River South HS; Beachwood, NJ; (2); Church Yth Grp; Girl Scts; Math Tm; JV Bsktbl; JV Fld Hcky; JV Sftbl; Hon Roll.

BIRO, PETER F; Princeton Day Schl; Lawrenceville, NJ; (4); Computer Clb; Math Clb; Math Tm; Model UN; Spanish Clb; Teachers Aide; Stage Crew; Nwsp Stf; Lit Mag; Rptr Sr Cls; Cum Laude Soc 86; NJ Schlrs Pgm 86; NJ Dstngshd Schlr 86; Duke U.

BISCHOFF, DOUG; Hunterdon Central HS; Flemington, NJ; (3); Computer Clb; Thesps; Acpl Chr; Band; Church Choir; Mrchg Band; Pep Band; School Musical; Stage Crew; Symp Band; MA Inst Of Tech; Comp Prgrmg.

BISHOP, JAMES; Arthur P Schalick HS; Bridgeton, NJ; (3); 4-H; Ftbl; 4-H Awd.

BISHOP, LORI; Brick Memorial HS; Brick, NJ; (3); Fld Hcky; Socr; Trk; Hon Roll.

BISIGNANO, MARK; Hamilton HS West; Yardville, NJ; (3); Band; Chorus; Concert Band; Madrigals; Mrchg Band; Pep Band; Symp Band; Variety Show; Lit Mag; JV Wrstlng; Trenton ST Coll; Elec Engr.

BISULCA, ANTHONY; Lodi HS; Lodi, NJ; (3); 10/200; Church Yth Grp; Leo Clb; Math Clb; Math Tm; Science Clb; Varsity Clb; Socr; High Hon Roll; Hon Roll; NHS; Capt JV Scr BPS King Div Chmpns 85; Mbr Ldi Vrsty Scr BPSL King Div Chmpns 85.

BITTLE, MARCY; Hillsborough HS; Somerville, NJ; (4); Band; Jazz Band; Mrchg Band; Pep Band; School Musical; Powder Puff Ftbl; JV Sftbl; Hon Roll; Directors Awd 87; Corp James Langdon Schlrshp 87; James Langdon Mem Schlrhsp 87; Mercer Cnty CC; Music Perf.

BITTNER, LAURA; Audubon HS; Audubon, NJ; (3); 1/110; Church Yth Grp; German Clb; Scholastic Bowl; SADD; Sec Sr Cls; Fld Hcky; Bausch & Lomb Sci Awd; Hon Roll; NHS.

BITTNER, NORMAN; Pitman HS; Pitman, NJ; (3); 20/183; Church Yth Grp; German Clb; Varsity Clb; Var Socr; JV Trk; Var Wt Lftg; Hon Roll; Bus.

BIVANS, LORENZO A; Cherokee HS; Marlton, NJ; (4); 18/411; Computer Clb; FCA; Capt Var Bsktbl; Capt Var Ftbl; Hon Roll; NHS; French Clb; Lit Mag; High Hon Roll; Natl Achvt Cmmnded Schlr Pgm; Garden ST Dstngshd Schlr; NJ Rep Ldrshp Conf Howard U; Princeton; Engrng.

BIVIANO, ANGELO; Wood-Ridge HS; Wood Ridge, NJ; (3); 1/100; Pres Computer Clb; Math Clb; Model UN; Nwsp Ed-Chief; Yrbk Stf; Ed Lit Mag; VP Stu Cncl; Var Trk; High Hon Roll; NHS; Natnl Latn Exm 2 Summa Cum Laude Cert & Gold Mdls 85 & 86; Yth & Govrnmnt.

BIVINS, DAVID; West-Windsor Plainsboro HS; Princeton Junct, NJ; (3); Math Clb; Orch; Var Socr; Acolyte Of Yr 87; Bus.

BIVONA, LAUREN; Red Bank Catholic HS; Red Bank, NJ; (4); 56/318; Trs French Clb; Intnl Clb; Yrbk Phtg; VP Sr Cls; Capt L Crs Cntry; Capt L Trk; High Hon Roll; Hon Roll; NHS; Excllence On The JEDTS; Ctznshp Awd; Trinity WA; Lbrl Arts.

BIXBY, DIANE A; Ocean City HS; Woobbine, NJ; (4); 19/285; Hst Drama Clb; Pres 4-H; Latin Clb; Science Clb; Chorus; School Musical; Var L Pom Pon; Hon Roll; NHS; Pres Schlr; U Of DE; Cvl Engrng.

BLACHER, MARK; Freehold HS; Freehold, NJ; (4); 3/240; Pres Debate Tm; Speech Tm; Ed Nwsp Stf; French Hon Soc; High Hon Roll; NHS; Ntl Merit SF; St Schlr; Best Frnch Stu 85-86; Med Sci Lrng Ctr 84-87; Liberal Arts Coll.

BLACK, DREW S; Mahwah HS; Mahwah, NJ; (4); 32/170; Boy Scts; FCA; Spanish Clb; Symp Band; Yrbk Stf; Stu Cncl; Crs Cntry; JV Ftbl; Socr; Trk; NJ ST Wrstlng Chmpn-#1-109, 87 & #3-101, 86; NJ ST Wrstlng Tm-IA Ntls 85 & 86; Syracuse; Sprts Med.

BLACK, MAUREEN; Middletown Twp South; Leonardo, NJ; (4); Band; Concert Band; Drill Tm; Jazz Band; Mrchg Band; Orch; Pep Band; School Musical; School Play; Symp Band; Directors Awd Band 85; All Shore Symphonic Band 87; NJ ST Youth Orchestra 87.

BLACK, REGINA MARIE; Mt St Dominic Acad; Boonton, NJ; (3); Chrmn Church Yth Grp; Dance Clb; Drama Clb; JCL; VP Chorus; Church Choir; Madrigals; School Play; Hon Roll; Latin Clb; Chrs Cncrt Slst; Cmmnctns.

BLACK, SUZANNE; Raritan HS; Hazlet, NJ; (3); Office Aide; Teachers Aide; Gym; Sftbl; Hon Roll; Scl Wrk.

BLACKBURN, DAWN; Paul VI HS; Haddon Heights, NJ; (4); 19/511; Drama Clb; Hon Roll; NHS; Spanish NHS; Comp Sci.

BLACKMAN JR, GERALD S; Overbrook SR HS; Lindenwold, NJ; (4); 4/350; French Clb; Scholastic Bowl; Science Clb; School Play; High Hon Roll; Hon Roll; Jr NHS; NHS; Futr Prob Slvg Tm NJ ST Fnls 84; Arch.

BLACKMAN, KIMBERLY; Manasquan HS; Spring Lake Hts, NJ; (3); 10/270; Church Yth Grp; Drama Clb; German Clb; Thesps; Acpl Chr; Chorus; Concert Band; School Musical; School Play; High Hon Roll; Acdmc Achvmnt Awds 85-87; Cmmnctns.

BLACKOWICZ, SUSAN; Thoms River High School East; Toms River, NJ; (3); #96 In Class; Q&S; Nwsp Rptr; Nwsp Stf; Var Capt Cheerleading; Hon Roll; Teaching.

BLACKWELL, SUE; Hunterdon Central HS; Ringoes, NJ; (3); 91/550; Church Yth Grp; Rep Frsh Cls; Var Cheerleading; High Hon Roll; Hon Roll; Child Dev Awd 86; Chrldng Ltrs/Numbers; Pre-Law.

BLAGBROUGH, JENNIFER; Hunterdon Central HS; Whitehouse Sta; (3); 110/543; Ski Clb; Rep Frsh Cls; Trs Sr Cls; Cheerleading; JV Sftbl; Psychlgy.

BLAIR, BEVERLY; Raritan HS; W Keansburg, NJ; (3); French Clb; Color Guard; Drill Tm; JV Bsktbl; Hon Roll.

BLAIR, DAWN LOUISE; Hillsborough HS; Hillsborough, NJ; (3); Church Yth Grp; Office Aide; Chorus; Church Choir; Madrigals; Stu Cncl; Hon Roll; Band Front-Tall Flgs-JV, V & Capt; Band Cncl; Westminster Coll Choir Smmr; Elem Math.

BLAIR, VALERIE; Cumberland Regional HS; Bridgeton, NJ; (4); Pres Drama Clb; 4-H; Chorus; Madrigals; School Musical; 4-H Awd; NHS; Cmnty Wkr; Office Aide; Jazz Band; Hugh Obrian Yth Fndtn Ambssdr 84; NJ Al ST Chrs 84-86; 4-H Clb Congrs Delg 86; Pharmacy.

BLAIR, WILLIAM; Madison HS; Madison, NJ; (3); Boy Scts; High Hon Roll; Spanish NHS; Bus.

BLAKE, CARLTON; Orange HS; Orange, NJ; (4); 27/150; Church Yth Grp; Debate Tm; Political Wkr; Spanish Clb; Drill Tm; Var Trk; High Hon Roll; Hon Roll; Schlrshp Rutgers U Newark NJ 87; Rutgers U; Pre Law.

BLAKE, DAHLIA; St Vincent Acad; Newark, NJ; (3); 14/64; Church Yth Grp; Hosp Aide; Church Choir; Stage Crew; Variety Show; Off Sr Cls; Rep Stu Cncl; High Hon Roll; Hon Roll; Cert Recog Vol Svc 86; Cert Spec Incntv Pgm Ramapo Coll NJ Slctd HS Stu 87; Howard U; Gen Practioner.

BLAKELOCK, CHRISTA; Hunterdon Central HS; Ringoes, NJ; (2); 130/460; Band; Concert Band; Symp Band; Var Capt Socr; Var Capt Swmmng; Hon Roll; Most Outstndng Cntrbtn For Smmr Swim Tm 87-88.

BLAKELY, CANDICE; Mt St Dominic Acad; E Orange, NJ; (3); Art Clb; Chess Clb; Church Yth Grp; Computer Clb; Dance Clb; French Clb; Library Aide; Pep Clb; Spanish Clb; SADD; Comp Club Essex Cnty Coll 85-86; Acad Awd Essex Cnty Coll 84-85; Kean Coll Acad Awd 85-86; Spellman; Business.

BLAKELY, DAWN; John F Kennedy HS; Paterson, NJ; (4); 32/356; Church Yth Grp; NAACP; Pres Chorus; Capt Color Guard; Nwsp Rptr; Nwsp Stf; Yrbk Rptr; Yrbk Stf; Rep Sr Cls; AM Len Ortrcl Cntst 2nd Pl 86; Hampton U; Accntng.

BLANAR, NATALIE; Raritan HS; Hazlet, NJ; (3); #32 In Class; Art Clb; Church Yth Grp; SADD; School Play; Stage Crew; Variety Show; Gov Hon Prg Awd; Hon Roll; NHS; Fine Arts.

BLANCO, JONATHAN; Lyndhurst HS; Lyndhurst, NJ; (3); 11/179; Church Yth Grp; Latin Clb; Church Choir; Concert Band; Socr; Hon Roll; Arch Engr.

BLANCO, MARIA; Union Hill HS; Union City, NJ; (3); Church Yth Grp; Spanish Clb; NHS; NGAT; Indstrl Engr.

BLANES, JOSEPH; Glen Ridge HS; Glen Ridge, NJ; (3); 18/115; Spanish Clb; Var Bsbl; Wt Lftg; Hon Roll; Lbrl Arts.

BLANEY, ANNEMARIE; Neptune SR HS; Neptune, NJ; (4); 25/355; Am Leg Aux Girls St; Church Yth Grp; GAA; Girl Scts; Letterman Clb; ROTC; Varsity Clb; Chorus; Variety Show; Trs Frsh Cls; NJ Schlr Athl Awd 86-87; Natl HS Chrl Awd 86-87; Presdntl Acadc Ftnss Awd 87; Temple U; Hlth Educ.

BLANK, GIL J; Morristown HS; Morris Plains, NJ; (3); 19/455; Am Leg Boys St; Capt Key Clb; VP Temple Yth Grp; Sec Sr Cls; Capt Diving; Var Ftbl; Trk; Hon Roll; NHS; Ntl Merit SF; NJ Key Clb Oratrcl Champ 86 & 87; NJ ST Rnkd Diver 87; Coach Awd Cmmtmt Excllnce Diving 86; MA Inst Tech; Biochem.

BLANK, KIMBERLY; Paul VI HS; Cherry Hill, NJ; (3); Camera Clb; Nwsp Bus Mgr; Nwsp Rptr; Brdcst Jrnlsm.

BLANTON, LISA; Vineland SR HS; Vineland, NJ; (3); 135/900; Church Yth Grp; Cmnty Wkr; DECA; FBLA; NAACP; SADD; Church Choir; Rep Frsh Cls; Rep Soph Cls; Rep Jr Cls; Blck Stu Assn Pres 86-87; Stu Cncl 85-87; Chef.

BLANZ, GWEN; Immaculate Heart Acad; Ho-Ho-Kus, NJ; (2); Cmnty Wkr; Model UN; Chorus; Church Choir; Orch; School Musical; School Play; Hon Roll.

BLASS, KEVIN; Gloucester Catholic HS; Sewell, NJ; (3); Bsbl; Bsktbl; Socr; Trk; Hon Roll.

BLATHERWICK, CHRISTINE; Hamilton East HS; Trenton, NJ; (2); AFS; Church Yth Grp; 4-H; FBLA; Stage Crew; JV Tennis; Hon Roll; Knights Of Col Essy Cont Awd-3rd Pl 86; Guide For New Stu Orientation At Schl 86; Anthrplgy.

BLATT, JOSHUA ALLAN; Manalapan HS; Manalapan, NJ; (3); Cmnty Wkr; Computer Clb; Political Wkr; Temple Yth Grp; Band; Hon Roll; Mnlpn Rec Bsktbl Champ 86-87; Bus.

BLAU, JENNY; Middletown South HS; Red Bank, NJ; (3); JV Bsktbl; Im Mgr(s); Im Powder Puff Ftbl; Im Socr; JV Sftbl; Hon Roll.

BLAUVELT, MELISSA; Passaic Valley HS; Little Falls, NJ; (2); Science Clb; Ski Clb; Spanish Clb; Lit Mag; Stu Cncl; JV Cheerleading; Var Tennis; Elks Awd; Hon Roll; Jrnlsm.

BLAUVELT, RICKY; Newton HS; Andover, NJ; (2); FFA; Military.

BLECKER, KATHY; Hunterdon Central HS; Ringoes, NJ; (3); Church Yth Grp; Band; Var L Fld Hcky; Var L Trk; Hon Roll.

BLEJWAS, AMY; Bridgewater Raritan HS East; Bridgewater, NJ; (4); Church Yth Grp; Intnl Clb; Ski Clb; Band; Off Stu Cncl; Cheerleading; Powder Puff Ftbl; Score Keeper; Hon Roll; German Clb; U Of DE; Bus.

BLENDER, BARA I; Spotswood HS; Milltown, NJ; (3); Intnl Clb; Color Guard; Stu Cncl; Var Crs Cntry; JV Trk; High Hon Roll; Hon Roll; NHS; Mst Imprvd Crss Cntry 86.

BLENKE, KATHLEEN; Immaculata HS; Neshanic, NJ; (3); 54/241; Church Yth Grp; Cmnty Wkr; Debate Tm; Drama Clb; French Clb; Hosp Aide; Intnl Clb; Ski Clb; Band; Concert Band.

BLESSING, THOMAS W; Watchung Hills Regional HS; Warren, NJ; (3); Drama Clb; Ski Clb; School Musical; School Play; Stage Crew; Off Frsh Cls; Off Soph Cls; Off Jr Cls; Off Sr Cls; Off Stu Cncl; Pres-Safe Rides 88; Chrmn-All Schl Cncl Elect Bd 88; Natl Cncl Tchrs Of Grmn Awd 86.

BLICH, JACQUELINE; Morris Catholic HS; Mine Hill Dover, NJ; (4); Church Yth Grp; Dance Clb; Hosp Aide; Chorus; Capt Color Guard; JV Var Sftbl; Frank J Porter Memorial Schlrshp 83; E Stroudsburg U; Phys Educ.

BLINEBURY, THOS; Riverside HS; Riverside, NJ; (3); Letterman Clb; Ski Clb; SADD; Varsity Clb; Pres Frsh Cls; Var Capt Ftbl; Var Trk; Var Wrstlng; Engl III 87; San Diego ST; Mrn Bio.

BLITSHTEYN, LEON; John P Stevens HS; Edison, NJ; (3); VP Art Clb; Cmnty Wkr; Intnl Clb; Key Clb; Model UN; Science Clb; Lit Mag; JV Socr; Gov Hon Prg Awd; Hon Roll; Smr Hnrs Prgm Bstn U 87; YMCA Spcl Olympcs Awd 87; Sci.

BLOCK, AMY; Hightstown HS; Roosevelt, NJ; (2); Ski Clb; Teachers Aide; Drill Tm; Yrbk Stf; Rep Stu Cncl; Stat Bsktbl; JV Fld Hcky; JV Mgr(s); Var JV Score Keeper; Hon Roll; JV Ltrs Fld Hcky 86-87; Delg Consttnl Cnvntn Cmte 87-88; UCLA; Psychanlyst.

BLOCK, GREG; South Plainfield HS; S Plainfield, NJ; (3); 17/260; Church Yth Grp; Drama Clb; Orch; School Play; Stage Crew; JV Bsbl; Var Bsktbl; High Hon Roll; NHS; Spanish NHS; Engr.

BLOCK, JASON; J P Stevens HS; Edison, NJ; (3); 19/458; Debate Tm; Ski Clb; SADD; Pres Y-Teens; Trs Sr Cls; Co-Capt Golf; NHS; Spanish NHS.

BLOCKER, ANGELA; Woodrow Wilson HS; Camden, NJ; (2); Church Yth Grp; Ski Clb; Tennis; Cit Awd; Hon Roll; NHS; Prfct Atten Awd; Elite Clb Recog 86-87; H S Prof Test Cert NJ 86-87; Enrgy Awd PRIME 87; Pre-Med.

BLOCKER, CHARLES; Atlantic City HS; Atlantic City, NJ; (3); High Hon Roll; Hon Roll; NHS; Schlrs Awd 85 & 86.

BLOCKER, LORI; Westfield HS; Westfield, NJ; (3); 158/469; 4-H; Girl Scts; Spanish Clb; Concert Band; Mrchg Band; Symp Band; Im Bsktbl; 4-H Awd; Hon Roll; Prfct Atten Awd; Cert Merit Spnsh 87; Dr Hubert G Humphrey Achvt Awd 83-86; Cert Merit Music 84-86; Bus Ed Awd 85; Acctng.

BLODGETT, SAMANTHA; J P Stevens HS; Edison, NJ; (3); 33/457; Exploring; Girl Scts; Model UN; Band; Mrchg Band; NHS; Ntl Merit Ltr; Acdmc All Am Schlr 84; Gntcs.

BLOM, DOUGLAS; Middlesex HS; Middlesex, NJ; (2); 1/171; German Clb; Math Clb; Concert Band; Jazz Band; Mrchg Band; School Musical; Rep Stu Cncl; High Hon Roll; Church Yth Grp; Computer Clb; Stu Mnth 85; HOBY Fndtn Ambssdr 86.

BLOOD, CHERYL LYN; Middle Township HS; Avalon Manor, NJ; (4); Dance Clb; Girl Scts; Intnl Clb; Key Clb; Fld Hcky; Mgr(s); Sftbl; High Hon Roll; NHS; Pres Schlr; Acad Achvmnt Awd; Rider Coll; Accntng.

BLOODGOOD, DAVID; Manasquan HS; Spring Lake Hts, NJ; (4); 30/225; Drama Clb; Latin Clb; Spanish Clb; Acpl Chr; Church Choir; School Musical; Stage Crew; Nwsp Rptr; Yrbk Stf; Bsktbl; Mary Washington Coll; Pltcl Sci.

BLOODGOOD, DEBORAH; Wall HS; Wall, NJ; (3); 3/289; VP Drama Clb; Spanish Clb; Thesps; Drm Mjr(t); School Musical; School Play; Symp Band; JV Var Fld Hcky; High Hon Roll; NHS; Engl.

BLOOM, DAVID P; Parsippany HS; Parsippany, NJ; (4); 1/320; Cmnty Wkr; Trs French Clb; Nwsp Stf; JV Bsktbl; Capt Tennis; Gov Hon Prg Awd; High Hon Roll; NHS; Ntl Merit SF; Rugers Schlr 86.

BLOOM, DAWSON; Belleville SR HS; Belleville, NJ; (3); 8/401; Boy Scts; Civic Clb; Key Clb; Spanish Clb; Varsity Clb; Stu Cncl; JV Var Bsbl; Var Ftbl; Var Tennis; Var Wrstlng; Newark NJ; Engrng.

BLOOM, DEBRA; Jackson Memorial HS; Jackson, NJ; (3); 5/416; Am Leg Aux Girls St; Pres Rptr 4-H; Math Tm; Pres VP Temple Yth Grp; Sec Frsh Cls; Sec Soph Cls; High Hon Roll; NHS; Art Clb; German Clb; Natl Art Hnr Socty Chrmn, Awds & Ceremn 85-88; NJ Govrnr Schl Publ Iss Fnlst 86-87; Advrtsg.

BLOOM, KAREN; Haddonfield Memorial HS; Haddonfield, NJ; (2); VP Frsh Cls; VP Soph Cls; VP Stu Cncl; Var Fld Hcky; JV Trk; High Hon Roll; Hon Roll; Lion Awd.

BLOOM, KENNETH; Columbia HS; South Orange, NJ; (3); Latin Clb; Science Clb; Mrchg Band; Orch; School Musical; Symp Band; 1st Pl NJ Sci League Bio I 85; Mang Cum Laude Ntl Ltn Exm, Ltn I 85.

BLOOMFIELD, JILL; Parsippany HS; Parsippany, NJ; (2); Intnl Clb; Ski Clb; Spanish Clb; SADD; VP Temple Yth Grp; Band; Mrchg Band; Yrbk Ed-Chief; Yrbk Stf; Hon Roll; Pre Law.

BLOUNT, JERRY; Lower Cape May Regional HS; Cape May, NJ; (3); 1/192; Chess Clb; Church Yth Grp; Computer Clb; Math Tm; Orch; JV Wrstlng; High Hon Roll; NHS; Ntl Merit SF; 1st Pl Gdm Monterey Cnty Mathletics 86; Schlr Wrstlr 86; Elec Engr.

BLOW, DENEEN K; Piscataway HS; Piscataway, NJ; (4); 62/493; Church Yth Grp; Political Wkr; Varsity Clb; Acpl Chr; Lit Mag; Stat Bsktbl; Var Stat Socr; Var L Sftbl; JV L Trk; Hon Roll; Commended Natl Achvmnt Schlrshp Pgm Outstndng Negro Stu 86; Lafayette Coll; Bus.

BLOXHAM, BRAD; Newton HS; Newton, NJ; (2); Chorus; Madrigals; JV Trk; Cert Cmndtn Outstndng Perf Alg I 86-87; Comp.

BLOXHAM, HEATHER; Newton HS; Andover, NJ; (2); 39/219; Latin Clb; SADD; Acpl Chr; School Musical; Nwsp Ed-Chief; Pres Frsh Cls; Pres Soph Cls; Pres Jr Cls; Rep Stu Cncl; Var Cheerleading; Slvr Awd-Grl Scts 87; HOBY Ambssdr 87.

BLOYER, DEBRA; Nutley HS; Nutley, NJ; (3); 41/306; Key Clb; Flag Corp; Rep Stu Cncl; NHS; Yth Deborah Hrt/Lng Assoc 84-87; Captn Morretti Amateur Dnce Co 85-86; Roche Amateur Plyrs 85-87; Finance.

BLUE, DENNIS; Mendham HS; Mendham, NJ; (2); Church Yth Grp; Ski Clb; Socr; Airplane Pilot.

BLUE, GEOFFREY N; Rumson-Fair Haven Regional HS; Fair Haven, NJ; (4); 13/220; Pres VP Stu Cncl; Var L Bsktbl; Var L Socr; NHS; St Schlr; Mry Wn Brdn Awd/Achlrshp 87; Wnthrp Smth Schlrshp 87; Princeton U; Cmptrs.

BLUM, LAURA; John P Stevens HS; Edison, NJ; (3); 131/475; Cmnty Wkr; Hosp Aide; Science Clb; Ski Clb; Temple Yth Grp.

BLUMENFELD, KARYN; Manalapan HS; Manalapan, NJ; (4); Sec Debate Tm; Office Aide; Chrmn Frsh Cls; Rep Soph Cls; Trs Jr Cls; Stu Cncl; Capt Twrlr; HOBY Awd 85; Clark U; Accntng.

BLUMENSTEEL, DONNA; Brick HS; Brick, NJ; (4); Church Yth Grp; FTA; SADD; Band; Drm Mjr(t); Jazz Band; Mrchg Band; Variety Show; Gov Hon Prg Awd; Hon Roll; Ocean County Coll; Legal Sec.

BLUSK, CHRISTINA; Buena Regional HS; Dorothy, NJ; (4); 21/180; Drama Clb; Varsity Clb; School Play; Ed Nwsp Rptr; JV Bsktbl; Var Capt Fld Hcky; Var Sftbl; Im NHS; Var Ltr Knowledge 86; Mst Imprvd Field Hcky 86; Drexel U; Cmmnctns.

BLYE, KRYSTAL; Clifford J Scott HS; East Orange, NJ; (3); French Clb; Intnl Clb; Office Aide; Lit Mag; Dept Hnrs Engl II, III 86-87; Frnch Cntst 86-87; Htl, Restrnt Mgmt.

BOATWRIGHT, KEISHA; West Side HS; Newark, NJ; (4); 13/246; Girl Scts; School Play; Rep Sr Cls; JV Crs Cntry; JV Trk; Hon Roll; Prfct Atten Awd; Rutgers Coll Engrng Schlrshp 87; Goal Card 84-86; Afro-Hstry & Bio Awds 85; Rutgers Coll Of Engrng; Elec En.

BOBINIS, MICHAEL A; Phillipsburg HS; Phillipsburg, NJ; (4); 70/360; Am Leg Boys St; Pres Exploring; Math Tm; Ftbl; Trk; Wt Lftg; Wrstlng; Prfct Atten Awd; Mst Outstndng FR Wrestler; No 1 Wrestlng Tm NJ; 1st Pl X-Mas Tourn; Rutgers Coll Engrng.

BOCCANFUSO, DENISE; Mc Corristin Catholic HS; Trenton, NJ; (3); Drama Clb; GAA; Teachers Aide; Chorus; School Musical; School Play; Variety Show; Capt Cheerleading; Swmmng; Hon Roll; THTR.

BOCCELLI, ANGELA; Sacred Heart HS; Landisville, NJ; (3); Art Clb; Office Aide; Pep Clb; Spanish Clb; Chorus; School Musical; JV Cheerleading; Var Capt Crs Cntry; JV Pom Pon; Prfct Atten Awd; Mst Vlbl Plyr X-Cntry 86; 2nd Pl Mllvl Run 85; Acctng.

BOCCIO, DAWN E; John F Kennedy HS; Willingboro, NJ; (2); Intnl Clb; SADD; Teachers Aide; Mgr Socr; Hon Roll; Drug Awareness Pgm 86-87; Law.

BOCCO, PATRICK; St Peters Prep; Hoboken, NJ; (4); 23/196; Cmnty Wkr; Science Clb; Im Bsbl; Im Bsktbl; Im Ftbl; High Hon Roll; NHS; Pres Schlr-Ath Awd 87; Gold Hnr Pin Acad Achvt 87; Rutgers Coll; Pre-Med.

BOCZKUS, TIFFANY; Lacey Township HS; Lanoka Harbor, NJ; (3); 47/317; Art Clb; Drama Clb; VP Gym; JV Powder Puff Ftbl; Var L Sftbl; Hon Roll; Educ.

BODEI, WILLIAM; Secaucus HS; Secaucus, NJ; (3); 32/168; Ski Clb; Varsity Clb; Band; Chorus; Concert Band; Jazz Band; Nwsp Ed-Chief; School Musical; Trs VP Stu Cncl; Hon Roll; Montclair ST Coll Pgm Acad Talented Yng Stu 86; Music.

BODEN, ELIZABETH; Cumberland Christian HS; Bridgeton, NJ; (3); 1/23; Church Yth Grp; Band; Chorus; Church Choir; High Hon Roll; Hon Roll; Bible Scripture Mstry Awd 85-86.

BODENCHAK, FRANK L; The Pingry Schl; Hillside, NJ; (4); Cmnty Wkr; Political Wkr; Quiz Bowl; Service Clb; Spanish Clb; Chorus; Ed Nwsp Ed-Chief; Ed Lit Mag; Var Crs Cntry; Var Trk; Hnrbl Mntn Scnd Hghst GPA 84-85.

BODINE, JANE; Gateway Regional HS; Westville, NJ; (4); 63/203; FHA; Office Aide; Spanish Clb; SADD; Varsity Clb; Rep Church Yth Grp; Var Capt Bsktbl; Im Coach Actv; Var Capt Fld Hcky; Var Sftbl; Outstndng Girl Ath Of Schl; Camden Cnty Coll; Bus.

BODNAR, DEBRA; South River HS; S River, NJ; (3); 5/150; Sec FNA; German Clb; Office Aide; Yrbk Stf; Stat Bsktbl; JV Sftbl; L Trk; Cit Awd; L Hon Roll; NHS; Loylty Day Qn VFW 86; Rutgers; Elem Ed.

BODNER JR, ANTON; St Joseph HS; Waterford, NJ; (3); 2/97; Pres 4-H; Cit Awd; 4-H Awd; High Hon Roll; Engr.

BODROG, HEATHER S; Washington Township HS; Sewell, NJ; (3); Church Yth Grp; Sec German Clb; Nwsp Rptr; Stu Cncl; Cheerleading; Mgr(s); Score Keeper; German Hnr Soc 86-87; German Exchng Stu 87-88; Rutgers; Commnctns.

BODZIAK, NICOLE; Toms River North HS; Toms River, NJ; (3); 106/482; Ski Clb; SADD; Band; Mrchg Band; Symp Band; Variety Show; Rep Sr Cls; Off Stu Cncl; Bsktbl; Var Diving; Intl PRIDE Conf Atlanta GA 87; 2 Yr Mbr Of TEAM 85-87; Vrsty Scr 85-88; Bus.

BOEHS, JOHN; Mendham HS; Chester, NJ; (2); Ski Clb; Var Socr; Hon Roll; Law.

BOETTICHER, KAROLEE; Passaic Valley HS; Totowa, NJ; (2); Concert Band; Mrchg Band; High Hon Roll; Pres Schlr; Mgr JV Wrstlng Tm 86-87; Med Asst.

BOGDA, MICHELE; Notre Dame HS; Trenton, NJ; (4); Drama Clb; School Musical; School Play; Rep Frsh Cls; Rep Soph Cls; Rep Jr Cls; Rep Sr Cls; Crs Cntry; NHS; German Hnr Scty 85-87; Rutgers Coll; Educ.

BOGER, PAUL; Bloomfield SR HS; Bloomfield, NJ; (3); Aud/Vis; Church Yth Grp; German Clb; JCL; VP Latin Clb; High Hon Roll; Hon Roll; Law.

BOGGIO, GLEN; Indian Hills HS; Franklin Lakes, NJ; (3); 101/306; Office Aide; Ski Clb; Var Ftbl; Var Trk; Wt Lftg; Hon Roll; TNT Athltc Corp 87; 1st Tm All-Lg Trk & Fld 87; Vsty Awd Trk & Fld 86-87; USC; Acctng.

BOGHOSIAN, JEFFREY; Oakcrest HS; Mays Landing, NJ; (3); Hst Frsh Cls; Var Capt Crs Cntry; JV Trk; High Hon Roll; NHS.

BOGOSIAN, JEFF E; Ridgefield HS; Ridgefield, NJ; (3); Am Leg Boys St; Church Yth Grp; Trs Soph Cls; Trs Jr Cls; Trs Sr Cls; Pres Stu Cncl; Bsbl; Crs Cntry; Wrstlng; Hon Roll.

BOHEIM, DEBORA; High Point Regional HS; Branchville, NJ; (3); 5/274; Debate Tm; Sec German Clb; Model UN; Ski Clb; Capt Cheerleading; Tennis; Trk; Wt Lftg; High Hon Roll; NHS; 4 Yr Vrsty Grls Trk 87; Grls Ski Rcng Tm NJ ST Champs 86-87; 4 Yr Vrsty Cheerldng; Bus.

BOHEM, CASANDRA; Willingboro HS; Willingboro, NJ; (2); Teachers Aide; Band; Color Guard; Concert Band; Mrchg Band; Orch; Socr; Swmmng; Twrlr; Stage Crew; U Of PA; Srgn.

BOHL, SANDRA; Secaucus HS; Secaucus, NJ; (3); 15/166; Church Yth Grp; VP Key Clb; Math Clb; Mu Alpha Theta; Stat Bsbl; High Hon Roll; Hon Roll; Mu Alpha Theta Awd.

BOHM, MICHELLE E; Manalapan HS; Manalapan, NJ; (3); 15/429; Teachers Aide; Lib Band; Lib Concert Band; Drill Tm; Mrchg Band; School Musical; Var Twrlr; NHS; Ntl Merit SF; JR All Am Hall Of Fame Band Hnrs 86-87; Bus.

BOHNER, GREGG; Christian Bros Acad; Pt Pleasant, NJ; (3); Boy Scts; Exploring; Im Socr; Hon Roll; Bus.

BOHRINGER, JOE; Millville SR HS; Millville, NJ; (3); 1/524; Am Leg Boys St; Church Yth Grp; Science Clb; Ski Clb; Sr Cls; Ftbl; JV L Trk; High Hon Roll; NHS; Ntl Merit Ltr; Math Awd 85; YMCA Yth Conf Natl Affairs 86-87; Gov Schl; Engr.

BOICE, WENDY; Lenape Regional HS; Vincentown, NJ; (4); 9/420; Church Yth Grp; FCA; Nwsp Stf; Rep Stu Cncl; JV Var Sftbl; NHS; Spanish NHS; JR Rtrn 86-87; W H Sassaman II Med Mem Awd 86-87; Southampton Twsp PTA Awd 86-87; Cedarville Coll; Nrsng.

BOISVERT, MICHELLE; Holy Spirit HS; Mays Landing, NJ; (2); 22/397; 4-H; Pep Clb; Chorus; School Musical; School Play; Rep Soph Cls; Stu Cncl; Var Fld Hcky; JV Sftbl; Hon Roll; Georgetown U; Law.

BOJARSKI, KIMBERLY; West Windsor-Plainsboro HS; Hamilton Sq, NJ; (3); Teachers Aide; Hst Band; Hst Concert Band; Hst Mrchg Band; Orch; School Musical; School Play; Symp Band; Rep Stu Cncl; Cit Awd; Music.

BOKER, LINDA; Gloucester HS; Gloucester Cty, NJ; (3); Trs French Clb; Girl Scts; Pep Clb; Capt Bowling; Hon Roll; NHS; Prfct Atten Awd; MVP-BWLNG Tm 84-87; Bwlng Conf All-Star Tm 84-87; Won Conf High Series In Bwlng 86-87; Rutgers U; Vet Med.

BOLAN, BRIAN; West Essex Regional HS; N Caldwell, NJ; (3); Band; Concert Band; Ftbl; Hon Roll; Vsty Lttr-Ftbl 85-86.

BOLAND, KATE; Morris Catholic HS; Montville, NJ; (4); 3/138; Church Yth Grp; Pres French Clb; Sec FBLA; Key Clb; Math Clb; Natl Beta Clb; Service Clb; Rptr Stu Cncl; JV Sftbl; NHS; Outstndng Transfer Stud 86-87; U Notre Dame; Bus Admin.

BOLANOWSKI, RICHARD; Oratory Prep; Cranford, NJ; (4); 2/44; Math Tm; Ski Clb; Nwsp Ed-Chief; Trs Frsh Cls; VP Soph Cls; Pres Jr Cls; Hon Roll; NHS; St Schlr; Med.

BOLAT, MINAT; Paterson Catholic Regional HS; Paterson, NJ; (3); Camera Clb; Computer Clb; Nwsp Rptr; Yrbk Ed-Chief; Rep Jr Cls; High Hon Roll; Hon Roll; Prfct Atten Awd; Simon Schlrshp Fnd 86-88; Corp Law.

BOLD, CHRISTINE; Collingswood SR HS; Collingswood, NJ; (3); Office Aide; Swmmng; Hon Roll; Med Tech.

BOLDERMAN, MARK; Manasquan HS; Manasquan, NJ; (2); 40/240; Church Yth Grp; Drama Clb; Thesps; Acpl Chr; Chorus; Church Choir; School Musical; School Play; Stage Crew; Hon Roll; Comm.

BOLDIZAR, JOHN; Florence Twp Mem HS; Florence, NJ; (3); Hosp Aide; Science Clb; High Hon Roll; Hon Roll; NHS; Rutgers; Sci.

BOLOGNESE, LORI; Mary Help Of Christns; Paterson, NJ; (4); Letterman Clb; SADD; School Play; Stage Crew; Im Bsktbl; JV Var Mgr(s); JV Var Score Keeper; JV Var Vllybl; Hon Roll; NHS; Phys Sci Awd & Hnr Chord 84; Montclair ST Coll; Bio.

BOLTON, SCOTT; Mount Olive HS; Flanders, NJ; (4); 17/285; AFS; Drama Clb; VP SADD; School Musical; Nwsp Rptr; Var L Socr; Im Vllybl; NHS; Varsity Clb; Chorus; Hnrbl Ment All Cty Soccer Tm 86; Study Tour London 87; Pre-Law.

BOLYN, BETH; Delaware Valley Regional HS; Frenchtown, NJ; (3); Church Yth Grp; Cmnty Wkr; French Clb; Teachers Aide; Band; Church Choir; Concert Band; School Musical; Fld Hcky; Sftbl; French.

BOMBA, KRISTIN; Penns Grove HS; Carneys Point, NJ; (3); Am Leg Aux Girls St; Spanish Clb; SADD; Rep Frsh Cls; Rep Jr Cls; Rep Stu Cncl; Var Sftbl; Intl Frgn Lang Awd 87; Intr Dsgn.

BOMBERGER, SHARON; Ocean City HS; Ocean City, NJ; (3); 40/341; Church Yth Grp; School Play; Yrbk Stf; Hon Roll; NHS; Chldhd Ed.

BOMBOLEVICZ, JAMES; Nutley HS; Nutley, NJ; (3); 106/367; Boy Scts; Ski Clb; Nwsp Stf; Var L Bsbl; Var Capt Ftbl; Grphc Arts.

BONA, DIANE; Elmwood Park Memorial HS; Elmwood Pk, NJ; (3); 4/170; Am Leg Aux Girls St; Church Yth Grp; Nwsp Ed-Chief; Nwsp Stf; Yrbk Ed-Chief; Yrbk Stf; Mgr(s); Score Keeper; High Hon Roll; NHS; Italian Natl Hnr Soc 86-87; CPA.

BONACCI, KARA; Hamilton HS West; Yarville, NJ; (3); Key Clb; Drill Tm; Off Jr Cls; Rep Stu Cncl; Score Keeper; Trk; Hon Roll.

BONADO, MARIDETH L; Shore Regional HS; W Long Br, NJ; (3); Ski Clb; Spanish Clb; Color Guard; Stage Crew; Var Mgr(s); Var Score Keeper; Stat Var Socr; Var Swmmng; Var Twrlr; Hon Roll; Bronze Congrssnl Awd 86; Acctng.

BONAGUARO, DAWN; Glen Rock HS; Glen Rock, NJ; (4); 14/150; Latin Clb; Library Aide; Spanish Clb; Capt Tennis; High Hon Roll; Jr NHS; NHS; Lyman Craig Humanitrn Awd 87; Rutgers U; Pre-Vet.

BONANNI, ANTHONY; Secaucus HS; Secaucus, NJ; (3); 26/168; Am Leg Boys St; Key Clb; Mu Alpha Theta; Hon Roll; Italian Hnr Soc 87; Seton Hall U; Pre Law.

BONCZEK, JOSEPH V; Neptune SR HS; Neptune, NJ; (3); Am Leg Boys St; Church Yth Grp; Ski Clb; SADD; Varsity Clb; Rep Sr Cls; Bsbl; Swmmng; High Hon Roll; Hon Roll.

BONCZEK, KIMBERLY; Toms River HS South; Beachwood, NJ; (3); Symp Band; Sec Frsh Cls; Rep Jr Cls; Rep Sr Cls; Sec Stu Cncl; Powder Puff Ftbl; Socr; Capt Twrlr; Hon Roll; NHS.

BONCZEK, MICHAEL; Bishop Ahr HS; Edison, NJ; (3); 3/275; Am Leg Boys St; Math Tm; Model UN; Spanish Clb; Var Crs Cntry; Var Trk; Im Vllybl; JV Wrstlng; High Hon Roll; NHS; Engr.

BOND, SHARON; Hunterdon Central HS; Flemington, NJ; (4); 4/560; Church Yth Grp; FCA; Hosp Aide; Orch; School Musical; High Hon Roll; Hon Roll; NHS; Ntl Merit SF; Spanish NHS; Grmn I & II 86-87; Bstn U Trstee Schlrshp 87; NCDE 86; Boston U; Med.

BOND-NELSON, STEPHEN G; North Plainfield HS; North Plainfield, NJ; (3); 19/160; Am Leg Boys St; Acpl Chr; Band; Jazz Band; Mrchg Band; French Hon Soc; Hon Roll; NHS; Boy Scts; Key Clb; NJ Rgn II & All ST Chorus 86-87.

BONDE, SUNITA; South Brunswick HS; Dayton, NJ; (2); 2/276; Am Leg Aux Girls St; VP FHA; Mu Alpha Theta; Ed Lit Mag; Var Tennis; Sal; Spanish NHS; Hosp Aide; Math Clb; Math Tm; Girls Ntn Sntr NJ 87; Awd Amer Auxlry; Indian Assn Music Awd 85; Med.

BONDS, SUSAN; Eastside HS; Paterson, NJ; (3); 88/540; NAACP; Mgr Mrchg Band; Rep Soph Cls; Rep Jr Cls; Mgr(s); Stat Sftbl; JV Vllybl; Child Psych.

BONER, MARY; Bridgeton HS; Bridgton, NJ; (3); Ski Clb; Teachers Aide; Varsity Clb; Yrbk Stf; Sec Soph Cls; Sec Jr Cls; Sec Sr Cls; Sec Stu Cncl; Mgr Bsbl; JV Var Cheerleading; Shwg Outstndg Wrk Lab Tech & Physics 85 & 87; Glassboro ST Coll; Crmnl Just.

BONET, PAULA; Hoboken HS; Hoboken, NJ; (3); Pace U; Psych.

BONIFACIO, MARK; Dwight-Englewood Schl; Leonia, NJ; (3); Cmnty Wkr; Ski Clb; L Bsbl; L Ftbl; Im Wt Lftg; Hon Roll; Med.

BONNELL, MARY; Frank H Morrell HS; Irvington, NJ; (3); Chorus; Hon Roll; Secy.

BONNER, CHRISTINA; Belvidere HS; Hope, NJ; (4); 2/122; Quiz Bowl; Ski Clb; SADD; JV Stat Bsktbl; Var Fld Hcky; Stat Ftbl; Var Golf; Hon Roll; NHS; St Schlr; Spnsh Awd 84; Girls St Delegate 86; Washing Wrkshps Smnr 86; Pre Med.

BONNER, ELLEN; Cranford HS; Cranford, NJ; (3); 59/276; Latin Clb; Math Clb; Stat Bsktbl; Var Fld Hcky; Hon Roll; Bus.

BONNER, MICHAEL; Belvidere HS; Hope, NJ; (3); 21/130; Am Leg Boys St; VP Frsh Cls; Rep Soph Cls; Rep Jr Cls; Var Bsbl; Var Bsktbl; Hon Roll.

BONSALL, MARIANNE; Paul VI HS; Lindenwold, NJ; (3); 65/418; Hon Roll.

BONWELL III, RAYMOND E; HS East; Toms River, NJ; (3); 8/509; Chess Clb; Church Yth Grp; Cmnty Wkr; FBLA; Key Clb; Scholastic Bowl; Bausch & Lomb Sci Awd; High Hon Roll; NHS; Ntl Merit Ltr; Shore Shop Stu Crftsmns Fair 1st Pl 86-87; 4th Pl Bus Law FBLA ST Comptn 86; Bus.

BONZEK, ANNE; Hamilton HS West; Trenton, NJ; (4); 21/309; Letterman Clb; SADD; Band; Rep Jr Cls; Rep Sr Cls; Swmmng; Tennis; Trk; NHS; Pres Schlr; All Cnty Swm Tm 2nd Tm; VA Commonwealth U; Phys Thrpy.

BOODY, PATRICIA; Paul VI HS; Magnolia, NJ; (4); 230/511; Spanish Clb; School Play; Glassboro ST Coll; Elem Educ.

BOOKER, DIONNE; Penns Grove HS; Penns Grove, NJ; (3); 6/135; Am Leg Aux Girls St; SADD; Chorus; Concert Band; Mrchg Band; School Play; Off Jr Cls; Trk; Hon Roll; NHS; Psychlgst.

BOOKER, LORA; Moorestown SR HS; Moorestown, NJ; (4); 39/230; French Clb; Model UN; School Play; Yrbk Phtg; Yrbk Stf; Ed Yrbk Stf; Stat Bsktbl; Hon Roll; Lion Awd; Rotary Awd; Steven Inst Tech Engrng Smnr, & Bill Bradley Ldrshp Smnrs 87; Lehigh U; Bio.

BOOS, KAREN; Scotch Plains Fanwood HS; Fanwood, NJ; (4); 14/350; German Clb; Key Clb; SADD; Var Diving; High Hon Roll; Hon Roll; Pres Schlr; 2nd Pl Union Cnty Divng 87; Wstfld YMCA Dvng Coaches Awd 84-87; Avon Schlrshp 87-91; Ithaca Coll; Phys Ther.

BOOZ, BRETT; Cumberland Regional HS; Bridgeton, NJ; (4); 8/298; Am Leg Boys St; Pres Church Yth Grp; Sec Drama Clb; 4-H; Jazz Band; Mrchg Band; School Musical; School Play; NJ All ST Chr 86; NJ All Sth Jrsy Chrs 84-87; JR/Sr All Amercn HS Band Hall Of Fame 86-87; U Of Miami; Rcrdng Engr.

BOPARAI, RICK; North Hunterdon HS; Annandale, NJ; (4); VICA; Outstndng Elec Awd 87; Vica Awd 87; Raritau Valley Coll; Comp.

BOPP, JAMES; Paramus HS; Paramus, NJ; (4); 49/330; 4-H; Ski Clb; Lit Mag; Var L Bsktbl; NHS; Ntl Merit Ltr; Pres Acad Fit Awd 87; Natl Soc Stud Olympd Awd 86; GA Inst Tech; Aero Engr.

BORAJKIEWICZ, JENNIFER L; Holy Cross HS; Willingboro, NJ; (3); 23/409; AFS; Spanish Clb; Rep Soph Cls; JV Capt Cheerleading; Mgr(s); Hon Roll.

BORCHERS, KATHLEEN; Raritan HS; Hazlet, NJ; (3); Hon Roll; Chld Psych.

BORDAMONTE, MAE HOPE; Paul VI Regional HS; Passaic, NJ; (4); Hosp Aide; Key Clb; Pep Clb; SADD; Chorus; School Play; Yrbk Stf; Cheerleading; Tennis; Hon Roll; Fnlst In Nrthn NJ Teen Pgnt 85; Pace U; Bio.

BORDAS, MONICA; Florence Twp Mem HS; Roebling, NJ; (3); Am Leg Aux Girls St; Church Yth Grp; Drama Clb; GAA; Letterman Clb; Varsity Clb; Nwsp Rptr; Nwsp Stf; Rep Stu Cncl; Var L Bsktbl; Cmnctns.

BORELLO, DANIELA; Fort Lee HS; Fort Lee, NJ; (3); Office Aide; Rep Frsh Cls; Rep Soph Cls; Rep Stu Cncl; Hon Roll; Italian Clb 85-87; AATI Natl Itln Cmptn Awd 86; Bus.

BORENSTEIN, SCOTT; Howell HS; Howell, NJ; (3); Latin Clb; Bsbl; Socr; Wrstlng; Hon Roll; NHS; Magna Cum Laude Natl Latin Exam.

BORER, ALLYSON; Hightstown HS; East Windsor, NJ; (3); FBLA; Key Clb; Spanish Clb; SADD; Yrbk Stf; Rep Frsh Cls; Stu Cncl; Tennis; High Hon Roll; Hon Roll; Socl Wrk.

BORGENICHT, GLEN; Parsippany HS; Parsippany, NJ; (2); FBLA; JV Bsbl; Im Bsktbl.

BORGES, CHERI; Brick Township HS; Brick, NJ; (3); ROTC; Color Guard; Drill Tm; Flag Corp; Mrchg Band; Var Bsktbl; Var Trk; Im Crs Cntry; Score Keeper; Im Sftbl; Military Order Of World Wars Acad Of Mrt 86-87; Natl Sojourners Awd 84-85; Outstndng Ldrshp Awd 85-86; Pilot.

BORGSTROM, HENRIK; West Essex SR HS; N Caldwell, NJ; (3); Drama Clb; French Clb; Hosp Aide; Library Aide; School Musical; School Play; Mgr Stage Crew; Ed Lit Mag; French Hon Soc; NHS; Intl Rltns.

BORINO JR, ANTHONY; Sussex County Vo Tech; Vernon, NJ; (2); Church Yth Grp; Computer Clb; Spanish Clb; Hon Roll; Merit Awd 86; Comp Sci.

BORINO, MARK; St Peters Prep Schl; Bayonne, NJ; (4); 70/196; Band; Jazz Band; Orch; Cmmnd Stud NMSQT 85; Rutgers U.

BORIS, MICHELE; Saureville War Memorial HS; Sayreville, NJ; (4); 70/353; Church Yth Grp; Spanish Clb; Varsity Clb; Rep Jr Cls; Rep Sr Cls; Rep Stu Cncl; Cheerleading; Hon Roll; U DE; Textile.

BOROTA, NICOLAE ANDREW; Fidrence Memorial HS; Roebling, NJ; (4); 7/88; Am Leg Boys St; Pres Latin Clb; Math Tm; Pres Science Clb; Hon Roll; Ntl Merit SF; John Politary Achvt Awd 87; Pres Acad Fit Awd 87; United Steel Wrkrs Schlrshp 87; TX A&M; Aerospace Engrg.

BOROWSKI, BRETT; Clifton HS; Clifton, NJ; (3); French Clb; VP Math Clb; School Play; Pres Stu Cncl; JV Vllybl; Bausch & Lomb Sci Awd; French Hon Soc; Church Yth Grp; Computer Clb; Science Clb; Clmba U Sci Hnrs Prgm 86-88; NJ Gvnrs Schl In Sci 87; Physcl Sci.

BOROWSKY, JOSEPH; St John Vianney HS; Morganville, NJ; (4); 10/253; Computer Clb; Math Clb; Stage Crew; High Hon Roll; NHS; Hugh O Brian Yth Fdtn Smnr 85; Texaco Philanthropic Fdtn Schlrshp 87; Pres Acad Fitness Awd Prgm 87; Rutgers Coll; Engr.

BORRELLI, PATRICK; Ridgefield Park HS; Ridgefield Pk, NJ; (3); Debate Tm; Ski Clb; JV Ftbl; JV Wrstlng; Clin Psych.

BORTHWICK, SUSAN; Immaculata HS; Manville, NJ; (3); 103/247; Church Yth Grp; Cmnty Wkr; Library Aide; Coach Actv; Crs Cntry; Vllybl; Hnrry Cert Cngrssnl Art Shw NJ 87; Fshn Dsgn.

BORYS, MICHAEL; North Arlington HS; N Arlington, NJ; (3); 16/116; Church Yth Grp; Cmnty Wkr; Computer Clb; Ski Clb; Rep Stu Cncl; JV Bsbl; JV Bsktbl; JV Ftbl.

BORZARO, ANNA; John F Kennedy HS; Paterson, NJ; (3); Computer Clb; Math Clb; Office Aide; Science Clb; Nwsp Ed-Chief; Rep Frsh Cls; Rep Soph Cls; Rep Jr Cls; Var Tennis; High Hon Roll; Hugh O Brien Yth Ldrshp Smnr 85-86; Sci.

BORZIO, MICHELLE; Kingsway Regional HS; Swedesboro, NJ; (2); JV Fld Hcky; Hon Roll.

BOSIE, JEFFREY; Perth Amboy HS; Perth Amboy, NJ; (3); Boys Clb Am; Pres Church Yth Grp; Varsity Clb; Nwsp Phtg; Yrbk Phtg; Rep Stu Cncl; Bsbl; Bowling; Socr; Tennis; Boys St Alt 87; Rutgers; Comms.

BOSIES, LOREN; Oakcrest HS; Egg Harbor, NJ; (4); 4/206; Sec Keywanettes; Drm Mjr(t); Yrbk Ed-Chief; Sec Jr Cls; JV Capt Sftbl; Hon Roll; Pres NHS; Pres Schlr; Amer Mngmnt Assoc Oprtn Entrprs 86; Girls Ctznshp Inst 86; Ocean Spray Awd Bus Schlrshp 87; Rochester Inst Of Tech; Htl Mgr.

BOSLAND, CHRISTOPHER; Wayne Hills HS; Wayne, NJ; (3); 1/335; Am Leg Boys St; Boy Scts; Drama Clb; GAA; Stage Crew; Nwsp Sprt Ed; Gov Hon Prg Awd; NHS; Ntl Merit Ltr; St Schlr.

BOSQUE, ADA; Our Lady Of Good Council HS; E Orange, NJ; (4); 11/112; Debate Tm; Drama Clb; Pres Science Clb; VP Ski Clb; Church Choir; School Musical; Capt Cheerleading; Hon Roll; VP NHS; Hstry Awd 84; Awd Wnng Essy 86; JR Ambssdr To UN 87; Boston U; Pol Sci.

BOSSERT, VERONICA; Nottingham HS; Trenton, NJ; (4); 44/298; Capt Var Cheerleading; Hon Roll; 2nd Rnnr Up Hmcmg Qn 86-87; Vet.

BOSTICK, TANGIE; Pemberton HS No 01; Browns Mills, NJ; (2); Cmnty Wkr; Math Clb; Band; Concert Band; Drill Tm; Mrchg Band; Nwsp Rptr; Nwsp Stf; Rep Stu Cncl; Hon Roll; ACCNTNG.

BOSTROM, MELANIE; Rahway HS; Rahway, NJ; (3); Church Yth Grp; Girl Scts; Church Choir; School Play; Yrbk Stf; Rep Jr Cls; Cheerleading; French Hon Soc; High Hon Roll; Jr NHS; Soph Prncs 85-86; Slvr Awd Girl Scts 84; Fshn Merch.

BOSWORTH, DEBORAH; Marylawn Of The Oranges HS; West Orange, NJ; (3); 4/68; Drama Clb; Pres NFL; School Musical; Lit Mag; Capt Cheerleading; Sftbl; Tennis; French Hon Soc; NHS; Advnc To Natl Forensic Grnd Trnmnt 85-86; Hghst Avg In Soph Cls In Religious Studies 85-86; Comm.

BOSZAK, DAVID; Hamilton High West; Yardville, NJ; (3); Boy Scts; Exploring; Ftbl; Im Ice Hcky; Var Trk; Im Vllybl; Wt Lftg; Wrstlng; Forestry.

BOSZAK, DAWN; Hamilton High West; Yardville, NJ; (4); 8/309; FBLA; GAA; JV Var Socr; Var Swmmng; Var Trk; Im Vllybl; Hon Roll; NHS; Pres Schlr; St Schlr; Hnrb Mntn Katharine Gibbs Ldrshp Awd 86; Hnrb Mntn All Cnty Grls Spring Trk 87; MIP Grls Spring Trk; Fairleigh Dickinson U; Comp Sci.

BOTERO, VIVIAN; Mary Help Of Christians Acad; Paterson, NJ; (3); 7/80; NFL; SADD; Drill Tm; Stage Crew; Im Bsktbl; Im Vllybl; Hon Roll.

BOTSCHKA, ROBERT; Don Bosco Prep HS; Franklin Lks, NJ; (4); Church Yth Grp; JV Var Socr; Hon Roll; Fairfield U; Psych.

BOTT, CHERRYL; Rutherford HS; Rutherford, NJ; (4); 2/167; Am Leg Aux Girls St; Church Yth Grp; Cmnty Wkr; GAA; Pep Clb; Varsity Clb; School Play; Sec Sr Cls; Stu Cncl; Bsktbl; Hnr Rl Bronbz Awd 84-85; Hnr Rl Silvr Awd 85-86.

BOTT, CHRISTOPHER; Burlington Township HS; Burlington Twp, NJ; (3); 10/129; Am Leg Boys St; Ski Clb; Varsity Clb; Band; Concert Band; Jazz Band; Mrchg Band; Socr; Tennis; Hon Roll; Comp Sci.

BOTT, MICHELLE; Long Branch HS; Long Branch, NJ; (4); Science Clb; Drm Mjr(t); Flag Corp; Mrchg Band; Yrbk Rptr; Yrbk Stf; Twrlr.

BOTTI, DAWN MARIE; West Morris Central HS; Long Valley, NJ; (4); 20/296; Debate Tm; Drama Clb; Acpl Chr; Pres Swing Chorus; Capt Twrlr; NHS; Chorus; Jazz Band; Sec Jr Cls; Rep Stu Cncl; James E Casey Schlrshp Awd; Lng Vly Wmns Clb Schlrshp; Lng Vly Chester Rtry Schlrshp; HOBY Ldrshp Smnr; Lafayette Coll; Engl.

BOTTINI, DOMENICK; Pascack Hills HS; Woodcliff Lake, NJ; (4); 127/245; Ski Clb; Spanish Clb; SADD; Im Bsbl; Im Bsktbl; JV Socr; Trk; Wrstlng; Hon Roll; York Coll PA; Bus.

BOTTONE, KRISTINE; South Plainfield HS; S Plainfield, NJ; (3); Camera Clb; Drama Clb; Radio Clb; Spanish Clb; Yrbk Phtg; Yrbk Rptr; Yrbk Sprt Ed; Yrbk Stf; Rep Jr Cls; Rep Sr Cls; Arts.

BOTTRILL, MICHAEL; Shore Regional HS; Monmouth Beach, NJ; (3); VP Key Clb; Thesps; School Musical; School Play; Stage Crew; Variety Show; Nwsp Rptr; Nwsp Stf; Crs Cntry; Tennis; Rutgers; Bus.

BOUCHARD, NATALIE; Phillipsburg HS; Phillipsburg, NJ; (3); 41/315; Ski Clb; Rep Stu Cncl; Cheerleading; High Hon Roll; NHS; Acctnt.

BOUCHER, MICHAEL; John F Kennedy HS; Willingboro, NJ; (3); Band; Concert Band; Jazz Band; Mrchg Band; Symp Band; Im Bsbl.

BOUCHER, MICHELLE; Camden Catholic HS; Marlton, NJ; (3); Church Yth Grp; French Clb; FTA; Hosp Aide; Teachers Aide; Hon Roll; Candystripe Awd 86; Tchr For Deaf.

BOUDOUGHIAN, ALICE; Pascack Hills HS; Woodcliff Lk, NJ; (4); 120/240; Church Yth Grp; Chorus; Church Choir; Bsktbl; Crs Cntry; Sftbl; Hon Roll; Hnr Pin 87; Cert Achvts 85-86; Phy Ed Awd 84; Montclair ST; Bus.

BOUDWIN, KIM; Life Center Acad; Burlington, NJ; (1); 1/11; Church Yth Grp; Cmnty Wkr; Chorus; Church Choir; Var Bsktbl; Var Sftbl; Var Trk; Var Vllybl; High Hon Roll; Prfct Atten Awd; Oral Roberts U; Tchr.

BOVE, MATTHEW; Highland Regional HS; Blackwood, NJ; (2); Var Ftbl; Hon Roll; Engrng.

BOWCOCK, DONNA; Toms River HS South; Toms River, NJ; (2).

BOWEN, STEPHANIE; Paramus Catholic HS; Garfield, NJ; (3); Church Yth Grp; Cmnty Wkr; Drama Clb; SADD; Teachers Aide; School Play; Yrbk Stf; Lit Mag; Rep Stu Cncl; Merit Awd 86; Psych.

BOWER, TINA; West Morris Central HS; Long Valley, NJ; (4); 7/297; Science Clb; Ski Clb; Capt Flag Corp; Off Jr Cls; Trs Sr Cls; Stu Cncl; Powder Puff Ftbl; NHS; Ntl Merit Ltr; Cmnty Wkr; Magna UM Laude Natl Latin Test 86; Soroptomist Interntl Schlrshp $500 87; Soc Of Plastic Engrs 87; William; Sci.

BOWERS, STEVEN; Bound Brook HS; S Bound Brook, NJ; (4); 14/128; Am Leg Boys St; VP French Clb; Key Clb; Sec Soph Cls; Trs Jr Cls; Rep Sr Cls; Var L Bsbl; Elks Awd; NHS; Church Yth Grp; Knights Of Altar Pres 83-87; Twin-Boro Comm Schlrshp 87; Rutgers U; Engrng.

BOWLES, RENEE; Riverside HS; Riverside, NJ; (3); Dance Clb; Hosp Aide; Office Aide; Ski Clb; High Hon Roll; Hon Roll; Htl Mgmt.

BOWMAN, DAMON; Bordentown Regional HS; Cookstown, NJ; (2); 15/141; Math Clb; Math Tm; JV Bsbl; JV Bsktbl; Hon Roll; Prfct Atten Awd; Peer Tutoring Pgm 86-87; U Of FL; Acctg.

BOWMAN, JENIFER; Salem HS; Salem, NJ; (3); Art Clb; Church Yth Grp; Computer Clb; English Clb; FBLA; JA; Library Aide; Math Clb; Math Tm; Office Aide.

BOWSER, KISHA; Camden Catholic HS; Glassboro, NJ; (3); Girl Scts; Office Aide; Spanish Clb; Capt Drill Tm; Yrbk Stf; Rep Soph Cls; Hon Roll; Mental Hlth.

BOXER, ARI; Lakewood HS; Lakewood, NJ; (3); 1/335; Political Wkr; Jazz Band; Var Trs Lit Mag; Var Trs Stu Cncl; JV Bsbl; High Hon Roll; NHS; Ntl Merit Ltr; Spanish NHS; English Clb; Rensselaer Awd Math & Sci 87.

BOYARSKY, LESLIE ANDREA; Howell HS; Howell, NJ; (3); 64/500; French Clb; Nwsp Stf; Engl Cert Of Excllnc 87; Tufts U; Bus.

BOYCE, CHERYL L; Lenape HS; Vincentown, NJ; (3); Latin Clb; Spanish Clb; Varsity Clb; Nwsp Rptr; Nwsp Stf; JV Var Bowling; JV Capt Cheerleading; JV Trk; Hon Roll; GAA; Journlsm.

BOYCE JR, H CHARLES; Raritan HS; W Keansburg, NJ; (4); 25/235; Boy Scts; Teachers Aide; Yrbk Ed-Chief; God Cntry Awd; NHS; Garden ST Schlrshp 87; Stevens Inst Tech Schlrshp 87; Ordr Arrw Eagle Sct 85; Stevens Inst Tech; Comp Engrng.

BOYCE, THOMAS; Palisades Park JR SR HS; Palisades Pk, NJ; (3); Cmnty Wkr; Computer Clb; Yrbk Stf; Var L Crs Cntry; Var L Trk; Wrstlng; Hon Roll; Comp Sci.

BOYDELL, TAMMIE; Hawthorne HS; Paterson, NJ; (3); SADD; Rep Frsh Cls; Rep Soph Cls; Hst Jr Cls; Rep Sr Cls; Stu Cncl; Var Capt Socr; Var Sftbl; Ski Clb; JV Bsktbl; Italian Clb, Scrtry For 86-87 84-87; Sftbl Awd 1st Team All Leg 86-87; CPA.

BOYE, HANK J; Shawnee HS; Tabernacle, NJ; (3); Am Leg Boys St; Church Yth Grp; Quiz Bowl; Varsity Clb; Var Bsbl; Var JV Wrstlng; Hon Roll; NHS; Ntl Merit Ltr; Rotary Awd; William & Gary; Sprts Med.

BOYER, JILL C; Hopewell Valley Central HS; Pennington, NJ; (4); Am Leg Boys St; Church Yth Grp; Spanish Clb; School Play; Stat Bsktbl; Fld Hcky; Var L Trk; Alpha Kappa Alpha Bk Awd 87-88; Harry R Davis Mem Schlrshp 87-88; Calvary Bapt Church Schlrshp 87-88; High Point Coll; Pre-Law.

BOYER, ROBERT L; Dunellen HS; Duneller, NJ; (4); Aud/Vis; Debate Tm; English Clb; Bsktbl; Ftbl; Score Keeper; Middlesex County Coll; Wrtr.

BOYER II, ROBERT LOUIS; Rahway HS; Rahway, NJ; (3); JV Var Bsbl; Var JV Bsktbl; Trk; Hon Roll; Prfct Atten Awd; Comp Sci.

BOYKINS, MICHELLE; New Brunswick HS; New Brunswick, NJ; (4); 12/110; Trs Sr Cls; Rep Stu Cncl; Hon Roll; Engrng.

BOYLE, CATHERINE; Manchester Township HS; Lakehurst, NJ; (3); 2/198; Am Leg Aux Girls St; VP Sec Drama Clb; Math Clb; School Play; Yrbk Stf; Tennis; High Hon Roll; NHS; Voice Dem Awd; Science Clb; Ambssdr Hgh Obrn Ldrshp Smnr 86; AM Assc-U Wmn Awd-Acdmc Achvt 85-87; Cornell; Law.

BOYLE, CHRISTOPHER; New Milford HS; New Milford, NJ; (3); Am Leg Boys St; Rep Soph Cls; Rep Jr Cls; Capt Var Ftbl; Var Trk; Capt Var Wrstlng; Cit Awd; Coachs Awd-Wrstlng 86-87; Accntng.

BOYLE, CHRISTOPHER; Vernon Twp HS; Sussex, NJ; (3); JCL; Quiz Bowl; Var Bsbl; Bsktbl; Var Bowling; Var Capt Crs Cntry; High Hon Roll; Hon Roll; NHS; Prfct Atten Awd.

BOYLE, ERIC; High Point Regional HS; Augusta, NJ; (3); 20/247; French Clb; Nwsp Rptr; Nwsp Stf; JV Trk; High Hon Roll; Hon Roll; Spcl Recgntn Awd Frgn Lang Tutr; Spcl Recgntn Awd Asst Sccr; Rutgers Schl Engrng; Mech Engr.

BOYLE, GEORGEANNE; Lakewood HS; Lakewood, NJ; (4); 50/336; Church Yth Grp; Cmnty Wkr; French Clb; Girl Scts; Church Choir; Yrbk Stf; Socr; Cit Awd; French Hon Soc; God Cntry Awd; Bill Bradley Yth Ctznshp Awd 87; US Slvr Cngrssnl Awd 86; Coll St Elizabeth Engl Schlrshp 87; Coll Of St Elizabeth; Engl.

BOYLE, JOSEPH; Toms River HS South; Pine Beach, NJ; (2); Math Tm; Var Trk; JV Wrstlng; Hon Roll; Pres Phys Ftnss Awd 87; Sci.

BOYLE, MICHELLE; Edgewood HS; Hamm Nton, NJ; (3); Latin Clb; Orch; Hon Roll; Prfct Atten Awd; JV Fld Hcky; Temple; Bus.

BOYLE, NANCY; Brick Memorial HS; Brick, NJ; (3); 41/370; Band; Concert Band; Drm Mjr(t); Jazz Band; Mrchg Band; Orch; Symp Band; Sec Soph Cls; Rep Jr Cls; NHS; Cmnctns.

BOYLE, TERESA; Rutherford HS; Rutherford, NJ; (4); 33/167; Key Clb; Acpl Chr; School Musical; Variety Show; Yrbk Ed-Chief; VP Sr Cls; Trs Stu Cncl; Co-Capt Cheerleading; High Hon Roll; Hon Roll; Bd Educ Bronze Awd GPA Excllnc 85; Superior Vocal Achvt Awd 86; MVP Chrldng Schlrshp 87; William Paterson; Public Rltns.

BOYLER, TRICIA; South River HS; South River, NJ; (2); Chorus; Pres Frsh Cls; Pres Soph Cls; Rep Stu Cncl; Chorus Awd 85-86; Ltrd Chorus 86-87.

BOYLES, MICHELE; Kingsway Regional HS; Swedesboro, NJ; (2); Hosp Aide; Score Keeper; Swmmng; Timer; ROTC; Phys Thrpst.

BOZEWSKI, ANDRE; St Anthony HS; Jersey City, NJ; (4); 6/59; Aud/Vis; Yrbk Stf; Hon Roll; Svc Libry Awd, Awd Merit Wrtng, Rdng Profcncy Tst 87; Mst Imprvd Stu Math 87; Jersey City ST Coll; Elem Ed.

BOZIAN, DIANA; Paramus Catholic Girls HS; Fort Lee, NJ; (3); Hosp Aide; High Hon Roll; NHS; Prfct Atten Awd; Hnrs Tutoring Chem 86-87; NY U; Med.

BOZOLUS, CHERYL; Roselle Catholic HS; Union, NJ; (4); 45/200; Rep Church Yth Grp; Hosp Aide; Service Clb; Lit Mag; Sftbl; Swmmng; Im Vllybl; High Hon Roll; NHS; Spanish NHS; Awds For Music 83; Kean Coll; Phy Thrpy.

BOZSIK, JENNIFER; Paramus Catholic Girls Rgnl HS; Elmwood Pk, NJ; (2); Hon Roll; NEDT Awd; Bus.

BOZZA, CHRISTINA; Morristown HS; Morris Plains, NJ; (2); 141/432; Stat Ice Hcky; Var L Socr; JV Im Sftbl; Im Badmtn; JV Bsktbl; Im Ftbl; Im Gym; Im Lcrss; Im Swmmng; Im Wt Lftg.

BRACEGIRDLE, THAD J; The Pennington Schl; Langhorne, PA; (1); 2/57; JV Bsktbl; Var Lcrss; Hon Roll; Drscll Mem Schlrshp 86-87.

BRACERAS, ROBBIE; James Caldwell HS; Caldwell, NJ; (4); 1/265; Ski Clb; VP Sr Cls; Stu Cncl; Var Ftbl; Var Capt Tennis; Bausch & Lomb Sci Awd; CC Awd; Kiwanis Awd; NHS; Ntl Merit Schol; Schlr-Athlete 87; Gridiron Sch 87; Rutgers Prsdntl Schlr 87; Dartmouth; Pre-Med.

BRACKEN, DAVE; West Morris Central HS; Long Valley, NJ; (4); 10/300; Debate Tm; Pres VP FBLA; Math Tm; VP Sr Cls; Pres Stu Cncl; Capt Swmmng; Mr FBLA NJ & ST VP FBLA; U Of MD-BALTIMORE.

BRACKETT, KENTON; Eastside HS; Paterson, NJ; (3); Elec Engrng.

BRADBURY, THERESA; Highland Reg HS; Erial, NJ; (4); 33/300; Church Yth Grp; Drama Clb; Band; Chorus; Church Choir; Concert Band; Capt Mrchg Band; JV Tennis; Capt Twrlr; Glassboro ST Coll; Math Ed.

BRADFORD, DIANE; Audubon HS; Mt Ephraim, NJ; (3); Church Yth Grp; Red Cross Aide; Chrmn SADD; Pres Jr Cls; Pres Stu Cncl; VP Stu Cncl; Fld Hcky; Capt Sftbl; Hon Roll; Band; Bill Bradley-Yng Ctzns Awd 87; Wheaton Coll; Scndry Ed.

BRADLEY, GALE; Toms River HS South; Toms River, NJ; (2); Math Tm; Ski Clb; Swmmng; Tennis; Im Vllybl; High Hon Roll; Hon Roll; Sailing Innr Ycht Clb Rcng Awds BBYRA Qlfr 86-87; Astrontcl Sci.

BRADLEY, MELISSA; James J Ferris HS; Jersey City, NJ; (3); Computer Clb; Drama Clb; Math Clb; Rep Soph Cls; Rep Jr Cls; Rep Stu Cncl; Mgr(s); Sftbl; Trk; Hgh Achvt Awds 86-87; West Palm Atlntc Coll; CPA.

BRADLEY, MICAH; Mc Corristin Catholic HS; Trenton, NJ; (3); Am Leg Aux Girls St; Church Yth Grp; English Clb; Library Aide; Math Tm; Political Wkr; Spanish Clb; Teachers Aide; Mrchg Band; Yrbk Stf; Morgan ST Coll; Acctng.

BRADLEY, PATRICK; Holy Spirit HS; Cardiff, NJ; (2); 20/397; Rep Frsh Cls; Hon Roll.

BRADLEY, STEVEN P; Florence Twp Memorial HS; Florence, NJ; (3); Am Leg Boys St; JA; Varsity Clb; Var Bsbl; Var Bsktbl; Var Ftbl; Bsbl Frdm Div 1st Team Allstar,Burlington Cnty 2nd Team & Mercer Cnty Amer Lgn Leag 87; Arch.

BRADLEY, TIMIA; Holy Spirit HS; Atlantic City, NJ; (4); Library Aide; Spanish Clb; Hon Roll; Glassboro ST; Mktg.

BRADSHAW, CASSANDRA; Riverside HS; Riverside, NJ; (3); Capt Drama Clb; SADD; Band; Chorus; Mrchg Band; School Musical; School Play; Ed Nwsp Stf; Yrbk Stf; VP Frsh Cls.

BRADY, CHRIS; Parsippany Hills HS; Morristown, NJ; (3); Church Yth Grp; Debate Tm; NFL; Speech Tm; Jazz Band; Variety Show; Var Trk; Chrstn Ldrshp Inst 85; Rutgers; Law.

BRADY, ERIN; Gloucester Catholic HS; Wenonah, NJ; (3); Cmnty Wkr; Dance Clb; Band; Chorus; School Musical; School Play; Var L Diving; Var Capt Socr; Var L Swmmng; Var L Tennis; Drexel U; Pre-Med.

BRADY, JAMES; Middletown HS South; Red Bank, NJ; (4); 78/436; High Hon Roll; Hon Roll; Rutgers Univ; Econmcs.

BRADY, KARREN; Clifford J Scott HS; East Orange, NJ; (3); French Clb; Library Aide; Band; Concert Band; Mrchg Band; Hon Roll; High Dept Hnrs In U S Hist & Instrumental Music 87; Honor Roll 86-87; Elec Engrng.

BRADY, MITCHELL; Matawan Regional HS; Aberdeen, NJ; (3); 49/320; Ski Clb; Spanish Clb; Temple Yth Grp; Band; Concert Band; Jazz Band; School Play; JV Bsbl; Var JV Socr; Var Trk; Soc Sci.

BRAIDWOOD, SCOTT; Washington Township HS; Turnersdille, NJ; (3); Church Yth Grp; Im Bsktbl; JV Golf; Hon Roll; Accntng.

BRAITHWAITE, DARREN; Burlington City HS; Edgewater Pk, NJ; (4); 31/191; Computer Clb; Exploring; Variety Show; Hon Roll; Kiwanis Awd; NHS; Wright Mem Fnd 87; Fabritiis Mem Schlrshp 87; NJ Grdn ST Schlrshp 87; Rutgers Coll; Elec Engrng.

BRAITHWAITE, JOCELYN; Victory Christian HS; Sicklerville, NJ; (2); 1/27; Drama Clb; Pep Clb; Yrbk Rptr; Var L Cheerleading; L Stat Sftbl; High Hon Roll; Schlstc All-Amrcn 86-87; Actrss.

BRAKE, PATRICK; Christian Brothers Academy; Hazlet, NJ; (3); Boy Scts; Church Yth Grp; French Clb; FBLA; Political Wkr; Ski Clb; Im Ftbl; Im Wt Lftg; Var JV Wrstlng; Hon Roll; Loyola Coll; Bus.

BRAMHALL, CATHERINE; Kent Place Schl; Morristown, NJ; (3); Pres Cmnty Wkr; Dance Clb; Intnl Clb; Political Wkr; Band; Lit Mag; DAR Awd; Ntl Merit Ltr; Frgn Affrs.

BRANAGH, WILLIAM; Waldwick HS; Waldwick, NJ; (3); 25/150; Rep Frsh Cls; Bsbl; Bsktbl; Ftbl; High Hon Roll; Hon Roll; Acctng.

BRANCA, DOMINIC; St Josephs Regional HS; Montvale, NJ; (3); JV Socr; High Hon Roll; Spanish NHS.

BRANCA, MICHAEL C; Camden Catholic HS; Pennsauken, NJ; (3); 29/279; Cmnty Wkr; German Clb; SADD; Ftbl; Golf; Swmmng; Wt Lftg; Wrstlng; Hon Roll; Math,German,Sci Hon Soc 86; Engr.

BRANCO, MICHELLE; Union HS; Union, NJ; (3); Yrbk Stf; Off Sr Cls; Hon Roll.

BRAND, DIANA LYNN; Brick Township HS; Brick Town, NJ; (4); Girl Scts; Radio Clb; Yrbk Stf; Lit Mag; High Hon Roll; Hon Roll; Treas OCUTS 85-87; VICA 86-87; Csmtlgy.

BRAND, JONATHAN D; Central Jersey Christian HS; Atlantic Highland, NJ; (2); Var Capt Bsktbl; Var Bowling; Var L Socr; Var Trk; High Hon Roll; NHS; All Conf Bsktbl 86 & 87; Pres Fit Awd 86.

BRAND, KIMBERLY; Lower Cape May Regional HS; Cape May, NJ; (3); Civic Clb; Pep Clb; Teachers Aide; Varsity Clb; Variety Show; Yrbk Stf; Sec Soph Cls; Stat Bsbl; Var Capt Cheerleading; Glassboro; Crmnl Just.

BRAND, MONICA L; Marlboro HS; Marlboro, NJ; (4); 2/529; French Clb; JCL; VP Latin Clb; Math Clb; Ski Clb; SADD; Varsity Clb; Rep Frsh Cls; Rep Soph Cls; Rep Jr Cls; Yth Yr Fnlst 87; JETS Tm Comptn 1st Pl Wnnr 87; Williams Coll.

BRANDS, RITA; Northwest Christian HS; Sussex, NJ; (3); Sec Church Yth Grp; Drama Clb; Ski Clb; SADD; Orch; School Play; Yrbk Phtg; Fld Hcky; High Hon Roll; Hon Roll; Natl Councl For Geogrphc Educ; Sprtsmnshp Awd; Elem Educ.

BRANDT, JENNIFER; Woodbridge HS; Woodbridge, NJ; (4); 9/386; Quiz Bowl; Ed Yrbk Stf; VP Soph Cls; Rep Jr Cls; Rep Sr Cls; Stu Cncl; Var Capt Cheerleading; Score Keeper; French Hon Soc; High Hon Roll; WA Wrkshps Schlrshp 86; Mddlsx Cnty JR Miss 87; George Washingtn U; Pre Law.

BRANDT, SHARON; Toms River HS East; Toms River, NJ; (3); 26/527; Hosp Aide; Band; Mrchg Band; Stage Crew; Yrbk Stf; Hon Roll; NHS; Church Yth Grp; Cmnty Wkr; Drama Clb; GS Silver Awd 84; Pres Phys Fit Awd 86-87; CPR Cert Red Cross 87; Chem.

BRANGMAN, RONALD; Essex Catholic Boys HS; Orange, NJ; (3); Drama Clb; NAACP; Church Choir; School Musical; School Play; Stage Crew; Pres Jr Cls; Rep Stu Cncl; Hon Roll; Prfct Atten Awd; Rutgers; Med.

BRANIC, LISA; Brick Memorial HS; Lakewood, NJ; (2); 20/510; French Clb; Bowling; High Hon Roll; Math.

BRANKER, HENRY; Essex Catholic Boys HS; Bloomfield, NJ; (3); Art Clb; JV Var Crs Cntry; JV Var Trk; Ntl Merit SF; Schlrshp Caldwell Coll 87; MIT; Phys.

BRANTLEY, ADRIA; Marylawn Of The Oranges HS; Newark, NJ; (3); 15/65; Art Clb; Civic Clb; Library Aide; Spanish Clb; Var Bsktbl; Vllybl; High Hon Roll; Hon Roll; NHS; Ntl Art Hnr Soc 87-88; Bus.

BRANTLEY-BUTLER, ERIC O; Buena Regional HS; Buena, NJ; (3); Drama Clb; NAACP; Madrigals; Nwsp Rptr; Trs Frsh Cls; Rep Soph Cls; Pres Sr Cls; Debate Tm; Office Aide; PAVAS; Schl Arts Scholar Glassboro ST Coll 87; All S Jersey Choir 87; All ST Choir 87-88; Advrtsng.

BRASEK, CARL; Holy Cross HS; Medford, NJ; (4); 58/355; Am Leg Boys St; Church Yth Grp; Cmnty Wkr; Political Wkr; Var Crs Cntry; Trk; Hon Roll; NHS; VFW Awd; German Clb; Awds/Trophies X-Cntry Open; Schlrshp US Acad Fndtn Pgm; US Naval Acad.

BRASZKO, NATALIE; Calvary Lighthouse Acad; Ft Monmouth, NJ; (1); Church Yth Grp; Yrbk Stf; Sec Stu Cncl; JV Sftbl; JV Vllybl; Hon Roll; Mst Chrstn, Ctzn Ldrshp; I Cor 13 Awd-Vllybl; Princeton U; Mdcl.

BRAUE, CHERYL; West Essex Regional HS; No Caldwell, NJ; (3); Drama Clb; Key Clb; Stage Crew; JV Sftbl; Hon Roll; NHS; Ntl Merit Ltr; Chem Olympcs NJIT, Key Club NJ Cnvntn 87; Physicl Sci.

BRAUN, PAUL; Rancocas Valley Regional HS; Mt Holly, NJ; (2); 1/317; German Clb; JA; Quiz Bowl; Science Clb; Band; JV Crs Cntry; Var Swmmng; JV Trk; High Hon Roll; NHS; Sci.

BRAUN, TANYA; Highland Regional HS; Blackwood, NJ; (2); Hon Roll; Camden County Coll; Bus.

BRAVACO, GUY; Bloomfield SR HS; Bloomfld, NJ; (4); 43/440; Computer Clb; Key Clb; Chorus; Soph Cls; Jr Cls; Sr Cls; Jr NHS; NHS; Hrn Roll 83-86; Seton Hall Univ; Acctng.

BRAVERMAN, MARCY; West Orange HS; W Orange, NJ; (3); Cmnty Wkr; Debate Tm; Trs French Clb; Service Clb; Temple Yth Grp; Y-Teens; Yrbk Rptr; Yrbk Stf; Lit Mag; Crs Cntry; Natl Fdrtn Pno Tchrs 86; Natl Pno Tchrs Gld 87; Hnr Exmplry Vlntr Srvc 86; Middlebury Coll; Psychlgy.

BRAVO JR, JOSE R; St Josephs Of Palisade; Union City, NJ; (4); 10/120; Spanish Clb; Variety Show; JV Var Bsbl; JV Var Bsktbl; High Hon Roll; Hon Roll; NHS; Spanish NHS; Stevens; Comp Sci.

BRAXTON, KIMBERLY; Immaculate Conception HS; East Orange, NJ; (3); Computer Clb; Debate Tm; Chorus; Church Choir; Rep Frsh Cls; Rep Soph Cls; Rep Jr Cls; JV Sftbl; Hon Roll; Hofstra U; Bus Adm.

BRAY, ERIK; Sparta HS; Sparta, NJ; (2); Key Clb; Off Frsh Cls; Rep Stu Cncl; Im Bsktbl; Arch.

BRAZINSKY, MICHAEL; Matawan Regional HS; Matawan, NJ; (2); Drama Clb; Variety Show; Var L Bsbl; Var L Bsktbl; Var Ftbl; Wt Lftg; Hon Roll; Rookie Yr Bsbl 87; USC MI; Law.

BREAULT, DENISE; Neumann Prep; Loomingdale, NJ; (3); 16/68; Hosp Aide; School Musical; School Play; Variety Show; Hon Roll; NHS; Spanish NHS; Peer Ministry Achvt Awd 86-87; Emerson Coll; Comm.

BREDAHL, MICHEL; Lawrenceville Schl; Bricktown, NJ; (3); French Clb; GAA; Yrbk Stf; Frsh Cls; Jr Cls; Stu Cncl; Fld Hcky; Socr; Swmmng; NHS; Comp Sci.

BREDDER, CHARLENE C; Randolph HS; Randolph, NJ; (4); 35/360; AFS; Church Yth Grp; Q&S; Nwsp Bus Mgr; Nwsp Ed-Chief; Nwsp Rptr; Nwsp Stf; Rep Frsh Cls; Rep Soph Cls; Rep Jr Cls; Quill & Scrll Hnr Awd 87; Intl Stds.

BREDEHOFT, MARY ALICE; Toms River H S North; Toms River, NJ; (4); Church Yth Grp; 4-H; Teachers Aide; Mrchg Band; Trk; 4-H Awd; Shippensburg U; Elem Ed.

BREEN, BRIAN; Washington Township HS; Turnersville, NJ; (3); Bsbl; JV Socr; Hon Roll; NHS; German Natl Hnr Soc 87.

BREEN, DANIEL; Fair Lawn HS; Fair Lawn, NJ; (3); Coach Actv; Ftbl; Lcrss; Wt Lftg; Arch.

BREEN, KIMBERLY; Lyndhurst HS; Lyndhurst, NJ; (3); 9/174; Am Leg Aux Girls St; Key Clb; Teachers Aide; Nwsp Rptr; Yrbk Stf; JV Bowling; JV Vllybl; High Hon Roll; Hon Roll; VP NHS; Jrnlsm.

BREIDT, KEITH; High Point Regional HS; Branchville, NJ; (3); 35/268; Am Leg Boys St; Cmnty Wkr; Science Clb; Teachers Aide; Nwsp Rptr; Var L Ftbl; Var L Swmmng; Var L Trk; Cit Awd; Hon Roll; Taught Frnch To Elem Stu 86-87; AF Acad; Aeronaut Engrng.

BREISH, BONNIE; Cinnaminson HS; Cinnaminson, NJ; (3); Art Clb; Church Yth Grp; German Clb; VICA; Chorus; Yrbk Stf; JV Socr; JV Sftbl; MIP Sccr 86; Montclair; Cmnctns.

BREITENBACH, MATTHEW; Shore Regional HS; Oceanport, NJ; (3); Chess Clb; Mrchg Band; Symp Band; Nwsp Stf; Var Golf; High Hon Roll; NHS; Drama Clb; Math Tm; Science Clb; Bronze & Slvr Congrsnl Mdls Hnr 86-87; Central Jersey Reg II Symp Band 86-87; New Jersey All Shore.

BREITENBACH, PAUL T; Shore Regional HS; Oceanport, NJ; (3); Am Leg Boys St; High Hon Roll; NHS; Chess Clb; Drama Clb; Key Clb; Q&S; Band; Concert Band; Jazz Band; Brnz & Slvr Cngrsnl Mdls Of Hnr 86&87; Cntrl Jrsy Rgn II Symphnc Band & NJ Shore Symphnc Bnd 85-87.

BREITHAUPT, CYNTHIA; Middletown H S South; Middletown, NJ; (4); 21/450; Camp Fr Inc; Capt Flag Corp; School Musical; Variety Show; Ed Nwsp Rptr; Lit Mag; Stu Cncl; Trk; Hon Roll; NHS; Brdcst Jrnlsm.

BRENNAN, DREW; St John Vianney HS; Manalapan, NJ; (2); JV Bsktbl; Ftbl; Hon Roll.

BRENNAN, ERIN M; Union Catholic Regional HS; Fanwood, NJ; (3); 4/317; Service Clb; SADD; Nwsp Stf; Var Bsktbl; Var Crs Cntry; French Hon Soc; High Hon Roll; NHS; Var Vllybl; Prtl Schlrshp Union Catholic Rgnl Hs 84-88.

BRENNAN, MARYANNE; Academy Of The Holy Angels; Bergenfield, NJ; (4); 5/152; Church Yth Grp; Mu Alpha Theta; Ski Clb; Spanish Clb; Nwsp Rptr; Yrbk Stf; Rep Stu Cncl; High Hon Roll; Trs NHS; St Schlr; Histry Hnr Soc 86-87; Summa Cum Laude Gold Mdl Ntl Latin Exam 84 & 85; Librl Arts.

BRENNAN, MICHAEL; Scotch Plains Fanwood HS; Fanwood, NJ; (3); Church Yth Grp; VP DECA; FBLA; Key Clb; Spanish Clb; SADD; VP Jr Cls; Stu Cncl; Var Ftbl; Hon Roll; Outstndng Svc Awd 86-87; Syracuse U; Mrktng.

BRENNAN, PATRICIA; Rutherford HS; Rutherford, NJ; (3); Key Clb; NFL; Pep Clb; Chorus; Stage Crew; High Hon Roll; NHS; Ntl Fnlst-Culnry Cmptn 85; Delg-Grls Ctzn Inst 87; Culnry Arts.

BRENNAN, PHILIP; Maple Shade HS; Maple Shade, NJ; (2); 1/170; Spanish Clb; Var Golf; High Hon Roll; Jr NHS; NHS; Prfct Atten Awd; Rotary Awd.

BRENNAN, TIMOTHY; Highstown HS; Hightstown, NJ; (3); Var Am Leg Boys St; Boy Scts; Political Wkr; Varsity Clb; Band; Chorus; Crs Cntry; Trk; Church Yth Grp; Cmnty Wkr; Pres Of Hightstown Interact 86 & 87; Winter Trk, Hnr Roll 87; AD AITARE DEI & Plus XII B S A Awds.

BRENNER, STACY; Livingston HS; Livingston, NJ; (3); 90/420; Var Cheerleading; Var Hon Roll; Bus.

BRESCH, KRISTEN; Riverside HS; Riverside, NJ; (4); 22/68; Am Leg Aux Girls St; SADD; Yrbk Ed-Chief; Sec Soph Cls; Sec Jr Cls; Pres Stu Cncl; Capt Var Fld Hcky; Capt Var Sftbl; Kiwanis Awd; Stu Cncl Schlrshp 87; Tom Nolder Schlrshp 87; Svc To The Schl Awd 87; Glassboro ST Coll; Cmmnctns.

BRESCIA, MICHELLE; Toms River HS East; Toms River, NJ; (4); 14/567; Am Leg Aux Girls St; Intnl Clb; Key Clb; Math Tm; Spanish Clb; SADD; Yrbk Stf; Stu Cncl; Powder Puff Ftbl; Socr; Toms Rvr Educ Assoc Schlrshp 87; Gelzer Pre-Legal Schlrshp 87; Natl Hnr Scty Schlrshp 87; James Madison U; Polt Sci.

BRESLIN, DANIEL P; Holy Cross HS; Moorestown, NJ; (3); 45/404; Am Leg Boys St; VP Church Yth Grp; Model UN; Nwsp Stf; Rep Frsh Cls; VP Soph Cls; VP Jr Cls; VP Sr Cls; JV Bsktbl; JV Crs Cntry; Poli Sci.

BRESLIN, SHANNON; Hanover Park Regional HS; Florham Park, NJ; (3); 27/273; Varsity Clb; Capt Bsktbl; Socr; High Hon Roll; Hon Roll; All Area, All Morris Girls Bsktbll 2nd Team Group 3 - State 86-87; Math.

BRESNAN, EILISH; Cresskill HS; Cresskill, NJ; (3); 48/103; Cmnty Wkr; DECA; Hosp Aide; Band; Color Guard; Mrchg Band; Capt Cheerleading; Var Mgr(s); Trk; Hon Roll; Bus.

BRESNYAN, NICHOLAS J; Pitman HS; Pitman, NJ; (2); Chess Clb; Library Aide; Lit Mag; Hon Roll; Ladies Auxlry VFW Awd-Outstndg Achvt In Currnt Affrs 84-85; James Madison U; Comp Prgmmg.

BRETT, JESSICA; Vineland HS; Vineland, NJ; (4); Art Clb; Drama Clb; French Clb; Socr; Mgr Tennis; Merit Roll 86; Mohowk Vly CC; Grphc Arts.

BREWER, CHRISTINE; De Paul HS; Pompton Lakes, NJ; (3); 5/190; Cmnty Wkr; Science Clb; Nwsp Stf; Yrbk Stf; Var Capt Cheerleading; Var Trk; High Hon Roll; Hon Roll; NHS; Ntl Merit SF.

BREWER, RICHARD; West Windsor Plainsboro HS; Princeton, NJ; (3); Boy Scts; German Clb; Red Cross Aide; Lit Mag; Var Swmmng; High Hon Roll; Hon Roll; Ntl Merit SF; Outstndg German Stu Awd 87; Princeton; Asian Stds.

BREWSTER, MATTHEW J; Bloomfield SR HS; Bloomfield, NJ; (3); VP Church Yth Grp; Chorus; Church Choir; School Musical; Nwsp Stf; Bsktbl; Ftbl; Hon Roll; Prfct Atten Awd; Pres Sr Cls; 1st Blk Yng Mn Pres SR Cls 87-88; Law.

BREY, LAUREN; Glen Ridge HS; Glen Ridge, NJ; (3); 33/108; Key Clb; Latin Clb; Chorus; Ed Nwsp Stf; Sec Jr Cls; Sec Stu Cncl; JV Var Cheerleading; Mgr(s); JV Trk; High Hon Roll; Peer Cnslg 86-88; AP Engl & Hstry 86-88; Humnties.

BRICE, TAMEKA; Woodstown HS; Bridgeton, NJ; (2); Var Bsktbl; JV Sftbl; JV Vllybl; Hon Roll; Prfct Atten Awd.

BRICE, TEA; Cumberland Regional HS; Bridgeton, NJ; (3); Church Yth Grp; JCL; Trk; Hon Roll; Oakwood Coll; Med Tech.

BRICENO, MARGARET; Roselle Catholic HS; Roselle, NJ; (4); 15/190; French Clb; Stage Crew; Yrbk Stf; Var Cheerleading; Im Gym; Var Mgr(s); Var Socr; Var Sftbl; Var Trk; Im Vllybl; Mens Assn Schlrshp, & Mst Schl Sprt Awd 87; Overall Sprt Grl Wnnr ACT Cheerng Cmp 86; Memphis ST U; Dirctng.

BRICKER, PHILIP; Burlington City HS; Edgewater Pk, NJ; (3); Crs Cntry; Ftbl; Wrstlng; EPAA Awd 84; Architect.

BRICKNER, KIM; Monsignor Donovan HS; Jackson, NJ; (3); 51/245; Church Yth Grp; Cmnty Wkr; GAA; SADD; Varsity Clb; Var Capt Bsktbl; Var Crs Cntry; Var Socr; High Hon Roll; NHS.

BRIDGES III, GEORGE W; Edgewood SR HS; Sicklerville, NJ; (2); Boy Scts; Varsity Clb; Ftbl; Golf; Hon Roll; Eagle Sct 87; Med.

BRIGGS, ANTHONY; Highland Regional HS; Sicklerville, NJ; (4); French Clb; Pres Band; Concert Band; Drm Mjr(t); Jazz Band; Mrchg Band; Yrbk Ed-Chief; Stu Cncl; Ntl Merit Ltr; Bus Mgmt.

BRIGHAM, BARBARA; Vineland HS; Vineland, NJ; (2); 1/925; Drama Clb; Key Clb; Spanish Clb; Chorus; High Hon Roll; Prfct Atten Awd.

BRIGHT, ROGER; Collingswood SR HS; Collingswood, NJ; (2); Boy Scts.

BRIGLIA, DAVID; Phillipsburg HS; Phillipsburg, NJ; (3); Model UN; Nwsp Stf; High Hon Roll; NHS; Pre Med.

BRIGNOLA, GEOFFREY; Shore Regional HS; Oceanport, NJ; (3); Spanish Clb; Pres Frsh Cls; Pres Soph Cls; Var JV Gym; Var JV Bsktbl; Var JV Socr; High Hon Roll; NHS; Cngressnl Awd Bronze 86; Intl Thesbns 87; Bus.

BRILL, KELLIE; Lacey Township HS; Forked River, NJ; (2); 17/317; Pep Clb; Variety Show; Off Soph Cls; Fld Hcky; Golf; Trk; Hon Roll; Everyday Hero Hist Clss 87; Educ.

BRINGHURST, MARK; Victory Christian HS; Berlin, NJ; (2); Church Yth Grp; Pres Frsh Cls; Hon Roll; Garden ST Assn Of Christian Schls ST Spelling Bee 1st Pl 86.

BRINK, INGRID; Middletown HS South; Locust, NJ; (3); Library Aide; Stage Crew; Nwsp Rptr; Nwsp Stf; Lit Mag; Im Fld Hcky; High Hon Roll; Hon Roll; Rutgers U; Engl.

BRINKERHOFF, STEPHEN G; Midland Park HS; Midland Park, NJ; (4); 6/130; Am Leg Boys St; Chess Clb; Math Clb; Science Clb; Ftbl; Wrstlng; NHS; Garden ST Schlr 86-87.

BRINKLEY, DE NARD; Hillside HS; Hillside, NJ; (4); 6/198; Am Leg Boys St; Boys Clb Am; Nwsp Stf; Yrbk Stf; Sr Cls; Gov Hon Prg Awd; Hon Roll; NHS; Ntl Merit Ltr; GA Tech; Elect Engrng.

BRINSON, REGINALD; Essex Catholic Boys HS; East Orange, NJ; (3); Boy Scts; Church Yth Grp; Church Choir; Nwsp Stf; Bsktbl; Gym; Powder Puff Ftbl; Swmmng; Hon Roll; Prfct Atten Awd; Georgetown U; Law.

BRINTZINGHOFFER, TAMMY; Holy Cross HS; Burlington, NJ; (4); 104/369; Camera Clb; Computer Clb; Drama Clb; Ski Clb; Spanish Clb; Band; Mrchg Band; School Musical; School Play; Stage Crew; Drama Awd; Spirt Awd; Svc & Ctznshp; Cabrine Coll; Bus.

BRISBON, AARON TYRONE; Paterson Catholic Regional HS; Paterson, NJ; (3); 34/98; Boys Clb Am; JV Bsktbl; Var Ftbl; Im Wt Lftg.

BRISTOW, AL C; Haddon Township HS; Westmont, NJ; (3); Am Leg Boys St; Varsity Clb; Var Gym; High Hon Roll; NHS; South Jersey Pommel Horse 3rd Tm 86.

BRITT, JO ANNE; Bishop Ahr-St Thomas HS; Iselin, NJ; (3); Intnl Clb; Ski Clb; SADD; School Play; Stage Crew; Variety Show; Yrbk Stf; Pres Stu Cncl; JV Socr; Hon Roll; Bus.

BRITTIN, BETH; Gloucester County Christian HS; Williamstown, NJ; (3); Church Yth Grp; Girl Scts; Church Choir; Nwsp Stf; Yrbk Stf; Var JV Bsktbl; Var L Sftbl; Trk; Var L Vllybl; Hon Roll; Sftbl Mst Home Run Awd 85; All Star Team Awd 85; Awana Schlrshp Camp Awd 85; Elem Educ.

BROADUS, SHARONDA; Abraham Clark HS; Roselle, NJ; (3); Lit Mag; Stu Cncl; Cheerleading; High Hon Roll; Hon Roll; NHS; KOFC Essy Awd 1st Pl 83; Duke U; Psych.

BROADWELL, LISA; Westfield SR HS; Westfield, NJ; (4); 3/450; Cmnty Wkr; VP French Clb; Model UN; Capt L Crs Cntry; Capt L Trk; French Hon Soc; NHS; Ntl Merit Ltr; Pres Schlr; Spanish NHS; FLE-NJ Awd For Outstndng Achiev In Frgn Lang Stu, NJ Schlr-Athlt Awd, Natl Hnr Scty Schlrshp 87; U Of PA; Frnch.

BROBERG, NOELLE; Howell HS; Howell, NJ; (2); 21/450; FBLA; German Clb; Color Guard; Stage Crew; Var Tennis; Math.

BROCKLEBANK, FAITH JOY; Toms River HS North; Toms River, NJ; (3); 23/467; German Clb; SADD; Orch; Yrbk Stf; Rep Soph Cls; High Hon Roll; Hon Roll; NHS; Acdmc Let 85; Acdmc Pin 86 & 87; Penn ST U; Geology.

BROCKLEHURST, JEANNINE M; Sterling HS; Somerdale, NJ; (4); 19/238; Drama Clb; Spanish Clb; Acpl Chr; Chorus; School Musical; School Play; Stage Crew; Variety Show; Lit Mag; High Hon Roll; Glassboro ST Coll; Drma.

BROCKMAN, KELLIE; Franklin HS; Franklin Pk, NJ; (3); Ski Clb; Band; Mrchg Band; School Musical; Bowling; Sftbl; High Hon Roll; Hon Roll.

BRODBECK, SUSAN C; Spotswood HS; Spotswood, NJ; (2); Yrbk Stf; Hon Roll; Photo Jrnlst.

BRODE, TERESA ANN; Vineland HS; Vineland, NJ; (4); 79/736; Am Leg Aux Girls St; Dance Clb; 4-H; Key Clb; Political Wkr; Spanish Clb; Stu Cncl; DAR Awd; Hon Roll; Rotary Awd; Cumberland Ctys Jr Mis 87; HOBY Amb 85; St Elizabeth; Hist.

BRODIE, ERIC; Ocean Township HS; Wayside, NJ; (3); 14/350; Capt Debate Tm; NFL; Speech Tm; Yrbk Bus Mgr; Var Crs Cntry; JV Tennis; Gov Hon Prg Awd; NHS; Ntl Merit Ltr; 1st Pl Monmouth JR Sci Sympsm 87; 1st Pl NJ JR Sci Acad 86; Hnry Membrshp Amer Assn Advcmt & Sci 87; Bus.

BRODIE, PAMELA; Indian Hills HS; Oakland, NJ; (3); 49/306; Boy Scts; Var L Gym; High Hon Roll; Spnsh PTO Awd 86; Bergen Cnty Gymnstcs Hnrb Mntn, Cnty Invttnl Gymnstcs Mt 1st Pl & All-Arnd 86-87; Marine Law.

BRODY, CARL E; New Milford HS; New Milford, NJ; (4); 7/136; Am Leg Boys St; Ski Clb; Drm & Bgl; Jazz Band; Orch; Sec Stu Cncl; Var Socr; Var Capt Trk; French Hon Soc; VP NHS; All-St Sccr Hnrbl Men 3rd Team All-Cnty 86-87; Leag Champ Long Jump Mile Relay 87; Top 10 Awd; U Of VT.

BRODZIAK, MICHAEL; St Marys HS; Sayreville, NJ; (4); 20/135; Church Yth Grp; Library Aide; Quiz Bowl; Spanish Clb; Bsktbl; Crs Cntry; Trk; High Hon Roll; Hon Roll; Spanish NHS; CYO Bsktbl 83-87; Bst Dfnsv Plyr 83-87; Rider Coll; Mrktng.

BROGAN, LAUREN; Hanover Park HS; Florham Park, NJ; (3); 25/271; Church Yth Grp; Cmnty Wkr; Rep Jr Cls; Rep Sr Cls; Sec Stu Cncl; JV Cheerleading; Capt Twrlr; Hon Roll; NHS.

BROGLE, STACYANN; Hamilton West HS; Trenton, NJ; (4); 5/309; Key Clb; Chorus; School Musical; Variety Show; Yrbk Stf; Stu Cncl; High Hon Roll; Hon Roll; Sec NHS; Rotary Awd; Cngrssnl Tchr Schlrshp 87-88; Hmltn Twsh Admin & Supv Schlrshp 87-88; Pres Acad Ftns Awd 87; Trenton ST Coll; Math Ed.

BROLLESY, HANY SAYED; Cedar Ridge HS; Matawan, NJ; (4); 4/371; Hosp Aide; Ski Clb; Rep Frsh Cls; Rep Stu Cncl; JV Bsktbl; French Hon Soc; Jr NHS; NHS; St Schlr; Garden ST Distngshd Schlr 86-87; PSAT-NMSQT Cmmnd Schlr 86-87; Rutgers U.

BROMLEY, STEVEN M; Haddonfield Memorial HS; Haddonfield, NJ; (3); Am Leg Boys St; Intnl Clb; Rep Stu Cncl; Im JV Bsktbl; Var Capt Golf; Hon Roll; NHS; Rotary Awd; UMDNJ Schlrs Progrm 88; Pre-Med.

BROOKS, APRIL L; Ewing HS; West Trenton, NJ; (4); 53/300; Sec Intnl Clb; Teachers Aide; Drill Tm; Rep Soph Cls; Rep Jr Cls; Rep Sr Cls; Stat Wrstlng; Ntl Merit SF; Rutgers U Deans Summr Schlr 86; Rep Princeton Model Congress 86; Wellesley Coll; Engl Tchr.

BROOKS, CHRISTY; Howell HS; Howell, NJ; (3); Drama Clb; Mrchg Band; School Musical; Rep Jr Cls; Rep Stu Cncl; NHS; Intnl Clb; NFL; SADD; Temple Yth Grp; Art.

BROOKS JR, JAMES TIMOTHY; Trenton Central HS; Trenton, NJ; (3); Boy Scts; Science Clb; Band; Concert Band; Drill Tm; Mrchg Band; Orch; Im Bsbl; Im Ftbl; Im Socr; VA ST U.

BROOKS, ONEIKA; Dwight Morrow HS; Englewood, NJ; (4); VP AFS; Camera Clb; Girl Scts; Pres JA; Sec Latin Clb; NAACP; Pep Clb; Church Choir; Trk; High Hon Roll; Hunter Coll; Psych.

BROOKS, PAULETTE; Clifford J Scott HS; East Orange, NJ; (3); Dance Clb; Drama Clb; Capt Color Guard; Nwsp Rptr; Trk; Hon Roll; Bst Female Model 87; Hnrs Awd Math 86-87; LTD Modelg Scholar 85-86; NYU; Brdcstg.

BROOKS, SHIRNETT; Dwight Morrow HS; Englewood, NJ; (3); 4/312; Church Yth Grp; Sec FBLA; Church Choir; Ed Nwsp Stf; Var Vllybl; Cit Awd; Gov Hon Prg Awd; High Hon Roll; NHS; Prfct Atten Awd; Pre-Med.

BROPHY, KELLY; Gloucester Catholic HS; Gloucester, NJ; (3); School Musical; Nwsp Ed-Chief; Nwsp Rptr; Rep Soph Cls; Rep Jr Cls; Pres Sr Cls; Stu Cncl; JV Bsktbl; Var Fld Hcky; Stu Mnth; Comm.

BROSEN, ANITA; Middlesex HS; Middlesex, NJ; (4); 49/157; Debate Tm; Off French Clb; SADD; Sec Band; Mrchg Band; Elks Awd; Hon Roll; Vrsty Lttr Mrchng & Cncrt Bands; Bllt 74-87; YEP 87; Cedar Crest Coll; Psychlgy.

BROSONSKI, DAWN; Pompton Lakes HS; Pompton Lakes, NJ; (4); 25/135; Math Clb; Q&S; Band; Concert Band; Mrchg Band; Yrbk Stf; Lit Mag; High Hon Roll; Hon Roll; Spanish Clb; Contentl Math League Awd; Wrtng.

BROSSE, MICHAEL A; S Brunswick HS; Monmouth Junction, NJ; (4); 2/250; Math Tm; Mu Alpha Theta; Temple Yth Grp; Var Tennis; Hon Roll; NHS; Ntl Merit Ltr; Sal; Spanish NHS; Rep Sr Cls.

BROSSOIE, NICOLE; Villa Victoria Acad; Trenton, NJ; (3); 5/22; Am Leg Aux Girls St; Cmnty Wkr; SADD; Chorus; School Musical; Lit Mag; VP Soph Cls; Sec Jr Cls; Socr; Trk; 2nd Bst-Spnsh 87; Mst Imprvd-Hist 87; Mst Imprvd-Chem 87; Cmmnctns.

BROSTROM, ERIKA; Glen Rock JR-SR HS; Glen Rock, NJ; (3); Art Clb; Cmnty Wkr; Dance Clb; DECA; Pep Clb; Spanish Clb; Teachers Aide; Varsity Clb; School Play; Variety Show; Dance Awd 85; Sales Awds 86-87; DECA Comp Medals 87; Track Medals 87; Art Thrpy.

BROUSSARD, ELIZABETH; Dwight-Englewood Schl; Ridgewood, NJ; (3); Cmnty Wkr; Spanish Clb; Yrbk Stf; Lit Mag; JV Var Sftbl; Hon Roll; Amnsty Intl Essay Cont 1st Pl Wnnr NJ 87; Natl Spnsh Exam 87; Engl.

BROWER, DAWN; Toms River H S East; Toms River, NJ; (3); 39/509; FBLA; Office Aide; Hon Roll; NHS; 6th Pl FBLA Rgnl Cmptn 87; Ocean Cnty Coll; Acctng.

BROWER, PAM; Midland Park HS; Midland Park, NJ; (4); 30/130; Church Yth Grp; DECA; Pep Clb; Varsity Clb; Band; Chorus; JV Var Cheerleading; Stat Wrstlng; High Hon Roll; Hon Roll; Kean Coll; Physcl Thrpy.

BROWN, ALIA; Edgewood SR HS; Sicklerville, NJ; (3); Drama Clb; Office Aide; VP Spanish Clb; Mrchg Band; School Play; Nwsp Rptr; Cheerleading; High Hon Roll; Hon Roll; Jr NHS; Ath Cert 85; Cert Apprctn 87; Pre Med.

BROWN, ARLISHA; Eastside HS; Paterson, NJ; (3); FBLA; JA; Chorus; Ldrshp Awd 87; Kathanne Gibbs; Bus Exec.

BROWN, CHERYL; Pitman HS; Pitman, NJ; (4); Church Yth Grp; Dance Clb; Band; Yrbk Stf; JV Bsktbl; JV Cheerleading; Var Mgr(s); Var Pom Pon; Var Tennis; Var Trk; Gloucester Cnty Coll; Bus.

BROWN, CLINT; Pennsville Memorial HS; Pennsville, NJ; (3); 53/225; Ski Clb; Spanish Clb; Concert Band; Socr; Hon Roll; Psych.

BROWN, CONNIE; Paulsboro HS; Paulsboro, NJ; (3); Cmnty Wkr; Computer Clb; VICA; Chorus; Yrbk Phtg; Off Jr Cls; Socr; Cit Awd; Secy.

BROWN, DANA; Maple Shade HS; Maple Shade, NJ; (2); Church Yth Grp; FBLA; Key Clb; Spanish Clb; Socr; Bus Admin.

BROWN, DANIEL; St John Vianney HS; Colts Neck, NJ; (2); Var Wrstlng.

BROWN, DAVID W; Bayonne HS; Bayonne, NJ; (3); Am Leg Boys St; Church Yth Grp; Rep Frsh Cls; Trs Soph Cls; Trs Jr Cls; Off Sr Cls; Rep Stu Cncl; Var Bsbl; Var Crs Cntry; Var Capt Ice Hcky; Sports Med.

BROWN, DENISE; Camden Catholic HS; Camden, NJ; (3); French Clb; FTA; Science Clb; Spanish Clb; Stage Crew; JV Sftbl; Hon Roll; Cert For Highest Avg-Spnsh & Frnch 85-86 & 85-87; Wheelock Coll; Chld Life Spclst.

BROWN, DIANE; Spotswood HS; Spotswood, NJ; (3); DECA; Drama Clb; Intnl Clb; School Musical; VP Sr Cls; Var Sftbl; Spanish NHS; NY U; Drama.

BROWN, FRED; Salem HS; Salem, NJ; (2); VP Art Clb; Chess Clb; Computer Clb; Library Aide; Pep Clb; Spanish Clb; SADD; Rep Stu Cncl; Bsbl; Bsktbl; MI ST; Comp Sci.

BROWN, JEN; Lakeland Reg HS; Ringwood, NJ; (4); 33/335; VP Acpl Chr; VP Madrigals; High Hon Roll; Hon Roll; NHS; Vrsty Capt Fncng Tm & Dist Chmps 86-87; Mt Holyoke Coll; Bio.

BROWN, JENE M; Eastside HS; Paterson, NJ; (2); Teachers Aide; Rep Soph Cls; JV Bsktbl; JV Crs Cntry; Var Trk; Cert Of Achvt-Engl I 85-86; Hrn-Passing HSPT 85-86; Mdcl Doc.

BROWN, JILL; Orange HS; Orange, NJ; (4); 6/147; High Hon Roll; Hon Roll; NHS; Montclair ST Coll; Psych.

BROWN, JILL P; Vineland HS; Vineland, NJ; (4); 15/736; Church Yth Grp; Sec French Clb; Key Clb; Varsity Clb; School Play; Var Capt Fld Hcky; French Hon Soc; High Hon Roll; NHS; Garden St Dstngshd Schlr 87-88.

BROWN, JOHN J; Burlington County Vo Tech HS; Edgewater Pk, NJ; (2); VICA; Var Bsktbl; Mgr(s); JV Socr; Prfct Atten Awd; Prfct Atten 85-87; VICA Awd 86-87; Stu Guides 86-87; Treton ST; Grphc Arts.

BROWN, JOLANDA; Vineland SR HS; Vineland, NJ; (3); JV Bsktbl; Arch.

BROWN, JULIE; Kings Christian HS; Delran, NJ; (2); Chorus; Yrbk Stf; Rep Soph Cls; High Hon Roll; Architect.

BROWN, KATHLEEN ANN; Pompton Lakes HS; Pompton Lakes, NJ; (1); Church Yth Grp; Girl Scts; Band; Church Choir; Color Guard; Mrchg Band; Bsktbl.

BROWN, KATHRYN; St John Vianney HS; Colts Neck, NJ; (3); Pres VP Intnl Clb; Library Aide; SADD; Chorus; Capt Flag Corp; School Play; Stage Crew; Yrbk Stf; Hon Roll; NHS; Gold & White Awd Wth Merit, Mrchng Unit Awd 85-87; Scl Sci.

BROWN, KATRINA; James J Ferris HS; Jersey City, NJ; (2); Church Yth Grp; Teachers Aide; Chorus; Nwsp Stf; Lit Mag; Mgr Bsbl; Mgr Bsktbl; Trk; Prfct Atten Awd; Howard U; Child Psychlgst.

BROWN, KIMBERLY; Gloucester Catholic HS; Woodbury, NJ; (3); Church Yth Grp; Computer Clb; French Clb; JA; School Play; Nwsp Stf; Yrbk Stf; Mgr(s); Hon Roll; Dance Clb; Prom Queen 87; Phys Fitness Test 86.

BROWN, LATRINA D; Neptune SR HS; Neptune, NJ; (2); Church Yth Grp; Latin Clb; Mgr Bsktbl; Mgr Ftbl; Mgr(s); Score Keeper; Vllybl; Secr.

BROWN, LAURA; Paul VI HS; Sewell, NJ; (4); 55/504; Math Clb; SADD; Sftbl; Hon Roll; Jr NHS; NHS; St Josephs Univ; Bus.

BROWN, LAWRENCE; John F Kennedy HS; Paterson, NJ; (4); 18/410; Am Leg Boys St; ROTC; Band; Drill Tm; Crs Cntry; Trk; Hon Roll; Engrng.

BROWN, LORETTA; Roselle Catholic HS; Roselle, NJ; (4); Church Yth Grp; GAA; Teachers Aide; JV Bowling; Var Socr; Im Vllybl; Hon Roll; NHS; Ntl Bus Hnr Soc 87; Actg Prfcncy 87; Un Co Coll; Scotch Plns; Acctg.

BROWN, MARC; Lower Cape May Regional HS; Cape May, NJ; (3); Church Yth Grp; Service Clb; Rep Stu Cncl; Var Ftbl; Var Tennis; Var Wrstlng; Hon Roll; 3rd Pl Dist 32 Wrstlng Champs 85-86; Bus.

BROWN, MARLO; St Mary HS; Jersey City, NJ; (3); Chorus; School Play; Nwsp Stf; Trs Jr Cls; Im Vllybl; High Hon Roll; NHS; Rotary Awd; Marian Awd 84; Chrstn Srv 86; Gnrl Excel Awd 87; Stevens Inst Of Tech; Sys Plnng.

BROWN, MAUREEN; Madison Central HS; Old Bridge, NJ; (3); 20/360; French Clb; Band; Concert Band; Mrchg Band; Stu Cncl; JV Capt Bsktbl; Gov Hon Prg Awd; High Hon Roll; Hon Roll; NHS; Governors Schl 86-87; Psych.

BROWN, MELANIE L; Columbia HS; Maplewood, NJ; (4); Church Yth Grp; Dance Clb; French Clb; Church Choir; Yrbk Phtg; Rep Stu Cncl; Var L Cheerleading; Rep Jr Cls; Rep Sr Cls; JV Trk; NAACP Cert Of Outstndng Acad Achvmnt 83; A T & T Engrnr Schlrshp Pgm 87; Certifctmerit Natl Frnce 86; Duke U; Engnrng.

BROWN, MICHAEL R; Eastside HS; Paterson, NJ; (2); Camera Clb; Drama Clb; FBLA; SADD; Yrbk Sprt Ed; Yrbk Stf; Bsbl; Bsktbl; JV Ftbl; Hon Roll; Acdmc Achvt 85; Super Achvt Excllnc HSPI 86; Gold Crd Hnr Rl 87; Hstry.

BROWN, RENATA; Weequahic HS; Irvington, NJ; (4); 6/350; Computer Clb; Capt Debate Tm; Model UN; Lit Mag; Stu Cncl; Cit Awd; NHS; Library Aide; Nwsp Rptr; Schlstc Mdlln 83; Ortrcl Mdlln 86; Nelson Mandella Frdm Awd 86; Drew U; Pol Sci.

BROWN, RICHARD; Monsignor Donovan HS; Jackson, NJ; (4); Ski Clb; Band; Jazz Band; Variety Show; Hon Roll; Ocean County Coll; Chem.

BROWN, ROBERT; Baptist HS; Medford, NJ; (4); 3/47; Chess Clb; Church Yth Grp; Var L Socr; Hon Roll; NHS; Grdn ST Dstngshd Schlr 87-88; Schl Sci Awd 85-86; Schl Hnr Soc 85-87; Acadmc All Star 86; Cvl Engrng.

BROWN, ROBERT; Essex Catholic Boys HS; Newark, NJ; (3); Church Yth Grp; Y-Teens; Acpl Chr; Chorus; Church Choir; Nwsp Stf; Yrbk Stf; Lit Mag; High Hon Roll; Hon Roll; Howard U; Law.

BROWN, SANDRA; Clifford J Scott HS; E Orange, NJ; (4); 21/251; Church Yth Grp; Quiz Bowl; Spanish Clb; Chorus; Church Choir; School Musical; Yrbk Stf; Lit Mag; Stu Cncl; Sec NHS; Dept Hgh Hnrs Spnsh 86; Glorious Church Of God In Christ-NE Diocese-Yng Person Of Yr 85 & 86; Rutgers U; Corp Law.

BROWN, SARA; Holy Spirit HS; Atlantic City, NJ; (4); 34/363; Dance Clb; French Clb; Yrbk Rptr; Yrbk Stf; Lit Mag; Hon Roll; NHS; Bus Adm.

BROWN, SEAN; Middletown HS South; Middletown, NJ; (3); Boy Scts; Drama Clb; Hosp Aide; Variety Show; Var L Socr; Var L Swmmng; Var Tennis; Hon Roll; MVP Sccr 86; VP Med Explorers 87; Rutgers; Med.

BROWN, SHERRI; High Point Regional HS; Sussex, NJ; (3); Spanish Clb; JV Bsktbl; JV Fld Hcky; Hon Roll; William Paterson Coll; Nrsng.

BROWN, STEFANIE; Paul VI HS; Magnolia, NJ; (4); 9/511; Church Yth Grp; Math Clb; Spanish Clb; SADD; School Play; Yrbk Stf; Co-Capt L Pom Pon; High Hon Roll; Hon Roll; NHS; Ped Surgn.

BROWN, SUZI; Vernon Township HS; Vernon, NJ; (3); Library Aide; Variety Show; Yrbk Stf; Lit Mag; Cheerleading; Hon Roll; Hlpd Spcl Olympcs 86; Fshn Show 85; Psych.

BROWN, TIMOTHY; Egg Harbor Twp HS; Egg Harbor Twp, NJ; (3); 21/376; Art Clb; 4-H; Ski Clb; Var Ftbl; JV Trk; 4-H Awd.

BROWN, TYESE; Essex Catholic Girls HS; S Orange, NJ; (3); Art Clb; Drama Clb; School Play; Variety Show; Hon Roll; NHS; Outstndng Musician Yr Awd Newark Cmnty Schl/Arts 85-87; Instr, Exprnc, Expsrs Gftd/Tlntd Std Awd 84; Howard U; Music Compstn.

BROWNA, MICHELE; Gateway Regional HS; Woodbury Hts, NJ; (4); 3/201; French Clb; Key Clb; Latin Clb; Science Clb; Yrbk Ed-Chief; JV Fld Hcky; Var Swmmng; French Hon Soc; NHS; NJ Gvrnrs Schl Scis Schlr 86; U Of PA; Pre Med.

BROWNE, SHARANDA; Immaculate Conception HS; Orange, NJ; (3); Church Yth Grp; Girl Scts; Church Choir; Cheerleading; Trk; Hon Roll; Bus Admin.

BROWNE, YEWANDE; Immaculate Conception HS; Orange, NJ; (3); Church Yth Grp; Girl Scts; Science Clb; Church Choir; Drill Tm; Stat Mgr(s); Score Keeper; Trk; NJ Piano Music Tchr Awd 76-87; Music Ed Assn Awd; Psych.

BROWNING, CATHERINE; West Windsor-Plainsboro HS; Princeton Junct, NJ; (3); Hosp Aide; Acpl Chr; School Play; Lit Mag; NHS; Model UN; Chorus; School Musical; Rep Frsh Cls; High Hon Roll; 600 Hr Svc Awd Pin-Med Ctr Princeton 87; Hosp Cmmndtn Excptnl Svc 86; Hosp Vlntr; Biochem Rsch.

BROWNING, KATHLEEN E; Academy Of The Holy Angels; New Milford, NJ; (3); Pres Chess Clb; Pres Computer Clb; 4-H; Math Tm; Mu Alpha Theta; Spanish Clb; Nwsp Stf; Lit Mag; 4-H Awd; Hon Roll.

BROZOSKI, BRENDA; Hunterdon Central HS; White House Sta, NJ; (2); 182/478; Radio Clb; Spanish Clb; Band; Stage Crew; Symp Band; Rep Frsh Cls; Rep Soph Cls; Rep Stu Cncl.

BROZYNA, ELIZABETH A; Toms River High School South; Toms River, NJ; (4); 3/316; Mrchg Band; Symp Band; High Hon Roll; Masonic Awd; VP NHS; Ntl Merit Ltr; St Schlr; Cit Awd; Teagle Fndtn Schlrshp 87; Oberlin Coll; Psych.

BRUBAKER, HARRY; Egg Harbor Twp HS; Mays Landing, NJ; (3); 21/339; Ski Clb; Bsbl; Var Ftbl; Trk; Wt Lftg; Hon Roll; Vrsty Schlr Grd 9-11; Achvt Acad Awds; Med Doc.

BRUBAKER, MICHELE; Egg Harbor Township HS; Mays Landing, NJ; (4); #21 In Class; French Clb; German Clb; Ski Clb; Spanish Clb; Trs Frsh Cls; Trs Soph Cls; Var Fld Hcky; Var Sftbl; Vrsty Schlr, All Acad Awd, Natl Eng Merit Awds 87; Vrsty Schlr 84-86; NY U; Intl Relat.

BRUCE, DANA; Middletown HS South; Middletown, NJ; (3); Model UN; Teachers Aide; Yrbk Stf; Lit Mag; Jr Cls; Var Fld Hcky; Var Lcrss; Var Trk; Hon Roll; Reiss Mem Awd; Lacrosse Bst Dfns Awd; Hcky Sprtsmnshp; Ntl Ltn Exm Cum Laude; Anml Bhvr.

BRUDER, BRYAN; J P Stevens HS; Edison, NJ; (3); Science Clb; Ski Clb; Temple Yth Grp; Band; School Play; Stage Crew; Trk; Phrmcy.

BRUEN, CHARLES J; Paramus Catholic Boys HS; Lodi, NJ; (3); 18/179; Am Leg Boys St; Computer Clb; Band; Drm & Bgl; Mrchg Band; Variety Show; Crs Cntry; Swmmng; Wrstlng; Hon Roll; Mltry Pilot.

BRUGAL, MAGGIN; Emerson HS; Union City, NJ; (4); 37/280; French Clb; Spanish Clb; Chorus; Yrbk Stf; Rep Frsh Cls; Rep Soph Cls; JV Bsktbl; JV Crs Cntry; Trk; Wt Lftg; Seton Hall U; Law.

BRUGMANS, TODD; Watchung Hills Reg HS; Warren, NJ; (3); Boy Scts; Intnl Clb; Chorus; BSA Egl Sct 86; Ordr De Molay Mstr Cnclr 87; Med.

BRUNGART, LAURA; Princeton HS; Princeton, NJ; (4); Church Yth Grp; Cmnty Wkr; Latin Clb; Mrchg Band; Rep Stu Cncl; Tennis; Vllybl; Gov Hon Prg Awd; Princeton Rgnl Schlrshp Fnd 87; Mary WA Coll.

BRUNO, CHRISTINA MARIE; Holy Spirit HS; Northfield, NJ; (4); 6/363; Dance Clb; Hosp Aide; Yrbk Stf; High Hon Roll; NHS; Silver Mdl Ntl Latin Exam 85; Englsh & Histry Awd 85; St Elizabeths; Pre-Med.

BRUNO, CHRISTY; Ramado HS; Franklin Lakes, NJ; (2); AFS; Camera Clb; Church Yth Grp; Exploring; French Clb; Trk; Hon Roll; Engrng.

BRUNO, ROBERT; Passaic County Tech; Ringwood, NJ; (4); 2/365; Dance Clb; VP VICA; VP Sr Cls; Hon Roll; NHS; St Schlr; NJIT; Elec Engrng.

BRUNOZZI, DOMINICK; Buena Regional HS; Vineland, NJ; (3); #11 In Class; Ski Clb; High Hon Roll; Hon Roll; Natl Sci Merit Awd 87; CPA.

BRUNSKI, AMY; Red Bank Regional HS; Shrewsbury, NJ; (3); 5/237; Band; Church Choir; Concert Band; Mrchg Band; Symp Band; High Hon Roll; NHS; Ntl Merit Ltr; Spanish NHS; Bst Spnsh Stu Schl 87.

BRUNSON, NIYA; University HS; Newark, NJ; (2); Church Yth Grp; Debate Tm; Drama Clb; Girl Scts; Leo Clb; Science Clb; Spanish Clb; Chorus; Church Choir; JV Trk; Dukes U; Med.

BRUNSON, SHERON; Toms River HS North; Toms River, NJ; (3); #74 In Class; Church Yth Grp; Exploring; Church Choir; Concert Band; Drm Mjr(t); Mrchg Band; JV Capt Bsktbl; High Hon Roll; Hon Roll; Acad Lttr 86-87; Med.

BRUSEO, PETE; Dover HS; Mine Hill, NJ; (3); Church Yth Grp; FCA; JV Bsbl; JV Var Ftbl; Wt Lftg; Carpenter.

BRUTHER, CHRIS; Manasquan HS; Brielle, NJ; (3); Church Yth Grp; Debate Tm; English Clb; FBLA; Spanish Clb; Var Bsbl; Var Bsktbl; Hon Roll.

BRUZAITIS, ERIC MASON; Manchester Township HS; Toms River, NJ; (4); Am Leg Boys St; French Clb; Socr; Hon Roll; Pres Drama Clb; School Play; Variety Show; Ed Nwsp Ed-Chief; Pres Stu Cncl; Corvinus Schlrshp 87; Journ Awd 87; Drama Awd 87; Seton Hall U; Engl Teacher.

BRYANT, CLAUDIUS L; Northern Burlington County HS; Mcguire Afb, NJ; (3); Am Leg Boys St; ROTC; Rep Stu Cncl; JV Bsktbl; Corp Lawyer.

BRYANT, DAWN; Vineland HS; Vineland, NJ; (2); Bus.

BRYANT, DEBBIE; Manalapan HS; Englishtown, NJ; (4); 95/417; Sec Church Yth Grp; Hosp Aide; Kiwanis Awd; Fairleigh Dickinson U; Bus Admn.

BRYANT, GUS; Essex Catholic Boys HS; Newark, NJ; (3); Church Yth Grp; JA; Var Crs Cntry; Var Trk; Variety Show; Im Bsbl; Im Bsktbl; Coach Actv; Score Keeper; Timer; Mst Vlubl Rnnr 84-85; Mst Vlubl Relay 86-87; Mst Vlubl Rnnr Of Yr 86-87; Georgetown; Law.

BRYANT, KELLIEANN; St John Vianney HS; Marlboro, NJ; (3); 22/264; Trs Church Yth Grp; Intnl Clb; Ed Yrbk Bus Mgr; Rep Jr Cls; JV Capt Socr; High Hon Roll; Hon Roll; NHS; Service Clb; Powder Puff Ftbl; Gold & White Awd 86-87; Pres Physical Ftnss Awd 86-87; Pltcl Sci.

BRYANT, MELISSA; Triton Regional HS; Runnemede, NJ; (3); 21/405; Latin Clb; Service Clb; Rep Jr Cls; Stat Bsktbl; JV Fld Hcky; Im Powder Puff Ftbl; Var L Trk; Hon Roll; NHS; Astronaut.

BRYANT, YOLANDA; Passaic County Tech-Voc HS; Passaic, NJ; (3); Computer Clb; Chorus 82-84; Hon Roll 84; Dance Clb 81-83.

BRYSON, DAWN; Buena Regional HS; Collings Lakes, NJ; (3); Dance Clb; Girl Scts; Ski Clb; SADD; Yrbk Stf; JV Cheerleading; Bus Admn.

BRZOSKO, JAN R; Hudson Catholic HS; Jersey City, NJ; (4); 8/175; Math Clb; Hon Roll; NHS; Westinghouse Sci Talent Srch 87; Hnrb Mntn NJ JR Acad Sci 87; 1st Pl Indvdl Awd Physics 87; Lawrence U; Laser Physics.

BRZOZOWSKA, BEATA; Lakeland Regional HS; Haskell, NJ; (4); 12/365; Math Tm; Ski Clb; Teachers Aide; Trs Soph Cls; Off Jr Cls; Off Sr Cls; Stu Cncl; Var Cheerleading; High Hon Roll; Sec NHS; Wanaque Womans Clb Nursing Schlrshp 87; U Vermont; Bio Sci.

BRZOZOWSKI, KEN; South River HS; S River, NJ; (4); 21/150; Am Leg Boys St; Computer Clb; French Clb; Math Clb; Varsity Clb; Var L Bsbl; Var Ftbl; L Socr; Capt L Trk; NHS; Natl Hnr Scty 85; NJ Boys ST 86; Arch Awds 87; U Of MD; Arch.

BUBNOWSKI, CINDY; Manalapan HS; Manalapan, NJ; (3); Girl Scts; Office Aide; Quiz Bowl; Rep Frsh Cls; Rep Soph Cls; Off Jr Cls; Stu Cncl; Hon Roll.

BUCARO, KRISTEN; Pequannock Township HS; Pompton Plains, NJ; (3); Church Yth Grp; Ski Clb; Varsity Clb; Sec Band; Concert Band; Jazz Band; Mrchg Band; Capt Bsktbl; Capt Fld Hcky; Var Sftbl; Rsrch & Dvlpmnt.

BUCCI, REBECCA; Princeton HS; Princeton, NJ; (3); Am Leg Aux Girls St; Dance Clb; Hosp Aide; Var Cheerleading; Bus.

BUCCIARELLI, NATALIE; Northern Valley Regional HS; Old Tappan, NJ; (3); 35/273; Drama Clb; Science Clb; Ski Clb; Band; Mgr Soph Cls; Var Cheerleading; JV Sftbl; Var Vllybl; Hon Roll; NHS; Engrng.

BUCCINO, GARY M; Memorial HS; Cedar Grove, NJ; (4); 14/123; Rep Soph Cls; Rep Jr Cls; Trs Sr Cls; Rep Stu Cncl; JV Var Bsbl; JV Var Ftbl; Hon Roll; NHS; Pres Schlr; APT Scholar; Black & Gold Club Scholar; PA ST.

BUCCOLO, ELISE; Toms River HS South; Beachwood, NJ; (2); Dance Clb; Intnl Clb; PAVAS; SADD; Mrchg Band; Pom Pon; Trk; High Hon Roll.

BUCHANAN, CHRISTINE; South Plainfield HS; S Plainfield, NJ; (3); 25/300; Computer Clb; Drama Clb; Ski Clb; SADD; School Musical; School Play; Stage Crew; Nwsp Ed-Chief; NHS; Spanish NHS.

BUCHMAN, NANCY; Belvidere HS; Phillipsburg, NJ; (3); 12/140; Church Yth Grp; Drama Clb; FFA; Church Choir; Hon Roll; Churchman Bus Schl; Secretary.

BUCHNER, BRIAN; Pennsville HS; Pennsville, NJ; (3); 24/240; Am Leg Boys St; Church Yth Grp; School Play; Nwsp Stf; Var Capt Bsktbl; Var Capt Socr; Im Vllybl; Hon Roll; Engrng.

BUCHOLTZ, CHRIS J; Cinnaminson HS; Cinnaminson, NJ; (3); Boy Scts; German Clb; JA; Ski Clb; Band; Orch; Trk; Concert Band; Mrchg Band; Symp Band; Outstndng Achvt Lang Arts, Engl Mech 84; Glassboro; Music.

BUCHOLTZ, MONIQUE; St Marys HS; S Amboy, NJ; (4); 12/125; Church Yth Grp; Library Aide; Spanish Clb; Hon Roll; Spanish NHS; Drmtlgst.

BUCHOLTZ, SARA; Soloman Schechter Day Schl; Maplewood, NJ; (4); 1/19; Trs Drama Clb; Yrbk Ed-Chief; Yrbk Phtg; Yrbk Stf; Rep Stu Cncl; Tennis; NHS; NEDT Awd; Val; USY Intl 86 Israel Affairs Co-Chrprsn; Barnard Coll.

BUCK, JESSE; Gloucester County Christian HS; Blackwood Terr, NJ; (3); Pres Frsh Cls; Lib Stu Cncl; Var Bsbl; Var Capt Bsktbl; Var Socr; High Hon Roll; Baptist Bible Coll; PE.

BUCKHOLZ, GERI-LYNN; Lakewood HS; Lakewood, NJ; (3); Am Leg Aux Girls St; Church Yth Grp; Exploring; Hosp Aide; JCL; Yrbk Stf; Lit Mag; Capt Crs Cntry; Var Trk; Hon Roll; Brnz Cngrsnl Awd 85; Slvr Cngrsnl Awd 87; Twrd Satori Schlr 84; Orthdntst.

BUCKLEY, ELLEN; St Rose HS; Sea Girt, NJ; (4); 4/207; Church Yth Grp; Key Clb; Math Tm; Spanish Clb; Stage Crew; Lit Mag; High Hon Roll; Hon Roll; NHS; Ntl Merit Ltr; Sea Girt Wmns Clb Scholar 87; Johns Hopkins U; Bio.

BUCKLEY, MICHAEL; B C V T S HS; Brtn Twp, NJ; (3); VICA; High Hon Roll; Hon Roll; Mnthly Attndnce Awd 85-86; Chef.

BUCSKU, TOM; Ewing HS; Ewing, NJ; (3); Boy Scts; Computer Clb; Math Clb; Spanish Clb; JV Bowling; Im Ftbl; JV Trk; Penn ST.

BUDACH, TAMMI; Marine Acad Of Science & Technlgy; Spring Lake, NJ; (3); 2/46; Drama Clb; Trs French Clb; ROTC; Church Choir; Drill Tm; High Hon Roll; Hon Roll; NHS; Prfct Atten Awd; Church Yth Grp; JR Gr Exec Comm Intl Ordr Of Rnbw Grls 86-87; Bio.

BUDAVARI, ADRIANE; Watching Hills Regional HS; Watchung, NJ; (4); 4/315; Pres Art Clb; Key Clb; Scholastic Bowl; Ski Clb; SADD; Var Bsktbl; Var Fld Hcky; JV Socr; Var Sftbl; High Hon Roll; J Kerrigan Mem Schlrshp 87; Chubb Top Ten 87; Swarthmore Coll; Med.

BUDD, CHRIS; North Warren Regional HS; Blairstown, NJ; (3); 3/150; Color Guard; Concert Band; Mrchg Band; Yrbk Stf; Trs Frsh Cls; Trs Soph Cls; Trs Jr Cls; Rep Stu Cncl; Var Capt Cheerleading; High Hon Roll; Rutgers U; Crmnl Jstc.

BUDD, HENRY; West Essex HS; No Caldwell, NJ; (3); Computer Clb; Science Clb; Ski Clb; Nwsp Rptr; Nwsp Stf; Stu Cncl; JV Bsbl; Im Socr; Var Capt Swmmng; Hon Roll; Invstmnt Bnkr.

BUDD, MICHAEL; Hamilton H S West; Yardville, NJ; (3); Am Leg Boys St; Cmnty Wkr; Var Golf; Var Swmmng; Hon Roll; NHS; Teen Arts-Cnty & ST 84-85; Gftd & Tlntd Engl 84-87; Golf MIP; Pre-Med.

BUDD, NANCY; Rancocas Valley Regl HS; Mt Holly, NJ; (3); Band; Concert Band; Mrchg Band; Vrsty Lttr Bnd 86.

BUDGIN, JEANNE; Morris Catholic HS; Boonton, NJ; (4); 17/138; Cmnty Wkr; Drama Clb; 4-H; Pres German Clb; Pep Clb; Ski Clb; Band; School Play; Powder Puff Ftbl; 4-H Awd; NC ST U; Vet Med.

BUDINICK, JOHN; Bayonne HS; Bayonne, NJ; (4); 60/350; Ski Clb; VP Frsh Cls; VP Soph Cls; VP Jr Cls; Var Capt Bsbl; Var Ftbl; Wt Lftg; Gov Hon Prg Awd; Hon Roll; NHS; Bill Armstrong Awd, US Army Rsrve Natl Schlr/Athl Awd 87; William Paterson; Bio.

BUEHLER, DENISE; Edgewood Regional SR HS; Elm, NJ; (3); 1/390; Latin Clb; Sec Pres Varsity Clb; Orch; Yrbk Stf; Var JV Bsktbl; Var Capt Fld Hcky; Sec Jr NHS; NHS; Val; Voice Dem Awd; Questor Awd 85-87; Dstngshd Prsn Awd 85-87; Rutgers Schl Pgm 86-87; Biochem Engr.

BUEHLER, KIMBERLY; Bridgeton HS; Bridgeton, NJ; (2); French Clb; Office Aide; SADD; Sec VICA; Nwsp Rptr; Sec Soph Cls; High Hon Roll; Hon Roll; NHS; NJ Cncl Soc Stu Excel 87; Roll Merit Hnr Roll 86; Top Ten Extmprns Spch Hlth Ocptnl Stu Am 87.

BUEHLER, MARJORIE; Overbrook Regional HS; Berlin, NJ; (3); German Clb; Concert Band; Mrchg Band; Hon Roll; Prfct Atten Awd; Vet.

BUEHLER, ROBIN; Overbrook Regional SR HS; Berlin, NJ; (3); Drama Clb; Spanish Clb; Mgr Mrchg Band; School Play; Ed Nwsp Stf; Mgr(s); Hon Roll; NHS; Prfct Atten Awd; 2 Gldn Poet Awds 85-86; 2 Hnrb Mntn Awd For Poetry 86 & 87; Jrnlsm.

BUEHLER, SHARON; Lower Cape May Regional HS; Villas, NJ; (3); 39/189; Sec Pres Church Yth Grp; Trs Pres Key Clb; Varsity Clb; Yrbk Sprt Ed; Var Swmmng; JV Tennis; Hon Roll; Camera Clb; 4-H; French Clb.

BUERCK, NAOMI; St John Vinney HS; Aberdeen, NJ; (3); 4/256; Math Tm; Band; School Musical; Yrbk Stf; Mgr(s); Var L Trk; High Hon Roll; NHS; Outstndng Achvt Hnrs Physcs 86-87; Gld & Wht Awd 85-87; Am Chem Soc Cont 85-87; Sci.

BUFANO, NICOLE; Sayreville War Memorial HS; Parlin, NJ; (4); 8/350; French Clb; Sec SADD; Nwsp Ed-Chief; Nwsp Stf; Ed Yrbk Stf; Ed Lit Mag; Cheerleading; Mat Maids; Score Keeper; French Hon Soc; Knghts Clmbus Essy Wnnr 84; Acadmc All Amer 84; Trustee Schlr :Nyu 87; NY U; Engl.

BUFF, TAMMY; Washington Township HS; Sewell, NJ; (2); Cmnty Wkr; French Clb; Color Guard; Mrchg Band; Hon Roll.

BUFFALINO, CARL; S River HS; So River, NJ; (4); 19/135; Ski Clb; Chorus; Im Bsbl; Var L Bsktbl; Im Ftbl; Var Capt Golf; Var Capt Socr; Im Tennis; Im Vllybl; NHS; Montclair St; Math.

BUFFO, TIMOTHY S; Overbrook SR HS; Albion, NJ; (4); Spanish Clb; Teachers Aide; Varsity Clb; Stage Crew; Bsktbl; Ftbl; Trk; Wt Lftg.

BUFORT, ANTHONY; Paramus HS; Paramus, NJ; (3); Computer Clb; Hon Roll; Cert Yth Speaks Out Spch Cont 87; Comp Sys Anlyst.

BUGAN, TINA; Dover HS; Branchville, NJ; (3); 21/226; Am Leg Aux Girls St; Key Clb; Ski Clb; Church Choir; School Musical; Yrbk Stf; High Hon Roll; NHS; East Stroudsburg; Math.

BUI, DA HAI; Dickinson HS; Jersey City, NJ; (2); Y-Teens; 2nd Hnr 85-86.

BUIRCH, LISA; Bridgeton HS; Bridgeton, NJ; (2); Art Clb; Drama Clb; French Clb; French Hon Soc; Voice Dem Awd; Fshn Dsgnr.

BUIS, ALISON; Kinnelon HS; Kinnelon, NJ; (2); Dance Clb; 4-H; French Clb; Girl Scts; Ski Clb; Varsity Clb; Var Trk; Hon Roll; Bio.

BUKATA, SUSAN V; New Milford HS; New Milford, NJ; (4); 2/143; Nwsp Ed-Chief; Yrbk Phtg; Sec Sr Cls; Var Trk; Gov Hon Prg Awd; NHS; Ntl Merit SF; Pres Schlr; Sal; St Schlr; Grls Ctznshp Inst 86; Biochem.

BUKLAD, JENNIFER; Columbia HS; Maplewood, NJ; (3); Church Yth Grp; Im Bsktbl.

BUKOWSKI, WILLIAM; Roselle Catholic HS; Linden, NJ; (4); 37/170; Church Yth Grp; Service Clb; Vllybl; High Hon Roll; Hon Roll; Spanish NHS; Union County; Comp Sci.

BULGACH, MARNI; Freehold Township HS; Freehold, NJ; (3); Art Clb; FBLA; Ed Yrbk Phtg; Sec Frsh Cls; VP Soph Cls; Grphc Dsgnr.

BULGER, JOSEPH B; Pequannock Twp HS; Pequannock, NJ; (4); 4/203; Am Leg Boys St; Varsity Clb; Rep Stu Cncl; Var Bsktbl; Var Ftbl; Var Capt Trk; VP NHS; Ntl Merit Schol; Garden St Distinguished Schlr 87; Twelve Pack 86-87; Rutgers U; Engrng.

BULLOCK, CALANDRA; Holy Spirit HS; Pleasantville, NJ; (4); Church Yth Grp; French Clb; Hosp Aide; Speech Tm; Chorus; Church Choir; School Play; VA Commonwealth U; Physcl Thrp.

BULLOCK, GEOFFREY; Marine Acad Of Science & Tech; East Keandburg, NJ; (4); 6/31; ROTC; Spanish Clb; Nwsp Ed-Chief; Yrbk Phtg; Var Swmmng; Im Wt Lftg; NHS; US Navy; Engrng.

BULLOCK, ROMAL DAVID; Seton Hall Prep Schl; East Orange, NJ; (4); Boy Scts; Church Yth Grp; Cmnty Wkr; English Clb; German Clb; Math Tm; Band; Church Choir; Nwsp Stf; Lit Mag; Drew U; Jrnlsm.

BULVANOSKI, CHRISTINA; Matawan Regional HS; Matawan, NJ; (4); 12/350; Math Clb; Band; Concert Band; Drm Mjr(t); Jazz Band; Mrchg Band; School Musical; Sec Soph Cls; Sec Jr Cls; Stu Cncl; Two Overall Drum Mjr Awds 86; Arch.

BULWIN, LORI ANN; Union HS; Union, NJ; (3); Church Yth Grp; German Clb; Library Aide; Service Clb; Concert Band; Orch; L JV Fld Hcky; JV L Sftbl; Jr NHS; Girls St 87; Girls Citizenship 87; Zoologist.

BUMBER, KIMBERLY; Southern Regional HS; Manahawkin, NJ; (4); 30/350; Dance Clb; VP Math Clb; Math Tm; Pres Spanish Clb; Ed Lit Mag; Cit Awd; Hon Roll; NHS; Cmnty Wkr; Concert Band; Exchng Clb Schlrshp 87; SGBA Chmpnshp Bsktbl Tm Coach 87; Sorptmst Yth Ctznshp Awd 87; Prft Atten 87; Glassboro ST Coll; Secndry Edu.

BUMGARNER, LAURA; Timothy Christian Schl; Somerset, NJ; (3); Church Yth Grp; Service Clb; Chorus; Var L Cheerleading; High Hon Roll; NHS; Elem Educ.

BUNCH, MICHELE; Marylawn Of The Oranges HS; Newark, NJ; (4); Church Yth Grp; Spanish Clb; Chorus; Church Choir; School Musical; School Play; Nwsp Phtg; Nwsp Stf; Yrbk Stf; Spanish NHS; Piano Perf Certs 85-86; NY U Schlrshp 87; NY U; Bio.

BUNCHE, SIMONE; Clifford J Scott HS; East Orange, NJ; (2); Spanish Clb; Flag Corp; Mrchg Band; Sec Frsh Cls; Rep Stu Cncl; Im Twrlr; Dept Hnrs-Spnsh 85-86; Dept Hnrs-Engl 86-87; Most Imprvd-Geo Hnrs 86-87; Acctg.

BUNDENS JR, DONALD J; Paulsboro HS; Gibbstown, NJ; (3); Quiz Bowl; JV L Bsktbl; Var L Crs Cntry; Hon Roll; Var L Swmmng; Bus.

BUNNELL, CHRISTINE; Gloucester County Christian HS; Mt Ephraim, NJ; (3); Yrbk Ed-Chief; Var L Bsktbl; Var L Fld Hcky; Var L Sftbl; High Hon Roll; Hon Roll; Prfct Atten Awd; Church Yth Grp; French Clb; Girl Scts; St Spelling Bee 3rd Pl 85, 4th Pl 86; 1st Pl Bible Memory St Comp 86; 19th Pl Bible Mem Ntl Comp 86; Pensacola Christian Coll; Engl.

BUOB, MAUREEN; Scotch Plains-Fanwood HS; Fanwood, NJ; (4); 100/325; AFS; FBLA; GAA; Service Clb; JV Var Cheerleading; JV Var Socr; Var Capt Sftbl; Im Vllybl; Accntng.

BUONDONNO, ROBERT T; Pennsauken HS; Pennsauken, NJ; (3); German Clb; Science Clb; Band; Variety Show; Im Bsbl; Im Bsktbl; Im Fld Hcky; Im Ice Hcky; Im Sftbl; Hon Roll; Engrng.

BUONO, LISA JOAN; St Marys HS; Garfield, NJ; (2); Drama Clb; Hosp Aide; PAVAS; Thesps; School Play; Rep Frsh Cls; Rep Soph Cls; Var Cheerleading; School Musical; Variety Show; Achvt Awd Outstndng Stdnt M Awd 85-86; Achvt Awd Oustndng Stdnt 86-87; NJ ST Fnlst Miss Amer Coed 87; Fshn & Dsgn.

BUONSANTO, DANNY P; Cliffside Park HS; Cliffside Park, NJ; (3); Am Leg Boys St; Exploring; Ski Clb; U Of Miami; Marine Bio.

BURCH, NANCY; Gateway Regional HS; Woodbury Hts, NJ; (2); Exploring; JCL; Key Clb; Latin Clb; SADD; Rep Stu Cncl; Bsktbl; Var L Swmmng; Var L Tennis; Var L Trk.

BURCH, SHERRI; Notre Dame HS; Trenton, NJ; (3); Hon Roll; Prfct Atten Awd; Trenton ST Coll; Dntstry.

BURCHETT, LAURA; Delaware Valley Regional HS; Milford, NJ; (4); 8/150; Pres VP Art Clb; Intnl Clb; Church Choir; School Play; Nwsp Rptr; JV Var Crs Cntry; Gov Hon Prg Awd; NHS; Pres Schlr; Trk; Outstndng Art Achvt Awd 87; Grad Hnrs 87; Acdmc All Amer 86; Beaver Coll; Sci.

BURCKBUCHLER, SCOTT; Brick Memorial HS; Bricktown, NJ; (3); Pres Frsh Cls; Rep Soph Cls; Pres Jr Cls; JV Socr; Wrstlng; High Hon Roll; Hon Roll; Georgetown U; Bus Admin.

BURDICK, IAN W; Egg Harbor Township HS; Mc Kee City, NJ; (4); 1/288; Trs Chess Clb; Model UN; Spanish Clb; Nwsp Ed-Chief; Lit Mag; Wrstlng; High Hon Roll; NHS; Ntl Merit SF; Val; Ivy League Clg; Chem Engrng.

BURDICK, KIM; West Morris Central HS; Long Valley, NJ; (3); 88/365; Sec Church Yth Grp; Chorus; Church Choir; School Musical; Lit Mag; Stu Cncl; Capt Var Cheerleading; Gym; Hon Roll; Cmmnctns.

BURDZY, THERESA; St Mary HS; Wallington, NJ; (3); Ski Clb; Varsity Clb; Yrbk Stf; Var Capt Cheerleading; Var Capt Pom Pon; High Hon Roll; NHS; All Am Acadc Achvt Awd 85-86; Berkley Bus Schl; Bus Adm.

BURGESS, KIMBERLY V; Burlington Co Vo Tech; Willingboro, NJ; (3); Exploring; VICA; VICA 86.

BURGHARDT, MARC; Ridgefield Park HS; Little Ferry, NJ; (3); 20/203; Cmnty Wkr; Drama Clb; NJIT; Elec Engr.

BURGOS, ISABEL; Dwight Morrow HS; Englewood, NJ; (4); High Hon Roll; Hon Roll; NHS; Prfsnl Model.

BURGWYN, DANETTE; Immaculate Conception HS; Vailsburg, NJ; (3); Art Clb; Church Yth Grp; Drama Clb; GAA; Girl Scts; Pep Clb; Chorus; Drill Tm; School Musical; Rep Soph Cls; Howard U; Psycht.

BURKE, BRIAN; Burlington City HS; Beverly, NJ; (4); 25/198; FBLA; Key Clb; Rep Stu Cncl; Var Socr; Elks Awd; Hon Roll; NHS; Ntl Merit Ltr; Drexel U; Elect Engrng.

BURKE, BRIAN; Paul VI HS; Somerdale, NJ; (3); #99 In Class; Ftbl; Trk; Wt Lftg; U Of Central FL; Engrng.

BURKE, CHRISTINE; St Rose HS; Neptune, NJ; (3); 19/240; Church Yth Grp; Key Clb; Math Tm; Stage Crew; Yrbk Stf; Rep Jr Cls; Rep Stu Cncl; Stat Socr; Im Vllybl; Hon Roll; Atten Awds 85-86; Ntl Ed Devpmnt Tst Top 10 Prcnt 85, 86 & 87; 2nd Pl CO CYO Bwlng Day 86; Gentc Engnrng.

BURKE, CRAIG; Wildwood HS; Wildwood Crest, NJ; (3); Rep Frsh Cls; Rep Jr Cls; JV Bsktbl; Var Ftbl; Var Trk; Im Vllybl; HOBY 86.

BURKE, DENNIS; A P Schlaick HS; Elmer, NJ; (3); 17/134; 4-H; Im JV Bsktbl; Capt JV Golf; Hon Roll; NHS; Comp Sci.

BURKE, JENNIFER; West Milford Township HS; West Milford, NJ; (3); 36/403; Church Yth Grp; Pres Spanish Clb; SADD; Nwsp Stf; Yrbk Phtg; Yrbk Stf; Hon Roll; NHS; Spanish NHS; Edtrl Edtr Schl Nwspr 86-87; Pre-Med.

BURKE, JONAS; Freehold Township HS; Freehold Twp, NJ; (4); 3/365; Drama Clb; Math Clb; Math Tm; Science Clb; Temple Yth Grp; Chorus; Madrigals; Bowling; NHS; NJ Dstngshd Schlr 86-87; All-Eastern Chorus 87; NJ Gvrnrs Schl In The Scncs 86; Rutgers; Engnrng.

BURKE, VICTORIA M; St Josephs Of The Palisade; W New York, NJ; (2); 24/108; Hosp Aide; Mgr School Play; Mgr Stage Crew; Score Keeper; Hon Roll; Vet.

BURKETT, MICHAEL; Lakewood HS; Lakewood, NJ; (3); 105/300; DECA; Drama Clb; French Clb; FBLA; Temple Yth Grp; Stage Crew; Yrbk Stf; Rep Jr Cls; DECA 1st Pl ST Awd Dsply Diorama 87; Fairleigh Dickinsons.

BURKHARDT, BETH; Gloucester Catholic HS; Haddonfield, NJ; (3); 16/205; Var Bsktbl; Var Socr; JV Sftbl; Hon Roll; NHS; Intl Frgn Lang Awd 85-86; Rep Stu Govt Day 85-86; Bus.

BURKLOW, TIMOTHY M; Pequannock Twnshp HS; Pompton Plains, NJ; (4); Am Leg Boys St; Church Yth Grp; Pres Band; Pres Sr Cls; Var L Ftbl; L Var Wrstlng; Cmnty Wkr; Varsity Clb; Concert Band; Jazz Band; Wm Marcy Agency Scholar 87; Stu Cncl Awd 87; Stu Cncl Scholar 87; 4 Yr Activity Awd; Phys Ed Sen Awd 87; Rutgers U; Bus.

BURLAK, LAURA; Egg Harbor Township HS; Bargaintown, NJ; (3); 5/349; VP French Clb; Key Clb; Model UN; Office Aide; Spanish Clb; Varsity Clb; Rep Jr Cls; JV Var Cheerleading; Var Crs Cntry; Gym; U PA; Med.

BURLEW, DAN; Dover HS; Dover, NJ; (4); 54/182; Boy Scts; Math Tm; Yrbk Ed-Chief; Yrbk Rptr; Yrbk Sprt Ed; Yrbk Stf; Var Capt Bsbl; Bowling; Hon Roll; Cntry 21 Accntng A Avg Awd 84-87; Mtchll Capidus Awd 87; JR Prm Kng 86; County Coll Morris; Accntng.

BURLEW, HEIDI; Arthur P Schalick HS; Elmer, NJ; (4); Church Yth Grp; Ski Clb; Sec Jr Cls; Stu Cncl; Mgr(s); Var Sftbl; Hon Roll; Ethnc Actvts; Athltc Awds & Hnrs; Glassboro ST Coll; Corp Law.

BURLING, JOHN; Pequannock Township HS; Pequannock, NJ; (3); Am Leg Boys St; Church Yth Grp; School Play; Var Bsktbl; Var Ftbl; Hon Roll; Prfct Atten Awd.

BURMEISTER, MARTA; Cherry Hill HS West; Cherry Hill, NJ; (4); 53/360; Office Aide; Spanish Clb; Mrchg Band; Bowling; High Hon Roll; Hon Roll; Home & Schl Assoc Awd 86-87; NJ Envrnmntl Ed Assoc Awd 86-87; Drexel U; Fash Merch.

BURNETTE, DAVID; Shore Regional HS; W Long Branch, NJ; (4); 7/210; Chess Clb; Math Clb; Math Tm; Science Clb; High Hon Roll; Ntl Merit Ltr; Garden ST Dstngshd Schlr 86; Share Schlr 87; Pres Acad Fit Awd 87; Embry-Riddle Aero U; Aero Engr.

BURNEY, ANTOINE; Essex Catholic Boys HS; Newark, NJ; (3); Boy Scts; Church Yth Grp; FBLA; SADD; Teachers Aide; Nwsp Stf; Yrbk Stf; Rep Frsh Cls; Rep Soph Cls; Sec Jr Cls; Hampton Inst; Bus Mgmt.

BURNS, AMY; Manasquan HS; Spring Lake, NJ; (2); 16/238; Spanish Clb; JV Var Bsktbl; JV Score Keeper; JV Var Sftbl; High Hon Roll; Hon Roll; Manasquan Brd Of Ed 87.

BURNS, EDWARD; Seton Hall Prep; Madison, NJ; (4); 10/187; Math Tm; Rep Jr Cls; Var L Bsbl; Var L Socr; Var Trk; High Hon Roll; NHS; Garden ST Dstngshd Schlr 86-87; U PA; Bus.

BURNS, KATHLEEN; Wallington HS; Wallington, NJ; (3); Am Leg Aux Girls St; Office Aide; Ski Clb; Band; Concert Band; School Play; Rep Stu Cncl; L Sftbl; JV Vllybl; Hon Roll.

BURNS, MONET; St Marys HS; E Brunswick, NJ; (4); 19/130; Church Yth Grp; French Clb; Girl Scts; Library Aide; School Musical; School Play; Ed Yrbk Stf; Ed Lit Mag; Rep Frsh Cls; Tennis; Art Awd 87; Mason Gross Schl; Vsl Arts.

BURNS, NANCY; Jackson Memorial HS; Jackson, NJ; (3); Dance Clb; Girl Scts; SADD; Band; School Play; Yrbk Stf; Badmtn; Fld Hcky; Vllybl; Hon Roll; Rider; Lab Tech.

BURNS, TARA; Bayonne HS; Bayonne, NJ; (3); Drama Clb; Key Clb; Concert Band; VP Stu Cncl; Cheerleading; Gym; Pom Pon; Trk; Vllybl; Wt Lftg; Douglass Coll 1 Wk; Girls Ctznshp Inst Awd-Womens Clb 87; Sprinter Of Month-Track Tm 87; Douglass Coll; Accntng.

BURNSTEIN, YISROEL; Jewish Educational Ctr; Elizabeth, NJ; (2); Math Clb; Quiz Bowl; Science Clb; JV Score Keeper; Hon Roll; NYS Sci Lg Hgh Ranking 86; Natl Bible Cont Fnls 86 & 87; Sci.

BUROW, HEATHER; Gateway Regional HS; Westville, NJ; (2); FHA; Fld Hcky; 1st Pl Pstr Cntst FHA Rgnl Cnvntn 86; Bus.

BURR, LORRAINE E; Ridge HS; Basking Ridge, NJ; (4); 19/200; Art Clb; VP Church Yth Grp; Ski Clb; L JV Trk; Hon Roll; Kiwanis Awd; NHS; NEDT Awd; Prfct Atten Awd; Pres Schlr; Bernards Twnshp Educ Assn Schlrshp, Bernards Area Schlrshp Assistnc Inc 87; Douglas Coll; Psych.

BURROUGHS, BRENDA; St Aloysius HS; Jersey City, NJ; (3); Boys Clb Am; Boy Scts; Church Yth Grp; Church Choir; Hon Roll; Awd Merit Typng 87; Comp Sci.

BURROWS, LOREE; Matawan Regional HS; Matawan, NJ; (4); Church Yth Grp; PAVAS; Chorus; Color Guard; Flag Corp; Madrigals; School Musical; Bsktbl; Mgr(s); Pom Pon; Trenton ST; Elem Ed.

BURROWS, LORRIN; St Mary HS; Spotswood, NJ; (3); 22/99; Church Choir; Yrbk Phtg; Lit Mag; Rep Soph Cls; Pres Jr Cls; High Hon Roll; Spanish NHS; Camera Clb; Spanish Clb; Variety Show; Jrnlsm.

BURROWS, RAQUEL; Holy Spiriy HS; Atlantic City, NJ; (3); 48/332; Church Yth Grp; Spanish Clb; Chorus; Hon Roll; Med Tech.

BURSACK, ERIC; John F Kennedy HS; Willingboro, NJ; (3); Key Clb; Off Stu Cncl; Wrstlng; Hon Roll; Soph Clss Rep 85-86; Arch.

BURSKI, HEATHER; West Windsor-Plainsboro HS; Robbinsville, NJ; (3); Am Leg Aux Girls St; Church Yth Grp; Pres French Clb; Mgr Nwsp Sprt Ed; Bausch & Lomb Sci Awd; NHS; Camera Clb; SADD; Nwsp Phtg; GATE Soc 85-87; Princeton Plasma Physcs Lab Smmr Sci Awd Prgm 87; Pblshd Essay Aspirations Coll 87; PHD; Chem Rsrch.

BURT, ROCHELLE; Vineland HS; Vineland, NJ; (4); 100/803; Cmnty Wkr; DECA; NAACP; Pep Clb; Pres Frsh Cls; Rep Soph Cls; Pres Jr Cls; Pres Sr Cls; Rep Stu Cncl; Stat Bsktbl; Pillsbury-Green Giant Schlrshp 87; Rutgers U; Acctg.

BURTON, ANNE; Hunterdon Central HS; Flemington, NJ; (3); 45/570; Key Clb; Pep Clb; Band; Concert Band; Jazz Band; Mrchg Band; Pep Band; Crs Cntry; Trk; Hon Roll.

BURTON, JAMES; Mainland Regional HS; Linwood, NJ; (3); 41/287; Boy Scts; Ski Clb; Church Choir; Rep Stu Cncl; Im Bowling; JV Ftbl; Var Trk; Trs NHS; Chief Of Order Arrow Lodge No 423 86-87; Boy Scouts Amer Eagle Scout Awd 87; Bus.

BURTON, KATHI; Holy Cross HS; Medford, NJ; (3); 112/301; Church Yth Grp; Hosp Aide; Ski Clb; Teachers Aide; Yrbk Stf; Rep Frsh Cls; Var Fld Hcky; JV Swmmng; JV Trk; Hon Roll; Phys Thrpy.

BURTON, KEVIN; Brick Twp HS; Brick Town, NJ; (3); VP JA; Ski Clb; Band; Jazz Band; Mrchg Band; JV Var Socr; High Hon Roll; Boy Scts; Church Yth Grp; HOSA Local Parlmntrn ST Pres 87-88; Am Leg Awd; Comp Engrng.

BURTON, RHONDA; Franklin HS; New Brunswick, NJ; (4); Church Yth Grp; DECA; FHA; SADD; Hon Roll; Computer Clb; FNA; Teachers Aide; JV Bsktbl; Var Mgr(s); 2nd Pl Splng Bee 84; Middlesex Vo Schl; Mgmnt.

BURTON, TRACI; Mt Olive HS; Flanders, NJ; (4); 66/280; SADD; High Hon Roll; Hon Roll; Rider Coll; Frgn Lang.

BURTT, CHRIS; Ocean Township HS; W Allenhurst, NJ; (4); 20/333; Boy Scts; Latin Clb; Band; Concert Band; Mrchg Band; Ntl Merit Schol; Pres Schlr; Latin Hnr Soc 84, 85; NJ Distngshd Schlr 87; Spartan Schlr 84-86; Coll Of William & Mary; Bus.

BURWELL, STEPHANIE; Camden Catholic HS; Camden, NJ; (3); 128/285; French Clb.

BURZYNSKI, DEBORAH; Toms River HS East; Toms River, NJ; (3); Intnl Clb; Key Clb; Q&S; Speech Tm; Mrchg Band; Nwsp Rptr; Nwsp Stf; Var Pom Pon; JV Swmmng; JV Trk; Comm.

BUSCH, JENNIFER L; Notre Dame HS; Lawrenceville, NJ; (3); Church Yth Grp; Red Cross Aide; Varsity Clb; Capt Cheerleading; Fld Hcky; Score Keeper; High Hon Roll; Hon Roll; Natl Bus Hnr Soc 86-87; Party Clb 85-87; Mst Spirtd Chrldng Captn Awd 86-87.

BUSER, CORNELIA; Wall HS; Wall, NJ; (4); 17/269; JCL; Latin Clb; Ski Clb; Band; Concert Band; Mrchg Band; Rep Soph Cls; Powder Puff Ftbl; Var L Socr; High Hon Roll; All Shre Band 84-85; NJ Dstngshd Schlr 86-87; Ntl Hnr Soc 85-87; Physcs.

BUSH, AMY; Morristown HS; Morristown, NJ; (2); Church Yth Grp; Chorus; Color Guard; Mrchg Band; Hon Roll; U Of CA Berkeley; Intl Rltns.

BUSH, KIM; Toms River HS North; Toms River, NJ; (3); 33/459; Spanish Clb; Yrbk Stf; High Hon Roll; Hon Roll; NHS; Capt Var Bsktbl; Capt Var Fld Hcky; Var L Socr; Psych.

BUSHELL JR, JOHN T; Central Regional HS; Seaside Park, NJ; (4); 24/230; Chess Clb; Capt Ftbl; Capt Trk; Wt Lftg; High Hon Roll; Mvp Ftbl & Weight Man Track 87; All Cnty Ftbl All Shore Ftbl 87; Mulhenberg Coll; Bus.

BUSHRA, JOSEPH; Baptist HS; Sicklerville, NJ; (3); Church Yth Grp; Drama Clb; Spanish Clb; Chorus; Church Choir; School Play; Stage Crew; Trs Frsh Cls; Trs Soph Cls; Score Keeper; Baptist Hnr Scty 87; Med.

BUSKIRK, JULIE A; Pennsville Memorial HS; Pennsville, NJ; (4); 8/200; Hosp Aide; Red Cross Aide; Orch; Rep Sr Cls; High Hon Roll; Hon Roll; NHS; Church Yth Grp; FHA; Grdn ST Dstngshd Schlr 87; Girls Ctznshp Inst Alt 86; Lafayette Coll; Cvl Engrng.

BUSS, TERI LEA; Moorestown HS; Moorestown, NJ; (4); 198/235; Church Yth Grp; French Clb; Teachers Aide; Yrbk Phtg; Stu Cncl; Var Capt Cheerleading; Gym; Hon Roll; Carol Anne Boehmler Memorial Awd & Dr Harold Paul Coxson Schlrshp 87; Shippensburg U; Comms.

BUSSANICH, MARIO; Secaucus HS; Secaucus, NJ; (3); 49/168; Key Clb; Math Clb; Mu Alpha Theta; Rep Jr Cls; Rep Sr Cls; Hon Roll; Voice Dem Awd; Mill Creek Art Expos 87.

BUTCHER, ANN; Newton HS; Greendell, NJ; (4); 24/196; 4-H; French Clb; Latin Clb; Capt Bsktbl; Fld Hcky; Sftbl; 4-H Awd; MVP Fld Hcky 86; Outstndng Frosh Girl Athlt 84; Penn ST; Athltc Traing.

BUTCHKO, ROBERT; Lenape Valley Regional HS; Andover, NJ; (3); 25/213; 4-H; Latin Clb; JV Socr; JV Var Trk; Hon Roll; Bio-Med Engrng.

BUTKOWSKI, LISA; Union Catholic HS; New Providence, NJ; (4); 30/300; Civic Clb; Drama Clb; PAVAS; Thesps; Chorus; School Musical; School Play; Golf; Hon Roll; Pres Schlr; Natl Sci Merit Awd 86; Rutgers Coll; Bio.

BUTLER, BRAD; Kittatinny Regional HS; Blairstown, NJ; (3); 19/220; Cmnty Wkr; School Musical; Stage Crew; Var Bsktbl; Var Socr; Im Wt Lftg; Hon Roll; NHS; Boys ST Nmnee AM Lgn 87; Lbrl Arts.

BUTLER, DANIELLE; Southern Regional HS; Barnegat, NJ; (3); Church Yth Grp; 4-H; Band; Concert Band; Mrchg Band; Rutgers; Vet Med.

BUTLER, DERRICK; Essex Catholic Boys Prep; East Orange, NJ; (3); Art Clb; Drama Clb; School Musical; School Play; Pres Frsh Cls; VP Soph Cls; Rep Jr Cls; Rep Stu Cncl; Bsktbl; Coach Actv; Assist Coach For E Orange US Yth Games Team 86; Ambssdr For E Orange US Yth Games Team 86; Mech Engr.

BUTLER, GREGORY E; Monmouth Regional HS; Tinton Falls, NJ; (3); Boy Scts; Trs French Clb; Ski Clb; Yrbk Ed-Chief; Off Jr Cls; Off Sr Cls; Rep Stu Cncl; JV Capt Socr; JV Capt Wrstlng; Ntl Merit Ltr; Bronze Cngrsnl Awd 86.

BUTLER, JENNIFER; Buena Regional HS; Vineland, NJ; (3); 11/250; Computer Clb; Dance Clb; JV Crs Cntry; JV Trk; NHS; Natl Sci Merit Awd 87; Penn ST; Bio.

BUTLER, JENNIFER; Rumson-Fair Haven Regional HS; Rumson, NJ; (3); 33/231; Girl Scts; Var Math Tm; Teachers Aide; Stage Crew; Nwsp Stf; Var Bowling; Var Trk; High Hon Roll; Hon Roll; School Musical; 1st Natl Sci Olympd Earth Sci 85; Mech Engrng.

BUTRYM, ALEXIS; Notre Dame HS; E Windsor, NJ; (2); Computer Clb; 4-H; Math Tm; Chorus; High Hon Roll; Grmn Hnr Soc 87; Frstry.

BUTTACAVOLI, MARY SUE; Howell HS; Howell, NJ; (4); 41/470; Pres Soph Cls; Pres Jr Cls; Pres Sr Cls; Var Cheerleading; Var Capt Gym; Var Trk; NHS; Tm Qlfd NCA Natl Chrldng Cmptn 86; Hmcnt Queen 86-87; Pace U; Accntng.

BUTTE, ATUL; Cherry Hill HS East; Cherry Hill, NJ; (4); 1/680; Am Leg Boys St; Boy Scts; Var Debate Tm; Hosp Aide; Pres Latin Clb; Capt Quiz Bowl; NHS; Ntl Merit Ltr; Voice Dem Awd; Ed Computer Clb; Medcl Schlrs Pgm Kennedy Hosp 86-87; Gov Schl Sci 85-86; Bornw U; Phy.

BUTTE, MANISH; Cherry Hill HS East; Cherry Hill, NJ; (2); Boy Scts; Chess Clb; Debate Tm; Hosp Aide; JCL; Pres Latin Clb; Library Aide; Science Clb; Ed Lit Mag; High Hon Roll; Eagle Sct 85; Physcn.

BUTTITTA, LISA; Belleville HS; Belleville, NJ; (2); Amer Assoc Of Tchrs Of Iltn Excel 87; Law.

BUTTON, CAROLYN; Summit HS; Summit, NJ; (3); 15/270; Ntl Merit SF; Ski Clb; Var Crs Cntry; Var Trk; Hon Roll; NHS; Anna Matilda Mc Neil Art Awd 87; Outstndg Athltc Achvt Ltr Awds 85-87.

BUTTON, SIBYL; Author P Schalick HS; Bridgeton, NJ; (3); 16/120; Sec Church Yth Grp; Trs Ski Clb; Speech Tm; Pres Chorus; Concert Band; Mrchg Band; Orch; JV Var Cheerleading; JV Var Tennis; NHS.

BUYTKINS JR, PAUL; Delaware Valley Regional HS; Milford, NJ; (3); Am Leg Boys St; Boy Scts; Letterman Clb; Quiz Bowl; Varsity Clb; Stu Cncl; Var L Bsbl; JV Bsktbl; Var L Ftbl; Im Vllybl; Engrng.

BYELICK, CHRISTOPHER J; Bound Brook HS; South Bound Brk, NJ; (4); Pres Drama Clb; NFL; Pres Speech Tm; Thesps; Band; Drm & Bgl; Jazz Band; School Musical; School Play; Stage Crew; Bst Actr Bucks Cnty, Govrs Schl Alt 85-86; 85 Awd Theatr 3 Spch Tm 83-87; Merit Schlrshp Smmr Art 87; Theater.

BYERS JR, EUGENE B; Hillside HS; Hillside, NJ; (3); Cmnty Wkr; Science Clb; Spanish Clb; Ed Nwsp Stf; Elks Awd; Hon Roll; Wnnr Ortry Cntst 87; Acctng.

BYERS, TOBI-LYN; Wayne Hills HS; Wayne, NJ; (3); 80/350; Drama Clb; Spanish Clb; Chorus; School Musical; School Play; Nwsp Stf; Yrbk Phtg; Yrbk Stf; Lit Mag; Rep Stu Cncl; Hnr Rl 84-87; Passaic Cnty Tn Arts Fstvl Actng; Drama.

BYK, KIMBERLEY; Mount Saint Mary Acad; Watchung, NJ; (4); Church Yth Grp; French Clb; GAA; Office Aide; Off Sr Cls; Tennis; French Hon Soc; Hon Roll; Superior Acad Xclnc/Frnch 5 Hnrs 86-87; Mercy Awd 86-87; Chrstn Ldrshp Awd 86-87; Mt St Marys Coll; Med.

BYRD, CARLA; Eastside HS; Paterson, NJ; (3); Band; Color Guard; Cheerleading; Hnr Rl 86; Prfct Atten 85; Med.

BYRD, KAREN; Lakeland Regional HS; Wanaque, NJ; (4); Math Clb; Lit Mag; High Hon Roll; Opt Clb Awd; Pres Acdmc Ftnss Awd, Brd Of Educ Schlrshp & Douglass Coll Schlrshp 87; Douglass Coll; Math.

BYRNE, DANIEL; Toms River HS East; Toms River, NJ; (3); 48/500; Am Leg Boys St; Math Tm; Quiz Bowl; JV Socr; NHS; Ntl Merit SF; Schlrshp-WA Wrkshps Cngrssnl Smnr 87; Hstry.

BYRNE, JAMES; Union HS; Union, NJ; (2); Boy Scts; ROTC; Science Clb; Rep Stu Cncl; JV Bsbl; Var Crs Cntry; Var Swmmng; High Hon Roll; NEDT Awd; Pres Schlr; Superior Cadet Decoration ROTC 85-86; Air Force Acad; Sci.

BYRNE, JENNIFER; Saint James HS; Gibbstown, NJ; (1); Drama Clb; SADD; Church Choir; School Musical; School Play; Hon Roll; Hon Outstndg Effort In Math 87; Law.

BYRNE, KEVIN; St Josephs HS; South Amboy, NJ; (4); 140/215; Am Leg Boys St; Drama Clb; Model UN; School Musical; School Play; Nwsp Ed-Chief; Nwsp Rptr; Yrbk Stf; Lit Mag; Stu Cncl; Lit Magzn Modrtrs Awd 87; Excllnc Arts 87; Drma Mst Vlbl 87; Le Moyne Coll; Engl.

BYRNE, KRISTIN; South Plainfield HS; So Plainfield, NJ; (4); 35/270; Drama Clb; Service Clb; SADD; Chorus; Jazz Band; Madrigals; Yrbk Bus Mgr; Yrbk Stf; French Hon Soc; High Hon Roll; F C Black Schlrshp 87; S Plfd Pop Warner Egls Assoc Schlrshp 87; Prncpls Awd Imprvmnt Ovrll 87; Douglass Coll; Pltcl Sci.

BYRNE, LISA M; Southern Regional HS; Cedar Run, NJ; (4); 13/392; Math Tm; Model UN; Trs Service Clb; VP Spanish Clb; Rep Stu Cncl; Var Cheerleading; High Hon Roll; NHS; Trs Church Yth Grp; Hosp Aide; Schlr Athlete Awd For Soccer 85 & 86; Sci Fair Hnrb Mntn 87; James Madison U; Accntng.

BYRNE, MICHAEL; De Paul Drocesan HS; Wayne, NJ; (4); 4/150; Math Tm; Capt Quiz Bowl; Ski Clb; Nwsp Stf; Yrbk Stf; Trs Sr Cls; NHS; Ntl Merit Ltr; St Schlr; Notre Dame.

BYRNE, MICHELLE; Washington Township HS; Sewell, NJ; (4); Chorus; JV Fld Hcky; Score Keeper; Swmmng; Trk; Hon Roll; Pre-Chldhd Educ.

BYRNE, STEPHEN; Manasquan HS; Manasquan, NJ; (2); 42/247; Church Yth Grp; Mrchg Band; Pep Band; Socr; High Hon Roll; Hon Roll; Arch.

BYRNES, COLLEEN; Holy Spirit HS; Brigantine, NJ; (2); 37/397; Drama Clb; Spanish Clb; Stage Crew; Nwsp Stf; Hon Roll; Drexel Hill; Comp Prgrmr.

BYRNES, CURTIS W; Cranford HS; Cranford, NJ; (4); 12/269; Math Clb; Science Clb; Spanish Clb; Yrbk Stf; Var Golf; Gov Hon Prg Awd; JC Awd; NHS; Pres Schlr; St Schlr; Rotary Clb & Parent-Tchr Schlrshp 87; Rutgers U; Med.

BYRON, ERIN; West Morris Mendham HS; Mendham, NJ; (2); 35/290; Church Yth Grp; French Clb; Ski Clb; Chorus; JV Bsktbl; JV Fld Hcky; JV Socr; Swmmng; Var L Trk; Hon Roll; WA DC Wrkshp 85; Hnrs Hstry 87; Georgetown; Jrnlsm.

CABACCANG, MICHELLE; Moutn St Dominic Acad; West Orange, NJ; (3); 3/57; Church Yth Grp; Cmnty Wkr; Hosp Aide; Office Aide; Spanish Clb; Chorus; Yrbk Bus Mgr; High Hon Roll; NHS; Elec Engrng.

CABALAR, MARIA SALOME; Toms River HS North; Toms River, NJ; (4); Chorus; Bsktbl; VP L Cheerleading; VP L Sftbl; High Hon Roll; Hon Roll; Coll Of Notre Dame; Lbrl Arts.

CABBA-GESTALK, SHAUNICE; Linden HS; Linden, NJ; (3); Cmnty Wkr; FBLA; FHA; ROTC; Temple Yth Grp; Drill Tm; Off Lit Mag; Rep Jr Cls; Rep Stu Cncl; Church Yth Grp; Cert Apprctn Hnds Acrss Amer 86; Gld Mdl 1 St Pl FHA 87; Cert Prmtn Exctv Offcr 87; Georgetown U; Intl Mrktr.

CABELL, ANN; South River HS; South River, NJ; (3); Church Yth Grp; FNA; Library Aide; Chorus; Color Guard; Stu Cncl; Crs Cntry; Tennis; Trk; Hon Roll; Rugers Coll; Psych.

CABRERA, LISSETTE; Immaculate Heart Acad; Nanuet, NY; (4); 16/168; Ed Lit Mag; Hon Roll; NHS; Spanish NHS; Natl Hispanic Schlr Awds Prg Semi Fnlst 86-87; Intl Bi-Lingual.

CABRERA, MAGGE; Chatham Twp HS; Chatham Twp, NJ; (3); Church Yth Grp; Drama Clb; Key Clb; Pep Clb; School Play; Swing Chorus; Yrbk Stf; JV Var Cheerleading; Hon Roll; Girl Scts; Vrsty Ltrs Cheerldng 86-87; English.

CACCAVELLI, MICHAEL; North Hunterdon HS; Hampton, NJ; (2); 60/340; Church Yth Grp; FCA; Trs Frsh Cls; JV Ftbl; JV Wt Lftg; JV Wrstlng; Gifted & Talented Camp-Blair Prep Schl 86; Law.

CACHOLA, YVETTE; Washington Twp HS; Sewell, NJ; (4); Var Fld Hcky; Glou Co Voc Schl; Nrsng.

CADENELLI, TARA; Wall HS; Manasquan, NJ; (3); 4/289; Pres Drama Clb; Key Clb; Quiz Bowl; Thesps; L Chorus; Orch; School Musical; Stat Trk; High Hon Roll; Hon Roll; Al-ST, Al-Shore Chorus NJ 86; Music.

CAESAR, MARK; West Side HS; Newark, NJ; (3); Church Yth Grp; Cmnty Wkr; Debate Tm; Political Wkr; Varsity Clb; Variety Show; Yrbk Sprt Ed; Rep Stu Cncl; Bsbl; Bsktbl; Plyr Yr & MVP 86-87; NJ Gvrnrs Cncl Sprts & Phys Ftns 86-87; All City & All Cnty Ftbl Tm 86-87; Acctng.

CAGNEY, LISA; Southern Regional HS; Ship Bottom, NJ; (3); Church Yth Grp; Library Aide; Pep Clb; Ski Clb; Variety Show; Rep Frsh Cls; Rep Soph Cls; Rep Jr Cls; Stu Cncl; Bsktbl; Intr Dsgnr.

CAHILL, ARLA DAWN; Randolph HS; Randolph, NJ; (4); Cmnty Wkr; Hosp Aide; Trs Key Clb; Ski Clb; Concert Band; Mrchg Band; Nwsp Stf; Ntl Merit SF; Smmr Inst-Gftd, Blr Acad 85; Montclair ST Coll; Biochem.

CAHILL, ELIZABETH; Pennsville Memorial HS; Pennsville, NJ; (3); Drama Clb; FBLA; Sec Spanish Clb; Stage Crew; Yrbk Stf; JV Fld Hcky; Hugh O Brien Youth Ldrshp Seminar 86; 1st Pl Rider Ccoll Foreign Lang Forensic Tournament; Communication.

CAHILL, SHAWN; Phillipsburg HS; Phillipsburg, NJ; (3); Church Yth Grp; Drama Clb; Band; Church Choir; Concert Band; Mrchg Band; School Musical; School Play; Stage Crew; Nwsp Phtg; Photo.

CAIN, BARBARA ANN; Manasquan HS; Brielle, NJ; (3); Art Clb; Church Yth Grp; Drama Clb; FBLA; School Play; Stage Crew.

CAIN, BRENDA; Cherokee HS; Marlton, NJ; (2); Var Crs Cntry; Var Trk; Hnr Rl 85-87; Acctng.

CAIN, MARK; Don Bosco Prep; Westwood, NJ; (4); 89/169; 4-H; Cit Awd; Dnfth Awd; 4-H Awd; OH U; Telecmnctns.

CAIRA, CHRISTOPHER; St James HS; Gibbstown, NJ; (2); Boy Scts; JV Ftbl; JV Golf; Hon Roll; Syracuse U; Prof Hcky Plyr.

CAIRNS, CHRISTINE; Central Regional HS; Bayville, NJ; (3); 70/240; SADD; JV Bsktbl; JV Fld Hcky; JV Sftbl; Flagler Coll; Hstry.

CAJIGAL, YSABEL; Pequannock Twsp HS; Pequannock, NJ; (3); Office Aide; Spanish Clb; Varsity Clb; Bsktbl; Var JV Socr; Cit Awd; Hon Roll; Spanish NHS; Intl Bus.

CALABRESE, ROSARIA; Weehawken HS; Weehawken, NJ; (3); 1/101; Yrbk Stf; Pres Frsh Cls; Pres Soph Cls; Pres Jr Cls; Var Cheerleading; High Hon Roll; NHS.

CALABRO, KRISTINE; Mahwah HS; Mahwah, NJ; (3); 24/165; Church Yth Grp; Cmnty Wkr; Debate Tm; Lit Mag; JV Var Socr; High Hon Roll; Spanish NHS; Algebra I Awd & Earth Sci Awd 84-85; Frgn Exchange Stu 87; Music.

CALAUTTI, LINDA; St Josephs HS; Ridgefield, NJ; (3); Model UN; Yrbk Stf; Score Keeper; Hon Roll; FIT; Fshn Byng.

CALBAZANA, CRYSTAL; Willingboro HS; Willingboro, NJ; (3); Am Leg Aux Girls St; Exploring; French Clb; FTA; Hosp Aide; Intnl Clb; Jr Civitan Int; Math Clb; Math Tm; Teachers Aide; Rutgers ST U; Math.

CALCAGNI, MELISSA; Washington Township HS; Sewell, NJ; (4); 64/490; Spanish Clb; Yrbk Stf; Stu Cncl; Mgr(s); Powder Puff Ftbl; Socr; Hon Roll; U Of DE.

CALDERA, LAUREN; Matawan Regional HS; Aberdeen, NJ; (4); 24/322; Math Clb; Off Stu Cncl; Bsktbl; Sftbl; High Hon Roll; Hon Roll; NHS; Mst Dedctd Bsktbl 86; Trenton ST Coll; Bus.

CALDWELL, CHERYL M; Rancocas Valley Regional HS; Mt Holly, NJ; (4); 15/254; Am Leg Aux Girls St; Church Yth Grp; Trs Key Clb; Math Tm; Church Choir; Yrbk Stf; Stu Cncl; Rutgers U; Accntng.

CALDWELL, ELIZABETH; Clifford J Scott HS; East Orange, NJ; (3); Church Yth Grp; Library Aide; Teachers Aide; Rptr Nwsp Stf; Hon Roll; Jr NHS; Dept Hnrs In Chem-Alg II-BUS-MTH-SPNSH III 86-87; Acctg.

CALDWELL, MICHAEL; West Windsor-Plainsboro HS; Princeton Junct, NJ; (3); FBLA; NAACP; Radio Clb; Pres Frsh Cls; Rep Jr Cls; VP Sr Cls; Rep Stu Cncl; JV Ftbl; Var Capt Tennis; Hon Roll; Mba.

CALHEIROS, DEBORAH; Toms River HS South; S Toms River, NJ; (3); 10/405; Band; Concert Band; Mrchg Band; Symp Band; High Hon Roll; Hon Roll; Amer Assn U Wmn; Anthrplgy.

CALHOUN, BETH; Rutherford HS; Rutherford, NJ; (4); 7/167; Nwsp Stf; Yrbk Bus Mgr; Stat Bsktbl; Stat Sftbl; High Hon Roll; Hon Roll; NHS; Ntl Merit Ltr; Math Tm; Spanish Clb; Grdn ST Dstngshd Schlr 86-87; Rutherford Bd Ed Brnz Awd 84-85; Rutherford Bd Educ Slvr Awd 85-86; Fairfield U; Fin.

CALHOUN, JENNICE; Paul VI HS; Turnersville, NJ; (3); Var Capt Fld Hcky; Var Capt Sftbl; La Salle U; Criminal Jstc.

CALHOUN, SEAN; Jackson Memorial HS; Jackson, NJ; (3); 2/444; Math Tm; Science Clb; Socr; Bausch & Lomb Sci Awd; High Hon Roll; NHS; Span Frgn Lang Awd; Genetic Engineering.

CALIENDO, BRENDA; Toms River North HS; Toms River, NJ; (4); 66/412; Key Clb; Ski Clb; Stage Crew; Yrbk Stf; Lit Mag; Stu Cncl; Socr; Tennis; Trk; Hon Roll; Grdn ST Rehab Hosp Schlrshp 87; U Of DE.

CALIENDO, PAUL; Manaipan HS; Englishtown, NJ; (3); 69/429; Latin Clb; Letterman Clb; Var Socr; Ntl Merit Ltr; Pre-Med.

CALILAP, CHARMANE B; St Aloysius HS; Jersey City, NJ; (3); Boys Clb Am; Church Yth Grp; Sec Dance Clb; Exploring; Hon Roll; Typng Skls & Tchnqs Cert Hnr & Awd Merit; Ped Nrs.

CALINDA, TINO; Parisppany Hills HS; Parsippany, NJ; (2); Church Yth Grp; Red Cross Aide; Stage Crew; Wt Lftg; JV Wrstlng; Cert Apprctn 87; Rutgers.

CALIZAYA, IVONNE; Mary Help Of Christians Acad; Cedar Grove, NJ; (2); Church Yth Grp; SADD; Teachers Aide; Church Choir; Orch; Sec Frsh Cls; Var Bsktbl; Tennis; Hon Roll; Prfct Atten Awd; Rutgers; Sci.

CALKIN, WENDY; A P Schalick HS; Elmer, NJ; (3); 1/120; Rep Soph Cls; Rep Jr Cls; Tennis.

CALL, MARY; Paramus Catholic Girls Regnl HS; Hasbrouck Hts, NJ; (2); Girl Scts; Political Wkr; Nwsp Stf; Lit Mag; Hon Roll; NEDT Awd; Jmp Rope Hrt 87; Psych.

CALLAHAN, BRENDA; Freehold HS; Freehold, NJ; (1); Church Yth Grp; FHA; JA; Church Choir; Tennis; Fshn Dsgnr.

CALLAHAN, KATHERINE; Highland Regional HS; Blackwood, NJ; (2); Latin Clb; Rep Stu Cncl; Var Socr; Hon Roll; Law.

CALLARD, GENEVIEVE; Passaic Collegiate Schl; Passaic, NJ; (4); Church Yth Grp; Exploring; Key Clb; Latin Clb; Ski Clb; Band; Yrbk Stf; Var Vllybl; Most Imprvd Vlybl 84.

CALLEGHER, AMY; Linden HS; Linden, NJ; (2); Civic Clb; Key Clb; Band; Drm Mjr(t); Mrchg Band; Trs Frsh Cls; Off Stu Cncl.

CALLEO, GINA; Union HS; Union, NJ; (2); Chess Clb; Spanish Clb; Chorus; Var L Crs Cntry; JV Fld Hcky; Var L Trk; Hon Roll; Pres Schlr; N Jersey Stu Crftmns Fair 3rd Pl-Photogrphy 87; Union Cnty 3rd Tm Crss Cntry 86; 5th P NJ Mrthn 87; Bus.

CALVANESE, DINA; St James HS; Gibbstown, NJ; (4); 7/69; Am Leg Aux Girls St; Art Clb; Yrbk Stf; Pres Soph Cls; Sftbl; Cit Awd; High Hon Roll; Hon Roll; Pres NHS; Ntl Merit Ltr; Immaculate Coll; Engl.

CALVIELLO, DAVID; St Mary HS; Rutherford, NJ; (4); 9/77; Am Leg Boys St; NFL; Political Wkr; Pres Soph Cls; Pres Jr Cls; Capt Var Bsktbl; Var Ftbl; Dnfth Awd; NHS; Kiwanis Clb Schlrshp 87; HS Athl Acdmc Awd 87; The Catholic U Am; Law.

CAMACHO JR, CARLOS; John F Kennedy HS; Willingboro, NJ; (2); 42/250; Trk; Hon Roll; Penn ST U; Law & Crmnl Jstc.

CAMADO, MARIA RONA; Belleville HS; Belleville, NJ; (3); Key Clb; Latin Clb; Spanish Clb; Rep Stu Cncl; Rutgers U; Engr.

CAMERON, AMY; Morristown HS; Normandy Pkwy, NJ; (2); Cmnty Wkr; Key Clb; Yrbk Stf; Trs Jr Cls; Ice Hcky; Lcrss; Socr; High Hon Roll; Hon Roll; Stanford U.

CAMERON, HEATHER; Butler HS; Butler, NJ; (4); 32/200; Math Tm; Yrbk Stf; Fld Hcky; Swmmng; Trk; High Hon Roll; Hon Roll; NHS; Charles K Payne Schlrshp Awd $500 87; Lakeland St Bnk Schlrshp Awd $600; William Paterson Coll; Psych.

CAMERON, KAREN JEANNE; Mountain Lakes HS; Mountain Lakes, NJ; (3); 16/116; Capt GAA; Math Tm; Gym; High Hon Roll; NHS; Spanish NHS; NJ ST All-Rnd Champ-Beam/Flr Champ, Estrn Rgnl All-Rnd Champ-Beam/Flr Champ,USAIGC Natl Tm Champ; Dance.

CAMERON, ROBERT; Ramapo Regional HS; Wyckoff, NJ; (4); 4/326; Cmnty Wkr; Hosp Aide; Radio Clb; Ed Lit Mag; Rep Frsh Cls; High Hon Roll; NHS; Ntl Merit Ltr; St Schlr; Colgate U.

CAMINITI, MELISSA; Paramus HS; Paramus, NJ; (4); 93/331; FBLA; Var L Cheerleading; Powder Puff Ftbl; Var L Sftbl; Italian Hnr Soc; Prom Cmte; Trenton ST Coll; Pre-Law.

CAMISA, TERESA; Bloomfield SR HS; Bloomfield, NJ; (3); Church Yth Grp; French Clb; Key Clb; Math Tm; Sec Soph Cls; VP Jr Cls; Trs Sr Cls; Trs Stu Cncl; Tennis; High Hon Roll.

CAMLIBEL, ALICIA; Mt St John Acad; Oxford, NJ; (2); Church Yth Grp; NFL; SADD; Chorus; Sec Frsh Cls; Sec Soph Cls; Var Cheerleading; Var Coach Actv; Hon Roll; Art Clb; 1st Pl-Frgn Lang Poetry Cont 87; 3rd Pl-Math Fair Poster Cont 87; Princeton; Psychrst.

CAMMA, FRANK; Clearview Regional HS; Sewell, NJ; (3); 6/181; Exploring; Var Ftbl; High Hon Roll; Hon Roll; Sntr Intrn Prog 87; Amer Lgn Boys St Nom 87; Rtry Ldrshp Prog Nom 87; U Of PA; Finance.

CAMMALLERI, ROBERTO; Bergenfield HS; Bergenfield, NJ; (3); 2/300; Chrmn Am Leg Boys St; Computer Clb; Math Tm; Quiz Bowl; Radio Clb; Var Bsktbl; Var Socr; Hon Roll; NHS; Rensselaer Poly Tech Inst Math & Sci Awd 87; Gvnrs Schl Of Sci Semfnlst 87; Amer Comp Sci Lgu Top Scor; Elec Engr.

CAMMAROTA, VICKY; Manchester Rgional HS; N Haledon, NJ; (3); GAA; Office Aide; Rep Frsh Cls; Rep Soph Cls; Rep Jr Cls; Rep Stu Cncl; JV Var Cheerleading; JV Powder Puff Ftbl; Var Trk; Hon Roll.

CAMMILLERI, ROXANNE; Mary Help Of Christians Acad; Clifton, NJ; (4); Art Clb; Dance Clb; Drama Clb; Letterman Clb; Service Clb; Drill Tm; School Play; Variety Show; Nwsp Ed-Chief; Hon Roll; Drozd-Skawinska Mem Schlrshp 87-88; Intl Frgn Lang Awd Ltn 87; Natl Ltn Exm Cum Laude Awd 87; Felician Coll; Art.

CAMMILLERI, SANDRA; Mary Help Of Christians Acad; Clifton, NJ; (4); Dance Clb; Drama Clb; Letterman Clb; Service Clb; Drill Tm; School Play; Variety Show; Nwsp Rptr; Nwsp Stf; Hon Roll; Ltn Hnr Soc 87; Pres Schlrshp 87-88fmaxima Cum Laude Slvr Mdl Natl Ltn Exm 87; Felician Coll.

CAMPANARO, FRANK; James Caldwell HS; W Caldwell, NJ; (3); Ski Clb; Wt Lftg; Wrstlng; High Hon Roll; Hon Roll; NHS.

CAMPANELLA, CRAIG; Park Ridge HS; Park Ridge, NJ; (3); 3/98; Am Leg Boys St; Math Clb; Scholastic Bowl; Spanish Clb; Varsity Clb; Stage Crew; Yrbk Sprt Ed; Bsbl; High Hon Roll; NHS; Outstndng Math Stu 86-87; 2nd Tm All Lg Var Bsbl 86-87; SF AISME Math Tst 86-87; Math.

CAMPANELLA, PETE; Washington Township HS; Sewell, NJ; (3); Church Yth Grp; Trs German Clb; Ski Clb; Crs Cntry; JV Socr; Trk; Hon Roll; Grmn Hnr Soc 86-87; Outstndng Fld Evnts 85-86; Dedctn Awd 86-87; Drexel U; Aero.

CAMPBELL, ALDON; Dwight Morrow HS; Englewood, NJ; (3); 19/312; High Hon Roll; Hon Roll; NHS; Prfct Atten Awd; Political Wkr; JV Trk; Sci Awd 87; Mech Engrng.

CAMPBELL, CELESTE; John F Kennedy HS; Willingboro, NJ; (4); 7/267; Am Leg Aux Girls St; Church Yth Grp; Band; Chorus; School Musical; Yrbk Stf; JV Var Tennis; Hon Roll; NHS; Ntl Merit Schol; Grdn ST Dstngshd Sclr 86-87; Rotary Ldrshp Awd 86, Stdnt Mnth 87; U Miami; Film Prod.

CAMPBELL, COLIN; Haddonfield Memorial HS; Haddonfield, NJ; (4); 13/152; Pres Drama Clb; German Clb; Intnl Clb; School Musical; School Play; Hon Roll; NHS; Ntl Merit SF; Chess Clb; Madrigals; German Natl Hnr Scty 86-87; Olympics Of The Mind Renatra Fusca Awd 84; U Of PA; Arch.

CAMPBELL, EDWARD; West Orange HS; W Orange, NJ; (4); Church Yth Grp; Office Aide; Seton Hall U; Eng.

CAMPBELL, KAREN; Holy Spirit HS; Margate, NJ; (2); 50/397; Church Yth Grp; Var Swmmng; Hon Roll; Rutgers U; Educ.

CAMPBELL, KAREN; Queen Of Peace HS; Kearny, NJ; (3); 50/279; NFL; VP Service Clb; Mgr Stage Crew; Rep Soph Cls; Rep Jr Cls; Rep Stu Cncl; Hon Roll; Kiwanis Awd; St Brother Miguel Hnr Soc 85-86; Scottish Champ 86; Highland Dancine Overall In US; Law.

CAMPBELL, SCOTT; Shore Regional HS; Oceanport, NJ; (3); JV Bsktbl; High Hon Roll; Hon Roll; Rutgers U; Mech Engr.

CAMPBELL, SHERRY; Hillside HS; Hillside, NJ; (3); Leo Clb; Spanish Clb; Nwsp Rptr; Yrbk Stf; Mgr(s); Hon Roll; Rep Frsh Cls; Sec Soph Cls; VP Jr Cls; Rep Sr Cls; Engl.

CAMPBELL, TRACY; Cherry Hill HS West; Cherry Hill, NJ; (3); Church Yth Grp; Cmnty Wkr; Office Aide; Spanish Clb; JV Capt Cheerleading; Hon Roll.

CAMPBELL, WAYNE; Parsippany Hills HS; Morris Plns, NJ; (4); German Clb; Key Clb; Office Aide; VP Science Clb; Ski Clb; Wrstlng; Hon Roll; NHS; PTA Awd 87; U CA, Berkeley.

CAMPBELL, WILLIAM; Immaculate HS; Somerville, NJ; (3); 32/254; Pres Intnl Clb; Math Clb; Model UN; Rep Jr Cls; Pres Sr Cls; Rep Stu Cncl; JV Bsktbl; JV Ftbl; Var L Golf; Var L Socr; Catholic Yth Chrties, Stu Athlete 87; Bus.

CAMPESI, MICHELLE; Mother Seton Regional HS; Roselle Park, NJ; (3); Drill Tm; Hon Roll; NHS; Geom Cert Achvt 85; Alg II Cert Achvt 86; Bus.

CAMPI JR, THOMAS; Wall HS; Allenwood, NJ; (3); 11/300; German Clb; Intnl Clb; Key Clb; Latin Clb; Ski Clb; Spanish Clb; SADD; Off Frsh Cls; Off Soph Cls; Off Jr Cls.

CAMPIS, JUAN E; Perth Amboy HS; Perth Amboy, NJ; (3); Computer Clb; ROTC; Band; Concert Band; Drill Tm; Jazz Band; Mrchg Band; Pep Band; Rep Jr Cls; Capt Trk; Comp Sci.

CAMPISANO, GINA MARIE; Wayne Valley HS; Wayne, NJ; (4); Cmnty Wkr; Computer Clb; Dance Clb; 4-H; French Clb; FBLA; GAA; JA; Office Aide; Red Cross Aide; Schlrshp Govrns Tchng Schlrs Prog 87; Parent Teacher Organztn Schlrshp 87; U CO; Math.

CAMPO, ALBA; Bricktownship HS; Brichtown, NJ; (4); Art Clb; Spanish Clb; Nwsp Rptr; High Hon Roll; Hon Roll; Spnsh Merit Awd 86; Awd Dept Lang & Lit Rider Coll 86; Mercer CC; Airline Stwrdss.

CAMPO, ANTOINETTE C; Shore Regional HS; W Long Branch, NJ; (3); Boy Scts; Computer Clb; Exploring; Math Clb; Science Clb; Variety Show; Socr; High Hon Roll; Chmstry League Awd 87; NY U; Cmmnctns.

CAMPOLI, MARY BETH; Southern Regional HS; Manahawkin, NJ; (3); Yrbk Stf; Off Frsh Cls; Off Jr Cls; Off Sr Cls; Stu Cncl; Fld Hcky; Mgr(s); Powder Puff Ftbl; Score Keeper; Sftbl; Fshn Dsgn.

CAMPOS, JAVIER; Paterson Catholic HS; Paterson, NJ; (3); DECA; Spanish Clb; Varsity Clb; Var Socr; Pres Vllybl; Rep Wt Lftg; Schl Of Media Art; Recrdng Engr.

CANADY, STEVEN L; Roselle Catholic HS; Roselle, NJ; (4); 119/190; Aud/Vis; Hosp Aide; School Play; JV Bsbl; Var Bsktbl; Var Crs Cntry; Ftbl; Trk; Olympics Of The Mind; Gftd & Tlntd Pgm; Intrmrl Hcky,Ftbl Bsktbl & Ping-Pong; Northeastern U; Phrmcy.

CANAVAN, KRISTIE; Middletown HS South; Red Bank, NJ; (3); Drama Clb; Variety Show; Yrbk Stf; Hon Roll; Dancer.

CANCILA, GREGORY; St James HS; Gibbstown, NJ; (4); 3/69; Am Leg Boys St; English Clb; Ski Clb; Spanish Clb; School Play; Stage Crew; Var Bsbl; JV Bsktbl; Var Ftbl; High Hon Roll; USAA Ldrshp Awd 85-86; Tutor In Engsh & Mth 86-87; Elec Engnrng.

CANDELARIA, HERIBERTO; New Brunswick HS; New Brunswick, NJ; (4); 1/150; Church Yth Grp; Math Tm; Spanish Clb; Lit Mag; Trs Jr Cls; Rep Pres Stu Cncl; Bausch & Lomb Sci Awd; NHS; Spanish NHS.

CANDELORI, NEEVA-GAYLE; Cherry Hill West HS; Cherry Hill, NJ; (4); Pres Trs Church Yth Grp; Dance Clb; French Clb; Office Aide; Acpl Chr; Chorus; Church Choir; Orch; Var Fld Hcky; Var Lcrss; Phila Coll Txtls & Sci; Fin.

CANDINO, KEVIN; Marist HS; Bayonne, NJ; (3); Drama Clb; Key Clb; Concert Band.

CANDON, CHRISTA; Union Catholic Regional HS; Clark, NJ; (4); Drama Clb; Hosp Aide; VP Thesps; Chorus; School Musical; School Play; Stage Crew; Nwsp Stf; Hon Roll; Extrordnry Stdnts Amer Prfrmg Arts 86-87; Montclair ST Coll.

CANE, JOANNE; Parsippany HS; Parsippany, NJ; (4); 95/321; Capt Cheerleading; Hon Roll; Church Yth Grp; FBLA; Pep Clb; Varsity Clb; Fld Hcky; Sftbl; Chrldng Schlrshp 87; MVP Chrldng 86-87; Hofstra U; Bus Fin.

CANGELOSI, JOANN; Washington Township HS; Sewell, NJ; (3); Am Leg Aux Girls St; French Clb; Hosp Aide; Sec Concert Band; Sec Mrchg Band; Nwsp Stf; Stu Cncl; NHS; Ntl Merit Schol.

CANGIALOSI, LISA; Memorial HS; Elmwood, NJ; (3); Math Clb; Concert Band; Mrchg Band; School Musical; NHS; St Schlr.

CANIZARES, LOURDES; Memorial HS; West New York, NJ; (4); 35/356; Art Clb; Cmnty Wkr; French Clb; Teachers Aide; Color Guard; Rep Frsh Cls; Rep Stu Cncl; Timer; Mgr Trk; Hon Roll; Urbn Schlrshp Awd Kean Coll 87; Kean Coll NJ.

CANNATA, CHRISTINE; Matawan Regional HS; Matawan, NJ; (3); Stu Cncl; Mgr(s); Score Keeper; Stat JV Socr.

CANNING, WALT; Gloucester City JR/Sr HS; Gloucester, NJ; (3); Church Yth Grp; Cmnty Wkr; DECA; FBLA; Lit Mag; Bsbl; Bsktbl; Crs Cntry; Mgr(s); Cit Awd; D Heart & Lng Ctr 82-87; FBLA 86-87; DE II 86-87; Camden Cnty Coll; Scndry Educ.

CANNON, KIMBLE; Neptune HS; Ocean Grove, NJ; (4); 2/400; Boy Scts; Pres Debate Tm; Drama Clb; Math Tm; Ski Clb; Pres Stu Cncl; Capt Swmmng; Trk; Voice Dem Awd; Slvr Cngrssnl Mdl; Duke U.

CANNON, MELISSA; Edgewood Regional HS; Sicklerville, NJ; (4); 7/321; Pres Latin Clb; Pres Varsity Clb; Rep Soph Cls; Sec Jr Cls; Rep Sr Cls; Var Bsktbl; Var Sftbl; Capt Var Tennis; DAR Awd; NHS; Penn ST U; Bus Admin.

CANSECO, EDUARDO; St Peters Prep; Bloomfield, NJ; (4); 45/196; Art Clb; Cmnty Wkr; Computer Clb; French Clb; Teachers Aide; Stage Crew; Var Trk; High Hon Roll; Prsdntl Acdmc Ftnss Awd 87; Boston U; Cmptr Engnr.

CANTELLO, PAUL; Hawthorne HS; Hawthorne, NJ; (3); Cmnty Wkr; Chorus; Jazz Band; Mrchg Band; Nwsp Rptr; Yrbk Ed-Chief; Var Tennis; High Hon Roll; NHS; Spanish NHS; Poli Sci.

CANZANO, CLAUDINE; Madison Central HS; Old Bridge, NJ; (3); FBLA; GAA; Varsity Clb; VP Frsh Cls; VP Soph Cls; Pres Jr Cls; Pres Sr Cls; Rep Stu Cncl; Stat Bsktbl; Capt Cheerleading; Middlesex Cnty Coll; Bus.

CAOLA, CHRISTINA; Paramus Catholic Girls Rgnl HS; Fort Lee, NJ; (3); 18/179; Camera Clb; Cmnty Wkr; Trs FBLA; Nwsp Stf; VP Soph Cls; VP Vllybl; Pres Sr Cls; Hon Roll; Prfct Atten Awd; Tutored Alg & Chem; Engrng Law.

CAPALBO, KAREN; Highland Regional HS; Erial, NJ; (4); Cmnty Wkr; Dance Clb; Drama Clb; Latin Clb; NFL; SADD; School Play; Pres Frsh Cls; Rep Soph Cls; Rep Sr Cls; Ntl Latin Ex Awd 86; La Salle; Mrktng.

CAPELLI, LISA; Hoboken HS; Hoboken, NJ; (3); 7/258; Var Sftbl; Var Tennis; Hon Roll; NHS; Trs Stu Cncl; Montclain ST Coll.

CAPESTRO, LISA; Matawan Regional HS; Matawan, NJ; (4); 10/316; French Clb; NFL; Color Guard; Ed Yrbk Ed-Chief; Jr Cls; Pres Sr Cls; Off Stu Cncl; French Hon Soc; NHS; Girls Ctznshp Awd, Gov Schl Arts; Teen Arts Fest Cmndtn; Lib Arts.

CAPITANO, ROSANNE; Rosella Catholic HS; Roselle, NJ; (4); 39/195; Stage Crew; Stat Bsbl; Stat Bsktbl; Hon Roll; Spanish NHS; 1st Yr Spn Awd 85; Seton Hall U; Psych.

CAPOBIANCO, JAMES M; Saddle Brook HS; Saddle Brook, NJ; (4); 15/116; Am Leg Boys St; Quiz Bowl; School Play; Nwsp Stf; Lit Mag; Stu Cncl; JC Awd; Art Awds 84-87; CA Inst Arts; Animation.

CAPOLI, ANTHONY; Eastern HS; West Berlin, NJ; (3); Drama Clb; Intnl Clb; Quiz Bowl; School Musical; Pres Soph Cls; Pres Jr Cls; Pres Stu Cncl; L Bsbl; High Hon Roll; Hon Roll; 2nd Pl Acad Of Karate Trnmnt 85; Marine Ftnss Awd 86; Villanova U; Bus Adm.

CAPONE, CARLA; Washington Township HS; Blackwood, NJ; (3); 80/530; Cmnty Wkr; Q&S; Spanish Clb; Glassboro ST Coll; Bio.

CAPORALETTI, MICHELLE; Holy Cross HS; Willingboro, NJ; (3); Var Sftbl; Hon Roll; Med.

CAPOZZA, RENEE; Brick Township HS; Brick Town, NJ; (3); 25/400; Key Clb; Ski Clb; Drill Tm; Flag Corp; Mrchg Band; Yrbk Stf; High Hon Roll; Hon Roll; Bus.

CAPOZZI, DANIELLE; Indian Hills HS; Franklin Lks, NJ; (3); 38/306; AFS; Spanish Clb; Stage Crew; Nwsp Stf; JV Trk; High Hon Roll; Hon Roll; Drama Clb; Vet Med.

CAPOZZOLI, MICHELE L; The Pennington Schl; Trenton, NJ; (1); 1/58; Chorus; Pres Frsh Cls; Rep Stu Cncl; Var L Cheerleading; Stat Score Keeper; Hon Roll.

CAPOZZOLO, ANTHONY; Morris Catholic HS; Parsippany, NJ; (4); 20/138; Church Yth Grp; FBLA; Var L Ftbl; Var Trk; High Hon Roll; Pres Acad Ftns Awd 87; Marist Coll; Info Sys.

CAPPELLINI, MARNIE; Northern Vly Rgnl HS At Old Tappan; Norwood, NJ; (3); 74/274; AFS; Ski Clb; Spanish Clb; SADD; Stage Crew; Hon Roll; Comms.

CAPPIELLO, STEVEN; Hudson Catholic HS; Hoboken, NJ; (3); 2/190; Debate Tm; Math Clb; Science Clb; Teachers Aide; Nwsp Rptr; Yrbk Stf; Var L Bowling; Var L Tennis; High Hon Roll; NHS; Hugh O Brien Yth Fndtn Ambsr 86; Joseph V Monaco Almn Schlrshp 86; Mens Clb Tutn Grnt SR Yr 87-88; Ivy Lgu Coll; Law.

CAPRA, SANDRA; Sacred Heart HS; Vineland, NJ; (3); French Clb; School Play; Yrbk Ed-Chief; Off Frsh Cls; Off Jr Cls; Var Capt Cheerleading; Mgr(s); High Hon Roll; NHS.

CAPRARI, ELENA; Bishop George Area HS; E Brunswick, NJ; (4); 37/265; Rep Church Yth Grp; Pres VP 4-H; VP Service Clb; Teachers Aide; Concert Band; Mrchg Band; School Musical; 4-H Awd; High Hon Roll; Hon Roll; Garden ST Schlrshp 87; Rider Coll; Bus Adm.

CAPRIGLIONE, RONNIE; Belleville HS; Belleville, NJ; (2); JV Bsbl; High Hon Roll; Hon Roll; Prfct Atten Awd.

CARABALLO, KIMBERLY; Monville Twp HS; Boonton, NJ; (4); 60/258; Drama Clb; Hosp Aide; Key Clb; School Musical; Hon Roll; NHS; Opt Clb Awd; Fairleigh Dickinson U; Psychlgy.

CARABALLO, MARIBEL; Orange HS; Orange, NJ; (2); High Hon Roll; NHS.

CARABALLO, MICHELE; Montville Township HS; Boonton, NJ; (2); FBLA; Key Clb; Var Capt Cheerleading; Mgr(s); High Hon Roll; Hon Roll; Law.

CARABELLESE, SANDI; Pinelands Regional HS; Tuckerton, NJ; (3); 9/190; Spanish Clb; Var Fld Hcky; Var Capt Trk; Hon Roll; NHS; Spanish NHS; Stu Mnth Awd 87; Sports Feature Ath Wk 87; Stockton ST Coll.

CARABELLESE, TRACI; Pinelands Regional HS; Mystic Island, NJ; (4); JV Fld Hcky; Var Trk; High Hon Roll; Hon Roll; NHS; Stuart Schl Schlrshp 86; Trck Sprtsprsn Awd 85-86; Track Most Helpful Awd 86; Stuart Schl; Legal Secy.

CARACCI, DOUGLAS; Holy Cross HS; Burlington, NJ; (3); 79/409; Chess Clb; Computer Clb; Science Clb; Golf; Hon Roll; Math.

CARAFELLO, JEANINE; Paramus Catholic HS; N Haledon, NJ; (3); Spanish Clb; Nwsp Rptr; Nwsp Sprt Ed; Lit Mag; NEDT Awd; Commnctns.

CARALLUZZO, KAREN L; Vineland HS; Vineland, NJ; (4); 200/653; Church Yth Grp; Office Aide; Italian Clb 85-86; Cncl Excptnl Chldrn Clb 85-86; Cumberland Cnty Coll; Music.

CARANO, SUZETTE; Buena Regional HS; Vineland, NJ; (4); 10/187; Drama Clb; Math Tm; Red Cross Aide; Ski Clb; School Play; Rep Frsh Cls; Rep Soph Cls; Rep Jr Cls; Rep Sr Cls; VP Pres Stu Cncl; Hugh O Brien Ldrshp Smnr 85; Merit Roll 86-87; Z-Club 86-87; Ursinus Coll; Vtrnry Med.

CARAVETTA, DENISE ANN; Nutley HS; Nutley, NJ; (3); 12/310; AFS; Am Leg Aux Girls St; Church Yth Grp; Key Clb; Spanish Clb; Stage Crew; Yrbk Stf; Pres Frsh Cls; Stu Cncl; Pres NHS; Girls ST Cnty Frhldr 87; Hugh O Brian Yth Fndtn Amb 86; Miss Teen NJ ST Pgnt Awareness Test Wnnr 87; Phy.

CARBERRY, DARCY; Jackson HS; Jackson, NJ; (2); 38/413; Sftbl; High Hon Roll; Hon Roll.

CARBONE, LAURA; Wood Ridge HS; Wood Ridge, NJ; (2); Art Clb; Model UN; Vllybl; Art.

CARBONE, RAYMOND; Passaic County Tech/Voc HS; Paterson, NJ; (4); 5/466; VICA; Band; Nwsp Rptr; High Hon Roll; Hon Roll; NHS; Prfct Atten Awd; NJ Inst Tech; Elect Engr.

CARCICH, JACQUI; Neptun SR HS; Neptune, NJ; (2); 5/350; Varsity Clb; Trs Jr Cls; Var L Bsktbl; Capt Var Sftbl; Var Tennis; High Hon Roll; Acctng.

CARDACI, MICHAEL P; Secaucus HS; Secaucus, NJ; (3); 20/176; Am Leg Boys St; Varsity Clb; Bsbl; Ftbl; Cit Awd; High Hon Roll; Hon Roll; Boys ST Am Lgn 87; Bus.

CARDENTEY, CATHLEEN; North Bergen HS; North Bergen, NJ; (3); JA; Chorus; School Musical; School Play; Variety Show; Hon Roll; Medical Tech.

CARDINEZ, NATALIE; North Bergen HS; N Bergen, NJ; (4); 210/435; Art Clb; Camera Clb; SADD; Chorus; Yrbk Bus Mgr; Yrbk Phtg; Yrbk Stf; Lcrss; Tennis; Wt Lftg.

CARDIS, BRIAN; Holy Cross HS; Florence, NJ; (3); 57/410; Chess Clb; Computer Clb; German Clb; Band; Concert Band; Jazz Band; Mrchg Band; Orch; Pep Band; School Musical; Bst Soloist Music In Parks Busch Grdns 87; Pharmacist.

CARDONA, ALFREDO JAVIER; Vineland SR HS; Vineland, NJ; (3); 79/820; Debate Tm; Library Aide; Political Wkr; Spanish Clb; SADD; Rep Frsh Cls; Rep Soph Cls; Rep Jr Cls; Rep Stu Cncl; Hon Roll; Chem Engr.

CARDONA, MARIBEL; Our Lady Of Good Counsel HS; Newark, NJ; (3); 55/122; FCA; Teachers Aide; Chorus; Gym.

CARDUCCI, ROBERT; Phillipsburg HS; Phillipsburg, NJ; (3); Var Crs Cntry; Trk; Wt Lftg; Comp Sci.

CAREY, DAVID; Lyndhurst HS; Lyndhurst, NJ; (2); Art Clb; German Clb; Ski Clb; VP Frsh Cls; Bsbl; Bsktbl; Ftbl; Seton Hall; Business.

CAREY, ERIN M; West Morris Central HS; Long Valley, NJ; (4); 43/290; Am Leg Aux Girls St; Science Clb; Ski Clb; Band; Concert Band; Mrchg Band; Orch; Rep Frsh Cls; Rep Soph Cls; Rep Jr Cls; Natl Hnr Soc Schlrshp, Outstndng Cls Stu Artst, Ed Asstnce Fnd Morris Cnty Schlrshp 87; St Marys Coll IN; Visual Arts.

CAREY, GINA; Florence Twp Memorial HS; Florence, NJ; (3); Am Leg Aux Girls St; GAA; Jazz Band; Off Frsh Cls; Off Soph Cls; VP Jr Cls; VP Sr Cls; Stu Cncl; Capt L Bsktbl; Capt L Fld Hcky; Trenton ST; Crmnl Just.

CAREY, LAURA E; West Morris Central HS; Long Valley, NJ; (4); 62/288; Drm Mjr(t); Jazz Band; High Hon Roll; Hon Roll; NHS; Natl Hnrs Soc Schlrshp 87; J Young Awd F Or Band 87; Barbara Martenis Schlrshp 87; Ithaca; Music Peformance.

CAREY, LYNNE; Notre Dame HS; Kendall Pk, NJ; (3); Church Yth Grp; Red Cross Aide; Service Clb; Ski Clb; SADD; Hon Roll; Jrnlst.

CAREY, STEVE; Vernon Township HS; Vernon, NJ; (3); Aud/Vis; Band; Yrbk Stf; Rep Frsh Cls; Rep Jr Cls; Hon Roll; Bus.

CARFAGNO, ASHLEE; Cherokee HS; Marlton, NJ; (2); Church Yth Grp; French Clb; Teachers Aide; Lit Mag; Hon Roll; NHS; Phy Thrpst.

CARFORA, ELAINE; St Aloysius HS; Jersey City, NJ; (2); Church Yth Grp; Exploring; SADD; School Play; Nwsp Rptr; Off Frsh Cls; Sec Soph Cls; Stu Cncl; Capt Bowling; Mgr(s); Outstndng Achvt-Wrld Hstry, Albr, Rlgn & Engl 86; Hghst Grd Pt Avg Physcl Sci 86 & Engl 87; Med.

CARIGA, ZOILA; Memorial HS; West New York, NJ; (3); Dance Clb; Debate Tm; English Clb; French Clb; Radio Clb; SADD; Nwsp Stf; Gym; Sftbl; Swmmng; Boyd Schl; Trvl.

CARINI, LAURIE; Millville SR HS; Millville, NJ; (4); Office Aide; Political Wkr; SADD; Color Guard; Mrchg Band; Variety Show; Sec Stu Cncl; Var Socr; Hon Roll; Stu Cncl Schlrshp 87; Cmbrlnd Cnty Coll; Bus Adm.

CARINO, THERESA; West Morris Mendham HS; Chester, NJ; (4); 2/318; Debate Tm; FBLA; Science Clb; Mrchg Band; High Hon Roll; NHS; St Schlr; The Wellesley JR Book Awd 86; U PA; Bus.

CARIS, JILL; Brick Memorial HS; Brick, NJ; (3); 61/380; Trs Key Clb; Temple Yth Grp; Var Capt Tennis; High Hon Roll; Hon Roll; Rutgers; Law.

CARLIN, ELIZABETH; Paulsboro HS; Paulsboro, NJ; (3); JV Bsktbl; JV Sftbl; JV Trk; Air Force.

CARLOWICZ, MICHAEL JAMES; St Joseph HS; Edison, NJ; (4); 1/206; Model UN; Nwsp Stf; Lit Mag; Var JV Bsbl; NHS; Ntl Merit Ltr; Val; Dance Clb; School Musical; Rep Jr Cls; Garden ST Distngshd Schlr 87; Outstndng Delg Harvard Mdl UN 85 & 86; Natl Merit Spc Scholar 87; Georgetown U; Bio Sci.

CARLSEN, MICHAEL; St Anthonys HS; Jersey Cty, NJ; (3); 4/80; Boy Scts; Bsbl; Bowling; Bus Mgmt.

CARLSON, MATTHEW; East Brunswick HS; E Brunswick, NJ; (3); Boy Scts; Chess Clb; Trs Church Yth Grp; German Clb; Science Clb; Symp Band; Ftbl; Vllybl; Wt Lftg; Hon Roll.

CARLSON, SCOTT; Morris Knolls HS; Denville, NJ; (3); 33/440; Boy Scts; Church Yth Grp; Debate Tm; Math Clb; Math Tm; Swmmng; Prfct Atten Awd; Summa Awd 85, 86 & 87; Dbtng Awd 87; Ntl Hnr Soc 87; Elctrcl Engrng.

CARLSON, TIMOTHY; North Warren Regional HS; Blairstown, NJ; (2); Ski Clb; Band; Concert Band; Mrchg Band; Pep Band; Bsbl; Socr; Hon Roll; Drum Captain 86-87; Air Force Acad; Pilot.

CARLSON, TINA; Sayreville War Memorial HS; Sayreville, NJ; (3); Church Yth Grp; Drama Clb; French Clb; Chorus; Stage Crew; Rep Soph Cls; Mgr Socr; Sftbl; Kean Coll; Elem Ed.

CARMELI, AUDREY; Parsippany HS; Parsippany, NJ; (4); 11/330; Church Yth Grp; Drama Clb; Trs Chorus; School Musical; School Play; Variety Show; High Hon Roll; Hon Roll; NHS; Ntl Merit SF; Natl Hispanic Schlr SF 86-87.

CARMICHAEL, MONICA; Burlington City HS; Edgewater, NJ; (3); Am Leg Aux Girls St; Exploring; Office Aide; Color Guard; Off Soph Cls; Stu Cncl; Var Cheerleading; Hon Roll; Minorities Engr Prog 85-86; Stu Cncl Rep 85-86; Stu Cncl Rep 86-87; Micro Bio.

CARMICHAEL, SHALEIM; Plainfield HS; Plainfield, NJ; (3); Debate Tm; Drama Clb; Model UN; Pep Clb; PAVAS; Church Choir; Pres Soph Cls; Vllybl; Hon Roll; Howard; Law.

CARMODY, DENNIS; St Rose HS; Neptune, NJ; (3); Chess Clb; Service Clb; Nwsp Rptr; Lit Mag; High Hon Roll; Hon Roll; NHS; NEDT Awd; Prfct Atten Awd; Rcgntn Excell Schlrshp 87; Jrnlsm.

CARNEIRO, AMALIA; East Side HS; Newark, NJ; (3); Church Yth Grp; Cmnty Wkr; Library Aide; Math Clb; Church Choir; Hon Roll; Nrsg.

CARNEVALE, LYNN; St John Vianney HS; Colts Neck, NJ; (3); 31/256; Church Yth Grp; Drama Clb; Spanish Clb; Thesps; Church Choir; School Musical; School Play; High Hon Roll; Hon Roll; Otstndng Achvt Spnsh 86 & 87; Gld & White Awd 87; Spnsh.

CARNIVALE III, MICHAEL; Burlington City HS; Burlington, NJ; (3); Am Leg Boys St; Church Yth Grp; Variety Show; Sec Stu Cncl; Var Crs Cntry; JV Trk; JV Wrstlng; Hon Roll; S Jersey Stu Crafts Fair - Outstndng & 2nd Fl 87; Civil Engrng.

CARO, ELLEN; Columbia HS; Maplewood, NJ; (3); Cmnty Wkr; Pep Clb; SADD; Temple Yth Grp; Y-Teens; Band; Chorus; Concert Band; Rep Frsh Cls; Rep Soph Cls; Gold Cert Music Ed Assn 82-84; Summer Arts Inst Cert 85-86; Natl Piano Plyng Audtns 81-82; Cmmnctns.

CAROE, CHRISTINA; Westfield HS; Westfield, NJ; (3); 14/469; Latin Clb; Concert Band; Var L Swmmng; High Hon Roll; Hon Roll; Bk Of Gold-Top 7 Pct Of Clss-Schltc/Ctznshp 84-85; Swmmng St Champs Tm 84-86; Lib Arts.

CAROLLA, AMY; Parsippany Hills HS; Parsippany, NJ; (3); Cmnty Wkr; FBLA; Hosp Aide; Key Clb; Service Clb; Stu Cncl; Powder Puff Ftbl.

CAROZZA, DEBRA; Academy Of Holy Angels HS; Upper Saddle Rive, NJ; (2); Church Yth Grp; Cmnty Wkr; Drama Clb; Ski Clb; Chorus; Church Choir; School Musical; Variety Show; Theater Arts.

CARPENTER, GAIL; Kent Place Schl; Short Hills, NJ; (4); VP Camera Clb; Church Yth Grp; Q&S; Variety Show; Ed Yrbk Phtg; Rep Frsh Cls; Rep Soph Cls; JV Fld Hcky; Achvt Vis Art Phopto Teen Arts Fstvl 86 & 87; Hnrs Art 87; William Smith; Engl.

CARPENTER, JEFFREY; Long Branch HS; Long Branch, NJ; (4); #1 In Class; French Clb; Mrchg Band; School Musical; Symp Band; Var L Bsbl; Bausch & Lomb Sci Awd; Gov Hon Prg Awd; Pres JETS Awd; NHS; Val; Garden ST Dstngshd Schlr Schlrshp 86; Rutgers Coll; Mech Engrng.

CARPENTER, KIM; Toms River East HS; Toms River, NJ; (3); 158/509; Camera Clb; Variety Show; Nwsp Phtg; Nwsp Stf; Yrbk Phtg; Mgr(s); Score Keeper; Wrstlng; Hon Roll; Fshn Merch.

CARPINELLO, CHRISTOPHER; Manasquan HS; Manasquan, NJ; (3); 22/240; Boy Scts; Drama Clb; French Clb; FBLA; Yrbk Stf; Var Crs Cntry; JV Socr; High Hon Roll; Jr NHS; Eagle Scout 86; NE U; Comp Sci.

CARPINELLO, KRISTINE; Jackson Memorial HS; Jackson, NJ; (4); 74/425; French Clb; Spanish Clb; Varsity Clb; Trs Jr Cls; Rep Sr Cls; JV Var Cheerleading; Powder Puff Ftbl; JV Var Socr; High Hon Roll; Hon Roll.

CARR, ALLISON; Cherokee HS; Atco, NJ; (2); Art Clb; Church Yth Grp; French Clb; Stage Crew; Hon Roll; Sci.

CARR, COLLEEN; Pinelands Regional HS; Tuckerton, NJ; (3); Am Leg Aux Girls St; Nwsp Ed-Chief; JV Bsktbl; JV Sftbl; Var Tennis; NHS; Sec Spanish NHS; Spanish Clb; Chorus; Nwsp Rptr; Sprtsmnshp Awd Girls Vrsty Tennis; Coachs Awd JV Girls Bsktbll; Full Schlrshp To 4 Yr Tennis Acad; James Madison U; Comm.

CARR, DAVID A; Manalapan HS; Manalapon, NJ; (3); 16/429; Cmnty Wkr; Drama Clb; JV Bsktbl; NHS.

CARR, KRISTINE; Holy Cross HS; Mount Laurel, NJ; (3); 78/400; Church Yth Grp; Rep Frsh Cls; Var Crs Cntry; JV Socr; Var Trk; Reg Hnrs 86-87; Advrtsng.

CARREA, JENNIFER; Arthur L Johnson HS; Clark, NJ; (4); 34/197; Pres German Clb; Chorus; Nwsp Stf; Ed Lit Mag; Stu Cncl; Hon Roll; German Natl Hnr Soc; Italian Clb; Intl Rltns.

CARREA, JULIE; Arthur L Johnson Regional HS; Clark, NJ; (4); 4/197; Trs German Clb; Nwsp Ed-Chief; Yrbk Stf; Lit Mag; Rep Stu Cncl; Hon Roll; Trs NHS; St Schlr; Art Clb; Chorus; German Natl Hnr Socty Pres; Outstnding Germn Stu Awd; Crusader Awd; Georgetown U; Intl Bus.

CARRELLE, RAYMOND; Don Bosco HS; Paramus, NJ; (2); #12 In Class; Bowling; Trk; Elks Awd; High Hon Roll.

CARRERA, MIRIAM; Hoboken HS; Hoboken, NJ; (4); 4/250; Spanish Clb; CC Awd; High Hon Roll; Stu Achvt Awd, Corp Schlrshp 87; Jersey City ST Coll; Bus Admin.

CARRERAS, ANA; Linden HS; Linden, NJ; (4); 53/350; Key Clb; Orch; School Musical; Yrbk Stf; Off Frsh Cls; Off Soph Cls; Off Jr Cls; Off Stu Cncl; Hon Roll; NHS; Debutante Schlrshp 87; Fshn Inst Tech; Adv.

CARRI, SUZANNE; Holy Spirit HS; Linwood, NJ; (4); Dance Clb; School Play; Bsktbl; Fld Hcky; Gym; Mgr(s); Sftbl; Trk; Hon Roll; US Achvt Acad & US Natl Ldrshp Mrt Awds 84 & 86; Vrsty Lttr Acad 86; Glassboro ST Coll.

CARRIGAN, JENNIFER; Gloucester Catholic HS; Deptford, NJ; (3); 1/177; Library Aide; Red Cross Aide; Church Choir; Nwsp Rptr; L Var Socr; L Var Trk; Bausch & Lomb Sci Awd; High Hon Roll; Hon Roll; NHS; Rutgers U Schlr 87; Rutgers U; Engrng.

CARRO, DENISE; Phillipsburg HS; Phillipsburg, NJ; (3); Hosp Aide; Ski Clb; Chorus; Drill Tm; JV Cheerleading; Bus Adm.

CARROCCIA, LISA; Watchung Hills Regional HS; Warren, NJ; (3); Key Clb; Sec Latin Clb; Band; Off Soph Cls; Off Jr Cls; Var L Tennis; High Hon Roll; Hon Roll; Natl Latin Exam Slvr Mdlst 87; Ecnmcs.

CARROLL, DAWN; Brick Township HS; Brick Town, NJ; (3); Church Yth Grp; Key Clb; Math Tm; Spanish Clb; Band; Concert Band; Mrchg Band; JV Sftbl; Hon Roll; Voice Dem Awd; Seton Hall; Law.

CARROLL, KEVIN; New Milford HS; New Milford, NJ; (4); 18/136; SADD; Rep Frsh Cls; Rep Soph Cls; Rep Jr Cls; Trs Stu Cncl; Cit Awd; High Hon Roll; Pres Schlr; Gld Nws Schlrshp 87; Hgh Acadc Achvt Math & Sci Awd 85-87; U DE; Engr.

CARROLL III, ROYAL J; West Windsor-Plainsboro HS; Princeton Jct, NJ; (3); Boy Scts; Computer Clb; Math Tm; Radio Clb; Mrchg Band; Lit Mag; Rep Stu Cncl; Im Mgr Vllybl; High Hon Roll; NHS; Chem Engrng.

CARROZZA, VICKI; Monsignor Donovan HS; Seaside Heights, NJ; (3); 52/245; Ski Clb; SADD; Rep Stu Cncl; Var Trk; High Hon Roll; NHS; Chem Paper Monmouth Coll Sci Symposium 86-87.

CARRUTH, KEVIN; Haddon Heights HS; Lawnside, NJ; (4); 20/161; Aud/Vis; Church Yth Grp; Cmnty Wkr; Computer Clb; JA; NAACP; SADD; Church Choir; Nwsp Rptr; Nwsp Stf; Gdn ST Schlrshp 87; U S Military Acad; Engnrng.

CARRUTH JR, SAMUEL; Pennsauken HS; Pennsauken, NJ; (4); 23/374; Math Clb; Science Clb; Ski Clb; Spanish Clb; Band; Mrchg Band; Yrbk Stf; Rep Frsh Cls; Rep Jr Cls; Rep Sr Cls; Hnrb Joseph E Coleman Acad Achvt Awd 86; U DE; Chem.

CARSON, DAVID; Immediate Conception HS; Orange, NJ; (3); Chorus; Bsbl; Ftbl.

CARSON, LAVONNE; Barrainger HS; Lincoln Univ, PA; (4); 5/449; Exploring; French Clb; Girl Scts; Math Clb; Math Tm; Teachers Aide; Acpl Chr; Band; Chorus; Church Choir; Dr Pfeffer Awd 84; Rutgers HS Mnrty Achvt Awd 87; Mxwll House Schlrshp 87; Lincoln U; Bio-Med.

CARSWELL III, JASPER LEE; St Pius X HS; Plainfield, NJ; (4); Church Yth Grp; School Play; Stage Crew; Bsktbl; Ftbl; Marine Corp JR ROTC 86-87; Sngng Grp 86-87; Ftbl Ath Of Wk & Game Ball 86-87; E Stroudsburg U.

CARTAGENA, TRINIDAD; North Bergen HS; North Bergen, NJ; (4); 10/430; Pres French Clb; Chorus; Color Guard; Yrbk Stf; Frsh Cls; French Hon Soc; Hon Roll; NHS; Svc Awds For Modelng Clb VP & Engl Dept Page 86; Barnard Coll; Bio.

CARTER, ALLEN G; Carteret HS; Carteret, NJ; (4); 44/200; Boy Scts; Math Tm; Science Clb; Nwsp Ed-Chief; Nwsp Sprt Ed; Yrbk Sprt Ed; Stu Cncl; Crs Cntry; Trk; AFROTC & Navy Srotc Scholar 87; The Citadel Scholar 87; The Citadel; Elec Engrng.

CARTER, AMY; Union HS; Union, NJ; (3); Pres Church Yth Grp; Band; Church Choir; Concert Band; Jazz Band; Mrchg Band; Pep Band; School Musical; School Play; Nwsp Stf; Rutgers; Sec.

CARTER, COLLEEN K; St Joseph HS; Franklinville, NJ; (4); SADD; Varsity Clb; Chorus; Lit Mag; Var Capt Cheerleading; Hon Roll; NHS; Widener Univ Schrlshp 87; Am Bus Womens Assoc Schlrshp 87; Carl D Perkins Grant 87; Widener Univ; Ped Nrsng.

CARTER, DAWN; Eastside HS; Paterson, NJ; (3); 28/600; Teachers Aide; Crs Cntry; Trk; Twrlr; Hon Roll; NHS; Rutgers U; Phrmcst.

CARTER JR, DONALD P; Seton Hall Prep; Newark, NJ; (4); 83/191; Boy Scts; Church Yth Grp; Key Clb; Pep Clb; Spanish Clb; Varsity Clb; Yrbk Stf; Bsbl; Bsktbl; Crs Cntry; Athletic Schlrshp For Track & Field 87; Monsignor William J Daly Athletic Awd 87; St James Schlrshp 87; U Of Georgia; Bio.

CARTER, ELIZABETH J; Edgewood Regional HS; Sicklerville, NJ; (4); 26/310; Concert Band; Jazz Band; Mrchg Band; Yrbk Stf; Rep Frsh Cls; Trs Soph Cls; Rep Jr Cls; Rep Sr Cls; Jr NHS; NHS; Ntl Commendtn Natl Achvt Schlrshp Pgm Outstndng Negro Stu; Distngushd Stu Awd; Kent ST U; Acctng.

CARTER, GLORIA; Linden HS; Linden, NJ; (3); Pres Church Yth Grp; FHA; Church Choir; Rep Soph Cls; Rep Jr Cls; Rep Stu Cncl; Hon Roll; Representing NJ In Washington DC W/Fha As St Ofcr 87; Law.

CARTER, JAVETTE SHAREE; Eastern Christian HS; Paterson, NJ; (3); 4/85; Pep Clb; Church Choir; Yrbk Stf; Bsktbl; Tennis; Cit Awd; Hon Roll; NHS; Pre-Med.

CARTER, JEFFREY; Baptist HS; Audobon, NJ; (3); 8/45; Church Yth Grp; Band; Yrbk Phtg; Var Bsbl; Bsktbl; Hon Roll; Ntl Merit SF; Hnr Soc 86-87.

CARTER, MARCIANNE; Burlington Twp HS; Burlington, NJ; (3); Chorus; Madrigals; Hon Roll; NHS; Penn ST; Aero Engr.

CARTER, MICHELLE; Gloucester City JR SR HS; Gloucester City, NJ; (3); Aud/Vis; Church Yth Grp; DECA; Pep Clb; School Play; Stage Crew; JV Fld Hcky; JV Sftbl; Im Swmmng; Hon Roll; Camden County Coll; Law Enfrcmt.

CARTER, MICHELLE M; Baptist HS; Haddon Heights, NJ; (3); Church Yth Grp; FCA; French Clb; Pep Clb; Ybrk Stf; Pres Frsh Cls; Var L Cheerleading; Sftbl; L Trk; Hon Roll; Bus.

CARTER, SHANNON; Arthur P Schalick HS; Bridgeton, NJ; (4) Chorus; Variety Show; Stat Trk; Hon Roll; 2nd Hnr Rll 86-87; NJ ST Teen Arts Fstvl & Music Awd 87; Salem Cnty Chorus 86-87.

CARTER, TAMIKO; Plainfield HS; Plainfield, NJ; (4); 29/371; Pep Clb Mrchg Band; Lit Mag; Rep Sr Cls; Rep Stu Cncl; Capt Pom Pon; Hon Roll Accounting.

CARTER, TARA; Cranford HS; Cranford, NJ; (2); Camera Clb; Rutgers Jrnlsm.

CARTER, TAWANDA; Millville SR HS; Millville, NJ; (3); DECA Drama Clb; Girl Scts; SADD; Variety Show; Rep Stu Cncl; JV Bsktbl; JV Cheerleading; JV Sftbl; Lgl Secy.

CARTER, TRESA; Washington Twp HS; Turnersville, NJ; (3); Church Yth Grp; Debate Tm; French Clb; Church Choir; Variety Show; Rep Frsh Cls; Sec Soph Cls; Rep Jr Cls; Sec Stu Cncl; Trk; Mst Imprvd Rnnr 85-87 Nwsppr Carrier Yr 83; Corp Law.

CARTMELL, DENISE; Matawan Regional HS; Matawan, NJ; (3); 25/310; Church Yth Grp; French Clb; Math Tm; Ski Clb; SADD; Concert Band; Mrchg Band; Fld Hcky; Trk.

CARUSO, DANTE V; Triton Regional HS; Somerdale, NJ; (4); 9/311 Yrbk Sprt Ed; Var L Crs Cntry; Var L Wrstlng; Hon Roll; Trs NHS; Pres Schlr; St Schlr; Am Leg Boys St; Key Clb; Latin Clb; Acdmc Stu Mnth 87 Marine Phys Fit Awd; Twnshp Schlr 87; U DE; Cvl Engrng.

CARUSO, DONNA; Cresskill HS; Cresskill, NJ; (3); Pep Clb; Ski Clb Band; Color Guard; Concert Band; Mrchg Band; Var JV Bsktbl; Var Cheerleading; Sftbl; Capt Trk; 1st Tm All Leag Trk 87; Music.

CARUSO, GIANNA L; Fair Lawn HS; Fair Lawn, NJ; (4); Rep Varsity Clb; Co-Capt Var Cheerleading; Coach Actv; Rep Frsh Cls; Rep Soph Cls Rep Jr Cls; Rep Sr Cls; Var Sftbl; Al-Sport Schlrshp 87; U Of MD; Bus Mgmt.

CARUSO, MICHAEL P; Hamilton HS North; Trenton, NJ; (3); Am Leg Boys St; CAP; Key Clb; Ski Clb; Varsity Clb; Bsbl; Socr; Trk; NHS; Natl Sci Merit Awd 84; Archit Engrng.

CARUSO, VINCENT; Rancocas Valley Regional HS; Mount Holly, NJ (4); DECA; Varsity Clb; Var L Trk; Im Wt Lftg; Perfect Attendance Acctng Awd; Phys Fitness Awd; Burlington Co Coll.

CARUSO, WILLIAM; Verona HS; Verona, NJ; (4); 15/189; Ski Clb Nwsp Rptr; Yrbk Sprt Ed; Lit Mag; Bsbl; Socr; Hon Roll; NHS; Pres Schlr; Spanish NHS; US Army ROTC Scholar 87; Essex Cnty Schlr-Ath 87; Outstndg Male Ath 87; Gettysburg Coll; Polit Sci.

CARVER, KEVIN; Baptist HS; Marlton, NJ; (3); Boy Scts; Church Yth Grp; Computer Clb; Var Stat Bsktbl; Var Socr; God Cntry Awd; Hon Roll NHS; Prfct Atten Awd; Prfct Atten Awd, Ntl Hnr Soc 87; Hnr Roll; God & Cntry Awd-Boy Scts 85; Eagle Sct; Comp Clb; Baptist Bible Coll; Rlgn

CARY, CHRISTINE; Gateway Regional HS; Woodbury Hts, NJ; (2) FHA; VP JA; JCL; SADD; Chorus; Mrchg Band; Hon Roll; Stu Cncl; Latin Clb; Nwsp Rptr; Intl Ord Of Rainbow For Girls 86-87; Rutgers U; Nrsng

CASADIA, TIFFANY; Sacred Heart HS; Vineland, NJ; (3); 12/56; Art Clb; Sec Spanish Clb; Pres SADD; School Musical; VP Stu Cncl; Var Cheerleading; Var Sftbl; Var Tennis; Hon Roll; NHS; Acadc All-Amer 87 Pres Physcl Ftns Awd 87; Mdlng Amer Assn Awd 86-87; Pre Med.

CASALE, JOHN C; Pompton Lakes HS; Pompton Lakes, NJ; (3); 30/134 Am Leg Boys St; French Clb; Math Clb; SADD; Varsity Clb; Yrbk Sprt Ed; Var L Ftbl; High Hon Roll; Hon Roll; Ftbll Lttr 85-87; Math League Hnr; Invlmnt In Town Politics Hnr 87; Accntng.

CASAROW, ANDREA; Cumberland Regional HS; Bridgeton, NJ; (4); 1/298; JCL; Quiz Bowl; Nwsp Rptr; Yrbk Stf; Lit Mag; High Hon Roll; NHS Pres Schlr; St Schlr; Val; Natl Latin Exam Schlrshp 87; Cumberland Cnty Cncl Soc Stds Awd 87; Italian Amrcn Civic Clb Awd 87; U Of PA; Attrny

CASCARELLI, FRANK; Linden HS; Linden, NJ; (3); Computer Clb VICA; Im Badmtn; JV Bsbl; Im Bsktbl; Im Fld Hcky; Im Ftbl; Im Sftbl Im Vllybl; Hon Roll; Accntnt.

CASCETTA, NUNZIO; Hudson Catholic HS; Hoboken, NJ; (3); Boy Scts; Nwsp Rptr; JV Socr; Im Vllybl; Cit Awd; Hon Roll.

CASCIANO, COLEEN; Phillipsburg Catholic HS; Phillipsburg, NJ; (4) 4/72; Cmnty Wkr; Drama Clb; Hosp Aide; School Musical; School Play Nwsp Rptr; Off Jr Cls; Trs Sr Cls; Off Stu Cncl; Capt Cheerleading; Hugh O Brian Yth Ldrshp Awd 85; Prsdntl Clssrm 86; Exchng Clb Yth Yr 87 Ursinus Coll; Cmmnctns.

CASCIANO, JENNIFER; Newton HS; Newton, NJ; (4); 22/196; SADD Trs Frsh Cls; Trs Soph Cls; Trs Jr Cls; Rep Stu Cncl; Ftbl; Capt Powder Puff Ftbl; Wrstlng; Hon Roll; NHS; Carnegie Mellon U; Bus.

CASCIATO, CELESTE; Haddon Township HS; Westmont, NJ; (4); 12/171; Hosp Aide; VP Service Clb; Yrbk Stf; Sftbl; Cit Awd; High Hon Roll NHS; Pres Schlr; Med Schlrs Pgm 86-87; Rutgers Coll; Bio.

CASCO, JACQUELINE; St Mary HS; Jersey City, NJ; (3); Church Yth Grp; Drama Clb; Pep Clb; Chorus; Church Choir; School Play; Yrbk Stf Var Mgr(s); Hon Roll; NHS; Chrstn Srvc Awd 87; Law.

CASCONE, JEFFREY; Northern Valley Regional HS; Norwood, NJ; (3) Cmrcl Art.

CASE, MICHELE; Henry Hudson Regional HS; Highlands, NJ; (2); Ski Clb; Stage Crew; Im Badmtn; Im Bsktbl; Im Socr; JV DECA; Var Tennis Im Vllybl; High Hon Roll; NHS; Frnch Awd 85-87; HOBY Fndtn Rep 87 Sci Olympd Awd 86; Intl Bus.

CASELLA, STEPHANIE; Friends Schl; Turnersville, NJ; (3); Stage Crew; Yrbk Stf; Lit Mag; Rep Stu Cncl; Moore Coll Of Art YAW Schlrshp 87; Lbrl Arts.

CASEY, JANET; Livingston HS; Livingston, NJ; (3); 22/417; AFS Cmnty Wkr; Key Clb; Math Tm; Band; Chorus; Drm Mjr(t); School Musical; Twrlr; High Hon Roll; US Twrlng Assc-NJ 2 Btn Chmpn 85; Wor Essx Cnty Math Leag Tm Cmptn 87; Won Rgnl Dnc Gld Cmptn 87; Math

CASEY, KATHLEEN; Matawan Regional HS; Matawan, NJ; (4); 19/311 Girl Scts; Math Tm; Speech Tm; Sec Concert Band; Jazz Band; Sec Mrchg Band; School Musical; Variety Show; Yrbk Stf; NHS; Math Hnr Soc 86-87

CASEY, LISA; Howell HS; Howell, NJ; (3); 46/450; Key Clb; NFL PAVAS; Band; Color Guard; Drm Mjr(t); Mrchg Band; Orch; Sftbl; NHS Jr Hall Of Fame Band Hnrs 87; Tremain Dance Convention Merit Awd 84-85; Vet Med.

CASEY, ROSEMARIE; Dickinson HS; Jersey City, NJ; (2); French Clb Band; Color Guard; Concert Band; Mrchg Band; Nwsp Bus Mgr; Nwsp Rptr; Swmmng; Comp/Algbra Awd 86; Seton Hall U; Pedtrcn.

CASEY, SARA ANN; Immaculate Heart Acad; New City, NY; (2); Cmnty Wkr; Exploring; Hosp Aide; Hon Roll; Psychology.

CASEY, WILLIAM; Madison Central HS; Old Bridge, NJ; (4); 3/370 Co-Capt Math Tm; Pres Stu Cncl; Im Bsbl; Var Bsktbl; Var Ftbl; Wt Lftg French Hon Soc; VP NHS; Ntl Merit Ltr; French Clb; NJ Dstngshd Schl Awd 86; Middlesex Cnty Outstndg Stu Awd 87; Grad Magna Cum Laud 87; Georgetown U; Bus Fin.

CASH, DEREK; Essex Catholic Boys HS; East Orange, NJ; (2); Art Clb; Aud/Vis; Math Clb; Spanish Clb; Yrbk Stf; Sftbl; Trk; Hon Roll; John F Kennedy Mem Hstry Awd 85; Cert Compltn Summer Pgm Cook Coll 87; Cert Achvt Upsala Coll 86; Comp Tech.

CASHION, BRANNON; Hightstown HS; E Windsor, NJ; (3); Church Yth Grp; FBLA; Key Clb; Ski Clb; Spanish Clb; Im Bsktbl; Im Lcrss; High Hon Roll; Hon Roll; Prfct Atten Awd; Bus Admin.

CASHION, KIMBERLY; Ridge HS; Basking Ridge, NJ; (3); 3/192; Trs AFS; Church Yth Grp; Cmnty Wkr; Ski Clb; Stat Ftbl; Powder Puff Ftbl; Var Trk; Hon Roll; Trs NHS; Spanish NHS.

CASIUS, MARIJKE; Bridgeton HS; Cedarville, NJ; (3); Art Clb; Aud/Vis; Church Yth Grp; Drama Clb; French Clb; Office Aide; Ski Clb; SADD; School Play; Jr NHS; Intl Rltns.

CASLANDER, MELISSA; Wayne Hills HS; Wayne, NJ; (1); Dance Clb; GAA; Girl Scts; Var Gym; Hon Roll.

CASOLA, CHRISTINA; Red Bank Catholic HS; Marlboro, NJ; (2); Cmnty Wkr; Drama Clb; Pep Clb; Ski Clb; Spanish Clb; Thesps; Color Guard; Flag Corp; Variety Show; L Twrlr; Int Dcrtng.

CASON, CATHERINE; Manville HS; Manville, NJ; (3); Band; Mrchg Band; Yrbk Phtg; Pres Frsh Cls; Sec Soph Cls; Rep Jr Cls; Sec Stu Cncl; NHS; SADD; Chorus; NJASC Exectv Mbr 87; Local Teen Arts Fnlst 87.

CASPER, CONNI; Salem HS; Salem, NJ; (2); Church Yth Grp; Drama Clb; Latin Clb; School Musical; School Play; Stage Crew; Fld Hcky; Mgr(s); Score Keeper; Hon Roll; Clse Up Fndtn Delg WA DC 87; JR Stsmn Fndtn Delg Anniv Cnstitnl Conv Phila 87; Socl Sci.

CASS, BRIAN; Boonton HS; Denville, NJ; (2); Concert Band; Jazz Band; Mrchg Band; JV Bsbl; Var Tennis; Hon Roll; North Jrsy Area Band Wnd Ensmbl 87; Natl Gld Yth Symphny Orchstra Crngie Hall 87; Smmr Arts Inst 86; Music.

CASSELLS, MATTHEW; Holy Cross HS; Edgewater Pk, NJ; (3); 45/405; Church Yth Grp; French Clb; Bsbl; Hon Roll; Sci.

CASSESE, JENNIFER; Livingston HS; Livingston, NJ; (3); 100/420; Church Yth Grp; Leo Clb; Color Guard; Var Vllybl; Hon Roll; Med.

CASSIDY, LYNNE; Westfield HS; Westfield, NJ; (3); 138/469; Church Yth Grp; Var L Swmmng; Hon Roll; Art Clb; Spanish Clb; Chorus; Nwsp Rptr; Nwsp Stf; Yrbk Stf; JV Socr; Swmmng Records 85-86; Lib Arts.

CASTAGNA, KATHLEEN; Notre Dame HS; Lawrenceville, NJ; (3); 16/400; AFS; Church Yth Grp; Hosp Aide; Red Cross Aide; Varsity Clb; Cheerleading; French Hon Soc; Hon Roll; NHS; Outstndng Achcvt Frnch II & III; Outstndng Achvt Hnrs Engl II; Outstndng Achvt Geom; Bus Mgmt.

CASTALDO, ANDREW P; River Dell HS; River Edge, NJ; (3); 1/225; Am Leg Boys St; Trs Latin Clb; Ski Clb; Nwsp Ed-Chief; Capt L Crs Cntry; Var Trk; Bausch & Lomb Sci Awd; Trs French Hon Soc; High Hon Roll; Pres NHS; Rutgers Schlr Prg 87; Summa Cum Laude Natl Latin Exam 86; Acdmc All Amer 87; Finance.

CASTELLANI, JOSEPH; Maple Shade HS; Maple Shade, NJ; (2); French Clb; Key Clb; VP Jr Cls; Socr; Trk; Wrstlng; High Hon Roll; Bus.

CASTELLANO, JENNIFER; Indian Hills HS; Oakland, NJ; (3); 81/306; Ski Clb; Spanish Clb; Stat Bsktbl; Score Keeper; JV Vllybl; Btty Crckr Awd; High Hon Roll; Hon Roll; Occu Thrpy.

CASTELLO, CHRISTOPHER; Union Catholic Regional HS; Scotch Plains, NJ; (4); 1/293; Math Tm; Capt Quiz Bowl; Science Clb; JV Golf; High Hon Roll; NHS; Prfct Atten Awd; Spanish NHS; Rutgers Schlr 86; Natl Merit Cmmnd Stu 86; Garden St Dist Schlr; Wharton Schl; Finance.

CASTELLUCCI, CHRISTINA; Saint Dominic Academy; Jersey City, NJ; (4); Dance Clb; Drama Clb; Pres NFL; PAVAS; SADD; Church Choir; School Musical; School Play; Hon Roll; Acdmc All Amer 87; Ice Sktg Brnz Metl NJ Cncl Figr Sktg Comptn 83; Seton Hall U; Elem Ed.

CASTILLO, BEATRIS; South River HS; S River, NJ; (2); Library Aide; Spanish Clb; Color Guard; Mgr(s); Hon Roll; Clr Grd Achvt Awd 87; Princeton; Dctr.

CASTNER, KAREN; Kittatinny Regional HS; Middleville, NJ; (4); 56/224; Spanish Clb; Band; Powder Puff Ftbl; JV Trk; Hon Roll; Trenton ST Coll; Psych.

CASTORO, CARLO; Hoboken HS; Hoboken, NJ; (3); 17/300; Capt Socr; JV Trk; Italian Clb 85-86.

CASTRILLON, DANIEL M; Don Bosco Prep; Montvale, NJ; (4); Boy Scts; Church Yth Grp; Cmnty Wkr; Pep Clb; SADD; Nwsp Phtg; Rep Frsh Cls; Rep Soph Cls; Rep Jr Cls; Var Ftbl; Schlrshp-Wagner Coll 87; Beagen Cnty Hnrs In Trk 87; All-Surburban Hnrs In Trk 86; Wagner Coll; Bus.

CASTRO, NORIEL; Leonia HS; Leonia, NJ; (3); 12/150; Camera Clb; Spanish Clb; JV Tennis; NHS; Med.

CASTRO, STEVE; Hoboken HS; Union City, NJ; (3); 18/300; Aud/Vis; Debate Tm; French Clb; Model UN; Spanish Clb; Chorus; Nwsp Ed-Chief; Nwsp Sprt Ed; Yrbk Sprt Ed; Rep Frsh Cls; Seton Hall; Crmnl Jstc.

CASTRO, WANDA; Buena Regional HS; Minotola, NJ; (2); Church Yth Grp; Chorus.

CASTRONVOVO, LYNNE; Cliffside Park HS; Fairview, NJ; (3); 7/234; Yrbk Bus Mgr; Yrbk Stf; Sec Stu Cncl; Var Bsktbl; Var Crs Cntry; Var Trk; Hon Roll; NHS; 2nd Tm All Leag BCSL Am-Bsktbl 86-87; 2nd Tm All Leag BCSL Am-Crs Cntry 86; Hrbl Mntn BCSL Trk 87; Boston U; Acctng.

CATALANO, DEAN J; Brick Township Memorial HS; Brick, NJ; (3); 38/385; Am Leg Boys St; Exploring; Off ROTC; Science Clb; Color Guard; Drill Tm; Dnfth Awd; High Hon Roll; NHS; SAR Awd; Amer Chem Soc Awd Achvt Chem 86; Aerontcl Engrng.

CATALANO, JAMES; St James HS; Woodstown, NJ; (4); 10/70; Chess Clb; Stage Crew; Hon Roll; Comp Excllnce Awd 86; Rlgn Awd 85; Bus Adm.

CATALLO, GINA; St Mary HS; Sayreville, NJ; (3); 10/100; Hosp Aide; Spanish Clb; Church Choir; Yrbk Stf; Off Frsh Cls; VP Soph Cls; Sec Jr Cls; JV Capt Cheerleading; Var Gym; Var Socr; 3 Coll Credits-Meddlesex Cnty Coll On Comp 86; Pre-Med.

CATANZARO, MARIA; Secaucus HS; Secaucus, NJ; (3); Dance Clb; GAA; JA; Key Clb; Math Clb; Mu Alpha Theta; Spanish Clb; Varsity Clb; Chorus; Cheerleading.

CATANZARO, SALLY; Secaucus HS; Secaucus, NJ; (1); 2/130; Mu Alpha Theta; Pres Frsh Cls; JV Cheerleading; JV Var Sftbl; Cit Awd; High Hon Roll; Jr NHS; Spanish NHS; Val; Art, Sprtsmnshp, Memrl Awds; Princeton.

CATERINI, CORINNE; Wildwood HS; Wildwood, NJ; (4); 21/111; Spanish Clb; School Musical; School Play; Variety Show; Yrbk Stf; Rep Jr Cls; Tennis; Hon Roll; Spanish NHS; Spnsh Achvt Awd 86-87; Eng Achvt Awd 87; La Salle U; Spnsh.

CATERSON, KATHERINE; Holy Spirit HS; Absecon, NJ; (2); 8/397; Debate Tm; Chorus; School Play; Pres Frsh Cls; Pres Soph Cls.

CATHCART, LAUREN; Delran HS; Delran, NJ; (4); Dance Clb; FBLA; Key Clb; Library Aide; Office Aide; Chorus; JV Cheerleading; Var Pom Pon; Parlmntrn FBLA 85-87; Capt JV Chrldg Sqd 84-85; Danc Marcia Hyland Danc Stdo Mt Laurel NJ 85-87; Berkeley Bus School; Exec Secy.

CATHERS, MELINDA; Warren Co Vo Tech; Phillipsburg, NJ; (3); Sec FBLA; Office Aide; Var Sftbl; Hon Roll; Sec.

CATHEY, HEATHER; North Hunterdon HS; Lebanon, NJ; (2); 122/335; Chorus; Crs Cntry.

CATLETT, CRYSTAL; Cinnaminson HS; Cinnaminson, NJ; (2); Chorus; Madrigals; Rep Frsh Cls; VP Soph Cls; Pres Jr Cls; JV Cheerleading; Sftbl; Hon Roll; Church Yth Grp; Church Choir; All S Jersey Chorus 85-87; Music.

CATONZARITI, RACQUEL; Montville Township HS; Pinebrook, NJ; (3); 38/273; FBLA; Sec Stu Cncl; Im Bsktbl; Var JV Lcrss; Var JV Mgr(s); L Powder Puff Ftbl; Var JV Score Keeper; High Hon Roll; NHS; Prjct Link-Up Awd 86-87; Bus.

CATOZZO, CHRISTIAN; Montville HS; Pinebrook, NJ; (2); FBLA; JV Lcrss; JV Socr; High Hon Roll; Hon Roll; Bus Admin.

CATRAL, JOHN; Cliffside Park HS; Cliffside Park, NJ; (2); Conduct Award 85-86; IFLA 86-87; Engr.

CATRINO, JO ANN; John P Stevens HS; Edison, NJ; (2); 26/452; Model UN; Office Aide; Nwsp Phtg; Hon Roll; Cmmnctns.

CATTELL, MEGAN; Clayton HS; Clayton, NJ; (4); 19/76; Drama Clb; English Clb; French Clb; VP Key Clb; PAVAS; Science Clb; Thesps; Chorus; Church Choir; Mrchg Band; Gloucester Cnty Clayton Hs JR Miss 86-87; NJ Schl Of Arts Schlr 86.

CAUALIERE, JOSEPH; St James HS; Monroeville, NJ; (3); Chess Clb; JV Var Bsktbl; JV Ftbl.

CAUDA, LISA; Montville Township HS; Pine Brook, NJ; (4); Cmnty Wkr; VP Key Clb; Spanish Clb; Ed Lit Mag; Cit Awd; Hon Roll; Kiwanis Awd; NHS; Parents Cncl Schlrshp, NJ Dist Key Clb Schlrshp, Mustangs Art Awd 87; U Of DE; Advrtsng.

CAULFIELD, MAUREEN; Rahway SR HS; Rahway, NJ; (3); Girl Scts; JA; School Play; Yrbk Stf; Rep Stu Cncl; Var Cheerleading; Capt Diving; Swmmng; Hon Roll; Grl Sct Slvr Awd 85; J Bona Awd 86; Mtl Brkng Schl Rcrd Dvng 87; Trenton ST; Phys Ed.

CAUSING, AILEEN; Princeton HS; Princeton, NJ; (4); Sec Church Yth Grp; Cmnty Wkr; Spanish Clb; Capt Var Fld Hcky; Capt Var Lcrss; Powder Puff Ftbl; Natl All Amer Field Hcky Plyr 86; Natl All Amer La Crosse Plyr 87; U Of PA; Arch.

CAUTHEN, KRAVEN; Passaic County Tech & Voc HS; Paterson, NJ; (4); 59/366; Spanish Clb; Variety Show; Yrbk Bus Mgr; VP Stu Cncl; JV Trk; Elks Awd; Hon Roll; Acctg.

CAVA, NEMESIO V; Passaic HS; Passaic, NJ; (3); Am Leg Boys St; Chess Clb; French Clb; Scholastic Bowl; Science Clb; Ski Clb; Var Tennis; High Hon Roll; Hon Roll; 3rd Pl Sci Fair 87; 3rd Pl NJUSTU Tae Kwon Do Championships 86; NJIT Urban Engrng Summer Pgm 87; Engrng.

CAVACIER, BUCK; Atlantic City HS; Margate, NJ; (4); Computer Clb; Key Clb; Office Aide; Teachers Aide; Hon Roll; NHS; St Schlr; Trs Jr Cls; JV Bsbl; JV Bsktbl; U Of Richmond; Golf Pro.

CAVALIERI, JEANNIE; Sacred Heart HS; Vineland, NJ; (3); Art Clb; French Clb; School Play; Nwsp Rptr; Yrbk Ed-Chief; Bsktbl; NJ Teen Visl Arts Awd 87; Coll Tlnt Srch Essy Awd 87; Cumbrland Cnty Teen Arts Fest Awd 87; Fshn Dsgn.

CAVALLARO, PAUL; Toms River HS East; Toms River, NJ; (3); 49/506; VP Key Clb; JV Bsbl; NHS; Pre-Law.

CAVALLARO, TROY; Holy Spirit HS; Absecon, NJ; (2); 25/397; Aud/Vis; Science Clb; Rep Soph Cls; JV Socr; Hon Roll.

CAVALLI, JOHN; Mc Corristin HS; Trenton, NJ; (3); 27/273; Drama Clb; FBLA; JA; Trs Stu Cncl; JV Socr; Var Tennis; Hon Roll; Jr NHS; NHS; Pre-Med.

CAVANAUGH, NANCY; Toms River HS North; Toms River, NJ; (3); 22/459; VP Key Clb; Science Clb; Concert Band; Drill Tm; Rep Frsh Cls; Rep Soph Cls; Rep Stu Cncl; Var Sftbl; Hon Roll; Stockton St Sci Fair Hnrb Mntn 84; DE Vly Sci Fair-3rd Pl 84; Advrtsng.

CAVE, MEGIN; Manasquan HS; Manasquan, NJ; (4); 36/224; VP Spanish Clb; Nwsp Stf; Mgr(s); Socr; High Hon Roll; Hon Roll; Ntl Merit SF; PTO Schlrshp 87; Libry Schlrshp 87; Hmcmng Queen 87; Widener U.

CAVENDER, TAMMIE; Central Jersey Christian Schl; Ocean Grove, NJ; (3); 1/28; Sec Church Yth Grp; Drama Clb; Ski Clb; Pres Chorus; Yrbk Stf; Sec Stu Cncl; Capt Cheerleading; Var L Sftbl; NHS; Spanish Awd 86; Bible Memorization Awd 85; Sci Awd 87; Public Admn.

CAVILHAS, CHRISTINE; Lacordaire Acad; Nutley, NJ; (3); Cmnty Wkr; Hosp Aide; Service Clb; School Play; Nwsp Stf; Yrbk Stf; Pres Sr Cls; Var Vllybl; High Hon Roll; NFL; Accptd To Engrng Pgm At NJ Inst Of Tech 87; Ntl Scl Stds Olympd Rcgtn Of Hnr 85; Pre-Med.

CAVLOV, ANNEMARIE; North Bergen HS; North Bergen, NJ; (4); Art Clb; Church Yth Grp; Rep Frsh Cls; Rep Soph Cls; Rep Jr Cls; Rep Sr Cls; William Paterson Coll; Lbrl Art.

CAVLOV, ANTHONY J; North Bergen HS; North Bergen, NJ; (3); Computer Clb; Stevens Tech; Elec Engrng.

CAYSON, SHELLY; Hillside HS; Hillside, NJ; (3); 30/238; VP Soph Cls; Rep Jr Cls; Rep Stu Cncl; Var Cheerleading; Stat Mgr(s); Rutgers U; Accntng.

CECALA, STANLEY J; St Josephs Of The Palisade; North Bergen, NJ; (3); 16/133; Im Vllybl; High Hon Roll; Hon Roll.

CECERE, JOSEPH; Bloomfield HS; Bloomfield, NJ; (3); Pre-Law.

CECIL, SHERRI; Union HS; Union, NJ; (4); 95/540; FNA; Pep Clb; Pres VICA; Band; Drm Mjr(t); Mrchg Band; Pep Band; Hon Roll; HOSA Natl Conf Dntl Splng 1st Pl Regnl,3rd Pl ST,3rd Pl Natlns 85-86; Most Moutstndg Dental Stud; Kean Coll; Scl Wrkr.

CEDFELDT, PAUL; Glen Rock HS; Glen Rock, NJ; (3); 19/145; Ski Clb; Spanish Clb; Trs Jr Cls; Var Socr; High Hon Roll; Hon Roll; Jr NHS; NHS; Lbrl Arts.

CELANO, CHRIS; Union Catholic Regional HS; Scotch Plains, NJ; (3); 17/330; Science Clb; Service Clb; Teachers Aide; High Hon Roll; Ntl Merit Ltr; Ntl Hnr Soc For Italian 86; Princton U; Laser Tech.

CELENTANA, MARC; Notre Dame HS; Mercerville, NJ; (3); 14/392; Am Leg Boys St; Pres Latin Clb; SADD; Rep Jr Cls; Rep Sr Cls; Rep Stu Cncl; Var Bsbl; Var Bsktbl; High Hon Roll; NHS; Engrng.

CELENTANO, TOM; Wayne Hills HS; Wayne, NJ; (2); Math Tm; Spanish Clb; Stu Cncl; JV Socr; Hon Roll; Arch.

CELENTANO, WILLIAM; St Peters Prep; Cliffside Pk, NJ; (4); Chess Clb; Cmnty Wkr; Computer Clb; Drama Clb; FBLA; Hosp Aide; School Play; Lit Mag; Stat Score Keeper; JV Tennis; Palisades Gen Hosp Vol Awd 86; Pace U; Fin.

CELENZA, CLAIRE; St Mary HS; Rutherford, NJ; (4); 9/78; Ski Clb; Stage Crew; Nwsp Stf; VP Stu Cncl; Var Bsktbl; Var Crs Cntry; Var Trk; French Hon Soc; Hon Roll; NHS; Drew U; Engl.

CELESTE, CATHERINE; Wayne Valley HS; Wayne, NJ; (4); Computer Clb; Service Clb; Ski Clb; Chorus; Church Choir; Yrbk Ed-Chief; JV Socr; Old Dominion U; Mgmt Info Systm.

CELLA, SIMONE; St John Vianney HS; Hazlet, NJ; (2); Church Yth Grp; Cmnty Wkr; Service Clb; Ski Clb; Stage Crew; Hon Roll.

CENGARLE, JULIO; Don Bosco Tech; Paterson, NJ; (2); 10/86; Boys Clb Am; Fld Hcky; Socr; JETS Awd.

CENICOLA, KEN; Dover HS; Mine Hill, NJ; (3); Computer Clb; Debate Tm; Teachers Aide; School Musical; School Play; Bsbl; Bowling; High Hon Roll; Hon Roll; NHS; Elect Engrng.

CENTENO, MARIA; Millville SR HS; Millville, NJ; (4); Art Clb; Church Yth Grp; FBLA; Spanish Clb; Teachers Aide; Church Choir; Cumberland Cnty Coll; Law.

CENTER, JILL; Phillipsburg HS; Phillipsburg, NJ; (3); 13/315; Church Yth Grp; Key Clb; Ski Clb; Pres SADD; School Play; Nwsp Ed-Chief; Trk; Capt Twrlr; High Hon Roll; Sec NHS; Chrch Cncl 86; Phy Thrpy.

CERALLI, WILLIAM; Glen Rock HS; Glen Rock, NJ; (3); 15/173; Boys Clb Am; Church Yth Grp; Ftbl; Wt Lftg; High Hon Roll; Hon Roll; NHS; Bus.

CERASI, VICTORIA; Highland Regional HS; Blackwood, NJ; (4); Computer Clb; Sec FTA; Service Clb; Band; Trs Soph Cls; VP Stu Cncl; JV Socr; NHS; VFW Awd; Glassboro ST Coll; Bus Mngmt.

CERE, KRISTEN; Abraham Clark HS; Roselle, NJ; (3); 3/175; Library Aide; Chorus; Madrigals; Var JV Tennis; High Hon Roll; Hon Roll; NHS; Sprtsmnshp Awd Grls Tnns 86-87; Span Lang Day Cont Natl Hon Men 87; 6 Flags Grt Advntr Choral Fest 86; Law.

CERES, JENNIFER L; Holy Spirit HS; Mays Landing, NJ; (3); Art Clb; French Clb; Pep Clb; Stage Crew; Hnrb Mntn Art Shw 86-87; Hostess Schl Hnr 84-85; Amer Coll Appld Arts; Fshn Mrch.

CERESI, DEBORAH; Morris Knolls HS; Denville, NJ; (4); 34/359; Pep Clb; Varsity Clb; Yrbk Stf; Sec Sr Cls; Cheerleading; Var Capt Fld Hcky; Trk; High Hon Roll; Summa Awd 83; Frshmn Awareness Ldr & Steering Cmmtte 85-86; Ski Club 86-87; Exec Cncl 86-87; Muhlenberg Coll; Bus Mngmnt.

CERNIGLIA, LISA; Kinnelon HS; Kinnelon, NJ; (4); 27/180; German Clb; Hosp Aide; Varsity Clb; Var Bsktbl; JV Sftbl; Hon Roll; NHS; Trs Spanish NHS; Art Clb; Church Yth Grp; Pres Acdmc Ftns Awd 87; Mrst Coll Pres Schlrshp 87; Marist Coll; Psychlgy.

CERNY, EDWARD CHARLES; Summit HS; Summit, NJ; (3); Boy Scts; Church Yth Grp; Model UN; Service Clb; Nwsp Rptr; Nwsp Stf; Rep Stu Cncl; Diving; JV Var Socr; Var Capt Swmmng; MV Swimmer 87; ST & City Govt Conf Rep 86-87.

CERONE, BERNADETTE; De Paul HS; Ringwood, NJ; (3); School Musical; Nwsp Stf; Yrbk Stf; Rep Frsh Cls; Pres Soph Cls; VP Jr Cls; VP Sr Cls; Rep Stu Cncl; Capt Bsktbl; Capt Var Socr; HOBY Fndtn, Alt For Rotary Yth Ldrshp Awds Pgm & Peer Counselor; Pre-Law.

CERONE, DEBBIE; Toms River HS North; Toms River, NJ; (3); 19/448; Dance Clb; Hosp Aide; Office Aide; SADD; School Musical; School Play; Fld Hcky; Pom Pon; High Hon Roll; Hon Roll; Elem Schl Tchr.

CERRITO, ERIC; Lyndhurst HS; Lyndhurst, NJ; (2); Boy Scts; Computer Clb; Political Wkr; Science Clb; Ski Clb; Elks Awd; Rcktry Clb 85-86; Cngrssmn Toricelli Stu Dbt 86-87; Law.

CERRONE, CYNTHIA; Holy Cross HS; Florence, NJ; (2); French Clb; Ski Clb; Yrbk Stf; Hon Roll; Psych.

CERRUTO, LAUREN; Glen Ridge HS; Glen Ridge, NJ; (3); 2/108; Spanish Clb; Concert Band; Jazz Band; Mrchg Band; Im Vllybl; Elks Awd; High Hon Roll; Ntl Merit Ltr; Rotary Awd; Aud/Vis; Smith Coll Awd 87; Creatv Wrtng.

CERVELLI, JOS; Bishop AHR HS; Fords, NJ; (3); 55/275; Cmnty Wkr; Computer Clb; Math Clb; Ski Clb; Spanish Clb; Nwsp Stf; Trk; Im Bsbl; Im Ftbl; High Hon Roll; Engrng.

CERVENAK, GEORGE; Toms River H S South; Toms River, NJ; (2); Boy Scts; Camera Clb; Chess Clb; Math Tm; JV Tennis; High Hon Roll; Schlrshp Monsignor Donovan 85-86; Rutgers ST U; Med.

CERVONE, EDMUND; The Pennington Schl; Pennington, NJ; (1); 1/57; JV Golf; JV Socr; Var Swmmng; High Hon Roll.

CESAREO, LISA ANNE; Bloomfield HS; Bloomfield, NJ; (3); Chorus; Montclair ST Coll; Bus.

CESARI, SCOTT; Phillipsburg HS; Phillipsburg, NJ; (3); 1/350; Civic Clb; Cmnty Wkr; VP Drama Clb; Lit Mag; JV Var Bsbl; High Hon Roll; NHS; St Schlr; Val; Best Supprtng Actor Awd Dramatics 85-86; Math.

CESARO, ROSE ANN; Steinert HS; Trenton, NJ; (3); Am Leg Aux Girls St; Exploring; JA; Sec Key Clb; Office Aide; SADD; Nwsp Sprt Ed; Nwsp Stf; Lit Mag; Var L Fld Hcky; Sftbl; 2nd Tm All CVC 87; Garden ST Games Fld Hockey Team 87; Speech Path.

CESTONE, MARIA; Mary Lawn Of The Oranges HS; West Orange, NJ; (2); Latin Clb; Spanish Clb; Nwsp Stf; Vllybl; High Hon Roll; Prfct Atten Awd; 2nd Spanish Lang Day Drew U 86.

CEVIK, ARZU; Passaic County Tech & Voc HS; Paterson, NJ; (3); Camera Clb; Computer Clb; Drama Clb; High Hon Roll; Hon Roll; Bus.

CHA, YOUNG; Franklin HS; Somerset, NJ; (3); Am Leg Boys St; Jazz Band; School Musical; Hon Roll; Var Socr; Im Vllybl; Im Wt Lftg; Elctrcl Engrng.

CHA, YOUNG; Parsipany HS; Lake Hiawatha, NJ; (3); Computer Clb; Ftbl; Hon Roll; Hnr Rll 85; Vrsty Ltr Ftbl 86; U Of CA; Aero Engr.

CHADOWITZ, MYRON; John P Stevens HS; Edison, NJ; (3); 21/456; Debate Tm; Key Clb; Math Tm; Model UN; Ski Clb; Trk; Hon Roll; NHS; Ntl Merit Ltr; Nwsp Phtg; Rep NJ-DEPT Energy HS Stu, Super Computing Hnrs Pgm Lawrence Livermore Natl Lab 87; Comp Sci.

CHADWICK, CHRISTOPHER; Admiral Farragut Acad; Lavallette, NJ; (3); 6/37; Pres Key Clb; Off ROTC; Concert Band; Jazz Band; Mrchg Band; Bowling; Ftbl; Vllybl; Wrstlng; Hon Roll; Head Masters Schlrshp Awd 84-85; AFA Gen Profiency Awd & Rsrv Offcrs Assn Of USMLTRY Excllnc 86-87; US Naval Acad; Mech Engrng.

CHAFAR, GIOMARA; Our Lady Of Good Counsel; Belleville, NJ; (4); 24/108; Office Aide; Pep Clb; Var Cheerleading; Var Vllybl; 2nd Hnrs 87; All Amer Schlrshp 87; Rutgers Of Nursing; Nrsng.

CHAFAR, JOSEPH; Essex Catholic HS Boys; Belleville, NJ; (3); Art Clb; Rep Frsh Cls; VP Soph Cls; Rep Stu Cncl; Var Bsbl; Var Socr; Hon Roll; Law.

CHAI, MARGARET; Pequannock Township HS; Pompton Plains, NJ; (3); 38/219; Am Leg Aux Girls St; Cmnty Wkr; Dance Clb; Drama Clb; German Clb; Political Wkr; Chorus; School Musical; Nwsp Ed-Chief; Lit Mag; Yth Chrprsn For IIF 86-87; Gov Schlr Public Issues 87; Yth Understndng 87; Mdl With J Meredith 85-87; Pltcl Sci.

CHAILLET, NICOLE; Rahway HS; Rahway, NJ; (3); Am Leg Aux Girls St; Hosp Aide; Nwsp Rptr; Yrbk Ed-Chief; Pres Stu Cncl; Cit Awd; High Hon Roll; Jr NHS; NHS; Spanish NHS; Nrsng.

CHAIN, WARREN; John F Kennedy HS; Willingboro, NJ; (2); 5/332; NAACP; Science Clb; Band; Concert Band; Jazz Band; Mrchg Band; VP Soph Cls; Trk; Cit Awd; High Hon Roll; Ctznshp Awd 85; Spllng Bee Wnnr, & Hnr Carrier 87; Engrng.

CHALMERS, TONYA MICHELE; Immaculate HS; East Orange, NJ; (2); Art Clb; Cmnty Wkr; Dance Clb; Pep Clb; Teachers Aide; Chorus; Drill Tm; School Musical; School Play; Stage Crew; Hampton U; Lawyer.

CHAMBERLAIN, C SUZANNE; Middletown South HS; Red Bank, NJ; (4); 22/450; Sec VP Church Yth Grp; Sec Girl Scts; Math Clb; Stage Crew; Yrbk Stf; High Hon Roll; Hon Roll; Sec NHS; Clemson U; Acctng.

CHAMBERLIN, GEORGE; Kittatinny Regional HS; Stillwater, NJ; (4); 29/230; Boy Scts; Church Yth Grp; 4-H; Scholastic Bowl; Band; Mrchg Band; Var Capt Socr; Var Capt Trk; Var Capt Wrstlng; Cit Awd; Marine Corps Res Offcr Training Corp Scholar 87-91; George Washington U; Bus Adm.

CHAMBERS, ALICIA; New Brunswick HS; New Brunswick, NJ; (3); Sec Church Yth Grp; Cmnty Wkr; Hosp Aide; VP Church Choir; Co-Capt Drill Tm; Rep Soph Cls; Rep Jr Cls; Rep Stu Cncl; JV Var Bsktbl; High Hon Roll; AT&T U; Elect Engineering.

CHAMBERS, MARQUIS ANGELO ST V; Manchester Township HS; Toms River, NJ; (3); Am Leg Boys St; Boy Scts; French Clb; Science Clb; Concert Band; Mrchg Band; Var Crs Cntry; Var Trk; Wt Lftg; Hon Roll; Manchester Twnshp 1st Aid Sqd 87; Frnch Clb-Paris Frnc 87; Cert Awd Dfnsv Drvng 87; Princeton U; Med.

CHAMBERS, NANCY; Westwood HS; Westwood, NJ; (3); 2/225; Drama Clb; Thesps; Drm Mjr(t); School Play; Variety Show; Rep Stu Cncl; Var Trk; High Hon Roll; NHS; Spanish NHS; Comms.

CHAMBERS, NICOLE; Eastern Regional HS; West Berlin, NJ; (3); School Play; Nwsp Stf; Off Soph Cls; Off Sr Cls; Off Stu Cncl; Tennis; Hon Roll; Jr NHS; Comm.

CHAN, GEOFFREY; Montville Township HS; Montville, NJ; (3); 11/276; Debate Tm; FBLA; Math Tm; NFL; Science Clb; Speech Tm; Nwsp Ed-Chief; JV Tennis; NHS; Ntl Merit Ltr; Layout Mgr Schl Nwsp; Pre Med.

CHAN, KIN H; Belleville HS; Belleville, NJ; (3); Aud/Vis; Computer Clb; Key Clb; Math Clb; Science Clb; Lit Mag; Off Stu Cncl; High Hon Roll; Hon Roll; NHS; NJIT; Elec Engr.

CHANCE, ANGELITA; Pemberton HS II; Pemberton, NJ; (4); 198/406; Science Clb; Church Choir; Yrbk Sprt Ed; Bsktbl; Gym; Socr; Trk; Vllybl; High Hon Roll; MVP Trk 85-86; 3 Yr Vrsty 86; All Star 86; Nrsng.

CHANDLER, CHRISTINE; Cresskill HS; Cresskill, NJ; (4); 18/112; Debate Tm; Drama Clb; Hosp Aide; Ski Clb; Spanish Clb; Band; Sec Chorus; Capt Color Guard; School Musical; Yrbk Stf; 3rd Pl Spkr Awd-Debate Tm 85; Bio.

CHANDLER, NATALIE; Triton Regional HS; Runnemede, NJ; (4); 7/309; Latin Clb; Pres Math Clb; Office Aide; SADD; Trs Soph Cls; Var Capt Fld Hcky; Powder Puff Ftbl; Var L Sftbl; High Hon Roll; NHS; Acad Stu Of Month 86; Tritons Rep 86; All Cnfrnc Fld Hcky 85 & 86.

CHANDLER, NICOLE JANEEN; Immaculate Conception HS; East Orange, NJ; (2); Church Yth Grp; Computer Clb; Teachers Aide; Y-Teens; Chorus; School Musical; Rep Stu Cncl; Nrsng.

CHANDRAKANTAN, ARUN; Manalapan HS; Manalapan, NJ; (4); 1/420; Pres Chess Clb; Debate Tm; Math Clb; Science Clb; Rep Frsh Cls; Rep Soph Cls; Sec Jr Cls; VP Sr Cls; Im Socr; L Tennis; Congressional Yth Ldrshp Awd & Rutgers U Summer Schlrshp 86; Yth Of The Yr 87; Rutgers U; Elec Engr.

CHANG, AERI; Dover HS; Mine Hill, NJ; (3); Ski Clb; Yrbk Stf; Sftbl; Hon Roll; Rep Sec Frsh Cls; Rep Soph Cls; Rep Jr Cls; Clthng Awd, Art Awd 85-86; Mth Awd 86-87; Bus.

CHANG, ALEX; Cherokee HS; Marlton, NJ; (2); Latin Clb; Math Clb; Math Tm; Quiz Bowl; Orch; Stage Crew; Im Tennis; JV Trk; Hon Roll; NHS; Bio.

CHANG, ATTICA; Paramus HS; Paramus, NJ; (4); 7/330; Camera Clb; Math Clb; Science Clb; Nwsp Stf; Lit Mag; Im Bsktbl; Im Trk; Hon Roll; Jr NHS; NHS; Schlrshps-Paramus, Hnr Scty & Cal Aggie Alumni 87; Awds-Waterloo Math, Frgn Lngs Bio & Physcl Ed 87; U Od CA Davis; Bio.

CHANG, CHEN; Cherry Hill East HS; Cherry Hill, NJ; (4); Chess Clb; Church Yth Grp; JCL; Latin Clb; Math Clb; Math Tm; Science Clb; Socr; Hon Roll; JETS Awd; Cheng Chang; Engrng.

CHANG, CHRISTOPHER; Morristown HS; Morris Plains, NJ; (1); Aud/Vis; Computer Clb; Math Clb; Math Tm; Orch; High Hon Roll; VFW Hstry Awd 86; Attened Coll Gftd Pgm 86; Princeton U; Comp Sci.

CHANG, CONRAD; Parsippany HS; Parsippany, NJ; (3); French Clb; Varsity Clb; Chorus; JV Bsktbl; Var L Tennis; Hon Roll; NHS.

CHANG, DAVID; Holy Spirit HS; Margate, NJ; (2); 6/397; High Hon Roll; Natl Latn Exm Magna Cum Ld 85-86; Actg.

CHANG, GRACE; Palisades Park HS; Palisades Pk, NJ; (4); 2/124; Pres Mu Alpha Theta; Q&S; Yrbk Ed-Chief; Ed Lit Mag; Bausch & Lomb Sci Awd; DAR Awd; Elks Awd; Gov Hon Prg Awd; NHS; Var Crs Cntry; Natl Hstry Day St Fnlst 84; NJ Dstngshd Schlr; Natl Merit Fnlst; Princeton U.

CHANG, HAEJIN; Holmdel HS; Holmdel, NJ; (3); 34/208; Aud/Vis; Cmnty Wkr; VP Debate Tm; German Clb; Trs Key Clb; Trs SADD; School Play; Nwsp Rptr; Yrbk Stf; Hon Roll; Pre-Med.

CHANG, ILEEN; Dumont HS; Dumont, NJ; (4); 19/217; Pres Mu Alpha Theta; Spanish Clb; SADD; Band; Chorus; Concert Band; Mrchg Band; Orch; School Musical; Stage Crew; High Achvt Awd 86.

CHANG, JASON; Newton HS; Lafayette, NJ; (2); Computer Clb; French Clb; Scholastic Bowl; Engrng.

CHANG, KO-CHIEN; Sayreville War Memorial HS; Belle Mead, NJ; (4); #16 In Class; French Clb; Math Clb; Teachers Aide; Yrbk Ed-Chief; VFW Awd; Gnrl Excllnc Math, Olympcs Mnd & Renatra Fusca Awds 86-87; Rutgers Coll; Elec Engr.

CHANG, LILY; Cherry Hill Hs East; Cherry Hill, NJ; (3); French Clb; Latin Clb; Science Clb; Spanish Clb; SADD; Im Badmtn; Im Bsktbl; Im Tennis; Im Vllybl; Hon Roll; Awd Excllnce Natl Sci Olympd 85; Awd Outstndng Schlr Alg I Exam Ind Math Cont 85.

CHANG, LYNDA; Memorial HS; West New York, NJ; (4); 42/358; Hosp Aide; Key Clb; Math Clb; Science Clb; Hon Roll; Rutgers Coll; Pharm.

CHANG, SOFIA; Maple Shade HS; Maple Shade, NJ; (4); 1/163; Computer Clb; Key Clb; Yrbk Stf; Var Badmtn; Var Capt Fld Hcky; Cit Awd; Gov Hon Prg Awd; Lion Awd; Pres NHS; Pres Schlr; Garden ST Dstngshd Schlr 86-87; Rotry Clb Awd 86; U Of PA.

CHANG, THOMAS; Watchung Hills Regional HS; Gillette, NJ; (3); JV L Bsbl; Bsktbl; JV Ftbl; Im Vllybl; Im Wt Lftg; Hon Roll; Prfct Atten Awd; Embrye-Riddle U; Aerntcl Sci.

CHANG, TINA; Newton HS; Newton, NJ; (4); 11/196; Math Clb; Yrbk Ed-Chief; Pres Sr Cls; Stat Wrstlng; DAR Awd; Sec NHS; Ntl Merit Ltr; St Schlr; Computer Clb; Quiz Bowl; Rtry Clb Yth Merit Awd 87; Dartmouth Coll; Comp Sci.

CHANG, UNJOO; North Bergen HS; N Bergen, NJ; (3); Art Clb; Math Tm; Band; Concert Band; Hon Roll; VFW Awd; Meadowlands Stu Art Expo Pncl Drwng 1st Pl 87; Graphic Art.

CHANTRE, MARLON; Dover HS; Dover, NJ; (3); French Clb; Nwsp Phtg; Im Ftbl; JV Socr; Var Swmmng; High Hon Roll; FL ST U; Hotel Mgmt.

CHAO, ANGELA; Parsippany Hills HS; Morris Plains, NJ; (4); 27/310; Sec Church Yth Grp; Debate Tm; Key Clb; Math Tm; Spanish Clb; Yrbk Stf; Var Trk; High Hon Roll; Hon Roll; NHS; Seton Hall U; Arch.

CHAO, EDWARD; West Windsor-Plainsboro HS; Lawrenceville, NJ; (3); AFS; Am Leg Boys St; Band; Chorus; Orch; JV Bsktbl; JV Crs Cntry; Hon Roll.

CHAO, JEFFREY; Holy Cross HS; Mount Laurel, NJ; (3); 5/403; Chess Clb; Computer Clb; Science Clb; Yrbk Stf; Rep Stu Cncl; High Hon Roll; Hon Roll; Hlth Rltd.

CHAPLIN, MICHELLE A; West Milford Township HS; West Milford, NJ; (4); 95/359; Art Clb; Church Yth Grp; DECA; Natl Art Hnr Soc 87; NJ ST Ldrshp Conf DECA 87; Comrcl Art.

CHAPMAN, ERICKA; Atlantic City HS; Atlantic City, NJ; (3); VP Church Yth Grp; Civic Clb; Cmnty Wkr; Key Clb; Latin Clb; Nwsp Stf; Rep Jr Cls; Rep Stu Cncl; Cheerleading; Hon Roll; Pre-Med.

CHAPMAN, MONIKA; Ramsey HS; Ramsey, NJ; (4); 26/256; Debate Tm; Girl Scts; Scholastic Bowl; Color Guard; Flag Corp; Stat Swmmng; Var L Trk; Hon Roll; NHS; Pres Acad Fit Awd 87; SUNY Oswego; Forestry.

CHAPMAN, VALERIE; Rancocas Valley Regional HS; Mt Holly, NJ; (2); Yrbk Rptr; Yrbk Stf; Lit Mag; Stat Bsktbl; Ftbl; Mgr(s); High Hon Roll; Hon Roll; Hnr Rl 85-87; Hgh Hnr Rl 86-87; Stu Dstnctn Strght A S 86; Real Est.

CHAPOT, WENDY; Princeton Day Schl; Neshanic Sta, NJ; (3); French Clb; Library Aide; Office Aide; Teachers Aide; JV Tennis; Hon Roll; Computer Clb; Math Tm; Science Clb; Equestrian Awds 84-87; Accntng.

CHAPPELL, MICHAEL; Bergen County Voc Tech; Saddle Brook, NJ; (3); JV Trk; Comp Repair.

CHARGUALAF, TRICIA; Monmouth Regional HS; Eatontown, NJ; (4); 40/234; Church Yth Grp; Office Aide; Spanish Clb; Chorus; Yrbk Stf; Rep Stu Cncl; Gov Hon Prg Awd; Hon Roll; Jr NHS; Latin Clb; Outstndg Excllnce Vocal Music Ind Living 87; Scholar Stuart Schl Bus Adm 87; Scholar Army Emerg Relief; The Stuart Schl; Ofc Mgmt.

CHARLES, DEBORAH; Vineland HS; Newfield, NJ; (1); Actng.

CHARLES, VERONICA; Vineland HS; Newfield, NJ; (2); Chorus; Drill Tm; Trk; Outstndng Prtcptn Pgnt Awd 86; Prfssnl Modelng.

CHARLTON, THOMAS; Southern Regional HS; Manahawkin, NJ; (3); 10/452; Boy Scts; Math Clb; Math Tm; Ski Clb; Hon Roll; NHS; Rep Frsh Cls; Rep Soph Cls; Rep Jr Cls; Rep Stu Cncl; Nuclear Pysics.

CHARNICK, BARRY; Monmouth Regional HS; Eatontown, NJ; (4); 1/250; Pres Chess Clb; Hosp Aide; Trs VP Math Clb; Capt Math Tm; Mu Alpha Theta; Ski Clb; Spanish Clb; Temple Yth Grp; Yrbk Sprt Ed; Yrbk Stf; NJ Govenors Schl Sci 86; Bronze Congrssnl Awd 86; Med.

CHASCSA, JOSEPH; Holy Cross HS; Beverly, NJ; (3); Chess Clb; S Jersey HS Champ 86-87; Rutgers; Accntng.

CHASE, JEFFREY G; Mainland Regional HS; Somers Point, NJ; (4); 15/278; Math Clb; Math Tm; Mgr Jazz Band; Mgr Mrchg Band; Im Bowling; Capt Vllybl; Pres NHS; Computer Clb; Mgr Band; Nwsp Stf; NJ Dstngshd Schlr 87; Am HS Math Hnr Roll 86 & 87; Top 5 Pct Of Clss 87; Stockton ST; Math.

CHASS, DAVID; Dwight Englewood HS; Paramus, NJ; (3); Cmnty Wkr; Math Tm; Ski Clb; Lit Mag; Var L Bsbl; Coach Actv; Var L Socr; Trk; Hon Roll; Johns Hopkins Schlr 82-83; Bus.

CHATTERJEE, SHILINA; Columbia HS; S Orange, NJ; (3); Cmnty Wkr; Girl Scts; Latin Clb; Pep Clb; JV Fld Hcky; PA ST U; Pltcl Sci.

CHAUBAL, CHARU; Christian Brothers Acad; Tinton Falls, NJ; (4); 13/216; Math Tm; Ski Clb; Thesps; Band; School Musical; School Play; Stage Crew; Nwsp Phtg; Nwsp Rptr; Nwsp Sprt Ed; U Of PA; Engr.

CHAUHAN, HARSHAL; Lodi HS; Lodi, NJ; (3); Science Clb; Spanish Clb; Temple Yth Grp; JV Socr; Hon Roll; Rutgers U; Med.

CHAUNCEY, JANE; Cranford HS; Cranford, NJ; (3); 93/298; Dance Clb; Gym; Trk; Fusion Dnc Theatre Cert Outstndng Prfrmnc 84 & Super Prfrmnc 85; Bio.

CHAVARRIA, EVELYN; St Joseph Of The Palisades HS; Guttenberg, NJ; (3); Art Clb; Camera Clb; Drama Clb; French Clb; Library Aide; Spanish Clb; Chorus; School Play; Nwsp Phtg; Nwsp Rptr; Gymnstcs Awds Medls 83-84; Bwlng Awds 86-87; Camera Clb Awd 88.

CHAZIN, MARTIN; Bridgewater-Raritan HS East; Bridgewater, NJ; (2); Debate Tm; Drama Clb; NFL; Speech Tm; Pres Temple Yth Grp; Chorus; School Musical; School Play; Rep Stu Cncl; Hon Roll; Jr/Sr Prom Co-Chrmn 87-88; Pre-Law.

CHEATHAM, INDYA; St Mary HS; Jersey City, NJ; (3); Church Yth Grp; NAACP; Pep Clb; U Of Bridgeport; Comm.

CHEDDAR, CHRISTINA; Woodbridge HS; Port Reading, NJ; (4); 20/386; Am Leg Aux Girls St; NFL; Pres SADD; Mrchg Band; School Musical; Nwsp Ed-Chief; Ed Lit Mag; Hon Roll; NHS; Drama Clb; James J Kerrigan Memrl Schlrshp, Emblem Clb Essy Cont Prtcpnt 87; Jrnlsm Awd 86; Hofstra U; Poli Jrnlsm.

CHEESMAN, DAWN; Vineland HS; Vineland, NJ; (2); Church Yth Grp; Cmnty Wkr; Hon Roll; Natl Hnr Scty For Typng I 85-86; Comp Prog.

CHELPATY, HEATHER; Lenape Valley Regional HS; Sparta, NJ; (4); 20/236; Key Clb; Yrbk Stf; Socr; Hon Roll; NHS; Pres Schlr; Bsktbl; Sftbl; Tennis; Vincenia Francom Acaro Romano Awd 87; Sussex Cnty Assoc Of Bus Offcls Schlrshp 87; Lenare Schlr 86; Wilkes Coll; Accntng.

CHELSTON, JOE; Brick Township HS; Brick, NJ; (3); Aud/Vis; Chess Clb; Computer Clb; FBLA; Leo Clb; Math Clb; Math Tm; SADD; Teachers Aide; VICA; OCC; Acctng.

CHEN, BETTY; Morris Catholic HS; Denville, NJ; (4); 4/142; Debat Tm; Pres FBLA; Math Clb; NFL; VP Spanish Clb; Pres Speech Tm School Play; High Hon Roll; Sec NHS; St Schlr; ST Chmpnshps J\ Debate 3rd Pl 85; Slvr Disc 4.0 Avg Full Acad Yr 87; Trnsfr Stu Dstnctr Slvr Disc 87; Wellesley Coll; Ec.

CHEN, CHARLENE; Montville Township HS; Pine Brook, NJ; (3); 3 277; Church Yth Grp; Capt FBLA; Hosp Aide; Key Clb; Office Aide Science Clb; Nwsp Stf; Cit Awd; High Hon Roll; Pres NHS; Gymnstcs Ms Imprvd Plyr 86; Northrn NJ Chnse Assn Teen Clb Treas 87; Key Cl Brthdy Clb Pres 86-87.

CHEN, CHIN-CHIN; Scotch Plains-Fanwood HS; Scotch Plains, NJ; (4) 2/300; Dance Clb; Drama Clb; French Clb; Math Tm; Model UN; Qui Bowl; Lit Mag; French Hon Soc; Gov Hon Prg Awd; High Hon Roll Stanford U.

CHEN, DEHAN; Millburn HS; Millburn, NJ; (4); 8/250; VP Church Yt Grp; Computer Clb; Math Tm; Spanish Clb; Jazz Band; Symp Band; Va L Tennis; Ntl Merit SF; Im Bsktbl; Presdntl Cmmndtn-Vlntr Wrk EP Lab RI 85; Biomdcl Engrng.

CHEN, ELSA YEE-FANG; Parisppany Hills HS; Morris Plains, NJ; (1) 8/321; Church Yth Grp; Math Tm; NFL; Capt Speech Tm; VP Soph Cls VP Jr Cls; Var L Tennis; Ntl Merit SF; Voice Dem Awd; Debate Tm Isshinryu Karate Awd; Nrthrn Nj Chiese Assoc; Asian Amer Club; Publ Reltns Dir.

CHEN, FANNIE; Cherokee HS; Marlton, NJ; (2); French Clb; Hos Aide; Latin Clb; Math Tm; Yrbk Stf; Lit Mag; Lcrss; High Hon Roll; NHS Genetics.

CHEN, HSUN-HYM; Mt Olive HS; Budd Lake, NJ; (3); 3/330; Scienc Clb; Ski Clb; Concert Band; Mrchg Band; School Musical; Tennis; Hig Hon Roll; Hon Roll; NHS; Ntl Merit Ltr; Mst Imprvd Plyr Awd-Tnns 87 Presdntl Physcl Ftns Awd 85-87; NJ Area Band 86.

CHEN, IRENE; South Brunswick HS; Kendall Park, NJ; (3); 1/274 Chess Clb; Pres FHA; Math Tm; Mu Alpha Theta; Science Clb; Nws Ed-Chief; Ed Lit Mag; French Hon Soc; High Hon Roll; NHS; Gov Sch Sci 87; Female Engrng 85; Rutgers Schlrs Pgm 87; Pre-Med.

CHEN, LI JEN; Dwight Morrow HS; Englewood Cliffs, NJ; (3); 17/32 Church Yth Grp; Math Tm; Variety Show; Yrbk Stf; Lit Mag; High Ho Roll; Hon Roll; NHS; Prfct Atten Awd; Rotary Awd.

CHEN, MAY; The Pennington Schl; San Carlos, CA; (3); 6/69; Dram Clb; German Clb; Intnl Clb; Library Aide; Political Wkr; School Musica School Play; Stage Crew; Stu Cncl; High Hon Roll; German I Awd, Acdm Top 20, & Wellesley Awd Outstndg Ldrshp & Schlrshp 87; Bus.

CHEN, PETER; Franklin Township HS; Somerset, NJ; (3); Compute Clb; Math Clb; Math Tm; Gov Hon Prg Awd; High Hon Roll; NHS; Com Awd From Comp Olympics 87; 8th Pl Cntrl Jersey Math Leag 87; 9th P Cntrl Jersey Math Leag 86; Rutgers U; Engr.

CHEN, YENG; Paramus HS; Paramus, NJ; (4); 3/330; Debate Tm; Mat Clb; Quiz Bowl; Ski Clb; Var Socr; NHS; Ntl Merit SF; German Hon So 85; Engrng.

CHENEY, MICHAEL; Pennington Prepratory HS; Robbinsville, NJ; (3) 30/82; Church Yth Grp; Chorus; Church Choir; Variety Show; JV L Bsb JV L Bsktbl; Var L Bowling; JV L Ftbl; Mgr(s); Im Wt Lftg; Untd Met Nw Dist Schlrshp 84; Genl Schlrshp 84; Engr.

CHENG, DORIS W; Bridgewater-Raritan HS West; Bridgewater, NJ; (4) Mrchg Band; Nwsp Stf; Yrbk Stf; Lit Mag; Stat Bsktbl; Powder Puff Ftb Hon Roll; NHS; Ntl Merit SF; Grdn ST Dstngshd Schlr 87.

CHENG, EDWARD; Parsippany Hills HS; Morris Plains, NJ; (3); Churc Yth Grp; Computer Clb; FBLA; Key Clb; NFL; Speech Tm; Thesp Y-Teens; Off Soph Cls; Off Jr Cls; NJ Foren ST Champ 86; Orignl Orator Champ 86; Oratory Govrns Awd Arts Educ 86.

CHENG, HONG Y; S Brunswick HS; Kendall Park, NJ; (3); 25/276 Chess Clb; Math Clb; Mu Alpha Theta; Science Clb; Var Trk; Hon Rol Math Clb; Yth Ftnss Achvmnt Awd 83-84; Elec Engnrng.

CHENG, JENFU; West Essex HS; No Caldwell, NJ; (2); Exploring; Hos Aide; Sec Key Clb; Science Clb; Spanish Clb; Lit Mag; Im Bsbl; JV Socr High Hon Roll; Vrsty Ltr Fencing 85-87; Key Clb Lieut Gov; Princeton.

CHENG, TERAVAT; Dickinson HS; Jersey City, NJ; (4); Camera Cl Computer Clb; Yrbk Phtg; Tennis; NHS; Prfct Atten Awd; Rutgers Coll O Engrng; Engrng.

CHENG, WEIYU; Clifton HS; Clifton, NJ; (3); Math Tm; High Hon Rol Hon Roll; Spanish NHS.

CHENVEN, ERIC; Park Ridge HS; Park Ridge, NJ; (3); 4/98; AFS; Bo Scts; Temple Yth Grp; School Play; Rep Frsh Cls; Rep Soph Cls; Rep St Cncl; Var JV Ftbl; High Hon Roll; Hon Roll; 19th Spnch Compttn Cert 8 Med.

CHERICHELLA, ROBERT; Wood-Ridge HS; Wood Ridge, NJ; (4); 2 75; Spanish Clb; Yrbk Stf; Sec Frsh Cls; Sec Soph Cls; Sec Jr Cls; Sec S Cls; Bsbl; Bsktbl; Wt Lftg; High Hon Roll; Green State Dist Schl Fairleigh Dickinson U; Bio.

CHERON, MONICA; Livingston HS; Livingston, NJ; (3); 102/416; Aud Vis; Key Clb; Leo Clb; Office Aide; Temple Yth Grp; Socr.

CHERRY, ASHLEN N; Cherry Hill HS East; Cherry Hill, NJ; (3); 37 714; Sec Am Leg Aux Girls St; Model UN; Nwsp Rptr; Var Bsktbl; Va Lcrss; Var Socr; Hon Roll; NHS; Ntl Merit Ltr; Bus.

CHERRY, BRADLEY; Phillipsburg HS; Phillipsburg, NJ; (4); 84/330 Cmnty Wkr; Ski Clb; Pres Frsh Cls; Pres Soph Cls; Var Ftbl; Im Wt Lftg JV Var Wrstlng; Cit Awd; Juniata Coll; Bus.

CHERRY, CARA; Tenafly HS; Tenafly, NJ; (4); Key Clb; Model UN School Musical; Pres Sec Stu Cncl; Var Capt Tennis; Cit Awd; High Ho Roll; Washington Wrkshp Sem 86; Delg Yth Pgm 87; Distngushd Schlr Pgm 86-87; Gov.

CHERRY, PAIGE; Hunterdon Central HS; Stockton, NJ; (2); 107/48 Sec Red Cross Aide; Sec 4-H Awd; Hon Roll; Ntl Pony Clb Rlly-3rd 8 Eastrn States Tm Indiv Chmpn 86; Ntl Pony Clb Tm Rlly-7th 85; U O New Hampshire.

CHERVIL, BALAGUER; Memorial HS; West New York, NJ; (4); 15 385; French Clb; Math Clb; Band; Bsbl; Socr; Trk; Hon Roll; NHS; NH Awd 86; AAA, NHS Awd 87; NY Inst Of Tech; Engrng.

CHESLAK, JOHN; Wall HS; Manasquan, NJ; (3); Computer Cl Spanish Clb; Stage Crew; Var Ftbl; Var Trk; Wt Lftg; High Hon Rol NHS; Natl Engl Merit Awd 86; Pre Med.

CHESNEY, SCOTT F; Verona HS; Verona, NJ; (3); Am Leg Boys S Cmnty Wkr; VP Frsh Cls; Pres Soph Cls; Pres Sr Cls; Rep Stu Cncl; V Stat Bsktbl; Stat Ftbl; Var Score Keeper; B Bradley Yng Ctzns Awd 8 Newark Bys & Grls Clb Amer Awd Courage 87; Cmnctns.

CHESSA, DAN; Manchester Regional HS; N Haledon, NJ; (3); Ski Cl Var Capt Ftbl; Var Golf; Ice Hcky; Hon Roll; Bio Engrng.

CHESTER, THOMAS; St John Vianney HS; Aberdeen, NJ; (2); Mat Tm; Off Soph Cls; JV Var Socr; JV Wrstlng; High Hon Roll; Hon Rol Prfct Atten Awd; Sea Cadets US Navy Supervision 87; US Svc Acad; La

CHESTNUT, KEITH; Morristown HS; Morris Plains, NJ; (1); Aud/Vis; Church Yth Grp; Key Clb; Radio Clb; Band; Concert Band; Jazz Band; Mrchg Band; Orch; Var Mgr Wrstlng.

CHEUNG, EDITH; Pitman HS; Pitman, NJ; (2); Phrmcst.

CHEUNG, FREDERICK; Franklin HS; Somerset, NJ; (3); Rep Church Yth Grp; Rep French Clb; Sec Key Clb; Rep Math Tm; Rep Model UN; Rep Soph Cls; High Hon Roll; Hon Roll; NHS; JV Tennis; Engrng.

CHEUNG, OCTAVIO; Matawan Regional HS; Aberdeen, NJ; (2); Boy Scts; Spanish Clb; Band; Concert Band; Jazz Band; Mrchg Band; School Musical; School Play; High Hon Roll; Pres Schlr; NJ ST Yth Orchstra 85-86; Al-Shore Symphnc Band 85-86; Cornell U; Vet Med.

CHEVALIER, DANIELLE; Henry Hudson Regional HS; Highlands, NJ; (2); Drama Clb; Acpl Chr; Band; Chorus; Concert Band; School Musical; Variety Show; Stat Bsktbl; Score Keeper; L Tennis.

CHEW, LILY; Secaucus HS; Secaucus, NJ; (3); 3/166; Computer Clb; Sec Intnl Clb; Mu Alpha Theta; Hon Roll; NHS; Spanish NHS; Voice Dem Awd; Columbia; Physcn.

CHEW, STEPHANIE; Gateway Regional HS; Wenonah, NJ; (3); 24/170; Pres Church Yth Grp; Latin Clb; SADD; Band; Chorus; Church Choir; Concert Band; Mrchg Band; School Musical; NHS; Vet.

CHHOWALLA, HEMA; Parsippany HS; Parsippany, NJ; (4); 39/330; FBLA; Yrbk Stf; NHS; Newark Hmn Rghts Cmmssn Annl Hmn Rghts Awd 84; Monclair ST Coll.

CHI, CARLIN L; Teaneck HS; Teaneck, NJ; (4); 1/375; Drama Clb; DECA; Debate Tm; Dance Clb; Computer Clb; Var L Crs Cntry; Var L Trk; Bausch & Lomb Sci Awd; Gov Hon Prg Awd; Hon Roll; Garden ST Dstngshd Schlr 86; Natl Latin Exm Magna Cum Laude 85-86; Physcs.

CHIACCHO, MARC; Penns Grove HS; Penns Grove, NJ; (4); #3 In Class; Key Clb; Latin Clb; JV Ftbl; Wt Lftg; Bausch & Lomb Sci Awd; 4-H Awd; Hon Roll; Physics Awd 87; Rutgers U; Physics.

CHIAFULLO, CHRIS; Long Branch HS; Long Br, NJ; (2); 5/314; Pres Drama Clb; Letterman Clb; NFL; School Play; JV Socr; Var Tennis; Hon Roll; Pres NHS; 1st Pl Earth Sci Olympiad; Boston Coll; Hotel-Rstrnt Mngt.

CHIANESE, KIMBERLY; Notre Dame HS; Yardville, NJ; (3); 10/370; Band; Concert Band; Drm Mjr(t); Mrchg Band; Orch; School Play; Rep Frsh Cls; Rep Jr Cls; Hon Roll; NHS; Math.

CHIANESE, SCOTT; Steinert HS; Trenton, NJ; (3); Lit Mag; JV Tennis; Poem Pblshd In Aspirations 86; Glassboro ST; Comm.

CHIAPPETTA, CHRISTOPHER; Christian Brothers Acad; Manalapan, NJ; (3); Boy Scts; Cmnty Wkr; Varsity Clb; Crs Cntry; Im Ftbl; Var L Trk; Hon Roll; Asbury Pk Press Carrier Schlrshp 87; All Monmth Indoor 1600 Meter Rely 87.

CHIAPPETTA, JASON; West Essex HS; N Caldwell, NJ; (3); Chess Clb; Computer Clb; Latin Clb; Natl Beta Clb; Band; Jazz Band; Golf; Tennis; Hon Roll; NHS; Hnrb Mntn Sci Project 84; Gold Mdl Acad Olympcs Physics 85; Pre-Med.

CHIARELLO, KARA; Mc Corristin Catholic HS; Trenton, NJ; (3); Drama Clb; FBLA; Science Clb; School Play; Hon Roll.

CHIAROLANZA, MARK; Parsippany Hills HS; Parsippany, NJ; (4); 49/330; Stage Crew; Ice Hcky; Wrstlng; ST U Of NY; Aerospc Engrng.

CHIAVETTA, CATHY; Northern Valley Regional HS; Harrington Pk, NJ; (3); 31/274; Sec AFS; Drama Clb; Ski Clb; Spanish Clb; Yrbk Stf; Ed Lit Mag; Rep Stu Cncl; Mgr(s); High Hon Roll; Hon Roll; Schl Rep Fdn Free Entrps LAB Sessn 87; Bus.

CHICHESTER, STEPHEN; Holy Cross HS; Mt Laurel, NJ; (3); JA; JV Wrstlng; Hon Roll; NHS Nmne 86-87; Comp Sci.

CHICKARA, CATHLEEN; Notre Dame HS; E Windsor, NJ; (3); 26/372; Drama Clb; Hosp Aide; Teachers Aide; JV Fld Hcky; High Hon Roll; NHS.

CHIDIAC, KATHLEEN; Brick Memorial HS; Bricktown, NJ; (1); Pres Frsh Cls; Pres Soph Cls; Rep Stu Cncl; Mgr Ftbl; Stat Mgr(s); JV Sftbl; Hon Roll; Brick Mem HS Booster Clb Sftbl Ldrshp Awd 86-87; Math.

CHIEFFO, DIANNE; Scotch Plains-Fanwood HS; Fanwood, NJ; (4); 69/355; Pres 4-H; Quiz Bowl; Teachers Aide; Band; Concert Band; Mrchg Band; Symp Band; Yrbk Stf; Sftbl; Ntl Merit Ltr; CPC Educ Fndtn Schlrshps 87-88; Penn ST; Wldlf Sci.

CHILCOTTE, DEBRA; St Joseph Of The Palisades HS; Jersey City, NJ; (3); Art Clb; SADD; Off Lit Mag; Pres Frsh Cls; High Hon Roll; NHS; Bus Adm.

CHILDS, ERIC; Rancocas Valley Regional HS; Mt Holly, NJ; (3); Spanish Clb; Varsity Clb; Rep Wrstlng; Prfct Atten Awd; Wrstlg Dist Rnnr Up & Regl Champ Awds 87; 1st Tm All Cnty 1st Tm All Div Awd 87.

CHILDS, JAMES; Collingswood SR HS; Woodlynne, NJ; (2); JCL; Latin Clb; Nwsp Ed-Chief; Rep Frsh Cls; Bowling; Hon Roll; Pres Schlr; Exemplar Awd 86; Jrnlst.

CHILIBERTI, DANIELLE; Paul VI HS; Laurel Sp, NJ; (3); 128/420; Art Clb; Bowling; Graphic Arts.

CHILSON, LYNETT; Red Bank Catholic HS; Eatontown, NJ; (4); 2/311; Q&S; Spanish Clb; SADD; Nwsp Ed-Chief; Hon Roll; Kiwanis Awd; Lion Awd; Sec Trs NHS; Sal; St Schlr; Bucknell U.

CHIMA, KULJIT; Mother Seton Regional HS; Carteret, NJ; (2); Computer Clb; Math Tm; Science Clb; Lit Mag; Off Frsh Cls; Off Soph Cls; High Hon Roll; Mthr Seton Rgnl Schlrshp 85; Top 10 Cpt In NC Sci League/Bio 86-87.

CHIN, DAVID H; Franklin HS; Somerset, NJ; (3); Sec Am Leg Boys St; Trs Art Clb; Trs Aud/Vis; Key Clb; Band; Rep Stu Cncl; Hon Roll; Cmnty Wkr; Concert Band; Mrchg Band; Itln Clb Pres 86-87; Schl HOSA Pres 86-87; NJ ST HOSA Hstrn/Rptr 87-88; Pre-Med.

CHIN, DERRICK; Paramus HS; Paramus, NJ; (3); JV Bsbl; Var Bsktbl; NHS; Engrng.

CHIN, LISA; Morris Catholic HS; Parsippany, NJ; (3); 14/150; Math Clb; Natl Beta Clb; Pep Clb; Nwsp Rptr; Yrbk Stf; Var Capt Sftbl; High Hon Roll; Hon Roll; Jr NHS; NHS.

CHINAPPI, MARISSA; Moorestown HS; Moorestown, NJ; (3); Am Leg Aux Girls St; Acpl Chr; Band; Nwsp Sprt Ed; Rep Jr Cls; Var Crs Cntry; God Cntry Awd.

CHIOCCO, FRANK; Don Bosco Prep; Ramsey, NJ; (2); 20/217; Band; Concert Band; Jazz Band; Mrchg Band; Orch; School Musical.

CHIORAZZI, EDWARD; Morris Catholic HS; Parsippany, NJ; (3); 17/148; Boy Scts; Library Aide; Natl Beta Clb; Scholastic Bowl; Yrbk Stf; JV Socr; JV Trk; Hon Roll; NHS; Brnz Mdl Acdmc Excllnc 85; Htl Mgmt.

CHIOVARI, AMY; Vineland HS; Vineland, NJ; (2); 53/868; Dance Clb; Drama Clb; Pep Clb; Spanish Clb; School Musical; School Play; Capt Cheerleading; Score Keeper; Hon Roll; Itln & Treasr Clb 85-87; Psych.

CHIPMAN, MICHELLE; Gateway Regional HS; National Pk, NJ; (2); Church Yth Grp; Rep French Clb; SADD; Psych.

CHIRICO, JOHN; Bloomfield HS; Bloomfield, NJ; (3); Hon Roll; Church Yth Grp; Cmnty Wkr; JA; Key Clb; Office Aide; Quiz Bowl; Ski Clb; Teachers Aide; School Play; Hnr Rll 85-87; Cls Rep 87; Ski Clb VP 87; Rutgers; Bus.

CHISHOLM, CHERYL; Linden HS; Linden, NJ; (3); Church Yth Grp; FBLA; FHA; Bsktbl; Cheerleading; Hon Roll; Kean Coll; Bus Adm.

CHMARA, REGINA; Brick Memorial HS; Brick, NJ; (3); Math Tm; Var Socr; Hon Roll; Acctng.

CHMIEL, ELIZABETH; Notre Dame HS; Hamilton Square, NJ; (3); 22/375; Hosp Aide; Math Tm; Red Cross Aide; Mrchg Band; Stat Bsktbl; Capt Pom Pon; High Hon Roll; Hon Roll; NHS; Excllnc Religious Studies; Excllnc Hnrs Eng II; Excllnc Hist; Bus Administration.

CHMIELEWSKI, RAYMOND; Lyndhurst HS; Lyndhurst, NJ; (3); 42/174; JV L Bsbl; JV L Bsktbl; Bus Mngmnt.

CHO, CHARLES Y; East Brunswick HS; East Brunswick, NJ; (4); Chess Clb; Church Yth Grp; German Clb; VP Math Clb; Math Tm; Science Clb; Nwsp Ed-Chief; Bausch & Lomb Sci Awd; High Hon Roll; NHS; German Hnr Soc Sec 86-87; Chem.

CHO, JUNG H; Northern Valley Regional HS; Demarest, NJ; (4); 7/235; Hosp Aide; Varsity Clb; Capt Ftbl; Hon Roll; NHS; Ntl Merit Ltr; Pres Schlr; St Schlr; All-League Ftbl 84-86; Wesleyan U; Med.

CHO, SONYA; Mainland Regional HS; Linwood, NJ; (4); 2/260; Church Yth Grp; Intnl Clb; Math Clb; Ed Nwsp Ed-Chief; Yrbk Stf; Trs Frsh Cls; VP Soph Cls; Hon Roll; Trs NHS; Ntl Merit Ltr; Sam Cohen Mrl Schlrshp 87; Columbia U.

CHOE, YUN-HUI; Northern Valley Regional HS; Norwood, NJ; (4); 15/270; AFS; Church Yth Grp; Hosp Aide; Intnl Clb; Ski Clb; Spanish Clb; Stage Crew; Yrbk Stf; High Hon Roll; Hon Roll; Rutgers U.

CHOEY, MARK; Teaneeck HS; Teaneck, NJ; (3); 121/417; Am Leg Boys St; JA; Math Tm; SADD; Nwsp Phtg; Nwsp Rptr; Ed Yrbk Phtg; JV Bsbl; Hon Roll; Prfct Atten Awd; Engrng.

CHOI, JENNY; Bayonne HS; Bayonne, NJ; (3); Chorus; Jazz Band; Mrchg Band; Vllybl; Jr NHS.

CHOI, JULIA; Northern Valley Regional HS; Norwood, NJ; (3); 6/274; Sec AFS; Sec Church Yth Grp; Intnl Clb; Model UN; Science Clb; Spanish Clb; Stage Crew; Yrbk Stf; Hon Roll; NHS; Smith Coll Bk Awd 86-87; Asian Clb Trea 86-87.

CHOI, MIKE; Cresskill HS; Cresskill, NJ; (3); 3/110; Am Leg Boys St; Church Yth Grp; Debate Tm; Ski Clb; Sec Concert Band; Jazz Band; Ed Yrbk Stf; JV Tennis; NHS; Ntl Merit Schol; Med.

CHOI, SANDRA; Northern Valley Regional HS; Norwood, NJ; (4); 6/270; AFS; VP Church Yth Grp; Intnl Clb; Library Aide; Science Clb; Soroptimist; Speech Tm; Band; Stage Crew; Nwsp Stf; Sci Wzrd-Physcs 85-86; Natl Sci Merit Awd 86-87; Sci Leag Awd 87; U Of MI Ann Arbor; Acctng.

CHOI, YOHAN; Shore Regional HS; Oceanport, NJ; (3); 1/222; Capt Chess Clb; Math Tm; Science Clb; Church Choir; Bausch & Lomb Sci Awd; NHS; Val; Boy Scts; Church Yth Grp; Math Clb; Rtgrs Schlr 87; Eagle Scout 86; Sci Hnrs Prgm Clmb U 86-87; Srgn.

CHOMINSKY, JOHN P; Wayne Hills HS; Wayne, NJ; (4); 41/292; Art Clb; FBLA; Math Clb; Spanish Clb; Jazz Band; JV Golf; Ice Hcky; Hon Roll; Ice Hcky Chmpshp; Vrsty Rifle Tm 83-85; Penn ST U; Advrtsng.

CHON, WONME; Cherry Hill West HS; Cherry Hill, NJ; (3); Pres Girl Scts; JCL; PAVAS; Orch; Off Frsh Cls; JV Bsktbl; Im Cheerleading; Cit Awd; Hon Roll; Korean Assn Southern NJ Schlrshp 86; U OfVA-RICHMOND; Dntstry.

CHONG, CHAE UN; Fort Lee HS; Fort Lee, NJ; (3); Trs Church Yth Grp; Band; Symp Band; Hon Roll; Rutgers U; Sci.

CHONG, STEPHEN; Rittatinny Reg HS; Stillwater, NJ; (4); 1/224; School Musical; Var Trk; Pres NHS; Ntl Merit SF; Pres Schlr; St Schlr; Val; Voice Dem Awd; Church Yth Grp; French Clb; 1st Pl Sussx Co Music Fndtn Schlrshp-Piano 85; Rbrt C Byrd Hnrs Schlrshp 87; Rtgrs Schlr; Johns Hopkins U; Mech Engrng.

CHONKO, EDWARD; Marist HS; Bayonne, NJ; (3); 24/108; Chess Clb; Church Yth Grp; Scholastic Bowl; Nwsp Rptr; Im Bsktbl; Ftbl; L Var Ice Hcky; Im Socr; Im Vllybl; HS Scholar 84; Rutgers Newark; Acctng.

CHOP, TRACY L; Morris Hill HS; Rockaway, NJ; (4); 2/265; Computer Clb; French Clb; Yrbk Stf; French Hon Soc; High Hon Roll; NHS; Sal; Exclsr Awds; ST U Of NY; Math.

CHOW, JEANNE M; Princeton HS; Princeton, NJ; (4); Y-Teens; Acpl Chr; Nwsp Phtg; Nwsp Rptr; Rep Frsh Cls; Rep Soph Cls; VP Jr Cls; VP Stu Cncl; Var Cheerleading; Var Capt Swmmng; Natl Merit Commended Stu 86-87; Gld Key Awd For Outstndng Svc 85-87; NJ Dstngshd Schlr 86-87; Med.

CHOW, KENNETH; The Pennington Schl; New York, NY; (2); #4 In Class; French Clb; Intnl Clb; Stage Crew; Crs Cntry; Vllybl; High Hon Roll; Hon Roll; NHS; Math, Physcs, Sci Awd 85-86; Arch.

CHOW, REBECCA; John P Stevens HS; Edison, NJ; (3); Church Yth Grp; Hosp Aide; Science Clb; Ski Clb; JV Powder Puff Ftbl; Hon Roll; NHS; 100 Hr/250 Hr Awds Cmmnty Svc Hosp 86.

CHRISBACHER, CARL; Wayne Valley HS; Wayne, NJ; (3); Ski Clb; Concert Band; Jazz Band; Mrchg Band; High Hon Roll; Hon Roll; NHS.

CHRIST, ANDREW; Raritan HS; Hazlet, NJ; (3); Am Leg Boys St; Socr; Hon Roll; Engrng.

CHRIST, MONICA; Paul VI HS; Turnerville, NJ; (4); 38/503; Math Clb; SADD; Hon Roll; NHS; Comp Sci.

CHRISTALDI, JOSEPH; Paul VI HS; Laurel Springs, NJ; (3); 10/418; Math Clb; Trs Jr Cls; JV Bsbl; High Hon Roll; Hon Roll; NHS; Italian Clb; Villanova; Bus.

CHRISTENSEN, CARMAN; Ocean Township HS; Ocean, NJ; (3); 21/344; Church Yth Grp; French Clb; Girl Scts; Science Clb; Band; Concert Band; Mrchg Band; Lit Mag; Jr NHS; NHS; Bioengrng.

CHRISTENSEN, KIRSTEN; Woodbridge HS; Woodbridge, NJ; (3); 1/300; Hosp Aide; Capt Quiz Bowl; Yrbk Phtg; Sec Jr Cls; High Hon Roll; Co-Capt NHS; Math Clb; Science Clb; Acpl Chr; Orch; Washington Wrkshp Trip Awd 87; John F Kennedy Hosptl Awd 87; Attitude Hnr Roll 85-87; Ed.

CHRISTENSON, ROBERT; Hammonton HS; Folsom, NJ; (4); Computer Clb; Exploring; Var Bsbl; Var Bowling; Hon Roll; NHS; Elec Engrng.

CHRISTIANA, RUSSELL; Wood-Ridge HS; Wood Ridge, NJ; (4); #16 In Class; Spanish Clb; Yrbk Stf; Pres Frsh Cls; Pres Soph Cls; Pres Jr Cls; Pres Sr Cls; Var Bsbl; Var Bsktbl; Capt Var Ftbl; Wt Lftg.

CHRISTIANSEN, LYNN; Timothy Christian HS; Matawan, NJ; (4); Church Yth Grp; Drama Clb; Chorus; School Musical; School Play; Yrbk Stf; JV Cheerleading; Var Sftbl; High Hon Roll; NHS; Valdctrn 83-84; Houghton Coll; Comm.

CHRISTIANSON, HOLLY; Notre Dame HS; Robbinsville, NJ; (3); Church Yth Grp; Hosp Aide; Yrbk Stf; JV Diving; Hon Roll; NHS.

CHRISTIE, DAVID A M; Bayley Ellard Catholic HS; Basking Ridge, NJ; (4); 2/90; Trs Church Yth Grp; NFL; Ski Clb; School Musical; Yrbk Bus Mgr; Capt Var Crs Cntry; Im Tennis; VP Sec NHS; Sal; Pres Spanish NHS; Holy Cross Coll; Theatre Arts.

CHRISTIE, DONNA-MARIE; Summit HS; Summit, NJ; (4); Orch; Yrbk Stf; Lit Mag; Crs Cntry; Capt Trk; Hon Roll; Prfct Atten Awd; Stu Month 86; Union Cnty Coaches MVP Trk & Field 86; Wesleyan Schlrshp 87; Wesleyan U.

CHRISTIE, LYNN ANNE; Paramus Catholic Girls Rgnl HS; Ho Ho Kus, NJ; (2); Church Yth Grp; Drama Clb; Science Clb; Chorus; School Musical; Variety Show; Lit Mag; Var Bowling; High Hon Roll; Dance Clb; Smmr Schlr St Peters Coll Jersy City Schlrshp 87; Acadmc Awds Eng, Jrnlsm; Gen Awd; Svc Actvty Awd 87; Music.

CHRISTIE, MICHELLE; Marylawn Of The Oranges; E Orange, NJ; (4); Pres Math Clb; Science Clb; Service Clb; Spanish Clb; School Play; Yrbk Stf; Bsktbl; Hon Roll; NHS; NEDT Awd 86; Sci Enrichment Hnrs Awd 85; U Of Rochester; Pre-Med.

CHRISTINE, COYLE; Paul VI HS; Laurel Springs, NJ; (4); 43/511; Math Clb; Spanish Clb; Rep Soph Cls; Hon Roll; NHS; Spanish NHS; Rutgers U; Accntng.

CHRISTOFILIS, CAROL; De Paul HS; Pompton Lakes, NJ; (4); German Clb; Hosp Aide; Office Aide; Teachers Aide; Chorus; Stage Crew; Stat Bsktbl; High Hon Roll; Psychlgy.

CHRISTOFORATOS, JERRY; Belleville HS; Belleville, NJ; (3); Hon Roll.

CHRISTOPHER, DAVE; Brick Township HS; Brick, NJ; (3); Cmnty Wkr; Drama Clb; Varsity Clb; School Musical; Ftbl; Trk; Wt Lftg; Phys Ed.

CHRISTOPHER, JULIA; Gloucester City HS; Gloucester Cty, NJ; (3); Art Clb; French Clb; Girl Scts; Q&S; Yrbk Stf; Lit Mag; Hon Roll; Intr Dsgn.

CHROBACK, DIANA LEA; Saddle Brook HS; Saddle Brook, NJ; (4); Am Leg Aux Girls St; Acpl Chr; Drm Mjr(t); Orch; Yrbk Rptr; Rep Stu Cncl; Var Sftbl; Gov Hon Prg Awd; NCTE Awd; Merit Pgm 86-88; Law.

CHRUPALA, KAREN; Holy Cross HS; Burlington, NJ; (3); 89/409; Ski Clb; Sftbl; Trk; Hon Roll.

CHRZANOWSKI JR, FRANK A; Cherokee HS; Marlton, NJ; (4); 2/398; Church Yth Grp; VP German Clb; Trs Math Clb; Var Swmmng; Pres NHS; Ntl Merit Schol; Sal; Computer Clb; Debate Tm; Scholastic Bowl; NJ Gov Schl Sci Drew U 86; Pres Clssrm Young Amer 87; Lenape Regnl HS Outstndng Stu 87; Ursinus Coll; Bio.

CHRZANOWSKI, JEFF; Cherokee HS; Marlton, NJ; (3); 1/454; Am Leg Boys St; Church Yth Grp; Computer Clb; German Clb; Math Tm; Scholastic Bowl; Var Trk; High Hon Roll; NHS; Ntl Merit Ltr; Outstndng Prfcncy Amer HS Math Exm, Gov Schl Sci NJ Fnlst 86-87; HOBY Fndtn Delg 85-86; Elec Engrng.

CHU, ALICE; Westfield SR HS; Westfield, NJ; (4); Science Clb; Spanish Clb; SADD; Chorus; NHS; Spanish NHS; Pres Acdmc Ftns Awd 87; Dgls Coll; Bus Mngmnt.

CHU, BRIAN; Matawan Regional HS; Matawan, NJ; (4); 1/316; School Musical; Yrbk Phtg; Trs Jr Cls; Pres Stu Cncl; Capt Crs Cntry; Var Trk; DAR Awd; NHS; Ntl Merit SF; Val; Garden ST Dstngshd Schlr 86.

CHU, KYONG; Fort Lee HS; Ft Lee, NJ; (4); 100/205; Boy Scts; Sec Camera Clb; Cmnty Wkr; Sec Trs Intnl Clb; Science Clb; Chorus; Pres Church Choir; Orch; School Play; Yrbk Rptr; Best Male Vclst 84-86; Rookie Thsbn Of Yr 84; Northeastern U; Hstry.

CHU, SHELLEY; Princeton HS; Princeton, NJ; (4); Cmnty Wkr; Q&S; Chorus; Pres Orch; Nwsp Stf; Off Frsh Cls; Rep Soph Cls; Off Jr Cls; Trs Stu Cncl; Var Swmmng.

CHUANG, JANETTE; Montville HS; Montville, NJ; (3); Art Clb; FBLA; Chorus; Hotel Mngt.

CHULIVER, ANTHONY; Holy Cross HS; Delran, NJ; (4); 10/350; Capt Math Clb; Spanish Clb; Concert Band; Mrchg Band; Orch; School Musical; Var Swmmng; High Hon Roll; NHS; Prfct Atten Awd; Math Awd, PTA Sprt Awd 87; Grdn ST Dstgngshd Schlr 86; Rensslar Poly Inst; Mech Engrng.

CHUN, DAL; Waldwick HS; Waldwick, NJ; (3); 1/136; Math Tm; Quiz Bowl; Yrbk Stf; Lit Mag; Var Tennis; High Hon Roll; NHS; Ntl Merit SF; St Schlr; Val; Lbrl Arts.

CHUN, JOYCE MOOYOUN; Northern Valley Regional HS; Northvale, NJ; (4); 32/273; AFS; Intnl Clb; Math Tm; Church Choir; Twrlr; NHS; Norwood Wmns Club Mst Imprvd 87; U MA Amherst; Bus.

CHUN, SAM H; Moorestown SR HS; Moorestown, NJ; (4); Am Leg Boys St; Church Yth Grp; Latin Clb; Band; Nwsp Stf; Sr Cls; Socr; Trk; Wrstlng; Quakeroots Hall Fame 87; U PA.

CHUNG, ARTHUR; J P Stevens HS; Edison, NJ; (2); 1/452; French Clb; Model UN; Science Clb; Nwsp Rptr; Trk; High Hon Roll; Concours Natl De Francais Level IB 11th NY/NJ Chptr 86; Dragon Relays Div 1 2nd Pl 4x800 86; Phys Sci.

CHUNG, JOON H; Delran HS; Delran, NJ; (4); 29/169; Art Clb; DECA; Math Tm; Science Clb; Var Bsbl; JV Bsktbl; Var Ftbl; Var Tennis; Var Wrstlng; Cit Awd; NJ Inst Of Tech; Arch.

CHUPAK, CAROL ANNE; Immaculate Conception HS; Lodi, NJ; (3); Drama Clb; English Clb; Spanish Clb; SADD; School Musical; School Play; Variety Show; Rep Frsh Cls; Rep Soph Cls; Var Cheerleading; Chrldng Cmptn Ind Awd & Tm Awd 86-87; Altrnt Grls St 87.

CHURCH, DEBORAH; The Pilgrim Acad; Cape May, NJ; (4); Church Yth Grp; FHA; Church Choir; Nwsp Stf; Yrbk Stf; Cit Awd; High Hon Roll; NHS; 2nd Sacred Kybd Grdn ST Assn Of Christian Schls 85; 4th Sacred Kybd 86; 4th Sacred Kybd 87; Bob Jones U; Educ.

CHWATKO, SHIRLEY; Rutgers Prep Schl; Old Bridge, NJ; (3); Pres French Clb; Hosp Aide; Model UN; Teachers Aide; Rep Stu Cncl; Var Crs Cntry; Hon Roll; Rep Frsh Cls; Rep Jr Cls; JV Sftbl; Blood Drive Ldr 86-87; Fin Miss Teen American Coed Pag 86; Schl Nwsp Writer 86-87; Pre-Med.

CIALINI, MIKE; Atlantic City HS; Margate, NJ; (4); 22/542; Computer Clb; Key Clb; Office Aide; SADD; Yrbk Stf; Var L Bsbl; Hon Roll; PA ST U; Bus.

CIAMPAGLIA, THOMAS; Lyndhurst HS; Lyndhurst, NJ; (3); 22/174; Seton Hall; Comp Sci.

CIAMPI, MARC; Holy Cross HS; Marlton, NJ; (3); Var JV Bsbl; Im Ftbl; Wt Lftg; Hon Roll; Rutgers U; Bus Mgmnt.

CIANCAGLINI, KELLI; Washington Twps HS; Turnersville, NJ; (4); 159/480; Hosp Aide; Office Aide; Q&S; School Musical; Sec Stu Cncl; Hon Roll; Stu Cncl Svc Awd 87; WA Twps Nrs Assoc Awd 87; Helene Fuld Schl Of Nrsng; Nrs.

CIANCIMINO, MARY; Bayonne HS; Bayonne, NJ; (3); Drama Clb; Office Aide; School Musical; Rep Jr Cls; Stu Cncl; Socr; Sftbl; Hon Roll; Comm.

CIARCO, SHAUNA; Lyndhurst HS; Lyndhurst, NJ; (3); 5/174; JV Var Bsktbl; JV Var Vllybl; Key Clb; Office Aide; Var Trk; High Hon Roll; Hon Roll; NHS; Prfct Atten Awd; Learn About Bus Seminr 86; Vet Med.

CICALE, LISA; Riverside HS; Riverside, NJ; (3); Cmnty Wkr; Drama Clb; SADD; Varsity Clb; Nwsp Rptr; Nwsp Stf; Yrbk Rptr; Yrbk Sprt Ed; Yrbk Stf; Pres Stu Cncl; LTC Delg 86; Outstndng Chrprsns Awd 85-87; Fire Mrshl 85-87; Montclair; Paralgl.

CICARDO, GINA; Lacey Twp HS; Forked River, NJ; (4); DECA; SADD; Yrbk Phtg; Var Capt Cheerleading; Pom Pon; Hon Roll; Pep Clb; Powder Puff Ftbl; Chrldng-Gldn Paw Awd, Outstndng SR Awd, 3 Yr Vrsty Ltr Wnnr 85-87; Raise-A-Cheer Trpl Comp 1st Pl 86; Broadcstng.

CICARELLI, JILL; Holy Spirit HS; Brigantine, NJ; (4); Cmnty Wkr; Nwsp Rptr; Nwsp Stf; Yrbk Stf; Stockton ST Coll; Bus.

CICCARELLA, JENNIFER; Mt Olive HS; Budd Lake, NJ; (3); Quiz Bowl; SADD; Acpl Chr; Rep Chorus; Madrigals; Orch; Var L Sftbl; High Hon Roll; Hon Roll; All St Chorus 86 & 87; Mdn Msc Mstr; Msc Hnr Scty 87; Law.

CICCARELLI, ROBERT; Haddonfield Memorial HS; Haddonfield, NJ; (4); Church Yth Grp; Yrbk Stf; JV Bsbl; Im Bsktbl; JV Socr; Var Capt Wrstlng; Hon Roll; NHS; Grmn Ntl Hnr Soc 86 & 87; Accntng.

CICCARELLI, STEVE; Haddonfield Memorial HS; Haddonfield, NJ; (3); 47/169; Sec Sr Cls; Bsbl; Golf; Socr; Wrstlng; High Hon Roll; Hon Roll; Wrstlng Iron Man Awd 87; Lwyr.

CICCARINO, CHRISTOPHER; Oratory Catholic Prep; Scotch Plains, NJ; (4); 9/44; Chess Clb; Church Yth Grp; Math Tm; Capt Quiz Bowl; Capt Scholastic Bowl; Service Clb; Nwsp Rptr; Nwsp Stf; Ed Yrbk Stf; Im Vllybl; NJ Schlr 86; Cngrssnl Yth Ldrshp Cncl 87; Amer Biogrphcl Soc 86; Bucknell U; Hstry.

CICCHINO, SUSAN E; Monsignor Donovan HS; Jackson, NJ; (3); 24/265; Drama Clb; Ski Clb; Stage Crew; High Hon Roll; NHS; Marine Bio.

CICERO, KELLYANNE; Parsippany HS; Parsippany, NJ; (3); Am Leg Aux Girls St; FBLA; GAA; Political Wkr; Varsity Clb; Sec Frsh Cls; Pres Soph Cls; VP Stu Cncl; Var L Bsktbl; Var Tennis; Rep Natl Assoc Stu Cncl Conv Buffalo NY 87; Franklin & Marshall; Govt.

CICIONE, TONIANN; Kingsway Regional HS; Mickleton, NJ; (4); 2/159; Pres French Clb; Key Clb; Yrbk Bus Mgr; Yrbk Stf; Ed Lit Mag; Rep Stu Cncl; Powder Puff Ftbl; Pres NHS; Sal; St Schlr; Natl Sci Mrt Awd 86; US Natl Math Awd 84-85; W Chest U; Bus Admin.

CIEMNOLONSKI, LAURA; Burlington City HS; Burlington, NJ; (4); 65/200; FBLA; Office Aide; Chorus; Mgr Trk; Hon Roll; Berkeley Bus Schl Schlrshp 87; Berkeley Bus Schl; Legal Secy.

CIERI, KATHERINE; Shore Regional HS; W Long Branch, NJ; (3); SADD; Color Guard; Flag Corp; Stage Crew; Nwsp Rptr; Twrlr; Hon Roll; Prfct Atten Awd; Comm.

CIERNIAK, BOZENA; Notre Dame HS; Trenton, NJ; (3); Hon Roll; Jr NHS; Accntng.

CIFELLI, FELICIA; Morristown HS; Morris Plains, NJ; (4); Crs Cntry; Trk; MVP Awd Trk 87; USMC; Admin.

CILIBERTI, DESIREE A; Morris Hills HS; Rockaway, NJ; (4); 6/264; Chorus; Concert Band; Orch; Symp Band; Gov Hon Prg Awd; High Hon Roll; JP Sousa Awd; Jr NHS; NHS; Govrs Awd Arts Educ 87; NJ Garden ST Art Ctr Talent Expo Wnnr 86; 1st Rnnr Up Miss Morris Cnty 87; Hartt Schl Of Music; Music Educ.

CIMA, CHRISTY; Washington Township HS; Turnersville, NJ; (4); Pres DECA; Key Clb; SADD; Nwsp Stf; Yrbk Stf; Rep Soph Cls; Rep Jr Cls; Rep Stu Cncl; JV Var Bsktbl; Var Capt Sftbl; Wshngtn DECA ST Fnlst-Gnrl Mrktng 86; Chrmn Hlth Fair 84-85; Penn ST U; Bus Admin.

CINALLI, BETH; Toms River High Schl South; Pine Bch, NJ; (2); Ski Clb; Drm Mjr(t); Mrchg Band; Variety Show; Powder Puff Ftbl; Elem Ed.

CINCOTTA, JANE; Pinelands Regional HS; Parkertown, NJ; (4); 17/190; Church Yth Grp; Nwsp Stf; Pres Stu Cncl; Var Bsktbl; Var Fld Hcky; Var Sftbl; Hon Roll; NHS; Ldrshp Awd Quncy Coll 87; Quincy Coll; Elem Educ.

CINEGE, CHRISTINE; Mount Saint Mary Acad; Linden, NJ; (4); GAA; Math Tm; Pres Ski Clb; Spanish Clb; Pres Band; Cheerleading; Var Gym; Swmmng; High Hon Roll; NHS; Cum Laude Scty 87; Duke; Med.

CINELLI, KIMBERLY; Cherokee HS; Atco, NJ; (2); Ski Clb; Rep Soph Cls; Gym; Hon Roll; Spcl Rcgntn Awd-Gymnstc Achvt 86-87.

CINQUINI, LISA; Cherokee HS; Marlton, NJ; (2); French Clb; Hon Roll; NHS; Law.

CIOCCO, SCOTT J; Overbrook HS; Pine Hill, NJ; (4); 14/350; Dance Clb; Ski Clb; Spanish Clb; Varsity Clb; Stage Crew; Trk; Hon Roll; NHS; Prfct Atten Awd.

CIOFFI, MICHELE; Saint John Vianney HS; Freehold, NJ; (3); Office Aide; Service Clb; Ski Clb; SADD; Yrbk Stf; JV Capt Cheerleading; Powder Puff Ftbl; High Hon Roll; NHS; Prfct Atten Awd; Gld, White Awd 86-87; Presdntl Phy Ftns Awd 86-87; Jr Vrsty Athltc Awd Ftbl, Bsktbl Chrldr 86-87; Comp Sci.

CIONCI, RICHARD; Cherry Hill H S West; Cherry Hill, NJ; (3); Chess Clb; Drama Clb; PAVAS; Band; Concert Band; Jazz Band; Mrchg Band; Orch; School Play; Symp Band; ST & Local Band Awds 85-87; Chess Club ST Awd Wnnr 87; Amer Music Abroad 86; U Sthrn CA; Phys Sci.

CIPERSKI, JILL; Wayne Hills SR HS; Wayne, NJ; (4); 72/289; Church Yth Grp; VP FBLA; Spanish Clb; Variety Show; Yrbk Stf; Capt Bsktbl; Sftbl; Vllybl; Hon Roll; Awd GPA Data Prcssng & Accntng 86-87; Stu Athl Assn Schlrshp 86-87; Rider Coll; Mrktng.

CIPOLLA, KELLY; Pennsville Memorial HS; Pennsville, NJ; (3); #6 In Class; FHA; Chorus; Lit Mag; Stu Cncl; Cheerleading; Mgr(s); High Hon Roll; Hon Roll; Psych.

CIPRIANI, DIANE; Hackettstown HS; Hackettstown, NJ; (4); 11/234; Teachers Aide; Chorus; Rep Stu Cncl; Hon Roll; Trs NHS; Fncng Co-Cptn Vrsty 84-87; Rookie Of The Yr Awd 84; Mst Imprvd Fncr 85; Rutgers Coll; Pltcl Sci.

CIPRIANI, LYDIA; Park Ridge HS; Park Ridge, NJ; (4); 7/106; Math Tm; Varsity Clb; Yrbk Sprt Ed; VP Soph Cls; VP Jr Cls; VP Sr Cls; Rep Stu Cncl; Var Capt Bsktbl; Var Capt Trk; High Hon Roll; Rutgers Coll; Econmcs.

CIRANNI, MARIA; Paul Vi HS; Atco, NJ; (1); GAA; Church Choir; School Play; Trk; Prfct Atten Awd; Itln Clb 86-87; Amer Assn Tchrs Itln Cert Of Awd Hnrb Mntn 87; Crmml Dfnse Lawyer.

CIRCONCISCO, ALFONSO; Secaucus HS; Secaucus, NJ; (4); 10/180; Computer Clb; Key Clb; Math Clb; Mu Alpha Theta; Yrbk Stf; High Hon Roll; Hon Roll; Mu Alpha Theta Awd; NHS; Ntl Merit Ltr; Frgn Lang Hnr Soc; Rutgers.

CIRCONCISO, ALFONSO; Secaucus HS; Secaucus, NJ; (4); 10/160; Intnl Clb; Key Clb; Math Clb; Mu Alpha Theta; Ed Lit Mag; High Hon Roll; Hon Roll; Mu Alpha Theta Awd; NHS; Pres Schlr; Italian Hnr Scty; Rutgers U.

CIRELLO, VINCENT ANTHONY; Fair Lawn HS; Fair Lawn, NJ; (4); French Clb; SADD; Varsity Clb; Coach Actv; Capt Ftbl; Capt Lcrss; Wt Lftg; Bergen Cnty Coaches Assn Schlrshp 87; BCCA Ftbl Schlrshp 87; Bergen Cnty Caring Awd 87; Hnrb Mntn-Ftbl; Randolph-Macon Coll; Psych.

CIRIANNI, SARINA; Bridgewater-Raritan HS; Raritan, NJ; (3); Pep Clb; Rep Frsh Cls; Rep Soph Cls; Rep Jr Cls; Rep Sr Cls; Rep Stu Cncl; Var Capt Cheerleading; Im Powder Puff Ftbl; JV Chrldng Cert 84; 1st Yr Vrsty Ltrs Chrldng 85 & 86; 2nd Yr Vrsty Awd Chrldng 86; 3rd Yr Chrldng 87.

CIRIGLIANO III, JOE; Oakcrest HS; Mays Lndg, NJ; (2); 9/293; Church Yth Grp; Computer Clb; French Clb; Ski Clb; School Play; Var JV Bsbl; JV Bsktbl; Hon Roll; Vrsty Schlr Awd 86-87; Fanny Schuler Math & Sci Awd 85; PTA Svc Awd 85; St Joseph U PA; Bus Mgmnt.

CIRILLO, KIM; Boonton HS; Boonton, NJ; (2); JV Fld Hcky; Mgr(s); Mat Maids; Score Keeper; Hon Roll; Psych.

CIRILLO JR, ROBERT; Livingston HS; Livingston, NJ; (3); 108/425; Band; Chorus; Concert Band; Madrigals; Mrchg Band; School Musical; Trk; JR Ntl Hnr Soc 84; N Jersey Rgnl Choir 84-86; Law.

CIRILLO, TARA; West Essex SR HS; Fairfield, NJ; (3); Varsity Clb; Socr; Sftbl; Hon Roll; All Cnty Scr Tm 86; Bus.

CIRONI, MICHEL VALENTYNA; Neumann Prep; Paterson, NJ; (3); #35 In Class; Chess Clb; Dance Clb; FBLA; Library Aide; Political Wkr; Spanish Clb; Varsity Clb; School Play; Lit Mag; Rep Frsh Cls.

CISZEWSKI, JENNIFER A; Sayreville War Memorial HS; Parlin, NJ; (3); German Clb; Rep GAA; Spanish Clb; School Musical; Stage Crew; Mgr Fld Hcky; Mgr Socr; Hon Roll; Pre Law.

CITRO, DOMINIC; Spotswood HS; Spotswood, NJ; (3); Pres Camera Clb; Model UN; Mrchg Band; Symp Band; Ed Nwsp Phtg; Ed Yrbk Phtg; JV Trk; JV Var Wrstlng; Vet.

CITRON, MIKE; Lakewood HS; Lakewood, NJ; (4); 17/336; Am Leg Boys St; Key Clb; JV Bsbl; Var L Socr; Var Trk; VP NHS; Pres Schlr; English Clb; Band; Rep Frsh Cls; Blck Hwks Schlrshp, Presdntl Acadc Ftns & Grdn ST Schlrshp Awds 87; U Of DE; Physcl Thrpy.

CIULLA JR, PETER; Nutley HS; Nutley, NJ; (4); 29/329; Exploring; Wrstlng; Hon Roll; NHS; Hgh Hnrs Math 83-87; OK U; Engrng.

CIVELLO, DONNA; Lakeland Reg HS; Ringwood, NJ; (4); French Clb; Ski Clb; Yrbk Stf; Rep Sr Cls; Trk; High Hon Roll; Hon Roll; Vrsty Lttr For Rnng Tr, De Paul HS 84-85; Hgh Hnr Roll 86-87; Hnr Roll 86-87; Ithaca Coll; Mrktng.

CIVIDANES, AME; Toms River HS North; Toms River, NJ; (3); 35/467; Intnl Clb; Spanish Clb; Orch; Stu Cncl; JV Capt Cheerleading; JV Socr; High Hon Roll; Hon Roll; NHS; Voice Dem Awd; NJ All ST Orchstra Violn 87-88; South Jrsy Rgnl Orchstra Violn 86-87; Grdn ST Philhrmnc Symp 86-88; Law.

CLAIR, COLLEEN; Mary Help Of Christians Acad; Suffern, NY; (3); Letterman Clb; Library Aide; Math Tm; Pep Clb; Variety Show; Nwsp Stf; Im Bsktbl; Im Vllybl; Hon Roll.

CLAIR, SUSAN; St John Vianney HS; Colts Neck, NJ; (4); 6/259; Drama Clb; Intnl Clb; School Musical; School Play; Ed Nwsp Ed-Chief; Yrbk Stf; Mgr Ftbl; High Hon Roll; NHS; Ntl Merit Ltr; Northwester U; Comm.

CLAIR, TIMOTHY; High Point Regional HS; Branchville, NJ; (1); Church Yth Grp; German Clb; Ski Clb; High Hon Roll.

CLANTON, ARLEEN; Linden HS; Linden, NJ; (3); Cmnty Wkr; Library Aide; Office Aide; Service Clb; Trs Chorus; School Musical; Rep Jr Cls; Capt Cheerleading; Hon Roll; NHS; Brd Of Trstees For L Mayors Yth Comm 86-87; Nmrs Dnc Awds 85-87; Bus.

CLARIZIO, JOSEPH; Lyndhurst HS; Lyndhurst, NJ; (3); 7/174; Cmnty Wkr; German Clb; Science Clb; Var Bsktbl; High Hon Roll; Hon Roll; NHS; NJS Crftsmn Fair 1st Pl 86; Columbia U; Engrng.

CLARK, ANDREW; Ridge HS; Basking Ridge, NJ; (4); 32/86; VP Church Yth Grp; Red Cross Aide; Ski Clb; Pres SADD; Off Stu Cncl; Var Socr; Stdnt Cncl Rep ST Cnvntn 86; Hnr Rll 86; Pedtrcn.

CLARK, CHERYL; Woodrow Wilson HS; Camden, NJ; (3); Varsity Clb; Yrbk Stf; Rep Frsh Cls; Rep Soph Cls; Sec Jr Cls; Sec Sr Cls; Pres Stu Cncl; Var Capt Bsktbl; Var Tennis; Var Capt Trk; Mst Vlbl Plyr Bsktbl, Mst Outstndng Field Perf Track 86-87; IN Inst Of Tech; Bus Admin.

CLARK, CHERYL A; Spotwood HS; Milltown, NJ; (3); 17/161; Church Yth Grp; 4-H; Intnl Clb; Ski Clb; Yrbk Stf; JV Sftbl; Hon Roll; NHS.

CLARK, FRED; Oakcrest HS; Mays Landing, NJ; (3); Computer Clb; ACC; Elec.

CLARK, GORDON; Brick Town HS; Brick Town, NJ; (3); 166/486; Am Leg Boys St; Nwsp Rptr; Lit Mag; Crs Cntry; Trk; Gov Hon Prg Awd; Jrnlsm.

CLARK, JEFF; Mahwah HS; Mahwah, NJ; (3); 13/161; Church Yth Grp; JCL; Rep Frsh Cls; Rep Soph Cls; Rep Jr Cls; JV Bsbl; JV Bsktbl; Var Capt Socr; High Hon Roll; NHS.

CLARK, JENNIFER; Ridge HS; Basking Ridge, NJ; (3); Pres AFS; Sec Church Yth Grp; Library Aide; Ski Clb; VP SADD; Chorus; Church Choir; Flag Corp; Nwsp Rptr; Rep Stu Cncl; Amer Field Stu Japan 87; Co-Pres AFS Clb 87-88; Hobby Rep Ldrshp Conf 86; Med.

CLARK, JENNIFER; Rutherford HS; Rutherford, NJ; (3); Chess Clb; Key Clb; Math Tm; Pres NFL; Science Clb; Var Tennis; High Hon Roll; NHS; Am Leg Aux Girls St; Computer Clb; Pres Clssrm 86; Fut Prob Slvg ST Comp Wnnr 84; Board Of Ed Slvr Awd Recip 86; Econ.

CLARK, JIM; Ocean City HS; Ocean City, NJ; (3); 9/355; SADD; Nwsp Ed-Chief; Pres Frsh Cls; High Hon Roll; NHS; Ntl Merit SF; NEDT Awd; Acdmc All Amrcn 84-85; 1st Grdn ST Schlstc Press Assoc Cont, Outstndng Socl Stds Stu 86-87; Jrnlsm.

CLARK, KENNY; Garden State Acad; New Rochelle, NY; (3); Wt Lftg; Wrstlng.

CLARK, LORETTA; Mc Corristin Catholic HS; Yardville, NJ; (3); Art Clb; Dance Clb; GAA; Girl Scts; Var JV Cheerleading; Var L Trk; Hampoton U; Crim Just.

CLARK, LORI; Bloomfield HS; Bloomfield, NJ; (3); Am Leg Aux Girls St; GAA; Spanish Clb; Capt Color Guard; Mrchg Band; Rep Soph Cls; Rep Jr Cls; Var Bsktbl; JV Sftbl; Hon Roll; Spec Ed.

CLARK, NAPOLEON D; Science HS; Irvington, NJ; (3); Am Leg Boys St; Im Bsktbl; Hon Roll; Math & Sci Pgm 85-87; HS Schlrs Recognition 86-87; Drexel U; Comp.

CLARK, SALLY E; Faith Christian HS; Cherry Hill, NJ; (4); 2/8; Drama Clb; Chorus; Church Choir; School Play; Yrbk Stf; Pres Frsh Cls; Pres Stu Cncl; Capt Var Cheerleading; Var Capt Fld Hcky; Gym; Pres Phys Fit Awd 85.

CLARK, SHARON; Monsignor Donovan HS; Bricktown, NJ; (3); 38/241; Drama Clb; Ski Clb; JV Var Cheerleading; High Hon Roll; Hon Roll; NHS; Psych.

CLARK, TIFFANI EVANGELINE; Garden State Acad; New Rochelle, NY; (3); 3/23; Church Yth Grp; Ski Clb; Chorus; Church Choir; Drill Tm; School Play; Bsktbl; Gym; Swmmng; Hon Roll; Med.

CLARK-CHRISTIE, JASON; John P Stevens HS; Edison, NJ; (3); 45/450; Debate Tm; Science Clb; Capt JV Bsktbl; Hon Roll; NHS; Aud/Vis; Band; Mrchg Band; Powder Puff Ftbl; Wt Lftg; Best Percussion Section 84.

CLARKE, DONALD; Millville SR HS; Millville, NJ; (4); Church Yth Grp; Cmnty Wkr; Variety Show; Bowling; Tennis; High Hon Roll; NHS; Sci Dept Awd, Bwlng Clb Schlrshp, Garden ST Schlr 87; Glassboro ST Coll; Bio.

CLARKE, KATHLEEN; Cranford HS; Cranford, NJ; (2); English Clb; Math Clb; Varsity Clb; Band; Mrchg Band; Rep Soph Cls; Rep Stu Cncl; JV Bsktbl; JV Fld Hcky; Var Trk; NY U-Rutgers; Physcl Thrpy.

CLARKE, KIM; Jackson Memorial HS; Jackson, NJ; (4); 7/403; VP Hst FNA; Hosp Aide; Mrchg Band; Orch; VP Jr Cls; Pom Pon; VP NHS; NEDT Awd; Math Tm; NAACP; Semi-Fnlst Ntl Hspnc Merit Schlrshp 86-87; NJ Dstngshd Schlr-Hnrbl Mntn; Hosp Adm.

CLARKE, LAUREN; The Ranney Schl; Monmouth Bch, NJ; (3); Dance Clb; Hosp Aide; Model UN; Red Cross Aide; Ski Clb; Spanish Clb; Chorus; Im Fld Hcky; JV L Sftbl; Var L Swmmng; Intra Mural Team Cap 84; Dancer Schl Play Anything Goes 84; Crimnl Just.

CLARKE, SHELLY; Kinsway Regional HS; Swedesboro, NJ; (2); Church Yth Grp; Teachers Aide; Hon Roll; Bus Admin.

CLARKSON, SHANNIN; Jackson Memorial HS; Jackson, NJ; (3); 171/416; Comendtn Typng 87-88; Sec.

CLAUSER, VERA; Delran HS; Delran, NJ; (4); VP DECA; Pep Clb; Chorus; JV Capt Cheerleading; Var JV Powder Puff Ftbl; High Hon Roll; Hon Roll; Mst Outstndng Stdnt DECA 87; NJ DECA Schlrshp 87; Burlington Co Coll; Own Bus.

CLAUSS, CRAIG; Westwood Regional HS; Westwood, NJ; (4); 24/220; Teachers Aide; Rep Soph Cls; Rep Jr Cls; Bsktbl; JV Golf; French Hon Soc; High Hon Roll; Hon Roll; NHS; Rensselaer Polytech Inst.

CLAXTON, HEATHER; Salem HS; Salem, NJ; (3); Church Yth Grp; Computer Clb; Math Clb; SADD; Teachers Aide; Tennis; Hon Roll; NHS; U Of HI; Archtctr.

CLAYMAN, AMY JILL; Westfield HS; Westfield, NJ; (2); Drama Clb; SADD; Chorus; School Musical; School Play; Swing Chorus; Sec Soph Cls; Ruth Tombacher Memorial Voice Schlrshp 86; Theatre.

CLAYTON, ELLIOTT; Weequahic HS; Newark, NJ; (4); 5/400; Boy Scts; Church Yth Grp; Computer Clb; Exploring; Letterman Clb; Spanish Clb; Nwsp Sprt Ed; Yrbk Stf; Pres Soph Cls; Stu Cncl; Grdn ST Dstgngshd Schlr Awd 87; FL A & M U; Bio-Med Engnrng.

CLAYTON, TAMMIE; Paterson Catholic Regional HS; Paterson, NJ; (2); Sec Church Yth Grp; NAACP; Pep Clb; Chorus; Sec Church Choir; Color Guard; Nwsp Stf; JV Bsktbl; Sal; Hal Jacksons Tlntd Teen 86; 2nd Runner Up NJ Tlntd Teens 86; Miss Paterson Pgnt 87; Law.

CLEAR, DYLAN; Metuchen HS; Metuchen, NJ; (4); Varsity Clb; Nwsp Rptr; Bsktbl; Ftbl; Powder Puff Ftbl; NHS; St Schlr; JNIHSAA Schlr Athlt, Ftbl All-Cnty Hnrb Mntn, Bsktbl All-Cnty Hnrb Mntn 87; U Of Rochester; Marine Bio.

CLEARY, CHERYL; Clifton HS; Clifton, NJ; (3); Cmnty Wkr; Pres Service Clb; Mrchg Band; Orch; Symp Band; Nwsp Stf; Cit Awd; High Hon Roll; Jr NHS; Spanish NHS.

CLEGG, MATTHEW; Toms River HS South; Toms River, NJ; (3); Church Yth Grp; Drama Clb; Thesps; School Musical; School Play; Am Leg Boys St; Boy Scts; NFL.

CLEMENS, LISA; Bordentown Regional HS; Bordentown, NJ; (2); 19/141; Church Yth Grp; Hosp Aide; Key Clb; Ski Clb; Church Choir; Yrbk Stf; Stat Bsktbl; Pom Pon; Hon Roll; Sci.

CLEMENSON, NEILS E; The Pilgrim Acad; Estell Manor, NJ; (3); Am Leg Boys St; Chess Clb; Debate Tm; Exploring; Radio Clb; Chorus; School Musical; School Play; Nwsp Rptr; Nwsp Stf; Comp Sci.

CLEMENTE, DONNA; Wood Ridge HS; Woodridge, NJ; (3); 36/91; Art Clb; Spanish Clb; VP Soph Cls; VP Jr Cls; Var Cheerleading; Var Sftbl; Accntng.

CLEMENTI, VINCENT; Immaculata HS; Somerville, NJ; (3); Var Bsbl; Bsktbl; Var Ftbl; Var Tennis; Wt Lftg; Rutgers U; Bus.

CLEMENTS III, JOHN E; Montville Township HS; Montville, NJ; (3); FBLA; Key Clb; Math Clb; Ski Clb; JV Crs Cntry; Var Socr; Tennis; High Hon Roll; NHS; Ntl Merit Ltr; Church Grp Guitarist; Gifted And Talented Pgm,Class Rep.

CLEMONS, LISA; Monmouth Regional HS; Neptune, NJ; (1); Girl Scts; Spanish Clb; Score Keeper; Doc.

CLEVELAND, DAVE; Washington Township HS; Sewell, NJ; (4); Letterman Clb; Math Clb; Model UN; Engrng Schlrshp 87; Pres Mr Bungle Clb 86-87; Bsktbl All Str 87; Sthrn Methodist U; Engrng.

CLIFFORD, ANNE; Morristown HS; Morris Plains, NJ; (1); Church Yth Grp; Hosp Aide; Key Clb; Chorus; Color Guard; Hon Roll; Med.

CLIFFORD, ERIC; Hoboken HS; Hoboken, NJ; (3); Aud/Vis; Boys Clb Am; Boy Scts; Cmnty Wkr; Latin Clb; Office Aide; VICA; School Play; Stage Crew; Variety Show; Mason.

CLINE, JASON; Vineland HS; Vineland, NJ; (2); English Clb; German Clb; Band; Stage Crew; Rep Stu Cncl; Church Yth Grp; Physics.

CLINK, BETH; High Point Regional HS; Lafayette, NJ; (3); Math Clb; Q&S; Yrbk Bus Mgr; Yrbk Ed-Chief; Yrbk Stf; Stat Fld Hcky; Mgr(s); JV Sftbl; High Hon Roll; Hon Roll.

CLINTON, BARBARA; Paramus Catholic Girls Regional; Leonia, NJ; (3); Church Yth Grp; Cmnty Wkr; Ski Clb; Teachers Aide; Coach Actv; Trk; High Hon Roll; Hon Roll; NHS; NEDT Awd; Schl Merit Awd For Cntrbtn 86-87; Ed.

CLOUSE, BERNADETTE; St Marys HS; Jersey City, NJ; (3); Church Yth Grp; Hosp Aide; Chorus; Church Choir; School Play; Yrbk Stf; Rep Jr Cls; Rep Sr Cls; Vllybl; Hon Roll; Gus Wellers Most Outstndng Volntr 86; Marion Awd Outstndng Achvr 86-87; Christ Hosp Schl Nrsng; Nrsng.

CLOWRY, CAROL; Holy Cross HS; Willingboro, NJ; (3); Hosp Aide; Ski Clb; Trs Band; Drm Mjr(t); VP Mrchg Band; School Musical; Swmmng; Hon Roll; DAAD Counselor 86; Guidance Aid; Rutgers; Fine Arts.

CLUNE, PATRICK; High Point Regional HS; Branchville, NJ; (3); 27/254; Boy Scts; Band; Concert Band; Jazz Band; Mrchg Band; JV Socr; Var Trk; Hon Roll; Pilot.

CO, KELVIN; Oakcrest HS; Philippines; (4); Hon Roll; Audio Engr.

COATES, DARIUS; Essex Catholic Boys HS; Irvington, NJ; (3); Art Clb; Var Ftbl; Var Wt Lftg; FL Southern Coll; Bus Admin.

COATES, RICK; Holy Cross HS; Willingboro, NJ; (4); Church Yth Grp; Red Cross Aide; Ski Clb; Varsity Clb; Off Jr Cls; Off Sr Cls; Off Stu Cncl; JV Bsktbl; Var Ftbl; Im Golf; Yth & Politcl Sys 86; The Citadel.

COBAS, LISBETH; Pararrius Catholic Girls HS; Hackensack, NJ; (3); Drama Clb; Service Clb; Church Choir; School Play; Nwsp Rptr; Lit Mag; NHS; Prfct Atten Awd; Hmrm Rep Christian Svc; Pre Law.

COBB, JACLYN; Bridgeton HS; Bridgeton, NJ; (4); 9/191; Ski Clb; Soroptimist; Var Tennis; NHS; Rensselaer Medal 86; Am Chem Soc Awd 87; Pres Acdmc Fit Awd 87; Clemson U; Chem Engrng.

COBERT, MARIANNE; Edgewood SR HS; Blue Anchor, NJ; (4); #10 In Class; Cmnty Wkr; Girl Scts; Yrbk Stf; Var Frsh Cls; Rep Jr Cls; Rep Sr Cls; Jr NHS; Hon Roll; NHS; Ntl Merit Ltr; Top Sls Grl Candian 50000 Club Awd 87; FIT NY; Merch.

COBO, GONZALO; Essex Catholic Boys HS; Kearny, NJ; (3); Rep Frsh Cls; Rep Soph Cls; Rep Stu Cncl; JV Fld Hcky; Var Socr; Hon Roll; Med.

COBUN, ELIZABETH; The Hun Schl; Mitchellville, MD; (3); Sftbl; Hon Roll; NHS.

COCEANO, THOMAS; St Marys Hall-Doane Acad; Willingboro, NJ; (4); 2/18; Am Leg Boys St; Drama Clb; VP Stu Cncl; Var Bsktbl; Bausch & Lomb Sci Awd; Cit Awd; High Hon Roll; VP Soph Cls; School Play; Garden ST Distngshd Schlr 87; Cum Laude Soc 87; Judicial Comm 87; Lehigh U; Engr.

COCHRAN, LORI; John E Kennedy HS; Willingboro, NJ; (3); 2/292; Am Leg Aux Girls St; Computer Clb; Intnl Clb; Yrbk Stf; Hon Roll; NHS.

COCHRANE, CHRISTINE A; Parsippany Hills HS; Parsippany, NJ; (4); 42/302; Church Yth Grp; Band; Church Choir; Concert Band; Drm Mjr(t); Jazz Band; Mrchg Band; School Musical; Variety Show; Hon Roll; Stewart Isler Awd 87; Concert Bnd Awd 87; Mt Tabor Bnd Awd 87; U Rhode Island; Dental Hygiene.

COCHRANE, CRAIG A; Lenape HS; Mt Laurel, NJ; (4); 13/434; Jazz Band; NHS; Ntl Merit Schol; Latin Clb; Variety Show; Lit Mag; Gym; High Hon Roll; St Schlr; At&t Schlr 87-91; Harvard U; Engr.

COCHRANE, HELEN; North Bergen HS; North Bergen, NJ; (3); French Clb; Key Clb; SADD; Chorus; Variety Show; Var Vllybl; Theatre.

COCHRANE, RENEE; John F Kennedy HS; Willingboro, NJ; (3); 10/292; Office Aide; Service Clb; Mgr(s); Trk; Cit Awd; Hon Roll; Jr NHS; Sec NHS; Prfct Atten Awd; Syracuse U; Brdcstr.

CODDAIRE, KATHLEEN; John F Kennedy HS; Willingboro, NJ; (2); 18/332; Latin Clb; L Stat Fld Hcky; Mgr(s); Score Keeper; Timer; Hon Roll; Psych.

CODY, ANN-MARGRET; St Peters HS; New Brunswick, NJ; (4); Hosp Aide; Chorus; School Musical; School Play; Yrbk Stf; Lit Mag; Sec Stu Cncl; Bowling; Cheerleading; Sftbl; Mst Profcnt Relig 83-84; Mst Profcnt Typng 85-86; Middlesex Cnty Coll.

CODY, DANIEL A; Ramapo HS; Wyckoff, NJ; (4); Debate Tm; Key Clb; Capt Ski Clb; Concert Band; Var Bsktbl; JV Socr; VP Jr Cls; Im Bsbl; Im Ftbl; Hon Roll; NYSSMA Fest Exclnt Piano; Swarthmore Coll; Econ.

COEFER, MATTHEW; Hamilton HS West; Trenton, NJ; (4); 17/320; Hosp Aide; Capt Swmmng; High Hon Roll; NHS; Presdntl Acadc Ftns Awd 87; Stockton ST Coll; Envrmntl Sci.

COELHO, CARLA A; Kearny HS; Kearny, NJ; (3); Art Clb; French Clb; Hosp Aide; School Musical; Yrbk Stf; Sec Soph Cls; Sec Rep Sr Cls; School Play; Stu Cncl; Trk; 2nd Pl Awd NJ Stu Crftsmn Fair 87; NY; Home Ec Tchr.

COFFARO, STEPHANIE; North Warren Regional HS; Hamburg, NJ; (4); 3/121; FBLA; Pep Clb; Ed Nwsp Stf; Stat Bsbl; JV Fld Hcky; Var Trk; JV Vllybl; Dnfth Awd; High Hon Roll; NHS; Blairstown Bus Assoc Schlr,FBLA Schlr 87; Rider Coll; Micro-Comp Acctg.

COFFEY, MAUREEN; Toms River HS East; Toms River, NJ; (4); Band; Concert Band; Drm & Bgl; Mrchg Band; Stage Crew; Symp Band; Hon Roll; Ntl Merit Ltr; Rotary Awd; U Of DE; Comp Sci.

COFIELD, STEVEN; Middletown South HS; Red Bank, NJ; (3); Church Yth Grp; Bsktbl; Ftbl; Im Golf; Vllybl; Hon Roll; Cmnctns.

COGAN, WILLIAM E; Paul VI Regional HS; Clifton, NJ; (4); Camera Clb; SADD; School Musical; Yrbk Ed-Chief; Yrbk Phtg; Yrbk Sprt Ed; Pres Trs Stu Cncl; Var Golf; Pep Clb; Nwsp Phtg; Chf Tax Assr Clifton 85; Myr Clifton 86; Montclair ST Coll; Bus Adm.

COGLIANESE, CHRISTOPHER; Linden HS; Linden, NJ; (3); 15/350; Am Leg Boys St; Boy Scts; VP Key Clb; ROTC; Pres Ski Clb; Drill Tm; Yrbk Stf; Rep Frsh Cls; Rep Jr Cls; Var L Trk; US Military Acad; Poltcl Sci.

COGNETTI, CHRISTOPHER; Westfield HS; Westfield, NJ; (2); Chorus; Church Choir; Orch; Bsbl; Ftbl; Nelson Keller Music Awd 86; NJ Yth Symphny Awd 86; NJ All ST Orch 86; Julliard Schl Music; Prof Music.

COHEN, BRIAN; Vineland HS; Vineland, NJ; (3); 17/824; French Clb; Temple Yth Grp; Varsity Clb; Stage Crew; Var L Swmmng; French Hon Soc; High Hon Roll; Hon Roll; NHS; Prfct Atten Awd; NISCA ST Top Ten Swmmng Awd 86-87; All Sth Jersey Swim Tm 86-87; Cape Atlntc League All Star Tn 87; Med.

COHEN, GEOFFREY; West Windsor-Plainsboro HS; Trenton, NJ; (3); Am Leg Boys St; Computer Clb; FBLA; Lit Mag; JV Trk; Cornell; Creatv Wrtng.

COHEN, JASON; Brick Memorial HS; Bricktown, NJ; (3); Im Bsktbl; Im Bowling; Var Crs Cntry; Im Ftbl; Im Ice Hcky; Im Tennis; Im Vllybl; Im Wt Lftg; Outstndg Runner Varsity Cross Country 86; Pilot.

COHEN, JULIAN M; Cherry Hill High School East; Cherry Hill, NJ; (4); 7/702; Am Leg Boys St; Q&S; Ed Nwsp Stf; Rep Stu Cncl; JV Tennis; Cit Awd; Ntl Merit Ltr; St Schlr; Model UN; Political Wkr; Drug,Chem & Allied Trades Assoc Schlrshp 87; Natl Cncl Jwsh Women Pres Merit Awd 87; U Chgo Hnr Schlrs; U Of Chicago; Lib Arts.

COHEN, LAURIE; Middletown South HS; Locust, NJ; (2); JCL; Math Tm; Model UN; Nwsp Stf; Yrbk Phtg; Var Fld Hcky; Lcrss; JV Socr; Var Trk; Cit Awd; Hghst Schlrshp Rnnr Up 86; Latin Awd 86; Math Awd 86; Law.

COHEN, MARC; Eastern HS; Voorhees, NJ; (3); 15/388; Debate Tm; Latin Clb; Speech Tm; Pres Temple Yth Grp; Nwsp Stf; Yrbk Stf; JV Var Tennis; High Hon Roll; Hon Roll; NHS; Pol Sci.

COHEN, MARCY; Middlesex HS; Middlesex, NJ; (3); 59/161; Key Clb; Spanish Clb; Trs SADD; School Musical; Hon Roll; Math.

COHEN, MARK; John P Stevens HS; Edison, NJ; (3); Science Clb; Temple Yth Grp; JV Bsbl; Im Vllybl; Hon Roll; NHS; Natl JR Clsscl Leag Latn Exmntn 87.

COHEN, NEIL; Shore Regional HS; W Long Branch, NJ; (4); 10/212; Am Leg Boys St; Concert Band; High Hon Roll; NHS; French Clb; Math Tm; Quiz Bowl; JV Bsbl; Var Capt Bowling; Var Golf.

COHEN, PHILIP; Jackson Memorial HS; Jackson, NJ; (4); 10/389; Am Leg Boys St; German Clb; Science Clb; Lit Mag; Capt Var Crs Cntry; Capt Var Trk; Co-Capt Wt Lftg; High Hon Roll; NHS; Ntl Merit Ltr; NROTC Primry Schlrshp 86-87; ADFPA Natl Champnshps 2nd Pl 86-87; NJ ST Rcrd Hldr 50 Mile Run 84-85; Yale U; Pre-Med.

COHEN, SAMARA; West Windsor-Plainsboro HS; Princeton Jct, NJ; (3); French Clb; Girl Scts; Ski Clb; Spanish Clb; Temple Yth Grp; Tennis; Trk; French Hon Soc; Hon Roll; Cert De Merite Concours Nationale De Francais 86 & 87; Rutgers; Frgn Langs.

COHEN, SETH D; Cedar Ridge HS; Matawan, NJ; (3); 16/354; Am Leg Boys St; Debate Tm; Math Tm; Ski Clb; SADD; JV Crs Cntry; Var Trk; VP French Hon Soc; High Hon Roll; Pres NHS; Bus.

COHEN, STUART; Fair Lawn HS; Fair Lawn, NJ; (4); 38/335; Cmnty Wkr; English Clb; Pep Clb; Political Wkr; Science Clb; Ski Clb; Temple Yth Grp; Varsity Clb; Off Frsh Cls; Off Soph Cls; David Bernickes Svc Awd 86; MPC Mem Schlrshp 87; Prncpls Hnrs 87; Rutgers Coll; Pltcl Sci.

COIN, ANGELA M; Prineton HS; Princeton, NJ; (3); Church Yth Grp; Debate Tm; VP French Clb; NFL; Band; Chorus; Jazz Band; Orch; School Musical; Stu Cncl; ST Chmpn Debte Prtnrs Novce Div 84-85; Schlrshp Smmr Art Inst 87; Law.

COKE, DONNA M; Vailsburg HS; Newark, NJ; (4); 3/205; Sec Church Yth Grp; Sec Church Choir; High Hon Roll; Hon Roll; NHS; Brd Of Educ Awd 87; The Adminstr Schlrshp Awd 87; Rutgers; Nrnsg.

COLAIACOVO, DAREN; Montville Township HS; Pine Brook, NJ; (4); 80/273; Art Clb; Church Yth Grp; FBLA; Key Clb; Letterman Clb; Ski Clb; Varsity Clb; High Hon Roll; Hon Roll; Rep Frsh Cls; Lacrosse Schlrshp Radfrd U 87; MVP Vrsty Lacrosse 87; All Conf Ftbl, All Leag Lacrosse 87; Radford U; Bus.

COLANERI, MARY K; Immaculate Heart Acad; Hasbrouck Heights, NJ; (2); Hosp Aide; Library Aide; High Hon Roll; Stu Ldrshp Cnfrnc 86-87; Prtcpnt Ldrhshp Frm Cthlc HS 86-87; Adpt Grndprnt Prgrm 86-87.

COLANGELO, DOREEN M; Shawnee HS; Medford, NJ; (4); 153/533; Variety Show; Pres Soph Cls; Pres Jr Cls; Off Sr Cls; Lcrss; Hon Roll; NHS; Dncd Wth Bllt Des Jeunes 76-87; Ntl Flute Assc & Flute Soc Phldlphia 79-87; Fairleigh Dickinson U; Lbrl Art.

COLANGELO, HARRY P; Raritan HS; W Keansburg, NJ; (3); 88/341; Am Leg Boys St; Library Aide; Trs Jr Cls; Trs Sr Cls; Var L Ftbl; Var L Trk; Im Wt Lftg; MVP Rnngbck Ftbl Cmp, 2nd Pl 200 M & 5th Pl 100 M Cnty Chmpnshps 85; Sprts Med.

COLARUSSO, FRANK; Cranford HS; Cranford, NJ; (3); 26/268; Art Clb; Science Clb; Band; Nwsp Rptr; Nwsp Sprt Ed; Var L Bsbl; JV Ftbl; Hon Roll; NHS; Pres Schlr; Pre-Med.

COLASURDO, JOSEPH; Hudson Catholic HS; Jersey Cty, NJ; (4); 20/180; Yrbk Stf; Hon Roll; NHS; U S Bus Ed Awd 86; Natl Ldrshp & Svc Awd 87; St Peters Coll; Accntnt.

COLAVITA, LESLIE; West Essex SR HS; Fairfield, NJ; (3); Am Leg Aux Girls St; French Clb; Key Clb; Nwsp Stf; Ed Lit Mag; Off Frsh Cls; VP Soph Cls; Stu Cncl; JV Capt Socr; Var Sftbl; Frnch Natl Hnr Soc, Natl Hnr Soc.

COLBY, CAROL IRENE; Carteret HS; Carteret, NJ; (4); 2/200; Capt Color Guard; Yrbk Ed-Chief; Trs Stu Cncl; High Hon Roll; Trs NHS; Ntl Merit Ltr; Sal; St Schlr; JCL; Math Clb; Pres Acdmc Ftnss Awd; Trenton ST Almni Schlrshp; Trenton ST Col6; Math.

COLDEBELLA, ROSEMARY; Nutley HS; Nutley, NJ; (3); 27/310; VP AFS; Church Yth Grp; Sec Key Clb; Stage Crew; JV Sftbl; Hon Roll; Trs NHS.

COLDENHOFF, TIMITY; Matawon Regional HS; Cliffwood Beach, NJ; (4); 21/311; Computer Clb; French Clb; Math Clb; Pres Radio Clb; Hon Roll; NHS; FL Inst Tech; Elect Engr.

COLDON, JED R; Don Bosco Tech HS; Paterson, NJ; (3); 17/91; Am Leg Boys St; Church Yth Grp; Cmnty Wkr; Rep Stu Cncl; Bsbl; Wt Lftg; Hon Roll; School Musical; Schrlshp Don Bosco HS Paterson 84-88; Rutgers New Brunswick NJ.

COLE, ALISHA; Lincoln HS; Jersey City, NJ; (3); Church Yth Grp; Hosp Aide; PAVAS; Variety Show; Hon Roll; Prfct Atten Awd; Rutgers U; Drama.

COLE, DANIEL; Dover HS; Dover, NJ; (4); Church Yth Grp; Computer Clb; Stage Crew; Scrkpr Ftbl; Hon Roll; Morris Cnty Coll; Elec Engr.

COLE, DOUGLAS; Washington Township HS; Sewell, NJ; (3); Exploring; French Clb; Ski Clb; High Hon Roll.

COLE, JOHN; Edgewood Regional SR HS; Berlin, NJ; (3); Exploring; Latin Clb; Concert Band; Drm Mjr(t); Jazz Band; VP Mrchg Band; Var Golf; Socr; All S Jersey Wind Ensmble 87.

COLE, JONATHAN; Long Branch HS; Elberon, NJ; (4); 3/230; Wrstlng; Hon Roll; Pres NHS; St Schlr; NROTC Schlrshp 87; Pilot.

COLE, SAMUEL; Long Branch HS; Long Br, NJ; (3); 1/280; Cmnty Wkr; Ed Lit Mag; Capt Wrstlng; Bausch & Lomb Sci Awd; Hon Roll; JETS Awd; NHS; Ntl Merit Ltr; St Schlr; Val; Acad Al Am HS Wrstlr 85; NJ ST Wrstlng Champ 86; St Wrstlng Champ Rnnr Up 87; NJ Gov Schl Sci 87; Med.

COLE, TIM; Newton HS; Andover, NJ; (3); German Clb; Rep Stu Cncl; High Hon Roll; Hon Roll; Stu Cncl Cmmtee; Amer Inds Arts Stu Assn; Wrtng.

COLE, VERONICA; Lyndhurst HS; Lyndhurst, NJ; (3); Art Clb; Cmnty Wkr; Pres Dance Clb; Ski Clb; School Play; Var Crs Cntry; Timer; Fshn.

COLELLO, JENNIFER; Westwood HS; Westwood, NJ; (3); 14/225; Church Choir; Concert Band; Jazz Band; Mrchg Band; Yrbk Stf; High Hon Roll; Hst NHS; Bst Prcssn Mscn Awd Band 87.

COLEMAN, ANGELA; Columbia HS; Maplewood, NJ; (3); Pep Clb; Science Clb; Pres Spanish Clb; Yrbk Stf; Rep Stu Cncl; JV Var Bsktbl; Var Trk; Hon Roll; Natl Heptathlon Champnshp Wnnr 87; Duke U LEAD Summer Schlrshp 87; Bkstbl Best Def Plyr Awd 85, 87; Premed.

COLEMAN, BETH ANN; De Paul Diocesan HS; Wayne, NJ; (3); Girl Scts; Ski Clb; Hon Roll; Church Yth Grp; Stage Crew; Nwsp Rptr; Im Tennis; Grl Scts Gld Awd 86.

COLEMAN, BRIAN; West Windsor Plainsboro HS; Princeton Junct, NJ; (3); Church Yth Grp; French Clb; FBLA; Model UN; Radio Clb; Var Crs Cntry; JV Socr; JV Var Tennis; High Hon Roll; Hon Roll; Outstndng Nwspr Car 85; Dist Car Wk 85; Mst Imprvd Plyr Vrsty Tnns 87; Tele Cmmnctns.

COLEMAN, LARRY; St John Vianney HS; Colts Neck, NJ; (3); 26/246; Church Yth Grp; JCL; Pres Latin Clb; VP Stu Cncl; JV Bsbl; Var L Bsktbl; L Capt Ftbl; Var L Trk; Hon Roll; NHS; 2nd Tm All-Cnty Ftbl; CYO-VLLYBL All-Star MVP; US Naval Acad; Sports Med.

COLEMAN, PENNY; Barnstable Acad; Upper Saddle Rive, NJ; (2); Cmnty Wkr; Dance Clb; Nwsp Stf; Bowling; Tennis; High Hon Roll; Frgn Lang Awd 85; Math Awd 86.

COLEMAN, SHAWN; Holy Spirit HS; Absecon, NJ; (3); School Play; Off Stu Cncl; Var L Socr; JV Tennis.

COLES, SHERI; Cumberland Regional HS; Brigeton, NJ; (2); 1/350; Church Yth Grp; French Clb; Intnl Clb; Yrbk Stf; High Hon Roll; Hon Roll; Top Reader MS Read-A-Thon 82-85; Gifted & Tlntd Hnrs Pgm 82-87; Horse Trainer.

COLGAN, TIMOTHY; Don Bosco Prep; Wyckoff, NJ; (4); 14/166; Pep Clb; Nwsp Rptr; Rep Frsh Cls; Stu Cncl; Bsbl; Bsktbl; Ftbl; High Hon Roll; Trs NHS; Rexnord Schlrshp, Lions Clb Schlrshp 87; Ramon J Casaprima Mem Awd & Ath Dep Awd In Appreciation 87; Penn St U; Law.

COLITSAS, MICHELLE; West Windsor-Plainsboro HS; Plainsboro, NJ; (3); Sec Cmnty Wkr; Hosp Aide; Model UN; Political Wkr; Nwsp Bus Mgr; Nwsp Rptr; Stu Cncl; Stat Bsbl; Stat Bsktbl; Hon Roll; Intl Rltns.

COLL, MELISSA; Woodstown HS; Woodstown, NJ; (4); 30/213; Church Yth Grp; FBLA; Hon Roll; Acad Schlrshp Elizabethtown Coll 87; 2nd Pl Thomas Edison Sci Fair 86; Elizabeth Coll; Med Lab.

COLLART, JULIE ANNE; Red Bank Regional HS; Red Bank, NJ; (3); Pres Art Clb; NFL; Service Clb; SADD; Nwsp Ed-Chief; Yrbk Ed-Chief; French Hon Soc; High Hon Roll; NHS; Ntl Merit Ltr.

COLLIER, LAYA; University HS; Newark, NJ; (2); Church Yth Grp; Exploring; JA; Church Choir; Hon Roll.

COLLIER, SHAWN; St James HS; Salem, NJ; (1); SADD; JV Fld Hcky; Sftbl; Navy; Instrctr.

COLLINS, BRIAN; Bayonne HS; Bayonne, NJ; (3); Hon Roll; NJIT; Elctrcl Engrng.

COLLINS, EDMOND A; The Pinry Schl; Short Hills, NJ; (4); Boy Scts; Orch; L Var Golf; Var L Swmmng; 4-H Awd; Ntl Merit Ltr; 4-H; German Clb; Acpl Chr; Band; Eastman Schl Of Music Schlrshp Merit 87-88; Tnglwd Inst Smmr Study Wth Empire Brass 86-87; Eastman Schl Of Music; Bus.

COLLINS, MARC; Princeton Day Schl; Trenton, NJ; (3); NFL; Jazz Band; School Musical; Nwsp Rptr; Rep Jr Cls; Pres Stu Cncl; Var Socr; Var Tennis; Hon Roll; Ntl Merit SF.

COLLINS, MELISSA; Ridge HS; Basking Ridge, NJ; (3); 26/192; 4-H; Latin Clb; Ski Clb; Bsktbl; Capt Socr; Swmmng; High Hon Roll; Hon Roll; NHS; Soccer 1st Tm All Mountain Vly Conf Forawd, 1st Tm All-Somerset Cnty & 2nd Tm All-ST 85-86.

COLLINS, MICHAEL; Holy Spirit HS; Ventnor, NJ; (4); 4/363; Pres VP Computer Clb; Exploring; Var Math Tm; VP Science Clb; Rep Soph Cls; Hon Roll; NHS; Nvl Acad; Engrng.

COLLINS, MICHAEL; Monmouth Regional HS; Eatontown, NJ; (3); 15/270; Sec Drama Clb; Political Wkr; Spanish Clb; SADD; Chorus; School Musical; School Play; Rep Jr Cls; Hon Roll; Rep Frsh Cls; All Shr Chrs Stu 85-87; Fnlst & Alt Gov Schl Of Arts 87; Prfrmr On Lcl TV Chrtbl Tlthns 86-87; Med.

COLLINS, NATALIE; Burlington Twp HS; Burlington, NJ; (3); 28/129; Chess Clb; FBLA; Key Clb; Band; Chorus; Mrchg Band; Rep Frsh Cls; Rep Soph Cls; Rep Jr Cls; Stu Cncl; Hstry.

COLLINS, SUSAN; Middletown S HS; Middletown, NJ; (4); 28/450; Band; Jazz Band; Mrchg Band; School Play; Symp Band; Crs Cntry; Trk; Hon Roll; Garden ST Distngshd Schlr Schrlshp 86; Math.

COLLINS, THOMAS; Morristown HS; Convent Station, NJ; (4); Hon Roll; NHS; NJ Distngshd Schlrshp 86; Rutgers Coll; Lbrl Arts.

COLLINS, TIMOTHY; Verona HS; Verona, NJ; (4); 16/182; Boy Scts; Q&S; Nwsp Sprt Ed; Yrbk Sprt Ed; Im Capt Bsktbl; Var Capt Crs Cntry; Var Capt Trk; High Hon Roll; NHS; Spanish NHS; Rutgers Coll; Pol Sci.

COLLIS, BRIAN; James Caldwell HS; Caldwell, NJ; (3); Art Clb; Lit Mag; AZ ST U; Arch.

COLOGNATO, HOLLY A; North Hunterdon HS; Clinton, NJ; (4); 30/348; Var Crs Cntry; Var Trk; Pre Med.

COLOMBO, ALEYNE; Triton Regional HS; Runnemede, NJ; (3); 51/405; Off Jr Cls; Rep Stu Cncl; JV Cheerleading; JV Powder Puff Ftbl; Hon Roll; Lion Awd; X-Ray Tech.

COLOMY, HEIDI; Sacred Heart HS; Newfield, NJ; (4); 6/61; VP German Clb; JA; Teachers Aide; Stat Bsktbl; Var Cheerleading; Capt Var Tennis; Hon Roll; VP NHS; G Aspius Awd-Hlth Field Schlrshp $500 87; Hlth Carriers Schlrshp Awd 87; Schlstc Acad Schlrshp 87-88; Beaver Coll; Bio.

COLON, ELOY; Buena Regional HS; Newtonvlle, NJ; (2); Varsity Clb; Var Crs Cntry; Var Trk; JV Wrstlng; Hon Roll; Airplane Engr.

COLONNA, TODD; Ridge HS; Basking Ridge, NJ; (3); 5/192; Nwsp Stf; Yrbk Stf; Off Stu Cncl; Var L Bsktbl; Var L Socr; Var Trk; Hon Roll; NHS; Spanish NHS; Gftd Tlntd Cls 84-88; All Smrset Cnty Boys Sccr Hnrbl Mntn 86; Summa Cum Laude Natl Latin Exam 86; Pre Med.

COLPAS, OSCAR; Eastside HS; Paterson, NJ; (3); 10/200; Church Yth Grp; Computer Clb; Dance Clb; NHS; Wrtg Cont Trphy 87; Sci.

COLSON, JOYCE; Middletown HS North; Middletown, NJ; (4); 39/415; Lit Mag; High Hon Roll; Hon Roll; NHS; Wmns Clb Schlrshp 87; Wmns Rpblcn Clb Schlrshp 87; Prsdntl Acadmc Ftns Awd Pgm 87; Brookdale CC; Acctng.

COLTELLARO, CATHY; Washington Township HS; Sewell, NJ; (3); Church Yth Grp; Office Aide; Spanish Clb; Powder Puff Ftbl; Sftbl; Hon Roll.

COLUCCI, LORELEI; Manchester Regional HS; Haledon, NJ; (3); 5/150; Art Clb; French Clb; Office Aide; Political Wkr; VP Frsh Cls; Pres Soph Cls; Trs Stu Cncl; Mat Maids; Var Powder Puff Ftbl; Hon Roll; Outstndg Achvt Frnch 87; Art Hstry.

COLUCCIO, ANTHONY; Notre Dame HS; E Windsor, NJ; (2); Var JV Bsbl; JV Bsktbl; Var JV Socr; Hon Roll; NHS.

COLUMBO, SHERRI; Pinelands Regional HS; Tuckerton, NJ; (4); 50/200; Stu Cncl; Var Bsktbl; Capt Var Fld Hcky; Var Sftbl; JV Trk; Al-Cnty Sftbl Tms 85-87; Al-Cnty Fld Hcky Tms 85 & 86; Hammonton Chptr Amer Bus Wmns Assn Schlrshp 87; Glassboro ST Coll.

COLWELL, CHRISTOPHER C; Hanover Park Regional HS; East Hanover, NJ; (3); 3/300; Am Leg Boys St; Church Yth Grp; Debate Tm; NFL; Sec Concert Band; Jazz Band; Rep Sr Cls; VP Stu Cncl; High Hon Roll; Pres NHS; Engrng.

COMEGYS, SUSAN; Holy Cross HS; Edgewater Park, NJ; (4); 16/365; Am Leg Aux Girls St; Church Yth Grp; French Clb; Yrbk Rptr; Yrbk Stf; High Hon Roll; Hon Roll; NHS; Italian Amer Roma Clb Schlrshp 87; Trenton ST Coll.

COMER, CHRISTIAN; Egg Harbor Township HS; Mays Landing, NJ; (4); 10/275; Var Golf; Hon Roll; NHS; Natl Engl Merit Awd 85-87; Intl Fgn Lang Awd 86-87; Computers.

COMIRE, ALBERT; St Rose HS; Wall, NJ; (3); JA; Ski Clb; School Musical; Stage Crew; Variety Show; Capt Bowling; Hon Roll; Berklee Coll Music; Perf.

COMISKY, LAURA; Bordentown Regional HS; Cookstown, NJ; (2); 14/120; Teachers Aide; Chorus; Var Pom Pon; Hon Roll; Nrsng.

COMITO, JONATHAN; Parsippany HS; Parsippany, NJ; (3); FBLA; Nwsp Sprt Ed; Lit Mag; VP Frsh Cls; VP Soph Cls; Pres Jr Cls; Pres Sr Cls; JV Var Bsbl; High Hon Roll; NHS; Finance.

COMMENT, BONNIE; Clifton HS; Clifton, NJ; (4); 10/590; Church Yth Grp; Office Aide; Chorus; High Hon Roll; Hon Roll; Jr NHS; NHS; Ntl Merit Ltr; Pres Schlr; Spanish NHS; W T Mayer Schlrshp 87; Montclair ST Coll; Bus Adm.

COMMINI, GINA; Notre Dame HS; Trenton, NJ; (2); Orch; JV Trk; Hon Roll; Outstndng Achvt Itln I & II 85-87; 2nd Pl Trk Awd 86; Rutgers U; Med.

COMMISSO, SANDRA; Gloucester Catholic HS; Woodbury, NJ; (3); JA; Chorus; Stage Crew; Nwsp Ed-Chief; Yrbk Stf; JV Bowling; JV Var Cheerleading; Gym; Var Mgr(s); Var Score Keeper; Awd Of Superiority Chrldng 87; Rutgers U; Paralegal.

COMPANO, ARLENE; Dover HS; Dover, NJ; (2); Office Aide; Chorus; Var Socr; Archtrl Engr.

COMPARRI, MELISSA; Buena Regional HS; Richland, NJ; (2); Spanish Clb; SADD; Varsity Clb; Band; Concert Band; Mrchg Band; Pep Band; Bsktbl; Sftbl; Prfct Atten Awd; Biol.

COMPETIELLO, LISA; St Aloysius HS; Jersey City, NJ; (3); Exploring; Hon Roll; Hnrs Cert; 2nd Hnrs; Fashion Insti Of Tech; Art.

COMPTON, JEAN; South Hunterdon Reg HS; Lambertville, NJ; (4); 9/73; Acpl Chr; Band; Chorus; Color Guard; Concert Band; Flag Corp; Jazz Band; Mrchg Band; School Play; Variety Show; Trenton ST Coll; Elem Music.

CONATON, ERIN; Immaculate Heart Acad; Rutherford, NJ; (3); Church Yth Grp; Model UN; Science Clb; Chorus; Yrbk Rptr; Trs Stu Cncl; Var Capt Cheerleading; French Hon Soc; High Hon Roll; NHS; Chem Team; Acad Decathln 2nd Pl ST Comp Public Spkng.

CONBOY, KIM; Sparta HS; Sparta, NJ; (4); Am Leg Aux Girls St; VP Key Clb; Soroptimist; SADD; VP Sr Cls; Church Yth Grp; Cmnty Wkr; Drama Clb; Nwsp Sprt Ed; Yrbk Phtg; ST Prty Chrmn Natl Prty Grls ST 86; JR Prom Qn 86; Hmcmg Ct Qn 86; OH U; Cmmnctns.

CONBOY, PATRICIA; Notre Dame HS; Lawrenceville, NJ; (3); Letterman Clb; Math Clb; Office Aide; Red Cross Aide; Service Clb; Ski Clb; SADD; Varsity Clb; Yrbk Stf; NHS; Psych.

CONCHA, MARCO; West Deptford HS; Woodbury, NJ; (4); 14/242; Computer Clb; French Clb; SADD; Nwsp Rptr; Var L Socr; Vllybl; NHS; St Schlr; JCL; Red Cross Aide; Ntl Hspnc Schlrs Awds Pgm Semi-Fnlst 86-87; Olympcs Of Mnd 85; Rtgrs Dns Smmr Schlr 86; U Of MD College Park; Aerospc.

CONDI, CHRISTINE; Shawnee HS; Medford, NJ; (3); Nwsp Phtg; Hst Soph Cls; Off Sr Cls; Hst Stu Cncl; JV Var Cheerleading; JV Var Sftbl; Rotary Awd; Phtgrphy.

CONDON, CHRISTOPHER; Holy Cross HS; Medford, NJ; (3); Chess Clb; Computer Clb; Science Clb; Elctrnc Engrng.

CONDON, JOY; Randolph HS; Randolph, NJ; (4); Church Yth Grp; Ski Clb; Orch; School Musical; JV Swmmng; Hon Roll; SR Strngs Awd Music 87; Lakeland Yth Symph 84-87; NJ Regn I Orch 1st Chair 84; Westchester U.

CONDON, KATHLEEN; Morristown HS; Morristown, NJ; (2); 67/432; Key Clb; Chorus; Rep Stu Cncl; Lcrss; Comm.

CONDRO, DOREEN; Paramus HS; Paramus, NJ; (3); JV Capt Cheerleading; JV Var Powder Puff Ftbl; Cmmnctns.

CONEY, SOPHIA; Trenton Central HS; Trenton, NJ; (3); Cmnty Wkr; Teachers Aide; Band; Yrbk Stf; Pres Frsh Cls; Pres Stu Cncl; Var Mgr(s); Cit Awd; Hon Roll; Prfct Atten Awd; Awd In Engrng Prog RCA 85-86; Close Up Prog WA DC 87; Delta Sigma Theta Qualities Lady Awd 85; Howard U; Nrsng.

CONEY, TRACY MARIE; Washington Township HS; Sewell, NJ; (3); Church Yth Grp; Hosp Aide; Teachers Aide; Chorus; Church Choir; Yrbk Stf; Rep Frsh Cls; Hon Roll; RN.

CONKLIN, CHRISTIAN; Waldwick HS; Waldwick, NJ; (3); Letterman Clb; Varsity Clb; Concert Band; Orch; Nwsp Rptr; Rep Frsh Cls; Var Capt Bsktbl; Var Tennis; Band; Mrchg Band; John Hpkns Stu Srch 85-87; Jrnlsm.

CONKLIN, CHRISTIE; Toms River HS East; Toms River, NJ; (4); Dance Clb; Chorus; Color Guard; Variety Show; Pom Pon; Powder Puff Ftbl; Sftbl; Swmmng; Stat Var Wrstlng; High Hon Roll; Vrsty Ltrs; Most Outstndg Lip Synch Perf; Ocean County Coll; Psych.

CONLEY, COLLEEN; Holy Cross HS; Cinnaminson, NJ; (3); Intnl Clb; Spanish Clb; Drill Tm; Yrbk Stf; Tennis.

CONLEY, DONNA LYNNE; Gloucester Catholic HS; Camden, NJ; (3); Church Yth Grp; JA; Spanish Clb; SADD; Stage Crew; Yrbk Stf; Hon Roll; NHS; Villanova; Psychlgy.

CONLON, MAUREEN; Sayreville War Memorial HS; Parlin, NJ; (2); Church Yth Grp; Dance Clb; French Clb; Varsity Clb; Rep Soph Cls; Var Cheerleading; Var JV Trk; Vllybl; Hon Roll; Comp.

CONN, VICKI; Notre Dame HS; Yardley, PA; (4); 36/370; Art Clb; Cmnty Wkr; Math Tm; Band; Nwsp Rptr; Yrbk Rptr; French Hon Soc; High Hon Roll; NHS; Key Clb; Engl Hnrs Awd 83; Art Awd 85-86; Art Schlrshp 87; Syracuse U; Art.

CONNELLY, CHRISANN; Holy Spirit HS; Absecon, NJ; (3); Spanish Clb; Bsktbl; Fld Hcky; Sftbl; NHS; Bloomsburg U; Elem Ed.

CONNELLY, PATRICIA; Highland Regional HS; Laurel Springs, NJ; (2); Stage Crew; Lit Mag; Hon Roll; Coll Of William & Mary; Archlgy.

CONNER JR, DANIEL J; Southern Regional HS; Waretown, NJ; (4); Trs Church Yth Grp; Ski Clb; JV Wrstlng; Hon Roll; NHS; Asbury Coll; Brdcst.

CONNER, ELIZABETH; Bridgewater-Raritan HS West; Bridgewater, NJ; (4); Sec Church Yth Grp; Sec Trs German Clb; Ski Clb; Ed Yrbk Stf; Rep Frsh Cls; Rep Soph Cls; Rep Jr Cls; Rep Sr Cls; Rep Stu Cncl; Stat Bsktbl.

CONNER, JASON; Don Bosco Prep; River Vale, NJ; (2); Chess Clb; JV Bsktbl; High Hon Roll; Scholar Awd 85; Bus.

CONNER, PAULA; Southern Regional HS; Waretown, NJ; (3); Sec Church Yth Grp; Computer Clb; Church Choir; Mrchg Band; Var Powder Puff Ftbl; Var Sftbl; Var Trk; High Hon Roll; Hon Roll; Prfct Atten Awd; Spec Ed.

CONNOLLY, CHRISTINE E; Kittatinny Regional HS; Newton, NJ; (4); 40/228; Pres 4-H; Girl Scts; Intnl Clb; Spanish Clb; School Musical; Rep Jr Cls; Var Capt Cheerleading; Var Crs Cntry; Wt Lftg; High Hon Roll; Silvr Awd-Girl Scouts 85; Psych.

CONNOLLY, ERIN; Manasquan HS; Manasquan, NJ; (2); 18/247; Sec Church Yth Grp; Drama Clb; Spanish Clb; Im Bsktbl; JV Cheerleading; JV Var Fld Hcky; Var Trk; High Hon Roll; Hon Roll; NHS; Acdmc Achvt Awd 86-87; Comms.

CONNOLLY, RYAN C; Monroe Township HS; Spotswood, NJ; (3); Am Leg Boys St; Boy Scts; Ski Clb; SADD; Band; Rep Stu Cncl; Im Bowling; Var L Socr; Im Vllybl; Im Wt Lftg; Pre-Law.

CONNOLLY, TARA; Ocean Twp HS; Ocean, NJ; (3); 153/304; Church Yth Grp; Dance Clb; Ski Clb; Spanish Clb; Drill Tm; Var JV Bsktbl.

CONNOR, MARGARET; Indian Hills HS; Oakland, NJ; (4); 7/282; Debate Tm; Letterman Clb; Spanish Clb; Varsity Clb; Yrbk Stf; JV Socr; Var L Sftbl; CC Awd; High Hon Roll; Hon Roll; John Steinkamp Awd Outstndng Achvt Hstry 87; U Of Notre Dame; Hstry.

CONNOR, MARGARET M; Villa Victoria Acad; Yardley, PA; (3); Pres Computer Clb; Pres Math Clb; Drill Tm; School Musical; Yrbk Stf; Pres Jr Cls; Var Bsktbl; Var Sftbl; Hon Roll; Art Piece Sent To ST Comptn 86.

CONNOR, WENDY; Salem HS; Salem, NJ; (3); Math Clb; Ski Clb; SADD; Band; Var Sftbl; Var Tennis; Hon Roll; NHS; Conflict Simulation Club 86-87; College Club 84-87.

CONNORS, BILLY; Manville HS; Manvill, NJ; (3); 1/108; Church Yth Grp; Var Bsbl; Var Bsktbl; Var Ftbl; High Hon Roll; Hon Roll; NHS; Var Ltrs 84-87; MVP JV Bsktbl 85-86; Hnr Rl 84-87; Notre Dame.

CONNORS, DEBBIE ANN; Sparta HS; Sparta, NJ; (4); Church Yth Grp; Key Clb; Ski Clb; Stat Bsbl; Cheerleading; Fashion Merchndsng.

CONOVER, GERALD; Highland Regional HS; Sicklerville, NJ; (3); 6/230; Latin Clb; Science Clb; Sec Jr Cls; JV Bsbl; Var Socr; Hon Roll; NHS; Boys Intrct Clb 85-88.

CONOVER, KIRSTEN; Brick Twp Memorial HS; Brick, NJ; (4); 6/290; Church Yth Grp; Capt Math Tm; Band; Jazz Band; Capt Mrchg Band; Stat Bsbl; JV Var Bowling; High Hon Roll; NHS; Rec Govrnrs Tchng Schlrs Prog 87; Govrnrs Schl Public Issues 86; Rutgers U; Sci.

CONOVER, NANCY; Egg Harbor Township HS; Linwood, NJ; (4); 15/300; Sec Dance Clb; Key Clb; Office Aide; School Musical; Nwsp Sprt Ed; Sec Stu Cncl; Bsbl; Capt Cheerleading; NHS; Natl Engl Merit Awd; Natl Jrnlsm Merit Awd; Natl Hnr Soc; Glassboro ST Coll; Elem Educ.

CONRAD, AMY; Glen Ridge HS; Glen Ridge, NJ; (3); AFS; Art Clb; Key Clb; PAVAS; Service Clb; Color Guard; School Musical; School Play; Stage Crew; Nwsp Rptr; Fnlst ST Sclptr Shw 87; 2nd Pl Smmrst Rgnl Art Shw; Natl Hnr Soc; Artst.

CONRAD, EILEEN; Immaculate Heart Acad; Twp Of Washington, NJ; (4); 1/171; Science Clb; Yrbk Bus Mgr; Var Sftbl; High Hon Roll; NHS; St Schlr; Quiz Bowl; Im Bsktbl; French Hon Soc; Ranked 8th In NJ Bio Awd 85; Ranked 10th In NJ Chem Awd 86; G Wshngtn U Awd Exclnc Math & Sci 86; Fairfield U; Bus.

CONRAD, ELLEN; Kearny HS; Kearny, NJ; (3); 24/300; German Clb; Hosp Aide; Capt Cheerleading; Sftbl; Cit Awd; High Hon Roll; Hon Roll; NHS; Princpls Hnr Awd 86; German Hnr Soc 87; Spec Ed.

CONRY, CAROLYN; Our Lady Of Good Counsel; Newark, NJ; (4); 2/102; Dance Clb; Science Clb; Ski Clb; Teachers Aide; Chorus; School Musical; Yrbk Phtg; Yrbk Rptr; Yrbk Stf; NHS; Rlgn Awd-Hrbl Mntn 87; Rider Coll; Fin.

CONSIDINE, PATRICIA; Shore Regional HS; Oceanport, NJ; (3); Debate Tm; French Clb; Key Clb; VP Frsh Cls; VP Soph Cls; JV Cheerleading; Powder Puff Ftbl; JV Sftbl; Var L Swmmng; Wt Lftg; Ldrshp Awd 85-86; YMCA Natl Qlfr Swmng 86; 1st Monmouth Cntys Swmng 87; Cmmnctns.

CONSTABLE, KATHLEEN; Sussex County Vo Tech; Newton, NJ; (4); 1/180; Chorus; High Hon Roll; Hon Roll; Jr NHS; Trs NHS; Glassboro; Fshn Merch.

CONSTABLE, RICHES-ANN; Lacordaire Acad; East Orange, NJ; (2); Church Yth Grp; Cmnty Wkr; Debate Tm; FNA; Madrigals; Yrbk Phtg; Lit Mag; VP Frsh Cls; JV Vllybl; Hon Roll; Rsrch Ascntst.

CONSTANCE, THOMAS; Mc Corristin HS; Trenton, NJ; (3); Hon Roll; Marine Bio.

CONSTANT, ALICIA; Cinnaminson HS; Cinnaminson, NJ; (3); Spanish Clb; Rep Frsh Cls; Rep Soph Cls; Rep Jr Cls; Rep Stu Cncl; Var JV Tennis; Prfct Atten Awd; Vrsty Awd In Tennis 85-86; Most Outstndng Plyr 84; Bus.

CONSTANTE, JOSEPH; Paterson Catholic HS; Paterson, NJ; (3); Church Yth Grp; Computer Clb; French Clb; Service Clb; Teachers Aide; Stage Crew; JV Crs Cntry; Var Socr; Library Aide; Hon Roll; Hnr Rl Achvmt Awds 85-86; Achvmt Awds Relgs Stdies, Spnsh I 85; Montclair Coll; Comp Engr.

CONSTANTINE, MICHAEL; Cresskill HS; Dumont, NJ; (3); 30/103; Band; Concert Band; Mrchg Band; JV Var Socr; JV Wrstlng.

CONTE, GARY; St John Vianney HS; Freehold, NJ; (2); Jazz Band; Symp Band; Rep Frsh Cls; JV Bsbl; Hon Roll; Berklee Schl Music; Musician.

CONTE, LUANN; Lawrence HS; Lawrenceville, NJ; (3); 4-H; FHA; Teachers Aide; Drill Tm; School Play; Capt Var Bsktbl; Stu Mnth 87; Bus.

CONTE, TRISH; Middletown HS South; Lincroft, NJ; (3); Office Aide; Nwsp Rptr; Nwsp Stf; Audio Engr.

CONTENTE, BILL; Saint Patrick HS; Linden, NJ; (4); 1/54; Church Yth Grp; Spanish Clb; School Musical; Nwsp Rptr; Yrbk Stf; Rep Frsh Cls; VP Stu Cncl; High Hon Roll; NHS; SAR Awd; NJ Dist Schlr 86-87; Portuguese Amer Schlrshp Assoc 86-87; Yale U; Law.

CONTESSA, ANTHONY; Lenape Valley Regional HS; Netcong, NJ; (3); Am Leg Boys St; Church Yth Grp; French Clb; JA; Letterman Clb; Ski Clb; Varsity Clb; Chorus; Lit Mag; JV Bowling; Bus Mgmt.

CONTI, LISA C; West Milford HS; Newfoundland, NJ; (3); Church Yth Grp; DECA; Varsity Clb; Rep Stu Cncl; JV Var Cheerleading; Jr NHS.

CONTILIANO, JIM; Hightsdown HS; E Windsor, NJ; (4); 10/441; Service Clb; Var Capt Bsbl; Socr; High Hon Roll; NHS; Prfct Atten Awd; All Cnty Bsbl 86-87; All St Sccr 86-87; Coll Of William & Mary; Med.

CONTILIANO, RICK; Hightstown HS; East Windsor, NJ; (4); 7/441; Service Clb; Var Capt Bsbl; Socr; High Hon Roll; NHS; Prfct Atten Awd; Alumni Hgh Acad Awd 87; All Cnty Cntrfldr 86-87; All St Sccr 86-87; Coll Of William & Mary; Med.

CONTINI, JENNIFER; Pitman HS; Pitman, NJ; (3); 14/154; Dance Clb; Chorus; Rep Frsh Cls; Rep Soph Cls; Var Jr Cls; Var Bsktbl; Var Fld Hcky; Var Sftbl; Var Trk; Hon Roll; Bus.

CONTROVICH, LISA; Camden Catholic HS; Berlin, NJ; (4); 57/263; Art Clb; French Clb; Teachers Aide; French Hon Soc; Bus.

CONVILLE, SUSAN; Washington Township HS; Blackwood, NJ; (3); Q&S; Ski Clb; High Hon Roll; Legal Sec.

CONWAY, CAROL L; Spotswood HS; Spotswood, NJ; (3); Spanish Clb; Band; Mrchg Band; Stu Cncl; Crs Cntry; Trk; High Hon Roll; Hon Roll; NHS; Sci.

CONWAY, CHRISTINE; Indian Hills HS; Oakland, NJ; (3); 109/306; Cmnty Wkr; Office Aide; Nwsp Rptr; Nwsp Stf; Yrbk Stf; Hon Roll; Jrnlsm.

CONWAY, DAVID S; Ocean City HS; Ocean City, NJ; (4); 49/273; Art Clb; Pres Drama Clb; Science Clb; School Musical; School Play; Stu Cncl; Var CAP; High Hon Roll; HS Drama Gld Awd 87; Nathan Heche Mem Awd 87; Tisch Scho Of Arts; Film & TV.

CONWAY, JENNIFER; St John Vianney HS; Aberdeen, NJ; (3); 50/250; Boy Scts; Church Yth Grp; Cmnty Wkr; Exploring; Hosp Aide; Ski Clb; SADD; Yrbk Phtg; Bsktbl; Mgr(s).

CONWAY, KEVIN; Essex Catholic Boys HS; East Orange, NJ; (2); 10/120; Church Yth Grp; Var JV Bsktbl; Var Socr; High Hon Roll; Stu Mnth 85; MVP Bsktbl 86; JV Bsktbl Most Dedicated Plyr 87; Lehigh U; Corp Law.

CONWAY, LAUREN; Highstown HS; E Windsor, NJ; (3); Aud/Vis; Yrbk Stf; High Hon Roll; Hon Roll; Hnr Roll Of Distnctn 84-85; Miss Teen All Amer Pageant 86; Miss NJ Teen USA Pageant Fnlst 87; Comms.

CONWAY, TODD; Immaculata HS; Flemington, NJ; (3); 78/246; Drama Clb; School Musical; School Play; Stage Crew; Stat L Bsktbl; Var Mgr(s); Var L Tennis; Cmnctns.

COO, MELANIE; Red Bank Catholic HS; Colts Neck, NJ; (3); Ski Clb; Var Gym; Var Trk; Vet Med.

COOK, ANDRIA; Morris Hills HS; Dover, NJ; (3); 38/159; Art Clb; Drama Clb; Hosp Aide; Ski Clb; Band; School Musical; Swing Chorus; Var Cheerleading; Hon Roll; Opt Clb Awd; Hist.

COOK, BETSY; Eastern Christian HS; Mahwah, NJ; (4); 1/83; Church Yth Grp; Nwsp Ed-Chief; Var Socr; Var Sftbl; NHS; Ntl Merit Ltr; Pres Schlr; Val; Computer Clb; Q&S; Dedication Awd 87; US Army Athl-Schlr Awd 87; Baylor U; Bus.

COOK, CHANEL; Mount Saint Mary Acad; Plainfield, NJ; (3); Art Clb; Camera Clb; Cmnty Wkr; GAA; Office Aide; Spanish Clb; L Pom Pon; Hon Roll; Science Clb; Band; Photo Awd 87; Hnrb Mntn Cmpstn Cls & Engrng Lab 87; Howard U; Frnsc Sci.

COOK, DOREEN D; Dover HS; Mine Hill, NJ; (3); Am Leg Aux Girls St; Debate Tm; French Clb; VP Ed JCL; PAVAS; Yrbk Sprt Ed; Gov Hon Prg Awd; NCTE Awd; Satori Rogate Awd Indpndt Rsrch 84-85; Psych.

COOK, GORDEN T; Hopewell Valley Central HS; Pennington, NJ; (4); Am Leg Boys St; Chorus; Jazz Band; Wrstlng; High Hon Roll; NHS; Hpwll Rpblcn Clb Schlrshp 87; Jhn Phllp Sousa Band Awd 87; U Of NH; Engrng.

COOK, JANET; N Burling Co Reg HS; Trenton, NJ; (4); 68/223; FFA; Teachers Aide; Chorus; Im Sftbl; Pres Acad Fit Awd Prgm 87.

COOK, KAREN; Park Ridge HS; Park Ridge, NJ; (2); 6/69; Service Clb; Varsity Clb; Band; Mrchg Band; Variety Show; Rep Frsh Cls; Rep Soph Cls; Trs Jr Cls; Var L Tennis; High Hon Roll; Mathematics.

COOK, KRISTY; Indian Hills HS; Franklin Lakes, NJ; (3); 12/306; Band; Concert Band; Jazz Band; Mrchg Band; School Musical; Symp Band; Variety Show; High Hon Roll; Hon Roll; NHS; Gym Awd 84-85; 1st & 2nd Pl Star Systems Natl Dance Cmpttn 87; Undergrad Awds 85-86.

COOK, LAUREN; Eastern Christian HS; Hawthorne, NJ; (4); Drama Clb; Acpl Chr; School Musical; Nwsp Rptr; JV Cheerleading; Hon Roll; Church Yth Grp; Chorus; School Play; Miss Amer Co-Ed ST Fnlst 87; NJ Regnl Chrs 83; Chrs Bergen Yth Orch 87; Messiah Coll.

COOK, LAURIE; Hackettstown HS; Hackettstown, NJ; (3); 28/191; Key Clb; JV Var Cheerleading; Powder Puff Ftbl; JV Var Sftbl; L Hon Roll; NHS; Stu Gov; All Star Chrldng.

COOK, MICHAEL; Maple Shade HS; Maple Shade, NJ; (3); Office Aide; Spanish Clb; JV L Bsbl; Var L Ftbl; High Hon Roll; Hon Roll; U S Air Force; Cmmnctns.

COOK, ROBERT; Timothy Christian HS; Edison, NJ; (2); 1/49; Church Yth Grp; Var Bsbl; Var Socr; High Hon Roll; Eastern Coll.

COOK, SHERI; Mount St Mary Acad; Milltown, NJ; (4); Art Clb; Hon Roll; Ntl Art Hnr Soc 87; Long Island U; Psych.

COOK, TRICIA E; Ewing HS; Trenton, NJ; (2); French Clb; VP Spanish Clb; Math.

COOKE, DAVID A; Midland Park HS; Midland Park, NJ; (3); 1/138; Am Leg Boys St; Capt Chess Clb; Scholastic Bowl; Bausch & Lomb Sci Awd; High Hon Roll; NHS; Voice Dem Awd; 1st Pl Humanities Awd 86; Cty Yng Schlr Awd Johns Hopkins U 86; America Mensa Rutgers Schlr 87; Med.

COOKE, DENNIS; Lyndhurst HS; Lyndhurst, NJ; (4); 21/180; Camera Clb; AFS; Computer Clb; Math Clb; Science Clb; JV Var Ftbl; JV Var Wrstlng; Kiwanis Awd; Schlrshp Awd $1000 Renewable Schlrshp 87; Fclty Bst Math Stu Awd 87; NJ Inst Of Tech; Elect Engrng.

COOKE, PAUL; De Paul Diocesan HS; Wayne, NJ; (4); 3/165; Am Leg Boys St; Exploring; Trs Latin Clb; Math Tm; Trs Jr Cls; Var Bsbl; JV Bsktbl; High Hon Roll; Pres NHS; Ntl Merit Ltr; 100 Hrs Vlntr Srvc Awd Chilton Mem Hosp, HS Engl Awd Exclnc Ovr 4 Yrs, NJ Dstngshd Schlr Awd 87; Princeton U; Bio.

COOKER, ALEX; Pennsgrove HS; Carneys Point, NJ; (3); Am Leg Boys St; Camera Clb; Church Yth Grp; Dance Clb; Drama Clb; Spanish Clb; SADD; Band; Chorus; Concert Band.

COOL, JENNIFER; Hammonton HS; Williamstown, NJ; (4); Trs Hosp Aide; Key Clb; Concert Band; Mrchg Band; Trs Stu Cncl; Hon Roll; NHS; 1st Pl Genl Bus Awd Atl CC Bus Symposium 83; Bio.

COOLEY, BRAD; Voorhees HS; Califon, NJ; (4); 2/276; Pres Latin Clb; School Musical; Bsktbl; VP Capt Tennis; Cit Awd; High Hon Roll; NHS; Sal; Natl Latin Exam 86; Bucknell U; Criminal Law.

COOLEY, LATRICIA; Trenton Central HS; Trenton, NJ; (3); French Clb; Office Aide; Acpl Chr; Chorus; Drill Tm; School Play; Variety Show; Lit Mag; JV Var Cheerleading; Var Mgr(s); Crimnl Justc.

COOMBS, SALVATORE; Kingsway Regional HS; Swedesboro, NJ; (2); Im Bsbl; Im Bsktbl; Im Ftbl; Im Vllybl; Im Wt Lftg; Bus Admin.

COON, JEFFREY; Lower Cape May Regional HS; Cape May, NJ; (3); 3/265; Am Leg Boys St; Drama Clb; Quiz Bowl; Chorus; School Musical; School Play; Yrbk Ed-Chief; High Hon Roll; NHS; Ntl Merit SF; U PA; Pre Med.

COON, RODNEY L; Palmyra HS; Riverton, NJ; (3); 40/115; Am Leg Boys St; Drama Clb; Letterman Clb; SADD; Varsity Clb; School Play; Stage Crew; Yrbk Rptr; Im Bsktbl; Var Capt Trk; St Chmpn Trk & Fld 85-87; Div All-Star 86-87; Jr Rtrn 87; Rider Coll; Mrktng & Mgmt.

COOPER, ALISON; Ocean Township HS; Asbury Park, NJ; (3); 76/357; Ski Clb; Spanish Clb; SADD; Yrbk Stf; Stat Ftbl; JV Swmmng; Bus.

COOPER, CHRISTOPHER; Brick HS; Brick, NJ; (3); Variety Show; Var Bsktbl; Var Socr; Bus.

COOPER, DANIEL; Overbrook Regional SR HS; W Berlin, NJ; (4); 34/365; Church Yth Grp; Cmnty Wkr; Computer Clb; Dance Clb; Drama Clb; Science Clb; Spanish Clb; Varsity Clb; Chorus; School Play; VRSTY Ltr Wnr Bsbl 86; Drexel U; Elec Engr.

COOPER, DUSTY; Williamstown HS; Williamstown, NJ; (1); Sec Church Yth Grp; Girl Scts; Drill Tm; Mrchg Band; Off Frsh Cls; JV Capt Cheerleading; JV Trk; Prfct Atten Awd; CPA.

COOPER, FAITH ANN; Paul VI HS; Runnemede, NJ; (3); 80/419; Hosp Aide; SADD; Flag Corp; Bowling; Hon Roll; Sci.

COOPER, JENNIFER; Delaware Valley Regional HS; Pittstown, NJ; (3); 11/200; Intnl Clb; Yrbk Ed-Chief; Yrbk Stf; Lit Mag; High Hon Roll; Hon Roll; Schlrshp Hnr Awd 86; Crtv Wrtng.

COOPER, JUMANNI; Immaculate Conception HS; E Orange, NJ; (3); Spanish Clb; Chorus; Hstry Awd 87; Rutgers U; Commnctns.

COOPER, MARY LYNN; Pennsauken HS; Pennsauken, NJ; (3); 23/372; Band; Concert Band; Mrchg Band; Symp Band; JV Swmmng; Hon Roll; NHS; Med.

COOPER, SCOTT P; Bogota HS; Bogota, NJ; (3); Am Leg Boys St; Cmnty Wkr; Science Clb; Concert Band; Drm Mjr(t); School Musical; Score Keeper; Gov Hon Prg Awd; VFW Awd; Voice Dem Awd; Excllnc Vcl Prfrmnc 84; Ridgewood Gilbert/Sullivan Prfrmng Troup 86; Advrtsng.

COOPER, TAMIKA; Clifford J Scott HS; East Orange, NJ; (3); 8/296; VP FBLA; Var Cheerleading; JV Var Sftbl; Hon Roll; Ldrshp Awd Ftr Secys Hnbl Mntn 87; Montclair ST Coll; Bus Law.

COOPERMAN, JOELLE; Cherry Hill East HS; Cherry Hill, NJ; (4); Art Clb; Church Yth Grp; PAVAS; Spanish Clb; High Hon Roll; NHS; Pres Schlr; St Schlr; Office Aide; Bd Of Educ Cmmndtn Acadc Achvt 87; Crimson Shld; Intrnshp W/WCAU TV 87; U Of Miami; Cmmnctns.

COOPERMAN, MARC S; Newark Acad; Short Hills, NJ; (4); Cmnty Wkr; Hosp Aide; Key Clb; Varsity Clb; Var Ftbl; Ntl Merit SF; 1st Tm All Conf, ST Ftbl 87; Mth.

COPE, JOSHUA S; Moorestown HS; Moorestown, NJ; (4); 3/230; Latin Clb; Math Tm; Chorus; Church Choir; Madrigals; School Play; JV Socr; High Hon Roll; Ntl Merit SF; St Schlr.

COPPER, JACQUELINE; Life Center Acad; Burlington, NJ; (3); Ski Clb; Color Guard; Bsktbl; Sftbl; Hon Roll; Legal Field.

COPPOLA, VINCENT; Paul VI HS; Bellmawr, NJ; (3); 211/500; Aud/Vis; Church Yth Grp; Key Clb; Pep Clb; SADD; Teachers Aide; Rep Frsh Cls; Rep Soph Cls; Rep Jr Cls; Bus.

CORACE, TRACY; Lenape Regional HS; Mt Laurel, NJ; (4); Church Yth Grp; FCA; Varsity Clb; Trs Sr Cls; Lcrss; Var L Trk; Hon Roll; NHS; Pres Schlr; 1st Gemtry Fnl 83-84; U Of DE; Acctng.

CORAGGIO, SUE; Morris Knolls HS; Rockaway, NJ; (3); 69/424; Church Yth Grp; SADD; Concert Band; Mrchg Band; VP Soph Cls; VP Jr Cls; Pres Sr Cls; High Hon Roll; Hon Roll; Stu Cncl; Fresh Awrnss Grp Ldr & SGA 86-87; Amercn Wmns All Str Hnr Band 84-87; Fnlst-Chnnl 13 Stu Art Fstvl 87; Bio.

CORAL, JULIE; Manchester Regional HS; Haledon, NJ; (4); 31/163; Art Clb; Yrbk Phtg; Hnr Rll 86 & 87; Art Dept Awd, Art Sply Grnt Frm William Paterson Coll 87; William Paterson Coll; Elem Ed.

CORALLO, DAVID; Passaic Valley HS; Little Falls, NJ; (4); 4/344; Am Leg Boys St; Cmnty Wkr; Science Clb; Gov Hon Prg Awd; High Hon Roll; NHS; Pres Schlr; Ntl Yng Ldrs Cnfrnc 86-87; UNICO Schlrshp 87; Grt Notch PTA Schlrshp 87; Rutgers Coll Of Pharm; Pharm.

CORALLO, JOSEPH; Montville HS; Pine Brook, NJ; (2); Hosp Aide; Ski Clb; JV Ftbl; JV Var Lcrss; Prfct Atten Awd; Med.

CORALLO, STACEY; Summit HS; Summit, NJ; (3); 104/276; Drama Clb; Acpl Chr; Chorus; Capt Color Guard; Capt Drill Tm; Drm Mjr(t); Madrigals; School Musical; Stage Crew; Yrbk Phtg; Music.

CORBO, TERRI LYNN; Hightstown HS; E Windsor, NJ; (4); Office Aide; Service Clb; SADD; Hon Roll; Drama Clb; Hosp Aide; Intnl Clb; Key Clb; Spanish Clb; School Musical; Schlstc Achvmnt Awd 85-87; East Stroudsburg U; Elem Ed.

CORBY, SUSAN; Mater Dei HS; Union Beach, NJ; (4); 24/147; Drama Clb; Math Clb; Spanish Clb; Ed Lit Mag; Powder Puff Ftbl; Hon Roll; NHS; Fclty Schrlshp Monmouth Coll 87-91; Frndly Sns Of ST Patrick Schlrshp 87; Chrstn Lfstyl Awd 87; Monmouth Coll.

CORCORAN, CHRISTIAN; Morris Catholic HS; Dover, NJ; (1); Church Yth Grp; FCA; Pep Clb; VP Soph Cls; JV Bsktbl; JV Socr; Var Trk; Engr.

CORCORAN, JOHN; Middlesex HS; Middlesex, NJ; (2); Computer Clb; French Clb; Key Clb; Math Clb; Sec Model UN; Ski Clb; SADD; Elks Awd; High Hon Roll; Hon Roll; Med Sci.

CORCORAN, NANCY; Lakeland Regional HS; Ringwood, NJ; (4); 63/345; Church Yth Grp; Ski Clb; Yrbk Stf; Off Frsh Cls; Rep Soph Cls; Rep Jr Cls; Rep Sr Cls; Rep Stu Cncl; Powder Puff Ftbl; JV Socr; Glassboro ST Coll.

CORDEIRO, BRENDA; St Mary HS; Spotswood, NJ; (2); Girl Scts; Library Aide; Stat Bsktbl; Mgr(s); Score Keeper; High Hon Roll; Hon Roll; NHS; Olympcs Of Mind 3rd Pl 87; Math.

CORDEIRO, MARICELLA; Ridgefield Park HS; Ridgefield Pk, NJ; (2); 18/183; Spanish Clb; Score Keeper; Vllybl; Hon Roll; Pedtrcn.

CORDERO, CHRISTINE; Parsippany Hills HS; Denville, NJ; (4); Church Yth Grp; Hosp Aide; Key Clb; Pep Clb; Color Guard; Capt Diving; Var Swmmng; Var Trk; Wt Lftg; Ntl Merit SF; Most Potntl Scriptre; Mech Engr.

CORDOVA, ELEANA; Wayne Valley HS; Wayne, NJ; (3); 75/290; Church Yth Grp; Intnl Clb; Ski Clb; Variety Show; Var Swmmng; Hon Roll; Swim Tm Vrsty Ltr, Natl Frnch Cntst 86-87; MEA Awd 85; Psych.

CORDTS, ERIKA; Collegiate Schl; Nutley, NJ; (4); 2/9; Office Aide; Ski Clb; Yrbk Bus Mgr; Rep Frsh Cls; Pres Soph Cls; Pres Jr Cls; Pres Sr Cls; Var Vllybl; Hon Roll.

CORES, ALVARO J; Union Hill HS; Union City, NJ; (3); Church Yth Grp; Math Clb; Mu Alpha Theta; Quiz Bowl; Spanish Clb; Nwsp Rptr; Rep Jr Cls; Rep Stu Cncl; Var Capt Bsbl; Var Ftbl; 1st Pl Piano Concrt 86; Coaches Awd Bsbll 86; 300 Pound Clb Bench Press Ftbll 87; Educ.

COREY, CHRISTINE; Manalapan HS; Manalapan, NJ; (3); 101/415; Bsktbl; Crs Cntry; Trk; All Dist Cross Cntry, Bsktbl, Track.

CORIELL, KAREN; Ocean Township HS; Oakhurst, NJ; (3); 116/334; Church Yth Grp; Cmnty Wkr; Girl Scts; Service Clb; Spanish Clb; SADD; Church Choir; Variety Show; JV Capt Socr; Girl Scouts Silver Awd 85; Bus.

CORLETT, MICHAEL; Lower Cape May Regional HS; Erma, NJ; (3); 5/170; Computer Clb; Math Tm; Spanish Clb; SADD; Varsity Clb; Nwsp Rptr; Sec Ed Yrbk Stf; Stat Ftbl; Stat Wrstlng; High Hon Roll; Gov Schl Sci 87; Rotary Yth Ldrshp Conf 87; Stevens Inst Tech; Comp Sci.

CORNEJO, JENNY; Dover HS; Dover, NJ; (3); Church Yth Grp; VP Pres Key Clb; Color Guard; Nwsp Phtg; Nwsp Rptr; Nwsp Stf; Lit Mag; Stat Bsbl; JV Bsktbl; Var Socr; Quill & Scrl Hnr Scty 85-87; Med.

CORNELL, TORIN; Middlesex HS; Middlesex, NJ; (4); 35/158; German Clb; Math Clb; Varsity Clb; Var Bsbl; Var Ftbl; Hon Roll; Hnrd Nmne Boys ST 86; ST Johns U; Athtc Admn.

CORNELY, CAROLINE; De Paul HS; Ringwood, NJ; (4); Cmnty Wkr; Pres Service Clb; Varsity Clb; Cheerleading; High Hon Roll; Hon Roll; U Of DE; Comms.

CORNETT, KIMBERLY; Hawthorne HS; Hawthorne, NJ; (3); Pep Clb; Ski Clb; SADD; Nwsp Stf; Rep Frsh Cls; Rep Jr Cls; Rep Sr Cls; Pres Stu Cncl; Capt Cheerleading; Sftbl; Ldrshp Training Camp Stu Cncl 87; Pol Sci.

CORNETTO, ANNA MARIE; Mary Help Of Christians Acad; Totowa, NJ; (3); Speech Tm; SADD; Nwsp Stf; Rep Soph Cls; Hon Roll; NHS; Ed.

CORNISH, MEGAN; Phillipsburg Catholic HS; Stewartsville, NJ; (3); Am Leg Aux Girls St; Science Clb; Pep Band; Sec Trs Frsh Cls; Pres Jr Cls; Bsktbl; Gov Hon Prg Awd.

CORNISH, RODNEY J; Eastside HS; Paterson, NJ; (3); 2/500; Key Clb; Nwsp Rptr; Var JV Bsktbl; Score Keeper; Cit Awd; High Hon Roll; Hon Roll; NHS; Prfct Atten Awd; Chem Engrng.

CORNWALL, RAYMOND; Highland Regional HS; Blackwood, NJ; (2); Drama Clb; Latin Clb; School Musical; School Play; VP Soph Cls; Bsktbl; Ftbl; Hon Roll; Rotary Awd; Temple U; Attrny.

CORONA, ROSA; Perth Amboy HS; Perth Amboy, NJ; (3); CAP; Computer Clb; Dance Clb; Drama Clb; Exploring; Nwsp Bus Mgr; Nwsp Ed-Chief; Nwsp Phtg; Nwsp Rptr; Nwsp Stf.

CORPUZ, MARIA; Academic HS; Jersey City, NJ; (4); 4/78; Chess Clb; Scholastic Bowl; Spanish Clb; Yrbk Phtg; Yrbk Stf; Bowling; Hon Roll; NHS; Boston U; Pre-Med.

CORRA, ANNA; Westwood HS; Washington Twns, NJ; (3); Intnl Clb; Hon Roll.

CORRAO, DENISE; North Arlington HS; N Arlington, NJ; (3); 40/106; Ski Clb; Spanish Clb; Varsity Clb; Band; Concert Band; Mrchg Band; Var L Crs Cntry; L Pom Pon; Var L Trk.

CORREA, ADRIANA; Paramus Catholic HS; Elmwood Park, NJ; (4); Church Yth Grp; Service Clb; Lit Mag; Mgr(s); Trk; Hon Roll; NHS; Cook Coll; Dntl.

CORREA JR, ANIBAL; Dover HS; Dover, NJ; (3); Hon Roll; Lincoln Tech; Auto Mech.

CORRELL, SHERRY; Toms River High School South; Beachwood, NJ; (4); Drama Clb; Hosp Aide; Ski Clb; School Musical; Variety Show; Var Capt Cheerleading; Var Mgr(s); High Hon Roll; Hon Roll; All Amercn Chrldr Awd 86; Acadmc All Amercn 87; Fshn Merch.

CORRENTI, ELIZABETH; Holy Cross HS; Roebling, NJ; (3); Church Yth Grp; Spanish Clb; Yrbk Stf; Fld Hcky; Pom Pon; Hon Roll; Pltcl Sci.

CORRIS, JEANETTE; North Bergen HS; N Bergen, NJ; (3); 11/453; Q&S; Ed Nwsp Sprt Ed; Stu Cncl; Var Capt Crs Cntry; Capt Var Trk; High Hon Roll; NHS; Spanish NHS; Sec Spanish Clb; Chorus; Hudson Cnty Interschlstc Athltc Assn Girls JV Cross Cntry Champ 84; Frshmn MVP & Tm Dedctn Awd 84-6; U Of PA; Bus Econ.

CORRY, DANIEL; Cumberland Regional HS; Bridgeton, NJ; (3); Pep Clb; Service Clb; Hon Roll; Engr Tech.

CORSEY, CATHLEEN; Monongahela JR HS; Woodbury, NJ; (1); Hosp Aide; Concert Band; Mrchg Band; Yrbk Sprt Ed; Yrbk Stf; Rep Frsh Cls; Sftbl; Twrlr; Cit Awd; Hon Roll; USN Acad; Pilot.

CORSIGLIA, STACY; Lakeland Regional HS; Ringwood, NJ; (4); 54/345; FBLA; Intnl Clb; Yrbk Bus Mgr; Yrbk Stf; Off Jr Cls; Rep Stu Cncl; CC Awd; Hon Roll; NHS; Art Clb; Trenton ST Coll; Acctng.

CORSINO, ANTHONY; Pope Paul Vi HS; Turnersville, NJ; (4); 10/503; Math Clb; Hon Roll; NHS; Pre Med.

CORSON, STACY; Middle Township HS; Cape May Court, NJ; (3); Dance Clb; Ski Clb; Flag Corp; Cheerleading; Pom Pon; Wt Lftg; Hon Roll; NJ ST Art Comptn Awd 86; Acad Exclnc Sci Awd 87; Art.

CORT, BRYAN; Roselle Catholic HS; Westfield, NJ; (4); Boy Scts; Red Cross Aide; JV Ftbl; Var Trk; Cit Awd; Hon Roll; Prfct Atten Awd; Amatr Athltc Union US Merit Hnrs; Schlrshp Achvt Awd; Howard U; Accntng.

CORT, KIMBERLY; Clifford J Scott HS; East Orange, NJ; (2); Computer Clb; Hon Roll; Dept High Hnr Awd Comp 87; Dept Hnr Awd Geom, Spanish II, Black Hstry 87; Hnr Roll Trphy 87; Howard U; Jrnlsm.

CORTES JR, JOSE; Perth Amboy HS; Perth Amboy, NJ; (4); 47/287; Dance Clb; Drama Clb; PAVAS; Thesps; Chorus; Madrigals; School Musical; School Play; Variety Show; Yrbk Stf; Best Thespian Awd 86-87; Performng Arts Awd 86-87; Urban Fndtn Wrkshp Minorities 86; Ridge Coll; Jrnslm.

CORTESE, CHRISSY; Morristown Beard HS; Roseland, NJ; (3); Hosp Aide; Yrbk Stf; Cheerleading; Hon Roll; Lib Arts.

CORTESE, MARIA; Bayonne HS; Bayonne, NJ; (3); Art Clb; Church Yth Grp; Cmnty Wkr; Drama Clb; Intnl Clb; Library Aide; Nwsp Ed-Chief; Rep Stu Cncl; Socr; Hon Roll; 2nd Pl Wnnr Fire Dept Art Cont 87; Fashion Inst Tech.

CORTESINI, GEORGE; Notre Dame HS; Hamilton Square, NJ; (4); 24/321; Political Wkr; Service Clb; Nwsp Stf; High Hon Roll; Hon Roll; NHS; Hnrb Mntn Gdn ST Distngshd Schlrs Pgm 86-87; Sfty, Ed, Training Trust Fund Scholar Wnnr 86-87; Trenton ST Coll; Econ.

CORTEZ, AMY; High Point Regional HS; Sussex, NJ; (3); Church Yth Grp; Spanish Clb; Band; Concert Band; Mrchg Band; Stat Bowling; Hon Roll; Rutgers; Chem.

CORTEZ, PERCY; Barringer HS; Newark, NJ; (2); Hosp Aide; Orch; Symp Band; Nwsp Rptr; Nwsp Stf; Yrbk Stf; Ftbl; Vllybl; Wt Lftg; Med.

CORTINAS, LINDA; Queen Of Peace HS; Newark, NJ; (4); 100/256; Church Yth Grp; French Clb; NFL; Ski Clb; School Play; JV Cheerleading; Var Crs Cntry; Hon Roll; SF Natl Hispnc Schlrs Awd Pgm 86-87; Stockton ST Coll; Psych.

CORTON, JANNETTE; St Josephs Of The Palisade; W New York, NJ; (3); Drama Clb; French Clb; Model UN; School Play; Yrbk Stf; Trk; Hon Roll.

CORY, MICHAEL; Manasquan HS; Belmar, NJ; (2); 17/229; Math Tm; Band; Mrchg Band; Crs Cntry; Ftbl; NHS; Voice Dem Awd; Clemson U; Math.

CORZINE, NICOLE; Madison HS; Madison, NJ; (2); Church Yth Grp; Exploring; Fld Hcky; Lcrss; Powder Puff Ftbl; Sftbl; Hon Roll; Lawyer.

COSENZA, DOREEN; St Pius X Regional HS; Plainfield, NJ; (3); Camera Clb; Church Yth Grp; Office Aide; Service Clb; Stage Crew; NHS; Ntl Merit Schol; Natl Sci Merit Awd 85; Merit Achvt Awd 86; Bus Mgt.

COSME, ELIZABETH; Paterson Catholic HS; Paterson, NJ; (3); 19/97; High Hon Roll; Scl Work.

COSPER, PAUL; Maple Shade HS; Maple Shade, NJ; (1); 5/147; Computer Clb; Key Clb; Spanish Clb; JV Bsbl; JV Socr; Var Trk; High Hon Roll; Jr NHS; Prfct Atten Awd; FL Inst Tech; Aerospc Engrng.

COSTA, LISA; Pitman HS; Pitman, NJ; (3); 1/162; Chorus; Concert Band; Mrchg Band; Var L Trk; High Hon Roll; Hon Roll; NHS; Mdrn Music Mstrs 86-87.

COSTA, VICTORIA; Holy Family Acad; Bayonne, NJ; (3); Cmnty Wkr; Dance Clb; Pep Clb; School Musical; Lit Mag; Rep Frsh Cls; Rep Stu Cncl; JV Capt Cheerleading; JV Coach Actv; Im Vllybl.

COSTALAS, MICHAEL; Marlboro HS; Englishtown, NJ; (4); 9/528; Science Clb; Acpl Chr; Chorus; School Musical; Ed Lit Mag; JV Trk; JETS Awd; Sec NHS; Ntl Merit Ltr; Drama Clb; Garden St Dstngshd Schlr Awd 86; Shield & Key Awd 84-87; NJ St Sci Day Awd 85-87; Rutgers Coll; Bio.

COSTANTINO, BRIAN; Paul VI HS; Laurel Springs, NJ; (3); Var Capt Ftbl; Var Capt Trk; Var Capt Wt Lftg; Olympc Conf Champ Discus 87; 3rd Pl ST Discus 87; 1st Pl Bench Press S Jersey 86; All Parochial Ftbl.

COSTANTINO, ROBERT; Ocean City HS; Sea Isle City, NJ; (3); 43/341; Boy Scts; SADD; JV Socr; Var Wt Lftg; High Hon Roll; Hon Roll; NHS; Trenton ST Coll; Accntng.

COSTANZA, JUSLAINE; West Windsor-Plainsboro HS; W Windsor, NJ; (3); Art Clb; Chorus; Variety Show; Lit Mag; Hon Roll; Church Yth Grp; French Clb; Stage Crew; High Hon Roll; Teen Arts Awds Rock Band Cnty, ST 87; Art.

COSTELLO, EUGENE; Marist HS; Bayonne, NJ; (3); 13/95; Church Yth Grp; Computer Clb; Drama Clb; Var Bsktbl; Im Ftbl; Im Vllybl; Hon Roll; Prncpls Schlstc Schlrshp 85-87; Bus Adm.

COSTELLO, JIMMY; Roselle Catholic HS; Elizabeth, NJ; (4); Art Clb; Church Yth Grp; Golf; Hon Roll; Bus Hnr Scty 86-87; The Cittone Inst; Crt Rprtng.

COSTELLO, KATHLEEN; Morristown Beard HS; Rockaway, NJ; (3); 4/81; Drama Clb; Teachers Aide; Thesps; School Musical; School Play; Capt Bsktbl; Capt Trk; High Hon Roll; Ntl Merit Ltr; Spanish NHS; Tri-M Natl Music Hnr Soc 85; Liberal Arts.

COSTELLO, LISA; Saint James HS; Pennsville, NJ; (2); 44/97; Drama Clb; Hosp Aide; School Play; Yrbk Stf; Art.

COSTER, CINDY; Chatham Township HS; Chatham Twp, NJ; (3); 41/159; Key Clb; Model UN; Band; Lib Concert Band; Nwsp Rptr; Sec Jr Cls; Var Capt Cheerleading; Hon Roll; Rep Frsh Cls; Rep Soph Cls; All Am Hall Fame Band Hnrs 86-87; Outstndng Musician Awd 85; Eng.

COSTINE, ANDREW; Middletown HS South; New Berlin, NY; (2); Socr; Hon Roll; Bus.

COSTINO, RACHEL ANNE; Paul VI HS; W Berlin, NJ; (3); 41/410; Spanish Clb; SADD; Yrbk Stf; Rep Frsh Cls; Bowling; Hon Roll; NHS; Spanish NHS; Pepperdine; Cmmrcl Art.

COTIGNOLA, JESSICA; Southern Regional HS; Barnegat, NJ; (2); Jazz Band; Orch; Variety Show; Lit Mag; Cheerleading; JV Fld Hcky; Hon Roll; Comptv Fig Sktng Ice Dncng 85-87; Peer Cnslng 86-87; Jrnlsm.

COTTMAN, DAWN; Delaware Valley Regional HS; Milford, NJ; (4); 30/165; Radio Clb; Acpl Chr; Band; Chorus; Concert Band; Mrchg Band; School Musical; Hon Roll; 1st Prfrmng Arts Class 86-87; Mrchng Bnd Awd 87; Somerset Cnty Coll; Mrktng.

COTTON, JENNIFER; Riverside HS; Riverside, NJ; (3); 44/120; Cmnty Wkr; Drama Clb; FTA; Political Wkr; School Musical; Nwsp Rptr; Yrbk Rptr; Trs Stu Cncl; Var Cheerleading; Stu Mth Spnsh, Bkkpng 84 & 86; Grls Ctznshp Inst 87; Alrnd Stu Govt 86-87; Comp Pgmng.

COUCHMAN, CLAIRE E; New Providence HS; New Providence, NJ; (4); Band; Concert Band; Mrchg Band; Orch; JV Tennis; OEA; Service Clb; George Eicher Meml Awd-Music 87; Stu Of Mnth 87; All Estrn Sts Orch 87; NJ All St Orch 84-86; Shenandoah Coll; Music.

COUGHLIN, CHRISTINE; Toms River High School South; Toms River, NJ; (2); Drama Clb; School Musical; Socr; Hon Roll.

COUGHLIN, JACQUELYN; Holy Spirit HS; Ocean City, NJ; (2); 37/397; Spanish Clb; High Hon Roll; Hon Roll; Berkely U; Psych.

COUGHLIN, JEFF; Linden HS; Linden, NJ; (3); Church Yth Grp; FBLA; Capt Bsbl; Score Keeper; Trk; Hon Roll; NHS; Garden ST Games Bsbl 86-87; All Star Am Leg Bsbl Tm 87; Union Cnty Yth Lg Bsbl Playoff & Champnshp 86; Math.

COUGHLIN, LAURIE; Linden HS; Linden, NJ; (3); FBLA; Key Clb; Science Clb; Color Guard; School Musical; Yrbk Stf; Sec Soph Cls; Stu Cncl; Hon Roll; Psych.

COUGHLIN, SCOTT; Glen Ridge HS; Glen Ridge, NJ; (3); 2/105; Boy Scts; Model UN; Band; Concert Band; Jazz Band; Mrchg Band; Im Vllybl; High Hon Roll; Ntl Merit Ltr; Rotary Awd; Hnr Guard 87; Natl Hnr Rl 87; Engrng.

COUNTERMAN, JODIE; Belvidere HS; Phillipsburg, NJ; (3); 8/140; Cmnty Wkr; Scholastic Bowl; Chorus; Hon Roll; NHS; Gftd & Tlntd 84; Hlth Care Admin.

COURTER, SHEILA; Memorial HS; Cedar Grove, NJ; (4); 2/123; Concert Band; Drm Mjr(t); Orch; Nwsp Ed-Chief; Var Crs Cntry; Var Fld Hcky; Var Capt Trk; High Hon Roll; NHS; French Clb; US Natl Ldrshp Merit Awd.

COURTRIGHT, CHERYL; Sussex County Vo-Tech HS; Franklin, NJ; (2); #4 In Class; SADD; Varsity Clb; Stu Cncl; Sftbl; High Hon Roll; Arch.

COUSOULIS, MARC; West Essex Reg HS; Fairfield, NJ; (2); Hon Roll; Physcs.

COUTO, BELEN; Manosquan HS; Spring Lake, NJ; (2); 31/246; Drama Clb; French Clb; Acpl Chr; Band; Chorus; Flag Corp; School Play; Stage Crew; High Hon Roll; Hon Roll; Rugers U; Chem Engr.

COVERDALE, CHRISTINE; Union Catholic Regional HS; Scotch Plains, NJ; (4); 13/308; Pres Service Clb; SADD; Ed Nwsp Phtg; Nwsp Sprt Ed; Yrbk Phtg; JV Capt Bsktbl; French Hon Soc; High Hon Roll; NHS; Rutgers Coll; 1st Wmn Pres.

COVERDALE, LAURA YVETTE; Buena Regional HS; Williamstown, NJ; (3); 1/236; Church Yth Grp; Math Clb; SADD; Varsity Clb; Rep Jr Cls; Stu Cncl; Crs Cntry; Trk; Wt Lftg; Hon Roll.

COVERT, HANNAH; Middletown High School South; Middletown, NJ; (3); Pres Church Yth Grp; Cmnty Wkr; Nwsp Rptr; Nwsp Stf; Var Fld Hcky; Var L Trk; Hon Roll; NHS; Spanish NHS; Cert Of Mert In Spnsh 86-87; Frgn Lngs.

COVINGTON, DESIRAE; University HS; Newark, NJ; (2); Cmnty Wkr; JA; Trk; NHS; Comp Scientist.

COVINGTON, JANINE; Camen HS; Camden, NJ; (3); Spanish Clb; Color Guard; Drill Tm; Flag Corp; Cheerleading; Hon Roll; JETS Awd; Jr NHS; NHS; Drexel U; Math.

COWAN, HELEN; Vineland HS; Vineland, NJ; (3); 28/824; Art Clb; Latin Clb; Yrbk Stf; Lit Mag; Italian Natl Hnr Soc-Pres 87-88; Lbrl Arts.

COWAN, MICHELLE; Scotch Plains-Fanwood HS; Scotch Plains, NJ; (3); Church Yth Grp; French Clb; Girl Scts; Bsktbl; Hon Roll; Teacher.

COWGILL, DAWN; Paulsboro HS; Paulsboro, NJ; (3); 28/130; Var Sftbl; Var Tennis; Hon Roll; Girl Scts; Office Aide; Varsity Clb; Band; Concert Band; Mrchg Band; Yrbk Stf; Popkin Schl Crt Rpt; Crt Stenog.

COX, ANNE-MARIE L; Collingswood SR HS; Woodlynne, NJ; (3); Rep Frsh Cls; Rep Soph Cls; JV Var Bsktbl; JV Sftbl; Hon Roll; Bus Mgmt.

COX, CHRISTINE; Morristown HS; Morristown, NJ; (2); 103/432; Church Yth Grp; Girl Scts; Key Clb; Pep Clb; Ski Clb; Band; Chorus; Color Guard; School Musical; Var Diving.

COX, GINNA; Point Pleasant Beach HS; Pt Pleasant, NJ; (3); Key Clb; Spanish Clb; Sec Frsh Cls; Sec Soph Cls; Sec Jr Cls; JV Bsktbl; Var Sftbl; Var Tennis; U Of Richmond; Psych.

COX, JOSEPH; Holy Cross HS; Mount Laurel, NJ; (3); 13/406; Chess Clb; Church Yth Grp; Computer Clb; Science Clb; Crs Cntry; Trk; High Hon Roll; Hon Roll; Ntl Merit SF; Natl Merit Schrlshp 87; Bio.

COX, MARY JUDE; Red Bank Regional HS; Little Silver, NJ; (2); Science Clb; Yrbk Stf; Rep Soph Cls; Rep Stu Cncl; Var L Golf; Var L Tennis; French Hon Soc; High Hon Roll; JETS Awd; Prfct Atten Awd; Acad Vrsty Lttr; Bus Ed Awd 86; Rutgers Girls Jr Open, Wnnr Of Girls Div 86; Net Wnnr At 36 Hole WMGA; Med.

COX, TERRI; Palmyra HS; Palmyra, NJ; (4); 5/115; Am Leg Aux Girls St; Drama Clb; FNA; School Play; Trs Stu Cncl; Mat Maids; Socr; Twrlr; High Hon Roll; Sec NHS; 3rd Tm Freedom Div All Star Socr 85; JR Rotarian Of Mnth 85; Burlington Cnty JR Freeholder 85; Nrsg.

COYLE, ALLYSON; Brick Memorial HS; Brick, NJ; (1); Cmnty Wkr; Bsktbl; Fld Hcky; Hon Roll; UCLA; Dr.

COYLE, COLLEEN; Atlantic Friends Schl; Somers Point, NJ; (3); Sec Thesps; Yrbk Stf; VP Stu Cncl; Var Socr; Cit Awd; High Hon Roll; NHS; Drama Clb; Hosp Aide; Headmstrs Awd Outstndng Contrbtns To Life Of Schl 86; Acad Ltrs High Hnrs 85-86; Comm Svc Lrdshp 85-86; Pre Med.

COYLE, COLLEEN; Mount Saint Mary Acad; Summit, NJ; (2); 16/93; Drama Clb; Spanish Clb; Chorus; School Musical; School Play; Hon Roll; YWCA Swim JR/Sr Ntls 87.

COYLE, CYNTHIA; Pope Paul VI HS; Laurel Springs, NJ; (3); 3/420; Math Clb; Spanish Clb; L Var Bsktbl; Var Fld Hcky; Im Powder Puff Ftbl; Hon Roll; NHS; Spanish NHS.

COYNE, COLLEEN; Neptune SR HS; Neptune, NJ; (4); 5/355; Drama Clb; GAA; Hosp Aide; Ski Clb; Chorus; Yrbk Stf; Trs Sr Cls; Swmmng; Elks Awd; Lion Awd; Elks Schlrshp 87; Lions Clb Schlrshp 87; Presdntl Acadc Ftns Awd 87; Trenton ST Coll; Nrsng.

CRAIG, CHRISTINE; Burlington City HS; Edgewater Pk, NJ; (3); JV Socr; JV Sftbl; High Hon Roll; Cognetics Toward Satori Awd 86-87; Extended Lrng Pgm 84-87; CPA.

CRAIG, TAGELINA; West Side HS; Newark, NJ; (4); 29/236; Art Clb; Cmnty Wkr; FBLA; Church Choir; Nwsp Rptr; Nwsp Stf; Yrbk Stf; Hon Roll; Nwspr Stf Awd 87; Natl Art Soc Awd 87; Montclair ST Coll; Bus Adm.

CRAIN, TOM; Teaneck HS; Teaneck, NJ; (2); JV L Bsbl; JV L Socr; JV L Trk; High Hon Roll; Hon Roll; N S Council Social Studies Oustndg Stu Awd 87.

CRAMER, ABBY; Ridge HS; Basking Ridge, NJ; (3); 29/192; Sec Drama Clb; French Clb; Acpl Chr; Chorus; School Musical; School Play; Stage Crew; Off Lit Mag; Hon Roll; NHS; Rotary Schlrshp 86; Kiwanis Schlrshp 86; Summer Arts Inst Schlrshp 86; Ballet.

CRAMER, CHRISTINE; Delaware Valley Regional HS; Milford, NJ; (3); 36/189; Church Yth Grp; Varsity Clb; Mrchg Band; School Play; Var JV Fld Hcky; Var JV Sftbl; Hon Roll.

CRAMER, GLENN; Teaneck HS; Teaneck, NJ; (4); 4/420; Pres Debate Tm; Drama Clb; NFL; Political Wkr; Nwsp Bus Mgr; Nwsp Ed-Chief; Tennis; NHS; Ntl Merit Ltr; St Schlr; NJ Schlrs Pgm 86; Scl Stds Dept Sr Awd; Williams Coll.

CRAMER, JOHN; Holy Spirit HS; Absecon, NJ; (4); 13/363; French Clb; Math Clb; Math Tm; Science Clb; JV Tennis; Hon Roll; NHS; Notre Dame; Sci.

CRAMER, MICHAEL; Holy Cross HS; Beverly, NJ; (3); Var L Ftbl; Bus Admn.

CRAMER, TRACY; Holy Spirit HS; Absecon, NJ; (3); 8/332; French Clb; FBLA; Off Stu Cncl; Mgr(s); Mgr Swmmng; Hon Roll; Jr NHS; Arch.

CRANDALL, JOANNA; Hunterdon Central HS; Flemington, NJ; (4); 51/543; Intnl Clb; Model UN; Spanish Clb; Varsity Clb; Nwsp Rptr; Rep Frsh Cls; Rep Soph Cls; Rep Co-Capt Jr Cls; Rep Sr Cls; Rep Stu Cncl; Boosters Clb Schlrshp 87; Soph Rcgntn Awd Wnnr Otstndng Achvt In Hstry & Svc To Fellow Stu 85; The American U; Intl Service.

CRANE, BRIAN E; Admiral Farragut Acad; Colts Neck, NJ; (4); 1/49; ROTC; Nwsp Ed-Chief; Sec Stu Cncl; Crs Cntry; DAR Awd; Sal; Vrsty Rifle Tm Capt 83-87; Cum Laude Soc 86-87; Am Leg Mltry Excllnc Awd 87; US Naval Acad; US Marine Corp.

CRANE, MARYBETH; Oakcrest HS; Egg Harbor, NJ; (1); 4-H; Key Clb; SADD; Band; Concert Band; Mrchg Band; School Musical; Yrbk Stf; Off Stu Cncl; Cit Awd; Schl Music Awd 86; Bst All Around Stu 86; Math.

CRANSTON, MICHAEL; Paul VI HS; Westmont, NJ; (4); 90/515; Am Leg Boys St; Church Yth Grp; Nwsp Ed-Chief; JV Crs Cntry; JV Trk; Hon Roll; NHS; Rutgers U; Accntng.

CRAPPS, MONIKA; Asbury Park HS; Asbury Park, NJ; (3); Church Yth Grp; Key Clb; Stat Mgr(s); Mgr Trk; Hon Roll; Jr NHS; PACE Awd Outstndng Stu In Mech Engrng 86; PACE Awd Mst Imprvd Stu In Geom 87; Elec Engrng.

CRATER, LOUISE; Sayreville War Memorial HS; Parlin, NJ; (3); French Clb; Ski Clb; Chorus; Church Choir; Color Guard; JV Cheerleading; Var Sftbl; Middlesex Cnty Coll; Med Lab.

CRAVER, WILLIAM; Spotswood HS; Helmetta, NJ; (3); Church Yth Grp; Computer Clb; Intnl Clb; Math Tm; Ski Clb; Spanish Clb; Varsity Clb; Church Choir; Stu Cncl; Var Socr; Engrng.

CRAWFORD, DAVID; Notre Dame HS; Mercerville, NJ; (3); Im Socr; Im Sftbl; Im Vllybl; High Hon Roll; Hon Roll; Natl Bus Hnr Soc 87-88; Advrtsng.

CRAWFORD, GLEN; Tenafly HS; Alpine, NJ; (3); Am Leg Boys St; Pres Exploring; Yrbk Ed-Chief; Stu Cncl; Hon Roll; Boy Scts; Church Yth Grp; Bsktbl; Ftbl; Exploring Post Safe Rds Pres.

CRAWFORD, JEFFREY; Mainland Regional HS; Somers Point, NJ; (3); VP Key Clb; VP Soph Cls; VP Jr Cls; Rep Stu Cncl; L Bsbl; JV Bsktbl; JV Ftbl; JV Socr; Hon Roll; NHS; Co-Capt JV Sccr Tm 85-86; Stockton ST Coll; Bus.

CRAWFORD, JOHANNA; Camden Catholic HS; Cherry Hill, NJ; (3); 24/256; Am Leg Aux Girls St; VP Art Clb; Pres Dance Clb; Pres 4-H; School Play; Vllybl; High Hon Roll; Hon Roll; NHS; Spanish NHS; Sci Hon Soc 87; Soc Sci Hon Soc 87; Emerald Hon Soc 87; Law.

CRAWFORD, OSMUND; Essex Catholic Boys HS; East Orange, NJ; (3); 15/250; Boy Scts; Yrbk Stf; Im JV Bsktbl; Hon Roll; U Of MD; Law.

CRAWFORD, VISTA; Millville SR HS; Millville, NJ; (4); Church Yth Grp; DECA; FBLA; FNA; Red Cross Aide; Teachers Aide; Church Choir; Atten Awd 84-87; Ms Cngnlty Jack & Jill Ctlln & 1st Rnnr Up 86-87; Cumberland Cnty Coll; Bus Admin.

CRAWFORD, ZULIEKA; Mt St Dominic Acad; East Orange, NJ; (3); French Clb; Library Aide; Spanish Clb; Variety Show; JV Bsktbl; Comp Engrng.

CRAWN, KATHERINE; Sussex Vo Tech; Sussex, NJ; (3); Church Yth Grp; Hosp Aide; Church Choir; Yrbk Phtg; Ntl Merit Ltr; Csmtlgy.

CREAGH, KEVIN; Cinnaminson HS; Cinnaminson, NJ; (3); JV Bsktbl; Im Vllybl; Wt Lftg; Bus Mgmt.

CREATHORNE, JENNIFER K; West Milford HS; West Milford, NJ; (3); Art Clb; Church Yth Grp; DECA; SADD; Varsity Clb; Flag Corp; JV Var Cheerleading; Stat Socr; Hon Roll; Jr NHS; Natl Art Hnr Scty 85-87; Advrtsng Art.

CREDE, SUSAN; Middlesex HS; Middlesex, NJ; (3); 4/161; Am Leg Aux Girls St; Cmnty Wkr; Drama Clb; Hosp Aide; Key Clb; Model UN; Spanish Clb; School Musical; Sec Frsh Cls; Sec Jr Cls; Stdnt Of The Month 87; St Francis Coll; Social Work.

CREED, LENORA; Toms River South HS; Beachwood, NJ; (2); Acpl Chr; Chorus; Orch; School Musical; Variety Show; Pom Pon; Swmmng; 1st Pl Solo Cltrl Olympcs; Athl Awd; Mdlng.

CREGAN, CHRISTINA; Morristown HS; Morristown, NJ; (1); Church Yth Grp; Latin Clb; Y-Teens; Concert Band; Var Swmmng; High Hon Roll; Jr NHS; GAA; Band; Hon Roll; Am Leg Cert Schl Awd 86; USS JR Natls FL 86-87; USS SR Natls CA 87.

CREIGHTON, COLLEEN; Paul IV HS; Williamstown, NJ; (3); 57/419; JV Crs Cntry; JV Trk; NHS; Spanish NHS; Teaching.

CRESSE, KAREN; Holy Spirit HS; Absecon, NJ; (3); 18/332; French Clb; NHS; Fash Merch.

CRESSEN, LYNN MARIE; Toms River East HS; Toms River, NJ; (4); 29/500; Chorus; Stu Cncl; Hon Roll; JC Awd; NHS; Exprt Rfl Shtr 85-87; NRA Awd 87; Ocean Cnty Coll; Vtrnry Med.

CREVELING, ERIC; Belvidere HS; Washington, NJ; (4); 9/130; Ski Clb; School Play; Sr Cls; Stu Cncl; Var L Ftbl; Var L Wrstlng; Hon Roll; NHS; Engl Hstry Awd; Best Back Ftbl; Mst Conscientious; Ocean Engrng.

CRIMMINS, JENNIFER; Montville Twp HS; Towaco, NJ; (3); 9/280; Exploring; Hosp Aide; Key Clb; NFL; Science Clb; Mrchg Band; Church Yth Grp; Debate Tm; Model UN; Speech Tm; NJ Gvrnrs Schl In The Sci 87; NJ St Forensics League Poetry Cmptn 86; 2nd In NJ St Bio League 86; Bio.

CRINCOLI, KRISTIN; S River HS; S River, NJ; (2); Cmnty Wkr; Dance Clb; FNA; German Clb; Spanish Clb; Concert Band; Mrchg Band; Symp Band; JV Bsktbl; Var Trk; Rutgers; Med.

CRINCOLI, ROCCO; Hudson Catholic HS; Jersey City, NJ; (3); Hon Roll; NHS; Law.

CRISANAZ, CYNTHIA; Long Branch HS; Long Branch, NJ; (2); 32/300; Drama Clb; Hosp Aide; NFL; School Musical; School Play; JV Sftbl; Var Tennis; Stu Ldr Awd 87; Varsity Awd-Tnns 86; Med.

CRISCIONE, SABRINA; Pequannock Township HS; Pequannock, NJ; (3); Drama Clb; Acpl Chr; Chorus; JV Var Cheerleading.

CRISPO, DANIELA; Vernon Township HS; Vernon, NJ; (3); Drama Clb; Hst Thesps; Acpl Chr; Chorus; School Musical; School Play; Stage Crew; Var Tennis; Gov Hon Prg Awd; NHS; Theatre Arts.

CRISTANTIELLO JR, VINCENT; Marist HS; Jersey City, NJ; (3); 5/160; Rep Frsh Cls; Rep Stu Cncl; Vllybl; High Hon Roll; Rutgers U; Acctg.

CRISTEA, MICHAEL; Passaic County Tech & Voc HS; Paterson, NJ; (3); 19/629; Chess Clb; Cmnty Wkr; Math Clb; Varsity Clb; VICA; Awd In Art 84; Csmtlgst.

CRISTELL, MARLA; Scotch Plains Fanwood HS; Scotch Plains, NJ; (3); Dance Clb; Key Clb; Concert Band; Mrchg Band; School Musical; Rep Frsh Cls; Rep Soph Cls; Rep Stu Cncl; Var Cheerleading; Hon Roll; Italian Natl Hon Soc 85-86; Med.

CRISTINZIO, TONI; Monongahela HS; Deptford, NJ; (2); Girl Scts; Color Guard; Flag Corp; Mrchg Band; Nwsp Rptr; Nwsp Stf; Math Awd Alg 87; Pres Awd Acad Achvt 87; Acad Awd Excllnce 87.

CROCCO, TODD; Hunterdon Central HS; Ringoes, NJ; (4); 5/559; FCA; German Clb; Variety Show; Rep Sr Cls; Capt Var Ftbl; Capt Var Wrstlng; Gov Hon Prg Awd; High Hon Roll; NHS; St Schlr; Sprtsmnshp Awd-Lacrss 84; Outstndng Stu 85; Bucknell U; Premed.

CROCE, STEPHEN L; Ewing HS; Trenton, NJ; (4); 2/302; Am Leg Boys St; Key Clb; Acpl Chr; Chorus; Stu Cncl; L Bsktbl; Capt Crs Cntry; Trk; High Hon Roll; Kiwanis Awd; N J Language Tchrs Spnsh Awd 87; Villamova U; Mech Engr.

CROKE, CATHERINE; Trenton Central HS; Trenton, NJ; (3); Computer Clb; JA; Red Cross Aide; Cit Awd; Hon Roll; NHS; Mayors Gold Mdl Awd 84; Mercer County CC; Compu.

CROMARTIE, ALICE; Essex County Voc Tech HS; Newark, NJ; (3); Church Yth Grp; Computer Clb; FBLA; Hosp Aide; Church Choir; Nwsp Stf; Yrbk Stf; Stu Cncl; Hon Roll; Jr NHS; Typg & Bkkpng Awd 85; Hghst Score Essex Cnty Coll Acctg 86; Katharine Gibbs; Bus.

CROMWELL, SHIQUONNE; University HS; Newark, NJ; (3); Cmnty Wkr; Hosp Aide; JA; Library Aide; Spanish Clb; Teachers Aide; Rep Jr Cls; Atten Awd 85-87; Rutgers U; Nrsg.

CRONCE, JOYCE; Hightstown HS; Hightstown, NJ; (4); Hon Roll; Rocky Brook Grdn Clb & Career Dvlpmnt Awds 87; Mercer Co Comm Coll; Hrtcltr.

CRONIN, JENNIFER; Montville Towhship HS; Montville, NJ; (4); 47/272; FBLA; Key Clb; Office Aide; Band; Var Cheerleading; Powder Puff Ftbl; High Hon Roll; Hon Roll; NHS; Pres Schlr; Natl Hnr Soc 87; Miss Natl Teen-Ager Pageant Schlrshp & MIP Chrldng Awd 86; Montclair ST Coll; Hotel Mgmt.

CROOM, LISA; Irvington HS; East Orange, NJ; (4); 34/452; Drama Clb; Hosp Aide; Key Clb; Nwsp Ed-Chief; Nwsp Rptr; Hon Roll; NHS; Jrnslm Awd; Frgn Exchng Stu; Taylor Pblc Rltns Awd; Franklin Coll; Telecomm.

CROPPER, JONATHAN; Williamstown HS; Williamstown, NJ; (3); Am Leg Boys St; French Clb; Key Clb; Red Cross Aide; SADD; Stage Crew; Pres Sr Cls; JV Var Socr; Hon Roll; JETS Awd; Schlrs Pgm-Schl Of Ostheopathic Med, JFK Hosp Stratford, NJ 87-88; JR Engrng Tech Soc Tm Cmptn 87; Cornell U; Mech Engrng.

CROSBY, BONNIE; Paul VI HS; W Berlin, NJ; (3); 103/416; Math Clb; Drill Tm; Var Mgr(s); Stat Wrstlng; Bus Admin.

CROSBY, KATHLEEN; St Pius X Regional HS; Parlin, NJ; (2); 11/83; Trs Church Yth Grp; Hosp Aide; Service Clb; Socr; JV Sftbl; Hon Roll; NHS; Rutgers U; Phrmcy.

CROSBY, KENNETH; Paramus Catholic Boys HS; Glen Rock, NJ; (3); 74/179; Am Leg Boys St; Church Yth Grp; Spanish Clb; School Play; Var JV Crs Cntry; Trk.

CROSIER, CHARLES; St James HS; Salem, NJ; (4); 2/69; Am Leg Boys St; Stage Crew; Yrbk Stf; Rep Soph Cls; Trs Sr Cls; Im Wt Lftg; Hon Roll; NHS; Rotary Awd; Acadmc All Amer 85.

CROSIER, JOHN; St James HS; Salem, NJ; (2); 29/105; SADD; School Play; Stage Crew; Yrbk Phtg; Yrbk Stf; Var Mgr(s); Hon Roll; M D.

CROSS, RICHARD C; Sacred Heart HS; Bridgeton, NJ; (3); French Clb; Teachers Aide; Stage Crew; Var L Swmmng; JV Tennis; Hon Roll.

CROSSAN, BRIAN; Hudson Catholic Regional HS; Weehawken, NJ; (3); Yrbk Stf; Im Bsktbl; Im Vllybl; Hon Roll.

CROSSLAND, BONNIE; Atlantic City HS; Ventnor, NJ; (4); 21/410; Model UN; Office Aide; Red Cross Aide; Sec Stu Cncl; Gov Hon Prg Awd; NHS; NJ Distngshd Schlr 87; ROTC Schlrshp 87; Rutgers U; Engr.

CROSSLAND, CHRISTY; Bridgewater-Raritan West HS; Bridgewater, NJ; (3); Pep Clb; SADD; Varsity Clb; Trs Soph Cls; VP Jr Cls; Pres Sr Cls; Rep Stu Cncl; Capt Var Cheerleading; Hon Roll; NHS; Chrldng Natls-Top 20 87; Penn ST U; Teaching.

CROTEAU, CHRISTOPHER L; South Hunterdon HS; Lambertville, NJ; (3); 8/80; Am Leg Boys St; Exploring; Key Clb; Stage Crew; Nwsp Rptr; Bsktbl; Golf; Hon Roll; Bus.

CROUCH, KEVIN; Woodstown HS; Woodstown, NJ; (3); Am Leg Boys St; Drama Clb; FBLA; VP Math Clb; Band; Symp Band; Nwsp Phtg; Yrbk Phtg; Hon Roll; JP Sousa Awd; Odsy Of Mind NJ ST Chmpnshp Tm 87; Altrnt RYLA 87; Engrng.

CROWE III, THOMAS A; Millville SR HS; Leesburg, NJ; (4); 45/450; Science Clb; Im Bowling; Capt Crs Cntry; Capt Trk; NHS; Sci Dept Awd, John Choko Memrl Trk Awd, Amrcn Assn Physcs Tchrs Awd 87; Stockton ST Coll; Engrng.

CROWELL, ANTHONY; Shore Regional HS; Oceanport, NJ; (3); Cmnty Wkr; Debate Tm; Pres Exploring; Sec French Clb; Hosp Aide; Key Clb; Capt Band; Capt Mrchg Band; Stage Crew; Capt Symp Band; Brnz Congrssnl Awd 87; Allnce Frncse Natl Frnch Essy Cont 7th Pl 87; 1st Pl Med/Hlth Div Sci Fair 87; Med.

CROWELL, SUSAN LENORE; Hunterdon Central HS; Ringoes, NJ; (4); 10/550; Drama Clb; Key Clb; Thesps; School Musical; School Play; Stage Crew; Variety Show; High Hon Roll; Hon Roll; VP NHS; Amnesty Intnl; Bst Actrss Bucks Cnty Comp; Wmns Clb Of Flemington Schlrshp; Dickinson Coll; Engl.

CROWLEY, ALISON M; Washington Twp HS; Sewell, NJ; (2); Church Yth Grp; Girl Scts; Rep Stu Cncl; JV Capt Cheerleading; Im Diving; Hon Roll; Stu Mnth 83; Prof Dncr.

CROWLEY, CARL C; Mainland Reg HS; Somers Point, NJ; (3); Cmnty Wkr; Pres Key Clb; Trs SADD; Pres Soph Cls; Pres Jr Cls; L Ftbl; Trk; Wt Lftg; Rotary Awd; Law.

CROWLEY, JOCELYN; Watchung Hills Regional HS; Warren, NJ; (3); 2/320; Debate Tm; Latin Clb; Sec Spanish Clb; Band; Off Frsh Cls; Rep Soph Cls; Off Jr Cls; Rep Stu Cncl; High Hon Roll; NHS; Cnty Rep NJ Schlr 87; Stu Of Mnth 86; Maxima Cum Laude Hnrs Natl Latin Exam 87.

CROWLEY, MARY; Park Ridge HS; Park Ridge, NJ; (3); 30/100; AFS; Church Yth Grp; Cmnty Wkr; Color Guard; High Hon Roll; Rutgers; Adv.

CROWLEY, TIMOTHY; Randolph HS; Ironia, NJ; (3); Church Yth Grp; Cmnty Wkr; Var Wt Lftg; High Hon Roll; Hon Roll; Lyndon ST Coll; Meteorolgy.

CRUCILI, STACIE; Notre Dame HS; Trenton, NJ; (3); 32/423; FBLA; Varsity Clb; School Musical; School Play; Variety Show; Cheerleading; NHS; Twrlr; Ms NJ Amer Coed Hstss 86; Ms Teen Hemsphr, Teen Tlnt Hemsphr 85; Bst Dncr Awd-Hemsphr Pgnt 85; Vet Med.

CRUICKSHANK, DENISE; Hopewell Valley Central HS; Pennington, NJ; (4); AFS; Church Yth Grp; FBLA; Ski Clb; Yrbk Stf; Bus Stu Mnth Mar 86; Mercer County; Soc Sci.

CRUIKSHANK, GINNIA; Point Pleasant Beach HS; Mantoloking, NJ; (2); Key Clb; Spanish Clb; Chorus; Nwsp Rptr; Yrbk Stf; Bsktbl; Sftbl; Tennis; VFW Awd.

CRUM, LAURIE; Pompton Lakes HS; Pompton Lakes, NJ; (4); SADD; School Play; Sec Frsh Cls; Rep Stu Cncl; L Cheerleading; High Hon Roll; Hon Roll; Pres Schlr; Glassboro ST Coll; Comm.

CRUMP, SHERI E; Vail-Deane HS; Newark, NJ; (2); Cmnty Wkr; Drama Clb; Latin Clb; Math Tm; NAACP; Political Wkr; Spanish Clb; Acpl Chr; Chorus; School Musical; Rider College Awd For Spanish 86; Radcliffe; Psychiatrist.

CRUTCHER, TERESA; High School South; S Toms River, NJ; (3); Computer Clb; DECA; Drama Clb; Radio Clb; Spanish Clb; Drill Tm; Nwsp Bus Mgr; Off Frsh Cls; 4-H Awd; Rutgers U; Bus Adm.

CRUZ, ANNE MARIE; Ridgewood HS; Ridgewood, NJ; (3); 2/450; Hosp Aide; Capt Math Tm; Sec Quiz Bowl; Science Clb; Sec Orch; Nwsp Stf; Gov Hon Prg Awd; High Hon Roll; NHS; Regnl Orch,All ST Orch 87; Rensselaer Polytech Medal 87; Columbia U Sci Hnrs Pgm 86; Math.

CRUZ, EDWIN; Essex Catholic Boys HS; Newark, NJ; (4); Boy Scts; French Clb; Math Clb; Spanish Clb; Ntl Merit Ltr; Auto Mech.

CRUZ, GLORIA; Cedar Ridge HS; Laurence Harbor, NJ; (3); Concert Band; Mrchg Band; Hon Roll; Spanish NHS; Delg GFWC-NJSFWC Wmns Clb Douglass Coll 87; Acct.

CRUZ, HEIDI; Paramus Catholic Girls Rgnl HS; Paramus, NJ; (3); Camera Clb; Church Yth Grp; Hosp Aide; Var Crs Cntry; Var Trk; High Hon Roll; NHS; Ntl Merit SF; Prfct Atten Awd; NEDTS Top 10 Percent Scorers & Montclair Coll Pgm Geol & Vocabulary 86; Engrng Pgm Notre Dame U 87.

CRUZ, ISRAEL; Perth Amboy HS; Perth Amboy, NJ; (3); Church Yth Grp; Var Bsbl; Hon Roll; Comp Engnr.

CRUZ, MAGDALA; St Joseph Of The Palisades HS; West New York, NJ; (4); 2/120; French Clb; Variety Show; Nwsp Ed-Chief; Yrbk Stf; Lit Mag; Rep Jr Cls; Im Bsktbl; French Hon Soc; NHS; LEAD Prg Bus Duke U 865; Acdmc All Amer 84-86; U Of PA; Finance.

CRUZ, MARIE; Park Ridge HS; Park Ridge, NJ; (2); AFS; Intnl Clb; Science Clb; Nwsp Stf; Lit Mag; JV Bsktbl; French Hon Soc; High Hon Roll; Prfct Atten Awd; Pres Schlr; Acdmc Ltr 86-87; Jrnlsm.

CRUZAN, MATTHEW; Hunterdon Central HS; Ringoes, NJ; (2); 24/478; Computer Clb; Stu Cncl; Hon Roll.

CRYAN, KELLY; Paul VI HS; Laurel Springs, NJ; (3); 18/418; Civic Clb; GAA; Math Clb; Teachers Aide; Var L Bsktbl; Var L Crs Cntry; JV L Sftbl; Hon Roll; Spanish NHS; U Of Notre Dame; Psychlgy.

CSAPO, KRISTA; Mc Corristin Catholic HS; Trenton, NJ; (3); 65/286; Church Yth Grp; Drama Clb; Hosp Aide; SADD; Thesps; Chorus; Madrigals; School Musical; School Play; Nwsp Rptr; Pblc Rltns.

CSERCSEVITS, MARY E; Holy Cross HS; Mt Holly, NJ; (3); 40/400; Cmnty Wkr; Spanish Clb; Y-Teens; Chorus; Church Choir; School Musical; Yrbk Rptr; Rep Sr Cls; Cit Awd; High Hon Roll; Sci Awds Of Achvt 85 & 86; Wrld Hngr Prjct Spksgrp 87; Acknwldgd At A Frshmn Crmny 85; Anthropology.

CSIPO, PAMELA M; John P Stevens HS; Edison, NJ; (4); Art Clb; Office Aide; Teachers Aide; Mrchg Band; Mgr Stage Crew; Socr; NHS; Dsgnd Logo Cmnty Rcyclng Pgm 87; Dsgnd Log Prjct Frnd 87; Safe Rides All Awarens Assoc Art Cont Wnnr; Trenton ST Coll; Art Ed.

CUARTAS, DORA; Paul VI Regional HS; Clifton, NJ; (3); 6/117; Yrbk Sprt Ed; Pres Jr Cls; Rep Stu Cncl; Var Cheerleading; Var Crs Cntry; Var Trk; French Hon Soc; High Hon Roll; Cert Natl Educ Dvlpmt Tsts 85; Chld Psych.

CUBEIRO, FERNANDO; Our Lady Of Good Counsel HS; Newark, NJ; (3); 28/140; Var Socr.

CUBELO, ANDREA; Toms River HS East; Toms River, NJ; (3); 5/509; Stat Bsbl; Var Capt Cheerleading; JV Swmmng; High Hon Roll; NHS; Amer Assn U Wmn Awd 85; Teens Edctng Alcohol Misuse Awd 86 & 87; Psych.

CUCCARESE, JON; Brick Township HS; Brick Town, NJ; (3); Varsity Clb; Var L Bsbl; Var L Bsktbl; Socr; Vrsty Bsktbl Awd Ms Imprvd 86; Vrsty Bsktbl Shrtsmnsp Awd 87; Arch.

CUCCI, CHRISTINE; Clifton HS; Clifton, NJ; (3); Math Clb; SADD; Chorus; Golf; JV Sftbl; Vllybl; Yrbk Stf; Hon Roll; Monclair ST Coll; Chiro.

CUCCIO, JANNA; Toms River HS East; Toms River, NJ; (3); Church Yth Grp; Cmnty Wkr; French Clb; Political Wkr; SADD; Variety Show; Rep Jr Cls; Stu Cncl; Crs Cntry; Trk; Engl.

CUCCUINI, JASON; Burlington City HS; Burlington, NJ; (2); Wrstlng; U Of AL; Bus.

CUCINOTTA, DENISE M; Florence Twp Memorial HS; Florence, NJ; (3); Aud/Vis; Church Yth Grp; FNA; Office Aide; Rep Stu Cncl; Var Fld Hcky; Hon Roll; St Francis Schl Nursing; Nrsng.

CUERVO, LILIANA; Fair Lawn HS; Fair Lawn, NJ; (4); 75/327; Church Yth Grp; Pres Trs Drama Clb; Acpl Chr; Sec Chorus; Church Choir; Madrigals; School Musical; School Play; Stage Crew; Variety Show; SF Hugh O Brien Awd Cont 85-86; Wm Patterson Coll; Early Ed.

CUEVA, ROBERT ANDREW; Belleville HS; Belleville, NJ; (3); Key Clb; Quiz Bowl; Spanish Clb; Rep Stu Cncl; Var Capt Tennis; Gov Hon Prg Awd; High Hon Roll; Pres NHS; Ntl Merit Ltr; Im Bsktbl; Founder & Pres Of Jr Engr Tech Scty Chptr 87; Engr.

CUILLO, PATRICK; De Paul HS; Bloomingdale, NJ; (4); JCL; Science Clb; JV Bsbl; Hon Roll; Blgy.

CULCASI, ROSEMARY; Hunterdon Central HS; Flemington, NJ; (2); 130/478; Art Clb; Church Yth Grp; Rep Frsh Cls; Stat Fld Hcky; Hon Roll.

CULLEN, COLLEEN; Red Bank Catholic HS; Lincroft, NJ; (3); Drama Clb; Latin Clb; Ski Clb; Spanish Clb; SADD; Yrbk Stf; Rep Frsh Cls; Rep Soph Cls; Powder Puff Ftbl; Sftbl; Pre Law.

CULLEN, GENE; Northwarren Regional HS; Blairstown, NJ; (4); 1/130; Church Yth Grp; Capt Scholastic Bowl; Rep Stu Cncl; Capt Ftbl; Capt Wrstlng; Bausch & Lomb Sci Awd; Gov Hon Prg Awd; NHS; Rotary Awd; Val; Rutgers U; Bio.

CULLEN, JOHN; Hackettstown HS; Hackettstown, NJ; (3); 29/180; Var Bsbl; Var Bsktbl; JV Ftbl; Hon Roll; NHS; 3rd Pl Crftsmn Fair Of NJ 85-86; 2nd Pl Crftsmn Fair Of NJ 86-87; Rutgers U; Cvl Engrng.

CULLEN, KIM; Cliffside Park HS; Cliffside Pk, NJ; (3); 42/243; Spanish Clb; Chorus; Stu Cncl; Bio Sci.

CULLEN, MICHAEL J; Paterson Catholic Regional HS; North Haledon, NJ; (4); 10/108; DECA; Political Wkr; Band; Nwsp Ed-Chief; Pres Jr Cls; Crs Cntry; High Hon Roll; NHS; Pres Schlr; Rep Soph Cls; Gov Tchng Schlrs Awd, Bishop Casey Svc Awd, & Wm Carlos Williams Engl Awd 87; Montelair ST Coll; Hstry.

CULVER, DAWN; Essex Catholic Giels HS; Irvington, NJ; (3); Church Yth Grp; Library Aide; Pep Clb; Church Choir; Hon Roll; Hghst Grd Avg Awd Algbr 85; Howard U; Bus Adm.

CUMBERLAND, JOSEPH; Burlington County Vo Tech; Fort Dix, NJ; (3); 22/200; FBLA; Sec VICA; Yrbk Ed-Chief; Yrbk Stf; Hon Roll; Prfct Atten Awd; Vica 2nd Pl Bus Procdure 86; FBLA 4th Pl; Rutgers; Comp Sci.

CUMMINGS, ELIZABETH; Westfield HS; Westfield, NJ; (4); 50/510; Am Leg Aux Girls St; Church Yth Grp; Latin Clb; SADD; Nwsp Sprt Ed; Sec Soph Cls; Socr; Swmmng; Hon Roll; Var Swim Tm Cap 86-87; Homecmng Queen 86-87; Duke U.

CUMMINGS, MICHAEL; Haddonfield Memorial HS; Haddonfield, NJ; (3); Church Yth Grp; JV Var Socr; Trk; High Hon Roll; Hon Roll; VP NHS; Athletic Recgntn Awd 87; US Air Force Acad; Pilot.

CUMMINGS, PAMELA; Holy Family Acad; Bayonne, NJ; (4); 4/130; Cmnty Wkr; French Clb; Orch; Var Tennis; High Hon Roll; VP NHS; NEDT Awd; Elks Clb Tnagr Mth 87; Hnrbl Mntn Grdn St Dstnghsd Schlr 87; Hghst Avg Awd-Pre-Calculus 87; Rutgers Coll; Biochem.

CUNEO, DONNA L; Paul VI HS; Somerdale, NJ; (2); Debate Tm; Drama Clb; Pres Exploring; NFL; SADD; Concert Band; Jazz Band; Mrchg Band; Bowling; Hon Roll; Mdl Of Yr Fnlst 86; Pope Pius XII Awd Sctng 87; Phila/NY Coll; Arts.

CUNHA, JOHN; Maple Shade HS; Maple Shade, NJ; (3); Am Leg Boys St; Boy Scts; Spanish Clb; Trs Jr Cls; Pres Sr Cls; Rep Stu Cncl; Var Ftbl; JV Trk; Hon Roll; Prfct Atten Awd; HOBY Awd Rnnr Up 85-86; Boy Sct Yr Awd 84-85; Sprts Med.

CUNINGHAM, SPENCER; Hamilton High West; Trenton, NJ; (3); Trk; Wt Lftg; Wrstlng.

CUNNINGHAM JR, DENNIS J; Mc Corristin HS; Trenton, NJ; (3); 3/67; Nwsp Sprt Ed; Ed Yrbk Stf; VP Frsh Cls; VP Soph Cls; VP Sr Cls; Trs Stu Cncl; Jr NHS; NHS; Ntl Merit Ltr; NEDT Awd; Stu Coun Excllnce Awd 86; Cert Of Part Schl Nwpr 87; 3rd Pl Schl Sci Fair 86-87; Physician.

CUNNINGHAM, JOHN; St Joseph Regional HS; Garnerville, NY; (3); 4/300; Boy Scts; Concert Band; Nwsp Stf; Crs Cntry; Trk; High Hon Roll; NHS; Computer Clb; JA; Math Tm; Egl Sct; AF Acad; Aerontcs.

CUNNINGHAM, KATHRYN; Faith Christian HS; Camden, NJ; (4); 5/; VP Chorus; Yrbk Stf; Pres Sr Cls; Var Capt Bsktbl; Var Capt Fld Hcky; Var Capt Sftbl; Hon Roll; NHS; 1st Pl Arts Lit Fair 86; 1st Pl Hstry Fair 86; All Star Tm Sftbl, Fld Hcky 86.

CUNNINGHAM, KIRA; Rancocas Valley Regional HS; Mt Holly, NJ; (3); Hosp Aide; Ski Clb; Band; Concert Band; Mrchg Band; Sec Frsh Cls; Sec Soph Cls; Lcrss; S Jersey Yth Cmssn 86-87; Lawyr.

CUNNINGHAM, MATTHEW E; Red Bank Catholic HS; W Allenhurst, NJ; (4); 8/311; Pres Exploring; Nwsp Rptr; Capt Ftbl; Capt Trk; Capt Wrstlng; Elks Awd; High Hon Roll; NHS; Ntl Merit Ltr; Silv Congrssnl Awd 86; Hmrm Pres 87; Schlr Ath 1st Tm 86; Outstndng Ldrshp Schl Actvts 87; Schlr Ath Awd; Johns Hopkins U; Pre-Med.

CUNNINGHAM, MICHAEL; Clearview Regional HS; Mullica Hill, NJ; (3); 15/185; Am Leg Boys St; Church Yth Grp; Exploring; Band; Mrchg Band; Im Bsktbl; Im Mgr(s); Hon Roll; NHS; Concert Band; Med.

CUNNINGHAM, TAMMY; Mc Corristin HS; Trenton, NJ; (3); Art Clb; Church Yth Grp; Debate Tm; Drama Clb; FNA; GAA; Hosp Aide; JA; Pep Clb; Teachers Aide; Outstndg Chrldr Scholar 86-87; Scholar St Francis Schl Nrsg 84-85; Nrsg.

CUNNINGHAM, TREMAYNE; Frank H Morrell HS; Irvington, NJ; (3); Church Yth Grp; Dance Clb; DECA; PAVAS; Church Choir; Cheerleading; Gym; High Hon Roll; Pres Schlr; Val; Hnr Rl 86-87; Parsons Schl Dsgn; Fshn Dsgnr.

CUNY, COLLEEN; Holy Family Acad; Bayonne, NJ; (2); 15/93; Church Yth Grp; School Musical; School Play; Stage Crew; Hon Roll; Med.

CUOZZO, JEANNE; West Windsor-Plainsboro HS; Princeton Junct, NJ; (3); AFS; Church Yth Grp; 4-H; Spanish Clb; Church Choir; JV Bsktbl; Capt Crs Cntry; Var Trk; High Hon Roll; Hon Roll; Sprtsmnshp Awd For Cross-Cntry 84-86; Elem Educ.

CUOZZO, THERESA; West Windsor-Plainsboro HS; Princeton Junct, NJ; (3); Church Yth Grp; Spanish Clb; Church Choir; Var Capt Crs Cntry; Var Trk; High Hon Roll; NHS; Orch; JV Bsktbl; JV Sftbl; MVP Awd Crss Cntry 84-86; Educ.

CUPAIUOLO, DANIELLE; Gateway R HS; Westville, NJ; (3); 35/200; FHA; Key Clb; Latin Clb; Office Aide; Spanish Clb; SADD; Yrbk Stf; Rep Frsh Cls; Rep Soph Cls; Rep Jr Cls; Glassboro ST Coll; Lbrl Arts.

CUPO, JASON; John P Stevens HS; Edison, NJ; (3); Ski Clb; Band; JV Bsbl; JV Ftbl; Powder Puff Ftbl; Wrstlng.

CUPON, LEANNE N; Phillipsburg HS; Alpha, NJ; (4); 36/329; Cmnty Wkr; Pres VP Exploring; Hosp Aide; Key Clb; Ski Clb; SADD; Church Choir; Variety Show; Nwsp Rptr; Ed Nwsp Stf; WA Wrkshps Cngrssnl Smnr 86; Cindy Vargo Mem Schlshp 87; Fairleigh Dickinson U.

CURCIO, EILEEN ALANA; Union HS; Union, NJ; (3); VP Church Yth Grp; Cmnty Wkr; Rep Stu Cncl; Var JV Bowling; Capt Var Fld Hcky; Cit Awd; Jr NHS; Key Clb; Letterman Clb; Spanish Clb; NJSF Of Wmns Clbs Girls Ciznshp 87; Exemplary Achvt Awd For Mech Drwng 86; Chrch Lector 85-86.

CURCIO, FRANCESCA; Holy Spirit HS; Ventnor, NJ; (4); 35/363.

CURCIO, GINA; Monsignor Donovan HS; Lavallette, NJ; (3); Ski Clb; Var JV Cheerleading; High Hon Roll; Hon Roll; NHS; Exc In Accntng I Awd 87; Hghst Avrg In Algebra I 87.

CURCIO, JOSEPH; Buena Regional HS; Newfield, NJ; (3); Debate Tm; Math Clb; Math Tm; Quiz Bowl; Varsity Clb; Var Capt Golf; Var Socr; Hon Roll; Jr NHS; Aerospc Engnr.

CURCURU, PROCOPIO; Vineland HS; Vineland, NJ; (1); Comp Prgrmmr.

CURE, JOAN ANN; Oak Knoll HS; Oldwick, NJ; (4); Ski Clb; Var Fld Hcky; Var Sftbl; Hon Roll; Math Awd 85; NJ ST Ski Tm 86-87; U NH; Math.

CURIO, NICOLE; Haddon Township HS; Westmont, NJ; (4); 58/179; Church Yth Grp; Political Wkr; Red Cross Aide; Varsity Clb; Orch; Nwsp Rptr; JV Bsktbl; Var Trk; Varsity Clb; School Musical; Mst Outstndng Stu In Industrial Arts, Co-Curricular Ldrshp Activity Awd & Dsgnd Cls Flag 87; Mercer Cnty Cmnty; Drafting.

CURLEY, MARGARET; Wayne Hills HS; Wayne, NJ; (3); 8/310; GAA; Latin Clb; Math Tm; Nwsp Stf; Yrbk Stf; Var Gym; JV Trk; High Hon Roll; Hon Roll; Sec NHS; Law.

CURLEY, PETER; Columbia HS; Maplewood, NJ; (3); Var Crs Cntry; Var Trk; Cross Country Tm Lttr Wnnr 84-86; Indoor Trk Lttr Wnnr 85-87; Outdoor Trk Lttr Wnnr 85-87; Law.

CURRAN, AMY LYNNE; Eastern HS; Voorhees, NJ; (3); 30/400; Intnl Clb; Political Wkr; Fld Hcky; JV Var Socr; High Hon Roll; Hon Roll; Jr NHS; Gym Aide; Intl Bus.

CURRAN, BRIDGET; De Paul HS; Ringwood, NJ; (3); 21/150; Ski Clb; Rep Stu Cncl; Var Capt Cheerleading; Var Capt Pom Pon; JV Sftbl; Trk; Im Vllybl; High Hon Roll; Lion Awd; NHS; Physcl Thrpy.

CURRAN, JOHN P; Ramapo HS; Wyckoff, NJ; (4); 23/329; Debate Tm; Ed Nwsp Stf; Im Bsktbl; Var Trk; Hon Roll; NHS; Ntl Merit SF; St Schlr; Im Socr; IBM Ldrshp Smnr; Stu Annl Intl Rltns Smnr; NJ Engrng Career Day Prtcpnt.

CURRERI, PETER; Pennsauken HS; Merchantville, NJ; (2); Ski Clb; Varsity Clb; Jazz Band; School Play; Stu Cncl; Bsktbl; Var Ftbl; Wt Lftg; Hon Roll; Science Clb; Jazz Band ST Chmpns 85-87; Ftbl Grp IV ST Chmpns 86-87; Elec Engr.

CURRY, CLAUDINE S; Essex Catholic Girls HS; East Orange, NJ; (4); 1/53; Spanish Clb; Sec Color Guard; Variety Show; Nwsp Ed-Chief; Yrbk Ed-Chief; High Hon Roll; Jr NHS; NHS; Ntl Merit Schol; Val; Garden ST Dist Schlr Prog 87; Princeton U; Engl.

CURRY, LAURA LYN; Lyndhurst HS; Lyndhurst, NJ; (3); 4/174; French Clb; VP Key Clb; Rep Frsh Cls; High Hon Roll; NHS; Rotary Awd; Stu Of Mnth-Engl Dept 84&85; Stu Of Mnth-Frnch Dept 85; Stu Of Mnth Hstry Dept 85; Rutgers; Corp Lwyr.

CURRY, STEPHEN; Monsignor Donovan HS; Toms River, NJ; (3); Aud/Vis; Boy Scts; Church Yth Grp; Library Aide; PAVAS; Band; Church Choir; Jazz Band; School Musical; School Play; Sr Altar Boy Awd 87; Stockton ST Coll; Music.

CURTIS, DAVID; A P Schalick HS; Elmer, NJ; (3); 3/125; Church Yth Grp; Band; Stage Crew; Trs Stu Cncl; Tennis; Hon Roll; NHS; Close-Up 86-87; Hugh O Brian Yth Fndtn 86; Amer Med Assoc Explorer 86-87; Bio.

CURTIS, GLENN; Deptford HS; Deptford, NJ; (4); 7/276; Band; Concert Band; Jazz Band; Rep Stu Cncl; Capt Var Bsbl; Var Crs Cntry; Capt Var Trk; Hon Roll; Jr NHS; NHS; Outstndng Electrnc Data Procsng Stu 86-87; Ntl Hnr Soc Awd 86-87; Ntl Schlr/Athlt Awd 86-87; Drexel U; Comp Info Systms.

CURTIS, JONATHAN T; Haddonfield Memorial HS; Haddonfield, NJ; (3); Am Leg Boys St; Church Yth Grp; Civic Clb; Drama Clb; French Clb; Intnl Clb; Varsity Clb; Chorus; Church Choir; School Musical; Ranatra Fusca Awd 87; Engrng.

CURTIS JR, KENNETH; Essex Catholic Boys HS; East Orange, NJ; (2); Church Yth Grp; Church Choir; Bsktbl; Ftbl; Sftbl; High Hon Roll; Hon Roll; Rotc.

CURTIS, MIKE; Abraham Clark HS; Roselle, NJ; (3); Boy Scts; Ski Clb; Coach Actv; Var Capt Ftbl; Mgr(s); Var Trk; Var Wt Lftg; Hon Roll; All Mtn Vly Conf Offnsve Guard 1st Team 86; Jackson ST; Comp Prog.

CURTIS, REBECCA; Warren Hills Regional HS; Washington, NJ; (4); Art Clb; Drama Clb; Lit Mag; Hon Roll; Moore Coll Art Mrt Schrlshp 86; Smmr Arts Inst 86; Moore Coll Of Art; BFA.

CURTIS, THOMAS J; Pope John XXIII Regional HS; Sparta, NJ; (3); Am Leg Boys St; Boy Scts; Cmnty Wkr; Latin Clb; Political Wkr; Ski Clb; Varsity Clb; Band; Im JV Bsbl; Var JV Bsktbl; Bus.

CUSH, PETRONELLA; Orange HS; Orange, NJ; (2); Church Yth Grp; Office Aide; Soroptimist; Score Keeper; Dentistry.

CUSICK, CHRISTOPHER J; West Milford HS; West Milford, NJ; (3); 95/410; Am Leg Boys St; Church Yth Grp; French Clb; SADD; Off Frsh Cls; Trs Soph Cls; Trs Jr Cls; Trs Sr Cls; Rep Stu Cncl; JV Bsbl; Gold Awd 87; Bus.

CUSUMANO, LEANNE; Manalapan HS; Manalapan, NJ; (4); 9/423; CAP; NFL; SADD; Drill Tm; Acpl Chr; Ed Lit Mag; Pres NHS; Ntl Merit SF; Color Guard; Stage Crew; COS Hnr Cadet 86; Grdn ST Dstngshd Schlr; CAP Cadet Major; Georgetown; Intl Rel.

CUTLER, LISA; Cherry Hill East HS; Cherry Hill, NJ; (4); Latin Clb; SADD; Nwsp Stf; Rep Frsh Cls; Rep Soph Cls; Rep Jr Cls; Rep Sr Cls; Rep Stu Cncl; Lcrss; Mgr(s); Garden St Distngshd Schlr 87; Cum Laude Society 87; U Of MI; Lib Arts.

CUTLIP, JUSTIN; Glen Ridge HS; Glen Ridge, NJ; (3); 41/108; Church Yth Grp; Cmnty Wkr; Key Clb; Varsity Clb; Var L Bsktbl; Var Capt Socr; Im Vllybl; Hon Roll; Gettysburg; Bus.

CUTTI, ERIC M; St John Vianney HS; Morganville, NJ; (3); Math Clb; Math Tm; Science Clb; Var Bsbl; High Hon Roll; Hon Roll; Top Math Stu Merit Awd 87.

CYBORSKI, LINDA; Mccorristin HS; Trenton, NJ; (3); 2/267; GAA; Pep Clb; Sec Frsh Cls; Rep Soph Cls; Rep Jr Cls; Stu Cncl; Var L Bsktbl; Var L Sftbl; High Hon Roll; Hon Roll; 1st Tm All Mercerry Cnty & All Conf Bsktbl 85-87; 2nd Tm All ST Parochial A Bsktbl 86-87JR Prom Qn.

CYBUCK, MOLLY; Mt Olive HS; Budd Lake, NJ; (3); AFS; Science Clb; Ski Clb; SADD; Varsity Clb; Yrbk Stf; Lit Mag; Var Crs Cntry; Var Trk; Natl Art Hnr Soc 86-88; 3 Yr Vrsty Awd Crs Cntry 86; Art Cmpttn Awds 86-87.

CYTRON, ANDREW; Mountain Lakes HS; Mountain Lakes, NJ; (4); 1/99; Math Tm; Science Clb; Trs Band; Var Capt Crs Cntry; Bausch & Lomb Sci Awd; Ntl Merit Schol; Spanish NHS; Val; Sec Model UN; Trs Mrchg Band; Gldn Nugget Schlrshp 87; Am Dfns Prprdnss Schlrshp 87; MIT; Physcs.

CZACHUR, CHRISTINE; Middlesex HS; Middlesex, NJ; (3); Church Yth Grp; Drama Clb; Math Clb; Model UN; Ski Clb; SADD; Nwsp Ed-Chief; Stat Ftbl; High Hon Roll; Elks Awd; Bus Admn.

CZAJKOWSKI, TRACY; Toms River HS HS; Toms River, NJ; (3); French Clb; Math Tm; Q&S; SADD; Nwsp Rptr; Nwsp Stf; Sec Frsh Cls; Tennis; Communications.

CZARNECKI, D MITRI J; Westfield HS; Westfield, NJ; (3); 19/470; Am Leg Boys St; Boy Scts; Off Latin Clb; Jazz Band; JV Capt Socr; Var L Wrstlng; High Hon Roll; JP Sousa Awd; NHS; Prfct Atten Awd; Union Cnty Coll Smnr Awds Prog 85-86; Gvrnrs Schl Sci 86-87; L Armstrong Awd Rnnr Up 84-85; Phrmcy.

CZARNIAK, LISA; Roselle Catholic HS; Linden, NJ; (4); 10/195; Hosp Aide; Math Clb; Ski Clb; School Play; Lit Mag; JV Var Tennis; Hon Roll; NHS; Spanish NHS; Rutgers Coll.

CZEBIENIAK, DANIEL J; Spotswood HS; Millton, NJ; (4); Am Leg Boys St; Drama Clb; Church Choir; School Musical; Capt Var Crs Cntry; Var Trk; Mst Imprvd Rnnr 86; Outstndng SR Awd Boys Cross Cntry 86-87; NJ Governors Cncl On Physcl Ftns 87; MUSIC.

CZECH, JEANNINE; Linden HS; Linden, NJ; (3); Library Aide; Acpl Chr; Madrigals; School Musical; High Hon Roll; NHS; Interior Design.

CZECHOWICZ, STACY; Highland Regional HS; Blackwood, NJ; (3); Church Yth Grp; French Clb; French Tchr.

CZECHOWSKI, SARAH; Delran HS; Delran, NJ; (4); 9/185; Debate Tm; FBLA; Math Tm; Spanish Clb; Nwsp Rptr; JV Socr; JV Sftbl; High Hon Roll; NHS; Brnz & Slvr Key Awds For Disting Acads 83-85; Chrmn Of Grt Amer Smkout At Delran 87; Glassboro ST Coll.

CZEKAJLO, MICHAEL; Marist HS; Bayonne, NJ; (3); #3 In Class; Boy Scts; Chess Clb; Church Yth Grp; Scholastic Bowl; Speech Tm; Crs Cntry; Hon Roll; Spanish NHS; Bayonne HS Boys CYO Champns 85-86; HCIAA X-Cntry-4th Pl Soph Boys 85.

CZERNIAWSKI, YOLANDA; Immaculate Conception HS; Wallington, NJ; (4); 3/92; Math Tm; Science Clb; Yrbk Stf; Rep Jr Cls; Rep Sr Cls; Bausch & Lomb Sci Awd; High Hon Roll; NEDT Awd; Prfct Atten Awd; St Schlr; Hghst Scorer Chem Lg 86; N Lentz Awd Hghst SAT Scores 86; Schl Mag Short Story Awd 86; Rutgers; Phrmcy.

CZERNIECKI, JEANNA; Paul Vi Regional HS; Clifton, NJ; (3); 7/120; Church Yth Grp; Girl Scts; Rep Frsh Cls; Pres Soph Cls; Var Cheerleading; French Hon Soc; High Hon Roll; NHS; Prsdntl Clsrm Fr Yng Amers 87; HOBY Ldrshp Fndtn 86; Z-Clb Pres 87-88; Early Chldhd Educ.

CZESAK, SCOTT; Lenape Valley Regional HS; Andover, NJ; (3); 16/252; Boy Scts; JV Golf; Hon Roll; NHS; Altrnt Dlgt Boys ST 87; Lenape Rgnl HS Dlgt To Lyl Ordr Of Moose Drg Congress 87; BSA Ldrshp Corp; Rutgers ST U; Meterology.

CZUJAK, BARBARA; St Mary Of The Assumption HS; Elizabeth, NJ; (2); Girl Scts; Englsh.

D ADDARIO, GINA; Rahway HS; Rahway, NJ; (3); Key Clb; Science Clb; School Musical; Variety Show; Stu Cncl; Var Capt Cheerleading; Tennis; High Hon Roll; Hon Roll; Prfct Atten Awd.

D ADDIO, DIANE; Cranford HS; Cranford, NJ; (3); 83/268; Church Yth Grp; Cmnty Wkr; Dance Clb; Chorus; School Play; Variety Show; Yrbk Stf; Cheerleading; Score Keeper; Cit Awd; Yth In Govt 87; Gld Cup In Ballet; U RI; Fine Arts.

D AGOSTINO, LEONARD; Holy Spirit HS; Atlantic City, NJ; (4); 46/363; School Play; High Hon Roll; JC Awd; NHS; Villonova; Bus Adm.

D ALESSANDRO, JAMES; Toms River HS South; Toms River, NJ; (3); 1/405; Boy Scts; Cmnty Wkr; Key Clb; Math Tm; Science Clb; Ski Clb; SADD; Teachers Aide; Capt Golf; Gov Hon Prg Awd; Vrsty Awd Acdmc Excllnce; MVP Golf; All Cnty Selectn Golf Tm.

D ALOISIO, SAMANTHA; Paramus Catholic Girls HS; Rochelle Park, NJ; (2); Dance Clb; SADD; NEDT Awd; Monmouth Coll; Vet.

D ALUSIO, JIM; Brick HS; Brick, NJ; (4); DECA; Letterman Clb; Ski Clb; Color Guard.

D AMATO, JAMIE; Toms River North HS; Toms River, NJ; (3); Band; Mrchg Band; School Musical; Symp Band; JV Sftbl; Var Trk; High Hon Roll; Hon Roll; Girls Ctznshp Inst 88; Acad Pin 87; Athltc Awd 85; Spts Psych.

D AMORE, PAUL; St Augustine Prep; Richland, NJ; (3); VP Frsh Cls; VP Soph Cls; JV Bsbl; Var Crs Cntry; Jr NHS; NHS; Bus.

D ANGELO, DANA KRISTIN; Neumann Prep HS; Paterson, NJ; (4); 1/84; Pep Clb; Lit Mag; Bausch & Lomb Sci Awd; High Hon Roll; NHS; Val; Gardn St Dstngshd Schlr 86-87; Amer Lgn Schl Awd 87; USAF Math & Sci Awd 87; Amer Cynamid Sci Awd 87; La Fayette Coll.

D ANGELO, ROBERT; Lodi HS; Lodi, NJ; (3); 5/130; French Clb; Science Clb; VP Pres Teachers Aide; Nwsp Stf; Hon Roll; NHS; Psych.

D ANIELLO, SUSAN; Immaculata HS; Somerville, NJ; (3); Rutgers U; Bus.

D ANNA, RITA KRISTINE; The Morristown Beard Schl; Oldwick, NJ; (3); VP AFS; Chorus; Yrbk Phtg; Yrbk Stf; Var Fld Hcky; Var Sftbl; JV Tennis; JV Vllybl; Hon Roll; Annl Art Awd 85; Fld Hcky & Sftbl Mst Imprvd Plyr 85; Commnctns.

D ANTHONY, MICHAEL; St John Vianney HS; Aberdeen, NJ; (3); 27/235; SADD; School Musical; School Play; Stage Crew; Lit Mag; Hon Roll; NHS; Gld,White Spch & Drm Awds.

D ANTUONO, CHRISTINE G; Scotch Plains-Fanwood HS; Fanwood, NJ; (3); Church Yth Grp; Dance Clb; FBLA; Key Clb; SADD; Band; Mrchg Band; Var L Cheerleading; Hon Roll; Prfct Atten Awd; Bus.

D ARCY, AMY; Holy Spirit HS; Northfield, NJ; (2); 37/397; Rep Stu Cncl; JV Swmmng.

D ARRIGO, ARTHUR; Bridgeton HS; Bridgeton, NJ; (4); 11/186; French Clb; Q&S; Ski Clb; Nwsp Ed-Chief; Yrbk Stf; Rep Frsh Cls; Rep Soph Cls; Rep Jr Cls; Capt Crs Cntry; Var Golf; Rutgers; Engl.

D AUGOSTINE, KIMBERLY; Buena Regional HS; Vineland, NJ; (2); Church Yth Grp; Dance Clb; PAVAS; Jr NHS; Prfrmng Arts.

D ESPIES, VERONICA; Lacey Township HS; Lanoka Harbor, NJ; (4); 14/270; Hosp Aide; Math Tm; Science Clb; JV Fld Hcky; JV Socr; High Hon Roll; Hon Roll; NHS; Prfct Atten Awd; Rep Frsh Cls; Rutgers Coll; Bio Sci.

D OVIDIO, LOU; Passaic County Vo-Tech HS; Paterson, NJ; (4); 15/366; Trs Spanish Clb; Yrbk Ed-Chief; Trs Jr Cls; Trs Sr Cls; Var L Bsbl; Hon Roll; Acdmc All Amer Awd; Fund Rsng Comm; Stu Guide; La Salle U; Finance.

D ZIO, DENA S; Lakewood HS; Lakewood, NJ; (3); 46/330; English Clb; Band; Mrchg Band; Orch; Symp Band; French Hon Soc; Hon Roll; Color Guard.

DA CRUZ, JOHN; Riverside HS; Riverside, NJ; (3); 7/120; Varsity Clb; JV Bsktbl; Var Capt Crs Cntry; JV Socr; Var Capt Trk; High Hon Roll; Hon Roll; Prfct Atten Awd; NJIT; Arch.

DA SALLA, SUZANNE; High Point Reg HS; Sussex, NJ; (3); Church Yth Grp; Spanish Clb; Rep Frsh Cls; Trs Soph Cls; Sec Jr Cls; Sec Stu Cncl; Stat Bsktbl; JV Sftbl; Var Tennis; Hon Roll; Svc Awd Stu Cncl 87; 3rd Vrsty Awd Tnns 86; 3rd Pl Awd Tnns Fstvl 86; Bus Admn.

DA SILVA, MICHELLE; Linden HS; Linden, NJ; (3); Key Clb; Political Wkr; Chorus; Church Choir; School Musical; School Play; Gym; La Danse Schl Prfrmng Arts Achvt Tap 86; La Danse Schl Prfrmng Arts Achvt Bllt 87; Chld Psych.

DABAGIAN, GAYE M; Ramapo Regional HS; Franklin Lks, NJ; (3); 102/322; AFS; Church Yth Grp; Cmnty Wkr; Library Aide; Hon Roll; Bio.

DABROWSKI, DIANA; Highland HS; Laurel Spgs, NJ; (4); FTA; JA; Spanish Clb; SADD; Teachers Aide; Varsity Clb; Stage Crew; Yrbk Stf; Bsktbl; Tennis; Vrsty Ltr Bsktbl Ten 85-87; Awds Clb.

DABROWSKI, KRISTEN; Stuart Country Day Schl; Trenton, NJ; (3); Cmnty Wkr; French Clb; Chorus; School Musical; Nwsp Rptr; Ed Lit Mag; High Hon Roll; Art Clb; Scholastic Bowl; Acpl Chr; Outstndng Achvt Crtcl & Creatv Wrtg 87; Outstndng Achvt Algbr 87; Spec Recog Achvt US Hstry 87; Engl.

DACRES, ANDREA; Eastside HS; Paterson, NJ; (3); Pres 4-H; Girl Scts; Key Clb; Red Cross Aide; School Play; VP Frsh Cls; 4-H Awd; Prfct Atten Awd; WPC Pre-Coll Acadc Pgm 86-87; Seton Hall U; Pre-Med.

DAGOGLIANO, CAROLYN; Palisades Park JR/Sr HS; Palisades Pk, NJ; (4); 1/125; Church Yth Grp; VP Mu Alpha Theta; Jazz Band; Nwsp Stf; Var Capt Bsktbl; Var Crs Cntry; Var Capt Vllybl; Cit Awd; Trs Sec NHS; Val; Am Leg Ortrcl Comptn 2nd Pl Bergen Cnty 87; Natl Schlr/Ath Awd US Army Res 87; Acad Excllce Awds 87; Rutgers Coll; Engrng.

DAGOSTINO, LISA S; Holmdel HS; Holmdel, NJ; (4); Drama Clb; Stage Crew; Nwsp Ed-Chief; Var Gym; Gov Hon Prg Awd; High Hon Roll; NHS; Ntl Merit SF; Spanish NHS; St Schlr.

DAIDONE, MICHELLE; Dover HS; Mine Hill-Dover, NJ; (2); Hosp Aide; Teachers Aide; Socr; Sftbl; Swmmng; Hon Roll; Humn Svcs.

DAILY III, ALBERT; Perth Amboy HS; Perth Amboy, NJ; (3); Camera Clb; NAACP; Spanish Clb; Varsity Clb; Band; Chorus; Madrigals; Mrchg Band; Var Ftbl; Var Wt Lftg; Natl Band Awd 83; Bio.

DAISEY, OWEN; Gloucester City HS; Gloucester, NJ; (3); #5 In Class; Am Leg Boys St; Math Clb; Red Cross Aide; Science Clb; Spanish Clb; Rep Stu Cncl; Capt Var Crs Cntry; Var L Trk; Wt Lftg; High Hon Roll; Tri-Cnty Conf Clssc Div 3200-M All Star 86 & 87; 3rd Pl Lcl Hampton Meml Race 86; Arch Engrng.

DAKWALA, PURVI; Dickenson HS; Jersey City, NJ; (2); Art Clb; French Clb; Intnl Clb; Nrsng.

DALAL, NEHA; Highland Regional HS; Laurel Springs, NJ; (2); Hosp Aide; Library Aide; Spanish Clb; Chorus; Mrchg Band; Pom Pon; Hon Roll; Med.

DALE, STEVE; Kearney HS; Kearny, NJ; (3); German Clb; Band; Chorus; Concert Band; Jazz Band; Mrchg Band; School Musical; Cit Awd; 2nd Chr Bass Clrnt N Jersey Rgn Bnd 85; Berklee Coll Music; Prfrmr.

DALE, TARA; Orange HS; Orange, NJ; (2); Hon Roll; Jr NHS; Masonic Awd; NHS; NYU; Pre Law.

DALESSANDRO, MICHAEL; Memorial HS; Elmwood Pk, NJ; (4); 36/161; Rep Frsh Cls; Rep Soph Cls; Var L Bsbl; Clemson U; Animal Sci.

DALESSIO, ARTHUR; Bloomfield SR HS; Bloomfield, NJ; (4); 13/450; Computer Clb; Debate Tm; Key Clb; Latin Clb; Math Clb; Math Tm; Quiz Bowl; Varsity Clb; Rep Frsh Cls; Rep Soph Cls; Itln Prz Best Rcrd In A Frgn Lang 87; Vrsty Lttrs In Tnns 86-87; Outstndng Athlt Awd 87; Stevens Inst Of Tech; Engnrng.

DALTON, JILL; Manasquan HS; Manasquan, NJ; (2); #21 In Class; Art Clb; DECA; Drama Clb; Spanish Clb; Stage Crew; JV Cheerleading; Var Gym; Var Trk; Hon Roll; NHS; Art.

DALTON, MELISSA; Pope Paul VI HS; Williamstown, NJ; (4); 56/511; Cmnty Wkr; French Clb; Stage Crew; Trk; NHS; St Josephs U; Mrktg.

DALY, CATHY; Roselle Park HS; Roselle Park, NJ; (3); Church Yth Grp; JA; Radio Clb; SADD; Trs Rep Frsh Cls; Rep Jr Cls; Var Fld Hcky; Var Sftbl; Art.

DALY, DEVIN; St John Vianney HS; Aberdeen, NJ; (3); Boy Scts; Church Yth Grp; Cmnty Wkr; Service Clb; SADD; Stage Crew; Rep Soph Cls; Rep Jr Cls; Trk; Wrstlng; Villanova; Acctng.

DALY, JEREMIAH; West Milford Township HS; West Milford, NJ; (3); 2/400; Am Leg Boys St; Art Clb; German Clb; Quiz Bowl; Varsity Clb; Var Crs Cntry; Jr NHS; NHS; Vrsty Capt Fncng; Grmn Hnr Soc; Med.

DALY, KIM; Holy Rosary Acad; N Bergen, NJ; (3); Art Clb; Dance Clb; Library Aide; Math Tm; Service Clb; Yrbk Stf; High Hon Roll; NHS; Prfct Atten Awd; Pharm.

DALY, MELISSA; Morristown HS; Morristown, NJ; (3); 4-H; Latin Clb; Math Tm; Diving; Swmmng; Bus Adm.

DALY, MICHAEL; Newton HS; Newton, NJ; (1); 1/190; Pres Church Yth Grp; Latin Clb; Math Tm; Scholastic Bowl; Science Clb; Off Lit Mag; Rep Frsh Cls; DAR Awd; High Hon Roll; Pres Schlr; Strght A Avg Awd Summa Cum Laude Latin 87; ST Sci Prtcptn Awd 87; Blair Acad Smmr Inst Gftd 86; Bio Chem.

DALZIEL, JAN; Neptune HS; Neptune, NJ; (2); Off Stu Cncl; Diving; Gym; Asbry Pk Press Athl Wk 86; Grdn ST Games Gymnstcs Gov Cup Awd 1st Pl 86; Natl Flr Exer Chmpn 87.

DAMASK, MICHELLE; The Pilgrim Acad; Mays Landing, NJ; (3); 3/20; Church Yth Grp; Teachers Aide; Chorus; Nwsp Sprt Ed; Yrbk Stf; Var Cheerleading; Var Sftbl; High Hon Roll; Prfct Atten Awd; Bst Typing Awd; Hghst Hstry Awd.

DAMBROSIO, JOHN; Newton HS; Newton, NJ; (3); 39/198; Varsity Clb; Var L Trk; Var Wt Lftg; High Hon Roll; Cert Commdentn Eng I, Latin I, Alg I 84-85; Cert Commdentn Eng II, Latin II & Eng III 85-87; Med.

DAMIANO, MELISSA; Hamilton HS West; Hamilton Square, NJ; (3); Office Aide; Teachers Aide; Stat Bsktbl; Mgr(s); Stat Socr; L Trk; Hon Roll; Trenton ST Coll; CPA.

DAMIS, DAVID; St Joseph Regional HS; Rivervale, NJ; (3); Church Yth Grp; Stu Cncl; Ftbl; Trk; Wt Lftg; Hon Roll; Spanish NHS; Natl Yng Ldrshp Awd 86-87; Bus.

DAMM, GARY; Edgewood RS HS; Sicklervle, NJ; (2); Latin Clb; L JV Socr; L JV Wrstlng; Hon Roll; Plntrs Pnts Phys Ftnss Awd 86; Gftd & Tlntd Prog 81-86 & 88; Pres Acad Ftnss Awd 86; Schlstc Awds 87; Naval Avtn.

DANDROW, STEPHEN; Cranford HS; Cranford, NJ; (2); Art Clb; French Clb; Latin Clb; Nwsp Rptr; French Hon Soc; Hon Roll; Columbia U; Frgn Correspondent.

DANESE, JOHN E; Ridgefield Memorial HS; Ridgefield, NJ; (4); 7/103; Ski Clb; School Play; Rep Jr Cls; Rep Stu Cncl; Bsbl; Ftbl; Hon Roll; NHS; St Schlr; Soc Acad Achvt 87; NJ Inst Tech; Elect Engrng.

DANESE, MICHELE; Shawnee HS; Medford, NJ; (4); 182/547; Var Cheerleading; Im Lcrss; Rep Jr Cls; Rep Stu Cncl; Miss Teen NJ North Amercn Teen 85; Bus.

DANESI, SHAWN; Kittatinny Regional HS; Newton, NJ; (3); 7/216; Math Clb; Science Clb; SADD; Chorus; Nwsp Stf; Rep Stu Cncl; Var Bowling; Var Stat Sftbl; High Hon Roll; NHS; Chemstry.

DANGELEWICZ, PETER M; Hackensack HS; Maywood, NJ; (3); 34/403; Am Leg Boys St; Letterman Clb; Teachers Aide; Varsity Clb; Var Bsbl; Cit Awd; Hon Roll; NHS; Spanish NHS; Ski Clb; Yth Of Mnth Awd 87; Aviation.

DANIEL, GREGORY; Wardlaw-Hartridge Schl; Cranford, NJ; (4); 6/48; Hosp Aide; Ski Clb; SADD; Concert Band; Jazz Band; Stage Crew; Rep Stu Cncl; JV Tennis; High Hon Roll; NHS; Bus.

DANIELS, BRADLEY; Pennington Prep; Hamilton Square, NJ; (2); 3/72; JV Ftbl; JV Golf; High Hon Roll; NHS; Lionel R Driscoll Merit Schlrshp 85-86; Hugh O Brien Yth Conf 87.

DANIELS JR, JAMES R; John F Kennedy HS; Willingboro, NJ; (3); 4/300; Am Leg Boys St; Church Yth Grp; Office Aide; Church Choir; Bsktbl; Var Capt Ftbl; High Hon Roll; Hon Roll; Jr NHS; NHS; Town Meeting On Tommorrow Schl Prog 86; Pre Med.

DANIELS, JEFFREY; John P Stevens HS; Edison, NJ; (2); 1/452; Church Yth Grp; French Clb; JV Bsbl; JV Bsktbl; High Hon Roll; Hon Roll; U Of MI; Aerospace Engr.

DANIELS, JENNIFER; Weequahic HS; Newark, NJ; (4); 10/370; Church Yth Grp; Drama Clb; Exploring; FNA; Hosp Aide; JA; Pres Spanish Clb; Band; Church Choir; Capt Color Guard; Peer Ldrshp Support Group 84-87; Drug Ed 83-87; David Toma TV Show 86; Rutgers Coll Nrsng; RN.

DANIELS, KEITH; Holy Spirit HS; Absecon, NJ; (3); 3/332; Boy Scts; Church Yth Grp; Math Tm; Pres Soph Cls; Rep Jr Cls; Stu Cncl; Im Bsktbl; Ftbl; Cit Awd; Hon Roll; HOBY Ldrshp Smnr 86; Yng Ldrs Amer 86; Crew Var; Princeton; Bus.

DANIELS, KIMBERLY; Passaic Valley HS; Little Falls, NJ; (4); 43/344; Sec Church Yth Grp; Dance Clb; Drama Clb; French Clb; Concert Band; Drm Mjr(t); Mrchg Band; Variety Show; Var Vllybl; High Hon Roll; Amer Leg Awd Ctznshp 83; Dance Awds 86; Bst Drum Mjr EMBA Champ 85; Douglas Coll; Cmmnctns.

DANIELS, LAURA; Clearview Reg HS; Mullica Hill, NJ; (3); 4/200; Church Yth Grp; Cmnty Wkr; Drama Clb; SADD; Band; Chorus; Church Choir; Concert Band; Mrchg Band; School Musical; 2 Mnths Boda Norway Teen Mssns Intl 86; 2 Mnths Bergen Norway 87.

DANIELS, SUZETTE; Weequahie HS; Newark, NJ; (4); 28/367; Church Yth Grp; Exploring; Spanish Clb; Church Choir; Drill Tm; Mrchg Band; Rep Jr Cls; Cheerleading; Cit Awd; Prfct Atten Awd; Franklin St John Schlrshp 87; Montclair ST Coll; Accntnt.

DANKO, NOELLE; Brick Memorial HS; Brick, NJ; (3); 7/375; FBLA; Hosp Aide; Key Clb; Yrbk Stf; Im Bsktbl; Sec Crs Cntry; High Hon Roll; NHS; ACCNTNG.

DANLEY, JENNIFER; Dover HS; Dover, NJ; (3); Am Leg Aux Girls St; French Clb; Intnl Clb; Office Aide; Ski Clb; Drm & Bgl; Capt Flag Corp; Variety Show; JV Sftbl; Hon Roll; Frnch & Psych Acadc Awd 87; Intl Bus.

DANN, PATRICIA; Glen Rock HS; Glen Rock, NJ; (3); 7/145; Red Cross Aide; Spanish Clb; Coach Actv; Sftbl; Swmmng; Tennis; Timer; High Hon Roll; Trs Jr NHS; NHS; Stu Mnth Socl Stds 86; Stu Mnth Sci & Phys Ed 87; Mst Vlbl Swmmr 85.

DANNA, MARK; Paul VI HS; Somerdale, NJ; (4); 92/511; Math Clb; Spanish Clb; Band; Concert Band; Mrchg Band; Im Bowling; JV Golf; Hon Roll; Spanish NHS; DE U; Accntng.

DANNER, RICHARD; St James HS; Woodstown, NJ; (3); 27/77; Cmnty Wkr; Ski Clb; Stage Crew; Var Ftbl; US Marine Corps Physcl Ftns Awd 87; St James Comp Sci Hnr 87; Natl Physcl Ftns Awd 87; Comp Sci.

DANSON JR, DONALD; Delran HS; Delran, NJ; (3); 23/200; JV Bsbl; Var Ftbl; JV Wrstlng; Hon Roll; Comp.

DAPONTE, NANCY; Linden HS; Linden, NJ; (3); DECA; FHA; High Hon Roll; Hon Roll; DECA 2nd Pl Aprl & Acsrs & 2 Certs For Top 80 Pct 87; Fash.

DARA, CHRISTINA; Hasbrouck Heights HS; Hasbrouck Hts, NJ; (3); Pres Church Yth Grp; Drama Clb; Trs Key Clb; Band; Chorus; Church Choir; School Play; Nwsp Ed-Chief; Yrbk Ed-Chief; High Hon Roll; 1st Pl Knghts Of Col Essy Cntst 87; 1st Pl BAR Assoc Law Day Essy Cntst 87; Pharm.

DARATA, MILISSA; Ridgefield Park HS; Little Ferry, NJ; (4); 72/180; Church Yth Grp; JV Cheerleading; Var Capt Sftbl; Var Vllybl; William Paterson; Nrsng.

DARBY, CHRISTOPHER; Teaneck HS; Teaneck, NJ; (4); 90/420; Boy Scts; Cmnty Wkr; Drama Clb; Exploring; JA; Bsktbl; Coach Actv; Mgr(s); Score Keeper; Jr NHS; Eagle Scout Awd; Stockton U; Pre-Law.

DARCHI, DEBBI; Central Regional HS; Bayville, NJ; (4); 1/243; Math Clb; Nwsp Stf; Yrbk Bus Mgr; Yrbk Ed-Chief; Var Tennis; Bausch & Lomb Sci Awd; French Hon Soc; Sec NHS; Pres Schlr; Val; SR Mnth Nov 86-87; CIBA-GEIGY Sci Awd 87; Grdn St Distngshd Schlr 86-87; Lebanon Vly Coll; Actrl Sci.

DARCY, KEVIN; Brick Township HS; Brick Town, NJ; (3); 101/486; Church Yth Grp; Political Wkr; Varsity Clb; Var Ftbl; Var Wt Lftg; Engrng.

DARDEN, NATALIE; Clifford J Scott HS; East Orange, NJ; (3); 1/250; Math Tm; Band; Mrchg Band; Nwsp Rptr; Lit Mag; Hon Roll; NHS; Ntl Merit Ltr; Prfct Atten Awd; St Schlr; Hgh Hnrs Frnch III 86; Hnrs Hstry, Engl Frnch IV 86 & 87; Rutgers ST U; Med.

DARECCA, JAMES; Christian Brothers Acad; E Brunswick, NJ; (3); 15/235; Church Yth Grp; Math Tm; Im Bsktbl; Im Sftbl; High Hon Roll; Business.

DAREN, HEATHER; Hamilton H S West; Trenton, NJ; (4); 10/341; Am Leg Aux Girls St; Hosp Aide; VP Intnl Clb; Pres Key Clb; Pres SADD; Madrigals; Rep Stu Cncl; NHS; Radio Clb; Nwsp Stf; Sen Bill Bradley NJ Yng Ctzns Awd 87; Soroptmst Yth Ctznshp Awd & Scholar 87; Trenton ST Coll; Spch Path.

DARIA, LAURA; Paul VI HS; Haddonfield, NJ; (3); 60/418; Church Yth Grp; Drama Clb; Chorus; School Play; Var Fld Hcky; Var Mgr(s); Powder Puff Ftbl; Hon Roll; NHS.

DARMINIO JR, JOSEPH T; Delsea Regional HS; Newfield, NJ; (3); Am Leg Boys St; Key Clb; Varsity Clb; Var Capt Bsbl; Var Capt Ftbl; Var Capt Wrstlng; High Hon Roll; NHS; Boy Scts; Spanish Clb; All-Area, All County, All South Jersey 2nd Tm Ftbll Guard 86-87; Marine Ldrshp Awd 86-87; Atheneum Lge.

DARNELL, JENNIFER; Rancocas Valley Regional HS; Lumberton, NJ; (2); Spanish Clb; Band; JV Cheerleading; Var Tennis; High Hon Roll; Hon Roll; Beauty Cltre.

DARROCH, SHANNON; Sayreville War Memorial HS; Parlin, NJ; (3); French Clb; FBLA; Spanish Clb; Rep Soph Cls; Trk; Hon Roll; Spanish NHS; US Acadc Achvt Awd 85; Berkeley Bus Coll; Bus.

DARTEY, CLEMENCE; Indian Hills HS; Oakland, NJ; (3); Computer Clb; JV Trk; Hon Roll; Law.

DAS, RAJNISH; Cherry Hill HS East; Cherry Hill, NJ; (2); Chess Clb; French Clb; JCL; Latin Clb; Math Tm; Model UN; High Hon Roll; U Of PA; Bus Mgmt.

DASARO, ANDREA; Bloomfield HS; Bloomfield, NJ; (4); 156/443; Drama Clb; Key Clb; Chorus; Color Guard; School Musical; School Play; Yrbk Phtg; Score Keeper; Stat Socr; Stat Wrstlng; Hrn Roll; Elizabethtown Coll; Cmmnctns.

DASGUPTA, SAYANTANI; Montville Twsp HS; Montville, NJ; (3); 1/273; Drama Clb; VP NFL; Science Clb; VP Speech Tm; Chorus; School Musical; School Play; Nwsp Stf; Lit Mag; Gov Hon Prg Awd; 14 Vars NJFL Trphs Pblc Spkng 84-87; 2nd Pl Tagor Soc Poetry Rdng 86; Govnrs Schl Arts Crtv Wrtng 87; Bio.

DASH, BEN; Cinnaminson HS; Cinnaminson, NJ; (3); 91/250; Cmnty Wkr; VP Trs DECA; FBLA; JA; Temple Yth Grp; Varsity Clb; Variety Show; Nwsp Stf; Im Badmtn; Capt Tennis; S Jersey Ten All Star 87; Burlington Cnty Ten Spotlght 87; DECA ST Ldrshp Conf Fnlst 87; Bus.

DASH, NANCY; Clearview Regional HS; Mullica Hill, NJ; (4); DECA; 4-H; JV Var Powder Puff Ftbl; Wilson Coll; Eqstrn Stdys.

DASILVA, ISABEL; St Marys Of The Assumption HS; Elizabeth, NJ; (2); 35/90; Chess Clb; Church Yth Grp; School Play; Rep Soph Cls; Vllybl; Hon Roll; Psych.

DASS, MICHAEL; Hamilton HS East; Trenton, NJ; (4); AFS; Camera Clb; Ftbl; Wrstlng; U MD.

DASTI, SOFIA; Piscataway HS; Piscataway, NJ; (4); 28/509; French Clb; JV Trk; Hon Roll; Jr NHS; NHS; Pres Schlr; Grdn St Dstngshd Schlrshp 87; Rutgers U; Phrmcy.

DAVDA, APARNA TINA; Parsippany Hills HS; Parsippany, NJ; (3); Am Leg Aux Girls St; Cmnty Wkr; Key Clb; Office Aide; Trs Spanish Clb; Yrbk Stf; Lit Mag; Hon Roll; NHS.

DAVENPORT, DANA; Holy Cross HS; Willingboro, NJ; (3); Hosp Aide; Soph Cls; Var Trk; Wt Lftg; JV Cheerleading; Gym; Hon Roll; Rutgers U New Brunswick ; Bio.

DAVENPORT, JAMES; Wall HS; Wall, NJ; (3); 29/286; German Clb; Ski Clb; Bsbl; Ftbl; Wrstlng; High Hon Roll; Hon Roll.

DAVENPORT, JENNIFER; Hunterdon Central HS; South Bound Brook, NJ; (4); 179/560; Stat Lcrss; Stat Socr; Stat Wrstlng; Hon Roll; Philadelphia Coll Text; Acctg.

DAVENPORT, MICHELLE; Mary Help Of Christians Acad; Paterson, NJ; (3); Cmnty Wkr; Computer Clb; NAACP; SADD; Chorus; Lit Mag; Cheerleading; NHS; Girl Scts; Hosp Aide; Rory Sparrows Tommrows Ldrshp Pgm Awd 87; U S Hstry Awd 87; Soclgy Awd 87; Law.

DAVENPORT, PAUL; Rancocas Valley Regional HS; Mt Holly, NJ; (3); 21/316; Cmnty Wkr; Spanish Clb; Band; Concert Band; Mrchg Band; Yrbk Rptr; Yrbk Stf; Stat Lcrss; Hon Roll; NHS; Architecture.

DAVENPORT, TED; Mt Olive Township HS; Flanders, NJ; (4); Ski Clb; VP Varsity Clb; Pres Sr Cls; Var Capt Ice Hcky; Var Capt Socr; Var Capt Tennis; Hon Roll; Mst All Arnd Cls Stu Awd 86-87; Muhlenberg Coll.

DAVENPORT, TONYA; Lincoln HS; Jersey City, NJ; (3); JA; Office Aide; Yrbk Phtg; Yrbk Rptr; Diving; Vllybl.

DAVEY, MAUREEN; St Rose HS; Brick, NJ; (3); Church Yth Grp; Girl Scts; Latin Clb; Math Tm; High Hon Roll; Hon Roll; Girl Sct Gold Awd 87; CYO Cheering Cmpttn 1st Pl 86; Asbury Pk Prss Nwsppr Educ Poetry Cntst 85; Pharmacy.

DAVIDOFF, MARC; Manalapan HS; Englishtown, NJ; (3); Elec.

DAVIDSON, CHRISTINA THERESA; Monsignor Donovan HS; Toms River, NJ; (4); 21/239; Am Leg Aux Girls St; Art Clb; Church Yth Grp; Drama Clb; German Clb; Scholastic Bowl; Spanish Clb; Teachers Aide; Orch; Pep Band; Montclair ST Coll Acadc Tlntd Young 85; Semi-Fnlst NJ Schlrs Prog 87; Bio Awd 85; Psych.

DAVIDSON, DEBRASU; Toms River North HS; Toms River, NJ; (3); 17/459; SADD; Orch; School Musical; Var JV Bsktbl; Mgr(s); Score Keeper; High Hon Roll; Hon Roll; NHS; NJ All ST Orchstra 86-88; NJ Al South Jrsy Rgnl Orchestra 85-87; Acdmc Awd Outstndng Acdmc Achvt Elizabethtown Coll; Phys Thrpy.

DAVIDSON, GUY; Pitman HS; Pitman, NJ; (4); 41/150; Am Leg Boys St; Cmnty Wkr; VP Spanish Clb; L Bsbl; Capt Ftbl; Wt Lftg; L Wrstlng All Tri-County Fullback 85 & 86; All Tri-County Heavywght 85-86; Phys Ed.

DAVIDSON, MICHELLE M; Burlington City HS; Edgewater Pk, NJ (2); Art Clb; FTA; Color Guard; Drill Tm; Mrchg Band; Elem Ed.

DAVIDSON, PATRICIA; Kearny HS; Kearny, NJ; (3); 75/372; Girl Scts Hon Roll; Bloomfield Coll; Paralgl.

DAVIDSON, PETER; Christian Brothers Acad; Pt Pleasant, NJ; (3) Varsity Clb; Chorus; Rep Jr Cls; Im Socr; Im Sftbl; JV Wrstlng; Caldwel Coll Schlrshp 87; Bus.

DAVILA, DIANA; Bayonne HS; Bayonne, NJ; (2); Church Yth Grp Church Choir; Hon Roll; Comp Prgmr.

DAVILA, JACQUELINE; West Orange HS; W Orange, NJ; (3); NFL; School Musical; School Play; Nwsp Rptr; Pres Frsh Cls; VP Soph Cls; Hon Roll; Cmnty Wkr; Stu Cncl; Tennis; Walk America 84-85; Ntl Latin Exam 84-86; Schl Art Cntst 1st Pl 86-87; Lang Cntst, Spanish Poetry 86-87; Intl Bus.

DAVILA, JUAN C; Ridgefield Memorial HS; Miami, FL; (2); Bsktbl; Crs Cntry; Trk; High Hon Roll; Hon Roll; Prfct Atten Awd; 2nd Tm All Leag Crs Cntry 86-87; Arch.

DAVIS, ARTEA; Linden HS; Linden, NJ; (3); Church Yth Grp; Trs FHA; Sec Church Choir; Rep Jr Cls; Rep Stu Cncl; Capt Bsktbl; Score Keeper; High Hon Roll; Hon Roll; NHS; Minorities Engr; Accntng.

DAVIS, CAROL; West Morris Central HS; Long Valley, NJ; (4); Band; Concert Band; Jazz Band; Mrchg Band; Rptr Yrbk Stf; Outstndng Musical Svc Awd 87; Mrchng Band Achiev Awd 84-87; Pfeiffer Coll; Elem Ed.

DAVIS, CHRISTINE; John F Kennedy HS; Willingboro, NJ; (2); Church Yth Grp; JCL; Latin Clb; Band; Church Choir; Concert Band; Jazz Band; Mrchg Band; Orch; Symp Band; Psych.

DAVIS, COLLEEN; Toms River HS East; Toms River, NJ; (4); 34/587; Drama Clb; Math Tm; Thesps; Jazz Band; Mrchg Band; School Musical; Stage Crew; NHS; Ntl Merit Ltr; Key Clb; Acad All Amer 86; Garden ST Dstngshd Schlrs Awd 87; Lehigh U; Comp Sci.

DAVIS, DEANNE; Saint James HS; Paulsboro, NJ; (2); Nwsp Stf; Cheerleading; Fshn Merch.

DAVIS, DEBORAH; Manalapan HS; Manalapan, NJ; (4); Cmnty Wkr; SADD; Temple Yth Grp; Stage Crew; Nwsp Rptr; Nwsp Stf; Lit Mag; Cmnctns.

DAVIS, ELISA; Kingsway Regional HS; Swedesboro, NJ; (3); Pres Church Yth Grp; Debate Tm; Var Capt Cheerleading; Powder Puff Ftbl; Var Trk; Wt Lftg; Stat Wrstlng; High Hon Roll; Hon Roll; NHS; Govnrs Schl Schlr Fut Of NJ Pub Issues 87; U Chicago; Lwyr.

DAVIS, ERICKA; Clifford J Scott HS; East Orange, NJ; (3); Cmnty Wkr; Exploring; JA; Cheerleading; Hon Roll; Commndtn US Hist 86-87; Intntl Bus.

DAVIS, GLENN H; Park Ridge HS; Park Ridge, NJ; (4); 48/106; AFS; VP Temple Yth Grp; Ed Lit Mag; Var L Socr; Hon Roll; Boston U; Cmmncntns.

DAVIS, GREGG S; Sayreville War Memorial HS; Parlin, NJ; (4); 27/363; Am Leg Boys St; Lit Mag; Var Diving; Var Capt Socr; Var Swmmng; Var Capt Trk; Cit Awd; Hon Roll; Lion Awd; NHS; All St Choris NJ 85 & 86; U Of DE; Bio.

DAVIS, GREGORY; Burlington County Vo Tech; Willingboro, NJ; (3); 5/192; Pres Computer Clb; FBLA; VICA; Im Ftbl; Im Socr; Im Sftbl; Im Vllybl; Hon Roll; NHS; Prfct Atten Awd; Air Force Acad; Pilot.

DAVIS, HEATHER; Sparta HS; Sparta, NJ; (3); Church Yth Grp; Hosp Aide; Key Clb; Stage Crew; Var Socr; Grad Barbizon Schl Modeling 86; Nursing.

DAVIS, JEFF; Manalapan HS; Manalapan, NJ; (4); Trs Church Yth Grp; JCL; Stage Crew; NJ Socty Public Accntnt Schlrshp 87; Pennsylvania ST U; Bus Mgmt.

DAVIS, LAUREN M; Immaculate Conception HS; Ridgefield Prk, NJ; (3); Church Yth Grp; Q&S; Ski Clb; SADD; Nwsp Phtg; Nwsp Rptr; Trs Frsh Cls; Rep Soph Cls; Rep Jr Cls; Quill & Scroll 86 & 87; Stu Cncl 85-87; Snow Capt 86 & 87; Bus.

DAVIS, LOUISE JANINE; Hamilton HS West; Trenton, NJ; (4); 42/309; Computer Clb; FBLA; Key Clb; Yrbk Stf; Badmtn; Stat Bsktbl; Mgr(s); Powder Puff Ftbl; Vllybl; Hon Roll; Exclinc Thrgh Educ Schlrshp 87; Douglass Coll; Comp Sci.

DAVIS, MARC; Bridgewater-Raritan West HS; Bridgewater, NJ; (4); Cmnty Wkr; Capt Math Tm; Sec Temple Yth Grp; Thesps; Nwsp Stf; Pres Soph Cls; Computer Clb; Drama Clb; Intnl Clb; Quiz Bowl; Bill Bradly Yng Ctzns Awd 87; Comp Sci Awd 87; U Of DE; Bus Admin.

DAVIS, MARIANNA; Salem HS; Salem, NJ; (4); 23/107; Library Aide; Teachers Aide; Thesps; Chorus; School Play; Stage Crew; Yrbk Stf; Hon Roll; NHS; U Of DE; Vet.

DAVIS, MARK G; Highland Park HS; Highland Park, NJ; (3); 17/123; Am Leg Boys St; Church Yth Grp; French Clb; Church Choir; Yrbk Rptr; Var Capt Crs Cntry; Var Capt Trk; High Hon Roll; Hon Roll; All Cnty Crs Cntry 86; MVP Crs Cntry 86; Chem Engrng.

DAVIS, MATTHEW D; Ocean Twp HS; Ocean, NJ; (3); 32/330; Church Yth Grp; Ski Clb; Ftbl; Wt Lftg; Wrstlng; High Hon Roll; NHS; Spartn Schlr 85-86; Cert Athltc Trnr 85-87; Ldrshp Pgm; Orthopedc Surgn.

DAVIS, MICHAEL; Bricktown HS; Brick Town, NJ; (3); 77/477; Drama Clb; German Clb; SADD; Church Choir; School Play; Variety Show; Var Crs Cntry; JV Socr; Var Trk; Hon Roll; Bus Mrktng.

DAVIS, MICHAEL SCOTT; Washington Township HS; Sewell, NJ; (4); Church Yth Grp; German Clb; Var JV Socr; Im Wrstlng; Messiah Coll; Bus Admin.

DAVIS, RANDY; Dover HS; Mine Hill, NJ; (3); 17/200; AFS; Debate Tm; German Clb; Math Tm; School Musical; School Play; Nwsp Sprt Ed; Trs Stu Cncl; JV Wrstlng; Hon Roll; Elec Engrng.

DAVIS, REGINA; Bridgeton HS; Bridgeton, NJ; (3); Library Aide; Teachers Aide; Church Choir; School Play; High Hon Roll; Hon Roll; Prfct Atten Awd; Comp Pgmmr.

DAVIS, ROLAND; Lakewood HS; Lakewood, NJ; (3); Latin Clb; Letterman Clb; Radio Clb; Spanish Clb; Varsity Clb; Socr; Hon Roll; Prfct Atten Awd; All ST 86; All Shr 86; Bus Mgmt.

DAVIS, RUSSELL; Holy Spirit HS; Absecon, NJ; (4); 52/363; Church Yth Grp; Var L Trk; Bus Adm.

DAVIS, SHARON; Lakewood HS; Lakewood, NJ; (3); 37/370; Church Yth Grp; English Clb; Var Tennis; High Hon Roll; Hon Roll; Vrsty Ltr Ten 86; Lat Hnr Soc Inductee 87; Bus Mgmt.

DAVIS, STEPHANY; Passaic County Tech VHS; Paterson, NJ; (3); 43/523; Rep Stu Cncl; JV Var Sftbl; Comp Pgmr.

DAVIS, TAMMY; Lower Cape May Regional HS; N Cape May, NJ; (4); Im Bsktbl; Capt Var Sftbl; Im Tennis; Var Im Vllybl; High Hon Roll; Hon Roll; All S Jersey 1st Tm Sftbl 85-86; All Cap Atlantic Lg Sftbl; Acad Achvt Awd 87; Elon Coll; Hstry.

DAVIS, TAMMY; Westwood HS; Westwood, NJ; (2); 10/200; Church Yth Grp; Band; Concert Band; Mrchg Band; Pep Band; JV Vllybl; High Hon Roll; Hon Roll; Knights Columbus Splng Bee 1st Prz 85; Hnrs Cls 85-87; Law.

DAVIS, TREENA; New Brunswick HS; New Brunswick, NJ; (4); #2 In Class; Yrbk Ed-Chief; VP Frsh Cls; VP Soph Cls; Var Bsktbl; Var Cheerleading; Var Trk; NHS; Sal; St Schlr; Voice Dem Awd.

DAVIS, VALERIE; Baptist HS; Woodbury Hts, NJ; (3); Church Yth Grp; Drama Clb; Chorus; School Play; Stage Crew; Hon Roll; JV Bsktbl.

DAVIS, VANESSA; Eastside HS; Paterson, NJ; (3); 3/600; Debate Tm; Pres Leo Clb; Science Clb; Church Choir; Mrchg Band; Yrbk Stf; VP Sr Cls; JV Crs Cntry; Mgr(s); Var Trk; Natl Merit Sci Awd Schlrshp 86; Miss Amer Coed Pgnt Trphy 87; Cornell U Minorty Engrng Pgm 86; Spelman Coll; Pre Law.

DAVIS, VICKI; Toms River East HS; Toms River, NJ; (3); 40/509; Exploring; Hosp Aide; Socr; Hon Roll; Phrmcst.

DAVIS, VINCENT; St Anthony HS; Jersey Cty, NJ; (3); Math Tm; JV Bsbl; Im Bsktbl; Var Bowling; Im Vllybl; Math Hnr Awd 87; Rutgers; Bus Adm.

DAVIS, VIRGIL; Mt Lakes HS; Fulton, MD; (3); 6/110; Aud/Vis; Math Clb; Science Clb; Band; Stage Crew; JV Trk; High Hon Roll; NHS; Ntl Merit SF; Physics ST Sci Day 87; Chem Leag 86; U MO Kansas City Schl Of Med.

DAWKINS, SANDRA; Plainfield HS; Plainfield, NJ; (2); Chorus; Rep Soph Cls; JV Mgr(s); Hon Roll; Alpha Theta Feta Teen Awd 87; De Vry; Word Processing.

DAWLEY, NANCY; Delaware Valley Regional HS; Pittstown, NJ; (3); 16/200; Am Leg Aux Girls St; Art Clb; Varsity Clb; Chrmn Jr Cls; Var L Fld Hcky; Var Capt Trk; High Hon Roll; NHS; All DRC Trk & Fld Hckey 86-87; Consmr Affrs.

DAWNSON, MARY; Cumberland Regional HS; Bridgeton, NJ; (4); Church Yth Grp; Joe Kubert Graphic Arts Schl.

DAWSON, KRISTA; Salem HS; Salem, NJ; (3); Art Clb; Computer Clb; Latin Clb; Ski Clb; Spanish Clb; SADD; Yrbk Stf; Trs Sr Cls; Hon Roll; NHS; Schltc Achvt Ad 84-85; Interior Dsgn.

DAWSON, MICHELE; Egg Harbor Township HS; Cardiff, NJ; (3); Pres Trs 4-H; Trs Math Clb; SADD; Drill Tm; Rep Soph Cls; Rep Jr Cls; Rep Stu Cncl; Jr NHS; Sec Computer Clb; EHTHS Top Wmns Bwlr, & Yrbk Actvts Ed 86-87; Phrmcy.

DAY, CHRISTOPHER; Delaware Valley Regional HS; Milford, NJ; (4); Key Clb; Q&S; Varsity Clb; Nwsp Sprt Ed; Var L Ftbl; Var L Wrstlng; Marine Corps Distngshd Athl Awd 87; US Marine Corps; Avionics.

DAY, PAMELA; St John Vianney HS; Colts Neck, NJ; (2); Ski Clb; School Play; Yrbk Stf; Rep Stu Cncl; JV Bsktbl; Mgr(s); High Hon Roll; Spanish NHS; 3rd Pl St Spnsh Cmptn 86; 4th Pl St Spnsh Cmptn 87; JV Athltc Awd 87; Intl Bus.

DE AMBROSE, JOANNE; Belleville HS; Belleville, NJ; (3); Spanish Clb; Chorus; Var JV Bsktbl; Mgr Crs Cntry; Var JV Trk; Hon Roll; Early Chldhd Educ.

DE ANGELIS, ANDREA; Paul IV HS; Turnersville, NJ; (3); 180/480; Church Yth Grp; Cmnty Wkr; Fld Hcky; Socr; S Jersey Girls Select Soccer Team 86-87; Athl Trng.

DE ANGELO, JO ANN; St James HS; Woodstown, NJ; (3); School Musical; Nwsp Rptr; Var JV Cheerleading; NHS; Glassboro ST Coll; Math Tchr.

DE BACCO, JANINE; Montville Twp HS; Pine Brook, NJ; (2); Art Clb; Computer Clb; Key Clb; Office Aide; Nwsp Stf; Lit Mag; JV Sftbl; High Hon Roll; Hon Roll; Pres Schlr.

DE BACKER, LAURA; Bernards HS; Bernardsville, NJ; (3); 33/185; Church Yth Grp; SADD; Church Choir; Color Guard; Mrchg Band; School Musical; Im Fld Hcky; Hon Roll.

DE BARI, ANTONELLE; Ridgefield Park HS; Little Ferry, NJ; (3); 5/215; Am Leg Aux Girls St; FBLA; Library Aide; Nwsp Rptr; Ed Yrbk Rptr; Rep Soph Cls; Rep Jr Cls; High Hon Roll; Hon Roll; NHS; Ntl Sci Olympiad Awd 86 & 87; NJ Sci Tchrs Assoc Awd 86; Rotary Yth Ldrshp Awd 87; Bus Adm.

DE BARI, MARTA M; South Brunswick HS; Kendall Pk, NJ; (3); Sec FHA; Math Tm; Mu Alpha Theta; Spanish Clb; Band; Crs Cntry; Trk; Hon Roll; NHS; Spanish NHS; 3rd Pl Stu Bdy Comp NJ ST FHA 86; Engrng.

DE BARO JR, JAMES; Brick Twp HS; Brick, NJ; (3); 114/471; Boy Scts; Ski Clb; Ryder Coll; Acctg.

DE BELLA, CANDICE; Highland Regional HS; Blackwood, NJ; (3); Trs French Clb; Hosp Aide; Mrchg Band; Yrbk Stf; Stu Cncl; Pom Pon; Rutgers U; Nrs.

DE BENEDETTO, DENISE; Toms River North HS; Toms River, NJ; (3); 52/458; Band; Mrchg Band; Stage Crew; Symp Band; Nwsp Rptr; Nwsp Stf; Off Frsh Cls; Off Soph Cls; Mgr(s); Hon Roll; Jrnlsm.

DE BLASI, FRANK; Manalapan HS; Manalapan, NJ; (3); Rep Sr Cls; Capt JV Bsbl; JV Ftbl; Hon Roll; Rutgers; Dentistry.

DE BLIECK, MARY; Manchester Regional HS; N Haledon, NJ; (1); Church Yth Grp; Rep Frsh Cls; Hon Roll; Intl Frgn Lang Awds 86.

DE BRUNO, ROSA; Mary Help Of Christian Acad; Mahwah, NJ; (4); Cmnty Wkr; Computer Clb; JCL; Latin Clb; Service Clb; SADD; Rep Sr Cls; Hon Roll; NHS; Maxima Cum Laude Natl Latin Exmntn 86; Italian 2 Yrs Engl 3 Yrs; Phar.

DE CANDIA, ROSEMARIE; Memorial HS; West New York, NJ; (3); FTA; JA; Spanish Clb; Rep Frsh Cls; Rep Soph Cls; Rep Jr Cls; Rep Stu Cncl; High Hon Roll; NHS; Ntl Merit Ltr; Jersey City ST Coll; Erly Chld.

DE CARLO, ANTHONY; Brick Memorial HS; Brick, NJ; (1); High Hon Roll; St Johns; Comp Sys Anlyst.

DE CARLO, TAMMY; Paramus HS; Paramus, NJ; (4); Church Yth Grp; Drama Clb; German Clb; Ski Clb; Yrbk Sprt Ed; Yrbk Stf; Rep Frsh Cls; Rep Stu Cncl; Socr; Rutgers; Pltcl Jrnslm.

DE CARLO, YVONNE; Wood-Ridge HS; Wood Ridge, NJ; (4); 6/75; Art Clb; Spanish Clb; Yrbk Stf; JV Bsktbl; Var Capt Sftbl; Var Capt Vllybl; High Hon Roll; NHS; De Vry; Comp.

DE CASTRO, JENNIFER; Manasquan HS; Sea Girt, NJ; (3); FBLA; Key Clb; Yrbk Stf; Stu Cncl; JV Bsktbl; JV Var Fld Hcky; JV Socr; JV Var Sftbl; High Hon Roll; Drama Clb; Acad Achvt 84-87.

DE CAUSEY, LAFAYETTE; Lakewood HS; Lakewood, NJ; (3); 150/351; Var Ftbl; Var Wrstlng; Comp Sci.

DE CESARE, R; Blair Acad; Portland, PA; (4); Ski Clb; Pres Concert Band; Mrchg Band; Rep Jr Cls; Trk; Wt Lftg; High Hon Roll; Lions Clb Ldrshp Seminar 86; Penn ST; Med.

DE CINQUE, JULIE; St James HS; Salem, NJ; (2); 15/93; SADD; Yrbk Stf; Trs Frsh Cls; Pres Soph Cls; Stat Bsbl; Var Bsktbl; Var Fld Hcky; Hon Roll; Physcl Ftnss Awd Frshmn 84-85.

DE COSTE, CHRISTINA; Middlesex HS; Middlesex, NJ; (4); 9/157; Girl Scts; Pres Key Clb; Pres Chorus; School Musical; Nwsp Stf; Capt Crs Cntry; High Hon Roll; Sec NHS; JV Trk; Gettysburg Pres Schlr 87; Gettysburg Coll.

DE COSTER, DAPHNE; Belvidere HS; Belvidere, NJ; (4); 6/150; VP Church Yth Grp; Drama Clb; Pres Band; Chorus; Drm Mjr(t); Madrigals; Pres Mrchg Band; School Musical; Hon Roll; NHS; Eng Hist Awd 84 & 85; Gov Schl Of Arts 86; Physical Therapy.

DE FILIPPIS, EILEEN; Manchester Regional HS; Haledon, NJ; (4); 5/156; Math Clb; Scholastic Bowl; Chorus; Capt Flag Corp; Madrigals; Score Keeper; Trk; Hon Roll; NHS; Pres Schlr; U Scranton Pres Schlrshp 87-88; U Scranton; Frgn Lang.

DE FILIPPIS, JILENE; Monsignor Donovan HS; Bayville, NJ; (3); 47/245; Pep Clb; SADD; Yrbk Stf; Rep Stu Cncl; Var Capt Bsktbl; Var Crs Cntry; Socr; Hon Roll; NHS; Rep Soph Cls; All Cnty Socr 87; All Class C Bsktbll 87; Hosptlty Mngmnt.

DE FREESE, CHRISTINE; Mahwah HS; Mahwah, NJ; (2); Girl Scts; Hon Roll; Spanish NHS; Ed.

DE FREESE, DAVID A; Rahway HS; Rahway, NJ; (4); 11/227; Model UN; Spanish Clb; Band; Jazz Band; Mrchg Band; Pep Band; VP Sr Cls; Mgr(s); Tennis; Mgr Wrstlng; Perfct Attndnc 85-86; Princeton U; Mech Engr.

DE GENNARO, ELIZABETH; Hoboken SR HS; Hoboken, NJ; (3); Teachers Aide; Band; Concert Band; Mrchg Band; Rep Stu Cncl; Var JV Bowling; Var Tennis.

DE GENNARO, GUY; Hudson Catholic HS; Jersey City, NJ; (3); 3/180; Science Clb; SADD; Var Swmmng; Hon Roll; NHS; De La Salle Schlrshp 84-88; 1st Pl Cummltve Scre Hudson Cnty Sci Tm 87.

DE GENNARO, JOSEPH; St Josephs Of The Palisades HS; N Bergen, NJ; (3); Band; Concert Band; Mrchg Band; Var Ftbl; High Hon Roll.

DE GREGORY, MARK; Ewing HS; W Trenton, NJ; (3); Band; Concert Band; Jazz Band; Orch; Nwsp Stf; Trs Soph Cls; JV Socr; Hon Roll; Knights Of Columbus Merit Awd 86 & 87; Stu Of Mnth Awd 86; Lib Arts.

DE GROAT, SANDRA; Toms River HS North; Toms River, NJ; (3); 50/459; Political Wkr; SADD; Chorus; Yrbk Phtg; Yrbk Stf; Stu Cncl; Sftbl; High Hon Roll; Hon Roll; Acadmc Ltr 87; Psych.

DE HART, HEATHER; Toms River HS East; Toms River, NJ; (4); Church Yth Grp; Dance Clb; Drama Clb; Science Clb; Church Choir; Color Guard; Mrchg Band; School Play; Var Pom Pon; Ocean Cnty Coll; Bus Admin.

DE JURA, CARLA MARIE; Union HS; Union, NJ; (2); Pres Art Clb; Church Yth Grp; Cmnty Wkr; Chorus; Color Guard; Drill Tm; Flag Corp; Mrchg Band; Hon Roll; Schl Lttr For Art Clb & Chorus 86; Vet Med.

DE LA CRUZ, ANNE; Bishop George Ahr HS; Edison, NJ; (4); Cmnty Wkr; French Clb; Ski Clb; Spanish Clb; SADD; Rep Frsh Cls; Sec Stu Cncl; Vllybl; High Hon Roll; Hon Roll; Dickinson Coll.

DE LA CRUZ, ENRIQUE M; Kearny HS; Kearny, NJ; (4); 25/383; Computer Clb; Math Tm; Rep Jr Cls; Hon Roll; NHS; Sci Olympd Tsts; ST Sci Leg Tst; Boys STALTRNT; Rutgers; Mlclr Bio.

DE LA CRUZ, IVETTE; St Mary Of Assumption HS; Elizabeth, NJ; (3); School Musical; School Play; Yrbk Ed-Chief; Rep Frsh Cls; Rep Soph Cls; Rep Jr Cls; Sec Sr Cls; Cheerleading; Hon Roll; NHS; Bio.

DE LA CRUZ, MICHAEL S; Perth Amboy HS; Perth Amboy, NJ; (4); 75/269; Chess Clb; French Clb; Key Clb; Ski Clb; Rep Soph Cls; Rep Jr Cls; Rep Sr Cls; Var Bowling; Var Tennis; JV Trk; St Johns U; Bus Admin.

DE LA ROI, COLLEEN; Florence Twp Memorial HS; Roebling, NJ; (3); FBLA; GAA; JV Var Fld Hcky; Hon Roll; Natl Bus Hnr Scty 87; Century 21 Acctng Cert Of Prof 87; Mgmt.

DE LATORRE, MICHELLE; St Josephs Of The Palaside; Guttenberg, NJ; (3); Yrbk Stf; JV Cheerleading; Var Sftbl; JV Swmmng; Acad All Amer 86; Natl Sci Merit Awds 86 & 87; Pre-Med.

DE LEON, SANDEE; Spotswood HS; Spotswood, NJ; (2); 8/127; Intnl Clb; Concert Band; Mrchg Band; Nwsp Stf; Stat Bsbl; JV Cheerleading; Stat Ftbl; JV Var Mgr(s); Hon Roll; Most Spirited 85-86; Mrktng.

DE LONG, LARA; Kittatinny Regional HS; Newton, NJ; (4); 2/224; Concert Band; School Musical; Bausch & Lomb Sci Awd; Gov Hon Prg Awd; High Hon Roll; NHS; Ntl Merit SF; Rotary Awd; Sal; St Schlr; Cornell U-Coll Art/Sci; Bio.

DE LORENZO, BRIAN T; Nottingham HS; Mercerville, NJ; (3); AFS; Am Leg Boys St; VP FBLA; Nwsp Sprt Ed; Wrstlng; Boston U; Comm.

DE LOS REYES, MARC; Marist HS; Jersey City, NJ; (3); 7/104; Hon Roll; NHS; 1st Hnr 84-86; Cvl Engr.

DE LUCA, SCOTT C; Nutley HS; Nutley, NJ; (4); 70/335; Am Leg Boys St; Key Clb; Spanish Clb; Stu Cncl; Im Bsbl; Var Bsktbl; Capt Ftbl; Im Sftbl; Im Vllybl; Im Wt Lftg; Full Schlrshp Ftbl Duke U 87; Duke; Bus.

DE LUCCIO, KIM; Vernon Township HS; Vernon, NJ; (3); Band; Concert Band; Jazz Band; Mrchg Band; School Musical; Symp Band; JV Trk; High Hon Roll; Hon Roll; NHS; Govrnrs Schl Of Arts NJ 87; All ST Wind Ens NJ 87; Hartt Summer Music Prog Orch 86; Music.

DE LUCIA, BRIAN; Union HS; Union, NJ; (3); Boys Clb Am; Church Yth Grp; Computer Clb; FBLA; Wt Lftg; Hon Roll; FBL Rgnl Comptn Accntng II 87; Hnr Roll 85-87; Distngshd Amer Stu Soc; Accntng.

DE LUCIA, DONNA M; Spotswood HS; Spotswood, NJ; (2); Girl Scts; Intnl Clb; Orch; Nwsp Stf; Var L Socr; Var L Trk; High Hon Roll; Hon Roll; Sci Lge Bio Tm 85-86.

DE MAIRA, ELAINE; Red Bank Catholic HS; Colts Neck, NJ; (4); 53/311; Intnl Clb; Spanish Clb; SADD; Teachers Aide; Nwsp Stf; Yrbk Stf; High Hon Roll; Hon Roll; Spanish NHS; Acctg I Hghst Hnr Awd 87; Loyola Coll; Lib Art.

DE MANSS, TONI; West Milford HS; West Milford, NJ; (3); 106/400; Art Clb; French Clb; Office Aide; Varsity Clb; Band; Mrchg Band; Yrbk Stf; Off Stu Cncl; Var JV Cheerleading; Prom Comm 87; Advrtsng Dsgn.

DE MARCO, ROBERT; Matawan Regional HS; Matawan, NJ; (3); 87/302; Boy Scts; Chess Clb; Church Yth Grp; Speech Tm; Stage Crew; Comp Engr.

DE MARCO, TONI ANN; Lakeland Regional HS; Wanaque, NJ; (3); Cmnty Wkr; Math Clb; SADD; Sec Soph Cls; Off Jr Cls; Off Sr Cls; Rep Stu Cncl; Var L Cheerleading; High Hon Roll; Ski Clb; Intl Cheerg Comptn 3rd Pl & Fnlst Nashvl TN 85-86; Road Shw Rep Schl At Othr Schls 86-87.

DE MARIA, FRANK; Marist HS; Bayonne, NJ; (3); 10/130; Bsktbl; Ftbl; Ice Hcky; Hon Roll; Ntl Merit Ltr; Engnrng.

DE MARRAIS, JENNIFER A; Teaneck HS; Teaneck, NJ; (4); 3/400; Church Yth Grp; Dance Clb; SADD; School Play; Nwsp Stf; Yrbk Ed-Chief; Stu Cncl; JV Sftbl; NHS; Ntl Merit SF; Garden ST Distngshd Schlr.

DE MARTINO, DAWN FRANCINE; Morris Catholic HS; Landing, NJ; (3); Church Yth Grp; French Clb; Natl Beta Clb; Nwsp Stf; Crs Cntry; Hon Roll; Best Essay 85; Engl.

DE MARY, ANGELA; Buena Regional HS; Richland, NJ; (2); NAACP; Hon Roll; Lamp Of Knowledge Lettr; Cultural Clb; Gifted And Talented; Law.

DE MATTEO, NICHOLAS; Highland Regional HS; Clementon, NJ; (4); 1/250; Aud/Vis; Pres Drama Clb; Trs Key Clb; VP Thesps; School Musical; School Play; VP Jr Cls; VP Sr Cls; Hon Roll; NHS; Mason-Gross; Actng.

DE MAYO, RALPH; Hanover Park HS; East Hanover, NJ; (3); Church Yth Grp; Ftbl; Hon Roll; Lang Arts III Hgh Achvt Awd 86; Accntng.

DE MIGLIO, DAWN; St Peters HS; New Brunswick, NJ; (4); Cmnty Wkr; Hosp Aide; Intnl Clb; Office Aide; Stage Crew; Yrbk Stf; Lit Mag; Gym; Hon Roll; TCI Schlrshp Awd 87; Middlesex Coll; Comp Pgmmng.

DE NICOLO, MARINA; New Milford HS; New Milford, NJ; (3); 39/150; VP French Clb; Girl Scts; Ski Clb; SADD; Varsity Clb; Band; Yrbk Stf; Rep Jr Cls; Rep Stu Cncl; Stat Bsktbl; Home Ec Acadmc Awd 86-87; HS Svc Awd 85-86; Elks Yth Day Awd 86; Mgmt.

DE NOIA, LAUREN; Bishop George Ahr/STA HS; Colonia, NJ; (4); French Clb; Science Clb; Teachers Aide; Pres Stu Cncl; Crs Cntry; Capt Sftbl; Hon Roll; Ldrshp Awd 87; All Conf Athlt 86; Rider Coll; Bus.

DE NUZZO, MARY ANNE; Southern Regional HS; Barnegat, NJ; (3); Cmnty Wkr; Hosp Aide; Band; Mrchg Band; JV Var Bsktbl; Var Mgr(s); JV Var Socr; Sftbl; Sprtsmnshp Awd-Socr 85; Elem Tchng.

DE OLD, CRAIG; Fair Lawn HS; Fairlawn, NJ; (2); Boy Scts; Church Yth Grp; Band; Concert Band; Mrchg Band; Rep Stu Cncl; JV Crs Cntry; Var L Swmmng; Var L Trk; Mst Imprvd Instrmntlst 87; Music.

DE PALMA, DANA; Fair Lawn HS; Fair Lawn, NJ; (3); 110/342; French Clb; JV Swmmng; JV Var Vllybl; Rutgers; Bus Mgmnt.

DE PETRIS, ANGELA; Arthur L Johnson Regional HS; Clark, NJ; (3); 43/189; Church Yth Grp; Sec Spanish Clb; Nwsp Rptr; Nwsp Stf; JV Var Cheerleading; JV Sftbl; Hon Roll; Spanish NHS; Jrnlsm.

DE PUY, CAROL; Immaculate Heart Acad; Allendale, NJ; (4); 51/165; Drama Clb; Exploring; Speech Tm; School Musical; Yrbk Stf; Var Hon Roll; Prfct Atten Awd; St Michaels Coll; Polit Sci.

DE RIENZO, DENISE; Paramus Catholic HS; Garfield, NJ; (4); 8/169; Cmnty Wkr; Dance Clb; 4-H; Library Aide; Church Choir; Elks Awd; 4-H Awd; Gov Hon Prg Awd; High Hon Roll; NHS; William Paterson; Elem Ed.

DE ROSA, CLARE; Glen Rock HS; Glen Rock, NJ; (3); French Clb; Nwsp Stf; Lit Mag; Var Vllybl; Hon Roll; Jr NHS; NHS.

DE SANDRE, JENNIFER; West Windsor Plainsboro HS; Cranbury, NJ; (3); Pres Sec 4-H; 4-H Awd; Hon Roll; Bus Adm.

DE SANTIS, JOLYN R; Rancocos Vly Reg HS; Vincentown, NJ; (4); Church Yth Grp; Spanish Clb; Ed Yrbk Stf; Lit Mag; JV Fld Hcky; Var Trk; High Hon Roll; Hon Roll; Pres Schlrshp Fairleigh-Dickinson 87; Montclair ST Coll; Mrktng.

DE SIMONE, TERESA; North Bergen HS; North Bergen, NJ; (3); Boy Scts; VP Church Yth Grp; Girl Scts; Teachers Aide; Band; Concert Band; Mrchg Band; Hon Roll; Jr NHS; NHS; Italian Hnr Scty 86-87; Early Educ.

DE SIMONE, TINA; Buena Regional HS; Collings Lakes, NJ; (4); 6/180; Math Clb; Ski Clb; Yrbk Stf; Rep Frsh Cls; Rep Soph Cls; Rep Jr Cls; Rep Stu Cncl; NHS; Natl Sci Merit Awd; Dental Hyg.

DE SOI, KANDICE; Pitman HS; Pitman, NJ; (3); 6/140; Church Yth Grp; Dance Clb; Teachers Aide; School Musical; Yrbk Phtg; JV Fld Hcky; Cit Awd; High Hon Roll; Hon Roll; NHS; Glassboro ST; Math.

DE SOLA, JAMEL; St Marys HS; Jersey, NJ; (3); Church Yth Grp; Cmnty Wkr; NAACP; Rep Frsh Cls; Mgr(s); Hon Roll; Comp Awd 84; Phy.

DE SOUSA, SHARON; Southern Regional HS; Barnegat, NJ; (3); Powder Puff Ftbl; Hon Roll; Commnctns.

DE STEFANO, LAURA; Hunterdon Central HS; White House Sta, NJ; (3); 79/543; Var L Bsktbl; Var L Fld Hcky; Var Capt Sftbl; Hon Roll; NHS.

DE STEFANO, ROBERT R; Spotswood HS; Spotswood, NJ; (3); Church Yth Grp; Intnl Clb; Science Clb; JV Var Socr; Trk; High Hon Roll; Hon Roll; NHS; Spanish NHS; Arch.

DE VINCENZO, ANN MARIE; Ridgefield Memorial HS; Ridgefield, NJ; (1); FHA; FTA; SADD; Church Choir; School Play; Off Frsh Cls; Badmtn; Swmmng; Cit Awd; Prfct Atten Awd; Jersey City ST Coll; Tchr.

DE VIRGILIO, PATRICIA ANNE; Parsippany Hills HS; Morris Plains, NJ; (4); 58/302; FBLA; Chorus; Variety Show; Yrbk Stf; Rep Frsh Cls; Rep Soph Cls; Rep Jr Cls; Rep Sr Cls; Var Powder Puff Ftbl; Hon Roll; FBLA Comp Regnl 8th Pl 86; FBLA Regnl & ST Comp 87; U S FL; Elem Ed.

DE VIVO, PAUL J; Randolph HS; Columbia, MD; (4); 21/360; Church Yth Grp; School Musical; Nwsp Rptr; Ftbl; Wrstlng; High Hon Roll; Hon Roll; NHS; Ntl Merit SF.

DE VOE, DANIELLE; Cumberland Regional HS; Bridgeton, NJ; (3); VP Church Yth Grp; JCL; Science Clb; Ski Clb; Chorus; Church Choir; Mrchg Band; High Hon Roll; Hon Roll; NHS; Ntnl Ltn Exm Of Hnrbl Mrt 85; Dntrstry.

DE YONGE, DEBORAH A; Cherry Hill HS East; Cherry Hill, NJ; (4); FBLA; Nwsp Ed-Chief; Crs Cntry; Lcrss; NJ Gov Awd 84; Hnrbl Mntn Natl Schltc Writng Awd 83; 2nd Pl NJ Crftsmn Fair 85; RI Schl Dsgn; Arch.

DEAN, DAVID; Lakeland Regional HS; Ringwood, NJ; (4); 93/365; Aud/Vis; Church Yth Grp; Letterman Clb; Red Cross Aide; Varsity Clb; Nwsp Stf; Yrbk Stf; Var Bsbl; Var Bsktbl; Hon Roll; Glassboro ST Coll.

DEANE, KAREN; Hightstown HS; E Windsor, NJ; (4); 32/441; French Clb; Ski Clb; Drill Tm; Rep Frsh Cls; Rep Soph Cls; Rep Jr Cls; Rep Sr Cls; Off Stu Cncl; JV Trk; NHS; Hgh Hnr Roll 83-87; Le High U; Econ.

DEANGELIS, MARISA; Parsippany Hills HS; Parsippany, NJ; (3); AFS; Cmnty Wkr; Trs German Clb; Political Wkr; Service Clb; Mdcl.

DEAS, GEOFFREY S; Rumson Fair Haven Regional HS; Rumson, NJ; (3); 57/231; Am Leg Boys St; Exploring; Varsity Clb; Stage Crew; Var Bowling; Cit Awd; Hon Roll; Cngrsnl Awd-Bronze 85; Cngrsnl Awd-Silver 86; Bill Bradley Outstndng Yng Ctzn 86.

DEATON, FRED; Paul Vi HS; Barrington, NJ; (3); 73/418; Im Crs Cntry; Hon Roll; Olympic Conf Chmpnshps 84 Plcd 15th; Bus.

DEAVER, JOHN; Notre Dame HS; Creamridge, NJ; (2); Drama Clb; Acpl Chr; Chorus; Madrigals; School Musical; School Play; Variety Show; Rep Frsh Cls; Rep Soph Cls.

DEBARI, NICK; Secaucus HS; Secaucus, NJ; (2); 25/125; Math Clb; Mu Alpha Theta; Varsity Clb; Var Bsbl; Var Bsktbl; Wt Lftg; Hon Roll; Vrsty Bsktbl, Bsbl 86-87.

DEBBS, JAMES W; Governor Livingston Regional HS; Berkeley Height, NJ; (4); 70/170; Drama Clb; Ski Clb; School Play; Yrbk Stf; Lit Mag; Tennis; Hon Roll; Hnrbl Ment Ntl Merit Schlr 86-87; Stu Run Berkeley Hts Day 87; U Richmond; Lib Arts.

DEBIAK, DEBBIE; Mary Help Of Christians Acad; West Paterson, NJ; (3); Pres JCL; Letterman Clb; Pres Jr Cls; Stu Cncl; Im Sftbl; Tennis; NHS; NEDT Awd; Ntl Latin Hnr Scty; Intl Affairs.

DEBONIS, FRANK; Northern Valley Regional HS; Harrington Pk, NJ; (3); 34/273; Var Capt Crs Cntry; Var Capt Trk; Hon Roll; NHS; Ntl Merit SF; Comms.

DEBUTIS, ERIN; Randolph HS; Randolph, NJ; (3); 135/352; Debate Tm; 4-H; Red Cross Aide; Speech Tm; Varsity Clb; Nwsp Stf; Crs Cntry; Trk; 4-H Awd; Hon Roll; Kate Peaslee Mem Sptsmnshp Hrsmnshp Awd 86; All-Area All-Cnty Grls Trck Tm 86; Outstndng Rnr 85-86; Sci.

DECKER, CHRISTINE; Notre Dame HS; East Windsor, NJ; (3); Hosp Aide; Varsity Clb; Nwsp Rptr; Rep Frsh Cls; Rep Jr Cls; Var L Gym; Mgr(s); Stat Wrstlng; High Hon Roll; Hon Roll; MI Gymnst 86; Engl Excel 86.

DECKER, DEBRA; Highland Rgnl; Sicklerville, NJ; (4); 12/297; French Clb; Service Clb; Office Aide; SADD; Varsity Clb; Stu Cncl; Var Cheerleading; Hon Roll; NHS; Seton Hall; Accntng.

DECKER, RUDY; Gloucester Catholic HS; Brooklawn, NJ; (3); Am Leg Boys St; Nwsp Stf; Stu Cncl; JV Bsbl; Var Ftbl; Var Wt Lftg.

DECKER, SHARON; Eastern Christian HS; Franklin Lakes, NJ; (3); VP Church Yth Grp; Yrbk Stf; Rep Stu Cncl; Mgr(s); Score Keeper; Var Stat Vllybl; Hon Roll; NHS; Calvin Coll MI; Math.

DECKER, TASHA; High Point Regional HS; Branchville, NJ; (3); Trs German Clb; Mrchg Band; JV Bowling; Hon Roll; Coachs Awd Bwlng 86; Spcl Rcgntn Awd Frgn Lang Tutor 86-87; NJ Inst Of Tech; Arch.

DECOU, SARAH; Collingswood SR HS; Collingswood, NJ; (2); JCL; Hst Latin Clb; JV Fld Hcky; JV Lcrss; High Hon Roll; Hon Roll; Jr NHS; NHS; VP Church Yth Grp; Band; Amer Lgn Auxlry Awd 85-86; Exemplar Awd 85-86; Presdntl Acadmc Ftns Awd 85-86.

DEEGAN, BARBARA; Manchester Township HS; Whiting, NJ; (3); Debate Tm; Library Aide; Band; Mrchg Band; School Play; Symp Band; Rep Jr Cls; JV Cheerleading; JV Var Diving; JV Var Socr; USMC; Fighter Piolet.

DEEGAN, DALE; Manasquan HS; Brielle, NJ; (3); Church Yth Grp; Drama Clb; FBLA; Spanish Clb; Flag Corp; Stage Crew; Hon Roll; Arch Dsgn.

DEEM, MICHAEL W; Bernards HS; Bernardsville, NJ; (4); 2/165; Math Tm; High Hon Roll; Ntl Merit SF; 2nd ST Sci Leag Chem Comp 86; Garden ST Dist Schlr 86; Chem Engr.

DEEMER, MICHELLE; Delaware Valley Reg HS; Milford, NJ; (4); 60/200; Church Yth Grp; Letterman Clb; Varsity Clb; Yrbk Sprt Ed; Yrbk Stf; VP Stu Cncl; Var Cheerleading; Var Fld Hcky; Var Capt Trk; Hon Roll; Coaches Athletic Awd 87; Hunterdon Drug Awarreness Awd 87; Hann Townsend Athletic Awd 87; West Chester U; Spch Cmmnctns.

DEFAZIO, ANNMARIE; Morristown HS; Morristown, NJ; (3); 96/404; Church Yth Grp; Cmnty Wkr; French Clb; Capt Math Tm; Political Wkr; Lit Mag; High Hon Roll; Hon Roll; Prfct Atten Awd; Hnrbl Mntn Knights Of Clumbus Essy 86; Bus.

DEFRANCESCO, DONNA; Glen Ridge HS; Glen Ridge, NJ; (3); AFS; Aud/Vis; Boys Clb Am; Band; Concert Band; Mrchg Band; Trk; Vllybl; High Hon Roll; Rotary Awd; Dodge Fndtn Schlrshp Chem Wrkshp 86; Schlrshp Grnt Nrthwstrn Smmr Prog 87; Astronomy.

DEGROFF, ALINA; Kinnelon HS; Riverdale, NJ; (4); FCA; Ski Clb; Varsity Clb; Pres Jr Cls; Off Stu Cncl; Cheerleading; Sftbl; Hon Roll; 4 Yrs Awd Vrsty Sftbl, Tm Capt Awd 87; U Of Kutztown; Crmnl Law.

DEGRUCCIO, SALLY ANN; Monsignor Donovan HS; Lavallette, NJ; (3); 21/245; Drama Clb; Ski Clb; Spanish Clb; SADD; Yrbk Stf; High Hon Roll; Hon Roll; NHS; U Of DE; Lib Arts.

DEGUTIS, ERIN; Randolph HS; Randolph, NJ; (3); 128/358; Debate Tm; Pres 4-H; Varsity Clb; Nwsp Rptr; Var Crs Cntry; Var Powder Puff Ftbl; Var Trk; 4-H Awd; Hon Roll; Kate Peaslee Hrsmnshp/Sprtsmnshp Mem 86; Amer Horse Show Assoc Zone Wnnr 85; Rnnr Up NJ 4-H Equestrn; Vet Sci.

DEGUZMAN, DAN; Parsippany HS; Parsippany, NJ; (2); Varsity Clb; Variety Show; JV Bsktbl; JV Socr; Var Tennis; Hon Roll; Prfct Atten Awd; Vrsty Lttr 85; Rutgers; Nuclear Med.

DEICKE, MARION; Manasquan HS; Belmar, NJ; (2); 11/235; FBLA; Key Clb; Spanish Clb; Band; Yrbk Stf; Trs Soph Cls; Pres Jr Cls; Var Crs Cntry; Var Socr; High Hon Roll; Villanova; Ed.

DEIS, JANET; West Morris Central HS; Long Valley, NJ; (3); French Clb; Key Clb; Spanish Clb; SADD; School Musical; Rep Frsh Cls; Rep Stu Cncl; JV Cheerleading; High Hon Roll; Hon Roll; Htl/Rest Mgmt.

DEITCH, DANY; Manalapan HS; Englishtown, NJ; (3); Office Aide; Temple Yth Grp; Chorus; Yrbk Stf; JV Var Bsbl; JV Var Bsktbl; JV Var Socr(s); Hotel Mgmnt.

DEITRICH, ERIC; Bayonne HS; Bayonne, NJ; (3); Ftbl; Cit Awd; Excptnl Police Svc Awd Bayonne Police Dept 86; Accntng.

DEJNEKA, MATTHEW; Hunterdon Central HS; Stockton, NJ; (4); 6/548; Boy Scts; Band; Jazz Band; Orch; Var Crs Cntry; JV L Socr; Capt L Trk; Im Vllybl; High Hon Roll; NHS; Garden State Distg Schlar 87; Vrsty Club Awd Winter & Spring Track 86-87; Rutgers U; Engr.

DEKLE, CRYSTAL; Manalapan HS; Englishtown, NJ; (2); Church Yth Grp; Church Choir; Brookdale CC; Pedtrcn.

DEL FAVERO, GLENN; Fair Lawn HS; Fair Lawn, NJ; (3); Boy Scts; Ski Clb; Off Soph Cls; Off Jr Cls; Socr; Hon Roll; 2nd Pl Awd NJ ST Crftsmns Fair Presntatn Drwng 86-87; Arch.

DEL VACCHIO, JANEEN; Carteret HS; Carteret, NJ; (4); 11/200; Am Leg Aux Girls St; Ski Clb; Band; Jazz Band; Capt Mrchg Band; School Play; Yrbk Ed-Chief; Stu Cncl; Swmmng; NHS; U Of DE.

DEL VECCHIO, MICHELE; Cranford HS; Cranford, NJ; (3); 81/268; Math Clb; Spanish Clb; Varsity Clb; Band; Concert Band; Mrchg Band; Nwsp Bus Mgr; Nwsp Stf; Yrbk Stf; Sftbl; Duquesne U; Jrnlsm.

DELA PENA, LORRAINE CHERYL; Sayreville War Memorial HS; Sayreville, NJ; (3); French Clb; FBLA; Pep Clb; Spanish Clb; Pom Pon; Hon Roll; Recog Awd Future Secr Amer 86; Accntng.

DELANEY, DENA; Ewing HS; Trenton, NJ; (3); Varsity Clb; Variety Show; Yrbk Bus Mgr; Yrbk Phtg; Yrbk Stf; L Var Sftbl; Tennis; Comm.

DELARGEY, RENEE; Triton Regional HS; Somerdale, NJ; (4); 66/309; Office Aide; Nwsp Stf; Yrbk Stf; Stu Cncl; Var Capt Socr; Var Sftbl; Var Hon Roll; MVP Soccer 86-87; Sunniest Smile 86-87; Glasboro ST Coll; Elem Ed.

DELATE, JOSEPH; Mc Corristin HS; Hamilton Sq, NJ; (3); 50/300; Art Clb; Pep Clb; Off Lit Mag; Jr NHS; Mercer Cnty Coll Lit Awd 86; Bus.

DELATORRE, PEDRO; Perth Amboy HS; Perth Amboy, NJ; (3); Pres Model UN; Bus.

DELEE, ADRIENNE; University HS; Newark, NJ; (3); JA; Spanish Clb; Chorus; VP Soph Cls; Rep Jr Cls; Rep Stu Cncl; Schlrshp Seton Hall Upward Bound 87; Douglass Coll; Bio Chem.

DELEON, MARY; St Marys HS; Sayreville, NJ; (4); Cmnty Wkr; Spanish Clb; High Hon Roll; Hon Roll; Hnr Roll 83-84; High Hnr Rll 86-87; Monmouth County Coll; Surgeon.

DELFINO, MARIE; Scotch Plains-Fanwood HS; Scotch Plains, NJ; (4); 58/329; Trs Drama Clb; Quiz Bowl; Spanish Clb; SADD; Acpl Chr; Chorus; Madrigals; School Musical; School Play; Lit Mag; Membr Of NJ Rgn Choir 85; 2 Yr Membr Of NJ All-ST Chorus 84 & 86; Membr Of All-Estrn Chorus 87; Douglass Coll; Italian.

DELGADO, ELAINE; Emerson HS; Union City, NJ; (4); 1/280; Am Leg Boys St; Trs French Clb; Co-Capt Color Guard; Ed Yrbk Stf; Trk; CC Awd; French Hon Soc; NHS; St Schlr; Val; Rutgers U Minority Merit Awd 87; Rutgers U.

DELGADO, LEON; St Joseph Regional HS; Hasbrouck Hts, NJ; (3); Comp Sci.

DELGADO, VIRGINIA; Fort Lee HS; Ft Lee, NJ; (3); Band; Concert Band; Jazz Band; Mrchg Band; Orch; Symp Band; Jazz Band Awd 84-85; Literature.

DELGARDIO, BRIDGID; Jackson Memorial HS; Jackson, NJ; (3); 20/420; Pres 4-H; Stat Score Keeper; Var Sftbl; Var Tennis; 4-H Awd; High Hon Roll; Hon Roll; NHS; Cert Of Achvt On NEDT 85; TAG 87; Mst Imprvd Vrsty Sftbl Plyr 87.

DELGUERCIO, CAROLYN; James Caldwell HS; W Caldwell, NJ; (2); Drama Clb; French Clb; GAA; Girl Scts; Key Clb; Im Var Cheerleading; Im Gym; Bus.

DELIA, ANTHONY; Glassboro HS; Glassboro, NJ; (3); Am Leg Boys St; Thesps; Varsity Clb; School Musical; Capt Crs Cntry; Var Trk; Hon Roll; NHS; Aerospace Engrng.

DELL, KRISTIE; Notre Dame HS; Trenton, NJ; (3); Service Clb; Hon Roll; Excell Engl 86-87; Law.

DELLA-FERA, DAVID N; Kearny HS; Kearny, NJ; (3); Am Leg Boys St; French Clb; Pres Jr Cls; Var JV Socr; French Hon Soc; High Hon Roll; Hon Roll; NHS; Columbia U; Poli Sci.

DELLANNO, ANTHONY; North Warren Regional HS; Blairstown, NJ; (4); 18/140; JV Var Bsbl; JV Socr; Hon Roll; MVP Bsbl All Area 2nd Team 86-87; All Conf; Montclair ST Coll; Comp Sci.

DELLERT, MICHAEL; Vernon Twsp HS; Highland Lakes, NJ; (3); Drama Clb; JCL; Chorus; School Musical; School Play; Stage Crew; Swing Chorus; Lit Mag; Hon Roll; Engl.

DELLI SANTI, ONDREA; Immaculate Conception HS; Newark, NJ; (4); Hosp Aide; Intnl Clb; Pep Clb; Chorus; Sec Trs Soph Cls; Stu Cncl; Trk; Advrtsng.

DELNERO, TARA; Union Catholic Regional HS; Roselle Park, NJ; (3); 27/317; Art Clb; Church Yth Grp; Cmnty Wkr; Office Aide; Political Wkr; Service Clb; SADD; Varsity Clb; Nwsp Rptr; Nwsp Stf; Fnlst Union Cthlc Slctd To Rprsnt Schl At UN 85-86; Mcrblgy.

DELORENZO, JANEL; Notre Dame HS; Trenton, NJ; (3); FBLA; Red Cross Aide; Ski Clb; Varsity Clb; Chorus; School Play; Rep Soph Cls; Tennis; Hon Roll; NHS; Princeton Pckt All-Area Tennis Tm 87; Colonial Vly Cnfrnc Tennis Tm 87.

DELOSSO, THOMAS NICHOLAS; Triton Regional HS; Runnemede, NJ; (4); 4/309; Aud/Vis; Boy Scts; Church Yth Grp; Key Clb; Political Wkr; Quiz Bowl; Pres Science Clb; Stu Cncl; Bausch & Lomb Sci Awd; DAR Awd; Eagle Scout Awd 84; Am Chem Soc Awd 85; Lit Vol Am Aws Pin 86; Physics.

DELP, BONNIE; West Orange HS; W Orange, NJ; (3); Pep Clb; Spanish Clb; Band; Chorus; Orch; Yrbk Stf; Capt Var Cheerleading; Var Sftbl; Trk; NHS; Adv.

DELUCA, PAUL; Marist HS; Bayonne, NJ; (4); 51/98; Key Clb; Stage Crew; Off Frsh Cls; Off Soph Cls; Off Jr Cls; Off Sr Cls; VP Stu Cncl; Var Tennis; Rotary Awd; St Ptrs Coll; Bus.

DELUZIO, CHRISTOPHER; Gloucester Catholic HS; Thorafare, NJ; (3); 27/175; Computer Clb; VP Sr Cls; Stu Cncl; JV Bsbl; Var Socr; Var Wrstlng; High Hon Roll; Hon Roll; NHS; Gettysburg Coll; Commmunication.

DELVALLE, CARMEN; Lakewood HS; Lakewood, NJ; (4); 42/287; Church Yth Grp; DECA; Pres FBLA; Hosp Aide; Spanish Clb; Rep Frsh Cls; Rep Stu Cncl; Var Trk; Hon Roll; Edward Williams Coll; Nrsng.

DEMAIO, JOHN; Hoboken HS; Hoboken, NJ; (3); Boy Scts; Banking.

DEMARCO, MELODIE; Ambassador Christian Acad; Toms River, NJ; (2); Church Yth Grp; Hosp Aide; Office Aide; Chorus; Yrbk Stf; Rep Soph Cls; Sftbl; Prfct Atten Awd; Ocean Cnty Coll Toms Rvr; Bus.

DEMARCO, NANCY; Immaculata HS; Green Br, NJ; (3); Dance Clb; Drama Clb; Pep Clb; School Play; Lit Mag; Psych.

DEMAREST, ANNETTE; West Milford HS; Hewitt, NJ; (4); 8/359; Am Leg Aux Girls St; Pres Varsity Clb; Var Capt Bsktbl; Stat Ftbl; Var Capt Sftbl; CC Awd; Pres NHS; German Clb; Band; Nwsp Rptr; NJ Chptr Natl Itln Amer Spts Hall Fame Scholar 87; Lioness Clb W Milford Scholar 87; Prncpls Scholar; Ithaca Coll; Phys Ther.

DEMAREST, JACQUELINE M; Scotch Plains-Fanwood HS; Scotch Plains, NJ; (4); Mgr Art Clb; Dance Clb; Pres Drama Clb; Trs PAVAS; Ed Political Wkr; School Play; Variety Show; Ed Lit Mag; NHS; Pres Schlr Tgl Schlrshp 87; Cmmnd Schlr 86-87; NJ Dstngshd Schlr 87; Rugers U; Advrtsng Artst.

DEMARTINI, JENNIFER; Bayonne HS; Bayonne, NJ; (3); Drama Clb; Key Clb; Library Aide; Thesps; School Play; Stage Crew; Lit Mag; Rep Frsh Cls; Rep Soph Cls; Rep Jr Cls; Psych.

DEMARTINO, JASON; Essex Catholic Boys HS; Montclair, NJ; (3); Boy Scts; Math Clb; Ski Clb; Rep Frsh Cls; Rep Soph Cls; VP Jr Cls; Rep Stu Cncl; Mgr Ftbl; Co-Capt Tennis; NHS.

DEMETRIOU, MARC; Lakeland Regional HS; Wanaque, NJ; (4); 68/354; Aud/Vis; Boy Scts; Ski Clb; Var L Ftbl; Socr; Wt Lftg; Hon Roll; Eagle Sct Awd 85; Stockton ST; Bus.

DEMILIA, CRAIG; Hillsborough HS; Belle Mead, NJ; (3); 102/328; Trk; Mrktng.

DEMITRIO, SUZANNE L; Jonathan Dayton Regional HS; Springfield, NJ; (4); 2/232; Hosp Aide; JCL; Quiz Bowl; Nwsp Ed-Chief; Bausch & Lomb Sci Awd; French Hon Soc; Ntl Merit SF; Sal; French Clb; Latin Clb; Natl Latin Exam Mdllst 84-86; St Sci Day Mdllst 84-86.

DEMKO, CRAIG; Waldwick HS; Waldwick, NJ; (3); Am Leg Boys St; Ski Clb; Varsity Clb; Var Bsktbl; Var Crs Cntry; JV Ftbl; JV Trk; Hon Roll; Prfct Atten Awd; Areo Engrng.

DEMM, MATTHEW; Morris Catholic HS; Morris Plns, NJ; (3); 15/135; Natl Beta Clb; Var Bsbl; Var Bsktbl; Var Ftbl; Hon Roll.

DEMO, DOUG; Pennsville Memorial HS; Pennsville, NJ; (3); 1/225; FBLA; Spanish Clb; Drill Tm; School Musical; Nwsp Stf; Lit Mag; Off Stu Cncl; High Hon Roll; Exploring; Q&S; Ray A Kroc Achvmnt Awd; Outstndng Rifle Awd; Rutgers U; Ecnmcs.

DEMORE, DARLENE; Vineland SR HS; Vineland, NJ; (3); 175/800; Church Yth Grp; Drama Clb; Pep Clb; Spanish Clb; Flag Corp; Nwsp Stf; Hon Roll; Merit Roll; USC; Arch.

DEMPSEY, ANN; Spotswood HS; Milltown, NJ; (3); Church Yth Grp; French Clb; Intnl Clb; Ski Clb; Varsity Clb; Rep Stu Cncl; Var Capt Cheerleading; JV Im Mgr(s); JV Var Trk; Hon Roll; Rutgers U; Educ.

DEMPSEY, MICHAEL; Edgewood Regional SR HS; Atco, NJ; (2); Boy Scts; JCL; Latin Clb; Stage Crew; Rep Frsh Cls; Rep Soph Cls; Rep Stu Cncl; JV Socr; High Hon Roll; Hon Roll; Egl Sct 86; Presdntl Acadc Ftns Awd 86; Ordr Arrow 86; Aero Engr.

DEMPSEY, MICHAEL; Matawan Regional HS; Matawan, NJ; (2); 12/346; Ski Clb; Concert Band; Stage Crew; Hon Roll; Archtl Engrng.

DENICE, SHARON; West Milford Township HS; West Milford, NJ; (3); 83/403; French Clb; Spanish Clb; SADD; Varsity Clb; Yrbk Bus Mgr; Rep Stu Cncl; Var Score Keeper; French Hon Soc; Hon Roll; Jr NHS; Fshn Merch.

DENICOLA, MATT; Northern Valley Regional HS; Northvale, NJ; (3); 16/274; Ski Clb; Bsktbl; JV Crs Cntry; JV Trk; Hon Roll.

DENKER, HEIDI; Belvidere HS; Belvidere, NJ; (4); Office Aide; Ski Clb; Teachers Aide; Variety Show; Yrbk Stf; Mgr Ftbl; JV Sftbl; Vllybl; Hon Roll; Martha S Johnson Schlrshp Cosmtlgy 87; Stroudsburg; Bus.

DENKOWYCZ, NICHOLAS; Cinnaminson HS; Cinnaminson, NJ; (3); Am Leg Boys St; Art Clb; Aud/Vis; Church Yth Grp; German Clb; Thesps; Stage Crew; Gov Hon Prg Awd; NHS; Philadelphia Coll Of Art Gold Key Wnnr 85; Dplma Ukrainian Stds 87; Comrcl Artst.

DENNERY, STEPHANIE; Wayne Hills HS; Wayne, NJ; (4); 35/287; French Clb; Variety Show; Yrbk Stf; Rep Frsh Cls; Rep Soph Cls; Rep Jr Cls; Var Cheerleading; Var Capt Gym; Hon Roll; NHS; Coachs Awd Gymnstcs 87; Athl Mnth 86; Douglass Coll; Bus.

DENNIS, SHAWN; De Paul Dioceram HS; Pompton Plains, NJ; (4); 69/167; Boy Scts; Nwsp Stf; Rep Frsh Cls; Var Bsktbl; JV Socr; Hon Roll; Bus Admin.

DENNY, JOHN; Hackettstown HS; Hackettstown, NJ; (2); Key Clb; Ski Clb; SADD; Bsbl; Bsktbl; Ftbl; Trk; God Cntry Awd; Mktg.

DENTE, SANDRA; Livingston HS; Livingston, NJ; (3); 70/417; Intnl Clb; Spanish Clb; Chorus; Flag Corp; Hon Roll; Spanish NHS; Church Yth Grp; Dance Clb; FBLA; Leo Clb.

DENTON, ERIC; Edgewood SR HS; Atco, NJ; (2); Hon Roll; Gftd & Tlntd 86-87; Convctn Future 86-87; Engrng.

DENTON, PETER; Paul VI HS; Williamstown, NJ; (3); 184/418; Art Clb; Concert Band; Nwsp Ed-Chief; Nwsp Rptr; Nwsp Stf; JV Var Ftbl; Var Ice Hcky; JV Wrstlng; VFW Awd; Comms.

DEORA, SONIA; John P Stevens HS; Edison, NJ; (3); Cmnty Wkr; Hosp Aide; Key Clb; Library Aide; Science Clb; High Hon Roll; Hon Roll; Jr NHS; NHS; 100 Hr Pin Awd JFK Hosp Svc 87; Treas Library Clb; Med.

DEPALMA, JANET; Paul VI HS; Waterford, NJ; (4); 224/544; Cmnty Wkr; Hon Roll; Scnd Hnrs 87; Bus Admn.

DERAAT, TEUNIS; Wayne Valley HS; Wayne, NJ; (3); Ski Clb; Band; Concert Band; Mrchg Band; Pep Band; Stage Crew; Hon Roll; Arch Engrng.

DERAMUS, FELICIA; Florence Township Mem HS; Florence, NJ; (2); Off Soph Cls; Comp.

DERIENZO, LAURA; Paramus Catholic Girls HS; Rochelle Pk, NJ; (3); Cmnty Wkr; Drama Clb; Science Clb; Nwsp Stf; Nwsp Stf; Ed Lit Mag; Rep Stu Cncl; High Hon Roll; NHS; NEDT Awd; Eng Awd JR Cls 86-87; Caldwell Coll Schlrshp 86-87; Bus Admin.

DERR, JEFFREY; Highland Regional HS; Blackwood, NJ; (2); Sec Latin Clb; Letterman Clb; Varsity Clb; Var Socr; JV Wrstlng.

DERRICK, ROSS; Mendham HS; Chester, NJ; (4); 79/318; Church Yth Grp; Cmnty Wkr; German Clb; Ski Clb; Var Bsbl; Wrstlng; Hon Roll; U Of MD; Engrng.

DERRIG, KATHY; Linden HS; Linden, NJ; (3); Church Yth Grp; Pres German Clb; Key Clb; Science Clb; Off Sr Cls; Var Tennis; High Hon Roll; NHS; Dance Clb; Stage Crew; Dlta Epsln Phi Grmn Hnr Soc 85-88; Mnrties In Engnrng 84-88; Math.

DERRINGER, ADAM; Franklin HS; Somerset, NJ; (3); Office Aide; Temple Yth Grp; Varsity Clb; Var Wrstlng; High Hon Roll; Hon Roll; Spts Med.

DERS, KIMBERLY; Cherokee HS; Marlton, NJ; (2); Drama Clb; Spanish Clb; Acpl Chr; Band; Chorus; Concert Band; Mrchg Band; School Musical; School Play; Hon Roll; Penn ST; Prfrmng Artist.

DESHPANDE, SARITA; East Brunswick HS; East Brunswick, NJ; (2); Cmnty Wkr; Dance Clb; Exploring; Hosp Aide; Intnl Clb; Key Clb; Library Aide; Office Aide; Off Temple Yth Grp; Rep Frsh Cls; Offcr Yth Grp, & Key Clb Rep 87; Hosp Aid Awd 86; Bus Admin.

DESINONE, MARCELLA; Monsignor Donovan HS; Jackson, NJ; (3); Dance Clb; Drama Clb; Intnl Clb; SADD; School Play; Hon Roll; NY U; Writer.

DESMOND, KELLEY; St John Vianney HS; Old Bridge, NJ; (4); 89/252; Church Yth Grp; FBLA; Hon Roll; Glassboro ST Coll.

DESORMES, SABRINA; Marylawn Of The Orangesw HS; Orange, NJ; (3); Chorus; Rep Soph Cls; Rep Jr Cls; Var Bsktbl; Var Sftbl; French Hon Soc; Acad All Amercn 87; Natl Hnr Roll 87; Fincng.

DESOUZA, TREVOR; Frank H Morrell HS; Irvington, NJ; (3); Church Yth Grp; Drama Clb; ROTC; Drill Tm; School Musical; Trk; Wt Lftg; Hon Roll; ROTC Good Cndct, Drll Tm, Ldrshp Rbbn, Fld Trnng Rbbn, Phys Ftnss Rbbn, Cadet Month 86-87; Law.

DESPINS, SUSAN; Gill-St Bernards Schl; Randolph, NJ; (4); Cmnty Wkr; Hosp Aide; Model UN; Co-Capt Scholastic Bowl; Pres Spanish Clb; Co-Capt Varsity Clb; Capt School Musical; School Play; Yrbk Ed-Chief; Lit Mag; Frances B Rohn Awd-Math 87; Bennett Svc Awd 87; Chrmns Prz For Outstndg Schlrshp-US Hstry 87; Rutgers Coll; Intl Bus.

DESPREAUX, JEFFREY; Memorial HS; Cedar Grove, NJ; (4); 5/123; Key Clb; Stage Crew; Nwsp Rptr; Yrbk Stf; Rep Stu Cncl; Bsbl; Var JV Bsktbl; Var Tennis; High Hon Roll; Hon Roll; Grdn St Disting Schlrs 86-87; U Of DE; Busi Admn.

DESROCHERS, LISA; Paul VI HS; Turnersville, NJ; (4); 31/511; French Clb; Math Clb; SADD; Powder Puff Ftbl; Hon Roll; JC Awd; NHS; Fnanc.

DESSICINO, ANDREA; The Pilgrim Acad; Egg Harbor, NJ; (4); Church Yth Grp; Yrbk Stf; Capt Cheerleading; High Hon Roll; Ntl Hnr Rlhgst GPA Spnsh 86; Geneva Coll; Spch Pathlgy.

DESTITO, ANTHONY; Bayonne HS; Bayonne, NJ; (3); Art Clb; Drama Clb; Fnlst-Fshn Dsgn Cmptn 87; Accptd To Trphgn Schl Of Dsgn 87; Clthng Dsgn.

DESTITO, ROSALINA; Holy Family Acad; Bayonne, NJ; (4); 6/130; Lit Mag; Vllybl; CC Awd; Hon Roll; NJ Garden ST Schlrshp & Hnrb Mntn-Physiology 87; Stevens Inst Of Tech; Biochem.

DETRICK, LAURA; Oakcrest HS; Mays Landing, NJ; (4); 6/212; GAA; Math Clb; Yrbk Ed-Chief; Yrbk Sprt Ed; Hst Soph Cls; Jr Cls; Mgr(s); Sftbl; Capt Tennis; NHS; Trenton ST Coll; Math.

DEUBEL, DONNA LYNN; St Pius X Regional HS; Spotswood, NJ; (4); 28/108; Varsity Clb; Drill Tm; Nwsp Stf; Yrbk Stf; Lit Mag; Cheerleading; Crs Cntry; Trk; High Hon Roll; Hon Roll; Georgian Ct Coll; Human Frnscs.

DEUSCH, MICHAEL; Shore Regional HS; Oceanport, NJ; (3); Ski Clb; Stage Crew; JV Bsbl; Var L Ftbl; Powder Puff Ftbl; Hon Roll; Prfct Atten Awd; Cnfrnc Ftbl Champs 86-87; Bus.

DEUSCHLE, KEVIN P; Columbia HS; South Orange, NJ; (4); Am Leg Boys St; Church Yth Grp; VP Stu Cncl; JV Socr; Var L Trk; Hon Roll; Ntl Merit Ltr; Prfct Atten Awd; Gayden St Dstngshd Schlr 86; Stbn Awd Outstndng Grmn Stu 86; Rugers Coll; Archlgst.

DEUTSCH, GREGG; Ramapo HS; Franklin Lakes, NJ; (3); 95/324; Drama Clb; French Clb; School Musical; School Play; Stage Crew; Rep Stu Cncl; Crs Cntry; Hon Roll; Drama Clb Awd 87; Engl Merit Awd 86; Bus.

DEUTSCH, JILL; Delran HS; Delran, NJ; (4); 19/188; Letterman Clb; JV Capt Bsktbl; Var Capt Socr; Var Capt Sftbl; High Hon Roll; Hon Roll; NHS; U S Army Rsrve Natl Schlr Athlte Awd, Gld Mdl Sprtng Gds Excllnce Acdmcs & Athltcs Awd 87; Monmouth Coll; Chld Psych.

DEUTSCH, JONATHAN; Hunterdon Central HS; Ringoes, NJ; (4); 200/517; Chess Clb; Computer Clb; Mrchg Band; Orch; School Musical; Variety Show; Im Bsktbl; Im Vllybl; Polish-Am Ctzn Schlrshp 87; Glassboro ST; Comp.

DEVINE, BRYCE D; Hackettstown HS; Hackettstown, NJ; (3); Am Leg Boys St; Drama Clb; Band; Concert Band; Jazz Band; Orch; Var Capt Bsbl; JV Var Ftbl; Var Capt Wrstlng; High Hon Roll; Bio Sci.

DEVINE, KATHLEEN M; John F Kennedy HS; Iselin, NJ; (3); German Clb; Girl Scts; Pep Clb; Spanish Clb; SADD; Yrbk Stf; Psych.

DEVINE, KERRY; Delran HS; Dania, FL; (4); 32/198; Pres French Clb; Yrbk Stf; Rep Stu Cncl; Var Stat Bsbl; Stat Bsktbl; JV Bowling; Var Fld Hcky; Im Vllybl; Outstndng Achvt Frgn Lang-Frnch 87; U Of Miami; Pol.

DEVINE, NORA; St Josephs Of The Palisades HS; Hoboken, NJ; (4); 1/115; School Play; Stage Crew; Variety Show; Nwsp Rptr; Lit Mag; High Hon Roll; NHS; St Schlr; Rtgrs Schlr 86; Outstndg JR 86; Rnsslr Mdl Awded Excllnc Math & Sci 86.

DEVINE, ROBERT; Morris Knolls HS; Wharton, NJ; (3); 52/424; High Hon Roll; Hon Roll; Bus.

DEVINE, SHANNAN; Lower Cape May Regional HS; Villas, NJ; (3); 87/188; French Clb; Hosp Aide; Spanish Clb; VP Pres SADD; Varsity Clb; Yrbk Stf; Var Mgr(s); Var Pom Pon; Stat Trk; Rotary Awd; Multi Lang.

DEVITIS, CYNTHIA; Jackson Memorial HS; Jackson, NJ; (3); 55/416; Library Aide; Quiz Bowl; SADD; Nwsp Rptr; Rep Jr Cls; Rep Sr Cls; VP Stu Cncl; Mgr Sftbl; High Hon Roll; Hon Roll; ST Cmpttns HOSA 2nd Pl & Natl Conf HOSA 5th Pl 87; Bio.

DEVITO, CAROL; Lakeland Regional HS; Ringwood, NJ; (4); 35/345; Church Yth Grp; Ski Clb; Varsity Clb; Chorus; Stu Cncl; JV Bsktbl; JV Sftbl; Capt Vllybl; High Hon Roll; NHS; Stu Cncl Schlrshp.

DEVLIN, JEFFREY; Essex Catholic Boys HS; Upr Montclair, NJ; (3); Boy Scts; Var Letterman Clb; Nwsp Rptr; Nwsp Stf; Church Yth Grp; French Clb; Service Clb; Varsity Clb; Pep Band; Rep Stu Cncl; Egl Sct 85; 2nd Hnrs 85-87; Ctznshp Awd 85; Arch Engrng.

DEVLIN III, LAURENCE; St James HS; Hancocks Bridge, NJ; (4); 1/68; Drama Clb; Band; Chorus; Orch; School Musical; School Play; Gov Hon Prg Awd; High Hon Roll; NHS; Ntl Merit Ltr; Trmpt In All E Cst Orch 87; Grdn ST Dist Schlrshp 87; All ST Orch/Bnd 84-86; Northwestern U; Orch.

DEVLIN, PATRICK; Matawan Regional HS; Matawan, NJ; (2); Church Yth Grp; Im Bsbl; JV Ftbl; Hon Roll; Rutgers U.

DEZSERAN, AMY E; Holycross HS; Delran, NJ; (3); Ski Clb; Fld Hcky; JV Tennis; Im Vllybl; High Hon Roll; Hon Roll; Intl Bus.

DHONDT, KRISTINA; Lakeland Regional HS; Ringwood, NJ; (3); 2/350; Stu Cncl; Var Bsktbl; Var Socr; Var Trk; High Hon Roll; NHS; Peer Cnlsng Club 86-87; Road Show Clb 86-87.

DHUPAR, SACHIV; Wood Ridge HS; Wood Ridge, NJ; (2); Art Clb; Computer Clb; Library Aide; Math Clb; Science Clb; Spanish Clb; Tennis; High Hon Roll; Med.

DI AMICO, MAUREEN; Passaic County Vo-Tech HS; Paterson, NJ; (4); Spanish Clb; Variety Show; Var Capt Cheerleading; Var Capt Pom Pon; Var Capt Sftbl; Hon Roll; Ntl Merit Ltr; Acad All-Amer 85-87; Natl Tm All-Amer Chrldng 85-87.

DI ANGELO, EDWARD; St Peters Prep; Jersey City, NJ; (4); Art Clb; Aud/Vis; Cmnty Wkr; Dance Clb; Library Aide; Pep Clb; Pres SADD; Lit Mag; Hon Roll; Lion Awd; ST Peters Prep-Prep Spirit Awd 86; ST Peters Coll; Accntng.

DI BABBO, ANTHONY J; St Augustine Prep; Turnersville, NJ; (3); 29/54; Cmnty Wkr; Varsity Clb; Nwsp Stf; Yrbk Stf; Rep Frsh Cls; Rep Soph Cls; Off Sr Cls; Bsbl; Socr; Swmmng; St Josephs U; Law.

DI BELLA, ALFRED; Gloucester County Christia; Swedesboro, NJ; (3); Church Yth Grp; French Clb; Sec Soph Cls; Trk; High Hon Roll; Hon Roll; Glassboro ST.

DI BELLA, CRAIG; Toms River HS North; Beachwood, NJ; (3); Stage Crew; Yrbk Stf; Rep Stu Cncl; Var Bsbl; Stat Bsktbl; JV Crs Cntry; Var Wrstlng; Hon Roll; OCC Bsbl Schl Coaches Awd 85; Bsbl Schl MVP 86; Crmnl Jstc.

DI BENEDETTO, AUDRA; Cliffside Park HS; Cliffside Park, NJ; (3); 1/234; Political Wkr; Yrbk Stf; Lit Mag; Stu Cncl; High Hon Roll; NHS; Rutgers Schlr 87; Italian Hnr Soc 86-87; Law.

DI BENEDETTO, CHERYL; Franklin HS; Somerset, NJ; (4); 6/318; Trs Drama Clb; Pres Chorus; School Musical; School Play; Stage Crew; Swing Chorus; High Hon Roll; NHS; Pres Schlr; Outstndg SR Vocal Music Awd; NY U; Lbrl Arts.

DI BRUNO, JOSEPH; Highland Regional HS; Laurel Springs, NJ; (4); 10/297; Pres Chess Clb; Computer Clb; Latin Clb; Scholastic Bowl; Science Clb; Hon Roll; NHS; 1st Co & Top Ten ST Sci League Chem Exm 86; Physics Olympic Tm Wnnr 86; Elec Engrng.

DI CARLO, DAWN; Highland Regional HS; Blackwood, NJ; (3); 50/250; Nwsp Rptr; JV Var Fld Hcky; Hon Roll; UCLA.

DI CARLO, FRANCINE; Morris Catholic HS; Boonton, NJ; (4); 88/138; Pep Clb; School Musical; Yrbk Stf; Cheerleading; Powder Puff Ftbl; Mst Spiritd, Mst Imprvd-Chrldr Awds 86-87, 85-86; County Coll Of Morris; Nrsng.

DI ENNA, MICHELLE; Haddonfield Memorial HS; Haddonfield, NJ; (4); Intnl Clb; Spanish Clb; Var Capt Cheerleading; Hon Roll; NHS; Spanish NHS; Accntng.

DI FABIO, CECELIA; Holy Spirit HS; Venthor Hts, NJ; (3); Camera Clb; Computer Clb; JA; Library Aide; Quiz Bowl; Radio Clb; Spanish Clb; Nwsp Phtg; Yrbk Phtg; Yrbk Stf; Lawyr.

DI FABRIZIO, LORENA; Marylawn Of The Oranges HS; Orange, NJ; (3); Service Clb; High Hon Roll; Hon Roll; NHS; Spanish NHS; Prfct Atten Awd; Spnsh Awd; Bus.

DI GANOVA, ANN MARIA; Paul XI HS; Somerdale, NJ; (3); 5/418; Math Clb; Pom Pon; Hon Roll; Spanish NHS; Nurse.

DI GASPER, LINDA R; Kearny HS; Kearny, NJ; (2); Band; Concert Band; Mrchg Band; Hon Roll; Biochem.

DI GIOVANNI, PETER; Immaculata HS; Belle Mead, NJ; (3); 10/245; Am Leg Boys St; Math Clb; Math Tm; Spanish Clb; SADD; L Var Bsktbl; Capt Socr; Elks Awd; NHS; Spanish NHS; Outstndng Achvt Math Leag 87; Sprts Med.

DI GIULIO, JENNIFER A; Pinelands Regional HS; Tuckerton, NJ; (3); SADD; Nwsp Rptr; Trs Soph Cls; Trs Jr Cls; Var L Fld Hcky; Var Capt Trk; Hon Roll; Cmnty Wkr; Teachers Aide; Rep Stu Cncl; HS Amer Athlt For Trck & Fld Hcky 86; $1000 Schlrshp To St Marys Of Plns Coll 87; Physcl Thrpy.

DI GREGORIO, NINA; Lenape Valley Regional HS; Netcong, NJ; (3); JV Var Bsktbl; French Hon Soc; Hon Roll; Prfct Atten Awd; Bus.

DI GUILIO, SUSAN; Belleville HS; Belleville, NJ; (3); Pres FTA; Hosp Aide; Key Clb; Chorus; Nwsp Rptr; Yrbk Stf; Rep Jr Cls; Rep Stu Cncl; JV Vllybl; Hon Roll; Adelphi U; Psych.

DI JOSEPH, ROBERT; Cumberland Regional HS; Bridgeton, NJ; (4); Ski Clb; Chorus; Madrigals; School Musical; Ftbl; Swmmng; Hon Roll; Debate Tm; Intnl Clb; Nwsp Rptr; NJ All ST Chorus; All South Jersey Chorus; Stockton ST Coll; Bio.

DI LORENZO, PETER; Audubon HS; Audubon, NJ; (3); Church Yth Grp; French Clb; Concert Band; Mrchg Band; School Musical; Sec Sr Cls; Var JV Bsbl; Var JV Bsktbl; Wt Lftg; Accntng.

DI LORETO, CRISTINA; Cranford HS; Cranford, NJ; (2); Band; Concert Band; Sftbl; Hon Roll; Montclair ST Coll; Acctng.

DI MARCO, DAMON; Steinert Memorial HS; Hamilton Square, NJ; (2); Church Yth Grp; Varsity Clb; Lit Mag; Var Crs Cntry; Var Trk; Hon Roll; Knghts Of Clmbs Dmcry Awd 86; Wrtng.

DI MATTIA, DEBBIE; Hightstown HS; Cranbury, NJ; (3); Hst FBLA; High Hon Roll; NHS; Prfct Atten Awd; Math Leag 86-87; Bus.

DI NARDO, MICHAEL; Lyndhurst HS; Lyndhurst, NJ; (2); 1/175; Symp Band; Pres Soph Cls; Rep Stu Cncl; JV Bsbl; JV Bsktbl; Capt L Ftbl; Cit Awd; Elks Awd; High Hon Roll; Prfct Atten Awd; Hugh O Brien Youth Fndtn Fnlst 87; Peer Counselor 86-87; Amer Legion Baseball; Dentistry.

DI PADOVA, CHRISTINE; Point Pleasant Borough HS; Point Pleasant, NJ; (4); 13/240; 4-H; Math Tm; Band; Concert Band; Mrchg Band; Hon Roll; NHS; Pres Schlr; Keyette Scholar 87; Alpha Delta Kappa Scholar 87; Steuben Soc Awd 87.

DI PASQUALE, FRANK; Manalapan HS; Englishtown, NJ; (4); 50/390; Var Bsbl; Im Ftbl; Rutgers U; Dentistry.

DI PASQUALE, JOHN; Pennsauken HS; Pennsauken, NJ; (3); 88/425; JA; Library Aide; Science Clb; Capt Crs Cntry; Capt Trk; VP Of Yr South Jersey JR Achvt 86.

DI PIETRO, ANTHONY; Vineland HS; Vineland, NJ; (3); Varsity Clb; Var L Tennis; Var Wrstlng; Ape Atlantic Leag Div I Tnns All-Star Tm 87; Med.

DI PIETRO, DARREN; St James HS; Gibbstown, NJ; (3); 11/79; Chess Clb; Drama Clb; NFL; School Musical; Yrbk Stf; Rotary Awd; Drexel U; Chem Engr.

DI PIETRO, MICHELE; Bishop Eustace Prep Schl; Cherry Hill, NJ; (3); 1/165; Cmnty Wkr; Hosp Aide; Trs Math Clb; Pep Clb; Pres Spanish Clb; SADD; Nwsp Stf; Yrbk Stf; Ed Lit Mag; VP NHS; Rutgers Schlr 87; Intl Finance.

DI RIENZO, ANTHONY; Glassboro HS; Glassboro, NJ; (3); SADD; Yrbk Sprt Ed; Bsbl; Bsktbl; Ftbl; Wt Lftg.

DI ROBERTO, FRANK; Hunterdon Central HS; Whitehouse Sta, NJ; (3); 65/545; Art Clb; Boy Scts; Trs Church Yth Grp; Ski Clb; Off Jr Cls; Socr; JV Var Tennis; Hon Roll.

DI SCIENZA, JOSEPH; Paul VI HS; Williamstown, NJ; (4); 1/511; School Play; Variety Show; Rep Soph Cls; Var Crs Cntry; Var Trk; NHS; Ntl Merit Ltr; Spanish NHS; St Schlr; Val; Pre-Dentstry.

DI STASO, MARISSA; Holy Family Acad; Bayonne, NJ; (3); 35/121; Dance Clb; Ski Clb; Var Capt Cheerleading; Var Capt Pom Pon; Hon Roll; Bus.

DIAMOND, CYNTHIA A; Riverside HS; Riverside, NJ; (3); 12/103; Drama Clb; FTA; Political Wkr; SADD; Off Stu Cncl; Hon Roll; NHS; Stu Govt Awd-Co-Chairing Spirit Wk Cmmttee 87; Acctg I 86, Acct II 87 Awds; Bus.

DIAMOND, KENT; St John Vianney HS; Marlboro, NJ; (4); 23/250; Stage Crew; Var JV Socr; Hon Roll; NHS; Prfct Atten Awd; Rutgers Coll.

DIAMOND, LARA; Maple Shade HS; Maple Shade, NJ; (3); 2/175; Drama Clb; JA; Pres Key Clb; Sec Spanish Clb; Chorus; School Musical; School Play; Yrbk Rptr; Trs Stu Cncl; Bsktbl; HOBY Fndtn Awd 86; Rotary Yth Ldrshp Awd 87; Gov Schl Publc Issues 87; Princeton U; Law.

DIAMOND, MARCI; Cinnaminson HS; Cinnaminson, NJ; (4); 10/228; Pres Debate Tm; Political Wkr; Service Clb; Nwsp Ed-Chief; Stu Cncl; JV Var Socr; Var Trk; Gov Hon Prg Awd; Ntl Merit SF; Rotary Awd; 1st High Jump; 1st Regnl Arco-Jesse Owens Games; Century III Schlrshp Cmptn; Pol Sci.

DIANA, DANIEL; Middlesex HS; Middlesex, NJ; (2); Boy Scts; Computer Clb; Ski Clb; Concert Band; Jazz Band; Mrchg Band; JV Trk; High Hon Roll; Hon Roll.

DIARAM, KUNTIE; Lincoln HS; Jersey Cty, NJ; (3); FNA; Hosp Aide; Red Cross Aide; Stu Cncl; Bowling; Coach Actv; Hon Roll; Prfct Atten Awd; Nrsng.

DIAZ, ANGIE; Passaic County Tech; Paterson, NJ; (4); 35/366; FNA; Hosp Aide; SADD; Drill Tm; Pep Band; Variety Show; Var Cheerleading; Pom Pon; Hon Roll; Farleigh Dickinson U; Dntl Hygn.

DIAZ, CELESTE B; Dover HS; Dover, NJ; (3); Spanish Clb; Hist & Eng; Lawyer.

DIAZ, HILARIO; Perth Amboy HS; Perth Amboy, NJ; (2); JV Bsbl; Gym; High Hon Roll; Hon Roll; Math.

DIAZ, JACQUELINE; Memorial HS; North Bergen, NJ; (3); Church Yth Grp; Drama Clb; Office Aide; Pres Stu Cncl; Gym; Pom Pon; Twrlr; Chld Psych.

DIAZ, JOHN; Cliffside Park HS; Fairview, NJ; (3); JV Crs Cntry; 3rd Prize Bookmark Cont 84; Art.

DIAZ, LILLIE; Pennsauken HS; Pennsauken, NJ; (2); Girl Scts; Spanish Clb; Co-Capt Drill Tm; Bus Exctive.

DIAZ, MARIA; Henry Hudson Regional HS; Atlntic Hglds, NJ; (3); Church Yth Grp; Girl Scts; Chorus; Brookdale; Nrs.

DIAZ, MARIO; Memorial HS; West New York, NJ; (3); AFS; Computer Clb; English Clb; FTA; Intnl Clb; Math Clb; Spanish Clb; Orch; Off Jr Cls; Hon Roll; COMP Prgmmr.

DIAZ, PILAR; Manville HS; Manville, NJ; (4); Quiz Bowl; High Hon Roll; Hon Roll; Sec NHS; Prsdntl Acad Fitness Awd 87; Rutgers U; Bus.

DIBEASE, JAMES; Edgewood Regional SR HS; Sicklerville, NJ; (3); 2/375; Drama Clb; Pres Latin Clb; Varsity Clb; Capt Bsbl; Var Capt Socr; High Hon Roll; NHS; VFW Awd; MVP Sccr Tm 84-85; Ltn Awd-Hghst Avg 85; Engrng.

DICARLO, ANDRIA; Washington Township HS; Turnersville, NJ; (3); Office Aide; Teachers Aide; Glassboro ST; Tchng Elem.

DICARLO, MARIA; Wayne Hills HS; Wayne, NJ; (3); 89/320; Dance Clb; Cheerleading; Italian Club; Douglas; Sttstcs.

DICKENS, ANGELIA; Atlantic City HS; Atlantic City, NJ; (2); French Clb; Model UN; Political Wkr; Band; Mrchg Band; Orch; Off Stu Cncl; Hon Roll; Delgtn Ldr U PA 86; Georgetown; Law.

DICKERSON, KAREN L; Highland Regional HS; Clementon, NJ; (3); Cmnty Wkr; Hosp Aide; Latin Clb; Spanish Clb; Sec Frsh Cls; Cheerleading; Sec Wrstlng; Hon Roll; UCLA; Bio.

DICKERSON, KIWON; St Marys HS; Jersey City, NJ; (2); 10/28; Computer Clb; FBLA; GAA; Math Clb; Var Frsh Cls; Var Bsktbl; Var Cheerleading; JV Sftbl; JV Vllybl; Hon Roll; VA ST U; Comp Pgmmng.

DICKERSON, LORI A; Ridge HS; Basking Ridge, NJ; (4); AFS; Church Yth Grp; Hosp Aide; Latin Clb; Political Wkr; Concert Band; Mrchg Band; Orch; Yrbk Stf; Pres Jr Cls; Jack & Jill America Inc Carol Robertson Scholar 87; Bernards Twp GOP Scholar 86; Princeton U; Intl Bus.

DICKEY, CHRISTINE; Pennsville HS; Pennsville, NJ; (3); 60/225; Drama Clb; JCL; Pres Latin Clb; SADD; Drm Mjr(t); School Musical; School Play; Nwsp Rptr; Lit Mag; Sec Stu Cncl; Jrnlst.

DICKEY, DAVID; Matawan Regional HS; Aberdeen, NJ; (4); 22/330; French Clb; Math Clb; NFL; Yrbk Stf; Var Ftbl; Trk; Wt Lftg; NHS; Schlr Athlt Lcl Paper 86; Elec Engr.

DICKINSON, BARRY; Middle Township HS; Cape May Ct House, NJ; (2); 2/180; Chess Clb; High Hon Roll; Outstndg Spnsh Stud Awd 85-87; Schlrshp Awd 85-87; Sci Fair 3rd Pl 85-87; Stockton ST Coll; Comp.

DICKINSON, CHRISTOPHER; Trenton Central HS; Trenton, NJ; (3); Chess Clb; Debate Tm; French Clb; Pres JA; Trs Key Clb; Scholastic Bowl; Capt Var Bsbl; High Hon Roll; Amer Legn Awd 84-85; Mayors Achvmnt Awd Acadmcs 85; Electncs.

DICKINSON, ERIC; Florence Twp Mem HS; Burlington, NJ; (3); 2/93; Am Leg Boys St; Church Yth Grp; Exploring; Math Clb; Math Tm; Quiz Bowl; Science Clb; Stage Crew; JV Bsbl; Im Wt Lftg; Fnlst For Gvrnrs Schl 86-87; U Of VT; Fish Mgmnt.

DICKSON, AMY; Rancocas Valley Regional HS; Mt Holly, NJ; (2); Church Yth Grp; Hosp Aide; Office Aide; Varsity Clb; VP Soph Cls; Stu Cncl; Coach Actv; Gym; Lcrss.

DICKSON, CHRIS; Paul VI HS; Somerdale, NJ; (3); Intl Rel.

DICKSON, DAVIDE; Toms River HS North; Toms River, NJ; (3); 26/448; Cmnty Wkr; German Clb; Science Clb; Drill Tm; Flag Corp; Mrchg Band; School Play; Stage Crew; Yrbk Stf; Rep Frsh Cls; Treas Of Posideon Chapter Of Natl Hnr Soc 87; Flag Squad Capt 87; Lifetime Of Hadassah 86; Vet.

DIEFENBACH, KIM; Paterson Catholic HS; Passaic, NJ; (3); 7/95; Computer Clb; High Hon Roll; Hon Roll; Tchng.

DIEFFENBACH, KRISTA N; Morris Catholic HS; Morris Plains, NJ; (4); 47/138; Art Clb; French Clb; Hosp Aide; Math Tm; Pep Clb; PAVAS; Service Clb; Ski Clb; School Musical; Pres Schlr; Art Cntst Wnnr 82; Voluntr Awd 100 Hrs 84; Pres Acadmc Awd 87; Catholic U Amer; Advrtsng.

DIEKER, MARYANN; Sayreville Mar Memorial HS; S Amboy, NJ; (2); Spanish Clb; SADD; Varsity Clb; Chorus; Rep Frsh Cls; Rep Soph Cls; Var L Crs Cntry; Hon Roll; Pres Schlr; Grtr Middlesez Cnty Conf All-Acdmc Hnr Roll 86-87.

DIEM JR, ARTHUR N; South River HS; South River, NJ; (4); 3/128; Am Leg Boys St; Var Bsktbl; Var Capt Ftbl; Hon Roll; NHS; Acadmc Vrsty Ltr 83-84; Schlr Athl, Wm C Denny Chapt Natl Ftbl Hall Fame 87; Pres Acad Ftnss Awd 87; Purdue U; Elec Engrng Tech.

DIETER, BRIAN; Victory Christian Schl; Williamstown, NJ; (4); Yrbk Stf; Off Soph Cls; Off Jr Cls; Off Sr Cls; Var Bsbl; Var Bsktbl; Var Mgr(s); Var Socr; Hon Roll; Letourneau; Comp Sci.

DIETERICH III, HENRY; Highland Regional HS; Blenheim, NJ; (3); AFS; Drama Clb; French Clb; School Musical; School Play; Pres Stage Crew; Variety Show; Nwsp Rptr; Emcee Tony Awds 87; Cert Merit Awd Actvty Pnts 86; Theatre Prg 86; Theatre.

DIFFLEY, EILEEN; Notre Dame HS; Kendall Pk, NJ; (2); 116/410; Church Yth Grp; Red Cross Aide; Speech Tm; Var L Mgr(s); Mount Saint Marys Coll.

DIFRANCO, DAWN; Hackettstown HS; Hackettstown, NJ; (3); 6/191; Q&S; Teachers Aide; Drm & Bgl; Yrbk Bus Mgr; Stu Cncl; Stat Bsktbl; Socr; High Hon Roll; Hon Roll; NHS; Teaching.

DIGAN, MARJORIE L; Southern Regional HS; Manahawkin, NJ; (3); 44/458; Church Yth Grp; Pep Clb; Off Stu Cncl; JV Fld Hcky; JV Powder Puff Ftbl; JV Capt Sftbl; DAR Awd; High Hon Roll; Hon Roll; NHS; Schlstc Athlt Acdmc Excllnc Drng Sftbl 85 & 86; Sprts Med.

DIGAN, MATTHEW; Pinelands Regional HS; Tuckerton, NJ; (3); 1/300; Aud/Vis; Drama Clb; French Clb; Science Clb; School Play; Stage Crew; Lit Mag; Vllybl; French Hon Soc; Gov Hon Prg Awd; Gov Schl Creatve Wrtng 87; Rutgers Hnr Schlr 87; Engrng.

DIGGS, KEVIN G; Montclair HS; Montclair, NJ; (4); Spanish Clb; Ftbl; Co-Capt Swmmng; Hon Roll; Natl Merit Scholar Outstndng Negro Stu 87; U MA; Engrng.

DIGIACOMO, ANGELA; Edgewood Regional SR HS; Sicklerville, NJ; (3); GAA; Red Cross Aide; ROTC; Lit Mag; Sftbl; Hnrbl Mntn Hnr Rl 86-87; Philadelphia Art Inst; Art.

DIGIACOMO, CARMELLA; Lyndhurst HS; Lyndhurst, NJ; (3); 16/175; Am Leg Aux Girls St; Pres Soph Cls; Pres Jr Cls; Hon Roll; NHS; Perfect Atten Awd 85; Berkely; Bus Mgmnt.

DIGIOVANNI, LAURA; Wildwood Catholic HS; Wildwood Crest, NJ; (4); 4/85; Exploring; Sec Stu Cncl; Mgr(s); Tennis; Hon Roll; NHS; Pres Schlr; Rotary Awd; US Math Awds 84-86; Putgers Schl; Engr.

DIGNEO, COSMO; Chery Hill HS West; Cherry Hill, NJ; (4); 101/360; JV Var Bsbl; JV Im Bsktbl; Var Capt Ftbl; Hon Roll; Italian Clb 84-86; Grant-Rutgers U 87; Rutgers U Camden; Acctng.

DILAURO, MICHELE; Parsippany HS; Parsippany, NJ; (3); FBLA; Latin Clb; Ski Clb; Pres Temple Yth Grp; Varsity Clb; Yrbk Phtg; Off Stu Cncl; Mat Maids; Stat Socr; Stat Wrstlng; John Hopkins ROGATE Pgm 84-86; Pharmclgy.

DILAURO, MICHELLE; Westfield HS; Westfield, NJ; (2); Math-A-Thon St Jude Chldrns Rsrch Hosp Hnr Awd, Art Poster Cont 1st Pl, Cert Rcgntn Excllnt Char 83; Grphc Arts.

DILEO, RICHARD; Hudson Catholic HS; Jersey City, NJ; (3); Var Bowling; Capt Crs Cntry; Im Vllybl; Hon Roll; NHS; Comp Sci.

DILEO, RUSSELL; Palmyra HS; Palmyra, NJ; (4); 19/121; Am Leg Boys St; Varsity Clb; Var Bsbl; JV Bsktbl; Var Socr; Hon Roll; Rotary Awd; All Conf Soccer 86; All Conf Bsbll 86; Shippensburg U.

DILKS, LISA; Sacred Heart HS; Bridgeton, NJ; (4); French Clb; Hosp Aide; SADD; Band; Variety Show; Yrbk Rptr; Lit Mag; 2nd Prz Schl Tlnt Shw; KFC Star; Cumberland Cnty Coll; Wrtng.

DILL, CHRIS; Ocean Township HS; Ocean, NJ; (4); Speech Tm; Band; Concert Band; Mrchg Band; School Musical; Lit Mag; Spartan Schlr Awd 83-84; Hartwick Coll; Med Stds.

DILL, KERI; West Milford Twp HS; West Milford, NJ; (4); 112/359; VP DECA; JV Gym; JV Trk; Hon Roll; Jr NHS; DECA 86; Psychology.

DILLON, CHERYL; Morris Knolls HS; Rockaway Twp, NJ; (3); 22/465; Hosp Aide; Varsity Clb; Lit Mag; Sec Stu Cncl; Capt Crs Cntry; Trk; High Hon Roll; NHS; Cmnty Wkr; Swmmng; Summa Awd For Acad Excel 85-86; Acad Decathalon 87; Med.

DILLON, JOSEPH F; Southern Regional HS; Manahawkin, NJ; (3); 3/450; Ski Clb; SADD; Pres Soph Cls; Pres Jr Cls; VP Stu Cncl; JV Bsbl; Var Socr; Bausch & Lomb Sci Awd; Gov Hon Prg Awd; High Hon Roll; HOBY 86; Wnnr Sthrn Rgnl HS Sci Fair 87; West Point; Engrng.

DILLON, TARA; St John Vianney HS; Hazlet, NJ; (2); 14/270; Service Clb; SADD; Nwsp Stf; Pres Frsh Cls; Sec Soph Cls; JV Var Tennis; Hon Roll; Gold & White Awd; Ecnmcs.

DILUZIO, ALAINE; Delran HS; Delran, NJ; (3); 30/185; Church Yth Grp; Yrbk Stf; Capt Bowling; Capt Fld Hcky; Var Lcrss; JR Mrksmn-Dstngshd Expert-Air Rifle 86; NRA JR Olympc Shootng Pgm-Dstngshd Expert 86; Bus.

DILZER, SCOTT; Butler HS; Butler, NJ; (3); 11/170; Am Leg Boys St; Boy Scts; Drama Clb; Math Clb; Band; Chorus; Concert Band; Mrchg Band; Pep Band; School Musical; U Of Richmond; Pre-Med.

DIMAGGIO, PETER; Leonia HS; Leonia, NJ; (3); 7/129; French Clb; Socr; Wrstlng; High Hon Roll; Hon Roll; East Coast Rgnl Slct Sccr Tm 86; Star Ldgr 1st Tm All ST Grp 1 Sccr 87; NJ ST Slct Sccr Tm 87; Engrng.

DIMENNA, ANGELA; Paul VI HS; Glendora, NJ; (4); 48/500; High Hon Roll; Hon Roll; NHS; Lincoln Bus Inst; Trvl.

DINALLO, DENNIS M; Hasbrouck Heights HS; Hasbrouck Heights, NJ; (4); 40/150; Art Clb; Church Yth Grp; Cmnty Wkr; Pres DECA; French Clb; Letterman Clb; Ski Clb; Varsity Clb; Stu Cncl; Capt Bsbl; Mst Vlbl Plyr Awd-Bsbl 87; Stu Of Yr Awd DECA & Pres Of DECA Hnr 86-87; St Thomas Aquinas Coll; Bus.

DINAPOLI, CARL D; St Marys HS; Carlstadt, NJ; (3); Am Leg Boys St; Chess Clb; Science Clb; Yrbk Phtg; Ftbl; Trk; ST Marys Gldn M Awds 85-87; Achvt In Math & Art 84-87; Arch.

DINARDO, CHRISTOPHER; Paulsboro HS; Gibbstown, NJ; (3); JV Bsbl; JV Ftbl; High Hon Roll; Hon Roll; Glassboro ST; Lbrl Arts.

DINCUFF, CHRISTOPHER; South River HS; South River, NJ; (3); 1/130; Am Leg Boys St; Pres Frsh Cls; Pres Soph Cls; Pres Jr Cls; Pres Sr Cls; Var L Bsbl; Var L Ftbl; NHS; French Clb; Quiz Bowl; Rutgers Schlr Pgm 87; Greater Middlesex Conf 86-87; Acdmc Ltr 86-87.

DINGERTOPADRE, DENISE; Cliffside Park HS; Fairview, NJ; (3); 36/234; Office Aide; Political Wkr; Sec Trs Spanish Clb; Yrbk Phtg; Yrbk Rptr; Yrbk Stf; Hon Roll; Erly Chldhd Ed.

DINH, NHAN; Dover HS; Dover, NJ; (3); 7/280; Key Clb; Math Tm; Yrbk Stf; JV Bsktbl; Var Trk; High Hon Roll; NHS; Grmn & Bio Awd 86; Acad All-Amer 86; Bus.

DINKLAGE, PETER H; Delbarton School; Brookside, NJ; (4); Church Yth Grp; Cmnty Wkr; Drama Clb; Chorus; School Musical; School Play; Stage Crew; Lit Mag; Outstdng Achvmnt Drama 87; Bennington Coll; Playwrtng.

DINKLER, DEBORAH; The Kings Christian HS; Burlington, NJ; (3); Band; Pres Chorus; Yrbk Stf; Trs Stu Cncl; L Var Bsktbl; L Var Fld Hcky; L Var Sftbl; High Hon Roll; NHS; Educ.

DINOFA, JEFFREY; Holy Spirit HS; Somers Pt, NJ; (3); 85/332; NHS; Stotesbury Cup, Gold Mdl Natl Chmpnshp 87; Phila City Chmpnshp Gold, Mdl, Stotesbury Cup Gold Mdl 86; Bus Admin.

DINOLA, RALPH; Kittatinny Regional HS; Newton, NJ; (4); 40/224; German Clb; Letterman Clb; Varsity Clb; Swmmng; Pres Schlr; Pratt Schl; Arch.

DINSHAH, ANNE; Delsea HS; Malaga, NJ; (4); 5/213; Concert Band; Mrchg Band; Rep Stu Cncl; Var Capt Diving; Var Capt Swmmng; Var Capt Trk; Im Wt Lftg; Hon Roll; JP Sousa Awd; NHS; Swmmng MVP 87; Grdn ST Dstngshd Schlrs 87; Buena Exhng Clb Stu Of Mon 87; U Of Notre Dame; Cvl Engnrng.

DIONISIO, FRANCIS; St Josephs Prep Seminary; Hazlet, NJ; (3); 1/9; Latin Clb; Spanish Clb; Chorus; Yrbk Stf; Rep Jr Cls; Var Socr; Hon Roll; NHS; St Josephs Awd Acad Achvt 86; St Johns U; Chem.

DIONISIO, ROMMEL T; Morristown-Beard Schl; Parsippany, NJ; (4); 1/81; Nwsp Ed-Chief; Capt Var Bsbl; DAR Awd; Ntl Merit Schol; St Schlr; Mrrstwn-Beard Schl Merit Schlr 81-87; Presdntl Schlr-Rutgers U; Natl Merit Schlrshp; St Schlr; Harvard; Med.

DIPOTO, MARC; Toms River HS North; Leawood, KS; (3); 29/438; Am Leg Boys St; Jazz Band; Mrchg Band; Nwsp Sprt Ed; Yrbk Rptr; JV Trk; High Hon Roll; Hon Roll; NHS; Law.

DIPOTO, NICOLE; Secaucus HS; Secaucus, NJ; (3); Key Clb; Math Clb; Varsity Clb; Bsbl; Bsktbl; Score Keeper; Hon Roll; Elem Ed.

DIPPLE, LINDA; Burlington Co Vo-Tech; Edgwater Park, NJ; (3); 20/198; Nwsp Stf; Pres Jr Cls; Bsbl; Sftbl; Hon Roll; Stu Ldrshp 86-87; Trenton ST; Physcgst.

DIPSEY, CHERIE; Passaic Valley HS; W Paterson, NJ; (2); 85/328; Drama Clb; GAA; School Play; Hon Roll; Journlsm.

DIRENZO, BETH; Cherry Hill West HS; Cherry Hill, NJ; (3); Am Leg Aux Girls St; GAA; Rep Stu Cncl; Capt Var Bsktbl; Capt Var Fld Hcky; Var Lcrss; Bktbl-1st Tm-All Grp 3 & Hnrbl Mntn 87; Lacrss-Mhwk Div-1st Tm 87; Educ.

DIRENZO, JENNIFER; Cherry Hill West HS; Cherry Hill, NJ; (3); Sr Cls; Rep Stu Cncl; Var Bsktbl; Var Fld Hcky; Var Lcrss; Hon Roll; Pre-Med.

DIRENZO, MARIA; Morris Catholic HS; Boonton, NJ; (4); 30/135; FBLA; Natl Beta Clb; Pres Pep Clb; Varsity Clb; Yrbk Stf; Rep Frsh Cls; Rep Soph Cls; VP Stu Cncl; JV Var Bsktbl; Hon Roll; Boston U; Bus.

DIRENZO, MARIELLA; Morris Catholic HS; Boonton, NJ; (3); 31/136; Cmnty Wkr; FBLA; VP JA; Natl Beta Clb; Varsity Clb; Yrbk Stf; Rep Frsh Cls; Rep Soph Cls; VP Stu Cncl; JV Var Bsktbl; Bus.

DIRUGGIERO, CATHERINE; Wayne Hills HS; Wayne, NJ; (3); 20/320; Church Yth Grp; GAA; Spanish Clb; Yrbk Stf; Lit Mag; NHS; Chorus; Church Choir; Hon Roll; Acdmc All-Amer Schlr & US Natl Art Awd 86; Liberal Arts.

DISCIASCIO, CHRISTOPHER; Ocean City HS; Ocean City, NJ; (3); 80/342; CAP; French Clb; Yrbk Stf; VP Frsh Cls; Pres Sr Cls; Rep Stu Cncl; Var Capt Crs Cntry; Var Capt Trk; Hon Roll; Crs Cntry All Star Tm Hnrb Mntn 86-87; Aerospc Engrng.

DISMUKES, REUBEN; Linden HS; Linden, NJ; (4); 13/345; Science Clb; Band; Jazz Band; Orch; School Musical; Bsbl; Kiwanis Awd; NHS; LHS Sprts Announcr/Mrng Show 87; Mst Frndly Boy 87; De Vry Tech Inst; Elec Tech.

DISPENZA, PHILIP; Memorial HS; West New York, NJ; (3); Chess Clb; Church Yth Grp; Math Clb; Church Choir; Bowling; Trk; Hon Roll; Jr NHS; NHS; Elec Engrng.

DITARANTO, LANA; Perth Amboy HS; Perth Amboy, NJ; (3); JA; Hon Roll; Drake Bus Schl; Bus.

DITTMAR, CHRISTIE; Mt Olive HS; Hackettstown, NJ; (3); Dance Clb; Drama Clb; FBLA; Science Clb; Ski Clb; SADD; Church Choir; School Musical; School Play; Nwsp Stf; Brdcstng.

DITURI, FRANK L; Morris Catholic HS; Morris Plains, NJ; (3); 6/136; German Clb; Math Tm; Natl Beta Clb; Scholastic Bowl; Concert Band; Rep Jr Cls; Hon Roll; NHS; Library Aide; Orch; 1st Pl Trophy Cath Math Lg 86; Bronze Mdl Regnl Acad Decthln 87; Hnr Rl Mdl 87; Med.

DIVERS, GEORGIANNA; Perth Amboy HS; Perth Amboy, NJ; (3); Drama Clb; German Clb; Model UN; Office Aide; Church Choir; Color Guard; Sec Sr Cls; Trk; Hon Roll; 2 Plus 2 Comp Pgm-Middlesex Cnty Coll 86-87; Princeton U; Corprt Atty.

DIX, JANET M; Montclair Kimberley Acad; Wayne, NJ; (4); Cmnty Wkr; School Play; Ed Nwsp Ed-Chief; Ed Lit Mag; Hon Roll; Ntl Merit Ltr; Brown U; Biomed Ethics.

DIXON, ANDREA; Delaware Valley Regional HS; Milford, NJ; (2); Pres Church Yth Grp; French Clb; GAA; Key Clb; Service Clb; Church Choir; Bsktbl; JV Crs Cntry; Stat Fld Hcky; Hon Roll; Berkeley; Intl Bus.

DIXON, JUSTINE; Paul VI Regional HS; Cedar Grove, NJ; (3); Key Clb; VP Science Clb; Rep Soph Cls; Sec Stu Cncl; Var Capt Bsktbl; Var Cheerleading; Stat Score Keeper; Var Sftbl; French Hon Soc; Hon Roll; Intl Frgn Lang Awd Frnch 85-87.

DIXON, RICHELLE; Cumberland Regional HS; Bridgeton, NJ; (3); 17/386; Trs Church Yth Grp; Spanish Clb; Teachers Aide; Var Bsktbl; Var Sftbl; High Hon Roll; Hon Roll; NHS; Fld Hcky; Tennis; Comm.

DJURASOVIC, GEORGE; Union HS; Union, NJ; (2); Science Clb; Service Clb; Spanish Clb; Off Soph Cls; Off Jr Cls; Off Stu Cncl; Crs Cntry; Trk; NEDT Awd; St Sci Lge Awd 87; Socl/Acadmc Awd 86; Pres Acadmc Ftns Awd 86.

DLABIK, KATHLEEN; Howell HS; Howell, NJ; (3); French Clb; Intnl Clb; Var JV Cheerleading; Var JV Socr; Hon Roll; NHS.

DOBIE, ROBERT DENNIS; Haddonfield Memorial HS; Haddonfield, NJ; (3); 65/180; Am Leg Boys St; Trs Church Yth Grp; Rep Soph Cls; Stu Cncl; Var Bsbl; Bsktbl; Var Socr; Hon Roll; Math.

DOBIES, JUSTINE; Paulsboro HS; Gibbstown, NJ; (3); 1/150; Hosp Aide; Nwsp Ed-Chief; Var Crs Cntry; Var Trk; High Hon Roll; NHS; St Schlr; Med.

DOBOVICH, SCOTT; Jackson Memorial HS; Jackson, NJ; (3); 39/416; Hosp Aide; ROTC; Varsity Clb; Drill Tm; JV Capt Ftbl; JV Var Wrstlng; High Hon Roll; Math Tm; Vrsty Wrstlng Sprtsmnshp Awd 85; Military Order Of Word Wars 86; Schlrshp Awd 85; Citadel; Pilot.

DOBRES, ROBT; North Arlington HS; N Arlington, NJ; (3); 20/120; Letterman Clb; Science Clb; Varsity Clb; Trs Band; Trs Concert Band; Trs Jazz Band; Trs Mrchg Band; NCTE Awd; Var Capt Bowling; Credit List; Sci.

DOBROW, LARRY; Ramapo HS; Franklin Lakes, NJ; (3); 16/322; Trs French Clb; Radio Clb; Temple Yth Grp; Nwsp Bus Mgr; Capt Yrbk Stf; Lit Mag; Rep Stu Cncl; Var Trk; NHS; Ntl Merit Ltr.

DOBROWOLSKI, SUZANNE J; Hopewell Valley Central HS; Pennington, NJ; (4); DECA; FBLA; Yrbk Stf; Hon Roll; Prfct Atten Awd; 1st Pl Cntrl Jersey Stu Crftsmn Fair 87; The Bobby Stover Memorial Schlrshp 87; Mercer Cnty Cmnty; Advrtsng Dsg.

DOBSON, BYRON; Atlantic City HS; Atlantic City, NJ; (2); Church Yth Grp; Computer Clb; Latin Clb; Model UN; Office Aide; Science Clb; Band; Concert Band; Jazz Band; Mrchg Band; Drexle Inst; Comp Engr.

DOCARMO, PETER; Toms River HS; Beachwood, NJ; (3); 28/405; Letterman Clb; Math Tm; Political Wkr; Ski Clb; Varsity Clb; Var Capt Ice Hcky; Im Powder Puff Ftbl; U Of NH; Mech Engr.

DODD, CHRISTIN; Middle Township HS; Avalon, NJ; (3); 2/250; Key Clb; Ski Clb; Chorus; Yrbk Stf; Trs Stu Cncl; Var Cheerleading; JV Fld Hcky; High Hon Roll; Jr NHS; NHS; Acad Excllnc Awd Frnch Achvmnt Awd; Math.

DODGE, JENNIFER; Vineland HS; Vineland, NJ; (3); 47/678; German Clb; Service Clb; Orch; Yrbk Stf; Hon Roll; NHS; All S Jrsy Orch 83-87; NJ ST Orch 85-87; All Estrn Orch Alt 87; Music.

DODGE, WILLIAM HEES; Montgomery HS; Princeton, NJ; (3); 2/103; Am Leg Boys St; Boy Scts; Drama Clb; Chrmn Model UN; Band; JV Tennis; Hon Roll; NHS; Ntl Merit Ltr; St Schlr; Rnk Exprt JR Natl Rfle Assn 87; NY Schlrs Pgm 87; Eagle Sct 85; Chem Engr.

DOE, RENEE; Bayonne HS; Bayonne, NJ; (4); 18/345; Computer Clb; Dance Clb; French Clb; FBLA; Key Clb; NAACP; Spanish Clb; Church Choir; School Musical; School Play; Old Dominion U Almnae Merit Schlrshp 87; Dr David G Morris Awd 87; Old Dominion U; Advrtsng.

DOERFLEIN, DENISE; Middletown HS South; Leonardo, NJ; (4); 127/478; Library Aide; Nwsp Ed-Chief; Nwsp Rptr; Yrbk Stf; Lit Mag; Rep Sr Cls; Fld Hcky; Twrlr; High Hon Roll; Hon Roll; Lit Cont Wnnr Poem 85; Montclaire ST Coll; Bus Mgmt.

DOERR, DIANE; East Brunswick HS; E Brunswick, NJ; (4); Varsity Clb; Chorus; Var Crs Cntry; JV Gym; Var Trk; Elon Coll; Psych.

DOHANICK, MICHELE; Pinelands Regional HS; Tuckerton, NJ; (3); #12 In Class; French Clb; Yrbk Stf; French Hon Soc; Hon Roll; NHS.

DOHERTY, DEBBIE; John P Stevens HS; Edison, NJ; (3); 41/485; Am Leg Aux Girls St; Hosp Aide; Key Clb; Ski Clb; SADD; Drill Tm; Powder Puff Ftbl; French Hon Soc; NHS; Band; Girls Ctznshp Nom 87; Bus Admn.

DOHERTY, DENA; Cranford HS; Cranford, NJ; (2); Stu Cncl; Bsktbl; Sftbl; Hon Roll; Score Keeper; Csmtlgy.

DOHERTY, DENISE; Bishop Ahr HS; Metuchen, NJ; (3); 64/267; Spanish Clb; Color Guard; Gym; High Hon Roll; Hon Roll; Cand Natl Hnr Soc, Chrstian Scl Actn Clb 86-87; Hnr Grd 85-86.

DOHERTY, SHEILA; Elizabeth HS; Elizabeth, NJ; (4); 131/841; Band; Bsktbl; Mgr(s); Var Capt Socr; Var Capt Sftbl; Schlrshps; Willm S Drby Mem Athltc Awd 87; Seton Hall U; Crmnl Jstc.

DOHMAN, DEANA; Parsippany HS; Lake Hiawatha, NJ; (3); Pres Church Yth Grp; Pep Clb; Spanish Clb; Concert Band; JV Var Sftbl; High Hon Roll; Hon Roll; NHS; Mrchg Band; Stage Crew; Sci.

DOLAN, CHARLES; Hawthorne HS; Hawthorne, NJ; (3); Am Leg Boys St; Boys Clb Am; Math Tm; Var Bsbl; Ftbl; Hon Roll; NHS; Rutgers U.

DOLAN, GEORGE M; Bergen Catholic HS; North Bergen, NJ; (3); 30/275; Am Leg Boys St; Political Wkr; Yrbk Phtg; Im Bowling; Im Tennis; Im Vllybl; High Hon Roll; NHS; Spanish NHS; Vlntr Amer Civil Liberties Union; Philosphy.

DOLAN, MICHAEL; Holy Spirit HS; Atlantic City, NJ; (2); 16/397; Drama Clb; School Play; Survyr.

DOLAN, MICHAEL K; Northern Burlington Co Reg HS; Columbus, NJ; (4); 4/238; Am Leg Boys St; Math Tm; Band; Var JV Ftbl; Var JV Trk; French Hon Soc; High Hon Roll; Hon Roll; NHS; Schlr Ldr Athl Awd Natl Ftbl Fndtn 87; Bucknell U.

DOLAN JR, ROBERT M; Msgr Donovan HS; Toms River, NJ; (3); 69/239; Drama Clb; PAVAS; Thesps; Jazz Band; School Musical; School Play; Stage Crew; Var L Socr; Hon Roll; NHS; Elect Engr.

DOLATLY, MARGUERITA; Lacordaire Acad; Clifton, NJ; (3); 1/33; Service Clb; Nwsp Ed-Chief; Ed Yrbk Stf; Lit Mag; High Hon Roll; NHS; Ntl Merit Ltr; NEDT Awd; Debate Tm; Intnl Clb; Yale 2ndry Schl Bk Awd 87; George Washngtn U Engrng Mdl 87; Latn Natl Hnr Soc 85-86.

DOLCE, DANNY; St Joseph Regional HS; Valley Cottage, NY; (3); Church Yth Grp; Rep Stu Cncl; Bsbl; Ftbl; Spanish NHS; Bus.

DOLCE, GINA; Triton Regional HS; Bellmawr, NJ; (4); 1/309; Capt Color Guard; Capt Mrchg Band; Sec Stu Cncl; High Hon Roll; NHS; Ntl Merit Ltr; St Schlr; Val; AFS; Camera Clb; Kennedy Hosp Schlrs Prog; George Washington U Awd Math & Sci Achvmnt; Girls Citznshp Inst Delegate; Psych.

DOLCE, NICHOLAS J; Vineland HS; Newfield, NJ; (3); Key Clb; Library Aide; Rep Sr Cls; Rep Stu Cncl; JV Socr; Var JV Wrstlng; High Hon Roll; NHS; Itln Ntl Hnr Scty 86-87; Prfct Atndnc 84-87; Elec Engr.

DOLL, LILYA A; Columbia HS; Maplewood, NJ; (4); Mrchg Band; Orch; School Musical; Stage Crew; Symp Band; Rep Soph Cls; Rep Jr Cls; Im Sftbl; Ntl Merit Ltr.

DOLLBAUM, DAN; Memorial JR-SR HS; Elmwood Park, NJ; (3); 6/168; Spanish Clb; Band; Concert Band; Mrchg Band; Var L Tennis; High Hon Roll; NHS; Spanish NHS; New Jersey Math Lge Schl Champ 85-86; Stats.

DOLQUEIST, LORI; Holy Spirit HS; Absecon, NJ; (3); 10/332; Exploring; Hosp Aide; Radio Clb; Spanish Clb; Nwsp Bus Mgr; High Hon Roll; Mock Trl Comptn 86; Englsh Achvt Awd 86; Histry Achvt Awd 85.

DOLSON, ANITA; Buena Reg HS; Vineland, NJ; (4); 4/180; Drama Clb; Math Clb; Pres Varsity Clb; Stage Crew; Pres Frsh Cls; Trs Soph Cls; Sec Stu Cncl; Capt Fld Hcky; Var Sftbl; NHS; Mrktg.

DOLSON, CANDY; A P Schalick HS; Elmer, NJ; (3); #27 In Class; Church Yth Grp; SADD; Off Band; Church Choir; Off Concert Band; Off Mrchg Band; Variety Show; JV L Bsktbl; JV L Sftbl; Tennis; Schalick Band Bst Sect Awd-Clarinet 84-85; All Salem Cnty Band 86-88; Music.

DOMINGO, ERNANI; Saint Peters Preparatory Schl; Jersey City, NJ; (4); 7/196; Sec Chess Clb; Sec SADD; Lit Mag; Pres Frsh Cls; CC Awd; High Hon Roll; NHS; Wrld Civlztn Gld Medl 84; Bio Gld Medl & Spnsh I Gld Medl 85; Spnsh II Gld Medl & 2nd Hnrs Cert 86; Boston Coll; Bio.

DOMOND, HERBY; Abraham Clark HS; Roselle, NJ; (3); Church Yth Grp; Model UN; Church Choir; Bsktbl; Ftbl; Score Keeper; Timer; Trk; Prfct Atten Awd.

DOMURAT, ERIN; Hunterdon Central HS; Stockton, NJ; (2); 57/478; Church Yth Grp; Cmnty Wkr; FCA; Service Clb; Ski Clb; JV Bsktbl; Stat Ftbl; Mgr(s); Score Keeper; Var Trk.

DOMZALSKI JR, JOSEPH L; Morris Hills HS; Rockaway, NJ; (3); 90/265; Science Clb; Trk; Comp Sci.

DON, COURTNEY; Holy Cross HS; Medford, NJ; (4); Pres Model UN; Service Clb; Ski Clb; Nwsp Rptr; Ed Nwsp Stf; Hon Roll; NHS; Burlington Cnty Mock Trl Chmpshp 87; American U; Intl Rltns.

DON, RICHARD E; Delran HS; Delran, NJ; (4); 21/189; Band; Chorus; Concert Band; Mrchg Band; School Musical; School Play; Pres Schlr; Color Guard; Jazz Band; Orch; Principals Awd Svc 86-87; Delran Parents Music Assn Music Achvt Awd 86-87; Acad Excllnce Scholar 86-87; Northwood Inst; Comp Sci.

DONAGHY, FRANK; Burlington City HS; Burlington, NJ; (3); Am Leg Boys St; Rep Frsh Cls; Rep Soph Cls; Bsbl; Ftbl; Hon Roll; Syracuse U; Elec Engr.

DONAGHY, KIMBERLY; Lakewood HS; Lakewood, NJ; (4); 55/267; GAA; Crs Cntry; Socr; Trk; Hon Roll; Capt Of Jr Vrsty Socr 85; Capt Of Girls Vrsty Socr 86-87; Vrsty Lttrs For Socr X-Cntry Trk 83-87; Montclair ST Coll.

DONAHUE, CRAIG W; Indian Hills Regional HS; Oakland, NJ; (4); 2/282; Am Leg Boys St; Boy Scts; Science Clb; Chorus; Var Bsbl; JV Bsktbl; Var Bowling; Ftbl; Trs NHS; Ntl Merit SF; Hgh Hnr Rll 83-86; Princeton; Cvl Engnr.

DONAHUE, LISA; Highland Regional HS; Blackwood, NJ; (3); 10/285; French Clb; Service Clb; NHS.

DONAHUE, MEGHAN; St John Vianney HS; Colts Neck, NJ; (2); Church Yth Grp; Office Aide; Ski Clb; SADD; School Play; Yrbk Stf; JV L Bsktbl; JV Crs Cntry; Stat Ftbl; Hon Roll.

DONAHUE, SEAN; Pinelands Regional HS; New Gretna, NJ; (3); SADD; Var Crs Cntry; Var Trk; JV Wrstlng; Hon Roll; Ldrshp Grp; Vrsty Cross Cntry Sprtsprsn Awd; Sprts Med.

DONALD, STEPHANIE L; Vernon Twp HS; Glenwood, NJ; (4); 5/250; Pres Thesps; Acpl Chr; Concert Band; Jazz Band; School Musical; NHS; Pres Schlr; Drama Clb; Band; Pres Chorus; Chopin Piano Awd & Excllnc Acting-Female 85-87; Natl Schl Choral Awd 87; FL ST U; Music Theory.

DONALDSON, LAURA; Washington Township HS; Sewell, NJ; (3); Am Leg Aux Girls St; Church Yth Grp; French Clb; Rep Stu Cncl; Stat Bsktbl; Fld Hcky; Capt Var Socr; JV Sftbl; Hon Roll; NHS; Pre-Med.

DONALDSON, PAMELA; Trenton Central HS; Trenton, NJ; (3); Dance Clb; Hosp Aide; Office Aide; Color Guard; Mrchg Band; School Play; Lit Mag; Rep Soph Cls; Pom Pon; Prfct Atten Awd; Acdmc Altamer Schlr & Volunteer Med File Clerk 84-85; Morris Brown Coll; Poltcl Sci.

DONALDSON, TIMOTHY; Gloucester County Christian HS; Pitman, NJ; (3); Church Yth Grp; French Clb; Library Aide; Trs Frsh Cls; High Hon Roll; Hon Roll; Telecmnctns.

DONAR, PAMELA; Roselle Catholic HS; Roselle, NJ; (4); Cmnty Wkr; Lit Mag; French Hon Soc; Hon Roll; Natl Bus Hnr Soc; Montclair ST; Bus Admin.

DONAT, CHRIS R; Summit HS; Summit, NJ; (4); 13/270; Model UN; Scholastic Bowl; Yrbk Stf; JV Im Bsktbl; Var L Lcrss; JV Socr; Wt Lftg; NHS; Ntl Merit SF.

DONATACCI, CHRIS; Perth Amboy HS; Perth Amboy, NJ; (3); French Clb; Bowling; Score Keeper; Sftbl; Mngt.

DONATH, ROBERT; Buena Reg HS; Estell Manor, NJ; (3); Lincoln Tech Schl; Elec.

DONATO, LESLIE; Paul VI HS; Medford, NJ; (4); 8/511; Math Clb; Chrmn SADD; Yrbk Sprt Ed; Capt L Tennis; French Hon Soc; High Hon Roll; Hon Roll; NHS; Ntl Merit Ltr; Tennis Plyr Yr, All South Jersey 86; Alumni Schlrshp Trenton ST Coll 86; Bus Admin.

DONDERO, LISA; Sacred Heart HS; Vineland, NJ; (4); French Clb; Girl Scts; Chorus; School Musical; School Play; Yrbk Stf; Im Mgr Bsktbl; Var Swmmng; Im Mgr Vllybl; Hon Roll; 3rd Pl In Sci Fair 84; Trenton ST Coll; Bio.

DONDERO, TOM; West Essex HS; No Caldwell, NJ; (3); Aud/Vis; Church Yth Grp; Scholastic Bowl; Varsity Clb; Rptr Frsh Cls; Rptr Soph Cls; Rptr Jr Cls; Stu Cncl; Var Ftbl; Im Swmmng; SR Ctzns Activities; Blood Bank; U VT; Bus Adm.

DONEGAN, COLLEEN; Jackson Memorial HS; Jackson, NJ; (3); 96/416; German Clb; Ski Clb; Varsity Clb; Band; Mrchg Band; Off Stu Cncl; Fld Hcky; Mgr(s); Sftbl; High Hon Roll; Nrsng.

DONEGAN, JAMES D; Wall Kill Valley Regional HS; Ogdensburg, NJ; (3); 18/180; Am Leg Boys St; Math Tm; SADD; Var L Crs Cntry; JV Socr; Var L Trk; Var L Wrstlng; Hon Roll; NHS.

DONEY, MARYANN; Linden HS; Linden, NJ; (3); Church Yth Grp; FHA; Girl Scts; Hosp Aide; Key Clb; Csmtlgy.

DONIA, MARIA; Holy Cross HS; Maple Shade, NJ; (4); 100/353; Church Yth Grp; Sftbl; Hon Roll; Drexel U; Acctng.

DONIA, SANTO; Paul VI HS; Sewell, NJ; (4); 17/503; Math Clb; NFL; Mrchg Band; VP Soph Cls; VP Jr Cls; VP Sr Cls; Swmmng; Trk; High Hon Roll; NHS; St Josephs U; Food Mrktng.

DONIO, ADRIENNE; St Joseph HS; Hammonton, NJ; (3); Cmnty Wkr; SADD; Stage Crew; Lit Mag; Stat Bsbl; JV Var Cheerleading; JV Fld Hcky; JV Mgr(s); JV Score Keeper; Hnr Rl Merit 84-86.

DONNANGELO II, JOHN A; Northern Valley Regional HS; Haworth, NJ; (4); Am Leg Boys St; Church Yth Grp; Political Wkr; Hon Roll; Acdmc Dcthln, Twn Ars Cncl 87; Congrssnl Intern 87-88; Washington, DC, Wrkshp Pgm 85-86; Law.

DONNELLY, BERNARD JAY; Shawnee HS; Medford, NJ; (4); 14/534; Math Tm; SADD; Hon Roll; NHS; Pres Acadmc Awd 87; Fin.

DONNELLY, JOHN; Bridgewater-Raritan HS West; Bridgewater, NJ; (4); Pres Key Clb; Office Aide; Science Clb; Yrbk Stf; Lit Mag; Var Golf; Hon Roll; Pres Schlr; Trenton ST Coll; Math Ed.

DONNELLY, KOFI; Boonton HS; Boonton, NJ; (2); Computer Clb; French Clb; Math Tm; Quiz Bowl; Ski Clb; High Hon Roll.

DONNELLY, MEAGAN; St Rose HS; Pt Pleasant, NJ; (3); Drama Clb; Ski Clb; Yrbk Stf; Var Trk; Im Vllybl; Hon Roll; NEDT Awd; Bio.

DONNELLY, TARA; Westfield HS; Westfield, NJ; (3); Church Yth Grp; Key Clb; SADD; Chorus; Yrbk Stf; Hon Roll; Fshn.

DONOFRIO, ALISON; James Caldwell HS; W Caldwell, NJ; (3); Key Clb; Off Frsh Cls; Off Soph Cls; Stu Cncl; Cheerleading; Hon Roll; Bus.

DONOFRIO, JEANNE; Waldwick HS; Waldwick, NJ; (3); 4/140; Math Clb; Concert Band; Mrchg Band; Sftbl; Tennis; Cit Awd; High Hon Roll; Hon Roll; Delgt For Ctznshp-Douglas Coll 87; Wrtrs Ad 87; Acctng.

DONOGHUE, JOANNA; Middletown HS South; Middletown, NJ; (3); Trs 4-H; Flag Corp; Mrchg Band; Nwsp Rptr; Nwsp Stf; Yrbk Stf; Trk; Cit Awd; 4-H Awd; Hon Roll; Pomona Grange Awd 86; Silver Congressional Awd 87; Brd Of Educ Cmmndnt 86-87; Bus.

DONOHUE JR, JAMES F; Clearview Regional HS; Mantua, NJ; (3); 24/191; Church Yth Grp; Exploring; JV L Bsbl; JV L Bsktbl; High Hon Roll; Hon Roll; NHS; Prfct Atten Awd; US Naval Acad; Pre Law.

DONOHUE, JENNIFER; North Warren Regional HS; Blairstown, NJ; (4); FBLA; Ski Clb; High Hon Roll; Hon Roll; Rotary Awd; Stat Bsktbl; Var Cheerleading; Var Fld Hcky; Stat Sftbl; Accntng Club Schlrshp, Rotary Anns Schlrshp 87; Rider Coll; Accntng.

DONOHUE, LORI J; West Milford HS; West Milford, NJ; (3); 89/400; French Clb; Varsity Clb; Nwsp Stf; Yrbk Stf; Socr; French Hon Soc; Hon Roll; Jr NHS; Bus.

DONOHUE, ROBERT; Clearview Regional HS; Mantua, NJ; (3); 29/191; Church Yth Grp; Exploring; Var L Bsbl; Var L Bsktbl; High Hon Roll; Hon Roll; NHS; Prfct Atten Awd; US Naval Acad; Pre-Law.

DONOHUE, THOMAS; Christian Brothers Acad; Middletown, NJ; (3); 33/240; Church Yth Grp; Rep Jr Cls; Trs Sr Cls; Trs Stu Cncl; Var L Bsktbl; Var L Socr; High Hon Roll; Hon Roll; NHS.

DONOVAN, JAMIE; Livingston HS; Livingston, NJ; (3); 20/417; Teachers Aide; Ed Lit Mag; Capt Wrstlng; High Hon Roll; Hon Roll; Spanish NHS; Eastr Seals Telethn Oprtr 84-86; 6th Pl-NJ Chptr Ntl Spnsh & Prtgus Tchrs Assc Exam 87; Intl Bus.

DONOVAN, JEAN D; Parsippany Hills HS; Parsippany, NJ; (3); Sec Key Clb; Spanish Clb; Sec Stu Cncl; Hon Roll; NHS.

DONOVAN, LORI; Piscataway HS; Piscataway, NJ; (4); 20/496; Math Clb; Varsity Clb; Color Guard; Drill Tm; Capt Flag Corp; Mrchg Band; Stat Bsbl; High Hon Roll; Hon Roll; Jr NHS; Grdn St Schlrshp 87; Wmn Engr Smmr Pgm Stevens Tech Inst 86; Band & Quibbletown PTA Schlrshp 87; Rutgers Coll ; Biomdcl Engr.

DONOVAN, RAYMOND; Marist HS; Jersey City, NJ; (3); Bsktbl; Vllybl; Hon Roll; Montclair ST Coll; Bus Admin.

DONOVAN, SHANNON; Maple Shade HS; Maple Shade, NJ; (4); 8/160; French Clb; Concert Band; Mrchg Band; Yrbk Stf; High Hon Roll; Hon Roll; Jr NHS; Pres Acdmc Fit Awd 87; Frnch Clb Schlrshp 87; Rutgers-Camden.

DONUS, DAVID C; West Milford HS; Hewitt, NJ; (3); 40/402; Am Leg Boys St; German Clb; SADD; Varsity Clb; Stu Cncl; Var Capt Socr; Var Tennis; Hon Roll; Church Yth Grp; Computer Clb; Ski Tm Vrsty Cptn 1st Tm, ST, 2nd Tm Conf, ST Chmpns 86-87; FAA Prvte Pilot 87; Natl Cert Scuba Dvr; Bus.

DOODY, PATRICK A; St Josephs Regional HS; Haworth, NJ; (4); Church Yth Grp; Crs Cntry; Tennis; Trk; Jr NHS; NHS; Western New England; Bus.

DOOLEY, CHRISTINE; Mt St Mary Acad; Bernardsville, NJ; (3); 3/82; Church Yth Grp; Science Clb; Var Bsktbl; Var Fld Hcky; Var Sftbl; NHS; VP Spanish NHS; GAA; Pep Clb; Service Clb; 1st Pl Drew U Spnsh Ortry Cntst 87; Geo Wshngtn U Engrng Mdl In Math & Sci 87; Math.

DOOLEY, MARY ELLEN; Immaculate Heart Acad; Ho-Ho-Kus, NJ; (4); 3/171; Cmnty Wkr; VP Model UN; Science Clb; Var Swmmng; Var Trk; French Hon Soc; Gov Hon Prg Awd; High Hon Roll; NHS; Ntl Merit Ltr; Acad Decthln Bronze Mdl NJ ST Level 87; Yrbk Lit Edtr 87; Classcl Piano Natl Wnnr; U VA; Econ.

DORAN, LORRAINE; Immaculate Conception HS; Wallington, NJ; (3); Church Yth Grp; NFL; Yrbk Stf; Rep Soph Cls; Vllybl; Hon Roll; Ntl Merit Ltr; 1st Pl Trphy Frnscs 86; Law.

DORELL, SHERRY; Oakcrest HS; Sweetwater, NJ; (3); Aud/Vis; French Clb; Key Clb; Mrchg Band; Yrbk Stf; Lit Mag; Var Cheerleading; Hon Roll; Jr NHS; Mtl Mngmt.

DOREN, KATHRYN; Immaculate Conception HS; Passaic, NJ; (3); 12/70; Cmnty Wkr; NFL; Scholastic Bowl; SADD; Chorus; School Musical; Lit Mag; Hon Roll; English Clb; Spanish Clb; Musical Outstndg Perf 86; Cath Forensic Lg Awd Wnr 86; ENGL.

DOREY, CATHERINE; East Brunswick HS; E Brunswick, NJ; (4); Art Clb; Cmnty Wkr; Drama Clb; GAA; Pep Clb; Ski Clb; SADD; Teachers Aide; Band; Chorus; Rutgers U; Comp Pgrmmng.

DORIO, CHRISTINE; Notre Dame HS; Trenton, NJ; (1); Dance Clb; 4-H; Band; Concert Band; Mrchg Band; School Musical; Rep Stu Cncl; Hon Roll; Pres Acad Ftns Awd 87; 1st Pl Dnc Mstrs Amer 87; Emory U; Med.

DORIZAS, DENISE; Belleville SR HS; Belleville, NJ; (3); Church Yth Grp; Hosp Aide; Key Clb; Chorus; Lit Mag; Gov Hon Prg Awd; High Hon Roll; NHS; 1st Pl Poetry Cntst 87; Srv Awd Clara Maass Hosp 86; Physcn.

DORNER, DEBRA ANN; West Essex Reg HS; Fairfield, NJ; (4); 15/345; Drama Clb; Chorus; School Musical; School Play; Sftbl; Hon Roll; NHS; Assoc Amer U Wmn Schlrshp 87-88; Fairfield Kofc 87-88; Fairfield Wmns Clb 87-88; Seton Hall U.

DORNEY, JOHN; St Josephs Regional HS; Westwood, NJ; (3); Boy Scts; Chess Clb; Computer Clb; Crs Cntry; Trk; High Hon Roll; Hon Roll; Spanish NHS; Model UN; Rutgers U; Engrng.

DORR, GENE; Notre Dame HS; Hamilton Sq, NJ; (3); 6/375; Varsity Clb; Stage Crew; Rep Soph Cls; Rep Jr Cls; Var L Crs Cntry; Var L Trk; High Hon Roll; NHS; Spanish NHS; MVP Crs Cntry Tm 86; Bioengnrg.

DORRALL, PATRICE; Camden Catholic HS; Sicklerville, NJ; (3); Church Yth Grp; Girl Scts; Hosp Aide; Spanish Clb; Band; Church Choir; Concert Band; Jazz Band; Mrchg Band; School Musical; Cmmnctns.

DORRIAN, JEFFREY; South River HS; South River, NJ; (3); Church Yth Grp; Letterman Clb; Office Aide; Spanish Clb; Varsity Clb; Yrbk Stf; Var Bsbl; Im Bsktbl; Var Capt Ftbl; Aeronautics.

DORSEY, BRIAN J; Weehawken HS; Weehawken, NJ; (4); 2/94; Math Tm; Nwsp Rptr; VP Stu Cncl; Var Capt Bsbl; Var Capt Bsktbl; Var Capt Socr; Elks Awd; High Hon Roll; Kiwanis Awd; NHS; Acad Schlrshp St Peters Coll 87-91; St Peters Coll; Acctg.

DORSEY, CHRISTIAN; Atlantic City HS; Atlantic City, NJ; (2); Church Yth Grp; Cmnty Wkr; Computer Clb; JCL; Key Clb; Latin Clb; Model UN; Political Wkr; Teachers Aide; Hon Roll; Grgtwn U; Corp Law.

DORSEY, JOY A; Acad Of Saint Aloysius; Jersey City, NJ; (2); Sec Church Yth Grp; NAACP; SADD; Teachers Aide; Sec Church Choir; Nwsp Rptr; Pres Frsh Cls; Pres Soph Cls; Var Mgr(s); Hon Roll; Hampton U; Pre-Med.

DORVAL, ROGER; Wayne Valley HS; Wayne, NJ; (4); 14/311; Am Leg Boys St; Boy Scts; Computer Clb; FBLA; JV Crs Cntry; Var Trk; Var Wrstlng; High Hon Roll; Hon Roll; Hst NHS; Mtn View Schlrshp 87; PTO Schlrshp 87; Trenton ST Coll; Elec Engr.

DOS SANTOS, JENNIFER; Parkridge HS; Park Ridge, NJ; (3); AFS; PAVAS; Ski Clb; Varsity Clb; School Musical; Lit Mag; Var Cheerleading; Var Socr; High Hon Roll; Hon Roll; Natl Hnr Roll Bk 87; Villanova; Engl.

DOSCHER, KERRIE; Monsignor Donovan HS; Bayville, NJ; (3); 39/245; Church Yth Grp; Drama Clb; French Clb; Trs Intnl Clb; Spanish Clb; SADD; Thesps; School Musical; Hon Roll; NHS; Hghst Avg Frnch 85-87; Spnsh I Hghst Avg 87; Frgn Bus.

DOSHI, MANISHA; Highland Regional HS; Blackwood, NJ; (2); Band; Concert Band; Jazz Band; Mrchg Band; Im Bsktbl; Var Crs Cntry; JV Diving; Law.

DOSHI, NEHA; Parsippany Hills HS; Morris Plains, NJ; (3); 20/360; AFS; Church Yth Grp; Cmnty Wkr; Hosp Aide; Key Clb; Math Tm; Sec Spanish Clb; Yrbk Stf; Stu Cncl; NHS; Phy Thrpy.

DOSSENA, CHRISTINE; Hackettstown HS; Great Meadows, NJ; (2); Computer Clb; Intnl Clb; Key Clb; Service Clb; Chorus; School Musical; Variety Show; Var JV Cheerleading; Score Keeper; Hon Roll; Csmtlgy.

DOSSENA, COLLEEN; Hjackettstown HS; Great Meadows, NJ; (4); 69/234; GAA; Q&S; Teachers Aide; Varsity Clb; Yrbk Stf; Bsktbl; Capt Cheerleading; Capt Sftbl; Hon Roll; Prfct Atten Awd; E Stroudsburg U; Elem Educ Tchr.

DOSTIE, YVETTE; Jackson Memorial HS; Jackson, NJ; (4); 19/387; 4-H; Yrbk Stf; High Hon Roll; NHS; Jackson PBA Schlrshp 87; Hgh Achvt Comp Awd 87; Phys Ed Awd 87; Montclair ST Coll; Soclgy.

DOTHARD, DAWN; Wash Twp HS; Sewell, NJ; (4); 17/480; French Clb; Ski Clb; Sftbl; High Hon Roll; Hon Roll; NHS; U DE; Acctg.

DOTOLI, ELIZABETH; Kent Place Schl; Far Hills, NJ; (3); Cmnty Wkr; Trs Debate Tm; VP Intnl Clb; Teachers Aide; Ed Yrbk Stf; Rep Soph Cls; Rep Sr Cls; Var JV Fld Hcky; JV Capt Lcrss; Var Sftbl; Coachs Awd Vrsty Sftbl 85; Coachs Awd JV Lacrosse 87; Intl Rltns.

DOTTER, KATHERINE; Bergenfield HS; Bergenfield, NJ; (4); Art Clb; Pres German Clb; Spanish Clb; Hon Roll; NHS; NJ Cngrssnl Tchng Schlrshp 87; Trenton ST Coll; Fine Arts.

DOUENIAS, MICKEY; Morris Hills HS; Rockaway, NJ; (3); 29/258; French Clb; Math Clb; Math Tm; Temple Yth Grp; JV Socr; JV Wrstlng; Cit Awd; French Hon Soc; High Hon Roll; Hon Roll; Rutgers; Mech Engrng.

DOUGHER, ELIZABETH; Ramapo HS; Wyckoff, NJ; (4); 26/329; Art Clb; Drama Clb; French Clb; Hosp Aide; Ed Yrbk Stf; Rptr Lit Mag; High Hon Roll; Hon Roll; NHS; Ntl Merit Ltr; Engl Merit Awd; Colgate U; Adv.

DOUGHERTY, PATRICK; St Augustine Prep; Franklinville, NJ; (3); 11/52; Pres Soph Cls; Pres Sr Cls; Var Crs Cntry; Var Wrstlng; Hon Roll; NHS; Hstry Clb 86-87; Villinova U; Bus Adm.

DOUGHERTY, PAUL; Paul VI HS; Collingswood, NJ; (4); 18/503; Church Yth Grp; Spanish Clb; SADD; School Play; Soph Cls; Bowling; Jr NHS; NHS; Spanish NHS; Rutgers U Summer Schlr 86; Pre-Law.

DOUGHTY, ANDREA; Pitman HS; Pitman, NJ; (3); 90/145; Chorus; JV Bsktbl; Var Tennis; English.

DOUGHTY, ED; St James HS; Salem, NJ; (1); SADD; School Musical; School Play; Rep Frsh Cls; Prfct Atten Awd.

DOUGHTY, WILLIAM; Burlington Township HS; Burlington, NJ; (3); 11/125; Am Leg Boys St; Ski Clb; Varsity Clb; Band; Concert Band; Jazz Band; Mrchg Band; JV Bsbl; Var L Socr; Hon Roll; Navy ROTC; Aerontcl Engrng.

DOUGLAS, CATHERINE; Buena Regional HS; Vineland, NJ; (3); Debate Tm; SADD; Band; Chorus; Concert Band; Madrigals; Mrchg Band; School Play; Hon Roll; Jr NHS; All S Jersey Jr Hgh Chrs 85; NJ Schl Arts Vocal 86-87; All S Jersey Chrs Alto II Sctn Ldr 87; Teaching.

DOUGLAS, DAVID; Lincoln HS; Jersey City, NJ; (3); Art Clb; Boy Scts; JA; Library Aide; Office Aide; Political Wkr; Hon Roll; Prfct Atten Awd; Achvt Roll 85; Acadc Bowl Tm 87; Montclaire Coll; Engrng.

DOUGLAS, GARTH; Vineland HS; Vineland, NJ; (3); Aud/Vis; Computer Clb; Rep Stu Cncl; Socr; Trk; Wrstlng; Hon Roll; Prfct Atten Awd; Comp Engrng.

DOUGLAS, JENNIFER; Morris Knolls HS; Denville, NJ; (2); Yrbk Stf; JV Var Fld Hcky; Trk; High Hon Roll; Hon Roll; Tchr.

DOVNER, SUSAN; South River HS; South River, NJ; (3); German Clb; Office Aide; High Hon Roll; Hon Roll; Bus Admin.

DOWD, JENNIFER; Waldwick HS; Waldwick, NJ; (3); 16/140; Ski Clb; Nwsp Rptr; Nwsp Stf; Lit Mag; Rep Soph Cls; Var Capt Tennis; Hon Roll; Outstndng Soph Hugh O Brien Yth Fnd, 1st Team AU Leag 86; WHS Bstr Clb Awd Sprts Queen 87; Fshn Edtr.

DOWD, TARA; St Mary HS; Matawan, NJ; (3); 9/100; French Clb; Chorus; Church Choir; School Musical; Stage Crew; Lit Mag; Var Tennis; French Hon Soc; High Hon Roll; NHS; Rcvd Hnrs On Rprt Crd HS 84-86; Rutgers; Spch Educ.

DOWNES, LEON; Asbury Park HS; Asbury Park, NJ; (3); Boys Clb Am; Church Yth Grp; Ftbl; Acctng.

DOWNES, MARIE LYNN; Riverside HS; Riverside, NJ; (3); Art Clb; Computer Clb; DECA; FBLA; Math Tm; Spanish Clb; SADD; Teachers Aide; Chorus; Swing Chorus; Mst Imprvmt & Effort; Ldrshp & Trustworthnss Amng Stu & Tchrs Mdl; Burlington Cnty Coll; Bus.

DOWNEY, CHRISTOPHER; Holy Spirit HS; Atlantic City, NJ; (4); 17/363; French Clb; Math Tm; Science Clb; Hon Roll; NHS; Rotary Yth Ldrshp Awd 86; Pre-Med.

DOWNEY, NORA; Cherry Hill HS East; Cherry Hill, NJ; (3); Church Yth Grp; Latin Clb; SADD; JV Fld Hcky; JV Lcrss; Powder Puff Ftbl; Trk; Hon Roll; Chrprsn Bi Annl Schl Blood Dr 86-87; Fratrnl Ordr Polc Rotry Xmas Prty 86; New England; Ed.

DOXEY, KERRY; Red Bank Catholic HS; Red Bank, NJ; (4); 41/319; Spanish Clb; Nwsp Rptr; Garden State Schlrshp 87; State Foreign Lang Awd 86; Acad All-Am At Large 86; Employee Of Month 86; Montclair ST Coll; Bus Admn.

DOYLE, KIMBERLY; High Point Regional HS; Lafayette, NJ; (3); Q&S; Spanish Clb; Yrbk Ed-Chief; Yrbk Stf; Bsktbl; Hon Roll; Svc Awd Yrbk Stff & Edtr 86-87; Bus Mgmt.

DOYLE, THOMAS; Bishop Goerge Ahr HS; Plainfield, NJ; (4); German Clb; Ftbl; Wt Lftg; Wrstlng; Hon Roll; 4th Pl NJ ADFPA Bench Press Chmpnshps 86; Kean Coll; Sports Med.

DOYLE, THOMAS M; Bishop George AHR HS; Old Bridge, NJ; (3); Church Yth Grp; Cmnty Wkr; Bowling; Socr; Sftbl; Hon Roll; NJ ST Certified EMT; Med Fld.

DOYLE, TIMOTHY; Atlantic City HS; Ventnor, NJ; (3); Model UN; Temple Yth Grp; Awd Distctn Ntl Model Un Nations 86; 2nd Pl Slvr Medal Garden ST Games 84; Penn ST U; Pre-Law.

DOYLE, TRACEY; Belleville HS; Belleville, NJ; (3); Key Clb; Spanish Clb; Jazz Band; Mrchg Band; Orch; Lit Mag; Rep Stu Cncl; High Hon Roll; Hon Roll; NHS; Washington Wrkshp Cngrsnl Smnr 87; Pres Sb JR Wmns Clb 85-87; Essex Cnty NJ JR Miss Schlrshp Pgm 88; Cprt Law.

DRABNIS, MARY; St Pius X Regional HS; Piscataway, NJ; (3); 2/105; ROTC; Var Crs Cntry; Var Twrlr; High Hon Roll; Hon Roll; NHS; Rutgers Schlr Awd 87; Chem.

DRACH, CHERYL; Highland Regional HS; Blackwood, NJ; (3); Science Clb; Spanish Clb; Yrbk Stf; Stu Cncl.

DRAEGERT, ELLEN M; Madison HS; Madison, NJ; (3); 19/199; Acpl Chr; Church Choir; Jazz Band; School Musical; Swing Chorus; Lit Mag; Var Trk; High Hon Roll; Hon Roll; NHS.

DRAGAN, DAN; Hunterdon Central HS; Flemington, NJ; (3); FBLA; Latin Clb; Ski Clb; Socr.

DRAGISH, BLYTHE; Collingswood SR HS; Woodlynne, NJ; (2); Church Yth Grp; Dance Clb; German Clb; Office Aide; Political Wkr; SADD; Varsity Clb; Church Choir; Im Fld Hcky; Stat Mgr(s); HS Cls Exmplr Awd 85-86; Arch.

DRAKE, DENNIS A; West Windsor-Plainsboro HS; Princeton, NJ; (3); Am Leg Boys St; Stage Crew; Var Swmmng; Var Trk; Archlgy.

DRAKE, JAMES; Ewing HS; Trenton, NJ; (4); 125/331; Boy Scts; Computer Clb; Pres DECA; JA; Science Clb; Orch; Stage Crew; Rep Frsh Cls; Stu Cncl; Hon Roll; 1st Pl ST DECA Cnfrnc 86; Rider Coll; Bus Adm.

DRAKE, KEVIN; Freehold Township HS; Freehold, NJ; (4); Chess Clb; Computer Clb; Varsity Clb; Nwsp Stf; Sec Frsh Cls; Rep Soph Cls; Rep Jr Cls; Rep Sr Cls; Rep Stu Cncl; Var Bowling; MVP Boys Vrsty Ten 87; Capt Vrsty Ten 85-87; Dist Tms Ten 84-87; Rutgers Coll; Econmcs.

DRAPER, JOHN; St Joseph Regional HS; Pearl River, NY; (3); Yrbk Stf; Hon Roll; Spanish NHS; Stff Achvt Awd 87; Intrmrl St Hcky 85-88; Bus.

DRAUCIK, EILEEN; Holy Family Acad; Bayonne, NJ; (4); Art Clb; Computer Clb; Math Clb; Spanish Clb; Nwsp Rptr; Hon Roll; NEDT Awd; St Peters Coll Sumr Schlr 85-86; NY U.

DRAYTON, GWENDOLYN S; Academy Of The Sacred Heart; Hoboken, NJ; (3); NAACP; Pep Clb; Variety Show; Yrbk Stf; Lit Mag; Pres Frsh Cls; Sec Stu Cncl; Im Stat Bsktbl; Coach Actv; Gym; Coaches Awd 87; Untd Eastrn ST Chmpns Dance 87; Excllnc Advncd Math 87; Med.

DREFKO, BILL; Kearny HS; Kearny, NJ; (3); Am Leg Boys St; Trs Aud/Vis; Sec German Clb; Library Aide; JV Bowling; French Hon Soc; Hon Roll; Optmtrst.

DREIFUS, ERIKA; Millburn HS; Short Hills, NJ; (4); 9/249; Cmnty Wkr; Quiz Bowl; Pres Temple Yth Grp; Nwsp Ed-Chief; Ed Lit Mag; Ntl Merit SF; NJ Schlrs Pgm 86; Frnch Lit Mag Creatv Wrtng Edtr 85-87; Garden ST Distngshd Schlr Pgm.

DRELLOCK, KAREN; Toms River H S South; Toms River, NJ; (2); Church Yth Grp; Key Clb; Teachers Aide; Drill Tm; Orch; School Musical; Stage Crew; Var L Mgr(s); Prfrmg Arts.

DRENNAN, LARISSA; The Holy Family Acad; Bayonne, NJ; (3); Cmnty Wkr; Computer Clb; Hosp Aide; Stage Crew; Im Bsktbl; Im Vllybl; High Hon Roll; NHS; Prfct Atten Awd.

DREW, DEVLIN; John F Kennedy HS; Willingboro, NJ; (3); Ftbl; Trk; Hon Roll; COMM Arts.

DREXLER, ANGELA J; James Caldwell HS; W Caldwell, NJ; (3); Bus.

DREXLER, HARRY JOHN; Lacey Township HS; Forked River, NJ; (4); 20/290; VP Stu Cncl; Ftbl; High Hon Roll; Hon Roll; Pres NHS; Rep Frsh Cls; Rep Soph Cls; Rep Jr Cls; Outstndng Engl Achvt Awd 85-86; Prsdntl Acdmc Fitness Awd & Outstndng Hstry Achvt Awd 87; Rutgers U; Poltcl Sci.

DREYER, CHRIS; Cherry Hill H S West; Cherry Hill, NJ; (3); Aud/Vis; Thesps; School Musical; School Play; Stage Crew; Hon Roll; NHS; Comp Tm Sth Jersey Basic 2nd Pl; Theater Wrkshp Treas; Prfmng & Visual Arts Soc; Engrng.

DRISCOLL, CHRISTOPHER; Holy Spirit HS; Brigantine, NJ; (3); 44/332; JV Bsbl; Var Swmmng; Im Vllybl.

DRISCOLL, DEBORAH; Pinelands Regional HS; Tuckertown, NJ; (4); 12/185; Art Clb; JV Fld Hcky; Var Socr; JV Trk; Hon Roll; Sec NHS; Stockton ST Coll; Bio.

DRISCOLL, MAUREEN; St Mary Of The Assumption HS; Hillside, NJ; (2); Service Clb; Speech Tm; Var L Sftbl; Hon Roll; Jr NHS.

DROHAN, AMY; Marylawn HS; West Orange, NJ; (2); Var Bsktbl; Var Sftbl; Hon Roll; Nwsp Rptr; Nwsp Stf; Wrld Geogrphy 86; Vet.

DROST, TERRY; Keansburg HS; Keansburg, NJ; (3); 4-H; German Clb; Key Clb; Science Clb; Tennis; 4-H Awd; Hon Roll; NHS; Prfct Atten Awd; Chem.

DRUCKER, DOUGLAS; West Windsor-Plainsboro HS; Robbinsville, NJ; (3); Model UN; Radio Clb; Nwsp Rptr; JV Crs Cntry; JV Tennis; Hon Roll; Cmnctns.

DRUMM, ANGELA; South HS; Beachwood, NJ; (3); 66/405; DECA; FBLA; Office Aide; OEA; Rep Frsh Cls; Fld Hcky; CC Awd; High Hon Roll; NHS; Ski Clb; Acctng.

DRUMMOND JR, ROBERT G; Salem HS; Hancocks Bridge, NJ; (3); Am Leg Boys St; Math Clb; Spanish Clb; Hon Roll; NHS; Ag Sci.

DU BOIS, HOLLY MARIE; Paul VI HS; Voorhees, NJ; (3); 14/419; Drama Clb; French Clb; French Hon Soc; Hon Roll; NHS; Stage Crew; Paint Mural Off Wall 86; Mock Awd Drama Clss 86; Top 5 Winners Of A Bty Pagnt 86; U Of PA; Sci.

DU BOIS, JEFFREY T; Cumberland Christian Schl; Estell Manor, NJ; (4); 1/29; Trs Frsh Cls; Pres Soph Cls; Pres Jr Cls; Trs Stu Cncl; Stat Bsktbl; Var Socr; Hon Roll; NHS; Val; Rutgers Schlr 86; Lawrence M Kimball Awd 87; Sccr Sprtsmnshp Awd 84 86; Stockton ST Coll.

DUBBS, EDWARD; Gloucester County Christian Schl; Woodbury, NJ; (3); Church Yth Grp; FCA; Sec Frsh Cls; VP Soph Cls; VP Jr Cls; Stu Cncl; Var Bsbl; Var Socr; Hon Roll; Timthy Awd 84.

DUBIN, LOUISE O; Bridgewater-Raritan HS East; Bridgewater, NJ; (4); Nwsp Rptr; Lit Mag; Var Capt Crs Cntry; JV Trk; NHS; Ntl Merit SF; St Schlr; French Clb; Math Tm; Science Clb; Grls Cross Cnty/Mst Vlbl Plyr Aweds 85; Wellesley Bk Awd Englsh Excllnc 86; Rutgers Schlr Awd 86.

DUBIN, STEVE; Buena Regional HS; Newfield, NJ; (2); Church Yth Grp; Debate Tm; Math Clb; Varsity Clb; Rep Frsh Cls; Rep Soph Cls; Var L Crs Cntry; Var L Trk; Hon Roll; Pres Schlr; Crss Cntry Mdls 86; Vrsty Debate Ltr 86; Schlrshp Ltr 87; Rutgers U; Law.

DUBLIN, TARA; Rantan HS; Hazlet, NJ; (4); 28/255; Drama Clb; French Clb; School Musical; School Play; Stage Crew; Yrbk Rptr; Drama Clb Awd 87; Rntn HS Awd 87; Emerson Coll; Actrss.

DUBOIS, LISA M; Maranatha Christian Acad; Freehold, NJ; (4); 1/7; Church Yth Grp; Teachers Aide; Chorus; Church Choir; School Play; Yrbk Ed-Chief; High Hon Roll; Val; Rep Stu Cncl; Bsktbl; Brookdale CC; Elem Ed.

DUCEY, JOHN; Monsignor Donovan HS; Toms River, NJ; (3); 14/234; Rep Church Yth Grp; SADD; Concert Band; Var JV Bsbl; JV Capt Bsktbl; Var L Crs Cntry; Var L Trk; Hon Roll; NHS.

DUCK, YVONNE R; Wallkill Valley Regional HS; Hamburg, NJ; (4); Art Clb; Church Yth Grp; Math Clb; Varsity Clb; Lit Mag; Bsktbl; Var Fld Hcky; Var Trk; Gov Hon Prg Awd; Pres Schlr; Pratt Natl Tlnt Srch Art & Dsgn 87; Pratt Inst; Fine Arts.

DUCKERS, LEE J; Manchester Twp HS; Toms River, NJ; (3); Am Leg Boys St; NHS; Comp.

DUCUSIN, MICHAEL; Hudson Catholic HS; Jersey City, NJ; (3); Boys Clb Am; Boy Scts; Dance Clb; Math Clb; Science Clb; Stage Crew; Yrbk Phtg; Im Bsktbl; Im Vllybl; NHS.

DUDAS, VICKY; Phillipsburg HS; Phillipsburg, NJ; (3); 22/315; Key Clb; Crs Cntry; High Hon Roll.

DUDASH, JOSEPH; Union HS; Union, NJ; (3); Am Leg Boys St; Rep Key Clb; Pres Spanish Clb; Sec Mrchg Band; Orch; Nwsp Rptr; Jr Cls; High Hon Roll; NHS; Boys Clb Am; Highest Acad Average; Amer Leg Boys ST; Boys Club Of Amer; Key Club; Span Club; Marching Band; Orch; Nwsp; Math.

DUDEK, DENNIS; John P Stevens HS; Menlo Park, NJ; (2); Ski Clb; Rep Soph Cls; Var Bsbl; L Ftbl; Var Wrstlng; Hon Roll; VFW Awd.

DUDLEY, TANAYO; West Side HS; Newark, NJ; (4); 19/250; Boys Clb Am; Girl Scts; Teachers Aide; Variety Show; Yrbk Ed-Chief; Rep Sr Cls; Bsktbl; Sftbl; Hon Roll; Rider Coll; Accntng.

DUDLING, MICHAEL G; Edison HS; Edison, NJ; (4); 23/402; Var Math Tm; Model UN; Science Clb; Lit Mag; JV Socr; Var Trk; NHS; St Schlr; Rep Jr Cls; Rep Sr Cls; Rutgers; Arch.

DUESPOHL, KRIS; Overbrook Regional SR HS; Pine Hill, NJ; (4); 36/335; 4-H; Hosp Aide; Band; Concert Band; Mrchg Band; Cheerleading; Twrlr; Hon Roll; NHS; VFW Awd; Century III Ldrs Schlrshp & JR Miss Repr 86-87; Philadelphia Coll; Phys Thrpy.

DUFF, DAWN MARIE; Clifton HS; Clifton, NJ; (4); 247/594; DECA; Yrbk Stf; Var Cheerleading; Var Pom Pon; ST Comptncy Awd Distrbtv Ed 85-86; Homerm Svc Awd 84; Delg ST Ldrshp Conv 87; Capri; Beautn.

DUFF, PATRICK; Madison HS; Madison, NJ; (3); Varsity Clb; Var Bsbl; Var Capt Socr; Im Wt Lftg; Hon Roll; 2nd Team All-Conf Sccr 86-87; Hnrbl Mntn All-Area Bsbl 87; Bus.

DUFFY, EDWARD; Highland HS; Clementon, NJ; (2); Church Yth Grp; Latin Clb; Band; Mrchg Band; Tennis; Wrstlng; Hon Roll.

DUFFY, ELIZABETH; Morristown HS; Morris Plains, NJ; (2); 37/432; Church Yth Grp; GAA; Key Clb; Office Aide; Pep Clb; Var L Cheerleading; Var L Crs Cntry; Var L Trk; Hon Roll.

DUFFY, FRANK; Parsippany HS; Parsippany, NJ; (3); Boy Scts; Chess Clb; Yrbk Stf; Hon Roll; Prfct Atten Awd; Rutgers U; Actuary.

DUFFY, JOSEPH; Holy Spirit HS; Absecon, NJ; (3); 11/332; Computer Clb; Hon Roll; Chem Awd 85-86.

DUFFY, LOIS; Immaculata HS; Flemington, NJ; (3); Library Aide; Math Tm; Model UN; School Play; Ed Yrbk Stf; Lit Mag; French Hon Soc; Gov Hon Prg Awd; NHS; Attnded Wmn In Engrng & Mgnt Smmr Pgm At Stevens Inst Of Tech 87; Intl Frgn Lang Awd Frnch III 87; Chem Engrng.

DUFFY, MISSY; Howell HS; Howell, NJ; (3); German Clb; Var L Bsktbl; Var Capt Sftbl; Hon Roll.

DUFFY, OBUN; St John Nianney HS; Marlboro, NJ; (2); CAP; Rep Frsh Cls; JV Ftbl; Var Trk; Career Explortn Awd 86; Pres Ftnss Awd 87; US Naval Acad; Nvl Aviator.

DUFFY, RICHARD; Tenafly HS; Tenafly, NJ; (4); Radio Clb; Rep Jr Cls; Rep Sr Cls; Rep Stu Cncl; JV Golf; JV Var Socr; JV Tennis; Engrng.

DUGGAN, DORIS; Mount St Dominic Acad; Bloomfield, NJ; (4); 11/53; Scholastic Bowl; Spanish Clb; Chorus; Yrbk Stf; Stu Cncl; Capt Crs Cntry; Capt Trk; Hon Roll; Sec NHS; NJ Gov Cncl Awd Phys Ftns & Sports 87; U RI; Math.

DUGGER, THOMAS; Randolph HS; Randolph, NJ; (3); 20/390; AFS; Camera Clb; Church Yth Grp; Math Clb; Math Tm; Ski Clb; Nwsp Stf; Tennis; Hon Roll; Catholic U Of America; Comp.

DUHNOSKI, CARL; Hamilton HS West; Yardville, NJ; (4); 21/323; Key Clb; Stage Crew; Trk; Vllybl; Hon Roll; Kiwanis Awd; NHS; Pres Schlr; Church Yth Grp; Diving; Hamilton Twnshp PBA Schlrshp 87; Top Tenpercnt 87; Pennsylvania ST U; Mrktng.

DUICK, MICHELE; Edison HS; Edison, NJ; (3); 30/471; Church Yth Grp; French Clb; Spanish Clb; Nwsp Rptr; Rep Soph Cls; Rep Jr Cls; JV Cheerleading; Hon Roll; NHS; Spnsh Merit Awds-Drew U Comptn 86-87; NJ Govs Schl Of Arts 86-87; Psych.

DUJNIC, JOANNE; Palisades Park HS; Palisades Park, NJ; (3); Drill Tm; Stat Bsbl; Var Capt Cheerleading; Hon Roll; NHS; Vtrnry Med.

DUKES, JAMES; Bridgeton HS; Cedarville, NJ; (3); Boy Scts; Teachers Aide; Im Bsktbl; Var Crs Cntry; Hon Roll; Jr NHS.

DUKIET, LINDA; John P Stevens HS; Edison, NJ; (4); 40/482; Church Yth Grp; Math Tm; Model UN; Nwsp Bus Mgr; Powder Puff Ftbl; French Hon Soc; NHS; Pres Acdmc Ftnss Awd 86-87; 4 Yr Gdn ST Dstngshd Schlrshp; 4 Yr Alumni Schlrshp; Trenton ST Coll; Elem Ed.

DUL, CHRISTINE; Garfield HS; Garfield, NJ; (3); 21/170; Dance Clb; Spanish Clb; Twrlr; Hon Roll; Art Awd 84-85.

DULL, GREGORY; Arthur P Schalick HS; Centerton, NJ; (3); 19/130; Am Leg Boys St; Pres Church Yth Grp; Pres Sr Cls; Var Capt Ftbl; Var L Trk; Var Capt Wrstlng; Ed Yearby Awd 86-87; Elec Engrng.

DULLY, GREGORY; St Rose HS; Pt Pleasant, NJ; (3); Aud/Vis; Camera Clb; Band; Stage Crew; Yrbk Stf; Lit Mag; Engrng.

DUMAN, CHERYL; Williamstown HS; Williamstown, NJ; (4); 1/267; Dance Clb; Drama Clb; Chorus; School Musical; School Play; Nwsp Ed-Chief; JV Tennis; High Hon Roll; Sec NHS; St Schlr; HS Jr Miss 87; NJ State Teen Arts Fest 85 & 86; Dance.

DUMANDAN, JOY MARIE; Saint Mary HS; Rutherford, NJ; (3); Drama Clb; FNA; Hosp Aide; Ski Clb; Thesps; Nwsp Rptr; VP Frsh Cls; Capt Cheerleading; French Hon Soc; NHS; Pre Med.

DUMOND, LORI; Hackettstown HS; Hackettstown, NJ; (4); 54/234; Church Yth Grp; Hosp Aide; Key Clb; Pep Clb; Rep Jr Cls; Rep Sr Cls; Rep Stu Cncl; Hon Roll; NHS; Cmnty Wkr; FL Southern Coll; Pltcl Sci.

DUNBAR, MATTHEW; Holy Spirit HS; Absecon, NJ; (4); 2/363; Math Tm; Chrmn Frsh Cls; Im Ftbl; Capt Socr; Im Vllybl; Jr NHS; NHS; Hnrb Mntn In Soccer 86; MVP In Soccer 86; Dartmouth; Engrng.

DUNCAN, AMY R; John P Stevens HS; Edison, NJ; (4); 196/485; Art Clb; Letterman Clb; Science Clb; VP Ski Clb; Rep Frsh Cls; Rep Soph Cls; Rep Jr Cls; Rep Sr Cls; Rep Stu Cncl; Var Capt Cheerleading; Art Awd 84; Chrldng Co Capt 86-87; AZ ST U; Bus.

DUNCAN, ERIN; Brick Memorial HS; Bricktown, NJ; (2); 43/400; Civic Clb; Red Cross Aide; Band; Concert Band; Mrchg Band; Socr; Prfct Atten Awd; Finance.

DUNGEE, PAMELA; Science HS; Newark, NJ; (4); 4/100; Hosp Aide; Office Aide; Chorus; Nwsp Rptr; Pres Jr Cls; VP Stu Cncl; High Hon Roll; NHS; Pres Schlr; U Of PA Wharton; Acctng.

DUNICAN, ANNMARIE L; Paramus Catholic Girls; Teaneck, NJ; (3); 6/169; Math Clb; VP Stu Cncl; JV Capt Bsktbl; Var L Sftbl; Mgr Capt Vllybl; High Hon Roll; Hon Roll; NHS; Variety Show; NEDT Awd; Top Frnch Stu Frnch III, Bst All-Arnd Vllybl Plyr Battag Cmp 85-86; Adv Plcmt Frnch Math & Bio 84-87; Bio.

DUNIGAN, MARY BETH; Mother Seton Regional HS; Woodbridge, NJ; (4); Sec Church Yth Grp; French Clb; Math Tm; Nwsp Stf; Lit Mag; Rep Jr Cls; JV Capt Bsktbl; Hon Roll; Sec Trs NHS; Seton Spirit Awd 87; St James Yth Grp Awd Outstndg Svc & Ldrshp 86-87; Gettysburg Coll; Polit Sci.

DUNLEAVY, CATHY; Paul VI HS; Berlin, NJ; (3); 45/418; Cmnty Wkr; French Clb; Church Choir; French Hon Soc; Hon Roll; Cert Of Merit Natl Frnch Exam 87; Rtgrs Coll; Psych.

DUNLEAVY, JACQUELYN; Paul VI HS; Haddonfield, NJ; (4); 63/511; SADD; Mrchg Band; Nwsp Rptr; Nwsp Stf; Var Pom Pon; Hon Roll; Church Yth Grp; Dance Clb; Math Clb; Spanish Clb; St Josephs U; Hist.

DUNLEAVY, TIMOTHY; Ramapo Regional HS; Wyckoff, NJ; (3); 126/332; Camera Clb; Lit Mag; High Hon Roll; Hon Roll; Ntl Merit Ltr; Cert Of Merit Hist 86-87; Archlgst.

DUNN, CHRIS; Haddonfield Memorial HS; Barrington, IL; (2); Varsity Clb; JV Bsktbl; JV Ftbl; Var Tennis; Hon Roll; Stanford.

DUNN, DAWN; Notre Dame HS; Trenton, NJ; (2); 23/403; Stat Bsbl; Bsktbl; Stat Socr; High Hon Roll; Hon Roll; NHS; Excllnc Religion II, Spnsh II 86-87; Excllnc Spnsh I 85-86; Law.

DUNN, JENNIFER; Manalapan HS; Manalapan, NJ; (3); 62/429; Dance Clb; Debate Tm; SADD; Yrbk Stf; Hon Roll; Bio Sci.

DUNN, NOELLE; Manasquan HS; Manasquan, NJ; (3); Drama Clb; Spanish Clb; School Musical; School Play; Stage Crew; JV Fld Hcky; High Hon Roll; Hon Roll; Jr NHS; Bd Educ Awd 85-87.

DUNN, PATRICIA; Hunterdon Central HS; White House Sta, NJ; (3); 43/550; Cmnty Wkr; Ski Clb; SADD; Stat Var Lcrss; Hon Roll; Bus.

DUNOFF, GLENN A; Cherry Hill HS East; Cherry Hill, NJ; (4); 28/690; Am Leg Boys St; Pres Aud/Vis; Trs French Clb; Radio Clb; Temple Yth Grp; Ntl Merit Ltr; NEDT Awd; VFW Awd; Voice Dem Awd; Hosp Aide; Commerce Bank Schlrshp & Grad Speaker 87; Garden ST Distngshd Schlr 86-87; U Of PA; Bus.

DUNPHY, THERESA; Toms River HS North; Toms River, NJ; (3); Church Yth Grp; Varsity Clb; Band; Color Guard; Concert Band; Mrchg Band; Crs Cntry; Var Swmmng; Hon Roll; Key Clb; TEAM 86-87; Elem Ed.

DUNSIZER, RANDALL TODD; Kinnelon HS; Kinnelon, NJ; (4); Boy Scts; Church Yth Grp; Math Tm; Stu Cncl; Socr; Hon Roll; JETS Awd; NHS; Pres Schlr; NJ Acdmc Decathlon 87, Home & Schl Assn Schlrshp, & Outstndng Physics Stu Awd 87; U Of Rochester; Optics.

DUNWOODY, KATE; Wildwood Catholic HS; Cape May, NJ; (3); 14/80; Drama Clb; French Clb; Girl Scts; Q&S; School Musical; School Play; Nwsp Bus Mgr; Nwsp Rptr; Nwsp Stf; Yrbk Bus Mgr; Media.

DUPIGNAC, EMILY; Toms River HS South; Toms River, NJ; (2); Ski Clb; Sec Frsh Cls; Var Sftbl; Var Swmmng; Var Tennis; High Hon Roll; Hon Roll; Hon Roll; NHS; Hnrb Mntn All Cnty Tnns Dbls 86; 1st Tm All Cnty Sftbl Ctchr 87; Math & Sci.

DUPUIS, COLLETTE; Westfield HS; Westfield, NJ; (2); Church Yth Grp; French Clb; Model UN; Boys Clb Am; L Trk.

DUPUIS, ELIZABETH A; Govewrnor Livingston Regional HS; Berkeley Heights, NJ; (4); 28/182; Girl Scts; Color Guard; Yrbk Phtg; Hon Roll; Spanish NHS; Library Aide; Spanish Clb; Yrbk Stf; Lit Mag; Girl Scout Gold Awd 84; Franklin & Marshall Book Awd 87; Pres Acad Fit Awd 87; U IL U/C; Engl.

DUPUY, ROBERT; Highland Regional HS; Blackwood, NJ; (2); Bsbl; Compu Archtctr.

DUQUE, CHARLES; North Bergen HS; North Bergen, NJ; (3); Art Clb; French Clb; SADD; Rutgers U; Comp.

DUQUE, SANDRA; Immaculate Conception HS; Ridgefield Prk, NJ; (3); 17/85; Cmnty Wkr; English Clb; Exploring; Q&S; SADD; Nwsp Ed-Chief; Nwsp Rptr; Nwsp Stf; Rep Frsh Cls; Rep Stu Cncl; NYU; Pub Rel.

DURANA, KAREN; Garden State Acad; Irvington, NJ; (3); 1/25; Sec Chorus; Off Concert Band; Variety Show; Bsktbl; High Hon Roll; NHS; St Schlr; School Play; Nwsp Rptr; Bowling; Stu Assoc Pres 87; Girls Club Music Coordinator 86; Stu Assoc Girls Spts Coord 86; Rutgers U; Med.

DURBIN, KIM; Toms River HS South; Beachwood, NJ; (3); 110/405; Church Yth Grp; Drama Clb; Key Clb; High Hon Roll; Hon Roll; OCC; Engl.

DURBORAW, KIM; Hunterdon Central HS; Flemington, NJ; (3); 61/550; Radio Clb; Ski Clb; Yrbk Bus Mgr; Im Lcrss; Hon Roll; Prfct Atten Awd; Spanish NHS; Outstndng Achvt-Chld Dvlpmnt 86; Accntng.

DURLAND, DARA; Rancocas Valley Reg HS; Mt Holly, NJ; (2); Fld Hcky; Lcrss; Hon Roll; Amer Lgn Essy Cont 2nd Pl 85; Pres Acdmc Ftnss Awd 85; Pre Lawyr.

DURNER, ALLISON; Notre Dame HS; Cranbury, NJ; (2); 78/372; Chorus; Madrigals; Mrchg Band; School Musical; School Play; NHS.

DUROSKY, JODI; Dover HS; Dover, NJ; (3); Pres Exploring; Office Aide; Red Cross Aide; Bsktbl; Socr; Sftbl; Psychlgy Acdmc Awd 87; Stu Tchr Of Tap Dancing 85; Office Asst Drug Cnslr 86-87; Rutgers U; Psychlgy.

DURRENBERGER, SHERI; Paramus HS; Paramus, NJ; (4); Ski Clb; CC Awd; Pace U Pleasantvl NY; Bus.

DURSKI, LEEANN; St Mary Regional HS; S Amboy, NJ; (3); 10/100; Computer Clb; Spanish Clb; Sec Soph Cls; Var Bsktbl; Var Crs Cntry; Var Capt Socr; Var Sftbl; High Hon Roll; NHS; Spanish NHS; Scranton U; Acctg.

DURST, THEODORE H; Notre Dame HS; Mercerville, NJ; (4); Art Clb; Computer Clb; Drama Clb; Office Aide; Political Wkr; School Musical; Stage Crew; Hon Roll; Guidnce Awd 85-86; Wrld Lit Awd 87; Mercer Cnty CC; Advrtsng.

DURYNSKI, JENNIFER; Saint Marys Regional HS; S Amboy, NJ; (3); 1/92; Church Yth Grp; Spanish Clb; Chorus; School Play; Nwsp Stf; Yrbk Stf; Lit Mag; High Hon Roll; Spanish NHS.

DUSTAL, DAWN S; Spotswood HS; Spotswood, NJ; (4); 24/189; Am Leg Aux Girls St; Cmnty Wkr; Concert Band; Drm Mjr(t); Mrchg Band; School Play; Trs Stu Cncl; Capt Cheerleading; JV Sftbl; Hon Roll; Hmrm Rep; Math.

DUSZKIEWICZ, PETER; Spotswood HS; Spotswood, NJ; (2); Hon Roll; Ftbl; Rutgers Coll; Comp Pgrmr.

DUTHALER, GREGG; Don Basco Prepatory HS; Maywood, NJ; (3); 2/200; Boy Scts; VP Debate Tm; Drama Clb; Math Tm; Ski Clb; School Musical; School Play; Nwsp Phtg; Nwsp Rptr; Rep Stu Cncl; Eagle Sct 86; Gnrl Escllnc Awd 85-86.

DUTHALER, TODD; Don Bosco Prep; Maywood, NJ; (4); Boy Scts; Ski Clb; Stage Crew; Yrbk Phtg; NHS; Eagle Sct 85; Syracuse U; Aerospc Engrng.

DUVE, MARK F; Warren Hills Regional HS; Washington, NJ; (4); 16/218; Am Leg Boys St; Boy Scts; Ski Clb; Crs Cntry; Socr; Hon Roll; NHS; Eagle Scout Awd 83; Stevens Inst Of Tech; Chem Engr.

DUYCK, KIMBERLY LYNN; Ocean City HS; Woodbine, NJ; (3); 2/350; Girl Scts; Science Clb; Spanish Clb; Co-Capt SADD; Mrchg Band; Orch; Lib Symp Band; Nwsp Rptr; High Hon Roll; Girl Sct Slvr Awd 85; Amer Lgn Ntl Ortrcl Cntst 2nd In Dist 86; Carnegie-Mellon; Prof Writing.

DVORAK, HEATHER; Lower Cape May Regional HS; Villas, NJ; (3); Drama Clb; French Clb; Girl Scts; SADD; Chorus; School Musical; School Play; Yrbk Phtg; Rep Frsh Cls; Rep Soph Cls; 2nd Hon Pres-Phys Fitness Awd 84-85; Acad Dinner Awd 2nd & 1st Honrs 85-86; Ntl Hon Soc 86-87; Acting.

DVORKIN, HEIDI; Toms River N HS; Toms River, NJ; (4); 4/396; FBLA; Ski Clb; Spanish Clb; Band; Yrbk Stf; Stu Cncl; Mgr Bsktbl; Fld Hcky; Sftbl; High Hon Roll; Garden St Dstngshd Schlrs Prgm Awd 87; Cornell U.

DWYER, COLLEEN; Kent Place Schl; Califon, NJ; (3); AFS; Ski Clb; JV Crs Cntry; JV Trk; Psych.

DYAL, MEGAN; Mercer Christin Acad; Cranbury, NJ; (2); 2/17; Church Yth Grp; Drama Clb; Rep Stu Cncl; Hon Roll; Yrbk Stf; Psych.

DYBICE, MIKE; Parsippany HS; Parsippany, NJ; (3); Chess Clb; Computer Clb; Math Clb; Math Tm; Ski Clb; Yrbk Stf; NHS; Prfct Atten Awd; 1st Pl Iron Hills Math Comp 87; Bio Engrng.

DYCHTWALD, DANA; Cherokee HS; Marlton, NJ; (3); Drama Clb; German Clb; Temple Yth Grp; Chorus; Nwsp Rptr; Rep Soph Cls; Rep Jr Cls; High Hon Roll; Hon Roll; NHS; Columbia; Comms.

DYER, JENNIFER; Vineland HS; Vineland, NJ; (3); 13/829; French Clb; Key Clb; Service Clb; NHS; Trk; Cmmnctns.

DYSON, DONNA; Pleasantville HS; Pleasantville, NJ; (3); Art Clb; Teachers Aide; Band; Yrbk Phtg; Frsh Cls; Soph Cls; Jr Cls; Gym; Swmmng; Tennis; Merit Roll; Pediatrcs.

DZENIS, VICTORIA; Manasquan HS; Brielle, NJ; (3); Drama Clb; French Clb; Thesps; Acpl Chr; Chorus; Church Choir; School Musical; School Play; Stage Crew; Variety Show; Montclair ST Coll; Speech.

DZIEMIAN, SUSAN; Bayonne HS; Bayonne, NJ; (3); Band; Var Capt Socr; Im Vllybl; Hon Roll; Jr NHS; All-Cnty Sccr Tm & NJ Grp IV 3rd Tm Sccr 86.

DZINGALA, CHRISTINA; Morris Knolls HS; Denville, NJ; (3); 68/450; Church Yth Grp; Cmnty Wkr; FBLA; Hosp Aide; JA; Color Guard; Lit Mag; High Hon Roll; Hon Roll; Ukrainian Saturday Schl Grad 86; 1st Pl Yth Group Beauty Pageant 84; Arch.

DZURY, ROBYN; Delaware Valley Regional HS; Milford, NJ; (3); 10/200; Key Clb; Varsity Clb; Chorus; School Musical; Off Soph Cls; Stat L Bsbl; Var Capt Cheerleading; JV Sftbl; High Hon Roll; Pres NHS; AZ ST; Psych.

E GENNARO, MICHELE; Secaucus HS; Secaucus, NJ; (3); 24/150; Math Clb; Mu Alpha Theta; NFL; High Hon Roll; Hon Roll; Jr NHS; Mu Alpha Theta Awd; 1st Pl ST Poetry Cntst 86; Recvd Bonds Best Stu In Italian 85-86; Berkeley Coll; Fshn Mdse.

EAGAN, TERENCE; Manasquan HS; Spring Lake Hts, NJ; (3); 45/250; Speech Tm; Science Clb; Var Ftbl; Wt Lftg; Hon Roll; Achvt Proj Soar Enrchmnt Pgm 87; Cornell U; Wldlfe Bio.

EARLEY, GRACIELA; Franklin HS; Somerset, NJ; (2); Art Clb; Church Yth Grp; SADD; Rep Soph Cls; Rep Jr Cls; High Hon Roll; Hon Roll; NHS; Frgn Lang Frnsc Trnmnt Awd 86; Bus.

EATON, HEATHER; Villa Victoria Acad; Trenton, NJ; (1); Chorus; School Musical; Trs Frsh Cls; Socr; Im Tennis; DAR Awd; Full Merit Schlrshp Villa Victoria Acad 86-90; John Hopkins U CTY 85-88.

EATON, NICOLE; Florence Twp Mem HS; Florence, NJ; (3); FTA; GAA; Letterman Clb; Math Clb; Math Tm; Varsity Clb; Rep Frsh Cls; Rep Soph Cls; Rep Jr Cls; Rep Stu Cncl; Math.

EAVES, DUANE; Egg Harbor Township HS; Cardiff, NJ; (3); 30/329; Church Yth Grp; Model UN; Spanish Clb; Hon Roll; Schlstc Ltr Awd; Phrmcst.

EBELING, MARY; Burlington Co Vo-Tech Schls; Willingboro, NJ; (4); 9/171; Church Yth Grp; VP FBLA; VICA; Yrbk Stf; Var Capt Bowling; Im Socr; Hon Roll; Trs NHS; 2nd Pl VICA ST Prlmtry Prcdr Cmptn 86; CPA.

EBERENZ, LYNN; West Morris Mendham HS; Mendham, NJ; (2); 25/292; Art Clb; Hon Roll; Gifted & Talented Pgm 85-86.

EBERSBACH, MICHELE; Sparta HS; Sparta, NJ; (2); Key Clb; SADD; Rep Soph Cls; Rep Stu Cncl; High Hon Roll; Hon Roll.

EBERT, CHRISTOPHER; Lakewood HS; Lakewood, NJ; (3); 24/354; Band; Jazz Band; JV Bsktbl; Var L Ftbl; Im Wt Lftg; Hon Roll.

EBLE, SHARON; Egg Harbor Township HS; Mays Landing, NJ; (3); 7/320; Mrchg Band; Yrbk Ed-Chief; Hst Jr Cls; Trs Stu Cncl; JV Var Sftbl; Hon Roll; Ntl Merit SF; Academic Varsity Letter Awd 85-87; All American Merit Awd 85; Rotary Yth Ldrshp Assn 87; U Of PA; Arch.

ECHANDY, MILTON A; Neptune SR HS; Neptune, NJ; (3); Am Leg Boys St; SADD; Varsity Clb; Var Bsbl; Var Bsktbl; Var Crs Cntry; Rider; Ed.

ECHAVARRIA, WANDA; Immaculate Conception HS; Maywood, NJ; (3); Church Yth Grp; Girl Scts; Spanish Clb; SADD; Stage Crew; Yrbk Stf; Trs Jr Cls; VP Sr Cls; Intl Bus.

ECHEVERRI, ANA ANA MARIA; Secaucus HS; Secaucus, NJ; (3); 13/166; Math Clb; Mu Alpha Theta; School Play; Nwsp Sprt Ed; French Hon Soc; High Hon Roll; Hon Roll; Mrt Crtfct 86; Bnd Hghst Achvr 85; Rutgers; Cmptr Sci.

ECKERT, JEFFREY; Toms River HS South; Toms River, NJ; (3); 7/406; Var Ftbl; Im Wt Lftg; High Hon Roll; Hon Roll; NHS; Amrcn Chem Soc Awd; NJ Gvrnrs Schl Fnlst; Biochem.

ECKERT, MARTA; Mother Seton Regional HS; Mountainside, NJ; (3); 1/75; Church Yth Grp; GAA; School Musical; Chess Clb; Pres Jr Cls; Pres Stu Cncl; Var Capt Vllybl; High Hon Roll; NHS; Ntl Merit Ltr; Rutgers Schlr 87; Hugh O Brian Ldrshp Smnr 86; Notre Dame U; Pre-Med.

ECKHAUS, JEFFREY; Wayne Hills HS; Wayne, NJ; (2); Aud/Vis; Math Clb; Spanish Clb; Temple Yth Grp; JV Trk; Hon Roll; VP Religs Cls.

ECKHOFF, SHARON; Cliffside Park HS; Cliffside Park, NJ; (1); Rep Stu Cncl; Trk; JV Vllybl.

ECKMAN, DAVID; Florence Twp Mem HS; Roebling, NJ; (3); 1/100; Am Leg Boys St; Church Yth Grp; Cmnty Wkr; Math Clb; Science Clb; JV Bsbl; JV Bsktbl; Var L Crs Cntry; Var JV Ftbl; Wt Lftg; Engrng.

ECOCHARD, LINDA; Southern Regional HS; Barnegat, NJ; (3); Dance Clb; Band; Concert Band; Mrchg Band; Pom Pon; Hon Roll; NHS; Elem Educ.

ECONOMIDES, JENNIFER; Indian Hills HS; Oakland, NJ; (3); 40/305; VP Church Yth Grp; Debate Tm; French Clb; Chorus; Nwsp Stf; JV Vllybl; Hon Roll; Cert Of Merit-Writers Wrkshp 84-85; Cert Of Merit-Frnch II 85-86; Ringwd Mnr Assoc Of Arts 85-86; Taxation.

EDA, PATRICIA; Secaucus HS; Secaucus, NJ; (3); 2/167; Key Clb; Mu Alpha Theta; Varsity Clb; Nwsp Ed-Chief; Pres Frsh Cls; Sec Stu Cncl; Var Tennis; JETS Awd; NHS; Spanish NHS; Hudson County Sci Fair-Top Awd 86; Engrng 4th Pl-Intl Sci & Engrng Fair 86.

EDELMAN, CARRIE; Matawan Regional HS; Aberdeen, NJ; (3); 1/306; Rep Frsh Cls; Trs Soph Cls; Trs Jr Cls; Stu Cncl; Var Fld Hcky; Trk; Hon Roll.

EDELMAYER, JILL; Kings Christian HS; Merchantville, NJ; (4); 2/23; Church Yth Grp; Drama Clb; Hosp Aide; VP Soph Cls; VP Jr Cls; Rep Sr Cls; Stat L Bsktbl; Capt L Fld Hcky; High Hon Roll; NHS; Hnrs Engl 83-87; Schlrshp From NJ St 86; Physical Thrpy.

EDELSON, CARYN; Cresskill HS; Cresskill, NJ; (4); 13/103; Cmnty Wkr; Debate Tm; Drama Clb; Ski Clb; Band; Concert Band; Mrchg Band; School Musical; Nwsp Stf; Yrbk Stf; Law.

EDELSTEIN, ANDREA B; Scotch Plains-Fanwood HS; Scotch Plns, NJ; (4); 89/300; FBLA; Key Clb; Temple Yth Grp; Concert Band; Mrchg Band; Symp Band; Hon Roll; George Washington U; Bus Admin.

EDENBAUM, SARAH; West Windsor-Plainsboro HS; Princeton Junct, NJ; (3); AFS; French Clb; Nwsp Stf; Var Swmmng; High Hon Roll; Hon Roll; Unsung Hero Awd Varsity Swimtm 86-87; Law.

EDGAR, JACQUELINE; Hamilton High West; Yardville, NJ; (4); 26/309; Math Clb; Yrbk Stf; JV Fld Hcky; Im Trk; Hon Roll; Timer; U Of CT; Bio.

EDGE, BRIAN; Burlington City HS; Edgewater Pk, NJ; (3); Band; Hon Roll; Prfct Atten Awd; Im Bsbl; Im Socr; Im Vllybl; Bio.

EDGECOMB, PATRICIA; Ambassador Christian Acad; Toms River, NJ; (2); 1/8; Hosp Aide; Yrbk Stf; Off Soph Cls; Rep Stu Cncl; Messiah Coll; Med.

EDMOND, CALANDRA; Essex Catholic Girls HS; Newark, NJ; (3); Church Yth Grp; NAACP; Church Choir; Effert 84; Spec Educ.

EDMONDS, MARIA; Schalick HS; Elmer, NJ; (3); Hosp Aide; Teachers Aide; Color Guard; Yrbk Stf; Rep Soph Cls; JV Cheerleading; Score Keeper; Hon Roll; VFW Awd; Chorus; Bsktbl Stats Awd 84-87; Band-Clrgd 84-87; VFW Awd 75; Glassboro ST; Childcare.

EDWARD, JENNIFER; Columbia HS; Maplewood, NJ; (4); Var Capt Socr; Var L Sftbl; Var L Swmmng; Sccr All Cnty 2nd Tm 85-86; Sccr All Conf 2nd Tm 86; Bus.

EDWARDS, BRIAN L; Kingsway Regional HS; Mickleton, NJ; (3); Am Leg Boys St; Aud/Vis; Church Yth Grp; School Musical; Var Crs Cntry; Hon Roll; NHS; Excptnl Ability Perf Arts 86; Iron Dragon Awd 86; Excllnce Audio Visual Slide Show Presentatn 86-87.

EDWARDS, CHARLES; Madison HS; Morristown, NJ; (3); 8/195; French Clb; Science Clb; Varsity Clb; VP Stu Cncl; Var L Socr; Var L Tennis; High Hon Roll; Hon Roll; NHS.

EDWARDS, DARRIN C; Hammonton HS; Hammonton, NJ; (3); 1/187; Church Yth Grp; French Clb; Math Clb; Science Clb; Band; Concert Band; Jazz Band; Mrchg Band; Pep Band; Symp Band; Acad Excellence Awd 86-87; Rutgers Scholar 87; Math.

EDWARDS, DONALD; Lenape Valley Regional HS; Stanhope, NJ; (3); 13/250; Varsity Clb; Chorus; Nwsp Rptr; Lit Mag; VP Ftbl; Var Trk; Wt Lftg; Hon Roll; HS Schlr Awd 86-87; Summer Arts Inst New Brunswick NJ 86-87; Co & St Tn Arts Fstvl 86-87; Englsh.

EDWARDS JR, JAMES; Bridgewater Raritan East HS; Bridgewater, NJ; (4); Pres Church Yth Grp; VP Spanish Clb; SADD; Rep Cmnty Wkr; Rep Sr Cls; Rep Stu Cncl; Crs Cntry; Stat Ftbl; Excell Awd Med Tech 87; Villanova U; Comm.

EDWARDS, JOEL EUGENE; Monmouth Regional HS; Tinton Falls, NJ; (4); Stage Crew; Ed Yrbk Ed-Chief; Ed Lit Mag; Rep Stu Cncl; Art Dept Awds 83-87; NJ Yng Flmmkrs Fest 1st & 3rd 83-84; WNET TV Chnl 13 Art Fest Artcls 84-85; MD Inst Coll; Art.

EDWARDS, JONATHAN D; Hackensack HS; Hackensack, NJ; (4); 1/412; Am Leg Boys St; Letterman Clb; Math Clb; Ski Clb; Spanish Clb; Lit Mag; L Tennis; High Hon Roll; Jr NHS; NHS; Golden Nugget Schlrshp 87; Music Schlrshp 87; Air Force Sci/Math Awds 87; Princeton; Physics.

EDWARDS, LISA; Eastern Christian HS; Paterson, NJ; (3); Church Yth Grp; Cmnty Wkr; Computer Clb; Dance Clb; Hosp Aide; Library Aide; Office Aide; Pep Clb; Church Choir; School Play; Hnr Grd 87; Debutante Frat Cotillion 85t; Princetown U; CPA.

EDWARDS, MICHAEL; Jefferson Twp HS; Lake Hopatcong, NJ; (3); 17/256; Am Leg Boys St; Computer Clb; Debate Tm; Math Tm; Science Clb; Chorus; Mrchg Band; Symp Band; Hon Roll; NHS; Chairmn Band & Choir 87-88; Medicine.

EDWARDS, NARONDA; West Side HS; Newark, NJ; (3); Cmnty Wkr; Girl Scts; Office Aide; Yrbk Stf; Hon Roll; Prfct Atten Awd; TNT/Ft 86; Catherine Gibbs Awd 87; Jersey City ST.

EDWARDS, NIJAH; Highland Regional HS; Blackwood, NJ; (2); Computer Clb; FHA; Latin Clb; Pep Clb; Nwsp Rptr; Lit Mag; JV Fld Hcky; Hon Roll; Comp Engrng.

EDWARDS, RENEE; Plainfield SR HS; Plainfield, NJ; (3); Dance Clb; Model UN; NAACP; School Musical; Nwsp Rptr; Yrbk Ed-Chief; Var Capt Cheerleading; Trk; Aud/Vis; Camera Clb; Ntl Lng Jmp Chmpn 84; Jack & Jill Of Amer Inc Teen Chptr Pres, Fndr Of Nae & J Prod Exctive Prdcr 87; Howard U; Mass Cmmnctns.

EDWARDS, ROBERT; The Pennington Schl; Neshanic Sta, NJ; (3); 36/82; Church Yth Grp; Spanish Clb; SADD; JV Var Bsbl; JV Bsktbl; Hon Roll; Bus.

EDWARDS, VICTORIA; Trinity Christian Acad; Hillside, NJ; (4); 1/2; Church Yth Grp; Band; Chorus; Mrchg Band; Yrbk Stf; Sftbl; Val; Jimmy Swaggart Bible; Secndr Ed.

EDWARDS, WENDY; Passaic County Tech & Voc HS; Haledon, NJ; (3); 3/524; Hon Roll; Trs NHS; US Natl Math Awds 85; Acad All Amer Schlrs 86; Commrcl Art.

EGAN, ANDREW J; Palisades Park JR-SR HS; Palisades Pk, NJ; (3); Boy Scts; JCL; Latin Clb; Concert Band; Mrchg Band; Pep Band; Stage Crew; Rep Stu Cncl; Var Crs Cntry; Var Co-Capt Wrstlng.

EGAN, MICHELE; Franklin HS; Somerset, NJ; (3); Church Yth Grp; Nwsp Rptr; Stu Cncl; Stat Bsbl; Var JV Fld Hcky; DAR Awd; Hon Roll; Educ.

EGAN, PATRICK; Christian Brothers Acad; Spring Lake Hts, NJ; (4); 24/219; Letterman Clb; Nwsp Rptr; Stu Cncl; Im Bsktbl; Im Ftbl; Var Capt Golf; Im Wt Lftg; Hon Roll; U Of Richmond; Bus.

EGAN, PATRICK; St Josephs HS; Westfield, NJ; (3); 4/219; Church Yth Grp; Political Wkr; Quiz Bowl; Jazz Band; School Play; Nwsp Rptr; Lit Mag; High Hon Roll; NHS; Ntl Merit Ltr; Holy Cross Book Awd 87; NJ Governors Schl Schlr 87; Full 4 Yr HS Schlrshp 84.

EGAN, WILLIAM J; Kittatinny Regional HS; Newton, NJ; (3); 12/224; Debate Tm; Math Tm; Science Clb; High Hon Roll; NHS; AIASA Treas 86-87; Lbrl Arts-Sci.

EGELAND, JENNIFER M; Toms River High School East; Toms River, NJ; (4); 6/567; Pres Church Yth Grp; Math Tm; Trs Band; Drm Mjr(t); Mrchg Band; Stage Crew; High Hon Roll; NHS; Ntl Merit SF; Comp Sci.

EGER, DEANA; Mainland Regional HS; Somers Pt, NJ; (4); Debate Tm; Pep Clb; Radio Clb; Pres SADD; School Play; Yrbk Rptr; Stat Trk; Bill Bradleys Yng Citzn Awd 87; Mainlands Assoc-Cncrnd Ctzns Awd 87; Stockton ST Coll; Pblc Rltns.

EGOAVIL, KEITH; Frank H Morrell HS; Irvington, NJ; (3); Boy Scts; Latin Clb; Var JV Socr; NJIT; Electrncs Engr.

EGOL, JONATHAN; Dwight Englewood Schl; Englewood, NJ; (3); 1/125; VP Debate Tm; Bausch & Lomb Sci Awd; Cmnty Wkr; Political Wkr; Orch; School Play; Var Lcrss; High Hon Roll; Rutgers ST Schlr 87; Faculty Cup Acdmc Excllnc 85; Natl Latin Cmpttn Gold Medal 84-87; Aerospace.

EHRHARDT, JULIA; Mother Seton Regional HS; Springfield, NJ; (4); 1/97; Math Tm; Science Clb; Yrbk Ed-Chief; Lit Mag; Stat Sftbl; Bausch & Lomb Sci Awd; NHS; Ntl Merit Ltr; St Schlr; Val; Prncpls Awd For Excllnc 87; Duke U; Physics.

EHRLICH, MARK F; Paramus Catholic HS; Wood Ridge, NJ; (4); 10/178; Capt Debate Tm; Pres Drama Clb; School Musical; Ed Lit Mag; JV VP Ice Hcky; JV VP Socr; Elks Awd; French Hon Soc; NHS; Ntl Merit Ltr; Egl Awd Brnz & Gold Plms BSA 85; Grdn ST Dstngshd Schlrshp 87; Rutgers Coll; Drama.

EIBLE, JEN; Mendham HS; Chester, NJ; (2); 93/300; Ski Clb; Stat Bsktbl; Var L Socr; Var L Sftbl; Hon Roll; 4-H; GAA; Mgr(s); Hnrb Mntn Grls Sftbl Catcher All Conf & All Area 87; Sftbl Sectional Champs 87; U MA; Sprts Mgmt.

EICHENBAUM, WENDY; Ridge HS; Basking Ridge, NJ; (3); 11/192; Drama Clb; Key Clb; Spanish Clb; Chorus; School Play; Stage Crew; High Hon Roll; Hon Roll; NHS.

EICHLIN, SCOTT; Delaware Valley Regional HS; Frenchtown, NJ; (3); 42/225; JV L Bsktbl; High Hon Roll; Hon Roll; Hnrs Bsktl Ltr; High Hnrs Bsktbl JV Ltr; Architectural.

EIDE, KAREN C; Steinert HS; Hamilton Sq, NJ; (3); AFS; Am Leg Aux Girls St; NFL; SADD; Nwsp Rptr; Lit Mag; Rep Soph Cls; Rep Jr Cls; Mgr(s); High Hon Roll; Frgn Svc.

EIFE, WALTER A; Haddon Township HS; Westmont, NJ; (3); Am Leg Boys St; Nwsp Stf; Pres Soph Cls; Sec Jr Cls; Pres Stu Cncl; Var L Bsktbl; Hon Roll; NHS; German Clb; Varsity Clb; Hugh O Brian Yth Ldrshp Conf; NJ St Stu Cncl Ldrshp Training Conf; Rutgers; Law.

EIKE, JASON C; Phillipsburg HS; Alpha, NJ; (3); Am Leg Boys St; Church Yth Grp; Pep Clb; Stage Crew; Rep Frsh Cls; Rep Soph Cls; JV Socr; JV Var Wrstlng; Bus.

EIRING, JENNIFER C; Spotswood HS; Milltown, NJ; (2); 13/127; Intnl Clb; Spanish Clb; Yrbk Stf; Var Trk; Hon Roll; Rutgers U; Phrmcy.

EISEN, JOSH; Dwight Morrow HS; Englewood, NJ; (4); 1/220; Cmnty Wkr; Drama Clb; Capt Math Tm; Yrbk Ed-Chief; Capt Var Tennis; High Hon Roll; NHS; Ntl Merit Ltr; St Schlr; Val; Rutgers Schlr 86; R C Byrd Schlrshp 87; Stanford U; Engrng.

EISENBEIS, AMEE; Matawan-Aberdeen Regional HS; Matawan, NJ; (2); Church Yth Grp; 4-H; Girl Scts; Math Tm; Ski Clb; Band; Concert Band; JV Bsktbl; JV Sftbl; Hon Roll.

EISNER, EDWARD C; New Providence HS; New Providence, NJ; (4); 1/167; Chess Clb; JV Var Bsbl; JV Var Bsktbl; Var Trk; Bausch & Lomb Sci Awd; NHS; Ntl Merit SF; High Hon Roll; Hon Roll; Prfct Atten Awd; NJ Gov Schl Sci 86; Rutgers Schlr 86; Grdn ST Distngshd Schlr 86; Yale U; Molecular Bio.

EISSING, TRACY; Central Regional HS; Bayville, NJ; (3); Church Yth Grp; FHA; SADD; Nwsp Rptr; JV Capt Fld Hcky; JV Socr; High Hon Roll; NHS; Awd Excllnc Outstndng Achvt Chld Dev 86-87; Awd Merit Stu Ath JV Sccr; Elem Ed.

EITEL, KRISTEN; West Windsor Plainsboro HS; Princeton Junct, NJ; (3); Church Yth Grp; Hosp Aide; Yrbk Stf; Stat Bsktbl; Stat Diving; Mgr(s); Score Keeper; JV Sftbl; Stat Swmmng; Mst Vlbl Plyr-Jr Varsity Sftbl 87; Intl Rltns.

EITNER, KEITH D; Newton HS; Lafayette, NJ; (3); 5/200; German Clb; Math Tm; Quiz Bowl; Science Clb; Ski Clb; Pres Stu Cncl; Var JV Bsbl; NHS; US Naval Acad; Naval Aviator.

EL, LISA; Our Lady Of Mercy Acad; Vineland, NJ; (3); Church Yth Grp; Dance Clb; NAACP; Mrchg Band; Trs Stu Cncl; High Hon Roll; Hon Roll; Jr NHS; Perfect Attndnc Awd 85-86; Calligraphy Clb 86-87; Wilfred Acad; Csmtc Cnsltnt.

EL, RUTH S; Irvington HS; Irvington, NJ; (3); Computer Clb; Dance Clb; Drama Clb; Temple Yth Grp; Varsity Clb; JV Crs Cntry; JV Score Keeper; JV Trk; Hon Roll; Prfct Atten Awd; Law.

ELBERTSON, TIMOTHY; Millville SR HS; Millville, NJ; (3); Debate Tm; Drama Clb; Trs Key Clb; Model UN; SADD; Mrchg Band; School Play; Nwsp Ed-Chief; Rep Stu Cncl; NHS; Comms.

ELDER, JANET; Pinelands Regional HS; Tuckertown, NJ; (4); 11/196; Church Yth Grp; Church Choir; Concert Band; High Hon Roll; Hon Roll; NHS; Ocean County Coll; Nrsg.

ELDER JR, WILLIAM; Parsippany HS; Parsippany, NJ; (4); 47/330; Model UN; Bsktbl; Capt Bowling; Capt Golf; Hon Roll; NHS; U MI Ann Arbor.

ELEFANTE, IRENE; Our Lady Of Good Counsel HS; Irvington, NJ; (3); 49/127; Brdcstng.

ELENBERG, IRVIN CHARLES; Hillel HS; Lakewood, NJ; (4); 1/31; Capt Math Tm; Quiz Bowl; Nwsp Stf; VP Stu Cncl; High Hon Roll; NHS; Ntl Merit Ltr; Val; Debate Tm; Math Clb; Rutgers Presdntl Schlrshp 86-87; NYU Schlrshp 86-87; U Of PA; Bus.

ELIKER, DARREN; Triton Regional HS; Somerdale, NJ; (4); 5/309; School Musical; NHS; French Clb; Key Clb; Band; Hon Roll; St Schlr; Carnegie-Mellon Univ; Music.

ELK, MONICA; Salem HS; Salem, NJ; (3); 44/165; FBLA; Spanish Clb; SADD; Teachers Aide; Varsity Clb; Yrbk Stf; Rep Stu Cncl; Fld Hcky; Hon Roll; Var Hockey Tri Cnty All Star Tm 85; Gifted & Tlntd 84; Bus Adm.

ELKADI, SHAHENAZ; Manalapan HS; Englishtown, NJ; (3); 73/433; Library Aide; Nwsp Rptr; Hon Roll; Prfct Atten Awd; Rutgers U; Bus Mgmt.

ELLEN, MARTIN; Wallington HS; Wallington, NJ; (2); Chess Clb; Stu Cncl; Tennis; NASA 87; Rutgers; Law.

ELLER, NICOLE; Mt Olive HS; Flanders, NJ; (3); Dance Clb; Exploring; FBLA; Hosp Aide; Science Clb; Ski Clb; SADD; Varsity Clb; Color Guard; JV Var Fld Hcky; Phys Thrpy.

ELLERMAN, PHYLLIS; Lenape HS; Medford, NJ; (3); Exploring; FBLA; Spanish Clb; SADD; Varsity Clb; Y-Teens; Acpl Chr; Var Cheerleading; High Hon Roll; FBLA Regnl Comptn Shrthnd 86.

ELLIOTT, BRIAN; Lakeland Regional HS; Ringwood, NJ; (4); 59/360; Church Yth Grp; Teachers Aide; Bsbl; Capt JV Bsktbl; Ftbl; Siena Coll; Bus.

ELLIOTT, CHRISTINA S; Cinnaminson HS; Cinnaminson, NJ; (4); 66/230; Church Yth Grp; Nwsp Stf; Lit Mag; Rep Sr Cls; Rep Stu Cncl; Pres Schlr; Art Awd; Cnnmnson Tchrs Assc Schlrshp; Taylor U; Educ.

ELLIOTT, CLIFFORD ALEXANDER; Edgewood Regional HS; Sicklerville, NJ; (3); JV Ftbl; Var Golf; JV Wrstlng; Questor Awd 85; Engr.

ELLIOTT, JAMIE; Freehold Township HS; Freehold, NJ; (3); Drama Clb; SADD; Sec Temple Yth Grp; School Musical; Yrbk Stf; Stat Bsbl; Cheerleading; Score Keeper; Sftbl; NHS; Monmouth Coll Govt Inst 2nd Pl Essay Comptn 87; Psych.

ELLIOTT, NATHAN J; Cinnaminson HS; Cinnaminson, NJ; (3); Am Leg Boys St; Chess Clb; Church Yth Grp; German Clb; Math Clb; Math Tm; Science Clb; Stage Crew; Stu Cncl; JV Bsktbl; German Mrt Awd 85-86.

ELLIOTT, TIMOTHY R; Cranford HS; Cranford, NJ; (3); 17/268; Am Leg Boys St; Math Clb; Spanish Clb; Jazz Band; Mrchg Band; VP Stu Cncl; Hon Roll; Spanish NHS; Boy Scts; Band; Eagle Sct Awd BSA 87; Cranford Mod Yth Govt 87; TV 35 Prodctn Clb 86-87; Engrng.

ELLIS, APRIL; Weequahic HS; Newark, NJ; (4); 30/349; Mrchg Band; Nwsp Rptr; Nwsp Stf; Ed Lit Mag; Rep Stu Cncl; Hon Roll; Alimni Schlrshp 87; Metropolitan Bapt Church Schlrshp 87; VA ST U; Chld Psych.

ELLIS, CHERYL; Pleasantville HS; Pleasantville, NJ; (4); 9/102; Church Yth Grp; Sec Computer Clb; Lib Band; Lib Concert Band; Lib Mrchg Band; Sec Yrbk Stf; Rep Jr Cls; Rep Sr Cls; Var Tennis; Marine Band Awd 86-87; Acad Achvt Awd 83-84, 86-87; Widener U; Pdtrc Nrsng.

ELLIS, JANE; Toms River HS South; Toms River, NJ; (3); 52/400; Math Tm; Ski Clb; Var Powder Puff Ftbl; Var Socr; Var Capt Swmmng; Var Capt Tennis; NHS; Amercn HS Athlt-Swmmng 85-86; Swmmr Of Yr-Observr 86-87; Indian Hostess 86-87.

ELLIS, KRISTIN; Ocean Township HS; Asbury Park, NJ; (3); 147/344; Pres Church Yth Grp; French Clb; Ski Clb; SADD; Church Choir; Stage Crew; Variety Show; Spcl Ed.

ELLIS, MATT; Warren Hills Regional HS; Washington, NJ; (4); AFS; Art Clb; Drama Clb; Intnl Clb; Drm & Bgl; Variety Show; Lit Mag; VP Frsh Cls; VP Soph Cls; High Hon Roll; Smmr Sclptr Cls Schlrshp 85; Invtn To Attnd Smmr Arts Institute 86; Portland Schl Of Art; Artst.

ELLIS, ROBERT; Kearney HS; Kearny, NJ; (2); Im Ice Hcky; Elks Awd; Hon Roll; Hnr Guard 87; Grphc Art.

ELLIS, STEVE ROGER; Rancocas Valley Regional HS; Lumberton, NJ; (3); 141/359; Band; Mrchg Band; JV Swmmng; JV Tennis; Hon Roll; Bus Admin.

ELLISON, LISA; Bishop George AHR St Thomas HS; Edison, NJ; (4); 104/267; Mgr Drama Clb; Hosp Aide; Spanish Clb; Capt Color Guard; Nwsp Stf; Yrbk Stf; High Hon Roll; Hon Roll; NEDT Awd; Prfct Atten Awd; Most Imprvd Awd Color Grd 85; U Of DE; Law.

ELMIGER, JOANN; Union Catholic Regional HS; Cranford, NJ; (3); 34/352; Church Yth Grp; Scholastic Bowl; Service Clb; Ski Clb; Spanish Clb; Nwsp Rptr; Yrbk Stf; Rep Bsbl; High Hon Roll; Hon Roll; Hnr Rll HS 84-87; Chrstn Ldrshp Awd 85; Marist Coll; Cmmnctns.

ELMO, LISA; Brick Memorial HS; Brick, NJ; (3); 79/350; Art Clb; Var Bowling; JV Capt Socr.

ELMORE, DWIGHT; Lakewood SR HS; Lakewood, NJ; (3); NAACP; Bsktbl; Hon Roll; Spcl Achvt Mech Drwng 84; Pgm Acclrtn Careers Engr 84-85; Arch.

ELSAID, ABIER; Dickinson HS; Jersey City, NJ; (3); Rep Jr Cls; Hon Roll; Prfct Atten Awd; Merit Rl 85-87; NY U; Lawyr.

ELY, PAM; Manalapan HS; Coltsneck, NJ; (4); 62/435; Temple Yth Grp; Rep Frsh Cls; Rep Soph Cls; Rep Jr Cls; Stu Cncl; JV Letterman Clb; JR Prom Crt; Homecomng Crt; SR Ball Crt; Boston U; Bus.

EMBLETON, MICHAEL; Vernon Township HS; Vernon, NJ; (3); Church Yth Grp; Concert Band; Jazz Band; Mrchg Band; VP Soph Cls; VP Jr Cls; JV Bsktbl; JV Trk; Hon Roll; Exploring; All Sussex Cnty Band 85 & 86; Air Pilot.

EMBLEY, GARY; Hamilton HS West; Trenton, NJ; (3); Am Leg Boys St; Hon Roll; Var L Bsbl; Var L Ftbl; Engrng.

EMEL, DEVEREAUE; Salem HS; Salem, NJ; (4); 7/170; Am Leg Aux Girls St; Pres Hosp Aide; Sec Soph Cls; Co-Capt Cheerleading; Hon Roll; Pres NHS; Rtry Stu Guest 86-87; Nrsng Schlrshp 87; Cndystrpr Of Yr 87; Trenton ST Coll; Nrsng.

EMENHEISER, RICK; Willingboro HS; Willingboro, NJ; (3); 14/350; Key Clb; Trs Sr Cls; Var L Golf; Var Wrstlng; Hon Roll; NHS; Prfct Atten Awd; Atl To Boys ST 87; Elec Engr.

EMENS II, GERALD; Millville SR HS; Millville, NJ; (3); Boy Scts; Camera Clb; Pres Church Yth Grp; Trs Soph Cls; Trs Sr Cls; Trs Stu Cncl; JV Ftbl; Var Wt Lftg; Var Wrstlng; Seton Hall U; Psych.

EMERSON, MICHAEL; Delaware Valley Regional HS; Frenchtown, NJ; (4); 15/150; Science Clb; Trs Soph Cls; Rep Stu Cncl; JV Bsktbl; Var Socr; JV Trk; Gardn ST Dstngshd Schlr 87; Pres Acdmc Ftnss Awd 87; Amer Lgn Cert Dstngshd Achvt 87; Mc Gill U; Poltcl Sci.

EMERY, JENNIFER L; Scotch Plains Fanwood HS; Scotch Plains, NJ; (3); 10/375; French Clb; Key Clb; Service Clb; SADD; Drill Tm; Mrchg Band; Symp Band; Var Socr; French Hon Soc; Hon Roll.

EMMERLING, LORIN E; West Milford HS; West Milford, NJ; (3); Ski Clb; Stu Cncl; Berkley Business Schl; Bus.

EMMERT, BONNIE; Toms River North HS; Toms River, NJ; (4); 3/391; Spanish Clb; SADD; Var Capt Bsktbl; Var Capt Tennis; Var L Trk; High Hon Roll; Hon Roll; NHS; ETS/NJSIAA Schlr-Ath Awd 87; Toms River Ed Assn Scholar 87; Army Rsrve Schlr-Ath Awd 87; Ursinus Coll; Hlth Sci.

EMMONS, DEBRA; St John Vianney HS; Keyport, NJ; (3); 1/235; Hosp Aide; Service Clb; SADD; Var Trk; NHS; Cmnty Wkr; Computer Clb; Math Tm; Stage Crew; Mgr Bsktbl; Cntry Clb Schlrshp Awd 85; Hgh Obrn Yth Fndtn Rep 86; Gov Schl Finlst Math, Sci 87; Merit Awds Math 87; Comp Engrng.

EMMONS, LISA; St John Vianney HS; Keyport, NJ; (2); 1/265; Cmnty Wkr; Service Clb; SADD; Var Trk; High Hon Roll; NHS; Computer Clb; Math Tm; Stage Crew; Stat Bsktbl; Gld, White Awd Curr, Intra Curr, Extra Curr Actvts 86-87; Cert Recog WNET 8th Annl Stu Arts Fest 86; Engrng.

EMRICH, ELLEN; Pinelands Regional HS; Tuckerton, NJ; (3); 6/190; Stat Ftbl; Var Trk; High Hon Roll; NHS; Spanish NHS; US Ntl Math Awd 87; Grls Ctznshp Inst 87; Jr Clss Exec & Prom Comm 87; Frgn Lang.

ENCARNACION, ANTONIO; Dickenson HS; Jersey City, NJ; (3); Boys Clb Am; Church Yth Grp; Key Clb; Band; Jr Cls; All Am Scholars Merit Awd 87; Ruthers Coll; Bus Mgmt.

ENCINOSA, MARITZA; Academic HS; Jersey City, NJ; (3); Boy Scts; Spanish Clb; Concert Band; Tennis; Rutgers Newark Coll; Acctng.

ENDE, PHILIP ERIC; West Orange HS; West Orange, NJ; (3); Am Leg Boys St; French Clb; Quiz Bowl; Nwsp Stf; Trs Soph Cls; VP Pres Stu Cncl; Var Bsktbl; Var Golf; Hugh O Brian Absdr 86; Bus & Alw.

ENDERLE, KRISTEN; Mt Saint Dominic HS; W Caldwell, NJ; (3); JCL; Latin Clb; Ski Clb; Nwsp Rptr; Nwsp Stf; Yrbk Phtg; Yrbk Stf; Pres Frsh Cls; Pres Soph Cls; Pres Sr Cls; Sprts Mgr.

ENG, GORDON W; Cliffside Park HS; Cliffside Park, NJ; (4); Chess Clb; Civic Clb; Cmnty Wkr; Hosp Aide; Concert Band; Jazz Band; Mrchg Band; Stu Cncl; Bsktbl; Var Tennis; Bill Bradleys Young Ctzns Awd 87; Rotary Clb Boy Of Mnth 86; Delegate Amer Lgn Boys St 86; Rutgers U; Hlth Rltd.

ENGEKE, SHELLY; Hunterdon Central HS; Lebanon, NJ; (2); Church Yth Grp; Rep Stu Cncl; Stat Bsktbl; JV Fld Hcky; JV Sftbl; Im Vllybl; Hon Roll; Clemson U; Bus.

ENGEL, ANDREW; Dwight Engelwood HS; Norwood, NJ; (3); Boy Scts; Chess Clb; Cmnty Wkr; Hosp Aide; Library Aide; Office Aide; Ski Clb; Band; Yrbk Phtg; Bowling; Olympics Of The Mind 84; Sci.

ENGEL, CHRISTINE; Mc Corristin Catholic HS; Trenton, NJ; (3); Drama Clb; FBLA; Pep Clb; Chorus; School Musical; School Play; Yrbk Stf; Cheerleading; Mgr(s); Hon Roll; Bus.

ENGLAND, KIMBERLEY; Delaware Valley Regional HS; Asbury, NJ; (4); 33/150; Art Clb; Ski Clb; Hon Roll; Bus Mgmt.

ENGLER, MARCY; West Windsor-Plainsboro HS; Princeton Junct, NJ; (3); Trs AFS; Model UN; Service Clb; Nwsp Ed-Chief; High Hon Roll; NHS; Poli Sci.

ENGLISH, VALERIE; Kearny HS; Kearny, NJ; (4); 17/383; Var Capt Socr; Var Capt Sftbl; High Hon Roll; NHS; Spanish NHS; KEA Philanthrpc Fund Inc 87; 1st Tm All Cnty Sftbl & Sccr 86-87; Acdmc Excllnc Awd 84; Kean Coll; Erly Chldhd Ed.

ENGWALL, KAREN; Waldwick HS; Waldwick, NJ; (3); Church Yth Grp; Drama Clb; French Clb; Spanish Clb; Band; Concert Band; Mrchg Band; Orch; Pep Band; Stage Crew; St Olaf Coll; French.

ENIS, STEVEN; Manalapan HS; Englishtown, NJ; (3); Latin Clb; L Var Tennis; MD; Law.

ENNICO, KIMBERLY; Immaculate Heart Acad; Westwood, NJ; (1); Girl Scts; Hosp Aide; Natl Beta Clb; Science Clb; Orch; JV Var Bsktbl; High Hon Roll; Stu Ldrshp Conf Wrkshp 87; Astrophysics.

ENSER, JON; Ramapo HS; Wyckoff, NJ; (3); 127/322; Boy Scts; Church Yth Grp; Hon Roll; Hnr Rll; Engrng.

ENTIS, IRA S; Morristown HS; Morristown, NJ; (3); 23/424; Am Leg Boys St; VP JA; Q&S; Temple Yth Grp; Nwsp Ed-Chief; Mgr Lit Mag; Hon Roll; NHS; Voice Dem Awd; Latin Clb; Sta Mgr Radio/TV Sta 87; Understndng Amer Bus Pgm 87; Bus.

ENTRUP, RONALD; Watchung Hills Regional HS; Warren, NJ; (3); Church Yth Grp; Ski Clb; Bus Accntng.

EPPS, ANDREA; Pennsauken HS; Delair, NJ; (3); 22/403; Church Yth Grp; Spanish Clb; Church Choir; Concert Band; Drm Mjr(t); Mrchg Band; Symp Band; Var Bsktbl; Var Tennis; JV Trk; Hnr Soc 87; Hgh Hnr Roll 87; Educ.

ERDMAN, RONNIE J; Haddon Township HS; Westmont, NJ; (3); Boy Scts; Letterman Clb; Varsity Clb; Var L Ftbl; Atten Annapolis Naval Acad Ftbl Cmp 86 3 87; JV MV Lnmn Awd 84-85; Bus.

ERDO, KRISTIANE; Toms River HS South; Beachwood, NJ; (2); Hosp Aide; Orch; JV Sftbl; Entrepreneur.

ERGOOD, RUSSELL; Bishop Eustace Preparatory Schl; Cherry Hill, NJ; (3); 70/170; Math Clb; Spanish Clb; JV Bsbl; JV Bsktbl; Var Socr; Spanish NHS; Bus Law.

ERIANNE, JOAN; Cumberland Regional HS; Bridgeton, NJ; (4); Chorus; Church Choir; Madrigals; Variety Show; High Hon Roll; Hon Roll; NHS; All S Jrsy Chrus 83-87; Brdgeton Symphny Chorus 86; Glassboro ST Coll; Music.

ERIANNE, KELLI; Schalick HS; Bridgeton, NJ; (3); 22/135; Church Yth Grp; Band; Concert Band; Mrchg Band; VP Frsh Cls; Pres Soph Cls; Rep Stu Cncl; Var Bsktbl; Var Fld Hcky; Var Sftbl; Unsung Hero Awd Bsktbll 87; 2nd Tm Allstr Awd Sftbll 87; Ed.

ERICKSEN, CHRISTINE; Brick Memorial HS; Bricktown, NJ; (1); FBLA; Hon Roll.

ERICKSON, ALICIA; Marine Acad Of Sciences & Technlgy; Long Branch, NJ; (3); #3 In Class; Drama Clb; French Clb; ROTC; Spanish Clb; Drill Tm; Nwsp Ed-Chief; Yrbk Bus Mgr; Rep Stu Cncl; Hon Roll; NHS; IFLA 84-85; Florida Inst Of Tech; Bio Chem.

ERICKSON, JIM; Bishop Eustace Prep; Medford, NJ; (3); Band; JV Golf; Var Ice Hcky; Hon Roll; JC Awd; NHS; Spanish NHS; Engrng.

ERICKSON, LORI BARTLETT; Kent Place Schl; Mountainside, NJ; (3); VP Pres Church Yth Grp; Acpl Chr; Chorus; Yrbk Bus Mgr; Rep Frsh Cls; Rep Soph Cls; Rep Jr Cls; Rep Sr Cls; Rep Stu Cncl; Fld Hcky; U Richmond; Intl Bus.

ERICSON, JESSICA; Delaware Valley Regional HS; Frenchtown, NJ; (3); Trs Key Clb; Varsity Clb; Hon Roll; Stat Bsbl; Var JV Cheerleading.

ERICSON, JOHN T; High Point Regional HS; Branchville, NJ; (4); 45/221; Am Leg Boys St; 4-H; Ski Clb; Tennis; Cit Awd; 4-H Awd; High Hon Roll; Hon Roll; Eastrn Str Magi Chptr 278 Awd 87; 4-H Schlrshp 87; Rotry Clb Schlrshp 87; Gettysburg Coll; Poltcl Sci.

ERICSON, SAMANTHA; Pennsville Memorial HS; Pennsville, NJ; (3); Drama Clb; Pres FHA; Girl Scts; JA; Office Aide; Red Cross Aide; Ski Clb; SADD; Band; Concert Band; Acctng.

ERKERT, STEVEN K; Burlington City HS; Edgewater Park, NJ; (3); Am Leg Boys St; Var Socr; Hon Roll; Elec Engr.

ERMINIO, MICHAEL; Lyndhurst HS; Lyndhurst, NJ; (3); 90/200; Spanish Clb; Varsity Clb; JV Var Bsbl; Bsktbl; JV Var Ftbl; Bus.

ERN, DAVID; Christian Brothers Acad; Lincroft, NJ; (3); 1/240; Boys Clb Am; Boy Scts; Im Bsktbl; Im Bowling; Im Ftbl; Im Sftbl; High Hon Roll; Hon Roll; Eagle Scout 87.

ERNANDES, JOANNE; Mc Corristin Catholic HS; Trenton, NJ; (3); 28/350; GAA; Hosp Aide; Rep Jr Cls; Socr; Hon Roll; NHS; Pep Clb; Scholastic Bowl; Yrbk Stf; Off Stu Cncl.

ERNST, KENDRA; Notre Dame HS; Titusville, NJ; (3); 86/400; Teachers Aide; Varsity Clb; Var Bsktbl; Var Fld Hcky; Var Trk; High Hon Roll; Hon Roll; NHS; Nutrtn Sci.

ERNST, ROBIN; Notre Dame HS; Titusville, NJ; (2); 8/400; Church Yth Grp; Math Tm; Capt Fld Hcky; VP Swmmng; JV Trk; Hon Roll; NHS; Church Yth Grp; Math Tm; Med.

ERRANDONEA, FRANCOIS; Hopatong HS; Hopatcong, NJ; (4); 13/299; Cmnty Wkr; Varsity Clb; Nwsp Stf; Stu Cncl; Capt Var Crs Cntry; JV Socr; Var Trk; High Hon Roll; NHS; St Schlr; Stevens Alumni Rgnl Schlrshp 87; NJ Dstngshd Schlr 87; US Army Rsrv Ntl Schlr Athlt Awd 87; Stevens Inst Of Tech; Bio Engr.

ERRANTE, CHRISTOPHER A; Nutley HS; Nutley, NJ; (3); 33/308; Am Leg Boys St; Spanish Clb; Varsity Clb; Stu Cncl; Var Bsbl; Var Ftbl; Hon Roll; Wrtng Awd 86; Princeton; Pol Sci.

ERRICKSON JR, DAVID; Middle Township HS; Del Haven, NJ; (4); 18/208; Ski Clb; Rep Stu Cncl; Var Crs Cntry; Var Trk; Hon Roll; Ntl Merit Ltr; Opt Clb Awd; Pres Schlr; Amer Legion Awd 87; Statler Fndtn 87; Johnson & Wales Coll; Htl Mgmt.

ERRICO, MARCUS R; Hunterdon Central HS; Sergeantsville, NJ; (4); 9/559; Boys Clb Am; Rptr Lit Mag; Var L Trk; Im Capt Vllybl; French Hon Soc; Gov Hon Prg Awd; NCTE Awd; NHS; Ntl Merit Ltr; St Schlr.

ERRICO, STEWART; High Point Regional HS; Sussex, NJ; (2); Boy Scts; Chess Clb; Computer Clb; Exploring; Concert Band; JV Ftbl; JV Trk; Var Wt Lftg; Hon Roll; Natl Sci Olympd; Air Force; Pilot.

ESCALANTE, JUDITH; Immaculate Conception HS; Wallington, NJ; (3); Hosp Aide; NFL; Stage Crew; Yrbk Stf; Rep Frsh Cls; VP Soph Cls; Pres Jr Cls; NEDT Awd; Spanish NHS.

ESCHLEMAN, ANNEMARIE; Notre Dame HS; West Trenton, NJ; (3); 12/300; Red Cross Aide; Spanish Clb; Nwsp Stf; High Hon Roll; Hon Roll; Spanish NHS; Bus.

ESCOBAR, MARTA; Immaculate Conception HS; Newark, NJ; (2); Aud/Vis; Camera Clb; Dance Clb; Office Aide; Chorus; Tennis; Spanish NHS; Social Worker.

ESCOBINAS, ARIEL A J; Essex Catholic Boys HS; Bloomfield, NJ; (2); 5/120; Boy Scts; Chess Clb; Church Yth Grp; Math Clb; Math Tm; Band; Im Bowling; JV Tennis; High Hon Roll; Schl Scholar 85-89.

ESMURDOC, CAROLINA FRANCES; Oak Knoll Schl; Elizabeth, NJ; (4); Art Clb; Church Yth Grp; Dance Clb; Hosp Aide; Service Clb; Nwsp Ed-Chief; Nwsp Rptr; High Hon Roll; Spanish NHS; Conrad & Marcel Schlumberger Schlrshp 87; Bucknell U; Chem.

ESPINOZA, DANNY; The Pingry Schl; Basking Ridge, NJ; (4); Key Clb; Spanish Clb; SADD; Lit Mag; JV Socr; Hon Roll; Ntl Merit Schol; Comp Sci.

ESPOSITO, GLEN; Hawthorne HS; Hawthorne, NJ; (3); Am Leg Boys St; SADD; Pres Frsh Cls; Rep Soph Cls; Pres Jr Cls; Pres Sr Cls; Rep Stu Cncl; Var Bsbl; JV Bsktbl; Hon Roll; Fndtn For Free Entrprs; Peer Cnslng TAF.

ESPOSITO, JEAN; Edgewood Regional HS; Sicklerville, NJ; (2); Church Yth Grp; Latin Clb; Office Aide; Varsity Clb; Yrbk Stf; Rep Frsh Cls; Rep Soph Cls; Stat Bsbl; Stat Ftbl; Hon Roll; Vrsty Lttr Sports; Distngshd Person; Med X-Ray Tech.

ESPOSITO, JENNIFER; Randolph HS; Ironia, NJ; (3); 48/350; French Clb; Band; Concert Band; Mrchg Band; Symp Band; Mat Maids; Powder Puff Ftbl; Score Keeper; French Hon Soc; Hon Roll; Exhbtr Stdnt Expstn Enrgy Resources 85; Cert Achvt Sci US Marn Corps 85.

ESPOSITO, LUISA; Lakeland Regional HS; Wanaque, NJ; (3); Dance Clb; Drama Clb; French Clb; Intnl Clb; Math Tm; PAVAS; Sec Sr Cls; Sec Stu Cncl; High Hon Roll; NHS; Schlrshp Awd Dnce Alvin Ailey Dance Co 87.

ESPOSITO, RENEE; Jackson Mem HS; Jackson, NJ; (4); 48/357; Church Yth Grp; Varsity Clb; Gym; Powder Puff Ftbl; Sftbl; Trk; Wt Lftg; High Hon Roll; Hon Roll; Jackson Twnshp HS Schlrshp Fund 87; Rider Coll; Bus Admin.

ESPOSITO, SANDRA; Ridge HS; Basking Ridge, NJ; (3); 32/192; Church Choir; JV Bsktbl; Coach Actv; Var Capt Crs Cntry; JV Fld Hcky; Var Capt Trk; Im Wt Lftg; Hon Roll; All-ST Crss Cntry Daily Record 85, Winter & Spring Trck Hnrb Mntn 86 & 87; Accntng.

ESPOSITO, SHARON; Dover HS; Dover, NJ; (3); 24/240; Girl Scts; Hosp Aide; Ski Clb; Spanish Clb; Concert Band; Mrchg Band; Bsktbl; Sftbl; High Hon Roll; Hon Roll; Bus.

ESPOSITO, TINA; Monsignor Donovan HS; Toms River, NJ; (3); Ski Clb; Var Sftbl; Hon Roll; NHS; Sociolgy.

ESQUIERES, RONALD; Indian Hills HS; Oakland, NJ; (3); 7/306; Varsity Clb; Band; Var Bsbl; Var Bsktbl; Var Ftbl; High Hon Roll; Hon Roll; NHS; Hnr Mntn All Cnty Bsbl 87; Elec Engr.

ESTELLE, EDDIE; Lakewood HS; Lakewood, NJ; (4); 38/270; Spanish Clb; Im Badmtn; Bsbl; Ftbl; Im Vllybl; High Hon Roll; Hon Roll; Spanish NHS; Black Hwks Schlrshp 87; Ocean Cnty Coll; Cvl Engrng.

ESTELLE, JENNIFER; Brick Memorial HS; Brick, NJ; (3); 10/380; FBLA; Rep Key Clb; Spanish Clb; Rep Jr Cls; Im Bsktbl; Crs Cntry; High Hon Roll; NHS.

ESTELLE, PAMELA; Notre Dame HS; Robbinsville, NJ; (3); Yrbk Phtg; Yrbk Rptr; Yrbk Stf; Rep Soph Cls; Hon Roll; Bus Admin.

ESTEVEZ, MARISOL; Memorial HS; W New York, NJ; (3); French Clb; Trs FHA; Flag Corp; Lit Mag; If I Were Pres-Essy Cntst-Knghts Clmbs 84; U Of Miami; Pltcl Sci.

ESTIS, MICHELLE; Manalapan HS; Manalapan, NJ; (3); 65/429; 4-H; Hosp Aide; Q&S; Yrbk Sprt Ed; Yrbk Stf; Var Bsktbl; Var Capt Sftbl; Var Tennis; Gov Hon Prg Awd; Ltn Hnr Scty; Ntrtn & Dtcs.

ESTLACK, AMY; Pitman HS; Pitman, NJ; (3); 29/147; Church Yth Grp; Key Clb; Political Wkr; Teachers Aide; Chorus; Nwsp Stf; Rep Frsh Cls; Rep Soph Cls; VP Stu Cncl; Var Stat Bsktbl; Miss Pitman Pgnt Cntst 87; Engl.

ESTLER, MELISSA; Dover HS; Dover, NJ; (4); 47/187; Church Yth Grp; French Clb; Band; Concert Band; Mrchg Band; Toccoa Falls Coll; Intr Dsgn.

ESTRADA, RAYMOND; Perth Amboy HS; Perth Amboy, NJ; (3); Model UN; Office Aide; ROTC; Science Clb; Stage Crew; Nwsp Ed-Chief; Trs Soph Cls; Stu Cncl; Hon Roll; Cert Recog Acdmc Excllnc 86; Dstngshd Cadet Awd ROTC 86 & 87; Rutgers U; Mltry Offcr.

ETHINGTON, JENNIFER; Franklin HS; Somerset, NJ; (3); Church Yth Grp; 4-H; German Clb; Band; Concert Band; Mrchg Band; Nwsp Rptr; Nwsp Stf; 4-H Awd; Prfct Atten Awd; Pres Italian Clb 86-87; Engl.

ETTER, KERRYLEA; Cherry Hill High School East; Cherry Hill, NJ; (4); PAVAS; Acpl Chr; Chorus; Church Choir; Concert Band; Madrigals; Mrchg Band; Orch; School Musical; Symp Band; Hnrs Div Schlrshp IN U 87-88; Martha Fletcher Schlrshp 87; Natl Choral Soc Awd 87; IN U Bloomington; Music.

EUBANKS III, JOHN SCOTT; Clifford J Scott HS; East Orange, NJ; (2); 6/257; Church Yth Grp; Latin Clb; Math Clb; Math Tm; Band; Church Choir; Concert Band; Drill Tm; Mrchg Band; Yrbk Stf; Air Force Acad; Pilot.

EUGSTER, LAURA; Woodbury HS; Woodbury, NJ; (2); Math Clb; Quiz Bowl; Chorus; Rep Stu Cncl; JV Fld Hcky; JV Capt Sftbl; Fshn Illustrtn.

EULER, CLAUDIA; Northern Valley Regional HS; Old Tappan, NJ; (3); 56/276; Church Yth Grp; Sec Intnl Clb; Ntl Merit SF; JV Crs Cntry; JV Trk; Hon Roll; AFS; FBLA; Math Tm; Office Aide; Socl Sci.

EVANGELIST, CAERY; High Point Regional HS; Agusta, NJ; (2); Chorus; High Hon Roll; Hon Roll; 2nd Pl Sussex Cnty Law Day Essy Cont 87; Archeolgy.

EVANGELISTA, JESSICA R; St Marys HS; Jersey City, NJ; (3); Pep Clb; Service Clb; Church Choir; Yrbk Stf; Chrstn Svc Awd 87; Nrsng.

EVANGELISTA, MARIA; Carteret HS; Carteret, NJ; (3); 80/217; FBLA; FTA; Pep Clb; Ski Clb; Spanish Clb; Band; Color Guard; Concert Band; Mrchg Band; Legal Secy.

EVANGELISTA, MARIA; St Mary HS; Jersey City, NJ; (3); Pep Clb; Service Clb; Church Choir; Yrbk Stf; Hon Roll; Christian Svc Awd 87; Sec Oriental Club Awd 87; Nrsng.

EVANGELISTA, THERESA; Pilgrim Acad; Nesco, NJ; (4); 2/23; Drama Clb; 4-H; Yrbk Stf; Sec Sr Cls; 4-H Awd; High Hon Roll; NHS; Amer Lgn Essy Cntst 87; Hstry Awd Frnch A D 84-86; TAG Schlrshp Grdn ST Schlrshp 87; Glassboro ST Col; Hstry.

EVANISH, DAWN; Holy Cross HS; Medford, NJ; (4); 22/360; Trs Spanish Clb; Nwsp Bus Mgr; Nwsp Stf; Yrbk Stf; Hon Roll; NHS; NEDT Awd; Chorus; Church Choir; Mock Trl Tm 85-87; Lit Ed Yrbk 86-87; Lncrs Life Crrspnd Sec 86-87; Douglass Coll; Comm.

EVANS, BONNIE; Central Regional HS; Bayville, NJ; (4); Letterman Clb; Varsity Clb; Var Capt Bsktbl; Var Sftbl; Var Tennis; NHS; Mock Trial Tm Ocean Cnty Champs; Natl Hnr Soc Scholar; Acad Athltc Awds Bsktbl & Sftbl; Temple U; Pre-Med.

EVANS, CARLA ANN; Trenton Central HS; Trenton, NJ; (3); Pep Clb; Color Guard; Drill Tm; Mrchg Band; Pom Pon; Trk; Prfct Atten Awd; 100 Behavior Crdts 85-87; Howard U; Law.

EVANS, ED; Mount Olive HS; Budd Lake, NJ; (3); Pres FBLA; Science Clb; Pres Jr Cls; Rep Stu Cncl; 1st Pl NJ DECA Gen Mrktg Awd 86; Busi Mktg.

EVANS, JAMES; Manasquaw HS; Spring Lk Hts, NJ; (3); 5/230; Math Clb; Science Clb; JV Bsbl; JV Ftbl; Wt Lftg; High Hon Roll; Kiwanis Awd; NHS; Bd Of Educ Awd 85-87; Bio.

EVANS, JOHN M; Cherokee HS; Marlton, NJ; (4); 33/411; Am Leg Boys St; French Clb; Pres Soph Cls; Pres Jr Cls; Pres Sr Cls; Rep Stu Cncl; Var Capt Ftbl; Var Capt Wrstlng; Hon Roll; NHS; U S Marines Ath Of Yr Awd 86-87; Columbia U; Law.

EVANS, KIMBERLY A; Holy Cross HS; Burlington, NJ; (4); 24/353; Drama Clb; French Clb; Ski Clb; Var L Color Guard; Mgr(s); Var JV Tennis; Hon Roll; Ntl Merit Ltr; St Schlr; R Stockton Fndtn Schlrshp 87; Sprt & Svc Awd HS 87; Stockton ST; Bio.

EVANS, PAUL J; Hamilton High School West; Trenton, NJ; (3); 1/330; Science Clb; Stu Cncl; Var Bsbl; Var Capt Ftbl; Var Wrstlng; NHS; Rutgers Schlr Hamilton W 87; Finlst NJ Govrns Schl The Sci 87; Biochem.

EVANS, ROBYN L; Hunterdon Central HS; Flemington, NJ; (3); 130/553; Service Clb; Ski Clb; Yrbk Ed-Chief; Yrbk Stf; Stu Cncl; JV Cheerleading; Hon Roll; Bio.

EVANS, SHERI; Randolph HS; Randolph, NJ; (4); Church Yth Grp; GAA; Varsity Clb; Band; Concert Band; Mrchg Band; Stu Cncl; Var Capt Fld Hcky; Var Sftbl; JV Swmmng; Pandolph Twnshp Womens Clb Schlrshp 87; Parent Tchr Assn Schlrshp 87; IN U Of PA; Comp Sci.

EVANS, SONYA; Edgewood Regional HS; Atco, NJ; (3); Office Aide; Sec Spanish Clb; Orch; JV Fld Hcky; Prfct Atten Awd; Spelman; Psych.

EVANS, THOMAS; Concord HS; Concord, NH; (2); Church Yth Grp; Band; Mrchg Band; Yrbk Stf; L Bsbl; L Im Bsktbl; Var JV Socr; Hon Roll; Finance Mgmt.

EVELYN, RENEE; Ferris HS; Jersey City, NJ; (3); Computer Clb; GAA; Math Clb; PAVAS; Varsity Clb; Chorus; VP Rep Soph Cls; Off Jr Cls; Var Bsktbl; Capt JV Cheerleading; Compu Whiz Awd 86; Compu Prgrmmr.

EVEREKLIAN, LENA; Wayne Hills HS; Wayne, NJ; (3); French Clb; GAA; Math Clb; Lit Mag; Mrktng.

EVERETT, ADOLPH; Saint Mary HS; Jersey City, NJ; (3); SADD; Stage Crew; Im Vllybl; Hon Roll; Chess Clb; Im Bsktbl; High Hon Roll; Christn Svc, Hnrs/Awds 86-87; Amer Stds Hnrs 86-87; Jersey City ST Coll; Accntng.

EVERETT, MARK; St Anthony HS; Jersey Cty, NJ; (3); Chess Clb; Bsbl; Bowling; Hon Roll; Ntl Merit Ltr; Hnr Roll 85-87; Natl Secndry Ed Cncl Schlr Pgm 86-87; Bio.

EVERETT, MICHELLE; Pleasantville HS; Pleasantville, NJ; (3); 15/109; Yrbk Stf; Rep Frsh Cls; Rep Soph Cls; Rep Jr Cls; JV Var Cheerleading.

EVERITT, CHRISTOPHER; Brick Township Memorial HS; Brick, NJ; (4); 7/280; Band; Concert Band; Jazz Band; Mrchg Band; School Musical; High Hon Roll; NHS; Ntl Merit Ltr; Outstndng Musicn Awd 84; U DE; Bus Adm.

EVERLY JR, DON; Cumberland Regional HS; Bridgeton, NJ; (4); 14/334; Church Yth Grp; Trs Exploring; Science Clb; Ski Clb; High Hon Roll; Hon Roll; NHS; Rotary Awd; Ursinus Coll; Pre-Med.

EVERTS, KRISTIN; Collingswood SR HS; Collingswood, NJ; (3); 12/242; Am Leg Aux Girls St; JCL; Latin Clb; Trs Soph Cls; Trs Jr Cls; Capt Bsktbl; Var L Lcrss; Capt Tennis; High Hon Roll; NHS; Physcl Thrpy.

EVOLA, MAURICE; Delran HS; Delran, NJ; (3); Church Yth Grp; Ski Clb; VICA; JV Bsbl; JV Socr; Hon Roll; San Jose ST U; Crim Just.

EWAN, JILL; Edgewood Regional HS; Cedar Brook, NJ; (2); 4-H; Latin Clb; Varsity Clb; Orch; Rep Soph Cls; Var JV Bsktbl; Stat Var Ftbl; 4-H Awd; Hon Roll; Sci Awd 85-86; 4-H Queen 1st Rnnr Up 85-87; US Air Force Acad.

EWAN, KIMBERLY; Buena Regional HS; Minotola, NJ; (3); 11/250; Math Clb; Pep Clb; Ski Clb; Hon Roll; Jr NHS; Ntl Merit Ltr.

EWELL, DARRYL; Essex Catholic Boys HS; Irvington, NJ; (3); Art Clb; Rep Frsh Cls; JV Ftbl; Im Sftbl; Var Wrstlng; Hon Roll; NJIT; Comm.

EWELL, JASON A; Ridgewood HS; Ridgewood, NJ; (3); Am Leg Boys St; Sec Jr Cls; Trs Sr Cls; JV Bsbl; Var Ftbl; Hon Roll; NHS.

EYERMAN, SONYA; Paramus Catholic Girls Regnl HS; Ridgefield, NJ; (3); Camera Clb; Dance Clb; Office Aide; Political Wkr; Lit Mag; Tennis; Art Awd 2nd Pl 87; Cert Awd Piano Stdy 84; Cert Awd Dance 85; Bus.

FAASSE, JEAN; West Milford Township HS; West Milford, NJ; (3); 8/403; Church Yth Grp; Spanish Clb; SADD; Varsity Clb; Yrbk Stf; Socr; Trk; Hon Roll; NHS; Ath Wk 86; Nwsp Features Edtr 86; Sports Med.

FAASSE, PATRICIA LYNN; Eastern Christian HS; N Haledon, NJ; (3); 1/88; Am Leg Aux Girls St; Church Yth Grp; Hosp Aide; Band; Orch; Nwsp Stf; JV Var Sftbl; Hon Roll; NHS; Ntl Merit Ltr.

FABER, JOHN; Eastern Christian HS; Midland Park, NJ; (3); 6/86; Chess Clb; Church Yth Grp; Computer Clb; 4-H; Band; School Play; Yrbk Stf; Crs Cntry; Hon Roll; NHS; Calvin Coll; Law.

FABISZEWSKI, WALTER; St Joseph Regional HS; Valley Cottage, NY; (3); 12/300; Math Tm; Nwsp Rptr; Im JV Bsktbl; Im Coach Actv; Hon Roll; Jr NHS; NHS; Spanish NHS; Bus.

FABOZZI, JASON; Dover HS; Mine Hill, NJ; (3); 1/225; Church Yth Grp; Capt Debate Tm; Drama Clb; School Musical; School Play; Nwsp Ed-Chief; Ed Lit Mag; High Hon Roll; NHS; Ntl Merit SF; Rutgers Schlrshp Pgm 87; Rogate Rsrch 84-86; Sympsm Of The Arts 84-87.

FACKELMAN, LORI ANN; Linden HS; Linden, NJ; (3); Trs Church Yth Grp; Mrchg Band; Rep Jr Cls; Rep Stu Cncl; Hon Roll; NHS; Bus Mgt.

FACUSE, MARY ANNE; Neumann Prep; Paterson, NJ; (3); French Clb; JA; Church Choir; Variety Show; Yrbk Bus Mgr; Yrbk Ed-Chief; Yrbk Phtg; Yrbk Stf; JV Capt Bsktbl; JV Fld Hcky; Peer Ministry; Psych.

FADEM, JONATHAN; Raritan HS; Hazlet, NJ; (3); Pres Drama Clb; French Clb; SADD; School Musical; School Play; Hon Roll; Natl Hnr Roll 86-87.

FAER, AMY CAREN; Jackson HS; Jackson, NJ; (3); 18/500; Am Leg Aux Girls St; Cmnty Wkr; Exploring; Hosp Aide; Science Clb; SADD; Yrbk Ed-Chief; Yrbk Rptr; JV Sftbl; High Hon Roll; High Hnr Roll Cert 80-87; Sftbl Cert 84-87; Law.

FAGAN, ABBY; Middle Township HS; Avalon, NJ; (3); 4/25; Church Yth Grp; Sec Key Clb; Chorus; Yrbk Rptr; Yrbk Stf; High Hon Roll; Jr NHS; NHS; Ntl Merit Ltr; Latin Hrn Soc 87; HS & Regnl 2nd Pl Wnnr Sci Fair; Math.

FAGLEY, DIANE; Palmyra HS; Riverton, NJ; (4); Am Leg Aux Girls St; Office Aide; VP Spanish Clb; Sec Jr Cls; Sec Sr Cls; Rep Stu Cncl; Var JV Cheerleading; JV L Fld Hcky; JV L Socr; JV L Sftbl; Kutztown U.

FAHERTY, SEAN; South Hunterdon Regional HS; Lambertville, NJ; (3); 12/76; Key Clb; School Play; Rep Jr Cls; Rep Sr Cls; Rep Stu Cncl; JV Var Bsbl; Stat Bsktbl; Bus.

FAHEY, DARYL; St John Vianney HS; Matawan, NJ; (3); Church Yth Grp; Girl Scts; Intnl Clb; Ski Clb; SADD; Teachers Aide; Im Bsktbl; Score Keeper; Var L Tennis; Hon Roll; Woods Hole Envrnmntl; Mrn Bio.

FAHEY, DIANE; Vineland HS; Vineland, NJ; (3); 88/825; Church Yth Grp; Drama Clb; English Clb; German Clb; Pep Clb; Band; Chorus; Mrchg Band; Stu Cncl; Hon Roll; Comm.

FAHEY, ROSALIND ANN; Bernards HS; Bernardsville, NJ; (3); 2/187; Q&S; Drill Tm; Yrbk Sprt Ed; JV Golf; Var Twrlr; High Hon Roll; Hon Roll; NHS; Church Yth Grp; French Clb; Scholastic Achvt Winner Miss NJ Coed Pageant & 4th Runner Up 87; Attorney.

FAHEY, SEAN; Point Pleasant Boro HS; Point Pleasant, NJ; (4); 26/240; Varsity Clb; School Play; Sec Frsh Cls; Trs Stu Cncl; Var JV Bsktbl; Var JV Ftbl; Var Trk; Cit Awd; NHS; Kiwanis Club Scholar 87; Pres Acad Fit Awd 87; Stu Govt Scholar 87; Villanova U; Pre-Law.

FAHEY, TIMOTHY F; Holy Cross HS; Burlington, NJ; (4); 109/355; Ski Clb; Band; Concert Band; Mrchg Band; Orch; School Musical; School Play; Stage Crew; Hon Roll; Ltr For Mrchng Bnd 84-85; Ltr Stage Crew Wk Schl Muscl 86-87; Cabrini Coll; Comp Sci.

FAHMI, TAMMY; Mount Olive HS; Hackestown, NJ; (3); 36/375; AFS; Cmnty Wkr; GAA; Hosp Aide; Spanish Clb; SADD; Varsity Clb; Bsktbl; Crs Cntry; Trk; MVP Awd & All Trnmnt Tm Vrsty Bsktbl 85-86; Med.

FAHNER, ROSEMARY; Rahway HS; Rahway, NJ; (3); Church Yth Grp; Dance Clb; Drama Clb; Capt Drill Tm; School Play; Yrbk Ed-Chief; Rep Stu Cncl; Capt Pom Pon; Var Tennis; Prfct Atten Awd; Ed.

FAHS, FRANK; Paulsboro HS; Gibbstown, NJ; (3); 7/130; Art Clb; Hon Roll; Amer Chem Soc Excllnc Chem Awd 87; Philadelphia Inst-Txtls & Sci.

FAILLA, CINDY; Jackson Memorial HS; Jackson, NJ; (4); 32/401; Ski Clb; SADD; VP Sr Cls; Stat Bsktbl; JV Fld Hcky; Var Powder Puff Ftbl; Var Socr; JV Tennis; Im Wt Lftg; High Hon Roll; Jcksn Educ Assn Schlrshp 87; Jcksn Phy Ed Schlrshp 87; Georgian Court Coll; Engl.

FAIRBANKS, HILLARY; Lenape Valley Regional HS; Stanhope, NJ; (4); 2/241; Key Clb; Chorus; Madrigals; School Musical; Rep Stu Cncl; Var Crs Cntry; High Hon Roll; Hst NHS; St Schlr; Rutgers Dean Smn Schlr 86; Sociolgy.

FAIRFIELD, RUSSELL; Central Regional HS; Seaside Park, NJ; (3); Boy Scts; School Musical; Stage Crew; Nwsp Rptr; Hon Roll; Ntl Merit Ltr; Law Club; Capt Mock Trial Team Cnty Champ; Bus Law.

FAKTOR, STACY; Freehold Township HS; Freehold, NJ; (3); 68/401; Dance Clb; Drama Clb; French Clb; FNA; SADD; Temple Yth Grp; Stage Crew; Yrbk Phtg; Yrbk Sprt Ed; Yrbk Stf; Boston U; Psych.

FALCO, DENISE; Morris Knolls HS; Denville, NJ; (3); Hosp Aide; Band; Concert Band; Socr; Hon Roll; Psych.

FALCO, PETER; Lakeland Reg HS; Ringwood, NJ; (3); 27/340; Boys Clb Am; Math Clb; Math Tm; Varsity Clb; Rep Jr Cls; Ftbl; Capt Wrstlng; High Hon Roll; Hon Roll; Pres NHS; Peer Cnclr 86-87; Engrng.

FALCO, THOMAS; St John Vianney HS; Aberdeen, NJ; (3); 91/253; Church Yth Grp; Computer Clb; Service Clb; Spanish Clb; Im Vllybl; Hon Roll; Law Enfrcmnt.

FALCONE, TOM; Verona HS; Verona, NJ; (3); Model UN; Rep Frsh Cls; Rep Soph Cls; Rep Jr Cls; Sec Stu Cncl; Var Bsktbl; Capt Var Socr; Var Trk; NHS; Spanish NHS.

FALIK, SELENA; Manalapan HS; Englishtown, NJ; (3); SADD; Nwsp Ed-Chief; Nwsp Rptr; Nwsp Stf; Rep Frsh Cls; Mass Cmmnctns.

FALIVENO, KARLEEN; Belleville HS; Belleville, NJ; (4); 98/400; Church Yth Grp; French Clb; FTA; Key Clb; Teachers Aide; Chorus; Yrbk Ed-Chief; Rep Stu Cncl; Var Trk; Hon Roll; Childrens Book Cont 1st Prz 87; Spec Educ Teacher.

FALK, RICHARD; Cumberland Regional HS; Bridgeton, NJ; (3); 7/385; German Clb; Nwsp Rptr; Var Socr; Jr NHS.

FALK, SUE; James Caldwell HS; West Caldwell, NJ; (3); Cmnty Wkr; FNA; Key Clb; Rep Frsh Cls; Rep Soph Cls; Rep Jr Cls; Off Stu Cncl; Var Cheerleading; Vrsty Ltr Awd In Chrldng 85-87.

FALLAH, MAZYAR; West Windsor HS; Robbinsville, NJ; (3); VP Chess Clb; Pres Debate Tm; French Clb; Math Tm; Model UN; High Hon Roll; NHS; Ntl Merit SF; NFL; NJ Govrs Schl Of Sci Drew U 86-87; George Washington U Schl Of Engrng Sci Awd 86-87; Med.

FALLAN, KRISTEN; Bishop George Ahr HS; Perth Amboy, NJ; (4); Church Yth Grp; Cmnty Wkr; French Clb; Service Clb; Ski Clb; Nwsp Rptr; Stu Cncl; Pom Pon; Hon Roll; NHS; Hugh O Brian Ldrshp Awd 85; Religion Awd 87; Jostens Ldrshp Awd 87; Villanova U.

FALLENI, DENA; Lenape Valley Regional HS; Stanhope, NJ; (4); 29/241; Church Yth Grp; Trs Chorus; Church Choir; Madrigals; Sec Stu Cncl; Capt Cheerleading; Capt Crs Cntry; Gym; Swmmng; Trk; Katherine Gibbs Ldrshp Awd 86; CC 84 ST Chmpn 84; MT Union.

FALLETTA, SALVATORE; Memorial JR/Sr HS; Elmwood Park, NJ; (4); 1/160; Am Leg Boys St; Math Clb; Band; Yrbk Phtg; Pres Soph Cls; Pres VP Stu Cncl; Var Capt Bsktbl; Var Capt Socr; NHS; Val; Garden ST Dstngshd Schlr 87; Rutgrs Schlr 86; 2nd Tm All Leag Sccr Goalie 87; Rutgers U; Pre-Med.

FALLON, LISA; Immaculate Conception HS; Ridgefield Pk, NJ; (4); Art Clb; Library Aide; Q&S; Pres Service Clb; Spanish Clb; Teachers Aide; Chorus; Rep Stu Cncl; Hon Roll; Natl Art Hnr Socty 85-87; Seton Hall Schlrshp 87-88; Seton Hall U; Elem Ed.

FALVO, DANIELA; Mc Corristin HS; Trenton, NJ; (3); School Play; JV Socr; Wt Lftg; Hon Roll; NHS.

FALVO, GINA; Watching Hills Regional HS; Stirling, NJ; (4); 50/318; Church Yth Grp; SADD; Yrbk Stf; Im Fld Hcky; Var Trk; Hon Roll; Pres Schlr; Italian Clb Schlrshp Awd, Passaic Twnshp Hill Wmns Clb Awd & Passaic Twnshp Salvation Army Awd 87; Fordham U; Child Psych.

FALVO, JAMES; South Hunterdon Regional HS; Lambertville, NJ; (3); 1/76; Am Leg Boys St; Debate Tm; Stage Crew; Yrbk Stf; JV Crs Cntry; High Hon Roll; NHS; Ntl Merit Ltr; Rutgers Schlrs 87; Bausch & Lomb Medlst Math/Sci 87; Somerset Cnty Coll Holocaust Studies Ctr Schlrshp; Bio.

FALZARANO, TONY; Montville HS; Montville, NJ; (3); Lndscpng.

FALZO, MARIA; Mt St Dominic Acad; North Caldwell, NJ; (3); Chorus; School Musical; School Play; Nwsp Stf; Yrbk Stf; Chess Clb; Pres Jr Cls; Capt Cheerleading; Hon Roll; NHS.

FALZON, MARK; Hudson Catholic HS; Hoboken, NJ; (3); Pep Clb; Var Bsktbl; Law.

FAMA, LISA; Manalapan HS; Englishtown, NJ; (3); Rep Frsh Cls; Rep Soph Cls; Rep Jr Cls; Rep Stu Cncl; Var Cheerleading; JV Gym; JV Socr; NHS; Natl Hnr Rl 87; Rutgers Coll Of Phrmcy; Phrmcy.

FAN, GRACE; West Windsor-Plainsboro HS; Princeton Jct, NJ; (3); Trs Art Clb; Chrmn Church Yth Grp; Hosp Aide; Math Tm; Yrbk Bus Mgr; Rep Stu Cncl; JV Socr; JV Trk; NHS; Med.

FAN, JESSIE; Holmdel HS; Holmdel, NJ; (1); Drama Clb; Hosp Aide; Key Clb; PAVAS; SADD; Chorus; Nwsp Stf; Hon Roll; Wnnr Eastrn Prfrmng Arts Compttn 87; Vrsty Cheerldng Sqd 87; Harvard Med Schl; Med.

FAN, SYLVIA; W Windsor Plainsboro HS; Robbinsville, NJ; (3); Cmnty Wkr; Chrmn English Clb; Ed Lit Mag; JV Tennis; High Hon Roll; NHS; Ntl Merit Ltr; AFS; Art Clb; French Clb; Wellesley Book Awd 87; Prnctn U Plasma Physcs Lab Smr Sci Awd Pgrm 87; Chrch Pianst, Orgnst 84-87; Med Rsrch.

FANCIS, STEPHANIE; Willingboro HS; Willingboro, NJ; (3); Girl Scts; Hosp Aide; Varsity Clb; Cheerleading; Gym; Sftbl; Hon Roll; Bio-Tech.

FANELLE, CARMINE; Paul VI HS; Stratford, NJ; (4); 39/512; Computer Clb; Math Clb; Concert Band; Jazz Band; Mrchg Band; Orch; Hon Roll; NHS; St Schlr; Grdn ST Dstngshd Schrlshp 86-87; Electrl Engnrng.

FANG, BONNY; Parsippany HS; Lake Hiawatha, NJ; (3); FBLA; JV Bsktbl; Var Trk; Hon Roll; NHS; FLBA ST Cmptn 3rd Plc 86-87; Vrsty Trck Lttr 86-87.

FANG, JEAN; Parsippany HS; Lake Hiawatha, NJ; (2); SADD; JV Bsktbl; JV Sftbl; Hon Roll.

FANTUZZI, LYNN; Toms River South HS; Toms River, NJ; (4); 7/350; Math Tm; Quiz Bowl; Variety Show; Sec Frsh Cls; Sec Soph Cls; Sec Jr Cls; Mgr(s); Powder Puff Ftbl; High Hon Roll; Hon Roll; Acadmc Ltr 83-87; Rollins Coll; Corp Lawyer.

FARAH, PAUL; Ferris HS; Jersey City, NJ; (3); VICA; Concert Band; JV Crs Cntry; JV Trk; Hon Roll; Prfct Atten Awd; Rutgers U; Tech.

FARELLA, ANGELINA; Brick Township HS; Brick, NJ; (4); 3/343; Drama Clb; SADD; Thesps; School Play; Yrbk Ed-Chief; Pres Stu Cncl; Var Capt Cheerleading; Trs NHS; High Hon Roll; Ms Teen Of Amer 86; Drma Awd 86; Med.

FARESE, JOSEPH; Clifton HS; Clifton, NJ; (4); 59/590; French Clb; Ftbl; Trk; Wt Lftg; High Hon Roll; Jr NHS; NHS; Rutgers; Bus Admin.

FARGO, ERIK; High Point Regiona HS; Agusta, NJ; (2); Ski Clb; Hon Roll; ROTC Schlrshp 89; Indstrl Arts Schlrshp 89; Indstrl Arts.

FARIAS, TAMARA; John P Stevens HS; Edison, NJ; (3); Drama Clb; Girl Scts; Thesps; Chorus; School Musical; School Play; Stage Crew; Swing Chorus; 3rd Pl NJ Dramatic Comptn 86; 1st Pl NJ Thespian Festvl 86; Comm.

FARINAS, LISSETTE; St Joseph Of The Palisades HS; W New York, NJ; (4); 9/120; Spanish Clb; Variety Show; Nwsp Rptr; Lit Mag; High Hon Roll; Hon Roll; NHS; Pres Schlr; Spanish NHS; St Schlr; Social Music 85; Grad Diploma Music Piano 86; 2 Yr Ntl Hnr Scty Awd 86-87; Hunter Coll; Bio-Chem.

FARINELLA, MARIA; Montville Township HS; Towaco, NJ; (3); 4/248; Capt FBLA; Key Clb; Model UN; VP SADD; JV Fld Hcky; JV Lcrss; Stat Swmmng; JV Trk; High Hon Roll; NHS; Rutgers Dean Summer Schlrs Pgm 87; Cert Appreciation 85; SOCIAL Sci.

FARINELLA, MICHELLE ALANE; Newton HS; Newton, NJ; (4); Dance Clb; Pres Drama Clb; Sec 4-H; Pres Thesps; Varsity Clb; Chorus; Madrigals; School Musical; School Play; Stage Crew; Dance Schlrshp & Thespian Schlrshp 87; John Cronin Vocal Awd & Arts Dance Azwd 87; Allentown Coll-St Francis; Danc.

FARLEY, BONNIE; Washington Township HS; Sewell, NJ; (3); Sec Church Yth Grp; Cmnty Wkr; Band; Concert Band; Mrchg Band; Music.

FARMER, EVELYN; Saint Aloysius HS; Jersey City, NJ; (3); Aud/Vis; Office Aide; Nwsp Stf; Stu Cncl; Hon Roll; NHS; Exploring; Chorus; Drill Tm; School Play; Schlrshp 87-88.

FARMER, SHANNON; Holy Spirit HS; Pleasantville, NJ; (3); Lawyer.

FARMER, WILLIAM; Cumberland Regional HS; Bridgeton, NJ; (4); 20/324; Am Leg Boys St; Intnl Clb; Science Clb; Ftbl; Trk; Wrstlng; High Hon Roll; NHS; West Pnt Admsns 87; Rotary Yth Ldrshp Awd 86; Model Cong Dlgt 87; West Point Acad; Aero Engr.

FARMIGA, NESTOR; Clifton HS; Clifton, NJ; (4); 4/580; German Clb; Math Clb; Math Tm; Science Clb; Ski Clb; Rep Soph Cls; JV Capt Socr; JV Trk; High Hon Roll; Hon Roll; Rbrt C Byrd Hnrs Schlrshp 87; Air Force Math & Sci Awd 87; AM Cynmd Sci Educ Awd 87; U Of Chicago; Physcs.

FARNAM, MEREDITH; Columbia HS; Maplewood, NJ; (3); 375/500; Church Yth Grp; Cmnty Wkr; Girl Scts; Latin Clb; Color Guard; School Musical; Vllybl; DAR Awd; Cntrl Jersey Cyclng Clb; Project 88.

FARNAN, MISSY; Ramapo HS; Wyckoff, NJ; (3); Pres Church Yth Grp; Nwsp Rptr; Chrmn Soph Cls; Rep Stu Cncl; Var Bsktbl; Var Crs Cntry; JV Trk; Hon Roll; All Lg Crs Cntry Tm; Villanova; Bus.

FARRAR, SUSAN; Rahway HS; Rahway, NJ; (4); 44/231; Am Leg Aux Girls St; Girl Scts; Hosp Aide; Color Guard; Yrbk Stf; Stu Cncl; Vllybl; Hon Roll; NHS; Med Tech.

FARRELL, CHRISTINA; Washington Township HS; Turnersville, NJ; (3); DECA; Library Aide; Color Guard; Mrchg Bnd Comptn Chptr I Champs 85-86; Miss Amer Co Ed Pagnt 87; NJ Frsh Egg Cookg Cntst 85-86; Fshn Mrch.

FARRELL, DAVID; Collingswood HS; Oaklyn, NJ; (3); Am Leg Boys St; Aud/Vis; Boy Scts; Church Yth Grp; French Clb; Band; Chorus; Concert Band; Jazz Band; Mrchg Band; Biochem.

FARRELL, DOUGLAS; Bordentown Regional HS; Bordentown, NJ; (2); 12/130; Drama Clb; Key Clb; Math Clb; School Musical; School Play; Stage Crew; Yrbk Stf; Im Bsktbl; Var JV Crs Cntry; Im Ftbl; S Jersey Wrstlg Coach & Offcls Awd 87.

FARRELL, EDDIE; Middletown South HS; Atl Highlands, NJ; (3); Var Bowling; Var Ftbl; Hon Roll.

FARRELL, ERIN; Mt St John Acad; Long Valley, NJ; (2); 1/24; Dance Clb; Drama Clb; Math Clb; Var Bsktbl; Var Socr; Im Tennis; Im Vllybl; Hon Roll; NEDT Awd; Pre-Law.

FARRELL, FRANK H; Sussex County Vo Tech; Andover, NJ; (4); 30/175; Drama Clb; School Musical; School Play; Stage Crew; High Hon Roll; Hon Roll; NHS; Cntry Theater Schlrshp 86; Smmr Arts Inst Schlrshp 86; Drama.

FARRELL, JAMES; Bordentown Regional HS; Bordentown, NJ; (3); Chess Clb; Drama Clb; Key Clb; School Musical; School Play; Stage Crew; Bsbl; Bowling; Ftbl; Hon Roll.

FARRELL II, JAMES; Pope John XXIII HS; Andover, NJ; (3); Boy Scts; Orch; JV Swmmng; Geom Awd Hghst Avg 85-86; Comp II Awd Hghst Avg 86-87; Life Scout 86; Cnty Coll Morris; MIS.

FARRELL, JANA; Union Catholic Regional HS; North Plainfield, NJ; (3); Science Clb; Yrbk Stf.

FARRELL, MEGHAN; Monsignor Donovan HS; Toms River, NJ; (3); 11/246; Am Leg Aux Girls St; Drama Clb; Math Clb; Math Tm; SADD; Varsity Clb; VP Sr Cls; Rep Stu Cncl; Capt Cheerleading; High Hon Roll; Attorney.

FARREN, CATHERINE; St Rose HS; Spring Lk, NJ; (3); 21/220; Rep Key Clb; Stat Bsktbl; Mgr(s); Score Keeper; Spanish NHS; Typg Awd; Awd Of Svc Key Clb.

FARREY, WENDY; Cinnaminson HS; Cinnaminson, NJ; (3); Latin Clb; Nwsp Stf; Rep Sec Stu Cncl; Bsktbl; Fld Hcky; Capt Sftbl; Trk; Trs NHS; All Grp III Hnrbl Mntn Fld Hcky 86; Coaches Awd Sftbl 87; Ath Mnth Fld Hcky, Sftbl 86-87; Elem Educ.

FARRIOR, JOCELYN; Notre Dame HS; Trenton, NJ; (3); Church Yth Grp; Cmnty Wkr; Hosp Aide; Chorus; School Play; Sec Civic Clb; Trk; DAR Awd; Hon Roll; NHS; VP Locl Yth Cncl Chrch 87-88; Las Chapernes Debutnts Chpln 86-87; Advrtsng.

FARRIS, TOBY; Howell HS; Howell, NJ; (2); Math Clb; Spanish Clb; Capt JV Bsbl; Var L Ftbl; Var L Wrstlng; Hon Roll; Jr NHS; Prfct Atten Awd; Varsity Clb; Bus.

FARRO, VALERIE; Mendham HS; Chester, NJ; (4); Yrbk Phtg; Rep Stu Cncl; Stat Lcrss; Fairleigh-Dickinson U; Bus Admn.

FARRY, WILLIAM; Manchester Regional HS; Haledon, NJ; (4); Am Leg Boys St; Chess Clb; Debate Tm; Nwsp Rptr; Yrbk Rptr; Lit Mag; Trk; Hon Roll; Bridgwtr ST Coll; Anthrplgy.

FARSCHON, CHRISTOPHER L; Woodstown HS; Bridgeton, NJ; (3); 5/186; English Clb; Key Clb; Math Clb; Ski Clb; Mrchg Band; Sec Stu Cncl; Swmmng; Trk; Hon Roll; NHS; Arch.

FARSIDE, BRENDA; Vineland HS; Vineland, NJ; (3); 75/800; Art Clb; Hosp Aide; Pep Clb; Political Wkr; Science Clb; Mgr Acpl Chr; Concert Band; JV Socr; Hon Roll; Olympics Of Mind Cmptn 2nd Pl 86; Olympics Of Mind Cmptn 2nd & 3rd Pl 87; Sec Of VHS Italian Clb; Law.

FASNACHT, ELIZABETH; Cherry Hill HS West; Cherry Hill, NJ; (3); #29 In Class; Church Yth Grp; Drama Clb; French Clb; PAVAS; Thesps; Chorus; Mrchg Band; School Musical; Swing Chorus; Variety Show; Tn Arts Cnty & ST 85; Tn Arts Cnty & ST All S Jersey Chrs 86; Chrgrphy.

FASS, PHILLIP; East Brunswick HS; E Brunswick, NJ; (3); Key Clb; SADD; Im Bsktbl; Stat Fld Hcky; Stat Sftbl; Im Vllybl; Brdcstng.

FATOUROS, TONY; Marist HS; Bayonne, NJ; (4); 1/98; Intnl Clb; Pres Key Clb; Nwsp Stf; Yrbk Stf; Bsbl; Vllybl; Hon Roll; NHS; Spanish NHS; Harvard Summr Schl 86; Garden ST Distngshd Schlrs Scholar 87; Marist Acad Achvt Awd 85.

FATUM, JUDI; Pemberton Twp HS; Browns Mills, NJ; (4); 18/406; FBLA; Office Aide; Capt Drill Tm; Nwsp Stf; Rep Stu Cncl; Capt Pom Pon; High Hon Roll; NHS; Mock Trl Cmptn Cert Of Hnr 87; Rutgers U; Comm.

FAULCON, NICOLE; Clifford J Scott HS; East Orange, NJ; (3); Art Clb; High Hon Roll; Hon Roll; Prfct Atten Awd; Brain Surgeon.

FAULLS, KATHY; Paul VI HS; Lindenwold, NJ; (3); 44/415; Church Yth Grp; French Clb; Math Clb; School Play; French Hon Soc; Hon Roll; Glassboro ST Coll; Elem Ed.

FAULSEIT, RONALD K; Kinnelon HS; Riverdale, NJ; (3); 29/159; Am Leg Boys St; Boy Scts; German Clb; Varsity Clb; Jazz Band; Rep Jr Cls; Lcrss; Wrstlng; Hon Roll; NHS; Penn ST; Music.

FAUSEL, DAVID; Waldwick HS; Waldwick, NJ; (3); #30 In Class; Jrnlsm.

FAUSTINI, ANN-MARIE BARBARA; River Dell SR HS; Oradell, NJ; (3); 5/232; Am Leg Aux Girls St; Cmnty Wkr; Hosp Aide; Capt Quiz Bowl; Speech Tm; Nwsp Ed-Chief; VP Jr Cls; VP Sr Cls; Capt Cheerleading; French Hon Soc; Columbia U Sci Hnr Pgm 87-88; Dartmouth Coll Bk Awd 87; Acadc Dcthdn Rgnl Lvl 87; Pre-Med.

FAVA, JENNIFER; Notre Dame HS; Trenton, NJ; (4); 60/330; Key Clb; Red Cross Aide; Ski Clb; SADD; Varsity Clb; JV Fld Hcky; Var Trk; High Hon Roll; Hon Roll; NHS; Trentoian, Trenton Times & CVC Coaches Hnrb Mntn Fld Hcky 86-87; Notre Dame Fld Hcky Most Imprdv Ply; Trenton ST Coll; Educ.

FAVILLA, DANIEL MARK; Edgewood SR HS; Hammonton, NJ; (4); 6/300; Quiz Bowl; Varsity Clb; Rep Jr Cls; JV Bsbl; JV Ftbl; Capt Trk; High Hon Roll; Hon Roll; Jr NHS; NHS; Farleigh Dickinson U Prsdntl Schlrshp 87; Rutgers U; Elec Engrng.

FAVOR, DENISE; Arthur L Johnson Regional HS; Clark, NJ; (3); 28/189; Hosp Aide; Thesps; School Musical; School Play; Sec Stu Cncl; Stat Bsktbl; Swmmng; Vllybl; Hon Roll; Italn Hnr Soc Gold Mdl 86; Phys Thrpy.

FAVORITE, TANYA; Collingswood SR HS; Collingswood, NJ; (2); Church Yth Grp; Latin Clb; Band; Mrchg Band; JV L Bsktbl; JV L Tennis; Hon Roll; All Str Tm Sftbl Leag, .667 Bttng Avg 87; Rutgers U; Accntng.

FAVORITO, DAWN; Paramus Catholic Girls HS; Maywood, NJ; (4); Church Yth Grp; Hosp Aide; Service Clb; Spanish Clb; Lit Mag; Cit Awd; Hon Roll; Kiwanis Awd; Seton Hall U; Elem Tchr.

FAVRETTO, SANDI; Vineland HS; Vineland, NJ; (2); 10/750; Hosp Aide; Key Clb; SADD; Jazz Band; Nwsp Ed-Chief; Rep Stu Cncl; Hon Roll; Jr Volntr 100 Hr Awd Pin 86; Socl Servcs.

FAY, JAMES; Norht Bergen HS; North Bergen, NJ; (4); 11/417; Computer Clb; German Clb; Key Clb; Spanish Clb; High Hon Roll; Hon Roll; Jr NHS; NHS; Spanish NHS; Frnkln Schl PTA Schlrshp 87; Rutgers Coll Of Engrng.

FAYNGOLD, JULIA; Livingston HS; Livingston, NJ; (4); 3/424; Ski Clb; Temple Yth Grp; Nwsp Ed-Chief; Ntl Merit SF; Pres Schlr; Pres Spanish NHS; St Schlr; Chrmn Civic Clb; Cmnty Wkr; Debate Tm; Hnr Ntl Cnfrnc Svt Jewry 86; Wrld Fdrlst Assoc Yth Ldrshp Cnfrnc 86; Crtv Wrtg Awd 86; Harvard U; Comp Sci.

FAZIO, LAUREN; De Paul HS; Kinnelon, NJ; (3); 10/150; JV Cheerleading; Var Fld Hcky; Var Trk; High Hon Roll; NHS.

FEARON, JOHN; Secaucus HS; Secaucus, NJ; (1); Key Clb; Mu Alpha Theta; Stage Crew; JV Bsbl; Ftbl; High Hon Roll; Hon Roll; Jr NHS; Penn ST; Prof Ftbl.

FEBINGER, EDWARD; South River HS; South River, NJ; (3); Am Leg Boys St; Boy Scts; French Clb; German Clb; Library Aide; Trs Stu Cncl; Crs Cntry; Trk; High Hon Roll; NHS; Accntng.

FEBINGER, RHONDA; South River HS; South River, NJ; (4); 8/130; Am Leg Aux Girls St; VP Church Yth Grp; Trs French Clb; German Clb; Pres Sr Cls; Rep Stu Cncl; Var L Trk; Cit Awd; Hon Roll; VP NHS; Hmcmng Queen 86-87; Schl Msct 86-87; Fash Inst Tech; Fach Merch.

FEBRES, GLORIA I; Morris Knolls HS; Denville, NJ; (4); 28/369; High Hon Roll; NHS; 4 Certs Of Achvt 85; Summa Awds For Acad Excllnc 86 & 87; Pres Acad Awd 87; Carnegie Mellon U; Bus.

FEBUS, ANNALISE; Summit HS; Summit, NJ; (3); Girl Scts; Model UN; Flag Corp; Yrbk Phtg; Yrbk Stf; JV Bsktbl; Im Bowling; Var Capt Vllybl; MVP Boostrs Awd Vllybl 87; Intrmrl Wmns Tm Chmpn 85-86; Eckerd Coll; Psych.

FECKO, BETH; Wayne Hills HS; Wayne, NJ; (3); Church Yth Grp; GAA; Math Clb; Ski Clb; Spanish Clb; JV Var Socr; JV Var Trk; High Hon Roll; Hon Roll; NHS; Art Awd 85; Physcl Thrpy.

FEDAK, RAYMOND PETER; Christian Brothers Acad; West Long Branch, NJ; (3); Capt Chess Clb; Church Yth Grp; Service Clb; Im Bowling; Im Fld Hcky; Im Golf; Im Sftbl; Im Tennis; Wrstlng; Hon Roll; Aviation.

FEDD, CRYSTAL; Mt St Dominic Acad; Newark, NJ; (3); Dance Clb; Library Aide; Drill Tm; Yrbk Stf; Trk; Howard U; Pre-Med.

FEDERAL, NATALIE; Emerson JR-SR HS; Emerson, NJ; (4); 10/95; School Play; Stage Crew; Trs Frsh Cls; Pres Soph Cls; Pres Jr Cls; Pres Sr Cls; Rep Trs Stu Cncl; Vllybl; Hon Roll; NHS; Am Leg James Hunter Awd 87; Fr Awd 87; Slvtn Army Schlrshp 87; Fshn Inst Tech; Fshn Dsgn.

FEDERICI, TRACEY; John F Kennedy HS; Willingboro, NJ; (3); 9/300; Am Leg Aux Girls St; Capt Band; Concert Band; Flag Corp; Mrchg Band; Fld Hcky; Sftbl; High Hon Roll; Jr NHS; Trs NHS; Accounting.

FEDERICO, ROBERT; Clifton HS; Clifton, NJ; (4); #189 In Class; Pres Art Clb; Pres German Clb; Library Aide; Var Ftbl; Opt Clb Awd; Cert Div Continuing Ed 86; Montclair ST U; Ecnmcs.

FEDORCHAK, JEFFREY; Lyndhurst HS; Lyndhurst, NJ; (2); Var Trk; Comp Sci.

FEENEY, CAROLINE; Chatham Township HS; Chatham, NJ; (4); 18/140; Church Yth Grp; Pep Clb; Yrbk Stf; Sec Frsh Cls; Sec Jr Cls; Sec Sr Cls; Tennis; Gov Hon Prg Awd; High Hon Roll; NHS; Bucknell U.

FEENEY, MICHAEL; Allentown HS; Cream Ridge, NJ; (3); 15/192; Math Clb; Scholastic Bowl; JV Mgr(s); JV Timer; Hon Roll; Case Wstrn U; Physcs.

FEENEY, THOMAS F X; Glen Rock HS; Glen Rock, NJ; (3); 18/145; Am Leg Boys St; Debate Tm; Quiz Bowl; Spanish Clb; School Play; Ed Lit Mag; Crs Cntry; Trk; NHS; NJ Governors Schl Of Arts 87; Law.

FEHRENBACK, KARL; Holy Spirit HS; Northfield, NJ; (2); 28/397; Church Yth Grp; Hon Roll; Prfct Atten Awd; US Naval Acad; Pilot.

FEIN, LAURA E; Cherry Hill HS East; Cherry Hill, NJ; (4); 7/700; Aud/Vis; Model UN; PAVAS; Capt Color Guard; Yrbk Ed-Chief; NHS; Ntl Merit SF; Im Bowling; Lcrss; French Hon Soc; Ntl Chrmn Us Div NAHSON; Intrnshp For Us Sntr Frank Lautenberg; Full Tuition Schlrshp MHJC.

FEIN, THOMAS; Wayne Hills SR HS; Wayne, NJ; (4); 19/287; Math Tm; Socr; Trk; Hon Roll; NHS; Grdn ST Dstngshd Schlr 87; Rutgers U; Bio.

FEINGOLD, KATHERINE; Gill/St Bernards HS; Westfield, NJ; (3); Rep SADD; Nwsp Sprt Ed; Rep Jr Cls; Rep Stu Cncl; Var Capt Bsktbl; Var Socr; Var Sftbl; Cit Awd; Pres French Hon Soc; High Hon Roll; Frnch, Math & Sci Acadc Awds 84; C Elliott Knoke Schlrshp 87; MVP Bsktbl, Sftbl, & Scr 87.

FEINSTEIN, ELLISA; Parsippany HS; Lake Hiawatha, NJ; (3); Cmnty Wkr; FBLA; SADD; Cmnty Wkr; Drama Clb; Pep Clb; Science Clb; Spanish Clb; JV Var Fld Hcky; Advrtsng.

FEITH, AMY; Roselle Park HS; Roselle Park, NJ; (3); 2/156; Am Leg Aux Girls St; Math Tm; Radio Clb; Spanish Clb; VP Jr Cls; Rep Stu Cncl; Var Cheerleading; Jr NHS; NHS; HOBY 85-86; Miss Schlrshp Rcgntn NJ 3rd Semifnlst 84-85; Coll St Eliz Sci Smnr 86-87; Chem.

FEIVELSON, NEAL K; Westfield HS; Westfield, NJ; (4); 16/484; Computer Clb; Drama Clb; Exploring; Science Clb; Temple Yth Grp; School Play; Stage Crew; God Cntry Awd; High Hon Roll; NHS; Engnrng.

FEKETE, ROBERT T; St Josephs HS; Piscataway, NJ; (4); 2/205; Model UN; Quiz Bowl; Lit Mag; JV Swmmng; NHS; Ntl Merit SF; Spanish NHS; Math Clb; Ski Clb; Spanish Clb; Spain Travl Study 84; Garden ST Schlr 86; Psychlgy.

FELD, JENNIFER; Pequannock Township HS; Pequannock, NJ; (3); 19/250; Church Yth Grp; Spanish Clb; Hon Roll; NHS; Bus.

FELDER, LANCE; St Anthony HS; Jersey Cty, NJ; (3); Cmnty Wkr; Stage Crew; Nwsp Rptr; Yrbk Stf; Rep Frsh Cls; Var L Bsbl; Im Vllybl; Im Ftbl; Acctnt.

FELDMAN, GLENN; Shore Regional HS; W Long Br, NJ; (3); Temple Yth Grp; Bsbl; Golf; High Hon Roll; Hon Roll; Acctng.

FELDMAN, RICHARD; East Brunswick HS; E Brunswick, NJ; (3); Debate Tm; Key Clb; Model UN; Spanish Clb; Temple Yth Grp; Varsity Clb; L Crs Cntry; Var Ftbl; L Wt Lftg; Hon Roll.

FELDT, ERIC; West Essex HS; Fairfield, NJ; (3); French Clb; Science Clb; Concert Band; Mrchg Band; School Play; Stage Crew; French Hon Soc; JP Sousa Awd; NHS.

FELICIANO, DENISE; N Bergen HS; North Bergen, NJ; (4); 14/480; High Hon Roll; Pres Acdmc Ftnss Awd 87; Soc Acdmc Achvt Awd 87; Plaque Hghst Av Stdy Italian Lang 4 Yrs 87.

FELICIANO, WILLIAM; Trenton Central HS; Trenton, NJ; (4); 6/500; Chess Clb; French Clb; Rep Key Clb; School Musical; Nwsp Rptr; Capt Socr; Cit Awd; Gov Hon Prg Awd; NHS; Ntl Merit Schol; Myrs Achvt Awd 83; Acadmc All Am 86; Gov Ctznshp Awd 87; Trenton ST Coll; COS Finance.

FELL, DEE ANN; Paulsboro HS; Bridgeport, NJ; (3); 19/133; Library Aide; Mrchg Band; Stage Crew; Score Keeper; Hon Roll; NHS; Katharine Gibbs Ldrshp Awd 87; Sec Sci.

FELLNER, MARY; Lenape Valley Regional HS; Netcong, NJ; (4); Key Clb; Red Cross Aide; Chorus; Concert Band; Mrchg Band; Nwsp Rptr; Cheerleading; High Hon Roll; Hon Roll; NHS; Dover Gen Hosp Schlrshp 87; Netcong-Stanhope Rotary Schlrshp 87; Garden ST Schlrshp 87; Rutgers Coll; Ped.

FELSMAN, KIM; Wayne Valley HS; Wayne, NJ; (3); 100/285; Church Yth Grp; Rep Soph Cls; Rep Jr Cls; Rep Sr Cls; L Capt Socr; Hon Roll; FBLA; GAA; Lit Mag; Var Bsktbl; Hnr Guard 87; One To One Steerng Commt 86-87; Stu Athltc Ftbl Tranr 86-87; Advstng.

FELT, KEVIN A; Pemberton Twp HS II; Browns Mills, NJ; (3); 7/440; Am Leg Boys St; Drama Clb; VP Exploring; Math Clb; Math Tm; Office Aide; School Play; Nwsp Rptr; Hon Roll; NHS; Ltr Grade Hnrs 86; Ride Alng Awd Law Enfrcmnt Explrs 86.

FELT, PAUL; Manasquan HS; Brielle, NJ; (2); 25/231; Art Clb; Pres Exploring; Spanish Clb; Ftbl; Wt Lftg; High Hon Roll; Hon Roll; Trs Jr Cls; Studnt Opprtnty Advncmnt & Rsrch Acad Awd Bd Of Educ; Med.

FELTEY, THOMAS; Kearny HS; Kearny, NJ; (2); Varsity Clb; Var Ftbl; Rutgers U; Engr.

FENDER, CHRIS; Livingston HS; Livingston, NJ; (3); Boy Scts; Chess Clb; Church Yth Grp; FCA; Varsity Clb; Var Bsbl; Var Ftbl; Var Wrstlng; Hon Roll; U Notre Dame; Pre-Law.

FENIMORE, MICHAEL; Hillsborough HS; Somerville, NJ; (3); 137/328; Kiwanis Awd; Avtn.

FENLON, MICHAEL; Marist HS; Bayonne, NJ; (3); 72/106; Ftbl; Timer; Wt Lftg; Med.

FENNAL, SONYA; Vineland HS; Vineland, NJ; (1); Mdcl Prfssn.

FENNELL, DOREEN; Abraham Clark HS; Roselle, NJ; (4); #6 In Class; Chorus; Color Guard; JV Var Vllybl; High Hon Roll; NHS; NJ Inst Of Tech Smr Hnrs Pgm 85; Rahwa Nrsng Schlrshp 87; Rutgers Schl Of Nrsng; Ped Nrsn.

FENNELL, PATRICK L; Lenape Valley Regional HS; Stanhope, NJ; (3); 11/224; Var Bsktbl; Var Socr; Var Trk; High Hon Roll; Hon Roll; Intl Frgn Lang Awds 86-87; Econ.

FENSTERMACHER, ROBERT; Madison HS; Madison, NJ; (3); 2/200; AFS; Pres Exploring; Pres German Clb; Band; Chorus; School Musical; Sec Sr Cls; Trk; High Hon Roll; NHS; Physics.

FENTON, JILL; West Deptford HS; Thorofare, NJ; (3); Church Yth Grp; Drama Clb; Pep Clb; School Musical; Nwsp Stf; JV Fld Hcky; JV Sftbl; Nrsng.

FEOLA, ANGELA; North Plainfield HS; North Plainfield, NJ; (4); 27/187; SADD; Yrbk Stf; Trs Frsh Cls; Trs Soph Cls; Trs Jr Cls; Off Stu Cncl; JV Var Cheerleading; Sftbl; NHS.

FERDINANDI, JOHN; Prsippany HS; Morris Plains, NJ; (3); Computer Clb; FBLA; High Hon Roll; Hon Roll.

FERDINANDI, PETER; Hudson Catholic HS; Jersey City, NJ; (3); 56/178; Boy Scts; Dance Clb; Pep Clb; SADD; VP Sr Cls; VP Stu Cncl; L Var Ftbl; Var Trk; Var Wt Lftg; Hon Roll; Life Boy Scout 86-87; Bus.

FERDINANDO, ANDREA; Kingsway Regional HS; Mullica Hl, NJ; (2); Ski Clb; Rep Frsh Cls; Stu Cncl; JV Fld Hcky; Hon Roll; Yrbk Stf; 3rd Pl Latin Poster Cont 85-86; 13th Pl Frshmn Yr; U Syracuse; Med.

FERENCZ, JENNIFER; Notre Dame HS; Hamilton Sq, NJ; (2); 32/374; Var Bowling; Hon Roll; NHS; All Star Employee 87; Hgh Hnrs Cls Phys Sci & Religion 86, Geom 87; Aerontcs.

FERENCZI, CHARMAINE; Bayonne HS; Bayonne, NJ; (3); Math Tm; Nwsp Ed-Chief; Lit Mag; High Hon Roll; Hon Roll; Jr NHS; Prncpl Hnrs 85; Art Hist.

FERENCZI, DESIREE; Bayonne HS; Bayonne, NJ; (4); 40/350; French Clb; Rptr FBLA; Science Clb; Spanish Clb; Nwsp Rptr; Nwsp Stf; Ed Lit Mag; Hon Roll; NCTE Awd; NHS; WA Wrkshps Cngrssnl Smnr, Ntl Stdnt Advsry Cncl 86; Rutgers U; Engl.

FERGUSON III, CLEVELAND; Neptune SR HS; Neptune, NJ; (2); Debate Tm; Model UN; Speech Tm; Tennis; Hon Roll; Prfct Atten Awd; Calligraphy Prosect For Neptune Brd Of Educ Pres 87; Monmouth; Jrnlst.

FERGUSON, JENNIFER; Cherry Hill West HS; Cherry Hill, NJ; (3); Church Yth Grp; Office Aide; Fld Hcky; Lcrss; Hon Roll.

FERGUSON, LAURA; Scotch Plains-Fanwood HS; Scotch Plains, NJ; (3); French Clb; Yrbk Bus Mgr; Yrbk Stf; L Trk; JV Vllybl; French Hon Soc.

FERGUSON, NANCY; Sayreville War Memorial HS; S Amboy, NJ; (4); 117/370; GAA; Spanish Clb; Varsity Clb; Band; Chorus; Concert Band; Jazz Band; Mrchg Band; Orch; School Musical; Governors Cncl Phys Ed Awd; Pres Phys Ftns Awd; William Paterson Coll; Commnctn.

FERGUSON, ROBIN; Jackson Memorial HS; Jackson, NJ; (3); 90/416; Art Clb; SADD; Lit Mag; Bsktbl; Sftbl; Vllybl; High Hon Roll; Hon Roll; 2nd Pl Dick Blick Natl Prntg Cont 85; Ocean Cnty Endngrd Spcies Cont 1st Pl 85 & 87; Govs Schl NJ 87; Schl Of Visual Arts; Illstrtn.

FERMAGLICH, MICHAEL; Ocean Township HS; Ocean Tsp, NJ; (3); Cmnty Wkr; French Clb; Ski Clb; Nwsp Stf; Im Bsktbl; Var Tennis; Bronze Cong Medal 87; Peer Ldrshp Prog 87-88; Accntng.

FERMIN, CARLOS M; Emerson HS; Neshanic Sta, NJ; (4); 36/280; Am Leg Boys St; Boy Scts; CAP; Cmnty Wkr; Var Capt Bowling; Var Ftbl; Cit Awd; Hon Roll; Pres Schlr; VFW Awd; Hdsn Cnty PTA Schlrshp 87; Rutgers Coll; Med Tech.

FERMIN, KONI; Mary Help Of Christians HS; Paterson, NJ; (3); Church Yth Grp; English Clb; Hosp Aide; JCL; Office Aide; Service Clb; Spanish Clb; SADD; School Musical; Sociology Awd 87; Drvrs Ed Awd 86; St Thomas Aquinas; Psych.

FERN, DAWN; Lakewood HS; Lakewood, NJ; (3); 143/400; French Clb; FBLA; Chorus; Yrbk Stf; JV Bowling; 40 WPM Typng 86; Rgnl Compttn 5th Pl Stengrph I 87; ST Compttn 5th Pl Stengrph I 87.

FERNANDES, CATHY; Cranford HS; Cranford, NJ; (2); Drama Clb; JCL; Latin Clb; Math Clb; Spanish Clb; Chorus; Nwsp Stf; Rep Frsh Cls; Rep Soph Cls; Rep Stu Cncl; Magna Cum Laude Natl Latn Exmntn 87; Magna Cum Laude Distngshd Annl Latn Wk Compttn 86; Vrsty Ltr Sccr; Psych.

FERNANDEZ, ELEANOR; Glassboro HS; Glassboro, NJ; (4); 7/151; Band; Chorus; Jazz Band; Trs Orch; Rep Stu Cncl; Var Cheerleading; Var Fld Hcky; Stat Wrstlng; NHS; Opt Clb Awd; Schlt Athl Awd-Chrldg 86; Glassboro Music Boostrs Schlrshp 87; Wmns Clb Schlrshp 87; Rutgers Coll; Pre-Med.

FERNANDEZ, FABIO; St Marys HS; Newark, NJ; (3); Church Yth Grp; Ski Clb; Spanish Clb; Nwsp Rptr; Crs Cntry; Trk; High Hon Roll; NHS; Rutgers; Busi.

FERNANDEZ, FERNANDO; Weehawken HS; Weehawken, NJ; (4); 17/200; Art Clb; Boy Scts; Drama Clb; Math Clb; Spanish Clb; Varsity Clb; Chorus; Nwsp Stf; Yrbk Stf; Sec Soph Cls; Vrsty Awd Wrstlng 85-86; Math Cls Hnr 86; Vrsty Awd Trck 85; Jersey City ST Coll; Engrng.

FERNANDEZ, JENNIFER; Fort Lee HS; Ft Lee, NJ; (2); FBLA; Pep Clb; Spanish Clb; SADD; Chorus; Color Guard; Flag Corp; Rep Soph Cls; Sec Jr Cls; JV Var Cheerleading; Rutgers U; Ed.

FERNANDEZ, KARINA; Red Bank Regional HS; Hazlet, NJ; (1); Cmnty Wkr; Dance Clb; Color Guard; Hon Roll; Computer Clb; Alvin Ailey Dance Wrkshp 87; Cert Of Achvt In Sci 87; Dance.

FERNANDEZ, MARIA; Saint John Vianney HS; Cliffwood, NJ; (2); Church Yth Grp; JV Var Bsktbl; Hon Roll; Jr NHS; Gold & White Awd; Cert Of Merit Outstndng Spanish III; John Hopkins U; Pre-Med.

FERNANDEZ, ROSA; St Aloysius HS; Jersey City, NJ; (4); 2/110; Chess Clb; Church Yth Grp; School Musical; Nwsp Stf; Stu Cncl; Capt Bowling; Gov Hon Prg Awd; High Hon Roll; NHS; Sal; Jersey Cty St Coll Pres Citatn Acad Achvt 87; Hudson Cnty Chbr Comm Ind Acad Achvt 87; Rugers Schlr 86; Rutgers U; Bus Admin.

FERNANDEZ, ROSEMARIE; Bridgewater-Raritan HS East; Boundbrook, NJ; (3); VP Latin Clb; Varsity Clb; Off Soph Cls; Off Jr Cls; Stat Bsbl; Var Cheerleading; Var Capt Gym; High Hon Roll; Church Yth Grp; Off Frsh Cls; Mid ST Gymnstcs Tm 86-87; ST Gymnstcs Chmpn USGF 84-85; US Air Force Acad; Aero Engr.

FERNANDEZ, VERONICA; Raritan HS; Hazlet, NJ; (4); Dance Clb; Ski Clb; Mrchg Band; Var Fld Hcky; Var Socr; Var Capt Trk; Spanish NHS; Cmnty Wkr; Band; Symp Band; Francis J Emery Schlrshp Awd 87; Spnsh Awd 87; Frgn Lang Edctrs Awd 87; Rutgers Coll; Trnsltr.

FERNICOLA, DANIELLE; Ramapo HS; Wyckoff, NJ; (3); 52/321; Camera Clb; French Clb; Latin Clb; Science Clb; Chorus; School Musical; Yrbk Phtg; High Hon Roll; Hon Roll; Frnch III Cert Merit 86; Frnch.

FERNICOLA, MICHAEL; Morris Catholic HS; Parsippany, NJ; (3); Aud/Vis; Bsbl; Bus.

FERNSTROM, KURT; Kinnelon HS; Kinnelon, NJ; (3); 6/159; Boy Scts; German Clb; Ski Clb; Varsity Clb; Var Swmmng; JV Tennis; Hon Roll; NHS; Ntl Merit SF; German Hnr Soc 87; Order Of Arrow-Boy Scouts 86; Engrng.

FERRAINOLO, KIM; Westwood HS; Washington Twp, NJ; (2); Math Clb; Quiz Bowl; Spanish Clb; Varsity Clb; Stu Cncl; Cheerleading; Btty Crckr Awd; Cit Awd; High Hon Roll; Hon Roll.

FERRAIUOLO, ANNE M; Morris Hills HS; Rockaway, NJ; (3); FBLA; Fld Hcky; Sftbl; Math.

FERRANTE, TINA; West Orange HS; W Orange, NJ; (3); JV Bsktbl; Powder Puff Ftbl; Var Sftbl; Hon Roll; Itln Hnr Soc 85; Schlr Athlt Awd 85; Allied Hlth.

FERRANTI, VINCENZO; Warren Technical HS; Phillipsburg, NJ; (2); VICA; Hon Roll; Prfct Atten Awd; Cnstrctn.

FERRARA, CATHY-JO; Kearny HS; Kearny, NJ; (4); Church Yth Grp; French Clb; FNA; Pep Clb; Cheerleading; Powder Puff Ftbl; Sftbl; Hon Roll; Wm Patterson Coll; Nrsng.

FERRARA, FRANK J; Hamilton HS East; Trenton, NJ; (3); FBLA; Crs Cntry; Socr; Trk; All Cnty Trck 1st & 2nd Tm 86-87; Georgetwn; Poltcl Sci.

FERRARA, LAURA; Bridgewater Raritan HS West; Bridgewater, NJ; (3); Cmnty Wkr; SADD; Teachers Aide; Capt Color Guard; Mrchg Band; Stage Crew; Stat Bsktbl; Powder Puff Ftbl; JV Sftbl; Elks Awd; Elks Awd-Stu Of Yr; Early Chld Devlpmnt.

FERRARA, LORI; Brick Town HS; Brick Town, NJ; (3); 29/440; Band; Yrbk Stf; Gym; High Hon Roll; NHS; UCLA; Bus.

FERRARI, DAVID; St Mary HS; Englewood Cliffs, NJ; (4); 10/74; Cmnty Wkr; Hosp Aide; Rep Stu Cncl; L Bsbl; L Vllybl; High Hon Roll; NHS; Rutgers U; Bus Admin.

FERRARI, GARRY; South River HS; South River, NJ; (3); Am Leg Boys St; Boy Scts; German Clb; Math Tm; Off Stu Cncl; L Tennis; Hon Roll; Amercn HS Math Exam Awd 87; Acamdc Ltr 86; Arch.

FERRARI, MICHAEL; Roselle Catholic HS; Roselle, NJ; (4); 3/189; Math Clb; Lit Mag; Im Fld Hcky; Wrstlng; High Hon Roll; NHS; Pres Schlr; Spanish NHS; St Schlr; Hghst Avg In Spnsh 87; 2nd Hghst Avg In Math 87; U Of Dayton; Engrng.

FERRARI, MICHAEL R; Brick Township Memorial HS; Brick, NJ; (4); 35/300; Rep Jr Cls; Rep Sr Cls; Trs Stu Cncl; Var Bsbl; Var L Bsktbl; Coach Actv; Var L Ice Hcky; Var Socr; High Hon Roll; NHS; Pres Acad Fit Awd 86-87; Hnrs Grad 86-87; Westchester U; Bus Finance.

FERRARIS, ERIC; Woodbridge HS; Sewaren, NJ; (3); 53/350; Am Leg Boys St; Cmnty Wkr; ROTC; Chorus; Color Guard; Rep Frsh Cls; JV Capt Socr; Var Tennis; High Hon Roll; Hon Roll; USNSCC M Demorest Awd Ldrshp 85 & 87; USNSCC Fago Awd-Cdt Of Yr 85; USCG Acad; Cvl Engrng.

FERRARO, ANITA; Pleasantville HS; Pleasantville, NJ; (3); Art Clb; Office Aide; Chorus; Wt Lftg; Val; HOSA 3rd Pl Dental Spllng 87; Dentl Asst.

FERRARO, SUSAN; Bayonne HS; Bayonne, NJ; (3); French Clb; Math Tm; Lit Mag; JV Bsktbl; Coach Actv; High Hon Roll; Jr NHS; Natl Frnch Cont Qualifier 85-87; Humanities.

FERRARO, SUSAN; Sayreville War Memorial HS; Parlin, NJ; (2); Varsity Clb; Band; Chorus; Concert Band; Jazz Band; Mrchg Band; School Musical; Rep Soph Cls; Var Swmmng; High Hon Roll; Math.

FERRE, ANDREW; Summit HS; Summit, NJ; (3); 35/270; Trs VP AFS; Aud/Vis; Church Yth Grp; Cmnty Wkr; Drama Clb; Exploring; Ski Clb; Spanish Clb; School Play; Lcrss; ASSE Exchng Stu Norway 87; Vlntr 1st Aid Sqd 87; VA Tech; Bldng Cnstrctn Mgmt.

FERREIRA, ISABEL; St Patricks HS; New York, NY; (4); 8/50; Boys Clb Am; Drama Clb; Hosp Aide; Sec Science Clb; Ski Clb; Church Choir; Nwsp Rptr; Yrbk Phtg; Lit Mag; CC Awd; Johanna Wolk Fndtn Schlrshp 87-88; Arabella Halsey Miller Trst Fnd Schlrshp 87-88; Parsons Schl Dsgn; Envrnmntl.

FERREIRA, NELSON ALEXANDER; East Side HS; Newark, NJ; (4); 1/488; Math Tm; Nwsp Rptr; Yrbk Sprt Ed; VP L Tennis; High Hon Roll; NHS; Opt Clb Awd; Val; Civic Clb; Computer Clb; R C Byrd Schlr 87; Esy Cont Wnnr 84-87; Peace Esy Cont Wnnr 87; Presdntl Acadc Ftns Awd; Achvt Awds; Colgate U; Pltcl Sci.

FERREIRO, GUADALUPE; Marylawn Of The Oranges HS; Newark, NJ; (3); 14/70; Math Clb; Science Clb; School Musical; French Hon Soc; Hon Roll; NHS; Ntl Merit Ltr; Prfct Atten Awd; Drama Clb; Lit Mag; Cstmr Svc Cert Burger King 87; Ntl Frnch Cntst Cert Of Merit 87; Span Schl 85-87; Psych.

FERRELL, CARIDAD; Immaculate Conception HS; Newark, NJ; (3); Church Yth Grp; Drama Clb; Pep Clb; Chorus; Church Choir; Off Soph Cls; Trk.

FERRIER, STEPHANIE; St Rose HS; Avon, NJ; (3); 22/225; Cmnty Wkr; Key Clb; Math Tm; Stage Crew; Yrbk Stf; Cheerleading; Hon Roll; NHS; Math.

FERRO, ANN MARIE; Jackson Memorial HS; Jackson, NJ; (4); 18/391; Hosp Aide; Yrbk Phtg; Yrbk Rptr; Ed Yrbk Stf; High Hon Roll; Hon Roll; NHS; NEDT Awd; Pres Schlr; Georgian Ct Coll; Bus Admn.

FERRO, CRISSY; South River HS; South River, NJ; (2); German Clb; Library Aide; JV Mgr(s); Score Keeper; Stat Socr; Var Timer; Var Trk; Mgr Stat Wrstlng; Hon Roll; Cup Knwldg Awd 86; Vrsty Lttr Grls Trk 87; FL ST U; Psych.

FERRY, MARY ANN; Dover HS; Dover, NJ; (4); 18/171; Hon Roll; NHS; Cntry 21 Accntg Awd 85-86.

FERRY, SHERYL; Kingsway Regional HS; Clarksboro, NJ; (4); 38/168; Cmnty Wkr; Yrbk Stf; Trs Soph Cls; Rep Stu Cncl; Capt Var Bsktbl; Capt Cheerleading; Capt Var Sftbl; High Hon Roll; Art Clb; GAA; Al Carino Bsktbl Schrlshp 86-87; All S Jersey All Group I Bsktbl & Sftbll Hnrs 86-87; Htsch Mem Awd 87; Drexel U; Accntng.

FERUS, BRIAN; Vineland HS; Millville, NJ; (2); Hon Roll; Engrng.

FETTER, ANDREA; Lakewood HS; Lakewood, NJ; (3); 20/330; French Clb; Band; Concert Band; Mrchg Band; Symp Band; Lit Mag; Stat Mgr Bsbl; French Hon Soc; Hon Roll; NHS.

FEUER, TEMA; Cherry Hill H S East; Cherry Hill, NJ; (4); Hosp Aide; Trs Latin Clb; Political Wkr; Spanish Clb; SADD; Temple Yth Grp; Rep Jr Cls; Rep Sr Cls; Stu Cncl; Mgr(s); Emory U; Intl Bus.

FIALA, DAWN; Middletown HS South; Red Bank, NJ; (3); Sec Church Yth Grp; Ski Clb; Church Choir; Drm Mjr(t); Var L Mrchg Band; Symp Band; Yrbk Stf; Powder Puff Ftbl; Var L Trk; High Hon Roll; German Natl Hnr Soc 86 & 87; 2 Crs Montclair ST Coll Thrgh Rogate 86; Intl Bus.

FICARA, BRIAN; Gateway Regional HS; Woodbury Hts, NJ; (3); 27/170; Trs German Clb; Bsktbl; Var Socr; Var Tennis; Wt Lftg; Hon Roll; NHS; IN U; Hotel Mgmt.

FICHNER, LISA JEAN; Mother Seton Regional HS; Linden, NJ; (2); Math Tm; Science Clb; School Musical; Nwsp Rptr; Pres Soph Cls; Var Cheerleading; High Hon Roll; Rep Frsh Cls; Drama Clb; Pep Clb; 4 Yr Schlrshp HS; Excel Geomtry, Alg II 86-87; Cert Merit Excel Frnch 86-87; Med.

FIEDLER, JENNIFER; Maple Shade HS; Maple Shade, NJ; (2); GAA; Key Clb; Spanish Clb; Stat Socr; High Hon Roll; Jr NHS; NHS; Yth Merit Awd Rotary Clb 86; Acad All Amer Awd 86; Comp Sci.

FIEDLER JR, PAUL; Holy Spirit HS; Pleasantville, NJ; (4); 125/357; FBLA; Letterman Clb; Hon Roll; Natl Rowing Champ JR 8 86, SR 8 87; FL Inst Tech; Comm Pilot.

FIELD, THOMAS; Holy Cross HS; Cinnaminson, NJ; (3); Ski Clb; Y-Teens; Golf; Socr; Trk; Hon Roll; Serra Clb Awd 84; Bus.

FIELDS, DAVID; Dover HS; Dover, NJ; (3); 3/240; Am Leg Boys St; Math Tm; Pres Soph Cls; Off Jr Cls; Off Stu Cncl; L Bsktbl; L Ftbl; High Hon Roll; Hon Roll; NHS; Psych, Bio & Ftbl Awds 85-87; Bus.

FIELDS, JESSICA; Asbury Park HS; Asbury Park, NJ; (2); 32/125; Church Yth Grp; Cmnty Wkr; Girl Scts; Intnl Clb; Key Clb; Pep Clb; Spanish Clb; Church Choir; Nwsp Ed-Chief; Yrbk Stf.

FIELDS, JOY; Vineland HS; Vineland, NJ; (3); #145 In Class; Dance Clb; English Clb; Acpl Chr; Church Choir; Rep Jr Cls; Outstndng Music Achvts 86-87; Lwyr.

FIELDS, ROSALIND; University HS; Newark, NJ; (2); Church Yth Grp; Hosp Aide; Church Choir; Rep Soph Cls; Upwrd Bound Learnng Pgm; VA ST Coll; Comp Sci.

FIELDSEND, GEORGE; Summit HS; Summit, NJ; (3); 120/245; Boy Scts; Band; Ftbl; Bus.

FIERSTEIN, LISA; Parsippany HS; Parsippany, NJ; (3); French Clb; Band; Var Cheerleading; JV Socr; High Hon Roll; NHS.

FIETKIEWICZ, PATRICIA; Holy Spirit HS; Absecon, NJ; (3); 22/332; French Clb; Im Vllybl.

FIEVET, TANIA; Franklin HS; Somerset, NJ; (3); Hon Roll; Cert Of Merit Amer Assn Of Tchrs Grmn Inc 85-87.

FIGAROTTA, ROBERT F; Bishop George Ahr HS; Colonia, NJ; (3); 51/275; Am Leg Boys St; SADD; Varsity Clb; Rep Soph Cls; Rep Jr Cls; JV Ftbl; Var Golf; JV Wrstlng; Hon Roll; Ntl Merit Ltr; Sci.

FIGLER, CINDY; Raritan HS; Hazlet, NJ; (3); French Clb; Ski Clb; Teachers Aide; Temple Yth Grp; Yrbk Phtg; Hon Roll; Pres NHS; Natl Hnr Soc Awd Grad 87; U Of MA Amherst; Law.

FIGLIO, MEAGAN L W; Woodtown HS; Elmer, NJ; (3); English Clb; French Clb; Math Clb; Band; Chorus; Concert Band; Mrchg Band; School Musical; Symp Band; NHS; Salem Cnty Band Awd Exclinc 85-87; S Jrsy Band Awd Exclinc 86-87; Art Awd Exclinc 87.

FIGUEROA, KELLY; Perth Amboy HS; Perth Amboy, NJ; (3); 7/564; Dance Clb; Hosp Aide; Model UN; School Musical; School Play; Variety Show; High Hon Roll; NHS; Chorus; Drama Clb; Girls Ctznshp Inst Delg 87; Gov Schl Arts 87; Perf Arts.

FIGUEROA, MARIETTE; Lakewood HS; Lakewood, NJ; (4); 36/270; Am Leg Aux Girls St; Church Yth Grp; Cmnty Wkr; FBLA; Hosp Aide; Key Clb; Church Choir; NHS; VP Spanish NHS; PTSA Awd Spnsh 87; Georgian Court Coll.

FIGUEROA, SAM; New Brunswick HS; New Brunswick, NJ; (3); Computer Clb; Hon Roll; Rutgers Coll; Comp Sci.

FIJALKOWSKI, JOY MICHELE; Holy Cross HS; Salisburg, NC; (4); Girl Scts; Scholastic Bowl; Yrbk Stf; Hon Roll; Catawba Coll; Bus.

FILAN, JOANNE; Toms River HS North; Toms River, NJ; (3); 42/459; Stat Bsktbl; High Hon Roll; Hon Roll; Acadmc Ltr 84-85; Marine Bio.

FILIP, MICHAEL SCOTT; Cresskill HS; Cresskill, NJ; (3); Ski Clb; Nwsp Rptr; Yrbk Rptr; Yrbk Stf; JV Tennis; JV Trk; Prfct Atten Awd; Boston U; Bus.

FILIPE, ANIBAL; East Side HS; Newark, NJ; (3); Computer Clb; French Clb; Math Tm; Rep Jr Cls; High Hon Roll; Hon Roll; Opt Clb Awd; H S Schlrs Recognition 86-87; NJ Inst Of Tech; Arch.

FILIPOWSKI, JOAN; Cinnaminson HS; Cinna, NJ; (4); 32/230; Am Leg Aux Girls St; Church Yth Grp; SADD; Off Stu Cncl; Bsktbl; Fld Hcky; Lcrss; Hon Roll; NHS; Outstndng Athlt Of The Yr 87; Natl Hnr Soc Awd 87; Penn ST U.

FILIPSKI, ROBERT; Union Catholic Regional HS; Fanwood, NJ; (3); Ski Clb; Concert Band; Bsbl; Hon Roll; Bus.

FILLIMAN, LISA; Passaic Valley HS; Little Falls, NJ; (4); 13/350; Am Leg Aux Girls St; Drama Clb; Drm Mjr(t); Orch; School Musical; Variety Show; Yrbk Stf; Var L Tennis; High Hon Roll; NHS; ITT Coll Schlrshp 87; Grls Ctznshp Inst Dlgt 86; Lafayette Coll; Psych.

FILOS, FAITH; Saint Mary HS; Rutherford, NJ; (3); Drama Clb; Thesps; School Play; Rep Frsh Cls; Rep Soph Cls; Rep Jr Cls; JV Bsktbl; JV Vllybl; Hon Roll; NHS; Frshm Year All Around Hnrs 84-85; Arts.

FINALDI, MELISSA; Mother Seton Regional HS; Pt Reading, NJ; (2); Drama Clb; Dstnctn Natl Lang Arts Olymp 85-86; Cert Super Prfrmnc Natl Ed Dvlpmt Tsts 86; Rutgers; Phrmcst.

FINAN, TOM; Red Bank Regional HS; Little Silver, NJ; (3); 8/320; Am Leg Boys St; Church Yth Grp; Cmnty Wkr; School Musical; Yrbk Ed-Chief; Yrbk Rptr; Cit Awd; French Hon Soc; High Hon Roll; Hon Roll; Slvr Congressnl Awd 87; Outstndng US Hstry II Stu Awd 87; Politcn.

FINCH, HOLLYANN; Edgewood Regional SR HS; Sicklerville, NJ; (3); #25 In Class; Latin Clb; Band; Concert Band; Jazz Band; Mrchg Band; Rep Soph Cls; Hon Roll; Sec Jr NHS; VP NHS; Pharm.

FINCH, LORI; Edgewood Regional SR HS; Atco, NJ; (3); #31 In Class; Library Aide; Hon Roll; NHS; SADD 87; Acctg.

FINCKEN, HEIDI; Kittatinny Regional HS; Newton, NJ; (4); 17/228; VP Church Yth Grp; Sec Trs 4-H; VP Spanish Clb; Nwsp Ed-Chief; Var Capt Cheerleading; JV Var Sftbl; Cit Awd; DAR Awd; 4-H Awd; NHS; Intl Rel.

FINDLAY, CHRISTINE; Middletown South HS; Middletown, NJ; (2); Variety Show; Score Keeper; Trk; Hon Roll; Bus.

FINDLAY, MATTHEW; West Essex HS; Roseland, NJ; (3); Key Clb; Ski Clb; Rep Frsh Cls; Rep Soph Cls; Crs Cntry; CO-BOULDER; Bus.

FINDLEY, SHARON; Morristown HS; Morristown, NJ; (3); Church Yth Grp; Cmnty Wkr; Hosp Aide; JA; Library Aide; NAACP; Teachers Aide; Chorus; Church Choir; Color Guard; Phrmcy.

FINE, BONNIE; Manalapan HS; Englishtown, NJ; (3); Drama Clb; SADD; Trk.

FINE, JOCELYN; Leonia HS; Leonia, NJ; (4); 9/150; AFS; VP Art Clb; Drama Clb; French Clb; Service Clb; Yrbk Stf; Trk; Vllybl; Hon Roll; Acdmc Decathlon Litry Awd 87; Pres Acdmc Ftns Awd 87; U Of VT; Studio Art.

FINELLO, LORRAINE; Academy Of St Aloysius; Jersey City, NJ; (3); SADD; Chorus; Nwsp Rptr; VP Soph Cls; Pres Jr Cls; NHS; Ntl Merit Ltr; Prfct Atten Awd; Miss Teenage Columbus Hdsn Cnty 85-86; HOBY Fndtn Smnnr 86; PA ST U; Mrktng.

FINEMAN, MELISSA J; John P Stevens HS; Edison, NJ; (4); 23/476; Thesps; Concert Band; Drm Mjr(t); Mrchg Band; Yrbk Stf; Sec Frsh Cls; High Hon Roll; NHS; 3rd Olympics Of The Mind Wrld Champs 84; Hugh O Brian Yth Awd Ldrshp Smnr 85; SUNY; Cmmrcl Art.

FINGER, CASSANDRA; Millville SR HS; Millville, NJ; (2); Church Yth Grp; Cmnty Wkr; Drama Clb; Spanish Clb; Acpl Chr; Band; Church Choir; Concert Band; Mrchg Band; School Play; Musicl Theatr.

FINI, CAROLYN; Highland Regional HS; Hilltop, NJ; (3); 9/350; Sec German Clb; JV Capt Bsbl; Var Cheerleading; Var Capt Socr; NHS; Rotary Awd; Rutgers.

FINK, RICHARD; Mc Corristin Catholic HS; Trenton, NJ; (3); 20/245; JA; Varsity Clb; Yrbk Rptr; JV Bsbl; Im Bsktbl; JV Var Ftbl; Im Vllybl; Hon Roll; NHS; NEDT Awd; Percival Sillas Mem Awd Soc Stds 85; Comp Sci.

FINK, STEPHEN; Freehold Township HS; Freehold, NJ; (3); 1/400; Math Tm; Band; Jazz Band; Mrchg Band; NHS; Ntl Merit Ltr; Louis Armstron Awd 86; Rensselr Mdl 87; Rgn II, All Shre Bands 86-87.

FINKELSTEIN, ARIANA; Hightstown HS; East Windsor, NJ; (3); Drama Clb; Key Clb; Service Clb; Thesps; Concert Band; School Musical; School Play; Stage Crew; Var Socr; High Hon Roll; Girls Citznshp Dougless Compass Rutgers Coll 87; MS Co-Ed Pagnt NJ Semi Fnlst 87; Vet Med.

FINKELSTEIN, JEFF; Montville HS; Montville, NJ; (4); 3/270; Cmnty Wkr; Key Clb; SADD; Temple Yth Grp; Yrbk Stf; JV Socr; Var Tennis; High Hon Roll; Pres NHS; Ntl Merit Ltr; Columbia U Sci Hnr 86-87; Med.

FINKELSTEIN, JUSTINE; Long Branch HS; Long Br, NJ; (3); 2/279; Science Clb; Band; Nwsp Ed-Chief; VP Frsh Cls; VP Jr Cls; Pres Sec Stu Cncl; Var Bowling; Hon Roll; NHS; School Musical; NJ Fed Of Wmns Clbs Grls Ctznshp Inst Douglass Coll Of Rutgers Univ 87; Bio Sci.

FINKEN, JEFFREY; Union HS; Union, NJ; (2); Boys Clb Am; VP Key Clb; Spanish Clb; Nwsp Rptr; Yrbk Rptr; Frsh Cls; Var L Crs Cntry; Var L Swmmng; Var L Trk; Hon Roll.

FINKLE, RISA; Paramus HS; Paramus, NJ; (3); VP Intnl Clb; Pres VP Orch; Nwsp Stf; Yrbk Ed-Chief; Sec Sr Cls; Rep Stu Cncl; NHS; VP Rotary Awd; Pres Spanish NHS; Cmnty Wkr; Rep At RYLA Ldrshp Conf 87; Phys Thrpy.

FINKLE, SETH; Bridgewater-Raritan E HS; Bridgewater, NJ; (3); Debate Tm; NFL; Chorus; Orch; Ed Lit Mag; Hon Roll; Ntl Merit Ltr; ST Teen Arts Fest Fnlst 87; Barbrshp Quartet 86-87; Acadmc Leag JV Capt 86-87.

FINLAY, SHANNON; Brick Township HS; Brick Town, NJ; (4); 1/354; Math Tm; Rep Stu Cncl; Var Tennis; High Hon Roll; NHS; St Schlr; Val; French Clb; Math Clb; Band; Mst Val Tennis 86-87; Greenbriar Home Owners Assoc 87; Old Guard Of Grtr Point Plesant 87; Boston U; Math.

FINN, BRIGID; St Rose HS; Avon By The Sea, NJ; (3); Church Yth Grp; Key Clb; Rep Frsh Cls; Bsktbl; Var Crs Cntry; Var Trk; Hon Roll; NEDT Awd.

FINN, RAYMOND; Christian Brothers Acad; Manalapan, NJ; (3); 46/250; Boy Scts; Hosp Aide; Political Wkr; Varsity Clb; Drm & Bgl; Nwsp Rptr; Rep Sr Cls; Im Capt Socr; Capt Trk; High Hon Roll; Eagle Sct 86; Asian Cltres.

FINN, RENEE; St Pius X Regional HS; New Brunswick, NJ; (3); 18/88; Church Yth Grp; School Play; Co-Capt Pom Pon; Hon Roll; NHS; Rep-HOBY Fndtn Smnr 86.

FINN, RONALD; Middletown HS South; Leonardo, NJ; (4); 16/453; Lit Mag; Jr Cls; Sr Cls; High Hon Roll; Hon Roll; Prncpls Awd-Acadmc Excllnc; Ntl Ltn Exam-Mgna Cum Laude; Arspc Engrng.

FINNEGAN, KATHLEEN; Belvidere HS; Belvidere, NJ; (3); Cmnty Wkr; Scholastic Bowl; Bsktbl; High Hon Roll; NHS; Camera Clb; Chorus; Color Guard; Rutgers; Pre Med.

FINNEGAN, SCOTT; Holy Cross HS; Marlton, NJ; (3); German Clb; JA; Wt Lftg; Var L Wrstlng; Hon Roll; Ntl Merit Ltr; U Of ME; FBI Fld Agnt.

FINNERAN, HEATHER; John P Stevens HS; Edison, NJ; (3); 100/500; Church Yth Grp; GAA; Key Clb; Science Clb; Nwsp Rptr; Nwsp Stf; Crs Cntry; Mgr(s); Trk; Hon Roll; Recgnt Hnry Awd Drmtc Arts 84-85; Wrstlng Mngr Outstndng Awd 85-86; UCLA; Bus.

FINNERAN, SHARON; Vineland HS; Vineland, NJ; (3); Art Clb; Drama Clb; FHA; GAA; Pep Clb; Spanish Clb; SADD; Teachers Aide; Varsity Clb; Acpl Chr; Grls Sccr All S Jersey 1st Team 86; Grls Sccr Coaches Awd Vrsty, Teams USA Soviet Tour Wmns Sccr 87.

FINNERTY, MAUREEN; TRHS South; Toms River, NJ; (3); Band; Crs Cntry; Trk; Wt Lftg; NHS; Upsala U; CPA.

FINNERTY, SEAN LAWRENCE; Middletown South HS; Lincroft, NJ; (4); 41/450; School Play; Nwsp Sprt Ed; Rep Soph Cls; Rep Jr Cls; Rep Stu Cncl; Var L Crs Cntry; Im Lcrss; Im Socr; Var L Trk; NHS; Bottlecappers Prog Govt Hnr 84-87; Villanova; Poli Sci.

FIORARANCIO, ROSANNA; Mary Help Of Christians Acad; Totowa, NJ; (3); 17/82; Letterman Clb; NFL; Yrbk Rptr; Lit Mag; Stu Cncl; Hon Roll; NHS; Pre-Law.

FIORE, KEVIN; West Essex HS; Roseland, NJ; (3); Math Tm; Science Clb; Rep Stu Cncl; Var Capt Bsbl; L Bsktbl; Var Socr; Im Vllybl; Hon Roll; NHS; Ntl Merit Ltr; U Of VA; Sprts Med.

FIORELLO, KATHLEEN; De Paul Diocesan HS; Wayne, NJ; (4); 66/178; Hosp Aide; Ski Clb; VP Frsh Cls; Rep Soph Cls; Rep Jr Cls; Rep Sr Cls; Sec Stu Cncl; JV Capt Cheerleading; L Golf; Sftbl; Phys Ed Awd; FL ST U; Pol Sci.

FIORELLO, TIMOTHY; Cranford HS; Cranford, NJ; (2); French Clb; Band; Chorus; Boy Scts; Concert Band; Mrchg Band; School Musical; Rep Frsh Cls; Rep Frsh Cls; French Hon Soc; Music.

FIORESI, JACKIE; Vineland HS; Vineland, NJ; (3); 45/800; Pep Clb; Im Gym; JV Im Sftbl; Var JV Tennis; Italian Clb; Rutgers U; Accntng.

FIORI, JENNIFER; Edgewood JR HS; Elm, NJ; (1); Church Yth Grp; Hon Roll; Jr NHS; Prfct Atten Awd.

FIORILLI, JOANNE MICHELE; Sayreville War Memorial HS; Parlin, NJ; (4); 4/353; VP Spanish Clb; SADD; Varsity Clb; Chorus; Color Guard; Stage Crew; Nwsp Ed-Chief; Rep Stu Cncl; Mgr(s); High Hon Roll; Garden St Distinguished Schlr 87; NY U; Jrnlsm.

FIORINI, PETER; Linden HS; Linden, NJ; (3); Cmnty Wkr; Var L Bsbl; JV Bsktbl; High Hon Roll; Hon Roll; NHS; Sports Awds 84-87; Math.

FIOTO, MICHELE; Manalapan HS; Manalapan, NJ; (3); Color Guard; Drill Tm; Hon Roll; NHS; Cert Merit Fren 86-87; Fashn Merch.

FIPPINGER, JEFFREY D; West Milford Township HS; West Milford, NJ; (3); Am Leg Boys St; Debate Tm; Model UN; Trs Spanish Clb; Varsity Clb; Concert Band; Mrchg Band; Nwsp Rptr; Jr NHS; Spanish NHS; NJ Frnsc League St Fnlsts 86; NJ Jr Philharmonic 85-86; W Milford Comp Fair 3rd Pl Wnnr 86; Intl Law.

FIRRIOLO, CHRISTOPHER; Howell HS; Howell, NJ; (3); 63/400; JCL; Band; Mrchg Band; Symp Band; Var Bsktbl; JV Crs Cntry; Hon Roll; Bsktbl Coach Awd 85 & 86; Mdcl.

FISCELLA, KERI; Paramus Catholic HS; Maywood, NJ; (2); Church Yth Grp; Spanish Clb; School Play; Nwsp Rptr; Lit Mag; Rep Frsh Cls; Crs Cntry; High Hon Roll; Farfield U; Teaching.

FISCHER, CHRISTINA; Mt St John Acad; Murray Hill, NJ; (2); 7/25; Cmnty Wkr; Drama Clb; GAA; Hosp Aide; SADD; Varsity Clb; Chorus; Rep Stu Cncl; Co-Capt Cheerleading; Var Score Keeper; Med.

FISCHER, CHRISTINE; Passaic Valley HS; Little Falls, NJ; (4); 50/350; Am Leg Aux Girls St; Church Yth Grp; Trs French Clb; Yrbk Stf; Sec Stu Cncl; JV Sftbl; JV Tennis; Pres High Hon Roll; Pres Acad Fit Awd 87; Girls Ctznshp Awd 86; Pace U.

FISCHER, DEBORAH E; South Brunswick HS; N Brunswick, NJ; (4); 10/255; Ski Clb; Spanish Clb; Varsity Clb; Var Capt Crs Cntry; Var Trk; Hon Roll; Trs NHS; Spanish NHS; St Schlr; South Bruns HS Schlr Athlt 86-87; U Of PA; Bio Engrng.

FISCHER, ERIC; Hillsborough HS; Neshanic, NJ; (4); 15/293; Math Tm; Trk; Ftbl; Tennis; High Hon Roll; Hon Roll; NHS; Cornell U; Math.

FISCHER, HARRY; Toms River HS South; Toms River, NJ; (3); Var L Ftbl; JV Trk; Im Wt Lftg; Var L Wrstlng; Sprts Med.

FISCHER, JENNIFER; East Burnswick HS; East Brunswick, NJ; (3); Am Leg Aux Girls St; Church Yth Grp; Cmnty Wkr; German Clb; JCL; Spanish Clb; Acpl Chr; Yrbk Rptr; NCTE Awd; German Hnr Scty.

FISCHER JR, MARTIN; Clifton HS; Clifton, NJ; (3); Off Intnl Clb; Math Clb; Science Clb; Service Clb; School Musical; School Play; Stage Crew; Var L Ftbl; Var L Trk; Var Wt Lftg; USAF Acad; Aerospace Engrng.

FISCHER, SARA; Union HS; Union, NJ; (2); Boys Clb Am; Dance Clb; German Clb; Band; Concert Band; Jazz Band; Orch; Nwsp Stf; Yrbk Stf; Hon Roll; Kawameehs MV Musician 86; Trenton ST Coll; Accountant.

FISCHER, TED; Cherry Hill High School HS; Cherry Hill, NJ; (3); Debate Tm; French Clb; Sec Model UN; Science Clb; Nwsp Stf; High Hon Roll; Hon Roll; NHS; Orwill & Irene Anderson Schlrshp 85.

FISH, ALEXANDER; Morris Knolls HS; Denville, NJ; (2); 63/376; Chorus; School Musical; School Play; Nwsp Rptr.

FISHBURN, DEBBIE; Kingsway Regional HS; Swedesboro, NJ; (2); Science Clb; Flag Corp; Mrchg Band; Hon Roll; NHS; JV Sftbl.

FISHBURN, PAUL T; Lenape HS; Mount Laurel, NJ; (4); 11/420; Am Leg Boys St; Math Tm; Concert Band; Jazz Band; Mrchg Band; School Musical; High Hon Roll; Hon Roll; NHS; Spanish NHS; Pres Clssrm 87; W H Hoskiss Scholar; Reno ST; Engrng.

FISHELBERG, JASON T; South Brunswick HS; Kendall Park, NJ; (3); 3/276; Am Leg Boys St; Mu Alpha Theta; Ski Clb; VP Soph Cls; VP Jr Cls; VP Stu Cncl; Var L Tennis; Hon Roll; NHS; Spanish NHS; Peer Ldrshp Prog 87-88; Vrsty Tennis MVP 86; Duke.

FISHER, DAVID; Holy Cross HS; Maple Shade, NJ; (3); Church Yth Grp; German Clb; Im Bsktbl; Im Bowling; Im Socr; Hon Roll; Elec Engrng.

FISHER, DONNA; Shore Regional HS; West Long Branch, NJ; (3); Hosp Aide; Pres Temple Yth Grp; Band; Chorus; Stage Crew; Nwsp Stf; Stat Trk; High Hon Roll; NHS; Ski Clb; Brnz Cngrssnl Awd 86; Phy Thrpy.

FISHER, DONNA JEAN; Cumberland Regional HS; Bridgeton, NJ; (3); Drama Clb; Library Aide; Flag Corp; Mgr(s); Score Keeper; Sftbl; Hon Roll; Cumberland Cnty Coll; Data Proc.

FISHER, JAMES; Holy Spirit HS; Margate, NJ; (4); 20/363; Math Tm; Im Ftbl; Im Vllybl; Jr NHS; NHS; George Washington U; Elec Engr.

FISHER, KATHY; Jefferson Township HS; Oak Ridge, NJ; (4); 5/226; Cmnty Wkr; SADD; Varsity Clb; Var Capt Bsktbl; Var Capt Fld Hcky; Var Sftbl; Cit Awd; NHS; Am Leg Aux Girls St; Exploring; Gov Tchng Schlrshp 87; U Of MD; Spch Thrpy.

FISHER, LARRY W; Penns Grove HS; Penns Grove, NJ; (3); Am Leg Boys St; JCL; Latin Clb; Band; Concert Band; Jazz Band; Mrchg Band; Symp Band; Meteorlgst.

FISHER, MARLO; Wildwood Catholic HS; Cape May, NJ; (3); French Clb; Hon Roll; Prfct Atten Awd; 1st Pl Sci Fair Chem 86-87; Hnrbl Mntn 5th Annl Marie Curie Sci Fair 87; US Metri Assn Awd 87; Pre Med.

FISHER, MATTHEW A; Vineland HS; Vineland, NJ; (3); 14/900; Church Yth Grp; Math Tm; Spanish Clb; Stage Crew; Var Mgr Bsktbl; Crs Cntry; Trk; NHS; Med Explrs Club Treas 86-87; Prncpls List; Med.

FISHER, NICOLE; Woodstown HS; Alloway, NJ; (3); English Clb; Key Clb; Ski Clb; Chorus; Trs Stu Cncl; Var L Fld Hcky; Wt Lftg; Drama Clb; SADD; Varsity Clb; All Tri Cnty Tm-Hcky 86; All Str Tm-Hcky 86; 2nd Pl-Sci Fair 85 & 3rd Pl 86; Mrchndsng.

FISHER, PAT; Delaware Valley Regional HS; Frenchtown, NJ; (4); 41/200; Am Leg Boys St; Church Yth Grp; VP Key Clb; Pep Clb; Varsity Clb; Yrbk Stf; Stu Cncl; Bsbl; Bsktbl; Socr; Rutgers U; Bus.

FISHER, SHAWN; Vineland SR HS; Vineland, NJ; (3); 113/800; Church Yth Grp; Drama Clb; Acpl Chr; Chorus; School Musical; Sec Sr Cls; L Var Crs Cntry; Var Mgr(s); Var Trk; Im Vllybl; 2nd Pl Pntng Ctgry VHS Art Exhbtn 87; Bus.

FISHER, TAUNYA; Neptune SR HS; Neptune, NJ; (2); SADD; Var Trk; Hon Roll; Exec Sec.

FISHMAN, RANDI; Bridgeton HS; Bridgeton, NJ; (3); 2/290; Am Leg Aux Girls St; Cmnty Wkr; SADD; Nwsp Stf; Yrbk Stf; Cit Awd; High Hon Roll; NHS; VFW Awd; Voice Dem Awd; Edgar M Bronfman Yth Fllwshp Israel 87; HOSA; Outstndng Socl Studies Stu Of Yr 87; Socl Sci.

FISHMAN, TODD; Clifton HS; Clifton, NJ; (4); 20/580; Am Leg Boys St; Ski Clb; Socr; Tennis; Pres Jr NHS; NHS; Opt Clb Awd; Spanish NHS; Sen Bill Bradley Stu Ldrshp Smnr 87; Mock Trial Def Atty 86 & 87; Brandeis U; Intl Rel.

FISK, ELIOT JAMES HYWEL; Haddonfield Memorial HS; Haddonfield, NJ; (3); Am Leg Boys St; Rep Soph Cls; Im JV Socr; Im JV Trk; High Hon Roll; Hon Roll; NHS; Ntl Merit Ltr; German Natl Hnr Soc & Yrbk Photo Editor 87; Engrng.

FITTON, DAVID; St Joseph Regional HS; West Nyack, NY; (3); 30/200; Church Yth Grp; Nwsp Rptr; Nwsp Stf; Yrbk Rptr; Yrbk Stf; JV Trk; High Hon Roll; Hon Roll; NHS; Spanish NHS; Lawyer.

FITTS, LISA; Morristown-Beard Schl; Rockaway, NJ; (3); 7/83; Intnl Clb; Model UN; School Play; Var Bsktbl; Var Cheerleading; JV Stat Lcrss; French Hon Soc; Hon Roll; Spanish NHS.

FITZGERALD, CAROLYN; Millville SR HS; Port Elizabeth, NJ; (4); 14/430; FBLA; Pres Girl Scts; Ed Lit Mag; Var JV Socr; NHS; Cmnty Wkr; Library Aide; Im Sftbl; High Hon Roll; Hon Roll; Girl Sct Gold Awd 85; SICO Fndtn Scholar 87; Chrst Episcopl Chrch Wmns Awd Fine Chrstn Traits & Char; Millersville U; Bus Adm.

FITZGERALD, CATHERINE; Jackson Memorial HS; Jackson, NJ; (3); German Clb; Band; Mrchg Band; JV Bsktbl; Powder Puff Ftbl; JV Var Sftbl; Preschl Tchr.

FITZGERALD, DANIEL; Pitman HS; Pitman, NJ; (2); Church Yth Grp; Band; Concert Band; Mrchg Band; Nwsp Rptr; Crs Cntry; Trk; Hon Roll; Vet.

FITZGERALD, JENNIFER; Middletown HS South; Red Bank, NJ; (3); VP Thesps; Variety Show; Yrbk Stf; Rep Soph Cls; Rep Jr Cls; Rep Stu Cncl; Golf; Powder Puff Ftbl; Tennis; Hon Roll; Bottlecapper Awd Rcgntn & Prtcptn 86-88; Glf Awds Bst Sprtmnshp 84&85; Finance.

FITZGERALD, LYNN; Monsignor Donovan HS; Toms River, NJ; (3); 106/236; Drama Clb; Pres 4-H; Band; Co-Capt Flag Corp; Jazz Band; Mgr(s); Hon Roll; NJ ST Chmpn 4-H Horse Jdgng 86; Educ.

FITZGERALD, TRACY; Pitman HS; Pitman, NJ; (4); 1/150; Church Yth Grp; Chorus; Trs Concert Band; Trs Mrchg Band; Nwsp Stf; Bsktbl; Crs Cntry; NHS; Ntl Merit Ltr; Rotary Awd; NJ All ST Chorus 85; Mdrn Msc Mstrs Scty 86; All Sth Jrsy Chrs 83-85.

FITZGIBBON, ELLEN E; Hackettstown HS; Hackettstown, NJ; (4); #7 In Class; 4-H; Key Clb; Chorus; Concert Band; Pep Band; High Hon Roll; NHS; Church Yth Grp; Band; Hon Roll; Gvrnrs Schl Of Fine Arts 86; Grls Ldrshp Douglas Coll 86; Gvrnrs Tchng Schlrs 87; Smith Coll; Tchng.

FITZHENRY, STEPHANIE ERIN; Mt Saint Dominic Acad; N Caldwell, NJ; (4); Intnl Clb; Library Aide; Service Clb; Variety Show; Nwsp Rptr; Socr; Hon Roll; NHS; Seton Hall U; Psych.

FITZMAURICE, SCOTT; Washington Tshp HS; Turnersville, NJ; (3); Church Yth Grp.

FITZPATRICK, CHRISTOPHER; Union HS; Union, NJ; (2); Computer Clb; Ski Clb; Spanish Clb; Var L Crs Cntry; Var L Trk; Jr NHS.

FITZPATRICK, JILL; St John Vianney HS; Colts Neck, NJ; (3); Yrbk Stf; Powder Puff Ftbl; Vllybl; Hon Roll; Anthrplgy.

FITZSIMMONS, CLARK; West Morris Mendham HS; Chester, NJ; (4); 9/320; Debate Tm; FBLA; German Clb; Intnl Clb; Pres JA; NFL; Ski Clb; Var Crs Cntry; JV Tennis; JV Trk; Outstndng Stu JA 85; Natl Hstry Day-ST Wnr Grp Presntatn 85; Acadmc Schlrshp U KS 87; Hsptl Adm.

FLAMM, STEPHEN; Chatham Township HS; Chatham Twp, NJ; (4); 8/140; Computer Clb; Exploring; Key Clb; Math Clb; Math Tm; Model UN; Science Clb; Band; Concert Band; Yrbk Phtg; MA Inst Of Tech; Elec Engrng.

FLANAGAN, DAWN; Paramus Catholic HS; New Milford, NJ; (3); Church Yth Grp; Intnl Clb; SADD; Teachers Aide; Church Choir; Variety Show; Tennis; Hon Roll; Engl.

FLANAGAN, KERRIN; Jackson Memorial HS; Jackson, NJ; (1); 1/394; Church Yth Grp; Drama Clb; Hosp Aide; Math Tm; School Play; Nwsp Rptr; Lit Mag; Rep Frsh Cls; High Hon Roll; Prfct Atten Awd; High Hnr Roll For 3 Cnsctive Mrkng Prds 86-87.

FLANAGAN, MICHAELA; Mt St Dominic Acad; Upper Montclair, NJ; (3); #18 In Class; Church Yth Grp; Latin Clb; Ski Clb; SADD; VP Frsh Cls; Hst Soph Cls; Sec Trs Jr Cls; Off Sr Cls; Var Capt Bsktbl; Var Socr; Fordham.

FLANAGAN, TERENCE M; St Rose HS; Belmar, NJ; (3); 16/229; Math Tm; Nwsp Stf; Yrbk Stf; Var Crs Cntry; Var Trk; Im Vllybl; Hon Roll; Ntl Merit Ltr; NEDT Awd; Prfct Atten Awd; Jrnlsm.

FLANIGAN, CATHLEEN; Buena Regional HS; Williamstown, NJ; (3); Drama Clb; English Clb; French Clb; Quiz Bowl; School Play; Yrbk Rptr; Socr; Tennis; French Hon Soc; Opt Clb Awd; Careers Awd, Hnr Rll Merit 85; Ecology.

FLANIGAN, SHERRI; Manasquan HS; Spring Lake, NJ; (2); 49/247; Drama Clb; FBLA; Hosp Aide; Math Tm; School Musical; School Play; Nwsp Stf; JV Socr; Hon Roll; Thesps; Smr Arts Inst 86; Prjct SOAR 86; Thesbian Soc; Engl.

FLANNERY, JUDITH; Paul VI HS; Runnemede, NJ; (4); 33/511; Drama Clb; French Clb; Math Clb; Color Guard; Stage Crew; French Hon Soc; Hon Roll; NHS; Rutgers U; Astrphyscs.

FLANNERY, PATRICIA; Jackson Memorial HS; Jackson, NJ; (3); 37/416; Church Yth Grp; Band; Concert Band; Mrchg Band; JV Bsktbl; High Hon Roll; Hon Roll; NHS.

FLECCA, JOSEPHINE; Roselle Park HS; Roselle Park, NJ; (4); 33/165; Spanish Clb; Chorus; School Play; Stage Crew; JV Fld Hcky; Moms Clb Schlrshp 87; Union Cnty Coll; Intrprtr.

FLECKE, THOMAS; Ramapo Indian Hills Regional HS; Wyckoff, NJ; (3); 94/322; AFS; Boy Scts; Radio Clb; Spanish Clb; JV Ice Hcky; Hon Roll; Cert Merit Sci 9; Cert Merit Spn 3; IBM Ldrshp Sem; Lawyer.

FLECKEN, SHAWN; Del Ran HS; Del Ran, NJ; (3); 29/259; Chorus; School Musical; VP Computer Clb; Stu Cncl; Hon Roll; Std Ldrshp Awd 87; Syracuse U; Archt.

FLEHER, LAURA; Bayonne HS; Bayonne, NJ; (4); 62/376; Sec Drama Clb; VP German Clb; Band; Concert Band; Mrchg Band; Orch; School Musical; School Play; Stage Crew; Yrbk Stf; Jersey City ST Coll; Chldhd Ed.

FLEISCHMAN, ROBERT; Monmouth Regional HS; Eatontown, NJ; (4); 5/232; Math Tm; Mu Alpha Theta; Mrchg Band; Orch; Stu Cncl; Var Wrstlng; High Hon Roll; Hon Roll; NHS; St Schlr; MA Inst Tech; Mech Engrng.

FLEISCHMANN, TOBI; Monsignor Donovan HS; Howell, NJ; (3); 122/239; French Clb; Yrbk Stf.

FLEMING, BARBARA; Fairlawn HS; Fair Lawn, NJ; (3); Church Yth Grp; Stu Cncl; Air Force Tstng Hgh Scre 87; Pre Law.

FLEMING, COSETHA; University HS; Newark, NJ; (2); Church Yth Grp; Cmnty Wkr; Drama Clb; Hosp Aide; JA; Pep Clb; School Play; Variety Show; High Hon Roll; Hon Roll; Penn ST U; Obsttrcn.

FLEMING, KEVIN; Christian Brothers Acad; Jackson, NJ; (3); 89/245; Varsity Clb; Im Bsktbl; Fld Hcky; Var L Mgr(s); JV Var Score Keeper; Im Vllybl; Hon Roll; St Johns U; Athltc Admin.

FLEMING, LEE ANN; Hamilton High West; Trenton, NJ; (4); 11/341; Intnl Clb; SADD; Band; Stu Cncl; Var Bsktbl; Capt Sftbl; Capt Tennis; High Hon Roll; Kiwanis Awd; NHS; Oglethorpe U; Intl Bus.

FLEMING, PAMELA; John F Kennedy HS; Willingboro, NJ; (4); 17/260; Nwsp Stf; Hon Roll; JC Awd; NHS; Willingboro Jaycees Schlrshp, Z-Clb Achvt Awd & Pres Acdmc Ftnss Awd 87; Rutgers U; Mgmt.

FLEMMING, AMY; Pitman HS; Pitman, NJ; (2); Dance Clb; JV Sftbl; Var Tennis; JV Trk; High Hon Roll; Hon Roll; Acmdc Excllnc Awds; Tennis Coachs Awd; Stdnt Crftmns Fair Awd Mech Drwg; Med.

FLEMMING, MAURIA A; Paul VI HS; Haddonfield, NJ; (4); 59/511; Drama Clb; Band; Church Choir; Concert Band; Mrchg Band; Orch; School Musical; Stage Crew; Variety Show; Im Bowling; Music Educ.

FLETCHER, CONNIE; Madison Central HS; Old Bridge, NJ; (4); 86/360; Drama Clb; German Clb; Chorus; Color Guard; Drill Tm; Flag Corp; School Play; Stage Crew; Hon Roll; Rep Frsh Cls; Middlesex County Coll; Bus.

FLETCHER, MARY; Monsignor Donovan HS; Toms River, NJ; (3); Church Yth Grp; Drama Clb; Ski Clb; SADD; Var Cheerleading; Im Swmmng; High Hon Roll; NHS.

FLICKER, MICHAEL T; Ocean City HS; Ocean City, NJ; (4); 18/286; Am Leg Boys St; Pres Church Yth Grp; Computer Clb; Math Clb; Spanish Clb; Hst Soph Cls; Var Socr; High Hon Roll; NHS; Pres Schlr; Mrch Rtry Schlr Of Mnth Awd 87; Schl Sprt Alunae Awd 87; Temple U; Sprts Med.

FLINTOSH, LAURA; Cherokee HS; Atco, NJ; (2); JV Bsktbl; High Hon Roll; Hon Roll; Spanish NHS; Church Yth Grp; Dance Clb; Girl Scts; Chorus; JV Powder Puff Ftbl; Swmmng; Hnr Roll 78-87; Admttnc To Spnsh Natl Hnr Scty 87; Offrd 3 Hnr Classes 87; Rutgers; Marine Bio.

FLITCROFT, STACEY; Toms River N HS; Toms River, NJ; (3); Church Yth Grp; Flag Corp; Orch; Yrbk Stf; Sftbl; Swmmng; High Hon Roll; Hon Roll; Ms Ocean Cnty Fair Qun 87; Flag Capt 87; Clark Coll Atlanta; Fshn Dsgn.

FLOOD, BRIAN L; Cinnaminson HS; Cinnaminson, NJ; (3); Camera Clb; Computer Clb; VICA; Stage Crew; Stat Bsktbl; JV Ftbl; L Score Keeper; Hon Roll; U CO; Aeros Engrng.

FLOOD, STEPHANIE; Gloucester City HS; Brooklawn, NJ; (3); 3/182; Am Leg Aux Girls St; Pep Clb; School Play; Yrbk Sprt Ed; Fld Hcky; Gov Hon Prg Awd; High Hon Roll; Hon Roll; NHS; St Schlr; 1 Act Plys Bst Actrss; Rutgers ST Schlr; Fnlst Govnrs Schl Prgm; Rutgers; Pre-Med.

FLOOK, RAYMOND; John F Kennedy HS; Willingboro, NJ; (3); 15/292; Hosp Aide; Key Clb; Nwsp Rptr; Nwsp Stf; Rep Jr Cls; Hon Roll; NHS; Fnlst-St Teen Arts Ftsvl 86-87; Jrnlsm.

FLORA, GLEN; Bayonne HS; Bayonne, NJ; (3); Science Clb; Socr; Var Wrstlng; Hon Roll; Sci Awd 86-87; US Air Force.

FLORENTO, VERONI C; St Marys HS; Jersey City, NJ; (4); Am Leg Boys St; Chorus; Concert Band; School Musical; School Play; Yrbk Phtg; Yrbk Stf; Pres Stu Cncl; Bowling; Vllybl.

FLORES, BYRON; St Mary HS; Jersey City, NJ; (4); 4/30; Boys Clb Am; Chess Clb; Computer Clb; Science Clb; Yrbk Stf; Rep Frsh Cls; Trs Soph Cls; VP Jr Cls; High Hon Roll; Hon Roll; Air Force; Mech Engrng.

FLORES, KELLY; Hopatcong HS; Stanhope, NJ; (4); 2/200; Drama Clb; Varsity Clb; Chorus; Concert Band; Lit Mag; Capt Bsktbl; Capt Socr; High Hon Roll; Trs NHS; Natl Hspnc Schlr Awd 87; ST Senate Yth Fnlst 86; Douglass Schlrs Fnlst 87; Rutgers U; Educ.

FLORES, LUIS; Don Basco Tech; Paterson, NJ; (3); 10/91; Flag Corp; Mrchg Band; High Hon Roll; Hon Roll; Systems Anlys.

FLORIN, ALEX; St John Vianney HS; Hazlet, NJ; (3); Computer Clb; Math Tm; Var Crs Cntry; Var Socr; Var Swmmng; Var Trk; Var Wrstlng; High Hon Roll; Hon Roll; NHS; Judo Tm; Engrng.

FLORIO, PEGGY; Waldwick HS; Waldwick, NJ; (4); 16/146; Church Yth Grp; Drama Clb; Girl Scts; Red Cross Aide; Nwsp Ed-Chief; Mgr Sr Cls; Lion Awd; NHS; Presdntl Acadc Ftns Awd; JR Lg Bergen Cnty Vlntr Schlrshp; Bloomsburg U; Spec Educ.

FLOWERS, JONATHAN D; Livingston HS; Livingston, NJ; (4); 16/425; Am Leg Boys St; Temple Yth Grp; Concert Band; Mrchg Band; Orch; School Musical; Nwsp Rptr; Ed Lit Mag; NHS; Ntl Merit SF; Schl Spirit Awd Compsg The Lancers March Band Awded By Big L Booster Clb 85; NJ All ST Cncrt 84-86; Music.

FLOYD, AMY; Ridgefield Park HS; Ridgefield Pk, NJ; (2); 1/204; Nwsp Rptr; Nwsp Stf; Yrbk Stf; Rep Stu Cncl; High Hon Roll; Hon Roll.

FLOYD, CARRIE; Timothy Christian HS; S Bound Brook, NJ; (1); Church Yth Grp; Hon Roll.

FLOYD, RODNEY; Asbury Park HS; Asbury Park, NJ; (3); #6 In Class; Key Clb; Yrbk Stf; Off Stu Cncl; Var Ftbl; Hon Roll; NHS; Vrsty Schlr 87; Accntng.

FLUEHR, CHRISTINA; The Pennington Schl; Richboro, PA; (3); 25/82; Cheerleading; Diving; Mgr(s); Marine Bio.

FLUHR, MELISSA; Howell HS; Howell, NJ; (3); 85/414; Spanish Clb; Socr.

FLUKEY, DIANE; Holy Spirit HS; Woodbine, NJ; (2); 50/397; Church Yth Grp; Spanish Clb; Var Trk; Im Vllybl; High Hon Roll; Hon Roll; Villanova; Fightr Pilot.

FLYNN, CORETTA; Plainfield HS; Plainfield, NJ; (3); 20/398; Church Yth Grp; Library Aide; Science Clb; Mrchg Band; Tennis; Hon Roll; NHS; Wrld Water Awd 87; 1st Clarinet Band 87; Garden Clb Awd 87; Rutgers; Biochem.

FLYNN, DANNY; Msgr Donovan HS; Toms River, NJ; (3); 81/245; FCA; FBLA; Math Clb; Ski Clb; SADD; Im Bsktbl; JV Ftbl; Var L Golf; Hon Roll; NHS; Bus.

FLYNN, DEIDRE; Lakewood HS; Northampton, PA; (3); 78/376; English Clb; Hosp Aide; Band; Color Guard; Drill Tm; Flag Corp; Mrchg Band; Lit Mag; Twrlr; Hon Roll; Penn ST; Bus Admin.

FLYNN, JASON; Jackson Memorial HS; Jackson, NJ; (3); 79/416; VP FBLA; Math Clb; Var Ftbl; JV Golf; High Hon Roll; Ntl Merit Ltr.

FLYNN, JOHN; Middletown HS South; Atlantic Highland, NJ; (3); Boy Scts; Pres Exploring; JV Ftbl; JV Wrstlng; Eagle Scout Awd 85; Bronze Cngrssnl Awd 87; Art Dir.

FLYNN, JOSEPH; Don Bosco Prep; Pearl River, NY; (3); 5/200; Debate Tm; Science Clb; Nwsp Rptr; JV Bsktbl; Var Crs Cntry; Var Trk; High Hon Roll; NHS; Prncpls Lst Awd 84-85; 1st Hon Awd 85-86; Sci Fair Wnnr 85-86; Invstmnt Bnkng.

FLYNN, KEITH; Ridge HS; Basking Ridge, NJ; (4); Aud/Vis; Church Yth Grp; FFA; Outstndng Effort Mrrstwn Flwr Shw 84-86; Ag Prfcncy Awd & Outstndng Accplshmnt 87; Somerset Cnty Tech Inst.

FLYNN, TIMOTHY; St Joseph Regional HS; Dumont, NJ; (3); JV Trk; Hon Roll; Spanish NHS.

FOGARTY, ALLISON; Mount St Mary Acad; Berkeley Hts, NJ; (4); Church Yth Grp; Dance Clb; French Clb; Pep Clb; Chorus; Hon Roll; Natl Latin Awd Cum Laude 83; Providence Coll; Polt Sci.

FOGLER, JENNIFER; High Point Regional HS; Branchville, NJ; (3); 22/254; Chorus; Mrchg Band; School Musical; School Play; Hon Roll; Rutgers; Bus Mngmnt.

FOJAS, CESAR F; Secaucus HS; Secaucus, NJ; (3); 5/166; Computer Clb; Key Clb; Mu Alpha Theta; Ski Clb; Varsity Clb; Var L Crs Cntry; Var L Tennis; High Hon Roll; Mu Alpha Theta Awd; NHS.

FOJAS, SERINA; Immaculate Conception HS; Secaucus, NJ; (3); 20/70; Yrbk Phtg; Yrbk Stf; JV Sftbl; Hon Roll; NY U; Bus.

FOLDESSY, HEATHER; Northern Highlands Regional HS; Allendale, NJ; (1); Church Yth Grp; Girl Scts; Band; Chorus; Concert Band; School Musical; Lit Mag; Var L Crs Cntry; Var Trk; Hnbl Mntn All Leg Crs Cntry 86; ST Fnlst NJ Miss Amer Coed Pgnt 86.

FOLESCU, SIMONA; James Caldwell HS; W Caldwell, NJ; (3); 9/200; Art Clb; Church Yth Grp; French Clb; Political Wkr; Trs VP Science Clb; Ski Clb; Yrbk Ed-Chief; Yrbk Stf; High Hon Roll; Hon Roll; Wellesley; Law.

FOLEY, BRIAN; Mount Olive HS; Long Valley, NJ; (3); 72/318; Debate Tm; Exploring; FBLA; Ski Clb; Concert Band; Sec Frsh Cls; Off Soph Cls; Trk; Twrlr; Bst Chem A Stu Of Yr 86-85.

FOLEY, DANIELLE; Reansburg HS; Keansburg, NJ; (3); 28/114; Art Clb; Science Clb; Trs Soph Cls; Trs Jr Cls; Trs Sr Cls; Trs Stu Cncl; JV Var Bsktbl; JV Socr; Gov Hon Prg Awd; Art Shw & Demo 85-86; Teen Arts Brookdale 86-87; Acad Art Awd 86-87; NY Schl Int Dsgn; Intr Dsgng.

FOLEY, SHARON; Cherry Hill HS East; Cherry Hill, NJ; (4); 135/670; Latin Clb; Rep Frsh Cls; Rep Soph Cls; Rep Sr Cls; Var Fld Hcky; Var Capt Lcrss; Swmmng; Trk; Hon Roll; Magna Cum Laude Awd Ntl Latin Exam 85-86; Bus.

FOLIO, AMY; St John Vianney HS; Colts Neck, NJ; (2); #1 In Class; Hosp Aide; Intnl Clb; Sec SADD; Yrbk Stf; Lit Mag; Sec Jr Cls; High Hon Roll; NHS.

FOLIO, KIM; St John Vianney HS; Colts Neck, NJ; (4); 50/251; Art Clb; Church Yth Grp; Hosp Aide; SADD; Yrbk Ed-Chief; Trs Soph Cls; Rep Jr Cls; VP Stu Cncl; High Hon Roll; Chnnl 13 Art Cont Wnnr 85-87; Law.

FOLIS, ELIZABETH; Lower Cape May Regional HS; Cold Spgs, NJ; (2); Hon Roll; U Of PA; Vet.

FONG, KIM; Academic HS; Jersey City, NJ; (4); 3/76; Art Clb; Chess Clb; Quiz Bowl; Scholastic Bowl; Nwsp Stf; Yrbk Stf; Lit Mag; Vllybl; Hon Roll; NHS; Geo Awd 84; Humnts Awd 86; Rutgers Coll Of Phar; Phar.

FONG, LINDA; Irvington HS; Irvington, NJ; (2); Teachers Aide; Band; Concert Band; Mrchg Band; Stu Cncl; Var Score Keeper; Var Tennis; High Hon Roll; Hon Roll.

FONTAINE, JANNETTE; Holy Cross HS; Medford, NJ; (3); Church Yth Grp; Ski Clb; Chorus; School Play; Rep Frsh Cls; Rep Soph Cls; VP Stu Cncl; Var Socr; Sftbl; Hon Roll; HOBY 85-86; U VT; Dntl Hygne.

FONTANEZ, CYNTHIA; Freehold Township HS; Freehold, NJ; (3); 14/385; Aud/Vis; Church Yth Grp; VP Drama Clb; Thesps; Band; Mrchg Band; School Play; Swmmng; Trk; NHS.

FOOTE, NICOLE; Immaculate Conception HS; Newark, NJ; (2); Church Yth Grp; Pep Clb; Chorus; Church Choir; Hon Roll; Acctng.

FORD, BRIAN; Brick Memorial HS; Brick, NJ; (2); Church Yth Grp; Hon Roll; Vet.

FORD, DEBORAH; Southern Regional HS; Beach Haven, NJ; (3); 52/475; Art Clb; Drama Clb; Q&S; Ski Clb; Spanish Clb; SADD; Var L Tennis; JV Trk; Hon Roll; NHS; Interior Dsgn.

FORD, ERIC; Passaic Valley HS; W Paterson, NJ; (4); 20/350; Rep Am Leg Boys St; Pres Church Yth Grp; VP German Clb; Var Capt Crs Cntry; Var Trk; Var JV Wrstlng; Kiwanis Awd; NHS; Pres Schlr; JV Bsktbl; Passaic Vly Hnr Socty 86-87; US Coast Grd Acad Appt 87; US Coast Acad; Engrng.

FORD, RICHARD; Burlington Township HS; Burlington, NJ; (3); Art Clb; Boy Scts; Chess Clb; Church Yth Grp; Var Mgr(s); Var Score Keeper; Trk; Jr Vrsty Ptch Trck 85-86; Lincoln Tech Inst; Mech Engr.

FORE, CHRISTINA A; Dickinson HS; Jersey City, NJ; (2); 4/600; Lit Mag; Hon Roll; NJ ST Sci Fair Awd 86; Hudson Conty NJ Sci Fair Awd 87; MA Inst Of Tech; Nclr Scintst.

FORESTA, VITA; Garfield HS; Garfield, NJ; (4); 8/170; Am Leg Aux Girls St; Drama Clb; Band; School Musical; School Play; Nwsp Rptr; Yrbk Stf; Rep Soph Cls; Rep Jr Cls; Rep Sr Cls; Math Hnr Soc 86-87; Unico Awd & Schlrshp 87; Leonardo Da Vinci Awd 87; Seton Hall U; Engl.

FORKER, URSULA; Pennsville Memorial HS; Pennsville, NJ; (3); Girl Scts; Latin Clb; Q&S; Teachers Aide; School Musical; School Play; Rutgers; Sci.

FORLENZA, ROBERT M; Toms River East HS; Toms River, NJ; (4); Church Yth Grp; Var L Ftbl; Var Trk; Var Wt Lftg; Hon Roll; Mech Drw Excllnc 85 & 86; Wght Lftng 200 Clb 86; Grove City Coll; Mech Engrng.

FORLENZA, STEVE; Rancocas Valley Regional HS; Mt Holly, NJ; (2); Boy Scts; Church Yth Grp; Cmnty Wkr; German Clb; Letterman Clb; SADD; Teachers Aide; Band; Chorus; Concert Band; US Band Achvt Awd 86.

FORMAN, ROBERT; Brick Memorial HS; Brick, NJ; (3); 5/382; Concert Band; Jazz Band; Capt Mrchg Band; School Musical; Im JV Trk; High Hon Roll; NHS; Band; Orch; Stage Crew; Best Drummer Marching Band 85; Outstndg Musicianship 87; Music.

FORMICA, MIMMA; North Brunswick Twp HS; N Brunswick, NJ; (4); Key Clb; Spanish Clb; Itln Hon Soc 85-87; Itln Awd 87; Cook Coll; Bio.

FORNACIARI, LORI; Phillipsburg HS; Bloomsbury, NJ; (4); 114/330; Model UN; Pep Clb; SADD; VP Frsh Cls; VP Soph Cls; Stu Cncl; JV Var Cheerleading; Pre-Law.

FORNAROTTO, ALYSA; Monsignor Donovan HS; Bricktown, NJ; (3); Church Yth Grp; Cmnty Wkr; Pep Clb; Service Clb; Ski Clb; SADD; Church Choir; Yrbk Stf; Capt Cheerleading; Stat Ftbl; All Cty Chrldr Catholic Yth Org 86.

FORRAR, JAYNE; Red Bank Regional HS; Shrewsbury, NJ; (2); SADD; Fld Hcky; Sftbl; Hon Roll; Spanish NHS; Georgetown U.

FORREST, BRIAN; Vineland HS North; Vineland, NJ; (2); 50/868; Debate Tm; Key Clb; Spanish Clb; SADD; Nwsp Sprt Ed; JV Cheerleading; Var L Swmmng; Hon Roll; Pep Clb; Rep Frsh Cls; Swimmng ST Champ 200 Medley Relay 87; Military.

FORSA, NICHOLAS; Lakeland Regional HS; Ringwood, NJ; (3); Boy Scts; Camera Clb; Ski Clb; Teachers Aide; Rep Frsh Cls; Rep Soph Cls; Rep Jr Cls; Stu Cncl; Trk; Hon Roll; Eagl Awd Sctg 86; Rd Shw For HS 86; Bus Adm.

FORSYTH, NORA; Red Bank Catholic HS; Red Bank, NJ; (3); Hosp Aide; SADD; Thesps; School Play; Yrbk Ed-Chief; L Tennis; JV Trk; NHS; NEDT Awd; Church Yth Grp; ST Of NJ Senate Citation For Tnns Tm ST Champnshp 86; Intl Bus Mgmnt.

FORSYTHE, JOANNE; Millville SR HS; Millville, NJ; (3); 38/524; Drama Clb; Girl Scts; Key Clb; Model UN; Political Wkr; Science Clb; School Musical; Bowling; Golf; NHS; Lit.

FORTE, KENNETH; Voorhees HS; Glen Gardner, NJ; (4); 25/275; Boy Scts; Latin Clb; Varsity Clb; Yrbk Bus Mgr; JV Socr; Hon Roll; NHS; Ntl Merit Ltr; JCL; Var Math Tm; Lat Hnr Soc 87; Rensselaer Polytech Inst; Aeron.

FORTE, ROBIN; Randolph HS; Randolph, NJ; (3); Church Yth Grp; Concert Band; Mrchg Band; Var Fld Hcky; Powder Puff Ftbl; Stat Wrstlng; French Hon Soc; Hon Roll; NHS; Hugh O Brien Yth Fdtn Smnr 86; Bus.

FORTESCUE, ROBERT; Middletown HS South; Red Bank, NJ; (3); Math Tm; Var L Crs Cntry; Var Trk; Ntl Merit SF; Natl Sci Olympiad Awd 85; Otstndng Achvmnt Eng Awd 85; Bus Admn.

FORTIS, STEPHEN F; Absegami HS; Egg Harbor City, NJ; (4); 10/225; Am Leg Boys St; Drama Clb; Pres FTA; Model UN; Stage Crew; VP Jr Cls; Pres Sr Cls; JV Capt Ftbl; Var Wrstlng; NHS; 2nd Pl ACC Soc Sci Fair Press Conf 85; ACC Stu Month 86; Directors Awd Drama Club 87; Widener U; Civil Engr.

FORTNA, CARL HUNTER; Elizabeth HS; Elizabeth, NJ; (4); 3/841; Pres Aud/Vis; Pres Church Yth Grp; Key Clb; Pres Science Clb; Var L Crs Cntry; High Hon Roll; Kiwanis Awd; NHS; Prfct Atten Awd; Spanish NHS; Pres Ldrshp Awd 87; PTA Ed Schlrshp 87; Suprntdnts Schlr 87; Lebanon Valley Coll; Vet.

FORTUNATO, JOHN E; Christian Brothers Acad; Freehold, NJ; (4); 2/220; Math Tm; Band; Jazz Band; Orch; School Musical; School Play; High Hon Roll; NHS; Sal; Hosp Aide; Gnrl Exclnc Mrt 87; VP Natl Hnr Scty 86-87; 4 Yr Schlrshp Manhattan Coll 87; Tufts U; Pre Med.

FORTUNATO, STEVEN; Don Bosco Prep; Ramsey, NJ; (3); 12/210; Chess Clb; Cmnty Wkr; Model UN; Nwsp Rptr; JV VP Bsbl; JV VP Ftbl; JV VP Trk; High Hon Roll; Hon Roll; 1st Hnrs Awd; Interml Sprots; Bus.

FORTUNE, ANNETTA; John F Kennedy HS; Willingboro, NJ; (2); 1/335; JV Bsktbl; Var Cheerleading; High Hon Roll; NHS; Engrng Careers Pgm 85-86; Political Sci.

FOSGREEN, MICHELE; Monsignor Donovan HS; Howell, NJ; (3); 118/245; SADD; Stat Bsktbl; Var L Crs Cntry; Var L Socr; Hon Roll; Coaches Varsity Girls Soccer 2nd Tm 85 & 87; Rutgers U; Teaching.

FOSS, LISA; Immaculate Heart Acad; Midland Park, NJ; (2); 6/169; Model UN; Science Clb; Nwsp Stf; High Hon Roll; Hon Roll; Latn Hnr Soc 86; Med.

FOSSETT, AMANDA L; Livingston HS; Livingston, NJ; (3); 20/420; AFS; Pres Church Yth Grp; Hosp Aide; Key Clb; Office Aide; Band; Concert Band; Mrchg Band; School Musical; High Hon Roll; Allright Coll; Dietcn.

FOSTER, DAMON; Essex Catholic Boys HS; Orange, NJ; (3); Art Clb; Var Math Clb; Acpl Chr; Chorus; Church Choir; Nwsp Phtg; Nwsp Stf; JV Bsktbl; Wt Lftg; Hon Roll; Frshmn Bstbl Most Improved 84; Syracuse; Accntng.

FOSTER, DEANNA; Hamilton HS; Trenton, NJ; (2); Sci Fair Proj 1st Pl 83; Cosmtlgst.

FOSTER, ERIC; Holy Spirit HS; Pleasantville, NJ; (4); 54/363; JV Bsbl; Hon Roll.

FOSTER, GOLDA; Abraham Clark HS; Roselle, NJ; (3); Latin Clb; Spanish Clb; Nwsp Rptr; Nwsp Stf; Lit Mag; Crs Cntry; Tennis; Trk; Hon Roll; NCTE Awd.

FOSTER, JEREL; Secaucus HS; Secaucus, NJ; (2); Dance Clb; Key Clb; Mu Alpha Theta; Ski Clb; Spanish Clb; Rep Frsh Cls; Im JV Bsktbl; Hon Roll; Prfct Atten Awd; Culinary.

FOSTER, JESSICA; Toms River South HS; Pine Beach, NJ; (3); 15/421; Am Leg Aux Girls St; Varsity Clb; Mrchg Band; Yrbk Ed-Chief; Fld Hcky; Var Swmmng; High Hon Roll; NHS; Extra Achvmnt In Comp Sailing 87; 2nd Pl Bay Head Jr Race Week 87; 9thpl Bluejay Natls 87; Med.

FOSTER, LAWRENCE; Memorial HS; West New York, NJ; (4); 20/400; Boy Scts; Chess Clb; Computer Clb; Sec Math Clb; Science Clb; Spanish Clb; Band; Pep Band; Symp Band; Rep Frsh Cls; Columbia WA U; Pre-Med.

FOSTER, MICHELE; Mt Olive HS; Flanders, NJ; (4); 34/384; AFS; Church Yth Grp; Dance Clb; Debate Tm; Ski Clb; Hon Roll; NHS; Pol Sci.

FOSTER, PATRICK; Essex Catholic Boys HS; Newark, NJ; (3); Art Clb; Math Clb; Nwsp Sprt Ed; Yrbk Stf; JV Crs Cntry; JV Trk; Hon Roll; NHS; Ntl Merit Schol; Engrng.

FOSTER, RICHARD; Toms River HS South; Pine Bch, NJ; (3); 26/405; Aud/Vis; Camera Clb; Computer Clb; Math Clb; Math Tm; Political Wkr; Yrbk Bus Mgr; Yrbk Rptr; Yrbk Stf; Crs Cntry; Smythe Sailing Area C 2nd 86; Atlantic Coast Champ Sailing 21st 87; Accntng.

FOTHERGILL, TISA; Orange HS; Orange, NJ; (2); Hosp Aide; Pep Clb; PAVAS; Spanish Clb; Speech Tm; Chorus; Color Guard; Flag Corp; Mrchg Band; School Musical; Vrsty Awd 86; Vrsty Awd Teens Arts Festvl 87; Bus.

FOTI, ROSARIO; St James HS; Carneys Point, NJ; (3); 3/89; Drama Clb; School Musical; Nwsp Ed-Chief; High Hon Roll; JR Rtrn 86; Amer Lgn Essy Cntst 1st Pl 84; Jrnlsm.

FOTIOU, BILL; Mainland Regional HS; Linwood, NJ; (4); 26/270; Church Yth Grp; Nwsp Rptr; Nwsp Stf; Var L Ftbl; Im Vllybl; Var Capt Wrstlng; High Hon Roll; NHS; Pres Schlr; Pres Acadmc Ftnss Awd 87; Coaches Awd Wrstlng 87; John & Irene Papines Schrshp 87; Rutgers Coll; Sprts Med.

FOUNTAIN, MICHELLE; Camden HS; Camden, NJ; (4); 2/300; Sec JA; Pep Clb; Rep Frsh Cls; Rep Sr Cls; Cheerleading; Pom Pon; High Hon Roll; Hon Roll; NHS; Prfct Atten Awd; Dukes Awd 87; CPA.

FOURNIER, MICHELLE S; W Morris Central HS; Califon, NJ; (4); 13/295; Sec Debate Tm; Pres Chorus; School Musical; Nwsp Rptr; Rep Stu Cncl; Var Cheerleading; Twrlr; VP NHS; Ntl Merit Ltr; St Schlr; Margaret T Ryan Awd-Chr 87; Most Acad Chrldr 85; Wake Forest U; Eclgy.

FOUTZ, JOANNA; Sacred Heart HS; Vineland, NJ; (3); 21/57; Spanish Clb; Mgr Bsktbl; Hon Roll; Marine Bio.

FOWLER, JAMEL DORENE; St Piux X Regional HS; Plainfield, NJ; (3); ROTC; Chorus; Trk; Hon Roll; Crimnl Law.

FOWLER, JENNIFER; Phillipsburg HS; Phillipsburg, NJ; (3); 47/315; Church Yth Grp; Rep Stu Cncl; Var Cheerleading; High Hon Roll; NHS; PHS Gftd & Tlntd Prog 86; Bloomsburg U; Comm.

FOWLER, MICHELLE; Lower Cape May Regional HS; Cape May, NJ; (3); Varsity Clb; Yrbk Stf; Rep Stu Cncl; JV Var Mgr(s); JV Stat Socr; Var Stat Trk; Hon Roll.

FOWLKES, LAWREN; Freehold HS; Freehold, NJ; (4); 125/240; Church Yth Grp; Office Aide; PAVAS; Teachers Aide; Nwsp Rptr; Yrbk Ed-Chief; Ed Lit Mag; Powder Puff Ftbl; Var Trk; Prfct Atten Awd; Delta Sigma Theta 87; Upwrd Bnd Georgian Ct Coll 87; Rutgers Coll; Cmnctns.

FOX, CARRIE; West Windsor-Plainsboro HS; Plainsboro, NJ; (3); 60/290; AFS; Pres VP Art Clb; School Musical; School Play; Yrbk Stf; Ed Lit Mag; High Hon Roll; Hon Roll; Natl Art Hon Soc 87; Schlstc Art Awds Gold Key Awd 87; Moore Coll Art Saturday Clsses Schlrshp 87; Fine Arts.

FOX, COLLEEN; Saint Peters HS; Milltown, NJ; (4); Cmnty Wkr; Intnl Clb; Chorus; Yrbk Stf; Hon Roll; Wrld History Mst Imprvd 84; Accntng I Most Profcnt 86; Accntng.

FOX, ERICA L; Anorthern Valley Regional HS; Haworth, NJ; (4); 4/217; Cmnty Wkr; Dance Clb; Political Wkr; School Play; Yrbk Ed-Chief; Stu Cncl; NCTE Awd; Pres NHS; St Schlr; Century III Ldrshp Pgm ST Finlst 86; Creative Writing.

FOX, JODY; Paul VI HS; Blackwood, NJ; (3); 76/410; Spanish Clb; Yrbk Stf; Off Pom Pon; Ntl Merit Schol; Spanish NHS; Acctg.

FOX, LIZA; Cherry Hill H S East; Cherry Hill, NJ; (4); Church Yth Grp; Latin Clb; Rep Stu Cncl; Var Capt Diving; Var Capt Fld Hcky; Var L Lcrss; Var L Swmmng; Cit Awd; High Hon Roll; NHS; All Conf 1st Tm All Group Four 3rd Tm 87; Georgetown; Bus.

FOX, PAM; Manatapan HS; Manalapan, NJ; (3); 96/430; Hosp Aide; SADD; Temple Yth Grp; Cert Achvmnt Vlnteer Svc To Cmnty 87; Psychology.

FOX, PETE; Hawthorne HS; Hawthorne, NJ; (3); Math Tm; Science Clb; SADD; Concert Band; Jazz Band; Mrchg Band; Yrbk Phtg; VP Frsh Cls; NHS; Church Yth Grp; Band Achvt Awds; Artifcl Intllgnc Course NJ Inst Tech Cert Compltn 86; Elec Engr.

FOXSON, JENNIFER; Wallkill Valley Regional HS; Hamburg, NJ; (4); 6/170; Math Clb; Pres SADD; Rep Stu Cncl; Var L Bsktbl; Var L Tennis; Var L Trk; NHS; FBLA; Band; Mrchg Band; Sussex Cnty Schlr Athl Schlrshp 87; HOBY 85; Rtry Schlrshp 87; Tufts U; Lbrl Arts.

FOYE, TANIKQUAA MALAYA; Northern Highlands Regional HS; Upr Saddle Rv, NJ; (3); Girl Scts; Library Aide; Office Aide; Pep Clb; Red Cross Aide; SADD; Stage Crew; Hon Roll; Bus.

FOYTLIN, DANIEL C; Toms River North HS; Toms River, NJ; (3); Aud/Vis; Boy Scts; Camera Clb; Church Yth Grp; Letterman Clb; VP Science Clb; Ski Clb; Spanish Clb; SADD; Varsity Clb; BSA Eagle Awd 87; Elec Engrng.

FRACASSO, JOSEPH; Marist HS; Bayonne, NJ; (4); Boy Scts; Computer Clb; Drama Clb; Pep Clb; Science Clb; Ski Clb; Varsity Clb; School Play; Nwsp Rptr; Trs Frsh Cls; Cchs Awd Ice Hcky Ldrshp On & Off Ice 87; Mst Vlbl Plyr Awd Vrsty Hcky 87; 1st Assist Hcky 87; UNV Of Hartford; Elec Engrng.

FRAGOLA, DEAN; Newton HS; Newton, NJ; (4); 22/210; Church Yth Grp; Cmnty Wkr; Computer Clb; Varsity Clb; Chorus; Jazz Band; Var Ftbl; Im Wt Lftg; Hon Roll; Ldrshp Cmp Rep; Engrng.

FRANCESCO, RORY; Immaculata HS; Somerset, NJ; (3); 26/240; Trs Chrmn Church Yth Grp; Math Tm; NFL; Office Aide; Ski Clb; Var JV Cheerleading; Coach Actv; NHS; Spanish NHS; Outstndng Spartan 86; Hotel Mgmnt.

FRANCHINO, ANGELA; High Point Regional HS; Branchville, NJ; (3); Cheerleading; Gym; Hon Roll; Jr NHS; Itln Clb Pres 84-85; Itln Hnr Soc 84-85; SALE Itln Clb 85-86; Bus Admin.

FRANCIS, CUTIE; Lincoln HS; Jersey City, NJ; (4); Art Clb; Church Yth Grp; Dance Clb; Debate Tm; Drama Clb; Exploring; FHA; GAA; Girl Scts; JA; Beauty Cntst; Miss JR; Bus.

FRANCIS, JO; Middle Township HS; Burleigh, NJ; (3); Pres Church Yth Grp; NAACP; Office Aide; Chorus; Pres Church Choir; Color Guard; Mrchg Band; NHS; Pres Sec 4-H; Rep Jr Cls; Bus Admin.

FRANCIS, LOUISE EMILY; St Dominic Acad; Jersey City, NJ; (4); 49/148; Church Yth Grp; Girl Scts; NAACP; Variety Show; Nwsp Sprt Ed; Rep Frsh Cls; Trk; Hon Roll; Prfct Atten Awd; Hosp Aide; 4 Yr Army QEP Schlrshp 87-91; Howard U; Radtn Thrpy Tech.

FRANCO, JENNIFER; Hightstown HS; Newtown, PA; (3); Ski Clb; Bsktbl; Var JV Diving; Var Fld Hcky; JV Sftbl; Hon Roll; U Of South FL; Bus Mgmnt.

FRANCO, KEVIN; Paramas HS; Paramus, NJ; (4); 34/330; Ski Clb; Yrbk Stf; Bsktbl; Vllybl; NHS; Ntl Merit SF; Peckway Schl Parent Tchrs Assn 87; Paramus Chmbr Of Commerce 87; Lehigh U; Bus.

FRANCO, RONNIE; Memorial HS; West New York, NJ; (3); 7/300; Cmnty Wkr; Library Aide; Political Wkr; JV Var Bsbl; JV Var Ftbl; High Hon Roll; Hon Roll; NHS; Prfct Atten Awd; Italian Club 87; Acctg.

FRANCO, THERESA; Lower Cape May Regional HS; N Cape May, NJ; (2); Varsity Clb; VP Frsh Cls; Rep Jr Cls; Rep Stu Cncl; JV Cheerleading; Var Mgr(s); Hon Roll; Office Aide; Prfct Atten Awd; Octgn Clb 86-89; Chrstms Qn Crt 86-87; Prm Cmte 87-88; Fshn.

FRANGOS, DIMITRIOS; Pennsauken HS; Pennsauken, NJ; (3); 81/417; Aud/Vis; Church Yth Grp; Math Clb; Math Tm; Spanish Clb; SADD; Varsity Clb; School Musical; School Play; Stage Crew; Pre-Med.

FRANK, BRIAN; St James HS; Mullica Hill, NJ; (2); Church Yth Grp; Latin Clb; Pres Frsh Cls; Rep Soph Cls; Sec Jr Cls; JV Var Bsbl; JV Bsktbl; Lion Awd; Ntl Merit Ltr; Bus.

FRANK, EMILY; Blair Acad; Blairstown, NJ; (3); Drama Clb; PAVAS; Acpl Chr; Chorus; Pres School Musical; Yrbk Stf; Fld Hcky; Score Keeper; Tennis; Hon Roll.

FRANK, JACK; Phillipsburg HS; Alpha, NJ; (3); Art Clb; Scholastic Bowl; Nwsp Rptr; York Coll; Art.

FRANK, KENNY; Beuna Regional HS; Milmay, NJ; (3); Ski Clb; Varsity Clb; Band; Bsbl; Trk; Wt Lftg; Hon Roll; Rutgers Sch Of Phrmcy; Phrmcst.

FRANK, SHARON; West Essex Regional HS; No Caldwell, NJ; (3); Pres Church Yth Grp; Drama Clb; French Clb; Office Aide; SADD; Color Guard; School Musical; School Play; Stage Crew; Yrbk Stf; Econ.

FRANKEL, MARK; Franklin HS; Somerset, NJ; (3); Chess Clb; Model UN; Teachers Aide; Lit Mag; Hon Roll; Bus.

FRANKEL, MOLLISSA; Montville HS; Sparta, NJ; (4); Computer Clb; FBLA; Key Clb; Ski Clb; SADD; JV Fld Hcky; Var Lcrss; Var Powder Puff Ftbl; High Hon Roll; Hon Roll; Fairleigh Dickenson U; Lbrl Art.

FRANKENBERG, BRETT; Toms River HS North; Toms River, NJ; (3); 10/459; Pres German Clb; Science Clb; Ftbl; Var JV Trk; High Hon Roll; Hon Roll; Prfct Atten Awd; VFW Awd; Voice Dem Awd; WA Wrkshps 87; St Sci Day 87; Engr.

FRANKIE, BRIAN; Hopewell Valley Central HS; Pennington, NJ; (4); 17/200; Boy Scts; Math Tm; Scholastic Bowl; Science Clb; Var Trk; High Hon Roll; NHS; Ntl Merit Schol; Cornell Univ; Chem Engrng.

FRANKLE, MICHELE; Fair Lawn HS; Fair Lawn, NJ; (3); 39/350; Spanish Clb; Color Guard; Hon Roll; Rep Frsh Cls; Rep Soph Cls; Bus.

FRANKLIN, DAWN; Manasquan HS; Belmar, NJ; (2); 72/247; DECA; Key Clb; Ski Clb; Spanish Clb; Band; Color Guard; Var JV Bsktbl; Var JV Socr; JV Sftbl; Hon Roll; Bus.

FRANKLIN, THOMAS; Paul VI HS; Williamstown, NJ; (3); Am Leg Boys St; Var L Ftbl; Capt Var Wrstlng; Hon Roll; NHS; German Ntl Hnr Scty; All Conf Hnrbl Mntn Ftbl; All Parochial Hnrble Mntn Ftbl; Engr.

FRANKS, CONNI L; Spotswood HS; Spotswood, NJ; (4); Intnl Clb; Rep Stu Cncl; JV Sftbl; Hon Roll; Art.

FRANKS, RALPH ROBERT; Highland Regional HS; Blackwood, NJ; (4); 5/297; Computer Clb; Nwsp Rptr; Pres Soph Cls; Pres Jr Cls; Pres Sr Cls; VP Stu Cncl; Capt Ftbl; Capt Wrstlng; Hon Roll; NHS; SJ All Acad Ftbl Team 86; Bio Team NJ ST Sci League 83-84; Boys Inter Club 84-87; Med.

FRANKS, STEPHANIE; Holy Cross HS; Medford, NJ; (4); Stu Cncl; Var Socr; JV Trk; High Hon Roll; Hon Roll; Villanova U; Nrsng.

FRANZ, MATTHEW; Weehawken HS; Weehawken, NJ; (2); 10/120; Chess Clb; Math Clb; SADD; Nwsp Stf; Yrbk Stf; Ftbl; Wt Lftg; Cit Awd; High Hon Roll; Kiwanis Awd; Prgrss Weightlifting 86-87; Naval Acad; Navy Pilot.

FRANZSON, LINDA; Brick Township HS; Downey, CA; (3); Church Yth Grp; Hosp Aide; JV Var Bsktbl; JV Crs Cntry; Var Gym; Var Trk; JV Vllybl; Nrsng.

FRASIER, MARVA VICTORIA; Dwight Morrow HS; Englewood, NJ; (4); Drama Clb; Pres Church Choir; Mrchg Band; Var Bsktbl; Trk; High Hon Roll; Hon Roll; Prfct Atten Awd; Alpha Phi Alpha Fraternity Alpha Kappa Alpha 87; Urban Leagide 87; Adelphi U; Psych.

FRASSETTO, JOHN ALBERT; Saint Joseph Reginol HS; Saddle River, NJ; (3); 80/250; Church Yth Grp; Varsity Clb; JV Var Coach Actv; Var Ftbl; Im Sftbl; Var Trk; Im Vllybl; Im Wt Lftg; Hon Roll; Spanish NHS; Bus Financer.

FRATELLO, DARLENE; Linden HS; Linden, NJ; (2); Key Clb; SADD; Band; Drill Tm; Mrchg Band; Trs Frsh Cls; Trs Soph Cls; High Hon Roll; Minorities Engrng 85-87.

FRATELLO, DONNA LYNN; Linden HS; Linden, NJ; (4); 74/380; Cmnty Wkr; Key Clb; SADD; Band; Concert Band; Mrchg Band; School Play; Rep Stu Cncl; Hon Roll; PTA Schlrshp Awd 87; Long Island U; Marine Bio.

FRATKIN, AMY; Manasquan HS; Manasquan, NJ; (3); VP Drama Clb; Key Clb; VP Thesps; Acpl Chr; Chorus; School Musical; Symp Band; Rep Stu Cncl; Capt Twrlr; Hon Roll; Spec Ed.

FRAYNE, STEVE; Bishop Eustace HS; Turnersville, NJ; (4); 4/193; Church Yth Grp; Cmnty Wkr; Drama Clb; School Play; Yrbk Stf; Crs Cntry; Trk; Gov Hon Prg Awd; High Hon Roll; NHS; Magna Cum Laude 87; Yale U; Econ.

FRAYSSE, SUSAN; Acad Of Holy Angels; Teaneck, NJ; (4); 24/153; Church Yth Grp; Sec French Clb; Math Clb; Chorus; Yrbk Stf; French Hon Soc; Hon Roll; Am Legion Awd 85; U S Cycling Fed Cert Official 81; Rutgers Coll; Communications.

FRAZEE, STEPHEN; St Mary HS; Keansburg, NJ; (4); 12/125; Church Yth Grp; Thesps; School Play; Bsbl; Bsktbl; Socr; High Hon Roll; NHS; Anthony Di Marzio Schlrshp Fund 87; Montclair Coll; Bio.

FRAZIER, ALLISON; Linden HS; Linden, NJ; (3); Cmnty Wkr; Trs French Clb; Key Clb; Science Clb; Chorus; Madrigals; School Musical; High Hon Roll; Hon Roll; NHS; NJ All ST Chorus 86; Boston Coll; Bus Mgmt.

FRAZIER, KIMBERLI; Immaculate Conception HS; Verona, NJ; (3); Church Yth Grp; Cmnty Wkr; Y-Teens; Chorus; Church Choir; JV Vllybl; Hon Roll; Prfct Atten Awd; Pre Law.

FRAZIER, LISA; Carringer HS; Newark, NJ; (4); 35/449; Drama Clb; Chorus; Color Guard; Variety Show; Yrbk Stf; VP Jr Cls; VP Sr Cls; Rep Stu Cncl; Bsktbl; Capt Twrlr; Montclair ST Coll; Bus Admin.

FRAZIER, NATUCHIA; Bridgeton HS; Bridgeton, NJ; (2); Church Yth Grp; Model UN; Pep Clb; Varsity Clb; Church Choir; Sec Frsh Cls; JV Var Bsktbl; Var Mgr(s); JV Var Sftbl; Var Trk; Social Wrkr.

FREAS, TARA ELIZABETH; Glenvar HS; Tuckertown, NJ; (4); 19/210; FCA; French Clb; Keywanettes; Yrbk Ed-Chief; Yrbk Phtg; Trs Frsh Cls; Var Socr; Trk; Chess Clb; NHS; PLUS 85-86; Advrtsng.

FRED, CARMEN; John F Kennedy HS; Paterson, NJ; (3); Intnl Clb; Office Aide; Chorus; Nwsp Phtg; Nwsp Rptr; Nwsp Sprt Ed; Nwsp Stf; Mgr Ftbl; Var Sftbl; Hon Roll; Montclair ST; Pre Law.

FREDA, ANTHONY; Newton HS; Newton, NJ; (4); 8/196; Pres German Clb; Math Tm; Science Clb; Rep Sr Cls; Off Stu Cncl; Bsktbl; Socr; Trk; NHS; U Scranton; Pre Med.

FREDA, DAWN-MARIE; Wood-Ridge HS; Wood Ridge, NJ; (3); 10/90; Spanish Clb; Band; Drm Mjr(t); Mrchg Band; Stu Cncl; Cheerleading; Trk; High Hon Roll; Hon Roll; NHS; Accntnt.

FREDENBURGH, LAURA; Holy Family Acad; Bayonne, NJ; (4); 2/131; Rep Church Yth Grp; Cmnty Wkr; French Clb; Hosp Aide; Key Clb; Band; Chorus; Orch; School Musical; Ed Nwsp Ed-Chief; NJ Distgshd Schlr 87; 4 Yr Schlrshp To Trenton ST 87; Schlrshp To Farleigh Dickinson, St Peters 87; Bryn Mawr Coll; Pre Med.

FREDERICK, DEBRA; Lakeland Regional HS; Ringwood, NJ; (4); 18/350; Art Clb; Math Tm; Var L Fld Hcky; Powder Puff Ftbl; High Hon Roll; Hon Roll; NHS; Ntl Merit Ltr; NJ Distngshd Schlr 86-87; Vrsty Lttr Fncng 84-85; U Of De; Psychology.

FREDERICK, NANCY; Sterling HS; Stratford, NJ; (3); Pep Clb; Band; Concert Band; Mrchg Band; Trs Soph Cls; Stu Cncl; JV Var Cheerleading; High Hon Roll; Hon Roll; Fash Merch.

FREDERICKS, LLOYD; Essex Catholic HS; E Orange, NJ; (2); Rep Frsh Cls; Cheerleading; Ftbl; Trk; High Hon Roll; Hon Roll.

FREDERICKS, MICHELE; Dover HS; Mine Hill, NJ; (3); 41/200; Var Crs Cntry; Stat Score Keeper; Var Trk; Tchng.

FREDHEIM, JENNIFERANNE; Hillside HS; Hillside, NJ; (3); 12/238; Computer Clb; Math Tm; Science Clb; Spanish Clb; Nwsp Ed-Chief; Nwsp Rptr; Nwsp Sprt Ed; Stat Socr; Var Sftbl; Hon Roll; Cmmnctns.

FREED, LISA; Indian Hills HS; Oakland, NJ; (3); 35/306; Nwsp Rptr; Nwsp Stf; Yrbk Bus Mgr; Yrbk Rptr; Yrbk Stf; High Hon Roll; Hon Roll; Dance Clb; Debate Tm; Spanish Clb; Ramapo Indian Hills PTSO Merit Awd In Span & Engl 85-86; Law.

FREELING, DAVID; Livingston HS; Livingston, NJ; (4); 8/425.

FREELY, MONICA; Immaculate Conception HS; Lyndhurst, NJ; (3); 7/84; Dance Clb; NFL; Spanish Clb; Speech Tm; Band; Nwsp Rptr; Ed Lit Mag; Rep Jr Cls; 1st Pl Lcl, 2nd Pl St & 3rd Pl Ntl Cthlcwar Vtrns Oratcl Cont 86.

FREEMAN, ALVIN; Middletown South HS; Atlantic Highland, NJ; (3); VP Soph Cls; Var Capt Bsktbl; Hon Roll; Spanish NHS; MVP 86-87; Spnsh Awd 86-87; Pharm.

FREEMAN, CONSWELLA; West Side HS; Newark, NJ; (3); Boys Clb Am; Church Yth Grp; JA; Church Choir; Color Guard; Off Jr Cls; Cheerleading; Gym; Ldrshp Awd 87; Katherine Gibbs; Secty.

FREEMAN III, HENRY J; Howell HS; Farmingdale, NJ; (3); German Clb; JV Bsbl; Im Bowling; Hon Roll; Rider Coll; Accntng.

FREEMAN, JACQULINE; Sparta HS; Sparta, NJ; (3); 14/275; Sec Key Clb; Pres Frsh Cls; Rep Soph Cls; Off Jr Cls; Chrmn Stu Cncl; Var Cheerleading; Var Swmmng; High Hon Roll; Hon Roll; NHS.

FREEMAN, NERETTA; Garfield HS; Garfield, NJ; (4); 13/162; Am Leg Aux Girls St; Church Yth Grp; Drama Clb; SADD; Varsity Clb; Variety Show; Yrbk Stf; Trs Jr Cls; Trs Sr Cls; Mgr(s); Greg Baron Awd 87; N Jersey Trck & Fld Schlrshp 87; 1st Tm St, Cnty & Leag Trck & Fld 87; Rutgers U; Chmstry.

FREEMAN, VERRAINA LYNN; John F Kennedy HS; Paterson, NJ; (3); Am Leg Aux Girls St; Church Yth Grp; Cmnty Wkr; NAACP; Capt Color Guard; Pres Sr Cls; Var Capt Bowling; CC Awd; Hon Roll; Pres NHS; Hampton; Med.

FREEMAN, YOLANDA RENEE; Trenton Central HS; Trenton, NJ; (3); Am Leg Aux Girls St; Dance Clb; Debate Tm; Pep Clb; Band; Chorus; Jazz Band; Nwsp Stf; Yrbk Stf; Off Frsh Cls; Schlstc Awd 84-85; Howard U; Law.

FREESTONE, FRED; Point Pleasant Boro HS; Point Pleasant, NJ; (4); 12/233; Computer Clb; Varsity Clb; Var Capt Bowling; Golf; High Hon Roll; Hon Roll; Pres Schlr; Nellie Bennett PTO Schlrshp 87; Ocean Cnty Coll; Acctnt.

FREESWICK, LISA; Clifton HS; Clifton, NJ; (3); Girl Scts; Library Aide; Nwsp Rptr; Yrbk Stf; JV Bowling; Hon Roll; Jr NHS; Word Prcsng.

FREI, RANDY; Newton HS; Newton, NJ; (3); Latin Clb; Math Tm; Science Clb; Ski Clb; Bsktbl; Capt Socr; Tennis; NHS; 1st Pl Chem Olypiad 86; Physics.

FREIMANIS, DENA; Vineland HS; Vineland, NJ; (4); 32/765; Pres German Clb; Varsity Clb; Var Capt Bsktbl; Var L Socr; Var Capt Trk; Track All Conf Hgh Jmp 86 & 85; Sccr All Conf 86; Slctd Yth Cngrss NJ-JUST Say No To Drugs 87; Susquehanna U.

FREIRE, ELLEN; Queen Of Peace HS; Lyndhurst, NJ; (3); Church Yth Grp; Spanish Clb; Rep Frsh Cls; Rep Stu Cncl; Church Yth Grp; Var JV Cheerleading; Berkeley Schl.

FREIS, CAROLYN; Bishop George Ahr HS; Metuchen, NJ; (4); Hosp Aide; Spanish Clb; SADD; Cheerleading; Crs Cntry; Trk; Hon Roll; Schlr Athlt Fll X-Cntry 85; 100 Hrs Awd 85; 250 Hrs Awd 87; U Of Scranton; Pre-Med.

FREIS, JEAN; Bishop George Ahr/St Thomas HS; Metuchen, NJ; (4); French Clb; VP German Clb; Ski Clb; School Play; Yrbk Stf; Mgr(s); Trk; Wt Lftg; U Of Scranton; Intl Lng.

FRENEY, DENISE; Oakcrest HS; Mays Landing, NJ; (3); 16/228; French Clb; Key Clb; Service Clb; Teachers Aide; Yrbk Stf; Off Jr Cls; Hon Roll; Jr NHS; NHS; Achvt Awd 86; Centenery; Eqstrn Stds.

FRENS, JACKIE; Eastern Christian HS; Prospect Pk, NJ; (3); 3/88; Church Yth Grp; Nwsp Rptr; Nwsp Stf; Stu Cncl; Var L Cheerleading; High Hon Roll; Hon Roll; NHS; Engl.

FREY, JULIE; St Joseph HS; Waterford, NJ; (4); 6/81; Am Leg Aux Girls St; SADD; Variety Show; Var Co-Capt Cheerleading; High Hon Roll; Hon Roll; Sec NHS; Lit Mag; Frnch Awd Excllnc; JR Miss Schlstc Awd; Glassboro ST Coll; Elem Ed.

FRIANT, KIMBERLY; Edgewood SR HS; Atco, NJ; (2); French Clb; Hnrbl Mntn Hnr Roll 87; Presdntl Acadc Ftns Awd 86; Cert Apprectn/Frnch Clb 87; Nrsng.

FRIBERG, ANDREW; Toms River High School South; Toms River, NJ; (2); Church Yth Grp; Pres Soph Cls; Rep Stu Cncl; Var JV Bsktbl; Var Golf; Var JV Socr; Hon Roll.

FRICKER, KURT; Middletown HS South; Middletown, NJ; (2); Socr; Var L Swmmng; Hon Roll; Grmn Hnr Soc 86-87; Rd Bnk YMCA Natl Swm Tm 86&87.

FRICKS, KATHRYN; Toms River HS North; Toms River, NJ; (3); 2/459; Off CAP; Sec German Clb; Math Tm; Orch; Pres Stu Cncl; NHS; Ntl Merit SF; Math Clb; Science Clb; School Musical; Rensselaer Poly Inst Awd Math & Sci 86-87; ST Sci Day 1st Pl Chem 85-86; Astro Engrng.

FRIDDELL, RANCE; Burlington Cty Vo-Tech Schl; Edgewater, NJ; (3); 13/192; Teachers Aide; VICA; Hon Roll; Elect Const.

FRIEDBERG, SANDI; Franklin HS; Somerset, NJ; (3); SADD; Rep Sec Temple Yth Grp; Yrbk Sprt Ed; Pres Soph Cls; Pres Jr Cls; Stu Cncl; Var Capt Tennis; Im Vllybl; High Hon Roll; Hon Roll; All Conf Tnns 84, 86; Bus.

FRIEDMAN, JEFF; West Orange HS; W Orange, NJ; (3); Wt Lftg; Hon Roll; Natl Hnr Awd Rcmdtn 87; 4th Pl NJ HS Power Lifting Chmpnshps 87; Econ.

FRIEDMAN, JENIFER; Delran HS; Delran, NJ; (4); 31/209; Drama Clb; Color Guard; School Musical; School Play; Stat Bsktbl; Hofstra Univ; Psych.

FRIEDMAN, JENNIFER; Dwight-Englewood HS; Cresskill, NJ; (3); Intnl Clb; Chorus; Jazz Band; Orch; Natl Latin Test Magra Cum Laude 87.

FRIEDMAN, JENNIFER; Tenafly HS; Tenafly, NJ; (3); Trs French Clb; Key Clb; Rep Jr Cls; Var Capt Sftbl; Var Vllybl; High Hon Roll; Ntl Merit Ltr; Hghst Hnrs Acad Awd 86; 2nd Team All-Leag Sftbl 86; Hon Ment All Leag Vlybl 86; Bio Sci.

FRIEDMAN, KAREN; Vineland HS; Vineland, NJ; (3); 31/870; French Clb; SADD; Stage Crew; Ed Nwsp Stf; Ed Yrbk Stf; Rep Jr Cls; Rep Stu Cncl; NHS; Co-Wrtr Of Wkly Column; JR Prom Committee; Penn ST; Commnctns.

FRIEDMAN, MARK; Parsippany HS; Parsippany, NJ; (3); FBLA; Letterman Clb; Varsity Clb; Stu Cncl; Var L Tennis; 1st Tm All-Conf Tnns Tm 87; Psych.

FRIEDMAN, MELISSA; West Morris Mendham HS; Chester, NJ; (2); 12/292; Debate Tm; Intnl Clb; Model UN; Ski Clb; Band; Mrchg Band; Pres Soph Cls; JV Crs Cntry; JV Trk; High Hon Roll; Psych.

FRIEDMAN, SAMANTHA; Freehold Township HS; Freehold, NJ; (3); 10/380; Drama Clb; French Clb; FBLA; Pres Trs Temple Yth Grp; Yrbk Stf; Powder Puff Ftbl; NHS; 6th Pl Ms FBLA Rgnl Cmptn 87; Lbrl Arts.

FRIEDMAN, TARA; Paramus Catholic Girls HS; Carlstadt, NJ; (3); 82/179; Aud/Vis; Math Tm; Spanish Clb; Rep Stu Cncl; JV Vllybl; Pre Med.

FRIEDMANN, GREGG; Nutley HS; Nutley, NJ; (3); 54/313; German Clb; Nwsp Rptr; Nwsp Stf; JV Bsktbl; Hon Roll; Cmnctns.

FRIEND, RENEE; Wall HS; Wall, NJ; (4); Ski Clb; Nwsp Rptr; Nwsp Sprt Ed; Nwsp Stf; Rep Soph Cls; Rep Jr Cls; JV Var Fld Hcky; JV Var Socr; High Hon Roll; Hon Roll; Marie Moen Atlantic Schlrhsp 87; E Carolina U.

FRIES, JOHN; Wildwood Catholic HS; N Wildwood, NJ; (3); 19/85; Q&S; Nwsp Rptr; Nwsp Stf; Var Tennis; Boy Scts; Math Clb; Im Vllybl; Hon Roll; Coachs Awd Tnns 86; Crtv Wrtng.

FRIEZO, CLAUDINE; Indian Hills HS; Franklin Lakes, NJ; (3); 12/306; AFS; Am Leg Aux Girls St; Camera Clb; Ski Clb; Spanish Clb; Yrbk Phtg; Var Cheerleading; Trk; High Hon Roll; VP NHS; NJ Grls St 87; NJ Tlnt Srch-Shw Of Strs-Garden St Piano Fnls 86; Med.

FRIGIOLA, MARK; N V R Old Tappan HS; Northvale, NJ; (3); 104/274; Cmnty Wkr; Var Bowling; Coach Actv.

FRIKERT, LAURA; Nutley HS; Nutley, NJ; (3); 36/304; French Clb; Office Aide; Capt Var Crs Cntry; Var Capt Trk; Hon Roll; NHS; Librl Arts.

FRIO, PAUL; Rutherford HS; Rutherford, NJ; (3); Key Clb; Math Tm; Ski Clb; School Play; Stage Crew; JV Tennis; High Hon Roll; NHS; The Rensselaer Mdl 87; Engrng.

FRITCH, MARY; Dover HS; Dover, NJ; (3); 5/289; Trs AFS; Am Leg Aux Girls St; Church Yth Grp; Computer Clb; Drama Clb; German Clb; Q&S; Scholastic Bowl; Service Clb; Ski Clb; Engl Literary Awd 1st Pl Prose 87; Bio Awd 86; Russian Studies.

FRITSCH, CHRISTINA E; Lenape Valley Regional HS; Stanhope, NJ; (4); Am Leg Aux Girls St; Church Yth Grp; Intnl Clb; Key Clb; Ski Clb; Spanish Clb; Sec SADD; Chorus; School Musical; Nwsp Rptr; WA Wrkshps Cngrssnl Smnr 86; 5th Dist Modl Cngrss 86; Century III Ldrshp Prog 87; Purdue U; Pol Sci.

FRITSCHIE, RENEE; Southern Regional HS; Barnegat, NJ; (3); 30/439; Church Yth Grp; Model UN; Service Clb; JV Trk; Hon Roll; NHS.

FRITTS, MARK; Middletown HS South; Middletown, NJ; (3); Math Clb; Ski Clb; Yrbk Phtg; Yrbk Stf; Golf; Socr; Tennis; Vllybl; Hon Roll; Arch.

FRITTS, PAULA; Mt Olive HS; Budd Lake, NJ; (3); 63/338; AFS; FBLA; Science Clb; Ski Clb; SADD; Yrbk Phtg; Yrbk Stf; Hon Roll; Natl Art Hnr Soc Pres 86-88; Advrtsng.

FRITZ, JOANNE; Collingswood HS; Camden, NJ; (3); Office Aide; Nwsp Stf; Yrbk Stf; Hon Roll; Bus.

FRITZ, TRACEY; Piscataway HS; Piscataway, NJ; (3); High Hon Roll; Hon Roll; Jr NHS; NHS; Rutgers; Math.

FRITZSCHA, SANDRA; Highland Regional HS; Erial, NJ; (3); 38/317; Camera Clb; Hon Roll; Business.

FROEHLICH, JOAN; Immaculate Conception HS; Rutherford, NJ; (2); 5/89; Debate Tm; Rep Frsh Cls; JV Var Sftbl; JV Capt Vllybl; Georgetown U.

FROST, JAN; Allentown HS; Clarksburg, NJ; (4); 27/175; Drama Clb; French Clb; FBLA; Ski Clb; School Play; Diving; Gym; Swmmng; Hon Roll; Hnr & Awd-1st Pl Lit NJ Teen Arts Fstvl 85-87; Wm Patterson ST Coll; Accntng.

FRUCHTMAN, HOPE; Clearview Regional HS; Mantua, NJ; (3); 3/195; Library Aide; Acpl Chr; Chorus; School Musical; School Play; Yrbk Sprt Ed; Yrbk Stf; Pres Stu Cncl; Stat Bsktbl; Var Tennis; 3rd Pl Spllng Bee 85; Prtcpnt NJ Mock Trial Cmptn 87; Pre-Law.

FRUEH, JENNIFER; River Dell SR HS; Oradell, NJ; (4); 31/207; GAA; Varsity Clb; Chorus; Yrbk Stf; JV Cheerleading; JV Sftbl; JV Var Vllybl; Hon Roll; NHS; Prfct Atten Awd; Lafayette Coll; Business.

FRUMOLT, BRIAN; Parsippany Hills HS; Morris Plains, NJ; (3); FBLA; Var L Ftbl; Wt Lftg; Hon Roll; Rogate SAT Awd 83; Air Force ROTC; Mrktng.

FRY, JENNIFER; Buena Regional HS; Newfield, NJ; (4); 10/180; Drama Clb; Ski Clb; Varsity Clb; Band; Rep Stu Cncl; Cheerleading; Masonic Awd; Sec NHS; SICO Schlrshp To Glassboro St Coll 87; Glassboro ST Coll; Bio.

FRY, RICHARD; Pitman HS; Pitman, NJ; (4); 17/149; Band; Chorus; Concert Band; Jazz Band; Mrchg Band; Socr; Trk; Hon Roll; Music Mstrs Hnr Sco 86-87; Rutgers; Engrng.

FRYER, KAREN; Edgewood SR HS; Atco, NJ; (3); 14/397; Am Leg Aux Girls St; Varsity Clb; Nwsp Stf; Yrbk Stf; Sec Frsh Cls; Rep Soph Cls; Var Stat Ftbl; Jr NHS; NHS; VFW Awd; Englsh Ed.

FUCHS, HEATHER; Indian Hills HS; Oakland, NJ; (3); 41/306; Church Yth Grp; Pep Clb; Varsity Clb; Socr; Hon Roll; PTSO Cert Merit Hstry, Engl, French 84-85; PTSO Cert Merit Engl 85-86; Bio.

FUENTES, DIANE; St Marys HS; Elizabeth, NJ; (2); Cmnty Wkr; Speech Tm; Pres Soph Cls; Stu Cncl; Sec Bsbl; Sec Bsktbl; Score Keeper; Im Vllybl; Svc Awd 86-87; Athltc Awd 86-87; Seton Hall; Psychology.

FUERNEISEN, CHARLOTTE; Salem HS; Salem, NJ; (3); Church Yth Grp; Pep Clb; Band; Concert Band; Rep Stu Cncl; Hon Roll; Exec Secty.

FUERTES, MELANIE R; Mt St Mary Acad; Piscataway, NJ; (2); 1/93; Cmnty Wkr; Hosp Aide; Intnl Clb; NAACP; Office Aide; Science Clb; Service Clb; Spanish Clb.

FUGES, CHRISTIN; Hopewell Valley Central HS; Titusville, NJ; (2); Church Yth Grp; French Clb; Chorus; School Play; JV Sftbl; High Hon Roll; Hon Roll.

FUHRMANN, JENNIFER; Notre Dame HS; Mercerville, NJ; (3); Red Cross Aide; Stage Crew; Var JV Tennis; JR Vrsty Tnns; Most Original Prjct Hstry Class; Pre-Med.

FULLAGAR, MELANIE; Ridge HS; Basking Ridge, NJ; (3); Hosp Aide; Service Clb; Flag Corp; Lit Mag; Hon Roll; NHS; Mrrstwn Memrl Hosp JR Vlnteer-Outstndng Svc Awd, Outstndng Achvt Awd 85, 87.

FULLAM, JENNIFER; Willingboro HS; Willingboro, NJ; (4); Pres 4-H; Hosp Aide; Latin Clb; Stage Crew; Hon Roll; Ntl Merit SF; St Schlr; Trenton ST Coll; Elem Ed.

FULLER, SCOTT; Lakeland Regional HS; Ringwood, NJ; (3); Computer Clb; Var JV Socr; Var Trk; Hon Roll; Comp Contest 3rd Pl 85-86; Rutgers; Comp Sci.

FULLERTON, FREDERIC; Toms River HS South; Toms River, NJ; (2); Exploring; Intnl Clb; Mrchg Band; Nwsp Bus Mgr; Yrbk Stf; Psych.

FULMER, LINDA; Toms River Norm HS; Toms River, NJ; (4); DECA; SADD; VP Soph Cls; Stu Cncl; Cheerleading; Gym; Church Yth Grp; Latin Clb; Library Aide; Spanish Clb; Prjct LEAD Ldr 85-86; Attndnc Cmmttee 86; Miss Teen NJ 86-87; Fshn Insti Of PA; Mdlng.

FULTON III, BERNARD; Atlantic Friends Schl; Atlantic City, NJ; (4); 1/14; Chess Clb; Cmnty Wkr; Drama Clb; Intnl Clb; NAACP; Political Wkr; Thesps; Chorus; School Play; Yrbk Stf; Headmstrs Ldrshp Awd 85-86; Mst Lkly To Sccd 86-87; Natl Achvt Schlrp Prog For Outstndg Negro Stus 86; Princeton; Law.

FULTON, MELISSA; Baptist HS; Voorhees, NJ; (2); 1/32; Church Yth Grp; French Clb; Var Fld Hcky; Var Sftbl; Cit Awd; 4-H Awd; High Hon Roll; Hon Roll; All Acdmc Tm Fld Hockey 86.

FURFARI, FRANK; Woodstown HS; Newfield, NJ; (3); English Clb; Key Clb; Spanish Clb; Off Frsh Cls; Off Jr Cls; Var L Bsktbl; Var Socr; Hon Roll; Sci Awd 86; Gftd & Tlntd Prog 86-87; Rogate 85-87; Bus.

FURFARO, CATHY; Paramus Catholic Girls HS; Cliffside Pk, NJ; (3); 7/179; SADD; Hon Roll; Jr NHS; Prfct Atten Awd; Prfncy In Frnch Awd 86; Hlth.

FURGIUELE, CATHERINE; Lenape Valley Regional HS; Andover, NJ; (4); 3/243; Hosp Aide; Key Clb; Nwsp Stf; Capt Bsktbl; Trk; NHS; Prfct Atten Awd; Pres Schlr; Spanish NHS; Rotary Schlrshp 87; Hugh O Brien Ldrshp Smnr Ambssdr 84-85; Suprndnt Rndtbl Awd 87; Boston U; Biomed.

FURGUIELE, CATHERINE; Lenape Vly Regional HS; Andover, NJ; (4); 3/253; Church Yth Grp; Hosp Aide; Key Clb; Var Capt Bsktbl; Var Fld Hcky; Var Trk; NHS; Pres Schlr; Spanish NHS; HOBY Ldrshp Ambssdr 85; Boston U; Bio Engr.

FURLONG, ROBERT; Jackson Memorial HS; Jackson, NJ; (4); 50/460; German Clb; Capt L Bsbl; Im Ftbl; JV Wt Lftg; High Hon Roll; Hon Roll; St Andrews Prsbytrn Coll.

FURMAN, LAURIE A; Spotswood HS; Spotswood, NJ; (4); 9/189; Drama Clb; Intnl Clb; Model UN; Concert Band; Mrchg Band; Ed Yrbk Stf; Pres Stu Cncl; NHS; Ntl Merit Ltr; Spanish NHS; Rtgrs U Deans Smmr Schlr 86; Pltcl Sci.

FURMAN, STEVEN; Shore Regional HS; W Long Branch, NJ; (3); Drama Clb; Q&S; Science Clb; Thesps; Band; Drm Mjr(t); Mrchg Band; School Musical; Nwsp Ed-Chief; High Hon Roll.

FURNISS, GREGG; Middletown South HS; Lincroft, NJ; (3); Church Yth Grp; Church Choir; Hon Roll; Ntl Merit Ltr; Engr.

FURY, SHANNON; Wall HS; Wall, NJ; (3); 15/315; Drama Clb; Key Clb; Acpl Chr; VP Chorus; Rep Frsh Cls; Mgr(s); High Hon Roll; Hon Roll; NHS; All Shore Chrs; NJOM Prgm.

FUSCO, DOMENICO; Don Bosco Tech; N Haledon, NJ; (3); 18/91; Yrbk Stf; JV Socr; Med.

FUSCO, ROBERT; Holy Spirit HS; Absecon, NJ; (2); 50/397; Church Yth Grp; Socr; VFW Awd; U Of PA; Ped.

FUSSELL, JENNIE; Essex Catholic Girls HS; Vailsburg, NJ; (4); 16/54; Art Clb; Computer Clb; FBLA; FHA; Model UN; Yrbk Stf; Rep Stu Cncl; Rep Stu Cncl; Badmtn; Montclair ST Coll; Accntng.

FUSTE, ANA PAULA; Riverside HS; Riverside, NJ; (3); 10/110; FBLA; FTA; Teachers Aide; Hon Roll; Jr NHS; NHS.

FUTERNIK, ALBERT; Fair Lawn HS; Fair Lawn, NJ; (2); Ski Clb; Band; Concert Band; Jazz Band; Mrchg Band; Orch; Pep Band; School Musical; High Hon Roll; Hon Roll; Elec Engr.

GABAEFF, DAVID; Bridgewater-Raritan HS East; Bridgewater, NJ; (3); Spanish Clb; Hon Roll; Pre-Law.

GABRIEL, RAINELDA; Belleville HS; Belleville, NJ; (3); Key Clb; Library Aide; Chorus; Rep Stu Cncl; Hon Roll; Illstrtn Bk Awd 85; Rutgers U; Bus.

GABURO, AL; Bridgewater-Raritan West HS; Raritan, NJ; (4); Letterman Clb; Pep Clb; Ski Clb; Varsity Clb; Var Capt Bsbl; Coach Actv; Var Capt Ftbl; Powder Puff Ftbl; Wt Lftg; U ME; Bnkg.

GADDIS, CHERIE; Raritan HS; Hazlet, NJ; (3); French Clb; Band; Chorus; Mrchg Band; Symp Band; Hon Roll; NHS; JV Crs Cntry; JV Socr; Var Capt Trk; Pre Med Bio.

GAETA, PATRICIA ANN; Memorial HS; Cedar Grove, NJ; (4); 23/123; Key Clb; Office Aide; Yrbk Stf; Hon Roll; NHS; Pres Schlr; The Coll Womens Clb Of Montclair 87; Nova U; Bus.

GAFFNEY, JENNIFER; Monsignor Donovan HS; Forked River, NJ; (3); 46/245; Art Clb; Ski Clb; Spanish Clb; SADD; Socr; High Hon Roll; NHS; Bus Adm.

GAFFNEY, LEIGH; Manasquan HS; Brielle, NJ; (3); FBLA; Spanish Clb; Stu Cncl; Hon Roll; Bus Mgmt.

GAFFOGLIO, LISA; Westwood HS; Washington Twp, NJ; (2); Church Yth Grp; Drama Clb; Spanish Clb; Chorus; Church Choir; School Play; Yrbk Stf; High Hon Roll; Spanish NHS.

GAGAS, LAURIE; Barnstable Acad; Teaneck, NJ; (3); Dance Clb; Service Clb; Teachers Aide; Powder Puff Ftbl; Score Keeper; Trk; Hon Roll; Sci Awd 85-86.

GAGLIANO, EUGENE; Waldwick HS; Waldwick, NJ; (4); 20/146; Church Yth Grp; Letterman Clb; Varsity Clb; Var Capt Ftbl; Var Capt Trk; JV Wrstlng; Hon Roll; U S GGA 87; All Leag Hnrs Offsve Guard 86; U S Coast Guard Acad; Engrng.

GAIDIS, JENNIFER; Secaucus HS; Secaucus, NJ; (3); Key Clb; Math Clb; Mu Alpha Theta; Spanish Clb; Chorus; Rep Frsh Cls; Stat Bsktbl; JV Tennis; High Hon Roll; Fin.

GAILLIOUT, MICHELLE; Lenape HS; Mt Laurel, NJ; (4); 104/434; JCL; Latin Clb; Varsity Clb; Var Capt Cheerleading; Hon Roll; Bus.

GAINER, ERICA; Clifford J Scott HS; East Orange, NJ; (3); English Clb; Off Jr Cls; Gym; Trphy For Best Secty In Cls 82; Trphy For 2nd Pl In Soc Stu Cls 82; Plaque For Engl Cls 86; Fairleigh Dickinson; Psych.

GAINES, JAMES; New Brunswick HS; New Brunswick, NJ; (4); 6/130; Church Yth Grp; NFL; Band; Yrbk Stf; Stu Cncl; Bsktbl; High Hon Roll; Hon Roll; Jr NHS; NHS; High Hnr Roll 83-87; Top Male Blck Stu 83-87; PA ST; Corp Attorney.

GAINEY, KERA LASHY; Dwight Morrow HS; Englewood, NJ; (3); 14/312; Church Choir; Yrbk Stf; VP Jr Cls; Rep Stu Cncl; Var Cheerleading; Trk; High Hon Roll; Hon Roll; NHS; Tlntd Teen Of Brgn Cnty 86-87; Clrksn U; Chem Engr.

GAITO, HEIDI; Montville HS; Towaco, NJ; (3); 50/350; FBLA; Ski Clb; Capt Fld Hcky; High Hon Roll; Prfct Atten Awd; Acctg Awd 87; Acctg.

GAJEWSKI II, STEPHEN J; St John Vianney HS; Laurence Hrbr, NJ; (1); Church Yth Grp; Band.

GALAIDA, ROBERT; Bishop AHR HS; Perth Amboy, NJ; (4); 123/265; JV Bsktbl; JV Ftbl; High Hon Roll; Hon Roll; Hnr Roll 87; 1st Hnrs 87; Rider Coll; Acctng.

GALANG, ANGEL; Hudson Catholic HS; Jersey City, NJ; (3); 30/220; Math Clb; High Hon Roll; Hon Roll; Chorus; Mgr Bsktbl; Stat Mgr(s); Mgr Trk; Hnr Roll 2nd Hnrs 86-87; High Hnr Roll 1st Hnrs 85; Rugers; Bus.

GALANO, SCOTT; Watchung Hills Regional HS; Watchung, NJ; (3); Boy Scts; Church Yth Grp; Key Clb; Ski Clb; Spanish Clb; Rep Soph Cls; JV Crs Cntry; Golf; Hon Roll; NHS; Med.

GALASSO, RANDY; J P Stevens HS; Edison, NJ; (2); 1/452; French Clb; Key Clb; Science Clb; Concert Band; Mrchg Band; Yrbk Stf; Rep Frsh Cls; Rep Soph Cls; Rep Stu Cncl; High Hon Roll; Bus.

GALATRO, BRYAN; Glen Rock SR HS; Glen Rock, NJ; (4); JCL; Latin Clb; Math Tm; Science Clb; Trk; Wrstlng; Hon Roll; Jr NHS; Ntl Merit Ltr; Manhattan Coll; Electrcl Engrng.

GALBRAITH, RENEE; East Brunswick HS; E Brunswick, NJ; (4); FBLA; Key Clb; Color Guard; Yrbk Stf; Trk; FBLA Outstndng Bus Stu Awd 87; Berkley Schl Annual Awd 87; FBLA Rgnl Cmptn Evnts 87; Bus Mgmnt.

GALE, GREGORY K; High Point Regional HS; Sussex, NJ; (3); 10/250; Am Leg Boys St; Debate Tm; Concert Band; Jazz Band; Bowling; Crs Cntry; Golf; Trk; High Hon Roll; NHS; Vet Med.

GALETTA, ANGELA; Pemberton Township HS No 1; Browns Mills, NJ; (2); Church Yth Grp; Nwsp Stf; Trs Frsh Cls; Stu Cncl; Mgr(s); Hon Roll; Rutgers U; Law.

GALIFI, FRANK; Shore Regional HS; West Long Branch, NJ; (4); 70/207; Capt Var Crs Cntry; Hon Roll; X-Cntry MVP Awd 85; Seton Hall U; Bus.

GALIN, MELISSA; Howell HS; Howell, NJ; (4); 75/355; Teachers Aide; Socr; U NC Greensboro.

GALIT, SCOTT; Freehold Township HS; Freehold, NJ; (3); Computer Clb; FBLA; Math Tm; NFL; Science Clb; Temple Yth Grp; Band; Lit Mag; NHS; Ntl Merit Ltr.

GALLACCIO, ANNE; Wildwood Catholic HS; N Cape May, NJ; (3); 25/80; School Musical; Nwsp Rptr; Nwsp Stf; Hon Roll; Cert Of Merit Sci & Lang Arts 85-86; Cert Of Merit Math & Lang Arts 86-87.

GALLAGHER, BARBARA; Egg Harbor Township HS; Pleasantville, NJ; (3); 21/329; AFS; Cmnty Wkr; Pres GAA; Spanish Clb; Var Capt Bsktbl; Var L Fld Hcky; JV Sftbl; Hon Roll; NHS; Hugh O Brien Yth Ldrshp Awd 85.

GALLAGHER, CHERIE; Union Catholic HS; Rahway, NJ; (3); Church Yth Grp; PAVAS; Service Clb; Chorus; Hon Roll.

GALLAGHER, JOHN M; Christian Brothers Acad; Colts Neck, NJ; (3); Chorus; School Musical; School Play; Stage Crew; Yrbk Ed-Chief; Yrbk Stf; Im Mgr Bsktbl; Im Mgr Sftbl; Trk; High Hon Roll; Ntl Hnr Soc 87-88; Undrclssmn 87; Edtr Asst Edtr In Chf Yrbk 88; Awd Drama 86-87; Lbrl Arts.

GALLAGHER, KARA; Bishop Fustace Prep HS; Laurel Springs, NJ; (3); Cmnty Wkr; French Clb; Pep Clb; SADD; Nwsp Rptr; Nwsp Stf; Cheerleading; High Hon Roll; NHS; Mgr(s); Chrldng Sqd Prtcptd Natl Cmptn 85-86; CA Plcd 4th Natn Dance 86-87; Georgetown; Finance.

GALLAGHER, KATHRYN M; Roselle Catholic HS; Port Reading, NJ; (4); Ski Clb; Stage Crew; Var Cheerleading; Gym; Stat Mgr(s); Var Trk; High Hon Roll; Hon Roll; NHS; Hnr Miss Amer Irish 87; Seton Hall U; Ed.

GALLAGHER, KRISTIN E; Ridge HS; Basking Ridge, NJ; (3); Church Yth Grp; Cmnty Wkr; Dance Clb; Band; Var JV Cheerleading; JV Swmmng; High Hon Roll; Hon Roll; NHS; Spanish NHS; Accntng.

GALLAGHER, MICHELE; Holy Spirit HS; Linwood, NJ; (4); 73/376; Spanish Clb; SADD; JV Bsktbl; Var Crs Cntry; Var Mgr(s); Hon Roll; NHS; Pres Schlr; Fairleigh Dickinson U; Bio.

GALLAGHER, MOURNA; Belvidere HS; Phillipsburg, NJ; (4); 54/120; Art Clb; Drama Clb; Hosp Aide; Model UN; Office Aide; Teachers Aide; Chorus; Flag Corp; Lit Mag; Hon Roll; Fashion Inst Tech; Fshn Merch.

GALLAGHER, PATRICK; West Essex SR HS; Fairfield, NJ; (3); Hon Roll; NHS; Arch.

GALLAGHER, TIMOTHY; Toms River HS East; Toms River, NJ; (4); Aud/Vis; Ski Clb; VICA; Band; Concert Band; Mrchg Band; BCSI; Data Prcssng.

GALLARDO, LINDA; St Joseph HS; W New York, NJ; (4); 17/130; French Clb; Variety Show; Nwsp Stf; Sftbl; Swmmng; Tennis; French Hon Soc; Hon Roll; Pres NHS; Optometry.

GALLARDO, LISSETTE; St Josephs Of The Palisads; Union City, NJ; (4); Church Yth Grp; Pep Clb; Spanish Clb; Yrbk Stf; Cheerleading; Pom Pon; Hon Roll; Spanish NHS; Rugers U.

GALLICCHIO, DIEGO J; Washington Township HS; Sewell, NJ; (3); Ski Clb; Spanish Clb; Socr; Tennis; Rutgers; Bus.

GALLIERA, GINA; Bishop Eustace Preparatory Schl; Audubon, NJ; (3); 9/171; Pres German Clb; Hosp Aide; Pep Clb; SADD; Nwsp Rptr; Pres Frsh Cls; Var Cheerleading; Var Score Keeper; High Hon Roll; NHS; 3rd Pl Natl Chrldng Cmptn CA 86; Grmn Hnr Socty 86.

GALLIGAN, PATRICK JOSEPH; Delbarton Schl; Morristown, NJ; (4); JV Bsktbl; Var L Ftbl; Lcrss; Hon Roll; Church Yth Grp; Cmnty Wkr; Latin Clb; Science Clb; All Nrthrn Hlls Dfnsv End, Ftbl-2nd Tm 85 & Hnrbl Mntn 86; Coll Of The Holy Cross; Law.

GALLIPOLI, KERRI; Toms River HS North; Toms River, NJ; (3); 7/459; Exploring; Science Clb; Spanish Clb; Stu Cncl; Fld Hcky; Socr; High Hon Roll; NHS; Med.

GALLMAN, JEANNE; Red Bank Regional HS; Union Bch, NJ; (3); FBLA; Sec FHA; SADD; Teachers Aide; High Hon Roll; Hon Roll; NHS; 1st Pl Cnsmr Mrktplc FHA, 2nd & 3rd Pl FHA Hero & NJ Prfct Tgthr 86-87; NC ST; Zoolgy.

GALLO, ANDREW; Glen Rock HS; Glen Rock, NJ; (4); 9/153; Am Leg Boys St; Model UN; Spanish Clb; Yrbk Sprt Ed; Var Bsktbl; Var Capt Socr; Gov Hon Prg Awd; High Hon Roll; NHS; Ntl Merit Ltr; Wesleyan U; Pol Sci.

GALLO, AURA; Eastside HS; Paterson, NJ; (4); 23/543; Church Yth Grp; FBLA; Office Aide; OEA; Church Choir; High Hon Roll; Hon Roll; Prfct Atten Awd; Fairleigh Dickinson; Acctng.

GALLO, GREGORY; Wood-Ridge HS; Moonachie, NJ; (3); 1/95; Latin Clb; Science Clb; Spanish Clb; Nwsp Stf; Rep Frsh Cls; Rep Soph Cls; Rep Jr Cls; Trs Stu Cncl; Var L Bsbl; Var L Bsktbl; Amer Clscl Leag Cert Cum Laude In Ltn 85-86.

GALLO, JENNIFER; Park Ridge HS; Park Ridge, NJ; (2); Church Yth Grp; Pres Girl Scts; Band; Mrchg Band; JV Vllybl; God Cntry Awd; PAVAS; Science Clb; High Hon Roll; GS Svlr Awd 85; Co Coach Smmr Swm Tm 87.

GALLO, JO ANN; Passaic Valley HS; Clifton, NJ; (4); Art Clb; Key Clb; JV Vllybl; High Hon Roll; Hon Roll; NHS; Wmns Clb Ltl Fals Bus & Prfssnl Schlrshp, Prsdntl Acdmc Ftnss Awd 87; Muhlenberg Coll; Pre-Law.

GALLO, JOHN; Franklin HS; Somerst, NJ; (3); 7/310; Key Clb; Model UN; SADD; Rep Soph Cls; Capt Swmmng; High Hon Roll; NHS; Golf; Somerset Cnty Swim Meet Champ & Coaches Awd-Somerset Vly YMCA Swim Tm 87; Engrng.

GALLO, STACEY; Weehawken HS; Weehawken, NJ; (3); 12/94; Office Aide; Nwsp Stf; Lit Mag; Rep Frsh Cls; Sec Soph Cls; Sec Jr Cls; Sec Sr Cls; Pres Stu Cncl; Sftbl; Hon Roll; HOBY Awd 85-86; Bus Admin.

GALLOWAY, LEONA; Manasquan HS; Brielle, NJ; (3); 63/239; Church Yth Grp; Dance Clb; FBLA; Hosp Aide; Lit Mag; Mltpl Sclerosis Citation Cert 86; Phys Thrpy.

GALLOZA, SERGIO; Dover HS; Dover, NJ; (2); Bus.

GALOFARO, DAVID A; Boonton HS; Lincoln Park, NJ; (3); Quiz Bowl; Ski Clb; SADD; Teachers Aide; Nwsp Rptr; Lit Mag; Rep Frsh Cls; Im Ftbl; JV Tennis; Hon Roll; Am Leg Boys ST 87; Chrstn Camp Cnslr 87; Pres War Games Clb 87; Physcn.

GALOSI, GINA; Cinnaminson HS; Cinnaminson, NJ; (3); Church Yth Grp; Sec Debate Tm; Drama Clb; Hosp Aide; Math Clb; Math Tm; Thesps; Chorus; School Musical; School Play; Law.

GALVES, DAN; Ridge HS; Basking Ridge, NJ; (3); 18/192; Latin Clb; Ski Clb; JV Socr; Var Tennis; Hon Roll; Ntl Merit Ltr.

GAMBA, CHRISTY; Leonia HS; Leonia, NJ; (3); 41/139; Pres Drama Clb; Thesps; Capt Color Guard; School Musical; School Play; Variety Show; Nwsp Stf; Yrbk Ed-Chief; Lit Mag; Trk; Bus Mngmnt.

GAMBERT, NANCY; Mary Help Of Christians Acad; Elmwood Park, NJ; (1); 4-H; Quiz Bowl; Nwsp Sprt Ed; 4-H Awd; High Hon Roll; Variety Show; Nwsp Rptr; Nwsp Stf; Cook Coll; Animal Sci.

GAMBINO, JEANNIE; St John Vianney HS; Matawan, NJ; (2); 43/270; SADD; Rep Soph Cls; Var Tennis; Hon Roll; 1st Tm All ST Porochial Tennis 86; 1st Tm All Shore Tennis 86 & 87; Broadcast Jrnlsm.

GAMBLE, JESSICA; Brick Township HS; Brick Town, NJ; (3); Pres Drama Clb; NFL; Thesps; Band; Chorus; Mrchg Band; School Musical; Stage Crew; Pom Pon; NHS; Cmmnctns.

GAMBUZZA, NORBERT; Middletown HS South; Lincroft, NJ; (3); Boy Scts; Y-Teens; Off Frsh Cls; Bsbl; Bsktbl; Ftbl; Hon Roll; Natl Conv Yth Covt 87; 2nd Tm All-St Bsbl 87; 1st Tm All Shr Bsbl 87.

GANDHI, NEERAJ; Wm L Dickinson HS; Jersey City, NJ; (3); Computer Clb; Math Clb; Math Tm; Scholastic Bowl; Science Clb; Nwsp Stf; Yrbk Stf; Lit Mag; Hon Roll; NHS; Gld Medl Sci Proj 85 & 87; Regl Wnnr Natl Sci Fair 87; Rep Hugh O Brian Yth Fndtn 86; Boston U; Med.

GANDY, KELLI; Bridgeton HS; Newport, NJ; (4); Art Clb; GAA; Service Clb; Varsity Clb; Pres Sr Cls; Var Fld Hcky; Sftbl; Var Swmmng; ST Teen Arts Festvl NJ 87; Won Schlrshp Art Srvc Art Lssns 87; Archtrl Stds.

GANESH, CHAMPAMATIE; Lincoln HS; Jersy City, NJ; (3); JA; Key Clb; Nwsp Rptr; Bowling; Tennis; JR Nurses Aide Work Study Pgm 86; Child Care Work Study Pgm 85; Med.

GANGES, BRIAN; Lawrence HS; Lawrencevlle, NJ; (2); Spanish Clb; Off Frsh Cls; Stu Cncl; Bsbl; Score Keeper; Socr; Wrstlng; Morehouse Coll; Pre Law.

GANGULY, NANDINI MOUMEE; Raritan HS; Hazlet, NJ; (3); 30/343; French Clb; Office Aide; Variety Show; Yrbk Stf; High Hon Roll; Hon Roll; NHS; Sci Awd 82-83; Perfect Attndnc Awd 82-83; Std Cncl Chorus Awd 83-84; Rutgers U; Biomed Engrng.

GANNING, KELLY; Monmouth Regional HS; Eatontown, NJ; (3); Cmnty Wkr; Drama Clb; Office Aide; Pep Clb; Spanish Clb; SADD; Flag Corp; Stage Crew; Sec Stu Cncl; Capt Cheerleading; Grls Ctznshp Awd Womns Clb 87; Brnz Cngrssnl Awd 86; Cmnctns.

GANNON, GIA; Camden Catholic HS; Tansboro, NJ; (2); French Clb; Off Soph Cls; Jr Cls; Stu Cncl; JV Fld Hcky; Hon Roll; Amb; Hmrm Rep; Ballet Dancer; Dance.

GANNON, JAMES; Vernon Township HS; Hewitt, NJ; (3); Quiz Bowl; JV Ftbl; Var L Wrstlng; Hon Roll; NHS; Stage Crew; Ntl Merit SF; Law.

GANNON, MONICA; Lower Cape May Regional HS; Villas, NJ; (2); 4/300; SADD; Chorus; Mgr(s); High Hon Roll; Hon Roll; Hnr Awd Having 1st Or 2nd Hnrs All Yr 85-86; Hnr Awd 86-87; Princeton; Law.

GANT, JEFF; Livingston HS; Livingston, NJ; (3); JA; Ski Clb; Wrstlng; Prfct Atten Awd; Elec Techncn.

GAPINSKI, AMY; Arthur P Schalick HS; Bridgeton, NJ; (3); 5/127; Drama Clb; SADD; Chorus; Color Guard; Rep Frsh Cls; Rep Soph Cls; Trs Jr Cls; Rep Stu Cncl; Var Cheerleading; Hon Roll; Drmtc Arts.

GARBACK, SHANNON; Washington Township HS; Sewell, NJ; (3); Sftbl; Swmmng.

GARBER, ALISON; Middletown HS South; Red Bank, NJ; (3); JV Bsktbl; Var Crs Cntry; JV Powder Puff Ftbl; Var Socr; Hon Roll.

GARBER, MARK; Waldwick HS; Waldwick, NJ; (2); Letterman Clb; Math Tm; Quiz Bowl; Ski Clb; Varsity Clb; Socr; Tennis; High Hon Roll; Hon Roll; Math, Sci, Lang Arts & Spnsh Hnrs; Advncd Plcmnt Soc Styds Cls; Math.

GARBER, MELISSA; Clifton HS; Clifton, NJ; (4); 47/580; Girl Scts; Capt Quiz Bowl; Science Clb; Chorus; Madrigals; School Play; Jr NHS; NHS; Ntl Merit Schol; St Schlr; Grl Sct Slvr Awd 84; Douglass Coll; Bio.

GARBOWSKI, ROBIN; Holy Spirit HS; Absecon, NJ; (2); 50/397; Pres Frsh Cls.

GARCIA, JORGE; Albert Emerson HS; Union City, NJ; (3); FCA; NFL; ROTC; Bsktbl; Socr; Swmmng; Wt Lftg; 2 Diplomas In Sci; Hnr Diploma A&b Avg; Military; Pilot.

GARCIA, KATHERINE; Passaic Valley HS; W Paterson, NJ; (2); 79/335; Drama Clb; GAA; Spanish Clb; Band; Chorus; Concert Band; Mrchg Band; Orch; School Play; Stage Crew; Band Music Awd 86-87; PA ST U; Psych.

GARCIA, LUCY; Our Lady Of Good Counsel HS; Newark, NJ; (3); 20/122; School Musical; NHS; Artist Of Yr Awd 86-87; MIT; Arch.

GARCIA, LYNN; Mary Help Of Christians Acad; Paterson, NJ; (1); SADD; Hon Roll; Acdmc Sklls Hnr 86; Outstndng Grds Grmmr Schl Schlrshp 86; Med Sci.

GARCIA, MARISOL; Mary Help Of Christians Acad; Paterson, NJ; (3); Church Yth Grp; Dance Clb; JCL; Letterman Clb; Math Tm; Quiz Bowl; School Play; Swmmng; Hon Roll; Prfct Atten Awd; Pre-Med.

GARCIA, MICHAEL; Rahway SR HS; Rahway, NJ; (4); 15/231; Am Leg Boys St; French Clb; Key Clb; Madrigals; Nwsp Stf; Yrbk Stf; VP Stu Cncl; Mgr Wrstlng; NHS; Pre-Law.

GARCIA, SANDRA; Passaic County Tech & Voc HS; Paterson, NJ; (3); 13/523; FNA; Hosp Aide; SADD; Yrbk Stf; JV Capt Cheerleading; Hon Roll; NHS.

GARCIA, SEAN MICHAEL; Ridgefield Park HS; Little Ferry, NJ; (3); Drama Clb; Ski Clb; Spanish Clb; Teachers Aide; VP Sr Cls; Var Capt Bsbl; Var Capt Bsktbl; Var Capt Ftbl; Wt Lftg; Football 3rd Team All County Punter & Honerable Mention 86-87; Accountant.

GARCIA, SONIA; Vineland SR HS; Millville, NJ; (4); 37/737; English Clb; Pres Spanish Clb; French Clb; Girl Scts; Political Wkr; Nwsp Rptr; Sec Stu Cncl; Sec NHS; Semi Fnlst Ntl Hspnc Schlr Awds 86-87; Gardn ST Dstngshd Schlrs 86-87; Rutgers U; Commnctns.

GARCIA, VIVIAN; John F Kennedy HS; Paterson, NJ; (4); 9/343; Science Clb; Rep Jr Cls; High Hon Roll; Hon Roll; Sec NHS; Pres Schlr; Cntrl HS Alumni Schlrshp, Outstndng Achvt 4 Yrs, Aspira Inc NJ-HNR Outstndng Achvts Educ 87; Rutgers U; Envrnmntl Sci.

GARCIA, YVETTE; Immaculate Conception HS; Ridgefield Park, NJ; (3); 9/70; NFL; Science Clb; Speech Tm; Church Choir; Yrbk Phtg; VP Jr Cls; Sftbl; Vllybl; Church Yth Grp; Frnscs 3rd Pl Trphy 85; Frnch Hnr Cert 85; NY U; Law.

GARD, DAVID; Southern Regional HS; Waretown, NJ; (3); Aud/Vis; Camera Clb; Church Yth Grp; Nwsp Phtg; Nwsp Rptr; Nwsp Stf; Yrbk Phtg; Yrbk Rptr; Yrbk Stf; Lit Mag; Photo-Jrnlsm.

GARDENHIRE, BARBARA ANNE; Vineland HS; Vineland, NJ; (4); 104/736; Church Yth Grp; English Clb; Pep Clb; Acpl Chr; Madrigals; School Play; Nwsp Rptr; Var L Trk; Ntl Merit Ltr; Cumberland CC; Pub Rel.

GARDNER, ANTHONY; Penns Grove HS; Carneys Point, NJ; (3); 11/270; German Clb; Band; Concert Band; Drill Tm; Drm & Bgl; Jazz Band; Mrchg Band; Orch; Pep Band; School Musical; Rutgers.

GARDNER, CAROLYN; Timothy Christian Schl; Milltown, NJ; (3); 1/44; Church Yth Grp; Chorus; High Hon Roll; Hon Roll; NHS; Elem Teacher.

GARDNER, ERICA; Vineland HS; Vineland, NJ; (4); 23/585; French Clb; French Hon Soc; High Hon Roll; Hnr Stu; Cumberlnd Cnty Coll; Bus Law.

GARDNER, KARRIE; Bricktownship HS; Brick Town, NJ; (3); 27/415; Art Clb; Drama Clb; Intnl Clb; Key Clb; Ski Clb; SADD; Thesps; Band; School Play; Stage Crew; Dir & Spcl Awd Drama Clb 87; Cmrcl Art.

GARDNER, PATRICIA; A P Schalick HS; Elmer, NJ; (4); 1/130; Math Tm; Variety Show; Pres Frsh Cls; Pres Soph Cls; Pres Rep Stu Cncl; Var Capt Fld Hcky; L Swmmng; Hon Roll; NHS; Val; Garden ST Distngshd Schlr 86-87; U DE.

GARFINKLE, JANICE; Jackson Memorial HS; Jackson, NJ; (3); 7/416; Am Leg Aux Girls St; Math Tm; Science Clb; Yrbk Stf; JV Sftbl; NHS; Ntl Merit Ltr; Spanish NHS; Voice Dem Awd; Nwsp Stf; Natl Art Hnr Soc 85-88; Sci.

GARFINKLE, NEIL; Fair Lawn HS; Fair Lawn, NJ; (2); Boy Scts; Cmnty Wkr; Drama Clb; PAVAS; Temple Yth Grp; Thesps; Y-Teens; Chorus; School Musical; School Play; Rutgers; Cmmnctns.

GARG, SAMPAK; Elizabeth HS; San Jose, CA; (2); French Clb; Leo Clb; Stage Crew; Nwsp Stf; Vllybl; Hon Roll; Schlrshp Frm Grammar Schl 85; Law.

GARGANIGO, MARC; Oratory Prep Schl; Westfield, NJ; (3); Service Clb; Nwsp Stf; VP Frsh Cls; Pres Soph Cls; JV Bsbl; Var Socr; Var Tennis; High Hon Roll; Hon Roll; NHS; Central Jersey Wrestling Champ 82; Law.

GARGANO, NICOLE; De Paul Diocesan HS; Lincoln Pk, NJ; (3); 30/160; Ski Clb; Pres Frsh Cls; Rep Soph Cls; Rep Jr Cls; Rep Sr Cls; Rep Stu Cncl; Var Fld Hcky; High Hon Roll; NHS; Pre-Med.

GARIBALDI, LAURIE; Spotswood HS; Spotswood, NJ; (2); 1/127; Intnl Clb; High Hon Roll; Hon Roll; Rutgers Univ; Phrmcst.

GARINO, PETER; Paterson Catholic Regional HS; Paterson, NJ; (3); 1/100; Am Leg Boys St; Cmnty Wkr; Library Aide; Model UN; Pep Clb; Science Clb; High Hon Roll; NHS; Prfct Atten Awd; 1st Pl NJ Chem Olympcs 85-86; Law.

GARLIC, KIM; Edgewood Regional SR HS; West Atco, NJ; (3); Church Yth Grp; Library Aide; Teachers Aide; Varsity Clb; Church Choir; Cheerleading; Trk; Hon Roll; Prfct Atten Awd; Music Mnstry Wrkshp 85; Varsty Awd 86-87; Spnsh & Foods Awd 85; Psych.

GARNER, JO ANN; Rancocas Valley Regional HS; Mt Holly, NJ; (4); French Clb; Hosp Aide; Ski Clb; Yrbk Stf; Lcrss; Hon Roll; Burlington County Coll; Thrpy.

GARNER, KIMBERLY; Washington Township HS; Turnersville, NJ; (3); German Clb; Hosp Aide; Hon Roll; Pre-Law.

GARNER, REINA; Freehold Township HS; Freehold, NJ; (4); Art Clb; Debate Tm; Spanish Clb; Yrbk Phtg; Lit Mag; Crs Cntry; Trk; High Hon Roll; NHS; Spanish NHS; Garden St Schlr 87; Schlrshp Trenton ST Coll Merit 87; Trenton ST Coll; Bus Adm.

GARNER, TYLEA; Mother Seton Regional HS; Irvington, NJ; (3); Cmnty Wkr; Hosp Aide; SADD; School Play; Yrbk Stf; Rep Frsh Cls; Rep Soph Cls; Rep Jr Cls; Off Sr Cls; Civic Clb; YMCA Cnslr 87; Orgnzr JR Ring Ceremoy 87; Prom Orgnzr 87; Bus Adm.

GARO, AILEEN; St Joseph Of The Palisades HS; Union City, NJ; (2); French Clb; Yrbk Stf; Soph Cls; Hon Roll; 1st & 2nd Hnrs 86 & 87; San Pedro De Macoris; Psych.

GAROFALO, ELKE; St Josephs Of The Palisades HS; North Bergen, NJ; (3); 11/155; Drama Clb; School Play; Ed Yrbk Stf; Pres Jr Cls; Stat Ftbl; Sftbl; Hon Roll; NHS; Fine Arts.

GAROFALO, MARCIA ANNE; Mary Help Of Christians Acad; N Haledon, NJ; (4); 10/80; Chorus; Orch; Stage Crew; Rep Jr Cls; Rep Sr Cls; Var Mgr(s); Vllybl; Hon Roll; NHS; Yth Mayor & Cncl 85-87; Marymount U; Bus Law.

GAROFANO, REBECCA; Middletown HS South; Middletown, NJ; (2); Office Aide; Yrbk Phtg; Mgr Bsktbl; Fld Hcky.

GARRABRANT, KAREN; Pitman HS; Pitman, NJ; (3); 40/143; Crs Cntry; Key Clb; Pres SADD; Concert Band; Ed Lit Mag; Stat Socr; Stat Trk; JC Awd; Rcrdng Scrtry S Jersey Yth Comm 87-88; Psych.

GARRAHAN, JENNIFER; Arthur P Schalick HS; Elmer, NJ; (3); 8/130; Math Tm; SADD; Concert Band; Mrchg Band; Yrbk Stf; Rep Sr Cls; Var JV Bsktbl; Var JV Sftbl; Tennis; Hon Roll; Coaches Awd Sftbl 86; Spirit Awd Bsktbl 86-87; Glassboro ST; Ed.

GARRETT, CAROLINE E; Scotch Plains-Fanwood HS; Scotch Plains, NJ; (4); 36/300; Model UN; Political Wkr; Q&S; Nwsp Ed-Chief; Lit Mag; French Hon Soc; Gov Hon Prg Awd; Ntl Merit SF; Pres Poltcl Afrs Clb; Jrnlsm.

GARRETT JR, DAVID G; Gloucester HS; Gloucester Cty, NJ; (3); French Clb; Math Clb; Var Ftbl; Var Trk; Im Wt Lftg; Cit Awd; Hon Roll.

GARRETT, MARY MARGARET; Hamilton HS West; Trenton, NJ; (4); 14/322; Am Leg Aux Girls St; Intnl Clb; SADD; Band; Madrigals; Symp Band; NHS; GAA; Mrchg Band; HOBY Fndtn Rep 85; Pres-Intl Clb 86-87; Editor-Spnsh Sectn Frgn Lang Nwsp 86-87; U Of West FL; Elem.

GARRIGAN, KATHY; Wayne Valley HS; Wayne, NJ; (3); 30/385; Church Yth Grp; Var L Crs Cntry; Var L Gym; Var L Trk; Hon Roll; 1st Tm All Cnty Hgh Jmp 87; 1st Tm All Conf Lng Jmp 87; 1st Tm All Conf, All Arnd Trk 86; U Of VA; Bnkng.

GARRIGANA, MICHELLE; Brick Township HS; Brick, NJ; (3); 48/358.

GARRIS, YVETTE; Mary Help Of Christians Acad; Paterson, NJ; (3); English Clb; SADD; Teachers Aide; JV Bsktbl; Prfct Atten Awd; Sociology 87; Hampton U; Secondary Educ.

GARRISON, BILLY; Cranford HS; Cranford, NJ; (3); Boy Scts; Wrstlng; Engrng.

GARRISON III, GEORGE C; Plainfield HS; Plainfield, NJ; (3); 8/563; FBLA; Band; Church Choir; Trs Stu Cncl; Var Bsktbl; Var Capt Crs Cntry; Var Trk; Var Hon Roll; NHS; Ntl Merit Ltr; Amng Top PSAT Scorer In Ntn 85; Gftd & Tlntd Prog 78-84; Nj Math Plcmnt Wnnr 84; Howard U; Elec Engr.

GARRITY, JOHN; Holy Spirit HS; Margate, NJ; (4); 51/363; Church Yth Grp; NHS; Crew Team; Trenton ST; Accntng.

GARRY, ELISE; St Mary Of The Assumption HS; Elizabeth, NJ; (2); Church Yth Grp; Hosp Aide; Chorus; Church Choir; School Musical; School Play; Variety Show; Var Bsktbl; Buyer.

GARTENBERG, JILL; Lakewood HS; Lakewood, NJ; (3); 10/300; Am Leg Aux Girls St; VP English Clb; Chorus; Var Tennis; Hon Roll; NHS; Spanish NHS.

GARUBO, CHRISTA NOEL; West Morris Mendham HS; Mendham, NJ; (4); 132/318; Art Clb; Cmnty Wkr; Hosp Aide; Office Aide; Yrbk Stf; Rep Stu Cncl; Var Socr; Var Capt Trk; Hon Roll; HOBY 84; Simmons.

GARWOOD, KATHLEEN M; Holy Cross HS; Willingboro, NJ; (4); 32/352; Yrbk Stf; Wt Lftg; Hon Roll; St Schlr; NJ ST & S Jersey Pstl Wrkrs Schlrshps, 1st Cthlc Slovak Ladies Assoc Schlrshp 87; Trenton ST Coll; Bus Admn.

GARZILLI, CHARLES; Sussex County Votech; Vernon, NJ; (2); Chess Clb; Computer Clb; JV Trk; Var Wt Lftg; Var Wrstlng; High Hon Roll; Comp Prgrmmr.

GARZO, MARY ANN; Greenbrook HS; Greenbrook, NJ; (2); High Hon Roll; Hon Roll; NHS; Rutgers U; Cmmrcl Artst.

GARZON, CHRISTINE; Holy Rosary Acad; Union City, NJ; (3); Math Tm; Spanish Clb; Teachers Aide; School Musical; Nwsp Stf; Yrbk Stf; Hon Roll; NHS; Prfct Atten Awd; Hnr Awds 85-87; Accntnt.

GASCOYNE, KERI; Wayne Hills HS; Wayne, NJ; (2); 24/350; Church Yth Grp; Spanish Clb; School Musical; Yrbk Stf; JV Bsktbl; Mgr(s); Score Keeper; Socr; Capt JV Sftbl; High Hon Roll; Librl Arts.

GASKILL, BRENDA; Cherryhill HS West; Cherry Hill, NJ; (3); Intnl Clb; Office Aide; Pres Sec SADD; School Play; Rep Jr Cls; Rep Sr Cls; Rep Stu Cncl; Var JV Cheerleading; Hon Roll; Italian Clb VP & Pres 86-88; Fraternal Order Of Police X-Mas Party 87-88; Spcl Needs Child Fld Day 87; Educ.

GASPARATOS, SUSIE; Fort Lee HS; Ft Lee, NJ; (3); Sec Camera Clb; Cmnty Wkr; VP FTA; Intnl Clb; Library Aide; SADD; Yrbk Phtg; Lit Mag; High Hon Roll; Hon Roll; Rutgers Coll; Engl Tchr.

GASPARRO, FRANK; Baptist HS; Mt Ephraim, NJ; (3); 20/50; Chorus; Yrbk Phtg; Yrbk Rptr; Yrbk Stf; Off Soph Cls; Off Jr Cls; Var JV Bsktbl; 4-H Awd; Bus.

GASS, SHELLY; Phillipsburg HS; Phillipsburg, NJ; (3); Pep Clb; Trs Frsh Cls; Trs Soph Cls; Var Capt Cheerleading; High Hon Roll; Hon Roll; NHS; Rep Stu Cncl.

GATELY, DINA; Raritan HS; Hazlet, NJ; (3); 18/327; Pres French Clb; SADD; Teachers Aide; Var Capt Cheerleading; High Hon Roll; Hon Roll; NHS; Educ.

GATELY, JOHN; Edgewood Regional SR HS; Hammonton, NJ; (2); Latin Clb; ROTC; Flag Corp; Ocngrphr.

GATERUD, MARY; North Hunterdon HS; Annandale, NJ; (3); 82/328; VP Drama Clb; Quiz Bowl; Scholastic Bowl; School Musical; School Play; Variety Show; Ed Lit Mag; Hon Roll; Vsl Dsgn Arts.

GATES, CAROLYN; Middletown HS South; Middletown, NJ; (4); 23/450; Intnl Clb; Political Wkr; SADD; Flag Corp; Stage Crew; Yrbk Ed-Chief; Rep Jr Cls; Rep Sr Cls; Hon Roll; Ntl Merit Ltr.

GATES, TARA; Pemberton TWP HS No II; Fort Dix, NJ; (3); Rep Jr Cls; Trk; NJ ST Semi-Fnls & Lttrd Trk 86-87; Miss NJ Coed Pgnt ST Fnlst 87; Howard U; Bus.

GATLIN, FAYE JEANNINE; Abraham Clark HS; Roselle, NJ; (3); Art Clb; Teachers Aide; MI ST U; Engrng.

GATTUSO, MARTHA; St James HS; Gibbstown, NJ; (3); French Clb; SADD; Chorus; Frnch.

GATZ, COLETTE; Sayreville War Memorial HS; Parlin, NJ; (2); Spanish Clb; Band; Color Guard; Concert Band; Mrchg Band; Stage Crew; Nwsp Stf; Hon Roll; Psych.

GAUDET, JEAN; Southern Regional HS; Spray Beach, NJ; (3); 15/350; Off Jr Cls; Stu Cncl; JV Var Fld Hcky; Var Powder Puff Ftbl; JV Var Sftbl; Im Vllybl; High Hon Roll; Hon Roll; Jr NHS; NHS; Acadc Athlt Awd 85; Bio.

GAUDIOSO, PETER A; West Milford Township HS; West Milford, NJ; (4); 23/351; Am Leg Boys St; Model UN; Band; Chorus; Concert Band; Jazz Band; Mrchg Band; School Musical; Rep Stu Cncl; Im Bsbl; Music Schlrshp 87; Hstry Awd-B Bradley Sntrl Cnfrnc 87; Syracuse U; Law.

GAUGHAN, SEAN A; Northrn Burlington Cnty Regnl HS; Allentown, NJ; (4); 7/236; Am Leg Boys St; Math Tm; Band; Jazz Band; School Musical; L Var Bsbl; L Var Crs Cntry; French Hon Soc; High Hon Roll; NHS; Jack/Edna Belasco Schlrshp87; Rutgers U; Materls Engrng.

GAUL, JEN; St Rose HS; Brick, NJ; (3); 80/240; Church Yth Grp; Ski Clb; School Musical; Yrbk Stf; Im Gym; Var Trk; Im Vllybl; Hon Roll; Industry Studies, Good Character 84; U MA Amherst; Psych.

GAULDEN, SHAUNDA D; Irvington HS; Irvington, NJ; (3); Church Yth Grp; Drama Clb; Girl Scts; Latin Clb; Spanish Clb; Bowling; Trk; Hon Roll; English Clb; Hosp Aide; Agran Clb 87; Bwlng-Mt Zion Bapt Chrch 86; Med.

GAURONSKI, JOSEPH C; Colonia HS; Colonia, NJ; (4); 1/244; Am Leg Boys St; Math Clb; Quiz Bowl; Scholastic Bowl; Ski Clb; Spanish Clb; SADD; Varsity Clb; Nwsp Sprt Ed; VP Soph Cls; Century III Ldrshp Awd 87; Faculty Bowl Wnnr 87; NJ Future Prob Solvng Bowl Champs 84-85; Princeton U; Pol Sci.

GAUS, JENNY; Bernards HS; Bernardsville, NJ; (3); 15/189; Cmnty Wkr; Band; Jazz Band; Orch; Nwsp Rptr; Crs Cntry; Trk; High Hon Roll; NHS; Intnl Clb; 4th Pl ST 55 Meter Hrdls 87; Instrmntlst Mgz Mscnshp Awd 86; Englsh.

GAUS, WILLIAM E; Paul VI HS; Turnersville, NJ; (4); 27/500; Church Yth Grp; Math Clb; Im Bowling; Socr; Hon Roll; NHS; Squires Columbus 83; Drexel; Arch.

GAUSEPOHL, STEVEN; Lenape Valley Regional HS; Andover, NJ; (3); 4/222; Boy Scts; JV Golf; JV Socr; French Hon Soc; High Hon Roll; Hon Roll; NHS; Ntl Merit Ltr; Lenape Vly Schr 85-86.

GAUTHIER, KATHRYN; Allentown HS; Allentown, NJ; (4); 12/184; Am Leg Aux Girls St; Girl Scts; Concert Band; Capt Drill Tm; Jazz Band; School Musical; Lit Mag; Hon Roll; NHS; Pres Acad Fit Awd 87; Rutgers Coll; Astrophyscs.

GAVIN, NANCY; Washington Township HS; Blackwood, NJ; (3); Hon Roll; Bus.

GAVINO, CONSUELO; Bloomfield HS; Bloomfield, NJ; (3); Library Aide; Band; Concert Band; Mrchg Band; Pep Band; Hon Roll; Montclair ST Coll; Accntnt.

GAVRILOVIC, IGOR; Wood-Ridge HS; Wood Ridge, NJ; (3); 1/90; French Clb; Math Clb; Model UN; Science Clb; Nwsp Stf; Var Trk; High Hon Roll; NHS; Med.

GAWRON, JAMES; Newton HS; Newton, NJ; (3); 23/210; Latin Clb; Math Clb; Science Clb; Concert Band; Mrchg Band; Hon Roll; Bio Sci Olympd; Chemstry.

GAWRONSKI, JOSEPH; Colonia HS; Colonia, NJ; (4); 1/244; Am Leg Boys St; VP Stu Cncl; Capt L Socr; NCTE Awd; VP NHS; Pres Spanish NHS; Val; Cmnty Wkr; Math Clb; Quiz Bowl; Rnnr Up Time Educ Wrtng Cont 86; ST Champ NJ Future Prblm Slvng Prg 84-85; Cntry III Ldrshp 87; Intl Reltns.

GAZZILLO, ANDREA; Immaculate Heart Acad; Ridgefield Park, NJ; (3); Spanish Clb; Yrbk Stf; Hon Roll; NHS; Prfct Atten Awd; Spanish NHS; Vol Religion Tchr 86-87; Pharm.

GAZZILLO, MIKE; Kinnelon HS; Kinnelon, NJ; (2); Art Clb; Aud/Vis; Boy Scts; Church Yth Grp; French Clb; Band; Concert Band; Jazz Band; Mrchg Band; Stage Crew; Stevens Ins; Elec Engr.

GEARING, MAUREEN; Toms River HS South; Pine Bch, NJ; (3); 20/405; Drm Mjr(t); Mrchg Band; Pres Stu Cncl; JV Socr; Im Sftbl; JV Swmmng; High Hon Roll; Hon Roll; NHS; Church Yth Grp; Elem Educ.

GEATENS, FRANCIS; Gloucester Catholic HS; Bellmawr, NJ; (3); 10/184; Am Leg Boys St; Computer Clb; Var Capt Bsbl; Im Bsktbl; Im Coach Actv; Im Golf; High Hon Roll; Hon Roll; Svc Acad; Engrng.

GECK, SCOTT; Union HS; Union, NJ; (2); Key Clb; Band; Concert Band; Jazz Band; Orch; Hon Roll; Sci.

GECZIK, LISA; Bishop AHR HS; Milltown, NJ; (4); 6/256; Hosp Aide; Service Clb; Spanish Clb; Teachers Aide; Lit Mag; Rep Stu Cncl; Gym; High Hon Roll; NHS; NEDT Awd; Full Tutn Gymnstcs Schlrshp George Washington U 87; Century III Ldrs Schl Rep 87; Rutgers Schlr 87; George Wasington U; Accnt.

GEDDES, ROBERT; Edison HS; Edison, NJ; (4); 22/417; Church Yth Grp; Spanish Clb; Rep Soph Cls; Rep Jr Cls; Rep Stu Cncl; Var L Crs Cntry; Var L Trk; Hon Roll; NHS; Spanish NHS; Ironman Crss Cntry 84-85; Rutgers Coll; Bus.

GEE, JOHN; Maple Shade HS; Maple Shade, NJ; (2); Capt Var Bsbl; Var Socr; High Hon Roll; Hon Roll.

GEE, WILLIAM; Gloucester Catholic HS; Deptford, NJ; (3); Chess Clb; Computer Clb; Varsity Clb; Capt Bowling; Golf; Var Tennis; High Hon Roll; Hon Roll; NHS; Prfct Atten Awd; All Conf Bowling 87; Mst Imprvd 85-87; Prchl B Chmps 85-87; Acctng.

GEHBAUER, JOHN C; Roxbury HS; Succasunna, NJ; (4); 38/391; Varsity Clb; Frsh Cls; Soph Cls; Stu Cncl; Var L Crs Cntry; Var L Trk; Hon Roll; Ntl Merit SF; Acad Awd 83-87; Penn ST U; Comm.

GEHLBACH, JENNIFER; Morris Catholic HS; Succasunna, NJ; (3); 53/135; Pep Clb; Yrbk Phtg; Sec Soph Cls; JV Bsktbl; Var Powder Puff Ftbl; Trk; Hon Roll; NCTE Awd; Engrng.

GEHRING, AMY; Holy Spirit HS; Ocean City, NJ; (4); 14/363; French Clb; Math Tm; Pep Clb; SADD; Nwsp Rptr; Stu Cncl; Fld Hcky; NHS.

GEIMES, TYE BROKER; Nutley HS; Nutley, NJ; (3); Aud/Vis; Boys Clb Am; Boy Scts; Church Yth Grp; Cmnty Wkr; Computer Clb; Library Aide; Ski Clb; Spanish Clb; Church Choir; Goodwork Inst 4 Yr Schlrshp Awd 87; Software Engrng Inc-Most Orig Comp Gm Awd 86; GA Tech; Bus Admin.

GEIS, TAMMY; Wareen Co Vo-Technical HS; Belvidere, NJ; (3); Church Yth Grp; Key Clb; VICA; Yrbk Stf; JV Cheerleading; Hon Roll; Prfct Atten Awd; Data Prcsng.

GEISLER, CHRISTINE; Bridgewater Raritan H S West; Bridgewater, NJ; (4); Pres Frsh Cls; Pres Soph Cls; Rep Jr Cls; Rep Jr Cls; Pres VP Stu Cncl; JV Var Cheerleading; NHS; Sal; SADD; Key Clb; WA Wrkshp Cngrssnl Smnr Cntry III Schlrshp Bill Bradley Ldrshp Smnr; Boston U; Pblc Rltns.

GEISLER, GEORGE; Brick Memorial HS; Brick, NJ; (3); 5/387; JV Bsktbl; JV Capt Socr; Var L Tennis; High Hon Roll; NHS.

GEISS, JACQUELINE; Ambassador Christian Acad; Farmingdale, NJ; (3); 1/6; Aud/Vis; Church Yth Grp; Office Aide; Chorus; Church Choir; Flag Corp; Yrbk Ed-Chief; Rep Stu Cncl; Score Keeper; High Hon Roll; Acadmc Hnr Awd 85-87; Chrstn Charctr Awd 85-86; Bus Mgmt.

GEISSEL, JENNIFER; Watchung Hills Regional HS; Watchung, NJ; (3); Sec Debate Tm; Rep Drama Clb; Hosp Aide; SADD; Capt Drill Tm; School Musical; Rep Jr Cls; Pres Stu Cncl; Stu Of The Mnth, 87 Lbrary Awd; Bus Mgmt.

GEIST, ERIC; St James HS; Salem, NJ; (2); 2/120; JV Bsktbl; High Hon Roll; Ntl Sci Merit Awd 86.

GELATO, LISA; Bayonne HS; Bayonne, NJ; (4); Varsity Clb; Drill Tm; Rep Frsh Cls; Rep Soph Cls; Rep Jr Cls; Rep Sr Cls; Twrlr; Hon Roll; NHS; Pres Schlr; Jersey City ST; Acctg.

GELB, JOSEPH; Union SR HS; Union, NJ; (4); 8/534; Boys Clb Am; Drama Clb; German Clb; Key Clb; Service Clb; Temple Yth Grp; Y-Teens; Concert Band; Nwsp Stf; Socr; Stevens Inst Tech Almni Schlr 87; Stevens Inst Of Tech; Engrng.

GELBSTEIN, JENNIFER; Toms River HS North; Toms River, NJ; (3); 6/459; Boy Scts; French Clb; Ski Clb; Band; Mrchg Band; Rep Frsh Cls; Rep Soph Cls; Rep Jr Cls; Rep Sr Cls; High Hon Roll; Grls Ctznshp Inst 87; Med.

GELLER, BETHE P; John P Stevens HS; Edison, NJ; (4); Art Clb; Ski Clb; SADD; Band; Yrbk Stf; Stu Cncl; Cheerleading; Powder Puff Ftbl; Socr; Swmmng; Syracuse U; Textile & Fshn Dsgn.

GELS, MICHELLE; Hamilton High West; Trenton, NJ; (4); 7/333; Sec Intnl Clb; Mrchg Band; Symp Band; Stu Cncl; Var Fld Hcky; Var Trk; VP NHS; Frgn Lang Nwsp Grmn Ed 87; Amer Logstcs Assn, Air Force Schlrshp 87; U Of DE; Pre Vet Med.

GELSINGER, JEFFREY; Gloucester Catholic HS; Mt Royal, NJ; (3); 37/188; Church Yth Grp; Hon Roll; Bsktbl All Str MVP 86; Mst Pts Scrd-Bsktbl Leag 86.

GEMELLI, MICHAEL; River Dell Regional HS; River Edge, NJ; (3); 57/224; Boy Scts; Church Yth Grp; Civic Clb; Exploring; Ski Clb; Band; Concert Band; Jazz Band; Mrchg Band; Im Bsbl; Most Imprvd Sccr Plyr; Engrng.

GEMINO, ERICSON A; Ridgefield Park HS; Ridgefield Pk, NJ; (4); 28/170; Aud/Vis; Nwsp Stf; Capt Var Trk; Hon Roll; Fairleigh Dickinson U; Engrng.

GEMMELL, ANNE; Pope Paul Vi HS; Haddon Heights, NJ; (3); 21/481; Church Yth Grp; Cmnty Wkr; Math Clb; Nwsp Rptr; Var Bsktbl; JV Crs Cntry; Hon Roll; NHS; Ntl Merit Schol; Bsktbl Top 20 Undrclssmn 87; All Parochial A 2nd Tm 87; All Sth Jersey 2nd Tm 87; Bus.

GENDRON, PAUL; Madison Central HS; Old Bridge, NJ; (3); 32/355; High Hon Roll; Hon Roll; NHS; Itln Clb 84-87; Itln Natl Hnr Socty 86; Phy Sci.

GENOVESE, CARMEN; Red Bank Catholic HS; Neptune, NJ; (3); Chess Clb; Cmnty Wkr; Math Clb; Math Tm; Var Ftbl; Var Capt Trk; High Hon Roll; Hon Roll; Varsity Clb; Im Vllybl; Chem Awd 87; Principals Awd Excllnce 87; Med.

GENSONE, GINA; Tenafly HS; Tenafly, NJ; (2); JV Capt Cheerleading; JV Sftbl.

GENTILE, KRISTIN; Millville SR HS; Millville, NJ; (4); 4/430; Church Yth Grp; Dance Clb; French Clb; Office Aide; SADD; Off Stu Cncl; Trk; Elks Awd; High Hon Roll; Hon Roll; Wmns Clb Rep 86; Beth Hiuel Sisterhood Awd 87; Joseph B Cox Mem Schlrshp 87; LA ST U; Bus.

GENTILE, LAURA A; Bishop Eustace Prep; Haddonfield, NJ; (3); French Clb; Pep Clb; SADD; Cheerleading; Fld Hcky; Trk; Hon Roll; NHS; Bus.

GENTILE, MICHELE; Montville Township HS; Montville, NJ; (3); #24 In Class; Capt FBLA; Key Clb; Varsity Clb; Fld Hcky; Lcrss; Mgr(s); Cit Awd; High Hon Roll; NHS.

GENTRY, ESTELLA; Academic HS; Jersey City, NJ; (3); Dance Clb; Band; Var Mgr Bsbl; Var Mgr Bsktbl; Ntl Dnc Inst Mbr 84-86; Prtcpnt Acdmy Awds TV Brdcst 84; Mrt Roll 84-87.

GENUS, MICHAEL; Holy Cross HS; Burlington, NJ; (4); 40/400; Ski Clb; Capt Var Bsbl; NHS; NJ Schlr Athltc 87; Syracuse U; Comp Sci.

GENZALE, THOMAS; Pope John HS; Oak Ridge, NJ; (4); Var Capt Bsbl; Var Capt Ftbl; Hon Roll; Coachs Awd-Bsbl 86; Lemoyne Coll; Bus.

GENZONE, TARA; Pinelands Regional HS; Tuckerton, NJ; (2); French Clb; Tennis; Im Wt Lftg; Hon Roll; Mrchg Band; Psych.

GEORGE, DAVID T; Delaware Valley Regional HS; Milford, NJ; (3); 31/215; Key Clb; Var Bsbl; Hon Roll; VA Polytech; Arspc Engrng.

GEORGE, ERIC; Union Catholic Regional HS; Newark, NJ; (4); Art Clb; JA; SADD; Chorus; Var Bsbl; Var Bsktbl; Hon Roll; MVP Bsktbl 87; Hmntrn Awd 87; Law.

GEORGE, JANET; Burlington Twp HS; Burlington Twnshp, NJ; (3); 6/128; Am Leg Aux Girls St; Spanish Clb; Pres Trs Varsity Clb; Chorus; Co-Capt Socr; Sftbl; High Hon Roll; Hon Roll; NHS; Right Field St Var Sftbl Champ 85; Centerfield Conf Champs Var Sftbll 87; Nrsng.

GEORGE, KIM; Delaware Valley Regional HS; Milford, NJ; (3); 17/208; JV Bsktbl; JV Var Sftbl; High Hon Roll; Hon Roll; Sec Soph Cls; Bus.

GEORGIOU, PARASKEVI; Fair Lawn HS; Fair Lawn, NJ; (4); 18/340; Church Yth Grp; Sec Math Clb; Sec Math Tm; Science Clb; Off Jr Cls; High Hon Roll; Hon Roll; Jr NHS; NHS; Sunday Schl Awd 84-87; Rutgers; Pharmacy.

GEORGIU, ANDREEA; Glen Ridge HS; Glen Ridge, NJ; (3); AFS; VP Key Clb; Yrbk Phtg; Pres Frsh Cls; Rep Stu Cncl; JV Trk; High Hon Roll; Rotary Awd.

GERACE, MELISSA; Holy Spirit HS; Northfield, NJ; (2); 22/397; Church Yth Grp; Hosp Aide; Church Choir; Var Fld Hcky; Var Trk; Hon Roll; Naval Acad; Engrng.

GERACI, COLLEEN; Vineland HS; Vineland, NJ; (4); 45/736; French Clb; Chorus; Pres Jazz Band; Mrchg Band; Orch; School Musical; Nwsp Stf; Stu Cncl; Hon Roll; NHS; NJ All-St Symph Band 85-87; Glassboro St Yth Orch 85-87; All S Jersey Wind Ensmbl 84-87; Westchester U; Music Ed.

GERACI, NICHOLAS; Freehold Township HS; Freehold, NJ; (3); Church Yth Grp; FCA; 4-H; Nwsp Stf; Rep Stu Cncl; Var Bsktbl; Var Capt Socr; Var Capt Trk; Jr NHS; NHS; All Dist All Conf Socr; All Dist Trk; NJ Shore Select Socr Tm; U S Socr Fed.

GERALD, ERICA LYNN; East Side HS; Paterson, NJ; (3); Drama Clb; Exploring; Girl Scts; PAVAS; Science Clb; F; Fashion Merch.

GERALDO, MARIA; Emerson HS; Union City, NJ; (4); 56/307; Cmnty Wkr; Sec FBLA; Y-Teens; Hon Roll; Prfct Atten Awd; Fairleigh Dickinson; Med Tech.

GERAN, COLLEEN; Immaculate Heart Acad; River Vale, NJ; (1); Ski Clb; School Musical; Var Swmmng; Hon Roll.

GERBER, BART; Lodi HS; Lodi, NJ; (3); 9/270; Am Leg Boys St; Leo Clb; Spanish Clb; Varsity Clb; Stu Cncl; Ftbl; Trk; Wt Lftg; Hon Roll; NHS; Sci.

GERBER, CHRISTOPHER; Holy Spirit HS; Absecon, NJ; (4); 29/363; French Clb; Pres Frsh Cls; Hon Roll; NHS; Pre-Law.

GERBER, NATALIE; Fair Lawn HS; Fair Lawn, NJ; (3); Aud/Vis; Drama Clb; Science Clb; Spanish Clb; Nwsp Ed-Chief; Nwsp Rptr; Ed Lit Mag; High Hon Roll; Hon Roll; NHS; Hnrbl Mntn Annual Poetry Cntst 87; JETS NJ Cmptn 2nd Pl 87; Jr Marshall 87; Comm.

GERBEREUX, KIRK; Millville SR HS; Mauricetown, NJ; (4); German Clb; Hon Roll; Achvt Awd Bio Amoeba Awd 83-84; Pres Awd Phys Ftnss 86-87; Law Enfrcmt.

GERCHICK, STUART; Franklin HS; Manalapan, NJ; (3); Computer Clb; Library Aide; Math Clb; Math Tm; Model UN; Var Socr; High Hon Roll; NHS; St Schlr; Deans Summer Schlrs Pgm At Rutgers Univ NJ 87; MIT; Bus Mgmnt.

GERCKENS, JOHN; Northern Valley Reg HS; Old Tappan, NJ; (4); 67/280; SADD; Lit Mag; VP Soph Cls; VP Jr Cls; VP Stu Cncl; Capt Bsbl; Capt Ftbl; NHS; Old Tppn Rep Clb Citznshp Awd 87; Brgn Cnty Coachs Awd-Sprtsmnshp 87; Old Tppn Ftbll Awd 87; Rutgers U; Bus Manag.

GERDES, MICHELE; St John Vianney HS; Port Monmouth, NJ; (4); 30/250; Drama Clb; Library Aide; Service Clb; SADD; Stage Crew; Hon Roll; Prfct Atten Awd; Pres Schlr; Secaucus PBA Schlrshp 87; Elizabethtown Coll; Vet Med.

GERECITANO, JOHN; Matawan Regional HS; Aberdeen, NJ; (4); 6/316; Math Tm; PAVAS; Teachers Aide; Thesps; Acpl Chr; Chorus; Madrigals; School Musical; School Play; NHS; Garden ST Distinguished Schlr 86; Natl Merit Commended Schlr 86; Trenton ST Alumni Schlrshp 86; Pre-Med.

GEREDIEN, ROSS; Bridgewater HS East; Martinsville, NJ; (3); German Clb; Science Clb; Acpl Chr; Chorus; Nwsp Phtg; Nwsp Stf; Lit Mag; Var Crs Cntry; Im Wt Lftg; High Hon Roll.

GERENETSKI, CAROLYN; Westwood HS; Wash Twp, NJ; (2); JV Sftbl; Hon Roll; Natl Art Honor Scty.

GERKENS, FRANCIS; Vernon Towmship HS; Highland Lks, NJ; (4); Boy Scts; FBLA; Scholastic Bowl; Varsity Clb; Chorus; Rep Stu Cncl; Swmmng; Cit Awd; Hon Roll; Eagl Sct 87; 1st Hstry-St Acadc Decthln 87; Loyola Coll; Intl Bus.

GERLACH, TANIA; Scotch Plains-Fanwood HS; Scotch Plains, NJ; (3); Key Clb; Spanish Clb; SADD; Chorus; Drill Tm; High Hon Roll; Hon Roll; Spanish NHS; Cert Apprctn-SADD Secr 87; Cert Mrt-Outstndng Achvt Ntl Stndrdzd Tst Grmn 85.

GERLING, WILLIAM; Brick HS; Brick Town, NJ; (4); 3/374; German Clb; Capt Math Tm; High Hon Roll; Pres Schlr; Parent Without Partners Schlrshp, Outstndng Achvt Frgn Lang & Pres Acdmc Ftnss Awd 87; Rutgers ST U; Engrng.

GERMAN, IBET; Memorial HS; West New York, NJ; (3); Sec Math Clb; JV Vllybl; Hon Roll; Rutgers U; Math.

GEROFSKY, TRACEY; Mc Corristin Catholic HS; Trenton, NJ; (3); Capt GAA; JA; Pep Clb; School Musical; Ed Yrbk Stf; Stu Cncl; JV Var Bsktbl; JV Var Sftbl; Hon Roll; NHS; Yng Columbus Club 86; Psych.

GERRATY, MICHELE; Manasquan HS; Brielle, NJ; (3); Girl Scts; Spanish Clb; Nwsp Stf; Yrbk Stf; Socr; High Hon Roll; Hon Roll; Old Dominion U.

GERSH, GARY; John P Stevens HS; Edison, NJ; (4); 48/482; Sec Thesps; Yrbk Ed-Chief; Pres Frsh Cls; Sec Stu Cncl; Var Tennis; French Hon Soc; NHS; Cmnty Wkr; French Clb; Office Aide; Intl Brnz & Gold Mdlst Olympcs Of Mind Div III 84; Bst Actr Awd 86.

GERSHMAN, DINA; Franklin HS; Somerset, NJ; (3); Key Clb; Ski Clb; SADD; Temple Yth Grp; Mrchg Band; JV Var Mgr(s); JV Sftbl; JV Var Tennis; Stat Wrstlng; Hon Roll.

GERTLER, MICHELLE; Freehold Borough HS; Freehold, NJ; (4); 34/247; Am Leg Aux Girls St; Political Wkr; Nwsp Stf; Yrbk Stf; High Hon Roll; Hon Roll; Trs Sec Spanish NHS; Drill Tm; Shield & Key Awd; Natl Jrnlsm Sem American U; Princeton Ballet Co JR Div; U Miami; Cmmnctns.

GERTNER, MIKE; Shore Regional HS; West Long Branc, NJ; (3); Chess Clb; Math Clb; Math Tm; Ski Clb; Spanish Clb; Temple Yth Grp; Variety Show; Off Sr Cls; Stu Cncl; Bsbl; ST Invntn Cont Wnnr; Capt Of Socr Tm 87-88; Tlnt Show Wnnr 86; Engnrg.

GETZINGER, WILLIAM G; Haddon Twp HS; Westmont, NJ; (3); Am Leg Boys St; French Clb; Ski Clb; Varsity Clb; Rep Stu Cncl; Capt Var Bsbl; Capt Var Ftbl; Var Wrstlng; High Hon Roll; Hon Roll.

GEURDS, STACEY; Mc Corrisitin Catholic HS; Trenton, NJ; (4); 12/249; Cmnty Wkr; GAA; Pres Sec Key Clb; Chorus; Nwsp Ed-Chief; Yrbk Ed-Chief; Rep Sr Cls; Cit Awd; NHS; Pres Schlr; Outstndg Achvt On NEDT 85; Italian Amer Schlr 87; Girls Ctznshp Inst At Douglass Coll 86; Trenton ST Coll; Lawyr.

GEVERT, MICHELLE; St James HS; Salem, NJ; (1); 31/73; JV Fld Hcky; Physlgst.

GEYDOSHEK, SHARON; Immaculate Conception HS; Garfield, NJ; (2); 6/89; Library Aide; Spanish Clb; Stage Crew; Yrbk Stf; High Hon Roll; Hon Roll; NEDT Awd; Prfct Atten Awd.

GEYER, MAYA; Hunterdon Central HS; Flemington, NJ; (3); 4/546; Art Clb; Drama Clb; French Clb; Key Clb; PAVAS; Ski Clb; Thesps; School Play; Variety Show; French Hon Soc; Mst Prmsng Yng Actress Awd Bucks Cnty Shs Comp 85.

GHANIM, CATHY; Middlesex HS; Middlesex, NJ; (3); Civic Clb; Cmnty Wkr; Dance Clb; Key Clb; SADD; Yrbk Stf; Tennis; Elks Awd; Girl Scts; Office Aide; Middlesex Mrchng Band Awd 86-87; Middlesex Music Dept Awd 85-86; Key Clb Actv Mem Awd 86; Rutgers ST U; Phrmcy.

GHANIM, ZIYAD; Plainfield HS; Plainfield, NJ; (3); Chess Clb; Church Yth Grp; Debate Tm; Socr; Var Wt Lftg; Var Wrstlng; Hon Roll; Engr.

GHIA, MARK; High Point Regional HS; Susex, NJ; (3); Pres Aud/Vis; German Clb; Ski Clb; Stage Crew; Variety Show; Nwsp Rptr; Nwsp Stf; JV Socr; Wt Lftg; Hon Roll; Mrktng.

GHIA, PAURAVI D; Holy Rosary Acad; Jersey City, NJ; (3); Art Clb; Computer Clb; French Clb; Rep Library Aide; Math Clb; Science Clb; Yrbk Stf; High Hon Roll; NHS; Slvr Mdl U S Hstry I 85-86; Cert Hnr Lat I 84-85; Cert Hnr Wrld Hstry 84-85; Micro-Biol.

GHIBERTI, LOUISA; Emerson HS; Jersey City, NJ; (3); Debate Tm; FBLA; Hosp Aide; Science Clb; Band; Chorus; Concert Band; Drm Mjr(t); Mrchg Band; Orch; Emrsn Awd 87; Band Awds Musicnshp 86&87; NYU; Med.

GHIGLIOTTI, ANDREA; Middletown HS South; Middletown, NJ; (2); Church Yth Grp; Cmnty Wkr; Ski Clb; Stage Crew; Yrbk Stf; JV Bsktbl; JV Fld Hcky; JV Socr; Hon Roll; Spnsh Acad Awd 85-86.

GHIO, CHRISTOPHER; Memorial HS; Cedar Grove, NJ; (4); 4/123; Pres Church Yth Grp; Nwsp Rptr; Yrbk Stf; Rep Stu Cncl; Var Capt Socr; Bausch & Lomb Sci Awd; High Hon Roll; NHS; Boy Scts; Stage Crew; Rutgers Scshlr, Bst Defnsve Sccr Plyr 86; Engrng.

GIACCHINO, SUZANNE; Mt Olive HS; Flanders, NJ; (3); Ski Clb; Teachers Aide; Band; Concert Band; Drm Mjr(t); Mrchg Band; Symp Band; Socr; Hon Roll; Outstndng Mscn 86-87; Mc Donalds All Amer Band 86-87; Area Band 86-87; Music.

GIACOBBE, LISA; Toms River HS East; Toms River, NJ; (4); Dance Clb; Debate Tm; Sec Drama Clb; Political Wkr; Thesps; Acpl Chr; Band; Chorus; Color Guard; Capt Pom Pon; Ocean Cnty Coll; Tchr.

GIACOBBE, PETER; Immaculata HS; Neshanic Station, NJ; (2); Quiz Bowl; Scholastic Bowl; Church Choir; Concert Band; Jazz Band; Pres Mrchg Band; School Musical; Var Bsbl; NHS; Spanish NHS; Rep For Band 85-87; High Music, Math, & Sci Awds 86-87; Engr.

GIALLOURAKIS, COSMAS CHRIS; Red Bank Regional HS; Shrewsbury, NJ; (3); Off Frsh Cls; JV Socr; VP L Tennis; Hon Roll; NHS; Spanish NHS; Stu Cncl; High Hon Roll; Brnz Cngrssnl Mdl 87; 2nd In NJ Jr Sci Symposium Envrnmntl Wtr Pollution 87; Div Spcl Summer Pgms 87; Mlclr Physics.

GIAMBRONE, DEBBIE; Paul VI HS; Passaic, NJ; (3); Girl Scts; Key Clb; Ski Clb; School Play; Yrbk Stf; Stat Bsktbl; Var Crs Cntry; Var Trk; Hon Roll; Jrnlst.

GIAMPAPA, BRIAN; Highland Regional HS; Sicklerville, NJ; (2); Latin Clb; Service Clb; JV Var Ftbl; Wt Lftg; High Hon Roll; Hon Roll.

GIAMPETRO, ANDREW; Eastern Regional HS; Voorhees, NJ; (4); 67/335; Computer Clb; Political Wkr; Service Clb; Yrbk Stf; Rep Stu Cncl; Var Trk; Hon Roll; Jr NHS; Varsity Ltr Winter & Spring Track 86-87; Livinston Coll; Comp Sci.

GIAMPILIS, MARLENA MARIA; The Wilson Schl HS; Succasunna, NJ; (4); 1/5; School Play; Yrbk Ed-Chief; Yrbk Phtg; Yrbk Stf; Pres Soph Cls; VP Sr Cls; Vllybl; High Hon Roll; NHS; Church Yth Grp; St Elizabeth Coll; Educ.

GIANCAMILLI, PAULA; Phillipsburg HS; Alpha, NJ; (3); 28/315; Drama Clb; PAVAS; Band; Chorus; Church Choir; Concert Band; Mrchg Band; School Musical; School Play; Rep Stu Cncl; Livingston Coll Rutgers; Bus.

GIANCASPRO, JOHN A; Becton Regional HS; Carlstadt, NJ; (3); Am Leg Boys St; Church Yth Grp; Cmnty Wkr; Political Wkr; Vllybl; High Hon Roll; Hon Roll; Rutgers U; Pre-Med.

GIANELLA, MICHAEL; John P Stevens HS; Edison, NJ; (3); 99/450; Cmnty Wkr; Nwsp Rptr; Cmnctns.

GIANGIORDANO, RICHARD; Shawnee HS; Medford, NJ; (4); 4/535; Am Leg Boys St; Science Clb; Var L Ftbl; Hon Roll; Ntl Merit Ltr; Pres Schlr; St Schlr; Rep Jr Cls; PASS Tutorial Awd 87; All Liberty Div Ftbl Team; U PA; Biophys.

GIANNANTONIO, JOHN P; Lenape Valley Regional HS; Netcong, NJ; (4); Church Yth Grp; Drama Clb; Chorus; Church Choir; Madrigals; School Musical; School Play; Variety Show; Bsktbl; Sftbl; NJ Tn Arts For St Wnnr 86; Rgnl Wnnr Hemisphere Cntst In Vcl Music 87; Morris County Coll; Music.

GIANNELLA, DAVID; Manchester HS; N Haledon, NJ; (4); Ftbl.

GIANNOBILE, JOAN; Holy Family Acad; Bayonne, NJ; (4); Church Yth Grp; Computer Clb; French Clb; Math Clb; Pep Clb; Im JV Bsktbl; Im Vllybl; NEDT Awd; Schlrshp-Cldwll Coll; Soph Dane & Jr Prm & Retrt Cmte; U Of San Francisco; Law.

GIAQUINTO, MARY; West Essex HS; Fairfield, NJ; (3); Rptr Aud/Vis; Cmnty Wkr; VP Spanish Clb; Stage Crew; Cmnctns.

GIARDIELLO, JOHNNA; Paramus Catholic Girls HS; Emerson, NJ; (3); Service Clb; Nwsp Phtg; Nwsp Stf; Yrbk Phtg; Yrbk Stf; Lit Mag; Cit Awd; Hon Roll; NHS; NEDT Awd; Law.

GIARDINA, JOSEPH; Holy Spirit HS; Ventnor, NJ; (3); 37/332; 4-H; Radio Clb; Science Clb; Sftbl; Hon Roll; Jr NHS; NHS; VFW Awd; Med.

GIARDINA, LORA; De Paul HS; Ringwood, NJ; (4); 86/156; Church Yth Grp; Var Capt Cheerleading; Coach Actv; JV Sftbl; Hon Roll; Pres Schlr; Quinnipiac Coll; Sci.

GIBBS, CANDICE; Jefferson Township HS; Lake Hopatcong, NJ; (3); Church Yth Grp; DECA; Band; Church Choir; Concert Band; Symp Band; Off Jr Cls; JV Sftbl; Sec Sci.

GIBSON, CORINNE; Woodrow Wilson HS; Camden, NJ; (2); Band; Chorus; Church Choir; Concert Band; Rep Stu Cncl; Hon Roll; Prfct Atten Awd; Psng HS Prfcncy Tst NJ 86; Glassboro ST Coll; Chem Engr.

GIBSON, CRYSTAL; Williamstown HS; Williamstown, NJ; (3); Key Clb; Math Clb; Math Tm; Science Clb; Spanish Clb; SADD; Bsktbl; Trk; Hon Roll; NHS; Drexel; Engr.

GIBSON, ELIZABETH ANNE; Jefferson Township HS; Milton, NJ; (4); 60/235; Church Yth Grp; 4-H; Math Clb; NFL; Pep Clb; Service Clb; Spanish Clb; Teachers Aide; Varsity Clb; School Musical; 3rd Pl Drew U Spnsh Ortry 87; Mst Imprvd Plyr Crs Cntry Team 83; 9th Pl Team Awd Acdmc Dcthln 87; Montclair ST Coll; Nutrtn.

GIBSON, MARNI; Middle Township HS; Cape May C H, NJ; (4); 25/200; Church Yth Grp; Dance Clb; Ski Clb; Capt Mrchg Band; School Musical; Gym; Socr; Hon Roll; NHS; Pres Schlr; Trenton ST Coll; Spch Pathlgy.

GIBSON, ORONDE; Woodrow Wilson HS; Camden, NJ; (3); Computer Clb; JA; Im JV Bsktbl; High Hon Roll; Chem Engr.

GIBSON, RAE; Toms River HS South; Beachwood, NJ; (3); 29/405; Fld Hcky; Socr; High Hon Roll; Hon Roll; Bus Admin.

GIBSON, STEPHANIE; Burlington City HS; Edgewater, NJ; (3); Dance Clb; GAA; Girl Scts; Scholastic Bowl; Chorus; Variety Show; Stu Cncl; Bsbl; Bsktbl; Bowling; Prfrmr Music.

GIDDENS, GAIL LATRESSE; Metuchen HS; Metuchen, NJ; (4); 69/177; Church Yth Grp; Civic Clb; Ski Clb; Acpl Chr; Church Choir; Concert Band; Mrchg Band; Orch; School Musical; Capt Crs Cntry; Syracuse U.

GIDDINGS, TARA; Lakewood HS; Lakewood, NJ; (4); 73/270; Art Clb; English Clb; Key Clb; Nwsp Phtg; Nwsp Rptr; Nwsp Stf; Yrbk Stf; Bsktbl; Capt Var Socr; Sftbl; MVP Sccr 2 Yrs; 1st Pl Indr Sccr; Glassboro ST.

GIFFORD, DAN; Central Jersey Christian HS; Brick, NJ; (3); 6/30; Church Yth Grp; Trs Frsh Cls; Trs Soph Cls; Trs Jr Cls; Var Bsbl; Var Bsktbl; High Hon Roll; Pres NHS; All Confrnce Bsbl, Bsktbl First Team 86-87; Sci Fair Hnrble Mntn 87; Messiah Coll; Acctng.

GIFFORD, GIANNA; West Essex Regional HS; Essex Fells, NJ; (3); Drama Clb; FTA; Political Wkr; Concert Band; Orch; Stage Crew; Symp Band; Lit Mag; Stu Cncl; Hon Roll; Law.

GIGLIO, DAWN; Roselle Catholic HS; Union, NJ; (4); 5/195; Church Yth Grp; Math Tm; School Musical; Lit Mag; High Hon Roll; Sec NHS; Spanish NHS; Seton Hall U Schlrshp, Desmond Costello Mem Schlrshp 87; Seton Hall U.

GIGLIOTTI, DEANA; Washington Township HS; Sewell, NJ; (3); 24/564; Spanish Clb; JV Bsktbl; JV Powder Puff Ftbl; Hon Roll; NHS.

GIGLIOTTI, FRANCES; Washington Township HS; Sewell, NJ; (3); 17/546; Spanish Clb; VP Frsh Cls; JV Powder Puff Ftbl; Hon Roll; NHS; Rotary Awd; Glassboro ST; Elem Ed.

GILBERT, EVELYN; Allentown HS; Allentown, NJ; (4); 2/175; Church Yth Grp; Dance Clb; NFL; Ski Clb; Orch; School Musical; Nwsp Rptr; Nwsp Stf; Yrbk Ed-Chief; Var Cheerleading; Garden ST Dstngshd Schlr 87; Engl Awd 83; Yale U.

GILBERT, STEVEN; Edgewood Regional SR HS; Sicklerville, NJ; (3); Chess Clb; Latin Clb; Lit Mag; High Hon Roll; Hon Roll; Jr NHS; Prfct Atten Awd; Engr.

GILBERT, TARAKA; Plainfield HS; Plainfield, NJ; (4); 43/371; Chorus; Variety Show; Nwsp Rptr; Yrbk Stf; Hon Roll; Voice Dem Awd; Rutgers Upward Bound 83-87; Peer Ldrshp 86-87; New Horizons Coll Clb 85-87; Model Congress 86; Temple U; Cmmnctns.

GILBERT, TIMOTHY; Dover HS; Mine Hill, NJ; (3); 108/228; Boy Scts; FCA; German Clb; Ski Clb; JV Var Bsbl; Im Bowling; JV Var Ftbl; JV Var Swmmng; Hon Roll; Coaches Awd Var Swim Tm 86; MVP Var Swim Tm 87; PA ST U; Arch.

GILBERT, TIMOTHY C; Middletown South HS; Lincroft, NJ; (4); 32/450; School Play; Variety Show; Yrbk Sprt Ed; Yrbk Stf; Lit Mag; JV Bsbl; Var L Ftbl; Im Vllybl; Im Wt Lftg; Cit Awd; Pres Acadmc Ftns Awd 87; Osborn Schlrshp 87; T E Mc Dermott Mem Schlrshp 87; U Of Richmond.

GILBERT, TRICIA; North Bergen HS; North Bergen, NJ; (1); 1/350; French Clb; Nwsp Rptr; Im Trk; High Hon Roll.

GILBRIDE, CINDY; Cherry Hill HS West; Cherry Hill, NJ; (3); Office Aide; Rep Jr Cls; Var Mgr(s); Swmmng; Hon Roll; Brd Ed Cert Cmmndtn Swmmng 86-87; Hm Schl Awd 86-87; Med.

GILBRIDE, DONNA; Camden Catholic HS; Pennsauken, NJ; (3); 13/283; French Clb; FBLA; Office Aide; Spanish Clb; Drill Tm; School Play; Hon Roll; NHS; Emerald Engl Litry Hnr Scty 87; Scl Sci Hnr Scty 86-87; Bus Adm.

GILCH, JESSICA; Paramus Catholic G R HS; N Bergen, NJ; (2); Dance Clb; Hon Roll; Columbia U; Psych.

GILHEANY, CYNTHIA J; Acad Of The Holy Angels; Montvale, NJ; (4); 8/152; Church Yth Grp; Pres Math Tm; Model UN; Pres Mu Alpha Theta; Service Clb; Spanish Clb; Church Choir; Ed Nwsp Stf; High Hon Roll; St Schlr; Natl Latin Exam Cum Laude 85; Bus.

GILL, CRAIG; Bridgewater Raritan HS East; Basking Ridge, NJ; (3); French Clb; Ski Clb; Off Stu Cncl; Var Ftbl; Var Lcrss; Powder Puff Ftbl; Hon Roll; NHS; All Cnty Plc Kckr-Ftbl, 1st Tm 85; Hnrbl Mntn-All Area & All Cnty Plc Kckr 85 & 86; Sprts Med.

GILL, HOLLIE; Burlington City HS; Edgewater Pk, NJ; (4); 9/209; Am Leg Aux Girls St; FBLA; Pres Jr Cls; Pres Sr Cls; Stu Cncl; Var Capt Bsktbl; VP Capt Socr; Var Sftbl; Hon Roll; Lion Awd; Schlrshp Bsktbll Lions Clb 87; Otstndng Hstry Stu 87; Ldrshp Awd 87; Trenton ST Coll.

GILL, KENNETH; Essex Catholic Boys HS; Newark, NJ; (2); Art Clb; Boy Scts; Service Clb; Ski Clb; Rep Stu Cncl; Bsbl; Bsktbl; Sftbl; JETS Awd; Fncng ST Champs; Sales.

GILLEECE, JENNIFER; Immaculate Heart Acad; Spring Valley, NY; (1); Church Yth Grp; Model UN; Hon Roll; Med.

GILLESPIE, BRIAN K; Bayonne HS; Bayonne, NJ; (4); 6/375; Am Leg Boys St; Boy Scts; Math Tm; School Play; Lit Mag; Swmmng; Jr NHS; NHS; Eagle Scout 86; Drew Schlr Awd 87; Drew U.

GILLESPIE, JAMES; Burlington Co Votech; Edgewater Park, NJ; (3); Boy Scts; Exploring; VICA; Chorus; Concert Band; Stu Cncl; Bsbl; Bsktbl; Socr; Wrstlng; Mechanic.

GILLESPIE, JOHN A; Hammonton HS; Hammonton, NJ; (4); 3/193; Am Leg Boys St; Intnl Clb; Band; Jazz Band; Nwsp Rptr; Nwsp Stf; Stu Cncl; High Hon Roll; Hon Roll; NHS; Locl Wnnr Knghts Columbus Essay Cont 84; Acad Excllnc Awd 84-86; Natural Sci.

GILLIAM, DAN; Lower Cape May Regional HS; N Cape May, NJ; (4); 32/240; French Clb; Pep Clb; Band; Concert Band; Drm Mjr(t); Jazz Band; Mrchg Band; Orch; Pep Band; School Musical; Strs For The Shire Schlrshp 87; L Armstrong Awd; Berklee Coll Of Music; Music.

GILLISPIE, MEGAN; Morristown-Beard HS; Morristown, NJ; (3); GAA; Hosp Aide; Nwsp Rptr; Nwsp Stf; Lit Mag; VP Soph Cls; VP Jr Cls; Pres Sr Cls; Var Lcrss; JV Capt Vllybl.

GILMAN, JANINE; South Plainfield HS; S Plainfield, NJ; (4); Art Clb; Drama Clb; Band; Mrchg Band; School Play; Nwsp Rptr; Yrbk Phtg; Lit Mag; Stu Cncl; Hon Roll; Wrtng Awds 87; Temple U; Advrtsng.

GILMARTIN, ELIZABETH; St John Vianney HS; Freehold, NJ; (2); Church Yth Grp; Concert Band; Mrchg Band; School Musical; Hon Roll; Music Awd Sphmr Yr Gld & Wht Awd 87.

GILMORE, APRIL; Rutherford HS; Rutherford, NJ; (3); Am Leg Aux Girls St; VP German Clb; Key Clb; Pep Clb; Chorus; VP Frsh Cls; VP Soph Cls; VP Jr Cls; VP Sr Cls; VP Stu Cncl; Bd Educ Awd Hgh Hnrs 84-86; Jersey Grls ST 87; U Of San Diego; Lwyr.

GILMORE, HEATHER; Newton HS; Andover, NJ; (2); Cmnty Wkr; Dance Clb; French Clb; Hosp Aide; Ski Clb; Variety Show; Jr NHS; Hghst All Arnd Eastern Perf Arts Dance Comptn 87; 1st Pl Natl Champ Encore Natl Tlnt Comptn 86; Perfrmng Arts.

GILMORE, KATHERINE; Toms River South HS; Toms River, NJ; (3); 65/425; Hosp Aide; Ski Clb; Chorus; Hon Roll; Bus Mgmt.

GILMORE, RUSSELL; St John Vianney HS; Manalapan, NJ; (2); JV Bsbl; Var Bsktbl; Var Ftbl; Hon Roll.

GILMOUR, BONNIE; The Kings Chritian HS; Cherry Hill, NJ; (3); Church Yth Grp; Pres Jr Cls; Stat Bsktbl; Var Fld Hcky; Var Sftbl; High Hon Roll; NHS; Chld Psych.

GILSTER, JEANA A; Cherokee HS; Marlton, NJ; (3); Cmnty Wkr; DECA; Intnl Clb; Service Clb; Nwsp Bus Mgr; Nwsp Phtg; Nwsp Rptr; Nwsp Stf; Yrbk Phtg; Stu Cncl; Mst Val Stff Ad Ed CHS Stehekin 86-87; Advrtsng.

GIMIGLIANO, MARK; Newton HS; Newton, NJ; (2); French Clb; JV Ftbl; Var JV Wrstlng; Hon Roll; Scl Sci.

GINCEL, GRETAL; Mount St John Acad; Hopatcong, NJ; (2); Drama Clb; Math Clb; Chorus; Var Bsktbl; Bus Mgmnt.

GINDHART, CHERYL; Mawah HS; Mahwah, NJ; (2); Church Yth Grp; Dance Clb; Drama Clb; Intnl Clb; Latin Clb; Ski Clb; Chorus; School Musical; School Play; DAR Awd; Marine Bio.

GINDOFF, ILANA; Manalapan HS; Manalapan, NJ; (3); Drama Clb; SADD; Sec Chorus; Madrigals; School Musical; School Play; Variety Show; Hon Roll; Gov Schl Fnls Singing 87; All Shore Chorus 86-87; Ithica Coll; Musical Theater.

GINELLI, JOHN; St John Vianney HS; Morganville, NJ; (3); Ski Clb; Rep Soph Cls; Var Ftbl; Hon Roll; Prfct Atten Awd; Bus.

GINN, COREY; Eastside HS; Paterson, NJ; (3); 48/500; Church Yth Grp; Drama Clb; Math Tm; Service Clb; Chorus; Church Choir; School Play; Hon Roll; Prfct Atten Awd; NJ Inst Of Tech; Elec Engrng.

GINSBERG, ANDREW R; Moorestown HS; Moorestown, NJ; (3); Am Leg Boys St; Trs French Clb; Band; Nwsp Stf; Var Socr; Ntl Merit Ltr; Rotary Awd; Rep Soph Cls; Var Tennis; Im Vllybl; Natl Freedms Fndtn Delg 87; Rotry Yth Ldrshp Awd RYLA Conf Delg 86; Cnsl 87; Phila Area Sccr Tm 86; Chem.

GIOCANNETTI, TANIA; Sacred Heart HS; Vineland, NJ; (3); French Clb; Stage Crew; Yrbk Stf; Hon Roll; Psych.

GIOIA, ANN MARIE; Pennsville Memorial HS; Pennsville, NJ; (1); 20/225; Am Leg Aux Girls St; Church Yth Grp; FBLA; Hosp Aide; Natl Beta Clb; Ski Clb; Spanish Clb; Orch; Pep Band; Nwsp Rptr; Med.

GIORDANO, ANDREA; Dover HS; Mine Hill, NJ; (3); 15/230; Spanish Clb; Var Bsktbl; Var Crs Cntry; Var Trk; Hon Roll; Jr NHS; All-Cnty Trck St Sect Chmps 86-87; All-Area Trck Hnrbl Mntn 87; All-Cnfrnc Hnrbl Mntn Bsktbl 87; Accntng.

GIORDANO, DEBORAH LYNN; Manalapan HS; Manalapan, NJ; (3); Teachers Aide; Swing Chorus; Variety Show; VP Soph Cls; Rep Jr Cls; Stu Cncl; Var Capt Cheerleading; Var Gym; Var Capt Pom Pon; NHS; Var Chrldng Capt 87; Natl Hnr Rl 87; Congrssnl Mdl Hnr 87; Perf Arts.

GIORDANO, ESTERINA; Marylawn Of The Oranges; Orange, NJ; (3); Church Yth Grp; Service Clb; Hon Roll; NHS; Spanish NHS.

GIORDANO, FLORENCE; Cedar Ridge HS; Parlin, NJ; (3); 64/369; Drama Clb; Hst FBLA; Rep Stu Cncl; Var Gym; JV Sftbl; JV Trk; Hon Roll; Gld Seal Awd 87; Grtr Mddlsx Cnfrnc All-Acad Tm 86; Med Tech.

GIORDANO, JENNIFER; Montville Township HS; Pinebrook, NJ; (2); 23/287; Art Clb; Camera Clb; Cmnty Wkr; FBLA; Key Clb; SADD; Lit Mag; Pres Stu Cncl; 4-H Awd; High Hon Roll; Kodak Grnd Prz Wnnr Drg Abuse No Excuse Phtgrphy 87; 3rd Prz Schl Art Shws 87; Duke; Neuro Srgry.

GIORGIANNI, NICK; St James HS; Gibbstown, NJ; (4); 24/79; Var Ftbl; Var Capt Wrstlng; Fathers Clb Awd Ctznshp-Ldrshp 87; DE Valley Coll; Pre Med.

GIOVACCO, TRICIA; Clifton HS; Clifton, NJ; (4); 56/600; Church Yth Grp; Drama Clb; French Clb; Girl Scts; Drm Mjr(t); School Play; French Hon Soc; High Hon Roll; Hon Roll; NHS; Lehigh U; Intl Rltns.

GIOVETSIS, MARYANN; Edgewood Regional SR HS; Atco, NJ; (2); Color Guard; Drill Tm; Mrchg Band; Hon Roll; Acadmc Ftnss Awd 85-86; Theatre.

GIRARDY, MATTHEW J; Bernards HS; Gladstone, NJ; (3); 27/185; Boy Scts; Church Yth Grp; Band; Concert Band; Mrchg Band; Orch; Crs Cntry; Trk; Hon Roll; Pdtrc Doctor.

GIRGENTI, KIMBERLY; Bishop Eustace Prep; Woodlynne, NJ; (3); Hosp Aide; Latin Clb; NFL; Office Aide; Spanish Clb; SADD; Capt Cheerleading; Hon Roll; Spanish NHS; NJ ST Chrldng Champs 86-87; Natl Jayvee Chrlsnd Champs 87; Air Force Acad; Aviation.

GIRON, FRANCISCO; James J Ferris HS; Jersey City, NJ; (3); Spanish Clb; Var Capt Socr; Math Tchr.

GIROUARD, JAMES; Newton HS; Andover, NJ; (2); 17/238; French Clb; Concert Band; Jazz Band; Mrchg Band; Pep Band; Symp Band; JV Socr; High Hon Roll; Hon Roll; Pres Schlr; Monmouth; Sys Analyst.

GISLER, SCOTT; Kitlatinny Regional HS; Newton, NJ; (4); 18/227; Band; Mrchg Band; Trs Frsh Cls; Trs Sr Cls; Var Bowling; Var Socr; Var Tennis; High Hon Roll; Hon Roll; NHS; All Lg Socr Tm 87; All Area Socr Tm 87; Comp Engrng.

GISO, ISABELLA; Linden HS; Linden, NJ; (3); Latin Clb; VICA; Sec Frsh Cls; Swmmng; Woodshop Trophy 84; Cosmetology Contest 87; Law.

GITLIN, RORI; Parsippany HS; Parsippany, NJ; (3); FBLA; Office Aide; Spanish Clb; Temple Yth Grp; Band; JV Bsktbl; Socr; Physcl Therapy.

GITTELMAN, DAVID; Verona HS; Verona, NJ; (3); Model UN; Spanish Clb; Temple Yth Grp; Nwsp Rptr; Yrbk Bus Mgr; Lit Mag; Socr; Trk; NHS; Spanish NHS.

GITTENS, SHARON; Pemberton HS; Pemberton, NJ; (4); 8/415; Am Leg Aux Girls St; Aud/Vis; Trs FBLA; Office Aide; Var Capt Bsktbl; Var Sftbl; Var Trk; Hon Roll; NHS; Cngrssnl Schlr 87; Trenton ST Coll; Acctg.

GIULIANO, ANGELA; Our Lady Of Mercy Acad; Sewell, NJ; (3); Computer Clb; Dance Clb; SADD; Teachers Aide; Chorus; Var Cheerleading; High Hon Roll; Hon Roll; Jr NHS; Frnch & Engl Awds 4.0 Avg; Elec Engrng.

GIULIANO, CONNIE; Vineland HS; Vineland, NJ; (4); 4/735; Cmnty Wkr; Exploring; Key Clb; Math Clb; Orch; Nwsp Stf; Rep Frsh Cls; Rep Jr Cls; Rep Badmtn; High Hon Roll; Hopwood Schlrshp Sci 86; Garden ST Schlr 86; ST Italian Comp 85; La Salle U; Med.

GIUNTA, ANDREA; Wall HS; Neptune, NJ; (3); VP FBLA; Ski Clb; Spanish Clb; Sec Bsktbl; Score Keeper; High Hon Roll; Hon Roll; NHS; Ntl Merit Ltr; Spanish NHS; Med.

GIUNTA, MARIA; Cumberland Regional HS; Bridgeton, NJ; (3); 15/384; Church Yth Grp; Debate Tm; Model UN; Science Clb; Ski Clb; Spanish Clb; Varsity Clb; Trs Frsh Cls; Trs Soph Cls; Trs Jr Cls; Comp Engr.

GIURICEO, NANCY; Marine Acad Of Sci And Tech; Belford, NJ; (3); 1/46; Hosp Aide; ROTC; Spanish Clb; Drill Tm; Nwsp Rptr; Yrbk Stf; Pres Jr Cls; High Hon Roll; NHS; Val; Nom For J Gilliam Awd JROTC 86-87; Promo To Cadet Ensgn In Schl JROTC 86; Bio.

GIVONE, RICHARD; Whippany Park HS; Whippany, NJ; (3); Church Yth Grp; Computer Clb; Office Aide; Varsity Clb; Chorus; Church Choir; Madrigals; School Musical; Var Tennis; JV Wt Lftg; Bus.

GIYANANI, RAVI; St Augustine Prep; Vineland, NJ; (3); 2/54; Chrmn Boy Scts; Chess Clb; 4-H; Hosp Aide; School Play; 4-H Awd; High Hon Roll; NEDT Awd; Prfct Atten Awd; Sal; Bwlng-2 Chmpnshp Tm Trphys 86 & 87; Al-Star Trphy Chess Tm 87; Bio.

GLAMKOWSKI, CATHY; Watchung Hills Regional HS; Warren, NJ; (3); Varsity Clb; Band; Concert Band; Mrchg Band; Off Stu Cncl; Var Capt Crs Cntry; Var Capt Trk; High Hon Roll; Hon Roll; Stu Of Mon 85; Mst Outstndng-Grls Trck 85; Hld Schl Rcd-400 Intrmdt Hrdls 85-87; Coachs Awd-Trck 86.

GLASER, JOHN; De Paul HS; Kinnelon, NJ; (4); Boy Scts; JCL; Latin Clb; Var Crs Cntry; JV Socr; Var Trk; Var Wrstlng; Emory U; Psychlgy.

GLASS, AMY SUE; Point Pleasant Beach HS; Pt Pleasant Beach, NJ; (2); Art Clb; Letterman Clb; Spanish Clb; Concert Band; Mrchg Band; Yrbk Stf; Rep Frsh Cls; JV Var Bsktbl; Var Crs Cntry; Var L Trk; Sprtsmnshp Awd Trck 87; WPIAL Fnlst ST Cmptn Rly Tm Trck 86; Art.

GLASS, COLLEENA; Central Regional HS; Bayville, NJ; (4); Political Wkr; Chorus; Nwsp Rptr; JV Bsktbl; Var JV Fld Hcky; Var Sftbl; JV Trk; High Hon Roll; Hon Roll; Jr NHS; Occup Thrpst.

GLASS, JAMES; Cinnaminson HS; Cinnaminson, NJ; (3); Camera Clb; Ski Clb; Band; JV Bsbl; JV Socr.

GLASSMACHER, JOSEPH; West Windsor Plainsboro HS; Princeton Jct, NJ; (3); Var Bsbl; Var Capt Bsktbl; Bus.

GLASSMAN, ROBIN; Columbia HS; Maplewood, NJ; (3); Spanish Clb; Concert Band; Mrchg Band; Orch; Symp Band; Rep Stu Cncl; Mgr Socr; Spanish NHS; 3 Yr Vrsty Ltr Mrchg Band 85-87; Intl Hotel Mgmt.

GLAYMON, SARAH; Atlantic City HS; Margate, NJ; (4); 11/407; Drama Clb; Pres Model UN; Office Aide; School Musical; School Play; Yrbk Phtg; JV Tennis; Hon Roll; NHS; NJ Distngshd Schlr 87; Frnch Embssy Awd Outstndng Frnch Stdnt 86.

GLAZER, LESLIE; Parsippany HS; Parsippany, NJ; (3); French Clb; FBLA; Pep Clb; VP Sec Temple Yth Grp; Varsity Clb; Y-Teens; Band; Rep Frsh Cls; Rep Soph Cls; Rep Stu Cncl.

GLAZER, MARK; New Milford HS; New Milford, NJ; (2); French Clb; Lit Mag; Rep Frsh Cls; Rep Stu Cncl; JV Socr; French Hon Soc; Hon Roll; NHS; Top 10 Cls 86-87; Ansthtc Med.

GLEMAN, HEATHER; Toms River HS South; Beachwood, NJ; (2); Church Yth Grp; Rep Frsh Cls; Rep Soph Cls; Rep Jr Cls; Var Fld Hcky; Stat Mgr(s); Var Socr.

GLENN, CHRISSY; Point Pleasant Borough HS; Point Pleasant, NJ; (4); 16/230; Var Bsktbl; Var Fld Hcky; Var Powder Puff Ftbl; Var Socr; Hon Roll; NHS; Pnthrs Athltc Bstr Schlrshp 87; NJ Schlr/Athlt Awd 87; US Marine Crps Dist Athlt Awd 87; Douglass Coll.

GLENN, ERIC; Trenton Central HS; Trenton, NJ; (4); 126/525; Church Yth Grp; Band; Jazz Band; Mrchg Band; Orch; Golf; Church Schlrshp 87; Bk Awd Schlrshp 87; Essay Wnnr 85; Johnson C Smith U; Acctng.

GLENN, ROBERT; Brick Memorial HS; Brick, NJ; (2); 33/386; Drama Clb; Band; Concert Band; Jazz Band; Mrchg Band; Orch; School Musical; Hon Roll; Church Yth Grp; School Play; 1st Pl Humorous Oral Interprtn Monmouth Coll 86; Best Actor For Schl Yr 87; Northwestern U; Fine Arts.

GLENN, TOKAR ELIZABETH; Southern Regional HS; Beach Haven, NJ; (4); 5/382; VP Soph Cls; Pres Jr Cls; Pres Sr Cls; VP Stu Cncl; Var L Cheerleading; Var L Trk; High Hon Roll; NHS; Teen Arts Fstvl-Pntg 85-87; Yth Of Mnth 86; Tufts U; Fine Arts.

GLENN, TRACY; Freeheld Twsp HS; Freehold, NJ; (3); 19/358; Drama Clb; French Clb; SADD; Chorus; Stage Crew; Stat Tennis; NHS.

GLETOW, DONNA; Jackson Memorial HS; Jackson, NJ; (3); 107/416; Nwsp Stf; Mercer Cnty Coll; Mrtcn.

GLICK, LINNEA; Montville Township HS; Montville, NJ; (2); Art Clb; Cmnty Wkr; FBLA; Girl Scts; Key Clb; Model UN; Chorus; JV Bsktbl; JV Fld Hcky; JV Lcrss.

GLICKMAN, DEANNA; Sparta HS; Sparta, NJ; (3); Hosp Aide; Chorus; School Musical; Socr; Swmmng; Trk; High Hon Roll; Hon Roll; Ntl Merit Ltr; Intl Law.

GLIK, ROBERT A; North Bergen HS; North Bergen, NJ; (3); 3/576; Am Leg Boys St; Chess Clb; Pres Key Clb; Stu Cncl; High Hon Roll; Hon Roll; NHS; Acad Decathlon USAD 86-88; Gold Medal Russian Olmypiad 86-87; Gold Medal GPA 85-87; Math.

GLOBIS, CATHERINE; Jackson Memorial HS; Jackson, NJ; (4); Art Clb; Library Aide; Office Aide; Yrbk Phtg; Var Trk; Im Wt Lftg; High Hon Roll; Hon Roll; Natl Art Hnr Soc Tech Advisr 85-87; Art Inst Of Phil; Photo.

GLOCK, NEAL; Voorhees HS; Hampton, NJ; (2); 42/292; Boy Scts; Latin Clb; Varsity Clb; Bsbl; Socr; Wrstlng; Cit Awd; Hon Roll; Pres Schlr; La Fayette Coll.

GLUCK, MARCI; West Windsor-Plainsboro HS; Princeton Junct, NJ; (3); Radio Clb; Pres SADD; Temple Yth Grp; Nwsp Rptr; Lit Mag; High Hon Roll; Hst Jr Cls; Stat Socr; Var Swmmng; Stat Trk; Sptsmnshp Awd Swmmng 87; Best Sttstcn Awd For Princeton Packet Soccer 87; Nice Person Awd 87; Psych.

GLUCKSMAN, SHARON; West Morris Mendham HS; Bernardsville, NJ; (3); Drama Clb; Hosp Aide; VP Trs Intnl Clb; PAVAS; Teachers Aide; Rep Temple Yth Grp; Thesps; Chorus; School Musical; School Play; Daryl Gehr Essy Schlrshp Israel 86; NJ Rep Untd Kubbutz Mvmnt Ldrshp Semnr 86; Prncpls Hnrs Lst 85-86; Advrtsng.

GLYNN, COLETTE; Pequannock Township HS; Pequannock, NJ; (3); 44/240; Orch; Off Frsh Cls; Off Soph Cls; Off Jr Cls; Bus.

GLYNN, DAVID; Park Ridge HS; Park Ridge, NJ; (2); 17/68; AFS; Church Yth Grp; Computer Clb; 4-H; Science Clb; Service Clb; Ski Clb; Concert Band; Mrchg Band; Hon Roll; Engrng.

GLYNN, MAUREEN; Cresskill HS; Cresskill, NJ; (3); French Clb; Acpl Chr; Chorus; Concert Band; Mrchg Band; Var Sftbl; Var Vllybl; Prfct Atten Awd; Vllybl Hnrb Mntn All Cnty 85-86, Bsktbl 84-86, Sftbl 84.

GLYNN, PATRICIA; Egg Harbor Township HS; Mays Landing, NJ; (4); 30/289; French Clb; Ski Clb; JV Cheerleading; JV Sftbl; Jr NHS; Am Leg Awd 83; E H Slaybaugh Tchrs Awd 83; Stockton ST Coll; Law.

GMACH, PAMELA; Edison HS; Edison, NJ; (4); 7/384; Art Clb; Sec Church Yth Grp; Trs Science Clb; Mrchg Band; Symp Band; Bsktbl; NHS; St Schlr; Rep Jr Cls; Rep Sr Cls; J C Penney Super Schlr Schlrshp; NJ Inst Tech Hnrs Schlrshp; NJ Inst Of Tech; Arch.

GNAS, JOSEPH; Manist HS; Bayonne, NJ; (3); Am Leg Boys St; Art Clb; French Clb; Key Clb; High Hon Roll.

GNIRREP, JOCELYN; Mt Olive HS; Budd Lake, NJ; (3); 57/319; Ski Clb; Var L Band; Chorus; Co-Capt Flag Corp; Jazz Band; Hon Roll; Ntl Merit Ltr; Aud/Vis; Drama Clb; School Musical; Mdrn Music Mstrs-Music Hnr Soc, NJ All-ST Chorus 87; Law.

GOAD, AMY; Bordentown Regional HS; Bordentown, NJ; (2); 15/112; Church Yth Grp; Capt Flag Corp; Var Trk; Hon Roll.

GOAD, BRIAN; Bordentown Regional HS; Bordentown, NJ; (4); 5/114; Computer Clb; French Clb; Math Clb; Math Tm; Trs Sr Cls; Var Crs Cntry; Var Trk; NHS; Ntl Merit Ltr; St Schlr; Rutgers Coll; Elec Engrng.

GOBIN, ANDRE; Memorial HS; West New York, NJ; (3); High Hon Roll; Hon Roll; Engrng.

GOBIN, DENISE; Spotswood HS; Spotswood, NJ; (2); 6/127; Trs FBLA; Intnl Clb; OEA; Spanish Clb; Chorus; Color Guard; Stu Cncl; Mgr Trk; High Hon Roll; Hon Roll; Bus Mgmt.

GOBO, MICHELE; Cliffside Park HS; Fairview, NJ; (3); 37/240; Yrbk Stf; Lit Mag; Pres Frsh Cls; Pres Soph Cls; Pres Jr Cls; Pres Sr Cls; JV Var Cheerleading; Hon Roll; Art Clb; Office Aide; Italian Clb Treas, Cert Merit 84-88; Frgn Lang Frnsc Trnmt 1st Pl 86; Chrldng Comptn Awd 87; Fairleigh Dcknsn U; Dntl.

GOEPEL, JAMES; Highland Regional HS; Laurel Springs, NJ; (3); 51/285; German Clb; Sec Science Clb; Swmmng; 1st Pl Physcs Olympcs Tm 86; Mbr 6th Pl Mdly Rly Tm 86; 13th Pl Bckstrk S Jrsy 86.

GOESSEL, CHUCK A; Cherokee HS; Marlton, NJ; (3); Am Leg Boys St; Letterman Clb; Ski Clb; Rep Frsh Cls; Rep Stu Cncl; Var Golf; Var Capt Socr; Hon Roll; Arch.

GOETZ, STEVEN; Highland Regnl HS; Blackwood, NJ; (3); 19/250; Latin Clb; Var JV Bsbl; Var JV Bsktbl; Hon Roll; NHS; Bus.

GOETZEL, ILENE; Manasquan HS; Brielle, NJ; (3); Drama Clb; Hosp Aide; Spanish Clb; Band; Yrbk Stf; Var Mgr(s); High Hon Roll; Kiwanis Awd; NHS; Ntl Merit SF.

GOFF, HEATHER; Holy Spirit HS; Margate, NJ; (2); 37/397; Tennis; High Hon Roll; Hon Roll.

GOFF, TERESA; Boonton HS; Canada; (3); Sec Church Yth Grp; French Clb; GAA; Radio Clb; Temple Yth Grp; Band; Color Guard; Variety Show; Sec Nwsp Stf; Lit Mag; Ms Am Coed Pgnt 87; CYO Bsktbl Cap 86-87; Model Hairshow 3rd Pl 86; Jrnlst.

GOKLANI, SASHA; Mount St John Acad; Gladstone, NJ; (2); Computer Clb; Im Tennis; Im Vllybl.

GOLABEK, ADAM; Linden HS; Linden, NJ; (3).

GOLD, JONATHAN; Northern Valley RHS; Harrington Pk, NJ; (3); 10/280; Var Am Leg Boys St; Debate Tm; French Clb; Ski Clb; Temple Yth Grp; Crs Cntry; Trk; Hon Roll; Ntl Merit SF; Med.

GOLDANI, SABENA; Mount Saint John Acad; Gladstone, NJ; (2); Art Clb; Computer Clb; Dance Clb; Math Clb; Science Clb; Chorus; Lit Mag; Sftbl; Tennis; Lawyer.

GOLDBERG, AMIE; Cherry Hill HS West; Cherry Hill, NJ; (4); Cmnty Wkr; Computer Clb; Intnl Clb; Spanish Clb; SADD; Yrbk Stf; Rep Frsh Cls; Rep Soph Cls; Rep Jr Cls; Ntl Merit Ltr; Trenton ST Coll; Lbrl Arts.

GOLDBERG, BRIAN; Jewish Educational Center; Hillside, NJ; (2); Aud/Vis; Chess Clb; Cmnty Wkr; Math Tm; Quiz Bowl; Science Clb; Service Clb; Temple Yth Grp; Y-Teens; Stat Bsktbl.

GOLDBERG, DOUGLAS; Westwood HS; Wash Twp, NJ; (2); Church Yth Grp; Church Choir; High Hon Roll; Hon Roll; Advtg.

GOLDBERG, JASON; Livingston HS; Livingston, NJ; (3); 100/420; Var Bsktbl; Var Ftbl; JV Lcrss; Wt Lftg; High Hon Roll; Hon Roll; Accntng.

GOLDBERG, KIMBERLY ANN; James Caldwell HS; W Caldwell, NJ; (3); Pep Clb; Science Clb; Flag Corp; Mrchg Band; Yrbk Phtg; Fash Mdsg.

GOLDBERG, SCOTT M; James Caldwell HS; W Caldwell, NJ; (4); 73/265; Key Clb; Band; Concert Band; Jazz Band; Mrchg Band; Nwsp Rptr; Ed Yrbk Stf; Mck Trl Clb; Lehigh U; Fin.

GOLDBLAT, HARRIS; Livingston HS; Livingston, NJ; (3); 39/424; Trs AFS; Pres FBLA; Model UN; Political Wkr; Spanish Clb; Temple Yth Grp; Band; Jazz Band; Mrchg Band; School Musical; Law.

GOLDBLATT, MICHAEL; Paramus HS; Paramus, NJ; (3); Aud/Vis; Computer Clb; Debate Tm; Intnl Clb; JV Var Trk; NHS; Rutgers; Bus.

GOLDEN, JOHN; Mc Corriston Catholic HS; Trenton, NJ; (3); Church Yth Grp; JV Bsbl; Hon Roll; Trenton ST Coll; Acctnt.

GOLDEN, LAUREN; Manchester Twp HS; Lakehurst, NJ; (3); Am Leg Aux Girls St; Art Clb; Church Yth Grp; Pres Cmnty Wkr; Drama Clb; SADD; School Play; Yrbk Stf; VP Sr Cls; Socr; HOBY Smnr 86; Hstry Stu Of Mnth 87; Bst Prsnlty & Mst Schl Sprtd 85; Trenton ST; Mscn.

GOLDEN, SHERRI; Bishop George AHR; Iselin, NJ; (4); Ski Clb; Drill Tm; Nwsp Stf; Pres Frsh Cls; Im Cheerleading; Hon Roll; Middlesex Cnty Coll; Paralgl.

GOLDEY, SHARON; Paul VI HS; Barrington, NJ; (3); 44/425; Drama Clb; French Clb; SADD; Yrbk Stf; Lit Mag; French Hon Soc; Hon Roll; NY U; Dramtc Wrtng.

GOLDFARB, JEFFREY; Glen Rock HS; Miami, FL; (3); 3/150; Capt Chess Clb; Capt Debate Tm; JCL; Science Clb; Ed Lit Mag; Var Crs Cntry; High Hon Roll; Ntl Merit SF; Law.

GOLDFEDER, MATT; Freehold Township HS; Freehold, NJ; (3); 18/385; Cmnty Wkr; Trs SADD; Nwsp Ed-Chief; Rep Soph Cls; Trs Stu Cncl; Coach Actv; Var L Socr; Wt Lftg; NHS; JV Trk; Bus.

GOLDMAN, BETH; Cherry Hill HS West; Cherry Hill, NJ; (3); Chess Clb; Drama Clb; French Clb; PAVAS; Band; Chorus; Concert Band; Jazz Band; Mrchg Band; Orch; Olympc Conf Sr Hnrs Band 86; Pol Sci.

GOLDSTEIN, BILLY; Saddle River Day Schl; Paramus, NJ; (2); Pres Soph Cls; Bsktbl; Crs Cntry; Score Keeper.

GOLDSTEIN, JOANNA; Bruriah HS; Teaneck, NJ; (3); Yrbk Stf; Hon Roll; Sci Fair Awd 1st Pl 86,2nd Pl 87.

GOLDSTEIN, JULIE; Matawan Regional HS; Aberdeen, NJ; (3); Ski Clb; Temple Yth Grp; Sec Band; Concert Band; Jazz Band; Mrchg Band; Trs Sr Cls; Tennis; Rep Frsh Cls; Rep Soph Cls; Israel Schlrshp 86; Ltr Rcgntn Wrkng Disabled Chldrn 86; Music.

GOLDSTEIN, RENEE M; Bruriah HS For Girls; Staten Island, NY; (3); Art Clb; Cmnty Wkr; SADD; Temple Yth Grp; Sec Jr Cls; NHS; NEDT Awd; Fashion.

GOLDSTONE, MALKA; Bruriah H S For Girls; Elizabeth, NJ; (3); Math Tm; Service Clb; Spanish Clb; Temple Yth Grp; NHS; NEDT Awd; Cmnty Wkr; Library Aide.

GOLDSWORTHY, AMY; Mainland Regional HS; Linwood, NJ; (1); 10/319; Drama Clb; Ski Clb; School Musical; School Play; Yrbk Stf; Trs Frsh Cls; VP Stu Cncl; Var Mgr(s); JV Tennis; Actress.

GOLEBIESKI, DAVID; Wallington HS; Wallington, NJ; (2); Boys Clb Am; Varsity Clb; Lit Mag; JV Bsbl; Var Bowling; JV Wt Lftg; Ntl Merit Ltr; MVP Awd Bwlng Hgh Avg Olympc Div 87; Natl Sci Merit Awd 86; Pilot.

GOLEBIEWSKI, AMELIA M; Ridgewood HS; Ridgewood, NJ; (4); 27/445; Church Yth Grp; Cmnty Wkr; Drama Clb; 4-H; Girl Scts; Intnl Clb; Acpl Chr; Madrigals; NHS; St Schlr; Coll Clb Wmns Clb Schlrshp, Drama Schlrshp 87; Coll Of The Holy Cross; Pre-Med.

GOLEMBESKI, DEIDRE; Central Regional HS; Seaside Pk, NJ; (3); 3/290; Am Leg Aux Girls St; Dance Clb; VP Frsh Cls; Stu Cncl; Fld Hcky; Socr; NHS; Athltc Acadc Awd Hcky & Sccr; Cert Rcgntn Outstndng Schlstc Achvt; 2nd Tm All Cnty Hcky; Grp III Chmps; Colgate; Fin.

GOLLIDAY, DANIELLE; Brhs East HS; Bridgewater, NJ; (4); Drama Clb; French Clb; Sec Frsh Cls; Sec Soph Cls; Sec Jr Cls; Sec Sr Cls; Sec Stu Cncl; Diving; Var Capt Gym; NHS; Lehigh U; Mrktng.

GOLOMB, NANCY; Wall HS; Wall, NJ; (4); 1/289; Computer Clb; French Clb; Key Clb; Capt Var Tennis; High Hon Roll; Kiwanis Awd; NHS.

GOLOMBOS, JOANNE; Manalapan HS; Manalapan, NJ; (3); Art Clb; Cmnty Wkr; Dance Clb; FBLA; FNA; SADD; School Play; Stage Crew; Yrbk Stf; Im Swmmng; Hotel-Bus Mgmt.

GOLUB, NEAL; Sayreville War Memorial HS; Sayreville, NJ; (3); Am Leg Boys St; French Clb; Quiz Bowl; Var L Bsbl; Var L Bsktbl; Pres French Hon Soc; High Hon Roll; Hon Roll; NHS; Fin.

GOMEZ, ANA; Mary Help Of Christians Acad; Paterson, NJ; (4); Church Yth Grp; Cmnty Wkr; French Clb; Hosp Aide; Teachers Aide; Chorus; Stage Crew; Hon Roll; Acad All Amer 87.

GOMEZ, GABRIELA; Secaucus HS; Secaucus, NJ; (4); 14/168; Dance Clb; Intnl Clb; Mu Alpha Theta; Ski Clb; Varsity Clb; Capt Color Guard; High Hon Roll; NHS; Spanish NHS; Math Clb.

GOMEZ, LUIS; Hillside HS; Hillside, NJ; (3); 12/238; ROTC; Rep Frsh Cls; JV Crs Cntry; Var Socr; Hon Roll; JROTC Clr Grd & Rngr Sqd Cmmndr 85-87; Aerntcs.

GOMEZ, MARY; Long Branch HS; Long Br, NJ; (3); 6/279; Vrsty Lttr 85-87; Hnr Rll 84-87; U Mayaguez; Elec Engr.

GOMEZ, RICHARD; Madison HS; Madison, NJ; (4); 14/208; Church Yth Grp; Nwsp Rptr; Yrbk Stf; Trs Sr Cls; Var Capt Swmmng; Var Tennis; VP NHS; Spanish NHS; St Schlr; Exploring; Ntl Hispanic SF 86; Dartmouth Coll; Engrng.

GOMINIAK, JOHN P; Notre Dame HS; East Windsor, NJ; (4); 7/336; Am Leg Boys St; Ski Clb; Varsity Clb; Nwsp Stf; Rep Soph Cls; L Tennis; High Hon Roll; Hon Roll; NHS; NROTC Schlrshp Wnr 87; Holy Cross Coll.

GOMORY, PAMELA; Abraham Clark HS; Roselle, NJ; (4); 9/170; Science Clb; Spanish Clb; Band; Chorus; Concert Band; Madrigals; Mrchg Band; Variety Show; Nwsp Rptr; Sec Sr Cls; Dance.

GONCEY, LISA; Delran HS; Delran, NJ; (4); Am Leg Aux Girls St; Computer Clb; Chorus; Nwsp Rptr; Stu Cncl; Var Bowling; Var Fld Hcky; Var Capt Lcrss; Trenton ST Coll; Phys Thrpy.

GONSEWSKI, DAVID; Brick Memorial HS; Brick, NJ; (3); Bsbl; Var Bsktbl; High Hon Roll; Hon Roll; FL ST.

GONZALEZ, ANGELO; Sacred Heart HS; Vineland, NJ; (3); 21/56; Spanish Clb; Bsbl; Bsktbl; Socr.

GONZALEZ, ANNIE; Paramus Catholic Girls HS; Teaneck, NJ; (1); Church Yth Grp; High Hon Roll; Hon Roll; Jrnlsm.

GONZALEZ, GABRIEL; Linden HS; Linden, NJ; (3); Var Socr; Hon Roll; Rutgers; Law.

GONZALEZ, GLADIBEL; Saint Mary HS; E Rutherford, NJ; (3); 1/81; Math Clb; Yrbk Stf; Lit Mag; Pres Jr Cls; Var Cheerleading; Var Trk; Var Vllybl; French Hon Soc; High Hon Roll; Pres NHS; Pre-Med.

GONZALEZ, GLADIBEL; St Mary HS; Howell, NJ; (3); 1/78; Drama Clb; French Clb; Library Aide; Math Clb; Pep Clb; SADD; School Play; Stage Crew; Lit Mag; Pres Jr Cls; Acad All-Amer Awd 85; Pre-Med.

GONZALEZ, GUILLERMO; North Bergen HS; North Bergen, NJ; (3); Art Clb; Church Yth Grp; Model UN; Spanish Clb; School Play; Rutgers; Advrtsng.

GONZALEZ, IRIS; Memoral HS; West New York, NJ; (3); FHA; Hosp Aide; Latin Clb; Rep Jr Cls; Rep Sr Cls; Rep Stu Cncl; Im Twrlr; Hon Roll; Hnr Rl 85-86; Citznshp Awd Hlth Clb 85-86; Nrsng.

GONZALEZ, ISAURA; St Joseph Of The Palisades HS; Guttenburg, NJ; (3); 5/133; Spanish Clb; Yrbk Stf; Cheerleading; Pom Pon; Hon Roll; Spanish NHS; Psychlgy.

GONZALEZ, JENNIFER; Bishop George Ahr HS; Plainfield, NJ; (4); 1/270; Am Leg Aux Girls St; Intnl Clb; Model UN; Pres Service Clb; Lit Mag; NHS; NEDT Awd; Val; Natl Hispanic Merit Scholar 87; Natl Affairs Conf 87; Distngshd NJ Schlr 86; Econ.

GONZALEZ, JENNIFER; Burlington County Vo-Tech; Mount Holly, NJ; (3); 13/192; Cmnty Wkr; Drama Clb; FHA; Stu Cncl; Fash Show; Fashions.

GONZALEZ, KENNETH; Perth Amboy HS; Perth Amboy, NJ; (4); 19/291; ROTC; Scholastic Bowl; Stage Crew; VP Soph Cls; Trs Jr Cls; Trs Sr Cls; Rep Stu Cncl; DAR Awd; Hon Roll; NHS; US Navl Inst Awd Excllnc 87; ROTC Outstndng Cadet Yr 84-87; James Dickson Car Schlrshp 87; Rutgers Coll; Bus Mngmt.

GONZALEZ, MANUEL; Elizabeth HS; Elizabeth, NJ; (4); 21/850; Church Yth Grp; Computer Clb; Sec Key Clb; Concert Band; Mrchg Band; Trs Jr Cls; Trs Sr Cls; NHS; Pres Spanish NHS; Comp Sci.

GONZALEZ, MARIA E; Barringer HS; Newark, NJ; (3); #1 In Class; Yrbk Phtg; Yrbk Stf; Bausch & Lomb Sci Awd; High Hon Roll; Hon Roll; NHS; Val; Rensselaer Math & Sci Awds 87.

GONZALEZ, MARIO; Emerson HS; Union City, NJ; (3); Yrbk Stf; Lit Mag; Wt Lftg; Hon Roll; NJIT; Arch.

GONZALEZ, MICHAEL; East Side HS; Newark, NJ; (3); Am Leg Boys St; Cmnty Wkr; Computer Clb; Exploring; Capt Math Tm; Variety Show; Nwsp Ed-Chief; Co-Capt Ftbl; Church Yth Grp; Mncipl Cncl Awds-Close-Up & Jbltn 86; Schlrshp-Irnbnd Cmmnty Cltrl Ctr 86; Princeton; Fnanc.

GONZALEZ, RONNIE; St Joseph Of The Palisades HS; North Bergen, NJ; (4); 19/135; Drama Clb; Political Wkr; Nwsp Rptr; VP Jr Cls; Trs Sr Cls; Swmmng; Tennis; High Hon Roll; NHS; Spanish NHS; Seton Hall; Real Estate.

GONZALEZ, THELMA; Bridgeton HS; Bridgeton, NJ; (3); Church Yth Grp; Dance Clb; 4-H; FNA; GAA; Library Aide; Science Clb; Varsity Clb; Yrbk Stf; Bsktbl; U Of Central FL; Mrn Bio.

GONZALEZ, WILLIAM; James Ferris HS; Jersey City, NJ; (3); Am Leg Boys St; JA; JV Socr; Gnrl Med.

GONZALEZ, YVONNE; Dover HS; Dover, NJ; (3); 62/280; AFS; Chorus; Hon Roll; Intl Bus.

GOOD, JUANITA; Overbrook HS; Lindenwold, NJ; (4); 80/236; Office Aide; SADD; Im Bsktbl; Var Cheerleading; Var JV Fld Hcky; Var Trk; Hon Roll; 2nd All Conf Tm Fld Hcky 86; Rutgers U; Scl Wrk.

GOOD, LORI; Burlington Co Vo Tech; Edgewater Park, NJ; (4); FBLA; Var Mgr Bsktbl; Var Mgr Socr; High Hon Roll; Hon Roll; Sec NHS; Bus Admin.

GOODMAN, BRUCE; Arthur L Johnson Regional HS; Clark, NJ; (3); 12/186; French Clb; Key Clb; Band; Concert Band; Mrchg Band; Variety Show; Bsktbl; Tennis; Hon Roll; U Of MA; Bus Adm.

GOODMAN, CAROLE; Edgewood Regional SR HS; Hammondton, NJ; (3); 5/390; Drama Clb; Sec Trs Latin Clb; Spanish Clb; School Play; Nwsp Rptr; Yrbk Stf; Sec Stu Cncl; Var Tennis; Hon Roll; Jr NHS; Schlrshp NJ Schl Arts Actng 86.

GOODMAN, DAVID J; Gateway Regional HS; Wenonah, NJ; (4); Am Leg Boys St; Exploring; German Clb; Key Clb; Math Tm; Science Clb; Yrbk Phtg; NHS; Ntl Merit Ltr; St Schlr; VA Tech; Arch.

GOODRICH, JAY; Montville HS; Pinebrook, NJ; (3); 86/275; Ski Clb; SADD; Concert Band; Var Golf; Im Lcrss; High Hon Roll; Hon Roll; Schl Arts Fstvl 2nd Pl 87; Arch.

GOODROE, MICHELE; Lower Cape May Regional HS; N Cape May, NJ; (4); 17/240; Church Yth Grp; Concert Band; Mrchg Band; Yrbk Stf; Lit Mag; Sftbl; Gov Hon Prg Awd; Hon Roll; NHS; Prnt Tchrs Assn Schlrshp 87; Gov Schl Schlr Monmth Coll 86; Cook Coll; Vet Med.

GOODSON, TALANI; Essex Catholic HS; Orange, NJ; (3); Computer Clb; Leo Clb; Y-Teens; Off Soph Cls; JV Bsbl; Im JV Bsktbl; Im Bowling; Im Ftbl; Im Sftbl; JV Trk; Bus.

GOODWIN, SHARON; Ramsey HS; Ramsey, NJ; (4); 14/256; Church Yth Grp; SADD; Teachers Aide; Var Bsktbl; Var Fld Hcky; Capt Sftbl; High Hon Roll; Hon Roll; NHS; Gov Tchng Schlrs Pgm 87; Pres Ftns Awd 87; Fld Hockey MVP,2nd Team All Cnty 86; Trenton ST Coll; Spec Ed.

GOOS, KEVIN; Atlantic Christian HS; Atlantic City, NJ; (3); 1/15; Church Yth Grp; Scholastic Bowl; Chorus; Church Choir; Yrbk Stf; VP Jr Cls; Var L Bsbl; Var L Bsktbl; Var L Ftbl; Var L Socr; All-Star Sccr Goalie 86-87; Pres Clssrm 87; United Wesleyan; Mnstr.

GORDON, COLLEEN; Gloucester City HS; Gloucester, NJ; (3); Science Clb; School Play; Nwsp Rptr; Yrbk Stf; Var Cheerleading; Var JV Fld Hcky; Var Mgr(s); Var Score Keeper; Hon Roll; Unsng Hero Awd-Fld Hcky 85-86; Lion Awd-Fld Hcky 86-87; Gvrnrs Schl NJ Fnlst.

GORDON, DOREEN; Highland Reginal HS; Somerdale, NJ; (3); 127/256; Drama Clb; Library Aide; VP Science Clb; Spanish Clb; Band; Chorus; Concert Band; Mrchg Band; School Musical; School Play; Theater Arts.

GORDON, ERIC; Scotch Plains-Fanwood HS; Scotch Plains, NJ; (4); 45/329; AFS; Leo Clb; Model UN; Quiz Bowl; Spanish Clb; Temple Yth Grp; Yrbk Stf; L Var Bsbl; Capt Var Crs Cntry; JV Trk; Pres Acdmc Ftns Awd 87; Spnsh Merit Awd 87; Villanova U; Bio.

GORDON, JAMIE; West Windsor Plainsboro HS; Princeton Jct, NJ; (3); Am Leg Aux Girls St; Temple Yth Grp; Mrchg Band; Nwsp Sprt Ed; Hst Frsh Cls; VP Soph Cls; VP Jr Cls; JV Capt Cheerleading; JV Var Tennis; Hon Roll; American U; Psych.

GORDON, JENNIFER; Teaneck HS; Teaneck, NJ; (4); 78/450; French Clb; Office Aide; SADD; Temple Yth Grp; School Play; Yrbk Stf; Hon Roll; NHS; Skidmore Coll; Psych.

GORDON, JILL; Mt Saint Mary Acad; Somerset, NJ; (3); 15/85; Trs Church Yth Grp; Cmnty Wkr; GAA; Hosp Aide; VP Science Clb; Church Choir; Nwsp Stf; Lit Mag; High Hon Roll; Spanish NHS; NJ Girls Ctznshp Inst 87; NJ Gov Schl 87; Music.

GORDON, LAURIE; West Essex Regional HS; Roseland, NJ; (3); Cmnty Wkr; SADD; Trs Soph Cls; Rep Jr Cls; Stu Cncl; Var Capt Sftbl; Var Capt Tennis; NHS; Spanish NHS; AFS; Rec Dir For Yth Wk In Roseland 86; Srvd On Roseland Yth Cmmtte 86-88; 2nd Tm All Cnfrnc For Tennis 87.

GORDON, MICHAEL; Dover HS; Dover, NJ; (3); Am Leg Boys St; Church Yth Grp; Key Clb; Chorus; School Musical; Trk; Hon Roll; NHS.

GORDON, STUART; Ocean Township HS; Ocean Twp, NJ; (4); Temple Yth Grp; Band; Pep Band; Crs Cntry; Stat Trk; Hon Roll; Gruenwald Schlrshp 87; Rutgers Coll; Engrng.

GORDON, SUSAN; Phillipsburg HS; Phillipsburg, NJ; (4); 53/292; Chorus; Tennis; Hon Roll; NHS.

GORMAN, KEVIN; Ocean Township HS; Ocean, NJ; (3); 17/344; Am Leg Boys St; Key Clb; Ski Clb; Var L Bsbl; Var L Socr; Im Wt Lftg; NHS; Sprtn Schlr Awd 85-87; Cntnentl Math Leag Wnnr 85; SR Ldrshp Pgm 87; Engrng.

GORMAN, LESLIE; Notre Dame HS; Lawrenceville, NJ; (3); 38/400; Latin Clb; Off Ski Clb; Stage Crew; Nwsp Rptr; Lit Mag; Off Stu Cncl; Fld Hcky; Hon Roll; NHS; Off Frsh Cls; Latin Hnr Soc 86-88; Pre Law.

GORMBOGI, DANIEL; Pitman HS; Pitman, NJ; (3); #113 In Class; AFS; Am Leg Boys St; Drama Clb; German Clb; School Play; Off Jr Cls; Capt Var Crs Cntry; Tennis; Trk; Hon Roll; Physics.

GORMLEY, LAURIE; Columbia HS; Maplewood, NJ; (3); Am Leg Aux Girls St; Cmnty Wkr; SADD; Var Capt Fld Hcky; Var L Lcrss; Sftbl; Lbrl Arts.

GORMLEY, PATRICIA; Scotch Plains-Fanwood HS; Scotch Plains, NJ; (3); French Clb; Hosp Aide; Latin Clb; Mrchg Band; Var L Swmmng; Var L Tennis; Var L Vllybl; Hon Roll; Math.

GORMLEY, SUE ANN; Scotch Plains-Fanwood HS; Scotch Plains, NJ; (4); 3/330; French Clb; Intnl Clb; Model UN; Yrbk Ed-Chief; Ed Lit Mag; Var Socr; Var Capt Vllybl; French Hon Soc; Ntl Merit Ltr; Rotary Awd; Tellurie Assn Summer Pgm Scholar 86; Robert C Byrd Scholar 87; Yale U; Engl.

GORNY, KIMBERLY; North Hunterdon HS; Lebanon, NJ; (4); 78/346; Thesps; Band; Chorus; Concert Band; Drm Mjr(t); Madrigals; Mrchg Band; School Musical; School Play; Drama Clb; NJ Gov Schl Of Arts Vcl Music 86; Music Ed.

GORSKI, BRIAN; Lower Cape May Regl HS; Villas, NJ; (4); Yrbk Stf; Atlantic CC; Clnry Arts.

GORSKI, JENNIFER; Red Bank Catholic HS; Rumsson, NJ; (4); 15/311; Latin Clb; Ski Clb; Drill Tm; Yrbk Ed-Chief; Powder Puff Ftbl; Trk; Twrlr; Hon Roll; NHS; VA Poly-Tech Inst; Arch.

GORSKI, SARA; Bridgewater-Maritan HS West; Bridgewater, NJ; (3); Church Yth Grp; 4-H; Hosp Aide; Im Powder Puff Ftbl; Im Score Keeper; 4-H Awd; Hon Roll; Intl Bus Mgmt.

GORZELANY, ROBERT J; Clifton HS; Clifton, NJ; (3); Am Leg Boys St; Spanish Clb; Nwsp Ed-Chief; Rep Soph Cls; Ntl Merit SF; Spanish NHS.

GOSNEY, JENNIFER; North Warren Regional HS; Blairstown, NJ; (2); Spanish Clb; Band; Concert Band; Drm Mjr(t); Mrchg Band; Orch; Var Cheerleading; Girl Scts.

GOSNEY, LAUREN; North Warren Regional HS; Blairstown, NJ; (3); 26/144; SADD; Band; Concert Band; Drm Mjr(t); Mrchg Band; Nwsp Phtg; Sec Stu Cncl; JV Bsktbl; JV Sftbl; Hon Roll.

GOSS, ABIGAIL; Marine Acad Of Sci & Tech; Little Silver, NJ; (3); Church Yth Grp; ROTC; Church Choir; Yrbk Stf; Var Fld Hcky; JV Socr; Hon Roll; NHS; Oceangrphy.

GOSSETT, KATHLEEN; St John Vianney HS; Aberdeen, NJ; (3); 18/270; Boy Scts; Church Yth Grp; Cmnty Wkr; Exploring; Girl Scts; Hosp Aide; Office Aide; Red Cross Aide; SADD; Ftbl; Gold & White Awd.

GOSTOVICH, STEVEN V; Overbrook Regional SR HS; Pine Hill, NJ; (3); Am Leg Boys St; Drama Clb; Letterman Clb; SADD; Varsity Clb; Nwsp Ed-Chief; Crs Cntry; Trk; Hon Roll; NHS; All Conf Awd Crss Cntry 86; MVP Overbrook Crss Cntry 86; Engr.

GOTO, KOJI; Cranford HS; Cranford, NJ; (3); 16/268; French Clb; Math Tm; Quiz Bowl; Science Clb; Science Clb; Orch; School Musical; Golf; French Hon Soc; NHS; NJ Music Educ Assoc Hgh Hnrs 81-87; Amer Clb 86-87; Math Leag.

GOTT, KAREN; Pennsville Memorial HS; Pennsville, NJ; (3); 3/225; Exploring; VP FBLA; Bsktbl; Var L Sftbl; Var L Tennis; High Hon Roll; Philadelphia Coll/Phrmcy; Phrmc.

GOTTDENKER, MARK; Matawan Regional HS; Matawan, NJ; (3); Letterman Clb; Ski Clb; Spanish Clb; Varsity Clb; Var Trk; Im Wt Lftg; Var Wrstlng; High Hon Roll; Hon Roll; Sprts Med.

GOTTESMAN, ADRIENE R; Delran HS; Delran, NJ; (4); 5/188; Trs Temple Yth Grp; Concert Band; Mrchg Band; Orch; School Musical; Var Fld Hcky; Var Lcrss; NHS; Pres Schlr; Garden ST Dstngshd Schlr 87; George Washington U; Intl Bus.

GOTTLIEB, MICHAEL; Parsippany HS; Parsippany, NJ; (3); Am Leg Boys St; FBLA; Varsity Clb; Nwsp Stf; Var L Bsktbl; Var L Ftbl; Var L Trk; Hon Roll; Cmmnts.

GOTTSCHALK, LISA; Ridgefield Park HS; Little Ferry, NJ; (3); 15/203; Debate Tm; Nwsp Bus Mgr; Hon Roll; Bus Mgmt.

GOTTSCHALL, JENNIFER; Holy Spirit HS; Margate, NJ; (2); 50/397; Var L Tennis; JV Wrstlng; High Hon Roll; Hon Roll.

GOTZIS, ANTHONY; Pennsauken HS; Pennsauken, NJ; (2); Church Yth Grp; Computer Clb; Science Clb; Spanish Clb; Band; Concert Band; Jazz Band; Mrchg Band; Var Tennis; Hon Roll.

GOUBEAUD, PAUL; Notre Dame HS; East Windsor, NJ; (3); 4/385; Am Leg Boys St; Church Yth Grp; Math Clb; Varsity Clb; Nwsp Sprt Ed; Lit Mag; Var Bsbl; Var Socr; High Hon Roll; Trs NHS.

GOULD, PATRICIA; J P Stevens HS; Edison, NJ; (3); 34/450; Art Clb; Science Clb; Ski Clb; Mrchg Band; Rep Frsh Cls; Rep Soph Cls; Jr Cls; Hon Roll; NHS; Spanish NHS; JR Prm Qun 87; Trenton ST; Mdcl.

GOULD, WILLIAM M; Toms River HS East; Toms River, NJ; (3); 46/509; Church Yth Grp; High Hon Roll; Hon Roll; Computer Engineering.

GOURDINE, DARRIUS; Essex Catholic Boys HS; East Orange, NJ; (4); 40/158; Spanish Clb; Yrbk Stf; Rep Frsh Cls; Rep Soph Cls; Rep Jr Cls; Rep Sr Cls; JV Ftbl; VP Trk; High Hon Roll; NHS; Howard U Of WA; Med.

GOVEIA, FRANK; Union HS; Union, NJ; (3); Math Clb; Spanish Clb; Rep Frsh Cls; JV Bsbl; JV Var Ftbl; High Hon Roll; Hon Roll; Jr NHS; NHS; Princeton; Mdcl Prfsn.

GOVETT, STACY; Pitman HS; Pitman, NJ; (4); 2/150; Am Leg Aux Girls St; Sec German Clb; Pres Key Clb; Office Aide; Teachers Aide; Chorus; Sec Jr Cls; Var Cheerleading; Im Vllybl; JETS Awd; Rutgers Schlr 85-86; U Of DE; Chem Engrng.

GRABELLE, DEAN; Ocean Township HS; Wayside, NJ; (3); 6/344; Key Clb; Ski Clb; Temple Yth Grp; JV Bsktbl; Var L Socr; Var L Trk; Im Wt Lftg; High Hon Roll; NHS; Ntl Merit SF; Natl Math League Cmptn 86.

GRABER, AMY; Timothy Christian Schl; Scotch Plains, NJ; (3); 1/44; Church Yth Grp; Service Clb; Chorus; High Hon Roll; NHS; Val; Hm Ec.

GRABERT, EILEEN; Holy Cross HS; Willingboro, NJ; (3); Intnl Clb; Hon Roll; Trenton ST Coll; Med.

GRACE, CULLEN M; Cedar Ridge HS; Old Bridge, NJ; (4); 12/371; German Clb; Science Clb; Stu Cncl; High Hon Roll; Hon Roll; Jr NHS; NHS; Ntl Merit SF; Lit Mag; German Hnr Soc Pres; Madison Twp Hstrcl Soc Awd; Archlgy.

GRACE, JONI; Maple Shade HS; Maple Shade, NJ; (4); 56/154; DECA; French Clb; GAA; Var Bsktbl; Var Capt Lcrss; Var Socr; Sftbl; Dera Sthrn Regn Schlrshp 87; Herbert Wiggins III Awd 87; Rider Coll.

GRACE, LISA; Neptune SR HS; Neptune, NJ; (2); JV Fld Hcky; Var Mgr(s); Var Score Keeper; Var Stat Sftbl; BYU; Intr Dsgn.

GRACE, ROBERT; Marlboro HS; Colts Neck, NJ; (3); 18/529; Science Clb; Concert Band; Exploring; Band; Mrchg Band; Symp Band; JETS Awd; NHS; St Schlr; 1st Pl Schl Am Chem Soc 85; MA Inst Tech; Elec Engr.

GRACEFFO, GERALD; Lakeland Regional HS; Wanaque, NJ; (3); 16/334; Ski Clb; VP Frsh Cls; VP Soph Cls; VP Jr Cls; VP Sr Cls; Rep Stu Cncl; Trk; Wrstlng; High Hon Roll; NHS; Rotary Yth Ldrshp Conf 87; Bus.

GRACEFFO, JOE; Ramapo Regional HS; Franklin Lakes, NJ; (3); 125/322; Church Yth Grp; Computer Clb; Debate Tm; Letterman Clb; Varsity Clb; Coach Actv; Ftbl; Trk; Rep Frsh Cls; Rep Soph Cls; Engr.

GRACON, ANNETTE; St John Vianney Regional HS; Englishtown, NJ; (4); Girl Scts; Intnl Clb; Math Tm; Yrbk Stf; Hon Roll; NHS; Prfct Atten Awd; Pres Schlrshp Loyola Coll; St John Vianney Gold & White Awd; Pres Acadmc Ftns Awd; Loyola Coll.

GRADY, KATHLEEN; Dumont HS; Dumont, NJ; (4); 14/217; Pres Girl Scts; Mu Alpha Theta; Trs Band; Trs Concert Band; Drm Mjr(t); Trs Mrchg Band; Yrbk Stf; VP NHS; Ntl Merit Ltr; NJ Dstngshd Schlr 86; Comptr Sci.

GRAETZ, TANIA; Msgr Donovan HS; Bricktown, NJ; (3); Sec Drama Clb; Hosp Aide; Thesps; Chorus; Church Choir; School Musical; School Play; Stage Crew; Stat Bsktbl; Life Chiropratic Coll; Med.

GRAF, MARTHA; Riverside HS; Delanco, NJ; (3); Church Yth Grp; Dance Clb; Drama Clb; Office Aide; Pres Pep Clb; SADD; Teachers Aide; Band; Church Choir; Concert Band; Outstndng Awd Piano 85-87; Most Imprvd Band Membr 87; Burlington Cnty Coll; Early Edu.

GRAHAM, ANDREW JAMES; North Hunterdon HS; Lebanon, NJ; (3); 67/329; Am Leg Boys St; Boy Scts; Stu Cncl; JV Var Socr; Var Trk; NHS; FBLA; Key Clb; Scholastic Bowl; JV Bsbl; Cngrssnl Awd Brnz & Slvr 86-87; Ambssdr HOBY Fndtn 85; 1st Pl ST Rsrch Papr 87; MIT; Finc.

GRAHAM, CHRISTINE; Gateway Regional HS; Woodbury Hts, NJ; (4); French Clb; FHA; Sec Key Clb; SADD; Teachers Aide; Off Stu Cncl; JV Fld Hcky; JV Mgr(s); JV Score Keeper; JV Swmmng; Gator Mnth 87; Glassboro ST Coll; Pblc Rltns.

GRAHAM, COLLEEN; St Mary HS; Keyport, NJ; (3); 1/99; Church Yth Grp; Yrbk Stf; Ed Lit Mag; JV Var Sftbl; High Hon Roll; NHS; NEDT Awd; Spanish NHS; Acdmc All AM 87; Math.

GRAHAM, CORETTA; Hackensack HS; Hackensack, NJ; (4); 35/402; Chess Clb; Church Yth Grp; Computer Clb; Exploring; FBLA; GAA; Hosp Aide; Intnl Clb; Key Clb; Letterman Clb; Black Schlr, Mary Mc Leod Bethone, 1st Rcpnt Louis Porter Schlrshp 87; Rutgers U-Douglass; Comp Sci.

GRAHAM, DORI LAINE; Northern Burlington Regional HS; Allentown, NJ; (4); 11/226; Church Yth Grp; Drama Clb; SADD; Teachers Aide; JV Capt Cheerleading; Var L Crs Cntry; Var L Mgr(s); Hon Roll; NHS; Spanish NHS; HOBY Ldrshp Sem 85; Rutgers U Coll Phrmcy; Phrmcy.

GRAHAM, JEROME; Immaculate Conception HS; East Orange, NJ; (2); Art Clb; Church Yth Grp; Office Aide; Science Clb; Chorus; Church Choir; School Play; Bsbl; Bsktbl; Ftbl; PA ST; Med.

GRAHAM, MARSHA DENISE; Camden HS; Camden, NJ; (3); JA; Drill Tm; Mrchg Band; Yrbk Stf; Rep Jr Cls; JV Tennis; Cit Awd; Hon Roll; Prfct Atten 85-86; Phila Rgnl Intrdctn Minrts Engrng 84-86; NY Inst Of Tech; Aerospac Tech.

GRAHAM, STEVEN WILLIAM; Parsippany HS; Parsippany, NJ; (4); 26/324; Var L Ftbl; Hon Roll; NHS; Pres Schlr; FBLA; Varsity Clb; Stu Cncl; Im Bsbl; Jr NHS; Prfct Atten Awd; Natl Elks Scholar Local & Natl Wnnr 87; Intrnshp Congressmn Dean Gallo 86-87; Boston U; Acctng.

GRAHAM, TASHAWNA; Snenery Snikver HS; Jersey City, NJ; (4); DECA; Girl Scts; Church Choir; School Musical; School Play; Bsktbl; Cheerleading; Prfct Atten Awd; Computer Awd 86; DECA Clb Awd 87; Morgan ST U; Psych.

GRAICHEN, GREGORY; Central Regional HS; Seaside Hts, NJ; (3); 10/243; Boy Scts; Key Clb; Nwsp Sprt Ed; JV Ftbl; L Trk; High Hon Roll; NHS; Ntl Merit Ltr; U Of Richmond; Phy Thrpy.

GRAICHEN, SUZANNE; Monsignor Donovan HS; Seaside Heights, NJ; (3); 61/250; Debate Tm; Ski Clb; JV Crs Cntry; Sftbl; Hon Roll; Rep Frsh Cls; Rep Soph Cls; Rep Sr Cls; Rep Stu Cncl; Law.

GRAMES, JOSEPH M; Clifton HS; Clifton, NJ; (3); Am Leg Boys St; Pres Math Clb; Math Tm; Science Clb; Nwsp Rptr; Stu Cncl; JV Tennis; High Hon Roll; Pres Jr NHS; Spanish NHS; Fin NJ Gov Schl Sci Drew U 87; Awd SAT Scores Rogate Pgm 84; Talntd & Giftd Pgm 82-88; Math.

GRAMKOWSKI, LAURIE; Haddenfield Memorial HS; Haddonfield, NJ; (2); AFS; Church Yth Grp; JV L Bsktbl; Stat Mgr(s); Stat Score Keeper; JV L Socr; JV L Trk; Hon Roll; Phys Ther.

GRAMLICH, S P; Delran HS; Delran, NJ; (3); Church Yth Grp; Pres Computer Clb; Exploring; Q&S; Spanish Clb; Lit Mag; Pres Sr Cls; Var Socr; Var Wrstlng; NHS; Acadmc All-Amer 85; Group II St Champs In Soccer 86; NJ Boys St Rep 87; Engrng.

GRAMLING, TIMOTHY S; John F Kennedy HS; Willingboro, NJ; (4); 2/280; Am Leg Boys St; Church Choir; Yrbk Bus Mgr; Var Tennis; Bausch & Lomb Sci Awd; Pres NHS; Ntl Merit Ltr; Sal; St Schlr; ROTC 87; Willingboro Yth Spcl Achvmnt Awd 86; Rutgers-New Brunswick Discvry 86 Prog 86; Harvard; Comp Engr.

GRAMM, KELLY; Lenape Regional HS; Mt Laurel, NJ; (1); Aud/Vis; Cmnty Wkr; Dance Clb; Drama Clb; Model UN; Fld Hcky; MDA Vnlntr Cmp Cnslr 87; Spcl Olympcs Vlntr 87; Ms Phtgnc 87; Fash & Mdlng.

GRANATA, MARYANN; Spotswood HS; Spotswood, NJ; (4); 41/187; DECA; FBLA; Model UN; OEA; Yrbk Stf; Hon Roll; Voice Dem Awd; 2nd DECA NJ Wnnr 87; Centanary Coll; Equine.

GRANDE, PAUL; Belleville SR HS; Belleville, NJ; (3); Boy Scts; Exploring; L Bsbl; Var Ftbl; JV Wrstlng; Hon Roll; Opt Clb Awd; Johnson & Wales Coll; Htl Mng.

GRANDE, SEBASTIAN; Holy Spirit HS; Margate, NJ; (3); 2/332; Speech Tm; High Hon Roll; Hon Roll; Bio Awd 85; Engr.

GRANDINETTI, TOM; Dover HS; Dover, NJ; (3); 15/250; JV Var Bsbl; High Hon Roll; Hon Roll; NHS; Century 21 Acctng Awd 86, 87; Acctng.

GRANESE, LYNN; West Milford HS; West Milford, NJ; (4); 180/359; Nwsp Stf; Yrbk Phtg; Yrbk Rptr; Yrbk Sprt Ed; Rep Soph Cls; Rep Jr Cls; Stat Bsktbl; Var Stat Gym; Score Keeper; Psychlgy.

GRANO, ELIZABETH; Indian Hills HS; Franklin Lakes, NJ; (3); 47/306; AFS; Church Yth Grp; Cmnty Wkr; French Clb; Hosp Aide; Nwsp Stf; Yrbk Stf; Rep Stu Cncl; Hon Roll; NHS; Bus.

GRANOFF, LORI; Parsippany HS; Parsippany, NJ; (3); FBLA; VP Cheerleading; Sftbl; Hon Roll; Child Psycht.

GRANT, AREATHA; Henry Snyder HS; Jersey City, NJ; (3); FBLA; Band; Mgr Nwsp Rptr; Sec Frsh Cls; Sec Jr Cls; Sec Stu Cncl; Capt Cheerleading; Sftbl; Hon Roll; NHS; Temple U; Pol Sci.

GRANT, DANIEL R; Montville HS; Towaco, NJ; (4); 41/270; VP Frsh Cls; Rep Soph Cls; Rep Jr Cls; Rep Sr Cls; Bsbl; Ftbl; Wrstlng; High Hon Roll; Hon Roll; NHS; Rutgers U; Law.

GRANT, FRANCINA; Senior HS; Cape May Ct House, NJ; (3); GAA; Rep Frsh Cls; Bsktbl; Tennis; Trk; Afro Amer Hist.

GRANT, GENEVIEVE; John P Stevens HS; Edison, NJ; (3); 57/457; Art Clb; Debate Tm; Exploring; Sec Girl Scts; Model UN; Acpl Chr; Chorus; Madrigals; School Musical; Variety Show; Slvr Ldrshp Awd Girl Scts Amer 85.

GRANT, JORDAN; Dwight Morrow HS; Englewood, NJ; (3); Am Leg Boys St; Debate Tm; Band; Jazz Band; Mrchg Band; Nwsp Rptr; Stu Cncl; JV Bsbl; Var Tennis; High Hon Roll; Acad Otstndng Achvmnt Awd Eng 87; Rep ST Mock Trls Tm 87; ST Model Cngrss Rep 86; Elec Engr.

GRANT, LESLIE; Lower Cape May Regional HS; Cape May, NJ; (3); Capt Dance Clb; Drama Clb; Jr Civitan Int; Spanish Clb; Variety Show; Cheerleading; Mgr(s).

GRANT, MEAGAN K; Metawan Regional HS; Matawan, NJ; (3); Drama Clb; French Clb; SADD; School Play; Nwsp Stf; Var Capt Fld Hcky; Var L Trk; High Hon Roll; 4 Time Vrsty Lttr Wnnr, Track, Winter, Track, Hockey 86-87; Childhood Education.

GRASMICK III, LOUIS F; Haddon Township HS; Westmont, NJ; (4); 90/171; Boy Scts; Church Yth Grp; German Clb; Varsity Clb; Rep Jr Cls; Var L Ftbl; Var L Trk; Im Wt Lftg; Hon Roll; Unsung Hero Awd Ftbl 86; John Bordner Schlrshp Church 87; Camden County Coll; Law.

GRATALE, DOMINICK; Secaucus HS; Secaucus, NJ; (4); 65/200; Boy Scts; Chess Clb; Church Yth Grp; Computer Clb; German Clb; Math Clb; Mu Alpha Theta; Hon Roll; Sci Schlrshp-Seton Hall U 87; Montclair ST Coll; Chem.

GRATER, JACQUELYN; Monongahela JR HS; Wenonah, NJ; (1); Career Clb 86-87; Hnr Rll 86-87; Gloucester County Coll; Nrsng.

GRAU, KIMBERLEY; Montville HS; Pinebrook, NJ; (3); Church Yth Grp; FBLA; Key Clb; Rep Frsh Cls; Rep Soph Cls; Rep Jr Cls; Sec Sr Cls; Sec Stu Cncl; Im Fld Hcky; Im Mgr(s); Psych.

GRAU, LISA; Kittatinny Regional HS; Newton, NJ; (4); 10/220; Math Clb; Math Tm; Chorus; School Play; Yrbk Stf; Stat Bsktbl; Var Fld Hcky; High Hon Roll; Hon Roll; NHS; Vet Med.

GRAUMANN, CHRISTEL M; Kittatinny Regional HS; Clinton, NY; (4); 30/227; Church Yth Grp; Hosp Aide; Chorus; Flag Corp; Yrbk Stf; VP Sr Cls; Cheerleading; Hon Roll; NHS; Rep Stu Cncl; Wmns Auxlry Sussex Cnty Mdcl Soc 87; U Of NH; Occptnl Thrpy.

GRAVATT, JO ANN; Bordentown Regional HS; Bordentown, NJ; (3); Dance Clb; French Clb; Math Clb; Math Tm; Chorus; Var Cheerleading; Var Score Keeper; Hon Roll; NHS; Rcvd Old Engl B 86; Frgn Rltns.

GRAVATT, WAYNE; Freehold Twp HS; Adelphia, NJ; (3); 32/375; Capt Cmnty Wkr; Trs FFA; JV Bsktbl; Var Mgr(s); JV Socr; Var Trk; NHS; Prfct Atten Awd; GMI; Auto Engrng.

GRAVES, KIM; Lenape Regional HS; Vincentown, NJ; (3); FBLA; FNA; Hosp Aide; Spanish Clb; Varsity Clb; Cheerleading; Gym; Trk; Hon Roll; Earth Sci Awd 84; Howard U; Bio.

GRAVES, MONIQUE; Our Lady Of Mercy Acad; Sicklerville, NJ; (3); Art Clb; Exploring; Chorus; Capt JV Cheerleading; Hon Roll; Pre Med.

GRAVES, RENE; Morristown HS; Morristown, NJ; (1); Church Yth Grp; Computer Clb; Girl Scts; NAACP; Office Aide; Chorus; Church Choir; Awf For Outstndng In Comp Scie Awd Math Awd 85-86; Yale; Law.

GRAVES, TODD; Deptford Township HS; Wenonah, NJ; (2); 31/294; Church Yth Grp; Cmnty Wkr; Ftbl; Var Trk; Wt Lftg; Hon Roll; Stu Of The Mnth; Carreer Clb; U Of NM.

GRAY, CAMERON; Northern Valley Reg HS At Demarest; Closter, NJ; (3); 2/250; Computer Clb; Debate Tm; Capt Math Tm; Science Clb; Stage Crew; Lit Mag; Rep Stu Cncl; JV Tennis; Gov Hon Prg Awd; High Hon Roll; AIME Rnd Of AHSME 86-87; ARML Tm 86 & 87; Schl Essay Wnr 86 & 87; Gold Mdl Overall Grade 87.

GRAY, CHRIS; Manalapan HS; Englishtown, NJ; (4); 100/500; L Bsktbl; Capt L Ftbl; Full Schlrshp U Of WV Ftbl; Coaches Awd 87; U Of WV; Engrng.

GRAY, EVELYN; Warren County Vo Tech; Washington, NJ; (4); Key Clb; VICA; Nwsp Stf; Yrbk Stf; Hon Roll; Coll; Data Entry.

GRAY, KIMBERLY; Pitman HS; Pitman, NJ; (2); Church Yth Grp; Dance Clb; Drama Clb; Mgr(s); JV Tennis; Hon Roll; Lawyer.

GRAY, MARIBEL; Notre Dame HS; Princeton, NJ; (2); 1/400; Art Clb; Math Tm; Service Clb; Stage Crew; High Hon Roll; NHS; Spanish NHS; NJ Mth Leag Soph Awd 86-87.

GRAY, MARILYN; Red Bank Regional HS; Little Silver, NJ; (3); Church Yth Grp; Stage Crew; Sec Stu Cncl; Var Fld Hcky; Var Socr; French Hon Soc; High Hon Roll; Hon Roll; NHS; Elect Engrng.

GRAY, NA TASHA GINISE; Teaneck HS; Teaneck, NJ; (4); Dance Clb; Drama Clb; Acpl Chr; High Hon Roll; Hon Roll; Prfct Atten Awd; Miss Hal Jacksons Talntd Teen Of Bergon Co 85-86; Howard U.

GRAY, SUSAN; Jackson Memorial HS; Jackson, NJ; (4); Cmnty Wkr; Pres PAVAS; SADD; Nwsp Ed-Chief; Cit Awd; VP Frsh Cls; Pres Jr Cls; VP Sr Cls; Rep Stu Cncl; Var Bsktbl; Senatr Bill Bradley Awd 86; Jacksn Meml Outstndng SR, Schlrshp 87; Ocean Cnty Coll; Comm.

GRAY, TAMMY; Buena Regional HS; Collings Lks, NJ; (2); Church Yth Grp; Acpl Chr; Chorus; Mrchg Band; Swing Chorus; Mgr(s); Hon Roll; Jr NHS; Pres Schlr; Rutgers Coll; Bus Mgmt.

GRAY, VICTORIA E; Southern Regional HS; Manahawkin, NJ; (4); 25/400; Church Yth Grp; Q&S; Sec Spanish Clb; School Musical; Yrbk Ed-Chief; Var Cheerleading; High Hon Roll; Hon Roll; NHS; Prfct Atten Awd; Barnegat Fdrtn Of Tchrs & S Rgnl Theatre Co Schlrshps 87; Trenton ST Coll; Comms.

GRAYBUSH, MARC; Randolph HS; Randolph, NJ; (4); Computer Clb; Ski Clb; Varsity Clb; VICA; Bsbl; Powder Puff Ftbl; Socr; Coop Indl Educ Outstndng Stu Awd 87; Johnson & Whales Schlrhsp 87; Johnson & Wales; Culinary N.

GRAZER, AMY; Cherokee HS; Marlton, NJ; (2); Hon Roll; French Clb; Yrbk Stf; Vllybl; Psych.

GRAZIANI, JOHN; Edgewood SR HS; Sicklerville, NJ; (3); Golf; Hon Roll; Pres Schlr; Rutgers U; Comps.

GRAZIANO, ANTHONY; Morristown Beard Schl; Short Hills, NJ; (3); 13/85; VP Intnl Clb; Service Clb; Ski Clb; JV Socr; MVP Skiing 86-87; No 1 NJ All Prep Lge Skiing 87 No 3 NJ All State Team Skiing 87; Law.

GRAZIANO, JOE; Toms River South HS; Toms River, NJ; (3); Am Leg Boys St; CAP; Intnl Clb; Math Clb; Ski Clb; Band; Color Guard; Mrchg Band; Stu Cncl; Socr; CAP Mtchl Awd 85; CAP Aerhart Awd 87; WA Wrkshps Cngsnl Smnr Schlrshp; Pltcl Sci.

GRAZIANO, LISA; Rutherford HS; Rutherford, NJ; (4); 10/170; Hosp Aide; Yrbk Phtg; High Hon Roll; Hon Roll; NHS; Natl Hnr Soc; Georgetown U; Nrsng.

GREANEY, JOE; Mount Olive HS; Flanders, NJ; (4); 22/365; Math Clb; High Hon Roll; Hon Roll; Mech Engnrng.

GRECCO, KIMBERLY ANN; Secaucus HS; Secaucus, NJ; (3); Art Clb; Key Clb; Chorus; Mrchg Band; Yrbk Stf.

GRECO, DENISE G; Bloomfield HS; Bloomfield, NJ; (2); Cmnty Wkr; Dance Clb; Key Clb; Pep Clb; Spanish Clb; SADD; Chorus; Yrbk Stf; Var Cheerleading; Hon Roll; Dance Schlrshp Debbie Mc Camis Schl 86; 1st Pl Amer Stars Tlnt Comptn 86; Barlingn Mdlng Schl Grad Cer; Montclair ST Coll; Actress.

GRECO, MARIA; Paramus Catholic Girls HS; Fair Lawn, NJ; (3); Dance Clb; Drama Clb; Hosp Aide; SADD; Nwsp Rptr; Lit Mag; Hon Roll; Cmnty Hosp Awd 86-87; Jmp Hrt Awd 86-87; Schl Merits 86-87; Nrsng.

GRECO, MELISSA; Spotswood HS; Spotswood, NJ; (3); Infnl Clb; SADD; Mrchg Band; Yrbk Stf; VP Jr Cls; JV Crs Cntry; Var Trk; NHS; Spanish NHS; Voice Dem Awd; Engrng.

GRECO, ROSEMARIE; Bridgewater-Raritan HS West; Raritan, NJ; (3); Cmnty Wkr; Sec Pep Clb; SADD; Yrbk Ed-Chief; Trs Frsh Cls; VP Soph Cls; Rep Stu Cncl; Var Cheerleading; Powder Puff Ftbl; Hon Roll.

GRECSEK, DAVID; West Windsor Plainsboro HS; Trenton, NJ; (3); French Clb; Radio Clb; Var Socr; Bus Mgmt.

GREELISH, MICHAEL; Summit HS; Summit, NJ; (3); Hon Roll; Ntl Merit Ltr; Liberal Arts Education.

GREEN, ARLENER; Malcolm X Shabazz HS; Newark, NJ; (2); Computer Clb; Drama Clb; Girl Scts; Chorus; School Play; Variety Show; Rep Stu Cncl; Hon Roll; NHS; Prfct Atten Awd; Comp Pgmmr.

GREEN, BERNARD; Central HS; Newark, NJ; (3); Var Capt Ftbl; Trk; Hon Roll; All Cty Ftbl 86; All Cty Indr Trck & Fld 86; Elec Engr.

GREEN, BRADLEY; Kittatinny Regional HS; Newton, NJ; (3); 2/227; Math Clb; Math Tm; Science Clb; Chorus; Church Choir; Madrigals; School Musical; High Hon Roll; Hon Roll; NHS; Mock Trl Tm 2nd Pl NJ 86; Engrng.

GREEN, CANDACE; Plainfield HS; Plainfield, NJ; (3); 49/400; Church Yth Grp; Office Aide; Co-Capt Pep Clb; Rep Jr Cls; Var Socr; Var Trk; Jr NHS; Minorities Engrng Pgms 84 & 85; Morgan ST U; Psych.

GREEN, CHARLEMAGNE; Kennedy HS; Willingboro, NJ; (3); 70/250; Chess Clb; Church Yth Grp; Trs Key Clb; Church Choir; Swmmng; Trk; Hon Roll; Rutgers U; Engr.

GREEN, DANA; Haddon Heights HS; Haddon Heights, NJ; (3); 16/166; Am Leg Aux Girls St; Girl Scts; Ski Clb; JV Var Bsktbl; JV Var Fld Hcky; Var L Sftbl; Hon Roll; Sprotsmnshp Awd Sftbl 85; Co-Sec Garnet & Gold Soc 87-88.

GREEN, DANA; Kent Place Schl; Basking Rifge, NJ; (4); Church Yth Grp; Cmnty Wkr; French Clb; Teachers Aide; School Musical; Trs Frsh Cls; Soph Cls; VP Sr Cls; Capt Fld Hcky; Capt Sftbl; Hdmstrs Awd 84; Sprtmnshp Awd 84; 1st Pl Dnc Pstr Cntst 87; Smith Coll; Hstry.

GREEN, EUGENE; Rahway SR HS; Rahway, NJ; (3); JA; Hon Roll; NHS; Rutgers U; Jrnlsm.

GREEN, FELICIA; Ferris HS; Jersey City, NJ; (3); Yrbk Phtg; Yrbk Rptr; Yrbk Stf; Sec Soph Cls; Trs Jr Cls; Rep Sr Cls; Rep Stu Cncl; JV Var Powder Puff Ftbl; Hon Roll; Prfct Atten Awd; Bus.

GREEN, JOSHUA A; Governor Livingston Regional HS; Berkeley Hts, NJ; (3); 50/200; Am Leg Boys St; Varsity Clb; Nwsp Ed-Chief; Nwsp Sprt Ed; Nwsp Stf; Rep Stu Cncl; Var Socr; Capt Var Swmmng; Capt Var Trk; Hon Roll; Mtn Vly All Conf Sccr Tm & Stu Ldrshp Day 86; Rec Cmmssn Teen Cmte 85-87; Engl.

GREEN, MATTHEW; Westwood HS; Washington Twp, NJ; (2); Band; Concert Band; Mrchg Band; Stage Crew; Off Soph Cls; Rep Stu Cncl; Hon Roll; Bus.

GREEN, MICHAEL; Morristown HS; Morristown, NJ; (3); 6/422; Church Yth Grp; Ski Clb; Y-Teens; JV Bsbl; Im Sftbl; Bus.

GREEN, PAUL; Sacred Heart HS; Vineland, NJ; (3); 13/57; Church Yth Grp; Computer Clb; German Clb; Im Bsktbl; Im Vllybl; Hon Roll; Prfct Atten Awd; Sr Vice Cmmndr, Cmmndr Son Amer Lgn 84 & 85; Glassboro ST; Acctng.

GREEN, WILLIAM; Holy Cross HS; Cinnaminson, NJ; (3); Ski Clb; VP Swmmng; JV VP Trk; VP Wrstlng; Hon Roll; Trntn ST; Mech Engrng.

GREENBERG, JEFFREY; Brick Township HS; Bricktown, NJ; (3); Bsbl; Wrstlng; Law.

GREENBERG, JEFFREY; Paramus HS; Paramus, NJ; (4); 31/330; Computer Clb; Math Clb; Math Tm; Band; Concert Band; Drm & Bgl; Jazz Band; Mrchg Band; Orch; Pep Band; All NJ 4R Rgn HS Band 84; Presdntl Acadc Ftnss Awd 87; Rutgers; Elec Engrng.

GREENBERG, MICHAEL D; Millburn HS; Millburn, NJ; (4); 7/249; Key Clb; Math Tm; Model UN; Quiz Bowl; Science Clb; Var Socr; Im Sftbl; Var Trk; High Hon Roll; Ntl Merit SF; Engr.

GREENBERG, ROBIN; Hightstown HS; East Windsor, NJ; (3); VP Spanish Clb; SADD; Temple Yth Grp; Yrbk Stf.

GREENE, CHRISTOPHER; Kittatinny Regional HS; Branchville, NJ; (3); 26/220; Boy Scts; Church Yth Grp; Exploring; Varsity Clb; Socr; Wt Lftg; Var JV Wrstlng; High Hon Roll; Hon Roll; NHS; 2 Wrstlng Trnmnt Trphys 84-85; Rtgrs Coll; Lndscpng.

GREENE, ERICH J; Waldwick HS; Midland Park, NJ; (4); 1/146; Capt Math Tm; School Play; Ed Nwsp Stf; Mgr Lit Mag; Gov Hon Prg Awd; High Hon Roll; NHS; Ntl Merit Schol; St Schlr; Val; Westinghouse Sci Tlnt Srch Hnr Grp, Am Acad Achvt Awd, & Robt C Byrd Hnrs Schlrshp 87; Princeton U; Physics.

GREENE, KIM; Franklin HS; Somerset, NJ; (3); Pres Civic Clb; VP DECA; NAACP; Varsity Clb; Var Trk; High Hon Roll; Hon Roll.

GREENE, SUSAN ANN; Freehold Township HS; Freehold, NJ; (4); French Clb; Pres Stu Cncl; Var Socr; Princpls Awd Scholar 87; Supt Awd Scholar 87; Var Soccr MVP 87; U CT.

GREENEMEIER, CARI; Piscataway HS; Piscataway, NJ; (3); Mgr Dance Clb; Key Clb; Hon Roll; NHS; Arch.

GREENSPUN, ROBERT; Atlantic City HS; Margate, NJ; (4); 35/402; Model UN; Pres Band; Pres Mrchg Band; Computer Clb; Latin Clb; Jazz Band; Symp Band; Hon Roll; Rotary Awd; Most Outstndng Dele Harvard Model UN 85; MVP Band 84-87.

GREENSTEIN, KAREN; Glen Rock HS; Glen Rock, NJ; (3); Drama Clb; French Clb; Acpl Chr; Band; Chorus; Pres Concert Band; Jazz Band; Madrigals; School Musical; Swing Chorus; Prfrmng Arts.

GREENSTEIN, MARC; Clifton HS; Clifton, NJ; (4); 95/580; Temple Yth Grp; Concert Band; Jazz Band; Mrchg Band; Orch; School Musical; Rep Soph Cls; Swmmng; Hon Roll; NHS; MIP Band 86-87; Band Schlrshp 87; Emory U.

GREENSTONE, SCOTT; Livingston HS; Livingston, NJ; (3); Leo Clb; Ski Clb; Temple Yth Grp; Nwsp Stf; Yrbk Stf; JV Tennis; Finnc.

GREENWOOD, KRISTEN; Mt Olive HS; Budd Lake, NJ; (3); #42 In Class; Math Tm; Ski Clb; Varsity Clb; Nwsp Rptr; JV Fld Hcky; Var Trk; Vllybl; High Hon Roll; Hon Roll; NHS; Indoor Track Coaches Awd 87; All-Conf Indoor Track 87; Math.

GREER, LISA; Pleasantville HS; Pleasantville, NJ; (4); 4/117; Dance Clb; VICA; Pom Pon; NHS; Capaldi Schalick & Reynolds Scholar 87; Katharine Gibbs Scholar 87; Atlantic Cnty Ed Sec Assn Bond 87; Katharine Gibbs Schl; Sec.

GREER, MICHELLE; Gateway Regional HS; Westville, NJ; (4); 46/205; Cmnty Wkr; French Clb; SADD; Var Capt Cheerleading; Hon Roll; Rotary Awd; Gloucester Cnty Coll; Ofc Sys.

GREER, RICHARD; Gateway Regional HS; Westville, NJ; (4); 42/205; Cmnty Wkr; SADD; JV Bsbl; Hon Roll; Prfct Atten Awd; Wenonah Lions Clb Outstndng Cmnty Svc 87; Crpntr.

GREFF, MICHELLE; Wayne Hills HS; Wayne, NJ; (3); 45/320; Am Leg Aux Girls St; GAA; Teachers Aide; Sec Band; School Musical; Nwsp Rptr; Rep Stu Cncl; High Hon Roll; NHS; Ed.

GREGER, CAROLINE; Lower Cape May Regional HS; Villas, NJ; (3); French Clb; Key Clb; Band; Concert Band; Mrchg Band; Orch; Pep Band; School Musical; Yrbk Stf; Im Vllybl; West Chester Coll; Math Tchr.

GREGG, VANESSA E; Nottingham HS; Mercerville, NJ; (4); Am Leg Aux Girls St; Church Choir; Drill Tm; Jazz Band; Madrigals; Sec Jr Cls; Var L Badmtn; Var L Sftbl; Var L Tennis; NCTE Awd; Sprts Med.

GREGOREC, GLENN; Lyndhurst HS; Lyndhurst, NJ; (3); 8/174; German Clb; JV Var Bsktbl; Var Crs Cntry; JV Var Trk; Hon Roll; NHS; Found Free Enterprise 86.

GREGORY, BRIAN; University HS; Newark, NJ; (3); JA; Teachers Aide; Hon Roll; Alg II Awd 86; Physics Lab Awd 87; AL ST Coll; Bus Admin.

GREGORY, LONNA; Clifford J Scott HS; East Orange, NJ; (3); #10 In Class; Band; Jazz Band; Mrchg Band; Hon Roll; PA ST; Engrng.

GREGORY, MICHELE; East Brunswick HS; E Brunswick, NJ; (4); FBLA; Key Clb; Band; Mrchg Band; Margaret Schoen Awd 87; Cntgrl Jersey Bank & Trust Co Awd 87; Outstndng Achvt In Bus Edu 87; Cittone Inst; Word Prcsng.

GREGORY, SHARIFA; Hillside HS; Hillside, NJ; (2); 6/66; Band; Church Choir; Color Guard; Mrchg Band; Cheerleading; Mnrts Engnrng 85-87; Rgt Pgm Gftd & Tlntd 85-86; Smile America Crtv Wrtg Cntst Wnnr 82; Brown U; Acctg.

GREIF, HAYLEY; Highstown HS; E Windsor, NJ; (4); 72/422; AFS; Intnl Clb; Trs SADD; Lit Mag; Rep Soph Cls; Hon Roll; College Of Wooster; Comm.

GRENTI, STEPHANIE MARIE; Hopatcong HS; Hopatcong, NJ; (3); 26/180; FHA; Ski Clb; School Play; Lit Mag; Powder Puff Ftbl; Socr; Trk; Wt Lftg; High Hon Roll; Hon Roll; Acad Achvt Awd 87; Gftd & Tlntd Pgm 87; Fnlst Sussex Cnty Tn Arts Fstvl 87; Textile Dsgn.

GRESKI, CAROL; Rancocas Valley Reg HS; Medford, NJ; (2); 28/316; Drama Clb; PAVAS; Thesps; Varsity Clb; Chorus; School Musical; Stage Crew; Variety Show; Mgr Bsktbl; JV Sftbl; PA ST.

GRETCHEN, LIPPERT; Life Center Acad; Willingboro, NJ; (2); 1/17; Church Yth Grp; Drama Clb; Spanish Clb; School Musical; School Play; Yrbk Phtg; Tennis; High Hon Roll; Outstndng Stu Sci Acad Achvt 85-8l; Adv.

GREY, ALICIA; Franklin HS; Somerset, NJ; (4); 30/327; Church Yth Grp; Hosp Aide; Teachers Aide; Jazz Band; Mrchg Band; Symp Band; Nwsp Bus Mgr; Nwsp Rptr; Var JV Fld Hcky; Wellesley Coll; Engl.

GRIBAS, ANGELA; West Morris Mendham HS; Chester, NJ; (3); 83/308; Church Yth Grp; Cmnty Wkr; Dance Clb; Drama Clb; Intnl Clb; Science Clb; School Musical; School Play; JV Trk; Hon Roll; AHEPA Awd Outstndng Schltc Achcvt Greek Lang & Clture 86; Hon Mntn Essay Wrtng Greek Yth Orgnztn 87; Art Hstry.

GRIBBIN, DOROTHY; Newton HS; Newton, NJ; (2); 6/219; French Clb; Latin Clb; Trs Flag Corp; Nwsp Stf; Yrbk Stf; Lit Mag; Hon Roll.

GRIBBIN, PETER; Newton HS; Newton, NJ; (2); 17/219; German Clb; Latin Clb; Concert Band; Mrchg Band; Lit Mag; Tennis; Hon Roll; No 1 Bio Sussex Cnty Sci Lg 87; No 1 Bio Natl Sci Olympd Tst 87.

GRIECO, ANNAMARIA; Mount Saint Dominic Acad; Bloomfield, NJ; (4); 3/53; Pres Intnl Clb; JCL; VP Latin Clb; Library Aide; Hst Frsh Cls; Hst Soph Cls; Stu Cncl; Crs Cntry; High Hon Roll; NHS; NJ Inst Of Tech; Elec Engrng.

GRIESSER, WILLIAM G; Middlesex HS; Middlesex, NJ; (3); 2/170; Am Leg Boys St; Computer Clb; Model UN; VP Band; Concert Band; Jazz Band; VP Mrchg Band; School Musical; VP Jr Cls; VP Sr Cls; Stu Of Mo 86 & 87; WA Wrkshp Dlgte 87; PBA Cert Meritorius Awd 87; Polit Sci.

GRIFF, DAVID M; Glen Rock HS; Glen Rock, NJ; (3); 14/145; Debate Tm; Drama Clb; French Clb; JCL; School Play; Pres Jr Cls; Pres Sr Cls; Var Socr; High Hon Roll; NHS; Ntl Hnr Soc 87; Am Lgn 87; Vrsty Trk 86; Law.

GRIFFIN, COLLEEN; Haddon Hts HS; Haddon Hts, NJ; (1); Church Yth Grp; 4-H; 4-H Awd; Hon Roll.

GRIFFIN, CYNTHIA; Asbury Park HS; Asbury Park, NJ; (4); 58/140; Pep Clb; Rep Frsh Cls; Rep Soph Cls; Rep Jr Cls; VP Stu Cncl; Bowling; Twrlr; Hon Roll; Hmcmng Qn 87; Tau Sigma Sorority 84-85; Cittone Inst Edison; Crt Reprtr.

GRIFFIN, ERIC F; Teaneck HS; Teaneck, NJ; (3); Am Leg Boys St; Church Yth Grp; Debate Tm; NFL; School Play; Yrbk Phtg; Yrbk Stf; Rep Soph Cls; Trs Jr Cls; Trs Stu Cncl; Rotary Yth Ldrshp Awd 87; Liberal Arts.

GRIFFIN, GINNY; Haddon Heights HS; Haddon Hts, NJ; (1); Church Yth Grp; 4-H; 4-H Awd; Hon Roll.

GRIFFIN, GRETCHEN; Toms River East HS; Toms River, NJ; (4); 18/580; Exploring; Intnl Clb; Math Tm; Mrchg Band; Orch; Ed Yrbk Rptr; Lit Mag; Hon Roll; NHS; Ntl Merit SF; Acamc Lttr 84; Rutgers; Vet.

GRIFFIN, JOHN; Toms River South HS; Beachwood, NJ; (2); Band; Mrchg Band; Symp Band; High Hon Roll; Hon Roll; Engrng.

GRIFFIN, KAREN; Pennsauken HS; Pennsauken, NJ; (2); JV VP Cheerleading; Hon Roll; Lwyr.

GRIFFIN, KIMBERLY ANN; Pennsville Memorial HS; Pennsville, NJ; (3); 1/225; Office Aide; Ski Clb; Rep Stu Cncl; Var Bsktbl; Var Sftbl; Var Tennis; High Hon Roll; NHS; Amer HS Athlt Awd 84; Salem Cnty All Star Tnns Tm 84-85; Tri Cnty All Star Sftbl Tm 86.

GRIFFIN, MARTY; Linden HS; Linden, NJ; (3); Church Yth Grp; Band; Chorus; Pres Church Choir; Concert Band; Mrchg Band; Pep Band; Rep Soph Cls; Rep Jr Cls; Var Bsktbl; Bus Mgmt.

GRIFFIN, TRACY; Ferris HS; Jersey City, NJ; (3); Boy Scts; Library Aide; Office Aide; Red Cross Aide; Teachers Aide; School Play; Hon Roll; Prfct Atten Awd; ABA; Court Reporter.

GRIFFIS, KATE; Morristown-Beard HS; Montclair, NJ; (3); 12/84; Pres Drama Clb; Sec Trs Q&S; Chorus; School Musical; School Play; Nwsp Stf; Lit Mag; Hon Roll; AFS; Art Clb; TRI M 85-86; Art Hnrs Soc 86-87; Intl Thespian Soc 86-87; Creative Wrtng.

GRIFFITH, ADRIENNE; Wall HS; Manasquan, NJ; (4); 26/269; Am Leg Aux Girls St; Church Yth Grp; Drama Clb; Ski Clb; Band; Nwsp Rptr; JV Bsktbl; High Hon Roll; NHS; Northwestern U; Cmmnctns.

GRIFFITH, JENNIFER; Edgewood SR HS; Waterford, NJ; (2); Fld Hcky; JV Stat Socr; Hon Roll; Pres Schlr; Stu Career Awrnss Pgm 85-86; Arch.

GRIFFITH, STACEY; Glen Rock HS; Glen Rock, NJ; (3); 26/150; AFS; Church Yth Grp; Band; Concert Band; Mrchg Band; Vllybl; Hon Roll; NHS; Psych.

GRIFFITTS, ERIC; Newton HS; Newton, NJ; (2); Church Yth Grp; Church Choir; Hon Roll; Prfct Atten Awd.

GRIFO, ANA; East Side HS; Newark, NJ; (3); Church Yth Grp; VP Math Clb; Pres Ski Clb; Variety Show; Rep Jr Cls; Rep Stu Cncl; Pratt Inst; Architect.

GRIGNI, LAURA; Carteret HS; Carteret, NJ; (4); 20/190; Drama Clb; Latin Clb; Concert Band; Drm Mjr(t); Mrchg Band; Sec Soph Cls; Sec Jr Cls; Pres Sr Cls; NHS; Trenton ST Coll.

GRILL, EMILY; Hunterdon Central HS; Whitehouse Sta, NJ; (3); 99/546; Am Leg Aux Girls St; French Clb; Ski Clb; Nwsp Rptr; Yrbk Stf; Stu Cncl; French Hon Soc; Hon Roll; Prfct Atten Awd; Intl Bus.

GRIM, KATHERINE; Delaware Valley Regional HS; Milford, NJ; (4); Am Leg Aux Girls St; Intnl Clb; School Play; Lit Mag; Rep Stu Cncl; JV Cheerleading; High Hon Roll; Hon Roll; Acad All Amer 86-87; Defnse Lwyr & Witnss Hunterdon Cnty Mock Trials Champs 87; Grant Ursinus Coll 87; Ursinus Coll; Engl.

GRIMALDI, CHRIS; Haddon Township HS; Westmont, NJ; (3); 10/200; Church Yth Grp; VP JA; JCL; Latin Clb; High Hon Roll; Hon Roll; Lat Hnrs 86-87; Jr Achiev Hnrs 84-86; Pre-Med.

GRIMES, DAWN MARIE; N Brunswick Township HS; N Brunswick, NJ; (4); Cmnty Wkr; Intnl Clb; Teachers Aide; Yrbk Stf; High Hon Roll; Hon Roll; NHS; 2 Certs Merit Le Grand Concour 85-86; Boston U; Culture.

GRIMES, JAMES T; Passaic Valley HS; West Paterson, NJ; (3); Am Leg Boys St; Cmnty Wkr; Var Capt Crs Cntry; Var L Trk; Cit Awd; Passaic Vly Hnr Society; U CA Los Angeles; Med.

GRIMES, KIMBERLY L; Franklin HS; Somerset, NJ; (4); 144/327; Drama Clb; Pres FHA; Key Clb; School Musical; Hampton; Bus.

GRIMES, PAULINE; Rancocas Valley Regional HS; Mt Holly, NJ; (2); 29/316; Church Yth Grp; Ski Clb; Concert Band; Mrchg Band; Fld Hcky; Var Sftbl; High Hon Roll; Hon Roll; NHS; Prfct Atten Awd; Math.

GRIMM, JANICE BETH; Bridgewater-Raritan HS West; Bridgewater, NJ; (3); Church Yth Grp; Band; Church Choir; Yrbk Bus Mgr; JV Sftbl; High Hon Roll; Hon Roll; NHS; Hotel Mngmnt.

GRINWIS, JOHN; High Point Regional HS; Sussex, NJ; (4); Aud/Vis; Band; Chorus; Jazz Band; School Musical; School Play; Bowling; High Hon Roll; Hon Roll; Drama Clb; Ntl Schl Choral Awd 87; HS Hrmnzrs Schlrshp 87; William Paterson Coll; CPA.

GRIPPALDI, CHRISTINA; Lacey Township HS; Forked River, NJ; (3); SADD; Nwsp Stf; Yrbk Stf; Stu Cncl; Bsktbl; Bowling; Powder Puff Ftbl; Sftbl; Swmmng; Hon Roll; MS Teen USA Pgnt Awd 87; Vrstyltr Sftbl 86; Law.

GRIPPE, MARYANN; Burlington Twp HS; Burlington, NJ; (3); 13/127; Am Leg Aux Girls St; French Clb; GAA; Key Clb; Bsktbl; Fld Hcky; High Hon Roll; Hon Roll; NHS; Acctg.

GRISCOM, CHRISTINA; Woodstown HS; Alloway, NJ; (3); English Clb; French Clb; Key Clb; Ski Clb; SADD; Varsity Clb; Yrbk Stf; Var Diving; Var Sftbl; Var Swmmng; Communications.

GRISCOM, MICHELLE; Pennsville Memorial HS; Salem, NJ; (3); 10/225; French Clb; Ski Clb; Rep Stu Cncl; JV Var Bsktbl; Var Fld Hcky; Var Trk; Hon Roll; NHS; Prfct Atten Awd; Exploring; Interntl Relations.

GRISSOM, DAWN M; Middletown H S South; Red Bank, NJ; (2); Hosp Aide; Nwsp Stf; Yrbk Ed-Chief; Score Keeper; Hon Roll; Acadmc All Amer Schlr 85-86; Schl Svc Awd 85-86; Psycht.

GRIZZLE, JOHN; Red Bank Regional HS; Red Bank, NJ; (3); Stat Bsbl; Stat Bsktbl; Var Mgr(s); Hon Roll; US Naval Acad; Aerospce Engrng.

GROCHOWSKI, JOHN; Kearny HS; Kearny, NJ; (4); 84/383; Var Capt Ftbl; Wt Lftg; Hon Roll; Boca Raton Coll; Bus Adm.

GRODMAN, JACQUELYN; Manalapan HS; Manalapan, NJ; (3); Church Yth Grp; SADD; Sec Band; Concert Band; Mrchg Band; Var Twrlr; NHS; Bus Admn.

GROELING, JAMES; Haddonfield Memorial HS; Haddonfield, NJ; (4); Trs Soph Cls; Trs Jr Cls; Off Stu Cncl; JV Var Socr; Var Capt Tennis; High Hon Roll; NHS; Spanish NHS; Tennis All ST 3 Yrs ST Champ 84-86; Ecnmcs.

GROFF, ROBERT; Buena Regional HS; Collings Lake, NJ; (4); 21/180; Pres Band; Pres Concert Band; Pres Jazz Band; Pres Mrchg Band; Pep Band; Hon Roll; Prfct Atten Awd; Vrsty Schlr Lttr 86; Drum Line Capt 85-87; Glassboro ST Coll; Bus Mngnt.

GROGAN, JAMES E; St Peters Prep; Wayne, NJ; (3); 16/187; Am Leg Boys St; NFL; Stu Cncl; Tennis; High Hon Roll; Hon Roll; Cmnty Wkr; Drama Clb; German Clb; Pol Sci.

GRONENTHAL, MICHELLE E; Newton HS; Newton, NJ; (2); Leo Clb; Math Tm; School Musical; School Play; Yrbk Stf; Cit Awd; Hon Roll; Art Bond 86; Pratt; Advrtsng.

GRONSKY, TANYA; North Hunterdon HS; Hampton, NJ; (3); Church Yth Grp; 4-H; FBLA; Key Clb; Color Guard; 4-H Awd; Ski Clb; VICA; Mrchg Band; Yrbk Stf; 8th Pl If FBLA Rgnl Competition 86-87; 4-H Ldrshp & Fashion Awds; ACCNTNT.

GROODY, DANIELLE; Kingsway Regional HS; Clarksboro, NJ; (2); 18/186; Church Yth Grp; Office Aide; Rep Stu Cncl; JV Fld Hcky; Var Sftbl; MI ST; Cmmnctn.

GROOF, DAVID; Millville SR HS; Millville, NJ; (3); Church Yth Grp; Key Clb; Office Aide; Red Cross Aide; VP SADD; Lit Mag; Bowling; JV Socr; Master Chef.

GROOKETT, TOM; Wildwood HS; Wildwood, NJ; (4); Varsity Clb; Rep Stu Cncl; Bsbl; Ftbl; MVP Sftbl; Rutgers U; Pre-Med.

GROOVER, ERIN; Immaculate Conception HS; Hasbrouck Heights, NJ; (4); 12/88; Chorus; School Musical; Off Frsh Cls; Off Soph Cls; Off Jr Cls; Off Sr Cls; Off Stu Cncl; Hon Roll; Art Ntnl Hnr Soc; Art.

GROSS, BRIAN; Collingswood SR HS; Collingswood, NJ; (2); Aud/Vis; Ski Clb; Stage Crew; Socr; Trk; Cit Awd; Hon Roll; Ntl Germn Hnr Soc 87; Schltc Awd Cert 86; VA Tech; Bus.

GROSS, CHRISTOPHER; Holy Spirit HS; Northfield, NJ; (4); 8/363; VP Science Clb; Spanish Clb; Im Vllybl; Ntl Merit SF; St Schlr; Grdn ST Dstngshd Schlr 86; Englsh Awd 85-86; Harvard; Astrnmy.

GROSS, JEANNIE; Cinnaminson HS; Cinnaminson, NJ; (3); Church Yth Grp; Dance Clb; Spanish Clb; Hon Roll; Bio Camp 86; Co-Op Prog 87; Med Fld.

GROSS, JENNIFER; Holy Spirit HS; Northfield, NJ; (2); 15/397; Spanish Clb; Church Choir; School Musical; JV Fld Hcky; Hon Roll; Natl Latin Exam Gold Mdl 85-86; U Notre Dame; Med.

GROSS, MELANIE; Morris Knolls HS; Denville, NJ; (3); 38/424; Art Clb; French Clb; Ski Clb; Varsity Clb; JV Var Socr; JV Var Sftbl; High Hon Roll; Hon Roll; Sec NHS; Suma Awd 85-87; Pol Sci.

GROSSMAN, DANIEL; Livingston HS; Livingston, NJ; (3); 19/420; Key Clb; Nwsp Rptr; Im Bsktbl; Im Fld Hcky; Im Sftbl; JV Trk; Hon Roll; Spanish NHS; Poli Sci.

GROSSMAN, SHOSHANA; Toms River HS East; Toms River, NJ; (4); JV Socr; Hon Roll; Ed.

GROSSWEILER, TINA; Lower Cape May Regional HS; North Cape May, NJ; (3); French Clb; Band; Chorus; Concert Band; Mrchg Band; School Musical; Nwsp Stf; JV Trk; Hon Roll; NHS; Mst Imprvd Music Stu Cortes Awd 84-85; Sci.

GROVE, RONALD A; University HS; Newark, NJ; (4); Church Yth Grp; English Clb; JA; Im Trk; High Hon Roll; Outstndng Awd Engl, Chem, Law Action 87; Rutgers U New Brunswick.

GROVEMAN, LYNN; Bordentown Regional HS; Bordentown, NJ; (4); 9/114; French Clb; Key Clb; Math Tm; Ski Clb; Capt Color Guard; Yrbk Stf; Rep Stu Cncl; Fld Hcky; Stat Trk; NHS; 1st Pl Champs Centrl Jersey Olmpcs Mnd 86.

GROVES, LEE; Victory Christian Schl; Blue Anchor, NJ; (3); 1/20; Art Clb; Science Clb; Stat Var Bsktbl; Capt Var Socr; Trk; Hon Roll; 2nd Degree Amer Tang Soo Do Assoc 86; GSACS Trck Meet Cmptn 86; GSACS Sci Fair 85.

GRUBER, DAWN E; Fair Lawn HS; Fair Lawn, NJ; (4); 26/320; Art Clb; Jr Cls; Rep Sr Cls; JV Var Trk; Hon Roll; NHS; Ntl Merit Ltr; Pres Schlr; Stage Crew; Yrbk Stf; 2nd Stu Art Cntst/Exhbtn Awd 86; AAA Poster Cntst 1st St 86; Parsons Schl Dsgn; Illstrn Dsgn.

GRUCCIO, MARIA; Sacred Heart HS; Vineland, NJ; (3); 1/60; Sec Trs French Clb; JA; SADD; School Play; Rep Frsh Cls; Var Cheerleading; High Hon Roll; Hon Roll; VP NHS; St Schlr; Hnry Rutgers Schlr Awd 87; US Sci Awd 85; US Hstry Awd 86; Bus.

GRUCHACZ, TODD M; Hunterdon Central HS; Stockton, NJ; (3); 192/543; Church Yth Grp; Hon Roll.

GRUNGO, JOE; Holy Cross HS; Mount Holly, NJ; (4); Boca Raton; Hosp Mgmt.

GRUNWALD, JASON P; Cherokee HS; Marlton, NJ; (3); Am Leg Boys St; Church Yth Grp; Ski Clb; SADD; JV Bsbl; Socr; JV Swmmng; Hon Roll.

GRYGLAK, JOLANTA; Sussex County Vo-Tech Schl; Stanhope, NJ; (2); Church Yth Grp; Achvt Awd 83; Med.

GRYGOTIS, LEIGH; Holy Spirit HS; Absecon, NJ; (4); 1/363; Math Clb; School Musical; Rep Stu Cncl; Var Capt Crs Cntry; Var Capt Swmmng; Var Capt Trk; High Hon Roll; Pres NHS; Math Awds; NJ ST Distngshd Schlr; Sci Awds; Elec Engr.

GRZYB, ANTONIA; Immaculate Conception HS; E Rutherford, NJ; (3); Art Clb; Church Yth Grp; Drama Clb; Spanish Clb; SADD; Chorus; Church Choir; School Musical; Stage Crew; Yrbk Phtg; Montclair; Bus.

GSTATTENBAUER, MICHELLE; Lenape Valley Regional HS; Sparta, NJ; (3); 8/220; Key Clb; NFL; Yrbk Stf; Lit Mag; Sec Frsh Cls; Pres Soph Cls; Trs Stu Cncl; Hon Roll; Trdr NY Stck Exch.

GUANZON, JAMES PAUL; Essex Catholic Boys HS; East Orange, NJ; (2); 3/30; Art Clb; Church Yth Grp; Math Clb; Nwsp Stf; Sec Frsh Cls; Pres Soph Cls; JV Crs Cntry; High Hon Roll; Acad All Amer; Comp Sci.

GUARINI, GEORGINA; St Aloysius HS; Jersey City, NJ; (3); Yrbk Stf; God Cntry Awd; High Hon Roll; NHS; Mission Rep 86-88; Typing Skills Awd 86; Fash Mrktg.

GUARINO, DONNA; Watchung Hills Regional HS; Warren, NJ; (3); Trs Debate Tm; Drama Clb; Pres Key Clb; Sec Spanish Clb; SADD; School Play; Trs Jr Cls; Rep Sr Cls; Tennis; NHS; Girls Ctznshp Inst Awd Douglass Coll 87; Econ.

GUARNACCIA, DARREN; Toms River East HS; Toms River, NJ; (3); 11/586; Boy Scts; Debate Tm; Exploring; French Clb; Key Clb; Science Clb; Speech Tm; JV Socr; JV Trk; Var NHS; Cook Coll; Vet.

GUBERMAN, MARK; Manalapan HS; Manalapan, NJ; (3); 29/429; Latin Clb; Science Clb; Temple Yth Grp; Nwsp Bus Mgr; Nwsp Rptr; JV Socr; L Tennis; Ntl Merit Schol; Magna Cum Laude In Natl Latin Exam 85; Mgmnt.

GUDEWITZ, MICHAEL; Howell HS; Howell, NJ; (3); 58/500; JCL; Latin Clb; SADD; Yrbk Phtg; Yrbk Sprt Ed; Yrbk Stf; Coach Actv; Socr; Wt Lftg; Wrstlng.

GUENESS, KIMBERLY; Paul VI HS; Somerdale, NJ; (3); 110/489; French Clb; Flag Corp; French Hon Soc; Ft Ldrdl Art Inst; Intr Dsgn.

GUENTHER, STEVEN A; Montgomery HS; Belle Mead, NJ; (3); Am Leg Boys St; Boy Scts; Church Yth Grp; Exploring; Math Tm; Science Clb; Concert Band; School Musical; Var Golf; NHS; Engr.

GUENTHER, VALERIE; Mount Olive HS; Budd Lake, NJ; (3); 4/340; AFS; Teachers Aide; Varsity Clb; Nwsp Ed-Chief; Nwsp Stf; Lit Mag; Var Swmmng; JV Var Tennis; JV Trk; High Hon Roll; Engrng.

GUERGUERIAN, CLAUDINE; John P Stevens HS; Edison, NJ; (4); 51/467; Art Clb; Thesps; Mrchg Band; School Musical; Stage Crew; Yrbk Stf; NHS; Corio Memrl Schlrshp 87; Achvt Fine Arts 87; Mrchg Band Frnt 87; Otis Art Inst Of Parsons Schl.

GUERRA, ALISSA R; Bishop Eustare Prep; Cinnaminson, NJ; (3); Dance Clb; Drama Clb; German Clb; Pep Clb; SADD; School Play; Lit Mag; Cheerleading; Hon Roll; Pre-Law.

GUERRA, JOHANNA; Passaic County Technical & Voc; Paterson, NJ; (3); 10/556; VP Pres Stu Cncl; Hon Roll; Bus.

GUERRA, NICANOR; Marist HS; Jersey City, NJ; (4); #2 In Class; Art Clb; Key Clb; Science Clb; Nwsp Rptr; Yrbk Stf; Im Bsktbl; Hon Roll; NHS; St Schlr; Acdmc All Amer 84; U Of CA; Pre Law.

GUERRERO, MILAGROS; Academic HS; Jersey City, NJ; (3); Church Yth Grp; Computer Clb; Hosp Aide; Spanish Clb; Chorus; Church Choir; Nwsp Stf; JV Tennis; Cit Awd; Hon Roll; Hugh O Brian Yth Fndtn Cert 86; 1st Plaque Music Cmptn Cnty & ST 2nd Natl 82; Accntng.

GUERRERO, NANCY; East Side HS; Newark, NJ; (4); 52/488; Dance Clb; Intnl Clb; Spanish Clb; Nwsp Stf; Rep Soph Cls; Hon Roll; Prfct Atten Awd; Rutgers U Newark; Chld Psych.

GUERRIERI, KATRINA ANN; Manchester Twp HS; Toms River, NJ; (3); Am Leg Aux Girls St; Sec Drama Clb; French Clb; Sec Frsh Cls; Sec Jr Cls; Sec Sr Cls; Sec Stu Cncl; Hon Roll; Science Clb; Rutgers U; Med.

GUERRIERO, JENINE; Mary Help Of Christians Acad; Totowa, NJ; (2); Dance Clb; Drama Clb; NFL; Quiz Bowl; SADD; High Hon Roll; Val; Church Yth Grp; School Play; HOBY Fndtn 87; Alg Awd 86; Law.

GUESS, LESTER; Camden HS; Camden, NJ; (4); 43/352; Drama Clb; Band; Concert Band; Drm Mjr(t); Jazz Band; Mrchg Band; School Musical; School Play; Rep Frsh Cls; Rep Soph Cls; Rutgers U; Bus Admin.

GUGLER, SEAN; Newton HS; Andover, NJ; (2); 1/219; Math Tm; Science Clb; Trs Chorus; Madrigals; School Musical; School Play; Lit Mag; Boys Clb Am; Rep Stu Cncl; NJ Mth Leag Awd, Natl Sci Olympd Test Awd, Cntntl Mth Leag Comp Sci Cont Awd 86-87; Comp Sci.

GUGLIELMO, LOUIS; East Brunswick HS; E Brunswick, NJ; (3); 65/504; Drama Clb; German Clb; Varsity Clb; School Musical; School Play; Stage Crew; L Var Bsktbl; Mgr(s); Acdmc All Amer 86; Arch.

GUIDA, LISA MARIE; Union HS; Union, NJ; (4); Dance Clb; Drama Clb; FBLA; Girl Scts; Key Clb; Varsity Clb; Chorus; School Musical; School Play; Bsktbl; Dance Awds Cmpttns 82-87; Rider Coll; Accntng.

GUIDO, NICOLE; Manchester Regional HS; N Haledon, NJ; (2); Bsktbl; Hon Roll.

GUIDRY, MARY; Holy Cross HS; Edgewater Park, NJ; (4); 14/370; Church Yth Grp; French Clb; Political Wkr; School Play; Nwsp Stf; Yrbk Stf; High Hon Roll; Hon Roll; NHS; Ntl Merit Ltr; Trenton ST Coll.

GUILES, STACEY; Belvidere HS; Belvidere, NJ; (4); 16/128; Church Yth Grp; 4-H; Ski Clb; Varsity Clb; Chorus; Rep Frsh Cls; Rep Soph Cls; Trs Sr Cls; Stat Bsktbl; High Hon Roll; Math.

GUIN, MARY; Morris Knolls HS; Rockaway Township, NJ; (4); Church Yth Grp; Key Clb; Pep Clb; Varsity Clb; Stu Cncl; Bsktbl; Stat Mgr(s); Tennis; Art Clb; GAA; Mst Imprvd Tnns 85; Outstndng Athlete Tnns 87; CCM; Bio.

GUIRE, MICHAEL; Bordentown Regional HS; Bordentown, NJ; (3); Drama Clb; Key Clb; School Musical; School Play; Stage Crew; Var Capt Bsbl; Var Bsktbl; Var Socr; Hon Roll; Olympics Of Mind 86-87.

GUIRGUIS, IRENE; Teaneck HS; Teaneck, NJ; (3); 50/412; Church Yth Grp; Church Choir; Hon Roll; Prfct Atten Awd; Hrn Scty 86-87; Rutgers Coll; Engrng.

GUJRATHI, SHEILA; Cherry Hill E HS; Cherry Hill, NJ; (3); French Clb; Hosp Aide; JA; JCL; Latin Clb; Model UN; Science Clb; SADD; Nwsp Rptr; Bowling; ST Champ Latin Crtmn; Med Field.

GULIZIA, CHRISTINE; Brick Memorial HS; Brick, NJ; (4); 23/290; Capt Band; Jazz Band; Mrchg Band; School Musical; Rep Soph Cls; Trk; High Hon Roll; NHS; Cls Musician 86-87; PTA Pres Cncl Schlrshp 86-87; GA Crt Coll; Bus Admin.

GUNNELL, COLLEEN; St Rose HS; Spring Lake Hts, NJ; (3); Drama Clb; Key Clb; Ski Clb; School Musical; School Play; Sftbl; Hon Roll; Coaches Awd Smmr Swm Tm 85; Psychlgy.

GUNTER, DAN; The Lawrenceville Schl; Hopewell, NJ; (3); Math Tm; Band; Orch; High Hon Roll; Ntl Merit Ltr; JV Fencing 86-87.

GUNTHER, RICHARD; Brick Township HS; Brick, NJ; (3); #45 In Class; Varsity Clb; JV Var Wrstlng; High Hon Roll; Rutgers; Comp Progrmmng.

GUPTA, ANITA; Franklin Twsp HS; Somerset, NJ; (3); Am Leg Aux Girls St; Rep Sr Cls; Pres German Clb; Ski Clb; SADD; Concert Band; Mrchg Band; Rep Frsh Cls; Rep Soph Cls; Rep Jr Cls; Pre-Law.

GUPTA, ATUL; Bloomfield HS; Bloomfield, NJ; (3); Computer Clb; Math Clb; Math Tm; Quiz Bowl; Scholastic Bowl; Science Clb; Chorus; High Hon Roll; Ntl Merit SF; Pres Schlr; NJ Govrs Schl Of Sci Fnlst 87; Med.

GUPTA, KAVITA; Paul VI HS; Lindenwold, NJ; (3); 8/396; Camera Clb; Drama Clb; Hosp Aide; NFL; Spanish Clb; Temple Yth Grp; Variety Show; Lit Mag; Hon Roll; Spanish NHS; Med.

GUPTA, MUNISH; Northern Valley Regional HS; Closter, NJ; (3); 1/250; Math Tm; Ski Clb; Ed Lit Mag; Rep Stu Cncl; JV Tennis; Bausch & Lomb Sci Awd; Gov Hon Prg Awd; High Hon Roll; NHS; Val.

GUPTA, SHILPI; Morristown HS; Morristown, NJ; (4); Latin Clb; Red Cross Aide; Nwsp Rptr; Pres Frsh Cls; Bsbl; Bsktbl; Gov Hon Prg Awd; High Hon Roll; Ntl Merit Ltr; Pres Schlr; Garden ST Schlr 87; Columbia U; Med.

GUPTA, SUNITA; Hackettstown HS; Hackettstown, NJ; (3); 5/191; Key Clb; Q&S; Chorus; Yrbk Stf; Off Jr Cls; Trs Sr Cls; Score Keeper; High Hon Roll; Hon Roll; NHS; Fnlst Gov Schl Pblc Issues 87; Colonial Msktrs Fife & Drm Corps 87 Nrtheastrn Champs 85-88; Pre Med.

GURAL, JOHN THOMAS; Central Regional HS; Bayville, NJ; (3); 29/239; Exploring; Ski Clb; Nwsp Rptr; Capt JV Bsbl; High Hon Roll; Hon Roll; NHS; Schlr Athlt Awd 87; Engr.

GUREVICH, TANYA; Cherry Hill HS East; Cherry Hill, NJ; (4); Latin Clb; Library Aide; Pep Clb; Bsktbl; Fld Hcky; Swmmng; Vllybl; High Hon Roll; Hon Roll; Cum Laud Awd 86; Drexel U; Fin.

GUROVICH, KATHY; Sayreville War Memorial HS; Parlin, NJ; (4); 97/353; Spanish Clb; Varsity Clb; School Play; Hon Roll; Ramapo Coll Of NJ; Bus Admin.

GURSKY, DAVID; Passaic Valley HS; Totowa, NJ; (4); Am Leg Boys St; Drama Clb; French Clb; School Musical; Ed Yrbk Stf; VP Stu Cncl; Pres NHS; Ntl Merit Ltr; Debate Tm; Am Leg Aux Girls St; Excllnc Mscl Drctn 87; Ski Clb; Yale U.

GURSKY, MELISSA; Notre Dame HS; Robbinsville, NJ; (2); 32/377; Drill Tm; Stat Bsbl; Stat Bsktbl; Pom Pon; Stat Socr; Hon Roll; NHS; Vrsty Ltr Awd Athl Training 86-8m; Pre Med.

GURWICH, TREVOR; Dwight Englewood HS; Englewood, NJ; (4); VP Debate Tm; Letterman Clb; Nwsp Rptr; Lit Mag; Rep Soph Cls; Rep Jr Cls; Var Socr; Var Capt Tennis; High Hon Roll; Fndr & Chrmn Of Cricket Clb 86; U Of PA; Lbrl Arts.

GUSTAFSON, STEPHANIE; Lakewood HS; Lakewood, NJ; (2); 105/335; Art Clb; Exploring; French Clb; Hosp Aide; Intnl Clb; Bio.

GUSTIS, JENNIFER; West Milford HS; W Milford, NJ; (4); 8/400; Ski Clb; SADD; Varsity Clb; Ed Yrbk Ed-Chief; Yrbk Phtg; Yrbk Stf; Var Capt Gym; High Hon Roll; Sec NHS; Spanish NHS; Rotary Clb Awd-Dedctd Athl 84; Lakeland Chemcl Inc Schlrshp 87; Gymnstcs 2nd All Cnty 86; Clemson U; Pre-Med.

GUTIERREZ, DAPHNE; St Josephs Of The Palisades HS; North Bergen, NJ; (2); Pep Clb; Lit Mag; VP Soph Cls; Capt Pom Pon; Swmmng; Hon Roll.

GUTIERREZ, JAVIER; Lakewood HS; Lakewood, NJ; (3); 104/330; Chess Clb; Cmnty Wkr; ROTC; Spanish Clb; Color Guard; Drill Tm; Socr; Vllybl; Wrstlng; Hon Roll; Aero Engr.

GUTMAN, JILL; Glen Rock HS; Glen Rock, NJ; (3); VP Trs AFS; Cmnty Wkr; Trs DECA; Hosp Aide; Chorus; Capt Color Guard; School Musical; Jr NHS; Office Aide; Pep Clb; DECA-ST Cmpttn & SAKS 5th Ave Teen Advisory Brd 86-87 & 86-88; Pediatric Nrsng.

GUY, DARREN; Cranford HS; Cranford, NJ; (2); JCL; Latin Clb; Model UN; Y-Teens; Nwsp Stf; Rep Frsh Cls; Rep Soph Cls; Stat Bsbl; Stat Bsktbl; Hon Roll; Ec.

GUYET, DANIELLE; Columbia HS; S Orange, NJ; (3); Church Yth Grp; Cmnty Wkr; Pres Frsh Cls; Pres Soph Cls; Rep Jr Cls; Var L Lcrss; Im Powder Puff Ftbl; Var L Socr; Cmmnctns.

GUZIEJEWSKI, DINA; Belleville HS; Belleville, NJ; (3); Chorus; High Hon Roll; Hon Roll; Bus.

GUZMAN, ANA; Pennsauken HS; Pennsauken, NJ; (3); Church Yth Grp; Leo Clb; Library Aide; Spanish Clb; SADD; Yrbk Phtg; Vllybl; Hon Roll; Spanish NHS; Temple U; Phys Thrpy.

GUZMAN, CARLOS M; St Joseph Of The Palisades HS; Secaucus, NJ; (3); Capt Var Bsbl; Hon Roll; NHS; Spanish NHS; FCA; Spanish Clb; Rep Frsh Cls; Im Vllybl; Acad All Amer Awd 86; Coaches Awd 85; Comp Sci.

GUZMAN, LUZ; St Aloysius HS; Jersey City, NJ; (4); Church Yth Grp; Library Aide; Spanish Clb; Nwsp Rptr; Ed Nwsp Stf; Bowling; Crs Cntry; Trk; NHS; Hstry Mdl, Relgs Stds Awd, Pres Acdmc Ftns Awd 87; NY U; Psych.

GWYNNE, KELLY; Immaculate Conception HS; Maywood, NJ; (4); 12/88; Rep Church Yth Grp; Hosp Aide; Library Aide; Chorus; Church Choir; School Musical; School Play; Nwsp Rptr; Sftbl; Swmmng; Swmmng Awds 1st 2nd & 3rd Pl 84-86; Nwspaper Awd 86; Williamer Paterson; Spch Pathlg.

GYORI, JENNIFER; Bridgewater-Raritan HS East; Bound Brook, NJ; (4); German Clb; Girl Scts; Math Tm; Orch; Var JV Socr; High Hon Roll; NHS; Church Yth Grp; Hosp Aide; Intnl Clb; Grls Ctznshp Inst NJSFWC 87; Math.

GYURO, KRISTI; Delaware Valley Regional HS; Milford, NJ; (3); 101/235; Varsity Clb; VP Stu Cncl; Crs Cntry; Var L Gym; Hon Roll; YMCA Floor-Ex ST Champ B Div 86-87; 2nd All Arnd ST Champ 86-87; Vet.

HAAS, CHRISTOPHER; Sacred Heart HS; N Wildwood, NJ; (3); Boy Scts; Varsity Clb; Nwsp Rptr; Rep Stu Cncl; Var Bsbl; JV Bsktbl; JV Crs Cntry; Hon Roll; Ntl Math Schlrs Soc 85-86; Ntl Hstry Schlrs Soc 8-87; AZ ST U; Sprts Med.

HAAS, EDWARD; Absegami HS; Egg Harbor, NJ; (4); Computer Clb; Ski Clb; JV Ftbl; Elec Tech.

HAASE, ALYSSA; Long Branch HS; Long Br, NJ; (3); #7 In Class; Sec Drama Clb; NFL; Concert Band; Jazz Band; Mrchg Band; School Musical; School Play; Symp Band; Nwsp Rptr; Lit Mag; NJ Drmtc Cmptn 4th Pl 86; Excllnc In Drama 86-87; Bst Spprtng Actress 87.

HABER, JOEL; Jewish Educational Ctr; Livingston, NJ; (2); Temple Yth Grp; Nwsp Rptr; Bsktbl; Ice Hcky; Pre Law.

HABERLE, FRANK; Rahway HS; Rahway, NJ; (4); Pres DECA; Band; Concert Band; Jazz Band; Mrchg Band; School Play; Ftbl; High Hon Roll; Hon Roll; NHS; DECA Schlrshp Wnnr 87; Culinary Inst Of America; Chef.

HABIB, ALFRED; St Josephs HS; Old Bridge, NJ; (3); 90/237; Am Leg Boys St; French Clb; Science Clb; Band; Var Crs Cntry; Var Trk; Hon Roll; NY U; Med.

HABICH, SHARON; Cranford HS; Cranford, NJ; (3); 54/268; Yrbk Stf; Var Stat Ftbl; Var Stat Wrstlng; Finance.

HACK, DAVID; Scotch Plains Fanwood HS; Fanwood, NJ; (3); Model UN; Quiz Bowl; Spanish Clb; Concert Band; Jazz Band; Var L Trk; Cit Awd; High Hon Roll; Opt Clb Awd; Spanish NHS; Premed.

HACKER, DAWN; Victory Christian Schl; Waterford Works, NJ; (3); FCA; GAA; Office Aide; Sec Frsh Cls; Sec Soph Cls; Sec Jr Cls; Var Mgr Bsktbl; Var L Fld Hcky; Mgr(s); Var Score Keeper; Best Hussle Awd Fld Hcky 87.

HACKER, JUNE S; Dumont HS; Dumont, NJ; (4); 2/219; Mu Alpha Theta; Pres Science Clb; Variety Show; Rep Stu Cncl; High Hon Roll; Sec NHS; Sal; Ski Clb; Spanish Clb; Dele Girls Citznshp Inst 86; U PA; Vet.

HACKETT, KAREN; Mt Olive HS; Budd Lake, NJ; (3); 34/370; AFS; SADD; Variety Show; Nwsp Stf; Yrbk Stf; Lit Mag; High Hon Roll; Jrnlsm.

HACKETT, KELLY; Hanover Park HS; East Hanover, NJ; (4); 11/300; Am Leg Aux Girls St; Pres Debate Tm; VP German Clb; NFL; Political Wkr; Band; Mrchg Band; Church Yth Grp; Pres NHS; Ntl Merit Ltr; Ntl Frnsc Leag Degree Of Hghst Dstntn 86; NJ Dstngshd Schlr 86; 1 Of 2 Grls Ntn Sntrs Rep NJ 86; Law.

HACKNEY, JANEL; Howell HS; Howell, NJ; (3); 5/344; Exploring; JCL; Sec Latin Clb; Math Tm; Band; Orch; Nwsp Rptr; Var Capt Cheerleading; Var Trk; Gov Hon Prg Awd; Pre Med.

HACKNEY, JOHN; Morristown HS; Morristown, NJ; (3); 38/451; Church Yth Grp; Cmnty Wkr; JCL; Latin Clb; Concert Band; Jazz Band; Mrchg Band; Wrstlng; Hon Roll; USNA Smmr Sem 87; Engrng.

HADDEN, SUSAN; Pitman HS; Pitman, NJ; (3); 21/145; Dance Clb; Hosp Aide; Chorus; Sec Frsh Cls; Rep Soph Cls; Rep Jr Cls; Stu Cncl; Fld Hcky; Sftbl; NHS; Psych.

HADLEY, RAKEIM J; The Pennington Schl; Newtonville, NJ; (4); 7/78; Boy Scts; Pres Church Yth Grp; Pres French Clb; Bsktbl; Crs Cntry; Cit Awd; DAR Awd; NHS; Rutgers Schlr 86; Dartmouth Coll; Bio.

HADNOTT, DANIELLE B; Teaneck HS; Teaneck, NJ; (4); 96/420; NAACP; Yrbk Phtg; Off Frsh Cls; Off Soph Cls; Off Jr Cls; Off Sr Cls; Stu Cncl; Trk; Ntl Merit SF; Cmnty Wkr; All Cty Track Awd 85; American U; Intl Bus.

HADRABA, HENRY; Ocean City HS; Ocean City, NJ; (3); Art Clb; Drama Clb; Latin Clb; NY U; Adv.

HAFERBIER, TRACY; Hunterdon Central HS; Flemington, NJ; (3); 105/543; Hon Roll; Comm.

HAFNER, JUDITH; Lakeland Regional HS; Ringwood, NJ; (4); 8/345; VP AFS; Teachers Aide; Sr Cls; Stu Cncl; Capt Cheerleading; High Hon Roll; NHS; Cupsaw Lk Athl Assn Schlrshp 87; Vrsty Ltr/Cap Fencng 84-87; Boston Coll Schlrshp 87; Boston Coll.

HAFTEL, VALERIE; Middletown HS South; Lincroft, NJ; (4); 11/453; Exploring; Science Clb; Acpl Chr; Chorus; Lit Mag; Var Capt Socr; High Hon Roll; Hon Roll; NHS; NJ All Shore Choir 85-87; Lincrft Sccr 86; Union Coll; Pre Med.

HAGAMIN, KIM; Camden HS; Camden, NJ; (3); Church Yth Grp; Off FBLA; JA; Pep Clb; Yrbk Ed-Chief; Ntl Merit Ltr; Prfct Atten Awd; Acctng.

HAGAN, DIANA; Lower Cape May Regional HS; Fishing Creek, NJ; (3); 27/240; Sec French Clb; Key Clb; Sec Spanish Clb; Varsity Clb; Yrbk Stf; Var Trk; Hon Roll; NHS; JV Mgr(s); Natl Lang Arts Olympd 84-85; Future Prblm Slvrs 86-87; NJ Math Lg 85-87.

HAGEN, TARA; Buena Regional HS; Newfield, NJ; (3); Church Yth Grp; FBLA; Ski Clb; Teachers Aide; Pres Varsity Clb; Stu Cncl; Cheerleading; Hon Roll; Atlntc CC; Lgl Scrtry.

HAGEN, TARA; Waldwick HS; Waldwick, NJ; (2); Drm & Bgl; Math Tm; Quiz Bowl; Rptr Nwsp Stf; Rptr Lit Mag; Mgr Soph Cls; JV Var Bsktbl; JV Var Socr; Var L Sftbl; Hon Roll.

HAGINS, TIA; Hillsborough HS; Somerville, NJ; (3); Rep Frsh Cls; Rep Soph Cls; Rep Jr Cls; Rep Stu Cncl; Var Capt Bsktbl; Capt Powder Puff Ftbl; Var Socr; JV Trk; Hon Roll.

HAGOOD, NATHANIEL T; Buena Regional HS; Vineland, NJ; (3); Computer Clb; Yrbk Stf; Rep Soph Cls; Hon Roll; Ltr Of Knwldg Acdmcs 85; Inroads Prospctv Career Yth 86; Brick Computer Inst; Comp Sci.

HAGOPIAN, DEBRA ANN; Timothy Christian Schl; East Brunswick, NJ; (3); 1/44; Camera Clb; Church Yth Grp; Chorus; Yrbk Phtg; Yrbk Stf; Rep Stu Cncl; Var Capt Cheerleading; High Hon Roll; NHS; Prfct Atten Awd; Gordon Coll; Marine Bio.

HAGUE, ERIK; St Pius X Regional HS; E Brunswick, NJ; (3); 16/102; Church Yth Grp; 4-H; Teachers Aide; Band; Orch; 4-H Awd; 4h Yr 85-86; 2 Mrt Awds Stu Mnth 86-87; All ST Rgnl Bnd NJ 87; Mnstr.

HAGY, MICHELLE; Overbrook Reg HS; Pine Hill, NJ; (4); 52/346; Am Leg Aux Girls St; Church Yth Grp; French Clb; SADD; Varsity Clb; Chorus; Rep Stu Cncl; JV Bsktbl; JV Var Sftbl; Var Capt Tennis; MVP Tennis; Glassboro; Art.

HAHN, KIM; Eastern Regional HS; Berlin, NJ; (3); 57/387; Trs Church Yth Grp; Girl Scts; Rep Church Choir; Voice Dem Awd; Messiah Coll; Acctng.

HAIKEN, LAURENCE; Livingston HS; Livingston, NJ; (3); 113/420; Key Clb; Math Clb; Rep Frsh Cls; Rep Soph Cls; Rep Stu Cncl; Capt Var Ftbl; Capt Var Lcrss; Powder Puff Ftbl; Wt Lftg; Hon Roll; Bst Ofnsv Lnmn 86-87; Bus.

HAILEY, ANGELA; John F Kennedy HS; Willingboro, NJ; (3); Church Choir; Capt Trk; Badmtn; Bsktbl; Var Crs Cntry; Sftbl; Hon Roll; Advrtsng.

HAINES, CHERI; A P Schalick HS; Bridgeton, NJ; (3); Library Aide; Chorus; Drill Tm; Flag Corp; Var Cheerleading; Sftbl; Hon Roll; Cumberland Cnty Coll; Wrd Prcsg.

HAINES, ROBERT; Southern Regional HS; Brant Beach, NJ; (3); 4/450; Ski Clb; Im JV Bsbl; High Hon Roll; NHS; Rotary Awd; Engrng.

AINES, TIM; Hillsborough HS; Bellemead, NJ; (4); 20/350; Math Clb; rm Mjr(t); Mrchg Band; Orch; Var Gym; JV Trk; Hon Roll; Ntl Merit tr; Fessenden-Trott Scholar Coll Engrng U Pittsburgh; Graden ST stngshd Schlrs Awd; Amer Liberty Scholar; U Pittsburgh; Engrng.

AIT, ARI; Livingston HS; Livingston, NJ; (3); 119/420; Chess Clb; Math lb; Math Tm; Varsity Clb; JV Bsbl; Im Sftbl; Var Swmmng; Im Tennis; on Roll; Ntl Merit Ltr.

AITHCOATH, CAROLINE; St Pius X Regional HS; New Brunswick, J; (3); Church Yth Grp; Computer Clb; Office Aide; Teachers Aide; hurch Choir; Vllybl; Howard U; Law.

ALBERT, HOLLY; Edgewood Regional SR HS; Atco, NJ; (3); 22/350; m Leg Aux Girls St; Dance Clb; Hosp Aide; Spanish Clb; Mrchg Band; ep Frsh Cls; Rep Soph Cls; Hon Roll; Jr NHS; NHS; Human Svcs.

ALDEMAN, MONTRELL; Edgewood Regional HS; Atco, NJ; (3); Boy cts; Cmnty Wkr; Exploring; 4-H; Hon Roll; Distngshd Persons Awd 87; on Men Hon Roll 87; Camden Cty Coll; Sci.

ALE, KATHLEEN; High Point Regional HS; Branchville, NJ; (3); 19/68; Church Yth Grp; Girl Scts; Trs Spanish Clb; Church Choir; Concert and; Jazz Band; Mrchg Band; Swmmng; High Hon Roll; NHS; All Sussex ounty Band Oboist 85; High Point Wind Ensemble 1st Oboist 86-87; cience.

ALE, WARNER; St Rose HS; Sea Girt, NJ; (3); Ski Clb; Trk; Intl Bus.

ALEN, SUSAN; Rancocas Valley Regional HS; Mount Holly, NJ; (4); rama Clb; PAVAS; School Play; Stage Crew; Trenton ST Coll; Psych.

ALEY, GLEN T; Bridgewater-Raritan East HS; Bridgewater, NJ; (3); rama Clb; Quiz Bowl; Acpl Chr; Chorus; Concert Band; School Play; Lit ag; Off Stu Cncl; JV Socr; High Hon Roll; NJ All ST Teen Arts Fnlst rbrshp Qurtet 87.

ALFORD, TIMOTHY; Manchester Twp HS; Toms River, NJ; (3); Am eg Boys St; Math Tm; Science Clb; L Var Bsbl; JV Bsktbl; L Var Ftbl; t Lftg; Arch.

ALIFKO, JODI; Woodbridge HS; Hopelawn, NJ; (4); 11/386; Acpl Chr; chool Musical; School Play; Swing Chorus; Trs Stu Cncl; NHS; 2nd Pl cl Mid Atlantic ST Chmpnshp 86; 3rd Pl Vcl Intl Skyln Fstvl 87; Fnlst dbg Twnshp Flg Dsgn 87; NY U; Scnc Dsgn.

ALINIEWSKI, BRIAN; Union HS; Union, NJ; (3); Boys Clb Am; erman Clb; Key Clb; Spanish Clb; Band; Concert Band; Jazz Band; rchg Band; Orch; Pep Band; Cntrl Jersey Reg Ii Symphnc Band 87; nion Bys & Grls Clb Yth Of Yr 85.

ALISKY, MERLAND G; Spotswood HS; Milltown, NJ; (4); 11/187; Am eg Boys St; Boy Scts; Drama Clb; School Musical; Yrbk Phtg; Yrbk Stf; V Var Socr; JV Var Trk; French Hon Soc; NHS; Rutgers U.

ALL JR, BILL; Absegami HS; Absecon, NJ; (3); Computer Clb; Office ide; Var L Ftbl; Var L Wrstlng; NHS.

ALL, BONNIE JOANNE; Cresskill HS; Cresskill, NJ; (3); Church Yth rp; Debate Tm; Temple Yth Grp; Chorus; Church Choir; Color Guard; it Mag; Stat Bsktbl; Coach Actv; Stat Vllybl; 2nd Pl Oil Pntng Paramus rt Shw 86-87; 1st Pl Spkr Nrthn NJ Debate Leg 85-86; Asst Dir Theatre rp; Theatre Arts.

ALL, DAVID; Bridgeton HS; Cedarville, NJ; (3); Am Leg Boys St; ffice Aide; Trs Stu Cncl; Var JV Crs Cntry; High Hon Roll; Hon Roll; HS; Cmnty Wkr; Teachers Aide; JV Im Bsktbl; Delg Rotry Yth Ldrshp onf 87; Acdmc Lttr 86-87; Math Dept Awd Adv Alg II 86-87; Oakwood oll; Accntng.

ALL, GLORIA; Vailsburg HS; Newark, NJ; (4); 87/290; Aud/Vis; hurch Yth Grp; FCA; Chorus; Church Choir; Concert Choir Awd 87; Cert f Mert 85; Seton Hall U; Bus Admin.

ALL, KATHY; Nutley HS; Nutley, NJ; (4); 41/335; Drama Clb; Chorus; chool Musical; School Play; Nwsp Rptr; Nwsp Stf; Yrbk Bus Mgr; Yrbk ptr; Yrbk Stf; Hon Roll.

ALL, KEVIN; The Kings Christian HS; Marlton, NJ; (3); 6/50; Church th Grp; Drama Clb; Church Choir; Var Socr; Hon Roll; NHS; 1st Pl Fine rts Fest Piano Solo 86; Orthdntst.

ALL, MICHELLE; Kingsway Regional HS; Swedesboro, NJ; (2); hurch Yth Grp; Chorus; Lcrss; Hon Roll; Mdlng.

ALL, SHERRY; Plainfield HS; Plainfield, NJ; (4); 235/408; Church Yth rp; Girl Scts; Pep Clb; Color Guard; Mrchg Band; Yrbk Stf; Rep Frsh ls; Rep Soph Cls; Rep Jr Cls; Rep Sr Cls; Schlrshp Jr Roses 87; Hnr Prfct ttndnce 83-85; Comp Sci.

ALL, TAWANDA; S Brunswick HS; E Orange, NJ; (3); Computer Clb; irl Scts; Model UN; NAACP; Pep Clb; Church Choir; Drill Tm; Variety how; Stat Bsktbl; Hon Roll; Howard U; Comp Sci.

ALL, THOMAS; Ridge HS; Basking Ridge, NJ; (2); VP Trs Church Yth rp; Var Swmmng; High Hon Roll; Hon Roll; Spanish NHS; Crmnl Law.

ALLER, KATHY; Palmyra HS; Palmyra, NJ; (3); 20/121; Drama Clb; ec Trs Key Clb; School Play; Stu Cncl; Stat Bsktbl; Var Capt Fld Hcky; on Roll; Thtre Arts.

ALLIDAY, WENDY; Brick Memorial HS; Brick, NJ; (4); Spanish Clb; m Gym; Art Clb; Variety Show; Yrbk Phtg; Ed Lit Mag; Var Bowling; igh Hon Roll; Hon Roll; Frgn Lang Club Schlrshp 87; Lebanon Vly; Bio.

ALLMAN, BRIAN; Holy Spirit HS; Absecon, NJ; (4); 125/355; Boy cts; Church Yth Grp; Teachers Aide; Yrbk Stf; Gym; Johnson & Wales oll; Food Svc.

ALM, EILEEN MICHELE; Saint Rose HS; Jackson, NJ; (3); 80/258; ey Clb; Ski Clb; Im Fld Hcky; Hon Roll; Outstndng Srvc Key Clb 86; U f DE; Marine Bio.

ALOSZ, DOREEN; Carteret HS; Carteret, NJ; (3); 29/217; Girl Scts; ftbl; Hon Roll; Berkeley; Bus Adm.

ALPIN, JOHN; Christian Brothers Acad; Middletown, NJ; (3); 30/230; hurch Yth Grp; Math Tm; Ski Clb; Chorus; Stage Crew; Yrbk Ed-Chief; us.

ALTER, DAVID; Cumberland Regional HS; Bridgeton, NJ; (3); Church th Grp; Drama Clb; Chorus; Church Choir; Madrigals; School Musical; chool Play; Capt Var Swmmng; Boy Scts; Intnl Clb; Music.

ALTERMAN, ERIC; Gloucester Catholic HS; Deptford, NJ; (3); Var L owling; JV Golf; Hon Roll; Frgn Lang Awd 86; Stockton; Marine Biology.

AMERSKY, MARK; Southern Regional HS; Manahawkin, NJ; (3); 2/00; Yrbk Phtg; Var Capt Bsktbl; Var Capt Socr; High Hon Roll; NHS; rfct Atten Awd; Le High U; Mech Engrng.

AMILOTHORIS, OURANIA; Millville SR HS; Millville, NJ; (3); 4/00; Sec Key Clb; Latin Clb; Office Aide; Sec SADD; Sr Cls; Stu Cncl; gr(s); Hon Roll; NHS; Sci Olympd-Chem 85-86; Pre Dntstry.

AMILTON, CARRIE; Cumberland Regional HS; Bridgeton, NJ; (4); /298; Sec Church Yth Grp; Intnl Clb; Office Aide; Science Clb; Spanish lb; Nwsp Rptr; Bsktbl; Var Mgr(s); NHS; Pres Schlr; Pres Scholar idener U 87-91; Hnrs Pgm U DE 87-91; Sci Recgntn 87; U DE; Mech ngrng.

HAMMA, AMY; Sayreville War Memorial HS; Parlin, NJ; (3); German Clb; Chorus; Concert Band; Mrchg Band; Stage Crew; Ed Lit Mag; High Hon Roll; Hon Roll; Band; Acctng.

HAMMELL, CHRISTOPHER; Rancocas Valley Regional HS; Mt Holly, NJ; (3); Hon Roll; Chef.

HAMMER, JANELLE; St James HS; Salem, NJ; (2); 13/75; Drama Clb; SADD; Band; Concert Band; Mrchg Band; JV Sftbl; JV Vllybl; Hon Roll.

HAMMOND, CATHERINE; Cherry Hill HS West; Cherry Hill, NJ; (3); 20/366; French Clb; Intnl Clb; SADD; VP Soph Cls; JV Fld Hcky; JV Lcrss; Hon Roll; NHS; Rotary Awd.

HAMMOND, CHRISTOPHER; Pinelands Regional HS; Tuckerton, NJ; (3); 17/210; Spanish Clb; SADD; JV Var Badmtn; Scrkpr Var Bsktbl; Hon Roll; NHS; Spanish NHS; Chem Engr.

HAMMOND, MICHELLE; Hackensack HS; Hackensack, NJ; (4); 4/400; Am Leg Aux Girls St; Church Yth Grp; JCL; Pres Frsh Cls; Pres Soph Cls; Pres Jr Cls; Pres Sr Cls; Rep Stu Cncl; Capt Bsktbl; Sftbl; LEAD Pgm 87; Cornell U; Law.

HAMMOND, MISSY; Baptist HS; Camden, NJ; (2); 1/32; Church Yth Grp; Spanish Clb; Varsity Clb; Chorus; Church Choir; Rep Stu Cncl; Var Bsktbl; High Hon Roll; Hon Roll; Atty.

HAMMOND, SHARON; Victory Christian Schl; Sicklerville, NJ; (3); 1/17; Sec Jr Cls; Capt Var Bsktbl; Var Fld Hcky; High Hon Roll; NHS; Ntl Merit Ltr; Bst Hustle Awd Bsktbll 85-87; Hghst Acdmc Avg 84-87; Bst All Around 84-87.

HAMORY, LARISSA; North Brunswick Twp HS; N Brunswick, NJ; (4); 10/280; Rep Stu Cncl; Var Bsktbl; Var Capt Socr; Var Sftbl; Hon Roll; Majors Awd For Cmmnty Svc 87; Sccr Clb Schlrshp 87; All Middlesex Cnty Tm Sccr 83-6; Villanova Univ; Mrktng.

HAMPSON, CRAIG; Bridgewater Raritan HS East; Bridgewater, NJ; (3); Boy Scts; Pres 4-H; Sec Chorus; Mrchg Band; Lit Mag; Im Capt Bowling; JV Trk; High Hon Roll; NHS; Acad Lge Tm 86-87; 4-H Pblc Prsntn ST Champ 87; Aerosp Engrng.

HAMPTON, KELLY; Holy Family Acad; Bayonne, NJ; (4); Church Yth Grp; JV Bsktbl; JV Socr; JV Sftbl; Hon Roll; Prfct Atten Awd; Outstndng Awd In HS Bus Ed 86-87; Typng Awd 86-87; Steno Awd 85-86; St Ptrs Coll; Bus Mngmnt.

HAMPTON, TRICIA; Rancocas Valley Regional HS; Mt Holly, NJ; (2); 30/316; Spanish Clb; JV L Mgr(s); JV L Score Keeper; JV L Sftbl; High Hon Roll; Hon Roll; Prfct Atten Awd; Lbrl Arts.

HAND, DENISE M; Randolph HS; Randolph, NJ; (4); 30/360; Church Yth Grp; Yrbk Phtg; Sec Frsh Cls; Rep Soph Cls; Rep Jr Cls; Rep Sr Cls; VP French Hon Soc; Hon Roll; Villanova U; Lib Arts.

HAND, KIMBERLY; Edgewood Regional HS; Sicklerville, NJ; (3); 10/371; Latin Clb; Spanish Clb; Varsity Clb; Nwsp Rptr; Yrbk Sprt Ed; Yrbk Stf; Var Socr; JV Var Sftbl; Cit Awd; High Hon Roll; Gftd/Tlntd 84-87; Treasr Vrsty Clb 86-87; Penn ST; Chem Engrng.

HAND, KYLE; Hunterdon Central HS; Flemington, NJ; (4).

HANDA, KIRAN; Immaculata HS; Middlesex, NJ; (3); Girl Scts; Stu Cncl; Hon Roll; Church Yth Grp; Debate Tm; French Clb; Lit Mag; Off Frsh Cls; Off Soph Cls; Off Jr Cls; Outstndng Spartan 87; Hnrb Mntn Alg 87; Syracuse U; Pol Sci.

HANDLER, JEFFREY; John P Stevens HS; Edison, NJ; (3); 15/457; Debate Tm; Sec Key Clb; Model UN; Mrchg Band; Nwsp Stf; JV Trk; Hon Roll; Sec NHS; Sec Spanish NHS; Mrchng Band Lttr Cont Achvt 86-87; Pol Sci.

HANDY, ANDREA; Highland HS; Erial, NJ; (3); 79/285; Computer Clb; Math Clb; Var JV Trk; Cit Awd; High Hon Roll; Hon Roll; Hon Ment 84; Hon Roll 85; GA Tech; Comp Prgrmmng.

HANFORD, MARK; St Joseph Of The Palisades HS; W New York, NJ; (4); 10/118; Church Yth Grp; Pres DECA; Stage Crew; Rep Stu Cncl; High Hon Roll; NHS; Spanish NHS; St Peters Clg; Accntng.

HANHAM, JEAN MARI; Lakeland Regional HS; Ringwood, NJ; (3); Rep Frsh Cls; Rep Soph Cls; Rep Jr Cls; Sec Stu Cncl; Var Capt Bsktbl; Var Capt Trk; Var Capt Vllybl; Hon Roll; NHS; All Cnty Grls Trk Hgh Jmp, & All Trends Grls Trk 1st Tm Hgh Jmp 85; Vrsty MVP Bsktbl 86-87; Psych.

HANISH, JOE; Perth Amboy HS; Perth Amboy, NJ; (3); Computer Clb; Science Clb; Band; Concert Band; Jazz Band; Mrchg Band; Pep Band; Var Crs Cntry; Stat Sftbl; Var Trk; Rutgers U; Music.

HANLEY, REBECCA; Glen Rock HS; Glen Rock, NJ; (3); 43/187; Am Leg Aux Girls St; Church Yth Grp; Varsity Clb; Nwsp Rptr; Pres Frsh Cls; Rep Stu Cncl; Var L Bsktbl; Var L Trk; High Hon Roll; Sec Jr NHS; Pre Law.

HANLON, PAMELA; Immaculata HS; Somerset, NJ; (3); Library Aide; Ski Clb; Lit Mag; Rcvd Plaque Spnsh Excel 84-85; Rider Coll; Accntng.

HANLON, TIMOTHY; Union HS; Union, NJ; (4); 84/534; Boy Scts; Church Yth Grp; Math Tm; Concert Band; Bsbl; Crs Cntry; Hon Roll; Band; Chorus; Jazz Band; USAF ROTC Typng II Scholar; Salvation Army Grant Scholar; Coll Holy Cross; Math.

HANN, TRUDY; South Hunterdon Regional HS; Lambertville, NJ; (4); 2/72; Red Cross Aide; Varsity Clb; Var Sftbl; Pres Schlr; Rotary Awd; Sal; St Schlr; French Clb; Key Clb; Spanish Clb; Cngrssnl Tchrs Scholar 87; Ann F Stout Awd 87; U S Army Rsrve Natl Schlr Ath 87; Trenton ST Coll; Elem Ed.

HANNAH III, DAVID CHARLES; Rancocas Valley Regional HS; Medford, NJ; (4); 42/307; Office Aide; Band; Concert Band; Jazz Band; Mrchg Band; Orch; School Musical; School Play; Stage Crew; High Hon Roll; Gold Pass 86-87; Pilot Cert 87; Burlington CC; Pilot.

HANNAH, RACHAEL; Manchester Twp HS; Whiting, NJ; (3); Church Yth Grp; FBLA; Office Aide; Color Guard; Yrbk Stf; Pom Pon; Hon Roll; NHS; Bus.

HANNAN, JOHN; Saint Joseph Regional HS; Wash Twp, NJ; (3); 8/225; Math Tm; Var Crs Cntry; JV Trk; Hon Roll; NHS; Spanish NHS; MIP Vrsty Cross Cntry 86,JV Sprng Trck 87; Engr.

HANNIGAN, JUDITH; Paul VI HS; Blenheim, NJ; (3); 74/418; Dance Clb; Nwsp Rptr; Nwsp Stf; Yrbk Stf; Var Capt Cheerleading; Im Powder Puff Ftbl; JV Trk; Hon Roll; NHS; Cmmnctns.

HANNON, MEAGAN; Cranford HS; Cranford, NJ; (3); Art Clb; Aud/Vis; Church Yth Grp; Chorus; Stage Crew; Sec Lit Mag; Hon Roll; Cranford Yth Govt Day 87; Art Hstry.

HANOVER, JASON; Manalapan HS; Manalapan, NJ; (3); 58/420; Drama Clb; Ski Clb; Thesps; Varsity Clb; Var L Ftbl.

HANRAHAN, KAREN; West Morris Mendham HS; Mendham, NJ; (3); Art Clb; 4-H; French Clb; FBLA; Hosp Aide; Intnl Clb; Yrbk Stf; JV Bsktbl; Stat Trk; Acctg.

HANSEN, CHRISSIE; Scotch Plains Fanwood HS; Scotch Plains, NJ; (3); French Clb; Key Clb; Yrbk Stf; Var JV Cheerleading; French Hon Soc; Hon Roll; Girls Ctznshp Inst 87; Lbrl Arts Ed.

HANSEN, CHRISTINE; Freehold Township HS; Freehold, NJ; (3); 55/485; Art Clb; Drama Clb; French Clb; Yrbk Stf; VP Stu Cncl; Var JV Cheerleading; Powder Puff Ftbl; JV Sftbl; NHS; Spirit Cmmtte Chrprsn 86-88; Lbrl Arts.

HANSEN, GREG C; Ridgefield Memorial HS; Ridgefield, NJ; (3); 5/110; Am Leg Boys St; Math Clb; Science Clb; Spanish Clb; Yrbk Ed-Chief; Bsbl; Hon Roll; NHS; Prfct Atten Awd; Comp Sci.

HANSEN, HEATHER; Delaware Valley Reg HS; Bloomsbury, NJ; (3); Dance Clb; Drama Clb; Chorus; School Musical; School Play; Stage Crew; High Hon Roll; Hon Roll; Governs Awd Arts Educ 87; Schlrshp Governs Schl 87; Schlrshp Princeton Ballet Schl 86-87; Schl Of Dance; Dancer.

HANSEN, MARYANN; Holy Rosary Acad; Jersey City, NJ; (3); Math Tm; Sec Spanish Clb; Yrbk Stf; Hon Roll; Jr NHS; Prfct Atten Awd; Natl Lang Arts Olympd 85; Stu Svc Awd 85-87; Cert Hnr Excllnc Relign III 87; Rutgers; Tchng.

HANSEN, MICHAEL; Kittatinny Regional HS; Stillwater, NJ; (4); 16/228; Math Tm; Teachers Aide; Bsbl; High Hon Roll; NHS; Rutgers Coll; Comp Cnsltng.

HANSON, DANIELLE; Kearny HS; Kearny, NJ; (3); Cmnty Wkr; Var Socr; Hon Roll; NHS; Spcl Ed.

HANSON, RYAN A; Pennsville Memorial HS; Pennsville, NJ; (4); 21/201; Am Leg Boys St; Aud/Vis; Camera Clb; Cmnty Wkr; Computer Clb; Teachers Aide; Var Golf; Comp Sci Awd 87; 1st Pl Team, Individ Comp Sci Cont 86-87; Rutgers Coll; Elec Engrng.

HANUSI, CHRISTINE; Mc Corristin Catholic HS; Trenton, NJ; (3); Art Clb; Capt Dance Clb; Girl Scts; Hosp Aide; Capt Variety Show; Lit Mag; Cheerleading; Gym; Score Keeper; Hon Roll; Trenton St; Art.

HAPIJ, LADA; Mt St Dominic Acad; Livingston, NJ; (3); 10/58; JCL; Library Aide; SADD; Nwsp Ed-Chief; Nwsp Rptr; Nwsp Stf; Yrbk Stf; Lit Mag; High Hon Roll; NHS; Schl Nwspaper Achvmnt Awd 85-86; SRA Tstng Pgm Awd 10 Pct Ntl 84-85; Spnsh Achvmnt Awd 86-87; Rutgers U; Engl.

HAQUE, KHALED K; Collingswood HS; Collingswood, NJ; (3); Am Leg Boys St; Boy Scts; Spanish Clb; Stage Crew; Var JV Socr; Hon Roll; Jr NHS; NHS; Comptv Chess Trnmnt 87; Acadmc Chllng Bwl 85-87; Med.

HARADA, AYAKO; Washington Township HS; Turnersville, NJ; (3); 1/550; High Hon Roll; Hon Roll; NHS; Rutgers Schlrs Prog 87; Annual ST Sci Day 87; Lawyer.

HARASZKO, COLLETTE; Red Bank Catholic HS; Eatontown, NJ; (3); Church Yth Grp; Drama Clb; VP Pres Key Clb; NFL; Red Cross Aide; Pres Chorus; School Play; Pres Soph Cls; High Hon Roll; NHS; Bst Spprtng Actrss 85-86; Tp 2% Clss 84-86; Pre-Law.

HARBISON, LISA; Westwood HS; Westwood, NJ; (2); Exploring; Girl Scts; Band; Color Guard; Concert Band; Mrchg Band; JV Sftbl; JV Vllybl; Hon Roll; U Of Miami; Mrn Bio.

HARCHOL, HANAN; S Brunswick HS; Dayton, NJ; (3); Drama Clb; Math Tm; Mu Alpha Theta; Jazz Band; Madrigals; School Musical; School Play; Crs Cntry; Hon Roll; NHS; Ply Clsscl Guitr Wqxr NY Mc Graw Hill Yng Artst Shwcs 86; Wnnr Tlnt Expo 86 Clsscl Guitr 86; Music.

HARDEK, SUSAN; Paramus Catholic Girls Regnl HS; Mahwah, NJ; (2); Science Clb; Spanish Clb; School Musical; Vllybl; High Hon Roll; Hon Roll; Hlth Awd 85-86; Latin Awd 86-87; UCLA; Mrktng.

HARDENBURG, ALAN WILLIAM; Jefferson Township HS; Wharton, NJ; (4); 5/235; Am Leg Boys St; Church Yth Grp; Debate Tm; Var Wrstlng; Bausch & Lomb Sci Awd; NHS; Ntl Merit Ltr; Math Tm; Science Clb; Symp Band; Air Force ROTC 4 Yr Schlrshp 87; Pres Acdmc Achvmnt Awd 87; Rose Hulman Inst Of Tech Hon Schlrshp 87; Rose Hulman Inst; Elec Engrng.

HARDIMAN, MICHAEL; Westwood HS; Washington Twp, NJ; (2); Ski Clb; Law.

HARDIN, BRIAN; Cherry Hill West HS; Cherry Hill, NJ; (2); 4-H; 4-H Awd; Hon Roll.

HARDING, FORREST; Notre Dame HS; Trenton, NJ; (2); Ski Clb; Chorus; School Play; Rep Soph Cls; JV Ftbl; Hon Roll; Excllnc Spnsh I 86.

HARDING, LESLIE; Madison HS; Madison, NJ; (3); Hon Roll; Spanish NHS.

HARDING, MICHAEL; Vail-Deane Schl; Westfield, NJ; (3); Rep Stu Cncl; Ntl Merit Schol; Vail Dean Prep Schlr Schlrshp.

HARDTMANN, JANET; Mary Help Of Christians Acad; Waldwick, NJ; (1); Girl Scts; Church Choir; Swmmng; Hon Roll; Math.

HARDTMANN, NANCY; Mary Help Of Christians Acad; Waldwick, NJ; (3); Girl Scts; JCL; Stage Crew; Coach Actv; Socr; Im Sftbl; Swmmng; Im Vllybl; Hon Roll; Dewitt-Wallce Rdrs Dgst WY Trk Grl Sct Cncl Berger Cnty 85; Sci.

HARDY, EDMOND; Morris Catholic HS; Denville, NJ; (1); Church Yth Grp; Im Bsktbl; JV Socr; Im Tennis; Seton Hall; Bus.

HARDY JR, LOUIS; Phillipsburg HS; Alpha, NJ; (3); Church Yth Grp; FFA; Ski Clb; Ag.

HARDY, STEPHANIE; Delran HS; Delran, NJ; (4); Hosp Aide; Science Clb; Ski Clb; SADD; Teachers Aide; Stat Bsktbl; JV Crs Cntry; JV Fld Hcky; Var Mgr(s); Var Trk; Millersville U; Envrmntl Sci.

HARE, TERRI; Roncocas Valley Regional HS; Mt Holly, NJ; (2); 85/298; Church Yth Grp; Varsity Clb; Yrbk Stf; Var JV Bsktbl; Var JV Mgr(s); Var Sftbl; Trenton ST Coll; Elem Ed.

HARELICK, GEORGIA; Parsippany HS; Parsippany, NJ; (3); Computer Clb; Off FBLA; Hon Roll; NHS; Ntl Merit Ltr; Acad Decthln 86-87; FBLA Natl Parlmntry Procudure Tm From NJ 86-87; Adv Div Hackney Stables Champ 86; Med.

HAREWOOD, MARY; Clifford J Scott HS; East Orange, NJ; (3); Hosp Aide; Intnl Clb; JA; Library Aide; Spanish Clb; SADD; Band; Concert Band; Jazz Band; Mrchg Band; Hgh Hnrs Spnsh & U S Hstry 87; Bio 87; Acdmc Excllnce 84; NY U; Med.

HARGIS, BRENDA LOUISE; Linden HS; Linden, NJ; (3); VP Pres Church Yth Grp; VP Pres French Clb; Key Clb; SADD; Nwsp Rptr; Rep Stu Cncl; Tennis; French Hon Soc; Hon Roll; NHS; Trenton ST.

HARGRAVE, STEWART; Vernon Twp HS; Mc Afee, NJ; (3); Boy Scts; High Hon Roll; Hon Roll; NHS; Bus.

HARGROVE, SCOTT R; Hillside HS; Hillside, NJ; (4); Cmnty Wkr; Computer Clb; Library Aide; U Of Pittsburg Bradford; Engr.

HARGROVE, TAMICA; Frank H Morrell HS; Irvington, NJ; (4); 19/460; Pres DECA; Ed Yrbk Stf; Rep Frsh Cls; Rep Soph Cls; High Hon Roll; Hon Roll; NHS; Church Yth Grp; Office Aide; Church Choir; Martin Luther King Jr Schrlshp 87; NANBPW Bk Schrlshp 87; Lcl Schrlshp 87; Seton Hall U; Accntng.

HARK, JILL; Whippany Park HS; Cedar Knolls, NJ; (3); Office Aide; Chorus; JV Cheerleading; Var Crs Cntry; Var Trk; Hon Roll; Cmmnctns.

HARKER, KIMBERLY; Baptist HS; Pennsauken, NJ; (4); 5/46; Church Yth Grp; Chorus; Stage Crew; Yrbk Stf; Sec Frsh Cls; VP Soph Cls; VP Jr Cls; VP Sr Cls; JV Var Bsktbl; JV Var Fld Hcky; Cedarville Coll; Psych.

HARKIN, EILEEN; Immaculate Heart Acad; Park Ridge, NJ; (3); Sec Model UN; Science Clb; Nwsp Rptr; Yrbk Ed-Chief; Hon Roll; NHS; Spanish NHS; Acad Decathlon 87; Sci.

HARKIN, ELEANOR; Immaculate Heart Acad; Park Ridge, NJ; (1); Church Yth Grp; Ed Yrbk Phtg; Var Cheerleading; Hon Roll; Interior Designer.

HARKINS, BRENDAN D; Camden Catholic HS; Pennsauken, NJ; (3); Am Leg Boys St; Aud/Vis; Church Yth Grp; FBLA; Varsity Clb; Var L Ftbl; Var L Trk; Hon Roll; Hstry NHS; Bus.

HARMON, YVONNE D; Mother Seton Regional HS; Rahway, NJ; (2); 10/128; Church Yth Grp; Drama Clb; Hosp Aide; Math Tm; NAACP; Science Clb; Church Choir; School Musical; School Play; Hon Roll; Volntr Svc Awd-Rahway Hosp 86; Georgetown; Obstetrcn.

HARPER, CYNTHIA; Cumberland Regional HS; Seabrook, NJ; (4); 30/309; Drama Clb; German Clb; Hosp Aide; Intnl Clb; Stage Crew; High Hon Roll; Hon Roll; Commndtn Physcs 86-87; Cmmndtn Chem 85-86; Acdmc Achvt Awd 84; U Of MD; Mech Engrng.

HARPER, RENEE; Lower Cape May Regional HS; Erma, NJ; (1); Drama Clb; School Play; Variety Show; Pres Frsh Cls; Rep Stu Cncl; Var Cheerleading; Var Trk; Coach Cmnty Grade Schl Chrldg Sqd 86-87; Lwyr.

HARRELL, RAINA; Paul VI HS; Williamstown, NJ; (3); 34/410; Church Yth Grp; Debate Tm; Spanish Clb; Church Choir; High Hon Roll; NHS; Spanish NHS; PRIME 87; Bus.

HARRINGTON, LISL; Red Bank Catholic HS; Neptune, NJ; (3); Church Yth Grp; Exploring; Trk.

HARRIOTT, FRANCHOT; Bridgeton HS; Bridgeton, NJ; (3); Hon Roll; NHS; U DE; Tech Engr.

HARRIS, CHAD; Rancocas Valley Regional HS; Mt Holly, NJ; (2); 22/298; Orch; School Musical; Im JV Socr; Im Trk; High Hon Roll; Hon Roll; NHS; Prfct Atten Awd; Yth Orch Glassboro ST Coll 86-87.

HARRIS, CHRISTOPHER; Overbrook SR HS; Berlin, NJ; (4); 15/350; Computer Clb; Trk; High Hon Roll; Hon Roll; NHS; Acad Awd 81; Acad Achvmnt Awd 83; Drexel U; Engr.

HARRIS, COLIN M; Hackettstown HS; Hackettstown, NJ; (3); Quiz Bowl; Scholastic Bowl; Ski Clb; JV Bsbl; JV Ftbl; JV Tennis; Im Wt Lftg; High Hon Roll; Hon Roll; 1st Hnrs St Peters Prep 84-85; High Hnrs 85-86; Zoolgy.

HARRIS, DAVID; Wayne Hills HS; Wayne, NJ; (3); #75 In Class; FBLA; Ski Clb; Spanish Clb; Varsity Clb; Yrbk Phtg; Var Capt Socr; Hon Roll; Merit Awd FBLA 88; Bus.

HARRIS, DAWN E; Paulsboro HS; Gibbstown, NJ; (4); 24/142; JA; Church Choir; Yrbk Stf; Sec Frsh Cls; Sec Soph Cls; Sec Jr Cls; Sec Sr Cls; Hon Roll; Mu Alpha Theta Awd; NHS; E T Fish Awd 87; Schlrshp By W Gaines & H Massey 87; Outstndng Acadc Achvt 87; Seton Hall U; Med.

HARRIS, DIANNA; Toms River HS South; Beachwood, NJ; (3); 87/438; Church Yth Grp; Band; Mrchg Band; School Musical; Symp Band; Sftbl; Trk; Wt Lftg; NHS; Lancaster PA; Mnstry.

HARRIS, INDIA; Columbia HS; Orange, NJ; (3); Church Yth Grp; English Clb; FBLA; Pep Clb; Spanish Clb; Church Choir; Drill Tm; Variety Show; Rep Frsh Cls; Rep Soph Cls; Acctnt.

HARRIS, JONATHAN; Summit HS; Summit, NJ; (3); 32/280; Am Leg Boys St; Boy Scts; Camera Clb; Spanish Clb; Varsity Clb; Band; Concert Band; Mrchg Band; Rep Frsh Cls; Var Socr; Bus Admin.

HARRIS, KENNETH E; Bridgeton HS; Bridgeton, NJ; (3); Church Yth Grp; Concert Band; Mrchg Band; Art Clb; JV Bsbl; Bowling; NHS; Sci Dept Awd Chem I, Cumberlnd Cnty Hnrs Bnd-Flute 87; Hd Acolyte St Andrews Episcopal Chrch 86-88; Engrng.

HARRIS, LISA; Linden HS; Linden, NJ; (3); VP FBLA; Church Yth Grp; Girl Scts; Office Aide; Service Clb; SADD; Teachers Aide; Church Choir; Pep Band; Nwsp Rptr; Acctg.

HARRIS, MARGO L; Our Lady Of Mercy Acad; Sicklerville, NJ; (3); Drama Clb; Girl Scts; Hosp Aide; Red Cross Aide; SADD; Chorus; School Play; Im Badmtn; Im Bsktbl; Im Vllybl; Volunteer Svc Awd 84; Northeastern U; Psych.

HARRIS, MICHELLE; Hackettstown HS; Hackettstown, NJ; (3); Church Yth Grp; Key Clb; Chorus; Church Choir; School Musical; Swing Chorus; Rep Stu Cncl; Mgr(s); Score Keeper; Trk; Acctg.

HARRIS, PAULETTE; Manchester Township HS; Toms River, NJ; (3); Church Choir; Stat Bsktbl; Mgr(s); Var Trk; Mrkt Rsrch Anlyst.

HARRIS, ROBYN; John F Kennedy HS; Willingboro, NJ; (3); 29/292; Trs Intnl Clb; Latin Clb; Math Tm; Service Clb; Flag Corp; Yrbk Stf; Hon Roll; Accntng.

HARRIS, VALERIE; Burlington Township HS; Burlington, NJ; (3); #39 In Class; Church Yth Grp; Debate Tm; Exploring; FCA; FTA; JA; Model UN; Pep Clb; Band; Chorus; Trenton ST; Psych.

HARRIS, YVETTE; West Side HS; Newark, NJ; (3); Boys Clb Am; Exploring; Science Clb; Mrchg Band; Trs Stu Cncl; NHS; Natl Hnr Soc 86; Attny.

HARRISON, BENJAMIN A; Dwight-Englewood Schl; Englewood, NJ; (3); Band; Chorus; Concert Band; Jazz Band; Orch; Bsbl; Bsktbl; Score Keeper; Psych.

HARRISON, DEAN; Atlantic City HS; Margate, NJ; (4); 40/475; Key Clb; Latin Clb; Office Aide; Red Cross Aide; Stu Cncl; Var Bsbl; JV Bsktbl; Var Crs Cntry; Var Ftbl; High Hon Roll; MVP Vrsty Bsbl 85 & 87; Gvrnrs Cncl Pyhscl Ftns Awd 87; Pres Acadc Ftns Awd 87; Duke U; Sprts Med.

HARRISON, KENNETH; Highland Regional HS; Erial, NJ; (3); Boy Scts; Trs Chess Clb; VP JA; Pres Latin Clb; Stu Cncl; JV Var Trk; Hon Roll; NHS; Mass Inst Tech; Comptr Sci.

HARRISON, LAURA LEA; Middle Township HS; Stone Harbor, NJ; (4); Dance Clb; Key Clb; Ski Clb; Band; Chorus; Mrchg Band; School Musical; Rep Frsh Cls; Rep Soph Cls; Rep Jr Cls; Sci Fair 2nd Pl; Best Sr Prom-Bnd; Key Clb Outstndng Part In Yrbk Staff; Boston U; Comm.

HARRISON, MARC; Woodburg HS; Woodbury, NJ; (3); 22/110; Am Leg Boys St; Varsity Clb; Chorus; School Play; Pres Soph Cls; Pres Jr Cls; Var Ftbl; Var Trk; Hon Roll; NHS; Tchr.

HARROD, JONATHAN; Summit HS; Summit, NJ; (3); Yrbk Phtg; Hon Roll; ST Physcs Cmptn Cmmndtn 87; Ntl HS Sci Inst 87; MIT; Comp Engr.

HART, COLLEEN; Holy Cross HS; Maple Shade, NJ; (3); 122/396; Church Yth Grp; SADD; School Musical; School Play; Rep Frsh Cls; Rep Soph Cls; Rep Jr Cls; JV Var Cheerleading; Hon Roll; NHS; Rutgers U; Bus.

HART, KATHLEEN; Gateway Regional HS; Wenonah, NJ; (3); 1/200; Church Yth Grp; JCL; Key Clb; Latin Clb; Science Clb; SADD; Chorus; Church Choir; Concert Band; Drm Mjr(t); NJ All ST Choir 87-88; NJ Schlr Lawrenceville Prep Schl 87; Educ.

HART, LAURA J; West Morris Mendham HS; Chester, NJ; (4); 111/318; Art Clb; Camera Clb; Church Yth Grp; Color Guard; Mrchg Band; Stage Crew; Lit Mag; Hon Roll; Moore Coll Of Art Frsmn Schlrshp 87; Moore Coll Of Art; Graphic Dsgn.

HARTLEY, KATHERINE; Bordentown Regional HS; Bordentown, NJ; (2); 11/141; Chorus; Church Choir; Concert Band; Var Mat Maids; JV Socr; Hon Roll; Church Yth Grp; Girl Scts; Math Tm; Mu Alpha Theta.

HARTLEY, SCOTT; Bordentown Regional HS; Bordentown, NJ; (4); 14/116; Am Leg Boys St; Church Yth Grp; Computer Clb; Mu Alpha Theta; Band; School Musical; NHS; Ntl Merit SF; Boy Scts; Math Clb; Olympics Of Mind Tm Capt Dist & Reg Champs ST Fnlst 84-87; Eagle Scout 86; Band Pres 87; Duke U; Engrng.

HARTMAN, NICHOLE; Monroe Township HS; Spotswood, NJ; (3); Church Yth Grp; Sec Key Clb; SADD; Hon Roll; NHS.

HARTMAN, TIFFANY; Chatham Township HS; Chatham, NJ; (4); 25/140; Key Clb; Yrbk Stf; Cheerleading; High Hon Roll; George Washington U.

HARTNETT, KAREN; Hackettstown HS; Hackettstown, NJ; (4); 6/240; Drama Clb; Pres Key Clb; Nwsp Bus Mgr; Stu Cncl; Crs Cntry; Trk; High Hon Roll; Pres Schlr; St Schlr; Voice Dem Awd; U Of Notre Dame; Gvt.

HARTRANFT, LISHA; Vineland HS; Vineland, NJ; (1); Church Yth Grp; Mrchg Band; Nwsp Stf; Yrbk Stf; Tennis; Pres Schlr; Presdntl Acad Ftnss Achvt Awd 86; Yrbk Staff 86-87; Chrch Yth Grp 86-87; Penn ST U; Law.

HARTUNG, JEANNE; Hightstown HS; East Windsor, NJ; (4); 13/407; Church Yth Grp; Drama Clb; Hosp Aide; Band; Mrchg Band; School Musical; School Play; Symp Band; High Hon Roll; Trs NHS; Stdnt Consrvtn Assoc 86; Allegheny Coll.

HARTWICH, JEFF; Vernon Twp HS; Sussex, NJ; (3); Drama Clb; Thesps; School Musical; School Play; Stage Crew; Variety Show; Airline Pilot.

HARTZ, CHRIS; Washington Township HS; Turnersville, NJ; (4); Camera Clb; Church Yth Grp; German Clb; Lit Mag; Im Tennis; Var Trk; Im Vllybl; Hon Roll; Hnr Roll; Mdrn Musicns Clb; Discvry Yth Retreat; Drexel; Elem Ed.

HARTZOG, JOANNE; Warren County Vo-Tech HS; Belvidere, NJ; (4); Key Clb; Library Aide; Ski Clb; VP VICA; Nwsp Stf; Yrbk Stf; Stu Cncl; Hon Roll; Grphc Arts Fld.

HARVEY, KEVIN; Hillsborough HS; Somerville, NJ; (4); 91/315; Ski Clb; Rep Soph Cls; Rep Jr Cls; JV Ftbl; High Hon Roll; Hon Roll; PA ST U; Bus Ecnmcs.

HARVEY, MARY K; Bishop Eustace Prep; Somerdale, NJ; (1); Church Yth Grp; JA; Teachers Aide; Cheerleading; JV Score Keeper; Sctry.

HARVEY, RANJA; Teaneck HS; Teaneck, NJ; (4); 10/450; Cmnty Wkr; Math Tm; Spanish Clb; SADD; Rep Stu Cncl; Cit Awd; DAR Awd; NHS; Ntl Merit SF; St Schlr; Cptn Vrsty Fncng 87; Ntl Achvt Fnlst 87; NNJIL Schlr Athlt Awd 87; Yale; Med.

HASA, KERRI; Bricktownship Memorial HS; Brick, NJ; (2); 11/381; Sec Church Yth Grp; FBLA; Rep Frsh Cls; Rep Soph Cls; Rep Jr Cls; Var JV Bsktbl; Var Socr; High Hon Roll.

HASANOEDDIN, RAZAK; Cedar Ridge HS; Matawan, NJ; (4); 116/360; Cmnty Wkr; VP SADD; Rep Soph Cls; Stu Cncl; Stat Bsktbl; Capt Pom Pon; Score Keeper; Trk; Spanish NHS; Capt Pep Clb; Mc Donalds Keyport NJ Month Crew 86; Stockton ST Coll; Bus.

HASBUN, ZAIDA; The Kings Christian HS; Dominican Repub; (3); Church Yth Grp; Chorus; Church Choir; Score Keeper; Sftbl; Hon Roll; Teen Tlnt Vcl Cmptn-2nd ST Fnls 86, 1st ST Fnls 87, 1st Dist Fnls 85; Acctnt.

HASKAMP, KERRIE; Toms River North HS; Toms River, NJ; (3); Church Yth Grp; Ski Clb; Spanish Clb; SADD; Varsity Clb; Y-Teens; Yrbk Sprt Ed; Stu Cncl; Crs Cntry; Swmmng; Rutgers Schl Dentstry; Dentstry.

HASSAN, DANIEL RICHARD; James J Ferris HS; Jersey City, NJ; (3); Am Leg Boys St; Spanish Clb; Rep Frsh Cls; Rep Soph Cls; Rep Jr Cls; Socr; Swmmng; Tennis; NHS; Achvt Awd 87; Montclair Coll; Bus.

HASSAN, DONNA; Hamilton High West; Trenton, NJ; (3); Art Clb; Aud/Vis; Nwsp Rptr; Mgr(s); Score Keeper; Stat Swmmng; Var Trk; Hon Roll; Hnrs Math & Specl Sci Cls 84-86; Glassborough ST; Comm Art.

HASSAN, GEORGE; Don Bosco Prep; Waldwick, NJ; (2); 5/214; Church Yth Grp; Crs Cntry; Socr; JV Wrstlng; High Hon Roll; Ntl Merit Ltr; Im Bsktbl; Theology I Gold Medal 85-86; Bus.

HASSE, SUSAN; Saint Alousius HS; Jersey City, NJ; (3); 2/118; Church Yth Grp; Exploring; SADD; Nwsp Rptr; Nwsp Stf; Im Vllybl; High Hon Roll; NHS; Sec Natl Hon Soc 87-88; Hghst Avg Hon Math 86-87; Hghst Avg Ecnmcs 86-87; Bus Adm.

HASSLER, JULIE; St James HS; Pennsville, NJ; (1); 3/73; Im Bsktbl; Var JV Fld Hcky; Hon Roll; Frnch Hnr 87; Rlgn Hnr 87.

HASSLER, MARSHA; St James HS; Salem, NJ; (3); 19/82; French Clb; JV Capt Cheerleading; JV Sftbl; Jr Rep Pro-Life 86-87; Elem Ed.

HASTINGS, JOHN; Wood-Ridge HS; Wood Ridge, NJ; (2); Art Clb; Boy Scts; Latin Clb; Model UN; Science Clb; Pres Frsh Cls; Pres Soph Cls; JV Bsbl; L Bowling; Im Fld Hcky; Ntl Latin Exam-Cum Laude Cert; Acadc All Amercn Schlrshp; Chmcl Engr.

HATALA, JOHN; North Hunterdon HS; Lebanon, NJ; (4); 41/365; Am Leg Boys St; Church Yth Grp; Pres Stu Cncl; L Ftbl; L Lcrss; Wt Lftg; Cit Awd; Hon Roll; Pres Schlr; US Marine Corps ROTC Schlrshp 87; US Naval Acad Cert Accmplshmnt 87; US Naval Acad.

HATCH, CLARENCE; East Side HS; Newark, NJ; (3); Mountcail ST Coll; Comp.

HATCH, MICHAEL; Paul VI HS; Oaklyn, NJ; (3); 146/410; Rep Soph Cls; JV Crs Cntry; Im Swmmng; JV Trk; Hon Roll; Dentstry.

HATEM, LISA; Summit HS; Summit, NJ; (3); Dance Clb; Sec Drama Clb; School Musical; School Play; Nwsp Stf; Lit Mag; Hon Roll; Teen Arts Fstvl-Rcgntn For Outstndng Achv Prfrmng Arts 86; New Jerseys Gvrnsrs Schl Of The Arts 87; Lbrl Arts.

HATTON, DARRYL; Mt Olive HS; Flanders, NJ; (3); Dance Clb; Ski Clb; SADD; Yrbk Stf; AFS; Camera Clb; Drama Clb; FBLA; Science Clb; Stage Crew; Pediatrc Thrpy.

HAUCK, CAROLINE; Linden HS; Linden, NJ; (3); French Clb; Science Clb; Nwsp Stf; Var Cheerleading; Var Gym; Minorites In Engnrng 81-87; Psych.

HAUCK, DOUG; Bridgewater Raritan HS West; Bridgewater, NJ; (4); Key Clb; Var Bsbl; JV Ftbl; Var Swmmng; Hon Roll; NHS; Pres Schlr; Penn ST; Fnncl.

HAUCK, KARL; Passaic County Tech; Paterson, NJ; (4); 7/365; Boy Scts; Spanish Clb; Off Frsh Cls; Off Soph Cls; Wt Lftg; Hon Roll; NHS; Natl Hnr Soc Pres; Rutgers U; Engrng.

HAUCK, MARY BERNADETTE; Waldwick HS; Waldwick, NJ; (3); 18/130; Rep Jr Cls; Bsktbl; Socr; Sftbl; Hon Roll; Sccr Vrsty Capt 86-88; Bsktbl Vrsty 85-88; Jr Clss Rep 86-87; Psych.

HAUG, DIANE; Paramus HS; Paramus, NJ; (4); 8/330; Girl Scts; VP Intnl Clb; Pres Spanish Clb; Pres Orch; Ed Nwsp Stf; Rep Stu Cncl; Stat Trk; NHS; Pres Spanish NHS; St Schlr; Chsn Ambssdr For USA To Itly Rtry Exchnge Stu 87-88; Rcpnt Of Jstn Fndtn Schlrshp, Yth Ldrshp 87 Lbrl Arts.

HAUGHEY, SEAN D; Willingboro HS; Willingboro, NJ; (3); 3/308; Am Leg Boys St; ROTC; Science Clb; Capt Color Guard; Orch; Rep Frsh Cls; JV Bsbl; JV Socr; Var L Swmmng; Hon Roll; Youth Advisory Board 86-87

HAUGHIAN, MARIA; Southern Regional HS; Barnegat, NJ; (3); Rep Soph Cls; Rep Jr Cls; Rep Stu Cncl; Im Sftbl; Hon Roll; Prfct Atten Awd; Rutgers; Scndry Educ.

HAUSCHILD JR, DANIEL C; The Pilgrim Acad; Absecon, NJ; (4); 3/24; Church Yth Grp; Debate Tm; Yrbk Stf; VP Sr Cls; Var L Bsbl; Var Capt Bsktbl; Var Capt Socr; High Hon Roll; NHS; Schl Soccer Lge MVP 86-87; US Naval Acad; Naval Arch.

HAUSWIRTH, LINDA; Toms River South HS; Beachwood, NJ; (2); Church Yth Grp; Girl Scts; Intnl Clb; JV Bsktbl; JV Fld Hcky; JV Sftbl; High Hon Roll; Hon Roll.

HAVERS, SHARON; Palmyra HS; Palmyra, NJ; (3); 24/100; Exploring; French Clb; SADD; Teachers Aide; Sec Stu Cncl; JV Fld Hcky; Stat Ftbl; Var JV Mat Maids; Var Tennis; Hon Roll; Math.

HAVILAND, CYNTHIA LYNN; John P Stevens HS; Edison, NJ; (3); Cmnty Wkr; Key Clb; Chorus; Color Guard; Drill Tm; Flag Corp; Mrchg Band; Powder Puff Ftbl; Hon Roll; NHS; John Hopkins Hrnbl Tltn Srch 84; Lib Arts.

HAWKINS, AARON; Millville SR HS; Millville, NJ; (4); Pres Church Yth Grp; Spanish Clb; Acpl Chr; Church Choir; Drill Tm; Oral Roberts Univ; Bus Admn.

HAWKS, SUSAN; Bayonne HS; Bayonne, NJ; (3); Drama Clb; Teachers Aide; Rep Jr Cls; Vllybl; Ed.

HAWTHORNE, AMY; West Windsor Plainsboro HS; Robbinsville, NJ (3); Art Clb; Church Yth Grp; SADD; Chorus; School Musical; Yrbk Phtg Rep Frsh Cls; Rep Soph Cls; Rep Jr Cls; Rep Stu Cncl; 2nd Pl Schl Art Shw 85-86; People To People Pgm Delg To Russia 86-87; Intr Dsgn.

HAY, MATT; Rancocas Valley Regional HS; Mt Holly, NJ; (2); 10/316 Church Yth Grp; Church Choir; JV Bsbl; JV Capt Socr; High Hon Roll Hon Roll; NHS; Ntl Piano Plyng Audtns 87; Sprts Med.

HAY, TRACY L; Central Regional HS; Seaside Park, NJ; (4); 16/242 Math Clb; Math Tm; Yrbk Bus Mgr; Yrbk Stf; High Hon Roll; Hon Roll NHS; Cook Coll; Pre-Med.

HAYDEN, ANDREA; Union Catholic Regional HS; Newark, NJ; (3) Church Yth Grp; Dance Clb; Drama Clb; Hosp Aide; Library Aide; Variety Show; Rep Soph Cls; JV Trk; High Hon Roll; Hon Roll; Rutgers U; Hlth Admin.

HAYDU, KATHLEEN; West Essex Regional HS; Essex Fells, NJ; (3) FTA; Hosp Aide; Key Clb; Teachers Aide; Stage Crew; Im Socr; Hon Roll Tchr.

HAYES, ANGELIQUE R; Abraham Clark HS; Roselle, NJ; (3); Sec Church Yth Grp; Girl Scts; Chorus; Stu Cncl; Cheerleading; Sftbl; Hon Roll; NHS; Probate Lawyer.

HAYES, CHERYL; University HS; Newark, NJ; (3); JA; Rep Frsh Cls Off Soph Cls; Off Jr Cls; JV Cheerleading; JV Crs Cntry; JV Sftbl; Va Trk; Hon Roll; Comms.

HAYES, DAVID; Freehold Township HS; Freehold, NJ; (3); 8/385; Chess Clb; Debate Tm; Exploring; Political Wkr; JV Crs Cntry; NHS; Ntl Merit Ltr; JV Trk; Rutgers Deans Smmr Schlr Awd 87; Natl Frat Stud Musicians 83-87; Pres Clsrm Yng Amer 87; Polt Sci.

HAYES, JOSEPH; Rahway HS; Rahway, NJ; (3); Aud/Vis; Rep Church Yth Grp; Stage Crew; Rep Stu Cncl; Bowling; Sec French Hon Soc; J NHS; VP NHS; Cmnty Wkr; High Hon Roll; Highest Avg-9th Gr 85; Peer Ed Prog 86-87; Deans Summer Schlr Prog; Model Congress 87; Rutgers Stage Tech.

HAYES, MICHELLE; Henry Snyder HS; Jersey City, NJ; (3); Hosp Aide JA; Quiz Bowl; Rep Stu Cncl; Hon Roll; NHS; Bus Admin.

HAYES, TRACY LYN; Overbrook Regional HS; Clementon, NJ; (4) 4-H; French Clb; SADD; Teachers Aide; Chorus; Variety Show; JV Cheerleading; Hon Roll; Yng Athrs Amer 84; Centennary Coll; Fshn Merc

HAYES, WARREN; Pascack Hills HS; Montvale, NJ; (4); Camera Clb Chess Clb; Computer Clb; Model UN; Political Wkr; SADD; Nwsp Phtg Yrbk Phtg; Bowling; Tennis; Albright Coll; Accntng.

HAYNER, MICHELLE; Brick Township Memorial HS; Brick, NJ; (2); 1 360; Rptr FBLA; Spanish Clb; Im Socr; High Hon Roll; Hon Roll; 1sp F Type-A-Thon 86; 1st Pl Olympc Typng Cntst 86-87; Bus.

HAYNES, JEFFREY; Marist HS; Jersey City, NJ; (3); 17/106; JA; Qui Bowl; Scholastic Bowl; Church Choir; Off Soph Cls; Off Jr Cls; Off Sr Cls Off Stu Cncl; Stat Bsbl; Stat Bsktbl; Accntnt.

HAYNES, MARC A; Gateway Regional HS; Wenonah, NJ; (3); 5/200 Cmnty Wkr; Pres Key Clb; Trs Latin Clb; SADD; Nwsp Ed-Chief; Rep St Cncl; Var Crs Cntry; Var Trk; High Hon Roll; Trs NHS; Lang Hnr Soc RVLA Conf Del; 1st NJJCL Southern Rgnl Latin Certamen; Intl Law.

HAYNES, PATRICK C; Cherokee HS; Marlton, NJ; (3); 77/454; Am Le Boys St; Boy Scts; Debate Tm; Math Clb; Math Tm; SADD; Var Trk; Va Wrstlng; Hon Roll; Black Belt Japanese Karate 87; US Naval Acad; Aer Sp Eng.

HAYNIE, LINDA; Glassboro HS; Glassboro, NJ; (3); Varsity Clb; Band Mrchg Band; Rep Dance Clb; Var Cheerleading; Mgr(s); Wt Lftg; Ho Roll; NHS.

HAYTHORN, STACEY LYNN; Dunellen HS; Dunellen, NJ; (3); 2/77 Am Leg Aux Girls St; Math Tm; Jazz Band; Mrchg Band; Yrbk Sprt Ed Bsktbl; Crs Cntry; Sftbl; Bausch & Lomb Sci Awd; Scholastic Bowl Ocngrphy.

HAYWOOD, DONNA; Arthur P Schalick HS; Elmer, NJ; (3); 2/150; Pre Church Yth Grp; Pres Exploring; Hosp Aide; SADD; Socr; High Hon Roll NHS; Ntl Merit SF; Chorus; Tennis; Close-Up Pgm 87; Pre-Med.

HAYWOOD, DOROTHY; Rahway HS; Rahway, NJ; (4); 35/210; Church Yth Grp; JA; ROTC; Church Choir; Cheerleading; High Hon Roll; Ho Roll; Jr NHS; NHS; E Ford Memrl Awd 87; Muhlenberg Regiona; RN.

HAZEL, ELAINE; Pennsauken HS; Pennsauken, NJ; (3); Variety Show Var Bsktbl; Hon Roll; Bus.

HAZELTON, JAMES E; Delran HS; Delran, NJ; (3); Band; Conce Band; Stage Crew; Bsbl; Prfct Atten Awd; Comms.

AZY, MICHAEL; Bridgewater-Raritan HS East; Bridgewater, NJ; (3); oy Scts; Var L Ftbl; Var L Lcrss; Powder Puff Ftbl; JV Wrstlng; God ntry Awd; Hon Roll; NHS.

EADLEY, CHRISTOPHER; Egg Harbor Township HS; Cardiff, NJ; 4); 3/288; Computer Clb; Drama Clb; Stage Crew; Nwsp Stf; Lit Mag; Var rs Cntry; JV Wrstlng; High Hon Roll; NHS; Stockton ST Coll; Med.

EADLEY, J STEVEN; Washington Twp HS; Turnersville, NJ; (4); 3/ 80; Rep Stu Cncl; Var Bsktbl; Capt Socr; NHS; Pres Intract; S NJ Yuth mmsn; 1st S Jrsy Sccr; Engrng.

EADY, LAURA; Northern Valley Regional HS; Northvale, NJ; (2); Art lb; Spanish Clb; Nwsp Stf; Lit Mag; Bsktbl; Sftbl; Hon Roll; Gftd/Tlntd gm 87; Fin/Educ.

EAL, JENNIFER; Burlington Township HS; Burlington, NJ; (3); 8/ 49; Drama Clb; FNA; Chorus; Madrigals; School Play; Nwsp Rptr; Yrbk tf; Mgr(s); NHS; Rotary Awd; Genetcs.

EALEY, MEGHAN; Cranford HS; Cranford, NJ; (2); Art Clb; Nwsp tf; Lit Mag; Hon Roll; Natl Art Hnr Soc, Art Cont Wnnr 86-87; Engrng.

EALEY, PATTI; Buena Regional HS; Williamstown, NJ; (4); 13/200; AA; PAVAS; Q&S; Speech Tm; Band; Color Guard; Mrchg Band; School lay; Stage Crew; Variety Show; Atlantic CC Annl Bus Sympsm 86; Procss Vrtng Awd, & Outstndng Ldrshpo Awd Stu Cncl 87; Coast Guard; Pblc ffairs.

EALY, KELLY ANN; Paul VI HS; Somerdale, NJ; (4); 24/514; Church th Grp; Hosp Aide; Math Clb; Spanish Clb; Drill Tm; Pom Pon; Hon oll; Philadelphia Coll Pharm; Pharm.

EALY, KEVIN; St Joseph Regioinal HS; Park Ridge, NJ; (4); 29/154; hurch Yth Grp; Ski Clb; JV Im Bsktbl; JV Golf; Var L Trk; Hon Roll; HS; Stevens Inst Of Tech 87; Park Ridge Rotary Clb 87; Stevens Inst Of ech; Cvl Engr.

EALY, LAURA; Pt Pleasant Beach HS; Pt Pleasant Bch, NJ; (2); ance Clb; French Clb; Key Clb; Nwsp Rptr; Yrbk Stf; Rep Frsh Cls; High on Roll; Frnch Achvt 86; Eng Achvt 87; Jrnlsm.

EALY, LEIGH ANN; Westfield HS; Westfield, NJ; (4); Girl Scts; JCL; atin Clb; SADD; Chorus; Hon Roll; NHS; Itln Clb Svc Awd 86-87; Itln lb Schlrshp 86-87; Amer U; Intl Bus.

EANEY, CYNTHIA; Oak Knoll Schl; Madison, NJ; (4); Drama Clb; rench Clb; Service Clb; Ski Clb; Nwsp Rptr; Nwsp Stf; Lit Mag; Hon oll; Ntl Merit Ltr; Boston Coll; Engl.

EANEY, JAMES; Monsignor Donovan HS; Manchester, NJ; (3); hurch Yth Grp; Latin Clb; Political Wkr; ROTC; SADD; Yrbk Stf; JV sbl; Var Ftbl; Wt Lftg; Hon Roll; Natl Guard ROTC 87; Hofstra U; re-Law.

EANEY, KARA; Lakeland Regional HS; Ringwood, NJ; (4); Church th Grp; Service Clb; Pres SADD; Yrbk Bus Mgr; Rep Yrbk Stf; Rep Jr ls; Var Stat Fld Hcky; Ski Clb; Teachers Aide; Rep Frsh Cls; Achvt Awd 7; NY Theatre Clb Actvties Coordntr & Pres 84-87; Coll St Rose; Spch thlgy.

EATER, JODIE; High Point Regional HS; Branchville, NJ; (3); Church th Grp; German Clb; Hosp Aide; Band; Concert Band; Mrchg Band; JV ar Cheerleading; JV Fld Hcky; Capt Pom Pon; JV Sftbl; Coachs Awd rsty Chrldng 85-87; Grmn Trnsltr.

EBBLE, CHRISTOPHER R; Highland Park HS; Highland Park, NJ;); AFS; Am Leg Boys St; Drama Clb; Math Clb; Math Tm; PAVAS; adio Clb; Science Clb; Spanish Clb; Rep Frsh Cls; Engrng.

EBER, KIMBERLY A; Overbrook Regional SR HS; Pine Hill, NJ; (3); rama Clb; French Clb; SADD; Yrbk Stf; Rep Stu Cncl; Var Cheerleading; ar Sftbl; JV Trk; Hon Roll; Sec Church Yth Grp; Chem.

ECK, MICHAEL; Pinelands Regional HS; Tuckerton, NJ; (4); Aud/ is; Capt CAP; Pres Science Clb; Spanish Clb; Nwsp Phtg; Yrbk Phtg; JV rs Cntry; JV Socr; NHS; Spanish NHS; Mitchell Awd Civil Air Patrol 86; arhart Awd 87; Capt Commndr CAP 85; Drexel Rutgers; Mech Engrng.

ECKEL, WINNIE; Paul VI Regional HS; Newark, NJ; (3); Trk; panish NHS; Engl Awd 85.

ECKMAN, ANDREW; Columbia HS; Maplewood, NJ; (3); Boy Scts; V Im Ftbl; L Var Wrstlng; Church Usher; Crmnl Jstc.

ECKMAN, MELYNDA; Newton HS; Newton, NJ; (3); 25/196; German lb; Hosp Aide; Science Clb; Varsity Clb; JV Bsktbl; Var Cheerleading; ar Crs Cntry; Trk; NHS; Girls Track MVP 86; Outstndng Frshmn Girl thlete 85.

EERY, MARY CATHERINE; Sacred Heart Regional HS; Vineland, J; (3); 7/59; German Clb; Yrbk Phtg; Stat Diving; Stat Swmmng; JV ennis; High Hon Roll; Hon Roll; Trs NHS; Cert Cumberland Cnty Coll nt Srch Career Options Essy Cntst 87; Women Engrng & Mngmnt 87; ngrng.

EFFRON, KATHLEEN; Manalapan HS; Manalapan, NJ; (4); Aud/Vis; ebate Tm; Library Aide; SADD; School Musical; School Play; Stage rew; NHS; Ntl Merit Schol; Pres Schlr; Prncpls Schlrshp 87; NJ istngshd Schlr 87; Rutgers Coll; Law.

EFFRON, WILLIAM; Madison Central HS; Old Bridge, NJ; (4); Trs omputer Clb; Math Tm; Spanish Clb; Varsity Clb; Var L Socr; Var L rk; Spanish NHS; Pres Yng Cptlsts 86-87; Mayors Schlrshp 87; U Of O-BOULDER; Aerospc Engr.

EFT, CORINNE; Morristown-Beard HS; Mendham, NJ; (2); 14/75; mnty Wkr; Drama Clb; French Clb; Ski Clb; School Play; Stage Crew; rbk Phtg; Sec Frsh Cls; Var Cheerleading; JV Lcrss.

EFTER, LINDA; Livingston HS; Livingston, NJ; (3); 118/420; Cmnty Vkr; Chorus; Stage Crew; Vllybl; Hon Roll; Jr NHS; Prfct Atten Awd; hrmcy.

EFTER, LISA; Newton HS; Newton, NJ; (4); 26/196; Sec German Clb; and; Concert Band; Mrchg Band; School Musical; Symp Band; Yrbk Stf; ar Capt Cheerleading; Powder Puff Ftbl; Trvl.

EGG, ERIC L; Morristown HS; Morristown, NJ; (4); Am Leg Boys St; oy Scts; Pres Church Yth Grp; Capt Debate Tm; Chorus; School Musical; ocr; Tennis; NHS; Ntl Merit Ltr; ADK Schlrshp For Exclinc In Music 87; Vashington Workshop Schlrshp 86; Kalamazoo Coll; Lbrl Arts.

EHIR, MICHAEL J; Mountain Lakes HS; Mountain Lakes, NJ; (4); 13/); Church Yth Grp; Math Tm; Concert Band; School Musical; Var Trk; igh Hon Roll; NHS; Ntl Merit SF; Irish Amer Cultural Inst Scholar 84; eorgetown.

EIL, EDWARD; Washington Township HS; Sewell, NJ; (3); Church th Grp; FCA; German Clb; Science Clb; Var Socr; JV Trk; Comp Engr.

EILMEIER, LORI; Morris Hills HS; Dover, NJ; (3); 41/365; French lb; FBLA; German Clb; VP Intnl Clb; Latin Clb; Lit Mag; Rep Stu Cncl; rench Hon Soc; Hon Roll; Masonic Awd; Altrnt Rcpnt Of Cngrssnl undestag Schlrshp To Study Abroad 85; Intl Public Svc.

EIM, LINDA; Pitman HS; Pitman, NJ; (2); Art Clb; Lit Mag; Fld Hcky; een Fest 3rd Pl-Self Portrait South Jersey Stu Craft Fair 87; Pitman iddle Schl Staff Art Awd 85; Art.

HEIN, JOANNE; Passaic County Tech & Voc HS; Paterson, NJ; (4); Hosp Aide; Spanish Clb; Ed Yrbk Stf; Var Capt Cheerleading; Var Capt Pom Pon; JV Sftbl; Hon Roll; NHS; Psychology.

HEINDRICHS, KURT M; Green Brook HS; Green Brook, NJ; (3); 10/56; Am Leg Boys St; JV Var Bsktbl; JV Var Ftbl; L Trk; NHS; Stage Crew; Yrbk Stf; Soc Stdys Achvt Awd 85; Hstry.

HEINE, JENNIFER; Paul VI HS; Lindenwold, NJ; (3); 150/417; English Clb; GAA; Pep Clb; Spanish Clb; School Musical; School Play; VP Sr Cls; Var L Cheerleading; Pom Pon; Var L Sftbl; Law.

HEINEMANN, ERIC; Don Bosco Prep HS; Wyckoff, NJ; (3); 12/190; German Clb; Science Clb; Var Socr; Var Trk; Hon Roll; NHS; Gld Mdl Grmn 85-86; Boston Coll; Acctng.

HEINEMANN, HANS; Faith Christian HS; Sewell, NJ; (4); 4/8; Church Yth Grp; Teachers Aide; Yrbk Ed-Chief; Yrbk Stf; Var Bsbl; Var Capt Socr; High Hon Roll; NEDT Awd; Chorus; Bst Def All Conf; Most Likely To Succeed; 7th KYU In Amer Goju Karate; Indoor Sccr Outside Of Schl; US Naval Acad; Aerontcl Engrng.

HEINEMANN, JOHN; Don Bosco Prep HS; Wyckoff, NJ; (2); 8/210; Chess Clb; German Clb; JV Bsktbl; Var Socr; JV Trk; High Hon Roll; Gold Mdl Hnrs Algebra & Trigmtry 86; Gold Mdl German I 86; Penn ST; Architect.

HEINRICHS, DALE; Pinelands Regional HS; Tuckerton, NJ; (3); Sec Spanish Clb; VP Soph Cls; Var Tennis; Var Trk; Hon Roll; NHS; Spanish NHS; Sci.

HEINZ, DIANE; Morris Catholic HS; Montville, NJ; (4); 36/138; Church Yth Grp; German Clb; Natl Beta Clb; SADD; School Musical; Bsktbl; Socr; Trk; High Hon Roll; Hon Roll; Bsktbl ST Chmps 86; Sccr Conf Champs 86; U Of DE.

HEITZMAN, JOSEPH; Notre Dame HS; Pennington, NJ; (2); 37/400; JV Socr; Var Trk; High Hon Roll; Hon Roll; NHS; Engr.

HELEMAN, BETH; Vineland HS; Vineland, NJ; (2); 5/850; Drama Clb; Key Clb; Spanish Clb; SADD; Chorus; Stage Crew; Yrbk Stf; Lit Mag; High Hon Roll; Brown U; Pdtrics.

HELLEIS, TRACY A; Northern Burlington Regional HS; Allentown, NJ; (4); 36/224; Hosp Aide; Teachers Aide; Color Guard; Yrbk Stf; Rep Frsh Cls; Rep Soph Cls; Rep Jr Cls; Rep Sr Cls; Sftbl; La Petite Dnce Studio Trphy; Pres Acdmc Ftns Awd 87; East Carolna U; Accntng.

HELLEN, TIMOTHY; Middletown South HS; Middletown, NJ; (2); Drama Clb; Pep Clb; Spanish Clb; Speech Tm; School Play; Rep Frsh Cls; Rep Soph Cls; Rep Jr Cls; Ftbl; Tennis; Gynclgst.

HELLER, JENNIFER; Audubon HS; Audubon, NJ; (3); Am Leg Aux Girls St; German Clb; Office Aide; Teachers Aide; Acpl Chr; Chorus; Church Choir; Madrigals; Mgr(s); Var JV Tennis; Hstry.

HELLMERS, CLIFF; Shore Regional HS; West Long Branch, NJ; (3); Cmnty Wkr; SADD; Var L Swmmng; Var L Trk; Wt Lftg; Hon Roll; Prfct Atten Awd; Swmng Monmouth Cnty Champ 86-87; HS Swmng Season 86-87; Sci Fair Regnl Qualfr 86.

HELMSTETTER, TOM; Immaculata HS; Pisataway, NJ; (3); Art Clb; Church Yth Grp; FCA; Varsity Clb; Yrbk Phtg; Im Bsktbl; Var L Ftbl; Im Socr; Im Sftbl; Var Wt Lftg; Embrey Riddle Aviat U; Pilot.

HELRIEGEL, VALERIE; Hunterdon Central HS; Whitehouse St, NJ; (4); 250/560; Church Yth Grp; Radio Clb; Band; Chorus; Church Choir; Concert Band; Jazz Band; Madrigals; Mrchg Band; Stat Ftbl; Dfrnt Drmr Awd 87; Montclair ST Coll; Brdcstng.

HELWANI, GHASSAN; Manchester Regional HS; P Dark, NJ; (3); Capt Crs Cntry; Var Socr; Var Trk; Wt Lftg; Hon Roll; Prfct Atten Awd; Rutgers U; Mech Engrng.

HELWIG, DONNA; Lower Cape May Regional HS; N Cape May, NJ; (4); 46/235; French Clb; SADD; Chorus; Flag Corp; Yrbk Stf; Hon Roll; Church Choir; Band Frnt Awd 87; Fine Arts Dept Awd Ntl Schl Chrl & Music Prfrmnc Awd 87; Brandywine JC; Trvl.

HELZER, CHRISTINA LYN; Park Bible Acad; Salem, NJ; (4); 3/5; Church Yth Grp; Drama Clb; Yrbk Ed-Chief; Pres Stu Cncl; Var Capt Bsktbl; Var Capt Sftbl; Var Capt Vllybl; Hon Roll; Amer Chrstn Hnr Scty 86; Pastors Awd 87; Stu Cncl Awd Schl Sprt 87; Salme Comm Coll; Elem Ed.

HEMBERGER, MICHAEL M; North Bergen HS; North Bergen, NJ; (3); Am Leg Boys St; Chrmn DECA; SADD; Nwsp Stf; Yrbk Stf; Pres Stu Cncl; JV Crs Cntry; Var Tennis; Hon Roll; VFW Awd; West Point; Bus Mgt.

HEMELESKI, THOMAS; Bloomfield HS; Bloomfield, NJ; (4); 31/444; Art Clb; Boy Scts; Computer Clb; Drama Clb; German Clb; Key Clb; Quiz Bowl; Scholastic Bowl; Band; Concert Band; Us Naval Smmr Sci Smnr 86.

HENBEST, JON CHARLES; Toms River HS South; Toms River, NJ; (4); Am Leg Boys St; Boy Scts; Church Yth Grp; Political Wkr; Church Choir; Mrchg Band; Ed Yrbk Stf; NHS; Pres Schlr; K M Beck Schlrshp Fndtn 87; Cty Indian Bndwgn Schlrshp 87; Oprtn Frndshp Of Amer Ntl Brd 85-87; Accntng.

HENCHES, ROBERT; Morris Catholic HS; Towaco, NJ; (3); Am Leg Boys St; Scholastic Bowl; Varsity Clb; Bsbl; Ftbl; Bus.

HENDERSHOT, STEVE; North Hunterdon Regional HS; Lebanon, NJ; (2); 135/450; FCA; JV Bsbl; Var Ftbl; Var L Wrstlng; Hon Roll; Law.

HENDERSON, FRANK J; West Milford Township HS; West Milford, NJ; (3); 42/402; Am Leg Boys St; Boys Clb Am; Model UN; VP Spanish Clb; VP Sr Cls; JV Ftbl; JV Wrstlng; Hon Roll; Poli Sci.

HENDERSON, JOE; Lyndhurst HS; Lyndhurst, NJ; (3); 2/174; JV Var Bsbl; JV Var Bsktbl; Gov Hon Prg Awd; High Hon Roll; Hon Roll; NHS; Rutgers U; Acctg.

HENDERSON, JOSEPH; Morristown HS; Morristown, NJ; (4); Band; Church Yth Grp; DECA; English Clb; FCA; Hosp Aide; JA; Office Aide; Ski Clb; ST Comp Petro Mktg Awd 87; Johnson & Wales Coll; Bus.

HENDERSON, JOSEPH; Passaic Valley Regional HS; W Paterson, NJ; (2); JV Bsbl; JV Ftbl; Hon Roll; Pres Schlr; 2nd Hnrs-3.0 GPA Or Better 86; Med.

HENDRICKS, DAVID; Pennsille HS; Pennsville, NJ; (3); 15/231; Am Leg Boys St; Cmnty Wkr; Exploring; Acpl Chr; Chorus; School Musical; Stu Cncl; Capt Var Socr; Hon Roll; NHS; Most Improved Vocalist 86; All Tri-Cnty Sccr 1st Tm 86; Sunbeam Sccr Plyr Yr 86; Med.

HENDRICKS, JAMIE; Pennsauken HS; Delair, NJ; (3); SADD; Teachers Aide; Score Keeper; Hon Roll; NHS; Fashion Show 84-85; 1st Pl PTA Cultural Enrchmnt Art Cntst 86-87; Maison De Paris; Hairdresser.

HENDRICKSON, TIM; Bloomfield HS; Bloomfield, NJ; (3); DECA; Hon Roll; Accntnt.

HENDRIX, MICHAEL; Lakeland Regional HS; Ringwood, NJ; (4); 50/ 360; Church Yth Grp; Letterman Clb; Math Tm; Var L Bsktbl; Hon Roll; NHS; JV Trk; Mgr(s); Score Keeper; Aud/Vis; Cngrsswmns Marge Roukema 1st Pl Model Cngrssmn 87; Cngrssmn Bill Bradleys H S Rep 87; Appalachian ST; Finance.

HENEL, CAROLYN; Ramapo HS; Franklin Lakes, NJ; (3); 7/322; Church Yth Grp; Trs Debate Tm; French Clb; Trk; Vllybl; High Hon Roll; Hon Roll; NHS; Ntl Merit SF; French Achvt Awd.

HENKEL, RICHIE; Secaucus HS; Secaucus, NJ; (3); Computer Clb; Math Clb; Mu Alpha Theta; Spanish Clb; Bsbl; Hon Roll; Mu Alpha Theta Awd; Spanish NHS; Bsbl Awd 86; Comp Awd 87; Math Awd 87; Rutgers U; Comp Engr.

HENLEY, KENDALL; Overbrook Regional SR HS; Pine Hill, NJ; (3); Drama Clb; 4-H; Chorus; Nwsp Rptr; Rep Jr Cls; Crs Cntry; Var Capt Trk; 4-H Awd; Hon Roll; Natl 4-H Congress 86fslvr Bowl ST Pblc Presentation 86; Camden Co 4-H King 86; USAF Acad; Intl Business.

HENNESSEY, MARY; Immaculate Conception HS; East Orange, NJ; (2); Crs Cntry; Trk; MVP-TRK 87; Coaches Awd-Crss Cntry 86.

HENNINGER, SUSAN; Union HS; Union, NJ; (4); Aud/Vis; Dance Clb; Drama Clb; FBLA; Chorus; Church Choir; Color Guard; School Play; Cheerleading; Drd Ed Vocal Schlrshp 83; Theatre Prfrmnc.

HENRY, ELIZABETH ANN; Randolph HS; Randolph, NJ; (4); 50/357; Pres AFS; Church Yth Grp; Sec Jr Civitan Int; Key Clb; Office Aide; Red Cross Aide; Service Clb; Nwsp Bus Mgr; Nwsp Stf; Yrbk Stf; Dstngshd Svc Awd 87; Miami U Of OH; Spch Pthlgy.

HENRY, FRANCILLE; Lincoln HS; Jersy City, NJ; (3); Nwsp Stf; Bowling; Tennis; LHS Hnr Soc 86; Audio Tech.

HENRY, KELLEY; Egg Harbor Township HS; Linwood, NJ; (4); 47/289; Art Clb; GAA; Spanish Clb; Sec Rep Frsh Cls; Sec Rep Soph Cls; Sec Rep Jr Cls; Sec Rep Sr Cls; Var JV Cheerleading; Sftbl; Hon Roll; Glassboro ST Coll; Elem Educ.

HENRY, LORI; Bordentown Regional HS; Bordentown, NJ; (3); Drama Clb; French Clb; FBLA; Math Tm; Mu Alpha Theta; SADD; Stat Bsbl; Hon Roll; Mu Alpha Theta Awd; NHS.

HENRY, MATTHEW; Pitman HS; Sewell, NJ; (2); Chorus; Bsktbl; Hon Roll; Math.

HENRY, PAUL; Pinelands Regional HS; Tuckerton, NJ; (3); 39/195; Church Yth Grp; Spanish Clb; SADD; School Play; Yrbk Stf; JV Bsktbl; Ftbl; Var Tennis; Hon Roll; Pres Phys Fit Awd 86-87; Bayshore SR Lg All Star Bsbl Dist Champs 84, Dist & Regnl Champs 86; Bus Adm.

HENSEL, MICHELE; Buena Regional HS; Milmay, NJ; (4); 3/190; Drama Clb; Math Clb; Ski Clb; SADD; School Play; Nwsp Stf; Rep Frsh Cls; VP Soph Cls; Pres Jr Cls; Sec Stu Cncl; Natl Yng Ldrs Confrnc WA DC.

HENSLEY, NICKOLAS; Delsea Regional HS; Malaga, NJ; (2); Var Crs Cntry; Var Ice Hcky; Hon Roll; Drftng.

HENSON, CHAVELLA; North Brunswick Township HS; N Brunswick, NJ; (4); 46/289; AFS; Model UN; Pres Soph Cls; Var Bsktbl; Var Sftbl; Var Trk; Var Vllybl; Hon Roll; Key Clb; Teachers Aide; Ladies Axlry Engn Co 1 Awd Cmmnty Svc 87; Easter Seal A86 & 87; Rutgers Coll.

HENSON, SHARON; University HS; Newark, NJ; (3); Church Yth Grp; JA; Church Choir; Hon Roll; Sec NHS; Future Actuary In Training Awd Prud Ins 85; Scholars Day Awd NBE 86; Bus Adm.

HENVICK JR, JAMES; Alma Prep; Warren, NJ; (2); 1/6; Boy Scts; Church Yth Grp; Spanish Clb; Church Choir; Nwsp Stf; Yrbk Stf; Bsbl; Bsktbl; God Cntry Awd; High Hon Roll; Med.

HERBERT, AMY; North Brunswick Township HS; N Brunswick, NJ; (4); Chess Clb; Church Yth Grp; Cmnty Wkr; Dance Clb; SADD; Yrbk Rptr; Yrbk Stf; Wt Lftg; Royal Acad Of Dance Hnr Awd 83; Ebony Sbrbnts Schlrshp 87; Barbados Dnc Thtre Schlrshp 82-84; Kean Coll; Rbtcs Engnrng.

HERBERT, CHRISTOPHER; Northern Burlington Regional HS; Wrightstown, NJ; (2); VP 4-H; FFA; 4-H Awd; FFA Awd-9th Pl ST Ag Mech Contest &goat Showing Awd 3rd Pl 87.

HERDMAN, AMANDA; MSGR Donovan HS; Lakewood, NJ; (3); Church Yth Grp; Cmnty Wkr; Hosp Aide; Intnl Clb; Ski Clb; SADD; Color Guard; Concert Band; Twrlr; Hon Roll; Congressional Yth Ldrshp Cncl 87; Bus.

HERDT, SUSIE; Notre Dame HS; Yardville, NJ; (3); German Clb; Acpl Chr; Chorus; Madrigals; School Musical; School Play; Variety Show; Hon Roll; NHS; Grmn Awd 86; Bus.

HERES, WILLIAM; Middletown HS South; Locust, NJ; (3); Am Leg Boys St; Boy Scts; School Play; Lit Mag; Rep Stu Cncl; French Hon Soc; Hon Roll; Chorus; Cornell U; Plot.

HERFLICKER, DARREN; Toms River High School North; Toms River, NJ; (3); 27/459; German Clb; Band; Mrchg Band; Hon Roll; Acdmc Ltr 85-87.

HERING, KATHLEEN GAIL; Spotswood HS; Spotswood, NJ; (3); 32/ 144; Am Leg Aux Girls St; Intnl Clb; Ski Clb; Nwsp Stf; Var Cheerleading; JV Mgr(s); Glassboro U; Lbrl Arts.

HERLIHY, TRISTIN; Mahwah HS; Mahwah, NJ; (4); Chorus; Rep Frsh Cls; Trk; Vllybl; Rep Soph Cls; Rep Jr Cls; Ramapo Coll; Bus.

HERMAN, LAUREN; Paulsboro HS; Gibbstown, NJ; (3); Band; Chorus; Concert Band; Drm Mjr(t); School Play; Nwsp Stf; Yrbk Stf; Rep Frsh Cls; Rep Soph Cls; Rep Jr Cls; Music In The Parks, Hershey Pk, PA Outstndng Drm Mjr, NJ Sentrs Awd 87; Stu Mnth Feb 86; Bio.

HERMANUS, MARVELA; Marylawn Of The Oranges; East Orange, NJ; (3); Math Clb; Science Clb; Service Clb; VP Spanish Clb; Rptr Nwsp Rptr; Trs Jr Cls; Hon Roll; NHS; Prfct Atten Awd; Spanish NHS; Latin Awd 85-86; Engl Awd 86; Natl Latin Exam Awd Cum Laude 85-86; Med.

HERNANDEZ, COLIN; Orange HS; Orange, NJ; (4); Pep Clb; Spanish Clb; Bsktbl; Socr; VA ST Coll; Bus.

HERNANDEZ, DIANE; Eastside HS; Paterson, NJ; (4); 5/600; Debate Tm; Speech Tm; Varsity Clb; Yrbk Rptr; Yrbk Sprt Ed; Sftbl; Vllybl; NHS; Ntl Merit Schol; Schlrshp William Paterson; Hstry Awd; William Paterson; Bus Admn.

HERNANDEZ, DIANE; Mary Help Of Christians Acad; Paterson, NJ; (3); Computer Clb; Drama Clb; Hosp Aide; Latin Clb; NFL; SADD; Teachers Aide; Im Cheerleading; Gym; Ntl Merit Ltr; Chld Psych.

HERNANDEZ, FELIPE; Perth Amboy HS; Perth Amboy, NJ; (1); Frsh Cls; Stu Cncl; Var Trk; Var Wt Lftg; Hon Roll; Dr Paul Zito Awd; Sp Tech.

HERNANDEZ, IDELSI; Secaucus HS; Secaucus, NJ; (4); 6/168; Church Yth Grp; Mu Alpha Theta; Spanish Clb; Church Choir; High Hon Roll; Hon Roll; NHS; Spanish NHS; 2nd Pl Spnsh Poetry Rectl Cntst 85; Dstngshed Amrcn High Schl Stu 85-86; Elec Engrng.

HERNANDEZ, ILEANA; Brick Memorial HS; Brick, NJ; (4); Drama Clb; Key Clb; Stage Crew; Trk; High Hon Roll; NHS; Seton Hall U Schlrshp 87; Seton Hall U; Pre-Law.

HERNANDEZ, JANETTE; North Bergen HS; N Bergen, NJ; (3); Cmnty Wkr; French Clb; Hosp Aide; Twrlr; Hon Roll; NYIT; Comp Accntng.

HERNANDEZ, NORMA; Orange HS; Orange, NJ; (3); Hon Roll.

HERNANDEZ, SONIA M; Holy Rosary Academy; Union City, NJ; (3); Drama Clb; French Clb; Math Clb; Spanish Clb; Varsity Clb; Nwsp Rptr; Nwsp Stf; Yrbk Stf; VP Soph Cls; Rep Sec Stu Cncl; Svc Awd-Nwspr Stff Awd; Svc Awd VP Soph Cls; Svc Awd Stu Cncl Sec; Crmnl Law.

HERNANEZ, NANCY; Perth Amboy HS; Perth Amboy, NJ; (3); Art Clb; Aud/Vis; Debate Tm; English Clb; Teachers Aide; Chorus; School Musical; School Play; Variety Show; Sr Cls; Hgh Hnr Roll 86; Middlesex Coll; Secy.

HERNE, KELLI; Hightstown HS; E Windsor, NJ; (2); Cmnty Wkr; Spanish Clb; Nwsp Rptr; Rep Stu Cncl; Var Stat Bsktbl; Var Socr; JV Sftbl; JV Trk; High Hon Roll; NHS; Hnrm Mnt For All Cnfrnc/Soccer 86; Psych.

HERR, LIZ; St John Vianney HS; Holmdel, NJ; (4); 11/250; SADD; Stage Crew; Lit Mag; Rep Frsh Cls; Rep Soph Cls; High Hon Roll; Hon Roll; NHS; Pres Acdmc Fit Awd 87; Grad Hgh Hon 87; Rutgers Coll; Bio Sci.

HERRERA JR, DANIEL F; Mc Corristin HS; Trenton, NJ; (3); 20/200; FBLA; Pep Clb; Lit Mag; Var Socr; Var Tennis; Hon Roll; Jr NHS; NHS; NEDT Awd; Natl Latn Awd Cum Laude 85; Rider; Accntng.

HERRERA, FABIAN A; Piscataway HS; Piscataway, NJ; (3); Cmnty Wkr; JA; Varsity Clb; Var Crs Cntry; Var Trk; Hon Roll; NHS; Ivy League Coll; Arch.

HERRERA, HECTOR; St Marys HS; Jersey City, NJ; (4); Church Yth Grp; Drama Clb; Chorus; Yrbk Phtg; Rep Frsh Cls; Rep Soph Cls; VP Sr Cls; Var Bsbl; Im Bsktbl; Im Bowling; Lylty Svc Awd 85-86; Math Awd 87; Bus Accntng.

HERRERA, TAMMY; Lakewood HS; Lakewood, NJ; (3); Drama Clb; Hosp Aide; Med.

HERRICK, MICHELLE; H G Hoffman HS; South Amboy, NJ; (3); 4/65; Math Clb; Ski Clb; Jr Cls; Cheerleading; Vllybl; Hon Roll; Finance.

HERRING, DAVID M; Spottswood HS; Spotswood, NJ; (4); Am Leg Boys St; Church Yth Grp; Sec Intnl Clb; Math Clb; Spanish Clb; Yrbk Stf; Off Sr Cls; High Hon Roll; Hon Roll; Spanish NHS; Congrssnl Art Comptn 84; Decthln Of Knldg 86.

HERRMANN, CHRISTOPHER; Lawrence HS; Lawrncevlle, NJ; (2); 77/218; Church Yth Grp; JV Swmmng; Hon Roll.

HERRMANN, FRED; Alma Prep Schl; Middlesex, NJ; (4); 2/5; Church Yth Grp; Pres Computer Clb; German Clb; Math Clb; Quiz Bowl; Nwsp Stf; Rep Jr Cls; JV Bsktbl; Hon Roll; VFW Awd; Kung Fu Blue Belt 85; Tae Kwon Do Yellow Belt 85; Missiah Coll; Communication.

HERRMANN, KARIN; Bridgewater East HS; Bound Brook, NJ; (4); Intnl Clb; Ski Clb; Varsity Clb; Band; Mrchg Band; Stage Crew; Yrbk Stf; Im Bsktbl; Var L Crs Cntry; JV Swmmng; Lafayette Coll; Elec Engrng.

HERRMANN, MELANIE; Delran HS; Delran, NJ; (4); 3/194; Am Leg Aux Girls St; Math Tm; Model UN; Quiz Bowl; Nwsp Rptr; Yrbk Stf; Lit Mag; Capt Bowling; Sec NHS; Pres Schlr; NJ Gvnrs Tchng Schlr; Dgls Coll Schlr; Dgls Coll; Englsh Tchr.

HERRMANN, ROBERT; Southern Regional HS; Manahawkin, NJ; (4); 14/361; VP Computer Clb; Math Clb; Math Tm; Im Bsktbl; Im Vllybl; High Hon Roll; Hon Roll; NHS; Widener U Pres Schlrshp 87; Widener U; Engrng.

HERRUP, AMY; Atlantic City HS; Margate, NJ; (4); 16/402; VP Drama Clb; Model UN; Service Clb; Sec Spanish Clb; Yrbk Ed-Chief; Sec Stu Cncl; Swmmng; High Hon Roll; Jr NHS; St Schlr; Most Outstndg Delgt At Harvard Mdl UN 86; Intl Relat.

HERSLOW, KRIS; Chatham Township HS; Chatham Twp, NJ; (4); 49/150; Drama Clb; Key Clb; Model UN; Chorus; Yrbk Ed-Chief; Yrbk Phtg; Yrbk Sprt Ed; Bsktbl; Trk; U CO; Comm Art.

HERTELL, KERRY; Westfield SR HS; Westfield, NJ; (3); 88/469; Church Yth Grp; Chorus; Church Choir; Rep Stu Cncl; Coach Actv; Socr; Swmmng; Wt Lftg; Hon Roll; 100 Yd Free Recrd Hldr 85; Pirate Invtnl 50 Yd Free Recrd Hldr 85; 100 Yrd Butterfly YMCA Natls 86; Ed.

HERTLEIN, HELENA; Gateway Reg HS; Wenonah, NJ; (4); 20/200; Exploring; Key Clb; Science Clb; Off SADD; Var Bsktbl; Var Sftbl; Var Capt Tennis; NHS; JCL; Latin Clb; All Gloucester Cnty 1st Dlbs 85; All South Jersey Dbls 85; Phys Therpst.

HERTZ, AMY; Livingston HS; Livingston, NJ; (3); 65/417; Cmnty Wkr; Leo Clb; Office Aide; Nwsp Stf; Yrbk Stf; Lit Mag; High Hon Roll; Hon Roll; Jr NHS; Spanish NHS.

HERTZBERG, LORI A; The Pingry Schl; Watchung, NJ; (4); French Clb; Spanish Clb; Yrbk Stf; Lit Mag; Var Crs Cntry; Var Trk; Ntl Merit SF; Cum Laude Scty 86; Rutgers Deans Smmr Schlr 86; MIP Cross Cntry 85-86.

HERZ, PETER; Ramapo HS; Wyckoff, NJ; (3); Nwsp Rptr; Trs Jr Cls; Rep Stu Cncl; Var Ftbl; Church Yth Grp; Drama Clb; Exploring; Radio Clb; Ski Clb; Varsity Clb; Bus.

HERZBERG, DAREN; Dwight Englewood HS; Up Saddle Riv, NJ; (3); Cmnty Wkr; Math Tm; Band; Jazz Band; School Musical; Nwsp Bus Mgr; Nwsp Stf; Yrbk Stf; JV Bsbl; JV Crs Cntry; Rotary Yth Ldrshp Awd 87; Bus.

HERZIG, VICTORIA; Park Ridge HS; Park Ridge, NJ; (4); 11/109; Math Clb; Science Clb; Variety Show; Lit Mag; NHS; Boston U; Med.

HESS, CYNTHIA; Maple Shade HS; Maple Shade, NJ; (3); VP Computer Clb; Key Clb; Spanish Clb; Yrbk Stf; Stat Bsbl; Var JV Cheerleading; JV Fld Hcky; Stat Ftbl; Var Lcrss; High Hon Roll; Rotary Yth Ldrshp Awd 87; Rotary Yth Merit Awd 86-87; Grls ST Alt.

HESTER, DANIEL; Manasquan HS; Brielle, NJ; (3); French Clb; FBLA; Math Clb; JV Bsbl; Hon Roll; Trea FBLA 87; Rgnl Qlfr Olympic Of The Minds 86-87; NANBAPW Clubs Inc 87; Howard U; Bus.

HETTESHEIMER, PAUL; Kearney HS; Kearny, NJ; (4); 36/383; Am Leg Boys St; Church Yth Grp; Latin Clb; Band; Concert Band; School Musical; Capt Swmmng; God Cntry Awd; NHS; Prfct Atten Awd; Ramapo Achvt Schlrshp 87; Wmns Clb Of Arlington Schlrshp 87; Rampao Coll NJ; Chemistry.

HETZEL, CYNTHIA; Toms River High School North; Toms River, NJ; (3); Church Yth Grp; 4-H; Girl Scts; Library Aide; Band; Concert Band; Mrchg Band; Pep Band; Symp Band; Capt Mgr(s); Cosmtlgy.

HETZEL, MOLLIE; West Windsor-Plainsboro HS; Princeton Jct, NJ; (3); Cmnty Wkr; French Clb; Model UN; Service Clb; Yrbk Stf; Rep Stu Cncl; Stat Bsbl; Cheerleading; JV Lcrss; JV Capt Tennis; Franklin Coll; Intl Pltcs.

HEUSCHKEL, GLEN A; Montgomery HS; Skillman, NJ; (3); Am Leg Boys St; Boy Scts; Church Yth Grp; Science Clb; Ski Clb; Band; Jazz Band; JV Tennis; Hon Roll; NHS; Outstndng Schl Svc & Spirt Awd 85-87.

HEWITT JR, JEFFREY; Pennsville Memorial HS; Pennsville, NJ; (3); JCL; Pres Latin Clb; Ski Clb; JV Bsbl; Bsktbl; Vllybl; Med.

HEWITT, JENNIFER; Toms River HS East; Toms River, NJ; (4); 62/567; Library Aide; Band; Concert Band; Mrchg Band; Nwsp Rptr; Powder Puff Ftbl; Capt Var Trk; High Hon Roll; NHS; Sons Of St Patricks Irish Schlrshp 87; Toms River Ed Assoc Schlrshp 87; Trenton ST Coll; Bio.

HEWITT, JOSEPH; Haddonfield Memorial HS; Haddonfield, NJ; (4); 2/160; Intnl Clb; Model UN; Yrbk Sprt Ed; Tennis; French Hon Soc; NHS; Ntl Merit Ltr; Garden ST Distngshd Schlr 86-87; Busns.

HEWITT, REBECCA; Millville SR HS; Millville, NJ; (3); Hosp Aide; Trs Soph Cls; Rep Stu Cncl; Bus Scrtry.

HEWITT, STEPHANIE; Cinnaminson HS; Cinnaminson, NJ; (3); Drama Clb; Key Clb; Spanish Clb; Temple Yth Grp; Thesps; School Musical; School Play; Var Cheerleading; Hon Roll; Sec NHS; Gov Schl 87; Frgn Lang.

HEYMAN, MARK; Ridgewood HS; Ridgewood, NJ; (3); 70/450; Am Leg Boys St; Drama Clb; French Clb; Ski Clb; Varsity Clb; Band; School Musical; Yrbk Stf; Stu Cncl; Ftbl; Bus.

HEYT, GREGORY J; Cherry Hill East HS; Cherry Hill, NJ; (3); 45/700; Am Leg Boys St; Radio Clb; Var L Crs Cntry; Var L Socr; Var L Trk; DAR Awd; High Hon Roll; Hon Roll; Ntl Merit Ltr; Natl Wnr Amer Essy Contst 86; Athlt Of Wk X-Cntry 86; Liberal Arts.

HIBBS, CONNIE; Paul VI HS; Haddon Hts, NJ; (3); Cmnty Wkr; Drama Clb; SADD; Rep Frsh Cls; Rep Soph Cls; Rep Jr Cls; Powder Puff Ftbl; Soc Psych.

HICKEY, DENISE E; West Morris Central HS; Long Valley, NJ; (4); 54/298; Art Clb; Church Yth Grp; GAA; Science Clb; Varsity Clb; Capt Gym; Var Trk; High Hon Roll; Hon Roll; NHS; 3rd Pl Ribbon Pencil Drawing 84; Bio League 85-86; Schlrhsp WA TWSP PD Local 301 87; TX A&M U; Civil Engrng.

HICKMAN, KELLY; Paulsboro HS; Gibbstown, NJ; (3); 32/150; Exploring; Chorus; Var Bsktbl; Var Fld Hcky; Var Capt Sftbl; Hon Roll; 3 Ltr Vrsty Awd 87; Glassboro ST Coll; Spts.

HICKMAN, ROBERT; Burl Co Voc & Tech HS; Mt Holly, NJ; (3); Computer Clb; VICA; Rep Jr Cls; Stu Cncl; Hon Roll; Elctrncs Shp Frmn 86-87; Elec Engr.

HICKMAN, SHERRI D; Hackettstown HS; Great Meadows, NJ; (3); 35/209; Chorus; Trs Jr Cls; Var Bsktbl; Var Cheerleading; Var Score Keeper; Capt Trk; Hon Roll; Blgy.

HICKMAN, THOMAS JOHN; Cumberland Christian Schl; Millville, NJ; (4); 5/29; Church Yth Grp; Band; Chorus; Church Choir; Yrbk Phtg; Lit Mag; L Mgr(s); Score Keeper; Mgr Socr; High Hon Roll; Hugh O Brien Yth Ldrshp Smnr 84-85; Pres Schlrshp To Nyack Coll 87-88; T C Davis Fmly Schlrshp 87-88; Nyack Coll; Elem Ed.

HICKS, JODI; Notre Dame HS; Kendall Pk, NJ; (2); Church Yth Grp; Chorus; High Hon Roll; Hon Roll; Hnrs-Hnrs Engl II 87.

HICKS, MICHELLE; Ridgefield Park HS; Ridgefield Pk, NJ; (3); 8/215; Math Clb; Math Tm; Science Clb; Trs Yrbk Bus Mgr; Yrbk Stf; Rep Sr Cls; JV Bsktbl; Score Keeper; Hon Roll; Sec NHS.

HICKS, NICOLE; Palisades Park JR-SR HS; Palisades Pk, NJ; (3); Yrbk Stf; Sec Frsh Cls; Sec Soph Cls; Sec Jr Cls; Rep Stu Cncl; Mat Maids; Btty Crckr Awd; Majorettes, Co-Capt 84-87; Bsbl Statscn 85-86; Tchr.

HICKS, TOM; Nanasquan HS; Sea Girt, NJ; (2); 50/216; Latin Clb; Spanish Clb; Yrbk Stf; JV Bsbl; Var Ftbl; Var Trk; Hon Roll.

HICKS, WILLENE A; Scoth Plains-Fanwood HS; Scotch Plains, NJ; (4); 15/300; Dance Clb; Model UN; Quiz Bowl; Chorus; Drill Tm; Mrchg Band; Orch; High Hon Roll; Hon Roll; Prfct Atten Awd; Gifted & Talented Prog 83-86; Georgetown U; Bus.

HICKS, YOLANDA; Weequahic HS; Newark, NJ; (4); #13 In Class; Cmnty Wkr; Capt Debate Tm; Pres Library Aide; Model UN; Quiz Bowl; Science Clb; Nwsp Rptr; Yrbk Stf; NHS; Opt Clb Awd.

HIDALGO, NELLY; Mary Help Of Christians Acad; Paterson, NJ; (3); SADD; Teachers Aide; JV Bsktbl; Stat Var Vllybl; Bus Mngt.

HIDALGO, PATRICIA E; Villa Walsh Acad; Basking Ridge, NJ; (4); Church Yth Grp; Girl Scts; Hosp Aide; Spanish Clb; Varsity Clb; Chorus; Var Socr; Hon Roll; Rotary Awd; Spanish NHS; Girl Sct Gold Awd 86; Independent B ST Socr Champ 83-87; Girl Sct Intl Wider Opportunity 85; Rutgers U; Bus.

HIERSPIEL, STACY; St John Vianney HS; Matawan, NJ; (3); Church Yth Grp; SADD; Stu Cncl; Powder Puff Ftbl; Score Keeper; Sftbl; Timer; 1st Degree Blackbelt 84; Instr Trainee 85; Psych.

HIGGENBOTHEM, THERESA; Bridgeton HS; Dividing Creek, NJ; (1); Church Yth Grp; Rep Stu Cncl; DAR Awd.

HIGGINS, CHRISTOPHER; Saint Rose HS; Neptune, NJ; (3); Boy Scts; Spanish Clb; Socr; Spanish NHS.

HIGH, STEPHANIE; Linden HS; Linden, NJ; (4); 72/350; DECA; FBLA; FHA; JA; Teachers Aide; Band; Mrchg Band; Off Jr Cls; Stu Cncl; Bsktbl; Baudes Fshn Coll; Fshn Merch.

HIGLEY, PEGGY; Freehold Boro HS; Freehold, NJ; (3); 13/249; Am Leg Aux Girls St; Church Yth Grp; JA; Capt Pep Clb; Spanish Clb; SADD; Varsity Clb; School Play; Nwsp Stf; Yrbk Stf; Shield & Key Awd 88; Excllnc In Phys Ed Awd 87; Prmry Ed.

HILD, JEFF; Boonton HS; Boonton, NJ; (1); Bsbl; Ftbl.

HILDEN, TARY; Toms River South HS; Toms River, NJ; (2); JV Fld Hcky; Var L Socr; Var L Trk; Hon Roll; Coachs Awd-Sccr 85-86; Most Imprvd V Sccr 86-87.

HILDICK, MIKE; Toms River HS North; Toms River, NJ; (3); Church Yth Grp; CAP; Cmnty Wkr; French Clb; Ski Clb; Varsity Clb; Nwsp Sprt Ed; L Bsbl; L Var Ftbl; Hon Roll; Captn, All Str Trvlng Tm 86; MVP Smmr Leag 86; Cls Advsr Chrch Yth Grp 87; VA Military Inst; Pilot.

HILL, APRIL; Pinelands Regional HS; Tuckerton, NJ; (2); School Play; Im Sftbl; DAR Awd; Bus.

HILL, DONNA; Cinnaminson HS; Cinnaminson, NJ; (3); Cmnty Wkr; Hosp Aide; Key Clb; SADD; Chorus; Yrbk Stf; Rep Jr Cls; Var Swmmng; Hon Roll; NHS; Med.

HILL, GWYNNE; Red Bank Reg HS; Little Silver, NJ; (4); 89/260; Exploring; Capt Color Guard; Spanish NHS; Miss Amer Coed Pgnt NJ 87; Howard Wilfield Fndtn Schlrshp 87; American U; Intl Bus.

HILL, HEATHER; High Point Regional HS; Branchville, NJ; (3); Am Leg Aux Girls St; Church Yth Grp; 4-H; Key Clb; SADD; Varsity Clb; Band; Chorus; Concert Band; Rep Frsh Cls; Prom Chrprsn 87; Treas-Sussex Cnty DWI Task Force 87; Phys Thrpy.

HILL, LARA; Triton Regional HS; Glendora, NJ; (4); 37/309; Cmnty Wkr; Drama Clb; Science Clb; Teachers Aide; Color Guard; Flag Corp; Mrchg Band; School Musical; School Play; Yrbk Rptr; Temple U; Real Est Apprsr.

HILL, LISA; Salem HS; Salem, NJ; (3); Art Clb; Teachers Aide; Hon Roll; Salem CC; Bus Accntng.

HILL, MATT; Baptist HS; Cherry Hill, NJ; (4); Church Yth Grp; Drama Clb; Chorus; Church Choir; Concert Band; Pep Band; School Play; Yrbk Phtg; Yrbk Rptr; Yrbk Stf; Camden Cnty Coll; Comp Sci.

HILL, REBEKAH; Bishop George Ahr HS; Piscataway, NJ; (4); 6/265 Band; Chorus; Concert Band; Jazz Band; Mrchg Band; School Musica Symp Band; High Hon Roll; NHS; NEDT Awd; Hartt Schl Of Music Tl Schlrshp 87; James J Kerrigan Mem Schlrshp 87; K Trautvetter Me Schlrshp 87; U Of Hartford; Piano.

HILL, SANDRA; Chatham Twp HS; Chatham Twp, NJ; (3); Church Yt Grp; Key Clb; Pep Clb; Yrbk Stf; Bsktbl; Fld Hcky; Hon Roll; NHS.

HILL, SONYA; John F Kennedy HS; Willingboro, NJ; (3); Art Clb Camera Clb; Church Yth Grp; FCA; GAA; Radio Clb; Church Choir; Va Bsktbl; Hon Roll; Gnrl Cmmnctns.

HILL, TORRANCE; Mc Coristin Catholic HS; Trenton, NJ; (3); Boy Clb Am; Boy Scts; Var Chess Clb; Ftbl; Trk; Masonic Awd; Fin.

HILLEN, KRISTIN; Hackettstown HS; Hackettstown, NJ; (2); Germa Clb; Key Clb; Latin Clb; Hon Roll; Bus.

HILLIARD, DENISE; Belvidere HS; Belvidere, NJ; (3); 16/135; Camer Clb; Church Yth Grp; English Clb; Scholastic Bowl; Chorus; Color Guar Hon Roll; Bus Mngmnt.

HILLIARD, KARLA; Lincoln HS; Jersey City, NJ; (4); Chorus; Rep St Cncl; Bsktbl; Bowling; Sftbl; Twrlr; Bus Secy.

HILLMAN, CHRISTINE; Paul VI HS; Williamstown, NJ; (3); Rutgers Law.

HILLMAN, IRA; Wayne Hills HS; Wayne, NJ; (3); 2/320; Spanish Cl Pres VP Temple Yth Grp; Nwsp Bus Mgr; Trs Frsh Cls; Trs Soph Cls; Tr Jr Cls; Trs Sr Cls; High Hon Roll; NHS; Ntl Merit Ltr; Tmple Yth Gr Ldrshp Awd 87.

HILLMAN, JO ANN; James Caldwell HS; W Caldwell, NJ; (3); Girl Scts Key Clb; Spanish Clb; Bryant; Acctg.

HILLMAN, RICHARD; St Augustine Prep; Newfield, NJ; (3); 17/5 Computer Clb; Var Crs Cntry; JV Golf; Hon Roll; Prfct Atten Awd; IL Ins Tech; Rbtcs.

HILLS, BETTINA; Vineland H S North; Vineland, NJ; (1); Church Yt Grp; DECA; Chorus; Church Choir; Prfct Attend Awd 84-86; Hnr Ro Awd 82-87; Merit Awd 84 & 86-87; Howard Univ; Tchng.

HILTON, BRYANT; Middletown High Schl South; Middletown, NJ; (4 10/450; Boy Scts; Cmnty Wkr; Political Wkr; Nwsp Rptr; Var L Crs Cntr Var L Trk; High Hon Roll; NHS; Ntl Merit Ltr; Math Tm; Grdn S Dstngshd Schlr 86-87; Dns Smmr Schlr Rtgrs U 86; Semi-Fnlst Gvrnr Schl Pblc Issues 86; Intl Bus.

HILWAY, VIKKI; Passaic Valley Regional HS; Totowa, NJ; (4); 300/35 Cmnty Wkr; Computer Clb; French Clb; JA; Jr Civitan Int; Math Cl Political Wkr; SADD; School Play; Variety Show; Monmouth Coll; In Bnkng.

HIMMEL, LYLE; Matawan Regional HS; Aberdeen, NJ; (3); 8/302; Mat Tm; Temple Yth Grp; Chorus; Madrigals; School Musical; JV Socr; Ho Roll; Debate Tm; Speech Tm; Stu Cncl; All Shore Chorus 86; NJ All S Chorus 86; 3rd Pl Contntl Math Leag Contst 85; Pol Sci.

HIMMELSBACH, KRISTINE; Montville HS; Towaco, NJ; (3); FBLA Key Clb; Hon Roll; Bus.

HINCKEN, JOHN; Washington Twp HS; Turnersville, NJ; (3); Ski Cl Var Swmmng; 1st Pl NJ Indstrl Arts Assn 87; Arch.

HINES, KEVIN; Parsippany HS; Parsippany, NJ; (2); Church Yth Gr FBLA; German Clb; JV Bsbl; Bsktbl; High Hon Roll; Hon Roll; Engrng.

HINRICHSEN, DAVID; Ocean Twp HS; Oakhurst, NJ; (3); 112/34 French Clb; L Band; Church Choir; Concert Band; Jazz Band; Mrch Band; Orch; Pep Band; School Musical; Symp Band; SR Ldrshp Pgm 8 Engr.

HINRICHSEN, MARIA; Lakeland Regional HS; Ringwood, NJ; (4); 1 345; Drama Clb; Math Clb; Quiz Bowl; Trs Yrbk Stf; High Hon Roll; NH Ntl Merit Ltr; NEDT Awd; St Schlr; Val; USN Acad Smmr Smnr 8 Rutgers Schlr Awd 86; Stevens Inst/Tech; Chem Engrng.

HINTON, KERRY; Camden Catholic HS; Mantua, NJ; (3); 6/283; Aud Vis; Camera Clb; Chess Clb; Nwsp Sprt Ed; Yrbk Phtg; Pres Stu Cncl; Ho Roll; NHS; Ntl Merit SF; Spanish NHS; Engl Hon Soc; Soc Sci Ho Society; PRTME At Villanova U; U Of PA Georgetown; Comp Sci.

HINTZ, CHRISTOPHER P; Randolph HS; Randolph, NJ; (4); Art Cl Camera Clb; CAP; German Clb; Stage Crew; Ed Nwsp Phtg; Gov Hon P Awd; Gvrnrs Schl Of Arts Trenton St Coll 86; Pratt Natl Tlnt Srch 3rd Schlrshp 87; NJ Schl Arts 86; Cleveland Inst Of Art; Grph Dsg.

HIOTT, NATALIE; Holy Family Acad; Bayonne, NJ; (3); 1/122; V Church Yth Grp; Cmnty Wkr; Scholastic Bowl; School Musical; Rep Frs Cls; Rep Soph Cls; VP Stu Cncl; Im Vllybl; High Hon Roll; NHS; Rutge Schlr 87 Rutgers Deans Summer Schlr 87.

HIPKO, TRACY; Spotswood HS; Milltown, NJ; (4); 4/187; Church Yt Grp; FBLA; Intnl Clb; Math Clb; SADD; Church Choir; School Play; Yrb Bus Mgr; Stu Cncl; Var Socr; Seton Hall U Acad Schlrshp 87-9 Outstndng Stu Span 87; William Martin Mc Donald Memrl Awd 87; Seto Hall U; Bus.

HIPPE, DANIEL; Brick Twsp Memorial HS; Brick, NJ; (2); Im Bsbl; I Bsktbl; Hon Roll; PTA Hghst Stu Hnr Awd 85.

HIPPENSTIEL, MARK; Holy Spirit HS; Absecon, NJ; (4); 40/363; Ma Tm; Im Crs Cntry; Im Vllybl; JV Wrstlng; JC Awd; NHS; Stotesburg C Gld Mdl & 2nd Pl Scl Sct Fair 86.

HIRA, ARCHANA; West Orange HS; West Orange, NJ; (4); 10/37 French Clb; Quiz Bowl; Color Guard; Mrchg Band; Stage Crew; Lit Ma French Hon Soc; Hon Roll; Jr NHS; NHS; Rutgers U Schlr Awd Schlrsh W Orange Schlrshp Fund 87; Cratv Wrtng Awd Engl 86-87; Rutgers U.

HIRKO, KIM; Phillipsburg HS; Phillipsburg, NJ; (4); 39/315; Cmnt Wkr; Sec Hst Drama Clb; VP Ed Key Clb; Rep Model UN; Thesps; Band Concert Band; Jazz Band; Mrchg Band; Pep Band; Muhlenberg Coll; P Med,Music.

HIRSCH, KEITH; Morris Hills HS; Rockaway, NJ; (4); 43/240; Var Bsb Var Bsktbl; Var Ftbl; U Of MD; Jrnlsm.

HIRSCH, KORINNA; South Plainfield HS; S Plainfield, NJ; (4); 24/21 Art Clb; Drama Clb; Radio Clb; SADD; Rep Stu Cncl; Cheerleading; Hig Hon Roll; NHS; Spanish NHS; St Schlr; Acdmc Ftnss Awd, Stu Rcgnt Awd Frm SPEA & MCEA 87; Chrng Tiger Awd 86; Glassboro ST Col Comms.

HIRSHORN, DAVID; Jewish Educational Center; Livingston, NJ; (3 Chrmn Aud/Vis; Trs Temple Yth Grp; School Musical; Nwsp Stf; Yrb Stf; Hon Roll; Biomed Engnrng.

HIRST, LINDA; Holy Spirit HS; Somers Pt, NJ; (4); 16/363; Art Cl French Clb; Yrbk Stf; JV Crs Cntry; Im Ftbl; JV Trk; Hon Roll; Jr NHS NHS.

HISLOP, LESLIE; Emerson HS; Union City, NJ; (3); FBLA; Capt Dri Tm; Yrbk Stf; Rep Jr Cls; Var Trk; Hon Roll; Bus Adm.

HITCH, MARCIUS; Pleasantville HS; Sicklerville, NJ; (4); Art Clb; Ftb Gym; Trk; Wt Lftg.

HITCHINGS, KIM; Holy Spirit HS; Atlantic City, NJ; (4); 47/363; French Clb; Hon Roll; Vrsty Crew 83-86; Ed.

HITCHNER, GRETCHEN; Woodstown HS; Alloway, NJ; (4); English Clb; German Clb; SADD; Chorus; Stage Crew; Nwsp Stf; Yrbk Stf; Ruritn Schlrshp 87-88; Widener U; Fshn Merch.

HITCHNER, JAY; Woodstown HS; Alloway, NJ; (3); 20/210; Church Yth Grp; English Clb; 4-H; Key Clb; Ski Clb; Spanish Clb; Var L Bsbl; Im Bsktbl; Var L Ftbl; Im Wt Lftg; Hnr Roll 84-87; Amer Lgn Awd 84; 4-H Awd 84; John Hopkins; Med Sci.

HITCHNER, LE ANN; Holy Spirit HS; Ventnor, NJ; (1); Red Cross Aide; Var Cheerleading; Jr NHS; JR Miss Shore Mall 86; JR Miss South Jrsy 87; Law.

HITCHOCK, JAMES; Pequannock HS; Pequannock, NJ; (3); 71/210; Am Leg Boys St; JA; Latin Clb; Math Clb; Varsity Clb; Nwsp Stf; Yrbk Rptr; Rep Jr Cls; Rep Sr Cls; JV Bsbl; All Cnty Bsktbl 85-87; Bus.

HIZA, LARUA; West Windsor-Plainsboro HS; Princeton Junct, NJ; (3); Off Am Leg Aux Girls St; Political Wkr; VP SADD; Nwsp Ed-Chief; Yrbk Rptr; Rep Stu Cncl; Var Cheerleading; Var Fld Hcky; Hon Roll; NHS; People To People Amer Stu Ambassador & Amer Mgmt Operation Enterprise Schl Rep 87; Poltcl Jrnlsm.

HLAVACH, NICOLE; Howell HS; Howell, NJ; (4); 80/355; Spanish Clb; Yrbk Stf; Sec Stu Cncl; Var Capt Cheerleading; Var Gym; Var Capt Pom Pon; Trk; Wt Lftg; Hon Roll; Katharine Gibb Ldrshp Awd For Ftr Secys 86; Douglass Coll; Crprt Ftns.

HLUDZIK, SUSAN; Linden HS; Linden, NJ; (3); Church Yth Grp; FBLA; Socr; Swmmng; Trk; Hon Roll; NHS; Var Ltr Soccer,Swmng & Track 84-87; Rutgers; Bus Mngmnt.

HMIRAK, KRISTIN; Hackettstown HS; Great Meadows, NJ; (3); 13/160; Exploring; Key Clb; Var L Bsktbl; Im Powder Puff Ftbl; Var Capt Socr; Var L Sftbl; High Hon Roll; Hon Roll; NHS; Pre Med.

HO, GRACE; Manalapan HS; Coltsneck, NJ; (2); 8/424; Drama Clb; Science Clb; School Play; Stage Crew; High Hon Roll; Yng Schlrs Inst 86; Hihg Hnrs Grmn Awd 87; Elecrnc Engnrng.

HO, MICHAEL; Matawan Regional SR HS; Matawan, NJ; (3); 9/304; Debate Tm; Math Tm; Speech Tm; Yrbk Stf; VP Jr Cls; Off Stu Cncl; Var Bsktbl; Crs Cntry; Socr; Trk.

HOANG, ANN; Morristown HS; Morristown, NJ; (3); JA; Score Keeper; Hon Roll; Fareleigh Dickenson Coll; Bus.

HOANG, DE; Waldwick HS; Waldwick, NJ; (3); 19/135; Chess Clb; Cmnty Wkr; Math Tm; Socr; Hon Roll; Prfct Atten Awd; Chem Engrng.

HOANG, YENNGA; Manasquan HS; Spring Lake Hghts, NJ; (1); French Clb; Math Tm; Science Clb; High Hon Roll.

HOAR, LISA; West Milford Township HS; West Milford, NJ; (4); 137/427; Church Yth Grp; Cmnty Wkr; Pres DECA; School Musical; JV Sftbl; Hon Roll; Girl Scts; School Play; Scholar Foundatn Free Enterprise 86; U MD; Intr Dsgn.

HOAR, TRACY A; West Milford HS; West Milford, NJ; (3); 33/402; Am Leg Aux Girls St; Pres DECA; SADD; Yrbk Stf; JV Var Cheerleading; JV Gym; Im JV Sftbl; NHS; Spanish NHS; Spanish Clb; Schlrshp For Free Entrprs 87; CPA.

HOBBIE, EDWARD; Westfield HS; Westfield, NJ; (2); Chorus; Concert Band; Bsbl; Co-Capt JV Bsktbl; Cit Awd; High Hon Roll; JP Sousa Awd; Pres Schlr; Music Awd-Musical Achvt & Outstndng Svc 86.

HOBBY, GAIL; Bayonne HS; Bayonne, NJ; (3); Color Guard; Drill Tm; Drm & Bgl; Flag Corp; Var JV Ice Hcky; Mrchg Band; Twrlr; Ice Sktng Awd 87; U ME; Psych.

HOBLITZELL, MARY; Westfield SR HS; Westfield, NJ; (4); 1/483; Spanish Clb; Rep Sr Cls; Var L Fld Hcky; NHS; Ntl Merit Ltr; Sal; Spanish NHS; St Schlr; Science Clb; Service Clb; Pres Acad Fit Awd 87; Mel Solbel Mcrscps Ltd Bio Awd 87; Engl, Sci Awd; Duke U; Bio.

HOBSON, KAREN; Manshester Twp HS; Whiting, NJ; (3); 4-H; French Clb; Science Clb; Var L Fld Hcky; 4-H Awd.

HOBSON, RENEE P; North Plainfield HS; N Plainfield, NJ; (4); 30/185; Art Clb; 4-H; French Clb; Girl Scts; Hosp Aide; SADD; Flag Corp; Capt Bsktbl; Cheerleading; Pom Pon; NJ Inst Of Tech; Arch.

HOCHMAN, IVY; Paramus HS; Paramus, NJ; (3); Debate Tm; FBLA; Math Clb; Math Tm; Ski Clb; School Play; Nwsp Stf; Yrbk Stf; Mgr(s); Trk; Mgr In Ftbl 85-86; Marine Bio Pres 86-87.

HOCHSTADTER, EDWARD; Hudson Catholic HS; Hoboken, NJ; (3); 40/200; Ice Hcky; High Hon Roll; Acctng.

HODDE, SHARON; Morris Hills HS; Dover, NJ; (2); 20/242; FBLA; Ski Clb; Stat Bsktbl; JV Fld Hcky; Hon Roll; Prfct Atten Awd; 4th Pl Rgnl FBLA Typng Compttn 87; 2nd Pl ST FBLA Typng Compttn 87; Psych.

HODEK, JEANETTE E; Belvidere HS; Great Meadows, NJ; (4); Chess Clb; French Clb; Hosp Aide; Flag Corp; Mrchg Band; Yrbk Stf; Hon Roll; Lena Mc Cain Schlrshp 87; Cnty Coll Morris; Jrnlsm.

HODGE, JUVONDA; Manalapan HS; Manalapan, NJ; (3); 56/429; Church Yth Grp; Girl Scts; JA; SADD; Flag Corp; Jazz Band; Mrchg Band; JV Var Bsktbl; JV Var Trk; Masonic Awd; Girl Scout Slvr Ldrshp Awd 86; 3rd Pl Prj Sci & Engrng Prg 85; Schlrshp Washington & Lee U 87; Med.

HODGE, MEGHAN; Morris Knolls HS; Denville, NJ; (2); Church Yth Grp; Yrbk Stf; JV Fld Hcky; Psychlgy.

HODGE, NICOLE; Union HS; Union, NJ; (2); Drama Clb; Math Clb; Ski Clb; School Play; Trs Soph Cls; Capt Fld Hcky; Mgr(s); Score Keeper; Hon Roll; Jr NHS; Psych.

HODGES, LAURIE; Morristown HS; Morristown, NJ; (2); Hosp Aide; Speech Tm; Teachers Aide; Chorus; Drill Tm; Mrchg Band; Nwsp Stf; Yrbk Stf; Lcrss; Hon Roll.

HODI, LISA; E Brunswick Vo-Tech HS; Spotswood, NJ; (3); Church Yth Grp; Drama Clb; VICA; School Play; Stage Crew; Rep Frsh Cls; Rep Soph Cls; VP Jr Cls; Rep Stu Cncl; Hon Roll; MAKEUP Artst.

HODSON, DARRYL; Arthur P Schalick HS; Elmer, NJ; (3); 4/120; Am Leg Boys St; Sec Boy Scts; Cmnty Wkr; Pres SADD; Var Bsktbl; Var Tennis; High Hon Roll; NHS; NJ Math Leag Awd 86-87; Salem Cnty Dbls Tm Tnns 87; Top 5 Stu Awd 86 & 87; Arthur P Schalick; Engrng.

HOEHLER, DAVID C; S Plainfield HS; S Plainfield, NJ; (4); 17/209; Computer Clb; Spanish Clb; Var Bsbl; Bowling; High Hon Roll; Pres Schlr; Spanish NHS; Joan Koziel Memrl Schlrshp 87; Rutgers U; Engrng.

HOELBINGER, JENNIFER; Gateway Regional HS; Woodbury Hts, NJ; (2); Art Clb; Key Clb; Latin Clb; SADD; Varsity Clb; Trs Frsh Cls; Trs Soph Cls; Stu Cncl; JV Bsktbl; Var Fld Hcky.

HOERSCH, TRACY L; Hasbrouck Hts HS; Hasbrouck Heights, NJ; (3); Trs Art Clb; Trs Camera Clb; DECA; Hosp Aide; Pep Clb; Spanish Clb; Capt Color Guard; Stage Crew; Yrbk Stf; JV Cheerleading; ST Fin Miss Amer Coed Pag 86; Berkeley Schl; Fash Merch.

HOFF, CATHY; Belvidere HS; Belvidere, NJ; (4); 5/122; Church Yth Grp; 4-H; French Clb; Varsity Clb; JV Var Bsktbl; JV Var Fld Hcky; JV Var Sftbl; 4-H Awd; Hon Roll; NHS; Grls St Alt 86; Top 10-HOBY Org 84; Cngrssnl Yth Ldrshp Cncl 86; Psych.

HOFFER, JANE; St John Vianney HS; Keyport, NJ; (2); 8/200; Intnl Clb; SADD; Stage Crew; Sftbl; High Hon Roll; Hon Roll; NHS; Bus Mrt Awd; Rutgers; Acctng.

HOFFMAN, BRIAN; St Rose HS; Neptune City, NJ; (3); Ski Clb; JV Var Socr; High Hon Roll; Hon Roll; Prfct Atten Awd.

HOFFMAN, DIANE; Millville SR HS; Dorchester, NJ; (3); 39/524; Hon Roll.

HOFFMAN, GREGG; Linden HS; Linden, NJ; (3); Ski Clb; Band; Concert Band; Jazz Band; Mrchg Band; School Musical; Golf; Hon Roll; NHS; Mac Donalds Mrchng Bnd 87.

HOFFMAN III, HARRY; Paulsboro HS; Paulsboro, NJ; (2); Church Yth Grp; SADD; Chorus; JV Bsktbl; Ftbl; Var Trk; Hon Roll; Prfct Atten Awd; Sprts Jrnlsm.

HOFFMAN, ROBIN; Voorhees HS; Califon, NJ; (4); 97/294; Church Yth Grp; Pres 4-H; FBLA; Pres FFA; Girl Scts; Color Guard; Hst Frsh Cls; Hst Soph Cls; Hst Jr Cls; 4-H Awd; Mst Imprvd Bus Ed 87; Katharin Gibbs Schl; Sec.

HOFFMAN, STEPHANIE; Millville SR HS; Millville, NJ; (3); GAA; Nwsp Rptr; Nwsp Stf; Var Fld Hcky; Var Trk; Hon Roll; Prfct Atten Awd; Gftd & Tlntd Prgm; Psych.

HOFFMAN, VANESSA; Freehold Township HS; Freehold, NJ; (3); 65/385; Art Clb; French Clb; Temple Yth Grp; Yrbk Stf; Fine Art.

HOFFMASTER, MIKE; Point Pleasant Borg HS; Point Pleasant, NJ; (4); 20/250; Key Clb; VP Frsh Cls; Var Crs Cntry; Hon Roll; Capt Wrstlng; NHS; VP Soph Cls; Sec Stu Cncl; Cook Coll Of Rutger U.

HOFMANN, ELIZABETH; Baptist HS; Tabernacle, NJ; (3); Church Yth Grp; Drama Clb; Sec Soph Cls; VP Jr Cls; Stat Bsktbl; Var Fld Hcky; Hon Roll; NHS; Ntl Merit Ltr; Cedarville Coll; Nrsng.

HOFMANN, LINDA; Bordentown Regional HS; Bordentown, NJ; (2); #1 In Class; Math Clb; Math Tm; Chorus; Rep Stu Cncl; JV Bsktbl; JV Fld Hcky; JV Sftbl; L Trk; Hon Roll.

HOGAN, JOHN; Florence Twp Mem HS; Florence, NJ; (3); Am Leg Boys St; FTA; Varsity Clb; Nwsp Stf; Trs Frsh Cls; Trs Soph Cls; Trs Jr Cls; Trs Sr Cls; Trs Sr Cls; Var Capt Bsktbl; Brlngtn Cnty Ftbl All Strs, 2nd Tm 87; Military Schl; Crmnl Jstc.

HOGAN, MARY; Parsppany HS; Parsippany, NJ; (3); VP FBLA; Lit Mag; VP NHS; Hosp Aide; Spanish Clb; Rep Stu Cncl; High Hon Roll; Prfct Atten Awd; Pres Classrm For Yng Amer 87; NJ FBLA St Prlmntrn & Pres Natl Parli Tm 87-88; Rcpnts Of FBLA-YFU 87; Pltcl Sci.

HOGAN, PATRICIA; St Aloysius HS; Jersey City, NJ; (3); Exploring; SADD; Chorus; School Play; Nwsp Rptr; Rep Soph Cls; Bowling; Hon Roll; J B Bealey Awd For Outstndng Chrstn Srv 86; Radio & Nwspr.

HOGG, ERICA; Vineland HS; Vineland, NJ; (3); Cmnty Wkr; SADD; Teachers Aide; Hon Roll; Stockton ST Coll; Phys Thrpst.

HOGGARD, SUZETTE; John F Kennedy HS; Willingboro, NJ; (3); Office Aide; Teachers Aide; Fld Hcky; Med Law.

HOHOLICK, ERICA; Bridgewater-Raritan HS West; Bridgewater, NJ; (4); Am Leg Aux Girls St; Cmnty Wkr; French Clb; Ski Clb; SADD; Yrbk Ed-Chief; Yrbk Stf; VP Jr Cls; VP Sr Cls; Stu Cncl; PA ST U; Lbrl Arts.

HOJNACKI, TODD; Bernards HS; Bernardsville, NJ; (3); 7/170; Cmnty Wkr; Spanish Clb; Band; Jazz Band; Mrchg Band; Orch; School Musical; Symp Band; JV Bsktbl; Var Golf; Stu Soloist In Symphnc & Jazz Bnd 85-86; Hstry.

HOLAHAN, KAREN; John F Kennedy HS; Willingboro, NJ; (3); 5/202; Exploring; Office Aide; Capt Flag Corp; Yrbk Stf; Lcrss; Mgr(s); Cit Awd; Pres NHS; Med.

HOLBROOK, NINA; Dwight Morow HS; Englewood, NJ; (4); 1/316; Hst FBLA; Stage Crew; Nwsp Rptr; Mgr(s); Score Keeper; Sftbl; Vllybl; High Hon Roll; Psychlgy.

HOLCOMB, JACQUELINE; Cloucester Catholic HS; Gloucester, NJ; (3); Art Clb; Hosp Aide; Office Aide; Red Cross Aide; Teachers Aide; JV Bowling; Stat Fld Hcky; JV Var Score Keeper; Hon Roll; Prfct Atten Awd; Phys Achvt Awd/Marine Phys Fitness 84-85; Cert In CPR 86-87; Self-Defense-Tang Soo Karate Acad 86-87; Rutgers In Camden; Specl Ed.

HOLDEN, MARC; Morristown HS; Morristown, NJ; (3); 17/422; Church Yth Grp; Exploring; Hosp Aide; Key Clb; Latin Clb; Concert Band; Mrchg Band; Swmmng; High Hon Roll; NHS; Cornell U; Med.

HOLEMON, ELISSA; Eastern Regional HS; West Berlin, NJ; (4); 25/300; Concert Band; Mrchg Band; Jr NHS; NHS; Pres Schlr; Bnkng.

HOLLAND, JANICE; Collingswood HS; Collingswood, NJ; (2); Church Yth Grp; Office Aide; Church Choir; Yrbk Stf; High Hon Roll; NHS; Presdntl Acadc Ftns Awd 86; Chester A Olinger Awd Excllnc Math 86; Bus Adm.

HOLLAND, JENNIFER; Immaculata HS; Hampton, NJ; (3); Spanish Clb; Teachers Aide; Sec Sr Cls; JV Bsktbl; Score Keeper; Stat Sftbl; Spanish NHS; Band; Concert Band; Mrchg Band; Excllnc Alg I 85; Excllnc Engl 87; Boston Coll; Bus.

HOLLAND, TRACY; University HS; Newark, NJ; (2); Church Yth Grp; Computer Clb; Exploring; JA; Red Cross Aide; Chorus; Church Choir; Key Clb; School Musical; Cert Accmplshmt Prjct Bus 86; Zoolgst.

HOLLDAND, SHANNON; Paul VI Regional HS; Cedar Grove, NJ; (3); Key Clb; Teachers Aide; Stage Crew; Rep Stu Cncl; Bsktbl; Cheerleading; Score Keeper; Trk; Hon Roll.

HOLLENBECK JR, ROBERT C; Middletown HS South; Red Bank, NJ; (2); Drama Clb; Quiz Bowl; Scholastic Bowl; School Musical; School Play; Variety Show; Nwsp Rptr; Nwsp Stf; Stu Cncl; Hon Roll; Cornell U; Engrng.

HOLLERON, ANDREW; South Plainfield HS; S Plainfield, NJ; (4); Drama Clb; Concert Band; Drm Mjr(t); Orch; Spanish Clb; SADD; Band; Mrchg Band; Pep Band; School Musical; Jerseyman Clb 82-87; Announcers Clb 85-87; Nrtheastrn Univ; Jnlsm.

HOLLICK, CHRISTINE; Pequannock Township HS; Pompton Plains, NJ; (3); 5/217; Drama Clb; Latin Clb; Ski Clb; Band; Chorus; School Play; Fld Hcky; Sftbl; High Hon Roll; NHS; Olympcs Mind 3rd Pl ST Wnnr 87.

HOLLIDAY, ERIC; Hamilton High Schl West; Trenton, NJ; (4); Trk; Track Team Cert Of Merit 86-87; Stu Of Mnth 86-87; Meritorious Stu Awd 86-87; Stu Of Yr Rotary Club 87; Law Enforcement.

HOLLIDAY, KATHY; Kittatinny Regional HS; Newton, NJ; (3); 22/226; Spanish Clb; Color Guard; Flag Corp; Swmmng; Hon Roll; NHS; VA Poly Tech Inst; Bus Adm.

HOLLIDAY, MICHAEL M; Westfield HS; Westfield, NJ; (4); 20/484; German Clb; Model UN; Var L Ftbl; Var L Trk; Cit Awd; DAR Awd; High Hon Roll; NHS; Ntl Merit SF; St Schlr; Arch.

HOLLISTER, BRIDGET; Vineland HS; Vineland, NJ; (4); 40/585; Cmnty Wkr; Debate Tm; English Clb; Key Clb; Latin Clb; Political Wkr; Band; Flag Corp; Trs Mrchg Band; Stu Cncl; Svc Citation-Mrchng Band 86; Svc Citation-Natl Hon Soc 87; La Salle; Sociology.

HOLLOWAY, GARY; Baptist HS; Maple Shade, NJ; (4); 9/45; Church Yth Grp; Drama Clb; French Clb; Pep Clb; Pres Chorus; Church Choir; School Play; Stu Cncl; Bsktbl; Hon Roll; Old Stonewall Awd 86; Mark Of Exclnc For Actng 86; Hnr Soc Indctn 85; Bob Jones U; Pastor.

HOLLOWAY, PURNELL; University HS; Newark, NJ; (2); Debate Tm; Drama Clb; Library Aide; Spanish Clb; Chorus; Church Choir; School Play; Stage Crew; Swing Chorus; Off Soph Cls; Law.

HOLLOWAY JR, RODRICK M; Roselle Catholic HS; Roselle, NJ; (4); Computer Clb; Drama Clb; French Clb; Lit Mag; French Hon Soc; High Hon Roll; Hon Roll; Mensa Soc & Intl Soc 86-87; Ntl Assoc Ltr Carries Outstndng Achvt 87; Dallas U Natl Comptv Schlrshp 86; Dallas U; Pre Med.

HOLLOWS, GREGORY; Haddon Township HS; Collingswood, NJ; (1); Church Yth Grp; JV Bsbl; JV L Crs Cntry; JV L Trk; High Hon Roll; Hon Roll; Mtrlgy.

HOLM, DAVID; Montgomery HS; Raleigh, NC; (3); Am Leg Boys St; Boy Scts; Pres Church Yth Grp; Pres Rep Band; Trs Frsh Cls; Trs Soph Cls; Trs Jr Cls; VP Sr Cls; JV Bsktbl; Var L Bsktbl; Bus.

HOLMBERG, ERIC; Waldwick HS; Waldwick, NJ; (3); Am Leg Boys St; Boy Scts; Computer Clb; Ski Clb; Socr; Wrstlng; Karate 1st Deg Blck Blt; Span Frnsc Trnmnt At Rider Coll; Tchng Elem Schl Span; Intl Business.

HOLMES, CAROLYN; Paul VI HS; Runnemede, NJ; (3); French Clb; Color Guard; Yrbk Stf; Var L Bsktbl; Mgr(s); Pom Pon; Var L Trk; Psych.

HOLMES III, JAMES; Gloucester Catholic HS; Wenonah, NJ; (3); 35/175; Quiz Bowl; VP Soph Cls; Rep Stu Cncl; Im Bsktbl; Var Ftbl; Hon Roll; Bus.

HOLMES, JEFFREY B; Lenape Regional HS; Mt Laurel, NJ; (4); 18/420; Am Leg Boys St; Boy Scts; Exploring; Latin Clb; Varsity Clb; Var JV Socr; Hon Roll; NHS; St Schlr; JR Rotarian 86-87; Bucknell U; Elec Engr.

HOLMES, LA COYYA JATON; Eastern Christian HS; Irvington, NJ; (3); 5/85; Church Yth Grp; Hosp Aide; Pep Clb; Chorus; Church Choir; Yrbk Stf; Stu Cncl; High Hon Roll; Hon Roll; NHS; Hnr Guard 87; 2nd VP NANBPW Clbs Inc 86-87; Rutgers U; Psych.

HOLMES, PATRICIA; Lenape Valley Regional HS; Netcong, NJ; (4); 5/236; Key Clb; Concert Band; Mrchg Band; Yrbk Stf; High Hon Roll; NHS; Pres Schlr; Spanish NHS; Orch; New Jersey Gvrnrs Tchng Schlr 87; Lenape Schlr 85-87; Montclair ST Coll; Tchr.

HOLMES, ROBIN; Collingswood HS; Collingswood, NJ; (2); French Clb; School Musical; School Play; Off Stu Cncl; Var Cheerleading; Gym; High Hon Roll; Jr NHS; NHS; NEDT Awd; Pres Acad Ftns Awd 86; Schlstc Achvt Awd; Med.

HOLMES, STACY; Lakewood HS; Lakewood, NJ; (3); Key Clb; Office Aide; Pres Jr Cls; VP Sr Cls; Cheerleading; Pre Law.

HOLMES, SUE; Delsea Regional HS; Newfield, NJ; (4); 2/213; Church Yth Grp; Sec Computer Clb; Drama Clb; Key Clb; School Musical; School Play; High Hon Roll; NHS; Sal; FTA; PSAT Commendtn; Exch Club Stu Of Month; Rutgers U; Visual Arts.

HOLMES, TONYA; Lincoln HS; Jersey City, NJ; (4); Comp.

HOLNESS, WAYNE; Essex Catholic Bays HS; East Orange, NJ; (4); 27/158; Art Clb; Pres Stu Cncl; Bsbl; Hon Roll; Penn ST U Black Achvt Awd 87; Drew Devney Comp Sci 87; Most Dedicated Plyr Vrsty Fencing 86-87; Air Force Acad; Aerosp Engr.

HOLOBOWSKI, WILLIAM F; Harold G Hoffman HS; South Amboy, NJ; (4); 2/70; Pres Chess Clb; Math Tm; SADD; Nwsp Rptr; Rep Frsh Cls; VP Soph Cls; Pres Jr Cls; Pres Sr Cls; Stu Cncl; JV Bsktbl; Spnsh II Awd 84-85; Compu Sci Awd 85-86; Attndd Washington Wrkshps 86; Rutgers; Cmmnctns.

HOLOWACHUK, STACIE; Wayne Hills HS; Wayne, NJ; (4); 32/287; French Clb; FBLA; Var Capt Bsktbl; Var Capt Socr; JV Sftbl; Var Trk; Hon Roll; NHS; Amer Lgn Awd For Outstndng Grl In Cls & Athlete Awd For Cls 87; Athlete Of Wk 86; U Of RI; Bus.

HOLOWIENKA, LINDA; Bayonne HS; Bayonne, NJ; (3); Church Choir; Hon Roll; St Peters Coll; Bus Mgnt.

HOLSTEIN, NEIL; Lakewood Prep; Middletown, NJ; (3); Latin Clb; Band; Concert Band; Jazz Band; Nwsp Rptr; Var Bsktbl; Var Socr; Var Tennis; Hon Roll; Ntl Ltn Exam Summa Cum Laude 85; Ntl Ltn Exam Cum Laude 86; Math.

HOLT, DIANE; Middletown HS; Lincroft, NJ; (3); Cmnty Wkr; 4-H; French Clb; Chorus; L Flag Corp; Mgr Stage Crew; Yrbk Stf; French Hon Soc; High Hon Roll; Hon Roll; Guidance Counselor.

HOLUB, DAVID C; Monmouth Regional HS; Eatontown, NJ; (4); 3/239; Mu Alpha Theta; Ski Clb; VP Trs Spanish Clb; Temple Yth Grp; Yrbk Bus Mgr; Tennis; High Hon Roll; Pres NHS; Ntl Merit SF; Chess Clb; Bronze Congressnl Awd; Duke U; Pre-Med.

HOLUB, FREDERICK N; Ocean Township HS; Wayside, NJ; (3); Church Yth Grp; Computer Clb; JCL; Latin Clb; Spanish Clb; Band; Concert Band; Mrchg Band; Jazz Band; Orch; All-Cnty Band & Orch, Matheletes-Math Tm 85; SR Ldrshp Pgm 87-88; Orthopdc Surgn.

HOLUB, LAURA; Middlesex HS; Middlesex, NJ; (3); 88/250; Pres Girl Scts; Ski Clb; Capt Color Guard; Concert Band; School Musical; Rep Jr Cls; Var Crs Cntry; Grl Sct Slvr & Gld Ldrshp Awds 87; Erly Ed.

HOLUBIAK, MYRON; Columbia HS; S Orange, NJ; (3); Computer Clb; Bsktbl; Lafayette; Physcs.

HOLVICK, MICHAEL; Oakcrest HS; Mays Landing, NJ; (4); 21/209; FFA; SADD; Yrbk Stf; Tennis; Vllybl; NHS; French Clb; JA; High Hon Roll; Hon Roll; Bio.

HOLZLI, TIM; De Paul Diocesan HS; Wayne, NJ; (3); 19/150; Aud/Vis; Math Tm; Quiz Bowl; Science Clb; Nwsp Phtg; Rep Jr Cls; Capt Bsbl; Im Bsktbl; Im Ftbl; Im Golf; Hnr Rl 4 Yrs; Scct Strtr 3 Yrs, Capt 2 Yrs; Bus.

HOM, ELAINE; John P Stevens HS; Edison, NJ; (3); 62/450; Key Clb; Library Aide; Science Clb; Service Clb; Powder Puff Ftbl; Hon Roll; NHS; Spanish NHS; Rutgers Univ; Med.

HOM, HENRY; Union Catholic Regional HS; Rahway, NJ; (3); 9/330; Art Clb; Library Aide; Science Clb; Service Clb; High Hon Roll; Hon Roll; Spanish NHS; Arch.

HOMAN, KAREN; Rancocas Valley Regional HS; Mt Holly, NJ; (2); 4/295; Yrbk Stf; Rep Soph Cls; JV L Gym; Var L Sftbl; High Hon Roll; NHS.

HOMCY, PAUL; Passaic Valley HS; W Paterson, NJ; (2); Rep Stu Cncl; JV Bsbl; Var L Bsktbl; JV Ftbl; Cit Awd; High Hon Roll; Hon Roll; Hnr Soc 87.

HOMER, DAWN; Nutley HS; Nutley, NJ; (3); Camera Clb; Key Clb; Red Cross Aide; Spanish Clb; Mrchg Band; Nwsp Rptr; Nwsp Stf; Lit Mag; Stu Cncl; Twrlr; Brdcst Cmmnctns.

HONDOWICZ, DAVID; John P Stevens HS; Edison, NJ; (4); 172/476; Debate Tm; Model UN; Band; Coach Actv; Cit Awd; Secy-Genl YMCA Hersey Middle Atlantic Model United Nations 86; Excllnc Hist 87; U Of DE; Polit Sci.

HONEYMAR JR, MICHAEL G; Union Catholic Regional HS; Elizabeth, NJ; (3); 12/350; Science Clb; Service Clb; High Hon Roll; Hon Roll; Spanish NHS.

HONG, JIMMY; Secaucus HS; Secaucus, NJ; (3); Math Clb; Mu Alpha Theta; Varsity Clb; Concert Band; Jazz Band; Mrchg Band; Rep Frsh Cls; Rep Soph Cls; Var Ftbl; Var Wt Lftg.

HONIG, DEIDRE; Cinnaminson HS; Cinna, NJ; (4); Aud/Vis; Church Yth Grp; Dance Clb; Color Guard; Schlstc Art Awd 86; Sound Engrng.

HONIGSBERG, MARTINE; Hackettstown HS; Great Meadows, NJ; (4); 25/238; Key Clb; Temple Yth Grp; Stat Socr; High Hon Roll; Hon Roll; NHS; PWP Schlrshp 87; Rutgers Coll; Bus.

HONIS, MONICA; Paramus Catholic Girls HS; Teaneck, NJ; (3); Church Yth Grp; Drama Clb; Hosp Aide; Spanish Clb; Ed Lit Mag; Mgr(s); Score Keeper; Hon Roll; Prfct Atten Awd; Atty.

HONKO, CURT ANDREW; Linden HS; Linden, NJ; (3); Chorus; Concert Band; Mrchg Band; School Play; JV L Bsbl; Im Bsktbl; JV Var Ftbl; Var L Swmmng; Hon Roll; NHS; Law.

HONORIO, MARIA; Cherry Hill HS West; Cherry Hill, NJ; (3); French Clb; Spanish Clb; SADD; Yrbk Stf; Var L Sftbl; Var L Tennis; Hon Roll; Unsung Hero Awd-Sftbl 85; MVP-TEN Tm 86.

HOOGERHEYDE, DAVID; Manchester Regional HS; N Haledon, NJ; (3); Church Yth Grp; Science Clb; Band; Concert Band; Jazz Band; Mrchg Band; Variety Show; Hon Roll; Vet.

HOOK, JERRY; Buena Regional HS; Buena Acers, NJ; (2); JV Trk; Hon Roll; Sci.

HOOKER, THOMAS F; Steinert HS; Hamilton, NJ; (3); Am Leg Boys St; Varsity Clb; Nwsp Ed-Chief; Crs Cntry; Trk; Hon Roll; NHS; NJ Cncl Soc Stud Outstndg Soc Stud Stu Awd 87; Phys Sci.

HOOKS, KIESHA; Marylawn Of The Oranges HS; E Orange, NJ; (4); Art Clb; Sec Camera Clb; Service Clb; Chorus; School Musical; School Play; Yrbk Stf; L Sftbl; French Hon Soc; NEDT Awd; Deans Summer Schl Merit Schlrshp 86; James Dickson Carr 4 Yr Schlrshp 87; Rutgers U; Bio.

HOOKS, KIMBERLY ANN; Monroe Twp HS; Spotswood, NJ; (4); Am Leg Aux Girls St; Key Clb; Ski Clb; SADD; VP Jr Cls; VP Sr Cls; Sec Stu Cncl; JV Var Cheerleading; Hon Roll; NHS; Stu Brd Of Educ 86-88; NJ Schlr Athlt Awd 85; USCA Natl 1st Pl Wnnr Chrldng 86; U Of NC Chapel Hill.

HOOSHMAND, SARAH; Mt St Dominic HS; N Caldwell, NJ; (3); Latin Clb; Library Aide; Yrbk Bus Mgr; High Hon Roll; NHS; Piano Awds Music Assn 81-84; Cert Awd Libry Ad 87; Cert Excllnc Frnch 87; Bus.

HOOVER, CHRISTY; Deptford HS; Wenonah, NJ; (1); Church Yth Grp; GAA; Office Aide; Spanish Clb; Chorus; Career Clb 86-87; Prfrmng Arts.

HOOVER, JEFFREY STEVEN; Schalick HS; Elmer, NJ; (3); Boy Scts; Bsbl; Ftbl.

HOOVER, LYNN CHRISTINE; South River HS; South River, NJ; (4); 4/130; Off Church Yth Grp; German Clb; Jazz Band; Mrchg Band; Pep Band; Pres Symp Band; Yrbk Stf; Stu Cncl; Pres NHS; Voice Dem Awd; MCASSPS Outstndng Stu Awd 87; SREA & MECA Stu Recogtn Awd 87; Outstndng Svc Marching Band 86; Rutguers U; Law.

HOPE, PATRICIA; Pennsville Memorial HS; Pennsville, NJ; (3); FBLA; Hosp Aide; Office Aide; Spanish Clb; SADD; Chorus; School Musical; Pom Pon; JV Sftbl; Im Vllybl; Accntng.

HOPECK, JOHN; Middlesex HS; Middlesex, NJ; (3); Ski Clb; Varsity Clb; Bsbl; Bsktbl; Ftbl; Hon Roll.

HOPF, NICOLE; Morris Catholic HS; Towaco, NJ; (3); Boy Scts; Church Yth Grp; Cmnty Wkr; Girl Scts; Red Cross Aide; JV Socr; Im Vllybl; Elem Educ.

HOPKINS, MICHAEL; Gloucester City JR SR HS; Gloucester, NJ; (4); 49/146; Cmnty Wkr; Computer Clb; Dance Clb; Model UN; Chorus; School Musical; School Play; Nwsp Stf; Yrbk Stf; Lit Mag; Cmmnty Svc Awd Rotary Clb 87; Camden Cnty Coll; Acctng.

HOPLER, TRACY; Morris Knolls HS; Rockaway, NJ; (4); 46/359; Church Yth Grp; Library Aide; Speech Tm; Nwsp Rptr; Nwsp Stf; High Hon Roll; Hon Roll; Pres Awd Outstndng Acdmc Achvt 87; Fairleigh Dickenson U; PHD.

HOPP, JULIE; Buena Regional HS; Newfield, NJ; (3); 29/250; Varsity Clb; Var Capt Bsktbl; Var Sftbl; Hon Roll; Jr NHS; Marketing.

HOPPE, BRENDA GAYLE; Delsea Regional HS; Monroeville, NJ; (3); Am Leg Aux Girls St; Hosp Aide; JCL; Yrbk Rptr; Var Badmtn; Gov Hon Prg Awd; NCTE Awd; Opt Clb Awd; Phys Thrpy.

HOPPER, MARY ELLEN; Queen Of Peace HS; Lyndhurst, NJ; (3); 7/279; French Clb; Ski Clb; Stage Crew; Var L Sftbl; Im Vllybl; High Hon Roll; Hon Roll; Phrmcy.

HOPSON, ANGELA L; Lenape HS; Mt Laurel, NJ; (4); 58/434; Exploring; FNA; Hosp Aide; Varsity Clb; Variety Show; Frsh Cls; Cheerleading; Var Trk; NHS; Spanish NHS; Minority Merit Schlrshp 87; Trenton ST Coll; Bio.

HOR, TRINA; Matawan Regional HS; Matawan, NJ; (3); Pres SADD; Yrbk Bus Mgr; Lit Mag; Gov Hon Prg Awd; NHS; Church Yth Grp; Nwsp Stf; Yrbk Stf; Stu Cncl; Hon Roll; Cmmrcl Art.

HORAN, LEANNE S; West Milford Twp HS; West Milford, NJ; (3); VP Church Yth Grp; DECA; Girl Scts; Office Aide; Spanish Clb; Concert Band; JV Bsktbl; JV Sftbl; Hon Roll; Spanish NHS; Fshn Mrktng Merch.

HORGAN, ELIZABETH; Notre Dame HS; Kendall Park, NJ; (3); Church Yth Grp; Cmnty Wkr; Color Guard; Mrchg Band; Stat Ftbl; JV Trk; Vrsty Ltr Atltc Trnr 85-87; Physcl Thrpy.

HORIN, BRIAN; Millville SR HS; Millville, NJ; (3); French Clb; Var Bsbl; Naval Acad; Engr.

HORN, DAN; Washington Township HS; Sewell, NJ; (3); 14/550; Hon Roll; NHS; Mech Engr.

HORNADAY, DAVID; South Brunswick HS; Monmouth Junction, NJ; (4); 10/267; FCA; Var Capt Bsbl; Var Bsktbl; High Hon Roll; NHS; NJ Grdn St Schlr 87; Outstndng Athlt 87; Schl Athlt 87; Rutgers U; Bus.

HORNBERGER, MARK; Holy Cross; Cinnaminson, NJ; (3); Am Leg Boys St; Boy Scts; Church Yth Grp; Exploring; German Clb; Bsbl; Bsktbl; Bowling; Tennis; Trk; Hotel Mgmt.

HORNER, MATT; Burlington Township HS; Beverly, NJ; (3); Am Leg Boys St; Aud/Vis; Cmnty Wkr; French Clb; Key Clb; Ski Clb; Hst Varsity Clb; Pres Frsh Cls; Pres Soph Cls; Pres Jr Cls; HOBY Ldrshp Conf; Excllnc In Educ Cntst Essay Wnnr; Bus Mgmt.

HORNER, REBECCA G; Pinelands Regional HS; Tuckerton, NJ; (4); 2/200; Math Tm; Teachers Aide; Yrbk Stf; JV Mgr Bsktbl; High Hon Roll; NHS; Ntl Merit SF; Pres Spanish NHS; St Schlr; Senator Bill Bradleys Yth Ctzn Awd 86; NJ Red Of Wmns Clbs Grls Ctznshp 86; Scrsis Soc 84-86; Mars Hill Coll; Math Tchr.

HORNER, SCOTT; Washington Township HS; Turnersville, NJ; (3); 51/542; German Clb; Band; Concert Band; Jazz Band; Mrchg Band; Germn Hnr Soc 84-87; Ntl Essy Cont-US Army Rsrv 86; Band Awds 84-87; OH ST U; Aerosp Engrng.

HORNER, SHERIE; Burlington City HS; Edgewater Pk, NJ; (4); 21/191; FNA; Var Mgr(s); Hon Roll; Pres Schlr; Friendly Inst Of City Of Burlington Schlrshp 87; Helene Field Schl Of Nrsg; Nrsg.

HORNIK JR, BRUCE; Notre Dame HS; Freehold, NJ; (2); 66/420; Church Yth Grp; Computer Clb; Hosp Aide; School Musical; School Play; Variety Show; Rep Frsh Cls; Rep Soph Cls; Rep Stu Cncl; JV Var Ftbl; Air Force Acad.

HOROWITZ, DEBORAH; Bloomfield HS; Bloomfield, NJ; (3); 1/460; Pres Key Clb; Math Tm; Scholastic Bowl; Science Clb; Temple Yth Grp; Concert Band; Jazz Band; Mrchg Band; St Schlr; Hugh O Brien Yth Fndtn ST Smnr 86.

HORTON, HEATHER; North Hunterdon Regional HS; Hampton, NJ; (4); 69/337; Pep Clb; Ski Clb; Varsity Clb; Mrchg Band; Symp Band; Variety Show; Sec Stu Cncl; Crs Cntry; Trk; U Of CA At Davis; Pol Sci.

HORTON, SUSAN; Point Pleasant Beach HS; Pt Pleasant Bch, NJ; (4); 3/100; Rep French Clb; Key Clb; Chorus; Variety Show; Capt Powder Puff Ftbl; High Hon Roll; Hon Roll; NHS; Pres Schlr; G Harold Antrim Schlrshp 87; Rotary Schlrshp 87; Frnch Merit Awd 87; Bd Of Educ Brnz Awd Hst 87; Trenton ST Coll; Fin.

HORVATH, ANGELA; Franklin HS; Somerset, NJ; (4); 133/327; Varsity Clb; Bowling; Cit Awd; Booster Clb 85-86; Vrsty Awd 85-86; Middlesex Cnty ; Accntng.

HORVATH, GAIL; St Peters HS; New Brunswick, NJ; (4); French Clb; Math Tm; Ski Clb; Yrbk Rptr; Yrbk Stf; Sec Soph Cls; Sec Jr Cls; Sec Sr Cls; Var Capt Cheerleading; NHS; Acdmc All Amer 86-87; Natl Merit Schlr 86; Knghts Columbs New Brunswck Schlrshp 87; Mercer Cnty CC; Flght Attndt.

HORVATH, NICK; Toms River North HS; Toms River, NJ; (3); Boy Scts; VICA; JV Bowling.

HORVATH, STEPHANIE; North Hunterdon HS; Clinton, NJ; (3); Chrmn 4-H; FFA; Chorus; Yrbk Stf; Cheerleading; Crs Cntry; Trk; FFA Sheerp Prodctn 86; U Of PA; Modeling.

HOSBACH, CHRISTIAN; Rancocas Valley Regional HS; Mt Holly, NJ; (3); Spanish Clb; Pres Band; Concert Band; Jazz Band; Mrchg Band; School Play; Stage Crew; Yrbk Stf; Rep Frsh Cls; Comp Repair.

HOSKING, STACEY; High Point Regional HS; Sussex, NJ; (1); Church Yth Grp; Yrbk Stf; L Sftbl; Hon Roll; Comp Fld.

HOTHEM, THOMAS; Park Ridge HS; Park Ridge, NJ; (4); 8/106; Boy Scts; Church Yth Grp; Capt Quiz Bowl; School Play; Yrbk Bus Mgr; Socr; NHS; Rutgers Coll.

HOTKO, DANIELLE; Hunterdon Central HS; Whitehouse Sta, NJ; (2); 108/487; Hosp Aide; Key Clb; Hon Roll.

HOU, ALEXANDER H; Wall HS; Wall, NJ; (4); 14/276; Computer Clb; German Clb; Key Clb; Ski Clb; Orch; Var L Crs Cntry; Var L Trk; High Hon Roll; Kiwanis Awd; NHS; Duke U; Pre Med.

HOU, NANCY; John P Stevens HS; Edison, NJ; (2); 12/452; Debate Tm; French Clb; Ski Clb; Ed Nwsp Stf; Lit Mag; Var Crs Cntry; High Hon Roll; Hon Roll; Concours Natl De Francais Lvl 1-B 16th In NY/NJ Chptr 86; Med.

HOULIHAN, LYNN; St John Vianney HS; Hazlet, NJ; (3); Church Yth Grp; Intnl Clb; School Play; Hon Roll; Bus.

HOULIHAN, PATRICE; St John Vianney HS; Hazlet, NJ; (4); FBLA; Intnl Clb; Yrbk Stf; Vrsty Let 85; Misericordia Coll; Bus Admin.

HOUNOS, KALI; Hammonton HS; Hammonton, NJ; (4); Sec Church Yth Grp; Key Clb; Color Guard; Yrbk Stf; Stu Cncl; Bsktbl; Pom Pon; Hon Roll; NHS; U S Natl Math Awd 83-85; Acdmc Awd 85-87; Schlstc Awd 87; Rutgers Coll.

HOUSE, CHRISTINE; Highland Regional HS; Erial, NJ; (3); Dance Clb; Drama Clb; FBLA; FHA; Service Clb; Thesps; School Musical; School Play; Nwsp Stf; Hon Roll; Miss Teen All-Amer Amity Awd 86-87; Girls Ineract Svcs & ST Finalist Miss Amer Co-Ed 87; Fashion Designer.

HOUSER, LESLIE; Dover HS; Mine Hill, NJ; (3); Band; Jazz Band; Mrchg Band; Orch; Pep Band; School Musical; Stage Crew; Symp Band; Bowling; Acdmc Awd Latin 86 & 87; SUNY-FREDONIA; Music.

HOUSTON, ED; Edison HS; Edison, NJ; (4); 6/417; Church Yth Grp; Math Tm; Model UN; Science Clb; Rep Stu Cncl; Var L Socr; Var L Tennis; Hon Roll; VP NHS; Grdn ST Dstngshd Schlrs Pgm; Grtst Schlstc Achvt-Sci; Athlt Wth Hghst Schlstc Rcrd; Lehigh U; Physcs.

HOUSTON, KIM; Lower Cape May Regional HS; N Cape May, NJ; (3); Spanish Clb; Varsity Clb; Band; Concert Band; Mrchg Band; Var Sftbl; JV Tennis; NHS; Physcl Ftnss Awd; Fshn Dsgn.

HOUSTON, LAURA; Toms River HS South; S Toms River, NJ; (3); 85/405; Band; Concert Band; Mrchg Band; FBLA; Intnl Clb; Fld Hcky; Tennis; Trk; Fshn Dsgn.

HOUSTON, TAMARA; Clifford J Scott HS; East Orange, NJ; (3); Nwsp Stf; Capt Cheerleading; Sftbl; Hon Roll; Frnch & Hist Awd 86-87; Nrsng.

HOUTS, RUTH; Glovecester Co Christian Schl; Westville Grove, NJ; (3); VP Church Yth Grp; Cmnty Wkr; Girl Scts; Library Aide; Var L Sftbl; Hon Roll; Bus.

HOWANITZ, AMBER; Lenape Valley Regional HS; Stanhope, NJ; (3); Church Yth Grp; VP Frsh Cls; Sec Stu Cncl; High Hon Roll; Hon Roll; English Clb; Pep Clb; Band; Concert Band; Jazz Band; Natl Hnr Roll Orgnztn 87; 3 Certs Apprctn 86; Schlr Music & Acadcs 84; Child Psych.

HOWARD, BILL; Holycross HS; Bordentown, NJ; (4); Church Yth Grp; Spanish Clb; Lit Mag; Im Trk; High Hon Roll; Hon Roll; Ntl Hnr Soc 85-87; U Scranton; Eng.

HOWARD, KISHA; Holy Spirit HS; Brigantine, NJ; (2); 33/397; Science Clb; Frsh Cls; Hon Roll.

HOWE, CHRISTINE; Burlington County Vo-Tech; Bordentown, NJ; (3); 8/192; FBLA; Hosp Aide; VICA; Yrbk Ed-Chief; Yrbk Stf; Rep Stu Cncl; Hon Roll; Secy.

HOWE, JEFFREY; Vineland SR HS; Vineland, NJ; (3); High Hon Roll; Hon Roll.

HOWE, THEODORE S; Cherry Hill High Schl East; Cherry Hill, NJ; (4); Church Yth Grp; Scholastic Bowl; Stage Crew; Im Bsktbl; Hon Roll; Ntl Merit SF; St Schlr; Engrng.

HOWELL, ABBIE; Shawnee HS; Medford, NJ; (3); Camp Fr Inc; Church Yth Grp; DECA; French Clb; Library Aide; SADD; Band; Church Choir; Concert Band; Mrchg Band.

HOWELL, LORRAINE; Central HS; Newark, NJ; (4); 24/148; Band; Va Capt Bsktbl; Crs Cntry; Mgr(s); Sftbl; Trk; Hon Roll; Prfct Atten Awd.

HOWELL, WADE C; Kittatinny Regional HS; Newton, NJ; (4); Am Le Boys St; 4-H; French Clb; Intnl Clb; Teachers Aide; Chorus; Madrigals School Musical; School Play; Trs Stu Cncl; VP Inter Act Clb JR Rotar 86-87; HS Plyrs Msk Awd 86-87; Sussex Co Arts Cncl Drama Awd 86-87 Bridgewater Coll; Frgn Rltn.

HOWLETT, DONNA; Paul VI Regional HS; W Orange, NJ; (4); 20/11 Key Clb; Yrbk Stf; High Hon Roll; Hon Roll; Spanish NHS; Acad A Amer 85-86; Excell Bus Awd 87; Montclair ST Coll; Bus Admin.

HOWLEY, MICHAEL; Holy Cross HS; Delran, NJ; (3); Church Yth Grp Cmnty Wkr; FCA; Rider Coll; Hlcptr Pilot.

HOXSEY JR, RICHARD L; Summit HS; Summit, NJ; (3); Model UN Rep Jr Cls; JV Lcrss; Outstndng Achvmnt Art 85-87; Penn ST U.

HOYER, THERESA; Columbia HS; S Orange, NJ; (3); Pres Church Yt Grp; Drama Clb; French Clb; Pres Latin Clb; Color Guard; School Musical School Play; Yrbk Ed-Chief; Yrbk Stf; French Hon Soc.

HRABAL, DARLENE; Vernon Township HS; Glenwood, NJ; (3); DECA FBLA; Flag Corp; Hon Roll; Fshn Merch.

HRATKO, THOMAS; Jackson Memorial HS; Jackson, NJ; (4); 57/450 Boy Scts; Exploring; ROTC; Color Guard; Drill Tm; Nwsp Ed-Chief; Hig Hon Roll; Hon Roll; Dayton Eleya Awd 87; ROTC Sqdrn Cmmndr Rnk O Capt 87; Life Scout BSA 88; Mercer County CC; Aviation.

HREBEK, JAMES; Wall HS; Manasquan, NJ; (3); 26/300; Cmnty Wkr Key Clb; Nwsp Rptr; Rep Frsh Cls; Rep Soph Cls; Stu Cncl; Tennis; Go Hon Prg Awd; Hon Roll; NHS; HOBY Ldrshp Smnr Ambsdr 86; Lawyer

HRNCIAR, KIM; Hackensack HS; Maywood, NJ; (3); Teachers Aide Band; Mrchg Band; Capt L Swmmng; Var Trk; Civic Clb; Hon Roll Spanish NHS; Grls Ctznshp Inst 87; Engr.

HROBAK JR, JAMES P; Holy Cross HS; Mt Laurel, NJ; (3); Chess Clb Im Vllybl; High Hon Roll; Hon Roll; Engrng.

HROMOHO, HEATHER; Immaculata HS; Middlesex, NJ; (3); Churc Yth Grp; Office Aide; Ski Clb; Bsktbl; Socr; Sftbl; NHS.

HRUNG, CATHY; Middletown SR HS; Lincroft, NJ; (2); Art Clb; Schoo Play; Nwsp Stf; Yrbk Ed-Chief; Stu Cncl; Bsktbl; High Hon Roll; Hgs Acad Avrge 85-86; 3rd Pl Math League; Comp Engrng.

HSIA, PHILIP H; Morris Knolls HS; Denville, NJ; (3); 22/424; Am Le Boys St; Math Clb; Quiz Bowl; Scholastic Bowl; Varsity Clb; Band; Yrb Stf; Coach Actv; JV Socr; High Hon Roll; 2 Yr Vrsty Lttr Wnnr Fencin Team 86-88; Bus.

HSIAO, MINA; West Essex SR HS; Roseland, NJ; (3); Drama Clb; Hos Aide; Band; Church Choir; Drm Mjr(t); Nwsp Rptr; French Hon Soc NHS; Am Leg Aux Girls St; Church Yth Grp; Smith Bk Awd 87; N Jerse Jr Rgn Band 85; N Jersey HS Area Band 87.

HSIEH, CHARLES; West Essex Regional SR HS; No Caldwell, NJ; (3) Church Yth Grp; Ski Clb; Spanish Clb; Yrbk Stf; Swmmng; Tennis; Ho Roll; West Essex Philsphcl Hnr Scty 87; Med.

HSIEH, DAVID; West Essex Regional HS; N Caldwell, NJ; (3); Mat Tm; Ski Clb; Orch; Var Swmmng; Var Tennis; Hon Roll; NHS; All Nort Jersey Rgnl & All State Orchestra 86; Med.

HSIEH, MARGARET; Middle Township HS; Cape May Court, NJ; (3) 1/200; Science Clb; Chorus; School Musical; Yrbk Stf; High Hon Roll Rutgers Schlr 87; 17th Pl NJ Sci Leag Bio 84-85; Latin Hnr Soc 86-87; Bio

HSIN, ROBERT; Montville Township HS; Montville, NJ; (4); 17/260 FBLA; Key Clb; Ski Clb; Bsktbl; Ftbl; High Hon Roll; NHS; Ntl Merit Ltr NJ Dstngshd Schl 86-87; Boston U; Med.

HSU, JULIE; West Windsor-Plainsboro HS; Princeton Junct, NJ; (3) Church Yth Grp; Hosp Aide; Ed Yrbk Bus Mgr; Rep Stu Cncl; JV Trk High Hon Roll; NHS; NJ Stdnt Cncl Ldrshp Trng Cmp 86; FBLA Reg Awds Acctg & Bus Math 86-87; Gindhart Piano Comptn 87; Med.

HSU, LILLIAN; Scotch Plains-Fanwood HS; Scotch Plains, NJ; (4); 4/ 300; VP French Clb; Model UN; Quiz Bowl; Mrchg Band; Nwsp Stf French Hon Soc; High Hon Roll; Pres Schlr; St Schlr; James J Kerrigar Mem Scholar 87; Cornell U; Econ.

HU, LAWRENCE; Nutley HS; Nutley, NJ; (3); 2/330; Am Leg Boys St AFS; VP Latin Clb; Stu Cncl; Capt Crs Cntry; Var Trk; Hon Roll; NHS Mech Engrng.

HUAMAN, JUANA; Kearny HS; Kearny, NJ; (3); Color Guard; Occptn Thrpst.

HUAMAN, RAFAEL; Kearny HS; Kearny, NJ; (4); 26/383; Science Clb Rep Jr Cls; High Hon Roll; Hon Roll; NHS; Acdmc Excllnc Awd 87 Garden ST Distgshd Schlr 87; Semi Finlst Nat Hispanic Schlrshp 87 Rutgers U; Biology.

HUANG, EUGENE; Montville HS; Towaco, NJ; (2); Key Clb; Var Cap Crs Cntry; Var Trk; High Hon Roll; Prfct Atten Awd; Outstndn Achvt-Grmn-Ltrary Soc Fndtn 86; 2nd Pl-Fstvl Of Arts-Wrkng Dfrwn Ctgry 86.

HUANG, PERRY; Roxbury HS; Succasunna, NJ; (3); FCA; Var Bsbl; Va Bsktbl; Var Ftbl; JV Tennis; High Hon Roll; Hon Roll.

HUANG, PHILIP; Parsippany Hills HS; Parsippany, NJ; (3); 2/329 Church Yth Grp; Exploring; Hosp Aide; Key Clb; Rep Jr Cls; Var Tennis High Hon Roll; NHS; Ntl Merit Ltr; Computer Clb; Cert Merit Superio Achvt NJ Math 87; Amer Math Comptn 87; AHSME Hnr Roll 87; Ame Invtnl Math Exam.

HUANG, RAYMOND; Matawan Regional HS; Matawan, NJ; (4); 5/316 Boy Scts; Church Yth Grp; Debate Tm; Math Tm; Radio Clb; Speech Tm Orch; School Musical; Nwsp Stf; Yrbk Stf; Natl Merit Schlr Commende 86; Garden ST Distinguished Schlr 86; NJ Gov Schl 86.

HUBBARD, ELIZABETH; Baptist HS; Stratford, NJ; (3); Rep Churc Yth Grp; Drama Clb; Chorus; Cheerleading; Hon Roll; NHS; Writer.

HUBBARD, ESMINE; Henry Synder HS; Jersey City, NJ; (3); Churc Yth Grp; Hosp Aide; Scholastic Bowl; Rep Stu Cncl; High Hon Roll; Ho Roll; Jr NHS; Prfct Atten Awd; Stu Achvmnt Awd 86 & 87; Pedtrcn.

HUBBARD, KELLY; Lyndhurst HS; Newark, NJ; (2); Chorus; Schoo Musical; Swing Chorus; Sftbl; Phys Thrpy.

HUBBARD, NANCI; Manchester Twshp HS; Toms River, NJ; (2) Church Yth Grp; Drama Clb; Pep Clb; SADD; Color Guard; Pom Pon Score Keeper; Sftbl; Tennis; Hon Roll; ST Fnlst Miss Amer Co-Ed 87.

HUBBARD, PAULA; Vineland HS; Vineland, NJ; (3); VP DECA; Ho Roll; Prfct Atten Awd; Fastest Typst 86; Bus Mang.

HUBBLE, BANE; Woodstown HS; Alloway, NJ; (3); English Clb Spanish Clb; Hon Roll; NHS.

HUBER, CHRIS; Brick Township Memorial HS; Brick, NJ; (3); 55/387 Aud/Vis; Cmnty Wkr; Computer Clb; Spanish Clb; Rep Frsh Cls; J Bsktbl; Var Bowling; Var Tennis; High Hon Roll; Hon Roll; U Of Rutgers Comp Sci.

HUBNER, MICHAEL; Paramus HS; Paramus, NJ; (2); Ftbl; Wt Lftg; Wrstlng; Grmn Natl Hnr Soc 87; Columbia U; Marine Bio.

HUDANICH, RON; Middle Twp HS; Avalon, NJ; (3); 12/209; Cmnty Wkr; Varsity Clb; Variety Show; Pres Jr Cls; Var Capt Socr; Hon Roll; NHS; Meteorlgst Awd DE Vly Sci Fair 85; Fbiol.

HUDDY, CORINNE; Hunterdon Central HS; Raritan, NJ; (1); 184/473; Rutgers U; Bus.

HUDSON, JANET; Cherokee HS; Tabernacle, NJ; (3); Stat Sftbl; Hon Roll; Art Inst Of Phila; Interior Dsn.

HUEBNER, MATTHEW; Southern Regional HS; Manahawkin, NJ; (4); 7/392; Dance Clb; Math Clb; Math Tm; Model UN; Off Stu Cncl; Var Ftbl; Im Vllybl; Elks Awd; Lion Awd; NHS; Widener U Pres Schlrshp 87; Widener U; Comp Engrng.

HUEBSCH, JULIE; Boonton HS; Boonton, NJ; (4); 8/230; Drama Clb; Hst French Clb; Jazz Band; VP Mrchg Band; Yrbk Stf; High Hon Roll; NHS; 4-H; Band; School Musical; Grdn ST Dstngshd Schlr 87; Douglass Coll; Arts Mgmt.

HUEBSCH, MICHELE; Boonton HS; Boonton, NJ; (3); 4-H; French Clb; Capt Color Guard; Rep Stu Cncl; Var Trk; High Hon Roll; NHS; Accntng.

HUERTA, CARLOS A; Don Bosco Tech; Paterson, NJ; (2); Boys Clb Am; Church Yth Grp; Spanish Clb; Physcn.

HUFF, ELIZABETH; West Side HS; Newark, NJ; (3); 1/250; Science Clb; VP Jr Cls; VP Sr Cls; Rep Stu Cncl; Var Bsktbl; Var Sftbl; High Hon Roll; Hon Roll; JETS Awd; NHS; Outstndg Frsmn Awd, Great Achvr 84-85; Outstndg Soph Awd, Great Achvr, Most Imprvd Bsktbl 85-86; Penn ST; Engr.

HUFF, KELLY L; Brick Township HS; Brick, NJ; (4); 15/400; Art Clb; Lit Mag; Rep Frsh Cls; Rep Soph Cls; Bsktbl; Var JV Sftbl; Var Tennis; Rep Gov Hon Prg Awd; High Hon Roll; Trenton SR; Art Therapy.

HUGHES, JASON; Red Bank Regional HS; Shrewsbury, NJ; (4); 47/250; Boy Scts; Church Yth Grp; French Clb; Ski Clb; Ntl Merit SF; Natl Merit Schlrshp Outstndng Negro Stu, Monmcth Cnty Cotlln Schlrshp 87; Morehouse Coll; Elec Engrng.

HUGHES, KARLTON; John F Kennedy HS; Willingboro, NJ; (3); Comp Sci.

HUGHES, KELLY; Wayne Valley HS; Wayne, NJ; (3); #13 In Class; Church Yth Grp; Ed Yrbk Stf; Lit Mag; Var Capt Crs Cntry; JV Socr; Var Trk; High Hon Roll; Sec NHS; Ntl Merit Ltr; Ski Clb; All Conf X Cntry 86.

HUGHES, KEVIN R; Paul VI Regional HS; Clifton, NJ; (4); 24/143; SADD; Stu Cncl; Var Capt Bsbl; Var Capt Bsktbl; Var Capt Ftbl; Hon Roll; Spanish NHS; All Cnty, Area & ST Hnrs Ftbl, Bsbl & Bsktbl 86-87; Schlr Athl Passaic Cnty Natl Ftbl Fndtn 87; Fordham U; Bus Adm.

HUGHES, NICOLE; Cinnaminson HS; Cinnaminson, NJ; (4); 89/231; Church Yth Grp; SADD; Chorus; JV Cheerleading; Var Capt Sftbl; Var Swmmng; Var Tennis; Cinnaminson Teachers Assn Schlrshp 87; Millersville U; Elem Educ.

HUGHES, SANDRA; Benedictine Acad; Newark, NJ; (4); Service Clb; Sec Spanish Clb; Chorus; School Play; Nwsp Rptr; Yrbk Stf; Capt Cheerleading; JV Vllybl; VP Frsh Cls; Union Cnty Schlr Athl Awd 87; Pol Sci.

HUGHES, SHAUNA; Bloomfield HS; Bloomfield, NJ; (3); Drama Clb; Key Clb; PAVAS; Chorus; Concert Band; Flag Corp; Madrigals; Mrchg Band; Yrbk Phtg; High Hon Roll; Bst Musician Chorus & Band 85; Seton Hall; Psych.

HUGHES, THERESA; John P Stevens HS; Edison, NJ; (4); 68/467; VP Art Clb; Key Clb; Model UN; School Play; Nwsp Stf; Yrbk Stf; Hon Roll; NHS; Pres Schlr; Debate Tm; Clara Barton Dmcrtc Club Awd 87; Douglass Coll; Pltcl Sci.

HUGHEY, MAGGIE; Holy Spirit HS; Margate, NJ; (2); 1/397; Var Swmmng; High Hon Roll; Hon Roll; Math.

HUHN, JENNIFER; Randolph HS; Ironia, NJ; (3); 12/353; Band; Concert Band; Mrchg Band; Symp Band; Yrbk Stf; Bsktbl; Sftbl; High Hon Roll; Jr NHS; NHS; Adv.

HUHN, PETER; Saint Joseph Regional HS; Park Ridge, NJ; (3); Computer Clb; George Washington U; Ecnmcs.

HUISMAN, KRISTEN; Manasquan HS; Belmar, NJ; (3); Spanish Clb; Varsity Clb; Trk; Hon Roll.

HULEHAN, LISA; Life Center Acad; Roebling, NJ; (2); Church Yth Grp; Chorus; Color Guard; School Musical; Var Cheerleading; Var Tennis; JV Var Vllybl; Highest Avg In US Hstry I & Scl Stds 86-87 & 85-86; Oral Roberts U; Jrnlsm.

HULITT, KIM; Vineland SR HS; Vineland, NJ; (3); Drama Clb; Spanish Clb; Nwsp Stf; Stockton Coll; Bus.

HULL, DONNA; Burlington County Vo-Tech Schl; Vincetown, NJ; (4); 7/166; Cmnty Wkr; FFA; Key Clb; SADD; VICA; Yrbk Stf; Stu Cncl; High Hon Roll; NHS; Crtv Flrl Dsgng Wnnr 85-86; Grnhnd Dgr FFA 85-86; Chptr Frmr Dgr FFA 86-87; Burlington County Coll; Bus Adm.

HULL, MATTHEW; Morristown-Beard Schl; Essex Falls, NJ; (3); 7/76; Art Clb; French Clb; Swmmng; Tennis; High Hon Roll; Hon Roll; Jr NHS; Advrtsng.

HULME, JOHN W; Highland Park HS; Highland Park, NJ; (4); Nwsp Stf; JV Bsbl; Var L Bsktbl; Var L Socr; Var L Tennis; Hon Roll; Ntl Merit SF; Cmnty Wkr; 3rd Tm All-St Group I Tennis 86; All-Conference Soccer 86; Broadcasting.

HULST, BURK; Kingsway Regional HS; Mickleton, NJ; (2); Cmnty Wkr; Latin Clb; Band; Jazz Band; Mrchg Band; High Hon Roll; Hon Roll; NHS; Psychlgst.

HUMINSKI, FRANK; Holy Cross HS; Edgewater Park, NJ; (3); 51/404; Computer Clb; School Musical; School Play; Stage Crew; Nwsp Rptr; Rep Stu Cncl; JV L Ftbl; Hon Roll; Ntl Merit Ltr; German Clb; Outstndng Rep Stu Cncl 86.

HUMPHREYS, MICHAEL; Penns Grove HS; Penns Grove, NJ; (4); 7/177; Am Leg Boys St; JCL; Chorus; School Play; Stage Crew; Socr; Trk; Elks Awd; NHS; St Schlr; 2nd Pl ST Cnsrvtn Essay Cntst 87; Schl Gftd & Tlntd Prg 85-87; U Of WY; Cnsrvtn.

HUMPHREYS, MICHELLE; Woodstown HS; Monroeville, NJ; (3); FBLA; VICA; Hon Roll.

HUMPHRIES, WILLIAM; Marist HS; Bayonne, NJ; (3); Rep Soph Cls; Rep Jr Cls; L Ftbl; Capt Trk; Atty.

HUNECKE, EDWARD; Dickinson HS; Jersey City, NJ; (3); Hnr Rl 86-87; St Peters Coll; Comp Pgm.

HUNG, ROBERT; Northern Valley Regional HS; Closter, NJ; (4); Computer Clb; Science Clb; Im Vllybl; High Hon Roll; North Jrsy Stu Crftmns Fair Elctrnc Crctry 2nd Plc/85 & 1st Plc/86; Prsdntl Acdmc Ftnss Awd 87; Livingston Coll; Comp Sci.

HUNG, SUSIE; Scotch Plains-Fanwood HS; Scotch Plain, NJ; (2); Key Clb; High Hon Roll; Hon Roll; Prfct Atten Awd; Outstndng Sci Awd 86; Itln Natl Hnr Soc 86; Fin.

HUNNEMAN, LEIF E; Lakewood HS; Lakewood, NJ; (3); 42/330; Am Leg Boys St; Aud/Vis; German Clb; Library Aide; Math Clb; Math Tm; Hon Roll; Comm.

HUNNEWELL, WENDY L; Morris Knolls HS; Denville, NJ; (4); 3/369; Cmnty Wkr; Pres French Clb; Sec Speech Tm; School Play; Lit Mag; NHS; Ntl Merit Ltr; Pres Schlr; St Schlr; Wrnr Lmbrt YFU Smmr Abrd Schlrshp Belgium 86, Spcl Merit Schlrshp; Shlrshp Frdms Fndtn Vly Frg 85; Cornell U; Bio.

HUNSINGER, DAVID; Gateway Regional HS; Wenonah, NJ; (2); Church Yth Grp; JCL; Chorus; Church Choir; Jazz Band; Mrchg Band; Nwsp Stf; Hon Roll; Boy Scts; Debate Tm; Sunday Schl Tchr 86-87; Best Spkr Awd 86-87; NJ All ST Chorus Bass II 87.

HUNSINGER, DOYLE; Watchung Hills Reg HS; Watchung, NJ; (3); Church Yth Grp; Cmnty Wkr; Latin Clb; Ski Clb; SADD; Off Soph Cls; Off Jr Cls; Stu Cncl; Im Bsbl; JV Crs Cntry; Bus.

HUNT, MARGUERITE; Gateway Regional HS; Wenonah, NJ; (3); 18/200; Drama Clb; Key Clb; Latin Clb; Ski Clb; School Musical; JV Tennis; Hon Roll; NHS; Grls Ctzshp Inst Awd From Rtgrs U 87.

HUNT, THOMAS; Hunterdon Central HS; Readington, NJ; (4); 113/548; Cmnty Wkr; Ski Clb; Chorus; Mrchg Band; School Musical; Variety Show; Stu Cncl; Im Badmtn; Im Vllybl; Hon Roll; Elizabeth Vosseller Mem Music Awd 87; Math Achvt Awd 85; Chorale Hnr 87; Seton Hall U; Sci.

HUNTER III, GEORGE K; Triton HS; Glendora, NJ; (3); 88/405; Am Leg Boys St; Aud/Vis; French Clb; Key Clb; Hon Roll; Kiwanis Awd; Outstndng Achvt Awd-Bio 86; Outstndng Svc Awd For Audio-Visual Clb 86; Elec Engrng.

HUNTER, NANCY; Hightstown HS; East Windsor, NJ; (4); AFS; Cmnty Wkr; Drama Clb; Pres French Clb; Hosp Aide; Service Clb; High Hon Roll; Hon Roll; NHS; Ntl Merit Ltr; Cert For Outstndng Acadc Prfrmnce 83-86; Hghst Acadc Avg Awd 86-87; Smith Coll; Lbrl Arts.

HUNTER, THERESA A; John F Kennedy Memorial HS; Avenel, NJ; (4); 65/274; Dance Clb; Concert Band; Drm Mjr(t); Mrchg Band; School Musical; Rep Jr Cls; Rep Sr Cls; R Sacarano Mem Schlrshp For Outstndng Achvt & Ldrshp In Msc 87; Pres Cncl Schlrshp 87; Mntclr ST Coll; Spch Thrpst.

HUNTZINGER, ESTHER; Wayne Hills HS; Wayne, NJ; (3); 2/330; Church Yth Grp; Math Clb; Band; Concert Band; Mrchg Band; Nwsp Ed-Chief; Nwsp Stf; Lit Mag; High Hon Roll; NHS; Del For Rotary Yth Ldrshp Awd 87; Del For Girl Ctznshp Inst 87; Educ.

HUNZIKER, JENNY; Point Pleasant Beach HS; Bay Head, NJ; (2); Key Clb; Spanish Clb; Varsity Clb; Chorus; Yrbk Stf; Var Cheerleading; Mgr(s); JV Socr; Comms.

HUQ, RUMANA; Ranney HS; Wall, NJ; (2); Dance Clb; Library Aide; NFL; Spanish Clb; Chorus; Nwsp Rptr; Nwsp Stf; Yrbk Stf; Var Swmmng; High Hon Roll; 1st Pl Kumite NJ Invt Karate Chmpshps 87; Silver Mdl Intl Piano Rcrdng Cmptn 86; Med.

HURFF, SANDRA; Paulsboro HS; Gibbstown, NJ; (4); 23/120; Drill Tm; Stage Crew; Yrbk Ed-Chief; Yrbk Stf; Twrlr; Hon Roll; NHS; Church Yth Grp; Ski Clb; Mrchg Band; Pres Acadc Ftns Awd 87; Mr Massey Schlrshp 87; Gloucester Co Coll; Spcl Ed.

HURLEY, BRETT; Southern Regional HS; Ship Bottom, NJ; (3); 54/492; Church Yth Grp; FBLA; Model UN; Ski Clb; Varsity Clb; Variety Show; Yrbk Stf; High Hon Roll; NHS; Rotary Awd; 1st Pl Trphy Bsbl 85; 3rd Pl Medl Wrstlng Headhntr Awd Wrstlng 86; Schlr/Athl Awd Wrstlng 87; Rutgers; Bus.

HURLEY, MICHELE; Acad Of The Holy Angels HS; Waldwick, NJ; (3); Church Yth Grp; Hosp Aide; Math Clb; Sec Spanish Clb; Lit Mag; Hon Roll; NHS; Sci.

HURLEY, TARA A; Academy Of The Holy Angels; Blauvelt, NY; (4); 5/152; Cmnty Wkr; Math Tm; Model UN; Mu Alpha Theta; Spanish Clb; Nwsp Ed-Chief; NHS; Ntl Merit SF; Ntl Ltn Exam Magna Cum Laude Cum Laude 84-85; Hstry Scty 86-87; Hstry Hnr Scty 86; Pltcl Sci.

HURST, HEATHER; Toms River HS South; Toms River, NJ; (3); 138/405; Art Clb; Church Yth Grp; Drama Clb; High Hon Roll; VP Voctnl Indstrl Clbs Amer 87; Int Dsgn.

HURTT, ALLISON; Westwood HS; Westwood, NJ; (2); Dance Clb; Pep Clb; Chorus; Variety Show; JV Cheerleading; JV Pom Pon; Trk; Bus.

HURWITZ, JEFFREY; Matawan-Aberdeen Regional HS; Matawan, NJ; (3); 12/300; Math Clb; Math Tm; Yrbk Stf; Off Stu Cncl; Tennis; Hon Roll.

HUSSAIN, DAVID; Orange HS; Orange, NJ; (2); Radio Clb; Hon Roll; NJIT; Elec Engr.

HUSSAIN, JAHANARA; Mary Help Of Christians Acad; Paterson, NJ; (3); Letterman Clb; Service Clb; SADD; Chorus; School Musical; Nwsp Stf; Gym; Spn Awd 84-85; Theology Awd 86-87; Soclgy Awd 86-87; Franklin Pierce; Pedtrc Thrpst.

HUSSAIN, NADEEM; Shawnee HS; Medford, NJ; (3); Am Leg Boys St; Chess Clb; Computer Clb; Latin Clb; VP Math Tm; Nwsp Rptr; Yrbk Stf; NHS; Boy Scts; Nwsp Stf; 2 Maxima Cum Laude Mdsl & 1 Summa Cum Laude 85-87; NJ Cvrnrs Schl Sci 87; MIT; Bio Med.

HUSSAIN, RHUKEA; Mary Help Of Christians Acad; Paterson, NJ; (1); SADD; Nwsp Stf; Off Frsh Cls; Stu Cncl; High Hon Roll; Val; Pro-Life 87; Toastmasters 87; Dartmouth U; Brain Surgeon.

HUSSAIN, SABEENA; West Windsor Plainsboro HS; Robbinsville, NJ; (4); 23/273; Cmnty Wkr; Hosp Aide; Intnl Clb; Math Clb; Political Wkr; Red Cross Aide; Service Clb; Concert Band; Ed Nwsp Rptr; Nwsp Stf; Acdmc Fit Awd 87; Pol Sci.

HUSTON, LYNETTE; Clearview HS; Mullica Hill, NJ; (3); DECA; FHA; Office Aide; Red Cross Aide; Teachers Aide; VICA; Chorus; Fld Hcky; Gym; Hon Roll; WRD Proccsor.

HUTCHERSON, DEBRA; Trenton HS; Trenton, NJ; (3); Art Clb; Office Aide; Band; Chorus; Stage Crew; Nwsp Rptr; Nwsp Stf; Cit Awd; High Hon Roll; Hon Roll; Nrsng.

HUTCHINS, JACKIE; Riverside HS; Riverside, NJ; (3); 21/188; DECA; Drama Clb; FBLA; SADD; Dance Clb; Var Capt Cheerleading; Burlington Cnty Coll; Accntnt.

HUTCHINSON, DEANNA; Vineland HS; Vineland, NJ; (3); 15/824; French Clb; Key Clb; Rep Stu Cncl; Var Fld Hcky; Hon Roll; NHS; Airline Pilot.

HUTCHINSON, KIMBERLY; Notre Dame HS; Trenton, NJ; (3); 40/373; Dance Clb; FBLA; Varsity Clb; Capt School Musical; School Play; Off Frsh Cls; Capt Cheerleading; High Hon Roll; NHS; 1st & 2nd Pl Bllt-Pointe-Shwstpprs Ntl Tlnt Cmptn 85 & 86; 1st Pl Bllt-Pointe-Ryl Strs 85; Arch.

HUTCHINSON, LISA; Lyndhurst HS; Lyndhurst, NJ; (4); 30/168; Church Yth Grp; Key Clb; Office Aide; Service Clb; Teachers Aide; 1st Pl Outstndng N Jersey Crftsmns Fair 86; Hnrbl Mntn Great Amer Poetry Cntst 87; PSYCH.

HUTCHINSON, RICH; Howell HS; Howell, NJ; (2); German Clb; Band; JV Ftbl; JV Wt Lftg; Hon Roll; Polit Sci.

HUTCHISON, DAVID; Bloomfield HS; Bloomfield, NJ; (3); Am Leg Boys St; Capt Aud/Vis; FHA; German Clb; Band; Madrigals; Stage Crew; Var Socr; Var Trk; Var Wrstlng; Culnry Arts.

HUTCHISON JR, DONALD; Bloomfield HS; Bloomfield, NJ; (3); German Clb; Jazz Band; Madrigals; Mrchg Band; Rep Jr Cls; Socr; Trk; Gov Hon Prg Awd; High Hon Roll; Hstrcl Soc Art Awd 87; Artst.

HUTCHISON, MONICA; Bloomfield HS; Bloomfield, NJ; (4); 22/437; Church Yth Grp; Sec French Clb; Key Clb; Drill Tm; Yrbk Stf; Rep Stu Cncl; French Hon Soc; Hon Roll; NHS; Pres Schlr; Rutgers U; Psych.

HUTMAKER, MICHAEL; South Brunswick HS; Monmouth Junction, NJ; (3); 18/256; Am Leg Boys St; Math Clb; Mu Alpha Theta; Spanish Clb; Var L Bsbl; Var L Socr; High Hon Roll; Mu Alpha Theta Awd; NHS; Spanish NHS.

HUTTER, DANIEL; Cherry Hill E HS; Cherry Hill, NJ; (3); Camera Clb; JCL; Band; Rep Jr Cls; JV Bsbl; JV Gym; High Hon Roll; MIP-BSBL 86; Cmnty Svc Awd 86; Bst Acadmc-Gymnstc Tm 86; Bio.

HUYNH, QUANG; Hillside HS; Union, NJ; (3); #6 In Class; Am Leg Boys St; Computer Clb; ROTC; Science Clb; Mgr(s); Var Socr; Hon Roll; Sci Awd 86; Rutgers; Pre-Med.

HWANG, GRACE; Parsippany HS; Parsippany, NJ; (3); Trs Church Yth Grp; VP French Clb; SADD; Yrbk Stf; Rep Stu Cncl; Var L Fld Hcky; Bausch & Lomb Sci Awd; High Hon Roll; Pres NHS; Stat Tennis; Rensselaer Medlst 87; ST Typng Cmptn 3rd Pl 85.

HWANG, HANS; Watchung Hills Regnl; Warren, NJ; (4); 10/311; Church Yth Grp; Math Tm; Var Crs Cntry; Var Trk; Hon Roll; Ntl Merit SF; St Schlr; Rutgers Deans Smr Schlr 86; Futr Prblm Slvrs 85-86; Evergrn Clb Bridge Chmpn 83-84; Princeton; Bio Sci.

HWANG, SON C; H P Becton Reg HS; East Rutherford, NJ; (3); 3/120; Am Leg Boys St; Pres Church Yth Grp; Pres Key Clb; Math Tm; Band; Jazz Band; Mrchg Band; Rep Stu Cncl; JV Bsbl; NHS.

HYATT, DAVID JAMES; Ridgewood HS; Ridgewood, NJ; (3); Trs Debate Tm; Math Tm; Capt Quiz Bowl; Jazz Band; VP Orch; Gov Hon Prg Awd; NHS; Ntl Merit Schol; Church Yth Grp; NFL; 2nd Chair Cellist All St Orchstra 87; 1st Pl Sci Chlng Esy Cont 85; Sci Hnrs Prg 85-86.

HYDE, CHRISTOPHER; Atlantic Friends Schl; Linwood, NJ; (4); Boy Scts; Pres Church Yth Grp; Model UN; Chorus; School Play; Mgr Lit Mag; Var Bsktbl; Im Bowling; Var Socr; St Schlr; Bio.

HYLAND, DON; Montville HS; Towaco, NJ; (3); 98/273; French Clb; Ski Clb; SADD; Ftbl; Lcrss; Tennis; Wrstlng; High Hon Roll; Hon Roll; Bus.

HYLAND, SUSAN; North Plainfield HS; N Plainfield, NJ; (4); 18/185; Girl Scts; Math Clb; Pep Clb; Capt Color Guard; Stat Var Bsbl; Stat Var Bsktbl; Var L Fld Hcky; Powder Puff Ftbl; Hon Roll; NHS; Trustee Schlrshp 87; Monmouth Coll; Phys Thrpy.

HYLE, STACEY; Immaculate Conception HS; Lodi, NJ; (3); 25/69; Trs NFL; Q&S; SADD; Chorus; Nwsp Rptr; Rep Jr Cls; Trs Stu Cncl; Var Cheerleading; Var Sftbl; Hon Roll; Rutgers; Bus.

HYLTON, RUDOLPH; Frank H Morrell HS; Irvington, NJ; (3); Art Clb; French Clb; Hosp Aide; SADD; Chorus; Var Socr; Var Tennis; French Hon Soc; Hon Roll; Prfct Atten Awd; Rutgers Coll; Airplane Tech.

HYMAN, HALLIE; Bayonne HS; Bayonne, NJ; (3); 10/450; Key Clb; Math Tm; Nwsp Rptr; Nwsp Sprt Ed; Lit Mag; Var Bsktbl; Stat Ice Hcky; Var Tennis; High Hon Roll; Jr NHS; All Cnty Tennis Team 84 & 86; Grls Bsktbl Natl AAU Jr Olympics 86-87; Pre Med.

HYMANS, MICHAEL; Morristown-Beard HS; Florham Pk, NJ; (3); Stu Cncl Treas; Yrbk Stf Editor; Vrsty Cross Cntry Co Capt; Vrsty Trk Co Capt; Drama Clb; Vrsty Cross Cty.

HYMES, LORI; Salem HS; Salem, NJ; (3); Computer Clb; Math Clb; Ski Clb; Teachers Aide; Rep Stu Cncl; Var Bsktbl; Stat Fld Hcky; Var Sftbl; Hon Roll; NHS; Bus Admn.

HYNDS, VICTORIA; Jackson Memorial HS; Jackson, NJ; (3); #51 In Class; Drama Clb; Ski Clb; Band; Mrchg Band; School Play; Stage Crew; Stat Bsktbl; Var Mgr(s); Im Powder Puff Ftbl; Var Socr; Physcl Educ.

HYNES, JOSEPH M; Edison HS; Edison, NJ; (3); 1/450; Church Yth Grp; French Clb; Math Tm; Science Clb; Lit Mag; Rep Frsh Cls; Rep Jr Cls; Crs Cntry; Trk; French Hon Soc; Operation Enterprise 87; MA Inst Of Tech; Engrng.

HYNES, LINDA; St John Vianney HS; Hazlet, NJ; (2); SADD; Band; Concert Band; Mrchg Band; JV Socr; High Hon Roll; Hon Roll; Vrsty Ltr Mrchng Band 85; Princeton.

HYSING, ANDREW; Manchester Twp HS; Lakehurst, NJ; (2); Capt Boy Scts; Church Yth Grp; Capt Exploring; Spanish Clb; Off Jr Cls; Var Socr; Var Tennis; Hon Roll; Med.

HYSING, KELLY; Manchester Twp HS; Lakehurst, NJ; (4); 10/180; Am Leg Aux Girls St; Trs Church Yth Grp; Hosp Aide; Math Tm; Science Clb; Spanish Clb; Trs Jr Cls; Mgr(s); Socr; NHS; Slipper Rock U; Intl Bus.

HYSON, SUZANNE; Lower Cape May Regional HS; Erma, NJ; (4); 1/230; Concert Band; Yrbk Stf; NHS; Val; Am Leg Aux Girls St; Band; Mrchg Band; High Hon Roll; St Schlr; School Musical; Rutgers Schlr 86; Washington Coll; Psych.

IACONE, KEVIN; Saint Joseph Of Palisades HS; Union City, NJ; (3); Bsktbl; Ftbl; High Hon Roll; Hon Roll.

IACONELLI, GINA; Holy Spirit HS; Absecon, NJ; (3); Church Yth Grp; Spanish Clb; Chorus; School Musical; School Play.

IACONO, JOSEPH; Middlesex HS; Middlesex, NJ; (2); French Clb; Key Clb; Varsity Clb; Rep Stu Cncl; JV Ftbl; JV Golf; Var L Wrstlng; Hon Roll; USNA; Engr.

IACOPONI, DAVID A; Northern Highlands HS; Upper Saddle Rvr, NJ; (4); 7/264; Boy Scts; Off Jr Cls; Off Sr Cls; Stu Cncl; VP Ftbl; Capt Wrstlng; NHS; Ntl Merit SF; Eagle Scout 86; Dartmouth Bk Awd; Engr.

IADANZA, RAYMOND; Jackson Memorial HS; Jackson, NJ; (3); 48/416; Art Clb; Var Bowling; High Hon Roll; Hon Roll; Natl Art Honor Soc 86-88; Automotive Design.

IANNACCONE, LYNN; Rutherford HS; Rutherford, NJ; (3); VP JCL; Key Clb; Science Clb; Spanish Clb; High Hon Roll; NHS; NEDT Awd.

IANNONE, JEFFREY M; Holy Cross HS; Willingboro, NJ; (3); 38/400; Am Leg Boys St; Chess Clb; Ski Clb; Spanish Clb; Pres Frsh Cls; Rep Jr Cls; Stu Cncl; Capt Var Tennis; High Hon Roll; NHS; Engrng.

IANNOTTA, STEVEN; Lenape Valley Regional HS; Stanhope, NJ; (3); Church Yth Grp; Mgr Color Guard; Var Ftbl; JV Ice Hcky; Var Trk; Wt Lftg; JV Wrstlng; High Hon Roll; Hon Roll; Rotary Awd; Mrn Bio.

IAZZETTA, DIANE; Union Catholic Regional HS; Cranford, NJ; (2); Hon Roll; Big Brthr-Big Sistr Peer Mnstry 87; Hlth Clb-VP 85-87; Hstry Clb 87; Rutgers; Phrmcy.

IBITOYE, DAVID; Dwight Morrow HS; Englewood, NJ; (4); 3/219; Church Yth Grp; Girl Scts; Library Aide; Math Tm; Chorus; Church Choir; Cit Awd; High Hon Roll; Trs NHS; Prfct Atten Awd; Natl Social Studies Olympiad Awd 87; Bergen Cnty Urban League Awd; Cornell U; Bio.

IBRAHIM, BERNIE; Timothy Christian Schl; Edison, NJ; (4); Church Yth Grp; Drama Clb; Church Choir; Trs Frsh Cls; Trs Soph Cls; Trs Jr Cls; Trs Sr Cls; Rep Stu Cncl; High Hon Roll; Trs NHS; Rutgers Coll/Engrng; Elec Engr.

ICKLAN, KAREN; St Rose HS; Brick, NJ; (4); 27/217; Latin Clb; Math Clb; Math Tm; Rep Soph Cls; Rep Jr Cls; Rep Sr Cls; Var Cheerleading; U Of IN Penn; Bus.

IDELCHIK, INNA; Fair Lawn HS; Fair Lawn, NJ; (3); 10/342; Cmnty Wkr; Drama Clb; Math Tm; Political Wkr; Science Clb; Color Guard; School Play; Yrbk Stf; Sec Soph Cls; NHS; Rensselaer Plytech Inst Math & Sci Awd 87.

IERVOLINO, JAMES; Hoboken HS; Hoboken, NJ; (3); Rep Jr Cls; Var Bsbl; Capt Var Bowling; High Hon Roll; Italian Clb Pres 86-87; NJ Inst Of Tech; Arch.

IGLAY, DEAN; Wall HS; Neptune, NJ; (3); 24/289; High Hon Roll; Hon Roll; HI Oceangrphy.

IGLESIAS, JOSE; Kearny HS; Kearny, NJ; (4); 4/383; Am Leg Boys St; Math Tm; Yrbk Sprt Ed; Rep Sr Cls; Var Swmmng; NHS; Spanish NHS; Cmnty Wkr; Intnl Clb; Spanish Clb; Acadmc Excel Awd 87; Stu Mnth 86; NJ Dstngshd Schlr 86; Arch Engrng.

IGNACCIO, ARLENE G; Leonia HS; Leonia, NJ; (3); 2/130; Quiz Bowl; Science Clb; Acpl Chr; Yrbk Stf; VP Frsh Cls; High Hon Roll; NHS; NEDT Awd; Latin Clb; Teachers Aide; Renssalaer Awd 87; Natl Latin Exm Cum Laude, USNMA US Natl Math Awd 85; Pre-Med.

IKEDA, TATSUHIRO; Hunterdon Central HS; Whitehouse Sta, NJ; (2); 47/478; Ski Clb; Rep Frsh Cls; Trs Soph Cls; Rep Stu Cncl; Tennis; Hon Roll; Teen Arts Fstvl 89; Artwk Dsplynd Untd Ntns, Arnd Wrld UN Pgm 89.

IM, SAMUEL; Union Catholic Regional HS; Browns Mills, NJ; (4); 9/295; Pres Chess Clb; Debate Tm; Math Tm; Science Clb; Service Clb; Var L Trk; High Hon Roll; NHS; Spanish NHS; Johns Hopkins U; Pre-Med.

INA, KYOKO; Cliffside Park HS; Cliffside Park, NJ; (1); Drama Clb; GAA; School Musical; School Play; Yrbk Stf; Gym; Swmmng; Tennis; French Hon Soc; Hon Roll; Intl Foreign Lang Awd 86; Law.

INAL, FIGEN; Lyndhurst HS; Lyndhurst, NJ; (2); Cmnty Wkr; German Clb; Leo Clb; Model UN; Office Aide; Science Clb; Chorus; Stage Crew; Yrbk Stf; VP Frsh Cls; 1st Pl Wrttn Engl Dialoge 83; Thank You Awd; 1st Pl Spkn Engl & Cmpstn.

INCARVITO, DOROTHY; Bishop Eustace Prep Schl; Delran, NJ; (4); 10/163; Drama Clb; Math Clb; VP Pres Pep Clb; SADD; Yrbk Sprt Ed; Var Capt Bowling; Var Capt Sftbl; High Hon Roll; NHS; Pres Schlr; Loyola Pres Schlrshp & ACDMC All-Amer 87; Bowling Conf Awds 83-87; Frnaklin & Marshall Coll; Hstry.

INCOLLA, JOSEPHINE; St Rose HS; Brielle, NJ; (3); Cmnty Wkr; Drama Clb; Chorus; School Musical; School Play; Variety Show; Nwsp Rptr; Lit Mag; Hon Roll; Magna Cum Laude Amer & Jr Classical Leagues Natl Latin Exam 85-86; Fine Arts Coll; Voice.

INCORVAIA, DENISE; Hopewell Valley Central HS; Hopewell, NJ; (4); 20/198; Drama Clb; Spanish Clb; Speech Tm; Band; Chorus; Concert Band; Mrchg Band; School Musical; School Play; Nwsp Rptr; Salisbury ST Acadmc Schlrshp, Pres Acadmc Ftns Awd 87; Salisbury ST Coll; Comnctn Art.

INFANTE, FRANCINE; Howell HS; Farmingdale, NJ; (4); NFL; PAVAS; Variety Show; Nwsp Stf; Yrbk Ed-Chief; Ed Lit Mag; Socr; Hghst Lvl Recgntn NJ ST Teen Arts 87; Bethany Coll; Englsh.

INFELD, KAREN; Montclair HS; Upper Montclair, NJ; (3); VP Temple Yth Grp; VP L Flag Corp; Ed Nwsp Rptr; Hon Roll; Jr NHS; Natl HS Inst At Northwestern U Jrnlsm Div 87; Jrnlsm.

INGALLS, DANIEL; Edgewood Regional HS; Sicklerville, NJ; (3); Latin Clb; ROTC; Stage Crew; JV Ftbl; Hon Roll; Jr NHS; Penn ST; Bus.

INGEMI, JOHN; Florence Twp Mem HS; Florence, NJ; (3); Science Clb; Capt Var Crs Cntry; Var Trk; Hon Roll.

INGLESE, CYNTHIA; Hmilton HS North NUM; Trenton, NJ; (3); Trs AFS; FBLA; Color Guard; JV Stat Bsktbl; JV Var Mgr(s); JV Var Socr; Stat Sftbl; High Hon Roll; Hon Roll; Accntng.

INGRAM, ALVIN; Burlinton City HS; Beverly, NJ; (3); Am Leg Boys St; Computer Clb; Hon Roll.

INGRAM, KEESHIA MONETTE; West Orange HS; W Orange, NJ; (4); 28/370; Pres Am Leg Aux Girls St; Pres Spanish Clb; Band; Church Choir; Mrchg Band; Var Capt Bsktbl; Var Capt Sftbl; NHS; Ntl Merit Ltr; Pres Spanish NHS; Richard Cataldo Awd For Schlr Athlete Of Yr 87; Unico Natl Schlrshp 87; Church Schlrshp & Awd 87; Coll William & Mary; Banking.

INSANA, PHYLLIS; Wood-Ridge HS; Wood-Ridge, NJ; (4); 10/76; Art Clb; Science Clb; Spanish Clb; Yrbk Stf; JV Capt Cheerleading; Hon Roll; Jr NHS; Trs NHS; Montclair ST Coll.

INSLICHT, SABRA; Cherry Hill H S West; Cherry Hill, NJ; (1); Dance Clb; Drama Clb; French Clb; School Play; Variety Show; Trk; Hon Roll; Pres Acad Fitness Awd 86; Bus.

INSPECTOR, AMY; Montville HS; Pine Brook, NJ; (3); 43/276; Art Clb; FBLA; Off Ski Clb; Off Frsh Cls; Trs Soph Cls; Off Jr Cls; Pres Stu Cncl; Var Lcrss; L Powder Puff Ftbl; High Hon Roll; 1000 Schlrshp To Caldwell CC 87; Frshmn La Crosse Tm Capt 85; Bus.

INTELISAWO, JOSEPH; Boonton HS; Lincoln Pk, NJ; (2); 86/196; Computer Clb; French Clb; Var JV Bsktbl; French Hon Soc; IN U; Comp Engr.

INTERMAGGIO, JAMES; Lakeland Regional HS; Wanaque, NJ; (3); Aud/Vis; Rep Frsh Cls; Rep Soph Cls; Rep Jr Cls; Rep Stu Cncl; JV Crs Cntry; Var Trk; Im Wt Lftg; Hon Roll; Var Ftbl; Eagle Scout Bronze Palm 84; Ntl Ldrshp Amer Awd NE Rgnl Wnnr Schlrshp 84; Bronze Congsnl Awd 86.

INTRIERI, SANDRA; Mary Help Of Christians Acad; Paterson, NJ; (4); 21/88; Computer Clb; GAA; Letterman Clb; Service Clb; Stage Crew; Yrbk Rptr; Yrbk Stf; VP Jr Cls; Rep Sr Cls; Vllybl; Hon Roll; Seton Hall U; Nrsng.

IOVINE, DAVID; Burlington City HS; Burlington, NJ; (3); Church Yth Grp; FBLA; JV L Socr; Hon Roll; Ntl Merit SF; O M St Comptn 85-87; Wrtr.

IOVINO, AMANDA; Middlesex HS; Middlesex, NJ; (3); DECA; French Clb; Ski Clb; Yrbk Stf; Var Capt Cheerleading; Fld Hcky; Im Powder Puff Ftbl; Stat Trk; Hon Roll; JR Clss Homecmng Rep 86-87; Foods.

IOVINO, THOMAS; De Paul Diocesan HS; Bloomingdale, NJ; (4); Am Leg Boys St; Church Yth Grp; Acpl Chr; School Play; Stage Crew; Variety Show; Nwsp Rptr; Nwsp Stf; Jrnlsm.

IPPOLITO, CYNTHIA; St Josephs HS; N Bergen, NJ; (3); Church Yth Grp; Political Wkr; Teachers Aide; Church Choir; Stat Score Keeper; Stat Socr; Hon Roll; Bergen CC; Comp.

IPRI, LINDA; Pope Paul VI HS; Deptford, NJ; (3); 133/500; Service Clb; Varsity Clb; Var Cheerleading; Powder Puff Ftbl; 2nd Hnrs 85; Vrsty Lttr 86; Pre Law.

IRBY, VINNETTA; Dwight Morrow HS; Englewood, NJ; (3); 78/388; Church Yth Grp; FBLA; GAA; JA; Spanish Clb; Church Choir; School Musical; Yrbk Stf; Sec Frsh Cls; Stu Cncl; Chrldng Awd 86-87; Bus Mngmt.

IREDELL, LEE ANN; Kittatinny Regional HS; Newton, NJ; (4); 17/222; Church Yth Grp; SADD; Church Choir; Madrigals; School Musical; Pres Soph Cls; Rep Stu Cncl; High Hon Roll; Hon Roll; NHS; Cngrss-Bndstg Fll 1 Yr Schlrshp-Wst Grmny 85-86; Hood Coll; Intl Rltns.

IRELAN, STEPHANIE; Freehold Twp HS; Freehold, NJ; (4); Church Yth Grp; Concert Band; Jazz Band; Mrchg Band; Sftbl; Trk; Berry Coll GA; Soclgy.

IRICK, CORINN; Buena Regional HS; Vineland, NJ; (3); 21/236; Sec Church Yth Grp; Girl Scts; Service Clb; Ski Clb; Yrbk Phtg; Yrbk Stf; Hon Roll; Jr NHS; Med.

IRINYI, ALEX; Boonton HS; Lincoln Park, NJ; (3); Arch.

IRVIN, KENNETH R; Vailsburg HS; Newark, NJ; (3); Am Leg Boys St; Church Yth Grp; Cmnty Wkr; Office Aide; Political Wkr; Teachers Aide; Church Choir; Drill Tm; JV Ftbl; Cit Awd; Cert Achvt Eagle Flght Pilot Ttrnng 87; Cert Ctznshp 87; Embry Riddle Aero U; Aero Engr.

IRVING, LAURI; Triton Regional HS; Runnemede, NJ; (3); French Clb; Latin Clb; Math Clb; Service Clb; Spanish Clb; Band; Church Choir; Concert Band; Mrchg Band; School Play; Rotary Intl Dist Rep To Santo Domingo 86; Frgn Lang.

IRWIN, MICHELE; Lyndhurst HS; Lyndhurst, NJ; (2); Color Guard; Med.

IRWIN, ROBERT; St James HS; Carneys Pt, NJ; (1); Art Clb; Drama Clb; ROTC; School Play; Stage Crew; Bsbl; Bsktbl; Socr; Swmmng; Wt Lftg; Drma Clb; Sccr; ROTC; UCLA; Bus.

ISAACSON, ADAM; Toms River South HS; Toms River, NJ; (3); 43/405; Am Leg Boys St; Intnl Clb; Math Tm; Temple Yth Grp; Orch; Swmmng; Hon Roll; NHS; Pre Law.

ISAACSON, STACEY; Dwight Englewood HS; Englewood, NJ; (3); Yrbk Stf; Tennis.

ISAACSON, STACY; Wayne Hills HS; Wayne, NJ; (2); VP Exploring; Model UN; Red Cross Aide; Spanish Clb; Chorus; School Play; Yrbk Stf; JV Fld Hcky; High Hon Roll; Hon Roll; Pre Med.

ISAJIW, ROMAN O; Kittatinny Regional HS; Newton, NJ; (3); 3/220; Am Leg Boys St; Trs 4-H; Var Capt Socr; Var Swmmng; Var Tennis; 4-H Awd; NHS; Math Clb; Varsity Clb; Band; Boys Natn Rep NJ 87; 4-H Clb Cong Rep 87; Natl Mke Wth Wl 2nd Pl 87; US Air Force Acad; Engrng.

ISNER, EMIL; Highland Regional HS; Blackwood, NJ; (3); Aud/Vis; Radio Clb; Hon Roll; JV Trk; JV Wrstlng; Cert Actvty Pts 86-87; Comm.

ISOLDI, ALEECE; Lyndhurst HS; Lyndhurst, NJ; (3); 24/174; Cmnty Wkr; Girl Scts; Service Clb; Stat Bsktbl; JV Var Sftbl; Elks Awd; High Hon Roll; Office Aide; JV Vllybl; Grl Sct Slvr Awd 84; Bergen Cnty Cnslrs Assn Caring Awd 86; Psych.

ISOLDI, PETER; Lyndhurst HS; Lyndhurst, NJ; (2); German Clb; Office Aide; JV Ftbl; JV Trk; Hon Roll; Acctng.

ISRANI, AJAY; Montville Township HS; Edison, NJ; (4); Cmnty Wkr; Science Clb; Nwsp Ed-Chief; High Hon Roll; Rotary Awd; High Hnr Roll Cert 87; Awd For Cmmnty Svc As First Aid Sqd 87; Awd Rtry Clb 87; Rutgers Coll; Bio.

ITA, ESSIEN; South River HS; South River, NJ; (3); Boy Scts; Church Yth Grp; French Clb; Rep Stu Cncl; Im Bsktbl; Var Socr; Cit Awd; God Cntry Awd; Brotherhd Order Arrow 87; Chem Engr.

ITALIANO, FRANK; Edgewood HS; Elm, NJ; (3); Wrstlng; Hon Roll; MIP Wrstlg 84-85; Utlty.

ITALIANO, JOE; Edgewood SR HS; Hammonton, NJ; (3); 11/390; Quiz Bowl; Varsity Clb; Capt Wrstlng; High Hon Roll; Hon Roll; Jr NHS; NHS; Questor Awd In Alg II 86; Dist Prsn Awd Mar 86-87; Med.

IULIANO, TINA MARIE; St Marys Of The Assumption HS; Elizabeth, NJ; (2); Church Yth Grp; Debate Tm; School Musical; Pres Frsh Cls; Rep Soph Cls; Stu Cncl; Vllybl; Music Achvt Cert 86-87; Cert Of Awd Hist Fair 1st Pl 86-87; Counciling.

IURATO, JOSEPHINE; Mary Help Of Christians Acad; Paterson, NJ; (3); SADD; Im Bsktbl; Computer Clb; Sftbl; Vllybl.

IVAHNENKO, GREG; Florence Twp Mem HS; Roebling, NJ; (3); Am Leg Boys St; Stage Crew; JV Bsbl.

IVERSON, BRADFORD; Cresskill HS; Cresskill, NJ; (2); 21/104; Debate Tm; Ski Clb; Nwsp Rptr; Rep Stu Cncl; JV Tennis; JV Trk; Hon Roll; Cornell; Bus.

IVES, CHARLES M; Blair Acad; Blairstown, NJ; (3); Art Clb; Pep Clb; Teachers Aide; Yrbk Rptr; Yrbk Stf; VP Bsbl; JV Bsktbl; VP Golf; VP Tennis; High Hon Roll.

IVESON, DAVID; Arthur P Schalick HS; Elmer, NJ; (4); 7/132; Library Aide; Golf; NHS; Arthr P Schlck Schlrshp 87; NJSIAA MJ Schlr/Athlt Awd 87; Widener U; Comp Pgmmr.

IVORY, PATRICE; Immaculate Conception HS; East Orange, NJ; (2); Chorus; Stu Cncl; Trk; High Hon Roll; Hon Roll; Prfct Atten Awd; Cert Achvt Engl 87-86; Hnr Roll Cert 87; Athltc Awd 86; Harvard; Law.

IZQUIERDO, XAVIER; Eastside HS; Paterson, NJ; (3); VP Chess Clb; Computer Clb; Science Clb; Nwsp Rptr; Nwsp Stf; Tennis; Pepsi Schlr Awd 86; WPC Cert Satisfctry Acad Perf Comp Sci 86; 1st Pl Indstrl Arts Crftmnshp 86; Stevens Inst Tech; Comp Sci.

IZURIETA, JEANNETTE; Wayne Hills HS; Wayne, NJ; (3); Church Yth Grp; Cmnty Wkr; French Clb; FBLA; Spanish Clb; Var Tennis; JV Trk; Hon Roll; 2nd Pl-Dbls, Tnns 87; Futurs Unlmtd 85; Exprncng Antch Wkend 86; Intl Stds.

IZZO, JOHN D; Don Bosco Technical HS; Paterson, NJ; (3); 33/90; Am Leg Boys St; Boy Scts; Pres Stu Cncl; Monclair ST; Contractor.

IZZO, JOSEPH; Wall HS; Wall, NJ; (3); 5/314; Boy Scts; Exploring; Var Bowling; High Hon Roll; Hon Roll; NHS; Tutrng Soc 85-87; Biochem.

JABIER, DOLORES; Holy Spirit HS; Absecon, NJ; (3); 40/332; French Clb; Off Jr Cls; Penn ST; Pre-Law.

JABLONSKI, DAVID; Middletown HS South; Red Bank, NJ; (3); Im Socr; Var Trk; JV Wrstlng; Hon Roll; Ntl Merit Ltr; Arch.

JABLONSKI, JEFFREY R; St Peters Prep; Kearny, NJ; (3); 25/178; Am Leg Boys St; Boy Scts; Nwsp Stf; Trs Stu Cncl; Hon Roll; Rep Soph Cls; Rep Jr Cls; HOBY Rep 86; Forn Tm 84-88, Capt 87; Yrbk SR Edtr 87-88; Natl Cath Forn Lg 3rd Pl 86; Modl Congress 86; Law.

JABLOW, LEON; St Peters Preparatory Schl; Jersey City, NJ; (4); 15/196; Mgr Aud/Vis; Chrmn Dance Clb; Drama Clb; French Clb; Mgr School Musical; Mgr School Play; Mgr Stage Crew; Mgr Variety Show; Swmmng; High Hon Roll; Magna Cum Laude Natl Latin Ex; Slv Latin Mdl, Slv Engl Mdl; Pres Acadmc Ftns Awd; USNA Anapolis; Marine Engnrg.

JACCO, JEANINE; Fair Lawn HS; Fair Lawn, NJ; (3); 31/342; Girl Scts; Sec Science Clb; School Musical; Frsh Cls; Soph Cls; Jr Cls; Hon Roll; NHS; Med.

JACELA, ELIZABETH; Immaculate Conception HS; Passaic, NJ; (3); French Clb; Girl Scts; Hosp Aide; JA; Chorus; Rep Frsh Cls; French Hon Soc; Hon Roll; Nrsng.

JACKMAN, BRIAN; Middletown Twp High North; E Keansburg, NJ (2); Boy Scts; Cmnty Wkr; Socr; Wt Lftg; JV Wrstlng; Hon Roll.

JACKOWSKI, MICHELE; Dover HS; Mine Hill, NJ; (3); 70/226; GAA; Latin Clb; Hon Roll.

JACKSON, AARON; Northern Burlington County HS; Mc Guire AFB NJ; (3); Am Leg Boys St; Computer Clb; Math Clb; Math Tm; Var Ftbl; Hon Roll; Ntl Bus Awd 85; Engr.

JACKSON, ADRIANE; Vailsburg HS; Newark, NJ; (3); Debate Tm; Drama Clb; FBLA; Church Choir; Color Guard; Yrbk Stf; Rep Jr Cls; Stu Cncl; Trk; Hon Roll; Seton Hall Upward Bound Stu 87; HS Schlrs Recgntn Awd 87; Bio Awd 86; Hampton U; Brdcst Jrnlsm.

JACKSON, AMY; Summit HS; Summit, NJ; (3); 27/275; Cmnty Wkr; Service Clb; Chorus; Rep Frsh Cls; Rep Soph Cls; Trs Jr Cls; Var JV Fld Hcky; Stat Lcrss; Hon Roll.

JACKSON, CARLA; Matawan Regional HS; Cliffwood Beach, NJ; (3); Aud/Vis; Library Aide; Office Aide; Drill Tm; Bsktbl; Crs Cntry; Var Mgr(s); Trk; Pres Ftnss Awd 83; St Johns; Phrmcy.

JACKSON, CHERYL; John F Kennedy HS; Willingboro, NJ; (3); 17/282; Am Leg Aux Girls St; Dance Clb; Yrbk Stf; VP Jr Cls; Cheerleading; Sftbl; Hon Roll; NHS; Rotary Awd; U IL; Med.

JACKSON, CHRISTINE; University HS; Newark, NJ; (3); Church Yth Grp; JA; Math Clb; Lit Mag; Off Jr Cls; Off Stu Cncl; Crs Cntry; Trk; Cit Awd; High Hon Roll; 1st Pl MLK Jr Essay 86; Awd Maintaning 3.5 GPA In Coll Prep 87; Awd For Cmnty Participation 87; Duke U; Biomedical Engr.

JACKSON, DAWN MICHELLE; Toms River H S South; Toms River NJ; (4); 26/344; OEA; High Hon Roll; Hon Roll; Outstndng Achvt Bus Ed 87; Berkeley Schls Annual Awd Outstndng Bus Achvt 87; Med Sec.

JACKSON, FRAN; Lanape HS; Tabernacle, NJ; (3); Rep Jr Cls; JV Cheerleading; JV Var Mgr(s); Var Mat Maids; JV Var Score Keeper; Stat Wrstlng; Hon Roll; Ballet/Pointe/Jazz Clss 84-87; Early Chldhd Ed.

JACKSON, GININA; Burlington City HS; Burlington, NJ; (2); Band; Chorus; Church Choir; Pres Frsh Cls; Pres Soph Cls; Sec Stu Cncl; Var Bsktbl; Var L Socr; Var L Sftbl; Hon Roll; Obstetrcs.

JACKSON, HARRY; Essex Catholic Boys HS; East Orange, NJ; (3); Var Ftbl; Sftbl; VP Capt Wrstlng; High Hon Roll; Hon Roll; Stdnt Mnth 87; Ply Yr Wrtlg 87; 3rd Dist 7 Wrstlg 140 Lbs 87; Hampton U; Bus Mgmt.

JACKSON, JENNIFER; Whippany Park HS; Whippany, NJ; (3); Exploring; 4-H; Key Clb; Band; Swing Chorus; Sec Frsh Cls; Rep Jr Cls; Var L Cheerleading; Church Yth Grp; Debate Tm; Citznshp Wshngtn Focus 4-H 86; Ldrshp Awd 4-H 86; Poltcl Sci.

JACKSON, KYA; Rancocas Valley Regional HS; Mt Holly, NJ; (2); Church Yth Grp; Debate Tm; Drama Clb; English Clb; Leo Clb; NAACP; PAVAS; Speech Tm; Thesps; Chorus; Theta Pi Omega Chptr, Alpha Kappa Alpha Soroity Ortrcl Cntst 86 & 87; Dstngshd Achvt Awd 86; Pre Law.

JACKSON, LATONYA; Monmouth Regional HS; Eatontown, NJ; (2); Pres Frsh Cls; Pres Soph Cls; Bsktbl; Stat Ftbl; Var Trk; Hon Roll; Stu Advsr To Frshmn 87-88; Paralgl.

JACKSON, MAKIBA ANASTASIA; Eastside HS; Paterson, NJ; (3); 21/500; Computer Clb; Debate Tm; Leo Clb; Science Clb; Chorus; Color Guard; Off Soph Cls; Off Jr Cls; Var JV Cheerleading; Im Sftbl; Chrldng-Varsity Mst Imprvd Tm 87; Engrng.

JACKSON, MARCIA; Vineland HS; Vineland, NJ; (1); Stu Cncl; Hon Roll; Bus.

JACKSON, MAUREEN; Northern Valley Regional HS; Norwood, NJ; (4); 11/270; Church Yth Grp; Yrbk Ed-Chief; Yrbk Stf; High Hon Roll; Hon Roll; NHS; Pres Schlr; John F Shine Schlrshp 87; Bio Awd 84; Stevens Inst Of Tech; Engrng.

JACKSON, RABIAH; Hillside HS; Hillside, NJ; (3); Aud/Vis; Computer Clb; GAA; Color Guard; Trk; Vllybl; Engrng.

JACKSON, SCOTT; Scotch Plain-Fanwood HS; Scotch Pl, NJ; (4); 64/329; AFS; Boy Scts; Quiz Bowl; Pres Mrchg Band; Stu Cncl; Var Capt Trk; JV Capt Vllybl; Cit Awd; Hon Roll; Boy Scouts JR Asst Scoutmstr 86-87; Trck MVP 87; U VA; Envrmntl Sci.

JACKSON, TASHIEKA; St Anthony HS; Jersey Cty, NJ; (3); Var Cheerleading; Co-Capt Sftbl; Hon Roll; Prfct Atten Awd; Pre-Med.

JACKSON, TISHA; Columbia HS; Maplewood, NJ; (3); Ski Clb; Yrbk Stf; Rep Jr Cls; JV Fld Hcky; JV Capt Lcrss; JV Socr.

JACOB, KELLYLYN; Paramus Catholic HS; Saddle Brk, NJ; (2); 30/157; Camera Clb; Church Yth Grp; GAA; Sec Trs Spanish Clb; School Musical; Var Bsktbl; Var Crs Cntry; Var Socr; Var Trk; Bus Mgmt.

JACOBASZ, MONICA; Hamilton-West HS; Yardville, NJ; (3); Am Leg Aux Girls St; GAA; SADD; Var JV Bsktbl; Var Powder Puff Ftbl; JV Sftbl; Hon Roll.

JACOBS, CARRIE; West Orange HS; West Orange, NJ; (4); 1/370; Sec French Clb; Variety Show; Ed Nwsp Stf; Lit Mag; Rep Stu Cncl; French Hon Soc; Jr NHS; NHS; Ntl Merit Ltr; Columbia Prss Assn 1st Plc Fiction 85; Allnc Frncs Awd Poetry Recitation 87; Prncpl Awd Engl & Frch 86; Amherst Coll.

JACOBS, DINA; Elmwood Park Memorial HS; Elmwood Pk, NJ; (3); 23/160; Cmnty Wkr; Dance Clb; Math Clb; Chorus; Nwsp Ed-Chief; Yrbk Phtg; Yrbk Stf; Sec Sr Cls; Hon Roll; Montclair ST; Acctng.

JACOBS, GINA MARIE; Hammonton HS; Hammonton, NJ; (3); Dance Clb; Lib Chorus; School Musical; Ed Nwsp Stf; Stu Cncl; Var Sftbl; NHS; Drama Clb; French Clb; School Play; Acadc Achvt Awd 86 & 87; Dance Awds 85-87; Chem.

JACOBS, JERRY; Linden HS; Linden, NJ; (3); FBLA; Political Wkr; Science Clb; Mrchg Band; School Musical; Nwsp Ed-Chief; Ed Lit Mag; Var L Crs Cntry; Hon Roll; NHS; Law.

JACOBS, JONATHAN R; Blair Acad; Abington, PA; (4); Aud/Vis; Drama Clb; School Play; Lcrss; Chorus; Stage Crew; Rep Frsh Cls; Rep Soph Cls; Var Ftbl.

JACOBS, KATHI; Edgewood Regional SR HS; Sicklerville, NJ; (4); 32/310; Hosp Aide; Yrbk Ed-Chief; Yrbk Stf; Fld Hcky; Hon Roll; Jr NHS; NHS; VFW Awd; Voice Dem Awd; Rider Coll; Bus Adm.

JACOBS, LYLE; Manalapan HS; Manalapan, NJ; (3); Art Clb; JA; Band; Im Badmtn; JV Crs Cntry; JV Ftbl; Im Lcrss; Im Sftbl; JV Trk; Im Vllybl; Intr Dsgn.

JACOBS, MARLENE; Atlantic City HS; Margate, NJ; (4); 3/650; Pres French Clb; Hosp Aide; Model UN; Service Clb; Yrbk Ed-Chief; VP Stu Cncl; NHS; Ntl Merit Ltr; Rutgers Schlr 86; NJ Distinguished Schlr 86; Pre Law.

JACOBS, PAUL; Brick Memorial HS; Lakewood, NJ; (4); 3/290; Math Tm; Concert Band; Jazz Band; Mrchg Band; School Musical; High Hon Roll; NHS; Outstndng Solost Awd Jzz Fstvl 87; Berklee Coll Music Schlrshp 87; Bst Trombn Solost Jzz Fstvl 87; Rutgers Coll; Dntstry.

JACOBS, VALERIE; Northern Valley HS; Old Tappan, NJ; (3); AFS; Ski Clb; SADD; Sec Jr Cls; Sec Sr Cls; JV Bsktbl; JV Sftbl; Var L Tennis; Hon Roll.

JACOBSEN, JANINE; Middletown HS; Middletown, NJ; (2); Teachers Aide.

JACOBSOHN, JUDITH; West Windsor-Plainsboro HS; Princeton Junct, NJ; (3); Model UN; Service Clb; Acpl Chr; Church Choir; Jazz Band; Yrbk Sprt Ed; Var Tennis; High Hon Roll; Church Yth Grp; French Clb; Cmmndd PSATS Ltr 86-87; Mst Imprvd Plyr Tnns 86; All Mercer Cnty Doubls Tm 86; Intl Rltns.

JACOBSON, CHARLES; Middlesex HS; Middlesex, NJ; (2); Ski Clb; Golf; Hon Roll.

JACOBSON, KRISTINE; Burlington City HS; Edgewater Pk, NJ; (4); 11/200; Church Yth Grp; Teachers Aide; Concert Band; Jazz Band; Mrchg Band; Rep Stu Cncl; JV Var Fld Hcky; NHS; Ntl Merit SF; Rotary Awd; Trenton ST Coll; Chem.

JACOBSON, RAYMOND; Livingston HS; Livingston, NJ; (3); 28/420; Am Leg Boys St; Chess Clb; Math Clb; Pres Science Clb; Im Bsktbl; Var Ftbl; Im Sftbl; Var Trk; High Hon Roll; Artrphyscst.

JACOBUS, ROBERT D; Bordentown Regional HS; Bordentown, NJ; (3); Am Leg Boys St; Art Clb; Chess Clb; VP Drama Clb; Key Clb; Q&S; School Musical; School Play; Stage Crew; Nwsp Ed-Chief; Film Maker.

JACOME, SONIA; Emerson HS; Union City, NJ; (3); French Clb; FBLA; Science Clb; Band; Color Guard; Nwsp Stf; Lit Mag; Rep Stu Cncl; French Hon Soc; Am Leg Aux Girls St; Music Awds 85-87; Outstndg Work Biol Awsd 86; Rutgers; Pedtrcn.

JADWINSKI, MICHAEL; Sayreville War Memorial HS; Parlin, NJ; (4); Church Yth Grp; Cmnty Wkr; Yrbk Stf; L JV Bsbl; L Var Ftbl; God Cntry Awd; Distngshd Achvt Varsity & Defensive Back Of Week 86; Catholic Yth Rep Natl Fdrtn Catholic Yth 85-87; Law Enforcement.

JAE, JO; South Brunswick HS; Kendall Pk, NJ; (2); Art Clb; Camera Clb; Church Yth Grp; CAP; Hon Roll; Aerospc Engrng.

JAFFE, DAVID; Fair Lawn HS; Fair Lawn, NJ; (3); 7/343; Am Leg Boys St; Computer Clb; Math Tm; Band; Sec Soph Cls; VP Jr Cls; Pres Sr Cls; Trk; High Hon Roll; NHS.

JAGERNAUTH, JACQUELINE; Columbia HS; Maplewood, NJ; (3); French Hon Soc; Engr.

JAIN, SANJAY; John Paul Stevens HS; Edison, NJ; (3); 4/450; Debate Tm; Hosp Aide; VP Pres Intnl Clb; Math Tm; Model UN; Science Clb; Nwsp Rptr; Yrbk Rptr; French Hon Soc; High Hon Roll; Bus Admin.

JAIN, SUSHIL; Parsippany Hills HS; Parsippany, NJ; (4); 2/305; Pres Computer Clb; Hosp Aide; Key Clb; VP Science Clb; Var L Tennis; Gov Hon Prg Awd; High Hon Roll; NHS; Ntl Merit SF; Sal; Hosp Vlnteer Awd For 300 Hrs 86; Med.

JAKABFI, EVA; St John Vianney HS; Morganville, NJ; (3); 31/275; Intnl Clb; Math Tm; SADD; School Musical; Rep Jr Cls; Var L Cheerleading; Var L Trk; Hon Roll; Math.

JAKIMOWICZ, JOSEPH; Kingsway Regional HS; Swedesboro, NJ; (2); Art Clb; Rep Soph Cls; Crs Cntry; Trk; X-Cntry Frank Marx Awd 87; Art.

JAKOWEICZUK, MICHELLE; Edgewood Regional SR HS; Berlin, NJ; (3); High Hon Roll; Hon Roll; 9th Grade Soc Stud Awd 84-85; Comm.

JAKUBOWSKI, ROBERT; Audubon HS; Audbon, NJ; (3); Am Leg Boys St; Scholastic Bowl; SADD; School Play; Trs Frsh Cls; VP Soph Cls; Trs Jr Cls; Trs Sr Cls; Trs Pres Stu Cncl; Var Capt Socr; Pre Law.

JAMES, BENJAMIN; Mc Corristin HS; Trenton, NJ; (3); Am Leg Boys St; Boy Scts; Cmnty Wkr; Pep Clb; Chorus; Rep Frsh Cls; Rep Soph Cls; Hon Roll; Amer Lgn Boys ST 87; 1st Pl Oratorcl Cnty Lvl Cntst 86; Military Pilot.

JAMES, CATHERINE A; Millburn SR HS; Short Hills, NJ; (4); 3/249; Math Tm; Science Clb; Band; Drm Mjr(t); Jazz Band; Orch; Ed Lit Mag; Ntl Merit SF; Church Yth Grp; Concert Band; RPI Sci Awd 86; NW Govrnrs Schl Sci 86.

JAMES, CHARISSE; Paterson Catholic HS; Paterson, NJ; (2); Church Yth Grp; Dance Clb; Red Cross Aide; Chorus; Church Choir; Color Guard; JV Var Cheerleading; Pom Pon; Vllybl.

JAMES, ELAINE; Linden HS; Linden, NJ; (3); FHA; Girl Scts; Bus.

JAMES, JENNIFER; Satinsky Inst; Camden, NJ; (4); French Clb; Latin Clb; Var Gym; Var Trk; Omega Inst; Law.

JAMES, SHAVONNE; Hillside HS; Hillside, NJ; (3); 25/238; Sec Leo Clb; Math Tm; Spanish Clb; Band; Concert Band; Mrchg Band; Rep Sr Cls; Capt Cheerleading; Mgr(s); Hon Roll; Chrldng Awds 86-87; Band Awd 85; U Of MD; Accntnt.

JAMES, SHERWIN; Dover HS; Dover, NJ; (4); 2/183; Trs Computer Clb; Math Tm; Yrbk Stf; Trs Stu Cncl; High Hon Roll; Masonic Awd; Pres NHS; Ntl Merit Schol; Prfct Atten Awd; Sal; Rensslr Math & Sci Awd 86; Grdn ST Distngshd Schlr 86-87; Rensselaer Polytech Inst.

JAMES, VENORA; Dwight Morrow HS; Ft Lauderdale, FL; (3); 43/312; Drama Clb; Hosp Aide; Hon Roll; Mdl 150 Hrs Candy Striping 85; U Of Miami; Psych.

JAMES, WANDA; University HS; Newark, NJ; (2); Yrbk Stf; VP Frsh Cls; Pres Soph Cls; VP Stu Cncl; Trenton ST Coll; Psych.

JAMIESON, SUE; Burlington Township HS; Burlington, NJ; (3); Varsity Clb; Band; Jazz Band; Fld Hcky; Trk; Hon Roll; Concert Band; Madrigals; Mrchg Band; Pep Band; Law.

JAN, STEPHEN Y; The Lawrenceville Schl; Cranbury, NJ; (4); VP Computer Clb; Math Tm; Sec Trs Science Clb; Lit Mag; Im Tennis; Hon Roll; Ntl Merit SF; Pres Schlr; Church Yth Grp; Library Aide; Corby Cmptr Mgr Prz 86; NJ Msc Tchrs Assoc Annl Adtns 83 Hnrs Awd 83; Med.

JANDOLI, DOUGLAS; West Orange HS; W Orange, NJ; (3); Var Bsbl; Var Ftbl; Hon Roll; Crmnl Jstc.

JANECZEK, SUSAN; East Brunswick HS; E Brunswick, NJ; (4); Dance Clb; Math Clb; Pep Clb; Red Cross Aide; Science Clb; Chorus; Lit Mag; Hon Roll; NHS; Rutgers U; Med.

JANNS, CATHERINE A; Spotswood HS; Spotswood, NJ; (4); 1/186; Am Leg Aux Girls St; Math Tm; Science Clb; Yrbk Ed-Chief; Socr; Tennis; Trk; High Hon Roll; Pres NHS; Trk Schlr Ath Awd 86; Ten Coach Awd 86; Med.

JANOSKY, GLENN; Newton HS; Newton, NJ; (2); 32/230; Church Yth Grp; Varsity Clb; Var Tennis; Hon Roll; Penn ST; Bus.

JANOWSKY, KAREN; North Hunterdon HS; Boca Raton, FL; (3); 18/328; Dance Clb; JA; Spanish Clb; Temple Yth Grp; Mrchg Band; Symp Band; Yrbk Rptr; Yrbk Stf; High Hon Roll; Jr NHS; Spnsh Acad Achvt Awd 86; NJ Yth Symphny Ensmbl Pgm 87; Acad Achvt Awd 86; Psych.

JANSEN, ELIZABETH; Manchester Regional HS; Haledon, NJ; (3); Church Yth Grp; Pep Clb; Science Clb; Yrbk Stf; Rep Frsh Cls; Rep Soph Cls; Rep Jr Cls; Rep Sr Cls; Rep Stu Cncl; JV Cheerleading; Pharm.

JANSKY, GREGORY; Red Bank Regional HS; Little Silver, NJ; (3); Boy Scts; Church Yth Grp; Nwsp Ed-Chief; Var Capt Socr; God Cntry Awd; Hon Roll; Eagle Sct 87; Ordr Arrow 85; Appalachian Srvc Prjct 86; Bus Admin.

JANSSEN, TIFANI; Wayne Hills HS; Wayne, NJ; (3); CAP; Band; Chorus; Mrchg Band; Bsktbl; Fld Hcky; Socr; Sftbl; Hon Roll.

JANTZ, JENNIFER; Middletown South HS; Lincroft, NJ; (2); Cmnty Wkr; 4-H; German Clb; Girl Scts; Chorus; Jazz Band; Mrchg Band; Sftbl; Twrlr; High Hon Roll; Dartmouth; Math.

JANULIN, CHRISTINE; High Point Regional HS; Sussex, NJ; (2); 3/300; Var Bsktbl; Wt Lftg; High Hon Roll; Intl Frgn Lang Awd Frnch 86-87; Pol Sci.

JANUSZ, ALINA; Wallington HS; Wallington, NJ; (2); Exploring; Chorus; Hon Roll; Med.

JANUZZI, GEORGE; Notre Dame HS; Monmouth Jct, NJ; (2); 32/385; Church Yth Grp; Ski Clb; Bsbl; Ftbl; Hon Roll; Ltn Hnr Soc 87; Ltn Achvt Awd 86-87.

JAO, JANE; Morris Catholic HS; Rockaway, NJ; (3); 2/135; Cmnty Wkr; Pres German Clb; Math Clb; Math Tm; Natl Beta Clb; Scholastic Bowl; Varsity Clb; JV Bsktbl; Var L Crs Cntry; Var Swmmng; Wrld Affr Smnr; Deans Smmr Schlr Pgm; Stevens Wmn Eng & Mng Smmr Pgm.

JAQUINET, MARIA; Memorial HS; West New York, NJ; (3); 10/300; Math Clb; Spanish Clb; Rep Frsh Cls; Rep Soph Cls; Rep Jr Cls; Rep Stu Cncl; High Hon Roll; Hon Roll; NHS; Engrng.

JARDINE, JAY; Dover HS; Mine Hill, NJ; (3); 18/228; German Clb; Math Tm; Q&S; School Musical; School Play; Nwsp Ed-Chief; JV Wrstlng; High Hon Roll; NHS; Ntl Merit Ltr; Century 21 Cert Prfcncy-Acctg 86 & 87.

JARIUS, LISA; Union Catholic HS; Roselle, NJ; (3); Office Aide; Service Clb; High Hon Roll; Hon Roll; NHS; Acctg Awd 87; Engl Awd 87; Religion Awd 87; Villanova; Acctg.

JASINSKI, MARK; Bruck HS; Brick, NJ; (4); 10/350; Varsity Clb; Band; Concert Band; Jazz Band; Mrchg Band; School Musical; Var L Bsktbl; High Hon Roll; NHS; Primerica Fndtn Scholar 87; Big A Awd Acad & Ath Achvt 87; Seton Hall U; Bus Mgmt.

JASKIEWICZ, FRANCINE; Bishop Eustace Prep Schl; Medford, NJ; (1); SADD; JV Cheerleading; Mgr Ice Hcky; Knghts Columbus Mrt Schlrshp 86; U Of Toronto; Ownr Mgr Pro Hcky.

JASPER, SALLIE; Plainfield HS; Plainfield, NJ; (3); 46/359; Camera Clb; Church Yth Grp; Girl Scts; VP Library Aide; Science Clb; Chorus; Rep Frsh Cls; Rep Soph Cls; Rep Jr Cls; Pom Pon; Lg Women Voters Scholar 87; Stu Mnth Hstry 86; NHS 87; Georgetown U; Pre-Med.

JASTRZEBSKI, MELODY; South River HS; S River, NJ; (2); VP Library Aide; Band; Mrchg Band; Pep Band; Symp Band; Lit Mag; Trk; Hon Roll; NHS; Schl Athl Awd 85-86; Future Problm Slvng Team 86-87; Rutgers; Med.

JAUREGUI, JOSE RODERICK; Marist HS; Bayonne, NJ; (4); 10/98; Trs Boys Clb Am; Key Clb; Nwsp Stf; Yrbk Stf; Rep Sr Cls; Rep Stu Cncl; Tennis; High Hon Roll; NHS; NY U; Bio.

JAVICK, MARGARET MARY; West Windsor Plainsboro HS; Princeton Jct, NJ; (3); VP Church Yth Grp; FBLA; Library Aide; Band; Chorus; Church Choir; JV Bsktbl; Score Keeper; Var Socr; Var JV Sftbl; Bus.

JAVIER, CESAR AUGUSTO T; William L Dickinson HS; Jersey City, NJ; (3); 2/400; Camera Clb; Computer Clb; Scholastic Bowl; Science Clb; Nwsp Stf; Yrbk Stf; Trs NHS; Prfct Atten Awd; St Sci Day Awd 86; Kean Coll; Physical Thrpst.

JAVIER, JOSEPH D; Hudson Catholic HS; Jersey City, NJ; (3); 5/168; Chess Clb; Math Clb; Science Clb; Im JV Socr; Im Vllybl; Hon Roll; NHS; Math Tm; De La Salle Acadc Schlrshp 84-87; Fine Art Awd 86; 1st Pl Chss Trphy 85; Arch.

JAY, KATHLEEN; Kent Place Schl; Chatham, NJ; (4); Art Clb; Cmnty Wkr; French Clb; Hosp Aide; Intnl Clb; Latin Clb; Spanish Clb; Teachers Aide; Concert Band; Nwsp Rptr; Rutgers U; Ecnmcs.

JEAN-LOUIS, CLIFFORD; St Joseph Regional HS; Spring Valley, NY; (3); 145/250; Var Church Yth Grp; Spanish Clb; Var Ftbl; Var Sftbl; Var Trk; Spanish NHS; MVP Trk & Fld 84-85; Law.

JECMENICA, KATHERINE; Cliffside Park HS; Cliffside Pk, NJ; (3); 5/234; Am Leg Aux Girls St; Math Tm; Sec VP Spanish Clb; Nwsp Rptr; Lit Mag; Var Tennis; NHS; Ntl Merit Ltr; Acad Decathlon NJ Gold Mdl Wnnr Essay 87; Foreing Lang Forensic Tourn Awd 86; U S Military Acad; Eng.

JEDZINAK, JENNIFER; Roselle Catholic HS; Roselle Park, NJ; (4); Drama Clb; Yrbk Stf; Rep Soph Cls; VP Stu Cncl; JV Capt Cheerleading; Var Swmmng; Var Tennis; French Hon Soc; NHS; Hon Roll; FL Int Of Tech; Marine Biol.

JEFFERIS, THYRA; South Hunterdon Regional HS; Lambertville, NJ; (3); 6/76; Key Clb; Var Capt Fld Hcky; Var Sftbl; NHS; Church Yth Grp; Spanish Clb; Chorus; Stage Crew; Sec Frsh Cls; Stu Cncl; MVP Field Hockey 85-86; Sftbl 87; All West Jersey Sftbl 87; 1st Team All Central Jersey Fld Hcky 85; James Madison U; Intl Bus.

JEFFERSON, KARYN; Immaculate Conception HS; Orange, NJ; (3); Girl Scts; Pep Clb; Chorus; Church Choir; Rep Frsh Cls; Pres Soph Cls; Rep Jr Cls; Stu Cncl; Bsktbl; Sftbl; Duke U; Engl.

JEFFERY, JOANNE; Pequamock Township HS; Pompton Plains, NJ; (3); 32/215; Church Yth Grp; Office Aide; Varsity Clb; Concert Band; Mrchg Band; Stat Gym; Var Socr; Var Stat Sftbl; Var Trk; NHS; Chem Engrng.

JEHLE, JENNIFER; Union HS; Union, NJ; (2); Drama Clb; Spanish Clb; Mgr Mrchg Band; Nwsp Stf; Im Fld Hcky; Mgr(s); Score Keeper; Stat Wrstlng; Hon Roll; Jr NHS; Pres Acad Fitness Awd 86.

JEKER, NATALIE; St James HS; Carneys Point, NJ; (3); Art Clb; French Clb; Stage Crew; Var Capt Cheerleading; Fld Hcky; Hon Roll; Comm Art.

JELINEK, MARGARET; Freehold Township HS; Freehold, NJ; (4); 9/353; Pres Drama Clb; Band; Drm Mjr(t); Mrchg Band; School Musical; School Play; Lit Mag; Cit Awd; JP Sousa Awd; NHS; Bst All Arnd Stu 87; Yth Yr 87; Soroptimist Schlrshp 87; Rice U; English.

JELINSKI, JODI; Edgewood Regional SR HS; Hammonton, NJ; (2); Chorus; Rep Soph Cls; Var Hon Roll; Ouestor Awd For Englsh 86-87; Bus.

JELVEH, NAZANIN; Paramus Catholic Girls HS; Dix Hills, NY; (3); Trk; Prfct Atten Awd; Med.

JENGEHINO, SUSAN; Cumberland Regional HS; Bridgeton, NJ; (4); Church Yth Grp; Hosp Aide; Intnl Clb; Trs Red Cross Aide; Spanish Clb; Mrchg Band; Yrbk Stf; High Hon Roll; Hon Roll; Millersville U Of PA; Lbrl Art.

JENKINS, ATHENA R; Millville SR HS; Cedarville, NJ; (3); DECA; Chorus; Brandywine; Fshn Merch.

JENKINS, DENISE; Holy Spirit HS; Absecon, NJ; (4); JV Bsktbl; L Var Socr; L Var Sftbl; Stockton ST Coll; Physcl Thrpy.

JENKINS, IRENE; Westfield SR HS; Westfield, NJ; (4); Church Yth Grp; JA; Orch; JV Bsktbl; Sftbl; Hon Roll; JC Awd; Rotary Club 87; Rutgers; Acctng.

JENKINS, JACKIE; Riverside HS; Delanco, NJ; (3); 8/111; Am Leg Aux Girls St; Church Yth Grp; Dance Clb; Nwsp Rptr; Yrbk Ed-Chief; Yrbk Phtg; Yrbk Stf; Band; Concert Band; Mrchg Band; Nwspr Asst Editor; Nwspr News Editor; Yrbk Acadmcs & Fclty Editor; Photography.

JENKINS, JOANN; New Brunswick HS; New Brunswick, NJ; (3); Church Yth Grp; Girl Scts; Hosp Aide; Church Choir; Capt Drill Tm; Rep Frsh Cls; Rep Stu Cncl; JV Var Bsktbl; Capt Pom Pon; Var Sftbl; Nrsng.

JENKINS, JOSEPH; Middle Township HS; Delhaven, NJ; (4); Ski Clb; Crs Cntry; Ftbl; Trk; Wt Lftg; Hon Roll.

JENKINS, KIMBERLEY B; Spotswood HS; Spotswood, NJ; (2); Intnl Clb; Concert Band; Nwsp Rptr; Yrbk Stf; Sec Frsh Cls; Rep Soph Cls; Off Stu Cncl; Var L Tennis; JV L Trk; Hon Roll; Retgers; Interntl Corp Law.

JENKINS, LA SHAWN ANTOINETTE; Red Bank Regional HS; Red Bank, NJ; (3); Church Yth Grp; Girl Scts; NAACP; Spanish Clb; Flag Corp; Cit Awd; God Cntry Awd; Hon Roll; Jr NHS; Spanish NHS; Candy Striper Red Bank Med Ctr; Flag Twirler 85; Spanish Hnr Soc 85; Silver Awd Girl Scouting 85; Comp Sci.

JENKINS, MICHAEL L; Northern Burlington Cnty Rgnl HS; Mc Guire Afb, NJ; (3); Am Leg Boys St; Church Yth Grp; FCA; JV Ftbl; L Trk; ST Cmpttn YMCA Rly Swm Tm 85; Math.

JENKINS, SAMUEL B; Rancocas Valley Regional HS; Mt Holly, NJ; (3); Am Leg Boys St; French Clb; Var Ftbl; Var Trk; Var Wrstlng; 2nd Tm All Stars Ftbl 86-87; Pittsburgh U; Engrng.

JENKINS, TINA; Cherokee HS; Marlton, NJ; (4); 113/413; Red Cross Aide; Spanish Clb; SADD; VP Stu Cncl; Var Capt Cheerleading; JV Sftbl; Hon Roll; Ntl Confrnc Stu Cncl OK City 86; Outstndng Chrldr Burlngtn CO 86; NJ ST Fnlst Miss AM Co-Ed 84-85; Educ.

JENKINS, VERONICA; Mount Saint Mary Acad; Plainfield, NJ; (3); 23/87; VP Band; Concert Band; Var Stat Bsktbl; Mgr(s); Var Tennis; French Hon Soc; Hon Roll; Drama Clb; French Clb; Office Aide; Hnrs Engl & Music 86-87; TAG Prog 86; Pharmcy.

JENNINGS, MARK; Allentown HS; Cream Ridge, NJ; (3); 9/205; Am Leg Boys St; Computer Clb; Math Clb; Math Tm; Scholastic Bowl; Stage Crew; Hon Roll; Ntl Merit Ltr; Comp Pgmr.

JENNINGS, PAUL; Lower Cape May Regional HS; N Cape May, NJ; (4); Chorus; Orch; School Musical; School Play; Stage Crew; Yrbk Stf; Boy Scts; Stockton ST Coll; Arts.

JENNISON, FIONA; Toms River North HS; Toms River, NJ; (3); 87/459; Nwsp Stf; Yrbk Stf; JV Tennis; Var Trk; Physcl Educ Ftnss Tst 86-87; AZ ST; Journalism.

JENSEN, KURT; Lower Cape May Regional HS; Cape May, NJ; (4); 50/220; Ski Clb; Varsity Clb; Bsktbl; Socr; Trk; Vllybl; Wt Lftg; Hon Roll; Rider Coll; Pre Law.

JENSH, VICTORIA; Haddonfield Memorial HS; Haddonfield, NJ; (4); Church Yth Grp; Intnl Clb; Church Choir; Mrchg Band; Variety Show; Yrbk Rptr; Yrbk Stf; JV Var Bowling; JV Mgr(s); Var Trk; Child Psych.

JENSSEN, JAMES; Indian Hills HS; Oakland, NJ; (3); 43/306; Boy Scts; Chess Clb; Church Yth Grp; Science Clb; Mgr Nwsp Stf; JV Bowling; Hon Roll; Ad Altare Dei Religious Awd 84; Chem.

JENT, ANGELA; Absegami HS; Mays Landing, NJ; (1); Band; Gym; Jazz Band; Mdls & Rbbns Gym Comp 83-87; Asst Tchr Gym; Intr Decor.

JERNG, DIANE; Montville Township HS; Montville, NJ; (3); 8/278; Key Clb; Math Clb; Science Clb; Concert Band; Mrchg Band; Trk; NHS; FBLA; Math Tm; Band; F Boughton Mem Piano Comp 1st 85; R E Lanning Mem Piano Comp 1st 86; Natl Merit Commnd Schlr 87; Med.

JERRIS, RANDON MATTHEW; Delbarton Schl; Brookside, NJ; (4); 4/109; Church Yth Grp; Cmnty Wkr; Math Tm; Model UN; Red Cross Aide; Science Clb; Ski Clb; JV Crs Cntry; Var L Golf; High Hon Roll; Warner-Lambert Schlrshp 87; Delbarton Mdl Excllnc In Engl Cmptn 87; Red Cross Outstndng Svc Awd 87; Williams Coll; Art Hstry.

JERROLD-JONES, TERESA; Rancocas Valley Regional HS; Mt Holly, NJ; (3); 45/286; Church Yth Grp; Band; Concert Band; School Musical; Rep Soph Cls; Rep Stu Cncl; Capt JV Fld Hcky; Var Sftbl; Hon Roll; Voice Dem Awd; Physcl Thrpy.

JESPERSEN, DAVID; Cumberland Regional HS; Bridgeton, NJ; (3); 6/384; Library Aide; Ski Clb; JV Socr; Var Capt Tennis; High Hon Roll.

JESSEN, LAUREN; Bayonne HS; Bayonne, NJ; (4); 39/350; School Play; Variety Show; Nwsp Stf; Lit Mag; Rep Jr Cls; Rep Sr Cls; Hon Roll; NHS; Bus Law Awd 87; Montclair ST Coll; Bus Admin.

JESTEADT, GREGORY; Hunterdon Central Regional HS; Flemington, NJ; (3); 200/550; Boy Scts; Church Yth Grp; JV Var Bsbl; Religion.

JETTER JR, CHRISTIAN; Pitman HS; Pitman, NJ; (3); 11/158; Cmnty Wkr; Key Clb; Rep Frsh Cls; VP Jr Cls; Rep Stu Cncl; Var Socr; Var Swmmng; Var Tennis; High Hon Roll; Hon Roll.

JEWELL JR, ELWIN E; Atlantic Christian Schl; Ventnor, NJ; (4); 4/14; School Play; Yrbk Stf; VP Frsh Cls; VP Soph Cls; VP Jr Cls; VP Sr Cls; Var Bsbl; JV Var Bsktbl; Var Capt Socr; NHS; Taylor U; Law.

JEWERS, BILLIE JO; Jackson Memorial HS; Jackson, NJ; (3); Aud/Vis; German Clb; Library Aide; SADD; Varsity Clb; Band; Mrchg Band; Nwsp Ed-Chief; Nwsp Rptr; Nwsp Sprt Ed; Socr Awd 85-86; Rutgers U; Psych.

JIMENEZ, BELINDA; Our Lady Of Good Counsel HS; Newark, NJ; (3); 40/120; Capt Pep Clb; Y-Teens; Chorus; Capt Sftbl; Wt Lftg.

JIMENEZ, CARLOS; Dwight Morrow HS; Englewood, NJ; (3); Chess Clb; Var Capt Bsbl; Var Socr; High Hon Roll; Prfct Atten Awd; Bus Admin.

JIMENEZ, CAROLINA; Washington Township HS; Sewell, NJ; (3); Church Yth Grp; French Clb; Spanish Clb; Sftbl; Tennis; Hon Roll; Psych.

JIMENEZ, DIANA; Mary Help Of Christians Acad; Paterson, NJ; (2); Church Yth Grp; SADD; Teachers Aide; Var Bsktbl; Im Vllybl; Hon Roll; Trust Funds 85-87; Farleigh Dickinson U; Acctg.

JIMENEZ, MAGDA; Weehawken HS; Weehawken, NJ; (3); 3/100; Intnl Clb; Math Clb; Yrbk Stf; Trs Rep Frsh Cls; Trs Rep Soph Cls; Trs Rep Jr Cls; Cheerleading; High Hon Roll; NHS; Pre-Law.

JO, ANNA; Burlington City HS; Edgewater Park, NJ; (4); 3/191; Trs Jr Cls; Trs Sr Cls; Rep Stu Cncl; JV Fld Hcky; Stat Trk; High Hon Roll; Pres NHS; Key Clb; Yrbk Stf; Pres Schlr; Rtry Clb Brlngtn Schlrshp; Ntl Hnr Soc Schlrshp; Untd Jrsy Bnk-Fdlty Bnk Schlrshp; Widener U; Mrchndsng.

JOANNIDIS, NICKOLAS; Saddle Brook HS; Saddle Brook, NJ; (4); 1/110; Am Leg Boys St; Math Clb; Quiz Bowl; Spanish Clb; Yrbk Sprt Ed; Crs Cntry; Trk; High Hon Roll; NHS; Val; PACE U Full Tuition, Interchange ST Bank & Cakulus Awds 87; PACE U; Accntng.

JOBES, CHRISTOPHER S; Paul VI HS; Turnersville, NJ; (3); Math Clb; Yrbk Stf; Bowling; U Of PA; Med.

JOBES, SANDRA; Wall High HS; Wall, NJ; (3); 8/350; Computer Clb; Drama Clb; French Clb; Girl Scts; Hosp Aide; Key Clb; High Hon Roll; Kiwanis Awd.

JOBIN, SARA E; Montclair HS; Toledo, OH; (4); 13/420; Church Yth Grp; Band; Church Choir; NHS; St Schlr; Concert Band; Jazz Band; Mrchg Band; Rep Stu Cncl; Hon Roll; NJ Music Eductrs Assn Adll Wllmns Cert 87; Natl Fedrtn Music Clbs Yng Artst Awd 86; Natl Yng Ldrs Cnf; Harvard; Music.

JOEHNK, TRACY; Secaucus HS; Secaucus, NJ; (3); Girl Scts; Library Aide; Spanish Clb; Variety Show; JV Stat Ftbl; JV Stat Mgr(s); Hon Roll; Berkeley; Exec Secy.

JOEL, PETER A; Riverdell Regional HS; Oradell, NJ; (3); 23/240; Am Leg Boys St; SADD; Nwsp Sprt Ed; Trs Jr Cls; Trs Sr Cls; Ftbl; Trk; Capt Wrstlng; NHS.

JOESTEN, ERIC; Bridgewater-Raritan HS East; Bridgewater, NJ; (3); Bsbl; Var L Diving; JV Socr; Var L Swmmng; JV Tennis; High Hon Roll; Hon Roll; NHS; Natl Intrschlstc Swmg Coachs Assn Of Amer ST Top 10 Awd Divg 87; Arch.

JOFFE, ELLIOTT S; Watchung Hills Regional HS; Watchung, NJ; (4); 7/330; Math Tm; Ed Lit Mag; Soph Cls; Hon Roll; Ntl Merit SF; Debtng Awd 85-87; Bus.

JOHANESSEN, HAROLD; Paramus Catholic Boys HS; Hackensack, NJ; (4); 67/223; Computer Clb; Math Clb; Math Tm; Lit Mag; Bergen CC; Psych.

JOHANSON, MARY; Washington Twp HS; Sewell, NJ; (3); German Clb; Jazz Band; Bsktbl; Tennis; Hon Roll; Germn.

JOHN, VARGHESE P; St Mary HS; Jersey City, NJ; (4); 5/102; Nwsp Stf; Yrbk Stf; CC Awd; High Hon Roll; NHS; Cmnty Wkr; Nwsp Rptr; Var Tennis; Im Vllybl; Hon Roll; Cert Hnr Recgntn Excllnce Scholar 87; Pres Citation Acad Achvt 86; Excllnce Awd Comp II; Marion Awd; NJ Inst Tech; Comp Sci.

JOHNSON, ANGELA; Washington Township HS; Sewell, NJ; (3); Art Clb; Church Yth Grp; DECA; Church Choir; Drama Clb; Q&S; Teachers Aide; Trk; Sun Schl Fin Sec 80-87; DECA Awd 86; Apprctn Awd-Svc To Chrch 87; Phila Coll Of Textiles & Sci.

JOHNSON, BARBARA ANNETTE; Moorestown Friends Schl; Riverside, NJ; (3); Pres French Clb; Chorus; School Musical; Ntl Merit Ltr; AFS; Am Leg Aux Girls St; School Play; Variety Show; Lit Mag; L JV Bsktbl; Cum Laude Soc 86-88; Le Grand Concours-Ntl Rnk 85-87; Rutgers Schlr 87; Chmbr Choir 3 Yrs; Econ.

JOHNSON, CARLA D; West Windsor Plainsboro HS; Princeton Jct, NJ; (4); 174/287; Church Yth Grp; Cmnty Wkr; Debate Tm; French Clb; Chorus; School Musical; Var L Fld Hcky; Schrlshp Pgm Outstndng Negro Stu 86; Afro Am Awareness Clb 86-87; Curry Coll; Mgmt.

JOHNSON, CHRISTOPHER; Trenton HS; Trenton, NJ; (3); JV Ftbl; JV Golf; Hon Roll; Hnr Awd Mst Imprvd Stu 86-87.

JOHNSON, CRAIG A; Plainfield HS; Plainfield, NJ; (4); 96/371; Pres DECA; Science Clb; Band; Concert Band; Jazz Band; Mrchg Band; Stu Cncl; Mgr Bsktbl; Mcs Hnrs 83-86; DECA Hnrs In Mgmt & Cmmnctns 85-86; Peer Ldrshp 86-87; Morgan; Ecnmcs.

JOHNSON, CRYSTAL; Camden Catholic HS; Camden, NJ; (2); 171/283; Hosp Aide; Chorus; JV Bowling; Trk; Hon Roll; Pre Med.

JOHNSON, CYNTHIA D; Ramapo HS; Franklin Lakes, NJ; (4); 6/329; Sec AFS; Church Yth Grp; Drama Clb; Thesps; Stage Crew; Ed Nwsp Stf; Lit Mag; Powder Puff Ftbl; High Hon Roll; Hon Roll; Natl Mrt Schlrshp 86; Supr List 86; Mrt Awd Physcs Pre-Cal Bio Eng Frnch 84-86; Biopsychology.

JOHNSON, DEBORAH; Benedictine Acad; Newark, NJ; (3); Cmnty Wkr; Drama Clb; GAA; Ski Clb; Church Choir; VP Jr Cls; JV Var Bsktbl; Hon Roll; Prfct Atten Awd; US Army Reserve Awd 87; Kean Coll; Chldhd Devlpmt.

JOHNSON, DEBORAH; Salem HS; Salem, NJ; (3); Exploring; 4-H; Hosp Aide; Math Clb; Spanish Clb; Thesps; Band; Chorus; 4-H Awd; NHS; NJ Gvrnrs Schl Sci 87; NJ Girls Ctznshp Inst 87.

JOHNSON, DEBRA; Glassboro HS; Glassboro, NJ; (3); Drama Clb; Hosp Aide; Thesps; Chorus; Madrigals; School Musical; School Play; Stage Crew; Hon Roll; NHS; Law.

JOHNSON, DUSTI; Salem HS; Salem, NJ; (3); Cmnty Wkr; Computer Clb; Pep Clb; SADD; Chorus; Yrbk Stf; Capt Cheerleading; Cit Awd; Hon Roll; NHS; Outstndng Stu Mth 86-87; Frnds Anmls Club 86-87; Stu Peer Cnslr 86-87; Elem Ed.

JOHNSON, EVERETT; University HS; Newark, NJ; (2); FBLA; Pep Clb; School Play; Stu Cncl; Trk; Hon Roll; NJ Inst Tech; Math-Sci.

JOHNSON, FALESHA; Trenton Central HS; Trenton, NJ; (3); Trk; Odom Awd 85; Hampton U; Law.

JOHNSON, HANS; Woodstown HS; Hixson, TN; (3); Chess Clb; Drama Clb; JA; Key Clb; Latin Clb; Ski Clb; JV Bsbl; JV Ftbl; JV Capt Socr; Var Swmmng; Embry-Riddel; Aviatn Manag.

JOHNSON, JACQUELINE; Our Lady Of Mercy Acad; Brigantine, NJ; (2); Computer Clb; Dance Clb; Yrbk Stf; Badmtn; Bsktbl; VP Crs Cntry; Swmmng; High Hon Roll; Hugh O Brian Awd 86-87; Rep Engl Dept Open Hse 86-87; Ntl Sci Merit Awd 86-87.

JOHNSON, JAY M; Cherokee HS; Marlton, NJ; (4); 93/398; Boy Scts; German Clb; Math Tm; Science Clb; SADD; JV Socr; JV Var Swmmng; JV Var Trk; Ntl Merit Ltr; Ntl Achvmnt Fnlst; Ntl Achvmnt Schlrshp; MI ST U; Chem.

JOHNSON, JENNY; South Hunterdon Regional HS; Lambertville, NJ; (4); 3/71; Drama Clb; Thesps; Chorus; Concert Band; Madrigals; Mrchg Band; School Musical; Variety Show; Ed Yrbk Stf; NHS; Spnsh-Intl Frgn Lang Awd 86-87; Douglass Coll; Advrtsng.

JOHNSON, JOAN; Orange HS; Orange, NJ; (3); Cmnty Wkr; GAA; Hosp Aide; JA; Service Clb; Y-Teens; Flag Corp; Bsktbl; Hon Roll; NHS; Princeton; Sci.

JOHNSON, JOANNA LEE; Neptune SR HS; Neptune, NJ; (4); 21/355; Drama Clb; GAA; Ski Clb; Varsity Clb; Mgr Stage Crew; Yrbk Ed-Chief; Lit Mag; Capt Swmmng; NHS; Pres Acdmc Ftnss Awd 87; James Madison U; Rcrtn Mgmt.

JOHNSON, JUSTINE; Lower Cape May Regional HS; Cape May, NJ; (3); Office Aide; Pep Clb; Ski Clb; Varsity Clb; Variety Show; Var L Cheerleading; JV L Sftbl; Im Wt Lftg; Presdntl Awd-Outstndng Physcl Ftnss 86-87; Var Awd-Stu Athltc Trnr-Ftbl & Wrstlng 86-87; Sprts Med.

JOHNSON, KATIE; Sparta HS; Sparta, NJ; (2); 4/325; Church Yth Grp; Cmnty Wkr; Key Clb; SADD; Rep Frsh Cls; Sec Soph Cls; Rep Jr Cls; Var JV Cheerleading; Stat Score Keeper; Var JV Swmmng; Acad Achvt Awd; Bio.

JOHNSON, KAVEL; Weeguahic HS; Newark, NJ; (3); Cmnty Wkr; Spanish Clb; Elec Engr.

JOHNSON, KENDALE; Egg Harbor Township HS; Pleasantville, NJ; (4); 15/289; FBLA; Model UN; Office Aide; Spanish Clb; SADD; Rep Stu Cncl; Trk; High Hon Roll; NHS; La Salle U; Spnsh.

JOHNSON, KENNY; Rahway HS; Rahway, NJ; (3); Intl Geneva Assn Meritrious Culinary Svc Awd 87.

JOHNSON, KIM-SU; Kearny HS; Kearny, NJ; (3); Sftbl; Hon Roll; Katherine Gibbs; Acctg.

JOHNSON, KIMBERLY; Middletown Township HS South; Middletown, NJ; (4); 24/453; Nwsp Rptr; Hon Roll; Ntl Merit Ltr; Acad All Amer 87.

JOHNSON, KYLE O; Burlington City HS; Burlingon, NJ; (3); Am Leg Boys St; FBLA; Pres Frsh Cls; Rep Soph Cls; Rep Jr Cls; Rep Sr Cls; Rep Stu Cncl; Stat Bsktbl; JV Var Crs Cntry; JV Tennis; Cmmnctns.

JOHNSON, LORIE N; Red Bank Catholic HS; Eatontown, NJ; (3); Pres Church Yth Grp; NAACP; VP Thesps; Chorus; Church Choir; Stage Crew; L Var Mgr(s); Var Trk; Hon Roll; NY U; Bio.

JOHNSON, LUCILLE; Barringer Prep; Newark, NJ; (1); FBLA; FTA; JA; Math Clb; Red Cross Aide; Science Clb; Teachers Aide; Chorus; Color Guard; Stu Cncl; R L Rice Cvc Assn Acad Cert 86; Mnclr ST Coll; Pdtrcn.

JOHNSON, MARLA; Lakewood HS; Lakewood, NJ; (4); 124/326; DECA; VP NAACP; Church Yth Grp; Civic Clb; Political Wkr; Chorus; Church Choir; Sec Frsh Cls; JV Bowling; Miss Sbdbtnte Of Ocean Cnty 85; Dist Ed Rgnl Mdl Wnnr 84-86; H Jacksons Tlntd Tns Cngnlty Awd 85; Ocean County Coll; Acctng.

JOHNSON, MATTHEW; Madison HS; Madison, NJ; (3); 10/212; German Clb; JV Capt Socr; Var Tennis; High Hon Roll; Hon Roll; NHS; Ntl Merit Ltr; MIP-TEN Tm 86; Hstry.

JOHNSON, MEGAN; Wildwood HS; Wildwood Crest, NJ; (3); Drama Clb; Sec Stat Service Clb; School Musical; School Play; Rep Soph Cls; Rep Jr Cls; Rep Stu Cncl; Sec Bsbl; Im Bowling; Var L Tennis; Advrtsng.

JOHNSON, MISTI; Salem HS; Salem, NJ; (3); Church Yth Grp; Cmnty Wkr; Computer Clb; Pep Clb; Spanish Clb; SADD; Teachers Aide; Band; Concert Band; Jazz Band; Rotry Yth Ldrshp Alt 87; Salem Cnty Band 5th Chair 86 & 87; Phys Thrpy.

JOHNSON, NATHANIEL M; Trenton Central HS; Trenton, NJ; (3); Computer Clb; Var Capt Bsbl; Var Capt Ftbl; Var Wt Lftg; Var Wrstlng; CC Awd; Hon Roll; Best Dfnsv Back 86-87; Rookie Yr Bsebl 86-87; Clemson U; Comp Sci.

JOHNSON, PATTIE; Middlesex HS; Middlesex, NJ; (4); Ski Clb.

JOHNSON, REBECCA HART; Point Pleasant Beach HS; Po Pleasant Bch, NJ; (4); 1/94; Sec French Clb; Sec Key Clb; Pres Jr Cls; Pres Sr Cls; VP Stu Cncl; Capt Cheerleading; Capt L Trk; High Hon Roll; NHS; St Schlr; Rutgers Schlr 86-87; Grls Ctznshp Delg; Ldrshp Training Conf Delg; Princeton U; Economics.

JOHNSON, REMONIA; Plainfield HS; Plainfield, NJ; (3); Political Wkr; Science Clb; Varsity Clb; Rep Jr Cls; Var Trk; Hon Roll; All Metro Trck & Fld 87; Sci Fair Awd 87; Phy Thrpst.

JOHNSON, RHONDA; West Side HS; Newark, NJ; (3); Boys Clb Am; Hosp Aide; Science Clb; Color Guard; Bsktbl; Mgr(s); Score Keeper; Sftbl; Jets Clb & Co-Ed Bsktbl Lg 87; Med.

JOHNSON, SCOTT; J P Stevens HS; Edison, NJ; (3); Science Clb; Ski Clb; Var JV Bsktbl; Im Wt Lftg.

JOHNSON, SOLOMON S; Montclair Kimberley Acad; Ft Orange, NJ; (4); Boy Scts; Debate Tm; FBLA; Radio Clb; Pres Varsity Clb; Band; Concert Band; Jazz Band; Capt Var Ftbl; Lcrss; Ntl H S Ftbl Hall Of Fame 87; Negro Schlr Merit Comm; Columbia Coll; Ec.

JOHNSON, STEPHANIE; Mt Olive HS; Flanders, NJ; (4); 3/275; Drama Clb; Pres Service Clb; Band; Concert Band; Jazz Band; Mrchg Band; School Musical; Ed Lit Mag; Stat L Swmmng; NHS; Mst Imprvd Frshmn Bnd 84; Frgn Lang.

JOHNSON, STEPHANIE; Pleasantville HS; Pleasantville, NJ; (4); 11/102; Exploring; Math Clb; Band; Chorus; Church Choir; Concert Band; Drill Tm; Mrchg Band; Capt Pom Pon; Glassboro ST Coll; Law.

JOHNSON, TAMMY; Triton Regional HS; Somerdale, NJ; (4); 2/309; Hosp Aide; Science Clb; Yrbk Stf; Sec Sr Cls; JV Capt Fld Hcky; Swmmng; NHS; Rotary Awd; Sal; St Schlr; U Of PA; Vet.

JOHNSON, TIFFINY; West Deptford HS; Mantua, NJ; (3); Natl Beta Clb; Quiz Bowl; Band; Chorus; Concert Band; Mrchg Band; Variety Show; Var JV Cheerleading; Var L Trk; High Hon Roll; MV Rnnr 87; South Jrsy Chr 87; Englsh Acad Excllnc Cert 85; U Of FL; Pharm.

JOHNSON, TRACY; Newton HS; Newton, NJ; (3); 21/194; Band; Concert Band; Mrchg Band; Powder Puff Ftbl; JV Sftbl; Hon Roll; NHS; Cert Commendation Engl I & II 84-86, Spn I & II 84-86, Typng II 85-86; Vet Med.

JOHNSON, TRECIA; Vailsburg HS; Newark, NJ; (4); 39/241; Dance Clb; FBLA; FNA; FTA; Pep Clb; SADD; Color Guard; Drill Tm; Im Pom Pon; Capt Twrlr; Bus Olympcs & Dept Awd 87; William Patterson; Bus Admin.

JOHNSON, TRISHA; Calvary Acad; Brick, NJ; (4); 1/25; FTA; Pres Jr Cls; VP Sr Cls; Stu Cncl; Bsktbl; Mgr(s); Vllybl; High Hon Roll; Val; Church Yth Grp; Kings Coll; Elem Educ.

JOHNSON, TROY; Egg Harbor Township HS; Mc Kee City, NJ; (3); 4/329; Chess Clb; Church Yth Grp; Model UN; Church Choir; Jazz Band; JV Bsktbl; Trk; High Hon Roll; Hon Roll; Jr NHS; Acad Vrsty Lttr 85-86; Elec Eng.

JOHNSON, VANESSA; Notre Dame HS; Lawrenceville, NJ; (2); Ski Clb; Chorus; Rep Frsh Cls; Rep Soph Cls; Score Keeper; Homeroom Rep Awd 86-87.

JOHNSON, WENDY; Buena Regional HS; Vineland, NJ; (3); 8/215; Church Yth Grp; Varsity Clb; VP Frsh Cls; Sec Soph Cls; VP Jr Cls; Rep Stu Cncl; Var Co-Capt Crs Cntry; Trk; Hon Roll; Jr NHS; Mst Dedctd Crss Cntry; Elem Ed.

JOHNSON, YASMIN; Weequahic HS; Newark, NJ; (4); 32/350; Computer Clb; Nwsp Stf; JV Trk; Cit Awd; Hon Roll; NHS; Spelman Coll; Child Psych.

JOHNSON, YVETTE; Acad Of The Holy Angels; Westwood, NJ; (2) Cmnty Wkr; Girl Scts; Hosp Aide; Color Guard; Drill Tm; JV Bsktbl; Capt Cheerleading; Var Sftbl; L Trk; Ntl Merit Ltr; MA Inst Of Tech; Engrng

JOHNSTON, KEVIN; Wall HS; Wall, NJ; (3); 29/320; Ski Clb; Variety Show; Bsktbl; L Crs Cntry; JV L Ftbl; Wt Lftg; Hon Roll; Comm.

JOHNSTON, LYNNE M; Mahwah HS; Worthington, OH; (4); 15/167 Pres Boy Scts; Church Yth Grp; Hosp Aide; Math Tm; Yrbk Stf; Rep Stu Cncl; VP Crs Cntry; High Hon Roll; NHS; Ntl Merit SF; Boston U; Bio.

JOHNSTON, PETER L; Hightstown HS; E Windsor, NJ; (4); 25/411 Church Yth Grp; Spanish Clb; Stage Crew; Nwsp Stf; Var Crs Cntry; Trk High Hon Roll; Hon Roll; NHS; Pres Schlr; 4 Yrs Hghst AVG Hstry-HS Clss 1944 Hstry Prz; Prsdntl Schlrshp St Joseph U; Mdl Cngrss Clb 3 Yrs St Joseph U-PA; Hstry.

JOHNSTON, ROBERT B; Hackensack HS; Maywood, NJ; (3); Am Leg Boys St; Letterman Clb; Varsity Clb; Ed Lit Mag; Stu Cncl; Var L Bowling; Cit Awd; Yth Mayor Maywood NJ 87; Natl Sci Day Prtcpnt 86.

JOHNSTON, TJIEN; Camden HS; Camden, NJ; (2); Dance Clb; Debate Tm; Latin Clb; Drill Tm; Nwsp Stf; Off Soph Cls; Hon Roll; Howard U; Gyn.

JOHNSTONE, CHRISTINE; Highland HS; Blackwood, NJ; (3); 32/285; Exploring; FTA; Science Clb; Band; Concert Band; Drm Mjr(t); Mrchg Band; High Hon Roll; Hon Roll; Elem Tchr.

JOHO, BRIAN; Abraham Clark HS; Roselle, NJ; (4); 5/165; Science Clb; Chorus; School Play; Nwsp Bus Mgr; Nwsp Phtg; Nwsp Rptr; Nwsp Sprt Ed; Stu Cncl; Bowling; High Hon Roll; Schlrshp Frm Upsala Col For Slctd Hnrs Prgm In The Fall; Upsala Col; Multntl Studies.

JONES, ANJINETTE; Plainfield HS; Plainfield, NJ; (3); 28/300; Chess Clb; Church Yth Grp; Chorus; Church Choir; Drill Tm; Hon Roll; Bus Admn.

JONES, BRUCE; Burlington City HS; Edgewater Pk, NJ; (2); JV Var Bsbl; JV Var Ftbl; 4-H Awd; Prfct Atten Awd.

JONES, CANDICE STARR; Union HS; Union, NJ; (4); 34/563; NAACP; Yrbk Phtg; Yrbk Rptr; Pres Stu Cncl; Bsktbl; Socr; Wt Lftg; Cit Awd; Hon Roll; Dpty Mayor Of Union Cnty 86-87; Pres Stu Cncl Awd 86-87; Fairleah Dcknsn U; Corp Law.

JONES, CAROL; Alma Preparatory Schl; Somerville, NJ; (4); Church Yth Grp; 4-H; Ski Clb; Band; Concert Band; Mrchg Band; Symp Band, Yrbk Phtg; Yrbk Stf; Bowling; Phy Thrpy.

JONES, CHARLENE; Plainfield HS; Plainfield, NJ; (3); 19/249; Teachers Aide; Mrchg Band; Var Trk; Hon Roll; NHS; Prfct Atten Awd; Office Aide; Band; Concert Band; JV Crs Cntry; Track, Field Awds 87; Honor Roll 84-86; Job Perfrmnc Awd 88; Acctg.

JONES, CHARLISSE R; Academic HS; Jersey City, NJ; (3); Chrmn PAVAS; Spanish Clb; Band; Chorus; Church Choir; Rep Frsh Cls; Cheerleading; Voice Dem Awd; Ophelia Devore Schl Charm/Modeling Grad 87; All Am Awd Schlr Pgm 86; Bus Admin.

JONES, CHRISTPHER; Paramus HS; Paramus, NJ; (2); Ski Clb; Socr; Wt Lftg; Wrstlng; Arch.

JONES, CORDELL TOMASSON; Pequannock Township HS; Pompton Plains, NJ; (3); 12/216; Am Leg Boys St; Yrbk Rptr; VP Frsh Cls; Pres Soph Cls; Pres Jr Cls; Pres Sr Cls; JV Var Bsktbl; Tennis; Hon Roll; NHS

JONES, DANA; Morristown HS; Morristown, NJ; (3); Key Clb; Pep Clb Sec Stu Cncl; Cheerleading; Sftbl; Hon Roll; NHS; Commnctns.

JONES, DEBORAH; Dwight Morrow HS; Englewood, NJ; (4); 51/247; Am Leg Aux Girls St; Yrbk Phtg; Yrbk Sprt Ed; Trs Jr Cls; VP Sr Cls; Trk; High Hon Roll; Phi Dlta Kppa Chap Delta Nu 85-87; Amrcn Leg Aux Schlrshp Awd, Phi Dlta Kppa Schlrshp Awd 87; Stockton ST Coll; Accntnt.

JONES, DENISE; Paramus Catholic Girls Reg HS; Teaneck, NJ; (3); Church Yth Grp; Drama Clb; Church Choir; School Play; Nwsp Rptr; Merit Awd Outstndng Schl Svc 87; Prfct Attendnc Awd 84-85; Psych.

JONES, DENISE; University HS; Newark, NJ; (3); Exploring; JA; Math Clb; Model UN; Hon Roll; Map III & IV 87-88; Saturday Acad 87; Bus Admin.

JONES, DEREK; Bridgewater-Raritan HS East; Basking Ridge, NJ; (3); Var L Ftbl; JV Lcrss; Powder Puff Ftbl; JV Wrstlng.

JONES, GREGG; Christian Brothers Acad; Colts Neck, NJ; (3); 20/250; Church Yth Grp; Math Tm; Chorus; Yrbk Rptr; Rep Soph Cls; Var Bsbl; Im Bsktbl; Im Ftbl; JV Socr; NHS; Engrng.

JONES, GWEN; Plainfield HS; Plainfield, NJ; (4); 26/396; Capt Color Guard; Mrchg Band; VP Sr Cls; Rep Stu Cncl; Var Cheerleading; Vllybl; Howard U; Comp Sci.

JONES, HERBERT; Montclair HS; Montclair, NJ; (3); Church Yth Grp; Spanish Clb; Church Choir; Yrbk Stf; Hon Roll; Outstndg Slsmnshp & Svc Cert Awd 85; Partcptn & Cntrbtns Cert Merit 85; Fashin Inst Tech; Fshn Dsgn.

JONES, JENNIFER; Haddon Township HS; Westmont, NJ; (3); Am Leg Aux Girls St; German Clb; Pep Clb; Varsity Clb; School Musical; School Play; Yrbk Stf; Rep Stu Cncl; Var Capt Cheerleading; Hon Roll; Scndry Tchr.

JONES, JENNIFER; Ridgefield Park HS; Ridgefield Pk, NJ; (3); Spanish Clb; Lit Mag; High Hon Roll; Hon Roll; Photogrphy.

JONES, JUANITA; Hillside HS; Hillside, NJ; (3); Pres Church Yth Grp; Trs Leo Clb; Math Tm; Trs Science Clb; Band; Concert Band; School Play; Hon Roll; Elec Engrng.

JONES, JULIAN; Toms River HS South; S Toms River, NJ; (3); 4/405; Math Tm; Science Clb; Im Wt Lftg; High Hon Roll; Hon Roll.

JONES, KERI; Burlington Township HS; Burlington, NJ; (3); Am Leg Aux Girls St; VP JA; Key Clb; Varsity Clb; Chorus; Church Choir; JV Fld Hcky; Capt Pom Pon; Hon Roll; NHS; Econ.

JONES, KESHA; Dwight Morrow HS; Englewood, NJ; (3); Church Yth Grp; Girl Scts; Spanish Clb; Sec Church Choir; Mrchg Band; Trs Jr Cls; Rep Stu Cncl; Var Cheerleading; High Hon Roll; Hon Roll; U MD Hmptn; Math.

JONES, KRISTYN MARIE; Garden State Acad; Pennsauken, NJ; (4); 1/24; German Clb; Concert Band; School Play; Yrbk Ed-Chief; Sec Soph Cls; Sec Jr Cls; Pres Sr Cls; Hon Roll; Pres Schlr; Val; Columbia Union Coll Merit Awd; Columbia Union Coll; Offc Adm.

JONES, L TANYA; Oakcrest HS; Mizpah, NJ; (4); 22/204; Key Clb; Church Choir; Color Guard; Nwsp Ed-Chief; VP Frsh Cls; VP Soph Cls; Var Bsktbl; Var Trk; Hon Roll; Jr NHS; Pres Physical Ftns Awd 87; Schlrshp Hugh N Boyd Minorities Journalism Wrkshp 87; Montclair ST Coll; Broadcastng.

JONES, LATRAIEL; Mc Corristin Catholic HS; Trenton, NJ; (3); Cmnty Wkr; Pep Clb; Yrbk Stf; Bowling; Tennis; Wt Lftg; Hon Roll; Outstndng Accmplshmnts In Frnch I & II 85-86.

JONES, LORI; Phillipsburg HS; Phillipsburg, NJ; (3); 54/314; Hosp Aide; Ski Clb; Flag Corp; Im Bowling; Hon Roll; Psych.

JONES, LYNNETTE; Egg Harbor Township HS; Ocean City, NJ; (4); 12/289; French Clb; Model UN; Office Aide; Ski Clb; Yrbk Stf; Hst Frsh Cls; Hst Soph Cls; Hst Jr Cls; Hst Sr Cls; NHS; Douglass Coll.

JONES, MARGARET; Linden HS; Linden, NJ; (4); Church Yth Grp; VICA; 6th Regionl Med Spelling Comp 87; Pres HOSA 86-87; Robert Walsh Bus Schl; Med.

JONES, MARIA; Southern Regional HS; Manahawkin, NJ; (3); Pres Ski Clb; Yrbk Stf; Rep Soph Cls; Rep Jr Cls; Var Capt Cheerleading; NHS; Clncl Psych.

JONES, MICHAEL; Pitman HS; Pitman, NJ; (3); 8/154; Key Clb; VP Frsh Cls; VP Jr Cls; Trs Stu Cncl; Var L Crs Cntry; JV Ftbl; Var L Trk; Hon Roll; Ntl Merit SF; Class V P; Stu Cncl Treas; Stu Cncl; Pepperdine; Corporate Law.

JONES, NICOLE; Frank H Morrell HS; Irvington, NJ; (3); Latin Clb; SADD; Chorus; Color Guard; Flag Corp; Swing Chorus; Off Sr Cls; Stu Cncl; JV Crs Cntry; JV Trk; NCS; Comp.

JONES, NIGERIA; Academic HS; Jersey City, NJ; (3); Hosp Aide; NAACP; Spanish Clb; Sec Stu Cncl; Bsktbl; Cheerleading; Voice Dem Awd; Bus Admin.

JONES, PAULETTE; Irvington HS; Irvington, NJ; (3); Drama Clb; Teachers Aide; Rep Stu Cncl; High Hon Roll; Hon Roll; NHS; Katherine Gibbs Ldrshp For Future Sec Awd 87; Bus Admin.

JONES, RANDY L; Piscataway HS; Piscataway, NJ; (4); 231/500; Boy Scts; Pres Church Yth Grp; CAP; Cmnty Wkr; ROTC; Varsity Clb; Color Guard; Drill Tm; Nwsp Ed-Chief; Rep Jr Cls; Stu Rep Board Ed 86-87; Senator Bill Bradley Good Ctzn Awd 87; AFJR ROTC Cadet NJ Hstry 86-87; DE ST Coll; Ofcr.

JONES, RICH; Westfield HS; Westfield, NJ; (2); 55/296; Math Tm; Pep Clb; Ski Clb; Spanish Clb; Concert Band; Stage Crew; Off Frsh Cls; Off Soph Cls; Lcrss; Socr; Ctznshp & Atten Awds 86; Rutgers Schl Of RX; Phrmcy.

JONES, ROBERT PETERSON; Morristown Beard Schl; Morris Plains, NJ; (3); 16/90; AFS; Camera Clb; Church Yth Grp; Model UN; Service Clb; Yrbk Phtg; Yrbk Stf; Bsktbl; Tennis; Intl Bus.

JONES, SHELLY; Clifford Scott HS; E Orange, NJ; (3); 40/280; Law.

JONES, SHERIL; Vineland HS North; Vineland, NJ; (1); Church Yth Grp; FCA; Library Aide; Chorus; Church Choir; Hon Roll; Acctng.

JONES, SHERWIN; James J Ferris HS; Jersey City, NJ; (3); Art Clb; Boys Clb Am; Boy Scts; Frsh Cls; Bowling; Crs Cntry; Swmmng; Tennis; Trk; Hon Roll; Hon Roll 85; U Of MD; Archtct.

JONES, SONYA; James J Ferris HS; Jersey, NJ; (3); Church Yth Grp; Computer Clb; Math Clb; Science Clb; Bsbl; Bsktbl; Crs Cntry; Sftbl; Hon Roll; Lawyr.

JONES, SOPHIA; Hillside HS; Hillside, NJ; (3); 32/238; Pres Frsh Cls; Var Bsktbl; Var Cheerleading; Var Sftbl; Var Trk.

JONES, STACEY; Manchester Township HS; Toms River, NJ; (3); Girl Scts; Chorus; L Fld Hcky; L Trk; Vrsty Wnnr Trk-N-Fld 85-87; Vrsty Wnnr Fld Hcky 86; Bus.

JONES, TANYA; Pennsauken SR HS; Pennsauken, NJ; (3); Band; Chorus; Bsktbl; Trk; Cit Awd; Hon Roll; Jr NHS; Prfct Atten Awd; Modelng Awd 85; Stenogrphy.

JONES, TIFFANY; Notre Dame HS; Trenton, NJ; (3); Church Yth Grp; Civic Clb; Cmnty Wkr; Dance Clb; Church Choir; Variety Show; Trk; Amer Fncl Svcs Corp Stu Achvt Awd 87; Ryl Flwr & Grdn Clb Bk Awd 87; Pre-Med.

JONES, TINA; Central Regional HS; Bayville, NJ; (3); Dance Clb; Exploring; Hosp Aide; VICA; Concert Band; Mrchg Band; Ann May Schl Of Nursing; Nrsng.

JONES, TONYA; Science HS; Orange, NJ; (4); 7/98; Orch; Nwsp Stf; Im Vllybl; High Hon Roll; Hon Roll; NHS; Pres Schlr; JETS Comptn 87; SR Music Awd 87; James Carr Schlrshp Awd 87; Douglass Coll; Bus.

JONES, VANESSA; Teaneck HS; Teaneck, NJ; (2); Pres Soph Cls; Cheerleading; Pre-Med.

JONKER, SHIRA; Wayne Hills HS; Wayne, NJ; (2); 15/290; Sec Church Yth Grp; French Clb; Math Clb; Model UN; Chorus; School Musical; Yrbk Stf; Lit Mag; Var Bsktbl; JV Trk; Elem Educ.

JONKER, TODD; Wayne Hills HS; Wayne, NJ; (4); 10/289; Pres Computer Clb; Concert Band; Drm Mjr(t); High Hon Roll; NHS; Ntl Merit Schol; St Schlr; Rep Church Yth Grp; Library Aide; Math Tm; Wayne PTO Brws & Shp Schlrshp 87; Amer Invt Math Exam 86 & 87; Comp Sci Awd 87; Rice U; Comp Sci.

JOO, RICHARD; Pemberton High School No 1; Browns Mills, NJ; (2); Boy Scts; Band; Concert Band; Mrchg Band; Bsbl; JV Socr; USAF Acad; Pilot.

JORDAN, AMY; Sacred Heart HS; Elmer, NJ; (4); 4-H; Spanish Clb; Variety Show; Lit Mag; 4-H Awd; Hon Roll; NHS; Ntl Merit Ltr; St Schlr; NJ Dstngshd Schlr Awd Schlrshp 86; Glassboro ST Coll; Math.

JORDAN, MAUREEN; Haddon Township HS; Oaklyn, NJ; (4); 25/171; Am Leg Aux Girls St; Madrigals; School Musical; Cit Awd; Hon Roll; NHS; Church Yth Grp; Dance Clb; German Clb; Acpl Chr; Modrn Music Mstrs; JR Miss Alt; Stu Athltc Trnr; West Chester U; Ed.

JORDAN, SUSAN A; West Windsor-Plainsboro HS; Plainsboro, NJ; (4); 94/281; Art Clb; Acpl Chr; School Musical; School Play; Ntl Merit SF.

JORDAN, VICKI; Egg Harbor Twnshp HS; English Creek, NJ; (3); 21/328; Exploring; Rep Stu Cncl; JV Fld Hcky; JV Sftbl; Hon Roll; Vrsty Schlr Awd; Field Hockey Awd JV; Sftbl Awd; Law Enfrcmnt.

JORDAN, VICTOR; St Marys Of The Assumpt; Elizabeth, NJ; (2); FBLA; Radio Clb; Ice Hcky; Socr; Hon Roll; NHS; Prfct Atten Awd; Bus.

JORGENSEN, EMILE; Teaneck HS; Teaneck, NJ; (3); Exploring; Math Tm; Yrbk Stf; Lit Mag; JV Socr; Hon Roll; NHS; Social Studies Awd.

JOSE JR, RENATO; Palisades Park JR SR HS; Palisades Pk, NJ; (3); Ftbl; High Hon Roll; Hon Roll; Jr NHS; Mu Alpha Theta; Awded-Svgs Bond Sci Fair 84; Excllnc-Spnsh 85-86; Arch.

JOSEPH, MARLENE; Plainfield HS; Plainfield, NJ; (4); Dance Clb; Drama Clb; FBLA; Concert Band; Mrchg Band; School Musical; School Play; Yrbk Stf; Rep Soph Cls; Rep Jr Cls; New Horizon 85-86; Bus Admin.

JOSEPH, NANCY; Linden HS; Linden, NJ; (3); Comp.

JOSEPH, REBECCA; Delaware Valley Regional HS; Frenchtown, NJ; (3); Trs Church Yth Grp; Key Clb; Ski Clb; Varsity Clb; Band; Chorus; Var Trk; Hon Roll.

JOSEPH, SIMONE; St Pius X Regional HS; Somerset, NJ; (3); Camera Clb; Debate Tm; Hosp Aide; JA; ROTC; Teachers Aide; School Play; Nwsp Phtg; Nwsp Rptr; Yrbk Phtg; Rutgers U Biomed Rsrchrs Assoc Schlrshp Pgm 86; Boston U; Pre Med.

JOSHI, ANITA; Hanover Park HS; Simsbury, CT; (4); 50/301; Sec Trs Drama Clb; VP German Clb; Chorus; Madrigals; School Musical; Yrbk Stf; Twrlr; NHS; HOBY Awd 86; Trinity Coll; Bio.

JOSHI, PARAG; Clifton HS; Clifton, NJ; (3); Am Leg Boys St; French Clb; Math Clb; Science Clb; Band; Jazz Band; School Play; French Hon Soc; Hon Roll; Jr NHS; Physcs Leag Awd 87; NYU; Bus.

JOST, AMANDA; Sacred Heart HS; Vineland, NJ; (4); 1/70; Pres German Clb; School Musical; Rep Frsh Cls; Off Jr Cls; Off Sr Cls; JV Var Cheerleading; JV Sftbl; High Hon Roll; Hon Roll; NHS; Dnstry.

JOST, MICHAEL; Vineland HS; Vineland, NJ; (3); Letterman Clb; Pep Clb; Varsity Clb; Rep Jr Cls; Rep Sr Cls; Rep Stu Cncl; Capt Var Golf; Capt Var Socr; Drexel; Civil Engrng.

JOST, MICHELE; Middle Township HS; Avalon, NJ; (3); 19/300; Church Yth Grp; Cmnty Wkr; Hosp Aide; Key Clb; Ski Clb; Chorus; Church Choir; School Musical; Yrbk Rptr; Yrbk Stf; ST Sci Fair Awd 1st Pl & 2nd Pl 85 & 87; DE Vly Sci Fair Awds Med & Hlth Tri-ST 3rd Pl Hnrbl Mntn; Physical Therapy.

JOYCE, JEANMARIE; Cliffside Park HS; Cliffside Park, NJ; (4); 13/236; Cmnty Wkr; Trs Spanish Clb; Yrbk Stf; Stu Cncl; Var JV Cheerleading; Sftbl; Hon Roll; Jr NHS; Pres NHS; Rotary Awd; St Ptrs Coll Smmr Schlrshp Schlrshp 86; Clffsd Prk Chptr UNICO Schlrshp 87; Rutgers U; Psychlgy.

JOYNER, ALEXANDER; Linden HS; Linden, NJ; (3); Computer Clb.

JUBA, ROBERT J; Passaic Valley Regional HS; West Paterson, NJ; (3); 1/329; Am Leg Boys St; Boys Clb Am; JA; Math Clb; Math Tm; Scholastic Bowl; Science Clb; Rep Jr Cls; Rep Sr Cls; Rep Stu Cncl; Boys ST Am Leg 87; Acad Committee Pres & Stu Rep Brd Ed 87-88.

JUCKETT, DANIEL; Maple Shade HS; Maple Shade, NJ; (3); Off Jr Cls; Var Bsbl; Var Capt Socr; NHS; Rotary Awd; Sccr-1st Tm All Frdm, 1st Tm All Grp 1 & 2nd Tm All Cnty 86-87; Bsbl-3rd Tm All Frdm 87; Johns Hopkins; Med.

JUDSON, STAN; South River HS; South River, NJ; (4); Band; VP Concert Band; VP Jazz Band; VP Mrchg Band; VP Pep Band; VP Symp Band; Imprl Music Ctr Awd 87; S River PTSO Schlrshp 87; Middlesex Cnty Arts HS 87; Brookdale CC; Auto Tech.

JUKNIEWICZ, LISA; Hillside HS; Hillside, NJ; (3); 23/238; Hon Roll; Rutgers; Elem Educ.

JULIANO, ANTHONY; Highland Regional HS; Blackwood, NJ; (3); Spanish Clb; Varsity Clb; Bsbl; Capt Ftbl; Wt Lftg; Wrstlng; Cit Awd; Hon Roll.

JULIANO, DEBRA; Edgewood Regional SR HS; Atco, NJ; (3); Spanish Clb; Varsity Clb; Trs Frsh Cls; JV Sftbl; Var Tennis; Hon Roll; Drftng Awd 85; Archt Engrng.

JULIANO, DIANA; Highland Regional HS; Blackwood, NJ; (4); #22 In Class; Pep Clb; Spanish Clb; SADD; Off Sr Cls; Sec Stu Cncl; Var Crs Cntry; Var Trk; NHS; Seton Hall Univ.

JULIANO, KAREN; Cinnaminson HS; Cinnaminson, NJ; (3); Drama Clb; Spanish Clb; Thesps; Chorus; Color Guard; Concert Band; Mrchg Band; School Musical; Yrbk Stf; Lit Mag; Bus.

JULIANO, NICK; Perth Amboy HS; Perth Amboy, NJ; (3); Varsity Clb; Var Capt Bsbl; Var Capt Bsktbl; Var Ftbl; Bus Mgmt.

JUN, JI YOUNG; Creeskill HS; Cresskill, NJ; (3); Office Aide; Ski Clb; Off Jr Cls; North Jersey Stu Crftsmns Fair 2nd Pl 87, Painting 87; Parsons Schl Of Dsgn; Art.

JUNGERMANN, SUZANNE; Immaculate Conception HS; Ft Lee, NJ; (3); Var Bsktbl; Var Sftbl; Hon Roll; Bus Admin.

JURADO, JOSE; Perth Amboy HS; Perth Amboy, NJ; (3); Computer Clb; De Vry Tech Schl; Comp Tech.

KACZALA, JENNIFER; South River HS; South River, NJ; (2); 21/124; German Clb; Pres Band; Pres Mrchg Band; Pres Pep Band; Pres Symp Band; Yrbk Stf; JV Sftbl; Hon Roll; Mrchng Band Lttr 85-86; 3rd Yr Band Awd 86-87.

KACZOROWSKI, CHRISTEN; Immaculata HS; Somerset, NJ; (3); 1/233; Pres Church Yth Grp; Church Choir; Rep Soph Cls; Pres Jr Cls; JV Var Bsktbl; Var Socr; Var Sftbl; NHS; Prfct Atten Awd; Spanish NHS; Educ.

KADEN, JENNIFER; Manalapan HS; Englishtown, NJ; (2); 68/400; Drama Clb; PAVAS; SADD; Thesps; Madrigals; School Musical; Stage Crew; All-Shore Chorus 87.

KAEBLE, CHRISTINE; Egg Harbor Township HS; Pleasantville, NJ; (2); 4/392; VP Girl Scts; Model UN; Nwsp Stf; Yrbk Stf; High Hon Roll; Hon Roll; Eqstrn Educ.

KAEPPLER, SUZANNE; Cumberland Christian HS; Millville, NJ; (4); 4/29; Church Yth Grp; German Clb; Teachers Aide; VP Frsh Cls; VP Soph Cls; VP Jr Cls; VP Sr Cls; Var L Sftbl; High Hon Roll; Hon Roll; Messiah Coll Deans Schlrshp 87; Scriptr Mstry Awd 83-87; Pres Phy Fit Awd Merit 83-87; Messiah Coll; Elem Ed.

KAFER, DONALD; Burlington County Vo Tech; Bordentown, NJ; (3); 3/192; Church Yth Grp; Cmnty Wkr; Rep Stu Cncl; Var Bsbl; Var Capt Bowling; Var Socr; Hon Roll; Prfct Atten Awd; All Star Team ST Scr 86; Elec Contrctr.

KAGAN, GARY; Madison Central HS; Old Bridge, NJ; (3); Trs Latin Clb; Spanish Clb; Hon Roll.

KAGAN, JAY; Cherry Hill H S West; Cherry Hill, NJ; (3); Aud/Vis; Model UN; Spanish Clb; Temple Yth Grp; Nwsp Rptr; Nwsp Stf; Var Crs Cntry; Var Swmmng; Hon Roll; Pres NHS; Pres Of Natl Hnr Scty 87-88; Ivy League; Med.

KAGAN, VERA; Belleville HS; Belleville, NJ; (4); 115/435; Office Aide; Teachers Aide; Bowling; Prfssnl Wmns Clb Amer Svngs Bnd 87; Shrthnd Awd, Cert 85; Wrd Prcssr Cert 86; Law.

KAHN, ROBERT; New Providence HS; New Providence, NJ; (4); 12/169; Boy Scts; Pres French Clb; Model UN; Varsity Clb; Flag Corp; School Play; Rep Frsh Cls; Swmmng; French Hon Soc; Trs NHS; U MI.

KAHN, RUSSELL; Brick Memorial HS; Bricktown, NJ; (1); English Clb; VP Scholastic Bowl; Sec Spanish Clb; Trs Temple Yth Grp; Lit Mag; Rep Dance Clb; JV Capt Bowling; Mgr(s); High Hon Roll; Spanish NHS; Yale; Med.

KAHN, STEVEN; Livingston HS; Livingston, NJ; (2); Key Clb; Off Frsh Cls; Off Soph Cls; JV Bsktbl; Socr; Hon Roll.

KAHNEY, ADRIENNE; South Hunterdon HS; Lambertville, NJ; (3); 17/84; Am Leg Aux Girls St; Cmnty Wkr; FBLA; Pres Key Clb; VP SADD; Band; Chorus; Concert Band; Jazz Band; Madrigals; Wm & Mry; Mrn Bio.

KAIAFAS, COSTAS A; Brick Township HS; Bricktown, NJ; (3); 5/410; Math Tm; Yrbk Stf; JV Bsktbl; JV Trk; High Hon Roll; NHS; Pre Med.

KAIN, MARIE; Gloucester Catholic HS; Woodbury, NJ; (3); Church Yth Grp; Computer Clb; English Clb; French Clb; Library Aide; Stage Crew; Yrbk Stf; JV Bsktbl; Hon Roll; Marine Corp Ftnss Awd 85-86; Accntng Bus.

KAIN III, PHILIP G; Bridgewater-Raritan West HS; Bridgewater, NJ; (4); Am Leg Boys St; Camp Drama Clb; NFL; Pres Spanish Clb; Band; Ed Nwsp Stf; Yrbk Bus Mgr; Sec Stu Cncl; Stu Rep Bd Of Ed 86-87; Ntl Spch & Debt Humor 87; NJ Ldrshp Counsel 86; Rutgers Coll; Museum Curation.

KAINE, SCOTT C; Dumont HS; Dumont, NJ; (3); 22/218; Am Leg Boys St; Spanish Clb; Yrbk Stf; Lit Mag; Pres Sr Cls; L Bsbl; Capt Var Socr; Var Civic Clb; Capt Var Wrstlng; NHS; Wrstlng-All Leag, Hnrb Mntn-All Cnty 87; West Point; Comp Pgmmng.

KAIRIS, LISA; St John Vianney HS; Keyport, NJ; (3); 6/350; Intnl Clb; Math Tm; Chorus; School Musical; Ed Yrbk Stf; Lit Mag; Gov Hon Prg Awd; High Hon Roll; NHS; Ntl Merit Ltr; Bus.

KALAJAINEN, KRISTIN; Bordentown Regional HS; Bordentown, NJ; (2); 1/135; Art Clb; Drama Clb; French Clb; Chorus; School Musical; Pom Pon; Elks Poster Cntst; 1st Brdntwn St Fair Art Show Teen Div 86; Art Thrpy.

KALAPOS, CONNIE; Linden HS; Linden, NJ; (3); High Hon Roll; Public Rltns.

KALDON, JACKIE; Arthur L Johnson Regional HS; Clark, NJ; (4); 59/197; Cmnty Wkr; Nwsp Stf; Lit Mag; Sec Soph Cls; Sec Jr Cls; Sec Sr Cls; Stu Cncl; Cheerleading; Sftbl; Homecoming Queen 86; Communications.

KALEDA, DAVID C; North Warren Regional HS; Blairstown, NJ; (3); Am Leg Boys St; Scholastic Bowl; VP Rep Stu Cncl; Var L Bsktbl; JV Crs Cntry; Hon Roll; NHS; Lawyer.

KALFRIN, VALERIE; Burlington Township HS; Burlington, NJ; (3); 1/120; Sec Church Yth Grp; Chrmn Model UN; Nwsp Ed-Chief; Nwsp Rptr; Yrbk Ed-Chief; Yrbk Rptr; High Hon Roll; NHS; Ntl Merit SF; Drama Clb; Hnrbl Mntn Schlstc Scospes Ntl Short Story Cntst 87; Highest Avg 84-86; Engl.

KALISCH, KIMBERLY; Bishop George Ahr HS; Woodbridge, NJ; (4); 11/267; French Clb; Math Tm; Science Clb; Teachers Aide; Lit Mag; High Hon Roll; Hon Roll; NHS; Excllnce Frnch 4 Yr Awd 87; Dstngshd SR Awd 87; Excllnce Scholar Awd 87; Svc Awd 87; NY ST U Binghamton; Biochem.

KALNINS, ANDIS; Wood-Ridge HS; Wood Ridge, NJ; (4); 3/76; Boy Scts; Math Clb; Model UN; Yrbk Ed-Chief; Var L Bsktbl; Var L Crs Cntry; Var L Trk; NHS; Eagle Scout 85; Engrng.

KALOKIRA, KAREN A; Parsippany Hills HS; Parsippany, NJ; (4); 43/325; Church Yth Grp; Pres VP FBLA; Political Wkr; Nwsp Stf; Pres Frsh Cls; Pres Soph Cls; Pres Jr Cls; Pres Sr Cls; Rotary Awd; Hosp Aide; Grls Citznshp Wnr 86; Natl Hnr Roll 87; Boston Coll; Spec Educ.

KALOLA, BINA; Parsippany Hills HS; Somerset, NJ; (4); 26/320; Pres Debate Tm; Pres FBLA; Math Tm; NFL; Political Wkr; Spanish Clb; Rep Stu Cncl; Cit Awd; Hon Roll; Trs NHS; HOBY ST Ldrshp Awd 84; NJ ST Ms FBLA 3rd Pl 87; NJ Mod Cngrss Party Whip 87; Barnard Coll; Law.

KALSER, ANNETTE; Red Bank Regional HS; Red Bank, NJ; (3); Art Clb; VP Pres Church Yth Grp; Ski Clb; Church Choir; Pres Frsh Cls; Pres Soph Cls; Var Diving; JV Var Sftbl.

KAM, PAUL; Matawan Regional HS; Matawan, NJ; (3); 13/302; Math Tm; Spanish Clb; Bsktbl; Crs Cntry; Socr; Tennis; High Hon Roll; Hon Roll; Prfct Atten Awd.

KAMATH, GAUTHAM D; Marlboro HS; Marlboro, NJ; (3); 2/529; Chess Clb; Math Tm; Science Clb; High Hon Roll; NHS; Ntl Merit SF; St Schlr; Ntl Sci Olympd Awd Physcs, ST Sci Day Cert Physcs 85; MIT; Electrncs.

KAMBACH, MELISSA; Lenape Valley Regional HS; Andover, NJ; (3); 6/274; Chorus; Madrigals; Swing Chorus; Sftbl; Swmmng; High Hon Roll; Hon Roll; NHS; Prfct Atten Awd; Spanish NHS.

KAMBECK, CHRISTINE; Spotswood HS; Milltown, NJ; (2); Church Yth Grp; Intnl Clb; Trk; Hon Roll; Btny.

KAMENETZ, BRYAN; Paramus HS; Paramus, NJ; (3); Aud/Vis; Chess Clb; Quiz Bowl; Temple Yth Grp; Nwsp Stf; Yrbk Stf; Rep Frsh Cls; Rep Soph Cls; Ntl Merit Ltr; Jrnlsm.

KAMIENSKI, JENNIFER; Florence Twp Memorial HS; Roebling, NJ; (3); GAA; Pep Clb; Varsity Clb; School Play; Variety Show; Nwsp Stf; Yrbk Stf; Cheerleading; Jrnlsm.

KAMINSKY, ROBERT; Freehold Twp HS; Freehold, NJ; (3); Trs Exploring; Intnl Clb; Yrbk Stf; Ntl Merit Ltr; Intl Bus.

KAMMERMAN, NEIL; Northern Valley Regional HS; Old Tappan, NJ; (3); 20/277; Political Wkr; Concert Band; Jazz Band; Mrchg Band; Symp Band; Rep Stu Cncl; Hon Roll; Rgn Bergen Champ Acad Decathln 87; 9th Pl Natl Acad Decthln Tm 87; Poltcl Sci.

KANALY, ROBERT; Southern Regional HS; Manahawkin, NJ; (3); 6/450; Computer Clb; Math Tm; Service Clb; Ski Clb; JV Crs Cntry; JV Socr; High Hon Roll; NHS; Schlr Athl 84-85; Awd No More Than Two B Grds In Yr 84-85; Chosn Amng Selct Fw Chem-Physcs Tstg 85-87; Biochem.

KANAZIK, CHRISTY-LYNN; Butler HS; Bloomingdale, NJ; (3); Church Yth Grp; Drama Clb; JCL; Latin Clb; Acpl Chr; Church Choir; School Musical; School Play; Hon Roll; Sci.

KANDRAVY, MICHAEL; Hawthorne HS; Hawthorne, NJ; (3); Math Tm; Ski Clb; Rep Stu Cncl; Bsktbl; L Var Ftbl; L Var Trk; Hon Roll; NHS; Prfct Atten Awd; Fin.

KANE, AILEEN; Mt Olive HS; Flanders, NJ; (4); 32/290; AFS; Math Tm; Nwsp Rptr; Hon Roll; NHS; Hnrble Schlrshp U Scranton 87; U Scranton; Education.

KANE, COLLEEN; Paul VI HS; Voorhees, NJ; (3); #17 In Class; French Clb; Math Clb; Office Aide; Rep Soph Cls; Rep Jr Cls; Sec Ftbl; Mgr(s); Score Keeper; Hon Roll; Intl Rltns.

KANE, KATHLEEN; Holy Cross HS; Moorestown, NJ; (3); 70/406; Capt Var Bsktbl; JV Fld Hcky; Var L Chess Clb; Hon Roll; Phys Ther.

KANE, KRISTEN; West Windsor-Plainsboro HS; Cranbury, NJ; (3); Cmnty Wkr; Exploring; Yrbk Phtg; Mgr(s); High Hon Roll; NHS; Ntl Merit Ltr; Camera Clb; Church Yth Grp; French Clb.

KANE, KRISTINA; Pinelands Regional HS; Tuckerton, NJ; (3); #16 In Class; JV Socr; Hon Roll; NHS; Trenton ST Coll; Jrnlsm.

KANE, NEISHA; Manchester Township HS; Lakehurst, NJ; (3); Am Leg Aux Girls St; Spanish Clb; Concert Band; Hon Roll; NHS; Prfct Atten Awd; Sci, Spnsh, & Engl Stu Of Mth.

KANE, R J; Manalapan HS; Englistown, NJ; (3); Boy Scts; Cmnty Wkr; Letterman Clb; Pep Clb; Service Clb; Varsity Clb; Yrbk Stf; Capt Var Bsktbl; Capt Var Socr; Capt Amer 70 Soccer Trvlng Team Germany Won Cup 84; Bus.

KANE JR, RICHARD; Manalapan HS; Englishtown, NJ; (3); Cmnty Wkr; Letterman Clb; Varsity Clb; Nwsp Stf; Yrbk Rptr; Rep Soph Cls; Rep Jr Cls; JV Bsbl; Var Capt Bsktbl; Var Capt Socr; 1st Tm-Cntrhlfbck-All-Dist-Frhld 86; 2nd Tm-Cntrhlfbck-All-Shore-Asbury Prk Press 86; Bus Mgmt.

KANE, WHITNEY; Madison HS; Madison, NJ; (3); Church Yth Grp; Varsity Clb; Trs Frsh Cls; VP Soph Cls; VP Jr Cls; VP Sr Cls; Trs Rep Stu Cncl; Var L Socr; Tennis; Var L Vllybl; Bus.

KANEFKE, PETER; Fair Lawn HS; Fair Lawn, NJ; (3); Aud/Vis; Boy Scts; Drama Clb; Hosp Aide; Varsity Clb; School Musical; School Play; Stage Crew; JV Lcrss; Var Socr.

KANG, EUN SOOK; Maple Shade HS; Maple Shade, NJ; (2); Church Yth Grp; French Clb; Girl Scts; Key Clb; Library Aide; Band; Color Guard; Mrchg Band; Yrbk Stf; Rep Frsh Cls; 3rd Pl-Tlnt Show 87; UP; Med.

KANG, HEESOOK; Maple Shade HS; Maple Shade, NJ; (3); Church Yth Grp; Drama Clb; Key Clb; Library Aide; School Play; Yrbk Stf; High Hon Roll; Hon Roll; Jr NHS; NHS; Intl Affrs.

KANG, KAREN; Glen Rock SR HS; Glen Rock, NJ; (3); 7/145; Hosp Aide; Math Tm; Science Clb; Nwsp Stf; Lit Mag; Cit Awd; High Hon Roll; Hon Roll; Jr NHS; NHS; Dsgnd Yrbk Cover 87; Rcvd Gold Cert For Piano By Music Edctrs Asso Of NJ 85-86; Exhbtd Art Expo 86-87; Med.

KANTENWEIN, DAVE; Newton HS; Newton, NJ; (2); 2/218; Pres VP 4-H; Math Tm; Science Clb; High Hon Roll; Hon Roll; Natl Sci Olympiad Chem 1 Of Top 20 NJ 87.

KANTNER, MICHAEL J; Shawnee HS; Medford Lakes, NJ; (3); 4/550; Am Leg Boys St; Math Tm; Science Clb; Band; Mrchg Band; Stage Crew; Gov Hon Prg Awd; NHS; Ntl Merit Ltr; French Clb; George Washington U Engr Awd 87.

KAPETANAKIS, KAREN; Ocean Township HS; Wanamassa, NJ; (3); Church Yth Grp; Dance Clb; French Clb; Key Clb; Chorus; Flag Corp; Co-Capt Twrlr.

KAPIT, RHONDA; Colonia HS; Colonia, NJ; (3); 41/348; German Clb; Temple Yth Grp; Chorus; School Play; Off Stu Cncl; Twrlr; NHS; Bus.

KAPITULA, JOHN; Passaic HS; Passaic, NJ; (4); 19/370; Nwsp Ed-Chief; Nwsp Stf; Elec Engr.

KAPLAN, ALYSSA; River Dell SR HS; River Edge, NJ; (4); 19/213; Teachers Aide; Temple Yth Grp; Nwsp Rptr; Nwsp Stf; High Hon Roll; Hon Roll; NHS; Spanish NHS; Paramus Red Wave & Ridgewood Breakers Swim Tms; Lifeguard Paramus Pool; Syracuse U; Comms.

KAPLAN, BRIAN S; East Brunswick HS; E Brunswick, NJ; (4); Key Clb; Spanish Clb; SADD; VP Stu Cncl; Capt Var Tennis; High Hon Roll; VP NHS; Ntl Merit SF; Spanish NHS; St Schlr.

KAPLAN, CONSTANCE; Scotch Plains Panwood HS; Scotch Plains, NJ; (3); Drama Clb; French Clb; Key Clb; Model UN; Quiz Bowl; SADD; School Play; Yrbk Stf; Rep Frsh Cls; French Hon Soc; Poli Sci.

KAPLAN, DOUGLAS; Middletown HS South; Middletown, NJ; (2); French Clb; VP Temple Yth Grp; Off Lit Mag; Rep Soph Cls; French Hon Soc; Hon Roll; Ntl Ltn Exm Slvr Mdl Maxima Cum Laude 86-87; Law.

KAPLAN, GEOFFREY; Parsippany HS; Parsippany, NJ; (3); Temple Yth Grp; Varsity Clb; Var L Ftbl; Wt Lftg; Var L Wrstlng; Hon Roll; Pyschl Thrpy.

KAPLAN, JAMES; Northern Valley-Old Tappan HS; Tappan, NJ; (3); 24/274; Debate Tm; Drama Clb; Science Clb; School Play; Nwsp Stf; Socr; NHS; NJ ST Champ Acad Dcthln Team 87; Ntl Slvr Mdlst In Ecs In Acad Dcthn 87; Ntl Bronze Mdlst 87.

KAPLAN, JENNIFER; Holy Spirit HS; Mays Landing, NJ; (2); 37/397; Girl Scts; Law.

KAPLAN, LAWRENCE; Middletown HS South; Red Bank, NJ; (3); Math Clb; VP Temple Yth Grp; Yrbk Phtg; Yrbk Stf; Lit Mag; Hon Roll.

KAPLAN, MICHAEL P; Jewish Educational Center HS; W Orange, NJ; (3); 1/27; Math Tm; Service Clb; Pres Temple Yth Grp; Nwsp Ed-Chief; Pres Soph Cls; Im JV Bsktbl; Im Capt Swmmng; Hon Roll; Office Aide; Scholastic Bowl; Rudgers Schlr 87; Rensselaer Awd Mth & Sci 87; U PA; Actuarial Sci.

KAPLAN, STACI; Wayne Valley HS; Wayne, NJ; (3); 71/350; FBLA; GAA; Ski Clb; Temple Yth Grp; Nwsp Stf; Lit Mag; Fld Hcky; Trk; Hon Roll; Psych.

KAPOCHUS, DAINA; Our Lady Of Mercy Acad: Milmay, NJ; (3); Church Yth Grp; Cmnty Wkr; SADD; Chorus; Nwsp Rptr; Yrbk Rptr; Yrbk Stf; Rep Jr Cls; VP Sr Cls; VP Rep Stu Cncl; Bio Sci.

KAPOOR, VANISH; Wayne Hills HS; Wayne, NJ; (3); Computer Clb; FBLA; Math Clb; Math Tm; Science Clb; Score Keeper; Socr; Trk; High Hon Roll; Hon Roll; Med.

KAPPATOS, NICK; Haddon Township HS; Westmont, NJ; (3); Ski Clb; Trs Frsh Cls; Trs Soph Cls; Trs Jr Cls; Var Ftbl; Var Golf; JV Wrstlng; High Hon Roll; Hon Roll; Coast Guard Acad; Bus Ecs.

KAPUS, SCOTT; Gateway Regional HS; Woodbury Heights, NJ; (3); Boys Clb Am; Church Yth Grp; Latin Clb; Science Clb; Varsity Clb; JV Bsbl; Var L Socr; Wt Lftg; High Hon Roll; Prfct Atten Awd; Latin Hon Soc 86-87; Gator Mnth Awd 85; S Jersey Coaches Asso 1st Tm Colnl Conf All Str Sccr 86; Engr.

KAPUSCINSKI, GREGG; Montville Township HS; Montville, NJ; (4); 32/263; Art Clb; Drama Clb; Chorus; School Musical; School Play; Lit Mag; Ntl Merit Schol; Ski Clb; Mrchg Band; High Hon Roll; Drama Mustang Awd 87; Male Voc Chrl Awd 87; Painting B/W Drawing 1st Pl Awds 87; Rutgers Coll; Theatre.

KARAGIANNIS, EVAGILIA; Cliffside Park HS; Cliffside Park, NJ; (2); Library Aide; Band; Concert Band; Mrchg Band; Nwsp Rptr; High Hon Roll; Hon Roll; Lion Awd.

KARAGIAS, KALLY; Manasquan HS; Brielle, NJ; (2); Art Clb; Drama Clb; French Clb; Thesps; Stage Crew; Nwsp Stf; Rep Soph Cls; Gym; Fash Dsgn.

KARAKOWSKI, JONATHAN; Christian Brothers Acad; Farmingdale, NJ; (3); 1/230; Chess Clb; Hosp Aide; Math Tm; Nwsp Stf; NHS; Val; Math & Sci Awd George Washington U.

KARAMINAS, GEORGE; Union HS; Union, NJ; (2); Church Yth Grp; Stage Crew; Im JV Socr; Stat Wt Lftg; High Hon Roll; Hon Roll; NHS.

KARAS JR, RICHARD; Huntedon Central HS; Flemington, NJ; (3); 37/543; Pres Church Yth Grp; Computer Clb; Im Bsktbl; JV Trk; Hon Roll; Excllnt Prfrmnce Piano 86; Interact Clb 86-87.

KARIM, AHMAD; Ocean Township HS; Wayside, NJ; (2); 31/344; Capt Debate Tm; Math Tm; NFL; Speech Tm; Concert Band; Var L Trk; Gov Hon Prg Awd; NHS; Spartan SR HS Awd Ocean Twnshp 86; Electrical Engineering.

KARMAZIN, LISA; Howell HS; Howell, NJ; (4); 5/254; Exploring; Math Clb; Quiz Bowl; Science Clb; Color Guard; Nwsp Rptr; Hon Roll; NHS; John Thumm PAT Schlrshp 87; Engl IV Hnrs & Spn IV Awd 87; Pres Acad Fitness Awd 87; Rutgers; Bio.

KARMILOVICH, STEPHEN; Howell HS; Howell, NJ; (3); 16/350; Cmnty Wkr; Capt Exploring; SADD; Var Bowling; Wt Lftg; High Hon Roll; NHS; Natl Law Enfrcmnt Conf Seattle, & Howell Twp Police Dept In-Svc Trning Acad 86; Crmnl Jstc.

KAROL, JACQUELINE; Abraham Clark HS; Roselle, NJ; (3); Drama Clb; French Clb; Red Cross Aide; Ski Clb; Chorus; Color Guard; Madrigals; School Play; Variety Show; Twrlr; Audition Trenton ST Govs Schl Drama 87; Intl Bus.

KAROSEN, SHERRY; Montville HS; Towaco, NJ; (2); Art Clb; Computer Clb; Key Clb; Office Aide; Teachers Aide; High Hon Roll; Hon Roll; Prfct Atten Awd; Merit Awd 87.

KARP, JEFFREY; Belvidere HS; Phillipsburg, NJ; (4); Aud/Vis; Chess Clb; Varsity Clb; Var Capt Bsktbl; Hon Roll; NHS; Mst Vlbl Plyr Bsktbl 85-86; ST Sci Day Tst 1st In Cnty.

KARR, MARK; Pennsville HS; Pennsville, NJ; (3); 12/235; Office Aide; Pres Soph Cls; Pres Jr Cls; Pres Sr Cls; Var Bsbl; Var Capt Ftbl; Var Wrstlng; Hon Roll; NHS; Boy Scts; Tri Cnty All Star Ftbl 85-86; Salem Cnty All Star Wrstlr 84-85; Schlrshp Awd 85-87; West Pt Acad; Phys Ther.

KARRA, RAMESH; John P Stevens HS; Edison, NJ; (3); Art Clb; Boy Scts; Chess Clb; Computer Clb; Hosp Aide; Intnl Clb; Library Aide; Math Clb; Ranatra Fusica Crtvty Awd OM 87; Engrng.

KARTATOS, MARIGGELA; Timothy Christian Schl; Piscataway, NJ; (2); Pres Soph Cls; Sec Stu Cncl; High Hon Roll; Hon Roll; Ahepa Medal Schltc Excllnce 84; Archiocesan Brd Ed Diploma 84; Rutgers U; Acctng.

KARTIKIS, JILL; Toms River HS South; Toms River, NJ; (2); SADD; JV Capt Fld Hcky; Var L Trk; High Hon Roll; Hon Roll; Most Vlbl Plyr Track 86; Most Vlbl Plyr Fresh & JV Field Hockey 85-86; Letter Acdmcs Fresh Yr 85-86; Art.

KASARDA, JOHN; Warren Hills Regional SR HS; Hackettstown, NJ; (3); Church Yth Grp; Ski Clb; Band; Concert Band; Stage Crew; Im Badmtn; JV Var Socr; Hon Roll; Bus.

KASCIK, MARY-ELLEN; Morris Catholic HS; Succasunna, NJ; (2); Dance Clb; Cheerleading; Sftbl; Poem Publshd Yrbk 87; Law.

KASE, DANIELLE; Spotswood HS; Spotswood, NJ; (3); 32/150; Intnl Clb; Flag Corp; JV Cheerleading; French Hon Soc.

KASHIAN, DARA; Secaucus HS; Secaucus, NJ; (3); 25/170; Camera Clb; Cmnty Wkr; Dance Clb; Key Clb; Letterman Clb; Math Clb; Math Tm; Mu Alpha Theta; Pep Clb; Ski Clb.

KASHPER, EUGENE M; The Lawrenceville Schl; Wayside, NJ; (4); Pres Chess Clb; Ed Lit Mag; JV Bsktbl; JV Swmmng; Hon Roll; Ntl Merit SF; French Clb; Math Tm; Im Ftbl; Im Socr; Law.

KASILAG, MARIA ZENAIDA; Saint Mary HS; Jersey City, NJ; (4); 7/102; Church Yth Grp; Intnl Clb; Pep Clb; Nwsp Stf; Yrbk Stf; High Hon Roll; Jr NHS; NHS; Pres Schlr; Pres Acad Ftns Awd 87; St Francis Schl Nrsng; Nrsng.

KASMER, KEIR; Raritan HS; Keyport, NJ; (3); 44/360; JV Bsbl; Hon Roll; NHS; Bst JV Bsbl Httr & Fldr 87; Phys Ftnss Awd 84-85; Bus.

KASOF, AMY; Freehold Township HS; Freehold, NJ; (3); Art Clb; French Clb; FBLA; Hosp Aide; Pep Clb; SADD; Pres Temple Yth Grp; Yrbk Stf; Lit Mag; NHS.

KASPARIAN, YERVANT; Ridgefield Park HS; Little Ferry, NJ; (3); 30/215; PAVAS; Varsity Clb; Lit Mag; Rep Stu Cncl; Capt Trk; Gov Hon Prg Awd; Hon Roll; NHS; Art Clb; Phila Coll Arts; Cmmrcl Art.

KASSAK, KAREN; Union HS; Union, NJ; (3); Church Yth Grp; Pres Drama Clb; Key Clb; Service Clb; Chorus; Hon Roll; Jr NHS; NCTE Awd; NHS; Rep Stu Cncl; Sci.

KASSOUF, EVELYN; Holy Spirit HS; Absecon, NJ; (4); 31/363; Church Yth Grp; Dance Clb; Drama Clb; French Clb; Chorus; School Musical; School Play; NHS; US History.

KASZA, KELLEY; Warren Co Vo Tech HS; Phillipsburg, NJ; (4); FBLA; Key Clb; Office Aide; Yrbk Stf; Cheerleading; Hon Roll; Acdmc All Amer Awd 85-86; Northampton Cnty CC; Travel.

KATARYNIAK, STEVEN; Bayonne HS; Bayonne, NJ; (3); 5/350; Chess Clb; Math Tm; Science Clb; Lit Mag; Hon Roll; Jr NHS; NHS; US Air Frc, US Army Certs Prtcptn Hudson Cnty Sci Fair 85; MA Coll Of Pharmacy; Phrmcy.

KATCHEN, DEBORAH; Mount Olive HS; Budd Lake, NJ; (4); 48/298; FBLA; Trs OEA; Varsity Clb; Yrbk Stf; JV Fld Hcky; Var L Sftbl; Hon Roll; Berkeley Schl Awd Outstndng Achvt Bus 87; US Army Spcl Act Awd & Cert 86 & 87; US Army Ltr Cmmdtn 86; County Coll Of Morris; Bus Admn.

KATSOULIS, DIMITRIOS; Edison HS; Edison, NJ; (4); #5 In Class; Math Clb; Math Tm; Science Clb; French Hon Soc; Hon Roll; Grdn ST Schlr Awd 87; Dstngshd Schlrs Prgm Awd 87; Rtgrs Schlr 86; Rtgrs U; Pre-Med.

KATZ, JULIE; Chery Hill H S West; Cherry Hill, NJ; (3); Sec Drama Clb; Spanish Clb; SADD; Teachers Aide; Thesps; Mrchg Band; School Musical; School Play; Stage Crew; Variety Show.

KATZ, LISA; East Brunswick HS; E Brunswick, NJ; (3); German Clb; Key Clb; Band; Color Guard; Nwsp Stf; Yrbk Stf; Hon Roll; Lbrl Arts.

KATZ, SHERI; Manalapan HS; Manalapan, NJ; (2); Drama Clb; Spanish Clb; Lit Mag; Coach Actv; Socr; Jersey Centrl Power & Light Best Music Video Awd 86; Advrtsng.

KAUFER, CHRISTINA; Secaucus HS; Secaucus, NJ; (4); 19/157; Church Yth Grp; Mu Alpha Theta; Office Aide; Varsity Clb; JV Var Cheerleading; JV Var Mgr(s); Stat Trk; Mu Alpha Theta Awd; Boston U Schlrshp 87; Boston U Schl Engrng; Aerospc.

KAUFFMAN, DONNA; Howell HS; Farmingdale, NJ; (3); 53/470; Drama Clb; Pres 4-H; VP French Clb; FBLA; Chorus; Church Choir; Capt Color Guard; Capt Drill Tm; Madrigals; Bowling; 4-H Queen Cont 2nd Rnnr Up 85; Wrd Encntr Top Speller 85 & 87,ST Fnlst 4th 85; Fash Inst Tech; Fshn Merch.

KAUFFMAN, KEVIN; Middletown South HS; Redbank, NJ; (4); 82/450; Var Capt Ftbl; Hon Roll; Holycross Fall-Ftbl Schlrshp 87; Vina Lombandi Awd-Ftbl 87; Gvrnrs Phys Fitness Awd 87; Holy Cross; Sclgy.

KAUFMAN, DANIEL; Dwight-Englewood Schlll; Wyckoff, NJ; (3); Sec Debate Tm; Intnl Clb; School Musical; School Play; Ed Lit Mag; Var Trk; Hon Roll; Ntl Merit Ltr; Ntl Ltn Exam Lvl II Mxma Cum Laude 85; Ntl Ltn Exam Lvl IV Mama Cum Laude 87.

KAUFMAN, SHARON; Livingston HS; Livingston, NJ; (4); 9/425; Hosp Aide; Model UN; Nwsp Stf; Yrbk Ed-Chief; Lit Mag; Gym; Pres French Hon Soc; NHS; Cornell Ntl Schlr 87-88; NJ Distngshd Schlr 86-87fyrbk Edtr In Chf 86-87; Cornell U; Law.

KAUFMANN, JODI; Salem HS; Salem, NJ; (3); Am Leg Aux Girls St; Drama Clb; Exploring; SADD; Thesps; School Play; Stage Crew; Stu Cncl; Hon Roll; NHS; Brthrhd Essay Awd Wnnr 87; Theatrical Awd 86; Pre-Med.

KAUFMANN, MELISSA; Montville HS; Pine Brook, NJ; (2); Boys Clb Am; Cmnty Wkr; FBLA; GAA; Key Clb; Ski Clb; Temple Yth Grp; Sec Soph Cls; Sec Jr Cls; Cheerleading.

KAUR, DVINDER; Indian Hills HS; Franklin Lks, NJ; (4); 33/282; Church Yth Grp; Hosp Aide; Chorus; Yrbk Stf; Hon Roll; NHS; Ntl Merit Ltr; Pres Schlr; Acdmc Decatholon 86-87; Franklin & Marshall; Bio Chem.

KAWASHIMA, JUN; Fort Lee HS; Ft Lee, NJ; (2); Rep Frsh Cls; Tennis; High Hon Roll; Jr NHS; Arch.

KAWUT, STEVEN M; The Pingry Schl; Clark, NJ; (4); Service Clb; Spanish Clb; Temple Yth Grp; School Play; Hon Roll; Ntl Merit SF; Grdn St Dstngshd Schlr 86; Wnnr Tlnt Expo 85; Jerome H Bentley 36th Annl Sci Day Awd 86; Lf Sci.

KAY, JOANNA; Hunterdon Central HS; Flemington, NJ; (2); 216/480; Band; Concert Band; Mrchg Band; Orch; Symp Band; Nwsp Stf; JP Sousa Awd; Engl.

KAY, TAMMY; James Caldwell HS; Caldwell, NJ; (3); Girl Scts; Key Clb; Chorus; Madrigals; Tennis; Hon Roll; Aerontcl Tech.

KAY, TROY; West Windsor Plainsboro HS; Princeton Junct, NJ; (3); Cmnty Wkr; FNA; Rep Math Tm; Office Aide; Radio Clb; Rep Science Clb; Teachers Aide; JV Var Tennis; High Hon Roll; Hon Roll; Acad Awds; Gifted Pgm; Hnrs Pgm; Psych.

KAYA, ENDER; Passaic Co Tech-Voc HS; Paterson, NJ; (3); JV Socr; Bus Adm.

KAYAL, JENNIFER; Ramapo HS; Wyckoff, NJ; (3); 120/322; Church Yth Grp; Spanish Clb; Band; Symp Band; Socr; Sftbl; Hon Roll; Intrmdt III & IV Math Merit Awd 85-87; Spnsh II Merit Awd 85-86; Educ.

KAYNE, ANDY; Voorhees HS; High Bridge, NJ; (2); 93/292; Varsity Clb; Golf; U Of DE; Golf Pro.

KAYSER, LEIGH ANN; Pequannock Township HS; Pequannock, NJ; (3); 27/240; Sec Trs Church Yth Grp; Acpl Chr; Capt Color Guard; School Play; Capt Cheerleading; Hon Roll; NHS; Comm.

KAZELIS, KAREN; Haddon Heights HS; Haddon Hts, NJ; (3); Stage Crew; Rep Frsh Cls; Stat Bsktbl; Var JV Fld Hcky; Powder Puff Ftbl; JV Sftbl; Stat Swmmng; High Hon Roll; Hon Roll; Rutgers Dean Summer Schlr Pgm 87; Garnet & Gld Soc 86-88; Marine Bio.

KEANE, BILL; St John Vianney HS; Freehold, NJ; (3); Capt Socr; JV Var Trk; Engrng.

KEARNEY, ERIN; Holy Spirit HS; Absecon, NJ; (2); 28/397; Cornell U; Restrnt Mgmt.

KEARNEY, LAURA; Spotswood HS; Spotswood, NJ; (3); Intnl Clb; Capt Color Guard; Orch; School Play; Trs Jr Cls; Trs Sr Cls; Capt Var Bsktbl; Var JV Sftbl; Hon Roll; Ldrshp Awd Bsktbl 86-87.

KEEFFE, NICOLE; Depaul HS; Pompton Plains, NJ; (4); 44/156; Am Leg Aux Girls St; Ski Clb; Nwsp Stf; Yrbk Ed-Chief; Var L Fld Hcky; Hon Roll; Rotary Awd; OH U.

KEEGAN, AMY; Mary Help Of Christians Acad; Paterson, NJ; (3); 1/86; JCL; Quiz Bowl; Chorus; School Musical; Variety Show; Nwsp Rptr; Nwsp Stf; Rep Soph Cls; Hon Roll; Law.

KEEGAN, CHRISTINA; Rutherford HS; Rutherford, NJ; (3); Church Yth Grp; Key Clb; Office Aide; School Play; Tchr-Hndcpd.

KEEGAN, PATRICIA ANNE; Westfield HS; Westfield, NJ; (2); Church Yth Grp; Cmnty Wkr; Hosp Aide; Library Aide; Office Aide; Pep Clb; Chorus; High Hon Roll.

KEELEY, STAN; R V R H S HS; Mt Holly, NJ; (3); Dance Clb; Varsity Clb; Var JV Socr; Cntrctr.

KEEN JR, THOMAS; Don Bosco Prep HS; Oakland, NJ; (2); 11/240; Boy Scts; Drama Clb; German Clb; Service Clb; School Play; Ice Hcky; High Hon Roll; Order Of Arrow Boy Scts Of Amer 85; Yth For Undrstndg Schlrshp Exchng Stud 86.

KEENAN, HAROLD; Marist HS; Bayonne, NJ; (3); 25/110; Church Yth Grp; Drama Clb; Letterman Clb; Ski Clb; Spanish Clb; School Play; Stage Crew; Var Capt Swmmng; Hon Roll; Acadc Achvt Awd-Prtl Schlrshp 87.

KEENAN, KIMBERLY; Rahway HS; Rahway, NJ; (4); 70/225; Chorus; School Play; High Hon Roll; Studio 7-Camino CA; Makeup Art.

KEENAN, MARY; Edgewood SR HS; Waterford, NJ; (3); French Clb; SADD; Yrbk Stf; JV Var Fld Hcky; Hon Roll; Jr NHS; Latin Clb; Commercial Art.

KEENE, NATALIE; Toms River HS North; Toms River, NJ; (3); 13/520; Church Yth Grp; French Clb; Ski Clb; Band; Church Choir; Concert Band; Jazz Band; Mrchg Band; Swmmng; High Hon Roll; Pre Med.

KEGEL, DAVID; Rutherford HS; Rutherford, NJ; (3); Trs French Clb; Key Clb; Rep Frsh Cls; Bsktbl; Var Mgr Tennis; NHS.

KEHLER, SEAN; West Windsor-Plainsboro HS; Lawrenceville, NJ; (3); FBLA; Model UN; Ski Clb; Concert Band; Mrchg Band; Hon Roll; WA Smnr 87.

KEHOE, MAUREEN E; Holy Cross HS; Cinnaminson, NJ; (4); 3/360; Church Yth Grp; French Clb; School Musical; School Play; Nwsp Ed-Chief; Yrbk Stf; NHS; Ntl Merit Ltr; St Schlr; Drama Clb; Engl Awd 87; Douglass Coll; Jrnlsm.

KEHOE, PATRICK; Bishop Ahr HS; Perth Amboy, NJ; (4); Church Yth Grp; Drama Clb; Im Bsbl; Im Bsktbl; Var Bowling; Var Trk; Var Capt Vllybl; Cit Awd; Hon Roll; Franklin Pierce Coll; Cmmnctns.

KEIL, JAMES R; Lenape HS; Pemberton, NJ; (4); 30/420; Am Leg Boys St; Church Yth Grp; Im Bsbl; Hon Roll; St Schlr; Bsbll All Star Tm Twnshp 84-85; Pres Acad Ftnss Awd Prgm 87; Rutgers U; Engrng.

KEISER, BENJAMIN; Central Regional HS; Bayville, NJ; (4); 4/220; Q&S; Ski Clb; Nwsp Sprt Ed; Stu Cncl; Crs Cntry; Trk; High Hon Roll; NHS; Pres Schlr; Spanish NHS; Congrssnl Yth Ldr Schlr 87; Lehigh U; Engrng.

KEKELIS, MICHAEL; Randolph HS; Randolph, NJ; (3); Church Yth Grp; Computer Clb; Dance Clb; Math Clb; Math Tm; Bsktbl; Natl Sci Olympiad-Chem A 87; Cmmndtn Form Fr II 86; Penn ST U; Comp Sci.

KEKESI, KRISTINE; Bordentown Regional HS; Bordentown, NJ; (4); 1/114; Computer Clb; French Clb; Pres Math Clb; Math Tm; Mu Alpha Theta; Chorus; Capt Drill Tm; Yrbk Stf; Var L Bowling; JV Fld Hcky; Rutgers Schlr, Garden ST Dstngshd Schlr & Cntrl Jersey Chmpns-Olympics Of Mind 86; Rutgers U; Engrng.

KELDER, LYNN; Bayonne HS; Bayonne, NJ; (3); Math Tm; Teachers Aide; Nwsp Stf; Stat Bsktbl; JV Var Cheerleading; High Hon Roll; Jr NHS; Med.

KELDSEN, DAVID P; Notre Dame HS; Clarksburg, NJ; (4); 92/352; Drama Clb; Ski Clb; Chorus; Madrigals; Mrchg Band; School Musical; School Play; Var JV Socr; Millstone Twnshp Wmns Org Schlrshp 86-87; Millstone Twnshp PTO Schlrshp 87; Wolinski Mem Schlrhsp 87; Mason Gross Schl Of PA; Theatr.

KELEHER, MICHAEL; Paulsboro HS; Gibbstown, NJ; (3); 12/150; Political Wkr; Nwsp Rptr; Pres Soph Cls; Rep Jr Cls; Rep Stu Cncl; JV Bsbl; Hon Roll; NHS; Law.

KELLEHER, PATRICIA; Haddonfield Memorial HS; Haddonfield, NJ; (3); Am Leg Aux Girls St; Intnl Clb; Spanish Clb; Nwsp Rptr; Yrbk Stf; Lit Mag; Fld Hcky; Hon Roll; NHS; Spanish NHS; Ntl Hnr Roll 87; Cntmpry Affrs Sympsm VP 87; Borough Of Hanndonfield Rec Cncl 87; Psych.

KELLER, CHERYL A; Spotswood HS; Spotswood, NJ; (2); Intnl Clb; Co-Capt Cheerleading; Crs Cntry; Trk; Hon Roll; Greater Middlesex Conf Blue Div All Star Tm 86; Outstndng Rnnr 86; Rookie Of Yr 86.

KELLER, DAVID R; Wood Ridge HS; Wood Ridge, NJ; (3); Am Leg Boys St; Boy Scts; Model UN; Yrbk Phtg; Rep Jr Cls; Var L Crs Cntry; Var L Trk; Cit Awd; VFW Awd; William T Hornaday Cnsrvtn Awd BSA 87; Pol Sci.

KELLER, EDWARD; Toms River High School East; Toms River, NJ; (4); Boy Scts; Q&S; Band; Nwsp Sprt Ed; Capt Ftbl; Trk; Wt Lftg; Eagle Scout Awd 87; Montclair ST Coll; Hist.

KELLER, GAYLE; Manasquan HS; Belmar, NJ; (2); 32/222; Church Yth Grp; Dance Clb; Band; Concert Band; Drill Tm; Mrchg Band; Twrlr; High Hon Roll; Hon Roll; 1st & 2nd Hnr Rll 85-86 & 86-87; Psych.

KELLER, J MICHAEL; Woodstown HS; Woodstown, NJ; (3); 12/205; Am Leg Boys St; English Clb; Key Clb; Ski Clb; Lit Mag; Rep Soph Cls; Var L Bsbl; Im Bsktbl; JV Ftbl; Hon Roll; Dist Wd Eductnl Cncl 84-87; Mltry.

KELLER, KRISTINA M; Spotswood HS; Milltown, NJ; (2); DECA; French Clb; Intnl Clb; Yrbk Stf; Var Mgr(s); JV Trk.

KELLER, LAURA; Manasquan HS; Belmar, NJ; (4); 29/225; Church Yth Grp; Math Tm; Band; Concert Band; Drm Mjr(t); Jazz Band; Mrchg Band; Twrlr; Cit Awd; High Hon Roll; Sndy Schl Schlrshp 87; Montclair ST Coll; Math.

KELLER, UNA; Bordentown Regional HS; Yardville, NJ; (3); Drama Clb; Hosp Aide; Key Clb; Math Clb; School Play; Lit Mag; Rep Stu Cncl; Bsktbl; Fld Hcky; Hon Roll; Obstetrcn.

KELLEY, BRIAN; Millville SR HS; Millville, NJ; (3); 21/545; Varsity Clb; Var Bowling; JV Tennis; Hon Roll; NHS; Rutgers U; Pharm.

KELLEY, JOHN A; Jackson Memorial HS; Jackson, NJ; (4); 57/390; Church Yth Grp; Ski Clb; JV Bsbl; Var Ftbl; Wt Lftg; High Hon Roll; James Madison U; Bus.

KELLEY, PETER; Jackson Memorial HS; Jackson, NJ; (3); 56/416; Pres Church Yth Grp; VP 4-H; German Clb; ROTC; Church Choir; JV Var Ftbl; Cit Awd; 4-H Awd; High Hon Roll; Aeronautical Engr.

KELLMYER, JEFF E; St James HS; Carneys Point, NJ; (3); 25/73; Rep Frsh Cls; Bsktbl; Var Mgr(s); Prfct Atten Awd; Acad Achvmnt Bus 85-86; Acad Achvmnt Hstry 86-87; Bus Admn.

KELLNER, STEPHEN; Mainland Regional HS; Linwood, NJ; (4); Church Yth Grp; Intnl Clb; Spanish Clb; Stocktn ST Coll.

KELLY JR, ALVIN T; Delsea Regional HS; Williamstown, NJ; (2); Rep Soph Cls; Coach Actv; JV L Ftbl; Var L Trk; Wt Lftg; Hon Roll; Prfct Atten Awd 86-87; Athenum Leag 87; Accntng.

KELLY, BRENDA; Mary Help Of Christian Acad; Clifton, NJ; (4); 6/80; GAA; JCL; Quiz Bowl; Service Clb; Yrbk Stf; Var Vllybl; High Hon Roll; NHS; Prfct Atten Awd; Summa Cum Laude Natl Latin Exam 86; Latin Hnr Scty 86; Letterman 85; Fairfield U; Bio.

KELLY, GREG; Ocean City HS; Marmora, NJ; (4); 4/291; Am Leg Boys St; VP Math Clb; Var Capt Crs Cntry; Var L Trk; High Hon Roll; NHS; Prfct Atten Awd; Rotary Awd; Science Clb; Spanish Clb; Conf All Star Team Cross Cntry 85-86; Garden St Dist Schlr 86-87; Conf Hnr Mntn Track 86; US Naval Acad; Engr.

KELLY, JOHN J; St Joseph Regional HS; Garnerville, NY; (4); Church Yth Grp; Ski Clb; Crs Cntry; Trk; Crdnl Spllmn Yth Awd 86; Dominican Coll; Spec Ed.

KELLY, JOSEPH P; Wayne Hills HS; Wayne, NJ; (3); 23/350; Trs French Clb; Chorus; Concert Band; Mrchg Band; Var Crs Cntry; JV Socr; Var JV Trk; Hon Roll; NHS; Bio.

KELLY, LAURA A; Acad Of The Holy Angels; Hasbrouck Heights, NJ; (4); 4/152; Mu Alpha Theta; Nwsp Rptr; Ed Nwsp Stf; Yrbk Rptr; Yrbk Stf; Hon Roll; VP NHS; St Schlr; Natl Merit Commnd Stud 86; Natl Latin Exam Silver Medal 84-85; Pre-Law.

KELLY, LEONARD; Mc Corristin Catholic HS; Allentown, NJ; (3); 59/100; Yrbk Stf; Rep Jr Cls; Bsktbl; Hon Roll; Jr NHS; NHS; Chiroprctc Med.

KELLY, SEAN; Bergen Catholic HS; Ho Ho Kus, NJ; (4); 161/261; French Clb; Varsity Clb; Var Bsbl; Var Ftbl; Var Wt Lftg; All NNJIL Placekicker 2nd Tm 85-86; U Of RI; Bus Finance.

KELLY, SHEILA; Stuart Country Day Schl; E Windsor, NJ; (3); Cmnty Wkr; French Clb; Model UN; Quiz Bowl; Radio Clb; Scholastic Bowl; Teachers Aide; Yrbk Bus Mgr; Rep Jr Cls; Sftbl; Commnd For Svc Admssns Comm; Outstndng Achvt Englsh.

KELLY, SUZANNE; Toms River HS East; Toms Rvr, NJ; (4); 98/635; Church Yth Grp; Cmnty Wkr; Hon Roll; Bus Adm.

KELLY, TERENCE P; Roselle Catholic HS; Union, NJ; (4); 1/195; French Clb; Math Clb; Math Tm; Science Clb; Lit Mag; Var L Crs Cntry; French Hon Soc; High Hon Roll; Hon Roll; NHS; Cornell U Summer Coll Scholar 86; 1st Pl ST Lev K Of C Essay Cont 83; Schl Scholar 83; US Naval Acad; Engrng.

KELMER, KENNETH J; Watchung Hills Regional HS; Millington, NJ; (4); Boy Scts; Church Yth Grp; Key Clb; Bsktbl; Var Capt Socr; Vllybl; Var Capt Wrstlng; Hon Roll; Parent Tchr Assn High Ranking Stu 87; Chubb & Son Inc Hgh Ranking Stu 87; Sons Poland Merit Awd 87; VA Polytech; Elec Engrng.

KELNER, SAUL; Manalapan HS; Manalapan, NJ; (4); 6/430; Chess Clb; Debate Tm; Science Clb; Temple Yth Grp; NHS; Ntl Merit Ltr; Acadc Ltns Awd 87; Tp Stu Scl Stdy 87; Knght Pythias Spch Cmptn Fnlst 87; G Washington U Hnrs Schlrshp; G Washington U; Bus.

KELSHAW, JENNIFER; Morris Hills HS; Wharton, NJ; (4); 36/285; Trs FBLA; Nwsp Stf; High Hon Roll; Hon Roll; K Gibbs Ldrshp Awd 86; Berkeley Schls Prsrvrnc Awd 87; FBLA Regnl Cmptns 86-87; County Coll Of Morris; Bus Mgmt.

KELUSAK, STEPHANIE; Lakewood HS; Lakewood, NJ; (1); Girl Scts; JV Sftbl; Hon Roll; Psychiatrist.

KEMLER, STACY; Notre Dame HS; Trenton, NJ; (2); 5/400; Rep Frsh Cls; Var Bsktbl; Var Socr; Var Sftbl; Elks Awd; High Hon Roll; Hon Roll; NHS; Girls Scr ST Tm 85-87; NJ AAU St Champs Bsktbl 84.

KEMME, GAIL; Hunterdon Central HS; Flemington, NJ; (4); 101/560; Pres Church Yth Grp; Church Choir; Stage Crew; Yrbk Stf; Hon Roll; NHS; Phy Ed Awd 87; Soph Rcgntn Pgm Svc & Math II 85; Messaih Coll; Home Ec.

KEMPER, CHRISTOPHER; Union Catholic Regional HS; Roselle, NJ; (2); 15/289; Hon Roll; 3rd Dgr Grn Blt Karate 85-87; Treas Hstry Clb 86-87; West Point Acad; Airbrn Rngr.

KENDEIGH, ANDREW E; Westfield HS; Westfield, NJ; (4); 100/490; Am Leg Boys St; SADD; Pres Frsh Cls; Pres Sec Stu Cncl; Var Bsbl; Capt JV Bsktbl; Capt Var Ftbl; Cit Awd; Schl Spirit Awd-Schlrshp 87; U Of WI-MADISON; Comms.

KENDZULK, BARBARA; Middlesex HS; Middlesex, NJ; (3); 39/162; Ski Clb; Spanish Clb; Yrbk Stf; Tennis; Mktg.

KENNARD, YOLANDA; Bordentown Regional HS; Wrightstown, NJ; (2); 20/141; SADD; Chorus; Flag Corp; Mrchg Band; Rep Stu Cncl; JV Bsktbl; English Clb; Rep Soph Cls; Stat Fld Hcky; JV Var Mgr(s); Howard U; Law.

KENNEDY, ARTHUR KYLE; Don Bosco Prep HS; Ramsey, NJ; (2); #13 In Class; Drama Clb; Pep Clb; Ski Clb; School Musical; School Play; Ftbl; High Hon Roll; 3rd Pl Phys Sci Fair 86; Hnrry Awd St Paul R C Chrch Altar Boy 86; Bus.

KENNEDY, BRIAN; Manalapan HS; Englishtown, NJ; (4); 88/417; Boy Scts; Exploring; Hosp Aide; Latin Clb; Ed Nwsp Phtg; Rep Jr Cls; Trs Sr Cls; Policemn Benevolent Assoc Awd 87; Sen Bill Bradly NJ Yng Citzns Awd 87; Jostens Stu Ldrshp Svcshp Awd; U Of Ed Stroudsburg; Phys Ther.

KENNEDY, JIM; Immaculata HS; Branchburg, NJ; (3); Pres Ski Clb; Concert Band; Jazz Band; Mrchg Band; Symp Band; Bus.

KENNEDY, KAREN; Piscataway HS; Piscataway, NJ; (4); 3/496; Band; Concert Band; Mrchg Band; Orch; Symp Band; Gov Hon Prg Awd; High Hon Roll; JP Sousa Awd; NHS; Natl H S Hnrs Orch 86; MENC All Eastrn Orch 87; All ST Wnd Ensmbl 84-87; Rutgers U; Pharm.

KENNEDY, KAREN; St John Vianney HS; Hazlet, NJ; (4); 17/258; Rep Frsh Cls; Rep Jr Cls; Rep Sr Cls; Rep Stu Cncl; Stat Bsbl; Var Cheerleading; Sftbl; Trk; High Hon Roll; NHS; Rutgers Coll; Mrktng.

KENNEDY, SHANNON; Our Lady Of Mercy Acad; Glassboro, NJ; (3); Church Yth Grp; Drama Clb; Chorus; Church Choir; School Play; Stage Crew; Im Bsktbl; Hon Roll; Prfct Atten Awd; Blk Belt In Karate 87; Water Ballet 84-87; Glcstr Cnty Coll; Psych.

KENNEY, CYNTHIA; Brick Memorial HS; Brick, NJ; (3); Office Aide; Band; Yrbk Stf; Sec Frsh Cls; VP Stu Cncl; Var JV Cheerleading; Mgr(s); Var JV Sftbl; Hon Roll; Most Spirited Chrldr Awd 86-87; Teaching.

KENNEY, MARGARET L; Cinnaminson HS; Cinnaminson, NJ; (4); 13/229; Key Clb; Thesps; Chorus; Mrchg Band; School Musical; Yrbk Ed-Chief; NHS; Ntl Merit Ltr; Pres Schlr; St Schlr; Drew U; Bus Admin.

KENNEY, NANCY JOAN ANNE; Riverside HS; Riverside, NJ; (3); Am Leg Aux Girls St; Hosp Aide; Varsity Clb; Rep Stu Cncl; JV Bsktbl; Var Capt Fld Hcky; Var Sftbl; Var Trk; Hon Roll; NJ St Certfd Firefghtr Sta 232 86; Nrsg.

KENNIE, SONJA; Washington Township HS; Sewell, NJ; (4); 15/480; French Clb; Var Capt Bsktbl; Var Fld Hcky; Var Capt Trk; Hon Roll; NHS; Mst Dedctd Bsktbll 87; Unsng Hero Fld Hcky 87; Mst Imprvd Bsktbll 86; U Of DE; Accntng.

KENNY, DAVID J; Saddlebrook HS; Saddle Brook, NJ; (3); 15/119; Am Leg Boys St; Latin Clb; Band; Jazz Band; Mrchg Band; Var Bsktbl; Capt Var Socr; Hon Roll; NHS; Mech Drwng Awd 86; Phys Ed Awd 87; Merit Pgm 86-87; Engrng.

KENT, ERIK; Columbia HS; South Orange, NJ; (3); Am Leg Boys St; Cmnty Wkr; Math Tm; Ski Clb; Temple Yth Grp; JV Socr; Var Tennis; French Hon Soc; 2nd Pl Indvdl Essex Cnty Math Cmpttn Geom 87; Music Ed Assc Adtns Awd Piano 84-85; Cornell U.

KENT, LAURA; St Mary HS; Teaneck, NJ; (3); Am Leg Aux Girls St; GAA; Ski Clb; SADD; Nwsp Stf; Yrbk Phtg; Rep Frsh Cls; Rep Soph Cls; Var L Bsktbl; Var L Crs Cntry; Bus Law.

KENT, SHEILA; Vineland HS; Vineland, NJ; (3); 81/827; VHS Select Choir-Strng Singer & Ftr Ldr Awd, Pitch Pipe Awd 86-87; Pre-Med.

KENT, TARA ANNE; Pope John XXIII HS; Vernon, NJ; (4); Var Capt Fld Hcky; Var Capt Trk; NHS; Hosp Aide; Red Cross Aide; Ski Clb; Teachers Aide; Chorus; Hon Roll; Cngrsnl Schlr Natl Yng Ldrs Conf 87; Capt Vrsty Ski Tm 86-87; Acadmc Excllnc Awd US Hstry II 87; Sprts Med.

KENTER, AMY; J P Stevens HS; Edison, NJ; (3); Art Clb; Key Clb; Office Aide; Science Clb; Temple Yth Grp; Powder Puff Ftbl; Hon Roll; NHS; Hand-In-Hand 87; Co-Curriculr Cncl 86; Stu Asstnc Tm 85; George Washington U; Acctg.

KENTOS, DEBBIE; Mount Olive HS; Flanders, NJ; (1); AFS; Church Yth Grp; Ski Clb; Trs Frsh Cls; Rep Stu Cncl; Cheerleading; Fld Hcky; Sftbl; Hon Roll; Sunday Bible Schl Tchr; PA ST; Photogrphy.

KENTOS, MARK; Mt Olive HS; Flanders, NJ; (3); 104/316; Church Yth Grp; Computer Clb; Science Clb; Ski Clb; Varsity Clb; JV Var Ftbl; JV Var Trk; Wt Lftg; Law.

KENWORTHY, KEVIN; Madison HS; Madison, NJ; (3); 95/228; Boy Scts; Church Yth Grp; Letterman Clb; Var Ftbl; Var Wt Lftg; Hon Roll; Star Sct 85; Bus.

KEOGH, MAUREEN; Immaculate Conception HS; West Orange, NJ; (3); Nwsp Rptr; Nwsp Stf; Rep Frsh Cls; Rep Jr Cls; Stu Cncl; Var Capt Bsktbl; Sftbl; High Hon Roll; NHS; Spanish NHS; Dntstry.

KEOGH, WEBSTER; Holy Spirit HS; Somers Point, NJ; (3); 30/332; Science Clb; Spanish Clb; Speech Tm; Stage Crew; Im Vllybl; Kiwanis Awd; Jr NHS; NHS; Med.

KEPHART, WILLIAM; Pitman HS; Pitman, NJ; (3); 8/150; Rep Frsh Cls; Rep Soph Cls; Rep Sr Cls; Rep Stu Cncl; Var Bsktbl; Var Ftbl; Var Tennis; Hon Roll; NHS.

KEPNER, TERRENCE J; Holy Spirit HS; Ventnor, NJ; (4); 33/363; Church Yth Grp; Cmnty Wkr; 4-H; Quiz Bowl; SADD; Varsity Clb; School Play; Rep Frsh Cls; Rep Soph Cls; Rep Jr Cls; Villanova; Fnc.

KERBAGE, TAREK; Ferris HS; Jersey City, NJ; (4); 2/270; Bowling; Tennis; Hon Roll; NHS; Rutgers; Elec Engrng.

KERCHUSKY, PAMELA; Immaculata HS; Belle Mead, NJ; (3); 7/241; Hosp Aide; Library Aide; Cheerleading; Coach Actv; NHS; Pres Spanish NHS; Acad All-Amer 87; Intl Frgn Lang All-Amer Spnsh 87; Bus.

KERN, EDWARD; Bridgewater-Raritan HS West; Bridgewater, NJ; (4); Drama Clb; Thesps; School Play; Stage Crew; Im Coach Actv; Var Ftbl; Powder Puff Ftbl; Im Wt Lftg; Hon Roll; Rutgers U; Pre-Law.

KERN, MAUREEN; Jackson Memorial HS; Jackson, NJ; (3); 58/416; VP FBLA; Drill Tm; Powder Puff Ftbl; Twrlr; Mgr Wrstlng; High Hon Roll; Hon Roll; Seton Hall U; Pyscl Ed.

KERN, TINA; Morris Knolls HS; Denville, NJ; (4); 2/383; Church Yth Grp; FBLA; Math Clb; Math Tm; Yrbk Stf; JV Sftbl; High Hon Roll; Lion Awd; NHS; Sal; Deans Hnr Schlrshp, Hme & Schl Assn Schlrshp 87; Eastern Nazarene Coll; Engrng.

KERNS, SCOTT; Holy Cross HS; Medford Lakes, NJ; (3); Am Leg Boys St; Ski Clb; Var VP Golf; Nvl Aviator.

KERR, BETH; West Morris Central HS; Long Valley, NJ; (3); Intnl Clb; Flag Corp; Stat Bsktbl; Hon Roll.

KERR, BRIDGET; Immaculata HS; Bridgewater, NJ; (3); Ski Clb; Spanish Clb; Band; Color Guard; Concert Band; Drill Tm; Flag Corp; Mrchg Band; School Musical; School Play; Math.

KERR, DONNA; Gloucester County Christian Schl; Sewell, NJ; (4); Church Yth Grp; Sec Jr Cls; Sec Sr Cls; Var L Bsktbl; Var L Fld Hcky; Var L Sftbl; Var L Vllybl; 4-H Awd; Hon Roll; NHS; Bus.

KERR, JESSICA; Kearny HS; Kearny, NJ; (1); Cmnty Wkr; Sat Frshmn Cls; HS Algebra Course; Vet.

KERR, KRISTIN; Central Regional HS; Seaside Park, NJ; (3); 1/216; Key Clb; Nwsp Rptr; VP Jr Cls; Bausch & Lomb Sci Awd; High Hon Roll; NHS; Spanish NHS; Rutgers Schlr 86-87; Engr.

KERR, MICHELE; Irvington HS; Irvington, NJ; (3); French Clb; Key Clb; Hon Roll; Comp Pgmmg.

KERR, TRACY; Central Regional HS; Seaside Park, NJ; (4); 3/213; Key Clb; Math Clb; Nwsp Rptr; Yrbk Stf; Var L Trk; French Hon Soc; High Hon Roll; VP NHS; Garden ST Dstngshd Schlr Awd 86-87; Slctd Attnd Stu Cngrs In Trenton 87; Lehigh U; Engrng.

KERRIGAN, CAROLYN; Saint John Vianney HS; Aberdeen, NJ; (4); 35/250; Church Yth Grp; Cmnty Wkr; Hosp Aide; Intnl Clb; SADD; Vllybl; Hon Roll; Vlntr Awd 84-85; Multpl Sclerosis Merit Awd 85-87; Forum Monmouth Coll 86; Pharmcy.

KERRIGAN, KATHLEEN A; Wayne Valley HS; Wayne, NJ; (3); 15/288; Am Leg Aux Girls St; Hosp Aide; JCL; Latin Clb; Lit Mag; Bowling; Socr; Trk; High Hon Roll; Hon Roll; US Mililtary Acad.

KERRIGAN, KELLIE; Holy Cross HS; Moorestown, NJ; (4); 31/370; Church Yth Grp; Pep Clb; Ski Clb; Cheerleading; High Hon Roll; Yth Amer Poltcl Sys 86; St Josephs U; Bus.

KERSEY, KIMBERLY; Morris Catholic HS; Dover, NJ; (3); Natl Beta Clb; Varsity Clb; Cheerleading; Coach Actv; Hon Roll; Natl Lang Arts Olympd 84-85.

KERSTNER, CHRISTINE; Newton HS; Andover, NJ; (4); 7/210; Latin Clb; Math Tm; Thesps; Madrigals; School Musical; School Play; Stage Crew; NHS; St Schlr; Fordham U; Brdcstng.

KERZIC, CATHERINE; Kearny HS; Kearny, NJ; (4); 71/383; Am Leg Aux Girls St; German Clb; Girl Scts; Bsktbl; Socr; Sftbl; French Hon Soc; Hon Roll; Kearny Bstr Clb Schlrshp 87; Polsh Wmns Clb Bond 87; Lincoln Schl PTA Schlrshp 87; Kean Coll Of NJ.

KESHIAN, PAUL; Northern Valley Regional HS; Northvale, NJ; (2); Latin Clb; Ski Clb; JV Bsbl; Im Ftbl; Hon Roll; Bus.

KESLER, CHARLES E; St Augustine Prep; Millville, NJ; (4); 27/53; Church Yth Grp; Computer Clb; Stat Bsktbl; Var L Golf; Hon Roll; Athl Awd Golf 87; Vrsty Athl Awd Golf 87; Prfct Atten Awd 83-87; Rider Coll; Bnkng.

KESSEL, MICHAEL H; Bayonne HS; Bayonne, NJ; (4); 5/350; Am Leg Boys St; VP Chess Clb; VP Science Clb; VP Temple Yth Grp; Lit Mag; JV Socr; Im Vllybl; Wt Lftg; Trs Jr NHS; Trs NHS; Grad Montclair ST Coll Acad Tlntd Yng Stu Pgm 87; Hudson Cnty Chamber Comm Acad Achvt Awd 87; Emory U; Pre-Med.

KESSELL, SCOTT; Ridge HS; Basking Ridge, NJ; (2); Rutgers-Newark NJ; Meteorology.

KESSLER, AIMEE; Livingston HS; Livingston, NJ; (2); AFS; Art Clb; Chorus; Rep Frsh Cls; Hon Roll; Show Chorus 85-87; Free Lnc Artst.

KESSLER, CHRISTA; Ocean Township HS; Oakhurst, NJ; (3); 41/344; Church Yth Grp; Hosp Aide; Key Clb; Spanish Clb; Color Guard; Ed Lit Mag; High Hon Roll; VP Jr NHS; NHS; Congressional Bronze Awd 86; Spartan Schlr 86-87; Munlenburg; Law.

KESTIN, MICHAEL; Dwight Morrow HS; Englewood Cliffs, NJ; (3); Boy Scts; Cmnty Wkr; Spanish Clb; Vllybl; Hon Roll; Law.

KETCHAM, CAROLYN; Toms River High Schl North; Toms River, NJ; (3); Am Leg Aux Girls St; Church Yth Grp; Capt Var Cheerleading; Stat Ftbl; Hon Roll; All Cnty CYO Chrldr 87; Arch.

KETCIK, SHANNON; Moorestown HS; Moorestown, NJ; (3); Church Yth Grp; Var Cheerleading; Hon Roll; Early Childhood Eductn.

KEVRA, ADAM; Vineland HS; Vineland, NJ; (3); Boy Scts; Key Clb; Math Clb; Math Tm; Political Wkr; Rep Soph Cls; Rep Jr Cls; Rep Stu Cncl; Var Stat Bsktbl; Var Mgr(s); Dlgtn Chrmn Mdl Cngrss Prty Caucus 86; Medcl Explrs Clb 85; Surgn.

KHAMMAR, ALEXANDER; Freehold Twnshp HS; Freehold, NJ; (3); 12/385; Exploring; Math Tm; Science Clb; Band; Mrchg Band; VP Jr Cls; Rep Stu Cncl; JV Trk; NHS; Deans Summer Schlr Rutgers U 87; Pre-Med.

KHAN, ERUM; James J Ferris HS; Jersey City, NJ; (3); Math Clb; Quiz Bowl; Nwsp Stf; Off Stu Cncl; Hon Roll; NHS; Hon Roll, Merit Roll, Schlstc Bowl Trphy & Plaque; Rutgers; Engrng.

KHAN, HASAN; Elizabeth HS; Hillside, NJ; (4); 14/850; Chess Clb; Civic Clb; Computer Clb; English Clb; Key Clb; Math Clb; Math Tm; Tennis; NHS; Rotary Awd; NJIT Fut Engrns 85; Cty Eliz Dpt Aging Svcs Awd 86; Supt Schlr Awd 86-87; Boston U; Biomed Engrng.

KHAN, MUNAZZA; Immaculate Heart Acad; New City, NY; (3); Hosp Aide; Yrbk Stf; Trk; High Hon Roll; Hon Roll; Rcgntn Awd 86; Cert Achvt 84; Aga Khan U; Bio.

KHAN, SHAFI; Steinert HS; Hamilton Square, NJ; (4); 5/302; Am Leg Boys St; Debate Tm; Math Tm; Quiz Bowl; Scholastic Bowl; School Play; Nwsp Stf; Yrbk Rptr; Yrbk Stf; Coach Actv; Engrs Clb Trenton Schlrshp, Natl Merit Schlrshp, & Gen Foods Corp Dir Schlrshp 87; Carnegie-Mellon U; Engrng.

KHAROD, AMIT; Saint Rose HS; Asbury Pk, NJ; (3); Chess Clb; Math Tm; Stage Crew; VP Jr Cls; Var L Trk; Hon Roll; NHS; NEDT Awd; Spanish NHS; Spanish Clb; Cert Of Hnrs In Spnsh II 86; Cert Of Hnr Schlrshp 87.

KHAWAJA, MUSTAFA; Parsippany Hills HS; Parsippany, NJ; (2); Symp Band; Harvard; Engr.

KHLYAVICH, ALEXANDRA; Randolph HS; Randolph, NJ; (3); 33/353; Lit Mag; JV Capt Fld Hcky; Hon Roll; Spanish NHS; Drama Clb; NFL; Chorus; Im Powder Puff Ftbl; Im Sftbl; Lbrl Arts.

KIANG, MARGARET E; Bridgewater-Raritan HS East; Bridgewater, NJ; (4); Hosp Aide; Math Tm; Science Clb; Spanish Clb; Orch; Nwsp Stf; Var Swmmng; NHS; Ntl Merit Schol; High Hon Roll; Westinghouse Hnrs Grp 87; Rensselaer Mdl 85; Dartmouth Coll; Med.

KIDD, JOE; Paulsboro HS; Paulsboro, NJ; (3); Computer Clb; Varsity Clb; Band; Concert Band; Jazz Band; Mrchg Band; Symp Band; Var Crs Cntry; Var Capt Trk; Wt Lftg; All Cnfrnc & All Cnty In Track 86 & 87; Hnrb Mntn In Track 87; Comp.

KIDD, TRACEY; Trenton Central HS; Trenton, NJ; (3); Pep Clb; Drill Tm; School Play; Hon Roll; Harvard U; Pre-Med.

KIEFER, DORI; Brick Memorial HS; Brick, NJ; (3); Church Yth Grp; Dance Clb; Mrchg Band; Variety Show; Pom Pon; Sftbl; Cit Awd; Band; Rep Frsh Cls; Rep Soph Cls; Do Mst Cmnty Awd Miss Amer Co-Ed Pgnt 86; Phys Thrpy.

KIEFER, KELLIE L; Union HS; Union, NJ; (3); Church Yth Grp; Key Clb; Spanish Clb; Nwsp Stf; Yrbk Stf; Capt Twrlr; High Hon Roll; Hon Roll; Jr NHS; NHS; Outstndg Achvt Spnsh; Corp Law.

KIEFER, STEPHANIE; Paul VI HS; Haddonfield, NJ; (3); 112/418; Var Bsktbl; Hon Roll; Physcl Thrpy.

KIELY, DANIELE; St Dominic Acad; Hoboken, NJ; (1); Service Clb; Var Swmmng; Hon Roll; Stevens Tech; Med.

KIENGST, SARA; Ridge HS; Far Hills, NJ; (3); Art Clb; Pres Church Yth Grp; Cmnty Wkr; Latin Clb; SADD; Var JV Bsktbl; Powder Puff Ftbl; Var Capt Socr; JV Var Sftbl; NHS; Summa Cum Ld Natl Latn Exm 87; Sccr 2nd Tm All Conf Hnbl Mntn All Cnty 87; Cmnctns.

KIERNAN, ROBERT; Monsignor Donovan HS; Howell, NJ; (3); 19/245; Boy Scts; Ski Clb; Crs Cntry; L Wrstlng; High Hon Roll; VFW Awd; BSA Eagle 87; Crmnl Just.

KIESZNOWSKI, SHERI ANNE; St John Vianney HS; Freehold, NJ; (4); 38/252; Sec Trs Church Yth Grp; Cmnty Wkr; Intnl Clb; Pres Service Clb; Church Choir; Concert Band; Yrbk Stf; Twrlr; Hon Roll; NHS; Gld & White Awd 83-87; Brookdale CC; Bus Admin.

KILAYKO, JASMIN; St John Vianney HS; Hazlet, NJ; (3); 11/200; Intnl Clb; JV Math Tm; Trs SADD; Ed Yrbk Stf; Stat Ftbl; JV Trk; High Hon Roll; NHS; Service Clb; Color Guard; Cert Merit Spnsh, Engl, Chem, & Anatomy; NJMTA Annl Piano Auditions; Med.

KILDUFF, EDWARD; Don Bosco Prep; Suffern, NY; (3); Art Clb; Chess Clb; Model UN; Science Clb; Varsity Clb; Yrbk Stf; Rep Soph Cls; Bsbl; JV Crs Cntry; Var Ice Hcky; Art Awd Achvmnt 84; Vrstyy Lttr Ice Hockey,Trck; Syracuse; Archtctrl Engr.

KILDUFF, PATRICK J; Don Bosco Prep; Tomkins Cove, NY; (3); 17/200; Church Yth Grp; Pres Debate Tm; Drama Clb; NFL; Rep Soph Cls; NHS.

KILEY, DEBI; Kingsway Regional HS; Mickleton, NJ; (2); Gordon Phillips Cosmetology.

KILGORE, ALISON; Bridgewater-Rantan HS East; Bridgewater, NJ; (3); Church Yth Grp; French Clb; SADD; Off Frsh Cls; Off Soph Cls; Off Jr Cls; Stu Cncl; Stat Bsktbl; JV Var Fld Hcky; Powder Puff Ftbl; Comp Sci.

KILLEEN, NANCY; Westfield HS; Westfield, NJ; (2); Church Yth Grp; French Clb; Key Clb; Political Wkr; Psych.

KILLMER, KIMBERLY; Manasquan HS; Spring Lake, NJ; (3); 7/241; Am Leg Aux Girls St; FBLA; Ski Clb; Band; Jazz Band; Orch; Var Trk; High Hon Roll; Kiwanis Awd; NHS; Acad Awd 86-87; FBLA 3rd Pl In Reg Comp For Bus Math 87; Girls State-Ward Secty, Justice Of Peace 87.

KILPATRICK, ANDREA; Cherry Hills HS West; Cherry Hill, NJ; (3); 15/389; French Clb; Hosp Aide; Library Aide; PAVAS; Mrchg Band; Symp Band; Lit Mag; Im Vllybl; Hon Roll; NHS.

KILPATRICK, CHRISTIAN; Manasquan HS; S Belmar, NJ; (3); 54/250; FBLA; Key Clb; Latin Clb; Concert Band; Jazz Band; Symp Band; Crs Cntry; Trk; High Hon Roll; Hon Roll; Church Yth Grp; Pre-Law.

KIM, BYUNG; Dickinson HS; Jersey City, NJ; (3); Computer Clb; Math Clb; Science Clb; Var Tennis; Hon Roll; Merit Rl 86-87; Cornell U; Med.

KIM, CATHY; Passaic Valley HS; W Paterson, NJ; (2); French Clb; Hon Roll; Schlrshp Domncn Acad NY 85-86.

KIM, CECILIA; Tenafly HS; Columbia, MO; (2); AFS; French Clb; Model UN; Engl Awd 85-86; Prof.

KIM, DAN; Garden State Acad; N Brunswick, NJ; (4); 1/32; Mgr Church Yth Grp; Teachers Aide; Ed Yrbk Stf; Rep Sr Cls; Capt Sftbl; Capt Vllybl; High Hon Roll; Prfct Atten Awd; Im Tennis; Pres Acad Ftns Awd 87; Mech Engr.

KIM, DANIEL; Montville Twsp HS; Towaco, NJ; (3); 10/270; Church Yth Grp; Hosp Aide; Key Clb; Ski Clb; Pres Frsh Cls; Rep Soph Cls; Pres Jr Cls; VP Stu Cncl; Var Lcrss; Var Capt Socr; Emergncy Dept Vol 100 Hrs 86; Boston U; Med.

KIM, DOO; Burlington Twp HS; Burlington, NJ; (3); Chess Clb; Church Yth Grp; Varsity Clb; Var Bsbl; Var Capt Socr; JV Trk; Engr.

KIM, ELLEN; Scotch Plains-Fanwood HS; Scotch Plains, NJ; (4); 2/300; Political Wkr; Jazz Band; Nwsp Stf; Bausch & Lomb Sci Awd; Gov Hon Prg Awd; NCTE Awd; Ntl Merit SF; Sal; St Schlr; German Clb; NJ Yth Symph 85-86; NJ All ST Band Orch 85.

KIM, ERIC; Maple Shade HS; Maple Shade, NJ; (3); Church Yth Grp; Computer Clb; FCA; Intnl Clb; Var Bsktbl; Coach Actv; JV Tennis; Var Trk; Hon Roll; Prfct Atten Awd; Cert Awd Comp I & Chem I 86-87; Engr.

KIM, HOE-CHIN; Rancocas Valley Regional HS; Mt Holly, NJ; (2); Quiz Bowl; Scholastic Bowl; Science Clb; Orch; Yrbk Stf; VP Frsh Cls; Rep Soph Cls; Rep Stu Cncl; High Hon Roll; NHS; Harvard U; Pol Sci.

KIM, JIYOUNG; Waldwick HS; Ramsey, NJ; (4); 3/136; Hosp Aide; Capt Math Tm; Orch; Nwsp Rptr; Yrbk Stf; Lit Mag; Tennis; Hon Roll; NHS; Prfct Atten Awd; Vly Hosp Aux Schlrshp 87; Pres Acdmc Ftnss Awd 87; Mst Imprvd Plyr Awd Tnns 86-87; Boston U; Biomed Engrng.

KIM, JOHN; N V R HS; Harrington Pk, NJ; (3); 1/274; Am Leg Boys St; VP Aud/Vis; Debate Tm; VP French Clb; Hosp Aide; Ski Clb; SADD; Rep Stu Cncl; Var Tennis; Bausch & Lomb Sci Awd.

KIM, JUNG H; Bridgewater-Raritan H S East; Bridgewater, NJ; (4); Church Yth Grp; Cmnty Wkr; German Clb; Hosp Aide; Math Tm; Quiz Bowl; Scholastic Bowl; Service Clb; Nwsp Bus Mgr; Yrbk Bus Mgr; Pre Med.

KIM, MIA; Northern Valley Regional HS; Harrington Pk, NJ; (3); 16/274; Church Yth Grp; Cmnty Wkr; Hosp Aide; Pres Intnl Clb; SADD; Mgr Stage Crew; Yrbk Stf; Rep Stu Cncl; High Hon Roll; Hon Roll; Englewood Hosp Svc 86; Ntrtn.

KIM, MOON-SOOK; Lakeland Regional HS; Haskell, NJ; (3); Cmnty Wkr; French Clb; Color Guard; Lit Mag; Trk; High Hon Roll; NHS; NEDT Awd; Art Clb; Math Tm; Sci Incentive Prog Ramapo Coll 86; Yth Scholars Inst For Comm Lebanon Vly Coll 87; Social Sci.

KIM, RICHARD; Palisades Park JR/Sr HS; Palisades Pk, NJ; (4); 7/126; Mu Alpha Theta; Nwsp Rptr; Lit Mag; Ftbl; Tennis; Trk; Wt Lftg; Hon Roll; NHS; Acdmc Decthln 87; U Of Rochester; Chem Engr.

KIM, SONNA; Bernards HS; Bedminster, NJ; (4); Q&S; VP Orch; Nwsp Rptr; Hon Roll; NHS; Ntl Merit Ltr; St Schlr; Chorus; Yrbk Stf; Prncpl Cellist, Juilliard Pre-Coll Orchstra 86-87; Fnlst Arts Rcgntn & Talent Srch 86-87; Princeton U.

KIM, SUHYON; Ocean Twsp HS; Asbury Park, NJ; (3); Boys Clb Am; Ski Clb; Trs Spanish Clb; Im Bsktbl; Spartan Schlr 85; Bus.

KIM, THOMAS; Paramus HS; Paramus, NJ; (3); Var NFL; Science Clb; Nwsp Ed-Chief; Ed Nwsp Stf; Ed Yrbk Stf; NHS; Ntl Merit Ltr; Spanish NHS; AFS; Chess Clb; Med.

KIMBLE, ANDREW; University HS; Newark, NJ; (2); Drama Clb; Church Choir; Variety Show; Nwsp Phtg; Nwsp Rptr; Nwsp Sprt Ed; Off Frsh Cls; Off Soph Cls; Stu Cncl; Bsktbl; MVP Chrch Bsktbl 87; Kudos Awd-Natl Phi Delta Kappa Delta Pi 87; Prjct Bus Awd 87; Vet.

KIMES, DAMON; Vineland HS; Vineland, NJ; (3); Political Wkr; Band; Chorus; Concert Band; Jazz Band; School Musical; School Play; Variety Show; Pres Frsh Cls; Rep Stu Cncl; V Wrstlng Rookie Of Yr 85; 3rd Pl Independnt Schls Wrstlng Tourn 85; Johns Hopkins; Psych.

KINDER, CONSTANCE; Benedictine Acad; Newark, NJ; (3); Church Yth Grp; Dance Clb; Drama Clb; Ski Clb; Spanish Clb; Teachers Aide; Drill Tm; Bowling; Coach Actv; Cotillion Awd 85; Miss Natl Teen Awd 87; Elec Engrng.

KING, CHRISTINE; Eastern HS; Berlin, NJ; (4); Church Yth Grp; Cmnty Wkr; French Clb; Hosp Aide; JV Bsktbl; JV Lcrss; Hon Roll; Glassboro ST Coll; Chldhd Educ.

KING, DANNY; Cranford HS; Cranford, NJ; (2); JCL; Latin Clb; Math Clb; JV Socr; L Var Swmmng; Hon Roll; Rcvd Slvr Medl-Ntl Latn Exm 86; Cum Laude-Philadelphia Latn Exm & Ntl Latn 87; Math.

KING, DOREEN; Toms River H S East; Glen Ridge, NJ; (4); 42/546; Drama Clb; Key Clb; Teachers Aide; Chorus; Church Choir; School Musical; School Play; Off Jr Cls; Off Sr Cls; Sftbl; Central Regnl Rotary Clb Scholar 87; Rutgers; Cmmnctns.

KING, EUREKA T; Kingsway Regional HS; Swedesboro, NJ; (2); Sec Church Choir; Flag Corp; Mrchg Band; Var Twrlr; Rutgers U Of NY; Nrsng.

KING, JEFF; Camden Catholic HS; Cinnaminson, NJ; (3); Var Capt Ftbl; Var Swmmng; JV Trk; JV Vllybl; Var Wt Lftg; Hon Roll; Prfct Atten Awd; All Conf Linebckr 86; All Parochial Linebckr 86; Hosp Adm.

KING, JENNIFER; Holy Spirit HS; Brigantine, NJ; (4); 72/375; Chorus; School Musical; Hon Roll; Grdn ST Schlrshp 87; Trenton ST Coll.

KING, KAREN; Holy Spirit HS; Ventnor, NJ; (4); 45/363; Off Cmnty Wkr; Off Pep Clb; School Musical; Variety Show; Rep Jr Cls; Rep Sr Cls; Stu Cncl; Var L Cheerleading; Hon Roll; NHS; Trntn ST; Elem Ed.

KING, KENRIC M; John F Kennedy HS; Paterson, NJ; (3); Am Leg Boys St; Nwsp Phtg; Nwsp Rptr; Nwsp Sprt Ed; Nwsp Stf; JV Bsbl; Crs Cntry; JV Wrstlng; Cert 6th Annual City Wide Ortrcl Cont 87; Cornell; Comp Engr.

KING, LEIDENE; Clifford J Scott HS; East Orange, NJ; (2); 1/382; Math Clb; Math Tm; Flag Corp; VP Frsh Cls; VP Soph Cls; Bowling; High Hon Roll; NHS; Hon Roll; Acad All-Amer 84-85; Gftd Stud Of Essex Cnty Awd 84-85; Csmtc Chem.

KING, MICHAEL; Woodstown HS; Woodstown, NJ; (3); 18/205; English Clb; VP German Clb; Math Clb; Rep Jr Cls; Crs Cntry; Socr; Tennis; Trk; Hon Roll; Sci Fr Lcl & ST 1st Pl & Hnrbl Mntn 85; Cngrssnl Yth Ldrshp Cncl Schlr 87; Colgate U; Bio.

KING, PATRICK; St John Vianney HS; Union Beach, NJ; (4); 23/250; Boy Scts; Nwsp Sprt Ed; Var L Crs Cntry; Var L Trk; Hon Roll; VP NHS; NROTC Schlrshp 87; Vgl Hnr, Ord Of Arrow & BSA; George Washington U; Pltcl Sci.

KING, RACHEL EDNA LUISE; Cumberland Regional HS; Bridgeton, NJ; (3); JV Fld Hcky; Hon Roll; Jr NHS; Church Yth Grp; Cmnty Wkr; Drama Clb; French Clb; School Play; Stage Crew; Lit Mag.

KING, RICHARD; Pinelands Regional HS; Tuckerton, NJ; (3); 5/200; Math Clb; Math Tm; Spanish Clb; Im Bsktbl; Im Bowling; Var L Tennis; Var L Trk; High Hon Roll; Hon Roll; Jr NHS; Boston U; Financial Mgmt.

KING, SHANNON; Middle Township HS; Dennisville, NJ; (3); 17/277; Quiz Bowl; Chorus; Mrchg Band; School Musical; Rep Frsh Cls; Rep Jr Cls; Stu Cncl; High Hon Roll; Hon Roll; NHS; Awd For Bst Frnch I Stu 85; Acad Awd For Frnch III 87; Acad Awd For Engl III 87; Ed.

KING, TEISHA; Plainfield HS; Plainfield, NJ; (3); 45/348; Trs Church Yth Grp; VP Library Aide; Church Choir; 4-H Awd; Isabell G Ross Memrl Citatn Excllnce Prsnl Grwth 83-84; Spellmen Coll; Lawyer.

KING, TREVA; Shawnee HS; Vincetown, NJ; (3); Trs Church Yth Grp; School Musical; Hon Roll; Jr NHS; Pres Stu Cncl; JV Bsktbl; JV Lcrss; NHS; VFW Awd; Prsdntl Clssrm Yg Amercns 87; Gvrns Schl Arts 86; Rtry Yth Ldrshp Cnfrnce 87; Duke U; Pre-Med.

KING, VIVIAN; Essex Catholic Girls HS; E Orange, NJ; (3); Church Yth Grp; Cmnty Wkr; Drama Clb; Girl Scts; Band; Chorus; Church Choir; Crs Cntry; Hon Roll; Non Schl Spnsrd Track Awds 84-87; Accordian Awds 84-86; Piano Awads 84-87; Rutgers Coll Newark; Stenogrphr.

KINGSLEY, MATTHEW P; Paramus HS; Paramus, NJ; (3); Am Leg Boys St; Varsity Clb; Rep Soph Cls; Im Var Bsktbl; Im Var Golf; Im Wt Lftg; Fairfield; Bus Finance.

KINGSTON, ELIZABETH; Manasquan HS; Spring Lake, NJ; (3); 62/239; Drama Clb; FBLA; Spanish Clb; High Hon Roll; Hon Roll; Liberal Arts.

KINGSTON, KEVIN; Essex Catholic Boys HS; East Orange, NJ; (3); Church Yth Grp; Ski Clb; Im Bsktbl; Im Fld Hcky; Im Sftbl; High Hon Roll; Hon Roll; Acctng.

KINKY, DENISE; Haddon Heights HS; Haddon Heights, NJ; (3); Am Leg Aux Girls St; JV Var Bsktbl; JV Sftbl; Cit Awd; High Hon Roll; Hon Roll; Garnet & Gold Soc 86-88; Bus.

KINNEALY, MICHELE; Morris Catholic HS; Boonton Twsp, NJ; (2); 82/166; Church Yth Grp; Hosp Aide; Office Aide; Pep Clb; Quiz Bowl; Red Cross Aide; Teachers Aide; CC Awd; Prfct Atten Awd; Nrsng.

KINNEY, JOHN; Ramapo HS; Franklin Lakes, NJ; (4); 18/332; Camera Clb; Computer Clb; Drama Clb; Quiz Bowl; Radio Clb; Scholastic Bowl; Science Clb; Spanish Clb; Thesps; School Musical; NJ Grdn St Schlr 87; Acadc Decthln 87; Presdntl Acadc Ftns Awd 87; PA ST U; Med.

KINNEY, KENNETH J; David Brearley Regional HS; Garwood, NJ; (3); 34/136; Am Leg Boys St; Madrigals; School Musical; Var L Bsbl; Var L Ftbl; Var L Wrstlng; Hon Roll; Amer Lgn Smmr Bsbll Cnfrnc 87; Eckert; Physcl Ed.

KINNEY, ROBERT; Roselle Park HS; Roselle Park, NJ; (3); 9/145; Am Leg Boys St; SADD; Trs Frsh Cls; Sec Soph Cls; Pres Jr Cls; Pres Sr Cls; Pres Stu Cncl; Var Ftbl; Var Wrstlng; Hon Roll; Sci.

KINNEY, TODD A; Cherry Hill HS East; Cherry Hill, NJ; (3); Am Leg Boys St; Varsity Clb; Capt Var Socr; Var Wrstlng; Hon Roll; NHS; Socr 1st Tm All Conf All Grp II All S Jersey 86; 2nd Tm ST; Bus.

KINSELLA, KEVIN; Dwight Morrow HS; Englewood, NJ; (3); 82/312; Ski Clb; Nwsp Rptr; Nwsp Stf; Castleton ST Coll; Comp.

KINSEY, DAVE; Vernon Twp HS; Glenwood, NJ; (3); Am Leg Boys St; Thesps; Chorus; Rep Soph Cls; Rep Jr Cls; Var Crs Cntry; JV Trk; Hon Roll; NHS; Ntl Merit Ltr; All-St Chorus 86 & 87; St Teen Arts 87; Physician.

KINSEY, KIM; Oakcrest HS; Mays Landing, NJ; (3); Drama Clb; GAA; JA; Band; Color Guard; Capt Flag Corp; Mrchg Band; School Play; Rep Soph Cls; Hon Roll; Vrsty Schlr; Tchng.

KIRBY, ADRIANNE; Woodbridge HS; Sewaren, NJ; (4); 28/368; Pres French Clb; Acpl Chr; Chorus; School Play; Yrbk Stf; Rep Stu Cncl; Stat Sftbl; French Hon Soc; NHS; Syracuse U; Bio Rsrch.

KIRBY II, CHARLES C; Princeton HS; Princeton, NJ; (3); Trs Churc Yth Grp; Drama Clb; Trs SADD; Pres Acpl Chr; Church Choir; VP Ja Band; School Musical; Stage Crew; Symp Band; Pres Frsh Cls; Gold K Awd 87; Theatre.

KIRBY, KRISTINE; Red Bank Catholic HS; Middletown, NJ; (Church Yth Grp; French Clb; Hosp Aide; SADD; Nwsp Rptr; Rep Fr Cls; Trk; Poli Sci.

KIRCHOFER, MAURICE; Green Brook HS; Green Brook, NJ; (3); 3/8 AFS; Am Leg Boys St; Key Clb; Lit Mag; Rep Stu Cncl; Var Co-Capt Bsk Var Co-Capt Bsktbl; High Hon Roll; VP NHS; Gov Schl 87; Senate Y Schlrshp 87.

KIRK, BONNIE; Union HS; Union, NJ; (4); 57/554; Church Yth Gr Concert Band; Var L Bsktbl; Capt L Fld Hcky; Var L Sftbl; Hon Ro NHS; Cmnty Wkr; Band; Church Choir; Union HS Fmle Schlr-Athlete 8 Acad Schrlshp Messiah Coll 87; Union Twnshp Educ Assn Schrlshp 8 Messiah Coll; Sports Med.

KIRK, JOHN; Pinelands Regional HS; Tuckerton, NJ; (3); 4/180; Scien Clb; Rep Stu Cncl; Var Crs Cntry; Var Trk; Bausch & Lomb Sci Awd; Hig Hon Roll; Hon Roll; NHS; Prfct Atten Awd; Pres Schlr; Amer Chmcl S Sci Awd 86-87; Prncpls Advsry Cmmttee; Bus.

KIRKENDALL, TARA; Phillipsburg HS; Phillipsburg, NJ; (3); 3/31 Am Leg Aux Girls St; Ski Clb; Concert Band; Mrchg Band; Nwsp Stf; R Stu Cncl; High Hon Roll; NHS; Pep Clb; Band; Scrtry Intrct Clb 87; La

KIRKPATRICK JR, CLAUDE R; Marine Academy Of Science & Tec Keansburg, NJ; (4); 7/31; Boy Scts; ROTC; Nwsp Rptr; Yrbk Phtg; VP S Cncl; Hon Roll; Pres NHS; Drill Tm; Nwsp Phtg; World Consrvtn Awd 8 US Air Force Acad; Aeronautics.

KIROUAC, SUSAN; Hunterdon Central HS; Flemington, NJ; (2); Dram Clb; Girl Scts; Hosp Aide; Quiz Bowl; School Play; Yrbk Stf; Hon Ro Rivier Coll Chllng Prog NH 86-87; Phys Thrpy.

KIRSCH, EDWARD; Woodstown HS; Woodstown, NJ; (3); English Cl Pres German Clb; Key Clb; Math Clb; Rep Frsh Cls; Rep Soph Cls; Rep Cls; Var Bsbl; Var Wrstlng; Hon Roll; Sci Fair Hnr Mntn 85-86; Sci Fa 1st Pl 86-87; ROGATE 84-87.

KIRSCHNER, BRIAN; Lakewood HS; Lakewood, NJ; (3); 16/354; A Leg Boys St; English Clb; JCL; Latin Clb; Temple Yth Grp; Nw Ed-Chief; JV Var Bsbl; Hon Roll; NCTE Awd; NHS; Clsscl Latn H Socty 85.

KIRSCHNER, SUSAN; Mt Olive HS; Flanders, NJ; (4); 20/280; Ho Aide; Science Clb; Ski Clb; Yrbk Stf; Ed Lit Mag; Stat Bsktbl; JV Sft NHS; Achvmnt Sci Chem 86; Sftbll Awds 84&85; Hours Cndystrppng 8 Penn ST U; Law.

KIRSH, MICHAEL A; Tenafly HS; Tenafly, NJ; (4); Model UN; Politic Wkr; Yrbk Stf; Pres Frsh Cls; Rep Soph Cls; Trs Jr Cls; Rep Stu Cncl; Hi Hon Roll; Ntl Merit Ltr; Pres Schlr; Home Schl Assn Schlrshp 87; Sta Fdntn Schlrshp 87; Brown U; Engrng.

KISALA, DOUGLAS; Mt Olive HS; Budd Lake, NJ; (3); 31/318; Bo Scts; Var Crs Cntry; Trk; High Hon Roll; Hon Roll; NHS; Ntl Merit S Lbrl Arts.

KISTLER, DONNA; Butler HS; Butler, NJ; (4); 30/200; Church Yth Gr Varsity Clb; Church Choir; Yrbk Stf; Rep Stu Cncl; Stat Bsktbl; Var F Hcky; Hon Roll; NHS; Pres Schlr; Pres Schlrshp Awd 87; William Guent Awd 87; Statler Fndtn Schlrshp 87; Keystone JC; Trvl/Trsm.

KISTLER, DYAN; Butler HS; Butler, NJ; (4); 40/200; Church Yth Gr Drama Clb; Thesps; Varsity Clb; Church Choir; School Musical; Rep S Cncl; Stat Fld Hcky; Ed Mitchel Schlrshp 87; Katharine Gibbs Schl; Sect

KISTLER, SUSAN; Elmwood Park Memorial HS; Elmwood Pk, NJ; (Church Yth Grp; French Clb; Hosp Aide; Intnl Clb; Nwsp Stf; Sft French Hon Soc; Hon Roll; Awd Plyg Sftbl 86; Nursing.

KITNER, RICHARD; Trenton Central HS; Trenton, NJ; (3); Drama Cl Stage Crew; Hon Roll; Mayors Hnr Awd Acdmc Excllnc & Delores Mu Memrl Awd 85; Lo Bue Phoenix Art Prz 1st Pl 87; Art.

KITTREDGE, NEIL; South Brunswick HS; Princeton, NJ; (3); 12/27 Drama Clb; Mu Alpha Theta; Stage Crew; Nwsp Rptr; Hon Roll; Engrn

KITZIS, ANDREA; Dwight-Englewood Schl; Englewood, NJ; (4); 2/11 Camera Clb; Latin Clb; Var Capt Bsktbl; Var Capt Lcrss; Var Capt So Var Swmmng; Im Vllybl; High Hon Roll; Ntl Merit Ltr; Prfct Atten Aw Cum Laude Soc 86-87; Mxma Cum Laude-Ntl Ltn Exm 84- Semifnlst-Ntl Hspnc Schlrshp Pgm 86-87; Bus.

KJELLBERG, THOMAS; Ramapo HS; Oakland, NJ; (3); 103/325; V Socr; High Hon Roll; Hon Roll; Cert Mrt Geo, Chem, Grmn & Engl 85-87; Engr.

KLAIMAN, JEAN M; The Pingry Schl; Summit, NJ; (4); Cmnty Wk Key Clb; Ski Clb; Orch; Ed Nwsp Phtg; JV Sftbl; High Hon Roll; Ntl Mer SF; Cum Laude Soc; Grdn St Distgshd Schlr.

KLAK, BARBARA; Immaculate Conception HS; Wallington, NJ; (3); 1 84; Q&S; Church Choir; Rep Frsh Cls; Rep Stu Cncl; Vllybl; Hon Roll; U Ntl Ldrshp Mrt Awd 86-87; US Ntl Math Awd 85-86; Acad All-Amer Large Div 85-86; Accntng.

KLAR, MICHAEL; Immaculata HS; Somerville, NJ; (2); 2/250; Boy Sc Intnl Clb; Math Clb; Math Tm.

KLATSKY, CARL; Matawan Regional HS; Aberdeen, NJ; (4); 34/31 Aud/Vis; Computer Clb; Math Clb; Math Tm; VP Radio Clb; JV Socr; J Wrstlng; Hon Roll; NHS; Videotext Proj Ldr 86-87; Stevens Inst Tec Elec Engrng.

KLAUBER, LISA; Cresskill HS; Cresskill, NJ; (4); 34/114; Pres Sr C Girl Scts; Ski Clb; Spanish Clb; Temple Yth Grp; Chorus; School Pla Nwsp Rptr; Nwsp Stf; Yrbk Phtg; Sr Svc Awd 87; Syracuse U; Bus.

KLEHM, ROBERT; Essex Catholic Boys HS; Newark, NJ; (3); JV Bs JV Ftbl; Im Sftbl; Var Trk; High Hon Roll; Hon Roll; ST Police Aca Criminal Jstc.

KLEIDERMACHER, DAVID N; Cherokee HS; Marlton, NJ; (4); 1/41 Trs Computer Clb; Debate Tm; Pres Math Tm; Temple Yth Grp; Tenni NHS; Pres Schlr; St Schlr; Chess Clb; Math Clb; MV Staffer Awd 86; Mo Likly Succeed 86; Gov Schl Schlr Sci 86; Comp Sci.

KLEIMAN, DENNIS; Cherry Hill West HS; Cherry Hill, NJ; (4); 32/36 Computer Clb; French Clb; Science Clb; Yrbk Phtg; Lit Mag; Tennis; Ho Roll; Ntl Merit SF; Bstn U; Lbrl Arts.

KLEIN, BILLY; West Orange HS; W Orange, NJ; (3); Aud/Vi Computer Clb; French Clb; Library Aide; Math Clb; Math Tm; Ban Concert Band; Nwsp Rptr; Nwsp Stf.

KLEIN, DEENA; Hightstown HS; East Windsor, NJ; (4); 60/407; AF Drama Clb; French Clb; Intnl Clb; Library Aide; PAVAS; SADD; Scho Musical; School Play; Stage Crew; U Of Colorado Schlrshp 86; U Delawar

KLEIN, DENNIS; Maple Shade HS; Maple Shade, NJ; (3); 4/110; A Leg Boys St; Boy Scts; Church Yth Grp; Cmnty Wkr; DECA; JA; Ma Clb; Varsity Clb; Band; Bsbl; Rutgers; Engrng.

KLEIN, GARY; Pequannock HS; Pequannock, NJ; (3); Am Leg Boys St; Chess Clb; Church Yth Grp; Yrbk Stf; Crs Cntry; Trk; U S Acad Decathlon 87; Electronics Clb 86-87; Vly Forge Chrstn Coll; Mnstry.

KLEIN, JASON; John P Stevens HS; Edison, NJ; (3); 22/465; Cmnty Wkr; Exploring; Science Clb; Spanish Clb; SADD; Temple Yth Grp; Rep Frsh Cls; Var JV Bsktbl; Powder Puff Ftbl; Var Socr.

KLEIN, JASON; Manalapan HS; Englishtown, NJ; (3); Boy Scts; Teachers Aide; VP Temple Yth Grp; Comp Sci.

KLEIN, MARGARET; St Pius V Regional HS; Parlin, NJ; (4); 18/115; Art Clb; Church Yth Grp; Office Aide; Teachers Aide; Varsity Clb; Church Choir; Nwsp Ed-Chief; Yrbk Rptr; Hon Roll; NHS; 3.5 GPA Awd 87; St John Fshr Coll; Bus Mgmt.

KLEIN, THOMAS; North Warren Regional HS; Newton, NJ; (4); 6/120; Scholastic Bowl; Nwsp Ed-Chief; VP Soph Cls; VP Jr Cls; Pres Stu Cncl; Capt Socr; NHS; VFW Vc Of Dmcrcy St Wnnr 86; NJ Schlr 86; Rutgers Coll.

KLEIN, TIMOTHY E; Upper Freehold Regional HS; New Egypt, NJ; (4); 11/175; Am Leg Boys St; Computer Clb; Math Tm; JV Ftbl; Var L Trk; High Hon Roll; Hon Roll; Sec NHS; Pres Schlr; Salvation Army Ctznshp Schlrshp 87; Fairleigh Dickinson U; Law.

KLEINBERG, ELIZABETH A; Mountain Lakes HS; Mountain Lakes, NJ; (4); 15/100; Capt GAA; Model UN; Political Wkr; Temple Yth Grp; Yrbk Stf; Var Capt Tennis; Hon Roll; NHS; Ntl Merit SF; Spanish NHS; Cngrssnl Intrn 86; Ldrshp Trng Smnrr 85; Cornell U; Poli Sci.

KLEKOS, CONNIE; Vineland HS; Vineland, NJ; (2); 122/865; Church Yth Grp; Cmnty Wkr; Dance Clb; English Clb; French Clb; Key Clb; Office Aide; Pep Clb; Teachers Aide; Varsity Clb; Law.

KLELE, FAITH; Secaucus HS; Secaucus, NJ; (3); Church Yth Grp; Math Clb; Mu Alpha Theta; Spanish Clb; High Hon Roll; Hon Roll; Bus.

KLEMICK, KATHARINE; Boonton HS; Lincoln Park, NJ; (3); Church Yth Grp; German Clb; Girl Scts; Hon Roll; Elem Schl Tchr.

KLERER, RACHEL L; Bruriah HS; Edison, NJ; (3); Cmnty Wkr; Math Tm; Spanish Clb; VP Temple Yth Grp; School Musical; Pres Soph Cls; NHS; Advtg.

KLEVA, JENNIFER; Central Regional HS; Seaside Park, NJ; (4); Church Yth Grp; Letterman Clb; Ski Clb; Varsity Clb; Sec Stu Cncl; Var Capt Fld Hcky; Var Capt Trk; Hon Roll; Oct Sr Of Month 87; US Army Resrv Natl Schlr Ath Awd 87; Outstndng Sr Of Yr 87; Springfield Coll; Athltc Trainr.

KLIDZIA, SHEILA; Ewing HS; West Trenton, NJ; (4); 159/300; DECA; Library Aide; Chorus; Rep Frsh Cls; Stat Bsbl; Score Keeper; Hon Roll; VP Cntrl Rgn DECA 86-87; Hon Mntn Rstrnt Mngmnt DECA Comptn 86; Acctng.

KLIMEK, ANDREW J; Pennsauken HS; Pennsauken, NJ; (4); 2/375; Am Leg Boys St; Pres French Clb; Leo Clb; Quiz Bowl; SADD; JV Var Socr; Pres French Hon Soc; VP NHS; Pres Schlr; Sal; Georgia-Pacific Fndtn Schlrshp 87; Frnch Lang Awd 87; Rotary Clb Awd 87; Juniata; Commnctns.

KLINCK, CHRISTINE; Millville SR HS; Millville, NJ; (3); Am Leg Aux Girls St; VP Key Clb; Chorus; Jazz Band; Orch; Variety Show; Hon Roll; NHS; Natl Choral Awd 86; Music.

KLINE, CHRISTOPHER; Cumberland Regional HS; Bridgeton, NJ; (3); 5/361; High Hon Roll; Hon Roll; Prfct Atten Awd; Recording Engr.

KLINE, DENISE; Hopewell Valley Central HS; Pennington, NJ; (2); AFS; Art Clb; 4-H; French Clb; High Hon Roll; Hon Roll; U Of Berkeley; Neuropsycht.

KLINKO, MICHELLE; Manchester Township HS; Whiting, NJ; (3); Girl Scts; Pep Clb; Yrbk Stf; Math Tm; Spanish Clb; Color Guard; Drill Tm; Flag Corp; Rep Soph Cls; JV Bowling; Band Front Captn Awd Flag Sqd Captn 86-88; Accntng.

KLINSKY, STEVEN J; Toms River High Schl North; Toms River, NJ; (3); Camera Clb; School Musical; School Play; Stage Crew; Nwsp Phtg; Yrbk Phtg; Yrbk Stf; Var L Trk; Capt Im Vllybl; Bus.

KLOTZ, TAMMY A; Bordentown Regional HS; Cookstown, NJ; (4); 7/114; FBLA; GAA; Hosp Aide; Q&S; Chorus; School Play; Nwsp Ed-Chief; Var Cheerleading; Hon Roll; NHS; Med.

KLOTZEK, NANETTE; St Peters HS; Piscataway, NJ; (4); 3/89; Math Clb; Concert Band; Mrchg Band; Ed Yrbk Stf; Lit Mag; High Hon Roll; Hon Roll; Spnsh Awd-Mst Profcnt 4 Yrs 87; Engl & Bio Awd-Mst Profcnt 87; Cook Coll; Ag.

KLUCK, KIMBERLY; Bridgewater Raritan HS East; Bound Brook, NJ; (3); Ski Clb; Spanish Clb; Chorus; Concert Band; Flag Corp; Mrchg Band; Symp Band; Stat Bsbl; Powder Puff Ftbl; Hon Roll; Acctng.

KLUCSARITS, LORI; Hunterdon Central HS; Flemington, NJ; (2); 13/480; Art Clb; Church Yth Grp; Hosp Aide; Ski Clb; Soph Cls; Stu Cncl; Sec Lcrss; Hon Roll; Schl Rep Tn Arts 85-87; Med.

KLUEG, BETH; Holy Spirit HS; Absecon, NJ; (4); 25/363; Pep Clb; SADD; Chrmn Stu Cncl; Var Co-Capt Cheerleading; High Hon Roll; Hon Roll; Jr NHS; NHS; Rutgers U; Bus.

KLUGMAN, CRAIG; Lakeland Regional HS; Wanaque, NJ; (3); 3/350; Trs Drama Clb; Math Tm; Quiz Bowl; SADD; Trs Thesps; School Musical; Nwsp Stf; High Hon Roll; NHS; Ntl Merit Ltr.

KLUMPP, JANET LYNN; Union HS; Union, NJ; (4); 152/534; Cmnty Wkr; FBLA; Girl Scts; Hosp Aide; JA; Church Choir; Cit Awd; Ntl Merit Ltr; Bus Merit Awd 85 & 86; Seton Hall U; Bus Mgmt.

KMECH, KENDRA; Secaucus HS; Secaucus, NJ; (4); 18/162; Key Clb; Mu Alpha Theta; Ski Clb; Mrchg Band; High Hon Roll; Hon Roll; Mu Alpha Theta Awd; Pres Schlr; SUNY New Paltz NY; Elem Educ.

KMETZ, PATRICIA; De Paul HS; Pompton Lakes, NJ; (3); 52/150; Am Leg Aux Girls St; Church Yth Grp; Chorus; School Musical; School Play; Stage Crew; Hon Roll; Peer Cnslr 86-87; Psychthrpy.

KMIEC, MIKE; Cherry Hill HS West; Cherry Hill, NJ; (3); Var L Swmmng; Philadelphia Coll Of Art.

KNAVER, CHRISTOPHER; Christian Brothers Acad; Lincroft, NJ; (3); 14/250; Math Tm; Var Capt Bsbl; Var Capt Bsktbl; Im Socr; Hon Roll; Engrng.

KNECHT, KERRI; Paul VI HS; Laurel Springs, NJ; (3); 81/416; Church Yth Grp; Cmnty Wkr; SADD; Drill Tm; Nwsp Rptr; Nwsp Stf; Yrbk Stf; Rep Jr Cls; Hon Roll; Prfct Atten Awd; Bus.

KNEHR, HELMUT T; Union HS; Union, NJ; (2); Sec Computer Clb; Science Clb; Orch; High Hon Roll; Hon Roll; Jr NHS; NEDT Awd; Pres Schlr; Math Clb; Spanish Clb; Ntl Sci Olympiad 86-87; NJS Sci Day 34th Pl 86-87; Engr.

KNEIS, HEIDI; Wayne Hills HS; Wayne, NJ; (3); Church Yth Grp; Dance Clb; Capt GAA; Var Fld Hcky; All Cnty Fld Hockey 1st Team 86,All Area 1st Team 86,All Leag Hon Ment 86.

KNEIS, MICHAEL J; Wayne Hills HS; Wayne, NJ; (4); 14/300; Rep German Clb; Math Tm; Varsity Clb; Nwsp Phtg; Var Crs Cntry; Var Trk; High Hon Roll; Trs NHS; Ntl Merit SF; St Schlr; Patriot Club Schlrshp 87; Rutgers Coll; Mech Engr.

KNEZEVIC, MICHAEL; Roselle Catholic HS; Roselle, NJ; (4); 40/187; JA; Im Bsktbl; Var Capt Socr; Im Vllybl; High Hon Roll; Jr NHS; NHS; US Army Most Vlbl Plyr-Sccr 86-87; All Mtn Vly Conf Sccr Tm 86-87; Mens Clb MVP 86-87; Rutgers Coll Arts/Sci; Psych.

KNICE, JENNIFER; Middletown S HS; Lincroft, NJ; (2); Cmnty Wkr; Hosp Aide; Rep Stu Cncl; Bsktbl; Fld Hcky; Socr; Sftbl; Vllybl; Hon Roll; Congressional Awd-Bronze 87.

KNIGHT, AMY; Manasquan HS; Belmar, NJ; (4); 4/225; Drama Clb; Hosp Aide; Key Clb; Thesps; Band; Chorus; Capt Flag Corp; DAR Awd; Gov Hon Prg Awd; Trs NHS; Elks Schrlshp 87; Natl Band Awd 87; Natl Merit Cmmdtn 86; Montclair ST Coll; Music Thrpy.

KNIGHT, TONYA; Toms River HS South; Beachwood, NJ; (4); 17/356; Church Yth Grp; French Clb; GAA; Girl Scts; Math Tm; Science Clb; Speech Tm; Church Choir; School Play; Var Crs Cntry; Early Admsn Coll 86-87; Natl Merit Schlrshp Ltr Cmmndtn 87; Clemson; Psych.

KNIPFELBERG, DEBORA; John P Stevens HS; Edison, NJ; (4); Drama Clb; Ski Clb; School Play; Rep Sr Cls; Rep Stu Cncl; Var Cheerleading; Powder Puff Ftbl; NHS; NJ 7th Annual Homecoming Queen 87; Yng Teens Theater Wrkshp Adjnt Prg Middlesex Cnty Coll 84; Rutgers U; Bus Mngmnt.

KNOLL, STEPHANIE; Atlantic Christian Schl; Ocean View, NJ; (3); Yrbk Stf; Pres Frsh Cls; Pres Soph Cls; Pres Jr Cls; Capt Bsktbl; Capt Fld Hcky; Capt Sftbl; Hon Roll; Sftbl MVP 85; Bsktbl All-Trnmnt Tm 86; Fld Hcky All-Trnmnt Tm 84; Phys Ed.

KNOWLES, AMY; Friends Schl; Monroeville, NJ; (3); Yrbk Stf; Socr; Sftbl; Doc.

KNOWLES, JAMIE; Highland Regional HS; Clementon, NJ; (4); 17/297; Computer Clb; FTA; Spanish Clb; Hon Roll; NHS; Highlnds Rep Govt Day 84-85; Elizabethtown Coll; Elem Educ.

KNOWLES, JOHN; Pemberton HS HS; Ft Dix, NJ; (1); Nwsp Stf; Socr; High Hon Roll; Hon Roll; CT U; Art.

KNUTELSKY, THOMAS; Wallkill Valley Regional HS; Franklin, NJ; (4); 3/170; Am Leg Boys St; Math Clb; Science Clb; SADD; Band; Jazz Band; Var L Bsbl; Var Capt Ftbl; Hon Roll; Pres NHS; Rutgers Coll Engrng; Mech Engr.

KOBER, KURT; Bridgewater Raritan HS East; Bridgewater, NJ; (3); Computer Clb; Band; Jazz Band; Mrchg Band; Orch; Symp Band; Im Bowling; High Hon Roll; Hon Roll; NHS.

KOBERNICK, GARY; Clifton HS; Clifton, NJ; (4); 146/587; Aud/Vis; Computer Clb; Intnl Clb; Ski Clb; VP Soph Cls; Rep Stu Cncl; JV Bsbl; Im Ftbl; Hon Roll; Rutgers U; Engrng.

KOBYLINSKI, MARK; Pitman HS; Pitman, NJ; (3); Var L Bsbl; Var Capt Bsktbl; Var L Socr; Im Vllybl; Im Wt Lftg; Soccer S Jersey Fnlst Grp I Tri-County Chmps 86; Intrmrl Vllybl Camp 86-87.

KOCH, A BRIDGET; Paul Vi HS; Haddonfield, NJ; (4); 180/512; VP Pres Drama Clb; French Clb; Drill Tm; School Musical; School Play; Variety Show; Pom Pon; Hon Roll; Elem Educ.

KOCH, JOSEPH F; Sussex County Vo-Tech HS; Montague, NJ; (2); Office Aide; Service Clb; Stu Cncl; Swmmng; Tennis; Trk; Hon Roll; Rep Ldrshp Trning Conf 87; Swm Team Plcd 11th & 12th Cnty Chmpnshps 87; Upsalla Coll 87; Rutgers U; Comp Sci.

KOCH, KENNETH; Kinnelon HS; Kinnelon, NJ; (2); Church Yth Grp; Drama Clb; Library Aide; PAVAS; Chorus; School Musical; School Play; Rep Stu Cncl; Hon Roll; HOBY 2nd Pl 87; Cornell U; Htl Rstrnt Mgmt.

KOCH, MARILYN; John P Stevens HS; Edison, NJ; (3); Church Yth Grp; Key Clb; Office Aide; Science Clb; Service Clb; Hon Roll; NHS; Phys Ther.

KOCH, RANDY; Garfield HS; Garfield, NJ; (3); 19/183; Ed Drama Clb; Math Tm; Speech Tm; Varsity Clb; School Play; Nwsp Rptr; Yrbk Stf; Rep Jr Cls; Rep Stu Cncl; Crs Cntry; Boys ST Delg 86-87; William Paterson Coll; Pre Vet.

KOCH, STEPHEN J; Collingswood HS; Collingswood, NJ; (3); 30/240; Am Leg Boys St; Boy Scts; Church Yth Grp; JA; Ski Clb; Spanish Clb; SADD; Band; Sec Sr Cls; JV Im Socr; USAF Acad; Engrng.

KOCHBERG, JOSEPH; Hightstown HS; East Windsor, NJ; (3); French Clb; Rep Frsh Cls; Rep Soph Cls; Rep Jr Cls; Var L Ice Hcky; Hon Roll; NHS; Ntl Merit Ltr; Pre Med.

KOCHER, DAVID; Hunterdon Central HS; Whitehouse Sta, NJ; (2); 76/485; Nwsp Sprt Ed; Var Bsbl; JV Ftbl; JV Trk; Outstndng Achvt In Math & Hstry 87; U Of FL; Nuclear Engrng.

KOCISCIN, MARK; St Pius X Regional HS; Piscataway, NJ; (4); Church Yth Grp; Computer Clb; Nwsp Bus Mgr; Var Bowling; Hon Roll; NHS; Chrstn Ldrshp 87; Hnrs Hgh GPA 87; Rochester Inst Of Tech; Elec.

KOCSIS, LORI ANNE; Sayreville War Memorial HS; S Amboy, NJ; (4); 13/353; Pres Science Clb; Pres Spanish Clb; Capt Flag Corp; School Musical; Nwsp Ed-Chief; Elks Awd; NHS; Spanish NHS; Intnl Clb; Library Aide; VFW Post 4699 Poppy Lylty Day Qn 86-87; Ithaca Coll; Phys Ther.

KODAMA, LIZETTE; Glen Rock HS; Glen Rock, NJ; (3); 29/145; Art Clb; Church Yth Grp; Drama Clb; Spanish Clb; School Play; Nwsp Stf; JV Socr; Hon Roll; Jr NHS; NHS; 3rd Pl Ovrall Rgnl Cmpttn Mdlng 86; 6th Pl Ovrall ST Cmpttn Mdlng 87; Spnsh.

KOEGEL, JENNIFER; Wood-Ridge HS; Wood Ridge, NJ; (2); French Clb; Model UN; Service Clb; Rep Stu Cncl; JV Sftbl; High Hon Roll; Burger King Schlrshp.

KOEHLER, VIRGINIA; Morristown Beard HS; Boonton, NJ; (2); Camp Fr Inc; Church Yth Grp; French Clb; Service Clb; Ski Clb; Pres Frsh Cls; JV Tennis; Var JV Vllybl; Hon Roll; Girl Scts; 2nd Pl-Frnch Pstr Awd 87; Math & Engl Awds 86.

KOEHN, DEANNE; Bishop Eustace Preparatory Schl; Woodbury, NJ; (3); 11/167; Am Leg Aux Girls St; Pres French Clb; NFL; SADD; Nwsp Bus Mgr; Nwsp Rptr; Score Keeper; Sftbl; Hon Roll; NHS; Cmnty Theater Grp 84-86; Yth Mnstry Pgm; Jrnlsm.

KOELLE, MICHAEL; Matawan Regional HS; Matawan, NJ; (3); 14/325; Math Tm; Ski Clb; Stage Crew; JV Socr; JV Trk; High Hon Roll; Engrng.

KOENIG, ANDREW S; Moorestown HS; Moorestown, NJ; (3); Am Leg Boys St; French Clb; Ed Nwsp Phtg; Ed Yrbk Phtg; Ed Lit Mag; JV Socr; Var Swmmng; High Hon Roll; Med.

KOENIG, PAUL T; Hopewell Valley Central HS; Pennington, NJ; (3); 1/220; Am Leg Boys St; Drama Clb; Math Tm; School Play; Nwsp Rptr; Rep Stu Cncl; Var Bsbl; Stat Bsktbl; High Hon Roll; NHS; Rutgers Schlr 86-87.

KOENIG, ROBERT H; Livingston HS; Livingston, NJ; (4); 25/423; Chess Clb; Computer Clb; Exploring; Math Clb; Lit Mag; French Hon Soc; High Hon Roll; Hon Roll; Jr NHS; NHS; US Naval Acad Smmr Sem 86; Comp Sci.

KOENIG, SCOTT; Livingston HS; Livingston, NJ; (2); Math Tm; VP Frsh Cls; VP Soph Cls; VP Jr Cls; JV Bsbl; Im Bsktbl; Var Socr; Im Sftbl; French Hon Soc; High Hon Roll; All-Essex Cnty Sccr Tm-Hnrbl Mntn 86.

KOERNER, DARLENE; Pennsauken HS; Pennsauken, NJ; (3); 29/419; Drama Clb; German Clb; Leo Clb; Ski Clb; School Musical; Var JV Mgr(s); Var JV Score Keeper; Tennis; Hon Roll; Jr NHS; Rutgers; Resrch-Devlp Bactrlgy.

KOERNER, DOROTHY; Immaculate Conception HS; Ridgefield Prk, NJ; (3); Q&S; Pres SADD; Nwsp Rptr; JV Var Bsktbl; Hon Roll; Hgh Hnrs Gym; Capt JV Bsktbl; Sci.

KOES, KRISTIN; Madison HS; Madison, NJ; (2); 18/200; Service Clb; JV Fld Hcky; Sftbl; High Hon Roll.

KOESTENBLATT, ERIK; Morristown HS; Morristownship, NJ; (3); Boy Scts; Chess Clb; Cmnty Wkr; Computer Clb; Hosp Aide; Radio Clb; Red Cross Aide; Chorus; Rep Frsh Cls; Hon Roll; Cnslr In Trngn 83; NC ST; Bus.

KOETS, TARA; Livingston HS; Livingston, NJ; (3); Church Yth Grp; Cmnty Wkr; Hosp Aide; Library Aide; Office Aide; Political Wkr; Service Clb; Teachers Aide; High Hon Roll; Hon Roll; Mayors Yth Grp 87; 1st Pl Art Show 84; Comm.

KOETTING, JACQUELYN; Paramus HS; Paramus, NJ; (4); 45/330; Drama Clb; Intnl Clb; Color Guard; Concert Band; Rep Orch; School Musical; School Play; Nwsp Rptr; Yrbk Stf; Rtry Stu Belgium 87-88; Trenton St Coll; Hstry.

KOHANE, DEBBI; Hunterdon Central HS; Flemington, NJ; (3); 161/543; Ski Clb; Band; Color Guard; Concert Band; Mrchg Band; School Musical; Stage Crew; Symp Band; Rep Civic Clb; Sec Stu Cncl; Bio.

KOHBERGER, CORTNEY; Northern Valley Regional HS; Harrington Pk, NJ; (3); Drama Clb; Trs French Clb; Band; Nwsp Rptr; Lit Mag.

KOHL, JAMES M; S Plainfield HS; S Plainfield, NJ; (4); 70/206; L Bsbl; L Bsktbl; Bowling; L Ftbl; Elks Awd; Hon Roll; Varsity Clb; Capt Badmtn; All Area, Cnty & ST, Grp II Bsbll 87; All Cnfrnc & ST, Grp II-3RD Tm Bsbll 86; Rutgers U; Bus Econ.

KOHN, NANCY; Montville Township HS; Montville, NJ; (3); 28/276; Drama Clb; Exploring; FBLA; Key Clb; Ski Clb; Chorus; Church Choir; School Musical; JV Var Fld Hcky; NHS; Cert Apprctn NJ Schl Brds Assn 85.

KOHUT, MARK; Linden HS; Linden, NJ; (3); Church Yth Grp; Ski Clb; Orch; School Musical; School Play; Variety Show; Hon Roll; Inst Of Audio Research; Music.

KOKOLA, CAROLEE; Franklin Twsp HS; Somerset, NJ; (3); Church Yth Grp; Cmnty Wkr; Drama Clb; 4-H; Ski Clb; Band; Color Guard; Concert Band; Mrchg Band; School Musical; Rutgers Schlr 87; Sci.

KOKOSKA, STEPHEN M; Spotswood HS; Spotswood, NJ; (3); High Hon Roll; Hon Roll; NHS.

KOLAKIOTIS, SONDRA; Bayonne HS; Bayonne, NJ; (3); Var Socr; Var Sftbl; Hon Roll; Devry Inst Of Tech; Tech.

KOLARSICK, JENNIFER LEE; Red Bank Catholic HS; Spring Lake, NJ; (4); 29/319; French Clb; Math Clb; Math Tm; Ski Clb; Yrbk Stf; Crs Cntry; Trk; Hon Roll; NHS; Douglass Coll.

KOLB, MELISSA; Watchung Hills Regional HS; Millington, NJ; (3); Band; Stat Crs Cntry; Mgr(s); Score Keeper; Stat Trk; Stat Wrstlng; Hon Roll; Law.

KOLESAR, JENNIFER; Middletown HS South; Locust, NJ; (2); US Naval Acad-Annapolis; Pilot.

KOLMER III, JOHN H; Christian Brothers Acad; Middletown, NJ; (3); 2/250; Church Yth Grp; Cmnty Wkr; Math Clb; Math Tm; Yrbk Stf; Im Lcrss; Var JV Trk; Im Vllybl; High Hon Roll; NHS; Cls Acadmc Achvt Awds 85-87; Bus.

KOLODIJ, CHRISTINE; St Aloysius HS; Jersey City, NJ; (4); 7/109; Church Yth Grp; Capt Bowling; Cit Awd; Hon Roll; Trs NHS; Pres Schlr; Accntng I Hnr Mntn 87; Schlrshps 87; St Peters Coll; Accntng.

KOLODZIEJ, STACEY ANN; Elizabeth HS; Elizabeth, NJ; (3); Key Clb; Hon Roll; NHS; VFW Awd; Voice Dem Awd; Bio.

KOMESHAK, PATRICK; Cherokee HS; Marlton, NJ; (3); Church Yth Grp; FFA; Science Clb; Im Bsbl; JV Bowling; JV Ftbl; Var Socr; JV Wt Lftg; Hon Roll; Jr NHS; Ldrshp Conf; USAF Acad; Vet.

KOMOROWSKI, DENISE; Lenape Valley Regional HS; Stanhope, NJ; (4); 19/236; Sec Key Clb; Yrbk Stf; Crs Cntry; French Hon Soc; Hon Roll; NHS; Intnl Clb; Concert Band; Stu Cncl; Presdntl Acad Fitness Awd 87; Trugman & Co CPA Schlrshp 87; Sussex Cnty Med Soc Bk Schlrshp 87; Rutgers U; Pharmacist.

KOMOROWSKI, DONNA; Sussex County Vo Tech; Stanhope, NJ; (2); Bowling; Mgr(s); Hon Roll.

KOMPA, JILL; Woodstown HS; Woodstown, NJ; (4); 1/215; Trs English Clb; Sec Band; VP Sr Cls; Var Socr; NHS; St Schlr; Val; Church Yth Grp; Exploring; Nwsp Rptr; Rutgers Schlr 86; Cngrssnl Schlr 87; Amer Chem Soc Awd 86; Trenton ST Coll; Med.

KOMPA, SCOTT; Woodstown HS; Woodstown, NJ; (3); Boy Scts; Computer Clb; English Clb; German Clb; Ski Clb; SADD; Nwsp Rptr; Nwsp Stf; Var Wrstlng; Med.

KONDEK, KAREN; Matawan Regional HS; Matawan, NJ; (3); 71/310; FBLA; School Play; Stage Crew; Bus.

KONG, ELAINE; Spotswood HS; Milltown, NJ; (4); 18/187; Math Clb; Math Tm; Yrbk Stf; Hon Roll; NHS; SUNY Binghamton; Econ.

KOOPS, SARAH; Eastern Christian HS; North Haledon, NJ; (3); Drama Clb; School Play; Stage Crew; Nwsp Rptr; Chrmn Frsh Cls; Crs Cntry; Tennis; Hon Roll; NHS; Arch.

KOPER, SHARON; Montville Twp HS; Pine Brook, NJ; (4); 50/267; Ski Clb; Varsity Clb; Yrbk Stf; Rep Stu Cncl; Var Capt Cheerleading; Powder Puff Ftbl; Sftbl; High Hon Roll; Hon Roll; NHS; Mst Vlbl Cheerldr Awd 87; Schlrshp Ntl Hnr Soc 87; Duquesne U; Bus.

KOPP, STEVEN A; Marlboro HS; Colts Neck, NJ; (4); Church Yth Grp; Exploring; German Clb; Ski Clb; NJSGA Caddy Schlrshp 87-88; U Of MD; Arch.

KOPPS, TRACY; Manalapan HS; Manalapan, NJ; (3); 20/429; Rep Soph Cls; Off Jr Cls; Off Sr Cls; Sec Stu Cncl; Capt Var Cheerleading; NHS; SUNY Fshn Inst Of Tech; Fshn.

KORALYCSIK, KEVIN; Wallington HS; Wallington, NJ; (3); Am Leg Boys St; Camera Clb; Church Yth Grp; Science Clb; Nwsp Stf; Yrbk Stf; JV Bsbl; Gov Hon Prg Awd; Hon Roll; NHS; Stu Wk 84-86.

KORANYI, PETER A; Tenafly HS; Tenafly, NJ; (4); 7/228; Pres Math Clb; Math Tm; Pres Science Clb; Orch; High Hon Roll; Ntl Merit SF; St Schlr; MIT; Biochmstry.

KORCHICK, ROBYN; Mc Corristin Catholic HS; Hamilton, NJ; (4); 11/280; VP Art Clb; Rotary Awd; Pep Clb; Varsity Clb; Yrbk Stf; Var Capt Bsktbl; Var Capt Sftbl; Hon Roll; NHS; Prfct Atten Awd; 3rd Tm All ST Bsktbl Prchl A 86-87; 2nd Tm All Mrcr Cnty-Bsktbl, Sftbl-Plyr Of Wk 87; Trenton ST Coll; Educ.

KOREN, GARRETT; Lakewood Prep; Howell, NJ; (2); 2/27; Math Tm; SADD; Variety Show; Lit Mag; Off Frsh Cls; Trs Soph Cls; Capt Tennis.

KORNICK, CARRIE; Lower Cape May Regional HS; North Cape May, NJ; (3); #8 In Class; Key Clb; Quiz Bowl; Scholastic Bowl; Spanish Clb; Varsity Clb; Yrbk Stf; Trs Jr Cls; Rep Stu Cncl; VP Capt Bsktbl; Var Trk; Japan-U S Schlrshp 86-87; Intl Law.

KORNMUELLER, JASON; West Morris-Mendham HS; Chester, NJ; (2); Chess Clb; Church Yth Grp; Computer Clb; FBLA; Ski Clb; SADD; Var Trk; Jr NHS; Annapls Naval Acad.

KORNREICH, JONATHAN; Parsippany Hills HS; Morris Plains, NJ; (4); 10/306; Trs FBLA; Quiz Bowl; Chorus; Madrigals; School Musical; Yrbk Rptr; Rep Jr Cls; Rep Sr Cls; Hon Roll; NHS; Pres Acad Fit Awd 87; ITT Coll Scholar Prgm 87; Natl Merit Ltr Cmmndtn 87; Brandeis U; Intl Fin.

KOSHLAP, KELLY; St John Vianney HS; Matawan, NJ; (3); 80/234; Church Yth Grp; Ski Clb; SADD; Rep Frsh Cls; Rep Soph Cls; JV L Bsbl; Var L Ftbl; Hon Roll; Presdntl Physcl Ftnss 85-87; Nvl Avtr.

KOSKO, JOHN; West Essex HS; Fairfield, NJ; (3); Am Leg Boys St; Science Clb; Drm Mjr(t); Jazz Band; Mrchg Band; School Musical; Symp Band; High Hon Roll; NHS; Spanish NHS.

KOSS, MICHAEL; Pingry Schl; Bridgewater, NJ; (4); Chess Clb; Debate Tm; Ntl Merit SF; St Schlr; Whitlock Prz For Math 86; Psych.

KOSTAL, GEOFFREY R; Governor Livingston Regional HS; Summit, NJ; (3); 2/200; Am Leg Boys St; Pres Exploring; NFL; School Musical; School Play; Pres Trs Stu Cncl; Var L Crs Cntry; French Hon Soc; NHS; Sal; Intl Commerce.

KOSTER, DANIEL; Hunterdon Central HS; White House Sta, NJ; (2); 9/485; Art Clb; Computer Clb; Spanish Clb; Stage Crew; High Hon Roll; Hon Roll; Spanish NHS; Exhbtr Tn Arts Fstvl Vsl Art 86-87; 3rd Pl Wldlf Pstr Cntst 86; Gftd & Tlntd Art III 87; Vsl Art.

KOSTIS, GEORGE; Union HS; Union, NJ; (3); Letterman Clb; Coach Actv; Ftbl; Wt Lftg; Wrstlng; Prfct Atten Awd.

KOSTY, LISA L; Colonia HS; Colonia, NJ; (4); 28/250; Key Clb; Capt Drill Tm; Mrchg Band; School Musical; School Play; Swing Chorus; Rep Stu Cncl; Mgr(s); Wrstlng; Sec Spanish NHS.

KOSYDAR, CHRISTIE JEAN; Bancocas Valley Regional HS; Mount Holly, NJ; (3); 5/316; Am Leg Aux Girls St; Service Clb; VP Frsh Cls; Sec Sr Cls; Rep Stu Cncl; Mgr Socr; JV Sftbl; High Hon Roll; Hon Roll; Messiah Coll PA; Pyscl Thrpst.

KOTCH, LIZ; Ocean Township HS; Asbury Park, NJ; (3); 44/344; Key Clb; Spanish Clb; SADD; Varsity Clb; Variety Show; Off Jr Cls; Var Capt Socr; High Hon Roll; Hon Roll; NHS; Spartan Schlr Awd; Penn ST; Phys Thrpst.

KOTLER, LISA; Hillsborough HS; Somerville, NJ; (3); Ski Clb; Off Frsh Cls; Off Soph Cls; Off Stu Cncl; Var Socr; Psycht.

KOTLIAR, TARAS; Toms River South HS; Toms River, NJ; (3); 3/405; Boy Scts; Sec Church Yth Grp; Key Clb; Math Tm; Science Clb; Band; Mrchg Band; Symp Band; High Hon Roll; Hon Roll; Rensselaer Medlst-Math & Sci 86-87; Comp Sci.

KOTOK, RACHEL; Vineland HS; Vineland, NJ; (2); 48/900; Debate Tm; Key Clb; Political Wkr; Spanish Clb; SADD; Chorus; Yrbk Stf; VP Frsh Cls; Sec Soph Cls; Sec Jr Cls; Hugh O Brian Yth Fndtn 87; Pltcl Sci.

KOTOVA, STANLEY; St Augustine Prep; Milmay, NJ; (3); 7/56; Chess Clb; Var Golf; Var Socr; Engrng.

KOTSAKIS, CHRIS; Cinnaminson HS; Cinnaminson, NJ; (3); Pres Aud/Vis; Church Yth Grp; Drama Clb; Thesps; School Play; Stage Crew; JV Trk; Hon Roll; NHS; Prfct Atten Awd; Cert Of Merit Philadelphia Coll Of Art Art Awd 85-86; Art Contest Sights & Sounds Fest 1st-3rd Pl 86; Schl Of Visual Arts; Cmmrcl Art.

KOTSEN, STEPHEN; Kinnelon HS; Kinnelon, NJ; (4); 1/165; Pres FBLA; Political Wkr; Church Yth Grp; Trs Stu Cncl; Var Capt Bsktbl; Var Capt Ftbl; Powder Puff Ftbl; CC Awd; Var NHS; Opt Clb Awd; Pres Colonial Hls Conf Stdnt Cncls 86-87; Charles K Payne Schlrshp; Womn Smoke Rise Schlrshp; Princeton U; Pol Sci.

KOTSIRIS, LISA; Arthur P Schalick HS; Bridgton, NJ; (4); 10/130; Teachers Aide; Band; Chorus; Concert Band; Mrchg Band; VP Jr Cls; Tennis; Hon Roll; NHS; Ntl Merit Schol; Penn ST U; Lbrl Arts.

KOTTAKIS, STEVE A; N Plainfield HS; N Plainfield, NJ; (4); 2/185; Am Leg Boys St; Boy Scts; Key Clb; Math Tm; Chorus; Jazz Band; Madrigals; Stage Crew; Variety Show; JV Bsbl; Lehigh U; Mech Engr.

KOTTARAS, JAMES; Sayreville War Memorial HS; Parlin, NJ; (4); Spanish Clb; Varsity Clb; L Var Trk; Outstndng Athlt Trk Plaq, Outstndng Trk SR Trphy 87; Sccr Trphys 83-87; Ramapo Coll; Fine Arts.

KOTYUK, KIM; Manville HS; Manville, NJ; (3); GAA; Var JV Bsktbl; Var Fld Hcky; Stat Ftbl; Var JV Sftbl; Hon Roll; NHS; Im Vllybl; Natl Hnr Soc Pres 88; Miss Hustle & Best Defense In Bsktbl 86 & 87.

KOUKOULIS, TRACIE; Pancocas Valley Regional HS; Mt Holly, NJ; (4); 50/270; VP Frsh Cls; Bsktbl; Var Fld Hcky; Var Lcrss; Mgr(s); Score Keeper; Stat Wrstlng; Salisbury ST Coll; Athltc Trng.

KOUKOURDELIS, TOM; South River HS; S River, NJ; (2); German Clb; JV Bsbl; Im JV Socr; JV Wrstlng; Hon Roll; Pilot.

KOUMARIANOS, KATHY; South River HS; South River, NJ; (3); Office Aide; Color Guard; Mrchg Band; Symp Band; Off Soph Cls; Off Jr Cls; Sec Sr Cls; Sftbl; Hon Roll; NHS; 7 Yr Awd Greek Lang 85.

KOVACH, KRISTIN; John P Stevens HS; Edison, NJ; (3); 87/450; Key Clb; Nwsp Stf; Yrbk Stf; Rep Jr Cls; Rep Stu Cncl; Var Bsktbl; Var Socr; NHS; Pres Of Prjct Friend-Big Sis/Brother 87-88.

KOVACH, MARK; Northern Burlington HS; Allentown, NJ; (4); Cmnty Wkr; 4-H; VP FFA; Office Aide; Ski Clb; Teachers Aide; Varsity Clb; Chorus; Ftbl; Wt Lftg; FFA-GRNHND, Chptr Frmr, Offcr Awd, Ftbl & Wrstlng Awds 83-87; Vail Tech.

KOVACS, ALBERT; Mc Corristin Catholic HS; Trenton, NJ; (3); 22/267; Off Pep Clb; Pres Frsh Cls; Pres Soph Cls; Pres Jr Cls; Pres Sr Cls; High Hon Roll; Hon Roll; Jr NHS; NHS; Stu Cncl Awd-Ldrshp 85 & 87; Schl Spirit Awd 86; Cert-Chrstn Svc 86; Elec Engrng.

KOVACS, BONNIE; St Pius X Regional HS; Somerset, NJ; (3); 2/88; Debate Tm; ROTC; Yrbk Stf; Sec Frsh Cls; Var Tennis; Hon Roll; NHS; Ntl Sci Olympiad & Bio Awd 85; Mdrn Lang Svc Awd 87; St Pius X HS Athltc Awd 87.

KOVACS, CAROLYN; Florence Twp Mem HS; Roebling, NJ; (3); GAA; Library Aide; JV Sftbl; Elks Awd; Hon Roll; Cmmrcl Artst.

KOVACS, KENNETH J; Morris Knolls HS; Denville, NJ; (3); 1/424; Am Leg Boys St; VP Trs Church Yth Grp; Sec VP Math Clb; Math Tm; Chorus; School Play; Yrbk Stf; Bausch & Lomb Sci Awd; High Hon Roll; NHS; N Jersey Rgnl Sci Fair 1st Pl Physics & US Army, Air Force, & Marines Awds; NJ Acdmc Decthln 87; VA Tech; Accntng.

KOVACS, LISA; Notre Dame HS; Mercerville, NJ; (3); Drama Clb; French Clb; PAVAS; School Play; Variety Show; Yrbk Stf; Rep Frsh Cls; Rep Soph Cls; Hon Roll; Rutgers U Trenton ST; Bus Adm.

KOVACS, MICHELLE; Notre Dame HS; Crosswicks, NJ; (2); 49/352; Debate Tm; Thesps; Chorus; School Musical; School Play; High Hon Roll; Hon Roll; Exclince Hnrs Eng I 86; Excptnl Perfrmnce Ita I II 86-87; Cert Awd Hnrs Eng II 87; Eng.

KOVALESKI, JOHN; Monsignor Donovan HS; Toms River, NJ; (3); 5/245; Math Tm; Science Clb; JV Ftbl; NHS; Chem Hnrs 87; Pre-Calculus Hnrs 87; Chem.

KOVALICK, KURT; Hunterdon Central HS; Flemington, NJ; (2); 61/478; Ski Clb; Varsity Clb; JV Bsktbl; Var L Ftbl; Var L Lcrss; Hon Roll; Engr.

KOVALY, MICHAEL; St Mary Of The Assmptn; Linden, NJ; (2); Service Clb; Rep Frsh Cls; Rep Soph Cls; Pres Jr Cls; Var JV Bsbl; Var JV Bsktbl; Im Vllybl; Hon Roll; NHS.

KOVAR, LANCE; Clifton HS; Clifton, NJ; (4); 22/589; Science Clb; Spanish Clb; Rep Frsh Cls; Rep Soph Cls; High Hon Roll; Hon Roll; NHS; Spanish NHS; Lafayette; Phycsn.

KOVITZ, ADAM JAY; Hightstown HS; East Windsor, NJ; (4); AFS; Drama Clb; Spanish Clb; Temple Yth Grp; Thesps; Chorus; School Musical; School Play; Hon Roll; NHS; Penn ST; Arch Engrng.

KOWALCZYK, KIM; Bayonne HS; Bayonne, NJ; (3); VP French Clb; Key Clb; Math Tm; Office Aide; Science Clb; High Hon Roll; Hon Roll; Jr NHS; Rutgers Coll Phrmcy; Phrmcy.

KOWALEWSKI, TRACY; Toms River HS South; Beachwood, NJ; (3); 129/406; Am Leg Aux Girls St; FBLA; Girl Scts; Political Wkr; Ski Clb; SADD; Mrchg Band; Var Powder Puff Ftbl; Var Vllybl; Church Yth Grp; Gregg JR Typng Awd 85-86; Polt Sci.

KOWALSKI, CAROLYN; Spotswood HS; Spotswood, NJ; (3); Dance Clb; Drama Clb; 4-H; Girl Scts; Band; Church Choir; Mrchg Band; School Musical; Pres Soph Cls; JV Bsktbl; Theatre Arts.

KOWALSKI, ELAINE; Manchester Regional HS; N Haledon, NJ; (2); GAA; Hon Roll; Tchr.

KOWALSKI, ELLEN; Paul VI Regional HS; Cedar Grove, NJ; (4); 11/127; Church Yth Grp; French Clb; Key Clb; Pep Clb; Service Clb; Ski Clb; SADD; Yrbk Stf; Stu Cncl; Cheerleading; Frnch Achvt Acad 86; Presdntl Acadc Ftns Awd 87; Acadc All Am Awd 86; Trenton ST Coll; Econ.

KOWALSKI, JILL; Hopewell Valley Central HS; Hopewell, NJ; (4); 16/200; French Clb; Service Clb; School Musical; Nwsp Rptr; Ed Yrbk Stf; Rep Stu Cncl; JV Var Tennis; High Hon Roll; Sec NHS; AFS; Gardn ST Distngshd Schlr 87; Lawrncvl Schl Smmr Sci Inst 86; Rev Clarence O Shea Memrl Schlrshp 87; Boston Coll; Bio.

KOWNACKY, KATHLEEN; Notre Dame HS; Ewing, NJ; (2); Drama Clb; Stat Bsbl; French Hon Soc; Hon Roll; Politcl Sci/Law.

KOWNATSKY, WADE; Cherry Hill West HS; Cherry Hill, NJ; (3); Library Aide; Stage Crew; JV Bsbl; JV Ftbl; NHS.

KOZA, MARGIE; Passaic Valley HS; Totowa, NJ; (4); 29/309; Church Yth Grp; Dance Clb; VP 4-H; Hosp Aide; Key Clb; Spanish Clb; Varsity Clb; Var Cheerleading; 4-H Awd; Variety Show; Fnlst Miss Coed Pgnt 84; William Paterson Coll; Nrsng.

KOZACHENKO, MICHAEL J; John F Kennedy HS; Willingboro, NJ; (3); 10/294; Am Leg Boys St; Church Yth Grp; Bsbl; Mgr(s); Socr; High Hon Roll; Hon Roll; NHS; NJ Grdn ST Schlr, Delg Rotary Yth Ldrshp Conf 87.

KOZAK, MICHAEL J; Hamilton High West; Trenton, NJ; (4); 61/341; Art Clb; Aud/Vis; Stage Crew; Capt L Bsbl; High Hon Roll; MIP Bsbl 87; Rider Coll NJ; Telecmmnctns.

KOZEJ, MATT; West Deptford HS; Woodbury, NJ; (3); Church Yth Grp; JA; Math Clb; Pep Clb; Spanish Clb; Rep Soph Cls; Rep Jr Cls; Coach Actv; Im Var Ftbl; Mgr(s); Pilot.

KOZIC, JODY; Middletown HS South; Navesink, NJ; (2); Church Yth Grp; Church Choir; JV Cheerleading; Var Diving; Var L Gym; Hon Roll; Arch.

KOZIMBO, KEVIN; Immaculata HS; Somerville, NJ; (3); 12/241; Am Leg Boys St; Computer Clb; Drama Clb; Math Tm; Ski Clb; Band; Concert Band; Drm & Bgl; Jazz Band; Mrchg Band; Natl Hon Soc Treas 87; Boys ST Altr 87; Awds Music & Comp; Engrng.

KOZIOL, KRISTINE; Manalapan HS; Manalapan, NJ; (3); 33/439; Hosp Aide; Sec SADD; Rep Soph Cls; Var Capt Cheerleading; NHS; Cert Hnr Scl Stds 86-87; Elem Ed.

KOZLOSKI JR, ANTHONY; Burlington City HS; Beverly, NJ; (3); Tennis; Indstrl Elec.

KOZLOW, ALEXANDRIA; Vailsburg HS; Newark, NJ; (4); 1/295; Debate Tm; Hosp Aide; Stu Cncl; Elks Awd; High Hon Roll; Jr NHS; VP NHS; St Schlr; Val; Seton Hall U; Nrsg.

KOZLOWSKI, DAWN; Wall HS; Wall, NJ; (4); 15/269; Computer Clb; Exploring; Ski Clb; Nwsp Phtg; Nwsp Rptr; Var L Fld Hcky; High Hon Roll; Kiwanis Awd; NHS; French Clb; All-Amer Schlr 86; Cmunctns.

KOZLOWSKI, SANDRA; Wall HS; Wall, NJ; (3); 14/289; AFS; French Clb; German Clb; Var L Tennis; High Hon Roll; Hon Roll; ASSE Intl Exchng Stu.

KOZLOWSKI, VINCENT; Belvidere HS; Belvidere, NJ; (4); 17/127; Varsity Clb; Yrbk Stf; Rep Soph Cls; VP Pres Stu Cncl; Var Bsktbl; JV Ftbl; Hon Roll; Mathmtcs.

KOZZI, JON; Monsignor Dovovan HS; Toms River, NJ; (4); 9/223; Drama Clb; Math Tm; Science Clb; Thesps; School Play; High Hon Roll; Hon Roll; NHS; Computer Clb; Intnl Clb; Sykes Schlr 87; Garden ST Distngshd Schlr 87; CT Coll.

KRAATZ, ROBIN; Dickinson HS; Jersey City, NJ; (3); Camera Clb; Office Aide; Teachers Aide; Chorus; School Musical; Yrbk Phtg; Rep Frsh Cls; High Hon Roll; Hon Roll; Prfct Atten Awd; Comp Opertr.

KRAEMER, PAUL; Toms River HS East; Toms River, NJ; (4); 5/544; Scholastic Bowl; Ski Clb; Tennis; High Hon Roll; JETS Awd; Jr NHS; Spanish NHS; Ntl Merit Schol; Schlr/Athl Awd 87; ST Sci Day Awd 87; Acdmc Ltr 86-87; Villanova; Engrng.

KRAEUTLER, TRACY; Mount St Dominic Acad; Livingston, NJ; (3); 14/63; Hon Roll; NHS.

KRAFT, ANDREAS W; Hamilton High East; Hamilton Square, NJ; (4); 34/300; Debate Tm; VP Exploring; Quiz Bowl; Speech Tm; Madrigals; School Musical; Nwsp Rptr; Yrbk Rptr; Var L Tennis; NHS; Knights Of Columbus Essay Awd 83; Rutgers Coll; Bio Sci.

KRAFT, JENNY; Manchester Twp HS; Toms River, NJ; (3); 4-H; Mat Tm; Science Clb; Spanish Clb; Yrbk Stf; Score Keeper; Hon Rol Outstndng Spnsh Awd 86; Kean Coll; Phys Thrpy.

KRAFT, RAINER R; Parsippany Hills HS; Morris Plains, NJ; (4); 8/30 Church Yth Grp; Exploring; Key Clb; Political Wkr; Symp Band; Lit Mag Off Stu Cncl; NHS; Ntl Merit Ltr; Pres Schlr; Rutgers Coll; Economics.

KRAJEWSKI, DANNY; West Orange HS; W Orange, NJ; (3).

KRAJEWSKI, DOROTHY; Passaic HS; Passaic, NJ; (4); 3/505; Dram Clb; Girl Scts; Office Aide; Yrbk Phtg; Yrbk Stf; Lit Mag; High Hon Rol NHS; Opt Clb Awd; Prfct Atten Awd; Wnnr WA Wrkshps Congrssnl Smr 86; Pres Acadmc Ftns Awd 87; Rutgers Coll; Comp Sci.

KRAJEWSKI, WENDY; Cumberland Regional HS; Bridgeton, NJ; (3 16/382; Band; Chorus; Color Guard; Drm Mjr(t); Mrchg Band; Var L C Cntry; Var L Diving; JV Swmmng; NHS; Mdl Cngrss Chrprsn 8 Cmmnctns.

KRAMER, CHAD; Edgewood SR HS; Cedar Brook, NJ; (2); Drama Cl JCL; SADD; Stage Crew; Rep Frsh Cls; Rep Soph Cls; Var Crs Cntry; J Tennis; JV Trk; Wrstlng; Law.

KRAMER, JEFFREY; Mount Olive HS; Budd Lake, NJ; (3); 18/320 FBLA; Ski Clb; Nwsp Rptr; VP Stu Cncl; Var Ftbl; Var Trk; Im Wt Lftg High Hon Roll; NHS; Ntl Merit Ltr; Comm.

KRAMER, SANDRA; Manalapan HS; Manalapan, NJ; (3); 67/42 SADD; Ed Nwsp Stf; Var Cheerleading; Edtr Awd Outstndng Wrk 8 Advrstng.

KRANKEL, DANIEL; Fair Lawn HS; Fair Lawn, NJ; (3); Var Ftbl; Va Lcrss; Wt Lftg; High Hon Roll; Hon Roll.

KRAPOHL, CHERYL; Wayne Hills HS; Wayne, NJ; (4); 12/287; Frenc Clb; Hosp Aide; Library Aide; Chorus; School Musical; Stage Crew; Yrb Stf; Lit Mag; NHS; Church Yth Grp; NJ All ST Choir 86; NJ Gvrnr Tchng Schlrs Pgm Schlrshp 87; Moravian Coll; Bio.

KRASILOVSKY, GALINA; Ridgefield Park HS; Ridgefield Pk, NJ; (2 2/204; Math Tm; Science Clb; Lit Mag; Off Stu Cncl; High Hon Roll; Ho Roll; Law.

KRASKA, JENNIFER L; Linden HS; Linden, NJ; (3); Am Leg Aux Girl St; Key Clb; Quiz Bowl; Service Clb; Speech Tm; Rep Stu Cncl; High Ho Roll; NHS; Art Clb; Computer Clb; JR Statesmn America Sec 87-8 Minorities Engrng 85-87; Lbrl Arts.

KRATT, EILEEN; Toms River East HS; Toms River, NJ; (3); 22/50 Var Crs Cntry; Var Trk; Hon Roll; All Amer Ftnss Awd 87; Vrsty Lttrs I Cross Cntry 85-87; Vrsty Lttrs In Trk 85-87; Wildlife.

KRAUS, KRISTINE M; South Plainfield HS; S Plainfield, NJ; (4); 11 193; Church Yth Grp; SADD; Varsity Clb; Chorus; Var Capt Crs Cntry Var Capt Trk; High Hon Roll; Hon Roll; NHS; Pres Schlr; Wagner Col Schlstc Schlrshp 87; Sport Wards; Wagner Coll; Bio.

KRAUS, PAUL; Holmdel HS; Holmdel, NJ; (3); 2/120; Boy Scts; Ches Clb; Nwsp Rptr; French Hon Soc; Gov Hon Prg Awd; Hon Roll; NHS; Nt Merit SF; Knghts Columbus Essy Cntst 1st Pl, Eagle Sct 87.

KRAUSE, BRENDA ALISHA; West Milford HS; W Milford, NJ; (2 Art Clb; Library Aide; Sec Frsh Cls; Im Gym; Im Sftbl; Hon Roll; Danc Clb; Pratt Inst; Comm Art.

KRAUSE, JOANNE; Sayreville War Memorial HS; Sayreville, NJ; (4 20/353; Church Yth Grp; Spanish Clb; Varsity Clb; Yrbk Sprt Ed; JV Fl Hcky; Var Tennis; High Hon Roll; NHS; Spanish NHS; Stage Crew Middlesex Cnty Coll Acad Scholar 87; Spec Ed Tchr.

KRAUSE, KIM; Pt Pleasant Boro HS; Pt Pleasant, NJ; (3); 21/221; Am Leg Aux Girls St; Capt Cheerleading; Hon Roll; Sec NHS; Band; Concer Band; Mrchg Band; Orch; Pep Band.

KRAUSE, PATRICIA H; Millville SR HS; Millville, NJ; (4); 82/40 Church Yth Grp; FBLA; Band; Chorus; Church Choir; Concert Band Mrchg Band; Symp Band; German Clb; Office Aide; Pfeiffer Coll; Acctng

KRAUTH, DEBORAH A; Hunterdon Central HS; Whitehouse, NJ; (3 Church Yth Grp; Computer Clb; FCA; 4-H; Key Clb; SADD; Thesps Chorus; Church Choir; Stage Crew.

KRAUTH, THOMAS; Union HS; Union, NJ; (3); Capt Aud/Vis; Germa Clb; Capt Stage Crew; Yrbk Stf; Rep Jr Cls; Stu Cncl; Ftbl; Var L Trk Hon Roll; NHS; U Of VA; Aero Engr.

KRELL, JUSTINE; Passiac Valley HS; Little Falls, NJ; (4); 1/349; Pre Church Yth Grp; Science Clb; Varsity Clb; Drm Mjr(t); Yrbk Stf; Va Bsktbl; Var Trk; Bausch & Lomb Sci Awd; Gov Hon Prg Awd; Val; Gd ST Dstngshd Schlr; Princeton U; Elec Engrng.

KRELL, SUSAN; Passaic Valley Regional HS; Little Falls, NJ; (2 Church Yth Grp; Ski Clb; Band; Concert Band; Mrchg Band; Orch; Bsbl Bsktbl; Gov Hon Prg Awd; High Hon Roll.

KREMER, JENNIFER; Paramus Catholic Girls Regional; Hasbrouck Hts, NJ; (2); Civic Clb; Spanish Clb; Nwsp Stf; Lit Mag; High Hon Roll Med.

KRESSLER, EDWARD; Riverside HS; Delanco, NJ; (3); 2/105; Am Le Boys St; VP Jr Cls; VP Sr Cls; JV Bsbl; JV Bsktbl; Var Ftbl; JV Trk; Hig Hon Roll; NHS; Service Clb; Pres Clsrm Young Amer 87; Natl Sci Meri Awd 86-87; NEDT Awd 86.

KREZEL, KENNETH W; Bayley Ellard Catholic HS; Whippany, NJ; (4) 13/86; Drama Clb; School Play; Stage Crew; Nwsp Ed-Chief; Yrbk Stf; Lit Mag; Hon Roll; Rider Coll; Engl.

KRIEG, PAUL; Oratory Prep HS; Morristown, NJ; (3); 5/45; Chess Clb Trs Computer Clb; Trs French Clb; Capt Math Tm; Ed Nwsp Stf; JV Bsbl High Hon Roll; NHS; Latin Clb; 14th Pl In Tri-ST Catholic HS Math Leag 85-86; Hstry.

KRIEGER, KIMBERLY; Delaware Valley Regional HS; Frenchtown NJ; (3); Am Leg Aux Girls St; Pres Key Clb; Thesps; Chorus; Church Choir; School Musical; School Play; VP Jr Cls; Stu Cncl; Hon Roll; Harry Bollback Awd For Outstndng Biblical Drama 86; U Of NC; Prfrmng Arts Tchr.

KRIEGSMAN, DEBRA; J P Stevens HS; Edison, NJ; (3); 87/450; Cmnty Wkr; Hosp Aide; Key Clb; Science Clb; Temple Yth Grp; Var Socr; Hon Roll; NHS.

KRIER, SIGNE; Brick HS; Brick Town, NJ; (3); 89/410; Drama Clb Math Tm; SADD; Thesps; Band; Concert Band; Mrchg Band; Schoo Musical; School Play; Variety Show; Jrnlsm.

KRIHAK, MICHAEL K; David Brearley Reg HS; Kenilworth, NJ; (4); 4 159; Trs Stu Cncl; Var L Bsktbl; Var L Crs Cntry; Var L Trk; Bausch & Lomb Sci Awd; Hon Roll; Jr NHS; NHS; Voice Dem Awd; Rensselaer Awd Math & Sci 86; Schlr Athl Awd 86-87; Rutgers U; Elec Engrng.

KRIMMEL III, JOSEPH K; Lacey Township HS; Forked River, NJ; (4) 10/276; Pres FBLA; Math Tm; Pres Science Clb; Pres SADD; Nwsp Ed-Chief; Var Capt Tennis; Elks Awd; High Hon Roll; NHS; HOBY Conf YMCA Yth Govt Outstndng Spkr Hse; PA ST U; Biomed Engrng.

RINSKY, TAMARA; Manalapan HS; Englishtown, NJ; (1); Drama Clb; ep Clb; SADD; Temple Yth Grp; Thesps; School Musical; School Play; it Mag; Rep Frsh Cls; Psych.

RISINSKI, SUSAN; Mount Saint Mary Acad; Edison, NJ; (3); 14/89; mnty Wkr; GAA; Library Aide; Pep Clb; Scholastic Bowl; Science Clb; panish Clb; Chorus; Nwsp Rptr; VP Soph Cls; Spn Lit Mag 85-87; GATE rgm 85-87; Pre-Vet Med.

RITTMAN, DANIEL; West Windsor-Plainsboro HS; W Windsor, NJ; 3); FBLA; SADD; Pres Frsh Cls; Pres Soph Cls; Rep Jr Cls; Pres Sr Cls; V Crs Cntry; Var Swmmng; JV Tennis; Socr; HOBY Fndtn Outstndng oph 86; Amer Lgn Boys ST 87; Htl-Rest Mgmt.

ROHN, JILL; Oakcrest HS; Mays Landing, NJ; (3); 4-H; Key Clb; Yrbk prt Ed; VP Jr Cls; VP Sr Cls; Var Fld Hcky; JV Sftbl; 4-H Awd; Hon oll; NHS; Vrsty Schlr 85-87; Trenton ST Coll; Socl Wrkr.

RUBNER, LEONARD F; Jackson HS; Jackson, NJ; (3); 20/450; Aud/ Vis; Cmnty Wkr; Concert Band; Nwsp Ed-Chief; High Hon Roll; HOSA 4-87; Early Admsn-Ocean Cnty CC 87-88; Ocean Cnty Coll Hnr Prgm 7-88; Ocean Cnty CC.

RUEGER, DAWN K; Rumson Fair Haven Regional HS; Fair Haven, J; (4); Dance Clb; Drama Clb; Pep Clb; Chorus; Madrigals; School Musical; Variety Show; Var Capt Cheerleading; Pom Pon; Performing Arts cty Schlrshp 87; Montclair ST Coll; Dance.

KRUEGER, TRICIA LYNN; Mc Corristin HS; Trenton, NJ; (4); 43/240; Church Yth Grp; GAA; Socr; Sftbl; Hon Roll; NHS; Stockton ST Coll; sych.

RUGE, KARISSA; Ramapo HS; Wyckoff, NJ; (3); 119/322; AFS; hurch Yth Grp; Drama Clb; French Clb; Var Powder Puff Ftbl; Var L ocr; JV Var Trk; Hon Roll; Psych.

RUITWAGEN, ANTOINETTE; Bridgeton SR HS; Bridgeton, NJ; (4); hurch Yth Grp; Political Wkr; Ski Clb; Soroptimist; Varsity Clb; Yrbk us Mgr; Yrbk Phtg; Var Fld Hcky; Mgr(s); Sftbl; Bus Admin.

RULEWICZ, JOSEPH; Belleville HS; Belleville, NJ; (3); High Hon oll; Hon Roll; Jr NHS; Prfct Atten Awd; Arch.

RULIKOWSKI, KIMBERLY; Overbrook SR Reg HS; Pine Hill, NJ; 3); Church Yth Grp; French Clb; SADD; Stu Cncl; Var JV Cheerleading; igh Hon Roll; Hon Roll; Prfct Atten Awd; Trenton ST Coll; Math.

RULIKOWSKI, LISA ANN; Mc Corristin Catholic HS; Hamilton Sq, J; (3); 21/267; Dance Clb; Chorus; Drill Tm; Rep Soph Cls; Capt Twrlr; on Roll; Awd For Exc In Frnch 87; Psychlgy.

RUPA, SCOTT; Marist HS; Jersey City, NJ; (3); 6/110; Nwsp Rptr; on Roll; Spanish NHS; Rutgers; Law.

RUPINSKI, JENNIFER; Bayonne HS; Bayonne, NJ; (3); Church Yth rp; Math Tm; Office Aide; Ski Clb; Rep Nwsp Stf; Rep Frsh Cls; Rep oph Cls; Capt Cheerleading; Capt Pom Pon; High Hon Roll; Boston Coll; in.

RUZE, JENNIFER; Bridgewater-Raritan H S East; Martinsville, NJ; 3); Cmnty Wkr; Hosp Aide; Ski Clb; SADD; Rep Frsh Cls; Rep Soph Cls; ec Jr Cls; Pres Sr Cls; Stu Cncl; JV Bsktbl; Pol Sci.

RZEMINSKI, CONNIE; Kearny HS; Kearny, NJ; (2); JV Score eeper; Hon Roll; Med.

RZEWICK, WILLIAM; St Pius X HS; Old Bridge, NJ; (3); ROTC; JV ar Bsbl; Var Ftbl; Marines.

RZNARIC, SNEZANA; Buena Regional HS; Estell Mnr, NJ; (2); horus; Flag Corp; Mrchg Band; Hon Roll; Sci.

SHATRIYA, KISHOR; Academic HS; Jersey City, NJ; (3); Chess Clb; omputer Clb; French Clb; Socr; Embry Riddle Aeron U; Aerospace.

U, ANTHONY; Tenafly HS; Tenafly, NJ; (4); Math Clb; Math Tm; VP rsh Cls; Trk; Go Clb Awd 87; Presdntl Acad Ftns Awd 87; Hghst Hnrs 87; ochester Inst Tech; Comp Engr.

UBAT, ANTHONY; Edgewood Regional HS; Hammonton, NJ; (3); mnty Wkr; Exploring; FBLA; Varsity Clb; Rep Soph Cls; Rep Jr Cls; VP tu Cncl; L Ftbl; Var Socr; Church Yth Grp; Bus Mgt.

UBIS, WILLIAM SCOTT; St Joseph Regional HS; Elmwood Pk, NJ; 3); 12/240; Boys Clb Am; Church Yth Grp; Cmnty Wkr; Math Tm; Im sktbl; Hon Roll; Jr NHS; NHS; Spanish NHS; Pharm.

UBU, WENDY; Manasquan HS; Manasquan, NJ; (2); 37/240; Spanish lb; SADD; Nwsp Stf; Rep Soph Cls; Stu Cncl; Bsktbl; Fld Hcky; Socr; on Roll; Trenton ST; Tchr.

UCHAR, CHRISTINE; Ridgefield Park HS; Ridgefield Pk, NJ; (3); 13/ 03; Debate Tm; English Clb; Q&S; Nwsp Stf; Yrbk Sprt Ed; Stat Crs ntry; Stat Wrstlng; Hon Roll; NHS; Elec Phalgrphr.

UCHAREZYK, MURIEL; Northern Burlington HS; Columbus, NJ; 3); 30/229; Am Leg Aux Girls St; Concert Band; Mrchg Band; Orch; Pep and; Rep Soph Cls; Rep Stu Cncl; Hon Roll; Spanish NHS; NJ Grls ST 7.

UCHERA, MICHELE; Toms River HS East; Toms River, NJ; (4); 64/ 50; Church Yth Grp; Ski Clb; School Play; Stage Crew; Nwsp Stf; Yrbk tf; Capt Cheerleading; JV Sftbl; JV Trk; Hon Roll; Ocean County Coll; rt.

UCINSKI, EDYTA; Dickinson HS; Jersey City, NJ; (4); Computer Clb; rench Clb; Chorus; Off Soph Cls; Bsbl; Vllybl; Cit Awd; NHS; Prfct Atten wd; 1st Prize Wnnr Natl Wide Essay Cont 85; Hnr Rl 85-87; Prfct Atten 5-86; FIT; Fash Buying.

UCSMA, DONNA; Scotch Plains Fanwood HS; Westfield, NJ; (3); Hst ECA; French Clb; Leo Clb; Service Clb; L Coach Actv; French Hon Soc; rfct Atten Awd; DECA Outstndng Svc Awd 85-86; Hnrb Mntn DECA mpttns 86-87; ST DECA Cmpttn 2nd Pl 86; Bus Mgmt.

UCZKUDA, MARIANNE; Sussex Vo Tech; Andover, NJ; (3); Stu ncl; Bsktbl; Cheerleading; Sftbl; Hon Roll; Computers.

UCZYKOWSKI, DAVID M; Pennsauken HS; Pennsauken, NJ; (4); 10/ 74; Am Leg Boys St; Math Clb; Math Tm; VP Sr Cls; Var L Ftbl; Gibb ndtn Awd 87; Rutgers; Engr.

UDLACIK, MICHAEL; Wallington HS; Wallington, NJ; (3); Am Leg oys St; School Musical; Yrbk Stf; Pres Frsh Cls; Sec Stu Cncl; Bsbl; ausch & Lomb Sci Awd; Hon Roll; NHS; Drama Clb; HOBY Fndtn 5-86; Gifted & Tlntd Pgm 84-88; UCLA; Comm Art.

UDLESS, CHRISTOPHER; Gloucester Catholic HS; Turnersville, NJ; 3); 10/202; Stage Crew; Nwsp Rptr; Yrbk Stf; JV Bowling; JV Ftbl; High on Roll; NHS; School Play; Yrbk Rptr; VP Natl Hnr Soc 87-88; Psych.

UEHL, TANYA; Northern Burlington Cty Rgnl HS; Juliustown, NJ;); Hon Roll.

UFCZYNSKI, ROBERT; Marist HS; Bayonne, NJ; (3); Church Yth rp; Cmnty Wkr; School Musical; Im Socr; Im Sftbl; Bus.

KUGEL, PRISCILLA MAYE; Mount St Mary Acad; Somerset, NJ; (2); 13/98; Church Yth Grp; Rep Intnl Clb; Political Wkr; Nwsp Ed-Chief; Pres Frsh Cls; Rep Stu Cncl; Hon Roll; Drama Clb; Hosp Aide; Teachers Aide; Knghts Columbs Essy Cont 1st Pl Rgnl Div 87; Natl Latn Exm 3rd Pl Magna Cum Laude 87.

KUGIT, KELLY; Freehold Township HS; Freehold, NJ; (4); 56/383; Drama Clb; Speech Tm; Chorus; Madrigals; School Musical; All Shore Choir 86; Trenton ST Coll; Psych.

KUHL, DONNA; Middletown HS South; Lincroft, NJ; (4); #39 In Class; Church Yth Grp; Girl Scts; Hosp Aide; Political Wkr; Flag Corp; Mgr(s); Hon Roll.

KUHN, ALYSSA G; Moorestown HS; Moorestown, NJ; (4); 3/230; Am Leg Aux Girls St; Debate Tm; Math Tm; Church Choir; Ed Yrbk Stf; Var Tennis; High Hon Roll; Ntl Merit SF; Pres Schlr; St Schlr; Schlrshp Attend Yth Schlrs Inst Lebanon Vly Coll 86; Burlingtn Cnty Schlstc Leag All Star Tenns 85; Chemical Engrng.

KUHN, HEIDI; Red Bank Regional HS; Red Bank, NJ; (3); Church Yth Grp; Ski Clb; Spanish Clb; Stu Cncl; Spanish NHS; Bus.

KUJAWSKI, STEPHANIE; Jackson Memorial HS; Jackson, NJ; (4); 105/410; Dance Clb; SADD; Bsktbl; Gym; Powder Puff Ftbl; High Hon Roll; Hon Roll; Rutgers U; Bus.

KUKAN, PATRICIA; Union Catholic Regional HS; Mountainside, NJ; (3); 5/328; Hosp Aide; Math Tm; Nwsp Rptr; Rep Soph Cls; VP Swmmng; VP Tennis; Cit Awd; French Hon Soc; NHS; Schl Rep NJ Hugh O Brian Ldrshp Sem 86; Comm.

KUKLA, JOSEPHINE MARY; Indian Hills HS; Oakland, NJ; (4); 118/ 278; VP Art Clb; Lit Mag; Hon Roll; Hnrbl Mntn Lcl Art Shw 87; Cert Rcgntn 87; Kean Coll Of NJ; Intr Dsgn.

KULA, MIRIAM; Bruriah HS; Woodbridge, NJ; (3); FHA; Math Clb; Spanish Clb; Temple Yth Grp; Yrbk Ed-Chief; Trs Frsh Cls; Sec Soph Cls; NHS; Sci Awd-Sci Fair 3rd Pl 86; Pharm.

KULBERDA, CAROLYN; Linden HS; Linden, NJ; (4); 17/347; FBLA; Key Clb; High Hon Roll; Hon Roll; NHS; Berkeleys Outstndng Achvt In Bus, Grad Bus Stu & Tremley Pt Civic Assn & Columbia Svngs & Ln Awds 87; Union Cnty Coll; Bus.

KULCZYNSKI, KAREN; Paul VI HS; Westmont, NJ; (3); Cmnty Wkr; FBLA; Spanish Clb; Chorus; Lit Mag; Var L Tennis; Spanish NHS; Spnsh Hnr Soc & Vrsty Ltr Tennis 87; U Of San Francisco; Phy Therapy.

KULDANEK, LORRAINE; Piscataway HS; Piscataway, NJ; (3); Church Yth Grp; Key Clb; Spanish Clb; Color Guard; Mrchg Band; Hon Roll; NHS; Wrld Of Music Fstvl Prtcpnt 87; Fshn Dsng.

KULESZCZYK, TERESA; Bridgewater-Raritan HS West; Raritan, NJ; (3); Key Clb; Trs Spanish Clb; Teachers Aide; Band; Concert Band; Mrchg Band; Stat Trk; Hon Roll; Prfct Atten Awd; Prom Chrprsn 87; Bus Mgmt.

KULIG, MICHAEL; Schalick HS; Elmer, NJ; (3); Church Yth Grp; JV Socr; Prfct Atten Awd; Top 5 Stu Awd 85-86.

KULINSKI, MICHAEL; Holy Cross HS; Cinnaminson, NJ; (3); Chess Clb; Computer Clb; Stage Crew; Hon Roll; Hnrb Mntn 84 & 86; Comp Sci.

KUMAR, VIMAL; Paramus HS; Paramus, NJ; (3); Science Clb; Nwsp Rptr; Lit Mag; Hon Roll; NHS; Sci Leag 86-87; Natl Scl Stds Olympd Amer Hstry & Wrld Hstry 86-87; Med.

KUNKEL, DAWN; Burlington City HS; Ddgewater Pk, NJ; (2); Cmnty Wkr; GAA; JV Bsktbl; JV Socr; JV Sftbl; Hon Roll; Csmtlgst.

KUNKLE, HONEY-L; Newton HS; Newton, NJ; (2); 3/199; French Clb; Lit Mag; DAR Awd; High Hon Roll; Acadc Excel Awd 84-85; Pres Acadc Ftns Awd 84-85; Foreign Lang.

KUNTZ, DAVID; Paul VI HS; Hoddon Heights, NJ; (3); 54/394; Math Clb; Band; Concert Band; Jazz Band; Mrchg Band; School Musical; JV Socr; JV Wrstlng; NHS; Rutgers; Law.

KUNZ, DAVID N; Don Bosco Technical HS; Totowa, NJ; (2); Boys Clb Am; JV Socr; Var Tennis; Comps.

KUNZ, JOSEPH; Midland Park HS; Midland Park, NJ; (4); 39/131; Boy Scts; FBLA; Yrbk Stf; High Hon Roll; Hon Roll; Montclair ST Coll; Acctng.

KUO, SHEREE; West Essex Regional HS; Roseland, NJ; (3); Drama Clb; Key Clb; Math Tm; Science Clb; Orch; Hon Roll; NHS; Spanish NHS; Fncng Tm JV & Vrsty Lttrs, Capt Of Team 85-88; North Jrsy Rgnl Orchstra 85,87,88; Med.

KUO, WEIKE; St Joseph HS; Orangeburg, NY; (3); Camera Clb; Computer Clb; Math Clb; Ski Clb; Spanish Clb; Stage Crew; Yrbk Stf; JV Tennis; JV Trk; High Hon Roll; Elec Engrng.

KUPCHA, KRISTINE; Sayreville War Memorial HS; Parlin, NJ; (3); Spanish Clb; SADD; Varsity Clb; Rep Frsh Cls; Var Crs Cntry; Var Socr; Var Swmmng; Var Trk; Im Vllybl; Hon Roll; Stockton ST U; Mrne Bio.

KUPPER, THOMAS; Madison HS; Madison, NJ; (4); 15/210; Jazz Band; Orch; School Musical; Symp Band; Var Tennis; NHS; Ntl Merit SF; Engl.

KURAS, MICHAEL J; Howell HS; Howell, NJ; (4); 16/380; Boy Scts; L Letterman Clb; VP Stu Cncl; Capt Ftbl; Var Capt Wrstlng; VP NHS; Service Clb; Band; Jazz Band; Voice Dem Awd; Wst Pt & Annapls ROTC Schl Acptd 87; Stu Yr 87; 3rd On Monouth Cnty Stu Athlt Tm 87; Coast Guard Acad; Comp Engr.

KUREK, KENNETH; Brick Memorial HS; Brick, NJ; (2); Band; Concert Band; Jazz Band; Mrchg Band; Orch; Pep Band; School Play; Symp Band; Hon Roll; Boy Scts; Trumpet Line Capt 87-88.

KURKEWICZ, DAVID; Mt Olive HS; Flanders, NJ; (3); 49/330; Science Clb; Ski Clb; Variety Show; Bsbl; Bsktbl; Hon Roll; Engrng.

KURLAND, MEREDITH; Parsippany HS; Parsippany, NJ; (3); Pres Latin Clb; VP Temple Yth Grp; Var Socr; Hon Roll; NHS; FBLA; Intnl Clb; Pep Clb; Service Clb; Spanish Clb; ROGATE 85; Spnsh Comp 2nd Pl Awd 86; Mayors Awd 85; Law.

KURLYCHEK, ANTHONY; Manchester Regional HS; Prospect Pk, NJ; (4); Pres English Clb; Band; Chorus; Concert Band; Mrchg Band; Yrbk Stf; Bsbl; Var Bsktbl; Ftbl; Rotary Awd; Pell Grant Awd 87-88; Penn ST U; Lwyr.

KUROKAWA, SHIN; Holy Spirit HS; Margate, NJ; (4); DAR Awd; Math Clb; Math Tm; Pres Science Clb; Teachers Aide; Orch; Hon Roll; Sec NHS; 1st Annual ST Sci Day 86; Physics Awd 86; 3rd AHSME 86; Caltech; Physics.

KUROWSKY, MELISSA; Wall HS; Manasquan, NJ; (4); 2/270; Pres Sec Church Yth Grp; Key Clb; Sec Spanish Clb; Church Choir; Jazz Band; School Musical; Cit Awd; Kiwanis Awd; NHS; St Schlr; Cntrl Jersey Rgn Ii Band 85&86; US Army Career Expl Awd 84; Daquesne U; Pharm.

KURTZ, DENA; West Essex HS; No Caldwell, NJ; (3); Key Clb; Temple Yth Grp; Yrbk Ed-Chief; Hon Roll; NHS; Highest Frnch II Grades & Exam Grades 87.

KURTZ, KIMBERLY; Buena Regional HS; Newfield, NJ; (3); 2/225; Key Clb; Pep Clb; Ski Clb; SADD; Yrbk Stf; Rep Frsh Cls; Rep Soph Cls; Sec Jr Cls; Rep Stu Cncl; Stat Bsbl; Rutgers Pharmacy Coll; Pharm.

KURZ, KELLY; Clifton HS; Clifton, NJ; (3); Spanish Clb; Chorus.

KURZWEIL, JORDAN; Montville Township HS; Montville, NJ; (3); Hst FBLA; Ski Clb; Lit Mag; VP Soph Cls; Jr Cls; Var Ftbl; Var Lcrss; High Hon Roll; Hon Roll; NHS; Bio Team ST Bio Leag 85-86; Pre Law.

KUSANT, SCOTT K; Hunterdon Central HS; Stockton, NJ; (2); 104/498; Pres Church Yth Grp; Church Choir; Nwsp Rptr; JV Bsbl; JV Bsktbl; Coach Actv; JV Ftbl; Im Vllybl; Im Wt Lftg; Hon Roll; Tchg.

KUSHNER, REBECCA; Parsippany HS; Parsippany, NJ; (2); Computer Clb; French Clb; Math Tm; Office Aide; SADD; Temple Yth Grp; Lit Mag; Stat Mgr Gym; High Hon Roll.

KUZIEMKO, THOMAS V; Bayonne HS; Bayonne, NJ; (4); 100/350; Computer Clb; Key Clb; Hon Roll; St Peters Coll.

KUZNIEWSKI, STEVEN; Monsignor Donovan HS; Toms River, NJ; (3); JV Var Bsktbl.

KWAN, DERRICK; Dwight Englewood HS; Saddle River, NJ; (3); Cmnty Wkr; Intnl Clb; Trk; DAR Awd; Lion Awd; Arch.

KWITKOSKI, DAWN; Sayreville War Memorial HS; Sayreville, NJ; (3); Church Yth Grp; GAA; Spanish Clb; JV Bsktbl; High Hon Roll; Hon Roll; Spanish NHS; Nrsng.

KYLE, HEATHER; Holy Spirit HS; Smithville, NJ; (4); 23/363; Drama Clb; Thesps; School Play; Pres Soph Cls; Cit Awd; Hon Roll; NHS; Var Co-Capt Fld Hcky; Tennis; Acdmc Awds 83 & 84; Cmnty Srv Awd 84; Drama Awd 84; Prnctn; Intl Rltns.

KYMICK, DAWN; Mt Olive HS; Budd Lake, NJ; (3); Office Aide; Ski Clb; JV Var Socr; Hon Roll; JV Sccr Awd Mst Imprvd 86; NC ST; Comp Sci.

LA BADIA, JILL; Indian Hills HS; Oakland, NJ; (4); Dance Clb; French Clb; Teachers Aide; Nwsp Ed-Chief; Nwsp Rptr; Lit Mag; Rep Soph Cls; Cit Awd; French Hon Soc; Hon Roll; NJ Cncl Socl Stds Awd, Educ Assn Schlrshp, & Awd & Schlrshp Excllnc Frnch 87; U DE; Lbrl Arts.

LA BARRE, LAURIE-ANN; Hackettstown HS; Belvidere, NJ; (3); 64/ 191; Red Cross Aide; Lit Mag; Bsktbl; Capt Var Cheerleading; Powder Puff Ftbl; Var L Sftbl; Hon Roll; Natl Merit & Leadrshp Awd 86; NCAA Cheerldng Awd 84 & 85; Honrbl Mentn-DRC All Star Catcher 86; Genetic Engrng.

LA BRIE, JEANNINE; Pennsauken SR HS; Pennsauken, NJ; (2); Church Yth Grp; Var JV Bsktbl; Mgr Ftbl; JV Sftbl; Bkkpng.

LA BRUNO, CHRISTINA; Bayonne HS; Bayonne, NJ; (3); Science Clb; Band; Concert Band; Mrchg Band; Orch; High Hon Roll; Jr NHS; Ntl Sci Merit Awd 84-85; Marine Bio.

LA CHANCE, JULIE; Pinkerton Acad; Windham, NH; (3); Crs Cntry; Trk; High Hon Roll; Hon Roll; Ntl Merit Ltr; Vet-Med.

LA CHANCE, NORMAN; Riverside HS; Riverside, NJ; (3); 5/101; Am Leg Boys St; Concert Band; Jazz Band; Mrchg Band; School Play; Crs Cntry; Trk; Hon Roll; NHS; La Salle; Music.

LA COGNATA, PATRICIA; Mary Help Of Christians Acad; Elmwood Pk, NJ; (2); Girl Scts; SADD; Chorus; Hon Roll; Physcl Sci Cert 85-86; Itln Cert 85-86; USNMA 86-87.

LA CROSSE, MICHELLE; Toms River HS South; Beachwood, NJ; (2); Intnl Clb; Sftbl; High Hon Roll; Math.

LA FARGA, DIANA B; Union Catholic Regional HS; Rahway, NJ; (3); 45/320; Church Yth Grp; GAA; Service Clb; SADD; Varsity Clb; JV Var Bsktbl; JV Var Sftbl; Hon Roll; Hstry Achvt Awd 87; Rutgers; Phrmcy.

LA FAZIA, CHRISTINE ROSE; Immaculate Conception HS; Fair Lawn, NJ; (4); Church Yth Grp; Computer Clb; FTA; Hosp Aide; Pep Clb; Q&S; SADD; Varsity Clb; Chorus; Church Choir; Honorary Hosp Vlntr, 2nd Pl Chrldng Compttn 85; William Paterson Coll; Elem Ed.

LA FORGE, DOUG; Passaic Cnty Tech & Voc HS; Hawthorne, NJ; (3); Boy Scts.

LA FRANCE, DAN; Ridgewood HS; Ridgewood, NJ; (3); 50/300; Boy Scts; Chess Clb; Debate Tm; Drama Clb; Exploring; Key Clb; Latin Clb; Letterman Clb; ROTC; Ski Clb; Pepperdine Yth Seminar 87; Villanova; Bus.

LA FRENIERE, NADINE; South Plainfield HS; S Plainfield, NJ; (3); 23/253; Varsity Clb; Sec Sr Cls; Trs Stu Cncl; L Var Bsbl; L Var Cheerleading; L Stat Gym; NHS; Spanish NHS; Computer Clb; VP Ski Clb; Mst Vlbl Chrldr 86-87; Schl Rep Grls Ctznshp Inst 87; Bus.

LA GRECA, KAREN M; Hopatcong HS; Hopatcong, NJ; (4); 2/210; FBLA; Scholastic Bowl; Varsity Clb; Yrbk Sprt Ed; Yrbk Stf; Var Capt Bsktbl; Var Sftbl; High Hon Roll; VP NHS; All Lge-All Area V Bsktbl/V Sftbl 85-86; Bloomsburg U; Bus Mgmt.

LA GRECA, SUSAN; Lakeland Regional HS; Ringwood, NJ; (4); 9/345; Trs AFS; Art Clb; Math Tm; Teachers Aide; Rep Stu Cncl; Var Stat Crs Cntry; NCTE Awd; NHS; Spanish NHS; Im Powder Puff Ftbl; Ntl Sci Olympiad-Bio-Cert Of Dstnctn 85-86; Pres Acad Ftnss Awd 86-87; Lklnd Rgnl Bd Of Ed Schlrshp 86; SNUY Binghamton; Bio.

LA GULLO, CHRISTOPHER S; Phillipsburg HS; Bloomsbury, NJ; (3); 6/315; Nwsp Stf; Pres Frsh Cls; Rep Stu Cncl; Var L Ftbl; Var L Wrstlng; High Hon Roll; NHS; Giftd & Tlntd Prgrm; US Naval Acad.

LA MAGRA, LINDA; Nutley HS; Nutley, NJ; (3); 3/304; Trs AFS; Am Leg Aux Girls St; Trs Key Clb; Math Tm; Sec Stu Cncl; Var Socr; Var Trk; High Hon Roll; Sec NHS; Ntl Merit Ltr; Math.

LA MANNA, MARIA; Secaucus HS; Secaucus, NJ; (4); 4/162; Math Clb; Mu Alpha Theta; Yrbk Stf; High Hon Roll; Hon Roll; NHS; Spanish NHS; Math.

LA MONACA, VINCENT; St Joseph HS; Hammonton, NJ; (3); 1/95; Drama Clb; Hosp Aide; Library Aide; Math Tm; Capt Quiz Bowl; Scholastic Bowl; Speech Tm; SADD; Teachers Aide; Orch; Camden Diocese Fornscs Leag 86; Rutgers Schlr 87; Rutgers Camden Smmr Schlrs Prog 87; Psych.

LA MOTTA, ALYSSA; Immaculata HS; Branchburg, NJ; (3); 11/250; 4-H; School Play; Rep Frsh Cls; Rep Soph Cls; Rep Jr Cls; Stat Bsbl; JV Var Cheerleading; Pres French Hon Soc; NHS; Am Leg Aux Girls St; Educ.

LA ROCCA, JOSEPH; Mc Corristin Catholic HS; New Egypt, NJ; (4); 60/250; Key Clb; SADD; Stage Crew; Var Bsbl; Hon Roll; NEDT Awd; Prfct Atten Awd; Ocean Cnty Coll; Cvl Engrng.

LA ROSA, KATHLEEN; Dumont HS; Dumont, NJ; (4); 7/217; Girl Scts; Mu Alpha Theta; Church Choir; Concert Band; Mrchg Band; Mgr Stage Crew; High Hon Roll; NHS; Church Yth Grp; Spanish Clb; Assoc Layout Yearbook Editor; Natl Art Hnr Soc; Dumont Swim Clb.

LA SASSO, MICHAEL; Pequannock Township HS; Pequannock, NJ; (3); 51/242; Stat Bsktbl; Mgr(s); Score Keeper; Tennis; Hon Roll; Bus.

LA TOURETTE, DENISE; Spotswood HS; Milltown, NJ; (3); FCA; Intnl Clb; Model UN; School Play; Crs Cntry; Swmmng; Trk; Mst Imprvd X-Cntry Rnnr 86; Sprts Med.

LA TRONICA, NICHOLAS; Steinert HS; Hamilton Sq, NJ; (3); AFS; Trenton ST Coll; Psychlgy.

LA VALLE, BRENDA; Vineland HS; Vineland, NJ; (3); 19/830; Church Yth Grp; Dance Clb; French Clb; Key Clb; Nwsp Stf; French Hon Soc; Hon Roll; Asbury Coll; Optmtry.

LA VECCHIA, CATHERINE; Marylawn Of The Oranges HS; South Orange, NJ; (4); 1/49; Pres Sec French Hon Soc; High Hon Roll; VP NHS; NEDT Awd; Prfct Atten Awd; St Schlr; Val; Church Yth Grp; Dance Clb; Drama Clb; Rtgrs Schlr-Deans Smmr Schlr Pgm 85-86; ISLI Confrnc-Ntr Dame 85-86; Almni Assoc Cls Agnt-Exec Brd; Psychlgy.

LAANINEN, JOHN; Lakeland Regional HS; Wanaque, NJ; (3); 8/430; Trs Intnl Clb; Math Clb; SADD; Variety Show; Nwsp Ed-Chief; Trs Yrbk Stf; High Hon Roll; Sec NHS; NEDT Awd; VP Spanish NHS; Cert Of Merit Frm Signa Delta Pi Chap At Drew U Fo Span, Lang 86; Cert Of Awd For Passaic Cnty Tenart; Bio.

LABARBERA, DONNA; Toms River South HS; Beachwood, NJ; (3); Library Aide; Nwsp Stf; Law.

LABAY, ROBERT; Union HS; Union, NJ; (2); Church Yth Grp; Sec Key Clb; Concert Band; Jazz Band; Mrchg Band; School Musical; Symp Band; Nwsp Stf; Gov Hon Prg Awd; High Hon Roll; Rgn II Symphonic Band, Jazz Ensmbl 87; All ST Jazz Ensmbl 87; Butler; Med.

LABBATE, VINCENT; Cranford HS; Cranford, NJ; (2); Latin Clb; JV Wrstlng; Geology.

LABOWICZ, JOANNE; South River HS; South River, NJ; (3); 10/130; Am Leg Aux Girls St; Office Aide; Spanish Clb; Stat Bsbl; Stat Wrstlng; High Hon Roll; Hon Roll; NHS.

LABOY, DELILAH; Lakewood HS; Lakewood, NJ; (3); 75/375; Spanish Clb; Bus Adm.

LACCITIELLO, FRANK; Passaic Valley HS; W Paterson, NJ; (2); JV Bsbl; JV Ftbl; Var L Wrstlng; High Hon Roll; Hon Roll.

LACERA, RUTH; Mary Help Of Christians Acad; Paterson, NJ; (1); Church Yth Grp; Pep Clb; SADD; Variety Show; Im Bsktbl; Gym; Score Keeper; Twrlr; Hon Roll; Doctor.

LACHER, BRITT; Franklin HS; Somerset, NJ; (4); 5/327; Rep Am Leg Aux Girls St; Hosp Aide; School Musical; Yrbk Ed-Chief; Var Capt Cheerleading; High Hon Roll; VP NHS; Prsdntl Acdmc Ftnss Awd, GFWC Franklin Wmns Clb Schlrshp, Cornell U Natl Schlr 87; Cornell U; Bio Sci.

LACHER, HILLARY; Bordentown Regional HS; Bordentown, NJ; (4); 12/114; Am Leg Aux Girls St; Art Clb; SADD; Yrbk Stf; Trs Stu Cncl; Elks Awd; Hon Roll; Jr NHS; Trs NHS; Trs Key Clb; Hmcmng Queen 86; Arts.

LACKEY, LISA; Vineland HS; Vineland, NJ; (3); Church Yth Grp; Dance Clb; 4-H; Hosp Aide; Spanish Clb; Chorus; Nwsp Rptr; Nwsp Stf; Lit Mag; Stu Cncl; Psych.

LACKI, JENNIFER; Kearny HS; Kearny, NJ; (3); German Clb; Concert Band; Mrchg Band; Rep Frsh Cls; Rep Soph Cls; Sec Stu Cncl; NHS; Band; Yrbk Stf; High Hon Roll; German Natl Hon Soc 87; Delegate NJ ST Fed Of Womens Club Girls Ctznshp Inst 87; Acdmc Excllnc Awd.

LACOMBA, ANNE MARIE; Paramus Catholic HS; Hackensack, NJ; (3); Art Clb; Church Yth Grp; French Clb; Girl Scts; SADD; Var Capt Trk; Hon Roll; Montclair ST; Frgn Lang.

LACOVARA, VINCENT; Morristown HS; Morristownship, NJ; (3); 5/422; Church Yth Grp; Cmnty Wkr; Key Clb; Nwsp Stf; Ed Yrbk Stf; Ed Lit Mag; Pres Stu Cncl; Var JV Bsbl; Swmmng; Wrstlng.

LACY, MATTHEW W; Monsignor Donovan HS; Toms River, NJ; (3); 7/241; Am Leg Boys St; Church Yth Grp; Off CAP; Science Clb; Socr; Wrstlng; High Hon Roll; NHS; B Mitchel Cvl Air Patrol Awd 86; Cvl Air Ptrl Cmndrs Cmndtn 86; USAF Acad; Pilot.

LACZKO, ILDIKO; St John Vianney HS; Hazlet, NJ; (1); Dance Clb; Intnl Clb; SADD; Stage Crew; Hon Roll; Dnce Awds 1st, 2nd, Hnr Mntn 87; Cosmtlgst.

LAFFERTY, CINDI; Overbrook SR HS; Lindenwald, NJ; (2); Drama Clb; GAA; Office Aide; Spanish Clb; SADD; Varsity Clb; Chorus; Stage Crew; Mgr(s); Sftbl; Mitchell JC; Law.

LAFFERTY, DAWN; Overbrook Regional HS; Pine Hill, NJ; (4); 73/365; Band; Concert Band; School Play; Capt Cheerleading; Var Capt Socr; JV Sftbl; Hon Roll; Vrsty Clb Schlrshp 87; Glassboro; Psych.

LAFFERTY, JOHN; Deptford Township HS; Deptford, NJ; (3); Chess Clb; Comp Sys Anlyst.

LAFFERTY, PATRICIA; Buena Regional HS; Williamstown, NJ; (3); 27/210; Dance Clb; Ski Clb; Swmmng; Vllybl; Wt Lftg; Hon Roll; Glassboro ST Coll.

LAFFEY, MICHELE; Wildwood Catholic HS; N Wildwood, NJ; (3); Church Yth Grp; Cmnty Wkr; Spanish Clb; SADD; Teachers Aide; School Play; Mgr Bsktbl; Capt Cheerleading; Mgr(s); Socr.

LAGAMBINA, SUSAN; Burlington Co Vo-Tech; Mt Holly, NJ; (3); Camera Clb; Off VICA; Chorus; Yrbk Stf; Stu Cncl; JV Var Bsktbl; Sftbl; Cit Awd; Hon Roll; Prfct Atten Awd; Hugh O Brien Awd 86; Most Imprvd Stud Plaq 86; Culinary Arts 1st Pl Mdl VICA 87.

LAGER, IRENA; New Milford HS; New Milford, NJ; (4); 8/141; Art Clb; Computer Clb; Math Tm; Spanish Clb; Yrbk Stf; Hon Roll; NHS; Natl Merit Commendation 86; Pres Acad Fit Awd 87; Acad Dechtln 85-87; Yrbk Bus Staff 86-87; Cooper Union; Engrng.

LAI, JOSEPHINE; South Brunswick HS; Kendall Park, NJ; (3); 3/277; Hst FHA; Math Tm; Nwsp Rptr; Rep Stu Cncl; Var Tennis; High Hon Roll; Mu Alpha Theta Awd; NHS; Spanish NHS; Mu Alpha Theta; Grtr Conf All Acad Hnr Rl 86; 7 Hnr Awds NJ Music Tchrs Assn 79-86; Prfrmd Natl Music Tchrs Assn 86; Aerosp Engrng.

LAIBSON, KEITH; Mt Olive HS; Flanders, NJ; (3); AFS; FBLA; Stage Crew; Yrbk Stf; JV Capt Wrstlng; Hon Roll; MVP & Mst Dedctd-Wrstlng Tm 87.

LAIKOWSKI, DONNA; Sayreville War Memorial HS; Parlin, NJ; (4); Church Yth Grp; Spanish Clb; Rep Frsh Cls; Rep Soph Cls; Rep Jr Cls; Rep Sr Cls; High Hon Roll; Hon Roll; Spanish NHS; Montclair ST Coll; Accntng.

LAINE, JANINE; Cresskill HS; Cresskill, NJ; (3); 28/113; Art Clb; Band; Chorus; Stage Crew; Sec Jr Cls; Sec Sr Cls; Var Bsktbl; JV Sftbl; Var Vllybl; Hon Roll; Cmmrcl Art.

LAING, TAMMY; Toms River HS South; Beachwood, NJ; (1); 4-H; Concert Band; Mrchg Band; Symp Band; Im Fld Hcky; Sprts Awd 86-87; Achvt Ltr-Band 86-87; Advncd Plcmnt-Hgh Hnrs Pgm 86-87; U Of PA; Vet.

LAIR, JAMES; Belleville HS; Belleville, NJ; (3); Aud/Vis; JV Bsktbl; Hon Roll; Accounting.

LAIRD, TRACY; Hamilton HS East; Trenton, NJ; (3); DECA; Drama Clb; School Musical; School Play; Stage Crew; Swing Chorus; High Hon Roll; Hon Roll; Prfct Atten Awd; Bus.

LAIRE, AMY; Warren Co Vo-Tech HS; Stewartsville, NJ; (3); Hosp Aide; Key Clb; Varsity Clb; VICA; Yrbk Stf; Sec Jr Cls; Bsbl; Cheerleading; Score Keeper; Sftbl; Trphy Chrldg 84-86; Data Prcssng.

LAKE, KELLEY ANN; Paulsboro HS; Paulsboro, NJ; (2); Debate Tm; Scholastic Bowl; Rep SADD; Acpl Chr; Mrchg Band; Nwsp Stf; Ed Lit Mag; Crs Cntry; Score Keeper; High Hon Roll; Med.

LAKE, LEEANN; Egg Harbor Township HS; Farmington, NJ; (4); 24/294; Office Aide; Hon Roll; Jr NHS; NHS; Brd Trustees Schlrshp 86-87; Schltc Ltr Awd 83-85; Atlantic CC; Acct.

LAKE JR, WILLIAM E; Sayreville War Memorial HS; S Amboy, NJ; (4); Trs Stu Cncl; Var L Ftbl; Var L Trk; Var L Wrstlng; FL ST U; Bus.

LAKISZAK, SUSAN; Madison Central HS; E Brunswick, NJ; (4); 1/370; Math Tm; Scholastic Bowl; Lit Mag; Var Crs Cntry; French Hon Soc; NHS; Pres Schlr; St Schlr; Val; Church Yth Grp; Old Bridge Twnshp Sci Awd 84-86; Hstry Awd 85; D Kiken Mem Schlrshp 87; U NC-CHAPEL Hill.

LAL, SANGEETA; Glen Rock SR HS; Glen Rock, NJ; (4); Am Leg Aux Girls St; Cmnty Wkr; Hosp Aide; Political Wkr; Temple Yth Grp; Varsity Clb; Chorus; Madrigals; School Musical; Vllybl; Glen Rock Cls 59 Schlrshp Awd 87; Susquehnna U; Psych.

LALAMA, JOHN; Hoboken HS; Hoboken, NJ; (3); Chess Clb; Church Yth Grp; French Clb; Band; Church Choir; Concert Band; Jazz Band; Mrchg Band; School Musical; School Play; Stevens Tech Enrchmt Prog 85; Hugh O Brien Yth Fndtn 86-87; Gvrnr Schl Monmouth Coll 87; Columbia U; Med.

LALBAHADUR, VIDESH; Acad HS; Jersey City, NJ; (4); Camera Clb; Chess Clb; Civic Clb; Cmnty Wkr; Computer Clb; Math Clb; Math Tm; Quiz Bowl; Scholastic Bowl; Science Clb; Citation From Mayor Of Jersey City CUCCI 86; 1st Pl Awd Acad Bowl League 87; Rcgntn City Sci Day 87; Coll Of Engrng; Biomed Engr.

LALLY, GILIAN; Verona HS; Verona, NJ; (3); French Clb; Band; Concert Band; JV Sftbl.

LALLY, KEVIN; Seton Hall Prep; Verona, NJ; (4); 5/187; Key Clb; Math Tm; Pres Pep Clb; Rptr Yrbk Stf; Rep Stu Cncl; Capt Swmmng; Gov Hon Prg Awd; High Hon Roll; NHS; Time Mag Essy Fnlst 87; Msgr T J Tuchy Awd 87; Msgr J L Mc Nulty Awd 87; U Of Notre Dame; Bus.

LALWANI, LEENA; Dwight Englewood HS; Englewood, NJ; (3); Dance Clb; Drama Clb; Intnl Clb; School Musical; School Play; Variety Show; Nwsp Ed-Chief; Nwsp Stf; Rep Soph Cls; Bus Admin.

LAM, CHRIS; Pennsauken HS; Pennsauken, NJ; (2); JV Socr; High Hon Roll; Schl Rep Cnty Stu Gov Day 87.

LAM, HELEN; Edison HS; Edison, NJ; (3); 14/469; Computer Clb; French Clb; Key Clb; Math Tm; Nwsp Rptr; Nwsp Stf; JV Socr; Var Trk; French Hon Soc; Hon Roll; 3rd Pl Dcthln Knwldg 85; 2nd Pl ST Olympcs Mnd 86; Med.

LAM, SHARON; Montville Township HS; Towaco, NJ; (3); 5/270; Church Yth Grp; Cmnty Wkr; French Clb; German Clb; Hosp Aide; Key Clb; Political Wkr; Ski Clb; Varsity Clb; Orch; Cornell U Smmr Schl 87; MIP Swmmng 85-86.

LAMANTEER, MICHAEL; Vineland SR HS; Vineland, NJ; (3); 4/820; Exploring; Key Clb; Socr; Cit Awd; High Hon Roll; NHS; Vrsty Ltr 87; Med.

LAMB, KATHLEEN; Mount St Dominic Acad; West Caldwell, NJ; (3); 23/56; Nwsp Stf; Yrbk Stf; Sec Soph Cls; Sec Jr Cls; VP Sr Cls; Var Capt Bsktbl; Var Capt Socr; Var Capt Sftbl; Hon Roll; Ski Clb; All ST Bsktbl 87; All Star Bsktbl 87.

LAMB, ROBERT; Maple Shade HS; Maple Shade, NJ; (4); 8/160; Am Leg Boys St; School Musical; Nwsp Stf; Yrbk Ed-Chief; High Hon Roll; NHS; Prfct Atten Awd; Pres Schlr; Rotary Awd; Drama Clb; Schl Blood Dr Chrmn 85-87; Gettysburg Coll; Bio.

LAMBERSKI, AMY; De Paul Diocesan HS; Wayne, NJ; (3); 1/150; Latin Clb; Math Tm; Nwsp Stf; Var Cheerleading; High Hon Roll; Jr NHS; NHS; Ntl Merit Ltr; Rotary Awd; Magna Cum Laud Natl Ltn Exm 84 & 86; Outstndng Achvt Hnrs Engl Lit, Pre-Calculus 86-87; Duke.

LAMBERSKY, DANA; Waldwick HS; Waldwick, NJ; (3); #27 In Class; Drama Clb; Chorus; Capt Color Guard; School Play; Stage Crew; Bowling; PWP THEA Intl Yth Actriv Awd 1st Tnil, 2nd Zone, 3rd Reg 82-86; Intl Yth Cncl PWP Sec 84-86; Tech Theatre.

LAMBERT, KIMBERLY; Clearview Regional HS; Sewell, NJ; (3); 14/171; Pres Church Yth Grp; Pres Chrmn 4-H; Church Choir; Var Swmmng; Cit Awd; Dnfth Awd; 4-H Awd; High Hon Roll; NHS; Prfct Atten Awd; Yth Triennium 86; Comp Sci.

LAMBERT, MATTHEW; Kittatinny Regional HS; Middleville, NJ; (4); 3/224; Boy Scts; Capt Quiz Bowl; Scholastic Bowl; Science Clb; Rep Stu Cncl; Var Capt Crs Cntry; Var Capt Trk; High Hon Roll; NHS; Rotary Awd; Drew U; Psych.

LAMBORNE, RENEE; Holy Cross HS; Marlton, NJ; (4); 16/366; Church Yth Grp; Spanish Clb; School Musical; Rep Soph Cls; Rep Stu Cncl; Var Capt Fld Hcky; Hon Roll; Pres NHS; Ski Clb; Church Choir; Natl Hnr Soc Awd 87; Schl Spirit & Svc Awd 87; U Of Richmond.

LAMBROS, ALEXANDER; Matawan Regional HS; Matawan, NJ; (2); Church Yth Grp; Ftbl; Var Trk; Med.

LAMEY, MICHELE; Pitman HS; Pitman, NJ; (3); 29/143; Church Yth Grp; Dance Clb; Hosp Aide; Stage Crew; Variety Show; Yrbk Stf; Stat Bsktbl; JV Fld Hcky; JV Var Socr; Hon Roll; Cndy Strpr Svc Cap, Typng Gold Pin 87; Prom Comm 87; Homecoming Comm 87.

LAMICELLA, PETER; Toms River HS South; Beachwood, NJ; (3); Rep Frsh Cls; Rep Soph Cls; Rep Jr Cls; Rep Sr Cls; Rep Stu Cncl; Var Bsbl; Var Ftbl.

LAMM, TAMMY; Cranford HS; Union, NJ; (3); 45/258; German Clb; Office Aide; Spanish Clb; Varsity Clb; Co-Capt Flag Corp; Mrchg Band; VP L Twrlr; Var L Vllybl; Hon Roll; Psychlgy.

LAMONT, MARGARET; Woodstown HS; Woodstown, NJ; (4); 27/240; Church Yth Grp; Cmnty Wkr; Drama Clb; 4-H; GAA; Key Clb; Spanish Clb; SADD; Nwsp Bus Mgr; Yrbk Phtg; Rrenton ST Coll; Marine Bio.

LAMONT, SARAH K; Lawrence HS; Lawrenceville, NJ; (4); 17/215; Drama Clb; Trs Latin Clb; Varsity Clb; School Play; Coach Actv; Var Capt Fld Hcky; Var Sftbl; Hon Roll; NHS; Rotary Awd; Brown U; Art Thrpy.

LAMORTE, MARC; Mc Cooristin HS; Trenton, NJ; (3); JA; Var Capt Bsktbl; Hon Roll; NHS.

LAMOTHE, REGINE; Marylawn Of The Oranges; Newark, NJ; (3); #12 In Class; Church Yth Grp; Latin Clb; Math Clb; Pep Clb; Spanish Clb; Church Choir; School Musical; Trs Soph Cls; Hon Roll; NHS.

LAMPE, CARYN; St John Vianney HS; Marlboro, NJ; (4); 8/257; Church Yth Grp; High Hon Roll; NHS; Cmnty Wkr; Math Clb; Teachers Aide; Drill Tm; Mrchg Band; Sftbl; Hon Roll; Natl Eagle Cross Awd-Dio Trenton 87; Awds Inter/Extra Curr Schl Act 83-87; Holmdel Kawanis Club Awd 84; Lehigh U; Math.

LAMSON, MARC L; Paulsboro HS; Gibbstown, NJ; (3); 2/150; Chur[...] Yth Grp; Chorus; Church Choir; Trs Soph Cls; Trs Jr Cls; JV Bsbl; V[...] Bsktbl; JV Ftbl; High Hon Roll; Trs NHS; Stu Mnth Awd 85; All Sou[...] Jersey Chorus 85; Elec Engrng.

LANCELLOTTI, ANTHONY; St James HS; Pennsville, NJ; (1); Cert [...] Hnrs In Englsh, Scl Stdys & Bus; Bus Math.

LAND, DAVID; Phillipsburg HS; Phillipsburg, NJ; (3); Church Yth G[...] Ski Clb; Sec Trs VICA; Score Keeper; Hon Roll.

LAND, MARGARET; Highland HS; Blackwood, NJ; (2); Rep Pep Cl[...] Rep Chorus; Capt Flag Corp; Rep Stu Cncl; Bsktbl; JV Trk; Hon Ro[...] Rutgers; Law.

LANDAU, DEBORAH; Middletown High Schl South; Leonardo, NJ; (3[...] Teachers Aide; Band; Mrchg Band; Pep Band; Stage Crew; Symp Ban[...] Hon Roll; Mgmt.

LANDIS, BETH; Lower Cape May Regional HS; Cape May, NJ; (2); 2[...] 263; Teachers Aide; Mgr(s); Tennis; Hon Roll; Outstndng Natl Aver CA[...] Testing 86-8m; Bus Mgr.

LANDRIEU, ERIC; Bernards HS; Bernardsville, NJ; (3); 20/186; Chur[...] Yth Grp; Chorus; Church Choir; Jazz Band; Mrchg Band; School Musica[...] Stage Crew; Hon Roll; JV Crs Cntry; JV Golf; 1st Chair Cnty Jazz Bar[...] 86-87; JR All Amer Hall Of Fame Band Hnrs Awds 86-87; 1st Contn[...] Comp 86-87; Engrng.

LANDRUD, LISA; Vernon Twp HS; Sussex, NJ; (3); Yrbk Bus Mgr; V[...] L Socr; High Hon Roll; Hon Roll; NHS; 4th Natl French Test Lvl III 8[...] Accntng.

LANDSMAN, HOWARD; J P Stevens HS; Edison, NJ; (3); Math Cl[...] Science Clb; Var JV Bsbl; Var JV Ftbl; Hon Roll; NHS; Spanish NHS; P[...] Med.

LANE, GREGORY JOSEPH; Notre Dame HS; Hamilton Sq, NJ; (3[...] SADD; School Play; Var JV Socr; JV Trk; Var Wrstlng; High Hon Ro[...] Hon Roll; NHS; Athltc Trnnr 85-86; Fld Hickey Ice Hockey & Ftbl Vrs[...] Ltr 85-86; Athltc Trnnr & Ftbl Vsty Ltrs 86-87; USNA; Pilot.

LANE, HEATHER; Lenape HS; Mt Laurel, NJ; (3); Dance Clb; Dram[...] Clb; Spanish Clb; Varsity Clb; Flag Corp; Variety Show; Nwsp Rptr; Re[...] Jr Cls; Var Cheerleading; High Hon Roll; Mrn Bio.

LANE, HEATHER; St Mary HS; Jersey City, NJ; (3); Hosp Aide; Churc[...] Choir; Yrbk Stf.

LANE, JAMES; Union Catholic Regional HS; Fanwood, NJ; (3); 17/31[...] Var L Bsktbl; Socr; Hon Roll.

LANE, JOANNE; Middletown HS South; Red Bank, NJ; (4); 1/450; A[...] Leg Aux Girls St; Concert Band; Jazz Band; Mrchg Band; Nwsp Sprt E[...] Lit Mag; Var L Socr; High Hon Roll; NHS; St Schlr.

LANE, JULIE; Indian Hills HS; Franklin Lakes, NJ; (3); 66/306; Cmn[...] Wkr; Q&S; Ski Clb; Varsity Clb; Nwsp Bus Mgr; Nwsp Stf; Rep Stu Cn[...] Bowling; Socr; Hon Roll; Hnrs Engl Merit Awd 86; Comms.

LANE, ROBIN; Summit HS; Summit, NJ; (3); Var Lcrss; Cmnty Wk[...] Rep Jr Cls; Powder Puff Ftbl; Hon Roll; Safe Rides 86-87; Grdn ST Game[...] 87.

LANE, RUSS; Manalapan HS; Manalapan, NJ; (3); 42/429; Cmnty Wk[...] 4-H; 4-H Awd; High Hon Roll; NHS; Vlntr Firefghtr 86-87; Bus Mgmt.

LANE, TISHA; Weequahic HS; Newark, NJ; (3); 12/376; Church Y[...] Grp; Sec Computer Clb; Chorus; Church Choir; Rep Jr Cls; Hon Roll; Bu[...] Admin.

LANE, TOM; Montville HS; Montville, NJ; (4); FBLA; Nwsp Rptr; J[...] Ftbl; Hon Roll; Polt Sci.

LANEY, JOHN; Haddonfield Memorial HS; Haddonfield, NJ; (4); 1[...] 155; Pres Church Yth Grp; Var L Bsktbl; Coach Actv; JV Socr; Frenc[...] Hon Soc; High Hon Roll; NHS; Rotary Awd; French Clb; Science Cl[...] Hstry.

LANG, BRIAN; Jackson Memorial HS; Jackson, NJ; (3); 12/42[...] Computer Clb; Drama Clb; Temple Yth Grp; Band; Concert Band; Ja[...] Band; Mrchg Band; School Musical; School Play; Stage Crew; Acad Aw[...] Bnqt 85-88; NEDT Mrt Cert 85; Odyssey Of The Mind St Lvl 87; Engrn[...]

LANG, JEANNETTE; Middlesex HS; Middlesex, NJ; (4); 19/157; O[...] Girl Scts; Model UN; Quiz Bowl; Spanish Clb; School Play; Trs Frsh Cl[...] Var Bsktbl; Var Capt Tennis; Hon Roll; NHS; Lockhead Schlrshp 2nd [...] 87; Acdmc Stu Awd Stu 87; Social Stu Awd 87; Penn St U.

LANGBEIN, TAMMY; Edgewood Regional SR HS; Sicklerville, NJ; (4[...] 15/310; Capt Drill Tm; Yrbk Sprt Ed; High Hon Roll; Hon Roll; Jr NHS[...] NHS; Soarng Eagle Awd 87; Acadmc Excllnc Spngh 87; Rider Coll Alumr[...] Schlrshp, Grdn ST Schlr 87; Rider Coll; Bus Admin.

LANGBERT, MARNI; East Brunswick HS; East Brunswick, NJ; (3); Se[...] Debate Tm; Rep Key Clb; Political Wkr; Spanish Clb; Gov Hon Prg Aw[...] Hon Roll; Spanish NHS; Model UN; Lit Mag; JV Trk; Rookie Of Yr In[...] Polcl Lgl Ed 86; Soph Hmcmng Queen 86; Tutorl Prog Eagleton Inst 8[...] Colgate U; Pol Sci.

LANGDON, DANNY; Oratory Prep; Manasquan, NJ; (3); French Cl[...] Service Clb; Stage Crew; Im Bsktbl; Im Ftbl; Im Vllybl; Rutgers; Bus.

LANGDON, SHIRLEY; Oakcrest HS; Mays Landing, NJ; (3); GA[...] Hosp Aide; SADD; Chorus; Lit Mag; JV Sftbl; Hon Roll; Jr NHS; Vrs[...] Schlr 86-87; Psych.

LANGE, CAROL; Edgewood HS; Atco, NJ; (3); Chorus; Yrbk Stf; O[...] Soph Cls; Off Jr Cls; Score Keeper; JV Socr; Hon Roll; Stu Gvrnmnt Aw[...] 86 & 87; Glassboro ST Coll; Bus.

LANGER, PHIL; Dwight Englewood Schl; Alpine, NJ; (3); Ski Clb; Yrb[...] Phtg; Yrbk Stf; Lit Mag; JV Var Lcrss; Tufts Coll; Bus.

LANGER, THOMAS; St Joseph Regional HS; Congers, NY; (3); 7/28[...] Boy Scts; Nwsp Rptr; Rep Frsh Cls; Pres Soph Cls; VP Jr Cls; JV Ftbl; J[...] Trk; Hon Roll; NHS; Spanish NHS; Albany ST; Bus.

LANGERMAN, SHERI; Ocean Township HS; Ocean, NJ; (4); 18/33[...] Yrbk Rptr; Capt Fld Hcky; Var Swmmng; High Hon Roll; Hon Roll; JET[...] Awd; NHS; Ntl Merit Ltr; Pres Schlr; St Schlr; Bowman Ashe A Schlrsh[...] 87; Rider Coll Foregin Lang Trnmnt 1st Pl 85-86; Kiwanas Schlrshp 87; [...] Of Miami; Marine Bio.

LANGLEY, DENISE; Arthur S Uchalick HS; Elmer, NJ; (3); Band[...] Concert Band; Mrchg Band; Pep Band; Yrbk Stf; Bus.

LANGLEY, GEORGE CHARLES; Cumberland Regional H[...] Rosenhayn, NJ; (4); 114/329; Art Clb; English Clb; Hon Roll; La Salle [...] Bus.

LANGON, GINA; Middle Twp HS; Goshen, NJ; (3); Church Yth Gr[...] 4-H; Quiz Bowl; Stat Mgr(s); 4-H Awd; Hon Roll.

LANGTON, JENNIFER; St John Vianney HS; Matawan, NJ; (4); JC[...] SADD; Yrbk Stf; Rep Soph Cls; JV Bsktbl; Stat Var Ftbl; Powder Pu[...] Ftbl; JV Var Sftbl; Im Swmmng; Hon Roll; Fordham U; Lbrl Arts.

ANING, CHRISTOPHER; Clearview Regional HS; Mullica Hill, NJ; 3); 22/172; Church Yth Grp; 4-H; Band; Chorus; Church Choir; Concert Band; Mrchg Band; School Musical; Yrbk Stf; Hon Roll; S Jersey Yth ommsn 86; Tlvsn Prdctn.

ANING, JAMES; Pinelands Regional HS; Tuckerton, NJ; (3); 17/200; Var L Bsbl; Var L Socr; Hon Roll; NHS; Prfct Atten Awd; Spanish NHS; Golden Glv Awd Vrsty Bsbl 87.

ANING, STEPHANIE; A P Schalick HS; Bridgeton, NJ; (3); 6/118; Math Tm; Chorus; Rep Frsh Cls; Capt Cheerleading; JV Trk; Hon Roll; NHS; Bus.

ANNI, JEREMY D; Bayonne HS; Bayonne, NJ; (4); 10/350; Am Leg Boys St; Art Clb; Science Clb; Nwsp Rptr; Lit Mag; Rep Frsh Cls; Rep Soph Cls; Rep Jr Cls; Rep Sr Cls; Elks Awd; Hugh O Brien Fndtn Rep 85; Bio Cmpttv Tm 85; Engl Awd 85&87; Boston U; Journlsm.

ANSING, LISA ANN; Acad Of The Sacred Heart; N Bergen, NJ; (3); Cmnty Wkr; Hosp Aide; Math Tm; Yrbk Bus Mgr; High Hon Roll; Hon Roll; Jr NHS; NHS; Algebra I & II, Geog, Engl, Spnsh, Bio & Hstry I Excllnc; NY U; Bus Admin.

ANTRY, MATTHEW F; Morris Knolls HS; Denville, NJ; (4); 15/359; JA; Nwsp Rptr; Nwsp Stf; Rep Stu Cncl; High Hon Roll; Lion Awd; NHS; Pres Schlr; St Schlr; George Washington U; Intl Affrs.

ANUTE, MICHELLE; Edgewood HS; Sicklerville, NJ; (4); 50/305; Exploring; Latin Clb; Hon Roll; Latn Awd 83-84; Glassboro ST; Math.

ANZ, SABRINA; Chatham Township HS; Chatham Twp, NJ; (4); Key Clb; Nwsp Ed-Chief; Lit Mag; Var Fld Hcky; Hon Roll; NHS; Ntl Merit Ltr; Prncpls Trphy 87; Jrnlsm & Pres Acad Ftns Awds 87; Colgate U; Englsh.

APIDUS, JACK; Steinert HS; Hamilton Square, NJ; (4); 15/294; Sec Am Leg Boys St; Hst Debate Tm; Exploring; NFL; Madrigals; School Musical; Nwsp Rptr; Yrbk Rptr; JV Tennis; NHS; Rutgers Coll; Law.

APUSHESKI, ANDREA; Holy Spirit HS; Northfield, NJ; (2); 49/397; Stage Crew; Hon Roll; U Of DE; Mrktng.

ARA, JENNIFER; Middletown HS South; Red Bank, NJ; (3); Church Yth Grp; Girl Scts; Ski Clb; Church Choir; Orch; JV Var Fld Hcky; Var Socr; Var Swmmng; Var Hon Roll; Psych.

ARACY, MICHAEL F; Pt Pleasant Boro HS; Pt Pleasant, NJ; (3); 56/252; Am Leg Boys St; Var Socr; Bus.

ARACY, RICH; Point Pleasant Boro HS; Point Pleasant, NJ; (4); 18/239; Am Leg Boys St; Exploring; VP Stu Cncl; Ftbl; Trk; Cit Awd; NHS; Bl Brdly Yng Ctzns Awd 87; Jstns Ctznshp Awd 87; Pres Acad Ftns Awd 87; Ursns Coll; Pre-Med.

ARAWAY II, JOHN STONE; Rancocas Valley Regional HS; Mt Holly, NJ; (3); Am Leg Boys St; Varsity Clb; Rep Soph Cls; Rep Jr Cls; Rep Sr Cls; Stu Cncl; Var Swmmng; JV Trk; JV Socr; Church Yth Grp; Intl All Stars Swim Tm Solar Cup 85; US Swim Aqua Devils Comptv Swim Tm 79-87; NJ Boys ST 87; Comp Engrng.

ARCERI, ANTOINETTE; Lenape Valley Regional HS; Stanhope, NJ; 2); JV Sftbl; High Hon Roll; Hon Roll; Comp Oper.

ARGEY, LORI; Middletown HS South; Middletown, NJ; (3); Am Leg Aux Girls St; Church Yth Grp; Letterman Clb; VP Ski Clb; Yrbk Stf; Pres Soph Cls; Rep Jr Cls; Rep Stu Cncl; JV Scrkpr Bsktbl; Var Crs Cntry; HOBY 85-86.

ARKIN, DOUGLAS; Hamilton High East; Allentown, NJ; (3); Am Leg Boys St; School Play; Yrbk Stf; Off Lit Mag; Stu Cncl; Var Crs Cntry; Var Trk; NHS; Ntl Merit Ltr.

ARKINS, ALVIN; Dwight Morrow HS; Englewood, NJ; (3); Debate Tm; Math Tm; Model UN; Ski Clb; Nwsp Sprt Ed; Yrbk Phtg; Var Ftbl; High Hon Roll; NHS; Acctng.

ARMORE, GERRI Y; Burlington City HS; Edgewater Park, NJ; (3); NA; Pep Clb; Pres Spanish Clb; Yrbk Stf; Rep Soph Cls; Trk; Hon Roll; Attended NJ Girls State 86-87; Philadelphia Coll/Phrmcy & Sci.

AROSA, ADAM; Middletown HS South; Middletown, NJ; (3); Hosp Aide; Ski Clb; Spanish Clb; Trs Jr Cls; Ftbl; Wt Lftg; Hon Roll; VP Spanish NHS; Bronze Congressnl Awd 87; Wagner Coll Camp Defnsv Linemn Awd 86; Med.

ARRAZ, LINA M; Paterson Catholic R HS; Paterson, NJ; (3); 20/100; Church Yth Grp; Girl Scts; Hosp Aide; Teachers Aide; Yrbk Ed-Chief; Yrbk Stf; Rep Jr Cls; High Hon Roll; Hon Roll.

ARSON, JENNIFER; Ocean Township HS; Ocean, NJ; (3); 43/344; Church Yth Grp; French Clb; Latin Clb; Ski Clb; Chorus; Ed Yrbk Phtg; JV Bsktbl; JV Sftbl; Paleontlgy.

ARSON, PATRICIA; Mater Dei HS; Hazlet, NJ; (4); 22/147; Pep Clb; Spanish Clb; Variety Show; Lit Mag; Var Trk; Hon Roll; NHS; Political Wkr; Awd Wnng Irish Step Dncr 83-87; Acad Excllnce Rlgn 83-87; Cert Hnr Chem & 1st Aid 87; Georgian Court Coll; Math.

ARUE, YOLETTE; Roselle Catholic HS; Roselle, NJ; (4); Church Yth Grp; French Clb; Girl Scts; Church Choir; School Play; Stage Crew; Variety Show; French Hon Soc; High Hon Roll; Hon Roll; Rutgers U; Psych.

ARWA, REGINA M; Camden Catholic HS; Audubon Pk, NJ; (4); 46/250; French Clb; Rep Stu Cncl; Var Cheerleading; Stat Score Keeper; JV Sftbl; Hon Roll; NHS; Prsdntl Acdmc Ftnss Awd 87; Frnch Achvmnt Awd 87; Drexel U; Mgmt Infrmtnl Systms.

ASCARIDES, MICHAEL; Millville SR HS; Millville, NJ; (3); CAP; Model UN; Varsity Clb; Yrbk Stf; Var Swmmng; NHS; Ntl Merit Ltr; AATG Natl German Schlrshp Wnnr 86; Govrs Schl In Math/Sci 87; Engrng.

ASH, ROBERT; Fair Lawn HS; Fair Lawn, NJ; (3); Aud/Vis; Political Wkr; Temple Yth Grp; Nwsp Stf; VP Stu Cncl; Capt Socr; Hon Roll; Ntl Merit Ltr; Voice Dem Awd; Pathgrn Math Awd; Bus Adm.

ASHLEY, SANDRA; Delran HS; Delran, NJ; (4); 42/211; Chorus; Bsktbl; Sftbl; E Stroudsburg; Bus.

ASPATA, SUSANNE; Delsea Regional HS; Monroeville, NJ; (4); #6 In Class; Exploring; Key Clb; Office Aide; School Play; Yrbk Stf; High Hon Roll; NHS; Flag Corp; Tennis; Hon Roll; Atheneum Leag, Sons Of Italy-John Moffa Jr Awd, Franklinville PTA Schlrshp Awd; York Coll Of PA; Med Tech.

ASSER, ROBERT; Don Bosco Prep HS; Wallington, NJ; (3); German Clb; JV Ice Hcky; Orthdntst.

ASSITER, MICHAEL J; Northern Burlington HS; Mc Guire Afb, NJ; 4); 5/235; Am Leg Boys St; Var L Ftbl; Var L Trk; JV Wrstlng; High Hon Roll; Hon Roll; VP NHS; Spanish NHS; Army ROTC Schlrshp 87; U S Military Acad Acceptnce 87; NJ Gvrnrs Tchng Schlrshp 87; Rugers; Tchng.

ASSMAN, JUDY; Morristown HS; Morristown, NJ; (3); 44/422; Cmnty Wkr; Hosp Aide; Key Clb; Red Cross Aide; Temple Yth Grp; Band; Color Guard; Concert Band; Flag Corp; Mrchg Band; Scl Wrk.

ATHAM, LISA; Manchester Rgional HS; N Haledon, NJ; (3); Office Aide; SADD; Teachers Aide; Color Guard; Yrbk Stf; Med Sec.

LATHBURY, GREG; Lower Cape May Regional HS; N Cape May, NJ; (4); Church Yth Grp; Computer Clb; Political Wkr; Stage Crew; Nwsp Stf; Var Socr; Var Trk; Vllybl; Hon Roll; Mock Trial 86-87; Widener U; Elec Engnrng.

LATORE, CHRISTINE; Middletown HS South; Middletown, NJ; (3); Ski Clb; Varsity Clb; Powder Puff Ftbl; Sftbl; Hon Roll; Lncrft Sftbl All Strs 85 & 86; Bttlcpprs Cert 86; Trvlng Tm-Sccr, Lncrft Tms 84; Engl.

LATOUR, RICHARD; North Bergen HS; North Bergen, NJ; (4); 71/420; Key Clb; SADD; Nwsp Phtg; Nwsp Stf; Capt Bowling; Hon Roll; Hmrm Rep 84-87; Outdrs Clb 84-87; NJSYABA Chmpnshp Tourn Bwlng-1st Pl 85-86; Penn ST U; Pre Med.

LATRONICA, JOSEPH E; West Milford Township HS; West Milford, NJ; (4); Am Leg Boys St; SADD; Varsity Clb; Band; Chorus; Concert Band; Jazz Band; Mrchg Band; School Musical; School Play; L Kocher & D Wertheim Mem Band Schlrshp; Greenwood Lake Pwrbt Assn Schlrshp; Mst Musical SR Cls 87; Roger Williams Coll; Cvl Engr.

LATTERNER, PEGGY; Waldwick HS; Waldwick, NJ; (3); 11/114; Church Yth Grp; Exploring; Nwsp Stf; Rep Soph Cls; Rep Jr Cls; Rep Stu Cncl; Sftbl; Hon Roll; NHS; MIP V Sftbl Awd 87; Boston Coll; Lawyr.

LAU, ARNOLD; Lakewood HS; Lakewood, NJ; (3); 11/370; Am Leg Boys St; JCL; Latin Clb; High Hon Roll; Hon Roll; NHS; Blk Blt In Krt & Stu Mdl 86; Geo Wshngtn U; Elec Engr.

LAUBSCH JR, ALFRED C; Vineland HS; Vineland, NJ; (3); 69/850; Cmnty Wkr; Debate Tm; German Clb; Library Aide; Math Tm; Nwsp Rptr; Nwsp Stf; Rep Frsh Cls; Rep Soph Cls; Rep Jr Cls; Law.

LAURINAITIS, JILL; Notre Dame HS; Mercerville, NJ; (3); Dance Clb; Service Clb; Varsity Clb; School Musical; Var Cheerleading; High Hon Roll; Hon Roll; NHS; Fnlst Miss NJ Natl Teen Pagnt 87; Mst Spirit Chrldr 87; Comm.

LAURY, CYNTHIA G; Ridge HS; Basking Ridge, NJ; (4); 3/205; VP AFS; Church Yth Grp; Capt Hosp Aide; Concert Band; Var L Crs Cntry; Var L Trk; Pres NHS; Ntl Merit SF; Cmnty Wkr; Quiz Bowl; NJ Grp II Chmpn Crss Cntry 86; Cntrl Jersey Rgnl Band 84; Psychlgy.

LAUTS, CHRIS; Vernon Township HS; Sussex, NJ; (3); Rep Frsh Cls; Rep Soph Cls; Var Bsktbl; MI ST; Accntng.

LAVAN, MICHELE; St John Vianney HS; Hazlet, NJ; (4); 91/259; Church Yth Grp; FBLA; Hosp Aide; Intnl Clb; Ski Clb; Nwsp Stf; Hon Roll; Hnr Rll 86-87; Kings Coll; Hstry.

LAVARRO JR, ROLANDO; St Peters Prep; Jersey City, NJ; (3); 6/178; Chess Clb; Computer Clb; Science Clb; Service Clb; Nwsp Stf; Var L Bowling; Var L Wrstlng; High Hon Roll; Im Bsktbl; St Peters Coll Smmr Schlr 87; Acctng.

LAVELLE, ANNMARIE; North Bergen HS; N Bergen, NJ; (4); 95/300; Var Crs Cntry; Var Sftbl; Var Trk; Hon Roll; St Peters Coll; Bus.

LAVENDER, JOSHUA; North Brunswick Top HS; N Brunswick, NJ; (4); Spanish Clb; Chorus; Nwsp Bus Mgr; Var Trk; Vllybl; High Hon Roll; Hon Roll; NHS; PBA Lcl 160 Mem Schlrshp 87; Pres Acadc Ftns Awd 87; Rutgers U; Corp Lwyr.

LAVIN, ANNE MARIE; Mount St Mary Acad; Edison, NJ; (3); Camera Clb; Computer Clb; GAA; Spanish Clb; Rep Soph Cls; JV Bsktbl; Var L Sftbl; Hon Roll.

LAVISH, JENNIFER; Hunterdon Central HS; Stockton, NJ; (2); 88/478; Chorus; Flag Corp; Mrchg Band; Off Soph Cls; Mrktng.

LAW, DIANE; Mainland Regional HS; Linwood, NJ; (4); 1/275; JCL; Math Clb; Ed Nwsp Stf; Ed Yrbk Stf; Rep Stu Cncl; Mgr(s); Var Tennis; NHS; Ntl Merit SF; Val; Grdn ST Schlr 86-87; NJ Mock Trial Tm Lwyr 86-87; Rutgers Schlr 85-86; Yale U; Asian Stds.

LAW, KATHLEEN; Middle Township HS; Avalon, NJ; (4); 42/222; Aud/Vis; Intnl Clb; Science Clb; Spanish Clb; School Musical; Yrbk Rptr; Yrbk Stf; Trk; Hon Roll; NHS; Elmer Smith Schlrshp 87; Rtry Schlrshp 87; Optmst Schlrshp 87; Stockton ST Coll; Psychlgy.

LAW, STACI L; Mc Corristin Catholic HS; Trenton, NJ; (3); Cmnty Wkr; DECA; GAA; Model UN; Pep Clb; Red Cross Aide; Y-Teens; Chorus; Yrbk Stf; Bowling; VA ST; Mktng.

LAWLER, BRIAN; Piscataway HS; Piscataway, NJ; (3); Band; Chorus; Concert Band; Mrchg Band; Orch; Hon Roll; Comp Sci.

LAWLER, EDWARD J; Rancocos Valley Regional HS; Mt Holly, NJ; (3); 44/305; Am Leg Boys St; Varsity Clb; JV Bsbl; Var Capt Crs Cntry; Var Trk; Air Force; Pilot.

LAWLER, NOELLE S; Immaculate Heart Acad; Ho Ho Kus, NJ; (4); 2/176; Cmnty Wkr; Model UN; Science Clb; Yrbk Sprt Ed; Sftbl; Capt Tennis; Bausch & Lomb Sci Awd; French Hon Soc; High Hon Roll; Hon Roll; Sci.

LAWLESS, DENISE; Pinelands Regional HS; West Creek, NJ; (3); #3 In Class; Am Leg Aux Girls St; Church Yth Grp; French Clb; Girl Scts; Sec Frsh Cls; JV Var Fld Hcky; JV Trk; Cit Awd; French Hon Soc; Hon Roll; Schlrshp Caldwell Coll 86; Gdn ST Games Fld Hcky 87; Villanova; Mech Engr.

LAWLESS, KATHLEEN; Monsignor Donovan HS; Howell, NJ; (3); Hosp Aide; Ski Clb; SADD; Teachers Aide; Nwsp Stf; Yrbk Stf; Score Keeper; High Hon Roll; Hon Roll; High Hnr Roll 84; Hnr Roll ,5-87; Vrsty Lttr In Sftbl Stats 86; Psych.

LAWLESS, MICHAEL; St Peters Prep Schl; Rutherford, NJ; (4); 3/197; Boy Scts; Camera Clb; Pres Church Yth Grp; Var Capt Crs Cntry; Mgr Ice Hcky; Var L Trk; NHS; Ntl Merit SF; Pres Schlr; St Schlr; Drw U Schlr II 87; J & N Mc Keen Schlrshp 87; Drew U; Rsrch Doctor.

LAWLOR, JASON; Morristown HS; Morris Plains, NJ; (3); 154/432; Church Yth Grp; Red Cross Aide; Y-Teens; 1st 2nd 3rd Yr Outstndng Volunteer Awds 85-87; Law.

LAWRENCE, JERRIE; Wayne Hills HS; Wayne, NJ; (3); 85/230; Rep GAA; Pep Clb; Spanish Clb; Varsity Clb; VP Bsktbl; Stat Ftbl; VP Socr; VP Sftbl; VP Trk; Sccr All-Cnty Hnbl Mntn All-Lg 86-87; Sccr Brgn Rcrd Athlt Of Wk 86-87; Sftbl Lg Champs; Rutgers Coll; Law.

LAWRENSON, ANNE; Oakcrest HS; Hammonton, NJ; (4); GAA; Q&S; Ski Clb; Nwsp Ed-Chief; Yrbk Stf; Var Bsktbl; Capt Tennis; Capt Trk; NHS; Pres Schlr; Prptl Plq 12 Vrsty Ltrs 87; Prncpls Awd Outstndng Engl Achvt 87; GAN Schlrshp & Army Awd Outstndg Ath; St Josephs U; Advrtsng.

LAWSON, CHRISTIE; High Point Regional HS; Branchville, NJ; (3); 12/275; French Clb; Teachers Aide; Concert Band; Mrchg Band; Nwsp Stf; Rep Stu Cncl; JV Bsktbl; JV Swmmng; High Hon Roll; NHS; Bus Mgmt.

LAWSON, EUGENE; University HS; Newark, NJ; (3); Lit Mag; VP Frsh Cls; VP Jr Cls; VP Sr Cls; Var JV Bsktbl; Var Tennis; Hon Roll; Jr NHS; NHS; Computer Clb; Martin Luther King Jr Sci Fair-1st Pl 86; Elec Engrng.

LAWSON, LAUREN; Plainfield HS; Plainfield, NJ; (3); Church Yth Grp; Office Aide; PAVAS; Acpl Chr; Chorus; Mrchg Band; School Musical; JV Var Cheerleading; Capt Pom Pon; Hon Roll; American Musical & Drama Acad.

LAWSON, LYANNE; East Brunswick HS; E Brunswick, NJ; (3); VP Church Yth Grp; Exploring; Sec German Clb; Key Clb; SADD; Varsity Clb; Crs Cntry; Fld Hcky; Hon Roll; NHS; Grmn Hnr Soc 86; History.

LAWTON, L GREGORY; Cherry Hill HS West; Cherry Hill, NJ; (3); 88/350; Boy Scts; Pres Church Yth Grp; Hosp Aide; Off Church Choir; Nwsp Ed-Chief; Rep Soph Cls; Rep Stu Cncl; Var Diving; Var Swmmng; Hon Roll; Union Leag Phil Awd Yth Wrk 87; Hm & Schl Awd 87; Bates; Bio.

LAWTON, VANESSA; John F Kennedy HS; Willingboro, NJ; (3); 17/256; Math Tm; Office Aide; Science Clb; Co-Capt Drill Tm; JV Lcrss; Hon Roll; Jr NHS; NHS; Elec Engrng.

LAWWILL, BRAD; Randolph HS; Randolph, NJ; (3); Church Yth Grp; Radio Clb; Band; Variety Show; JV Bsbl; JV Ftbl; Im Sftbl; High Hon Roll; Hon Roll; Rudgers U; Bus.

LAYHEW, DENISE; Baptist HS; Haddon Hts, NJ; (3); 1/50; Spanish Clb; Sec Jr Cls; Rep Stu Cncl; L Var Bsktbl; L Var Fld Hcky; L Var Sftbl; High Hon Roll; NHS; Math Tm; All Acdmc Fld Hcky, Bsktbll 86-87; St Talents Christ 1st Pl Bible $400 Schlrshp 86; Cedarville Coll; Elem Ed.

LAYTON, MARSHA; Teaneck HS; Teaneck, NJ; (3); 147/412; JA; Church Choir; JV Trk; Hon Roll; Hnrd Natl Hnr Rll 87; Troph NJ Fed Music Clbs 86; Fnlst Miss NJ Amer Coed Pagnt & Troph 85; FL ST; Advrtsg.

LAYTON, SEAN; Lakewood HS; Lakewood, NJ; (3); Civic Clb; CAP; Computer Clb; German Clb; Intnl Clb; Im Ftbl; Billy Mitchell Awd 86; Photogrphy 85; Rocketry Comp 85; Oglethorpe U; Pre Law.

LAZAR, JODI; Northern Valley Regional HS; Norwood, NJ; (3); 12/275; Hosp Aide; Ski Clb; Temple Yth Grp; Band; Mrchg Band; Nwsp Rptr; Yrbk Stf; Hon Roll; Jr NHS; NHS; Acctng.

LAZARUS, NICOLE; Freehold Township HS; Freehold, NJ; (3); French Clb; Temple Yth Grp; Off Jr Cls; Rep Stu Cncl; Powder Puff Ftbl; Capt JV Sftbl; Var Tennis; Law.

LAZELL, PAMELA; Acad Of The Holy Angels; Englewood Cliffs, NJ; (2); Math Tm; Spanish Clb; Chorus; Color Guard; Lit Mag; Tchr.

LAZZARA, JANELLE; Paramus Catholic Girls Regionl HS; Teaneck, NJ; (4); 33/167; Church Yth Grp; Hosp Aide; Nwsp Ed-Chief; Capt Bowling; Cit Awd; Hon Roll; Trs NHS; Nwsp Rptr; Brn Pcclo Athlt Of Yr Awd 87; Hcknsck Hsptl Nrses Alumni Schlrshp Awd 87; VFW Nrsng Schlrshp 87; William Paterson Coll; Nrsng.

LAZZARO, FRANK; J P Stevens HS; Edison, NJ; (3); Spanish Clb; Acpl Chr; Chorus; Rep Frsh Cls; Sec Soph Cls; Stu Cncl; Crs Cntry; Socr; Trk; Hon Roll; 2nd Pl Drwng Cont-Twp 82; Montclair; Comp Tech.

LE, DAN; Ridge HS; Basking Ridge, NJ; (2); French Clb; Wrstlng; Hon Roll; Med.

LE DELL, ARIC; Ridge HS; Basking Ridge, NJ; (2); Church Yth Grp; Latin Clb; JV L Wrstlng; Slctn Chem Olympiad Infrml Accptnce Ltn Ntl Hnr Soc Chrch Bell Choir 85-86; Chem Cmptr.

LE DONNE, ANNETTE; Sayreville War Memorial HS; Sayreville, NJ; (2); Church Yth Grp; Spanish Clb; SADD; Band; Concert Band; Mrchg Band; Rep Soph Cls; Hon Roll.

LE PAGE, MARK; Paramus HS; Paramus, NJ; (3); School Musical; School Play; Stage Crew; Variety Show; Yrbk Stf; Bsktbl; Score Keeper; Wt Lftg; Hon Roll; NHS; Arch.

LE SCHACK, SHARON A; St Pius X HS; Somerset, NJ; (4); Aud/Vis; Church Yth Grp; Dance Clb; Drama Clb; PAVAS; ROTC; Stage Crew; Variety Show; Hon Roll; Marion Medal; Arts Recog & Tlnt Srch 87; Middlesex; Archlgy.

LEACH, JOSEPH J; Hackettstown HS; Hackettstown, NJ; (4); 21/234; High Hon Roll; Hon Roll; NHS; Pres Schlr; NJ Distgshd Schlr Prog; Hackettstwn Trd Assoc Bus Awd; Part Tm Job; Penn ST; Bus.

LEADBEATER, HOLLY; Central Jersey Christian HS; Eatontown, NJ; (3); Church Yth Grp; Drama Clb; Office Aide; Chorus; Yrbk Bus Mgr; Stu Cncl; High Hon Roll; NHS; Congrssnl Awd Brnz Lvl 87; Sci Fair 3rd Pl 86; Sci Fair 2nd Pl 87.

LEAHY, JENNIFER; Bishop Eustace Prep; Medford, NJ; (3); 2/164; Am Leg Aux Girls St; Cmnty Wkr; Drama Clb; French Clb; Spanish Clb; Teachers Aide; Orch; Trs Lit Mag; Ice Hcky; God Cntry Awd; Yth Schlr Inst Schlrshp 87; Knghts Columbs Schlrshp 84.

LEAHY, JENNIFER; Jackson Memorial HS; Jackson, NJ; (3); 19/425; Ski Clb; Concert Band; Mrchg Band; Socr; Tennis; High Hon Roll; NHS; Utica Syracuse; Hosp Admn.

LEAK, RISHIE; Lincoln HS; Jersy City, NJ; (4); 1/90; Church Yth Grp; FBLA; JA; Key Clb; Math Clb; Church Choir; Trk; Hon Roll; NHS; Garden St Dstngshd Schlr 86; Bus.

LEAP, HEATHER; Delaware Valley Regional HS; Frenchtown, NJ; (3); 26/180; Concert Band; Stat L Bsktbl; Var L Crs Cntry; Stat L Fld Hcky; Stat L Sftbl; JV L Trk; High Hon Roll; Hon Roll; Elem Ed.

LEAP, WAYNE; Pitman HS; Pitman, NJ; (3); 2/150; Church Yth Grp; High Hon Roll; Hon Roll; NHS.

LEASH, DAINNA COLLEEN; West Deptford HS; Mantua, NJ; (4); 10/260; Church Yth Grp; French Clb; Chorus; Church Choir; School Musical; Var L Cheerleading; High Hon Roll; NHS; Pres Schlr; Schl & Gloucestr Cnty JR Miss 87; Scrpt Tear Tlnt Schlrshp 87; Gov Schl Fne Arts Schlrshp 86; NY U.

LEASH, ROBERT; Paulsboro HS; Gibbstown, NJ; (3); Spanish Clb; SADD; Y-Teens; Bus Admin.

LEAVITT, CRAIG; Fair Lawn HS; Fair Lawn, NJ; (3); Band; Concert Band; Mrchg Band; JV Socr; Var Trk; Pdtrcs.

LECAROS, JORGE; Passaic County Voc-Tech HS; Paterson, NJ; (3); 25/520; Boys Clb Am; Computer Clb; Spanish Clb; Var Socr; Hon Roll; Compu Sci.

LEDDY, DENISE; Wall HS; Manasquan, NJ; (4); 12/269; Drama Clb; Ski Clb; Spanish Clb; School Play; Fld Hcky; High Hon Roll; Hon Roll; Kiwanis Awd; NHS; Acad All Amer Schlr 85-86; Bryant Coll; Acctng.

LEE, BARBARA; Parsippany HS; Parsippany, NJ; (4); 22/330; Spanish Clb; Concert Band; Jazz Band; School Musical; Stage Crew; Yrbk Stf; High Hon Roll; Hon Roll; NHS; Aud/Vis; Recvd Mexico Gvnmnt Mdl For All Amer Yth Hnr Musicians 84; Hnrbl Mntn Schlrs Awd 86-87; DE U; Comm.

LEE, CHANG HYUN; Cherry Hill HS West; Cherry Hill, NJ; (3); French Clb; JCL; Latin Clb; Bsktbl; Gym; NHS; Med.

LEE, CHAO-YING; Nutley HS; Nutley, NJ; (3); 8/350; Computer Clb; German Clb; Math Clb; Orch; Stu Cncl; JV Bsktbl; JV Sftbl; Var Tennis; Hon Roll; Jr NHS; NNJIL 1st Tm Tennis 86-87.

LEE, CHRISTINE; Bridgeton HS; Bridgeton, NJ; (4); Ski Clb; Soroptimist; Mrchg Band; Pom Pon; High Hon Roll; Hon Roll; Ntl Merit Schol; Cumberland County Coll; Elem Ed.

LEE, DANIEL; Ramapo HS; Wyckoff, NJ; (3); 17/322; VP Debate Tm; VP Spanish Clb; Temple Yth Grp; Var Socr; High Hon Roll; Hon Roll; NHS; Ntl Merit Ltr; Fndtn Free Enterprise 87-88; Engl III Awd 86-87; Spn IV Awd 86-87.

LEE, HAEMIN; Cresskill HS; Cresskill, NJ; (3); 4/104; Debate Tm; Ski Clb; Stage Crew; Yrbk Ed-Chief; Var Capt Trk; NHS; Math Tm; Yrbk Stf; Lit Mag; JV Tennis; NJ Stu Crftmns Fair 1st 86, 2nd 85, 3rd 84; Arch.

LEE, HARVEY; Bishop Eustace HS; Ewan, NJ; (4); 54/179; Spanish Clb; SADD; Yrbk Sprt Ed; JV Golf; Var Wrstlng; Spanish NHS; Penn ST; Bus.

LEE, JAE; Bordentown Regional HS; Cookstown, NJ; (3); French Clb; Math Clb; Pres Soph Cls; Rep Stu Cncl; Im Ftbl; JV Socr; Wt Lftg; Var JV Wrstlng; Columbia; Jrnlsm.

LEE, JAE JUN; Northern Valley R HS; Haworth, NJ; (3); 9/250; Pres Church Yth Grp; Computer Clb; Pres Intnl Clb; Math Tm; Varsity Clb; Var Crs Cntry; Var Trk; Vllybl; High Hon Roll; NHS; Am Invttnl Math Exam 87; Fairleigh Dickinson U Pgmmng Cont 3rd Pl 86, 2nd Pl 87.

LEE, JANE A; Princeton Day Schl; Trenton, NJ; (4); AFS; Pres Church Yth Grp; French Clb; Hosp Aide; Model UN; Orch; Var Tennis; Ntl Merit SF; St Schlr; Cum Laude 86.

LEE, JEANNY; Ft Lee HS; Fort Lee, NJ; (4); Gov Hon Prg Awd; Edward John Noble Fndtn Schlrshp, NJ Symphony Orchester League Awd, NJ Governors Awd 86; The Juilliard Schl; Piano.

LEE, JEFFREY F; Haddon Township HS; Westmont, NJ; (3); Am Leg Boys St; Nwsp Rptr; Pres Frsh Cls; Sec Soph Cls; Trs Jr Cls; Stu Cncl; Var Socr; Var Swmmng; Var Tennis; Hon Roll; World Affrs Cncl 85; Bar Assoc Law Day 86; Duke U; Phy Therapist.

LEE, JOHN; John P Stevens HS; Edison, NJ; (2); 12/452; Debate Tm; Model UN; Ski Clb; Var L Crs Cntry; Var Trk; Hon Roll; 2nd Pl Tm Cntrl Jersey Group IV ST Chmpnshp 85; 2nd Pl Tm Group IV ST Chmpnshps 85; Intrnl Ecn.

LEE, JUNG EUN; West Windsor-Plainsboro HS; Princeton Jct, NJ; (3); Am Leg Aux Girls St; Church Yth Grp; French Clb; Model UN; Church Choir; Orch; School Musical; Lit Mag; JV Fld Hcky; High Hon Roll; Concrt 1st Chair Regn II NJ Orchstra, Asst Cncrt Mistrss All ST Orchstra 86-87; Mbr Vrsty Fld Hcky; Sci.

LEE, KENTON; Livingston HS; Livingston, NJ; (3); 16/420; AFS; Debate Tm; Math Clb; Chorus; Orch; School Musical; School Play; Variety Show; Hon Roll; Jr NHS; Cvl Engrng.

LEE, MARK T; Whippany Park HS; Whippany, NJ; (4); 20/180; Am Leg Boys St; Church Yth Grp; Varsity Clb; Church Choir; Capt Var Socr; Capt Var Trk; NHS; Hnbl Mntn Sccr; 2nd Tm All Conf Sccr; Capt Clb; Trenton ST; Comp Sci.

LEE, MILLYS; Pascack Hills HS; Woodcliff Lake, NJ; (3); Camera Clb; Hosp Aide; Pres Service Clb; Drill Tm; School Musical; School Play; Stage Crew; Nwsp Rptr; Yrbk Phtg; Lit Mag; 3rd Pl Bergen CC Wrtng Cntst Poetry 86; Hnrbl Mntn NJ Inst Of Tech Wrtg Cntst 87; Oberlin Coll; Photojournalist.

LEE, NANCY; Parsippany HS; Parsippany, NJ; (4); 7/330; AFS; Church Yth Grp; Cmnty Wkr; Computer Clb; Debate Tm; FCA; FBLA; German Clb; Hosp Aide; Intnl Clb; Mrrs Cnty PTSA & 200 Clb Of USA Schlrshps 87; Spcl Olympcs Awd 87; Barnard Coll; Med.

LEE, OSWALD; John F Kennedy HS; Paterson, NJ; (3); Orch; JV Ftbl; Var Golf; High Hon Roll; Hon Roll; Cmmrcl Airln Pilot.

LEE, RONALD; Brick Township HS; Brick Town, NJ; (3); 1/475; Computer Clb; Debate Tm; Key Clb; Math Clb; Math Tm; Ski Clb; SADD; Yrbk Phtg; Yrbk Stf; Rep Frsh Cls; Cornell; Bus.

LEE, SE-YOUNG; Tenafly HS; Cresskill, NJ; (4); 5/228; Pres Church Yth Grp; Hosp Aide; Math Clb; Math Tm; Model UN; Spanish Clb; VP Chorus; Concert Band; Madrigals; Mrchg Band; Svrl Chmpnshp Awds In Golf 85; Med.

LEE, SHAWN; Hillsborough HS; Somerville, NJ; (4); 8/285; Math Tm; Rep Soph Cls; Rep Sr Cls; JV Trk; High Hon Roll; Hon Roll; Trs NHS; St Schlr; Outstndng Math Stu, Comptng Cert Excllnce, Hnry Awd, N Amrcn Phlps Schlrshp Compttn; Rutgers U; Comp Sci.

LEE, STEVEN; Kennelon HS; Smoke Rise, NJ; (4); 12/168; FBLA; Ski Clb; Spanish Clb; Nwsp Stf; Ed Yrbk Stf; Lit Mag; Var Capt Tennis; Trs NHS; Ntl Merit Ltr; Spanish NHS; Grdn ST Dstngshd Schlr 86-87; Lehigh U; Med.

LEE, SYLVIA; Lincoln HS; Jersy City, NJ; (4); 4/213; FBLA; FHA; JA; VP Jr Cls; VP Sr Cls; Pres Stu Cncl; Jr NHS; NHS; Ntl Merit Ltr; Benedict Coll; Bus Mgmt.

LEE, TERRY; Bridgewater Raritan HS; Bridgewater, NJ; (3); Key Clb; Ski Clb; Var Tennis; High Hon Roll.

LEE, TINA T; Holmdel HS; Holmdel, NJ; (4); 5/190; Pres Key Clb; Rptr Yrbk Rptr; Var L Cheerleading; Var L Sftbl; French Hon Soc; High Hon Roll; Kiwanis Awd; NHS; Ntl Merit Ltr; St Schlr; Deans Summer Schlr 86; MA Inst Of Tech; Bio.

LEE, VIVIAN; Indian Hills HS; Franklin Lakes, NJ; (4); 23/282; AFS; Church Yth Grp; Hosp Aide; JCL; Latin Clb; Ski Clb; Ed Yrbk Stf; Lit Mag; Ntl Merit Ltr; Grdn ST Dstngshd Scholr 87; Barnard Coll; Econ.

LEE, WILLIAM; Sparta HS; Alexandria, VA; (3); 84/215; Church Yth Grp; Concert Band; Jazz Band; Mrchg Band; Symp Band; Socr; Trk; High Hon Roll; Hon Roll; Outstndg Achvt Acad Stud 86-87; U VA; Econ.

LEE, YOUNG; Holy Spirit HS; Ocean City, NJ; (2); 33/397; NFL; Hon Roll; Cornell U.

LEE, YU; St Mary HS; Rutherford, NJ; (3); Comp Sci.

LEE, YUN-CHIN; Sayreville War Memorial HS; Parlin, NJ; (4); 2/350; Am Leg Aux Girls St; Trs French Clb; Mgr Stage Crew; Ed Yrbk Stf; French Hon Soc; High Hon Roll; NHS; Prfct Atten Awd; Sal; Chorus; Lehigh U; Engrng.

LEEDS, DANIEL D; Boonton HS; Lincoln Park, NJ; (4); 4/230; Pres Am Leg Boys St; Capt Math Tm; Lit Mag; L Socr; L Trk; Capt Vllybl; High Hon Roll; NHS; St Schlr; Lehigh U; Math.

LEEDS, DOUGLAS; Baptist HS; Lindenwold, NJ; (3); VP Church Yth Grp; Drama Clb; Chorus; Var Capt Bsbl; Var Capt Bsktbl; Var Capt Socr; Trk; Acctng.

LEEGWATER-KIM, JULIE R; Stuart Country Day Schl; Skillman, NJ; (4); 1/30; Science Clb; Acpl Chr; Orch; Nwsp Rptr; Lit Mag; Bausch & Lomb Sci Awd; Gov Hon Prg Awd; High Hon Roll; Ntl Merit Schol; Geraldine R Dodge Fndtn Educ Awd 87; NJ Govs Jersey Pride Awd 87; Golden Nugget Schlrshp 87; Princeton U; Molecular Bio.

LEEKS, DLONTAY; Barringer HS; Newark, NJ; (3); Boy Scts; English Clb; Science Clb; Off Frsh Cls; Ftbl; Trk; Hon Roll; Prfct Atten Awd.

LEEMANN, GARY; Toms River South HS; Toms River, NJ; (3); 10/405; Var JV Crs Cntry; Var JV Trk; NHS.

LEEN, JOAN; Toms River HS East; Toms River, NJ; (3); Ski Clb; Chorus; JV Fld Hcky; JV Swmmng; JV Trk; Hon Roll; Embry-Riddle; Aeronautcl Engrng.

LEESTMA, JAMES L; Elmwood Park Memorial HS; Elmwood Park, NJ; (3); 15/150; Am Leg Boys St; Nwsp Rptr; Yrbk Stf; Var Bsbl; Var Capt Bsktbl; Im Wt Lftg; Hon Roll; Spanish NHS; Pre-Law.

LEFF, BRIAN; Jackson Memorial HS; Jackson, NJ; (3); 66/425; Ski Clb; SADD; Band; Concert Band; Mrchg Band; Golf; High Hon Roll; Hon Roll; Artistic Rllrsktng Natl 5th 85; Lndscp Arch.

LEGACKI, JAMES; Immaculata HS; Middlesex, NJ; (3); 52/250; Library Aide; Math Tm; JV Crs Cntry; Prfct Atten Awd; Spanish NHS; Cthlc Math Leag Vrsty Div Outstndng Achvt 87.

LEGER, MARIE; Columbia HS; South Orange, NJ; (3); 75/513; French Clb; Girl Scts; Latin Clb; Service Clb; French Hon Soc; Merit Cert-Ntl Frnch Cmptn 86 & 87; ST Fnlst-Miss Amercn Coed Pgnt 87; Soclgst.

LEGG, JODI M; Spotswood HS; Spotswood, NJ; (3); 7/172; Ski Clb; Chorus; Concert Band; Drm Mjr(t); Mrchg Band; Pres Jr Cls; JV Var Cheerleading; JV Sftbl; High Hon Roll; Hon Roll; Most Stolen Bases In Sftbl 86; 1st Seat Clarinet Cncrt Band 84; Homerm Rep For Brd Of Ed 86; Chiroprctr.

LEGG, KIMBERLY A; Spotswood HS; Spotswood, NJ; (4); 10/189; Intnl Clb; Model UN; Ski Clb; Concert Band; Mrchg Band; VP Stu Cncl; JV Var Cheerleading; High Hon Roll; NHS; Spanish NHS; Pre-Law.

LEGGIN, JULIANNE S; Lenape Valley Regional HS; Stanhope, NJ; (4); Var Capt Swmmng; Hon Roll; NHS; Pres Schlr; NJ Schlr Athlt Awd 87; D Fergussen Memrl Schlr Athlt 87; Dover Gen Sci Awd Lds Auxlry 87; Cornell U; Resrch Sci.

LEGGIN, PATRICIA; Hillsborough HS; Belle Mead, NJ; (4); 13/285; Cmnty Wkr; Latin Clb; Service Clb; Teachers Aide; High Hon Roll; Hon Roll; Jr NHS; NHS; Ntl Merit Ltr; Misericordia Coll Schlrshp 87; Good Stu Recgntn ST, Mayor & Fed Grvntmnt 87; Foothills Nrsng Hm Schlr; Misericordia Coll; Pre-Optmtry.

LEHANE, MICHAEL P; Cherokee HS; Marlton, NJ; (4); Off Church Yth Grp; Drama Clb; French Clb; Chorus; School Musical; School Play; Nwsp Stf; Var Swmmng; Hon Roll; NHS; Trenton ST Coll.

LEHANSKI, DEBRA F; Academy Of The Holy Angels; Washington Twp, NJ; (3); Cmnty Wkr; Library Aide; Model UN; Ski Clb; Band; Ed Nwsp Stf; Mu Alpha Theta Awd; NHS; Natl History Day-Cnty 2nd & ST Grade Of Excllnc 86; Schlrshp To Yth Schlrs Pgm 86; Pre-Med.

LEHMANN, KEITH; St John Vianney HS; Old Bridge, NJ; (3); Im Ftbl; JV Trk; Hon Roll; Stetson U; Accntng.

LEHNER, RICHARD A; Cherokee HS; Marlton, NJ; (3); Am Leg Boys St; Church Yth Grp; JV Socr; Vllybl; JV Wrstlng; Hon Roll; Aviation.

LEHR, MICHAEL; Toms River South HS; Toms River, NJ; (2); CAP; Math Tm; Red Cross Aide; Ski Clb; Golf; JV Swmmng; High Hon Roll; Hon Roll; Billy Mitchell Awd 87; Plt.

LEHR, RODGER B; Pennsville Memorial HS; Pennsville, NJ; (3); 35/225; Am Leg Boys St; Pres VICA; JV Socr; Var Tennis; JV Trk; Hon Roll; Sthrn NJ Stu Crfts Fair 3rd Pl Automtd Tech 87; NU VICA Skl Olympcs Opng Clsng Cermns 87; US Army; Robtcs Engrng.

LEIB, JULIE; Red Bank Regional HS; Red Bank, NJ; (3); Latin Clb; Yrbk Stf; Var L Bsktbl; Var L Socr; Var L Socr; JV High Hon Roll; Hon Roll; NHS; Outstndng Bio Stu 84-85; Med.

LEIB, MICHAEL S; Paramus HS; Paramus, NJ; (4); 6/330; Math Clb; NFL; Temple Yth Grp; School Play; Nwsp Rptr; Tennis; NHS; Ntl Merit SF; St Schlr; Hbrw Hnr Soc 85-87.

LEIDENFROST, STEVE; Paramus Catholic HS; Hasbrouck Hts, NJ; (4); 44/178; Church Yth Grp; JA; Lit Mag; Acadc All Am Awd 87; Mnhttn Coll Schlrshp 87; Manhattan Coll.

LEIMKUHLER, WILLIAM JAMES; West Windsor-Plainsboro HS; Princeton Junct, NJ; (3); Church Yth Grp; Var L Swmmng; JV L Trk; Hon Roll; Engr.

LEISER, GAIL; Spotswood HS; Spotswood, NJ; (3); Am Leg Aux Girls St; Drama Clb; Band; School Play; Nwsp Stf; Stu Cncl; Hon Roll.

LEISNER III, THOMAS; St James HS; Pennsville, NJ; (2); 11/100; Church Yth Grp; Bsktbl; Var Crs Cntry; Socr; Wt Lftg; High Hon Roll; Acad All Amercn 86.

LEIT, DAVID; Livingston HS; Livingston, NJ; (4); 13/424; Chrmn Debate Tm; Chorus; School Musical; Swing Chorus; Nwsp Ed-Chief; Gov Hon Prg Awd; NHS; St Schlr; Cmnty Wkr; Leo Clb; Fclty Hnr Awd 84; Acdmc Excllnc Medlln 87; David Starr Jordan Schlr Stanford U 87; Stanford U; Law.

LEITMAN, JENNIFER; Wayne Hills HS; Wayne, NJ; (3); Ski Clb; Spanish Clb; Temple Yth Grp; Concert Band; Mrchg Band; Nwsp Rptr; Nwsp Stf; Yrbk Stf; JV Capt Sftbl; Var Trk; Sprts Brdcstng.

LEITNER, MARTY; Rancocas Valley Regional HS; Mt Holly, NJ; (2); 9/297; Varsity Clb; JV Bsbl; Var Socr; Var Wt Lftg; Im Wrstlng; High Hon Roll; Hon Roll; NHS; Comp Sci.

LEKATIS, KIKI; Mother Seton Regional HS; Irvington, NJ; (2); FBLA; Var Powder Puff Ftbl; JV Vllybl; High Hon Roll; Hon Roll; Hghst Avg Geom 87.

LELYO, JENNIFER; Paramus Catholic Girls HS; Saddle Brk, NJ; (3); Church Yth Grp; Drama Clb; JV Bsktbl; Var Mgr(s); Var Score Keeper; JV Var Socr; Hon Roll; Jr NHS; NHS; Bio.

LEMALDI, MARIA; Monsignor Donovan HS; Toms River, NJ; (3); Debate Tm; Drama Clb; Ski Clb; SADD; Stat Sftbl; High Hon Roll; Hon Roll; Law.

LEMASTERS, JENNIFER LYNN; Hackettstown HS; Hackettstown, NJ; (4); 75/234; Church Yth Grp; Intnl Clb; Key Clb; SADD; Teachers Aide; Band; Concert Band; Jazz Band; Mrchg Band; Hon Roll; Pres Acdmc Fit Awd Cert & Pin 87; Loylty & Excptnl Intrst Mrchg Band 87; Bst Wrk Penmnshp 87; Bloomsburg U; Fshn Merch.

LEMBO, NICHOLAS; Don Bosco Prep; Franklin Lakes, NJ; (4); 17/200; Boys Clb Am; Rep Stu Cncl; Var Capt Wrstlng; Hon Roll; NHS; Penn ST; Bus.

LEMING, EMILY; Summit HS; Summit, NJ; (4); Church Yth Grp; Cmnty Wkr; Library Aide; Pep Clb; Mrchg Band; Symp Band; Twrlr; Hon Roll; Stat Bowling; Stat Ftbl; Bus & Prfnsl Wmns Clb Of Smt Schlrshp 87; Smt Ed Assn Schlrshp 87; Sweet Briar Coll; Hstry.

LEMISE, MICHELE; De Paul Butler HS; Bloomingdale, NJ; (3); Dance Clb; Drama Clb; Chorus; Church Choir; School Musical; School Play; Stage Crew; Swing Chorus; High Hon Roll; Hon Roll; Actng.

LEMP, DEBRA; St John Vianney HS; Hazlet, NJ; (4); 51/250; Hosp Aide; Intnl Clb; JCL; Trs Service Clb; Yrbk Stf; Capt Twrlr; Hon Roll; Church Yth Grp; Dance Clb; Girl Scts; Pres Acdmc Ftnss Awd 87; Gold & White Awd 85-87; Girl Scout Gold Awd 84; Trenton ST Coll; Chem.

LEMP, KATHRYN; St John Vianney HS; Hazlet, NJ; (4); 50/250; Girl Scts; Intnl Clb; Service Clb; Ski Clb; Band; Drill Tm; Mrchg Band; Yrbk Stf; Hon Roll; Pres Acdmc Ftnss Awd 87; Gold & White Awd 85-87; Girl Scout Silver 84; Trenton ST Coll; Elec Engrng.

LEMPFERT, STACEY; Indian Hills HS; Oakland, NJ; (3); Drama Clb; Hosp Aide; Red Cross Aide; Acpl Chr; Chorus; School Musical; School Play; Nwsp Stf; Cit Awd; Hon Roll; Med.

LENGA, KIRK; Manalapan HS; Westfield, NJ; (4); 48/417; Political Wkr; Temple Yth Grp; JV Golf; US Coast Grd AIM Pgm Fnlst 86; Carnegi Mellon U; Ecnmcs.

LENGA, SAMARA; Manalapan HS; Englishtown, NJ; (3); 25/435; Nwsp Bus Mgr; Nwsp Rptr; Mgr(s); JV Socr.

LENGE, ALLISON; Paramus Catholic Girls HS; Little Ferry, NJ; (2' Church Yth Grp; Cmnty Wkr; Hosp Aide; Math Tm; SADD; School Play Nwsp Stf; Yrbk Stf; Lit Mag; Hon Roll; Engl Awds 86; Lawyer.

LENGE, CHRISTOPHER; Leonia HS; Leonia, NJ; (3); Computer Clb Spanish Clb; Pres Jr Cls; Pres Sr Cls; Capt Bsbl; Capt JV Bsktbl; Hig Hon Roll; Hon Roll; NHS; Bus.

LENGE, DEBORAH; Paramus Catholic Girls HS; Little Ferry, NJ; (3 Church Yth Grp; Cmnty Wkr; Hosp Aide; Math Clb; SADD; School Play Trk; French Hon Soc; Hon Roll; Prfct Atten Awd; St Peters Coll; Accntng

LENGYEL, PETER; Ewing HS; Trenton, NJ; (4); Am Leg Boys S Cmnty Wkr; Key Clb; Political Wkr; Ski Clb; Varsity Clb; Nwsp Sprt E Nwsp Stf; Off Soph Cls; Off Jr Cls; WA Wrkshp 85; Outstndng S Athlt-Tnns 87; Stu Of The Mnth 87; Tulane U; Pol Sci.

LENK, MEREDITH; Lakewood Prep; Brick Town, NJ; (1); 3/23; Art Clb German Clb; GAA; Letterman Clb; Science Clb; Varsity Clb; Stat Scor Keeper; Socr; Hon Roll; Athl Dir Awd Outstdng Acdmc & Athl Excln Art Awd 1st 85-86; Law.

LENKEY, ROBIN; St Pius X Regional HS; Milltown, NJ; (3); Dance Clb Chorus; School Musical; Yrbk Phtg; Yrbk Stf; Cheerleading; Glassboro Psych.

LENNON JR, BYRON; Clifford J Scott HS; East Orange, NJ; (3); 13 280; Church Yth Grp; JA; Church Choir; Trk; Hon Roll; Dept Hnrs Gft 85-87; Dept Hgh Hnrs 85-86; Bus.

LENNON, COLLEEN; Union Catholic Regional HS; Elizabeth, NJ; (3 22/308; Service Clb; SADD; JV Var Bsktbl; Hon Roll; Chem.

LENNON, JOHN; Phillipsburg HS; Phillipsburg, NJ; (3); 15/350; Dram Clb; Math Tm; Quiz Bowl; Thesps; School Musical; School Play; Variet Show; Off Frsh Cls; Var Crs Cntry; Trk; Olympcs Mind Cptn 2nd S Chmpnshp 87; Sci.

LENNON, KATHLEEN; Paramus Catholic Girls HS; Paramus, NJ; (3 Cmnty Wkr; Ski Clb; Cheerleading; Hon Roll; Rutgers.

LENNON, SHAREEN; Pinelands Regional HS; Tuckerton, NJ; (3 Spanish Clb; Band; Concert Band; Mrchg Band; Twrlr; Hon Roll; NHS Prfct Atten Awd; Natl Hnr Soc 87; Hnr Rll; Natl Awd Wnnr Hnr Rl Schlstc Awd 87; Elem Educ.

LENTINE, MICHELLE; Our Lady Of Mercy Acad; Wmstown, NJ; (4 7/34; Art Clb; Cmnty Wkr; Science Clb; SADD; Nwsp Stf; Yrbk Stf; L Mag; High Hon Roll; NHS; Pres Schlr; Sr Marie Galetto Schlrshp, N Frgn Lang Awd-Spanish 87; Amrcn Chemcl Soc Awd 86; Monmouth Col Intl Bus.

LENZ, CHERYL; Morris Knolls HS; Denville, NJ; (4); 117/359; FBLA Hosp Aide; High Hon Roll; Fairleigh Dickinsn U; Phys Ther.

LENZEN, JOHN; Christian Brothers Acad; Brielle, NJ; (3); 15/260; In Ftbl; Im Sftbl; Wt Lftg; High Hon Roll; Ntl Merit Ltr; :Financl Consult.

LEON, PAMELA; Memorial HS; W New York, NJ; (4); 2/300; Frenc Clb; Key Clb; Math Clb; Trk; High Hon Roll; NHS; Sal; NJ Distingsh Schlr Awd 87; Rensselaer Schlrshp 87; Math Clb Schlrshp 87; Rensselae Poly Tech; Comp Sci.

LEONARD, ANTOINETTE; St John Vianney HS; Hazlet, NJ; (4 FBLA; Intnl Clb; Political Wkr; Nwsp Rptr; Lit Mag; Tennis; Hon Rol Stat Ftbl; Poetry Awds 84-87; Asst Edtr-Schl Nwspr 85-86; Vrsty Ltr 8 La Salle U; Comms.

LEONARD, CHRIS; Morris Knolls HS; Denville, NJ; (3); Exploring Summa Awd 86 & 87.

LEONARD, JAMES; Southern Regional HS; Barnegat, NJ; (3); 7/40 PAVAS; Pres Band; Jazz Band; Capt Mrchg Band; School Musical; Hig Hon Roll; Hon Roll; NHS; Church Yth Grp; Service Clb; Sci Fair 1st P 86-87; Outstndg Scl Stds Stu 86-87; Gov Schl Arts 86-87; Law.

LEONARD, LAWRENCE; Hoboken HS; Hoboken, NJ; (3); #2 In Clas Rep Frsh Cls; Rep Soph Cls; Rep Jr Cls; Var Bsktbl; High Hon Roll; NHS Prfct Atten Awd; Membr Inroads/Northern NJ 86-88; Cornell; Actuari Science.

LEONARD, OPAL; Toms River HS East; Toms River, NJ; (4); 148/56 Church Yth Grp; Intnl Clb; Trs Q&S; Spanish Clb; Church Choir; Nws Bus Mgr; Nwsp Rptr; Nwsp Stf; JV Crs Cntry; Powder Puff Ftbl; Fnlst Fo Hmecmng Queen 86; Psych.

LEONARD, STEPHEN; The Hun Schl; Somerset, NJ; (3); 13/123; Ches Clb; Cmnty Wkr; Computer Clb; Latin Clb; Math Tm; Teachers Aid Nwsp Phtg; Im Vllybl; High Hon Roll; Church Yth Grp; Mst Imprvd Aw Smmr Swmmng 85.

LEONARD, STEVEN; Bridgewater-Raritara HS East; Bridgewater, N (3); Varsity Clb; Var Capt Ftbl; Powder Puff Ftbl; Im Wt Lftg; Var Cap Wrstlng; Bus Admin.

LEONARD, SUSAN; Immaculate Conception HS; Secaucus, NJ; (4 Dance Clb; Stage Crew; Hon Roll; Girls Ctznshp Inst 86; Katherine Gibb Schlrshp 87; Katherine Gibbs SchlSECY.

LEONARDIS, JOANNE; Kearny HS; Kearny, NJ; (2); Band; Mrch Band; Pep Band; Stage Crew; Stat Bsktbl; Var L Mgr(s); Var JV Scor Keeper; Hon Roll; Concert Band; Frshmn & JV Awds Crew Rowing; Vrst Ltr & Awd In Band; Pre Law.

LEONE, CAROL; Cherry Hill East HS; Cherry Hill, NJ; (2); Church Yt Grp; Cmnty Wkr; English Clb; Yrbk Stf; Bsktbl; Sftbl; Stu Congress 86-8 Fshn.

LEONE, JUSTINE; Saint John Vianney HS; Keyport, NJ; (3); Churc Yth Grp; Intnl Clb; School Musical; Variety Show; Stat Ftbl; Powder Pu Ftbl; Hon Roll; Gld & Wht Awds 85-87; Spcl Ed.

LEONETTI, MICHELE; Arthur P Schalick HS; Elmer, NJ; (4); 6/13 Church Yth Grp; Math Clb; Ski Clb; Capt Color Guard; Rep Frsh Cls; St Cncl; Score Keeper; Hon Roll; NHS; Intl Frgn Lang Awd 87; Pionee Amer Scholar 87; Bloomsburg U; Bus.

LEONETTI, RHONDA; St James HS; Gibbstown, NJ; (1); 15/72; Danc Clb; Debate Tm; Drama Clb; NFL; VP Frsh Cls; JV Cheerleading; J Score Keeper; Var Hon Roll; Frnsc Awd 1st Pl In Dclmtn, Grad Of Casablancas Mdl & Tlnt Agncy, 1st & 2nd Pl-Dance Comp 87.

LEONTE, KEVIN; Lyndhurst HS; Lyndhurst, NJ; (3); 17/174; JV Bsb JV Var Bsktbl; Bus.

LEPORE, MATTHEW; Butler HS; Butler, NJ; (3); Computer Cl Letterman Clb; Math Clb; Math Tm; Scholastic Bowl; Varsity Clb; Re Stu Cncl; Var L Bsbl; Var L Ftbl; Wt Lftg; Bes In Fair In Hist Fai Pre-Prof.

LEPOSFKY, CAROLYN; Randolph HS; Randolph, NJ; (4); 19/365; Church Yth Grp; Band; Mrchg Band; Rep Frsh Cls; Rep Soph Cls; Rep Jr Cls; Rep Sr Cls; Var JV Bsktbl; Powder Puff Ftbl; High Hon Roll; NSH; Spnsh Natl Hnr Soc; Bsktbl; IN U; Frgn Lang.

LEPPIN, CHRISSY; Union HS; Union, NJ; (3); French Clb; FBLA; Teachers Aide; Band; Yrbk Stf; Var Cheerleading; Var Gym; Var Twrlr; Hon Roll; Svc Awd 85; Montclair ST.

LERMAN, DAWN; Northern Valley Reg HS; Harrington Pk, NJ; (3); Drama Clb; Pres French Clb; Ski Clb; SADD; Pres VP Temple Yth Grp; Nwsp Rptr; Rep Stu Cncl; Stat Bsktbl; Hon Roll; AFS; Rutgers U Girls Citiznshp Inst 87.

LESKO, JO ANN; Madison Central HS; Old Bridge, NJ; (4); Church Yth Grp; Cmnty Wkr; VP Girl Scts; Hosp Aide; Red Cross Aide; Color Guard; Var Socr; Var Trk; Frst Aid & Rescue Sqd 85-86; Stu Athltc Trnr 86-87; Grl Sct Slvr Awd 85; Middlesex Cnty; Police Officer.

LESNIAK, RENEE; Mother Seton Regional HS; Rahway, NJ; (2); 36/85; Art Clb; Church Yth Grp; Computer Clb; Dance Clb; English Clb; Latin Clb; Math Clb; Science Clb; Spanish Clb; Chorus; Cert Awd Rcrutmnt 87; Csmtlgst.

LESSIG, SCOTT; Phillipsburg HS; Phillipsburg, NJ; (3); 135/365; Var Bsbl; JV Bsktbl; Williamsport CC; Cnstrctn.

LESTER, SIMON; Holy Spirit HS; Absecon, NJ; (2); 9/397; Var Socr; Var Trk; High Hon Roll; Hon Roll; Gold Medal Natl Latin Test 85-86; Econ.

LETTERIE, BARBARA; Cinaminson HS; Cinnaminson, NJ; (3); Church Yth Grp; Cmnty Wkr; German Clb; Ski Clb; SADD; Band; Concert Band; Mrchg Band; Hon Roll; NHS; Phrmcy.

LEUITSKY, JOHN; Pequannock Township HS; Pompton Plains, NJ; (3); 27/150; Am Leg Boys St; Boy Scts; Chess Clb; Band; Concert Band; Jazz Band; Mrchg Band; Crs Cntry; High Hon Roll; NHS; Cmmnctns.

LEUNG, JAMES; Hasbrouck Heights HS; Hasbrouck Hts, NJ; (3); Am Leg Boys St; VP Key Clb; L Letterman Clb; Spanish Clb; Stage Crew; Yrbk Stf; Var Bowling; Var Crs Cntry; Var Trk; Voice Dem Awd.

LEUNG, JOSEPH; Don Bosco Prep HS; Mahwah, NJ; (2); 6/214; Dance Clb; Rep Soph Cls; JV Crs Cntry; Trk; High Hon Roll; 1st Pl Physcl Sci & 4th Annl Fr Anthony Midura Sci Fair & Mst Outstndng Proj 86; Arch.

LEUNG, KENNETH; Madison Central HS; Old Bridge, NJ; (3); French Clb; Hon Roll; Med Sci Inst 86; NYU; Phys Thrpy.

LEUZZI, MARILYN; Paramus Catholic Girls HS; Little Ferry, NJ; (3); Camera Clb; Dance Clb; Library Aide; Teachers Aide; F Dickenson; Dntstry.

LEV, ELI; Wayne Hills HS; Wayne, NJ; (4); 4/285; Math Clb; Nwsp Rptr; Yrbk Stf; High Hon Roll; Hon Roll; NHS; Ntl Merit Ltr; NJ Dstngshd Schlr 87; Won Essy Cntst-WPC 86; NJ Inst Of Tech; Engnrng.

LEV, VICTORIA; Columbia HS; Maplewood, NJ; (3); French Clb; Key Clb; Math Clb; Spanish Clb; Yrbk Stf; Stat Bsktbl; Var L Fld Hcky; Mgr(s); Hon Roll; Jr NHS; Columbia U; Invstmnt.

LEVENTHAL, MICHAEL; J P Stevens HS; Edison, NJ; (3); 9/450; Math Tm; Science Clb; Trs Frsh Cls; Trs Soph Cls; Trs Jr Cls; Trs Stu Cncl; Tennis; High Hon Roll; NHS; Ntl Merit Ltr; Fnc.

LEVERE, LISA; Mc Corristin Catholic HS; Trenton, NJ; (3); Church Yth Grp; Debate Tm; JA; Red Cross Aide; Church Choir; Stage Crew; Nwsp Rptr; Nwsp Stf; Hon Roll; Mayors Achvt Awd Art 85; All Amer Schlr Awd 85-86; Cert Hnr Art 85; Georgetown U; Engl.

LEVERINGTON, TOMLYN; Dover HS; Dover, NJ; (4); 6/183; Office Aide; Spanish Clb; Yrbk Stf; Trs Stu Cncl; Var Bsktbl; Var Capt Socr; Var Capt Sftbl; High Hon Roll; NHS; NJ Schlr Athlt Awd 87; HS Coachs Awd 87; Elon Col NC; Phy Ed.

LEVI, DANIEL S; Marlboro HS; Colts Neck, NJ; (3); 9/615; Math Tm; Capt Tennis; Var Trk; JV Wrstlng; Gov Hon Prg Awd; JETS Awd; Ntl Merit SF; St Schlr; Cngrssnl Page US Hse Reps 86; Capt Chem Leag 87; Cornell Scty Engrs Excell Awd 87; Chem.

LEVI, JEANINE; Morris Catholic HS; Parsippany, NJ; (4); Cmnty Wkr; VP French Clb; Hosp Aide; Red Cross Aide; Teachers Aide; Chorus; JV Var Powder Puff Ftbl; Sftbl; Fairleigh Dickinson U; Comm Art.

LEVIN, ROBERT; Cinnaminser HS; Cinnaminson, NJ; (3); English Clb; Speech Tm; SADD; Temple Yth Grp; Nwsp Stf; Yrbk Stf; Bsktbl; Tennis; Hon Roll; Finance.

LEVINE, AMY; South Hunterdam Regional HS; Stockton, NJ; (4); Drama Clb; Exploring; Key Clb; SADD; Thesps; School Play; Variety Show; Nwsp Rptr; Rep Soph Cls; Rep Jr Cls; Kalmia Clb Excllnc Engl Awd 87; Dickinson Coll; Poltcl Sci.

LEVINE, DAN; Mainland Regional HS; Linwood, NJ; (3); 3/263; Computer Clb; Spanish Clb; Band; Concert Band; Jazz Band; Mrchg Band; Nwsp Stf; Yrbk Rptr; Yrbk Stf; Var L Bsktbl; 1st Prize Comp In Ed 87; Rose Hulman; Comp.

LEVINE, HEATHER; Lakewood HS; Lakewood, NJ; (3); 22/330; Am Leg Aux Girls St; English Clb; Latin Clb; Chorus; Lit Mag; Tennis; High Hon Roll; Hon Roll; Jr NHS; Spanish NHS; Law.

LEVINE, STEPHEN; Franklin HS; Somerset, NJ; (3); Boy Scts; Church Yth Grp; Ski Clb; Varsity Clb; Band; Concert Band; Jazz Band; Mrchg Band; Orch; Symp Band; Fist Aie Squad 87; All ST Band 86; I Floor Hockey 86-87; 7ed.

LEVINE, STEPHEN; West Essex Regional HS; No Caldwell, NJ; (3); Varsity Clb; Jazz Band; Var Socr; Im Swmmng; Var Wrstlng; Hon Roll; Poli Sci.

LEVINE, TODD; Manalapan HS; Englishtown, NJ; (3); Ski Clb; VP Frsh Cls; Rep Soph Cls; Stu Cncl; Var Ftbl; Var Trk; Notre Dame; Psychology.

LEVISS, JONATHAN A; Mountain Lakes HS; Mountain Lakes, NJ; (4); 4/98; Model UN; Quiz Bowl; Pres Temple Yth Grp; Varsity Clb; Concert Band; Nwsp Bus Mgr; Var Socr; Var Trk; High Hon Roll; Ntl Merit SF.

LEVIT, GABRIELA; Cedar Ridge HS; South Amboy, NJ; (4); 46/372; FBLA; Math Tm; Pep Clb; SADD; Temple Yth Grp; Stu Cncl; Hon Roll; Spanish NHS; Smi-Fnlst-Ntl Hspnc Schlr Awds Pgm 85; Engrng.

LEVITOV, LORI; Bayonne HS; Bayonne, NJ; (3); 20/400; Mgr Drama Clb; Office Aide; VP Temple Yth Grp; School Musical; Nwsp Stf; Rep Frsh Cls; Rep Soph Cls; Rep Jr Cls; Jr NHS.

LEVITT, LAURIE; Montville HS; Montville, NJ; (3); 51/280; VP Cmnty Wkr; FBLA; Ski Clb; Yrbk Ed-Chief; Yrbk Stf; Rep Frsh Cls; Rep Soph Cls; Off Stu Cncl; High Hon Roll; NHS; Bus.

LEVONAITIS, BARBARA; Bridgewater-Raritan HS West; Bridgewater, NJ; (3); Var Capt Bsktbl; Var Fld Hcky; Var Swmmng; Var Tennis; Hon Roll; Bsktbll All ST Tm, Bsktbl Plyr Yr Cnty, Cnty Scrng Title, All Cnty Tm, All Mid-ST Stfl, Bsktbl.

LEVY, BETH M; Mount Olive HS; Flanders, NJ; (4); 95/298; AFS; Cmnty Wkr; Drama Clb; Hosp Aide; SADD; Temple Yth Grp; Varsity Clb; Yrbk Bus Mgr; Yrbk Stf; Rep Jr Cls; Mt Olive Rotry Schlrshp 87; Morris Cnty Fld Hcky Chmpns 86; A C Mabee St Frm Ins Agncy Schlrshp 87; NYS U Stony Brook; Phy Thrpy.

LEVY, DANIEL; Fairlawn HS; Fair Lawn, NJ; (3); 1/341; Computer Clb; Math Tm; Science Clb; Yrbk Phtg; Yrbk Stf; Soph Cls; Var Capt Tennis; NHS; Ntl Merit Ltr; St Schlr; NHS; Vrsty Cpt Tnns; Rutgers Schlr; Lwyr.

LEVY, JENNIFER; Atlantic City HS; Margate, NJ; (3); Camera Clb; Latin Clb; Model UN; Office Aide; Ski Clb; Temple Yth Grp; School Play; Off Jr Cls; Var Cheerleading; Hon Roll; NY U; Pre-Law.

LEVY, MARK; Manalapan HS; Manalapan, NJ; (4); 50/417; NHS; Congrssnl Schlr Awd 86; JR Stsmn Amer 86-87; Rutgers Coll; Bus Admin.

LEW, HOWARD; Manalapan HS; Manalapan, NJ; (3); 153/433.

LEW, JOANNE; Eastern HS; W Berlin, NJ; (3); French Clb; Latin Clb; Chorus; Orch; School Musical; Stage Crew; Yrbk Stf; L Pom Pon; Hon Roll; NHS; Biomed.

LEW, RICHARD; Ocean Township HS; Ocean, NJ; (3); 13/344; Debate Tm; Library Aide; Math Tm; NFL; Thesps; Orch; School Musical; School Play; High Hon Roll; Hon Roll; 3rd Pl-NJ ST Debate Trnmnt 87; Sprtn Schlr Awd 85-87; Tpzo-NJ ST Sci Day-Chmstry-16th Pl 87; Elec Engnrng.

LEWANDOWSKI, KAREN; Florence Twp Mem HS; Roebling, NJ; (4); 31/83; Drama Clb; Latin Clb; Office Aide; Band; Mrchg Band; School Musical; School Play; Yrbk Ed-Chief; Yrbk Stf; Mgr(s); Burlington Co Coll.

LEWANDOWSKI, MELISSA; Lenape Valley Regional HS; Andover, NJ; (3); 9/240; Latin Clb; Nwsp Rptr; Sec Jr Cls; Rep Stu Cncl; Var Crs Cntry; JV Trk; High Hon Roll; Hon Roll; Ntl Achvt Acad Awd-Spnsh 86; Attrny.

LEWANDOWSKI, MICHAEL T; Marist HS; Bayonne, NJ; (4); 11/106; Key Clb; Spanish Clb; Yrbk Rptr; Yrbk Sprt Ed; Capt Var Bsbl; Wt Lftg; Hon Roll; Spanish NHS; MVP Vrsty Bsbl; Seton Hall U; Lawyer.

LEWIS, ALICIA; Weequahic HS; Newark, NJ; (3); #10 In Class; Drama Clb; Exploring; Spanish Clb; Teachers Aide; Drill Tm; Mrchg Band; Stage Crew; Variety Show; Stu Cncl; Jr NHS; Fashion Show Trphy 87; Air Force; Comp Sys Anlyst.

LEWIS, ALLISON K; Pequannock Township HS; Pompton Plains, NJ; (2); Science Clb; Concert Band; Mrchg Band; School Play; Nwsp Rptr; Bsktbl; Var Socr; Hon Roll; Spanish NHS; Cmnty Wkr; Phys Ther.

LEWIS, ANDREA; Clifford J Scott HS; E Orange, NJ; (4); Pres FBLA; Hosp Aide; Math Clb; Quiz Bowl; Nwsp Rptr; Lit Mag; Hon Roll; NHS; Douglass Coll; Bio.

LEWIS, DOUGLAS; Cherokee HS; Marlton, NJ; (4); 9/398; Boy Scts; Church Yth Grp; Off Jr Cls; Off Sr Cls; JV Crs Cntry; Var Trk; God Cntry Awd; NHS; St Schlr; Presdntl Acadc Ftnss Awd 86-87; USAF Acad.

LEWIS, JACQUELINE; Holy Cross HS; Medford, NJ; (4); 2/356; Model UN; Ski Clb; Pres Spanish Clb; Nwsp Stf; High Hon Roll; VP NHS; Ntl Merit Ltr; Sal; St Schlr; Govs Schl In Sci 86; USMA Invitnl Acadmc Wrkshp 86; K Of C Chrctr & Ldrshp Awd 87; Boston Coll; Pre-Law.

LEWIS, JEFF; Toms River HS South; Pine Beach, NJ; (3); 1/408; Math Tm; Var Crs Cntry; Var Socr; Capt Var Trk; High Hon Roll; NHS; Ntl Merit SF; MVP-WNTR Trck & Sprng Trck Awds 86-87.

LEWIS, LISA; Vineland SR HS; Vineland, NJ; (4); 38/753; Pres Church Yth Grp; Drama Clb; Off Key Clb; VP Latin Clb; Acpl Chr; Stu Cncl; Var L Fld Hcky; Hon Roll; NHS; Air Force; Poli Sci.

LEWIS, MARYELLEN; Camden Catholic HS; Hennsuaken, NJ; (3); 162/300; Spanish Clb; Chorus; Bsktbl; Hon Roll; Howard U; Med.

LEWIS, MONICA; Red Bank Catholic HS; Brielle, NJ; (3); Dance Clb; German Clb; Hosp Aide; PAVAS; Ski Clb; SADD; Im Vllybl; Phil Coll Text & Sci; Mrktg.

LEWIS, MONIQUE; Lacordaire Acad; Newark, NJ; (4); 10/42; Art Clb; Mrchg Band; School Musical; School Play; Yrbk Sprt Ed; Var Capt Bsktbl; Im Sftbl; Im Vllybl; Hon Roll; NHS; Schlr Athlete 87; Bst Math Grd Schl 87; Bsktbll All Star Tm Div B 87; Rutgers U; Accntng.

LEWIS, PAMELA B; Monsignor Donovan HS; Toms River, NJ; (3); 51/213; Church Yth Grp; Drama Clb; Hosp Aide; Service Clb; Ski Clb; SADD; Crs Cntry; Trk; Hon Roll; Intl Piano Recording Comptn 84; Nrsng.

LEWIS, SAUNDRA; Essex Catholic Girls HS; Newark, NJ; (3); Art Clb; NAACP; Science Clb; Rutgers; Psych.

LEWIS, TOWANNA; Essex Catholic Girls HS; Newark, NJ; (3); Computer Clb; Math Clb; Science Clb; Drill Tm; Variety Show; Yrbk Stf; Pres Stu Cncl; Trk; Voice Dem Awd; Spelman U; Law.

LEWIS, TYWANNA; University HS; Newark, NJ; (3); Computer Clb; FNA; Hosp Aide; JA; NAACP; Chorus; Drill Tm; Lit Mag; Rep Civic Clb; Pres Jr Cls; Mst Outstndng Physcs Lab Trophy; Math.

LEWIS, VICKI; Riverside HS; Riverside, NJ; (3); 35/111; Trs DECA; Varsity Clb; Mgr Stu Cncl; Var L Bsktbl; Var L Trk; Most Imprvd Plyr Vrsty Bsktbl 86-87; Top 10 Pct DECA Comptn 87; Burlington County Coll.

LEWIS, YUENGE; St James HS; Salem, NJ; (2); 2/100; Church Yth Grp; Girl Scts; Pep Clb; Spanish Clb; SADD; Yrbk Stf; High Hon Roll; VFW Awd; Sci, English & Math Awds; Comp Engr.

LEWIS, YVETTE; Teaneck HS; Teaneck, NJ; (4); 35/420; Church Yth Grp; Drama Clb; NAACP; Chorus; Lit Mag; Gov Hon Prg Awd; High Hon Roll; Jr NHS; NHS; Prfct Atten Awd; Natl Mrt Awd Soc Stds 87; Bergen Cnty Urbn Lg Awd 87; Fnlst Miss Ntl Tngr Pgnt 86; Rutgers U; Jrnlsm.

LEY, GREGORY S; Gateway Regional HS; Woodbury Hts, NJ; (4); German Clb; Key Clb; Letterman Clb; Library Aide; Office Aide; VP Spanish Clb; SADD; VP Stu Cncl; L Bsbl; L Ftbl; Gator Of Mnth-Sept 86; Mrn Corps Leag-Ntl Yth Phys Ftns Pgm-Cert Of Athltc Accmplshmnt 87; Glassboro ST Coll-NJ; Law.

LEYFMAN, YELENA; Bruriah HS; Elizabeth, NJ; (3); Computer Clb; Yrbk Stf; Trs Soph Cls; Trs Jr Cls; Sci Fair Awd 83-87; Fairleigh Dickinson U; Thrpy.

LEYVA, EDWARD; Paramus Catholic HS; Teaneck, NJ; (3); Church Yth Grp; Teachers Aide; Im Bowling; Im Fld Hcky; JV Wrstlng.

LI, CHRISTINE; Montville HS; Montville, NJ; (2); FBLA; Pres Intnl Clb; Sec Key Clb; NFL; Chorus; Color Guard; Nwsp Stf; Lit Mag; Hon Roll; Creative Wrtng Awd For Merit, N NJ Chinese Assn Teen Clb Sec & Jr Statesmen Of Amer VP 87; Comms.

LI, LINDA; Parsippany HS; Lk Hiawatha, NJ; (3); Sec French Clb; Yrbk Stf; Lit Mag; Gov Hon Prg Awd; High Hon Roll; Hon Roll; NHS; VP Pres Ntl Arts Hnrs Soc 86-88; Artstc Dscvry Art Exhbtn 86-87; Rutgers Schlr 86; Wu Li Mstr.

LI, YIM; Burlington Township HS; Burlington Townsh, NJ; (4); 6/119; Color Guard; Gym; Socr; Tennis; Cit Awd; Hon Roll; NHS; Hghst Avg Phys Educ; Pres Acad Ftnss Awd; Rutgers; Intl Bus.

LI CALSI, LINDA; Immaculate Conception HS; Ridgefield Pk, NJ; (3); VP SADD; Stage Crew; Nwsp Rptr; Nwsp Sprt Ed; JV Capt Bsktbl; Mgr(s); Hon Roll; Spanish NHS; Drama Clb; Q&S; Accomendation In Basic Skills & Spnsh II 84-85 & 85-86; Cert Of Appreciation 86-87; Rutgers U; Psych.

LIAKOPOULOS, C VALERIE; Secaucus HS; Secaucus, NJ; (3); 61/166; Church Yth Grp; Key Clb; Spanish Clb; Mrchg Band; Nwsp Rptr; Lit Mag; Trs Soph Cls; Rep Jr Cls; Off Sr Cls; Hon Roll; Stockton ST Coll; Bus Mgmt.

LIAO, LINDA; Cherry Hill H S East; Cherry Hill, NJ; (3); Latin Clb; Chorus; Yrbk Stf; JV Fld Hcky; JV Sftbl; Var Trk; High Hon Roll; Hon Roll; DE Vly Tri-St Regnl Schlstc Art Awds 87.

LIAO, THERESA; West Windsor-Plainsboro HS; Princeton Junct, NJ; (3); Hosp Aide; Ed Nwsp Stf; Trs Jr Cls; Trs Sr Cls; JV Capt Bsktbl; JV Capt Fld Hcky; JV Var Sftbl; Gov Hon Prg Awd; NHS; AFS; Trentonian All Area Field Hcky Hnrb Mntn 86; All Area Sftbl 2nd Tm 87; All Star Fld Hcky Hnrb Mntn 86.

LIBROJO, DONATA; Academic HS; Jersey City, NJ; (4); 18/78; Lit Mag; Var Capt Bowling; Capt Var Vllybl; Hon Roll; NHS; Art Clb; Nwsp Stf; Prfct Atten Awd; 1st Sci Awd 84; Military Awd 84; Hudson Cinema Pntng Cntst 86; Rutgers Coll; Accntng.

LICCIARDIELLO, DONA; Mount Olive HS; Budd Lake, NJ; (4); 60/297; AFS; Drama Clb; FBLA; Ski Clb; Concert Band; Mrchg Band; Yrbk Stf; Hon Roll; Grad Most Prsnlty & Common Sense 87; Slippery Rock U; Bus.

LICHTENBERGER, WALTER; Secaucus HS; Secaucus, NJ; (2); Pres Computer Clb; VP Mu Alpha Theta; Varsity Clb; Nwsp Stf; Var Crs Cntry; Var Trk; High Hon Roll; Jr NHS; Mu Alpha Theta Awd; Voice Dem Awd.

LICHTER, PAUL; Middletown High School South; Middletown, NJ; (4); 7/452; Exploring; Hosp Aide; Math Tm; Science Clb; Ski Clb; Lit Mag; Var L Golf; JV Socr; High Hon Roll; Elctrcl Engrng.

LIDOR, ANNE; Union HS; Union, NJ; (3); Am Leg Aux Girls St; Pres Drama Clb; Trs Spanish Clb; Pres Temple Yth Grp; Band; Var Crs Cntry; Var Trk; Hon Roll; NHS; Ntl Merit Ltr.

LIEBMANN, MARJORIE BETH; Fair Lawn HS; Fair Lawn, NJ; (3); 36/341; Math Tm; Trs Spanish Clb; Temple Yth Grp; Chorus; Off Frsh Cls; Off Soph Cls; Off Jr Cls; High Hon Roll; Hon Roll; NHS; Chem Awd 86-87; Rutgers U; Chldhd Educ.

LIEDL, JEFFREY M; Hillsborough HS; Somerville, NJ; (4); 20/285; Var Bsktbl; Var Crs Cntry; Hon Roll; NHS; Prfct Atten Awd; Schlrshp Trenton ST Coll Almni Assoc 87; NJ Garden St Dstngshd Schlr 87; Trenton ST Coll; Acctng.

LIEDTKA, KARL; Notre Dame HS; Trenton, NJ; (4); Cmnty Wkr; Letterman Clb; Ftbl; All Colnl Vly Conf Ftbl 87; All Mercer Cnty Ftbl 87; Lebanon Vly Coll; Psych.

LIER, CHRISTINA; Eastern Christian HS; Allendale, NJ; (4); 8/81; Church Yth Grp; Acpl Chr; Chorus; Concert Band; Var Tennis; Hon Roll; NHS; Drama Clb; Orch; Bsktbl; Sportsmanship Awd 84-85; Calvin Coll; Elementary Educ.

LIFSHEY, JOANNA; Cherry Hill High School West; Cherry Hill, NJ; (3); PAVAS; Spanish Clb; Speech Tm; SADD; Temple Yth Grp; School Musical; Nwsp Rptr; Nwsp Sprt Ed; Nwsp Stf; Lit Mag; News Edtr Schl Nwspr 87-88.

LIGERALDE, DAVIDSON; Glen Ridge HS; Glen Ridge, NJ; (4); 2/122; Trs AFS; Pres Spanish Clb; Trs Sr Cls; Elks Awd; High Hon Roll; Ntl Merit Ltr; Rotary Awd; Sal; Church Yth Grp; JA; Cngrssnl Yth Schlr 87; Grdn ST Dstngshd Schlr 87; Affrmtv Actn Cmmtt Stu Rep 85-87; Muhlenberg; Comp Sci.

LIGGON JR, ROGER W; Plainfield HS; Plainfield, NJ; (3); 32/351; Boys Clb Am; Church Yth Grp; 4-H; Band; Var L Bsbl; Var L Crs Cntry; High Hon Roll; Hon Roll; NHS; Minorities In Engr 84-87; Rutgers U.

LIGHT, LIZ; Burlington Twp HS; Burlington, NJ; (3); Cmnty Wkr; Socr.

LIGON, GREG; Ridge HS; Basking Ridge, NJ; (3); 15/193; Church Yth Grp; Ski Clb; JV Var Tennis; High Hon Roll; Hon Roll; NHS; Spanish NHS; Gftd & Tlntd Pgm Schl 86; Schl Rep Bus Smnr The Foundtn For Free Entrprs 87; Baylor U; Bus Admin.

LIGORNER, KARYN LESLI; Newark Acad; Springfield, NJ; (4); AFS; Yrbk Ed-Chief; Yrbk Phtg; Lit Mag; Var Capt Vllybl; St Schlr; Cum Laude Soc 87; Headmasters Mdl 87; Smith Coll Awd 86; Mc Gill U; Intl Rel.

LILLIE, SANDRA; North Brunswick Twp HS; North Brunswick, NJ; (4); 47/300; Spanish Clb; Nwsp Stf; Var Sftbl; Hon Roll; NHS; Mst Imprvd Stu Schlrshp 87; Pres Acad Ftns & Nbths SR Sprts Awds 87; Rutgers Cook Coll.

LIM, ANNE; John P Stevens HS; Edison, NJ; (3); 67/450; Cmnty Wkr; Science Clb; Hon Roll.

LIM, ELIZABETH; West Essex HS; No Caldwell, NJ; (3); Hosp Aide; Mrchg Band; VP Orch; Stage Crew; Hon Roll; NHS; Natl Ldrshp & Svc Awd 87.

LIM, EUGENE; Hillsborough HS; Neshanic, NJ; (4); 20/293; Latin Clb; Math Tm; Spanish Clb; Rep Frsh Cls; Var L Ftbl; Var L Trk; Im Wt Lftg; Hon Roll; NHS; Spanish NHS; Coll Engrng Rutgers U; Elec Eng.

LIM, JOANNE; Bridgewater-Raritan East HS; Bridgewater, NJ; (4); Intnl Clb; Math Tm; Capt Quiz Bowl; Spanish Clb; Nwsp Rptr; Elks Awd; High Hon Roll; VP NHS; Ntl Merit Ltr; St Schlr; Pres Acad Ftns Awd 87; Fratrnl Order Eagles Svc, Acad Awd 87; Foreign Lang Educators NJ Awd 87; Harvard U; Asian Studies.

LIM, VICTORIA; Delran HS; Delran, NJ; (4); Am Leg Aux Girls St; Math Tm; Q&S; Science Clb; Chorus; School Musical; Nwsp Ed-Chief; Lit Mag; Stu Cncl; Var Lcrss; NBC/Maceys Dept Store Natl Essy Cont Wnnr 86; KYW Radio 1060 Stu Reprtr Pgm 87; Mst Val Staff Awd 87; Temple U; TV Brdcstr.

LIMA JR, PETER D; Westfield SR HS; Westfield, NJ; (3); 87/470; Church Yth Grp; FCA; Spanish Clb; Chorus; School Play; Var L Bsbl; Var Ftbl; Wt Lftg; Hon Roll; MVP Awd Bsbl 85; MVP Awd JV Bsbl 86; Penn ST; Metrlgy.

LIMBARDO, MICHELLE; Paramus Catholic HS; Fort Lee, NJ; (3); Camera Clb; Church Yth Grp; Cmnty Wkr; Dance Clb; Drama Clb; Math Clb; Math Tm; Cvl Engr.

LIMJUCO, GARY; Union Catholic Regional HS; Rahway, NJ; (3); Debate Tm; Math Tm; Science Clb; Service Clb; VP Spanish Clb; Ed Nwsp Stf; High Hon Roll; NHS; Spanish NHS; Engrng.

LIMJUCO, ROBERT; Union Catholic Regional HS; Rahway, NJ; (1); 5/293; Debate Tm; Science Clb; Nwsp Rptr; High Hon Roll; NHS; Spanish NHS; Engrng.

LIMONE, HEATHER; Mc Corristin Catholic HS; Trenton, NJ; (3); 52/260; GAA; Chorus; School Musical; Sec Jr Cls; Sec Sr Cls; Var Capt Cheerleading; Stat Socr; Hon Roll; Jr NHS; NHS; Amer Achvt Awd Chrldg 86; Amer Achvt Awd Acdmc 85.

LIMONE, JERRILYN; Union Catholic Regional HS; Cranford, NJ; (3); 98/304; PAVAS; SADD; Thesps; Stage Crew; High Hon Roll; Hon Roll; Tech Crw Prfrmng Arts 86-87; Steno 1 Stght A 87; Typng 33 Wrds Pr Min 87; Exec Secr.

LIMOSNERO, MARIA; Southern Regional HS; Manahawkin, NJ; (3); 22/350; Spanish Clb; VP Frsh Cls; Rep Soph Cls; Rep Jr Cls; Rep Sr Cls; Rep Stu Cncl; Stat Bsktbl; Mgr(s); Capt L Socr; High Hon Roll.

LIMOUZE, ROBERT; Westwood HS; Westwood, NJ; (2); Boy Scts; Exploring; JV Var Ftbl; Hon Roll; Opt Clb Awd; Mech Engrng.

LIN, DAVID; Parsippany Hills HS; Morris Plns, NJ; (3); Exploring; FBLA; Key Clb; Math Tm; VP Sec Science Clb; Tennis; High Hon Roll; Hon Roll; NHS; Certfd Lifegrd 87.

LIN, DAVID Y; Paramus HS; Paramus, NJ; (4); 3/330; Am Leg Boys St; Computer Clb; Ski Clb; Ed Yrbk Stf; Im JV Socr; High Hon Roll; NHS; German Clb; Math Clb; Math Tm; Garden ST Dstngshd Schlr; Ger Hnr Soc; Bergen Cnty Soc Profssnl Engrs; Cornell U; Elctrcl Engrng.

LIN, DOROTHY; Parsippany Hills HS; Morris Plains, NJ; (4); 20/309; Exploring; Hosp Aide; Key Clb; Science Clb; Variety Show; Hon Roll; NHS; Music Eductrs Assn NJ Annl Audtn Awd 83-87; Awd Exclln Lang Grmn 87; Gldn Poet Awd 85-86; Rutgers; Engrng.

LIN, JULIE; Howell HS; Howell, NJ; (4); Math Tm; Bowling; Monmouth Coll; Acctg.

LIN, MARGARET; Parsippany HS; Parsippany, NJ; (3); FBLA; Math Clb; Math Tm; Pep Clb; Service Clb; Spanish Clb; Trk; Dentistry.

LIN, TED; Hoboken HS; Hoboken, NJ; (3); 3/350; Chess Clb; Church Yth Grp; French Clb; Service Clb; Church Choir; Capt Tennis; Gov Hon Prg Awd; High Hon Roll; Hon Roll; NHS; Elect Engrng.

LIN, TINA; Northern Valley Regional HS; Norwood, NJ; (4); 14/270; AFS; Art Clb; Cmnty Wkr; Intnl Clb; Nwsp Stf; Rep Stu Cncl; Trk; High Hon Roll; NHS; Bus.

LINAHAN, MICHAEL J; Ewing HS; Trenton, NJ; (3); Am Leg Boys St; Cmnty Wkr; Key Clb; Rep Jr Cls; Var Capt Ftbl; Var Trk; Ntl Merit Ltr; Bus.

LINARDAKIS, PATRICIA; Brick Memorial HS; Brick, NJ; (4); 34/365; Pres Church Yth Grp; Dance Clb; Rep Frsh Cls; Rep Soph Cls; VP Jr Cls; Rep Sr Cls; Pres Stu Cncl; Coach Actv; JV Var Socr; High Hon Roll; Glassboro ST Coll; Cmmnctns.

LIND, JEANNE S; Westfield SR HS; Westfield, NJ; (4); Key Clb; Spanish Clb; Teachers Aide; Band; High Hon Roll; Hon Roll; Psych Awd 87; Montclair ST Coll.

LIND, KRISTEN; Maple Shade HS; Maple Shade, NJ; (4); 9/170; French Clb; Trs Key Clb; Stat Bsbl; Capt Var Cheerleading; High Hon Roll; NHS; Acadc All Am 85-87; U UT.

LINDABERRY, JEFFREY S; Faith Christian HS; Willingboro, NJ; (1); 1/11; Church Yth Grp; Latin Clb; Math Clb; Chorus; Trs Frsh Cls; Var Bsbl; Var Bsktbl; High Hon Roll; NEDT Awd; Maxima Cum Laude Nationn Latin Lg Tst 86-87; Mst Sprtsmlk Trphy Vrsty Bsktbl 86-87; Bob Jones U; Comp.

LINDARDAKIS, ERICA; Manasquan HS; Brielle, NJ; (2); FBLA; Spanish Clb; Mrchg Band; Hon Roll.

LINDEMAN, JENNIFER; Madison HS; Madison, NJ; (3); 69/200; Aud/Vis; French Clb; Yrbk Stf; JV Vllybl; French Hon Soc; High Hon Roll; Hon Roll; Bus.

LINDEN, STACEY ANN; Teaneck HS; Teaneck, NJ; (4); 6/420; Drama Clb; VP SADD; Pres Temple Yth Grp; Band; Nwsp Sprt Ed; Sec NHS; Thspn Yr 87; Spnsh Awd 87; NJ Cncl Scl Stds Outstndng Stu Awd 87; Tufts U.

LINDER, DYAN; South Plainfield HS; South Plainfield, NJ; (2); Hosp Aide; Ski Clb; Spanish Clb; SADD; Flag Corp; Variety Show; Yrbk Stf; Sec Soph Cls; Stu Cncl; Hon Roll; 100 Hr Awd Cndy Strpng 86; Acdmc Awd Hnr Rll 87; Rutgers; Psych.

LINDER, JUZETTA; Paterson Catholic Regional HS; Paterson, NJ; (3); Capt Dance Clb; Drama Clb; Church Choir; Yrbk Stf; Rep Frsh Cls; Rep Soph Cls; Rep Jr Cls; Var Cheerleading; Prfct Atten Awd; Pep Clb; Vietnam Vet Essay Cont 2nd Pl 87; Seton Hall U; Media Comms.

LINDLAR, COLLEEN; St John Vianney HS; Old Bridge, NJ; (3); 28/300; Church Yth Grp; SADD; Stage Crew; Yrbk Stf; High Hon Roll; Hon Roll; NHS.

LINDNER, CRISTIN; Mount St Dominic Acad; Roseland, NJ; (3); Dance Clb; School Musical; School Play; Yrbk Stf; Lit Mag; Pres Stu Cncl; Mgr(s); Socr; Trk; Hon Roll; Engl.

LINDNER, STEVEN J; Lenape Valley Regional HS; Netcong, NJ; (4); Boy Scts; Drama Clb; French Clb; Ski Clb; Band; Madrigals; School Musical; School Play; French Hon Soc; Mc Guffy Scholar 87; OH U; Psych.

LINDOR, NIRVA MARIE; Academic HS; Jersey City, NJ; (3); Am Leg Aux Girls St; Church Yth Grp; French Clb; Scholastic Bowl; Chorus; Church Choir; Yrbk Stf; Trophy Comp Lab STEP Pgm 87; Cert Humanities STEP Pgm 87; Cert Alg II STEP Pgm 86; Optometry.

LINDSEY, TONYA; Lakewood HS; Lakewood, NJ; (3); 12/331; Am Leg Aux Girls St; Hosp Aide; Mrchg Band; Yrbk Rptr; JV Bowling; JV Trk; NHS; Accptnc Discovery Smmr Pgm Mnrty Stu Excl 86; HI-STEP AT&T, Congrssnl Schlr Natl Yng Ldrs Conf 87; Arch.

LINFANTE, LENNY; Belleville HS; Belleville, NJ; (3); Varsity Clb; Hon Roll; Var Letters Rowing 86-87; Rutgers U.

LING, JONATHAN; Bridgewater East HS; Bridgewater, NJ; (3); Computer Clb; German Clb; Math Tm; Radio Clb; Im Bowling; Hon Roll; NJIT Comp Semi-Fnlst 86; Natl Duracell Cmptn Semi-Fnlst 87.

LINGER, KEN; Bridgewater-Raritan High Schl East; Bridgewater, NJ; (3); Computer Clb; German Clb; Math Tm; Band; Concert Band; Jazz Band; Mrchg Band; Orch; Im Bowling; Hon Roll; Aerospc.

LINK, CHRISTINA; Clifton HS; Clifton, NJ; (3); Ed Key Clb; Sec Math Clb; Yrbk Stf; Off Frsh Cls; Sec Soph Cls; Sec Jr Cls; Var Swmmng; Var Tennis; Timer; Cit Awd; Rensellar Polytech Inst.

LINK, FAITH; Secaucus HS; Secaucus, NJ; (3); 66/166; Church Yth Grp; Key Clb; Band; Concert Band; Stage Crew; Hon Roll; V Awd For Band 87.

LINK, MICHELE; St Peters HS; Highland Park, NJ; (4); 10/89; Math Clb; Yrbk Stf; Ed Lit Mag; Cheerleading; Trk; Hon Roll; NHS; Syracuse U; Elem Ed.

LINNEHAN, MARY JANE; Marlboro HS; Morganville, NJ; (4); 142/528; Cmnty Wkr; Drama Clb; Pres Exploring; Hosp Aide; Pres Service Clb; Stage Crew; Ed Lit Mag; Hon Roll; Congrssnl Awd 86; Grdn ST Schlrshp 87; Monclair ST Coll; Pblc Hlth.

LIOU, JAMES; Absegami HS; Egg Harbor City, NJ; (3); 3/290; Am Leg Boys St; Math Clb; Math Tm; Quiz Bowl; Var Tennis; High Hon Roll; VP NHS; Ntl Merit Ltr; Hosp Aide; Acdmc Lttr Awd 86; 1st Pl Cnty Math Leags 87; Med.

LIPARI, ELIZABETH; Cinnaminson HS; Cinnaminson, NJ; (3); Am Leg Aux Girls St; Church Yth Grp; SADD; Concert Band; Drm Mjr(t); Yrbk Stf; Rep Stu Cncl; Var Bsktbl; Hon Roll; NHS; Clsc Tours Music Schlrshp 87; Ldrshp Awd Mrchng Band 87; JV Capt 85; Sci.

LIPARI, PATRICIA; St Mary HS; Rassaic, NJ; (4); 7/74; FBLA; Service Clb; Varsity Clb; Yrbk Stf; Sftbl; Hon Roll; NHS; Montclair ST.

LIPAT, CHRISTINE; West Essex SR Regional HS; No Caldwell, NJ; (3); Hosp Aide; Science Clb; Color Guard; Trs Orch; School Play; Stage Crew; NHS; Ntl Merit Ltr; Spanish NHS; Fncng 1 JV Ltr 1 Var Ltr; Rgn I SR HS Orch 87; All ST Orch 87; Outstndng Achvt NJSA 85-87; Bio Sci.

LIPINSKI, BEATA; Linden HS; Linden, NJ; (4); 11/345; Church Yth Grp; VP FBLA; Ski Clb; Sec Sr Cls; Capt Cheerleading; Gym; High Hon Roll; NHS; Yrbk Stf; Rep Frsh Cls; HOBY Ambssdr 85; A R Taranto Awd Bst All Arnd Stu 87; Rutgers U; Pre-Law.

LIPOFF, DEAN; Atlantic City HS; Atlantic City, NJ; (3); Model UN; Off Jr Cls; Tennis; Hon Roll; Bus Admin.

LIPPAI, STEPHEN P; Woodbridge HS; Fords, NJ; (4); 49/386; Church Yth Grp; Rep Jr Cls; JV Socr; High Hon Roll; Prfct Atten Awd; Gldn Key Awd Natl Assn Accntnts, & Michael J Barenti Mem Schlrshp 87; Palm Bch Atlantic Coll; Accntng.

LIPPERT, BRIDGET; Burlington City HS; Beverly, NJ; (3); VP Drama Clb; Sec Pres Girl Scts; Co-Capt Color Guard; Drill Tm; School Musical; Nwsp Rptr; Ed Lit Mag; Hon Roll; Prncpls Nmbr 1 Clb 85-86; Extndd Lrnng Pgm 84-87; Cognetcs 86-87; Theatre Arts.

LIPPINCOTT, DAVID; Immaculata HS; Piscataway, NJ; (3); Boy Scts; Math Tm; Office Aide; Ski Clb; Yrbk Phtg; Yrbk Stf; Awd Comp Sci 87; Awd Excllnc Math 86.

LIPPINCOTT, JENNIFER; Riverside HS; Delanco, NJ; (3); 25/110; Art Clb; Church Yth Grp; Computer Clb; Chorus; Off Stu Cncl; Var Bsktbl; Stat Crs Cntry; JV Sftbl; Unsng Heros Awd-Bsktbl 86 & 87; Cmmrcl Artst.

LIPPOLIS, JENNIFER; J P Stevens HS; Edison, NJ; (3); Hosp Aide; Powder Puff Ftbl; Comm.

LISA, CATHERINE; St James HS; Swedesboro, NJ; (4); Sec Hosp Aide; Yrbk Stf; JV Bsktbl; JV Sftbl; Var Tennis; Pres Cit Awd; NHS; Prfct Atten Awd; Merid Awd-Relgious Stdy, Geom Effrt 85 & 86; Goldey Beacom Coll; Secy.

LISA, JOSEPH; Dover HS; Dover, NJ; (3); 46/228; Band; Concert Band; Jazz Band; Mrchg Band; School Musical; Variety Show; Hon Roll; Music.

LISEHORA, KATHLEEN E; St Marys Hall-Doane Acad; Trenton, NJ; (3); #2 In Class; Am Leg Aux Girls St; Library Aide; Yrbk Stf; Rep Stu Cncl; Stat Bsbl; Capt Var Cheerleading; Var Mgr(s); Var Score Keeper; Cit Awd; High Hon Roll; Mck Trl Tm 86-87; JETS Tm Comptn 86-87; Acolyte Christ Epscpl Chch; Acctg.

LISH, STEPHANIE; Middle Twp HS; Cape May Crthse, NJ; (3); 5/220; Church Yth Grp; Hosp Aide; Ski Clb; Concert Band; Drm & Bgl; Capt Mrchg Band; Symp Band; Rep Stu Cncl; High Hon Roll; Jr NHS; Chem Engrng.

LISS, LOUISA; Edison HS; Edison, NJ; (3); 7/471; French Clb; Temple Yth Grp; Rep Frsh Cls; Rep Soph Cls; Rep Jr Cls; Rep Stu Cncl; Swmmng; Var Tennis; French Hon Soc; Hon Roll; Athlete Mth Cntrl Jrsys Outstndng Athlete Pgm 86; Dbl Mddlsx CO Chmpnshps Wnnr 200 & 500 Yd Frstyl86.

LIST, DARREN; Montclair HS; Montclair, NJ; (3); Am Leg Boys St; Spanish Clb; Var L Ice Hcky; Hon Roll; Hon Roll; Hcky 2nd Tm A Leag All Str 87; 3rd Tm All ST Stu Grdn ST Gms 87; Chmpnshp Tm W.

LIST, PETER; Madison HS; Madison, NJ; (3); 16/211; Art Clb; Drama Clb; Exploring; School Musical; School Play; Socr; Gov Hon Prg Awd; High Hon Roll; NHS; Ntl Merit Ltr; Rotry Intl Yth Exchng Stu Japan 86; Visual Fine Arts.

LISTER, DANIELLE; Manasquan HS; Manasquan, NJ; (3); 17/226; Spanish Clb; Thesps; Band; Drm Mjr(t); School Musical; Var Crs Cntry; Var Socr; Var Trk; Var Twrlr; Sec NHS; Soccer Hustle & Dedication Awd 85; Brd Of Educ Awd 86 & 87; Pharmacy.

LISZEWSKI, MARGE; Eastern HS; Voorhees, NJ; (4); Yrbk Stf; Hon Roll; NHS; Pres Schlr; Grad W/Hgh Hnrs; Rutgers U.

LISZEWSKI, SCOTT; Marist HS; Bayonne, NJ; (3); 18/120; Key Clb; Engr.

LITTEN, JORDAN; Cinnaminson HS; Riverton, NJ; (3); Am Leg Boys St; Math Tm; SADD; Rep Jr Cls; Pres Sr Cls; Var Bsbl; JV Bsktbl; Capt Socr; Bus Mgt.

LITTLE, KIM; Madison Avenue Baptist Acad; Mahwah, NJ; (1); 2/10; Church Yth Grp; Church Choir; Cheerleading; Hon Roll.

LITTLE, ROMONDA; Academic HS; Jersey City, NJ; (4); 1/78; Art Clb; Sec Church Yth Grp; Pres Church Choir; Lit Mag; Hon Roll; NHS; Yth Excllnce 87; Rutgers Schlr 86; Garden ST Schlr 87; Bus Admin.

LITTLEFIELD, PAUL; Dwight Morrow HS; Englewood, NJ; (4); 20/219; Math Tm; Var Crs Cntry; Var Swmmng; High Hon Roll; NHS; Band; Concert Band; Jazz Band; Mrchg Band; JV Socr; 5th Pl H S ST Swmg Champ 87; Hnbl Mntn All Leag Crss Cntry 86; Acdmc Excllnc Physcs & Pre Calcls 87; Lehigh U; Engrng.

LITTLES, DENISE; William L Dickinson HS; Highland Pk, NJ; (4); Latin Clb; OEA; Lit Mag; Wrstlng; Hon Roll; Garden ST Schlr 87; Delta Schlrshp 87; Morgan ST; Howard U; Bio Chem.

LITYNSKI, JOHN; Saint Joseph Regional HS; West Point, NY; (3); Boy Scts; Chess Clb; Church Yth Grp; Ski Clb; Off Stu Cncl; Var L Golf; Var L Socr; Hon Mntn ST NJ Golf 86-87; W Pt JR Clb Champ Golf 85; Purdue; Robotics.

LIU, CHRISTINA K; West Windsor-Plainsboro HS; Princeton Jnctn, NJ; (4); 1/278; Am Leg Aux Girls St; Hosp Aide; Pres Intnl Clb; Sec Orch; Nwsp Ed-Chief; Lit Mag; JV Trk; NHS; Ntl Merit SF; Val; Youth For Understndng Intl Schlrshp 86.

LIU, EDWARD; Parsippany Hills HS; Morris Plains, NJ; (3); Computer Clb; Key Clb; Math Tm; NFL; Sec Science Clb; JV Tennis; Hon Roll; Gvrnrs Schl Smmr Pgm 87; Bio Chem.

LIU, LISA; Watchung Hills Regional HS; Warren, NJ; (4); 30/320; Cmnty Wkr; Pres German Clb; Nwsp Ed-Chief; Cit Awd; NHS; St Schlr; Blck Blt-Karate 76-85; Cum Laude Awd-Ntl Exam 87; Prsdntl Acdmc Ftnss Awd 87; US Merchant Marine Acad.

LIVE, HENRY P; Emerson HS; Union City, NJ; (3); Am Leg Boys St; Chess Clb; French Clb; FBLA; Ski Clb; Band; Concert Band; Mrchg Band; Pep Band; Yrbk Stf; Air Frc Acad; Aerntcl Engr.

LIVINGOOD, WENDY; Hunterdon Central HS; Bethlehem, PA; (4); 98/548; Sec Art Clb; Church Yth Grp; German Clb; Stage Crew; Gym; Trk; Hon Roll; Hnr Awd Oil Paintg 87; Hnr Gftd & Tlntd Art 87; Kutztown U; Visl Fine Arts.

LIVINGSTON, JENNIFER ANNE; Hunterdon Central HS; Whitehouse Sta, NJ; (3); 101/550; Am Leg Aux Girls St; DECA; FCA; Science Clb; Yrbk Rptr; JV Cheerleading; JV Crs Cntry; JV Score Keeper; Twrlr; Gov Hon Prg Awd; Altnt For Grls Ctznshp Pgm 87; Offcr Of Intrct Clb 87-88; Chld Dvlpmnt Awd 86; Cornell; Hotel Mngmt.

LIVINGSTON, KENNETH; Salem HS; Salem, NJ; (3); 3/185; Chess Clb; Yrbk Stf; High Hon Roll; Hon Roll; NHS; Lincoln Tech; Comp Aided Drftg.

LIVINGSTON, LAURI SUZANNE; Hunterson Central HS; Whi House Sta, NJ; (4); 30/550; Church Yth Grp; FCA; Intnl Clb; Model UN Crs Cntry; Civic Clb; NHS; Cmnty Wkr; Computer Clb; SADD; Gir Ctznshp Inst Delg 86; JR Miss Hunterdon Cnty 87; Pres Clsrm 8 Vanderbilt U; Intl.

LIZ, CHARLES; Memorial HS; West New York, NJ; (3); Varsity Cl Bsktbl; Cmmnctns.

LJUBICICH, HELEN; Paramus HS; Paramus, NJ; (2); 3rd Hnrs Acad; Sec.

LLANES, JUAN; Memorial HS; West New York, NJ; (3); Var Capt Bsb Var Trk; Cit Awd; Hon Roll; B Sherman Mem Awd 87; Mst Vlbl Plyr Bs 87; Jersey Jrnl All Cnty 2nd Bsmn 86-87.

LLOYD, SUSAN; Salem HS; Salem, NJ; (2); Pep Clb; Spanish Cl Teachers Aide; JV Cheerleading; Cosmtlgst.

LLUMIQUINGA, NELSON; Frank H Morrell HS; Irvington, NJ; (4 150/550; Art Clb; Church Yth Grp; Key Clb; Library Aide; Office Aid Political Wkr; SADD; Yrbk Stf; Socr; Prfct Atten Awd; NJ ST Bar Ass Mock Trl 2nd Pl 87; William Paterson Coll; Poli Sci.

LO BELLO, ROSE; St Mary HS; Rutherford, NJ; (3); 21/85; Ski Cl Thesps; Trs Jr Cls; Capt Bsktbl; Sftbl; Vllybl; Hon Roll; NHS.

LO BIONDO, ADINA; Vineland SR HS; Vineland, NJ; (3); 11/824; V Church Yth Grp; French Clb; VP Pres Key Clb; Letterman Clb; Pep Cl SADD; Rep Stu Cncl; Var L Tennis; High Hon Roll; NHS.

LO CASCIO, FRANK; Arthur L Johnson HS; Clark, NJ; (4); 7/200; Hig Hon Roll; NHS; Italian Honor Scty Awd 86; Le High U; Chem.

LO CASTRO, FLORENCE; Mary Help Of Christians Acad; Mahwa NJ; (4); 13/77; Letterman Clb; Stage Crew; Bsktbl; Var Vllybl; Hon Ro NHS; Sci Awd 83; Engl & Itln Awd 85; Stockston ST Coll; Bio.

LO GRECO, JOANN; Bloomfield HS; Bloomfield, NJ; (3); GAA; Hos Aide; Key Clb; Chorus; Var L Vllybl; High Hon Roll; Hon Roll; S JR H Schlstc Achvt Awd 85; Vlntr Recntn Awd Svc 85; TV Prodctn.

LO RICCO, MICHAEL; Hillsborough HS; Belle Mead, NJ; (3); 39/32 Hosp Aide; SADD; Rep Frsh Cls; Stu Cncl; JV Var Socr; High Hon Ro Hon Roll; Trenton ST; Accntng.

LO SAPIO, JEFFREY; Randolph HS; Randolph, NJ; (3); Intnl Clb; Ke Clb; Latin Clb; Ski Clb; Band; Concert Band; Mrchg Band; Yrbk Phtg; W Lftg; Wrstlng; VA Tech; Law.

LOBB, DUSTY; Buena Regional HS; Newfield, NJ; (3); 30/250; Ma Clb; Ski Clb; Varsity Clb; Pres Frsh Cls; Pres Soph Cls; Rep Stu Cnc Bsbl; Bsktbl; Socr; Hon Roll; Sprts Mgmt.

LOBB, WILLIAM JAMES; Bishop Eustace Prep Schl; Medford, NJ; (4 36/166; JA; Science Clb; Spanish Clb; Nwsp Rptr; Ed Nwsp Stf; Im Vllyb Hon Roll; NHS; La Salle U; Ecnmcs.

LOBIANCO, JOHN; Hillsborough HS; Belle Mead, NJ; (3); 18/328; Hos Aide; Latin Clb; Crs Cntry; Vllybl; Hon Roll; NHS; Acdmc Tm 86-87.

LOBOSCO, CINDY; Brick Memorial HS; Brick, NJ; (3); French Cl Spanish Clb; Yrbk Stf; Rep Frsh Cls; Rep Soph Cls; Rep Stu Cncl; Var F Hcky; JV Im Socr; Hon Roll; Rutgers.

LOCASCIO, JOSEPH; North Brunswick Township HS; N Brunswic NJ; (4); 6/300; Church Yth Grp; Latin Clb; Chorus; Rep Stu Cncl; Va Bsbl; Var Bsktbl; Var Ftbl; High Hon Roll; Hon Roll; NHS; Natl Jr Clss Leag Awd Excllnc Latin 87; Ftbl Schl Athl Schlrshp 87; Army, Nav ROTC Schlrshp 87; Bucknell U; Law.

LOCASCIO, MICHAEL; Westfield SR HS; Westfield, NJ; (4); 23/49 Key Clb; Spanish Clb; Sec Frsh Cls; Rep Soph Cls; Rep Sr Cls; Rep St Cncl; Var L Lcrss; JV Socr; High Hon Roll; NHS; U Of Notre Dame.

LOCASTRO, FLORENCE; Mary Help Of Christians Acad; Mahwah, N (4); 13/78; Computer Clb; GAA; Letterman Clb; Service Clb; Var I Bsktbl; Var Im Vllybl; Hon Roll; NHS; Stockton ST Coll; Bio.

LOCK, TIMOTHY; Morristown-Beard Schl; Chatham Twp, NJ; (3); A Leg Boys St; Boy Scts; Church Yth Grp; Trs Drama Clb; Trs Service Cl School Musical; Lit Mag; VP Sr Cls; AFS; Chorus; Order Of Arrow Lodg Chf 87; Intl Thespian Soc 86; Vice Chf Admin Order Of Arrow 85.

LOCK, WALTER G; Red Bank Regional HS; Pt Monmouth, NJ; (3 Church Yth Grp; Cmnty Wkr; Computer Clb; SADD; Pres VICA; Band Mrchg Band; Nwsp Rptr; Yrbk Rptr; Rep Stu Cncl; Brnz Cngrssnl Awd 8 Slvr Cngrssnl Awd 87; VICA NJ Skll Olympcs-1st Comp Sci 86 & 8 Comp Sci.

LOCKART, STUART; Holy Spirit HS; Linwood, NJ; (4); 15/36 Exploring; Speech Tm; VP Sr Cls; High Hon Roll; NHS; Voice Dem Awd U S Nvl Acad; Hstry.

LOCKHART, SEANNA; Ridgefield Memorial HS; Ridgefield, NJ; (3 Church Yth Grp; Cmnty Wkr; School Play; Variety Show; High Hon Rol Hon Roll; Acdmc Decathalon 86; Aeronautics Tech.

LOCKO, DANA; Hamilton High West; Trenton, NJ; (4); 29/350; Band Concert Band; Mrchg Band; Stat Bsktbl; Sftbl; Stat Wrstlng; Pres Schl Top 10 Pct Cls 87; Trenton ST Coll; Acctng.

LOCKS, JAMIE; Moatville HS; Towaco, NJ; (2); FBLA; Trk; Villanov Tchng.

LOCKWOOD, CHARLES; Mainland Regional HS; Linwood, NJ; (3 JCL; Key Clb; SADD; School Play; Nwsp Bus Mgr; Yrbk Sprt Ed; Off Frs Cls; Off Soph Cls; Off Jr Cls; NHS; Arch.

LOCKWOOD, STEPHEN; Brick Memorial HS; Bricktown, NJ; (2 Varsity Clb; JV Golf; Var Score Keeper; JV Socr; Wrstlng; Hon Roll; Ag

LODESTRO, DAVID; St John Vianney HS; Matawan, NJ; (3); 82/24 FBLA; Intnl Clb; Band; Concert Band; School Musical; School Play; Ho Roll; Prfct Atten Awd; Gld & Wht Awd 85-87; Yth Life; Bus.

LOFARO, STEPHANIE; Matawan Regional HS; Matawan, NJ; (3 Cmnty Wkr; Hosp Aide; Political Wkr; Ski Clb; Var JV Fld Hcky; J Sftbl; Cmmnty Svc Awd 100 Hrs 85; Mst Outstndng Plyr JV Field Hck 86; Gov Keans Re-Electn Recgntn 85; Marine Bio.

LOFLAND, KELLY; Woodrow Wilson HS; Camden, NJ; (3); Church Yt Grp; Teachers Aide; Chorus; Church Choir; School Musical; School Pla Variety Show; Trk; Hon Roll; Prfct Atten Awd; RN.

LOFTUS, PATRICIA; St Marys HS; Old Bridge, NJ; (4); 4/125; Spanis Clb; Bsktbl; Socr; Vllybl; NHS; Spanish NHS; Girls ST Alt 86; Schlr At Awd 87; Trenton ST Coll.

LOGAN, JANICE; Brick Memorial HS; Brick, NJ; (2); 12/350; Intnl Cl Key Clb; VP Soph Cls; Pres Jr Cls; Stat Mgr(s); High Hon Roll; Hon Ro Bus.

LOGAN, JENNIFER A; Southern Regional HS; Manahawkin, NJ; (3 56/426; French Clb; Latin Clb; Lit Mag; French Hon Soc; Hon Roll; NHS Ntl Merit SF.

LOGAN, MATTHEW; Middle Township HS; Cape May Ct House, NJ (3); Capt Church Yth Grp; Cmnty Wkr; Drama Clb; Varsity Clb; Schoo Play; L Ftbl; Wt Lftg; Hon Roll; Elec Engr.

LOMANTO, CHRISTINE; Brick Memorial HS; Bricktown, NJ; (4); 25/ 190; French Clb; Color Guard; Mrchg Band; Lit Mag; Sftbl; High Hon Roll; NHS; Schlrshp Patrsn Cthlc HS 83-84; Cert Of Excllnc Fdrtn Allncs Frances 85-86; Embry-Riddle U; Aerospc Engnr.

LOMAX, MITZI; Plainfield HS; Plainfield, NJ; (3); 9/354; Church Yth Grp; Debate Tm; French Clb; JA; Library Aide; Math Clb; Model UN; Science Clb; Teachers Aide; Chorus; Boston Coll; Engl.

LOMBARD, TRACIE A; West Milford Township HS; West Milford, NJ; (3); 133/400; Church Yth Grp; DECA; French Clb; Pep Clb; Ski Clb; SADD; Hon Roll; Bus.

LOMBARDI, OWEN; Dwight-Englewood Prep Schl; Leonia, NJ; (3); Am Leg Boys St; Cmnty Wkr; Nwsp Rptr; VP Soph Cls; VP Jr Cls; Off Sr Cls; JV Capt Ftbl; Var Lcrss; Hon Roll; Ntl Merit SF; Hutchins Awd Crtv Wrtng 85; Bailey Awd Prsnl Cmmttmnt Scl Chng 87; Poli Sci.

LOMBARDI, REGINA; Pinelands Regional HS; Mystic Island, NJ; (3); Art Clb; Band; Color Guard; Mrchg Band; Yrbk Stf; Twrlr; High Hon Roll; Hon Roll; Hnr Blll 82-87; Miss Amer Co Ed Pagnt Fnlsts 86; Art Awd 87; Intr Dsgn.

LOMBARDI, VICTOR; Piscataway HS; Piscataway, NJ; (3); Aud/Vis; Radio Clb; Band; Concert Band; Im Vllybl; Hon Roll; Acceptance To Natl Guitar Workshop 87; Composer.

LOMBARDO, ERIKA; Fair Lawn HS; Fair Lawn, NJ; (3); 84/342; Dance Clb; Exploring; FHA; Hosp Aide; Variety Show; Swmmng; Trk; High Hon Roll; Rutgers; Phrmcy.

LONDON, DAVID; Oakcrest HS; Mays Landing, NJ; (3); Trs Church Yth Grp; VP French Clb; Band; Mrchg Band; Pres Stu Cncl; Trk; Gov Hon Prg Awd; High Hon Roll; NHS; Prfct Atten Awd; Law.

LONDON, SCOTT; Lakewood HS; Lakewood, NJ; (4); 60/330; Am Leg Boys St; Yrbk Ed-Chief; VP Stu Cncl; Var L Bsbl; English Clb; French Clb; Latin Clb; Temple Yth Grp; Nwsp Sprt Ed; Hon Roll; Widener U; Bus.

LONG, ANDREE G; Middle Township HS; Cape May C H, NJ; (4); Drama Clb; High Hon Roll; Masonic Awd; NHS; Publshd Poems 85-86; Great Stry Awd Atlantic Elctrc Cont 84; Rutgers Coll; Psych.

LONG, JOAN M; Bayonne HS; Bayonne, NJ; (4); Am Leg Aux Girls St; Church Yth Grp; DECA; Rep Stu Cncl; Score Keeper; Hon Roll; Amer Lgn Girl ST 86; Bergen Cnty CC; Htl-Rest Mgmt.

LONG, MELISSA; Edgewood Regional SR HS; Atco, NJ; (3); 10/375; Drama Clb; Sec French Clb; Nwsp Rptr; Yrbk Stf; Rep Soph Cls; Rep Jr Cls; Trs Stu Cncl; Hon Roll; Jr NHS; NHS; Natl Ldrshp & Svc Awd 87; Natl Sci Merit Awd 86; Comms.

LONG, MICHAEL; Paul VI HS; Sicklerville, NJ; (3); 88/395; Boy Scts; Math Clb; Var Crs Cntry; Var Trk; Prfct Atten Awd; SAR Awd; Boys Scouts Am Eagle Scout & Sr Ptrl Ldr 84-87; St John Neumann Altar Boy & Usher 83-87; Chem Engr.

LONG, ROBIN; Gloucester HS; Gloucester Cty, NJ; (3); French Clb; Concert Band; Jazz Band; Mrchg Band; Lit Mag; NHS.

LONG, VANESSA; Orange HS; Orange, NJ; (3); Church Yth Grp; Band; Concert Band; Mrchg Band; Mgr(s); Vllybl; Hon Roll; Mrchng Bnd Awd 84-86; Morgan ST; Bus.

LONGO, BRIAN; Mt Olive HS; Budd Lake, NJ; (3); 75/275; Science Clb; Ski Clb; SADD; VICA; Lit Mag; Var L Swmmng; Ntl Merit Ltr.

LONGO, DANIELLE; Newton HS; Newton, NJ; (2); 11/219; Latin Clb; Yrbk Stf; Rep Frsh Cls; Rep Soph Cls; Rep Stu Cncl; JV Fld Hcky; Stat Sftbl; Hon Roll; Lang.

LONZISERO, NICHOLAS; Ridgefield Memorial HS; Ridgefield, NJ; (3); Computer Clb; Science Clb; Yrbk Stf; Hon Roll; Engr.

LOOBY, KEVIN; Brick Memorial HS; Ricktown, NJ; (3); 160/375; Ski Clb; Var Socr; Team Mens 19 & Under Soccer 86-87; Bus.

LOONAM, PATRICIA A; Immaculate Conception HS; Lodi, NJ; (4); Q&S; Chorus; School Musical; Nwsp Rptr; Nwsp Stf; Lit Mag; Sftbl; Hon Roll; Intr Dsgn.

LOORY, LARA; Dover HS; Dover, NJ; (3); 1/218; Am Leg Aux Girls St; Debate Tm; Math Tm; Q&S; Spanish Clb; Lib Band; Concert Band; Drm Mjr(t); Mrchg Band; Orch.

LOOSE, DEANNA A; Faith Christian HS; Cherry Hill, NJ; (4); 1/8; Chorus; Yrbk Bus Mgr; Lit Mag; Sec Frsh Cls; Sec Soph Cls; Sec Stu Cncl; Capt Bsktbl; Capt Fld Hcky; Capt Sftbl; High Hon Roll; Math League Awd; Tri-ST Athltc Cnfrnc All Star Team/Bsktbl; Yrbk Ltry Edtr; Cdrvl Coll; Accntng.

LOPER, ELINDA; Cumberland Regional HS; Bridgeton, NJ; (3); 22/384; Church Yth Grp; Drama Clb; German Clb; Intnl Clb; Model UN; Science Clb; Ski Clb; School Play; High Hon Roll; Hon Roll; Phrmcy.

LOPES, MARLA; St James HS; Carneys Point, NJ; (3); 2/79; Drama Clb; Hosp Aide; SADD; School Musical; Yrbk Stf; Var Cheerleading; High Hon Roll; Prfct Atten Awd; Rotrn Mnth 86; Psych.

LOPEZ, ADRIANA; Mother Seton Regional HS; Hillside, NJ; (3); Debate Tm; School Play; Yrbk Stf; Rep Soph Cls; Sec Jr Cls; Stu Cncl; Sftbl; Trk; NHS; Prfct Atten Awd; Sprt Awd 86; Prom Cmte Srvc Awd, Recrtmnt Awd 87; Bus.

LOPEZ, ANTHONY; Bordentown Regional HS; Bordentown, NJ; (4); 13/ 113; Pres Spanish Clb; Rep Sr Cls; Var Bsbl; Ftbl; Capt Wrstlng; Hon Roll; NHS; FL Inst Tech; Space Sci.

LOPEZ, ARDITH M; Perth Amboy HS; Perth Amboy, NJ; (2); 56/457; Church Yth Grp; Cmnty Wkr; French Clb; Library Aide; Science Clb; Rep Soph Cls; Rep Stu Cncl; Hon Roll; 2nd Anl Schlr Awd Peth 87; Miss Amer Coed Pgnt Outstndng Prog Part Trphy 86; Rutgers; Pediatrician.

LOPEZ, DIANA M; St Joseph Of The Palisades HS; Union City, NJ; (3); Spanish Clb; High Hon Roll; Hon Roll; Spanish NHS; NY U; Drama.

LOPEZ, FELIX; Marist HS; Jersey City, NJ; (3); Aud/Vis; Cmnty Wkr; Bsbl; JV Crs Cntry; JV Ftbl; Var Timer; JV Trk; JV Vllybl; JV Wt Lftg; Accntng.

LOPEZ, HENRY; Hudson Catholic HS; Jersey City, NJ; (3); Dance Clb; Spanish Clb; Mgr School Play; Yrbk Phtg; Yrbk Rptr; Im Capt Bsktbl; JV Var Socr; Im Vllybl; Systms Anlyst.

LOPEZ, JEANETTE; Our Lady Of Good Councel HS; Newark, NJ; (3); 50/121; Church Yth Grp; Hosp Aide; Teachers Aide; Chorus; Church Choir; Stage Crew.

LOPEZ, JENNY; Howell HS; Howell, NJ; (3); German Clb; School Musical; Hon Roll; Drexel; Veterinarian.

LOPEZ, LAURA E; Oakcrest HS; Hammonton, NJ; (4); 89/214; FBLA; GAA; Hosp Aide; Model UN; Office Aide; SADD; Teachers Aide; Var Capt Bsktbl; Var Capt Sftbl; Var Capt Tennis; Athltc Schlrshp 87; All Cnfrnc In 3 Var Sprts, MVP Bsktbl & Ten, Bst All Arnd Sftbl All Str 87; Glassboro ST Coll; Elem Educ.

LOPEZ, LYDIA; Millville SR HS; Millville, NJ; (3); Sec FBLA; Key Clb; Mrchg Band; Rep Frsh Cls; VP Soph Cls; Rep Stu Cncl; Mgr(s); Score Keeper; Mgr Sftbl; Acctg I 1st Pl 86; Modern Ms Cert Of Achvt 87; Cert Of Recgntn Brd Of Ed 86; Rider Coll; CPA.

LOPEZ, MARIA; Hoboken HS; Hoboken, NJ; (2); Exploring; Chorus; Rep Soph Cls; Sftbl; Schl Mem Faculty Awd 85; Med.

LOPEZ, MICHAEL; Union HS; Union, NJ; (3); Pres German Clb; Var L Trk; NHS; Mst Imprvd Stu 85; US Naval Acad Smmr Smnr 87.

LOPEZ, MICHELE; Hightstown HS; East Windsor, NJ; (4); Spanish Clb; High Hon Roll; Dstngshd Minrty Schlr 87; Trenton ST Coll.

LOPEZ, NANCY; Mother Seton Regional HS; Elizabeth, NJ; (4); 16/92; Drama Clb; GAA; Hosp Aide; Science Clb; Hon Roll; Katherine Gibbs Ldrshp Awd 86; Stu In Govt Day Awd 87; Excllnc-Acctng Awd 86; Rutgers U; Crmnl Jstc.

LOPEZ, RENE; Bloomfield SR HS; Bloomfield, NJ; (3); Key Clb; Math Tm; Quiz Bowl; Science Clb; Spanish Clb; Hon Roll; Bio-Med Engrng.

LOPEZ, SONIA; University HS; Newark, NJ; (3); Exploring; JA; High Hon Roll; NHS; Dr Mrtn Lthr Kng Sci Fair Wnnr 86; STEP Outstndng Achvt Awd-Engnrng & Albgr II 87; Phsycs.

LOPIPARO, SUSAN; Freehold Township HS; Freehold, NJ; (4); 29/353; Drama Clb; Nwsp Stf; Ed Yrbk Stf; Lit Mag; Co-Capt Stu Cncl; Score Keeper; NHS; Presdntl Acad Ftnss Awd 87; Lafayette Coll; Law.

LORA, ANGELA; Memorial HS; West New York, NJ; (3); Cmnty Wkr; Var Office Aide; Var Political Wkr; Teachers Aide; Rep Frsh Cls; Rep Soph Cls; Rep Jr Cls; Rep Stu Cncl; Var Hon Roll; Rutgers; Pol Sci.

LORENTZ, PAMELA; A P Schalick HS; Elmer, NJ; (4); Sftbl; Hon Roll; Salem Cnty Mncpl Clrk & Treas Assoctn Schlrshp 87; Berkeley Awd For Outstndng Achvt In HS Bus Euc 87; Cumberland Cnty Coll; Data Proc.

LORENZO, MICHAEL; Parsippany Hills HS; Parsippany, NJ; (2); Key Clb; Spanish Clb; Hon Roll; Engrng.

LORENZO, PETER; Morristown HS; Morristown, NJ; (1); Var L Lcrss; Penn St; Arch.

LORETANGELI, KATHRYN; Bordentown Regional HS; Bordentown, NJ; (2); 20/162; Ski Clb; Socr; Sftbl; Hon Roll; Sci.

LORETTO, KATHLEEN; Cliffside Park HS; Cliffside Pk, NJ; (3); 8/236; Color Guard; Flag Corp; Stu Cncl; Score Keeper; JV Sftbl; High Hon Roll; Hon Roll; NHS; Italn Hon Scty 87; Guardn Of Svcs Natl Hon Scty 88; Bus.

LORFINK, ROBERT; Hudson Catholic HS; Jersey City, NJ; (3); Dance Clb; Letterman Clb; Pep Clb; Varsity Clb; Y-Teens; Var Bsbl; L Bsktbl; JV Ftbl; Rutgers U; CPA.

LORMAN, JEFF; Burlington City HS; Edgewater Pk, NJ; (2); Boy Scts; JV Bsbl; JV Ftbl; Wt Lftg; Law.

LORO, STEPHANIE; Pennsauken HS; Pennsauken, NJ; (3); 31/417; Spanish Clb; Hon Roll; Spanish NHS; Pnnskn Hnr Soc 87; Rutgers U; Vet Med.

LOSCH, DANA; South Hunterdon Regional HS; Lambertville, NJ; (3); 4/ 85; Am Leg Aux Girls St; Key Clb; Sec Frsh Cls; VP Soph Cls; VP Jr Cls; Pres Sr Cls; Sec Stu Cncl; Fld Hcky; Hon Roll; NHS; Psychlgy.

LOSITO, ALBERT; Burlington Co Vo-Tech; Riverside, NJ; (3); VICA; Wt Lftg; High Hon Roll; Hon Roll; NHS; Ntl Merit Ltr; Prfct Atten Awd; CIA Amer; Chef.

LOSITO, MARTHA; Edison HS; Edison, NJ; (3); 20/469; Math Tm; Pres Spanish Clb; Rep Frsh Cls; L Trk; Hon Roll; NHS; Spanish NHS; Cmnty Wkr; Computer Clb; Office Aide; Hrnbl Mntn NJ Chptr Ntl Spnsh Exam 86f1st In Natl St Bank Essay Cntst 85; Hnrbl Mntn Oratry Cntst 87; Rutgers U; Psych.

LOTA, KATHLEEN; Hawthorne HS; Hawthorne, NJ; (3); Art Clb; Camera Clb; Hosp Aide; Pep Clb; Ski Clb; Yrbk Phtg; Yrbk Stf; Stu Cncl; Powder Puff Ftbl; Hon Roll; Adv.

LOTITO, ELIZABETH ANNE L; St Rose HS; Spring Lk, NJ; (3); 1/217; Key Clb; Latin Clb; Math Tm; Service Clb; Chorus; Stu Cncl; High Hon Roll; NHS; Computer Clb; Debate Tm; HOBY Rep, Finlst, & Ambassador 86-87; Spring Lake Historical Soc; Political Sci.

LOUGHNER, DIANA; West Morris Central HS; Long Valley, NJ; (4); 14/340; Am Leg Aux Girls St; Church Yth Grp; Drama Clb; Intnl Clb; Spanish Clb; Acpl Chr; Church Choir; Drill Tm; Jazz Band; Bus Admin.

LOUGHRAN, KIMBERLY; Henry Hudson Regional HS; Atlntic Hglds, NJ; (2); Church Yth Grp; SADD; Jazz Band; School Play; Variety Show; Pres Frsh Cls; Pres Soph Cls; Pres Jr Cls; Crs Cntry; High Hon Roll; Hugh O Brien Yth Fndtn Ldrshp Semnr 87; Comm.

LOUIE, CARYN; Paul VI HS; Runnemede, NJ; (3); 15/418; Cmnty Wkr; Math Clb; Hon Roll; Spanish NHS; Med.

LOUIS, CLAIRE; Wardlaw-Hartridge HS; Newark, NJ; (2); 23/54; Aud/ Vis; Key Clb; Library Aide; Acpl Chr; Chorus; Nwsp Stf; Yrbk Sprt Ed; Var JV Bsktbl; Var JV Fld Hcky; Var JV Lcrss; Howard U; Psych.

LOUNSBURY, ELIZABETH; Ranney Schl; Lincroft, NJ; (3); 7/45; Church Yth Grp; Sec French Clb; Library Aide; NFL; Chorus; Nwsp Ed-Chief; Yrbk Stf; Lit Mag; High Hon Roll; Ntl Merit Ltr; English.

LOVE, KIRK; Paulsboro HS; Gibbstown, NJ; (3); 4/125; Quiz Bowl; SADD; Pres Jr Cls; Pres Stu Cncl; Var Crs Cntry; Var Golf; Var Tennis; Var Wrstlng; Hon Roll; NHS; Acdmc Wrestler Awd 85-87; Stu Athl Schlr Awd Courier Post 87; Advertsng.

LOVE, SCOTT; St James HS; Salem, NJ; (2); French Clb; Ski Clb; Off Soph Cls; Bsbl; Bsktbl; Ftbl; French Hon Soc; Hon Roll.

LOVE, THOMAS; Clearview Regional HS; Sewell, NJ; (4); 5/157; Pres 4-H; SADD; VP Jr Cls; Pres Sr Cls; Var Capt Ftbl; Var Co-Capt Wrstlng; Cit Awd; 4-H Awd; Hon Roll; NHS; Ursinus; Physcn.

LOVELACE, LAMONT; Plainfield HS; Plainfield, NJ; (3); Art Clb; Church Clb; Church Yth Grp; Cmnty Wkr; DECA; English Clb; FBLA; Science Clb; SADD; VICA; Church Choir; Bus.

LOVELAND, JANA; Lakeland Regional HS; Ringwood, NJ; (2); Church Yth Grp; Drama Clb; SADD; School Play; Yrbk Phtg; Hon Roll; Acad Tlntd Yng Stu Pgm Montclair ST Coll 85.

LOVELESS, JAMES; West Orange HS; W Orange, NJ; (3); Band; Concert Band; Mrchg Band; Model UN; Montclair ST; Aviation.

LOVELL, EILEEN; Our Lady Of Mercy Acad; Franklinville, NJ; (3); 16/ 46; Cmnty Wkr; Science Clb; Sec Stu Cncl; JV Var Cheerleading; Hon Roll; Prfct Atten Awd; Dance Clb; SADD; Nwsp Rptr; Lit Mag; Newcomb Med Ctr Med Explrs Pres 86-87; Natl Wthr Svc Bureau Wthr Spttr 87; Pres Phys Ftns Awd 87; Pre-Med.

LOVELY, KISHA; John F Kennedy HS; Willingboro, NJ; (3); Mgr(s); Var Trk; High Hon Roll; Hon Roll; NHS; Jr Prom Queen Class 88; Comp Oprtr.

LOWE, JENNIFER; Plainfield HS; Plainfield, NJ; (3); 1/300; Am Leg Aux Girls St; Math Tm; Science Clb; Nwsp Rptr; Cit Awd; High Hon Roll; NHS; Ntl Merit SF; Val; Rnsslr Awd & Schlrshp 87; Rtgrs Schlr 87; Acdmc All Amer 86; Bio Chem.

LOWE, JOSEPH; Kingsway Regional HS; Clarksboro, NJ; (2); Ski Clb; Bsktbl; Gd Ctznshp Awd 86; 3 Yrs Svc US Nvl Sea Cdts Corps; Ltr Cmmndtn Svc USCG; Mtrlgy.

LOWE, KARIN; Cumberland Regional HS; Bridgeton, NJ; (3); Debate Tm; Intnl Clb; JCL; Latin Clb; Science Clb; Ski Clb; Varsity Clb; Yrbk Stf; Mgr(s); Tennis; Comm.

LOWNEY, JAMES; Msgr Donovan HS; Toms River, NJ; (3); Church Yth Grp; Nwsp Phtg; Nwsp Rptr; Nwsp Stf; Cmmnctns.

LOWRIE, MICHELE; Delaware Valley Regional HS; Milford, NJ; (4); 28/165; Key Clb; Yrbk Rptr; Yrbk Stf; Trs Jr Cls; JV Fld Hcky; Hon Roll; Rider Coll.

LOWRY, STEVEN; Paul VI HS; Berlin, NJ; (3); 13/450; Math Clb; Spanish Clb; JV Bsktbl; Im Bowling; Hon Roll; Spanish NHS; Medical.

LOZA, HEATHER; Cinnaminson HS; Cinnaminson, NJ; (2); Church Yth Grp; Rep SADD; Rep Frsh Cls; Rep Soph Cls; Var Crs Cntry; Lcrss; Mgr(s); Var Swmmng; Hon Roll; Elem Educ.

LOZADA, GRACE; Hunterdon Central HS; Lebanon, NJ; (2); Key Clb; Stage Crew; Off Soph Cls; Psycht.

LU, ALBERT; S Brunswick HS; Kendall Park, NJ; (3); 7/276; Chess Clb; French Clb; Math Clb; Capt Math Tm; Mu Alpha Theta; JV Trk; French Hon Soc; NHS; $1,000 Awd In Piano Rctl 82; Prnctn U; Med.

LUBAS, MARK J; Pompton Lakes HS; Pompton Lakes, NJ; (3); 33/154; Am Leg Boys St; Chess Clb; Computer Clb; Intnl Clb; Spanish Clb; SADD; JV Bsbl; Var Wrstlng; Rutgrs St Johns; Bus Adm.

LUBENOW, ANNE ELIZABETH; Overbrook Regional HS; Lindenwold, NJ; (4); 5/335; French Clb; Science Clb; Chorus; Yrbk Stf; Stu Cncl; Crs Cntry; Trk; Hon Roll; NHS; Aero Engrng.

LUBIAK, MICHAEL; Franklin HS; Somerset, NJ; (3); German Clb; Ski Clb; SADD; Var JV Bsbl; Coach Actv; Var JV Socr.

LUBIN, DAVID C; Randolph HS; Randolph, NJ; (3); 23/353; Ftbl; Im Wt Lftg; JV Wrstlng; High Hon Roll; Hon Roll; JETS Awd; AT&T Bell Lab Corp Awd Natl Energy Fndtn SEER Comp 85; Princeton Physcs Lab Awd 85; Hnrb Mntn SEER; Mech Engrng.

LUBKEMANN, SHARON; Highland Regional HS; Laurel Springs, NJ; (4); 6/300; Art Clb; Church Yth Grp; Drama Clb; School Play; Ed Yrbk Ed-Chief; Co-Capt Bsktbl; Crs Cntry; Trk; High Hon Roll; NHS; Art Awds-Bst Shw, Bst Blck & Wht 86; Pres Ftnss Awd 85 & 86; Wrtr.

LUBRANO, TREASA; Villa Walsh Acad; Mendham, NJ; (3); Church Yth Grp; 4-H; NFL; Quiz Bowl; Service Clb; Chorus; Orch; School Musical; School Play; Nwsp Stf; Natl Piano Playing Auditions 86-87; Jr All-Amer Hall Of Fame Band Hnrs 86; Swim Team Spirit Awd 85.

LUCARELLI, ROSANNE C; Ocean Twp HS; West Deal, NJ; (3); Dance Clb; Drama Clb; Ski Clb; SADD; Varsity Clb; Variety Show; Stu Cncl; Capt Cheerleading; Powder Puff Ftbl; Sftbl; Hnr Hmcmng Atten 84-86; Hmcmng Queen 85; Best Cheer, Dance Awds; 95 Avg Italian Mdls; Performng Arts.

LUCAS, CINDY; Gloucester County Christian HS; Elmer, NJ; (2); Church Yth Grp; 4-H; Chorus; Trs Soph Cls; Var Bsktbl; Var Fld Hcky; Var Sftbl; Var Trk; Var Vllybl; 4-H Awd.

LUCAS, DANIELLE; Bayonne HS; Bayonne, NJ; (2); Dance Clb; French Clb; FBLA; Science Clb; Teachers Aide; NJ Coll Med; Csmtc Srgry.

LUCAS, NICHOLAS; Brick Township HS; Brick Town, NJ; (4); 23/347; German Clb; JV Var Bowling; Acad Schlrshp $250 87; WV U; Chem Engrng.

LUCCA, TRACY; St Joseph HS; Hammonton, NJ; (4); Cmnty Wkr; Dance Clb; Pep Clb; Soroptimist; SADD; School Play; Yrbk Phtg; Yrbk Stf; Trs Jr Cls; Var Capt Cheerleading; Amer Alumni Schlrshp 87; Our Lady Of Mount Carmel 87; MVP Chrldng 86-87; PA ST U; Bus Admin.

LUCCHESI, ERIC; Rigefield Park HS; Cliffside Park, NJ; (4); 38/175; Yrbk Stf; PTA Rdgfld Pk St Frncs Mthrs Gld 87-88; Roger Williams Coll; Arch.

LUCCIOLA, VICTOR; Marist HS; Bayonne, NJ; (3); 60/110; Bsbl; Capt Ftbl; Wt Lftg; Crmnl Jstc.

LUCIANO, KIM-THU; Neptune SR HS; Wall Township, NJ; (4); 33/355; Art Clb; Ski Clb; Stage Crew; Lit Mag; Rep Stu Cncl; JV Fld Hcky; Var Socr; Var Tennis; Hon Roll; Tae Kwon Do Blue Blt 87; Sci Fair Hnrbl Mntn 84; J Murrays USTF Regn IV Tae Kwon Do Smr Camp 87; Parsons Schl Dsgn NY; Intr Dsn.

LUCKENBILL, HOLLY; Hillbrough HS; Somerville, NJ; (3); Cmnty Wkr; Pep Clb; Variety Show; Capt Cheerleading; Gym; Powder Puff Ftbl; FL ST U; Mngmnt.

LUCZKIEWICZ, CHRISSY; Highland Reginal HS; Blackwood, NJ; (3); 15/300; Computer Clb; Science Clb; JV Golf; Hon Roll; Sports Med.

LUDDEN, ROBERT; Chrisian Brothers Acad; Middletown, NJ; (3); 50/ 225; Drama Clb; Band; Chorus; Orch; School Musical; School Play; Stage Crew; Im Sftbl; Var JV Wrstlng; Hon Roll; William & Mary; Bus Admin.

LUDOVICH, JOEL; Edgewood Regional SR HS; Waterford, NJ; (3); Drama Clb; 4-H; Varsity Clb; Stage Crew; JV Socr; JV Sftbl; Var Tennis; Hon Roll; Jr NHS.

LUDOVICO, FELICIA MARIA; Park Ridge HS; Park Ridge, NJ; (3); 19/98; AFS; Camera Clb; Church Yth Grp; PAVAS; Rep Frsh Cls; VP Soph Cls; Pres Jr Cls; Vllybl; Hon Roll; NHS; Chem.

LUDVIGSEN, MARK; Voorhees HS; Pottersville, NJ; (4); 5/277; Math Tm; Yrbk Stf; Lit Mag; Crs Cntry; Trk; Wrstlng; High Hon Roll; Hon Roll; NHS; Ntl Merit Ltr; Grdn ST Dstngshd Schlr 87; Natl Yng Ldrs Conf Cngrsnl Schlr Rep 87; Wrstlng Awd 87; Coll William & Mary.

LUDWIG, COURTNEY; Manalapan HS; Manalapan, NJ; (3); Yrbk Stf; Arch.

LUDWIG, DOUG; Bridgewater-Raritan West HS; Bridgewater, NJ; (4); Varsity Clb; Var Bsbl; Capt Var Ftbl; Powder Puff Ftbl; Wt Lftg; Hon Roll; Phys Ed.

LUDWIG, JON; West Morris Mendham HS; Morristown, NJ; (2); FBLA; German Clb; Trk; High Hon Roll; Hon Roll; Prfct Atten Awd; U Of FL Gainesville; Corp Law.

LUDWIG, KYLE; Manalapan HS; Manalapan, NJ; (3); Dance Clb; SADD; Yrbk Stf; Arch.

LUDWIG, MICHAEL; Buena Regional HS; Collings Lks, NJ; (2); Ski Clb; Varsity Clb; JV Bsbl; JV Bsktbl; Var Ftbl; JV Trk; Forstry Mgmt.

LUDWIG, PATRICIA; Parsippany HS; Parsippany, NJ; (3); Exploring; Mrchg Band; Symp Band; JV Bsktbl; Var Trk; Hon Roll; NHS; Prfct Atten Awd; Law.

LUEDER, LUCIANO J; Ambassador Christian Acad; Aura, NJ; (4); 2/14; Church Yth Grp; Rep Sr Cls; VP Stu Cncl; Var Bsktbl; Var Capt Socr; NHS; Sal; Rep Frsh Cls; High Hon Roll; Grdn ST Dstngshd Schlr Awd, Sccr MVP Awd 86-87; Fnnc.

LUETH, SABRINA; North Hunterdon HS; Annandale, NJ; (3); 74/328; Church Yth Grp; Latin Clb; SADD; Church Choir; School Play; Tennis; Hon Roll; Latn Hnr Soc 87.

LUETKEMEYER, SHARON; Secaucus HS; Secaucus, NJ; (3); 9/176; Mu Alpha Theta; Quiz Bowl; Mrchg Band; Orch; School Musical; Nwsp Rptr; Sec Soph Cls; High Hon Roll; Hon Roll; NHS; Bus Adm.

LUGO, DENISE; Ferris HS; Jersey City, NJ; (3); Am Leg Aux Girls St; Church Yth Grp; Computer Clb; Math Clb; Sec Band; Trk; Trs Sec NHS; Prfct Atten Awd; High Achvr 87; Opthlmc Tech.

LUISI, ROCCO; Parsippany Hills HS; Augusta, NJ; (2); Chess Clb; Concert Band; Var Crs Cntry; Var Trk; Hon Roll; Eng.

LUISI, STEPHANIE; Immaculate Heart Acad; Moonachie, NJ; (2); Pep Clb; JV Sftbl; JV Swmmng; Hon Roll; Rutgers; Med.

LUKACS, TRACEY; St Rose HS; Lakewood, NJ; (3); Key Clb; Math Tm; Ski Clb; School Musical; Mgr(s); JV L Socr; Var L Trk; French Hon Soc; Hon Roll; NEDT Awd; Bio.

LUKARIC, JOSEPHINE; Academy Of The Sacred Heart; Hoboken, NJ; (3); Hosp Aide; Math Tm; Quiz Bowl; Yrbk Stf; High Hon Roll; Hon Roll; Jr NHS; VP NHS; Achvt Cthlc HS Math League, Exclinc-Advncd Math, Chmstry & Engl 86-87 & Spnsh II & Engl II 85-86.

LUKAS, DAVID; Don Bosco Technical HS; Clifton, NJ; (2); 2/90; Boy Scts; Chess Clb; Hosp Aide; Im Bowling; Var Trk; High Hon Roll; NHS; Prfct Atten Awd.

LUKAS, DIANE; Clifton HS; Clifton, NJ; (4); 24/589; Girl Scts; Math Clb; SADD; Capt Var Bowling; Capt Var Fld Hcky; Capt Var Socr; L Var Sftbl; L Twrlr; High Hon Roll; NHS; Gold C Awd 87; C Club Awd 87; Clifton Coll Wmns Club Schlrshp 87; Trenton ST Coll; Acctng.

LUKIS, RICHARD; Burlington City HS; Beverly, NJ; (3); Am Leg Boys St; Cmnty Wkr; Teachers Aide; Nwsp Stf; Rep Stu Cncl; Var Ftbl; Var Trk; Wt Lftg; Hon Roll; All Lg Suburban Ftbl 86; 2nd Mr South Jersey Bench Press Champ 87; 51 Shot Put 87; Physlgy.

LUKOWIAK III, GEORGE S; Don Bosco Tech HS; Belleville, NJ; (2); 23/90; Aud/Vis; Chess Clb; Var Tennis; Hon Roll; NJIT; Arch.

LULL, MATT; Hunterdon Central HS; Ringoes, NJ; (3); 164/543; Ski Clb; Wrstlng; Hon Roll; NJ St Champ Freestyle 3rd, Dance 3rd, Rllrsktng 84; PA St Champ 2nd Dance Rllrsktng 85; Bus.

LULLO, TINA; William L Dickinson HS; Jersey City, NJ; (3); SADD; Yrbk Stf; Rep Soph Cls; Hon Roll; NHS; Comm Arts.

LUM, LINDA; Cherry Hill HS West; Cherry Hill, NJ; (4); Church Yth Grp; Intnl Clb; JCL; Spanish Clb; Chorus; Color Guard; Stage Crew; Yrbk Ed-Chief; Yrbk Stf; Stu Cncl; Columbia Schlstc Press Awd 86; Rampant Awd 87; Home & Schl Assoc Awd 87; Philadelphia Coll Pharm.

LUM, LINDA; Hackensack HS; Maywood, NJ; (4); 6/406; Cmnty Wkr; Radio Clb; Teachers Aide; Varsity Clb; Off Jr Cls; Var L Vllybl; High Hon Roll; NHS; Pres Schlr; Colgate U; Bio.

LUMER, MARY A; Governor Livingston Reg HS; Murray Hill, NJ; (4); Church Yth Grp; School Musical; Nwsp Rptr; Yrbk Rptr; Lit Mag; Cheerleading; Trk; Alt Gov Schl Creatv Wrtng 86; NJ ST Teen Arts Fest 86; ST Teen Arts 87; U AZ.

LUNA, PEARLIE; Lyndhurst HS; Lyndhurst, NJ; (4); 1/168; German Clb; VP Library Aide; Stat Sftbl; Var Vllybl; Elks Awd; High Hon Roll; NHS; St Schlr; Val; Lrn About Bus Rep 86; Acad Decathalon 8l; Rutgers U; Phrmcy.

LUNA, SHERI; Lodi HS; Lodi, NJ; (3); Leo Clb; Pep Clb; Varsity Clb; Yrbk Stf; VP Frsh Cls; VP Jr Cls; Pres Sr Cls; Var Capt Cheerleading; Montclair ST Coll; Accntng.

LUND, THEODORE; Manasquan HS; Manasquan, NJ; (2); 35/247; French Clb; Math Clb; Band; Concert Band; Jazz Band; Mrchg Band; JV Bsktbl; Hon Roll; Acad All Amer 87; Engrng.

LUNDE, LISA; West Windsor-Plainsboro HS; Lawrenceville, NJ; (3); Church Yth Grp; JV Socr; High Hon Roll; NHS; German Awd; Spelng Awd.

LUNGARETTI, MICHAEL; West Essex HS; Fairfield, NJ; (3); Var Capt Bsktbl; High Hon Roll; Hon Roll; NHS.

LUONGO, JOYCE; Belleville HS; Belleville, NJ; (3); 5/436; Church Yth Grp; Science Clb; Spanish Clb; Chorus; Rep Sr Cls; Pres Stu Cncl; Capt Crs Cntry; Capt Trk; NHS; Poetry Awd JR Wmns Club 87; 2nd Tm All NNJIL Cross-Cntry 86; Hnrbl Mntn All Essex Crss-Cntry 85.

LUPI, TRICIA; Lakeland Regional HS; Wanaque, NJ; (3); 15/343; Off Frsh Cls; Off Soph Cls; Off Jr Cls; Off Sr Cls; Var L Fld Hcky; High Hon Roll; NHS; AFS; Art Clb; Church Yth Grp; Grls Ctzshp Inst Dgls Coll 87; JR Olympc Natl Fncng 87; 1st Pl Math Exam 87; Phys Thrpy.

LUPPINO, CATHY; Bayonne HS; Bayonne, NJ; (4); 102/350; Church Yth Grp; Cmnty Wkr; Library Aide; Office Aide; Political Wkr; SADD; Teachers Aide; Nwsp Rptr; Lit Mag; Rep Stu Cncl; Christ Hosp Schl Nrsng; Nrsng.

LUSCAN, CHRISTINE; Clearview Reg HS; Mullica Hill, NJ; (3); 28/198; SADD; Ed Yrbk Ed-Chief; Var Fld Hcky; JV Sftbl; Var Swmmng; Hon Roll; NHS; George W Trautwein Memorial Awd 86; Cpa.

LUSZIK, ANN MARIE; St John Vianney HS; Englishtown, NJ; (2); 14/270; Cmnty Wkr; Math Tm; Office Aide; Ski Clb; SADD; Jazz Band; High Hon Roll; Hon Roll; NHS; Prfct Atten Awd; Gold & White Awd 87; Spn Comptn Drew U 3rd Pl 86, Hnrb Mntn 87; Rutgers; Phrmcst.

LUTCHMIDAT, HAIMANAND; Dickinson HS; Jersey Cty, NJ; (3); 1/23; Computer Clb; Off Frsh Cls; Off Soph Cls; Off Jr Cls; Bsbl; Bsktbl; Ftbl; Gym; Socr; Merit & Achvt Awds 87; Jersey City ST Coll; Comp Prgm.

LUTHIN, CLAIRE; Northern Valley Regional HS; Old Tappan, NJ; (3); 24/247; AFS; Yrbk Sprt Ed; Rep Stu Cncl; Var Bsktbl; Var Sftbl; Var Vllybl; High Hon Roll; NHS; Ski Clb; Hon Roll; Grls Ctznshp Inst-Douglass Coll 87; 1st Tm All-County Vllybl 86; 1st Tm All League-Vllybl 86.

LUTKINS, TRACEY; West Orange HS; W Orange, NJ; (3); Varsity Clb; Band; Concert Band; Mrchg Band; Yrbk Stf; Powder Puff Ftbl; Sftbl; Capt Swmmng; Hon Roll; Bus Mgmt.

LUTTGENS, PAMELA; Linden HS; Linden, NJ; (4); 67/345; Service Clb; Yrbk Stf; Rep Sr Cls; VP Stu Cncl; High Hon Roll; Hon Roll; NHS; PTA Schlrshp 87; Fashion Inst Of Tech; Fshn Byng.

LUTTMAN, TAMMI; Wall HS; Wall, NJ; (3); Church Yth Grp; Key Clb; Ski Clb; Spanish Clb; Crs Cntry; Socr; Trk; High Hon Roll; NHS; Ntnl Tutoring Scty 85-87; UNC Chapel Hill; Englsh Lit.

LUTZ, ANDREW; Mt Olive HS; Budd Lake, NJ; (3); 55/316; Debate Tm; Science Clb; Nwsp Rptr; Nwsp Stf; Pres Soph Cls; Stu Cncl; VP Trk; SUNY Binghamton; Pltcl Sci.

LUTZ, KRISTEN; Waldwick HS; Waldwick, NJ; (3); 34/140; Church Yth Grp; Teachers Aide; Yrbk Phtg; Yrbk Stf; Rep Jr Cls; Var Powder Puff Ftbl; Cert Awd Typng I 85-86; Cert Awd Home Ec I 86-87; Montclair ST Coll; Elem Ed.

LUTZ, LYNDA; Hunterdon Central HS; Flemington, NJ; (3); 113/543; Band; Flag Corp; Mrchg Band; Stage Crew; Stu Cncl; Hon Roll.

LUTZ, NICHOLAS; Verona HS; Verona, NJ; (4); 28/184; French Clb; French Hon Soc; High Hon Roll; Hon Roll; Pres Schlr; B Weller Comp Sci Schlrshp 87; Pres Acadc Ftns Awd; Montclair St Coll; Comp Sci.

LUTZ, PETER J; Mt Olive HS; Budd Lake, NJ; (4); Art Clb; School Musical; School Play; Pres Soph Cls; Pres Jr Cls; Rep Sr Cls; Stu Cncl; Var JV Ftbl; Var JV Wrstlng; Natl Art Hnr Soc; Smr Arts Inst At Rutgers Univ Schlrshp 86; Kutztown U; Art Education.

LUTZ, STUART; Ocean Township HS; Asbury Park, NJ; (3); 40/344; Temple Yth Grp; Band; Concert Band; Mrchg Band; Nwsp Rptr; Var Trk; Hon Roll; Voice Dem Awd; Voice Demcrcy 3rd Pl 86; Pol Sci.

LUVERA, MARIA DEL CARMEN; Cliffside Park HS; Fairview, NJ; (3); 10/234; Spanish Clb; Capt Color Guard; Lit Mag; Stu Cncl; Sftbl; Hon Roll; NHS; Spnsh Schlstc Awd 86; Intl Stdys.

LUY, TIFFANY; Watchung Hills Reg HS; Ellicott City, MD; (2); Drama Clb; Variety Show; Var Capt Cheerleading; Hon Roll; Phsycl Thrpy.

LUYBER, WENDY; Florence Twp Mem HS; Florence, NJ; (3); Am Leg Aux Girls St; Pres FTA; Math Clb; Varsity Clb; Nwsp Stf; Sec Soph Cls; Sec Jr Cls; Rep Stu Cncl; Var L Cheerleading; Hon Roll; Secondary Math Educ.

LUZAR, TINA; Middlesex HS; Middlesex, NJ; (4); Color Guard; Mrchg Band; School Musical; Hon Roll; Brkley Schls Annl Bus Educ Awd 87; Ldrshp Awd Fut Secy 86; Cmmndtn Comp IV Pascal 86; Rider Coll; Bus Educ.

LUZZI, ROSEANN; Lyndhurst HS; Lyndhurst, NJ; (2); Church Yth Grp; Girl Scts; Key Clb; Chorus; Mgr(s); 3rd Pl Cnty Art Shw 85; Rutgers; Arch.

LY, HUY; Dickinson HS; Jersey City, NJ; (3); NFL; Teachers Aide; Socr; Vllybl; Rutgers; Comp Sci.

LYLES, CALVIN; Franklin Township HS; Somerset, NJ; (3); VP Church Yth Grp; Var Bsktbl; Hon Roll; Varsity Clb; Minorities In Engrng 85; Bus Adm.

LYLES, DE ANNA ATHENYA; Eastside HS; Paterson, NJ; (3); 22/640; Chorus; Stage Crew; Rep Frsh Cls; Rep Soph Cls; Rep Jr Cls; Rep Stu Cncl; Mgr(s); Vllybl; Dnfth Awd; NHS; Havard U; Pharm.

LYLES, DEANNA; Eastside HS; Paterson, NJ; (3); 22/640; NAACP; Chorus; Variety Show; Stu Cncl; Mgr(s); Vllybl; Dnfth Awd; NHS; Ntl Merit SF; Howard U; Phrmcy.

LYNCH, BRENDAN; Morristown HS; Morristown, NJ; (3); 19/451; Church Yth Grp; Hosp Aide; Key Clb; Concert Band; Mrchg Band; JV Var Crs Cntry; JV Var Trk; High Hon Roll; Hon Roll; NHS.

LYNCH, CHRISTINA; Middletown HS South; Lincroft, NJ; (3); Church Yth Grp; Hosp Aide; Thesps; Nwsp Rptr; French Hon Soc; High Hon Roll; Hon Roll; NHS; Rider Coll Frgn Lang Tourn 1st Pl Adv French Orgnl Skit; Jrnlsm.

LYNCH, ERINN JANE; West Essex Regional HS; Fairfield, NJ; (3); Church Yth Grp; French Clb; Key Clb; Pep Clb; Nwsp Stf; Var Capt Cheerleading; Cmmnctns.

LYNCH, JENNIFER; Toms River H S North; Toms River, NJ; (4); Ski Clb; Capt Var Bsktbl; L Sftbl; L Tennis; L Trk; Hon Roll; NHS; Pres Schlr; MVP Bsktbl 87; Springfield Coll; Sprts Med.

LYNCH, MICHAEL; West Windsor Plainsboro HS; Princeton Junct, NJ; (3); Art Clb; Chess Clb; Radio Clb; School Play; Variety Show; Ed Lit Mag; Sec Soph Cls; VP Stu Cncl; Lion Awd; Mdl Cngrss Dlgt; Head Dlgt NJBA Mck Trl; James Madison U; Bus Admin.

LYNCH, NICOLE A; South Plainfield HS; S Plainfield, NJ; (3); Dance Clb; Band; Mrchg Band; Orch; Bsktbl; Trk; Hon Roll; Rtlng Sales.

LYNCH, PATRICIA; Immaculata HS; Somerset, NJ; (3); Church Yth Grp; VP Girl Scts; Lit Mag; Capt Soph Cls; Rep Stu Cncl; High Hon Roll; NHS; Spanish NHS; Chess Clb; Cmnty Wkr; Exclinc-Engl Awd 87; Slvr Awd-2nd Hghst Awd-Grl Scts 87; Outstndng Sprtn 86; Vet Med.

LYNCH, SUSAN; Lacey Township HS; Lanoka Harbor, NJ; (4); 11/298; DECA; Sec Frsh Cls; Sec Soph Cls; Sec Stu Cncl; Capt Var Cheerleading; Stat Mgr(s); Var Pom Pon; Powder Puff Ftbl; High Hon Roll; Hst NHS; Mac Millan Text Publctn 85; PA ST U; Bus Adm.

LYNCH, THOMAS; Bridgewater Raritan West HS; Bridgewater, NJ; (3); Ski Clb; Spanish Clb; JV Ftbl; Var Tennis; Im Vllybl; Hon Roll; Bus Admin.

LYNES, DAVID; St Marys Hall Doane Acad; Cherry Hill, NJ; (4); Am Leg Boys St; Computer Clb; Drama Clb; Red Cross Aide; Stage Crew; Rep Sr Cls; Capt Bsbl; Var Socr; Cit Awd; VP Frsh Cls; Gettysburg Coll; Bus Mgmt.

LYNN, MEGHAN; Manchester Township HS; Whiting, NJ; (3); Dance Clb; Drama Clb; Hosp Aide; Science Clb; Spanish Clb; School Play; Variety Show; Nwsp Rptr; Nwsp Stf; Stat Bsktbl; Semi-Fnlst Govnrs Schl Dance 87; Law.

LYNNE JR, LEO D; Nutley HS; Nutley, NJ; (2); 15/320; Church Yth Grp; Key Clb; Ski Clb; Variety Show; JV Ftbl; Socr; Wt Lftg; JV Wrstlng; Hon Roll; Princeton; Arch.

LYON, FIONA; Brick HS; Brick Town, NJ; (4); 7/400; Am Leg Aux Girls St; Dance Clb; Mrchg Band; High Hon Roll; Cll Prep Sci.

LYONS, BRIDGET; Dwight-Englewood Schl; Allendale, NJ; (3); Girl Scts; Orch; School Musical; School Play; Var Sftbl; Hon Roll; St Schlr; Headmasters Awd Dwight Englewood 87; Frnch Natl Cntst 1st In Chap 5th Natl 85 & 87; GS Slvr Awd.

LYONS, KATHLEEN; Immaculata HS; Neshanic Sta, NJ; (3); Ski Clb; Band; Concert Band; Mrchg Band; Stage Crew; Tennis; Vllybl; Hnrb Mntn Alg I 85; Adpt Grndprnt Pgm, Spartan Sprt Cmtes 84-86.

LYONS, KELLY; Manasquan HS; Brielle, NJ; (2); 34/250; Drama Clb; FBLA; Spanish Clb; Chorus; School Play; Mgr(s); Score Keeper; Hon Roll; Hnr Rl 86-87; Howard U; Law.

LYONS, STEPHANIE; Our Lady Of Good Counsel HS; Newark, NJ; (3); Camera Clb; Church Yth Grp; Letterman Clb; Pep Clb; Church Choir; Rep Sr Cls; Stu Cncl; Cheerleading; Intl Yr Homeless 86-87; U CA, Los Angeles; Comp Engrng.

LYONS, TRICIA M; Acad Of The Holy Angels; Oradell, NJ; (4); 14/152; French Clb; Mu Alpha Theta; Nwsp Rptr; Yrbk Stf; Cheerleading; NHS; Garden ST Distngshd Schlr 87; Hstry Hnr Socty 87; Ed.

MA, JUI C; Holy Spirit HS; Somers Point, NJ; (3); 29/332; Drama Clb; French Clb; Chorus; School Play; Mgr(s); Im Vllybl; Comp Sci.

MA, JUI SUN; Holy Spirit HS; Somers Pt, NJ; (3); 27/332; French Clb; Chorus; School Play; Yrbk Stf; Var Tennis; Var Hon Roll; NHS; Acad Math Awd 85-86; U Of Penn; Intl Econ.

MA, STEPHEN C; Dumont HS; Dumont, NJ; (3); Am Leg Boys St; M Alpha Theta; Science Clb; Variety Show; Yrbk Stf; Rep Stu Cncl; Im Soc High Hon Roll; NHS; Spanish NHS; Acad Decathlon Bronze Mdl Ess Wrtng; Rensselaer Medal; Chem Engrng.

MAASS, KELLIE; Gloucester City JR/Sr HS; Brooklawn, NJ; (3); GA Pep Clb; Science Clb; Band; School Play; Yrbk Stf; JV Fld Hcky; JV Sftb Hon Roll; Church Yth Grp; Mst Imprvd Sftbl 87; Rutgers Coll; Psych.

MAC CREGOR, SHARON; Sussex County Vo-Tech HS; Sparta, NJ; (3 Am Leg Aux Girls St; Art Clb; Camera Clb; Church Yth Grp; Spanish Cl Band; Pep Band; Nwsp Bus Mgr; Yrbk Bus Mgr; Rep Lit Mag; Spar Wmns Clb Art Awd 87; NJ ST Teen Arts Fstvl 87; Stheastern Bibl Co Art.

MAC DONNELL, TIMOTHY W; Saint Joseph Regional HS; Westwoo NJ; (4); Art Clb; Aud/Vis; Chess Clb; Pep Band; JV Tennis; Hon Ro NHS; Spanish NHS; Fordham U; Comp Sci.

MAC ELRATH, DONALD V; Overbrook Regional SR HS; Pine Hill, N (4); 30/335; French Clb; Band; High Hon Roll; Hon Roll; Prfct Atten Aw Elect Engr.

MAC FARLANE, GENE; Oakcrest HS; Sweetwater, NJ; (3); Boy Sct German Clb; JV Var Ftbl; Var Trk; Hon Roll; 1st Pl Acadc Excel 84; Vrs Schlr 87; Aero.

MAC LACHLAN, LISA; Bloomfield HS; Bloomfield, NJ; (3); Rep Jr Cl Fshn Inti Tech; Intr Dsgn.

MAC LEAN, H BARRY; New Milford HS; New Milford, NJ; (4); 23/13 Church Yth Grp; JV Bsbl; Var Wrstlng; French Hon Soc; Hon Roll; Pr Schlr; Muhlenberg Coll; Math.

MAC MILLAN, SCOTT TAYLOR; Aububon HS; Audubon, NJ; (4 Pres Ski Clb; Am Leg Boys St; Church Yth Grp; Computer Clb; Choru Capt Var Bsktbl; Capt Var Socr; High Hon Roll; Hon Roll; NJ Boys S Dlgt Amer Lgn 86-87; Med.

MAC NAMARA, JULIE; Collingswood HS; Collingswood, NJ; (3 Church Yth Grp; Office Aide; Nwsp Stf; Pres Frsh Cls; Rep Pres Stu Cn Cheerleading; High Hon Roll; Jr NHS; NHS.

MAC NIVEN, JILL; Parsippany Hills HS; Parsippany, NJ; (3); 2/30 Church Yth Grp; Letterman Clb; Off Jr Cls; Capt Swmmng; Trk.

MACAULAY, ALICE; Phillipsburg HS; Phillipsburg, NJ; (3); Dram Clb; FNA; Chorus; Church Choir; School Play; VP Frsh Cls; Ca Cheerleading; Hon Roll; Church Yth Grp; Natl Essay Awd 85; Bus Admi

MACAULAY, HELEN; Phillipsburg HS; Phillipsburg, NJ; (3); 110/31 Church Yth Grp; Pres Drama Clb; School Play; Trs Frsh Cls; Var Bsktb Stat Var Fld Hcky; Stat Var Sftbl; Hon Roll; School Musical; KCEA 1st ST Cmptn 84; Photo.

MACAULAY, MELISSA; Phillipsburg HS; Phillipsburg, NJ; (4); 35/31 Ski Clb; Band; Concert Band; Rep Stu Cncl; Fld Hcky; Sftbl; Hon Rol NHS; NE U; Chem.

MACCARONE, DONNA; St James HS; Swedesboro, NJ; (1); JV Bsktb JV Fld Hcky; Accntng.

MACCARONE, JOSEPH; St James HS; Swedesboro, NJ; (3); JV V Ftbl; Var Wrstlng; Marines Phys Ftnss Awd 87; Agri Bus.

MACCARONE, SAMUEL; St James HS; Swedesboro, NJ; (3); JV V Ftbl; Var Wrstlng; French Hon Soc; Marine Ftns Awd; Bus Mgmt.

MACDONALD, MICHELLE; Delaware Valley Regional HS; Milfor NJ; (4); Church Yth Grp; Band; Chorus; Concert Band; Mrchg Ban School Musical; DE Vly Rgnl Band Bstr Clb-Mrchng Band Awd 8 Mercer County CC; Photo.

MACEIA, ANTONIO; Oakcrest HS; Elwood, NJ; (3); Church Yth Gr French Clb; Spanish Clb; SADD; Wrstlng; Hon Roll; Vet.

MACGREGOR, JENNIFER; Lakewood HS; Lakewood, NJ; (3); 33/33 Hst FBLA; German Clb; Band; Concert Band; VP Mrchg Band; Orc Symp Band; High Hon Roll; Hon Roll; Rutgers; Mktng.

MACHAK, JILL ALLISON; Pequannock Township HS; Pompto Plains, NJ; (3); Camera Clb; Drama Clb; PAVAS; Acpl Chr; Chorus School Musical; Yrbk Phtg; Lit Mag; Varsity Clb; Stage Crew; Chem Hn Cls 85-86; Sci Awd 2nd Pl Proj 81; FL Inst Tech; Photogrphy.

MACHOS, GREGORY; S Plainfield HS; S Plainfield, NJ; (3); 10/30 Computer Clb; Science Clb; Spanish Clb; Mrchg Band; Rep Stu Cncl; J Bsktbl; Hon Roll; Spanish NHS; Rutgers; Comp Sci.

MACHTEMES, DONNA; Lyndhurst HS; Lyndhurst, NJ; (3); Germa Clb; Key Clb; Var Cheerleading; JV Trk; Inter Dsgn.

MACIEJUNES, DIANE; Ridgefield Park HS; Ridgefield Pk, NJ; (3); 34 200; Am Leg Aux Girls St; Cmnty Wkr; Girl Scts; Spanish Clb; Teacher Aide; Yrbk Stf; Lit Mag; Stat Crs Cntry; Ftbl; Stat Wrstlng; Hugh O Bria Delg 85; Trenton ST U; Kndrgrtn Tchr.

MACIOCH, CHERYL; Woodbridge HS; Woodbridge, NJ; (4); 30/38 Var Capt Crs Cntry; Var Trk; French Hon Soc; Hon Roll; NHS; Sun Tr Sun Rlty Awd 87; J P Lozo Mem Awd 87; Rutgers U; Mktg.

MACIURAK, M STEPHANIE; Bishop George Ahr/ST Thomas A H Perth Amboy, NJ; (4); Church Yth Grp; Dance Clb; Hosp Aide; Intnl Cl Spanish Clb; School Musical; Nwsp Stf; Lit Mag; JV Capt Socr; Art Cl Lit Mag Awd 85-87; Jrnlsm Cont 86-87; U Of DE; Psych.

MACK, EDWIN; Holy Spirit HS; Ventnor, NJ; (4); 41/363; JV Bsbl; Ho Roll; NHS.

MACK, MYRIA; Whippany Park HS; Whippany, NJ; (4); 22/171; Churc Yth Grp; Cmnty Wkr; Exploring; NAACP; Church Choir; Co-Capt Colo Guard; Madrigals; Yrbk Stf; Hon Roll; NHS; Cmmndtn High Achvmn Bio/Eng 83; Cmmndtn Outstndng Achvmnt Physics 86; Cmmndt Outstndng Achvmnt 83-86; Pre-Med.

MACK, PATRICK C; Piscatauay HS; Piscatawa Y, NJ; (3); Math Tm Radio Clb; Varsity Clb; Im Bsbl; Im Bsktbl; Im Coach Actv; Var L Soc Im Sftbl; Im Tennis; Hon Roll; Med.

MACK, SHARON; Immaculate Conception HS; Paterson, NJ; (3 Church Yth Grp; Cmnty Wkr; Pres Drama Clb; FCA; FBLA; Math Cl PAVAS; SADD; Chorus; School Play; Hi Hnrs Chorus 86; Notre Dame Psychlgy.

MACKE, NATALIE; Ranapo Regional HS; Franklin Lakes, NJ; (3); 42 323; AFS; Camera Clb; Church Yth Grp; Spanish Clb; Church Choir; Yrb Stf; Bsktbl; Socr; Hon Roll; NHS; Sbjct Merit Achvt Awd-Engl, Hstry & Spnsh 85-87; VP, Pres-Chrch Yth Grp 86, 87; Sci.

MACKEY, CHERYL; St Joseph Schl; Berlin, NJ; (3); Hosp Aide; Schoo Play; Yrbk Stf; Lit Mag; Sec Frsh Cls; Pres Soph Cls; Sec Jr Cls; Var Cap Cheerleading; High Hon Roll; Prfct Atten Awd; NCA All Ame Fnlst-Cheerldng 86; St Joseph U; Pediatrcn.

MACKEY, LAURA; Manchester Township HS; Lakehurst, NJ; (4) Drama Clb; Math Clb; Math Tm; Pres Spanish Clb; Chorus; Schoo Musical; School Play; Stage Crew; Ed Nwsp Ed-Chief; Nwsp Phtg; Mat Leag Awd, Drama Clb Awd 85 & 86; Spnsh Clb Awd 86; Glassboro ST Col Psych.

MACKIE, JEANINE; Cumberland Regional HS; Bridgeton, NJ; (3); 13/437; Intnl Clb; JV Trk; High Hon Roll; Hon Roll; Drexel; Chem Engrng.

MACKIEWICZ, JAMES; South River HS; South River, NJ; (3); 21/140; Boy Scts; Church Yth Grp; French Clb; Letterman Clb; Pep Clb; Political Wkr; SADD; Varsity Clb; Rep Stu Cncl; Var L Bsbl; Home News Allstar Bsbl Tm & Middlesex Cnty Arch Awd 87; Cntrl Jersey Dist 2nd Tm Quarterback 86; Arch.

MACKIN, LAUREL; Summit HS; Summit, NJ; (3); 21/270; Ski Clb; Nwsp Stf; Rep Soph Cls; Rep Jr Cls; Pres Stu Cncl; Var L Fld Hcky; Var L Sftbl; High Hon Roll; Hon Roll; NHS.

MACKINTOSH, VICTORIA E; BCVTS-MEDFORD HS; Pemberton, NJ; (4); 16/152; 4-H; FFA; SADD; Varsity Clb; VICA; Nwsp Rptr; Stu Cncl; Bowling; Cit Awd; DAR Awd; Govrnr Awd Pride In The Best Of NJ 87; Burlington CC; Envrnmnt Sci.

MACKLIN, FRANCESCA; Malcolm X Shabazz HS; Newark, NJ; (3); Cmnty Wkr; Yrbk Stf; Hon Roll; NHS; Comp Prgrmng.

MACKTA, JESSICA; Morristown HS; Morristown, NJ; (2); 1/450; French Clb; Hosp Aide; JCL; Latin Clb; Yrbk Phtg; Yrbk Stf; High Hon Roll; Hon Roll; Jr NHS; Magna Cum Laude On Natl Latin Exam; Photo.

MACNAMARA JR, JAMES F; Haddon Twp HS; Westmont, NJ; (4); 1/173; Am Leg Boys St; Aud/Vis; Boy Scts; FBLA; German Clb; Red Cross Aide; Varsity Clb; Stage Crew; Nwsp Rptr; Yrbk Stf; Eagle Scout Schlrshp 87; Cornell U; Chem Engrng.

MACRINA, CHRISTINE; Paul VI HS; Magnolia, NJ; (3); 88/400; Bowling; Im Sftbl; Hon Roll.

MACUR, JULIET; Bridgewater-Raritan West HS; Bridgewater, NJ; (3); Hosp Aide; SADD; Nwsp Stf; Lit Mag; Rep Stu Cncl; Var JV Bsktbl; High Hon Roll; Hon Roll; NHS; Church Yth Grp; Miss Teen NJ Scholar & Recgntn Pag 2nd Rnnr Up 86; Engl.

MACZKO, KRISTIE; Montville Township HS; Towaco, NJ; (4); 25/264; VP Church Yth Grp; Ski Clb; Capt Mrchg Band; Nwsp Phtg; Lit Mag; Trk; High Hon Roll; NHS; Ntl Merit SF; Rotary Awd; Rutgers U; Journalism.

MADAMA LAWSON, REENAH ANN; Toms River HS South; Toms River, NJ; (4); 118/328; Flag Corp; High Hon Roll; Ocean Co CC; Arch.

MADAMBA, AARON; Pinelands Regional HS; Mystic Island, NJ; (4); Pres VP Aud/Vis; Capt CAP; VP Science Clb; Stage Crew; Yrbk Phtg; JV Var Tennis; Elks Awd; Hon Roll; Sen Bill Bradley Stu Ldrshp Smnr 87; US Army.

MADARA, BELINDA; Holy Cross HS; Mount Holly, NJ; (3); 45/440; Drama Clb; Ski Clb; Chorus; Drill Tm; Mrchg Band; School Musical; Rep Sr Cls; Hon Roll; Lancers For Life; Nrsng.

MADAS, PAMELA; Lakewood HS; Lakewood, NJ; (3); 2/330; Am Leg Aux Girls St; Church Choir; Jazz Band; Yrbk Ed-Chief; Yrbk Stf; French Hon Soc; High Hon Roll; NHS; Chorus; School Musical; Congressional Schlr 87.

MADDEN, SUZANNE E; Teaneck HS; Teaneck, NJ; (4); 11/400; Sec VP Drama Clb; SADD; School Musical; School Play; Nwsp Rptr; Yrbk Phtg; Yrbk Stf; Hon Roll; NHS; Ntl Merit Ltr; Garden ST Dist, Douglass Schlr 87; Hnrs Div Schlrshp-IN U 87; VA Plytchnc Inst & St U; Thtre.

MADDOCKS, BRIAN; Pennsville Memorial HS; Pennsville, NJ; (4); 1/200; Am Leg Boys St; CAP; Pres Ski Clb; Rep Stu Cncl; Var Ftbl; Bausch & Lomb Sci Awd; NHS; NJ Gvrnrs Schl In Sci 86; NJ JR Acad Sci Grnts In Aid Wnnr 87; South Jrsy TD Clb All Acdmc Tm 86; U S Air Force Acad; Engnrng.

MADER, MIKE; Lower Cape May Regional HS; N Cape May, NJ; (3); Varsity Clb; Rep Frsh Cls; Rep Soph Cls; Rep Jr Cls; Ftbl; Im Wt Lftg; Var Wrstlng; Hon Roll; NHS; Opt Clb Awd; 1st & 3rd In Indust Arts Show 86-87; LCMR Wrstng Trnmnt Champ & JV MVP 87; Outstndng Indust Art 86; Arch.

MADGEY, ALLAN; Gateway R HS; Westville, NJ; (4); 25/205; Boy Scts; VICA; High Hon Roll; Hon Roll; Prfct Atten Awd; Rotary Awd; Spanish NHS; Outstndng Awd S Jersey Crftsmns Fair 85; U AK Fairbanks; Cvl Engrng.

MADORRAN, JEAN; Palisades Park HS; Palisades Pk, NJ; (3); JCL; Mu Alpha Theta; Concert Band; Nwsp Bus Mgr; Yrbk Stf; JV Bsktbl; Capt Twrlr; High Hon Roll; NHS; Ntl Merit Ltr; Grls Ctznshp Inst-Douglass Coll, JR Vstng Day-Lafayette Coll 87.

MADRID, DAVID; Don Bosco Prep HS; Dumont, NJ; (3); Var Crs Cntry; Var High Hon Roll.

MADRY, ANNA; Wallington HS; Wallington, NJ; (2); Service Clb; Mrchg Band; School Play; Stage Crew; Rep Stu Cncl; JV Stat Bsktbl; Hon Roll; Stu Of Wk 86; Educ.

MADSON, BETHANY; Bloomfield SR HS; Bloomfield, NJ; (3); Livingston Coll; Spch Thrpy.

MAESTRALE, MICHELLE; Paul Vi HS; Laurel Springs, NJ; (4); 39/503; Math Clb; Spanish Clb; School Play; Yrbk Sprt Ed; Lit Mag; Rep Soph Cls; Stat Bsbl; Var CAP; Var Score Keeper; Var Hon Roll; Finance.

MAFFEI, LOUIS; Oratory Catholic Prep Schl; Denville, NJ; (3); 9/45; Boy Scts; Computer Clb; Library Aide; Math Tm; Science Clb; High Hon Roll; NHS; Outstndng Achvt Ltn II Awd 86; Elec Engrng.

MAFFUCCI, ELISE; West Orange HS; W Orange, NJ; (3); French Clb; Hosp Aide; Band; Mrchg Band; Yrbk Stf; Lit Mag; Rep Stu Cncl; Var Cheerleading; French Hon Soc; Hon Roll.

MAGALETTA, LYNN; Mt St Dominic Acad; W Caldwell, NJ; (4); Dance Clb; Spanish Clb; Var Bsktbl; Stat Sftbl; Hon Roll; NHS; Prfct Atten Awd; Seton Hall U; Bus.

MAGAW, BETH; South River HS; South River, NJ; (3); Aud/Vis; Trs Church Yth Grp; German Clb; Band; Concert Band; Jazz Band; Mrchg Band; Pep Band; Stage Crew; Symp Band; Middlesex Cnty Coll; Radiolgy.

MAGEE, JENNIFER; Linden HS; Linden, NJ; (3); Pres Church Yth Grp; German Clb; Sec Key Clb; Chorus; Color Guard; L Mrchg Band; School Musical; Swmmng; NHS; Physcl Thrpy.

MAGEE, THOMAS; Gloucester Catholic HS; Woodbury, NJ; (3); Bsktbl; JV Capt Bowling; Var Capt Crs Cntry; Var Capt Trk; Most Spirited Player Bowling 86-87; Trenton ST Coll.

MAGENHEIMER, PATRICIA; Pinelands Regional HS; Tuckerton, NJ; (4); 4/190; Am Leg Aux Girls St; Math Clb; Science Clb; Spanish Clb; Nwsp Stf; Sec Stu Cncl; JV Cheerleading; Var Tennis; JV Trk; Hon Roll; Tulano U; Engrng.

MAGERA, MICHAEL J; Union Catholic Regional HS; Mountainside, NJ; (4); 7/294; Art Clb; Chess Clb; Pres Debate Tm; Science Clb; Ski Clb; Nwsp Stf; Lit Mag; NHS; Spanish NHS; Natl Sci Olympd 86; Acad All-Amer 86; Natl Sci Merit Awd 86; Biol.

MAGGS, ROBERT; Cinnaminson HS; Cinnaminson, NJ; (3); Am Leg Boys St; Math Clb; Yrbk Stf; Rep Soph Cls; Rep Jr Cls; Ftbl; Var Tennis; High Hon Roll; Hon Roll; NHS; S Jersey All Str Tennis 86-87; Gld Medl Athl Mnth May Tennis 86-87.

MAGIN, LAURA; Gateway Regional HS; Wenonah, NJ; (2); Exploring; JCL; Key Clb; Latin Clb; SADD; JV Fld Hcky; Swmmng; Var L Trk; Latin Natl Hnr Soc 87.

MAGISTRO, ELIZABETH; Long Branch HS; Long Branch, NJ; (4); 7/257; FBLA; Church Choir; Color Guard; DAR Awd; JETS Awd; NHS; Concert Band; Mrchg Band; VP Frsh Cls; Trs Jr Cls; PA Textile & Sci; Fshn Merch.

MAGLALANG, MICHAEL; Holly Spirit HS; Absecon, NJ; (2); 24/397; Boy Scts; Church Yth Grp; French Clb; Orch; School Play; Rep Soph Cls; JV Socr; Tennis; Latn Wd Ntl Tst Magna Cum Ld 85-86; Aerosp Engrng.

MAGLALANG, MICHELLE; Holy Spirit HS; Absecon, NJ; (3); 1/332; Orch; School Musical; Variety Show; Nwsp Stf; Lit Mag; Pres Soph Cls; NHS; NJ Music Tchrs Assoc Piano 1st Pl 86; Hgh Hns Ntl Piano Adtns 85; Smmnr Arts Inst 86; Med.

MAGNOTTI, LAURI; Clifton HS; Clifton, NJ; (3); Hosp Aide; Teachers Aide; Band; Concert Band; Mrchg Band; Mgr(s); Score Keeper; Hon Roll; Jr NHS; Scndry Educ.

MAGUIRE, BRENDAN; Haddon Township HS; Westmont, NJ; (2); 1/175; Chess Clb; Church Yth Grp; Debate Tm; Rep Frsh Cls; JV Socr; JV Tennis; High Hon Roll; NHS; Ntl Merit SF; Val; Natl Latin Exam-Slvr Mdl 86; Natl Latin Exam Cum Laude Cert 87; 1st Pl Indvdl In S Jersey In Mth 85; MIT; Rad.

MAGUIRE, MARIANNE; Ocean City HS; Ocean City, NJ; (2); 86/314; Art Clb; Spanish Clb; Socr; Trk; High Hon Roll; Hon Roll; NY U; Psych.

MAGUIRE, MEGHAN; Villa Victoria Acad; Jacobstown, NJ; (2); 1/18; Hosp Aide; Pres Soph Cls; Rep Stu Cncl; Var Bsktbl; L Var Socr; L Var Sftbl; High Hon Roll; Mock Trial 85-86; Schlrshp Villa Victoria Acad 85-87.

MAHER, HEATHER; Pequannock Township HS; Pequannock, NJ; (3); Church Yth Grp; Cmnty Wkr; Dance Clb; Band; Chorus; Capt Color Guard; Concert Band; Yrbk Ed-Chief; Var Twrlr; Hon Roll; Bio.

MAHER, JENNIFER; Mount Olive HS; Budd Lake, NJ; (3); 14/330; AFS; Drama Clb; Ski Clb; Nwsp Phtg; Yrbk Phtg; Yrbk Stf; Lit Mag; High Hon Roll; Prfct Atten Awd; School Play; Ntl Art Hnr Scty Treas 87-88; Comm.

MAHMOUD, EPTISAM; St Aloysius HS; Jersey City, NJ; (3).

MAHMOUD, GERMINE; Mother Seton Regional HS; Hillside, NJ; (2); Library Aide; Science Clb; SADD; Trs Soph Cls; Hon Roll; 2nd Hnr; Sci & Math Awd; Princton; Pediatrics.

MAHON, DEBRA ANNE; Notre Dame HS; Trenton, NJ; (4); 19/324; Varsity Clb; Capt Crs Cntry; Trk; High Hon Roll; Hon Roll; NHS; Natl Bus Hnr Scty Sec 85-87; NJ Schlr Ath Awd 86-87; Trenton ST Coll.

MAHONEY, KEVIN; Hillsborough HS; Somerville, NJ; (4); 7/300; Math Tm; Science Clb; Jr Cls; Tennis; High Hon Roll; NHS; Ntl Merit Ltr; Pres Schlr; St Schlr; Penn ST U Schlr 87; Acadmc Tm Capt 85-87; Span Achvt Awd 87; Penn ST; Finance.

MAHONEY, LYNN; Holy Rosary Acad; Jersey City, NJ; (3); Mgr Church Yth Grp; Mgr Drama Clb; Pres Library Aide; Math Tm; Mgr Spanish Clb; VP Soph Cls; Accntng.

MAHONY, JOHN J; Phillipsburg Catholic HS; Stewartsville, NJ; (3); 32/90; Am Leg Boys St; Church Yth Grp; Ski Clb; Varsity Clb; Var Capt Ftbl; Var Capt Wrstlng; Hon Roll; Vet Med.

MAHR, CHRISTOPHER; Belvidere HS; Arnold, CA; (4); Am Leg Boys St; Chess Clb; Letterman Clb; Math Tm; Varsity Clb; VICA; Stage Crew; Yrbk Stf; Off Jr Cls; Off Sr Cls; Bsktbl-Dfnsv Plyr Of Yr Coaches Awd 86-87; Glf-Capt Cnfrnc All Str MVP 86-87; AIASA ST Cnfrnc 84; Boston U; Acctng.

MAIER, CHRISTOPHER; Paul VI HS; Voorhees, NJ; (4); 21/503; French Clb; Math Clb; Capt Bowling; Co-Capt Tennis; Hon Roll; NHS; Grdn ST Dstngshd Schlr 86-87; Bio Sci.

MAIER, ELIZABETH; Paramus HS; Paramus, NJ; (2); Drama Clb; Band; Chorus; Mrchg Band; Orch; School Musical; School Play; Stage Crew; Yrbk Stf; Lit Mag; Grmn Hnr Socty 87; Psych.

MAIER, JENNIFER; Highland HS; Blackwood, NJ; (2); French Clb; Rep Frsh Cls; Rep Soph Cls; Rep Stu Cncl; JV Cheerleading; JV Socr; Hon Roll; Drexel; CPA.

MAIESE, TINA; Edgewood HS; Berlin, NJ; (3); 6/360; Latin Clb; Varsity Clb; Bsktbl; Var Socr; Var Capt Sftbl; High Hon Roll; Hon Roll; Jr NHS; NHS; Prfct Atten Awd; Play Of Wk Sftbl 87; Olympic All Conf Awd Sftbll Ptchr 87; Accntng.

MAILISCH, CHRISTOPHER; Morristown HS; Morris Plains, NJ; (3); Boy Scts; Latin Clb; Radio Clb; Hon Roll; Ntl Merit SF; Yrbk Phtg; Arch.

MAILLARO, KATHLEEN; Holy Spirit HS; Brigantine, NJ; (4); 120/400; Dance Clb; Drama Clb; SADD; School Musical; School Play; Nwsp Bus Mgr; Nwsp Rptr; Yrbk Stf; Off Stu Cncl; Elks Awd; Miss NJ USA 87; Cathlc Dghtrs Amer Awd 83; Wall St Wiz Awd 83; Salisbury ST Coll; Cmnctns Art.

MAILLOUX, THERESA; Hamilton W HS; Yardville, NJ; (4); 18/322; Band; Concert Band; Mrchg Band; Symp Band; Yrbk Stf; Diving; NHS; Pres Schlr; Edward C Levy Schlrshp 87-88; Hamilton Tnshp Educ Assn Awd 87; Trenton ST Coll; Engl.

MAIN, LYNNAIA; Egg Harbor Township HS; Cardiff, NJ; (4); 4/289; French Clb; Model UN; Ski Clb; Sec Soph Cls; Sec Jr Cls; Rep Stu Cncl; High Hon Roll; VP NHS; Intl Dir Distngushd Ldrshp 86; Ntl Ldrshp Merit Awd 86; Pres Schlrshp Am U 87; The American U; Intl Rel.

MAIRONE, KERRY; Wildwood Catholic HS; N Wildwood, NJ; (3); 4-H; Spanish Clb; Bsktbl; 4-H Awd; High Hon Roll; NHS; Spanish NHS; Englsh Exc Awd 86; Rlgn Achvt Awd 86-87; Equine Stdys.

MAIRONE, RICHARD; Holy Spirit HS; Northfield, NJ; (4); 12/363; Spanish Clb; Pres SADD; Nwsp Ed-Chief; Nwsp Rptr; Pres Jr Cls; Var Capt Bsktbl; Hon Roll; NHS; Rep Frsh Cls; Duke Coll; Accntng.

MAISTO, BARBARA; John P Stevens HS; Edison, NJ; (3); 66/469; Science Clb; SADD; Orch; Rep Stu Cncl; Var L Cheerleading; Powder Puff Ftbl; Var L Sftbl; Hon Roll; NHS; Colonia Iselin Athltc Assoc Awd 85; Lwyr.

MAITRE, MARY ANN; Asbury Park HS; Asbury Park, NJ; (3); French Clb; Sec Key Clb; Yrbk Stf; Tennis; High Hon Roll; Kiwanis Awd; Voice Dem Awd; Var Schlr 85-87; Omega Psi Phi Awd 86-87; Forensics 85-87; Engr.

MAKAREWICZ, MONICA; Edison HS; Hampstead, NH; (4); 1/390; Pres Jr Cls; Sr Cls; Twrlr; Trs French Hon Soc; NHS; Pres Schlr; Val; Church Yth Grp; French Clb; FTA; Miss NJ Coed Pageant 3rd Runner Up, Challenger Schlrshp 87; NJ St Baton Chmpnshps 2nd Pl 86; Amer U; Law.

MAKAROW, TIM; Millville SR HS; Millville, NJ; (4); 89/482; Chess Clb; Concert Band; Jazz Band; School Musical; Variety Show; Lois Armstrong Jazz Awd 87; Glassboro ST Coll.

MAKO, MATTHEW; Freehold Township HS; Freehold, NJ; (4); Chess Clb; Lit Mag; Ntl Merit SF.

MAKOWKA, DAVID J; Paramus Catholic Boys HS; Rochelle Park, NJ; (3); Am Leg Boys St; JV Wrstlng; Brnz Mdl 3rd-4th Pl Indian Hills Wrstlngtrnmnt 85-87.

MAKOWSKI, KIM; Weehawken HS; Weehawken, NJ; (4); 18/94; Nwsp Stf; Yrbk Ed-Chief; Yrbk Stf; Pres Soph Cls; Pres Jr Cls; Pres Sr Cls; Stat Ftbl; Twrlr; Stat Wrstlng; High Hon Roll; Cls Recgntn Awd 87; Richard Arricale Mem Awd 87; Weehawken Ed Assn Awd 87; Fashion Inst Tech; Fash Buyer.

MAKRANSKY, JIM; Sayreville War Memorial HS; Parlin, NJ; (4); 158/438; Var L Ftbl; Im Wt Lftg; Hon Roll; Distngshd Achvt Awd Ftbl, & Offnsv Lnmn Wk 87; Kean Coll; Accntng.

MALABE, FLOR; Wm L Dickinson HS; Jersey Cty, NJ; (2); GAA; School Play; Bsktbl; Hon Roll; Police Offcr.

MALANGA, JOHN; Immaculate Conception HS; Newark, NJ; (4); 18/76; Boys Clb Am; School Musical; Nwsp Rptr; Yrbk Stf; Var Bsbl; Var Ftbl; Var Capt Wrstlng; Hon Roll; MVP Wrstlng 86-87; Essex Cnty Coaches Schlr/Athlete Awd 87; Rutgers Newark; Accntnt.

MALANIAK, CHARLES; Lyndhurst HS; Lyndhurst, NJ; (2); 15/75; Key Clb; Latin Clb; Band; Concert Band; Mrchg Band; Orch; Pep Band; Bsktbl; Var Socr; Var Trk; Hartwick; Psych.

MALANTIC, GRACE; Saddle River Day HS; Oradell, NJ; (3); Math Tm; Lit Mag; Stu Cncl; Bsktbl; Socr; Sftbl; High Hon Roll; Spanish NHS; Jr Athl Of Yr; Certs Exc Alg, Biol & Engl 84-85; MVP Grls Vars Sccr 85-86; Certs Exc Span, US Hist 85.

MALATESTA, RALPH; Watchung Hills Regional HS; Warren, NJ; (4); 150/325; Key Clb; SADD; Varsity Clb; JV Bsbl; Im Bsktbl; Var Capt Ftbl; Im Lcrss; Im Sftbl; Im Vllybl; Im Wt Lftg; All Cnty Ftbl Ply 86; All ST, Area, Cnty Ftbl Plyr 87; SADD 87; WV U; Bus.

MALDONADO JR, JESUS; Barringer HS; Newark, NJ; (1); Red Cross Aide; JV Bsbl; Hon Roll; Prfct Atten Awd; Sci B Avg 87; IN U; Engr.

MALDONY, MAURA; Mother Seton Reg HS; Edison, NJ; (4); 19/100; Hosp Aide; Library Aide; Science Clb; School Play; Yrbk Stf; Lit Mag; Rep Soph Cls; Hon Roll; Draw Me A Story Cont Semi-Fnlst 87; Dept Awd For Art; Marymount Coll; Intr Dsgn.

MALESICH, RICHARD C; Camden Catholic HS; Cherry Hill, NJ; (4); 80/276; Am Leg Boys St; Computer Clb; FBLA; German Clb; Political Wkr; JV Bsbl; Im Bsktbl; Hon Roll; Rutgers; Bus.

MALETSKY, LORIN; Pompton Lakes HS; Pompton Lakes, NJ; (3); 1/124; Am Leg Boys St; Boy Scts; Church Yth Grp; Computer Clb; Math Tm; Q&S; Quiz Bowl; Band; Nwsp Phtg; Yrbk Ed-Chief; Rensselaer Math & Sci Mdl; Comp Engrng.

MALIA, BOBBI O MALLEY; Immaculate Heart Acad; Emerson, NJ; (2); Natl Beta Clb; Var Capt Cheerleading; Im Gym; Hon Roll; Lake Forest; Sci.

MALIK, CHRISTINE; Middletown High School South; Middletown, NJ; (3); Church Yth Grp; Trs Girl Scts; Thesps; Chorus; School Musical; School Play; High Hon Roll; NHS; Pres Spanish NHS; Bronze Congressional Medal 86; Sen Bradley Young Citzns Awd 86; Girl Scout Gold Awd 87; Bus.

MALINOWSKI, MICHELLE; Jackson Memorial HS; Jackson, NJ; (4); 14/391; Sec French Clb; School Musical; Lit Mag; Wt Lftg; French Hon Soc; High Hon Roll; NHS; Pres Acdmc Fit Awd 87; Fitnss Awd 84; Rutgers Coll; Engl.

MALINOWSKI, ROBERT A; Piscataway Voctnl & Techncl HS; Piscataway, NJ; (4); 15/163; VICA; Var Capt Bsbl; Var Bsktbl; Var Capt Socr; Hon Roll; Schrl Athlete Awd 87; Democratic Social Clb Schrlshp 87; Polish Natl Hme Schrlshp 87; Middlesex County Coll; Clnry Ar.

MALINOWSKI, TARA; Salem HS; Salem, NJ; (3); Office Aide; SADD; JV Capt Cheerleading; Trvl Agnt.

MALINOWSKI, WILLIAM; Bayonne HS; Bayonne, NJ; (3); Key Clb; JV Bsktbl; Acctng.

MALISZEWSKI, JANETTE; Highland Regional HS; Blackwood, NJ; (3); 23/285; FBLA; Yrbk Stf; Rep Frsh Cls; Sec Soph Cls; VP Jr Cls; Stat Wrstlng; NHS; Prof Secy.

MALLARI, CHRIS; St James HS; Pennsvlle, NJ; (1); Stu Rep Ideals St Marys Schl 86; Princeton.

MALLIK, KAMALA; Pequannock Township HS; Pequannock, NJ; (3); 2/215; Dance Clb; German Clb; Hosp Aide; Band; Chorus; JV Tennis; Hon Roll; NHS; Ntl Merit SF; Pres Clssrm 87.

MALLORY, YVETTE; Buena Regional HS; Richland, NJ; (3); 51/218; Drama Clb; Hosp Aide; Varsity Clb; Church Choir; Yrbk Stf; JV Var Fld Hcky; Mgr(s); Sftbl; Hon Roll; Jr NHS; Rutgers U; Fshn Merch.

MALMENDIER, JACQUELINE; Brick Township HS; Brick Town, NJ; (3); 11/420; Dance Clb; Drama Clb; French Clb; Key Clb; Teachers Aide; Thesps; Pres Chorus; Capt Mrchg Band; School Musical; School Play; Julliard; Voice.

MALONE, CHARLENE; Clifford J Scott HS; E Orange, NJ; (3); 6/280; Math Tm; Hon Roll; NHS; NJ Inst Tech; Mech Engr.

MALONE, JEFFREY; Seton Hall Preparatory Schl; West Orange, NJ; (3); 15/212; Church Yth Grp; German Clb; Var L Crs Cntry; Var L Trk; High Hon Roll; Hon Roll; Pilot In US Military.

MALONEY, CHRIS; Paul VI HS; Haddon Field, NJ; (4); 220/511; Boy Scts; Church Yth Grp; Capt Crs Cntry; Trk; Temple U; Hstry.

MALONEY, CHRISTINE; Toms River South HS; Pine Beach, NJ; (4); 9/324; Varsity Clb; Mrchg Band; School Play; Ed Yrbk Stf; Bsktbl; High Hon Roll; Hon Roll; NHS; Acad Ltr 86 & 87; GA Court Coll; Elem Ed.

MALONEY, ERIN; Paramus Catholic HS; Upr Saddle Rvr, NJ; (3); Art Clb; Church Yth Grp; Exploring; Chorus; Lit Mag; Capt Var Tennis; Hon Roll; Purdue U; Pre-Law.

MALONEY, LANCE; Holy Cross HS; Florence, NJ; (3); JV Bsbl; JV Crs Cntry; Hon Roll; VFW Awd; Law.

MALONEY, ROBERT; Hudson Catholic HS; Hoboken, NJ; (3); Computer Clb; Science Clb; Hon Roll; NHS; Tutored Fresh 86-87; Strtgy Clb 86-87; Accntng.

MALTESE, LISA; Buena Regional HS; Vineland, NJ; (3); Drama Clb; SADD; School Play; Rep Stu Cncl; Trk; Hon Roll; Jr NHS.

MALTMAN, MELISSA; Kingsway Regional HS; Swedesboro, NJ; (3); Church Yth Grp; French Clb; Office Aide; Pep Clb; Science Clb; Varsity Clb; Trs VP Stu Cncl; Var JV Cheerleading; Powder Puff Ftbl; Var Swmmng; Chld Psych.

MALTZ, MELANIE; Cherry Hill West HS; Cherry Hill, NJ; (3); Intnl Clb; Spanish Clb; Teachers Aide; Stu Cncl; Var L Lcrss; Var L Tennis; Hon Roll; Var Let Tennis 86-87; Trenton ST Coll.

MALUSIS, JOHN; Pennsville Memorial HS; Pennsville, NJ; (3); 23/231; Trs Frsh Cls; Trs Soph Cls; Trs Jr Cls; Trs Sr Cls; Rep Stu Cncl; Var L Ftbl; Hon Roll; Var L Bsbl; Bsktbl; Ftbl-1st Tm All Tri-Cnty Conf All Star, Wd Rcvr, Salem Cnty Wd Rcvr & Crnr Bk 86; Bsbl Star Ctchr 87.

MAMALIAN, PAUL; New Milford HS; New Milford, NJ; (4); 8/136; Pres Church Yth Grp; Ski Clb; Yrbk Bus Mgr; Var Socr; Var Capt Trk; Pres French Hon Soc; NHS; Ntl Merit Schol; St Schlr; SADD; Armenian Missnry Assn Amer Schlrshp, Armenian Rlf Soc Merit Awd 87-88; George Washington U; Pre-Law.

MAMCZAK, NATALIE DENISE; Mother Seton Regional HS; Rahway, NJ; (3); 4/90; Cmnty Wkr; Hosp Aide; Math Tm; Quiz Bowl; Science Clb; Yrbk Stf; Sec Stu Cncl; Var Vllybl; Hon Roll; NHS.

MAMUNES, MELANIE; Ridgewood HS; Ridgewood, NJ; (3); Cmnty Wkr; Trs French Clb; Scholastic Bowl; SADD; Yrbk Stf; Rep Frsh Cls; Rep Soph Cls; Rep Jr Cls; Rep Sr Cls; JV Bsktbl.

MANCHAND, SHAUN; Montclair HS; Montclair, NJ; (3); 75/404; Am Leg Boys St; FBLA; FTA; Pres Spanish Clb; Pres Jr Cls; Rep Stu Cncl; Capt Var Socr; Hon Roll; Srvc Awd, Spcl Olympics Vlntr, Hd Prom Cmte 87; Finnc.

MANDAK, GREGORY; Clifton HS; Clifton, NJ; (4); 5/580; German Clb; Math Clb; Science Clb; Capt Lcrss; High Hon Roll; NHS; Garden ST Distngshd Schlr 87; Dr Elinor E Hanna Schlrshp 87; Outstndng Achvt Forgn Lang Germ 87; Middlebury Coll.

MANDARA, BILL; Paramus HS; Paramus, NJ; (2); Church Yth Grp; Band; Church Choir; Concert Band; Arch.

MANDELL, BEVERLY; Lakewood HS; Lakewood, NJ; (3); 43/360; Am Leg Aux Girls St; Rep Frsh Cls; Rep Soph Cls; Sec VP Stu Cncl; JV Var Cheerleading; JV Mgr(s); JV Score Keeper; Var L Socr; English Clb; Spanish Clb; U Of VA.

MANEELY, CHRISTINA; Holy Cross HS; Riverside, NJ; (3); 90/403; Church Yth Grp; French Clb; Hosp Aide; SADD; Yrbk Stf; Stat Crs Cntry; Mgr(s); Score Keeper; Stat Trk; Vllybl; Phila Coll Of Textiles/Sci; Bus.

MANEGOLD, MARK; Pompton Lakes HS; Pompton Lakes, NJ; (2); Boy Scts; Pres Computer Clb; Math Clb; Spanish Clb; SADD; Concert Band; Jazz Band; Mrchg Band; Rep Frsh Cls; Rep Stu Cncl; Aero Engr.

MANEKAS, KAY; Madison Central HS; Old Bridge, NJ; (3); 111/370; FBLA; Spanish Clb; Varsity Clb; Chorus; Rep Frsh Cls; Rep Soph Cls; Rep Jr Cls; Sec Sr Cls; Rep Stu Cncl; Var Capt Cheerleading; Rutgers U; Psych.

MANELL, JILL; Paramus Catholic Grls Regional HS; Ridgefield, NJ; (3); Art Clb; Church Yth Grp; Dance Clb; Hosp Aide; Church Choir; Nwsp Rptr; Explorers Clb-Sec & Bergen News-Sun Bulletn 86-87; Miss Amer Co-Ed NJ & Outstndng Awd 85; Educ.

MANFRA, LAUREEN; Brich Township HS; Brick Town, NJ; (3); 74/400; Capt Color Guard; JV Bsktbl; JV Trk; High Hon Roll; Hon Roll; Psych.

MANFREDI, JESSICA; Indian Hills HS; Franklin Lks, NJ; (3); 27/303; Co-Capt French Clb; High Hon Roll; Hon Roll.

MANGAN, JENNIFER; Roselle Catholic HS; Roselle, NJ; (4); Drama Clb; Church Choir; School Musical; Stage Crew; Lit Mag; French Hon Soc; High Hon Roll; Hon Roll; NHS; School Play; Natl Merit Cmmnd Stu 86-87; U Of MD.

MANGANO, MICHAEL; Pitman HS; Pitman, NJ; (3); #6 In Class; Teachers Aide; Band; Var Bsbl; JV Bsktbl; Var Socr; Hon Roll; NHS.

MANGAROO, ROBERT; Don Bosco Tech; Paterson, NJ; (2); 12/86; JV Bsbl; Var Bsktbl; Hon Roll.

MANGIONE, JIM; Mc Corristin HS; Mercerville, NJ; (3); Off Art Clb; Off Camera Clb; Y-Teens; Band; Chorus; Concert Band; Jazz Band; Mrchg Band; School Musical; Nwsp Phtg; Svc Awd Music 85-87; Comp Sci.

MANGIONE, NAOMI; High Point Regional HS; Augusta, NJ; (4); 13/230; Church Yth Grp; Concert Band; School Play; Sftbl; Pres Frsh Cls; Tennis; Jr NHS; NHS; Spanish Clb; Band; Acad Awd For Spnsh Slvr Mdl 83-84; Acad Awd For Msc Gold Mdl 83-84.

MANGOLD, SCOTT; Haddonfield Memorial HS; Haddonfield, NJ; (3); Trs Frsh Cls; Trs Soph Cls; Var Bsbl; Var Socr; Hon Roll; Bus Mgmt.

MANHEIMER, KRISTA; Morristown HS; Morris Plains, NJ; (2); 20/450; Sec Key Clb; Red Cross Aide; Nwsp Rptr; Var Cheerleading; JV Socr; High Hon Roll; Hon Roll; Duke U; Bus Admin.

MANI, NARAYAN; West Essex SR HS; Fairfield, NJ; (3); Debate Tm; French Clb; Key Clb; Socr; Wrstlng; Hon Roll; Econ.

MANION, KIMBERLY; Rutherford HS; Rutherford, NJ; (3); Art Clb; Drama Clb; Key Clb; Science Clb; Variety Show; Rep Frsh Cls; Sec Stu Cncl; Var Cheerleading; Var Swmmng; JV Tennis; MVP Swmmng 87.

MANKOWSKI, KEN; Delran HS; Delran, NJ; (4); 36/188; Church Yth Grp; Pres Computer Clb; FBLA; Math Tm; Pep Clb; Rep Soph Cls; Rep Stu Cncl; Im Bsktbl; Im Vllybl; Hon Roll; Prfct Attnd Awd 83-87; Drexel U; Comp Sci.

MANN, EDWARD; River Dell SR HS; Oradell, NJ; (4); Spanish Clb; Pres Band; Chorus; Drm Mjr(t); Jazz Band; Mrchg Band; School Play; Symp Band; JP Sousa Awd; NHS; B Nai B Rith Oradell Awd 87; IN U.

MANNING, CAROL; Madison HS; Madison, NJ; (3); 56/212; Church Yth Grp; French Clb; GAA; Yrbk Stf; Rep Stu Cncl; JV Bsktbl; Score Keeper; Hon Roll; Crmnl Jstc.

MANNING, MARLISE; Immaculata HS; Bridgewater, NJ; (3); 4-H; Office Aide; Ski Clb; Bryant Coll RI; Finance.

MANNING, SUSAN; Middletown South HS; Middletown, NJ; (3); Church Yth Grp; Yrbk Stf; Rep Stu Cncl; Var Ftbl; Score Keeper; Var Swmmng; Hon Roll; Bus.

MANNION, DEBBIE; Manalapan HS; Manalapan, NJ; (3); SADD; Crs Cntry; NHS; Bus Admin.

MANOLAKIS, ALEXIA EVA; Union HS; Union, NJ; (3); Dance Clb; Drama Clb; French Clb; School Musical; School Play; Yrbk Stf; Im Bowling; Im Gym; Sftbl; Im Swmmng; NYU; Dnc.

MANSUETO, ANNAMARIA; Immaculate Conception HS; Leonia, NJ; (3); Art Clb; Camera Clb; Drama Clb; Ski Clb; Spanish Clb; SADD; Chorus; School Play; Stage Crew; Yrbk Stf; NY U; Bus.

MANTILLA, CHANTE MARIE; Dumont HS; Dumont, NJ; (4); 24/217; Mu Alpha Theta; Service Clb; Spanish Clb; Stage Crew; Variety Show; Yrbk Stf; Ftbl; High Hon Roll; Mu Alpha Theta Awd; Pres Schlr; Montclair ST; Psych.

MANTYLA, MICHAEL; Don Bosco Prep; Suffern, NY; (2); 5/215; Computer Clb; Hosp Aide; Im Trk; High Hon Roll; Amer Leg Awd 85; Schl Scholar 85; Stephen Gangone Mem Scholar 86.

MANVELE, NANCY L; Haddon Township HS; Collingswood, NJ; (4); 31/171; Church Yth Grp; Dance Clb; Varsity Clb; School Musical; School Play; Rep Frsh Cls; Mgr(s); Timer; Gov Hon Prg Awd; Stockton ST Coll; Pol Sci.

MANZ, MARK; Montville HS; Montville, NJ; (2); Key Clb; Ski Clb; Spanish Clb; JV Socr; High Hon Roll; Hon Roll; Engrng.

MANZELLA, JOANN; Queen Of Peace HS; Lyndhurst, NJ; (3); 126/280; Church Yth Grp; Debate Tm; NFL; Teachers Aide; Nwsp Stf; Rep Soph Cls; VP Capt Crs Cntry; Var L Trk; Hon Roll; Cmnty Wkr; Arch Diocese Nawarks Ldrshp Wrkshp 86; Nrsng.

MANZO, ROBERT; Passaic County Tech; Paterson, NJ; (4); 1/366; Am Leg Boys St; Varsity Clb; VICA; Nwsp Stf; Bsbl; Hon Roll; NHS; St Schlr; Val; Garden ST Dist Schlr 86; NJIT; Elec Engr.

MAPPIN, KENT; St Joseph Regional HS; Mahwah, NJ; (3); 156/280; JV Lcrss; Im Wt Lftg; Stockton ST Coll; Mrktng.

MAPPS, MAURICE; Central HS; Newark, NJ; (4); VP Stu Cncl; Var Capt Ftbl; NC A&T; Mech Engr.

MAQSUDI, MAHNAZ; Parsippany Hills HS; Parsippany, NJ; (3); DECA; French Clb; Office Aide; Varsity Clb; Variety Show; JV Bsktbl; Var Powder Puff Ftbl; Var Socr; Hon Roll; Compltd Fnl 2 Grdes 1 Yr 86-87; Utica Coll; Brdcstng.

MARAMANGALAM, MARY; Paramus Catholic Girls Regnl HS; Englewood, NJ; (3); Hosp Aide; Nwsp Stf; Lit Mag; Hon Roll; 150 Hrs Srvc Pin Vlntr Srvcs Englewood Hosp 87; MA Scl Wrk.

MARANDINO, JARED; Buena Regional HS; Newfield, NJ; (2); Ski Clb; JV Bsbl; JV Var Ftbl; Cvl Engrng.

MARANDOLA, FRANCO; Ferris HS; Jersey City, NJ; (3); Am Leg Boys St; Yrbk Stf; Rutgers; Comp Sci.

MARANT, DONNA; Eastside HS; Paterson, NJ; (3); Dance Clb; GAA; Varsity Clb; Acpl Chr; Chorus; Rep Jr Cls; Rep Stu Cncl; JV Crs Cntry; JV Trk; Awd Vocal Prfrmnce 86-87; Awd In-Door Trck 85-86; Awd Crss Cntry 85-86; Psych.

MARASCIO, FRANK; Rutherford HS; Rutherford, NJ; (3); Boys Clb Am; Spanish Clb; Hon Roll; Prfct Atten Awd; Monclair ST Coll; Math.

MARASHLIAN, ALEXANDER; Parsippany Hills HS; Morris Plains, NJ; (2); Church Yth Grp; Symp Band; Bsbl.

MARASPIN, GLENN M; Bridgewater-Raritan H S West; Raritan, NJ; (3); Am Leg Boys St; Pep Clb; SADD; Off Frsh Cls; Pres Soph Cls; Pres Jr Cls; Off Sr Cls; Pres Stu Cncl; Var JV Socr; Hon Roll; Natl Grd Bsc Trng Hnr Grad 87; Stu Brd Of Ed Spksmn 85-87.

MARAZITI, DEBORAH L; Morris Catholic HS; Boonton Twp, NJ; (4); 1/138; Girl Scts; Hosp Aide; Capt Color Guard; School Musical; School Play; Bausch & Lomb Sci Awd; Pres NHS; Ntl Merit Ltr; Val; Allied Sgnl Sci Awd; Chrstn Svc Awd; Swarthmore Coll; Astrophyscs.

MARCANTUONO, STACEY; Maple Shade HS; Maple Shade, NJ; (2); FBLA; GAA; Spanish Clb; JV Bowling; JV Socr; High Hon Roll; Hon Roll; Prfct Atten Awd; Rotary Club Yth Merit Awd 86; Hrse Show 3rd Pl Ylw Rbbn 86; Soccer Day Camp Cert 86; Burlington CC; Bus.

MARCEL, DANIELLE; Kittatinny Regional HS; Newton, NJ; (3); 35/216; SADD; Pres Frsh Cls; Pres Soph Cls; Pres Jr Cls; Rep Stu Cncl; JV Cheerleading; Trk; High Hon Roll; Hugh O Brien Awd 86.

MARCEL, JOSEPH R; Kittatinny Regional HS; Newton, NJ; (4); 26/222; Var Bsktbl; Var Capt Socr; Var Trk; High Hon Roll; NHS; Pres Schlr; Outstndng Stu-Athl 87; Natl Schlr Athl Awd-US Army Rsrv 87; Shippensburg U Of PA; Comp Sci.

MARCELLE, JILL; Middletown HS South; Middletown, NJ; (3); Church Yth Grp; Cmnty Wkr; Stage Crew; Variety Show; Sec Soph Cls; Im Fld Hcky; Im Socr; Hon Roll; Acdmc Excel Sci & Engl 85; Boston Coll; Bus Admin.

MARCELO, RONALD; Oratory Prep; Springfield, NJ; (3); 1/46; Chess Clb; Math Tm; Service Clb; Ski Clb; Nwsp Rptr; Pres Frsh Cls; Trs Sec Stu Cncl; Var Crs Cntry; Var Trk; NHS; Kennedy Mem Schlrshp 83-88.

MARCH, JULIE; Depaul Diocesan HS; Wayne, NJ; (4); 40/156; Cmnty Wkr; VP Sr Cls; Rep Stu Cncl; Var Capt Bsktbl; Var Capt Cheerleading; JV Fld Hcky; Sftbl; Im Vllybl; Hon Roll; All Cnty Bsktbll 87; North-South All ST Bsktbl Game 87; Peer Cnslr 87; Syracuse U; Publc Rltns.

MARCHESE, JOSEPH; Kittatinny Regional HS; Newton, NJ; (3); 17/216; Var Bowling; JV Trk; High Hon Roll; Hon Roll; NHS; 1st Pl Outstndng Mchncl Drwng NJ Stu Crftsmns Fair 86; 1st Pl Arch Rndrng NJ Stu Fair 86.

MARCHESE, RALPH; Wayne Hills HS; Wayne, NJ; (3); 72/370; Jazz Band; JV Socr; Var Wrstlng; Hon Roll.

MARCHESE, VALERIE; Brick Township HS; Brick, NJ; (4); 65/343; Dance Clb; Varsity Clb; Yrbk Stf; Rep Frsh Cls; Rep Soph Cls; Rep Jr Cls; Rep Sr Cls; Capt Cheerleading; Coach Actv; Powder Puff Ftbl; Hnr Awds 83-87; Voice Of Dmcrcy 87; Montclair ST; Math.

MARCHIONE, DAVID C; Holy Cross HS; Moorestown, NJ; (3); 64/410; Am Leg Boys St; Boy Scts; Band; School Musical; Yrbk Ed-Chief; Rep Soph Cls; Rep Jr Cls; Rep Sr Cls; Hon Roll; NHS.

MARCHITTO, CHRISTA; Bayonne HS; Bayonne, NJ; (3); Office Aide; Nwsp Rptr; Var Bsktbl; Var Tennis; Hon Roll; Arch.

MARCIAL, WILLIAM; Bridgeton HS; Pt Norris, NJ; (3); Chess Clb; Spanish Clb; Var Crs Cntry; Var Socr; Var Trk; Var Wrstlng; Hon Roll; Prfct Atten Awd; Business Management.

MARCIANTE, MISSY; Central Regional HS; Bayville, NJ; (3); 10/245; Sec Key Clb; Math Clb; Band; Nwsp Rptr; Yrbk Stf; Crs Cntry; Trk; French Hon Soc; High Hon Roll; NHS.

MARCUS, ALEXANDER M; Millburn HS; Short Hills, NJ; (3); 18/259; Sec Am Leg Boys St; Math Tm; Science Clb; Pres Temple Yth Grp; Ntl Merit SF; Im Sftbl; JV Wrstlng; Abraham Joshua Heschel Hnr Soc 86-88; Sci.

MARCUS, DEBORAH; Ocean Township HS; Wayside, NJ; (3); 12/344; Cmnty Wkr; Hosp Aide; Nwsp Rptr; Var Bowling; High Hon Roll; St Schlr; NJ Rgte Schlrs 83-86; Yng Schlrs Inst Monmth Coll 83-86; Spartn Schlr 85-87; Law.

MARDAGA, CLAUDINE; Paramus Catholic Girls HS; Fort Lee, NJ; (3); Pres SADD; High Hon Roll; Hon Roll; Prfct Atten Awd; Yrly Sci Awd 84-85; Pre Med.

MARDER, MELISSA; Holy Cross HS; Browns Mills, NJ; (4); 63/366; Cmnty Wkr; Drama Clb; Band; Mrchg Band; School Musical; Socr; Vllybl; Wt Lftg; Hon Roll; NHS; Athltc Trng Clb Pres, Interact Clb VP 86-87; Vrsty Lts Band & Athltcs 84-87; Elizabethtown Coll.

MARDIROSIAN, SUSAN; Baptist HS; Cherry Hill, NJ; (3); Church Yth Grp; Chorus; Church Choir; Stage Crew; Drama Tech Pin 86; Psych.

MARGHELLA, JAYNE; Vineland HS; Vineland, NJ; (3); Church Yth Grp; Varsity Clb; JV Fld Hcky; Var Sftbl; 2nd Tm All Conf Sftbl Ptchr 87; 2nd Tm All Area Sftbl Ptchr 87; Fshn Merch.

MARGICIN, ANN-MARGARET; Notre Dame HS; Hamilton Sq, NJ; (2); 38/385; Latin Clb; Red Cross Aide; Ski Clb; JV Fld Hcky; Im Sftbl; Hon Roll; NHS; Latin Hnr Soc 86-87; Vet.

MARGIOTTA, DEANNA; Paramus Catholic Girls HS; Park Ridge, NJ; (3); Drama Clb; School Musical; School Play; Variety Show; Nwsp Stf; JV Socr; JV Sftbl; High Hon Roll; NHS; NEDT Awd; 1st Pl Tlnt Shw; Advrtsng.

MARGOLIES, STACY; Sayreville War Memorial HS; Parlin, NJ; (4); 1/353; Pres Math Clb; Spanish Clb; Stage Crew; High Hon Roll; NHS; Spanish NHS; Val; Hon Roll; St Schlr; Garden St Dstngshd Schlr Awd 87; PA ST U; Engrng.

MARGRE, JOSEPH; Paul VI HS; Voorhees, NJ; (3); Im Bowling; Var L Crs Cntry; Var L Trk; Acctg.

MARIANI, FRANCESCA; Hillsborough HS; Neshanic, NJ; (4); 6/300; Church Yth Grp; Orch; Var Trk; Hon Roll; NHS; Bryn Mawr Coll; Bio.

MARIANO, DENISE; South River HS; S River, NJ; (2); Band; Mrchg Band; Symp Band; Cheerleading; Coach Actv; Crs Cntry; Mgr(s); Trk; Hon Roll; Kearn Coll; Athltc Trnng.

MARIANO, GIA; Arthur L Johnson Regional HS; Clark, NJ; (3); 22/189; Trs Spanish Clb; Drill Tm; School Musical; Nwsp Stf; Rep Stu Cncl; Var Trk; High Hon Roll; Spanish NHS; Church Yth Grp; Science Clb; Gftd & Tlntd Prog 86-87; Poem Pblshd 86; Awd Of Part In NJ Sci 86; Wrtr For Nwswk.

MARIANO, JOSEPH; South River HS; South River, NJ; (3); Var Capt Socr; Var Capt Wrstlng; Hon Roll; Soccer All Div 1st Tm 86-87; Wrstlng 1st Tm All Div 85-87.

MARIANO, MARJORIE MAY; River Dell SR HS; Oradell, NJ; (2); Orch; Hon Roll; Cert Acad Excllnce Wrld Hstry 86; Cert Acad Excllnce Engl 86; Cert Acad Excllnce Spn I 86; Arch.

MARIN, ALEX; Don Bosco Prep; No Bergen, NJ; (3); 40/213; JV Var Trk; Sci Fair Awd 85; Jr Var Lttr Outdoor Track 86; Var Lttr Indoor Track 87; USC; Aero Engr.

MARINACCIO, LANNA; James Caldwell HS; W Caldwell, NJ; (3); Co-Capt Flag Corp; Ed Nwsp Rptr; Sec Sr Cls; Science Clb; Gym; Hon Roll.

MARINARI, CHRISTOPHER; Allentown HS; New Egypt, NJ; (3); Computer Clb; Math Tm; Science Clb; High Hon Roll; Hon Roll; Distngshd Hnrs Awd 84-86; Aerospace Engrng.

MARINARO, TRICIA; Manasquan HS; Manasquan, NJ; (1); Stat Bsktbl; High Hon Roll; Hon Roll; Stanford; Fshn.

MARINELLI, MICHAEL; Holy Cross HS; Medford, NJ; (3); 64/410; Am Leg Boys St; Church Yth Grp; Computer Clb; Ski Clb; Im Bsbl; Im Bsktbl; Var Golf; Hon Roll.

MARINELLI, MICHELE; Phillipsburg HS; Phillipsburg, NJ; (3); 16/315; Sec SADD; Variety Show; Var Fld Hcky; Var Sftbl; High Hon Roll; NHS; Sci.

MARINER, ANDREA M; Buena Regional HS; Mays Landing, NJ; (3); Camera Clb; Ski Clb; Wt Lftg; 4-H; Temple Yth Grp; Church Choir; Rep Frsh Cls; 4-H Awd; Alantic CC; Bus.

MARINKOVIC, PETRIJA; Mary Help Of Christians Acad; Paterson, NJ; (4); 9/80; Computer Clb; Hosp Aide; Var JV Bsktbl; Gym; Var Vllybl; High Hon Roll; Hon Roll; NHS; Prfct Atten Awd; Span I Span II 84-85; W Hist I W Hist II 84-85; Comp I 86; IN U Pennsylvania; Pre-Med.

MARINO, ANDREW; West Essex Regional HS; Fairfield, NJ; (3); 221/340; Am Leg Boys St; Pres Band; Pres Concert Band; Pres Jazz Band; Pres Mrchg Band; Pres Symp Band; Ed Nwsp Stf; NHS; Orch; Hon Roll; Philisophical Soc 87; Villanova U; Mech Engrng.

MARINO, ANTHONY; Palmyra HS; Palmyra, NJ; (3); 21/125; Am Leg Boys St; Church Yth Grp; Key Clb; Latin Clb; Spanish Clb; Rep Stu Cncl; Ftbl; Tennis; Hon Roll; Accntng.

MARINO, DONNA; Wayne Hills HS; Wayne, NJ; (3); 19/330; Ski Clb; Spanish Clb; Varsity Clb; Variety Show; VP Frsh Cls; VP Soph Cls; VP Jr Cls; VP Sr Cls; Rep Stu Cncl; JV Socr; Colgate; Liberal Arts.

MARINO, JACK; Paul VI HS; Blackwood, NJ; (3); Var Capt Crs Cntry; Var L Trk; Hon Roll; NHS; Engr.

MARINO, JOHN; Manasquar HS; Belmar, NJ; (2); 28/240; Math Tm; Spanish Clb; Wt Lftg; Var Wrstlng; High Hon Roll; Hon Roll; NHS; HS Brd Educ Hnr 87; Culinary Inst Of America; Chef.

MARINO, JOSEPHINE; Nutley HS; Nutley, NJ; (4); 18/315; Camera Clb; Spanish Clb; Var Bsktbl; High Hon Roll; Hon Roll; NHS; Slvr N Awd Schltc Achvt 85; Hnr Grad 87; Presdntl Awd Schltc Ftnss 87; FL Inst Tech; Engrng.

MARINO, KENNETH J; Saddle Brook HS; Saddle Brook, NJ; (3); 22/120; Am Leg Boys St; Letterman Clb; Model UN; Varsity Clb; Pres Jr Cls; Pres Sr Cls; Rep Stu Cncl; Var L Socr; Var L Wrstlng; Hon Roll; Seton Hall; Bus Engrng.

MARINO, MICHAEL; West Essex Regional HS; Fairfield, NJ; (4); 68/345; Drm Mjr(t); Jazz Band; Pres Mrchg Band; Pres Symp Band; Pres Frsh Cls; Sec Sr Cls; Hon Roll; Stu Voice Awd 87; Bnd Booster Awd 87; Villanova U; Fnc.

MARINO, STEPHANIE; Glen Rock HS; Glen Rock, NJ; (3); 71/155; AFS; Art Clb; Debate Tm; French Clb; Pep Clb; Ski Clb; Varsity Clb; Nwsp Rptr; Tennis; Hon Roll.

MARINUS, KEVIN; Toms River South HS; Beachwood, NJ; (3); 29/406; Var Capt Crs Cntry; Var Capt Trk.

MARION, ELLEN; Middletown HS South; Lincroft, NJ; (4); 6/450; Cmnty Wkr; Political Wkr; Flag Corp; Yrbk Stf; Rep Sr Cls; DAR Awd; French Hon Soc; High Hon Roll; NHS; Ntl Merit Ltr.

MARION III, JAMES W; Wallkill Valley Reg HS; Franklin, NJ; (3); 1/160; Am Leg Boys St; SADD; Band; Yrbk Stf; Lit Mag; Pres Jr Cls; Pres Sr Cls; Ftbl; Swmmng; Trk; Soph Math Clb Scores Awd 86; Teen Arts Awd For Poetry 86; Awd For Swmmng Vrsty 87; Biochem.

MARION, KATHLEEN N; Middletown HS South; Lincroft, NJ; (3); Church Yth Grp; Cmnty Wkr; Math Tm; Yrbk Stf; Powder Puff Ftbl; JV Sftbl; High Hon Roll; Hon Roll; NHS.

MARIONE, TRICIA; Westfield HS; Westfield, NJ; (2); Church Yth Grp; Key Clb; Latin Clb; Quiz Bowl; Science Clb; Spanish Clb; SADD; Socr; Trk; Hon Roll; Bio.

MARK, NANCY; Manalapan HS; Englishtown, NJ; (3); 16/422; Rep Frsh Cls; Rep Jr Cls; VP Sr Cls; Rep Stu Cncl; Var JV Mgr(s); Im Socr; NHS; Cert Hnr Alg I 85; Cert Hnr Socl Stds 87.

MARKERT, ROSEANN; Paramus Catholic Girls HS; Dumont, NJ; (3); Dance Clb; Exploring; French Clb; Hosp Aide; Library Aide; Red Cross Aide; School Musical; School Play; Stage Crew; Lit Mag; Natl Educ Dvlpmnt 86; Knights F Columbus Schlrshp 84; John Hopkins U Talent Srch 87; Marine Bio.

MARKEY, CRISTY M; John F Kennedy HS; Willingboro, NJ; (3); 30/297; Art Clb; Sec Stu Cncl; Var Capt Cheerleading; Hon Roll; Ntl Hnr Rll 86-87; Capt Vrsty Chrldng 87; Pre Law.

MARKLEY, CRAIG; Lower Cape May Regional HS; North Cape May, NJ; (3); Church Yth Grp; Varsity Clb; Var Capt Bsbl; JV Bsktbl; Var Capt Ftbl; Im Vllybl; Im Wt Lftg; Hon Roll; NHS; Mst Coachable Vrsty Ftbl 86.

MARKO, TAMMY; East Brunswick HS; East Brunswick, NJ; (3); Spanish Clb; High Hon Roll; Hon Roll; Spanish NHS.

MARKOVICH, MICHAEL; Toms River North HS; Toms River, NJ; (4); Var Capt Ftbl; Hon Roll; Outstndng SR Awd, Booster MVP Awd, Anchor Awd, Outstndng SR Ftbl Plyr Awd 87; W Chester U; Physcl Ed.

MARKOVITCH, LORIANN; Riverside HS; Riverside, NJ; (3); Dance Clb; VP DECA; SADD; Hon Roll; Best Dancer 84; 3rd Pl Fshn Mdlng DECA 86; Prof Cert 85; Pierce Coll Bus; Accntng.

MARKOWITZ, GINA; Wall HS; Wall, NJ; (3); 13/289; Exploring; Ski Clb; Spanish Clb; High Hon Roll; NHS; Princeton U; Lwyr.

MARKS, E MICHELLE; Cumberland Regional HS; Bridgeton, NJ; (4); 130/329; Church Yth Grp; Exploring; Church Choir; Capt Color Guard; Capt Flag Corp; Capt Mrchg Band; Outstndng Achvt Bnd Frnt 87; Air Force; Pre-Med.

MARKS, ERICA L; Burlington City HS; Burlington, NJ; (3); Church Yth Grp; VP Exploring; Thesps; Church Choir; Yrbk Stf; Rep Stu Cncl; Var Cheerleading; Hon Roll; Prfct Atten Awd; Voice Dem Awd; Burlington Cnty Bible Bowl-3rd Pl 86; Fnlst In Voice Of Democrcy Essy/Spch Cont 86; Pedtrcs.

MARKS, JANET; Collings HS; Collingswood, NJ; (3); French Clb; School Play; Yrbk Stf; Im Cheerleading; Im Fld Hcky; JV Var Lcrss; Hon Roll; Philadelphia Coll Of Pharmacy.

MARLER, REBECCA; Watchung Hills Regional HS; Warren, NJ; (3); Church Yth Grp; Key Clb; SADD; Church Choir; Nwsp Stf; Off Soph Cls; Powder Puff Ftbl; Sftbl; Hon Roll; Nrsng.

MARLIN, JASON; Pitman HS; Pitman, NJ; (3); Church Yth Grp; Computer Clb; Letterman Clb; Varsity Clb; Trs Band; Concert Band; Jazz Band; Mrchg Band; Pep Band; Off Jr Cls; Tri-M Music Honor Soc 87; Hon Mention All-Tri-County-Trk-Pole Vault 87; Most Outstndng Field Event 87; U Of IL; Aeronautical Engrng.

MARLOW, DENISE THERESE; Pope Paul VI HS; Williamstown, NJ; (3); 71/416; Pres Church Yth Grp; Drama Clb; FCA; German Clb; Teachers Aide; Church Choir; School Musical; Hon Roll; Grmn Natl Hnr Soc 86; Marine Mammal Bio.

MARLOW, RICH; Washington Township HS; Turnersville, NJ; (4); Church Yth Grp; Band; Concert Band; Jazz Band; Mrchg Band; School Musical; Trk; Temple U; Bus Admin.

MARLOWE, JOSH; Christian Brothers Acad; Middletown, NJ; (3); Nwsp Rptr; Lit Mag; Hon Roll; Creative Wrtng.

MAROLD, JOHN; Watchung Hills Reg HS; Stirling, NJ; (3); Spanish Clb; Variety Show; Bsbl; Golf; IN U; Pilot.

MAROON, JENIFER; Mc Corristin HS; E Windsor, NJ; (3); Drama Clb; JA; Key Clb; Chorus; School Musical; Yrbk Phtg; Yrbk Stf; Camera Clb; School Play; Nwsp Stf; Syracuse; Advrtsng.

MAROTTA, ANN; West Orange HS; W Orange, NJ; (3); French Clb; Band; Concert Band; Mrchg Band; Orch; French Hon Soc; High Hon Roll; Hon Roll; Jr NHS; Ntl Merit Ltr.

MAROUSIS, DESPINA; Brick Memorial HS; Brick, NJ; (3); 16/380; Church Yth Grp; Intnl Clb; Variety Show; Lit Mag; Sec Jr Cls; Stat Bsktbl; JV Socr; High Hon Roll; Hon Roll; NHS; Ldrshp Awd Sccr Tm 85-86; Intl Relatns.

MARQUARD, JESSICA; Kittatinny Regional HS; Newton, NJ; (3); 20/220; Church Yth Grp; Ski Clb; Church Choir; Chorus; Madrigals; School Musical; Stat Bsktbl; Var Fld Hcky; Var Sftbl; Hon Roll; NJ All ST Chrs 86 & 87; CPA.

MARQUARDT, LOREN; Parsippany Hills HS; Parsippany, NJ; (3); French Clb; Varsity Clb; Lit Mag; Fld Hcky; Sftbl; Hon Roll; Natl Arts Hnr Scty 86-87; Fine Arts.

MARQUES, ANABELA ALVES; East Side SR HS; Newark, NJ; (4); 21/488; Sec Computer Clb; Service Clb; Rep Soph Cls; Rep Jr Cls; Rep Sr Cls; Rep Stu Cncl; Hon Roll; NHS; Church Yth Grp; Library Aide; Gold Crd Awd 84-85; Chrctr Awd 87; Tlnt Srch Awd 86; Rutgers U.

MARQUES, CARLA; Our Lady Of Good Counsel HS; Newark, NJ; (3); 1/122; School Play; Rep Soph Cls; Rep Jr Cls; Rep Stu Cncl; Hon Roll; NHS; NEDT Awd; Studnt Of Mnth 85; Rutgers U; Psych.

MARQUES, ISABEL; Toms River HS; Toms River, NJ; (3); High Hon Roll; Amer Assn U Wmn Awd 86; Pedtrcn.

MARQUEZ, ALEXANDRA; Dover HS; Mine Hill, NJ; (3); 28/228; French Clb; Hosp Aide; Math Tm; Ski Clb; School Musical; Trs Soph Cls; Off Jr Cls; VP Sr Cls; Cheerleading; Sftbl; U Of DE; Med Tech.

MARQUEZ, EILEEN; Sacred Heart HS; Vineland, NJ; (3); Church Yth Grp; 4-H; Church Choir; Var Bsktbl; JV Crs Cntry; Im Vllybl; Health Careers Clb 84-87; Prom Committee 87-88; Rutgers U; Bus.

MARRELLO JR, ANGELO N; Phillipsburg Catholic HS; Phillipsburg, NJ; (3); Am Leg Boys St; Band; Concert Band; Jazz Band; Orch; School Musical; School Play; Symp Band; Bsktbl; Ftbl; MVP KC, DE Rvr Conf, Schl 86; Crmnl Just.

MARRERO, JULIETA; Our Lady Of Good Counsel HS; Newark, NJ; (3); 13/122; Camera Clb; Drama Clb; Chorus; School Musical; School Play; Yrbk Stf; Hon Roll; Spnsh Awd 86; 2nd Hnrs 86; Rutgers; Educ.

MARRERO, LUIS; Jackson Memorial HS; Jackson, NJ; (3); 18/416; Computer Clb; Sec Exploring; JV Ftbl; JV Trk; Im Vllybl; High Hon Roll; NHS; Spanish NHS; Schlrshp Awd Const Outstndng Schlrshp 85-86; Auto Engrng.

MARRIOTT, LAURI; Washington Township HS; Sewell, NJ; (2); Art Clb; Cmnty Wkr; Drama Clb; Girl Scts; Hosp Aide; PAVAS; Political Wkr; Church Choir; Church Yth Grp; Blk Cltr Clb 86-87; Widener; Scl Wrk.

MARRO, DANETTE; Mt St Mary Acad; Westfield, NJ; (3); Church Yth Grp; Drama Clb; French Clb; Model UN; Spanish Clb; Acpl Chr; Chorus; School Musical; School Play; Nwsp Rptr; Peeks Edtrl Stf 87-88; Law.

MARROCCO, MONICA; Immaculate Conception HS; Passaic, NJ; (4); 9/100; Science Clb; VP Spanish Clb; Nwsp Rptr; Ed Lit Mag; Stu Cncl; VP Spanish NHS; Quill & Scroll 86; Art Natl Hnr Scty 85.

MARRRA, MAUREEN; Scotch Plains-Fanwood HS; Scotch Plains, NJ; (3); AFS; French Clb; Key Clb; Spanish Clb; Variety Show; Cheerleading; High Hon Roll; Spanish NHS; Dnc Mstrs Amer 1st Pl Jazz Schlr 86; Dnc Mstrs Amer 2nd Pl Acrbtcs 85; Shwstppr Natl Comtn 2nd Pl 84; Dance.

MARSAN, ENA; Dwight Morrow HS; Englewood, NJ; (3); Hosp Aide; Spanish Clb; Ed Nwsp Rptr; Ed Yrbk Stf; Sec Jr Cls; Stat Bsktbl; Var L Cheerleading; High Hon Roll; NHS; Mrchg Band; Columbia U Alumni Clb Bk Awd 87; Frgn Lang 87; Pediatrcn.

MARSDEN, MONICA R; Pitmna HS; Pitman, NJ; (3); Dance Clb; Capt Debate Tm; Exploring; French Clb; JA; Key Clb; Nwsp Stf; Yrbk Rptr; Twrlr; Hon Roll; PHS Hnr Stu 84-88; Rutgers U; Bus Admin.

MARSEGLIA, MICHAEL F; Hackensack HS; Hackensack, NJ; (4); 42/402; Am Leg Boys St; Aud/Vis; Letterman Clb; Radio Clb; Ski Clb; Varsity Clb; Stage Crew; Var Bsbl; Var Ftbl; Im Vllybl; Presdntl Phys Ftns Awd; U Scranton; Electronic Engr.

MARSEILLE, PHILIPPE; Linden HS; Linden, NJ; (4); 36/345; FBLA; Capt Socr; Tennis; Trk; Hon Roll; NHS; Jersey City ST Coll; Acctnt.

MARSH, AMY; Neptune SR HS; Neptune City, NJ; (4); 20/355; Exploring; GAA; Ski Clb; Varsity Clb; JV Var Fld Hcky; Var JV Socr; NHS; St Schlr; Var JV Bsktbl; Prsdntl Acdmc Fitness Awd 87; William Patterson Coll; Bus Adm.

MARSH, JENNIFER; Timothy Christian HS; Rahway, NJ; (4); Church Yth Grp; Cmnty Wkr; School Play; VP Sr Cls; Stu Cncl; Bsktbl; Socr; NHS; Val; School Musical; Garden ST Distngshd Schlr 87; Spansh Awd 84-85; Acadmcs & Character Excllnc 83-84; Electrcl Engrng.

MARSH, JENNIFER; Warren County Vo-Tech HS; Phillipsburg, NJ; (3); Key Clb; VICA; Nwsp Stf; Yrbk Stf; Hon Roll; Graphic Arts.

MARSHALL, CURT; Warren Technical HS; Belvidere, NJ; (3); Key Clb; VICA; Yrbk Stf; Bsbl; Crs Cntry; Score Keeper; Socr; Trphys In Bsebl 84-85; Cabinet Mkr.

MARSHALL, DINI; Lakewood Prep; Lanoka Harbor, NJ; (4); Drama Clb; Thesps; School Play; Nwsp Phtg; Nwsp Rptr; VP Capt Socr; Athletic Dir Awd 87; Montclair; Cmmnctns.

MARSHALL, HEIDI; West Windsor-Plainsboro HS; Princeton, NJ; (3); German Clb; SADD; High Hon Roll; NHS; Semi Fnlst Cngrss Bundestag Yth Exchng Pgm 87; Lang.

MARSHALL, JACINDA; St Mary Of The Assumption HS; Hillside, NJ; (3); Service Clb; School Play; Yrbk Stf; Rep Stu Cncl; Hon Roll; NHS; Pre Med.

MARSHALL, KIMBERLY; Burlington City HS; Beverly, NJ; (3); Sec Church Yth Grp; Cmnty Wkr; Trs FTA; SADD; Chorus; Church Choir; Yrbk Stf; Rep Stu Cncl; Var Cheerleading; RCA Minorty Engrng Pgm 86; Chld Psych.

MARSHALL, ROBERT A; Northern Valley Regional HS; Harrington Park, NJ; (3); Debate Tm; Var Crs Cntry; Var Trk; Hon Roll; French Clb; N Jersey Debate League 1st Pl Spkr 87; Peer Counselor 87; NJ Boys ST Delegate 87.

MARSHALL, SUZANNE; Holy Spirit HS; Absecon, NJ; (3); 13/332; Church Yth Grp; Spanish Clb; Speech Tm; Church Choir; School Musical; Rptr Nwsp Rptr; Yrbk Rptr; Off Soph Cls; Mgr(s); Hon Roll.

MARSHELLO, META; Oakcrest HS; Mays Landing, NJ; (4); 30/242; Keywanettes; Varsity Clb; School Play; Variety Show; Yrbk Ed-Chief; Yrbk Stf; Rep Jr Cls; CC Awd; Cit Awd; Sec Jr NHS; Miss NJ Natl Teenager 87; Vlntr Cmnty Srv Awd 87; Pres Physcl Ftns Awd 87; Cmnctns.

MARSIGLIO, PETER; Mahwah HS; Mahwah, NJ; (2); 4-H; Hon Roll; Elec Engrng.

MARSZALEK, SHERYL; Lodi HS; Lodi, NJ; (3); Art Clb; Church Yth Grp; Key Clb; Spanish Clb; Varsity Clb; Yrbk Stf; Stu Cncl; Bsktbl; Sftbl; Tennis; Hon Mntn All BPSL Sftbl 87; Comm Art.

MARSZALEK III, STAN J; Christian Brothers Acad; Middletown, NJ; (3); Boy Scts; Band; Chorus; Jazz Band; Stage Crew; Hon Roll; Envrnmntl Sci.

MARTELL, ERICA LYNNE; Our Lady Of Mercy Acad; Williamstown, NJ; (3); 13/47; Dance Clb; SADD; Chorus; Variety Show; Nwsp Rptr; Nwsp Stf; Var JV Cheerleading; Hon Roll; Cert Of Recgntn Oracal Staff 85; Cert Of Achvtmnt Cheerldng Camp 86; Bus.

MARTELL, LYNETTE; St James HS; Carneys Point, NJ; (2); French Clb; Ski Clb; Varsity Clb; School Play; Yrbk Stf; VP Frsh Cls; Stu Cncl; Cheerleading; Hon Roll; Fashn Merch.

MARTELLO, MARIA; Fort Lee HS; Fort Lee, NJ; (3); Cmnty Wkr; Chorus; Bsktbl; Hon Roll; Italian Hnr Soc 86; Italian Cb 84-87; Ntl Cntst Italian Hnrbl Ment 85-86; Bus.

MARTIN, ALEC; Saint Peter HS; Somerset, NJ; (4); Am Leg Boys St; Intnl Clb; Band; Lit Mag; Var Capt Ftbl; Var Trk; Var Capt Wrstlng; Du Cret Schl Arts Scholar 87; William J O Rourke Awd Track 87; Du Cret Schl Arts; Comm Art.

MARTIN, CARLA; Emerson HS; Union City, NJ; (4); 2/281; Am Leg Aux Girls St; Sec French Clb; Co-Capt Flag Corp; Yrbk Stf; Stu Cncl; French Hon Soc; NHS; Sal; Lit Mag; CC Awd; Garden ST Dstngshd Schlr 86; NJ Regnl Acad Decath Stu 87; Brown U.

MARTIN, CHRISTOPHER; Essex Catholic Boys HS; Bloomfield, NJ; (3); 9/156; Math Clb; Math Tm; Service Clb; Ski Clb; Rep Stu Cncl; Var JV Bsktbl; Mgr(s); Socr; High Hon Roll; NHS; Coll Of Holy Cross; Bus.

MARTIN, CLARISSA; Watchung Hius Regional HS; Martinsville, NJ; (3); 23/384; SADD; School Musical; Lit Mag; Socr; Sftbl; Swmmng; Tennis; Trk; Vllybl; Hon Roll; Berkeley; Intl Bnkng.

MARTIN, DAVID R; Willingboro HS; Willingboro, NJ; (3); 1/350; Am Leg Boys St; CAP; Latin Clb; Math Clb; ROTC; Science Clb; Gov Hon Prg Awd; High Hon Roll; NHS; Rutgers U Schlr; RCA MEP Engrng Pgm; Aerospce Engrng.

MARTIN, DENISE; Edgewood Regional HS; Sicklerville, NJ; (2); Hosp Aide; Yrbk Stf; Var Stat Bsktbl; Stat Fld Hcky; High Hon Roll; Hon Roll; Prfct Atten Awd; Spcl Svc Awd W Jersey Hosp 86; 100 Hr Pin W Jersey Hosp 86; Photo Jrnlsm.

MARTIN, EDWARD; Westfield HS; Westfield, NJ; (4); Science Clb; Nwsp Phtg; JV Bsktbl; JV Socr; Var Trk; Lehigh U; Engrng.

MARTIN JR, EDWARD R; St Peters Prep Schl; White House Sta, NJ; (3); 11/187; Am Leg Boys St; Pep Clb; SADD; Nwsp Ed-Chief; Stu Cncl; L Var Bsktbl; Wt Lftg; High Hon Roll; Church Yth Grp; Dance Clb; Eucharistic Minstr 87-88; Prep Spirit Awd 85-86; Classcs.

MARTIN, ELLEN; Bridgewater Raritan HS West; Bridgewater, NJ; (3); SADD; Rep Sr Cls; Rep Stu Cncl; Var Capt Cheerleading; Var Capt Diving; Var Swmmng; High Hon Roll; Church Yth Grp; Pep Clb; Acpl Chr; All Amer Diver Status 87-88; Smrst Vly YMCA Ntl Diving Team 87-88; Ntl Chrldng Champs 86-87; Accntng.

MARTIN, ESTHER; Union Hill HS; Union City, NJ; (4); Math Clb; Mu Alpha Theta; Ski Clb; Spanish Clb; Teachers Aide; Color Guard; Yrbk Stf; High Hon Roll; Hon Roll; NHS; Spnch Awd High Grd Avrg 83-84; Rutgers U; Pharmacy.

MARTIN, HEATHER; Pinelands Regional HS; Tuckerton, NJ; (3); 21/200; SADD; Yrbk Phtg; Trs Frsh Cls; JV Socr; Var Tennis; JV Trk; Hon Roll; NHS; Bus Mgmt.

MARTIN, HERBIE; Burlington County Vo-Tech HS; Willingboro, NJ; (2); Acpl Chr; JV Bsbl; JV Bowling; Prfct Atten Awd.

MARTIN, HOLLY; Morris Knolls HS; Green Pond, NJ; (3); 45/424; Sec Church Yth Grp; Dance Clb; Cheerleading; JV Tennis; High Hon Roll; NHS; Page US Senate 86.

MARTIN, JOHN; Collingswood SR HS; Collingswood, NJ; (4); 77/235; Am Leg Boys St; Aud/Vis; Boy Scts; Quiz Bowl; Chorus; School Musical; NHS; NEDT Awd; PA ST U; Bio.

MARTIN JR, JOSEPH A; Southern Regional HS; Manahawkin, NJ; (3); Yrbk Stf; Off Frsh Cls; Off Soph Cls; Off Jr Cls; Off Sr Cls; Rep Stu Cncl; JV Var Bsbl; JV Bsktbl; Hon Roll; NHS; Schlr Athlt Awd-Vrsty Bsbl 87; Boston Coll; Poli Sci.

MARTIN, KIM; Marylawn Of The Oranges; Newark, NJ; (4); NFL; Chorus; School Musical; School Play; Nwsp Rptr; Sec Jr Cls; Stu Cncl; Sftbl; Vllybl; Cert Of Awd Intrmrls & Glee Clb 86; Jrnlsm.

MARTIN, KIM; Our Lady Of Mercy Acad; Millville, NJ; (4); Art Clb; Dance Clb; Sec Jr Cls; Sec Stu Cncl; High Hon Roll; Hon Roll; Art Awd; Glassboro ST Coll; Phyclgy.

MARTIN, LESLEE; Immaculate Heart Acad; Fairlawn, NJ; (1); Pep Clb; Chorus; High Hon Roll; Hon Roll; Bowling Trophies-High Team Series 86-87; Rutgers U; Pharmacy.

MARTIN, MARIE; Matawan Regional HS; Matawan, NJ; (2); Church Yth Grp; Girl Scts; Sftbl; Trk; Prfct Atten Awd; Drftg.

MARTINELLI, ANGELA; Sacred Heart HS; Vineland, NJ; (4); 12/64; Hosp Aide; Sec Spanish Clb; School Play; Yrbk Sprt Ed; Im Vllybl; Hon Roll; Var NHS; Minitola Ntl Bk Awd, Italilan-Amer Clb Awd 87; Ntl Merit Awd 86; Douglass Coll; Accntng.

MARTINELLI, JANNA; Our Lady Of Mercy Acad; Vineland, NJ; (3); 1/47; Church Yth Grp; SADD; Chorus; Nwsp Rptr; Trs Frsh Cls; Pres Soph Cls; Pres Jr Cls; Pres Stu Cncl; Var Cheerleading; NHS; Natl Sci Merit Awd 85-86; Acdmc All Amer Schlr 86; Orthodontist.

MARTINETTI, PAUL; Mc Corriston HS; Trenton, NJ; (3); 9/260; Varsity Clb; Rep Jr Cls; Sec Stu Cncl; Var Golf; Var Trk; Hon Roll; NHS; JV Wrstlng; Jr NHS; Natl Latin Exam-Cum Laude; Tutoring; Pre-Med.

MARTINEZ, ALMA; Memorial HS; West New York, NJ; (3); Church Yth Grp; FBLA; Math Clb; Spanish Clb; Hon Roll; NHS; Bus Adm.

MARTINEZ, BARBARA; Our Lady Of Good Counsel HS; Newark, NJ; (3); 6/126; Drama Clb; Chorus; School Play; Yrbk Stf; Mgr(s); Sftbl; Timer; NHS; NEDT Awd; Span Excllnc Awd; Communications.

MARTINEZ, CHRISTINE; Morris Catholic HS; Succasunna, NJ; (1); 7/157; FTA; SADD; Pres Stu Cncl; Capt Cheerleading; Sftbl; High Hon Roll; Hon Roll; NHS; Ntl Merit Schol; St Schlr; Princeton; Teacher.

MARTINEZ, ESPERANZA; Ridgefield Park HS; Little Ferry, NJ; (4); 29/172; French Clb; Spanish Clb; French Hon Soc; Rutgers U; Comp Sci.

MARTINEZ, HUMBERTO; St Joseph Of The Palisades HS; W New York, NJ; (4); 6/120; Spanish Clb; Nwsp Stf; Hon Roll; NHS; Spanish NHS; St Schlr; Acad All-Amer 84; Ntl Ldrshp & Svc Awds 85; Finance.

MARTINEZ, MARC A; Bergen Catholic HS; Ho-Ho-Kus, NJ; (3); 66/273; Am Leg Boys St; Cmnty Wkr; School Musical; Yrbk Stf; Bowling; Crs Cntry; Trk; Hon Roll; Sci.

MARTINEZ, MICHAEL; John P Stevens HS; Edison, NJ; (3); 1/450; Am Leg Boys St; Model UN; Science Clb; High Hon Roll; NHS; Ntl Merit Ltr; Pres Spanish NHS; 2nd Degree Blck Blt Tae Kwon Do Cert ATA 85-87; ATA Instrctr Trnee 84-87; Capt Edison JR ATA Tm 85; Law.

MARTINEZ, ROBERT; West Windsor-Plainsboro HS; Princeton Junct, NJ; (3); Chess Clb; FBLA; Radio Clb; Tennis; Hon Roll; David Sarnoff Res Ctr Minorities In Engrng Prog Awd 87; Bus Admin.

MARTINEZ, ROSA; Eastside HS; Paterson, NJ; (3); Library Aide; Office Aide; Cit Awd; Awd Englsh Poetry Cntst 86; Acad Excllnc Awd 85; De Vry.

MARTINO, ANGELINA; Woodbridge HS; Port Reading, NJ; (4); 16/385; Quiz Bowl; Ski Clb; Spanish Clb; Chorus; Capt Flag Corp; Hon Roll; Sec NHS; Ntl Merit Ltr; Pres Spanish NHS; Scholastic Bowl; Prom & Dance Cmtes; Gov Tchng Schlr 87; Seton Hall U; Educ.

MARTINO, ANNAMARIE; Wayne HS; Wayne, NJ; (3); 65/250; Hon Roll; Cert Of Recgntn Accntng Awd FBLA 87; Italian Club; Bus.

MARTINO, JENNIFER; Arthur L Johnson Regional HS; Clark, NJ; (4); 2/214; Am Leg Aux Girls St; Sec Art Clb; Yrbk Rptr; Lit Mag; High Hon Roll; NHS; Ntl Merit Ltr; Sal; Spanish NHS; Voice Dem Awd; Gdn St Dstngshd Schlr 86; Unico Schlrshp 87; Sandoz Schlrshp 87; Coll Of St Elizabeth; Biochem.

MARTINO JR, THOMAS J; Palmyra HS; Palmyra, NJ; (3); 11/121; Church Yth Grp; SADD; Pres Frsh Cls; Pres Soph Cls; Pres Jr Cls; Pres Sr Cls; VP Stu Cncl; Var Capt Socr; Var Capt Trk; Trs NHS; Marine Corp Outstndg Stu Ath 86-87; JR Rotarian.

MARTINOVICH, KRISTIN; Maple Shade HS; Maple Shade, NJ; (3); Var Capt Bsktbl; Var Socr; Var Sftbl; Hon Roll; 3rd Team Div Socr Sftbl; 2nd Team Freedom Div Socr, Sftbl & Bsktbl; 1st Team Group Sftbl.

MARTINS, CARLOS; East Side HS; Newark, NJ; (4); 110/488; Varsity Clb; Crs Cntry; Trk; Cit Awd; Men Of Essx Trck Awd 87; Cmnty Pride Awd 87; Schlr Atlt Awd 87; Fairleigh Dickson U; Bus Admn.

MARTON, KEVIN; Bridgewater-Raritan HS East; Martinsville, NJ; (3); Boy Scts; Camp Fr Inc; Church Yth Grp; Letterman Clb; Ski Clb; Varsity Clb; Church Choir; Var Crs Cntry; Var Golf; Var Wrstlng; Soc Sci.

MARTORANA, MARIBETH; Pope Paul VI Regional HS; Clifton, NJ; (3); Key Clb; Teachers Aide; Yrbk Stf; JV Vllybl; Gov Hon Prg Awd; High Hon Roll; NHS; Sec Spanish NHS; Z-Clb Brd; Art.

MARTORANA, TARA; Mt Saint Mary Acad; Colts Neck, NJ; (3); Aud/Vis; Church Yth Grp; Computer Clb; Dance Clb; 4-H; Service Clb; Spanish Clb; School Musical; Variety Show; Nwsp Rptr; Svc Awd To Acad-Typng Hnr 86; Svc Awd To Acad 87; 4 Yrs Equestrian Awds; Bus Mgmt.

MARTORANO, DENNIS; Ridgefield Park HS; Little Ferry, NJ; (3); 44/203; Cmnty Wkr; Hon Roll; Awd EMS Training 86; Engrng.

MARTS, JONEL; St James HS; Salem, NJ; (2); 9/120; Hosp Aide; Pep Clb; Spanish Clb; SADD; Yrbk Stf; Var Bsbl; JV Var Fld Hcky; High Hon Roll; Lawyer.

MARTZ, GARY R; Gloucester HS; Gloucester, NJ; (3); 4/175; Am Leg Boys St; FBLA; Yrbk Stf; Pres Soph Cls; Pres Jr Cls; High Hon Roll; Hon Roll; NHS; Drama Clb; Frnch Grammatical Knowledge Awd; Trenton ST; Banking.

MARTZ, KIMBERLY; Manalapan HS; Manalapan, NJ; (2); Cmnty Wkr; Rep SADD; Rep Frsh Cls; Rep Soph Cls; Var Bsktbl; Swmmng; Rep Stu Cncl; JV Mgr(s); JV Score Keeper; Var Socr; Psychlgy.

MARTZ, PAUL; Camden Catholic HS; Camden, NJ; (3); 110/300; Art Clb; Boy Scts; French Clb; Varsity Clb; Rep Frsh Cls; Var Capt Ftbl; Wt Lftg; Var Wrstlng; Cit Awd; Union Lge Awd 85-86; Phila Little Qtr Ftbl Team 85-86; Sports Med.

MARUCCI JR, ANTHONY C; Mount Olive HS; Flanders, NJ; (3); 160/375; Aud/Vis; Political Wkr; SADD; Chorus; Concert Band; Jazz Band; Mrchg Band; Nwsp Rptr; Lit Mag; Stu Cncl; Cngrsmn Dean Gallo Spcl Intern 87; Hugh O Brian Yth Fndtn Ambsdr 86; MIP Music 85-86; Polt Sci.

MARULANDA, RICHARD; Morris Catholic HS; Denville, NJ; (3); Aud/Vis; Dance Clb; Pres FBLA; Pep Clb; Scholastic Bowl; Trs Spanish Clb; Stage Crew; Tennis; Vrsty Ltr For Acad Decathlaon 86-8m; Attorney.

MARULLO, JOE; Toms River South HS; Beachwood, NJ; (2); JV Var Bsbl; Ftbl; JV Socr; High Hon Roll; Hon Roll; Beechwood-Pine Bch Al-Star Tm Bsbl 85; Comp Sci.

MARULLO, LORI ROSE; Sayreville War Memorial HS; Parlin, NJ; (4); 67/357; Pres Drama Clb; French Clb; Chorus; School Musical; School Play; Swing Chorus; Nwsp Stf; Lit Mag; Hon Roll; VFW Awd; Plyrs Awd-Theatre 87; NJ All ST Choir 86; Fnlst Grdn ST Arts Ctr Tlnt Expstn 85 & 86; Douglass Coll; Pltcl Sci.

MARX, MITCHELL; J P Stevens HS; Edison, NJ; (3); 11/450; Math Tm; Science Clb; Temple Yth Grp; Nwsp Stf; NHS; Ntl Merit SF; Spanish NHS; Arch.

MARX JR, RONALD; Sussex Vo Tech; Hopatcong, NJ; (3); High Hon Roll; Acad All-Amer Schlrs 87; Comp Sci.

MARZUCCA, ANTHONY C; Paulsboro HS; Gibbstown, NJ; (3); Band; Concert Band; Jazz Band; Mrchg Band; Symp Band; Jr All Amer Hall Fame Band Hnrs 86; Emery-Riddle Coll; Pilot.

MARZULLO, ANDREA; Eastern HS; Voorhees, NJ; (3); 24/350; Cmnty Wkr; Hosp Aide; Intnl Clb; Temple Yth Grp; Yrbk Stf; JV Tennis; Hon Roll; Jr NHS; NHS; Commended Perf PSAT 86; Med.

MASCARO, JULIE ANN; Kingsway Regional HS; Mickleton, NJ; (3); French Clb; Hosp Aide; Key Clb; Office Aide; Capt Band; Chorus; School Musical; Powder Puff Ftbl; Var Sftbl; High Hon Roll; Bio Awd 85-86; Supt Awd 84-85; Sports Med.

MASCENIK, NANETTE; Woodbridge SR HS; Woodbridge, NJ; (3); Art Clb; Dance Clb; Varsity Clb; Chorus; Stage Crew; Var Bowling; Hon Roll; Phrmcy Sci.

MASCIA, JACQUELINE; St John Vianney HS; Marlboro, NJ; (4); 54/250; SADD; Rep Frsh Cls; Rep Soph Cls; Rep Jr Cls; Rep Sr Cls; Rep Stu Cncl; Var Stat Ftbl; Capt Powder Puff Ftbl; Var L Sftbl; Hon Roll; Gold & White Awd; Loyola Coll; Mrktng.

MASCIANTONIO, STELLAMARIE; Cherry Hill West HS; Cherry Hill, NJ; (3); Art Clb; PAVAS; Hon Roll; Rutgers; Psych.

MASCIOCCO, BETTY JEAN; James Caldwell HS; West Caldwell, NJ; (3); Key Clb; Science Clb; Mgr(s); Socr; Hon Roll; Prfct Atten Awd.

MASCOLA, JOHN; John P Stevens HS; Edison, NJ; (3); 145/450; Boy Scts; Cmnty Wkr; Science Clb; Ski Clb; Band; Concert Band; Mrchg Band; Powder Puff Ftbl; Prjct Gifted 85; Bio.

MASCULLO, RAYMOND; Secaucus HS; Secaucus, NJ; (3); Seton Hall U; Broadcasting.

MASIN, ERIN; Voorhees HS; Hampton, NJ; (2); 74/292; Key Clb; Chorus; Variety Show; Stat Socr; Trk.

MASINO, ANGELA; Newton HS; Newton, NJ; (2); 23/222; Chorus; Drill Tm; Yrbk Bus Mgr; Yrbk Ed-Chief; Yrbk Stf; Hon Roll; Law.

MASINO, DAVE; J P Stevens HS; Edison, NJ; (3); 35/454; Exploring; Science Clb; SADD; Hon Roll; Rugers Schl Of Acctg; CPA.

MASLO, KAREN E; Holmdel HS; Holmdel, NJ; (3); Church Yth Grp; Band; Stage Crew; Pres Frsh Cls; Pres Soph Cls; VP Stu Cncl; Capt Bsktbl; Var Crs Cntry; Var Sftbl; Var Tennis; Cngrssnl Awd Brz 85; Sftbll Hons All Monmouth, Shore 1st Tm 85-87; All ST Grp I, II 3rd Tm 85-87; Educ.

MASON, DAVID; Egg Harbor Twp HS; Linwood, NJ; (3); 27/335; Pres Computer Clb; Science Clb; Ski Clb; Spanish Clb; Var Swmmng; JV Tennis; JV Trk; Im Mgr Wt Lftg; Vrsty Ltr Acad 85-87.

MASON, JACKIE; Ocean City HS; Woodbine, NJ; (3); 30/341; Chorus; JV Sftbl; Hon Roll; Glassboro ST; Law.

MASON, MELISSA; Paul VI HS; Audubon, NJ; (3); 180/450; German Clb; SADD; Drill Tm; Nwsp Rptr; Crs Cntry; Trk; CPA.

MASON, MICHAEL; Paul VI HS; Bellmawr, NJ; (4); 41/514; Church Yth Grp; Math Clb; SADD; Var L Bsktbl; Camden Cnty Govt Day 85; Bus.

MASON, SHERI; Bridgeton HS; Bridgeton, NJ; (3); Girl Scts; Church Choir; Bsktbl; Crs Cntry; Trk.

MASSA, LINDA; Immaculate Conception HS; Kearny, NJ; (3); 2/70; Math Tm; NFL; SADD; Nwsp Rptr; Yrbk Stf; Rep Jr Cls; Var Vllybl; NHS; Spanish NHS; Hgh Hnr Rll; Ntl Educ Dvlpmnt Tst Awd; Duke U; Engnrng.

MASSARI, BETHANN; Mc Corrishn Catholic HS; Bordentown, NJ; (3).

MASSENAT, VERTULIE; Mc Corristain Catholic HS; Trenton, NJ; (3); Pre-Med.

MASSEY, HEATHER; Woodstown HS; Elmer, NJ; (3); Church Yth Grp; Pres 4-H; German Clb; Sec Math Clb; Yrbk Stf; Var Twrlr; Hon Roll; Prfct Atten Awd; Olympcs Mnd 86-87; Grmn Hnr Soc 86-87; Aeronautcl Engrng.

MASSEY, RAZIAH; Immaculate Conception HS; Newark, NJ; (3); Church Yth Grp; Debate Tm; Science Clb; Chorus; Church Choir; Rep Stu Cncl; Hon Roll; NHS; Psych.

MASSING, JACKIE; St James HS; Salem, NJ; (2); Spanish Clb; SADD; Stu Cncl; Fld Hcky; Sftbl; High Hon Roll; Physcl Thrpst.

MASTERS, MARGARET; St Marys HS; Rutherford, NJ; (4); 6/74; Math Clb; NFL; VP Thesps; Nwsp Rptr; Yrbk Ed-Chief; Stat Bsktbl; Capt Sftbl; High Hon Roll; VFW Awd; Girl Scout Gold Awd 85; Law.

MASTERSON, CHRISTINA; Boonton HS; Boonton, NJ; (3); GAA; Radio Clb; Ski Clb; SADD; Variety Show; Yrbk Rptr; Yrbk Stf; High Hon Roll; Hon Roll; Rutgers Schl Of Phrmcy; Phrmcy.

MASTIN, JANET; Florence Township Memorial HS; Florence, NJ; (4); 25/80; Church Yth Grp; DECA; French Clb; Teachers Aide; Pres Rep Stu Cncl; Elks Awd; Hon Roll; William Paterson Coll; Bus Admn.

MASTORIO, TRACIE; Cedar Ridge HS; Cliffwood Bch, NJ; (3); 74/330; FBLA; Ski Clb; Band; Concert Band; Mrchg Band; Cheerleading; Swmmng; Hon Roll; BUS Admin.

MASTRO, ELENA MICHELE; West Windsor-Plainsboro HS; Lawrenceville, NJ; (3); Trs AFS; Trs Church Yth Grp; Pres 4-H; SADD; Concert Band; Rep Stu Cncl; Capt Var Cheerleading; Cit Awd; 4-H Awd; Hon Roll; Outstndng 4-H 86-87; Fshn Review Awd 85-86; Ldrshp Awd 86; Rutgers U; Acctng.

MASTRO, MICHAEL C; Delsea Regional HS; Vineland, NJ; (3); Am Leg Boys St; Pres Key Clb; Nwsp Stf; Yrbk Stf; Rep Frsh Cls; Rep Soph Cls; Pres Trs Stu Cncl; Var Tennis; Hon Roll; NHS; Athnm League Acad Exc 87.

MATARI, NUHA; Mary Help Of Christians Acad; Paterson, NJ; (3); Cmnty Wkr; Latin Clb; Letterman Clb; Library Aide; Service Clb; Sec SADD; Varsity Clb; Chorus; School Play; Nwsp Rptr; Natl Lat Exm 86-87; Psych.

MATEO-NUNEZ, MONICA; Camden Catholic HS; Pennsauken, NJ; (3); VP Spanish Clb; Rep Frsh Cls; BUS.

MATHER, DON; Watchung Hills Regional HS; Millington, NJ; (3); Boy Scts; Church Yth Grp; Cmnty Wkr; Spanish Clb; Golf; Spanish NHS; Acctg.

MATHEWS, HEATHER R; West Windsor-Plainsboro HS; Princeton Jct, NJ; (4); 56/287; Pres AFS; Concert Band; Mrchg Band; Orch; School Musical; Stage Crew; Yrbk Stf; JV Fld Hcky; Hon Roll; Ntl Merit Ltr; U NC Chapel Hill; Ntrl Sci.

MATHIAS, ROBERT; Toms River HS South; Pine Bch, NJ; (3); 21/420; Rep Jr Cls; Rep Sr Cls; Rep Stu Cncl; JV Bsbl; JV Ftbl; L Var Golf; Hon Roll; NHS; Bus Mngmt.

MATHUVIRAN, SELENE; Dickinson HS; Jersey City, NJ; (3); JA; Merit Roll 85; Pace U; Bus Admin.

MATLACK, JACQUELINE; Glassboro HS; Glassboro, NJ; (4); 22/106; Church Yth Grp; Dance Clb; Drama Clb; Exploring; Q&S; Thesps; Chorus; School Musical; School Play; Fld Hcky; Hnr-Jack Collins-Acadc Achvt 87; Awd-Mobil Rsrch-Chmcl Engrng 86; Chr Awd 87; Penn ST; Bus.

MATO, SHAWN; West Milford Township HS; W Milford, NJ; (2); SADD; Var L Socr; Var JV Tennis; Hon Roll; Vrsty Ski Tm-MVP, 1st Tm NJ All-ST, 1st Tm All-City 85-86; Vrsty Ski Tm-MVP, 1st Tm NJ ST 86-87.

MATONTI, JOHN; Montville Twsp HS; Montville, NJ; (3); Art Clb; Pres FBLA; Key Clb; Ski Clb; School Musical; Var Capt Swmmng; JV Capt Tennis; High Hon Roll; NHS; 1st Pl FBLA St Comp Bus Graphics 86; Won New Mntvll Mstng Logo Dsgn 86; 12th & 10th Pl Awds Smmg 86; Bus Comm.

MATOS, ARWEN; John F Kennedy HS; Willingboro, NJ; (2); 32/332; Computer Clb; Intnl Clb; School Musical; Yrbk Stf; JV Fld Hcky; JV Lcrss; Mgr(s); JETS Awd; Mgr Bsktbl; Mgr Tennis; RCA Minorities Prog 85-86; Z-Club 10th Grade Rep 86-87; Project Shark Tutor 85-87; Trenton ST; Fash Merch.

MATOS, JACQUELYN; Central Regional HS; Bayville, NJ; (3); Nwsp Rptr; Nwsp Stf; Lit Mag; Stat Bsbl; Stat Ftbl; Var Trk; Writer.

MATOS, LIDIA; East Side HS; Newark, NJ; (3); Hosp Aide; Math Clb; Yrbk Stf; High Hon Roll; Hon Roll; B Avg Awd 87; Engrng.

MATOS, SARAH; Our Lady Of Good Counsel HS; Newark, NJ; (3); 15/122; Drama Clb; Chorus; Rep Soph Cls; Rep Jr Cls; Rep Sr Cls; Sftbl; Hon Roll; NHS; Spnsh Merit Awd 85-86; Csmtlgy.

MATREYEK, RYAN; Newton HS; Newton, NJ; (1); Boy Scts; Ski Clb; Swmmng; Hon Roll; U S Air Force Acad; Pilot.

MATRISCIANO, TERESA; Rancocas Valley Regional HS; Mt Holly, NJ; (4); 3/260; Am Leg Aux Girls St; Hosp Aide; Math Tm; Concert Band; Mrchg Band; Ed Lit Mag; Var Trk; High Hon Roll; NHS; Bsktbl; Mt Holly Rotary Scholar 87; 1st Catholic Slovak Ladies Assn Scholar 87; Pres Acad Fit Awd 87; Rutgers U.

MATT, LISA; Fort Lee HS; Ft Lee, NJ; (4); 51/216; Sec Thesps; School Musical; School Play; Stage Crew; Nwsp Ed-Chief; Nwsp Rptr; Nwsp Stf; Lit Mag; Hon Roll; French Clb; Fred Witte, PBA Lcl 245 & Jrnlsm Schlrshps 87; Goucher Coll; Jrnlsm.

MATTERA, DEANNA; Oakcrest HS; Mays Landing, NJ; (3); Trs French Clb; Drill Tm; JV Fld Hcky; Var JV Sftbl.

MATTESON, SUSANN; Southern Regional HS; Surf City, NJ; (3); 23/420; Concert Band; Jazz Band; Mrchg Band; Stage Crew; Var Socr; High Hon Roll; Hon Roll; NHS; Orch; Schlr Athlt Awd 85; Best Marcher Awd 85-86; Prfct Attndnc Band 84-86; Intr Dcrtng.

MATTHEWS, BURNELL K; Trenton Central HS; Trenton, NJ; (4); Church Yth Grp; Red Cross Aide; Science Clb; Band; Church Choir; Trk; High Hon Roll; Hon Roll; Blck Hstry Essy Cntst 83-84; Navy; Elctrncs.

MATTHEWS, CALANDRA; Mary Help Of Christians Acad; Paterson, NJ; (3); Sec Church Yth Grp; SADD; Sec Church Choir; Yrbk Rptr; Cheerleading; Hon Roll; NHS; NEDT Awd; Bsktbl; Acad All Am Schlr Awd, Ltrmn Sweater, 2nd Rnnr Up Miss Pop/Congeniality-Miss Paterson Pgnt 86; Cmmnctns.

MATTHEWS, DONALD; Northern Burlington Cnty Regnl HS; Jobstown, NJ; (4); 4-H; FFA; Bsbl; Ftbl; Hon Roll; Pennco Tech Schlrshp 87; FFA Chaptr ST, Regl, Natl 83-84; Pennco Tech; Auto Tech.

MATTHEWS JR, JAMES J; Memorial HS; Cedar Grove, NJ; (4); 13/123; Church Yth Grp; Key Clb; Ski Clb; Var JV Socr; High Hon Roll; Hon Roll; NHS; Pres Schlr; Prsdntl Acad Ftns Awd 83-87; 4 Yr Schlrshp Rutgers U-Newark NJ 87; Schlrshp Senton Hall U 87; Rutgers U; Accntng.

MATTHEWS, ROGER C; West Morris Mendham HS; Mendham, NJ; (4); 2/330; Capt Debate Tm; School Play; Nwsp Rptr; Rep Stu Cncl; Sec Trk; High Hon Roll; Ntl Merit Schol; Opt Clb Awd; Sal; Time Mag Essy Cntst Fnlst 86-87; NY Schlrs Pgm 86; Yth For Undrstndng Frgn Exchng Schlrshp France 85; U Of VA; Pre Law.

MATTHEWSON, SHAWN; Orange HS; Orange, NJ; (2); Rep Soph Cls; Rep Stu Cncl; JV Ftbl; Hon Roll; Howard U; Engrng.

MATTIELLI, JENNIFER; Bayonne HS; Bayonne, NJ; (3); Drama Clb; JA; Key Clb; Nwsp Stf; Rep Frsh Cls; Pres Soph Cls; Rep Jr Cls; Gym; High Hon Roll; Jr NHS.

MATTIO, SUSAN; Highland HS; Blackwood, NJ; (2); Latin Clb; Tennis; High Hon Roll; Library Aide; School Play.

MATTIOLI, THERESA; Paul VI HS; Williamstown, NJ; (3); 16/418; Math Clb; Trs Frsh Cls; Sec Stu Cncl; Var L Sftbl; Hon Roll; NHS; Hugh O Brien Yth Ldrshp Semnr 86; Bio.

MATTIOLI, THOMAS; Penns Grove HS; Penns Grove, NJ; (3); Cmnty Wkr; Computer Clb; Exploring; JCL; Political Wkr; Band; Concert Band; Jazz Band; Mrchg Band; Symp Band; Drexel U; Comp Engrng.

MATULA, KARIANNE; Perth Amboy HS; Perth Amboy, NJ; (3); 1/400; Model UN; Mu Alpha Theta; Rep Jr Cls; Rep Stu Cncl; Var Cheerleading; Var Trk; High Hon Roll; NHS; Rutgrs Schlr 87; Art.

MATULAC, KIT; Ridgefield Park HS; Ridgefield Pk, NJ; (3); 49/204; Score Keeper; Vet Med.

MATULLO, CHRISTINE; Lenape Valley Regional HS; Stanhope, NJ; (3); 45/213; Off Frsh Cls; Stat Crs Cntry; Hon Roll; CPA.

MATUS, CHRISTINE LIM; Monsignor Donovan HS; Toms River, NJ; (3); 16/239; Art Clb; Hosp Aide; Math Tm; Spanish Clb; Yrbk Stf; Var Tennis; Hon Roll; Sec NHS; Spnsh Awd 85; Bus.

MATUS, VALERIE; Baptist HS; Gloucester City, NJ; (3); 6/50; Church Yth Grp; Drama Clb; Chorus; School Play; Stage Crew; Yrbk Stf; VP Frsh Cls; Rep Stu Cncl; Bsktbl; Hon Roll; Mark Of Excl Awd Tech Prod/Drama 86; Baptist Hnr Scty 87; Carnegie Mellon U 87; Dmcrcy Is Us Schlrshp; Tech Theater.

MATUSIK, RENEE; Randolph HS; Randolph, NJ; (3); 21/328; Church Yth Grp; French Clb; Hosp Aide; Letterman Clb; Band; Concert Band; Jazz Band; Mrchg Band; Orch; Stage Crew; Ymca Natl Gymnstc Meet Qualfr 85-87; U Of NE-VALPARAISO; Bus.

MATZ, RAE A; Hasbrouck Heights HS; Hasbrouck Heights, NJ; (4); 33/110; Spanish Clb; VICA; Color Guard; Mrchg Band; Rep Jr Cls; Rep Stu Cncl; Stat Bsktbl; JV Trk; Hon Roll; Hazel Tanner Schlrshp, Pres Acdmc Ftnss Awd, & DECA Stu Yr Awd 87; Accntng.

MAUGER, CHRISTOPHER M; Haddonfield Memorial HS; Haddonfield, NJ; (3); Am Leg Boys St; Drama Clb; Pres Band; Jazz Band; Orch; School Musical; Stage Crew; NHS; Spanish NHS.

MAUGHAM, CHRISTOPHER; East Brunswick HS; E Brunswick, NJ; (3); 105/618; German Clb; Math Clb; Science Clb; Band; Jazz Band; Yrbk Stf; Hon Roll; Grmn Hnr Scty 86-88; Aerospc Engnrng.

MAURER, DARRIN; Vineland H S North; Vineland, NJ; (2); 49/793; Key Clb; SADD; Drill Tm; Mrchg Band; Nwsp Rptr; Ed Yrbk Stf; Hon Roll; Prfct Atten Awd; Brdcstng.

MAURER, FRANK; St James HS; Salem, NJ; (4); 10/68; SADD; School Play; Yrbk Ed-Chief; Stu Cncl; Hon Roll; NHS; Ntl Merit Ltr; Ntl Frgn Lng Awd; Prom King; Glsbr ST Coll.

MAURER, GEOFFREY M; West Windsor Plainsboro HS; Plainsboro, NJ; (3); Am Leg Boys St; Boy Scts; Exploring; Lit Mag; Pblshd Wrtngs In Asperations Ltry Mag Svrl Times 84-85; Norwich U; Pol Sci.

MAURIELLO, ROBERT; Edgewood Regional SR HS; Berlin, NJ; (2); Latin Clb; Hon Roll; Prfct Atten Awd; Pres Phys Ftnss Awd 86; Med.

MAURO, MICHELE; Linden HS; Linden, NJ; (4); 10/345; Pres Church Yth Grp; Hosp Aide; Ed Yrbk Stf; Capt Cheerleading; High Hon Roll; Hon Roll; Lion Awd; NHS; VP Frsh Cls; Rutgers Coll Nrsng Merit Scholar 87; Lionness Scholar 87; PTA Scholar 87; Rutgers Coll Nrsng; Nrsng.

MAURO JR, ROBERT D; St John Vianney HS; Hazlet, NJ; (4); 17/249; Pres Computer Clb; Math Tm; Office Aide; SADD; Nwsp Sprt Ed; JV Var Bsbl; Mgr Bsktbl; High Hon Roll; Hon Roll; NHS; Comp Sci Awd, Pres Acdmc Ftns Awd 87; Gld & Whte Awd Invlvmnt & Actvts 83-87; Trenton ST Coll; Comp Inf Sys.

MAURO, SUSAN; Cresskill HS; Cresskill, NJ; (4); 27/113; Ski Clb; Band; Chorus; Drm Mjr(t); Jazz Band; Mrchg Band; Yrbk Phtg; Lit Mag; Var Crs Cntry; High Hon Roll; Ntl Hnr Soc 86-87; Sec Stu Body 86-87; Int Design.

MAUROFF, KIMBERLY; Lenape Regional HS; Vincentown, NJ; (4); Church Yth Grp; SADD; Sec Varsity Clb; School Play; Rep Frsh Cls; Rep Soph Cls; Rep Jr Cls; Rep Sr Cls; Rep Stu Cncl; Bsktbl; Ramapo ST Coll.

MAURONE, BRENDA; Vineland HS; Millville, NJ; (4); 34/656; English Clb; Latin Clb; Pep Clb; Lit Mag; Hon Stu 86-87; Rutgers-Livingston; Pre Law.

MAUSER, ALICIA; Pennsville HS; Pennsville, NJ; (3); #41 In Class; Drama Clb; Latin Clb; Q&S; Band; Concert Band; Drill Tm; Mrchg Band; School Play; Rep Sr Cls; Hon Roll; Fshn Merch.

MAUTE, LINDA; Cherry Hill East HS; Cherry Hill, NJ; (4); Am Leg Aux Girls St; Dance Clb; Teachers Aide; Orch; School Musical; Variety Show; Nwsp Rptr; Capt Pom Pon; Trk; Hon Roll; Gov Schl Arts Fnlst 87; All S Jersey Orchstra 85-87; Featrd Dnc Miss Brlngtn Cnty Pgnt 87; Law.

MAVIGLIA, ANTONELLA; Freehold HS; Manalapon, NJ; (3); 3/250; Math Tm; Science Clb; Capt Color Guard; Nwsp Stf; Yrbk Bus Mgr; Stat Ftbl; JV Trk; VP NHS; Prfct Atten Awd; Spanish NHS; Grls Ctznshp Inst 87; Spnsh Awd Frgn Lang Awd 86-87; Pre Med.

MAVIGLIA, SAVERIO M; Freehold HS; Manalapan, NJ; (4); 1/250; Computer Clb; Exploring; Math Tm; Jazz Band; Mrchg Band; JV Trk; Bausch & Lomb Sci Awd; Pres NHS; Ntl Merit SF; Spanish NHS; Rensselaer Poly Inst Math,Sci Awd 86; Comp Sci.

MAVORAH, IAN; Ocean Township HS; Oakhurst, NJ; (3); 74/370; Im Bsktbl; Im Tennis; NYU; Stock Mrkt.

MAVROS, STUART; Indian Hills HS; Franklin Lakes, NJ; (3); Boy Scts; Church Yth Grp; Debate Tm; Ed Yrbk Phtg; Acad Dcthln 86-87; Frst Fire Svc & Srch & Rescue Inc 87; Army Rsrve Mdcl Spclst 87; Vet Med.

MAXWELL, MICHAEL; Immaculata HS; Piscataway, NJ; (3); Boy Scts; Church Yth Grp; Office Aide; Teachers Aide; Varsity Clb; Variety Show; Lit Mag; Var Ftbl; Wt Lftg; Law.

MAXWELL, ORVIL; Orange HS; Orange, NJ; (2); Art Clb; Boy Scts; Church Yth Grp; French Clb; Church Choir; Nwsp Stf; Bsbl; Bsktbl; Ftbl; Wrstlng; Mech Drwng Cert 87; NJIT; Mech Ngr.

MAXWELL, PATRICIA; Orange HS; Orange, NJ; (4); 34/160; Church Yth Grp; Pres DECA; PAVAS; Y-Teens; Chorus; Church Choir; School Musical; Variety Show; Rep Stu Cncl; JP Sousa Awd; Galloway Polhill Jr Awd, AT&T Schlrshp, Trphs Voice & Chorus 87; Greensboro Coll; Voice Music.

MAY, GREG; Bridgeton HS; Bridgeton, NJ; (3); Am Leg Boys St; Concert Band; Mrchg Band; School Musical; NHS; Drama Clb; HOSA ST Offcr; Parlmntry Procdre Tm; Olympcs Mind/Cogntcs Tm; Chem Engrng.

MAY, JOHN D; Absegami HS; Cologne, NJ; (3); 17/287; Am Leg Boys St; VP Science Clb; Ski Clb; Rep Stu Cncl; Var Bsbl; Var Crs Cntry; Hon Roll; Ntl Merit Ltr; Library Aide; Stage Crew; Math League Awd Computer Progrmng 86; Elec Engr.

MAY, JOSEPH C; South River HS; S River, NJ; (4); 15/132; Am Leg Boys St; German Clb; Bsktbl; JV Ftbl; Golf; Marine Bio.

MAY, MARLENE; Middlesex HS; Middlesex, NJ; (3); 39/167; Key Clb; Model UN; Cheerleading; Crs Cntry; Sftbl; Hon Roll; Acctng.

MAY, PAULA; Rahway HS; Rahway, NJ; (3); Chorus; Off Soph Cls; Off Jr Cls; Trk; Hon Roll; Rutgers Coll; Crmnl Jstc.

MAY, STEPHANIE; A P Schalick HS; Elmer, NJ; (3); Office Aide; Chorus; Cumberland; Bus.

MAYADAS, PRIYA; Dwight Englewood HS; Englewood, NJ; (4); Orch; School Play; Lit Mag; High Hon Roll; Cum Laude 87; Brdcst Music Inc Compstn Prz 81; Outstndng Stu Manhatten Schl Music 87; New England Consrvtry; Musician.

MAYBERRY, CAROLYN; Manasquan HS; Manasquan, NJ; (3); French Clb; FBLA; Ski Clb; Spanish Clb; Stage Crew; Yrbk Stf; Crs Cntry; Socr; Tennis; Trk; Comm Art.

MAYBERRY, DEBORAH; Westfield HS; Westfield, NJ; (2); Ambassador Coll; Commrcl Arts.

MAYER, BETH; Parsippany HS; Parsippany, NJ; (3); French Clb; FBLA; Pep Clb; Mgr(s); Var L Tennis; Hon Roll; NHS; Pres Bnai Brith Grls 86; Explors Law 87; Untd Syngog Yth 85-87; Librl Arts.

MAYER, LAURIE GAIL; J P Stevens HS; Edison, NJ; (4); 31/467; Hosp Aide; Model UN; VP Science Clb; School Musical; Stage Crew; Ed Yrbk Stf; Lit Mag; Stat Bsktbl; Trs NHS; Hlth Achvt Awd 84; Rutgers Coll; Psych.

MAYER, ROBERT; Cresskill HS; Cresskill, NJ; (3); 18/103; Am Leg Boys St; Debate Tm; Ski Clb; Trs Band; Concert Band; Jazz Band; Nwsp Phtg; Ed Nwsp Stf; JV Tennis; Photogrphy.

MAYER-COSTA, PAULO; Essex Catholic Boys HS; East Orange, NJ; (3); Library Aide; Ski Clb; School Musical; Ed Yrbk Phtg; VP Frsh Cls; Rep Soph Cls; Im Bowling; Var Golf; Swmmng; NHS; Intrmrl Sftbl Chmps 84-85; Frst Hnrs 84-88; NJ Inst Technlgy; Indus Admins.

MAYES, GRACE; James Caldwell HS; W Caldwell, NJ; (3); Am Leg Aux Girls St; Church Yth Grp; Pres Key Clb; Band; Mrchg Band; Var Bsktbl; Var Capt Crs Cntry; Var Capt Trk; High Hon Roll; NHS; Phys Thrpy.

MAYES, TOM; Dover HS; Dover, NJ; (4); 13/187; Am Leg Boys St; FCA; VP Ski Clb; Variety Show; Bsktbl; Capt Ftbl; Vllybl; High Hon Roll; NHS; N Dover PTA Schlrshp 87; Ftbl Schlrshp 87; Natl Hnr Soc Schlrshp 87; FL ST U; Bus Mngmnt.

MAYNARD, ROBIN; West Orange HS; West Orange, NJ; (1); French Clb; Swmmng; Jr NHS; Mdlng.

MAYO, AMIRI; Dwight Morrow HS; Englewood, NJ; (1); Hosp Aide; Band; Jazz Band; Mrchg Band; JV Bsktbl; Hon Roll; Cornell; Vet.

MAYO, ERIKE; St Mary HS; Teaneck, NJ; (3); Am Leg Boys St; Church Yth Grp; Church Choir; School Play; Var L Bsktbl; Hon Roll; NHS; Prfct Atten Awd; Aud/Vis; Boy Scts; MIT Inst; Elctrl Engrng.

MAYO, SHAWN; Glen Rock HS; Glen Rock, NJ; (3); 33/157; Nwsp Stf; Yrbk Stf; JV Bsbl; JV Bsktbl; Var JV Ftbl; JV Socr; Hon Roll; Bus.

MAYR, ANNABELLE; Vineland SR HS; Vineland, NJ; (4); #6 In Class; Letterman Clb; Math Clb; Pep Clb; Spanish Clb; Varsity Clb; Band; Mrchg Band; Var Capt Crs Cntry; Trk; St Schlr; Mc Donalds Schlrshp 86; Early Dcsn Accptnc Johns Hopkins U 86; John Hopkins U; Med.

MAYRIDES, MARK; Immaculata HS; Belle Mead, NJ; (3); 15/240; Church Yth Grp; Office Aide; Ski Clb; Thesps; School Play; Yrbk Stf; Var Golf; Var Socr; French Hon Soc; NHS; Law.

MAYS, JENNIFER; Vineland HS; Vineland, NJ; (3); 12/824; Key Clb; Orch; Hon Roll; Elem Eductn.

MAYS, MIKE; De Paul HS; Wayne, NJ; (3); Am Leg Boys St; JCL; Pres Sr Cls; Bsktbl; Hon Roll; Arch.

MAZAK, MICHELLE; Hunterdon Central HS; Flemington, NJ; (2); 32/496; Service Clb; Socr; JV Sftbl; Hon Roll; John Hopkins; Med.

MAZE, ADAM K; Sayreville War Memorial HS; Sayreville, NJ; (3); Am Leg Boys St; Math Tm; Temple Yth Grp; Mrchg Band; Yrbk Sprt Ed; Yrbk Stf; Var L Tennis; High Hon Roll; NHS; Spanish NHS; Aerospc-Biomed Engr.

MAZEFFA, ROBERT M; Hunterdon Central HS; Flemington, NJ; (3); 8/543; Church Yth Grp; Ski Clb; Trs Jr Cls; Rep Stu Cncl; JV Socr; Var L Tennis; High Hon Roll; NHS; Spanish NHS; Semifnlst Natl Merit Schlrshp, Eductnl Comm 87; Engrng.

MAZEL, JOSEPH W; Fair Lawn HS; Fair Lawn, NJ; (3); Aud/Vis; Cmnty Wkr; Computer Clb; Drama Clb; Letterman Clb; Ski Clb; Varsity Clb; Acpl Chr; Stage Crew; Nwsp Stf; Med.

MAZER, JONATHAN; Central Regional HS; Seaside Hts, NJ; (3); Spanish Clb; SADD; Bsktbl.

MAZO, VERA; Paul VI HS; Springfield, VA; (3); 26/300; Dance Clb; Latin Clb; Math Tm; Var L Drill Tm; School Musical; Nwsp Rptr; Nwsp Stf; Nwsp Staff Hgh Hnrs, Rptr Hnrs 86-87; Latin Tm Capt 86-87; Math Tutorl Soc 86-87; Natl Lat Exam Gld Mdl.

MAZOR, TANYA; Bruriah HS; Staten Isl, NY; (4); 20/46; Cmnty Wkr; Dance Clb; Debate Tm; Hosp Aide; Teachers Aide; Temple Yth Grp; Chorus; School Musical; Nwsp Rptr; Yrbk Stf; Pres Acdmc Fit Awd 87; Baruch Coll; Bus.

MAZUR, BETH; Bricktownship Memorial HS; Brick, NJ; (2); 15/381; Spanish Clb; High Hon Roll; Hon Roll; NHS; Pratt; Art.

MAZUR, JOANN; Dover HS; Dover, NJ; (3); 23/210; Debate Tm; Key Clb; Political Wkr; Chorus; Color Guard; School Musical; Rep Stu Cncl; High Hon Roll; Hon Roll; NHS; Peer Ldrshp Awd 86-87; JR Bnd Awd 86-87; Psychlgy Awd 86-87; U Of Southern CA; Lwyr.

MAZUR, LORI; Immaculate Conception HS; Lodi, NJ; (3); #19 In Class; Math Clb; NFL; Q&S; Speech Tm; Church Choir; School Musical; Nwsp Rptr; Lit Mag; Hon Roll; NEDT Awd; Frnscs Extmprns Spkng Awd, Ntl Ldr Math,Sci, Drama & Speech Awd 85-86; Engl Mjr.

MAZURCZYK, MATTHEW; Manalapan HS; Manalapan, NJ; (3); Computer Clb; Science Clb; Natl Sci Day 17th ST 86-87; Elctrcl Engrng.

MAZURE, TRACY LYN; Rutherford HS; Rutherford, NJ; (3); Cmnty Wkr; Key Clb; Library Aide; VP Science Clb; Ed Yrbk Ed-Chief; Yrbk Stf; JV Bowling; Cit Awd; High Hon Roll; NHS; Brnz & Gld Awds 85 & 86; Attnd Grls Ctznshp Inst-Rtgrs 87.

MAZUREK, RICHARD MICHAEL; Midland Park HS; Midland Park, NJ; (4); 18/131; Camera Clb; Chess Clb; Library Aide; Scholastic Bowl; Yrbk Phtg; Lit Mag; Stu Cncl; High Hon Roll; NHS; Ntl Merit Ltr; NYU Trustee Scholar 87; Pres Acad Fit Awd 87; NYU.

MAZURKIEWICZ, STANLEY PAUL; Sayreville War Memorial HS; Parlin, NJ; (4); Spanish Clb; Concert Band; Jazz Band; School Musical; Symp Band; Var Ftbl; Var Wrstlng; Hon Roll; 1st Chair Rgn II Symphnc Band 87; Middlesex Cnty Art 86-87; Seton Hall U; Bus.

MAZZA, LISA; Toms River HS North; Toms River, NJ; (4); 82/410; SADD; Band; Mrchg Band; Rep Jr Cls; JV Var Bsktbl; JV Var Socr; JV Var Tennis; Wt Lftg; Observer All Cnty & All Shore Ten Tm Awd 84; Flagler U; Engl.

MAZZA, ROMA; Highland Regional HS; Blackwood, NJ; (4); 40/297; Hon Roll; Wagner Coll; Acctng.

MAZZITELLI, CHRIS; Atlantic Christian Schl; Marmora, NJ; (3); Church Yth Grp; Trs Jr Cls; Var Co-Capt Bsktbl; Var Socr; High Hon Roll; Messiah Coll; Sports Fld.

MAZZITELLI, JOHN; Washington Township HS; Turnersville, NJ; (3); JV Tennis; Hnr Rl 83-84; Rutgers U; Comp Engr.

MAZZO, DAWN; Paul VI HS; Runnemede, NJ; (3); Intnl Clb; Math Tm; High Hon Roll; Hon Roll.

MAZZOCCOLI, ROSANNA; Mary Help Of Christians Acad; Paterson, NJ; (2); English Clb; SADD; Chorus; Church Choir; Gym; Hon Roll; Alg Awd 85-86; Italian Awd 85-86; Sci Awd 85-86; Health Awd; Acctng.

MAZZOCHI, LESLIE; Vineland SR HS; Vineland, NJ; (3); Art Clb; Office Aide; Spanish Clb; Glasboro; Graphic Dsgn.

MAZZOLA, PAUL; Vineland H S North; Vineland, NJ; (1); Ski Clb; Yrbk Stf; Rep Stu Cncl; Bsbl; Hon Roll; Stu Of Wk Awd-Wrld Hist & Geo 86-87; Alg Achvr Awd 86-87; Medicine.

MAZZONI, KRISTIN; Buena Regional HS; Vineland, NJ; (3); 3/220; Rep Frsh Cls; Rep Soph Cls; Rep Stu Cncl; High Hon Roll; Hon Roll; Jr NHS; NHS; Vineland Regnl Dance Co; Natl Sci Merit Awd; Villanova U; Law.

MC ADAMS, JIM; Paul VI HS; Sewell, NJ; (3); Letterman Clb; Math Clb; Varsity Clb; Var Capt Socr; Drexel U; Engr.

MC ADAMS, KRISTIN M; Hanover Park HS; East Hanover, NJ; (4); 2/301; Church Yth Grp; Science Clb; Jazz Band; Mrchg Band; Nwsp Rptr; JV Var Sftbl; NHS; Ntl Merit SF; Sal; St Schlr; Engrng.

MC ALEER, SUSAN; Shawnee HS; Medford, NJ; (4); 23/533; Yrbk Stf; JV Lcrss; Hon Roll; NHS; Medford Educ Assn Awd 87; U Of MD College Park; Spch Pth.

MC ANDREW, KEVIN; Don Bosco Prep; Pearl River, NY; (3); 25/200; Nwsp Rptr; Lit Mag; Im Bsktbl; Im Ftbl; Hon Roll; Don Bosco Sci Fair-1st Pl Physics, Mst Outstndng Proj 85; Intramural Floor Hcky 84-86; Aerontcs.

MC ANDREW, MARK; Don Bosco Preparatory HS; Upr Saddle River, NJ; (4); 8/178; Model UN; Quiz Bowl; Golf; Ice Hcky; Socr; High Hon Roll; NHS; Acad All-Amer 85-86; Acad Decathalon 86-87.

MC ANDREW, NORVILLE; Wayne Hills HS; Wayne, NJ; (4); Math Clb; Spanish Clb; Varsity Clb; Jazz Band; Variety Show; Bsbl; Bsktbl; Ftbl; Hon Roll; Rutgers Coll; Pre Law.

MC ANDREW, PATRICK J; Freehold Township HS; Freehold, NJ; (4); 6/350; Cmnty Wkr; Ftbl; Var L Trk; Wt Lftg; NHS; Pres Schlr; Hnry Kng Stnfrd Schlrshp U Miami FL 87; Grdn ST Dstngd Schlrs NJ 87; Pres Acdmc Ftnss Awd 87; U Of Notre Dame; Engrng.

MC ARTHUR, JOHN; Rancocas Valley Regional HS; Mt Holly, NJ; (2); 12/300; Ski Clb; Varsity Clb; Bsbl; Bsktbl; Ftbl; Swmmng; High Hon Roll; NHS; Med.

MC ATEER, ROBIN; Warren County Vo-Technical HS; Hackettstown, NJ; (3); FBLA; Pres Key Clb; Varsity Clb; VICA; Off Jr Cls; Stat Bsbl; Stat Bsktbl; Mgr(s); Score Keeper; Hon Roll; Wrd Prcssng.

MC BREEN, KELLEY; St John Vianney HS; Freehold, NJ; (4); 3/252; Ski Clb; SADD; Ed Yrbk Bus Mgr; Rep Sr Cls; Var Capt Trk; High Hon Roll; Hon Roll; Pres VP NHS; Sal; NJ Dist Schlr Hon Ment 86-87; Outstndg Spnsh Achvt Awd 87; Bucknell U; Bio.

MC BRIDE, CHRISTOPHER; Holy Spirit HS; Brigantine, NJ; (2); 50/397; Crs Cntry; High Hon Roll; Hon Roll; Penn ST; Arch.

MC BRIDE, ELLEN; Wildwood Catholic HS; Cape May, NJ; (4); Bsktbl; Glasboro ST Coll; Cmnctns.

MC BURNEY, JENNIFER; Pequannock Township HS; Pompton Plains, NJ; (3); 40/200; Trs Church Yth Grp; Mgr FBLA; Mgr Varsity Clb; Chorus; Mgr Church Choir; Rep Frsh Cls; JV Stat Bsktbl; Var Socr; JV Sftbl; Hon Roll; Bus.

MC BURROWS, SHANTA; Hillside HS; Hillside, NJ; (3); Cmnty Wkr; Hosp Aide; Math Tm; Teachers Aide; Nwsp Stf; Rep Frsh Cls; JV Var Bsktbl; Sftbl; Temple U; Comm.

MC CABE, EUGENE; Brick Memorial HS; Brick, NJ; (3); 22/380; Church Yth Grp; Exploring; ROTC; Drill Tm; High Hon Roll; NHS; Air Force Assoc Awd 86; Amer Leg Awd Schltc Exclince 86; Reserve Offcrs Assoc Awd 87; Aero Engrng.

MC CABE, JENNIFER; Kinnelon HS; Kinnelon, NJ; (4); 17/169; Camera Clb; Spanish Clb; Stat Bsbl; Stat Bsktbl; JV Cheerleading; Powder Puff Ftbl; Stat Socr; Hon Roll; NHS; Pres Schlr; NY Inst Tech Renew Scholar 87; Caldwell Coll Renew Scholar 87; Rutgers Coll Engrng; Comp Engrg.

MC CABE, MICHELE; Egg Harbor Towpship HS; Linwood, NJ; (4); 20/289; Stu Cncl; JV Bsktbl; Var Tennis; High Hon Roll; Hon Roll; Sec NHS; Ntl Merit Schol; Schltc Vrsty Ltr Wnnr; Cape Atantic Div I Conf Tm Tennis; All Sth Jersey Grp III Tm; Comm.

MC CABE, ROSEMARY; Monsignor Donovan HS; Howell, NJ; (3); French Clb; Color Guard; Mrchg Band; Yrbk Stf; Hnr Athltc Awd 86; Rutgers U; Med.

MC CABE, STEPHEN; St Joseph Regional HS; Park Ridge, NJ; (3); 61/250; Boy Scts; Im Bsbl; Im Fld Hcky; Im Ftbl; Im Ice Hcky; Im Socr; High Hon Roll; Hon Roll; Prfct Atten Awd; Spanish NHS; U Scranton; Penn Crmnl Just.

MC CAFFREY, EILEEN; Morris Catholic HS; Denville, NJ; (4); 7/138; German Clb; Girl Scts; Math Clb; Natl Beta Clb; Thesps; School Musical; NHS; Ntl Merit Ltr; Drama Clb; Exploring; Bill Bradley Yng Ctzn Awd 86; Girl Scout Gold Awd 87; Garden St Schlr 87; St Michaels Coll.

MC CAIN, DEBBIE; Lincoln HS; Jersy City, NJ; (3); Sec Soph Cls; VP Stu Cncl; Var Cheerleading; NHS; Schlrshp Chrm Schl 86; Cert Frshmn Achiev Clb 85; Cert Sphmr Achiev Clb 86; Sain & Peter Coll; Comptr Sci.

MC CALL, ANGELA; Hillside HS; Hillside, NJ; (3); 26/238; Leo Clb; Science Clb; Spanish Clb; Band; Chorus; Church Choir; Rep Stu Cncl; Im Bsktbl; Var Cheerleading; High Hon Roll; PA ST; Pedtrcn.

MC CALL, COLLEEN; Overbrook SR HS; Sanford, FL; (1); SADD; Cheerleading; Drama Clb; Girl Scts; Teachers Aide; Chorus; Crs Cntry; Trk; Ms NJ Coed Pgnt Fnlst 87; Comp Pgmmng.

MC CALL, KELLY; Franklin HS; Somerset, NJ; (3); Church Yth Grp; Ski Clb; Chorus; Church Choir; Var Capt Cheerleading; Gym; JV Sftbl; JV Swmmng; Tennis; Hon Roll; Vrsty Awd 3 Yr Cncrt Chrs 87; Accptd Fnlst Miss Teen Amer 86; Biol.

MC CALL, ORLINDA; Camden County Voc & Tech HS; Atco, NJ; (1); 4-H; Office Aide; SADD; Teachers Aide; VICA; Rep Frsh Cls; Var Bsktbl; JV Crs Cntry; Var Trk; 4-H Awd; Laser Tech.

MC CALL, SHAWNETTE; Villa Victoria Acad; Trenton, NJ; (3); 1/22; Cmnty Wkr; Hosp Aide; Yrbk Stf; Lit Mag; Pres Frsh Cls; VP Jr Cls; DAR Awd; Hon Roll; John Hopkins U; Pre Med.

MC CANN, CHERIE; Edgewood HS; Chesilhurst, NJ; (3); Church Yth Grp; Varsity Clb; Church Choir; Bsktbl; Trk; Hon Roll; Glassboro ST U; Engr Sci.

MC CANN, LOIS; Highland Regional HS; Blackwood, NJ; (2); Art Clb; Church Yth Grp; Band; Concert Band; Mrchg Band; Stage Crew; Hon Roll.

MC CANTS, DAVID; Montclair Kimberley Acad; East Orange, NJ; (4); Varsity Clb; Orch; VP Soph Cls; VP Jr Cls; Var Capt Bsktbl; Var Capt Ftbl; Var Lcrss; Hon Roll; Klein Awd For Outstndng Commitment To Acad & Athletics 84-86; Brown U.

MC CARRON, KIMBERLY; Holy Spirit HS; Ventnor, NJ; (2); 1/397; High Hon Roll; Hon Roll; Sci Awd 85-86; Sci.

MC CARRON, PETER; Don Bosco Prep; Tappan, NY; (2); Church Yth Grp; Cmnty Wkr; SADD; Im Bsktbl; Ftbl; Trk; Wt Lftg; Law.

MC CART, KERI; Washington Township HS; Turnersville, NJ; (2); Mgr(s); JC Awd; Hnr Role 85; Rutgers U; Chld Psych.

MC CARTAN, THOMAS; Middletown South HS; Red Bank, NJ; (2); Boys Clb Am; Boy Scts; Camera Clb; Ski Clb; Bsbl; Ftbl; Hon Roll; Brookdall Coll; Mgmt.

MC CARTER, CHRISTINA; Highpoint Regional HS; Sussex, NJ; (4); Am Leg Aux Girls St; German Clb; Science Clb; Im Sftbl; Var Capt Swmmng; High Hon Roll; NHS; Im Vllybl; Wallkill Vlly Rtry Clb Schlrshp 87; U S Army Rsve Schlr Athltc Awd 87; Acad Coll Schlrshp 87; St Peters Coll; Vet Med.

MC CARTER, JENNIFER; High Point Regional HS; Sussex, NJ; (2); German Clb; Im Bsktbl; Var Swmmng; Im Vllybl; Im Wt Lftg; Hon Roll; Peer Cnslng 87; Sftbl Fres Team 85-86; Intr Dcrtr.

MC CARTHY, CHRISTINA; Lyndhurst HS; Lyndhurst, NJ; (3); Office Aide; Chorus; Nwsp Rptr; JV Cheerleading; Sftbl; High Hon Roll; Hon Roll; PTA Cltrl Arts Cntst 86; PTA Cltrl Arts Cntst 86; Arts Fest Awd Otstndng Prfrmr 86; Fairleigh Dickinson U; Accntng.

MC CARTHY, HUGH; Mt Olive HS; Flanders, NJ; (4); 67/296; Pres Church Yth Grp; Varsity Clb; VP Stu Cncl; Var Crs Cntry; Var L Socr; Var L Trk; Im Vllybl; Quiz Bowl; Ski Clb; School Musical; Natl Art Hnr Soc; Cmunctns.

MC CARTHY, JENNIFER; Morris Catholic HS; Lake Hiawatha, NJ; (2); 9/127; Drama Clb; Pep Clb; Chorus; School Musical; School Play; Hon Roll; Sal; Princeton; Tchr.

MC CARTHY, KARA; Waldwick HS; Wladwick, NJ; (3); 6/138; Church Yth Grp; Service Clb; Ski Clb; Spanish Clb; Yrbk Stf; Socr; Trk; High Hon Roll; Hon Roll; NHS; Outstndg JR-LANG Arts 87; Peer Cnslng Lttr-Svc Awd 86; Cert-Vlntr Wrk-Bergen Pns Co Hosp 85-86; Georgetown U; Lbrl Arts.

MC CARTHY, KATIE; Red Bank Regional HS; Little Silver, NJ; (3); Nwsp Rptr; Lit Mag; French Hon Soc; High Hon Roll; Hon Roll; NHS; Ntl Merit Ltr; Spanish NHS; Hnr Courses; Advncd Placement Courses; Frgn Lang.

MC CARTHY, KERRY; Waldwick HS; Waldwick, NJ; (4); 23/146; Cmnty Wkr; Math Tm; Ski Clb; Varsity Clb; Stage Crew; Nwsp Rptr; Yrbk Stf; Powder Puff Ftbl; JV Socr; JV Sftbl; Providence Coll; Bio.

MC CARTHY, KEVIN; Brick Township Memorial HS; Brick, NJ; (2); 5/381; Rep Frsh Cls; JV Bsbl; JV Capt Bsktbl; JV Ftbl.

MC CARTHY, STEPHEN G; Dwight-Englewood HS; Englewood, NJ; (4); Stu Cncl; Var Co-Capt Ice Hcky; Var Co-Capt Lcrss; Var Socr; Cum Laude Soc 87; Haverford.

MC CARTNEY, MEGHAN; Rutherford HS; Rutherford, NJ; (4); 14/167; Key Clb; Math Tm; School Musical; Yrbk Stf; Rep Frsh Cls; Rep Soph Cls; Rep Sr Cls; Var L Crs Cntry; Var L Trk; Ntl Merit Ltr; Wllm Carlos Williams Wrtng Awd Hon Mntn; Mrtn Lthr Kng JR Wrtng Cont Hon Mntn; Fairfield U.

MC CARTY, BETH; Victory Christian Schl; Blue Anchor, NJ; (3); Capt Bsktbl; High Hon Roll; Ntl Sci Merit Awd 87; Indstrl Psych.

MC CARVILLE, LAURA; Buena Regional HS; Newfield, NJ; (4); 9/220; Chorus; Yrbk Rptr; Sec Frsh Cls; JV Stat Bsktbl; Var JV Sftbl; Hon Roll; Jr NHS; NHS; Stu Mth 87; Vrsty Acadmc Ltr 86; La Salle; Cmnctns.

MC CARVILLE, LISA; Buena Regional HS; Newfield, NJ; (3); 2/250; Trs Pres Art Clb; Varsity Clb; Hon Roll; NHS; Sal; Ski Clb; Color Guard; Nwsp Rptr; Rep Frsh Cls; NJ Schl Arts 86-87; Zonta Z Clb-Sec & Pres 85-87; U DE; Vet Med.

MC CAULEY, JENNIFER; St John Vianney HS; Freehold, NJ; (4); 99/256; Church Yth Grp; Cmnty Wkr; FBLA; JCL; Service Clb; Ski Clb; SADD; Yrbk Stf; Lit Mag; Fld Hcky; Christian Svc Awd; Allentown Coll; Bus Law.

MC CAULEY, STACEY; Roselle Park HS; Roselle Park, NJ; (3); 8/190; Computer Clb; Debate Tm; Math Clb; Radio Clb; Speech Tm; Nwsp Rptr; High Hon Roll; NHS; Apple II Comp Chlng Awd 87; Cmnctns.

MC CAULLEY, PATRICE; Holy Spirit HS; Longport, NJ; (4); 27/363; Yrbk Ed-Chief; Hon Roll; NHS; Garden ST Distngshd Schlr 86; Attorney.

MC CLAMMY, JAMES I; West Windsor-Plainsboro HS; Princeton, NJ; (4); 19/287; Am Leg Boys St; Model UN; Orch; School Musical; Symp Band; High Hon Roll; Ntl Merit Ltr; St Schlr; Computer Clb; Jazz Band; Ntl Achvt Schlrshp-Outstndng Negro Stu 87; Gvrnrs Schl Of Pblc Issues & Ftur Of NJ 86; Yale U; Plcl Sci.

MC CLANE, JAMES; Park Ridge HS; Park Ridge, NJ; (4); 1/115; Am Leg Boys St; VP Scholastic Bowl; Var Bsbl; Capt Bsktbl; Pres NHS; St Schlr; Val; Scholastic Bowl; Varsity Clb; Sobel Bio Awd 87; 1st Tm Al-Leag Bsktbl 87; UNICO Awd 87; Duke U; Bio-Med Engr.

MC CLANE, SHARON; Park Ridge HS; Park Ridge, NJ; (3); 8/92; Church Yth Grp; Cmnty Wkr; Yrbk Stf; Var Bsktbl; Var Socr; Var Sftbl; High Hon Roll; NHS; Record Schlrshp 87; 1st Tm All-League Sftbll 87.

MC CLEISH, ROB; Pitman HS; Pitman, NJ; (3); Band; Concert Band; Jazz Band; Mrchg Band; Socr; Trk; Hon Roll; NHS; Math.

MC CLENAHAN, JENNIFER; West Windsor-Plainsboro HS; Robbinsville, NJ; (3); Diving; Var Capt Socr; JV Sftbl; MVP Socr 86; All Mrcr Tm-Socr 86; Pucket/Ledger All Area G Rls Socr Tm 84-86; Phy Ed.

MC CLOSKEY, SANDRA; Madison HS; Madison, NJ; (3); 75/212; Church Yth Grp; Cmnty Wkr; Dance Clb; French Clb; Hosp Aide; Varsity Clb; Rep Soph Cls; Rep Stu Cncl; JV Var Cheerleading; Var Gym; Soclgy.

MC CLURG, MATT; High Point Regional HS; Sussex, NJ; (2); Wt Lftg; JV Wrstlng; Arch.

MC COMB, ALISON; Middletown HS North; Middletown, NJ; (2); Band; Concert Band; Mrchg Band; Hon Roll; Arch.

MC CONNELL, JASON; Millville SR HS; Pt Norris, NJ; (4); 104/417; Trs Church Yth Grp; Computer Clb; Hon Roll; Honor Roll Twice 83; Honor Roll 87; Cumberland County Coll; Lib Art.

MC CONNELL, STACEY; Middlesex HS; Middlesex, NJ; (4); 26/157; Girl Scts; Spanish Clb; Band; Concert Band; Jazz Band; Mrchg Band; Crs Cntry; Capt Trk; Prfct Atten Awd; JBEW Local Union 262 Scholar 87; Bond Exclince Crs Cntry & Track $100 87; Outstndng Girl Ath Trck 87; Bloomsburg U; Elem Ed.

MC CONVILLE, MARGARET; Marylawn Of The Oranges HS; South Orange, NJ; (3); 8/65; Chorus; School Play; Rep Jr Cls; Tennis; French Hon Soc; Dance Clb; Hosp Aide; Cheerleading; Sftbl; Intl Stu Ldrshp Conf 86; Comm.

MC COOG, KAREN; Maple Shade HS; Maple Shade, NJ; (3); Key Clb; Spanish Clb; Rep Soph Cls; Trs Jr Cls; Rep Stu Cncl; Capt Fld Hcky; Var JV Lcrss.

MC COOL, JENNIFER; John F Kennedy HS; Willingboro, NJ; (2); Dance Clb; Drama Clb; Spanish Clb; Chorus; School Musical; Yrbk Stf; Rep Frsh Cls; Var Socr; Mst Imprvd Girls Vrsty Sccr 85; Penn ST; Htl Mgmt.

MC CORD, LA NISSA; Hillsborough HS; Piscataway, NJ; (4); Cmnty Wkr; Dance Clb; Drama Clb; Library Aide; NAACP; Pep Clb; Chorus; Church Choir; Madrigals; School Musical; Outstndng Fine Arts Stu $100 Schlrshp 87; Outstndng Dnc Stu Hnr 87; Outstndng Music Stu $25 Sclrshp 87; Rutgers; Dance.

MC CORMACK, DARREN; Morris Catholic HS; Montville, NJ; (3); Letterman Clb; Math Clb; Pep Clb; Science Clb; Service Clb; Ski Clb; SADD; Varsity Clb; Rep Soph Cls; Rep Sr Cls; Hnbl Mntn All Cnty & 2nd Tm All Conf Crss Cntry 86; 2nd Hnrs 86-87; Comp Sci.

MC CORMACK, KARYN; St John Vianney HS; Colts Neck, NJ; (3); 23/240; Church Yth Grp; Yrbk Stf; Trs Sr Cls; JV Capt Socr; Hon Roll; NHS; Cmmnctns.

MC CORMACK, KELLI; Vernon Township HS; Glenwood, NJ; (3); DECA; Drama Clb; School Musical; School Play; Stage Crew; JV Trk; Hon Roll; DECA Natl Cmptn 3rd Pl 86-87; SCJAL Trck Chmps 85-86; Fine Arts Invlmnt Cert Awd; Advrtsng.

MC CORMICK, MEGHAN; Bridgeton HS; Bridgeton, NJ; (3); Nwsp Ed-Chief; Yrbk Stf; Var Tennis; High Hon Roll; NHS; Drama Clb; GAA; Office Aide; Political Wkr; Ski Clb; Girls St 87; Schltc Lttr 85 & 86; Rotary Yth Ldrshp Assn Alt 87.

MC CORMICK, SHANNON; Keansburg HS; Keansburg, NJ; (3); Church Yth Grp; Exploring; Library Aide; VICA; Bowling; Tennis; Hon Roll; NHS; Top 10% Vocatnl Schl Cmrcl Art 86-87; Bible Coll; Mnstr.

MC COY, DEIDRE; Holy Spirit HS; Atlantic City, NJ; (2); 50/397; Hon Roll; Pro Ice Sktr.

MC COY, DENEB; Holy Spirit HS; Atlantic City, NJ; (2); 50/397; Hon Roll; Prof Ice Sktr.

MC COY, FRANCIS; St James HS; Salem, NJ; (3); SADD; Var Bsbl; Intl Frgn Lang Awd Frnch 85-86; Pro Athl.

MC COY, JAMES; Collingswood SR HS; Collingswood, NJ; (3); Am Leg Boys St; German Clb; Ski Clb; Rep Frsh Cls; Var Drama Clb; Var Socr; NHS; Grmn Hnr Soc 86-87; Chem.

MC COY, JAMES; Southern Regional HS; Waretown, NJ; (4); 9/398; Chess Clb; Computer Clb; Math Tm; High Hon Roll; Hon Roll; NHS; St Schlr; 1st Pl Libry Shrt Stry Cont 87; Pres Acdmc Ftnss Awd 87; Trenton ST Coll; Math Ed.

MC COY, MONIQUE; Neptune SR HS; Neptune, NJ; (2); Drama Clb; Library Aide; Church Choir; School Musical; School Play; High Hon Roll; Hon Roll; NHS; Prfct Atten Awd; Sci Fair 3rd Pl 86; Varsty Ltr Drama 87; Vrsty Ltr High Hnr Roll 87; Psych.

MC CRACKEN, CAROLINE; Cumberland Regional HS; Bridgeton, NJ; (3); 34/384; Church Yth Grp; Exploring; German Clb; Intnl Clb; JCL; Science Clb; Variety Show; Jr NHS; Psych.

MC CRACKEN, CAROLYN; Watchung Hills Regional HS; Warren, NJ; (3); 3/321; Sec Drama Clb; Trs Girl Scts; Hosp Aide; Scholastic Bowl; Chorus; Church Choir; Stage Crew; JV Fld Hcky; High Hon Roll; NHS; Schl Wnnr Bcntnnl Cnstn Essy Cntst 87; Bst Dfnsv Plyr JV Fld Hcky 86; Gld Ldrshp Grl Scts 87; Med.

MC CRAE, WANDA L; E Orange HS; E Orange, NJ; (4); 1/310; Church Yth Grp; Hosp Aide; Math Tm; Church Choir; High Hon Roll; Hon Roll; NHS; Prfct Atten Awd; St Schlr; Val; Rutgers Schlr 86; Stevesn Inst Alumni Schlr 87; James Dickson Carr Schlr Rutgers U 87; NJ Inst Of Tech; Elect Engr.

MC CREDY, MICHAEL; Overbrook SR HS; Pine Hill, NJ; (3); Socr; Prfct Atten Awd; Constrctn.

MC CUE, SUSAN; St Mary Of The Assumption HS; Elizabeth, NJ; (2); 3/85; Church Yth Grp; Hosp Aide; Service Clb; Church Choir; Var Sftbl; Hon Roll; Jr NHS; HOBY Fndtn Ambssdr 87; Law.

MC CURDY, PAULA; Delsea Regional HS; Wenonah, NJ; (4); 1/213; Am Leg Aux Girls St; Drama Clb; Yrbk Ed-Chief; Trk; Cit Awd; DAR Awd; High Hon Roll; NHS; St Schlr; Val; Montclair ST Coll; Bio.

MC CURDY II, ROGER B; Saint Augustine Prep; Turnersville, NJ; (3); 1/53; Chess Clb; Church Yth Grp; Nwsp Ed-Chief; Yrbk Stf; Lit Mag; Trs Soph Cls; L Golf; NHS; Prfct Atten Awd; Boy Scts; Eagle Scout 84; Medicine.

MC CUSKER, ED; Haddon Heights HS; Barrington, NJ; (3); L Bsbl; L Bsktbl; L Socr; Hon Roll; Education.

MC CUTCHEON, GWEN LEA; Washington Twp HS; Turnersville, NJ; (3); Church Yth Grp; Cmnty Wkr; Office Aide; Band; Concert Band; Mrchg Band; School Musical; Hon Roll; Prfct Atten Awd; Olympic Conf Hnrs Band 86; Genetic Engrng.

MC DANIEL, MARIA ANTOINETTE; Edgewood SR HS; Sicklerville, NJ; (2); Dance Clb; Drama Clb; Hosp Aide; Latin Clb; Church Choir; Mrchg Band; Nwsp Rptr; Off Stu Cncl; Capt Cheerleading; Hon Roll; Distrct Math Awd 84; Hnr Rll; Howard U Washington DC; Law.

MC DANIEL, SHEILAREE; Academic HS; Jersey City, NJ; (4); 18/78; Church Yth Grp; Chorus; Church Choir; Variety Show; Alpha Kappa Alpha Schlrshp, AFL-CIO Educ Scshlrshp Fund, Prfct Attndnce 83-87; Trenton ST Coll; Bus Admin.

MC DERMOTT, CATHERINE; Sayreville War Memorial HS; Sayreville, NJ; (2); Church Yth Grp; Hosp Aide; Spanish Clb; Stage Crew; Stu Cncl; Hon Roll; Edu.

MC DERMOTT, JOAN; Holy Spirit HS; Margate, NJ; (4); 32/363; Spanish Clb; Stage Crew; Rep Frsh Cls; Rep Soph Cls; Rep Jr Cls; Rep Sr Cls; Stu Cncl; Ftbl; Mgr(s); High Hon Roll; Temple; Psychlgy.

MC DERMOTT, MARCIE; Notre Dame HS; Lawrenceville, NJ; (3); 125/400; Church Yth Grp; French Clb; Red Cross Aide; Ski Clb; SADD; Stat JV Bsbl; JV Var Cheerleading; Fld Hcky; Hon Roll; NHS; Pre-Med.

MC DERMOTT, MARY; De Paul HS; Ringwood, NJ; (3); 65/150; Sec Sr Cls; JV Fld Hcky; Var Socr; Var Trk.

MC DERMOTT, MARYANN; Sayreville War Memorial HS; Sayreville, NJ; (3); Church Yth Grp; Spanish Clb; Color Guard; Concert Band; Flag Corp; Mrchg Band; Yrbk Stf; Hon Roll; Spanish NHS; Librl Arts.

MC DERMOTT, VIRGINIA; Riverside HS; Riverside, NJ; (4); 5/75; SADD; Varsity Clb; Nwsp Stf; Yrbk Stf; Stu Cncl; Cheerleading; NEDT Awd; Sftbl; Hon Roll; Pres Schlr; Garden ST Distngshd Schlr; Trenton ST Alumni Scholar; Independent Ins Agent Scholar; Trenton ST U; Mgmt.

MC DEVITT, JOHN; Hackettstown HS; Hackettstown, NJ; (4); 12/234; Aud/Vis; Drama Clb; Pres Q&S; Yrbk Bus Mgr; Yrbk Stf; VP Sr Cls; Var JV Crs Cntry; Var JV Trk; Hon Roll; NHS; U Notre Dame; Chem Engrng.

MC DEVITT, JOHN BARRY; Bishop Ahr HS; Scotch Plains, NJ; (4); 42/268; Am Leg Boys St; German Clb; Math Tm; Band; Nwsp Stf; Rep Chrmn Stu Cncl; Capt Var Bsbl; Var Bsktbl; Capt Var Socr; High Hon Roll; Schlr Athl 87; U Of Notre Dame; Sports Med.

MC DEVITT, MEGHAN; St Rose HS; Avon, NJ; (4); 26/214; Var Capt Cheerleading; NHS; Clemson U; Marketing.

MC DONALD, DANIELLE; Gloucester JR-SR HS; Gloucester, NJ; (4); 2/140; French Clb; Math Clb; Spanish Clb; Band; Concert Band; Mrchg Band; Lit Mag; NHS; Sal; St Schlr; H R Young Schlrshp 87; Monmouth Coll; Hstry.

MC DONALD, EDWARD; Notre Dame HS; Trenton, NJ; (2); Math Tm; Crs Cntry; Trk; High Hon Roll; Hon Roll; NHS; Engrng.

MC DONALD, GEOFF; Southern Regional HS; Manahawkin, NJ; (3); 90/450; Lit Mag; Var Trk; Hon Roll; Milestones Freedm Lcl Exchng Clb; Interact Clb-Rotary; USAF; Militry Sci.

MC DONALD, JOHN; St Joseph Regional HS; Demarest, NJ; (4); Nwsp Rptr; Svc Awd 87; Outstanding Achvt-The Guardian Schl Newspaper 87; Seton Hall U; Broadcst Journlsm.

MC DONALD, KEELEY; Roxbury HS; Landing, NJ; (4); 37/391; Political Wkr; Ski Clb; Pres Orch; Rep Stu Cncl; Var Fld Hcky; NHS; Pres Schlr; Debate Tm; Natl Schl Orchstr Awd 87; PBA Schlrshp 87; All Cnty, St, Cnfrnc & Area Fld Hcky Goalie 86; Old Dmn U; Lawyer.

MC DONALD, MARK; Orange HS; Orange, NJ; (2); Band; Var Bsbl; JV Wrstlng; Optometrist.

MC DONALD, RENFORD; Clifford J Scott HS; E Orange, NJ; (4); Boy Scts; Church Yth Grp; Pres Computer Clb; 4-H; Intnl Clb; Math Clb; Red Cross Aide; Socr; Trk; Hon Roll; Cert AT&T Sci Prgrm 86; Rutgers U; Comp Sci.

MC DONNELL, KEVIN G; Piscataway HS; Piscataway, NJ; (4); 47/496; Drama Clb; Math Tm; Chorus; Concert Band; Jazz Band; Madrigals; Mrchg Band; Orch; School Musical; School Play; Central Jersey Music Ed Assn Orch 87; Central Jersey Music Ed Assn Concert Band 86; Naval Sci.

MC DONNELL, STACEY; Mt St Mary Acad; Spotswood, NJ; (4); 13/79; Cmnty Wkr; Office Aide; Q&S; Sec Spanish Clb; Chorus; Nwsp Ed-Chief; Nwsp Rptr; Nwsp Sprt Ed; Hon Roll; Computer Clb; Congrsnl Yth Ldrshp Conf 86; NJ Spcl Olympcs Cert 84-86; Marist Coll; Jrnlsm.

MC DONOUGH, THOMAS; St Peters Prep; Bayonne, NJ; (4); 11/196; Boy Scts; Cmnty Wkr; Debate Tm; German Clb; Political Wkr; School Musical; Pres Sr Cls; High Hon Roll; Ntl Merit SF; St Schlr; Rutgers Coll.

MC DUFFIE, IVAN; Eastside HS; Paterson, NJ; (3); 50/700; Computer Clb; FCA; Math Tm; SADD; Var Bsbl; Var Bsktbl; Cit Awd; High Hon Roll; Sptsmnshp Awd Bsktbl Tm 86-87; Comp Sci.

MC DUFFIE, MICHELLE B; Abraham Clark HS; Roselle, NJ; (3); Girl Scts; Spanish Clb; Drill Tm; Variety Show; JV Cheerleading; JV Gym; JV Trk; Fshn Merch.

MC ELFISH, DONNA; Triton Regional HS; Somerdale, NJ; (4); 13/295; Sec AFS; French Clb; Science Clb; Nwsp Rptr; Stu Cncl; NHS; Outstndg Achvmnt Lab Chem 85; Outstndg Achvmnt Lab Physcs 86; Prncpls Hnr Rll 84-87; Baylor U; Engnrng.

MC ELGIN JR, JAMES F; Ocean City HS; Ocean City, NJ; (3); Church Yth Grp; Drama Clb; School Play; Trs Stu Cncl; Coach Actv; Socr; Tennis; Ranked 9th Intl Sabre Fencer 84-85; Fenced In US Sprts Fstvl 84-85; 4th & 5th Pl JR Olympics 84-85.

MC ELHONE, CAROLYN; John F Kennedy HS; Willingboro, NJ; (3); Hosp Aide; Office Aide; Flag Corp; Mrchg Band; Nwsp Rptr; Yrbk Stf; Flagler Coll; Poltcl Sci.

MC ELROY, EILEEN; Cinnaminson HS; Cinna, NJ; (4); 31/231; Church Yth Grp; Off Frsh Cls; Off Soph Cls; Off Jr Cls; Off Sr Cls; Off Stu Cncl; Capt Var Fld Hcky; Var Lcrss; Hon Roll; NHS; 1st Tm All South Jersey La Crosse 87; Trenton ST Coll; Health.

MC ELROY, MELISSA; North Warren Regional HS; Columbia, NJ; (3); Am Leg Aux Girls St; Exploring; 4-H; Nwsp Rptr; Yrbk Ed-Chief; Lit Mag; Bsktbl; Dnfth Awd; 4-H Awd; Hon Roll; Specl Hon Raising Seeing Eye Dogs 77-87; 4-H Clb Congrss Chgo 86; Rotary Ldrshp Awd 87; Rutgers/Rider; Engl/Germn Ed.

MC ELROY, PAMELA; Cinnaminson HS; Cinnaminson, NJ; (3); Am Leg Aux Girls St; Church Yth Grp; Rep Jr Cls; Bsktbl; Var Fld Hcky; Var Lcrss; Hon Roll; Hnr Mntn All S Jersey La Crosse 87; 2nd Tm Sioux Div La Crosse 87; Fld Hcky Capt 84; Hstry.

MC FADDEN, RITA; Paul VI HS; Atco, NJ; (4); 77/503; Am Leg Aux Girls St; Chorus; Church Choir; School Musical; School Play; Variety Show; Sec Frsh Cls; Sec Trs Stu Cncl; Hon Roll; NHS; Waterford Twp Mayors Awd Outstndng Civic Contrbtn 86; Assumption Schl Awd 83; Catholic Dghtrs Amer Awd; Music Ed.

MC FALL, KATHLEEN; Glen Rock SR HS; Glen Rock, NJ; (3); 32/145; Sec AFS; Sec Church Yth Grp; Debate Tm; Hosp Aide; Pep Clb; Teachers Aide; Chorus; Church Choir; School Musical; JV Var Trk; Afro-Amer Clb Secy 86-87; PASS 87 Pgm Skidmore Coll 87; Bergen Cnty Chorus 86-87.

MC FALL, PATRICIA; Lacey Township HS; Forked River, NJ; (3); 56/260; Church Yth Grp; Cmnty Wkr; Drama Clb; Trs FBLA; Hosp Aide; Spanish Clb; SADD; Chorus; Nwsp Stf; Ed Yrbk Stf; :Educ.

MC FARLAND, DEBROAH; Sussex Vo-Tech HS; Ogdensburg, NJ; (2); Dance Clb; Ski Clb; Varsity Clb; School Musical; Rep Frsh Cls; Pres Soph Cls; Bowling; Cheerleading; Trk; Hon Roll; The Hugh Obrien Yth Fndtn 86-87; Cosm.

MC FARLAND, THOMAS F; St Joseph Regional HS; Spring Valley, NY; (3); 5/225; Pres Church Yth Grp; Math Tm; Yrbk Stf; Rep Stu Cncl; Var Golf; Hon Roll; NHS; Spanish NHS; St Boniface Acad Schlrshp 86-87; Treas Rcklnd Cnty Cathlc Yth Org 87-88; Bus.

MC FARLANE, MICHELLE; Sparta HS; Sparta, NJ; (3); Key Clb; Ski Clb; Jr Cls; JV Cheerleading; AZ ST U; Fshn Mrchndsr.

MC FILLIN, TERRI; Holy Spirit HS; Margate, NJ; (4); 44/363; French Clb; Stage Crew; Nwsp Rptr; Stu Cncl; Var Bsktbl; Var Gym; Bausch & Lomb Sci Awd; Hon Roll; Physcl Sci Awd; La Salle; Psychlgy.

MC GAHN, DANIEL; Atlantic City HS; Brigantine, NJ; (2); Computer Clb; Model UN; Office Aide; Science Clb; Teachers Aide; Lit Mag; Var Golf; Var Swmmng; High Hon Roll; Sci Resrch Pgm 86-87; JR Natl Sailng Champ 85; Mid Atlntc Sailing Cham 2nd Pl 85.

MC GARRITY, JAYNE; Millville SR HS; Millville, NJ; (4); 10/400; Church Yth Grp; Im Badmtn; JV Bsktbl; Im Bowling; JV Fld Hcky; L Var Socr; JV Var Sftbl; Im Vllybl; High Hon Roll; NHS; Wmns Clb 87; Bio Awd 84; GPA Awd 84; Messiah Coll; Veterinary Med.

MC GARRY, KATHLEEN; Notre Dame HS; Dallas, TX; (2); Church Yth Grp; Rep Frsh Cls; Socr; Var Socr; High Hon Roll; Hon Roll; NHS.

MC GAY, KELLY; Lower Cape May Regional HS; Townbank, NJ; (3); 12/205; Girl Scts; Band; Concert Band; Mrchg Band; Orch; Hon Roll; NHS; 3rd Pl Typng Compttn 86; Glassboro ST Coll; Ed.

MC GEE, VOLANTE; Mt St Dominic Acad; East Orange, NJ; (3); 15/75; Library Aide; Chorus; Nwsp Stf; Stat Bsktbl; Hon Roll; NHS; Chem Engrng.

MC GILL, GRETCHEN ANN; Bloomfield HS; Bloomfld, NJ; (4); 20/442; Hosp Aide; VP Key Clb; Capt Drill Tm; Yrbk Stf; Rep Stu Cncl; VP L Trk; High Hon Roll; NHS; Ntl Merit Ltr; GAA; W R Hotchkiss Fdtn Schlrshp 87; East Carolina U; Acctg.

MC GINN, ROBERT; Paulsboro HS; Paulsboro, NJ; (3); 56/120; Rep Stu Cncl; JV Bsbl; JV Bsktbl; Crpntry.

MC GOVERN, ANNE; Maple Shade HS; Maple Shade, NJ; (2); French Clb; Key Clb; Trs Frsh Cls; Trs Soph Cls; JV Lcrss; JV Stat Socr; Hon Roll; NHS; Rtry Clb Yth Merit Awd 86; Pre-Med.

MC GOVERN, CHRISTOPHER; Clearview Regional HS; Sewell, NJ; (3); 42/171; Church Yth Grp; Rep Stu Cncl; Var L Swmmng; Var Trk; Hon Roll; NHS; Coachs Awd Smmr Smmmng 85; Aerospc Engrng.

MC GOVERN, MICHAEL; Vernon Township HS; Sussex, NJ; (3); Chorus; School Musical; Pres Frsh Cls; Stu Cncl; Trk; Hon Roll; Prfct Atten Awd; NJ Assctn Stu Cncl Trsr & Rgnl Chrs 84-87; Sussex Cnty Chrs 84-85; Mrn Engr.

MC GOWAN, COLLEEN; Holy Spirit HS; Longport, NJ; (3); Spanish Clb; SADD; Yrbk Stf; Rep Frsh Cls; Rep Jr Cls; Rep Sr Cls; Mgr(s); Var Tennis; Hon Roll; NHS.

MC GOWAN, JENNIFER; Mt St Dominic HS; Caldwell, NJ; (3); GAA; JCL; Latin Clb; Ski Clb; Nwsp Phtg; Nwsp Rptr; Nwsp Stf; Yrbk Stf; Lit Mag; Rep Frsh Cls.

MC GOWAN, JOHN D; Wildwood HS; W Wildwood, NJ; (3); 1/109; Am Leg Boys St; Math Tm; Capt Scholastic Bowl; Lit Mag; Im Bowling; Var L Trk; Im Vllybl; High Hon Roll; NHS; JV Ftbl; Rutgers Schlr 87.

MC GOWAN, PATRICIA; Williamstown HS; Williamstown, NJ; (3); 1/280; Hosp Aide; Pres Key Clb; SADD; Nwsp Ed-Chief; Yrbk Stf; Sec Jr Cls; Rep Stu Cncl; Var Fld Hcky; High Hon Roll; JETS Awd; Engrng.

MC GRATH, COLLEEN; Brick Township HS; Brick, NJ; (4); 18/343; Key Clb; Color Guard; Lit Mag; Powder Puff Ftbl; High Hon Roll; Cert Of Excllnc, Ocean Cnty & ST Teen Arts Fstvl 86; Cert Of Excllnc Teen Fine Arts Exhbtn 85; Trenton ST Coll; Intr Dsgn.

MC GRATH, EDWARD; Southern Regional HS; Barnegat, NJ; (3); 112/460; Rep Soph Cls; Rep Stu Cncl; JV Var Socr; JV Var Trk.

MC GRATH, MICHAEL; Notre Dame HS; Hamilton Sq, NJ; (2); Math Tm; Varsity Clb; Yrbk Stf; Var L Crs Cntry; Var L Trk.

MC GRATH, TARA A; Jonathan Dayton Regional HS; Mountainside, NJ; (4); 67/232; Church Yth Grp; Q&S; Spanish Clb; Nwsp Stf; Yrbk Stf; Crs Cntry; Trk; Hon Roll; Varsity Clb; Fine Art Awd-Outstndng Art Stu 87; Mtn Vly Conf Schl-Athlt Awd Trk 87; Fshn Inst Tech NY; Adv Dsgn.

MC GUIGAN, MICHAEL; Notre Dome HS; Trenton, NJ; (3); FBLA; Latin Clb; Ski Clb; Varsity Clb; Rep Frsh Cls; Rep Soph Cls; Rep Jr Cls; Var Bsbl; Var Trk; Hon Roll; Biomed Engr.

MC GUINNES, DAN; John F Kennedy HS; Willingboro, NJ; (2); 16/332.

MC GUIRE, CAROLINE; Academy Of The Holy Angels; Ridgewood, NJ; (3); Church Yth Grp; Exploring; French Clb; Hosp Aide; Math Clb; Mu Alpha Theta; Ski Clb; Chorus.

MC GUIRE, JUDE A; Summit HS; Summit, NJ; (3); Ski Clb; Stat Bsbl; Var Cheerleading; Stat Ftbl; Var Score Keeper; Hon Roll.

MC GUIRE, KELLY; Bayonne HS; Bayonne, NJ; (3); Dance Clb; Ski Clb; Cheerleading; Gym; Swmmng; Trk; French Clb; Wt Lftg.

MC GUIRE, KEVIN; Roselle Catholic HS; Roselle, NJ; (4); 28/190; Variety Show; Nwsp Rptr; Var Capt Bsbl; Var Capt Bsktbl; Capt Socr; Hon Roll; VA Weslyan Gen Schlrshp 87; Sam Sadorkis Mem Schlrshp 87; Alumni Mothers Club Schlrshp 87; Dayton U; Bus.

MC GUIRE, MAUREEN; Linden HS; Linden, NJ; (3); Church Yth Grp; French Clb; Key Clb; Acpl Chr; Band; Chorus; Madrigals; School Musical; School Play; Wrk Hndcpd Chldrn.

MC GUIRE, SHERRI L; Hopewell Vally Central HS; Pennington, NJ; (3); DECA; FBLA; Var Bsktbl; Var Socr; Var Sftbl; 1st L Ovrll In Rgnl Conf 86-87; 2nd In NJ For Rsrch Proj 86-87; Rider Coll; Bus.

MC GUIRK, SANDI; West Essex SR HS; Roseland, NJ; (3); Church Yth Grp; Church Choir; Concert Band; Orch; JV Var Socr; Var Trk; Hon Roll; Comm.

MC GURR, ANDREW R; Teaneck HS; Teaneck, NJ; (3); 30/412; Am Leg Boys St; Ftbl; Capt Var Trk; Wrstlng; Hon Roll; NHS; Elect Engrg.

MC HENRY, LISA; Paul VI HS; Lindenwold, NJ; (3); 7/431; Art Clb; Math Clb; Drill Tm; School Musical; JV Trk; Hon Roll; NHS; Spanish NHS; Eng.

MC HORNEY, DIANA; Vernon Twp HS; Highland Lakes, NJ; (4); 54/240; Exploring; JCL; Pep Clb; Ski Clb; Varsity Clb; Variety Show; Rep Jr Cls; Rep Sr Cls; Rep Stu Cncl; Im Bowling; WA Coll; Pre-Medical.

MC HOSE, JAMIE; Holy Spirit HS; Brigantine, NJ; (2); 25/397; Drama Clb; Pep Clb; Church Choir; Mgr(s); Hosp Aide; SADD; School Play; Score Keeper; Berkly; Journslm.

MC HUGH, EDWARD; Lakeland Reg HS; Ringwood, NJ; (4); 30/345; Aud/Vis; Church Yth Grp; Cmnty Wkr; Rep Sr Cls; Var Capt Bsbl; Var L Socr; High Hon Roll; Hon Roll; Jr NHS; NHS; Lakeland Alumni Schlrshp 87; Villanova U; Law.

MC ILHENNY, STACIE; Deptford HS; Mantua, NJ; (1); Band; Concert Band; Yrbk Stf; JV Bowling; High Hon Roll; JC Awd; Jr NHS.

MC INTOSH, DENISE; Eastside HS; Lauderdale Lakes, FL; (2); #8 In Class; Computer Clb; Rep Frsh Cls; High Hon Roll; Hon Roll; 2nd Pl H S Sci Fair Awd 86-87; Stu Of Mnth Alg I 85-86.

MC INTOSH, DENNIS; Baptist HS; Woodlynne, NJ; (1); Church Yth Grp; Pep Clb; Rep Stu Cncl; JV Bsktbl; JV Socr; Hon Roll; Scty Of Dstngshd Amer HS Stud 86; Phila Coll Of Pharm; Sci.

MC INTOSH, LISA; Overbrook SR HS; Sicklerville, NJ; (3); Pres Church Yth Grp; Dance Clb; DECA; Church Choir; Variety Show; JV Bsktbl; JV Fld Hcky; JV Trk; Teachers Aide; Chorus; Radio Brdcstng.

MC INTOSH, TARA; Buena Regional HS; Buena, NJ; (4); 30/170; Dance Clb; Pep Clb; Ski Clb; SADD; Varsity Clb; Chorus; Rep Frsh Cls; Rep Soph Cls; Rep Jr Cls; Rep Sr Cls; Prsdntl Acdmc Ftnss Awds Pgm 87; Glassboro ST Coll; Elem Ed.

MC INTOSH, TERRY; Cumberland Regional HS; Bridgeton, NJ; (3); 1/386; Church Yth Grp; Intnl Clb; JCL; Latin Clb; Science Clb; Lit Mag; High Hon Roll; Jr NHS; NHS; 1st Art Wrk Schl Literary Mgzn, Hnrb Mntn Natl Latin Exam, Art Wrk Dsplyd Teen Arts Fstvl 85; Pre-Med.

MC INTYRE, DEIDRE; Gloucester City JE SR HS; Brooklawn, NJ; (3); Pep Clb; Band; Concert Band; School Play; Yrbk Stf; JV Cheerleading; Hon Roll; Nrsng.

MC INTYRE, JEANNE; River Dell SR HS; River Edge, NJ; (2); Church Yth Grp; Pep Clb; Chorus; Girl Scts; Psych.

MC IVOR, MAUREEN; Sayreville War Memorial HS; Sayreville, NJ; (3); Church Yth Grp; Pep Clb; Spanish Clb; Yrbk Stf; Rep Sr Cls; Hon Roll; Accntng.

MC KAY, LINDA; Timothy Christian Schl; Piscataway, NJ; (2); 1/50; Church Yth Grp; Var Score Keeper; Var L Socr; Var Sftbl; High Hon Roll; NHS; Prfct Atten Awd; Math Awd 85-86.

MC KEAN, JULIE; Red Bank Catholic HS; Middletown, NJ; (4); 103/319; Church Yth Grp; Civic Clb; Cmnty Wkr; Drama Clb; 4-H; French Clb; Pep Clb; Political Wkr; Ski Clb; Speech Tm; Yr End Awds MCHSA Chldrns Equitatn 85-86; 4-H Pamona Grange Awd 83; U Of NC; Pre-Law.

MC KEE, JULIE ELLEN; Holy Cross HS; Maple Shade, NJ; (3); SADD; Band; Drm & Bgl; Mrchg Band; Schl Lttr Band Bar 87; Scl Svc.

MC KEEVER, JOHN; Belvidere HS; Phillipsburg, NJ; (3); 9/125; Var Ftbl; Var Golf; Im Wt Lftg; Var Wrstlng; Engrng.

MC KENNA, JAMES; Oratory Prep; Millburn, NJ; (1); 7/45; Boy Scts; Math Tm; Ski Clb; High Hon Roll; NHS; Eagle Sct 86; Rutgers U.

MC KENNA, JOHN; St John Vianney HS; Matawan, NJ; (3); 5/250; Math Clb; Math Tm; Band; Concert Band; Jazz Band; Mrchg Band; Orch; School Musical; School Play; Symp Band; Outstndng Music Awd 85 & 87; Outstndng Rgn Awd 86; Geo Wshngtn U Awd-Excllnc Math & Sci 87; VA Polytech; Arch.

MC KENNA, JULIA; John P Stevens HS; Edison, NJ; (3); 112/450; Var Crs Cntry; JV Socr; Var Trk; Hon Roll.

MC KENNA, KATHLEEN ANN MARIE; Belvidere HS; Hope, NJ; (4); Am Leg Aux Girls St; 4-H; Office Aide; Ski Clb; Teachers Aide; Varsity Clb; Cheerleading; Hon Roll; Pom Pon; Human Ecol Achvt Awd 87; Warren Cnty Home Ec Advsry Cncl Scholar 87; Coll St Elizabeth; Dietetics.

MC KENNA, KEITH; Don Bosco Prep; Hasbrouck Heights, NJ; (2); Drama Clb; Ski Clb; School Musical; School Play; JV Ftbl; High Hon Roll; NHS; Ntl Merit Ltr.

MC KENNA, KEVIN; Christian Brothers Academy; Belford, NJ; (4); 6/230; Varsity Clb; Nwsp Rptr; Yrbk Rptr; Crs Cntry; Trk; High Hon Roll; NHS; St Schlr; NJ Dstngshd Schlr 87; Schlr Athlt Awd 87; Mst Vlbl Mdl Dstnc Rnnr 87; Rugers Coll; Pre-Med.

MC KENNA, PAMELA; Immaculate Heart Acad; Oakland, NJ; (1); Church Yth Grp; Socr; Trk; Hon Roll; Prfct Atten Awd; Math.

MC KENNA, RACHEL; St John Vianney HS; Keyport, NJ; (4); 79/250; Cmnty Wkr; FBLA; Spanish Clb; Im Powder Puff Ftbl; High Hon Roll; Hon Roll; Garden ST Schlrshp; Montclair ST Coll; Paralgl.

MC KENZIE, DAVID L; West Windsor-Plainsboro HS; Lawrenceville, NJ; (3); Boy Scts; Ski Clb; SADD; Band; School Play; Stage Crew; Rep Stu Cncl; Hon Roll; Bus.

MC KENZIE, KURT; Essex Catholic Boys HS; Irvington, NJ; (3); Art Clb; Jazz Band; Wt Lftg; Wrstlng; High Hon Roll.

MC KENZIE, MICHAEL; Woodtown HS; Alloway, NJ; (4); Spanish Clb; JV Ftbl; JV Wrstlng; Stockton ST Coll; Bus Mgmt.

MC KEON, ALISON; Waldwick HS; Waldwick, NJ; (3); Church Yth Grp; Cmnty Wkr; Spanish Clb; Nwsp Rptr; Nwsp Stf; Score Keeper; Hon Roll; Bus Mgmt.

MC KEON, BRIDGET; St John Vianney HS; Manalapan, NJ; (2); Church Yth Grp; Rep Frsh Cls; Var Cheerleading; JV Capt Sftbl; Hon Roll; Gld & Wht Awds-Srv, Schlrshp & Actvty 86 & 87; Vrsty Awds-Chrldng 86; Boston Coll; Comms.

MC KEON, JEAN; Indian Hills HS; Franklin Lks, NJ; (3); Cmnty Wkr; French Clb; GAA; Chorus; School Play; Variety Show; Yrbk Stf; Sec Stu Cncl; Var Capt Cheerleading; Coach Actv; Rutgers-Douglass Coll; Comrcl.

MC KEOWN, ELLEN; Matawan Regional HS; Aberdeen, NJ; (2); French Clb; Ski Clb; Sftbl; Stat Wrstlng.

MC KINNEY, CHERIE; Lower Cape May Regional HS; Cape May, NJ; (3); GAA; Math Tm; Office Aide; Pep Clb; Spanish Clb; Teachers Aide; Varsity Clb; Rep Frsh Cls; Rep Soph Cls; Rep Jr Cls; Octagon Clb Treasr 88; Comp Sci.

MC KINNEY, DALLAS; Gloucester City HS; Brooklawn, NJ; (3); Boy Scts; Library Aide; SADD; Nwsp Stf; Bsktbl; Ftbl; Trk; Wt Lftg; Hon Roll; Eppleman Ftbl Awd 87; Crmnl Law.

MC KIVER, TARA; James J Ferris HS; Jersey City, NJ; (3); Trs Church Yth Grp; DECA; Drama Clb; Ed Nwsp Stf; Rep Soph Cls; Pres Jr Cls; Rep Stu Cncl; Vllybl; Hon Roll; Prfct Atten Awd; Hampton U; Child Psych.

MC KNIGHT, LEIGHA; Holy Spirit HS; Brigantine, NJ; (2); 28/397; Spanish Clb; Nwsp Rptr; Hon Roll.

MC KNIGHT, MADELYN; Lincoln HS; Jersy City, NJ; (3); FBLA; Yrbk Stf; Co-Capt Cheerleading; Prfct Atten Awd; Katherine Kibbs; Exec Sec.

MC LAIN, SUSAN; Bricktownship HS; Brick Town, NJ; (4); Drama Clb; Band; Concert Band; Mrchg Band; Stage Crew; High Hon Roll; Hon Roll; NHS; Frostburg ST Coll.

MC LAUGHLIN, CHRISTOPHER B; New Milford HS; New Milford, NJ; (4); 3/141; Am Leg Boys St; Nwsp Sprt Ed; Yrbk Stf; Var Socr; Capt Var Trk; Pres NHS; Ntl Merit Schol; ITT Coll Schlrshp Recpnt 87; U Of PA; Ecnmcs.

MC LAUGHLIN, COLETTE; Bayonne HS; Bayonne, NJ; (4); 8/320; U Of DE; Lwyr.

MC LAUGHLIN, DONALD; St Joseph Regional HS; Ramsey, NJ; (3); 19/225; Am Leg Boys St; Hosp Aide; Math Tm; Ski Clb; Sec SADD; Varsity Clb; Nwsp Rptr; Nwsp Stf; Yrbk Phtg; Yrbk Rptr; Hnbl Mntn All Lge Tnns 85-87; MVP Tnns Mst Imprvd Plyr Hockey 86-87; U Of VT; Spts Mgmnt.

MC LAUGHLIN, JOSEPH; Holy Spirit HS; Atlantic City, NJ; (4); 25/363; French Clb; French Hon Soc; High Hon Roll; Hon Roll; NHS; Garden ST Distngshd Schlr 86; Holy Spirit Crew Tm 83-87; Engr.

MC LAUGHLIN, KELLY; Sparta HS; Sparta, NJ; (3); 68/268; Church Yth Grp; Key Clb; SADD; VP Jr Cls; VP Sr Cls; Rep Stu Cncl; Tennis; Hon Roll; Educ.

MC LAUGHLIN, KEVIN; Phillipsburg HS; Phillipsburg, NJ; (3); Cmnty Wkr; Ski Clb; Rep Stu Cncl; JV Bsbl; Var Ftbl; Im Wt Lftg; Hon Roll; 3 Time All Str Bsbl Plyr 85-87.

MC LAUGHLIN, NANCY; Sacred Heart HS; Clayton, NJ; (3); Girl Scts; Office Aide; Spanish Clb; SADD; School Play; Lit Mag; Rep Frsh Cls; Var Crs Cntry; JV Mgr(s); JV Score Keeper; Barry U; Nrsg.

MC LAUGHLIN, PATRICIA; Arthur P Schalick HS; Newfield, NJ; (3); 25/145; DECA; Spanish Clb; Teachers Aide; Yrbk Stf; Rep Frsh Cls; Rep Soph Cls; Rep Stu Cncl; Var Capt Fld Hcky; Score Keeper; Hon Roll; Acctng.

MC LAUGHLIN, SHANNON; Highland Regional HS; Clementon, NJ; (2); Drama Clb; Hosp Aide; Chorus; Mrchg Band; School Play; Stage Crew; Pom Pon; Schl Music Awd; Psyclgy.

MC LOUGHLIN, EILISH; Paramus Catholic Girls HS; Westwood, NJ; (3); 14/180; Cmnty Wkr; French Clb; Service Clb; Chorus; School Musical; School Play; Trk; Hon Roll; NHS; NEDT Awd; Eng Awd; Psych.

MC MAHON, BRIDGET; Holy Spirit HS; Palermo, NJ; (3); 42/332; Spanish Clb; Off Stu Cncl; Var L Swmmng; JV Var Trk; Hon Roll; NHS; Comm.

MC MAHON, CHUCK; Washington Township HS; Turnersville, NJ; (3); Bsktbl; Socr; Hon Roll; Vrsty Ltrs Soccr & Bsktbll 86; Rutgers U; Comp Sci.

MC MAHON, MARY; Lenape Valley Regional HS; Sparta, NJ; (3); 11/210; French Clb; Key Clb; JV Bsktbl; Crs Cntry; Trk; French Hon Soc; Hon Roll; NHS; Lenape Schlr Awd 86; French Frnsc Trnmnt Wnnr 86.

MC MAHON, MARYBETH; St Rose HS; Brick Town, NJ; (3); Key Clb; Church Choir; School Play; Yrbk Stf; Hon Roll; Spanish NHS; Int Dsgn.

MC MAHON, MICHAEL; Morristown HS; Morristown, NJ; (2); Church Yth Grp; Letterman Clb; Yrbk Stf; Bsbl; Ftbl; Lcrss; Hnr Rll.

MC MAHON, THERESA; Bishop Ahr HS; Colonia, NJ; (4); 74/277; Spanish Clb; Var Bsktbl; Var Mgr(s); Capt Sftbl; DAR Awd; High Hon Roll; Hon Roll; Ntl Merit SF; Lock Haven U; Athltc Trng.

MC MANUS, JENNIFER; Rancocas Valley Regional HS; Hainesport, NJ; (2); 34/298; Cmnty Wkr; School Play; JV Bsktbl; JV Fld Hcky; High Hon Roll; Hon Roll; NJ Schl Arts Schlrshp 87; Librl Arts.

MC MANUS, KRISTEN; Randolph HS; Randolph, NJ; (3); 40/353; Am Leg Aux Girls St; Church Yth Grp; Ski Clb; Powder Puff Ftbl; Var Tennis; High Hon Roll; Hon Roll; William & Mary.

MC MARTIN, BETH; Hunterdon Central HS; Flemington, NJ; (4); 12/548; Pres Church Yth Grp; Chorus; Jazz Band; Mrchg Band; School Musical; Symp Band; NHS; St Schlr; Church Choir; Variety Show; Music Dept Awd 87; Amer Cyanmd Excllnc Stdy Sci Awd 87; IN U Bloomington; Anthrplgy.

MC MEEKIN, JENNIFER; Atlantic City HS; Atlantic City, NJ; (3); Bowling; Var Fld Hcky; Hon Roll; U Sthrn FL; Psych.

MC MILLIAN, JACQUELINE; Paul VI HS; Williamstown, NJ; (3); Church Yth Grp; Spanish Clb; Chorus; Var Capt Crs Cntry; Var Trk; Prfct Atten Awd; All S Jersey X Country 84 & 86; Sports Medicine.

MC MONAGLE, KRISTINE; Haddon Heights HS; Barrington, NJ; (3); Church Yth Grp; Band; Concert Band; Mrchg Band; Mgr Sftbl; Hon Roll; JV Mgr(s); JV Score Keeper.

MC MULLEN, CARRIE; Columbia HS; Bayville, NJ; (3); Dance Clb; Radio Clb; Spanish Clb; Variety Show; Trs Frsh Cls; Rep Soph Cls; Rep Jr Cls; Cheerleading; Penn ST U; Resp Thrpst.

MC NAIR, KEVIN; Highland Regional HS; Clementon, NJ; (3); 43/290; Church Yth Grp; Spanish Clb; Band; Church Choir; Concert Band; Jazz Band; Mrchg Band; School Musical; JV Var Bsktbl; Hon Roll; Music Awd 85; Physcl Achvt Awd 85; U PA; Med.

MC NAIR, SHANTESIA; Our Lady Of Good Counsel HS; Newark, NJ; (3); Chorus; School Musical; Hnrb Mntn Art Awd 87; Rutgers U.

MC NALLY, MAUREEN; Red Bank Regional HS; Little Silver, NJ; (4); 10/260; Church Yth Grp; Concert Band; Drm Mjr(t); School Musical; Cit Awd; Elks Awd; Kiwanis Awd; NHS; Sec Spanish NHS; Trenton Sister-City Yth Orch 87; VA Tech; Cmmnctns.

MC NALLY, MEAVE; Bayonne HS; Bayonne, NJ; (4); 26/300; French Clb; Math Tm; Chorus; Orch; School Musical; Gym; High Hon Roll; Jr NHS; Cert Of Chem Lab 85; Smmr Schlr U Of Caen France 85; Music Awd 85; Physcl Anthrplgst.

MC NAMARA, DIANE; Memorial HS; Cedar Grove, NJ; (4); 16/123; Key Clb; Spanish Clb; Mrchg Band; Yrbk Ed-Chief; Var Bsktbl; Var Capt Tennis; Var Capt Trk; High Hon Roll; Jr NHS; NHS; Acadmic Excllnc Spnsh III Awd; Excllnc Phy Ed III Awd; Music Awd.

MC NEE, RICHIE; Gloucester City HS; Gloucester Cty, NJ; (3); Am Leg Boys St; English Clb; Math Clb; Pep Clb; Science Clb; Spanish Clb; School Play; Var Capt Bsbl; Var Bsktbl; Var Ftbl; All Tri Cnty Bsbl 1st Team 86-87.

MC NEILA, TOM; Lakeland Regional HS; Wanaque, NJ; (3); Ski Clb; SADD; Var Crs Cntry; JV Trk; Hon Roll; Bus.

MC NEILLY, CHRIS; Paulsboro HS; Paulsboro, NJ; (3); 34/130; Yrbk Stf; Stat Bsbl; Stat Ftbl; Mat Maids; Sftbl; Hon Roll; Katherine Gibbs Secy Awd 87; Omega Bus Schl; Trvl Agent.

MC NELIS, MICHELLE; Holy Cross HS; Browns Mills, NJ; (3); 30/409; Cmnty Wkr; Spanish Clb; Rep Stu Cncl; JV Trk; Hon Roll; Pre Law.

MC NICHOLAS, CORI; Bricktown HS; Brick Town, NJ; (3); 24/410; Key Clb; Math Tm; SADD; Trs Band; Trs Concert Band; Trs Mrchg Band; Var Stat Score Keeper; JV Var Sftbl; High Hon Roll; NHS.

MC NICOL, DUNCAN; Long Branch HS; Long Branch, NJ; (4); #2 In Class; Boy Scts; Band; Concert Band; Mrchg Band; School Musical; Socr; Hon Roll; NHS; Sal; Grdn ST Dstngstd Schlr 86-87; Rtgrs Schlr 85-86; Rutgers Coll; Pre Med.

MC NULTY, MAUREEN THERESA; St Marys HS; Keansburg, NJ; (4); 7/130; Church Yth Grp; Library Aide; Office Aide; Stage Crew; Yrbk Stf; Lit Mag; Bsktbl; High Hon Roll; Hon Roll; Spanish NHS; COA Schlrshp 83-87; Rutgers U; Elem Ed.

MC PARTLAND, JILL; Mother Seton Regional HS; Linden, NJ; (3); GAA; Hosp Aide; Service Clb; Drill Tm; Stage Crew; Hon Roll; NHS; Dance Clb; Im Bsktbl; Var Sftbl; Seton Spirit Awd 87; 3rd Pl Awd Knights Of Pythias Hwy Sfty Pstr Cntst 87; 200 Hrs Awd Pin Cndystrpng.

MC PHERSON, CYNTHIA S; Randolph HS; Mendham, NJ; (3); 4/360; AFS; Church Yth Grp; VP Key Clb; Concert Band; Mrchg Band; Nwsp Sprt Ed; Sec French Hon Soc; High Hon Roll; Hon Roll; NHS; NJ Inst Tech 2nd Pl Essy 86; NJ Dstngshd Schlr 87; Psychlgy.

MC PHERSON, PAM; Montville Township HS; Montville, NJ; (3); 40/248; Boy Scts; Church Yth Grp; Key Clb; SADD; Varsity Clb; Band; Church Choir; Concert Band; Drm Mjr(t); Mrchg Band; Capt Var Swim 87-88; Deacon 1st Presbyterian Church Boonton 87-88.

MC QUAID, KATHLEEN; Southern Regional HS; Barnegat, NJ; (4); 34/340; Trs Church Yth Grp; Teachers Aide; Lit Mag; Bsktbl; Capt Cheerleading; Hon Roll; NHS; Associated Schls Inc; Entrtnmnt.

MC QUIGGAN, MARIANNE; Burl Co Vo-Tech HS; Burlington, NJ; (3); 17/192; FBLA; Fld Hcky; Hon Roll; 5th Plc Wrd Prcssng FBLA Southern Rgnl Cmptn 87; Ntl Hnr Rll Lttr 86; Bus.

MC QUILLAR, TONIA; Trenton Central HS; Trenton, NJ; (3); Church Yth Grp; Hosp Aide; Church Choir; Color Guard; Mrchg Band; JV Var Cheerleading; Var Crs Cntry; Var JV Trk; Hon Roll; Nrsng.

MC REE, BARBARA; Lakewood HS; Lakewood, NJ; (3); Hst FBLA; German Clb; Girl Scts; Hosp Aide; Band; Mrchg Band; Nwsp Rptr; Yrbk Stf; Cit Awd; Sen Bradley Yng Ctzen Awd 87; German Natl Hnr Soc 86; Physical Therapy.

MC SHANE, CAROLINE; Paul VI HS; Lindenwold, NJ; (4); 63/504; Pres Church Yth Grp; Math Clb; Office Aide; Chorus; Bsktbl; Var Crs Cntry; Var Sftbl; Var Tennis; Var Trk; Hon Roll; Rutgers.

MC SHANE, SARAH ANNE; Mahwah HS; Mahwah, NJ; (4); Drama Clb; Ski Clb; Spanish Clb; Chorus; School Musical; Nwsp Phtg; Nwsp Rptr; Lit Mag; Hon Roll; Spanish NHS; Thndrbrd Schlrshp 87; Monmouth Coll; Educ.

MC SWEENEY, REBECCA; John F Kennedy HS; Willingboro, NJ; (3); Spanish Clb; Orch; Fld Hcky; Lcrss; Swmmng; Hon Roll; Jr NHS.

MC TONIC, NICOLE; Perth Amboy HS; Perth Amboy, NJ; (3); French Clb; Science Clb; Band; Chorus; Concert Band; Mrchg Band; Capt Cheerleading; Gym; Hon Roll; Vet.

MC VEIGH, JEFFREY S; Moorestown HS; Moorestown, NJ; (3); Am Leg Boys St; Cmnty Wkr; Latin Clb; Ski Clb; Var L Ftbl; Var L Trk; High Hon Roll; Jr Rotarian 87; Elect Engr.

MC VEY, SCOTT; Pennsville Memorial HS; Pennsville, NJ; (3); 3/231; Band; Concert Band; Jazz Band; Mrchg Band; Orch; Pep Band; School Musical; JV Wrstlng; High Hon Roll; Engrng.

MCALARY, DAVID LEE; Marist HS; Bayonne, NJ; (3); 19/96; Cmnty Wkr; Key Clb; Ski Clb; Spanish Clb; Rep Frsh Cls; Rep Soph Cls; Rep Stu Cncl; JV Socr; Im Wt Lftg; Hon Roll; Med.

MEAD, PATRICK; Cherry Hill H S East; Cherry Hill, NJ; (3); Church Yth Grp; Cmnty Wkr; Latin Clb; Im Capt Bsktbl; Var Diving; Var Swmmng; Hon Roll; Variety Show; Top 10 ST Swmmng 86; 2nd Tm All South Jersey Swmmng Awd 86; Var Swim Tm 85-87.

MEADE, JENNIFER; Saint Rose HS; Bricktown, NJ; (3); Math Tm; Ski Clb; Rep Frsh Cls; Rep Soph Cls; Sec Trs Jr Cls; Var Socr; High Hon Roll; NHS; NEDT Awd; Cngrssnl Schlr Rep NJ Natl Yng Ldrs Cnfrnc 87; Frshmn All Arnd Art Awd 84-85.

MEADE, MICHELLE; Cranford HS; Cranford, NJ; (3); 19/266; AFS; Math Clb; Model UN; Quiz Bowl; Science Clb; Band; Mrchg Band; School Musical; JV Cheerleading; Hon Roll; Law Clb; 1st Aid Sqd Cadet Corp.

MEADE, STEVEN M; Bergenfield HS; Bergenfield, NJ; (3); 1/300; Am Leg Boys St; Quiz Bowl; Mrchg Band; Pres Soph Cls; Rep Stu Cncl; Capt Tennis; NHS; Chess Clb; Spanish Clb; Band; Outstndng Jr 87; Rutgers Scholar 87; Brown U Bk Awd 87; Math.

MEADOWS, TYRETTA; Essex Catholic Girls HS; Hillside, NJ; (4); 2/51; Co-Capt Pep Clb; Science Clb; Chorus; Co-Capt Drill Tm; Variety Show; Ed Yrbk Stf; Rep Jr Cls; VP Sr Cls; High Hon Roll; NHS; Dstngshd Schlrs Awd 87; High Hnr Roll 83-87; Douglass Coll; Accntng.

MEAGHER, RICHARD J; Glassboro HS; Glassboro, NJ; (3); 1/160; Am Leg Boys St; Science Clb; School Play; Pres Stu Cncl; Capt Socr; Gov Hon Prg Awd; NHS; St Schlr; Nwsp Stf; Rep Frsh Cls; NJ Governors Schl In Sci 87; Henry Rutgers Schlr 87; Dstngshd NJ Schlr 87; Physics.

MEARS, MARY BETH; Glassboro HS; Glassboro, NJ; (4); 1/141; Office Aide; Mrchg Band; Bausch & Lomb Sci Awd; High Hon Roll; NHS; Val; Drill Tm; Im Bsktbl; Im Fld Hcky; Hon Roll; Govnrs Tchg Schlrs Awd 87; Grdn St Dstgsgd Schlr Awd 87; Phi Beta Kappa Bk Awd 87; U Of Rocheser; Engrng Optics.

MEASDAY, REBECCA; Livingston HS; Livingston, NJ; (3); 148/417; Dance Clb; Math Tm; Pep Clb; Acpl Chr; Chorus; Church Choir; Madrigals; School Musical; School Play; Swing Chorus; Drama.

MEDICI, NICOLE; Manchester Reg HS; N Haledon, NJ; (3); Chorus; Church Choir; Capt Color Guard; Powder Puff Ftbl; Hon Roll; Rutgers U; Bus Law.

MEDINA, ERIBERTO L; Dickinson HS; Lakewood, NJ; (3); Computer Clb; Math Clb; Science Clb; JV Var Bsktbl; JV Var Bowling; Var Score Keeper; Hon Roll; Prfct Atten Awd; Merit Roll 84-86; Chem Engrng.

MEDINA, MARILYN; Lincoln HS; Jersey City, NJ; (2); Church Yth Grp; DECA; Math Clb; Spanish Clb; Church Choir; Lit Mag; Rep Stu Cncl; Cit Awd; Hon Roll; Prfct Atten Awd; Engl, Math, HSPT Awds.

MEDINA, SEAN; Cliffside Park HS; Fairview, NJ; (3); 62/234; Rep Stu Cncl; Bsbl; Ftbl; Hon Roll; Brdcstng.

MEDORA, CHRISTINE; West Windsor-Plainsboro HS; Princeton Junct, NJ; (3); French Clb; Chorus; Nwsp Rptr; Lit Mag; High Hon Roll; Hon Roll; NHS; Play Guitar Band Won 3rd Pl Schl Talent Shw 86; Aspirations Cnty Literary Mag 85-86; Lib Arts.

MEDURI, ANNE; Clearview HS; Mantua, NJ; (3); 37/171; DECA; Pep Clb; Spanish Clb; SADD; Varsity Clb; Stage Crew; Pres Soph Cls; Pres Jr Cls; Rep Stu Cncl; Capt Cheerleading; HOBY-1 86; Gftd Tlntd Clss 84-87; Bus Admin.

MEDVEDZ, ROBERT; St Josephs HS; Fords, NJ; (3); Art Clb; Boy Scts; Church Yth Grp; Computer Clb; School Musical; School Play; Nwsp Stf; Yrbk Stf; Lit Mag; Robert Frost Lit Cont 86 & 85; RI Schl Of Design; Graphics.

MEEGAN, JOHN; MSGR Donovan HS; Jackson, NJ; (3); Boy Scts; FCA; Ski Clb; Socr; Trk; Rbtcs.

MEEHAN, KRISTA; Edgewood SR HS; Las Vegas, NV; (3); Cmnty Wkr; Drama Clb; Library Aide; Spanish Clb; SADD; Stage Crew; JV Fld Hcky; Jr NHS; NHS; S Jersey Yth Cmmssn 86-87.

MEEHAN, MICHELLE; Cumberland Regional HS; Bridgeton, NJ; (3); 24/384; Church Yth Grp; Exploring; Science Clb; Teachers Aide; Sftbl; Hon Roll; Jr NHS; Phys Ther.

MEEK, AMANDA SUE; Lyndhurst HS; Lyndhurst, NJ; (4); 6/168; French Clb; High Hon Roll; Hon Roll; NHS; Strlng Frst Cnfrnce Ctr Bus Lab 86; John Mc Walters Soc Studies Awd, Lyndhurst Ind Assn Schlrshp 87; Fshn Inst Tech; Ptrn Mkng.

MEEK, BRIAN; Pequannock Township HS; Pompton Plains, NJ; (3); Chess Clb; Library Aide; Hon Roll; Marine Engrng.

MEEKER, DAWNMARIE; Lakewood HS; Lakewood, NJ; (3); 45/330; English Clb; Office Aide; Spanish Clb; Chorus; Var Capt Cheerleading; Hon Roll.

MEEKS, MARCY A; Howell HS; Farmingdale, NJ; (4); 20/354; Chess Clb; Church Yth Grp; Math Tm; Church Choir; School Musical; School Play; Nwsp Rptr; Lit Mag; Ntl Merit Ltr; St Schlr; Drew Schlr & Drew Elsie Fishen Schlrshps 87-88; New Transcript Stu Of Wk 87; Drew U; Writer.

MEENAN, BERNIE; Holy Cross HS; Riverside, NJ; (4); Boy Scts; Model UN; Stage Crew; Hon Roll; Rutgers Coll Of Engrng; Engrng.

MEGLIS, EDWARD; Holy Cross HS; Mt Laurel, NJ; (3); Computer Clb; Band; Concert Band; Mrchg Band; School Musical; JV Crs Cntry; Hon Roll; Prfct Atten Awd; Comp Sci.

MEHR, JAY; Union HS; Union, NJ; (3); German Clb; Key Clb; Jazz Band; Mrchg Band; Bsktbl; Diving; Golf; Swmmng; Hon Roll; NHS; Amrcn Lgn Boys ST Cand 87; Law.

MEHTA, MONICA; Lakeland Regional HS; Ringwood, NJ; (4); 9/345; Drama Clb; Math Tm; Quiz Bowl; Teachers Aide; High Hon Roll; NHS; NEDT Awd; NY U Trustees Schlrshp 87; NY U; Polt Sci.

MEHTA, RUPAL; Eastern HS; Voorhees, NJ; (3); 1/406; Hosp Aide; VP Service Clb; Drm Mjr(t); Stu Cncl; Bausch & Lomb Sci Awd; Gov Hon Prg Awd; High Hon Roll; NHS; Quiz Bowl; Band; Intl Ambssdr Hugh O Brien Yth Fndtn 86; Rep/Schlr U Mdcn, Dntstry 87; Rep Cngrssnl Yth Ldrshp Cncl 86; Mdcn.

MEICKE, LISA; Secaucus HS; Secaucus, NJ; (4); 28/150; Dance Clb; Key Clb; Math Clb; Mu Alpha Theta; Band; Chorus; Color Guard; Mrchg Band; Vllybl; Bergen CC; Secr.

MEININGER, GARY; Fair Lawn HS; Fair Lawn, NJ; (3); 2/330; Am Leg Boys St; VP Computer Clb; Math Tm; Temple Yth Grp; Sec Stu Cncl; High Hon Roll; Hon Roll; NHS; Bio Team 85-86; Amer Comptr Sci League Natl Comptn 84-87.

MEININGER, MICHAEL; Fair Lawn HS; Fair Lawn, NJ; (3); 2/330; Computer Clb; Math Clb; Math Tm; Temple Yth Grp; Trs Stu Cncl; High Hon Roll; Hon Roll; NHS; Bio Team 85-86; Chem Team 86-87.

MEISENBACHER, MARK A; Immaculata HS; Middlesex, NJ; (3); 14/250; Am Leg Boys St; Church Yth Grp; Library Aide; Math Clb; Spanish Clb; Varsity Clb; Rep Jr Cls; Rep Stu Cncl; Var Bsbl; Bsktbl; Stu Yr 86; Atty.

MEISSNER, KARL; Westfield HS; Westfield, NJ; (3); 155/459; Boy Scts; Church Yth Grp; Im Wrstlng; Comptr Sci.

MEISSNER, ROBERT; Mt Olive HS; Budd Lake, NJ; (2); AFS; Debate Tm; Drama Clb; Math Tm; School Play; Variety Show; High Hon Roll; Hon Roll; Stdied-Coll Gftd Pgms The Smmr Inst-Blair 85; Stdyng Thtre-NJ Schl Of Arts-Montclair 87.

MEJIA, KARLA; Dickinson HS; Jersey City, NJ; (3); Computer Clb; French Clb; Hon Roll; Prfct Atten Awd; Comp Info Sys.

MEJZAK, RONALD; Paul VI HS; Williamstown, NJ; (3); 60/480; Boy Scts; Math Clb; Math Tm; Spanish Clb; JV Trk; JV Wt Lftg; JV Wrstlng; Hon Roll; Prfct Atten Awd; Spanish NHS; Natl Spn Hnr Soc 85-87; Go-Ju-Rye-U Karate Purple Belt 85-87; Med.

MELCHIONNE, SANDI; Waldwick HS; Waldwick, NJ; (3); 45/150; Church Yth Grp; Ski Clb; Church Choir; Orch; Nwsp Rptr; Cheerleading; Trk; Comm.

MELE, GOACHIM; Marist HS; Jersey City, NJ; (3); #15 In Class; Hon Roll; Acctng.

MELENDEZ, LISSETTE; Academic HS; Jersey City, NJ; (4); 40/78; Spanish Clb; JV Bowling; Jersey City ST Coll; Accntng.

MELENDEZ, MADELINE; William L Dickinson HS; Jersey City, NJ; (4); Prfct Atten Awd; Bus & Law Clb Pres 86-87; Merit Awd 86 & 87; Rutgers; Accntng.

MELIA, DAWN; Union Catholic Regional HS; Scotch Plains, NJ; (3); 116/330; Key Clb; Service Clb; Ski Clb; Yrbk Sprt Ed; Rep Soph Cls; VP Sr Cls; VP Stu Cncl; Cheerleading; Hon Roll; Human Phisiology.

MELILLO, MICHELE; Bloomfield SR HS; Bloomfield, NJ; (3); Drama Clb; Band; Chorus; School Play; Capt Cheerleading; Hon Roll; Cosmetologist.

MELKO, GLENN J; Paul VI HS; Blackwood, NJ; (3); 129/511; Rep Soph Cls; Rep Jr Cls; Var Bsbl; Capt Bowling; JV Var Socr; Wt Lftg; Rutgers U; Phrmcy.

MELLBERG, LAURA; Voorhees HS; Pottersville, NJ; (4); 2/264; Debate Tm; VP Key Clb; Pres SADD; Mrchg Band; Swing Chorus; High Hon Roll; NHS; Ntl Merit Ltr; St Schlr; Schlrs Awd-Lamp Of Lrng 87; U Of Rochester; Optcl Engrng.

MELLENO, LISA; Peguannock Township HS; Pompton Plains, NJ; (3); Hosp Aide; Orch; Yrbk Stf; JV Var Fld Hcky; Ice Hcky; Hon Roll; 100 Hr Awd-Candi Strpr 86; Med.

MELLY, MARY BETH; De Paul Diocesan HS; Riverdale, NJ; (4); 50/178; Girl Scts; Nwsp Stf; JV Bsktbl; Capt L Crs Cntry; Var L Trk; Cit Awd; High Hon Roll; Hon Roll; Rvrdl Ctznshp Awd 87; Lklnd ST Bank 87; Douglass Coll.

MELLY, MICHELE; De Paul Diocesan HS; Riverdale, NJ; (3); 54/150; Girl Scts; Ski Clb; Var Bsktbl; Var Crs Cntry; Var Trk; High Hon Roll; Hon Roll; 2nd Tm All Cnty & All Conf-Crss Cntry 84; Art Thrpy.

MELNICK, DANNY; St Pius X HS; Edison, NJ; (3); Art Clb; Computer Clb; Exploring; Scholastic Bowl; Var Ftbl; Var Wt Lftg; Hon Roll; Outstndng Score Amer Sci Tst 86; Sports Med.

MELODY, KEVIN; Holy Spirit HS; Egg Harbor City, NJ; (3); 46/332; JV Socr; US Navy; Aerntcl Engr.

MELOGRANA JR, LOUIS F; Rumson-Fair Haven Regional HS; Fair Haven, NJ; (4); 29/219; Am Leg Boys St; Pres Debate Tm; Pres Speech Tm; Variety Show; Im Crs Cntry; Elks Awd; Hon Roll; NHS; Home & Schl Assn Scholar 87; Rutgers Coll; Hstry Ed.

MELTON, ANDREA; Kittantinny Regional HS; Newton, NJ; (2); Chorus; School Musical; JV Swmmng; Sussex Cnty Chorus 85-86; Rgnl Chorus 87; Bob Jones U; Vocal Prefmnc.

MELTON, GARY P; Absegami HS; Egg Harbor City, NJ; (4); Am Leg Boys St; Aud/Vis; Nwsp Rptr; Pres Jr Cls; VP Sr Cls; Capt Var Bsktbl; Capt Var Fthl; Capt Var Trk; Dnfth Awd; Hon Roll; 4 Yr-Full Ftbll Schlrshp 87; Acadmc All Amer 87; Old Grad Awd-Counties Bst Athlt Ovver 4 Yrs 87; Rutgers U; Pre Med.

MELUSKY, ROBERT L; Manville HS; Manville, NJ; (3); Capt Band; Sec Frsh Cls; Trs Soph Cls; Rep Jr Cls; Rep Sr Cls; Var L Bsktbl; Var Capt Crs Cntry; Var Capt Trk; High Hon Roll; VP NHS; Lock Haven U; Sports Med.

MELUSO, KAREN; Park Ridge HS; Park Ridge, NJ; (3); 35/98; Church Yth Grp; PAVAS; Stage Crew; Hon Roll; AFS; Interact; Yrbk Fclty Editor; Erly Chldhd Educ.

MELZAK, LORI; Raritan HS; Hazlet, NJ; (4); Drama Clb; Nwsp Rptr; Nwsp Stf; U Of Bridgeport; Jrnlsm.

MENDEZ, DIANE; Hoboken HS; Hoboken, NJ; (3); Hon Roll; Prfct Atten Awd; Val; Comp.

MENDEZ, JAMES; E Exxex Catholic HS; E Orange, NJ; (4); Boy Scts; Debate Tm; French Clb; Intnl Clb; Spanish Clb; Church Choir; Bsbl; Bsktbl; Crs Cntry; Fld Hcky; Bus Adm.

MENDEZ, JOSE; Vineland HS; Vineland, NJ; (2); Off Soph Cls; Bsbl; Arch.

MENDEZ, MILADIZ; Eastside HS; Paterson, NJ; (2); 9/516; Hon Roll; Comp.

MENDEZ, OSWALD; North Bergen HS; Guttenberg, NJ; (3); Drama Clb; French Clb; Spanish Clb; Speech Tm; French Hon Soc; Hon Roll; Valdctrn 84; Pub Spkng Awds 86-87; Frnch Cntst Awd 85-86; Mrktng.

MENDEZ, YOLANDA; Our Lady Of Good Counsel HS; Newark, NJ; (3); Camera Clb; Sec Church Yth Grp; Debate Tm; Drama Clb; Office Aide; Pep Clb; Ski Clb; Temple Yth Grp; Band; Chorus; Acad All Amer Schlr Pgm 86-87; Natl Sci Olympd Cert 86-87; Vice Sec NJ Spn Bapt Yth 86; U PA; Acctng.

MENDIZABAL, JOANNA; Manchester Regional HS; N Haledon, NJ; (3); Camera Clb; Yrbk Stf; Rep Jr Cls; Hon Roll; Travel/Trsm.

MENDOKER, LYNN; South River HS; South River, NJ; (3); 8/140; Dance Clb; Drama Clb; Math Tm; Spanish Clb; Rep Stu Cncl; Var Cheerleading; Var Sftbl; NHS; VFW Awd; Voice Dem Awd.

MENDOLERA, ANN MARIE; Bridgeton HS; Bridgeton, NJ; (2); GAA; SADD; Yrbk Stf; Stat Mgr(s); Score Keeper; JV L Tennis; Vllybl; Sci Olympics 85 & 86; Tchng.

MENDONCA, FRANCISCO M; East Side HS; Newark, NJ; (4); Am Leg Boys St; Art Clb; Stage Crew; Yrbk Ed-Chief; Stu Cncl; Opt Clb Awd; Church Yth Grp; Exploring; Hosp Aide; Intnl Clb; Close Up Pgm 86; Ldrshp Pgm W/Brd Educ 86; Montclair ST Coll; Pltcs.

MENDOZA, DIANA; Dover HS; Dover, NJ; (3); Dance Clb; Crs Cntry; Trk; Wt Lftg; On The Spot Awd 87.

MENDOZA, GEORGE; Memorial HS; West New York, NJ; (3); Computer Clb; Varsity Clb; Var Capt Bsbl; Hon Roll; Prfct Atten Awd; NJIT; Elec.

MENDOZA, JEWEL; Vineland HS; Vineland, NJ; (2); 21/793; Drama Clb; French Clb; Key Clb; SADD; Nwsp Rptr; Ed Nwsp Stf; Yrbk Stf; Hon Roll; High Hnr Roll; Dentistry.

MENDOZA, MARIA C; Oak Knoll Schl; Livingston, NJ; (4); 2/54; Pep Clb; Ski Clb; Spanish Clb; Stage Crew; Soph Cls; Var Bsktbl; Var Fld Hcky; Var Capt Sftbl; Im Vllybl; High Hon Roll; Cornelian Schlrshp 83-87; Rensselear Mdl Excel Math & Sci 86; Cum Laude Soc 86; Comp Sci Awd 86; Columbia U; Comp Sci.

MENDYK III, ANTHONY; Lower Cape May Regional HS; Villas, NJ; (3); 4-H; Key Clb; Band; Concert Band; Mrchg Band; Orch; School Musical; Yrbk Stf; 4-H Awd; Comp Sci.

MENEGHELLO, LAURA; St Aloysius HS; Jersey City, NJ; (4); 10/112; Nwsp Ed-Chief; High Hon Roll; NHS; Pres Athl Awd 87; Jersey City ST Coll; Bus Admin.

MENEI, LYNNE; Highland Reg HS; Laurel Springs, NJ; (2); FTA; German Clb; GAA; Office Aide; Service Clb; SADD; VP Soph Cls; Cheerleading; Ursinus; Soclgy.

MENENDEZ, ALEX; Secaucus HS; Secaucus, NJ; (4); 35/153; Am Leg Boys St; Key Clb; Mu Alpha Theta; VP Frsh Cls; VP Soph Cls; VP Jr Cls; Pres Sr Cls; Pres Stu Cncl; Bsktbl; Tennis; Fordham U; Accntng.

MENENDEZ, CHRISTINE; Secaucus HS; Secaucus, NJ; (4); 10/160; Mu Alpha Theta; Varsity Clb; Var L Cheerleading; High Hon Roll; Hon Roll; NHS; Spanish NHS; Altrnte ST Douglass Coll 86; Pre-Med.

MENEREY, LAURIE ANNE K; Glassboro HS; Glassboro, NJ; (4); Cmnty Wkr; Drama Clb; Exploring; Intnl Clb; Math Tm; Political Wkr; Science Clb; Thesps; Band; Chorus; AMA Explr Awd 87; Mst Drmtc 87; Gov Awd-Crtv Wrtng 87; U Of PA; Nrsng.

MENEVE JR, RUSSELL; Hawthorne HS; Hawthorne, NJ; (3); 10/250; Var Tennis; NHS; Chess Clb; Cmnty Wkr; Ski Clb; Varsity Clb; Rep Frsh Cls; Rep Soph Cls; Rep Jr Cls; Rep Sr Cls; 2nd Pl Passaic Cnty Tourn Tennis 86; All Cnty Tm Tennis 84-88; Pres Phy Fit Awd 87; U S Air Force Acad.

MENICHELLI, SANDI; Hamilton High North; Mercerville, NJ; (3); AFS; L Var Cheerleading; JV L Sftbl; High Hon Roll; Hon Roll; Rutgers U; Psycht.

MENICOLA, ANTHONY; Paramus Catholic Boys HS; Maywood, NJ; (3); 71/195; Computer Clb; Spanish Clb; Var Bsbl; Var Bsktbl; Var Ftbl; Var Vllybl; Var Wt Lftg; Hon Roll; NHS; Spanish NHS; Treas Spnsh Ntl Hnr Soc 85-86; Arch.

MENKIN, ANDREA; Mt Olive HS; Flanders, NJ; (3); Var Capt Cheerleading; Hon Roll; AFS; Dance Clb; Hst FBLA; Ski Clb; SADD; Temple Yth Grp; Varsity Clb; Ntl Fnlst Arabian Horses Equtnt 87; Intl Open Chrldng Ntl Fnlst 85; IOCC Compted 86; Horse Trainer.

MENZ, MICHAEL; Jackson Memorial HS; Jackson, NJ; (4); 45/397; FBLA; Yrbk Phtg; JV Bsbl; Im Bsktbl; Im Ice Hcky; High Hon Roll; Hon Roll; U Of Pittsburgh Schlrshp 87; U Of Pittsburgh; Ecnmcs.

MENZAK, SANDY; Hunterdon Central HS; White House Sta, NJ; (3); 67/543; Rptr 4-H; Varsity Clb; Symp Band; Im Gym; Var Sftbl; Var Trk; Im Vllybl; 4-H Awd; Hon Roll; Spanish NHS; Eng Ridger Reserve Hi-Point Earner 86; Felmintgon Fair Grand Champn Western Hi-Point 86; SR Champn 86; Astronomy.

MEOLA, MARK; Wayne Hills HS; Wayne, NJ; (3); FBLA; JV Wrstlng; Hon Roll; U Of NC Chapel Hill; Fin.

MERANDINO, ANN MARIE; Clifton HS; Clifton, NJ; (4); 35/589; Concert Band; Drm Mjr(t); Mrchg Band; Var Capt Bsktbl; Key Clb; High Hon Roll; Hon Roll; NHS; Bsktbl Bstr Clb Schlrshp Awd; Montclair ST Coll.

MERCADO, AARON; Cranford HS; Cranford, NJ; (3); 15/268; Art Clb; Church Yth Grp; Math Clb; Math Tm; Quiz Bowl; Science Clb; Band; Concert Band; Jazz Band; Mrchg Band; Pioneers Of Amer AT & T Essay Cont 85; Natl Spnsh II Exam 85; Natl Spnsh IV Exam 87; Comp Sci.

MERCADO, GRISELL; Perth Amboy HS; Perth Amboy, NJ; (3); French Clb; Hon Roll; Comp Sci.

MERCADO, JERRY B; Our Lady Of Good Counsel HS; Newark, NJ; (4); 17/102; Yrbk Phtg; Rep Frsh Cls; Rep Soph Cls; Rep Jr Cls; Pres Sr Cls; Var L Bsbl; Var L Bsktbl; Var L Socr; NHS; Ntl Merit Ltr; FDU; Ind Engrng.

MERCE, SUZANNE B; Spotswood HS; Spotswood, NJ; (3); Pres Church Yth Grp; Intnl Clb; Band; Orch; Yrbk Stf; Stu Cncl; Hon Roll; NHS; Speech Pathology.

MERCEDES, ROSSINA B; St Josephs Of The Palisades HS; Union City, NJ; (3); French Clb; Yrbk Stf; Bowling; Cheerleading; Sftbl; Hon Roll; Hnr Roll; Sftbl; Chrldng; Bus Mngmnt.

MERCHAK, ANN MARIE; Dover HS; Mine Hill, NJ; (3); 4/200; Key Clb; Ski Clb; Spanish Clb; Var Capt Sftbl; High Hon Roll; Hon Roll; NHS; Sftbl Awd 86; Psych & Peer Ldrshp Awds 87; Psych.

MERCHAK, JOSEPH; Dover HS; Mine Hill, NJ; (4); 17/180; Hon Roll; NHS; John Spinny Alperti Memorial Awd; Elect Tech.

MERCOGLIANO, VICTORIA; Neptune SR HS; Neptune City, NJ; (2); Yrbk Stf; Lit Mag; Fld Hcky; Sftbl; Swmmng; Htl/Rest Mgmt.

MERCURIO, MICHELE; Livingston HS; Livingston, NJ; (4); 143/420; Church Yth Grp; FBLA; Hosp Aide; Leo Clb; Stage Crew; Lit Mag; Mgr(s); Twrlr; Hon Roll; U Of DE; Educ.

MERIDA, MARLYSE; St John Vianney HS; Hazlet, NJ; (3); 6/256; Math Tm; Chorus; School Musical; Stage Crew; Rep Jr Cls; Capt L Cheerleading; High Hon Roll; NHS; Pres Schlr; Intnl Clb; Frnch Awd Merit 86-87; Socl Stds Awd Merit 85-87; Engl Awd Merit 85; Bio Rsrch.

MERIGHI, DANIELLE; Sacred Heart HS; Vineland, NJ; (3); 6/60; French Clb; VP SADD; School Play; Yrbk Rptr; Var Bsktbl; Var Sftbl; Var Tennis; Hon Roll; NHS; Sec Frsh Cls; Cape-Atlntc League All Strs-Sftbll 87; All Tms Jrnl, Mllvll Dly 2nd Tm-Tnns 86-87.

MERKLE, ROBERT; Oratory Prep; New Providence, NJ; (4); 5/50; Math Tm; Capt Varsity Clb; Nwsp Rptr; Yrbk Phtg; Var Capt Bsktbl; Var Capt Socr; High Hon Roll; Pres NHS; NEDT Awd; Outstndng Algbr I-II Awd 84-86; Notre Dame; Elc Engr.

MERLETTO, TRACEY; Secaucus HS; Secaucus, NJ; (3); 4/167; Ski Clb; Spanish Clb; Varsity Clb; Chorus; Color Guard; Mrchg Band; Rep Frsh Cls; Rep Soph Cls; JV Bsktbl; High Hon Roll; Engl Essay Contst 84; Spnsh X Mas Crd Contst 85-86; Rutgers U; Math.

MERLINO, JEFFREY; Hawthorne HS; Hawthorne, NJ; (3); Var Wrstlng; NHS.

MERLINO, SHERRIANN; Burlington Co Vo-Tech; Mt Holly, NJ; (3); 6/192; VICA; Nwsp Stf; Yrbk Stf; Hon Roll; Grphc Arts.

MERO, ANTHONY; East Side HS; Newark, NJ; (3); Am Leg Boys St; Math Clb; Math Tm; Band; Yrbk Stf; High Hon Roll; Rensiller Math & Sci Awd 87; Acctng.

MEROLA, JOSEPH; Brick Memorial HS; Brick, NJ; (3); 50/375; Computer Clb; English Clb; Varsity Clb; Rep Jr Cls; Capt Var Bsbl; Coach Actv; Wt Lftg; High Hon Roll; Hon Roll; Bus.

MEROLA, MICHAEL; Cranford HS; Cranford, NJ; (3); 10/280; Am Leg Boys St; Art Clb; Boy Scts; Church Yth Grp; Math Clb; Science Clb; Chorus; Hon Roll; Intl Affairs.

MEROLA, STEPHEN; Parsippany Hills HS; Morris Plains, NJ; (4); 3/300; Exploring; Hosp Aide; Key Clb; Math Tm; Science Clb; Hon Roll; NHS; Ntl Merit Ltr; NJ Garden St Dstngshd Schlr 86; Nabisco Brands Spec Schlrshp 87; Unico Parsippany 87; Franklin Coll; Med.

MERONE, JENNIFER; Mount Olive HS; Budd Lake, NJ; (2); 50/325; Church Yth Grp; Drama Clb; Varsity Clb; Chorus; Church Choir; School Musical; School Play; Stage Crew; Variety Show; Swmmng.

MERRICK, GEOFFREY W; Madison HS; Madison, NJ; (3); 15/215; Am Leg Boys St; Church Yth Grp; Letterman Clb; Varsity Clb; Bsbl; Var Capt Bsktbl; Var Capt Socr; Vllybl; High Hon Roll; NHS; Engrng.

MERRIGAN, KATHLEEN; Hunterdon Central HS; Whitehouse Sta, NJ; (3); Church Yth Grp; Pres 4-H; Service Clb; Ski Clb; School Play; Stage Crew; Rep Jr Cls; Rep Stu Cncl; L JV Trk; 4-H Awd; Elem Educ.

MERRIGAN, THUY; Toms River HS South; Beachwood, NJ; (3); Am Leg Aux Girls St; Camera Clb; FBLA; GAA; Girl Scts; Math Tm; Ski Clb; SADD; Stage Crew; Variety Show; Bus Stckbrkr.

MERRITT, HEATHER; Montgomery HS; Skillman, NJ; (3); Church Yth Grp; Hosp Aide; Ski Clb; Band; Yrbk Stf; Capt Cheerleading; JV Socr; Hon Roll; NHS; Wellsley Coll Awd Eng Achvmnt 87; Psych.

MERRITT, JOAN; Bridgewater HS; Bound Brook, NJ; (3); JV Bsktbl; Var Crs Cntry; Var JV Socr; JV Sftbl; Var Trk; Frnch Exchng Stu 87; U Of NC; Intl Bus.

MERRITT, TINA; Montville Township HS; Towaco, NJ; (4); 41/258; FBLA; Rep Sec Intnl Clb; Key Clb; OEA; High Hon Roll; NHS; Church Yth Grp; Cmnty Wkr; Teachers Aide; Church Choir; K Gibbs Schlrshp, Coop Ofc Ed Schlrshp 87; FBLA Cmptns-Job Intrvw Cat 87; Mustang Plq Bus Awd 87; Katharine Gibbs Schl; Bus.

MERTZ, SUZANNE; Mount Saint Mary Acad; Watchung, NJ; (4); 6/79; Service Clb; Pres Frsh Cls; Pres Soph Cls; Pres Stu Cncl; JV Fld Hcky; Var Tennis; French Hon Soc; NHS; Opt Clb Awd; Hon Roll; Sister Eloise Clair Schl Ldrshp Awd 87; Sommma Cum Laude 87; Hugh O Briann Ldrshp 2nd Pl 85; Drew U; Poltcl Sci.

MESA, ANTOLIN; Roselle Catholic HS; Elizabeth, NJ; (4); 13/200; Latin Clb; Math Tm; Spanish Clb; Lit Mag; Var L Wrstlng; Hon Roll; NHS; Spanish NHS; Art Clb; Peer Grp 84-85; Intrmrl Bsktbll & Ping Png; Smfnlst Ntl Hspnc Schlr Awds Pgm 86-87; Rutgers Coll; Law.

MESKIS, RUSS; Wood-Ridge HS; Wood Ridge, NJ; (3); Art Clb; Church Yth Grp; Computer Clb; Science Clb; Spanish Clb; Band; Var Ftbl; High Hon Roll; Hon Roll; Music.

MESSAM, PETERKAYE; Plainfield HS; Plainfield, NJ; (3); 21/398; Dance Clb; Drama Clb; JA; Math Tm; School Musical; Mgr(s); Tennis; Hon Roll; Jr NHS; NHS; Bst Dncr 84-86; Mst Cooprtv 86; Mst Lkly Scceed 86; Comp.

MESSENGER, KIM; Toms River East HS; Toms River, NJ; (3); 29/520; Ski Clb; Yrbk Stf; Bsktbl; Im Bowling; Var Swmmng; High Hon Roll; Hon Roll; NHS; Pres Physcl Ftns Awd 87; Pre-Law.

MESSINA, LOREN; James Caldwell HS; W Caldwell, NJ; (4); Key Clb; High Hon Roll; Hon Roll; Hnr Rll 87; Montclair ST Coll.

MESSINA, LORI; St Pius X Regional HS; Sayreville, NJ; (4); 22/108; Church Yth Grp; Teachers Aide; Chorus; Church Choir; Flag Corp; School Musical; Stage Crew; Nwsp Stf; Pom Pon; Hon Roll; Hnr Rl 83-87; Sports Awd; Merit Awd; GA Court Coll; Engrng.

MESSINA, MARY; Paul IV HS; Haddonfield, NJ; (4); 48/511; Cmnty Wkr; Math Clb; Im Bowling; Var Crs Cntry; Mgr(s); Hon Roll; NHS; Engl.

MESSINGER, MITCHELL; Manalapan HS; Manalapan, NJ; (3); Sec Drama Clb; Hosp Aide; Sec Temple Yth Grp; Sec Thesps; School Musical; School Play; Stage Crew; Nwsp Rptr; Bst Jrnlsm Stu 86; Cmnty Svc Awd 86-87; Studyng Video Prodctn; Flm.

MESZAROS, JAMES A; Parsippany Hills HS; Morris Plains, NJ; (2); Debate Tm; Band; Jazz Band; Nwsp Rptr; Nwsp Sprt Ed; Ed Lit Mag; Var L Crs Cntry; Var L Trk; Hon Roll; Voice Dem Awd; Career Wk Essay Cntst 1s Pl Wnnr 86; HOB 1st Rnnr Up 86; 1st Pl Impromptu Spkng Wnnr 87; Jrnlsm.

METALLO, VICTOR N; Seton Hall Prep; Montclair, NJ; (4); Art Clb; Church Yth Grp; Key Clb; Hon Roll; Pres Schlr; Black Belt 83; Sr Prfct Alter Boy 86; 100 Clb Schlrshp 87; Seton Hall U; Med.

METTEE, GAYLE; Clifton HS; Clifton, NJ; (4); 193/636; Drama Clb; Spanish Clb; Band; Chorus; JV Cheerleading; Coach Actv; Var Co-Capt Gym; Im Tennis; Hon Roll; Jr NHS; MVP-GYMNSTCS 86-87; All Cnty Hon Men Gumnstcs Beam & Vault 87; NNJIL League Hon Men Gymnstcs Beam 87; William Paterson Coll; Speech.

METZ, KELLY; Ocean Township HS; Oakhurst, NJ; (3); 93/344; Hosp Aide; Key Clb; Yrbk Stf; Var JV Socr; Psych.

METZGAR, ALICE; Sussex County Vo Tech; Sussex, NJ; (3); Var Sftbl; High Hon Roll; Hon Roll.

METZGER, CINDY; West Essex SR HS; No Caldwell, NJ; (3); Cmnty Wkr; Nwsp Rptr; Badmtn; Bsktbl; Coach Actv; Socr; Sftbl; Trk; Vllybl; Indoor All Star Sccr-All Star Tm 85-6; AZ ST; Comm.

METZGER, NICOLE; Mount Olive HS; Flanders, NJ; (3); Computer Clb; Science Clb; Ski Clb; Varsity Clb; Nwsp Stf; Var Tennis; High Hon Roll; NCTE Awd; NHS; Ntl Merit SF; VA Polytchnc; Aerontcl Engrng.

METZGER, VICTORIA; Dwight-Englewood HS; Englewood, NJ; (3); Yrbk Bus Mgr; Yrbk Stf; JV Var Sftbl; JV Capt Tennis; Var Trk; Ntl Merit Ltr.

METZLER, SHARON; Cherry Hill HS West; Cherry Hill, NJ; (3); Drama Clb; Intnl Clb; Office Aide; Spanish Clb; Mrchg Band; School Musical; Stage Crew; Yrbk Phtg; Off Frsh Cls; Off Soph Cls; Green Blt Karte 86; Culinry Arts.

MEYER, J BRENDAN; Scotch Plains-Fanwood Regional HS; Scotch Plains, NJ; (3); German Clb; Model UN; Quiz Bowl; Concert Band; L Var Socr; L Var Trk; Im Vllybl; Hon Roll; Prfct Atten Awd; Grmn Ntl Hnr Soc 86; Arch.

MEYER, KAREN; Paramus Catholic Girls Reg HS; Oradell, NJ; (3); 31/179; Church Yth Grp; Math Clb; Church Choir; Nwsp Ed-Chief; Nwsp Stf; Lit Mag; Rep Stu Cncl; Hon Roll; NHS; U PA; Bnkg.

MEYER, MICHAEL; Cherry Hill West HS; Cherry Hill, NJ; (3); PAVAS; Concert Band; Jazz Band; Mrchg Band; Orch; Var Crs Cntry; High Hon Roll; NHS; Ntl Merit Ltr; Natl Beta Clb; All Regn Band 1st Chr 84-86; All Olmpc Conf Band 1st Chr 87; Music Comp.

MEYER, R WESLEY; Pt Plsnt Bch HS; Pt Plsnt Bch, NJ; (2); Church Yth Grp; Key Clb; Varsity Clb; Concert Band; Orch; Stage Crew; Im Bsktbl; Var Ftbl; JV Trk; Wt Lftg; Penn ST; Archt,Aero Engr.

MEYER, ROCHELLE; West Windsor-Plainsboro HS; Trenton, NJ; (3); Pres AFS; Am Leg Aux Girls St; Camera Clb; SADD; Temple Yth Grp; Orch; High Hon Roll; Hon Roll; NHS; People To People Soviet-Amer Yth Exhcange 87.

MEYERHARDT, JEFF; Northern Valley Reg HS; Closter, NJ; (2); 2/250; Office Aide; Science Clb; Spanish Clb; Teachers Aide; Temple Yth Grp; School Musical; Off Frsh Cls; Pres Stu Cncl; Capt Var Crs Cntry; Var Tennis; Scndry Stu Training Pgm 87; Sci.

MEYERS, ANDREW; Saint Josephs Regional HS; Ramsey, NJ; (3); 6/225; Math Tm; SADD; Nwsp Stf; Yrbk Stf; Frsh Cls; Soph Cls; Jr Cls; Sr Cls; Stu Cncl; JV Var Ftbl; NHS; Vlntr Wrk Valley Hosp Ridgewood; Cnslng; Georgetown; Econ.

MEYERS JR, GERARD; Camden Catholic HS; Berlin, NJ; (3); 30/283; Am Leg Boys St; German Clb; Band; Concert Band; Jazz Band; Mrchg Band; Pep Band; School Musical; NHS; German Natl Hnr Soc 85; Sci Hnr Soc 85.

MEYERS, KRISTEN; Holy Cross HS; Delran, NJ; (3); 38/407; Church Yth Grp; Hosp Aide; Key Clb; Natl Beta Clb; Service Clb; Spanish Clb; Teachers Aide; Yrbk Stf; JV Var Mgr(s); Hon Roll; Bus.

MEYERSON, JOSEPH; Secaucus HS; Secaucus, NJ; (4); 8/156; Mu Alpha Theta; Ski Clb; Yrbk Stf; Ed Lit Mag; High Hon Roll; NHS; Ntl Merit SF; St Schlr.

MEYERSON, SHARI L; Lenape Valley Regional HS; Stanhope, NJ; (3); 2/224; Key Clb; Latin Clb; SADD; Nwsp Rptr; Yrbk Stf; Lit Mag; Rep Stu Cncl; JV Sftbl; JV Swmmng; FBLA; Clemon U Sci & Engrng Hnrs Pgm; Latin Hnr Soc; Intl Frgn Lang Awd; Civil Engrng.

MEZGER, JUDITH; Shore Regional HS; Oceanport, NJ; (3); Yrbk Stf; Trs Frsh Cls; Trs Soph Cls; Trs Jr Cls; Trs Sr Cls; JV Var Bsktbl; Stat Fld Hcky; Mgr(s); JV Var Socr; Hon Roll; Accntng.

MICALE, DEAN; Notre Dame HS; Hamilton, NJ; (2); Var L Swmmng; Hon Roll; NHS.

MICELI, ROSINA; Essex Catholic Girls HS; Irvington, NJ; (4); 15/55; Art Clb; Camera Clb; Service Clb; Yrbk Phtg; Bowling; Socr; Sftbl; Vllybl; Hon Roll; Sen Bill Bradley Yng Ctzns Awd 86-87; Ministries To The Agina Awd 86-87; Outstndng Volntr Svc Awd 86-7; Kean Coll; Spch Pathology.

MICHAEL, VICKI; Kearny HS; Kearny, NJ; (3); Var Gym; Gymstc Awd 84; Dancing Awds 84-85; Hnr Roll 83-84.

MICHAIL, JOHN; Brick Memorial HS; Bricktown, NJ; (1); Drama Clb; Band; Concert Band; Mrchg Band; School Musical; School Play; Crs Cntry; Trk; Boy Scts; Drm & Bgl; Lord Mayor Westminister Parade-London, England-Prtcpnt, Yth Music Fr Wrld-London, England 88; Music.

MICHALLIS, KELLY; Manasquan HS; Brielle, NJ; (3); 48/226; FNA; Hosp Aide; Latin Clb; JV Bsktbl; Var Socr; Im Sftbl; Im Vllybl; High Hon Roll; Hon Roll; Spcl Ed.

MICHEL, ALISON R; Hopatcong HS; Andover, NJ; (4); 5/200; Drama Clb; Thesps; Chorus; School Musical; School Play; Variety Show; Sec Soph Cls; Trs Sr Cls; High Hon Roll; NHS; Sussex Cnty Teen Arts Fest Wnnr 86-87; NJ ST Teen Arts Fest 86-87; SR Stu Arts Awd Sussex Cnty 87; U Of NC Chapel Hill; Theatre.

MICHEL, CHRISTIAN C; Bishop Eustace Prep; Cherry Hill, NJ; (3); 27/170; Am Leg Boys St; Church Yth Grp; French Clb; Math Clb; Science Clb; JV Crs Cntry; Ftbl; JV Capt Wrstlng; French Hon Soc; High Hon Roll; Am Chem Soc Chem Awd 87; Cum Laude Prog 85-87; Air Force; Med.

MICHEL, ERICH; Bogota HS; Bogota, NJ; (4); 28/113; Am Leg Boys St; Math Tm; Quiz Bowl; Pres Trs Science Clb; Spanish Clb; Teachers Aide; Yrbk Stf; Var Bsbl; Cit Awd; Hon Roll; Bill Bradley NJ Yng Ctzns Awd 87; NJ Inst Tech; Elctrcl Engrng.

MICHEL, MARK E; Ewing HS; Trenton, NJ; (3); Am Leg Boys St; Boy Scts; Church Yth Grp; Key Clb; Nwsp Sprt Ed; VP Sr Cls; Rep Stu Cncl; Var Capt Bsbl; JV Bsktbl; Var Capt Ftbl; Frsh Bsktbl Sptsmnshp & Dedictn Awd 84-85; Vrsty Bsbl All Cnty Selctn 85-86; Am Leg Rookie Yr 86-87.

MICHITSCH, EDWARD F; Bergen Catholic HS; Hackensack, NJ; (4); 19/261; Pres Church Yth Grp; Yrbk Phtg; Var Trk; High Hon Roll; NHS; Spanish NHS; St Schlr; Rnk Cho Dan 1st Degr Blck Blt Tang Soo Do Moo Duk Kwan Karate 87; NY U; Corp Fin.

MICHLESKI, DOREEN; Wallington HS; Wallington, NJ; (2); Quiz Bowl; Scholastic Bowl; Stage Crew; Nwsp Rptr; Nwsp Stf; High Hon Roll; Hon Roll; Engl Lit.

MICHLESKI, MARK; Wallington HS; Wallington, NJ; (2); Quiz Bowl; Scholastic Bowl; Stage Crew; Nwsp Rptr; Nwsp Stf; High Hon Roll; Hon Roll; VFW Awd; Voice Dem Awd; Engl Litrtr.

MICK, FREDERICK; Delsea Regional HS; Malaga, NJ; (2); Spanish Clb; JV Bsktbl; Var Crs Cntry; High Hon Roll; Hon Roll; Atheneum League 86-87; Astrnmy Clb 87-88; Math.

MICKENS, FELIX; Plainfield HS; Plainfield, NJ; (4); Art Clb; Hon Roll; Morehouse Coll; Comp Sci.

MICKUS, SHAUN; Abraham Clark HS; Roselle, NJ; (4); 3/165; Chorus; School Play; Nwsp Ed-Chief; Nwsp Rptr; Nwsp Sprt Ed; Nwsp Stf; Stu Cncl; High Hon Roll; Hon Roll; NHS; Olympcs Of Mnd 83-84; Chlng Team 86; Ftr Prblm Slvng Team 85-87; Cmnctns.

MICOU, PAUL D; North Hunterdon HS; Annandale, NJ; (4); 13/342; Church Yth Grp; JCL; Key Clb; Pres VP Latin Clb; Math Tm; Ski Clb; Chorus; High Hon Roll; Ntl Merit SF; Math Clb; Ntl Ltn Hnr Soc; Engrng.

MIDDAUGH, GINA; Warren Tech HS; Hackettstown, NJ; (3); Computer Clb; FBLA; Key Clb; Varsity Clb; Cheerleading; Comp.

MIDDLEBROOK, JAMES; Bridgewater-Raritan Hs East; Bridgewater, NJ; (3); Boy Scts; Computer Clb; Math Clb; Scholastic Bowl; Lit Mag; Bowling; High Hon Roll; Hon Roll; NHS; Ntl Merit Ltr; Bus.

MIDDLETON, MICHAEL; Immaculata HS; Belle Mead, NJ; (3); 124/250; Library Aide; Ski Clb; Ftbl; Tennis; Wt Lftg; Rutgers; Acctng Admn.

MIDDLETON, PATTY; Millville SR HS; Millville, NJ; (3); #14 In Class; Camera Clb; Church Yth Grp; Drama Clb; French Clb; GAA; Key Clb; Office Aide; Radio Clb; Speech Tm; SADD; Jv Glf 87; Elon Coll; Advtsng.

MIDELTON, GARY; Atlantic City HS; Ventnor, NJ; (2); Boy Scts; Model UN; Office Aide; Crs Cntry; Trk; Wrstlng; Hon Roll; Med.

MIEDEL, WENDY; Jackson Memorial HS; Jackson, NJ; (3); 40/416; Drama Clb; Ski Clb; School Musical; School Play; Var Capt Fld Hcky; High Hon Roll; NEDT Awd; Voice Dem Awd; Varsity Clb; Yrbk Stf; Mst Imprvd Plyr Fld Hcky 85; Ed.

MIEDEL, WILLIAM; Jackson Memorial HS; Jackson, NJ; (3); 17/247; Drama Clb; Ski Clb; Chorus; School Musical; Variety Show; High Hon Roll; NHS; Prtcpd In Ocean Cnty Teen Arts Fstvl 87; Arch.

MIELE, ANDREA; John P Stevens HS; Edison, NJ; (3); 39/450; Cmnty Wkr; French Clb; Hosp Aide; Science Clb; Ski Clb; Acpl Chr; Rep Frsh Cls; JV Bsktbl; Var Bowling; Capt Powder Puff Ftbl.

MIELECHOWSKY III, ALEX; Gateway Regional HS; National Park, NJ; (4); 40/203; German Clb; Math Tm; Science Clb; SADD; JV Golf; NHS; Prfct Atten Awd; W Chester U; Accntnt.

MIEROP, KIM; Eastern Christian HS; North Haledon, NJ; (4); 6/80; Am Leg Aux Girls St; Church Yth Grp; Drama Clb; Office Aide; Yrbk Stf; VP Frsh Cls; Hon Roll; NHS; Hnrs Schlrshp Calvin Coll 87-88; Calvin Coll; Psychology.

MIGLIACCI, KEVIN; Newton HS; Newton, NJ; (2); Math Tm; Rep Stu Cncl; High Hon Roll; Prfct Atten Awd; Cert Of Commndtn Engl 87; Natl Sci Olympd Awd Chem & Biol 86-87; Aerospace Engr.

MIGLIN, PATRICIA E; Spotswood HS; Spotswood, NJ; (2); Church Yth Grp; Drama Clb; FBLA; Intnl Clb; School Play; Nwsp Stf; Stu Cncl; Crs Cntry; Trk; Hon Roll; Rutgers U; Sci.

MIGNONE, CHRISTOPHER; Brick Memorial HS; Brick, NJ; (1); Art Clb; School Musical; Capt Bsbl; Bsktbl; Ftbl; Ldrshp Awd Bsbl, Ltrmn-Bsbl, Bsktbl & Ftbl 87; Seton Hall U; Hstry Tchr.

MIGUEL, ELIZABETH; Immaculate Conception HS; Paterson, NJ; (3); Science Clb; Spanish Clb; School Musical; Stage Crew; Yrbk Stf; Sec Jr Cls; Vllybl; Hon Roll; Spanish NHS; Jr Cls Secy 86-87; Spnsh Natl Hnr Soc 85-87; Psych.

MIHALECZ, MICHAEL; Arthur P Schalick HS; Elmer, NJ; (3); Drama Clb; VP Exploring; Mrchg Band; School Play; Yrbk Stf; Rep Sr Cls; Tennis; Hon Roll; Church Yth Grp; Trs Band; De Molay; Close Up; Jr NRA; Olympcs Mind Rentra Fusca Awd; Pharm.

MIHM, THOMAS; Paul VI HS; Lindenwold, NJ; (3); Im Bowling; Var L Crs Cntry; Var Trk; LAW.

MIHOK, MICHAEL; Central Regional HS; Bayville, NJ; (3); Score Keeper; JV Trk; High Hon Roll; Hon Roll; NHS; Legal Eagles Mock Trl Team 84-85; Ocean-Moumouth Drftng Comptn 85-86; Mech Engrng.

MIHOVCH, JOHN; Keansburg HS; Keansburg, NJ; (3); Var Bsbl; Var Bsktbl; Var Ftbl; Cit Awd; Hon Roll; NHS; Acad All Amer Natl Ed Cncl 87.

MIKAELIAN, VICKI; Toms River HS South; Toms River, NJ; (2); Off Soph Cls; Var Capt Cheerleading; JV Socr; Hon Roll; Gld Ky Awd; PA ST; Mrchndsng.

MIKESELL, ANDREW; Parsippany HS; Parsippany, NJ; (3); Church Yth Grp; Cmnty Wkr; Ski Clb; Mrchg Band; School Musical; School Play; Stage Crew; Var L Crs Cntry; Var Swmmng; Var L Trk; Swmmr Bst Cls Lk Hiawatha Cntry Clb 86; Mst Vlbl Swmmr, Mst Apprctd Swmmr Lk Hiawatha Cntry Clb 85; Pre Dntstry.

MIKESELL, CORINNE; Parsippany HS; Parsippany, NJ; (4); 98/330; Church Yth Grp; DECA; French Clb; Hosp Aide; Q&S; Ski Clb; Nwsp Ed-Chief; Yrbk Bus Mgr; Lit Mag; L Tennis; DECA Regnl 1st Pl Advrtsng 87; DECA ST Fin Mktng 87; U GA; Publshng.

MIKUCKI, PAUL; Toms River HS South; Toms River, NJ; (2); Church Choir; Mrchg Band; Var L Trk; CC Awd; Cit Awd; SAR Awd; VFW Awd; Boy Scts; Church Yth Grp; School Musical; Boy Sct Eagl Awd 86; Pope Pius XII Awd 87; Stf Diocs Trentn Sct Retrts 86; Engrng.

MIKUSI, CORRINE; John P Stevens HS; Edison, NJ; (3); 72/450; Hosp Aide; Science Clb; Thesps; Concert Band; Drm Mjr(t); Jazz Band; School Musical; Capt Twrlr; Hon Roll; NHS.

MILANESI, GLENN H; Vineland HS; Vineland, NJ; (2); 1/700; Concert Band; High Hon Roll; Engnrng.

MILANO, MARC; Union HS; Union, NJ; (3); Am Leg Boys St; Key Clb; Spanish Clb; Rep Soph Cls; Rep Jr Cls; Var Ftbl; Var Wt Lftg; Hon Roll; NHS; Ntl Merit SF; Am Lgn Jersey Boys ST Dir Pblc Wrks 87; Sci Leag 85-87; Cornell; Engrng.

MILAS, LINDA; Maple Shade HS; Maple Shade, NJ; (4); DECA; Capt Socr; Sftbl; High Hon Roll; DECA Apprl & Accsrs 2nd Pl ST Comptn 87; Gordon Phillips Bty Schl; Cosmt.

MILES, RENE; Saint Joseph HS; Williamstown, NJ; (3); 10/95; SADD; Teachers Aide; Pres Jr Cls; Var Cheerleading; Var Capt Sftbl; High Hon Roll; NHS; Cmnty Wkr; Drama Clb; Letterman Clb; Prncpls List; Glassboro ST Coll; Elem Educ.

MILES, TAMIEQKYA; John F Kennedy HS; Willingboro, NJ; (3); Chorus; Church Choir; School Musical; Hon Roll; NHS; Accntng.

MILES, TRICIA; Kinnelon HS; Kinnelon, NJ; (3); Art Clb; Camera Clb; Church Yth Grp; French Clb; Girl Scts; Yrbk Ed-Chief; Yrbk Phtg; Rep Stu Cncl; Score Keeper; Commnctns.

MILEY, FRANCIS; Sacred Heart HS; Vineland, NJ; (4); Am Leg Boys St; German Clb; SADD; Chorus; School Play; Sec Trs Sr Cls; Var Tennis; Pres NHS; Ntl Merit Ltr; Hugh Obrien Yth Ldrshp Smnr 85.

MILIAN, JOHN; Columbia HS; Orange, NJ; (4); 3/480; Aud/Vis; Spanish Clb; School Play; Stage Crew; Spnsh Hnr Scty 86; Montclair Coll; TV.

MILIOTE, ANTHONY; Manalapan HS; Manalapan, NJ; (4); 15/600; Boy Scts; Chess Clb; Drama Clb; Stu Cncl; Badmtn; Bsbl; Bsktbl; Ftbl; Golf; Socr; Clemson U; Mgmt.

MILISITS, ANDREW; The Lawrenceville Schl; New Kensington, PA; (2); Art Clb; Cmnty Wkr; Debate Tm; Chorus; Pres Jr Cls; Stu Cncl; Im Bsktbl; Hon Roll; Rotary Awd; Im Sftbl; All Amercn Clb 86; Black Cltrl Orgnztn 87.

MILL, ALEXANDER; Vineland HS; Vineland, NJ; (3); 72/824; VP Art Clb; French Clb; Ed Lit Mag; French Hon Soc; Gov Hon Prg Awd; High Hon Roll; Hon Roll; Olympics Mind 85-86 & 86-87; Earnest Fiore Awd Best Of Show Stu Art Exhibit 86; Comm Art.

MILLAR, JUDITH; Paramus Catholic HS; Moonachie, NJ; (4); GAA; Hosp Aide; Political Wkr; Teachers Aide; Varsity Clb; Capt L Socr; JV Capt Sftbl; Hon Roll; Psychologist.

MILLAR, MICHAEL; Holy Spirit HS; Ocean City, NJ; (4); JA; Varsity Clb; Swmmng; Rwng Tm 84-87; Pblc Rltns; Northeastern; Rl Est.

MILLAR, ROBERT; North Arlington HS; N Arlington, NJ; (3); Boy Scts; Ski Clb; Yrbk Stf; Bsbl; Bsktbl; Ftbl; Wt Lftg; High Hon Roll; Hon Roll; Bus.

MILLEMANN, MIKE; Jackson Memorial HS; Jackson, NJ; (4); 68/413; Ski Clb; L Capt Trk; Var Vllybl; Var Wt Lftg; High Hon Roll; Hon Roll; U S Phy Ed Achvt Acad 87; NJ Inst Of Tech; Arch.

MILLEMANN, SHARON; Immaculata HS; Somerset, NJ; (3); Cmnty Wkr; Hosp Aide; Var Capt Cheerleading; Hon Roll; Bus Cmnctns.

MILLER, ADAM; Mount Olive HS; Flanders, NJ; (4); 13/275; Ski Clb; VP Temple Yth Grp; School Play; Nwsp Ed-Chief; Pres Stu Cncl; Var Socr; Var Swmmng; NCTE Awd; NHS; St Schlr; Govt.

MILLER, ADRIENNE; West Windsor-Plainsboro HS; Princeton Jct, NJ; (3); Cmnty Wkr; French Clb; Service Clb; SADD; School Play; Nwsp Rptr; Lit Mag; Trk; Hon Roll; NHS; Schlrshp-Chstnt Hill Coll Ldrshp Pgm 87; Psychlgy.

MILLER, ANDREA; Pitman HS; Pitman, NJ; (4); Rep Frsh Cls; Rep Soph Cls; Rep Jr Cls; Stu Cncl; Pom Pon; Stat Socr; Im Vllybl; Hon Roll; Hubertys Phrmcy Schlrshp 87; Philadelphia Coll; Phrmcy.

MILLER, ANDREA; Ranoocas Vly Regional HS; Rancocas, NJ; (2); 10/337; Teachers Aide; Varsity Clb; Bsktbl; Fld Hcky; Sftbl; High Hon Roll; NHS; Burlngtn Cnty 2nd Tm All Str Sftbl, Offnsve Plyr Yr Awd Sftbl 87.

MILLER, AUTHERENE; Immaculate Conception HS; Bloomfield, NJ; (2); Church Yth Grp; Dance Clb; Pep Clb; Church Choir; School Musical; Mgr Bsktbl; JV Var Mgr(s); JV Var Score Keeper; Var Trk; Capts Awd Trk & Fld Wght Tm 86; Vet Med.

MILLER, CARRIE; Parsippany Hills HS; Morris Plns, NJ; (3); Am Leg Aux Girls St; Cmnty Wkr; Drama Clb; Service Clb; Spanish Clb; Temple Yth Grp; School Play; Yrbk Stf; Lit Mag; Stu Cncl; Pblc Rltns.

MILLER, CHRISTINE; Scotch Plains Fanwood HS; Scotch Plains, NJ; (3); AFS; Church Yth Grp; FBLA; Spanish Clb; Band; Chorus; Sec Frsh Cls; Sec Soph Cls; Pres Stu Cncl; Cheerleading; Bus.

MILLER, DEBBIE; Camden County Vo Tech Schl; Camden, NJ; (3); Pres DECA; Yrbk Stf; NHS; Deca Awds Rgnl And St Lvl; Gvrnrs Schl Of The Arts; Coll Prfrmng Arts Phil; Dancer.

MILLER, DEBRA; Highland Regional HS; Blackwood, NJ; (4); 26/297; VP Art Clb; Camera Clb; Spanish Clb; Concert Band; Mrchg Band; Socr; Trk; Hon Roll; NHS; Comm Art.

MILLER, DIANA; High Point Regional HS; Branchville, NJ; (3); 24/268; Am Leg Aux Girls St; VP Sec Church Yth Grp; Pres German Clb; Math Clb; SADD; Band; Concert Band; Co-Capt Drill Tm; Mrchg Band; Rep Sr Cls.

MILLER, ERIC; St Marys HS; Teaneck, NJ; (2); Church Yth Grp; Var Ftbl.

MILLER, ERIK; South Plainfield HS; S Plainfield, NJ; (3); 6/265; Am Leg Boys St; SADD; Jazz Band; Mrchg Band; Trs Sr Cls; Rep Stu Cncl; High Hon Roll; Jr NHS; NHS; Spanish NHS; Boston Coll; Bus Admin.

MILLER, FRANKIE BETH; Cinnaminson HS; Cinnaminson, NJ; (3); JV Bsktbl; Lcrss; JV Socr; JV Tennis; High Hon Roll; Pres Jr NHS; NHS; Girls ST 86-87.

MILLER, GARY; Linden HS; Linden, NJ; (3); German Clb; Nwsp Rptr; Nwsp Stf; JV Var Ftbl; Hon Roll; Delta Epsilon Phi 86-88; Jrnlsm.

MILLER, GARY; Paul IV HS; Bellmawr, NJ; (3); JV Bsbl; Bus.

MILLER, GLENN E; Pennsville Memorial HS; Pennsville, NJ; (3); German Clb; Chorus; Concert Band; Hon Roll; All Cnty Chorus & All S Jersey Chorus 85-87; NJ All ST Chorus 86-87; Choir Dir Awd 85; Music.

MILLER, JANICE; Passiac Country Tech; Paterson, NJ; (3); Church Yth Grp; SADD; Sftbl; Vllybl; 3rd Pl Cosmtlgy Awd 85, 1st Pl 86; Cosmtlgst.

MILLER, JEFFERY HART; St Joseph Regional HS; Ramsey, NJ; (3); 23/225; Math Tm; Yrbk Stf; JV Trk; Cit Awd; High Hon Roll; Yrbk Awd Layout Ed 87; Finance.

MILLER, JENNIFER; West Milford Township HS; Hewitt, NJ; (3); 53/406; Debate Tm; Spanish Clb; SADD; Nwsp Sprt Ed; Nwsp Stf; Socr; High Hon Roll; Hon Roll; NHS; Spanish NHS; Marine Bio.

MILLER, KOREY B; Saddle Brook HS; Saddle Brook, NJ; (4); 3/110; Am Leg Boys St; Math Clb; Capt Scholastic Bowl; Nwsp Ed-Chief; Var L Ftbl; Var L Trk; High Hon Roll; NHS; Acad Math Awd Outstndng Stu 87; Excllnce Math/Sci Irene Dellon Awd 87; U MI; Aerospc Engrng.

MILLER, LAUREN; Atlantic City HS; Margate, NJ; (4); 28/402; Debate Tm; Girl Scts; Model UN; Rep Stu Cncl; Var L Crs Cntry; Hon Roll; Sec NHS; Outstndng Del Mdl Cngrss 84-85; Pol Sci.

MILLER, LAWRENCE J; Lenape HS; Vincentown, NJ; (3); 36/520; Am Leg Boys St; Exploring; German Clb; Intnl Clb; Service Clb; SADD; Nwsp Rptr; Yrbk Phtg; Trk; Hon Roll; Rotary Intl Paul Harris Fellow 85; 2 Vrsty Ltrs & 6 Mdls South Jersey Trck Coaches Assoc In Trck; US Naval Acad; Aero Engr.

MILLER, LINDA; Highland Regional HS; Blackwood, NJ; (3); 17/385; French Clb; Science Clb; Spanish Clb; Mrchg Band; Stu Cncl; Twrlr; Hon Roll; NHS; Spec Ed Tchr.

MILLER, MELISSA; Florence Twp Mem HS; Roebling, NJ; (3); Girl Scts; Science Clb; Band; Mrchg Band; Sftbl; Hon Roll; Spanish NHS; Excllnce Chem 87; Excllnce Spn 86-87; Nrsg.

MILLER, MICHAEL; Rancolas Valley Regional HS; Mt Holly, NJ; (2); 24/338; Boy Scts; Var Bsktbl; JV Golf; High Hon Roll; Hon Roll; Engr.

MILLER, MICHELLE; Hamilton High West; Yardville, NJ; (4); 15/270; Math Tm; Co-Capt Drill Tm; School Musical; Variety Show; Rep Stu Cncl; Score Keeper; Hon Roll; NHS; Pres Schlr; ST Teen Arts Fstvl 87; PTA Schlrshp 87; Garden ST Schlrshp 87; Fairleigh Dickenson U; Ballet.

MILLER, NAOMI; Millville SR HS; Millville, NJ; (3); 88/524; Church Yth Grp; Cmnty Wkr; SADD; Yrbk Rptr; Mgr(s); French Hon Soc; Prfct Atten Awd; French Clb; Office Aide; Rep Stu Cncl; Olympcs Of The Mind Tm Awd 86-87; Gftd & Tlntd Prg 84-87; Host Frnch Exch Stu 86; Stdy Abrd France 87; Med.

MILLER, PATRICIA ANN; Eastern Regional HS; Berlin, NJ; (4); 23/342; Color Guard; Drill Tm; Mrchg Band; Capt Pom Pon; High Hon Roll; Hon Roll; NHS; Gold Medallion Awds 85-86 & 86-87; Berkeley Schl Awd Outstndng Achvt Bus Ed 87; Du Pont Sec Scholar 87; Goldey Beacom Coll; Exec Sec.

MILLER, RACHEL; Pleasantville HS; Pleasantville, NJ; (3); 6/135; Trs Church Yth Grp; Sec Library Aide; Sec Math Clb; Red Cross Aide; Church Choir; Sec Frsh Cls; Tennis; NHS; Bus Adm.

MILLER, ROBIN; Middletown South HS; Lincroft, NJ; (4); 8/450; Math Clb; Political Wkr; Ski Clb; Chorus; Trk; French Hon Soc; High Hon Roll; Ntl Merit Ltr; Garden ST Distngshd Schlr Awd 86.

MILLER JR, RONALD K; Pinelands Regional HS; Tuckertown, NJ; (4); 16/200; Art Clb; Church Yth Grp; Variety Show; High Hon Roll; Hon Roll; Jr NHS; NHS; Half Schlrshp Lincoln Tech 87; Lincoln Tech; Drftng.

MILLER, SANDEE; Middletown HS; Leonardo, NJ; (4); 50/413; Trs Drama Clb; Pres SADD; Capt Flag Corp; School Musical; School Play; Ed Lit Mag; Aud/Vis; Church Yth Grp; Cmnty Wkr; US Congrssnl Awd Bronz Mdl 84; Golden Poet Awd Wrld Poetry 86; Thorne Art Scholar 87; Syracuse U; Art.

MILLER, SCOTT; Delran HS; Delran, NJ; (4); 51/189; Var Ftbl; Var Capt Trk; Var Capt Wrstlng; Gov Hon Prg Awd; No 1 Clb Burlington Cnty Schltc Wrstlg 86-87; Prncpl Awd 87; 1st Pl Schltc Lg 86-87; Wrstlg Clb Scholar; Glassboro Coll; Bus.

MILLER, SCOTT P; Randolph HS; Randolph, NJ; (3); 24/353; Math Tm; Ski Clb; SADD; Temple Yth Grp; Yrbk Sprt Ed; Var Ftbl; JV Trk; High Hon Roll; NHS.

MILLER, STACE; Garden State Acad; Andover, NJ; (4); Church Yth Grp; Drama Clb; 4-H; Concert Band; Stage Crew; Nwsp Ed-Chief; Nwsp Phtg; Nwsp Rptr; Rep Jr Cls; Hon Roll; Columbia Union Coll Ldrshp Schlrshp 87; Columbia Union Coll; Psych.

MILLER, STEPHANIE L; Lower Cape Max Regional HS; Cape May, NJ; (4); 27/240; Girl Scts; Concert Band; Jazz Band; Mrchg Band; School Play; Stage Crew; Nwsp Ed-Chief; Yrbk Bus Mgr; Lit Mag; NHS; NY ST U; Bus Admin.

MILLER, STEPHEN T; Bishop Eustace Prep; Medford, NJ; (3); 2/165; Am Leg Boys St; Boy Scts; NFL; Speech Tm; Bsktbl; Bausch & Lomb Sci Awd; High Hon Roll; Pres NHS; Ntl Merit Ltr; German Natl Hnr Soc 86; Amer Lgn Ortrcl Cntst ST Chmpn 87; Natl Cathlc Frnsc Lg 85-87; Molclr Bio.

MILLER, SUSAN; Ocean Township HS; Ocean, NJ; (3); 37/344; Ski Clb; Sec VP Spanish Clb; SADD; Pres Varsity Clb; Sec Frsh Cls; Sec Soph Cls; Trs Jr Cls; VP Sr Cls; Var L Socr; NHS; Spartan Schlr 85-87; Bus.

MILLER, TONYA; Irvington HS; Irvington, NJ; (3); Yrbk Stf; Cheerleading; High Hon Roll; Hon Roll; NHS; Drama Clb; Band; Chorus; Concert Band; Drill Tm; US Constitution Awd 87; Pre-Med.

MILLER, TRACEY; Morristown HS; Morristown, NJ; (3); Exploring; VP Sec JA; Speech Tm; Church Choir; Concert Band; Mrchg Band; Rep Jr Cls; Powder Puff Ftbl; Trk; Hon Roll; U Of Pittsburg; Law.

MILLER, TRACY T; Chatham Twp HS; Chatham, NJ; (4); 14/140; VP Church Yth Grp; Girl Scts; Key Clb; Model UN; Var JV Sftbl; CC Awd; High Hon Roll; Hon Roll; Sec NHS; JV Fld Hcky; Beatty-Hughes Schlrshp 87; Pres Acdmc Fitness Awd 87; Mock Trial Awd 87; Trinity Coll.

MILLER, WESTON C; Bernards HS; Bernardsville, NJ; (4); 10/165; Church Yth Grp; Band; Church Choir; Jazz Band; JV Bsbl; Var L Bsktbl; Sec NHS; Ntl Merit SF; Presbytrn Church Elder 86-87.

MILLET, LEITHA; Ferris HS; Jersey City, NJ; (3); Church Yth Grp; English Clb; GAA; Office Aide; Spanish Clb; Varsity Clb; Chorus; School Play; Off Jr Cls; Sftbl; St Peters Coll; Pedtrcn.

MILLEY, RODNEY; Williamstown HS; Williamstown, NJ; (4); 42/269; JV Bsbl; Var JV Ftbl; Var Trk; Wt Lftg; Hon Roll; Brks Irvine Unsung Hero Ftbl Awd 86; Insprtnl Awd Ftbl 87; Karate Achvt Awd 87; Stockton ST Coll; Premed.

MILLIRON, RICK; South Hunterdor Regional HS; Lambertville, NJ; (4); 25/77; School Play; Rep Frsh Cls; Ftbl; Var Capt Wrstlng; York Coll Of PA; Scrty.

MILLS, CHARLENE; Willingbor HS; Willingboro, NJ; (4); Church Yth Grp; Trs Sr Cls; Rep Stu Cncl; Var Capt Bsktbl; Lcrss; Sftbl; Trs NHS; Yth Achvt Awds 86; Army ROTC Scholar 87; US Military Acad; Info Systems.

MILLS, KATHY; Bridgewater Raritan East HS; Bridgewater, NJ; (3); Intnl Clb; Ski Clb; Rep Frsh Cls; Rep Soph Cls; Rep Jr Cls; Trs Stu Cncl; Var Capt Cheerleading; Powder Puff Ftbl; High Hon Roll; NHS; Mrktng.

MILLS, KEN; Delran HS; Delran, NJ; (4); 25/190; Aud/Vis; Church Yth Grp; German Clb; Stage Crew; Variety Show; Capt Crs Cntry; Capt Trk; Hon Roll; Penn ST; Arch Engrng.

MILLSTEIN, PAMELA; Manalapan HS; Englishtown, NJ; (2); Library Aide; Nwsp Rptr; Nwsp Stf; Engl.

MILNE, JOHN; Holobken HS; Hoboken, NJ; (4); 44/280; VP Key Clb; Chorus; School Musical; School Play; Stage Crew; Variety Show; Nwsp Rptr; Yrbk Stf; Trs Soph Cls; Rep Sr Cls; Top 10 87; Marine Mdlnd Bnk Arw Schl Achvt 87; Tchrs Assoc Awd; Montclair St Col; Kndrgrtn Tchr.

MILONE, KRISTIN; Kittatinny Regional HS; Newton, NJ; (4); Math Tm; Office Aide; Science Clb; Spanish Clb; Trk; High Hon Roll; Hon Roll; NHS; Voice Dem Awd; Bio Sci.

MILOS, SEAN; Morris Catholic Regional HS; Denville, NJ; (2); 35/157; JV Bsktbl; Hon Roll.

MILOSEVIC, VLADIMIR; Passaic County Vo-Tech HS; Paterson, NJ; (4); SADD; Yrbk Stf; Hon Roll; N Jersey Stu Crftsmns Fair 85; NJ Inst Of Tech; Elctrcl Engr.

MILTON, LIZ; Madison Avenue Baptist Acad; Paterson, NJ; (4); Church Choir; School Musical; Sec Jr Cls; Var Bsktbl; Var Cheerleading; Var Vllybl; High Hon Roll; Hon Roll; Prfct Atten Awd; Val; Bio Awd 85; Phys Sci Awd 84; Chancelors Scholar 87; Liberty U; Fash Merch.

MINERVINI, ANNA; Emerson HS; Weehawken, NJ; (4); 31/288; Art Clb; Debate Tm; Library Aide; Teachers Aide; Yrbk Stf; Rep Pres Jr Cls; Rep Pres Sr Cls; Rep Stu Cncl; Jr NHS; NHS; Frgn Natl Hnr Soc 86; Hnrbl Mntn-Natl Italian Cntst 85-87; Presdntl Acad Fitness Awds Prog 87; Fashion Inst; Merch.

MINERVINI, LUCIA; Secaucus HS; Secaucus, NJ; (4); 3/160; Am Leg Aux Girls St; VP Computer Clb; Key Clb; Pres Mu Alpha Theta; Varsity Clb; Nwsp Rptr; Rep Soph Cls; Rep Jr Cls; Var L Tennis; NHS; Itl Hnr Society 85; Itln Ptry Cntst; Safe Energy Clb; Phrmcy.

MINERVINI, MICHAEL; Hoboken HS; Hoboken, NJ; (3); Boy Scts; Drftng.

MINERVINI, THERESA; Wood-Ridge HS; Wood Ridge, NJ; (2); Art Clb; Latin Clb; Model UN; Service Clb; Lit Mag; VP Frsh Cls; VP Soph Cls; JV Cheerleading; JV Vllybl; High Hon Roll; Natl Latin Exam Cum Laude 86.

MINGO, NICOLE; Plainfield HS; Plainfield, NJ; (3); 10/500; Aud/Vis; Math Tm; Band; Rep Jr Cls; Rep Stu Cncl; Swmmng; Var Capt Tennis; Trk; Hon Roll; NHS; US Achvt Awd Math Awd 85; NJ Math League Awd Wnner 87; Howard U; Pre-Med.

MINHAS, KIRNJIT KOUR; Parsippany Hills HS; Parsippany, NJ; (4); 4/304; French Clb; FBLA; Hosp Aide; Science Clb; Symp Band; Yrbk Stf; Off Stu Cncl; High Hon Roll; VP NHS; Inst Of Womens Schlrs; Rutgers; Engnrng.

MINICHINO, MARY BETH; Glen Rock HS; Glen Rock, NJ; (3); 30/141; DECA; Drama Clb; Spanish Clb; Varsity Clb; School Play; Var Capt Cheerleading; High Hon Roll; Hon Roll; Jr NHS; NHS.

MINIERI, MICHAEL A; Union HS; Union, NJ; (4); 3/534; Am Leg Boys St; Bsktbl; Ftbl; Socr; Trk; High Hon Roll; NHS; Church Yth Grp; German Clb; Pres Clssrm 86; Knights Of Pythias Schlrshp; William & Mary; Bus.

MINNER, MARC; Saint Augustine Prep; Williamstown, NJ; (3); 4/55; Cmnty Wkr; Pep Clb; Trs Sr Cls; Im Bsktbl; Im Ftbl; Im Socr; Im Sftbl; Im Vllybl; High Hon Roll; Hon Roll; 1st & 2nd Hnrs 84-87; NEDT Awd 84-87; Temple; Med.

MINNICK, DAVID F; Hamilton High School East; Trenton, NJ; (3); Church Yth Grp; Exploring; FBLA; Madrigals; School Musical; Var L Ftbl; Var L Trk; Im Vllybl; Wt Lftg; Hon Roll; Finance.

MINNITI, ANTHONY; Cinnaminson HS; Cinnaminson, NJ; (3); Science Clb; SADD; Nwsp Stf; Rep Frsh Cls; Rep Soph Cls; Rep Jr Cls; Rep Stu Cncl; Tchr, Hon Roll; Prfct Atten Awd; Phila Coll Of Pharm/Sci; Pharm.

MINOGUE, GEORGENE; Pequannock Township HS; Pompton Plains, NJ; (3); 48/215; Office Aide; Yrbk Stf; Hon Roll; Spanish NHS; Montclair ST Coll; Psych.

MINOR, MICHELE; Jackson Memorial HS; Jackson, NJ; (3); 43/416; High Hon Roll; Hon Roll; Frgn Lang Frnscs Cmptn Kean Coll 87; Acadc Awds Upwrd Bnd, Georgian Ct Coll 85-87; U Of Pittsburgh; Petroleum Tech.

MINORE, DOMINICA; Washington Township HS; Turnersville, NJ; (4); 77/480; Spanish Clb; Cheerleading; Hon Roll; AZ ST U; Bus.

MINOTT, JANICE; Dwight Morrow HS; Englewood, NJ; (4); 47/229; Dance Clb; Debate Tm; Rep Stu Cncl; High Hon Roll; Hon Roll; Prfct Atten Awd; Bio Awd 85; Outstndng Persevrnc In HS Bus Educ 87; ST U Of NY Albany; Acctng.

MINSKY, JENIFER; Fair Lawn HS; Fair Lawn, NJ; (3); 99/346; Drama Clb; Ski Clb; VP Temple Yth Grp; School Musical; School Play; Stage Crew; Variety Show; Yrbk Stf; Rep Jr Cls; Rep Stu Cncl; Bus.

MINTSCHEKNO, NOEL; Southern Regional HS; Manahawkin, NJ; (3); 83/460; Cmnty Wkr; GAA; Intnl Clb; Varsity Clb; Yrbk Stf; Frsh Cls; Soph Cls; Jr Cls; Stu Cncl; Fld Hcky; TV Rptr For S News Ntwrk Sta 86-87; Stu Rep For Brd Of Ed Prjct 86-87; Sprts Wrtr For S Rgnl News Shw; Ithica; Comm.

MINUTELLA, ANTHONY; Passaic County Tech & Voc HS; Passaic, NJ; (3); 40/523; Boys Clb Am; Library Aide; Bowling.

MIOLOVIC, MIRIJANA; Elmwood Park Memorial JR SR HS; Elmwood Pk, NJ; (3); Am Leg Aux Girls St; Hosp Aide; Math Clb; Band; Mrchg Band; School Musical; Yrbk Phtg; Sec Stu Cncl; Sftbl; Hon Roll; Bus.

MIOZZI, ROBIN MARIE; Kingsway HS; Swedesboro, NJ; (2); CAP; Cmnty Wkr; Chorus; Var Cheerleading; Mgr Stat Ftbl; Mgr Stat Wrstlng; School Musical; Stage Crew; Var Mgr(s); JV Trk; Amercn Red Crss Cert Of Apprctn 85; Cvl Air Ptrl Mrtrious Svc Awd 85; Rutger U; Grphc Illstrtr.

MIRAGLIA, MARIA; Rancocas Valley Regional HS; Mt Holly, NJ; (2); Drama Clb; Sftbl; High Hon Roll; Hon Roll; Med.

MIRAGLIOTTA, TINA; Kittatinny Regional HS; Newton, NJ; (4); 6/222; Science Clb; Spanish Clb; Teachers Aide; Nwsp Rptr; Nwsp Stf; High Hon Roll; NHS; Rotary Awd; Sci Achvt Awd 86-87; Pres Acad Ftns Awd 86-87; Bucknell U; Bio.

MIRANDA, JANET; Academic HS; Jersey City, NJ; (3); Science Clb; Spanish Clb; Rep Jr Cls; Rep Stu Cncl; Var Bowling; Bus Mgmt.

MIRANDA, REENA; St Mary HS; Rutherford, NJ; (3); Math Clb; Thesps; Nwsp Rptr; Yrbk Rptr; Lit Mag; Pres Frsh Cls; Pres Stu Cncl; Var Cheerleading; Hon Roll; Sec NHS.

MIRANDE, THOMAS M; Monroe Township HS; Spotswood, NJ; (3); Am Leg Boys St; Ski Clb; Nwsp Rptr; Rep Stu Cncl; JV Bsbl; Var Golf; Var Capt Socr; Var Wrstlng; Hon Roll; NHS; Grtr Middlesex Cnty Schlr-Athlt Awd 86; U Of NC; Poli Sci.

MIRANDI, VINCENT; Whippany Park HS; Whippany, NJ; (4); 16/180; Am Leg Boys St; Debate Tm; Thesps; Jazz Band; Yrbk Ed-Chief; Yrbk Stf; Pres Frsh Cls; Pres Soph Cls; Gov Hon Prg Awd; Hon Roll; The Cooper Union; Grphc Dsgn.

MIRZAI, HOSSEIN; Washington Township HS; Sewell, NJ; (4); 40/490; French Clb; JV Tennis; High Hon Roll; Hon Roll; NHS; Hnr Grad, Prsdntl Ftnss Acdmc Awd 87; Glassboro ST Coll; Engrng.

MISASI, ANTHONY; Lakeland Regional HS; Wanaque, NJ; (3); 79/340; Church Yth Grp; Pres Band; Concert Band; Drm & Bgl; Jazz Band; Mrchg Band; Pep Band; Hon Roll; NHS.

MISE, KATRINA; Montville Township HS; Montville, NJ; (3); 73/266; Church Yth Grp; FBLA; High Hon Roll; Hon Roll; Natl Awd Kids Clay 87.

MISHOE, SHALINNI ANIQUE; St Pius X Regional HS; Plainfield, NJ; (3); Church Yth Grp; GAA; Red Cross Aide; Science Clb; Chorus; Church Choir; Variety Show; VP Frsh Cls; Rep Soph Cls; Rep Jr Cls; Accntng.

MISKO, SUSAN; Belleville HS; Belleville, NJ; (4); 19/324; Chorus; High Hon Roll; Hon Roll; NHS; Rutgers-Newark; Comp Sci.

MISKOVKSY, JOHN; Collegiate Schl; Passaic, NJ; (3); 1/11; Chess Clb; Pres JCL; Ed Key Clb; Math Tm; Scholastic Bowl; Nwsp Ed-Chief; Ed Lit Mag; Rep Stu Cncl; High Hon Roll; NEDT Awd; 1st Pl Sci Fair 85-86; 3rd Prz Trntn ST Coll NJ Cntst 84-85; Captain N NJ Chmpn Certamen Tms 85-86.

MISLOW, JOHN; Princeton Day Schl; Princeton, NJ; (3); French Clb; Hosp Aide; Latin Clb; Red Cross Aide; Orch; Nwsp Ed-Chief; Nwsp Stf; High Hon Roll; Hon Roll; Ntl Merit Ltr.

MISSAGGIA, LISA; Mt Olive HS; Flanders, NJ; (2); 37/325; FBLA; Spanish Clb; Yrbk Stf; Bsktbl; JV Fld Hcky; Sftbl; Hon Roll; Hnrs Math, Engl & Sci 86-87; Hnrs Math & Engl 85-86; Princeton; Accntng.

MISSAK, EMAD; Hudson Catholic HS; Dayton, NJ; (3); Camera Clb; Chess Clb; Computer Clb; Science Clb; Church Choir; Im Vllybl; Radiolgy.

MISSONELLIE, CHRISTINA; Paramus Catholic Girls HS; Elmwood Pk, NJ; (3); Art Clb; Hosp Aide; PAVAS; Stat Gym; Stat Vllybl; Hon Roll; Ntl Merit Schol; Art Achvt Awd 86-87; Crtvty Hnr 85-86; Fashion Inst Of Tech; Hrdrssr.

MISTRY, KAVITA; W L Dickinson HS; Jersey City, NJ; (3); Trs Computer Clb; Math Clb; Scholastic Bowl; Science Clb; Yrbk Stf; Lit Mag; Hon Roll; Pres NHS; Prfct Atten Awd.

MISUCK, PAUL; Gloucester HS; Brooklawn, NJ; (4); 68/149; Math Clb; Chorus; Concert Band; Jazz Band; Mrchg Band; Orch; School Play; Nwsp Rptr; Bowling; Hon Roll; Glassboro ST Coll; Cmmnctns.

MITCHELL, AUDRA I; Southern Regional HS; Manahawkin, NJ; (4); Dance Clb; Band; Jazz Band; Hon Roll; Georgian Ct Coll; Invstmnt Adv.

MITCHELL, DESIREE; Asbury Park HS; Asbury Park, NJ; (3); Dance Clb; Drama Clb; JA; Spanish Clb; Flag Corp; Yrbk Stf; Var Bsktbl; Var Cheerleading; Var Crs Cntry; Pres Trk.

MITCHELL, KAREN; Red Bank Catholic HS; Freehold, NJ; (3); SADD; Nwsp Rptr; Socr; High Hon Roll; Hon Roll; NHS; Intl Bus.

MITCHELL, MARTIN; Cherokee HS; Marlton, NJ; (4); 12/397; Am Leg Boys St; Debate Tm; VP Math Tm; Lit Mag; Trk; NHS; Ntl Merit Schol; Grdn St Dstngshd Schlr 86-87; Presdntl Acadc Ftns Awd 87; Marlton Grdn Clb Schlrshp 87; U DE; Chem.

MITCHELL, MEGAN; Madison Avenue Baptist Acad; Lake Hiawatha, NY; (1); Church Yth Grp; Office Aide; Church Choir; Cheerleading; Pom Pon; Score Keeper; Hon Roll; Prfct Atten Awd.

MITCHELL, SAMANTHA L; Morristown HS; Morristown, NJ; (4); Cmnty Wkr; JA; Im Fld Hcky; Hon Roll; U Of MD; Psychlgy.

MITCHELL, SHANNON; A P Schalick HS; Elmer, NJ; (3); 10/137; Varsity Clb; Sec Stu Cncl; Bsktbl; Sftbl; Hon Roll; NHS.

MITCHELL, SHAVON; Frank H Morrell HS; Irvington, NJ; (3); Band.

MITCHELL, STEPHANIE; Bridgeton HS; Bridgeton, NJ; (3); Dance Clb; Sec 4-H; Office Aide; Church Choir; 4-H Awd; Cmmnctns.

MITCHELL, SUZANNE; Woodstown HS; Woodstown, NJ; (3); VP FBLA; Office Aide; Band; Concert Band; Mrchg Band; Stu Cncl; Hon Roll; Katherine Gibbs Ldrshp Awd 87; Salem Cnty Band 86-87; Goldey Beacom Coll; Hotel Mgmt.

MITCHELL, TANYA CHERIE; Dwight Morrow HS; Englewood, NJ; (4); Church Yth Grp; Y-Teens; Color Guard; Drm Mjr(t); Flag Corp; Mrchg Band; Rep Soph Cls; Rep Sr Cls; Hon Roll; William Paterson Coll; Bus Mgt.

MITCHELL, TIMOTHY; Pitman HS; Pitman, NJ; (3); 18/143; Am Leg Boys St; Ftbl; Engrng.

MITCHELL, TRACY; Washington Township HS; Sewell, NJ; (2); Church Yth Grp; Spanish Clb; Fld Hcky; Hon Roll; Psych.

MITCHELL, VALERIE; Kent Place Schl; Chatham, NJ; (3); 1/56; Trs Church Yth Grp; Hosp Aide; Science Clb; Chorus; Nwsp Ed-Chief; Nwsp Sprt Ed; Nwsp Stf; Lit Mag; Sec Trs Soph Cls; Sec Trs Sr Cls; Gov Schlr Gov Schl Sci 87; Natl Merit Ltr 87; Physics.

MITCHELL, YVONNE; Notre Dame HS; Trenton, NJ; (2); Computer Clb; English Clb; French Clb; FBLA; Intnl Clb; Model UN; Pep Clb; Political Wkr; Science Clb; SADD; Intl Bus.

MITCHKO, RYAN; Warren County Vo-Tech; Oxford, NJ; (2); VICA; High Hon Roll; Hon Roll; Prfct Atten Awd; Drftng.

MITKUS, ROBERT; Holy Cross HS; Medford, NJ; (4); 14/369; Church Yth Grp; Debate Tm; Var L Socr; High Hon Roll; Hon Roll; NHS; Loyola Coll; Bio.

MITRIK, KATHRYN MARIE; Linden HS; Linden, NJ; (1); Church Yth Grp; Cmnty Wkr; Hosp Aide; Key Clb; Band; Concert Band; Mrchg Band; High Hon Roll; Prfct Atten Awd; Minorities In Engrng 86-87; Math.

MITTERANDO, DANIELLE; Middletown H S North; New Monmouth, NJ; (3); JV Fld Hcky; Var L Sftbl; Hon Roll; Acad All-Amer 87.

MITZNER, DAWN L; Watchung Hills Regional HS; Watchung, NJ; (4); 1/320; Sec Key Clb; Scholastic Bowl; Gov Hon Prg Awd; NHS; Ntl Merit Schol; St Schlr; Val; VP Frsh Cls; NJ Govs Schl For Sci 86; Westinghouse Sci Tlnt Srch-Hnrs Grp 87; Robert Byrd Schlrshp 87; MIT; Gntc Engnrng.

MIZAK, JOHN C; Colonia HS; Avenel, NJ; (4); 21/244; Am Leg Boys St; Cmnty Wkr; Varsity Clb; Yrbk Sprt Ed; Capt Crs Cntry; Capt Trk; Hon Roll; Jr NHS; NHS; NJIT; Elec Engr.

MOCREIA, PAUL; East Side HS; Newark, NJ; (3); Cmnty Wkr; Stage Crew; Swmmng; Drftng.

MODERNEL, ERIC; St Marys Of The Assmptn; Elizabeth, NJ; (2); Service Clb; JV Bsbl; JV Score Keeper; Hon Roll; Svc Awd 86-87; Union Cnty Coll; Bus.

MOELLER, MELISSA; West Windsor-Plainsboro HS; Princeton, NJ; (3); AFS; Art Clb; 4-H; Spanish Clb; Concert Band; JV Bsktbl; Bus.

MOFFA, KATHLEEN; Paul VI HS; Erial, NJ; (3); 93/415; Camera Clb; Church Yth Grp; Drama Clb; Chorus; Variety Show; Hon Roll.

MOFFETT, JASON; Collingswood HS; Oaklyn, NJ; (3); Am Leg Boys St; Ski Clb; Spanish Clb; Concert Band; School Play; Yrbk Stf; Rep Stu Cncl; Capt Var Bsbl; Var Ftbl; Im Wt Lftg; Ctznshp Awd; Hnr Mntn Conf Bsbl 87; Lions Clb Awd; Bus Admin.

MOFFITT, KEVIN; Ocean City HS; Ocean View, NJ; (3); 59/341; Drama Clb; French Clb; SADD; School Musical; School Play; Stage Crew; Var Diving; Var Swmmng; DAR Awd; Johnson & Wales Coll; Cul Art.

MOFFITT, MARC C; West Morris Mendham HS; Chester, NJ; (3); Church Yth Grp; FBLA; Library Aide; Ski Clb; Nwsp Stf; JV Bsbl; Bus.

MOG, MEREDITH; Timothy Christian Schl; North Plainfield, NJ; (2); 1/45; Church Yth Grp; Teachers Aide; Chorus; Variety Show; Yrbk Phtg; Var L Bsktbl; Var L Socr; Var L Sftbl; High Hon Roll; Val; Chopins Revolutionary Etude Piano 86; John Casablancas Modeling Agncy 86; Timothian Awd 85; Marine Bio.

MOGAN, KIMBERLY; Holy Spirit HS; Brigantine, NJ; (2); 28/397; Var L Bsktbl; Var L Tennis; Hon Roll.

MOGENSEN, KRISTEN; Kearny HS; Kearny, NJ; (3); Am Leg Aux Girls St; Color Guard; Rep Frsh Cls; Rep Soph Cls; Rep Jr Cls; Trs Sr Cls; Rep Stu Cncl; NHS; German Clb; Yrbk Stf; Varsty Crew Tm Coxswain 87; German Natl Hnr Soc 87; Johnson & Wales Coll; Culinary.

MOGLIA, GINA; Parsippany Hills HS; Parsippany, NJ; (3); Hosp Aide; Library Aide; Varsity Clb; Band; Concert Band; Symp Band; Rep Jr Cls; Stat Ftbl; Powder Puff Ftbl; Score Keeper; 2 Vrsty Lttrs & Cert Scr Screkeepr 85-87; Vrsty Ltr Band 86-87; Caldwell Coll; Elem Ed.

MOHAMED-TAKI, ASSIF; Lakeland Regional HS; Ringwood, NJ; (4); Cmnty Wkr; Computer Clb; Math Clb; Science Clb; Teachers Aide; Nwsp Stf; Swmmng; Hon Roll; Intnl Clb; Natl Sci Olympcs Physcs Dstnctn Awd 87; Sci Proj Cont Merit Awd 84; Clarkson U; Pre-Med.

MOHAN, JOHN; Buena Regional HS; Vineland, NJ; (3); 3/225; Math Tm; Quiz Bowl; Yrbk Stf; Var Socr; Var Tennis; High Hon Roll; Hon Roll; Jr NHS; Acdmc Let Achvng 90 Or Better Avg 84-85; Princeton; Law.

MOHN, ROBERT; St John Vianney HS; Matawan, NJ; (3); CAP; Computer Clb; SADD; Teachers Aide; Var L Crs Cntry; Var Trk; Hon Roll; Prfct Atten Awd; Physics.

MOHR, ANNE MARIE; Paul VI HS; Somerdale, NJ; (3); 20/419; German Clb; Math Clb; Bsktbl; JV Crs Cntry; JV Fld Hcky; Var L Trk; NHS; Grmn Ntl Hnr Soc 85-86.

MOHR, STACEY; Burlington Twp HS; Burlington, NJ; (3); 14/132; French Clb; Quiz Bowl; Varsity Clb; Chorus; Madrigals; Bsbl; Var JV Fld Hcky; Mgr(s); Score Keeper; NHS; Psych.

MOHSEN, NANCY; Ocean Township HS; Wayside, NJ; (3); 5/344; Cmnty Wkr; Key Clb; SADD; Ntl Merit SF; Muslim Yth Grp 85-87; Wrld Famine Rld Cmte Treas 87; Grls Ctznshp Inst 87; Ldrshp Pgm 87; Chem Engrng.

MOJARES, RICHARD; Oratory Prep Schl; New Providence, NJ; (4); 6/44; Math Tm; Nwsp Rptr; Pres Frsh Cls; Pres Soph Cls; Sec Pres Stu Cncl; Var Bsktbl; Var L Socr; Hon Roll; NHS; Tennis.

MOKOID, JACQUELINE; Pennsville Memorial HS; Pennsville, NJ; (3); 18/228; Cmnty Wkr; FBLA; Spanish Clb; Nwsp Stf; Rep Jr Cls; Rep Stu Cncl; Var Sftbl; Capt Var Tennis; Hon Roll; Trs NHS; Girls Ctznshp Inst Dlgt 87; Plyr Yr Girls Ten 86; Tri-Co Conf All Str Tm Sftbl 87; Poltcl Sci.

MOLENARO, MARK; Don Bosco Tech HS; Paterson, NJ; (3); 36/91; Exploring; PAVAS; Q&S; SADD; Concert Band; School Musical; JV Crs Cntry; Var Ice Hcky; Var Socr; Hon Roll; Ldrshp Retreat 86-87; Wdwrkng Awd 83-86; Natl Art Awd 84-85; Art.

MOLFETTA, ANGELO; W L Dickinson HS; Jersey City, NJ; (2); Bus.

MOLINARO, MELISSA; Bishop Eustace Prep; Cherry Hill, NJ; (3); Drama Clb; Math Clb; Office Aide; Pep Clb; SADD; School Play; Cheerleading; Crs Cntry; Gym; Trk; Bus.

MOLINELLI, KATHLYNN; Buena HS; Milmay, NJ; (3); #13 In Class; Flag Corp; Mrchg Band; Hon Roll; Glsboro ST Coll; (3); Tchr.

MOLLACH, LAURA; Union HS; Union, NJ; (3); 1/505; Boys Clb Am; Key Clb; Science Clb; Ed Nwsp Sprt Ed; Yrbk Stf; Fld Hcky; Capt Trk; High Hon Roll; Trs Jr NHS; NHS; Outstndng Svc Schl 85; Biochem.

MOLLENKOPF, RICHARD; Friends Schl; Glassboro, NJ; (3); Socr; Sftbl; Im Tennis.

MOLLET, PETRA; Academy Of The Holy Angels; River Vale, NJ; (3); French Clb; Model UN; Var Capt Crs Cntry; Var Vllybl; High Hon Roll; Hon Roll; Trs NHS.

MOLNAR, HEATHER; Morris Catholic HS; Flanders, NJ; (1); 34/156; Chorus; JV Cheerleading; Trk; Hon Roll; UCLA; Psych.

MOLONEY, MARY; Holy Spirit HS; Northfield, NJ; (2); 11/397; Spanish Clb; Hon Roll; Sprts Med.

MOLOUGHNEY, KRISTEN; St Marys HS; Secaucus, NJ; (4); Ski Clb; Spanish Clb; Capt Vllybl; High Hon Roll; Hon Roll; Prfct Atten Awd; Spanish NHS; Widener U.

MONAGHAN, PATRICIA; Queen Of Peace HS; Kearny, NJ; (3); 54/279; Cmnty Wkr; Hosp Aide; Library Aide; Service Clb; Ski Clb; Stage Crew; Off Soph Cls; Rep Jr Cls; Hon Roll; Hghst Av Accntng Awd 87; Accntng.

MONAHAN, ANDREA; Paul VI HS; Blackwood, NJ; (3); Church Yth Grp; Dance Clb; Hon Roll; Seton Hall; Psych.

MONAHAN, ERIC; Belleville HS; Belleville, NJ; (3); Boy Scts; Ski Clb; JV Var Trk; Elec Engrng.

MONFARDINI, MICHAEL; Buena Regional HS; Landisville, NJ; (3); 15/236; Socr; Trk; Hon Roll; Jr NHS; Aeronautical Engr.

MONFORT, OSCAR; Memorial HS; West New York, NJ; (3); 35/350; Boy Scts; Leo Clb; Rep Frsh Cls; Rep Soph Cls; Rep Jr Cls; Trs Stu Cncl; Var Crs Cntry; Var Trk; Hon Roll; Jr NHS; Math.

MONG, JESSICA; Holy Spirit HS; Absecon, NJ; (4); 10/363; Church Yth Grp; French Clb; Red Cross Aide; Rep Frsh Cls; Rep Soph Cls; Rep Jr Cls; Rep Sr Cls; Var Tennis; Bio.

MONGELLI, ELIZABETH; Immaculate Conception HS; Secaucus, NJ; (2); Debate Tm; Hosp Aide; NFL; Chorus; Yrbk Stf; Tennis; Hon Roll; NEDT Awd; Newark Catholic Frnsc Leag 2nd Pl 86; NYU; Ped.

MONGEY, MARY DENICE; Villa Walsh Acad; Morristown, NJ; (2); Red Cross Aide; Chorus; School Play; Stage Crew; VP L Bsktbl; L Tennis; L Trk; Church Yth Grp; Cmnty Wkr; School Musical; Olympcs Of Mind 86-87; Task Frc 86-87; Cngrssnl Yth Ldrshp Cncl Awd 87; Providence Coll; Law.

MONINGHOFF, LARA; Belvidere HS; Belvidere, NJ; (4); 4/122; Am Leg Aux Girls St; Model UN; Red Cross Aide; Capt Scholastic Bowl; Service Clb; Yrbk Stf; Stat Bsktbl; NHS; Ntl Merit Ltr; Gftd & Tlntd Prgm; Outstndng Achvt In Physlgy; Scl Sctys Tchrd Awd; Outstndng Achvt In Spnsh; Pediatric Srgn.

MONITZER, DIANE; Overbrook Regional SR HS; Lindenwold, NJ; (4); 86/346; Var Sftbl; Hon Roll; Camden Cnty Coll; Bus Mgmt.

MONROE, AMANDA; St Rose HS; Brick, NJ; (3); Hosp Aide; Red Cross Aide; Ski Clb; SADD; Silver Cngrssnl Awd 87; Prncpl Awd Otstndng Stu 84; Blnd Vet Assoc Aux Awd 86; Je Rsey Shore Med Ctr 87; West VA U; Bio Engrng.

MONROY, CHRISTINA; Elizabeth HS; Elizabeth, NJ; (4); 54/803; French Clb; Hosp Aide; Key Clb; Library Aide; Socr; Cit Awd; Hon Roll; NHS; Pres Schlr; Ramapo Coll Of NJ; Psych.

MONSEN, ERIK; Highstown HS; East Windsor, NJ; (4); 2/407; Pres Trs AFS; Am Leg Boys St; Church Yth Grp; Drama Clb; Exploring; Capt Math Tm; Chorus; School Musical; School Play; Stage Crew; Rensselaes Poly Insti; Aerontcl.

MONSORNO, CHERYL; Roselle Catholic HS; Linden, NJ; (3); Church Yth Grp; Drama Clb; School Musical; JV Var Cheerleading; Var Gym; High Hon Roll; NHS; Spanish NHS; Varsity Clb; Nalt Ldrshp & Svc Awd 87; US Chrldng Achvt Awd 86; Eng.

MONTALBANO, ROSA; West Essex Regional HS; Fairfield, NJ; (3); Cmnty Wkr; French Clb; French Hon Soc; Hon Roll; Jr NHS; NHS; Wst Essex Phlsphcl Soc 86-87; Cornell U Of Miami; Law.

MONTANINO JR, WILLIAM; Clifton HS; Clifton, NJ; (4); 48/589; Boys Clb Am; DECA; Office Aide; SADD; Rep Sr Cls; Hon Roll; NHS; Johnson & Wales Schlrshp 87; Clifton DECA Top Slsmn 86-87; Army Culnry Schl; Chef.

MONTANO, MARC; Bridgewater-Raritan H S East; Bridgewater, NJ; (3); Church Yth Grp; 4-H; Var Socr; Var Tennis; Trk; High Hon Roll; Hon Roll; Elect Engrng.

MONTEAU, DANIELLE; Shore Regional HS; Oceanport, NJ; (3); French Clb; Science Clb; Fld Hcky; Socr; High Hon Roll; NHS; Ldrshp Awd Sci Clb 86; Vet.

MONTELEONE, DONALD A II; Oak Crest HS; Mays Landing, NJ; (2); All Amer Awd 86; Lndscpr.

MONTELEONE, VINCENT; Boonton HS; Lincoln Pk, NJ; (2); Boy Scts; Church Yth Grp; Exploring; SADD; Varsity Clb; Var Lcrss; Var Socr; Var Capt Vllybl; JV Wrstlng; Teenag Coach Awd-Sccr 86; Rutgers; Law.

MONTEMURRO, RITA; Toms River HS East; Toms River, NJ; (4); 26/567; Key Clb; Political Wkr; Chorus; Capt Drill Tm; Mrchg Band; School Musical; Capt Pom Pon; High Hon Roll; Hon Roll; NHS; Acdmc All Amer 86-87; Pre Law.

MONTEROSA, CARRIE ANNE; Parsippany Hills HS; Morris Plains, NJ; (3); Dance Clb; Drama Clb; Nwsp Rptr; Var Fld Hcky; Mgr(s); Score Keeper; Hon Roll.

MONTESINOS, DIANA; Parsippany Hills HS; Parsippany, NJ; (4); 40/301; Service Clb; Spanish Clb; Chorus; School Musical; Variety Show; Stu Cncl; High Hon Roll; Hon Roll; Exploring; Office Aide; Natl Merit Hspnc Schlrs Semifnlst 87; MORRIS Cnty Mock-Trl Tm Champs Law 87; PA ST U; Pre-Law.

MONTREUIL, FRANCE; Jackson Memorial HS; Jackson, NJ; (3); 6/430; Am Leg Aux Girls St; Hosp Aide; Red Cross Aide; Ski Clb; Jr Cls; Bsktbl; Powder Puff Ftbl; Wt Lftg; High Hon Roll; NHS; Phys Thrpy.

MOODY, KARL; Edgewood Regional SR HS; Sickelerville, NJ; (3); Socr; Wrstlng; Hon Roll; Jr NHS; PSAT Awd 87; Bus Admin.

MOODY, MALIK; Eastside HS; Paterson, NJ; (2); 34/535; Church Yth Grp; Debate Tm; Varsity Clb; Band; Nwsp Phtg; Rep Stu Cncl; Var Ftbl; Var Trk; Capt Var Wrstlng; HOBY 87; Pre-Law.

MOODY, VANESSA; Camden HS; Camden, NJ; (4); 69/401; Cmnty Wkr; Debate Tm; JA; Model UN; Political Wkr; School Play; Yrbk Sprt Ed; VP Frsh Cls; Var Capt Bsktbl; Crs Cntry; Cert Of Cmmndtn Mayor 85-86; Bsktbll Unsung Hero 85-86; Citation Senator NJ 85-86; Wilberforce U; Corp Law.

MOODY, VINCENT G; Scotch Plains-Fanwood HS; Scotch Plains, NJ; (4); 90/300; Quiz Bowl; Stage Crew; Rep Jr Cls; Rep Sr Cls; GA Tech; Info Sci.

MOON, MICHELLE N; Red Bank Regional HS; Red Park, NJ; (4); 90/256; Girl Scts; Hosp Aide; Chorus; Nwsp Rptr; Lit Mag; Art Recog Talent Srch Hnbl Men Creative Wrtng 87; NJ Govrs Schl Of Arts 86; Columbia Schlstc Press 87; Anthro.

MOON, TRACY; Orange HS; Orange, NJ; (2); Art Clb; FNA; Hosp Aide; Mgr Pep Clb; Mgr Cheerleading; Prfct Atten Awd; U VA; Phys Thrpst.

MOONEY, STAYCE; Holy Family Acad; Bayonne, NJ; (3); 2/130; Church Yth Grp; Dance Clb; Spanish Clb; School Musical; Stage Crew; Nwsp Rptr; Yrbk Stf; High Hon Roll; NHS; NEDT Awd; St Peters Coll Smmr Schlr 86-87; Bio.

MOONEY, THOMAS; Cranford HS; Cranford, NJ; (3); 68/269; Drama Clb; Spanish Clb; Thesps; Acpl Chr; School Musical; Bsbl; Ftbl; Peer Develpmnt Facilitator; Psych Club; Leg Aide Assemblyman Chuck Hardwick 87; Bio.

MOONSAMMY, ANN; Dickinson HS; Jersey City, NJ; (4); 17/450; Computer Clb; Exploring; Math Clb; Q&S; Scholastic Bowl; Science Clb; Nwsp Rptr; Nwsp Stf; Yrbk Stf; Lit Mag; Rutgers Newark; Sci.

MOORE, ANGELA; Irvington HS; Irvington, NJ; (4); 21/466; Art Clb; Sec Church Yth Grp; Latin Clb; Church Choir; Color Guard; Flag Corp; Stage Crew; Hon Roll; NHS.

MOORE, ARTHUR; Essex Catholic Boys HS; East Orange, NJ; (3); Church Yth Grp; Im Sftbl; Im Wt Lftg; Hon Roll; NJ Inst Of Tech; Arch.

MOORE, BARBARA ANN; Southern Regional HS; Barnegat, NJ; (3); 12/440; Concert Band; Mrchg Band; Trk; High Hon Roll; Hon Roll; NHS; Rotary Awd; CPA.

MOORE, BESTY; West Morris Mendham HS; Mendham, NJ; (2); 25/300; Art Clb; Church Yth Grp; Drama Clb; Intnl Clb; Model UN; PAVAS; School Play; Stage Crew.

MOORE, JAMES; Middle Township HS; Cape May Court, NJ; (3); 25/300; Key Clb; Capt Band; Chorus; Concert Band; Jazz Band; Mrchg Band; School Musical; Variety Show; Yrbk Stf; NHS; Dir Awd Mrchng Band Excptnl Prfrmnc 86; U Rochester; Pol Sci.

MOORE, JEANNINE A; Kearny HS; Kearny, NJ; (4); 50/383; Church Yth Grp; Hosp Aide; Spanish Clb; Yrbk Stf; Im Bowling; JV Gym; Hon Roll; NHS; PTA Schlrshp, Tuition Aid Grant 87-88; Kean Coll Of NJ; Early Chldhd.

MOORE, JENNIFER; Hunterdon Central HS; Flemington, NJ; (2); 112/478; Rep Frsh Cls; Rep Soph Cls; Rep Stu Cncl; Fld Hcky; Lcrss; Med.

MOORE, JOE; Franklin HS; Somerset, NJ; (3); Art Clb; Boy Scts; Camera Clb; Drama Clb; Scholastic Bowl; School Musical; School Play; Stage Crew; Socr; NHS; Studio Art.

MOORE, KEVIN; West Orange HS; West Orange, NJ; (4); 8/370; Math Tm; Science Clb; Ski Clb; Jazz Band; Mrchg Band; Var Capt Crs Cntry; Var Trk; French Hon Soc; Gov Hon Prg Awd; Ntl Merit SF; 1st Pl Chem Olympcs Wrkng Model 87; 1st Pl NJ Amer HS Math Exam 86; Princeton U; Elec Engr.

MOORE, LAURIE; Watchung Hills Regional HS; Watchung, NJ; (2); Church Yth Grp; Drama Clb; Key Clb; Ski Clb; SADD; Chorus; School Musical; School Play; Stage Crew; Yrbk Stf.

MOORE, LLOYD E; Frank H Morrell HS; Irvington, NJ; (3); Cmnty Wkr; Dance Clb; Latin Clb; Band; Chorus; Church Choir; Concert Band; Crs Cntry; Swmmng; Hon Roll; Latn Hnr Soc 86; Natl Hnr Rl 87; Maritl Arts Cert Advncmt 86-87; St Johns; Comp Sci.

MOORE, MARC L; Piscataway HS; Piscataway, NJ; (4); 38/498; Church Yth Grp; Science Clb; Varsity Clb; Off Jr Cls; Off Sr Cls; Stu Cncl; Var L Trk; NHS; St Schlr; Spanish Clb; Natl Merit Fin 87; Brown U; Pre-Med.

MOORE, RONALD; Cumberland Regional HS; Bridgeton, NJ; (4); 5/300; Debate Tm; Intnl Clb; Science Clb; Varsity Clb; VP Soph Cls; VP Jr Cls; VP Stu Cncl; Tennis; Cit Awd; High Hon Roll; Natl Conf Christians & Jews Brthrhd Awd 87; All S Jersey Tennis Doubles 87; U Of DE; Civil Engrng.

MOORE, SUSAN; Triton Regional HS; Glendora, NJ; (2); AFS; Math Clb; Office Aide; Spanish Clb; Rep Soph Cls; High Hon Roll; Hon Roll.

MOORE, TAWANNA; James J Ferris HS; Jersey City, NJ; (2); FTA; VP Soph Cls; JV Var Cheerleading; Prfct Atten Awd; Merit Awd; FL Southern Coll; Jrnlsm.

MOORMAN, MARLENE; Edgewood SR HS; Berlin, NJ; (3); 4-H; ROTC; Band; Color Guard; Drill Tm; Sftbl; Tennis; Trk; ROTC Awdds Bnqt 10 Rbbns 86-87; USN; Air Trffc Cntrllr.

MOOYMAN, CYNTHIA; North Brunswick Townhip HS; North Brunswick, NJ; (4); 67/297; Cmnty Wkr; JCL; Latin Clb; Spanish Clb; SADD; Varsity Clb; Drama Clb; Swmmng; Trk; Hon Roll; All Cnty, All Conf Swimming; Rutgers Coll; Bus.

MORACA, MICHAEL; Paul VI HS; Deptford, NJ; (4); 14/503; Cmnty Wkr; SADD; Lit Mag; Im Bsktbl; Im Bowling; Im Tennis; NHS; Bryant Coll; Actrl Math.

MORALES, DANIA; Dover HS; Dover, NJ; (3); Sec AFS; Church Yth Grp; German Clb; Pep Clb; Science Clb; Ski Clb; Band; Orch; Nwsp Phtg; Yrbk Stf; Excllnc Bio Awd 86.

MORALES, GRECIA; Ridgefield Park HS; Ridgefield Park, NJ; (2); 37/183; Science Clb; Spanish Clb; Nwsp Rptr.

MORALES, MARGARET; Matawan Reg HS; Cliffwood Beach, NJ; (4); 19/316; Church Yth Grp; FBLA; Math Clb; Nwsp Stf; Cit Awd; High Hon Roll; NHS; Spanish NHS; Harvard Smr Sch 86; Rutgers Smr Schlr 86; Acad All-Amrcn 86; Harvard U; Econ.

MORALES, TRACY; Mary Help Of Chritians Acad; Paterson, NJ; (3); 4/85; French Clb; JCL; Drill Tm; JV Vllybl; Hon Roll; NHS; Prfct Atten Awd; Pre-Med.

MORALES, YASMINNIE; Holy Spirit HS; Pleasantville, NJ; (3); Church Yth Grp; Cmnty Wkr; Hosp Aide; Library Aide; SADD; Chorus; Cert Pin-ACMC 85-86; Cert-Emplye Of Mnth 87; Med.

MORAN, DONNA; Pinelands Regional HS; Tuckerton, NJ; (3); Church Yth Grp; Drama Clb; Science Clb; Spanish Clb; Variety Show; Yrbk Stf; Rep Soph Cls; Hon Roll; Prfrmng Arts.

MORAN, EDWARD; St Joseph Regional HS; New City, NY; (4); 96/185; Camera Clb; Cmnty Wkr; Computer Clb; Ski Clb; Spanish Clb; Varsity Clb; Bsbl; Bsktbl; Coach Actv; Ftbl; All Cnty, All ST, MVP-MVP Thanksgiving Day Game & All League & All Surburban 86-87; Muhlenberg Coll; Bus.

MORAN, JOEL; Morris Hills HS; Rockaway, NJ; (3); 109/249; Boy Scts; Computer Clb; Wt Lftg; Wrstlng; Denver Deisle Awd-Auto Mech.

MORAN, KATIE; Morristown HS; Convent Sta, NJ; (2); 118/432; Key Clb; Latin Clb; Varsity Clb; Sec Soph Cls; Swmmng; Tennis; Hon Roll; Svrl Awds For Swmng 86-87; MIP Swmr 86; Intr Dcrtr.

MORAN, MARTIN; Sparta HS; Sparta, NJ; (3); 90/264; Varsity Clb; Jazz Band; Mrchg Band; Symp Band; Var Capt Crs Cntry; Var L Swmmng; Var L Trk; Mst Imprvd Swmmr 85-86; Hawthorne Coll; Aviation.

MORAN, ROCCO; Southern Regional HS; Tuckerton, NJ; (2); Art Clb; Camp Fr Inc; Computer Clb; English Clb; Exploring; PAVAS; Science Clb; SADD; VICA; Nwsp Phtg; Art.

MORANO, ANTHONY; Holy Spirit HS; Ventnor, NJ; (2); 21/397; Spanish Clb; Varsity Clb; Orch; School Musical; Var Trk; Hon Roll; Jr NHS; Music Awd 85; Rutgers U; Corp Law.

MORASKI, CHRISTINA; Holy Spirit HS; Ventnor, NJ; (3); 39/332; Spanish Clb; Off Jr Cls; Phrmcy.

MOREIRA, MARIA; Pequannock Township HS; Pompton Plains, NJ; (3); 1/220; Science Clb; Chorus; Var Socr; JV Trk; High Hon Roll; Hon Roll; Jr NHS; Spanish NHS; Acad All Amer 87; Rutgers Schlr 87; Biol.

MOREJON, EBERTO; Memorial HS; Hialeah, FL; (3); Nwsp Rptr; Nwsp Sprt Ed; Nwsp Stf; Tennis; Hon Roll; Law.

MORELLA, LISA; Highland Regional HS; Blackwood, NJ; (3); #25 In Class; Trs Art Clb; Hon Roll; Med Tech.

MORELLI, DAYNA MICHELE; John P Stevens HS; Edison, NJ; (4); School Musical; School Play; Variety Show; Rep Soph Cls; Rep Jr Cls; Rep Sr Cls; Rep Stu Cncl; Capt Powder Puff Ftbl; Middlesex Cnty Arts HS 83-86; Ntrl Mtn Inst; Hrdrssr.

MORELLO, JENNIFER A; Vineland HS; Vineland, NJ; (2); 12/800; French Clb; Key Clb; Latin Clb; SADD; Yrbk Ed-Chief; Yrbk Stf; Stu Cncl; Mgr(s); Sci.

MORELLO, RICHARD; Indian Hills HS; Oakland, NJ; (3); 8/306; Am Leg Boys St; Var Letterman Clb; Q&S; Nwsp Ed-Chief; Nwsp Rptr; Var Bsbl; Var Bsktbl; NHS; Amer Schltc Press Assn 86; NJ Press Wmn 1st Pl Feature Story St 87; Nwstrn U; Comm.

MORENO, ANA; Roselle Park HS; Roselle Park, NJ; (3); #15 In Class; Hosp Aide; Library Aide; Band; Concert Band; Mrchg Band; Capt Pom Pon; Hon Roll; JP Sousa Awd; NHS; Phy Therapy.

MORENO, MARIA; Columbia HS; Maplewood, NJ; (3); Church Yth Grp; Cmnty Wkr; Library Aide; Chorus; Yrbk Phtg; Yrbk Stf; Mgr(s); NHS; Natl Spn Lev III Tst Hnrb Mntn 87; MEA NJ Aud Awd 1st Pl 82 & 84-86; Seton Hall U; Intl Bus Mgr.

MORENO, TONY; Kearny HS; Kearny, NJ; (4); Art Clb; Camera Clb; Cmnty Wkr; Spanish Clb; JV Bowling; JV Socr; JV Sftbl; Giordano Arthur J Mem Schlrshp 87; Teterboro Schl; Airplane Mech.

MORERO, VANNA; Mary Help Of Christian Acad; Paterson, NJ; (3); Computer Clb; Service Clb; SADD; Chorus; Hon Roll; Geometry Awd 85-86.

MORESCO, ALISON; Msgr Donovan HS; Lakewood, NJ; (3); 45/275; Hosp Aide; Capt Color Guard; JV Var Sftbl; Hon Roll; 100 Hrs Svc Candy Strpr 85; Bio.

MOREYRA, MARIA; Immaculata HS; Piscataway, NJ; (4); 6/120; Intnl Clb; Math Tm; Ski Clb; Color Guard; Yrbk Phtg; Rep Stu Cncl; Tennis; Pres French Hon Soc; Sec NHS; Engrng.

MORGAN, ADAM; Madison HS; Madison, NJ; (3); 44/212; Church Yth Grp; Exploring; French Clb; SADD; Score Keeper; Capt Var Socr; JV Trk; Hon Roll.

MORGAN, BECKY; Washington Township HS; Sewell, NJ; (2); Hon Roll; Spnsh I Awd; Glasboro ST Coll; Tchng.

MORGAN, CANDICE L; Newton HS; Newton, NJ; (2); Church Yth Grp; Sec 4-H; German Clb; Hst Service Clb; Chorus; School Musical; Lit Mag; JV Fld Hcky; 4-H Awd; Hon Roll; FFA Vegetable Awds 86-87; Home Ec Baking Awds 86-87; Sci.

MORGAN, CHRISTINE; Southern Regional HS; Manahawkin, NJ; (3); 29/435; Church Yth Grp; Soroptimist; Spanish Clb; Trs Frsh Cls; Hon Roll; NHS; Rep Soph Cls; Rep Jr Cls; JV Sftbl; Bus Admn.

MORGAN, DORION; Burlington TWP HS; Burlington, NJ; (3); 31/149; Aud/Vis; VP Church Yth Grp; Cmnty Wkr; Debate Tm; FCA; Chrmn Model UN; Speech Tm; Band; Chorus; Pres Church Choir; Syracuse U; Pre Law.

MORGAN, JANE; Warren Vo Tech; Asbury, NJ; (2); Church Yth Grp; Key Clb; Ski Clb; Varsity Clb; VICA; Church Choir; Bsktbl; Hon Roll.

MORGAN, JULIE; Belvidere HS; Belvidere, NJ; (3); 13/135; Pres Sec Church Yth Grp; Drama Clb; GAA; VP Band; Chorus; Sec Church Choir; Concert Band; VP Mrchg Band; Bsktbl; Fld Hcky; Sci.

MORGAN, KAREN; Paramus Catholic HS; Saddle Brk, NJ; (2); Church Yth Grp; Dance Clb; School Musical; Lit Mag; JV Socr; Var Trk; Hon Roll; NEDT Awd; Prfct Atten Awd; Bus.

MORGAN, KRISTINE; Mount Olive HS; Flanders, NJ; (3); 20/340; AFS; Sec FBLA; Teachers Aide; Var Trk; High Hon Roll; Hon Roll; NHS; Cert Of Acadmc Rcgntn-Chem, Erth Sci 87, 85; Bus Mgmt.

MORGAN, MICHAEL; Haddonfield Memorial HS; Haddonfield, NJ; (2); JV Socr; Trk; Hon Roll.

MORGAN, STEVE; Seton Hall Prep; Clifton, NJ; (3); 40/250; Pep Clb; Science Clb; School Musical; School Play; Stage Crew; Trk; Wt Lftg; Wrstlng; Hon Roll; Flght.

MORIELLO, CARMINE; Linden HS; Linden, NJ; (4); 149/365; VICA; CC Awd; High Hon Roll; Hon Roll; Kiwanis Awd; The Cittone Inst Schlrshp 87; Italian Ladies Clb Schlrshp 87; Co-Op Indstrl Ed Voc Tech Awd 87; Cittone Inst; Comp.

MORITA, KATHERINE; Bridgeton HS; Bridgeton, NJ; (3); Art Clb; Aud/Vis; Drama Clb; Ski Clb; School Musical; School Play; Nwsp Stf; Sec Soph Cls; Tennis; NHS; Full Yr Schlrshp NJ Schl Arts 86-87; Comm Art.

MORLEY, DARIN; Pitman HS; Pitman, NJ; (2); Church Yth Grp; Band; Concert Band; Jazz Band; Mrchg Band; Trk; Hon Roll; Coaches Awd Track Team 86-87; Fine Arts.

MOROSINE, HILDEANN; Hackettstown HS; Hackettstown, NJ; (4); Latin Clb; Band; Chorus; Color Guard; Mrchg Band; Symp Band; Hon Roll; Annual Schl Awd Outstndng Perserverance HS Bus Classes 87; Dover Bus Coll; Wrd Proc.

MORRA, DANNY; James Caldwell HS; W Caldwell, NJ; (3); VP Math Clb; Math Tm; Sec Orch; High Hon Roll; Hon Roll; NHS; Natl Hnr Roll 86-87; Outstndng Biolgcl Achvt 85; Hgh Acadmc Achvt 85; Bio.

MORRELL, SHERRI; Delsea Regional HS; Williamstown, NJ; (4); 50/202; SADD; Var Capt Bsktbl; Var Capt Fld Hcky; Var Capt Sftbl; Wt Lftg; High Hon Roll; Kay Frey Mem Athltc Scholar 87; Rider Coll; Law.

MORRIELLO, GREGORI; Belleville HS; Belleville, NJ; (3); Cmnty Wkr; Key Clb; Band; Jazz Band; Mrchg Band; Stage Crew; Yrbk Stf; Off Jr Cls; Var Crs Cntry; Var Trk; Chem.

MORRIS, AMY; Boonton HS; Boonton, NJ; (2); Church Yth Grp; Dance Clb; Exploring; GAA; Pep Clb; SADD; Varsity Clb; Yrbk Stf; Var Cheerleading; Hon Roll; Law.

MORRIS, BETH; Hamilton West HS; Trenton, NJ; (3); Spanish Clb; Nwsp Stf; Rep Stu Cncl; Sftbl; Vllybl; Hon Roll; Trenton ST; Pediatric Nrsng.

MORRIS, DAWN; Highland Regional HS; Erial, NJ; (3); 3/375; Cmnty Wkr; Political Wkr; Science Clb; Service Clb; Stu Cncl; Bsktbl; NHS; Sci.

MORRIS, DEANNA; Sussex Vo-Tech; Stanhope, NJ; (3); Am Leg Aux Girls St; Girl Scts; Rep Stu Cncl; JV Bsktbl; JV Swmmng; High Hon Roll; Hon Roll; Morris Cnty Coll; Bus Mgmt.

MORRIS, DONNA; Sussex Vo Tech; Newton, NJ; (3); Library Aide; Office Aide; SADD; Hon Roll.

MORRIS, ESTHER; Asbury Park HS; Asbury Park, NJ; (4); 9/117; Key Clb; Hon Roll; Var Schlr 85-87; Bus Admin.

MORRIS, FRED; Parsippany Hills HS; Morris Plns, NJ; (3); Key Clb; Political Wkr; Trs Temple Yth Grp; JV Crs Cntry; Im Wt Lftg; JV Wrstlng; Hon Roll; NHS; Ntl Merit SF; Bus.

MORRIS, HEATHER; Phillipsburg HS; Phillipsburg, NJ; (3); 21/315; GAA; Ski Clb; Sec SADD; Stu Cncl; JV Var Trk; High Hon Roll; Criminal Justc.

MORRIS, JAYME; Villa Victoria Acad; New Hope, PA; (2); 2/35; DAR Awd; High Hon Roll.

MORRIS, JODI; Mc Corristin Catholic HS; Trenton, NJ; (3); GAA; Pep Clb; Chorus; Rep Frsh Cls; Tennis; Scl Sci.

MORRIS, LESLEE; Mainland Regional HS; Linwood, NJ; (3); Drama Clb; Key Clb; Model UN; Political Wkr; Sec Pres SADD; Nwsp Rptr; Sec Jr Cls; Dance Clb; Debate Tm; Intnl Clb; Operation Enterprise Ldrshp Semnr Colgate U 87; Monmouth Coll Govt Inst 87; Natl Yth Ldrshp Congress; American U; Political Science.

MORRIS, LINDA L; Florence Twp Mem HS; Roebling, NJ; (3); Pres GAA; Letterman Clb; Varsity Clb; Rep Stu Cncl; Var L Bsktbl; Var L Fld Hcky; Var L Sftbl; FTA; Teachers Aide; Nwsp Stf; Sftbll-NJ St Chmps/ Hnrbl Mntn All-South Jersey 87; Florence Twp Mem Athltc Assn Pres & VP 86-88; Pltcl Sci.

MORRIS, MARIANNE; Middletown HS South; Middletown, NJ; (4); 43/444; Camera Clb; Math Tm; Stage Crew; Yrbk Stf; High Hon Roll; Hon Roll; Osbourne Bus Schlrshp 87; Montclair ST Coll; Bus Adm.

MORRIS, PHYLLIS; Ocean Township HS; Ocean Twp, NJ; (3); 56/344; Key Clb; Math Clb; Math Tm; Pres Temple Yth Grp; Band; Concert Band; Jazz Band; Mrchg Band; School Musical; Spartan Schlr Awd 85; Mst Imprvd Soph Musicn 86; ACE Band Awd 87; Bus.

MORRIS, SHAWN; Hudson Catholic HS; Jersey City, NJ; (3); Delasalle Schlrshp Acdmc 84-86; Sci.

MORRIS, TANYA; Weegwahic HS; Newark, NJ; (3); Cmnty Wkr; Computer Clb; Hosp Aide; Math Clb; Pep Clb; Science Clb; Chorus; Pep Band; Variety Show; JV Badmtn; Engl Awd 85; Sci Awd 85; Acctnt.

MORRISON, CHRISTOPHER; Palmyra HS; Palmyra, NJ; (3); 17/147; Aud/Vis; Computer Clb; Pres Exploring; Key Clb; Library Aide; Teachers Aide; Nwsp Rptr; Yrbk Stf; Hon Roll; NHS; NJ Teen Arts Awd 86-87; Drexel U; Comp.

MORRISON, CHRISTY; West Windsor-Mainsbon HS; Princeton, NJ; (3); FBLA; Art Clb; Hosp Aide; Hon Roll; Chem.

MORRISON, DEBORAH; The Morristown-Beard Schl; Short Hills, NJ; (3); Pres AFS; Intnl Clb; Service Clb; School Play; Nwsp Stf; Sec Soph Cls; JV Capt Fld Hcky; Mgr(s); Var Sftbl; Hon Roll.

MORRISSEY, SEAN; Holy Cross HS; Willingboro, NJ; (4); Sftbl; Capt Var Swmmng; Hon Roll; NHS; NJ ST Swm Chmp 100 Yd Frstyle 87; MVP Swm Tm 84-87; South Jersey All Star Swm Tm 85-87; Southern IL U; Med.

MORRONE, THOMAS; Paul Vi HS; Sicklerville, NJ; (4); 13/514; Math Clb; Hon Roll; NHS; Ntl Merit Ltr; Spanish NHS; NMSAT Mth Awd 85-86; NLSA Ldrshp, Svc Awd 85-86; Rutgers; Law.

MORROW, LISA; Brick Memorial HS; Brick, NJ; (3); Drama Clb; School Play; Swmmng; Hon Roll; Art.

MORSCH, KELLY LEIGH; Paul VI Regional HS; Newark, NJ; (3); Church Yth Grp; Civic Clb; Spanish Clb; SADD; School Play; Stu Cncl; JV Bsktbl; Var JV Cheerleading; Cit Awd; Hon Roll; Csmtlgy.

MORSE, SHERRY; Mt Olive HS; Flanders, NJ; (3); 2/315; Hosp Aide; Science Clb; Ed Lit Mag; High Hon Roll; NHS; Strght A's Physcs 86-87; Anml Care.

MORTENSEN, TAMMY L; Dumont HS; Dumont, NJ; (4); 10/217; VP Chorus; Co-Capt Color Guard; Concert Band; School Musical; School Play; Yrbk Stf; High Hon Roll; Mu Alpha Theta Awd; NHS; St Schlr; Lwyr.

MORTON, ALICIA S; Woodrow Wilson HS; Camden, NJ; (3); JA; Spanish Clb; SADD; Yrbk Stf; Computer Clb; Comp Sci Tech.

MOSCA, JACQUELINE; Paramus Catholic Girls Regionl HS; Hasbrouck Hts, NJ; (3); Cmnty Wkr; Drama Clb; English Clb; French Clb; Office Aide; Teachers Aide; School Play; Nwsp Bus Mgr; Nwsp Ed-Chief; Nwsp Rptr; Merit Awd 87; Penn ST; Pre Law.

MOSCARELLO, MARY; Mc Corristin Catholic HS; Trenton, NJ; (3); Art Clb; GAA; Pep Clb; Chorus; Yrbk Stf; Rep Soph Cls; Sftbl; Hon Roll; Jr NHS; NHS; Rutgers U; Photo.

MOSCHETTI, ANGELA; Immaculate Heart Acad; Nanuet, NY; (4); 9/171; Church Yth Grp; Cmnty Wkr; Yrbk Stf; Cheerleading; Coach Actv; Sftbl; Vllybl; High Hon Roll; NHS; Acadmc Al-Amer 86; Arch.

MOSER, DENISE; Phillipsburg HS; Phillipsburg, NJ; (3); 91/356; Drama Clb; Hosp Aide; Ski Clb; Thesps; Chorus; School Play; Nrsng.

MOSERY, NIZAN BUD; Cresskill HS; Cresskill, NJ; (3); Boy Scts; Temple Yth Grp; Socr; Trk; Technion Haifa Israel; Aero Eng.

MOSES, DENISE; Essex Catholic Girls HS; Newark, NJ; (4); 3/52; Church Yth Grp; FBLA; Library Aide; Yrbk Stf; High Hon Roll; Hon Roll; Rutgers HS Stu Achvt Awd 87; Pace U; Bus Mgmnt.

MOSES, MICHAEL; Mt Olive HS; Flanders, NJ; (3); 50/320; Aud/Vis; Math Tm; Science Clb; Hon Roll; Sci Achvt Awd-Earth Sci 84-85; Hnr Roll 84-85; PA ST U; Pre-Med.

MOSHEN, MATTHEW H; Matawan Regional HS; Matawan, NJ; (3); 7/360; Math Tm; Soroptimist; Speech Tm; Concert Band; Jazz Band; Mrchg Band; School Musical; Variety Show; Nwsp Rptr; Nwsp Sprt Ed; Regn II Concrt Band 85; Pol Sci.

MOSHINSKY, DEBORAH; Paul VI HS; Turnersville, NJ; (3); 12/416; Rptr German Clb; Math Clb; Band; Concert Band; Mrchg Band; Bowling; Hon Roll; German Hnr Soc 86; Med.

MOSHO, AMY; Manalapan HS; Englishtown, NJ; (4); 110/530; Boy Scts; Cmnty Wkr; Drama Clb; Girl Scts; Hosp Aide; JCL; Latin Clb; Temple Yth Grp; Thesps; School Musical; Hofstra U; TV Brdcstg.

MOSIELLO, LAURA; Hunterdon Central HS; Flemington, NJ; (4); 204/548; Drama Clb; Thesps; Chorus; Madrigals; School Musical; School Play; Nwsp Rptr; Hon Roll; VFW Awd; Voice Dem Awd; Wheaton Clg; Intrntnl Rltns.

MOSKOW, BARBARA; Manalapan HS; Manalapan, NJ; (3); Cmnty Wkr; Dance Clb; SADD; VP Temple Yth Grp; Psych.

MOSKOWITZ, LIZ; Cliffside Park HS; Cliffside Park, NJ; (3); Spanish Clb; Hon Roll; Hnr Rll 86; IFIA Bio Intrntn Frgn Lang Awds 86; Montclair ST Clg; Tchng.

MOSKWA, KIMBERLY; Rahway HS; Rahway, NJ; (3); Service Clb; Thesps; Chorus; School Musical; Nwsp Stf; Rep Jr Cls; Var Tennis; Cit Awd; Hon Roll; NHS; Prsnlty Of Mnths Oct & Nov 86; Law.

MOSLEY, BANESSA; Highland Regional HS; Clementon, NJ; (2); Library Aide; Spanish Clb; Band; Chorus; Concert Band; Jazz Band; Mrchg Band; Nwsp Stf; Stu Cncl; High Hon Roll.

MOSLEY, CYNTHIA; Bridgeton SR HS; Bridgeton, NJ; (2); Hosp Aide; Latin Clb; Flag Corp; Mrchg Band; Off Soph Cls; Trk; Bus Law.

MOSLEY, MARIA; Pemberton Township HS; Fort Dix, NJ; (2); Exploring; FBLA; Math Clb; Math Tm; Red Cross Aide; Band; Concert Band; Drm Mjr(t); Mrchg Band; Nwsp Rptr; Bus Law.

MOSLEY, MICHAEL; West Windsor Plainsboro HS; Plainsboro, NJ; (3); Am Leg Boys St; Art Clb; Boy Scts; Cmnty Wkr; Trs French Clb; Rep Ski Clb; Acpl Chr; VP Chorus; High Hon Roll; NHS; Engrng.

MOSLEY, MICHELLE ERICA; John F Kennedy HS; Willingboro, NJ; (3); Art Clb; Spanish Clb; Mrchg Band; Stat Sftbl; Stat Vllybl; Stat Wt Lftg; Teen Arts Fstvl Cert 86; U NM; Nrsng.

MOSS, ANDREA; Bordentown Regional HS; Wrightstown, NJ; (2); 9/140; Chorus; Var Color Guard; Var Drill Tm; Var Pom Pon; High Hon Roll; Hon Roll; Howard U; Pdtrcs.

MOSS, JOMARIE; Spotswood HS; Spotswood, NJ; (4); Dance Clb; Drama Clb; Intnl Clb; Science Clb; School Musical; School Play; Variety Show; Lit Mag; VP Frsh Cls; Mgr(s); Excllnc Drama Awd 87; Pace U; Cmmnctns.

MOSSMAN, TIMOTHY; Ptiman HS; Pitman, NJ; (4); 7/150; Computer Clb; Teachers Aide; Nwsp Sprt Ed; Rep Stu Cncl; Var Crs Cntry; Var Trk; NHS; Ntl Merit Ltr; St Schlr; Olympc Of Th Mnd Wrld Chmpn 85; U VA; Elec Engrng.

MOSTAFAVI, RAMIN; Secaucus HS; Secaucus, NJ; (2); Math Clb.

MOTEK, DOUG; Spotswood HS; Spotswood, NJ; (3); 1/150; Am Leg Boys St; Boy Scts; FBLA; Model UN; Var Bsbl; Var Ftbl; French Hon Soc; NHS; Hugh O Brien Yth Fndtn ST Fnlst 86; Engrng.

MOTLEY, BYRON; Lincoln HS; Jersey City, NJ; (3); JA; SADD; School Play; Var Bsbl; Var Bsktbl; Var L Ftbl; Trk; High Hon Roll; Hon Roll; MVP Ftbl 85; Hudson Cnty 5th Qtr Clb Offnsv Plyr Of Wk 85; Law.

MOTLEY, VERONICA; University HS; Newark, NJ; (2); Lawyer.

MOTON, DARNETIA; Camden HS; Camden, NJ; (3); Church Yth Grp; Pep Clb; Rep Frsh Cls; Rep Soph Cls; Rep Jr Cls; Trk; Cit Awd; High Hon Roll; Hon Roll; Prfct Atten Awd; Acctnt.

MOTT, JENNIFER; Paramus Catholic HS; Hawthorne, NJ; (3); Bus.

MOTT, KIM; Ocean Twp HS; Ocean, NJ; (3); Girl Scts; Key Clb; SADD; Capt L Flag Corp; Stage Crew; L Bowling; Hon Roll; Rutgers; Math.

MOTT, ROBERT; Egg Harbor Township HS; Linwood, NJ; (3); 11/364; Pres Church Yth Grp; Model UN; Yrbk Stf; Pres Bowling; High Hon Roll; Hon Roll; Ntl Merit SF; History Awd 84; Comp Sci.

MOTTA, ALICIA; James J Ferris HS; Jersey City, NJ; (3); 1/27; Computer Clb; Math Clb; Office Aide; Science Clb; Spanish Clb; Teachers Aide; Yrbk Stf; Lit Mag; Trs Soph Cls; VP Jr Cls; Rutgers Schlrshp Prg JRS 87; Citations Acad Achvt 87; 2nd Pl Fire Smart Wrtng Contest 87; Rutgers U; Journlsm.

MOTTER, LAURA; Highland Regional HS; Blackwood, NJ; (4); German Clb; Band; Chorus; Mrchg Band; Stage Crew; Pom Pon; Camden Cty Coll; Wrd Prcsng.

MOTWANI, BOBBY; Raritan HS; Hazlet, NJ; (3); 3/340; French Clb; Math Tm; Science Clb; Spanish Clb; Var Crs Cntry; Var Trk; High Hon Roll; Hon Roll; NHS; Math Clb; Law.

MOUNT, MEGAN; Immaculata HS; Somerset, NJ; (3); Church Yth Grp; Concert Band; Mrchg Band; Rep Frsh Cls; Var JV Bsktbl; Var JV Socr; Var JV Sftbl; Swmmng; Prfct Atten Awd; Band; Eng-Hrbl Mntn Awd; Psych.

MOUROVIC, PAULA; Jackson Memorial HS; Jackson, NJ; (3); 122/416; DECA; Drama Clb; Chorus; Hon Roll; Regnl DECA 2nd Pl Role Plyng 87; Ocean County Coll; Rsrt Mgmt.

MOWBRAY, JAMES; Holy Spirit HS; Brigantine, NJ; (2); 16/397; Hon Roll.

MOWEN, JEFF; Point Pleasant Boro HS; Brielle, NJ; (4); 7/235; Key Clb; Quiz Bowl; Scholastic Bowl; JV Bsbl; Tennis; Wrstlng; NHS; Pres Schlr; HS Schlrshp 87; Gvnrs Cncl Physcl Ftns Awd 87; Outstndng Achvt-Physcl Educ 87; Presdntl Acadc Awd 87; U Of DE; Mrn Bio.

MOWERY, KRISTINE; Highland HS; Blackwood, NJ; (2); Church Yth Grp; English Clb; Service Clb; Spanish Clb; SADD; Stu Cncl; Bsktbl; Var Tennis.

MOWRY, BETH; Burlington City HS; Burlington, NJ; (3); Church Yth Grp; Hosp Aide; Off Frsh Cls; Hon Roll; Socl Wrkr.

MOY, CATHERINE; Freehold HS; Englishtown, NJ; (4); 4/240; Ski Clb; Orch; Ed Nwsp Stf; Ed Yrbk Stf; Hon Roll; Sec NHS; VP Spanish NHS; Monmouth Jr Sci Sympsm Spkr 87; NJ St Teen Arb Fest-Dist Wnnr 87; Garden St Dstngshd Schlr 87; Columbia Coll; Engl.

MOY, TRACY; Delran HS; Delran, NJ; (3); Drama Clb; FBLA; Hosp Aide; Office Aide; Ski Clb; SADD; Yrbk Stf; Powder Puff Ftbl; Hon Roll; Spirt Wk; Soph Clss Actvts; JR Clss Actvts; Bus.

MOYER, COLETTE; Palmyra HS; Palmyra, NJ; (3); Church Yth Grp; Drama Clb; French Clb; Key Clb; SADD; Teachers Aide; Chorus; Church Choir; School Play; Variety Show.

MOYER, MICHAEL G; Haddonfield Memorial HS; Haddonfield, NJ; (4); Church Yth Grp; Cmnty Wkr; Sec Intnl Clb; Rep Stu Cncl; Var Socr; Hon Roll; Spanish NHS; Loyola Coll; Blngl Lwyr.

MOYER, STEPHEN; Holy Spirit HS; Northfield, NJ; (4); 37/363; Church Yth Grp; Spanish Clb; VP Frsh Cls; Rep Jr Cls; JV Var Swmmng; Var Tennis; Hon Roll; NHS; Rchstr Inst Of Tech; Cnmtgrphy.

MOYLE, JEFF; Eastern HS; Voorhees, NJ; (4); Rep Frsh Cls; JV Bsbl; Var Swmmng; Hon Roll; NHS; Pres Schlr; Robt Marshall Schlrshp Mjrng Elec Engrng 87; Rutgers U; Elec Engrng.

MOZER, RICHARD; Paul VI Regional HS; Clifton, NJ; (3); Am Leg Boys St; Boy Scts; Cmnty Wkr; Key Clb; Ski Clb; SADD; Ed Yrbk Rptr; Hon Roll; St Andrews Schl HS Schlrshp 84; Bus.

MROTEK, DOUGLAS M; Spotswood HS; Spotswood, NJ; (3); 1/170; Boy Scts; Computer Clb; FBLA; Math Tm; Model UN; Science Clb; JV Bsbl; Var L Ftbl; High Hon Roll; NHS; Hugh Obrian Yth Fndtn ST Fnlst 86; Engr.

MUCCIA, MAGGIE; Edison HS; Edison, NJ; (3); 34/479; Church Yth Grp; Dance Clb; Drama Clb; School Play; Variety Show; Sec Sr Cls; Capt Cheerleading; Hon Roll; NHS; Spanish NHS; Psychlgy.

MUCHAYPINA, JOSE; Perth Amboy HS; Perth Amboy, NJ; (3); Art Clb; Chess Clb; Computer Clb; Math Clb; Hon Roll; Prfct Atten Awd; Var Bowling; JV Var Socr; Var Tennis; Rutgers Coll; Engrng.

MUDALEL, BERNADETTE; Jackson Memorial HS; Jackson, NJ; (4); 155/387; Ski Clb; Yrbk Stf; Cheerleading; Powder Puff Ftbl; High Hon Roll; Hon Roll; Food Service Awd 87; Ocean Cnty Coll; Bus.

MUELLER, KRIS ANN; Woodbridge HS; Fords, NJ; (3); Ski Clb; SADD; Acpl Chr; Chorus; Swing Chorus; Yrbk Stf; Bsktbl; Bowling; JV Var Cheerleading; Sftbl; Barbizon Schlrshp 87; Hlth Sci.

MUELLER, ROSEMARIE; Teaneck HS; Teaneck, NJ; (4); 21/420; Math Tm; Band; Chorus; Concert Band; Mrchg Band; School Musical; Hon Roll; JP Sousa Awd; NHS; Rep Stu Cncl; ST La Salle Hnr Scty Mnhtn Coll 87; Manhattan Coll; Engr.

MUELLER, SIEGFRIED; Kittatinny Reg HS; Newton, NJ; (3); 20/230; Drama Clb; Latin Clb; Science Clb; Band; School Musical; Yrbk Bus Mgr; Lit Mag; Pres Stu Cncl; Hon Roll; NHS; Ldrshp Trnng Conf, Boys ST 87; Governors Schl 86; U Of PA; Biochem.

MUELLER, THEREESE L; Riverside HS; Riverside, NJ; (3); Sec DECA; SADD; Rep Soph Cls; Rep Jr Cls; Sec Stu Cncl; Var Cheerleading; Prom Ct 87; Trenton ST; Crmnl Jstc.

MUENZ, HEATHER LEIGH; Hawthorne HS; Hawthorne, NJ; (3); Pep Clb; Hon Roll; Fashn Merch.

MUENZENBERGER, DIANA; Gateway Regional HS; Woodbury Heights, NJ; (4); 33/206; Church Yth Grp; German Clb; Office Aide; Science Clb; SADD; Var Fld Hcky; Im Vllybl; Hon Roll; NHS; Church Choir; Bond Frm SADD 87; Gloucester Cnty; Nrsng.

MUFSON, DAN; John P Stevens HS; Edison, NJ; (4); 8/476; Model UN; VP Thesps; Acpl Chr; School Play; Variety Show; Ed Nwsp Ed-Chief; Ed Lit Mag; French Hon Soc; NHS; Ntl Merit Ltr; Slctd Gvrns Chl Pblc Issus Ftr NJ 86; Nancy Carter Mrl Awd 83-84; Awd Otstndng Achvmnt Eng 83-84; Pltcl Sci.

MUGNO, ALBERT M; Don Bosco Tech; W Paterson, NJ; (4); 4/68; Am Leg Boys St; Church Yth Grp; Pep Clb; SADD; Pres Frsh Cls; Pres Soph Cls; Pres Jr Cls; Pres Stu Cncl; Var Bsktbl; Var Socr; Alumni Achvt Awd, UNICO Schlrshp; Outstndg Stu; NJ Schlrs Athlt Awd; Montclair ST Coll; Indust Arts.

MUIA, ANGELA; Bishop Ahr HS; Sewaren, NJ; (4); Drama Clb; Thesps; Capt Chorus; Color Guard; School Musical; Trk; Vllybl; Hon Roll; Outstndg Prfrmr Color Guard 84-86; Rutgers U; Acctg.

MUIR, MARK A; Eastside HS; Paterson, NJ; (3); 143/500; Chess Clb; Computer Clb; Varsity Clb; Variety Show; Var Capt Crs Cntry; Trk; Accntnt.

MUKHERJEE, MOON; Parsippany Hills HS; Parsippany, NJ; (4); FBLA; Spanish Clb; SADD; Band; Color Guard; Off Frsh Cls; Off Soph Cls; Off Jr Cls; Off Sr Cls; Hon Roll; Berkeley Schl Outstndng Achvt Bus Educ; Educ Sec Assn Awd; CUNY; Bus Admin.

MUKODA, STEPHANIE; Cumberland Regional HS; Bridgeton, NJ; (3); 12/368; JCL; Latin Clb; Model UN; Science Clb; Sec Jr Cls; Mgr(s); JV Tennis; High Hon Roll; Jr NHS; NHS; Rutgers; Phrmcy.

MULARZ, JEFFREY; Union Catholic Regional HS; Elizabeth, NJ; (4); 19/293; Ski Clb; Tennis; 2nd Hnr Role 84-86; NJ Inst Of Tech; Elec Engr.

MULBAUER, VICTORIA; Fair Lawn HS; Fair Lawn, NJ; (3); 40/341; Drama Clb; Political Wkr; VP Temple Yth Grp; School Musical; School Play; Yrbk Stf; Rep Frsh Cls; Rep Jr Cls; Rep Stu Cncl; Cmnty Wkr; Gld & Slvr Awd 86 & 87; Hnrbl Mntn 85; Fnc.

MULDER, PAMELA T; Buena Regional HS; Newfield, NJ; (2); Art Clb; Ski Clb; SADD; Rep Frsh Cls; Sec Soph Cls; Sec Jr Cls; Rep Stu Cncl; JV Cheerleading; Photogrphy.

MULFORD, AMY; John F Kennedy HS; Willingboro, NJ; (3); Drama Clb; Chorus; School Musical; School Play; Stage Crew; Cheerleading; NHS; Burlington Cnty & NJ ST Teen Arts Fstvs 85-87.

MULLAN, STACEY; Holy Cross HS; Cinnaminson, NJ; (3); Spanish Clb; SADD; Color Guard; Mrchg Band; Var Cheerleading; Var Pom Pon; JV Tennis; Hon Roll; Founder Of DAAD 86-87.

MULLANE, LISA M; Holy Family Acad; Bayonne, NJ; (4); 38/130; Sec Exploring; Pres Chorus; Church Choir; Orch; School Musical; Trs Stu Cncl; Cit Awd; Elks Awd; NHS; Music Highest Grade 86; Specl Music Awd 87; Govrnrs Schl Fnlst Music 86; Montclair ST Coll; Music Educ.

MULLEN, KEVIN; Florence Township HS; Roebling, NJ; (4); Am Leg Boys St; Church Yth Grp; FBLA; Nwsp Rptr; Nwsp Stf; Rider Coll; Accntng.

MULLENS III, JOHN; Gateway Regional HS; Wenonah, NJ; (3); 33/200; Am Leg Boys St; Church Yth Grp; Cmnty Wkr; German Clb; Science Clb; SADD; Jazz Band; Rep Stu Cncl; Var JV Ftbl; Var Capt Trk; Bio.

MULLENS, MELANIE; Gloucester Catholic HS; Sewell, NJ; (3); Dance Clb; Drama Clb; Pep Band; School Musical; Variety Show; Yrbk Phtg; Var Crs Cntry; Mgr(s); Var Trk; Hon Roll; Mst Sprtd Awd-Crss Cntry Rnng 85; 3rd Mst Imprvd-Karate Tst 85; 3rd Pl-Prchl B Chmpnshp-Crss Cntry 85; Music.

MULLER, ALLISON; Bayonne HS; Bayonne, NJ; (3); Office Aide; JV Cheerleading; Hon Roll; Fishing Club; Hostess Schl Office; Psychtry.

MULLER, SCOTT J; Secaucus HS; Secaucus, NJ; (3); Church Yth Grp; Cmnty Wkr; Math Clb; Mu Alpha Theta; Ski Clb; Varsity Clb; JV Bsbl; Var Bsktbl; Var Ftbl; Mu Alpha Theta Awd; Stevens Tech Inst; Math.

MULLIGAN, MAUREEN; St Mary HS; Rutherford, NJ; (3); Thesps; Varsity Clb; School Musical; Nwsp Rptr; Yrbk Sprt Ed; VP Stu Cncl; Capt Bsktbl; Capt Sftbl; Capt Vllybl; Trs NHS; Acdmc All Amer Schlr Pgm 85.

MULLIN, KATHLEEN; Hawthorne HS; Hawthorne, NJ; (4); 43/174; CAP; Pres Girl Scts; Band; Jazz Band; Mrchg Band; School Play; Yrbk Stf; L Mgr(s); Rotary Awd; Lbry Schlrshp 87; Grl Sct Gld Awd 86; Rutgers U; Math.

MULLINS JR, LEE W; Immaculate Conception HS; Orange, NJ; (2); Art Clb; Camera Clb; Chorus; Var Bsktbl; Trk; Wt Lftg; All Conf Bsktbl 87; Mst Imprvd Trophy Fresh Yr 86; Setor Hall U; Engl.

MULROONEY, HELEN; Middlesex HS; Middlesex, NJ; (4); 53/168; Yrbk Bus Mgr; Yrbk Ed-Chief; Yrbk Phtg; Yrbk Rptr; Yrbk Sprt Ed; Yrbk Stf; Var Stat Bsktbl; Var Powder Puff Ftbl; Var Trk; Hon Roll; The Body Schl Of Travel; Trvl.

MULVIHILL, BRIDGET; Immaculate Conception HS; Orange, NJ; (3); Art Clb; Drama Clb; Girl Scts; NFL; Pep Clb; School Play; Stage Crew; Capt Var Cheerleading; Capt Var Sftbl; Law.

MUMFORD, CAMERON T; Dickinson HS; Jersey City, NJ; (2); Nwsp Stf; Stu Cncl; Prfct Atten Awd; Merit Roll 86; Jersey City ST Coll; Comp Prgm.

MUMSCHIEW, STACEY; Cumberland Regional HS; Bridgeton, NJ; (3); Exploring; JCL; Latin Clb; Science Clb; Med.

MUND, MARY JEAN; Westfield SR HS; Westfield, NJ; (4); Art Clb; Church Yth Grp; French Clb; Hon Roll; Art Purchse Awd 86; Pro Art Awd 86; Distngshd Acdmc Achvt 87; Tulane U; Bio.

MUND, MEREDITH; Mt Olive HS; Flanders, NJ; (3); AFS; Dance Clb; FBLA; Science Clb; SADD; Varsity Clb; JV Var Cheerleading; Hon Roll; Mst Sprt Chrldng 86-87; Mst Imprvd 86; Spec Ed.

MUNDASSERY, APPU J; The Lawrenceville Schl; Princeton Jct, NJ; (4); Drama Clb; Hosp Aide; Spanish Clb; School Play; Ed Lit Mag; Rep Jr Cls; High Hon Roll; Ntl Merit SF.

MUNN, MELISSA; Cherry Hill HS West; Cherry Hill, NJ; (3); Am Leg Aux Girls St; PAVAS; Thesps; Drm Mjr(t); Orch; School Musical; School Play; Yrbk Ed-Chief; Rep Soph Cls; JV Tennis; Yrbk Faclty & Undrclssmn Edtr; Yrbk Actvts Edtr; Rutgers Coll; Secdry Ed.

MUNNA, RAJESH; Dickinson HS; Jersey City, NJ; (3); Sci Proj Awd 84; Cert For Engl Lang 84; Rutgers; Acctg.

MUNOZ, ALEX; South River HS; S River, NJ; (3); 20/150; Church Yth Grp; Ski Clb; Rep Frsh Cls; Var L Bsbl; Var L Ftbl; Hon Roll; Elec Engrng.

MUNOZ, ANITA; Hunterdon Central HS; Flemington, NJ; (2); 21/478; Intnl Clb; Frsh Cls; Soph Cls; Stu Cncl; Hon Roll; Art.

MUNSON, EUGENE; Triton Regional HS; Somerdale, NJ; (4); 2/309; Am Leg Boys St; Key Clb; Yrbk Stf; Stu Cncl; Crs Cntry; Pres NHS; Ntl Merit Schol; Sal; St Schlr; Chess Clb; Cnty Govrnmnt Smnr 84-85; U Of DE; Accntng.

MUNSON, T EUGENE; Teiton Regional HS; Somerdale, NJ; (4); 2/325; Am Leg Boys St; Key Clb; Yrbk Stf; Stu Cncl; Var Crs Cntry; Pres NHS; Ntl Merit Schol; Sal; St Schlr; Chess Clb; U DE; Accntng.

MUNVER, RAVI; Dwight Englewood Schl; Englewood Cliffs, NJ; (3); Cmnty Wkr; Hosp Aide; Math Clb; Math Tm; Ski Clb; Temple Yth Grp; Var Trk; Hon Roll; Atlntc Pacifc Math Leag 3rd Pl Schl Cert 87; Bergen Cnty Math Leag Cert Merit 87; Trck Schl Recd 87.

MUNZING JR, GEORGE R; Piscataway HS; Piscataway, NJ; (3); Hon Roll; Spanish NHS; NJIT; Elec Engnrng.

MURCHISON, TARA; Asbury Park HS; Asbury Pk, NJ; (2); 5/163; Rep Soph Cls; Var Cheerleading; High Hon Roll; Hon Roll; Varsity Scholar Awd 86-87; Math Achvmnt Awd 86-87; Lawyer.

MURDOCH, JENNIFER; St Rose HS; Manasquan, NJ; (3); 31/221; Chess Clb; VP NFL; Stat Var Bsktbl; Score Keeper; Timer; Stat Var Trk; Hon Roll; Spanish NHS; Marist Pouk NY; Psych.

MURDOCH, KAREN; Spotswood HS; Spotswood, NJ; (4); 40/189; Intnl Clb; SADD; Concert Band; Orch; Stage Crew; Symp Band; Rep Stu Cncl; Hon Roll; JP Sousa Awd; Band; Middlesex Cnty Arts HS 86; Music.

MURDOCK, RUSSELL; Bridgewater-Raritan HS West; Bridgewater, NJ; (3); FCA; FBLA; Spanish Clb; Drill Tm; Nwsp Bus Mgr; Bsktbl; Ftbl; Hon Roll; Ntl Merit Schol; Spanish NHS; Mrktng.

MURNANE, PAULA; Morris Knolls HS; Dover, NJ; (4); 29/353; Cmnty Wkr; Girl Scts; Letterman Clb; Ski Clb; Varsity Clb; Chorus; Yrbk Phtg; Yrbk Stf; Var Crs Cntry; Var Trk; Summa & Dover Gnrl Awds 87; Natl Hnr Scty 87; Clemson U; Nrsng.

MUROSKI, MATTHEW; Sayreville War Memorial HS; Parlin, NJ; (4); 121/365; Church Yth Grp; L Var Bsbl; Middlesex Cnty Coll; Engrng Sci.

MURPHY, COLLEEN; Oceantownship HS; Wanamassa, NJ; (4); 49/344; Spanish Clb; Varsity Clb; Yrbk Stf; Fld Hcky; High Hon Roll; NHS; PA ST U; Foods.

MURPHY, COREEN; Westwood HS; Washington Twns, NJ; (4); 30/220; French Clb; Band; Concert Band; Mrchg Band; Var Sftbl; CC Awd; French Hon Soc; High Hon Roll; Hon Roll; Opt Clb Awd; WA Twnshp Wmns Cntmpry Club Schlrshp 87; Fordham U; Pre-Med.

MURPHY, DARLENE; Pitman HS; Pitman, NJ; (3); 44/149; Yrbk Stf; Sec Soph Cls; Sec Stu Cncl; Var Pom Pon; JV Socr; Stat Sftbl; Hon Roll; Cntry 21 Typwrtng Awd 85-86; Bus Admnstrtn.

MURPHY, DOUG; Bon Bosco Prep; Monsey, NY; (3); 6/200; Nwsp Stf; Yrbk Stf; Lit Mag; Var L Bsbl; Var L Bsktbl; High Hon Roll; NHS; Pres Schlr; Hstry Mdl Hghst Avg 85-86.

MURPHY, ELIZABETH; West Windsor Plainsboro HS; Princeton Junct, NJ; (3); French Clb; Hosp Aide; Acpl Chr; School Musical; School Play; Variety Show; Hon Roll; Engrng.

MURPHY, ERIN; West Windsor-Plainsboro HS; Plainsboro, NJ; (2); FBLA; Radio Clb; Ski Clb; Nwsp Stf; Yrbk Stf; JV Capt Cheerleading; Score Keeper; Hon Roll; Mrktng Cmmnctn.

MURPHY, GARY; Maple Shade HS; Maple Shade, NJ; (3); 1/140; Am Leg Boys St; Boy Scts; Computer Clb; Pres Spanish Clb; Rep Sr Cls; Var Socr; High Hon Roll; Jr NHS; NHS; Rotary Yth Ldrshp Awd 87; Lawyer.

MURPHY, JESSICA E; Mount St Mary Acad; Edison, NJ; (4); 1/78; French Clb; JCL; Office Aide; Band; Symp Band; Nwsp Ed-Chief; Nwsp Rptr; Yrbk Ed-Chief; Lit Mag; French Hon Soc; Rtgrs Schlr 86; Cntrl Jrsy Rgn II Bnds 84-86; Bstn Coll Exprnc 86; Frdhm U; Svt Stdys.

MURPHY, JILL; Gloucester County Christian HS; Glassboro, NJ; (2); Church Yth Grp; Quiz Bowl; Sec Frsh Cls; Sec Soph Cls; Fld Hcky; High Hon Roll; Hon Roll.

MURPHY, JOANNA; St Rose HS; Manasquan, NJ; (3); Drama Clb; Key Clb; Library Aide; School Play; Rep Frsh Cls; JV Socr; Psychlgy.

MURPHY, JUDITH ANN; North Bergen HS; Guttenberg, NJ; (4); FHA; Girl Scts; JV Var Crs Cntry; Var JV Trk; Var Hon Roll; Athltc Awd 85; Awd Of Mrt 85; St Peters; Real Est Bus.

MURPHY, KATHLEEN; Wall HS; Wall, NJ; (3); 22/289; L Bsktbl; L Capt Fld Hcky; L Sftbl; High Hon Roll; Hon Roll; Optmtry.

MURPHY, KATHY JO; Ewing HS; Trenton, NJ; (3); Variety Show; Var Mgr(s); Var Score Keeper; Temple U; Forgn Lang.

MURPHY, KELLY; Holy Spirit HS; Margate, NJ; (4); 163/373; Stat Bsktbl; Arch.

MURPHY, MICHAEL; Sparta HS; Sparta, NJ; (3); Cmnty Wkr; Key Clb; School Play; Var Capt Socr; JV Trk; Sussex Cnty Teen Arts 85; NJ ST Teen Arts; 5th Congrssnl Dist Art 85.

MURPHY, SUZANNE; Brick Township HS; Brick Town, NJ; (3); French Clb; Ski Clb; Yrbk Stf; Var Fld Hcky; Var Powder Puff Ftbl; Trk; Hon Roll; Fashion Inst Of Tech.

MURPHY, TARA; Lenape Valley Regional HS; Andover, NJ; (3); 54/252; Key Clb; Yrbk Stf; Stu Cncl; Comm.

MURPHY, TRACEY; De Paul HS; Wayne, NJ; (3); 35/170; Cheerleading; Pom Pon; Trk; High Hon Roll; Hon Roll; Health Awd; Syracuse; Psych.

MURRAY, ARLENE; Washington Township HS; Sewell, NJ; (3); Cmnty Wkr; French Clb; Office Aide; Q&S; Science Clb; Stage Crew; Variety Show; Yrbk Stf; Lit Mag; Stat Bowling; Bus Adm.

MURRAY, CHRISTINE; West Morris Central Regional HS; Long Valley, NJ; (4); 8/289; Cmnty Wkr; Hosp Aide; Band; Concert Band; Sec Ed Yrbk Stf; Fld Hcky; High Hon Roll; Hon Roll; NHS; Ntl Merit Ltr; Outstndng Socl Stds Stu 87; Our Lady Mtn Chrch Schlrshp 87; George Washingtom U.

MURRAY, DEATRIX L; Toms River South HS; Beachwood, NJ; (3); 36/405; Drama Clb; VP Key Clb; Spanish Clb; Speech Tm; Thesps; Pres Chorus; Mrchg Band; School Musical; Yrbk Stf; NHS; Attrny.

MURRAY, GEORGENE; Manasquan HS; Brielle, NJ; (2); DECA; Drama Clb; French Clb; Thesps; Acpl Chr; Chorus; School Musical; School Play; Stage Crew; Fld Hcky.

MURRAY, HOLLY; West Deptford HS; Woodbury, NJ; (3); Key Clb; Political Wkr; Stu Cncl; Intr Dsgn.

MURRAY, MICHELE K; Millburn HS; Short Hills, NJ; (4); 23/260; Key Clb; Nwsp Rptr; Rptr Yrbk Stf; Var Capt Tennis; Ntl Merit SF; St Schlr; All St 1st Tm Grp II Tennis 1st Dbls 85-87.

MURRAY, MICHELE L; Princeton HS; Pricenton, NJ; (3); Cmnty Wkr; Pep Clb; Var Cheerleading; Stat Mgr(s); Stat Score Keeper; Clb Mbrshp Italian Clb 86-87; Accntng.

MURRAY, ROBERT; Middle Township HS; Cape May Court, NJ; (3); 16/247; Am Leg Boys St; Computer Clb; Math Tm; Science Clb; Yrbk Stf; VP Jr Cls; Im Golf; Hon Roll; NHS; Ntl Merit SF; US Army Mdln Sci & Engr Fairs 85; Atlntc Co Commt Coll Bus Sympsum Comp Prog 3rd Pl 86; NJ Sci Cert; US Naval Acad; Comp Sci.

MURRAY, RUSSEL; Don Bosco Prep HS; Hawthorne, NJ; (4); Boy Scts; Concert Band; Mrchg Band; Stage Crew; Nwsp Stf; L Trk; CC Awd; Hon Roll; NHS; Eagle Sct 85; Fordham U; Bus.

MURRAY, SEAN P; West Essex Regional HS; Roseland, NJ; (2); Church Yth Grp; French Clb; Band; Concert Band; Jazz Band; Mrchg Band; Symp Band; JV Bsktbl; Socr; Hon Roll; Yth Of Amer Hon Band 87; Villanova; Law.

MURRAY, THEODORE; Admiral Farragut Acad; Manasquan, NJ; (3); 14/37; Boy Scts; Church Yth Grp; ROTC; Band; JV Bsktbl; Law Enfrcmnt.

MURRAY, TIM; Bishop George Ahr HS; Iselin, NJ; (4); 45/267; Yrbk Sprt Ed; Bsktbl; Var JV Ftbl; Hon Roll; Yrbk Achvt Awd & Acdmc Hnr Roll 87.

MURRRAY, BRAD; West Windsor-Plainsboro HS; Princeton Junct, NJ; (3); Model UN; Spanish Clb; Variety Show; JV Crs Cntry; JV Ftbl; JV Trk; High Hon Roll; Hon Roll; Audo Engrng.

MURSCHELL, JASON; Paulsboro HS; Gibbstown, NJ; (3); 25/150; Boy Scts; Library Aide; School Musical; Nwsp Rptr; Sec Jr Cls; JV Crs Cntry; JV Trk; JV Wrstlng; Hon Roll; Engr.

MURSCHELL II, WAYNE M; Pitman HS; Pitman, NJ; (4); 59/150; Cmnty Wkr; FCA; Key Clb; Political Wkr; Varsity Clb; VP Capt Socr; VP Capt Wrstlng; Bus Mgmt.

MURTHA, NOREEN; Manasquan HS; Belmar, NJ; (2); Church Yth Grp; Drama Clb; Color Guard; School Musical; School Play; Stage Crew; Lit Mag; Stat Bsbl; Stat Bsktbl; Hon Roll; Educ.

MURZENSKI, STEVEN; Linden HS; Linden, NJ; (3); Cmnty Wkr; German Clb; Political Wkr; Wt Lftg; Hon Roll; Natl Sci Olpympd Bio 87; Crmnl Jstc.

MUSACCHIO, DONALD J; Colonia HS; Colonia, NJ; (3); 22/302; Boy Scts; Debate Tm; NFL; Quiz Bowl; Pres Science Clb; Band; Concert Band; Jazz Band; Mrchg Band; Orch; Rutgers Coll; Cermc Engrng.

MUSCARELLE, DANIELLE; Clifton SR HS; Clifton, NJ; (4); DECA; Girl Scts; Chorus; Hnrb Mntn NJ DECA Regional Rest Mgt 87; Banking.

MUSICO, LARRY; Passaic Valley HS; W Paterson, NJ; (2); Rep Soph Cls; Bsbl; Hon Roll; Rutgers; Med.

MUSILLO, TERESA; Paterson Catholic HS; Paterson, NJ; (3); Camera Clb; French Clb; Powder Puff Ftbl; Hon Roll; Law.

MUSKETT, ANTONIA; Cinnaminson HS; Cinnaminson, NJ; (3); Art Clb; Church Yth Grp; Dance Clb; DECA; Drama Clb; FBLA; Intnl Clb; PAVAS; Ski Clb; SADD; S Blue VP Or NJ Dist Ed Clbs Of Amer 87-88; JR Rotnan Intrct Clb 87; Mrktng.

MUSSER, ERICA LYNN; Williamston HS; Williamstown, NJ; (4); 6/269; Am Leg Aux Girls St; French Clb; Nwsp Stf; Lit Mag; JV Var Fld Hcky; Hon Roll; NHS; Pres Schlr; Rotary Awd; Voice Dem Awd; Schlrs Pgm Kennedy Memorial Hosp 86-87; SICO 4000 Awd For Millersville U 87; Millersville U; Biology.

MUSTER, MARLO; Middletown H S South; Lincroft, NJ; (4); 14/470; School Musical; Variety Show; Lit Mag; Capt JV Cheerleading; JV Var Socr; Trk; Vllybl; High Hon Roll; Trs NHS; St Schlr; Bio.

MUSTO, BARBARA; Long Branch HS; Long Branch, NJ; (4); 12/247; Church Yth Grp; Drama Clb; Girl Scts; Key Clb; NFL; Speech Tm; Chorus; School Play; Yrbk Bus Mgr; Yrbk Phtg; Var Schlr Awd 85; Natl Forensic Dist Fnlst 86; Cmmnctns.

MUSTO, DINA; Paramus Catholic Girls HS; Little Ferry, NJ; (2); 3/157; Cheerleading; Trk; Sal; Prfct Atten Awd; Drama Clb; VP Frsh Cls; Soph Cls; Prncpls Lst & 1st Hnrs 86-87; Cert For Prfcncy In Thlgy 87; Law.

MUSTO, MICHELE; Manalapan HS; Manalapan, NJ; (3); 62/429; JV Gym; JV Capt Socr; Hon Roll; Bus Mgmt.

MUSUMECI, GINA; St James HS; Swedesboro, NJ; (4); 11/68; Yrbk Stf; Pres Frsh Cls; Pres Jr Cls; Stat Bsbl; Var Cheerleading; Rotary Awd; Church Yth Grp; SADD; School Musical; Stu Gvrnmnt Awd 87; La Salle U; Mrktng.

MUTH, DAVID; West Morris Central HS; Long Valley, NJ; (4); Sec FBLA; Hon Roll; Bus Ed Wad 87; IN ST U; Sci.

MUTH, ROBERT; Mount Olive HS; Hackettstown, NJ; (4); 9/275; Drm Mjr(t); Jazz Band; Mrchg Band; School Musical; Symp Band; High Hon Roll; Hon Roll; NHS; St Schlr; Math Clb; NJ Dstngshd Schlr 87; Louis Armstrong Jazz Awd 86; All Area Brd 87; Stevens Inst Of Tech; Elec Engr.

MUUSS, THERESA A; Edison HS; Edison, NJ; (4); 32/493; Pres Drama Clb; Key Clb; Spanish Clb; Chorus; School Play; Variety Show; Nwsp Stf; NHS; Spanish NHS; Kean Coll; Theatr.

MUZAFFAR, AYESHA; Mullica Hill-Friends HS; Woodstown, NJ; (4); 2/10; Cmnty Wkr; Dance Clb; Hosp Aide; Model UN; Yrbk Phtg; Yrbk Stf; Off Soph Cls; Off Jr Cls; Mgr(s); Score Keeper; Miss TEEN NJH 1st Rnnr-Up 86; George Washington U; Sci.

MUZYK, DAWN; Princeton HS; Princeton, NJ; (2); CAP; Debate Tm; Band; Drill Tm; Orch; Symp Band; Lit Mag; JV Bsktbl; Lcrss; JV Trk; USAF Acad; Pilot.

MYERS, AMY; John F Kennedy HS; Willingboro, NJ; (3); 28/300; FBLA; Hosp Aide; Concert Band; Mrchg Band; Orch; Mgr(s); Hon Roll.

MYERS, AMY; Lower Cape May Regional HS; Erma, NJ; (3); Church Yth Grp; SADD; Teachers Aide; Chorus; Church Choir; School Musical; Stage Crew; Swing Chorus; Yrbk Bus Mgr; Hon Roll; Lawyer.

MYERS, BRIAN G; Gloucester HS; Gloucester, NJ; (3); Am Leg Boys St; German Clb; School Play; Rep Frsh Cls; Rep Soph Cls; Trs Jr Cls; Stu Cncl; Im Bsktbl; Capt Socr; Var Tennis; Bst Actr Awd-1 Act Plays 85 & 86; Acctg.

MYERS, ELIZABETH C; Somerville HS; Somerville, NJ; (4); Dance Clb; Drama Clb; SADD; Thesps; Acpl Chr; Color Guard; School Musical; School Play; Yrbk Rptr; Hon Roll; Most Outstndng Achvt 87; Silver Poet Awd 87; Douglass Coll; Jrnlsm.

MYERS, IRENE ROCHELLE; Gloucester City JR SR HS; Gloucester, NJ; (4); 5/147; Chorus; Capt Color Guard; Concert Band; Drm Mjr(t); Flag Corp; Mrchg Band; School Play; Capt Bowling; Sftbl; NHS; Louis Stief Mem Schlrshp, Jean Walker Mem Schlrshp 87; Kean Coll; Physcl Thrpy.

MYERS, LENON PAGE; Timothy Christian HS; Piscataway, NJ; (3); Church Yth Grp; Computer Clb; Ski Clb; Pres Frsh Cls; Var Bsbl; JV Capt Bsktbl; Var Socr; High Hon Roll; Hon Roll; Bus Admin.

MYERS, MARCIA; Clayton High HS; Clayton, NJ; (4); 3/75; Am Leg Aux Girls St; Key Clb; School Play; Nwsp Rptr; Yrbk Rptr; Pres Soph Cls; Pres Jr Cls; Pres Sr Cls; Stu Cncl; NHS; Garden ST Distngshd Schlr 86; Rutgers Schlr 86; Studnt Of Mnth 85; Eng.

MYERS, MARK; Holy Cross HS; Willingboro, NJ; (3); Jr Cls; JV Var Bsktbl; Var Trk; Willingboro Twnshp Yth Achvt Awd 86; Burlington Cnty All Str Trck 2nd Tm 87; Natl Hnr Rl 87; Envrnmtl Engrng.

MYERS, MARSHANETTE; Plainfield HS; Plainfield, NJ; (3); Chorus; Trk; Wt Lftg; Hon Roll; Trenton ST Coll; Crmnl Law.

MYERS, MATT; Delran HS; Delran, NJ; (4); Nwsp Rptr; Var Socr; Hon Roll; Lynchburg Coll Schlrshp 87-88; Lynchburg Coll; Bus Mgmnt.

MYERS, SCOTT; St James HS; Swedesboro, NJ; (2); Church Yth Grp; Bsktbl; Ftbl; Kiwanis Awd.

MYTROWITZ, CHERYL; John P Stevens HS; Edison, NJ; (3); Varsity Clb; Rep Frsh Cls; Var Bsktbl; Powder Puff Ftbl; Sftbl.

NACION, ROMUALD; St Marys HS; Jersey City, NJ; (3); 30/105; Drama Clb; Pep Clb; SADD; Varsity Clb; School Musical; Socr; Im Tennis; Chorus; Church Choir; School Play; Pre Cep Prog St Peters Coll Schlrshp 86-88; Prep Prog Georgetown U Schlrshp 87; Georgetown U; Bus.

NADDEO, LISA; Brick Township Memorial HS; Brick, NJ; (3); Intnl Clb; Variety Show; Rep Soph Cls; Pom Pon; JV Socr; Var Trk; High Hon Roll; Gym Shw JR Cls Capt; Teen Arts Fstvl; Mock Trial; Bus.

NAGANAND, MANEESH; Emerson HS; Union City, NJ; (4); 14/280; Chess Clb; Pres Computer Clb; Debate Tm; Nwsp Stf; Yrbk Stf; Rep Stu Cncl; Bausch & Lomb Sci Awd; French Hon Soc; Hon Roll; Pres Schlr; Edison Schl PTA Awd 87; Faculty Schlr Book Awd 87; Stevens Inst Of Tech; Elec Eng.

NAGATSUKA, GEORGE; Ocean City HS; Ocean View, NJ; (3); 11/341; Trs Am Leg Boys St; Sec Church Yth Grp; Latin Clb; Math Clb; Science Clb; Var L Wrstlng; High Hon Roll; Hst NHS; US Navel Acad; Sci.

NAGLE, JENNIFER; Paul IV HS; Voorhees, NJ; (4); 22/503; VP French Clb; Rep Frsh Cls; Var Bsktbl; Im Bowling; French Hon Soc; Hon Roll; Natl Frnch Cont Awd 84-85; Bio.

NAGLE, KARA; Manasquan HS; Spring Lake Hts, NJ; (3); Sec Drama Clb; French Clb; Latin Clb; Spanish Clb; Thesps; Pres Chorus; Stage Crew; Hon Roll; Kiwanis Awd; NHS; Brd Of Educ Awd; Fshn Merch.

NAGLER, ANASTASIA; Ambassoador Christian Acad; Gibbstown, NJ; (4); 1/14; Yrbk Ed-Chief; Pres Sr Cls; Pres Stu Cncl; High Hon Roll; Pres NHS; Val; Church Yth Grp; Exploring; Trs 4-H; Frsh Cls; Pres Scholar St Josephs U 87; Gorden ST Dstnghsd Schlr 87; Good Samaritan Awd 86; St Josephs U; Pre-Med.

NAGY, CHRISTOPHER J; Montville Township HS; Montville, NJ; (3); 49/276; Concert Band; Jazz Band; Mrchg Band; School Musical; Nwsp Phtg; Rep Frsh Cls; Rep Soph Cls; Rep Jr Cls; Trk; High Hon Roll; Acolyte Svc Awd Bible Prsntd For Srvng 79-86; Pltcl Sci.

NAGY, DONNA; Paramus Catholic HS; Fairlawn, NJ; (4); Art Clb; Cmnty Wkr; Dance Clb; Drama Clb; Ski Clb; School Musical; Variety Show; Nwsp Rptr; Rep Frsh Cls; Hon Roll; Outstndng Achvt Awd Schl Arts 86; Awd Mss NJ USA Pgnt 86; William Paterson Coll; Cmmnctns.

NAGY, JEANETTE; Mc Corristin HS; Wrightstown, NJ; (3); Pres Pep Clb; Rep Jr Cls; Rep Sr Cls; JV NHS; Hstry.

NAHAS, SARA; Chatham Township HS; Chatham, NJ; (2); Church Yth Grp; Chorus; School Musical; Swing Chorus; Yrbk Stf; Pres Jr Cls; Rep Stu Cncl; JV Fld Hcky; JV Lcrss.

NAIK, AMISH; Randolph HS; Randolph, NJ; (3); 19/350; Am Leg Boys St; Math Clb; Ski Clb; Yrbk Stf; Im Bsbl; Var Ftbl; Wt Lftg; High Hon Roll; Hon Roll; NHS; Bus Admn.

NAIK, ARPANA; Hackettstown HS; Hackettstown, NJ; (3); 1/191; Q&S; Drm & Bgl; Stu Cncl; Gov Hon Prg Awd; High Hon Roll; NHS; Ntl Merit Ltr; Church Yth Grp; Cmnty Wkr; Drama Clb; Nwspr Copy Editor 86-87; Key Of Knowledge JR Val 86-87; Yth For Understandg Corporate Schlrshp 87; Medicine.

NAIMOLI, DENISE; Washington Township HS; Blackwood, NJ; (3); Girl Scts; JV Fld Hcky; Hon Roll; Bus.

NAIPAWER, MICHELE; Immaculate Conception HS; Wallington, NJ; (4); 1/92; NFL; Q&S; Pres Speech Tm; Nwsp Stf; Rep Frsh Cls; Rep Soph Cls; High Hon Roll; NHS; NEDT Awd; Intl Pltcs.

NAJARIAN, DAVID; Hudson Catholic HS; Jersey City, NJ; (3); 60/203; Cmnty Wkr; Varsity Clb; Stu Cncl; Bsbl; Ftbl; Wt Lftg; Hon Roll; Rutgers; Bio Tchr.

NAJWER, KATHERINE; Morristown HS; Morristown, NJ; (2); Art Clb; Dance Clb; Hosp Aide; Ski Clb; Chorus; Hon Roll; Part Time Job 86-87; Hosp Volunteer; Exploring Med Prog Morristown Memrl Hosp.

NALEY, BRUCE; J P Stevens HS; Edison, NJ; (3); Boy Scts; Exploring; Science Clb; Ski Clb; Band; Concert Band; Mrchg Band; Var Trk; French Hon Soc; Hon Roll; Eagle Sct 86; Natl Ygh Sci Cmp 87; Sci.

NALLY, CLARA; Bayonne HS; Bayonne, NJ; (3); Church Yth Grp; Hosp Aide; Key Clb; Ski Clb; Yrbk Stf; Fashion Buyer.

NAM, SOEUN; Parsippany HS; Lake Hiawatha, NJ; (3); Church Yth Grp; FBLA; Intnl Clb; Spanish Clb; Yrbk Stf; Prfct Atten Awd; 2nd Pl Trphy Ping Pong Chrch Yth Grp Trnmnt 86; 2nd Pl Yth Grp Vllybl Trnmnt 85; Rutgers U; Math.

NANFELDT, CHRISTINE; St John Vianney HS; Holmdel, NJ; (2); 47/300; Church Yth Grp; Drama Clb; Hosp Aide; Service Clb; Stage Crew; Nwsp Rptr; High Hon Roll; Mdcl Explrs Post 727 VP 87; Chrch Lector 83-87; Offc Radio Anncr; Med.

NANNI, KIMBERLY SUE; Delaware Valley Regional HS; Frenchtown, NJ; (4); Art Clb; Ski Clb; Yrbk Rptr; Yrbk Stf; Lit Mag; JV Bsktbl; Trk; Awd Prtcptn Teen Arts Fstvl 85-87; Art Inst Of PA; Visul Cmmnctns.

NAPARANO, DENISE; Mary Help Of Christians Acad; Paterson, NJ; (3); Computer Clb; Office Aide; Service Clb; SADD; Chorus; Hon Roll.

NAPIWOCKI, SHARON L; Roxbury HS; Succasunna, NJ; (3); 40/425; Pres 4-H; Art Clb; Orch; 4-H Awd; Hon Roll; Acdmc Awds GPA 3.692 85-86.

NAPODANO, GINA; Passaic Valley HS; W Paterson, NJ; (4); Key Clb; Hon Roll; Amer Bus Acad Schlrshp 87; Ammeron Bus Acad; Crt Reporting.

NAPOLEON, DENISE; South Plainfield HS; S Plainfield, NJ; (3); Mrchg Band; Yrbk Stf; Sec Frsh Cls; Sec Soph Cls; Sec Jr Cls; Rep Stu Cncl; Var Cheerleading; JV Sftbl; NHS; Spanish NHS; Bus.

NAPOLI, ELIZABETH; St James HS; Gibbstown, NJ; (1); 5/73; Art Clb; JV Bsktbl; JV Sftbl; High Hon Roll; NHS; Ntl Merit Schol; VFW Awd.

NAPOLI, KAREN; St Pius X Regional HS; Milltown, NJ; (4); 13/108; Teachers Aide; Chorus; Madrigals; School Musical; School Play; Variety Show; Score Keeper; French Hon Soc; Hon Roll; NHS; Bishops Awd Excllnc Religion 87; Hnrs Stu 87; Glassboro St Coll; Teacher.

NAPOLI, PETER C; Salem HS; Salem, NJ; (4); 2/170; Am Leg Boys St; Computer Clb; Pres JA; Math Tm; VP Sr Cls; Off Stu Cncl; Bsbl; Capt Ftbl; Wrstlng; Elks Awd; Garden ST Distngshd Schlr, Elks Fndtn Schlrshp 87; All Acdmc Tm Ftbl 86-87; Rutgers U; Ecnmcs.

NAPOLIELLO, DENNIS; Morris Catholic HS; Ironia, NJ; (3); 46/135; Boy Scts; Church Yth Grp; Cmnty Wkr; French Clb; Pep Clb; Ski Clb; Varsity Clb; Variety Show; JV Bsbl; JV Bsktbl; Hon Roll 86-87; Bus.

NAPOLITANO, JANINE; Paamus Catholic Girls Regional HS; Wood Ridge, NJ; (2); Cmnty Wkr; Dance Clb; FBLA; Lit Mag; Hon Roll; Pres Acdmc Awd 85; 8 Yrs Piano Stdy.

NAPOLITANO, KIM; Secaucus HS; Secaucus, NJ; (2); 4/130; Key Clb; Mu Alpha Theta; Spanish Clb; Tennis; High Hon Roll; Jr NHS; ROGATE John Hopkins Gftd & Tlntd Prgm 85-87.

NAPP, SUSAN; Manchester Regional HS; Prospect Pk, NJ; (3); Chorus; Concert Band; Madrigals; Mrchg Band; Vllybl.

NAPPI, STEPHANIE; Manosquan HS; Manasquan, NJ; (2); 15/247; Drama Clb; Math Tm; Spanish Clb; Color Guard; JV Cheerleading; Twrlr; High Hon Roll; Kiwanis Awd; Elem Tchr.

NARCISI, JOSEPHINE; Bayonne HS; Bayonne, NJ; (3); Intnl Clb; Science Clb; Band; Concert Band; Drill Tm; Mrchg Band; Orch; Hon Roll; Pre-Med.

NARDI, CHRIS; Morris Catholic HS; Lake Hopatcong, NJ; (1); 67/156; JV Bsbl; JV Bsktbl.

NASEEF III, GEORGE S; Parsippany Hills HS; Parsippany, NJ; (3); Chess Clb; FBLA; Bsbl; Ftbl; Boston U; Pre Med.

NASH, BRIAN; Christian Brothers Acad; Neptune City, NJ; (4); Hosp Aide; Stage Crew; Nwsp Stf; Im Bsktbl; Im Capt Socr; Im Sftbl; Hon Roll; Intl Union Oprtng Engrs Schlrshp Wnnr; Providence Coll; Lbrl Arts.

NASH, CHRISTINE; University HS; Newark, NJ; (2); Church Yth Grp; Cmnty Wkr; English Clb; Spanish Clb; Chorus; Church Choir; School Play; Variety Show; Yrbk Stf; Sec Soph Cls.

NASH, SIBYLLA; Neptune SR HS; Neptune, NJ; (3); 84/359; Drama Clb; FTA; Girl Scts; Teachers Aide; School Play; Stage Crew; Lit Mag; Trs Jr Cls; Hon Roll; Prfct Atten Awd; Delegate Ms Teen NJ Pgnt 87; Cmpltd John Roberts Powers Mdlng Schl; Mass Media.

NASKIEWICZ, JASON; John F Kennedy HS; Willingboro, NJ; (2); 1/300; Key Clb; Im Bsbl; JV Var Socr; Swmmng; High Hon Roll; Hon Roll; NHS; Bus.

NATALE, FILOMENA; Bridgewater Raritan HS West; Raritan, NJ; (4); Spanish Clb; Concert Band; Mrchg Band; Pep Band; Nwsp Stf; Mgr(s); Hon Roll; Lion Awd; NHS; Pres Acdmc Fit Awd 87; Brdgwatr Rartn HS West Achvt Bus Ed & PTO Jt Schlrshp Fnd 87; U Of Scranton; Mktg.

NATALE, PATRICK; Summit HS; Summit, NJ; (3); Computer Clb; Varsity Clb; Rep Frsh Cls; Bsbl; Ftbl; Im Wt Lftg; Var Wrstlng; Var Hon Roll; Dist II Champ Wrstlg 87; Comp Sci.

NATHAN, EDWARD; Manalapan HS; Englishtown, NJ; (4); 40/425; Temple Yth Grp; Madrigals; School Play; Nwsp Rptr; Ftbl; Wrstlng; NHS; Variety Show; Wt Lftg; Pres Awd Acad Fit 87; Garden ST Dstngshd Schlrs Awd 87; Rutgers Coll; Psych.

NATHANSON, CORTNEY; John P Stevens HS; Edison, NJ; (3); Exploring; Key Clb; VP Temple Yth Grp; Concert Band; Yrbk Stf; Rep Frsh Cls; Rep Soph Cls; Pom Pon; Powder Puff Ftbl; Hon Roll; Vrsty Ltr 3 Yrs Pompom Sqd/Mrchng Band 84-87; Appntd Stu Advsr 1991 Cls 87-88; Advrtsng.

NATHANSON, ERIC; Atlantic City HS; Ventnor, NJ; (3); Model UN; Office Aide; Spanish Clb; Sec Jr Cls; Hon Roll; Vars Ltr Insignia Crew 85-86; Med.

NATICCHIA, STEPHANIE; Haddonfield Memorial HS; Haddonfield, NJ; (4); Pres Intnl Clb; Sec Frsh Cls; Rep Stu Cncl; Var Capt Bsktbl; Var Capt Fld Hcky; Var Capt Trk; Cit Awd; Hon Roll; NHS; Spanish NHS; Offnsv Plyr Yr Fld Hcky 86; DAR Swng Cont 1st Pl 83; All S Jersey Fld Hcky Team 85-86; Pre-Med.

NATOLI, WILLIAM; Highland Regional HS; Erial, NJ; (4); Im JV Bsbl; JV Var Ftbl; JV Var Socr; JV Wrstlng; Bys Intrct; Widener U; Cvl Engr.

NAU, WESLEY; Hightstown HS; Hightstown, NJ; (3); Boy Scts; Cmnty Wkr; French Clb; Ski Clb; SADD; Rep Stu Cncl; Im Ice Hcky; High Hon Roll; Hon Roll; Lehigh; Engrng.

NAUGHTON, LISA; Central Regional HS; Bayville, NJ; (3); Drama Clb; Chorus; Stage Crew; Bsktbl; Fld Hcky; Vllybl.

NAUMCHIK, THERESA; Dover HS; Dover, NJ; (3); Chorus; High Hon Roll; Hon Roll; County Coll Of Morris; Radiolog.

NAUTA, THOMAS; Lenape Valley Reg HS; Andover, NJ; (3); 10/224; Var Bsbl; JV Ftbl; Im Wt Lftg; Cit Awd; High Hon Roll; Hon Roll; NHS; German Honor Scty 87; Lenape Schlr Awd 86; Engr.

NAVARRO, ADRIANA; St Joseph Of The Palisades HS; Union City, NJ; (2); Church Yth Grp; Spanish Clb; Var Diving; Var Swmmng; Hon Roll; Tchng.

NAVARRO, CHRYSTAL A; Lakewood HS; Lakewood, NJ; (3); 51/357; Hosp Aide; Spanish Clb; Band; Concert Band; Symp Band; Rep Frsh Cls; Rep Soph Cls; Rep Jr Cls; Var Bsktbl; JV Mgr(s); All ST Grp III Girls Bsktbl 86-87; Personal Mgmt.

NAVARRO, JOEL; West Essex HS; Fairfield, NJ; (3); Boy Scts; Chess Clb; Science Clb; Varsity Clb; Var JV Bsktbl; Var JV Socr; Var Trk; Hon Roll; Med.

NAVAS, JULIO C; Ocean Township HS; Ocean, NJ; (4); 26/320; Chess Clb; Computer Clb; Ski Clb; Band; Concert Band; Mrchg Band; Trk; High Hon Roll; NHS; St Schlr; Spartan Schlr 84-86; Ntl Hispanic Schlrshp Awd 87; Cmptr Comp 1st Pl 84; Engrng.

NAVON, AMY; Hillsborough HS; Somerville, NJ; (3); 32/328; Camera Clb; Hosp Aide; Library Aide; Ski Clb; SADD; Temple Yth Grp; JV Bsktbl; Crs Cntry; Powder Puff Ftbl; Hon Roll; Phys Thrpst.

NAYAR, NARAYAN; West Essex HS; No Caldwell, NJ; (3); Rep Stu Cncl; Var Tennis; NHS.

NAYLOR, BONNIE; Riverside HS; Riverside, NJ; (4); 20/74; DECA; Hon Roll; DEAC Coop & Ed Awd 87; Zurbrug Mem Hosp Scholar Med Assn 87; Delanco PTA Mst Imprvd Stu 87; Harcum JC; Anim Hlth Tech.

NAYLOR, CRAIG; Woodstown HS; Woodstown, NJ; (4); 4/220; Am Leg Boys St; Off Jr Cls; Off Sr Cls; Swmmng; DAR Awd; High Hon Roll; Hon Roll; NHS; Pres Schlr; US Naval Acad.

NAZAROK, BRET; Haddon Township HS; Westmont, NJ; (3); Varsity Clb; Nwsp Stf; Rep Frsh Cls; Rep Soph Cls; Im Bsbl; Var Golf; Var Gym; Var Wrstlng; Hon Roll; Bus.

NAZZARETTO, TERESA; Bergen County Vo-Tech HS; Fairlawn, NJ; (2); AFS; Church Yth Grp; Cmnty Wkr; Computer Clb; Drama Clb; English Clb; Hosp Aide; Key Clb; Pep Clb; Varsity Clb; Med.

NEALL, LESLIE; Ocean City HS; Ocean City, NJ; (3); 8/341; Dance Clb; Drama Clb; Model UN; Spanish Clb; Variety Show; Rep Frsh Cls; Rep Soph Cls; Rep Jr Cls; Rep Stu Cncl; Cheerleading; Rotary Clb Stu Yr 86-87; Gifted & Talented Awd 84-85; Psych.

NEALON, JOSEPH; St Joseph Regional HS; Spring Valley, NY; (4); 45/180; Church Yth Grp; SADD; Rep Stu Cncl; Bsktbl; Capt Var Socr; Capt Var Trk; Spanish NHS; Brian Maher Mem Schlrshp Sccr 87; Duquesne U; Bus.

NEBEL, NICOLE; West Milford Township HS; West Milford, NJ; (4); 26/359; Nwsp Bus Mgr; Nwsp Ed-Chief; Nwsp Rptr; Yrbk Rptr; Rep Stu Cncl; High Hon Roll; Hon Roll; NHS; Hnrbl Mntn NJ Dstngsh Schlr 87; Marktng.

NEELY, DEBORAH; Weequahic HS; Newark, NJ; (4); 8/347; Sec Church Yth Grp; Exploring; Pres Band; Concert Band; Pres Mrchg Band; Pres Frsh Cls; VP Soph Cls; Jr NHS; NHS; Rutgers; Bus.

NEGRIN, JOANNE; John F Kennedy HS; Willingboro, NJ; (4); 12/270; Pres Intnl Clb; Concert Band; Mrchg Band; Yrbk Ed-Chief; Yrbk Stf; Mgr Socr; Mgr Sftbl; Gov Hon Prg Awd; High Hon Roll; Hon Roll; Amer U Pres Scholar 87; 8th Pl Regnl Part Natl French Exam 85; 1st Pl Dist Spellng Bee 86; American U; Intl Rltns.

NEGRON, ANA L; Dover HS; Dover, NJ; (4); 27/187; Hon Roll; Rutgers U; Nrsg.

NEHILA, NANCY; Howell HS; Howell, NJ; (3); French Clb; Chorus; Color Guard; School Play; Howell Music Parents Awd 86; Sci & Engrng Prog Brookdane CC 86; Rutgers Schl; Sci Engr.

NEILAN, SIOBHAN; Morris Catholic HS; Mount Tabor, NJ; (1); 24/156; Church Yth Grp; Hosp Aide; Band; Hon Roll; Law.

NEIMAN, DAVID; Paul VI HS; Clementon, NJ; (3); Nwsp Rptr; Nwsp Sprt Ed; Soph Cls; Jr Cls; L Capt Bsbl; L Capt Ftbl; L Capt Wrstlng; VFW Awd; Church Yth Grp; Acadc All Am 87; Athltc All Am 87; Capt Of Ftbl, Wrstlng, & Basbl Tms 87 & 88; Pre-Law.

NEIVERT, EDNA W; Columbia HS; Maplewood, NJ; (4); Dance Clb; Hosp Aide; Capt L Crs Cntry; Capt L Swmmng; Ntl Merit SF; St Schlr; German Clb; Intnl Clb; Latin Clb; Variety Show; Brown U Book Awd 86; Garden ST Dstngshd Schlr 86; Internatl Rltns.

NELL, MARY KAY; Holy Spirit HS; Absecon, NJ; (3); 47/332; Spanish Clb; High Hon Roll; Hon Roll; Penn ST; Zoology.

NELLANY, JENNIFER; Paul VI HS; Deptford, NJ; (3); 42/420; Math Clb; NFL; Spanish Clb; Trs Stu Cncl; JV Cheerleading; JV Fld Hcky; Im Powder Puff Ftbl; Hon Roll; NHS; Spanish NHS; Acctng.

NELSON, CHERYL A; Parsippany HS; Parsippany, NJ; (4); 192/374; Church Yth Grp; Drama Clb; FBLA; OEA; Church Choir; Ed Secrs Assn Awd 87; PTA Schlrshp & N Thurmond Lattimore Awd 87; Greggs Shrthnd Spd Awd 87; Cnty Coll Morris; Bus Adm.

NELSON, CORNELL; Mc Corristin Catholic HS; Trenton, NJ; (3); Am Leg Boys St; Church Yth Grp; FCA; JA; Church Choir; Yrbk Stf; Var L Bsktbl; Hon Roll; Comp.

NELSON, DAVID S; Woodstown HS; Woodstown, NJ; (3); Computer Clb; German Clb; Key Clb; Ski Clb; Var Bsbl; Ftbl; Var Capt Wrstlng; LAW.

NELSON, DAWN; Indian Hills HS; Oakland, NJ; (3); 110/306; Cmnty Wkr; Debate Tm; Spanish Clb; Varsity Clb; Nwsp Stf; Yrbk Stf; Mgr(s); L Trk; Hon Roll; Crmnl Justice.

NELSON, DENIS; Pequannock Township HS; Pequannock, NJ; (3); 30/220; Boys Clb Am; JV Var Ftbl; Wt Lftg; JV Var Wrstlng; Hon Roll; NHS; Bus Adm.

NELSON, DONYALE Y; Cherry Hill H S West; Cherry Hill, NJ; (3); 50/340; French Clb; Rep Frsh Cls; Var Cheerleading; Trk; Hon Roll; Rutgers Deans Summer Schlrs Prog 87; AB Hnr Roll 85-87; Ped.

NELSON, GINA; Linden HS; Linden, NJ; (3); Church Yth Grp; Girl Scts; Hosp Aide; Pep Clb; Drill Tm; Var Bsktbl; Var Cheerleading; Var Pom Pon; Gov Hon Prg Awd; Stonewall; Banking.

NELSON, GREGORY; Hackettstown HS; Hackettstown, NJ; (2); Church Yth Grp; Key Clb; JV Bsbl; Fncng JR Awd 86-87; Mth.

NELSON, JESSE; Audubon HS; Audubon, NJ; (3); Varsity Clb; Socr; Hon Roll; Cmmnctns.

NELSON, KELLI; A P Schalick HS; Elmer, NJ; (3); 7/120; Math Tm; Spanish Clb; Trs Soph Cls; VP Stu Cncl; Mat Maids; JV Stat Socr; Hon Roll; NHS; SADD; Variety Show; Chld Psychlgy.

NELSON, KENNETH; Arthur L Johnson Regional HS; Clark, NJ; (3); Boy Scts; Church Yth Grp; Stat Bsbl; JV Bsktbl; JV Var Ftbl; Var Trk; Im Wt Lftg; God Cntry Awd.

NELSON, SIMONE; West Essex Regional HS; North Caldwell, NJ; (4); 21/349; Am Leg Aux Girls St; Drama Clb; Thesps; School Musical; School Play; Lit Mag; Var Cheerleading; French Hon Soc; NHS; Ntl Merit Ltr; Frnkln & Mrshl Coll Bk Prz Of Exc In Hmnts 87; Outstndng Achvt In Scl Stdys Awd 87; Nrthwstrn U; Theatre.

NELSON, TIM D; John F Kennedy HS; Willingboro, NJ; (2); #5 In Class; NAACP; Science Clb; Concert Band; Mrchg Band; Orch; Pep Band; School Musical; Symp Band; Hon Roll; Jr NHS; 2nd Spllng Bee 86; 1st Phila Inqr Spllng Bee 85; Sctn Ldr Mrchng Band 87; Princeton U; Mech Engrng.

NELSON, TINA MARIE; Sussex Vo Tech; Stanhope, NJ; (3); Hosp Aide; SADD; Drm & Bgl; Off Stu Cncl; Gym; Mgr(s); Hon Roll; Safty Cmte Ofcr; Dover Bus Coll; Law.

NEMETH, ANDREA; Clifton HS; Clifton, NJ; (3); Am Leg Aux Girls St; German Clb; Girl Scts; Library Aide; Chorus; Nwsp Rptr; Nwsp Stf; Hon Roll; Jr NHS; Hnr Grd; Pharm.

NEMETH, MICHELLE; John P Stevens HS; Edison, NJ; (3); Acpl Chr; Chorus; Drm Mjr(t); Mrchg Band; Rep Jr Cls; Pom Pon; Hon Roll; All ST Chorus 87; Region II Chorus 85; Baylor U; Surgeon.

NERI, MICHAEL L; Vineland SR HS; Vineland, NJ; (3); Church Yth Grp; Pep Clb; Red Cross Aide; Trs Science Clb; JV Bsbl; JV Bsktbl; JV Tennis; Hon Roll; Lawyer.

NESBITT, DONALD; Riverside HS; Delanco, NJ; (3); 6/101; FTA; Concert Band; Jazz Band; Hon Roll; NHS; Drama Clb; Trs Band; Drm Mjr(t); Mrchg Band; School Musical; Math Educ.

NESMITH, ARETHA; Woodrow Wilson HS; Camden, NJ; (4); Aud/Vis; Cmnty Wkr; Computer Clb; Drama Clb; FTA; Key Clb; Library Aide; Ski Clb; Church Choir.

NESTER, MEREDITH; Maple Shade HS; Maple Shade, NJ; (4); Church Yth Grp; DECA; Yrbk Stf; Rep Frsh Cls; Rep Soph Cls; Rep Jr Cls; Rep Sr Cls; Rep Stu Cncl; JV Cheerleading; High Hon Roll; Full Svc Rest Mrktng NJ St DECA Comptn 87; Achvmnt Of Excel Awd Natl DECA Comptn 86; Glassboro ST Clg; Mrktng Educ.

NETTLEFORD, PAUL; Long Branch HS; Long Br, NJ; (3); 39/279; FBLA; Concert Band; Mrchg Band; Symp Band; Crs Cntry; Law.

NEUBIG, JEFFREY P; Blair Acad; Stockholm, NJ; (2); Scholastic Bowl; Pres Frsh Cls; VP Soph Cls; JV Socr; Var Swmmng; Hon Roll; Debate Tm; Quiz Bowl; Spanish Clb; JV Lcrss; Project Rogate 84-86; Richard M Schute Schlrshp 86-87; John Hopkins; Sci.

NEUMAIER, ANDREA L; Rutgers Preparatory Schl; Edison, NJ; (4); Key Clb; Q&S; Nwsp Ed-Chief; Var Lcrss; Var Capt Swmmng; High Hon Roll; Ntl Merit SF; St Schlr; Hosp Aide; Model UN; Austn W Sctt Schlrshp; Cum Laude Soc.

NEUMANN, SPENCER; Ocean Township HS; Ocean, NJ; (3); 2/344; Am Leg Boys St; VP Key Clb; Ski Clb; Spanish Clb; Var Capt Ftbl; Wt Lftg; Wrstlng; Ntl Merit Ltr; Rnsslr Mdl Recpnt 87; NJ Jr Acad Sci 86; Spartn Schlr 86-87; Bus.

NEUNER, DEBORAH; New Milford HS; New Milford, NJ; (3); FFA; Girl Scts; Trk; Vet.

NEUSTEIN, DAVID; John P Stevens HS; Edison, NJ; (3); 125/437; Girl Scts; Office Aide; Science Clb; Pres Temple Yth Grp; Im Socr; Im Trk.

NEVAREZ, IVAN M; Hillside HS; Hillside, NJ; (3); 4/200; Computer Clb; Leo Clb; Math Clb; Math Tm; Science Clb; Bsbl; Var Crs Cntry; Var Socr; Im Vllybl; High Hon Roll; MIT; Engrng.

NEW, SUZANNE; Monsignor Donovan HS; Howell, NJ; (3); Drama Clb; Ski Clb; Band; Church Choir; Color Guard; Concert Band; Stage Crew; Bus Mgmt.

NEWBILL, JANICKA; Camden HS; Camden, NJ; (2); Church Yth Grp; Debate Tm; Spanish Clb; Church Choir; Jazz Band; Nwsp Rptr; Yrbk Stf; Rep Soph Cls; Cit Awd; Hon Roll; George Washington U; Obstet.

NEWELL, COLLEEN; Paul VI HS; Somerdale, NJ; (4); 28/500; French Clb; FBLA; Flag Corp; NHS; Intl Bus.

NEWELL, STEPHANIE; Paul VI HS; Somerdale, NJ; (3); 24/418; Drama Clb; French Clb; Pom Pon; French Hon Soc; Hon Roll; NHS; Aerospc Engrng.

NEWHARD, STEFANIE; St James HS; Pennsville, NJ; (4); Hosp Aide; SADD; School Musical; Yrbk Stf; Rotary Awd; Pro-Life Coord 86-87; Full Two Yr Schlrshp To Salem CC; Salem CC; Pre Schl Teachr.

NEWKIRK, CHRIS; Timothy Christian HS; Cranford, NJ; (3); 2/45; Church Yth Grp; Yrbk Stf; Var Bsktbl; Var Socr; High Hon Roll; Hon Roll.

NEWKIRK, FELICIA LOUISE; Hillside HS; Hillside, NJ; (3); 18/252; Girl Scts; VP Leo Clb; Math Tm; Science Clb; Sec Spanish Clb; Band; Mrchg Band; Yrbk Phtg; Yrbk Rptr; Yrbk Stf; Msc Educ Assn Of NJ-ANNL Audition Awd Hhnrs 85 & 87; Piano Tchrs Soc-Amer Inc Annl Piano Exam 87; Fshn Merch.

NEWKIRK, KENNETH DALE; Cumberland Regional HS; Bridgeton, NJ; (2); FFA; Grnhnd Awd FFA 85-86; Chptr Frmr FFA 86-87; Prof Awd Veg Prod FFA 86-87; Frmg.

NEWMAN, JENNIFER G; West Windsor Plainsboro HS; West Windsor, NJ; (3); Am Leg Aux Girls St; Debate Tm; Drama Clb; French Clb; Model UN; SADD; School Play; High Hon Roll; NHS; Mdl Cngrss 87; Law.

NEWMAN, KAREN; Long Branch HS; Long Branch, NJ; (4); 10/247; Pres Keywanettes; School Play; Yrbk Stf; Trs Frsh Cls; Trs Soph Cls; Var Capt Gym; NHS; Science Clb; Temple Yth Grp; Capt Bsbl; Vrsty Schlr Awd; Psych.

NEWMAN, NICOLE; Lakewood HS; Lakewood, NJ; (3); Computer Clb; Dance Clb; DECA; Pep Clb; SADD; Varsity Clb; Cheerleading; Vllybl; Hon Roll; Ntl Merit Ltr; Rutgers U; Comp Sci.

NEWMAN, SCOTT; Monmouth Regional HS; Eatontown, NJ; (4); 17/250; Math Clb; Math Tm; Mu Alpha Theta; Ski Clb; Bsktbl; Var Capt Tennis; High Hon Roll; Hon Roll; Mu Alpha Theta Awd; NHS; Prfct Atten Awd 84; Math Team Awd 86; Frschmn Bsktbll Awd 84; Brandeis U.

NEWSOME, JOE; Williamstown HS; Williamstown, NJ; (4); 96/267; Varsity Clb; Rep Frsh Cls; Rep Stu Cncl; Socr; Michael T O Keefe Mem Awd 87; Schlr-Ath Awd US Army 87; All Conf All Cnty Hnrb Mntn All SJ 87; Mt Union Coll; Biol.

NEWTON, LISA MARIE; Haddon Township JR SR HS; Westmont, NJ; (4); #60 In Class; Varsity Clb; School Play; Variety Show; Sec Frsh Cls; Sec Soph Cls; Rep Stu Cncl; Var Fld Hcky; JV Swmmng; High Hon Roll; Hon Roll; NJ ST Govt Convntn Delg, & Camden Cnty Govt Day Cnvntn Delg 84; Spotlght 87; Elon Coll; Pol Sci.

NEWTON, SHARON; Wayne Hills HS; Wayne, NJ; (3); 37/320; Church Yth Grp; Cmnty Wkr; Hosp Aide; Math Clb; Varsity Clb; JV Sftbl; Var Tennis; Var Trk; High Hon Roll; Hon Roll; Tnns Tm Awd For 2nd Pl In Cnty Trnmnt 85-87; Chsn As Peer Ldr For Schl Scrtry 85-87; Awd Vlntry Svc 87; Nrsng.

NEWTON, TARA; Franklin HS; Somerset, NJ; (3); Church Yth Grp; FBLA; Library Aide; Office Aide; Pep Clb; Spanish Clb; SADD; Church Choir; Rep Frsh Cls; Badmtn; U Of NC At Chapel Hill; Accntg.

NG, PAULINE; West Windsor-Plainsboro HS; Princeton Junct, NJ; (3); Exploring; Commercial Art.

NGO, TRANG; Dover HS; Dover, NJ; (3); Key Clb; Yrbk Stf; Sftbl; Hon Roll; NHS; Rutgers U; Accntng Bus.

NGUYEN, BICH; Mt St Dominic Acad; Little Falls, NJ; (3); 7/60; Intnl Clb; JCL; Latin Clb; Library Aide; Lit Mag; Stu Cncl; Crs Cntry; High Hon Roll; NHS; Elec Engr.

NGUYEN, DUY; Oakcrest HS; Hammonton, NJ; (4); 3/212; Pres French Clb; Math Clb; Var Socr; Capt Var Tennis; High Hon Roll; Hon Roll; Sec NHS; NJ Govnrs Cncl Phy Ftns, Sport Awd 87; Presdntl Acadc Ftns Awds Pgm Awd 87; Tchrs Assn Schlrshp 87; Rutgers U; Pre-Med.

NGUYEN, HUYEN; Manchester HS; Manchester, NJ; (3); Math Clb; Math Tm; Science Clb; Advrstng.

NGUYEN, KIM-NGOC; Fair Lawn HS; Fair Lawn, NJ; (1); Computer Clb; Quiz Bowl; Science Clb; High Hon Roll; Natl Sci Leag Awd-Bio 86-87; Natl Sci Olympd Awd-Bio 86-87; Amer Comp Sci Leag Natl Cmptn 86-87; Med.

NGUYEN, KY; Woodstown HS; Woodstown, NJ; (4); Am Leg Boys St; VP Key Clb; SADD; Trs Sr Cls; Rep Stu Cncl; Capt Var Socr; Var L Swmmng; Capt Var Tennis; Var L Wrstlng; English Clb; Mock Trl Tm 85-86; Francis Marion Coll; Finance.

NGUYEN, LINH; Atlantic Friends Schl; Ventnor, NJ; (2); Computer Clb; French Clb; Spanish Clb; Chorus; Stage Crew; Yrbk Stf; Rep Frsh Cls; Rep Soph Cls; Stu Cncl; Var Socr; Socl Ltr Acdmc, Ctzn & Ldrshp 86; MIT; Sci.

NGUYEN, NHAN; Middlesex HS; Middlesex, NJ; (3); #6 In Class; Computer Clb; Trs German Clb; Latin Clb; Math Clb; Math Tm; Varsity Clb; Tennis; High Hon Roll; Hon Roll; NHS; Elec Engrng.

NGUYEN, TAM; Middlesex HS; Middlesex, NJ; (4); 10/158; French Clb; Model UN; Nwsp Rptr; Var Tennis; Hon Roll; Sec NHS; Rutgers U; Acctg.

NGUYEN, THANG; Burlington County Vo Tech; Willingboro, NJ; (3); 3/192; Computer Clb; SADD; Var Bowling; Im Ftbl; Var Capt Socr; Im Vllybl; Hon Roll; Jr NHS; Prfct Atten Awd; Pelle Lindbergh Mem; Hockey Clb Awd 85-86; Burlington Cnty Coll; Comp Prog.

NGUYEN, THANG D; Fair Lawn HS; Fair Lawn, NJ; (4); Computer Clb; Science Clb; Off Jr Cls; Off Sr Cls; Bsbl; Socr; Vllybl; Hon Roll; JETS Awd; VP NHS.

NGUYEN, THUY; South Brunswick HS; Dayton, NJ; (3); 9/274; FHA; Ed Lit Mag; JV Tennis; French Hon Soc; High Hon Roll; NHS; Prfct Atten Awd; Awds For Tennis 87; Intl Bus.

NGUYEN, TI; South Brunswick HS; Dayton, NJ; (2); Var Bsktbl; JV Socr; Hon Roll; U Of PA; Engr.

NGUYEN, TRAM; St Rose HS; Spring Lk Hts, NJ; (3); 3/210; Cmnty Wkr; Latin Clb; Library Aide; Math Tm; Lit Mag; NCTE Awd; Trs NHS; Am Leg Aux Girls St; Trs Computer Clb; Key Clb; Natl Piano Plyng Adtns Natl Stu Mscns 85-87; Pblctn Poem Bk 87; Gldn Poet Awd 87; Law.

NIBBS, ANGELA; Notre Dame HS; Trenton, NJ; (4); Red Cross Aide; SADD; Im JV Socr; Im Vllybl; Hon Roll; Excllnc-Frnch $200 Awd 86-87; Awd Of Merit-Spnsh 84-85; Schiller Intl U-Paris; Frnch.

NICASTRO, TINA MARIE; Lyndhurst HS; Lyndhurst, NJ; (3); 20/176; Am Leg Aux Girls St; Church Yth Grp; Girl Scts; Key Clb; Teachers Aide; Chorus; High Hon Roll; Hon Roll; Rutgers Newark; Acctg.

NICHOLAS, EVE; Central Regional HS; Bayville, NJ; (3); Drama Clb; Intnl Clb; SADD; Chorus; School Musical; School Play; Nwsp Stf; JV Var Socr; Stat Trk; High Hon Roll; Schlr Athl Awd; Theatr.

NICHOLAS, MARK; Central Regional HS; Bayville, NJ; (4); Aud/Vis; Key Clb; Pep Clb; Ski Clb; Temple Yth Grp; Coach Actv; Var L Ftbl; Var Capt Trk; Im Wt Lftg; Outstndng Athl 86-87; Susquehanna U; Bus Ecnmcs.

NICHOLS, CATHERINE; St James HS; Mickleton, NJ; (4); 14/68; Church Yth Grp; Drama Clb; JA; SADD; School Musical; School Play; Yrbk Stf; Hon Roll; NHS; U Tampa Svc, Ldrshp Schlrshp 87; US Bond Svc, Ldrshp, Dedicatn 87; U Of Tampa; Marine Sci.

NICHOLS, JONI; Bridgeton HS; Bridgeton, NJ; (3); GAA; Office Aide; Ski Clb; Varsity Clb; Yrbk Rptr; Yrbk Stf; Var Fld Hcky; Var Sftbl; Var Swmmng; Hon Roll; Phrmcy.

NICHOLS, MATTHEW; Southern Regional HS; Manahawkin, NJ; (3); 3/435; Church Yth Grp; French Clb; Model UN; Ski Clb; Yrbk Stf; JV Tennis; Gov Hon Prg Awd; High Hon Roll; NHS; Ntl Merit SF; Outstndng Acdmcs; Intl Rltns.

NICINSKI, TIMOTHY; Union HS; Union, NJ; (3); Chorus; JV Bsbl; JV Ftbl; JV Wrstlng; James P Dow Awd 85; Sci.

NICK, CYNTHIA; Morris Catholic HS; Sparks, MD; (2); 53/167; Church Yth Grp; Hosp Aide; Spanish Clb; JV Bsktbl; Im Score Keeper; Hon Roll.

NICKEL, APRIL; Pinelands Regional HS; Tuckerton, NJ; (3); #2 In Class; Lit Mag; Stat Mgr Bsktbl; Stat Mgr Fld Hcky; Mgr(s); Score Keeper; Stat Mgr Trk; Hon Roll; Phys Ther.

NICOLAI, JOHN C; Notre Dame HS; Trenton, NJ; (2); Aud/Vis; Computer Clb; Stage Crew; Var Bowling; High Hon Roll; NHS; Hghst Hnrs In Hnrs Geom 87; Merit Of Achvt In Bowling Excllnc 87; 38th Annual AHSME 87; Wildlife Exploration.

NICOLICH, ANTHONY; St Joseph Of Palisades HS; Weehaven, NJ; (2); Church Yth Grp; Stage Crew; Bsbl; Bsktbl; High Hon Roll; Political Wkr; School Play; Score Keeper; Vllybl; Hon Roll.

NICOLL, PAMELA R; Middlesex Cnty Vo-Tech East Brunswck; Spotswood P O, NJ; (4); 14/168; Church Yth Grp; Cmnty Wkr; Library Aide; VICA; Rep Frsh Cls; Hon Roll; ST VICA Chmpn Bkng 87; Cooprtv Voctnl Ed Outstndng Stu 87; Congrssnl Schlr 87; Hudson CC; Culnry Arts.

NICOSIA, SCOTT; Toms River South HS; Toms River, NJ; (2); Cmnty Wkr; FFA; Political Wkr; Ski Clb; JV Crs Cntry; JV Trk; Lndscpr.

NICZEWSKA, JOANNA; Bayonne HS; Bayonne, NJ; (4); Dance Clb; German Clb; Hon Roll; Jeanne O Connr Schlrshp 87; Christ Hosp Schl Nrsng; RN.

NIECE, KATHRYN; Warren Hills Regional SR HS; Oxford, NJ; (4); 2/218; Pres AFS; Pres German Clb; Key Clb; JV Var Bsktbl; High Hon Roll; VP NHS; Sal; Jerome H Bentley ST Sci Day Awd 85; Hnrs Prog Upsala Coll 87; Warren Hls Regnl Schlrshp 87; Upsala Coll; Bus.

NIED, ALLISON; West Windsor-Plainsboro HS; Lawrenceville, NJ; (3); Trs Art Clb; Exploring; Radio Clb; Trs Frsh Cls; Trs Soph Cls; Pres Jr Cls; Pres Stu Cncl; JV Capt Socr; High Hon Roll; Hon Roll; Zenith Chptr NHS 87; NJ Teen Arts Fest Painting 85.

NIEDERER, TARA; Hunterdon Central HS; Ringoes, NJ; (3); 30/542; Trs Church Yth Grp; Dance Clb; Trs German Clb; Church Choir; Stage Crew; Variety Show; Yrbk Stf; Rep Frsh Cls; Rep Soph Cls; Rep Jr Cls; Artwork UN Display 87; Vet.

NIEMAN, NICOLE; Collingswood SR HS; Collingswood, NJ; (2); Church Yth Grp; Office Aide; Nwsp Rptr; High Hon Roll; Hon Roll; Jr NHS; NHS; Princeton U; Psych.

NIEMIEC, EUGENE S; Memorial HS; Cedar Grove, NJ; (4); Drama Clb; Red Cross Aide; Band; Mrchg Band; School Play; Nwsp Stf; Var Socr; High Hon Roll; Hon Roll; NHS; Rutgers U; Pre-Med.

NIENART, LYDIA; Kittatinny Regional HS; Lafayette, NJ; (3); 32/216; Yrbk Stf; Var JV Fld Hcky; Gov Hon Prg Awd; Hon Roll; 1st Prize Teen Arts Fstvl 1st Prize Crftsmn Fair 84-85; 1st Prize Teen Arts Fstvl 85-86; Cmmrcl Arts.

NIERADKA, LAURA; Wood-Ridge HS; Wood Ridge, NJ; (2); Art Clb; Model UN; Color Guard; Trs Frsh Cls; Trs Soph Cls; JV Sftbl; JV Vllybl; High Hon Roll.

NIERAOKA, JAMIE; Keansburg HS; Keansburg, NJ; (3); 1/120; German Clb; Key Clb; VP Frsh Cls; VP Jr Cls; Pres Stu Cncl; JV Bsktbl; Var Ftbl; Bausch & Lomb Sci Awd; High Hon Roll; NHS; Stu Mnth Elks 86; 1st Pl Rutgers Grmn Declmtn Cont 86; Engl, Grmn, Math, Sci, Socl Stds Awds 85-87; Law.

NIESHALLA, THOMAS; Don Bosco Prep; Oakland, NJ; (4); 1/180; Church Yth Grp; German Clb; Orch; Nwsp Rptr; Rep Stu Cncl; Socr; High Hon Roll; NHS; Mech Engrg.

NIETO, HERNAN; Dickinson HS; Jersey City, NJ; (4); Spanish Clb; Im Ftbl; JV Var Socr; David City Proj Awd 83; City & Cnty Soccer Champns 85; Intl Busnss.

NIEVES, CARMENCITA; Our Lady Of Good Counsel HS; Newark, NJ; (4); 3/102; Cmnty Wkr; Hosp Aide; School Musical; School Play; Hon Roll; NHS; Prfct Atten Awd; Pres Schlr; Prsdnt III Schlrshp 87; Spnsh Awd 84 & 85; Chrldng Awd 86; U Of Scranton; Nrsng.

NIEVES, ELIAS; Perth Amboy HS; Perth Amboy, NJ; (3); 35/564; Church Yth Grp; Computer Clb; Im Bsktbl; Schlr Awd 85-87; De Vry Tech Schl; Comp Pgmmr.

NIEVES, HENRY; Dover HS; Dover, NJ; (3); Exploring; Ftbl; Wt Lftg; Var Capt Wrstlng; Hon Roll.

NIEVES, MELISA; Ralph Waldo Emerson HS; Union City, NJ; (3); Am Leg Aux Girls St; Cmnty Wkr; Office Aide; Political Wkr; Chorus; School Play; Pom Pon; Vllybl; Hon Roll; Prfct Atten Awd; Kiwanis Awd 84; Crmnl Law.

NIEVES, SONIA; Oakcrest HS; Elwood, NJ; (4); GAA; VP Spanish Clb; Trs SADD; Church Choir; Ed Yrbk Stf; Var Tennis; Capt Var Trk; Prfct Atten Awd; St Schlr; Varsity Schlr 83-87; Trenton ST Coll; Spcl Educ.

NIGEL, DAVID; Florence Twp Memorial HS; Bordentown, NJ; (3); Computer Clb; Latin Clb; Quiz Bowl; Band; Jazz Band; Variety Show; Wt Lftg; Cit Awd; Comp Tech.

NIGRO, MARIA; Triton Regional HS; Blackwood, NJ; (4); 12/309; Cmnty Wkr; Sec Math Clb; Nwsp Rptr; Nwsp Stf; Yrbk Stf; Trs Sr Cls; Stu Cncl; Powder Puff Ftbl; Sftbl; Trk; Grls Ctznshp Inst 85-86; Outstndng Achvt Bio 84-85; Rutgers; Acctnt.

NIKOLOF, VELIKA; J P Stevens HS; Edison, NJ; (4); 73/550; Spanish NHS; Cert Merit Natl Frnsc Trnmt 1st Pl Spnsh 84-85; Natl Spnsh Exm 6th Pl 85-86; Cmmrcl Photo.

NILAND, KERRY; Randolph HS; Ironia, NJ; (3); 36/350; Church Yth Grp; Cmnty Wkr; Band; Concert Band; Mrchg Band; Stu Cncl; Var JV Fld Hcky; Trs Powder Puff Ftbl; Hon Roll; NHS; Mrchndsng.

NILES, LYNN E; Montville Township HS; Towaco, NJ; (3); 7/276; Key Clb; Library Aide; Science Clb; Concert Band; Drm Mjr(t); Mrchg Band; School Musical; Var Capt Trk; NHS; Ntl Merit Ltr; Mst Imprvd Plyr Awd-Grls Trck 86 & 87; Chem.

NILLES, BONNIE; Toms River HS South; Toms River, NJ; (4); 29/329; Art Clb; Church Yth Grp; Hosp Aide; Var Mgr(s); Powder Puff Ftbl; JV Var Socr; JV Tennis; High Hon Roll; Hon Roll; Rutgers U; Advrtsng.

NIMON, JENNIFER; Red Bank Catholic HS; Lincroft, NJ; (3); Sec Church Yth Grp; Art Clb; Chorus; Nwsp Rptr; Var Powder Puff Ftbl; JV Sftbl; Hon Roll; Engl.

NINE, JENNA; Chatham Township HS; Chatham, NJ; (4); Sec Church Yth Grp; Key Clb; Model UN; Pep Clb; Concert Band; Jazz Band; School Musical; Yrbk Stf; Sec Stu Cncl; Stat Trk; Purdue U; Pharm.

NINTZEL, KEN F; Sparta HS; Sparta, NJ; (4); Church Yth Grp; Debate Tm; Drama Clb; Band; Chorus; Concert Band; Jazz Band; Mrchg Band; School Musical; High Hon Roll; Sr Stu Art Awd-Crtv Wrtng 87; Prtl Schlrshp 87; Tisch Schl Of Arts; Theatre.

NIPPS, SUSAN RAY; Manville HS; Manville, NJ; (3); Dance Clb; Office Aide; PAVAS; Variety Show; Trs Frsh Cls; Rep Stu Cncl; Var Cheerleading; Stat Trk; Hon Roll; NHS; Teen Arts; Gov Schl.

NISBET, KIMBERLY; Immaculata HS; Bridgewater, NJ; (3); 95/256; Hosp Aide; JA; Science Clb; Service Clb; Ski Clb; Variety Show; Rep Stu Cncl; Stat Bsbl; JV Cheerleading; Im Vllybl; Mgmnt.

NISLER, JASON; Newton HS; Newton, NJ; (3); 40/200; German Clb; Political Wkr; Ski Clb; Varsity Clb; Rep Jr Cls; VP Sr Cls; Var Ftbl; JV Trk; Wt Lftg; High Hon Roll; Natl Sci Olympiad, Cedrt Of Accomondation In Trig & Anylitic Geom 86-87.

NITTI, TARA; Toms River HS East; Toms River, NJ; (4); 70/567; Intnl Clb; Math Tm; Ski Clb; Yrbk Stf; Off Jr Cls; Off Sr Cls; Stu Cncl; Stat Bsktbl; JV Fld Hcky; NHS; Temple U; Finance.

NIX, TULIN L; Abraham Clark HS; Roselle, NJ; (3); FHA; Hosp Aide; Library Aide; NAACP; Chorus; Lit Mag; Rep Jr Cls; Var Trk; Hon Roll; Rutgers Coll; Nrsng.

NIXON, JOAN; Newton HS; Newton, NJ; (4); 23/196; Spanish Clb; Yrbk Stf; Lit Mag; Hon Roll; Rotary Awd; Cmnctns.

NIXON, KIM; Matawan Regional HS; Cliffwood Bch, NJ; (2); 27/310; Math Tm; Spanish Clb; Var L Bsktbl; JV Sftbl; Var L Tennis; High Hon Roll; Grls Tnns Rookie Yr 85-86.

NIZIOL, STEPHEN; Middlesex HS; Middlesex, NJ; (4); 28/160; Key Clb; Math Tm; Ski Clb; Concert Band; Mrchg Band; Trs Stu Cncl; Var Bsbl; Var Capt Bsktbl; Var Capt Crs Cntry; All Vlly Conf Tm In Cross Cntry 85-86.

NIZIOLEK, CHRISTINE; Abraham Clark HS; Roselle, NJ; (3); Library Aide; Chorus; Madrigals; High Hon Roll; NHS; Sec Frsh Cls; Sec Soph Cls; Sec Jr Cls; Bus Mgr.

NIZNIK, JENNIFER; Hawthorne HS; Hawthorne, NJ; (3); Hosp Aide; Math Tm; Variety Show; Rep Frsh Cls; Rep Soph Cls; Var Capt Crs Cntry; Var Capt Trk; Cit Awd; High Hon Roll; Trs NHS; Physcl Thrpy.

NIZOLAK, PAUL; Cranford HS; Cranford, NJ; (3); 168/300; Aud/Vis; Church Yth Grp; Radio Clb; Ski Clb; SADD; Ftbl; Wrstlng; De Vry; Elec.

NOAKES, LAURA; St James HS; Carneys Point, NJ; (2); #12 In Class; Girl Scts; Spanish Clb; SADD; Yrbk Stf; Stat Bsktbl; Hon Roll; Acad All Am 86; Elem Ed.

NOBLES, SUSANNE; Ridge HS; Basking Ridge, NJ; (2); 3/169; Latin Clb; Science Clb; Acpl Chr; Chorus; Concert Band; School Musical; Ed Lit Mag; Off Soph Cls; Tennis; High Hon Roll; Latin Hnr Soc; Law.

NOBRE, SANDRA; East Side HS; Newark, NJ; (3); Computer Clb; Math Clb; Chorus; Rutgers; Word Processor.

NOCELLA, LAWRENCE; Gateway Regional HS; Woodbury Hts, NJ; (3); 37/190; Exploring; Band; Chorus; Mrchg Band; School Musical; Stage Crew; All S Jersey Chorus Tenor II 86-87; W Deptford Tn Mscl Thtre 86-87; Wrtr For Jersey Atari Comp 84-87; Drexel U; Engrng.

NOCELLA JR, LOUIS THEODORE; Gateway Regional HS; Woodbury Hts, NJ; (2); German Clb; Science Clb; Concert Band; Mrchg Band; Hon Roll.

NOCELLA, RICHARD J; Cherokee HS; Marlton, NJ; (3); Am Leg Boys St; Trs Soph Cls; Stu Cncl; Var Ftbl; JV Trk; Var Wt Lftg; Hon Roll; Engr.

NOEL, ROBERTA; Orange HS; Orange, NJ; (3); Art Clb; Debate Tm; FBLA; NAACP; Pep Clb; Y-Teens; Yrbk Stf; Off Soph Cls; Stu Cncl; Tennis; U Of CA Los Angeles; Psych.

NOGUEIRA, JUDI; Red Bank Catholic HS; Little Silver, NJ; (3); Church Yth Grp; Girl Scts; SADD; Thesps; School Play; Yrbk Stf; Capt Twrlr; Excllnce Religion Awd 85.

NOLAN, COLLEEN; Southern Regional HS; Barnegat, NJ; (3); Nwsp Stf; Yrbk Stf; Pres Sr Cls; Rep Stu Cncl; Stat Bsktbl; JV Tennis; High Hon Roll; Hon Roll; NHS; Nwsp Rptr; Beaver Coll; Phys Thrpy.

NOLAN, JOHN P; Moorestown HS; Moorestown, NJ; (4); 30/230; Am Leg Boys St; Church Yth Grp; Cmnty Wkr; Latin Clb; Y-Teens; Lit Mag; Bsbl; Var Capt Socr; Var Capt Swmmng; High Hon Roll; All Nj Scr 87; Rotry Clb Schlrshp 87; U S Coast Guard Acad; Govnmt.

NOLDER, DONNA; Pitman HS; Pitman, NJ; (3); 8/146; Chorus; Rep Stu Cncl; Pom Pon; Hon Roll; Albright; Pre-Med.

NOLL, BERNADETTE; Immaculata HS; Somerville, NJ; (3); Church Yth Grp; Drama Clb; Hosp Aide; JA; Office Aide; School Musical; School Play; Variety Show; Off Frsh Cls; Off Soph Cls; Engl Awd 85-86.

NOLLAR, LINDA; Allentown HS; Cream Ridge, NJ; (4); Pres FFA; Chorus; School Musical; Nwsp Sprt Ed; Yrbk Stf; Var L Fld Hcky; High Hon Roll; Hon Roll; NHS; Star St Ag Busmn NJ FFA 87; Flrclture Prfcncy Awd FFA 86-87; De Kalb Awd FFA 87; Floral Shop.

NOLTE, VERA; Kingsway Regional HS; Clarksboro, NJ; (2); Church Yth Grp; NFL; Im Bsktbl; Im Sftbl; JV Tennis; Mock Trial-Gloucestr Cnty Chmpns 86-87; Cmmrcl Artst.

NOONE, SHEILA; De Paul Diocesan HS; Ringwood, NJ; (4); 55/155; Dance Clb; Teachers Aide; School Play; Stage Crew; Hon Roll; Psychlgy.

NORBE, TRACY; Manchester Regionial HS; North Haledon, NJ; (3); GAA; Yrbk Stf; Pres Frsh Cls; Rep Soph Cls; Rep Jr Cls; Capt Civic Clb; Capt Powder Puff Ftbl; Trk; Cit Awd; Hon Roll.

NORBECK JR, ROBERT; St Joes HS; Mt Laurel, NJ; (3); Hnr Rl 2 Yrs; U Of PA; Law.

NORDONE, TONY; Lower Cape May Regional HS; Erma, NJ; (2); 11/263; Math Tm; Var Socr; JV Trk; Hon Roll; Prfct Atten Awd; Princeton U; Math Sci.

NORGARD, DEBORAH D; Mt Olive HS; Flanders, NJ; (1); Church Yth Grp; Ski Clb; Var Sftbl; Sftbl; Hon Roll; NJBEA Typng Awd 87; Ftns Awd 87; Most Outstndg Earth Sci 87; Bus.

NORMANN, HOLLY; Howell HS; Freehold, NJ; (4); 28/400; German Clb; Girl Scts; Bowling; Sftbl; Hon Roll; Monmouth Coll; Mrktng/Mgmt.

NOROD, ANDREA; Kittatinny Regional HS; Newton, NJ; (3); 47/224; GAA; Ski Clb; Spanish Clb; Varsity Clb; Band; Var Bsktbl; Var Fld Hcky; Var Trk; Hon Mntn All Area Fld Hcky 85; All Area, Leag Fld Hcky, 3rd Tm Wst Jrsy Fld Hcky,Mst Imprvd Trk 86; Brdcst Commnctns.

NORRIS, KRISTA; Madison HS; Madison, NJ; (3); German Clb; Hosp Aide; Flag Corp; Hon Roll; Kessler Inst Rehab Vol Wrk 85; Overlook Hosp Vol Work 87; Gov Awd Ger Achvt 87; Soc Wrk.

NORRIS, MELISSA A; Academy Of The Holy Angels; Palisades Pk, NJ; (4); 13/152; Mu Alpha Theta; Nwsp Rptr; Yrbk Stf; Hon Roll; NHS; Magna Cub Laude-Natl Latin Exam 85; Cert Of Achvt-Ntl Bio Exam 85; Cert Of Excllnc-Ntl Hstry Contst 85; Teacher.

NORRIS, SHANNON; Clearview Regional HS; Sewell, NJ; (3); 23/171; DECA; Trs Rep Stu Cncl; Cheerleading; JV Var Fld Hcky; Stat Wrstlng; High Hon Roll; Hon Roll; NHS; JV Sftbl; 3rd Ovrll Finance/Crdt DECA Rgnl Conf 87; Accntng.

NORTH, JOHN H; Hunterdon Central HS; Whitehouse, NJ; (2); 76/478; Church Yth Grp; JV L Bsbl; JV L Bsktbl; Ftbl; Hon Roll; Soph Rcgntn Pgm-Bsktbl 86-87; Hrn Rll-All 4 Mrkng Periods-Rcgntn Pgm 85-86.

NORTH, MELISSA; Middlesex HS; Middlesex, NJ; (3); 9/171; French Clb; Model UN; Var Bsktbl; Var Fld Hcky; Var Sftbl; Hon Roll; NHS; Sprts Med.

NORTON, SEBRINA; Cinnaminson HS; Englewood, CO; (3); Sec Church Yth Grp; Drama Clb; Intnl Clb; Math Clb; PAVAS; Sec Science Clb; Chorus; Yrbk Rptr; Rep Stu Cncl; Prfct Atten Awd; Thspn Actrs Achvt Awd 86; Affrmtv Actn Cmte 87; CO ST U; Theatre Arts.

NORVELL, JOANNA; Hunterdon Central HS; Ringoes, NJ; (3); 28/540; Service Clb; Varsity Clb; Yrbk Sprt Ed; Var Crs Cntry; Var Trk; Hon Roll; NHS; Ntl Merit Ltr; Russian Hnr Soc 85-88.

NORWITZ, NICOLE; Middletown H S South; Locust, NJ; (4); Cmnty Wkr; Hosp Aide; Office Aide; Ski Clb; SADD; Color Guard; Flag Corp; Yrbk Stf; High Hon Roll; Hon Roll; Awd-Hlpng Spec Olympcs 86; Piano Recital 87; Pre Med.

NOSEK, SHARON; Woodstown HS; Woodstown, NJ; (4); 9/209; Drama Clb; Key Clb; SADD; School Play; Yrbk Bus Mgr; Yrbk Phtg; Stat Bsktbl; JV Swmmng; High Hon Roll; NHS; T Edison Sci Fr 84-85; DE Vly Sci Fr 84-85; Presdntl Acadc Ftns Awd 87; Trenton ST Coll; Vet.

NOTARO, NOELLE; Eastern HS; Berlin, NJ; (3); Camera Clb; Service Clb; Yrbk Stf; Rep Frsh Cls; Rep Soph Cls; Rep Jr Cls; Trs Sr Cls; Rep Stu Cncl; Var Cheerleading; Stat Ftbl; Pre-Med.

NOVAK, KAREN; Millburn HS; Millburn, NJ; (3); Church Yth Grp; Library Aide; Office Aide; Quiz Bowl; Pine Manor; Culnary Arts.

NOVAK, KAREN; Spotswood HS; Spotswood, NJ; (4); 31/187; Am Leg Aux Girls St; Cmnty Wkr; Model UN; Office Aide; SADD; Ed Yrbk Stf; Trk; Hon Roll; Douglass Coll; Prsnl Mgmt.

NOVAK, KEVIN E; Spotswood HS; Spotswood, NJ; (2); Science Clb; Band; VP Frsh Cls; JV Bsbl; JV Var Ftbl; Hon Roll; Economics.

NOVAK, MARGO; Columbia HS; S Orange, NJ; (4); Church Yth Grp; Latin Clb; SADD; Chorus; Concert Band; Im Vllybl; Im Sftbl; St Schlr; NE Conf Awd Excel Ltn 87; Outstndng Hstry Paper 87; Dickinson Coll; Elem Educ.

NOVAK, YVONNE; Columbia HS; S Orange, NJ; (3); 99/514; VP Church Yth Grp; JCL; Pres Latin Clb; Math Tm; Varsity Clb; Church Choir; School Musical; Yrbk Stf; Socr; High Hon Roll.

NOVAKOWSKI, JOELLE; Woodstown HS; Alloway, NJ; (3); English Clb; Exploring; French Clb; Hosp Aide; Key Clb; Capt SADD; Sec Jr Cls; VP Sr Cls; JV Tennis.

NOVEMBRE, MARK; Hamilton HS West; Trenton, NJ; (3); Band; Concert Band; Var Tennis; Hon Roll; NHS; Phrmcy.

NOVICK, BROOKE; Cherry Hill HS West; Cherry Hill, NJ; (3); Am Leg Aux Girls St; Spanish Clb; SADD; Temple Yth Grp; Stage Crew; Rep Soph Cls; JV Capt Cheerleading; Hon Roll; NHS; Eng.

NOVICK, STEVEN; Scotch Plains-Fanwood HS; Scotch Plains, NJ; (3); Model UN; Spanish Clb; Temple Yth Grp; Band; Concert Band; Jazz Band; Mrchg Band; School Musical; Symp Band; Im Vllybl; Emery; Dntstry.

NOVIELLO JR, NICHOLAS R; Bridgewater-Raritan H S West; Bridgewater, NJ; (4); Scholastic Bowl; Ski Clb; SADD; Nwsp Ed-Chief; Ed Nwsp Stf; Pres Frsh Cls; Trs Sr Cls; Trs NHS; Rutgers U Deans Summer Schlr 87; Schltc Mag Hnrb Mntn Essay 84; Boston U Schl Mgmt; Finance.

NOVY, BRIAN; Bayonne HS; Bayonne, NJ; (4); German Clb; Pres Temple Yth Grp; Stage Crew; Nwsp Ed-Chief; Lit Mag; Hon Roll; Jr NHS; NHS; Knights Of Pythias Pblc Spkng Awd 86; Morris Tosk Mem Awd 85; Carleton Coll.

NOWAK, BERK; Morristown-Beard HS; New Vernon, NJ; (3); 10/83; Pres Intnl Clb; Math Tm; Band; Yrbk Stf; Capt Var Bsbl; Var Ftbl; Hon Roll; 1st Pl-Schl NJ Math Leag Compttn 87; Schlrshp Cldwll Coll 86; Bus.

NOWAKIWSKY, LISA; Mt St Dominic Acad; S Orange, NJ; (4); VP Sec Church Yth Grp; Cmnty Wkr; VP Girl Scts; Intnl Clb; Spanish Clb; Lit Mag; VP Jr Cls; Rep Stu Cncl; High Hon Roll; Hon Roll; Rutgers U; Art Hist.

NOWICKI, AGNES; Wallington HS; Wallington, NJ; (3); Am Leg Aux Girls St; Camera Clb; Service Clb; Stu Cncl; Trk; NHS; Rutgers U; Phrmcy.

NOWICKI, KATIE; Toms River High Schl HS; Toms River, NJ; (4); 23/340; Am Leg Aux Girls St; Church Yth Grp; Quiz Bowl; Ski Clb; Trs Frsh Cls; Off Stu Cncl; Var Capt Cheerleading; Hon Roll; NHS; Voice Dem Awd; Villanova U; Bus.

NOWICKI, NICOLE; Holy Spirit HS; Pomona, NJ; (2); 33/397; Dance Clb; Chorus; School Musical; Variety Show; Yrbk Stf; Hon Roll; Cmmnctns.

NOWICKI, TAMMY; Life Center Acad; Willingboro, NJ; (2); 3/16; Church Yth Grp; Chorus; School Play; Stage Crew; Var Bsktbl; Var Sftbl; Var Vllybl; PHY Educ.

NOWYGROD, KAREN; Dwight Englewood Schl; Englewood, NJ; (3); Cmnty Wkr; Chorus; School Musical; Lit Mag; Var Fld Hcky; JV Lcrss; Capt Mgr(s); Hon Roll; Jrnlsm.

NOYES, JENNIFER; Ridge HS; Basking Ridge, NJ; (3); 72/192; Church Yth Grp; CAP; Hosp Aide; Service Clb; Ski Clb; Nwsp Stf; Fld Hcky; Swmmng; Hon Roll; Pres Grls Svc Orgnztn Vlntr Prog 86-87; Psych.

NSHAIWAT, FLORIDA FERIAL; Dickinson HS; Jersey City, NJ; (3); Lit Mag; Hon Roll; Prfct Atten Awd; Jersey City ST Coll; Acting.

NUCCI, ROBYNNE; Toms River North HS; Toms River, NJ; (3); 64/460; French Clb; Ski Clb; Pres SADD; Nwsp Stf; Yrbk Stf; Trs Jr Cls; Trs Sr Cls; JV Fld Hcky; Hon Roll; NHS; Brdcst Jrnlsm.

NUGENT, CHRISTINE; North Arlington HS; N Arlington, NJ; (3); 1/110; Church Yth Grp; Hosp Aide; VP Band; Sec Sr Cls; Rep Stu Cncl; Var Bowling; Var Crs Cntry; Var Trk; NHS; Pres Spanish NHS; Rutgers Schlr 87; Girls Ctznshp Inst Delg 87; Natl Sci Merit Awd 85; Rutgers; Engr.

NUGUID, MARIEPAZ; Marylawn Of The Oranges HS; Maplewood, NJ; (4); 14/49; Camera Clb; Computer Clb; Dance Clb; French Clb; FTA; Rep Sr Cls; Im Badmtn; Im Tennis; French Hon Soc; Hon Roll; Congrssnl Schlr Natl Congrssnl Yng Ldrshp Conf 87; Seton Hall U; Corp Law.

NUNES, EMILIA; East Side HS; Newark, NJ; (4); 2/490; Church Yth Grp; Sec Civic Clb; Cmnty Wkr; English Clb; Library Aide; Math Clb; Math Tm; Nwsp Rptr; Yrbk Ed-Chief; Lit Mag; Dstnghsd Schlr Garden St; Govnrs Schl Schlr; Roster Of Superior Merit; Drew U.

NUNES, KENNETH J; Raritan HS; Keyport, NJ; (4); 1/298; Am Leg Boys St; Math Clb; Science Clb; Spanish Clb; Varsity Clb; Tennis; Bausch & Lomb Sci Awd; High Hon Roll; NHS; Val; Garden ST Dist Schlr 86; Duke U; Pre Med.

NUNES, RICHARD; Essex Catholic HS For Boys; East Orange, NJ; (3); Church Yth Grp; Spanish Clb; Church Choir; Off Stu Cncl; Bsktbl; Sftbl; Wrstlng; High Hon Roll; Hon Roll; NHS; Law.

NUNEZ, LISA; Immaculate Conception HS; Lodi, NJ; (2); Ski Clb; SADD; Yrbk Stf; Bsktbl; Hon Roll; Marine Bio.

NUNEZ, LISETTE; Immaculate Conception HS; Wallington, NJ; (3); 3/70; Q&S; Spanish Clb; School Musical; Lit Mag; Vllybl; High Hon Roll; Trs NHS; Prfct Atten Awd; Spanish NHS; Acad All Amercn 86; Bus.

NUNEZ, ROBERT A; Union Catholic HS; Kenilworth, NJ; (3); 5/300; Am Leg Boys St; Math Tm; Science Clb; Spanish Clb; Nwsp Rptr; Lit Mag; High Hon Roll; NHS; Med.

NUNNENKAMP, HEIDI; Edgewood Regional SR HS; Berlin, NJ; (2); Church Yth Grp; Latin Clb; Stat Bsbl; L Cheerleading; Stat Socr; Stat Sftbl; Hon Roll; Jr NHS; VFW Awd; Mayors Awd 86; Chld Psych.

NUTLAY, PAMELA; Hunterdon Central HS; Ringoes, NJ; (4); 15/548; Hosp Aide; Temple Yth Grp; Chorus; Nwsp Ed-Chief; Nwsp Stf; French Hon Soc; NHS; Ntl Merit Ltr; High Hon Roll; Hon Roll; Amnesty Interntl Actvt; Mock Trl Tm Attrny; Rutgers Coll; Pre-Law.

NUTRY, LAURA; Toms River HS South; Beachwood, NJ; (3); 36/405; Intnl Clb; Math Clb; Math Tm; Band; Concert Band; Mrchg Band; Symp Band; Tennis; Psych.

NUZZOLO, DEBORAH; Elmwood Park Memorial HS; Elmwood Pk, NJ; (3); 8/150; Church Yth Grp; School Musical; Stu Cncl; Hon Roll; NHS; Montclair ST Coll.

NYAZI, BURHAN; Passaic County Tech & Voc HS; Prospect Pk, NJ; (3); Comp Proc.

NYNKA, MARK; Franklin HS; Franklin Pk, NJ; (3); Am Leg Boys St; Boy Scts; Church Yth Grp; German Clb; Ski Clb; Var L Socr; Im Sftbl; Im Vllybl; USN Acad Annapolis MD.

O BOYLE, BRIAN F; Union HS; Union, NJ; (4); Aud/Vis; Camera Clb; Civic Clb; School Play; Nwsp Phtg; Yrbk Ed-Chief; Yrbk Phtg; Rep Stu Cncl; Ftbl; Hon Roll; Montclaire ST Coll; Bus.

O BOYLE, THOMAS J; Dover HS; Dover, NJ; (3); Aud/Vis; Ski Clb; Band; Concert Band; Jazz Band; Mrchg Band; Orch; School Musical; Stage Crew; Wt Lftg; Tech Schl; Electronics.

O BRIEN, DANIEL; Northwest Christian Schl; Hamburg, NJ; (1); Hosp Aide.

O BRIEN, DARRAUGH; Wesfield SR HS; Westfield, NJ; (4); 104/489; Cmnty Wkr; Latin Clb; Capt Diving; Capt Swmmng; Hon Roll; Psych.

O BRIEN, DAVID; Edgewood Regional HS; Hammonton, NJ; (2); Boy Scts; FBLA; Latin Clb; JV Bsbl; JV Socr; Hon Roll; Pharm.

O BRIEN, DINA; Mainland Regional HS; Northfield, NJ; (3); Var Crs Cntry; Var Trk; High Hon Roll; Hon Roll; NHS; Glassboro ST Coll; Bus.

O BRIEN, KATHIE; Mainland Regional HS; Somers Pt, NJ; (4); 60/270; Trs Jr Cls; Trs Sr Cls; Stu Cncl; Mgr(s); Sftbl; Trk; Hon Roll; La Salle U-Phila PA; Bus Admin.

O BRIEN, KENNETH; Park Ridge HS; Park Ridge, NJ; (3); 30/100; Art Clb; Camera Clb; Church Yth Grp; Computer Clb; Math Clb; Science Clb; Varsity Clb; Var Ftbl; Var Trk; Hon Roll; Bus.

O BRIEN, KEVIN; Mount Olive HS; Flanders, NJ; (3); Debate Tm; Drama Clb; Acpl Chr; Chorus; Variety Show; Off Lit Mag; Hon Roll; Nal Hnr Soc 86; Trphy Tlnt Cntst 86; Berkley; Musician.

O BRIEN, KEVIN; Westfield SR HS; Westfield, NJ; (4); 47/526; Aud/Vis; Boy Scts; Pres Chess Clb; Pres Spanish Clb; Nwsp Phtg; Ed Nwsp Rptr; Hon Roll; NHS; Spanish NHS; Debate Tm; Eagle Sct 85; Pres Acad Ftnss Awd 87; CT Coll; Lawyr.

O BRIEN, MAUREEN; Immaculate Heart Acad; Saddle Brook, NJ; (4); 21/171; Drama Clb; Exploring; Model UN; Ski Clb; Swmmng; Trk; Hon Roll; NHS; Schlrshp Civic Awrnss Prog Wash Wrkshps 87; Loyola Coll; Bus Adm.

O BRIEN, MICHAEL; Cinnaminson HS; East Riverton, NJ; (3); Am Leg Boys St; Church Yth Grp; Nwsp Stf; Pres Jr Cls; Var Crs Cntry; JV Trk; NHS.

O BRIEN, MICHELE; Pequannock Township HS; Pompton Plains, NJ; (3); 42/230; Spanish Clb; Varsity Clb; Yrbk Stf; Cheerleading; Sftbl; Hon Roll; Psych.

O BRIEN, PATRICIA; Morris Catholic HS; Morris Plains, NJ; (3); 50/135; Church Yth Grp; Dance Clb; Ski Clb; Pres Spanish Clb; Teachers Aide; Stu Cncl; Sftbl; Hon Roll; Cheerleading; Spnsh Awd 86; 2nd Rnnr-Up Miss Amer Coed Pgnt 87; Villa Nova U; Pre-Law.

O BRIEN, SHAUN; Southern Regional HS; Manahawkin, NJ; (4); 11/361; Model UN; Nwsp Ed-Chief; Bausch & Lomb Sci Awd; High Hon Roll; Ntl Merit Ltr; Pres Schlr; St Schlr; French Clb; Capt JV Bowling; NHS; NJ Forgn Lang Edtrs Awd 86-87; Outstndng SR Engl 86-87; Quill & Scrll Awd Jrnlsm 8-87; American U; Grmn Stds.

O BRIEN, TRACEY; John P Stevens HS; Edison, NJ; (3); Art Clb; Debate Tm; Drama Clb; Key Clb; Model UN; School Musical; Yrbk Stf; Stu Cncl; Stat Mgr(s); Powder Puff Ftbl.

O BRIEN JR, WILLIAM E; Oratory Prep Schl; Morristown, NJ; (3); Computer Clb; French Clb; VP Math Clb; Math Tm; Quiz Bowl; Science Clb; JV Bsktbl; Swmmng; High Hon Roll; NHS; Knghts Of Clmbs Michael J Doody Schlrshp 85-88; Elec Engrng.

O CONNELL, KERRI; Morris Catholic HS; Succasunna, NJ; (1); 49/156; Stat Bsktbl; JV Trk.

O CONNOR, DONNA; Bordentown Regional HS; Bordentown, NJ; (3); 17/147; FBLA; Math Clb; Chorus; JV Bsktbl; Im Sftbl; Hon Roll; Bus Admins.

O CONNOR, JENNIFER; Notre Dame HS; E Windsor, NJ; (3); 23/380; Debate Tm; Drama Clb; FBLA; Red Cross Aide; Ski Clb; Variety Show; Rep Soph Cls; Sftbl; High Hon Roll; NHS; Hnrs Alg I Awd 84-85; Spnsh II Awd 85-86; Finance.

O CONNOR, KELLY; Parsippany Hills HS; Denville, NJ; (3); Art Clb; Office Aide; Ski Clb; Teachers Aide; Lit Mag; Var L Fld Hcky; Powder Puff Ftbl; AFS; Church Yth Grp; FBLA; 2 Wk Art Shwcse 86; 1 Wk Art Shwcse 87; Var Lttr Club 87; Bio.

O CONNOR, MAUREEN; Delran HS; Delran, NJ; (4); Intnl Clb; Model UN; Varsity Clb; Band; Off Frsh Cls; Off Soph Cls; Sec Sr Cls; Var Capt Fld Hcky; Powder Puff Ftbl; Var Sftbl; Prncpl Awd 87; Hnr Soc, No 1 Club; Towson ST U.

O CONNOR, WILLIAM; Holy Spirit HS; Avalon, NJ; (4); 3/363; Am Leg Boys St; Math Tm; Nwsp Ed-Chief; Nwsp Phtg; Jr NHS; NHS; Naval Acad; Engr.

O DARE, KELLY; Holy Cross HS; Mt Laurel, NJ; (3); Ski Clb; Spanish Clb; Varsity Clb; Yrbk Stf; JV Cheerleading; JV Trk; High Hon Roll; Hon Roll; Law.

O DONNELL, KEVIN; Oratory Prep Schl; Mountain Lakes, NJ; (3); Service Clb; Band; Var Crs Cntry; Var Trk; Im Vllybl; Hon Roll; NHS; Im Bsktbl; Im Ftbl; Music-Piano, Guitar & Drum 81 To Present; Econ.

O DWYER, MICHELE; Hightstown HS; Hightstown, NJ; (4); Church Yth Grp; VICA; Elks Awd; Hon Roll; Prfct Atten Awd; Wnnr-Teen Arts Fstvl 86; Chnl 13 Art Cmptn-Draw Me A Story-Wnnr 87; Art Inst/Philadlphia; Cmrcl Art.

O GRADY, CORNELIUS; Pirelands Regional HS; New Gretna, NJ; (4); 3/190; Am Leg Boys St; Science Clb; Trs Jr Cls; Trs Sr Cls; Var Ftbl; JV Socr; Capt Tennis; High Hon Roll; Hon Roll; NHS; Rnslr Poly Tech; Bus Adm.

O HARA, DANIEL P; Pemberton Township HS; Browns Mills, NJ; (4); 40/406; Am Leg Boys St; Camera Clb; Nwsp Ed-Chief; Ed Nwsp Phtg; Yrbk Phtg; JV Trk; High Hon Roll; NHS; Rotary Awd; Kent ST U; Aerospc Engr.

O KEEFE, ANA; North Bergen HS; North Bergen, NJ; (4); 8/470; Key Clb; Rep Jr Cls; Rep Sr Cls; Var Bsktbl; Var Crs Cntry; Var Sftbl; Var Trk; High Hon Roll; NHS; Spanish NHS; Fnlst Ntl Hispanic Schlrshp Competn 87.

O KEEFE, JEFFREY T; Toms River HS South; Toms River, NJ; (3); 43/410; Church Yth Grp; Ski Clb; JV Bsbl; JV Bsktbl; L Var Socr; Hon Roll; ROTC; Engrng.

O KEEFE, KAREN; Notre Dame HS; Mercerville, NJ; (4); 25/336; Red Cross Aide; Yrbk Stf; Capt Pom Pon; Stat Wrstlng; High Hon Roll; Hon Roll; NHS; Spanish NHS; ST Librty Drll Tm 86; Rutgers Coll; Ecnmcs.

O LEARY, JUDITH; Central Regional HS; Bayville, NJ; (4); 9/213; Am Leg Aux Girls St; Pres Drama Clb; Math Clb; Q&S; Sec Band; Chorus; Color Guard; Concert Band; Drm Mjr(t); Jazz Band; Arian Music Awd 87; Rutgers Coll.

O LEARY, KELLIE; Timothy Christian HS; South Plainfield, NJ; (4); 1/40; Drama Clb; Church Choir; Yrbk Stf; Sec Sr Cls; Var Capt Cheerleading; Im VP Socr; High Hon Roll; Pres NHS; Sal; St Schlr; Intl Singng Comptn 1st & 2nd Pl 84-86; Svc Awd 83; Wheaton Coll; Tchr.

O LOUGHLIN, FLORENCE; Central Regional HS; Ocean Gate, NJ; (4); PAVAS; Hon Roll; Schlrshp Stuarts Bus Schl 87; Outstndng Achvt In Bus Berkely Schls 87; Outstndng Achvt Steno II 87; Stuarts Bus Schl; Bus.

O MALLEY, MATT; Warren Hills Regional SR HS; Washington, NJ; (4); Am Leg Boys St; Concert Band; Jazz Band; Kiwanis Awd; NHS; Ntl Merit Ltr; Rotary Awd; St Schlr; Trk; High Hon Roll; Yrbk Stu Life Edtr 86-87; Orgnztn Of Amer States Dlgt 85-86; Hoyens Gftd & Tlntd Prgm; Grgtwn; Law.

O MARA, DEBRA; Highland Regional HS; Blackwood, NJ; (4); Chess Clb; Band; Concert Band; Jazz Band; Mrchg Band; Glassboro ST Coll; Musicn.

O NEAL III, JOSEPH M; Paul VI HS; Runnemede, NJ; (3); 139/418; Math Clb; Hon Roll; Prfct Atten 85 & 87; Vet Med.

O NEAL, KIMBERLY; Paterson Catholic Regional HS; Paterson, NJ; (2); Church Yth Grp; Computer Clb; FHA; Sec Church Choir; Hon Roll; Plays Piano & Organ Sun Schl 85-87; Comp.

O NEIL, MAURA K; Saint Rose HS; Wall, NJ; (3); Latin Clb; Ski Clb; Var Socr; Var Sftbl; Law.

O NEILL, BRENDA J; Toms River HS South; Toms River, NJ; (3); 104/405; DECA; Hosp Aide; Rep Frsh Cls; Rep Jr Cls; JV Sftbl; High Hon Roll; Hon Roll; Med.

O NEILL, KELLY; Bridgewater Raritan H S East; Basking Ridge, NJ; (3); Church Yth Grp; Red Cross Aide; Powder Puff Ftbl; Var L Socr; Var L Swmmng; Hon Roll; NHS; Grls Vrsty Sccr Tm ST Cmps 86-87; Pre Med.

O NEILL, MICHAEL; St Josephs Prep Seminary; Philadelphia, PA; (4); Boy Scts; Church Yth Grp; Debate Tm; Chorus; School Play; Var Capt Bsbl; Im Bsktbl; Var Socr; Cit Awd; Spanish Clb; Ad Altar Dei Rlgs Awd 83; Pope Pius XII Rlgs Awd 84; Hmntrn Awd 87; St Johns U; Math.

O REILLY, SHERYL; Lakeland Regional HS; Ringwood, NJ; (4); 16/345; Art Clb; Church Yth Grp; Intnl Clb; Yrbk Stf; Lit Mag; VP Sr Cls; Rep Stu Cncl; Var Crs Cntry; High Hon Roll; NHS; Tchrs Assn Awd 87; Bucknell U.

O ROURKE, HEATHER; Indian Hills HS; Franklin Lks, NJ; (3); Ski Clb; Rep Stu Cncl; Var Cheerleading; Var Gym; Hon Roll; Chrldng Cert 87; Psych.

O ROURKE, MARY; Montville Twp HS; Towaco, NJ; (4); 88/277; Church Yth Grp; Girl Scts; Chorus; High Hon Roll; Hon Roll; Lion Awd; Boonton Montville Lions Ben Yanowski Mem Schlrshp 87; Montville Twp Educ Assn Schlrshp 87; William Paterson Coll; Elem Ed.

O SHAUGHNESSY, KATHLEEN; St John Vianney HS; Freehold, NJ; (4); 6/250; Ski Clb; SADD; Yrbk Stf; Off Stu Cncl; High Hon Roll; Trs NHS; St Schlr; Pres Acadmc Ftns Awd; Holy Cross Coll; Bio.

O SHEA, BRENDAN J; Scotch Plains-Fanwood HS; Scotch Plains, NJ; (3); Am Leg Boys St; Church Yth Grp; French Clb; Var L Bsbl; Var L Bsktbl; French Hon Soc; High Hon Roll; Hon Roll.

O SUCH JR, ROBERT; Sayreville War Memorial HS; Parlin, NJ; (4); 37/358; Church Yth Grp; Math Clb; Spanish Clb; Var Gym; Trk; Var Wrstlng; Hon Roll; NHS; Spanish NHS; Cook Coll; Bus.

O TOOLE, JIM; Paul VI HS; Williamstown, NJ; (3); 156/418; School Musical; School Play; Nwsp Rptr; Nwsp Stf; Hon Roll; Cmmnctns.

OAKLEY, CRISTIN; Phillpsburg HS; Phillipsburg, NJ; (4); Church Yth Grp; Cmnty Wkr; Dance Clb; FFA; Key Clb; Office Aide; Pep Clb; Chorus; Church Choir; School Musical; Out Of ST Awd From Pinebrook Jr Coll 87-88; Pinebrook JR Coll; Sclgy.

OATES, MAUREEN; West Essex HS; North Caldwell, NJ; (3); Church Yth Grp; Cmnty Wkr; Hosp Aide; Key Clb; Varsity Clb; Nwsp Stf; Yrbk Stf; Lit Mag; Fld Hcky; Socr; U Scranton; Law.

OBAL, KATHLEEN; Pascack Valley HS; Hillsdale, NJ; (4); 243/270; Art Clb; Yrbk Stf; High Hon Roll; Hon Roll; Montclair ST Coll; Fine Arts.

OBARA, JOANNE; St Mary HS; Wallington, NJ; (3); Drama Clb; Hosp Aide; Thesps; Lit Mag; Rep Jr Cls; Stu Cncl; Cheerleading; Sftbl; Hon Roll; NHS; Psych.

OBED, LEONORA; Notre Dame HS; West Trenton, NJ; (2); 56/376; Church Yth Grp; Debate Tm; Yrbk Rptr; Yrbk Stf; DAR Awd; Hon Roll; NHS; Spanish NHS; Yrbk Phtg; Lit Mag; Miss NJ Cinderella Teen Pgnt 87; Cert Of Achvt-Piano 87; NJ Miss Amer Coed Pgnt 87; Rider Coll; Cmmnctns.

OBERHAUSER, GLEN; Manasquan HS; Sea Girt, NJ; (3); 1/226; Math Tm; Spanish Clb; Nwsp Stf; Var Bsbl; JV Bsktbl; High Hon Roll; Kiwanis Awd; NHS; Ntl Merit Ltr; Rutgers Schlr 87; NJ Schlrs Prog Semi-Fnlst 87.

OBERTI, FELICIA; Toms River East HS; Toms River, NJ; (4); 13/540; Cmnty Wkr; Debate Tm; French Clb; Hosp Aide; VP Key Clb; Political Wkr; Chorus; JV Powder Puff Ftbl; Sftbl; High Hon Roll; Kiwanis Ldrshp Trnng Schlrshp; Outstndng PLE Stu; Acdmc All Am; Clemson U; Poli Sci.

OBERTUBBESING, EDWIN; Middletown HS South; Leonardo, NJ; (3); Cmnty Wkr; Drama Clb; VP Band; Drill Tm; School Play; Variety Show; Lit Mag; Rep Stu Cncl; High Hon Roll; Capt Mrchg Band; Outstndng Drama Prrmnc 85; VP Locl Vlntr 1st Aid Sqd Cadets 86; VP Band Pgm 85 88; Liberal Arts.

OBERTUBBESING, MARY ANN; Middletown H S South; Leonardo, NJ; (4); 171/444; Cmnty Wkr; Hosp Aide; Teachers Aide; Band; Concert Band; Mrchg Band; Pep Band; School Musical; School Play; Symp Band; Louise Groff Fndtn Awd 87; Middletown Schl Of Nursing Schlrshp 87; Howard Osborn Schlrshp Awd 87; Brookdale CC; Nursing.

OBERUCH, WILLIAM; Sayreville War Memorial HS; Parlin, NJ; (3); Var Crs Cntry; Var Trk; Im Wrstlng; Hon Roll; Montclair ST; Math.

OBFENDA, TONY; Holy Cross HS; Mount Laurel, NJ; (4); 134/355; Church Yth Grp; Church Choir; JV Trk; Hon Roll; La Salle U; Comp Sci.

OBISO, RICK; High Point Regional HS; Sussex, NJ; (2); Church Yth Grp; Office Aide; Spanish Clb; Teachers Aide; School Musical; School Play; Stage Crew; Wt Lftg; Hon Roll; Chorus; Tchrs Asstnt Srv Awd 86-87; U NC; Tchr.

OBITZ, MICHELLE; Watchung Hills Regional HS; Watchung, NJ; (4); 66/318; Key Clb; Ski Clb; SADD; Band; Color Guard; School Musical; Stat Bsktbl; Var Cheerleading; Hon Roll; Band Parnts Assn Schlrshp 87; U Of DE; Acctng.

OBOYLE, TIMMY; Secaucus HS; Secaucus, NJ; (3); Varsity Clb; Bsktbl; Ftbl; Wt Lftg; Hon Roll; Rutgers; Bus Mngmnt.

OBRIEN, DAN; Point Pleasant Beach HS; Bay Head, NJ; (2); 2/103; CAP; JV Bsktbl; JV Tennis; High Hon Roll; Hon Roll; Pres Schlr; Pres Acad Ftnss Awd 87; Purdue; Aviation.

OBRIEN, GEOFFREY; Columbia HS; Maplewood, NJ; (3); Church Yth Grp; Cmnty Wkr.

OCALLAGHAN, KATHLEEN; Lakeland Regional HS; Bethlehem, PA; (3); 13/340; Math Tm; School Musical; Stage Crew; Variety Show; Capt JV Fld Hcky; High Hon Roll; Hon Roll; NHS; NEDT Awd; Drama Clb; Fencing Varsity 85-87; Ed.

OCCHIPINTI, BRIDGET; Butler HS; Butler, NJ; (4); 32/200; Church Yth Grp; Cmnty Wkr; Hosp Aide; Varsity Clb; Sec Stu Cncl; Cheerleading; Fld Hcky; Sftbl; Hon Roll; Bloomsburg U; Bus.

OCCHIPINTI, DANIELA M; Marylawn Of The Oranges HS; Orange, NJ; (3); Spanish Clb; Hon Roll; Spanish NHS; Dance Clb.

OCCHIUZZO, MARRIANNA; Pemberton Twp HS C 2; Browns Mills, NJ; (4); 7/369; Church Yth Grp; SADD; Band; Yrbk Ed-Chief; Yrbk Stf; Stat Bsbl; Hon Roll; NHS; Rotary Awd; Drama Clb; Miss Amer COED ST Fnlst 87; Burling County Coll; Engrng.

OCONNOR, CHRISTINE; Pinelands Regional HS; Tuckerton, NJ; (3); Chorus; School Musical; JV Var Tennis; Hon Roll; Cmmnctns.

OCONNOR, KELLY; Southern Regional HS; Brant Bch, NJ; (3); 19/437; Church Yth Grp; SADD; Yrbk Stf; Rep Frsh Cls; Rep Soph Cls; Rep Jr Cls; Off Stu Cncl; Tennis; Hon Roll; NHS; Schlr Athlt Awd For Vrsty Tnns 84; Mst Imprvd For Vrsty Tnns 84; Vet.

OCONNOR, SHIVAUN; Immaculate Conception HS; Secaucus, NJ; (4); Art Clb; Dance Clb; Stage Crew; Swmmng; Hon Roll; Montclair ST Coll.

ODELL, KATHY; Middlesex HS; Middlesex, NJ; (4); 30/160; Church Yth Grp; Girl Scts; Key Clb; Ski Clb; Spanish Clb; Drill Tm; School Musical; Yrbk Bus Mgr; Var Pom Pon; Im Powder Puff Ftbl; Bloomsburg U; Accntng.

ODGERS, CARRIE; Kittatinny Regional HS; Newton, NJ; (3); 11/216; Science Clb; Chorus; Madrigals; Mrchg Band; School Musical; School Play; Yrbk Stf; JV Stat Fld Hcky; NHS; NJ All ST Chorus 85 & 87; NJ Rgn I Chorus 85-87; Sprts Med.

ODIO, VERONICA; Hillside HS; Hillside, NJ; (3); 16/235; Boys Clb Am; Hosp Aide; Leo Clb; Science Clb; VP Spanish Clb; Band; Concert Band; Mrchg Band; Yrbk Stf; Off Stu Cncl; Rutgers U; Pre-Med.

ODOM III, RAYMOND; Mercer Christian Acad; Philadelphia, PA; (3); Church Yth Grp; Church Choir; Mrchg Band; Var Bsktbl; Var Socr; Elctrcl Engrng.

ODONOVAN, KEVIN; Notre Dame HS; Trenton, NJ; (3); FBLA; Latin Clb; Political Wkr; SADD; JV Ftbl; Hon Roll; Accntng.

OESTERLE, MARK; De Paul HS; Wayne, NJ; (4); 40/150; Church Yth Grp; Intnl Clb; Latin Clb; Pep Clb; Service Clb; Bsktbl; JV Ftbl; Capt Golf; Vllybl; Hon Roll; Villanova U; Poly Sci.

OESTREICHER, KURT; Freehold Township HS; Freehold, NJ; (3); 20/385; Church Yth Grp; CAP; Pres Trs Drama Clb; Science Clb; Sec Spanish Clb; School Musical; Rep Jr Cls; NHS; Chorus; Madrigals; Mst Imprvd JR Choir 86-87; 1st Pl Rider Coll Frnsc Lang Tour Spnsh 85-86; 1st Pl Co Theatr Comptn 85; Engr.

OFFERDAHL, THOMAS; Marine Acad Of Science & Tech; Little Silver, NJ; (3); #4 In Class; Church Yth Grp; ROTC; Sec Spanish Clb; Drill Tm; Nwsp Rptr; Yrbk Ed-Chief; Pres Soph Cls; Socr; Hon Roll; NHS; Cdt Of Mnth 85; Dstngshd Cdt Awd; US Mltry Ofcr.

OGILVIE, FAITH; Orange HS; Orange, NJ; (3); VP DECA; Trs FBLA; VP Soph Cls; Pres Jr Cls; Rep Stu Cncl; Hon Roll; Natl Ldrshp Awd 87; Rutgers-New Brunswick; CPA.

OGILVIE, WAYNE; East Side HS; Paterson, NJ; (2); Am Leg Boys St; Boys Clb Am; Camera Clb; English Clb; Exploring; JA; Quiz Bowl; Spanish Clb; School Musical; Nwsp Sprt Ed.

OGLESBY, TRINA; Saint Mary HS; Jersey City, NJ; (3); Church Yth Grp; Cmnty Wkr; Computer Clb; Hosp Aide; Teachers Aide; Church Choir; School Play; Trk; Hon Roll; Prfct Atten Awd; Fshn Dsgnr.

OGRADY, PHILIP; Mt Olive HS; Flanders, NJ; (3); 25/342; FBLA; Math Clb; Science Clb; Varsity Clb; L Bsktbl; L Socr; L Tennis; Hon Roll; NHS; Rep Jr Cls; Mst Imprvd Tnns 86.

OHARE, MAURA; Paramus Catholic Girls Regionl HS; Fairview, NJ; (2); Church Yth Grp; Science Clb; Nwsp Rptr; Nwsp Stf; Rep Stu Cncl; High Hon Roll; NEDT Tp 10 Pct Natl 87.

OKEEFE, KERRY; St Marys HS; Rutherford, NJ; (3); 6/85; Hosp Aide; Library Aide; Band; Concert Band; Yrbk Stf; Var L Bsktbl; Capt Crs Cntry; Var L Trk; High Hon Roll; Spanish NHS; Coachs Awd-Crss Cntry & Trk 86; Acadc Achvt Awds 85-87; Arts Mgmt.

OKONSKY, TOM; Bridgewater Raritan HS West; Raritan, NJ; (4); Drama Clb; Pep Clb; Science Clb; Ski Clb; School Play; Ftbl; Trk; Vllybl; Rutgers ST U; Pre-Med.

OKUN, SCOTT; Wayne Hills HS; Wayne, NJ; (2); Boy Scts; Temple Yth Grp; Varsity Clb; Concert Band; Rep Frsh Cls; Rep Soph Cls; Bowling; Hon Roll; Engr.

OLAN, LOU; Hudson Catholic HS; Jersey City, NJ; (3); Chess Clb; Science Clb; Speech Tm; JV Socr; Var L Tennis; Hon Roll; Jr NHS; Biol.

OLANDER, DALE; Wall HS; Wall, NJ; (4); Chess Clb; Computer Clb; JCL; Latin Clb; ROTC; Ski Clb; Crs Cntry; Ftbl; Trk; High Hon Roll; VP Natl Hon Soc 87; Penn ST U; Bus.

OLANO, EVONNE; Dover HS; Dover, NJ; (3); 12/240; Cmnty Wkr; French Clb; Hosp Aide; Math Tm; Ski Clb; Spanish Clb; School Musical; School Play; High Hon Roll; NHS; Ped.

OLAYAN, OMAR A; River Dell SR HS; River Edge, NJ; (3); Am Leg Boys St; Boy Scts; Church Yth Grp; Exploring; Model UN; Varsity Clb; Stage Crew; Trk; Wrstlng; Cit Awd; Prncpls Advsry Cncl, & Peer Ldrshp Advsry Netwrk 87; Envrnmntl Sci.

OLCHASKEY, DIANE; Sayreville War Memorial HS; Sayreville, NJ; (3); Church Yth Grp; Concert Band; School Musical; High Hon Roll; Hon Roll; Accntng.

OLDOERP, AUDREY; St John Vianney HS; Hazlet, NJ; (2); Church Yth Grp; Ski Clb; School Musical; School Play; Yrbk Phtg; Var Mgr(s); NHS.

OLDROYD, MATTHEW; Holy Spirit HS; Absecon, NJ; (3); 14/332; Var L Socr; Var L Tennis; High Hon Roll; Hon Roll; Jr NHS; NHS; Magne Cum Laude Ntl Latin Awd 84-85; Law.

OLEAR, CONRAD; Fair Lawn HS; Fair Lawn, NJ; (3); Camera Clb; Exploring; Var Ftbl; Ski Clb; Rep Frsh Cls; Var Bsbl; Var Mat Maids; Wt Lftg; U DE; Pre-Law.

OLEAR, JENNIFER; Holy Family Acad; Bayonne, NJ; (3); Church Yth Grp; Cmnty Wkr; Dance Clb; Spanish Clb; Stage Crew; Yrbk Stf; Im Vllybl; NHS.

OLEGARIO, LISA; Mount Saint Marys Acad; Edison, NJ; (3); 8/85; GAA; Hosp Aide; Science Clb; Spanish Clb; Lit Mag; High Hon Roll; NHS; Spanish NHS; Art Clb; Computer Clb; Spn Awd 85-86; Engl Awd 86-87; Art Awd 85-86 & 86-87; Cook Coll; Pre-Med.

OLEKNA, MICHELLE; St Pius X Regional HS; Highland Park, NJ; (3); 1/80; Hosp Aide; Chorus; Concert Band; School Play; Var Bowling; Hon Roll; NHS; 2 French Acdmc Awds 86-87; Fine Arts Svc & Religion Acdmc Awd 87; Montclair ST Coll; Dance.

OLESKE, SUZANNE; Monsignor Donovan HS; Bay Head, NJ; (3); Art Clb; Drama Clb; Ski Clb; SADD; Nwsp Ed-Chief; Yrbk Rptr; Lit Mag; Cheerleading; Hon Roll; Goldn Post Awd Poem Whispers 87; Wrtr.

OLESNICKI, ANNETTE; Union HS; Union, NJ; (4); 126/534; Church Yth Grp; French Clb; JA; Key Clb; Office Aide; Yrbk Stf; Off Soph Cls; Catholic U Of Amer; Pltcs.

OLIVER, CHRISTY M; Academy Of St Aloysius; Jersy City, NJ; (2); Church Yth Grp; Civic Clb; Cmnty Wkr; Library Aide; NAACP; Speech Tm; Teachers Aide; Church Choir; Nwsp Stf; Prfct Atten Awd; Sister Helen Frnch Schlrshp 85; Acad Recog In Frnch 86; Acad Recog For Hstry 86; Intl Rltns Spec.

OLIVER, DAVID-HENRY; Montclair HS; Montclair, NJ; (4); 46/408; Am Leg Boys St; VP Chess Clb; Cmnty Wkr; Computer Clb; Math Tm; Science Clb; Teachers Aide; Off Soph Cls; Off Jr Cls; Sec Sr Cls; Natl Achvt Fin 87; Physics Tm 87; Chem Tm 86; MIT; Bio-Med Engrng.

OLIVER, SUSAN D; Spotswood HS; Spotswood, NJ; (2); 6/127; Girl Scts; Intnl Clb; Chorus; Color Guard; Mrchg Band; Stu Cncl; Hon Roll.

OLIVERI, CHARLES; Middlesex County Vo-Tech Schl; New Brunswick, NJ; (3); VICA; Hon Roll; Outstndng Awd & 2nd Pl Awd Cntrl Jersey Crftsmns Fair, & 4th Pl NJ VICA Skll Olympcs 87; Tech Drftsmn.

OLIVERI, JOSEPH; Wayne Valley HS; Wayne, NJ; (4); 21/317; Aud/Vis; FBLA; Yrbk Rptr; JV Var Bsktbl; JV Var Golf; Hon Roll; NHS; NJ Distgshd Scholar Awd 87; Anthony Wayne PTO Awd 87; Rutgers U; Bus.

OLIVERI, MARIJO; Mt St Mary Acad; Hillside, NJ; (3); Aud/Vis; Dance Clb; Pep Clb; Service Clb; Spanish Clb; Rep Jr Cls; Pres Sr Cls; Rep Stu Cncl; Var Pom Pon; Im Swmmng; Pre-Law.

OLIVERI, MARY E; Saint James HS; Gibbstown, NJ; (4); 21/68; Exploring; Red Cross Aide; High Hon Roll; Hon Roll; Acad Exlnc Soc Sci & Theol 87; Biol Mrt Awd & Pope Pius IV 84; Natl Hnr Roll 86; Glassboro ST Coll.

OLIVERO, NOEL; Toms River HS North; Toms River, NJ; (4); 18/425; Boy Scts; Pres German Clb; Orch; School Musical; School Play; Swmmng; Trk; High Hon Roll; NHS; U Of Richmond; Bio.

OLIVETO, GERARDO; Paul VI Regional HS; Bloomfield, NJ; (4); 3/119; Camera Clb; Chess Clb; Math Clb; Science Clb; JV Bsbl; High Hon Roll; Hon Roll; Jr NHS; Kiwanis Awd; NHS; Stevens Inst Of Tech; Elec Engr.

OLMO, JACKIE; Vineland HS; Vineland, NJ; (3); 89/824; Pep Clb; SADD; Chorus; Stage Crew; Rep Frsh Cls; Rep Soph Cls; Rep Jr Cls; Rep Stu Cncl; JV Cheerleading; Hon Roll; Bus Admin.

OLSEN, JOHN; St John Vianney HS; Aberdeen, NJ; (2); Church Yth Grp; JV Ftbl.

OLSEN, KRISTINA; Central Regional HS; Bayville, NJ; (3); Nwsp Rptr; Nwsp Stf; Sec Jr Cls; Off Stu Cncl; Var Crs Cntry; High Hon Roll; Hon Roll; Sec NHS; Sec NHS 87-88; Bus.

OLSEN, LAURIE; Secaucus HS; Secaucus, NJ; (2); 14/170; Cmnty Wkr; Math Clb; Spanish Clb; Chorus; Co-Capt Color Guard; Mrchg Band; School Musical; Stat Bsktbl; Mgr(s); Hon Roll; Blgy.

OLSEN, MELANIE; Vineland SR HS; Vineland, NJ; (3); English Clb; GAA; Yrbk Stf; JV Bsktbl; Phys Thrpst.

OLSEN, SHANNON; Matawan-Aberdeen Regional HS; Matawan, NJ; (4); 8/340; Hosp Aide; Math Tm; SADD; Color Guard; Concert Band; Mrchg Band; Sec Frsh Cls; Pres Soph Cls; VP Jr Cls; VP Sr Cls.

OLSHAKER, MEREDITH; Matawan Regional HS; Matawan, NJ; (3); 34/318; Math Tm; Ski Clb; Spanish Clb; Stage Crew; Yrbk Stf; Var Capt Bowling; Var L Sftbl; Wt Lftg; High Hon Roll; NHS; Srvng Hnr Grd Grad; Rutgers; Physcl Thrpy.

OLSON, JAMIE; Manasquan HS; Sea Girt, NJ; (2); 1/212; VP Church Yth Grp; Latin Clb; High Hon Roll; Hon Roll; Kiwanis Awd; SOAR-CREATV Wrtng 85-87 & Envrnmntl Prtctn 86-87; Hlth Careers Clb 86-87; Psychlgy.

OLVEIRA, MARIA; Mary Help Of Christians HS; Paterson, NJ; (3); 25/83; Church Yth Grp; Dance Clb; French Clb; Hosp Aide; Spanish Clb; SADD; Teachers Aide; Church Choir; Drill Tm; School Play; Med Tech.

OMIATEK, CHRISTINA M; St James HS; Gibbstown, NJ; (1); Drama Clb; Temple; Socl Sci.

ONARTECHEVARRIA, JON; Dover HS; Dover, NJ; (3); Hnr Rl 86-87.

ONEILL, MARTIN; Brick Memorial HS; Brick, NJ; (3); Lit Mag; Var Bsktbl; Debate Tm; Hon Roll; Rutgers; Law.

ONOREVOLE, KEVIN; Nutley HS; Nutley, NJ; (4); 99/330; Office Aide; Orch; Stage Crew; Variety Show; Yrbk Phtg; Rep Stu Cncl; Montclair ST Coll; Law Enfrcmt.

ONYSKOW, STEVE; Waren Coutny Vocational Tech HS; Port Murray, NJ; (3); Key Clb; VICA; Bsbl; Crs Cntry; Automtv.

OOLIE, TARA; Morristown Beard HS; N Caldwell, NJ; (3); AFS; Drama Clb; Intnl Clb; Service Clb; Temple Yth Grp; School Play; Attny.

OPALSKI, MARK; West Windsor-Plainsboro HS; Plainsboro, NJ; (3); Am Leg Boys St; Art Clb; Boy Scts; Church Yth Grp; PAVAS; Red Cross Aide; Ski Clb; Teachers Aide; Lit Mag; Crs Cntry; Outwrd Bnd JR Pgm Awd 85; U Of NC; Psych.

ORABONI, NADINE; Brick Memorial HS; Brick, NJ; (3); Drama Clb; NFL; Thesps; Flag Corp; Mrchg Band; Stage Crew; Im Bsktbl; High Hon Roll; NHS; Cmmnty Svc Awd 85-86; Law.

ORAM, RICKI; John F Kennedy HS; Willingboro, NJ; (4); FBLA; Intnl Clb; Teachers Aide; Color Guard; Mrchg Band; Yrbk Stf; Pom Pon; Hon Roll; Jr NHS; Atlantic City CC; Crd Dlr.

ORANTES, MARIA; William Dickinson HS; Jersey City, NJ; (3); Computer Clb; Merit Awd 85-86; St Peters Coll; Accntng.

ORBAN, TIMOTHY; Wayne Hills HS; Wayne, NJ; (3); 70/300; Church Yth Grp; JV Bsbl; JV Ftbl; High Hon Roll; Hon Roll; 1st Pl-JV Bsbll Tourney 87; Group Mag-Wrk Cmp 85; Math.

ORDILE, SUZANN; Mainland Regional HS; Linwood, NJ; (3); 9/350; Cmnty Wkr; Hosp Aide; Service Clb; Nwsp Stf; Rep Frsh Cls; Rep Soph Cls; Rep Jr Cls; Rep Sr Cls; Rep Stu Cncl; NHS; Rotary Yth Ldrshp Awd 87; Rogate - NJ G/T Pgm 84-88; Georgetown U; Pre-Med.

ORDINO, KEITH; Lakewood HS; Lakewood, NJ; (3); 73/330; Art Clb; Spanish Clb; MIT; Arch.

ORDONEZ, IVAN; North Bergen HS; North Bergen, NJ; (4); Key Clb; ROTC; Drill Tm; JV Var Wrstlng; Hon Roll; Color Guard; Var Gym; JV Socr; Im Wt Lftg; High Hon Roll; N J ROTC Coast Guard Reserve Offcr Awd 87; Natl Russian Olympiada 5th Pl In Nation 87; Marine Corps.

ORE, LAVETT; Essex Catholic Girls HS; Irvington, NJ; (3); Am Leg Aux Girls St; Art Clb; Library Aide; Stage Crew; Rep Stu Cncl; Stu Cncl Awd 86-87; Fine & Vsl Arts Cert 86; Amer Lgn Aux Cert 87; FIT; Fash Dsgn.

OREFICE, PAUL C; Ridgefield Memorial HS; Ridgefield, NJ; (3); 3/100; Am Leg Boys St; Church Yth Grp; Math Clb; Ski Clb; Yrbk Bus Mgr; Trs Frsh Cls; Rep Soph Cls; Rep Jr Cls; Var Crs Cntry; Cit Awd; Acdmc Decathlon Bronze Medalist For Essay.

ORFANELLI, ALYSSA; Phillipsburg HS; Alpha, NJ; (3); 57/359; Church Yth Grp; Drama Clb; Girl Scts; Library Aide; Ski Clb; School Musical; School Play; Stage Crew; Hon Roll; Schlr/Athlt Of Alpha 84.

ORFE, JAMES; Riverside HS; Delanco, NJ; (3); 16/108; Am Leg Boys St; Chess Clb; Nwsp Stf; L JV Bsktbl; JV L Score Keeper; Gov Hon Prg Awd; Hon Roll; Comm.

ORILLE, JOHN; Saint John Vianney HS; Hazlet, NJ; (3); Rep Jr Cls; Pres Sr Cls; Var Ftbl; Var Trk; Im Wt Lftg; US Naval Acad; Engr.

ORIO, GINA; Saint John Vianney HS; Hazlet, NJ; (3); 47/280; Intnl Clb; SADD; Yrbk Stf; Powder Puff Ftbl; High Hon Roll; Hon Roll; Prfct Atten Awd; Seton Hall U.

ORLANDO, CINDY; Rutherford HS; Rutherford, NJ; (4); 8/167; Nwsp Stf; Yrbk Stf; JV L Tennis; JV Trk; High Hon Roll; Hon Roll; NHS; Rutherford Board Of Educ Schlstc Awds-Bronze 84-85 & Silver 85-86; Natl Eng Merit Awd; Rutgers U Coll Arts/Sci.

ORLANDO, MARCELLA; Academy Of The Sacred Heart; Little Ferry, NJ; (3); Hosp Aide; JA; Math Tm; Sec NHS; Acadmc Excllnc Advncd Math, Hist, Eng, & Chem 87; Pre-Med.

ORLANDO, PETER; Christian Brothers Acad; Freehold, NJ; (3); Varsity Clb; JV Bsbl; Var JV Socr; Im Sftbl; High Hon Roll; Hon Roll; Air Force Acad; Aerospc Engrng.

ORLINA, CLARINDA; Saint Marys HS; Jersey City, NJ; (3); 2/125; Civic Clb; Drama Clb; Intnl Clb; JA; Pep Clb; PAVAS; Service Clb; Chorus; Church Choir; Concert Band; Sci & Bus Awds 85-87; Rutgers; Pre Med.

ORONSKY, CARL; John P Stevens HS; Edison, NJ; (3); 68/457; Chess Clb; Cmnty Wkr; Science Clb; Ski Clb; Var JV Bsbl; JV Bowling; JV Socr; Hon Roll; Law.

OROSA, LLIMA; Memorial HS; West New York, NJ; (3); Office Aide; Spanish Clb; NHS; Top 25 Of Soph Cls & Wrtn Excllnc 85-86; Rutgers Coll; Engl.

OROSZ, SHERYL; Mary Help Of Christians Acad; Paterson, NJ; (3); 11/86; Church Yth Grp; Red Cross Aide; SADD; VP Soph Cls; VP Jr Cls; Var Bsktbl; Var Vllybl; Hon Roll; NHS; Physcl Thrpy.

ORR, ALEXANDER; Wood-Ridge HS; Wood Ridge, NJ; (4); 9/76; French Clb; Yrbk Sprt Ed; Rep Stu Cncl; Var Bsbl; Var Ftbl; High Hon Roll; Hon Roll; NHS; St Schlr; HS Rep-Sntr Bill Brdly Stu Ldrshp Smnr 87.

ORR, KEITH M; Ridgewood High HS; Ridgewood, NJ; (3); Boy Scts; CAP; Exploring; FBLA; Math Clb; Science Clb; Band; CC Awd; Hon Roll; NHS; Aerontcl Engr.

ORRISS, CHRISTOPHER; John P Stevens HS; Edison, NJ; (3); Am Leg Boys St; Church Yth Grp; Political Wkr; Science Clb; JV Bsbl; Poltcl Sci.

ORTEGA, BLANCA; Hamilton High West Schl; Yardville, NJ; (3); Spanish Clb; Teachers Aide; Nwsp Stf; Stu Cncl; Hon Roll; Accntg.

ORTEGA, JOHNNY; Feris HS; Jersey City, NJ; (3); Boys Clb Am; Varsity Clb; Var Bsbl; Engrng.

ORTH, WENDY M; West Morris Mendham HS; Chester, NJ; (3); 123/308; Dance Clb; 4-H; Sec FHA; Pep Clb; Swing Chorus; Yrbk Stf; Rep Stu Cncl; Mgr(s); Sftbl; High Hon Roll; Fshn.

ORTIZ, CAMILLE; Hoboken HS; Hoboken, NJ; (3); Office Aide; Spanish Clb; Chorus; Sec Frsh Cls; Sec Soph Cls; Sec Jr Cls; JV Var Cheerleading.

ORTIZ, ELI; Bridgeton HS; Bridgeton, NJ; (3); High Hon Roll; Hon Roll; ID ST U; Comp Sci.

ORTIZ, JOSE; Perth Amboy HS; Perth Amboy, NJ; (3); French Clb; Office Aide; ROTC; Chorus; Rep Jr Cls; Rep Stu Cncl; Hon Roll; Annl Schlrs Dnnr 86; ROTC Acdmc Tm 85; Arch.

ORTIZ, LANDY; Perth Amboy HS; Perth Amboy, NJ; (2); High Hon Roll; Lwyr.

ORTIZ, LISA; Millville SR HS; Laurel Lake, NJ; (3); Band; Hon Roll; Barbizon; Mdlng.

ORTIZ, NOEMI; Hoboken HS; Hoboken, NJ; (3); Chorus; Color Guard; Pom Pon; Drma.

ORTIZ, PRISCILLA; Edgewood Regional Sr HS; Sicklerville, NJ; (3); 9/390; Sec French Clb; Spanish Clb; Varsity Clb; Stage Crew; Nwsp Ed-Chief; Off Lit Mag; Stat Sftbl; Jr NHS; Trs NHS; Frgn Lang.

ORTIZ, YVONNE; Hightstown HS; Hightstown, NJ; (3); Cmnty Wkr; Drama Clb; Key Clb; Library Aide; Spanish Clb; Band; Concert Band; Mrchg Band; Hon Roll; Mrktng.

ORTLOFF, WAYNE; Highland Regional HS; Blackwood, NJ; (3); 2/350; Church Yth Grp; Computer Clb; Band; Concert Band; Jazz Band; Mrchg Band; School Musical; NHS; Voice Dem Awd.

ORTON, ADAM; Central Regional HS; Seaside Hgts, NJ; (4); Ski Clb; Band; Concert Band; Var Ftbl; Var Tennis; JV Trk; High Hon Roll; Hon Roll.

ORZECHOWSKI, JULIA; Camden Catholic HS; Cherry Hill, NJ; (3); 15/349; Am Leg Aux Girls St; Nwsp Ed-Chief; Off Jr Cls; High Hon Roll; NHS; FTA; Girl Scts; Latin Clb; Mgr(s); Mat Maids; Ltn Hnr & Emerald Hnr Sctys.

OSAR, VINCENT; Vernon HS; Sussex, NJ; (3); Nwsp Stf; Lit Mag; Var Crs Cntry; Var Trk; Hon Roll; Prfct Atten Awd; Rotary Awd; Cong Yth Ldrshp Cncl Ntl Young Ldrs Cntst 87; Rotary Intntl Yth Ldrshp Conf 86; Pltcl Sci.

OSBORN, ROBINLYNN; Brick Township HS; Brick Town, NJ; (4); Drama Clb; Thesps; Nwsp Ed-Chief; Rep Frsh Cls; High Hon Roll; NHS; John Brasca Mem COE Awd 87; Katherine Gibbs Ldrshp Awd 86-87; Berkeley Schl Awd Outstndng Achvt 87; Bus Admin.

OSBORNE, DAVID; Franklin Twp HS; Somerset, NJ; (4); 4/327; Ski Clb; Concert Band; Jazz Band; Mrchg Band; Nwsp Rptr; Nwsp Sprt Ed; Pres Frsh Cls; Stat Bsktbl; Gov Hon Prg Awd; NHS; All- ST Symphonic Bnd 1st Chair 86; NJ Yth Symphony 2nd Chair 86-87; High Hnr Roll 86-87; Boston U; Jrnlsm.

OSBORNE, PATRICIA A; Carteret HS; Carteret, NJ; (3); 18/214; Am Leg Aux Girls St; Mgr Drama Clb; JCL; Sec Latin Clb; Capt Color Guard; Concert Band; Ed Nwsp Rptr; Ed Yrbk Rptr; Sec Frsh Cls; Pres Soph Cls; Rutgers; Bus Admin.

OSBORNE, RITA; Pennsauken HS; Pennsauken, NJ; (3); Camp Fr Inc; Office Aide; Rep Frsh Cls; JV Bsktbl; Hotel Mgmt.

OSER, COREY J; Rumson-Fair Haven HS; Fair Haven, NJ; (4); Trs Church Yth Grp; Drama Clb; Madrigals; School Musical; School Play; Variety Show; Ed Nwsp Stf; Var Crs Cntry; Elks Awd; High Hon Roll; NE Conf Awd Frgn Lang 87; NJ Gov Schl Altrnt Theatre 86; Bates Schlrshp 87; Bates Coll; Law.

OSGOOD, GRETCHEN; Westwood HS; Ridgewood, NJ; (2); Drama Clb; Teachers Aide; School Play; Stage Crew; Variety Show; Rep Stu Cncl; JV Vllybl; High Hon Roll; Jr NHS; NHS; Opt Clb Awd; Crtcs Awd For Exc In Cameo Role 87; Actress.

OSHEROW, LISA; Dwight-Englewood HS; Englewood, NJ; (3); Camera Clb; Dance Clb; Mgr(s); Broker.

OSHVA, PHILIP; Bridgewater-Raritan H S East; Martinsville, NJ; (4); Boy Scts; Cmnty Wkr; Debate Tm; Intnl Clb; Math Clb; Math Tm; Scholastic Bowl; Science Clb; Spanish Clb; Speech Tm; Garden St Dstngshd Schlr 86-87; U Of PA; Chem.

OSLACKY, PAUL; Don Bosco Prep HS; Tuxedo, NY; (3); SADD; Yrbk Stf; JV Crs Cntry; JV Trk; JV Wrstlng.

OSMAN, GIHAN; Madison Central HS; Old Bridge, NJ; (4); 15/367; Cmnty Wkr; Computer Clb; Pres French Clb; Key Clb; Scholastic Bowl; Spanish Clb; SADD; Pres French Hon Soc; NHS; Pres Schlr; Acdmc Letter 86-87; Rutgers Coll Of Pharmacy; Pharm.

OSMUN, MAUREEN; Phillpsburg HS; Phillipsburg, NJ; (1); Drama Clb; GAA; Sec Key Clb; Band; Drill Tm; School Play; Stage Crew; Nwsp Rptr; Cheerleading; JV Sftbl; Vet.

OSSOWSKI, DAVID; Jackson Memorial HS; Jackson, NJ; (4); 78/387; Socr; Hon Roll; Var Most Imprvd Scrr Awd 86; SR Awd 87; Ocean County Coll; Bus Mngmnt.

OST, JAMES JUSTIN; Bridgewater-Raritan West HS; Bridgewater, NJ; (3); Key Clb; Math Clb; Science Clb; Nwsp Stf; VP Capt Swmmng; JV Tennis; Hon Roll; Lehigh U; Mech Engr.

OSTAPOVICH, LYNN; Bound Brook HS; S Bound Brook, NJ; (4); 12/131; Sec Trs French Clb; Girl Scts; Pres Key Clb; Sec Concert Band; Sec Mrchg Band; Off Sr Cls; Rep Stu Cncl; Lion Awd; NHS; Ntl Merit SF.

OSTREGA, MARC; Manalapan HS; Englishtown, NJ; (3); Temple Yth Grp; Band; Concert Band; Jazz Band; Mrchg Band; School Musical; Symp Band; Yrbk Stf; Cert Hnr Outstndng Achvt Peer Cnslng 86-87; Natl Conf Christns/Jews Cert 87; Clncl Psych.

OSWALD, STACEY; Manalapan HS; Manalapan, NJ; (3); Var JV Bsktbl; Var JV Socr; Var JV Sftbl; Cert Of Hnr-Math 86-87; Bus.

OTCHET, FELICIA; Raritan HS; Hazlet, NJ; (4); 5/250; French Clb; Math Tm; Mrchg Band; Yrbk Stf; Rep Frsh Cls; Pres Soph Cls; Bsktbl; Var Capt Tennis; NHS; Science Clb; Rutgers Deans Smmr Schlr 86; Smith Coll.

OTERO, VICTORIA; Passaic County Tech Vocational HS; Paterson, NJ; (3); 4/465; Spanish Clb; Varsity Clb; Crs Cntry; Trk; High Hon Roll; Hon Roll; NHS; Mech Engr.

OTT, BRIAN; Gloucester Co Christian Schl; Turnersville, NJ; (4); 1/16; Debate Tm; Quiz Bowl; Chorus; Yrbk Stf; VP Sr Cls; Var Socr; High Hon Roll; NHS; Ntl Merit Ltr; Val; AWANA Yth Ldr; Pensacola Chrstn Coll; Mech Eng.

OTT, CHARLES; Westfield HS; Westfield, NJ; (3); 43/469; Church Yth Grp; SADD; Concert Band; Jazz Band; Orch; Bsbl; Bsktbl; Ftbl; Wt Lftg; Hon Roll; Don Larg Mem MVP Awd Ftbl & Bsbl 85; Vrsty Ftbl Ltrmn 86.

OTT, CHRISTINE N; Howell HS; Howell, NJ; (4); 38/375; VP Church Yth Grp; French Clb; FBLA; Office Aide; Chorus; Church Choir; Nwsp Stf; Lit Mag; God Cntry Awd; Jr NHS; Schlrshp From Howell Police Benevolent Assn $500; Acad Fitness Awd; Anthrplgy Awd; Trenton ST Coll; Crmnl Justice.

OTT, HEATHER; Paul VI HS; Somerdale, NJ; (4); 92/500; French Clb; Varsity Clb; Nwsp Phtg; Yrbk Sprt Ed; Rep Frsh Cls; Rep Soph Cls; Rep Jr Cls; Var L Fld Hcky; Var L Trk; NHS; Natl Frnch Cont 87.

OTT, THERESA; St James HS; Mantua, NJ; (4); 13/69; Hon Roll; Gloucester Cnty Coll; Lgl Secr.

OTTEN, JILL; Paulsboro HS; Paulsboro, NJ; (4); Art Clb; Camera Clb; Ski Clb; Teachers Aide; Lit Mag; Rep Stu Cncl; Trk; Wt Lftg; Hon Roll; Gloucester Cnty Teen Arts Fest Hnbl Mntn 86; Southern NJ Stdnt Crfts Fair 2nd Pl 87; Gloucester Cnty Coll.

OTTEN, JOY; De Paul HS; Pompton Lakes, NJ; (4); 62/156; Am Leg Aux Girls St; Church Yth Grp; GAA; Spanish Clb; Varsity Clb; L Capt Bsktbl; Var L Fld Hcky; Var L Socr; L Capt Sftbl; High Hon Roll; Vrsty Strtr Fld Hcky, Bsktbl, Sftbl ST Champs 84-85, Sftbl MVP, Bsktbl Hgh Scrер 1st Team All Cnty; Rutgers U; Accntng.

OTTEN, THEODORE; St James HS; Paulsboro, NJ; (4); 5/72; Am Leg Boys St; VP Jr Cls; Var Bsbl; Capt Bsktbl; Hon Roll; VP NHS.

OTTER, ANDREA; Hamilton High West; Trenton, NJ; (4); 3/309; Exploring; Science Clb; SADD; Chorus; Madrigals; Yrbk Ed-Chief; Lit Mag; Mgr Bsktbl; Mgr(s); High Hon Roll; Garden St Distngshd Schlr 87; Mc Galliard PTA Schlrshp 87; PBA Local 66 Wives Schlrshp 87; Trenton ST Coll; Crmnl Jstc.

OTTO, CRAIG; Livingston HS; Livingston, NJ; (3); Boy Scts; Church Yth Grp; Dance Clb; Drama Clb; PAVAS; Chorus; Orch; Swing Chorus; Variety Show; Var Crs Cntry; Theatre.

OTTO, KEVIN; Jackson Memorial HS; Jackson, NJ; (3); 68/426; Boy Scts; German Clb; Math Clb; Band; Concert Band; Mrchg Band; Ftbl; Wt Lftg; Hon Roll; German Awd 86; Acctng.

OTTO, ONEAL; Essex Catholic Boys HS; East Orange, NJ; (4); 54/99; Nwsp Rptr; Off Stu Cncl; Var Cheerleading; Capt Socr; Var Trk; High Hon Roll; Hon Roll; Cert Awd Spnsh II; Fairleigh Dickinson U; Bio.

OUDEH, ABDULAH; Hillside HS; Hillside, NJ; (1); ROTC; Drill Tm; Im Ftbl; JV Wrstlng; Montclair ST; Acctng.

OUGHOURLI, DEENA; Manchester Regional HS; Prospect Pk, NJ; (3); French Clb; GAA; Yrbk Stf; Bsktbl; Powder Puff Ftbl; Cit Awd; Amer Hstry Awd 86-87; Accntng.

OUTERBRIDGE, LEU VORNIA; Essex County Voc & Tech HS; Irvington, NJ; (2); 19/200; Church Yth Grp; FBLA; Church Choir; Rep Stu Cncl; Cit Awd; Prfct Atten Awd; Comp Prgrmr.

OUTLAW, YOLANDA; Clifford J Scott HS; E Orange, NJ; (3); 6/280; Exploring; Library Aide; Math Tm; Office Aide; Spanish Clb; Nwsp Stf; Yrbk Stf; High Hon Roll; Hon Roll; NHS; Achvmnt Awd For Upsalas Sci Enrchmnt Pgm 86; Comp Sci.

OUTWATER, NICOLE; Brick Township HS; Brick Town, NJ; (3); 9/400; German Clb; Crs Cntry; Trk; High Hon Roll; NHS.

OVERBECK, SCOTT J; Holy Cross HS; Mt Laurel, NJ; (3); 5/404; Am Leg Boys St; Boy Scts; Church Yth Grp; JV Crs Cntry; L Var Wrstlng; High Hon Roll; Hon Roll.

OWCA, BRIAN S; Clifton HS; Clifton, NJ; (3); Am Leg Boys St; Drama Clb; Math Clb; Spanish Clb; Teachers Aide; School Play; Tennis; Vllybl; Cit Awd; Hon Roll; Law.

OWCHARIW, SONIA; Abraham Clark HS; Roselle, NJ; (4); 16/130; Band; Chorus; Concert Band; Drm Mjr(t); Jazz Band; Madrigals; Mrchg Band; Swing Chorus; Variety Show; Nwsp Rptr; Mont Clair ST Coll; Intl Affrs.

OWENS, DAWN; Woodrow Wilson HS; Camden, NJ; (3); Church Yth Grp; Computer Clb; JA; Library Aide; SADD; Flag Corp; Mrchg Band; Yrbk Stf; Off Frsh Cls; Off Soph Cls; Office Bus 84-87; Co-Op 86-87; Trenton ST Coll; Bus Adm.

OWENS, GAY; Bridgeton HS; Dividing Creek, NJ; (4); Sec Church Yth Grp; Civic Clb; Soroptimist; Teachers Aide; Yrbk Stf; Rep Soph Cls; Rep Jr Cls; Rep Sr Cls; Gov Hon Prg Awd; High Hon Roll; Edward Paullin Balon II Schlrshp 87; George Washington U Mdl 86; Pres Acadmc Ftns Awd 87; Ursinus Coll; Bio.

OWENS, JOSEPH; Westside HS; Newark, NJ; (3); 22/429; Church Yth Grp; Drama Clb; FCA; Var Bsbl; Var Bsktbl; Var Crs Cntry; Var Socr; Var Trk; Cit Awd; Hon Roll; MVP-PATTERSON Bsktbl League 87; Seton Hall; Bus.

OWENS, KIMBERLY; Manasquan HS; Brielle, NJ; (3); 19/239; Art Clb; Hosp Aide; Spanish Clb; JV Bsktbl; JV Sftbl; High Hon Roll; Hon Roll; NHS; Comm.

OWENS, MONIQUE N; Monmouth Regional HS; Eatontown, NJ; (4); Trs DECA; Rep FBLA; Office Aide; Pep Clb; VP SADD; Church Choir; Hon Roll; Rep Stu Cncl; Var JV Cheerleading; Dbtnt-Mnmth Cnty Ctlln 87; Morgan ST U; Bus Admin.

OWENS, RONI; Brick HS; Brick Town, NJ; (3); Church Yth Grp; GAA; Hosp Aide; Latin Clb; Spanish Clb; SADD; Bsktbl; Bowling; Sftbl; Vllybl; Nrs.

OXTON, LORI; Palisades Park JR SR HS; Palisades Pk, NJ; (3); Cmnty Wkr; FBLA; Service Clb; Yrbk Ed-Chief; Yrbk Stf; JV Capt Cheerleading; Twrlr; Spnsh I Awd 85; Schl Svc 86; Shrthnd Spd 86; Ct Reporting Insti; Crt Rptr.

OXX, JEFF; Kearny HS; Kearny, NJ; (3); German Clb; Band; Concert Band; Mrchg Band; School Musical; Grmn Ntl Hnr Soc 87; Navy; Pilot.

OZGA, SHERYL; Cinnaminson HS; Cinnaminson, NJ; (3); Am Leg Aux Girls St; Church Yth Grp; Drama Clb; Exploring; German Clb; Hosp Aide; Science Clb; VP Thesps; Band; Chorus; Alto II Sctn Ldr Of All-S Jersey Rgnl Chorus 85; All-St Chorus 85-87; Engrng.

PAARZ, STACY; Holy Spirit HS; Absecon, NJ; (3); 17/332; Var L Cheerleading; Hon Roll; Kiwanis Awd; NHS; 2nd Rnr Up Ms NJ Teen 86.

PABLO, LETTIE A; North Middle Schl; Bloomfield, NJ; (1); Stu Yr Awd 86; Pres Phys Ftnss Awd 86; Hnr Rl 84-87; Bus Admin.

PACCIONE, JOE; Toms River HS South; Toms River, NJ; (1); JV Bowling; Hon Roll; Bus.

PACHECO, TINA MARIE; Camden Catholic HS; Camden, NJ; (3); Chorus; Church Choir; Variety Show; Northern U; Comp.

PACI, GEORGE; Princeton Day Schl; Trenton, NJ; (3); Computer Clb; Math Tm; Madrigals; Var JV Diving; Hon Roll; Telluride Assoc Smmr Pgm 87; Peer Grp Ldr 87-88; 6th ST NJ Fncng, Foil 85; Sci.

PACI JR, ROBERT J; The Lawrenceville Schl; Trenton, NJ; (4); Church Yth Grp; Chorus; Church Choir; School Play; Nwsp Stf; JV Crs Cntry; JV Wrstlng; Hon Roll; Ntl Merit SF; Im Wt Lftg; NJ Garden ST Distngushd Schlr 86-87; Rensselaer Plytch Medal Math,Sci 86; Peer Group Ldr; Williams Coll.

PACICHELLI, ANGELA; Sacred Heart HS; Bridgeton, NJ; (3); 8/56; Spanish Clb; SADD; School Musical; Yrbk Stf; Sec Trs Sr Cls; Cheerleading; Mgr(s); High Hon Roll; NHS; Secondary Educ Teacher.

PACIORKOWSKI, PATRICK JAMES; Bayonne HS; Bayonne, NJ; (4); 45/360; Boy Scts; Church Yth Grp; Cmnty Wkr; Rep Stu Cncl; Wt Lftg; High Hon Roll; Hon Roll; Lockheed Elctrncs Mgmt Assn Scholar 87; Prncpls Hnr Tech Field 87; NJIT; Elctrcl Engrng.

PACK, CHRIS; Red Bank Regional HS; Little Silver, NJ; (3); JV Bsbl; Socr; Sftbl; Trk; High Hon Roll; Hon Roll; NHS; Ntl Merit Ltr; Spanish NHS; Essay Pblshd Voices Of Conflict 87; Math Leag Awd 87; Comp Sci.

PADILLA, DIEGO; Passaic County Tech; Paterson, NJ; (3); NHS; NJIT; Engnrng.

PADRON, DOUG; Jackson Memorial HS; Jackson, NJ; (3); 130/416; Var L Ftbl; Powder Puff Ftbl; JV Trk; Var Wt Lftg; JV Wrstlng; Hon Roll; Bus Admin.

PAES, STEPHANIE; Montville Township HS; Towaco, NJ; (3); 60/240; Church Yth Grp; FBLA; JV Bsbl; High Hon Roll; Hon Roll; Literary Soc Fdn Awd 86 & 87; Am Assn Of Tchrs Of Grmn Total Immersion Wknd 87; K Gibbs Ldrshp Awd 87; Para-Legal.

PAESE, KAREN; Belvidere HS; Phillipsburg, NJ; (3); 1/135; Cmnty Wkr; Scholastic Bowl; Band; School Musical; VP Jr Cls; Rep Stu Cncl; JV Bsktbl; NHS; High Hon Roll; Chorus; Hugh O Brian Yth Fndtn Ambssdr & Miss Teen Of Amer Schlrshp & Recgntn Pgnt 86; Genetics.

PAEZ, VIVIAN; William Dickinson HS; Jersey City, NJ; (4); 43/365; Church Yth Grp; Dance Clb; Pep Clb; Church Choir; Drill Tm; Flag Corp; School Musical; School Play; VP Sr Cls; Rep Stu Cncl; The Berkeley Schls; Busnss Admn.

PAGAN, ANTONIO; Woodrow Wilson HS; Camden, NJ; (3); JV Bsbl; Hon Roll; Air Force Acad; Pilot.

PAGAN, OMAIRA; Vineland HS; Vineland, NJ; (3); Pep Clb; Rep Jr Cls; Rep Stu Cncl; Var Cheerleading; Hon Roll; Spanish NHS; Phys Thrpy.

PAGAN, PETRA; Passaic County Tech & Voc HS; Paterson, NJ; (4); 6/340; Off Jr Cls; Off Sr Cls; Stu Cncl; Bsktbl; Sftbl; Vllybl; High Hon Roll; Hon Roll; NHS; Ntl Merit Ltr; Smmr Schlr Comp 86; Ldrshp Awd All-Am 85; Math Merit Awd 85-87; Stevens Tech; Mach Engrng.

PAGE, CHRISTOPHER C; Piscataway HS; Piscataway, NJ; (4); 9/496; Math Tm; Science Clb; Rep Soph Cls; Trs Jr Cls; Rep Sr Cls; High Hon Roll; Hon Roll; NHS; Ntl Merit SF; Math.

PAGLIONE, CHERYL; Notre Dame HS; Robbinsville, NJ; (3); 3/373; Service Clb; Varsity Clb; Chorus; School Musical; Nwsp Stf; Tennis; High Hon Roll; NHS; Spanish NHS; Voice Dem Awd; U PA; Intl Bus.

PAGLIONE, LISA; Life Center Acad; Burlington, NJ; (3); 4/28; Drama Clb; School Play; Nwsp Ed-Chief; Trs Jr Cls; Tennis; Congressnl Yth Ldrshp Cncl 86-87; 2nd & 3rd Pl Photogrphy Comptn 85 & 86; 1st Ping Pong Comptn 85 & 86; Zoolgy.

PAGLIUCA, CAROLYN; Cresskill HS; Cresskill, NJ; (4); 28/115; Ski Clb; Spanish Clb; Stage Crew; Pres Jr Cls; VP Sr Cls; Rep Stu Cncl; Sftbl; Vllybl; High Hon Roll; Hon Roll; Natl Hnr Scty Grnt 87; CHS PTSA SR Svc Awd 87; Pace U; Bus.

PAIK, EDWARD Y; Glen Rock HS; Glen Rock, NJ; (4); 7/153; Am Leg Boys St; Band; Concert Band; Jazz Band; Mrchg Band; Orch; School Musical; Capt Trk; Vllybl; St Schlr; Natl Mrt Semi Fnlst 87; Instrmntl Music Acad Awd 87; Columbia U; Engr.

PAINI, CRISSY; Phillipsburg HS; Phillipsburg, NJ; (3); 42/315; Drama Clb; Thesps; Chorus; School Musical; School Play; Variety Show; Sec Jr Cls; JV Var Cheerleading; Hon Roll; NHS; Natl Hnr Soc; Hnr Roll; Talnt Awds; Music Mjr.

PAJAK, KAREN ANNETTE; Sayreville War Memorial HS; Sayreville, NJ; (4); Church Yth Grp; Pres Dance Clb; School Musical; Lit Mag; Stu Cncl; VFW Awd; Voice Dem Awd; Al-Estrn Chorus 87; Al-ST Chorus 86; Smmr Arts Inst Schlrshp Rutgers U New Brunswck 85 & 86; Rutgers U; Music.

PAJAK, SUSAN ELLEN; Sayreville War Memorial HS; Sayreville, NJ; (2); Church Yth Grp; Pres Dance Clb; Drama Clb; PAVAS; Chorus; School Musical; Nwsp Rptr; Lit Mag; Rep Stu Cncl; Cheerleading; Summer Art Inst Scholar Awd Rutgers U 85-87; Dance.

PAJARILLO, KAREN; Union HS; Union, NJ; (3); Sec French Clb; Hosp Aide; Key Clb; Science Clb; Jazz Band; Mrchg Band; Orch; Nwsp Sprt Ed; Rep Stu Cncl; Fld Hcky; Outstndng Achvt Sci 84-85; ST Sci Day Awd, 41st Grls Ctznshp Inst Spnsrd NJ St Fdrtn Wmn Clbs 87; Med.

PAK, KI YOUNG; Rutherford HS; Rutherford, NJ; (3); JV Bsbl; JV Ftbl; JV Trk; Acctng.

PAK, RICHARD; Vineland HS; Vineland, NJ; (2); 1/818; Computer Clb; Key Clb; Latin Clb; Stu Cncl; High Hon Roll; Hon Roll; Prfct Atten Awd; U PA; Doctor.

PAK, SANGWOO; Pemberton Township HS II; Browns Mills, NJ; (3); 1/454; Am Leg Boys St; Church Yth Grp; Cmnty Wkr; Math Tm; Scholastic Bowl; Nwsp Rptr; Yrbk Stf; JV Socr; Var Tennis; NHS.

PALAMARA, LISA; Paramus HS; Paramus, NJ; (4); 12/330; Cmnty Wkr; Trs VP Service Clb; Nwsp Stf; Rep Sr Cls; Stat Trk; NHS; Ntl Merit SF; Nwsp Rptr; Yrbk Stf; Lit Mag; Italian Hnr Soc Sec & Pres 83-87; Leonardo Da Vinci Soc Awd Outstndng Achvt 87; Pres Phys Fit 83-87; Rutgers U; Phrmcy.

PALANGIO, FRANCO; Marist HS; Bayonne, NJ; (3); AFS; Camera Clb; Dance Clb; English Clb; French Clb; German Clb; Key Clb; Political Wkr; Scholastic Bowl; Service Clb; Phy Thrpst.

PALASITS, JENNIFER; Union HS; Union, NJ; (3); Am Leg Aux Girls St; Church Yth Grp; Key Clb; Science Clb; Spanish Clb; Band; JV Fld Hcky; Capt Trk; Hon Roll; NHS.

PALLANTE, SHIRLEY; Gateway Reg HS; Westville, NJ; (4); 55/205; FHA; Key Clb; Latin Clb; VP SADD; Rep Stu Cncl; Stat Bsktbl; Var Fld Hcky; JV Sftbl; Stat Trk; Hon Roll; Alt Rtry Yth Ldrshp 86; 3 Letter Vrsty Sprts Awd 86; Misericordia; Bus Admn.

PALLIS, MARK P; High Point Regional HS; Branchville, NJ; (3); 3/268; Am Leg Boys St; Debate Tm; Science Clb; Pres Sr Cls; Rep Stu Cncl; Var Ftbl; Var Trk; Var Wrstlng; NHS; Ntl Merit Ltr; Acdmc All Amer Awd, Acdmc Enrchmnt Pgm Outstndng Achvt 87; Med.

PALMA, DOUGLAS; Ranlucas Vly Regional HS; Mount Holly, NJ; (4 1/248; Am Leg Boys St; Varsity Clb; Capt Var Golf; Var Socr; Capt Va Swmmng; Elks Awd; High Hon Roll; NHS; Val; VFW Awd; Mt Holl Wmns Leag Schlrshp 87; Tmpl U Pres Awd 87; Mt Holly Rtry Cl Schlrshp 87; Temple U; Phys Ther.

PALMER, KELLY; Clayton HS; Clayton, NJ; (4); 25/75; Key Clb; Nws Bus Mgr; Nwsp Stf; Yrbk Bus Mgr; Yrbk Stf; Trs Soph Cls; Trs Sr Cl Rep Stu Cncl; Sftbl; Lt Gov Of NJ Dist Of Key Clb Intl 85-86; Secy Of N Dist Of Key Clb Intl 86-87; Widener U; Htl-Rstrnt Admin.

PALMER, KIMBERLEY; Asbury Park HS; Avon, NJ; (3); 4/190; Offic Aide; Pep Clb; Nwsp Ed-Chief; Nwsp Rptr; Yrbk Rptr; Var Bsktbl; Va Bowling; Var Sftbl; Hon Roll; NHS; Vrsty Schlr 85-87; Omega Psi Ph Frtnrty Ctznshp 86; Jrnlsm.

PALMER, MICHAEL; Southern Regional HS; Manahawkin, NJ; (4); 400; Model UN; Q&S; Yrbk Ed-Chief; Var Capt Crs Cntry; Golf; High Ho Roll; NHS; Sal; St Schlr; Cmnty Wkr; Exchng Clb Schlrshp, Rbrt C Byr Schlrshp 87; U Of PA; Bus.

PALMER, QUANAE; Rahway SR HS; Rahway, NJ; (4); 51/239; Se Church Yth Grp; JA; Pres NAACP; Teachers Aide; Pres Chorus; Churc Choir; Madrigals; Yrbk Rptr; Pres Sr Cls; Jr NHS; NAACP Yth ST Bd 8 Hnr Rl Stu; Rutgers U; Pre-Law.

PALMIERI, AMY; Gloucestor County Christian Schl; Woodbury, NJ; (1 Spanish Clb; Chorus; School Musical; Sec Stu Cncl; Var Bsktbl; Var Fl Hcky; Var Sftbl; Var Trk; Hon Roll.

PALMIERI, JODI; Wall HS; Manasquan, NJ; (3); 27/289; Sec Dram Clb; Ski Clb; Spanish Clb; School Musical; School Play; High Hon Rol Hon Roll; Chmstry.

PALMIERI JR, VINCENT J; Southern Regional HS; Barnegat, NJ; (4 17/383; Model UN; Variety Show; Stu Cncl; Var Bsbl; Var Bowling; JV C Cntry; High Hon Roll; Hon Roll; NHS; Pres Schlr; 1st Pl Essy Wnnr 8 Am HS Athlt 84; PA ST; Bus Adm.

PALMUCCI, ANTHONY; Bricktownship Memorial HS; Bricktown, N (3); Band; Concert Band; Jazz Band; Mrchg Band; Hon Roll; Musician Inst; Music Career.

PALMUCCI, SUSAN; Rahway HS; Rahway, NJ; (3); Church Yth Gr Girl Scts; Hosp Aide; Sec JA; Sec Service Clb; Capt Color Guard; Yrb Ed-Chief; Rep Jr Cls; High Hon Roll; Hon Roll; Bus Mngmnt.

PALOMO, KIMBERLY A; Atlantic City HS; Atlantic City, NJ; (4); 3 402; Drama Clb; Chorus; Jazz Band; Orch; School Musical; School Pla Var Cheerleading; JV Fld Hcky; Var Sftbl; Hon Roll; Semi-Finalist Talent Expo 86; Maude Norris Awd For Outstndng Stu 87; Els Mechaskie Music Awd 87; Carnegie-Mellon U; Music.

PALUCH, MOTRJA; Collegiate HS; Rutherford, NJ; (1); Art Cl Church Yth Grp; Dance Clb; Drama Clb; Latin Clb; Church Choir; J Socr; Var Vllybl; Hon Roll; Ukranian Am Yth Assoc 77-87; Arch.

PALUCH, ULJANA; Collegiate HS; Rutherford, NJ; (1); Church Yt Grp; Girl Scts; JCL; Latin Clb; Teachers Aide; JV Socr; JV Capt Vllyb Hon Roll.

PALUMBO, CAROL-LYNN; St John Vianney HS; Holmdel, NJ; (2 Intnl Clb; Service Clb; Ski Clb; Bsktbl; Var Crs Cntry; JV Trk; Hon Ro Acad Awd, Var Ltr X-Cntry 86-87; Villanova; Pharm.

PALUMBO, GINA; Ocean Township HS; Ocean, NJ; (3); Key Cl SADD; Yrbk Phtg; Yrbk Stf; Bus.

PALUMBO, LENNY; Belleville HS; Belleville, NJ; (3); Boy Scts; Ban Concert Band; Jazz Band; Mrchg Band; Stage Crew; Off Jr Cls; Stu Cn Acctg.

PALUS, MARK; Indian Hills HS; Franklin Lks, NJ; (4); 10/283; Am L Boys St; Cmnty Wkr; Math Tm; Red Cross Aide; Science Clb; Ski Cl Nwsp Stf; Yrbk Stf; JV Bsbl; NHS; Rotary & Rutgers Deans Me Schlrshps 87; Natl Merit Ltr Commendation 87; Rutgers U; Engrng.

PAMPANIN, TINA; Paul VI Regional HS; Clifton, NJ; (3); Pres Chur Yth Grp; Pres Key Clb; Ski Clb; Pres Spanish Clb; JV Sftbl; JV Vllyb High Hon Roll; Hon Roll; Pres Spanish NHS; Lawyer.

PANAROTTO, ANNMARIE; Parsippany HS; Lake Hiawatha, NJ; (3 Math Tm; Pep Clb; Varsity Clb; Rep Frsh Cls; Rep Soph Cls; Rep Jr C JV Var Cheerleading; High Hon Roll; Hon Roll.

PANAS, RICHARD; Millville SR HS; Millville, NJ; (3); 44/524; Churc Yth Grp; FCA; VICA; Band; Church Choir; Concert Band; Mrchg Ban Hon Roll; U MD College Park; Drftng.

PANCERI, DONNA; Sacred Heart HS; Richland, NJ; (3); Art Cl German Clb; Mgr Stage Crew; Yrbk Ed-Chief; Lit Mag; Mgr(s); Hon Ro Sec NHS; Prfct Atten Awd.

PANCIONE, DANIELLE; Mount St Mary Acad; Piscataway, NJ; (4 GAA; Pep Clb; Service Clb; Spanish Clb; VP Frsh Cls; Rep Soph Cls; Re Jr Cls; Hon Roll; Spanish NHS; VP Nat Spnsh Hnr Soc 86-87; Cum Lau Natl Latin Exam 83; Marymount Coll; Intl Bus.

PANDYA, RUPAM; Metuchen HS; Metuchen, NJ; (4); 33/164; Frenc Clb; Math Tm; Science Clb; Var Fld Hcky; Hon Roll; NHS; Rutgers U Biochem.

PANEK, DAVE; Audubon HS; Audubon, NJ; (3); German Clb; JV Bsktbl; Var L Golf; Hon Roll; Elec Engr.

PANELLA, TARA; Bloomfield HS; Bloomfield, NJ; (3); Sec Am Leg A Girls St; Drama Clb; German Clb; Hosp Aide; Key Clb; Rep Soph Cls; V Trk; High Hon Roll; Ntl Merit SF; Opt Clb Awd.

PANFEN, MARISOL; Long Branch HS; Long Br, NJ; (3); 9/314; J Band; Concert Band; Mrchg Band; Symp Band; Var Bowling; Var Socr; J Var Sftbl; Var Twrlr; Econ Awd 86; 4.0 Avg Awd 86-87; Engr.

PANGIA, KAREN; Edgewood Regional SR HS; Atco, NJ; (3); Deba Tm; Quiz Bowl; Spanish Clb; Yrbk Stf; Stat Bsbl; JV Cheerleading; H Roll; Bus.

PANGILINAN, ALMA; Secaucus HS; Secaucus, NJ; (3); 18/166; Dram Clb; Key Clb; Ski Clb; Mrchg Band; School Play; Off Frsh Cls; Sec S Cncl; Stat Bsktbl; Stat Ftbl; High Hon Roll; Frgn Lang Dept Awd, S Cncl Merit Awd 85; Prfrmng Arts Awd-Dance & Stage 86; Columbia Bus.

PANGILINAN, ROEHL; Academic HS; Jersey City, NJ; (3); Am Le Boys St; Computer Clb; Stage Crew; Trs Stu Cncl; JV Bowling; JV So Computer Clb; Hon Roll; NHS; Ntl Merit Schol; City Acad Achvt Citatio 87; Columbia; Comm.

PANICHELLI, ANGELA; Sacred Heart HS; Bridgetown, NJ; (3); 9/5 Spanish Clb; SADD; School Play; Yrbk Stf; Sec Trs Cls; V Cheerleading; Stat Socr; High Hon Roll; NHS; Sec Ed.

PANICO, MICHAEL A; Fair Lawn HS; Fair Lawn, NJ; (4); 1/329; A Leg Boys St; Math Tm; Varsity Clb; Rep Frsh Cls; Rep Soph Cls; Rep Cls; Rep Sr Cls; Capt Wrstlng; Bausch & Lomb Sci Awd; High Hon Ro Robert C Byrd Schlrshp, Grdn ST Dstngshd Schlr, NJ ST Intr Schls Athltc Assn Schlr Athlt Awd 87; Harvard; Bio.

PANICO, RICHARD; Holy Spirit HS; Ventnor, NJ; (4); #36 In Class; Church Yth Grp; Varsity Clb; Church Choir; Im Bsktbl; Im Powder Puff Ftbl; Capt Swmmng; Im Wt Lftg; High Hon Roll; Hon Roll; Jr NHS; Ntl Latin Awd 86; Ntl Rowing Chmpn 85 & 86; U PA.

PANICOE, DANIEL; West Essex Regional HS; Fairfield, NJ; (3); Drama Clb; Intnl Clb; Key Clb; Variety Show; Rep Jr Cls; Pres Sr Cls; Pres Stu Cncl; Stat Ftbl; Wt Lftg; High Hon Roll; Toyota Sports Awd 85; Outstndng Ctznshp, Schlrshp Awd 85; FBI.

PANICUCCI, MARIANNE; Bridgewater-Raritan HS East; Martinsville, NJ; (3); Church Yth Grp; Cmnty Wkr; Spanish Clb; Chorus; Church Choir; Jazz Band; Mrchg Band; High Hon Roll; Hon Roll; NHS; Vrsty Lrrd Mrchng & Jazz 86 & 87; Law.

PANNER, TAMMY; Washington Twp HS; Turnersville, NJ; (3); 2/540; French Clb; Sec Girl Scts; Trs Soph Cls; Rep Stu Cncl; Sftbl; High Hon Roll; Jr NHS; NHS; Rotary Awd; Pre-Med.

PANNONE, PAUL; Brick Memorial HS; Brick, NJ; (3); Band; Concert Band; Capt Mrchg Band; Pep Band; Variety Show; Hon Roll.

PANNUCCI, JAMES; Columbia HS; Maplewood, NJ; (3); 82/513; Ski Clb; Ftbl; Wt Lftg; Chem.

PANOCEK, JAMES; Mc Corristin Catholic HS; Trenton, NJ; (3); 6/230; Trs Frsh Cls; JV Bsbl; Var Socr; Var Tennis; Hon Roll; Debate Tm; Sci Fair Awd 86-87.

PANSERA, ANGELA; Kingsway Regional HS; Swedesboro, NJ; (4); 1/160; Key Clb; Science Clb; Yrbk Stf; Powder Puff Ftbl; Bausch & Lomb Sci Awd; High Hon Roll; NHS; Prfct Atten Awd; St Schlr; Kingsway-Rutgers Schlrshp 87; Best Avg/Math 87; Best Sci Stu 87; Rutgers U; Chem.

PANSTER, MIKE; J P Stevens HS; Edison, NJ; (3); 125/450; Debate Tm; Key Clb; Ski Clb; Temple Yth Grp; Pres Y-Teens; Stage Crew; Nwsp Bus Mgr; Yrbk Stf; Rep Frsh Cls; Rep Soph Cls; Bus.

PANTELIONE, CYNTHIA; Middle Township HS; Belleplain, NJ; (4); 8/228; Church Yth Grp; Stage Crew; Pres Schlr; Elmer Smith & Frances Nelson & Elizabeth Soeder Schlrshps 87; PR Inter American U; Chem.

PANTOS, DAVID M; Madison Central HS; Old Bridge, NJ; (3); 15/360; Am Leg Boys St; Debate Tm; Pres Soph Cls; Stu Cncl; Var L Trk; High Hon Roll; Hon Roll; Pres NHS; Ntl Merit Ltr; Math Tm; Gov Schl Of Public Issues-Finalist 87; Ldr Of Yth Political Awareness Grp 87-88; Bus Mgmt.

PANZITTA, THOMAS; Notre Dame HS; Trenton, NJ; (3); Art II Awd 85-86; Art III Advncd Awd 86-87; Hnr Roll 85-86; :Comp Grphcs.

PAOLA, MARYANN DI; Hamilton HS; Trenton, NJ; (4); 21/298; Hosp Aide; Key Clb; Concert Band; Mrchg Band; Stage Crew; Nwsp Phtg; Yrbk Phtg; Stat Swmmng; Voice Dem Awd; Hnr Grad 87; Pres Schlrshp At U Scrntn 87; Elem Schl PTA Schlrshp 87; U Scrntn; Physcl Thrpy.

PAOLILLO, NADINE; St John Vianney HS; Morganville, NJ; (4); 90/249; Art Clb; Church Yth Grp; FBLA; Library Aide; Ski Clb; SADD; Yrbk Stf; Rep Jr Cls; Rep Sr Cls; Mgr(s); Loyola Coll.

PAOLINE, JOSEPH; Paul VI HS; Runnemede, NJ; (4); 3/501; Math Clb; Spanish Clb; Cit Awd; Hon Roll; NHS; NJ Grdn ST Schlrshp 87; Phila Coll Of Phrmcy & Sci Pres Schlrshp 87; Phrmcy.

PAOLINI, DAVE; Holy Cross HS; Palmyra, NJ; (4); 42/366; Ski Clb; Church Choir; Yrbk Phtg; JV Im Bsbl; Hon Roll; Trenton ST Coll; Comp Sci.

PAOLINI, GLORIA; Hillsborough HS; S Somerville, NJ; (3); 67/328; Library Aide; Band; Color Guard; Hon Roll; :Astrnmy.

PAPADATOS, LOUIS; West Milford HS; W Milford, NJ; (3); 1/408; Chrmn Am Leg Boys St; German Clb; Quiz Bowl; Hon Roll; NHS; Val; Ger Hnr Soc 87; Strategy & Mltry Hstry Clb 86-87; Learning Unltd 87.

PAPAGELOPOULOS, MARIA; Dover HS; Dover, NJ; (4); 21/187; VP Church Yth Grp; French Clb; Office Aide; Q&S; VP Spanish Clb; Chorus; Nwsp Stf; Lit Mag; High Hon Roll; Hon Roll; Dover Fire Dept Schlrshp 87; St Andrews Phlptchs Schlrshp 87; La Roche Coll.

PAPALEO, BETSY; Cherry Hill H S East; Cherry Hill, NJ; (4); Drama Clb; French Clb; Letterman Clb; Cheerleading; Powder Puff Ftbl; Sftbl; Hon Roll; Pres Schlr; Ball ST U; Gen Bus.

PAPENBERG, JIM; Rutherford HS; Rutherford, NJ; (3); 7/177; Am Leg Boys St; Spanish Clb; Var Capt Bsbl; Var Capt Ftbl; Var Trk; Var Wrstlng; High Hon Roll; Hon Roll; NHS; Bsbll All-Lg 86-87; Ftbll All-Lg 85-86.

PAPP, ALBERT; Columbia HS; Maplewood, NJ; (4); Chess Clb; Computer Clb; German Clb; Jazz Band; Mrchg Band; Orch; School Musical; Symp Band; Vllybl; Grmn Achvt Steuben Awd 87fdelta Epsilon Phi 86-87; Rutgers Coll; Comp Sci.

PAPP, LISA; Bordentown Reg HS; Bordentown, NJ; (4); 2/114; Am Leg Aux Girls St; Drama Clb; Key Clb; Ski Clb; Chorus; Yrbk Stf; Var Bowling; Var Cheerleading; Pres NHS; Sal; NJ; Coca-Cola Bwlng Schlrshp 86; Grdn ST Dstnbgshd Schlr 87; 1st Tm All Cnty Bwlng 84-87; Pre-Law.

PAPPALARDO, MARC; Toms River East HS; Toms River, NJ; (3); 52/459; Varsity Clb; Var Bsbl; Var Ftbl; Var Trk; Hon Roll; NHS; Acadc Ltr 84-85; Presdntl Physcl Ftns Awd 84-86; S Jersey St Bsbl Chmpns 87.

PAPPALARDO, VINCENT; Lenape Valley Regional HS; Sparta, NJ; (4); 14/241; Pres Frsh Cls; Pres Jr Cls; Pres Sr Cls; Stu Cncl; Var Ftbl; Var Trk; VP NHS; Grdn ST Dstngshd Schlr 86; Pres Acadmc Ftns Awd, Sussex Cnty All Leag Awd Trk 87; Rutgers U; Engrng.

PAPPAS, ELENI; St Dominic Acad; Bayonne, NJ; (4); 9/148; French Clb; GAA; JCL; Service Clb; SADD; Acpl Chr; Yrbk Rptr; L Var Fld Hcky; High Hon Roll; NHS; Outstndng Achvt Frnch & Hstry; U Southern CA; Aerospc Engr.

PAPPAS, EMANUEL; Cherry Hill HS West; Cherry Hill, NJ; (3); Am Leg Boys St; Science Clb; Spanish Clb; Band; Symp Band; Rep Frsh Cls; Rep Soph Cls; Bsbl; Socr; NHS; Biomed Engr.

PAPPAS, MARIA; Highland Regional HS; Clementon, NJ; (3); 43/300; Computer Clb; Stat Bsbl; Im Cheerleading; Stat Socr; Hon Roll; Drexel U; Finance.

PARADISE, ELAINE; Toms River North HS; Toms River, NJ; (3); Var L Cheerleading; Hon Roll; UNC Wilmington.

PARAMESWARAN, MAHESH; Fair Lawn HS; Fair Lawn, NJ; (3); 13/543; Math Clb; Math Tm; Science Clb; Rep Soph Cls; Rep Jr Cls; Rep Stu Cncl; Var Tennis; Hon Roll; NHS; Vrsty Fencing 86-87; Pre-Med.

PARDINI, JOHN; Gloucester Catholic HS; Wenonah, NJ; (3); NFL; Science Clb; Nwsp Rptr; Yrbk Stf; Var Bsktbl; Var Crs Cntry; Var Score Keeper; Var Timer; Var Trk; Im Wt Lftg; Outstndg Sls Awd Radio Shack 87; Pres NHS 87; Temple U; Med.

PARDO, EDDIE; Perth Amboy HS; Perth Amboy, NJ; (3); JA; Varsity Clb; Stage Crew; Variety Show; Var JV Bsktbl; Var JV Crs Cntry; JV Ftbl; Var Wt Lftg; Hon Roll; Bsktbl Hnr 84-85; Crss Cntry Ltr 86-87; Acctng.

PAREKH, NICKEN; William L Dickinson HS; Jersey City, NJ; (3); Math Clb; Scholastic Bowl; VP Science Clb; Nwsp Rptr; Yrbk Stf; Lit Mag; CC Awd; Hon Roll; NCTE Awd; VP NHS; Compltn Guitar & Piano Course 85; Stevens Tech Explres Clb 86; Awd HS Schlrs Comp Sci Prog 87; Columbia U; Med.

PARENT, NICOLE; Toms River North HS; Toms River, NJ; (3); 78/459; Spanish Clb; JV Fld Hcky; Rutgers U; Erly Chldhd Educ.

PARETTI, JOSEPH; Elmwood Park Memorial HS; Elmwood Park, NJ; (4); 5/175; Library Aide; Math Clb; Band; Concert Band; Mrchg Band; School Musical; School Play; Stage Crew; Tennis; Hon Roll.

PARETTI, LISA; Memorial HS; Elmwood Park, NJ; (4); 1/150; Math Clb; Band; Yrbk Stf; Rep Stu Cncl; Sftbl; High Hon Roll; NHS; Spanish NHS.

PARGOT, LYNN; Gill St Bernards HS; Martinsville, NJ; (3); Hosp Aide; School Musical; Variety Show; Bsktbl; Cheerleading; Sftbl; Psych.

PARINELLO, DANIEL; Sayreville War Memorial HS; Parlin, NJ; (4); Drm & Bgl; Capt Mrchg Band; Church Yth Grp; Cmnty Wkr; Band; Concert Band; Stage Crew; Nwsp Rptr; Outstndng Muscn-Band 87; Wesley Coll.

PARIS, PETER B; Princeton HS; Princeton, NJ; (4); Church Yth Grp; Pres Sr Cls; Var Bsktbl; Var Ftbl; Im Lcrss; Powder Puff Ftbl; Var Trk; Harvard.

PARIS, PETER F; Glen Rock SR HS; Glen Rock, NJ; (4); DECA; Library Aide; Ski Clb; Nwsp Phtg; Nwsp Stf; Yrbk Phtg; Ed Yrbk Stf; JV Var Ftbl; Fnlst Schl Vsl Arts Schlrshp Cmpttn 87; Top 20 Ovrll Rgnl DECA Cmpttn ST Lvl 87; School Of Visual Arts; Photo.

PARISI, DAVID EDWARD; Ridgefield Park HS; Little Ferry, NJ; (4); 13/190; Chess Clb; Debate Tm; Concert Band; Capt Crs Cntry; Trk; Hon Roll; NHS; Aero Schlrshp Teterboro Arprt 87; Rutgers Coll; Engr.

PARK, CHRISTINA; Eastern Christian HS; Wyckoff, NJ; (4); #10 In Class; Cmnty Wkr; Drama Clb; Chorus; School Play; Nwsp Rptr; Ed Nwsp Stf; Sec Jr Cls; Hon Roll; Lion Awd; NHS; Messiah Acdmc Schlrshp $500 Per Yr 87; Messiah Coll; Art Teach.

PARK, EDWARD; Wayne Valley HS; Wayne, NJ; (3); 1/285; Am Leg Boys St; Hosp Aide; Model UN; Ed Nwsp Stf; Ed Yrbk Stf; Ed Lit Mag; VP Pres Stu Cncl; Cit Awd; High Hon Roll; NHS; Medicine.

PARK, JAMES; Northern Valley Regional HS; Harrington Park, NJ; (4); 2/270; Boy Scts; Computer Clb; Debate Tm; Drama Clb; Math Tm; Science Clb; Nwsp Rptr; Lit Mag; Rep Stu Cncl; JV Tennis; Debate Tm & Spkr Awds 84-87; 2nd ST NJ Bio 83; NJ ST Sci Day 2nd ST 83, 10th ST 86; Harvard U; Lawyer.

PARK, MARY; Fort Lee HS; Ft Lee, NJ; (3); Art Clb; Camera Clb; Church Yth Grp; Cmnty Wkr; Computer Clb; Key Clb; Math Tm; Science Clb; Salvation Army Schlrshp 87; Tri-M Music Hnr Soc 85; Rutgers Coll; Engrng.

PARKE, MARK; Kittatinny Regional HS; Newton, NJ; (4); 50/230; Boy Scts; Teachers Aide; Varsity Clb; JV Bsbl; Var Socr; JV Trk; Var Wrstlng; Hon Roll; Temple U; Cvl Cnstrctn Engrng.

PARKER, BRAD; Washington Township HS; Turnersville, NJ; (3); Ski Clb; Im Bsktbl; L Golf; Im Wt Lftg; Hon Roll.

PARKER, BRUCE; Burlington Twp HS; Burlington, NJ; (3); 39/129; Am Leg Boys St; Hosp Aide; Church Yth Grp; Drama Clb; Chorus; Madrigals; Mock Trial 87; Mdl Cngrss 88; Trenton ST; Hstry.

PARKER, BRUCE; John F Kennedy HS; Willingboro, NJ; (3); 26/293; Boy Scts; Trs Computer Clb; Key Clb; Latin Clb; Science Clb; Concert Band; Jazz Band; Yrbk Sprt Ed; Tennis; Hon Roll; Natl Hnr Rl 87; RCA Engrng Pgm 85; MIT; Engrng.

PARKER, GEORGE F; St Rose HS; Belmar, NJ; (4); 6/207; Nwsp Stf; Lit Mag; Pres Soph Cls; Rep Jr Cls; Sec Stu Cncl; Capt Var Bsktbl; Var Tennis; High Hon Roll; Kiwanis Awd; Ntl Merit SF; CYO Bsktbl Schlrshp 87; Rutgers Coll; Engl.

PARKER, JENNIFER; Bridgewater-Rantan High Schl East; Bridgewater, NJ; (3); Church Yth Grp; Intnl Clb; Spanish Clb; SADD; Chorus; School Musical; Stu Cncl; Powder Puff Ftbl; Hon Roll; NHS; Psnsh Tutoring Cert 85-86; Educ.

PARKER, KARIN; Middle Township HS; Cmch, NJ; (3); Church Yth Grp; Key Clb; Spanish Clb; Trs Frsh Cls; Trs Soph Cls; Trs Jr Cls; Rep Stu Cncl; Stat Bsktbl; Mgr(s); JV Var Sftbl; NY U; Bus.

PARKER, KATHI; Rancocas Valley Regional HS; Mt Holly, NJ; (2); Var Gym; JV Lcrss.

PARKER, KATRINA; Franklin HS; Somerset, NJ; (3); Church Yth Grp; Cmnty Wkr; FBLA; Hosp Aide; Church Choir; Color Guard; Rep Soph Cls; Stat Bsktbl; Sftbl; Library Aide; Progressive Natl Baptist Assoc 87; Comp Engr.

PARKER, MELISSA; Shore Regional HS; Oceanport, NJ; (3); Trs Key Clb; Chorus; School Musical; Stage Crew; JV Bsktbl; Var JV Socr; High Hon Roll; NHS; Chem Yth Schlrs Inst 87; Hnrb Mntn Tri-State Sci Fair 87; All Shore Choir 87.

PARKER, NICKOLE; Pleasantville HS; Pleasantville, NJ; (3); Church Yth Grp; Band; Church Choir; Concert Band; Mrchg Band; Pep Band; Yrbk Stf; Sec Mgr(s); Capt Pom Pon; Var Sftbl; Pre Law.

PARKER, SCOTT; Riverside HS; Riverside, NJ; (3); Chess Clb; Church Yth Grp; Concert Band; Mrchg Band; Bsbl; Hon Roll; Ntl Merit Ltr.

PARKER, SHARON; Summit HS; Summit, NJ; (4); 50/278; Drama Clb; Concert Band; Mrchg Band; School Musical; Yrbk Stf; Rep Stu Cncl; JV Sftbl; Var Swmmng; High Hon Roll; Capt YMCA Swm Tm 86-87; MVP Swm Tm 86-87; Providence Coll.

PARKER, SKIP; Madison Avenue Baptist Acad; Elmwood Park, NJ; (3); Church Yth Grp; Church Choir; Bsktbl; L Socr; Hon Roll; Garden ST Assn Chrstn Schl Comptn 1st & 2nd Pl Spch 86-87, 2nd Pol Sci & Econ 87; Geom Achvt Awd 86; US Military Acad.

PARKER JR, STEPHEN R; Egg Harbor Township HS; Pleasantville, NJ; (3); 9/360; Stat Cmnty Wkr; Computer Clb; Hon Roll; Vrsty Schlstc Awd 85-86; Comm Jstc Inst Of Atlantic Cnty Schl Mdtr 86; Otstndng Svc Awd; Psb Trenton ST U; Comp Eng.

PARKER, W LARRY; Eatontown HS; Eatontown, NJ; (4); 4/234; Exploring; Political Wkr; SADD; School Musical; Nwsp Stf; Sr Cls; Mgr(s); Score Keeper; NHS; Ntl Merit SF; Edtrl Antrbtr Lcl Nwsppr 85-87; Mmbr Monmouth Rgnl Mck Trl Tm 85-87; Peer Tutor 85-87; Pltcl Sci.

PARKER, WENDY; Mendham HS; Chester, NJ; (2); 4-H; Intnl Clb; Ski Clb; Stu Cncl; Hon Roll; Campus Life.

PARKERSON, ROBIN; Clayton HS; Clayton, NJ; (3); Yrbk Ed-Chief; Yrbk Rptr; Yrbk Stf; Bsktbl; Hon Roll; Drftng.

PARKHOUSE, JASON; Sussex County Vo-Tech; Montague, NJ; (4); 2/175; SADD; Yrbk Sprt Ed; VP Stu Cncl; Socr; Swmmng; High Hon Roll; Pres NHS; Garden ST Dist Schlr 86-87; Auburn Univ; Engrng.

PARKHURST, PAMELA R; Middle Township HS; Cape May C H, NJ; (4); 47/228; Church Yth Grp; Ski Clb; Band; Jazz Band; Mrchg Band; Symp Band; Var Golf; Hon Roll; William T Douglass Schlrshp 87; Ursinus Coll; Bus Admin.

PARKS, AMY C; Vineland HS; Vineland, NJ; (4); 2/736; Key Clb; Acpl Chr; Drm Mjr(t); Sec Mrchg Band; Orch; Symp Band; NHS; Ntl Merit Ltr; All-Cmbrlnd Cnty Hnrs Bnd 83-87; Grdn ST Dstngshd Schlr 86-87; Snd Engr.

PARKS, JUDITH A; Buena Regional HS; Dorothy, NJ; (4); 16/180; Acpl Chr; Chorus; Ltr Knwldg 83-86; Atlantic Co CC Schlrshp 86-87; Bus Admin.

PARKS, KATHLEEN; Bishop George Ahr HS; Edison, NJ; (4); Exploring; Intnl Clb; Math Tm; Model UN; Science Clb; Ski Clb; Nwsp Rptr; Nwsp Stf; Lit Mag; Mgr(s); Amer Lgn Awd 87; Bucknell U; Bio.

PARKS, PIERRE; Hillside HS; Hillside, NJ; (2); Church Yth Grp; Hosp Aide; Leo Clb; Spanish Clb; Church Choir; Stu Cncl; Hon Roll; U Of PA; Med.

PARKS, ROBERT E; Christian Brothers Acad; Bricktown, NJ; (3); Chorus; Ed Lit Mag; Rep Jr Cls; Mgr Wrstlng; Hon Roll; NHS; Ntl Merit Ltr; Gen Excllnc Awd 84; Am Legion Awd 84; Business.

PARLACOSKI, KATHLEEN; Linden HS; Linden, NJ; (3); Key Clb; SADD; Orch; Sec Yrbk Stf; Hon Roll; NHS; Prfct Atten Awd; Med.

PARLAPANIDES, ANTONIA; Central Regional HS; Seaside, NJ; (3); Church Yth Grp; Cmnty Wkr; Dance Clb; Drama Clb; Hosp Aide; Key Clb; Math Clb; Math Tm; Political Wkr; SADD.

PARLATO, CHRISTINE; Parsippany HS; Parsippany, NJ; (3); Pep Clb; PAVAS; Band; Concert Band; Jazz Band; Mrchg Band; Orch; Pep Band; School Musical; School Play; Rutgers; Psychlgy.

PARLIN, ALLISON; Atlantic City HS; Margate, NJ; (4); 2/402; Trs French Clb; Model UN; VP Temple Yth Grp; Yrbk Stf; Stu Cncl; Var L Crs Cntry; NHS; Sal; St Schlr; Office Aide; Abraham Toshua Hesehel Hnr Soc; Outstndng Delgt-Model UN Conf 85 & 86; Max Siegel Memrl Schlrshp 86; Intl Relatns.

PARRILLO, CHRISTINE; Wayne Valley HS; Wayne, NJ; (4); 17/319; Capt Color Guard; Yrbk Stf; High Hon Roll; NHS; Grdn ST Dstngshd Schlr 87; Lehigh U Schlrshp 87; Lehigh U; Math.

PARRILLO, RICKIE ANN; Belleville HS; Belleville, NJ; (3); Cmnty Wkr; French Clb; Intnl Clb; Political Wkr; Yrbk Stf; Off Jr Cls; Off Sr Cls; Stu Cncl; Rutgers U.

PARRINELLO, LORI A; Spotswood HS; Spotswood, NJ; (2); Cmnty Wkr; Intnl Clb; Band; Chorus; Concert Band; Capt Bsktbl; Hon Roll; Comp Tech.

PARRISH, MICHAEL; Burlington County Vo Tech HS; Bordentown, NJ; (3); 19/181; Var JV Bowling; Im Socr; Im Vllybl; Hon Roll; Church Yth Grp; VICA; NROTC Marines; Comp Tech.

PARRY, DEBRA; Bishop George AHR HS; Colonia, NJ; (4); Capt Cmnty Wkr; Ski Clb; Sec Trs Jr Cls; Sec Trs Sr Cls; Capt Cheerleading; Coach Actv; Hon Roll; Stn Hall U; Bus.

PARRY, WARREN K; South Hunterdon Regional HS; Lambertville, NJ; (3); 2/80; Am Leg Boys St; Church Yth Grp; Key Clb; Stu Cncl; Crs Cntry; Golf; Vllybl; Wrstlng; High Hon Roll; NHS; Rutgers U; Engrng.

PARSON, KIM; Baptist HS; Mt Laurel, NJ; (2); Church Yth Grp; Drama Clb; French Clb; Church Choir; School Play; Stage Crew; Frsh Cls; Stu Cncl; Var L Cheerleading; JV L Fld Hcky; Liberty U; Computers.

PARSONS, ANDREA; Summit HS; Summit, NJ; (3); 80/270; Church Yth Grp; Girl Scts; JA; Concert Band; Jazz Band; Mrchg Band; School Musical; Symp Band; Swmmng; Hon Roll; Elizabeth Bullard Schlrshp Piano 84; Mrchg Band Schlrshp Wstchstr Band Cmp 87.

PARSONS, CRAIG; Hunterdon Central HS; White House Sta, NJ; (3); Am Leg Boys St; Model UN; Rep Stu Cncl; JV Lcrss; Wrstlng; French Hon Soc; 4-H Awd; High Hon Roll; Spanish NHS; Frnch I Awd 85.

PARSONS, KRISTIN; Haddonfield Memorial HS; Haddonfield, NJ; (4); Drama Clb; SADD; Mrchg Band; School Play; Off Stu Cncl; Stat Mgr(s); Var Swmmng; Hstry Tchr.

PARSONS, SANDRA S; Somerville HS; Somerville, NJ; (4); 1/260; Pres Drama Clb; Math Clb; Model UN; Spanish Clb; Thesps; Capt Color Guard; NHS; Ntl Merit SF; Val; NJ Distinguished Schlr 86; Hugh O Brian Ambsdr 85; Rutgers Schlr 86.

PARSZIK, CHRISTINE; Waldwick HS; Waldwick, NJ; (3); 31/130; Church Yth Grp; Varsity Clb; Chorus; Yrbk Stf; Mgr Jr Cls; Rep Stu Cncl; Cheerleading; Socr; Hon Roll; Montclair ST Coll; Elem Educ.

PARTLOW, SANDRA; North Hunterdon HS; Annandale, NJ; (4); 8/346; Sec VP Church Yth Grp; Sec Chorus; Church Choir; Madrigals; School Musical; School Play; Swing Chorus; French Hon Soc; NHS; Drama Clb; NJ All St Chorus, Outstndng Voc Mus 86; Vocal Perf.

PARTON, CHRISTOPHER B; Rumson-Fair Haven Regional HS; Rumson, NJ; (3); 16/231; Am Leg Boys St; Capt Swmmng; NCTE Awd; NHS; YMCA Vrsty Swim Tm-Tm Record 200 Butterfly & Natl Tm 87; Guitarist & Vocalist Local Rock Band 85-7.

PARTRIDGE, STEVE; Pennsauken HS; Pennsauken, NJ; (2); 44/350; Leo Clb; Science Clb; Ski Clb; Spanish Clb; SADD; Var Bsbl; Var Socr; Hon Roll; Spanish NHS; Aud/Vis; Med.

PARZERO, TAMMY; Dover HS; Mine Hill, NJ; (3); 22/228; Church Yth Grp; Drama Clb; French Clb; Letterman Clb; Ski Clb; Church Choir; School Play; Yrbk Stf; Capt Bowling; Var Cheerleading; Gen Assmbly Yth Advsry Delgt 87; Typng I Awd 86; Psych.

PASAMIHALIS, NICK; Pennsauken HS; Pennsauken, NJ; (2); Boy Scts; Church Yth Grp; Science Clb; Spanish Clb; Band; Concert Band; Mrchg Band; School Musical; Symp Band; JV Socr.

PASCALE, ANTHONY L; Triron Regional HS; Bellmawr, NJ; (3); Am Leg Boys St; Drama Clb; Pep Clb; Chorus; Church Choir; School Musical; School Play; Crs Cntry; Ftbl; High Hon Roll; Annl Ldrshp Bnqt Cls 88, Schlrshps To NJ Schl Of Arts 86 & 87; Glassboro ST; Engl.

PASCHER, LEAH J; Bruriah HS For Girls; Elizabeth, NJ; (3); 1/44; Math Tm; Service Clb; Spanish Clb; Teachers Aide; Pres Soph Cls; NHS.

PASCHER, MOSHE C; Jewish Eductional Ctr; Elizabeth, NJ; (4); 2/12; Chess Clb; Chrmn Math Tm; Nwsp Stf; Im Bsktbl; Im Vllybl; Bausch & Lomb Sci Awd; High Hon Roll; NHS; Ntl Merit SF; St Schlr; Pre-Med.

PASCUZZI, JESSICA; Hightstown HS; East Windsor, NJ; (3); Church Yth Grp; Drama Clb; Key Clb; Ski Clb; Spanish Clb; Stage Crew; Art.

PASECHNICK, WENDY; Immaculate Conception HS; Little Ferry, NJ; (3); 18/84; Cmnty Wkr; Exploring; VP NFL; SADD; Chorus; School Play; Stage Crew; Nwsp Phtg; Var Cheerleading; Var Vllybl; 1st Hnr Awd 84; 2nd Hnr Awd 86; 2nd Pl Trphy Rdng NFL 86; Pace-White Plns NY; Law.

PASHMAN, ROBERT; Clifton HS; Clifton, NJ; (3); Church Yth Grp; Nwsp Ed-Chief; Comms.

PASOLA, JENNY; Point Pleasant Beach HS; Pt Plsnt Bch, NJ; (2); Cmnty Wkr; French Clb; Hosp Aide; Sec Key Clb; Band; Concert Band; Mrchg Band; School Play; Symp Band; JV Crs Cntry; Nrsng.

PASSADOR, MARYANN; Lodi HS; Lodi, NJ; (4); 1/137; Key Clb; Math Tm; Science Clb; Flag Corp; Stat Socr; Co-Capt Trk; High Hon Roll; Kiwanis Awd; NHS; Ntl Merit SF; Rensselaer Math & Sci Awd 85-86; Rutgers Coll; Biochem.

PASSANO, CHERIE; Hawthorne HS; Hawthorne, NJ; (4); 9/174; Math Tm; Pep Clb; Pres SADD; Pres Sr Cls; Stu Cncl; Var Sftbl; Hon Roll; NHS; Spanish NHS; Voice Dem Awd; Gldn H Awd 87; Montclair ST; Bio.

PASSANTE, KEVIN; Nothern Valley Old Tappan HS; Old Tappan, NJ; (3); 104/274; AFS; Chorus; School Musical; JV Bsktbl; Ftbl Anncr 86; Rochester Inst Of Tech; Prntng.

PASSARELLI, DANIEL F; North Plainfield HS; N Plainfield, NJ; (4); 47/180; Boy Scts; Church Yth Grp; Band; Jazz Band; Ftbl; Wt Lftg; Glassboro ST Coll; Crmnl Justc.

PASSARO, GINA MARIE; Pequannock Township HS; Pompton Plains, NJ; (3); 15/233; Am Leg Aux Girls St; Chorus; Color Guard; School Musical; School Play; VP Rep Stu Cncl; Var Stat Bsktbl; High Hon Roll; Hon Roll; NHS; Jrsy Cntrl Pwr & Lght Co Cnsrvtn Hm Music Video Cont Wnnr 85-86; Law.

PASSUCCI, OLIVIA; Scotch Plains Fanwood HS; Scotch Plains, NJ; (3); French Clb; Key Clb; Var Cheerleading.

PASTER, THOMAS M; Cranford HS; Cranford, NJ; (4); Acpl Chr; Band; Concert Band; Drm Mjr(t); Jazz Band; Madrigals; Orch; School Musical; JP Sousa Awd; Pres Thespian Soc 86-87; Natl Assn Tchrs Singing Comptn 1st Pl 86; Rgn & All-St Chorus & Orch 84-87; Ithaca Coll; Perfrmng Music Ed.

PASTERNACK, SCOTT M; Marlboro HS; Colts Neck, NJ; (4); 4/529; Boy Scts; Model UN; NFL; Ski Clb; Pres Speech Tm; Sec Temple Yth Grp; Lit Mag; Gov Hon Prg Awd; High Hon Roll; NHS; Mnmth Refrm Tmpl Smmr Yth Israel Schlrshp 85; Recpnt Stu Cncl Schlrshp 87; Wnnr NJ Poetry Intrp 86; William & Mary Coll; Law.

PASTOR, TARA; Kittatinny Reg HS; Layton, NJ; (4); 61/228; Drama Clb; Pres SADD; Chorus; School Musical; School Play; Stu Cncl; JV Var Cheerleading; Cit Awd; Hon Roll; Kenneth H Beck Mem Schlrshp 87; Womens Clb Schlrshp 87; Kittatinny Masks Awd Dramatic Achvt 87; OH U; Comm.

PASTORE, FRED; Don Bosco HS; Ramsey, NJ; (3); 43/180; Band; Concert Band; Jazz Band; Mrchg Band; JV Tennis; Hon Roll.

PATANE, FRED; Washington Township HS; Sewell, NJ; (3); Band; Concert Band; Tennis; Bus Adm.

PATANE, THERESA; Holy Spirit HS; Ocean City, NJ; (2); 37/397; Speech Tm; Hon Roll; Jr NHS; Law.

PATCH JR, THOMAS J; Vineland HS; Vineland, NJ; (2); 200/800; Debate Tm; Drama Clb; French Clb; JV Bsbl; JV Ftbl; Temple U; Law.

PATEL, AJAY; Wm L Dickinson HS; Jersey City, NJ; (4); Library Aide; Math Clb; Science Clb; CC Awd; Hon Roll; Acad All Amer 87; Rutgers; Elec Engrng.

PATEL, ANILA; St Anthony HS; Jersey Cty, NJ; (3); Computer Clb; JA; Hon Roll; Prfct Atten Awd; Pres Citations For Acad Achvt 87.

PATEL, ASHISH; Union HS; Union, NJ; (3); Am Leg Boys St; VP Computer Clb; German Clb; Science Clb; Service Clb; High Hon Roll; Hon Roll; NHS; Ntl Merit Ltr; Opt Clb Awd; Essay Cont Bnai Brith On Holacaust 86; 3rd Pl Essay Cont 87; Highest Schltc Achvt Awd 85; Elec Engr.

PATEL, BELLA; Acad Of St Aloysius; Jersey City, NJ; (4); Pres Library Aide; Math Tm; NFL; Nwsp Stf; Ed Yrbk Stf; Rep Stu Cncl; Vllybl; CC Awd; NHS; St Schlr; Gold Mdl Natl Latin Exam 86; Grad With High Hons Gold Mdl Rcvd 87; Dept Awd Rlgn Dept 87; Seton Hall U; Med.

PATEL, DAHESH; Union HS; Westfield, NJ; (3); Computer Clb; German Clb; High Hon Roll; NHS; Exemplry Achvt Awd Bus Law 86-87; UCLA; Tax Atty.

PATEL, HARNISH; Elmwood Park Memorial HS; Elmwood Pk, NJ; (3); #16 In Class; Computer Clb; Library Aide; Math Clb; Yrbk Stf; Var Socr; Var Tennis; Var Capt Trk; Hon Roll; Rotary Awd; MIT; Aero Engrng.

PATEL, HIREN R; Cliffside Park HS; Fairview, NJ; (3); 3/243; Am Leg Boys St; Camera Clb; German Clb; Hosp Aide; Math Tm; Political Wkr; Lit Mag; Var Crs Cntry; Var Tennis; High Hon Roll; Rensselaer Polytechnic Inst Math & Sci Awd 87; Rider Coll Frnsc Trnmt Wnnr 86 & 87; Govs Sch Of Sci 87; Medicine.

PATEL, HITESH; Dickinson HS; Jersey City, NJ; (3); Computer Clb; Exploring; Math Clb; Scholastic Bowl; Science Clb; Lit Mag; Hon Roll; NHS; Prfct Atten Awd; Sal; Soc Stud, Read Awds; Merit Roll; Rutgers U; Elec Engrng.

PATEL, KETAN; Piscataway HS; Piscataway, NJ; (4); 36/496; Boy Scts; Hon Roll; NHS; St Schlr; Gov Alive With Studnts 86; Presdntl Acad Ftns Awd 87; NJ Inst Of Tech; Elec Engr.

PATEL, KEYUR; Long Branch HS; Long Br, NJ; (3); 4/220; Church Yth Grp; Cmnty Wkr; Math Clb; Math Tm; Science Clb; JV Var Bsbl; JV Var Bsktbl; JV Var Socr; High Hon Roll; NHS; Phy Natl Test Awd 87; Rutgers; Elec Engr.

PATEL, KRINAL; Florence Twp Mem HS; Bordentown, NJ; (4); 8/84; Math Clb; Math Tm; Science Clb; School Play; High Hon Roll; Pres Schlr; Drama Clb; FBLA; Latin Clb; Acad Exc In US II & Chem II 85-86; Hghst Avrg In Us I & II 87; Boys ST; Rtgrs Coll Phrmcy; Phrmcst.

PATEL, MANISH; Memorial HS; Cedar Grove, NJ; (4); 6/123; Boy Scts; Church Yth Grp; Nwsp Rptr; Rep Stu Cncl; Var Socr; Var Capt Tennis; High Hon Roll; NHS; Chem Achvt Awd 86; Pharmacy.

PATEL, MANISH; West Essex HS; Fairfield, NJ; (3); French Clb; Temple Yth Grp; Variety Show; Rep Stu Cncl; Bsktbl; L JV Debate Tm; Hon Roll; NHS; Bus.

PATEL, MAYANK; Dickinson HS; Jersey City, NJ; (2); Rep Stu Cncl; High Hon Roll; Hon Roll; Rutgers Coll Of Engrng; Elctrcl.

PATEL, MEHUL; Highland Regional HS; Blackwood, NJ; (3); Comp Sci.

PATEL, NEELAM P; John P Stevens HS; Edison, NJ; (4); Library Aide; Math Tm; Speech Tm; Orch; Lit Mag; High Hon Roll; NHS; Pres Schlr; Spanish NHS; Chess Clb; Otto Burgdorf Sci Comptn Wnnr 86; Math Assn Amer Cntst Wnnr 85; Acad Sci 87; Rutgers Coll; Comp Sci.

PATEL, NILESH; Abraham Clark HS; Roselle, NJ; (3); Math Clb; Spanish Clb; Bsbl; Sftbl; Vllybl; Hon Roll; Lion Awd; Prfct Atten Awd; Spanish NHS; Merit Roll 84-87; Rutgers U; Elec Engr.

PATEL, NISHUTA; Cinnaminson HS; Cinnaminson, NJ; (3); Dance Clb; Chorus; Bowling; Socr; Trk; Prfct Atten Awd; Indn Yth Dnce Awd 86-87; Spnsh Awd 84-85; Bus.

PATEL, PARESH P; Sayreville War Memorial HS; Parlin, NJ; (3); Boy Scts; Band; School Play; Nwsp Stf; Yrbk Stf; Var Swmmng; High Hon Roll; Voice Dem Awd; Olympc Minds Tm 86-87; Med.

PATEL, RUPAL; Holy Spirit HS; Absecon, NJ; (3); 28/332; Spanish Clb; Yrbk Stf; Engr.

PATEL, SAMIR; John P Stevens HS; Edison, NJ; (3); Hosp Aide; Ski Clb; Trk; Med.

PATEL, SEJAL; Florence Twp Mem HS; Florence, NJ; (3); Math Clb; Math Tm; Science Clb; Rep Soph Cls; JV Sftbl; High Hon Roll; Hon Roll.

PATEL, SHALINI; Kingsway Regional HS; Mickleton, NJ; (3); ROTC; Band; Concert Band; Drill Tm; Mrchg Band; Pep Band; Symp Band; JV Var Vllybl; Pep Clb; Teachers Aide; Bst Lnsmn Awd Vlybl 84-85; Athltc Awd Trk Mgr 85-86; Cert Fstvl India Clbrtn 85-86; U WA; Phrmcy.

PATEL, SHEETAL; Rutherford HS; Rutherford, NJ; (4); 8/150; French Clb; Key Clb; Library Aide; Math Tm; Science Clb; Spanish Clb; Teachers Aide; Stat Tennis; Hon Roll; NHS; Brown U; Med.

PATEL, SUKETU; Cresskill HS; Cresskill, NJ; (3); 5/104; Boy Scts; Cmnty Wkr; Office Aide; Nwsp Rptr; Stu Cncl; Bsbl; Ftbl; High Hon Roll; NHS.

PATEL, VISHAL; North Bergen HS; North Bergen, NJ; (4); 15/419; Spanish Clb; High Hon Roll; Hon Roll; NHS; Spanish NHS; Pres Fit Awd 87; Soc Acad Achvt 87; Intl Frgn Lang Awd 86; Boston U; Pre-Med.

PATERNOSTER, JOSEPH; St Marys Of The Assumption HS; Elizabeth, NJ; (4); 3/59; JV Var Drama Clb; Im Bsktbl; Im Socr; Im Vllybl; NHS; SETON Hall U; Bus.

PATERSON, BRANDON; Toms River South HS; Toms River, NJ; (3); FBLA; Spanish Clb; Varsity Clb; Capt Crs Cntry; Socr; Capt Trk; Engrng.

PATERSON, GEORGE; Brick Memorial HS; Brick, NJ; (4); 4/290; Am Leg Boys St; Boy Scts; Key Clb; Co-Capt Math Tm; JV Crs Cntry; JV Trk; Bausch & Lomb Sci Awd; High Hon Roll; NHS; Ntl Merit SF; Trenton ST Coll; Psychlgy.

PATERSON, LARA; Vineland HS; Vineland, NJ; (3); Pep Clb; Sec Trs SADD; Rep Frsh Cls; Rep Soph Cls; Rep Jr Cls; Rep Stu Cncl; Capt JV Cheerleading; Cit Awd; Hon Roll; Child Dvlpmnt.

PATERSON, MARGARET; Mc Corristin Catholic HS; Trenton, NJ; (3); 26/267; Drama Clb; JA; Pep Clb; Chorus; Church Choir; School Musical; School Play; Yrbk Stf; NHS; NEDT Awd; French III & Chem Awd 86-87.

PATEY, ROBERT; Marist HS; Jersey, NJ; (3); Varsity Clb; Var Bsbl; JV Bsktbl; Im Vllybl; Professional Baseball Player.

PATRICK, CAROLYN; Monmouth Regional HS; Ft Monmouth, NJ; (3); Church Yth Grp; 4-H; FHA; 4-H Awd; Jr NHS; Southern OR Coll; Home Ec.

PATRICK, CHARLES; Whippany Park HS; Whippany, NJ; (3); Am Leg Boys St; Church Yth Grp; Cmnty Wkr; Ski Clb; Nwsp Stf; Ftbl; Hon Roll; Arch.

PATRICK, MARGARET; Holy Spirit HS; Northfield, NJ; (2); 25/397; Church Yth Grp; Church Choir; School Musical.

PATRICK, PAUL E; Spotswood HS; Spotswood, NJ; (4); 19/189; Am Leg Boys St; Math Tm; Band; Concert Band; Jazz Band; Mrchg Band; School Play; Symp Band; Variety Show; Var Capt Ftbl; Music.

PATRICK, SCOTT; West Essex Regional HS; No Caldwell, NJ; (3); Am Leg Boys St; JCL; Math Tm; JV Socr; Var Tennis; High Hon Roll; NCTE Awd; Ntl Merit Schol; Spanish NHS; Natl Latin Exam Cum Laude 85-86; Bus Admin.

PATTERSON, BONITA YVETTE; Henry Snyder HS; Jersey City, NJ; (4); 7/214; Church Yth Grp; FHA; Church Choir; Yrbk Stf; CC Awd; NHS; JCSC Corp Schlrshp 87; Prjct PRIME Ed Grnt 86; Jersey City ST Coll; Chldhd Ed.

PATTERSON, DANETTE; Ocean Township HS; Ocean Tsp, NJ; (3); 88/344; Girl Scts; Spanish Clb; Band; Capt Flag Corp; Mrchg Band; Orch; Awd Of Merit-Envrmntl Commission Ocean Twnshp 86; Comp Sci.

PATTERSON, WILLIAM; Collingswood SR HS; Camden, NJ; (3); JV Bsbl; Var Bowling; Var Socr; Vllybl; Hon Roll; Drexel; Drftng.

PATTON, LORI; Baptist HS; Sicklerville, NJ; (4); 1/45; Capt Church Yth Grp; Band; Chorus; Orch; School Play; Yrbk Bus Mgr; Pres Frsh Cls; Rep Stu Cncl; High Hon Roll; Var Fld Hcky; Mst Lkly To Succeed 87; Bob Jones U; Brdcstng.

PATTON, PENNI; Toms River HS South; Toms River, NJ; (4); 2/320; Church Yth Grp; Church Choir; Flag Corp; Lit Mag; VP Frsh Cls; Stat Ftbl; Var L Swmmng; High Hon Roll; Jr NHS; NHS; Ldrshp Cup 87; J C Penney Ctznshp Awd 87; Most Val Swmmr 84-87; U Of DE; Comm.

PAUGH, AMY; High Point Regional HS; Sussex, NJ; (3); 22/247; French Clb; Office Aide; Stat Timer; JV Trk; Wt Lftg; Hon Roll; Psych.

PAUGH, JUDITH; St Mary HS; Sayreville, NJ; (4); Library Aide; SADD; Chorus; Cheerleading; Gym; Pom Pon; Score Keeper; High Hon Roll; Church Yth Grp; Office Aide; Prtl Schlrshp To Brkly Bus Schl 87; Outstndng Ldrshp Ablty Prsntd By Kthrn Gibbs 86; Berkeley Bus Schl; Exec Secy.

PAUL, HILLARY; Florence Twp Mem HS; Florence, NJ; (3); Am Leg Aux Girls St; FTA; GAA; Nwsp Rptr; Ed Nwsp Stf; Yrbk Stf; Score Keeper; Sftbl.

PAUL, MONIK; South Brunswick HS; Kendall Pk, NJ; (2); Dance Clb; French Clb; Latin Clb; High Hon Roll; Hon Roll; Hosp Aide; School Play; Stage Crew; Nwsp Stf; Yrbk Stf; Med.

PAULSEN, THOMAS; Paulsboro HS; Paulsboro, NJ; (3); 39/150; Chorus; Var Bsbl; Var Bsktbl; Var Ftbl.

PAUWELS, SUSAN; Wood-Ridge HS; Wood Ridge, NJ; (3); 1/90; Pres Computer Clb; Sec VP Library Aide; Math Tm; Model UN; Sec Stu Cncl; Var Bowling; Var Gym; Var Vllybl; NHS; Genetics.

PAUZNER, JEFFREY J; Clifton HS; Clifton, NJ; (3); Am Leg Boys St; Library Aide; Science Clb; Spanish Clb; Variety Show; Nwsp Phtg; Yrbk Phtg; Spanish NHS; Wrld Hist Achvt Awd 84-85; Electrcty & Electrncs I Achvt Awd 85-86; Humanities.

PAVLIK, TERESA; Gloucester Catholic HS; Glendora, NJ; (3); Glassboro ST; Bus.

PAW, KRISTIN; Randolph HS; Randolph, NJ; (3); Latin Clb; Ski Clb; Cheerleading; Powder Puff Ftbl; Coachng, Vrsty Ftbll & Bsktbll Awds 86.

PAWELEK, JOSEPH EDWARD; St Piux X Regional HS; So Rvr, NJ; (4); Church Yth Grp; Computer Clb; Drama Clb; ROTC; Stage Crew; JV Bsbl; Monmouth Coll; Med.

PAYLAGO, BRIAN; St John Vianney HS; Freehold, NJ; (3); FBLA; Math Tm; Service Clb; Ski Clb; SADD; Crs Cntry; Var Trk; Hon Roll; Law.

PAYNE, JOHN; Montville HS; Montville, NJ; (3); Church Yth Grp; Key Clb; Ski Clb; Varsity Clb; Var Capt Crs Cntry; Var Capt Trk; Engrng.

PAYNE, NANCY; Paul VI HS; Audubon, NJ; (3); 130/400; Church Yth Grp; Latin Clb; Red Cross Aide; Nwsp Stf; Lit Mag; Pres Soph Cls; Pres Jr Cls; Var Cheerleading; Cmnty Wkr; Office Aide; Govt Day Camden NJ 86; Hugh Obrien Yth Fndtn HOBY 86; Intervwee Reel To Reel 87; Marywood Coll; Eng.

PAYNE, SANDRA L; Delaware Valley Regional HS; Bloomsbury, N (4); Sec Key Clb; SADD; Varsity Clb; Yrbk Rptr; Lit Mag; Rep Frsh Cl Rep Stu Cncl; Capt Cheerleading; High Hon Roll; Hon Roll; Memrl Aw 87; 1st Tm All DE Rvr Conf Chrldg 87; Mst Vlbl Chrldr Awd 87; Lafayet Coll; Psych.

PAZOS, VIVIAN; Memorial HS; West New York, NJ; (3); Intnl Cl Math Clb; Spanish Clb; Hon Roll; NHS.

PEACOCK, KRISTIN M; Palmyra HS; Palmyra, NJ; (3); #6 In Clas Cmnty Wkr; German Clb; Key Clb; SADD; Nwsp Stf; VP Stu Cncl; Tennis; L Trk; Cit Awd; Hon Roll; NJ Grls Ctznshp ST Inst 87; U Of P Med.

PEAK, KELLY; Cherry Hill West HS; Cherry Hill, NJ; (4); Chorus; P Band; JV VP Bsktbl; Sftbl; Vllybl; Brndywn Coll; Fash Merch.

PEAR, DEBBIE; Wall HS; Neptune, NJ; (3); 50/294; Key Clb; Variet Show; Var Capt Bsktbl; Coach Actv; Var Crs Cntry; Var Fld Hcky; Powd Puff Ftbl; Score Keeper; Var Socr; High Hon Roll; Boston U; Phys Thrpy.

PEARCE, DONALD; Sussex Cnty Vctnl Tech Schl; Sparta, NJ; (3); Ho Roll; Best Math Avg 85-86; Mst Improvd Bio Stu 86-87; Mech.

PEARCE, MIKE; Jefferson Township HS; Oak Ridge, NJ; (4); 23/23 Computer Clb; Math Tm; Varsity Clb; Rep Frsh Cls; Rep Soph Cls; Re Jr Cls; Var JV Socr; Im Vllybl; Hon Roll; NHS; Frgn Lang Cmptn 1st 84-85; Grt Amer Smkt Comp Poster Awd 2nd Pl Hnrb Mntn; VA Tec Comp Sci.

PEARCE, THOMAS; Camden Catholic HS; Collingswood, NJ; (3); Bo Scts; FBLA; German Clb; Science Clb; Teachers Aide; JV Ftbl; Var Gol Im Wt Lftg; JV Wrstlng; BSA 85; Eagle Sct 87; Bus.

PEARSON, KRISTEN; Newton HS; Andover, NJ; (3); 5/197; Frenc Clb; Hosp Aide; Latin Clb; Lit Mag; JV Trk; High Hon Roll; NHS; Ntl S Olympd 86; Engl.

PEARSON, ROBERT; Collingswood HS; Collingswood, NJ; (2); Frenc Clb; JCL; Latin Clb; Office Aide; SADD; Hon Roll; Americanism Essay Aw 86; Med.

PEART, DANA; West Orange HS; W Orange, NJ; (3); AFS; French Cl Spanish Clb; Var JV Trk; French Hon Soc; Hon Roll; Cert Merit Am Assc Frnch Tchrs 87; Mst Dedctd Gymnst & Cert Of Achvmnt In Gymnstcs Trnng Camp 84; Intl Bus.

PECK, JAMES; Toms River HS South; Beachwood, NJ; (2); Socr; Hig Hon Roll; Hon Roll; Engrng.

PECK, ROBERT; Linden HS; Linden, NJ; (3); Office Aide; Bsktbl; Ftl Accntng.

PECK, THOMAS; Hunterdon Central HS; Flemington, NJ; (3); 28/55 Am Leg Boys St; Church Yth Grp; Cmnty Wkr; Ski Clb; Soph Cls; VP Pr Stu Cncl; JV Bsktbl; JV Var Socr; Hon Roll; Spanish NHS; U PA; Atty

PECK, WENDY; St James HS; Gibbstown, NJ; (3); 9/84; Church Yt Grp; Drama Clb; Pep Clb; SADD; Nwsp Rptr; JV Bsktbl; JV Var F Hcky; Sftbl; Hon Roll; Ed.

PECKER, MICHELLE; Parsippany HS; Parsippany, NJ; (3); FBL Spanish Clb; VP Temple Yth Grp; Band; Chorus; Color Guard; Sta Crew; Symp Band; Off Jr Cls; Lbrl Arts.

PECKMAN, CYNTHIA; Gill/St Bernards HS; Maplewood, NJ; (3); Yrb Stf; Cheerleading; Mgr(s); Sftbl; Hon Roll; Intl Bus.

PECORA, RAYMOND; Bloomfield HS; Bloomfield, NJ; (3); Hon Ro Hnrs Mrkng 87; Hnrb Mntn Mrkng 86; Hnrll 85-87.

PECORARO, DIANNE; Immaculate Conception HS; Wallington, N (2); English Clb; Spanish Clb; Stage Crew; Yrbk Stf; Bowling; Vllybl; Hi Hon Roll; NHS; Spanish NHS; Swmmng; USNMA Awd 85-6; Soc C Distinguished Amer HS Stu 86-7; Stevens Inst; Med.

PEDERSEN, JACQUELINE; Holy Family Acad; Bayonne, NJ; (2); In Decrtr.

PEDERSEN, KARIN; Newton HS; Newton, NJ; (3); 12/194; Church Yt Grp; French Clb; GAA; Band; Chorus; Church Choir; Mrchg Band; Re Frsh Cls; Rep Soph Cls; Rep Jr Cls; Archit.

PEDICONE, CHRISTOPHER; Holy Spirit HS; Absecon, NJ; (3); 14 332; Off Soph Cls; JV Bsktbl; Im Ftbl; Im Vllybl; Hon Roll; NHS; Ed.

PEEK, EMILY; Millville SR HS; Millville, NJ; (4); 57/417; French Cl JV Im Fld Hcky; Im Trk; Im Prfct Atten Awd; Bus.

PEEPLES, ANGELA CORETTA; Willingboro HS; Willingboro, NJ; (3 10/308; Am Leg Aux Girls St; Church Yth Grp; Girl Scts; Acpl Chr; Pr Band; Co-Capt Drm & Bgl; Madrigals; Tennis; NCTE Awd; Girl Scout G Ldrshp Awd 86; Elec Engrng.

PEER, CHRISTOPHER; Dover HS; Dover, NJ; (3); Am Leg Boys S German Clb; Math Tm; Scholastic Bowl; Science Clb; Band; Var JV Ftb Var JV Wrstlng; AFS; Boy Scts; Satori 86-87; Marine Sci.

PEET, FAITH V; Woodstown HS; Woodstown, NJ; (3); 20/162; Lat Clb; Office Aide; SADD; Chorus; Flag Corp; Rep Soph Cls; Rep Jr Cls; St Cncl; Var Pom Pon; Swmmng; Southern NJ Intl Sunshine Pageant Rep 8 Math.

PEIL, STEVEN E; Phillipsburg HS; Phillipsburg, NJ; (3); 4/315; Pr Church Yth Grp; Ski Clb; Im Trk; High Hon Roll; NHS; Athlt Awd Sch Bsbl & Bsktbl 84; All-Star Game Bsbl & Bsbl Tm Batting Crown 8 Chem.

PEKAROFSKI, JAMES; Linden HS; Linden, NJ; (3); Church Yth Gr Key Clb; Library Aide; Yrbk Stf; Hon Roll; Jr NHS; NHS; Union Cn Coll; Bus Admin.

PELKEY, MIKE; Brick Memorial HS; Brick, NJ; (2); 69/400; Var Bs Var Bsktbl; Var Socr; Hon Roll; Rutgers U; Tchng.

PELLEGRINI, JEFFREY; Buena Regional HS; Buena, NJ; (3); Ski Cl Varsity Clb; Var Bsbl; JV Bsktbl; Wt Lftg; Hstry.

PELLEGRINO, VICKY; Mother Seton Regional HS; Perth Amboy, N (2); Hosp Aide; Chorus; School Musical; Sec Jr Cls; Var Cheerleading; Ho Roll; Nrsg.

PELLOT, MICHELLE; Cherry Hill High School West; Cherry Hill, N (3); School Play; Stage Crew; Rep Frsh Cls; Rep Soph Cls; Rep Jr Cls; V Sr Cls; JV Bsktbl; French Clb; Church Choir; Nwsp Rptr; Hm & Schl Awd 86-87; Bus.

PELOQUIN, MICHEL; Notre Dame HS; Kendall Pk, NJ; (2); 50/40 Boy Scts; Church Yth Grp; Computer Clb; Off Frsh Cls; Off Soph Cls; C Cntry; Trk; Wt Lftg; Wrstlng; NHS; Air Force Acad; Aero Space.

PELOSI, GILDA; Manchester Regional HS; Haledon, NJ; (4); 19/15 French Clb; Science Clb; French Hon Soc; Hon Roll; William Paterso Coll; Bio.

PELOUZE, MARK P; Cherry Hill HS; Cherry Hill, NJ; (3); Am Leg Boy St; Cmnty Wkr; Var Bsbl; Var Bsktbl; Var Capt Socr; Hon Roll; JV MV Bsktbl 85-86; Dan Bubser Awd Outstndng Dedctn Tm Spirit Bsktbl 86-8 MV Ptchr Bsbl 86-87; Bus.

PELUSO, MIKE; Piscataway HS; Piscataway, NJ; (3); Church Yth Grp; English Clb; Variety Show; Im Bsbl; Im Bsktbl; JV Ftbl; Im Ice Hcky; JV Wrstlng; Hon Roll; NHS; Poems Pblshd Litry Mgzn; Italian II Hghst Grade; Chrch Folk Grp-Guitar; Nazareth Coll; Music Thrpy.

PELUSO, ROSEANN; Cliffside Park HS; Fairview, NJ; (4); 10/236; Church Yth Grp; Exploring; Nwsp Stf; Yrbk Ed-Chief; Off Stu Cncl; Hon Roll; Jr NHS; Rotary Awd; AARP Schlrshp 87; Itln Merit Awd 86; Natl Hnr Soc 86-87; Rutgers; Phrmcy.

PENA, ANNA; St Josephs Of The Palisades HS; W New York, NJ; (1); 15/130; VP Spanish Clb; Nwsp Stf; Ed Yrbk Stf; Hon Roll; NHS; Spanish NHS; Natl Guild Piano Tchrs 85; St Johns U; Phrmcy.

PENA, JEANETTE; Emerson HS; Union City, NJ; (3); Camera Clb; Hosp Aide; Office Aide; Political Wkr; Spanish Clb; Color Guard; Drill Tm; Yrbk Stf; Lit Mag; Off Jr Cls; Pre-Med.

PENARANDA, AUGUSTO; Passaic County Tech & Voc HS; Pompton Lakes, NJ; (4); 20/366; Trs Spanish Clb; Yrbk Bus Mgr; Rep Frsh Cls; Rep Jr Cls; Pres Stu Cncl; Socr; Cit Awd; Attnd Sen Bill Bradleys Ldrshp Smnr 87; Yth Govt Day 86; Wnnr-Ntl Ldrshp & Svc Awd 86-87; Trenton ST Coll; Fin.

PENEIRAS, HELENA; Queen Of Peace HS; Kearny, NJ; (3); 72/278; French Clb; Hosp Aide; Hon Roll; Med Lab Tech.

PENENO, DENISE; Waldwick HS; Waldwick, NJ; (3); Church Yth Grp; French Clb; Letterman Clb; Varsity Clb; Chorus; Yrbk Phtg; Yrbk Stf; Im Sftbl; Var L Tennis; Var L Trk; Pharmacist.

PENICK, JOSH; Columbia HS; South Orange, NJ; (3); 74/513; Am Leg Boys St; Pres Jr Cls; Var L Bsktbl; Kiwanis Awd; Church Yth Grp; Spanish Clb; SADD; Nwsp Phtg; Nwsp Rptr; Nwsp Stf; Outstndng Stu Of Yr 83; Engrng.

PENN, STEPHANIE; Freehold Township HS; Freehold, NJ; (3); Art Clb; Variety Show; Pres Jr Cls; Sec Stu Cncl; Stat Bsktbl; Var JV Cheerleading; Mgr(s); JV Sftbl; NHS; Jack & Jill Of Amer Rec Secy; Adv.

PENN, TAMMATHA LOUISE; Cumberland Regional HS; Bridgeton, NJ; (4); 96/329; Church Yth Grp; FBLA; SADD; JV Mgr(s); Var Sftbl; High Hon Roll; Hon Roll; Prfct Atten Awd; Data & Wrd Prcsng Cert 87; Edsn CC; Comp Sci.

PENNA, JUDY; Rutherford HS; Rutherford, NJ; (1); 1/168; Church Yth Grp; Cmnty Wkr; Band; Chorus; Flag Corp; Rep Jr Cls; Rep Sr Cls; High Hon Roll; Hon Roll; Kiwanis Awd; Renssalaer Awd Math & Sci 86; Unico Schlrshp 87; Profssnl Womens Schlrshp 87; Rutgers U; Prsthtcs.

PENNELL, HEATHER; Voorhees HS; Port Murray, NJ; (2); 74/292; Church Yth Grp; Ski Clb; Chorus; School Musical; Variety Show; Rep Frsh Cls; VP Stu Cncl; Bowling; Tennis; Vllybl; Oral Roberts U; Dr.

PENNIX, JOEY; Orange HS; Orange, NJ; (2); Computer Clb; Spanish Clb; Rep Frsh Cls; Sec Soph Cls; Rep Stu Cncl; High Hon Roll; Hon Roll; NHS; Sal; Spanish NHS; Elec Engrng.

PENQUE, THOMAS DILLON; Hackensack HS; Maywood, NJ; (4); 32/400; Am Leg Boys St; Boy Scts; Pres Key Clb; School Play; Yrbk Ed-Chief; VP Jr Cls; Pres Sr Cls; Hon Roll; VP NHS; Pres Schlr; Hugh O Brian Ldrshp Smnr 85; World Affrs Smnr 86; Exchng Stu Mexico 87; Boston Coll; Finance,Ecnmcs.

PENROSE, MICHAEL C; Pompton Lakes HS; Pompton Lakes, NJ; (4); 5/132; Church Yth Grp; Exploring; Math Clb; Co-Capt Scholastic Bowl; Trs Spanish Clb; Yrbk Bus Mgr; High Hon Roll; NHS; Prfct Atten Awd; Pres Schlr; Awd-Outstndng Stu-Scl Sci 87; $500 Gallo & $350 Ntl Hnrs Soc Schlrshps 87; $375 Acadc Tm Schlrshp 86; St Josephs U; Chem.

PENSWATER, JOHN J; Holy Cross HS; Delran, NJ; (4); Am Leg Boys St; Rep Frsh Cls; Rep Soph Cls; Rep Jr Cls; Rep Sr Cls; Rep Stu Cncl; JV Var Bsbl; Im JV Socr; NHS; Outstndng Rep 86; La Salle U; Pltcl Sci.

PENTZ, INGRID; Holy Cross HS; Cinnaminson, NJ; (3); Church Yth Grp; Hosp Aide; Ski Clb; Spanish Clb; Stage Crew; Hon Roll; Nrsng.

PEPPER, ROBERT; The Pennington Schl; Somerset, NJ; (3); 15/80; Boy Scts; Church Yth Grp; Ski Clb; VP Chorus; School Musical; Yrbk Stf; Var Lcrss; JV Socr; Im Vllybl; God Cntry Awd.

PERAGINO, THERESA; Kittatinny Regional HS; Newton, NJ; (3); 21/216; Var JV Bsktbl; Var JV Fld Hcky; Var Trk; High Hon Roll; Hon Roll; NHS; Field Hockey-Sussex Cnty All-Area Hnrb Mntn 85-86; Field Hockey-Sussex Cnty All-League Hnrb Mntn 86; Pt.

PERALTA, JORGE L; Passaic HS; Passaic, NJ; (3); Am Leg Boys St; Sec Computer Clb; Ski Clb; Var Socr; Cit Awd; Prfct Atten Awd; Seton Hall U; Corp Law.

PERCARIO, CRISTY; Hillsborough HS; Neshanic, NJ; (3); 126/328; Camera Clb; Cmnty Wkr; Sftbl; Hon Roll; Crmnl Jstcs.

PERCARIO, NANCY; East Brunswick HS; E Brunswick, NJ; (4); Var Capt Fld Hcky; Var Trk; NHS; Ntl Merit Ltr; St Schlr; James J Kerrigan Mem Schlrshp 87; Natl Art Hnr Soc Secy 87; U Of AZ; Arch.

PERCARPIO, MICHAEL; Don Bosco Tech; Paterson, NJ; (3); 1/100; Church Yth Grp; Yrbk Rptr; High Hon Roll; NHS; 1st Pl Sci Fair Elec 86; Elec Engr.

PERDOMO, CHRIS ANN; North Bergen HS; N Bergen, NJ; (3); Art Clb; Dance Clb; Drama Clb; Model UN; PAVAS; Spanish Clb; School Play; Off Frsh Cls; Off Soph Cls; Off Jr Cls; Trvl Agnt.

PEREIA, ANTONIO; East Side HS; Nwark, NJ; (3); Boy Scts; Church Yth Grp; Debate Tm; Drama Clb; Ski Clb; School Musical; School Play; Pres Jr Cls; Rep Stu Cncl; Hon Roll; Bus Admin.

PEREIRA, ANTONIO; Essex Catholic Boys HS; Newark, NJ; (2); JV Crs Cntry; Im Trk; Mt St Marys MD; Acctng.

PEREIRA, CLARA; East Side HS; Newark, NJ; (3); Bus.

PEREIRA, FELICIANO H; East Side HS; Newark, NJ; (3); JA; Crs Cntry; Socr; Trk; High Hon Roll; Hon Roll; Engl Awd 85-86; Comp Engr.

PEREIRA, JORGE; Eastside HS; Paterson, NJ; (2); Boys Clb Am; Cmnty Wkr; Hon Roll; Med.

PEREZ, ANA; Hoboken HS; Hoboken, NJ; (3); Int Amer U PR; Law.

PEREZ, BARBARA; Holy Rosary Acad; Union City, NJ; (3); Art Clb; Dance Clb; French Clb; Math Tm; Trs Spanish Clb; Variety Show; Spnsh Clb Awd 87; Dance Awds 85-87; Shwstpprs Ntl Dance Compttn-1st Pl 85; Miami U; Arch.

PEREZ, EFERN R; Union Hill HS; Union City, NJ; (3); 12/232; Am Leg Boys St; Church Yth Grp; Mu Alpha Theta; Teachers Aide; Pres Stu Cncl; Var Ftbl; High Hon Roll; Hon Roll; NHS; Im Vllybl; LEAD Pgm 87; Acad Decthln Tm 87; Mech Engr.

PEREZ JR, GERMAN W; Memorial HS; West New York, NJ; (3); 9/300; Chess Clb; Computer Clb; French Clb; Math Clb; Band; Mrchg Band; Orch; High Hon Roll; Hon Roll; Natl Hnr Soc 86; Rutgers U; Biochem.

PEREZ, JULIA; Bayonne HS; Bayonne, NJ; (3); Sec French Clb; Key Clb; Math Tm; High Hon Roll; Hon Roll; Lawyer.

PEREZ, LIZETTE; St Josephs HS; Union City, NJ; (4); FCA; French Clb; Hosp Aide; Yrbk Phtg; Yrbk Stf; Bsktbl; Twrlr; French Hon Soc; Hon Roll; NHS; Montclair ST Coll; Crmnl Law.

PEREZ, NELSON; Delsea Regional HS; Williamstown, NJ; (2); Arch.

PEREZ, ROBERT; Indian Hills HS; Oakland, NJ; (3); 105/316; Computer Clb; Science Clb; Swmmng; Hon Roll; Schlrshp Hudson Catholic 84-85; Athl Awd Swmmng 85; NJ Inst Tech; Elec Engrng.

PEREZ, ROBERT; Manchester Twp HS; Toms River, NJ; (2); Drama Clb; NFL; Science Clb; Band; Nwsp Rptr; Yrbk Stf; Music.

PEREZ, SARA; Buena Regional HS; Buena, NJ; (3); Church Yth Grp; Chorus; Church Choir; Acctg.

PERFIDIO, PATTY; Paul VI HS; Williamstown, NJ; (4); 110/511; Church Yth Grp; Hosp Aide; JA; Spanish Clb; Rep Soph Cls; Bowling; Powder Puff Ftbl; Trk; Hon Roll; Spanish NHS; La Salle U; Lawyer.

PERFIT, TAMAR; Lakewood Prep; Freehold, NJ; (2); 1/15; Drama Clb; Exploring; Thesps; School Play; VP Frsh Cls; VP Soph Cls; Socr; Pblshd Bst Stu Poetry NJ 86; Math League Cmptn 86-87; Russian Hnr Soc 86-87.

PERIC, ELIZABETH; Immaculate Conception HS; Guttenberg, NJ; (3); Church Yth Grp; Dance Clb; Spanish Clb; SADD; Stage Crew; Variety Show; Lentz & Lentz Awd-Hgh SAT Scrs 87; Rutgers U; CPA.

PERIS, MARSHAL; Scotch Plains-Fanwood HS; Scotch Plains, NJ; (3); German Clb; Model UN; Concert Band; Mrchg Band; Rep Stu Cncl; JV Bsbl; JV Socr; Gov Hon Prg Awd; Hon Roll; NHS; Pre Med.

PERKINS, SHERRY; Manchester Twp HS; Lakehurst, NJ; (4); 36/186; Sec Drama Clb; Math Tm; Sec Spanish Clb; School Musical; Nwsp Rptr; Nwsp Stf; Rep Soph Cls; Stat Bsbl; Stat Bsktbl; Hon Roll; Montclair ST Coll; Psych.

PERLER, MICHAEL; Vernon Twp HS; Mcafee, NJ; (3); Ski Clb; Yrbk Stf; Off Lit Mag; Bsbl; High Hon Roll; Hon Roll; NHS; Prfct Atten Awd; Rutgers Deans Smmr Schlr 87; Comp Engrng.

PERLMAN, LAURA; West Windsor-Plainsboro HS; Plainsboro, NJ; (3); French Clb; Radio Clb; JV Socr; High Hon Roll; NHS; Band; Concert Band; Mrchg Band; School Musical; Hon Roll; Psych.

PERLMUTTER, DIANA; Kittatinny Regional HS; Newton, NJ; (3); 22/230; Debate Tm; Chorus; Madrigals; School Musical; Yrbk Sprt Ed; JV Fld Hcky; NHS; Am Leg Aux Girls St; Drama Clb; School Play; Acadmc Decathln Slvr Mdl Spch, Gld Mdl Essay 87; All Sussex Cnty Chorus, All NJ Regn Chorus 84-87; Liberal Arts.

PERNELL, DAVID; Plainfield HS; Plainfield, NJ; (3); Pres Art Clb; CAP; Dance Clb; Debate Tm; Library Aide; Office Aide; ROTC; Chorus; Church Choir; Off Jr Cls; Black Woman Conf & Acdmc Achvt 85-86; Stu Of Month 86-87; Rutgers; Mech Drawing.

PERNELL, DAWN; Vineland HS; Vineland, NJ; (3); 178/848; Office Aide; Teachers Aide; Mrchg Band; Lit Mag; Prfct Atten Awd; Glassboro ST Coll; Cmptr Sci.

PERPETUA, BONNIE; Notre Dame HS; Lawrenceville, NJ; (2); SADD; Hon Roll; Frnch Awd 86.

PERREN, KEVIN; A P Schalick HS; Bridgeton, NJ; (3); High Hon Roll; Hon Roll; NHS; 3rd Pl NJ Crftsmn Fr 87; Elec Engr.

PERREN, LEE; Braick Township HS; Brick Town, NJ; (3); 19/400; Boy Scts; Church Yth Grp; Computer Clb; Math Clb; Math Tm; Lit Mag; High Hon Roll; Rutgers; Comp.

PERREN, LISA; West Morris HS; Long Valley, NJ; (3); 30/495; Key Clb; Stu Cncl; JV Trk; Gov Hon Prg Awd; High Hon Roll; Acdmc Schl Ltr 85; Fnlst Gov Schl 86-87; St Elizabeth; Intl Bus Admin.

PERRI JR, FRANK R; St Joseph HS; Hammonton, NJ; (4); Aud/Vis; SADD; Stage Crew; Trs Frsh Cls; JV Bsbl; JV Var Ftbl; JV Var Wt Lftg; Cit Awd; Hon Roll; Kiwanis Awd; Hnrs Cert Art & Music Hstry 84; Pres Phys Fit Awd 84-87; Widener U; Acctng.

PERRICONE, PAM; Mater Dei HS; Union Beach, NJ; (4); Church Yth Grp; Pep Clb; Hon Roll; NHS; Kean Coll; Tchg.

PERRINE, DINA; Hackettstown HS; Hackettstown, NJ; (4); 29/220; Hosp Aide; Key Clb; Concert Band; Jazz Band; Mrchg Band; Stu Cncl; Trk; Hon Roll; NHS; Chorus; Az ST U.

PERRON, KELLEY; Garden State Acad; Hackettstown, NJ; (4); 4/31; Church Yth Grp; Office Aide; Church Choir; Nwsp Ed-Chief; Nwsp Rptr; Nwsp Stf; High Hon Roll; Hon Roll; Pres Schlr; Pres Acad Ftns Awd 87; Columbia Union Coll Schlrshp 87; Southern Coll; Med.

PERRONE, TARA; Red Bank Regional HS; Little Silver, NJ; (3); Art Clb; Church Yth Grp; Dance Clb; French Clb; PAVAS; Chorus; Church Choir; French Hon Soc; Hon Roll.

PERRUZZI, SEAN; Columbia HS; Maplewood, NJ; (3); Chess Clb; Church Yth Grp; Drama Clb; Math Tm; Quiz Bowl; Science Clb; Thesps; School Musical; Nwsp Stf; Yrbk Stf; Yng Ctzns Awd & Spec Recgntn Awd 87; Yth Rep Family Svc & Child Guidnce Ctr 86-88; Italian Club 85-87.

PERRY, ALEXANDER; Long Branch HS; Long Branch, NJ; (3); 14/287; FBLA; Letterman Clb; Red Cross Aide; Varsity Clb; Var L Ftbl; Var Trk; High Hon Roll; Hon Roll; Prfct Atten Awd; Schlr Ltrmn 86; Comp Sci.

PERRY, DANNETTA; Buena Regional HS; Newtonville, NJ; (3); Camera Clb; Computer Clb; Yrbk Phtg; Yrbk Stf; Stat Bsktbl; Scrkpr Score Keeper; Hon Roll; Comp Tech.

PERRY, DEAN; Toms River East HS; Toms River, NJ; (3); 64/505; Church Yth Grp; Cmnty Wkr; JV Capt Wrstlng; Hon Roll; Acad Lttr 84-85; Comm.

PERRY, DIANNE; Highland Regional HS; Erial, NJ; (3); 63/298; JV Bsktbl; Var Fld Hcky; JV Sftbl; Hon Roll; Artisans Club-Theatre.

PERRY, GRETCHEN; Riverside HS; Delanco, NJ; (3); 11/138; Am Leg Aux Girls St; Dance Clb; SADD; Rep Frsh Cls; Trs Soph Cls; Trs Jr Cls; Trs Sr Cls; VP Stu Cncl; Var Cheerleading; Var Fld Hcky; HOBY Fndtn 86; Intr Dsgn.

PERRY, KEVIN; Jefferson Township HS; Oak Ridge, NJ; (4); 1/235; Science Clb; SADD; Varsity Clb; Var Crs Cntry; JV Trk; NHS; St Schlr; Val; Navy ROTC Schlrshp 87; Rutgers Dist Schlr 85; U Of Notre Dame; Engrng.

PERRY, LAURA; Holy Cross HS; Willingboro, NJ; (4); 110/352; Church Yth Grp; Im Pom Pon; Im Trk; William Patterson Coll; Cmmnctn.

PERRY, PHILIP; Barnstable Acad; Garnerville, NY; (4); 2/29; Rep Soph Cls; High Hon Roll; Hon Roll; Achvt Sci 84-86; MIT; Physcst.

PERSAK, ALLISON; Glen Ridge HS; Glen Ridge, NJ; (3); Hosp Aide; Key Clb; Ski Clb; Mgr(s); Hon Roll; Natl Art Hnr Soc 86-87; United Nations Art Expo 87; Art.

PERSAUD, MANDOEDARI; Hillside HS; Hillside, NJ; (3); 2/58; School Play; Hon Roll; Rugers U; Med.

PESDA, JOHN; Edgewood SR HS; Sicklerville, NJ; (2); Var Socr; Var Tennis; JV Wrstlng; Law.

PESTRICHELLI, JOHN A; River Dell Regional HS; River Edge, NJ; (3); 29/228; Am Leg Boys St; Boy Scts; Ski Clb; SADD; Var L Bowling; Var L Socr; Var L Trk; NHS; Acad Dcthln Tm; Sci Tm; Engrng.

PETER, JOYCE; Clayton HS; Clayton, NJ; (3); FBLA; FHA; Key Clb; Office Aide; SADD; Drill Tm; Yrbk Stf; Merit Achvt Awd 87; Glassboro ST; Comp Sci.

PETERS, ANDREW; Howell HS; Howell, NJ; (4); 23/360; Jazz Band; Mrchg Band; School Musical; Nwsp Ed-Chief; JP Sousa Awd; NHS; Drama Clb; Q&S; Acpl Chr; Cecilian Music Clb Schlrshp 87; All Shore, Regn, Estrn & Ntl Bands & Chr 84-87; J Thumm Schlrshp 87; Oberlin Conservatory; Music.

PETERS, BONNIE LYNN; Riverside HS; Delanco, NJ; (4); Dance Clb; Hosp Aide; Spanish Clb; SADD; Off Stu Cncl; Var Stat Fld Hcky; JV Var Mgr(s); JV Var Score Keeper; JV Stat Sftbl; Vllybl; West Chester U; Elem Ed.

PETERS, MARIA; Eastern HS; Voorhees, NJ; (4); 29/335; Church Yth Grp; Intnl Clb; Service Clb; Mrchg Band; Capt Var Sftbl; Hon Roll; NHS; Rotgers U; Vet Med.

PETERS, MELANIE; The Friends Schl; Brooklawn, NJ; (3); VP Church Yth Grp; Teachers Aide; Variety Show; Yrbk Phtg; Yrbk Stf; Rep Frsh Cls; Rep Soph Cls; Rep Jr Cls; Off Stu Cncl; Capt Cheerleading; Dnce & Gymnstcs Awds 87; Mdlng & Cmmrcl Awds 85-86; Dr Sprts Med.

PETERSEN, KATHY; Morris Catholic HS; Boonton, NJ; (3); German Clb; Hosp Aide; Latin Clb; Spanish Clb; Varsity Clb; Nwsp Stf; Var Crs Cntry; Var Trk; Hon Roll; Vet.

PETERSEN, KEN; North Warren Regional HS; Blairstown, NJ; (4); Boy Scts; Pres FFA; Chorus; Concert Band; Mrchg Band; School Musical; Nwsp Stf; Rep Stu Cncl; JV Bsktbl; Band; Natl FFA Natl Band 87; Rutgers Cook Coll; Ag.

PETERSEN, LISA; Toms River HS South; Toms River, NJ; (2); Church Yth Grp; Drama Clb; Thesps; Chorus; Color Guard; School Musical; School Play; Variety Show; JV Sftbl; Hon Roll; Bst Actrss-Frnscs Tm.

PETERSEN, LOU ANNE; South River HS; South River, NJ; (3); Red Cross Aide; Spanish Clb; Lit Mag; Sec Stu Cncl; JV Capt Cheerleading; Hon Roll; VFW Awd; Ice Skater RVFSC 86-87floyalty Day Queen VFW 87; Phys Therapist.

PETERSEN, ROBERT N; Arthur L Johnson Reg HS; Westfield, NJ; (4); 33/200; Aud/Vis; Trs Spanish Clb; Stage Crew; Yrbk Stf; Off Stu Cncl; Capt Socr; JV Trk; Spanish NHS; Clark Soccer Club Schlrshp 87; Arthur F Johnson PTA 87; Cark Kumph PTA 87; Rutgers ST U; Bio.

PETERSON, DANIEL; Hunterdon Central HS; Whitehouse, NJ; (3); 95/543; VP Church Yth Grp; Computer Clb; Concert Band; Jazz Band; Mrchg Band; Symp Band; Ed Nwsp Phtg; Hon Roll; Ski Clb; Marine Tech Fld.

PETERSON, KELLY PATRICIA; Lacey Twp HS; Forked River, NJ; (3); 1/300; Am Leg Aux Girls St; Art Clb; DECA; Trs Stu Cncl; JV Bsktbl; Var Fld Hcky; Powder Puff Ftbl; Var Socr; JV Tennis; High Hon Roll; Unsng Hero Vrsty Sccr 86; Schlr Athlt Vrsty Sccr 87; 4th Plc Ovrll ST NJ DECA Advrtsng 87; Advrtsng.

PETERSON, KIMBERLY; Woodstown HS; Alloway, NJ; (3); Church Yth Grp; English Clb; SADD; Church Choir; Hon Roll; Comp Elec.

PETERSON, PAM; Shawnee HS; Medford, NJ; (3); Hosp Aide; Teachers Aide; JV Capt Lcrss; JV Socr; Hon Roll; Medford Girls Travling Soccr Clb 85 & 86; Pres Phys Fit Awd 86 & 87; Miss Amer Co-Ed Pag ST Fin 87; Sports Med.

PETERSON, PAMELA; Monsignor Donovan HS; Brick, NJ; (4); Cmnty Wkr; French Clb; Latin Clb; Nwsp Ed-Chief; Lit Mag; L Trk; NHS; Ntl Merit SF; Manhattanville Coll Hnrs Schlrshp 87; Seton Hall U Hnrs Schlrshp 87; Drew U Hnrs Schlrshp 87; Manhattanville Coll.

PETERSON, REBECCA; Saint John Vianney HS; Matawan, NJ; (2); #2 In Class; CAP; Intnl Clb; JCL; Latin Clb; Rep Frsh Cls; Stat L Crs Cntry; Stat L Trk; High Hon Roll; NHS; Outstndng Achvt Hstry, Hugh O Brien Yth Smnr 86-87; Outstndng Achvt In Ltn 85-87; Annapolis; Engrng.

PETERSON, SIGURD; Paul VI HS; Gibbsboro, NJ; (4); 11/504; Boy Scts; French Clb; Math Clb; Political Wkr; SADD; Band; Concert Band; Jazz Band; NHS; Engnrng.

PETERSON, STEVEN; Elizabeth HS; Elizabeth, NJ; (4); Church Yth Grp; Rep Frsh Cls; Rep Soph Cls; Rep Jr Cls; Var JV Bsbl; Im Wt Lftg; High Hon Roll; Hon Roll; Seton Hall U; Bus.

PETERSON, TARALEE; De Paul HS; Butler, NJ; (4); 50/164; Yrbk Stf; Var Capt Cheerleading; Var Socr; JV Sftbl; Var Trk; Hon Roll; De Paul Art Show 3rd Pl 85; Preakness Art Show 2nd Pl 87; Beaver Coll; Sci Illustration.

PETILLO, ALYSSA; St John Vianney HS; Colts Neck, NJ; (3); 38/246; Teachers Aide; Chorus; Flag Corp; School Musical; School Play; Stage Crew; Nwsp Rptr; Nwsp Stf; Hon Roll; Drama Clb; Gold & White Awd.

PETRANINO, ELIZABETH; Kinnelon HS; Kinnelon, NJ; (3); 44/180; Art Clb; Church Yth Grp; French Clb; NFL; Speech Tm; Stage Crew; Yrbk Stf; Rep Frsh Cls; Capt JV Socr; Trk; Amnesty Intl.

PETRASEK, RICHARD; Wood-Ridge HS; Wood Ridge, NJ; (3); 1/90; Latin Clb; Library Aide; Math Clb; Model UN; Nwsp Sprt Ed; Var Stu Cncl; Co-Capt Bowling; Tennis; High Hon Roll; NHS; Natnl Latin Exam Silver Medls 85 & 86.

PETRAT, ELIZABETH; Belleville HS; Belleville, NJ; (3); Computer Clb; Key Clb; Service Clb; Flag Corp; Off Jr Cls; High Hon Roll; Hon Roll; NHS; Comp Pgmmr.

PETRECCA, LAURA; Wayne Hills HS; Wayne, NJ; (3); Spanish Clb; Yrbk Stf; Lit Mag; Rep Jr Cls; JV Bsktbl; Stat Ftbl; Var Trk; Commnctns.

PETRECCA, LISA; Wayne Hills HS; Wayne, NJ; (2); 10/300; Spanish Clb; Yrbk Sprt Ed; Yrbk Stf; Stu Cncl; Bsktbl; Socr; Trk; Math.

PETRICK, BETH; Perth Amboy HS; Perth Amboy, NJ; (2); Model UN; PAVAS; Chorus; School Musical; School Play; Variety Show; Nwsp Stf; Rep Stu Cncl; Mst Hmrs 85; 2nd Plc Lip Sync Cntst 86; NY U; Actg.

PETRIN, DANIEL; Woodstown HS; Woodstown, NJ; (3); Am Leg Boys St; Drama Clb; Pres Band; School Musical; Var Crs Cntry; Capt Tennis; NHS; Church Yth Grp; French Clb; Pres Concert Band; Outstndng Bandsman Awd 86-87; Diploma For Am Legion Boys State 87; Most Imprvd Band Membr Awd 87; Rutgers Coll Of Phrmcy; Phrmcy.

PETRINO, JOANNE; Trenton Central HS; Trenton, NJ; (3); Key Clb; Chorus; Mgr Socr; Hon Roll; Advrtsng.

PETRIZZI, SUZANNE; Manalapan HS; Manalapan, NJ; (3); Dance Clb; PAVAS; SADD; Chorus; Variety Show; Yrbk Stf; Rep Frsh Cls; Rep Soph Cls; Rep Sr Cls; Off Stu Cncl; Cert Hnr-Geomtry 86-87; Frhld Rgnl 3rd Yr Music Awd 86-87; Advrtsng.

PETRO, JANE; Holy Spirit HS; Pleasantville, NJ; (4); 59/354; Am Leg Aux Girls St; Pres Sec 4-H; Quiz Bowl; Teachers Aide; Church Choir; School Musical; 4-H Awd; High Hon Roll; Hon Roll; Church Yth Grp; Bus Symposium 86; Young United Ch Wmn Schlrshp 87; Kean Coll Of NJ; Occup Therapy.

PETROCHKO, JOSEPH; Maple Shade HS; Maple Shade, NJ; (3); Boy Scts; French Clb; Var JV Bsbl; Var JV Crs Cntry; Var JV Socr; Var JV Trk; Var Wrstlng; High Hon Roll; NHS; Computer Clb; Boy Scts-Eagle Awd 87.

PETRONE, MARIA A; Acad Of The Holy Angels; Old Tappan, NJ; (4); 16/152; Drama Clb; Chorus; School Musical; School Play; Yrbk Stf; High Hon Roll; NHS; Opt Clb Awd; Church Yth Grp; Natl Ltn Exam Cum Laude 84; U Sthrn CA; Actng.

PETRONELLA, MICHELE L; Hamilton HS West; Trenton, NJ; (4); 39/343; Dance Clb; Girl Scts; Key Clb; Band; Concert Band; Mrchg Band; Variety Show; Sr Cls; Cheerleading; Hon Roll; Robinson Schl PTA Schlrshp & Pres Acdmc Ftnss Awd 87; Exec Cmte Band 85-87; U Of Miami; Dance.

PETROSKI, EILEEN E; Bishop George HS; Carteret, NJ; (4); 60/270; Red Cross Aide; Concert Band; Jazz Band; Mrchg Band; School Musical; Swmmng; JP Sousa Awd; Hosp Aide; Band; Esprt De Corp Awd, Ldrshp Awd, Jrnlsm Awd, Awd Of Excllnc, Stu Tchr-Music 86-87; Susquehanna U; Tchng.

PETROZELLI, THERESA; Hunterdon Central HS; White House Sta, NJ; (3); Church Yth Grp; Key Clb; Chorus; Church Choir; Variety Show; Hon Roll; Prfct Atten Awd; Cntrl Jrsy Rgn II Chorus 87; Music Ther.

PETROZZA, CARMELA; Mary Help Of Christians HS; Paterson, NJ; (2); SADD; Chorus; Church Choir; Gym; Hon Roll; Achvt World Hist,Physcl Sci,Alg Cert Awd 84-85.

PETRUCELLI, LISA; Belvidere HS; Belvidere, NJ; (4); 15/128; Am Leg Aux Girls St; Church Yth Grp; Sec Drama Clb; Model UN; Pres Chorus; Madrigals; School Musical; School Play; Stage Crew; Nwsp Rptr; Chrs Awd 85-86; Ntl Yng Ldrs Conf 86-87; Psychlgy.

PETRULLO, JOHN; Kittatinny Regional HS; Newton, NJ; (3); 30/216; Am Leg Boys St; JV Wrstlng; Hon Roll; NHS; Ishnryu Karate 3 Yrs Won Trophs & 1st Pl Rbbns 84-86; Engrng.

PETTI, CATHY; Nutley HS; Nutley, NJ; (4); 1/280; AFS; Am Leg Aux Girls St; Drama Clb; School Play; Capt Tennis; Trk; NHS; Ntl Merit Ltr; St Schlr; Val; Rnsslr & Govnrs Schlr 86; Law.

PETTINELLI, DINO; Phillipsburg HS; Alpha, NJ; (3); 23/315; Cmnty Wkr; Band; Chorus; Concert Band; Jazz Band; Mrchg Band; Orch; Pep Band; Nwsp Rptr; Nwsp Stf; King Of The Alpha Diamond Jubilee Celebtn Parade 86; Pat Reilly Wrstlng Trnmnt Trphy 85; Ed.

PETTIS, TONDALAYA; Frank H Morrell HS; Irvington, NJ; (3); Art Clb; Computer Clb; SADD; Rep Soph Cls; Hon Roll; Cheyney U; Comp Sci.

PETWAY, RANDY E; Vindland HS; Vineland, NJ; (4); 42/750; French Clb; Political Wkr; Rep Jr Cls; Var Bsbl; Var Ftbl; Im Wrstlng; Ntl Merit SF; St Schlr; James Dickenson Carr Scholar Rutgers Coll 87; PA ST U Achvt Scholar 87; Natl Achvt Scholar SF 86; Rutgers Coll; Comp Sci.

PETZINGER, KRISTEN; Timothy Christian Schl; Woodbridge, NJ; (3); #6 In Class; Church Yth Grp; Girl Scts; Chorus; God Cntry Awd; High Hon Roll; Hon Roll; Calvin MI; Psychlgy.

PEVNY, MICHAEL; St Joseph Regional HS; River Vale, NJ; (3); 65/230; Spanish Clb; Varsity Clb; JV Wrstlng; Spanish NHS; Sports Med.

PEYPOCH III, RAMON J; Christian Brothers Acad; Middletown, NJ; (3); 21/240; Math Tm; Chorus; Nwsp Sprt Ed; Yrbk Sprt Ed; VP Stu Cncl; JV Bsbl; JV Bsktbl; Im Socr; High Hon Roll; Rep NHS; Ivy Leag Schl; Mdcn Tech.

PEYSER, JEFF; West Essex HS; No Caldwell, NJ; (2); Computer Clb; Key Clb; Math Tm; Science Clb; Spanish Clb; Rep Frsh Cls; JV Crs Cntry; Bus.

PEZZA, KELLY ANN; Westwood HS; Westwood, NJ; (4); Drama Clb; Nwsp Stf; Yrbk Stf; Hon Roll; ST Fnlst Awd-Miss Teen Coed 87; Caldwell Coll; Comm.

PEZZANO, RENEE; Lyndhurst HS; Lyndhurst, NJ; (2); Varsity Clb; Bsktbl; Sftbl; High Hon Roll; Poem Awd 87; Phy Thrpst.

PEZZUTI, DEBORAH; West Essex HS; Fairfield, NJ; (4); 44/345; Drama Clb; Chorus; School Musical; School Play; Stage Crew; JV Sftbl; Hon Roll; Montclair ST Coll; Art Ed.

PFEFFER, MICHELLE; Penns Grove HS; Penns Grove, NJ; (3); Am Leg Aux Girls St; Pres Church Yth Grp; JCL; SADD; VP Sr Cls; Var Capt Cheerleading; Gym; Var Sftbl; Bausch & Lomb Sci Awd; Sec NHS; Physcl Thrpy.

PFEIFFER, CONSTANCE; Spotswood HS; Spotswood, NJ; (4); 3/189; Trs Intnl Clb; Model UN; Co-Capt Color Guard; Ed Yrbk Stf; Var Socr; High Hon Roll; VP NHS; Ntl Merit Schol; Pres Schlr; Sec Spanish NHS; Grdn ST Dstngshd Schlr; Cngrssnl Clssrm; Rutgers U; Phrmcy.

PFEIFFER, GLORIA ANN; Cinnaminson HS; Cinnaminson, NJ; (4); Am Leg Aux Girls St; Church Yth Grp; Drama Clb; Pres German Clb; Hosp Aide; Intnl Clb; SADD; Thesps; Acpl Chr; Chorus; All S Jrsy Rgnl Choir 85-87; Cmnctns.

PFEIFFER, MARIE; E P Memorial HS; Elmwood Pk, NJ; (3); Spanish Clb; Band; Concert Band; Mrchg Band; JV Var Bsktbl; Hon Roll.

PFEIFFER, MONICA; Florence Twp Memorial HS; Roebling, NJ; (3); JV Fld Hcky; Hon Roll; Natl Bus Hnr Scty 87; Mrktng.

PFLAUM, WENDY; Oak Knoll Schl; Scotch Plns, NJ; (4); Art Clb; Pep Clb; Service Clb; Ski Clb; Acpl Chr; Chorus; Madrigals; School Musical; Nwsp Phtg; Nwsp Stf; U Of MD; Intr Dsgn.

PHADIA, SONIA; Wayne Valley HS; Wayne, NJ; (3); Hosp Aide; Library Aide; Math Tm; Band; Lit Mag; Mgr(s); High Hon Roll; Hon Roll; NHS; GAA; Natl Frnch Cont Merit Cert 86; Pre Med.

PHAIR, REGINA MARIE; Madison Central HS; Old Bridge, NJ; (4); 11/355; Trs French Clb; Lit Mag; French Hon Soc; NHS; Italian Club 85-87; Italian Hnr Soc 87; Dance-Ballet, Jazz Club 85-87; Rutgers Coll.

PHAM, ANH; William L Dickinson HS; Orange, NJ; (4); Intnl Clb; VICA; Var Bsktbl; Var Vllybl; Var Wrstlng; Lincoln Tech Inst; Automotive.

PHAM, CHUONG; Dover HS; Dover, NJ; (3); Am Leg Boys St; Exploring; JV Crs Cntry; JV Socr; JV Var Trk; Hon Roll.

PHAM, THANG; Egg Harbor Township HS; Mckee City, NJ; (3); 16/329; French Clb; JV Socr; Schltc Ltr Awd 85-86; Stevens Inst Tech; Mech Engrng.

PHELAN, CATHY; Matawan Regional HS; Matawan, NJ; (3); 31/302; Cmnty Wkr; Bsktbl; Cheerleading; Sftbl; High Hon Roll; NHS.

PHELAN, EDWARD; The Kings Christian Schl; Lumberton, NJ; (2); 1/55; Church Yth Grp; Drama Clb; VP Frsh Cls; VP Soph Cls; Var Socr; High Hon Roll; Engrng.

PHELPS, DENISE; Highland HS; Erial, NJ; (3); DECA; Drama Clb; Thesps; School Play; Prfct Atten Awd; DECA Awds 2nd Pl Finance & Credit Regnl Div 86; DECA Hnry Mention Finance & Credit ST Lvl 87; Acctng.

PHIFER, STEVEN; Gloucester County Christian HS; Mantua, NJ; (2); Socr; Trk; Hon Roll; Prfct Atten Awd.

PHILIPP, DENISE; Pualsboro HS; Gibbstown, NJ; (2); Chorus; School Musical; School Play; Rep Soph Cls; Var Cheerleading; Stat Mat Maids; High Hon Roll; Hon Roll; Pres Phys Fit Mst Outstndng 86; Ed.

PHILLIPS, LOUIS; Paulsboro HS; Gibbstown, NJ; (4); 20/135; Hon Roll; VFW Awd; Presdntl Acadc Ftns Awd 87; Awd Acadc Achvt 86; N Amer Schl Cnsrvtn Diplma 87; Frostburg ST Coll; Wldlf Mgmt.

PHILLIPS, RIKKI; Fair Lawn HS; Fair Lawn, NJ; (3); FHA; CUNY Tech Schl; Grphc Arts.

PHILLIPS, TRACY; Ocean Township HS; Asbury Park, NJ; (3); 72/345; Ski Clb; JV Var Crs Cntry.

PHILLPS, NICOLE; Cherokee HS; Marlton, NJ; (3); Dance Clb; Hosp Aide; Ski Clb; Spanish Clb; Rep Jr Cls; Rep Stu Cncl; JV Var Cheerleading; High Hon Roll; Nrsng.

PHILPOTT, MICHELLE F; Spotswood HS; Spotswood, NJ; (2); Intnl Clb; Model UN; Orch; Rep Frsh Cls; Pres Soph Cls; Var Tennis; JV Trk; High Hon Roll; Hon Roll; Sci Leag 85-86.

PHILPOTT, STEPHEN; Overbrook Regional HS; Lindenwold, NJ; (4); 2/335; Am Leg Boys St; Church Yth Grp; Science Clb; Concert Band; Drm Mjr(t); Mrchg Band; Var Capt Tennis; Hst NHS; Sal; St Schlr; NROTC Schlrshp Awd 86; U S Naval Acad; Engrng.

PHRANER, TERESALEE; Fairlawn HS; Fair Lawn, NJ; (3); 129/363; Exploring; Girl Scts; World Tae Kwon Do Karate Fed Cert 87; Monclair ST U; Bus.

PIATT JR, RICHARD J; Phillipsburg Catholic HS; Easton, PA; (4); 14/72; Drama Clb; Chorus; School Musical; School Play; Stage Crew; Nwsp Rptr; Yrbk Ed-Chief; Yrbk Stf; Hon Roll; VP NHS; Yth Mnth Exch Clb 87; Stu Mnth Phllpsbrg Rotary Clb 8 7; Lafayette Coll.

PICA, NICOLE; Carteret HS; Carteret, NJ; (3); 84/222; Pres Pep Clb; Ski Clb; Spanish Clb; Nwsp Stf; Yrbk Stf; Var L Bsktbl; Crs Cntry; JV Var Sftbl; JV Tennis; GAA; SOCL Wrk.

PICCOLA, RICHARD; Maple Shade HS; Maple Shade, NJ; (3); 3/200; Computer Clb; FBLA; Library Aide; Yrbk Rptr; Yrbk Sprt Ed; Yrbk Stf; JV Crs Cntry; JV Trk; Cit Awd; High Hon Roll.

PICILLO, KELLI; Madison HS; Madison, NJ; (3); 78/214; Church Yth Grp; JV Bsktbl; Var Socr; Var Sftbl; Hon Roll; Cnslr Cmp Fatima Hndcppd Chldrn Vlntr 86-87; Cnslr Cmp Lincoln Hndcppd Chldrn 80-87.

PICIONE, ANTHONY; Phillipsburg HS; Phillipsburg, NJ; (3); 11/300; High Hon Roll; Ntl Merit Ltr; Warren Cnty Champnshp Mock Trl Team 86-87; Lawyr.

PICK, CHRISTINE; Lakeland Regional HS; Wanaque, NJ; (3); 25/356; Math Tm; Rep Jr Cls; VP Stu Cncl; Var Bsktbl; Var Capt Fld Hcky; Sftbl; Var Capt Trk; High Hon Roll; NHS; Trs Spanish NHS; 2nd Tm All Conf Discus Throw 87; Hnbl Mntn All Cnty Fld Hockey & Mem On Grdn ST Tm 85 & 87; Restarnt Mgmnt.

PICONE, DONNA MARIE; Brick Memorial HS; Brick, NJ; (4); 4/290; Key Clb; Math Tm; Office Aide; Concert Band; Jazz Band; Mrchg Band; Stage Crew; High Hon Roll; NHS; U Of DE; Bus Admin.

PICONE, RACHAEL; Hunterdon Central HS; Whitehouse Sta, NJ; (4); 142/548; Sec Art Clb; JA; Thesps; Capt Color Guard; Jazz Band; School Musical; Variety Show; Yrbk Phtg; Pres Jr Cls; Hon Roll; Rcgntn Outstndg Activities 84-85; Rutgers Coll; Ftns & Hlth Spcls.

PIDANE, DONNA; Holy Family Acad; Bayonne, NJ; (4); 1/150; Nwsp Ed-Chief; Nwsp Rptr; Nwsp Stf; Rep Sr Cls; CC Awd; Elks Awd; High Hon Roll; NHS; St Schlr; Val; Rutgers Schlr 86; St Peters Summer Schlr 85-86; George Washington Awd Achvmnt In Math & Sci 86; Rutgers U; Biochem.

PIDDINGTON, JOSEPH; Jackson HS; Jackson, NJ; (4); Stage Crew; Bsbl; JV Ftbl; Swmmng; 2nd Pl Wnnr-SSSCF-GN Cbnt 87; Atlantic CC; Clnry Arts.

PIELL, FRED; Delaware Valley Regional HS; Pittstown, NJ; (3); 9/220; Am Leg Boys St; Pep Clb; Varsity Clb; Var Bsktbl; Var Crs Cntry; Var Trk; High Hon Roll; NHS; Bus Admin.

PIENTA, KAREN; Buena Regional HS; Vineland, NJ; (2); Pep Clb; Ski Clb; Rep Frsh Cls; Rep Soph Cls; Cheerleading; Mgr Stat Fld Hcky; Mgr(s); Score Keeper.

PIEPSZAK, CHRIS; Pennington HS; West Trenton, NJ; (2); French Clb; Q&S; Nwsp Rptr; Yrbk Stf; Lit Mag; Socr; Sftbl; Hon Roll; NHS; French I Awd 85-86; Moch Trial Tm 86-87; Campus Guides 86-87.

PIERCE, EDWARD D; West Morris Mendham HS; Cliffside Park, NJ; (3); 50/308; Am Leg Boys St; Math Tm; Var L Ftbl; Wt Lftg; Hon Roll; MIP Ftbl 86; West Point; Engrng.

PIERCE, JENNIFER; Bridgeton HS; Bridgeton, NJ; (3); 4-H; Girl Scts; 4-H Awd.

PIERCE, KELLY; Camden HS; Camden, NJ; (2); Debate Tm; 4-H; Church Choir; Mrchg Band; Nwsp Stf; Yrbk Bus Mgr; Sec Soph Cls; Var Cheerleading; Hon Roll; Pres Schlr; Mst Sprt-Chrldng 86-87; Temple; Bus Admin.

PIERCE, LAZETTE; St Vincent Acad; Newark, NJ; (3); Hosp Aide; Service Clb; JV Cheerleading; Prfct Atten Awd; Honor Athl Yr Trck Newark Y Trck Tm 83; Crmnl Jstc.

PIERCE, MICHAEL; Voohees HS; High Bridge, NJ; (2); 72/292; Var Crs Cntry; Var Golf; Bus.

PIERCE, RUTH; Cumberland Regional HS; Bridgeton, NJ; (3); 11/384; Science Clb; High Hon Roll; Hon Roll; Jr NHS; NHS; Prfct Atten Awd; Temple; Med.

PIERCE, VALERIE A; Columbia HS; South Orange, NJ; (4); Drama Clb; French Clb; Library Aide; Math Clb; Math Tm; Science Clb; Lit Mag; Ntl Merit SF; St Schlr; NJ ST Sci Lg Awd Chem 86; Princeton; Bio Rsrch.

PIERFY, DAVID; Hamilton HS East; Trenton, NJ; (3); Exploring; FBLA; JV Crs Cntry; Var L Tennis; Var L Wrstlng; Hon Roll; NHS; Ntl Merit Ltr; 1st Pl Accntng I 86; Independent Stdy 86-87; Accntng.

PIERRE, GINIA; Abraham Clark HS; Roselle, NJ; (4); 4/166; Drama Clb; Pep Clb; Madrigals; Ed Lit Mag; Rep Jr Cls; Rep Stu Cncl; Hon Roll; NHS; Rtgts Acdmc Achvmnt Awd 87; Acdmc All-Amrcn 87; Ntl Assn Negro Bus & Pro Wmns Clbs Inc Schlrshp 87; Rutgers U; Med.

PIERSON, DAVID; Kingsway Regional HS; Mickleton, NJ; (2); Chess Clb; Church Yth Grp; Computer Clb; Science Clb; Jazz Band; Mrchg Band; Rep Frsh Cls; Rep Soph Cls; Stu Cncl; Hon Roll; Comp Sci.

PIERSON, GINA; Lenape Valley Regional HS; Andover, NJ; (3); Church Yth Grp; Dance Clb; Girl Scts; Hosp Aide; Intnl Clb; Trs Jr Cls; Rep Stu Cncl; Fld Hcky; Sftbl; Hon Roll; Variety Show 85; MI ST; Bus Adm.

PIERSON, KEITH; Boonton HS; Lincoln Park, NJ; (2); Boy Scts; Var L Crs Cntry; JV Lcrss; Im Vllybl; High Hon Roll; Hon Roll; OH ST U; Engl.

PIETRANGELO, GINA; Toms River HS East; Toms River, NJ; (3); 17/504; Church Yth Grp; Girl Scts; Hosp Aide; Ski Clb; SADD; Cit Awd; High Hon Roll; Cmnty Wkr; French Clb; Math Clb; Acad Ltr/Pin 87; Cert Rcgntn Amer Assn U Wmn 87; Rugers U Smnr, Douglass Cmps Wmn In Engrng 87; VA Polytech; Engrng.

PIETRO, LAURA ANN; Central Regional HS; Bayville, NJ; (4); 28/210 Am Leg Aux Girls St; Pres Key Clb; Chorus; Sec Sr Cls; Var Capt Trk Kiwanis Awd; NHS; Pres Schlr; Sec Soph Cls; Sec Jr Cls; Salutn Army Schlrshp 87; Slvr Rdg Pk West Wmns Clb Schlrshp 87; Bombert Schlrshp 87; Ursinus Coll; Comms.

PIETROWICZ, MARNI; Hopewell Valley Central HS; Titusville, NJ (3); 48/216; AFS; Art Clb; French Clb; Latin Clb; Lit Mag; Rep Frsh Cls Rep Soph Cls; Rep Jr Cls; Rep Sr Cls; Rep Stu Cncl; Cmnctns.

PIETRUSKA, DANNY; St Peters Prep; Bayonne, NJ; (4); 69/191; Computer Clb; High Hon Roll; Hon Roll; St Peters Coll; Cmptr Sci.

PIETRYKOSKI, ELIZABETH; Bloomfield SR HS; Bloomfield, NJ; (4); Band; Chorus; Hon Roll; Clara E Schauffler Hm Ec Awd 87; Montclair ST Coll; Int Dsgn.

PIETRYKOSKI, JOHN; Bloomfield SR HS; Bloomfield, NJ; (3); Aud/Vis; Hon Roll; Bus.

PIETSCH, CHRYSSA; Steinert HS; Crosswicks, NJ; (3); Exploring; Key Clb; Acpl Chr; Chorus; Drill Tm; Madrigals; Mrchg Band; School Musical; School Play; Pom Pon; Orthdntst.

PIETSCH, JOSEPH; Lodi HS; Lodi, NJ; (4); 50/147; VP Key Clb; Leo Clb; Varsity Clb; Var L Tennis; Kiwanis Awd; William Paterson Coll; Bus

PIEZEMA, DENNIS; East Orange HS; E Orange, NJ; (3); Art Clb, Cmnty Wkr; Drama Clb; JA; NAACP; PAVAS; Spanish Clb; Speech Tm Stage Crew; Variety Show; Drama.

PIFFATH, MICHELE; Notre Dame HS; Trenton, NJ; (3); Church Yth Grp; Red Cross Aide; Service Clb; Stage Crew; Yrbk Stf; JV Socr; Stat Sftbl; Swmmng; Hon Roll; Montclair ST Coll.

PIGAGE, JOY; Long Branch HS; Long Branch, NJ; (4); 22/240; Yrbk Ed-Chief; Lit Mag; Sec Soph Cls; Sec Jr Cls; Sec Sr Cls; Socr; Twrlr; Prfct Atten Awd; U S Jrnslm Awd 86; Cmmnctns.

PIIZZI, DONNA; Cranford HS; Cranford, NJ; (4); 33/270; FBLA; Chorus Yrbk Bus Mgr; Stu Cncl; Crs Cntry; Trk; Hon Roll; NHS; Katharine Gibbs Ldrshp Awd 86 & Schlrsh P 87; Katharine Gibbs; Exec Secy.

PIKE, LEANNE; Cherry Hill HS East; Cherry Hill, NJ; (4); Church Yth Grp; SADD; Nwsp Stf; Lit Mag; Rep Stu Cncl; Var Capt Crs Cntry; Var Trk; Hon Roll; Lafayette Coll; Engl.

PILCH, LANCE; Hunterdon Central HS; Stockton, NJ; (2); 33/478; FCA; Hosp Aide; Rptr Frsh Cls; Rptr Soph Cls; Rptr Stu Cncl; JV Bsbl; JV Socr; Hon Roll; Socr; Vllybl; Soph Recog Awd-Eng 86-87; Aviation.

PILKINGTON, ERIC; Wallkill Valley Regional HS; Stockholm, NJ; (3); Computer Clb; Math Clb; Lib Band; Jazz Band; Off Lib Mrchg Band; Lib Symp Band; Var Ftbl; JV Tennis; Hon Roll; All Sussx Cnty Band 85-86, Bus Admin.

PILLA, MICHAEL; Bridgeton SR HS; Bridgeton, NJ; (3); Am Leg Boys St; Church Yth Grp; Varsity Clb; Church Choir; VP Jr Cls; VP Sr Cls; Var Bsbl; JV Bsktbl; Var Ftbl; High Hon Roll; 2nd Tm All-Conf-Ftbl 86; Accntng.

PILLAI, SHIBA; Immaculate Heart Acad; Demarest, NJ; (3); 2/180; Aud/Vis; Hosp Aide; Model UN; Science Clb; Chorus; Orch; Stage Crew; Nwsp Rptr; Yrbk Stf; Lit Mag; Princeton U; Sci.

PILLARI, BRENDA; Ridgefield Park HS; Little Ferry, NJ; (3); 7/215 Computer Clb; Debate Tm; Math Clb; Math Tm; Science Clb; Spanish Clb; Y-Teens; Off Frsh Cls; Off Soph Cls; Sec Stu Cncl; Ramapo Spec Incntv Prog 87; Unsung HERO Awd Bsktbl 85; Med.

PINCKNEY, LISA; Delaware Valley Regional HS; Frenchtown, NJ; (3); 50/220; Art Clb; Ski Clb; Yrbk Stf; Trs Rep Stu Cncl; Hon Roll; Math.

PINCKNEY, ROBIN; Immaculate Conception HS; Orange, NJ; (2); Hosp Aide; PAVAS; Spanish Clb; Art Clb; Church Yth Grp; Drama Clb; Var Cheerleading; Hon Roll; Prfct Atten Awd; 3rd Pl Spnsh Vcblry Cntst 87; Sci Achvt Awd 86; Hwrd U; Pre-Med.

PINDER, LOUVENIA; Edgewood Regional HS; Chesilhurst, NJ; (3); Dance Clb; JA; Mrchg Band; Rep Frsh Cls; Rep Jr Cls; Rep Sr Cls; Hon Roll; Pres Jr NHS; Prfct Atten Awd; Medicine.

PINEDA, EVELYN; Paterson Catholic Reg HS; Paterson, NJ; (3); Church Yth Grp; Library Aide; JV Bsktbl; JV Cheerleading; Var Score Keeper; JV Vllybl.

PINEIRO, JUDY; Newton HS; Newton, NJ; (2); 39/219; SADD; Concert Band; Mrchg Band; Yrbk Stf; Lit Mag; Rep Frsh Cls; Sec Soph Cls; Trs Jr Cls; Rep Stu Cncl; Var L Cheerleading.

PINGITORE, JOHNNA; Middletown HS South; Red Bank, NJ; (3), Church Yth Grp; Girl Scts; Chorus; Church Choir; Socr; French Hon Soc; Hon Roll; 4 1st Pl Trphys Dnc 86-87; 4 2nd Pl Trphys Dnc 86-87; Towson; Dnc.

PINIAK, ANDREW; Red Bank Regional HS; Red Bank, NJ; (4); Nwsp Sprt Ed; Nwsp Stf; Stu Cncl; Bsbl; Var Trk; Hon Roll; Lab Asst Cert 84; Adult Dscssn Group 87; Swmthn For Cancer Cert 87; Spllthn For M S Cert 86; Rutgers U.

PINILLA, FREDY; Ferris HS; Jersey City, NJ; (3); Church Yth Grp; Spanish Clb; Yrbk Stf; Var JV Socr; Tennis; Hon Roll; NHS; Prfct Atten Awd; Outstndng Bilingal Stu 86; Stu Achvt Awd 87; Atlantic Union Coll; Theology.

PINKSTONE, RAYMOND; Pennsauken HS; Pennsauken, NJ; (3); 25/420; German Clb; Leo Clb; Science Clb; Ski Clb; Yrbk Stf; VP Jr Cls; VP Stu Cncl; Trk; Hon Roll; Jr NHS; Rutgers U; Bus.

PINNIX, CHARLETTE; Mt St Dominic Acad; East Orange, NJ; (3) Church Yth Grp; Hosp Aide; Church Choir; School Musical; School Play Trk; Hon Roll; Pre Med.

PINO, GERARDO; Dickinson HS; Jersey City, NJ; (4); Art Clb; Church Yth Grp; Cmnty Wkr; Dance Clb; Red Cross Aide; Science Clb; SADD; Var Capt Socr; JV Vllybl; High Hon Roll; Achvt Roll 85-86; Dentist.

PINO, JOSEPH; Toms River HS North; Toms River, NJ; (3); 7/450; Boy Scts; Science Clb; Ski Clb; Spanish Clb; Rep Stu Cncl; JV Socr; Var Wrstlng; Gov Hon Prg Awd; High Hon Roll; Pres NHS; Eagle Sct 85; USSF Sccr Rfree 84; Wrstlng 2nd Pl Dist 87; Sci.

PINO, STEFANIE; Edgewood SR HS; Blue Anchor, NJ; (2); Yrbk Stf Tennis; High Hon Roll; Hon Roll; Jr NHS; Pres Acdmc Ftnss Awd 86, Spnsh Schlr Awd 85-86; Rutgers U; Bus.

PINS, RICHARD; Northern Valley Regional HS; Norwood, NJ; (3); 75/275; Art Clb; Pres Aud/Vis; Boy Scts; Debate Tm; French Clb; Ski Clb; Teachers Aide; Temple Yth Grp; School Musical; School Play; Political Sci.

PINTO, ALBERT; John F Kennedy HS; Metuchen, NJ; (3); 18/249; Am Leg Boys St; High Hon Roll; PA ST U; Physcs.

PINTO, ANDREW; De Paul Didlesan HS; Wayne, NJ; (4); 11/164; Pep Clb; Nwsp Stf; Bsktbl; Im Vllybl; High Hon Roll; NHS; Ntl Merit Ltr; St Schlr; Spnsh,Acctng Acad Awd 85-86; Villanova U; Acctng.

PINTO, BEATRICE; Memorial HS; West New York, NJ; (3); Cmnty Wkr; Office Aide; Teachers Aide; Chorus; VP Bsktbl; Capt JV Sftbl; JV Vllybl; Athltc Awd Vrsty Bsktbll Sftbll 86; Certf Hon Accmplshmnt Arts Art Expo 87; Eugene Lang Coll; Art Mgmt.

PINTO, CONSUELA; Mt St Dominic Acad; Belleville, NJ; (3); 6/56; Hosp Aide; Intnl Clb; Library Aide; Service Clb; Ed Nwsp Stf; Mgr Lit Mag; High Hon Roll; NHS; 1st Hnrs 84-87; Atty.

PINZON, CLAUDIA; Henry Hudson Regional HS; Highlands, NJ; (3); French Clb; SADD; Yrbk Stf; Var Bowling; Var Fld Hcky; Ltr Fld Hcky & Bowlng 87; Cert Chem Tstng 86.

PIOTROWSKI, MICHAEL; Saint John Vianney HS; Colts Neck, NJ; (3); FBLA; Rep Soph Cls; Rep Jr Cls; JV Socr.

PIPERNO, ROBERT; Pennsauken HS; Pennsauken, NJ; (2); 52/350; Boy Scts; Spanish Clb; JV Golf; JV Socr; Var L Swmmng; Hon Roll; Spanish NHS; Cert Tchg Swmg Learn To Swim Prog Spnsrd By Pennsauken PTA 87; Law.

PIPPITT, NANCY; Riverside HS; Riverside, NJ; (3); 19/101; Drama Clb; FBLA; Key Clb; SADD; Chorus; Off Stu Cncl; Im JV Bsktbl; JV Var Fld Hcky; Var Sftbl; Hon Roll; Vrsty Sftbl Coaches Awd 86; Hnrbl Mntn All S Jrsy Grp Fld Hcky 86; Advrtsng.

PIRET, BRIAN; Wood-Ridge HS; Wood Ridge, NJ; (3); 7/90; Spanish Clb; Var Bsbl; JV Var Bsktbl; Var Socr; High Hon Roll; NHS; 2nd Team-All Conf Soccer 86.

PIRO, CHRISTINE; Manalapan HS; Manalapan, NJ; (3); Nwsp Rptr; JV Mgr(s); Score Keeper; Socr; JV Sftbl; Hon Roll; Cmnctns.

PIROZZI, RICH; Wayne Hills HS; Wayne, NJ; (3); 29/310; French Clb; Var Ftbl; JV Golf; Im Wt Lftg; Capt Wrstlng; High Hon Roll; Hon Roll; NHS.

PISANSKY, JANET; Arthur L Johnson Regional HS; Clark, NJ; (4); 3/196; Art Clb; Drm Mjr(t); Mrchg Band; Orch; Stu Cncl; Stat L Bowling; VP NHS; Ntl Merit Ltr; Spanish NHS; Am Leg Aux Girls St; NJ Garden ST Dist Schlr 86; Poltcl Sci.

PISAPIA, JESSICA; Timothy Chrstn; North Plainfield, NJ; (1); 1/39; Camera Clb; Church Yth Grp; Spanish Clb; Chorus; High Hon Roll; Val; Spanish, Algebra, Civics,English, Science Awd 86; Princeton; Arch.

PISCHEDDA, DEANNA; Lacey Township HS; Forked River, NJ; (3); Pres DECA; Rep Soph Cls; Rep Stu Cncl; Capt Cheerleading; Powder Puff Ftbl; Hon Roll; Trenton ST Coll; Bus Frgn Affr.

PISCITELLI, KAREN; South River HS; South River, NJ; (3); 11/147; Church Yth Grp; Dance Clb; VP German Clb; Library Aide; Math Clb; Band; Yrbk Stf; Rep VP Stu Cncl; Mgr Var Bsbl; Mgr JV Bsktbl; Vrsty Ltrd Ftbl & Field Hcky 84-85; Penn ST; Lawyer.

PISCITELLI, NANCY; Hoboken HS; Hoboken, NJ; (3); #3 In Class; Aud/Vis; Cmnty Wkr; Frsh Cls; Rep Soph Cls; Rep Jr Cls; Rep Stu Cncl; High Hon Roll; VP NHS; Peef Ldrshp Cmte; Acctng.

PISCITELLO, MICHELLE L; Livingston HS; Livingston, NJ; (4); 85/424; French Clb; Pep Clb; Varsity Clb; Var Cheerleading; Powder Puff Ftbl; Vrsty Chrldng Ltrs 83-87; Fairleigh Dickinson U Madison.

PISKADLO, BRYAN; Ramapo Regional HS; Wyckoff, NJ; (4); 95/328; Hon Roll; Cert Merit Alg II 85-86; Cert Merit Geom 84-85; Cert Merit Engl 83-84; Rutgers U; Phrmclgy.

PISKOROWSKI, LORIE; Middlesex HS; Middlesex, NJ; (3); 16/161; Trs German Clb; Key Clb; SADD; Chorus; Concert Band; Drm Mjr(t); Mrchg Band; Orch; Hon Roll; NHS; Math.

PITARO, EUGENE A; Hudson Catholic HS; Neshanic, NJ; (3); 40/200; Art Clb; Camera Clb; Cmnty Wkr; Computer Clb; English Clb; FBLA; Intnl Clb; Library Aide; Science Clb; Spanish Clb; Elect Engr.

PITCHER, BRIAN S; Pemberton Twp H S II; Fayetteville, NC; (4); Am Leg Boys St; Math Tm; Quiz Bowl; ROTC; Drill Tm; NHS; Boy Scts; Church Yth Grp; Exploring; Pep Clb; AFROTC Scholar 87; HOBY Ldrshp Sem 85; U Cntrl FL; Elec Engrng.

PITLIUK, LISA; Parsippany HS; Parsippany, NJ; (3); Cmnty Wkr; Exploring; FBLA; PAVAS; Ski Clb; Spanish Clb; Thesps; Lit Mag; Off Stu Cncl; Tennis; Rutgers Coll; Comm.

PITROWSKI, STEVEN; Wildwood Catholic HS; N Wildwood, NJ; (3); Art Clb; Library Aide; Spanish Clb; Tennis; Comp Pgmmr.

PITT, PATRICIA; Plainfield HS; Plainfield, NJ; (3); Hosp Aide; JA; VICA; Chorus; Hon Roll; Teachers Aide; Chorus; Vllybl; Voctnl Awd Csmtlgy 86-87; Money Schlrshp 86-87.

PITTENGER, WILLIAM; Newton HS; Newton, NJ; (2); 24/200; Computer Clb; Stage Crew; Bsbl; Hon Roll; Compu Prgrmng.

PITTMAN, GREGORY; Dickinson HS; Jersey City, NJ; (3); Camera Clb; Church Yth Grp; Key Clb; Q&S; Lit Mag; Rep Jr Cls; Off Stu Cncl; Hon Roll; NCTE Awd; Prfct Atten Awd; Liberty U; Pre-Law.

PITTMAN, MELISSA; Sussex Vo Tech; Franklin, NJ; (3); Girl Scts; VICA; Sr Cls; JV Bowling; Im Powder Puff Ftbl; Var Sftbl; Var Tennis; JV Vllybl; Hon Roll; JETS Awd; Auto Body.

PITTS, DANIEL; Rahway HS; Rahway, NJ; (3); Boy Scts; JA; Political Wkr; Var Crs Cntry; Var Wrstlng; Hon Roll; US Naval Acad; Med.

PITTS, KIMYATTA; Woodrow Wilson HS; Camden, NJ; (3); Computer Clb; Drill Tm; School Play; Off Frsh Cls; Off Soph Cls; Bsktbl; Pom Pon; Sftbl; Hon Roll; NHS; Engrng.

PITTS, LEKESHA; Edgewood SR HS; Atco, NJ; (2); Church Yth Grp; Girl Scts; Hosp Aide; JA; Latin Clb; Spanish Clb; Band; Church Choir; Concert Band; School Play; Amateur Athltc US 85; Acad Excllnc Io & Gmtry 86; NY U; Bus.

PITTS, LISA; Franklin HS; Somerset, NJ; (3); School Musical; School Play; Hon Roll; Jr NHS; Drama.

PIZANIE, JACQUELYN M; Lacey Township HS; Forked River, NJ; (3); 4/300; Am Leg Aux Girls St; Church Yth Grp; FBLA; Science Clb; Var Yrbk Stf; VP Sr Cls; JV Capt Fld Hcky; JV Socr; High Hon Roll; VP NHS; 3rd Sci Fair 87; Acadc Achvt Awd-Ms Amer Co-Ed Pgnt 86; 7th Rgnl Cmptn FBLA Bus Math 86; Drew U; Comp Sci.

PIZARRO, MAXIMILIANO F; Christian Brothers Acad; Holmdel, NJ; (4); 96/220; Cmnty Wkr; Hosp Aide; Nwsp Rptr; Lit Mag; Crs Cntry; Trk; US Brnz Cngrssnl Awd 85; Cathloic U Of Amer; Phlsphy.

PIZARRO, MINA; Mary Help Of Christians Acad; Paterson, NJ; (3); Computer Clb; SADD; Stage Crew; Im Vllybl.

PIZZUTILLA, GINA A; Overbrook Regional HS; West Berlin, NJ; (4); 30/365; Pres Spanish Clb; SADD; Band; Concert Band; Mrchg Band; Orch; Symp Band; Off Frsh Cls; Off Soph Cls; Off Jr Cls; Immclt Tltn Schlrshp 87; Gvrnrs Awd Art Ed 87; Hll Fm Bnd Awd 87; Immaculate Coll; Music.

PLACEK, DANIANNE; Brick Township HS; Brick Town, NJ; (3); High Hon Roll; Dental Hyg.

PLANER, KAREN; Wall HS; Wall, NJ; (3); 18/289; Computer Clb; French Clb; Key Clb; Im Fld Hcky; High Hon Roll; Hon Roll; Acctng.

PLATEK, LISA; Delran HS; Delran, NJ; (3); Sftbl; Swmmng; Acctng.

PLATT, CORRY T; Pequannock Township HS; Pompton Pl, NJ; (3); 21/210; Am Leg Boys St; Office Aide; Science Clb; Pres SADD; Rep Frsh Cls; Rep Soph Cls; Pres Stu Cncl; Stat Bsbl; Stat Bsktbl; NHS; Hugh O Brian Yth Ldrshp Smnr; Pres Clsrm For Yng Amers; NJ Boys ST 87.

PLATT, JENNIFER; Gateway Regional HS; Wenonah, NJ; (3); 8/200; Church Yth Grp; JCL; Key Clb; Latin Clb; Library Aide; Chorus; Church Choir; School Musical; Hon Roll; NHS.

PLEUNE, KRISTA; Randolph HS; Randolph, NJ; (3); 119/253; Church Yth Grp; GAA; Band; Bowling; Hon Roll.

PLOETZ, JANINE; Neumann Prep Schl; Ringwood, NJ; (4); 4/84; Library Aide; Office Aide; Variety Show; Yrbk Phtg; Fld Hcky; High Hon Roll; Jr NHS; NHS; Pres Schlr; Spanish NHS; Acdmc All-Amrcn Schlr 85; Ldrshp & Svc Awd 85; George Washington U; Intl Bus.

PLOSKY, JOSHUA; Union HS; Union, NJ; (2); Debate Tm; French Clb; Math Clb; Science Clb; Speech Tm; Im Crs Cntry; Hon Roll; Jr NHS; NEDT Awd; Biophyscs.

PLOTNER, MATTHEW; Matawan Regional HS; Matawan, NJ; (3); 2/300; Math Tm; PAVAS; Band; Chorus; Concert Band; Madrigals; Mrchg Band; School Musical.

PLUCKTER, TAMMY; Lakewood HS; Lakewood, NJ; (3); 39/345; Am Leg Aux Girls St; Pres English Clb; French Clb; Key Clb; Ed Yrbk Stf; Trk; French Hon Soc; High Hon Roll; NHS; James Madison U; Bus Admin.

PLUHAR, PATRICIA ANN; Wayne Valley HS; Wayne, NJ; (4); Trs FBLA; Pres German Clb; JCL; Latin Clb; Ski Clb; Spanish Clb; School Play; Nwsp Stf; Lit Mag; Rep Sr Cls; Z-Clb Dir Chrmn Of Bd 86-87; Stu Athltc Assn Awd 86-87; Magna Cum Ld Nation Ltn Exam 85; Keene ST Coll; Bus.

PLUMMER, PATRICIA; Dwight Morrow HS; Englewood, NJ; (4); JA; Math Clb; Math Tm; Spanish Clb; Band; Concert Band; Jazz Band; Mrchg Band; Hon Roll; Prfct Atten Awd; Cert Apprctn Day Care 86; Cert Merit Music Parnts Clb 84; Berklee Coll Of Music; Music.

PLUMMER, THOMAS; Cherry Hill HS West; Cherry Hill, NJ; (3); Am Leg Boys St; Sec Band; Sec Concert Band; Sec Jazz Band; Sec Mrchg Band; Sec Orch; School Musical; School Play; Sec Symp Band; Camden Cnty Comp Cont Basic Prgrmmng Awd 1st & 2nd Pl Tm 87; Engrng.

PLUSCH, STEVEN; Buena Regional HS; Williamstown, NJ; (3); 15/225; Q&S; Ski Clb; Nwsp Stf; Yrbk Stf; JV Var Bsbl; Hon Roll; Jr NHS; U DE; Physcl Thrpst.

PLUTA, MARK; Clayton HS; Clayton, NJ; (3); 26/85; Boy Scts; FBLA; FHA; JA; Key Clb; VICA; Yrbk Stf; High Hon Roll; Hon Roll; Gloucester Cty Coll; Bus Admnst.

PO, GENALYN; Union Catholic Regional HS; Hillside, NJ; (4); 25/298; Hosp Aide; Latin Clb; Service Clb; Nwsp Stf; Yrbk Stf; Hon Roll; Spanish NHS; NYU; Bio.

POBLETE, CHRISTINE MARIE; St John Vianney HS; Marlboro, NJ; (4); 34/260; Church Yth Grp; Intnl Clb; Ed Yrbk Stf; Rep Soph Cls; Im Cheerleading; Stat Var Trk; High Hon Roll; Pres Acad Ftns Awd 87; Outstdng Awd Bio, Hstry, Cmmnty Invlmnt 85; Auxlry Mssnrs Of Assmptn 84-85; Lehigh U; Premed.

POCCIA, CATERINA MARIA; Parsippany Hills HS; Morris Plains, NJ; (4); 17/301; FBLA; CC Awd; Cit Awd; High Hon Roll; Hon Roll; Jr NHS; NHS; Italian Clb Pres 87; Nrthestrn Conf Outstndng Frgn Lang Awd 87; PTSA Jefferson Cup Acadmc Awd 87; Montclair ST Coll; Bus Mgmt.

PODELL, ALISSA; Fairlawn HS; Fair Lawn, NJ; (3); JV Cheerleading; Coach Actv; Stat Lcrss; Accntng.

PODESZWA, TINA; Morristown HS; Denville, NJ; (3); Key Clb; Yrbk Stf; Cheerleading; Cit Awd; Hon Roll; Chldhd Educ.

PODOLL, NATHAN; Newton HS; Newton, NJ; (2); Church Yth Grp; German Clb; Science Clb; Church Choir; Bsktbl; L Socr; L Trk; High Hon Roll.

PODURGIEL, JANE C; Princeton Day Schl; Princeton, NJ; (4); Chorus; Nwsp Stf; Rep Sr Cls; Var Gym; Ntl Merit SF; Magna Cum Laude Natl Latin Exam 84; FCC Radio License 86; Var Fncng Tm 86; Intl Bus.

POEDUBICKY, JEFFREY S; Northern Burlington Regional HS; Columbus, NJ; (3); Am Leg Boys St; Church Yth Grp; VP Soph Cls; Var Ftbl; Var Golf; JV Trk; Var Wrstlng; Hon Roll; Spanish NHS.

POGUE, KERRY; Abraham Clark HS; Roselle, NJ; (4); 27/150; Chorus; Church Choir; Capt Bsktbl; Var Trk; Hon Roll; Berkley Schl Bus Otstndng HS Stu Bus 87; Union Cntys Prfsnl Wmns Clb Negro Bus Schlrshp 87; Drew U Madison; Pol Sci.

POIRIER, ALANNA; Mt Olive HS; Budd Lake, NJ; (4); 22/280; Varsity Clb; Bsktbl; Var Crs Cntry; Var Fld Hcky; Var Capt Trk; Hon Roll; NHS; Outstndng Fml Athl 87; 3rd Tm All ST Hgh Hrdls 87; Advncd Envrnmntl Tech Corp Schlrshp 87; Rutgers U; Chem.

POIRIER, JENNIFER; Holy Cross HS; Delran, NJ; (3); Chess Clb; Church Yth Grp; Cmnty Wkr; Girl Scts; Hosp Aide; Band; Mrchg Band; Yrbk Stf; Hon Roll; Med.

POIST, ANDREA; Voorhees HS; Rochester, NY; (4); 10/264; Am Leg Aux Girls St; Varsity Clb; Off Stu Cncl; Var Bsktbl; Var Fld Hcky; Var Sftbl; Cit Awd; High Hon Roll; NHS; Pres Spanish NHS; Janine Zehner Meml Awd 87; Hnterdn Wmns Fndtn Dffrnt Drmmr Awd 87; PBA Local 188 Awd 87; SC Coll; Law.

POLAK, ALICIA; Cinnaminson HS; Cinnaminson, NJ; (4); 79/229; Debate Tm; Sec DECA; Nwsp Rptr; Nwsp Stf; Rep Frsh Cls; Rep Soph Cls; Stu Cncl; Swmmng; Hon Roll; DECA Reg 2nd & 3rd Pl 86; 1st Pl St Natl Conf 86; Reg 4 1st Pl Awds 87; C W Post; Journ.

POLAND, DAWN; Mc Corristin Catholic HS; Hamilton Sq, NJ; (3); Camera Clb; Band; Chorus; Concert Band; Mrchg Band; Bsktbl; Hon Roll; Spcl Svcs.

POLANSKY, ROBERT; Dwight-Englewood HS; Fairlawn, NJ; (3); Cmnty Wkr; Computer Clb; Debate Tm; Math Tm; Temple Yth Grp; Nwsp Stf; Var L Crs Cntry; Var L Trk; Hon Roll; Cert Of Merit-NJ Math Leag 86; 3rd Pl Medl 4x400m Relay MAAPS Trck Chmpnshps 85 & 87.

POLASZEK, CHRISTOPHER; Lenape Valley Regional HS; Stanhope, NJ; (3); JV Bsbl; Var Bsktbl; Hon Roll; NHS; Acdmc All- Amer NSEC, Intl Foreign Lang Awd 87.

POLCINI, JOHN A; Atlantic Christian Schl; Ocean City, NJ; (2); Chorus; Yrbk Sprt Ed; Yrbk Stf; Pres Soph Cls; Bsbl; JV Capt Bsktbl; Mgr(s); Score Keeper; Socr; Hon Roll.

POLEN, NANCY; Parsippany HS; Parsippany, NJ; (2); Sec Church Yth Grp; Cmnty Wkr; Girl Scts; Q&S; Sec Science Clb; Mrchg Band; Ed Yrbk Phtg; Swmmng; High Hon Roll; Prfct Atten Awd; Bio.

POLERA, MICHELLE; Holy Family Acad; Bayonne, NJ; (2); Vllybl; Hon Roll.

POLIMENI, MARIA; Paulsboro HS; Paulsboro, NJ; (3); 13/150; Cmnty Wkr; Office Aide; Fld Hcky; Sftbl; High Hon Roll; Hon Roll.

POLINIAK, SUSAN; Holy Cross HS; Willingboro, NJ; (4); Chess Clb; Scholastic Bowl; School Musical; Ed Lit Mag; High Hon Roll; NHS; Ntl Merit Ltr; Chorus; Stage Crew; Almni Awd 87; Rtgrs Smmr Schlr 86; Dstngshd Schlr Awd 86; U Of PA; Mech Engrng.

POLITE, KAMAL; Frank H Morrell HS; Irvington, NJ; (3); Exploring; Drill Tm; Hon Roll; Eagle Flight Perfect Atten Awd 84-87; Airmen 1st Cls 87; Cert Of Appreciation Eagle Flight 87; Air Force Acad; Aeronauticl Eng.

POLITO, BETH; Scotch Plains Fanwood HS; Scotch Plains, NJ; (4); 43/300; SADD; Chorus; Var L Sftbl; Var L Tennis; High Hon Roll; Hon Roll; Prfct Atten Awd; Spanish NHS; SPF Chptr UNICO All Bertilotti Awd 87; SPF Scholar Fndtn 87; Pres Acad Fit Awd 87; Montclair ST Coll; Cmmnctn Sci.

POLIZZOTTO, MICHELLE; Belvidere HS; Belvidere, NJ; (3); 4/135; Scholastic Bowl; Band; Concert Band; Mrchg Band; Nwsp Rptr; Nwsp Stf; JV Bsktbl; JV Sftbl; Hon Roll; NHS; Outstndng Achvt-Frnch 84-85; Math.

POLK, KATHERINE M; Acad Of The Holy Angels; River Vale, NJ; (4); 1/152; Church Yth Grp; Mu Alpha Theta; Yrbk Stf; Bausch & Lomb Sci Awd; High Hon Roll; NHS; Ntl Merit Ltr; Ntl Ltn Exm 84&85; Ntl Sci Olympd 85; Ntl Hstry Day 85; Hstry.

POLK, SYLVIA S; Glen Rock HS; Glen Rock, NJ; (4); 29/162; Cmnty Wkr; Debate Tm; Spanish Clb; Nwsp Stf; Mgr Lit Mag; Hon Roll; Jr NHS; NHS; Pres Stu Cncl BCHSJS 86-87; Stephen Erlich Awd BCHSJS Acdmc Exclnnc 87; Barnard Coll.

POLLARO, NICK; Wallington HS; Wallington, NJ; (4); 16/87; Teachers Aide; Varsity Clb; School Play; Trs Jr Cls; Trs Stu Cncl; Bsbl; Bowling; Ftbl; NHS; FL Southern Coll; Sprts.

POLLITT, AMY; Hopewell Valley Central HS; Titusville, NJ; (2); Cmnty Wkr; FBLA; Red Cross Aide; Service Clb; Spanish Clb; SADD; Teachers Aide; Chorus; School Musical; School Play; Spec Ed.

POLLOCK, LISA; Highland Regional HS; Blackwood, NJ; (3); Church Yth Grp; French Clb; Chorus; Stu Cncl; Temple Yth Grp; Schlrshp Midrasha Hbrw JC 86-87; Ms Glcstr Twnshp Dnc Co 84-85; Local ST/Natl Awds Dnc Comptn 80-86; Chld Psychlgst.

POLLOCK, MINDY; Vineland HS; Vineland, NJ; (3); 74/824; Drama Clb; Hosp Aide; Library Aide; Model UN; Office Aide; Political Wkr; Spanish Clb; Acpl Chr; Chorus; School Musical; Music.

POLSTER, ELIZABETH; Mc Corristin Catholic HS; Mercerville, NJ; (3); 34/270; JA; Service Clb; Nwsp Ed-Chief; Nwsp Rptr; Lit Mag; NHS; Nwsp Sprt Ed; Nwsp Stf; Gov Hon Prg Awd; Hon Roll; Ladies Ancnt Ordr Hbrnians Natl Irsh Hstry Essy Cont 1st NJ & 3rd US 86, 1st NJ 87; Vet Med.

POMATTO, MICHAEL M; Egg Harbor Twp HS; Scullville, NJ; (3); 4/350; Ski Clb; JV Var Ftbl; Trk; Hon Roll; Jr NHS; NHS; Stock Mrkt Game Awd 1st Pl 87; All Conf Javelin Trck All Cnty Trck 86; Bronze Mdlst NJSAA Trck Schl; Biologist.

POMERANTZ, JENNIFER; Newton HS; Newton, NJ; (4); 4/196; Church Yth Grp; Math Tm; Scholastic Bowl; Science Clb; Concert Band; Lit Mag; Rep Stu Cncl; Powder Puff Ftbl; Stat Tennis; NHS.

POMERANTZ, RACHEL; Newton HS; Newton, NJ; (2); 6/230; Church Yth Grp; Cmnty Wkr; Latin Clb; Concert Band; Mrchg Band; Yrbk Rptr; Ed Lit Mag; Rep Frsh Cls; Rep Stu Cncl; High Hon Roll.

POMETTI, FRANK; Howell HS; Howell, NJ; (3); 9/414; JCL; SADD; Drm Mjr(t); Jazz Band; Mrchg Band; School Musical; Symp Band; JV Trk; Var Wrstlng; NHS; USMA; Engrng.

POMILIO, ANGELA; Cherokee HS; Marlton, NJ; (1); Church Yth Grp; Pres 4-H; GAA; Mrchg Band; Mgr(s); JV Socr; JV Trk; 4-H Awd; Hon Roll.

POMPEO, JENNIFER; Montville HS; Montville, NJ; (3); 43/266; Cmnty Wkr; FBLA; Key Clb; Ski Clb; Varsity Clb; Var Fld Hcky; Var Lcrss; High Hon Roll; NHS; Gftd & Tlntnd 84-87; 1st Pl-Swng-Sprng Arts Fstvl 86; Bus.

PONTANO, MARIANNE; Edgewood Regional SR HS; Sicklerville, NJ; (2); Sec 4-H; JA; Teachers Aide; Tennis; 4-H Awd; Hon Roll; Prfct Atten Awd; Hrse Awds 86-87; Hrse Jdgng Awds 84; Accntnt.

PONTICIELLO, MICHAEL; Notre Dame HS; Trenton, NJ; (2); Rep Soph Cls; High Hon Roll; NHS.

PONTORIERO, ROSA; Mother Seton Regional HS; Union, NJ; (3); 17/86; Yrbk Stf; Hon Roll; Jr NHS; NHS; Prfct Atten Awd; Spnsh Awd 86; Cert Awd 87; Natl Sci Olympiad 87; Rutgers Coll; Lib Arts.

POOLE, KELLY; Holy Spirit HS; Linwood, NJ; (3); 24/332; FTA; Yrbk Stf; Im Vllybl; Hon Roll; NHS; Ed.

POOLE, LAURA; Holy Spirit HS; Linwood, NJ; (2); 16/397; Girl Scts; Stage Crew; Yrbk Stf; Hon Roll; Villanova U.

POPE, TAMMY; Toms River HS East; Toms River, NJ; (4); Church Yth Grp; Cmnty Wkr; Pep Clb; Ski Clb; SADD; Rep Frsh Cls; Rep Stu Cncl; Stat Bsbl; Capt Cheerleading; Mgr(s); JR Wmns Clb Chrldng Awd 87; E Stroudsburg U; Psych.

POPIEL, KATARZYNA; Vernon Twp HS; Hamburg, NJ; (4); 8/265; Boy Scts; Chorus; Nwsp Stf; Yrbk Stf; Lit Mag; Hon Roll; NHS; Ntl Merit Ltr; Pres Schlr; VTEA Jean Krauss Mem Schlrshp 87; Rutgers U.

PORCELLI, JOSEPH; Toms River HS East; Toms River, NJ; (4); 5/567; Am Leg Boys St; Computer Clb; FBLA; Intnl Clb; Math Tm; Quiz Bowl; Scholastic Bowl; Science Clb; Varsity Clb; Var Socr; Natl Socty Profssnl Engrs 87; Ciba Geigy Schlrshp 87; East Dover PTA Schlrshp 87; U Of PA; Frnchs Mgmt.

POREDA, STANLEY; Burlington Cnty Vo-Tech; Riverside, NJ; (4); VICA; Yrbk Bus Mgr; Im Socr; Im Sftbl; Im Vllybl; Hon Roll; Pres NHS; St Schlr; Garden ST Distgsd Schlr Awd 86-87; De Vry Inst Of Tech; Comp Mgmnt.

POREDA, STEPHEN; The Pennington Schl; Yardley, PA; (3); Spanish Clb; JV Bsktbl; JV Socr; Var Tennis.

PORETTA, TRINA; Phillipsburg HS; Phillipsburg, NJ; (3); 9/329; Church Yth Grp; SADD; Sec Frsh Cls; Sec Soph Cls; Sec Stu Cncl; JV Var Cheerleading; High Hon Roll; NHS; NJ Assn Stu Cncls 87.

PORFANO, DAWN; Hackensack HS; Hackensack, NJ; (4); 13/401; Yrbk Sprt Ed; Yrbk Stf; Var L CAP; Var Trk; NHS; Am Leg Aux Girls St; Teachers Aide; Hon Roll; Cls Top 20, Actvty H Awd 87; SUNY Coll-Cortland; Phys Ed.

PORPORA, GINA; Holy Spirit HS; Brigantine, NJ; (2); 37/397; Drama Clb; Girl Scts; Spanish Clb; Church Choir; Stage Crew; Nwsp Stf; Hon Roll; Bus.

PORRECA, CHRISTOPHER G; Montville Township HS; Pine Brook, NJ; (2); FBLA; Key Clb; Ski Clb; Spanish Clb; SADD; Yrbk Stf; Capt Ftbl; JV Lcrss; Wt Lftg; Hon Roll; West Point; Military.

PORREDON, ISABEL; Holy Rosary Acad; Union City, NJ; (3); Drama Clb; French Clb; VP GAA; Math Tm; Trs Stu Cncl; Var Co-Capt Bsktbl; Trphy Bsktbl Mst Dedctd 86-87; Natl Lang Arts Olympd 85; Contntl Math Leag 85; Boston Coll; Pre-Law.

PORRO, JEANINE; Rutherford HS; Rutherford, NJ; (4); 18/167; Off Teachers Aide; Pres Varsity Clb; School Play; Pep Clb; DECA; Pres Sr Cls; Var Bsktbl; Var Sftbl; Var Capt Vllybl; NHS; HOBY Fndtn-Outstndng Sophs 85; Grls Ctznshp Inst 86; Gvrnrs Physcl Ftns & Sprts Awd 87; Drew U; Pre-Law.

PORTA, COSMO; Hoboken HS; Hoboken, NJ; (3); NJ Inst Of Tech; Elect Engr.

PORTER, EVELYN; University HS; Newark, NJ; (3); Church Yth Grp; JA; Spanish Clb; Chorus; Church Choir; Rep Soph Cls; Bsktbl; Vllybl; Hon Roll; NHS; Prfct Attndnc Outstndng Achiev In Afro-Amer Hstry 84-85; Bus Admn.

PORTER, JOHN; Deptford Township HS; Deptford, NJ; (2); 28/293; Rep Frsh Cls; Rep Stu Cncl; Im Bsktbl; Hon Roll; Jr NHS; U S Air Frc Acad; Nvl Avtr.

PORTIK, JEFFREY M; Dunellen HS; Dunellen, NJ; (3); Am Leg Boys St; Drama Clb; VP Key Clb; Band; Chorus; Concert Band; Madrigals; Mrchg Band; Var L Bsktbl; Var L Ftbl; Bus.

PORTNOV, YAN; Wayne Hills HS; Wayne, NJ; (3); Spanish Clb; Nwsp Rptr; Socr; Swmmng; Trk; Hon Roll.

PORTNOY, JESSICA; John P Stevens HS; Edison, NJ; (3); Cmnty Wkr; Drama Clb; Science Clb; Temple Yth Grp; School Musical; Rep Stu Cncl; Mgr Powder Puff Ftbl; Middlesex Arts HS Hon Awd.

PORTNOY, SEAN; Cherry Hill HS West; Cherry Hill, NJ; (3); 3/350; Am Leg Boys St; Drama Clb; French Clb; Intnl Clb; PAVAS; School Play; Nwsp Bus Mgr; Nwsp Ed-Chief; Nwsp Rptr; Nwsp Stf.

PORTO, JOSEPH; Marist HS; Jersey City, NJ; (4); 22/98; Chess Clb; Computer Clb; Key Clb; Nwsp Rptr; Yrbk Stf; Bowling; Hon Roll; NHS; Hnrs Cmmndtn 84&87; De Vry; Comp.

PORTO, LORI; Montville Township HS; Montville, NJ; (2); FBLA; Key Clb; Cheerleading; Mgr(s); Score Keeper; Timer; High Hon Roll; Hon Roll; Bus.

PORTO, MARY ANN; Academic HS; Jersey City, NJ; (3); Computer Clb; Office Aide; Spanish Clb; Chorus; Church Choir; School Musical; Stu Cncl; Tennis; Trk; Rutgers; Bus.

PORTSMORE, PAUL E; Don Bosco Prep; Ho Ho Kus, NJ; (3); 25/176; Church Yth Grp; Model UN; Pep Clb; Service Clb; Lit Mag; Bsbl; Var L Socr; Hon Roll; NHS; Law.

PORZIO, RAY; St John Vianney HS; Morganville, NJ; (2); Computer Clb; English Clb; FBLA; Intnl Clb; Math Clb; Science Clb; Ski Clb; SADD; Yrbk Sprt Ed; Rep Soph Cls; Stndrd Physcl Ftns Awd 85-87; Ltl League All Star Team 86; AZ ST U; Accntng.

POSCH, STEPHEN; Manchester Regional HS; N Haledon, NJ; (4); Church Yth Grp; Computer Clb; Exploring; Math Tm; Stage Crew; Trk; NJ Inst Of Tech; Comp Sci.

POST, CHRISTOPHER; Don Bosco Prep; Hawthorne, NJ; (2); 22/217; Boys Clb Am; Crs Cntry; Trk; High Hon Roll; Ntl Merit Ltr; Spirit Club; Wilderness Adventure; Culinary.

POST, MEGAN ANNE; Our Lady Of Mercy Acad; Marmora, NJ; (4); Art Clb; Drama Clb; Library Aide; Yrbk Stf; Sec Frsh Cls; Pres Sr Cls; Rep Stu Cncl; Im Badmtn; Im Bsktbl; Cheerleading; Stu Yr 83-84; Cabrini Coll; Spec Ed.

POST, WILLIAM; Don Bosco Prep HS; Hawthorne, NJ; (3); 11/220; Rep Stu Cncl; High Hon Roll; NHS.

POSTEN III, SAMUEL; Middletown HS South; Navesink, NJ; (3); Boy Scts; School Play; Stu Cncl; JV Ftbl; Im Wt Lftg; Brnz Cngrsnl Awd 87; Comp Tchr 86-87; Archlgy.

POSTMA, KRISTA; Eastern Christian HS; N Haledon, NJ; (4); 8/81; Cmnty Wkr; Varsity Clb; Chorus; Church Choir; Yrbk Ed-Chief; Stu Cncl; Var Capt Crs Cntry; JV Sftbl; Capt Trk; Hon Roll; Crss Cntry-1st Tm All Leag 2nd Tm All Cnty 86; Trck 2nd Tm All Leag 87; Ntl Hnr Soc 85-87; Gordon Coll.

POSTMA, LAUREN; Eastern Christian HS; Towaco, NJ; (4); 13/90; Church Yth Grp; Cmnty Wkr; Office Aide; Band; Concert Band; Orch; Stage Crew; Stu Cncl; Var Capt Socr; Hon Roll; Gordon Coll; Phy Ed.

POTENZA, LOUIS; Wayne Hills HS; Wayne, NJ; (3); Math Tm; Spanish Clb; JV Trk; Hon Roll; Civil Engrng.

POTOCHAR, RONALD; Freehold Boro HS; Freehold, NJ; (4); 35/240; JA; Hon Roll; NHS; Prfct Atten Awd; Spanish NHS; Presdntl Schlrshp 87; NASA/Morgan Engrng Enrchmt Pgm 87; Morgan ST U; Indstrl Engr.

POTTER, DEBBIE; Cinnaminson HS; Cinnaminson, NJ; (3); Church Yth Grp; Service Clb; JV Fld Hcky; JV Lcrss; Swmmng; Hon Roll; Prfct Atten Awd; Rotary Awd; Jr Rotarian February 87; Rogate.

POTTER, KATHRYN M; Toms River North HS; Toms River, NJ; (4); 129/391; Band; Concert Band; Drm Mjr(t); Jazz Band; Mrchg Band; Orch; School Musical; School Play; Symp Band; Var L Cheerleading; Music.

POTTER, MICHAELA; Morristown HS; Morristown, NJ; (1); Church Yth Grp; Key Clb; SADD; Band; Church Choir; Concert Band; Variety Show; Nwsp Phtg; Yrbk Phtg; High Hon Roll; Georgetown; Advtg.

POTTS, GARY; Gateway Regional HS; Wenonah, NJ; (2); Exploring; French Clb; JCL; Latin Clb; VP Stu Cncl; Bsbl; Bsktbl; Capt Socr; Wt Lftg; Hon Roll; Gator Mnth 85; Sports Med.

POTTS, KRISTA; Holy Cross HS; Delran, NJ; (4); 163/366; Drill Tm; Bsktbl; Score Keeper; Tennis; Vllybl; Hon Roll; Burlington County Coll.

POUNCEL, HOLLI; Orange HS; Orange, NJ; (4); 5/160; Am Leg Aux Girls St; FBLA; Library Aide; Color Guard; Sec Frsh Cls; VP Soph Cls; Sec Jr Cls; Sec Stu Cncl; Twrlr; Hon Roll; Delta Sigma Theta Acad Merit Awd 87; Trenton ST Coll; Bus Admin.

POUNTNEY, SHANA; Gloucester City HS; Brooklawn, NJ; (3); French Clb; Library Aide; Science Clb; Concert Band; School Play; Yrbk Stf; Hon Roll; Glassboro Coll; Psychlgy.

POWELL, CHERYL; John F Kennedy HS; Paterson, NJ; (3); Camera Clb; Intnl Clb; Trk; Hon Roll; NHS; Mech Engrng.

POWELL, JAMES; Mt Olive HS; Flanders, NJ; (3); 2/328; AFS; Math Tm; Varsity Clb; Var L Socr; High Hon Roll; Hon Roll; NHS; Sal; Rutgers Schlrs 87; Amer Hstry.

POWELL, JENNIFER; Rahway HS; Rahway, NJ; (2); NAACP; Stu Cncl; Vllybl; Hon Roll; Natl Cncl Negro Wmn Inc 87; Hampton U; Law.

POWELL, PETER; Rancocas Valley Regional HS; Medford, NJ; (2); High Hon Roll; Hon Roll.

POWELL, SCOTT; Wayne Hills HS; Wayne, NJ; (3); 19/323; Am Leg Boys St; Boy Scts; French Clb; FBLA; Math Tm; Model UN; Spanish Clb; JV Wrstlng; High Hon Roll; Hon Roll; Intl Law.

POWELL, STEFAN; St James HS; Salem, NJ; (1); 10/75; SADD; JV Bsktbl; JV Scrkpr Ftbl; Math Awd 86.

POWELL, STEVEN; Glassboro HS; Glassboro, NJ; (3); Am Leg Boys St; VP Sec Science Clb; Thesps; Concert Band; Mrchg Band; School Musical; School Play; JV L Bsbl; High Hon Roll; NHS; Aerospc Engrng.

POWER, BARBARA; Burlington City HS; Edgewater Park, NJ; (3); Am Leg Aux Girls St; Exploring; Rep Frsh Cls; Trs Soph Cls; Rep Jr Cls; JV Bsktbl; JV Sftbl; Hon Roll; Hosp Aide; Yrbk Stf; Rider Coll; Lbrl Arts.

POWER, THEODORE; Notre Dame HS; Mercerville, NJ; (3); Church Yth Grp; Ski Clb; Varsity Clb; JV Var Ftbl; Wt Lftg; Hon Roll; Rutgers U.

POWERS, CYNTHIA; Cumberland Regional HS; Bridgeton, NJ; (3); Drama Clb; FBLA; Intnl Clb; JCL; High Hon Roll; Sec Jr NHS; NHS; Math.

POWERS, JAMES; Red Bank Regional HS; Red Bank, NJ; (3); Ski Clb; Sr Cls; Ftbl; Capt Trk; High Hon Roll; Hon Roll; NHS; Bus.

POWERS, SCOTT W; Pequannock Township HS; Pompton Plains, NJ; (4); 15/217; Am Leg Boys St; DECA; Varsity Clb; JV Bsbl; JV Bsktbl; Var Capt Ftbl; Var Golf; Cit Awd; Hon Roll; Jr NHS; Ftbl Shlrshp 87; Montclair ST Coll; Bus.

POWERS, WENDY; Pemberton HS II; Ft Leavenworth, KS; (4); 32/428; Church Yth Grp; Girl Scts; Band; Concert Band; Mrchg Band; Yrbk Rptr; Yrbk Stf; Rep Frsh Cls; Rep Jr Cls; Rep Stu Cncl; Tchrs Assn Scholar 87; Ladies Aux Scholar 87; Hnr Band 83; NIU; Bus Mgmt.

PRACHAR, CYNTHIA ANN; Bishop AHR HS; Iselin, NJ; (4); 96/277; Dance Clb; Drama Clb; French Clb; Ski Clb; Thesps; Capt Color Guard; School Musical; School Play; Stage Crew; Hon Roll; Police Firemns Ins Co 87; Ldrshp Awd Colr Grd 86-87; MVP Colr Grd 87; Bryant Coll; Mktg.

PRAGER, STACEY; Hightstown HS; Cranbury, NJ; (4); Church Yth Grp; Cmnty Wkr; Drama Clb; Acpl Chr; Chorus; Church Choir; School Play; Variety Show; Sftbl; Hon Roll; Monmouth Coll; CPA.

PRAML, HEATHER; Wayne Hills SR HS; Wayne, NJ; (2); Church Yth Grp; French Clb; GAA; Band; Concert Band; Flag Corp; Mrchg Band; Yrbk Stf; JV Cheerleading; Hon Roll; UVA; Cmmnctns.

PRATICO, CATHERINE; Belvidere HS; Belvidere, NJ; (3); 3/137; Girl Scts; Scholastic Bowl; Band; Chorus; Concert Band; Madrigals; Mrchg Band; Nwsp Ed-Chief; Nwsp Rptr; Hon Roll; Outstndng Frnch Awd 85; Frnch.

PREBICH, KRISTEN; Bishop Eustace Prep; Cherry Hill, NJ; (3); French Clb; Math Clb; Pep Clb; SADD; Nwsp Stf; Yrbk Stf; Var Cheerleading; French Hon Soc; Hon Roll; NHS; Frnch Tutor 86; Pre-Law.

PREEDE, KATHY; Westwood HS; Westwood, NJ; (2); Church Yth Grp; Library Aide; Church Choir; Stat Bsbl; Stat Sftbl; JV Vllybl; High Hon Roll; Elem Ed.

PREGO, MARIA; De Paul HS; Wayne, NJ; (3); 59/150; JV Fld Hcky; JV Sftbl; Hon Roll; Rutgers; Intl Bus.

PREHN, DAWN; St Pius X HS; Dunellen, NJ; (4); 18/108; Sec Church Yth Grp; Dance Clb; Library Aide; Nwsp Stf; Hon Roll; NHS; Bus Awd 85 & 87; Awd For Excel In Spnsh 86; Kean Coll; Bus.

PRELICH, KAREN ANN; Paramus Catholic Girls HS; Lodi, NJ; (3); Church Yth Grp; Cmnty Wkr; French Clb; Ski Clb; SADD; Sec Rep Stu Cncl; Var L Cheerleading; Hon Roll; NHS; NEDT Awd; Christian Svc Awd 86-87; 3rd Prz HS Short Story Cont 86; Bus.

PRELOG, STEFAN; Pompton Lakes HS; Pompton Lakes, NJ; (3); 32/134; French Clb; Q&S; Nwsp Stf; VP Frsh Cls; Rep Soph Cls; Rep Jr Cls; Pres Stu Cncl; L Trk; Hon Roll; Prfct Atten Awd; Jr Mayor Pompton Lakes 87; Pol Sci.

PRENDERGAST, CATHARINE; Villa Victoria Acad; Yardley, PA; (3); 2/24; Drama Clb; Math Clb; Drill Tm; Lit Mag; VP Frsh Cls; Pres Soph Cls; Off Stu Cncl; Tennis; High Hon Roll; Hon Roll; Wrtng Competition Pblshd Mercer Cnty Coll Pblctn 86; Villanova U; Prntng.

PRENDERGAST, TAMMI; James Caldwell HS; W Caldwell, NJ; (3); Var L Cheerleading; Var L Gym.

PRENTICE, BRIAN; Rutherford HS; Rutherford, NJ; (4); 54/168; Key Clb; Ski Clb; Varsity Clb; Im Bsbl; Im Bsktbl; Im Socr; Im Swmmng; Im Vllybl; Im Wt Lftg; Hon Roll; Fordham U; Finance.

PREOLO, SUSAN; Ridgefield Park HS; Ridgefield Pk, NJ; (3); 26/203; Debate Tm; Yrbk Stf; Var L Crs Cntry; Score Keeper; Var L Trk; Wrstlng; Hon Roll; NJ ST Sci Leag 85-87; Theatrical Enrichment Prgm 86-87; PA ST U; Vet.

PRESCOTT, C CHRISTOPHER; Rancocas Vly Regional HS; Mt Holly, NJ; (2); Computer Clb; Science Clb; High Hon Roll; Hon Roll; Prfct Atten Awd; Comp Tech.

PRESCOTT, RANCE; Oratory Prep Schl; Union, NJ; (4); Im Bsktbl; Hon Roll; U Of Scranton.

PRESCOTT, SARAH; Pleasantville HS; Absecon, NJ; (4); 8/120; VP Computer Clb; Sec SADD; Yrbk Stf; Trs Sr Cls; Stu Cncl; Bsktbl; Golf; Rugers U; Accntng.

PRESLEY, SONYA; Franklin HS; Somerset, NJ; (3); Church Yth Grp; Dance Clb; DECA; FBLA; NAACP; Office Aide; Pep Clb; SADD; Varsity Clb; Rep Frsh Cls; Chrldng Awd 85-87; Spellman Coll; Bus Admin.

PRESNELL, KATHERINE; Madison HS; Madison, NJ; (2); Church Yth Grp; Band; Chorus; Church Choir; Mrchg Band; Orch; School Musical; Var Twrlr; High Hon Roll; Hon Roll; Regn I Chorus NJSMA 87.

PRESSLER, ESTHER; Ridgefield Park HS; Little Ferry, NJ; (4); 3/172; Am Leg Aux Girls St; Church Yth Grp; Computer Clb; Debate Tm; Sec Latin Clb; Math Tm; Ski Clb; Ed Nwsp Rptr; Nwsp Stf; Stu Cncl; Piano Comp Two Times Natls; Sci Tm; Hiba Bible Stdy Clb; Stevens Inst Tech; Engrng.

PRESTIFILIPPO, ROSEMARY; Secaucus HS; Secaucus, NJ; (2); 1/130; Math Clb; Mu Alpha Theta; Spanish Clb; Band; Concert Band; Jazz Band; Mrchg Band; School Musical; School Play; Nwsp Rptr.

PREVOSTI III, GEORGE A; Howell HS; Howell, NJ; (3); German Clb; Band; Concert Band; Mrchg Band; Symp Band; Bowling; Golf; Hon Roll.

PREZIOSI, MARIO; Lyndhurst HS; Lyndhurst, NJ; (2); Ski Clb; Var Socr; Hon Roll.

PREZIOSO, JOHN; Essex Catholic Boys HS; Bloomfield, NJ; (3); Boy Scts; JV Fld Hcky; Im Ftbl; High Hon Roll; Fire Sfty Essy Cntst; Knights Of Columbus 84.

PRICE, BETH; Pennsville Memorial HS; Pennsville, NJ; (3); Boy Scts; Pres German Clb; Office Aide; Pep Clb; Yrbk Stf; Rep Stu Cncl; JV Bsktbl; JV Var Cheerleading; JV Sftbl; Grmn Hnr Socty-Delta Epsln Phi 86-87; Radiolgy.

PRICE, CARLA; St James HS; Gibbstown, NJ; (3); Hosp Aide; Spanish Clb; Color Guard; Jazz Band; Mrchg Band; Nwsp Rptr; Lit Mag; Hon Roll; Effort Awds Engl, Art, Math 87; Cmnctns.

PRICE, GIOVINA; Pope Paul VI HS; Runnemede, NJ; (3); 48/414; Math Clb; SADD; Mrchg Band; Variety Show; Bowling; Hon Roll; NHS.

PRICE, JAY; Manasquan HS; Manasquan, NJ; (3); 45/250; Church Yth Grp; Cmnty Wkr; FBLA; Var Bsbl; Var Ftbl; Im Wt Lftg; Hon Roll; Homecoming Ct 84-86; Lbrl Arts.

PRICE, JENNIFER; Middletown HS South; Middletown, NJ; (4); 3 450; Stage Crew; Rep Frsh Cls; Powder Puff Ftbl; French Hon Soc; Hig Hon Roll; Hon Roll; Psychlgy.

PRICE, JUDITH; Secaucus HS; Secaucus, NJ; (4); 5/160; Sec Mu Alph Theta; Varsity Clb; Yrbk Stf; Capt Vllybl; Mgr Wrstlng; High Hon Ro Sec NHS; Spanish NHS; 2nd Tm All Lge Vllybl 85-86; Hnrbl Ment Vlly 84; 1st Tm Hudson Cnty Vllbl 85-86.

PRICE, LILIANNE; Edgewood HS; Hammonton, NJ; (3); #30 In Clas 4-H; Girl Scts; Varsity Clb; Orch; Cheerleading; Sftbl; Wrstlng; Hon Ro Vrsty Clb 86-87; Vet Med.

PRICE, PAULA; Bloomfield HS; Bloomfield, NJ; (3); 5/400; Key Clb; Se Spanish Clb; Sec Jr Cls; Sftbl; High Hon Roll; Hon Roll; NHS; Homeroo Rep 86-87; JU Prom Cmmtte 86-87; Wrstlng Mgr 85-86; Child Psych.

PRICE, ROBERT G; Jackson Memorial HS; Jackson, NJ; (3); 31/41 Am Leg Boys St; Chess Clb; Math Tm; Band; Mrchg Band; Trk; NHS Elec Engr.

PRICE, TRACY; Bunea Regional HS; Vineland, NJ; (3); Hon Roll.

PRICKETT, DEANNA; West Windsor-Plainsboro HS; Plainsboro, N (3); Church Yth Grp; Rep Soph Cls; Rep Jr Cls; Var JV Bsktbl; Var J Socr; Var L Sftbl; Hon Roll; Mst Imprvd Bsktbl 85-86; Mst Imprvd Sftb All-Trnmnt Tm-Bsktbl 86-87; Bus Mgmt.

PRIESTLEY, VANJIA; Lower Cape May Regional HS; Cape May, N (3); 38/195; Cmnty Wkr; Varsity Clb; Bsktbl; Var Sftbl; JV Var Tenni Hon Roll; NHS; Acdmc Achvt Awd 85-86; Med.

PRIMAVERA, ANNA; Linden HS; Linden, NJ; (3); FBLA; Office Aid School Musical; School Play; Rep Frsh Cls; Rep Soph Cls; JV Capt Vllyb Wt Lftg; Cert Of Commendation On Eliz HS Volleyball Tm 86; Cert O Proficiency-Gram 45-86; Cert Of Stdnt 87; Berkeley; Bus Educ.

PRIMUS, SYBILREE; Paterson Catholic Regional HS; Paterson, N (3); 17/100; Hosp Aide; NAACP; Band; Church Choir; Nwsp Bus Mgr; Re Frsh Cls; Pres Soph Cls; Pres Jr Cls; Var Capt Cheerleading; Var Sftb Rep Of Schl Day In Yth Govt 86 & 87; Qn Of Hal Jcksn Tlntd Tn Pgnt 8 Rep Schl In NJ Blk Cnvntn 86; Morgan ST U; Neurosci.

PRISCO, ROBERT R; Riverside HS; Riverside, NJ; (3); 1/110; Varsit Clb; VP Soph Cls; Pres Jr Cls; Pres Sr Cls; Var Bsbl; Var Bsktbl; Bausc & Lomb Sci Awd; High Hon Roll; NHS; Prfct Atten Awd; Trgnmtry Aw Spnsh III & IV Awds; NEDT Tst Awd; Law.

PRITCHETT, DENINNE; Salem HS; Salem, NJ; (2); JA; SADD; Churc Choir; Cheerleading; Sftbl; Penn ST; Bus.

PRITZLAFF, ODE; Middletown HS South; Lincroft, NJ; (3); Am Le Boys St; Var Ftbl; Var Wt Lftg; Var Wrstlng; Hon Roll; Natl JR Jud Chmpn 84-87; NJ Outstndng JR Judo Plyr 85; Bus Admin.

PROBST, ERIC; Don Bosco Prep HS; Oakland, NJ; (4); 3/167; Ski Cl Nwsp Sprt Ed; Nwsp Stf; Socr; Trk; NHS; Hstry Mdl, Spnsh Mdl 87; Co Of Holy Cross; Lawyer.

PROCOPIO, JON; Waldwich HS; Waldwick, NJ; (3); 8/130; Lit Ma High Hon Roll; Hon Roll; Arch.

PROCTOR, TONYA; Burlington City HS; Beverly, NJ; (4); 39/197; Pre Church Yth Grp; Exploring; Co-Capt Drill Tm; Yrbk Stf; Capt Mg Bowling; Hon Roll; Edgwtr Pk Brd Ed 87; Cook Coll.

PROHOWICH, THEODORE; Millville SR HS; Millville, NJ; (3); Churc Yth Grp; Key Clb; Latin Clb; Science Clb; Rep Stu Cncl; Im Bowling; J Crs Cntry; JV Trk; Hon Roll; NHS; Engrng.

PROLEIKA, SUE; Edison HS; Edison, NJ; (4); 3/390; Quiz Bowl; Spanis Clb; High Hon Roll; NCTE Awd; Pres NHS; Spanish NHS; St Schlr; Sch Stff Schlrshp, Trenton ST Coll Schlrshp, Chem Csh Awd Union Carbi Corp 87; Trenton ST Coll-NJ; Comms.

PRONTI, JOSEPH; Brick Memorial HS; Brick, NJ; (4); 39/290; Cmnt Wkr; Math Tm; Office Aide; Varsity Clb; Ftbl; Wt Lftg; Cit Awd; Hig Hon Roll; Hon Roll; NHS; Ftbll Ldrshp Awd 86; Ftbll Big A Awd 87; Ftbl MIP Awd 87; Fairleigh Dickinson; Accntng.

PROPHETT, CARRIE; Notre Dame HS; Belle Mead, NJ; (3); Varsit Clb; Off Soph Cls; Off Jr Cls; Off Sr Cls; Trk; High Hon Roll; NHS Church Yth Grp; Chorus; Bsktbl; NJ Parochial S ST Long Jum Cham 84-86; Athlete Of Wk 87; JR Olympcs Track Lincoln NE 86.

PROSPERI, PAULA; Southern Regional HS; Barnegat, NJ; (3); Camer Clb; Pep Clb; Chorus; Yrbk Stf; Var Cheerleading; JV Gym; JV Socr; Ho Roll; Med.

PROTTER, DEBBIE; Morris Knolls HS; Dover, NJ; (2); 37/376; French Clb; Temple Yth Grp; Chorus; Yrbk Stf; Lit Mag; High Hon Roll; Ho Roll.

PROUDMAN, SARA; Gill St Bernards HS; Watchung, NJ; (3); Cmnt Wkr; Hosp Aide; Nwsp Rptr; Nwsp Sprt Ed; Nwsp Stf; Var Socr; Va Sftbl; Var Tennis; Hon Roll; Spanish NHS; Vrsty Lttrs 85-87; Law.

PROVENCHER, CHRIS; Lakeland Regional HS; Ringwood, NJ; (3); 38 400; Math Clb; Var Socr; Var Trk; Im Wt Lftg; JV Wrstlng; Hon Roll NHS; Blckblt Karate 87; Law Enfrcmnt.

PROVOST, ALDEN; Glen Ridge HS; Glen Ridge, NJ; (4); 29/117; AFS Model UN; Varsity Clb; Yrbk Phtg; Var Capt Socr; Var Capt Tennis; Ho Roll; U Of Richmond.

PRUDEN, DAWN; Lenape Valley Regional HS; Stanhope, NJ; (3); 51 240; DECA; FBLA; Sftbl; Trk; Devry; Data Prcssng.

PRUDEN, GINGER; Henape Valley Regional HS; Stanhope, NJ; (3) DECA; Fld Hcky; Hon Roll; Katherine Gibbs Ldrshpshp 87; Katherin Gibbs; Bus.

PRUDENTI, DEBORAH; Mt Olive HS; Flanders, NJ; (4); 25/286 Drama Clb; PAVAS; Band; Chorus; Drm Mjr(t); Jazz Band; Gov Hon Pr Awd; High Hon Roll; JP Sousa Awd; NHS; Mc Donald All Am HS Ban 86; Natl Chrl Awd 87; Instrmntlst Mag Merit & Mscnshp Awd 87; Trento ST Coll; Music Educ.

PRUITT, PATRICK; Holy Spirit HS; Linwood, NJ; (3); 11/332; Nws Rptr; Off Stu Cncl; Var L Bsktbl; Var L Golf; High Hon Roll; Hon Roll NHS; Cum Laude Ntl Latin Exam 85; Accntng.

PRUKSA, PETER; Clifton HS; Clifton, NJ; (3); Comp Sci.

PRYDULUK, DEANA; St Pius Regional HS; Piscataway, NJ; (3); Gi Scts; Ski Clb; Spanish Clb; Church Choir; Yrbk Phtg; Yrbk Rptr; Yrbk Stf Pres Stu Cncl; Cheerleading; Capt Vllybl; Somerset CC; Speech Thrpst.

PRYOR, CYNTHIA; Camden HS; Camden, NJ; (4); Church Yth Grp Teachers Aide; Church Choir; Hon Roll; Prfct Atten Awd; Prfct Atten Aw 85-86; Montclair ST Coll; Bus Admin.

PRZEKOP, DEBBIE; Immaculate Conception HS; Secaucus, NJ; (3) Dance Clb; SADD; School Musical; School Play; Stage Crew; Yrbk Stf Hon Roll; Acctng.

PSARAS, BARBARA; Monsignor Donovan HS; Toms River, NJ; (3); 13 276; Am Leg Aux Girls St; Art Clb; Church Yth Grp; Math Tm; Ski Clb Spanish Clb; Flag Corp; High Hon Roll; NHS; Math.

PSEJA, DAVID; Pascack Valley HS; River Vale, NJ; (4); Church Yth Grp; Computer Clb; Science Clb; Stage Crew; Hon Roll; Pres Schlr; Valparaiso U; Envrnmtl Sci.

PTASNIK, MICHELE; Monroe Twp HS; Jamesburg, NJ; (3); Church Yth Grp; Rep Stu Cncl; JV Socr; Hon Roll; NHS; Exclnt Grds Theory Accntng I & II 86-87; 2nd Hghst Grd Accntng I 86; 1st Hghst Grd Accntng II 87; Byrant Coll; Accntng.

PUCCI, MICHAEL; Belleville HS; Belleville, NJ; (2); Computer Clb; Ski Clb; JV Bsktbl; Hon Roll.

PUCCINI, LAURA; W Milford Twp HS; W Milford, NJ; (2); Varsity Clb; Bsktbl; Cheerleading; Trk.

PUCHALSKI, STEVE; Dover HS; Dover, NJ; (4); 18/187; Am Leg Boys St; Latin Clb; Var Crs Cntry; Var Trk; Var Capt Wrstlng; High Hon Roll; Hon Roll; NHS.

PUCHOWSKI, DAVID A; Brick Memorial HS; Brick, NJ; (1); Bsbl; Hon Roll.

PUCILLO, PHILIP A; Passaic Valley HS; Little Falls, NJ; (3); Am Leg Boys St; Science Clb; Ski Clb; Trs Stu Cncl; Var Bsbl; JV Scrkpr Ftbl; JV Wrstlng; High Hon Roll; Pres Schlr; Lafayette; Law.

PUCYLOWSKI, JEFF; Lakewood HS; Lakewood, NJ; (3); 70/330; Church Yth Grp; English Clb; Latin Clb; Var Bsbl; JV Bowling; Hon Roll; Engrng.

PUENTE, ARISTIDES; St Joseph HS; Union City, NJ; (4); 16/118; Boy Scts; Intnl Clb; Chorus; High Hon Roll; Hon Roll; 1st Hnrs Alg 85; 1st Hnrs Intl Clb 84; 1st Hnrs Vlybl Intrmrls 87; Rutgers; Engrng.

PUERLING, CHERYL; Red Bank Regional HS; Little Silver, NJ; (4); 23/257; Library Aide; Service Clb; Nwsp Bus Mgr; Nwsp Rptr; Ed Nwsp Stf; French Hon Soc; Hon Roll; NHS; St Schlr; Natl Piano Plyng Audtns 84-87; Pres Acadmc Ftns Awd 87; Frnkln Mrshal Coll; Psych.

PUGLISI, ROBERT; Keansburg HS; Keansburg, NJ; (3); 2/115; German Clb; Math Clb; Science Clb; Rep Stu Cncl; Var Bsbl; Var Bsktbl; Hon Roll; NHS; Sal; St Schlr.

PUKASH, TRACY; Toms River South HS; Beachwood, NJ; (3); 123/400; Powder Puff Ftbl; Var L Sftbl; Im Vllybl; MVP Sftbl Frshmn Yr 84-85; Unsung Hero Vrsty Sftbl 86-87; Tchr.

PULASKI, JENNIFER; Toms River HS East; Toms River, NJ; (2); Ski Clb; SADD; Rep Soph Cls; Rep Stu Cncl; JV Fld Hcky; JV Tennis; JV Trk; Rcvd Prsdntl Physcl Ftns Awd 85-87; Cmptv Figure Sktr Rcvng Awds For Cmptns In Ice Sktng 85-87; Trenton ST Coll; Interior Dsgn.

PULEO, LISA; Central Regional HS; Bayville, NJ; (3); Pres Intnl Clb; Nwsp Rptr; Pres Jr Cls; Stu Cncl; Var Crs Cntry; High Hon Roll; Hon Roll; NHS; Spanish NHS; JV Mgr(s); Washington Workshops Model Cngrssnl Seminar 87; Mock Trial Tm Won County Chmpsnshp.

PULMANO, JULIUS; West Essex SR HS; Roseland, NJ; (3); Trs Computer Clb; VP Key Clb; Science Clb; Band; Rep Jr Cls; Trs Stu Cncl; Im Bsktbl; Hon Roll; NHS; Bus Admin.

PUOPOLO, TARA; Jackson Memorial HS; Jackson, NJ; (4); 27/397; Var Ftbl; Powder Puff Ftbl; High Hon Roll; Ntl Merit Schol; VFW Awd; Presdntl Ftns Awd; Jackson Twnshp Chmbr Cmmrc; Vrsty Athltc Awd-Mgr; Steockton ST Coll; Bnkng.

PURCELL, DENISE; Cliffside Park HS; Fairview, NJ; (3); Political Wkr; Spanish Clb; Color Guard; Yrbk Stf; Lit Mag; Stu Cncl; High Hon Roll; Hon Roll; NHS; Jrnlsm.

PURCELL, SHEREE; Ridgefield Dark HS; Little Ferry, NJ; (3); 2/215; Math Tm; Yrbk Bus Mgr; Yrbk Stf; Sr Cls; Var Capt Crs Cntry; Var Trk; High Hon Roll; Trs NHS; Off Frsh Cls; JV Bsktbl; Girls Ctznshp Inst 87; Italian Club 86-87; Med.

PURI, PAVAN; Cherry Hill East HS; Cherry Hill, NJ; (4); Chess Clb; Math Tm; Co-Capt Science Clb; Band; Mrchg Band; JV Tennis; High Hon Roll; St Schlr; German Clb; Symp Band; Rensselaer Mdl Outstndg Achvt Math & Sci 86; Vrsty Ltr 87; JV Chess Tm ST & Natl Champ 87; Cornell U; Elect Engrng.

PURSEL, VICTORIA; Phillipsburg HS; Phillipsburg, NJ; (3); Key Clb; Varsity Clb; Fld Hcky; Swmmng; Trk; NHS; Bus.

PURSLEY, DIANE; Ridgewood HS; Ridgewood, NJ; (3); AFS; Cmnty Wkr; Hosp Aide; Band; Concert Band; Mrchg Band; Orch; High Hon Roll; NHS; Ntl Merit Ltr; Natl Ltn Exm Cert 84 & 87; N Jersey Rgnl Bank 85.

PURYAR, MARC; Long Branch HS; Long Branch, NJ; (4); Pres French Clb; Band; Concert Band; Drm & Bgl; Jazz Band; Mrchg Band; Orch; School Play; Symp Band; Var L Bsbl; W P Beatty Mem Schlrshp 87; Outstndng Frgn Lang Stdnt 86; Kean Coll NJ; Soclgy.

PURZNER, CHRIS; West Morris Mendham HS; Morristown, NJ; (2); JV Bsktbl; Hon Roll.

PUSCIAN, LISA; Eastern Regional HS; Voorhees, NJ; (4); 27/330; Yrbk Ed-Chief; Yrbk Phtg; Yrbk Sprt Ed; Stu Cncl; Var Socr; Capt Var Trk; Mgr Wrstlng; Hon Roll; NHS; Pres Schlr; Un Sung Hero For Vrsty Sccr 86-87; Prs Acad Fit Awd 87; U Of Dayton; Advrtsng.

PUTLOCK, DOUG; Pequannolk Township HS; Pequannock, NJ; (3); 60/241; Aud/Vis; Boy Scts; Church Yth Grp; Ski Clb; JV Var Bsbl; JV Var Ftbl; Hon Roll; Arch.

PUZIO, RAYMOND; Collegiate Schl; Passaic, NJ; (3); Chess Clb; Drama Clb; VP Exploring; VP JCL; Sec Key Clb; Nwsp Ed-Chief; Off Lit Mag; Mgr Bsbl; Mgr Trk; High Hon Roll; Math.

PUZO, EMILIO; West Essex SR HS; Fairfield, NJ; (3); Science Clb; SADD; Band; Concert Band; Jazz Band; Mrchg Band; Orch; Symp Band; Lit Mag; High Hon Roll; VP Of Italian Clb 87; NJIT Chemistry Olympics 87; 1st Pl Poetry Reciting-Italian Fest 87; Columbia U; Medicine.

PYLE, CYNTHIA; Kent Place HS; Short Hills, NJ; (2); Church Yth Grp; Cmnty Wkr; Band; Chorus; Rep Soph Cls; Var Gym; JV Lcrss; Im Swmmng; JV Vllybl; Ftnss USA-AAHPERD SR Merit 85; Econ.

PYLE, MARYANNE; Holy Spirit HS; Northfield, NJ; (2); 54/313; Var Capt Crs Cntry; Gym; Var L Trk; Hon Roll; Ntl Hnr Roll 87; Atlantic Gymn Team 84-86; Elem Ed.

PYNE, BRADLEY; Holy Cross HS; Medford, NJ; (3); Var Bsbl; Var Bsktbl; Var Capt Ftbl; Hon Roll; Rep Frsh Cls; Rep Soph Cls; Rep Jr Cls; MVP Awd V Ftbl 86; AF Acad; Avtn.

PYNE, JANICE; Plainfield HS; Plainfield, NJ; (3); 39/375; Church Yth Grp; Varsity Clb; Church Choir; Vllybl; Hon Roll; Prfct Atten Awd; Howard U; Premed.

PYRH, SANDY; Saint Mary HS; Spotswood, NJ; (3); Var Socr; Im Vllybl; Stat Wrstlng; Rutgers U; Psych.

PYTAL, JENNIFER L; Passaic Valley HS; Little Falls, NJ; (4); 12/344; Am Leg Aux Girls St; Church Yth Grp; Cmnty Wkr; French Clb; Yrbk Stf; Var Tennis; High Hon Roll; NHS; Hnr Scty 86-87; WA DC Cngrssnl Ldr Invitatn 86; Presdntl Acadmc Ftns Awd 86-87; Bus Mgmt.

QAQISH, EVA; Holy Rosary Acad; Union City, NJ; (3); Computer Clb; Intnl Clb; Math Clb; Spanish Clb; Pres Soph Cls; Bsktbl; Span Awd; Prfct Atten; NJ Inst Of Tech; Comp Sci.

QUADIR, ASHRAFUL; Kingsway Regional HS; Swedesboro, NJ; (4); 6/155; Latin Clb; Band; Yrbk Ed-Chief; Mgr(s); Socr; Tennis; High Hon Roll; Hon Roll; NHS; Rutgers U; Elec Engr.

QUAN, ERIC; Don Bosco Prep; Waldwick, NJ; (3); Boy Scts; Pres Church Yth Grp; SADD; Church Choir; Socr; Trk; God Cntry Awd; Lutheran Living Faith Awd 86; Ophthalmolgst.

QUAN, LISA; John P Stevens HS; Edison, NJ; (3); 16/450; Hosp Aide; Key Clb; Math Tm; Ski Clb; Yrbk Sprt Ed; VP Stat Tennis; High Hon Roll; NHS; Vrsty Awd Tennis 86; NJAATSP Outstnd Stu Cert Span 86; 250 Hr Pin Vltnrng John F Kennedy Hsop 87; Bus Admin.

QUANTZ, SHERWOOD; Kent Place Schl; Summit, NJ; (4); Church Yth Grp; Cmnty Wkr; Hosp Aide; Ski Clb; Rep Sr Cls; Davidson Coll; Econ.

QUARTIER, SCOTT; Ridgefield Park HS; Ridgefield Park, NJ; (3); 61/208; Q&S; Band; Chorus; Concert Band; Mrchg Band; Pep Band; School Play; Stage Crew; Yrbk Ed-Chief; Rep Stu Cncl; Hartwick Coll; Chem.

QUEEN, NYA; Linden HS; Linden, NJ; (3); Chess Clb; Cmnty Wkr; 4-H; Key Clb; Math Tm; NFL; Red Cross Aide; ROTC; Science Clb; Band; Physics.

QUICK, AMY JANE; S Hunterdon Regional HS; Lambertville, NJ; (4); 16/80; Am Leg Aux Girls St; Church Yth Grp; Drama Clb; FBLA; JCL; Acpl Chr; Chorus; Nwsp Sprt Ed; Cheerleading; NCTE Awd; Hnr Rll 86-87; Psych.

QUICK, DAVID; North Warren Regional HS; Columbia, NJ; (4); Church Yth Grp; Cmnty Wkr; FFA; Letterman Clb; Varsity Clb; Wrstlng; Hon Roll; Wrstlr-4th Regn & 3rd Dist 86-87; Morris County; Lndscp Arch.

QUICK, JEFFREY; Belvidere HS; Belvidere, NJ; (4); Office Aide; Var Bsbl; Ftbl; Hon Roll; US Air Force.

QUILES, DIANA; Morristown HS; Morristown, NJ; (1); FBLA; Hosp Aide; Color Guard; Bsktbl; Socr; Trk; DAR Awd; Gov Hon Prg Awd; Spanish NHS; Soc Wrkr.

QUILES, MADDIE; Perth Amboy HS; Perth Amboy, NJ; (3); Camera Clb; Dance Clb; French Clb; FBLA; Library Aide; Math Clb; Ski Clb; Spanish Clb; VICA; Sftbl; Drake Secr Coll; Secr.

QUIMBY, KELLIE; Belleville HS; Belleville, NJ; (3); Acpl Chr; Chorus; Madrigals; School Musical; School Play; Stage Crew; Swing Chorus; Nwsp Rptr; Nwsp Stf; Yrbk Stf; Hon Rl 86-87; Itln Clb 86-87; Educ.

QUINLAN, MICHAEL; Lenape Valley Regional HS; Stanhope, NJ; (3); 18/224; Church Yth Grp; Drama Clb; Acpl Chr; Chorus; Madrigals; School Musical; School Play; Yrbk Stf; Hon Roll; NHS; Secondary Educ.

QUINN, A ROBYN; Bridgeton HS; Bridgeton, NJ; (4); 1/150; Am Leg Aux Girls St; VP Debate Tm; GAA; Latin Clb; Pres Science Clb; Soroptimist; SADD; Teachers Aide; Varsity Clb; Yrbk Sprt Ed; Baush Lomb Sci Awd ; Hortense Headley Memrl Schlrshp; Rutgers Schlr; Ursinus Coll; Pre-Med.

QUINN, CARI; Howell HS; Howell, NJ; (3); 171/358; Color Guard; Pom Pon; Twrlr; Glassboro Coll; Phys Thrpst.

QUINN, COLLEEN; Lakewood HS; Lakewood, NJ; (1); Art Clb; Church Yth Grp; Girl Scts; Hosp Aide; Church Choir; Hon Roll; Geriatric.

QUINN, DEVON; Madison HS; Madison, NJ; (3); Art Clb; Church Yth Grp; French Clb; Band; Chorus; Jazz Band; Mrchg Band; Orch; Pep Band; School Musical; Music.

QUINN, EUGENE; Christian Brothers Acad; Freehold, NJ; (3); 40/230; Church Yth Grp; High Hon Roll; Hon Roll; Cmnty Wkr; Letterman Clb; Varsity Clb; Variety Show; Var L Mgr(s); Var Score Keeper; Achvd Blck Blt Karate 85; Eng.

QUINN, JASON M; Hackensack HS; Rochelle Park, NJ; (3); 208/410; Am Leg Boys St; Aud/Vis; Boy Scts; Chess Clb; Computer Clb; Key Clb; Library Aide; Ski Clb; Teachers Aide; Varsity Clb; Ad Altare Dei 85; Eagle Sct 87; Amer Lgn Schl Awd 84; Annapolis; Accntng.

QUINN, JOHN; Indian Hills HS; Franklin Lks, NJ; (4); 55/286; AFS; Cmnty Wkr; Radio Clb; ROTC; Science Clb; Yrbk Sprt Ed; Yrbk Stf; Hon Roll; NHS; PTSO Schlrshp 87; Laura S Potters Schlrshp 87; U Of VT; Vet.

QUINN, KAREN ANNE; Lakewood HS; Lakewood, NJ; (3); Art Clb; Church Yth Grp; Cmnty Wkr; Drama Clb; French Clb; Girl Scts; Yrbk Stf; Var Fld Hcky; French Hon Soc; Natl Art Hnr Scty 87; Philadelphia Art Inst; Comm Art.

QUINN, KERRY; James Caldwell HS; W Caldwell, NJ; (3); Trs Church Yth Grp; Key Clb; Ski Clb; Spanish Clb; Color Guard; Yrbk Stf; Sec Frsh Cls; Soph Cls; High Hon Roll; Hon Roll; Elem Educ.

QUINN, MARYJO; Lower Cape May Regional HS; N Cape May, NJ; (2); Exploring; Art Awd 2nd Pl & 3rd Pl 84-85; Psych.

QUINN, TERRANCE J; Christian Bros Acad; Spring Lake, NJ; (3); Am Leg Boys St; Boy Scts; Camera Clb; Debate Tm; Drama Clb; Stage Crew; Im Bsktbl; Im Bowling; Im Ftbl; Im Socr; Eagle Scout Awd 86; West Point; Elec.

QUINONES, MARILYN; Pleasantville HS; Pleasantville, NJ; (3); Library Aide; Math Clb; Mrchg Band; Stu Cncl; Sftbl; Swmmng; Tennis; Prfct Atten Awd; Comp Dataprocssr.

QUINONEZ, ANTHONY; Edgewood Regional SR HS; Blue Anchor, NJ; (2); Wrstlng; Hon Roll; Prsdntl Acdmc Ftnss Awd 86; Amateur Athlc Union US Cert Attnmnt 85 & 86.

QUINTAVALLE, ALISA; Jackson Memorial HS; Jackson, NJ; (3); 83/416; Hon Roll; Frnch Tchr.

QUIREZ, ALTAGRACIA; Memorial HS; West New York, NJ; (2); #19 In Class; French Clb; Scholastic Bowl; Rep Frsh Cls; High Hon Roll; Hon Roll; Acctnt.

QUIRING, STEVEN; Plainfield HS; Plainfield, NJ; (3); 2/500; Math Tm; Quiz Bowl; JV Bsbl; Var L Golf; JV Socr; Var L Swmmng; High Hon Roll; NHS.

QUIRK, JACQUELINE P; Middletown HS; Middletown, NJ; (4); 160/464; VP Thesps; Acpl Chr; Chorus; Color Guard; Flag Corp; Mrchg Band; School Musical; School Play; Variety Show; Nwsp Rptr; Music Merit Scholar Carnegie Mellon U 87; ST Thespian Scholar 87; Music Scholar Monmouth Arts Fndntn; Carnegie Mellon U; Musical Thtr.

QUOW, NICOLE; Newark Acad; Irvington, NJ; (4); Church Yth Grp; Cmnty Wkr; Girl Scts; Hosp Aide; Key Clb; NAACP; Chorus; Church Choir; Capt Trk; Cit Awd; Robert C Byrd Hnrs Schlrshp 87; Men Of Essex Schlr-Athlete Awd 87; Bethany Baptist Church 87; Brown U RI; Bio.

RA, JEANNIE; Woodbridge HS; Woodbridge, NJ; (4); 72/387; Art Clb; Chorus; Rep Frsh Cls; Rep Soph Cls; Rep Jr Cls; Rep Sr Cls; Rep Stu Cncl; Capt Var Cheerleading; Hon Roll; Ski Clb; GSS 87; NJIT; Arch.

RABBITO, JANET; St John Vianney HS; Freehold, NJ; (3); 13/235; Church Yth Grp; Cmnty Wkr; Intnl Clb; Service Clb; Yrbk Stf; High Hon Roll; Hon Roll; Prfct Atten Awd; Mrktng.

RABEL, SUSAN E; Hopewell Valley Central HS; Trenton, NJ; (3); AFS; Church Yth Grp; DECA; Service Clb; Stat Bsktbl; High Hon Roll; Hon Roll; 2nd Pl Overall Display Diorama-Food Ind St DECA Comptn 87; Outstndng Achvt DECA Comptn Awd 87; Nursery Schl Tchr.

RABEY, SUZANNE; Mainland Regional HS; Somers Point, NJ; (3); 37/317; Capt Drill Tm; Flag Corp; Stat Diving; Mgr(s); Hon Roll; NHS; Rainbow Girls ST Ofcr,Grand Cross Color 85-86; Most Outstndg Band Stud 84-86; Most Outstndg Mrchr 86.

RACIOPPI, GERARD; Essex Catholic Boys HS; Verona, NJ; (3); 3/136; Aud/Vis; Chess Clb; Office Aide; Nwsp Ed-Chief; High Hon Roll; Jr NHS; NHS; Prfct Atten Awd; Finance.

RACK, LAURA M; W Milford HS; West Milford, NJ; (3); 16/400; Church Yth Grp; French Clb; Pres Ski Clb; SADD; Band; Concert Band; Mrchg Band; Nwsp Phtg; Yrbk Phtg; Rep Frsh Cls; Jrnlsm.

RACZYNSKI, WENDI; Roselle Park HS; Roselle Park, NJ; (3); #28 In Class; Color Guard; Concert Band; Drill Tm; School Musical; Nwsp Phtg; Nwsp Rptr; Nwsp Stf; Twrlr; Hon Roll; Merti Awd For Band 87; Comms.

RADA, PAULETTE; Florence Twp Mem HS; Burlington, NJ; (3); Nrsng.

RADER, DANA; Newton HS; Newton, NJ; (2); Hosp Aide; Band; Concert Band; Mrchg Band; Pep Band; JV Tennis.

RADICE, GERARD; Bloomfield HS; Bloomifled, NJ; (3); Hon Roll; Bus.

RADICK, ROBERT; Morristown HS; Morristown, NJ; (3); 1/422; Exploring; Hosp Aide; JCL; Latin Clb; Math Tm; Off Lit Mag; High Hon Roll; Ntl Merit SF; Schlrshp Wshngtn Wrkshp Pgm 87; Natl Ltn Exm Maxima Cum Laude 87; NCTE Achvmnt Awd Wrtg 87.

RADITZ, NANCY L; Cherokee HS; Marlton, NJ; (4); 1/411; Am Leg Aux Girls St; Cmnty Wkr; French Clb; SADD; Yrbk Sprt Ed; Rep Sr Cls; JV Cheerleading; High Hon Roll; VP NHS; Ntl Merit SF; George Washington U Schl Engr Awd 86; Rutgers Schlr 86; Garden ST Distngushd Schlr 86; Engrng.

RADWANSKI, PATRICIA; Saint Marys HS; Parlin, NJ; (4); 1/127; Var Capt Bsktbl; Var Crs Cntry; Var Capt Socr; JV Sftbl; French Hon Soc; High Hon Roll; VP NHS; Ntl Merit Ltr; St Schlr; Val; Congressional Teacher Schlrshp 87; Distinguished Schlr 86; Phi Betta Kappa Schlrshp 87; Trenton St Coll; Elem Educ.

RADZIETA, JOHN; Middle Township HS; Cape May Ct House, NJ; (2); 2/175; VP Key Clb; Pres Frsh Cls; JV Bsktbl; High Hon Roll; Hon Roll.

RADZIK, JOSEPH; De Paul HS; Wayne, NJ; (4); 72/156; Boy Scts; Socr; Wrstlng; Hon Roll; Eagle Scout 86; U Of RI; Bio Rsrch.

RADZIK, MARK; De Paul HS; Wayne, NJ; (3); 26/150; Am Leg Boys St; JCL; Latin Clb; Ski Clb; Nwsp Rptr; L Golf; JV Capt Socr; Hon Roll; NHS; Continental Math Leag Awd 85.

RAFAEL, JILL; Bayonne HS; Bayonne, NJ; (4); 2/350; Drama Clb; Math Tm; Temple Yth Grp; Nwsp Ed-Chief; Rep Frsh Cls; High Hon Roll; Jr NHS; St Schlr; Ntl Jrnlsm Awds 86; Princpls Hnrs 83; Gov Schl Sci 86; Bio.

RAFALSKI, MATTHEW E; Washington Twp HS; Sewell, NJ; (3); Boy Scts; German Clb; Latin Clb; Science Clb; Band; Pres Chorus; Concert Band; Drm & Bgl; Jazz Band; Sec Mrchg Band; NJ All ST Chorus 86-88; South Jersey Chorus & Band 85-88; Atted HOBY Week-End 85-86; Bio Chem.

RAFANAN, MARICEL; Saint Mary HS; Jersey City, NJ; (3); Service Clb; Chorus; Hon Roll; 1st & 2nd Hnrs 84-85; Awd Music 1st Hnrs 85-86; Awd Rlgn 2nd Hnrs 86-87; Christian Svc Awd 86-87; Rutgers; Nrsng.

RAFFAELE, TINA; Gloucester Catholic HS; Glassboro, NJ; (3); 63/195; Church Yth Grp; Dance Clb; Drama Clb; School Play; Diving; Fld Hcky; Mgr(s); Swmmng; Hon Roll; Sci.

RAFFERTY, MARY; Monsignor Donovan HS; Jackson, NJ; (4); 5/223; Drama Clb; Intnl Clb; Thesps; School Musical; School Play; High Hon Roll; NHS; Ntl Merit Ltr; St Schlr; Church Yth Grp; Allianc Frncaise Frnch Achvt Schlrshp 87; Untd Food Cmmrcl Wrkrs Un Lcl Schlrshp 87; Gld Mdl Grad 87; Georgetwn U; Mdrn Lang.

RAGAZZO, CHRISTOPHER; J P Stevens HS; Edison, NJ; (3); 70/425; Ski Clb; Bowling; Golf.

RAGGI, MICHAEL; Parsippany HS; Parsippany, NJ; (3); Boy Scts; FBLA; Var L Bsbl; Var L Socr; Hon Roll; Prfct Atten Awd; U Of VA; Accntng.

RAGLAND, MAURICE; Parsippany HS; Parsippany, NJ; (3); Church Yth Grp; Cmnty Wkr; Intnl Clb; NAACP; Spanish Clb; Varsity Clb; Church Choir; Bsktbl; Ftbl; Trk; Engrng.

RAGO, CHRISTOPHER; Washington Township HS; Sewell, NJ; (4); 41/490; Pres Art Clb; Pres Church Yth Grp; DECA; Drama Clb; Service Clb; Spanish Clb; School Musical; School Play; Yrbk Stf; NHS; Wedgewd Wmns Clb Schlrshp 87; Harold Parent Memrl Schlrshp 87; Spotliters Schlrshp 87; Syracuse U; Spch Comms.

RAGONE, DAVE; Cherry Hill West HS; Cherry Hill, NJ; (3); Spanish Clb; Rep Jr Cls; Var Ftbl; L Wt Lftg; Hon Roll; Prfct Atten Awd; Respect For Drugs Prog 87-88; Sports Med.

RAGONE, JOE; Victory Christian HS; Elmer, NJ; (4); 3/22; Church Yth Grp; Yrbk Phtg; Capt Bsktbl; Capt Ftbl; Var L Socr; JV L Trk; US Nvl Acad; Engrng.

RAGONESE, GREGORY ALAN; Paulsboro HS; Gibbstown, NJ; (4); 40/160; Boy Scts; Church Yth Grp; Library Aide; Crs Cntry; Basic Training At Ft Dix-Early Entry Pgm For Army Rsrv 87; Military.

RAGOSA, LAURA; Manalapan HS; Manalapan, NJ; (2); Yrbk Stf; Hon Roll; Gerantlgst.

RAGUCCI, MARY ELIZABETH; East HS; Toms River, NJ; (4); French Clb; Q&S; Ski Clb; SADD; Nwsp Rptr; Nwsp Stf; Crs Cntry; Powder Puff Ftbl; Trk; High Hon Roll.

RAIA, CHRIS; Monsignor Donovan HS; Toms River, NJ; (3); Church Yth Grp; Drama Clb; Thesps; Stage Crew.

RAICHEL, ROBERT; Clifton HS; Clifton, NJ; (4); German Clb; JV Var Bsbl; JV Bsktbl; Jr NHS; NHS; Slovak Cathlc Sokol Schlrshp 87; St Bonaventure U; Accntng.

RAIMATO, CANIO; Bloomfield HS; Bloomfield, NJ; (3); Boy Scts; Nwsp Stf; JV Bsbl; JV Ftbl; Ice Hcky; JV Socr; JV Tennis; Hon Roll; NHS; Prfct Atten Awd; Spnsh Awd 83-84; Montclair St; Bus.

RAINESS, JEFF; Morris Knolls HS; Dover, NJ; (3); Ski Clb; Varsity Clb; Rep Jr Cls; Var Capt Ftbl; Var Wt Lftg; Hon Roll; Bus.

RAINIER, CHRISTINE; Bordentown Regional HS; Bordentown, NJ; (3); Hosp Aide; Lcrss; Athltc Trnr.

RAINIER, PAUL; Edgewood Regional HS; Hammonton, NJ; (3); 3/375; Latin Clb; Yrbk Phtg; Bsbl; High Hon Roll; Hon Roll; NHS; Ntl Merit SF.

RAINNER, LASHAWN; Senior HS; Bridgeton, NJ; (2); Computer Clb; Math Clb; Office Aide; SADD; Mrchg Band; Var Cheerleading; Var Pom Pon; JV Vllybl; Hon Roll; Prfct Atten Awd; Comp Progrmmng.

RAINS JR, JIMMIE; Arthur P Schalick HS; Newfield, NJ; (3); 12/134; Math Clb; Concert Band; Mrchg Band; Variety Show; Bsbl; Hon Roll; NHS; Rep Stu Cncl; Olympcs Of Minds 84-87.

RAISSIS, IRENE; Woodbridge HS; Colonia, NJ; (2); 52/346; Trs Church Yth Grp; Ski Clb; Acpl Chr; School Play; Nwsp Rptr; VP Frsh Cls; VP Soph Cls; VP Jr Cls; Capt Cheerleading; Var Trk; ST Fnslst Miss Amer Coed Pageant Of NJ 87; Miss Jr Goya Of Perth Amboy 87-88; Chrldng Captain 85-87.

RAITH, KATHERINE; Holy Cross HS; Mt Holly, NJ; (3); 25/420; Spanish Clb; Stage Crew; Yrbk Stf; Rep Frsh Cls; High Hon Roll; Hon Roll; Design.

RAIVELY, KRISTIE; Paulsboro HS; Paulsboro, NJ; (3); #7 In Class; Trs Church Yth Grp; Girl Scts; Chorus; Church Choir; School Musical; Hon Roll; NHS; Stu Mnth; All S Jrsy Chorus 86-87; All ST Chorus 87; Nrsng.

RAJHANSA, DIPAK; Washington Township HS; Turnersville, NJ; (3); Am Leg Boys St; Exploring; VP Stu Cncl; JV Bsktbl; JV Socr; Var Trk; Hon Roll; NHS; Prfct Atten Awd; Peer Facilitator 85-87; Med.

RAK, ANDREW; Morris Catholic HS; Pine Brook, NJ; (4); 33/138; Boy Scts; Trs FBLA; German Clb; Natl Beta Clb; Service Clb; Varsity Clb; Lit Mag; Im Bsktbl; Var L Crs Cntry; Var L Trk; 2nd Pl NJ ST Parocial B Pole Vlt 87; Pres Acdmc Fit Awd 87; Clark U; Lib Arts.

RALEIGH, JONATHAN C; Lakeland Regional HS; Ringwood, NJ; (3); 45/370; Math Clb; Math Tm; Ski Clb; Rep Frsh Cls; Rep Soph Cls; Rep Jr Cls; Bsbl; Bsktbl; Var Socr; Var Wrstlng; NEDT Awd 86; Cnty 6 League Soccer Chmpns 86; Peer Cnslr; U WI Mdsn; Intl Fnc.

RALLIS, GEORGIA; Morristown HS; Morristown, NJ; (2); Girl Scts; Chorus; Hon Roll; Engl Hnr Awd 84; Hnr Roll & Awds 85; UCLA; TV Actng.

RAMAKRISHNAN, LAKSHMI; Lodi HS; Lodi, NJ; (4); 4/137; Key Clb; Math Tm; Spanish Clb; Hon Roll; NHS; Lodi Brd Ed Essay Cont 1st Prz 86; NHS Scholar 87; Rutgers; Phrmcy.

RAMBARAN, VIOLET; St Mary HS; Jersey City, NJ; (3); 1/120; Drama Clb; Chorus; Church Choir; School Play; Nwsp Rptr; Yrbk Stf; VP Soph Cls; VP Jr Cls; NHS; Cmnty Wkr; Rutgers Mnrty Achvt Awd, & Chrstn Svc Awd 86; Outstndng Achvt Awd 84-85; UCLA; Jrnlsm.

RAMBO, MATTHEW; Edgewood SR HS; Hammonton, NJ; (2); Debate Tm; Latin Clb; JV Wrstlng; Hon Roll; NHS; Pres Schlr.

RAMELLA, MICHAEL; Marist HS; Bayonne, NJ; (3); Boy Scts; Key Clb; Science Clb; Rep Soph Cls; Rep Jr Cls; Pres Stu Cncl; Var Mgr(s); Var Score Keeper; Bus.

RAMER, HELENE; H G Hoffman HS; South Amboy, NJ; (3); Sec Chess Clb; Dance Clb; Drama Clb; Girl Scts; Hosp Aide; PAVAS; Ski Clb; Chorus; Drm & Bgl; School Play; Middlesex Arts 86-87; Arts & Sci Fair 84-85; Middlesec Cnty Coll; Music.

RAMIREZ, LILIANA; Elizabeth HS; Elizabeth, NJ; (4); 69/850; Church Yth Grp; Band; Church Choir; Mrchg Band; Rep Jr Cls; Rep Sr Cls; Cit Awd; Trenton ST Merit Schlrshp 87; Trenton ST Coll; Intr Dsgn.

RAMIREZ, MARISOL; Our Lady Of Good Counsel HS; E Orange, NJ; (3); 15/122; Church Yth Grp; Dance Clb; Science Clb; School Musical; Rep Frsh Cls; Capt Var Cheerleading; Hon Roll; Acdmc All-Am Schlr Awd 84-87; Natl Svc & Ldrshp Awd 84-85; Fin.

RAMIREZ, TIFFANY; Timothy Christian Schl; Freehold, NJ; (2); Church Yth Grp; Hosp Aide; High Hon Roll; Prfct Atten Awd.

RAMIREZ, WILFREDO; Camden HS; Camden, NJ; (3); Boy Scts; JA; Latin Clb; Spanish Clb; SADD; Bsbl; Ftbl; Wt Lftg; Montclair ST Coll; Accntng.

RAMOS, ELIZABETH; Queen Of Peace HS; North Arlington, NJ; (3); 26/280; Church Yth Grp; Cmnty Wkr; Model UN; NFL; Church Choir; Stage Crew; Nwsp Stf; Yrbk Stf; Sec Stu Cncl; NHS; Semi Fnlst Hgh O Brn Yth Fndtn 86; 1st Plc JV Rdng Frncscs 86; Schlrshp Hague Model U N 87; Rutgers U; Poly Sci.

RAMOS, GERALDO; Hoboken HS; Hoboken, NJ; (4); Electrncs.

RAMOS, MARIA; Belleville HS; Belleville, NJ; (3); Chorus; Lit Mag; Hon Roll.

RAMOS II, OSCAR; Paul VI HS; Passaic, NJ; (3); Aud/Vis; Church Yth Grp; Civic Clb; Cmnty Wkr; Church Choir; Yrbk Phtg; Yrbk Stf; Im Ftbl.

RAMOS, VANESSA; Roselle Catholic HS; South Plainfield, NJ; (4); 88/198; Ski Clb; Stage Crew; Lit Mag; Rep Stu Cncl; Var Socr; French Hon Soc; High Hon Roll; Hon Roll; Bus Hnr Soc 86-87; Middlesex County Coll.

RAMSARAN, TREVOR; Camden HS; Camden, NJ; (2); Chess Clb; NHS; Pres Schlr; Pres Frsh Cls; High Hon Roll; Comp Engr.

RAMSEY, PORTIA; Clifford J Scott HS; E Orange, NJ; (4); 3/251; Math Clb; Math Tm; Varsity Clb; Flag Corp; Nwsp Rptr; Trk; Hon Roll; NHS; Men Of Essex Schlr Ath Awd 87; U Of DE; Accntng.

RANA, ILAXI; Passaic HS; Passaic, NJ; (3); 20/486; Computer Clb; Intnl Clb; Office Aide; Science Clb; Spanish Clb; Teachers Aide; Orch; Tennis; Cit Awd; Hon Roll; Indian Cl, Medcl Clb 86-87; Med.

RANA, MANOJ; Passaic HS; Passaic, NJ; (3); Am Leg Boys St; VP Computer Clb; Math Clb; Science Clb; Spanish Clb; Teachers Aide; JV Bsbl; Var Wrstlng; Hon Roll; NHS; Sci Fair Wnnr 2nd Pl 85-86; Stevens Inst Of Tech; Elec Engr.

RANA, SHAMSA; Eastside HS; Paterson, NJ; (3); Capt Scholastic Bowl; Pres Science Clb; Nwsp Rptr; Cit Awd; Elks Awd; High Hon Roll; Hon Roll; NHS; Prfct Atten Awd; Capt Debate Tm; Schlrshp-Smmr Prgrm-Sci 87; Acdmc All AM 87; 3rd Pl NJ ST Edctnl Dept Ortrcl Cntst 87; Harvard; Med.

RAND, HEATHER; Hammonton HS; Hammonton, NJ; (4); Intnl Clb; Sec Chorus; School Musical; School Play; Swing Chorus; Nwsp Rptr; Yrbk Stf; Var JV Mgr(s); Hon Roll; NHS; Acad Achvt Awd 85; Muscl Theatr.

RAND, JAMIE; Bayonne HS; Bayonne, NJ; (3); Var Socr; Jr NHS; Physcl Thrpst.

RANDAZZO, TERRI; Bishop Eustace Prep; Turnersville, NJ; (2); Latin Clb; Math Clb; Office Aide; SADD; JV Cheerleading; Stat Sftbl; Im Vllybl.

RANDOLPH, AICHA D; Eastside HS; Paterson, NJ; (4); 18/500; Mgr(s); Pres Schlr; Trenton ST Coll; Bus Adm.

RANDOLPH, JILL; Cresskill HS; Cresskill, NJ; (4); 5/114; Debate Tm; VP French Clb; Ski Clb; Chorus; Color Guard; High Hon Roll; NHS; Pres Schlr; St Schlr; Full Tuition Schlrshp Trntn ST Coll 87; Grnt Amrcn Scty Wmn Accnts 87; Trenton ST Coll; Bus Mgmt.

RANDOW, PATRICK; Mc Corristin Catholic HS; Trenton, NJ; (3); 23/215; Aud/Vis; Camera Clb; Chess Clb; Computer Clb; Drama Clb; English Clb; Math Clb; Quiz Bowl; Varsity Clb; Stage Crew; Systm Anlyst.

RANELLI III, FRANK; Bishop HHR/St Thomas HS; Fords, NJ; (4); Boy Scts; Church Yth Grp; Ski Clb; Chorus; Socr; Var L Trk; Wt Lftg; JV Wt Lftg; Hon Roll; All Conf-1st Tm Sccr 86; All Cnty-2nd Tm Sccr 86; Sccr Schlrshp; St Francis Coll; Arts/Sci.

RANI, SUSIE; Belleville HS; Belleville, NJ; (3); Hosp Aide; Radio Clb; SADD; Rutgers Coll Of Phrmcy; Phrmcy.

RANIERI, STEPHANIE; De Paul Diocesan HS; Wayne, NJ; (3); 40/150; Am Leg Aux Girls St; Ski Clb; Nwsp Stf; Yrbk Rptr; Yrbk Stf; JV Fld Hcky; Stat Sftbl; Hon Roll; Bus Mgmt.

RANKIN, KELLY; Bridgewater-Raritan HS East; Bridgewater, NJ; (3); 4-H; Science Clb; Chorus; Rep Sr Cls; Stu Cncl; Var Swmmng; 4-H Awd; High Hon Roll; Hon Roll; NHS; Capt-Smrst Cnty Eqstrn Drll Tm 85; Smrst Cnty Cttl Jdgng Tm 85-87; Vet.

RANKIN, KIESHA; Pawsboro HS; Paulsboro, NJ; (3); 86/150; JA; SADD; Stat Trk; 4-H Awd; JR Achvt Awd Citation Cert Sales Club 86; Tuskegee U; Elec Engrng.

RANSOM, TURIA; South River HS; S River, NJ; (2); Var Bsktbl; Var Lttrmn Bsktbll 86-87; AAU Jr Olympc Prtcpnt 87.

RANSON, JOHN; Monsignor Donovan HS; Toms River, NJ; (3); 8/342; Am Leg Boys St; Hon Roll; NHS; Distngshd Achvmnt Soc Sci 86; Finlst 4 Yr NROTC Schlrshp Prog 87; Candidate Clss US Naval Acad 87; US Naval Acad; Naval Offcr.

RANUCCI, MICHELLE M; Scotch Plains-Fanwood HS; Scotch Plains, NJ; (4); 102/300; DECA; Union Cnty Coll; Accntng.

RAO, JAY B; Colonia HS; Avenel, NJ; (3); Am Leg Boys St; Pres Chess Clb; Debate Tm; Trs German Clb; NFL; Capt Quiz Bowl; Pres Science Clb; Speech Tm; Ed Nwsp Stf; Yrbk Ed-Chief; ST Fnlst Extmprns Spch 87; Ftre Pblm Slvng Semi Fnlst Intl Compttn 87; Acdmc Chllnge Tm ST Wnnr 86.

RAO, RAM; Lakeland Regional HS; Wanaque, NJ; (3); 1/350; Latin Clb; Math Clb; Math Tm; Quiz Bowl; Var Crs Cntry; JV Trk; Gov Hon Prg Awd; High Hon Roll; NHS; Ntl Merit Ltr; Electrical Engrng.

RAO, SUMANA D; East Brunswick HS; East Brunswick, NJ; (4); Cmnty Wkr; Dance Clb; French Clb; Hosp Aide; Pres Intnl Clb; School Play; Lit Mag; VP French Hon Soc; NHS; Ntl Merit SF; Merit Semi Fnlst 86; VP Frnch Hnr Soc 86; Interntnl Relations.

RAPAPORT, JERROLD; Jewish Educational Ctr; W Orange, NJ; (3); Chess Clb; Cmnty Wkr; Math Tm; Service Clb; Nwsp Ed-Chief; Lib Ed Yrbk Stf; Hon Roll; NHS; Vtrnry Med.

RAPP, TAMMY; Woodbridge HS; Iselin, NJ; (4); 36/376; Church Yth Grp; Hosp Aide; Chorus; Flag Corp; Variety Show; Nwsp Bus Mgr; Yrbk Stf; Lit Mag; Hon Roll; NHS; Helen Nessler Awd 87; 250 Hrs Hosp Svc 86; Acadmc Excllnc Plq 87; Douglass Coll; Spch.

RAPPE, DAMON; Paul VI HS; Barrington, NJ; (3); Bowling; Bus.

RAPPOPORT, LAWRENCE H; Madison Central HS; Old Bridge, NJ; (3); 5/360; Chrmn Am Leg Boys St; Trs Spanish Clb; Nwsp Ed-Chief; Trk; Gov Hon Prg Awd; High Hon Roll; Hon Roll; NHS; Prfct Atten Awd; Spanish NHS; Sci Awd; Sci.

RAPS, ROBERT J; Spotswood HS; Spotswood, NJ; (3); 6/171; Boy Scts; FBLA; Science Clb; VP Soph Cls; JV L Bsktbl; Var L Ftbl; Var L Trk; Hon Roll; NHS.

RAQUET, EVELYN; Wayne Hills HS; Wayne, NJ; (4); 9/287; Cmnty Wkr; Pres FBLA; Math Clb; Math Tm; Variety Show; High Hon Roll; NHS; St Schlr; Garden ST Distngshd Schlr 86-87; U Of DE; Accntng.

RARING, KRISTEN; Holy Spirit HS; Absecon, NJ; (3); 38/332; Var Fld Hcky; JV Sftbl; Hon Roll; NHS; Lasalle Coll; Accntng.

RASCHDORF, WERNER; De Paul HS; Kinnelon, NJ; (4); 39/153; Boy Scts; Church Yth Grp; CAP; Exploring; German Clb; Ski Clb; Varsity Clb; Chorus; Color Guard; Yrbk Phtg; Ski Tm Racer 86-87; Air Force Acad; Aerontcl Engrng.

RASCIO, LAUREN L; Saddle River Day Schl; N Haledon, NJ; (3); 6/50; Church Yth Grp; Cmnty Wkr; Library Aide; Math Tm; Pres Spanish Clb; Chorus; Church Choir; Madrigals; School Musical; Yrbk Ed-Chief; Schl Schlrshp 85-88; Wrtg Cntst Schlrshp 85; Mss Teen USA Acdmc Pgnt 86; Bio.

RASHDUNI, DAVID; Glen Rock JR SR HS; Glen Rock, NJ; (3); Boy Scts; Science Clb; High Hon Roll; Hon Roll; Frnch Stu Of Mnth Awd 86; Med.

RASKIND, CRAIG H; The Frisch Schl; West Orange, NJ; (4); Drama Clb; Mu Alpha Theta; Science Clb; Sec Temple Yth Grp; VP Tennis; VP Trk; Sec Cit Awd; Hon Roll; NHS; W Orange Frst Aid Sqd-Yth Sqd Emer Rdr 86-87; AABJ&D Chvra Kdsha 86-87; SBMC-350 Hr Jr Vlntr Awd 87; Yeshiva U; Pre Med.

RASMUSSEN, MICAH; Vineland HS; Vineland, NJ; (3); 30/850; Pres Church Yth Grp; Key Clb; Chorus; Mrchg Band; School Musical; Ed Nwsp Sprt Ed; Rep Stu Cncl; Gov Hon Prg Awd; Drama Clb; Library Aide; Mdl Cngrss Comm Chrmn 86; OM Rantra Fusca Awd 84-86; Mrchg Band Svc Cit 85; Law.

RASMUSSEN, MICHAEL; Monsignor Donovan HS; Toms River, NJ; (3); Aud/Vis; Ski Clb; Jazz Band; Mrchg Band; Pep Band; Variety Show; Camden Cnty Coll; Opthmlgy.

RASO, HECTOR; Paterson Catholic HS; Paterson, NJ; (2); Hon Roll; Earth Sci Awd 86; Art.

RAST, MICHELLE; Henry Hudson Regional HS; Atlntic Hglds, NJ; (3); 1/95; Off SADD; Band; Yrbk Ed-Chief; VP Frsh Cls; VP Soph Cls; Pres Jr Cls; VP Sr Cls; Var L Tennis; NHS; St Schlr; Cngrssnl Bronze Awd 85-86; William & Mary; Adv.

RASZKIEWICZ, BARBARA; Immaculate Conception HS; Lyndhurst, NJ; (3); Drama Clb; Q&S; Chorus; School Musical; Stage Crew; Lit Mag; Hon Roll; Frnch Awd 84-86; Montclair ST Coll.

RATHBONE, LARRY J; Woodstown HS; Alloway, NJ; (4); Boy Scts; Drama Clb; English Clb; Chorus; School Musical; Nwsp Rptr; Lit Mag; Capt Crs Cntry; Capt Trk; Hon Roll; Salem Cnty, Tri Cnty & Hnrbl Mntn Crs Cntry Trck 86 & 87; USAF; Physcl Thrpy.

RATHOD, MIHIR; Saddle River Day Schl; Paramus, NJ; (3); Computer Clb; Math Tm; Scholastic Bowl; JV Bsbl; JV Socr; Var Wrstlng; Hon Roll; Prfct Atten Awd; Steven David Bader Mem Scholar Awd 85-86; Bus.

RATLEFF, HOPE; Woodrow Wilson HS; Camden, NJ; (1); Civic Clb; Computer Clb; Vllybl; Hon Roll; JETS Awd; Stdy Drxl U 85; Stdy Glassboro SC Cmps 86; Elec Engr.

RATTAZZI, SUZANNE; Franklin HS; Somerset, NJ; (3); Church Yth Grp; Girl Scts; Band; Concert Band; Mrchg Band; Symp Band; Bus.

RATYCZ, CHRISTINA; Bishop Ahr HS; Edison, NJ; (4); French Clb; VP German Clb; Hosp Aide; Ski Clb; SADD; Yrbk Stf; Var Trk; Hon Roll; Scholar Ukrainian Natl Assn 87; Bus Adm.

RATZIN, PATRICIA; Immaculate Conception HS; Passaic, NJ; (3); 21/70; Spanish Clb; SADD; Chorus; Church Choir; School Musical; School Play; Stage Crew; Yrbk Stf; NEDT Awd; Accntng.

RAU, FRANK; Red Bank Regional HS; Little Silver, NJ; (4); 1/260; High Hon Roll; JETS Awd; Kiwanis Awd; Lion Awd; NHS; Spanish NHS; St Schlr; Val; George Washington U Mdl 86; Rensselaer Mdl Scholar 87; Rensselaer Polytech; Math Sci.

RAU, JENNIFER; Monsignor Donovan HS; Lakewood, NJ; (3); 74/265; Drama Clb; SADD; Thesps; Chorus; School Musical; School Play; Hon Roll; Dancer.

RAUCHBERG, TRACY; Parsippany HS; Parsippany, NJ; (3); Office Aide; Temple Yth Grp; Hon Roll; NJ Figure Skating Cncl Ann Marie Dunn Trphy 87; Independent Stdy Prog For Figure Skating 84-87; Sports Psychlgy.

RAULLI, KAREN; Manasquan HS; Manasquan, NJ; (2); 8/245; Church Yth Grp; DECA; Drama Clb; French Clb; FBLA; Var Tennis; High Hon Roll; Hon Roll; Broad Of Educ Awd.

RAVAL, SHILPA; Academy Of St Aloysius; Jersey City, NJ; (4); 1/112; Pres Aud/Vis; Intnl Clb; NFL; VP Chorus; School Play; Nwsp Ed-Chief; Lit Mag; CC Awd; NHS; Val; Grdn ST Dstngshd Schlr 87; R Byrd Hnr Schlr 87; Drew U; Pltcl Sci.

RAVEN, SHARON; Bruriah High School For Girls; Old Bridge, NJ; (4); Pres Art Clb; Pres Temple Yth Grp; Mgr Stage Crew; Rptr Nwsp Stf; Ed Yrbk Stf; Trs Soph Cls; Pres Sr Cls; Svc Citation Yth Group 87; 2nd Pl Sci Fair 86; Stern Coll; Tchng.

RAVENELL III, SAUL; Orange HS; Orange, NJ; (3); Boys Clb Am; Boy Scts; Civic Clb; Cmnty Wkr; FBLA; NAACP; VP Y-Teens; Wrstlng; Trp To Wshngtn DC For Clsd Sessions & Smnr On Govt 87; Bus Mngmnt.

RAVO, TINA; Kittatinny Regional HS; Branchville, NJ; (4); 23/222; Spanish Clb; High Hon Roll; Hon Roll; NHS; Pres Schlr; Achvt Awd Bus Educ 87; Achvt Awd Spnsh 87; Secy Ldrshp Awd 86; K Gibbs Schlrshp 87; Dover Bus Coll; Exec Secy.

RAWS, TIM; Highland Regional HS; Blackwood, NJ; (2); Latin Clb; Im Bsktbl; JV Socr.

RAY, TERESA; Monongahela JR HS; Wenonah, NJ; (1); Var Trk; Crls Vrsty Trk & Wntr Trk, & Career Clb Awd 86-87; Law.

RAYNOR, REBECCA; Newton HS; Newton, NJ; (2); 47/214; Girl Scts; Red Cross Aide; Thesps; Off Lit Mag; Rptr Stu Cncl; Mgr(s); Score Keeper; Stat Trk; JV Vllybl; Trenton ST Coll; Bus Admn.

RAYNOR, SCOTT; Washington Township HS; Turnersville, NJ; (2); Pres VP Exploring; Stu Cncl; Crs Cntry; Trk; Glassboro ST; Law Enfrcmnt.

REA, CAROL; Lower Cape May Regional HS; W Cape May, NJ; (3); 1/193; Pres Trs 4-H; Key Clb; Trs Spanish Clb; Band; Trs Soph Cls; Trs Jr Cls; Trs Sr Cls; Var Sftbl; Var Swmmng; High Hon Roll; Optmst Stu Of Yr 85; Outstndg 4-H Wmn Of Yr 86; Washington Ctznshp Focus 85; Engrng.

REA, HERB; Toms River South HS; Pine Bch, NJ; (2); Math Tm; Bsktbl; Tennis; High Hon Roll; Hon Roll.

READE, JAMES P; Phillipsburg Catholic HS; Phillipsburg, NJ; (3); 35/87; Am Leg Boys St; Ftbl; Wrstlng; Hon Roll; Wrstlng Capt 85-87; Comm.

READE, JOHN A; Ocean City HS; Beesleys Pt, NJ; (3); 18/341; Am Leg Boys St; Bsktbl; Var Golf; High Hon Roll; Hon Roll; NHS; Rep Model Cong 85-87; Delg Amer Lgn Jrsy Boys ST 87; Pre Med.

REAGAN, MICHELLE; Toms River East HS; Toms River, NJ; (4); 68/585; Sec Art Clb; Key Clb; Math Tm; Pep Clb; Ski Clb; Off Lit Mag; Off Soph Cls; Jr Cls; Sr Cls; Stu Cncl; Acctng.

REAGLE, DEBRA LEE; Central Regional HS; Bayville, NJ; (4); 46/220; Church Yth Grp; Drama Clb; Pres Band; Chorus; Color Guard; Pres Concert Band; Jazz Band; Pres Mrchg Band; School Musical; School Play; Arian Awd 87; Northern Lghts Thtr Schlrshp 87; Lebanon Valley Coll; Music.

REAHM, JEFFREY; Holy Spirit HS; Mays Landing, NJ; (3); 26/332; JA; Nwsp Bus Mgr; High Hon Roll; Hon Roll; Pre Law.

REAMER III, RAYMOND V; Don Bosco Preparatory HS; Fairlawn, NJ; (4); 85/170; Church Yth Grp; Cmnty Wkr; Letterman Clb; Pep Clb; Varsity Clb; Bsbl; Bsktbl; Coach Actv; Ftbl; Socr; Roger Williams Coll; Crmnl Jstc.

REAMS, SHIKIETA J; John F Kennedy HS; Paterson, NJ; (2); Rep Soph Cls; Hon Roll; Spanish NHS; HERO 86-87; Howard U; Crmnl Just.

REARDON, CHRISTINE; Holy Spirit HS; Margate, NJ; (4); 30/363; French Clb; Quiz Bowl; Yrbk Rptr; Rep Stu Cncl; Cheerleading; Mgr(s); High Hon Roll; Hon Roll; NHS; Rutgers U; Bio.

REARDON, DON; Washington Township HS; Sewell, NJ; (3); Spanish Clb; Im Bsbl; Im Bsktbl; Im Ftbl.

REAVES, CASPER M; Crawford HS; Cranford, NJ; (4); 2/267; Band; Var Capt Crs Cntry; Var Capt Trk; Bausch & Lomb Sci Awd; French Hon Soc; High Hon Roll; Sal; St Schlr; Boy Scts; Chess Clb; NJ Schlr Ath 87; Natl Achvt Schlrshp 87; Schl Math Awd 87; Princeton U; Elec Engrng.

REAVES, JA MEDA A; St Vincent Acad; Newark, NJ; (4); 12/63; Yrbk Phtg; Yrbk Rptr; Rep Jr Cls; Pres Sr Cls; Rep Stu Cncl; L Cheerleading; Var Trk; Ntl Merit Ltr; Cmnty Wkr; Girl Scts; NSFONS 86-87; Hnrble Mntn PSAT/NMSQT 85-86; Fairleigh Dickinson U; Psych.

REBELES, LISA; Florence Twp Memorial HS; Roebling, NJ; (3); Am Leg Aux Girls St; GAA; Math Clb; Varsity Clb; Trs Jr Cls; Trs Sr Cls; Rep Stu Cncl; Var Fld Hcky; Var Sftbl; High Hon Roll; Math.

REBELS, STEPHANIE; Morris Knolls HS; Dover, NJ; (3); NFL; Varsity Clb; Chorus; Color Guard; Drill Tm; Drm & Bgl; Flag Corp; Mrchg Band; School Musical; Stage Crew; Vrsty Lttr In Mrchng Band 86; Color Grd & Wntr Grd; Med.

REBENACK, ED; Wayne Hills HS; Wayne, NJ; (3); 34/320; JV Bsbl; Var Bsktbl; Hon Roll; NHS.

REBER, HOPE; Mount Olive HS; Flanders, NJ; (3); 77/350; AFS; Aud/Vis; 4-H; Varsity Clb; School Play; Yrbk Stf; Lit Mag; Var Swmmng; JV Trk; 4-H Phtgrphy ST Cmpnshp 85; Swmng Most Imprvd 86; Physcl Ftnss Pres Awd 87; CA U Berkly; Math.

REBOLI, DENISE; Mt St Dominic Acad; W Caldwell, NJ; (3); Nwsp Rptr; Yrbk Bus Mgr; JV Coach Actv; L Socr; Var L Trk; Gov Hon Prg Awd; High Hon Roll; NHS; Church Yth Grp; JCL; St Peters Smmr Schlrs Pgm; Montcliar ST Gftd & Tlntd Pgm; NJ Inst Tech Femme Pgm; Math.

RECCHION, MICHELE; Toms River HS South; Pine Beach, NJ; (4); 13/360; Math Tm; Variety Show; JV Bsktbl; Powder Puff Ftbl; Var Capt Sftbl; Var L Tennis; High Hon Roll; Hon Roll; NHS; Pres Schlr; Vrsty Sftbl MVP 87; Acdmc Ltrs 83-84, 86-87; JV Bsktbl MVP 84-85; Georgian Court Coll.

RECINIELLO, JOSEPH; Queen Of Peace HS; Rutherford, NJ; (3); 44/277; Boy Scts; French Clb; Model UN; Nwsp Stf; Ed Hon Roll; Accntng.

REDD, TOYA; Manchester Township HS; Lakehurst, NJ; (2); Girl Scts; Chorus; Church Choir; Sftbl; Hon Roll; Spanish NHS; Med.

REDDICK, AILEEN; Marylawn Of The Oranges HS; Irvington, NJ; (2); Church Yth Grp; Drama Clb; Pep Clb; Spanish Clb; School Musical; Hon Roll; NEDT Awd; 1st Prz Jr Div-Essay Cntst-Irvington Pblc Libry 85; Dist Wnr-Intrmdt Cls Natl Piano Audtns 86.

REDDICK IV, WILLIAM J; Seton Hall Prep; Union, NJ; (4); Trs Church Yth Grp; Pep Clb; Var Capt Bsbl; Hon Roll; Pres Schlr; Bsbl Schlrshp-Seton Hall U 87; CYO Outstndng Yth Rep-Union Cty 87; Prsh Cncl-Electd Yth Rep; Seton Hall U; Coach.

REDI, JASON; West Windsor-Plainsboro HS; Princeton, NJ; (3); Aud/Vis; Computer Clb; Jazz Band; Hst Orch; School Musical; School Play; Stage Crew; Symp Band; Hon Roll; Elec Comp Engr.

REDISH, STEPHANIE; Monsignor Donovan HS; Jackson, NJ; (4); 31/223; Am Leg Aux Girls St; Ski Clb; SADD; Yrbk Stf; Sec Jr Cls; Rep Stu Cncl; Capt Var Cheerleading; Coach Actv; JV Capt Sftbl; High Hon Roll; Century III Ldrshp Scholar Schl Rnr-Up 86; Fclty & Staff Scholar 87; Chrldg MVP 87; Penn ST; Comm.

REDMAN, ERICA; Paulsboro HS; Paulsboro, NJ; (3); Church Yth Grp; Office Aide; Band; Chorus; Church Choir; Color Guard; Mrchg Band; Rep Frsh Cls; Rep Stu Cncl; Var Trk.

REDMAN, JOSEPH; Paulsboro HS; Paulsboro, NJ; (3); Var Bsbl; Var Ftbl; Var Wrstlng; Outstndng Wrstlr Of Yr 87.

REDMER, GAY; Paul VI HS; Oaklyn, NJ; (3); Political Wkr; JV Crs Cntry; Hstry.

REDMOND, JACK; Brick Twp HS; Brick Town, NJ; (3); 24/390; Latin Clb; Varsity Clb; Bsbl; Var Bsktbl; Ftbl; Wt Lftg; NHS.

REDMOND, KATHLEEN; Manville HS; Manville, NJ; (3); Pres Drama Clb; French Clb; Girl Scts; Band; Concert Band; Concert Band; Mrchg Band; Variety Show; Yrbk Stf; Rep Stu Cncl; HS Yr France Pgm 86-87; Girl Scout Wider Opportunity Pgm 86; Linguistics.

REED, BRENDA; West Windsor-Plainsboro HS; Dutch Neck, NJ; (3); 83/290; Church Yth Grp; 4-H; Ski Clb; Acpl Chr; Stat Diving; Stat Sftbl; Stat Swmmng; 4-H Awd; Hon Roll; W New England Coll; Bus.

REED, CHRISTOPHER E; Essex Catholic HS; Orange, NJ; (2); Chess Clb; Church Yth Grp; Math Clb; JV Bsbl; High Hon Roll; Natl Awd Merit Outstndng Achvt Bio 85; Natl Sci Merit Awd 86; Engrng.

REED, GLEN; Mount Olvie HS; Flanders, NJ; (3); Civic Clb; Computer Clb; Math Tm; Political Wkr; Ski Clb; Band; Concert Band; Mrchg Band; Stage Crew; Lit Mag; Achvmnt Natl Hist Day 85; Schlrshp Awd 86.

REED, JOHN P; Overbrook Regional HS; Pine Hill, NJ; (4); 21/335; Church Yth Grp; French Clb; Var Crs Cntry; Socr; JV Var Trk; Hon Roll; NHS; Rutgers Dean Smmr Schlr; Phila Coll Of Phrmcy; Phrmcy.

REED, KEITH; East Orange HS; East Orange, NJ; (4); Pres Jr Cls; Var Bsktbl; Fairleigh Dickinson U; Bus.

REED, LA ONQUE; Clifford J Scott HS; East Orange, NJ; (3); 18/210; Dance Clb; Varsity Clb; Band; Concert Band; Nwsp Rptr; Yrbk Stf; Pres Sr Cls; Sftbl; Trk; Hon Roll; Comp Sci.

REED, MELISSA; Hopewell Valley Central HS; Hamilton, NJ; (4); Chorus; School Musical; School Play; Stage Crew; Lit Mag; Rep Stu Cncl; JV Crs Cntry; Hon Roll; Hussian Schl Of Art Schlrshp, Awd 85; Mercer County CC; Aviatn.

REED, MICHAEL; Paulsboro HS; Paulsboro, NJ; (4); 6/145; Computer Clb; Band; Chorus; Jazz Band; Mrchg Band; School Play; Trk; JP Sousa Awd; Kiwanis Awd; NHS; 3rd Gloucester Cnty Coll Comp Cntst 87; Colonial Conf Hnrs Band-Tnr Sax 86-87; Gloucester Cnty Coll; Acctng.

REED, MICHAEL; Vineland HS; Newfield, NJ; (4); Var Trk; Cumberland Cnty Coll; Bio.

REED, MONIQUE; Eastside HS; Paterson, NJ; (4); 17/543; Science Clb; Acpl Chr; Yrbk Stf; Rep Stu Cncl; Var Cheerleading; Bausch & Lomb Sci Awd; Hon Roll; Masonic Awd; Ntl Merit Schol; Prfct Atten Awd; HS Schlrshp Cert 84; Outstndng Acadc Achvt Sci 86; William Paterson Coll; Jrnlsm.

REED, PAUL; Franklin HS; Somerset, NJ; (3); Cnty, St Teen Arts-Guitar 87; U Of MT; Wldlf Cnsrvtn.

REED, PENNY; Holy Spirit HS; Absecon, NJ; (4); 39/363; Pep Clb; Yrbk Stf; JV Cheerleading; NHS; Stocton ST Coll; Accntng.

REED, ROBERT; Bloomfield HS; Bloomfield, NJ; (3); Hon Roll; Engr.

REED, SUSAN; Woodstown HS; Monroeville, NJ; (3); 1/180; Art Clb; English Clb; Yrbk Stf; Lit Mag; High Hon Roll; NHS; St Schlr; Thomas Edison Sci Fair 1st Pl 87; Amer Chem Scty Exclince Awd 87; Prom Comm 87; Early Chldhd Educ.

REESE, JOHN; Fair Lawn HS; Fair Lawn, NJ; (3); 29/340; Am Leg Boys St; Varsity Clb; Rep Frsh Cls; Pres Soph Cls; Pres Jr Cls; Rep Sr Cls; Capt Ftbl; Capt Wrstlng; NHS; USMA; Mltry Ofcr.

REESE, MARLO; Essex Catholic Girls HS; E Orange, NJ; (3); Cmnty Wkr; Library Aide; Pep Clb; Teachers Aide; Hon Roll; Acctg.

REETZ, CAROLYN; Hamilton HS East; Hamilton Square, NJ; (3); AFS; Sec Church Yth Grp; Cmnty Wkr; Exploring; JA; Service Clb; Chorus; Church Choir; Mgr(s); Score Keeper; Southrn NJ Untd Methdst Conf Yth Delg 2 Yrs; Elem Ed Tchr.

REEVES, DIANA; Millvelle HS; Millville, NJ; (3); Church Yth Grp; French Clb; Ski Clb; SADD; Rep Stu Cncl; Var Socr; Hon Roll; NHS; Boy Scts; Science Clb; Ldrs Clb; Unsung Hero Awd Soccer & Yth In Govt; Biochem.

REEVES, HAROLD S; Cranford HS; Cranford, NJ; (4); 4/267; Trs AFS; Trs Chess Clb; JCL; Latin Clb; Math Tm; Quiz Bowl; Trs Spanish Clb; Lit Mag; Trs Sr Cls; Hon Roll; Nat Hispnc SF Merit Harvard Smmr Schl 86; Magna Cum Ld Natl Latn Exm 86; Amer Club Pres; Clssc Law.

REEVES, KATHERINE; Kent Place Schl; Summit, NJ; (3); Cmnty Wkr; Hosp Aide; Chorus; Yrbk Bus Mgr; VP Frsh Cls; Rep Soph Cls; VP Jr Cls; VP Sr Cls; Rep Stu Cncl; Im Ice Hcky.

REGAN, COURTNEY; Glen Rock HS; Glen Rock, NJ; (3); Drama Clb; Ski Clb; Varsity Clb; School Play; Nwsp Stf; Sec CAP; Sec Jr Cls; Sec Sr Cls; JV Sftbl; Var Vllybl.

REGAN, LINDA; James Caldwell HS; West Caldwell, NJ; (4); 70/265; Sec Trs Spanish Clb; Nwsp Rptr; Nwsp Stf; Yrbk Stf; Stu Cncl; Capt Cheerleading; Trk; Bloomsburg U; Ed.

REGAN, MARGARET; Immaculate Conception HS; E Orange, NJ; (4); 9/78; Office Aide; Teachers Aide; School Musical; Nwsp Rptr; Pres Stu Cncl; Sftbl; NHS; Chorus; Yrbk Ed-Chief; Rep Jr Cls; James J Mc Mahon Ctznshp & Ldrshp Hnrs 86-87; Coll Wmn Clb Schlrshp 87; Utica Coll; Engl.

REGAN, MARIA; Phillipsburg HS; Phillipsburg, NJ; (3); 18/315; Boy Scts; Cmnty Wkr; SADD; Stu Cncl; High Hon Roll; NHS; Prfct Atten Awd; Rutgers; Nrsng.

REGECI, KRISTEN; Johnson Regional HS; Clark, NJ; (4); Pres French Clb; Stage Crew; Variety Show; Nwsp Rptr; Yrbk Stf; Trs Pres Stu Cncl; Cheerleading; L Score Keeper; L Trk; Natl Ldrshp Merit Awd 85-86; Enrlld In Gifted & Tlntd Pgm 86-87.

REGELSKI, MARIANNE; Dover HS; Dover, NJ; (3); 11/210; AFS; Am Leg Aux Girls St; Ski Clb; Drm Mjr(t); School Musical; Yrbk Stf; VP Stu Cncl; Bowling; High Hon Roll; NHS; Bus.

REGER, CHRISTINA; Notre Dame HS; Robbinsville, NJ; (2); Hosp Aide; Flag Corp; Stage Crew; Lit Mag; Rep Frsh Cls; Mgr(s); Swmmng; Timer; Hon Roll; NHS; Intl Order Rainbow 87-88; Grnd Rep W Grmny Org 86-87; Bus Mng.

REGETZ, STEPHANIE; Secaucus HS; Secaucus, NJ; (3); Key Clb; Math Clb; Mu Alpha Theta; Varsity Clb; Concert Band; Mrchg Band; Yrbk Stf; Rep Jr Cls; Rep Sr Cls; Hon Roll; Engrng.

REHA, GEORGE; Monalapan HS; Englishtown, NJ; (2); CAP; Avioncs.

REHBERG, KRISTON J; Don Bosco Prep HS; Monroe, NY; (2); Boy Scts; Computer Clb; Pep Clb; High Hon Roll; Hon Roll; Life Sct 86; First Hnrs 85-86; Comp Sci.

REHBERG, MICHAEL; Don Bosco Prep; Monroe, NY; (4); Boy Scts; Exploring; Nwsp Phtg; Nwsp Stf; Hon Roll; NHS; NY Rgnts Schlr 87; Rochester Inst Tech; Comp Sci.

REHBORN, DIANA C; Edgewood Regional SR HS; Berlin, NJ; (3); 7/375; Hosp Aide; Sec Trs Latin Clb; Sec Spanish Clb; Varsity Clb; Nwsp Stf; Yrbk Stf; Var Stat Bsbl; Var Cheerleading; NHS; Acdmc All Amer Awd 86; NJ Med Schlrs Pgm 87-88; NJ Schlrs Pgm Semifnlst 87; Bio.

REHMANN, RICHARD S; Hammonton HS; Hammonton, NJ; (3); Pres Key Clb; Band; Concert Band; Mrchg Band; Var Bsktbl; Var Golf; Var Socr; High Hon Roll; NHS; Hugh O Brian Yth Ldrshp; Civil Eng.

REHO, JAMES; St Josephs Prep Seminary; Princeton, NJ; (4); 1/16; Drama Clb; Pres NFL; School Play; Nwsp Ed-Chief; Yrbk Phtg; Rep Sr Cls; NHS; Ntl Merit Ltr; Spanish NHS; High Hon Roll; St Josephs Awd Hghst Avg Grd 9-12; St Johns Schlrshp Wnnr; Intro Phys Sci Awd; St Johns U; Math.

REICH, BENJAMIN; Pennsauken HS; Merchantville, NJ; (2); Jazz Band; School Musical; Swing Chorus; Spanish NHS; Berklee Coll; Musician.

REICH, BRIAN; West Orange HS; West Orange, NJ; (4); 7/370; Am Leg Boys St; Math Tm; Quiz Bowl; Nwsp Sprt Ed; Var Crs Cntry; Socr; Var Tennis; Var Wrstlng; Gov Hon Prg Awd; NHS; Hugh Obrian St Rep To Interntl Conf 85; St Schlrshp Jewish War Vet 87; 1st Tm Math St Of NJ 86; Harvard.

REID, AMEE SUZANNE; Kingsway Regional HS; Mullica Hill, NJ; (4); 25/161; Art Clb; Church Yth Grp; Key Clb; Teachers Aide; VICA; Yrbk Stf; Fld Hcky; High Hon Roll; VICA Offcr 86-87; Archtct.

REID, MICHAEL; Immaculate Conception HS; Orange, NJ; (3); Art Clb; Var Capt Ftbl; Var Trk; Wt Lftg; Trck Mst Imprvd & Coaches Awds 86 & 87; Ftbll AVCA Hnrbl Mntn 87; Prof Athlt.

REID, PATRICIA; Paulsboro HS; Paulsboro, NJ; (3); 98/150; Girl Scts; Spanish Clb; SADD; Stat Bsktbl; Var Capt Fld Hcky; Var Trk; Omega Insti; Law.

REIDEL, LAURIE; Ridgefield Park HS; Little Ferry, NJ; (4); 8/190; Spanish Clb; Teachers Aide; Yrbk Stf; Lit Mag; Trs Sr Cls; Off Stu Cncl; Var Capt Bsktbl; Stat Trk; Capt Var Vllybl; Hon Roll; Spanish Awd 87; Montclair ST Coll; Bus.

REIDY, JAMES; St Joseph Regional HS; Spring Valley, NY; (3); 10/225; SADD; Nwsp Stf; Rep Stu Cncl; Bsbl; Ftbl; Capt Trk; Capt Wrstlng; High Hon Roll; NHS; Spanish NHS; Mst Imprvd Ftbl, MIP Wrstlng 85; JV Wrstlng & Track MVP 86; U Of TX; Stock Broker.

REIF, CARL J; Bishop Eustace Prep Schl; Bellmawr, NJ; (3); Am Leg Boys St; Pres Jr Cls; Pres Stu Cncl; Var L Ftbl; Var Capt Ice Hcky; Im Capt Vllybl; Var Wt Lftg; NHS; Garden ST Ice Hockey Team Brnz Medal 87; Spirit Awd 84; 2(d Pl Rgnls,1st Dist Ice Hockey 86; Pre-Med.

REIFENBERGER, KRISTIN; West Windsor-Plainsboro HS; Princeton Jct, NJ; (3); AFS; Radio Clb; Ed Nwsp Sprt Ed; Nwsp Stf; Ed Yrbk Ed-Chief; Lit Mag; Rep Frsh Cls; Rep Soph Cls; Rep Jr Cls; Stat Bsbl; Mercer Cnty Lit Magazine Aspirations 87; Princeton Packet 86-88; Comms.

REIGHN, DONALD; Haddonfield HS; Haddonfield, NJ; (3); Var Capt Crs Cntry; Var Trk; Acctg.

REIGHN, MIKE; Deptford HS; Wenonah, NJ; (1); VP Frsh Cls; JV Ftbl; Wt Lftg; JV Wrstlng; Hon Roll; Rutgers; AF Offcr.

REILLY, BRIAN; Green Brook HS; Green Brook, NJ; (3); Chess Clb; Church Yth Grp; Drama Clb; Key Clb; Ski Clb; Band; Chorus; Concert Band; Jazz Band; Mrchg Band; All Hntrdn-Smrst Cnty Band 88; Cntrl Jrsy Gr 1, 4th Pl Dscs & 5th Pl Sht Put 88; Law.

REILLY, CHRISTOPHER; Haddonfield Memorial HS; Haddonfield, NJ; (2); 30/142; Art Clb; Service Clb; SADD; Lit Mag; Rep Stu Cncl; Bsbl; JV Socr; Envrnmntl Cnsrvtn Grp 87; U DE; Art.

REILLY, JACQUELINE; Gateway Regional HS; Woodbury Hts, NJ; (2); VP FHA; Key Clb; SADD; Pres Frsh Cls; Pres Soph Cls; JV Bsktbl; Var Fld Hcky; Var Sftbl.

REILLY, JOSEPH; De Paul HS; Wayne, NJ; (4); 29/170; Am Leg Boys St; Chess Clb; Church Yth Grp; Ski Clb; High Hon Roll; Busi Admn.

REILLY, KAREN; Roselle Park HS; Roselle Park, NJ; (4); 21/161; Pres German Clb; Political Wkr; Radio Clb; Score Keeper; NHS; Ctznshp Inst Alt 85-86; Montclair St Coll; Acctng.

REILLY, LISA; Parsippany HS; Parsippany, NJ; (3); Dance Clb; SADD; Chorus; School Musical; Stage Crew; Lit Mag; Hon Roll; French Clb; Intl Ordr Rainbow Grls Grnd Wrthy Assoc Advsr 86-87; Mstr Grnd Crss Color IORG 87.

REILLY, NORA; Mount Saint Marys Acad; Plainfield, NJ; (2); 26/92; Off Church Yth Grp; Off Lit Mag; Rep Frsh Cls; Stu Cncl; Score Keeper; Hon Roll; Peer Minister 87-88; Parish Cncl 86-89; Psych.

REIM, DEANNE; Buena Regional HS; Newfield, NJ; (4); 23/180; SADD; Chorus; Rep Stu Cncl; Stat Bsktbl; Stat Fld Hcky; JV Sftbl; Hon Roll; NHS; Physcl Thrpy.

REIMELS, DAWN; Cumberland Christian Schl; Vineland, NJ; (4); 7/31; Church Yth Grp; Hosp Aide; Yrbk Stf; Sec Soph Cls; Var L Bsktbl; Var L Fld Hcky; Hon Roll; Dance Clb; Var L Cheerleading; Pres Phy Ftnss Awd 82-86; Towson ST U; Occup Thrpy.

REINDLE, TRACI; Wayne Hills HS; Wayne, NJ; (3); 49/400; GAA; Spanish Clb; Nwsp Stf; Var Capt Bsktbl; Coach Actv; Var Socr; Var Sftbl; Hon Roll; :Sports Med.

REINGOLD, CAREN; Wayne Hills HS; Wayne, NJ; (4); 53/320; FBLA; Capt GAA; Yrbk Phtg; Var Cheerleading; High Hon Roll.

REINHARD, STEPHEN; Parsippany HS; Parsippany, NJ; (3); Am Leg Boys St; Pres VP FBLA; Pres Intnl Clb; Trs Spanish Clb; Lit Mag; Rep Stu Cncl; Stat Bsbl; Trs NHS; Rep Frsh Cls; Rep Soph Cls; FBLA ST VP Nrthrn Rgn 87-88; FBLA NJ ST Exec Brd 87-88; Stanford U; Econ.

REINHOLD, LOIS IDA; Scotch Plains-Fanwood HS; Scotch Plains, NJ; (3); FBLA; Spanish Clb; JV Sftbl; Spanish NHS; Manhattenville; Hstry Ed.

REINHOLD, ROBYN; Pinelands Regionall HS; Tuckerton, NJ; (4); SADD; Fld Hcky; Socr; DAR Awd; Hon Roll; Schlrshp Of 1500 From Stuart Bus Schl 87; Stuart Bus Schl; Bus.

REINISCH, ADAM; Parsippany HS; Lk Hiawatha, NJ; (2); Aud/Vis; Boy Scts; FBLA; Ski Clb; Spanish Clb; Band.

REINKNECHT, JANET; High Point Regional HS; Sussex, NJ; (2); 37/300; Church Yth Grp; GAA; SADD; Varsity Clb; Rep Frsh Cls; Rep Soph Cls; Trs Stu Cncl; Fld Hcky; JV Sftbl; High Hon Roll; J V Defnsv Plyr Fld Hocky 85; J V Constnt Plyr Awd Sftbl 87; Math.

REINOLD, ERIK; Matawan Aberdeen HS; Matawan, NJ; (3); 67/302; Ski Clb; Varsity Clb; School Musical; Stage Crew; Crs Cntry; Mgr(s); Trk; Hon Roll; Captn Boys Crss Cntry & Trk 87-88; Bus.

REISDORF, CHRISTINA; Chatham HS; Chatham, NJ; (2); Art Clb; Model UN; Pep Clb; Yrbk Ed-Chief; Stu Cncl; JV Var Cheerleading; Var Trk; Latin Clb; Spanish Clb; Trs Frsh Cls; Smmr Inst For Gftd & Tlntd 85 & 86; Track & Chrldng Awds 85-87; Boston U; Arch.

REISER, JOHN; Watchung Hills Regional HS; Warren, NJ; (2); Key Clb; Ski Clb; SADD; Yrbk Stf; JV Var Bsbl; JV Var Bsktbl; Hon Roll; U Of NC; Bus Mgmt.

REISER, JOSH; James Caldwell HS; W Caldwell, NJ; (4); 20/265; Key Clb; Ski Clb; Temple Yth Grp; Band; Lit Mag; Rep Stu Cncl; JV Trk; High Hon Roll; NHS; St Schlr; Washington U-St Louis; Arts.

REISS, ADAM; John P Stevens HS; Edison, NJ; (3); 72/450; Key Clb; Science Clb; Temple Yth Grp; Band; Concert Band; Mrchg Band; Nwsp Stf; Crs Cntry; NHS; Spanish NHS; Accntng.

REISS, JOEL; John F Kennedy HS; Willingboro, NJ; (3); Am Leg Boys St; Pres Key Clb; Math Tm; Science Clb; Pres Temple Yth Grp; Ed Yrbk Stf; Var Crs Cntry; Hon Roll; Jr NHS; NHS; Elctrcl Engrng.

REITMAIER, CHRIS; Egg Harbor Township HS; Pleasantville, NJ; (3); 38/378; Chess Clb; Cmnty Wkr; Jr Cls; Stu Cncl; Bsktbl; Socr; Tennis; Stockton ST Coll; Bus Adm.

REITZ, KATHLEEN; Toms River HS South; S Toms River, NJ; (3); 29/405; Math Tm; Political Wkr; SADD; Band; Concert Band; Drm Mjr(t); Mrchg Band; Symp Band; Variety Show; Pom Pon; Pres Phys Ftnss Awd; Phrmcst.

REKKER, ROBERT; Collegiate HS; Passaic, NJ; (1); Computer Clb; Exploring; Latin Clb; Stu Cncl.

RELOVSKY, DAN; Holy Cross HS; Mount Laurel, NJ; (4); Church Yth Grp; Church Choir; School Musical; Rep Soph Cls; Im JV Bsbl; JV Var Bsktbl; Hon Roll; NHS; Sr Awd Bsktbl 87; Drexel U; Commerce,Engr.

REMBELLES, CHRISTINA MARIE E; Manville HS; Manville, NJ; (3); Church Yth Grp; Chorus; Concert Band; Mrchg Band; Nwsp Rptr; Yrbk Phtg; Yrbk Rptr; High Hon Roll; Hon Roll; NHS; Awd Of Hnr Bi-Cnty Bnd Chrs 85-87; Awd Seargeat-At-Arms 87; Music Awd 85; Trenton ST Coll; Bus.

REMBERT, DIANE; Mount St Dominic Acad; East Orange, NJ; (3); Library Aide; Pep Clb; Ski Clb; Chorus; Church Choir; Nwsp Rptr; Prfct Atten Awd; Med.

REMCHICK, TANYA; Highland Regional HS; Blanheim, NJ; (2); Im Fld Hcky; Music.

REMELGADO, LISA; Mother Seton Regional HS; Elizabeth, NJ; (3); GAA; JA; SADD; Pom Pon; Sftbl; Hon Roll; Drill Tm; Im Bsktbl; Im Vllybl; Katharine Gibbs Ldrshp Awd 87; Schl Spotlght Awd For Schl Sprt 87; Acad Awd In Accntng, Steno & Typng; Accntng.

REMENTOV, TAMMY; Kings Christian Schl; Cherry Hill, NJ; (4); 3/23; Art Clb; Church Yth Grp; GAA; Latin Clb; Letterman Clb; Varsity Clb; Chorus; Church Choir; Yrbk Ed-Chief; Yrbk Stf; Supr Achvt Art-Mid-Atlntc Chrstn Schl Assn 84-86; Bio.

REMES, JOSEPH R; Hackensack HS; Maywood, NJ; (3); 30/410; Am Leg Boys St; Ski Clb; Teachers Aide; Bsbl; Var Capt Tennis; Cit Awd; Hon Roll; NHS; Prfct Atten Awd; Spanish NHS; Montclair ST Coll; Bus Mgmt.

REMIG, EDWARD W; Millburn HS; Short Hills, NJ; (3); 27/259; Am Leg Boys St; VP Church Yth Grp; Math Tm; Red Cross Aide; Nwsp Stf; Var Capt Bsbl; Im Bsktbl; Var L Ftbl; Var Capt Ice Hcky; High Hon Roll; Chrchs Mst Outstndng Neophyte 86; Area, Conf Bsbl Tm 86; Sci Tm 86-87.

REMY, STEPHEN; Lower Cape May Regional HS; N Cape May, NJ; (1); Spanish Clb; VP Rep Frsh Cls; VP Rep Stu Cncl; JV Var Bsbl; JV Bsktbl; Var Im Socr; Im Sftbl; Im Vllybl; High Hon Roll; Hon Roll; Law.

RENART, KRYSTAL; Mainland Regional HS; Northfield, NJ; (3); 66/317; Pres Church Yth Grp; Church Choir; Nwsp Stf; Frgn Langs.

RENCHER, KELLY; Hunterdon Central HS; Flemington, NJ; (4); 102/548; Church Yth Grp; FCA; German Clb; Intnl Clb; Church Choir; Color Guard; Hon Roll; Intl Stds.

RENDA, GUY; Carteret HS; Carteret, NJ; (3); 28/217; Var Capt Bsbl; Var Capt Ftbl; All Acadc Bsbl Tm 86; Bl Div All Str Bsbl Tm 87; Monclair ST.

RENDEIRO, NELLY; East Side HS; Newark, NJ; (3); Girl Scts; Band; Church Choir; Concert Band; Mrchg Band; Orch; Rep Jr Cls; Rep Stu Cncl; Hon Roll; Rutgers U; Law.

RENDLEMAN, THIALAND LA-VAUGHN; West Side HS; Newark, NJ; (3); Boy Scts; Church Yth Grp; Pres JA; Band; Church Choir; Concert Band; Mrchg Band; 1 Of 3 Fnlst Pres Yr 86; USC Columbia; Aviation.

RENICK, HEATHER; Lakeland Regional HS; Wanaque, NJ; (3); 5/300; French Clb; Math Tm; SADD; Nwsp Sprt Ed; Sec Nwsp Stf; Var L Crs Cntry; JV Socr; Var L Trk; High Hon Roll; NHS; Natl Merit Awd Frnch, Chem 86; Recrd Vltnr Wk 87; Phys Thrpy.

RENN, THERESA; Egg Harbor Township HS; Mays Landing, NJ; (4); 13/287; Office Aide; Yrbk Stf; Hon Roll; Jr NHS; NHS; Berkeley Schls Awd Outstndng Achvt Bus Ed 87; Sectrl.

RENNER, CRYSTAL; Lyndhurst HS; Lyndhurst, NJ; (3); 6/174; VP Pres Key Clb; Service Clb; Color Guard; Variety Show; High Hon Roll; NHS; Ntl Merit Ltr; Cmnty Wkr; Girl Scts; Science Clb; Kiwanis Ldrshp Trng Inst Trenton St 85; Golden Poet Awd 86; Acad Decthln Hnrs Tm 87; Jrnlsm.

RENNER, KELLY; James Caldwell HS; West Caldwell, NJ; (3); Key Clb; Science Clb; Capt Cheerleading; High Hon Roll; Hon Roll; Bus.

RENNER, MICHELLE; Rancocas Valley Regional HS; Mt Holly, NJ; (2); Ski Clb; Cheerleading; Lcrss; High Hon Roll; Hon Roll.

RENOLD, LENA; Montville Township HS; Montville, NJ; (2); Key Clb; Varsity Clb; Mrchg Band; Swmmng; Trk; High Hon Roll; Hon Roll; Frgn Lng.

RENSHAW, APRIL; Overbrook SR HS; Pine Hill, NJ; (4); 8/350; French Clb; Band; Concert Band; Mrchg Band; Symp Band; Stu Cncl; Bsktbl; Sftbl; Jr NHS; Stockton ST; Oceanography.

RENSKY, GABRIELLE; Holy Cross HS; Burlington, NJ; (3); Spanish Clb; Church Choir; Drm Mjr(t); Off Soph Cls; Hon Roll; US Amtr Cnfdrtn Of Rllr Sktng 1st Pl NJ ST, 1st Pl Estrn Rgnls, 5th Pl Ntls US 85; Dntl Hygnst.

RENTA, PRISCILLA; St Joseph Of The Palisades HS; Jersey City, NJ; (3); Hosp Aide; Spanish Clb; JC Awd; Spanish NHS; NY U; Psych.

RENTAS, AMY; Orange HS; Orange, NJ; (4); FNA; Hosp Aide; Band; Concert Band; Mrchg Band; Yrbk Stf; Stu Cncl; Sftbl; Hon Roll; Natl Sci Olympiad 84; All City Instrumental Concert 82; Rutgers U; RN.

RENTON, SANDRA; Newton HS; Newton, NJ; (4); 5/196; Cmnty Wkr; Pres 4-H; French Clb; Hosp Aide; Latin Clb; Math Tm; Scholastic Bowl; Science Clb; Madrigals; Rep Stu Cncl; Medcl Tech.

RENWICK, IAN; Wayne Hills HS; Wayne, NJ; (4); 25/288; Math Clb; Chorus; Pres Concert Band; Pres Mrchg Band; School Musical; School Play; Gov Hon Prg Awd; High Hon Roll; JP Sousa Awd; NHS; NJ Are, Rgnl & All ST Bands Wnd Ensmbls 84-87; Music Awd 87; Tufts U; Engrng.

RENZ, PATRICIA; Holy Cross HS; Cinnaminson, NJ; (4); French Clb; High Hon Roll; Hon Roll; Cabrini Coll Acad Schlrshp 87; Cabrini Coll Hnrs Prog 87; Congrsnl Schlr Natl Yng Ldrs Conf 87; Cabrini Coll; Bus Admin.

REPKO, SUSAN; Notre Dame HS; Mercerville, NJ; (3); Red Cross Aide; Var Bsktbl; Var Crs Cntry; Var Sftbl; High Hon Roll; Hon Roll; NHS; Ntl Bus Hnr Soc.

RESAL, PARBATIE; Ferris HS; Jersey City, NJ; (3); Church Yth Grp; Cmnty Wkr; Church Choir.

RESCIGNO, THERESA; Shore Regional HS; W Long Branch, NJ; (3); Spanish Clb; SADD; JV Capt Cheerleading; JV Var Fld Hcky; Hon Roll; Fld Hcky Ltr; Chrldng Ltr; Hnr Rl; Fshn Dsgnr.

RESENDE, VICTORINO; East Side HS; Newark, NJ; (3); Computer Clb; French Clb; Math Clb; Chorus; Yrbk Stf; Off Soph Cls; Bsbl; Socr; Wt Lftg; Wrstlng; Comp.

RESIDE, ROBIN; Hopewell Valley Central HS; Titusville, NJ; (4); 94/199; Sec FBLA; Lit Mag; High Hon Roll; AFS; Church Yth Grp; Chorus; School Play; Stage Crew; Hon Roll; Pblshd Mercer Co CC Ltry Mag 86; 3rd Pl Typing I FBLA Reg Cmptn 86; 2nd Pl Wrd Prcsng FBLA Reg 87; Bucks Co CC; Bus Admn.

RESNICK, HELAINE; Livingston HS; Livingston, NJ; (4); 71/420; FBLA; Leo Clb; Office Aide; Temple Yth Grp; Yrbk Stf; Spanish NHS; U Of MI; Bus.

RESNICK, ROBERT; Glen Rock HS; Glen Rock, NJ; (4); 22/160; Debate Tm; Nwsp Ed-Chief; Trs Soph Cls; Trs Jr Cls; Var Bsbl; Cit Awd; NHS; Ntl Merit Ltr; St Schlr; Cmnty Wkr; Tufts U; Pol Sci.

RESNICK, SANDRA G; Verona HS; Verona, NJ; (4); 4/182; Drama Clb; Intnl Clb; Model UN; Jazz Band; School Musical; Swing Chorus; Lit Mag; High Hon Roll; NHS; French Hon Soc; Sylvia Strauss Memrl Schlrshp Frgn Lang 87; Smith Coll Clb Bk Awd 86; Tufts U; Psych.

RESTIVO, FRANK ANTHONY; St Marys HS; Jersey City, NJ; (3); 1st Hnr 84-85; Rutgers; Comp.

RESTO, ANA; Barringer Prep; Newark, NJ; (1); JA; Nwsp Ed-Chief; Barringer High; Beautician.

RETTEW, JAMES H; Moorestown HS; Moorestown, NJ; (3); Off Church Yth Grp; French Clb; NFL; Ed Nwsp Phtg; Var L Ftbl; Hon Roll; Drama Clb; Thesps; Band; Variety Show; NJ Summer Arts Inst 87; Poli Sci.

REU, RAYMOND; Watchung Hills Regional HS; Warren, NJ; (3); Civic Clb.

REUBEN, EDWARD; Wecquakie HS; Newark, NJ; (3); 1/400; Church Yth Grp; Computer Clb; Church Choir; Rep Stu Cncl; Bsbl; High Hon Roll; Jr NHS; NHS; Comp Sci Awd & Mst Vlbl Rookie 87; Rutgers Coll; Engr.

REUBEN, LARISSA; Mt St Dominic Acad; Newark, NJ; (3); 19/55; Intnl Clb; Trs Library Aide; Yrbk Stf; Trk; NHS; Advncd Basic Comp Mt Clair ST Coll 86; Layout Edtr Yrbk 87-88; Comp Sci.

REUSS, JUDITH; Sacred Heart HS; Vineland, NJ; (3); 7/60; Am Leg Aux Girls St; SADD; Yrbk Stf; Lit Mag; Rep Frsh Cls; Pres Soph Cls; Off Jr Cls; Capt Var Cheerleading; Hon Roll; NHS.

REUTER, RONALD; Mc Corriston Catholic HS; Allentown, NJ; (3); #15 In Class; Lit Mag; Im Bsktbl; Im Bowling; Var Tennis; Im Vllybl; High Hon Roll; Trs NHS; NEDT Awd; Engrng.

REUTER, STAFANIE; Union Catholic Regional HS; Berkeley Hts, NJ; (4); 6/296; Latin Clb; Math Tm; Science Clb; Boys Clb Am; Yrbk Stf; Vllybl; French Hon Soc; High Hon Roll; NHS; Wnnr Ntl Latin Exam 85; Wnnr In Physcs Olympd 86; Lttr Of Excllnce In Frnch 86; Sci.

REUTHER, DANA; Manalapan HS; Manalapan, NJ; (3); Color Guard; Drill Tm; Nwsp Rptr; Yrbk Stf; Hon Roll; NHS; Psych.

REUTTER, ANN CARDER; Woodbury HS; Woodbury, NJ; (2); 6/100; Am Leg Aux Girls St; Sec Exploring; Hosp Aide; Math Clb; Scholastic Bowl; Varsity Clb; Chorus; Rep Frsh Cls; Rep Soph Cls; Rep Jr Cls; Stdnt Cncl Secy 87-88; Coachs Smg Awd 87; Hld Hgh Swmg Recd 86-87; Phy Thrpy.

REUTTER, T R CHRISTIAN; Woodbury HS; Woodbury, NJ; (4); #6 In Class; Am Leg Boys St; Boy Scts; Scholastic Bowl; Varsity Clb; Pres Chorus; Sec Stu Cncl; Capt Swmmng; NHS; Pres Schlr; Math Clb; Engl Awd 86; Rtry Clb Schlrshp 87; Wdbury Old Rrtrtn Cmte Awd 87; John Hopkns U; Intl Rltns.

REVAK, SANDRA; Florence Twp Memorial HS; Roebling, NJ; (4); 2/87; Church Yth Grp; Hosp Aide; Science Clb; Spanish Clb; Church Choir; Var Bsktbl; JV Fld Hcky; Hon Roll; NHS; Sal; Amer Lgn Schlrshp 87; Stockton ST Coll; Phys Thrpy.

REVER, SCOTT; Union HS; Union, NJ; (4); 41/534; FBLA; Key Clb; Math Tm; Temple Yth Grp; Nwsp Rptr; Nwsp Sprt Ed; Yrbk Rptr; Yrbk Sprt Ed; Var Bsbl; Var Bsktbl; PTA Schlrshp Outstndng Stdnt, Gdn ST Schlrshp 87; Rutgers Coll; Bus.

REY, CRISTIAN; Memorial HS; West New York, NJ; (3); Hon Roll; Engrng.

REYES, ERNEST; St Joseph Of The Palisades HS; Cliffside Park, NJ; (4); 12/135; Church Yth Grp; Drama Clb; Science Clb; Church Choir; Nwsp Stf; Yrbk Stf; Vllybl; Hon Roll; NHS; 3 Yr Awd Stage Assts Drama Clb 87; Rutgers; Phrmcy.

REYES, MARTA; Perth Amboy HS; Perth Amboy, NJ; (3); Cmnty Wkr; Model UN; Concert Band; School Play; Variety Show; Rep Jr Cls; Rep Stu Cncl; Hon Roll; Office Aide; Pep Clb; Band Awd 85-87; Culinary Inst Amer; Restrnt Mgt.

REYES, SUSANA; Bridgewater-Raritan High Schl East; Bridgewater, NJ; (3); Art Clb; Debate Tm; English Clb; Girl Scts; Math Clb; Science Clb; School Play; Sftbl; Hon Roll; 3rd Pl Writing Contest 85; Acctg.

REYNOLDS, DAWN; Vineland HS; Vineland, NJ; (3); Drama Clb; Acpl Chr; Church Choir; School Play; Church Yth Grp; 4-H; Hosp Aide; Key Clb; Office Aide; Teachers Aide; Theatre.

REYNOLDS, FREDERICK; Secaucus HS; Secaucus, NJ; (3); 7/166; Computer Clb; Key Clb; Mu Alpha Theta; Ski Clb; Spanish Clb; Sec Jr Cls; JV Tennis; NHS; SAR Awd; Spanish NHS; Jersey City Med Dntl Gldn Pin Mst Outstndng Med Prjct 82; Acad Tlntd Yng Stu Prog Monclair ST 83-86; Yale; Med.

REYNOLDS, GEORGIANNA; Brick Memorial HS; Brick, NJ; (3); 1/300; Capt Drill Tm; Jazz Band; Mrchg Band; JV Socr; High Hon Roll; NHS; Rutgers Schlr 87; Am Chem Soc Awd 87; Girls Citznshp Inst 87.

REYNOLDS, KIMBERLY; Pennsauken HS; Pennsauken, NJ; (2); 4/403; Church Yth Grp; Science Clb; Chorus; Church Choir; Color Guard; Mrchg Band; School Musical; Yrbk Stf; High Hon Roll; Spanish NHS; All S Jrsy Chorus 85-87; Music Ed.

REYNOLDS, MATTHEW; Holy Spirit HS; Margate, NJ; (3); 32/332; Church Yth Grp; Off Stu Cncl; JV Socr; Var Swmmng; High Hon Roll; NHS; Notre Dame; Pre-Med.

REYNOLDS, MELISSA; West Morns Mendham HS; Mendham, NJ; (4); Chorus; School Musical; School Play; VP Jr Cls; NEDT Awd; Dance Clb; Hosp Aide; Rep Frsh Cls; Rep Soph Cls; Intl Rel.

REZAC, PATRICIA; Toms River HS South; Beachwood, NJ; (3); 12/400; Hosp Aide; Key Clb; SADD; Varsity Clb; Var Crs Cntry; JV Var Fld Hcky; Var Trk; High Hon Roll; Hon Roll; NHS; TEAM 85-87; Engr.

RHATIGAN, DEBORAH; Chatham Twp HS; Chatham, NJ; (4); 26/140; Drama Clb; Girl Scts; Key Clb; Model UN; Chorus; School Musical; School Play; Swing Chorus; Nwsp Stf; Yrbk Stf; Presdntl Acadc Ftnss Awd 87; HS Vcl Awd; Trenton ST Coll.

RHINEHART, ANDREA; Hunterdon Central HS; Flemington, NJ; (3); 24/550; Sec FCA; Ski Clb; Stu Cncl; Var JV Fld Hcky; Im Lcrss; Var Mgr(s); High Hon Roll; Hon Roll; Spanish NHS; Arch.

RHODES, REBECCA; W Windsor Plainsboro Regional HS; Princeton, NJ; (3); 1/350; Drama Clb; English Clb; French Clb; Spanish Clb; SADD; Stage Crew; Nwsp Rptr; Nwsp Stf; High Hon Roll; NHS; Smith Coll Bk Awd 86-87; Natl Japan Schlrshp Cmptn 86-87; Tellwride Assn Prog 87.

RIANHARD, JAMES L; Blair Acad; Blairstown, NJ; (4); Church Yth Grp; Rep Sr Cls; JV Bsbl; JV Ftbl; JV Socr; Var Tennis; Tablefoot 86-87; Schlstc Bwl Tm Cptn 86-87; Econ.

RIBA, OSCAR; Kearny HS; Kearny, NJ; (3); Am Leg Boys St; Pres Art Clb; Chorus; Mrchg Band; School Play; Pres Soph Cls; Pres Stu Cncl; French Hon Soc; High Hon Roll; NHS Pres 87; US Achvmnt Acad 85; Amrcn Lgn Awd 84; Theatre.

RIBARDO, DONNA; Vineland HS; Vineland, NJ; (2); Lit Mag; Rep Soph Cls; Crs Cntry; Trk; Air Force Acad; Psycht.

RIBAUDO, GINA V; St Rose HS; Oakhurst, NJ; (4); 12/214; Key Clb; Latin Clb; Pep Clb; Stage Crew; Pres Jr Cls; Cheerleading; Pom Pon; High Hon Roll; Hon Roll; Pres NHS; Pltcl Gvrnmnt.

RIBAVARO, RUTHANN; John F Kennedy HS; Willingboro, NJ; (3); 2/250; Band; Concert Band; Mrchg Band; Symp Band; Var Fld Hcky; Var Capt Lcrss; Mgr Sftbl; High Hon Roll; Hon Roll; NHS; Natl Hnr Rll Natl Ldrshp Orgnztn 87; Math.

RIBEIRO, FERNANDO; Essex Catholic Boys HS; Newark, NJ; (2); Boys Clb Am; Boy Scts; Church Yth Grp; Hosp Aide; Y-Teens; Orch; Var Bowling; Var Socr; Sftbl; High Hon Roll; Lang.

RIBEIRO, MARIA; Riverside HS; Riverside, NJ; (4); 4/80; Pres FTA; Hon Roll; NHS; Prfct Atten Awd; St Schlr; CAP Kudy Schlrshp 87; Nicholas Lombardi Mem Awd 87; Twnshp Cmmtt Awd 87; Glassboro ST Coll.

RIBEIRO, MICHAEL; Middle Township HS; Cape May C H, NJ; (4); 12/228; Key Clb; Ski Clb; Socr; Elmer Smith Schlrshp 87; S Jersey Grp II Al-Star Tm Sccr 87; ST Al-Star Sccr Tm Rnr Up 87; Rutgers U; Comp Sci.

RIBEIRO, NANCY J; Kearny HS; Kearny, NJ; (4); 17/383; Am Leg Aux Girls St; Pres French Clb; Var Crs Cntry; Var Trk; French Hon Soc; Hon Roll; NHS; Albion Hale Brainard Stu Asst Fnd Schlrshp 87; Teddy Gleason Schlrshp 87; Rutgers Coll; Lawyer.

RIBON, NELSON; Keansburg HS; Keansburg, NJ; (3); DECA; German Clb; Yrbk Phtg; Yrbk Stf; Lit Mag; Rep Stu Cncl; Stat JV Bsktbl; Score Keeper; Tennis; Hon Roll; Var Ltr Ten 84-88; Bus Adm.

RICCA, MAURIZIO; Union Hill HS; Union City, NJ; (4); Latin Clb; Mu Alpha Theta; Mu Alpha Theta Awd; NY Rest Schl; Culinary Arts.

RICCARDI, CHRISTOPHER L; Delaware Valley Regional HS; Milford, NJ; (3); 15/235; Art Clb; Church Yth Grp; Debate Tm; Drama Clb; Intnl Clb; Scholastic Bowl; Thesps; Chorus; Church Choir; School Musical; NJ ST Gov Schl Of Pblc Issues & Future Of NJ 87; NJ ST Teen-Arts Fnlst 86 & 87; Bio-Tech.

RICCARDI, KRISTINE; Bayonne HS; Bayonne, NJ; (3); Gym; Sftbl; Wt Lftg; Hon Roll.

RICCARDI, MARK; Toms River HS South; Beachwood, NJ; (1); Rep Stu Cncl; Gym; Med.

RICCARDI, ROBIN; Toms River HS South; Beachwood, NJ; (3); 32/405; Am Leg Aux Girls St; Frsh Cls; Jr Cls; Sr Cls; Rep Stu Cncl; Hon Roll; NHS; Hgh Obrn Yth Fndtn ST Conf 86; Ldrshp Trnng Conf 86; Natl Ldrshp Trnng Conf 87; Engl.

RICCI, KAREN; Columbia HS; Maplewood, NJ; (3); Fld Hcky; Sftbl; Hcky 86-87; Sftbll MVP Sph Yr 85-86; Commnctns.

RICCI, KRISTINE; Bridgeton HS; Port Norris, NJ; (3); Drama Clb; French Clb; Var Mgr(s); Var Score Keeper; Cit Awd; High Hon Roll; Hon Roll; Jr NHS; NHS; Rotary Awd; Congressional & Rotary Yth Ldrshp Awds 87; Fshn Mrchndsng.

RICCIARDI, KAREN; St Rose HS; Allenwood, NJ; (3); Am Leg Aux Girls St; VP Key Clb; Math Tm; Yrbk Stf; Rep Jr Cls; Var Socr; Gov Hon Prg Awd; Pres NHS; NEDT Awd; Drama Clb; Geom & Algebra II/Trig Awd 86; Math.

RICCIARDI, MICHAEL; Lakewood HS; Lakewood, NJ; (4); 69/270; Church Yth Grp; CAP; French Clb; FBLA; JCL; Latin Clb; JV Bsktbl; Chrstn Yth Schlrshp 87; Capt CYO Bsktbl Tm 87; Ltn Hnr Soc 87; Glassboro ST Coll; Cmnctns.

RICCIARDI, SUSAN E; Madison Central HS; Old Bridge, NJ; (3); 2/355; French Clb; Scholastic Bowl; Varsity Clb; Yrbk Stf; Stu Cncl; Cheerleading; French Hon Soc; Gov Hon Prg Awd; High Hon Roll; Hon Roll; Fnlst Govnrs Schl Sci 86-87; Qlfd Fnlst All Amer Chlrldg Natl 85-86; Middlesex Cnty Coll Frgn Lang; Phrmcy.

RICCO, DEBBIE; John F Kennedy Memorial HS; Iselin, NJ; (4); 46/274; Church Yth Grp; Dance Clb; FBLA; Spanish Clb; School Play; Yrbk Stf; Hon Roll; NHS; Pres Schlr; Bus.

RICCO, TRICIA; Wildwood Catholic HS; Wildwood Crest, NJ; (3); Spanish Clb; SADD; School Play; Pres Stu Cncl; Var Cheerleading; Hon Roll; Spanish NHS; School Musical; Rep Frsh Cls; Rep Soph Cls; 1st Pl Sci Fair, Hnrbl Mntn Stockton Coll 86; 1st Pl Sci Fair 87; Bloomsburg U; Math Tchr.

RICE, AARON; St Mary HS; Jersey City, NJ; (3); JV Capt Bsktbl; Hon Roll; Pres Schlr; Pittsburg U; Electrcl Engrng.

RICE, SHELLY; Bridgeton HS; Bridgeton, NJ; (4); 2/191; French Clb; Q&S; Ed Nwsp Rptr; Yrbk Stf; VP Soph Cls; Pres Jr Cls; NHS; Sal; Voice Dem Awd; Rep Pres Clssrm 86; Hghst Schltc Ltr B 83-86; Rep HOBY Ldrshp Sem 84; Drexel; Elec Engrng.

RICH, LINDA; Gateway Reg HS; Woodbury Height, NJ; (3); Chef.

RICH, RAMONA J; Barringer HS; Newark, NJ; (4); Drama Clb Exploring; French Clb; Chorus; School Musical; School Play; Yrbk Phtg Yrbk Stf; Trk; Comp Sci.

RICHARD JR, JOHN W; Shawnee HS; Vincentown, NJ; (4); 57/534 Teachers Aide; Hon Roll; NHS; Outstndng Achvt & Pres Acad Fit Awd 87 NJ Teen Fine Arts Film Prod 85; NJ JR Acad Of Sci 83; Marietta Coll Cmmnctns.

RICHARDS, JAMES; Haddon Township HS; W Collingswd Ht, NJ; (3) German Clb; Varsity Clb; Var JV Bsbl; Bsktbl; Hon Roll; Comp Prgrmmng Cntst 3rd Pl Tm Cmpttn 86; Bus.

RICHARDS, JANE; Our Lady Of Mercy Acad; Ventnor, NJ; (3); Aud/Vis; Stage Crew; Ed Yrbk Stf; VP Jr Cls; Bsktbl; Hon Roll; Ntl Merit Ltr; Crew Tm 84; Prom Cmmtte 86-87; NY U; Engl.

RICHARDS, MICHELLE; Bishop George AHR/St Thomas HS Plainfield, NJ; (4); Church Yth Grp; Chorus; Stat Bsktbl; High Hon Roll; Hon Roll; Ntl Merit Ltr; Union Cnty Coll; Psych.

RICHARDS, ROSANN E; Benedictine Acad; Newark, NJ; (3); Church Yth Grp; French Clb; JCL; Latin Clb; Pep Clb; Church Choir; L Var Vllybl; Prfct Atten Awd.

RICHARDSON, ANDREW; Bergen County Vo Tech HS; Lodi, NJ; (4); Varsity Clb; VICA; Stu Cncl; Capt Bsktbl; Trk; MVP Bsktbl 86-87; All Co Trk 86-87; U Of Louisville; Accntng.

RICHARDSON, DANA; Hackettstown HS; Belvidere, NJ; (4); FBLA Off Sr Cls; Orange Coast Coll; Bus Admin.

RICHARDSON, DORI; Jackson Memorial HS; Jackson, NJ; (4); #94 In Class; Drama Clb; SADD; Acpl Chr; Chorus; School Musical; School Play; Variety Show; Var Capt Bowling; Church Yth Grp; Hon Roll; Frgn Lng Outstndng Achvt Awd 87; Cert Of Recgntn For Musical Escllnc 86; MVP Athltc Excllnc Awd 87; Georgian Court Coll; Jrnlsm.

RICHARDSON, ERIKKA; University HS; Newark, NJ; (2); Chorus; Color Guard; Drill Tm; School Play; Stage Crew; Hon Roll; Harvard U; Srgn.

RICHARDSON, GEOFFREY; Morristown HS; Morristown, NJ; (3); Band; Concert Band; Mrchg Band; High Hon Roll; Hon Roll; Attrny.

RICHARDSON, GEORGETTE; Mt St Dominic Acad; East Orange, NJ; (3); 10/60; Church Yth Grp; Dance Clb; Drama Clb; JCL; Latin Clb; Office Aide; Band; Chorus; Church Choir; Madrigals; Geo Cshnl Outstndng Yth Awd 86; MA Coll Of Phrmcy; Phrmcy.

RICHARDSON, KRISTINE; Ridgefield Park HS; Ridgefield Pk, NJ; (2); 6/183; Nwsp Stf; Yrbk Stf; Bsktbl; Trk; Capt Vllybl; Hon Roll; 1st Team All Leag Grls Bsktbll 86-87; Hnrb Mntn All Leag Grls Trck 87.

RICHARDSON, MARCIA; Newton HS; Newton, NJ; (3); Latin Clb; Varsity Clb; Rep Frsh Cls; Rep Soph Cls; Rep Jr Cls; Stat Bsbl; Var Bsktbl; Var Fld Hcky; JV Trk; Hon Roll; Fld Hocky Tm SCIL Champs & Sctnl Champs 86; Spcl Olympics 84-85.

RICHARDSON, NIKKI; Cinnaminson HS; Cinnaminson, NJ; (3); Church Yth Grp; Chorus; Church Choir; JV Fld Hcky; Var Gym; JV Lcrss; Var Mgr(s); Hon Roll; JV Field Hockey Coaches Awd 86; Jr Hmcmng Rep 86; Jr Prom Ct 87.

RICHARDSON, PAMELA S; Camden HS; Camden, NJ; (4); 77/300; Dance Clb; German Clb; Pep Clb; Sec Frsh Cls; Sec Soph Cls; Rep Jr Cls; Rep Sr Cls; JV Var Civic Clb; Mgr(s); Pom Pon; Most Creatve Shrt Rods Chrldg 87; Bus Adm.

RICHARDSON, SABRINA; East Side HS; Newark, NJ; (4); 197/488; Church Yth Grp; Band; Chorus; Church Choir; Color Guard; Concert Band; Mrchg Band; Stu Cncl; Mgr(s); Sftbl; Wilber Force U; Sclgy.

RICHARDSON, TRACY; Toms River High School North; Toms River, NJ; (3); 10/459; Var Tennis; High Hon Roll; Hon Roll; Acadmc Lttr 85-87; Pre-Law.

RICHARDSON, VICKI; Saint James HS; Salem, NJ; (3); 13/79; Mgr SADD; Var Bsktbl; Var Crs Cntry; Var Fld Hcky.

RICHES, ERIKA; Lakewood HS; Lakewood, NJ; (1); Church Yth Grp; Hon Roll; Art.

RICHIE JR, WILLIAM; Salem HS; Salem, NJ; (4); 13/187; Am Leg Boys St; Chess Clb; Computer Clb; Latin Clb; Math Clb; Ski Clb; Teachers Aide; Var Tennis; Var Trk; Bausch & Lomb Sci Awd; Schlrshp Pats Pizzeria 87; Trenton ST Coll; Elec Engrng.

RICHKUS, LORI; Waldwick HS; Waldwick, NJ; (3); 2/114; Church Yth Grp; Math Tm; Ski Clb; Im Socr; Im Sftbl; High Hon Roll; Hon Roll; Sal; HS Network 86-87; Math.

RICHLAN, KRISTY; Nutley HS; Nutley, NJ; (3); Am Leg Aux Girls St; Drama Clb; JCL; Acpl Chr; Orch; Pep Band; Swing Chorus; Yrbk Rptr; Rep Lit Mag; Interior Dsgn.

RICHMAN, BETH; Montville Township HS; Montville, NJ; (4); Pres Drama Clb; NFL; VP Speech Tm; School Musical; School Play; Ed Lit Mag; Rep Stu Cncl; High Hon Roll; NHS; Ntl Merit Schol; Gov Schlr Sch Arts 86; ST Champ Hmrs Interp NJ Frnscs Leag 86-87; Gdn ST Schlr 87 Amherst Coll.

RICHMOND, ERIC C; Woodstown HS; Elmer, NJ; (3); Spanish Clb; Var Bsbl; Hon Roll; U Of ME:Wldlf Mgmt.

RICHMOND, FREDRICK; Teaneck HS; Teaneck, NJ; (4); 51/420; SADD; Nwsp Sprt Ed; Yrbk Sprt Ed; Sec Sr Cls; Rep Stu Cncl; Capt Var Tennis; Hon Roll; Sec NHS; Acadc All Am Schlr 86-87; USBEA US Bus Ed Awd Wnr 87; Vrsty Tennis MVP 2yrs; Rutgers Coll; Ec Bus.

RICHMOND, KEITH; Lakeland Regional HS; Wanaque, NJ; (3); 4/350; Church Yth Grp; Pres Latin Clb; Math Clb; SADD; Teachers Aide; Var Trk; Cit Awd; High Hon Roll; NHS.

RICHMOND, KELLY; Hightstown HS; E Windsor, NJ; (4); Key Clb; Ski Clb; SADD; Rep Jr Cls; Rep Sr Cls; Capt Swmmng; Trk; Hnrs 3 Periods Row; U Of RI.

RICHMOND, SUSAN; Wall Township HS; Farmingdale, NJ; (4); 5/269; AFS; German Clb; Library Aide; Library Aide; Ski Clb; Band; High Hon Roll; Kiwanis Awd; Ntl Merit Ltr; German.

RICHNER, RANDAL; Gateway Regional HS; Woodbury, NJ; (2); Church Yth Grp; Exploring; Science Clb; School Musical; VP Stu Cncl; JV Bsbl; JV Bsktbl; JV Socr; Hon Roll; Voice Dem Awd; MD.

RICHTER, LEON; West Essex HS; No Caldwell, NJ; (3); VP Rep Temple Yth Grp; Nwsp Ed-Chief; Ed Lit Mag; Stu Cncl; Gov Hon Prg Awd; High Hon Roll; NHS; French Clb; Math Tm; 1st Wrld Yth Assembly 86; HS Sports Mag Edtr 86-87; Brd Philisophcl Soc 86-87.

RICHTERS, AMY; Middletown HS South; Middletown, NJ; (3); Pres Girl Scts; Library Aide; Math Tm; Co-Capt Science Clb; Concert Band; Mrchg Band; High Hon Roll; NHS; Church Yth Grp; Cmnty Wkr; Brnz Cngrssnl Awd 87; Grl Sct Gld Awd 87.

RICKER, MICHELE; Kittatinny Regional HS; Newton, NJ; (3); 11/220; Am Leg Aux Girls St; Church Yth Grp; 4-H; Spanish Clb; Band; Trs Stu Cncl; High Hon Roll; Hon Roll; NHS; Nrth Jrsy Crftsmns Fair 1st Pl & 1st Outstndng 87; Socl Wrk.

RICKERT, CAROLYN; Vineland HS; Vineland, NJ; (4); 4-H; Key Clb; Varsity Clb; Fld Hcky; Mgr(s); Mgr Wrstlng; 4-H Awd; Hon Roll; Stockton ST Coll; Phys Thrpy.

RICKERT, JOHN W; Holy Cross HS; Edgewater Park, NJ; (3); 93/412; Am Leg Boys St; Nwsp Stf; Stu Cncl; Var Ftbl; NHS; Spanish Clb; Varsity Clb; Rep Frsh Cls; Rep Soph Cls; JV Bsktbl; Brdcst Jrnlsm.

RICKERT, LISA; East Brunswick HS; E Brunswick, NJ; (4); Pres Stu Cncl; Pres Soph Cls; Pres FBLA; NHS; St Schlr; Spanish NHS; Socr; Ed Yrbk Stf; Ski Clb; Var Trk; Amer H S Athl; Outstndng Ldrshp Quals A Ldrshp Positn Model Cngrss; Outstndng Svc Stdnt Cncl; Georgetown U; Finc.

RICKERT, MISTY; Kingsway Regional HS; Mullica Hl, NJ; (2); Nwsp Stf; Hon Roll; Art Inst Philadelphia; Comm Art.

RICKS, JAMIE; Perth Amboy HS; Perth Amboy, NJ; (3); 2/26; Im Trk; Hon Roll; Middlessec Cnty Coll; Sci.

RICKWALDER, DANIEL; Whippany Park HS; Whippany, NJ; (3); 24/86; Am Leg Boys St; Church Yth Grp; Varsity Clb; Chorus; Madrigals; School Musical; Pres Frsh Cls; Pres Soph Cls; Ftbl; NHS.

RIDDLE, DEAUN; Randolph HS; Randolph, NJ; (3); Church Yth Grp; Debate Tm; Pep Clb; Capt Var Cheerleading; Var Coach Actv; Mgr(s); Pom Pon; Powder Puff Ftbl; Sftbl; Hon Roll; Intr Dsgn.

RIDDLE, JOANNE; Belvidere HS; Belvidere, NJ; (3); 4/130; Church Yth Grp; Model UN; Scholastic Bowl; Chorus; Church Choir; School Play; Stage Crew; Hon Roll; NHS; Partcptd In Gftd & Tlntn Prog 84-87; Cnty Chorus 86-87; Comm.

RIDEOUT, DAVID; Glen Ridge HS; Glen Ridge, NJ; (3); Boy Scts; Concert Band; Jazz Band; Mrchg Band; Var Capt Trk; High Hon Roll; Hon Roll; 82nd Prcntl Ntl Chem Exam-Amercn Chmcl Soc 87; Arspc Engrng.

RIDGEWAY, NICOLE; Penns Grove Carneys Point HS; Carneys Point, NJ; (3); 2/213; Am Leg Aux Girls St; Latin Clb; Varsity Clb; Pres Frsh Cls; VP Soph Cls; VP Jr Cls; Sr Cls; Rep Stu Cncl; Var Capt Cheerleading; Elks Awd; Gov Schl NJ 87; Gifted & Tlntd Pgm 84-88; Elks Lodge Pride 87; John Hopkins U; Ped.

RIDGWAY, CHARLES; Cumberland Regional HS; Bridgeton, NJ; (3); Boy Scts; Exploring; FFA; Hon Roll; Fire Fghtr I, II 86-87; US Navy; Comp Tech.

RIDOLFO, ROD; Montville HS; Montville, NJ; (4); Computer Clb; FBLA; Key Clb; SADD; Var Bsbl; JV Bsktbl; AZ ST U; Pre-Law.

RIEBEL, CHRISTINE; Camden Catholic HS; Pennsauken, NJ; (4); 45/286; FTA; SADD; Chorus; Drill Tm; Sftbl; Hon Roll; NHS; Pres Schlr; Sec.

RIEGER, LORI; Cumberland Regional HS; Bridgeton, NJ; (4); 4/350; Drama Clb; Pres Intnl Clb; Soroptimist; Pres Spanish Clb; Stage Crew; Nwsp Stf; Yrbk Sprt Ed; High Hon Roll; NHS; Pres Schlr; Spnsh Awd 87; Cngrssnl Yth Ldrshp Cnfrnc 87; U Of Richmond; Cmnl Law.

RIEHMAN, LAURA; Madison HS; Bridgewater, NJ; (3); GAA; Varsity Clb; Yrbk Stf; Var Capt Bsktbl; Var Powder Puff Ftbl; Var Socr; Var Sftbl; JV Hon Roll; All Conf Hon Ment Bsktbl; MIP Sftbl; 2nd Team All Conf Sftbl.

RIESS, PATRICIA; Ridge HS; Basking Ridge, NJ; (3); 19/192; Church Yth Grp; Drama Clb; Acpl Chr; Church Choir; Drm Mjr(t); Madrigals; School Musical; Stage Crew; NHS; Ntl Merit Ltr; Bio.

RIFKIND, ADAM; West Windsoro-Plainsboro HS; Trenton, NJ; (3); German Clb; Model UN; Political Wkr; Radio Clb; Temple Yth Grp; Im Bsbl; Im Socr; George Washington U; Govt.

RIGGERT, JENNIFER; North Hunterdon HS; Annandale, NJ; (3); 3/328; Pres Church Yth Grp; German Clb; Band; Church Choir; Jazz Band; Madrigals; Mrchg Band; Orch; High Hon Roll; Acad Achvt Scty 86.

RIGGIO, KERRY KERSTIN; Morris Knolls HS; Denville, NJ; (2); 14/400; Cmnty Wkr; Debate Tm; Library Aide; Scholastic Bowl; Science Clb; Service Clb; Chorus; Off Lit Mag; High Hon Roll; Art Clb; Physics Wrkshp Seton Hall U 87; Summa Awd 86; Sci League Awd 87; Replc Constl Conv Cnty Coll Morris 87; Sci.

RIGOLIZZO, STEVEN; Holy Spirit HS; Linwood, NJ; (2); 37/397; JV Crs Cntry; JV Socr.

RIKEMAN, MARYKAY; Southern Regional HS; Barnegat, NJ; (3); 129/485; 4-H; Girl Scts; Ski Clb; Band; Concert Band; Jazz Band; Mrchg Band; School Musical; School Play; Socr; Stockton ST Coll; Accntng.

RIKER, ELIZABETH; Phillipsburg HS; Alpha, NJ; (3); 135/360; SADD; Sec Thesps; Band; Chorus; School Musical; School Play; Stage Crew; Variety Show; Nwsp Stf; Lit Mag; Libral Arts Coll; Elem Educ.

RILEY, CHRISSY; Eastern Regional HS; West Berlin, NJ; (4); Stu Cncl; Cheerleading; Trk; Outstndng Weigh Prsn Girls Trck 85; Freshmn & Sr Hmcmng Court 83-87; 3rd Pl Metal Camden Co Trckmt; Widener U; Psych.

RILEY, JAMES; St James HS; Carneys Point, NJ; (2); Im Wt Lftg; Hstry & Alg 86-87; Acctnt.

RILEY, JOHN; North Warren Regional HS; Columbia, NJ; (4); 10/132; Ski Clb; Var Crs Cntry; JV Wrstlng; NHS; Pres Acdmc Fit Awds Prog 87; Navy Nuclr Prog.

RILEY, KIMBERLY; Red Bank Catholic HS; Neptune, NJ; (4); Art Clb; Cmnty Wkr; Political Wkr; Ski Clb; Mgr(s); Powder Puff Ftbl; Twrlr; AFS; Exploring; Math Clb; GCI Delg 86; Lifeguard 85-87; Sci Resrch 87; U Of DE; Intl Relations.

RILEY, LAURA; Notre Dame HS; Kendall Pk, NJ; (2); Hosp Aide; Office Aide; Service Clb; Spanish Clb; Church Choir; High Hon Roll; Hon Roll; Spnsh II Awd 87; U Of Penn; Bus.

RILEY, LINDA; Pennsauken HS; Pennsauken, NJ; (3); 23/417; Leo Clb; Spanish Clb; Drill Tm; Yrbk Stf; Fld Hcky; Lcrss; Hon Roll; VP NHS; Spanish NHS.

RILEY, MEGAN; St Peters HS; Milltown, NJ; (4); GAA; Pep Clb; Ski Clb; Varsity Clb; Stage Crew; Sr Cls; Bsktbl; Sftbl; NHS; Prfct Atten Awd; Glassboro ST; Elem Ed.

RILEY, SUSAN; Cumberland Regional HS; Bridgeton, NJ; (4); 3/298; Office Aide; Soroptimist; Sec Spanish Clb; JV Fld Hcky; Var Capt Sftbl; High Hon Roll; NHS; Garden St Schlrshp 87; Trenton St Alumni Schlrshp 87; Prsdntl Acad Fitness Awd 87; Trenton ST Coll.

RIMM, HARRY; Atlantic City HS; Margate, NJ; (3); Church Yth Grp; Cmnty Wkr; Office Aide; Radio Clb; Teachers Aide; Off Stu Cncl; Capt Bsktbl; JV Tennis; High Hon Roll; NHS; Yth Dbls Tnns Trnmnt Wnr 85.

RINALDI, CHRISTOPHER J; River Dell SR HS; Oradell, NJ; (4); 90/214; Am Leg Boys St; Ski Clb; Var Bsbl; Var Capt Ftbl; Im Vllybl; Hon Roll; All-Cnty, All-League, & All-Suburban Ftbl, Stu Teacher Recognition Awd 87; Gettysburg Coll.

RINALDI, GISELE; Mother Seton Regional HS; Hillside, NJ; (2); 13/129; GAA; Math Tm; Science Clb; Stage Crew; Stage Crew; Yrbk Phtg; Var Bowling; JV Capt Vllybl; Hon Roll; NEDT Awd; Spirt Awd 87; Chld Psych.

RINALDI, STEVEN; Union HS; Union, NJ; (4); 156/550; Civic Clb; Computer Clb; Ski Clb; Crs Cntry; Var L Tennis; Aud/Vis; Exploring; Service Clb; Yrbk Stf; Prfct Atten Awd; N Jersey Stu Craftsman Fair 2nd Pl & Resolution Outstndng Achvt 86; N Jersey Stu Craftsman Fair 87; Union Cnty Coll; Civil Tech.

RINCAVAGE, LORI A; Monroe Twp HS; Spotswood, NJ; (4); DECA; Yrbk Phtg; Yrbk Stf; Rep Stu Cncl; Hon Roll; Home Schl Assn Awd 87; 1st Pl-Casual Mdlng Rgnl/St 87; Top 10 Sls Mtng Rgnl/Natl 87; Middlesex Cnty Coll; Mktg Mgmt.

RINEER, DIANA; Roselle Park HS; Ossining, NY; (4); 7/161; Library Aide; Office Aide; Speech Tm; Flag Corp; School Musical; School Play; NHS; Rutgers U; Cmmnctns.

RING, MARGOT; Summit HS; Summit, NJ; (3); Church Yth Grp; Rep Soph Cls; Rep Jr Cls; Var Fld Hcky; Var Lcrss; Hon Roll; Hon Arthur Switt Awd, Mst Imprvd Plyr Vrsty Lacrosse Tm 87; 1st Tm All-Union Cnty Fld Hcky 85 & 86.

RINGEL, MATTHEW L; Millburn HS; Short Hills, NJ; (4); 2/249; Chorus; Jazz Band; School Musical; Var Stu Cncl; Ntl Merit SF; Sal; St Schlr; High Hon Roll; NHS; Williams Clg Bk Awd, Attnd Boston U Tanglewood Inst-Piano & Attnd Inst British/Irish Stds-Oxford.

RINGLE, JEFF; West Essex HS; Fairfield, NJ; (4); Key Clb; Acpl Chr; Chorus; Stage Crew; Swing Chorus; Rep Stu Cncl; JV Bsbl; Var Ftbl; Im Vllybl; Hon Roll; Jacksonville U; Vet.

RINKOWSKI, KIM; Pinelands Regional HS; Tuckertown, NJ; (4); 6/204; Off Jr Cls; Rep Sr Cls; Bsktbl; JV Sftbl; Hon Roll; NHS; Physcl Thrpy.

RIOPEL, MARY ANNE; Saint John Vianney HS; Morganville, NJ; (3); Service Clb; SADD; Var Crs Cntry; Powder Puff Ftbl; Var Trk; Wt Lftg; High Hon Roll; Hon Roll; NHS; Gld & White Awd For Inter & Extra Curricular Actvts 86-87; Pres Phy Fit Awd 86-87; Spts Med.

RIORDAN, TRICIA; St John Vianney HS; Hazlet, NJ; (2); 75/250; Var L Bsktbl; Var L Sftbl; High Hon Roll; Hon Roll; Gym Awd 86; Notre Dame; Bus.

RIOS, ENID; Vineland HS; Vineland, NJ; (3).

RIOS, LUZ; Passaic County Tech & Voc HS; Paterson, NJ; (3); Law.

RIPPEL, JENNIFER; Matawan Regional HS; Matawan, NJ; (3); #5 In Class; Trs Civic Clb; Math Clb; Math Tm; Spanish Clb; Band; Concert Band; Mrchg Band; Yrbk Stf; Hon Roll.

RIPPER, JASON; Bridgeton HS; Newport, NJ; (3); Boy Scts; Church Yth Grp; Bsktbl; Crs Cntry; Data Prcsng.

RIPPEY, RONALD; De Paul Diocesan HS; Kinnelon, NJ; (4); Math Tm; Pres Jr Cls; Var L Bsbl; Im Bsktbl; Var L Ftbl; Im Wt Lftg; Hon Roll; Pre-Med.

RIPPEY, TRACY; Pennsauken HS; Pennsauken, NJ; (3); Science Clb; Spanish Clb; Chorus; Drill Tm; Mrchg Band; Rep Frsh Cls; Trs Soph Cls; Trs Jr Cls; Pom Pon; Hon Roll; Med.

RISKO, DAWN; Parsippany Hills HS; Parsippany, NJ; (2); Church Yth Grp; Computer Clb; FBLA; Spanish Clb; Yrbk Stf; Hon Roll; Natl Bicentennial Compttn On The Constitution & Bill Of Rights 87.

RISKO, LORI; Hunterdon Central HS; Flemington, NJ; (3); 218/545; 4-H; Jr Cls; Cit Awd; 4-H Awd; Hon Roll; Pblc Spkng Awd 86; Ldrshp Awd 86; Cert Of Merit Outstndng Clb Wrk 86; Clthng Awd 85.

RISLEY, CHRISTINE ROSE; Pemberton HS; Browns Mills, NJ; (4); 3/406; Church Yth Grp; Service Clb; Nwsp Rptr; Yrbk Stf; Rep Soph Cls; Var Tennis; High Hon Roll; Hon Roll; NHS; Pres Schlr; Ft Dix Ofcrs Wvs Schlrshp 87; Grm Lang Awd 87; Hrnt Awd Ten 86; Trenton St Coll; Intl Rltns.

RISLEY, DAWN MARIE; Egg Harbor Township HS; Cardiff, NJ; (4); 6/282; Hosp Aide; Chrmn Model UN; Trs SADD; Rep Stu Cncl; Var Crs Cntry; Var Trk; High Hon Roll; Jr NHS; Ntl Merit Ltr; Schlstc Vrsty Lttr Awd 84-87; Franklin; Obstetrics.

RISOR, ADRIENNE LYNN; Brick HS; Bricktownship, NJ; (1); Prntng.

RITACCO, DOMINICK F; Nutley HS; Nutley, NJ; (3); 18/304; Am Leg Boys St; Hon Roll; NHS; Prfct Atten Awd; Wrstlng; Italian Clb 85-87.

RITCHEY JR, DANIEL E; Lakewood HS; Lakewood, NJ; (3); 47/330; SADD; Var L Bsbl; Var L Cheerleading; Var L Ftbl; Im Vllybl; Im Wt Lftg; Yrbk Stf; Hon Roll; Prfct Atten Awd; Phys Thrpy.

RITTER, AMY; Academy Of St Elizabet; Morristown, NJ; (1); School Musical; Lit Mag; JV Cheerleading; Socr; Trk; High Hon Roll; Pres Schlr; Church Yth Grp; Dance Clb; Office Aide; Knights Of Columbus Schlrshp 86-87; St Elizabeths Acad Schlrshp 86-87; Mdl For Outstndng Achvt Sci 86; Med.

RITTER, BENTLEY; Paul VI HS; Somerdale, NJ; (3); 21/417; Church Yth Grp; Pres Frsh Cls; VP Stu Cncl; Var L Ftbl; Var L Trk; Hon Roll; Bio Chem Engr.

RITTER, JACQUELINE; Notre Dame HS; Lawrenceville, NJ; (2); 89/400; Church Yth Grp; Drama Clb; Chorus; Trk; Hon Roll; Accntng.

RITTER, JULIA; Mainland Pegional HS; Linwood, NJ; (3); 25/193; Drama Clb; Intnl Clb; PAVAS; Chorus; School Play; Stage Crew; Nwsp Rptr; Nwsp Stf; Hon Roll; NHS; Natl Hnr Soc 87; Prfrmng Arts.

RITTER, MATTHEW; Saint Augustine Preparatory Schl; Vineland, NJ; (3); Computer Clb; Nwsp Sprt Ed; Yrbk Stf; Hon Roll; Nwsp Rptr; Nwsp Stf; Yrbk Phtg; Millersville U; Meterlgy.

RITTER, TERRY A; Bridgewater Raritan HS East; Basking Ridge, NJ; (3); Am Leg Boys St; Ski Clb; Var L Ftbl; Var L Tennis; Mid ST Chmps Tenns 86; Conf Chmps Tnns 86; Sprts Med.

RIVAS, ROSARIO; Essex County Voc HS; Newark, NJ; (3); Computer Clb; FBLA; School Musical; School Play; Stu Cncl; Bsktbl; Sftbl; Cit Awd; Hon Roll; NHS; Achvt Awd Accntng 85-87; Trphy For Being Pres Of FBLA 86-87; Honorary Awd Of FBLA 86-87; Rutgers New Brunswick; CPA.

RIVERA, CHRISTINE ANNE; New Provicence HS; New Providence, NJ; (4); 10/169; Cmnty Wkr; Hosp Aide; Model UN; Chorus; Color Guard; Yrbk Stf; French Hon Soc; High Hon Roll; NHS; Stu Of Month October 87; Garden St Dstngshd Schlr 87; Rtry Clb Schrlshp 87; Villanova U; Bus Admin.

RIVERA, EDWIN; Dover HS; Dover, NJ; (3); Computer Clb; Band; Concert Band; Mrchg Band; Pep Band; Tennis; High Hon Roll; Hon Roll; NHS; Princeton U; Comp Sci.

RIVERA, ELBA; East Orange Adult HS; Irvington, NJ; (3); Church Yth Grp; Office Aide; Service Clb; Spanish Clb; Teachers Aide; Tennis; Vllybl; Sec.

RIVERA, GRISELLS; Good Counsel HS; Newark, NJ; (3); Camera Clb; FNA; FTA; Hosp Aide; Chorus; Prfct Atten Awd; Prfct Atten Awd 84-85; Rutgers U; Psych.

RIVERA JR, HUMBERTO; Perth Amboy HS; Perth Amboy, NJ; (2); German Clb; Math Clb; Science Clb; Var Ftbl; Var Wrstlng; Gen Excllnce Awd 85; Hnr Rl 86 & 87; Comp Engr.

RIVERA, LISSETTE; Mc Corristin Catholic HS; Trenton, NJ; (3); Church Yth Grp; Dance Clb; GAA; Band; Chorus; Sec Frsh Cls; Off Stu Cncl; Swmmng; High Hon Roll; Hon Roll; Cty Trntn Schltc Awd 83-85; Acdmc Excllnc 85; Cert Excllnc Spnsh III 87; Med Secr.

RIVERA, MARIA; Woodrow Wilson HS; Camden, NJ; (3); Aud/Vis; Rep Frsh Cls; Sftbl; Prfct Atten 86-87; Coll For Recordng Arts; Rcrdng.

RIVERA, MAURICIO; Eastside HS; Paterson, NJ; (2); Spanish Clb; Off Soph Cls; High Hon Roll; Trenton ST; Microbio.

RIVERA, RAFAEL; Woodrow Wilson HS; Camden, NJ; (4); Church Yth Grp; Band; Chorus; Church Choir; Temple U; Bus.

RIVERA, TANYA; Lincoln HS; Jersy City, NJ; (2); Art Clb; Yrbk Stf; Vllybl; Math Clb; Nwsp Stf; Stu Cncl; Prfct Atten Awd.

RIVERS, ALISA; Red Bank Regional HS; Neptune, NJ; (3); NAACP; Chorus; Mrchg Band; Mgr(s); Score Keeper; Prfct Atten Awd; Rep Jr Cls; JR Vrsty Lttrs 83-84; Vrsty Lttrs 84-86; Psychlgy.

RIVERS, FRED; University HS; Newark, NJ; (2); Boys Clb Am; Boy Scts; Church Yth Grp; Computer Clb; 4-H; Girl Scts; JA; Math Clb; NAACP; SADD.

RIVIELLO, KRISTIN; Hunterdon Central HS; Whitehouse Sta, NJ; (3); 128/556; Church Yth Grp; Cmnty Wkr; Key Clb; Teachers Aide; Stat Sftbl; Hon Roll; Kings Coll; Psych.

RIZK, CHRISTINE; Southern Regional HS; Ship Bottom, NJ; (3); 88/500; Hon Roll; Bio.

RIZO, MARIA; Palisades Park HS; Palisades Pk, NJ; (3); Q&S; Teachers Aide; Mrchg Band; Nwsp Stf; Yrbk Stf; Var JV Bsktbl; Swmmng; Piano 1st Pl 81 & 2nd Pl 82; Comp.

RIZZO, FRANK; St James HS; Gibbstown, NJ; (4); Cmnty Wkr; Yrbk Stf; Trs Frsh Cls; Trs Soph Cls; JV Var Bsbl; JV Var Bsktbl; JV Var Ftbl; Hon Roll; La Salle Coll; Psychlgy.

RIZZO, JEFF; Gateway Regional HS; Woodbury Heights, NJ; (3); 10/180; German Clb; Rep Stu Cncl; Stat Score Keeper; JV Var Socr; Var Capt Tennis; Im Wt Lftg; Hon Roll; NHS; Accounting.

RIZZO, JILL; Bloomfield HS; Bloomfield, NJ; (3); Church Yth Grp; Key Clb; Rep Stu Cncl; Var Cheerleading; Var Sftbl; Hon Roll; Frgn Lang Hnr Corps Italn 3 85-86; Dstngshd Svc Awd 85-86.

RIZZO, MICHELE; Passaic County Tech; Paterson, NJ; (2); VICA; Cheerleading; Cosmetlgy.

ROA, CAROLINA; Dickinson HS; Jersey City, NJ; (3); Spanish Clb; Hon Roll; Hnr Roll 86-87; Rutgers U; Dentist.

ROACH, GARY R; Middle Township HS; Rio Grande, NJ; (4); 23/208; Boy Scts; Scholastic Bowl; Socr; God Cntry Awd; NHS; Appntmnt-US Air Frc Acad Schlrshp-CO Sprngs 87; USAF Acad.

ROAKE, ELAINE; Bayonne HS; Bayonne, NJ; (2); Drama Clb; French Clb; Office Aide; Stage Crew; Nwsp Bus Mgr; Nwsp Stf; Lit Mag; Brooks Coll; Interior Designer.

ROANE, VALVIN; Paulsboro HS; Paulsboro, NJ; (4); 25/135; Red Cross Aide; Chorus; School Musical; School Play; Bsbl; Bsktbl; Ftbl; Wt Lftg; Hon Roll; S Jersey Choir 84-87; All State Chours 84; Pres Acadc Ftns Awd Prog 87; Drexel U; Elec Engr.

ROASARIO, GLADYS; Camden HS; Camden, NJ; (3); Church Yth Grp; Computer Clb; Dance Clb; Drama Clb; English Clb; Frsh Cls; Soph Cls; Jr Cls; Stu Cncl; Socr; Drexel; Comp Engr.

ROBART, FORREST; Linden HS; Linden, NJ; (4); 9/345; Key Clb; Science Clb; Ski Clb; Band; Chorus; Concert Band; Madrigals; Mrchg Band; School Musical; NHS; Linden Kiwanis Clb Scholar 87; Linden Lions Clb Scholar 87; Emmanuel Bedrick Mem SS & PTA 87; Rutgers U; Bio-Chem.

ROBB, ASHLEIGH; Notre Dame HS; Hamilton Sq, NJ; (1); Church Yth Grp; Drama Clb; Math Clb; Chorus; Church Choir; Variety Show; High Hon Roll; Hon Roll; Bus.

ROBBINS, APRIL; Hunterdon Central HS; Ringoes, NJ; (3); Sec Church Yth Grp; Church Choir; Lit Mag; JV Socr; Hon Roll; Beautician.

ROBBINS, FRANK; Penns Grove HS; Penns Grove, NJ; (3); 13/177; Church Yth Grp; Latin Clb; Pres Sr Cls; Var L Ftbl; Var Capt Trk; Wt Lftg; Gftd Tlntd Prgm 85-87; Tri Cnty Trk All Str 87; Bio.

ROBBINS, TAVETTE; Cumberland Regional HS; Bridgeton, NJ; (3); Church Yth Grp; 4-H; French Clb; Trs Girl Scts; Chorus; Church Choir; Nwsp Stf; Yrbk Stf; Trk; Prfct Atten Awd; Bus Mgmt.

ROBERSON, BRIAN W; Ewing HS; Trenton, NJ; (3); Am Leg Boys St; Yrbk Stf; Capt Crs Cntry; Capt Wrstlng; Key Clb; Stu Cncl; Ftbl; Crs Cntry Rnnr Of Yr 86-87; Bst Wrstlr Of Yr 86-87; Wrk Slctd For Mercer Cnty Teen Arts Fest 85-86.

ROBERTS, ANDREW L; Lawrence HS; Lawrenceville, NJ; (3); 2/210; Am Leg Boys St; JV Bsktbl; JV Tennis; High Hon Roll; NHS; Ntl Merit SF; Rotary Awd; Amer Invtnl Math Exam 87; Ntl Sci Olympd Chem Awd 86; Med.

ROBERTS JR, BRUCE S; Ridgefield Park HS; Ridgefield Pk, NJ; (3); 88/203; Boys Clb Am; Boy Scts; Intnl Clb; Office Aide; Varsity Clb; Band; Bsbl; Bowling; Var Ftbl; Var Wrstlng; Mitchell Coll; Educ.

ROBERTS, CHARLENE; Hillside HS; Hillside, NJ; (4); 4/196; Church Yth Grp; Leo Clb; Math Clb; Spanish Clb; Concert Band; Mrchg Band; Stu Cncl; Trk; Hon Roll; NHS; Penn ST; Indstrl Engr.

ROBERTS JR, GERALD; Ridgefield Park HS; Little Ferry, NJ; (3); 12/215; Am Leg Boys St; Spanish Clb; Yrbk Stf; JV Bsktbl; Hon Roll; Bus.

ROBERTS, JESSICA; Burlington City HS; Edgewater, NJ; (3); German Clb; JA; JV Var Mgr(s); Accrcy Typng Hnr Rll, Rhythmic Typing 86-87; Psych.

ROBERTS, JOHN; Northern Vly Regional HS; Norwood, NJ; (3); 6/274; AFS; Church Yth Grp; Ski Clb; JV Ftbl; Var Trk; High Hon Roll; Hon Roll; NHS; U Of FL; Psych.

ROBERTS, KATHLEEN M; Cherry Hill HS West; Cherry Hill, NJ; (3); French Clb; Thesps; Concert Band; Mrchg Band; School Musical; School Play; Stage Crew; Symp Band; Hon Roll.

ROBERTS, KENNETH; Ridgefield Memorial HS; Ridgefield, NJ; (3); Boy Scts; Cmnty Wkr; SADD; School Play; Variety Show; Var Ftbl; Var Trk; Hon Roll; FL U; Aerospc Engrng.

ROBERTS, LISA; Elmwood Park Memorial HS; Elmwood Pk, NJ; (4); 28/160; Girl Scts; Sftbl; Hon Roll; William Paterson Coll; Comp Prc.

ROBERTS, NATHANIEL; Arts HS; Newark, NJ; (3); Am Leg Boys St; Drama Clb; Chorus; Stage Crew; Rep Stu Cncl; Crs Cntry; Hon Roll; Ntl Merit Ltr; St Schlr; Smmr Arts Inst Schlrshp 85; Bible Schlr 84; NJ ST Teen Arts Fest 86; Morehouse Coll; Engrng.

ROBERTS, VICTORIA; St James HS; Gibbstown, NJ; (3); 1/79; Pep Clb; SADD; Yrbk Stf; JV Var Bsktbl; High Hon Roll; Astrnmy.

ROBERTSON, BRIAN; John F Kennedy HS; Willingboro, NJ; (2); 26/366; Nwsp Rptr; Nwsp Sprt Ed; Nwsp Stf; JV Bsbl; Ftbl; Score Keeper; Hon Roll.

ROBERTSON, BRYAN S; Mount Olive HS; Budd Lake, NJ; (4); 103/393; Art Clb; Camera Clb; Chess Clb; PAVAS; Q&S; Ski Clb; Yrbk Phtg; JV Socr; Var Wt Lftg; JV Wrstlng; Fanny B Thalheimer Merit Scholar 87; Aaronson Merit Scholar 87; 3rd Pl Corklins Photo Tourn 87; Philadelphia Coll Art; Fine Art.

ROBERTSON, JOHN; Holy Cross HS; Delran, NJ; (2); Church Yth Grp; Boys Clb Am; Var L Swmmng; Var L Trk; High Hon Roll; All Cnty Tm Swmmng; Law.

ROBERTSON, PAMELA; Haddon Twp HS; Haddonfield, NJ; (4); 1/171; Church Yth Grp; Debate Tm; Chorus; Madrigals; School Musical; Cit Awd; High Hon Roll; NHS; Ntl Merit Ltr; Val; Drew Schlr Category 1 87-91; Garden St Distngshd Schlr 87-91; Outstndng Stu Awd Math, Soc Stu 87; Drew U; Psychology.

ROBERTSON, PAMELA; Matawan Regional HS; Cliffwood Bch, NJ; (2); French Clb; Hon Roll; Sci.

ROBERTSON, RAQUEL; Weeguahic HS; Newark, NJ; (3); 7/370; GAA; Trs Jr Cls; Var Capt Bsktbl; Var Sftbl; Drug Peer Ldr-Stu Agnst Drugs 86-87; Actng Jr Clss Tres 86-87; Fayetteville ST U; Bus Admin.

ROBERTSON, TAMMI; South River HS; South River, NJ; (3); 17/150; Office Aide; Spanish Clb; Band; Color Guard; Concert Band; Mrchg Band; Trs Sr Cls; Var JV Cheerleading; Sftbl; NHS; Natl Hnr Soc 87-88; Physical Educ.

ROBICHAUD, MICHAEL; Verona HS; Verona, NJ; (4); 27/182; Band; Concert Band; Drm Mjr(t); Jazz Band; Mrchg Band; School Musical; Tennis; Hon Roll; NJ Rgn Band, All-St Band 86; VA Military Inst; Mech Engrng.

ROBIN, SAMANTHA; St Rose HS; Brick, NJ; (3); Key Clb; Ski Clb; Stat Bsktbl; Var Capt Cheerleading; Var Socr; Socl Wrkr.

ROBINSON, AME; Franklin HS; Somerset, NJ; (3); Dance Clb; Rep Jr Cls; Bsktbl; JV Capt Cheerleading; Pblc Rltns.

ROBINSON, BERNARD; Marist HS; Jersey City, NJ; (3); Church Yth Grp; 4-H; Var Bsbl; Var Ftbl; Score Keeper; Var Trk; Capt Wt Lftg; MVP Bsbl 84-85; Trk Team Of Mnth 86-87; FL ST; Bus Mgnt.

ROBINSON, BRUCE; M C V T HS; New Bruns, NJ; (3); Boy Scts; Computer Clb; Math Clb; Band; Chorus; Orch; Off Jr Cls; Var Bsbl; Var Bsktbl; Prfct Atten Awd.

ROBINSON, CAROL; Woodstown HS; Elmer, NJ; (3); FBLA; Concert Band; Mrchg Band; Var Bsktbl; Var Pom Pon; Var Sftbl; Hon Roll; Pres Church Yth Grp; English Clb; German Clb; ROGATE 86 & 87; Sci Fair-1st Pl Lcl, 1st Pl Dist, 1st Pl Rgnls 86; Ldrshp Awd-Hnrbl Mntn 87; Law.

ROBINSON, CIAN; Newton HS; Andover, NJ; (4); 10/196; Am Leg Boys St; Latin Clb; Math Tm; Science Clb; JV Bsbl; JV Bsktbl; Var Socr; Hon Roll; NHS; Natl Sci Olympd 1st Bio, 2nd Physics Hnrb Mntn 83 & 85-86.

ROBINSON, CLARENCE; Woodstown HS; Elmer, NJ; (4); 23/225; Math Clb; SADD; Yrbk Stf; High Hon Roll; Hon Roll; NHS; English Clb; Spanish Clb; Variety Show; Nwsp Rptr; Clement Newkirk Awd 87; U DE; Elec Engr.

ROBINSON, DEMETRIUS; Edgewood SR HS; Sicklerville, NJ; (2); JV Ftbl; Var Trk; Hon Roll; Dstngshd Person Awd 87; Drexel U; Enviro Engr.

ROBINSON, DOUG; Boonton HS; Lincoln Park, NJ; (3); 12/280; Am Leg Boys St; High Hon Roll; NHS; JV Bsbl; Im Ice Hcky; JV Socr; Var L Tennis; Im Vllybl; Rep NJ Boys ST 87.

ROBINSON, FRANCINE; Morris Catholic HS; Wharton, NJ; (3); French Clb; Hosp Aide; Spanish Clb; Hon Roll; Ice Fgre Sktng Compttn Awds; Frgn Lang.

ROBINSON, GINA; Paterson Catholic Regional HS; Paterson, NJ; (3); Hosp Aide; NAACP; Capt Pep Clb; Chorus; Color Guard; School Musical; High Hon Roll; Hon Roll; Prfct Atten Awd; Achvt Awd Bio 85; Excell Awd Engl 86; Ped.

ROBINSON, GLENN; Ocean City HS; Sea Isle City, NJ; (4); 2/296; Pres Math Clb; JV Bsktbl; High Hon Roll; Kiwanis Awd; Pres NHS; Ntl Merit Ltr; Sal; St Schlr; Latin Clb; Science Clb; Gov Schl Giftd Sci Stu 86; Distngushd Schlr Awd 86-87; Bus.

ROBINSON, HEIDI; Middle Twp HS; Dennisville, NJ; (4); 10/210; Band; Mrchg Band; Yrbk Stf; High Hon Roll; Pres Acad Fit Awd 87; Outstndg OEA Stu 87; Full Tuition Brd Trustee Scholar 87; Atlantic CC; Exec Sec.

ROBINSON, HOWARD A; Millville SR HS; Millville, NJ; (3); 16/520; Church Yth Grp; Civic Clb; Cmnty Wkr; Im Bowling; God Cntry Awd; High Hon Roll; Prfct Atten Awd; US Govt Copyright Comp Pgm 1st Pl 84; Acad Achvt Awd 85; Alg II Acad Awd 86; Air Force; Chem.

ROBINSON, JANNA; Cumberland Regional HS; Bridgeton, NJ; (1); Church Yth Grp; 4-H; French Clb; Band; Church Choir; Concert Band; Mrchg Band; Var Fld Hcky; Var Sftbl; Hon Roll; US Nvl Acad; Nvl Officer.

ROBINSON, JILL; Manasquan HS; Manasquan, NJ; (3); 12/250; Drama Clb; French Clb; Key Clb; Trs Frsh Cls; Rep Stu Cncl; Var Gym; Var Socr; Var Trk; High Hon Roll; NHS; Brd Ed Awd 86 & 87; Acadmc Al-Amer Awd 86; US Stu Cncl Awd 86.

ROBINSON, KAREN; Paul VI HS; Turnersville, NJ; (4); 149/514; Dance Clb; GAA; Service Clb; SADD; Sr Cls; Bsktbl; Coach Actv; Crs Cntry; Fld Hcky; Socr; Bsktbl Schlrhsp To Notre Dame 87-88; Street & Smith Bsktbl All Amer 86-87; 1000 Careet Pt In Bsktbl 87; Notre Dame.

ROBINSON, LILLIAN; Buena Regional HS; Richland, NJ; (4); 36/172; Library Aide; SADD; Chorus; Mrchg Band; Yrbk Stf; Rep Frsh Cls; Rep Soph Cls; Rep Jr Cls; Rep Sr Cls; Rep Stu Cncl; Otstndng Child Devp 86-87; Awd 20 Or Mor Credits 90 Or Above Avg Social Studies 86-87; Atlantia CC; Child Devp.

ROBINSON, MARGO; Northern Burlington Cnty Rgnl HS; Wrightstown, NJ; (1); Hosp Aide; Band; Concert Band; Symp Band; Frsh Cls; Cheerleading; Score Keeper; Hon Roll.

ROBINSON, NICHOLE; Trenton Central HS; Trenton, NJ; (2); Sec Key Clb; Nwsp Rptr; Nwsp Stf; Trk; Cit Awd; Hon Roll; Prfct Atten Awd; 1st Pl Dist Sci Fair 87; Awd Amer Soc Microbio 87; Bio Sci.

ROBINSON, ROBYN; Middletown HS HS; Middletown, NJ; (4); 33/450; Church Yth Grp; Sr Cls; Var Coach Actv; Var L Swmmng; Var Capt Trk; Hon Roll; Variety Show; Lit Mag; Jr Cls; Hon Roll; U Of NC; Physcl Thrpy.

ROBINSON, VICKI; Bridgeton HS; Bridgeton, NJ; (4); Church Yth Grp; Hosp Aide; Acpl Chr; Church Choir; Capt Trk; Hon Roll; Prfct Atten Awd; Schl Sve Adln Outstndng Vcl Awd 87; Morale Bstrs Merit Awd 86; Mst Dedicated Trck Rnr 87; Comp Prgmng.

ROBINSON, WILLIAM; Atlantic Christian Schl; Ocean View, NJ; (4); 3/15; Church Yth Grp; Chorus; School Play; Yrbk Stf; Pres Sr Cls; Capt Bsbl; Capt Bsktbl; Capt Socr; Pres Frsh Cls; USA Todays Natns Bsktbl Scorer 85-86; USA Todays Hnbl Men All Amer Bstbl 85-86; Phy Ed.

ROBSON, ALICIA; Nutley HS; Nutley, NJ; (4); 28/317; Sec French Clb; Key Clb; Ski Clb; Stu Cncl; Mgr(s); Hon Roll; NHS; James E Casey Scholar 87; Cook Coll; Biol.

ROCCO, MARY CATHERINE; Bricktownship HS; Brick, NJ; (4); Girl Scts; SADD; Teachers Aide; Masonic Awd; Prfct Atten Awd; Rotary Awd; Pell Grnt 87; Ocean Cnty Coll; Nrsng.

ROCHA, MARIA; South River HS; S River, NJ; (4); 26/125; Sec Church Yth Grp; Pres French Clb; Sec FNA; Radio Clb; Cit Awd; French Hon Soc; Hon Roll; Kean Coll; Speech Therapy.

ROCHE, DONNA MARIE; Metuchen HS; Edison, NJ; (4); 10/174; DECA; Pres French Clb; Key Clb; Math Tm; Pres Science Clb; Var Fld Hcky; Elks Awd; French Hon Soc; High Hon Roll; NHS; Worcester Poly Inst; Engrng.

ROCHE, KELLYANN; J F Kennedy HS; Willingboro, NJ; (2); English Clb; Girl Scts; Spanish Clb; Teachers Aide; Church Choir; JV Fld Hcky; Im Vllybl; Wt Lftg; Hon Roll; Knghts Clmbs Essy Awd 85; Cmnctns.

ROCHE, MICHAEL; St Joseph Regional HS; Valley Cottage, NY; (3); Computer Clb; Im Trk; Hon Roll; Spanish NHS; Arch.

ROCHE, PAUL; Saint Marys HS; Old Bridge, NJ; (3); Spanish Clb; Off Sr Cls; JV Bsbl; Var Socr; Vllybl; Var Co-Capt Wrstlng; High Hon Roll; Hon Roll; NHS; Olympics Of The Mind 85-86.

ROCHON, DAWN; Woodrow Wilson HS; Camden, NJ; (3); Church Yth Grp; GAA; Church Choir; Yrbk Stf; Bsktbl; Sftbl; Hon Roll; Prfct Atten Awd; Hampton U.

ROCK, LISA; Howell HS; Howell, NJ; (4); 6/380; Exploring; Rep Stu Cncl; Stat Bsktbl; JV Sftbl; DAR Awd; NHS; CC Awd; E Stroudsburg U Hnr & Deans Schlrshps 87; Central Jersey Italian-Amer Wmns Auxiliary Clb Schlrshp 87; E Stroudsburg U; Nrsng.

ROCKE, ROBERT; Bloomfield HS; Bloomfield, NJ; (4); 11/442; Church Yth Grp; Computer Clb; Drama Clb; Key Clb; Math Tm; Science Clb; Band; Concert Band; Drm Mjr(t); Jazz Band; Stevens Inst Of Tech Alumni Rgnl Schlrshp 87; Air Frc ROTC Schlrshp 87; Pres Ftnss Awd 87; Stevens Inst Of Tech; Bio Med.

ROCKHOLD, KIM; Absegami HS; Absecon, NJ; (4); 36/202; Church Yth Grp; Computer Clb; French Clb; SADD; High Hon Roll; Hon Roll; WV U; Physics.

ROCKWELL, CHRISTINA; Vineland HS; Vineland, NJ; (2); Lit Mag; Crs Cntry; Trk; Air Force; Reporter.

ROCKWELL, GLENN; De Paul HS; Newfoundland, NJ; (4); 59/156; Im Bsktbl; JV Ftbl; Im Vllybl; Hon Roll; Marist Coll; Accntng.

ROCKY, RUTH; Carteret HS; Carteret, NJ; (3); 27/226; Cmnty Wkr; Drama Clb; Girl Scts; JCL; Latin Clb; Band; Concert Band; Mrchg Band; School Play; Nwsp Stf; Phys Ftnss Awd 84; Drama.

RODEN, FREDERICK; The Oratory Schl; Springfield, NJ; (3); 2/45; Pres French Clb; Latin Clb; Quiz Bowl; Scholastic Bowl; Sec Science Clb; Service Clb; Nwsp Rptr; Hon Roll; NHS; Hmnties.

RODGERS, MARY JO; Mount St Dominic Acad; Verona, NJ; (2); 1/37; Church Yth Grp; Drama Clb; Spanish Clb; Hst Frsh Cls; Soph Cls; Var Crs Cntry; Var Trk; High Hon Roll; Pres Jr NHS; NHS; Summer Schlr St Peters Coll 87.

RODOLA, TOM; Essex Catholic HS; Newark, NJ; (3); Boy Scts; Math Clb; Stage Crew; Nwsp Bus Mgr; Yrbk Sprt Ed; Var Ftbl; Im Sftbl; High Hon Roll; NHS; Accntng.

RODRICKS, MICHAEL; Oakcrest HS; Pleasantville, NJ; (4); 2/200; Aud/Vis; Concert Band; Mrchg Band; Symp Band; Co-Capt Socr; Wt Lftg; High Hon Roll; JP Sousa Awd; Sal; St Schlr; U Of Notre Dame; Pre Pro Stds.

RODRIGUES, ALBERTO; East Side HS; Newark, NJ; (3); Hon Roll; NJIT; Mech Engr.

RODRIGUES, MAURICE; Union HS; Union, NJ; (2); Boys Clb Am; High Hon Roll.

RODRIGUEZ, CARMEN; Perth Amboy HS; Perth Amboy, NJ; (4); Off Sr Cls; Gym; Lawyer.

RODRIGUEZ, EDWARD L; Randolph HS; Randolph, NJ; (4); 4/390; Nwsp Stf; Lit Mag; Crs Cntry; Trk; NHS; Spanish NHS; St Schlr; Chess Clb; Computer Clb; Intnl Clb; Natl Merit Fnlst 87; U Of CA Rgnt Schlrshp 87-90; B Dickinson Schlrshp 87-90; U Of CA Berkeley; Med.

RODRIGUEZ, ELSA; Union Hill HS; Union City, NJ; (4); Math Clb; Spanish Clb; Teachers Aide; Flag Corp; Cheerleading; Gym; Twrlr; Vllybl; Hon Roll; Spanish NHS; Comp Sci.

RODRIGUEZ, ELVIN; Passaic County Vo-Tech HS; Paterson, NJ; (4); 10/366; Boy Scts; Co-Capt Chess Clb; Spanish Clb; Hon Roll; NHS; St Schlr; Natl Hispanic Schlrs SF 87; De Vry Tech Inst; Comp Info.

RODRIGUEZ, ESTHER LIDIA; Holy Rosary Acad; North Bergern, NJ; (3); Church Yth Grp; French Clb; Math Tm; Teachers Aide; Church Choir; Cert Hnr Geom 86; Cert Hnr For Religion III 87; Cert Merit Fren I 85; Elem Educ.

RODRIGUEZ, FRANCISCO; Perth Amboy HS; Perth Amboy, NJ; (3); Ftbl; Wt Lftg; Wrstlng; Arch.

RODRIGUEZ, GABRIELA; Perth Amboy HS; Perth Amboy, NJ; (2); French Clb; Library Aide; Ski Clb; Yrbk Stf; Rep Jr Cls; Rep Stu Cncl; Hon Roll; Govnrs ST Schl 87; Nrs.

RODRIGUEZ, HELEN; Memorial HS; West New York, NJ; (3); Debate Tm; Pep Clb; Science Clb; School Play; Nwsp Stf; Coach Actv; Vllybl; JETS Awd; NHS; Prfct Atten Awd; Hnr Rl 84 Thru 86; Rutger U; Engrng.

RODRIGUEZ, LAURA; Holy Rosary Acad; W New York, NJ; (3); VP Trs Spanish Clb; Nwsp Ed-Chief; High Hon Roll; Hon Roll; Trs NHS; Sal; Val; Drama Clb; French Clb; Math Clb; Sbjct Awds For 95 Pct 85-87; Prncpls List Cert 85-87; Service Awds 85-87; St Johns U; Pharm.

RODRIGUEZ, LETICIA; Science HS; Newark, NJ; (4); 6/99; Church Yth Grp; Yrbk Stf; Var Crs Cntry; Im Vllybl; Hon Roll; JCI Senator Schlrshp 87; Fannie P Woodie Schlrshp 87; Stevns Inst Tech; Chem Engrng.

RODRIGUEZ, LILLIAN; Bloomfield HS; Bloomfield, NJ; (3); French Clb; Orch; Var Trk; Var Capt Vllybl; Psych.

RODRIGUEZ, LUIS; Emerson HS; Union City, NJ; (3); Art Clb; FBLA; Spanish Clb; Yrbk Rptr; Yrbk Stf; Lit Mag; Stu Cncl; Tennis; Hon Roll; NJ Inst; Arch.

RODRIGUEZ, MARIA; Orange HS; Orange, NJ; (3); Girl Scts; Yrbk Stf; Stu Cncl; Var L Tennis; High Hon Roll; Hon Roll; VP NHS; Rutgers U Schlr 86-87; Spnsh & Sci Awds 86-87; Rutgers U; Bus Admin.

RODRIGUEZ, MARITZA; Trenton Central HS; Trenton, NJ; (3); Art Clb; Office Aide; Spanish Clb; Teachers Aide; Lit Mag; Rep Soph Cls; Bowling; Tennis; Cit Awd; Hon Roll; RCA Mnrts Engr Pgm 85-86; Nrsng.

RODRIGUEZ, MELISSA; Millville SR HS; Woodbine, NJ; (4); Boy Scts; Pres Exploring; GAA; Office Aide; Trs SADD; Band; Concert Band; Mrch Band; Pep Band; Variety Show; Mrchng Band Awd 86 & 87; Mrt Schrlsh 87; NHS Fndrsng Schlrshp 87; Trenton ST; Accntng.

RODRIGUEZ, MICHAEL; Passaic County Tech HS; Paterson, NJ; (3 Am Leg Boys St; Boys Clb Am; Scts; CAP; Dance Clb; Exploring; JA Math Tm; ROTC; Spanish Clb; Boy Scts Of Amer; USAF Acad; Arnt Engrng.

RODRIGUEZ, PATRICIA; Woodrow Wilson HS; Camden, NJ; (3); Gi Scts; Spanish Clb; Varsity Clb; Yrbk Stf; Cheerleading; Swmmng; Tenni High Hon Roll; NHS; Spanish NHS.

RODRIGUEZ, REBECA; Trenton Central HS; Trenton, NJ; (3); Churc Yth Grp; Dance Clb; Debate Tm; Drama Clb; French Clb; School Musica NHS; Acdmc Achvmnt Awd 85; Amrcn Lgn Axlry Awd 85; Lngst.

RODRIGUEZ, RUTH; Camderl Catholic HS; Camden, NJ; (3); Churc Yth Grp; Latin Clb; Spanish Clb.

RODRIGUEZ, STEVE R; Hasbrouck Heights HS; Hasbrouck Height NJ; (3); Am Leg Boys St; Aud/Vis; Drama Clb; Key Clb; Ski Clb; Spanis Clb; Acpl Chr; Chorus; Concert Band; Drm & Bgl; Hugh O Brien Yt Ldrshp Rep 86; Oxford; Bio Chem.

RODRIGUEZ, YANIRA; Our Lady Of Good Counsel HS; Newark, N (3); 56/122; Camera Clb; Church Yth Grp; Civic Clb; Computer Clb; Gi Scts; Office Aide; Chorus; Church Choir; Spanish NHS; Bus.

RODRIQUEZ, RUTH; Dickinson HS; Jersey City, NJ; (3); Office Aide Rep Soph Cls; Rep Jr Cls; Prfct Atten Awd; NJ Inst Tech; Engrng.

ROE, BRIAN; Wayne Hills HS; Wayne, NJ; (3); 15/300; Math Tm; Mod UN; Spanish Clb; Concert Band; School Musical; Nwsp Stf; High Ho Roll; Hon Roll; NHS; Sci.

ROE, JENNIFER; Lakewood HS; Lakewood, NJ; (4); 80/270; Drama Cl German Clb; Girl Scts; Office Aide; Mrchg Band; Symp Band; Hon Rol Fairleigh Dickinson; Banking.

ROEBUCK, GLORIA; Camden College Vo-Tech Schl; Camden, NJ; (3 Sec DECA; Yrbk Stf; Sec Frsh Cls; Sec Soph Cls; Sec Jr Cls; Rep Stu Cnc Mgr Socr; High Hon Roll; Hon Roll; DECA Reg Conf Genl Mktg 1st 87.

ROESEL, STEVEN P; Scotch Plains-Fanwood HS; Fanwood, NJ; (4 100/300; Boy Scts; Church Yth Grp; Pres DECA; Drm Mjr(t); Jazz Ban Mrchg Band; Symp Band; Hon Roll; St Schlr; Band; 1st Atlantic Svn Schlrshp Awd $1000 87; Deca Cmptn-1st Pl Overall Finance & Crdt Re 87; St Cmptn 87; Union Coll; Comp Sci.

ROEVER, KATHLEEN A; Hunterdan Central HS; Flemington, NJ; (3 69/550; SADD; Band; Concert Band; Mrchg Band; Var JV Sftbl; Im Vllyb Hon Roll; Vrsty Ltr Wnnr Sftbl 87; Vrsty Ltr 3 Yrs Mrchg Band 87 Chiroprctr.

ROG, MARGARET; South River HS; South River, NJ; (4); 30/130 German Clb; Library Aide; Yrbk Stf; JV Fld Hcky; Rutgers U; Comms.

ROGERS, DANA; Brick Twp Memorial HS; Brick, NJ; (3); 3/390; Frenc Clb; VP Key Clb; Var Trk; High Hon Roll; NHS; Prfct Atten Awd Alternate-Amer Lgn Auxiliary Grls ST 87; Med.

ROGERS, ELIZABETH; Manasquan HS; Belmar, NJ; (4); Art Cl Church Yth Grp; Dance Clb; Drama Clb; Latin Clb; Spanish Clb; Acpl Ch Chorus; Nwsp Rptr; Nwsp Stf; Psych.

ROGERS, JANICE; Toms River North HS; Toms River, NJ; (3); 10/45 Var L Gym; JV Sftbl; L High Hon Roll; NHS; Lwyr.

ROGERS, KRISTINE; Toms River HS East; Toms River, NJ; (4); 60 567; French Clb; Hon Roll; Trooper Phillip Lamonaco Schlrshp 87; Ocea Cnty Coll; Child Psych.

ROGERS, LINDA; Bishop George Ahr/St Thomas HS; Perth Ambo NJ; (4); 106/267; ROTC; Concert Band; Mrchg Band; Yrbk Phtg; Rep Frs Cls; Rep Soph Cls; Rep Jr Cls; Band; Symp Band; Lit Mag; JROT Knockout Drill Cmptn-4th Pl 84; Rochester Inst Tech; Photo.

ROGERS, MICHAEL J; Rancross Valley Regional HS; Mt Holly, NJ; (3 1/317; Am Leg Boys St; Math Tm; Capt Quiz Bowl; Lit Mag; Pres Sr Cl Var Bsktbl; High Hon Roll; NHS; Val; Rutgers U Schlr.

ROGERS, MONICA; Neptune SR HS; Neptune, NJ; (4); 11/356; Am Le Aux Girls St; GAA; Letterman Clb; Math Tm; Pres SADD; Yrbk Stf; Cap L Trk; Trs Jr NHS; NHS; Pres Schlr; Sptsmnshp Awd Indr/Outdr Tr 86-87; Alpha Kappa Alpha Sorority Scholar 87; Douglass Coll; Law.

ROGERS, SCOTT; Ridge HS; Stamford, CT; (4); 30/220; Trs VP Germa Clb; Ski Clb; Yrbk Stf; Var JV Bsktbl; Var Capt Golf; Hon Roll; NH Emory U.

ROGERS, SHARON; Buena Regional HS; Newfield, NJ; (4); 7/18 Drama Clb; Pep Clb; Ski Clb; Trs Varsity Clb; Stu Cncl; Co-Capt Va Cheerleading; Hon Roll; NHS; Glassboro ST Coll; Fshn Merch.

ROGERS, TED; Vernon Township HS; Sussex, NJ; (3); Sr Cls; Stu Cnc Var L Bsbl; Var L Ftbl; Wt Lftg; Var L Wrstlng; Hon Roll; NHS; Vrst Awd Vkng Wrstlng 87.

ROGERS, VIRGINIA ANNE; Bishop Eustace Prep Schl; Mount Laure NJ; (3); Spanish Clb; SADD; Cheerleading; Hon Roll; NHS; Spanish NH

ROGOW, DEBBIE; Hunterdon Central HS; Flemington, NJ; (4); 8/54 Quiz Bowl; School Musical; Nwsp Stf; Trs Stu Cncl; Band; Mrchg Band Symp Band; Nwsp Rptr; Bsktbl; Elks Awd; NJ Schlr 86; Garden ST Di Schlr 87; Cornell U; Hist.

ROHATY, DEBORAH; Mt St Mary Acad; Flemington, NJ; (3); 11/8 Church Yth Grp; Girl Scts; Hosp Aide; School Musical; Rep Soph Cl High Hon Roll; Hon Roll; NHS; Cmnty Wkr; Chem Achvt Awd, Schl Sv Awds 87; Mock Trial Comp 86-87.

ROHDE, CHRISTOPHER; Paul VI Regional HS; Clifton, NJ; (3); 1 132; Ski Clb; Rep Frsh Cls; Rep Soph Cls; Rep Jr Cls; Rep Sr Cls; Var Bs Var Capt Socr; Rep Spanish NHS; Law.

ROIG, MELINDA; St John Vianney HS; Marlboro, NJ; (3); Dance Cl Drama Clb; VP French Clb; Math Tm; Thesps; Chorus; School Musica French Hon Soc; High Hon Roll; NHS; Rlgn Awd 87; Frnch Awd 8 Comm.

ROITMAN, MARA; Maple Shade HS; Maple Shade, NJ; (3); Am Le Aux Girls St; VP Key Clb; Trs Spanish Clb; Pres Jr Cls; Cheerleadin Mgr(s); Stat Sftbl; Hon Roll; NHS; Voice Dem Awd; Rutgers Schlr, Acdm All Am Schlr, Rtry Clb Yth Merit Awd; Psych.

ROJAS, CATALINA; Mary Help Of Christians Acad; Paterson, NJ; (4 4/78; Church Yth Grp; Band; Pres Soph Cls; Rep Pres Stu Cncl; High Ho Roll; Hon Roll; NHS; Ntl Merit Ltr; St Schlr; Trenton ST Full Schlrsh 87; Acadmc All-Am 86-87; Distngshd Schlr 87; Trenton ST Coll; Psych.

ROJAS, DIANA; Mary Help Of Christians Acad; Paterson, NJ; (3); 5/8 Church Yth Grp; Letterman Clb; Chorus; School Musical; Rptr Lit Ma Rep Stu Cncl; High Hon Roll; Hon Roll; NHS; Ntl Merit Ltr; Jrnlsm.

ROJAS, JEANNETTE; St Joseph Of The Palisades HS; Union City, N (4); Model UN; Spanish Clb; Stage Crew; Variety Show; Yrbk Stf; Spanis NHS; St Johns U; Pharm.

ROJEK, JEFF; Lodi HS; Lodi, NJ; (4); 18/140; Capt Quiz Bowl; L Bsbl; Capt Bsktbl; L Ftbl; Hon Roll; NHS; 2dn Tm All Leag WR Ftbl 86; Hnrb Mntn All Leag Grd-Bsktbl 87; Fordham U.

ROKUSKIE, KEVIN; Kingsway Regional HS; Swedesboro, NJ; (2); VP Church Yth Grp; Rep Stu Cncl; Var Ftbl; Var Trk; Im Wt Lftg; Var Wrstlng; Hon Roll; NHS; Coaches Awd Wrstlng 85-86; Dennis Martin Peace Awd Wrstlng 86-87; Most Dedicated Ftbl 86.

ROLENC, JOE; Toms River North HS; Toms River, NJ; (1); Band; Jazz Band; Mrchg Band; Orch; School Musical; School Play; Symp Band; Bsbl; Hon Roll; Prfct Atten Awd.

ROLLAND, TIMOTHY M; The Pennington Schl; Trenton, NJ; (4); 4/80; Spanish Clb; SADD; Sec Jr Cls; VP Sr Cls; Var Capt Diving; Capt Swmmng; Var Trk; High Hon Roll; NHS; Hnrs Spnsh IV Awd; Ltn I Hnrs Awd; NY U.

ROLLER, RHONDA C; Lenape Valley Regional HS; Netcong, NJ; (4); FBLA; Bowling; High Hon Roll; Hon Roll; Katherine Gibbs JR Achvt Hnrb Mntn 86; Berkeley Schls Outstndng Achvt Awd 87; Thomas V Romano Awd 87; County Coll Of Morris; Sys Tech.

ROLLINSON, JAMES; Morristown-Beard Schl; New Vernon, NJ; (3); 8/83; French Clb; Varsity Clb; Pres Soph Cls; Pres Jr Cls; Pres Stu Cncl; Var Bsktbl; Var Golf; Cit Awd; French Hon Soc; High Hon Roll; Joseph Ryer Awd 84; Schlrshp Awd 84; Pre-Law.

ROLNICK, JOSHUA N; Highland Park HS; Highland Park, NJ; (3); 12/121; Am Leg Boys St; Radio Clb; Ski Clb; Mrchg Band; Nwsp Bus Mgr; Nwsp Phtg; Nwsp Rptr; Nwsp Sprt Ed; Yrbk Phtg; Yrbk Stf; Cmnctns.

ROMAN, LAURA; Raritan HS; Hazlet, NJ; (4); Yrbk Stf; Var Fld Hcky; Socr; Hon Roll; NHS; Rutgers Coll; Psych.

ROMAN, LISA; Red Bank Regional HS; Little Silver, NJ; (3); Key Clb; Ski Clb; Hon Roll; NHS; Spanish NHS; Rep Frsh Cls; Rep Soph Cls; Rep Stu Cncl; Var JV Cheerleading; JV L Socr.

ROMAN, ORLANDO; Passaic County Tech & Voc HS; Paterson, NJ; (3); Boy Scts; Color Guard; Rep Stu Cncl; JV Var Bsbl; Prfct Atten Awd; Designed H S Logo 86; Professional Logos 86; Design Dinner Programs For Schl 87; Schl Of Visual Arts; Comm Art.

ROMAN, ROBERT; Roselle Park HS; Roselle Park, NJ; (3); 30/166; Camera Clb; JA; Nwsp Phtg; Nwsp Rptr; VP Capt Bsbl; VP Crs Cntry; VP Trk; Hon Roll; Acctng.

ROMAN, SONIA; Vineland HS; Vineland, NJ; (2); 10 Merit Rlls 84-85; Cert Rcgntn 85; 2 Achvt Math Cert 85 87; Data Prcssng.

ROMANELLI, PHILIP F; Lawrenceville School HS; Havertown, PA; (3); Am Leg Boys St; Boy Scts; Drama Clb; Pres Service Clb; Acpl Chr; Chorus; School Musical; Nwsp Stf; Crs Cntry; Hon Roll; Eagle Scout; Fr Hist & English Prizes 1985; Bertolet-O'neill Prize 1987; Ad Altare Dei Awd.

ROMANO, LAURA; West Essex Regional HS; Fairfield, NJ; (2); Chorus; JV Bsktbl; JV Coach Actv; Var JV Sftbl; Hon Roll; Elec.

ROMANO, ROSALIE; Bayonne HS; Bayonne, NJ; (3); Drama Clb; Pres Intnl Clb; Math Tm; Stage Crew; Hon Roll; Jr NHS; Intl Bus.

ROMANOWSKI, WILLIAM; Gloucester City JR SR HS; Gloucester, NJ; (4); 26/141; Computer Clb; Bowling; Socr; Vllybl; Wt Lftg; High Hon Roll; Hon Roll; Grphc Arts 86-87; Camden Co Coll.

ROMANS, TAMMY; Toms River South HS; Beachwood, NJ; (3); 98/405; Aud/Vis; Church Yth Grp; Library Aide; Cheerleading; Sftbl; Hon Roll; Educ.

ROMANSKI, JOYCE; Wayne Valley HS; Wayne, NJ; (4); 30/317; Latin Clb; Jazz Band; Madrigals; Mrchg Band; Orch; School Musical; School Play; Lit Mag; High Hon Roll; NHS; Cum Laude Ntl Latin Exam; Ntl Latin Hnr Soc; Wayne Vly PTO Schlrshp; Rutgers Coll; Jrnlst.

ROMANSKY, BRIAN; Lakeland Regional HS; Ringwood, NJ; (3); 53/400; Rep Stu Cncl; High Hon Roll; Ntl Merit Ltr; Natl Sci Olympiad-Chem 86; Cert Of Educ Devel NEDT 85; Elec Engrng.

ROMEO, JASON; Buena Regional HS; Newfield, NJ; (3); Drama Clb; Pep Clb; Ski Clb; Varsity Clb; School Musical; School Play; Stage Crew; Variety Show; Var L Golf; JV Socr; Comp Tech.

ROMERO, ANA; Memorial HS; West New York, NJ; (3); Var Pom Pon; Hon Roll; Graphics 86; Psych.

RONNEN, DAN; Ocean Township HS; Wayside, NJ; (3); Cmnty Wkr; French Clb; Library Aide; Temple Yth Grp; Nwsp Stf; Im Bsktbl; Im Coach Actv; Var L Tennis; Im Vllybl; Deans Smmr Schlr Pgm Rutgers U 87; Bus Law.

ROO, CAROL; Freehold Township HS; Freehold, NJ; (3); 6/285; Drama Clb; French Clb; Hosp Aide; Math Tm; Science Clb; Speech Tm; Concert Band; Mrchg Band; JV Trk; NHS.

ROONEY, THERESA; Immaculate Heart Acad; Hillsdale, NJ; (3); Var Trk; NHS; Prfct Atten Awd; Hnr Roll 84-87; Lat Hnr Soc 85; Manhattan Coll; Acctg.

ROOST, TINA; Waldwick HS; Waldwick, NJ; (3); 23/140; Church Yth Grp; Cmnty Wkr; Rptr 4-H; Political Wkr; Nwsp Rptr; Lit Mag; Marketing.

ROOTH, MICHELE; Holy Family Acad; Bayonne, NJ; (4); 10/130; VP French Clb; Orch; Yrbk Stf; Var Tennis; High Hon Roll; Hon Roll; NHS; NEDT Awd; Tnns Rookie Of Yr 84; Tnns MIP 87; All-Cnty 1st Dbls 86; Rutgers U.

RORRO, MARY; Villa Victoria Acad; Trenton, NJ; (4); Spanish Clb; Chorus; Orch; Lit Mag; Rep Jr Cls; Gov Hon Prg Awd; Lion Awd; Spanish NHS; Cntry III Ldrshp Awd 87; US Marine Crps Sci Fair Awd Wnnr 86; Ntl Assc Tchrs-Inaln Awd Wnnr 87; Bryn Mawr Coll.

ROSA, BLANCA; Garden State Acad; Tampa, FL; (4); Art Clb; Church Yth Grp; German Clb; Hosp Aide; Office Aide; Red Cross Aide; Science Clb; Spanish Clb; Teachers Aide; Chorus; Southern Coll TN; Nrsng.

ROSA, DENISE; Trenton Central HS; Trenton, NJ; (3); Church Yth Grp; Latin Clb; High Hon Roll; Hon Roll; JETS Awd; Socl Wrk.

ROSADO, SHARON LEE; Eastside HS; Paterson, NJ; (3); JA; Office Aide; Teachers Aide; Rep Jr Cls; Bsbl; Ntl Merit Schol; Engl Awd 86; Clifton Schl Of Bus; Exec Secy.

ROSANDER, DAVID; Timothy Christian Schl; Piscataway, NJ; (3); 1/35; AFS; Cmnty Wkr; Computer Clb; Drama Clb; Political Wkr; Radio Clb; Chorus; School Play; Stage Crew; VP Stu Cncl; Rutgers Coll Deans Smmr Schlr 86; Grdn St Dstngshd Schlr Schlrshp; Rutgers Sch Of Engrng; Engrng.

ROSARIO, LOURDES; Paramus Catholic Girls Regnl HS; Montvale, NJ; (3); Math Clb; Nwsp Rptr; Lit Mag; Hon Roll; Jr NHS; 1st Prz Uterary Mag Bylines Short Stry Cntst 86 & 87; NCTE Achvt Awd Wrtg 87; Awd Prfcncy Eng 86 & 87; English.

ROSARIO, ONEIDA; Warren County Vo-Tech HS; Washington, NJ; (4); Key Clb; VICA; Nwsp Stf; Yrbk Stf; Pres Sr Cls; Pres Stu Cncl; High Hon Roll; Hon Roll; NHS; Rep Frsh Cls; Comp.

ROSATI, ELAINE; Washington Township HS; Blackwood, NJ; (4); 1/480; Chorus; School Musical; School Play; Lit Mag; Rep Jr Cls; Hon Roll; NHS; Ntl Merit Schol; St Schlr; Val; Rutgers Schlr 86; WA Twnshps JR Miss 86; Best Cls 87; WFIL TV 6 87; Trenton ST Coll; Psych.

ROSCHER, BRIAN; Hunterdon Central HS; Flemington, NJ; (2); 59/478; Chess Clb; CAP; Im Vllybl; Prfct Atten Awd; Soph Recog Prgm Geom 87; Rutgers Coll; Engrng.

ROSCISZEWSKI, KAREN; Bayonne HS; Bayonne, NJ; (3); Am Leg Aux Girls St; Drama Clb; Jazz Band; Orch; Nwsp Stf; Lit Mag; Var Mgr(s); Var Score Keeper; Var Timer; Im Vllybl; Schlrshp-Cathlc HS 84-85; Grls Nation Senator 87; Penn ST; Bus.

ROSE, BRANDON; Brick Township HS; Brick, NJ; (4); 55/360; German Clb; Trs Varsity Clb; Var Ftbl; Var Trk; High Hon Roll; Var Wrstlng; Alt To Bys ST Rider Coll 86; 2 Time Wnnracad & Ath Awd Wrstlng 86-87; Outstndng Lnmn Awd 87; Trenton ST; Pol Sci.

ROSE, GWENDOLYN; Belvidere HS; Oxford, NJ; (4); 19/122; Am Leg Aux Girls St; Trs Drama Clb; 4-H; Trs SADD; Varsity Clb; Chorus; School Musical; Yrbk Stf; Stat Bsbl; JV Bsktbl; Stu Of Mon 86; Moravian Coll; Elem Ed.

ROSE, ROB; Cumberland Chrstn HS; Bridgeton, NJ; (3); 2/23; Church Yth Grp; Chorus; Pres Frsh Cls; Pres Soph Cls; Stu Cncl; Var L Bsbl; Var L Bsktbl; Var L Socr; Var Trk; High Hon Roll; Law.

ROSE, SHERYL; Matawan Regional HS; Matawan, NJ; (3); Temple Yth Grp; Band; Concert Band; Jazz Band; Mrchg Band; Orch; Pep Band; School Musical; School Play; Yrbk Stf.

ROSEBERRY, JAMES; Gloucester County Christian HS; Monroeville, NJ; (2); Church Yth Grp; Pres Frsh Cls; Pres Soph Cls; Var Bsbl; Var Bsktbl; Var Socr; Hon Roll.

ROSEN, MELISSA; Manacapan HS; Englishtown, NJ; (3); Exploring; Nwsp Rptr; Yrbk Stf; Cheerleading; NHS; Opt Clb Awd; Pres Frsh Cls; Pres Soph Cls; Pres Stu Cncl; Rutgers; Attrny.

ROSEN, PAM; Parsippany HS; Parsippany, NJ; (3); Sec Key Clb; Spanish Clb; SADD; Temple Yth Grp; Varsity Clb; Capt Color Guard; VP Concert Band; Stage Crew; Hon Roll; Sec NHS; JR Hall Of Fm Band Hnrs 86; Psychlgy.

ROSEN, STACEY; Manalapan HS; Manalapan, NJ; (3); Girl Scts; SADD; Temple Yth Grp; Drill Tm; Nwsp Rptr; Accntng.

ROSENBAUM, EVAN; Triton Regional HS; Somerdale, NJ; (4); 17/305; Latin Clb; Science Clb; School Musical; Hon Roll; Ntl Merit Ltr; NJ Dist Schlrs Awd 86; Mech Engr.

ROSENBAUM, MATT; Montville HS; Montville, NJ; (4); 35/257; VP Cmnty Wkr; FBLA; Key Clb; Pres Ski Clb; SADD; VP Stu Cncl; JV Golf; JV Socr; High Hon Roll; NHS; North Jersey Crftmns Fair 2nd Pl 86-87; Sprg Teen Arts Fstvl 2nd Pl 86-87; Syracuse Schlrshp 86-87; Syracuse U; Arch.

ROSENBERG, ADAM C; East Brunswick HS; E Brunswick, NJ; (3); Rep Key Clb; Latin Clb; Model UN; Teachers Aide; Temple Yth Grp; Concert Band; Mrchg Band; Nwsp Stf; Rep Stu Cncl; Hon Roll; Most Outstndng Del Model UN U PA 87; Law.

ROSENBERG, AMY; Waldwick HS; Waldwick, NJ; (3); 15/140; Cmnty Wkr; Spanish Clb; Veterinary Medicine.

ROSENBERG, MARK; Jackson Memorial HS; Jackson, NJ; (3); 1/425; Ski Clb; High Hon Roll; NHS; Rutgers Schlr 87; Med.

ROSENBERG, SHARON; Manalapan HS; Manalapan, NJ; (3); Cmnty Wkr; Color Guard; Drill Tm; Stage Crew; Socr; Fashn Merchndsng.

ROSENBLATT, HUGH; Manalapan HS; Manalapan, NJ; (2).

ROSENBLATT, TODD; Ocean Township HS; Ocean, NJ; (3); 86/344; Key Clb; VP Science Clb; Spanish Clb; VP Temple Yth Grp; Rep Stu Cncl; JV Bsktbl; Socr; JV Tennis; Engrng.

ROSENBLUM, ADAM; Lakewood HS; Lakewood, NJ; (3); 30/330; Am Leg Boys St; Debate Tm; English Clb; Latin Clb; Political Wkr; Temple Yth Grp; Varsity Clb; Rep Jr Cls; JV Bowling; Var Tennis; All Ocean Cnty Dbls Tnns Chmpn 86; Law.

ROSENDALE, TIMOTHY; Eastern Christian HS; Hawthorne, NJ; (4); 2/83; Concert Band; Nwsp Ed-Chief; Pres Frsh Cls; Pres Soph Cls; Coach Actv; Var L Socr; Hon Roll; NHS; Ntl Merit SF; Val; Schl Svc Awds 85-86; Pres NHS Chptr 87-88; Soccr Coach 87; Calvin Coll; Engl.

ROSENFARB, JASON; Randolph HS; Randolph, NJ; (4); Am Leg Boys St; Exploring; Political Wkr; Temple Yth Grp; Wt Lftg; Var Wrstlng; Hon Roll; Emory U; Pltcl Sci.

ROSENFELD, CLINT; High Point Regional HS; Branchville, NJ; (3); Am Leg Boys St; Variety Show; Var Bsbl; Var Capt Ftbl; Wt Lftg; Wrstlng; Hon Roll; Engr.

ROSENFELD, MARISSA BETH; The Pilgrim Acad; Egg Harbor City, NJ; (3); Art Clb; Pres Church Yth Grp; Chorus; Church Choir; Nwsp Stf; Yrbk Stf; Lit Mag; Var Cheerleading; Hon Roll; Sci Fair Awd 86; Fine Arts Awd Pntng & Choir 86.

ROSENGARTEN, SPENCER A; Columbia HS; Maplewood, NJ; (3); Am Leg Boys St; Chess Clb; Science Clb; Rep Stu Cncl; Crs Cntry; French Hon Soc; Chem.

ROSENSON, GARY; Matawan Regional HS; Aberdeen, NJ; (4); 14/336; Math Clb; School Musical; Yrbk Bus Mgr; VP Stu Cncl; Socr; Var L Tennis; Hon Roll; NHS; Ski Clb; Temple Yth Grp; Outstndg Acdmc Achvmnt & Ldrshp Awd 84; Math Hon Soc 86-87.

ROSENSTEIN, ALIX; Morristown HS; Morris Plains, NJ; (1); Hosp Aide; Key Clb; Rep Stu Cncl; Bsktbl; JV Tennis; High Hon Roll; Psychtrst.

ROSENSTEIN, ARI; Jewish Educational Ctr; Elizabeth, NJ; (2); Boy Scts; Chess Clb; Math Tm; Nwsp Rptr; Off Jr Cls; Var Fld Hcky; Hon Roll; Columbia; Arch.

ROSI, MICHELLE; Vineland HS; Vineland, NJ; (4); 3/736; VP Exploring; Key Clb; Math Clb; Varsity Clb; Chorus; Madrigals; Yrbk Ed-Chief; Rep Stu Cncl; Var Fld Hcky; Hon Roll; Unsung Hero Field Hcky 86; Natl Merit SF 86; U DE; Chem.

ROSLAN, CHRIS; Kittatinny Regional HS; Newton, NJ; (4); 40/230; Latin Clb; PAVAS; Band; Jazz Band; School Musical; School Play; Variety Show; Tennis; Hon Roll; Smmr Arts Inst NJ Schl Of Arts 84; NJ ST Tn Arts Fstvl 84-86; W Paterson Coll Smmr Jazz Ensbl 87; William Paterson; Music Mgmt.

ROSMAITA, KAREN; The Morristown Beard Schl; N Caldwell, NJ; (3); 11/89; Sec Drama Clb; Intnl Clb; Library Aide; Thesps; School Musical; School Play; Nwsp Stf; Yrbk Stf; Lit Mag.

ROSPOND, KATHRYN; West Orange HS; W Orange, NJ; (3); Aud/Vis; Pres French Clb; Chorus; Jazz Band; Mrchg Band; Pres French Hon Soc; High Hon Roll; Hon Roll; Jr NHS; Science Clb; Girls Ctzn Inst Rep 87; Intl Rec Cmptn Hnbl Mntn 85; Schlstc Awd 85; Jrnlsm.

ROSS, AMY; Bloomfield HS; Bloomfield, NJ; (3); Band; Chorus; Concert Band; Jazz Band; Mrchg Band; Orch; School Musical; Yrbk Stf; Music Ed.

ROSS, CHARLES; Secaucus HS; Secaucus, NJ; (3); Am Leg Boys St; Mu Alpha Theta; Ski Clb; Var L Bsbl; JV Bsktbl; Var L Ftbl; Bus Admn.

ROSS, DEBRA; Hightstown HS; East Windsor, NJ; (3); 54/357; Spanish Clb; VP L Bsktbl; VP L Fld Hcky; VP L Sftbl; Hon Roll; NHS; Grls Ctznshp Inst 87; Sftbl Sprtsmnshp Awd 87; Nmd 3rd Tm All Cnty Sftbl 87; Psych.

ROSS, JACQUELINE; Kearny HS; Kearny, NJ; (3); Ski Clb; Drill Tm; Mrchg Band; Yrbk Stf; JV Cheerleading; JV Var Powder Puff Ftbl; Marn Bio.

ROSS, JENNIFER; Raritan HS; Hazlet, NJ; (3); 91/327; Spanish Clb; Band; Concert Band; JV Capt Cheerleading; Hon Roll; Peer Grp Cnslng 87; Sprts Thrpst.

ROSS, KARLENE; Cherry Hills HS West; Cherry Hill, NJ; (3); Am Leg Aux Girls St; French Clb; Intnl Clb; Ed Yrbk Phtg; Off Frsh Cls; Off Soph Cls; Off Jr Cls; Hon Roll; Teachers Aide; Stage Crew; Hm & Schl Assn Awd 87; Pre Med.

ROSS, MICA; Faith Christian Schl; Blackwood, NJ; (3); 2/4; Church Yth Grp; Scholastic Bowl; Service Clb; Chorus; Yrbk Stf; Pres Stu Cncl; Var Sftbl; High Hon Roll; Hon Roll; Prfct Atten Awd; Yth Essy Cont 1st Pl Awd CME Chrch 86; Georgetown U; Tech Engrng.

ROSS, NEIL A; Randolph HS; Randolph, NJ; (4); 1/360; Temple Yth Grp; JV Tennis; High Hon Roll; Ntl Merit SF; Garden St Schlr 86; NJ St Sci Day Comp 86; Ntl Sci Olympd 85-86.

ROSS, ROSEMARIE; St James HS; Alloway, NJ; (1); 23/73; Drama Clb; Hosp Aide; SADD; Hon Roll; Actng.

ROSSELLI, MICHAEL; Mendham HS; Mendham, NJ; (4); 69/318; FBLA; Math Tm; Yrbk Sprt Ed; Rep Stu Cncl; Var Bsbl; Var Bsktbl; JV Ftbl; Im Vllybl; Hon Roll; Athltc Awd 87; Princpls Hnr Lst 84-87; U Richmond; Bus Mngmnt.

ROSSETTI, CAROLYN; Saint Mary HS; Keansburg, NJ; (3); 1/97; Church Yth Grp; Yrbk Stf; JV Var Cheerleading; Var Crs Cntry; French Hon Soc; High Hon Roll; NHS; NEDT Awd; Rutgers Schlr 87.

ROSSHIRT, KENNETH; Manchester Twp HS; Whiting, NJ; (3); 1/200; Math Tm; Science Clb; Bausch & Lomb Sci Awd; High Hon Roll; Hon Roll; NHS; Rutgers Schlr Prog 87; Bausch & Lomb Mth 87.

ROSSI, KIRK; Wood-Ridge HS; Wood-Ridge, NJ; (3); 19/90; Boy Scts; Church Yth Grp; Latin Clb; Math Clb; Model UN; Yrbk Bus Mgr; JV Var Bsbl; Hon Roll; Rutgers U; Sprtswrtr.

ROSSI, MICHAEL; Bishop Eustace Preparatory Schl; Sewell, NJ; (3); 5/165; Am Leg Boys St; Church Yth Grp; Cmnty Wkr; Pres Math Clb; Sec Trs Spanish Clb; SADD; Bsbl; High Hon Roll; NHS; Spanish NHS; U Of DE.

ROSSI, PAMELA; Brick Memorial HS; Brick, NJ; (2); Chorus; JV Fld Hcky; Hon Roll.

ROSSI, ROBERT; Nutley HS; Nutley, NJ; (3); 21/299; Am Leg Boys St; Drama Clb; Latin Clb; Office Aide; School Musical; Trs Jr Cls; VP Sr Cls; JV Var Bsktbl; Var Trk; NHS; Bio Sci.

ROSSITER, RUSSELL; Gloucester Catholic HS; National Pk, NJ; (3); 5/200; Boy Scts; Library Aide; U Of PA; Surgeon.

ROSSMELL, PATTI ANN; North Arlington HS; N Arlington, NJ; (3); Ski Clb; Trs Soph Cls; Trs Jr Cls; Trs Sr Cls; Hst Stu Cncl; Var Bsktbl; Var Cheerleading; Var Sftbl; Trs NHS; Spanish NHS; Elem Ed.

ROSWECH, MARC; Toms River High School South; Beachwood, NJ; (4); 15/326; Am Leg Boys St; Hosp Aide; Math Tm; Ski Clb; JV Bsktbl; High Hon Roll; Trs NHS; Pres Adac Ftnss Awd 87; Natl Hnr Scty Schlrhsp 87; Stu Athlt Trnr Vrst Let 87; PA ST U; Engrng.

ROTANTE, JAMES; St Josephs Regional HS; Wyckoff, NJ; (4); 8/154; Church Yth Grp; Math Tm; Off Stu Cncl; Crs Cntry; Socr; Hon Roll; NHS; Ntl Merit SF; Spanish NHS; St Schlr; Knghts Columbs ST Schlrshp 87; Italn Labr Brd Schlrshp; Penn ST; Elec Engr.

ROTBERG, TAMARA LEE; Washington Township HS; Turnersville, NJ; (4); 52/480; Cmnty Wkr; Spanish Clb; Chorus; Color Guard; Nwsp Rptr; Coach Actv; Var L Swmmng; Hon Roll; NJ Gvrnrs Tchng Schlrshp 87; Presdntl Acadc Ftns Awd 87; Yvonne Ferrari Memrl Awd 87; Trenton ST Coll; Spcl Ed Tchr.

ROTH, CARL; Henry Hudson Regional HS; Atlntic Hglds, NJ; (3); Spanish Clb; SADD; Yrbk Rptr; Stu Cncl; JV Bsbl; Capt L Bsktbl; Var L Crs Cntry; L Var Tennis; NHS; Bus.

ROTH, JENNIFER; Middletown HS South; Leonardo, NJ; (3); Yrbk Stf; Powder Puff Ftbl; L Socr; JV Swmmng; Hon Roll; Rcrtnl Sccr Tm Dvsn II 86-87; ST Cp Chmpns Brnz Mdl; Cmmnctns.

ROTH, SANDRA LEE; Bayley Ellard Catholic HS; Whippany, NJ; (4); School Play; Nwsp Rptr; Yrbk Ed-Chief; Rep Frsh Cls; Rep Soph Cls; VP Jr Cls; Trs Stu Cncl; Socr; NHS; HOBY Awd 84-85; Fairleigh Dickinson U; Bus Mngt.

ROTHERY, RICHARD; Wall HS; Wall, NJ; (4); 20/269; German Clb; Variety Show; Pres Sr Cls; Stu Cncl; Var L Bsbl; Var L Crs Cntry; JV Ftbl; Hon Roll; Nuclear Engrng.

ROTHSTEIN, MICHELE DENISE; West Milford Township HS; West Milford, NJ; (3); 18/405; Am Leg Aux Girls St; Spanish Clb; SADD; Concert Band; Mrchg Band; School Musical; NHS; Spanish NHS; Cmnty Wkr; Office Aide; Pblshd In Grt Poems Tdy 87; Lbn Vly Coll Yth Schlrs Inst 87; Pltcl Sci.

ROTHWELL, JEANNE; Immaculate Conception HS; Newark, NJ; (3); Drama Clb; Chorus; School Play; Trk; Spanish NHS.

ROTONDO, DANIELLE; Notre Dame HS; Trenton, NJ; (3); 56/348; Drama Clb; Chorus; School Musical; School Play; Rep Soph Cls; JV Socr; NHS; Spanish NHS; DE U; Comm.

ROTTER, BETH; Manalapan HS; Manalapan, NJ; (3); 56/429; Hosp Aide; SADD; Nwsp Stf; Mgr Gym.

ROTUNNO, MARK; South River HS; S River, NJ; (2); Art Clb; Church Yth Grp; Y-Teens; Seton Hall U.

ROUDEZ, KIM; Immaculate Conception HS; Newark, NJ; (4); 38/77; Cmnty Wkr; Red Cross Aide; Chorus; School Musical; School Play; Variety Show; Rep Stu Cncl; Trk; Hon Roll; Acad Achvmnt Hist 87; Stockton St Coll; Psych.

ROUNDS, JULIE; Middletown H S South; Red Bank, NJ; (3); Am Leg Aux Girls St; Cmnty Wkr; Powder Puff Ftbl; Trk; High Hon Roll; Hon Roll; NHS; Mst Vlbl Plyr Awd Grls Indoor Trck Tm 86; Educ.

ROUNDTREE, WILLAM; Asbury Park HS; Asbury Park, NJ; (4); Church Yth Grp; Dance Clb; Office Aide; Spanish Clb; SADD; Band; School Musical; Pres Stu Cncl; Cit Awd; High Hon Roll; Omega Psi Phi Fraternity 83-84 & 85-86; Elion Workers Schlrshp 87-88; Norfolk ST; Bus Admin.

ROUNTREE, TISA; Essex Catholic Girls HS; Newark, NJ; (3); Pep Clb; Rep Soph Cls; Rep Jr Cls; Trs Sr Cls; Hon Roll; Acad All-Amer 86; Hampton U; Acctg.

ROURKE, MARY ELLEN; West Essex SR HS; Roseland, NJ; (3); Am Leg Boys St; Am Leg Aux Girls St; French Clb; Key Clb; Latin Clb; SADD; Var L Socr; Var L Trk; Hon Roll; NHS; Prsh Cncl 87; Pltcl Sci.

ROUSCULP, MATTHEW; Jackson Memorial HS; Marietta, GA; (4); 17/390; Am Leg Boys St; Ski Clb; Sec Sr Cls; Pres Stu Cncl; Capt Var Ftbl; JV Trk; Var Wt Lftg; JV Wrstlng; High Hon Roll; NHS; N J Distingshd Schlr 86; Pop Warner Schlr Athlete 84; VFW Schlr 87; Rutgers; Pre-Med.

ROUSE, JAMES; Henry Snyder HS; Jersey City, NJ; (3); NHS.

ROUSE, JOANN; Haddon Heights HS; Lawnside, NJ; (4); 28/160; Debate Tm; French Clb; Hosp Aide; Nwsp Ed-Chief; Yrbk Stf; Lit Mag; Rep Frsh Cls; Rep Soph Cls; Rep Jr Cls; NHS; Temple U; Jrnlsm.

ROUTON, CAROL ANN; Haddon Heights HS; Haddonfield, NJ; (4); 21/160; French Clb; Nwsp Phtg; Nwsp Rptr; Yrbk Stf; JV Mgr(s); Powder Puff Ftbl; JV Score Keeper; JV Tennis; Hon Roll; Church Yth Grp; Parent-Teacher Group Bk Awd 87-88; U Of DE; Bus.

ROUX, LISA; Pennsville HS; Pennsville, NJ; (4); Am Leg Aux Girls St; Chorus; Concert Band; Mrchg Band; Rep Soph Cls; Rep Jr Cls; Rep Sr Cls; Rep Stu Cncl; Stat Mgr Ftbl; Hon Roll; W Chester U; Accntng.

ROVEE, CHRIS K; Hunterdon Central HS; Stockton, NJ; (4); 53/542; Variety Show; Nwsp Sprt Ed; Capt Gym; JV Wrstlng; High Hon Roll; NCTE Awd; Sec NHS; Ntl Merit Ltr; Yrbk Rptr; JV Bsktbl; Garden ST Dstngshd Schlr 87; NJ Al-ST Gymnsts Tm 86; U Of CA Berkeley; Engl.

ROVELLI, JOSEPH D; Bergen Catholic HS; Dumont, NJ; (3); Am Leg Boys St; Church Yth Grp; Lit Mag; Bsbl; Socr; High Hon Roll; Hon Roll; MVP In Soccer 84 & 86; Brd Of Chsn Frhldrs At Boys ST 87; Accntng.

ROVICK, PETER; Chathan Twp HS; Chatham Twp, NJ; (4); Sec Soph Cls; VP Jr Cls; Trs Sr Cls; Rep Stu Cncl; Var Capt Crs Cntry; Var Trk; Hon Roll; NHS.

ROWE, ED; Pinelands Regional HS; Tuckerton, NJ; (3); SADD; Var Bsbl; Hon Roll; Acad All Amer; Ntl Math Achvt Awd.

ROWE, JEANNE ANNE; Teaneck HS; Teaneck, NJ; (4); 60/420; Church Yth Grp; NAACP; Spanish Clb; SADD; Ed Yrbk Stf; JV Swmmng; Var L Trk; Hon Roll; NHS; Cert Outstndng Acadmc Achvmnt 83; Sequence Hnrs 80-83; Urban Lge Cert Outstndng Acadmc Achvmnt 87; Douglass Coll; Bio.

ROWE, MICHAEL J; Don Bosco Prep; N Haldeon, NJ; (4); Pep Clb; Ski Clb; Yrbk Stf; Rep Sr Cls; Stu Cncl; JV Var Ftbl; Hon Roll; Yng Schlrs Conf 86-87; Found For Free Enterprise 86-87; STYLE 85-87; Siena Coll; Naval Aviator.

ROWE, RONNIE; North Warren Regional HS; Blairstown, NJ; (2); Church Yth Grp; Quiz Bowl; Spanish Clb; Band; Concert Band; Mrchg Band; Yrbk Stf; Rep Frsh Cls; High Hon Roll; Drill Tm; All Cnty Band 85-87; Gftd & Tlntd Pgm 84-87; Rutgers Coll; Bus Ecs.

ROWLAND, ELIZABETH; Memorial HS; Cedar Grove, NJ; (4); 2/123; Spanish Clb; Mrchg Band; Nwsp Sprt Ed; Rep Stu Cncl; Capt Bsktbl; Sftbl; Tennis; High Hon Roll; Pres NHS; Garden ST Distinguished Schlr 87-88.

ROWLEY, JENNIFER; Notre Dame HS; Trenton, NJ; (3); 7/375; CAP; Latin Clb; Service Clb; Lit Mag; Crs Cntry; Score Keeper; High Hon Roll; Hon Roll; NHS; Latn Hnr Soc 85-88; Chrstn Clowning 86-88; Amherst Coll; Bio.

ROY, MARC; Pennsville Memorial HS; Pennsville, NJ; (3); 2/275; Boy Scts; Chess Clb; Computer Clb; Drama Clb; Math Clb; PAVAS; Band; Concert Band; Jazz Band; School Musical; Eastman Coll; Music.

ROY, PRYIA; Rahway SR HS; Rahway, NJ; (4); 37/230; Quiz Bowl; Variety Show; Nwsp Rptr; Nwsp Stf; Yrbk Rptr; Yrbk Stf; Rep Sr Cls; Var Bsktbl; Cit Awd; Hon Roll; Unicefs 1st Earth Run For Peace Prtcpnt 86-87; Pres Sr Productions Jr Achvt/Apld Ecmncs 86-87; Villanova U; Lwyr.

ROYAL, TAKESHA; Mainland Regional HS; Somers Pt, NJ; (3); Church Yth Grp; Band; Chorus; Church Choir; Concert Band; Trk; Hon Roll; Rotary Awd; Hnr Rl 84-87; Rotary Intl 87; Med.

ROYDS, ROBERT K; John F Kennedy HS; Willingboro, NJ; (3); Drama Clb; Chorus; School Musical; School Play; Stage Crew; JV Ftbl; Hon Roll; Ntl Merit Ltr; Variety Show; Stage Mgr ST Teen Arts Champ 86-87; Acctg.

ROYSTER JR, JAMES L; Lincoln HS; Jersey City, NJ; (4); Camera Clb; Computer Clb; FBLA; Math Clb; Var Bsbl; Im Bsktbl; JV Var Bowling; Capt Ftbl; Im Sftbl; Im Vllybl; Cmptr Sci.

ROYSTER, JASON; Immaculata HS; Piscataway, NJ; (2); Cmnty Wkr; SADD; Band; Concert Band; Rep Frsh Cls; Rep Soph Cls; Rep Stu Cncl; Co-Capt Bsktbl; Co-Capt Ftbl; JV Trk; Math.

ROZANSKY, DANA; Cherry Hill East HS; Cherry Hill, NJ; (3); Am Leg Aux Girls St; French Clb; Model UN; Var JV Score Keeper; Var Sftbl; Gov Hon Prg Awd; NCTE Awd; 2nd Pl Spch Rptrng Cntst 87; Cum Laude 87; Hold Ranking In NJ & Middle States In Tennis 87.

ROZELL, FRED; Brick Township HS; Brick Town, NJ; (4); Varsity Clb; JV Ftbl; Var Ice Hcky; Ocean County Coll; Bus.

ROZZO, CHRISTINE; Wayne Hills HS; Wayne, NJ; (3); 99/330; Hosp Aide; Pep Clb; Band; Concert Band; Variety Show; Sec Jr Cls; Sec Sr Cls; Var Capt Cheerleading; Var Capt Pom Pon; Trk; Chrldng Coach Awd 85; Essay Cntst Awd 84.

RUBAN, MICHELLE; Parsippany HS; Parsippany, NJ; (3); FBLA; Spanish Clb; Band; Yrbk Stf; High Hon Roll; NHS; Girls Ctznshp Inst 87; 2nd Pl Spnsh Natl Hnr Scty Cmptn 86.

RUBANO, ANGELO; Lakewood HS; Lakewood, NJ; (3); 6/350; Am Leg Boys St; Band; Concert Band; Jazz Band; Mrchg Band; Var L Bsbl; Hon Roll; NHS; Spanish NHS; VFW Schlrshp Essy Cntst 86; Chrprctc Med.

RUBEL, WILLIAM; Wayne Valley HS; Paterson, NJ; (4); Model UN; Ed Lit Mag; High Hon Roll; Hon Roll; NCTE Awd; NHS; Ntl Merit Ltr; Grdr ST Dstngshd Schlr 86-87; Engl.

RUBIANO, BETTINA; Union Hill HS; Union City, NJ; (3); Math Clb; Mu Alpha Theta; Spanish Clb; Drill Tm; Off Jr Cls; Pom Pon; Hon Roll; Mu Alpha Theta Awd; Pre Med.

RUBIN, BRYON; Hackensack HS; Hackensack, NJ; (3); 7/400; Am Leg Boys St; Spanish Clb; Varsity Clb; Rep Frsh Cls; Rep Soph Cls; Var L Bsbl; Im Vllybl; High Hon Roll; NHS; Spanish NHS; Achvt Engl I 85; Mickey Mantle Hackensack Bsbl Co-MVP, 100 Pct Awd 85; Med.

RUBIN, DAVID M; Wayne Valley HS; Wayne, NJ; (3); Am Leg Boys St; Model UN; Band; Jazz Band; Mrchg Band; Yrbk Stf; Lit Mag; Var Tennis; High Hon Roll; Hst NHS; Yale Bk Awd Bst Acad 87; Pre-Med.

RUBIN, RACHEL; Bridgewater-Raritan HS East; Bridgewater, NJ; (3); French Clb; Chorus; Nwsp Stf; Stat Swmmng; Hon Roll; Intr Dsgn.

RUBIN, SARAH; Bridgewater Raritain HS East; Bridgewater, NJ; (2); Spanish Clb; SADD; Nwsp Ed-Chief; Rep Frsh Cls; Rep Soph Cls; Rep Stu Cncl; JV Fld Hcky; Hon Roll; Vlntr Spcl Olympcs 87; Bus.

RUBIN, SUSAN; Colonia HS; Colonia, NJ; (4); 1/244; Math Clb; Scholastic Bowl; Temple Yth Grp; Yrbk Ed-Chief; Bausch & Lomb Sci Awd; NCTE Awd; Val; Am Leg Aux Girls St; NFL; SADD; Futr Prblm Slvng Bwl-Tp 15 Inatl; NJ Govs Schl Math, Sci; Prjct Gftd Course-Envrnmntl Sci; Biolgcl Sci.

RUBINSTEIN, MICHELE; Freehold Township HS; Freehold, NJ; (3); Art Clb; Pep Clb; SADD; Temple Yth Grp; JV Cheerleading; Pom Pon; Stat Trk; NHS; Prtnrs In Pcmkng-Art Aprtcn Awd; Fash Dsgn.

RUBIO, ROSA; Hoboken HS; Hoboken, NJ; (3); Church Yth Grp; French Clb; Church Choir; Pom Pon; Med.

RUBLE, CHRISTINA; Rancocas Valley Regional HS; Mt Holly, NJ; (2); 20/316; Art Clb; Church Yth Grp; High Hon Roll; Hon Roll.

RUDDOCK, MICHELLE; Perth Amboy HS; Perth Amboy, NJ; (3); 10/350; Hosp Aide; Science Clb; Ski Clb; Spanish Clb; Varsity Clb; Band; Concert Band; Mrchg Band; Crs Cntry; Socr; Sftbll,Bsktbll & Hnr Rll 87.

RUDERFER, STUART B; Livingston HS; Livingston, NJ; (3); Sec FBLA; Sec Key Clb; Political Wkr; VP Temple Yth Grp; School Musical; Swing Chorus; Yrbk Ed-Chief; Pres Frsh Cls; Hon Roll; Jr NHS; Law.

RUDEWICK, JACK; Belvidere HS; Washington, NJ; (4); 9/130; Am Leg Boys St; Varsity Clb; Im Ftbl; Var Capt Golf; Im Socr; Im Sftbl; Im Vllybl; High Hon Roll; Hon Roll; Clnry Arts.

RUDING, JENNIFER; Neptune SR HS; Ocean Grove, NJ; (4); Lit Mag; Rep Jr Cls; Rep Sr Cls; High Hon Roll; Hon Roll; Jr NHS; NHS; Prsdntl Acad Ftns Awd 87; Outstndng Sr Grdtng-Dstnctn-Indstrl Art 87; Trsts Schlrshp-Sprng Grdn Clg 87; Spring Garden Coll; Arch.

RUDISILL, ROSEMARIE; Egg Harbor Township HS; W Atlantic City, NJ; (3); 5/372; Art Clb; Church Yth Grp; School Musical; JV Cheerleading; JV Fld Hcky; JV Swmmng; High Hon Roll; Jr NHS; NHS; Ntl Merit Ltr; Law.

RUDNICK, HOLLY; Union HS; Union, NJ; (4); Key Clb; Service Clb; Temple Yth Grp; Concert Band; Jazz Band; Mrchg Band; Orch; School Musical; Mgr(s); Mgr Trk; All State Orch 85-87; Pres Acdmc Achvmnt Awd 87; Music Tchrs Schlrshp 87; Natl Hnrs Bnd 86-87; Cook Coll; Sci.

RUE, CHRIS; Rancocas Valley Regional HS; Mount Holly, NJ; (2); Church Yth Grp; Drama Clb; Band; JV Bsbl; JV Socr; High Hon Roll; Prfct Atten Awd; Stu Of Dstnctn 86-87; Penn ST.

RUECK, CHRISTINE; Middletown North HS; Middletown, NJ; (2); Library Aide; Office Aide; SADD; Teachers Aide; Chorus; Nwsp Rptr; Lit Mag; Bowling; JV Tennis; Hon Roll; Sports Med.

RUEDIGER, ARTHUR; Cumberland Regional HS; Bridgeton, NJ; (4); 58/334; Var Crs Cntry; JV Wrstlng; Hon Roll; Acad Schlrshp 87-88; Model Cngrss Team 87; Polt Sci Club 87; DE Valley Coll; Bio.

RUFF, DAWN MARIE; Maple Shade HS; Maple Shade, NJ; (3); Am Leg Aux Girls St; French Clb; FBLA; Spanish Clb; Rep Stu Cncl; Var JV Bsktbl; Var Socr; Var Sftbl; Prfct Atten Awd; Trenton ST; Spcl Ed.

RUFFIN, DAMON J; Passaic County HS; Paterson, NJ; (3); Art Clb; Boys Clb Am; Church Yth Grp; Computer Clb; NAACP; Teachers Aide; Stage Crew; Yrbk Stf; Im Badmtn; Im Bsbl; Paterson Math Sci Ft 84; Montclair ST Coll; Cmrcl Arts.

RUGARBER, PAUL; St John Vianney HS; Freehold, NJ; (3); 19/246; Church Yth Grp; Cmnty Wkr; Service Clb; SADD; JV Capt Socr; Vllybl; High Hon Roll; Hon Roll; NHS; 1st Pl-Rcqutbll Leag; Trenton ST Coll; Arch.

RUGER IV, A NELSON; Atlantic Friends Schl; Mays Landing, NJ; (2); Cmnty Wkr; Computer Clb; Drama Clb; Thesps; School Play; Stage Crew; Lit Mag; Socr; K R Morgan Schlrshp Awd 86; Perf Arts.

RUIBAL, GLORIA; Lakeland Regional HS; Ringwood, NJ; (4); 3/345; Church Yth Grp; Drama Clb; Math Clb; Thesps; School Play; Variety Show; CC Awd; Gov Hon Prg Awd; NHS; Spanish NHS; Lakeland ST Bank Schlrshp 87; U Notre Dame; Chem Engrng.

RUIZ, ANDREW; Union HS; Union, NJ; (2); Chess Clb; Math Clb; Im Bsktbl; Var Crs Cntry; Im Tennis; Wt Lftg; Hon Roll; Jr NHS; Comprehnsv German Lang Course 87; Engr.

RUIZ, CARMEN M; Camden County Voc; Camden, NJ; (1); Drama Clb; FFA; VICA; School Play; Nwsp Stf; Yrbk Stf; Frsh Cls; Fld Hcky; Prfct Atten Awd; SCM Awd Plq 83; Glassboro ST Coll; Law.

RUIZ, ELSIE; Mary Help Of Christians Acad; Paterson, NJ; (3); SADD; Teachers Aide; Pharmacy.

RUIZ, JOSE; Dover HS; Dover, NJ; (3); 10/210; AFS; VP Frsh Cls; Swmmng; High Hon Roll; NHS; 1st Prz Physcs Ponce 4 Sci Fair & Southrn Area PR.

RUIZ, JUDY; Eastside HS; Paterson, NJ; (3); Hon Roll; Hnr Roll 87; Rutgers U; Chem.

RUIZ, MARISOL; Woodrow Wilson HS; Camden, NJ; (3); Church Yth Grp; Cmnty Wkr; Debate Tm; Quiz Bowl; Church Choir; Rep Soph Cls; PRIME 86-87; Philadelphia C Parh & Sci; Med.

RUIZ, RAOUL; Edison HS; Edison, NJ; (4); 4/384; Math Tm; Science Clb; Chorus; Orch; JV Bowling; Trk; Hon Roll; NHS; Columbia Sci Hnrs Pgm; Cntnntl Math Leg Awd; Colubmia Engrng; Bioengrng.

RUIZ, REX B; Bergen Catholic HS; Oradell, NJ; (3); Am Leg Boys St; Hosp Aide; Nwsp Stf; Sec Rep Soph Cls; Off Jr Cls; Off Sr Cls; Im Bowling; Im Vllybl; High Hon Roll; Spanish NHS; Columbia Coll Bk Awd 87; Ntl Spanish Contest Wnnr 85; Medicine.

RUIZ, TANYA; Wayne Hills HS; Wayne, NJ; (3); 60/328; Cmnty Wkr; Capt GAA; Pep Clb; Ski Clb; Spanish Clb; Rep Stu Cncl; Capt Var Cheerleading; Pom Pon; Trk; High Hon Roll; Vlntr Coaches Awd Chrldng 85; Criminal Law.

RUIZ, YESENIA; Eastside HS; Paterson, NJ; (2); #7 In Class; Science Clb; High Hon Roll; Hon Roll; Rutgers; Cvl Engr.

RULLO, MELISSA; Notre Dame HS; Lawrenceville, NJ; (3); VP Art Clb; Hosp Aide; Latin Clb; Red Cross Aide; Ski Clb; Hon Roll; U Of Bridgeport; Advrtsmt.

RUNGE, THOMAS H; Toms River High School North; Toms River, NJ; (3); JV Var Bsbl; JV Var Bsktbl; Var Crs Cntry; NHS; 1st Pl Sci Fair Awd 85; Engr.

RUNKO, AARON; Howell HS; Howell, NJ; (3); 60/450; JCL; Latin Clb; Spanish Clb; SADD; Varsity Clb; Var L Bsbl; Var Capt Socr; NHS; Pres Schlr; Var Trk; Natl Hnr Soc Treas 87-88; Acctng.

RUNNELLS-GREEN, CRYSTAL M; Jackson Memorial HS; Lakewood, NJ; (3); 79/433; Art Clb; Church Yth Grp; NAACP; Office Aide; ROTC; Spanish Clb; Church Choir; Color Guard; JV Trk; Hon Roll; Debutante Cotillion Ms Congnlty 86-87; Prfct Atten Awd 86-87; Spn Clb Hnr Soc 86-87; Temple U; Bus Entrprnr.

RUNYON, KERRY; Point Pleasant Boro HS; Point Pleasant, NJ; (4); 12/250; Chorus; Church Choir; School Musical; JV Fld Hcky; JV Trk; NHS; Chrstrs Guild Awd 83-84; Chamberlayne JC; Fshn Dsgn.

RUPERTUS, ADRIANE; Highland Regional HS; Blackwood, NJ; (2); JV Fld Hcky; Musician.

RUPP, CARLA; Gloucester Catholic HS; Woodbury, NJ; (3); Compute Clb; Stage Crew; JV Var Bowling; Var Swmmng; Im Mgr Vllybl; Hon Roll Intl Frgn Lang Awd 86; Bus.

RUPP, KRISTIN; North Brunswick Twp HS; N Brunswick, NJ; (4) Drama Clb; Pres Trs Key Clb; Model UN; Rep Stu Cncl; Cit Awd; Hor Roll; Kiwanis Awd; NHS; Latin Clb; Math Tm; Century III Ldrshp Aw 87; Mrl Schlrshp Female Entrng Non Tradtnl Fld 87; Rutgers U; E Frcstng Poltcs.

RUPPERT, SUSANNE; Watchung Regional HS; Gillette, NJ; (3); Ke Clb; SADD; Off Stu Cncl; Var Tennis; Var Trk; Cit Awd; Hon Roll; Op Clb Awd; Church Yth Grp; Cmnty Wkr; Tnns Intructior 87; Mass Comms

RUPPRECHT, DESIRE; Mc Corristin Catholic HS; Bordentown, NJ (3); JA; JV Bsktbl; Hon Roll; NHS; Sci.

RUSCONI, SHERYL; Clifton HS; Clifton, NJ; (4); 55/589; French Clb Key Clb; Library Aide; Band; Mrchg Band; Bowling; French Hon Soc; Hor Roll; Jr NHS; NHS; W R Hotchkiss Fndtn Schlrshp; Pres Acdmc Ftns Awd 87; Montclair ST Coll; Bus Admn.

RUSEK, CHRISTOPHER; Ridge HS; Basking Ridge, NJ; (2); 8/190; Boy Scts; Church Yth Grp; Math Tm; Quiz Bowl; Science Clb; Ski Clb; Spanish Clb; Concert Band; Stage Crew; JV Socr; United Way Yth Ldrs Conf 87 Gifted & Tlntd Pgm 87; Harvard; Crmnl Law.

RUSH, LINDA; Warren Co-Vo Technical HS; Washington, NJ; (3); Hosp Aide; Key Clb; Library Aide; Ski Clb; Varsity Clb; Var L Cheerleading; Va L Sftbl; Hon Roll; Prfct Atten Awd; Accntng.

RUSH, MICHAEL; Paul VI Regional HS; Clifton, NJ; (3); Church Yt Grp; Cmnty Wkr; Drama Clb; French Clb; Office Aide; School Musical; Li Mag; Var Tennis; French Hon Soc; Hon Roll; Theatre Arts.

RUSH, REBECCA; Kearny HS; Kearny, NJ; (4); 13/383; Computer Clb French Clb; Capt Gym; French Hon Soc; High Hon Roll; Hon Roll; NHS Milton Bock Alumni Awd 87; PTA Awd 87; Booster Clb Schlrshp 87 Montclair ST Coll; Comp Sci.

RUSH, SCOTT; Indian Hills HS; Oakland, NJ; (3); 26/303; Chess Clb Q&S; Temple Yth Grp; Varsity Clb; Nwsp Rptr; Nwsp Sprt Ed; Im Socr Hon Roll; NHS; Ntl Merit Ltr; Boys Var Fncng Tm 85-87; Epee Nat Chmpn Fncng 87tmpl Yth Grp Treas 85.

RUSIN, DIANE; Immaculate Conception HS; Wallington, NJ; (2); 9/89 Debate Tm; English Clb; NFL; Yrbk Stf; Var Bsktbl; JV Vllybl; High Hor Roll; NHS; Spanish NHS.

RUSSELL, ERNEST; Linden HS; Linden, NJ; (3); Church Yth Grp Exploring; JA; Scholastic Bowl; Science Clb; Var Bsbl; Var Ftbl; Va Tennis; Bausch & Lomb Sci Awd; High Hon Roll; U Notre Dame; Engrng

RUSSELL, HEATHER; Shore Regional HS; Oceanport, NJ; (3); Latin Clb; VP Stu Cncl; Var Bsktbl; Fld Hcky; Sftbl; High Hon Roll; Brnz Cngrssnl Awd 86.

RUSSELL, KELLIE; Burlington County Vo-Tech; Willingboro, NJ; (3) Camera Clb; Dance Clb; DECA; French Clb; Library Aide; SADD Teachers Aide; VICA; Band; Chorus; Chorus, Libraray Aide & Gymnastics Rutgers U; Bus Admin.

RUSSELL, KIMBERLY; Washington Township HS; Turnersville, NJ (3); Art Clb; Ski Clb; Spanish Clb; Rep Soph Cls; Rep Jr Cls; Hon Roll Drexel; Intr Dsgn.

RUSSELL, LINDA; Union HS; Union, NJ; (4); FFA; Teachers Aide School Play; Variety Show; Nwsp Rptr; Nwsp Stf; Elks Awd; Poster Cntst Awd; FFA Flwr Arrngmnt; Own Animal Shelter.

RUSSELL, LORI; Brick HS; Brick, NJ; (3); Church Yth Grp; Variety Show; Socl Wrk.

RUSSELL, MARY LYNN; Randolph HS; Randolph, NJ; (4); Church Yth Grp; Chorus; Capt Drill Tm; Trs Jr Cls; Trs Sr Cls; Powder Puff Ftbl Hon Roll; Svc Awd, Ldrshp Awd 87; Rutgers U.

RUSSELL, MELISSA; Woodstown HS; Woodstown, NJ; (4); 43/210 Church Yth Grp; FBLA; Hosp Aide; SADD; SADD; Rep Sr Cls; Bsktbl Cheerleading; 2nd Pl Regnl Comp FBLA 87; Widener U; Bus Mgmt.

RUSSELL, ROBERT KEITH; Whippany Park HS; Whippany, NJ; (3) 45/187; Church Yth Grp; Stage Crew; Golf; Hon Roll; Engrng.

RUSSINKO, PAUL; Pinelands Regional HS; Tuckerton, NJ; (3); 10/200 Am Leg Boys St; Var L Crs Cntry; Var L Trk; Pres French Hon Soc; Hon Roll; Trs NHS; Sprts Persn-Sprg Trck 87; Most Impvd Rnnr-Crss Cntry 84 & 86; Grp I ST Chmpn Crss Cntry Tm 84; Pre-Med.

RUSSO, AMY KRISTINE; Shawnee HS; Medford, NJ; (4); 26/535; Latin Clb; Pep Clb; Varsity Clb; Yrbk Stf; JV Var Sftbl; Hon Roll; NHS; Pres Acad Fit Awd Pgm 87; Gdn ST Dstngshd Schlr Pgm 86-87; Rutgers Coll; Acctng.

RUSSO, CHRISTOPHER A; Bridgewater Raritan HS West; Bridgewater, NJ; (3); Church Yth Grp; German Clb; Rep Frsh Cls; JV Bsbl; Coach Actv; Var L Ftbl; Powder Puff Ftbl; High Hon Roll; Hon Roll; NHS; Sci.

RUSSO, JAMES; De Paul Diocesan HS; Wayne, NJ; (4); 7/154; Church Yth Grp; JCL; Pres Latin Clb; Nwsp Stf; Var L Bsbl; Var L Bsktbl; DAR Awd; NHS.

RUSSO, JOANN; Phillipsburg HS; Phillipsburg, NJ; (4); 69/292; Drama Clb; Ski Clb; Band; Chorus; Concert Band; Mrchg Band; School Musical; Nwsp Stf; Rep Stu Cncl; Hon Roll; Barber Schl PTO Schlrshp; Bloomsburg U; Elem Educ.

RUSSO, PAULA; Wayne Hills HS; Wayne, NJ; (3); 7/350; French Clb; Math Tm; Science Clb; School Musical; Stage Crew; Var Fld Hcky; Var Mgr(s); Mgr Wrstlng; High Hon Roll; NHS; Chem.

RUSSO, STEPHANIE; Morris Hills HS; Rockaway, NJ; (4); 1/289; French Clb; Intnl Clb; Capt Scholastic Bowl; Thesps; Mrchg Band; VP Sr Cls; Stu Cncl; NHS; St Schlr; Val; Japan US Senate Schlrshp Prgrm 86; Morris Hills Frgn Lng Awd 87; Georgetown U; Japanese.

RUSSO, STEVEN; Fair Lawn HS; Fair Lawn, NJ; (3); Ski Clb; Stage Crew; JV Bsbl; JV Ftbl; Ice Hcky; Var Lcrss; Wt Lftg; Cvl Engr.

RUSSONIELLO, JANINE; Saint Rose HS; Pt Pleasant, NJ; (3); 23/220; Dance Clb; Rptr Key Clb; School Play; Nwsp Rptr; Lit Mag; Stu Cncl; Var Bsktbl; Var Crs Cntry; Sftbl; Hon Roll; Job At Rest 86-87; Cmmnctns.

RUSSUP, DAWN; New Brunswick HS; New Brunswick, NJ; (4); 9/110; Math Tm; Nwsp Stf; Var Sftbl; Sec NHS; Rnnr Up NJ Young Playwrights Fest 86; Princpls Awd Acad Excllnce Sftbl 86; Conf All Amer Hnr Rl 86; Marist Coll; Cmmnctns.

RUTBERG, MELANIE; Atlantic City HS; Atlantic City, NJ; (4); 150/402; Key Clb; Model UN; Lawyer.

RUTNIK, TRACEY; Ramapo HS; Wyckoff, NJ; (4); 42/329; Sec VP Spanish Clb; Ed Yrbk Stf; Powder Puff Ftbl; High Hon Roll; Hon Roll; NHS; Rep Frsh Cls; Off Soph Cls; VP Jr Cls; Rep Stu Cncl; Engl, Span, Socl Studies Achvt Awds; Outstndng Yrbk Contrib Awd; APTS Schlrshp; Rutgers Coll.

UTOWSKI, JEFF; Secaucus HS; Secaucus, NJ; (3); Boy Scts; Key Clb; nd; Concert Band; Jazz Band; Mrchg Band; Orch; School Play; Ftbl; Ice cky.

VAN, THOMAS; St John Vianney HS; Hazlet, NJ; (2); Pres JCL; Latin b; Rep Frsh Cls; JV Bsbl; Hon Roll; Princeton; Accntng.

YAN, CATHERINE; Keansburg HS; Keansburg, NJ; (3); Art Clb; hurch Yth Grp; Cmnty Wkr; Off Key Clb; Varsity Clb; Yrbk Stf; Stu ncl; Cheerleading; Score Keeper; Sftbl; Cert Hnr High Achvmt Indl Arts ; St Anns CYO Achvmt Awd 86-87; Funeral Dir.

YAN, CHRIS S; Haddonfield Memorial HS; Haddonfield, NJ; (3); Am eg Boys St; Church Yth Grp; Intnl Clb; Varsity Clb; Var Bsbl; Var Socr; HS; Spanish NHS; Hnrb Mntn Walt Whitman Poems Submttd 87; Bldg anning.

YAN, DANIEL PATRICK; Monroe Township HS; Spotswood, NJ; (4); /196; Stu Cncl; Coach Actv; Capt Ftbl; Wt Lftg; Gov Hon Prg Awd; HS; St Schlr; Am Leg Boys St; Cmnty Wkr; Science Clb; Bill Denny ntrl NJ Chptr Natl Ftbl Fndtn, All-Cnty Ftbl Tm 87; All Acdmc Tm chlr/Athl 86-87; Glassboro ST Coll; Comms.

YAN, ERIN; West Windsor Plainsboro HS; Princeton Junct, NJ; (3); hurch Yth Grp; Latin Clb; Spanish Clb; Teachers Aide; Yrbk Stf; Fld cky; Lcrss; High Hon Roll; Hon Roll; Ten Trphy-Mst Imprvd Cmpr 84; d Hcky Awd-Mst Imprvd Plyr Of Yr 86; Bus Mgmt.

YAN, JENNIFER; Manasquan HS; Manasquan, NJ; (4); 1/220; Math lb; Science Clb; Spanish Clb; Lit Mag; Var L Trk; High Hon Roll; iwanis Awd; NHS; St Schlr; Val; Garden ST Distngshd Schlr Scholar 86; utgers Schlr; Rutgers Coll; Bio Sci.

YAN, JOHN; Lower Cape May Regional HS; N Cape May, NJ; (2); 23/ 34; Hon Roll; NJ ST Future Problem Solvers Pgm 86-87; Asst Soccer oach Township League 86-87.

YAN III, JOHN T; Seton Hall Prep Schl; New Providence, NJ; (4); 23/ 93; Church Yth Grp; Key Clb; Pep Clb; Spanish Clb; Varsity Clb; Rep rsh Cls; Var L Socr; High Hon Roll; Hon Roll; Kiwanis Awd; Seton Hall ; Bus.

YAN, JUDY; Northern Valley Regional Old Tappan; Old Tappan, NJ;); AFS; 4-H; Concert Band; Jazz Band; School Musical; Symp Band; wsp Rptr; High Hon Roll; Hon Roll; NHS.

YAN, KELLIE; Woodstown HS; Alloway, NJ; (3); English Clb; Sec rench Clb; Key Clb; Sec SADD; Chorus; Pres Stu Cncl; Var Cheerleading; ar Fld Hcky; Hon Roll; Ski Clb; Ruritan Natl Yth Ldrship Conf 87.

YAN, KRISTINE; Marylawn Of The Oranges HS; West Orange, NJ;); 6/52; Service Clb; Spanish Clb; Nwsp Rptr; Yrbk Stf; Sftbl; Bausch & omb Sci Awd; High Hon Roll; NHS; Spanish NHS; Pep Clb; Fnlst NJ iovnr Schl Sci 86; Liberal Arts.

YAN, MARZETTE; Central Regional HS; Bayville, NJ; (3); Girl Scts; ICA; Twrlr; 3rd Pl In Cnty VCA Extmprns Spch 86-87; 1st Pl Dsgn Cont 5-86; Art Dsgn.

YAN, MICHELLE; Paul VI HS; Laurel Springs, NJ; (3); 116/418; Rep oph Cls; Rep Jr Cls; Var Fld Hcky; Powder Puff Ftbl; Var Trk; Hon Roll; NHS; Psych.

YAN, ROBERT; Bridgewater Raritan HS East; Bridgewater, NJ; (4); Church Yth Grp; French Clb; Intnl Clb; Ski Clb; Stage Crew; JV Bsbl; JV ocr; U DE; Mech Engrng.

YAN, SARAH; Mother Seton Regional HS; Elizabeth, NJ; (4); Pres Drama Clb; Pep Clb; Teachers Aide; Thesps; School Musical; School Play; Stage Crew; Nwsp Ed-Chief; Nwsp Rptr; Nwsp Sprt Ed; Montclair ST Coll; Theater.

YAN, SUSAN; Monsunor Donovan HS; Jackson, NJ; (3); 43/245; Ski Clb; Var Cheerleading; Hon Roll; Mc Donalds Rstrnt 86-87; Pre-Law.

YAN, TOM; Morristown HS; Morris Plains, NJ; (3); Key Clb; Varsity Clb; Bsbl; Bsktbl; Coach Actv; Ftbl; Powder Puff Ftbl; Wt Lftg.

YBACKI, ANDREW; Edgewood Regional HS; Atco, NJ; (3); Jazz Band; Mrchg Band; Comm.

RYDER, MICHAEL; Watchung Hills Regional HS; Warren, NJ; (4); 79/ 315; Computer Clb; Math Clb; Math Tm; Scholastic Bowl; Band; Chorus; Concert Band; Jazz Band; Mrchg Band; School Play; Bst Actr Musicl 87; Stevens Inst Tech; Comp Engrng.

RYDSTROM, CHRIS; Spotswood HS; Milltown, NJ; (3); 46/159; Am Leg Boys St; Ski Clb; Band; Variety Show; Hon Roll; Musician.

RYDZEWSKI, STEPHEN T; Bishop Eustace HS; Collingswood, NJ; (3); Am Leg Boys St; Cmnty Wkr; Spanish Clb; Bsbl; Bsktbl; NHS; Spanish NHS; Best Hitter Bsbl Team Awd 87; Bus Admin.

RYERSON, ANNE MARIE; Morris Catholic HS; Boonton, NJ; (4); 10/ 138; Church Yth Grp; Natl Beta Clb; Yrbk Ed-Chief; Pres Sr Cls; Var Capt Sftbl; High Hon Roll; NHS; Latin Clb; Pep Clb; Off Lit Mag; Brnrd Flynn Mem Schlrshp 87; 1st Tm All ST Par B Sftbll 86; NJ Stu/Athlt Awd 87; Donglass Coll; Psychlgy.

RYKIEL, DAWN; Wall HS; Wall, NJ; (4); 16/269; JCL; Latin Clb; Sftbl; Letterman Clb; High Hon Roll; Hon Roll; Kiwanis Awd; NHS; Rutgers Coll; Gntcs.

RYNKIEWICZ, JOHN; Holy Spirit HS; Brigantine, NJ; (3); 6/332; Im Vllybl; High Hon Roll; Hon Roll; NHS; Math Awd 84-85.

RZEPNICKI, MATTHEW; Cherry Hill HS West; Cherry Hill, NJ; (3); JV Ftbl; Var Trk; JV Wrstlng; Brdcstng.

SAAM, BILL; Voorhees HS; Hampton, NJ; (4); 25/264; German Clb; JCL; Key Clb; Latin Clb; Math Tm; Varsity Clb; Capt Var Crs Cntry; JV Socr; Var Trk; Im Vllybl; Vrsty Fencng ST Champs 86; VA Tech; Engrng.

SAAVEDRA, ALICIA M; Mount St Mary Acad; Hillside, NJ; (3); Art Clb; Dance Clb; Leo Clb; Service Clb; Pres Sec Spanish Clb; Teachers Aide; Yrbk Stf; Rep Stu Cncl; Hon Roll; Pres Sec Spanish NHS; 1st Pl Natl Spnsh Exam, & Hon Mntn Drew U Spnsh Lang Day 87; Acdmc Awds Theolgy, Bus, & Svc 85-87; Law.

SABA, ROY M; Moorestown SR HS; Moorestown, NJ; (3); Am Leg Boys St; Debate Tm; German Clb; Sec Intnl Clb; NFL; JV Var Socr; JV Tennis; JV Trk; High Hon Roll; Hon Roll; Social Studies Stu Of Mnth 86; Amer Lgn NJ Boys ST 87; Sci.

SABATINO, ANTHONY; Metuchen HS; Metuchen, NJ; (4); 4/178; Am Leg Boys St; Boy Scts; Sec French Clb; Capt Math Tm; Sec Science Clb; French Hon Soc; Pres NHS; Pres Schlr; St Schlr; Rensselaer Medal 86.

SABELLA, RICHELLE; Secaucus HS; Secaucus, NJ; (3); Key Clb; Math Clb; Mu Alpha Theta; Varsity Clb; Off Frsh Cls; JV Sftbl; Var Tennis; High Hon Roll; Hon Roll; Spanish NHS; Lawyr.

SABER, KRISTINE L; Williamstown HS; Williamstown, NJ; (4); 38/267; Cmnty Wkr; Mgr(s); Score Keeper; Outstndng Frgn Lang Awd-Spnsh 84; Montclair ST Coll; Nrsry Schl.

SABIN, GLENN H; Bound Brook HS; Bound Brook, NJ; (4); 1/136; Boy Scts; VP Key Clb; Pres Latin Clb; Capt Speech Tm; Pres Science Clb; Trs Sr Cls; Capt Var Ftbl; Capt Var Trk; NHS; Ntl Merit SF; Rutgers Schlr 86; Garden ST Schlr 86.

SABINE, CHERYL; Morristown HS; Morris Plains, NJ; (3); 4-H; Hosp Aide; Chorus; Capt Color Guard; Concert Band; Mrchg Band; Nwsp Phtg; Nwsp Stf; Yrbk Stf; Lit Mag.

SABLE, CARL; Fair Lawn HS; Fair Lawn, NJ; (2); 3/300; Chess Clb; Computer Clb; Math Clb; Math Tm; Science Clb; High Hon Roll; JETS Awd; AIME 87; ACSL 86-87; EDU Prog Cntst 1st Prize 87; Robotics.

SABO, GREG P; Lawrence HS; Lawrenceville, NJ; (3); 30/225; VP Pres FBLA; Quiz Bowl; Ski Clb; SADD; Varsity Clb; Trs Stu Cncl; Bsktbl; Var Crs Cntry; Var Tennis; Hon Roll; Bus & Stu Mnth 85 & 87; Otstndng Plyr Tns Tm 87; Bnkng.

SABOGAL, CYBELE; Academic HS; Jersey City, NJ; (3); Computer Clb; French Clb; Spanish Clb; SADD; School Play; Stu Cncl; Bowling; Cheerleading; Powder Puff Ftbl; Sftbl; Trenton ST Coll; Pre-Law.

SACCO III, ANTHONY MICHAEL; Buena Regional HS; Minotola, NJ; (3); Y-Teens; Trs Band; Concert Band; Jazz Band; Mrchg Band; Im Wt Lftg; Best 1st Yr Musician 85; Musician.

SACCONE, PAUL; Notre Dame HS; Clarksburg, NJ; (3); 135/375; Am Leg Boys St; Band; Chorus; Concert Band; Jazz Band; Madrigals; Mrchg Band; School Musical; Rep Stu Cncl; NHS; Excllnc Chem 85-86; Excllnc Comp Prgrmng 83-84; Hofstra; Med.

SADATI, ARASH; Middlesex HS; Middlesex, NJ; (4); Aud/Vis; Chess Clb; Drama Clb; Math Clb; Math Tm; Red Cross Aide; Trs Nwsp Stf; Sec Stu Cncl; Capt Socr; Capt Vllybl; Best Essay; Phlsphy People Relgn Awd 83; Psychlgy.

SADOW, AUDREY; Freehold Township HS; Freehold, NJ; (4); 48/353; French Clb; Pep Clb; Varsity Clb; Yrbk Stf; Stat Mgr(s); Powder Puff Ftbl; Score Keeper; Var Socr; NHS; All-Dist Sccr Tm 87; Athlt Of Wk 87; Mst Vlbl Offnsv Plyr 87; U Of MD; Psych.

SADOWSKI, DOUGLAS J; Fair Lawn HS; Fair Lawn, NJ; (4); Am Leg Boys St; Im Coach Actv; Var Socr; NHS; Fairlawn H S Svc Awd 87; Fairlawn All Sports Robert Wright Schlrshp 87; Rutgers U; Mech Engr.

SAFONT, JACQUELINE; Mary Help Of Christian Acad; Paterson, NJ; (1); Quiz Bowl; SADD; Hon Roll; Lawyer.

SAGRESTANO, BRIAN M; Bridgewater-Raritan HS East; Bridgewater, NJ; (3); Boy Scts; Pres Acpl Chr; Mrchg Band; Var Swmmng; Var Tennis; Elks Awd; Gov Hon Prg Awd; NHS; VP Church Yth Grp; Drama Clb; NJ All ST Chorus 85-87; NJ ST Teen Arts Fstvl Slctn Brbrshp Qrtet 87; Pol Sci.

SAHARIG, ELIZABETH; Clifton HS; Clifton, NJ; (3); French Clb; Math Clb; JV Var Vllybl; Dance Clb; Am Leg Aux Girls St; Hosp Aide; Chorus; Med.

SAHI, AVINASH; John P Stevens HS; Edison, NJ; (3); 41/457; Chess Clb; Debate Tm; Intnl Clb; Math Clb; Math Tm; Model UN; Temple Yth Grp; School Musical; Variety Show; Im Badmtn; 3rd NJ Olympics Mind Comp 87; Boston U; Dntstry.

SAHLI, JENNIFER E; Spotswood HS; Spotswood, NJ; (3); Office Aide; Color Guard; Mrchg Band; Nwsp Rptr; Nwsp Stf; Yrbk Bus Mgr; Yrbk Stf; Var Crs Cntry; Var Trk; Hon Roll; Track 2nd Team All Blue Div Hnrs; DECA Rgnl Comp Hnrble Mntn; 86 Cntrl Chmpn Group 1 Track 3rd Pl; Rutgers ST; Jrnlsm.

SAILER, GREGORY TROY; Manchester Twp HS; Whiting, NJ; (4); 2/ 186; Am Leg Boys St; Drama Clb; Science Clb; Spanish Clb; Tennis; Hon Roll; NHS; Pres Schlr; Sal; St Schlr; Trinity U; Cmmnctns.

SAINI, TINA; West Windsor-Plainsboro HS; Princeton Junct, NJ; (3); FBLA; Hosp Aide; Model UN; Nwsp Rptr; Yrbk Stf; JV Socr; JV Trk; High Hon Roll; AFS; Art Clb; Deans Smmr Scholars Prog Schlrshp Rutgers U 87; Poetry In Tri-Cnty Cncls Yng Arthors Comp 87; Med.

SAINI, VANITA; Montville HS; Montville, NJ; (2); Key Clb; SADD; Lit Mag; Y-Teens; JV Trk; High Hon Roll; Prfct Atten Awd; Arch.

SAINTE, CATHERINE; Plainfield HS; Plainfield, NJ; (3); Am Leg Aux Girls St; Church Yth Grp; Chorus; Church Choir; JV Bsktbl; Var Fld Hcky; Stat Sftbl; Pltcl Sci.

SAJNANI, SUNITA; Glen Rock JRSR HS; Glen Rock, NJ; (3); 58/145; Trs AFS; Cmnty Wkr; Debate Tm; Orch; Nwsp Rptr; High Hon Roll; Hon Roll; Jrnlst.

SAKAMOTO, HIROKO; Dwight-Englewood Schl; Cliffside Pk, NJ; (3); Art Clb; Camera Clb; Cmnty Wkr; Dance Clb; Intnl Clb; Bsktbl; ICU; Translator.

SAKARIA, RAVI; Chatham Twp HS; Chatham Twp, NJ; (3); 35/168; Computer Clb; Science Clb; Yrbk Stf; Lit Mag; Trs Frsh Cls; Trs Sr Cls; Hon Roll; NHS; Ntl Merit SF; Prfct Atten Awd; Yth For Understndng Schlrshp To West Germany 87; Duke,Bus.

SAKIN, GEORGE; Red Bank Regional HS; Little Silver, NJ; (3); Boy Scts; Church Yth Grp; Var Swmmng; Var Trk; High Hon Roll; AAV Bhyscl Ftns Tst Outstndng Achvt 87; Engrng.

SAKS, WILLIAM; Dover HS; Mine Hill, NJ; (2); Latin Clb; Ski Clb; Var Bsbl; Var Bsktbl; Var Ftbl; Wt Lftg; Hon Roll.

SAL CERO, MARY ANN; North Valley Regional HS; Northvale, NJ; (3); Hosp Aide; Band; Chorus; Church Choir; Concert Band; Mrchg Band; School Musical; Gergen Cnty Proffesional Cnslrs Assoc Caring Awd 87; Speech Thrpy.

SALAAM, COREY K; Ferris HS; Jersey City, NJ; (4); 69/277; Art Clb; Capt Bowling; Crs Cntry; Trk; Prfct Atten Awd; DE ST; Comp Engr.

SALAMON, ERIC; Sayreville War Memorial HS; Old Bridge, NJ; (3); Boy Scts; German Clb; Science Clb; Spanish Clb; Mgr Stage Crew; Ed Yrbk Rptr; Var L Swmmng; NHS; Spanish NHS; Psychlgy.

SALCEDO, MARIEFEL; William L Dickinson HS; Jersey City, NJ; (3); Office Aide; Nwsp Stf; Rep Stu Cncl; 3 Merit Rlls 84-85; Achvt Rl 86-87; Prfct Atten Awd 84-85; Pace U; Accntng.

SALEM, SUSAN; John P Stevens HS; Edison, NJ; (3); OEA; Varsity Clb; Band; Mrchg Band; Var Bowling; Var Sftbl; Trk; Hon Roll.

SALERNO, ANN MARIE; Roselle Catholic HS; Roselle, NJ; (4); 29/195; Yrbk Stf; Off Soph Cls; Cheerleading; Mgr(s); Tennis; High Hon Roll; Hon Roll; Northwood Inst Acad Excllnce Scholar 87; Walbro Scholar Fund 87; Northwood Inst; Hotel Rest Mgmt.

SALERNO, KAREN A; Spotswood HS; Spotswood, NJ; (2); 15/127; French Clb; Girl Scts; Intnl Clb; Ski Clb; Mrchg Band; Capt Cheerleading; Hon Roll; Mst Imprvd Chrldng 86; Rutgers U; Acctng.

SALERNO, LAURA; Immaculate Conception HS; Lodi, NJ; (3); Drama Clb; SADD; School Musical; School Play; Stage Crew; Yrbk Stf; Mrktng.

SALERNO, MARCY MARIE; Mount Saint Mary Acad; Kenilworth, NJ; (4); 10/80; GAA; Pep Clb; Service Clb; Pres Spanish Clb; Chorus; Pres Stu Cncl; Bowling; Mgr Fld Hcky; Mgr Sftbl; Hon Roll; Schl Spirit Awd; Top 10 Mdl; Ldrshp Awd; Fairfield U; Acctng.

SALERNO, MIKE; Union HS; Union, NJ; (4); 51/534; Am Leg Boys St; Ski Clb; Trs Stu Cncl; Var L Socr; Var Capt Swmmng; Hon Roll; NHS; Rotary Awd; Boston U; Engrng.

SALES, IVAN; Hoboken HS; Hoboken, NJ; (3); Var Socr; Var Mgr(s); Var Socr; Wt Lftg; Bus.

SALES, MICHELE; Mary Help Of Christians HS; Wayne, NJ; (2); Hosp Aide; SADD; Teachers Aide; Varsity Clb; Variety Show; Nwsp Stf; Var Bsktbl; Im Gym; Im Sftbl; Im Vllybl; Alg 86; Hstry 86; Rugers-Syracuse; Jrnlsm.

SALFELDER, MARK; Sussex County Vo Tech; Sparta, NJ; (4); Scholastic Bowl; Varsity Clb; JV L Bsbl; Var Capt Bowling; Var L Ftbl; Var Capt Trk; Hon Roll; Sparta Wmns Clb Schlrshp 87; Twnshp Cncl Dstngshd Stu Awd 87; Morris Cnty Coll; Bus.

SALGADO, CARLO; Ocean Twp HS; Ocean Twp, NJ; (4); 148/330; Boys Clb Am; French Clb; Nwsp Stf; Im Bsktbl; Rutgers-Livingston; Politcl Sci.

SALGADO, JANINE; Watchung Hills Regional HS; Gillette, NJ; (3); 29/ 300; Drama Clb; Key Clb; Ski Clb; SADD; Stage Crew; Tennis; High Hon Roll; Hon Roll; NHS; Bus.

SALGADO, KATHERINE; St Anthony HS; Jersey Cty, NJ; (3); Church Yth Grp; Church Choir; Hon Roll; St Porters Coll; Comp Sci.

SALGADO, MARILYN; Perth Amboy HS; Perth Amboy, NJ; (3); Dance Clb; Drama Clb; French Clb; Chorus; Mrchg Band; School Play; Twrlr; High Hon Roll; Hon Roll; Bus.

SALIM, JENNIFER; Dwight Morrow HS; Englewood, NJ; (3); 22/312; Church Yth Grp; GAA; Spanish Clb; School Play; Stu Cncl; Var Sftbl; JV Capt Vllybl; High Hon Roll; Hon Roll; Prfct Atten Awd; Fshn Mrchndsng.

SALIS, ARI; Manalapan HS; Manalapan, NJ; (3); Hosp Aide; Temple Yth Grp; Var Socr; Var Capt Trk; NHS; 1st Pl 200 Mtr/Trk 85; Hnrb Mntn In Trck 86; Med Doctor.

SALKELD, LESLIE; Manasquan HS; Brielle, NJ; (3); 4/230; FBLA; Math Tm; Spanish Clb; JV Capt Fld Hcky; Cit Awd; DAR Awd; High Hon Roll; Kiwanis Awd; NHS; Pres Schlr; Bd Of Educ Awd 85-86 & 86-87; Bus.

SALLATA, SUZANNE; Atlantic City HS; Ventnor, NJ; (4); 45/402; Dance Clb; Office Aide; Variety Show; Stat Bsbl; Cheerleading; Capt Var Diving; Capt Var Swmmng; Hon Roll; Rotary Awd; U Miami.

SALLEY, DOLLY; Immaculate Conception HS; East Orange, NJ; (3); Art Clb; Spanish Clb; Chorus; Var Cheerleading; Hon Roll; Spanish NHS; Highest Average Spanish Ii & Iii; Spanish Honor Society Pres 87; Pre Dentistry/Advertising.

SALLIS, YOLANDA; Passaic County Tech; Paterson, NJ; (4); Hosp Aide; Var Cheerleading; Trk.

SALM, ROBERT; Oratory Catholic Prep Schl; Fanwood, NJ; (4); 1/44; Boy Scts; Chess Clb; Pres Math Clb; Capt Math Tm; Quiz Bowl; Yrbk Ed-Chief; Var Bsbl; High Hon Roll; NHS; Val; Eagle Sct 85; Garden ST Dstngshd Schlrs Pgm 86; Chem.

SALMANOWITZ, LORI; Parsippany Hills HS; Parsippany, NJ; (3); Debate Tm; Hosp Aide; NFL; Service Clb; Temple Yth Grp; Y-Teens; Color Guard; Flag Corp; Mrchg Band; Yrbk Stf; Northeastern U; Socl Wrkr.

SALSBERG, STEPHANIE; Boonton HS; Boonton, NJ; (2); Radio Clb; Ski Clb; Temple Yth Grp; Rep Frsh Cls; Rep Stu Cncl; High Hon Roll; Hon Roll.

SALTARELLI, MARY; Holy Rosary Acad; Jersey City, NJ; (3); Art Clb; Hosp Aide; Latin Clb; Math Clb; Science Clb; Badmtn; Socr; NHS; Ntl Merit Schol; Algebra I, Prfct Atten, Art I & Spnsh I Awds 84; Spnsh II, Religion II, Hnr Roll & Art II Awds 86; Rutgers Coll; Phrmcy.

SALTZMAN, DAVID; Morristown HS; Morris Plains, NJ; (3); 5/422; Cmnty Wkr; JA; JCL; Latin Clb; Temple Yth Grp; Lit Mag; High Hon Roll; Hon Roll; Summa Cum Laude Natl Latin Exam 86; Maxima Cum Laude Natl Latin Exam 87; Best Selling JR Achvt Co NJ.

SALUTI, JOE; West Essex SR HS; N Caldwell, NJ; (3); Am Leg Boys St; Math Tm; Science Clb; Nwsp Rptr; Nwsp Sprt Ed; Var Socr; Var Tennis; Im Vllybl; JV Wrstlng; Bausch & Lomb Sci Awd; Dartmouth Bk Awd 87; Harvard; Bus.

SALVATORE, ALLISON; Clayton HS; Clayton, NJ; (4); #4 In Class; Drama Clb; Key Clb; Science Clb; Chorus; School Musical; Rep Stu Cncl; Cheerleading; DAR Awd; NHS; St Schlr; Hugh O Brien Yth Fndtn Smnr Rep 85-86; Glassboro ST Coll; Psych.

SALVATORE, DAVE; Paulsboro HS; Paulsboro, NJ; (3); Debate Tm; Political Wkr; Scholastic Bowl; Rep SADD; Acpl Chr; Chorus; VP Mrchg Band; School Musical; Lit Mag; Socr; Acctng.

SALVATORE, KENNETH J; Bound Brook HS; Bound Brook, NJ; (3); Am Leg Boys St; Science Clb; Yrbk Rptr; Rep Soph Cls; Rep Jr Cls; Stu Cncl; Var Trk; Stu Wk 85.

SAMBADE, MARY J; Bayonne HS; Bayonne, NJ; (3); Science Clb; Jazz Band; Mrchg Band; Nwsp Stf; Lit Mag; High Hon Roll; Math Clb; Band; Concert Band; Nwsp Rptr; St Peters Coll Smmr Schlrs Prgm 86.

SAMBORN, KIMBERLY; Bruriah HS For Girls; Fair Lawn, NJ; (3); Drama Clb; Temple Yth Grp; Fld Hcky; Sftbl; 3rd Sci Fair 85-87; Pre Med.

SAMITT, ALISON; Parsippany HS; Parsippany, NJ; (4); 3/330; Hosp Aide; Pres Science Clb; Rep Temple Yth Grp; Flag Corp; School Musical; Bausch & Lomb Sci Awd; High Hon Roll; NHS; French Clb; Intnl Clb; NJ Gvrnrs Schlr-Sci 86; Grdn ST Dstngshd Schlr 87; Johns Hopkins U; Bio.

SAMMAK, JILL; Vernon Township HS; Sussex, NJ; (3); Lit Mag; Pres Jr Cls; Stat Bsbl; Var Tennis; High Hon Roll; Hon Roll; NHS; Viking Clb Tnns Awd 87; 1st Pl SCIL Tnns Trnmnt Mdl 87; All Area & Lge In Nwsp For Tnns 87.

SAMMORS, ROBBY; Paulsboro HS; Paulsboro, NJ; (2); JV Bsbl; JV Wrstlng; Navy Career.

SAMONSKI, LEAH; Northern Burlington Regional HS; Columbus, NJ; (1); Chorus; Bsbl; Hon Roll; Nrsry Schl Tchr.

SAMORA, DAVID; Middletown South HS; Middletown, NJ; (3); JV Bsbl; JV Ftbl; JV Wrstlng; Hon Roll; Cornell U.

SAMPSON, CHRISTIANE; Buena Regional HS; Williamstown, NJ; (4); 21/174; Office Aide; Hon Roll; Secy.

SAMRA, DAVID; Sayreville War Memorial HS; Sayreville, NJ; (4); Spanish Clb; Hon Roll; Middlesex Cnty Coll; Accntng.

SAMSON, ELIZABETH; Toms River North HS; Toms River, NJ; (3); 57/459; German Clb; Ski Clb; VP SADD; Orch; Yrbk Stf; Off Frsh Cls; Off Soph Cls; Off Jr Cls; JV Cheerleading; High Hon Roll; WA Workshops Congressional Seminar 87; Bus Mngmnt.

SAMUEL JR, LAWRENCE A; South River HS; South River, NJ; (3); Chorus; Jazz Band; Mrchg Band; Pep Band; Symp Band; Capt L Crs Cntry; L Ftbl; Capt L Trk; Wrstlng; Rutgers Mason Gross Schl; Music.

SAMUELS, ROBIN L; West Morris Central HS; Hackettstown, NJ; (3); 109/337; Am Leg Boys St; Pres Art Clb; Boy Scts; FBLA; School Musical; School Play; Stage Crew; Socr; Art.

SANCHEZ, BENJAMIN; Hillside HS; Hillside, NJ; (4); 1/188; Math Clb; Science Clb; Service Clb; Concert Band; Mrchg Band; Bausch & Lomb Sci Awd; High Hon Roll; Pres NHS; St Schlr; Val; Gvrnrs Pride Awd 87; Grdn ST Dstngshd Schlr Awd, Byrd Schlrshp 87; Stevens Inst Of Tech; Chem.

SANCHEZ, JORGE IVAN; Perth Amboy HS; Perth Amboy, NJ; (3); 19/535; Am Leg Boys St; Boy Scts; Computer Clb; French Clb; Math Tm; Model UN; Scholastic Bowl; School Play; Stu Cncl; JV Bsbl; Awds Night Hnr 8; Engnrng.

SANCHEZ, LILIBETH; Watchung Hills R HS; Watchung, NJ; (3); 19/321; Math Tm; Science Clb; Spanish Clb; Nwsp Rptr; Hon Roll; NHS; Spanish NHS; 2nd Pl Sci Leag 85; 4th Pl Math Cmpttn 85; Med.

SANCHEZ, ROSEMARY E; Mount Saint Dominic Acad; Paterson, NJ; (2); Drama Clb; Intnl Clb; Lit Mag; Sec Trs Jr Cls; Var Socr; Var Trk; Hon Roll; Jr NHS; NHS; Prfct Atten Awd; Wnnr Sister Germaine Clark Full Tuitn Schlrshp Mt St Dominic Acad 85; Spring Courses 86-87; Ed.

SANCHEZ, SANDRA; Immaculate Conception HS; Passaic Pk, NJ; (4); 20/92; Church Yth Grp; Drama Clb; Ski Clb; Spanish Clb; Stage Crew; Yrbk Stf; Hon Roll; High Hnrs Histry & Religion Awd 87; Penn ST; Bus.

SANCHEZ, TANIA G; Glen Ridge HS; Glen Ridge, NJ; (3); 5/101; AFS; Key Clb; Library Aide; Nwsp Rptr; Nwsp Stf; VP Frsh Cls; Sec Sr Cls; JV Var Sftbl; High Hon Roll; Natl Young Leaders Conf; Bus.

SANDERS, RAQUEL; Dover HS; Dover, NJ; (3); Sec Church Yth Grp; VP Key Clb; Spanish Clb; Chorus; Church Choir; Swing Chorus; Vllybl; Hon Roll; Hampton Inst; Bus Admin.

SANDERS, SHARON; Lakewood HS; Lakewood, NJ; (3); 4/330; Am Leg Aux Girls St; Pres English Clb; FBLA; Latin Clb; Mrchg Band; L Stat Bsbl; High Hon Roll; Hon Roll; NHS; Spanish NHS; Bus.

SANDERSON, KRISTEN; St John Vianney HS; Colts Neck, NJ; (2); #8 In Class; SADD; Yrbk Stf; Var Crs Cntry; Var Socr; Var Trk; High Hon Roll; Prfct Atten Awd; Gold & White Awd 85-87; Yth Fr Life Clb 86-87.

SANDFORD, RICHARD; Wall HS; Manasquaw, NJ; (4); 4/250; Am Leg Boys St; VP German Clb; Ski Clb; Var Socr; High Hon Roll; Kiwanis Awd; NHS; Kiwanis Hnr Soc; Natl Engl Mrt Awd; Acad All Amer; U Of DE; Engrng.

SANDFORD, STEPHEN L; Wall HS; Manasquan, NJ; (3); 35/350; Am Leg Boys St; Rep Church Yth Grp; Rep German Clb; Varsity Clb; Var Bsbl; Var Bsktbl; Var Socr; High Hon Roll; Hon Roll; Law.

SANDHAM, AIMEE; Notre Dame HS; Kendall Pk, NJ; (4); 46/336; SADD; Color Guard; Rep Frsh Cls; Rep Soph Cls; Var Capt Swmmng; Timer; Im Vllybl; High Hon Roll; Hon Roll; Swimming Schlrshp 87; Trenton ST Coll.

SANDLER, AMY; Hightstown HS; E Windsor, NJ; (4); 81/422; Cmnty Wkr; French Clb; Sec FBLA; Intnl Clb; Yrbk Stf; Stu Cncl; High Hon Roll; Hon Roll; U Of RI; Erly Chldhd Ed.

SANDMAN, LISA M; Shawnee HS; Tabernacle, NJ; (4); 52/535; Cmnty Wkr; Drama Clb; Political Wkr; Chorus; Jazz Band; School Musical; Stage Crew; Yrbk Stf; Hon Roll; NHS; Gvrnrs Tchng Schlrshp 87; Lenape Dist Educ Assn Awd 87; Trenton ST Coll; Spcl Educ.

SANDONE, HOLLY M; Cherokee HS; Atco, NJ; (4); 159/411; Am Leg Aux Girls St; FCA; French Clb; Ski Clb; Pres Frsh Cls; VP Soph Cls; Rep Jr Cls; Pres Stu Cncl; Var Cheerleading; Var Trk; Pres Clssrm 86; Ldrshp Training Camp 86; Wanesburg Coll; State Trooper.

SANDONE, LORI; Washington Township HS; Sewell, NJ; (2); French Clb; Teachers Aide; JV Cheerleading; Nrsng.

SANDOVAL, OSCAR; Passaic Ounty Tech & Voc HS; Passaic, NJ; (4); 4/366; Latin Clb; Math Tm; Stat Bsbl; Stat Ftbl; High Hon Roll; Hon Roll; NHS; Comp Prgmmr.

SANDS, RACHEL; Vineland HS; Newfield, NJ; (3); 162/800; Yrbk Stf; Prfct Atten Awd; Flght Attdnt.

SANDT, NANCY; Phillipsburg HS; Phillipsburg, NJ; (2); Church Yth Grp; FFA; Band; Chorus; Church Choir; Stage Crew; Pop N Rock Shw Bnd Bass Gtr 87; Phys Thrpy.

SANDY, JOHN; Clifton HS; Clifton, NJ; (3); Office Aide; Ski Clb; JV Bsbl; JV Bsktbl; Hon Roll; Prfct Atten Awd; Montclair ST.

SANDY, SCOTT; Arthur L Johnson Regional HS; Clark, NJ; (3); 34/211; Pres Stu Cncl; Cit Awd; High Hon Roll; NHS; Bus.

SANFORD, JENNIFER; Linden HS; Linden, NJ; (3); Church Yth Grp; VP Science Clb; Color Guard; Orch; School Play; Stage Crew; Nwsp Stf; Swmmng; High Hon Roll; NHS; Hnr Mntn Sci Cllng Awd; Vet Med.

SANG, JANSEW; Memorial HS; W New York, NJ; (4); 10/358; Dance Clb; Key Clb; Sec Math Clb; Science Clb; Band; Concert Band; Mrchg Band; School Play; High Hon Roll; Jr NHS; Knights Pythias Essay Awd 83; Italian Cmmty Ctr Awd 87; Rutgers U; Sci.

SANKAR, NANDHINI; Montville Township HS; Montville, NJ; (3); Intnl Clb; Key Clb; Yrbk Stf; JV Gym; Dental.

SANNEY, STACIE; Hopewell Valley Central HS; Hopewell, NJ; (4); DECA; FBLA; German Clb; High Hon Roll; Hon Roll; Berkley Bus Schl Awd Outstndng Prsrvrnc 87; Katherine Gibbs Schl Annl Sec Achvt Hon Mntn 86; Centenary Coll; Accntng.

SANTAELLA, STEPHEN; Teaneck HS; Teaneck, NJ; (4); 138/400; Boy Scts; Church Yth Grp; Math Tm; SADD; Stu Cncl; JV Var Bsbl; Var Ftbl; JV Trk; Im Vllybl; Semi-Fnlst Ntl Hispanic Schlrs Awd 86-87; Engr.

SANTANELLO, PAUL; Middletown HS South; Middletown, NJ; (3); Drama Clb; SADD; School Play; Var L Crs Cntry; Var Trk; Hon Roll; Ltrs For Crs Cntry 85-87; Pre-Law.

SANTANEN, ERIC; Lenape Valley Regional HS; Stanhope, NJ; (3); 3/240; Am Leg Boys St; Trs FBLA; Rptr Nwsp Rptr; Rep Stu Cncl; Var Trk; High Hon Roll; Hon Roll; NHS; Prfct Atten Awd; Spanish NHS; Comp Sci.

SANTANGELO, DONALD; Bridgewater Raritan HS East; Bridgewater, NJ; (4); 98/260; Boy Scts; Radio Clb; Science Clb; School Play; Yrbk Stf; Cit Awd; Elks Awd; High Hon Roll; Jr NHS; NHS; Hiram Percy Maxim Schlrshp Mem Awd 85; Pblc Svc Awd 84-87; Rutgers; Elec Eng.

SANTANGINI, PAUL; Washington Township HS; Sewell, NJ; (3); Chess Clb; Church Yth Grp; Civic Clb; Computer Clb; German Clb; Model UN; Q&S; Science Clb; Yrbk Stf; Lit Mag; Bus Admin.

SANTANNA, MARGARET; Bishop George Ahr HS; Edison, NJ; (4); 34/267; Cmnty Wkr; Hosp Aide; Intnl Clb; Math Tm; Model UN; Color Guard; Concert Band; Mrchg Band; Symp Band; Nwsp Stf; Providence Coll.

SANTANTONIO, DEAN; Parsippany HS; Parsippany, NJ; (3); FBLA; Varsity Clb; Socr; Wrstlng; High Hon Roll; Hon Roll; NHS; Bus.

SANTAVICCA, NANCY; Spotswood HS; Spotswood, NJ; (3); FBLA; Cheerleading; High Hon Roll; Hon Roll; Word Proc.

SANTIAGO, DOUGLASS; Hoboken HS; Hoboken, NJ; (3); Art Clb; Boys Clb Am; Drama Clb; Chorus; School Musical; School Play; Variety Show; Off Sr Cls; Stu Cncl; Trk; NJ Schl Of Arts MSC 86; Montclair ST Coll Nght Cls 86; Gulean Arts Schl; Thtr.

SANTIAGO JR, HECTOR; Riverside HS; Riverside, NJ; (3); Varsity Clb; Var Crs Cntry; Var Trk; Wt Lftg; JV Wrstlng; Hon Roll; Prfct Atten Awd.

SANTIAGO, MARC; Pasamus Catholic Boys HS; Fort Lee, NJ; (4); Computer Clb; Math Tm; Ed Lit Mag; NHS; Ntl Merit SF; Natl Hispanic Schlrshp Awd Fnlst 87; Mechncl Engrng.

SANTIAGO, NOEMI; Passaic County Tech V HS; Paterson, NJ; (3); 72/400; US Natl Math Awd 87; Lawyer.

SANTIAGO, ROSIE; Edgewood Reg HS; Hammonton, NJ; (3); Civic Clb; Cmnty Wkr; Office Aide; Sec Spanish Clb; Church Choir; Mgr Fld Hcky; Mgr(s); Score Keeper; Hon Roll; Prfct Atten Awd; Kane Bus Inst; Data Prcsng.

SANTIAGO, WANDA; Perth Amboy HS; Perth Amboy, NJ; (3); French Clb; Band; Chorus; High Hon Roll; Kean Coll; Phys Thrpy.

SANTILLI, CLAUDIA; Cliffside Park HS; Cliffside Pk, NJ; (3); 103/443; Am Leg Aux Girls St; Drama Clb; Spanish Clb; Nwsp Rptr; Nwsp Stf; Rep Stu Cncl; Tennis; Acad Deca NJ 87; Foresic Lang Awd 86; Pol Sci.

SANTINI, LAURIE; Saint John Vianney HS; Colts Neck, NJ; (2); 1/276; Intnl Clb; SADD; Yrbk Phtg; Capt Cheerleading; JV Trk; High Hon Roll; Schl Gold & White Awd 86-87; Duke; Med.

SANTITORO, LUANN; Mc Corristin Catholic HS; Trenton, NJ; (3); 8/266; Drama Clb; Pres Pep Clb; Chorus; School Musical; School Play; Nwsp Stf; Lit Mag; Rep Soph Cls; Rep Jr Cls; Hon Roll; Chrstn Srvc Awd 86; Magna Cum Laude Natl Latin Exm 85.

SANTONE, GINA; Maple Shade HS; Maple Shade, NJ; (3); Am Leg Aux Girls St; DECA; SADD; Rep Frsh Cls; Sec Soph Cls; VP Stu Cncl; Yrbk Stf; Spanish NHS.

SANTORA, ROBIN; Our Lady Of Good Counsel; Newark, NJ; (4); 1/102; Cmnty Wkr; Science Clb; Chorus; School Musical; Yrbk Stf; High Hon Roll; NHS; Garden ST Dstngshd Schlrs, Acdmc All-Amrcn Awd 87; Purdue U; Astrophysics.

SANTORINI, VICKI; Hillsborough HS; Belle Mead, NJ; (2); Art Clb; Latin Clb; Varsity Clb; Concert Band; Sec Trs Frsh Cls; Sftbl; Var Trk; Hon Roll; Stu Of Mnth 5/87; PUSH 86-87; Marine Bio.

SANTORO, CHUCK; Paramus HS; Paramus, NJ; (4); 75/340; Am Leg Boys St; VP Drama Clb; VP Chorus; School Musical; School Play; Yrbk Ed-Chief; Stu Cncl; Bergan Cnty Choir 85-87; Renaissance Scty Pres; Syracuse U; Musical Theatre.

SANTOS, ISABEL; Our Lady Of Good Counsel HS; Newark, NJ; (3); 8/122; Var Vllybl; NHS; Cert Awd Stngrphy 87; Schl 2nd Hnrs Clss 86; Athltc Awd Vllybll 87.

SANTRONI, ANASTASIA; Gloucester Catholic HS; Wenonah, NJ; (3); 2/198; Dance Clb; Chorus; School Musical; Nwsp Stf; Pres Soph Cls; Pres Jr Cls; Gov Hon Prg Awd; High Hon Roll; Hon Roll; NHS; Stu Mnth 85; Intl Frgn Lang Awd 86.

SANTUCCI, LISA; St James HS; Penns Grove, NJ; (2); Church Yth Grp; Dance Clb; Drama Clb; Church Choir; Yrbk Stf; JV Sftbl; Sunshine Compttn 3rd Pl Mdlng 85; Intl Tchrs Dnc Compttn 3rd Pl Ballt 86; Media Jrnlsm.

SAO, SHAM; Bridgewater-Raritan H S East; Bridgewater, NJ; (3); Chess Clb; Pres Computer Clb; Math Tm; Quiz Bowl; Spanish Clb; Chorus; Lit Mag; Im Bowling; JV Tennis; JV Trk; Top 10% Sci Leag, Top 40 ST Sci Day Compttn 88.

SAPERSTEIN, DAWN L; Roxbury HS; Succasunna, NJ; (4); 1/422; AFS; French Clb; Pres Temple Yth Grp; Chorus; Ed Lit Mag; Rep Stu Cncl; High Hon Roll; NHS; Ntl Merit SF; Rotary Awd; Hist.

SAPHERSTEIN, MICHAEL; Fair Lawn HS; Fair Lawn, NJ; (3); 2/341; Computer Clb; Drama Clb; Math Clb; Science Clb; Temple Yth Grp; Stage Crew; VP Stu Cncl; High Hon Roll; NHS; Ntl Merit Ltr; Semi-Fnlst Gov Schl Pblc Issues 87; Bus.

SAPORITO, MARIA; Clifton HS; Clifton, NJ; (4); 44/689; Key Clb; Math Clb; Office Aide; Spanish Clb; Bsbl; Cheerleading; Spanish NHS; Natl Jr Hnr Socty; Pres Acad Physical Ftns Awd; Douglass Coll; Liberal Arts.

SARACENI, FRANK; North Bergen HS; North Bergen, NJ; (4); 17/400; Var JV Ftbl; Hon Roll; NHS; N Bergen HS PTSA Schlrshp Awd 87; Rutgers U.

SARACEVIC, ALAN; Hillsborough HS; Hillsborough, NJ; (3); 20/538; Ski Clb; JV Bsbl; Var L Ftbl; High Hon Roll; Hon Roll; Ntl Merit SF; Rutgers U; Lbrl Arts.

SARACINO, PIERINA; Arthur L Johnson Reg HS; Clark, NJ; (4); 17/207; Aud/Vis; French Clb; Key Clb; Science Clb; Ski Clb; Band; Concert Band; Drm Mjr(t); Jazz Band; Mrchg Band; Gld Mdlln Excel Itln 84-86.

SARAGUSA, ANGELA; Saint Rose HS; Bradley Bch, NY; (3); 55/241; Dance Clb; Drama Clb; Hosp Aide; Ski Clb; Variety Show; Nwsp Phtg; Nwsp Rptr; Yrbk Stf; Hon Roll; Prfct Atten Awd; Multiple Sclerosis Hon Awd Raising Money 85-86; Seton Hall U; Hist.

SARAIYA, RAKESH; Roselle Park HS; Roselle Park, NJ; (3); Am Leg Boys St; Art Clb; Cmnty Wkr; Computer Clb; Hosp Aide; Math Clb; Capt Math Tm; Nwsp Stf; Yrbk Phtg; Yrbk Stf; Chem Caravan NJ 87; Physician.

SARAMBO, CHRISTINE M; Neptune SR HS; Neptune City, NJ; (3); Church Yth Grp; Debate Tm; Girl Scts; Model UN; Church Choir; Yrbk Stf; Rep Soph Cls; God Cntry Awd; Hon Roll; Jr NHS; Arts.

SARAN, RAJESH; The Pennington Schl; Susquehanna, PA; (3); 1/81; VP French Clb; JV Wrstlng; High Hon Roll; NHS; Elec Engr.

SARCHIO, CHAD T; Wayne Hills HS; Wayne, NJ; (3); 4/335; Am Leg Boys St; Boy Scts; Pres Band; Nwsp Ed-Chief; Yrbk Stf; Pres Stu Cncl; Var Swmmng; Gov Hon Prg Awd; Pres NHS; Drama Clb; Pres Med Explrs Post 645 86-87; NROTC Fnlst 87; Golf Caddy Preakness Hills Cntry Clb; Law.

SARCONE, ANTHONY; Saint Mary HS; Holmdel, NJ; (4); 30/130; Nwsp Rptr; Yrbk Ed-Chief; Rep Soph Cls; Rep Jr Cls; Rep Sr Cls; High Hon Roll; NHS; NEDT Awd; Prncpls Awd 87; Snt Awd 87; Montclair ST Coll; Psych.

SARDANA, SEEMA; Cedar Ridge HS; Old Bridge, NJ; (4); 5/360; Computer Clb; French Clb; FBLA; Intnl Clb; Key Clb; Library Aide; Math Tm; SADD; Chorus; Orch; Stevens Inst Tech; Engrng.

SARDELLA, GIANNA; Acad Of Sacred Heart; Hoboken, NJ; (4); 3/54; Cmnty Wkr; Dance Clb; GAA; Hosp Aide; Rep Frsh Cls; Rep Soph Cls; Rep Jr Cls; Sec Sr Cls; Pres Stu Cncl; Vllybl; Montclair ST Schlrshp 87; 1st Hnrs & 2nd Hnrs 87; Excel Engl, Econ, Geogrphy, Alg, Geo, & Hstry; Seton Hall U; Bus.

SARGENTI, JOSEPH; Essex Catholic HS For Boys; Clifton, NJ; (3); JV Bsktbl; JV Ftbl; Hon Roll; Bus.

SARKISIAN, DAVID; Kinnelon HS; Kinnelon, NJ; (4); 9/176; Church Yth Grp; Pres German Clb; School Musical; JV Var Socr; JV Tennis; High Hon Roll; Hon Roll; NHS; Pres Schlr; Rotary Awd; Grmn Clb Schlrshp 87; Purdue U; Aviation Tech.

SARMIENTO, REZELIE; St Aloysius HS; Jersey City, NJ; (3); 1/12(Boy Scts; Capt Bowling; Bausch & Lomb Sci Awd; High Hon Roll; Ho Roll; NHS; Rtgrs Schlr 86-87; Prsdnts Ctatn Awd 86-87; Rutgers; Bnkn

SARMIERE, JENNIFER; West Mulford Township HS; W Milford, N (2); Hosp Aide; Nwsp Stf; Mgr(s); Hon Roll; Phys Therapy.

SARN, SUSAN; Red Bank Catholic HS; Little Silver, NJ; (3); Girl Scts SADD; Coach Actv; JV Crs Cntry; Capt Var Trk; NHS; NEDT Awd; Spe Educ.

SARNO, FELECIA; Manchester Twp HS; Lakehurst, NJ; (3); Dram Clb; French Clb; Science Clb; Teachers Aide; Hon Roll; Frnch Stu Of Y Awd 87.

SAROKAS, CHRISTINE; Clifton HS; Clifton, NJ; (4); Computer Cl Hosp Aide; Office Aide; Science Clb; Spanish Clb; Teachers Aide; Thesp School Play; Nwsp Ed-Chief; Nwsp Rptr; Robert Mills Foundation Trus Schlrshp 87-88; Felician Coll Lodi NJ; Nursing.

SAROSHINSKY, DONNA; Bayonne HS; Bayonne, NJ; (3); Key Cl Math Tm; JV Bsktbl; Var Sftbl; Var Tennis; Hon Roll; Acctg.

SARREL, MATTHEW D; Millburn HS; Millburn, NJ; (3); Debate T Pres English Clb; Science Clb; Concert Band; Mrchg Band; Var Trk; J Wrstlng; High Hon Roll; Ntl Merit Ltr.

SARRO, ANGELO; Bloomfield SR HS; Bloomfield, NJ; (3); Boy Scts Computer Clb; Bsbl; Trk; Wt Lftg; High Hon Roll; Hon Roll; Cert O Avg-Italian, Math, Hstry & Sci 85; Hnrb Mntn 85-87; Seton Hall; Pre-Law

SARTORI, STEPHEN; Morris Knolls HS; Rockaway, NJ; (3); 16/426 Am Leg Boys St; Varsity Clb; Im JV Bsbl; Var JV Bsktbl; Var JV Ftb High Hon Roll; Hon Roll; Jr NHS; NHS.

SARY, CHRISTEN; Florence Twp Mem HS; Roebling, NJ; (3); Am Le Aux Girls St; Pres FTA; Math Clb; Pres Band; Concert Band; Jazz Banc Pres Mrchg Band; Nwsp Rptr; Yrbk Stf; Sec Frsh Cls; 3rd Prz In Essa Cntst 87; Penn ST; Criminolgy.

SASSAMAN, DONNA; Florence Township Memorial HS; Florence, NJ (4); 1/77; Am Leg Aux Girls St; Chorus; Variety Show; Pres Jr Cls; Rep St Cncl; Var Bsktbl; Var Capt Fld Hcky; Var Sftbl; Trs NHS; Val; Garden S Distngshd Schlr 87; NJ Schlr Athlt 87; Presdntl Acadmc Ftnss Awd 8 Drew U; Biolgcl Sci.

SASSE, CHRISTOPHER; Edgewood Regional SR HS; Sicklerville, NJ (2); Pres Latin Clb; Varsity Clb; Rep Stu Cncl; Var L Ftbl; Var L Wrstlng Hon Roll; Jr NHS; Prfct Atten Awd; Pres Schlr; Voice Dem Awd; NJ Lati Convntn Achvt Awd 86; Dstngshd Stu Cert Merit 86 & 87; Questor Aw Engl 87; Aerospc Engrng.

SASSO, ROBERT; Lodi HS; Lodi, NJ; (4); 27/137; Boys Clb Am; Mat Clb; Math Tm; Var L Bsbl; Hon Roll; VP NHS; US Army Rsrv Ntl Schlr Athlt Awd 87; Brgn CO Athlt Of Wk 87; Athlt Of Mon-Bsbll 87; Willian Patterson Coll; Bus.

SATORSKI, ANDREA; South River HS; S River, NJ; (2); Church Yt Grp; Spanish Clb; Sec Band; Trs Chorus; Church Choir; Concert Band Mrchg Band; Pep Band; Symp Band; Var Trk; Tchr.

SATTAN, SCOTT; Southern Regional HS; Barnegat, NJ; (3); 56/400 Aud/Vis; Cmnty Wkr; Latin Clb; Lit Mag; JV Socr; Var Wrstlng; Hon Roll NHS; Wrstlng Var Lttrs; Wrstlng Scholar Athl Awd; Soccer Mos Dedicated; Phys Therapy.

SAUCHELLI, CHRISTINE; Morris Catholic HS; Rockaway, NJ; (4); 13 138; Nwsp Ed-Chief; Yrbk Stf; Score Keeper; High Hon Roll; NHS Fairfield U; Jrnlsm.

SAUER, JAMES; Union Catholic HS; Cranford, NJ; (3); 11/317; Bo Scts; Ski Clb; Eagle Scout; Attnry.

SAUERWALD III, WILLIAM; Egg Harbor Hownship HS; Pleasantville NJ; (3); 19/329; JV Bsbl; Acad All Amer 86; JR Vrsty Awd Bsbl 86; Vrst Lttr Acad 85-86; Sci.

SAUL, MELISSA; A P Schalick HS; Elmer, NJ; (4); Art Clb; JA; JV Va Bsktbl; JV Sftbl; Hon Roll; Chld Dvlpmnt Asst.

SAULOG, AIMEE E; St Plus X Regional HS; Piscataway, NJ; (4); 2/108 Math Tm; Quiz Bowl; Teachers Aide; School Play; Nwsp Stf; Yrb Ed-Chief; Bowling; Capt Tennis; High Hon Roll; NHS; Sltrn 87; Grdn S Dstngshd Schlr 87; Ntl Edctnl Dvlpmnt Tst Awd 83-84; Rutgers Coll Chem Engnrng.

SAUNDERS, DIONICIA K; Egg Harbor Township HS; W Atlantic City NJ; (3); Sec Drama Clb; French Clb; PAVAS; SADD; Sec Chorus; Churc Choir; School Musical; School Play; Pres Frsh Cls; 1st Pl Wnnr Talent Sh 85-86; Outstndg Prgm 84-85; Music Schls Week 84-85; Howard U; Music

SAUNDERS, EMILY; Hunterdon Central HS; Flemington, NJ; (4); 150 543; JA; Key Clb; Stage Crew; Off Frsh Cls; Off Soph Cls; Off Jr Cls; St Cncl; JV Bsktbl; Hon Roll; 3 On 3 Comp Awd Bsktbl 86; Foul Shoot Aw 86; Rutgers; Phrmcy.

SAVAGE, AMY; South Plainfield HS; S Plainfield, NJ; (4); Hosp Aide Ski Clb; Spanish Clb; SADD; Acpl Chr; Band; Chorus; Church Choir Concert Band; Mrchg Band; Hampton U; Psych.

SAVAGE, JON; Monsignor Donovan HS; Toms River, NJ; (3); 31/245 Church Yth Grp; SADD; Var Crs Cntry; Var Trk; Hon Roll; NHS; Ele Engrng.

SAVAGE, TIMOTHY; Trenton Central HS; Trenton, NJ; (3); Cit Awd Gov Hon Prg Awd; Hon Roll; U Of NC A&F; Elec Engrng.

SAVARD, JOANNE; Mt Olive HS; Flanders, NJ; (3); 142/318; AFS Dance Clb; Sec Science Clb; SADD; Varsity Clb; Yrbk Stf; Sec Frsh Cls Sec Soph Cls; Rep Stu Cncl; Var Fld Hcky; MVP Awd Fld Hcky 85; A ST; Psychlgy.

SAVATORE, ALLISON; Clayton HS; Clayton, NJ; (4); 4/72; Drama Clb Key Clb; Chorus; School Musical; Stu Cncl; Var Cheerleading; Var Fl Hcky; NHS; FHA; Science Clb; Schl Rep HOBY Fndtn Sem 85; Psych.

SAVERIANO, STEPHANIE; Holy Spirit HS; Absecon, NJ; (3); Churc Yth Grp; Cmnty Wkr; Off SADD; Nwsp Rptr; Lit Mag; Pres Frsh Cls; Of VP Jr Cls; Var L Sftbl; Var L Tennis; Hon Roll; Commnctns.

SAVERINO, DENISE; Monsignor Donovan HS; Brick Town, NJ; (3) Church Yth Grp; Cmnty Wkr; Girl Scts; Hosp Aide; Library Aide; Office Aide; Political Wkr; Ski Clb; Spanish Clb; SADD; Seton Hall U; Attorney.

SAVICH, NATALIE; Shawnee HS; Medford, NJ; (3); DECA; Colo Guard; Yrbk Stf; Stat Trk; Hon Roll; Young Schlr Summer Session U CC 87; Top 20 Entrenprenshp DECA Natl Career Conf 86; Magna Cum Laude; Journlsm.

SAVINO, GINA; Academic HS; Jersey City, NJ; (3); French Clb; Spanis Clb; Yrbk Stf; Math.

SAVITSKY, ANNE P; Pascack Valley HS; River Vale, NJ; (4); 94/261 Church Yth Grp; Red Cross Aide; Spanish Clb; Mrchg Band; Schoo Musical; Symp Band; Variety Show; Nwsp Rptr; Var Bowling; Hon Roll Marist Coll.

SAVOLA, STACIE L; Spotswood HS; Milltown, NJ; (3); Intnl Clb; Sk Clb; Stage Crew; Nwsp Stf; Yrbk Stf; Stu Cncl; JV Var Cheerleading; Trk Hon Roll; NHS.

SAWHNEY, ROGER ANU; Wardlaw-Hartridge HS; Edison, NJ; (4); 3/49; Pres Civic Clb; Cmnty Wkr; Computer Clb; Pres Debate Tm; Hosp Aide; Speech Tm; SADD; Acpl Chr; School Musical; School Play; JR Vlntr Srv Awd 87; Pan Amer Scty Mdl 87; Ntl Ltn Exam Awds 84-85; Stnfrd U; Bus.

SAWICKI, ELIZABETH; Kingsway Regional HS; Clarksboro, NJ; (4); 16/150; Am Leg Aux Girls St; Key Clb; Soroptimist; VP Frsh Cls; Pres Stu Cncl; Capt Cheerleading; Stat Swmmng; Trs NHS; Im Powder Puff Ftbl; Hon Roll; Swm Tm Mngr Of Yr 85-86; KRHS SR Stud Of Mnth 84-86; Bio.

SAWIRIS, HANI; Sayreville War Memorial HS; Parlin, NJ; (4); 18/353; VP Science Clb; Spanish Clb; Yrbk Bus Mgr; Yrbk Phtg; Yrbk Rptr; Rep Sr Cls; Cit Awd; Hon Roll; NHS; Spanish NHS; J J Weber Mem Awd Hghst Achvt Math $25 87; Outstndng Cntrbtns Eclgy/Bio Clb $50 & Spnsh Clb $25 87; Rutgers Coll Engrng; Elec Engrg.

SAWYER, KEVIN; West Essex HS; Essex Falls, NJ; (3); Computer Clb; Drama Clb; Key Clb; Latin Clb; Math Tm; Spanish Clb; Stu Cncl; Socr; Hon Roll; Prfct Atten Awd.

SAWYER, MICHAEL; West Essex HS; Essex Fells, NJ; (3); Computer Clb; Key Clb; Stage Crew; Stu Cncl; Hon Roll; NHS.

SAWYER, SEAN; Essex Catholic Boys HS; E Orange, NJ; (3); Bsktbl; JV Var Ftbl; Im Sftbl; Hon Roll; Norfolk ST Univ; Mrktng.

SAXON, JERILYN; Rutherford HS; Rutherford, NJ; (4); 5/167; Library Aide; Acpl Chr; Chorus; School Musical; Variety Show; Nwsp Ed-Chief; Rep Sr Cls; High Hon Roll; NHS; Trs Frsh Cls; Pres Clsrm Young Amer 86; Intl Rltns.

SAXTON, ERIN EILEEN; Whippany Park HS; Whippany, NJ; (3); Varsity Clb; Chorus; Madrigals; Sec Soph Cls; Sec Jr Cls; VP Stu Cncl; Stat Bsktbl; Var Capt Fld Hcky; JV Sftbl.

SAYBE, WILL; Florence Township Memorial HS; Florence, NJ; (3); Am Leg Boys St; Bsktbl; Ftbl; All Brlngtn Cnty Bsktbl Tm-1st 87; All SJ Grp I-1st Tm 87; All Freedom Div 1st Tm 87; Hstry.

SAYEGH, ROBERT B; Fair Lawn HS; Fair Lawn, NJ; (4); 93/327; Am Leg Boys St; Pres Varsity Clb; Trs Jr Cls; Pres Sr Cls; Rep Stu Cncl; Var Crs Cntry; Ftbl; Var Capt Trk; Wrstlng; VFW Awd; 1st Tm All Leag Crss Cntry; 3rd All Cnty Trck & 2nd Tm All Cnty; 2nd Tm All Cnty Trck Rlay; VA Military Inst; Bus.

SBLENDORIO, TARA; Nutley HS; Nutley, NJ; (3); 61/299; AFS; Camera Clb; FBLA; Key Clb; Spanish Clb; Yrbk Phtg; Sec Stu Cncl; Bsktbl; Hon Roll; Bus Adm.

SCAGLIONE, KRISTIN; St Pius X Regional HS; Dunellen, NJ; (4); 8/109; Dance Clb; Chorus; School Musical; Variety Show; Nwsp Ed-Chief; Var Cheerleading; Hon Roll; NHS; JA; Yrbk Sprt Ed; MCASSPS Outstndng Stu Awd 87; Cngrsnl Schlr 87; Syracuse U; Jrnlst.

SCAGLIONE, VINCENZA; Mount St Dominic Acad; Newark, NJ; (3); Intnl Clb; JCL; Latin Clb; Library Aide; High Hon Roll; Hon Roll; NHS; 2nd Hnrs 84-86; 1st Hnrs 86-87; Mdcn.

SCALA, MARISA; Union Catholic Reg HS; N Plainfield, NJ; (3); 1/330; Scholastic Bowl; Service Clb; Ski Clb; Church Choir; Nwsp Ed-Chief; High Hon Roll; NHS; Spanish NHS; Church Yth Grp; Science Clb; HS Schlrshp 84-88; NJAATSP Lvl I Reg ST Spnsh Exam 1st Pl 85; Outstndng Achvt Sci 85-86; Spnsh.

SCALA, MICHAEL; Secaucus HS; Secaucus, NJ; (3); 12/166; Varsity Clb; Nwsp Rptr; High Hon Roll; Hon Roll; Spanish NHS; VP Math Clb; VP Mu Alpha Theta; JV Bsbl; Stat Bsktbl; JV Capt Ftbl.

SCALA, ROSINA; St Aloysius HS; Jersey City, NJ; (4); Boy Scts; Exploring; Spanish Clb; Yrbk Stf; Hon Roll; Pres Schlr; Yrbk Stf Awd Of Merit 87; Pres Acad Ftns Awd 87; Coburn; Fshn Mrktng.

SCALER, KATHLEEN; Somerville HS; Somerville, NJ; (4); 8/249; Sec French Clb; Girl Scts; Hosp Aide; Band; Concert Band; Mrchg Band; High Hon Roll; NHS; Gov Tchng Schlrs Pgm; Douglass Coll; Speech Thrpy.

SCALES, RAISHAWN; University HS; Newark, NJ; (3); Cmnty Wkr; JA; Office Aide; Spanish Clb; Teachers Aide; Chorus; Hon Roll; Bus Mgmt.

SCALES, TARA; Marylawn Of The Oranges; East Orange, NJ; (4); 8/49; School Musical; Nwsp Rptr; Yrbk Stf; Trs Jr Cls; High Hon Roll; NHS; Spanish NHS; Cmmnd Schlr 87; Natl Achvt Schlrshp Prog Outstndng Black Stu 87; Intl Stu Ldrshp Inst Notre Dame 86; Bus Mngmnt.

SCALPATI, CARROLL; Ocean Township HS; Ocean, NJ; (4); Cmnty Wkr; Office Aide; SADD; Stat Bsbl; Powder Puff Ftbl; Guidance Dept Schlrshp 87; Italian Amer Assoc Schlrshp 87; Jhnsn/Wls Coll; Htl & Rest Mngm.

SCALZO, NICOLE; Secaucus HS; Secaucus, NJ; (3); Dance Clb; Hosp Aide; Ski Clb; Chorus; JV Cheerleading; Pom Pon; Hon Roll; Vis Prfrmng Arts.

SCANLON, MICHAEL; Kearny HS; Kearny, NJ; (4); 94/383; German Clb; Ftbl; Wrstlng; Hon Roll; Vrsty Ftbl Ltr 84; Hnr Roll 87; Wrstlg Cert 84; Kean Coll; Phys Ther.

SCANLON JR, ROBERT A; Don Bosco Prep HS; Fairlawn, NJ; (4); Aud/Vis; Letterman Clb; Science Clb; Ski Clb; Varsity Clb; Yrbk Phtg; Trk; Wt Lftg; Wrstlng; High Hon Roll; Bergen Co PBA Schlrshp Awd 86-87; U Of Scranton; Pre Med.

SCANNAPIECO, ROBERT W; Edgewood Regional HS; Cedar Brook, NJ; (3); Am Leg Boys St; Church Yth Grp; Cmnty Wkr; Key Clb; SADD; School Play; Nwsp Bus Mgr; Aud/Vis; Camera Clb; Drama Clb; Pres Of Sth Jersey Yth Cmssn 85-87; Amer Lgn Hnr Svc Dedctn Loyalty Awd 85; Soarng Eagle Awd 87; Bible Psych.

SCARANI, GIA; Sacred Heart HS; Bridgeton, NJ; (4); German Clb; Hosp Aide; Crs Cntry; Mgr(s); Sftbl; Prfct Atten Awd; Monmouth Coll; Pltcl Sci.

SCARPA, DAN; Vineland HS; Vineland, NJ; (3); Aud/Vis; Library Aide; SADD; Nwsp Phtg; Yrbk Phtg; Yrbk Stf; Rep Stu Cncl; Var Trk; Stockton ST Coll; Med.

SCARPA, SALVATORE; Kearny Christian Comm Ed Ctr; Kearny, NJ; (4); Church Yth Grp; School Musical; School Play; Nwsp Rptr; Yrbk Ed-Chief; High Hon Roll; Hon Roll; Ntl Merit Ltr; Spanish NHS; Val; Schlrshp Awd 84-85; Stevens Inst Of Tech; Comp Sci.

SCARPATI, PETER; Holy Cross HS; Mt Laurel, NJ; (3); 46/415; Church Yth Grp; Rep Sr Cls; JV Bsbl; JV Capt Socr; Hon Roll; Math.

SCARPATI, STEPHANIE; Hopewell Valley Central HS; Hopewell, NJ; (2); Service Clb; JV Var Bsktbl; Var JV Sftbl; Var Tennis; High Hon Roll; Hon Roll.

SCATTONE, VICTORIA; Camden Catholic HS; Pennsauken, NJ; (3); 17/283; Am Leg Aux Girls St; Church Yth Grp; FBLA; Nwsp Rptr; Yrbk Stu Cncl; NHS; Voice Dem Awd; Latin Hnr Soc 86; Emrld Soc Engl 87; Pol Sci.

SCATURO, JENNIFER; Roselle Catholic HS; Elizabeth, NJ; (4); 36/190; Drama Clb; School Musical; School Play; Yrbk Stf; Rep Sr Cls; Capt Cheerleading; Capt Tennis; French Hon Soc; NHS; VA Weslyan Schlrshp 87; Marist Brthrs Hnr Awd 87; Loyola Coll; Psych.

SCAVUZZO, PAUL; Toms River HS; Toms River, NJ; (3); 24/405; Church Yth Grp; Jazz Band; Mrchg Band; Orch; Symp Band; JV Bsbl; JV Bsktbl; Hon Roll; NHS; Natl Arion Fndtn Awd Music 87.

SCERBO, CAROLYN; De Paul Diocesan HS; Lincoln Park, NJ; (4); 44/156; Am Leg Aux Girls St; Cmnty Wkr; Dance Clb; Twrlr; High Hon Roll; Hon Roll; NHS; Pres Schlrshp-Felician Coll $1000 87; Erly Brd Smmr Pgm-Cnty Coll Of Morris 85; Seton Hall U; Med Tech.

SCHAAL, CRAIG; Maple Shade HS; Maple Shade, NJ; (3); Spanish Clb; Socr; Wrstlng; High Hon Roll; Hon Roll.

SCHACHMAN, ANDREW D; Governor Livingston HS; Berkeley Hgts, NJ; (4); Key Clb; Model UN; Service Clb; Ski Clb; Soroptimist; School Play; Yrbk Stf; Lit Mag; JV Lcrss; JV Var Socr; SR Cls Schlrshp Awd; Chicago U; English.

SCHACHTER, SHARON; Ocean Township HS; Ocean, NJ; (3); 58/344; VP Key Clb; Latin Clb; Varsity Clb; Band; Concert Band; Mrchg Band; School Musical; Rptr Yrbk Stf; Stat Bsbl; Stat Bsktbl; PHD.

SCHAD, DONALD; Washington Twp HS; Turnersville, NJ; (3); Boy Scts; Church Yth Grp; Stage Crew; Hon Roll; Optmtrst.

SCHAEFER, CHARLES; Collingswood HS; Oaklyn, NJ; (2); Church Yth Grp; JV Bsbl; Var Ftbl; Wt Lftg; High Hon Roll; Lion Awd; NHS; Air Force Acad; Engr.

SCHAEFER, CYNTHIA; Ocean Township HS; Ocean, NJ; (3); 36/350; Pres Trs Aud/Vis; Debate Tm; VP Trs Service Clb; NHS; Voice Dem Awd; JCL; Latin Clb; Library Aide; Spanish Clb; School Musical; Gov Schl Publc Issues 87; Brnz Cngrsnl Awd 86; NJ Novice ST Chmpn 85; Intl Bus.

SCHAEFER, KRISTINE; Pennsville HS; Pennsville, NJ; (3); 2/225; French Clb; Chorus; Flag Corp; Mrchg Band; Orch; School Musical; School Play; Hon Roll; NHS.

SCHAEFER, STEPHANIE A; Pope Paul Vi HS; Haddonfield, NJ; (4); 19/511; Church Yth Grp; Drama Clb; Math Clb; Spanish Clb; School Musical; Hon Roll; NHS; Ntl Merit Ltr; Spanish NHS; Dstngshd Schlr; Drew Schlr; Fairleigh Dickinson Pres Schlr.

SCHAEFER, STUART; Don Bosco Prep; Wayne, NJ; (2); 1/220; Computer Clb; German Clb; Science Clb; Yrbk Rptr; Yrbk Stf; Var Ice Hcky; High Hon Roll; 2nd Pl Sci Fair Phy Categ 86; Awd Excllnce Hnrs Geom, Bio, & Latin I 85-86; MIT; Comp.

SCHAEFER, SUSAN; Paul VI HS; Clementon, NJ; (3); 5/416; Drama Clb; Sec German Clb; Hosp Aide; Spanish Clb; Speech Tm; Variety Show; High Hon Roll; Hon Roll; NHS; Spanish NHS; Germn Hnr Soc 87; Foreign Lang.

SCHAFER, GENE; Paramus Catholic HS; Rochelle Pk, NJ; (4); #26 In Class; Lit Mag; Kings Coll Scholar 87; Caldwell U Scholar 87; Seton Hall U; Pre-Med.

SCHAFFER, LYNN; Paul VI HS; Stratford, NJ; (3); 26/423; Spanish Clb; Band; Concert Band; Mrchg Band; Yrbk Stf; Lit Mag; Hon Roll; Spanish NHS.

SCHAFFER, SCOTT; Toms River HS North; Toms River, NJ; (3); 35/460; Trs German Clb; Intnl Clb; Science Clb; Ski Clb; Var L Socr; Var L Trk; Hon Roll; NHS; Neurosrgry.

SCHAFFLER, DAVID; Woodstown HS; Woodstown, NJ; (3); Boy Scts; German Clb; Key Clb; Math Clb; Rep Stu Cncl; Var Capt Bsbl; JV Var Socr; Tri-Cnty Chmpns Bsbl 86; South Jersey Chmpns Bsbl 85; Econ.

SCHAFLE, MICHELLE; Rancocas Valley Regional HS; Mt Holly, NJ; (3); Aud/Vis; Hosp Aide; Spanish Clb; Lcrss; High Hon Roll; Hon Roll; NHS; Gifted And Tlntd 85-88; Glassboro ST Coll; Com Dsgn.

SCHAIBLE, JEAN; Morristown HS; Morristown, NJ; (4); 8/418; Pep Clb; Ski Clb; Band; Chorus; Co-Capt Cheerleading; Socr; High Hon Roll; NHS; Cmnty Wkr; Hosp Aide; Key Clb Outstndng Pres 87; Presdntl Acadc Ftnss Awd 87; Wmns Clb Schlrshp 87; U Of DE; Lbrl Arts.

SCHAPPELL, WILLIAM; Warren County Vo Tech HS; Port Murray, NJ; (4); Ski Clb; Varsity Clb; VICA; Yrbk Phtg; Yrbk Stf; Trs Soph Cls; JV Bsbl; Var Socr; High Hon Roll; Prfct Atten Awd; Graphic Arts.

SCHARR, DONNA; Overbrook Reg SR HS; Pine Hill, NJ; (4); 32/335; French Clb; Trs Chorus; Stat Bsktbl; Cheerleading; Var Crs Cntry; Var Trk; Hon Roll; NHS; NJSIAA-ETS Schlr/Athlt Awd 87; Crss Cntry-Mst Dedictd Awd/Mst Imprvd 85-87; Choral Awd-Dedctd Svcs; Elizabethtown Coll; Acctng.

SCHARR, MARK W; Overbrook Regional SR HS; Pine Hill, NJ; (3); Am Leg Boys St; Crs Cntry; Trk; Hon Roll; Prfct Atten Awd.

SCHATZ, STEPHEN M; Morris Hills Regional HS; Rockaway, NJ; (3); 6/265; Am Leg Boys St; Drama Clb; Trs Thesps; School Musical; School Play; Nwsp Rptr; Nwsp Stf; Lit Mag; St Schlr; Library Aide; Eng.

SCHATZEL, KRISTIN; Hunterdon Central HS; Flemington, NJ; (4); 30/584; AFS; Nwsp Stf; Yrbk Stf; Rep Stu Cncl; Var Capt Crs Cntry; Var Capt Trk; NHS; Voice Dem Awd; 4-H; Rep Frsh Cls; Sen Wm Bradley ST Stu Ldrshp Conf Rep 87; Nrtheastrn U; Pre-Law.

SCHAUM, MATTHEW; North Bergen HS; North Bergen, NJ; (4); 35/425; German Clb; Drm Mjr(t); Jazz Band; Mrchg Band; Pep Band; Symp Band; Var JV Bowling; High Hon Roll; Garden St Schlrshp Awd 87; Rutgers U; Hist.

SCHAUMBURG, JEFF; Kittatinny Reg HS; Newton, NJ; (4); 3/228; Math Tm; Science Clb; Service Clb; Wt Lftg; High Hon Roll; NHS; Ntl Merit Ltr; St Schlr; Elec Engrng.

SCHEELE, MELISSA; Ridgewood HS; Ridgewood, NJ; (3); Orch; High Hon Roll; NHS; Chem Tm Ltr 86-87.

SCHEESE, AMY LOUISE; Lenape Valley Regional HS; Netcong, NJ; (3); 5/225; Church Yth Grp; Girl Scts; Key Clb; Office Aide; Yrbk Stf; Jr Cls; Stu Cncl; Bsktbl; Trk; High Hon Roll; Lenape Vly Schlr 86; Acctg.

SCHEETZ, STEVEN; Gloucester Catholic HS; Wenonah, NJ; (3); Intl Frgn Lang Awd Frnch 85; Aero Engr.

SCHEIBLE, ROBERT; Belleville HS; Belleville, NJ; (3); 5/401; Key Clb; Ski Clb; Spanish Clb; Varsity Clb; Var Crs Cntry; Var Trk; High Hon Roll; VP NHS; Rep Soph Cls; Rep Stu Cncl.

SCHELLER, SUSAN; Mary Helpof Christians Acad; Paterson, NJ; (4); Computer Clb; SADD; Chorus; Nwsp Stf; Hon Roll; Farleigh Dickinson U; Law.

SCHENKEL, LINDA; Overbrook Regional SR HS; Lindenwold, NJ; (4); 20/346; Yrbk Stf; High Hon Roll; Hon Roll; NHS.

SCHENSKI, BRIAN; Riverside HS; Delanco, NJ; (3); 19/103; Church Yth Grp; Varsity Clb; Off Stu Cncl; Var Capt Crs Cntry; Var Trk; Var Wrstlng; Prfct Atten Awd; Delanco Ed Assc Citznshp Awd 84; Electronics.

SCHERER, LISA; Toms River HS; Toms River, NJ; (3); Ski Clb; SADD; Yrbk Stf; Rep Frsh Cls; Rep Soph Cls; Rep Jr Cls; Rep Sr Cls; Rep Stu Cncl; JV Capt Cheerleading; Im Sftbl.

SCHERFF, SUSAN; Sparta HS; Sparta, NJ; (3); Key Clb; Nwsp Rptr; Var Swmmng; Peer Cnclr Prsnl Devlpmt Pgm 86-88; Miami U; Pblc Rltns.

SCHERI, RANDALL P; Jefferson Twp HS; Oak Ridge, NJ; (3); 2/270; Am Leg Boys St; Boy Scts; Math Tm; Science Clb; Ski Clb; Mrchg Band; School Musical; Bausch & Lomb Sci Awd; High Hon Roll; NHS.

SCHERTZER, LORI; John P Stevens HS; Edison, NJ; (3); 50/450; Cmnty Wkr; Key Clb; VP Library Aide; Model UN; Office Aide; Science Clb; SADD; Temple Yth Grp; Y-Teens; Flag Corp; Accntng.

SCHIERECK, KERI; Sayreville War Memorial HS; Sayreville, NJ; (4); 20/350; Church Yth Grp; Sec German Clb; Math Clb; Nwsp Rptr; JV Sftbl; High Hon Roll; NHS; Ntl Merit Ltr; NJ Inst Of Tech; Arch.

SCHIETTINO, ANTOINETTE; Cliffside Park HS; Cliffside Pk, NJ; (4); 21/254; Camera Clb; Intnl Clb; Letterman Clb; Pep Clb; Yrbk Phtg; Lit Mag; Cheerleading; Pom Pon; High Hon Roll; NHS; Glassboro ST Coll; Elem Ed.

SCHILL JR, JAMES M; Holy Cross HS; Riverton, NJ; (4); Chess Clb; German Clb; Quiz Bowl; Science Clb; Stage Crew; Hon Roll; Jr NHS; NHS; Stockton ST Coll.

SCHILLER, JAMES; Central Regional HS; Ocean Gates, NJ; (3); Church Yth Grp; Cmnty Wkr; Drama Clb; Key Clb; Service Clb; Spanish Clb; Band; Chorus; Concert Band; Drm Mjr(t).

SCHILLER, JEAN; Marlboro HS; Colts Neck, NJ; (2); 120/450; Drama Clb; 4-H; Girl Scts; Spanish Clb; Temple Yth Grp; Stage Crew; Yrbk Phtg; Yrbk Stf; Stu Cncl; Mgr(s); 4-H Schlrshp; Ptry Awd; Georgian Ct Coll; Psych.

SCHILTER, LARA; Brick Memorial HS; Brick, NJ; (3); 35/320; Church Yth Grp; Quiz Bowl; Red Cross Aide; Ski Clb; Chorus; Stage Crew; Fld Hcky; Mgr(s); Trk; NHS; HOSA-VP & Hstrn Rprtr; Mck Trl; HOPE; Music Thrpst.

SCHIMMINGER, THOMAS; Bayley Ellard HS; E Hanover, NJ; (4); Var Bsbl; Capt Ftbl; Wt Lftg; Capt Wrstlng; W J Ftbl Coaches Assoc All St 87; MVP Ftbl 86; MVP Wrstlng 84-87.

SCHIMPF, KENNETH; Clifton HS; Clifton, NJ; (3); Boys Clb Am; JV Var Socr; Rutgers; Vet.

SCHINDEL, RACHEL SHARON; Kingsway Regional HS; Swedesboro, NJ; (4); 4/159; Drama Clb; French Clb; Chorus; Church Choir; School Musical; Nwsp Ed-Chief; Yrbk Ed-Chief; Off Lit Mag; High Hon Roll; NHS; American U; Intl Rel.

SCHINDLER, JEFFREY; Fair Lawn HS; Fairlawn, NJ; (3); 34/350; Ski Clb; Temple Yth Grp; Pres Frsh Cls; Rep Soph Cls; Rep Stu Cncl; Var L Lcrss; Hon Roll; Prncpls List; Med.

SCHINELLER, CRISTA; Park Ridge HS; Park Ridge, NJ; (4); 2/106; 4-H; Sec Trs Jr Cls; Sec Trs Sr Cls; Var Capt Socr; Var Capt Trk; Twrlr; High Hon Roll; NHS; Sal; St Schlr; Army Res Schlr Ath Awd 87; Outstndng Frgn Lang Awd 87; Outstndng Stu 85; U PA; Sports Med.

SCHININA, JOANNE; Immaculate Conception HS; Lodi, NJ; (4); Spanish Clb; Hon Roll; William Paterson; Bus Admin.

SCHIRALDI, MICHELE; St Aloysius HS; Jersey City, NJ; (3); Girl Scts; Swmmng; Mssn Rep 86; John Jay Coll; Crmnl Jstc.

SCHLATE, INGEBORG; Morristown Beard HS; Morristown, NJ; (4); 3/80; AFS; Intnl Clb; Model UN; Q&S; Yrbk Bus Mgr; Var Bsktbl; Var Fld Hcky; Var Lcrss; Var Swmmng; Hon Roll; Cum Laude Soc 87; Pres Acadmc Ftns Awd 87; Dickinson W Richards Awd Human & Admc Grwth 87; Johns Hopkins U; Intl Stds.

SCHLENKER, SALLY K; Academy Of The Holy Angels; Old Tappan, NJ; (3); Church Yth Grp; Math Tm; Mu Alpha Theta; Chorus; Color Guard; Stage Crew; Yrbk Stf; Vllybl; Hon Roll; NHS; Schl Actn Clb; Natl Hist Soc; Aclyte In Parish; Mngmnt.

SCHLISSEL, JENNIFER; Mt Olive HS; Flanders, NJ; (3); 20/314; AFS; FBLA; SADD; Temple Yth Grp; Varsity Clb; Sec Jr Cls; Sec Stu Cncl; Var Capt Tennis; Var Trk; Hon Roll; MIP Tennis 84; Most Dedicated Tennis 85-86; MIP Track 85-86; Sports Med.

SCHMAUDER, VALERIE M; Bernards HS; Bernardsville, NJ; (4); 6/165; Exploring; Teachers Aide; Chorus; Nwsp Stf; Var Fld Hcky; NHS; Ntl Merit SF; Grdn ST Distngshd Schlr 86; Vrsty Ski Tm Capt 85-87; Math.

SCHMELTER, ROBYN; Immaculate Conception HS; Bogota, NJ; (3); Art Clb; Cmnty Wkr; Q&S; SADD; Nwsp Rptr; Rep Frsh Cls; Drama Clb; Spanish Clb; Chorus; Church Choir; 6th Annl NJ Dept Envrnmntl Prtctn Poster Cont Hon Mntn 85; Cert Apprctn Echoes Grphcs Ed 87; Comm Art.

SCHMIDBERGER, TOM; Randolph HS; Randolph, NJ; (3); Church Yth Grp; Trs 4-H; German Clb; Radio Clb; Ski Clb; Band; Mrchg Band; Dnfth Awd; 4-H Awd; Bus Mgmt.

SCHMIDHEISER, BRAD; Clearview Regional HS; Mullica Hill, NJ; (3); 75/178; Boy Scts; Band; Rep Stu Cncl; Capt Var Socr; L Var Trk; Wt Lftg; Var Wrstlng; Prfct Atten Awd; Eagle Scout Awd 85; Glassboro ST Coll; Bus.

SCHMIDLING, DONNA; Brick Twp Memorial HS; Brick, NJ; (4); 24/290; German Clb; Key Clb; Math Tm; Trk; High Hon Roll; NHS; Drama Clb; Math Clb; Office Aide; Band; Gvrnrs Tchng Schlrshp 87; Eleanor Gruppuso Schlrshp 87; U Of RI; Elem Tchr.

SCHMIDT, CONNIE; Howell HS; Howell, NJ; (3); Church Yth Grp; French Clb; JCL; Pres Latin Clb; Pres SADD; Rep Soph Cls; Var Tennis; Hon Roll; Pblc Reltns.

SCHMIDT, DAWN; Mount Olive HS; Budd Lake, NJ; (3); Church Yth Grp; Dance Clb; JV Stat Fld Hcky; Hon Roll; Earth Sci Hnr Awd 85; Acctg.

SCHMIDT, ERIK; Wall HS; Allenwood, NJ; (3); 10/289; Church Yth Grp; VP FBLA; German Clb; Nwsp Rptr; Nwsp Stf; L JV Socr; Wrstlng; High Hon Roll; Hon Roll; Syracuse; Brdcst Jrnlsm.

SCHMIDT, ERIKA; Lodi HS; Lodi, NJ; (3); 6/160; Pres Key Clb; Yrbk Phtg; Var Capt Bowling; NHS; Boy Scts; French Clb; Math Clb; Math Tm; Service Clb; Varsity Clb; Plyr Yr Bowling 87; 1st Tm All Lgue Bwlng 87.

SCHMIDT, JON; Hunterdon Central HS; Whitehouse Sta, NJ; (3); 1/556; Church Yth Grp; German Clb; Math Clb; Math Tm; Orch; School Musical; High Hon Roll; German II Awd 86; German Hnr Soc 86; Sci Lg 86; Civil Engrng.

SCHMIDT, JOSEPH; Bordentown Regional HS; Bordentown, NJ; (4); 19/114; Computer Clb; Math Tm; Mu Alpha Theta; Chorus; Yrbk Bus Mgr; JV Var Socr; Hon Roll; NHS; Prfct Atten Awd; Drama Clb; Olympics Of Mind; Compu.

SCHMIDT, KRISTIN; Union HS; Union, NJ; (3); Trs Church Yth Grp; Key Clb; Nwsp Stf; Rep Frsh Cls; Var L Fld Hcky; Var L Sftbl; Sec Jr NHS; NHS; VFW Awd; Hopwood Summer Schlrshp Prog 87; Acctng.

SCHMIDT, LINDA; South River HS; S River, NJ; (4); 13/130; German Clb; Library Aide; Math Clb; Yrbk Stf; Var JV Fld Hcky; Trk; NHS; Prsdntl Acdmc Ftns Awd 87; PTSO Schrshp 87; Rutgers Coll; Bio.

SCHMIDT, LISSA; Long Branch HS; Long Branch, NJ; (3); FBLA; PAVAS; Science Clb; Concert Band; Jazz Band; Mrchg Band; Symp Band; Capt Bowling; Im Wt Lftg; Church Yth Grp; Ldrshp Awd 87; Vrsty Schlr Awd 87; All Shore Band 85-87; Ctl Rgn Band Grp III St 87; NJ ST Yth Orchst; Studio Engr.

SCHMIDT, RYAN; Randolph HS; Randolph, NJ; (3); 28/355; Bsbl; Bowling; Tennis; Hon Roll; NHS; Bus.

SCHMIDT, STEPHEN; North Plainfield HS; N Plainfield, NJ; (3); 24/179; Am Leg Boys St; Boys Clb Am; Debate Tm; Political Wkr; Mrchg Band; Orch; VP Sr Cls; Ftbl; NHS; Scholastic Bowl; Chrmn Model Congress 87; Georgetown U; Pol Sci.

SCHMIEDER, LORI; Manchester HS; Whiting, NJ; (2); Drama Clb; Girl Scts; NFL; Lit Mag; Sftbl; Tennis; High Hon Roll; Hon Roll; Engl Lit.

SCHMITT, ERICA; Bricktownship HS; Jupiter, FL; (3); 16/450; Pep Clb; Spanish Clb; Stu Cncl; Crs Cntry; Tennis; Trk; Dnfth Awd; High Hon Roll; Hon Roll; NHS; U Of FL; Med.

SCHMITT, JOANNE; Spotswood HS; Milltown, NJ; (3); Church Yth Grp; Intnl Clb; Ski Clb; Yrbk Stf; Score Keeper; High Hon Roll; Hon Roll; NHS; Bus.

SCHMITT, MIKE; Holy Cross HS; Medford, NJ; (3); Church Yth Grp; Cmnty Wkr; Ski Clb; Rep Jr Cls; Rep Stu Cncl; JV Bsbl; JV Bsktbl; Hon Roll; JV Ltr Bsbl 85-86; JV Ltr Bsktbl 84-85; Syracuse U; Engrng.

SCHMITZ, PAUL A; Spotswood HS; Spotswood, NJ; (3); Ski Clb; Socr; Pilot.

SCHMON, KERRY; Passaic Valley Regional HS; Totowa, NJ; (2); Art Clb; Dance Clb; Science Clb; Spanish Clb; Teachers Aide; JV Bsktbl; High Hon Roll; Pres Schlr; AIDS Research Foundtn 87; Intl Beauty Show 87; UCLA; Acting.

SCHNABEL, SUSAN; Monsignor Donovan HS; Bricktown, NJ; (3); Art Clb; Girl Scts; Ski Clb; Stage Crew; Cheerleading; JV Socr.

SCHNACKENBERG, LYNN; Mahwah HS; Mahwah, NJ; (2); Capt Dance Clb; Girl Scts; Library Aide; Chorus; Mrchg Band; Var Cheerleading; Hon Roll; Hnr Rl; Bus.

SCHNEEMAN, LAURIE; Victory Christian Schl; Monroeville, NJ; (3); Pres Rptr 4-H; Office Aide; Chorus; Church Choir; School Musical; Nwsp Ed-Chief; Yrbk Stf; Var Cheerleading; Var Sftbl; Hon Roll; Thrpy.

SCHNEIDER, BETH; Southern Regional HS; Manahawkin, NJ; (4); 24/396; Band; School Musical; Variety Show; Yrbk Stf; Computer Clb; Stu Cncl; Var Socr; Trk; High Hon Roll; NHS; Ursinus Coll; Liberal Arts.

SCHNEIDER, JENNIFER M; S Brunswick HS; Kendall Park, NJ; (3); 28/286; Art Clb; Camera Clb; Sec 4-H; Math Tm; Mu Alpha Theta; French Hon Soc; 4-H Awd; Hon Roll; NHS; Prfct Atten Awd; Animal.

SCHNEIDER, WALTER; St Peters Prep; Bayonne, NJ; (3); Am Leg Boys St; Boy Scts; Church Yth Grp; German Clb; Teachers Aide; Rep Frsh Cls; Off Soph Cls; Off Jr Cls; Sec Sr Cls; Sec Stu Cncl; Slavic Clb-Sec, Treas, VP 84-85, 85-86, 86-87; Miltry Sci.

SCHNETTLER, MARCELO; Academic HS; Jersey City, NJ; (3); Am Leg Boys St; French Clb; School Play; Stage Crew; Variety Show; Lit Mag; Swmmng; Trk; Embry-Riddle U; Aerospce Engrng.

SCHNIPPER, STEVEN; Jewish Educational Center HS; Elizabeth, NJ; (2); Am Leg Aux Girls St; Chess Clb; Math Tm; Y-Teens; Im Bsktbl; Im Sftbl; Hon Roll; Prtcpnt Jerome G Bentley JR Annl ST Sci Day 86.

SCHNITZER, LORI; Linden HS; Linden, NJ; (4); Drama Clb; Key Clb; Office Aide; Spanish Clb; School Play; Capt Fld Hcky; High Hon Roll; NHS; PBA & Pta Schlrshp 87; Philadelphia Coll Pharm; Pharm.

SCHNOCK, CHRISTINA MARIE; Manalapan HS; Manalapan, NJ; (3); Drama Clb; Thesps; Church Choir; Madrigals; School Musical; School Play; Stage Crew; Silver Congressnl Medal 87; Religious Educ Teacher 86; Music.

SCHNOLL, RACHEL; Summit HS; Summit, NJ; (4); 70/275; Drama Clb; Model UN; VP Temple Yth Grp; Chorus; Madrigals; School Musical; School Play; Nwsp Bus Mgr; Stat Sftbl; Hon Roll; Best Drama Plyr Awd 84; Brandeis U.

SCHOCH, GAIL; Washington Twp HS; Turnersville, NJ; (4); Chorus; School Play; Chorus Awd 87; Grnd Rep KY & Jr Grnd Ex Comm Rainbw 86-88; Wrthy Advsr, Mystc #5 86.

SCHOEN, LINDSAY; Dwight Morrow HS; Englewood, NJ; (3); 5/312; Drama Clb; School Musical; School Play; Yrbk Stf; High Hon Roll; Prfct Atten Awd.

SCHOEN, MICHAEL; E Brunswick HS; E Brunswick, NJ; (2); Key Clb; Science Clb; Ski Clb; Nwsp Rptr; Nwsp Stf; High Hon Roll; Hon Roll; Awd Scoring High Chem League 86-87.

SCHOENBERG, AMANDA; Dwight Englewood HS; Tenafly, NJ; (3); Dance Clb; Debate Tm; Math Tm; School Musical; Ed Nwsp Bus Mgr; Cheerleading; Gym; Lcrss; Socr; Hon Roll; Bergen Cnty Math Leag Merit Awd 87; Med.

SCHOENBERG, JOSH; Livingston HS; Livingston, NJ; (3); 72/417; FBLA; Leo Clb; Nwsp Rptr; Nwsp Sprt Ed; Nwsp Stf; Im Bsktbl; Im Sftbl.

SCHOENBERGER, JEREMY; Vineland HS; Vineland, NJ; (2); CAP; Computer Clb; Key Clb; Political Wkr; Spanish Clb; Rep Stu Cncl; Hon Roll; Civil Air Ptrl Cert 86; Awd Svc Vet NJ Memrl Home 87; Avtn Engr.

SCHOENBERGER, LYNN A; Passaic Valley HS; Little Falls, NJ; (4); 140/337; Church Yth Grp; Cmnty Wkr; Computer Clb; DECA; Drama Clb; French Clb; Girl Scts; Key Clb; Library Aide; Spanish Clb; Wm Paterson Coll.

SCHOENEICK, KATHLEEN; Toms River H S South; Toms River, NJ; (2); Chorus; Fash Merch.

SCHOENEWOLF, BRENDA J; Manasquan HS; Spring Lake, NJ; (2); 50/256; Church Yth Grp; Key Clb; Ski Clb; Spanish Clb; SADD; Bsktbl; Fld Hcky; Sftbl; Hon Roll; Lwyr.

SCHOFIELD, KRISTEN; Maple Shade HS; Maple Shade, NJ; (3); JA; Red Cross Aide; Spanish Clb; SADD; Rep Frsh Cls; Rep Soph Cls; Sec Jr Cls; Var Cheerleading; Spanish NHS; Rotary Clb Ldrshp Awd 85; Stu Cncl Achvt Acad 86; DECA Conf Fin 87; James Madison U; Phys Thrpy.

SCHOLTZ, HEATHER ANN; Brick Memorial HS; Brick, NJ; (3); 9/370; Cmnty Wkr; Key Clb; Latin Clb; Math Tm; Science Clb; Spanish Clb; Gov Hon Prg Awd; High Hon Roll; Jr NHS; NHS; Mock Trial Comptn Ocean County 4th Pl 87; Latin Hnr Scty 85-86; Mulitple Sclerosis Spellathon 85; Johns Hopkins U; Surgery.

SCHONENBERGER, SIMONE; Park Ridge HS; Park Ridge, NJ; (4); 6/106; Nwsp Ed-Chief; Lit Mag; Rep Jr Cls; High Hon Roll; VP NHS; Gardn St Dstngshd Schlr 87; Amer Assn Tchrs Of German Inc-Cert Of Merit 85; Washington & Lee U; Pol Sci.

SCHONFELD, DAN; Livingston HS; Livingston, NJ; (4); 1/424; Pres Computer Clb; Pres Math Clb; Capt Math Tm; Var Socr; Var Trk; CC Awd; French Hon Soc; Gov Hon Prg Awd; JETS Awd; NHS; 1st Pl Cnty Math Comp Calculus 86; Acad Medallions Acad Excell 87; Yale U; Comp Sci.

SCHOONOVER, ANNE; Manasquan HS; Sea Girt, NJ; (3); 6/230; Cmnty Wkr; Drama Clb; Hosp Aide; Math Tm; Spanish Clb; Stage Crew; Mgr(s); High Hon Roll; Kiwanis Awd; NHS; Brd Educ Awd 86-87.

SCHOONOVER, REGINA; Pope John XXIII HS; Lake Hoptacong, NJ; (4); 3/130; Church Yth Grp; Cmnty Wkr; Drama Clb; Chorus; School Musical; Ed Lit Mag; Rep Sr Cls; Var Capt Cheerleading; Var Capt Trk; High Hon Roll; Chrldng Schlrshp Awd 87; Sussex Cnty SR Stu Arts Awd Vcl Music 87; John Joseph Frank Mem Awd 87; PA ST U; Gntcs.

SCHOR, JUSTIN; Waldwick SR HS; Waldwick, NJ; (2); Math Tm; NFL; Service Clb; School Play; Nwsp Rptr; Nwsp Sprt Ed; JV Bsktbl; Var L Socr; Var L Trk; Kiwanis Awd; Stanford U.

SCHORR, HEATHER; Mendham HS; Brookside, NJ; (4); Intnl Clb; Band; Color Guard; Concert Band; Mrchg Band; Symp Band; High Hon Roll; Hon Roll; NHS; Pres Schlr; Wmns Clb Schlrshp 87; Rcgntn 16 Cnstv Hnr Rl 83-87; Lehigh U; Bus Mgmt.

SCHOTT, DARLENE; Mahwah HS; Mahwah, NJ; (4); Drama Clb; Red Cross Aide; Stu Cncl; Capt Cheerleading; Gym; Capt Pom Pon; Cit Awd; High Hon Roll; NHS; St Schlr; Thndrbrd Schlrshp $350 87; Schlrshp From Mahwah Police Dept 87; Ctznshp Awd For Douglass Coll 86; Glassboro ST; Crmnl Jstc.

SCHOTT, JENNIFER; Rd Bank Catholic HS; Colts Neck, NJ; (3); Band; Concert Band; Jazz Band; Mrchg Band; Var Bsktbl; Var Socr; NHS; Accntng.

SCHOWN, JOHN RUSSELL; Piscataway HS; Piscataway, NJ; (4); 29/496; Boy Scts; VP Church Yth Grp; Math Tm; Varsity Clb; Chorus; Var Swmmng; Hon Roll; NHS; Ntl Merit Ltr; Rutgers Coll Of Engrng.

SCHRANTZ, ALEX; Morristown-Beard HS; Madison, NJ; (3); 3/83; Am Leg Boys St; Teachers Aide; Concert Band; Var Ftbl; Var Trk; DAR Awd; High Hon Roll; Jr NHS; NHS; Ntl Merit Ltr; Cum Laude 87; Economics.

SCHRANTZ, JENNIFER; Toms River High School East; Toms River, NJ; (3); 75/510; French Clb; Intnl Clb; Library Aide; Yrbk Stf; Mgr(s); Hon Roll; Hnr Roll 85-86; Lib Arts.

SCHREIER, MARY; Central Regional HS; Bayville, NJ; (4); 17/250; Math Clb; Teachers Aide; Band; Concert Band; Jazz Band; Mrchg Band; Var Tennis; Var Trk; High Hon Roll; NHS; Personl Typng Awd 87; Kean Coll; Elem Educ.

SCHREIER, MATT; Highstown HS; East Windsor, NJ; (3); Cmnty Wkr; French Clb; Ski Clb; SADD; Jazz Band; Yrbk Stf; Im Lcrss; Var L Trk; Hon Roll.

SCHREINER, ERIC; Holy Spirit HS; Brigantine, NJ; (3); 3/332; Im Vllybl; Hon Roll; NHS; Englsh Awd 84-85; Histry Awd 85-86.

SCHREINER, LEE ANN; Holy Spirit HS; Brigantine, NJ; (3); 49/332; Dance Clb; Spanish Clb; SADD; Hon Roll; Villanova; Nrsng.

SCHREINER, MARK; Holy Spirit HS; Brigantine, NJ; (2); 50/397; JV Bsbl; Ftbl; Hon Roll.

SCHROEDER, DONALD; St Peters Prep; Lyndhurst, NJ; (4); 13/197; Boy Scts; Church Yth Grp; German Clb; NFL; Nwsp Rptr; God Cntry Awd; High Hon Roll; Acad Schlrshp To Holy Cross 87-88; Holy Cross; Engl.

SCHROETER, LISA; Newton HS; Newton, NJ; (3); 3/194; Drama Clb; French Clb; German Clb; SADD; Band; Concert Band; Drm Mjr(t); Mrchg Band; School Musical; Stage Crew; Cnty Band 85-86; Cnty Area & Regnl I Band 87; Govrs Schl For Music 87; Boston Coll; Psych.

SCHROETTER, THOMAS; Mater Del HS; Hazlet, NJ; (4); Boy Scts; Church Yth Grp; Cmnty Wkr; School Play; Rep Frsh Cls; Rep Soph Cls; Trs Jr Cls; Off Stu Cncl; Capt Var Golf; Rlgn Awd-4 Yrs 87; Spch Awd 87; Coaches Awd/Plyrs Awd-Golf 87; Glassboro ST Coll; Bus.

SCHROLLER, DIANE; Belleville HS; Belleville, NJ; (3); DECA; Library Aide; Band; Chorus; Jazz Band; Mrchg Band; School Musical; Variety Show; Stu Cncl; Hon Roll; Tourism & Recrtn.

SCHUBEL, LIAM P; Freehold Township HS; Freehold, NJ; (4); Boy Scts; Church Yth Grp; Spanish Clb; Concert Band; Jazz Band; Bowling; Crs Cntry; Trk; Wrstlng; NHS; Trenton ST Coll; Comp Sci.

SCHUESSLER, LAURIE; Bordentown Regional HS; Bordentown, NJ; (2); 6/140; Pres Hst 4-H; Math Tm; SADD; Chorus; School Play; Yrbk Stf; VP Soph Cls; Rep Stu Cncl; Mgr(s); Pom Pon; 4-H Awd 81-85; Hnr Roll; Marine Bio.

SCHUETZ, TRACI; Waldwick HS; Waldwick, NJ; (3); 9/134; Lit Mag; Mgr(s); High Hon Roll; Hon Roll; NHS.

SCHUETZLER, BRIAN; Sparta HS; Sparta, NJ; (3); Church Yth Grp; Drama Clb; Acpl Chr; Sec Chorus; Church Choir; Madrigals; School Musical; School Play; Hon Roll; Scndry Ed.

SCHUIL, SUSAN; Eastern Christian HS; Prospect Park, NJ; (3); 8/88; Art Clb; Sec Church Yth Grp; Drama Clb; Spanish Clb; School Play; VP NHS; The Berkely Schl; Fshn Mktg.

SCHUJKO, JO ANNE; Bordentown Regional HS; Yardville, NJ; (2); #4 In Class; Church Yth Grp; Chorus; Church Choir; Sec Soph Cls; High Hon Roll; Hon Roll; Prfct Atten Awd; Math.

SCHULDES, FELICIA; Notre Dame HS; Trenton, NJ; (4); Church Yth Grp; Cmnty Wkr; Hosp Aide; JA; Office Aide; Yrbk Stf; Cit Awd; Awd Kids Say Know Drg Abuse 87; Koinonia Clb 85-87; Marine Bio.

SCHULER, CYNTHIA M; Morristown HS; Morristown, NJ; (4); 124/418; Am Leg Aux Girls St; Cmnty Wkr; Latin Clb; Office Aide; Band; Rep Soph Cls; Capt Bsktbl; Trk; Hon Roll; Powder Puff Ftbl; Wmns Clb Schlrshp, PBA Schlrshp, & Finalst Ms US Teen 87; U MD; Pre Med.

SCHULTZ, AMY; Hunterdon Central HS; Flemington, NJ; (3); Pres Sec Church Yth Grp; 4-H; Science Clb; Chorus; Church Choir; Orch; Crs Cntry; Swmmng; Trk; Hon Roll; Grmn Hnr Scty 86-88; Schlrshp Intl Chrstn Yth Exchng 86; Physcl Ftnss Awd 85-86; Dctr Of Oncology.

SCHULTZ, CHERYL; East Brunswick HS; East Brunswick, NJ; (4); Ftbl; Vllybl; High Hon Roll; Hon Roll; Johnson & Wales Coll; Hotel Mgm.

SCHULTZ, JEFFREY; Caldwell HS; Caldwell, NJ; (4); 29/250; Key Clb; Var Trs Sr Cls; Stu Cncl; Var Golf; High Hon Roll; NHS; High Hnr Rl 85-87; Penn ST U; Bus.

SCHULTZ, RUTHANN; Lower Cape May Regional HS; N Cape May, NJ; (3); 54/192; Office Aide; SADD; Chorus; Flag Corp; Hon Roll; Glassboro; Elem Ed.

SCHULTZ, TRICIA; Millville JR SR HS; Dorchester, NJ; (3); FCA; Hosp Aide; Stat English Clb; Trk; Hon Roll; Natl Yth Phys Ftnss Pgm Marine Corps Leag 86-87; Med.

SCHULTZE, LYNN; Parsippany HS; Lk Hiawatha, NJ; (2); VP German Clb; Band; Concert Band; Mrchg Band; Stage Crew; Symp Band; Home Ec Awd 85; Bus Admin.

SCHULTZE, WENDY; Toms River High School East; Toms Rvr, NJ; (4); 178/531; Church Yth Grp; Cmnty Wkr; Drama Clb; SADD; Chorus; Mrchg Band; School Play; Variety Show; Pom Pon; Trphs Prfct Attndc Dance; Columbia Coll SC; Pro Dance.

SCHULZ, JAMES; Hamilton High West; Yardville, NJ; (4); Am Leg Boys St; Cmnty Wkr; FBLA; Political Wkr; SADD; Varsity Clb; Var Socr; NJ ST Sfty Cncl Svd By The Blt 87; Intl Law.

SCHULZ, ROBIN ANN; Burlington City HS; Edgewater Pk, NJ; (3); Am Leg Aux Girls St; FTA; Concert Band; Drill Tm; Mrchg Band; Sec Stu Cncl; Fld Hcky; Mgr(s); Sftbl; Tchr.

SCHUMACHER, DONALD; St John Vianney HS; Freehold, NJ; (3); 25/250; Art Clb; Church Yth Grp; Service Clb; SADD; L Var Crs Cntry; L Var Trk; Hon Roll; Gold & White Awd 85; Aero Engr.

SCHUMACHER, JANE; St John Vianney HS; Freehold, NJ; (4); 9/250; Art Clb; Church Yth Grp; Drama Clb; Girl Scts; Math Tm; Ski Clb; SADD; Teachers Aide; Mrchg Band; Stage Crew; Gold & White Awd 84-87; Garden State Dist Scholars Schlrshp 87; U Of Pittsburgh; Occ Therapy.

SCHUMACHER, LISA; Newton HS; Newton, NJ; (3); 1/194; Latin Clb; Math Tm; Nwsp Stf; Yrbk Stf; Lit Mag; Rep Stu Cncl; Var Bsktbl; Var Trk; NHS; Church Yth Grp; Arthur Disque Awd-Outstndng Fresmn Girl Athlete 84-85; Coaches Awd-Girls Track 86; Communctns.

SCHUPANSKY, ANDRES; Dickinson HS; Jersey City, NJ; (3); Camera Clb; Computer Clb; Exploring; Math Clb; Scholastic Bowl; Science Clb; Hon Roll; NHS; Rutgrs Schlr 87; Tech Engnrng.

SCHUSTER, RON; John P Stevens HS; Edison, NJ; (3); Am Leg Boys St; Debate Tm; Model UN; Var L Socr; NHS; YMCA Natl Affairs Conf 87; Operation Enterprise Pgm 87; Model UN Distngshd Hnrs Delegatn 87; Intl Rltns.

SCHUTZBANK, MICHAEL; Lakewood HS; Lakewood, NJ; (3); 29/330; Am Leg Boys St; Trs FBLA; German Clb; Hosp Aide; Hon Roll; Var L Ftbl; Im Wrstlng; Sntrl Bill Bradley Young Citizens Awd 87.

SCHUTZER, ROMI; Secaucus HS; Secaucus, NJ; (3); 16/166; Key Clb; Ski Clb; Varsity Clb; School Play; Lit Mag; Pres Jr Cls; Var Cheerleading; High Hon Roll; Spanish NHS; Hugh O Brian Yuth Fdtn Ldrshmp Smnr, Ntl Ldrshp Trng Ctr NJASC 86; UCLA; Bus Admn.

SCHWAB, SUSAN M; Holy Cross HS; Medford, NJ; (3); 68/400; Am Leg Aux Girls St; Girl Scts; Science Clb; Spanish Clb; Yrbk Sprt Ed; Var L Cheerleading; Var L Tennis; Grl Scts Of Amer Slvr Ldrshp Gld Ldrshp & Slvr Awd 85; Bus.

SCHWAEBLE, DIANA; West Morris Mendham HS; Mendham, NJ; (4); 162/322; Art Clb; Church Yth Grp; Cmnty Wkr; Dance Clb; Drama Clb; Ski Clb; Chorus; School Play; Fld Hcky; Am Legion Awd 83; Miss Teen Rnnr Up 86; Mason Gross Schl Arts; Drama.

SCHWAGER, DAVID; Steinert HS; North Crosswicks, NJ; (3); Am Leg Boys St; Church Yth Grp; Band; Concert Band; Mrchg Band; Orch; School Musical; School Play; JV Tennis; NHS.

SCHWARTZ, CAYE; John P Stevens HS; Edison, NJ; (3); 37/450; Key Clb; Model UN; Office Aide; Sec Science Clb; Mrchg Band; French Hon Soc; Hon Roll; NHS; St Schlr; Psych.

SCHWARTZ, DEBBIE; Brurial H S For Girls; West Orange, NJ; (3); Temple Yth Grp; Rptr Yrbk Bus Mgr; Sec Frsh Cls; VP Soph Cls; Sec Jr Cls; NHS.

SCHWARTZ, ELIZABETH; Mary Help Of Christians Acad; Sloatsburg, NY; (3); 18/85; Hosp Aide; Library Aide; Teachers Aide; Chorus; Im Bsktbl; Im Ftbl; Hon Roll; Frnch Hnr Cert 85 & 86; Wrld Hstry Cert 86; Geometry Cert 86.

SCHWARTZ, JEFFREY; Raritan HS; Hazlet, NJ; (3); 1/340; Drama Clb; Pres VP French Clb; Capt Math Tm; Science Clb; Band; Jazz Band; School Play; Yrbk Stf; High Hon Roll; NHS; NJ Govs Schl In Sci 84-87; Math Lg Best Frshmn, Soph, & JR 85-87.

SCHWARTZ, JENNIFER; Watchung Hills Regional HS; Watchung, NJ; (4); 7/310; Am Leg Aux Girls St; Latin Clb; Capt JV Bsktbl; Capt Fld Hcky; Capt JV Sftbl; High Hon Roll; Hon Roll; NHS; Opt Clb Awd; NY U Schlrshp 87; Chubb & Son Awd 87; Ntl Ltn Exm 87; NY U; Mrktng Rsrch.

SCHWARTZ, JENNIFER; West Essex SR HS; Roseland, NJ; (3); Key Clb; Spanish Clb; SADD; Temple Yth Grp; Nwsp Stf; Yrbk Bus Mgr; Yrbk Stf; Tennis; Hon Roll; NHS; Ina Wolfe Schlrshp 87.

SCHWARTZ, MATTHEW; Lenape Valley Regional HS; Andover, NJ; (3); 1/224; FBLA; Office Aide; Temple Yth Grp; High Hon Roll; Hon Roll; Prfct Atten Awd; Lenape Valley Schlr Awd 85.

SCHWARTZ, MELISSA; Kinnelon HS; Kinnelon, NJ; (3); Debate Tm; Drama Clb; French Clb; NFL; Pres PAVAS; Ski Clb; School Musical; School Play; Nwsp Rptr; Nwsp Stf; Hugh Obrian Yth Fndtn Cert Of Reg 87.

SCHWARTZ, SAMUEL W; The Frisch Schl; Wyckoff, NJ; (4); L Debate Tm; Varsity Clb; Jazz Band; Rep Stu Cncl; Capt Socr; Pres NHS; Yale U.

SCHWARZ, BARBARA; Pt Pleasant Boro HS; Pt Pleasant Bch, NJ; (3); Drama Clb; Chorus; School Musical; Ocean Cnty Coll; Pschology.

SCHWARZ, ERIC; Holy Spirit HS; Brigantine, NJ; (3); 20/332; Hon Roll; Rutgers U; Comm.

SCHWARZ, KENNETH; Somerset County Vo Tech HS; Princeton, NJ; (4); 1/141; Ski Clb; Hon Roll; Pres Schlr; Val; Nchls Thul Awd 87; Natl Bnk Of Cntrl Jrsy Schlstc Exc Awd 87; Exc In Vo-Tech Shp Prgm 86-87; Auto Body.

SCHWARZE, STACY; Memorial HS; West New York, NJ; (3); Chorus; Lit Mag; Rep Soph Cls; Rep Stu Cncl; Hon Roll; Rutgers Schl Of Nursing; Nrsng.

SCHWARZMAN, MARK; Metuchen HS; Metuchen, NJ; (4); 39/177; Var L Bsbl; Var L Ftbl; Wt Lftg; Hon Roll; Ftbl Div All Star Team 86; Booster Club Cert Of Merit Acad & Athl Exc 87; Rutgers U; Bus.

SCHWEID, BRET; Fair Lawn HS; Fair Lawn, NJ; (3); 20/340; Math Tm; Science Clb; Service Clb; JV Socr; Hon Roll; NHS; Sci.

SCHWENGER, COLLEEN; Absegami HS; Port Republic, NJ; (3); 13/284; 4-H; French Clb; VP Pres FBLA; Key Clb; Ski Clb; Nwsp Stf; Ed Lit Mag; Mgr Fld Hcky; Tennis; 4-H Awd; Acadmcs Vrsty Ltr 84-86; Duke U; Poli Sci.

SCHWIER, CATHERINE; Manasquan HS; Spring Lake, NJ; (3); Church Yth Grp; Cmnty Wkr; Drama Clb; FBLA; Key Clb; Latin Clb; Ski Clb; Spanish Clb; Tennis; Hon Roll.

SCHWINDT, KAREN; St John Vianney HS; Keyport, NJ; (2); GAA; Intnl Clb; SADD; Yrbk Stf; JV Bsktbl; Im Crs Cntry; JV Sftbl; High Hon Roll; Hon Roll; Gold & White Awd 86-87; Lbrl Arts.

SCHWINGEL, COLLEEN; Parsippany Hills HS; Dover, NJ; (3); Church Yth Grp; FBLA; Thesps; School Play; Pres Soph Cls; Pres Jr Cls; Rep Stu Cncl; Powder Puff Ftbl; High Hon Roll; Bambergers Comm Svc Awd 86; Peer Cnslng Pgm 85-87; Pub Rel Commtte 86-87; Engrng.

SCHWORK, STEVE; Allentown HS; Robbinsville, NJ; (2); Band; Drm Mjr(t); Jazz Band; School Play; Stage Crew; Symp Band; Var L Bsktbl; Var L Socr; Var L Trk; Law.

SCIABARASI, LORRIE; James Caldwell HS; W Caldwell, NJ; (3); Art Clb; Ski Clb; Stat Bsktbl; JV Mgr(s); JV Capt Sftbl; Hon Roll; Arch.

SCIACCA, MICHAEL; Don Bosco Prep HS; Stony Point, NY; (3); 12/225; Hosp Aide; Varsity Clb; Var Bowling; Im Fld Hcky; High Hon Roll; NHS.

SCIARRILLO, TINA; Hanover Park HS; E Hanover, NJ; (3); 18/273; Exploring; NAACP; Science Clb; Spanish Clb; SADD; Teachers Aide; Lit Mag; Hon Roll; Psych.

SCIBEK, TAMARA; Sayreville War Memorial HS; Sayreville, NJ; (4); 69/340; Pres German Clb; Varsity Clb; Church Choir; Jazz Band; JV Bsktbl; Capt Var Sftbl; Hon Roll; Church Yth Grp; Chorus; Pres Grmn Hnr Soc 85-87; All Middlesex Cnty Sftbl Awd 3rd Tm 85 & 1st Tm 87; Johnson & Wales Coll; Trvl.

SCIGLITANO, CHRISTOPHER D; Paramus Catholic Boys HS; Ridgefield, NJ; (4); 1/178; Math Tm; Band; Nwsp Ed-Chief; Lit Mag; VP Sr Cls; Rep Stu Cncl; Var Capt Ice Hcky; French Hon Soc; High Hon Roll; Pres NHS; Ridgefield Chptr Unico Natl Schlrshp 87; Robert A Byrd NJ Dept Ed Schlrshp 87; Dartmouth Coll.

SCILLA, TRACY; Manchester Twp HS; Toms River, NJ; (3); Math Tm; Science Clb; High Hon Roll; Fshn Mdse.

SCILLIERI, CHRISTOPHER; Memorial HS; Elmwood Pk, NJ; (3); 20/160; Am Leg Boys St; Math Clb; Nwsp Sprt Ed; Yrbk Sprt Ed; Pres Sr Cls; Rep Stu Cncl; Var Ftbl; Var Trk; Hon Roll; 2nd Tm All Lg Track 87; Bus Mgmt.

SCILLIERI, JANICE; Lyndhurst HS; Lyndhurst, NJ; (4); 2/168; Sec German Clb; JV Sftbl; JV Vllybl; Elks Awd; High Hon Roll; VP NHS; Sal; Garden St Dstngshd Schlr 86-87; Trenton ST Coll.

SCIMECA, BETTY; Lodi HS; Lodi, NJ; (4); 69/135; Church Yth Grp; Girl Scts; Varsity Clb; Concert Band; Mrchg Band; Orch; Var Socr; Sftbl; Var Trk; Bergen CC; Elec Engrng Tech.

SCIMEME, DORIANN; Bishop George AHR HS; Milltown, NJ; (4); 21/265; Drama Clb; Pres Service Clb; Thesps; Chorus; School Musical; School Play; High Hon Roll; Hon Roll; NHS; ST Sub JR Yr Awd 85-86; Trenton ST Coll; Deaf Ed.

SCIMENE, DORIANN; Bishop George Ahr HS; Milltown, NJ; (4); 21/267; Drama Clb; Pres Service Clb; Thesps; Chorus; School Musical; School Play; High Hon Roll; Hon Roll; NHS; Band; Ntl Sci Merit Awd 83 & 87; St Sub-Jr Of Yr 86; Miss Mltwn 86; Trntn ST Coll; Tchr.

SCIORRA, VICKI ANN; Wayne Hills HS; Wayne, NJ; (4); 2/288; Art Clb; Cmnty Wkr; Dance Clb; Exploring; Math Clb; Spanish Clb; Lit Mag; Ed Lit Mag; High Hon Roll; Hon Roll; Passiac Cnty Achvt Awd 87; Rutgers Schlr 6; Wmns Club Of Preakness Mem Scrhlshp 87; Lehigh U; Bio.

SCOLA, LARISSA; West Essex SR HS; Roseland, NJ; (3); Church Yth Grp; Drama Clb; French Clb; Chorus; Church Choir; School Musical; School Play; Stage Crew; Hon Roll; NHS; Law.

SCOLLO, JOHN; Hunterdon Central HS; Flemington, NJ; (2); 87/485; Debate Tm; Nwsp Stf; Off Soph Cls; Crs Cntry; Trk.

SCOPELLITI, PAULINA; Pennsauken HS; Pennsauken, NJ; (2); Spanish Clb; Mrchg Band; Hon Roll; Med.

SCORDATO, ADRIENNE; Matawan Regional HS; Marlboro, NJ; (3); 63/350; Cmnty Wkr; Pres DECA; SADD; Band; Concert Band; School Musical; Hon Roll; DECA Adv & Display 1st,2nd & 1st Plcs 86,2nd Pl 87; Adv.

SCORNAVACCA, THOMAS; Paul VI HS; Haddonfield, NJ; (3); 30/428; AFS; Church Yth Grp; Band; Concert Band; Jazz Band; Mrchg Band; Pep Band; Var Tennis; Hon Roll; NHS; Princeton U; Pre Med.

SCOTT, CHRISTOPHER; High Point Regional HS; Branchville, NJ; (2); German Clb; Swmmng; Pre-Law.

SCOTT, DEXTER L; Florence Twp Memorial HS; Edgewater Park, NJ; (4); 26/88; French Clb; FBLA; FTA; Varsity Clb; Nwsp Rptr; Pres Sr Cls; Var L Trk; Cit Awd; Elks Awd; Am Leg Boys St; Bus Hnr Soc 86-87; Renaissance Soc; Montclair ST Coll; Lawyer.

SCOTT JR, EVAN PAUL; Pennsville Memorial HS; Pennsville, NJ; (3); Am Leg Boys St; Church Yth Grp; Political Wkr; Spanish Clb; JV Ftbl; JV Trk; Hon Roll; Senator Bill Bradleys Ldrshp Semr 87; Pol Sci.

SCOTT, JOHNETTA; Plainfield HS; Plainfield, NJ; (3); 12/300; Math Tm; Science Clb; Band; Concert Band; Hon Roll; Jr NHS; NHS; Prfct Atten Awd; 1st Pl Stevens Tech Inst Sci Fair 87; 3rd Pl Chem Div North Jersey Sci Fair 87; Chem Engrng.

SCOTT, KARL; Gateway Regional HS; Westville, NJ; (2); German Clb; Latin Clb; Band; Concert Band; Jazz Band; Mrchg Band; School Musical; Tennis; Law.

SCOTT, KELLY; Morristown HS; Morristown, NJ; (1); Aud/Vis; Girl Scts; Radio Clb; Band; Chorus; Church Choir; Concert Band; JV Bsktbl; JV Socr; Var Sftbl; Sftbl Frelinghuysen Schl Rookie Yr & MVP 84-86; Bsktbll Schl Co-Cptn 85-86; Syracuse; Psycl Ed.

SCOTT, MARIE; Maple Shade HS; Maple Shade, NJ; (3); Am Leg Aux Girls St; DECA; FBLA; Key Clb; Spanish Clb; Cheerleading; Socr; High Hon Roll; Hon Roll; Prfct Atten Awd.

SCOTT, ROBERT; Parsippany Hills HS; Putnam Valley, NY; (3); Am Leg Boys St; Cmnty Wkr; Key Clb; Chorus; Stu Cncl; Swmmng; Wrstlng; Hon Roll; NHS; Ntl Merit Ltr; Rsrvd Chmpn JR Nvce Equittn Ovr Fnces 86; Cornell U; Vet.

SCOTT, SABURNIA; Belvidere HS; Belvidere, NJ; (3); Church Yth Grp; French Clb; Ski Clb; Varsity Clb; Stage Crew; Rep Frsh Cls; Rep Soph Cls; Rep Jr Cls; Stu Cncl; Fld Hcky; Frnch Awd Fresh Clss 84; Varsity B 87.

SCOTT, STEPHANIE; Monsignor Donovan HS; Bayville, NJ; (4); 18/226; Cmnty Wkr; French Clb; SADD; Yrbk Stf; Trk; Gov Hon Prg Awd; High Hon Roll; Hon Roll; NHS; Fnlst Gov Schl NJ 86; Hnr Rl, Natl Hnr Soc 85-87; Trenton ST Coll; Engl.

SCOTT, TAMARA; St Marys Hall Doane Acad; Medford, NJ; (4); 6/18; Hosp Aide; Library Aide; Pep Clb; Yrbk Stf; Sec Sr Cls; Mgr Bsktbl; Sftbl; Trk; High Hon Roll; Hon Roll; Intramural Champ 85-87; Vassar; Psych.

SCOTT, TAMMY; Camden HS; Camden, NJ; (3); Pres Band; Pres Church Choir; Concert Band; Jazz Band; Mrchg Band; Yrbk Phtg; Yrbk Rptr; Pres Soph Cls; Rep Jr Cls; Cit Awd; Howard U; Law.

SCOTT, VICKI; Toms River HS South; Pine Beach, NJ; (1); Key Clb; Im JV Bsktbl; Im JV Fld Hcky; Wt Lftg; Hon Roll.

SCOTT, WILLIAM; Glen Rock HS; Glen Rock, NJ; (3); 26/146; Spanish Clb; Band; Concert Band; Nwsp Stf; Yrbk Stf; JV Bsktbl; Var Ftbl; High Hon Roll; Jr NHS; NHS; Notre Dame; Business.

SCOTTI, REGINA; Glen Rock SR HS; Glen Rock, NJ; (2); AFS; Church Yth Grp; Debate Tm; French Clb; Nwsp Stf; JV Trk; JV Vllybl; Cit Awd; Hon Roll; VP Jr NHS; Advrtsng.

SCOVELL, VICTORIA; Vernon Township HS; Vernon, NJ; (3); 39/245; Varsity Clb; Band; Color Guard; School Musical; Lit Mag; Rep Stu Cncl; JV Var Swmmng; Stat Trk; Hon Roll; NHS; Cnslr-6th Grd Outdr Ed Cmp 87; Sr Advsr 87-88; Ecud.

SCOVISH, DORI; Mary Help Of Christians HS; Pompton Plains, NJ; (3); 9/84; Computer Clb; SADD; Teachers Aide; Hon Roll; Prfct Atten Awd; Mst Outstndng Awd 85; Acad All Amer 87; Engl, Hstry, Sci Awds 86; Seton Hall U; Law.

SCRITTORALE, ANTHONY; West Esser HS; No Caldwell, NJ; (3); Boy Scts; Key Clb; Hon Roll; Sci.

SCRIVEN, ANGELA DAWN; Paterson Catholic HS; Paterson, NJ; (3); 13/97; NAACP; Church Choir; Color Guard; Rep Jr Cls; Rep Stu Cncl; Trk; High Hon Roll; Prfct Atten Awd; Pre Med.

SCRUGGS, NATOSHA; Lincoln HS; Jersy City, NJ; (3); Camera Clb; Church Yth Grp; Drama Clb; Teachers Aide; Church Choir; Yrbk Phtg; Yrbk Rptr; Stu Cncl; Co-Capt Cheerleading; Prfct Atten Awd; Nrsng.

SCULL, BARBARA; Florence Twp Mem HS; Florence, NJ; (3); FBLA; GAA; Drill Tm; Drm Mjr(t); Mrchg Band; Variety Show; Nwsp Rptr; VP Frsh Cls; Pres Stu Cncl; Cheerleading; Admin Bus.

SCULL, CYNTHIA; Paul VI HS; Sicklerville, NJ; (3); Hosp Aide; Band; Concert Band; Mrchg Band; Camden County Coll; Admin Asstn.

SCULL, SUSAN; Florence Twp Mem HS; Florence, NJ; (3); Am Leg Aux Girls St; German Clb; Girl Scts; Varsity Clb; Yrbk Stf; Pres Frsh Cls; Pres Soph Cls; Pres Jr Cls; Rep Stu Cncl; Co-Capt Cheerleading; Nrsng.

SCULLY, MARNIE; Maralapan HS; Manalapan, NJ; (2); Drama Clb; Girl Scts; Chorus; Stage Crew; Drama.

SCULLY, MICHAEL; Burlington Twp HS; Burlington, NJ; (3); 13/123; Key Clb; Var Tennis; Hon Roll; NHS.

SCYTHES, JAMES; Bridgeton HS; Bridgeton, NJ; (2); Bowling; JV Crs Cntry; Hon Roll.

SEAFORD, MATTHEW; Watchung Hills Regional HS; Millington, NJ; (3); Boy Scts; Church Yth Grp; Computer Clb; Debate Tm; French Clb; Ski Clb; JV Trk; Hon Roll; JV Crs Cntry; Eagle Scout 86; VA Poly Tech Inst; Sci.

SEAGER, JENNIFER; Lower Cape May Regional HS; Cape May, NJ; (3); 20/192; Dance Clb; Sec Key Clb; Church Choir; School Musical; Lit Mag; Hon Roll; NHS; Church Yth Grp; Cmnty Wkr; Band; Accmpnst-Piano, Rctl-Glssboro Coll 87; Solo Rctlst-Prsbytrn Chrch 83, 85 & 87; 1st Pl MEC Piano 86; Temple U; Music.

SEAMAN, ANN; John P Stevens HS; Edison, NJ; (3); 4/450; Cmnty Wkr; Girl Scts; Library Aide; Science Clb; Sec Jr Cls; Mgr(s); High Hon Roll; NHS; Ntl Merit Ltr; Spanish NHS; Natl Sci Olympd 86; Proj Gifted Middlesex Cnty Coll 86; Lib Arts.

SEAMAN, LORI; Bordentown Regional HS; Bordentown, NJ; (3); 7/142; Church Yth Grp; French Clb; Key Clb; Math Clb; Math Tm; Ski Clb; School Musical; JV Var Bsktbl; Var Capt Socr; Var Sftbl; 2nd Team All Cnty Sccr Team & All Sbrbn Sccr Team All Star Teams 85; Girls Soccer Team Trvl Team 84; Bio Chenm.

SEBBEN, TRISH; Belleville HS; Belleville, NJ; (3); Church Yth Grp; Drama Clb; French Clb; Chorus; Church Choir; Color Guard; Drm & Bgl; Mrchg Band; School Musical; Stu Cncl.

SEBESTA, MICHAEL; Admiral Farragut Acad; Solvay, NY; (3); 2/37; Church Yth Grp; Hosp Aide; Jr Civitan Int; ROTC; Teachers Aide; Off Stu Cncl; Var Lcrss; High Hon Roll; NHS; Engl Dept Awd; US Naval Acad; Flght Srgn.

SECCO, MICHELE ANNE; Dover HS; Dover, NJ; (4); 13/171; Ski Clb; Concert Band; Mrchg Band; Yrbk Stf; Sec Stu Cncl; Var Capt Socr; Var Sftbl; High Hon Roll; NHS; Schl Scholar 87; Rogate Schlr 84; U MD; Bus.

SECH, KRISTINE; Notre Dame HS; New Egypt, NJ; (3); 23/373; High Hon Roll; Hon Roll; NHS; Cert Of Awd French 85-86; Hon Roll A & B 85-86; Cert Of Hon Roll Of Dist A 85-86; Rider Coll; Lib Arts.

SEDLOCK, TRACY; Egg Harbor Twnshp HS; Mayslanding, NJ; (4); 2/289; DECA; Math Clb; Model UN; Spanish Clb; Nwsp Ed-Chief; Yrbk Ed-Chief; Trs Jr Cls; Trs Sr Cls; Stat Bsktbl; Score Keeper; Garden ST Distngushd Schlr Awd 87; Rutgers Schlr Awd 86; Stu Rotarian Mnth 86; Rutgers U; Acctng.

SEES, PHYLLIS; Paramus Catholic Girls HS; Hasbrouck Hts, NJ; (2); Service Clb; Ski Clb; Rep Frsh Cls; VP Soph Cls; JV Socr; Var Trk; Hon Roll; Bus.

SEETOO, ELLEN; Brick Memorial HS; Brick, NJ; (4); Yrbk Bus Mgr; Yrbk Ed-Chief; Yrbk Sprt Ed; Yrbk Stf; JV Var Trk; High Hon Roll; NHS; Trenton ST Coll; Health Educ.

SEETOO, PATTI; Brick Township Memorial HS; Brick, NJ; (3); #2 In Class; Church Yth Grp; Drill Tm; Stage Crew; Yrbk Phtg; High Hon Roll; NHS; Girls St Pgm 87; Comp Prgmmng.

SEGAL, YAEL; Morristown HS; Morris Plains, NJ; (1); Temple Yth Grp; JV Sftbl; Hon Roll; Htl Mgmt.

SEGAR, VALERIE; Paulsboro HS; Paulsboro, NJ; (3); Church Yth Grp; Drama Clb; FBLA; Office Aide; Band; Chorus; Church Choir; Concert Band; Drm Mjr(t); Jazz Band; Law.

SEGLETES, JENNIFER; Phillipsburg HS; Phillipsburg, NJ; (3); 15/315; Cmnty Wkr; Hosp Aide; Key Clb; Im Bowling; High Hon Roll; NHS; Gftd & Tlntd Pgm; Occptnl Thrpy.

SEIB, LORRAINE; Holy Spirit HS; Brigantine, NJ; (4); 51/363; French Clb; Girl Scts; Hosp Aide; Church Choir; Orch; Fld Hcky; Capt L Sftbl; French Hon Soc; High Hon Roll; Hon Roll; Carmen C Bonnani Mem Scholar Awd 87; Holy Spirit Excllnce Frnch Awd 87; St Josephs U; Chem.

SEIBERT, KERRY; Newton HS; Newton, NJ; (4); 13/200; Latin Clb; Ski Clb; Concert Band; Mrchg Band; Symp Band; Bowling; Powder Puff Ftbl; Trk; High Hon Roll; NHS; Cmnty Coll Of Morris Cnty; Law.

SEIDEL, ROBERT; Brick Memorial HS; Brick, NJ; (4); 32/290; Key Clb; JV Wrstlng; High Hon Roll; Hon Roll; NHS; Navy.

SEIDELMANN, CHRIS; Toms River HS North; Toms River, NJ; (1); Band; Concert Band; Mrchg Band; Orch; School Musical.

SEIDENGLANZ, ELIZABETH; Notre Dame HS; Trenton, NJ; (4); 60/332; Hosp Aide; Key Clb; Office Aide; Red Cross Aide; SADD; Varsity Clb; School Play; Rep Frsh Cls; Rep Soph Cls; Rep Jr Cls; Cmnty Svc Frm Mrymnt Coll 87; Athltc Achvt Frm Mrymnt Coll; Marymount Coll; Fshn Mrchndsng.

SEIDLE JR, JOHN; Burl Co Vo Tech; Burlington, NJ; (3); 6/192; Church Yth Grp; FBLA; Church Choir; JV Bowling; Hon Roll; NHS; Prfct Atten Awd; Aud/Vis; Boy Scts; U Of Hartford; Comp Sys.

SEIJAS, CARLOS; St Joseph Of The Palisades HS; W New York, NJ; (4); 6/130; Math Clb; Spanish Clb; Variety Show; Nwsp Rptr; Var Tennis; High Hon Roll; NHS; Spanish NHS; Finance.

SEITZ, NICOLE; Red Bank Regional HS; Little Silver, NJ; (2); German Clb; French Hon Soc; Hon Roll; John Hopkins Rogate Pgm 84; Intl Scenario Wrtng Proj Awd 83; Markham Pl Schl Gifted & Tlntd Pgm 82; Frgn Lang.

SEKULA, JEFFREY J; De Paul Diocesan HS; Wayne, NJ; (3); 4/150; Am Leg Boys St; Quiz Bowl; Ski Clb; Nwsp Rptr; Rep Stu Cncl; Var Capt Socr; Hon Roll; NHS; Rotary Awd.

SELBY, ALESHIA; Weequahic HS; Newark, NJ; (4); 50/373; Cmnty Wkr; Exploring; SADD; Pres Jr Cls; Pres Sr Cls; Rep Stu Cncl; JV Var Sftbl; Gov Hon Prg Awd; Boys Clb Am; Church Yth Grp; Posner Lab Awd 87; Svc Awds 83-87; Ldrshp Awds 83-87; William Patterson Coll; Socilgy.

SELBY, HELEN; Audubon HS; Mt Ephraim, NJ; (4); French Clb; Chorus; Concert Band; Nwsp Stf; Stu Cncl; Bsktbl; Cheerleading; Crs Cntry; Sftbl; Trk; Dmcrt 86; Mth.

SELFRIDGE, PAT; Haddonfield Memorial HS; Haddonfield, NJ; (4); Var Capt Ftbl; Var Trk; Im Wt Lftg; Thms A Kehoe Mem Schlrshp 87; Mulhenberg Coll.

SELLECK, JOHN; Don Bosco Prep; Suffern, NY; (4); 5/190; Cmnty Wkr; Key Clb; Quiz Bowl; Pres Service Clb; Ed Yrbk Stf; Var JV Tennis; Var Trk; High Hon Roll; NHS; Acad All-Amrcn 86; Knights Of Columbus Schlrshp 84-87; Bus Mgmt.

SELLERS, JENNIFER; Ramapo Regional HS; Wyckoff, NJ; (3); 72/366; VP Camera Clb; French Clb; Hon Roll; Franklin Lakis Vlntr Amblnce Corps 87; Secy/Sgt At Arms Chrch Yth Grp 86-87; Optometry.

SEMANCHIK, DAVID M; Voorhees HS; Lebanon, NJ; (4); 18/274; Am Leg Boys St; French Clb; Key Clb; Capt Quiz Bowl; Rep Stu Cncl; French Hon Soc; Hon Roll; Pres NHS; AM Lgn Boys Ntn Sntr 86; Ntl Tchrs Englsh Wrtng Awd 86; Law.

SEMIDEY, MELISSA; Dickinson HS; Jersey City, NJ; (3); Church Yth Grp; Computer Clb; Model UN; Pep Clb; Spanish Clb; Teachers Aide; Varsity Clb; Cheerleading; Pom Pon; Sftbl; Accntng.

SEMIRARO, RICH; Hunterdon Central HS; Flemington, NJ; (3); 10/543; Computer Clb; Science Clb; Ski Clb; JV Ftbl; Var Trk; Hon Roll; NCTE Awd; NHS; Ntl Merit Ltr; Spanish NHS; Bus.

SEMITSCHEW, SHARON; Bridgewater-Raritan West HS; Raritan, NJ; (4); Drama Clb; JV Cheerleading; Powder Puff Ftbl; Hon Roll; Pres Schlr; Somerset County; Bus Admin.

SENA, FRANK; Somerville HS; Neshanic Sta, NJ; (3); Chess Clb; Church Yth Grp; Math Tm; Spanish Clb; Var Socr; Var Tennis; JV Trk; High Hon Roll; NHS; Ntl Merit Ltr; Engrng.

SENG, CHRIS; Edgewood Regional HS; Hammonton, NJ; (3); JV Var Socr; JV Sftbl; Hon Roll; Prfct Atten Awd; Cert Achvt Purchsng Clrk 87; Olympia Natl Schlstc Typing Cntst 87.

SENGUPTA, SHAMPA; St Anthonys HS; Jersey Cty, NJ; (3); Cmnty Wkr; Girl Scts; Library Aide; NFL; Pep Clb; Teachers Aide; Nwsp Rptr; Nwsp Stf; Hon Roll; Hnr Rl 85-87; Bio.

SENKOVICH, MICHAEL; Elmwood Park Memorial HS; Elmwood Park, NJ; (4); 4/160; Am Leg Boys St; Band; School Musical; Rep Stu Cncl; L Trk; French Hon Soc; NHS; St Schlr; Voice Dem Awd; AM HS Math Exam Hnrbl Men 85-86; Natl Band Awd Wnnr 86-87; Engnrng.

SENN, DAVID; Ocean City HS; Oceanview, NJ; (3); 12/345; Am Leg Boys St; Math Clb; Science Clb; Spanish Clb; Var Socr; Pres NHS; Prfct Atten Awd; Engrng.

SENNER, SUSAN; Paul VI HS; Williamstown, NJ; (4); 12/511; Drama Clb; Hosp Aide; Math Clb; Hon Roll; NHS; Italn Clb; Distngshd Stu Amrca; Hon Mntn Garden ST Dstngshd Schlr Pgm; Accntng.

SENNETT, BRAD; Woodbury JR/Sr HS; Woodbury, NJ; (4); Boy Scts; Church Yth Grp; Pres VP FFA; Office Aide; Chorus; Ftbl; Wrstlng; DE Valley Coll Of Sci & Ag Schl 87-88; Mouth Encmpmnt Schlrshp-Rebekahs 87-88; FTD Schlrshp 87-88; DE Valley Coll/Sci/Ag; Hrtcltr.

SENTNOR, DAVID; Hightstown HS; East Windsor, NJ; (4); 42/422; Drama Clb; FBLA; Var Crs Cntry; JV Socr; Var Trk; Hon Roll; NHS; Prfct Atten Awd; Northwestern U; Acctg.

SEPP, JAMES; Bogota HS; Bogota, NJ; (3); 11/100; Am Leg Boys St; VP Sr Cls; Trs Stu Cncl; Bsktbl; Ftbl; Trk; Hon Roll; Varsity Clb; Yrbk Stf; Wt Lftg; LAB 87; TLC 87; Rep Bd Ed 86-87; Med.

SERAFIN, KARL; Vineland HS; Vineland, NJ; (2); 1/700; Rep Stu Cncl; JV Ftbl; Var JV Trk; High Hon Roll; Air Force Acad; Spc Prgrm.

SERAFIN, ROBERT; Marist HS; Bayonne, NJ; (3); Scholastic Bowl; Spanish Clb; Nwsp Rptr; Yrbk Rptr; Trk; High Hon Roll; Bus.

SERIN, AMY C; Wallkill Valley Regional HS; Franklin, NJ; (4); 27/170; French Clb; FBLA; Math Tm; SADD; Nwsp Rptr; Pres Frsh Cls; Pres Soph Cls; Pres VP Stu Cncl; Hon Roll; NHS; NJASC Ntl Conv Dlgt 86; Ldrshp Trainng Cmp Dlgt 85; Seton Hall U; Bus.

SERIO, ALEX; Rutherford HS; Rutherford, NJ; (4); 41/168; Varsity Clb; Chorus; Var Ftbl; Var Capt Wrstlng; FL Ist Of Tech; Aerontcl Sci.

SERIO, TRICIA; Belleville SR HS; Belleville, NJ; (3); 1/385; Church Yth Grp; Key Clb; Science Clb; Spanish Clb; VP Stu Cncl; Score Keeper; Sftbl; High Hon Roll; NHS; Montclair ST Coll Tlntd St Pgm 85-86; Secr Octagon Clb, Fnlst Govnrs Schl Arts & Sci 86-87; Dntstry.

SERRA, CHRISTINE; Lyndhurst HS; Lyndhurst, NJ; (4); 30/182; Church Yth Grp; Key Clb; Yrbk Sprt Ed; Sec Stu Cncl; Mgr(s); Pom Pon; Trk; Twrlr; Elks Awd; Kiwanis Awd; William Paterson Coll; Law.

SERRAN, FITZGERALD; Frank H Morrell HS; Irvington, NJ; (3); Am Leg Boys St; Drama Clb; School Play; Nwsp Rptr; Sec Stu Cncl; JV Socr; Var Trk; High Hon Roll; Hon Roll; NHS; Temple U; Med.

SERRANO, JOHNNY; Bayonne HS; Bayonne, NJ; (3); Am Leg Boys St; Concert Band; Crs Cntry; Trk; Wt Lftg; Jr NHS; Sci.

SERRANO, MONSERRATE; Vineland HS; Vineland, NJ; (3); Spanish Clb; Yrbk Stf; Bsktbl; Tennis; Hon Roll; Merit Rll 84-85; Glassboro Coll; Tchr.

SERRETTI, KRISTIN; Roselle Park HS; Roselle Park, NJ; (3); 26/144; Church Yth Grp; Hosp Aide; Radio Clb; Varsity Clb; Yrbk Stf; Rep Soph Cls; Rep Jr Cls; Stu Cncl; Var L Fld Hcky; Hon Roll; Schlrshp Trenton Close-Up Prgm 87; Marine Bio.

SERVEDIO, JAMES L; Abraham Clark HS; Roselle, NJ; (3); Math Clb; Political Wkr; JV Socr; Ntl Merit SF; MA Inst Tech; Engr.

SERWIN, LINDA; St Marys HS; E Rutherford, NJ; (3); Drama Clb; Thesps; School Play; Nwsp Rptr; Lit Mag; Sec Jr Cls; Stat Bsktbl; Var Cheerleading; Hon Roll; NHS; T J Diffily Schlrshp 84; Acad All Amer 85; Comm.

SESOK, CHRISTINE; Vineland SR HS; Vineland, NJ; (3); 4/827; Math Clb; Pres Red Cross Aide; Spanish Clb; Concert Band; Sec Stu Cncl; Var Mgr(s); JV Tennis; Hon Roll; NHS; Spanish NHS; Villanova; Bus Mgmt.

SESSA, AL; Saint John Vianney HS; Colts Neck, NJ; (3); 4-H; Ski Clb; Rep Soph Cls; JV Var Bsbl; Im Bsktbl; JV Ftbl; Im Wt Lftg; Hon Roll; Bus.

SETESCAK, STEPHEN; Hillsborough HS; Somerville, NJ; (3); 12/326; Science Clb; Wt Lftg; Wrstlng; Bausch & Lomb Sci Awd; High Hon Roll; NHS; Mech Engr.

SETOODEH, SHARVIN; West Orange HS; W Orange, NJ; (3); Chess Clb; Computer Clb; Math Clb; Math Tm; Science Clb; Spanish Clb; Var Wrstlng; Hon Roll; NHS; Spanish NHS; Pre Med.

SETRAKIAN, ANAHID; Fairlawn HS; Fairlawn, NJ; (4); Church Yth Grp; Girl Scts; Teachers Aide; Var Frsh Cls; Var Soph Cls; Var Jr Cls; Var Sr Cls; Sftbl; Trk; High Hon Roll; Gdn ST Dstngshd Schlr 87; Armenian Rlf Soc Schrlshp 87; Armenian Genl Athltc Union Schrlshp 87; Rutgers U; Bus.

SETTANNI, ANDREA MARIE; Haddonfield Memorial HS; Haddonfield, NJ; (3); Rep Church Yth Grp; Intnl Clb; Spanish Clb; Sec Concert Band; Sec Mrchg Band; Ed Yrbk Bus Mgr; JV Tennis; Hon Roll; NHS; Spanish NHS; Smmr Schlrs Prg Rutgers U 87.

SEVERINI, GABRIELLA; Mensignor Donovan HS; Bricktown, NJ; (3); 29/265; Art Clb; Cmnty Wkr; Ski Clb; SADD; VICA; Cheerleading; Hon Roll; NHS; Publ Rel.

SEVERINO, KERRY; Secaucus HS; Secaucus, NJ; (3); Math Clb; Mu Alpha Theta; Spanish Clb; Varsity Clb; Chorus; Cheerleading; High Hon Roll; Mu Alpha Theta Awd; Spanish NHS; Lit Mag; UCLA; Psycht.

SEXTON, MARILYN; Hillside HS; Hillside, NJ; (3); 7/256; Church Yth Grp; Nwsp Rptr; Yrbk Stf; Sec Frsh Cls; Capt Socr; Sftbl; High Hon Roll; Jr NHS; Pres Interact Clb 87-88; Chld Psychlgy.

SEXTON, MATT; Madison Avenue Baptist Acad; Paterson, NJ; (2); 1/10; Church Yth Grp; Cmnty Wkr; FCA; Letterman Clb; Varsity Clb; Church Choir; Var Capt Bsktbl; Var Capt Socr; High Hon Roll.

SEXTON, SEAN; Bergen Catholic HS; Teaneck, NJ; (4); Church Yth Grp; Office Aide; Teachers Aide; Acpl Chr; Chorus; Im Bsktbl; Im Fld Hcky; JV Socr; Bus.

SEYLER, STEPHANIE; Holy Spirit HS; Absecon, NJ; (3); 41/332.

SHABABB, ROBERT; Emerson HS; Union City, NJ; (4); Am Leg Boys St; Church Yth Grp; Cmnty Wkr; Political Wkr; Yrbk Ed-Chief; Off Sr Cls; Var Bsktbl; Capt Tennis; Al County Ten 87; Rutgers U.

SHABLESKI, LYNN; Monsignor Donovan HS; Lavallette, NJ; (3); 13/245; Am Leg Aux Girls St; Latin Clb; Math Clb; Rep SADD; Rep Stu Cncl; JV Trk; Var Cit Awd; High Hon Roll; VP NHS; Ntl Merit Ltr; Bus.

SHACK, STEPHANIE; Mt Olive HS; Flanders, NJ; (3); 15/319; Dance Clb; Band; Chorus; Lit Mag; High Hon Roll; NHS; AFS; Drama Clb; Temple Yth Grp; Concert Band; Choral Camp Schlrshp; Modern Music Masters Induction Natl Music Hnr Soc; Schl Tlnt Contest 1st Pl; Pre-Law.

SHADE, DAWN; Marine Acad; Union Beach, NJ; (4); 8/32; French Clb; ROTC; Drill Tm; Trs Sr Cls; Math Awd 85-86; Cadet Of Mnth 85-86; Outstndng Cadet For Annual Navy Inspection 85-86; Monmouth Coll; Microbio.

SHADE, JENNIFER; Belvidere HS; Phillipsburg, NJ; (4); Am Leg Aux Girls St; Art Clb; Library Aide; Office Aide; Ski Clb; SADD; Yrbk Phtg; Yrbk Stf; Monmouth Coll; Crmnl Jstc.

SHAGAWAT, JENNIFER; Wayne Hills HS; Wayne, NJ; (3); FBLA; GAA; Spanish Clb; Varsity Clb; Stage Crew; Sftbl; Hon Roll; FBLA Awd 87; Sftbl NJ ST Intrschlstc Sectnl Champs 87; Cmmnctns.

SHAH, ANJU; Holy Rosary Acad; Jersey City, NJ; (3); 7/30; Art Clb; French Clb; FFA; Library Aide; Math Clb; Math Tm; Science Clb; SADD; Yrbk Stf; Hon Roll; All Marcn Achvmnt Acad 85; Natl Ldrshp & Svc 86; Pre-Med.

SHAH, DARSHAN; Memorial HS; Cedar Grove, NJ; (1); Boys Clb Am; Boy Scts; Computer Clb; Red Cross Aide; Spanish Clb; Crs Cntry; Trk; Hon Roll; Pres Schlr; 100%-HSPT Test-Math, 99%-Engl 87; Med.

SHAH, DEVAL; Lodi HS; Lodi, NJ; (3); #8 In Class; Boys Clb Am; Exploring; Math Clb; Math Tm; Varsity Clb; Tennis; NHS; Math.

SHAH, MITESH; Emerson HS; Union City, NJ; (4); 15/280; Computer Clb; FHA; JA; Library Aide; Math Clb; Math Tm; Teachers Aide; High Hon Roll; Hon Roll; NHS; Typng Bus Awd; Sci Awd; Rutgers U; Engnrng.

SHAH, NILESH A; Bound Brook HS; S Bound Brook, NJ; (3); 2/178; Am Leg Boys St; Latin Clb; NFL; Speech Tm; Var Socr; Var Tennis; Hon Roll; NHS; MVP In Tnns 86-87; Arspc Engrng.

SHAH, NRUPA; Bishop George Ahr HS; Edison, NJ; (3); 16/272; Hosp Aide; Service Clb; Spanish Clb; Stage Crew; Nwsp Stf; Yrbk Stf; High Hon Roll; NHS; Volunteer Serv Hosp 87; Pre-Med.

SHAH, PINAL; Hoboken HS; Hoboken, NJ; (3); Chess Clb; Exploring; Teachers Aide; High Hon Roll; NHS; Library Aide; Varsity Clb; Nwsp Stf; JV Tennis; Hon Roll; Top 10 Stu Schl Natl Hnr Soc 87; Stevens; Engrng.

SHAH, PURVIN B; Emerson HS; Union City, NJ; (3); 1/20; Computer Clb; Library Aide; High Hon Roll; Hon Roll; NHS; Prfct Atten Awd; Stevens Inst; Med.

SHAH, SHILPA; Boonton HS; Boonton, NJ; (3); Exploring; French Clb; Nwsp Stf; Yrbk Stf; Lit Mag; Stat Socr; Law.

SHAH, SHISHIR; North Bergen HS; North Bergen, NJ; (3); 4/400; Camera Clb; Chess Clb; CAP; Debate Tm; Math Tm; Scholastic Bowl; Stu Cncl; Tennis; NHS; Natl Russn Olymph Brnz Medlst 86, Slvr 87; Rgnl Sci Fair Slvr Medlst Area Physcs 87; MIT; Aerospce Engrng.

SHAH, SONYA; Columbia HS; Maplewood, NJ; (3).

SHAH, TEJAL; St Marys HS; Carlstadt, NJ; (3); 8/82; Dance Clb; SADD; Stage Crew; Variety Show; Yrbk Stf; Var Crs Cntry; Var Trk; Hon Roll; NHS.

SHAKER, BASEM; Manchester Regional HS; Haledon, NJ; (3); Socr; Wt Lftg; Hon Roll; Outstnding Athltc Achvt Vrsty Tm 3 Yrs 86-87; Engr.

SHALAWAY, JEFF; Pitman HS; Pitman, NJ; (2); Trs Church Yth Grp; Rep Stu Cncl; Bsktbl; Var Crs Cntry; Var Golf; Im Vllybl; Hon Roll.

SHALAWAY, STACEY; Pitman HS; Pitman, NJ; (4); 9/150; Pres Church Yth Grp; Teachers Aide; Var Bsktbl; Var Sftbl; Im Vllybl; Hon Roll; NHS; Physcl Thrpy.

SHALFOROOSH, SORAYA; Waldwick HS; Waldwick, NJ; (4); Intnl Clb; Nwsp Rptr; Ed Lit Mag; CARE Fndrsr Orgnzr 85; Poetry Cont Wnnr 87; Emerson Coll; Adv.

SHALLCROSS, WILLIAM; St James HS; Elmer, NJ; (4); 9/83; Church Yth Grp; CAP; School Play; Prfct Atten Awd; Citatn Meritorious Svc 85; Cert Apprectn 85; Cert Accmplshmnt 85; U S FL; Crmnl Justice.

SHANDOR, JENNIFER; Belvidere HS; Phillipsburg, NJ; (4); 14/125; Varsity Clb; Rep Sr Cls; JV Var Bsktbl; JV Var Fld Hcky; Var Golf; JV Var Sftbl; Hon Roll; NHS; Penn ST; Elem Ed.

SHANNON JR, DONALD R; Neumann Prep; Hawthorne, NJ; (3); #20 In Class; Am Leg Boys St; Pres Exploring; JV Crs Cntry; Im Golf; JV Trk; High Hon Roll; NHS; VP Rotary Awd; Pres Clssrm 87; Modl Cong 86; Miltry Offcr.

SHANNON, MARY JO; Paul VI HS; Laurel Springs, NJ; (3); Hosp Aide; Latin Clb; Spanish Clb; Phrmcy.

SHAPIRO, CAMI; Manalapan HS; Manalapan, NJ; (3); SADD; Yrbk Stf; Socr.

SHAPIRO, DOUGLAS S; Northern Valley Regional HS; Haworth, NJ; (4); 2/250; Am Leg Boys St; Science Clb; Temple Yth Grp; Nwsp Ed-Chief; Yrbk Bus Mgr; Rep Stu Cncl; JV Var Bsbl; High Hon Roll; NHS; Ntl Merit SF; Grdn St Dstngshd Shlr Awd; 1st Pl-Frnch Drama Comptn; Pre Med.

SHAPIRO, HAROLD; Morris Knolls HS; Rockaway, NJ; (3); 5/424; Pres Science Clb; VP Temple Yth Grp; Nwsp Phtg; Yrbk Phtg; High Hon Roll; NHS; Comp Sci.

SHAPIRO, KENNETH; West Essex SR HS; No Caldwell, NJ; (3); Math Tm; SADD; Nwsp Stf; Ed Lit Mag; Hon Roll; VP NHS; Opt Clb Awd; Key Clb; Science Clb; Stage Crew; Vrsty Fncng 87-88; NJ Cncl Tchrs Engl 1st, 3rd Pl Short Story 85-87; Gov Schl Arts Creatv Wrtng 87; Magz Edtr.

SHAPIRO, MEREDITH; Madison Central HS; Old Bridge, NJ; (3); 4/365; FBLA; Spanish Clb; SADD; Varsity Clb; Yrbk Stf; Rep Stu Cncl; Var L Sftbl; Var Trk; High Hon Roll; NHS; Bus, Math Awds 85, 86; Bus.

SHAPRIO, JAKE; Bridgewater Raritan East HS; Bridgewater, NJ; (2); Aud/Vis; Debate Tm; Drama Clb; Key Clb; NFL; Ski Clb; Spanish Clb; Speech Tm; SADD; Temple Yth Grp; Hgh Hnr Roll 86; Bus.

SHARIF, DAVID; Clifford J Scott HS; East Orange, NJ; (3); Band; Concert Band; Mrchg Band; Var JV Bsbl; Var Ftbl; Swmmng; Hon Roll; Deptmntl Hnrs Chem, Hstry & Alg 87; Engr.

SHARKEY, PATTI; Our Lady Of Mercy Acad; Cape May Ct Hse, NJ; (3); Cmnty Wkr; Computer Clb; Yrbk Phtg; Yrbk Stf; Lit Mag; Im Badmtn; Im Bsktbl; Im Vllybl; Hon Roll; Ntl Merit Schol; Bus.

SHARMA, AKHIL; John P Stevens HS; Edison, NJ; (3); 1/464; Debate Tm; Math Clb; Science Clb; Nwsp Rptr; Nwsp Stf; Crs Cntry; Trk; Hon Roll; Harvard; Bus Mngnt.

SHARP, ARDAN; Edgewood Regional SR HS; Tansboro, NJ; (3); #17 In Class; Hosp Aide; Latin Clb; Nwsp Rptr; Nwsp Stf; Yrbk Stf; Im Fld Hcky; JV Socr; Hon Roll; Jr NHS; Sec NHS; Gifted & Talented Pgm 84-87; Fash Desgnr.

SHARP, DUER; Woodrow Wilson HS; Camden, NJ; (3); Boys Clb Am; Cmnty Wkr; Leo Clb; Letterman Clb; Varsity Clb; Rep Frsh Cls; Rep Soph Cls; Var Bsktbl; Var Capt Ftbl; Var Trk; All Conf-Ftbl 86-87; All Group-Ftbl 86-87; Cmnctns.

SHARP, JENNIFER; Middlesex HS; Middlesex, NJ; (4); 14/158; French Clb; SADD; Chorus; School Musical; High Hon Roll; Hon Roll; Artstclly Tlntd Kybrd 85-87; Brkly Schls; Micro Comp Accntg.

SHARP, KAREN; Gloucester HS; Gloucester Cty, NJ; (3); Library Aide; Pep Clb; VP Fld Hcky; Im Mgr Gym; VP Sftbl; Hon Roll.

SHARP, KEN; Ocean City HS; Ocean City, NJ; (3); 41/341; Hon Roll; NHS; Carpenter.

SHARP, ROBIN; Paulsboro HS; Gibbstown, NJ; (3); 21/130; Drama Clb; Band; Chorus; Flag Corp; Mrchg Band; School Musical; School Play; High Hon Roll; Hon Roll; K Gibbs Bus Schl; Exec Secy.

SHARPE, KIMBERLY; Manchester Township HS; Toms River, NJ; (2); Girl Scts; Color Guard; Mrchg Band; Stat Bsktbl; JV Sftbl.

SHARPLESS, ANNE MARIE; Bridgeton HS; Bridgeton, NJ; (3); Sec Church Yth Grp; Drama Clb; 4-H; Pres Spanish Clb; Flag Corp; Yrbk Stf; Sec Jr Cls; Rep Stu Cncl; 4-H Awd; Hon Roll; Psych.

SHARPLESS, KEYONA; Hillside HS; Hillside, NJ; (3); 4/238; Dance Clb; Leo Clb; Math Tm; Hon Roll; Jr NHS; NHS; 1st Rnnr-Up Grls Ctznshp Inst 87; Mrktng.

SHARPLEY, BETH; Lower Cape May Regional HS; N Cape May, NJ; (3); Sec Church Yth Grp; Varsity Clb; VP Soph Cls; Rep Stu Cncl; Stat Bsbl; Var L Cheerleading; Stat Ftbl; Var Stat Mgr(s); Im Vllybl; Hon Roll; Secy Octagon Clb 87-88; Advrtsg.

SHAW, DEBORAH JEAN; Haddonfield Memorial HS; Haddonfield, NJ; (4); Church Yth Grp; Intnl Clb; Red Cross Aide; Spanish Clb; Drm Mjr(t); Mrchg Band; Orch; Yrbk Stf; Rep Soph Cls; Rep Stu Cncl; Bnd Ldrshp Awd 87; Elizabethtown Coll; Accntnt.

SHAW, JENNIFER; Maple Shade HS; Maple Shade, NJ; (3); Cmnty Wkr; VP French Clb; Key Clb; Library Aide; Office Aide; Spanish Clb; Teachers Aide; JV Bowling; Yth In Govt Town Clrk; Burlington Cnty Uth In Govt Supt Of Elctns; Tutor; Spcl Ed Tchr.

SHAW, KELLY; Holy Spirit HS; Ventnor, NJ; (3); 49/332; Pep Clb; JV VP Cheerleading; VP JV Sftbl; Hon Roll; Syracuse U; Advrtsmnt.

SHAW, ROBYE; Morris Hills HS; Rockaway, NJ; (2); 14/244; Cmnty Wkr; Exploring; Office Aide; Ski Clb; JV Fld Hcky; High Hon Roll; Hon Roll; Exclsr Awd 86; Prjct Lead 87; Law.

SHAW, TRACEE; Freehold Township HS; Freehold Twp, NJ; (4); 19/353; Aud/Vis; FBLA; Hosp Aide; JA; Spanish Clb; Capt Drill Tm; Stat Bsktbl; Var Powder Puff Ftbl; Var Trk; NHS; Most Sprtd & Dedctd Band Stu 86; Most Outstndng Band Front Stu 87; Untd Black Families Schlrshp 87; U Of MI; Acctg.

SHEA, CATHERINE; H G Hoffman HS; South Amboy, NJ; (3); 16/59; Ski Clb; VP Soph Cls; Rep Stu Cncl; JV Bsktbl; VP Socr; JV Sftbl; Im Vllybl; Cit Awd; Hon Roll; NHS; Phys Thrpy.

SHEA, DANIEL C; Lawrence HS; Lawrenceville, NJ; (3); Am Leg Boys St; Cmnty Wkr; Spanish Clb; Varsity Clb; Mrchg Band; Sec Frsh Cls; Stu Cncl; Var Socr; Var Tennis; Hon Roll; Cornell; Engr.

SHEA, DENNIS; Christian Brothers Acad; Freehold, NJ; (4); 40/230; Pep Clb; Ski Clb; Varsity Clb; Yrbk Stf; Rep Jr Cls; Im Bsktbl; Var L Golf; Var L Socr; Im Sftbl; High Hon Roll; Bus Mgmt.

SHEA, JOHN; Waldwick HS; Waldwick, NJ; (3); 32/135; Am Leg Boys St; Letterman Clb; Concert Band; Var JV Bsbl; Var JV Ftbl; Cmnty Wkr; Ski Clb; Varsity Clb; Chorus; Jazz Band; Hnr Mntn All Leag Def Bk Ftbl 86; Hnr Mntn All Leag/Subrbn 2nd Bsmn Bsbl 87; Unicp Achvrs Awd 86.

SHEAHAN, JENN; Paramus Catholic HS; Fair Lawn, NJ; (3); 24/174; CAP; Dance Clb; SADD; Stage Crew; Nwsp Rptr; Nwsp Stf; Lit Mag; VP Frsh Cls; Im Cheerleading; Scranton U; Psych.

SHEEHAN, COLLEEN; Newton HS; Newton, NJ; (4); 3/186; Sec French Clb; Scholastic Bowl; Madrigals; Rep Stu Cncl; Stat Bsbl; Capt Cheerleading; Stat Ftbl; God Cntry Awd; NHS; St Schlr; NJ Grls Ctznshp Inst 86; Ntl Merit Schlrshp Commendation 86; Cnty & Rgnl Chorus 86-87; Engl.

SHEEHAN, ELIZABETH; Manasquan HS; Brielle, NJ; (3); 10/248; Am Leg Aux Girls St; French Clb; FBLA; Key Clb; Math Tm; Yrbk Stf; Rep Frsh Cls; Sec Sr Cls; Sftbl; Var Capt Tennis; Brd Educ Awd 86-87.

SHEEHAN, GARRETT; Brick Township HS; Brick, NJ; (3); Computer Clb; Exploring; UNEXSO-UNDERWATER Explorers Soc, MAUG & Natl Geogrphc Soc; Comp Operations.

SHEEHAN, JENNIFER; Indian Hills HS; Oakland, NJ; (4); 69/282; Trs AFS; Cmnty Wkr; Debate Tm; Drama Clb; French Clb; Hosp Aide; High Hon Roll; Hon Roll; Emory U; Bus Admin.

SHEETS JR, JAMES W; Warren Hills Regional HS; Belvidere, NJ; (4); Church Yth Grp; Computer Clb; SADD; Church Choir; Nwsp Bus Mgr; Var Bsbl; Bowling; Im Swmmng; Drftng.

SHEETS, SCOTT; Belvidere HS; Belvidere, NJ; (4); Camera Clb; Church Yth Grp; Key Clb; Office Aide; SADD; Trs VICA; Church Choir; JV Bsktbl; L Crs Cntry; Socat Cert 87; Cert Jb Sklls Achvmnt/Cbntmkg 84-87; Lincoln Tech Inst; Elctrncs.

SHEETZ, LORI; The Kings Christian HS; Somerdale, NJ; (2); 5/53; Band; Chorus; Church Choir; Concert Band; Yrbk Stf; Var L Bsktbl; Var L Fld Hcky; Var L Sftbl; High Hon Roll; Hon Roll; Fld Hcky, Sftbl, Bsktbl MVP & All-Star Lg 85-86; Fld Hcky MVP Div 86; Phys Ed.

SHEILS, CAROLYN; Villa Walsh Acad; Morristown, NJ; (4); Church Yth Grp; Drama Clb; Orch; School Musical; Yrbk Stf; Lit Mag; VP Stu Cncl; Capt Socr; Army ROTC Schlrshp 87; Fordham U; Poli Sci.

SHELAT, SURESH G; Emerson JR-SR HS; Emerson, NJ; (4); 1/100; Yrbk Ed-Chief; Trs Soph Cls; Trs Jr Cls; Trs Sr Cls; JV Bsktbl; Capt Tennis; Bausch & Lomb Sci Awd; CC Awd; Gov Hon Prg Awd; Ntl Merit Ltr; B Franklin Reinaver II Free Enterprise Awd 86; Pres Schlr-Ath 87; TIME Mag Writing Cont Fnlst 87; MA Inst Tech; Biomed Engrng.

SHELDON, LISA; Hamilton High West; Trenton, NJ; (3); FBLA; Chorus; Capt Color Guard; Madrigals; 6th Pl For Clrk Typst I At Cntr Rgnl Cmptn 86; Bloomfield Coll; Chrprctc.

SHELDON, STEVE; Bridgeton HS; Bridgeton, NJ; (3); Boy Scts; French Clb; Ski Clb; JV Var Crs Cntry; Var Capt Swmmng; God Cntry Awd; Acctg.

SHELL, KEVIN; Paul VI HS; Haddonfield, NJ; (3); 193/418; Church Yth Grp; Cmnty Wkr; Math Clb; Spanish Clb; Varsity Clb; Var Bsbl; Var Capt Bsktbl; Accntng.

SHELLHAMMER, JOE; St Peters HS; Somerset, NJ; (4); School Musical; Yrbk Stf; Bsbl; Capt Ftbl; George Krauszer Mem Scholar Ftbl Ldrshp Acad 87; Bernie Duff Mem Awd Outstndg Vrsty Ftbl Plyr 86-87; Ramapo Coll NJ; Envr Stud.

SHELTON, DAWN; High Point Regional HS; Newton, NJ; (3); 49/268; Church Yth Grp; Girl Scts; Band; Church Choir; Mrchg Band; Nwsp Rptr; Nwsp Stf; High Hon Roll; Hon Roll; Girl Scout Slvr Awd 85; Stud Tchng Frnch 86-87; Ed.

SHEN, ELLEN; Leonia HS; Leonia, NJ; (3); 8/130; Art Clb; Scholastic Bowl; Science Clb; Sec Spanish Clb; Teachers Aide; Yrbk Stf; Hon Roll; Sec NHS; Hgh ScrER Sci Leag, & Hon Mntn Yrbk Stff 86-87; Biochem.

SHENTON, PHILIP; Millville HS; Millville, NJ; (4); 19/400; Drama Clb; German Clb; Mrchg Band; School Musical; Stage Crew; Trs Stu Cncl; Var L Trk; NHS; Pres Schlr; Trs Church Yth Grp; Christian Svc Awd 87; Beta Sigma Phi Engl Awd 87; Hofstra U.

SHEPHERD, BOB; Bricktown HS; Bricktown, NJ; (3); 80/460; VICA; JV Bsktbl; Hon Roll; NHS; Jackson Vo-Tech Schl; Auto Tech.

SHEPPARD, SEAN; Toms River South HS; Beachwood, NJ; (3); Ski Clb; Band; Concert Band; Mrchg Band; Stage Crew; Bsbl; Mgr(s); Score Keeper; Socr; Trk; Sccr-2nd Tm Clss A South-Hrbl Mntn All Cnty 86-87; Crmnlgy.

SHEPPARD, SHERRI; Lower Cape May Regional HS; Cape May, NJ; (3); 17/190; Key Clb; Varsity Clb; Jr Cls; Sr Cls; Sftbl; Tennis; Cit Awd; NHS; Tennis MVP 85-86; Softball Best Defensive Plyr 87; Bus.

SHEPPARD, THOMAS; Hunterdon Central HS; Ringoes, NJ; (2); Boy Scts; Computer Clb; Exploring; German Clb; Hon Roll; Natl Grmn Hnr Soc 87; Accntng.

SHERARD, ALEXIS; Lakewood Prep; Lakewood, NJ; (3); Band; School Play; Capt Var Bsktbl; JV Socr; Hon Roll; Math Tchr.

SHERIDAN, ANDREA J; St Rose HS; Spring Lake, NJ; (3); 1/225; Drama Clb; Latin Clb; Math Clb; Math Tm; Nwsp Rptr; Trk; High Hon Roll; NHS; Ntl Merit Ltr; Gen Excel Awd 85 & 86; VP Natl Hnr Soc 87-88; Coll William & Mary; Corp Lwyr.

SHERIDAN, JOHN; Seton Hall Preparatory Schl; Whippany, NJ; (3); 15/229; 4-H; Math Clb; Math Tm; Spanish Clb; High Hon Roll; NHS; Law.

SHERIDAN, JOSEPH; Highland Regional HS; Erial, NJ; (4); 11/297; Chess Clb; Drama Clb; Latin Clb; Band; Concert Band; Jazz Band; Mrchg Band; School Musical; School Play; Yrbk Stf; All-Cnfrnc Band; Med.

SHERIDAN, MARY; Acad Of The Holy Angels; Teaneck, NJ; (1); Church Yth Grp; School Musical; School Play; Stage Crew; Bus.

SHERIDAN, MICHAEL; Egg Harbor Township HS; Mayslanding, NJ; (3); 11/376; Ski Clb; Rep Frsh Cls; Rep Soph Cls; Rep Jr Cls; JV Var Ftbl; Var Trk; Hon Roll; Jr NHS; Acad Ltr 85-86; Temple; Spts Med.

SHERIDAN, SHAWN; Madison Central HS; Old Bridge, NJ; (3); 91/356; JV Ftbl; JV Wt Lftg; Hon Roll; Comp Sci.

SHERLOCK, ALLISON; Victory Christian Schl; Sicklerville, NJ; (4); 2/22; Church Yth Grp; Hosp Aide; Teachers Aide; Church Choir; School Musical; School Play; Yrbk Rptr; Cheerleading; High Hon Roll; NHS; Music Awds 84-85; Chrstn Schls Hnr Soc; Engl.

SHERMAN, ANDREW; Toms River North HS; Toms River, NJ; (3); #42 In Class; Ski Clb; Crs Cntry; Wt Lftg; Var L Wrstlng; Hon Roll; NHS.

SHERMAN, JOHN; Bridgeton HS; Cedarville, NJ; (4); Boy Scts; Church Yth Grp; Ski Clb; Variety Show; JV Socr; Berkley Coll Of Music; Music.

SHERMER, DONNA; Holy Cross HS; Mt Laurel, NJ; (3); Rep Stu Cncl; Cheerleading; Hon Roll; Prfct Atten Awd; Capt-Chrldng Sqd; Hmcmng & Sprt Wk; Psychlgy.

SHERRON, JAMES A; Hammonton HS; Hammonton, NJ; (4); 5/190; Boy Scts; Pres Trs Church Yth Grp; JV Bsbl; Var JV Bowling; JV Golf; High Hon Roll; Hon Roll; NHS; Garden St Dstngshd Schlr 86; Acadmc Achvt Awds 85-86; Frgn Lang Clb 86-87; Princeton U; Aerosp Engrng.

SHERWOOD, JOSHUA; Glen Rock JR SR HS; Glen Rock, NJ; (3); AFS; Debate Tm; Library Aide; Nwsp Rptr; Nwsp Stf; Lit Mag; Crs Cntry; Trk; Hon Roll; Jrnlsm.

SHETH, NISHA; J P Stevens HS; Edison, NJ; (4); 125/450; Intnl Clb; Key Clb; Library Aide; Science Clb; Stage Crew; Off Sr Cls; Swmmng; ESL Achvt 87; Good Athltc 85; Nuclear Med.

SHETH, SHEFALI; James Caldwell HS; W Caldwell, NJ; (3); Art Clb; Key Clb; Spanish Clb; Color Guard; Yrbk Stf; Off Jr Cls; Off Sr Cls; Stu Cncl; High Hon Roll; Hon Roll; Bus.

SHETTY, SMITHA; Immaculata HS; Bridgewater, NJ; (3); Yrbk Stf; Rep Stu Cncl; Var Tennis; Bio.

SHEVCHUK, NATALIE; Hamilton HS; Trenton, NJ; (4); 2/309; Church Yth Grp; Pres Science Clb; SADD; Church Choir; Yrbk Sprt Ed; Co-Capt Lit Mag; Stat Bsktbl; Fld Hcky; Bausch & Lomb Sci Awd; Cit Awd; US Ntl Math Awd 84-87; Am Cynmd Excel Study Sci 87; Rtry Clb Schlrshp; The Kings Coll; Med.

SHEVLIN, MEG; Ranney Schl; Wayside, NJ; (2); 4/45; French Clb; Quiz Bowl; Scholastic Bowl; Nwsp Ed-Chief; JV Sftbl; Var Sftbl; Srch Excel Schlrshp 85-87; Mock Trl Tm 86-87.

SHEVRIN, JILL; Manalapan HS; Manalapan, NJ; (3); 67/403; SADD; Pres Temple Yth Grp.

SHIBATA, LISA; Scotch-Plains Fanwood HS; Fanwood, NJ; (2); AFS; High Hon Roll; Appld Dsgn.

SHICK, DEBRA; Cinnaminson HS; Cinnaminson, NJ; (3); Key Clb; VP SADD; Yrbk Stf; JV Var Bowling; JV Sftbl; NHS; Prfct Atten Awd; Sec Rotary Awd; MIP Sftbl 86; Bus Admin.

SHIELDS, JENNIFER; Toms River H S North; Toms River, NJ; (3); 50/459; Off Jr Cls; Var Cheerleading; Mgr(s); High Hon Roll; Hon Roll; NHS; Vrsty Ltr Acad 85; Vrsty Pin Acad 87; Biol.

SHIELDS, LESLIE; Hunterdon Central HS; Neshanic Sta, NJ; (3); 23/556; Civic Clb; Pres Sec 4-H; French Clb; Concert Band; Mrchg Band; Nwsp Rptr; Yrbk Stf; 4-H Awd; High Hon Roll; NHS; Scl Sci.

SHIELDS, LISA; Paul VI HS; Bellmawr, NJ; (3); 114/480; Cmnty Wkr; Spanish Clb; Im Cheerleading; Hon Roll; NHS; Pierce JR Bus Coll; Bus.

SHIELS, CATHERINE; Hillsborough HS; Neshanic, NJ; (3); 17/328; Dance Clb; Girl Scts; Var L Cheerleading; Var Stat Ftbl; Gym; Pom Pon; Powder Puff Ftbl; Hon Roll; Wt Lftg; Chrprsn Yth Svc Cmmssn 86; Spec Olympcs Vlntr 87; Bus.

SHIFFMAN, SCOTT; Jackson Memorial HS; Jackson, NJ; (4); 5/390; JV Bsktbl; JV Socr; High Hon Roll; NHS; Prfct Atten Awd; Pres Schlr; Jackson Rtry Schlrshp 87; Acad All Amer 87; Rutgers U; Med.

SHIH, FLORENCE S; Bridgewater-Raritan HS East; Bridgewater, NJ; (4); French Clb; Hosp Aide; Library Aide; Chorus; Nwsp Stf; Yrbk Stf; Im Bowling; Hon Roll; NHS; Pres Schlr; Rutgers Univ.

SHIH, JAMES; West Essex Regional HS; No Caldwell, NJ; (2); Computer Clb; Exploring; Key Clb; Math Clb; Math Tm; Science Clb; JV Trk; Hon Roll; Fncng Vrsty Ltr 85-87; Hnr Roll 85-87; Masth & Sci Cert; Elctrncs.

SHIH, KATHLEEN; Middletown HS South; Middletown, NJ; (3); 4-H; Math Tm; Science Clb; Flag Corp; Yrbk Sprt Ed; High Hon Roll; Spanish NHS; Exploring; Math Clb; Spanish Clb; Dept Prks & Rec Yth Art Shw-2 1st-S & 3rd Pl-Wtrclr 85, 86 & 87; Hgh Prfrmnc-Annl Assc Math 86.

SHIM, CAROLINE; Millvill SR HS; Millville, NJ; (3); 2/500; Orch; Trs Stu Cncl; Var Swmmng; Var Tennis; Gov Hon Prg Awd; High Hon Roll; Church Yth Grp; Cmnty Wkr; JV Golf; NHS; Math Awd; Grls Ctznshp Inst-Douglas Coll, Thunderbolt Awd Tnns; Yale U; Bio.

SHIM, KATHERINE; John P Stevens HS; Edison, NJ; (2); 11/452; French Clb; Hosp Aide; Math Tm; Model UN; Science Clb; Nwsp Stf; Lit Mag; High Hon Roll; Church Yth Grp; Hon Roll; Cncrs Natl De Francais Lvl IB 86; Schlr Of The Wk 85; Yng Schlrs Excel Awd; Princeton U; Gntcs.

SHIM, YEONAH; Vail Deane HS; Elizabeth, NJ; (3); Dance Clb; Drama Clb; French Clb; Hosp Aide; Science Clb; Spanish Clb; Chorus; School Play; Yrbk Phtg; Pres Frsh Cls; Bio.

SHIMP, RICHARD; Bridgewater Raritan West HS; Bridgewater, NJ; (4); Var JV Bsbl; Var L Ftbl; Cvl Engnrng.

SHIMP JR, RICHARD; Woodstown HS; Woodstown, NJ; (3); Church Yth Grp; Drama Clb; English Clb; 4-H; German Clb; Bsbl; Ftbl; 4-H Awd; Bio.

SHIN, GINA; Glen Rock SR HS; Glen Rock, NJ; (3); 13/160; Art Clb; Church Yth Grp; Cmnty Wkr; Drama Clb; Hosp Aide; Varsity Clb; Stage Crew; Yrbk Stf; Stu Cncl; Var Tennis; Artcls NY Korea Times 86; U Of PA.

SHIN, TOMMY; Pemberton Twp HS; Browns Mills, NJ; (3); 52/405; Quiz Bowl; Scholastic Bowl; Tennis; Hon Roll; Prfct Atten Awd; Comp Sci.

SHINN, RACHEL; Burlington Township HS; Burlington Townsh, NJ; (3); Key Clb; Scholastic Bowl; Varsity Clb; Lib Band; Chorus; Lib Concert Band; Lib Jazz Band; Lib Mrchg Band; Lib Orch; Rep Frsh Cls; Temple Coll; Music Ed.

SHIPLEY JR, JOHN C; Cherry Hill East HS; Cherry Hill, NJ; (4); 5/717; Am Leg Boys St; Debate Tm; Political Wkr; Var Capt Tennis; DAR Awd; Pres NHS; Ntl Merit Schol; Model UN; Radio Clb; High Hon Roll; New Jersey Schlsrs Prog 86; Robert C Byrd Schlrshp 87; Repb Clb Awd Stdy Of Pol Sci 87; Princeton 1; Intl Affairs.

SHIPMAN, SYLVIA J; John F Kennedy HS; Paterson, NJ; (2); Church Yth Grp; Varsity Clb; Chorus; Church Choir; Rep Soph Cls; Ice Hcky; Sftbl; Cit Awd; Hon Roll; US Air Force.

SHONE, JENNIFER B; Pitman HS; Pitman, NJ; (3); 43/154; Capt Debate Tm; French Clb; FBLA; Mgr JA; Sec Key Clb; SADD; Chorus; Drill Tm; Yrbk Stf; Tri-M Natl Music Honor Soc 86; S Jersey Youth Commission 86; Law.

SHOPLOCK, BARBARA; Ewing HS; Trenton, NJ; (2); JA; Letterman Clb; Ski Clb; Varsity Clb; Sec Frsh Cls; Rep Soph Cls; Trs Jr Cls; Off Sr Cls; Rep Stu Cncl; Prfct Atten Awd; Ski Rc Wnnr 84-87; USC San Diego; Mrn Bio.

SHORT, KRISTINE; Manalapan HS; Manalapan, NJ; (4); Church Yth Grp; Drama Clb; School Play; Nwsp Rptr; Nwsp Stf; PBA Schlrshp 87; Trenton ST Coll; Communication.

SHORT, SAMANTHA; Bridgewater-Raritan HS East; Bridgewater, NJ; (2); French Clb; SADD; Yrbk Stf; Off Frsh Cls; Rep Soph Cls; Var Cheerleading; Powder Puff Ftbl; JV Trk; Stat Wrstlng.

SHOTWELL, CHRIS; Newton HS; Newton, NJ; (2); 81/231; Church Yth Grp; French Clb; FFA; Ski Clb; SADD; Rep Frsh Cls; Rep Soph Cls; JV Ftbl; JV Golf.

SHOTWELL, KRISTI; Newton HS; Newton, NJ; (2); 30/219; Rep French Clb; Ski Clb; Chorus; Rep Stu Cncl; Cheerleading; Stat Ftbl; Score Keeper; Hon Roll; Bus.

SHOTWELL, MICHELLE; New Milford HS; New Milford, NJ; (3); 27/141; Drama Clb; Off Band; Concert Band; Drm Mjr(t); Jazz Band; Mrchg Band; Orch; Pep Band; Nwsp Stf; Yrbk Stf; Outstndg Achvt Band 86 & 87; Jazz Band Svc Awd 86 & 87; Ofcr Awd Band 87; Music.

SHOUP, ERIC; Manalapan HS; Manalapan, NJ; (3); Exploring; Pres Explr Pst 951 86-88; Engrng.

SHOVLIN, ROBERT; Westfield SR HS; Westfield, NJ; (3); 81/469; Am Leg Boys St; Church Yth Grp; SADD; Chorus; Im Bsktbl; Var L Ftbl; Wt Lftg; Cit Awd; High Hon Roll; Spanish Clb; Hugh O Brian Yth Ldrship Smnr 86; Bk Of Emeralds 85; Chrl Awd 85.

SHRANK, MARC; John P Stevens HS; Edison, NJ; (3); 38/436; Key Clb; Nwsp Ed-Chief; Nwsp Sprt Ed; JV Trk; NHS; Spanish NHS.

SHREKGAST, GREG; Wall HS; Wall Twp, NJ; (4); 81/269; Cmnty Wkr; Varsity Clb; L Var Bsbl; L Bsktbl; L Var Ftbl; JV Ice Hcky; L Var Trk; Hon Roll; Shore Conf Div Awd-Ftbl 84; Pace U-NY; Accntng.

SHREM, ANDREA J; Red Bank Regional HS; Bradley Beach, NJ; (3); Dance Clb; Drama Clb; Office Aide; PAVAS; Ski Clb; Temple Yth Grp; Pom Pon; Gov Hon Prg Awd; Hon Roll; Outstnding Dance Mjr In Perf Arts Prog 86-87; 3rd Pl In Voc Indstrl Clbs Of Amer Cmptn 86-87; Dance.

SHU, JOYCE; West Windsor-Plainsboro HS; Princeton Junct, NJ; (3); Nwsp Stf; Swmmng; Sportsmanshp Awd Swmmng 86; Swmmng Records 85, 86; Child Psychlgy.

SHUI, CONWAY; Montville Township HS; Pine Brook, NJ; (3); 31/276; Capt VP FBLA; Ski Clb; Sec Sr Cls; Var JV Socr; High Hon Roll; Hon Roll; NHS; Key Clb; Varsity Clb; Ftbl; Vsty Plaque & Ltr For Sccr 87; Tnns Trphy 86; U Of PA; Law.

SHUKLA, SHILPA; Montville HS; Montville, NJ; (3); Cmnty Wkr; Dance Clb; FBLA; Hosp Aide; Key Clb; Library Aide; Service Clb; Sec Spanish Clb; Temple Yth Grp; Varsity Clb; Pre-Law.

SHULMAN, REBECCA; Dwight-Englewood HS; Leonia, NJ; (3); Camera Clb; Dance Clb; School Musical; Rptr Lit Mag; JC Awd; Dance.

SHULTIS, MICHELE; North Warren Regional HS; Blairstown, NJ; (4); Church Yth Grp; Nwsp Rptr; Yrbk Ed-Chief; Yrbk Rptr; Rep Frsh Cls; Rep Soph Cls; Hon Roll; Pres Acadmc Ftns Awd 87; Messiah Coll; Psych.

SHULTZ, LISA; Cumberland Regional HS; Bridgeton, NJ; (3); Church Yth Grp; Drama Clb; 4-H; Girl Scts; Teachers Aide; School Play; Bsktbl; Sftbl; Tennis; High Hon Roll; Cumberland County CC.

SHUM, CHARLOTTE; Livingston HS; Livingston, NJ; (4); 7/424; Church Yth Grp; Yrbk Sprt Ed; JV Var Fld Hcky; Mgr(s); Var Vllybl; High Hon Roll; Jr NHS; NHS; Ntl Merit Ltr; Spanish NHS; 3rd Pl Hnrb Mntn NJAATSP Exm 86; HS Spnsh IV Hnrs Stu 86; 2nd Tm All Metro Vllybl Leag 87; U Of PA; Bio.

SHUMAKER, DEBBIE; Bridgewater-Raritan HS West; Raritan, NJ; (3); Hosp Aide; Yrbk Stf; Stat Bsktbl; JV Socr; Trenton ST U; Med.

SHUPE, CHARLES; Lakewood HS; Lakewood, NJ; (3); 19/300; German Clb; Band; Jazz Band.

SHUPP, THERESA; Mother Seton Regional HS; Rahway, NJ; (3); 14/74; Hosp Aide; Co-Capt Pom Pon; Dnfth Awd; High Hon Roll; Hon Roll; NHS; Seton Spotlight Awd 87; Spnsh & Bio Awds 86; St Johns U; Liberal Arts.

SHURELDS, INDIA; Camden HS; Camden, NJ; (3); Dance Clb; Drama Clb; Office Aide; School Play; Nwsp Stf; Yrbk Stf; Lit Mag; Rep Soph Cls; JV Cheerleading; Vllybl; Engrng.

SHUTE, DONNA; Cherokee HS; Marlton, NJ; (4); 12/411; Dance Clb; Sec Latin Clb; Trs Stu Cncl; Var Capt Cheerleading; Cit Awd; Hon Roll; NHS; St Schlr; Church Yth Grp; FBLA; Burlington Cnty Outstndng Chrldr Awd 86; Presdntl Clsrm Conf Delgt 87; JR Ms Fnlst-Ms Burlngtn Co 86; Bus Mgmt.

SHUTE, MICHAEL; Highland Regional HS; Erial, NJ; (2); VP Frsh Cls; JV Bsktbl; Var JV Socr; Hon Roll; Rotary Awd.

SHUTE, ROSE ANN; Kingsway Regional HS; Swedesboro, NJ; (2); 4-H; Ski Clb; Band; Concert Band; Mrchg Band; Bsktbl; Cit Awd; 4-H Awd; Ctznshp Awd 85-86; 4-H Awd 86-87; Cosmetologist.

SHUTTLESWORTH, MELISSA; Madison HS; Madison, NJ; (2); Band; Chorus; Concert Band; Orch; School Musical; High Hon Roll; Hon Roll; ST Fnlst Miss Amer Coed Beauty Pageant 87; Apprenticed Of NJ Ballet Co 86-87; Ballet Dancer.

SIANO, ANNA; Essex Catholic Girls HS; Irvington, NJ; (3); Art Clb; PAVAS; School Play; Variety Show; Yrbk Stf; Lit Mag; Rep Stu Cncl; High Hon Roll; Hon Roll; Library Aide; Art Hnrs 86-87; St Peters Coll; Elem Educ.

SIANO, SALVATORE R; Passaic Valley HS; W Paterson, NJ; (3); 4/315; Am Leg Boys St; Yrbk Stf; Trs Sr Cls; JV Var Bsktbl; Var Golf; Var Socr; High Hon Roll; NHS; Pres Schlr; Rutgers Schlr Awd 87; Rugers; Lwyr.

SIBILIA, NICHOLAS; Belleville HS; Belleville, NJ; (3); Hon Roll; Pre-Law.

SIBRIAN, GUADALUPE; Union Hill HS; Union City, NJ; (4); Trs Church Yth Grp; Pres Math Clb; Mu Alpha Theta; Pres Spanish Clb; Drm Mjr(t); Yrbk Stf; NHS; Spanish NHS; Rutgers; Bio.

SICA, MATTHEW; North Arlington HS; N Arlington, NJ; (4); 3/141; Math Clb; Yrbk Sprt Ed; Pres Stu Cncl; Var Bsbl; Var Bsktbl; Var Ftbl; Cit Awd; Lion Awd; Trs NHS; Spanish NHS; Pres Acad Fit Awd 87; UAF Outstndng Achvt In Math & Sci 87; U Of CT; Bus Admin.

SICILIANO, JAMES L; Paul VI HS; Somerdale, NJ; (3); 36/415; Am Leg Boys St; Math Clb; JV Bsbl; JV Ftbl; Hon Roll; NHS; Villanova; Engr.

SICILIANO, PAMELA; Paul VI HS; Bellmawr, NJ; (3); 38/420; Cmnty Wkr; Dance Clb; Math Clb; Pep Clb; Red Cross Aide; SADD; VP Frsh Cls; VP Soph Cls; VP Jr Cls; VP Stu Cncl; Hnrbl Mntn-Italian 84-86; Villanova U.

SICKELS, DAWN; Matawan Regional HS; Matawan, NJ; (4); 17/310; Math Tm; Trs Stu Cncl; Var Crs Cntry; Stat Trk; Cit Awd; NHS; Hon Roll; Phrmcy.

SICOLI, ANTHONY G; Union HS; Union, NJ; (4); 3/534; Am Leg Boys St; Church Yth Grp; Spanish Clb; JV Trk; JV Wt Lftg; Hon Roll; NHS; Spanish NHS; Villanova U; Bus Admin.

SIDERS, ERIN; Montclair HS; Montclair, NJ; (3); AFS; Cmnty Wkr; Latin Clb; Office Aide; Political Wkr; SADD; Stu Cncl; Hon Roll; 2nd Prz Library Book Review Cont 87; Task Force To Promote A Positive Schl Image 86-87; Archtctr.

SIEBERT, SUSAN; Pitman HS; Pitman, NJ; (3); 5/130; Key Clb; VP Soph Cls; Rep Stu Cncl; Var Fld Hcky; Capt Trk; High Hon Roll; Hon Roll; NHS; Teachers Aide; Chorus; HOBY Awd 85; Tri-M Msc Hnr Scty 86-87; Jr Exec Brd Mbr 86-87; Bus.

SIEGEL, LISA; Toms River HS North; Toms River, NJ; (1); Band; Concert Band; Mrchg Band; Orch; School Musical; Symp Band; Coach Actv; Mgr(s); Score Keeper; Timer; Acad Ltr 86; All S Jersey Symph Band 87; Music.

SIEGEL, STEVEN; Lakewood HS; Lakewood, NJ; (3); English Clb; SADD; Temple Yth Grp; Crs Cntry; Hon Roll; Arch.

SIEGEL, SUSAN; Middletown HS South; Red Bank, NJ; (2); Drama Clb; Library Aide; Ski Clb; Chorus; Variety Show; Gym; Dncng.

SIEGEL, WENDY; West Orange HS; W Orange, NJ; (3); French Clb; Temple Yth Grp; Nwsp Stf; Yrbk Stf; French Hon Soc; Hon Roll; Bus.

SIEIRA, ANA; East Side HS; Newark, NJ; (3); Computer Clb; French Clb; Spanish Clb; Orch; School Musical; Hon Roll; Rutgers; Bus.

SIEIRA, MARIA; East Side HS; Newark, NJ; (3); French Clb; Spanish Clb; School Musical; Off Jr Cls; Swmmng; Rutgers.

SIERADZKI, KAREN; Paramus Catholic Girls Rgnl HS; Garfield, NJ; (2); Nwsp Stf; NEDT Awd; Engl Prfcncy Awd 86; Rght To Life Clb 86-87; Engl Tchr.

SIFFORD, VANESSA; Clifford J Scott HS; Piscataway, NJ; (4); 10/250; Flag Corp; Engl Hnrs 86; Typng Hnrs 87; Rutgers Coll; Gyn.

SIGEL, KIRK; Ocean City HS; Ocean City, NJ; (3); 1/344; Trs Church Yth Grp; Pres Computer Clb; Latin Clb; Math Clb; Quiz Bowl; Science Clb; Var Tennis; High Hon Roll; Rotary Awd; Distngshd Acadmc Awd 86; Hnry Mntn Natl Latin Exam 86; MA Inst Tech; Elec Entr.

SIGGINS, LISA; High Point Regional HS; Branchville, NJ; (4); 23/232; Debate Tm; German Clb; Stat Bsktbl; Var Mgr(s); Stat Trk; High Hon Roll; Hon Roll; Natl Bk Sussex Cnty Schlrshp 87; Voc Guidnc Stu Asst Awd 87; Wildcat Booster Club SR Awd 87; U Of Scranton; Accntng.

SIGNORELLA, MARIA; Rosell Park HS; Roselle Park, NJ; (3); 1/150; PAVAS; Chorus; Concert Band; Jazz Band; Mrchg Band; School Musical; Sec Sr Cls; Stu Cncl; Var L Fld Hcky; High Hon Roll; WA DC Schlrshp 86-87; Bus.

SIKORA, LOREN; Toms River South HS; Toms River, NJ; (3); 35/505; FBLA; Lgl Scrtry.

SILCOX, CHERI; Palmyra HS; Palmyra, NJ; (3); 22/124; Church Yth Grp; Drama Clb; Key Clb; Office Aide; Color Guard; Mgr(s); Hon Roll.

SILKOWSKI, MARGARET D; Ocean Township HS; Ocean, NJ; (3); 63/344; French Clb; Latin Clb; JV Fld Hcky; Natl Latn Hnr Soc; Adelphi; JR Clsscl Leag; CPA.

SILLS, TAUNYA LYNNETTE; East Orange HS; East Orange, NJ; (3); French Clb; Girl Scts; Variety Show; Yrbk Stf; Rep Jr Cls; Sec Sr Cls; Hon Roll; Prfct Atten Awd; Fnlst Miss Amer Coed Pgnt 86; Grad Barbzn Mdlng Schl 85; Hampton U; Bus Admin.

SILVA, MARIA; Long Branch HS; Long Br, NJ; (3); #12 In Class; Church Choir; Nwsp Stf; Vrsty Schlr Awd 86-87; Stock Mrkt Game Awd 87; Bus Admin.

SILVA, MAURICIO; Watchung Hills Regional HS; Watchung, NJ; (3); Variety Show; High Hon Roll; Hon Roll.

SILVANI, VALERIE; Secaucus HS; Secaucus, NJ; (3); 8/170; Dance Clb; Hosp Aide; Mu Alpha Theta; School Musical; Mgr(s); JV Vllybl; High Hon Roll; NHS; Spanish NHS; Bst Spnsh I 85, Spnsh II Stdnt 86.

SILVER, JILL; Pompton Lakes HS; Pompton Lakes, NJ; (4); 9/150; Math Clb; SADD; Capt Band; Concert Band; Mrchg Band; School Play; Ed Yrbk Stf; Cheerleading; Capt Gym; NHS; Bus.

SILVERMAN, IAN; Highland HS; Clementon, NJ; (2); Spanish Clb; Nwsp Stf; Writer.

SILVERMAN, JENNIFER; Mount Olive HS; Budd Lake, NJ; (3); 18/318; AFS; VP FBLA; Library Aide; Ski Clb; SADD; Varsity Clb; Rep Soph Cls; Var Cheerleading; High Hon Roll; NHS; Poem Pblshd Amercn Poetry Anthlgy 87; ST Fnlst Miss Amer Co Ed Pgnt 87; Outstndng Stenogrphy Stu 86; Advrtsng.

SILVERS, COLLEEN; Kearny HS; Kearny, NJ; (3); 75/383; Yrbk Stf; Var Capt Cheerleading; Coach Actv; Var Powder Puff Ftbl; Im Socr; Var Sftbl; Hon Roll; Friends Of Erin Schlrshp 87; Glassboro ST Schlrshp 87; V Sftbl MVP 87; Glassboro ST Coll.

SILVESTRI, MARIANNE; Manchester Regional HS; N Haledon, NJ; (4); GAA; Hosp Aide; Yrbk Stf; Rep Frsh Cls; Rep Soph Cls; Rep Jr Cls; Rep Sr Cls; Rep Stu Cncl; Powder Puff Ftbl; Capt Vllybl; Cmmnctns.

SIMBER, MATTHEW W; Collingswood HS; Collingswood, NJ; (3); Am Leg Boys St; Church Yth Grp; JCL; Latin Clb; Band; Concert Band; Jazz Band; Mrchg Band; Orch; JV Tennis; Achvt Mech Drwg 84-85; Math.

SIMEK, ROBERT; Paulsboro HS; Gibbstown, NJ; (3); 9/150; Office Aide; Nwsp Bus Mgr; Nwsp Rptr; Hon Roll; Hst NHS; VFW Awd; Cmcrcl Art.

SIMINOFF, RUSSELL; South Plainfield HS; S Plainfield, NJ; (3); Im Bowling; Var Capt Tennis; Elks Awd; Hon Roll; Ntl Merit Ltr; Rookie Of Yr Tennis 85; Bus.

SIMIONE, ELIZABETH; Cumberland Reg HS; Bridgeton, NJ; (3); 93/384; Dance Clb; French Clb; RN.

SIMMERMAN, DAWN; Brick Twp Memorial HS; Brick, NJ; (4); 1/290; Key Clb; Latin Clb; Co-Capt Math Tm; Stat Bsktbl; Capt Trk; High Hon Roll; NHS; Val; Garden ST Dstngshd Schlr Awd 87; Cook Coll; Vet Med.

SIMMERMAN, LORNA; Pitman HS; Pitman, NJ; (3); 23/138; Key Clb; Teachers Aide; Chorus; Nwsp Stf; Var Capt Tennis; Hon Roll; Tri-M Mdrn Music Mstrs 86-87; Tri-Cnty Conf Tnns All Star 1st Dbls 85-86; Outstndng Plyr Awd Tnns 86-7; Bio.

SIMMONS, JACQUELINE A; Howell HS; Howell, NJ; (3); 29/460; FBLA; Spanish Clb; Speech Tm; SADD; Nwsp Ed-Chief; Nwsp Rptr; Nwsp Stf; Yrbk Stf; NHS; Bus.

SIMMONS, JOHN; Ewing HS; Trenton, NJ; (2); Boy Scts; Church Yth Grp; Computer Clb; JA; Chorus; Bowling; Ftbl; French Hon Soc; High Hon Roll; Hon Roll; V Letter Bwlng 86-87; Math Awd 85-86; MIT; Elec Engrng.

SIMMONS, SEAN; Belvidere HS; Belvidere, NJ; (3); JV Ftbl; Im Wt Lftg; Var JV Wrstlng; Hon Roll; NHS.

SIMMONS, STEVEN; Jackson Memorial HS; Jackson, NJ; (3); 10/145; Math Clb; Science Clb; Spanish Clb; Ntl Merit Ltr; Spanish NHS; High Hon Roll; Hon Roll; Comp Sci.

SIMMONSKI, DAWN R; Moorestown HS; Moorestown, NJ; (2); Church Yth Grp; Dance Clb; Drama Clb; Acpl Chr; Chorus; JV Cheerleading; Tennis; Psych.

SIMON, AMY; Union HS; Union, NJ; (2); Science Clb; Service Clb; Spanish Clb; Mrchg Band; Orch; School Musical; Gym; JV Tennis; JV Twrlr; Hon Roll; Pres Acadmc Ftns Awd 86; Astront.

SIMON, DONNA; Union HS; Union, NJ; (3); French Clb; FBLA; Key Clb; Hon Roll; Bus Adm.

SIMON, JAMES; Essex Catholic Boys HS; E Orange, NJ; (3); Dance Clb; Chorus; VP Soph Cls; Var L Bsbl; Var L Bowling; Var L Ftbl; Hon Roll; Jr NHS; NHS; Stu Of Mo 85; Natl Hnr Soc 86; Acctg.

SIMONE, FRANCES; Buena Regional HS; Vineland, NJ; (2); Service Clb; Varsity Clb; JV Bsktbl; Var Fld Hcky; Var Sftbl; Hon Roll; U Of TX; Bio.

SIMONE, LEAH; Watching Hills Regional HS; Gillette, NJ; (3); 116/350; French Clb; Key Clb; SADD; Stage Crew; Off Soph Cls; Off Jr Cls; Rep Sr Cls; Stat Ftbl; Powder Puff Ftbl; Twrlr; Prm Cmte 87-88; Safe Rdes Sec 86-88; John Hopkns Tlnt Srch 83; Poltcl Sci.

SIMONE, MONIQUE; Manchester Regional HS; N Haledon, NJ; (3); Camera Clb; Dance Clb; DECA; GAA; Rep Stu Cncl; JV Var Powder Puff Ftbl; Var L Trk; Hon Roll; Rep Frsh Cls; Trs Soph Cls; Peer Cnslg 87-88; Capri Hair Inst; Cmstlgy.

SIMONE, NANCY U; Faith Christian Schl; Berlin, NJ; (4); 3/8; Drama Clb; Chorus; Yrbk Bus Mgr; Bsktbl; Cheerleading; Fld Hcky; Sftbl; High Hon Roll; Hon Roll; Mst Sportsmanlike Plyr Bsktbl 85-86; Glassboro Coll; Elem Ed.

SIMONE, STEPHEN; St Augustine Prep; Vineland, NJ; (4); 11/53; Computer Clb; Yrbk Phtg; Tennis; Wrstlng; NHS; Prfct Atten Awd; Lit Mag; Temple U; Pre-Med.

SIMONELLI, JILL; Metuchen HS; Metuchen, NJ; (4); 40/162; Church Yth Grp; Church Choir; JV Var Bsktbl; Var Capt Sftbl; Elks Awd; Hon Roll; Booster Clb Awd, Excllnc Athltc & Acdmc Achvt 87; Mst Imprvd Sftbl Plyr 87; Moravian Coll; Art.

SIMONETTI, MICHELLE; Toms River East HS; Toms River, NJ; (4); Im Crs Cntry; Im Fld Hcky; Im Trk; Hon Roll; Med.

SIMONETTI, PAUL; Notre Dame HS; E Windsor, NJ; (2); Ftbl.

SIMPKINS, JEFFREY R; Highland Regional HS; Blackwood, NJ; (3); Art Clb; Chess Clb; Church Yth Grp; Latin Clb; Bsktbl; Score Keeper; Tennis; Drexel U; Engrng.

SIMPSON, ERIN; Brick Memorial HS; Brick, NJ; (3); 21/384; Drama Clb; FBLA; Color Guard; Capt Flag Corp; Mrchg Band; Stage Crew; High Hon Roll; NHS.

SIMPSON, HENRY L; J P Stevens HS; Rahway, NJ; (4); Art Clb; Letterman Clb; Varsity Clb; Im Wt Lftg; Var Wrstlng; Chess Clb; Dist 19 Wrstlng Finals 2nd Pl & Cert Of Awd Achvt Graphic Arts 86-87; Mst Imprvd Acdmc Wrstlr 85-86; Fshn Inst Of Tech; Adv Dsgn.

SMITH, JENNIFER; John F Kennedy HS; Willingboro, NJ; (2); 5/300; JCL; Latin Clb; Color Guard; Flag Corp; Yrbk Stf; Var Fld Hcky; Var Lcrss; Mgr Swmmng; Hon Roll; NHS.

SMITH, JENNIFER; Overbrook Reg SR HS; Berlin, NJ; (3); Church Yth Grp; VP Spanish Clb; SADD; Chorus; Church Choir; Var Bsktbl; Stat Trk; Hon Roll; NHS.

SMITH, JESSICA; Montville Twnshp HS; Pinebrook, NJ; (3); 55/267; FBLA; Sftbl; High Hon Roll; Hon Roll; HS In Israel Schlrshp Pgm 86; JEA Schlrshp 86; Law.

SMITH, JIM; Kearny HS; Kearny, NJ; (3); Computer Clb; German Clb; Im Bowling; Im Ice Hcky; Im Sftbl; Im Vllybl; Hon Roll; NHS; German Hnr Scty 87; Boston U; Film Making.

SMITH, JOSEPH; De Paul HS; Wayne, NJ; (3); 48/150; Chem Tm Awd 85-86; Achvt Awd Accntng 86-87; William Paterson Coll; Bus.

SMITH, JUDITH A; Princeton Day Schl; East Brunswick, NJ; (4); 1/89; NFL; Orch; School Musical; Yrbk Stf; Lit Mag; High Hon Roll; NHS; Ntl Merit SF; St Schlr; Bl Rbbn Schltc Art Cmptn 87; Grnd Cncrs Rgnl Frnch Prz 85; Prz For Eng, Frnch, Art & Sci 86-87; Yale U.

SMITH, JULIE; Friends Schl; Sicklerville, NJ; (3); 1/20; Dance Clb; Variety Show; Yrbk Stf; Off Soph Cls; Jr Cls; Stu Cncl; High Hon Roll; Scholar,Rutgers 87; Smmr Coll Cornell U Pre-Med 87; Obstetrics.

SMITH, JUSTIN M; Madison HS; Madison, NJ; (4); 5/208; Cmnty Wkr; French Clb; Political Wkr; Orch; School Musical; Nwsp Rptr; Nwsp Rptr; Yrbk Phtg; Lit Mag; French Hon Soc; Co-Editor-In-Chf Glyphs Lit Mgzn 86-87; Physics.

SMITH, KATHLEEN; Phillipsburg HS; Phillipsburg, NJ; (3); 51/315; Ski Clb; SADD; Stu Cncl; Tennis; Hon Roll; NHS; Comms.

SMITH, KELLY; Marine Acad Of Science & Technlgy; Union Beach, NJ; (3); 12/45; Church Yth Grp; Drama Clb; Exploring; French Clb; Girl Scts; ROTC; Drill Tm; Variety Show; Nwsp Stf; Hon Roll.

SMITH, KIM; Secaucus HS; Secaucus, NJ; (2); 3/123; Mu Alpha Theta; Ski Clb; Color Guard; Stage Crew; VP Frsh Cls; VP Soph Cls; JV Tennis; High Hon Roll; Hon Roll; Jr NHS.

SMITH, KIMBERLY; Hackettstown HS; Great Meadows, NJ; (4); 50/234; Trs FFA; Office Aide; Spanish Clb; Teachers Aide; Stage Crew; Stat Trk; High Hon Roll; Hon Roll; NHS; Co Coll Of Morris; Bus Admn.

SMITH, KIMBERLY; Voorhees HS; Glen Gardner, NJ; (4); French Clb; Key Clb; Red Cross Aide; Concert Band; Mrchg Band; Variety Show; Lit Mag; French Hon Soc; Hon Roll; VA Wesleyan Coll Schlrshp 87; VA Wesleyan Coll; Engl.

SMITH, LA SHONDA; Bridgeton HS; Bridgeton, NJ; (2); Crs Cntry; Fld Hcky; Hon Roll; Data Prcssr.

SMITH, LA VEETA; Eastside HS; Paterson, NJ; (3); NAACP; SADD; Mrchg Band; School Musical; Nwsp Ed-Chief; Rep Sec Jr Cls; Var Capt Trk; NHS; Church Yth Grp; FL A&M U; Aerontcs.

SMITH, LESLIE LYNN; Haddonfield Memorial HS; Haddonfield, NJ; (4); 15/162; Am Leg Aux Girls St; Yrbk Bus Mgr; Var Capt Golf; Var JV Swmmng; DAR Awd; NHS; St Schlr; Church Yth Grp; FCA; Varsity Clb; Rotary Yth Ldrshp Awds Conf; Rutgers JR Grls Amat Golf Champ; NJ JR Grls Golf Champ; Vanderbilt U; Intl Reltns.

SMITH, LINDA; St James HS; Wenonah, NJ; (2); #1 In Class; Drama Clb; SADD; School Musical; School Play; Sftbl; High Hon Roll; Georgetown; Pre-Med.

SMITH, LORA JANE; Mount Olive HS; Budd Lake, NJ; (4); 47/275; Church Yth Grp; Drama Clb; SADD; Acpl Chr; Band; Chorus; Flag Corp; School Musical; Yrbk Stf; Hon Roll; DE Vly Coll Hnr Schlrshp, Stu Cncl Svc Schlrshp, & Advncd Envrnmntl Tech Corp Schlrshp 87; DE Vly Coll; Bio.

SMITH, MAASI; Irvington HS; Irvington, NJ; (3); Boys Clb Am; Rep Frsh Cls; Rep Soph Cls; Rep Stu Cncl; Hon Roll; Acad All Amer; US Ldrshp Soc; Bus.

SMITH, MARGARET E; Union Catholic Regional HS; Fanwood, NJ; (4); 16/293; VP Pres Girl Scts; Hosp Aide; Service Clb; Sec Spanish Clb; Nwsp Rptr; Nwsp Stf; Ed Lit Mag; Rep Frsh Cls; Hon Roll; NHS; UN Mvmnt Better Wrld Rep 86-87.

SMITH, MARK; Burlington City HS; Burlington, NJ; (3); Chess Clb; Church Yth Grp; JV Tennis; Machinist Of Yr 87; Engl Awds 85 & 86; Physics.

SMITH, MICHAEL; Toms River HS South; Pine Beach, NJ; (4); Cmnty Wkr; Math Tm; Spanish Clb; Teachers Aide; Concert Band; Mrchg Band; High Hon Roll; Band; Hon Roll; Math Lttr 84-5; Band Lttr 84-6; Acad Lttr 86-7; Stockton ST Coll; Math.

SMITH, MITCHELL; Manchester Regional HS; Prospect Pk, NJ; (2); Computer Clb; School Play; Im Bsbl; Im Bowling; Im Coach Actv; Im Diving; Im Mgr(s); Im Score Keeper; Im Sftbl; Im Swmmng; ST Polc Safety Patrol 84; Comp Pgmmr.

SMITH, MONICA Y; Metuchen HS; Metuchen, NJ; (4); 7/175; French Clb; Science Clb; Orch; Nwsp Rptr; Fld Hcky; French Hon Soc; Hon Roll; NHS; Pres Schlr; Golden Poet Awds 85; U Of CA Los Angeles; Arabic.

SMITH, NIGEL; Perth Amboy HS; Perth Amboy, NJ; (3); Church Yth Grp; UCLA; Med.

SMITH, PAMELA; West Windsor-Plainsboro HS; Lawrenceville, NJ; (3); Camera Clb; Debate Tm; Drama Clb; French Clb; Intnl Clb; Model UN; Speech Tm; Lit Mag; Rsrch Mrn Bio.

SMITH, PAMELA M; Middletown HS; Leonardo, NJ; (4); 37/450; Dance Clb; Girl Scts; Acpl Chr; Chorus; School Musical; Variety Show; Rep Sr Cls; High Hon Roll; Hon Roll; Summa Awd 84; Magna Com Laude In Latin 84-85; Physcl Thrpy.

SMITH, PETE; Morris Catholic HS; Rockaway, NJ; (3); 43/140; Var L Ftbl; Im Vllybl; Im Wt Lftg; Var L Wrstlng; Church Yth Grp; Natl Beta Clb; Pep Clb; Quiz Bowl; Varsity Clb; Powder Puff Ftbl; Psych.

SMITH, PHILBERT; West Side HS; Newark, NJ; (3); Boy Scts; Hosp Aide; NAACP; Band; Concert Band; Nwsp Rptr; Pres Jr Cls; Pres Stu Cncl; Var Ftbl; Var Capt Wrstlng; MVP & Wrstlr Of Yr 85-87; Outstndng Stu Of Yr 85-87; Stu Ldr Gvrnmnt & 1st VP 87-88; Bus.

SMITH, RAYMOND SCOTT; Burlington County Vo Tech; Riverside, NJ; (4); VICA; Stu Cncl; Eckenrode Mem Awd 87; Comp Sci.

SMITH, REBECCA; Summit HS; Summit, NJ; (3); Church Yth Grp; FBLA; Model UN; Orch; JV Var Cheerleading; High Hon Roll; Hon Roll.

SMITH, RENEE P; Allentown HS; Robbinsville, NJ; (4); Am Leg Aux Girls St; Cmnty Wkr; Hosp Aide; Library Aide; Teachers Aide; Hon Roll; Masonic Awd; Pres Schlr; Lions Clb 87; Wstchstr U; Psych.

SMITH, RHONDA; Abraham Clark HS; Roselle, NJ; (3); 15/171; Church Yth Grp; Cmnty Wkr; Hosp Aide; Band; Chorus; Church Choir; Color Guard; Mrchg Band; Stu Cncl; Cheerleading; 1st Prize Hlth Fair Comp 86; Psych.

SMITH, ROBERT J; Atlantic City HS; Margate, NJ; (3); Model UN; Rep Jr Cls; Var L Bsbl; Var Ftbl; Hon Roll; NHS; Pre-Med.

SMITH JR, ROBERT W; Atlantic Christian Schl; Ocean City, NJ; (4); 5/14; Chess Clb; Church Yth Grp; Speech Tm; Chorus; School Play; Yrbk Ed-Chief; Trs Sr Cls; Var Capt Socr; Hon Roll; NHS; Gordon Coll; Bus Adm.

SMITH, ROGER; Bayonne HS; Bayonne, NJ; (4); 17/345; Pres Chess Clb; Drama Clb; Math Tm; Science Clb; Im Ftbl; Im Trk; NHS; Ntl Merit Schol; NJ Govrnrs Schlr, Elks Clb Outstndng Stu 86; U Of MD College Pk; Poltcl Sci.

SMITH, RONALD V; Bishop Eustace Prep; Medford, NJ; (3); 32/169; Am Leg Boys St; Cmnty Wkr; Drama Clb; German Clb; Band; Orch; School Musical; School Play; Stage Crew; JV Bsbl; Bio.

SMITH, SHARON; St Rose HS; Brick, NJ; (3); 31/245; Ski Clb; School Play; Stage Crew; Yrbk Phtg; Yrbk Stf; Sec Crs Cntry; Mgr(s); Sec Trk; High Hon Roll; Hon Roll; Hnrs Engl 86; Physcl Thrpy.

SMITH, SHAUN; Essex Catholic Boys HS; East Orange, NJ; (2); Math Clb; Math Tm; Im Bsktbl; Im Sftbl; High Hon Roll; Comp Sci.

SMITH JR, SHELDON V; Summit HS; Summit, NJ; (3); Band; Concert Band; Jazz Band; Mrchg Band; Orch; Pep Band; School Play; Lcrss; High Hon Roll; Sprtsmnshp Awd La Crosse 86; Sci.

SMITH, STACEY; Montville Township HS; Montville, NJ; (2); Key Clb; Co-Capt Color Guard; Jazz Band; School Musical; Var JV Mgr(s); Mgr Tennis; High Hon Roll; Hon Roll; Cmnty Svc Awd 87; Music Awd 87; Math.

SMITH, STACY; Manchester Regional HS; Haledon, NJ; (3); Church Yth Grp; Dance Clb; German Clb; Girl Scts; Variety Show; Yrbk Stf; Rep Frsh Cls; Rep Soph Cls; Rep Jr Cls; Rep Stu Cncl; 4-H Clb-Babysitting & Essay Cntst Awd 84; Dance Awds 84-86; Early Childhood Educ.

SMITH, TIM; Atlantic City HS; Brigantine, NJ; (2); Model UN; Yrbk Sprt Ed; Yrbk Stf; Rep Soph Cls; Var Swmmng; Astrntcl Engnr.

SMITH, TINA; Glen Rock SR HS; Glen Rock, NJ; (3); AFS; Art Clb; Church Yth Grp; Drama Clb; Ski Clb; School Play; Ed Nwsp Stf; L Trk; Hon Roll; Jr NHS; Ridgwd Art Assn Hnr Mntn Waterclr 85; Bates Coll; Psych.

SMITH, TRACY; Morristown HS; Morris Plains, NJ; (1); Key Clb; Church Choir; Socr.

SMITH, VERNON; Egg Harbor Twp HS; Pleasantville, NJ; (4); 38/290; Spanish Clb; Stu Cncl; Bsktbl; Crimnl Justice.

SMITH, VINCENT J; Millburn SR HS; Millburn, NJ; (4); 70/250; Church Yth Grp; JV Ftbl; Var Trk; Hon Roll; Ntl Merit SF; Annapolis Navan Acad; Engr.

SMITH, VIRGINIA; Bound Brook HS; South Bound Brook, NJ; (3); Drama Clb; French Clb; Intnl Clb; School Play; Nwsp Stf; Rutgers U; Jrnlsm.

SMITH, WAYNE; Riverside HS; Riverside, NJ; (3); 20/120; FBLA; Intnl Clb; SADD; Varsity Clb; Off Jr Cls; Off Sr Cls; Var Capt Bsbl; JV Bsktbl; JV Ftbl; Im Vllybl; Outstndng Stu Phy Educ 87; Stockton-Rutgers; Bus Admin.

SMITH, WESLEY; Edgewood Regional HS; Chesilhurst, NJ; (3); 29/390; Latin Clb; Scholastic Bowl; Spanish Clb; Varsity Clb; Var Capt Tennis; Hon Roll; NHS; Prfct Atten Awd; Soaring Eagle Awd 86-87; Law.

SMOLEN, HEATHER L; Bishop Ahr HS; Edison, NJ; (4); 78/240; Drama Clb; French Clb; Chorus; Drill Tm; School Musical; School Play; Stage Crew; Lit Mag; Rep Jr Cls; Hon Roll; Prtl Schlrshp Wagner Coll SI NY 87-88; Lstd In All Amer Acad Hgh Achvrs 87-88; Amer Spch Drama Gftd; Wagner Coll; Drama.

SMUTZ, STEPHANIE; West Windsor Plainsburo HS; Princeton Jct, NJ; (3); Am Leg Aux Girls St; Church Yth Grp; Mrchg Band; Rep Stu Cncl; Capt JV Bsktbl; Var L Socr; Var L Trk; Cit Awd; NHS; Prfct Atten Awd; PA Coll Of The Arts Gld Key Awd 86.

SMYTH, LAURA; Immaculate Conception HS; Lyndhurst, NJ; (4); 12/92; Q&S; Quiz Bowl; VP Speech Tm; Nwsp Sprt Ed; Pres Stu Cncl; Hon Roll; NEDT Awd; Prfct Atten Awd; Hugh O Brien ST Ldrshp Sem; Century III Ldrs Schl Wnnr; St Peters Coll Smmr Schlr; Engl.

SNEAD, KIMBERLY; Our Lady Of Good Councel; Newark, NJ; (3); 28/122; Sec Church Yth Grp; Hosp Aide; Scholastic Bowl; Science Clb; Chorus; Church Choir; Hon Roll; Rcvd 2nd Hnrs 86; Ped.

SNEAD, NANCY LYNN; Essex Catholic Girls HS; Irvington, NJ; (4); 22/52; VP Drama Clb; FHA; Pep Clb; Drill Tm; School Play; Stage Crew; Nwsp Rptr; Nwsp Stf; Yrbk Phtg; Yrbk Rptr.

SNEDDEN, GEORGE; Wall HS; Wall, NJ; (3); 26/289; Church Yth Grp; JV Ftbl; Hon Roll; Monmouth Coll; Psych.

SNEDEKER, SCOTT; Middletown South HS; Middletown, NJ; (4); Ski Clb; Varsity Clb; Stage Crew; Rep Soph Cls; Rep Jr Cls; Rep Sr Cls; JV Socr; Var Capt Trk; Roanoke Coll Grant 87; Roanoke Coll; Bus Admin.

SNEED, SUZANNE; Mt Olive HS; Flanders, NJ; (3); 21/316; Dance Clb; Debate Tm; Ski Clb; Nwsp Ed-Chief; Nwsp Stf; Yrbk Ed-Chief; Ed Yrbk Stf; JV Var Fld Hcky; Hon Roll; Hst NHS; Natl Art Hnr Soc.

SNIDER, GREGORY; Memorial HS; Cedar Grove, NJ; (1); 9/123; Math Tm; Nwsp Rptr; Nwsp Stf; Yrbk Rptr; Yrbk Sprt Ed; Yrbk Stf; Rep Stu Cncl; Var Crs Cntry; JV Trk; NHS; 2nd Pl Alg I & II Essex Cnty Math Leag 84-86; Pascal Awd 86; Fnlst Govs Schl NJ Drew U 85; Math Tchr.

SNIVELY, STEVE P; Buena Regional HS; Buena, NJ; (2).

SNODGRASS, MATTHEW R; Woodbury HS; Woodbury, NJ; (3); Am Leg Boys St; Boy Scts; Band; Pres Chorus; JV Socr; Var Tennis; God Cntry Awd; High Hon Roll; JC Awd; NHS; God & Life Awd 86; Math.

SNOVER, KATHLEEN; Belvidere HS; Belvidere, NJ; (4); 11/125; Pres Drama Clb; SADD; Varsity Clb; Madrigals; School Musical; Lit Mag; Capt Cheerleading; NHS; French Clb; Quiz Bowl; Frnch II Acdmc Awd 84-85; Frnch III Acdmc Awd 85-86; Hugh O Brien Yth Ldrshp Semnr Rep & Fin 84-85; Theatr Arts.

SNOW, STEPHANIE; Gateway Regional HS; Woodbury Hts, NJ; (3); 7/120; German Clb; Band; Chorus; Concert Band; Jazz Band; Mrchg Band; School Musical; Hon Roll; NHS; Prfct Atten Awd; Rtry Clb RYLA 87; Rutgers U.

SNOW, STEPHANIE; St John Vianney HS; Englishtown, NJ; (2); Sec Church Yth Grp; Drama Clb; Intnl Clb; SADD; Trs Church Choir; Yrbk Stf; Trk; Hon Roll; Girl Scts; Hosp Aide.

SNYDER, DEBRA; Maple Shade HS; Maple Shade, NJ; (2); Church Yth Grp; GAA; Girl Scts; Spanish Clb; Pres Soph Cls; Trs Stu Cncl; JV L Bsktbl; Var L Socr; JV L Sftbl; HOBY Ambssdr 87.

SNYDER, JACQUELYN; Raritan HS; Hazlet, NJ; (3); 8/340; Sec French Clb; Bsktbl; JV Gym; Socr; Var Trk; Var L High Hon Roll; NHS; Natl Sci Olympd Chem Cert Merit 86; Monmth Cnty Teens Arts Fest Cert Merit 86; 3rd Pl Recylcng Essy 87; Aeronautcs.

SNYDER, JASON; Wallington HS; Wallington, NJ; (4); 25/90; Boy Scts; Church Yth Grp; Ski Clb; Chorus; School Play; Bsbl; Bsktbl; Bowling; Trk; Wt Lftg; Restrnt-Hotel Mgmnt.

SNYDER, JULIE; Columbia HS; Maplewood, NJ; (1); French Clb; Hosp Aide; Library Aide; Service Clb; Fld Hcky; Swmmng; Sci.

SNYDER JR, ROBERT N; Baptist HS; Gloucester City, NJ; (4); 4/45; Church Yth Grp; Drama Clb; Band; Church Choir; School Musical; School Play; Yrbk Ed-Chief; VP Stu Cncl; Stat Wrstlng; Ntl Merit Ltr; PA Nwsps Inc Schlrshp Asst Awd Wnnr 86; PA Nwsps Inc An Outstndng Crrier Of Yr 86; Grdn ST Dstngshd; Warner Southern; Chrstn Mnstrs.

SNYDER, STEVEN; Toms River North HS; Fontana, CA; (3); Church Yth Grp; Cmnty Wkr; 4-H; Chorus; School Musical; School Play; Variety Show; 4-H Awd; Natl Amer Stars Tlnt 1st Pl Wnnr Sngr 86-87; Natl Hemisphere Tlnt Pgnt 1st Pl Wnnr Sngr 85-86; Music.

SNYDER, TAMMY; Belvidere HS; Belvidere, NJ; (4); 29/122; Computer Clb; Band; Color Guard; Mrchg Band; School Musical; School Play; Northampton Cnty Area CC; Educ.

SOBELMAN, JOSHUA; Pennsville Memorial HS; Pennsville, NJ; (3); Am Leg Boys St; Office Aide; JV Bsbl; Marine Bio.

SOBHI, NIMA; Hackettstown HS; Hackettstown, NJ; (2); Drm Mjr(t); Hnr Hackettstown HS Centennial Cls 85; Cnty Coll-Morris; Elec Engrng.

SOBIESKI, ALLISON; Ocean Township HS; Wayside, NJ; (3); Nwsp Rptr; JV Bsktbl; Score Keeper; Spnsh Clb; SR Ldrshp Prjct; Bus.

SOBIESKI, SONYA M; Columbia HS; Maplewood, NJ; (4); 11/498; Pres Drama Clb; Chorus; School Musical; School Play; Variety Show; Nwsp Stf; Yrbk Ed-Chief; Hosp Aide; Nwsp Rptr; Yrbk Stf; Winner-NJ Young Playwrites Fest 85; NJ Governors Awds-Arts Educ/Creative Wrtng 85; Vrsty Lttr Drama; Humanities.

SOBIESZCZYK, AMY E; Saint Rose HS; Interlaken, NJ; (4); 22/214; Key Clb; Latin Clb; School Musical; Var Cheerleading; High Hon Roll; Hon Roll; NHS; Hnrb Mntn Garden ST Dist Schlr Awd 87; Bus.

SOBOLESKI JR, LAWRENCE C; Marlboro HS; Morganville, NJ; (4); 3/529; Pres Math Tm; NFL; VP Science Clb; Speech Tm; JV Trk; Capt JETS Awd; VP NHS; Ntl Merit Ltr; Opt Clb Awd; St Schlr; Amer Invtnl Math Exm 85 & 87; Mst Lkly To Succeed 87; Cornell U; Chmcl Engrng.

SODANO, PAT; Madison HS; Madison, NJ; (3); Art Clb; Music Cmpstn.

SODERBERG, ERICA A; Ridge HS; Basking Ridge, NJ; (4); 46/239; Church Yth Grp; Drama Clb; French Clb; Ski Clb; Chorus; Capt Drill Tm; School Musical; School Play; Hon Roll; Bio.

SODERMAN, ELSA; Howell HS; Farmingdale, NJ; (3); 7/428; VP Church Yth Grp; Exploring; Pres Trs French Clb; Church Choir; Nwsp Stf; NHS; Awd Excllnc Engl 87; Sci.

SOECHTING, CHRISTINE; Matawan Regional HS; Matawan, NJ; (4); 12/310; French Clb; SADD; Chorus; Madrigals; School Musical; Yrbk Stf; Rep Sr Cls; Rep Stu Cncl; JV Fld Hcky; Hon Roll; NJ All-St Chorus 85.

SOECHTING, DOROTHEE; Matawan Regional HS; Matawan, NJ; (3); 3/364; Art Clb; Stage Crew; Ed Nwsp Phtg; Nwsp Rptr; Off Soph Cls; Off Jr Cls; Stu Cncl; Var JV Fld Hcky; Trk; Hon Roll.

SOFIELD, KEVIN; Ocean TWP HS; Oakhurst, NJ; (4); 5/320; Nwsp Sprt Ed; Sec Sr Cls; Var Capt Bsbl; Var L Bsktbl; JV Var Ftbl; Socr; Im Wt Lftg; Bausch & Lomb Sci Awd; High Hon Roll; VP NHS; NROTC Schlrshp 87; US Army Rsrve Natl Schlr/Athlt Awd 87; NJ Schlr Athlt 87; US Naval Acad; Engrng.

SOFMAN, KRIS; Kearny HS; Kearny, NJ; (4); DECA; Var Bsktbl; JV Cheerleading; JV Gym; 1st Pl Awd On A Tst Cncrning Food Mrktng DECCA 87; Kean Coll; Elem Ed.

SOFRAN, SHARON; Woodbridge HS; Port Reading, NJ; (3); 49/350; Ski Clb; Off Stu Cncl; Hon Roll; Spanish NHS; Bus.

SOHN, CHRISTOPHER; Edgewood Regional HS; Sicklerville, NJ; (2); Im Socr; Lincoln Tech Schl; Auto Engrng.

SOLANKA, HEATHER; Vernon Township HS; Highland Lakes, NJ; (3); Score Keeper; JV Socr; JV Stat Sftbl; Var L Swmmng; Hon Roll; NHS; Rep Frsh Cls; Rep Soph Cls; Rep Jr Cls; Rep Stu Cncl; Civil Engrng.

SOLANKI, RITA; Dickinson HS; Jersey City, NJ; (3); Computer Clb; French Clb; Mdcl.

SOLANKO, KARIN; Manasquan HS; Brielle, NJ; (2); 8/256; French Clb; FBLA; Key Clb; Nwsp Stf; Cheerleading; High Hon Roll; Kiwanis Awd; NHS; Hugh O Brien Ldrshp Awd 86-87; Bd Of Educ Schlstc Awd 86-87.

SOLARI, ANDREA; Holy Spirit HS; Brigantine, NJ; (3); 42/332; French Clb; School Musical; School Play; VP Frsh Cls; VP Soph Cls; Im Vllybl; High Hon Roll; Nrs.

SOLDA, SUSAN; Imamaculate Conception HS; Woodridge, NJ; (3); Math Tm; Ski Clb; Spanish Clb; SADD; School Musical; School Play; Yrbk Stf; Cheerleading; Capt Sftbl; Cit Awd; Seton Hall U; Crim Just.

SOLDO, DAVID; Paul VI HS; Cherry Hill, NJ; (3); 118/462; SADD; Rep Frsh Cls; Bsbl; Var Ftbl; Im Ice Hcky; Im Wt Lftg; JV Wrstlng; Acad All Amer 87; Outstndng HS Ath In Amer 87; Lafanette; Bus Adm.

SOLER, WILLIAM; Essex Catholic Boys HS; East Orange, NJ; (3); 2/117; Chess Clb; Math Clb; Math Tm; Nwsp Rptr; Sftbl; High Hon Roll; Jr NHS; JR Class VP Soph Yr 87; Outstndng Achvt Bio 86; Elec Engrng.

SOLETTO, MICHELLE; Watchung Hills Regional HS; Warren, NJ; (4); Chrmn Church Yth Grp; Drama Clb; School Play; Yrbk Sprt Ed; Lit Mag; Var JV Trk; Stat Wrstlng; Hon Roll; Pres Schlr; Voice Dem Awd; Mc Dougal & Lttl Yng Wrtrs Cert Of Merit 86; ST Entry-Litrary Wrk-Teen Arts Fstvl 87; Flagler Coll; Hearng Imprd Educ.

SOLIMAN, MONA; Red Bank Regional HS; Little Silver, NJ; (3); Art Clb; German Clb; Latin Clb; Varsity Clb; Yrbk Stf; Rep Jr Cls; Fld Hcky; Swmmng; Trk; Cit Awd; Pre-Med.

SOLOMON, AMY; Morristown/Bayley HS; Convent Sta, NJ; (2); Key Clb; Pep Clb; JV Cheerleading; U Boca Raton; Bus.

SOLOMON, ANTHONY; Barringer HS; Newark, NJ; (3); Boys Clb Am; Boy Scts; Computer Clb; Chorus; Var JV Bsktbl; Var JV Ftbl; Var Wt Lftg; Comp Prgmmr.

SOLOMON, JAMES; Newton HS; Newton, NJ; (2); 3/219; Math Tm; SADD; Stu Cncl; Ftbl; High Hon Roll; Dntstry.

SOLOMON, SHARON; Morristown-Beard HS; Budd Lake, NJ; (3); 1/83; AFS; VP Boy Scts; Intnl Clb; Sec Model UN; Sec Q&S; Science Clb; Spanish Clb; Chorus; Nwsp Bus Mgr; Yrbk Phtg; Rensaleer Polytech Inst Awd Math & Sci Excllnc 87; Rutgers Schlr 87; Elias Lieberman Poetry Awd 87; Med.

SOLOSHATZ, DAVID A; Manalapan HS; Englishtown, NJ; (3); 2/420; Am Leg Boys St; Math Tm; Trs Soph Cls; Trs Stu Cncl; JV Tennis; High Hon Roll; NHS; Ntl Merit Ltr; Computer Clb; Nwsp Stf; Rensselaer Math & Sci Medl 87; Columbia U Sci Hnrs Pgm 86-87; John Hopkins Ctr Tlntd Yth 84-86.

SOLTESZ, SUSAN; Woodbridge HS; Woodbridge, NJ; (4); 20/386; French Clb; Acpl Chr; Chorus; Swing Chorus; Rep Frsh Cls; Rep Soph Cls; Rep Stu Cncl; JV Bsktbl; JV Sftbl; Elks Awd; Ursinus Coll Freeland Schlrshp, Bruce O Stout Schlrshp 87; Ursinus Coll; Bus.

SOMAR, KHALMANIE; Dickinson HS; Jersey City, NJ; (3); Computer Clb; Office Aide; Science Clb; Yrbk Phtg; Yrbk Rptr; Yrbk Sprt Ed; Yrbk Stf; Rep Jr Cls; Rep Stu Cncl; Twrlr; Cert Compltng Hghr Effcncy Pgm 84; Plaq Smmr Job Plcmnt Org 84.

SOME, LESLIE; Livingston HS; Livingston, NJ; (3); Key Clb; Temple Yth Grp; Lit Mag; Mgr(s); JV Trk; High Hon Roll; Hon Roll; Jr NHS; Spanish NHS; U Of PA; Bus.

SOMERSTEIN, EVAN; Memorial HS; Elmwood Pk, NJ; (3); 9/160; Math Clb; Yrbk Sprt Ed; JV Ftbl; Hon Roll; NHS.

SOMERVILLE, TINA; Wall Twp HS; Sea Girt, NJ; (4); 22/269; Ski Clb; Nwsp Rptr; Yrbk Bus Mgr; Stat Bsbl; Var Fld Hcky; Powder Puff Ftbl; JV Socr; High Hon Roll; Kiwanis Awd; NHS; Bus Adm.

SOMMA, GRETCHEN; Middlesex HS; Middlesex, NJ; (4); 1/175; Key Clb; SADD; School Play; Trs Jr Cls; Sec Sr Cls; Stu Cncl; Capt Cheerleading; High Hon Roll; NHS; St Schlr; Rutgers Schlr 86; Garden St Dstgshd Schlr Awd 86; Phrmcy.

SOMMER, JULIE; Parsippany Hills HS; Denville, NJ; (3); Political Wkr; School Musical; Yrbk Ed-Chief; Lit Mag; Off Frsh Cls; Off Soph Cls; Off Jr Cls; Off Sr Cls; Off Stu Cncl; Var Stat Bsbl; Villanova; Lawyer.

SON, JOSEPHINE; Saint Mary HS; Rutherford, NJ; (3); Drama Clb; Math Clb; Thesps; School Musical; School Play; Stage Crew; Nwsp Rptr; Var Bsktbl; Stat Sftbl; Var Vllybl; Arch.

SON, YOUNG; John P Stevens HS; Edison, NJ; (4); 26/476; Church Yth Grp; Hosp Aide; Math Tm; Science Clb; JV Ftbl; Hon Roll; NHS; Prfct Atten Awd; St Schlr; Natl Sci Olympd Cert Dstnctn 86; Rensselaer Polytech; Mech Engr.

SONDEEN, LESLIE; Cinnaminson HS; Cinnaminson, NJ; (3); Church Yth Grp; Hosp Aide; Key Clb; SADD; Concert Band; Mrchg Band; Rep Frsh Cls; Rep Soph Cls; Rep Jr Cls; NHS; Pedtrc Nrsng Prctnr.

SONG, BYUNGHO; North Bergen HS; N Bergen, NJ; (3); 29/450; Debate Tm; Hosp Aide; Key Clb; Office Aide; Socr; Hon Roll; 4th Pl Math Leag 87; Slvr Mdl Russian Olympd 87; Russian Clb Awd-Rcgntn Acadc Decthln NJ 87; Math.

SONG, ELISA; Dwight-Englewood Schl; Demarest, NJ; (3); Cmnty Wkr; Hosp Aide; Orch; Lit Mag; High Hon Roll; Hon Roll; Ntl Merit SF; Psychtrst.

SONG, TAE; Cliffside Park HS; Cliffside Pk, NJ; (3); 70/250; Church Yth Grp; Church Choir; Stu Cncl; Var L Ftbl; Var L Trk; Hon Roll; Rep Church Conv 87; Standard Achvt Latin Cls 86; PA ST; Arch.

SONI, RAJESH N; Mount Olive HS; Flanders, NJ; (4); 2/276; Aud/Vis; Math Tm; Ski Clb; Concert Band; Jazz Band; JV Trk; VP NHS; Ntl Merit SF; St Schlr; Quiz Bowl; Area Band; Rgn Band; Modern Music Mstrs-Treas; Engrng.

SONTAKAY, ARATI; Summit HS; Summit, NJ; (3); 35/270; Cmnty Wkr; Drama Clb; French Clb; Hosp Aide; Orch; Chess Clb; Lit Mag; Hon Roll; Biol.

SONZ, LORRETTA; Union Catholic Reg HS; Scotch Plains, NJ; (4); Latin Clb; Service Clb; Ski Clb; Spanish Clb; SADD; Nwsp Rptr; Rep Stu Cncl; Swmmng; Tennis; Hon Roll; J Wilk Mem Schlrshp; Ursinus Coll.

SOOKRAM, ARNOLD; Paramus HS; Paramus, NJ; (4); 9/335; VP Debate Tm; Trs German Clb; Intnl Clb; Math Clb; NFL; Ski Clb; School Play; Nwsp Stf; Lit Mag; Rep Sr Cls; Premed.

SOOS, JEFFREY; St Josephs HS; Edison, NJ; (4); 35/205; Trs Church Yth Grp; Cmnty Wkr; Political Wkr; Ski Clb; Var Tennis; High Hon Roll; Syracuse U; Bus.

SOOY, CHRISTINA; Holy Spirit HS; Absecon, NJ; (2); 28/397; Pep Clb; Spanish Clb; Var L Crs Cntry; JV Trk.

SOOY, KAREN; Parsippany Hills HS; Denville, NJ; (4); 37/305; AFS; Trs Spanish Clb; SADD; Mrchg Band; Variety Show; Var Fld Hcky; Powder Puff Ftbl; Hon Roll; NHS; Presdntl Schlrshp 87; Valparaiso U; Pre Med.

SOOY, REGINA; Pennsauken HS; Pennsauken, NJ; (3); JV Bowling; JV Cheerleading; Spanish NHS.

SOPKO, BETH; Notre Dame HS; Ewing, NJ; (2); Math Clb; Concert Band; Mrchg Band; School Musical; Nwsp Stf; Hon Roll; NHS; Hgh Hnrs Engl Awd 87; Dir Awd Band 86-87.

SOPRYCH, CHRIS; Notre Dame HS; Trenton, NJ; (2); 13/373; Math Tm; Wt Lftg; French Hon Soc; High Hon Roll; Hon Roll; NHS; Frnch I Awd 85-86; Frnch II Awd 86-87; Hnrs Alg I Awd 85-86.

SORACE, MICHAEL; Marist HS; Bayonne, NJ; (3); 20/150; Nwsp Stf; Yrbk Stf; Var JV Bowling; Var Socr; 2nd Hnrs 86-87.

SORBELLO, ALFIO; St James HS; Swedesboro, NJ; (2); 7/101; Church Yth Grp; Var Bsbl; JV Var Bsktbl; Var Ftbl; High Hon Roll.

SORG, KATHERINE; Collingswood SR HS; Collingswood, NJ; (2); JCL; Latin Clb; Color Guard; Concert Band; Im Bsktbl; Var Sftbl; High Hon Roll; Hon Roll; NHS; Pres Schlr; Law.

SORGE, THOMAS; West Windsor Plainsboro HS; Plainsboro, NJ; (3); Boy Scts; Varsity Clb; Band; Concert Band; Orch; Yrbk Phtg; Im Bsbl; Var Ftbl; Im Lcrss; Im Sftbl; Band Gld Mdl 85; Natl Sci Awd 85; Soc Stds Achvt 85; Arch.

SORI, TARA; Washington Twp HS; Sewell, NJ; (4); 110/480; Church Yth Grp; Cmnty Wkr; Dance Clb; Office Aide; Political Wkr; Ski Clb; Spanish Clb; Teachers Aide; Stu Cncl; JV Cheerleading; Rtgrs U; Psych.

SORIANO, CLAUDIA; St Marys Of The Assn; Irvington, NJ; (2); Art Clb; Chess Clb; Dance Clb; Math Clb; Spanish Clb; SADD; Chorus; Yrbk Phtg; Sftbl; Vllybl.

SORRELL, TERRENCE M; Salem HS; Salem, NJ; (3); Am Leg Boys St; Computer Clb; Latin Clb; Office Aide; Pep Clb; Pres Sr Cls; Var Capt Bsktbl; Var L Crs Cntry; Var L Ftbl; Var L Trk; Brthrhd Awd 87; Schlr Athlt Feb 87; Mst Crgs Athlt Trk Rlys 87; Engr.

SORRENTINO, SUSAN; East Brunswick HS; E Brunswick, NJ; (4); Variety Show; Stu Cncl; Capt Cheerleading; Dance Clb; Drama Clb; Key Clb; Pep Clb; SADD; Chorus; Trk; Iona Coll; Real Est Law.

SORRENTINO, VIRGINIA D; Hunterton Central HS; Flemington, NJ; (4); 61/565; Orch; Off Stu Cncl; Hon Roll; Sweet Adelines Music Schlrshp 87; Schlrshp To Juilliard 86-87; Schlrshp To Aspen Music Fstvl 85-86; New England Cnsrvtry; Violin.

SORRENTINO, WILLIAM; Toms River H S South; Beachwood, NJ; (2); Bsbl; Bsktbl; Ftbl; Swmmng; High Hon Roll; Legal Prof.

SOSA, HEIDI; St Marys Of The Assumpti; Irvington, NJ; (2); Chess Clb; Computer Clb; Dance Clb; FNA; Model UN; Spanish Clb; Chorus.

SOTAK II, RONALD P; Sacred Heart HS; Vineland, NJ; (3); Im Bsktbl; Var Socr; Var Swmmng; Im Vllybl; Pol Sci.

SOTINSKY, SONYA; Matawan Regional HS; Aberdeen, NJ; (3); 4/320; Math Tm; Spanish Clb; Stage Crew; Yrbk Stf; Rep Soph Cls; Rep Jr Cls; Rep Stu Cncl; Trk; High Hon Roll; Arch.

SOTO, LU ANN; Paterson Catholic HS; Paterson, NJ; (2); GAA; SADD; Varsity Clb; Band; Bsktbl; Score Keeper; Sftbl; Wt Lftg; Hon Roll; Boston U; Law.

SOTO, LUZ; Perth Amboy HS; Perth Amboy, NJ; (2); Hon Roll; Trntn ST Coll; Psych.

SOTO, MIGDALIA; Phillipsburg HS; Phillipsburg, NJ; (3); SADD; Chorus; School Musical; Nwsp Stf; Yrbk Stf; Spnsh.

SOTO, NORBERTO; Our Lady Of Good Counsel HS; Newark, NJ; (3); 1/150; Chess Clb; Drama Clb; Capt Quiz Bowl; Scholastic Bowl; Science Clb; School Musical; School Play; Yrbk Stf; Trk; Pres NHS; Schlrshp Of Our Lady Of Good Counsel 84; Thespian Critics Awd-Dramatic Perf 87; Rutgers Schl Of Pharmacy.

SOTOMAYOR, MARCELA; Holy Rosary Acad; Union City, NJ; (3); Drama Clb; Sec French Clb; Math Clb; Spanish Clb; Nwsp Rptr; Nwsp Stf; Yrbk Stf; VP Frsh Cls; Engl Awd & Sci Cmptn 85; Secy & Staff Wrtr French Club 87; Nutrition.

SOUCHAK, STEPHANIE; Wildwood Catholic HS; Wildwood Crest, NJ; (3); 2/73; Var Scholastic Bowl; Var Spanish Clb; Var School Musical; Pres Stu Cncl; Var Cheerleading; DAR Awd; High Hon Roll; NHS; Rotary Awd; Spanish NHS; US Military Acad Engr Wrkshp 87; Rotary Intl Ldrshp Conf 87; Sci Fair 2nd Pl 85-86,3rd Pl 87; Treas 87; Penn ST; Engr.

SOUDAH, RANDA; Mt St Mary Acad; Somerset, NJ; (4); 7/79; Church Yth Grp; Nwsp Ed-Chief; Stu Cncl; JV Fld Hcky; French Hon Soc; High Hon Roll; NHS; Ntl Merit SF; Q&S; Nwsp Rptr; Ntl Art Hnr Soc Sec; Gifted & Tlntd Prog.

SOUTHARD, JAMES T; Florence Twp Mem HS; Roebling, NJ; (3); Am Leg Boys St; Concert Band; Jazz Band; Trs Mrchg Band; School Musical; School Play; Nwsp Rptr; Nwsp Sprt Ed; Nwsp Stf; Band; Post Bglr Opre Larson Pst 8838 VFW Roebing NJ; Trenton ST; Cmnctns.

SOWERS, TERESA; Penns Grove HS; Carneys Point, NJ; (3); 1/172; Nwsp Ed-Chief; Yrbk Ed-Chief; Pres Jr Cls; Var Pom Pon; Var Sftbl; NHS; Rotary Awd; Camera Clb; Church Yth Grp; Computer Clb; Miss Teen Of Amer Pageant 86; Rutgers Schlr 87; Hugh O Brian Yth Ldrshp Ambassador 86; Jrnlst.

SOWERS, TRACY; Mainland Regional HS; Linwood, NJ; (4); Church Yth Grp; Drama Clb; SADD; Thesps; School Play; Stage Crew; Variety Show; Nwsp Rptr; Yrbk Rptr; Stu Cncl; Stockton ST Coll; Pre-Law.

SPADAVECCHIA, MARK; Hoboken HS; Hoboken, NJ; (3); Boy Scts; Computer Clb; Ftbl; Wt Lftg; Hon Roll; St Peters Coll; Accntng.

SPAGNOLA, DAWN; Brick Township HS; Brick Town, NJ; (4); Band; Concert Band; Mrchg Band; Yrbk Stf; Powder Puff Ftbl; Socr; High Hon Roll; Hon Roll; NHS; Schlrshp Natl Hnr Soc 87; Acdmc Achvmnt Awds 84-87; Music Achvmnt Awds 85; Trenton ST Coll.

SPAGNOLO, MARY; Brick Township Memorial HS; Brick, NJ; (3); 14/360; Church Yth Grp; Cmnty Wkr; FBLA; Spanish Clb; Rep Frsh Cls; Mgr(s); High Hon Roll; NHS; Bus Admn.

SPAGNOLO, MATT; Ridgefield Park HS; Ridgefield Pk, NJ; (3); 9/205; Am Leg Boys St; Computer Clb; Debate Tm; Lit Mag; Hon Roll; Pres NHS; Rtry Clb Yth Ldrshp Awd 86-87; Arch.

SPAIHTS, JONATHAN S; Ewing HS; Ewing, NJ; (4); 35/302; Church Yth Grp; Acpl Chr; School Musical; Swing Chorus; Yrbk Stf; Lit Mag; Ntl Merit SF; Princeton U; Engl.

SPALETA, BRONKO; Hoboken HS; Hoboken, NJ; (3); Stat Bsktbl; Mgr(s); Score Keeper; Hon Roll.

SPALL, LYNLEY; Vineland HS; Vineland, NJ; (2); 8/900; Key Clb; Latin Clb; Chorus; Pres Frsh Cls; Pres Soph Cls; Fld Hcky; Mgr(s); Sftbl; Swmmng; Hon Roll.

SPANN, CARLA JUNE; Rutherford HS; Rutherford, NJ; (3); Computer Clb; Drama Clb; Trs French Clb; Science Clb; Varsity Clb; Math Clb; Math Tm; Science Clb; Varsity Clb; Band; MA Inst Of Tech; Engrng.

SPANTON, DANIEL; St Joseph HS; West New York, NJ; (4); 18/155; Camera Clb; Pres Drama Clb; Latin Clb; Math Clb; School Musical; School Play; Stage Crew; Variety Show; Nwsp Stf; Yrbk Stf; Schltc Awd Lcl 144 87; NJ Inst Of Tech; Arch.

SPARACIO, DANIELLE; Sacred Heart HS; Estell Manor, NJ; (3); 4/65; Spanish Clb; SADD; School Play; Off Soph Cls; Sec Trs Jr Cls; Trs Stu Cncl; JV Bsktbl; Mgr(s); Hon Roll; NHS; Math & Sci Merit Awds 85-86; Natl History & Govt Awd 86; Atnd 25th Annl Chmcl Caravan Rutgers Univ 87; Engrng.

SPARANO, GINA; Middletown HS South; Middletown, NJ; (3); Hosp Aide; Drm Mjr(t); Mrchg Band; Trs Soph Cls; Thesps; Band; Concert Band; Pep Band; Stu Cncl; Powder Puff Ftbl; Bottlecapper Awd 87; Exec Cmmtte Bottlecappers 87; Elem Educ.

SPARANO, NICOLE; Manchester Regional HS; N Haledon, NJ; (2); Church Yth Grp; Stu Cncl; Socr; Sftbl; Hon Roll; Rtgrs Coll; Phrmcst.

SPARKS, KELLY; Kingsway Regional HS; Swedesboro, NJ; (2); 33/186; Ski Clb; JV Bsktbl; JV Fld Hcky; JV Swmmng; Hon Roll; NHS; Orthdntst.

SPARKS, SHARRON; Manalapan HS; Englishtown, NJ; (3); #147 In Class; JA; Band; Church Choir; Concert Band; Mrchg Band; Orch; School Musical; Trk; Hon Roll; Yth Ldrshp Dvlpmnt Inst Of NJ BIC 87; Dscvry Pgm 87; Rutgers ST U; Bus Admin.

SPARROCK, DAVID; Ocean Township HS; Ocean Twp, NJ; (3); 106/344; Boy Scts; Computer Clb; Debate Tm; French Clb; NFL; JV Crs Cntry; Ftbl; JV Swmmng; JV Trk; 3rd Pl ST JV Debte Trnmt 87; Aerospce Engr.

SPATOLA, JEFFREY; Middletown HS South; Leonardo, NJ; (2); Computer Clb; JA; Science Clb; Rep Frsh Cls; Golf; French Hon Soc; High Hon Roll; Prfct Atten Awd; French Clb; Latin Clb; Ltn Hnr Scty 86-87; Pres Physcl Ftns Awd 86-87; Georgetown U; Arch.

SPEAREL, ANDREA; Shore Regional HS; Monmouth Beach, NJ; (3); Church Yth Grp; Key Clb; Ski Clb; Thesps; Band; Mrchg Band; School Play; Var Socr; Var Tennis; Hon Roll.

SPEARS, JAMES; Pennsville HS; Pennsville, NJ; (3); CAP; Debate Tm; Spanish Clb; Band; Concert Band; Jazz Band; Mrchg Band; Pep Band; School Musical; Symp Band; All Salem Cnty HS Bnd 86-87; Prcssn Sctn Ldr 86-87; Engr.

SPECTOR, JENNIFER; Manalapan HS; Manalapan, NJ; (3); 27/523; Cmnty Wkr; SADD; Temple Yth Grp; Lit Mag; Hon Roll; NHS; Cert Hnr Geom I 86; Cert Hnr Alg II 87; Cert Hnr Soc Studs 87.

SPEED, LA-SHANNA D LAINE; Vailsburg HS; Newark, NJ; (4); Church Yth Grp; FHA; Pep Clb; Lit Mag; High Hon Roll; Hon Roll; Bloomfield Coll; Acctg.

SPEED, MARGARET; Bloomfield SR HS; Bloomfld, NJ; (4); 1/447; Math Tm; Science Clb; Church Choir; Elks Awd; Gov Hon Prg Awd; High Hon Roll; NHS; Ntl Merit SF; St Schlr; Val; Princeton U; Chem Engrng.

SPEENEY, JOHN; Madison Central HS; Old Bridge, NJ; (3); 60/365; Varsity Clb; Var Bsbl; Var Crs Cntry; JV Ftbl; Var Trk; Im Wt Lftg; Hon Roll; 3-M Awd, Vrsty Ltrs-Bsktbl, Crss Cntry & Trck, 1st Tm All-Cnty Crss-Cntry 87; Peer Ldr 88.

SPEER, DAVID; Wayne Hills HS; Wayne, NJ; (3); 81/350; JV Bsktbl; JV Golf; Communciations.

SPEICH, LAURA; Delsea Regional HS; Monroeville, NJ; (2); Church Yth Grp; Band; Church Choir; Concert Band; Mrchg Band; Wrd Prcssng.

SPEICHER, CHRISTINA; Central Regional HS; Bayville, NJ; (3) Cmnty Wkr; Chorus; Drill Tm; Mrchg Band; Nwsp Rptr; Yrbk Stf; Li Mag; Var Crs Cntry; Capt Var Twrlr; Capt Im Vllybl; Sara C Merrick Spnsh Schlrshp 87; Pres Natl Hnr Scty 87-88; Law.

SPELKER, KIMBERLY; Madison HS; Madison, NJ; (3); 56/211; Orch JV Var Bsktbl; Var Tennis; Advrtsng.

SPENCE, STACEY; Pleasantville HS; Pleasantville, NJ; (4); Cit Awd Hon Roll; Prfct Atten Awd; Bradford Bus Schl; Acctg.

SPENCE, ZELDA; Buena Regional HS; Newtonville, NJ; (4); 15/180 Church Yth Grp; Q&S; Varsity Clb; Variety Show; Nwsp Stf; Rep Stu Cncl; Var Crs Cntry; Stat Tennis; Capt Var Trk; NHS; Scty Dstngshd Am HS Stu 86-87; Hnr Rll 84-87; S Jersey Grp II Trck Chmp 85-86; Ruters U Psychlgy.

SPENCER, ALYSSA K; Hillsborough HS; Neshanic, NJ; (4); Church Yth Grp; Dance Clb; Drama Clb; Trs Chorus; Mrchg Band; Orch; School Musical; School Play; Variety Show; Rep Stu Cncl; Rider Coll; Bus Admin

SPENCER, JOHN C; Pequannock Township HS; Pompton Plains, NJ (4); 2/203; Math Clb; Varsity Clb; Capt Ftbl; JV Golf; Capt Wrstlng; Go Hon Prg Awd; Hon Roll; Pres NHS; Ntl Merit SF; Spanish NHS; 1st Pl N Math League Cmptn 85; Qlfd Score Amer Hs Math Exam 86; W Poin Invtnl Acad Wrkshp 86; U Of PA; Finance.

SPENCER, SLADE; Clearview Regional HS; Mantua, NJ; (4); 25/160 Drama Clb; VP Band; VP Concert Band; VP Mrchg Band; School Musical School Play; Stage Crew; Hon Roll; Prfct Atten Awd; Mrchng Awd 82-87 Physcs Awd 87; Papr Sci & Engrn Schlrshp 89; SUNY Coll; Paper Sci.

SPERA, FRANK; St James HS; Gibbstown, NJ; (2); 7/99; SADD; Hon Roll; U Miami FL; Law.

SPERBER, CHRISTINE; Red Bank Regional HS; Shrewsbury, NJ; (3) Ski Clb; Rep Frsh Cls; Rep Soph Cls; VP Jr Cls; Rep Stu Cncl; Var Fl Hcky; Var Socr; Var Swmmng; All Star Tm-Princeton Fld Hcky Cmp 86 Philosphy.

SPERO, DREW; Toms River HS North; Toms River, NJ; (3); SADD Temple Yth Grp; Concert Band; Mrchg Band; Socr; Tennis; High Hon Roll; Hon Roll; Acad Lttr 85 & 87; Bus.

SPICER, JILL; Shawnee HS; Medford, NJ; (1); Girl Scts; Stage Crew; Li Mag; Cheerleading; Pom Pon; Elem Tchr.

SPICER, ROBERT; The Kings Christian HS; Somerdale, NJ; (2) Church Yth Grp; Drama Clb; School Play; JV Bsktbl; Var Socr; High Hon Roll; Hon Roll.

SPICHIGER, JOHN; Lenape Valley HS; Andover, NJ; (3); 17/225; Bo Scts; FBLA; Socr; Tennis; Hon Roll; NHS; Engrng.

SPIDALETTO, TRISTA; Academic HS; Jersey City, NJ; (4); 15/78 Spanish Clb; Lit Mag; Rep Stu Cncl; Capt Crs Cntry; L Trk; High Hon Roll; Hon Roll; Drama Clb; Nwsp Rptr; Yrbk Stf; Smth Coll Bk Awd 8 JCEA Schlrshp 87; Jrsy Cty Wmns Clb Schlrshp 87; Smith Coll; Engnrng

SPIEGELMAN, JENNIFER; Wayne Hills HS; Wayne, NJ; (4); 12/30 French Clb; FBLA; GAA; Ski Clb; Varsity Clb; Yrbk Phtg; Var Capt Fl Hcky; NHS; 1st Tm All Cnty Vrsty Fld Hcky 86-87; Gardn ST Distngsh Schlr 86-87; Rutgers Coll; Ecnmcs.

SPIGNER, CHARLENE; Hillside HS; Hillside, NJ; (4); 38/194; Civ Clb; Cmnty Wkr; Hosp Aide; Service Clb; Church Choir; Var Capt Bsktb Stat Ftbl; Var Mgr(s); JV Var Score Keeper; Hon Roll; Cvc Awd 8 Hillside Schlrshp Fund Awd 87; Bloomfield Coll; Accntng.

SPIKES, APRIL; West Side HS; Newark, NJ; (4); 63/240; Bloomfiel Coll; Nrsng.

SPILLMAN, SANDRA A; David Brearley Regional HS; Kenilworth, N (4); 21/163; Cmnty Wkr; Drama Clb; German Clb; Acpl Chr; Chorus School Musical; School Play; Nwsp Rptr; Capt Cheerleading; Gym; S Teen Arts Grp Drama 86-87; Montclair ST Coll; Music.

SPILSBURY, JEFF; Belleville HS; Belleville, NJ; (3); Key Clb; Var Bsbl; JV Bsktbl; Var L Ftbl; Hon Roll.

SPINA, LAURA; Holy Spirit HS; Absecon, NJ; (3); 14/332; French Cl School Musical; Chrmn Soph Cls; Chrmn Jr Cls; NHS; Drama Clb; Orc Religion Awd High Achvmnt 85-86; Lbrl Arts.

SPINA, MARY ANN; Immaculate Conception HS; Saddle Brook, N (3); 7/70; Q&S; Rep Jr Cls; Tennis; Hon Roll; NEDT Awd; Yrbk Stf; Am Legn Aux Cert Of Particptn 85; Art.

SPINA, MICHAEL E; Salem HS; Salem, NJ; (3); Am Leg Boys St; Pr Stu Cncl; Capt Tennis; NHS; Sci.

SPINELLA, GRAZIELLA; Immaculate Conception HS; Lodi, NJ; (Am Leg Aux Girls St; Church Yth Grp; Spanish Clb; Chorus; Churc Choir; Prfct Atten Awd; 2nd Hnrs Awd 86-87; Montclair ST Coll; Acctn

SPINELLI, CHRISTOPHER; Vineland HS; Vineland, NJ; (3); 38/84 Aud/Vis; Boy Scts; Key Clb; Math Tm; Pep Clb; Ski Clb; Nwsp Rpt Nwsp Stf; Yrbk Rptr; Yrbk Stf; Perfct Atten 86-87; A Avg 84-85; Rutge U; Pre Med.

SPINKS, JUSTINE; Paulsboro HS; Paulsboro, NJ; (3); 6/150; Churc Yth Grp; Drama Clb; Girl Scts; Quiz Bowl; Scholastic Bowl; SAD Chorus; Church Choir; School Musical; Variety Show; United Way Be Teen Model Yr 85; Outstndng Soph Yr-Hugh O Brian Yth Sem 86; Fnl Acceptance Gov Schl; Rutgers; Pol Sci.

SPIRKO, CAROL; Colonia HS; Colonia, NJ; (4); Church Yth Gr Varsity Clb; Var Capt Bsktbl; Var L Socr; Var L Sftbl; Hon Roll; Sftbl A Cnty, All ST 2nd Tm Grp 3 84; Sftbl All Cnty 86; Sftbl All Cnty, All S Grp 3 87; Trenton ST Coll; Phys Ed.

SPIRT, MELISSA H; Livingston HS; Livingston, NJ; (4); 97/424; Cmn Wkr; Hosp Aide; Leo Clb; Model UN; VP Frsh Cls; Sec Sr Cls; Rep St Cncl; Var Capt Cheerleading; Powder Puff Ftbl; Cit Awd; John M Too Schlrshp Outstndng Svc 87; Parent/Teacher Cncl Top 25 Pct 87; Rutge Coll; Engl.

SPITALE, EMILY; St James HS; Carneys Point, NJ; (2); 16/101; SAD Nwsp Phtg; Nwsp Stf; Yrbk Phtg; Yrbk Stf; Rep Soph Cls; Hon Roll.

SPITALE, JOSEPH; Brick HS; Brick, NJ; (3); 100/420; Letterman Cl Political Wkr; Var Capt Bsktbl; Hon Roll; Crimnl Justc.

SPITZER, STEPHEN; Holy Spirit HS; Margate, NJ; (2); 1/397; H Roll; Natl Latin Exam Hon Ment 86; Accntng.

SPIZZUCO JR, DANIEL; Toms River HS East; Toms River, NJ; (Church Choir; Variety Show; Ftbl; Hon Roll; Montclair ST Coll.

SPOELSTRA, CHARLES G; Indian Hills HS; Oakland, NJ; (4); 4/28 Church Yth Grp; German Clb; Socr; High Hon Roll; Hon Roll; Jr NH NHS; Ntl Merit SF; St Schlr; PTSO Awds; Bio Lg Comptn; Chem I Comptn; Physcs Lg Comptn; Chem Lg Comptn; Congrsssnl Yth Ldrs Conf; Wheaton Coll; Pre-Med.

SPONG, LAURA; Memorial HS; Cedar Grove, NJ; (2); Trs 4-H; Pres French Clb; Math Tm; Scholastic Bowl; Chorus; School Musical; Rep Soph Cls; 4-H Awd; High Hon Roll; Voice Dem Awd; Outstndng Geomtry Stu Acad Awd 87; Twnshp Rcreatn Advsry Bd Stu Rep 87-89; Pub Rltns.

SPORER JR, JAMES F; Linden HS; Linden, NJ; (3); Cmnty Wkr; Teachers Aide; VICA; School Play; Bsbl; Bsktbl; Coach Actv; Var Ftbl; Sftbl; Trk; All Cnty Ftbl Tm, Wtch Wng Chmps 86; ST Chmps 85.

SPORTELLI, NICOLE; Monseignor Donovan HS; Bricktown, NJ; (3); Rep Frsh Cls; Sftbl; Hon Roll; Intl Rel.

SPRAGUE, LINDA; Matawan Regional HS; Cliffwood Bch, NJ; (3); #55 In Class; Spanish Clb; Pres SADD; Color Guard; Mrchg Band; Yrbk Phtg; Lit Mag; Hon Roll; NHS.

SPRAGUE, SCOTT; Brick Memorial HS; Bricktown, NJ; (1); Trk; High Hon Roll; Prfct Atten Awd; Lawyer.

SPRATLEY, SANDRA; Paulsboro HS; Paulsboro, NJ; (3); 75/158; Chorus; Color Guard; Yrbk Stf; Stat Bsktbl; Var Trk; Htl/Mtl Mgmt.

SPRING, DAWN; Clifton HS; Clifton, NJ; (3); Math Clb; Rep Frsh Cls; Rep Soph Cls; Var Sftbl; Hon Roll.

SPRINGER, ADAM; Montville HS; Montville, NJ; (4); 15/265; Computer Clb; FBLA; Key Clb; VP Math Clb; Nwsp Rptr; Lit Mag; Capt Trk; High Hon Roll; Hon Roll; NHS; NJ Dstngshd Schlr 86-87; Columbia U; Ecnmcs.

SPRINGER, DOUGLAS W; Hillside HS; Hillside, NJ; (3); 10/269; Am Leg Boys St; Aud/Vis; Math Tm; Ski Clb; Concert Band; Drm Mjr(t); Mrchg Band; Rep Stu Cncl; L Capt Gym; L Trk; USNA Annapls.

SPROUL, MARK; Christian Brothers Acad; Brielle, NJ; (3); 16/250; Math Tm; Im Bsktbl; Im Mgr Ice Hcky; Im Socr; Im Sftbl; High Hon Roll; Engrng.

SPULER, ALBERT; Washington Twp HS; Sewell, NJ; (4); 5/480; Church Yth Grp; Civic Clb; Drama Clb; Spanish Clb; School Musical; Mgr Stage Crew; Nwsp Stf; Yrbk Stf; Trs Frsh Cls; Rep Stu Cncl; Rutgers U; Intl Rltns.

SPURR, DAVID; Parsippany Hills HS; Morris Plns, NJ; (3); 1/340; Am Leg Boys St; Pres Debate Tm; Math Tm; Pres NFL; Concert Band; Mrchg Band; Lit Mag; Rep Jr Cls; Rep Sr Cls; Hon Roll; Rutgers Schlr 87; Acdmc Decathln 87; ST Sci Day Chem Team 1st Morris Cnty 87; Law.

SPYCHALSKI, STACIE; Bridgewater-Raritan West HS; Bridgewater, NJ; (3); Hosp Aide; Scholastic Bowl; Science Clb; SADD; Jr Cls; Stu Cncl; High Hon Roll; Hon Roll; NHS; Dctr.

SQUADRITO, JOSEPHINE; Glassboro HS; Glassboro, NJ; (3); Hosp Aide; Hon Roll; NHS; Achvt Awd Outstndng Perfrmnce Soc Stud 86-87; Hnrs Acad Achvt 86-87; Gloucester Cnty Coll; Nrsng.

SQUEO, ROBYN; Dwight-Englewood Schl; Alpine, NJ; (3); Math Clb; Math Tm; School Musical; School Play; JV Bsktbl; Var Socr; Var Sftbl; Var Trk; Var Wt Lftg; Citizenship Awd 84; Law.

SQUICCIMARRA, LYNN; Spotswood HS; Spotswood, NJ; (4); Drama Clb; Band; Concert Band; Orch; School Musical; School Play; Symp Band; Ed Lit Mag; Mgr(s); Hon Roll; Mddlsx Cnty Hgh Schl Arts Music 86; Crtv Wrtng Awd Grad 87; U Miami; Music.

SQUIER, STEPHANIE; Pennsville Memorial HS; Pennsville, NJ; (4); 1/201; Camp Fr Inc; Exploring; Office Aide; Spanish Clb; Color Guard; Stu Cncl; Pom Pon; Hon Roll; Sec Amer Industl Arts Stu Assn & Hmcmg Queen 86-87; Elem Educ.

SRAY, KAREN; Cumberland Regional HS; Bridgeton, NJ; (2); Church Yth Grp; French Clb; Office Aide; Science Clb; Ski Clb; Hon Roll; Jr NHS.

SRIVASTAVA, ANJALI; Hunterdon Central HS; Whitehouse Sta, NJ; (3); 18/543; Rep Key Clb; Orch; School Musical; French Hon Soc; Hon Roll; NHS; Ntl Merit SF.

SROLOVITZ, STEVEN R; Willingboro HS; Willingboro, NJ; (4); 2/308; Am Leg Boys St; Key Clb; Science Clb; Mgr(s); Var Tennis; Hon Roll; NHS; Ntl Merit Ltr; Natl Hebrew Hnr Scty; Amer Chem Scty Awd 87; Cooper Union; Elec Engr.

ST HILAIRE, NICOLE; La Cordaire Acad; Bloomfield, NJ; (3); Art Clb; Church Yth Grp; Dance Clb; Debate Tm; French Clb; Intnl Clb; Service Clb; Chorus; School Play; Stage Crew; Recvd A Schlrshp To Traphgan Fshn Inst 87; Modern Miss 87; Loras IA; Psychologist.

ST JOHN, CHRISTOPHER; Union Cathlic Regional HS; Roselle, NJ; (2); 90/190; Ski Clb; Hon Roll; Prfct Atten Awd; Cert Of Awd Geom 87; Cert Of Awd U S Hstry 87; Stanford U; Sci.

ST JOHN, MICHAEL; Lower Cape May Regional HS; Villas, NJ; (3); Thesps; Concert Band; Drm Mjr(t); Jazz Band; School Musical; School Play; Hon Roll; JP Sousa Awd; Rotary Awd; Boy Scts; Eagle Sct 85; Ad Altare Dei Cthlc Rlgs Awd 83; Rutgers; Theatre.

ST LOUIS, RACHELLE; St Aloysius HS; Jersey City, NJ; (3); Cmnty Wkr; Office Aide; Vllybl; Hon Roll; Montclair ST Coll; Law.

STACH, MELINDA; Mahwah HS; Mahwah, NJ; (2); 30/120; Pres Band; Pres Concert Band; Pres Mrchg Band; Pres Pep Band; Hon Roll; Prfct Atten Awd; Music Hnr Awd 85-86; Cert Dstngshd Srvc, Drctrs Awd Mrchng Band 86-87; U Of CA; Berkeley; Math.

STACKHOUSE, BETHANN; Trenton Central HS; Trenton, NJ; (4); Hosp Aide; Bsbl; Fld Hcky; Swmmng; Trk; Vllybl; High Hon Roll; Hon Roll; Luke Achvt Awd 87; Albert B Kahn TCHS Schlrshp Awd 87; Data Prcssr.

STAFFIERI, KIMBERLY; Cumberland Regional HS; Bridgeton, NJ; (3); Dance Clb; Intnl Clb; JCL; Cheerleading; Hon Roll; Jr NHS.

STAFFORD, ANDREA LYNN; Paterson Catholic Regional HS; Passaic, NJ; (2); Cmnty Wkr; Computer Clb; Dance Clb; Chorus; Church Choir; Cheerleading; Hon Roll; Georgetown; Med.

STAFFORD, BOB; Gloucester JRSR HS; Gloucester, NJ; (4); Stage Crew; Var Bsbl; JV Bsktbl; Var Ftbl; Im Wt Lftg; Cit Awd; Hon Roll.

STAGGERS, LYNADA; Hillside HS; Hillside, NJ; (3); Church Yth Grp; Cmnty Wkr; Leo Clb; Math Tm; Spanish Clb; Church Choir; School Play; Yrbk Stf; Var Mgr(s); Hon Roll; Natl Sorority Phi Delta Kappa 87; Winter Track Cert Awd 86-87.

STAHL, MATTHEW; Borrentown Regional HS; Bordentown, NJ; (4); 4/114; Am Leg Boys St; Computer Clb; Mu Alpha Theta; Var Bsktbl; JV Bowling; Var Capt Golf; Im Tennis; Im Wt Lftg; High Hon Roll; Hon Roll; Air Force ROTC Schlrshp 86; Olympcs Of Mnd ST Fnlst; GA Tech; Comp Sci.

STALLINGS, SHERRY; Scotch Plains-Fanwood HS; Scotch Plains, NJ; (4); 9/330; AFS; Am Leg Aux Girls St; Church Yth Grp; Dance Clb; Debate Tm; German Clb; Girl Scts; Hosp Aide; Key Clb; Math Tm; Natl Achvt Outstndng Negro Stdnts 87; Unico Schlrshp & AKA Schlrshp 87; Johns Hopkins U; Pedtrcn.

STALLONE, PAMELA; Raristan HS; Hazlet, NJ; (3); 6/340; Drama Clb; French Clb; Chorus; Concert Band; Drm Mjr(t); Jazz Band; Mrchg Band; School Musical; High Hon Roll; NHS; Girl Scout Silv Awd 85; Schlr Var Ltr 87; Music Ed.

STAMBONI, CHRISTINE; Sayreville War Memorial HS; Parlin, NJ; (3); Hon Roll; Pres Acad Ftns Awd 84; Rutgers; Art.

STAMOS, BRUCE; Pt Pleasant Borough HS; Pt Pleasant, NJ; (4); 4/250; Am Leg Boys St; Key Clb; Scholastic Bowl; Varsity Clb; Var Socr; Cit Awd; High Hon Roll; Kiwanis Awd; NHS; Pres Schlr; U Of Richmond; Bio.

STANCATI, CAROLYN; Mc Corristin Catholic HS; Trenton, NJ; (3); Camera Clb; GAA; Pep Clb; Spanish Clb; Chorus; Bowling; Tennis; Vllybl; Wt Lftg; Hon Roll; Culinary.

STANCZAK, JOHN; St Peters Prep; Kearny, NJ; (4); 30/200; Drama Clb; Pres German Clb; Capt NFL; School Musical; School Play; Cmnty Wkr; Hosp Aide; JCL; Speech Tm; SADD; Schl Sprt Awd 85; Georgetown U; Law.

STANCZAK, TOM; Manchester Regional HS; N Haledon, NJ; (3); Church Yth Grp; Var JV Ftbl; Var Trk; 2nd Tm All ST Fncg 86-87; Comp Sci.

STANFORD, CHRISTINE; Huntendon HS; Stockton, NJ; (2); 192/478; Pres Church Yth Grp; FCA; Hosp Aide; Chorus; Church Choir; JV Var Cheerleading; NJ ST Teen Arts Fest & St Tour 86-87; Private Art Show 87; Fashion.

STANGER, REGAN; Vineland HS; Vineland, NJ; (2); 5/900; Sec Church Yth Grp; 4-H; French Clb; Church Choir; JV Fld Hcky; Var Mgr(s); Var Swmmng; JV Trk; 4-H Awd; Hon Roll; Cert Of Merit French 85-86; Play In Recital For Piano 87; Business.

STANKAVAGE, GORDON; Riverside HS; Riverside, NJ; (3); 15/100; Drama Clb; Political Wkr; Chorus; School Musical; Nwsp Rptr; Nwsp Stf; JV Crs Cntry; Hon Roll; NEDT Awd; Cngrss Bundestag Schlrshp Germany 1 Yr 87-88; Physics.

STANKIEWICZ, MICHAEL D; Millburn HS; Short Hills, NJ; (4); 3/257; Am Leg Boys St; Math Tm; Band; Jazz Band; Orch; Nwsp Stf; Var L Bsktbl; High Hon Roll; Ntl Merit Ltr; Tgle Fndntn Hnry Schlrshp 87; Harvard U.

STANKOWITZ, DENISE; Mother Seton Regional HS; Perth Amboy, NJ; (2); Nwsp Rptr; Lit Mag; NEDT Awd; Shrt Stry Publshd Lit Mag 86; Shrt Stry Pblshd Geom Mag 87; Fut Entry Teen Art Fstvl 87-88; Rutgers U; Acctg.

STANTON, JOHN J; Maple Shade HS; Maple Shade, NJ; (3); 93/160; FCA; Ftbl; Wt Lftg; Wrstlng.

STAPLETON, SCOTT; Burlington Township HS; Burlington, NJ; (3); 18/139; Ski Clb; Varsity Clb; Bsbl; Socr; Hon Roll; Elec Engr.

STARACE, KIMBERLY; Paramus HS; Paramus, NJ; (3); Church Yth Grp; Cmnty Wkr; Exploring; Library Aide; Ski Clb; SADD; Ed Lit Mag; Rep Jr Cls; Capt Socr; Cit Awd; Pres Phy Fit Awd; Yng Ctzns Awd; Pre-Med.

STARCHER, DAVID M; Millville SR HS; Millville, NJ; (3); Im Bowling; JV Ftbl; Im Wt Lftg; Comp Pgmmng.

STARK, CRAIG GARRETT; Highland Regional HS; Clementon, NJ; (2); German Clb; Intnl Clb; Model UN; Science Clb; Lit Mag; L Crs Cntry; Trk; High Hon Roll; Hon Roll; Med.

STARK, DAVID A; East Brunswick HS; East Brunswick, NJ; (4); Pres Art Clb; Key Clb; SADD; Ed Nwsp Stf; Ed Yrbk Stf; Pom Pon; NHS; Beth Plotz-Goldberg Art Schlrshp 87; 1st Rnnr-Up St Peters H S Art Comp 87; 1st Pl Awd Art Exhbt 84; RI Schl Of Dsgn; Ill.

STARK, ERIC DAVID; Highalnd Regional HS; Clementon, NJ; (3); 21/285; German Clb; Intnl Clb; Model UN; Political Wkr; Crs Cntry; Hon Roll; NHS; Library Aide; Science Clb; Trk; Schl Rep Annual Camden Cnty Govt Day 86; Blck Blt Tang Soo Karate 84; ST Fnls 1st Pl Physcs Olymp Tm; Polit Sci.

STARK, JOSEPH; Highland Regional HS; Blackwood, NJ; (4); Pres AFS; Aud/Vis; Drama Clb; Band; Chorus; Concert Band; Jazz Band; Mrchg Band; Pep Band; School Musical; Glassboro ST; Bus.

STARK, JULIE ANNE; Northwest Christian HS; Branchville, NJ; (3); Ski Clb; Orch; School Play; Var Fld Hcky; Art.

STARKE, TODD; Vernon Township HS; Sussex, NJ; (3); Aud/Vis; German Clb; Library Aide; Stage Crew; JV Swmmng; Mst Outstndng Indvdl Intl Aerospace Cmp 84; Gftd & Tlntd Pgm 84-87; Hstry.

STARR, KELLI; Egg Harbor TWP HS; Pleasantville, NJ; (4); 6/260; Ski Clb; Nwsp Rptr; Crs Cntry; Trk; High Hon Roll; NHS; Athlete Of Mnth-Feb 87; U Of DE; Athletic Trng.

STARRETT, CYNTHIA; Brick Memorial HS; Brick, NJ; (4); 38/210; Key Clb; Nwsp Stf; Yrbk Stf; JV Capt Cheerleading; Powder Puff Ftbl; JV Trk; Cit Awd; Hon Roll; Epphny Yth Grp Pres 82-87; Shippensburg U.

STASOLLA, VINCENTE; Don Bosco Prep HS; Highland Mill, NY; (3); 40/200; Rep Jr Cls; Rep Stu Cncl; Var Tennis; Hon Roll; Ten Scholar Nick Bollettieri Ten Acad 85; Fin.

STASSOU, ANDREA; Dwight Morrow HS; Englewood Cliffs, NJ; (3); 3/312; Trs Church Yth Grp; Chrmn Hosp Aide; Pres Latin Clb; Teachers Aide; Ed Nwsp Stf; Rep Stu Cncl; Var L Sftbl; High Hon Roll; Civic Clb; Drama Clb; Alpha Omega Awd 85; 2nd Pl Piano Solo 85; Chrch Sndy Schl Grad Vldctrn 85; Law.

STATMORE, DEBBIE; Montville HS; Pinebrook, NJ; (3); FBLA; Key Clb; Ski Clb; Temple Yth Grp; JV Powder Puff Ftbl; JV Tennis; Hon Roll; Bus Mgmt.

STATON, RANDY; Eastside HS; Paterson, NJ; (3); Boys Clb Am; Debate Tm; NAACP; Var Capt Ftbl; Var Capt Wt Lftg; Pres Schlr; Rotary Awd; Ntl Yth Ldrshp Cnfrnc 86-87; Pres Oa A Fanics Clb 86-87; U Of MD; Mech Engr.

STATON, TIFFANY; John F Kennedy HS; Willingboro, NJ; (2); 1/340; Church Yth Grp; Pres Frsh Cls; Pres Soph Cls; Pres Jr Cls; Cit Awd; High Hon Roll; Pres Jr NHS; NHS; Phildlphia Yth Orchstra 85; All South Jrsy/ All ST Orchstras 85.

STEAKLEY, KRIS; Manchester Regional HS; Prospect Park, NJ; (3); Church Yth Grp; Chorus; School Play; Nwsp Rptr; High Hon Roll; Hon Roll; Outstndng Achvt Awd Engl, Geom, Wrld Hstry, 86; Outstndng Achvt Awd Engl, Sci 852nd Spllng Bee 85; Engl.

STEARNE, DANIEL; Paul VI HS; Bellmawr, NJ; (3); 99/450; French Clb; Rep Soph Cls; Rep Jr Cls; JV Crs Cntry; Hon Roll; NHS; 2nd Hnr Roll 87; Villanova U; Law.

STECKLER, ADAM; Jackson Memorial HS; Jackson, NJ; (1); 2/394; Math Tm; Science Clb; Band; Concert Band; Jazz Band; Mrchg Band; Ftbl; Wt Lftg; High Hon Roll; NEDT Awd; Engrng.

STEELE, SONDRA; Paul VI HS; Haddon Hts, NJ; (3); 23/420; Church Yth Grp; French Clb; Math Clb; Chorus; Rep Jr Cls; JV Crs Cntry; JV Sftbl; French Hon Soc; Hon Roll; NHS; Swmng Awd; Lafayette Coll; Comp Sci.

STEELMAN, LYNDA; Bridgeton HS; Bridgeton, NJ; (1); Church Yth Grp; High Hon Roll; Sci Dept Awd 87; NJ Cncl Soc Stds Awd 87; Vet Med.

STEEN, SHELLEY; Eastern Christian HS; Franklin Lakes, NJ; (4); 7/81; Church Yth Grp; Cmnty Wkr; Drama Clb; Orch; School Play; Nwsp Rptr; Var Socr; Var Capt Sftbl; Hon Roll; NHS; Hnrs Schlrshp For Calvin Coll 87; Sprtsmnshp Awd 85-86; Calvin Coll; Bus Mgmt.

STEENSMA, DAVID; Eastern Christian HS; North Haledon, NJ; (3); Am Leg Boys St; Aud/Vis; Chess Clb; Church Yth Grp; Orch; Nwsp Rptr; Yrbk Ed-Chief; Hon Roll; NHS; Ntl Merit Ltr; Elec Engnrng.

STEFAN, ANTON CHRISTOPHER; Jackson Memorial HS; Jackson, NJ; (4); Band; Concert Band; Jazz Band; Mrchg Band; School Musical; High Hon Roll; Eagle Scout 87; Music Scholar Band Parents Assn 87; Yth Ldrshp Amer Awd 86; Music Perf.

STEFANELLI, STEVEN; St John Vianney HS; Hazlet, NJ; (3); 42/285; Var Ftbl; JV Trk; Hon Roll; Bus Admn.

STEFANI, JULIE; West Windsor-Plainsboro HS; Lawrenceville, NJ; (3); FBLA; Acpl Chr; Chorus; School Musical; Stage Crew; Swing Chorus; Stat Ftbl; Hon Roll; Intl Bus.

STEFANO, DOUGLAS JOHN; Highland Regional HS; Blackwood, NJ; (3); 29/285; Boys Clb Am; Latin Clb; Science Clb; Rep Stu Cncl; JV Bsbl; Var JV Bsktbl; JV Capt Socr; Hon Roll; Mst Coachbl Plyr Scr; Phila Coll Phrmcy; Sprts Med.

STEFFENS, PATRICIA; Secaucus HS; Secaucus, NJ; (3); Math Clb; Math Tm; Mu Alpha Theta; Varsity Clb; Band; Concert Band; Drm Mjr(t); Mrchg Band; Orch; School Musical; 3rd Tm All Cnty 86; 1st Tm All Cnty 87.

STEFFICK, DIANE E; South Brunswick HS; Kendall Park, NJ; (4); 8/255; Mu Alpha Theta; Political Wkr; Color Guard; Mrchg Band; Hon Roll; NHS; Ntl Merit Ltr; Rotary Awd; Spanish NHS; PA ST U U Schlrs Pgm 87; IN U Hnrs Div 87; Garden ST Schlrs Awd 87; Bus.

STEGER, CHRISTOPHER D; Christian Brothers Acad; Manasquan, NJ; (3); 17/250; Math Tm; Chorus; Orch; Yrbk Rptr; Yrbk Stf; Im Capt Sftbl; High Hon Roll; NHS; Chsn As Eucharistic Mnstr 86; Acctng.

STEGWAY, LISA; Hoffman HS; South Amboy, NJ; (3); 11/54; Chorus; Rep Soph Cls; Hon Roll; Jr NHS; Secy.

STEIGERWALT, LISA; Vineland HS; Vineland, NJ; (4); 5/700; Cmnty Wkr; Sec German Clb; Hosp Aide; Key Clb; Math Clb; Pep Clb; Varsity Clb; Yrbk Stf; JV Var Socr; NHS; Med.

STEIL, LAURA; Watching Hills Regional HS; Warren, NJ; (4); Art Clb; German Clb; Ski Clb; SADD; Chorus; Flag Corp; Orch; School Musical; Var Swmmng; Var Trk; AATG Awd-German 86.

STEIN, DEBORAH; Egg Harbor Township HS; Scullville, NJ; (3); 31/320; Exploring; French Clb; Girl Scts; Temple Yth Grp; Variety Show; Hon Roll; Rutgers.

STEIN, JENNIFER ANN; Toms River H S East; Toms River, NJ; (4); 4/567; Aud/Vis; Exploring; FBLA; Intnl Clb; Math Tm; Quiz Bowl; Ski Clb; Trs Spanish Clb; Yrbk Stf; Off Soph Cls; Certs Rcgntn Amrcn Assn U Wmn 84-86; NYU; Flm Drctr/Wrtr.

STEIN, WILLIAM; Maple Shade HS; Maple Shade, NJ; (2); Drama Clb; School Musical; Yrbk Rptr; Im Bsktbl; JV Crs Cntry; Var JV Ftbl; Var Trk; High Hon Roll; Yrbk Stf; Hon Roll; Yth Merit Awd Svc, Dependblty & Lrdshp Rotary Club 86; Stud Govt Day Bus Adminstry 86; Geo.

STEINMACHER, KIMBERLY; Rahway HS; Rahway, NJ; (4); 22/231; Girl Scts; Hosp Aide; Key Clb; Mrchg Band; Off Stu Cncl; Swmmng; Capt Twrlr; Hon Roll; NHS; Spanish NHS; Union Cnty 200 Clb Schlrshp 87; Wesley Coll; Fshn Merch.

STEINMETZ, THOMAS; Camden Catholic HS; Pennsauken, NJ; (3); 89/320; Chess Clb; Nwsp Sprt Ed; Var Golf; JV Socr; Var Trk; JV Wrstlng; Hon Roll; Sci Hnr Soc 85-86; Schl Rep Ambssdr 85-87; Engr.

STEINMEYER, DEBRA; Passaic Valley HS; Little Falls, NJ; (4); 50/351; Cmnty Wkr; GAA; Office Aide; Service Clb; Yrbk Stf; Sec Frsh Cls; Sec Soph Cls; Sec Jr Cls; Sec Sr Cls; Stu Cncl; UNICO Schlrshp 87; PTA Schlrshp 87; Katharine Gibbs Ldrshp Awd 86; Rider Coll; Bus Admin.

STEINWEHR JR, GEORGE; Toms River HS East; Toms River, NJ; (4); 185/587; Church Yth Grp; Key Clb; Lit Mag; Stu Tchr 87; Ocean Cnty Brd Rltrs Essay Cntst 1st Pl 87; Key Clb Serv Awd 87; Penn ST; Compu Prgrmr.

STEISKAL, SUSAN; Pennsville HS; Pennsville, NJ; (3); 42/229; Drama Clb; French Clb; Office Aide; Spanish Clb; SADD; Band; Concert Band; Mrchg Band; Orch; School Musical; Social Wrk.

STELL, LOUIS; Manchester Regional HS; Haledon, NJ; (2); Vocalist.

STELLA, JENNIFER; Ridgefield Park HS; Ridgefield Pk, NJ; (3); 3/203; Church Yth Grp; Debate Tm; Science Clb; Service Clb; Spanish Clb; Ed Lit Mag; Hon Roll; NHS; Grls Ctzn Inst NJ St Fed Wmns Clbs 87; Acad Decathln 87; Psych.

STELLING, SANDRA; South Brunswick HS; Kendall Park, NJ; (4); 12/255; Am Leg Aux Girls St; Church Yth Grp; VP Mu Alpha Theta; Color Guard; Mrchg Band; Coach Actv; Var Capt Socr; Var Trk; NHS; Spanish NHS; Bill Bradley Ldrshp Smnr Rep 86; Hnr Grad 87; Lehigh U; Engrng.

STELLMAN, JAIME; Morris Knolls HS; Rockaway, NJ; (3); Teachers Aide; Concert Band; Jazz Band; Mrchg Band; Yrbk Stf; Lit Mag; Stu Cncl; JV Trk; Hon Roll; Vrsty Ltr Mrchng Band 86; Optmtry.

STELTZER, JODI; Parsippany Hills HS; Parsippany, NJ; (4); 72/130; Pres Varsity Clb; Variety Show; Nwsp Rptr; Trs Sr Cls; Off Stu Cncl; Capt Fld Hcky; Powder Puff Ftbl; Sftbl; Hon Roll; Fclty Awd, Outstndng Svc Schlrshp, MVP Fld Hcky 87; Vrsty Clb Schlrshp; Syracuse U; Commnctns.

STEMMLE, JONATHAN; Howell HS; Howell, NJ; (2); JCL; Latin Clb; Math Clb; Math Tm; L Var Tennis; L Trk; Bus.

STENGEL, BROOKE A; Princeton HS; Princeton, NJ; (4); Church Yth Grp; Trs French Clb; Acpl Chr; Church Choir; Swing Chorus; Sr Cls; HS Gld Ky Awd 87; Bshps Awd Vcl Excllnc & Achvmnt 86; Career Awrnss Cmmnty Svc SR Ldrshp 86-87; Bryn Mawr Coll.

STEPANIAN, RICHARD; Queen Of Peace HS; Newark, NJ; (3); Im Var Bsbl; Im Bsktbl; Im Coach Actv; Im Var Ftbl; AR U; Bus Admin.

STEPHANICK, MARYANN; Hoffman HS; South Amboy, NJ; (3); Ski Clb; Trs Soph Cls; JV Var Bsktbl; Var Capt Crs Cntry; JV Sftbl; Hon Roll; NHS; Girls Cross Cntry Grp I ST Champs 85-86; NJ Grp I ST Champs Bsktbl 84-86; Natl JR Olympics Awd 85; Ed.

STEPHEN, SHARON; John P Stevens HS; Edison, NJ; (3); 30/450; Math Clb; Science Clb; Ski Clb; SADD; Rep Soph Cls; Rep Jr Cls; JV Var Bsktbl; Powder Puff Ftbl; Hon Roll; NHS; Med.

STEPHENS, BRIAN; Columbia HS; Maplewood, NJ; (2); Med.

STEPHENSON, B MICHELLE; Bridgeton HS; Bridgeton, NJ; (3); Church Yth Grp; Cmnty Wkr; Hosp Aide; Ski Clb; Varsity Clb; Band; Concert Band; Mrchg Band; Bowling; Capt Cheerleading; Nrsg.

STEPHENSON, ERIC; Mc Corristin Catholic HS; Trenton, NJ; (3); Boy Scts; Camera Clb; Church Yth Grp; Chorus; School Musical; Stage Crew; JV Bsbl; Var L Socr; Hon Roll; USAA 87; Arch.

STEPHENSON, ERICA L; Montclair HS; Upper Montclair, NJ; (4); 125/408; Sec Art Clb; Church Yth Grp; Sec Computer Clb; Teachers Aide; Ed Yrbk Ed-Chief; Ed Lit Mag; Rep Stu Cncl; High Hon Roll; Ntl Merit SF; Debate Tm; Artist Of The Spring 85-86; EOF Tutor Motclair ST Coll 85-86; NJIT HS Schlr Comp Sci 86-87; Comp Sci.

STEPIKURA, TRACY ANN; Manalapan HS; Englishtown, NJ; (4); 21/417; Church Yth Grp; Girl Scts; Science Clb; Teachers Aide; Nwsp Rptr; Socr; NHS; Chess Clb; Hon Roll; Half Tuition To Wagner Coll 87; Cngrssnl Brnz Mdl 85; Wagner Coll; Med Tech.

STERN, AL; Paramus HS; Paramus, NJ; (3); Lit Mag; 3rd Pl Story Cont Bergen CC 87; 2nd Pl Kata Karate Trnmnt 87.

STERN, AMY; Fair Lawn HS; Fair Lawn, NJ; (2); Computer Clb; Math Clb; Math Tm; Science Clb; Spanish Clb; Rep Frsh Cls; Rep Soph Cls; Hon Roll; JETS Awd; Awd Yng Schlrs 86-87; Natl Sci Leag, 6th Natn Chem 86-87; Cal Tech; Comp Sci.

STERN, CANDICE; Holy Spirit HS; Linwood, NJ; (2); 13/397; Spanish Clb; Pres Soph Cls; Hon Roll; Jr NHS; 2 1st Prz Art Awds 86; 1 3rd Prz Art Awd 85; Intr Dsgn.

STERN, DAN; Cherry Hill High School West; Cherry Hill, NJ; (3); JA; Spanish Clb; Nwsp Phtg; Nwsp Rptr; Nwsp Stf; Lit Mag; Frsh Cls; Soph Cls; Htl-Rstrnt Mgmt.

STERN, STACEY J; The Pingry Schl; Livingston, NJ; (4); Pres AFS; Temple Yth Grp; Yrbk Sprt Ed; JV Trk; Ntl Merit SF; Pres Schlr; St Schlr; French Clb; Key Clb; Spanish Clb; Ntl Merit SF, Gdn ST Dstngshd Schlr, Pres Schlr 86.

STEVEN, MURIELLE; St Rose HS; Neptune, NJ; (3); 34/243; Dance Clb; Exploring; Math Tm; Ski Clb; Stage Crew; Variety Show; French Hon Soc; Hon Roll; Ntl Merit Ltr; NEDT 86; Frnch Awd 84; Accptnc To Red Bnk Rgnl Perf Arts 85; Law.

STEVENS, CHRISTINE; Rantan HS; Hazlet, NJ; (3); Aud/Vis; Off Co-Capt Flag Corp; Rep Frsh Cls; Rep Soph Cls; Rep Jr Cls; Rep Sr Cls; Stu Cncl; JV Var Score Keeper; Sftbl; Band; Montclair U; Bus.

STEVENS, KELLY; Clifton HS; Clifton, NJ; (3); Cmnty Wkr; Band; Concert Band; Mrchg Band; Orch; Pep Band; Symp Band; Trs Stu Cncl; Im Bsktbl; Region Band Jr 85; Spec Educ.

STEVENS, MARK; Newton HS; Newton, NJ; (2); Hon Roll.

STEVENS, MARY ANN; Wall Township HS; Manasquan Park, NJ; (4); AFS; Art Clb; Ski Clb; Yrbk Stf; Var Trk; NHS; Natl Art Hnr Soc; U DE; Elem Spec Ed.

STEVENS, SCOTT; Hamilton High School North Nvm; Mercerville, NJ; (4); 43/291; Church Yth Grp; Hon Roll; VFW Awd; Principals List 87; Trenton ST Coll; Bus Admin.

STEVENS, TRACEY LYNN; Boonton HS; Lincoln Park, NJ; (3); Am Leg Aux Girls St; Sec Church Yth Grp; Radio Clb; Spanish Clb; Variety Show; Lit Mag; Capt Cheerleading; Trk; Hon Roll; Comm.

STEWARD, JAMES; Paterson Catholic Regional HS; Paterson, NJ; (3); 18/101; DECA; Varsity Clb; Lit Mag; Rep Frsh Cls; Rep Soph Cls; Rep Jr Cls; Rep Stu Cncl; Bsbl; Bsktbl; Fld Hcky; Hnr Roll 84-85 & 85-86; Hgh Hnr Roll 86-87; Engnrng.

STEWARD, NORMAN; Woodstown HS; Woodstown, NJ; (3); Am Leg Boys St; Trs French Clb; Hosp Aide; Pres Frsh Cls; Trs Sr Cls; Var Crs Cntry; Var Trk; Capt Wrstlng; Hon Roll; Rotary Awd; Emergncy Med Techncn Certf NJ 86-89; Various 1st Plc Sci Fr Awds 84-86; US Naval Acad; Chem.

STEWART, CHRIS; Middletown North HS; Middletown, NJ; (2); Ski Clb; JV Ftbl; Wt Lftg; High Hon Roll; Hon Roll; Bus.

STEWART, COLIN G; Piscataway HS; Piscataway, NJ; (4); 6/496; VP Computer Clb; Key Clb; Lit Mag; NHS; St Schlr; Natl Achvt Schlr Outstndng Black Stu 87; Harvard U; Comp Sci.

STEWART, DONNA; Columbia HS; South Orange, NJ; (3); Capt Dance Clb; French Clb; Natl Beta Clb; Chorus; School Musical; School Play; Capt Var Cheerleading; Trk; CC Awd; Cmmnctns.

STEWART, ERICA; Orange HS; Orange, NJ; (4); 2/160; Color Guard; Pres Stu Cncl; Sftbl; Twrlr; Masonic Awd; NHS; Sal; J D Carr Mnrty Schlrshp 87; AT&T Schlrshp 87; ILA Lcl 1233 Schlrshp 87; Douglass Coll.

STEWART, JAMI; West Milford HS; Hewitt, NJ; (3); 54/408; Intnl Clb; Latin Clb; SADD; Varsity Clb; Nwsp Stf; Yrbk Stf; Trs Frsh Cls; Jr Cls; Stat Bsbl; Stat Ftbl; Hotel Mgmt.

STEWART, JEFFREY T; Butler HS; Bloomingdale, NJ; (3); Am Leg Boys St; Church Yth Grp; Math Clb; Radio Clb; Varsity Clb; Var L Bowling; Hon Roll; NHS; Vllybl; Cmnty Wkr; MVP Vrsty Bwlng 87; 1st Pl Elec Arts Awd 85; Jvnl & Dmstc Rltns Judge & St Hghr Educ Chncllr 87; Pre-Dntstry.

STEWART, JENNIFER; Wayne Hills HS; Wayne, NJ; (3); Girl Scts; Stage Crew; Yrbk Bus Mgr; JV Vllybl; Hon Roll; Vrsty Fncng Tm 84-87; Slvr Awd Grl Sct 85.

STEWART, KATHY; Paulsboro HS; Paulsboro, NJ; (4); Sec Trs VICA; Bsktbl; Gym; Mgr(s); Hon Roll; Prfct Atten Awd; Excllnc Awd Teen Art Fest Mxd Media Postr 87; 1st & 3rd Pl Stdnt Cfts Fair 87; Paste Up Mech.

STEWART, KELLY; Paramus Catholic Girls Reginl HS; Saddle Brk, NJ; (3); 17/174; Drama Clb; Rep Stu Cncl; Var Crs Cntry; Var Capt Trk; High Hon Roll; NHS; Ntl Merit Schol; NEDT Awd; Aud/Vis; Pep Clb; Achvt Awd In Frnch & Physcl Ed 87; 1st Pl Amer Lgn Axlry Essay Cntst 85; Tchr.

STEWART, MARK; Dwight Morrow HS; Englewood, NJ; (4); Boy Scts; Debate Tm; Drama Clb; Math Tm; School Play; Lit Mag; Socr; Trk; Vllybl; Wrstlng; Rutgers; Engrng.

STEWART, MICHELE; Pennsville Memorial HS; Pennsville, NJ; (3); Am Leg Aux Girls St; Office Aide; VICA; Chorus; Yrbk Stf; Pom Pon; Hon Roll; Hotel Mgt.

STEWART, REED; Glen Rock HS; Glen Rock, NJ; (3); AFS; Art Clb; Camera Clb; Civic Clb; Cmnty Wkr; Drama Clb; Intnl Clb; Model UN; PAVAS; SADD; Exchng Stu Australia With Experiment In Intl Living 87; Lib Arts.

STEWART, SUSAN; Morris Catholic HS; Dover, NJ; (3); Church Yth Grp; Hosp Aide; Pep Clb; Yrbk Stf; JV Cheerleading; Powder Puff Ftbl; Sftbl; Hon Roll; Nrsg.

STEYN, GAVIN R; Morristown HS; Morristown, NJ; (4); 16/441; Debate Tm; Math Tm; Band; Exploring; JA; JCL; Office Aide; Temple Yth Grp; High Hon Roll; Hon Roll; Garden ST Dist Schlr 86; Comp Sci.

STIBITZ, RUSS; Southern Regional HS; Manahawkin, NJ; (4); 22/392; Chess Clb; Model UN; Chorus; School Musical; Lit Mag; High Hon Roll; Hon Roll; NHS; Knghts Columbus Essy Cont 1st Pl 87; Gordon Coll; Biblicl Stds.

STIFT, KRISTIN; Watchung Hills Regional HS; Watchung, NJ; (3); Church Yth Grp; Concert Band; Mrchg Band; Stage Crew; Symp Band; JV Var Cheerleading; JV Trk; Bus.

STILE, GEMMA; Passaic Valley HS; Totowa, NJ; (4); 210/380; Church Yth Grp; Drama Clb; Office Aide; Chorus; Church Choir; School Musical; School Play; Lit Mag; Mgr(s); Hon Roll; Berkely Coll; Bus Admin.

STILES, ERIC; Mainland Regional HS; Linwood, NJ; (3); 6/290; Church Yth Grp; Drama Clb; Key Clb; Math Clb; School Musical; School Play; Nwsp Ed-Chief; Nwsp Stf; JV Crs Cntry; NHS; Math Awd 86; Psych.

STILL, YOLANDA J; Overbrook Reg SR HS; Lindenwold, NJ; (4); 7/324; Spanish Clb; Stat Bsktbl; JV Stat Fld Hcky; Mgr(s); Stat Trk; High Hon Roll; Hon Roll; Jr NHS; NHS.

STINSON, DANNY; Upper Freehold Regional HS; New Egypt, NJ; (1); Church Yth Grp; 4-H; FFA; High Hon Roll; Hon Roll; Bio.

STINSON, EVETTE; Frank H Morrell HS; Irvington, NJ; (3); Aud/Vis; ROTC; Band; Mrchg Band; Yrbk Stf; Rep Stu Cncl; Hon Roll; Kean Coll Awd 87; Technlgy.

STINTON, CHRISTINE ANN; Randolph HS; Randolph, NJ; (3); 26/353; Am Leg Aux Girls St; Church Yth Grp; Key Clb; Socr; High Hon Roll; Hon Roll; Law.

STIPES, DOUG; Cumberland Regional HS; Bridgeton, NJ; (3); High Hon Roll; Jr NHS; Cumberland Cnty Coll.

STIRITZ, SARAH; Bloomfield SR HS; Bloomfield, NJ; (4); 22/465; Camera Clb; Sec Church Yth Grp; French Clb; Chorus; French Hon Soc; High Hon Roll; Hon Roll; NHS; SR Awd Bloomfield JR Wmns Clb, Prsdntl Ftnss Awd 87; William Paterson Coll; Elem Edu.

STITES, CHERYL; Bridgeton HS; Bridgeton, NJ; (4); Aud/Vis; Camera Clb; Computer Clb; French Clb; Office Aide; Ski Clb; Spanish Clb; Varsity Clb; Stat Bsbl; Capt Cheerleading; Cumberland County Coll; Acctg.

STITT, WAYNE; Pitman HS; Pitman, NJ; (2); Church Yth Grp; Dance Clb; Var Mgr(s); Var Score Keeper; Hon Roll; Vrsty Grls Sccr Mgr Awd & Lttr 86; Cert Achvt 87; Jersey Stu Crftmmns Fair; Arch.

STIVALE, RENEE; Glen Ridge HS; Glen Ridge, NJ; (3); 6/105; Varsity Clb; Yrbk Stf; Rep Frsh Cls; JV Capt Cheerleading; High Hon Roll; NHS; Bus Mngmt.

STOCKL, SHARON; Baptist HS; Vincentown, NJ; (3); Church Yth Grp; French Clb; Capt Cheerleading; Lcrss; Mgr(s); Hon Roll; Socl Commtt 86-87; Mjr Char Cls Play 86-87; Trenton ST Coll; Chem.

STOEDTER, REBECCA; Manchester Township HS; Toms River, NJ; (2); French Clb; Math Clb; Math Tm; Science Clb; SADD; Mgr(s); French Hon Soc; Bus.

STOHRER, KRISTEN; Southern Regional HS; Beach Haven, NJ; (3); Church Yth Grp; Cmnty Wkr; Sec Frsh Cls; Sec Soph Cls; Rep Jr Cls; Stu Cncl; Var Bsktbl; Var Fld Hcky; Var Sftbl; Hon Roll; MVP Vrsty Fld Hcky 86; MIP JV & Frshmn Y Bsktbl 85 & 86; U Of Delaware; Sports Medicine.

STOINSKI, TARA; Haddonfield Memorial HS; Haddonfield, NJ; (4); AFS; Am Leg Aux Girls St; Church Yth Grp; Cmnty Wkr; Latin Clb; Model UN; Q&S; Service Clb; SADD; Nwsp Stf; George Washington U Engrng Awd; Latin Natl Hon Soc.

STOKES, JON L; St James HS; Carneys Point, NJ; (2); Crs Cntry; Socr; Wt Lftg; Natl Hnr Rll 87; U Of PA; Opthlmlgst.

STOKES, LISA WILLIE; Lincoln HS; Jersy City, NJ; (3); JA; Q&S; Varsity Clb; Nwsp Stf; Yrbk Stf; Lit Mag; Soph Cls; Stu Cncl; High Hon Roll; Hon Roll; Hall Fame Essayist 85.

STOKES, THERESA; Edgewood Regional HS; Chesilhurst, NJ; (2); Church Yth Grp; Civic Clb; French Clb; Yrbk Stf; Hon Roll; Pres Schlr; Xavier U; Bus.

STOLL, ERICA RYE; Northern Valley Regional HS; Demarest, NJ; (4); 15/228; Pres Church Yth Grp; Sec French Clb; Yrbk Sprt Ed; Bsktbl; Sftbl; Vllybl; Hon Roll; NHS; St Schlr; Pres Acadmc Ftns Awd 87; Lafayette Coll.

STOMBER, KAREN; De Paul HS; Wayne, NJ; (3); 21/150; Ski Clb; Nwsp Rptr; Yrbk Stf; High Hon Roll; NHS; Swim Awds 84-87; Bus.

STONE, CHRISTINE; Bloomfield SR HS; Bloomfield, NJ; (3); 17/501; Teachers Aide; Chorus; Color Guard; Mrchg Band; Orch; Fld Hcky; Girl Scts; Key Clb; Service Clb; Spanish Clb; Montclair ST Coll; Vocal Music.

STONE, DEIRDRE ANNE; Red Bank Catholic HS; Freehold, NJ; (3); Political Wkr; Yrbk Stf; Rep Stu Cncl; Im Powder Puff Ftbl; Var JV Trk; High Hon Roll; Hon Roll; Gnrl Excel 86; Relgn Awd 87; Bus.

STONE, FRANK; West Milford Township HS; West Milford, NJ; (4); Nwsp Rptr; High Hon Roll; Hon Roll; Georg E Rth Schlrshp 87; Hnrbl Mntn-NJ ST Ptry Cntst 86-87; Macalester Coll; Engl.

STONE, JONATHAN; Hackettstown HS; Allamuchy, NJ; (4); 39/234; Boy Scts; Chess Clb; Sec Band; Jazz Band; Mrchg Band; Hon Roll; NHS; Montclair ST Coll; Bus Admin.

STONE, JULIE; Clearview Regional HS; Sewell, NJ; (3); 90/170; Church Yth Grp; Church Choir; Yrbk Stf; Hon Roll; Comp Pgmmr.

STONE, KIMBERLY; Franklin HS; Somerset, NJ; (4); 13/327; Pres Intnl Clb; Key Clb; Office Aide; VP Varsity Clb; Color Guard; Nwsp Stf; Capt Var Cheerleading; Trk; High Hon Roll; NHS; Garden ST Dstngshd Schlr 86-87; Pres Acad Ftns Awd 87; U Of MI.

STONE, MICHAEL; Passaic HS; Passaic, NJ; (4); 4/503; Bausch & Lomb Medl Excllnc Sci RIT NY; Medl Exclln Math & Sci Renssl r Polytchnc Inst NY; Stevens Inst Of Tech; Comp Sci.

STONE, TRENIESE; Parsippany Hills HS; Morris Plains, NJ; (3); FBLA; Spanish Clb; Band; Symp Band; Dover Bus Coll; Bus Educ.

STONEHAM, KEVIN; Brick HS; Brick Town, NJ; (3); 39/420; Variety Show; Yrbk Stf; Lit Mag; JV Bowling; Mgr(s); Var Trk; 4-H Awd; High Hon Roll; Hon Roll; Financial Accntnt.

STOOPAK, GAIL; James Caldwell HS; W Caldwell, NJ; (3); 4-H; Key Clb; Spanish Clb; Temple Yth Grp; Stu Cncl; JV Vllybl; High Hon Roll; Hon Roll; NHS.

STOOR, SHELLIE; Holy Cross HS; Willingboro, NJ; (4); 82/386; Chess Clb; Hosp Aide; JA; Library Aide; Drm Mjr(t); Twrlr; High Hon Roll; Hon Roll; Trenton ST; Acctg.

STOOTS, TERESA; Medford Technical HS; Browns Mills, NJ; (3); FFA; Varsity Clb; Nwsp Stf; Yrbk Stf; Trs Jr Cls; Trs Sr Cls; Var Socr; Hon Roll; Prfct Atten Awd; GAA; VP FFA Chptr Frmr Degree 86-87; Grnhnd Degree 85-86; Ag.

STOPPIELLO, COLLEEN; Immaculate Heart Acad; Hawthorne, NJ; (1); Hon Roll.

STOPYRA, CHRIS; Freehold Township HS; Howell, NJ; (3); 19/485; Latin Clb; SADD; Mgr(s); Var Socr; Var Wrstlng; NHS; Ntl Merit Ltr; U S Nvl Acad Smmr Smnr & Wrkshp 87; U S Mltry Acad Acdmc Wrkshp 87; U S Cst Gd AIM Prncpl 87; Engnrng.

STORCH, AMIJOY; Scotch Plains Fanwood HS; Westfield, NJ; (4); 16/300; Dance Clb; Model UN; Chorus; School Musical; French Hon Soc; Hon Roll; NHS; Pres Schlr; French Clb; Quiz Bowl; Bio Tm 85; College Clb Awd 87; Kerrigan Schlr 87; Rutgers Coll; Biochem.

STORCH, TERRI; West Essex Regional HS; Fairfield, NJ; (3); Art Clb; Church Yth Grp; FTA; Color Guard; Mrchg Band; Yrbk Stf; Off Stu Cncl; Twrlr; Hon Roll; Advrtsng.

STOUDT, CHRISTIAAN; Monmouth Regional HS; Eatontown, NJ; (3); Drama Clb; Socr; Hon Roll; U TX; Engrng.

STOUT, VICTORIA; Phillipsburg HS; Phillipsburg, NJ; (3); 143/315; Trs SADD; Chorus; Stu Cncl; Var JV Cheerleading; Var JV Fld Hcky; Nrsg.

STOWELL, BRUCE; Edgewood Regional HS; Cedarbrook, NJ; (2); Varsity Clb; Yrbk Phtg; Yrbk Stf; Rep Soph Cls; Var Bsbl; Ftbl; Var Wrstlng; Hon Roll; Prfct Atten Awd.

STRADA, DINA; Wall HS; Wall, NJ; (3); 10/285; Key Clb; Ski Clb; Spanish Clb; Yrbk Stf; Trs Frsh Cls; Rep Soph Cls; JV Fld Hcky; Score Keeper; JV Var Sftbl; High Hon Roll; Psych.

STRALEY, JULIANNE; Matawan Regional SR HS; Matawan, NJ; (3); 17/319; Color Guard; Mrchg Band; School Musical; Yrbk Ed-Chief; Yrbk Phtg; VP Soph Cls; Pres Jr Cls; Rep Stu Cncl; Cit Awd; Hon Roll.

STRANG, SCOTT; Buena Regional HS; Newfield, NJ; (4); 1/180; Stage Crew; Yrbk Ed-Chief; Pres Soph Cls; Trs Sr Cls; Bsktbl; Crs Cntry; Pres NHS; Val; NJ Govrs Schl In The Sci 86; Rutgers Schlrs Pgm 86; GA Tech; Elec Engrng.

STRANO, STEPHEN; Highland Regional HS; Blackwood, NJ; (4); 4/325; Am Leg Boys St; Sec Chess Clb; Computer Clb; Letterman Clb; Quiz Bowl; Trs Science Clb; Service Clb; Var Tennis; Hon Roll; NHS; Engrng.

STRASFELD, LYNNE; Fort Lee HS; Ft Lee, NJ; (3); Service Clb; Yrbk Stf; Stu Cncl; Trk; High Hon Roll; NHS; Sec Spanish Clb; Librl Arts.

STRATER, KAREN; Morristown HS; Morristown, NJ; (4); 12/418; Church Yth Grp; Cmnty Wkr; Exploring; 4-H; JA; Key Clb; NAACP; Lit Mag; JV Var Bsktbl; NHS; Deans Smr Schlrs Prgm/Rtgrs U; Duke U; Doctor.

STRATER, SHARON; Norristown HS; Morristown, NJ; (4); 57/418; Church Yth Grp; Cmnty Wkr; Hosp Aide; JA; Key Clb; Powder Puff Ftbl; NHS; Lit Mag; Bsktbl; Hon Roll; Pres Morris Cty Urban Leag Yth Cncl 86-87; Deans Summer Schlr Pgm 86; Acad Deca 86-87; Duke U; Med.

STRATTON, JOHN; Holy Spirit HS; Ocean City, NJ; (3); 20/332; Aud/Vis; Sec Computer Clb; Hon Roll; NHS; Ntl Hnr Soc 85-86; Physics.

STRAUB, PAUL; Pope Paul VI HS; Laurel Springs, NJ; (3); 9/417; French Clb; Math Clb; JV Bsbl; Im Bowling; French Hon Soc; Hon Roll; Villanova; Law.

STRAUSS, JEN; Wayne Hills HS; Wayne, NJ; (3); 14/330; Var Capt Swmmng; Var Capt Trk; Var Socr; Hon Roll; NHS; Sprts Med.

STRAUT, MICHELE; Waldwick HS; Waldwick, NJ; (3); 35/137; Nwsp Rptr; Nwsp Sprt Ed; Lit Mag; Mgr Soph Cls; Coach Actv; Var Capt Crs Cntry; Var Capt Trk; High Hon Roll; Hon Roll; Mst Vluble Plyr Trck 86-87; 1st Tm All-League & Hnrbl Mntn All-Cnty Trck 87.

STRAWDERMAN, MARK A; Woodbury HS; Woodbury, NJ; (3); 4/100; Am Leg Boys St; Math Clb; Scholastic Bowl; Science Clb; Varsity Clb; Band; Chorus; Drm Mjr(t); Jazz Band; Mrchg Band; All St Chorus 86 & 88; All South Chorus 85-88; Rensselaer Polytech Inst; Aero.

STRAWN, SHANNON; Burlington City HS; Beverly, NJ; (3); Church Yth Grp; Dance Clb; Debate Tm; Pep Clb; Varsity Clb; Nwsp Rptr; Lit Mag; Stu Cncl; Cheerleading; Fld Hcky; Attd Rotry Yth Ldrshp Awds 86-87; Attd YMCA Yth & Govt 86-87; Educ.

STRAYTON, GEORGE R; St Josephs Regional HS; Valley Cottage, NY; (3); 2/225; Boy Scts; Trs Church Yth Grp; Computer Clb; Band; Tennis; Trk; High Hon Roll; Jr NHS; NHS; Ntl Merit Ltr; Holy Cross Awd 87; Comp Engr.

STREELMAN, JODY; Union HS; Union, NJ; (4); French Clb; Hosp Aide; Key Clb; Stat Fld Hcky; Mgr(s); Charlstn Baptist Coll; Bus.

STREET, LAWRENCE E; South Plainfield HS; S Plainfield, NJ; (3); 24/300; VP Drama Clb; French Clb; Chorus; Madrigals; Mrchg Band; Orch; School Musical; French Hon Soc; Hon Roll; NHS; NJ All-State Chorus 85-87; NJ All-State Opera Festival Soloist 86-87; NJ Govnrs Schl Of Arts 87; Music.

STREKER, CLIFF; Parsippany HS; Lake Hiawatha, NJ; (4); 70/330; Hon Roll; Pres Acdmc Fit Awd 86-87; ASU; Engrng.

STRILLACCI, JILL; Mt Olive HS; Flanders, NJ; (2); 37/320; Varsity Clb; Band; Concert Band; Mrchg Band; Bsktbl; High Hon Roll; Hon Roll; Church Yth Grp; Church Choir; Symp Band; Trim-M Music Hnr Soc & Soph Band Awd 86-87; Bsktbl MVP & Typing Awd 85-86; Accntnt.

STRIPPOLI, MARISA; Clifton HS; Clifton, NJ; (3); Spanish Clb; Chorus; Madrigals; Nwsp Stf; Yrbk Stf; Var JV Cheerleading; Mgr(s); Hon Roll; Jr NHS; Spanish NHS; Grad Hnr Guard 87; Tlntd & Gftd Pgm 84-87; Over-All Chrldng Chmps 86; Boston Coll; Financing.

STROBER, JAMIE S; Spotswood HS; Milltown, NJ; (4); 24/185; Cmnty Wkr; Drama Clb; Intnl Clb; Ski Clb; School Musical; Var Cap Cheerleading; Hon Roll; Voice Dem Awd; Vrsty Lttr 85; Pres Of Ecnmcs Clb 86; Advrstng Dsgn.

STROHL, JOAN; Warren Technical HS; Washington, NJ; (4); Key Clb; Ski Clb; VICA; Nwsp Stf; Yrbk Stf; Bsktbl; Var Mgr(s); Var Sftbl; Hon Roll; Antonelli Schl Of Arts; Arts.

STROLI, DANIELLE; Bruriah HS For Girls; Passaic, NJ; (4); Debate Tm; Drama Clb; Sec Temple Yth Grp; Y-Teens; School Play; Variety Show; Nwsp Ed-Chief; Nwsp Rptr; Yrbk Rptr; Ntl Merit Ltr; Schlrshp 87-88; Touro Coll; Pltcl Sci.

STROTHERS, SHARONDA; University HS; Newark, NJ; (2); Church Yth Grp; GAA; Chorus; Church Choir; School Play; JV Capt Bsktbl; Sftbl Qn Of Gnl Bapt ST Cnvntn Of NJ 87; VP Of Yth Under Womens Dept Of GBC Of NJ 86; Howard; Med.

STROUT, ELLEN; West Morris Central HS; Long Valley, NJ; (4); 42/280; Band; Mrchg Band; Var Socr; Var Trk; High Hon Roll; NHS; Art Clb; Stage Crew; Yrbk Stf; Lit Mag; Andrew Bradiccich Memrl & Art Awds 87; John W Ginty Memrl Schlrshp 87; Syracuse U; Ad Dsgn.

STRUBBE JR, WALTER; Waldwick HS; Waldwick, NJ; (3); 10/136; Computer Clb; Math Tm; Quiz Bowl; Concert Band; Jazz Band; Mrchg Band; Ntl Merit Ltr; US Naval Acad Smmr Semnr; Boys ST Alt; Rider Coll Frnsc Trnmnt Spnsh Coll Bowl; US Naval Acad; Engrng.

STRUMOLO, TRACY; Raritan HS; Hazlet, NJ; (4); Hosp Aide; Office Aide; SADD; Teachers Aide; Chorus; Var Bsktbl; Hon Roll; Kean Coll Spcl Ed.

STRUNK, SCOTT; Life Center Acad; Burlington, NJ; (3); Aud/Vis; Church Yth Grp; Band; Chorus; Concert Band; Jazz Band; Symp Band; Var Bsbl; Var Socr; Hon Roll; Hghst Avg In Amer Hist 85-86; Sptsmnsh Awd In Bsbl 84-85 & Sccr 85-86.

STRUTHERS, MEREDITH; Delaware Valley Regional HS; Frenchtown, NJ; (3); 7/208; Church Yth Grp; Teachers Aide; Acpl Chr; Chorus; Church Choir; Orch; School Musical; Stage Crew; High Hon Roll; Hon Roll; Cer Hnr Excel Schlrshp 86; St Tn Arts Fstvl Choir 86-87; Cngrsmn J Courter Smnr 87; Psych.

STRUTZEL, LAUREN; Boonton HS; Lincoln Park, NJ; (3); French Clb; Capt GAA; Pres Radio Clb; Chorus; Variety Show; Fld Hcky; Sftbl; High Hon Roll; Hon Roll; Music.

STRYDESKY, ALBERT; Linden HS; Linden, NJ; (1); Key Clb; ROTC; Band; Mrchg Band.

STRYKER, JERI; Brick Memorial HS; Brick, NJ; (2); French Clb; FBLA; Trk; High Hon Roll; Hon Roll; Prfct Atten Awd.

STRZEMINSKI, MARK; Saddle Brook HS; Saddle Brook, NJ; (4); 23/115; Am Leg Boys St; Varsity Clb; Lit Mag; Stu Cncl; Var Capt Ftbl; JV Trk; PRESV-U Of Scranton 87-88; Rtry Clb Of Sddl Brk-Acad/Chrctr 87; Slvtn Army-Hmnts-Acad-SBHS Ftbl Prnt; U Of Scranton; Bio.

STUART, NICHOLAS; Dwight Morrow HS; Englewood, NJ; (3); 44/321; Cmnty Wkr; Nwsp Ed-Chief; Ed Lit Mag; Pres Soph Cls; Pres Jr Cls; School Play; Stage Crew; Nwsp Rptr; Nwsp Stf; Rep Stu Cncl; Hnr Rll Awd, Vrsty Ltr Awd 86; Natl Soc Stds Olympiad 85; Med.

STUART, SHARON; Mother Seton Regional HS; Newark, NJ; (3); SADD; Drill Tm; School Musical; Seton Sptlght Awd 87.

STUBBMANN, ALLISON; Raritan HS; Hazlet, NJ; (3); 69/339; SADD; Capt Flag Corp; Nwsp Phtg; L Stat Bsbl; L Score Keeper; Stat Socr; Capt Twrlr; Hosp Aide; SADD; Nwsp Rptr; Hazlet Brd Educ 87-88; Mock Trial 86-87; Broadcast Journalism.

STUBBS, PEICHA; Washington Township HS; Turnersville, NJ; (3); Office Aide; Spanish Clb; High Hon Roll; NHS; Engr.

STUDER, DEIRDRE; De Paul HS; Ringwood, NJ; (3); Church Yth Grp; Ski Clb; Nwsp Stf; Rep Stu Cncl; Capt L Socr; Var L Trk; High Hon Roll; NHS; Math Awd 85-86; Soc Studs Awd 86-87; Engl Lit Hnr Awd 86-87.

STUDIVANT, DONNA; Weequahic HS; Newark, NJ; (3); 26/360; Boys Clb Am; Rutgers U; Spec Ed.

STULIK, JESSICA L; Waldwick HS; Waldwick, NJ; (4); Church Yth Grp; Orch; High Hon Roll; NHS; Aspen Summer Dnc Pgm Schlrshp 86; Prfrmng Arts Schlrshp 87; Ballet Wst Prfssnl Dncr 86-87; Bllt Dncr.

STURGIS, MERISHA; John F Kennedy HS; Willingboro, NJ; (3); Pres Church Yth Grp; Church Choir; Mrchg Band; Rep Frsh Cls; Rep Soph Cls; Rep Jr Cls; Hon Roll; Exploring; Hosp Aide; Band; Stephen Long Guild Awd Pgnt 85 & 87; Natl Hnr Rl 87; Drew U; Bio.

STURM, GRETA M; Paramus Catholic Girls Regionl HS; Rochelle Pk, NJ; (3); Cmnty Wkr; Library Aide; Spanish Clb; Lit Mag; High Hon Roll; Hon Roll; NHS; Prfct Atten Awd; Chrctr Awd 84-85; Svc Awd 86-87; Holy Crss Bk Prize 86-87; Math.

STURM, JASON; Don Bosco Prep; No Haledon, NJ; (3); Ski Clb; Socr; Wrstlng.

STUTESMAN, NANCY; Brick Memorial HS; Brick, NJ; (1); Bsktbl; Capt Socr; Var Tennis; High Hon Roll; Hon Roll; Prnctn; Lawyer.

STUTMAN, KIMBERLY; Wayne Hills HS; Wayne, NJ; (3); Debate Tm; Pep Clb; Y-Teens.

STUTZMANN, KONRAD; Bridgeton HS; Bridgeton, NJ; (3); Am Leg Boys St; Band; Concert Band; Mrchg Band; Nwsp Stf; Yrbk Stf; VP Jr Cls; Var Golf; High Hon Roll; NHS; Rotc.

STYLES, SANDRA; Clayton HS; Clayton, NJ; (4); 19/75; Key Clb; Library Aide; Chorus; Mrchg Band; Stage Crew; Yrbk Stf; Hon Roll; NHS; Prfct Atten Awd; Tang Soo Karate Awd 2nd Imprvd Orange Belt 86; Gloucester Cnty Coll.

SU, TINA; Manchester Township HS; Lakehurst, NJ; (3); Am Leg Aux Girls St; Drama Clb; Math Clb; Science Clb; Spanish Clb; Fld Hcky; Tennis; Hon Roll; NHS; 1st Pl Tlnt Shws Piano Solo 85-87; Bus.

SUAREZ, ESTHER; Holy Family Acad; Bayonne, NJ; (3); Church Yth Grp; Cmnty Wkr; Computer Clb; Dance Clb; French Clb; Office Aide; Spanish Clb; Teachers Aide; Yrbk Stf; Rep Stu Cncl; Frnch Awds; Maria Limon Awd 85-86; Intl Bus.

SUAREZ, JENNIFER; Brik Memorial HS; Brick, NJ; (4); 26/295; Office Aide; Rep Frsh Cls; Rep Soph Cls; Rep Jr Cls; Rep Sr Cls; Sec Stu Cncl; Stat Bsbl; JV Capt Socr; High Hon Roll; NHS; Ocean County Coll; Nursing.

SUAREZ, JOYCEANN; Lodi HS; Lodi, NJ; (4); 8/137; Church Yth Grp; Sec Hosp Aide; Key Clb; Leo Clb; VP Spanish Clb; Off VICA; Sec NHS; Chem Lab Asst 86; William Paterson Coll; Nrsg.

SUAREZ, MARIA; St Marys HS; Rutherford, NJ; (4); 10/74; Am Leg Aux Girls St; Drama Clb; School Musical; Yrbk Stf; Cheerleading; Sftbl; High Hon Roll; NHS; Spanish NHS; Acad All Amer 86; Coll St Elizabeths; Pre-Med.

SUAREZ, ROSA; Ridgefield Park HS; Ridgefield Pk, NJ; (3); 78/205; Church Yth Grp; Spanish Clb; Teachers Aide; Church Choir; Mgr Nwsp Stf; Tennis; Hon Roll; Cert Working Schls Newspaper 85-86; Rutgers U; Commercial Art.

SUBBARAO, KAVERI; West Windsor-Plainsboro HS; Princeton Junct, NJ; (3); AFS; Debate Tm; Drama Clb; French Clb; Sec Hst Model UN; Pres SADD; Pres Orch; Rep Jr Cls; JV Tennis; High Hon Roll; Visited USSR As Stu Ambssdr In The Public People Pgm 87; Tophies For Outstndng Plyr 86-87; William & Mary; Frgn Relatns.

SUBER, WAYNE; Essex Catholic Boys HS; Newark, NJ; (3); Boys Clb Am; JV Ftbl; Im Sftbl; JV Trk; Im Wt Lftg; Var Wrstlng; Hon Roll; Smmr Coll Pgm NJ Inst Tech 85; Bus Educ.

SUBIN, DANIEL; Holy Spirit HS; Margate, NJ; (2); 1/397; Bsktbl; High Hon Roll; Engl Awd 85-86; Natl Latin Exam Slvr Mdl 85-86.

SUBOURNE, JOELLE; Hunterdon Central HS; Flemington, NJ; (4); 85/517; Am Leg Aux Girls St; Ski Clb; SADD; Chorus; Var Color Guard; Mrchg Band; School Musical; Stage Crew; Rep Jr Cls; Off Sr Cls; Outstndng Stu In Chld Dev 87; U Of Cntrl FL; Comps.

SUDEN, LORA TUM; Southern Regional HS; Surf City, NJ; (3); Cmnty Wkr; French Clb; Math Tm; Capt Color Guard; Coach Actv; Hon Roll; NHS; Prfct Atten Awd; Frnch Hnr Awd 85; Psych.

SUE, KYUNG; Paramus HS; Paramus, NJ; (3); Art Clb; Trs Church Yth Grp; Service Clb; Church Choir; JV Bsktbl; JV Trk; JV Vllybl; Im Wt Lftg; 2nd Pl NJ Stu Crftsmns Fair 85; Outstndg Prfrmnce Art Svc 87; RI Schl Dsgn; Archit.

SUESSMUTH, HEATHER; Kingsway Regional HS; Mickleton, NJ; (4); 19/175; Church Yth Grp; Key Clb; Lit Mag; Stu Cncl; Bsktbl; Fld Hcky; Trk; Cit Awd; Hon Roll; JR Miss 86-87; Stu Mnth 86; W Jersey Field Hockey Assn Scholar 86-87; Fash Merch.

SUGARMAN, IAN K; Pascak Hills HS; Woodcliff Lake, NJ; (3); Am Leg Boys St; Var Debate Tm; Model UN; Political Wkr; Nwsp Rptr; Sec Jr Cls; Trs Sr Cls; Var Socr; Ntl Merit Ltr; Rotary Awd; Hrns US Hstry I Awd 87; Math Leg Cmptn Awd 87; Hnr Pin 86-87; MED.

SUGG, ANGELA; Highland Regional HS; Somerdale, NJ; (3); 140/288; Camera Clb; French Clb; German Clb; Nwsp Phtg; Yrbk Phtg; Yrbk Stf; Stu Cncl; Cheerleading; Trk; Vllybl; Phil Inqr Jrnlsm Career & Dev Wrkshp 87; Chrldng Awd 84; U Of MD; Jrnlsm.

SUGGS, RENEE; Westside HS; Newark, NJ; (3); Church Yth Grp; Cmnty Wkr; Hosp Aide; Teachers Aide; School Play; Sftbl; Vllybl; High Hon Roll; Jr NHS; NHS; Stu Of Mnth 84; Rutgers U; Data Entry.

SUH, YOUN JOO; Dwight-Englewood HS; Tenafly, NJ; (3); Church Yth Grp; Cmnty Wkr; Intnl Clb; Church Choir; Orch; School Musical; Lit Mag; Bsktbl; Hon Roll; Dwght Englewd Music Schlrshp Awd 85-88; Asian Stds.

SUH, YOUNG; Ridgefield Park HS; Ridgefield Pk, NJ; (3); 26/203; Science Clb; Ski Clb; High Hon Roll; Hon Roll.

SUKHU, KAREN I; South Plainfield HS; S Plainfield, NJ; (4); 6/193; Pres French Clb; VP SADD; Chorus; VP Frsh Cls; Trs Soph Cls; Rep Stu Cncl; L Var Tennis; Pres French Hon Soc; Gov Hon Prg Awd; Pres NHS; FLE NJ Awd Excllnce Frnch, Grmn, & Spnsh 87; Deleg Grls Ctznshp Inst 86; Yrbk Sectnl Ed 86-87; Rutgers U; Engrng.

SUKINIK, AMY; Shore Regional HS; Oceanport, NJ; (3); Drama Clb; French Clb; Temple Yth Grp; Thesps; Chorus; School Musical; Mgr(s); Score Keeper; High Hon Roll; NHS; Cngrssnl Awd 86; Frnch Lang Forn Wd 87; Pride NJ Cont Wnnr 86; Pre-Law.

SUKOLA, ELIZABETH; Bordentown Regional HS; Fieldsboro, NJ; (2); 10/140; Art Clb; Ski Clb; Var Cheerleading; Elks Awd; Marketing.

SULIK, PAULA; Woodstown HS; Monroeville, NJ; (3); English Clb; Bsktbl; Mgr(s); Score Keeper; Psychtry.

SULKOWSKI, COLLEEN M; Spotswood HS; Helmetta, NJ; (2); 13/127; Intnl Clb; Mrchg Band; Pep Band; Nwsp Rptr; Stu Cncl; JV Sftbl; Hon Roll; 3rd Yr Mrchng Band Awd 85-86; Desgnr.

SULLIVAN, BRIAN; Florence Twp Memorial HS; Roebling, NJ; (2); Science Clb; Penn ST; Bus Mgmt.

SULLIVAN, DAWN; Morris Hills HS; Dover, NJ; (3); 41/265; Latin Clb; Varsity Clb; Nwsp Stf; Crs Cntry; L Var Trk; High Hon Roll; Hon Roll; All Cnty Tm Winter & Spring 85-87; All Area 1st Tm 87; Bus.

SULLIVAN, JENNIFER; Kinnelon HS; Kinnelon, NJ; (2); French Clb; Varsity Clb; Chorus; Yrbk Stf; Trs Soph Cls; Var Stat Lcrss; Swmmng; Var Tennis; French Hon Soc; NHS; Actrss.

SULLIVAN, JOHN; Monsignor Donovan HS; Toms River, NJ; (3); Church Yth Grp; Ski Clb; SADD; Varsity Clb; Variety Show; JV Var Bsbl; JV Var Bsktbl; L Var Ftbl; L Var Trk; Parocial A Sst Mt Shot Put 87.

SULLIVAN, JOSEPH; Ramapo Regional HS; Wyckoff, NJ; (3); 44/322; Boy Scts; Church Yth Grp; Spanish Clb; Teachers Aide; Nwsp Rptr; Trk; Hon Roll; NHS; Achvt Awd Geom 84-85; Achvt Awd Span II 85-86; Civil Egnrng.

SULLIVAN, KATE; Holy Cross HS; Burlington, NJ; (4); 21/365; JA; Drill Tm; Rep Soph Cls; Rep Jr Cls; Rep Sr Cls; Rep Stu Cncl; Tennis; Trk; High Hon Roll; Hon Roll; Uf Of Notre Dame; Civil Engrng.

SULLIVAN, KELLI; Union Catholic HS; Linden, NJ; (4); Art Clb; Church Yth Grp; Pep Clb; Q&S; Service Clb; Ski Clb; SADD; Church Choir; Yrbk Stf; Berkeley Schl; Fshn Merch.

SULLIVAN, LON L; Woodstown HS; Woodstown, NJ; (3); French Clb; SADD; School Play; Nwsp Rptr; Crs Cntry; Trk; Prfct Atten Awd; Tri-County Conf Awd Cross Country 85 & 86; Jrnlsm.

SULLIVAN, MARK; Voorhees HS; Hampton, NJ; (2); 23/292; Boy Scts; Latin Clb; Bsktbl; JV Crs Cntry; JV Trk; Hon Roll.

SULLIVAN, MARY ELIZABETH; Mount Saint Mary Academy; Elizabeth, NJ; (3); GAA; Library Aide; Acpl Chr; Chorus; School Musical; Nwsp Rptr; Gov Hon Prg Awd; Outstndng Achvt Music Awd No 185-87; Cntrl Jersey Rgnl Chorus 87; Music.

SULLIVAN, MEGHAN; Saint Rose HS; Belmar, NJ; (3); 53/225; Camera Clb; Pres Church Yth Grp; Service Clb; SADD; Rep Frsh Cls; JV Bsktbl; Hon Roll; Spanish NHS; Chestnut Hill Coll; Psych.

SULLIVAN, ROBERT; Morris Catholic HS; Dover, NJ; (3); 20/135; Drama Clb; German Clb; Natl Beta Clb; Quiz Bowl; JV Scholastic Bowl; Band; School Musical; Ed Nwsp Rptr; High Hon Roll; NHS; Acdmc Decathlon Tm & Hnrb Mntn Awd Schl Musical 87; Engl Awd-Creative Wrtng 86; Corp Law.

SULLIVAN, SCOTT J; West Milford Township HS; W Milford, NJ; (3); 53/406; Am Leg Boys St; Pres Frsh Cls; Var Bsktbl; French Hon Soc; Hon Roll; Opt Clb Awd; Varsity Clb; Rep Stu Cncl; 1st Rnnr Up-Bys St Gov 87; MVP-JV Bys Bsktbl 86; Seton Hall; Ed.

SULLIVAN, STACIE ANN; Dover HS; Dover, NJ; (3); 25/228; Debate Tm; Key Clb; Latin Clb; Chorus; Jazz Band; School Musical; Nwsp Rptr; Lit Mag; Hon Roll; NHS; Lit & Latin Awds 85; Ldrshp Awd 87; Am U; Pre Law.

SULLIVAN, TANYA; Frank H Morrell HS; Irvington, NJ; (4); 107/460; Exploring; Hosp Aide; ROTC; Band; Concert Band; Mrchg Band; Cheerleading; Trk; Hon Roll; RN.

SULTAN, MARA; Schalick HS; Elmer, NJ; (3); 12/130; Drama Clb; Chorus; Color Guard; School Play; Sec Frsh Cls; Rep Soph Cls; Sec Jr Cls; Sec Sr Cls; Rep Stu Cncl; Tennis; All St Chorus NJ 87; South Jersey Chorus 84-87; Lib Arts.

SULTAN, ROGER M; Morris Catholic HS; Flanders, NJ; (1); 25/156; French Clb; Latin Clb; Bsbl; Ftbl; Wt Lftg; Hon Roll; Air Force Acad; Plot.

SULZNER, DEBBIE; Overbrook SR HS; West Berlin, NJ; (3); Church Yth Grp; Sec 4-H; French Clb; Girl Scts; Chorus; Hon Roll; Slvr Awd Girl Scts 86; Lake Erie Coll; Frnch.

SUMEY, WILLIAM; Penns Grove HS; Penns Grove, NJ; (3); JCL; Latin Clb; Sec Band; Sec Mrchg Band; Rep Stu Cncl; Var JV Bsbl; Var L Wrstlng; Prfct Atten Awd; US Marine Corps; Mltry Police.

SUN, STEPHEN; Sayreville War Memorial HS; Parlin, NJ; (3); Pres Computer Clb; German Clb; Math Tm; Quiz Bowl; Yrbk Ed-Chief; Swmmng; Hon Roll; NHS; Pres Schlr; VFW Awd; Rensselaer Smmr Pgm Schlrshp 87; 3rd Pl ST Olympcs Mnd Cmpttn 86; Rensselaer Polytechnic; Pre Med.

SUNA, DAVE; New Milford HS; New Milford, NJ; (3); Ski Clb; Trs Frsh Cls; Rep Soph Cls; JV Socr; Var Tennis; French Hon Soc; Basic Programming Awd 86-87; Liberal Arts.

SUNDER, MADHAVI; Mainland Regional HS; Northfield, NJ; (3); 1/320; Dance Clb; Drama Clb; Intnl Clb; JCL; Key Clb; Math Clb; SADD; School Musical; School Play; Nwsp Ed-Chief; Gvrnrs Schl On Public Issues Schlr 87; Hugh O Brian Yth Ldrshp Smnr 86; Mock Trial Tm-Atty 85-87.

SUNDERMANN, WILLIAM; Pinelands Regional HS; Tuckerton, NJ; (4); #1 In Class; SADD; Pres Frsh Cls; Pres Soph Cls; Pres Jr Cls; Pres Sr Cls; Bsktbl; Ftbl; Mgr(s); Socr; Trk; Bus Adm.

SUNGENIS, PAUL; Sacred Heart HS; Vineland, NJ; (4); #7 In Class; Boy Scts; Political Wkr; Science Clb; Spanish Clb; SADD; School Musical; Yrbk Phtg; Yrbk Stf; Pres Soph Cls; Mgr(s); Law.

SUPPA, SHEPHEN; St Augustine Prep; Vineland, NJ; (3); 6/55; Socr; Hon Roll; NEDT Awd; Prfct Atten Awd; Brdcstng.

SURLES, PRISCILLA; Essex Catholic Girls Schl; Union, NJ; (3); Am Leg Aux Girls St; Girl Scts; Science Clb; Chorus; Pep Band; Off Frsh Cls; Off Soph Cls; Off Jr Cls; Stu Cncl; Timer; Temple U; Clncl Psych.

SURRETTE, DANIELLE; Wall HS; Wall, NJ; (4); 16/274; AFS; Drama Clb; French Clb; Ski Clb; Thesps; Band; Mrchg Band; School Musical; School Play; Nwsp Rptr; Ntl Piano Plyrs Gld 83-87; Cmmnctns.

SUSHKO, PETER; Our Lady Of Good Counsel HS; Newark, NJ; (4); 8/102; Boy Scts; Chess Clb; Computer Clb; Im Socr; 2nd Hnrs Acdmcs 87; Ctznshp 84; Kings Coll; Bus Admin.

SUSKO, ANDREW; Woodbridge HS; Sewaren, NJ; (3); 48/380; Am Leg Boys St; Chess Clb; Church Yth Grp; Computer Clb; Dance Clb; Debate Tm; NFL; SADD; Teachers Aide; Chorus; Rutgers U; Bus Mgmt.

SUTERA, MARYANNE; Fort Lee HS; Fort Lee, NJ; (3); Church Yth Grp; FBLA; FTA; Teachers Aide; Yrbk Stf; Cit Awd; Hon Roll; Italian Clb 85-87; Italian Hnr Soc 86-87; Tchr.

SUTH JR, J RICHARD; Notre Dame HS; Trenton, NJ; (3); Varsity Clb; Rep Stu Cncl; Var Ftbl; Var Trk; NHS; Elec Engnrng.

SUTOR, JOANNE; West Orange HS; W Orange, NJ; (3); Computer Clb; French Clb; Lit Mag; JV Socr; Hon Roll; Sci Expo 86; Schlrshp Comp Schl; Bus.

SUTTER, KRISTEEN; Boonton HS; Boonton, NJ; (4); 60/232; Church Yth Grp; SADD; Stu Cncl; Var Capt Cheerleading; Var Sftbl; Var Trk; High Hon Roll; Hon Roll; Rutgers U.

SUTTON, CAROL; Orange HS; Orange, NJ; (2); VP Band; VP Concert Band; VP Mrchg Band; Sec Frsh Cls; Rep Stu Cncl; Stat Bsktbl; Capt Sftbl; Acctnt.

SUTTON, JIMMY; University HS; Newark, NJ; (2); JA; Stu Cncl; Hon Roll; Montclair ST Coll; Anmtn Art.

SUWAK, JENNIFER; Monsignor Donovan HS; Toms River, NJ; (3); Art Clb; Church Yth Grp; Political Wkr; Service Clb; Ski Clb; SADD; Hon Roll; Office Aide; Y-Teens; Church Choir; Nwspr Hnr Outstndng Summer Camp Cnslr Manchester Day Camp 86; Acad Achvt Scholar 85; Johns Hopkins CTY; Boston U; Law.

SUYDAM, DWAYNE; Warren County Technical Schl; Phillipsburg, NJ; (2); VICA; Var Bsbl; High Hon Roll; Hon Roll; Prfct Atten Awd; Grphcs.

SUYDAM, NICOLE; Overbrook Regional HS; Pine Hill, NJ; (4); 31/335; Im JV Bsktbl; JV Var Crs Cntry; Hon Roll; St Josephs; Crmnl Jstc.

SVENNINGSEN, SUSANNE; Watchung Hills Regional HS; Watchung, NJ; (4); 17/311; AFS; Key Clb; SADD; Var Capt Fld Hcky; Var Capt Swmmng; High Hon Roll; Hon Roll; NHS; Garden ST Dstngshd Schlr, Wesley J Hodge Mem Schlrshp 87; Georgetown U; Intl Rltns.

SVETLOV, MARINA; North Brunswick Township HS; N Brunswick, NJ; (4); AFS; French Clb; Key Clb; Latin Clb; Library Aide; Math Tm; Nwsp Stf; Sftbl; Trk; High Hon Roll; Gosden St Dstgshd Schlrs Pgm 87; Awd Excel Stdy 2 Langs 87; Awd Outstndng Acad Achvt 87; John Hopkins U; Intl Stds.

SWAIN JR, JOSEPH B; Cumberland Regional HS; Fairton, NJ; (3); Church Yth Grp; Intnl Clb; JCL; Church Choir; Drill Tm; Yrbk Phtg; Yrbk Stf; Rep Frsh Cls; Rep Soph Cls; Rep Jr Cls; Trenton ST Coll; Ofcr Army.

SWALES, LINDA; Belvidere HS; Phillipsburg, NJ; (4); 8/123; Church Yth Grp; SADD; Stat Crs Cntry; Hon Roll; NHS; Exec Secty.

SWALINA, CAROLYN; Middlesex HS; Middlesex, NJ; (4); 39/157; Spanish Clb; SADD; Awd Excllnc-Creatv Wrtng 87; Artstclly Tlntd Creatv Wrtng 86-87; Wilkes Coll; Comms.

SWAMINATHAN, ASHVIN; Middletown South HS; Middletown, NJ; (2); Band; Concert Band; Drm & Bgl; Drm Mjr(t); Mrchg Band; Lit Mag; High Hon Roll; Hon Roll; U Of CA Santa Cruz.

SWANFELD, PATRICIA; Buena Regional HS; Collings Lakes, NJ; (3); Math Clb; Office Aide; SADD; Color Guard; Mrchg Band; School Play; Rep Jr Cls; Trs Stu Cncl; High Hon Roll; Hon Roll; Lamp Of Knwldg 87; Acctg.

SWANK, MEREDITH; Cumberland Regional HS; Shiloh, NJ; (4); Church Yth Grp; JCL; Spanish Clb; High Hon Roll; Hon Roll; Jr NHS; NHS; Ornmntl Hrtcltr.

SWANSON, ANITA; Morristown HS; Morristown, NJ; (2); 125/446.

SWARTLEY, BRANDON; The Kings Christian Schl; Haddonfield, NJ; (2); 3/55; Church Yth Grp; Cmnty Wkr; Stage Crew; Bsktbl; High Hon Roll; 1st Pl Piano Wnr Mid Atlantic Chrstn Schls Assoc SR High Fine Arts 86; 1st Pl Piano Wnr Fine Arts 86; Drexel U; Elec Engrng.

SWARTZ, ANDREW; Hunterdon Central HS; Flemington, NJ; (3); 137/534; Computer Clb; Science Clb; Ski Clb; Stage Crew; Nwsp Ed-Chief; JV L Socr; JV L Trk; JV L Wrstlng; NJ Chem Olympcs 3rd Pl Lab Evnt 87; Mech Engrng.

SWARTZ, JENNIFER; Park Ridge HS; Park Ridge, NJ; (3); 26/85; Camp Fr Inc; French Clb; Teachers Aide; Chorus; School Musical; Yrbk Ed-Chief; Prfct Atten Awd; Intl Mrktng.

SWAYZE, DANIEL; Dover HS; Dover, NJ; (3); 7/230; Am Leg Boys St; Ski Clb; Nwsp Rptr; Stu Cncl; Ftbl; Wt Lftg; Cit Awd; High Hon Roll; JC Awd; NHS; Otstndng Frshmn Ftbll Plyr; U Of Delaware.

SWEENEY, DAVID; Holy Spirit HS; Somers Point, NJ; (4); 43/363; Pres Church Yth Grp; Debate Tm; Drama Clb; NFL; Spanish Clb; School Musical; Nwsp Rptr; Nwsp Stf; Pres Sr Cls; Bsbl; Elzbthtwn Acdmc Schlrshp 87; Cmnctns.

SWEENEY, JAMES; Paul VI HS; Laurel Springs, NJ; (3); 86/418; Var Trk; Spanish NHS.

SWEENEY, KATHLEEN; Holy Cross HS; Riverside, NJ; (4); 30/376; Ski Clb; Spanish Clb; Yrbk Stf; High Hon Roll; Hon Roll; 1st Pl-US Eastern Rgnl Rllr Sktng Champs 87; NJ St Champ 86; U Of DE.

SWEENEY, KELLY A; West Milford Township HS; West Milford, NJ; (3); Art Clb; DECA; FCA; Latin Clb; Model UN; Office Aide; Spanish Clb; SADD; Rep Frsh Cls; Im Cheerleading; Natl Art Hnr Scty 86-87.

SWEENEY, MICHAEL; St John Vianney HS; Hazlet, NJ; (2); 1/250; High Hon Roll.

SWEENEY, SHAWN; St Joseph Regional HS; Upr Saddle Rvr, NJ; (3); 166/225; Camera Clb; Church Yth Grp; Computer Clb; Nwsp Phtg; Yrbk Phtg; Yrbk Stf; Hon Roll; Genrs & Dedctd Svc Yrbk Layout Awd 86-87; Bus Mgmt.

SWEENEY, WILLIAM; Bordentown Regional HS; Bordentown, NJ; (3); 2/142; Chess Clb; Math Tm; Trs Concert Band; Jazz Band; Mrchg Band; Lit Mag; Crs Cntry; Trk; High Hon Roll; NHS; Cmmrcl Pilot.

SWEET, JARED; Lakewood Prep; Freehold, NJ; (1); Boy Scts; Exploring; Math Tm; Pres Frsh Cls; Pres Soph Cls; Var Socr; High Hon Roll; Bowling; JETS Tm Stu 87; Sci Tm-NJ Sci Leag Cmptn 86-87; Lead Fifer-Joshua Huddy Fife & Drum Corps 86-87.

SWEETEN, EDWIN; Kingway Regional HS; Mt Royal, NJ; (3); Aud/Vis; Schl Tchr.

SWEETWOOD, DAWN; Oakcrest Regional HS; Hammonton, NJ; (4); 7/204; Hosp Aide; SADD; Teachers Aide; Mrchg Band; Ed Yrbk Stf; Mgr(s); Hon Roll; Jr NHS; NHS; Trenton ST Coll; Nrsng.

SWELLER, SANDRA; Newton HS; Newton, NJ; (3); 1/191; Pres Latin Clb; Math Tm; Science Clb; Capt Flag Corp; Madrigals; Lit Mag; Sec Jr Cls; Var Trk; NHS; Scholastic Bowl; Rutgers Schlr 87; ST Fin Gov Schl Sci 87; NJ Sci Supv Assn 3rd Pl Essay Cont 85; Sci.

SWENSON, STACEY; Millville SR HS; Millville, NJ; (3); Hosp Aide; Bowling; Sftbl.

SWEZEY, WAYNE W; Midland Park HS; Midland Park, NJ; (4); 24/130; Am Leg Boys St; Drm Mjr(t); JV Capt Socr; Gov Hon Prg Awd; JP Sousa Awd; NHS; Band; Chorus; Concert Band; Natl Choral Awd 87; U MA/Amherst New Englnd Hnr Band 87; All ST/Rgn Band & All ST/Cnty Chorus 84-87; U Of MI; Music Compstn.

SWIATEK, EDWARD; Bishop George Ahr/St Thomas HS; S Plainfield, NJ; (4); Computer Clb; VP Band; Concert Band; Jazz Band; Mrchg Band; Pep Band; School Musical; Symp Band; JP Sousa Awd; Drew U; Comp Sci.

SWICKER, DONNA; Wall HS; Wall, NJ; (3); 12/289; French Clb; Yrbk Stf; Var Capt Crs Cntry; Var Capt Trk; High Hon Roll; Hon Roll; NHS; Bus.

SWIFT, JANET; Secaucus HS; Secaucus, NJ; (4); 9/162; Hosp Aide; Math Clb; Mu Alpha Theta; Ski Clb; Band; Concert Band; Mrchg Band; High Hon Roll; Hon Roll; NHS; Calculus Lg 86-87; Pace U; Acctg.

SWIFT, TOM; Hunterdon Central HS; Flemington, NJ; (3); 207/543; Art Clb; Chorus; Concert Band; School Musical; School Play; Stage Crew; Symp Band; Im Bsktbl; NBL 16 ST Of NJ, 14 Exprt Clss BMX 84; Gftd & Tlntd Crtv Wrtng 87; Eng.

SWINDLE, ROBYN; Matawan Regional HS; Cliffwood, NJ; (3); Sec Church Yth Grp; FBLA; Hosp Aide; Office Aide; Spanish Clb; SADD; Church Choir; Rep Stu Cncl; Hon Roll; Prfct Atten Awd; Phy.

SWINTON, PAUL; Arthur P Schalick HS; Bridgeton, NJ; (4); 19/132; Math Clb; Teachers Aide; JV Bsktbl; JV Ftbl; Var Trk; Alumni & Frnds Schlrshp 87; Embry-Riddle Arntcl U; Cptr Sci.

SWON, KIMBERLY A; West Morris Mendham HS; Brookside, NJ; (4); Dance Clb; Yrbk Stf; Capt Cheerleading; Hon Roll; Cmptv Ice Skater 4th Rnnr Up Miss Teen 86; St Fnlst Outstndng Yng Amer 84; Colby Coll; Ecnmcs.

SYKES, KATHERINE J; Lakeland Regional HS; Ringwood, NJ; (4); 26/349; High Hon Roll; Spanish NHS; Ringwood Lg Wmns Voters Awd 87; 3rd Pl Scrtchbrd Ringwood Mnrs Yth Art Expo 86; Yrbk Cover Dsgnr 87; Longwood Coll; Commrcl Art.

SYKES, LISA; Victory Christian Schl; Franklinville, NJ; (2); Drama Clb; Yrbk Stf; Cheerleading; Bus Mngmt.

SYLVESTER, LAUREN; Middletown HS South; Red Bank, NJ; (3); Cmnty Wkr; Dance Clb; Drama Clb; English Clb; Hosp Aide; Intnl Clb; Latin Clb; Pep Clb; SADD; Teachers Aide; Congrssnl Slvr Awd 86-87; Israel Schlrshp Awd 86-87.

SYME, GEOFFREY; James Caldwell HS; Caldwell, NJ; (3); Boy Scts; Cmnty Wkr; 4-H; PAVAS; Political Wkr; Radio Clb; Science Clb; Band; Chorus; Concert Band.

SYRE, STEPHANIE; Middletown H S South; Middletown, NJ; (3); Drama Clb; Ski Clb; SADD; School Musical; School Play; Variety Show; Mgr(s); Var Tennis; Hon Roll; Bottle Capper Exec Commtte Mem 86-87; Comm.

SZABO, GABRIELLA; North Warren Regional HS; Delaware, NJ; (4); 9/140; Spanish Clb; Teachers Aide; Nwsp Ed-Chief; Rep Frsh Cls; Rep Soph Cls; Rep Jr Cls; Rep Sr Cls; Hon Roll; VP NHS; World Affairs Sem 85-86; U DE; Bus.

SZAFRANKSI, MICHELE; Paul VI HS; Audubon, NJ; (3); 25/418; Church Yth Grp; Drama Clb; French Clb; Math Clb; Church Choir; School Musical; School Play; French Hon Soc; Hon Roll; NHS; Chem Engrng.

SZALMA, SAMANTHA; W/T HS; Sewell, NJ; (2); Art Clb; Debate Tm; VICA; Acpl Chr; Chorus; School Musical; School Play; Hon Roll; VFW Awd; Baking.

SZAP, MATTHEW; Toms River H S East; Toms River, NJ; (4); 30/567; Exploring; Math Tm; Concert Band; Jazz Band; Pres Mrchg Band; Var Trk; VP NHS; NHS Scholar 87; Raider Brigade Scholar 87; Gettysburg Coll; Pre-Health.

SZCYKALSKI, LISA; Maple Shade HS; Maple Shade, NJ; (2); Spanish Clb; JV Bsktbl; Var Bowling; Mgr(s); Var Stat Socr; High Hon Roll; Prfct Atten Awd.

SZCZEPANIAK, NANCY; Matawan Regional HS; Matawan, NJ; (4); French Clb; Hosp Aide; Latin Clb; Science Clb; Teachers Aide; Chorus; School Musical; French Hon Soc; Hon Roll; ST Wnnr Med Tech HOSA 87; Med Explrs Sec 87; Cook Coll; Pre Med.

SZCZEPANIAK, RICHARD J; Matawan Regional HS; Matawan, NJ; (3); Cmnty Wkr; Im Bsbl; Im Coach Actv; Var Wrstlng; Hon Roll; NHS; Math.

SZCZERBA, KIMBERLY; Brick Memorial HS; Brick, NJ; (4); 16/307; Capt Math Tm; Yrbk Stf; JV Var Cheerleading; Powder Puff Ftbl; High Hon Roll; Hon Roll; NHS; MVP Chrldng 86-87; Chrldng Ldrshp 84-85; Natl Chrldng CA 87-88, Hoola-Bowl HI 87; U DE; Acctng.

SZELINGOSKI, WILLIAM P; Mc Corristin HS; Bordentown, NJ; (3); 20/265; Engrng.

SZEMIOT, CAROL; Manalapan HS; Manalapan, NJ; (3); Hon Roll; Bio.

SZETO, LESTER; Howell HS; Howell, NJ; (3); Stage Crew; Nwsp Ed-Chief; Nwsp Sprt Ed; Var Crs Cntry; Var Tennis; JV Trk; Tennis Mst Imprvd 86.

SZEWCZYK, CHRISTINE; Wayne Hills HS; Wayne, NJ; (3); 10/350; Ski Clb; Spanish Clb; Color Guard; Concert Band; JV Sftbl; JV Swmmng; Var Trk; High Hon Roll; NHS; Outstndng Prfrmnc Awd FBLA 87.

SZLAGA, STACY; Lakewood Prep; Brick, NJ; (4); Art Clb; German Clb; Library Aide; Math Clb; Science Clb; Ski Clb; Spanish Clb; SADD; Band; Chorus; Med.

SZOBOTA, JENNIFER; Morristown HS; Morristown, NJ; (3); Exploring; Var Crs Cntry; Im Powder Puff Ftbl; Var Swmmng; Var Trk; All Area Swm Tm; YMCA Natls; Bus.

SZOT, CARRIE; Sparta HS; Sparta, NJ; (3); GAA; SADD; Varsity Clb; Stage Crew; Var Capt Socr; Var Sftbl; Var Swmmng; Im Vllybl; Cit Awd; Hon Roll; Art Major 88.

SZOT, CHRISTINA; Paramus Cath Girls Regional HS; Hasbrouck Hts, NJ; (2); Ski Clb; Sec Soph Cls; JV Tennis; High Hon Roll; Hon Roll; NEDT Awd.

SZOTAK, SUSANN; Union HS; Union, NJ; (3); Am Leg Aux Girls St; Key Clb; Drm Mjr(t); Jazz Band; NHS; Ntl Merit Ltr; Voice Dem Awd; Boys Clb Am; Dance Clb; Sec German Clb; Boys Clb Am Yth Yr, 1st Rnnr Up ST NJ 86; Natl Spc Sci Ed Fndtns Spc Sci Acad Stanford U 86; Stanford; Law.

SZPYT, CORINNE; Wallington HS; Wallington, NJ; (2); Varsity Clb; Lit Mag; Pres Soph Cls; Var L Bsktbl; Stat Ftbl; Var L Sftbl; JV Vllybl; Hon Roll; Stu Of Week Awd 85-86; Athlete Of Week Awd 86-87; Elem Educ.

SZURA, BRIAN P; Rutherford HS; Rutherford, NJ; (3); Am Leg Boys St; Boy Scts; Camera Clb; Civic Clb; Key Clb; Math Tm; NFL; Scholastic Bowl; Thesps; Acpl Chr; NJ ST Bwl & Intl Future Prblm Slvng-JR Div 85; NJ ST Bwl 3rd Pl 87; Envrnmntl Sci.

SZURA, JONATHAN E; Rutherford HS; Rutherford, NJ; (3); Boy Scts; Camera Clb; Computer Clb; German Clb; Scholastic Bowl; Band; Concert Band; Jazz Band; Mrchg Band; Orch; NJ ST Bwl Future Prblm Slvng JR Div & Intl Bwl 84-85; Humanties.

SZURKO, HELEN; Linden HS; Linden, NJ; (3); Church Yth Grp; FNA; Library Aide; Office Aide; Red Cross Aide; Chorus; Yrbk Stf; Stu Cncl; Sftbl; Prfct Atten Awd; Lib Aide 85; Dntl Asst.

SZURKO, JENNIFER; John P Stevens HS; Edison, NJ; (3); 46/450; Drama Clb; Science Clb; Ski Clb; Capt Color Guard; School Play; Stage Crew; Powder Puff Ftbl; Hon Roll; NHS; Psych.

TABAK, SHARON DEE; Pascack Hills HS; Woodcliff Lake, NJ; (4); 74/232; Spanish Clb; SADD; Chorus; Ed Lit Mag; Hon Roll; 2nd Prz In Alfred U Wrtg Cont 87; 3rd Prz In Bergen Cnty Wrtng Awds For Poetry 87; Poem Pblshd 87; Goucher Coll; Crtv Wrtg.

TABERNA, VERONICA; Orange HS; Orange, NJ; (3); Library Aide; Stu Cncl; Tennis; Bausch & Lomb Sci Awd; Hon Roll; Jr NHS; NHS.

TABERT, KRISTEN; Saint John Vianney Regional HS; Old Bridge, NJ; (2); 21/267; Teachers Aide; School Musical; School Play; Stage Crew; Lit Mag; Hon Roll; Drama Awd 85-87; Psych.

TABOR, DAN; Buena Regional HS; Vineland, NJ; (2); French Clb; Ski Clb; Band; School Play; Stage Crew; Yrbk Stf; Rep Frsh Cls; Rep Soph Cls; Rep Stu Cncl; Hon Roll; Adam Comp Schlrshp 85; Stockton ST Coll; Comp.

TACCONE, GERARD A; Montville HS; Montville, NJ; (3); 42/272; Church Yth Grp; FBLA; Key Clb; Ski Clb; Var Bsbl; JV Bsktbl; Var Ftbl; High Hon Roll; NHS; Engrng.

TACKETT, HEATHER; W Essex HS; No Caldwell, NJ; (3); FTA; Chorus; Var Bsktbl; Var Fld Hcky; Var Tennis; All Star Field Hockey 3rd Tm 86-87; Boston U; Liberal Arts.

TACOVELLI, BRIAN; West Orange HS; W Orange, NJ; (3); Ski Clb; Spanish Clb; Band; Nwsp Ed-Chief; Nwsp Rptr; Nwsp Stf; Ed Lit Mag; Rep Jr Cls; Rep Stu Cncl; Im Tennis; Corp Law.

TAFURI, ROBERT; Manchester Regional HS; N Haledon, NJ; (2); JV Bsktbl; Golf; Hon Roll; Engr.

TAFURI, SANDRA; Manchester Regional HS; N Haledon, NJ; (3); German Clb; Hosp Aide; Yrbk Stf; Sec Stu Cncl; Stat Bsktbl; Var Socr; Hon Roll; NHS; Girls Ctzn Inst Douglass Coll 86; Intl Bus.

TAHA, DARYOUSH; Edgewood HS; Sicklerlve, NJ; (2); Bio.

TAHAN, DAVID G; Wayne Hills HS; Wayne, NJ; (2); Red Cross Aide; Band; Concert Band; Jazz Band; Mrchg Band; Ftbl; Swmmng; Wt Lftg; Hon Roll.

TAHANEY, KELLY; Princeton HS; Princeton, NJ; (4); AFS; Cmnty Wkr; Hosp Aide; Lit Mag; Sec Stu Cncl; Var Capt Bsktbl; Var Capt Socr; Senator Bill Bradleys Young Ctzn Awd NJ 87; Crew 85-87; Rutges U; Ped.

TAHANEY, KRISTEN; Bishop Eustace Prep; Atco, NJ; (4); Church Yth Grp; French Clb; Pep Clb; Yrbk Stf; Rep Sr Cls; Stat Bsktbl; Stat Socr; Hon Roll; VP NHS; Pres Schlrshp 87; Loyola Coll; Psych.

TAHERIPOUR, MORVARID; Dwight Englewood Schl; Wash Township, NJ; (3); Dance Clb; Hosp Aide; Stage Crew; Yrbk Stf; Lit Mag; Hon Roll; Frnch Natl Cont 10th Pl Lvl I 85; Frnch Natl Con 11th Pl Lvl II 86; Frnch Natl Cont 15th Pl Lvl III; Pre Law.

TAHMOOSH, SUSAN; John F Kennedy HS; Paterson, NJ; (4); 10/343; Art Clb; French Clb; German Clb; Intnl Clb; Orch; Nwsp Stf; Yrbk Stf; Jr NHS; NHS; Hon Roll; Outstndng Acad Achvt 87; Outstndg Achvt Frgn Lang 87; Art Awd 87; Montclair ST Coll; Comm Art.

TAI, CHAU; Hillsborough HS; Somerville, NJ; (3); 5/328; Science Clb; School Musical; School Play; Capt Vllybl; High Hon Roll; Hon Roll; NHS; Drama Clb; Yrbk Stf; Powder Puff Ftbl; Rutgers Coll Of Engrng; Mgnt.

TAILOR, MAMTA; Clifton HS; Clifton, NJ; (4); 187/555; Key Clb; Spanish Clb; Yrbk Ed-Chief; Yrbk Stf; Var Crs Cntry; Var Trk; Spanish NHS; Wm Ptrsn Coll; Nrsng.

TAKACS, CHRISTINE; Hopewell Valley Central HS; Titusville, NJ; (4); AFS; Church Yth Grp; FBLA; Service Clb; Spanish Clb; School Musical; Stage Crew; Hon Roll; Fairleigh Dickinson U Madison.

TAKACS, DOREEN; Clifton HS; Clifton, NJ; (4); DECA; Hosp Aide; Office Aide; Computer Clb; JV Mgr(s); Hon Roll; DE NJ Ldrshp Conf Overall 2nd Pl Dioraa 2nd Pl Interview & 2nd Pl Visual Merch 87; Berkeley Schl; AOT.

TAKAKI, FREDERICK; Vineland HS; Vineland, NJ; (4); US Army; Aviator.

TALADA, J REED; Hunterdon Central HS; Stockton, NJ; (3); 55/560; Am Leg Boys St; Cmnty Wkr; German Clb; Latin Clb; Nwsp Stf; Trs Frsh Cls; Trs Soph Cls; Rep Soph Cls; Rep Stu Cncl; Hon Roll; Wake Forest U; Law.

TALAG, MARY ROSE; Academic HS; Jersey City, NJ; (3); Computer Clb; Exploring; Science Clb; Nwsp Rptr; Nwsp Stf; Yrbk Phtg; Yrbk Rptr; Yrbk Stf; Prfct Atten Awd; U Of Philippines; Intl Bus.

TALARICO, MARIA; North Bergen HS; North Bergen, NJ; (4); 124/390; Capt Color Guard; Yrbk Stf; Bst Prsnlty & Mst Frndly 87; Awded Mdl-Actvties-Sec Of Italian Clb 87; Lab Inst Of Merch-NY; Advrtsng.

TALBOT, JOANNE; Haddon Township HS; Westmont, NJ; (3); Am Leg Aux Girls St; JCL; Latin Clb; Band; Jazz Band; Orch; Hon Roll; Science Clb; Chorus; Concert Band; Cum Laude Awd Jr Clsscl Leag 85; Latin Hon Soc 86-87; Interact Clb 86-87; Vet.

TALDELORE, VIVIAN; Rutherford HS; Rutherford, NJ; (3); Cmnty Wkr; Concert Band; Mrchg Band; Lit Mag; High Hon Roll; Cmnty Wkr; Debate Tm; Awd Congrssmn Robert G Torricellis Mdl Cngrss 87; Mock Assmbly In Trenton 87; U Of South FL; Med.

TALIAFERRO, JAMES; Essex Catholic Boys HS; Montclair, NJ; (3); Nwsp Rptr; Stu Cncl; Im Bsktbl; JV Ftbl; Im Sftbl; JV Trk; High Hon Roll; Hon Roll; Vrsty Fencg Tm 86-87; Pol Sci.

TALIAFERRO, JEFFREY W; Wardlaw-Hartridge Schl; Plainfield, NJ; (4); 9/48; Debate Tm; Drama Clb; SADD; Chorus; School Musical; School Play; Lit Mag; Sec Stu Cncl; Stat Ftbl; Stat Swmmng; W-H Pin Acdmc Excllnc & Cntrbtns Schl Cmnty, Mary B Wells Hstry Prz, Natl Schlchoral Awd 87; Duke U; Lawyer.

TALISH, CHRIS; West Essex SR HS; Fairfield, NJ; (2); French Clb; Socr; Trk; Hon Roll.

TALLARIDA, VALERIE; Maple Shade HS; Maple Shade, NJ; (4); 24/167; DECA; French Clb; GAA; Key Clb; Pres Frsh Cls; Rep Jr Cls; Rep Sr Cls; Rep Stu Cncl; Var Cheerleading; Var High Hon Roll; Sparc Plug Awd Var Chrldng 85-86; 2nd Pl DECA A/A Wrttn Evnt 86; Rider Coll.

TALLEYRAND, REGINE; Columbia HS; South Orange, NJ; (4); Cmnty Wkr; Var L Socr; Var L Trk; Ntl Merit Ltr; Sec Spanish NHS; St Schlr; Mst Vlbl Plyr Awd JV Sccr Tm 84; Most Imprvd Plyr Vrsty Sccr Tm 86; Ldrshp Educ & Devlopmnt Pgm 86.

TALLO, SUZANNE; East Brunswick HS; E Brunswick, NJ; (3); German Clb; Key Clb; Bsktbl; Co-Capt JV Fld Hcky; NHS; Grmn Hnr Soc 86-87; Med.

TALPAS, CHRIS; Phillipsburg HS; Phillipsburg, NJ; (4); 90/350; Office Aide; Wrstlng; Hon Roll; Hnr Rl.

TALT, MICHELLE; Vernon Township HS; Highland Lks, NJ; (3); Church Yth Grp; Rutgers U; Comp Sci.

TAMASHUNAS, BRUCE A; Shawnee HS; Medfod, NJ; (4); 2/535; Church Yth Grp; Cmnty Wkr; Latin Clb; Library Aide; Math Tm; Jazz Band; Madrigals; School Musical; High Hon Roll; NHS; INPO Schlrshp 87-88; Ntl Schlr Harvard 86; Stanford U Jordan Schlr; Engr.

TAMBARO, JOSEPH; Christian Brothers Acad; Holmdel, NJ; (3); 7/229; Hosp Aide; Stage Crew; Nwsp Rptr; Ed Yrbk Stf; Im Ftbl; Im Sftbl; Swmmng; High Hon Roll; Coach Awd Holmdel Swim Tm 86; Jr Hosp Vlntr 86; Johns Hopkins U; Med.

TAMBONE, LOUIS; Don Bosco Tech; Paterson, NJ; (3); 6/91; Am Leg Boys St; Hosp Aide; Chorus; Variety Show; Nwsp Stf; VP Frsh Cls; VP Soph Cls; Pres Jr Cls; Rep Stu Cncl; Hon Roll; 4 Yr Schlrshp To Don Bosco Tech 84.

TAMMANA, NANDINI; Parsippany Hills HS; Parsippany, NJ; (3); AFS; Cmnty Wkr; German Clb; Hosp Aide; Service Clb; Band; Mrchg Band; Im Trk; Hon Roll; NHS.

TANAKA, ASAKO; Fort Lee HS; Ft Lee, NJ; (3); Camera Clb; Drm Mjr(t); Jazz Band; Mrchg Band; Orch; School Musical; Symp Band; Hon Roll; NHS; Mdrn Music Mstrs.

TANG, NEIL; Monroe Township HS; Spotswood, NJ; (3); Am Leg Boys St; Math Tm; Science Clb; Concert Band; Mrchg Band; Capt Var Crs Cntry; Var Trk; Im Vllybl; Im Wt Lftg; High Hon Roll; Elec Engnrng.

TANIER, MICHAEL; Gloucester Catholic HS; Mt Ephraim, NJ; (3); Cmnty Wkr; JA; SADD; Band; School Musical; High Hon Roll; Frnch Frgn Lang Awd 86-87; Tchr.

TANK, TUSHAR; John P Stevens HS; Edison, NJ; (3); 19/405; Chess Clb; Debate Tm; Math Tm; Model UN; Science Clb; Hon Roll; NHS; Olympics Of Mind-2nd In ST & Amer Invitational Math Exam 87; Elec Engrng.

TANNENBAUM, SALLY; Atlantic City HS; Margate City, NJ; (3); Drama Clb; Sec Latin Clb; Model UN; Office Aide; VP Temple Yth Grp; School Musical; School Play; Stu Cncl; Var L Cheerleading; Hon Roll.

TANNER, DELISA R; Ramsey HS; Saddle River, NJ; (3); Church Yth Grp; Rep Stu Cncl; Var Capt Cheerleading; Hon Roll; Ntl Merit SF; HOBY Fndtn Ldrshp-Schlrshp Awd 86; Fndr & Pres Fnancl Clb 86-87; Schlstc R Awd 86.

TANTOSCA, JENNIFER; St Elizabeth Acad; South Orange, NJ; (1); Hon Roll; Schlrshp Acad St Elizabeth, Achvt Awds Alg I, Hstry I, Theolgy 86-87; Art.

TANTUM, DONALD; Oakcrest HS; Mays Lndg, NJ; (2); 20/292; French Clb; School Musical; Nwsp Rptr; JV Capt Bsbl; JV Bsktbl; Var Socr; Comm.

TANUDTANUD, LYNLEE; St John Vianney HS; Freehold, NJ; (3); Hosp Aide; Math Tm; Service Clb; SADD; Yrbk Rptr; Ed Yrbk Sprt Ed; Score Keeper; High Hon Roll; Hon Roll; NHS; Gold & White Awd; Pre-Med.

TAPPER, DIANA; Edgewood Regional SR HS; Atco, NJ; (3); 4/390; Exploring; FBLA; Latin Clb; Fld Hcky; Hon Roll; Jr NHS; Entrprnr.

TARANTINO, COLLEEN; Newton HS; Newton, NJ; (4); 19/196; Hosp Aide; Varsity Clb; Chorus; Madrigals; VP Soph Cls; Capt Fld Hcky; NHS; All Leag Fld Hcky 86; All Area Fld Hcky 86; Coachs Awd Fld Hcky 86; U Of Pittsburgh; Physcl Thrpy.

TARANTINO, TODD D; Brick Township HS; Brick Town, NJ; (3); 125/430; Key Clb; Dance Clb; Csmtlgst.

TARANTO, TAMI; Burlington City HS; Edgewater Park, NJ; (2); FNA; Chorus; Var L Cheerleading; Mgr(s); Score Keeper; Hon Roll; Soph Rllrsktg Pairs Champ S E Rgn 84; S E JR Rllrsktg Pairs Chmp 85; NJ ST Frshmn Lds Fgrs Chmp 86; Nrsng.

TARANTOLO, PATRICIA ANN; Monmouth Regional HS; Eatontown, NJ; (4); 28/236; Chorus; Drm Mjr(t); School Musical; School Play; Pres Frsh Cls; Pres Soph Cls; VP Jr Cls; Var Cheerleading; Capt Twrlr; Hon Roll; Exc llnc Actng Awd Rider Coll Drma Fstvl 86; Red Bnk Rgstr Tlnt Shwcse Fnlst Awd 84; Miss Tntn Flls Qn; Villanova U; Comms.

TARASEVITSCH, NINA LEE; Woodbridge HS; Iselin, NJ; (4); 18/386; Am Leg Aux Girls St; SADD; Flag Corp; Yrbk Ed-Chief; High Hon Roll; Hon Roll; Jr NHS; NHS; Hugh O Biran Yth Ldrshp Ambsdr 85; Rutgers Coll; Elec Engr.

TARAZONA, LANCE; Kearny HS; Kearny, NJ; (3); Boys Clb Am; Church Yth Grp; Cmnty Wkr; Drama Clb; German Clb; Varsity Clb; Band; Concert Band; Jazz Band; Mrchg Band; Recpnt Prncpls Hnr Awd 84-85; Intl Musical Prsntn 86; Invtnl Tour Germny 87; Rutgers U; Bus.

TARBOX, ERIC ALEXANDER; Morristown HS; Morristown, NJ; (3); Am Leg Boys St; Boy Scts; CAP; Key Clb; School Musical; School Play; Trk; Hon Roll; Cvl Air Patrol NJ Wing Drll Tm 87; Air Force Acad; Bus Econ.

TARDITI, LAURA; Haddonfield Memorial HS; Haddonfield, NJ; (4); VP Key Clb; Yrbk Ed-Chief; JV Bsktbl; Mgr(s); Capt Twrlr; French Hon Soc; High Hon Roll; NHS; Rotary Awd; St Schlr; CPA.

TARNOWSKI, ANN MARIE; Bridgewater Raritan West HS; Raritan, NJ; (4); Am Leg Aux Girls St; Spanish Clb; Nwsp Rptr; Yrbk Sprt Ed; Bsktbl; Capt Powder Puff Ftbl; Var Sftbl; Capt Vllybl; High Hon Roll; NHS; Gov Cncl Phy Ftns Awd 87; Villanova U; Lib Arts.

TARQUINTO, ANTHONY J; West Deptford HS; Woodbury, NJ; (3); 39/256; Am Leg Boys St; JV Bsbl; Var Bsktbl; Var Ftbl; Hon Roll; NHS; Prfct Atten Awd; Finance.

TARTAGLIONE, KEVIN; Immaculata HS; Belle Mead, NJ; (3); 40/246; Dance Clb; Math Clb; Ski Clb; Varsity Clb; Rep Frsh Cls; Im Bsktbl; Im Bsktbl; Var Ftbl; Hon Roll; NHS; Hnr Roll & Varsity Clb; Math Clb; Bio Med.

TARVER, THOMAS; Jackson Memorial HS; Jackson, NJ; (4); 162/417; Varsity Clb; Capt Var Ftbl; High Hon Roll; Rutgers U Ftbl Schlrshp 87; High Hnr Roll; Rutgers; Bus Mrktng.

TARVES, LORI ANN V; Paul VI HS; Somerdale, NJ; (3); Drama Clb; Sec French Clb; NFL; Chorus; School Musical; Variety Show; Lit Mag; Pom Pon; Hon Roll; NHS.

TARZAISKI, CHRISTINE; Paul VI HS; Magnolia, NJ; (3); Church Yth Grp; Drama Clb; French Clb; Hosp Aide; Math Clb; Chorus; Stage Crew; French Hon Soc; Hon Roll; NHS; Phila Coll Pharm; Phrmcy.

TASH, JEFF; Hightstown HS; Hightstown, NJ; (3); French Clb; JV Bsbl; Ftbl; Pre-Med.

TASKOWITZ, GREGG; South River HS; S River, NJ; (2); German Clb; Letterman Clb; Varsity Clb; Pres Jr Cls; Bsktbl; Score Keeper; Socr; Tennis; Wrstlng.

TASSONE, JUDI L; Hammonton HS; Hammonton, NJ; (3); Key Clb; School Musical; Sec Stu Cncl; Var Fld Hcky; High Hon Roll; Hon Roll; NHS; Dance Clb; School Play; Variety Show; Acad Excllnc Awd 86; Dance Educs Of Amer Rengl Dance Comp 1st Pl 85; Shwstpr Natl Tltn Comp 2nd Pl 86.

TATE, AMANDA; Ocean City HS; Ocean City, NJ; (3); 49/324; Art Clb; Drama Clb; Science Clb; Spanish Clb; Speech Tm; Pres SADD; School Musical; Nwsp Rptr; Nwsp Stf; Yrbk Stf; Gvrnrs Schl Of Arts For Creatve Wrtng 87; Cmmnctns.

TATORIS, JOSEPH; Parsippany Hills HS; Parsippany, NJ; (3); Spanish Clb; Ftbl; Wt Lftg; Hon Roll; Rutgers; Mech Engr.

TAUB, LARA; Hightstown HS; East Windsor, NJ; (3); 16/400; Am Leg Aux Girls St; Spanish Clb; SADD; Rep Soph Cls; Sec Jr Cls; VP Sr Cls; Rep Stu Cncl; Socr; NHS; Ski Clb; Pre-Law.

TAVAGLIONE, ANNELIESE; Howell HS; Howell, NJ; (2); 73/400; Teachers Aide; Variety Show; Nwsp Bus Mgr; Nwsp Stf; Yrbk Stf; Mgr Mgr(s); JV Socr; Hon Roll; Eng Awd 87; Boston Coll; Math.

TAVARES, JAMES; Regis HS; Cedar Grove, NJ; (3); Church Yth Grp; Ski Clb; Band; School Musical; VP Jr Cls; JV Crs Cntry; Order Owl Acad Hnrs 85.

TAVASKA, HOLLY; Morristown HS; Morristown, NJ; (2); 67/446; Church Yth Grp; Band; Concert Band; Mrchg Band; Orch; School Musical; Symp Band; Hon Roll; Pres Schlr; Music Bstr Awd 87; Area Band 87; Dntl Hygnst.

TAWIL, ESTHER; Asbury Park HS; Deal, NJ; (4); Var Capt Tennis; NY U.

TAYLOR, ANITA; Bordentown Regioanl HS; Bordentown, NJ; (3); 10/142; Church Yth Grp; Church Choir; Stu Cncl; Bowling; Trk; Hon Roll; NHS; Sci.

TAYLOR, AUDREY; Dwight Morrow HS; Englewood, NJ; (3); Civic Clb; Office Aide; Pep Clb; Political Wkr; Band; Yrbk Stf; Rep Frsh Cls; Rep Soph Cls; Rep Stu Cncl; Cheerleading; Pharmacy.

TAYLOR, BENJAMIN BAKAAR; Essex Catholic Boys HS; Irvington, NJ; (3); Church Yth Grp; Drama Clb; Service Clb; Chorus; School Play; Nwsp Sprt Ed; Pres Jr Cls; Pres Stu Cncl; Cit Awd; NHS; Arch.

TAYLOR, BRANDES; John F Kennedy HS; Willingboro, NJ; (2); Dance Clb; Intnl Clb; Teachers Aide; Mrchg Band; Pom Pon; Swmmng; High Hon Roll; Z-Clb 85-87; Brown U; Cmmnctns.

TAYLOR, CHRISTOPHER; West Morris Mendham HS; Mendham, NJ; (2); Church Yth Grp; Cmnty Wkr; Red Cross Aide; Wrstlng; Engr.

TAYLOR, DARRYL; Williamstown HS; Williamstown, NJ; (2); Stage Crew; JV Tennis; Hon Roll; NHS; Frnch Hghst Aver Awd 85-87; Acad Excel Awd 85-87; U Penn; Aerosp Engrng.

TAYLOR, JEFFREY P; West Milford Township HS; W Milford, NJ; (3); Am Leg Boys St; SADD; Varsity Clb; VP Jr Cls; VP Stu Cncl; Var Bsbl; Capt Socr; ST Assembly NJ Boys ST 87; Rutgers; Acctng.

TAYLOR, JENNIFER; Westfield HS; Westfield, NJ; (4); 39/484; French Clb; Trs Latin Clb; Science Clb; Chorus; Yrbk Ed-Chief; Var Trk; High Hon Roll; NHS; Pres Schlr; Congrssnl Schlr 87; Wellesley Coll.

TAYLOR, JERRY MARK; Manchester HS; Toms River, NJ; (3); Science Clb; Var Socr; Air Force; Arch.

TAYLOR, JOHN; Oakcrest HS; Mays Landing, NJ; (3); 4/228; Math Clb; Band; Concert Band; Mrchg Band; High Hon Roll; Hon Roll; Jr NHS; NHS; Engrng.

TAYLOR, JOHN; The Kings Christian HS; Medford, NJ; (3); Pres Frsh Cls; VP Stu Cncl; Var L Bsbl; JV L Bsktbl; Var Capt Socr; High Hon Roll; Hon Roll; NHS; Ski Clb; Sccr League All-Star; Engrng.

TAYLOR, KEN; Lower Cape May Regional HS; Cape May, NJ; (2); 31/256; Church Yth Grp; 4-H; JV Bsbl; JV Ftbl; Im Vllybl; Wt Lftg; 4-H Awd.

TAYLOR, KENNETH; West Side HS; Newark, NJ; (3); Computer Clb; Drama Clb; FBLA; Math Clb; Chorus; Bsktbl; Ftbl; Hon Roll; Prfct Atten Awd; Trphy Bst In Shape Frsh 84-85; Comp Prg.

TAYLOR, MICHELE; Manchester Twp HS; Toms River, NJ; (3); Am Leg Aux Girls St; Math Tm; Spanish Clb; Capt Flag Corp; Trs Frsh Cls; Var L Fld Hcky; Var L Sftbl; High Hon Roll; Kiwanis Awd; NY U; Accntng.

TAYLOR, PETER J; Delaware Valley Regional HS; Milford, NJ; (3); Boy Scts; Cmnty Wkr; Exploring; Ski Clb; Var Trk; JV Wrstlng; Crimneolgy.

TAYLOR, SCOTT; Shore Regional HS; Oceanport, NJ; (3); 63/240; Stage Crew; Nwsp Rptr; JV Trk; Var Wrstlng; High Hon Roll; 2nd Pl Holmdel Wrstlng Trnmnt 87; Elec Engr.

TAYLOR, SHARON; Milville HS; Millville, NJ; (4); 20/420; FBLA; OEA; Hnr Stu 87; Pres Acad Ftnss Awd 87; Kiwanis Schlrshp Awd 87; Cumberland Cnty Coll; Elem Educ.

TAYLOR, SHARON D; Gill/St Bernards HS; Piscataway, NJ; (4); Varsity Clb; Variety Show; Rep Frsh Cls; Rep Soph Cls; Rep Jr Cls; Var Capt Bsktbl; Var Capt Socr; Var Capt Sftbl; Cit Awd; High Hon Roll; E Gill Awd 87; MVP Scr 86; M D Jefferson Awd 85; J Creasey Awd 87; U Of NC Chapel Hill; Engr.

TAYLOR, STEVE; Toms River North HS; Toms River, NJ; (2); Drama Clb; Ski Clb; School Play; Variety Show.

TAYLOR, SUSAN; St James HS; Wenonah, NJ; (1); 2/92; Hon Roll; Ntl Sci Merit Awd 86-87; Schlstc All Amer 86-87; Ntl Hnr Roll 86-87; Ntl Englsh Awd 86-87.

TAYLOR, THERESA; Weequahic HS; Newark, NJ; (3); 5/400; Church Yth Grp; Sec Jr Cls; Var Cheerleading; Var Sftbl; NHS; NC ST U; Bus Admin.

TAYLOR, TOSCHIA; Burlington Township HS; Burlington, NJ; (3); 27/129; FBLA; JA; Office Aide; Chorus; Color Guard; Mrchg Band; Rep Frsh Cls; VP Sr Cls; Rep Stu Cncl; JV Bsktbl; Katherine Gibbs JR Achvt Hgh Hnrs Awd 86-87; Bus Admin.

TAYLOR, TYRONE; Montclair HS; Montclair, NJ; (4); 117/410; Drama Clb; PAVAS; Jazz Band; Madrigals; School Musical; School Play; Swing Chorus; Variety Show; Gym; Hon Roll; Schl Prfrmng Arts Awd 87; Natl Arts Rcgntn Awd 87; Estrn US Latin Dnc Chmpn 87; Dnc Tchr Elem Schl Stu; Carnegie Melln U; Musical Theat.

TAYLOR, VERONICA; Egg Harbor Township HS; Pleasantville, NJ; (3); #2 In Class; Math Clb; SADD; Band; Concert Band; Mrchg Band; Trs Frsh Cls; Trs Soph Cls; Trs Jr Cls; Var Trk; Hon Roll; Bio Med Engr.

TAYLOR, WILLIAM; Jackson Memorial HS; Jackson, NJ; (4); Pres Exploring; VP Math Clb; Math Tm; Science Clb; Yrbk Stf; High Hon Roll; Ntl Merit Schol; NEDT Awd; Coll Coll; Math.

TEDESCO, DREW; Lenape Valley Regional HS; Andover, NJ; (3); 34/213; French Clb; Key Clb; Concert Band; JV Socr; Prfct Atten Awd 84-87; Cert Merit Frnch 84-87.

TEDESCO, ROBERT; Middlesex HS; Middlesex, NJ; (3); Ski Clb; JV Bsbl; Var Bsktbl; Hon Roll.

TEDESCO, SHARON; Cinnaminson HS; Cinnaminson, NJ; (3); French Clb; Girl Scts; Office Aide; Teachers Aide; Yrbk Phtg; Yrbk Stf; Im Powder Puff Ftbl; Im Sftbl; Hon Roll; Acctg.

TEEVAN, JOHN; Christian Brothers Acad; Holmdel, NJ; (4); 14/216; Computer Clb; Math Tm; Ski Clb; Nwsp Stf; Im Bsktbl; Im Ftbl; Im Sftbl; Im Wt Lftg; Capt L Wrstlng; High Hon Roll; Frndly Sons Of St Patrick Schlrshp; Coll Of Holy Cross; Bio.

TEEVAN, MARTIN; Christian Brothers Acad; Holmdel, NJ; (4); Hosp Aide; Math Tm; School Musical; Nwsp Sprt Ed; Im Ftbl; Var Wrstlng; High Hon Roll; NHS; Bishop George Ahr Chrstn Svc Awd 87; Congrssnl Awd 86; Coll Holy Cross; Econ.

TEGER, MICHAEL R; Morristown HS; Morris Plains, NJ; (4); 31/445; Am Leg Boys St; CAP; Cmnty Wkr; Exploring; Ski Clb; Rep Frsh Cls; Rep Soph Cls; NHS; Pres Schlr; Billy Mitchell Awd 85; A Earhart Awd, Stdnt Pilots Lic 86; U CO; Aerosp Engrng.

TEITELBAUM, SHERYL; Raritan HS; Hazlet, NJ; (3); Ski Clb; Varsity Clb; Bsktbl; Socr; Tennis; Math Tchr.

TEITELMAN, STEPHEN A; St Marys Hall-Doane Acad; Camden, NJ; (3); 9/22; Am Leg Boys St; Library Aide; SADD; Varsity Clb; Variety Show; Yrbk Stf; High Hon Roll; Hon Roll; Rep Sr Cls; Rep Stu Cncl; Lebanon Valley Coll; Pre-Med.

TEIXEIRA, ANA; East Side HS; Newark, NJ; (3); 1/500; VP Computer Clb; Exploring; Math Clb; Math Tm; Yrbk Stf; Bausch & Lomb Sci Awd; High Hon Roll; NHS; Opt Clb Awd; St Schlr; Cert-Tutrng At Irnbnd Eductnl & Cltrl Ctr 85-87; Awd & Intrnshp-Wrk Sntr Ltnbrg 87; Bus Admin.

TEJANI, SHAMIM; Paul VI HS; Williamstown, NJ; (4); 7/503; Math Clb; Spanish Clb; High Hon Roll; Hon Roll; NHS; St Schlr; Bio.

TELEMAQUE, VLADIMIR; St Joseph Regional HS; Spring Valley, NY; (3); Art Clb; Cmnty Wkr; Hosp Aide; Teachers Aide; Chorus; Swing Chorus; Bsbl; Bsktbl; Crs Cntry; Ftbl; Cert Merit US Govt 86; Cert Apprctn US Govt 86; Math Hnr Awd 85; Arch.

TELEMDSCHINOW, JO ANN; New Brunswick HS; New Brunswick, NJ; (4); 4/110; Ed Lit Mag; Jr Cls; High Hon Roll; Hon Roll; Trs NHS; Ntl Merit SF; Garden St Dstngshd Schlr 86-87; Acad All Amer Schlr 85-86; Rutgers Univ.

TELESH, JOHN; Hopatcong HS; Hopatcong, NJ; (4); Church Yth Grp; Orch; Nwsp Phtg; Nwsp Rptr; Nwsp Stf; Yrbk Ed-Chief; Yrbk Phtg; Yrbk Stf; Hon Roll; Prfct Atten Awd; Messiah Coll; Accntng.

TELLEFSEN, CORA; Spotswood HS; Spotswood, NJ; (3); SADD; Yrbk Ed-Chief; Yrbk Phtg; Yrbk Sprt Ed; Yrbk Stf; JV Cheerleading; Hon Roll; Arch.

TELLERIA, OLGA M; St Josephs Of The Palisades HS; Union City, NJ; (3); Spanish Clb; Yrbk Stf; High Hon Roll; Hon Roll; Spanish NHS; Med.

TELLO, WENDY; Holy Family Acad; Bayonne, NJ; (2); 30/85; Im Vllybl; Hon Roll; Bus.

TELONIDIS, JULIA; Ocean Township HS; Oakhurst, NJ; (3); Church Yth Grp; Lit Mag; Art.

TEMPLE, AMY; Hamilton H S West; Trenton, NJ; (3); Church Yth Grp; Office Aide; VP SADD; Science Clb; Yrbk Stf; Rep Frsh Cls; Rep Soph Cls; VP Jr Cls; VP Sr Cls; Rep Stu Cncl; Stu Govt; Trntn ST Coll; Cmnctns.

TENDLER, JODI; Paramus HS; Paramus, NJ; (2); Art Clb; Drama Clb; Intnl Clb; SADD; Temple Yth Grp; Drill Tm; Flag Corp; Lit Mag; Wt Lftg; Bus.

TENNANT, SUSAN; Southern Regional HS; Barnegat Light, NJ; (3); 12/470; Church Yth Grp; Trs French Clb; Spanish Clb; Yrbk Ed-Chief; Rep Frsh Cls; Rep Soph Cls; Rep Jr Cls; Rep Stu Cncl; JV Trk; High Hon Roll; Southern Reg Awds Banquet Acadcs 86 & 87; Optometry.

TERCEK, KRISTIN L; Dumont HS; Dumont, NJ; (4); 4/210; Art Clb; Mu Alpha Theta; Science Clb; Ski Clb; School Play; Variety Show; Ed Yrbk Phtg; Ed Lit Mag; High Hon Roll; NHS; Prsdnt Ntl Art Hnr Soc 86-87; Chsn Reprsntv World Affrs Semnr U Of WI 86; George Wshngtn Awd Math 86; NW U; Film.

TERHUNE, JASON; Ramsey HS; Ramsey, NJ; (3); Sftbl; Wt Lftg.

TERHUNE, KEVIN; Ocean Township HS; Ocean, NJ; (3); Key Clb; PAVAS; Band; Concert Band; Mrchg Band; JV Bsbl; JV Bsktbl; JV Var Socr; Stu Ldrshp Pgm 86-88; Cngrssnl Awd Pgm 87-88; Optmtrst.

TERIFAY, COLLEEN; Paul VI HS; Laurel Springs, NJ; (3); Powder Puff Ftbl; Drexel U; Court Rprtr.

TERLEMEZIAN, GABE; Waldwick HS; Waldwick, NJ; (3); Ski Clb; Varsity Clb; JV Var Bsbl; JV Var Ftbl; Bus.

TERRA-NOVA, JEFFREY M; Pt Pleasant Beach HS; Lavallette, NJ; (2); Bsbl; JV Bsktbl; Ftbl; Hon Roll; Prfct Atten Awd.

TERRACCIANO, ROSE; Kingsway Regional HS; Clarksboro, NJ; (2); Ski Clb; JV Fld Hcky; Var Sftbl; Hon Roll; La Salle; Psych.

TERRANOVA, ROMINA; Belleville HS; Belleville, NJ; (3); Rep Key Clb; Rep Jr Cls; Hon Roll; Bus.

TERRELL, JEN; Morristown-Beard HS; New Vernon, NJ; (2); 3/76; Camera Clb; French Clb; Lit Mag; JV Fld Hcky; French Hon Soc; Hon Roll; Chnnl 13, WNET, Chldrns Art Fstvl 87; Hnrbl Mntn, Bst Stu-Ptry 83.

TERRIS, MARC; Vineland HS; Vineland, NJ; (3); Chess Clb; French Clb; Scholastic Bowl; Science Clb; Temple Yth Grp; JV Var Crs Cntry; Ftbl; Var JV Trk; Gov Hon Prg Awd; High Hon Roll; Cmp Cnclr-Jwsh Smmr Cmp 85-87; Ldr Lcl Jwsh Yth Grp 85-87; Accntng.

TERRY, JENNIFER; Toms River HS South; Pine Beach, NJ; (3); 70/405; Church Yth Grp; JV Bsktbl; JV Sftbl; Var Tennis; Hon Roll; Elem Educ.

TERRY, NORNA; Life Center Acad; Mt Holly, NJ; (2); VP Church Yth Grp; Drama Clb; School Play; Var Bsktbl; Hon Roll; Keyboard Music Awd 85-86; Princeton U; Psych.

TERRY, RALPH; Essek Catholic Boys HS; East Orange, NJ; (3); Aud/Vis; Library Aide; USC; Bus.

TERRY, SHERYL; Ramsey HS; Ramsey, NJ; (3); 30/244; GAA; Trs Soph Cls; JV Bsktbl; Var Capt Fld Hcky; Var Capt Sftbl; High Hon Roll; Hon Roll; Jr NHS; NHS; Bst Indstrl Arts Stu 85-86; 1st Pl Awd NJ Crtfmns Fair Archt 86; 1st Tm Lg & 2nd Tm All Cnty Sftbl 86; VA Tech; Archt.

TERTZAGIAN, CHRISTINE; Ocean Township HS; Oakhurst, NJ; (3); 62/344; Key Clb; Ski Clb; Sec Spanish Clb; Socr; Swmmng; JV Let Swmmng 87; JV Let Soccer 85-87.

TESLENKO, VIC; Hopewell Valley Central HS; Princeton, NJ; (3); 18/213; Trs AFS; Am Leg Boys St; Math Tm; Nwsp Rptr; JV Tennis; High Hon Roll; NHS; Ntl Merit Ltr; Prfct Atten Awd; Amer Invitational Math Exam 86; Bio.

TESMAN, KOREN; Washington Township HS; Blenheim, NJ; (3); Trs English Clb; Hosp Aide; Library Aide.

TESORIERO, VIKKI; Jackson Memorial HS; Jackson, NJ; (3); 32/416; Art Clb; FBLA; Ski Clb; Stage Crew; Trk; High Hon Roll; Color Guard; Wt Lftg; Natl Art Honor Soc; Sons Of Norway Schlrshp 87; Natl Power Lifting Drug-Free Champ 87; Art.

TESORO, MARIA; Villa Victoria Acad; Trenton, NJ; (1); Library Aide; Chorus; Church Choir; School Musical; School Play; Stage Crew; Hon Roll; Bus.

TESTA, DAVID; James Caldwell HS; W Caldwell, NJ; (3); Key Clb; Science Clb; Band; Concert Band; Jazz Band; Mrchg Band; Orch; JV Golf; High Hon Roll; Sec NHS; NJ Regl Band 85; Bio.

TESTA, FRANK C; Vineland HS; Vineland, NJ; (4); 1/585; Key Clb; Latin Clb; Math Clb; High Hon Roll; NHS; Ntl Merit Ltr; Val; VP Jr Cls; VP Sr Cls; Rep Stu Cncl; Myer & Sarah Rotok Math Awd, Moose Awd Hghst Hstry Av, & Rtry Clb Awd Male Hghst Overall Av 87; Rutgers Coll.

TESTA, JEANNINE; Highland Regional HS; Erial, NJ; (3); 34/285; Sec AFS; Pres Camera Clb; French Clb; Band; Chorus; Mrchg Band; Nwsp Phtg; JV Pom Pon; Hon Roll; Law.

TETI, ALLYN M; The Pingry Schl; Chatham, NJ; (1); AFS; French Clb; Key Clb; Spanish Clb; Var Mgr Bsbl; JV Diving; Mgr(s); Swmmng; Hon Roll; Ntl Merit SF; Pltcl Sci.

TETLEY, KIM; Egg Harbor Township HS; Mays Landing, NJ; (4); 17/289; Hst French Clb; German Clb; Model UN; Office Aide; Sec Band; School Musical; Ed Yrbk Stf; NHS; Ntl Merit Ltr; Vrsty Schlr 84-86; Rutgers U; Frgn Lang.

TETTAMANTI, ROSEMARIE; Bayonne HS; Bayonne, NJ; (3); U Of Las Vegas; Med.

TETZ, DEBRA; Buena Regional HS; Richland, NJ; (3); 21/220; Ski Clb; Jr Cls; Hon Roll; Jr NHS; Bus Mgmt.

TEZA, DENNIS L; Newton HS; Newton, NJ; (3); 58/200; Am Leg Boys St; Latin Clb; Ski Clb; SADD; Band; Rep Frsh Cls; Rep Soph Cls; VP Stu Cncl; Var Bsbl; Var Ftbl; VP ST Stu Cncl 87; Bus Adm.

THATCH, SUSAN; St Pius X HS; Piscataway, NJ; (3); 8/88; Church Yth Grp; Office Aide; Scholastic Bowl; Stage Crew; Rep Jr Cls; Var Bsktbl; Var Crs Cntry; Sftbl; High Hon Roll; Pres NHS; St Pius Sci Awd 87; St Pius Spn Awd 87; Schl Svc Awd 87; Nrsng.

THATCHER, BARBARA; Belvidere HS; Belvidere, NJ; (4); Office Aide; Pep Clb; Teachers Aide; Varsity Clb; Yrbk Phtg; Yrbk Rptr; Yrbk Stf; Var Capt Cheerleading; Im Wt Lftg; Hon Roll; Empire Beauty Schl Schlrshp 87; Empire Beauty Schl; Csmtlgst.

THATCHER, CYNTHIA; Central Regional HS; Bayville, NJ; (3); VP FHA; Spanish Clb; Band; Yrbk Stf; VP Stu Cncl; Capt Cheerleading; Gym; Sftbl; Trk; High Hon Roll.

THAXTON, CHERYL; Orange HS; East Orange, NJ; (4); 38/162; Dance Clb; DECA; Hosp Aide; Variety Show; Nwsp Rptr; Nwsp Sprt Ed; Stu Cncl; Score Keeper; Hon Roll; NHS; Hampton U; Pre-Med.

THAYER, CHRISTOPHER; Morristown-Beard HS; Madison, NJ; (2); Band; Chorus; Orch; School Play; JV Socr; Hon Roll; Tri-M Music Hnr Soc 87.

THEDFORD, JENNIFER; Vineland HS; Vineland, NJ; (3); 8/827; French Clb; Key Clb; Varsity Clb; Trs Frsh Cls; Rep Jr Cls; Cheerleading; Swmmng; French Hon Soc; Gov Hon Prg Awd; Hon Roll.

THEOBALD, STACEY; St Joseph Of The Palisade HS; W New York, NJ; (2); Church Yth Grp; GAA; VICA; Church Choir; Yrbk Stf; Bowling; Swmmng; Hon Roll; St Peters Coll; Accounting.

THIER, DEBORAH; Madison Central HS; Old Bridge, NJ; (3); 160/350; Chorus; School Play; Hon Roll; Actg.

THINSCHMIDT, JILL; Mainland Regional HS; Northfield, NJ; (4); 26/390; Church Yth Grp; German Clb; Ski Clb; Sec Band; Sec Concert Band; Sec Mrchg Band; Nwsp Stf; Var Capt Crs Cntry; Var L Trk; Sec NHS; Pace U Merit Schlrshp 87; Mainland Band Schlrshp 87; Stu Cncl Schlrshp 87; Pace U; Equine Breedr.

THOELE, VICKI; West Morris Central HS; Long Valley, NJ; (4); 12/298; Pres Church Yth Grp; Band; Concert Band; Mrchg Band; Nwsp Stf; Co-Capt Tennis; High Hon Roll; Hon Roll; NHS; St Schlr; NJ Dist Schlr 87; Alumni Schlrshp 87; Trenton ST Coll; Bus Admin.

THOMAS, ALEX; Brick Memorial HS; Brick, NJ; (3); Var Ice Hcky; High Hon Roll.

THOMAS, DENISE; Belleville HS; Belleville, NJ; (3); Library Aide; Yrbk Stf; Hon Roll; Rutgers U; Comp Pgmmr.

THOMAS, DENNE; John F Kennedy HS; Willingboro, NJ; (4); 18/267; Dance Clb; Drama Clb; Church Choir; School Musical; Yrbk Stf; Sr Cls; Capt Pom Pon; Cit Awd; Hon Roll; Sec NHS; Marching Band Ldrshp Recgntn 86-87; Comm Svc Awd 84-85; Outstndng Dance Awd 85-86; Spelman; Bio.

THOMAS, KAREN E; Governor Livingston Reg HS; Berkeley Height, NJ; (4); 48/186; Pres Art Clb; Church Yth Grp; Drama Clb; Lit Mag; Hon Roll; Ntl Merit Ltr; Mrchg Band; School Musical; Rhode Island Schl Dsgn Annl Art Awd 87; Gov Livingston SR Clss Schlrshp Awd 87; Vtd Best Art 87; U MI; Visual Arts.

THOMAS, KENNETH; Morris Hills HS; Rockaway, NJ; (3); Capt Ski Clb; Hon Roll; Engrng.

THOMAS, KIMO; Grace A Dunn HS; Trenton, NJ; (1); Boys Clb Am; Church Yth Grp; Spanish Clb; Church Choir; Drill Tm; VP Frsh Cls; Cit Awd; Hon Roll; Prfct Atten Awd; Nwsp In Ed Awd 86; Harvard U; Acctng.

THOMAS, LISA; Pemberton Township HS; Pemberton, NJ; (2); FBLA; Band; Concert Band; Mrchg Band; Nwsp Stf; Trs Stu Cncl; Hon Roll.

THOMAS, LISA C; Clifton HS; Clifton, NJ; (4); 260/589; DECA; Library Aide; Chorus; Crs Cntry; Swmmng; Trk; Lancaster Bible Coll; Chrstn Ed.

THOMAS, ROBERT W; Chatham Township HS; Chatham, NJ; (3); 36/159; Am Leg Boys St; Varsity Clb; Nwsp Rptr; Pres Jr Cls; Pres Sr Cls; Rep Stu Cncl; Var L Bsbl; Var L Ice Hcky; Hon Roll; Al-Area, Cnty Ice Hcky Tm 86-87; Law.

THOMAS, RUSSELL; Hightstown HS; E Windsor, NJ; (3); AFS; Aud/Vis; Drama Clb; PAVAS; Service Clb; Spanish Clb; Acpl Chr; School Musical; Stage Crew; Yrbk Stf; Flm Mkng.

THOMAS, SHAWN EUGENE; Essex Catholic Boys HS; Orange, NJ; (3); Church Yth Grp; JA; Letterman Clb; Red Cross Aide; Service Clb; Varsity Clb; Y-Teens; Church Choir; Rep Soph Cls; Rep Jr Cls; Alpha Kappa Alpha-Yng Achvr Awd 85; Jersey City NJ-NOVICE Swmng Rcrd Hldr 85; Citation-Myr Of Orange; Howard U; Elec Engr.

THOMAS, TESSIE; Paramus Cathlic Girls Regional HS; Little Ferry, NJ; (2); Hosp Aide; SADD; Teachers Aide; Variety Show; Lit Mag; High Hon Roll; Hon Roll; Prfct Atten Awd; Camera Clb; Bst Chrctr Awd 87; Spnsh Awd 87; Wstrn Cvlztn 86; NY U; Bus.

THOMAS, TIFFANIE C; Cumberland Regional HS; Bridgeton, NJ; (3); French Clb; NAACP; Trs Church Choir; Yrbk Phtg; Capt Trk; Church Yth Grp; VP Girl Scts; Intnl Clb; Ski Clb; Drill Tm; Cmmndbl Achvt Sci 84-85; Faithful & Cnscrtd Svc Awd 86; Rutges U; Crmnlgy.

THOMAS, TUESDAY; Kent Place Schl; Irvington, NJ; (3); Dance Clb; Library Aide; Math Tm; VP NAACP; Lit Mag; Rep Soph Cls; High Hon Roll; Hon Roll; Jr NHS; Schlrhsp Gallmans Newark Dance Theatre 87; Engrng.

THOMAS, TYRONE; Essex Catholic Boys HS; Montclair, NJ; (3); Art Clb; Chess Clb; Drama Clb; Math Clb; Math Tm; School Musical; Stage Crew; High Hon Roll; Hon Roll; Ntl Merit SF; Fencing JV & Weapons Repair, Unofcl Team Vllybl; Duke U; Physics.

THOMAS, VANETTA; University HS; Newark, NJ; (2); Exploring; Cert Accmplshmnt 86; Fairleigh Dickinson U; Corp Law.

THOMAS, VELISSA; Paterson Catholic HS; Paterson, NJ; (3); NAACP; Pep Clb; Color Guard; Pep Band; Nwsp Stf; Yrbk Stf; Rep Frsh Cls; Rep Soph Cls; Stu Cncl; Vllybl; Mdl DECA Rgnl Conf 87; Bus Admin.

THOMAS, WILLIAM; Dwight Morrow HS; Englewood, NJ; (3); Trk; High Hon Roll; Hon Roll; Atten Awd 87; Track Awd 87; Morehouse Coll; Theolgy.

THOMPSON, AMY YVETTE; Penns Grove HS; Penns Grove, NJ; (3); 15/162; Am Leg Aux Girls St; JCL; Latin Clb; Flag Corp; Nwsp Ed-Chief; Ed Yrbk Stf; Trs Frsh Cls; Trs Soph Cls; Trs Jr Cls; Trs Sr Cls; Comp Engrng.

THOMPSON, ARTHUR; Bridgeton SR HS; Bridgeton, NJ; (4); Cmnty Wkr; VICA; Band; High Hon Roll; Hon Roll; Awd Outstndng Crpntry Stu 86-87.

THOMPSON, BONNIE; Sussex County Vo-Tech; Glenwood, NJ; (3); Chorus; Church Choir; School Musical; Stage Crew; Htl/Rest Mgmt.

THOMPSON, ECHAINNA; Franklin HS; Somerset, NJ; (3); Church Choir; Rep Soph Cls; Trk.

THOMPSON, ELIZABETH; Dwight-Englewood Schl; Englewood, NJ; (3); Camera Clb; Church Yth Grp; Cmnty Wkr; Hosp Aide; Teachers Aide; Chorus; Church Choir; School Musical; School Play; Lit Mag; Medal-Trck 87; Med.

THOMPSON, JILL; Middletown HS South; Red Bank, NJ; (3); VP Church Yth Grp; Cmnty Wkr; Ski Clb; Stage Crew; Rep Stu Cncl; High Hon Roll; NHS; Outstndng Achvt Civics & Earth Sci 84-85; Merit Awd Am Auto Assoc 86-87; Intr Dsgnr.

THOMPSON, LEON; Niddlesex Co Voch Tech HS; New Brunswick, NJ; (3); 5/13; Church Yth Grp; Math Clb; Pep Clb; SADD; Teachers Aide; Chorus; Church Choir; Sec Stu Cncl; Hon Roll; Prfct Atten Awd; Hon Playing SR Grad 87; Awd 1st Pl Cont Mechncl Drftng 87; Hon Having Most Respect Toward Tchrs Schl; Rutgers Coll; Architect.

THOMPSON, MELISSA; Eastern Christian HS; Paterson, NJ; (3); 12/85; Pep Clb; Yrbk Stf; Sec Stu Cncl; Cit Awd; Hon Roll; NHS; Trenton ST; Psych.

THOMPSON, MICHAEL; Belleville HS; Belleville, NJ; (3); Var Bsbl; Var Ftbl.

THOMPSON, NYKITA; Mother Seton Regional HS; Irvington, NJ; (2); Drama Clb; GAA; Varsity Clb; Yrbk Stf; Pres Jr Cls; Bsktbl; Bowling; Var Trk; Hon Roll; Delta 89; Ed.

THOMPSON, ROTANDA; John F Kennedy HS; Willingboro, NJ; (2); 5/297; Sec Church Yth Grp; Dance Clb; Intnl Clb; Latin Clb; Church Choir; Orch; VP Soph Cls; High Hon Roll; Jr NHS; NHS; HOBY Rep-HS 87; Good Ctznshp Awd 84-85; RCA Mnrty Engr Trner 85; George Washington U; Bus Mgmt.

THOMPSON, SANDRA; James Caldwell HS; West Caldwell, NJ; (4); 53/265; Key Clb; Sec Jr Cls; Sec Sr Cls; Var Cheerleading; Var Gym; JV Sftbl; High Hon Roll; Hon Roll; Bus.

THOMPSON, SANDRA ANN; Toms River HS South; Beachwood, NJ; (2); Intnl Clb; Science Clb; Flag Corp; Mgr(s); High Hon Roll; Hon Roll; Acdmc Ltr 86; Engrng.

THOMPSON, SCOTT E; Randolph HS; Randolph, NJ; (3); 43/438; Am Leg Boys St; Church Yth Grp; Debate Tm; Key Clb; Math Clb; Math Tm; Mu Alpha Theta; Chorus; Church Choir; Stage Crew; Am Leg Jrsy Bys ST Dlgt 87.

THOMPSON, SHANNON; Manalapan HS; Manalapan, NJ; (3); Dance Clb; PAVAS; Varsity Clb; Chorus; Var Stat Trk; Bus.

THOMPSON, SHEILA; Scotch Plains Fanwood HS; Scotch Pl, NJ; (4); 22/329; Church Yth Grp; German Clb; Varsity Clb; Drill Tm; Drm Mjr(t); Jazz Band; Off Stu Cncl; Sftbl; NHS; Rotary Awd; American U; Pol Sci.

THOMPSON JR, WILLIAM; Paul IV HS; Collingswood, NJ; (3); Church Yth Grp; Math Clb; Math Tm; Im Bowling; Var Crs Cntry; NHS; Engrng.

THOMSEN, LINDA J; Park Ridge HS; Park Ridge, NJ; (3); 13/98; AFS; VP Sec Intnl Clb; Library Aide; Math Clb; Drm Mjr(t); Mrchg Band; Sec Trs Sr Cls; Hon Roll; NHS; Rotary Awd; NRA Pro Mrksmn 87; Indstrl Engr.

THOMSON, BARBARA; Sacred Heart HS; Vineland, NJ; (4); 3/63; Art Clb; Dance Clb; Sec Spanish Clb; Teachers Aide; School Play; Stage Crew; Variety Show; Hon Roll; NHS; Natl Sci Merit Awd 85; Schlrshp-Cthlc Dghtrs Of Amer 83.

THOMSON, KENNETH; Wall HS; Manasquan, NJ; (3); Cmnty Wkr; German Clb; Political Wkr; Rep Stu Cncl; Crs Cntry; Wrstlng; High Hon Roll; Bus.

THOMSON, KEVIN; Gloucester City HS; Gloucester, NJ; (3); Am Leg Boys St; Model UN; Chorus; School Musical; School Play; Stu Cncl; Var Bsktbl; Var Ftbl; Var Trk; Hon Roll; Bus Mgmt.

THORN, RODGER; Clifton HS; Clifton, NJ; (3); Science Clb; Band; Concert Band; Jazz Band; Mrchg Band; Stage Crew; Nwsp Stf; JV Lcrss; JV Socr; Hon Roll; Biochem.

THORNTON, CHRISTINE; Monsignor Donovan HS; Jackson, NJ; (3); 29/243; Church Yth Grp; Dance Clb; Drama Clb; Math Tm; Service Clb; SADD; Thesps; School Musical; School Play; Var Cheerleading; Natl Honor Scty 86; Honor Roll 84-86; Cathl U Of Amer; Physics Tchr.

THORNTON, MARC; Essex Catholic HS; E Orange, NJ; (4); 63/150; Pres Stu Cncl; Im Bsktbl; Var Ftbl; Im Sftbl; Trk; Hon Roll; Rochester Natl Schlrshp 87; U Of Rochester.

THORNTON, SHEILA T; Academy Of The Holy Angels; Dumont, NJ; (4); 3/152; Pres Math Clb; Mu Alpha Theta; Spanish Clb; Yrbk Stf; Gov Hon Prg Awd; High Hon Roll; Hon Roll; NHS; Ntl Merit Ltr.

THORPE, ALEXIA; Plainfield HS; Plainfield, NJ; (3); 56/400; Sec FBLA; Sec Sr Cls; Rep Stu Cncl; Mgr(s); Capt Tennis; Hon Roll; Tennis Trophies; Bus Admin.

THORPE, TOM; Hunterdon Central HS; Flemington, NJ; (4); Computer Clb; Band; Concert Band; Jazz Band; Mrchg Band; Pep Band; School Musical; Symp Band; Variety Show; Somerset Coll; Comp Sci.

THOUROT, MICHELE; Victory Christian Schl; Atco, NJ; (4); 2/22; Church Yth Grp; Library Aide; Teachers Aide; High Hon Roll; Hon Roll; Jr NHS; NHS; Elem Educ.

THOUROT, NICOLE; Victory Christian HS; Atco, NJ; (4); 3/22; Church Yth Grp; Library Aide; Teachers Aide; High Hon Roll; Hon Roll; Jr NHS; NHS; Bus Admin.

THURKOW, LINDA; Linden HS; Linden, NJ; (3); Church Yth Grp; JV Var Bowling; Hon Roll; NHS.

THURSTON, NATHANIEL; Princeton HS; Princeton, NJ; (4); Debate Tm; Math Tm; Model UN; NFL; Ntl Merit Ltr; Physcs Olympd Tm 87; Reed Coll.

TIEMAN, TAMARA; Southern Regional HS; Barnegat, NJ; (4); 6/389; Concert Band; Yrbk Stf; Rep Frsh Cls; Rep Soph Cls; Rep Jr Cls; Rep Sr Cls; Rep Stu Cncl; JV Fld Hcky; Im Vllybl; High Hon Roll; Barnegat Reg Repblcn CC Schlrshp 87; Rutgers Schlr 86; Coll Of William & Mary; Mktg.

TIEN, DAVID; Bridgewater-Raritan High Schl West; Bridgewater, NJ; (3); Math Tm; Scholastic Bowl; Band; Stage Crew; Nwsp Phtg; Nwsp Rptr; Yrbk Phtg; Yrbk Stf; Trk; NHS; Engrng.

TIERNEY, ALYSSA; Morristown-Beard Schl; Morristown, NJ; (3); AFS; Sec Intnl Clb; Teachers Aide; Yrbk Ed-Chief; Yrbk Stf; Var Lcrss; Var Swmmng; JV Var Tennis.

TIERNEY, MICHAEL; Holy Spirit HS; Ventnor, NJ; (4); 42/363; Church Yth Grp; Civic Clb; Cmnty Wkr; SADD; Soph Cls; Jr Cls; Sr Cls; Stu Cncl; Capt L Bsbl; Capt L Ftbl; KOP Awd Amer Lgn Awd 83; Rutgers U; Sports Med.

TIERNEY, RODERIC; Princeton HS; Princeton, NJ; (4); Am Leg Boys St; Computer Clb; Var Debate Tm; Math Tm; Model UN; NFL; Scholastic Bowl; Science Clb; Var Speech Tm; Var Tennis; Lwyr.

TIESLAU, CHRIS; Millville SR HS; Millville, NJ; (3); Chess Clb; Computer Clb; 4-H; L Swmmng; 4-H Awd; Electro Mech.

TIETJEN, JUSTINE; Voorhees HS; Califon, NJ; (3); 6/277; Chrmn Church Yth Grp; Key Clb; Spanish Clb; Church Choir; Madrigals; Orch; School Musical; High Hon Roll; Hon Roll; Akron U; Bio Med Engrng.

TIGHE, COLEEN P; Linden HS; Linden, NJ; (4); 14/346; French Clb; Trs Key Clb; Science Clb; Ski Clb; Band; Capt Mrchg Band; School Musical; Nwsp Rptr; High Hon Roll; Hon Roll; U Of DE; Lbrl Arts.

TIGNOR II, THOMAS P; West Morris Mendham HS; Mendham, NJ; (4); 1/318; Debate Tm; Math Tm; NHS; Ntl Merit SF; Opt Clb Awd; Church Yth Grp; Cmnty Wkr; Service Clb; Chorus; Church Choir; Asthma Ath Of Yr 86; Master Clsses Piano Accptnce 86; All ST Chrs 86; Hgh Pt Achvt Awd 84; Comp Sci.

TILLIS, APRIL; West Orange HS; W Orange, NJ; (3); Sec French Clb; Temple Yth Grp; Band; Chorus; Mrchg Band; Nwsp Rptr; Cheerleading; Gym; Mgr(s); Swmmng.

TILLMAN, BOBBY; Dwight Morrow HS; Englewood, NJ; (4); 75/229; Church Yth Grp; FBLA; Latin Clb; Library Aide; Spanish Clb; Chorus; Yrbk Stf; Lit Mag; Bsbl; Mgr(s); Acctg.

TILTON, CORI; Woodstown HS; Elmer, NJ; (4); 17/220; Drama Clb; English Clb; 4-H; Chrmn German Clb; Key Clb; Library Aide; SADD; School Musical; School Play; Rep Sr Cls; Hwrd Fld Hcky Awd 87; Tri Cntry All Star 87; Drama Clb 87; Mary Washington; Bio.

TIMKO, DONNA; Spotswood HS; Milltown, NJ; (4); Church Yth Grp; Girl Scts; Library Aide; Church Choir; School Play; Nwsp Stf; Socr; Trk; Hon Roll; David Podlesny Art Awd 87; Montclair U; Fine Art.

TIMKO, ELIZABETH; Immaculata HS; Somerville, NJ; (3); Camera Clb; Church Yth Grp; Drama Clb; Math Tm; Ski Clb; Thesps; Band; Church Choir; Concert Band; Drm Mjr(t); Comp Sci.

TIMMONS, ROBERT; North Bergen HS; N Bergen, NJ; (3); German Clb; ROTC; Drill Tm; Crs Cntry; Trk; Merit Soc 87; Navy; Comp Oper.

TIMMONS, SUSAN; Cinnaminson HS; Cinnaminson, NJ; (3); GAA; JA; JV Bsktbl; Var Fld Hcky; JV Lcrss; Var Capt Swmmng; Rotary Awd; Mst Dedctd Plyr-Fld Hcky 85; Mst Vlbl Swmmr 86; Coachs Awd-Swmmng 87; Bus.

TIMONERA, MAYDA; Washington Township HS; Sewell, NJ; (4); 35/470; Church Yth Grp; Cmnty Wkr; Hosp Aide; Ski Clb; Spanish Clb; Color Guard; Mrchg Band; Hon Roll; NHS; Rotry Yth Ldrs Awd 86; Trenton ST Coll; Bio.

TIMPANARO, ANTHONY; Bayonne HS; Bayonne, NJ; (3); High Hon Roll; Math Hnrs 86-88.

TIMPONE, JOSEPH M; Immaculata HS; Somerville, NJ; (4); CAP; Math Tm; Red Cross Aide; Spanish Clb; Rep Stu Cncl; Var JV Ftbl; Hon Roll; NHS; Spanish NHS; Voice Dem Awd; Dr Scholl Wrldwd Fndtn Schlrshp 87; Lehigh U; Chem Engrng.

TINDELL, SHANNAN; Benedictine Acad; Newark, NJ; (4); Church Yth Grp; French Clb; Hosp Aide; Church Choir; Nwsp Rptr; Nwsp Sprt Ed; Yrbk Stf; Twrlr; Cit Awd; Trenton ST Coll; Spch Pathlgy.

TING, MICHAEL; Bridgewater-Raritan HS East; Bridgewater, NJ; (3); Computer Clb; Debate Tm; Math Clb; NFL; Speech Tm; Yrbk Ed-Chief; High Hon Roll; Ntl Merit Ltr; Rensslr Medl 87; Rutgers Schlr 87; NJ Frnscs Leag Fnlst 87; Engrng.

TINLEY, MICHAEL; Red Bank Regional HS; Red Bank, NJ; (3); Var Capt Bsktbl; Var Trk; Hnrbl Mntn-All Mnmth Bsktbl Tm 87; Scrng Ldrs-Shr 87; Accntng.

TIONGSON, ROSA; West Orange HS; West Orange, NJ; (2); Church Yth Grp; Hosp Aide; PAVAS; Acpl Chr; Art Clb; Drama Clb; Girl Scts; Band; Chorus; Church Choir; Chrldng Awds Artstc Awds 84-87; Violin Ansmbl & Schlrshp 85; All Cty Orchstra 83; Music Arts.

TIRENIN, MICHAEL; Hopewell Valley Central HS; Trenton, NJ; (4); 40/194; Sec Art Clb; Science Clb; Spanish Clb; High Hon Roll; Hon Roll; Hopewell Twnshp Lioness Clb Schlrshp, RISD Outstndng Achv, Excel Art Awd, Pres Acad Ftnss Awd 87; Drexel U; Bio.

TIRITILLI, CHRISTINE; Matawan Rehional HS; Cliffwood Bch, NJ; (3); 21/320; SADD; Color Guard; School Musical; Nwsp Rptr; Yrbk Stf; Rep Stu Cncl; Spanish Clb; Chorus.

TITTEL, DAWN; Rahway HS; Rahway, NJ; (3); Aud/Vis; Church Yth Grp; GAA; JA; Library Aide; Service Clb; Nwsp Stf; Yrbk Rptr; Yrbk Stf; Sec Frsh Cls; Bus Mgnt.

TITUS, TERESA; Middletown HS South; Middletown, NJ; (3); Yrbk Ed-Chief; VP Soph Cls; Jr Cls; Sec Stu Cncl; Stat Bsktbl; JV Socr; French Hon Soc; NHS; Ntl Merit SF; Most Outstndng Stu, Natl Olympic Bio Contest 2nd Highest Score & Subject Awds 85; Phys Thrpst.

TJALMA, MICHELE; Belvidere HS; Phillipsburg, NJ; (4); 3/125; Am Leg Aux Girls St; Pres Church Yth Grp; Key Clb; Library Aide; Model UN; Pep Clb; Var Sftbl; Bausch & Lomb Sci Awd; Hon Roll; Sec NHS Girls Citizenshp Inst Delgte 86; Elem Ed.

TKATSCHENKO, TAMARA; Williamstown HS; Williamstown, NJ; (4) 2/267; Am Leg Aux Girls St; Var Capt Cheerleading; NHS; Rotary Awd; St Schlr; Voice Dem Awd; Homecmng Rep; Prom Qn; French Merit Awd; Stu Councl Recogntn Awd; Trenton ST Coll; Nursing.

TOBEY, JENNIFER; Dwight Englewood Schl; Fort Lee, NJ; (3); Hosp Aide; Math Tm; Yrbk Stf; Lit Mag; Var Crs Cntry; Var Trk; High Hon Roll; Hon Roll; Ntl Merit Ltr; Prfct Atten Awd; Atlntc-Pcfc Math Leag Awd 87; Johns Hopkins Gftd Pgm 85-87; Genetic Cnslr.

TOBEY, PATRICK; Marist HS; Bayonne, NJ; (4); 29/103; Science Clb; Nwsp Rptr; Nwsp Stf; Yrbk Stf; Bsktbl; Golf; Score Keeper; Vllybl; High Hon Roll; Hon Roll; Stdlr Fndtn-NJ Htl/Mtl Assn 87-88; Mrst Schlrshp 83-84; Johnson & Wales; Clnry Arts.

TOBEY, PHIL; Marist HS; Bayonne, NJ; (3); 29/110; Boy Scts; Key Clb; Coach Actv; Var Capt Ftbl; Mgr(s); Var Trk; Im Vllybl; Var Wt Lftg; Hon Roll; Prfct Atten Awd; MVP Indr Trck; Bus Mngmnt.

TOBIA, CHRISTOPHER; Paul VI HS; Laurel Spr, NJ; (4); 49/504; Am Leg Boys St; Math Clb; Rep Sr Cls; Var L Bsbl; Bsktbl; Hon Roll; NHS; Accntng.

TOBIA, LISA; James Caldwell HS; W Caldwell, NJ; (3); Sec Key Clb; Yrbk Stf; Var Capt Socr; Var Sftbl; High Hon Roll; NHS; 1st Tm All Cnty Sccr 85 & 86; 1st Tm All Conf Sftbll 86; Pilot.

TODD, BERNADETTE; Holy Spirit HS; Linwood, NJ; (2); 16/397 French Clb; Rep Frsh Cls; Fld Hcky.

TODD, JILL M; Warren Hills Regional SR HS; Washington, NJ; (3); Rep DECA; Pep Clb; Yrbk Stf; JV Cheerleading; Powder Puff Ftbl; Hon Roll

TODD, KEVIN; Baptist HS; Pine Hill, NJ; (1); Church Yth Grp; Trs Frsh Cls; JV Bsktbl; Hon Roll; PA U; Med.

TODD, MICHAEL; Florence TWP HS; Roebling, NJ; (3); Boy Scts; Stage Crew; Var L Ftbl; Trk; Wt Lftg; Engrng.

TODD, MICHAEL; Regis HS; Jersey City, NJ; (3); Ski Clb; Band; Concert Band; Yrbk Stf; Wt Lftg; Wrstlng; Psych.

TOLEDO, ALAN; Memeorial HS; West New York, NJ; (3); Var Bsbl; Var Trk; Prfct Atten Awd; Comp Engrng.

TOLENTINO, CARMEN; St Anthonys HS; Jersey City, NJ; (4); 2/60; JV Var Bowling; Grdn St Dstngshd Schlr 87; Montclair ST Coll.

TOLIVER, KARLA DARIENNE; Hillside HS; Hillside, NJ; (3); 8/238; Cmnty Wkr; Leo Clb; Math Tm; Science Clb; Spanish Clb; Nwsp Phtg; Nwsp Rptr; Nwsp Stf; Hon Roll; Cert Of Mbrshp From LEO Clb 87; Cert Of Cmpltn Awd By NJ Inst Of Tech Comp Based Phys 87; Med.

TOLMAYER, ROBERT J; Rancocas Valley Regional HS; Mt Holly, NJ; (4); 6/254; Am Leg Boys St; JV Capt Bsktbl; Var Capt Socr; Var L Trk; Hon Roll; NHS; Pres Schlr; Ski Clb; Band; JV Tennis; Rtgrs U Deans Smmr Schlrs Pgm 86; US Air Frc Acad; Aerosp Engrng.

TOLOCKA, ALLISON; Southern Regional HS; Shipbottom, NJ; (3); 13/420; Band; Mrchg Band; Orch; Rep Soph Cls; Rep Stu Cncl; JV Cheerleading; High Hon Roll; Hon Roll; NHS.

TOMARO, ROBERT; Phillipsburg Catholic HS; Asbury, NJ; (4); 1/73; Math Tm; Pres Soph Cls; Stu Cncl; Var Socr; Bausch & Lomb Sci Awd; High Hon Roll; Pres NHS; Val; Quiz Bowl; Scholastic Bowl; All ST Scr Private & Pariochl 2nd Team 85-87; 1st All Conf Scr 84-87; MVP Scr Off Plyr Yr 85-87; GA Inst Tech; Aero Engrng.

TOMASELLO, CLAUDIA; Morristown-Beard HS; Morris Plains, NJ; (3); 24/77; Trs AFS; Church Yth Grp; Hosp Aide; Teachers Aide; Lit Mag; JV Tennis; Stat Trk; Var Vllybl; Hon Roll; Mst Imprvd Plyr Awd Vllybll 87; Mrn Bio.

TOMASI III, PETER; Hawthorne HS; Hawthorne, NJ; (3); Aud/Vis; Boy Scts; Var L Chess Clb; Band; Chorus; Church Choir; Concert Band; Jazz Band; L Mrchg Band; Var L Socr; Band Achvmnt Awd 85-86; Cert Of Recognition Audio/Visual 87; Elec.

TOMASINI, ELIZABETH; Paramus Catholic Girls HS; New Milford, NJ; (3); Church Yth Grp; Variety Show; Hon Roll; Prfct Atten Awd; CYO Retreat Tm & Accptnc Nght Tm Stu 87; Christn Svc Awd Out Stndng Stu 85-87; Bio.

TOMASKO, MICHELE; Holy Cross HS; Marlton, NJ; (3); French Clb; Girl Scts; Pep Clb; Ski Clb; Pep Band; Yrbk Stf; Rep Soph Cls; Rep Jr Cls; Rep Sr Cls; Cheerleading; Cls Homecoming Rep 84-85; Acctng.

TOMASSO, DEANNA; Vineland HS; Vineland, NJ; (3); 149/733; Drama Clb; French Clb; School Play; Stage Crew; JV Tennis; Dance Clb; Library Aide; Office Aide; NJ Schl Arts Glassboro ST Coll Dnce 85-86; Alvin Ailey Dnce Wrkshp Stocktn ST 86-87; Dance Ed.

TOMBACK, JEFF; Wayne Hills HS; Wayne, NJ; (3); #30 In Class; Pep Clb; Spanish Clb; Y-Teens; JV Var Bsbl; JV Var Bsktbl; Hon Roll; NHS; Penn ST.

TOMBLIN, BROOKE ELIZABETH; Gill/St Bernards HS; Mendham, NJ; (3); Pres Church Yth Grp; Dance Clb; Ski Clb; Spanish Clb; Church Choir; School Musical; Variety Show; Yrbk Stf; Var Bsktbl; Stat Sftbl; Meredith Pyne Awd Scholar 86-87; Excllnce Spn II 85-86; Scripps Coll; Humanities.

TOMLINSON, SHARON LYNN; Sayreville War Memorial HS; Sayreville, NJ; (4); Church Yth Grp; Dance Clb; DECA; Spanish Clb; Hnbl Mntn, Gen Merch Supv 87; Actv DECA Stu Awd 87; Jhnsn & Wls Schlrshp For DECA Achvt 87; Johnson & Wales Coll; Trl Trsm.

TOMMASO, ALBERTINA; Immaculate Heart Acad; Waldwick, NJ; (3); 13/160; Church Yth Grp; Dance Clb; Drama Clb; Red Cross Aide; Var Trk; Hon Roll; Piano 83-87; Karate 85; Italian Club 85; PA ST; Science.

TOMMINELLI, LORI; Toms River East HS; Toms River, NJ; (4); FBLA; Intnl Clb; Hon Roll; Rider Coll; Bus.

TOMSON, BRUCE; Hunterdon Central HS; Flemington, NJ; (3); 56/543; Boy Scts; Church Yth Grp; Key Clb; Ski Clb; SADD; Varsity Clb; Band; Ftbl; Hon Roll; Spanish NHS; Vrsty Lttrmn 86; Marine Bio.

TONER, EILEEN; Roselle Catholic HS; Roselle, NJ; (4); Drama Clb; Chorus; School Musical; School Play; Stage Crew; High Hon Roll; Hon Roll; Kean Coll; Theatre.

TONER, MICHAEL; Sacred Heart HS; Millville, NJ; (3); 4/62; Spanish Clb; Rep Frsh Cls; Rep Soph Cls; Rep Jr Cls; Pres Stu Cncl; Var Bsktbl; Var Golf; Var JV Socr; High Hon Roll; Hon Roll; Monchito Diaz Awd 85; ACPR 85; Leag Soccer All Star 1st Team Awd 86; Leag Golf All Star 2nd Team 87; Bus.

TONEY, KATRINA; Mother Seton Regional HS; Rahway, NJ; (2); GAA; Hosp Aide; Library Aide; NAACP; Yrbk Phtg; Yrbk Stf; Geom Hnr 87; Hampton; Chem.

TONGES, SANDRA; Middlesex HS; Middlesex, NJ; (4); 3/168; Math Tm; Quiz Bowl; Scholastic Bowl; Ski Clb; Stat Bsktbl; Var Capt Fld Hcky; High Hon Roll; Hon Roll; NHS; HOBY Ldrshp Semnrs; Grdn ST Dstngshd Schlr Awd; Rutgers U; Mrktng.

TOOHEY, SUZANNE; Highland Regional HS; Blackwood, NJ; (4); 56/297; JV Var Bsktbl; Var Capt Socr; Var Capt Sftbl; 1st Tm Sccr Al-Conf, Al-Group 3 86; Contrbtn Awd Sftbl 86; Comp Sci.

TOOLE, LESLEY; Mt Olive HS; Budd Lake, NJ; (4); Dance Clb; Ski Clb; JV Cheerleading; High Hon Roll; Hon Roll; Natl Hnr Art Soc 86-87; Rutgers; Bus.

TOOMEY, JENNIFER; Highland Regional HS; Sicklerville, NJ; (3); Art Clb; Camera Clb; Spanish Clb; Var L Fld Hcky; Var L Trk; Aud/Vis; Library Aide; Hon Roll; Track Contrubtn Outstndng Rnnr Awds 86; Pres Physcl Ftns Awd 84-85; Drexel U; Int Design.

TOPOLSKI, MARK; Cinnaminson Township HS; Cinnaminson, NJ; (3); 8/268; Am Leg Boys St; Church Yth Grp; Cmnty Wkr; German Clb; Math Tm; Science Clb; SADD; Varsity Clb; Concert Band; Rep Frsh Cls; John Hopkins Tlnt Fr Gftd Stu 82; NJ ROGATE Prgrm 84; AUS Svc Acad; Nclr Engr.

TOPPER, RENEE; Notre Dame HS; Trenton, NJ; (2); Church Yth Grp; Dance Clb; Thesps; Church Choir; School Musical; School Play; Stage Crew; Off Soph Cls; Hon Roll; NHS.

TORCHIA, KRIS; Monowgahela JR HS; Wenonah, NJ; (1); VP Pres Frsh Cls; VP Pres Stu Cncl; JV Socr; Hon Roll; Prfct Atten Awd; Sci.

TORCHIA, MARIA; Our Lady Of Mercy Acad; Turnersville, NJ; (3); FNA; Hosp Aide; Chorus; Pres Frsh Cls; Im Badmtn; Im Bsktbl; Var Cheerleading; Im Vllybl; Hon Roll; NHS; Ntl Sci Merit Awd; Ntl Scndry Ed Cncl Acad All-Amer 86; Prncpls List 84-87; Pre-Med.

TORCHON, MARJORIE; Saint Dominic Acad; Jersey City, NJ; (4); 44/149; Art Clb; Computer Clb; Intnl Clb; NAACP; SADD; Nwsp Rptr; Pres Sr Cls; Stu Cncl; Crs Cntry; Trk; 2nd Team In Crs Cntry 85; 1st Team In Crs Cntry 86; Mrtn Lthr King Schlrshp 87-88; Prvdnc Coll; Pltcl Sci.

TORIELLO, PETER J; Westwood HS; Westwood, NJ; (2); Jazz Band; Variety Show; Hon Roll; Ldr Corps Ridgewood YMCA 87; Jazz Band Hnrs Awd 87; Berklee Coll Music; Musician.

TORIGIAN, CHRISTINE; Paramus HS; Paramus, NJ; (3); Trs Church Yth Grp; French Clb; Library Aide; Ski Clb; Off Jr Cls; Trs Stu Cncl; VP L Socr; French Hon Soc; NHS.

TORIGIAN, DREW A; Paramus HS; Paramus, NJ; (4); 14/330; Am Leg Boys St; French Clb; Pres Math Clb; Pres Science Clb; Pres Band; Jazz Band; French Hon Soc; High Hon Roll; NHS; Johns Hopkins U; Math.

TORO, MIRIAM; Mc Corristin Cath HS; Trenton, NJ; (3); Church Yth Grp; Dance Clb; Drama Clb; GAA; Pep Clb; Chorus; School Musical; School Play; Rep Stu Cncl; Hon Roll; Syracuse U; Bus.

TORREGROZA, INGRID; Mary Help Of Christians Acad; Haledon, NJ; (1); JCL; SADD; Im Bsktbl; Gym; Tennis; High Hon Roll; Hon Roll; Natl Sci Merit Awd 86-87; Math.

TORRES, CARIDAD; Dover HS; Dover, NJ; (2); Key Clb; Band; Concert Band; Mrchg Band; High Hon Roll; Hon Roll; Svc Awd 85-86; Bio Awd 86-87; Sci Engnrng.

TORRES, CARMELO; East Side HS; Newark, NJ; (3); Am Leg Boys St; Computer Clb; Math Clb; Hon Roll; HS Schlrs Recgntn 87; Rutgers; Pol Sci.

TORRES, DIANNE; New Brunswick HS; New Brunswick, NJ; (3); Spanish Clb; Flag Corp; Rep Stu Cncl; Cheerleading; Hon Roll; Prfct Atten Awd; Rutgers; Bio.

TORRES, MANUEL; Burlington Township HS; Burlington, NJ; (3); 19/143; Am Leg Boys St; Var Capt Ftbl; NHS; Chess Clb; Varsity Clb; JV Bsktbl; Prfct Atten Awd; 2nd Team All Div Ftbl Defensive Back 86; Engr.

TORRES, OMAYRA; Perth Amboy HS; Perth Amboy, NJ; (4); Church Yth Grp; Office Aide; OEA; Teachers Aide; Stu Recog Prgm Schl Awd 87; Acctg.

TORRES, SANTOS; Perth Amboy HS; Perth Amboy, NJ; (4); 16/290; Library Aide; Math Tm; Spanish Clb; Yrbk Stf; Off Sr Cls; Stu Cncl; Tennis; Vllybl; High Hon Roll; Hon Roll; Kwns Awd-Irwng Gldstn 87; Ntl Hnr Soc 87; Schlrshp-Trntn ST Coll 87; Rider Coll; Bus.

TORRINGTON, ANDREW; Steinert HS; Hamilton, NJ; (3); Varsity Clb; Var Capt Swmmng; Im Capt Vllybl; Hon Roll; NHS; FBLA; Letterman Clb; Red Cross Aide; MVP Varsity Swmmng.

TORRISI, JENNIFER L; Cherry Hill E HS; Cherry Hill, NJ; (3); Church Yth Grp; Dance Clb; Latin Clb; Stu Cncl; Var Powder Puff Ftbl; Var Swmmng; Spirit Wk 84-86; Cotillion-Publcty 86; Engrng.

TORTORA, FRANK; Secaucus HS; Secaucus, NJ; (3); Math Clb; Mu Alpha Theta; L Bsbl; L Ftbl; Wt Lftg; Hon Roll; MVP Ftbl, All Leag & Cnty Hnr Rl Ftbl 86; Roston Coll.

TORTORIELLO, ANNA; Toms River HS North; Toms River, NJ; (3); High Hon Roll; Hon Roll; Ocean County Coll; Mgmt.

TOSADO, LORENZO; Memorial HS; West New York, NJ; (2); Band; Var Bsbl; JV Crs Cntry; Var Mgr(s); Var Trk; Princeton U; Comp Analyst.

TOSCANO, ALISA; Notre Dame HS; Robbinsville, NJ; (2); 43/409; Chorus; School Musical; NHS; Spanish NHS; Bsktbl; U Of PA; Pre Dentl.

TOSCANO, AMY; H G Hoffman HS; South Amboy, NJ; (3); 1/70; Office Aide; Ski Clb; Pres Frsh Cls; Pres Soph Cls; Rep Jr Cls; Var Cheerleading; Var Crs Cntry; Var Sftbl; High Hon Roll; NHS; Voice Of Dmcrcy Dist Wnr 86-87; Mthmtcs.

TOSCANO, ANGELO; Passaic Valley HS; W Paterson, NJ; (4); 5/353; Science Clb; High Hon Roll; NHS; Ntl Merit Ltr; NJ Hnrs Schlrshp 87-91; High GPA For HS Career 83-87; NJ Sci League 84-87; NJ Inst Of Tech; Engr.

TOSSOUNIAN, NORA; Montville Township HS; Pine Brook, NJ; (4); 10/254; Trs Church Yth Grp; Hosp Aide; Key Clb; Orch; Nwsp Stf; High Hon Roll; NHS; Garden ST Distngshd Schlr 86; Columbia Sci Hnrs Pgm 86-87; Wmns Clb Awd 87; Columbia U; Med.

TOTH, DAVID; Woodbridge HS; Woodbridge, NJ; (3); 5/350; Boy Scts; Church Yth Grp; VP Computer Clb; Math Clb; Capt Quiz Bowl; Science Clb; Rep Stu Cncl; NHS; Ntl Merit Ltr; NJ Gvrns Schl Sci Fnlst 87; Carnegie Mellon AP Early Adm 87; Biochem.

TOTH, JACQUELINE; St John Vianney HS; Union Beach, NJ; (4); 68/250; Hosp Aide; Rep Soph Cls; Rep Jr Cls; Rep Sr Cls; Var Socr; Hon Roll; Paralegal.

TOTH, TARA; Bordentown Regional HS; Bordentown, NJ; (3); 6/150; Drama Clb; Key Clb; Chorus; School Play; Stu Cncl; Cheerleading; Trk; Hon Roll; NHS; Prfct Atten Awd; Old Engl B; Counslr Stokes ST Natl Park.

TOTO, KATHERINE; Pennsauken HS; Pennsauken, NJ; (1); GAA; JA; Varsity Clb; Off Jr Cls; Off Sr Cls; NHS; St Schlr; Bsktbl; Fld Hcky; Sftbl; Med.

TOTO, MATTHEW; Middlesex HS; Middlesex, NJ; (3); German Clb; Ski Clb; Bsbl; Bsktbl; Ftbl; Villanova U; Law.

TOTTON, STEPHANIE; Morristown-Beard HS; Convent Station, NJ; (2); French Clb; Service Clb; Fld Hcky; Lcrss; Sftbl; Hon Roll; Peer Grp 87-89.

TOUB, KIMBERLY; Pequannock Township HS; Pompton Plains, NJ; (3); 21/218; Hosp Aide; Spanish Clb; Pres Temple Yth Grp; School Play; Lit Mag; Mat Maids; Hon Roll; NHS; Spanish NHS.

TOUZALIN, MONTY; Jackson HS; Jackson, NJ; (3); 54/416; JA; Bsktbl; Socr; High Hon Roll; Hon Roll; Outstndng Spksmn Frdm 86; Bus Mgmt.

TOWER, SCOTT; Holy Spirit HS; Linwood, NJ; (3); 34/332; Nwsp Rptr; JV Golf.

TOWEY, JOYCELYN; Bishop George Ahr HS; S Plainfield, NJ; (4); 95/265; Spanish Clb; SADD; Drill Tm; School Play; Crs Cntry; Pom Pon; Trk; Vllybl; High Hon Roll; Hon Roll; Prncpl List Strght A 84-85; Middlesex Cnty Coll; Bus Adm.

TOWNES, JEANETTE; East Side HS; Newark, NJ; (3); Cmnty Wkr; Exploring; FNA; Hosp Aide; Service Clb; Y-Teens; Church Choir; Sftbl; Trk; Ntl Merit Ltr; VA U; Nrsng.

TOWNSEND, LAURA ANNE; Holy Spirit HS; Marmora, NJ; (3); 105/313; Dance Clb; Drama Clb; Latin Clb; PAVAS; Red Cross Aide; Spanish Clb; SADD; Pep Band; School Play; Yrbk Stf; Mgr Surf Team & Natl Schltc Surfing Assoc 86-87.

TOZER, BEVERLY; Middle Township HS; Cape May Court, NJ; (3); Mrchg Band; L Mgr(s); High Hon Roll; Hon Roll; Engl Achvmnt Awd 85-87; Dir Awd 85-86; Stockton ST Coll; Bus.

TOZER, RENEE LYNN; Middle Township HS; Cape May C H, NJ; (4); 6/210; Key Clb; Color Guard; Mrchg Band; Hon Roll; NHS; Opt Clb Awd; Pres Schlr; Ski Clb; Stage Crew; Yrbk Rptr; Bst Bio Stu; Mock Trl Team; Acad Exc Awd; Albrght Coll; Bio.

TOZOUR, JENNIFER; Gloucester County Christian HS; Sewell, NJ; (2); Church Yth Grp; Cmnty Wkr; Spanish Clb; Chorus; Bsktbl; Fld Hcky; Sftbl; High Hon Roll; Sci Fair 1st Prz 86; Pensacola Chrstn Coll; Nrsng.

TRACEY, TARA; Brick Memorial HS; Brick, NJ; (1); Frsh Cls; Cheerleading; Socr; High Hon Roll; Soph Cls Treas 87-88; Vrsty Chrng Sqd 87-88; ST Champ For JV Trio Chrng Comp 87.

TRACEY, TERESA; Howell HS; Howell, NJ; (3); French Clb; Pep Clb; Ski Clb; Spanish Clb; Chorus; High Hon Roll; Hon Roll.

TRACY, DANIELLE; Boonton HS; Lincoln Pk, NJ; (2); Off Frsh Cls; Off Soph Cls; Bsktbl; Fld Hcky; Sftbl; Hon Roll; Mst Prmsg Plyr Awd Fld Hcky 85; Morris Cnty Fld Coachs Assoc Elctd All Cnty Tm 86.

TRACY, THOMAS; Buena Regional HS; Buena, NJ; (3); 33/200; Church Yth Grp; Cmnty Wkr; Teachers Aide; Glsbr ST; Elem Tchr.

TRACY, TOBY; Holy Spirit HS; Brigantine, NJ; (2); 37/397; Bsktbl; Im Vllybl; Hon Roll.

TRAEGER, GEOFFREY; Lenape Valley Regional HS; Andover, NJ; (4); 40/240; Am Leg Boys St; VP German Clb; Intnl Clb; Key Clb; Lit Mag; Var Bsbl; Var Socr; Hon Roll; Giftd Talntd Pgm 87; Auburn U; Pilot.

TRAFICANT, LISA; Central Regional HS; Bayville, NJ; (4); 28/243; Church Yth Grp; Cmnty Wkr; Letterman Clb; Var JV Bsktbl; Coach Actv; Var Capt Socr; Var Capt Tennis; High Hon Roll; Hon Roll; NHS; Roanoke Awd, Pell Grant & Lutheran Brotherhood Schlrshp 87-88; Roanoke Coll; Physcl Thrpy.

TRAFLET, JANICE; Immaculate Conception HS; Elmwood Park, NJ; (3); 4/70; Spanish Clb; SADD; Stage Crew; Nwsp Rptr; Lit Mag; Tennis; NHS; NEDT Awd; Ntl Ldrshp Awd 86.

TRAFLET, JEANNE; Immaculate Conception HS; Elmwood Park, NJ; (3); 14/70; English Clb; Q&S; Spanish Clb; Nwsp Rptr; Yrbk Rptr; Lit Mag; High Hon Roll; NEDT Awd; Poltcl Sci.

TRAHAN, DAVID; Monsignor Donovan HS; Jackson, NJ; (3); Boy Scts; Church Yth Grp; DECA; FHA; German Clb; Hosp Aide; JA; Red Cross Aide; Ski Clb; Teachers Aide; Natl Rifle Assoc 85; Monsignor Donovan Athltc Awd 84-87; Army; Law Enfrcmnt.

TRAINOR, MICHAEL; Jackson Memorial HS; Jackson, NJ; (4); 130/387; DECA; Rgnl Comp Fo DECA 87; Pres DECA Class 86-87; Trenton ST; Lawyer.

TRAJKOVSKA, VIOLET; Garfield HS; Garfield, NJ; (2); 8/200; Trs Art Clb; Exploring; SADD; Sec Teachers Aide; Color Guard; Nwsp Stf; Yrbk Stf; JV Tennis; Elks Awd; Med.

TRAN, MAI-ANH; Rutherford HS; Rutherford, NJ; (3); Math Tm; Tennis; Trk; High Hon Roll; Rep Frsh Cls; Computer Clb; Key Clb; NFL; Ski Clb; Chorus; Futre Pblm Slvng Tm 3rd ST 87; Acdmc Decthln; Bergen Cnty Choir; Intl Ecnmcs.

TRAN, NGUYEN; Dickinson HS; Jersey City, NJ; (4); Office Aide; Science Clb; Teachers Aide; Socr; Capt Swmmng; Ntl Merit Schol; Rutgers; Electrl.

TRAN, THAO; William L Dickinson HS; Jersey City, NJ; (4); FNA; Girl Scts; Library Aide; Red Cross Aide; Church Choir; Pres Frsh Cls; Rep Soph Cls; Badmtn; Vllybl; High Hon Roll; Biliogo Pgm Awd 86; Rutgers; Bio Chem.

TRANTHAM, TAMMI; Baptist HS; Cherry Hill, NJ; (3); Church Yth Grp; Cmnty Wkr; Drama Clb; Hosp Aide; Chorus; Church Choir; School Play; Stage Crew; Var Cheerleading; Educ.

TRAPANESE, JEFFREY; Wayne Hills HS; Wayne, NJ; (3); 74/350; Am Leg Boys St; Church Yth Grp; JV Bsbl; JV Bsktbl; Hon Roll.

TRAUSE, HOLLY; Wood-Ridge HS; Wood-Ridge, NJ; (3); Latin Clb; Sftbl; High Hon Roll; Cum Ld & Magna Cum Ld 86-87; Natl Latn Exam 85-87; Bio.

TRAVALINE, STEFANIE; Cumberland Regional HS; Bridgeton, NJ; (3); 31/385; French Clb; Intnl Clb; JV Bsktbl; JV Var Fld Hcky; Stat Mgr(s); Var Score Keeper; JV Stat Sftbl; Hon Roll; Jr NHS; NJ Math Leag Awd 85; Frnch.

TRAVERSO, ROBYN; Paramus Catholic Girls HS; Fair Lawn, NJ; (3); Ski Clb; SADD; Nwsp Stf; Var Co-Capt Cheerleading; Pom Pon; Socr; Elem Ed.

TRAVEZANO, ANGELA; Paterson Catholic Regional HS; Paterson, NJ; (3); 5/97; Camera Clb; Computer Clb; Var Capt Sftbl; Hon Roll; Prfct Atten Awd; Rutgers U; Bus.

TRAWINSKI, JANICE; West Milford Township HS; West Milford, NJ; (3); 19/402; Dance Clb; Rep Frsh Cls; Coach Actv; Var Gym; Hon Roll; JETS Awd; Jr NHS; NHS; Dnce Schlrshp-Dnc Edctrs Amer 86.

TREFERO, TAMMY; Absegami HS; Absecon, NJ; (3); #24 In Class; Art Clb; Drama Clb; Key Clb; Science Clb; SADD; School Play; Yrbk Stf; Hst Stu Cncl; Hon Roll.

TREITEL, ANDREW J; The Frisch Schl; Englewood, NJ; (4); Capt Debate Tm; Hosp Aide; Trs Science Clb; Temple Yth Grp; Varsity Clb; Band; Nwsp Ed-Chief; Yrbk Stf; Lit Mag; Rep Frsh Cls; Nrth Jersey Debate Leag-Spcl Tm Awd, Trnmt Trophy; Sci Fair 3rd Pl; Columbia U.

TRELSTAD, BRIAN; Princeton HS; Princeton, NJ; (4); Q&S; Nwsp Sprt Ed; Pres Soph Cls; Pres Stu Cncl; Var L Bsktbl; Var L Socr; Var L Trk; High Hon Roll; Nicholas Arcaro Schlr Athlt 87; Florence Burke Awd 87; Harvard U; Hist.

TREMEL II, CHARLES; Brick Memorial HS; Brick, NJ; (4); 19/290; Var Capt Crs Cntry; Var Trk; High Hon Roll; St Schlr; Exchng Clb Stu Rcgntn Awd 87; Schlr Athlt Crss Cnty 85-87; Montclair St.

TREOLE, KATHLEEN M; Clifton HS; Clifton, NJ; (4); 25/589; Girl Scts; Library Aide; Band; Concert Band; Mrchg Band; Rptr Soph Cls; Bsktbl; Hon Roll; Jr NHS; NHS; Mustang Band Schlrshp 87; Christopher Columbs Mddle Schl Almni Schlrhsp; 1st Fmle Qrtrmstr 50 Yr Hstry; Ithaca Coll; Spch Pathlgy.

TRESSLER, BRIAN; Raritan HS; W Keansburg, NJ; (3); 113/340; Hon Roll; Arthtctr.

TRIANT, JENNIFER K; Cresskill HS; Cresskill, NJ; (3); 11/103; Church Yth Grp; French Clb; Ski Clb; Nwsp Rptr; High Hon Roll; NHS; Rep Stu Cncl; Var Mgr(s); JV Sftbl; Stat Vllybl; Bus.

TRIAS, MERILEE; Bishop Eustace Prep; Somerdale, NJ; (4); Dance Clb; Drama Clb; Math Clb; Pep Clb; Spanish Clb; School Musical; School Play; Frsh Cls; Cheerleading; Trk; All Amer Chrldr Fnlst 86; Drexel U; Fash Merch.

TRIBLEHORN, JEFF; Middletown HS South; Red Bank, NJ; (3); Am Leg Boys St; Church Yth Grp; Var Stat Bsktbl; L Bowling; Stat Ftbl; Hon Roll; Lwyr.

TRILONE, DONNA; Manville HS; Manville, NJ; (4); 14/92; Church Yth Grp; Library Aide; Hon Roll; Union Cnty Coll; Dntl Hgnst.

TRIMBLE, COLLEEN; Lower Cape May Regional HS; Cape May, NJ; (3); 13/248; Church Yth Grp; Key Clb; Spanish Clb; Mrchg Band; Capt Pom Pon; High Hon Roll; Hon Roll; NHS; Prfct Atten Awd; Rotary Intl Exchng Pgm-Spain 87.

TRIMBLE, KELLY; Lenape Regional HS; Vincentown, NJ; (3); Spanish Clb; Varsity Clb; Var JV Cheerleading; Trk; Hon Roll; Won 1st & 3rd Pl Lenapes Ltrry Mag Poetry Cntst 86-87; Temple; Engl.

TRINIDAD, VICTOR JOEL; Municipal Schl Of Princetn; Williamson, WV; (3); Art Clb; French Clb; Radio Clb; SADD; Nwsp Phtg; Yrbk Phtg; Crs Cntry; Lcrss; Wrstlng; Arch.

TRIOLO, BOBBI; Manchester Regional HS; Haledon, NJ; (2); Church Yth Grp; Teachers Aide; Band; Chorus; Church Choir; Color Guard; Drill Tm; Mrchg Band; JV Sftbl; Ptry Awd 87; Bio.

TRIOLO, CHRISTINE; Monsignor Donovan HS; Toms River, NJ; (3); 32/260; Drama Clb; Model UN; Ski Clb; Stage Crew; Cheerleading; Score Keeper; Trk; Hon Roll; NHS; Georgetown U Intl Rltns Prog 87; Dplmtc Rltns.

TRIPODI, VINCENZO; North Bergen HS; N Bergen, NJ; (3); 150/453; Computer Clb; Off Stu Cncl; Var Trk; Stu Cncl Awd 87; Rugers U; Comp Bus.

TRIVEDI, SUNIL J; West Milford HS; West Milford, NJ; (4); 2/360; Am Leg Boys St; SADD; Varsity Clb; VP Sr Cls; Var Wrstlng; NHS; Sal; Garden ST Dist Schlr; Mel Sobel Microscoper LTD Bio Awd; U S Air Force Math & Sci Awd; U Of MI; Med.

TROGDON, MELISSA L; Overbrook SR HS; Clementon, NJ; (4); 3/335; Girl Scts; Mrchg Band; Bsktbl; Crs Cntry; Trk; High Hon Roll; Hon Roll; Pres NHS; U Of NH; Hosp Admn.

TROIA, JULIA L; Middlesex HS; Middlesex, NJ; (4); 80/157; Key Clb; Ski Clb; Chorus; School Musical; Merit Awd Bond 87; Middlesex County Coll.

TROIDL, LISA E; The Hun School Of Princetn; Pennington, NJ; (4); 6/109; Drama Clb; French Clb; Trs German Clb; Chorus; School Musical; School Play; Variety Show; High Hon Roll; Pres Schlr; St Schlr; 2nd Pl Classcl Vocal Comptn Stokes Cnty; Henry King Stanford Acad Scholar; Schl Vocal Music Prz; U Miami; Studio Music.

TROMER, DOTAN; Morris Hills HS; Wharton, NJ; (3); 50/266; Math Tm; Socr; MIT; Elctrncs.

TRONCONE, ADRIENNE; Columbia HS; Maplewood, NJ; (3); Cmnty Wkr; Library Aide; Teachers Aide; Cert Hnrb Merit Outstndng Prfrmnc Natl Latin Exm, HS Rep Grls ST 87; Bus.

TRONCONE, NICOLE; Columbia HS; Maplewood, NJ; (1); Church Yth Grp; Library Aide.

TROPEANO, DANIEL; Arthur L Johnson HS; Clark, NJ; (3); Rep Frsh Cls; Rep Soph Cls; Rep Jr Cls; Rep Sr Cls; Var L Ftbl; Var L Lcrss; Hon Roll.

TROST, JEFFREY; John P Stevens HS; Edison, NJ; (3); 1/456; Trs Cmnty Wkr; Sec Debate Tm; Sec Model UN; Pres Science Clb; Spanish Clb; Nwsp Bus Mgr; Rep Frsh Cls; Rep Soph Cls; Rep Jr Cls; Rep Stu Cncl; Olympics Of The Mind 87; Rider Coll Frgn Lang Forencis Trnmnt 1st Pl 86; Natl Chmpnshp 1st Pl 85-87; Nuclear Physics.

TROTMAN, KAREN; Haddonfield Memorial HS; Haddonfield, NJ; (3); JV Var Cheerleading; Acctng.

TROTMAN, VICKI; Toms River High School North; Toms River, NJ; (3); 94/459; Var Fld Hcky; Var Socr; Var Trk; Hon Roll; Elem Educ.

TROTTA, FRANK B; Ridgefield Memorial HS; Ridgefield, NJ; (4); Ski Clb; Bsktbl; Trk; Montclair ST Coll; Pol Sci.

TROUTMAN, ABIGAIL; Montville Township HS; Montville, NJ; (3); 62/248; Church Yth Grp; Ski Clb; JV Capt Fld Hcky; JV Powder Puff Ftbl; Var Trk; High Hon Roll; Hon Roll; NHS; Law.

TROVATO, LAURA; Queen Of Peace HS; Kearny, NJ; (3); Teachers Aide; Bowling; Tennis; Vllybl; Hon Roll; Spanish NHS; Rutgers U.

TRUEHART, TERRY; J F K HS; Willingboro, NJ; (2); Church Yth Grp; Latin Clb; Office Aide; Color Guard; Trs Frsh Cls; Trs Soph Cls; Trs Jr Cls; Pom Pon; Hon Roll; Engr.

TRUESDELL, STEPHANIE; Stuart Country Day Schl; Lawrenceville, NJ; (3); Cmnty Wkr; French Clb; School Play; VP Frsh Cls; VP Soph Cls; VP Jr Cls; Pres Sr Cls; JV Bsktbl.

TRUITT, KRISHNA S; Grace A Dunn JR HS; Trenton, NJ; (1); Political Wkr; Sec Spanish Clb; Chorus; Church Choir; Drill Tm; School Play; Lit Mag; Mgr Trk; Hon Roll; Prfct Atten Awd; Drug Essay Contest Wnnr 1st Pl 87; Judge.

TRUITT, SUE; West Morris Mendham HS; Mendham, NJ; (4); 16/320; FBLA; Intnl Clb; Stat Ftbl; High Hon Roll; Hon Roll; St Schlr; Alt Wmns Ctznshp Pgm 86; Albright Coll; Bus Mgmt.

TRUJILLO, BARBARA; Memorial HS; West New York, NJ; (3); Teachers Aide; Lit Mag; Rep Frsh Cls; Rep Soph Cls; Rep Pres Jr Cls; Rep Sr Cls; Rep Stu Cncl; Var Cheerleading; Hon Roll; Govt Hstry.

TRUKOWSKI, STACY; Randolph HS; Randolph, NJ; (3); 92/390; Church Yth Grp; Latin Clb; Ski Clb; Capt Color Guard; Yrbk Stf; Capt Var Cheerleading; Powder Puff Ftbl; Htl Rest Mgmnt.

TRULUCK, VIVIAN; Pennsauken HS; Pennsauken, NJ; (3); Library Aide; Trs Spanish Clb; Nwsp Rptr; Mgr Bsktbl; Mgr Crs Cntry; Hon Roll; Sec Spanish NHS; Honor Soc 86-87; Engl.

TRUMAN, CHRISTINE; Mainland Regional HS; Linwood, NJ; (3); Church Yth Grp; Church Choir; Bus.

TRUMBAUER, SUSAN M; Westfield HS; Westfield, NJ; (3); Hosp Aide; Pep Clb; Band; Chorus; Color Guard; Concert Band; Drill Tm; Flag Corp; Mrchg Band; Orch; Clemson U; Phrmcy.

TRUNCELLITO, DAVID; Toms River HS East; Toms River, NJ; (3); 3/540; Am Leg Boys St; Pres FBLA; Pres Math Tm; JV Socr; Trs NHS; Ntl Merit SF; Church Yth Grp; Intnl Clb; Scholastic Bowl; Ski Clb; 1st Pl Indvdl & Tm Ocean Cnty Mth Leg 86-87; SAT Mth 800 Vrbl 640 87; FBLA 3rd ST Acctng-Bus 86-87; Engrng.

TRUONG, HUNG; North Bergen HS; North Bergen, NJ; (4); 46/400; VP French Clb; Var Tennis; French Hon Soc; Rutgers U; Elect Engr.

TRUONG, THANH; Morris Knolls HS; Denville, NJ; (3); French Clb; Math Clb; NHS; Chem Hnrs, Merit Awd 86-87; Frnch, Pre Calculs Merit Awds 86-87; Boston U; Natl Sci.

TRUONG, TRI M; Monroe Township HS; Spotswood, NJ; (4); 4/198; Am Leg Boys St; Computer Clb; Math Clb; Math Tm; Quiz Bowl; Scholastic Bowl; Science Clb; JV Socr; Im Tennis; Bausch & Lomb Sci Awd; Princeton; Engrng.

TRUPPA, ROBERT J; Lacey Twp HS; Forked River, NJ; (3); 11/306; Am Leg Boys St; Boy Scts; Science Clb; Rep Frsh Cls; Rep Soph Cls; Cit Awd; Hon Roll; NHS; Prfct Atten Awd.

TRUPPO, CINDY; Randolph HS; Randolph, NJ; (3); 81/350; Girl Scts; VP Key Clb; Lit Mag; Sec Frsh Cls; Rep Soph Cls; Rep Jr Cls; Capt Tennis; Hon Roll; Spanish NHS; NFL; P E Hoffman Awd 87; Spec Ed.

TRUSKOWSKI, ELLEN; T R HS South; Beachwood, NJ; (2); Girl Scts; Stage Crew; Yrbk Stf; L Bsktbl; L Fld Hcky; L Socr; Hon Roll; Del To HOBY Fndtn Sem 87; VP Of Beachwood Jr Rec Cmmttee, CCD Tchr 86-87; Sci.

TSAI, JERRY; The Lawrenceville Schl; Princeton, NJ; (3); Pres Math Tm; Pres Science Clb; Mgr Orch; Nwsp Stf; Hon Roll; JETS Awd; Ntl Merit SF.

TSAI, KURCHIA; Montville HS; Montville, NJ; (3); Drama Clb; FBLA; NFL; Capt Scholastic Bowl; Chorus; School Musical; Nwsp Bus Mgr; Var Trk; NHS; Ntl Merit Ltr; Rep-Sntrs Stu Ldrshp Smnr 87; Hgh Hnr Roll 85-87; Vet Med.

TSENG, LILY; Paramus HS; Elmhurst, NY; (4); 39/336; Art Clb; Church Yth Grp; Intnl Clb; Math Clb; Spanish Clb; Orch; Jr NHS; NHS; Pres Schlr; Bus Schlrshp 87; Paramus Run Schlrshp 87; Baruch Coll; Acctg.

TSENG, YI PING; Passaic County Tech & Voc HS; Passaic, NJ; (3); 33/523; Hon Roll; Berkeley; Comp.

TUBBS, LAURA; Montville Twp HS; Pinebrook, NJ; (3); 92/276; Church Yth Grp; Drama Clb; Chorus; Church Choir; Socr; Dance Clb; FBLA; GAA; Varsity Clb; School Musical; Runnr Up Miss Chrldr NJ; Music Lssn Schlrshp; Phrmcy.

TUBER, MICHELLE; Livingston HS; Livingston, NJ; (3); AFS; Chorus; JV Sftbl; Hon Roll; Cmnctns.

TUCCILLO, ANNA M; Bordentown Regional HS; Bordentown, NJ; (4); 7/114; Am Leg Aux Girls St; Church Yth Grp; Cmnty Wkr; Drama Clb; Capt Math Tm; Mu Alpha Theta; Capt Color Guard; Var Bowling; Stat Fld Hcky; Hon Roll; Olympics Of Mind Cntrl Jersey Champs 86; Pre-Med.

TUCKER, BRADFORD; Holy Spirit HS; Ocean City, NJ; (3); 45/332; JV Ftbl; VP L Wrstlng; Hon Roll; Jr NHS; Physcs Airplane Cntst Wnnr 86; Pre Med.

TUCKER II, CHARLES B; Lenape HS; Vincentown, NJ; (3); 2/531; Am Leg Boys St; German Clb; Math Tm; Scholastic Bowl; Varsity Clb; Var L Trk; High Hon Roll; NHS; Ntl Merit Ltr; Church Yth Grp; German Ntl Hnr Soc 86-87; Chem Engrng.

TUCKER, EBONY; Weequyahie HS; Newak, NJ; (4); 7/390; Hosp Aide; Teachers Aide; Bsktbl; Trk; Hon Roll; Newark Human Rights Commsn Annl Human Rights Awds 85; Monclair ST Coll; Med Phycn.

TUCKER, KATHRYN; Burlington County Vo-Tech; Beverly, NJ; (3); 1/192; Dance Clb; FBLA; Chorus; Yrbk Stf; Hon Roll; Prfct Atten Awd; Stenogphr I 4th FBLA Regnl Cmptn 86; Berkley; Bus Mgmt.

TUDJEK, KRISTA; Wildwood Catholic HS; Wildwood Crest, NJ; (3); 9/90; JA; Spanish Clb; School Musical; Stage Crew; Var Fld Hcky; JV Tennis; Hon Roll; NHS; Spanish NHS; Relgn Awd 85; Bus.

TUELLA, KETHLEY ANN; Rutherford HS; Rutherford, NJ; (3); Am Leg Aux Girls St; French Clb; Pres Key Clb; NFL; Nwsp Stf; Lit Mag; Rep Sr Cls; Tennis; Decthlt-Acadc Decthln 87; Ftur Prblm Slvng Tm-3rd Pl-ST 86; NYU-COLUMBIA; Jrnlsm.

TUFARO, CHRISTINA; Bishop George Ahr HS; S Plainfield, NJ; (3); Cmnty Wkr; Debate Tm; Intnl Clb; Model UN; Ski Clb; JV Tennis; High Hon Roll; Occptnl Ther.

TUFTS, RICK; Madison Central HS; Old Bridge, NJ; (3); 70/360; Varsity Clb; Var Bsktbl; JV Socr; Var Tennis; Hon Roll.

TUIN, MARC; Warren County Vo-Technical HS; Phillipsburg, NJ; (3); Boy Scts; Church Yth Grp; 4-H; VICA; JV Bsktbl; Var Crs Cntry; Var Trk; Hon Roll; Lincoln Tech Schl; Diesel.

TUITE, JOSEPH M; Kearny HS; Kearny, NJ; (3); 8/400; Am Leg Boys St; Var L Bsktbl; Var Socr; High Hon Roll; NHS; Acdmc Excllnc Awd 85; Engrng.

TULL, DAWN; Gateway Regional HS; Westville, NJ; (3); #9 In Class; French Clb; German Clb; Spanish Clb; SADD; Sftbl; Trk; Ntl Frgn Lang Hnr Soc; Wrtr.

TULL, WENDY; Holy Spirit HS; Ventnor, NJ; (4); 5/363; Stage Crew; Trk; Hon Roll; NHS; Distngshd Schlr 86; Gvnrs Schl Of Sci Fnlst 86; Rotary Yth Ldrshp Awd 86; Engr.

TULLAI, JOHN; Notre Dame HS; West Trenton, NJ; (3); Math Tm; Nwsp Ed-Chief; JV Var Bsktbl; High Hon Roll; Pres NHS; Pres Spanish NHS; Spnsh II, III, IV Awds; NJ Chem Caravan Delg; Excllnc Religious Stds; Med.

TUMANG, MICHELE; Academic HS; Jersey City, NJ; (3); Computer Clb; Dance Clb; French Clb; Science Clb; Nwsp Rptr; Yrbk Ed-Chief; Yrbk Phtg; Yrbk Stf; Ed Lit Mag; Swmmng; Hnr Stu 84-87; Northeastern U; Phys Thrpy.

TUMARKIN, ANDREA; John P Stevens HS; Edison, NJ; (3); Cmnty Wkr; Drama Clb; Girl Scts; Office Aide; Temple Yth Grp; Y-Teens; Chorus; Nwsp Rptr; Nwsp Stf; Lit Mag; Middlesex Cnty Arts 85-87; Commnctns.

TUMBARELLO, JOSEPHINE; Sacred Heart HS; Vineland, NJ; (3); Spanish Clb; Chorus; School Musical; School Play; Lit Mag; Glassboro ST; Tchr.

TUNC, FEZA; East Brunswick HS; E Brunswick, NJ; (3); FBLA; German Clb; Hosp Aide; Key Clb; Math Clb; Science Clb; Ski Clb; SADD; Im Bowling; High Hon Roll; Grmn Hnr Soc 86-87; Amer Invtnl Math Exam 87; Pre-Med.

TUNISON, AUDRA; Hunterdon Central HS; Whitehouse Sta, NJ; (4); 151/550; Trs Art Clb; Sec Church Yth Grp; Cmnty Wkr; Latin Clb; Church Choir; Stage Crew; Jordan S Doyle Scholar PBA Scholar 87; Fairleigh Dickinson U; Psych.

TUNSTALL, VAUGHN S; Woodbury JR SR HS; Woodbury, NJ; (3); 10/107; Am Leg Boys St; Church Yth Grp; Exploring; Math Tm; Science Clb; Varsity Clb; Band; Chorus; VP Church Choir; Concert Band; John Hopkins Talent Search Schlrshp $50 82; $1500 Schlrshp To Math Prgm At Howard U 87; Doctor.

TUOHY, THOMAS; St Peters Prep; Jersey City, NJ; (4); 26/196; Pres Soph Cls; Stu Cncl; Bsbl; Capt L Ftbl; Wt Lftg; High Hon Roll; NHS; Letterman Clb; Varsity Clb; Prep Spirit Awd II 85; All-Cnty Hnrb Mntn & Outstdng Defensive Perf Awd 85-86; Montclair ST Coll; Bus Admin.

TUPACZEWSKI, PAUL; Boonton HS; Boonton, NJ; (2); Pres Computer Clb; French Clb; Math Clb; Math Tm; Nwsp Ed-Chief; Rep Stu Cncl; JV Vllybl; High Hon Roll; Hon Roll; Comp Engrng.

TUPAJ, IRENE; Wallington HS; Wallington, NJ; (3); Chorus; School Play; Yrbk Stf; Trk; Hon Roll; NHS; Grls ST Alt 87; Stu Of Wk 87; Wnnr Art Cntst 85.

TUPLER, TERI; Franklin HS; Somerset, NJ; (3); Key Clb; SADD; Temple Yth Grp; VP Jr Cls; VP Sr Cls; Var Capt Fld Hcky; JV Sftbl; High Hon Roll; Hon Roll; NHS; Occ Ther.

TUPPER, JAMES EDWARD; Brick Memorial HS; Brick, NJ; (2); 10/360; High Hon Roll; Comp Tech.

TURANCHIK, STEPHEN; Glen Rock HS; Glen Rock, NJ; (3); 20/145; Am Leg Boys St; Boy Scts; Capt Chess Clb; Trs Band; Capt Pep Band; VP Socr; Capt Trk; NHS; Ntl Merit Ltr; Prfct Atten Awd; 1st Tm All League Chess 85-87; Frgn Lng Std Month April/May 87; Holy Cross Coll; Econmcs.

TURI, STEVEN; Wood-Ridge HS; Wood Ridge, NJ; (3); 9/90; Art Clb; Computer Clb; Math Clb; Spanish Clb; JV Bsbl; Var Ftbl; Var Wrstlng; High Hon Roll; Hon Roll; NHS; 1st Tm All Lg Running Back 86; 2nd Tm All Area Running Back 86; 3rd Tm All Cnty Running Back 86.

TURNA, CHAINCHAL; Elwood Park Memorial HS; Elmwood Pk, NJ; (3); Cmnty Wkr; Trs French Clb; Hosp Aide; Trs Intnl Clb; Trs Library Aide; Chorus; School Musical; Nwsp Rptr; French Hon Soc; High Hon Roll; Bio.

TURNBULL, MONIQUE; Nottingham HS; Mercerville, NJ; (3); Dance Clb; Girl Scts; Teachers Aide; Cheerleading; Fld Hcky; Sftbl; High Hon Roll; Hon Roll; Med.

TURNER, AMANDA; Ewing HS; Trenton, NJ; (2); Dance Clb; Key Clb; Chorus; School Musical; Off Frsh Cls; Off Soph Cls; Rep Stu Cncl; Stat Bsbl; Mgr(s); Stat Var Socr.

TURNER, BETH; Delawrae Valley Regional HS; Milford, NJ; (4); Rep Stu Cncl; Im Bsktbl; L Var Fld Hcky; L Var Trk; Hon Roll; Glassboro ST Coll; Bus.

TURNER, CHRISTINE; West Milford Townshop HS; Hewitt, NJ; (4); 12/400; Art Clb; Cmnty Wkr; DECA; FTA; Intnl Clb; Spanish Clb; High Hon Roll; NHS; Olymp Mind 2nd Pl Regnl 84-86; DECA 1st,3rd Pl Hnrbl Ment 86; Adv.

TURNER, DAVID; Morristown HS; Morristown, NJ; (2); Church Yth Grp; CAP; Exploring; Ski Clb; Band; Church Choir; Concert Band; Mrchg Band; JV Socr; Hon Roll; Bus Mgmt.

TURNER, HEATHER; Atlantic Christian HS; Mays Landing, NJ; (1); 1/9; Church Yth Grp; Chorus; Pres Frsh Cls; Var Bsktbl; Var Fld Hcky; Var Sftbl; Hon Roll; PHYS Ed Tchr.

TURNER, JILL L; The Pilgrim Acad; Absecon, NJ; (3); Church Yth Grp; FHA; Capt Cheerleading; Swmmng; Tennis; High Hon Roll; VFW Awd; Sci Fair Awd 2nd Plc 85; Tri-ST Sci Fair Awd 1st Plc 86; Liberty U; Elem Educ.

TURNER, MICHAEL; Morristown HS; Morristown, NJ; (2); 22/446; CAP; Pres Key Clb; Ski Clb; JV Socr; High Hon Roll; Hon Roll; Sci Engrng.

TURNER, MYLO; Asbury Park HS; Asbury Park, NJ; (4); 3/142; Service Clb; Yrbk Ed-Chief; Trk; Co-Capt Twrlr; Cmnty Wkr; High Hon Roll; Kiwanis Awd; NHS; Drill Tm; Drm Mjr(t); Omega Psi Phi Frat Awd Acad Achvt 86; Var Schlr Awd Acad Achvt 85-86; Princeton; Med.

TURNER, PATTI; Peqvannvek Township HS; Pompton Plains, NJ; (3); 89/215; Hosp Aide; Varsity Clb; Band; Concert Band; Mrchg Band; Var Socr; Hon Roll; Phy Fit Achvt Awd 86-87; Vrsty Ltr Sccr 85-86; Johnson & Wales Coll; Baking.

TURNER, STEPHEN; Sacred Heart HS; Vineland, NJ; (4); 6/63; Church Yth Grp; Orch; Variety Show; Lit Mag; High Hon Roll; Hon Roll; NHS; Ntl Merit SF; Prfct Atten Awd; St Schlr; Natl Hstry/Govt Awd 86-87; Villanova; Lib Arts.

TURNER, TERRI L; Audubon HS; Mt Ephraim, NJ; (3); DECA; Office Aide; Spanish Clb; Teachers Aide; Variety Show; Wt Lftg; NC ST.

TURNER, TERRY L; Cherry Hill HS West; Cherry Hill, NJ; (4); French Clb; Intnl Clb; PAVAS; Mrchg Band; Yrbk Stf; Lit Mag; Rep Soph Cls; NHS; Ntl Merit Ltr; Garden ST Dstngshd Schlr 87; Presdntl Acadc Ftns Awd 87; NYU; Bus.

TURNER, TODD; Boonton HS; Boonton, NJ; (3); French Clb; Ski Clb; High Hon Roll; Hon Roll; Econ.

TURNEY, REGINA; Oak Knoll Schl; Berkeley Hts, NJ; (2); Hosp Aide; Key Clb; Pep Clb; Red Cross Aide; Service Clb; Ski Clb; Varsity Clb; Church Choir; Nwsp Rptr; Nwsp Stf; Lttr-Fncg Tm 87; Achvt Cert-Adv 1st Aid & CPR 87; Engr.

TUROFF, CHERYLL; Immaculate Conception HS; Elmwood Park, NJ; (3); SADD; Pres Stage Crew; Lit Mag; Var Bsktbl; JV Mgr(s); JV Sftbl; Prfct Atten Awd; Physical Educ Cert Of Hnr 85-86; Outstndng Svc Trophy Stage Crew 87; Accntng.

TURQMAN, LOUISA; Watchung Hills Reg HS; Millington, NJ; (4); VP Drama Clb; Girl Scts; Ski Clb; Speech Tm; SADD; Pres Chorus; Capt Flag Corp; VP Trk; NHS; Thesps; Natl Schl Choral Awd 87; Govnrs Tchng Schlr 87; Coll Of Wm & Mary; Amer Hstry.

TURSI, MARIA; Paul VI HS; Sewell, NJ; (4); 33/503; French Clb; School Play; Lit Mag; French Hon Soc; Hon Roll; NHS; Philadelphia Coll/Pharm & Sci.

TURSKY, DAWN; Morristown HS; Morristown, NJ; (3); Dance Clb; Hosp Aide; Key Clb; Office Aide; Pep Clb; Ski Clb; Im Badmtn; JV Powder Puff Ftbl; Hon Roll; 1 Yr Pin-Outstndng Svc-Frndlys Frnchs 87; Cert Of Achvt-Memrl Hosp-Vlnteer Wrk 85; Rutgers U; Bus Mgmt.

TURTON IV, ROBERT S; Alma Prep Schl; Zarephath, NJ; (2); Church Yth Grp; CAP; Yrbk Stf; Score Keeper; Hon Roll; US Navy.

TUTTLE, APRIL; Middletown South HS; Leonard, NJ; (4); 110/445; Church Yth Grp; Variety Show; Var JV Powder Puff Ftbl; Hosp Aide; Cheerleading; Sftbl; Hon Roll; Brookdale CC; Rec Mgmt.

TUTTLE, STEVE; Don Bosco Prep; Ringwood, NJ; (4); Capt Ice Hcky; NHS; St Michaels U.

TWOHY, JOHN; Christian Brothers Acad; Matawan, NJ; (3); 70/245; School Play; Stage Crew; Yrbk Stf; JV Stat Bsktbl; JV Mgr(s); Vllybl; Hon Roll; Bus.

TWOHY, MARY SUE; St John Vianney HS; Aberdeen, NJ; (4); 6/250; Church Yth Grp; Office Aide; Chorus; Concert Band; Jazz Band; Capt Mrchg Band; School Musical; Mgr Stu Cncl; High Hon Roll; NHS; Gld & Wht Awd 83-87; Excllnc In Music 86 & 87; Brkle Coll Of Music Cert Of Musicnshp 85; U Of Notre Dame; Bus.

TWOMBLY, JONATHAN D; Dwight Morrow HS; Englewood, NJ; (4); 5/220; School Play; Ed Yrbk Phtg; Lit Mag; Pres Stu Cncl; Var Bsbl; Var Crs Cntry; Var Vllybl; DAR Awd; NHS; Ntl Merit SF; Natl Socl Stdy Olympd Mdllst 86; Acadc Decthln Rgnl Slvr Mdl-Hstry 87; Harvard; Politcn.

TWOMEY, JOHN; Lakewood HS; Lakewood, NJ; (3); 33/330; Church Yth Grp; Latin Clb; Var Bsbl; Var Bowling; Im Vllybl; Hon Roll; HS TV Cmmrcl-Drg Pgm 87; George Washington U; Bus Mgmt.

TYAS, KIM; Clearview SR HS; Mantua, NJ; (3); 87/171; Bsktbl; Cheerleading; Stat Ftbl; Score Keeper; Sftbl; Stat Wrstlng; Gloucster County; Sec Off Wrk.

TYKOTSKAYA, ILONA; Academic HS; Jersey City, NJ; (3); Nwsp Rptr; Lit Mag; Dramatic Arts.

TYLER, DIANE; Central Regional HS; Bayville, NJ; (3); 22/236; Hosp Aide; Nwsp Rptr; JV Var Socr; High Hon Roll; Hon Roll; Grl Sccr MVP Awd 87; Awd Excllnc Phys Ed 87; Schlr Athl Awd 87.

TYLER, MARY E; Immaculata HS; Pittstown, NJ; (3); JA; Math Tm; Band; Chorus; Church Choir; Concert Band; School Musical; School Play; Symp Band; Lit Mag; Natl Merit Cmmnded Schlr 86-87; Carnegie-Mellon; Math.

TYLER, PHILIP; Clifford J Scott HS; E Orange, NJ; (4); Hosp Aide; Math Clb; Varsity Clb; Band; Nwsp Rptr; Rep Stu Cncl; Bowling; Mgr(s); Hon Roll; Jr NHS; Upsala Sci Enrchmnt Awd 85-86; Bethany Baptist Schlrshp 87; VA Tech; Comp Engr.

TYNDALL, ESTHER; Hillside HS; Hillside, NJ; (3); 21/238; Church Yth Grp; Hosp Aide; Math Tm; Science Clb; High Hon Roll; Rutgers U; Pre Law.

TYNER, DAMON; Holy Spirit HS; Atlantic City, NJ; (3); 31/332; Spanish Clb; VP L Bsktbl; Hon Roll; NHS; Villanova U; Sprts Med.

TYSEN, LISA; Dwight Morrow HS; Englewood, NJ; (4); 23/229; Church Yth Grp; Drama Clb; JA; School Musical; School Play; Variety Show; Lit Mag; High Hon Roll; Hon Roll; NHS; Art Awd Frm Bergen Cnty Artists Gld 86; Westminster Coll; Art.

TZENG, JAUSHENG; Paramus HS; Paramus, NJ; (3); Math Clb; Science Clb; Service Clb; Ed Yrbk Stf; Im Vllybl; NHS; Top 10 Pct Of All Stud NJ Sci Leag Comptn 85-86; 4th Pl Category Of 2nd Yr Bio 86-87.

UBER, PATTY; Paramus HS; Paramus, NJ; (3); Rptr Yrbk Stf; NHS; Bus Admin.

UDVARHELY, DENISE; St John Vianney HS; Freehold, NJ; (3); Church Yth Grp; Intnl Clb; VP Service Clb; SADD; Rep Jr Cls; JV Var Tennis; High Hon Roll; Hon Roll; NHS; Pres Phys Ftns Awd 83-87; French IV Merit Awd 87; Gold & White Schl Awd 86&87; Phys Ther.

UHDEN, LORELLE; Red Bank Regional HS; Little Silver, NJ; (3); SADD; French Hon Soc; High Hon Roll; Hon Roll; NHS; Sec Rotary Awd; Acdmc Awd Vrsty Ltrs 86 & 87; Chem Engr.

UHER, BRIAN F; Paul VI HS; Gibbsboro, NJ; (4); 11/502; Am Leg Boys St; Church Yth Grp; Quiz Bowl; Stage Crew; Yrbk Stf; Ed Lit Mag; Wrstlng; Hon Roll; NHS; Ntl Merit SF; Tulluridge Assoc Summr Prog 86; Kennedy Mem Hosp Sclrs Prog 86.

UHLER, LISA ANNE; Triton Regional HS; Somerdale, NJ; (4); 26/309; French Clb; Math Clb; Concert Band; Mrchg Band; Trs Jr Cls; Powder Puff Ftbl; Stat Socr; NHS; Nrs.

ULASEWICH, TIMOTHY; Toms River HS South; Toms River, NJ; (3); 14/405; Church Yth Grp; Cmnty Wkr; Band; Church Choir; Concert Band; Mrchg Band; Im JV Bsktbl; Im Socr; High Hon Roll; Hon Roll; Archtctr.

ULASHKEVICH, PAUL; Saint John Vianney HS; Marlboro, NJ; (4); 39/250; Computer Clb; FBLA; Hosp Aide; Intnl Clb; Service Clb; SADD; Yrbk Sprt Ed; Var Tennis; High Hon Roll; Hon Roll; Cert Of Merit Spnsh III 86; Cert Of Achvt-Vlntry Svc To Cmnty 87; Disciplinary Awd 87; Loyola Coll Of MD; Pre-Med.

ULISSI, KIM L; Pennsville Memorial HS; Pennsville, NJ; (3); 38/235; GAA; JCL; Latin Clb; Office Aide; Ski Clb; Spanish Clb; SADD; Varsity Clb; Rep Jr Cls; Lib Stu Cncl; Sci.

ULLOA, JEAN MARIE; Vernon Township HS; Sussex, NJ; (3); Dance Clb; Hosp Aide; Varsity Clb; Stat Var Ftbl; JV Swmmng; Hon Roll; Englewood Hosp Schl-Nrsng; Nrs.

ULREY, BRENDA MICHELLE; Haddon Township HS; Westmont, NJ; (1); GAA; Letterman Clb; Varsity Clb; Bsktbl; Var Crs Cntry; JV Trk; Im Vllybl; Soc Wrkr.

ULRICH, GREGG; Lyndhurst HS; Lyndhurst, NJ; (3); 13/150; Nwsp Rptr; Nwsp Stf; JV Var Bsbl; Bsktbl; Hon Roll; NHS; Cmptr Sci.

ULRICH, LINDA SUSAN; Montclair HS; Montclair, NJ; (4); 14/408; AFS; Red Cross Aide; Concert Band; Madrigals; Mrchg Band; School Musical; Off Lit Mag; High Hon Roll; Ntl Merit SF; Church Yth Grp; Cngrs Bundestag Schlrshp To West Germany 85-86; Sign Lang Clb Trsr 84-85; Amnesty Intl Vlntr 86; MA Inst Of Tech; Physics.

ULRICH, NANCY; De Paul HS; Pompton Plains, NJ; (3); Aud/Vis; Church Yth Grp; Drama Clb; Hosp Aide; Band; Chorus; School Musical; School Play; Stage Crew; Yrbk Stf; Parsons Schl Dsgn; Intr Dsgn.

ULRICH, WILLIAM S; Paul VI HS; Somerdale, NJ; (4); 118/511; Drama Clb; German Clb; Math Clb; School Musical; Stage Crew; JV Tennis; Ntl Merit SF; Pol Sci.

UMANZOR, SAUL; Union Catholic Regional HS; Elizabeth, NJ; (4); Band; Jazz Band; Hon Roll; Rutgers Univ; Pro Musician.

UMLAND, DAWN RENEE; Cliffside Park HS; Cliffside Pk, NJ; (4); 16/236; French Clb; Nwsp Stf; Rep Frsh Cls; Rep Soph Cls; Rep Jr Cls; Rep Sr Cls; Rep Stu Cncl; Trk; Vllybl; High Hon Roll; Fred E Witte Schlrshp 87-88; BCSL 1st Tm All League Discus 86-87; Std Athl Awd 87; Lehigh U; Pol Sci.

UMSTEAD, JEFFREY; Manchester Regional HS; Haledon, NJ; (3); Am Leg Boys St; JV Var Bsbl; JV Wrstlng.

UMSTEAD, STEPHEN; Burlington City HS; Burlington, NJ; (3); Am Leg Boys St; JV Ftbl; Var L Trk; U PA; Comp Sci.

UNDERWALD, SUZANNE; Summit HS; Summit, NJ; (3); 1/275; Drama Clb; School Play; Stage Crew; Nwsp Stf; Lit Mag; Capt Twrlr; High Hon Roll; St Schlr; Hosp Aide; Pep Clb; Sept Stu Of Mo 86; Awd Of Excllnc Soc Studies 87; Rutgers Schlr 87; Law.

UNDERWOOD, KIM; Millville SR HS; Millville, NJ; (3); 17/526; Church Yth Grp; 4-H; SADD; Band; Mrchg Band; Variety Show; Nwsp Rptr; Nwsp Stf; Off Stu Cncl; Cheerleading; Stu Hghst Grd Pt Avg; Erly Chldhd Ed.

UNDERWOOD, KIMBERLY; Haddonfield Memorial HS; Haddonfield, NJ; (4); Drama Clb; Latin Clb; Q&S; Concert Band; Jazz Band; Mrchg Band; Nwsp Ed-Chief; Lit Mag; NHS; Church Yth Grp; Latn Ntl Hnr Soc 86-87; Srgn.

UNG, ALICE; Whippany Park HS; Whippany, NJ; (3); 28/187; Band; Concert Band; Mrchg Band; Stage Crew; Yrbk Stf; Hon Roll; Phrmcy.

UNGAR, JEFFREY J; Lenape HS; Mt Laurel, NJ; (4); 3/420; Capt Chess Clb; Capt Math Tm; JV Crs Cntry; JV Trk; High Hon Roll; Hon Roll; NHS; Top Indvdl Co Math Lg, German Hnr Soc; U Waterloo; Comp Sci.

UNGAR, TRACEY; Lodi HS; Lodi, NJ; (4); 7/147; Boys Clb Am; Sec Exploring; Key Clb; Quiz Bowl; Science Clb; Pres Spanish Clb; Chorus; Madrigals; NHS; Pres Schlr; Grls Voc Clb Schlrshp 87; Span Clb Schlrhsp 87; PTA Schlrshp 87; NY U; Psychlgy.

UNGARO, ANGELA; Holy Spirit HS; Northfield, NJ; (3); High Hon Roll; Hon Roll; Tchr Hstry.

UNGARO, MARIA; Immaculate Heart Acad; Suffern, NY; (4); 7/171; Trs Model UN; Science Clb; Yrbk Stf; Var Capt Cheerleading; Hon Roll; VP NHS; Spanish NHS; Acad All Amer 86; Fordham U; Lawyer.

UNGER, JENNIFER; Delaware Valley Regional HS; Pittstown, NJ; (3); 2/208; Art Clb; Acpl Chr; Chorus; School Musical; School Play; Hon Roll; Cmmrcl Art.

UNICE, BRIDGET R; Watchung Hills Regional HS; Warren, NJ; (4); Church Yth Grp; Dance Clb; PAVAS; Chorus; Drill Tm; Variety Show; NJ Ballet Co Apprentice 86-87; Somerset Cnty Perf Arts SR Awd 87; U UT; Ballet.

UNKER, LISA; West Essex SR HS; No Caldwell, NJ; (3); Key Clb; Temple Yth Grp; Nwsp Stf; Yrbk Ed-Chief; Hon Roll; NHS; Ntl Merit Ltr.

UPDEGROVE, JENNIFER; Wesdt Windsor-Plainsboro HS; Princeton Junct, NJ; (3); Cmnty Wkr; Spanish Clb; SADD; Powder Puff Ftbl; Vllybl; High Hon Roll; Hon Roll; Dev Psych.

URBAN, KATHRYN; Pitman HS; Pitman, NJ; (3); 13/180; Spanish Clb; Teachers Aide; Bsktbl; Fld Hcky; High Hon Roll; NHS; 2nd Pl In Crftmns Fair For Dsgn Category 86.

URBANO, CHRISTIAN; Timothy Christian Schl; Plainfield, NJ; (4); 5/36; Band; Chorus; Madrigals; Rep Stu Cncl; Var Bsbl; Var Capt Bsktbl; Var Capt Socr; High Hon Roll; NHS; Mst Outstndng Frnch & Bible 85; 2nd Highst Avrg Chemstry 86; Salve Regin Coll; FBI.

URBANO, MICHAEL A; Passaic HS; Passaic, NJ; (4); 23/500; Am Leg Boys St; Cmnty Wkr; Science Clb; Ski Clb; Im Bsbl; NHS; SAR Awd; Italian-Marecn Forum-Lodi Schlrshp 87; Annl Math Exam Awd 87; Presdntl Acadc Ftns Awd 87; U Of VT; Biolgcl Sci.

URBANSKI, DARLENE; Mc Corristin Catholic HS; Trenton, NJ; (3); 17/248; Drama Clb; JA; Pres Key Clb; Capt Color Guard; Mgr Stage Crew; Hon Roll; NHS; 2 Vrsty Lts Clrgrd 86 & 87; Mc Corristin Srvc Awd 87; Bus Admin.

URIBE, GLADYS; Memorial HS; West New York, NJ; (3); Intnl Clb; Vllybl; High Hon Roll; Pedtry.

URICHER, AMY; Kingsway Regional HS; Mickleton, NJ; (3); Hosp Aide; Key Clb; Ski Clb; School Musical; Lit Mag; Rep Stu Cncl; Stat Bsbl; Var Cheerleading; Gov Hon Prg Awd; Hon Roll; Mod Miss 1st Rnnr-Up 87; JR Vol Convntn Rep 86; Spec Ed.

URKUMYAN, MARAL; Fort Lee HS; Ft Lee, NJ; (3); Trs Camera Clb; FTA; Spanish Clb; SADD; Yrbk Phtg; Lit Mag; Hon Roll; NHS.

USARZEWICZ, MARK J; St Peters Prep Schl; Bayonne, NJ; (4); 62/196; Am Leg Boys St; Boy Scts; Cmnty Wkr; Jr Cls; Sr Cls; JV Bsktbl; Church Yth Grp; Stu Cncl; Elks Awd; Hon Roll; Elks Tngr Of Mnth 87; Parish Rep Ythdnry Cncl 86-87; NY U; Rstrnt Owner.

USATINE, WARREN; Lakewood HS; Lakewood, NJ; (3); 10/330; English Clb; Latin Clb; Concert Band; VP Jazz Band; Mrchg Band; Trs Lit Mag; JV Var Bsbl; Capt Var Bowling; High Hon Roll; NHS; Boys ST Delegate 87; All Cnty Bowling Tm 86-87; Business Economics.

USCHAK, CHRISTOPHER VINCENT; Union HS; Union, NJ; (2); Church Yth Grp; Science Clb; Jazz Band; Orch; Ice Hcky; Cit Awd; High Hon Roll; Hon Roll; Pres Schlr; Band; MVP In Ice Hcky 84-87; 1st Pl Hlwn Art Cntst 84-85; Bstn Coll; Pdtrcn.

USCHAK, ROMAN JOHN; Union HS; Union, NJ; (4); 22/534; Off Am Leg Boys St; Church Yth Grp; Sec Science Clb; Band; Orch; Ed Nwsp Stf; Rep Frsh Cls; Rep Soph Cls; Rep Jr Cls; Rep Sr Cls; Boston Coll Schlrshp 87-88; Guidnce Cnslrs Awd, Anthny Petosa Memrl, PTA Awd 87; Boston Coll; Chem.

UTZ, ANNEMARIE; Ridge HS; Basking Ridge, NJ; (3); 1/192; Church Yth Grp; VP Sec German Clb; Scholastic Bowl; Nwsp Rptr; JV Bsktbl; Var Cheerleading; Var JV Sftbl; JV Swmmng; High Hon Roll; NHS; Congress-Bundestag Yth Exchng Schlrshp 87; German Natl Hnr Scty 86-88; St Elizabeths Chem Wrkshp 87; Physician.

VACCA, THOMAS; Lakeland Regional HS; Wanaque, NJ; (3); Math Tm; Rep Frsh Cls; Rep Soph Cls; Rep Jr Cls; Rep Stu Cncl; Var Ftbl; Var Trk; NHS; Bus.

VACHA, JEFFREY; Phillipsburg HS; Phillipsburg, NJ; (3); Trs Church Yth Grp; Computer Clb; Concert Band; Jazz Band; Mrchg Band; School Musical; Hon Roll; Prfct Atten Awd; Wrrn Cnty Band; Olympcs Of Mnd; Gftd & Tlntd; Comp Sci.

VACLAVICEK, RENEE; Immaculate Conception HS; Little Falls, NJ; (4); Exploring; Q&S; Spanish Clb; Nwsp Stf; Rep Stu Cncl; Bowling; Var Capt Sftbl; Hon Roll; Schlrshp Cath Dghtrs Amrc 87; Immaculate Conception; Bus.

VADEHRA, VIVEK; Hudson Catholic HS; Jersey City, NJ; (4); Computer Clb; Math Clb; Science Clb; Nwsp Rptr; High Hon Roll; NHS; Service Clb; Hon Roll; Pres Citation Acadmc Achvt Awd 87; Excllnc Religion Awd 86; De La Salle Schlrshp 84-87; Boston U; Med.

VAGG, DINA; St Aloysius HS; Jersey City, NJ; (3); Church Yth Grp; Cmnty Wkr; SADD; Yrbk Stf; Stu Cncl; Var Capt Bsktbl; Var Capt Sftbl; Hon Roll; Jr NHS; VP NHS; Ithaca Coll; Bus Mgmt.

VAGHANI, KAVITA; North Arlington HS; N Arlington, NJ; (3); 3/109; Hosp Aide; Spanish Clb; Color Guard; Hon Roll; NHS; VP Spanish NHS; Best Span Stu I, II & III 85-87; VP Span Hnr Scty 87; Span Tutor Awd 86-87; Rutgers U; Bio Tech.

VAIDMAN, GREGORY; Arthur L Johnson Regional HS; Clark, NJ; (3); 12/190; Chess Clb; Exploring; Hon Roll; Ntl Merit Ltr; Prfct Atten Awd; Spanish NHS; Math Assn Of Amer Awd 1st 87; NJ Assn Math Techrs Awd 1st 87; Rgnl Math Day Cmptn Lvl II 1st 86; Comp.

VAIDYANATHAN, RAJEEV; Kingsway Regional HS; Mantua, NJ; (3); Am Leg Boys St; Nwsp Ed-Chief; Yrbk Ed-Chief; Cit Awd; High Hon Roll; NHS; Ntl Merit Ltr; Cmnty Wkr; Drama Clb; Outstndng Rcgntn Writing Comp,Supr Achvtexcllnce Algebra 85; Med.

VALATKA, MICHELE; Notre Dame HS; Trenton, NJ; (4); Cmnty Wkr; Dance Clb; Drama Clb; Math Clb; Red Cross Aide; School Musical; School Play; Hon Roll; NHS; Rutgers U; Pre Med.

VALCARCEL, HEATHER; John F Kennedy HS; Camden, NJ; (2); Church Yth Grp; Church Choir; Hon Roll; Accntng.

VALDES, JORGE; Tenafly HS; Tenafly, NJ; (4); School Play; Var Bsbl; Var Wt Lftg; Ntl Merit SF; Penn ST U; Finance.

VALDES, LINDA; Monsignor Donovan HS; Lakewood, NJ; (3); Debate Tm; Drama Clb; Latin Clb; Science Clb; SADD; Stage Crew; Yrbk Rptr; Yrbk Stf; Hon Roll; NHS; Certif In NJ Mock Trial 87; Pre Law.

VALDES, SAADIA; Parsippany Hills HS; Parsippany, NJ; (3); Church Yth Grp; Service Clb; Spanish Clb; Varsity Clb; Co-Capt Color Guard; Co-Capt Flag Corp; Mrchg Band; Ed Yrbk Stf; Capt Var Powder Puff Ftbl; Itlian Club 84-87; Forgn Lang.

VALENCIA, JUAN; Hillside HS; Elizabeth, NJ; (4); 7/198; Am Leg Boys St; Math Clb; ROTC; Var Capt Crs Cntry; Var Capt Trk; Var Capt Wrstlng; Hon Roll; Sec NHS; Outstndng Cadet JROTC Pgm 85-86; Dr Wayne T Branom Awd Schlrshp 87; Rutgers Coll Engrng; Elec Engr.

VALENSI, LISA; N Valley Reg HS; Harrington Pk, NJ; (3); VP French Clb; Ski Clb; Yrbk Ed-Chief; Pres Stu Cncl; Var Capt Cheerleading; JV Sftbl; NHS; Law.

VALENTA, JAY K; West Milford HS; West Milford, NJ; (3); Am Leg Boys St; Dance Clb; German Clb; Red Cross Aide; SADD; JV Golf; JV Trk; High Hon Roll; NHS; Arch.

VALENTIN, LUIS; Woodrow Wilson HS; Camden, NJ; (3); Church Yth Grp; Yrbk Stf; Pres Frsh Cls; VP Soph Cls; Rep Jr Cls; JV Bsbl; Hon Roll; Prfct Atten Awd; Hugh O Brian Yth Ldrshp 86; Ntl Sci Merit Awds 86-87; Princeton; Math.

VALENTIN, MARIA D; Our Lady Of Good Counsel HS; Newark, NJ; (4); 20/108; Art Clb; Pep Clb; Chorus; Stage Crew; Yrbk Stf; Bsbl; Bsktbl; Gym; Socr; Vllybl; Awd Art Cntst 87; Awd Art Cntst All HS Stu NJ 87; Rutgers U; Bus Admn.

VALENTIN, MICHELE; Parsippany HS; Parsippany, NJ; (4); 126/303; Cmnty Wkr; FBLA; Pep Clb; Ski Clb; Spanish Clb; Crs Cntry; Trk; High Hon Roll; Hon Roll; PAL Plc Athltc Awd 87; Lock Haven U; Vet-Med.

VALENTINE JR, ARTHUR; Oakcrest HS; Mays Landing, NJ; (3); Computer Clb; Math Clb; JV Var Bsktbl; JV Var Ftbl; Var Trk; High Hon Roll; Jr NHS; NHS; Var Schlr 85-87; Elec Engr.

VALENTINE, EILEEN; Paramus Catholic Girls Regionl HS; Waldwick, NJ; (2); Drama Clb; Stage Crew; Lit Mag; Hon Roll; NEDT Awd; Studio Arts.

VALENTINE, JOSEPH M; Livingston HS; Livingston, NJ; (4); 71/415; Am Leg Boys St; Boy Scts; Varsity Clb; Var Capt Bsbl; Var Ftbl; Var Wrstlng; Hon Roll; VFW Awd; Sprtsmnshp Awd 87; Ftbl Hll Fame Awd 87; Rutgers; Accntng.

VALENTINE, MICHAEL; Pope John XXIII HS; Oak Ridge, NJ; (4); 7/140; French Clb; Quiz Bowl; Teachers Aide; Varsity Clb; School Play; Lit Mag; Var Capt Bsbl; Var Capt Ftbl; High Hon Roll; NHS; WV Wesleyan Coll 87; Brown U Schlrshp 87; NJ Schlr-Athl Awd 87; Brown U; Pre-Law.

VALENTINE, TARA; Lenape Valley Regional HS; Andover, NJ; (4); 55/250; Lit Mag; Pres Soph Cls; Rep Jr Cls; Rep Sr Cls; Rep Stu Cncl; Sftbl; Swmmng; Tennis; Hon Roll; Spanish NHS; Atlantic Cst Conf Schlrshp 87; NC ST U; Pltcl Sci.

VALENTINE, WALTER; Brick Memorial HS; Brick, NJ; (3); Band; Concert Band; Mrchg Band; Bsktbl; Crs Cntry; Trk; Hon Roll; Med.

VALENTINI, KIMBERLY; Monsignor Donovan HS; Seaside Hts, NJ; (3); 150/245; 4-H; Ski Clb; Hon Roll; NHS; Fashion Merch.

VALENTINO, JACQUELINE; Oakcrest HS; Hammonton, NJ; (3); 2/228; Aud/Vis; Dance Clb; Debate Tm; Drama Clb; French Clb; Varsity Clb; Chorus; Flag Corp; School Musical; School Play.

VALENTINO, JACQUELINE; Toms River HS North; Toms River, NJ; (3); High Hon Roll; Hon Roll; Ntl Merit Ltr; Chem.

VALENZA, JOSEPH; Lodi HS; Lodi, NJ; (3); 23/153; Camera Clb; Leo Clb; Science Clb; Varsity Clb; Variety Show; Yrbk Phtg; Yrbk Stf; Stu Cncl; JV Var Bsbl; Bsktbl; Educ Assoc Essay Cont Hon Ment 86; 2nd Honor Roll 84-86; 3rd Honor Roll 86-87; Bus Mgmt.

VALINOTI, ANN MARIE; Lodi HS; Lodi, NJ; (3); 22/153; French Clb; Key Clb; Leo Clb; Varsity Clb; Sec Soph Cls; Sec Stu Cncl; JV Bsktbl; Var JV Sftbl; High Hon Roll; Hon Roll; Vrsty Sftbl ST Chmpns 87; Bus.

VALKEMA, HOLLY; Northwest Christian HS; Sussex, NJ; (2); Church Yth Grp; 4-H; Ski Clb; School Play; Yrbk Stf; Var Fld Hcky; Calvin Coll; Bus.

VALLANCOURT, NANCY; Immaculate Heart Acad; Park Ridge, NJ; (4); 30/171; Cmnty Wkr; Lit Mag; Hon Roll; NHS; Rutgers U; Bus.

VALLANDINGHAM, TRACI; Paulsboro HS; Swedesboro, NJ; (4); FNA; Library Aide; Office Aide; Rep Stu Cncl; Var JV Cheerleading; Fld Hcky; Mat Maids; Btty Crckr Awd; Cit Awd; Gov Hon Prg Awd; Mck Trial 87; Gloucester County Coll; Nrsng.

VALLE, ROXANA; Mary Help Of Christians Acad; Paterson, NJ; (1); Library Aide; Chorus; Bsktbl; Gym; Socr; Vllybl; Hon Roll; Acad All Amrcn Awd 87; US Natl Math Awds 87; Med.

VALLE, SOCORRO; Dover HS; Dover, NJ; (4); 14/187; Church Yth Grp; Drama Clb; Chorus; Church Choir; Variety Show; Cheerleading; High Hon Roll; Hon Roll; NHS; Rutgers U; Psych.

VALLELEY, TRACIE; Haddon Heights HS; Barrington, NJ; (3); French Clb; Office Aide; Quiz Bowl; Scholastic Bowl; Chorus; School Musical; Yrbk Stf; Off Stu Cncl; JV Var Fld Hcky; High Hon Roll; Duke; Pre-Med.

VALLEY, ELI; Cherry Hill HS West; Cherry Hill, NJ; (3); PAVAS; School Play; Nwsp Rptr; Nwsp Stf; Yrbk Stf; Lit Mag; Off Soph Cls; Off Sr Cls; Gov Hon Prg Awd; NHS; 2nd Prz Crtv Wrtng Contst, Schlwd Hnrs Stu Catgry 87; Colmba Prss Assn Awd Excell In Yrbk 86; U Of PA; Pltcl Cartoong.

VALLIER, ERIN; John P Stevens HS; Edison, NJ; (3); 52/452; French Hon Soc; Hon Roll.

VALLONE, BRETT; Abraham Clark HS; Roselle, NJ; (3); Aud/Vis; Boy Scts; Church Yth Grp; Library Aide; Rep Stu Cncl; Hon Roll; Comp Sftwre Dsgn.

VAN BLARCOM, CHRISTINE; Mary Help Of Christians Acad; Midland Park, NJ; (3); Computer Clb; GAA; SADD; Teachers Aide; Chorus; Drill Tm; Nwsp Stf; Comp Ltrcy & Itln I Awd 85 & 87; Berkley; Comp.

VAN BOERUM, SCOTT; Eastern Christian HS; Prospect Park, NJ; (4); 12/81; Chess Clb; Church Yth Grp; Computer Clb; Ski Clb; Bsbl; Hon Roll; Pres Schlr; Computer Sci Stu Of Yr 86; Faculty Scholrs Pgm NJIT 87; NJ Inst Of Tech; Architecture.

VAN BRUMMELEN, DANIEL; High School North; Toms River, NJ; (3); Church Yth Grp; JV Tennis; High Hon Roll; Hon Roll; Accntng.

VAN BRUMMELEN, JAMES; Calvary Acad; Toms River, NJ; (4); 2/8; Church Yth Grp; Yrbk Stf; Pres Sr Cls; Trs Stu Cncl; Var Bsbl; Var Bsktbl; Socr; Hon Roll; Sal; Kings Coll; Acctng.

VAN BUSKIRK, AMY N; Madison HS; Madison, NJ; (3); 6/212; French Clb; VP German Clb; Chorus; School Musical; Yrbk Stf; Rep Stu Cncl; High Hon Roll; Hon Roll; NHS; Personal Devel Pgm Ldr 86-88; Math.

VAN DER GROEF, MARIE; Northwest Christian HS; Sussex, NJ; (3); Church Yth Grp; Ski Clb; School Play; Yrbk Bus Mgr; Fld Hcky; Sftbl; Cit Awd; High Hon Roll; Hon Roll; Drama Clb; Calvin Coll; Bus Mgmt.

VAN DIEN, STEPHEN; Voorhees HS; Pottersville, NJ; (4); 3/264; Boy Scts; Var Math Tm; Var Golf; Var Socr; Bausch & Lomb Sci Awd; High Hon Roll; NHS; Spanish NHS; Voorhees HS Sci, Math & Spnsh Awds 85-87; Rice U; Chem Engr.

VAN DORN, DOROTHY; Manasquan HS; Mt Desert, ME; (3); 42/283; Art Clb; Drama Clb; French Clb; FNA; Band; Socr; French Hon Soc; 2nd Hnr Rl 85-86; 1st Hnr Rl 85-86; 2nd Hnr Rl 86-87; BU; Artst.

VAN DYK, VICTOR S; Saddle Brook HS; Saddle Brook, NJ; (3); 31/119; Am Leg Boys St; Latin Clb; Spanish Clb; SADD; School Play; JV Ftbl; Var JV Socr; Var JV Trk; Wt Lftg; Phys Ed Tchr.

VAN DYKE, MARC; Princeton Day Schl; Perrineville, NJ; (3); Math Tm; Nwsp Ed-Chief; Trs Soph Cls; Sec Stu Cncl; JV Crs Cntry; Gov Hon Prg Awd; High Hon Roll; NHS; Ntl Merit Ltr; Chess Clb; Advncd Physics Princeton U With A Avg; Telluride Finlst; Biophyscs.

VAN GROFSKI, TOM; West Windsor-Plainsboro HS; Plainsboro, NJ; (3); Capt L Trk; Hon Roll; Prfct Atten Awd; Sprtsmnshp Awd 85-87; Physcl Edu.

VAN HASSEL, STEPHEN; Glen Rock JR SR HS; Glen Rock, NJ; (4); 4/170; Hosp Aide; Spanish Clb; Stage Crew; Bsbl; Socr; High Hon Roll; Jr NHS; NHS; Ntl Merit Ltr; Garden State Dstgshd Schlr 86-87; Coll William & Mary.

VAN HATTEM, MATTHEW; Midland Park HS; Ho Ho Kus, NJ; (4); 7/130; Debate Tm; Quiz Bowl; Lib Chorus; Church Choir; Nwsp Rptr; NHS; Cit Awd; High Hon Roll; Cnty Fnlst Amer Lgn Ortrcl Cntst 86; Bergen Cnty Model Cngrss 86; Amer Lgn Gld Mdl Awd 87; Frankln & Mrshll Coll; Engl.

VAN HORN, DENISE; Delsea Regional HS; Franklinville, NJ; (4); 34/202; Key Clb; Yrbk Stf; Sftbl; Hon Roll; NHS; Pres Acdmc Ftnss Awd 87; Widener U; Accntng.

VAN HORN, HEATHER; James Caldwell HS; Caldwell, NJ; (4); 17/265; Band; Concert Band; Mrchg Band; Orch; School Musical; School Play; Stat Bsktbl; Var Socr; High Hon Roll; NHS; Acad Merit Schlrshp 87; Musical Excllnc 86-87; VA Polytech Inst; Animal Sci.

VAN KOUTEREN, MARK A; Roxbury Public HS; Flanders, NJ; (4); 48/432; Boy Scts; Pres Model UN; Pres Spanish Clb; Band; Chorus; Jazz Band; Mrchg Band; Mc Donalds All Am Marching Band Nom 86; N Jersey Symphonic Hnr Band, N Jersey Area Hnr Band 86&87; Counly Coll Morris; Bus Admin.

VAN MEIR, VICKIE; Secaucus HS; Secaucus, NJ; (4); Trs Key Clb; Mu Alpha Theta; Pres Ski Clb; Varsity Clb; Rep Jr Cls; Stu Cncl; Var Trk; Capt Vllybl; High Hon Roll; Hon Roll; Acad Summer Camp; Gifted & Tlntd Acad Studs; U Of NC Charlotte; Arch.

VAN NAMEE, ANNE; St James HS; Carneys Point, NJ; (3); SADD; School Musical; Rep Soph Cls; JV Cheerleading; JV Sftbl; Psych.

VAN NEST, MEGAN; Manasquan HS; Manasquan, NJ; (2); Dance Clb; Drama Clb; Math Clb; Pep Clb; Spanish Clb; Band; School Play; Stage Crew; Cheerleading; Hon Roll.

VAN NOSTRAN, KIRSTEN; Lenape Valley Regional HS; Stanhope, NJ; (4); 24/240; Sec SADD; Band; Chorus; Orch; School Musical; Stage Crew; Stu Cncl; NHS; German Hnr Soc 86; Region I Band 87; Music.

VAN NUYS, ADRIENNE; Hunterdon Central HS; Ringoes, NJ; (4); 35/557; French Clb; Yrbk Stf; Lit Mag; Stu Cncl; Co-Capt Var Bsktbl; Wt Lftg; DAR Awd; Sec French Hon Soc; Hon Roll; NHS; Schlr Athlt Awd 86; Engl.

VAN ORDEN, AMY; Northern Highlands Regional HS; Allendale, NJ; (4); 61/257; Church Yth Grp; Chorus; Madrigals; School Musical; Lit Mag; Stat Wrstlng; NHS; Ntl Merit Ltr; Betty Jane D Amore Creatve Wrtng Awd 87; Columba Schlstc Prss Awd 84; Trenton ST Coll; Engl.

VAN RIPER, LISA; Newton HS; Andover, NJ; (4); 41/197; Spanish Clb; Drill Tm; School Play; Yrbk Stf; Var Cheerleading; JV Var Trk; Twrlr; Berkley Schl Awd Outstndng Perseverance 87; Daughters Of Amer Rev Good Ctznshp Awd 83; Joe Kubert Schl; Cartoonist.

VAN SANT, BRADLEY; Vineland North HS; Vineland, NJ; (2); 36/868; French Clb; Golf; Socr; Hon Roll; Clemson U Smmr Prog 87; Engr.

VAN SCIVER, CHANCELLOR; St Marys Hall-Doane Acad; Beverly, NJ; (3); 2/22; Am Leg Boys St; Nwsp Rptr; Off Frsh Cls; Off Soph Cls; Stu Cncl; Var L Socr; Cit Awd; High Hon Roll; Ntl Merit Ltr; NEDT Awd; U Of PA; Bus.

VAN SYCKLE, SUZANNE M; Warren Hills SR HS; Washington, NJ; (3); DECA; Pep Clb; Bus.

VAN TASSELL, CHRISTINA; Watchung Hills Reg HS; Watchung, NJ; (3); Trs Key Clb; SADD; Lit Mag; Off Jr Cls; Stu Cncl; Var Bsktbl; JV Sftbl; Hon Roll; Coachs Awd Bst Attitude Vrsty Bsktbl 86-87.

VAN TOL, INGRID; Montville Township HS; Montville, NJ; (4); 24/260; Church Yth Grp; Hosp Aide; Key Clb; Ski Clb; Varsity Clb; Band; School Musical; Var Capt Gym; Var Capt Trk; High Hon Roll; 1st Tm All Conf All Around 84-86; Pre-View Magazine Schlr Athlete Of The Mo 86; Army Resv Schlr 86-87; Valparaiso U; Bio.

VAN WINKLE, JAMES; Hudson Catholic HS; Secaucus, NJ; (4); 30/182; Church Yth Grp; Cmnty Wkr; Dance Clb; Hosp Aide; Key Clb; SADD; Rep Frsh Cls; VP Stu Cncl; Var Drama Clb; Im Bsktbl; Baseball, Ice Hockey, Stu Cncl, & Peer Minestry Awds 86-87; Drexel U; Civil Engrng.

VAN ZANDT, KIM; Vineland SR HS; Vineland, NJ; (3); Office Aide; Teachers Aide; Hon Roll; March Dimes 80; Mrt Stu 84; Stu Mnth 82; AF; Pre Law.

VANACKER, JODY; Sussex County Vocational HS; Hamburg, NJ; (4); 6/175; High Hon Roll; Hon Roll; NHS.

VANAMAN, ROBERT; Millville SR HS; Millville, NJ; (4); SADD; JV Bsbl; Var JV Bowling; Var JV Ftbl; Hon Roll; NHS; Prfct Atten Awd; Pres Schlr; Rotary Awd; Rugers Coll Of Engrng.

VANDER MEER, DAVID; Toms River HS South; Toms River, NJ; (2); JV Bsktbl; JV Ftbl; L Golf; Im Vllybl; Bsktbl Coaches Awd 86; Bus Admin.

VANDERHOOF, KIM; Jefferson Township HS; Lake Hopatcong, NJ; (3); Church Yth Grp; Cmnty Wkr; DECA; FBLA; Chorus; School Play; Stage Crew; VP Stu Cncl; Score Keeper; Hon Roll.

VANDERLIP, KAREN; Deptford Township HS; Wenonah, NJ; (3); 9/310; Band; Concert Band; Yrbk Stf; JV Bowling; JV Cheerleading; High Hon Roll; Hon Roll; Jr NHS; NHS; Med.

VANDERSLICE, JEFFREY C; Collingswood SR HS; Oaklyn, NJ; (3); Am Leg Boys St; Church Yth Grp; School Musical; School Play; Trs Frsh Cls; Off Sr Cls; Bsbl; Bsktbl; Hon Roll; Htl/Rstrnt Mgmt.

VANDERSLICE, PATRICK C; Collingswood SR HS; Oaklyn, NJ; (3); Am Leg Boys St; Church Yth Grp; Rep Frsh Cls; Off Sr Cls; Stu Cncl; Bsbl; Bsktbl; Hon Roll; Phys Ed.

VANEGAS, VERONICA; Ferris HS; Jersey City, NJ; (3); Mgr Computer Clb; Mgr English Clb; Mgr French Clb; Mgr JA; Mgr Spanish Clb; Mgr School Musical; Mgr French Hon Soc; Mgr Spanish NHS; Im Gym; Merit Cert 85 & 86; Comp Pgmmr.

VANKIRK, MATT; Wayne Hills HS; Wayne, NJ; (3); 17/350; Math Tm; Ski Clb; Varsity Clb; Var Trk; High Hon Roll; NHS; Law.

VANLEER, COLLEEN; Pitman HS; Pitman, NJ; (2); Exploring; Var Fld Hcky; JV Sftbl; Lawyer.

VANLEER, THOS; Pitman HS; Pitman, NJ; (3); 32/155; French Clb; JA; Spanish Clb; JV Bsbl; JV Bsktbl; Ftbl; Hon Roll; Acdmc Hnr Awd 86-87; St Joes; Accntng.

VANLENTEN, JENNIFER L; Lakeland Regional HS; Ringwood, NJ; (4); 13/345; Capt Quiz Bowl; Trs Band; Church Choir; High Hon Roll; NHS; Ntl Merit SF; Engl.

VANN, KAREN; Bridgeton HS; Bridgeton, NJ; (2); 4-H; Girl Scts; Spanish Clb; SADD; Church Choir; Mrchg Band; Nwsp Stf; Trs Frsh Cls; Trs Soph Cls; Trs Stu Cncl; Natl Yth Phy Ftns Awd 87; U Of GA-ATLANTA; Comm.

VANNELLA, ELIZABETH; Notre Dame HS; Bordentown, NJ; (2); 42/400; French Clb; SADD; Varsity Clb; Chorus; Rep Stu Cncl; Var Fld Hcky; JV Sftbl; French Hon Soc; Hon Roll; NHS; Schlr-Athlt Awd 85; Amer Leg Courage Hnr Ldrshp Patrtsm Awd 85.

VANVOURELLIS, JOYCE; Colonia HS; Colonia, NJ; (4); 63/244; Yrbk Stf; Hon Roll; Jr NHS; NHS; Prfct Atten Awd; Bus Admin.

VARALLO, FRANKLIN; Vineland HS; Vineland, NJ; (3); 138/824; Church Yth Grp; Cmnty Wkr; Spanish Clb; Varsity Clb; Socr.

VARANO, MICHAEL; Westfield HS; Westfield, NJ; (4); 98/483; Spanish Clb; Jr Cls; Stu Cncl; Bsbl; Ftbl; Hon Roll; U VT; Finance.

VARGA, DONNA MARIE; St Rose HS; Wall, NJ; (3); Key Clb; Math Clb; Math Tm; Service Clb; Spanish Clb; Variety Show; Hon Roll; Spanish NHS; VFW Awd; Fash Indstry.

VARGA, TED; Notre Dame HS; Trenton, NJ; (2); Boy Scts; Debate Tm; German Clb; School Musical; Lit Mag; Wrstlng; High Hon Roll; Hon Roll; NHS; William & Mary Law Schl; Law.

VARGAS, ENEIDA; Passaic County Tech & Voc HS; Paterson, NJ; (3); VICA; Chrldng Awd 84.

VARGAS, JUAN; Academic HS; Jersey City, NJ; (3); Spanish Clb; Var Capt Socr; Hon Roll; Stu Of Mnth 86-87; Elec Engrng.

VARGHESE, SANTOSH; Hillside HS; Hillside, NJ; (3); 2/200; Am Leg Boys St; Computer Clb; Leo Clb; Math Tm; Pres Trs Science Clb; JV Bsbl; Var Socr; High Hon Roll; Jr NHS; NHS; Ntl Hnr Rl 87; Srgn.

VARGOS, ANNIS; Emerson HS; Union City, NJ; (3); Flag Corp; Yrbk Stf; Sec Jr Cls; Sec Sr Cls; Hon Roll; NY U; Acctng.

VARISCO, ELEANOR; Notre Dame HS; Kendall Park, NJ; (3); 23/385; Church Yth Grp; FBLA; Latin Clb; SADD; Yrbk Stf; Sec Ftbl; High Hon Roll; Hon Roll; NHS; Ntl Bus Hnr Soc 87; Ntl Ltn Hnr Soc 86; Outstndng Achvt Ltn 85-86; Psych.

VARONA, LYDIA; North Arlington HS; N Arlington, NJ; (3); 9/109; Band; Capt Color Guard; Concert Band; Yrbk Ed-Chief; JV Trk; Hon Roll; NHS; Spanish NHS; Hosp Aide; Spanish Clb; Natl Piano Playing Auditions Amer Coll Of Musicians USA 86-87; Rider Coll Cmptn Spnsh Awd 87; Rutgers; Bus Admin.

VARVATSOULIS, MARIA; Bayonne HS; Bayonne, NJ; (3); Sec Trs Church Yth Grp; French Clb; Math Tm; Science Clb; Co-Capt Color Guard; Mrchg Band; Orch; Variety Show; Hon Roll; Co-Capt Drill Tm; Sci Leag Tm 86-87; Math.

VASAN, SANDHYA; West Windsor-Plainsboro HS; Princeton Junct, NJ; (3); Debate Tm; Hosp Aide; Model UN; Band; Orch; School Musical; Var Tennis; High Hon Roll; NHS; Ntl Merit Ltr; Engrng.

VASI, CHERYL M; Hopatcong HS; Hopatcong, NJ; (4); 9/199; FHA; Concert Band; School Musical; Yrbk Stf; VP Frsh Cls; Pres Soph Cls; JV Var Cheerleading; High Hon Roll; Hon Roll; NHS; FL ST U; Hotel.

VASQUEZ, DAMARIS; Lakewood HS; Lakewood, NJ; (1); Spanish Clb; Hon Roll.

VASQUEZ, IRIS; Asbury Park HS; Bradley Bch, NJ; (3); High Hon Roll; Hon Roll; NHS; Vrsty Schlr 1st Awd, Frnsc Trnmnt 1st Pl 87; Med.

VASQUEZ, JAMES; Hoboken HS; Hoboken, NJ; (3); French Clb; Hon Roll.

VASTA, LORI; Montville HS; Montville, NJ; (3); 113/280; Church Yth Grp; FBLA; Key Clb; Im Bsktbl; Im JV Fld Hcky; Powder Puff Ftbl; Powder Puff Ftbl; Hon Roll.

VASTEY, GARDY; Essex Catholic Boys; Newark, NJ; (3); Chess Clb; Spanish Clb; Yrbk Stf; Socr; Wt Lftg; Rutgers; Med.

VATH, FREDERICK; Oratory Prep; Watchung, NJ; (4); Ski Clb; Pres Jr Cls; VP Stu Cncl; Var Crs Cntry; Var Trk; Hon Roll; NHS; Rutgers U; Engrng.

VAUGHAN, VERA; Red Bank Regional HS; Little Silver, NJ; (3); 4/320; Cmnty Wkr; French Clb; Chorus; School Musical; School Play; Yrbk Stf; French Hon Soc; NCTE Awd; NHS; Ntl Merit SF; Eng.

VAUGHN, DANETTE; Essex Catholic Girls HS; Newark, NJ; (3); Art Clb; Church Yth Grp; Drama Clb; Model UN; Pep Clb; Chorus; Church Choir; Rep Soph Cls; Rep Jr Cls; VP Sr Cls; All-Amer Acads Schlr Awd 86; Natl Ldrshp,Svc Awd 86; Syracuse U; Media Comm.

VAUGHN, JERMAINE; Timothy Christian Schl; Plainfield, NJ; (1); 2/45; VP Frsh Cls; Var Bsktbl; High Hon Roll; Orthdmstry.

VAUGHN, ROBERT; West Morris Mendham HS; Chester, NJ; (1); Ski Clb; School Musical; School Play; God Cntry Awd; High Hon Roll; Hon Roll; Acting.

VAUGHN, SHAWN ANTONIO; Williamston HS; Williamstown, NJ; (3); Am Leg Boys St; Key Clb; SADD; Bsktbl; High Hon Roll; Hon Roll; NHS; Engr Career Day 87; Math Olympcs 87; Navy; Math.

VAZQUEZ, BETTY; Mary Help Of Christians Acad; Paterson, NJ; (4); Computer Clb; Math Tm; Model UN; SADD; Chorus; School Musical; Nwsp Stf; Hon Roll; NHS; Prfct Atten Awd; NJ Inst Tech; Chem Engrng.

VAZQUEZ, DENNIS; North Bergen HS; N Bergen, NJ; (3); Church Yth Grp; Computer Clb; Band; Concert Band; Mrchg Band; Crs Cntry; Trk; Russian Olympiad 3rd Pl-Essay Catagory 86-7; Engrng.

VAZQUEZ, DILYS; St Josephs Of The Palisades HS; Union City, NJ; (2); 7/130; Yrbk Stf; Rep Soph Cls; Hon Roll; NY U; Stck Brkr.

VAZQUEZ, ELENA; Dickinson HS; Jersey Cty, NJ; (2); Nrsg.

VAZQUEZ, ILLEAN; Saint Marys HS; Jersey City, NJ; (3); Dance Clb; Drama Clb; Pep Clb; Service Clb; Chorus; Church Choir; School Musical; School Play; Stage Crew; Sec Sr Cls; Spnshs Awd A Avg 85-86; Flight Attendant.

VAZQUEZ, ISABEL; St Mary Of The Assumption HS; Elizabeth, NJ; (2); Church Choir; School Musical; School Play; Rep Frsh Cls; Rep Soph Cls; Rep Stu Cncl; Var Cheerleading; Var Tennis; Hon Roll; Jr NHS; Tnns Awd Trphy 86-87; Chrldng Awd 86-87; JR Natl Hnr Soc Awd Cert 86; Rutgers U; Psych.

VAZQUEZ, JUAN; Dover HS; Dover, NJ; (2); Church Yth Grp; Math Tm; Bsbl; Bsktbl; Socr; Hon Roll; Mech Engrng.

VAZQUEZ, JULIO; Saint Anthonys HS; Jersey, NJ; (4); 6/60; Library Aide; Var Bsbl; JV Bsktbl; Dnfth Awd; Hon Roll; Outstndng Stu Athlt Awd 87; St Johns U; Bus.

VAZQUEZ, MARISOL; East Side HS; Newark, NJ; (3); Chorus; Off Jr Cls; High Hon Roll; Hon Roll; Rutgers U; Phrmcy.

VAZQUEZ III, VICTOR; Hoboken HS; Hoboken, NJ; (3); Boys Clb Am; Golf; Hon Roll; Prfct Atten Awd; Chess Clb; Church Yth Grp; Chorus; Sci Awd 85; Hudson County CC; Chef.

VEARY, DAVID; Matawan Regional HS; Matawan, NJ; (3); 72/350; Bsbl; Prsdntl Acdmc Ftnss Awd 85; Trenton ST Coll; Engrng.

VEASEY, ELAINE; Monongahela JR HS; Deptford, NJ; (1); Art Clb; Spanish Clb; Rep Stu Cncl; Var Bowling; Hon Roll.

VEATCH, LISA; North Hunterdon HS; Asbury, NJ; (3); 131/328; Drama Clb; Chorus; Madrigals; School Musical; School Play; Swing Chorus; Var Socr; Var Sftbl; Key Clb; Yrbk Stf; San Francisco Consrvtry Music.

VECCHIONE, PAUL; T R HS South; So Toms River, NJ; (4); 28/322; FBLA; Math Tm; Quiz Bowl; Spanish Clb; Stage Crew; Variety Show; Yrbk Ed-Chief; Capt Bsbl; Ftbl; Wt Lftg; Pre-Legal Schlrshp, Ruth Cline Schlrhp For Exclnce 87; Rutgers U; Econ.

VECHESKY, MICHAEL; Burlington City HS; Burlington, NJ; (2); 5/250; Am Leg Boys St; Varsity Clb; L Capt Bsbl; Capt Bsktbl; Var L Ftbl; Wt Lftg; High Hon Roll; Hon Roll; Val; Civil Engr.

VEDA, LORINES; St Josephs Of The Palisades HS; Union City, NJ; (3); GAA; Spanish Clb; Var Bsktbl; Var Sftbl; High Hon Roll; Ntl Merit Ltr; Ntl Sci Merit Awd 85; Bus Mngmnt.

VEGA, GRACE; St Aloysius HS; Jersey City, NJ; (3); Teachers Aide; Vet.

VEGA, MICHAEL; Pemberton Twp H S II; Browns Mills, NJ; (4); 21/406; Drama Clb; FBLA; Concert Band; Jazz Band; Mrchg Band; School Play; Yrbk Stf; Rep Frsh Cls; Im Socr; VP NHS; Garden ST Schlrshp 87; Minority Garden ST Schlrshp 87; Interact Rep 87; Trenton ST Coll; Theatre.

VEGA, MINDY; Hoboken HS; Hoboken, NJ; (3); Exploring; French Clb; Spanish Clb; Chorus; Yrbk Stf; Var Capt Sftbl; Var Capt Swmmng; Acctng.

VEGA, RICARDO; Our Lady Of Good Counsel HS; Newark, NJ; (3); 22/122; Hosp Aide; Teachers Aide; NY U; Bus Admin.

VEGA, VERONICA; Mary Help Of Christians Acad; Paterson, NJ; (2); Hon Roll; Med.

VEINTIMILLA, ALEXCEY; Marist HS; Jersey City, NJ; (3); Boy Scts; Computer Clb; High Hon Roll; Hon Roll; Spanish NHS; Stevens Tech; Elec Engrng.

VEITH, JENNIFER; Paul VI HS; Atco, NJ; (4); 23/511; Am Leg Aux Girls St; Drama Clb; Pres German Clb; Math Clb; Math Tm; Pep Clb; Chrmn SADD; School Musical; School Play; Stage Crew; Natl Germn Hnr Soc 84-87; Garden ST Fin 87; Cmmndtn Mayor Cmmnty Svc 86; U DE; Cmmnctns.

VEITH, KEVIN R; Jefferson Twp HS; Oak Ridge, NJ; (3); Am Leg Boys St; Church Yth Grp; SADD; L Var Bsbl; Capt L Bsktbl; L Var Ftbl; Capt Var Ice Hcky; Hon Roll; NHS; Math Tm; Prsnl Dvlpmnt Pgm Steerng Cmte; Safe Ride Vol; Psych.

VELA, VILMA; Emerson HS; Union City, NJ; (3); Cmnty Wkr; FBLA; SADD; Nwsp Ed-Chief; Nwsp Rptr; Yrbk Stf; Lit Mag; Rep Stu Cncl; Vllybl; Hon Roll; Recog Prtcptn Acdmc Dcthln 87; Cert Recog Excptnl Prfrmnc Bio 86; Jrnlsm.

VELASCO, JULIAN; Bishop George AHR HS; Perth Amboy, NJ; (4); 14/267; Am Leg Boys St; Boy Scts; Intnl Clb; Model UN; Sec Trs Thesps; Nwsp Stf; Lit Mag; High Hon Roll; NHS; NEDT Awd; Grdn ST Dstngshd Schlr; Ntl Hspnc Schlr Awds Semi Fnlst; Dcthln Of Knwldg; Bus Admin.

VELASCO, ROBERT; John P Stevens HS; Edison, NJ; (3); Cmnty Wkr; Ski Clb; Im Coach Actv; Im Powder Puff Ftbl; JV Var Wrstlng; Rutgers Coll; Advertsng.

VELASQUEZ, DAWN; St Mary HS; S Amboy, NJ; (3); 16/100; Church Yth Grp; VP Computer Clb; Stage Crew; Hon Roll; Psych.

VELAZQUEZ, SOBEIDA; Barringer Prep; Newark, NJ; (2); Chorus; School Musical; Gym; Trk; Cit Awd; Hon Roll; Prfct Atten Awd; Comp Sci.

VELDEN, KIRSTEN; Bridgewater Raritan High Schl East; Bridgewater, NJ; (3); Church Yth Grp; Girl Scts; Hosp Aide; Spanish Clb; Acpl Chr; Church Choir; Flag Corp; Mrchg Band; Powder Puff Ftbl; Hon Roll; 6 1st Pl Trphs & 2nd Pl NJ Chmpnshps 87; Bus.

VELECHKO, SCOTT; Paul VI Regional HS; Clifton, NJ; (4); 4/125; Am Leg Boys St; Computer Clb; SADD; Nwsp Sprt Ed; Rep Sr Cls; Trs Stu Cncl; JV Crs Cntry; Var L Socr; NHS; Pres Schlr; Rensselaer Polytech Inst; Comp.

VELEZ, VICTOR; Long Branch HS; Long Br, NJ; (3); 3/279; Cmnty Wkr; Computer Clb; FBLA; High Hon Roll; Hon Roll.

VELIZ, JAVIER; Clifford J Scott HS; E Orange, NJ; (3); 8/250; Boy Scts; Computer Clb; Hst Exploring; Office Aide; Varsity Clb; JV Bsbl; Score Keeper; Var Socr; Hon Roll; Hst NHS; Bio.

VELIZ, PAULINA; Morris Catholic HS; Dover, NJ; (2); 21/156; AFS; CAP; French Clb; Intnl Clb; Math Clb; SADD; Bsktbl; French Hon Soc; Hon Roll; Ntl Merit Schol; Fairleigh Dickinson U; Sci.

VELLIOS, CHRIS; Dover HS; Dover, NJ; (3); Hon Roll; NHS; Acctng.

VELLIOS, FRANCES; Morris Catholic HS; Dover, NJ; (4); 26/13 French Clb; Cheerleading; Hon Roll; Frnch Awd 85; Drew U.

VELLUTO, MIKE; Wildwood Catholic HS; Avalon, NJ; (4); 29/93; Aut Desiel Coll Of Nashville.

VELTRI, ANTHONY; Don Bosco Tech HS; Elmwood Park, NJ; (3); 2 91; Rep Jr Cls; Rep Sr Cls; Rep Stu Cncl; JV Bsbl; Im Ftbl; Hon Roll; Religion Awd 86; NJ Rogate/Acad Tlntd Yng Stu 83; Cmpltd Coll Leve Etymology & Basic Comp Sci; Corp Law.

VENABLE, AMY; Princeton Day Schl; Lawrenceville, NJ; (3); Churc Yth Grp; Drama Clb; Pres GAA; Latin Clb; Stage Crew; Nwsp Phtg; Yrb Sprt Ed; Rep Stu Cncl; Stat Fld Hcky; Stat Lcrss; MVP JV Fencing Squa 86-87; Peer Grp Ldr 87-88.

VENABLE, NATASHA; St Marys HS; Elizabeth, NJ; (2); Church Yt Grp; Drama Clb; Service Clb; Church Choir; School Musical; School Pla Easter Assy Cntst 86; Essay Cntst 82; Elec Engr.

VENANZI, JOHN PAUL; Bordentown Regional HS; Trenton, NJ; (3); 140; Church Yth Grp; NFL; Spanish Clb; JV Bsbl; Im Bsktbl; Var Bowling JV Socr; High Hon Roll; NHS; Prfct Atten Awd; Schlrshp Caldwell Co 86; JR SR Prom Committee 87; Acctng.

VENAZIO, JOE; Cherry Hill High Schl West; Cherry Hill, NJ; (3); Ar Leg Boys St; Rep Jr Cls; Socr; Accntng.

VENE, DOMINICK; Paramus HS; Paramus, NJ; (3); Drama Clb; Schoo Play; Ed Lit Mag; JV Bsbl; Var Trk; JV Wrstlng; Fnlst Spch Cntst 8 Psych.

VENESKY, JOLENE; Belvidere HS; Belvidere, NJ; (4); Office Aid Capt Drm Mjr(t); Mrchg Band; Variety Show; Nwsp Stf; Yrbk St Northampton CC; Fashn Merchnsn.

VENEZIAN, JONATHAN J; Montclair Kimberly Acad; Essex Falls, N (4); Chess Clb; Civic Clb; Math Tm; Ski Clb; Lit Mag; Fencng MVP; Vrst Water Polo; Smltn Clb Pres; Chem Engrng.

VENEZZIO, BRIDGET; Toms River HS South; S Toms River, NJ; (3 70/405; Nwsp Stf; JV Socr; Hon Roll; Soccer Awd, Coaches Awd/Plaqu 85.

VENOUZICU, ESTER; Manalapan HS; Manalapan, NJ; (3); 15/45 Temple Yth Grp; Band; Color Guard; Concert Band; Mrchg Band; Nws Rptr; Yrbk Ed-Chief; Ed Yrbk Sprt Ed; Lit Mag; NHS; Natl Hnr Rll Aw 86-87.

VENOUZIOU, SILVANA; Manalapan HS; Manalapan, NJ; (4); Dram Clb; Nwsp Rptr; Yrbk Ed-Chief; NHS; Pres Schlr; Debate Tm; Exploring JCL; Math Clb; Temple Yth Grp; Garden ST Dstngshd Schlr 86-87; Lt Magna Cm Laud 85; Rutgers Coll; Cmnctns.

VENTOLA, JOSEPH; Immaculate Conception HS; Newark, NJ; (4 Science Clb; Spanish Clb; Chorus; Hon Roll; Spanish NHS; Hstry Awd- Avg 87; Rlgn Awd-A Avg 87; NJ Sci Leag 86; Montclair ST Coll.

VENTURA, HILDA; Henry Snyder HS; Jersey City, NJ; (3); Trs Spanis Clb; Rep Frsh Cls; Jr NHS; Prfct Atten Awd; Rutgers U; Med.

VENTURA, MINERVA; Academic HS; Jersey City, NJ; (3); Cmnty Wk Office Aide; Spanish Clb; Nwsp Stf; Yrbk Stf; Hofstra U; Jrnlsm.

VENTURA, SUSAN; Matawan Regional HS; Matawan, NJ; (3); 72/12 FNA; Hosp Aide; High Hon Roll; Hon Roll; Lab Tech 2nd Pl States 8 Nrs Aide 2nd Pl States 87; Fairleigh Dickenson U; Nrs.

VENUTO, DEBBIE; Washington Township HS; Sewell, NJ; (3); Churc Yth Grp; Cmnty Wkr; French Clb; Rep Stu Cncl; Hon Roll.

VENUTO, MICHAEL; Highland Reg HS; Blackwood, NJ; (2); Spanis Clb; Nwsp Stf; Trs Frsh Cls; Im Bowling; Var Capt Socr; Im Wt Lftg; Ho Roll; Rotary Awd; U Of PA; Pre-Med.

VERA, MARIANELA; Emerson HS; Union City, NJ; (4); 4/280; Debat Tm; Drama Clb; Political Wkr; School Play; Nwsp Stf; Yrbk Stf; Off St Cncl; Cheerleading; Cit Awd; NHS; Kiwanis Clb Ldrshp Smnr 84; HOB Ldrshp Smnr 85; Georgetown U; Law.

VERCELLI, THOMAS C; Ridgefield Park HS; Ridgefield, NJ; (3); 20 215; Am Leg Boys St; Stu Cncl; JV Bsbl; Var Capt Bsktbl; Var Ftbl; Va Trk; Hon Roll; Engrng.

VERDECCHIA, DAVID; Palmyra HS; Palmyra, NJ; (3); Am Leg Boy St; Aud/Vis; Chess Clb; Cmnty Wkr; Computer Clb; French Clb; SADD JV Bsbl; Elctrnc Engr.

VERDI, ALANNA; Ridgefield Park HS; Little Ferry, NJ; (4); 3/27 Computer Clb; Capt Debate Tm; Girl Scts; Math Tm; Quiz Bowl; Scienc Clb; Spanish Clb; Teachers Aide; Band; Mrchg Band; Vrsty Fensing Capt Law.

VERGA, CRAIG; Manchester HS; Haledon, NJ; (2); French Clb; Varsit Clb; Var Bsbl; Frgn Lang.

VERGEL, JESENIA; Memorial HS; W New York, NJ; (4); 4/365; Cmnt Wkr; Computer Clb; Debate Tm; JA; Science Clb; CC Awd; Kiwanis Awd NHS; Ntl Merit Ltr; Voice Dem Awd; U S Air Force Awd Exclnce Mat & Sci, Stu Cncl Awd Cmmnty Svc, Minorty Stu Achvt Awd 86-87; NY U Biolgcl Sci.

VERHOEVEN, MICHELLE; Mahwah HS; Mahwah, NJ; (4); Cmnt Wkr; Dance Clb; Drama Clb; French Clb; Math Tm; Red Cross Aide; Orch School Play; Nwsp Stf; Lit Mag; Coll Of St Elizabeth; Math.

VERISH, SANDRA; Delaware Valley Regional HS; Milford, NJ; (4); 3 189; Intnl Clb; Sec Key Clb; Scholastic Bowl; Stat Bsbl; JV Bsktbl; Sta Crs Cntry; High Hon Roll; Trs NHS; Pres Schlr; St Schlr; Lehigh U Engrng.

VERMEULEN, KRISTIN; Eastern Christian HS; Towaco, NJ; (4); 3/81 Acpl Chr; Chorus; Nwsp Rptr; Yrbk Bus Mgr; Hon Roll; NHS; Pres Schlr U Of MA; Hotel Mngmnt.

VERNY, GAIL; Union HS; Union, NJ; (4); 16/536; Cmnty Wkr; Englis Clb; FBLA; Hosp Aide; JA; Math Clb; Office Aide; Science Clb; Spanis Clb; Teachers Aide; Kean Coll; Bus.

VERRONE, ROSEANNE; Immaculate Heart Acad; N Haledon, NJ; (3) Yrbk Bus Mgr; Trk; Vllybl; Hon Roll; Spanish NHS; Attrny.

VESPA, JOHN FRANK; Nutley HS; Nutley, NJ; (3); Pres AFS; Am Le Boys St; Pres Chess Clb; Trs Latin Clb; Pres Political Wkr; VP SADD Drm Mjr(t); Jazz Band; Orch; VP Stu Cncl; Region Band Clarinet & Teno Sax 84-85; Amer Leg Jersey Bys ST Band 87; Music.

VESPOLI, CHRISTINE; Rutherford HS; Rutherford, NJ; (4); 36/168 Math Clb; Math Tm; Pep Clb; Ski Clb; Chorus; Nwsp Rptr; Nwsp Stf Yrbk Stf; Rep Sr Cls; Hon Roll; Presdntl Acad Ftns Awd, 1st Pl Essay Wn Brgn Cnty Bd Of Reltrs 87; Rutgers U; Comp Sci.

VESTERGAARD, KAREN; West Windsor Plainsboro HS; Princeto Jct, NJ; (4); 83/290; Service Clb; Im Badmtn; Var Capt Tennis; Var Trk NHS; Mst Imprvd Plyr Awd-Tnns & Wntr Trck 85 87; Bst Sprtsmnsh Awd-Tnns 86; Jhn James Adbrn Schlrshp 87; U Of DE; Vet Med.

VESTERMAN, WILLIAM J; Piscataway HS; Piscataway, NJ; (4); 3/49 Church Yth Grp; Key Clb; Science Clb; Concert Band; Jazz Band; Pre Mrchg Band; Orch; High Hon Roll; NHS; Ntl Merit SF.

VETRATI, ARIANNA; Monsignor Donovan HS; Lakewood, NJ; (3); 74/250; Church Yth Grp; Drama Clb; Pres Intnl Clb; Spanish Clb; SADD; Teachers Aide; Stage Crew; Trk; Hon Roll; Awd No 1 Clss Spnsh Hnrs 84-85; Law.

VIANI, CRAIG; Christian Brothers Acad; Middletown, NJ; (3); Dance Clb; Drama Clb; School Play; Nwsp Stf; Yrbk Stf; Im Mgr Bowling; Var Socr; Im Mgr Sftbl; Im Mgr Vllybl; Comm.

VIAU, FLORENCE; Emerson HS; Union City, NJ; (4); 3/280; VP Art Clb; Radio Clb; Scholastic Bowl; Ed Lit Mag; Rep Stu Cncl; JV Trk; CC Awd; French Hon Soc; NHS; St Schlr; Rutgers Schlr 86; Dept Of Air Force Math & Sci Awd 87; Floretta Witzig Sci Awd 87; Stevens Tech; Elec Engr.

VIAU, MIREILLE; Emerson HS; Union City, NJ; (3); Am Leg Aux Girls St; Pres Art Clb; FBLA; Scholastic Bowl; Nwsp Ed-Chief; Sec Stu Cncl; JV Trk; French Hon Soc; NHS; Camera Clb; Rutgers Schlr 87; Engrng.

VICARI, DANIELLE; Brick Twp HS; Brick, NJ; (3); 92/481; Church Yth Grp; VICA; Socr; High Hon Roll; Hon Roll; Prfct Atten Awd; Beautcn.

VICENTE, LISA; Paramus Catholic Girls HS; New Milford, NJ; (3); Stage Crew; Lit Mag; Rep Soph Cls; Bowling.

VICHENGRAD, KIRK; Parsippany HS; Parsippany, NJ; (3); Pres Drama Clb; French Clb; Pres NFL; SADD; School Musical; Pres School Play; Nwsp Stf; Lit Mag; High Hon Roll; NHS; Svrl Prstgus Drama & Frnscis Awds 87; Fnlst Nmn Byst 87; Slvr Cp Wnr Hrvd U 86; Drmtc Arts.

VICHNESS, BECKY; West Essex Regional HS; Roseland, NJ; (3); Pres VP Temple Yth Grp; Yrbk Ed-Chief; Score Keeper; Hon Roll; NHS; Sociology.

VICINELLI, CRISTINA; Summit HS; Summit, NJ; (3); 21/280; Cmnty Wkr; French Clb; Ski Clb; Yrbk Phtg; VP Frsh Cls; Var Stat Ice Hcky; Powder Puff Ftbl; High Hon Roll; Hon Roll; 3rd Pl Natl Frnch Cont Metro Area 85; Hnr Rll 84-87; Intl Stds Abrd Schlrshp U Of Madrid 87; Lingstcs.

VICINO, MARYANN; Sayreville War Memorial HS; Parlin, NJ; (2); Sec Church Yth Grp; Drama Clb; Hosp Aide; Spanish Clb; Varsity Clb; Chorus; Flag Corp; Mrchg Band; School Play; Stage Crew; Putgers; Med.

VICKERS, LAWANDA; Abraham Clark HS; Roselle, NJ; (3); Church Yth Grp; 4-H; FNA; Office Aide; Chorus; Church Choir; Madrigals; Hon Roll; Crtcl Care Nrsng.

VICKERS, MARY; St John Vianney HS; Colts Neck, NJ; (3); 46/289; Art Clb; Church Yth Grp; Cmnty Wkr; Office Aide; SADD; Stage Crew; Sec Frsh Cls; Sec Soph Cls; Sec Jr Cls; Sec Sr Cls.

VICKERS, RICHARD A; Pennsauken HS; Pennsauken, NJ; (3); 18/370; Am Leg Boys St; Science Clb; Spanish Clb; JV Socr; Hon Roll; NHS.

VICTOR, SHERYL; Livingston HS; Livingston, NJ; (3); 270/424; FBLA; Band; JV Var Fld Hcky; Peer Counseling; Stock Club; George WA U; Arch.

VIDAL, MARY; Notre Dame HS; Clarksburg, NJ; (3); 7/374; Church Yth Grp; Drama Clb; Math Tm; Chorus; School Musical; School Play; High Hon Roll; NHS; Spanish NHS; Candy Striper 86.

VIDRO, MIKE; Millville SR HS; Millville, NJ; (3); ROTC; Cit Awd; SUNY; Sci.

VIDUCIC, ANTHONY; Dumont HS; Dumont, NJ; (4); 15/217; Math Clb; Mu Alpha Theta; Bsktbl; High Hon Roll; NY U; Law.

VIEIRA, ISABEL; Benedictine Acad; Newark, NJ; (4); 7/39; Sec French Clb; Sec Latin Clb; Trs Math Clb; Ed Mgr Nwsp Bus Mgr; Nwsp Phtg; Nwsp Rptr; Ed Mgr Yrbk Bus Mgr; Rep Stu Cncl; Sftbl; Var Vllybl; Slvtn Army Awd 83; Fshn Byng.

VIEIRA, KRISTIE; Arthur L Johnso Reg HS; Clark, NJ; (3); Art Clb; GAA; Letterman Clb; School Play; Nwsp Rptr; Nwsp Stf; Yrbk Rptr; Yrbk Stf; Var L Bsktbl; JV Var Vllybl; MIP Bsktbl 84-85; Nrsg.

VIEIRA, SONYA; De Paul Diocesan HS; Pompton Lakes, NJ; (3); 1/150; Church Yth Grp; Nwsp Stf; Bausch & Lomb Sci Awd; High Hon Roll; NHS; Chem I & II & Sci Teams 86-87; Engl Awd 85-87; Frnch Awd 86-87; Bio.

VIERECK, MICHELLE; Gloucester City JR SR HS; Gloucester, NJ; (3); Pep Clb; Trs Frsh Cls; Stu Cncl; Bsktbl; JV Fld Hcky; Mgr(s); Score Keeper; JV L Sftbl; Timer; Hon Roll; Unsung Hero 86-87; Float Cmmtt; Dance Cmmtt.

VIGNOLA, AIMEE; Roxbury HS; Succasunna, NJ; (4); 2/422; VP Sec AFS; Am Leg Aux Girls St; French Clb; Math Tm; Sec Stu Cncl; High Hon Roll; NHS; Sal; St Schlr; Cmnty Wkr; Dept Awd For Excllnce Math, Fren & Soc Stud 87; Dickinson Coll; Math.

VIGORITO, KAREN; Manchester Regional HS; N Haledon, NJ; (4); GAA; Yrbk Stf; Stat Bsktbl; Powder Puff Ftbl; Stat Socr; Hon Roll; H S Bowl 85; Intl Frgn Lang Awd 86.

VIGORITO, KELLY A; Manchester Reg HS; N Haledon, NJ; (2); GAA; Hon Roll; Intl Frgn Lang Awd 85 & 86.

VIGUE, RACHEL; Atlantic Friends Schl; Pleasantville, NJ; (3); Pres Church Yth Grp; Drama Clb; Hosp Aide; Pres Service Clb; Chorus; Church Choir; School Play; Lit Mag; Var L Bsktbl; Cit Awd; Ltr In Comm Svc 86; Seminary VP 86; Ltr In Ldrshp 86; Brigham Young U; Soc Sci.

VIJ, POONAM; Holy Rosary Acad; Union City, NJ; (3); French Clb; Math Clb; Science Clb; Teachers Aide; Yrbk Stf; High Hon Roll; NHS; Prncpls List 84-87; Natl Sci Olympiad Awd Bio & Chem 84-87; Cert & Awds Of Hnr Engl I II II 84-87; Med.

VILACHA, BOBBI JO; Union HS; Union, NJ; (4); 143/535; Church Yth Grp; Dance Clb; FBLA; Service Clb; Spanish Clb; Swmmng; Hon Roll; Salvation Army Schlrshp 87; Future Bus Ldrs Of Amer St Ldrshp 86-87; Conf 5th Pl Otstndg Prjt 87; Drew U; Psych.

VILLA, JOHN; St Joseph Regional HS; Pearl River, NY; (4); 3/154; Church Yth Grp; Rep Jr Cls; Var L Trk; High Hon Roll; Jr NHS; NHS; Spanish NHS; Cmnty Wkr; Pep Clb; Service Clb; Intl Youth Achvt 3rd Edition 86; Shirley K Bender Schrlshp Grant 87; NJ St Interschlstc Assoc Schlr; U Of Notre Dame; Pre-Prof.

VILLA, RAMON; Shore Regional HS; West Long Branc, NJ; (3); 47/200; Boy Scts; Ski Clb; Spanish Clb; JV Crs Cntry; JV Socr; High Hon Roll; Hon Roll; Bus.

VILLABON, LUIS; Boonton HS; Wayne, NJ; (2); High Hon Roll; Drama Clb; Sec VP French Clb; PAVAS; Chorus; Concert Band; Jazz Band; Mrchg Band; School Musical; Nwsp Stf; Svc Fren Club 86-87; Schlrshp Worth-Tyrrell Schl Of Prfmng Arts 86-87; 1st Profsnl Actng Job NJ Fest; Singer.

VILLALOBOS, ROLANDO; St Anthonys HS; Jersey Cty, NJ; (3); Law.

VILLANI, CHERYL; Middlesex HS; Middlesex, NJ; (4); 16/158; Pres French Clb; Hosp Aide; Chorus; Nwsp Rptr; Var Stat Tennis; Elks Awd; High Hon Roll; Hon Roll; NHS; Voice Dem Awd; Natl Piano Playng Aud-ST Winner 85-86; Artistically Talnted-Keybrd 83-87; Stu Of Mnth Awd 87; U Of RI; Pharmacy.

VILLANI, FRANK; Hawthorne HS; Paterson, NJ; (3); Boys Clb Am; Chess Clb; Hon Roll; Optmtry.

VILLANI, KATRINA; Toms River High School South; Beachwood, NJ; (3); 14/405; FBLA; Math Tm; Band; Variety Show; Yrbk Stf; Sec Sr Cls; Pom Pon; Socr; Hon Roll; NHS; Accntng.

VILLANUEVA, GRACE; Academic HS; Jersey City, NJ; (3); Yrbk Phtg; Yrbk Stf; Var Cheerleading; Bus Adm.

VILLANUEVA, PATTY; Perth Amboy HS; Perth Amboy, NJ; (3); French Clb; FBLA; Chorus; Bus.

VILLASENOR, ANNE-MARIE PUNZALAN; Bishop Eustace Prep; Seaford, DE; (4); Math Clb; Pep Clb; Spanish Clb; SADD; Nwsp Stf; Lit Mag; Var Trk; Hon Roll; NHS; Spanish NHS; U DE; Lbrl Arts.

VILLEPIQUE, HOLLYANN; Bernards HS; Bernardsville, NJ; (3); 24/186; Q&S; Band; Chorus; Concert Band; Mrchg Band; Orch; Nwsp Stf; Yrbk Stf; Lit Mag; NHS; Cty Chorus 87; Exc Band Awd 86; All Am Hall Fame Band Hnrs 86; Pre-Med.

VILORD, KIMBERLY; Washington Twp HS; Turnersville, NJ; (4); 98/480; Am Leg Aux Girls St; Church Yth Grp; French Clb; Mrchg Band; Trs Sr Cls; Off Stu Cncl; Sftbl; Hon Roll; Office Aide; Ski Clb; Rotary Yth Ldrshp Awd 86; Girls St Alternate 86; Svc Awd 87; Rutgers U; Mrktng.

VINCENT, MARGARET; Camden Catholic HS; Camden, NJ; (3); 57/287; VP Church Yth Grp; Spanish Clb; Hon Roll; Spanish NHS; Hstry Hnr Soc 87; Merit Awd 86; Yth Awd 87; Georgetown U; Bus Adm.

VINCI, JUDY; Red Bank Catholic HS; Long Branch, NJ; (3); Church Yth Grp; JA; SADD; Capt Flag Corp; Hon Roll; Mary Carmody Awd Recgntn Acad Imprvmnt 87.

VINDEL, MARIA; William L Dickinson HS; Jersey City, NJ; (4); Computer Clb; Library Aide; Science Clb; Lit Mag; Off Jr Cls; Off Sr Cls; Stu Cncl; NHS; Montclair ST Coll; Psych.

VINING, PATRICK J T; St Peters Prep; Essex Fells, NJ; (3); Am Leg Boys St; Boy Scts; Capt Debate Tm; NFL; Var L Speech Tm; NHS; German Clb; Service Clb; Capt Vllybl; Oratorical Declamation NCFL 5th 86; Awded Dplma Frm Albeniz Inst For Inter Piano Pgm 87; Classics.

VIOLA, MARIA; Marylawn Of The Oranges HS; Orange, NJ; (4); 3/49; Hosp Aide; Service Clb; Chorus; Nwsp Rptr; Nwsp Stf; VP Pres Stu Cncl; NHS; NEDT Awd; Sec Spanish NHS.

VIOLA, SILVIA; Marylawn Of The Oranges HS; Orange, NJ; (2); 8/63; Cmnty Wkr; Latin Clb; Math Clb; Service Clb; Spanish Clb; Chorus; Stage Crew; Sec Frsh Cls; Trs Stu Cncl; Sftbl; Svc Awd 86; 2nd Pl Lvl I Drew U Spnsh Lang Day 86.

VIRA, ANNA; Manville HS; Manville, NJ; (3); 16/115; Band; Chorus; Mrchg Band; Orch; Variety Show; Yrbk Stf; Rep Frsh Cls; Pres Soph Cls; Pres Jr Cls; Stu Cncl; Cnty & Schl Level Teen Arts; Underclsm Yrbk Editor; Encharged Hmncng Rcptn; Columbia U; Bus.

VIRGILIO, RICHARD; Paul VI HS; Voorhees, NJ; (4); 47/503; Math Clb; NFL; Red Cross Aide; SADD; Pres Stu Cncl; Var L Ftbl; High Hon Roll; Hon Roll; NHS; Biology.

VIRKLER, STEPHEN; Montville Township HS; Towaco, NJ; (3); 56/276; Church Yth Grp; Key Clb; Church Choir; JV Tennis; High Hon Roll; Hon Roll; Cmmnctns.

VIRUET, SUSANA; East Side HS; Newark, NJ; (3); Church Yth Grp; Civic Clb; Cmnty Wkr; Computer Clb; Model UN; Office Aide; Spanish Clb; Drill Tm; Rep Jr Cls; JV Var Cheerleading; Comp Pgmmr.

VISCARDI, CELESTE; Immaculate Heart Acad; Hillsdale, NJ; (1); Art Clb; Church Yth Grp; Science Clb; Chorus; High Hon Roll; Ltn Hnr Scty 87; Sci.

VISCONTI, GEORGE J; Arthur L Johnson Regional HS; Clark, NJ; (3); 105/191; Nwsp Stf; Var Bsbl; Var Bsktbl; Var Ftbl; Wt Lftg; Engrng.

VISCONTI, SCOTT; Edgewood SR HS; Waterford Works, NJ; (3); Boy Scts; German Clb; JV Var Bsbl; Cit Awd; Prfct Atten Awd; VFW Awd; NJ Gen Assmbly/NJ Senate Citations 85 & 86; Natl Soc Sons Of Amer Rvltn Cert Rcgntns 85; Bus Admin.

VISCUSO, MARC; Livingston HS; Livingston, NJ; (3); 45/440; Trs Frsh Cls; JV Lcrss; Var Socr; Var Trk; Var Wrstlng; High Hon Roll; Hon Roll; Jr NHS; NJ St Soccer Tm 86; NJ St Soccer Tm B 85; Bus.

VISICARO, JENNIFER; Monsignor Donovan HS; Bayville, NJ; (3); 66/237; Church Yth Grp; Cmnty Wkr; Ski Clb; Color Guard; Im Cheerleading; JV Trk; Hon Roll; NHS; Boston Coll; Bus.

VISSCHER, THEODORE; Clifton HS; Old Bridge, NJ; (4); 33/580; CAP; Key Clb; Science Clb; High Hon Roll; NHS; Pres Schlr; Stevens Inst Of Tech; Mech Engr.

VITALE, HEATHER; Spotswood HS; Helmetta, NJ; (4); Ski Clb; SADD; Variety Show; Nwsp Ed-Chief; Nwsp Rptr; Nwsp Stf; Hon Roll; Jrnlsm Awd & Acdmc Achvt Awd 87; Rider Coll; Liberal Arts.

VITALE, JEFFREY; Manasquan HS; Spring Lake Hts, NJ; (3); 61/226; Art Clb; FBLA; Spanish Clb; JV Bsbl; JV Var Socr; JV Wrstlng; Hon Roll; Bus.

VITETTA, ROSA; Fort Lee HS; Fort Lee, NJ; (3); Cheerleading; Hon Roll; Fshn Dsgn.

VITIELLO, MARK; Nutley HS; Nutley, NJ; (3); Computer Clb; Stage Crew; Hon Roll; Arch.

VITTORELLI, DANIELLE; Paul VI HS; Glendora, NJ; (4); 32/503; GAA; Math Clb; Service Clb; Hon Roll; Geo Awd 84; Rutgers; Math.

VITTORINO, STACEY; Holy Cross HS; Delanco, NJ; (3); 239/409; Church Yth Grp; Ski Clb; Drill Tm; Mrchg Band; Capt Pom Pon; Hon Roll; Super Star Drll Tm 1st, 2nd & 3rd Pl 85 & 86; Nrs.

VITULANO, STEVEN; Secaucus Secondary Schl; Secaucus, NJ; (3); 11/166; Church Yth Grp; JA; Varsity Clb; Variety Show; Var L Bsbl; Var L Ftbl; Wt Lftg; High Hon Roll; Hon Roll; Kiwanis Awd; Babe Ruth Baseball Home Run Trophy 84; Babe Ruth Baseball All Star Tm 84.

VIVAS, ADRIANA MARIA; St Josephs Of The Palisades HS; North Bergen, NJ; (2); 16/34; Church Yth Grp; Spanish Clb; Hon Roll; Psych.

VIVIAN, PAMELA LYNN; Phillipsburg HS; Phillipsburg, NJ; (3); 27/315; Church Yth Grp; Pres Key Clb; Chorus; Variety Show; Nwsp Rptr; Stu Cncl; Var Twrlr; High Hon Roll; Hon Roll; NHS; Ky Clb VP 86-87; Bus Admin.

VIVONA, DAVID; St John Vianney HS; Colts Neck, NJ; (4); Cmnty Wkr; Math Tm; Nwsp Rptr; Lit Mag; Rep Soph Cls; Rep Jr Cls; JV Bsbl; JV Bsktbl; JV Ftbl; Var Golf; Clemson U; Mrktng.

VIZZINI, JOSEPH; Vernon HS; Vernon, NJ; (3); Letterman Clb; Ski Clb; Band; Mrchg Band; Var Socr; Var Tennis; NHS; Spanish NHS; Spanish Clb; Varsity Clb.

VOEHL, SALLY ANN; Montville Township HS; Pine Brook, NJ; (2); Church Yth Grp; Trs Drama Clb; FBLA; Key Clb; Model UN; NFL; Scholastic Bowl; Science Clb; Chorus; Concert Band; 1st Pl Bus Engl Rgnl FBLA Compttn 87; 2nd Pl Imprmptu Essy Compttn Dist Key Clb Cnvntn 87; Sci.

VOELLMICKE, JOHN; Ramapo Regional HS; Franklin Lakes, NJ; (3); 8/320; Math Tm; Radio Clb; Nwsp Rptr; Var Bsktbl; High Hon Roll; NHS; Attnd Rotary Yth Ldrshp Conf 87; IBM Ldrshp Sem 86; Engrng.

VOELLMICKE, KURT; Ramado HS; Franklin Lakes, NJ; (3); 11/320; Civic Clb; VP Math Tm; Radio Clb; Nwsp Sprt Ed; Var Bsktbl; Crs Cntry; High Hon Roll; NHS; Certs Merit Spanish III & IV, Engl I, II & III, Alg II, Hstry 84-87; Engrng.

VOGEDING, JASON; Paulsboro HS; Paulsboro, NJ; (3); 20/150; Cmnty Wkr; Stu Cncl; Capt Crs Cntry; Tennis; JV Wrstlng; Hon Roll; Hnrs Engl 85-87.

VOGEL, CHRISTOPHER; Manasquan HS; Brielle, NJ; (2); French Clb; Band; Concert Band; Jazz Band; Madrigals; Mrchg Band; Hon Roll.

VOGEL, JEFFREY; Manasquan HS; Brielle, NJ; (4); 13/225; Math Tm; Spanish Clb; Band; Concert Band; Jazz Band; Mrchg Band; High Hon Roll; NHS; Presdntl Acadc Ftnss Awd 86-87; Brielle PTO Top Schlrshp Acadc Achvt 86-87; Tufts U; Engrng.

VOGEL, LISA MARIE; Wildwood Catholic HS; N Wildwood, NJ; (3); Church Yth Grp; JA; Spanish Clb; School Musical; School Play; Yrbk Stf; Rep Jr Cls; Fld Hcky; Librl Arts.

VOGEL JR, ROBERT A; Randolph HS; Randolph, NJ; (4); Am Leg Boys St; VP Jr Cls; Pres Sr Cls; Var Socr; High Hon Roll; Hon Roll; Pres NHS; Ldrshp Cncl JR & SR Yr 85-87; B Bowyer Mem Schlrshp 87; All ST Socr 86-87; Loyola Coll; Bio.

VOGEL, SUZANNE; Highstown HS; East Windsor, NJ; (4); Sec 4-H; French Clb; Drill Tm; School Play; Capt Var Crs Cntry; Mgr(s); Stat Sftbl; Var Trk; Prfct Atten Awd; Bowling; MVP Cross Cntry 85-86; Cross Cntry Sprtsmshp 86-87; Most Imprvd Athl Spring Track 85-86; IN U Of PA; Bus.

VOGELAAR, AMY; Kittatinny Regional HS; Newton, NJ; (3); 5/220; Drama Clb; 4-H; Chorus; School Musical; School Play; High Hon Roll; Hon Roll; NHS; Ntl Merit Ltr; Lbrl Arts.

VOGL, JEFFREY; Holy Spirit HS; Absecon, NJ; (3); 49/332; Pres Aud/Vis; Stage Crew; Swmmng.

VOGLESONG, JOHN; Collingswood SR HS; Collingswood, NJ; (2); Church Yth Grp; French Clb; Rep Stu Cncl; Var Bsbl; Var Ftbl; Wt Lftg; JV Wrstlng; Hon Roll; Pres Schlr; Marine Bio.

VOGT, ELIZABETH; N Burlington Cnty Reg JR/Sr HS; Medford, NJ; (1); Cmnty Wkr; 4-H; FFA; Office Aide; Teachers Aide; Nwsp Rptr; Cit Awd; 4-H Awd; Hon Roll; Kiwanis Awd; ST FFA Cnvnt Dlgt 87; Star FFA Greenhand 87; DE Valey Coll; Agribus.

VOJACK, DANIELA ANN; Ridgewood HS; Midland Park, NJ; (3); 8/450; Pres AFS; Am Leg Aux Girls St; French Clb; Stage Crew; Rep Soph Cls; Rep Stu Cncl; High Hon Roll; NHS; HOBY 86; Drtmth Bk Awd 87; Frnch Awd 85; Dnc Educ.

VOLCKHAUSEN, MARGARET; Ramapo Regional HS; Wyckoff, NJ; (3); 60/322; Church Yth Grp; Capt Var Cheerleading; Hon Roll; Assn PTS 85-86; Cert Merit Frnch & Engl III, Sen Cit Eastrn Conf Chmp V Bsktbl Chrldng Sqd 86-87.

VOLCY, HARRY CASSELL; Essex Catholic Boys HS; East Orange, NJ; (3); Art Clb; Chess Clb; Math Clb; Math Tm; Nwsp Ed-Chief; Nwsp Rptr; Yrbk Stf; JV Bsktbl; Hon Roll; NHS; Mech Engr.

VOLCY, JERRY; Essex Catholic Boys HS; East Orange, NJ; (3); 10/125; Aud/Vis; Chess Clb; Library Aide; Math Clb; Math Tm; Nwsp Stf; High Hon Roll; Engrng.

VOLL, AMY; Monsignor Donovan HS; Toms River, NJ; (3); Art Clb; Church Yth Grp; French Clb; Ski Clb; SADD; Var Cheerleading; Var Trk; Hon Roll; NHS.

VOLPITTA, RICHARD; Paramus Catholic Boys HS; Wood Ridge, NJ; (4); 15/178; Am Leg Boys St; Boy Scts; VP Computer Clb; Hosp Aide; Var Swmmng; Hon Roll; NHS; Wood-Ridge Mem Fund Scholar 87; Fairfield U Scholar 87; Fairfield U.

VOLZ, KIMBERLEY A; Kittatinny Regional HS; Newton, NJ; (3); 42/270; Pep Clb; SADD; Varsity Clb; Band; Frsh Cls; Cheerleading; Gym; Score Keeper; Trk; God Cntry Awd; Fshn Mrchndsg.

VON BUSCH, NICOLE; Toms River HS South; Toms River, NJ; (3); 87/405; Math Clb; Mrchg Band; Variety Show; Pom Pon; Socr; Schlrshp Alfred Univ For Summer Art Prog 87; Art.

VON DOEHREN, MICHELINE; Port Jervis HS; Montague, NJ; (3); Church Yth Grp; French Clb; Spanish Clb; SADD; Varsity Clb; Church Choir; Yrbk Phtg; Yrbk Sprt Ed; Yrbk Stf; Bsktbl; Lang.

VON ENDE, JODI; De Paul Dioccsan HS; Ringwood, NJ; (3); 25/150; Church Yth Grp; High Hon Roll; NHS; Alge II Hghst Achvmnt Awd 86-87; Elem Ed.

VON FABRICE, BRIANNE; Bridgewater-Raritan East HS; Bridgewater, NJ; (3); Am Leg Aux Girls St; Speech Tm; Trs Frsh Cls; Pres Soph Cls; Pres Jr Cls; Rep Stu Cncl; Var Capt Cheerleading; Var Tennis; Hon Roll; NHS.

VON GLAHN, JOHN; Cresskill HS; Cresskill, NJ; (4); 24/114; Church Yth Grp; Band; Chorus; Concert Band; Jazz Band; Mrchg Band; Capt Crs Cntry; Trk; Hon Roll; NHS; Music Ed.

VON MINDEN, ANNIKA; Lenape Valley Regional HS; Andover, NJ; (3); Drama Clb; Hosp Aide; Thesps; Chorus; School Musical; School Play; Stage Crew; Nwsp Stf; French Hon Soc; Hon Roll; Physcl Thrpy.

VOORHEES, BILL; Phillipsburg HS; Maroa, IL; (4); 153/297; Boy Scts; FFA; VICA; Stage Crew; Var Socr; Ag.

VOORMAN, MARINUS; Eastern Christian HS; Allendale, NJ; (4); 5/83; Church Yth Grp; Computer Clb; Trs Pep Clb; Yrbk Stf; Trs Soph Cls; VP Jr Cls; Trs Sr Cls; Var Tennis; Hon Roll; Trs NHS; Math Awd Schl-Bst Math Stu 4 Yrs 87; Hnr Guard 86; Tennis Hnrbl Mntn; Calvin Coll; Accntnt.

VOS, ANGELA; Mary Help Of Christians Acad; Paterson, NJ; (1); Church Yth Grp; SADD; Nwsp Ed-Chief; Nwsp Stf; Bsbl; Sftbl; Hon Roll; Val; Pstrs Awd Schlrshp 86; Ntl Mrt Sci Awd 87; Gld Mtl For Exc In Acdmc Sbjcts 86; Doctor.

VOSINAKIS, VASILIOS; Madison Central HS; Old Bridge, NJ; (4); Art Clb; JV Var Bsktbl; JV Ftbl; JV Var Trk; Rutgers; Elec Engrng.

VOSS, HEATHER; Hamilton HS East; Yardville, NJ; (4); 12/309; Cmnty Wkr; Hosp Aide; Church Choir; Concert Band; Mrchg Band; School Musical; Sec Stu Cncl; Hon Roll; NHS; St Schlr; Tourn Bands Atlantic Coast Champs 83-85; Eastern Mrch Bnd Assoc Champs 83-85; Spartan Wk 85&86; Phys Ther.

VOSSELLER, DAVID; Middlesex HS; Middlesex, NJ; (4); #16 In Class; Boy Scts; Church Yth Grp; German Clb; School Musical; Capt Var Trk; Hon Roll; Kiwanis Awd; Masonic Awd; NHS; Mtn Vly Conf-All Conf Team 87; Outstndng Athlt Trck 87; Presdtns Acad Ftns Awd 87; Bucknell U; Hstry/Lwyr.

VOSSHALL, PETER; Kinnelon HS; Kinnelon, NJ; (3); 1/159; Boy Scts; Math Tm; Science Clb; Jazz Band; Yrbk Stf; Rep Trs Stu Cncl; Var Capt Crs Cntry; Var Trk; Gov Hon Prg Awd; Am Leg Boys St; NJ All-State Chorus 86-87; Rensselaer Math & Sci Awd 87; Rutgers Schlr 87; Princeton; Sci.

VOWELL, AMY; Toms River South HS; Beachwood, NJ; (1); Cmnty Wkr; Bsktbl; Capt Fld Hcky; Var Capt Sftbl; Field Hcky MVP 86; Sftbl Coaches Awd 87; Princeton; Dermatologist.

VRANCIK, LAURA; Notre Dame HS; Trenton, NJ; (3); 37/380; Latin Clb; Political Wkr; Red Cross Aide; Teachers Aide; Rep Soph Cls; Rep Jr Cls; Hon Roll; NHS; VP-LATIN Hnr Soc 86-87.

VRECENAT, KIMBERLE; Secaucus HS; Secaucus, NJ; (3); GAA; Key Clb; Math Clb; Spanish Clb; Band; Chorus; Drill Tm; Nwsp Stf; Rep Jr Cls; JV Sftbl; Rutgers U; Accntng.

VREELAND, MICHAEL; Montville HS; Pinebrook, NJ; (3); Bsbl; Bsktbl; Ftbl; Wt Lftg; High Hon Roll; Hon Roll; Frosh Athl Of Yr 85; All-Conf & All-Cnty Ftbl 87; Most Imprvd Ftbl 87; Rutgers; Real Estate.

VREELAND, SHERRY; Brick Mem HS; Brick, NJ; (3); FBLA; OEA; Hon Roll; Busnss.

VU, TANIA; West Windsor Plainsboro HS; Plainsboro, NJ; (3); Hosp Aide; Math Tm; Model UN; Trs Orch; JV Tennis; NJ All ST Orchstra 86; Natl HS Mun Dlgtn Awd 87; Poetry Pub Mercer Cnty Lit Mag 87; Bio.

VURTSER, VICTORIA; Wayne Hills HS; Wayne, NJ; (3); 33/330; Cmnty Wkr; Exploring; French Clb; GAA; Hosp Aide; Office Aide; Trs Temple Yth Grp; Hon Roll; NHS; Med.

WABAYASHI, MAKIKO; Mary Help Of Christians Acad; Ridgewood, NJ; (3); 12/83; JCL; Math Tm; School Musical; Yrbk Stf; Lit Mag; Hon Roll; NEDT Awd.

WACHELKA, JEFFERY; Belvidere HS; Phillipsburg, NJ; (3); 18/135; Ski Clb; Socr; Hon Roll; Prfct Atten Awd.

WACHTER, MARY; St James HS; Repaupo, NJ; (3); 6/84; Debate Tm; Drama Clb; SADD; VP Frsh Cls; Pres Soph Cls; Pres Jr Cls; Capt Var Bsktbl; Var Fld Hcky; Var Sftbl; Mbr Hugh O Brien Yth Ldrshp Fndtn S Jersey 86; Life Sci.

WACHTER, REGINA; St James HS; Repaupo, NJ; (2); 8/73; SADD; Rep Frsh Cls; JV Bsktbl; JV Fld Hcky; JV Sftbl; High Hon Roll; Ntl Merit Ltr; U Of Notre Dame; Acctng.

WADDELL, JENNIFER; Manasquan HS; Brielle, NJ; (2); 23/242; Church Yth Grp; Drama Clb; French Clb; Stage Crew; Nwsp Stf; Hon Roll; NHS; Brd Ed Awd 3.4 GPA 86-87.

WADDINGTON, STEPHEN; Pennsville Memorial HS; Pennsville, NJ; (4); 14/220; Am Leg Boys St; Computer Clb; Nwsp Rptr; Rep Jr Cls; Stat Bsbl; Var Bsktbl; Var JV Socr; High Hon Roll; NHS; Acctg.

WADE, TRACY LYNN; Immaculate HS; Middlesex, NJ; (4); 14/214; Camera Clb; Hosp Aide; Library Aide; Science Clb; Ski Clb; Lit Mag; Bowling; Hon Roll; NHS; Prfct Atten Awd; Stevens Inst Of Tech; Engrng.

WADE, ZESLYN; Trenton Central HS; Trenton, NJ; (3); Trk; Cit Awd; High Hon Roll; Hon Roll; Ntl Merit Ltr; Comp Engrng.

WADSACK, JENNIFER; Chatham Twp HS; Chatham Twp, NJ; (4); 15/140; Am Leg Aux Girls St; Pres Church Yth Grp; Drama Clb; Scholastic Bowl; Pres Chorus; Ed Yrbk Stf; Ed Lit Mag; High Hon Roll; NHS; Ntl Merit Schol; Ezra Taft Benson Schlrshp 87; Natl Schl Choral Awd, Res Acad Ftnss Awd 87; Brigham Yng U; Pol Sci.

WAGNER, ANISIA CHERYL; Westwood HS; Westwood, NJ; (4); 70/219; Church Yth Grp; Cmnty Wkr; Varsity Clb; Band; Chorus; Variety Show; Var Capt Crs Cntry; Var Capt Trk; Hon Roll; Rep Frsh Cls; Schlrshp Pascack Vly Police Wives Assoc 87; Joan Daun Music Schlrhsp 87; Booster Schlrshp Awd 87; Rutgers U; Acctng.

WAGNER, EDWARD; Westwood HS; Westwood, NJ; (4); 41/219; Am Leg Boys St; Church Yth Grp; Varsity Clb; Nwsp Rptr; Var Capt Crs Cntry; Var Capt Trk; Hon Roll; Jr NHS; Natl Art Hnr Socty 86-87; 1st Pl Nrthrn NJ Crftsmn Fair 86; Vrsty Indr Trck Capt 86-87; Pratt; Art.

WAGNER, ELIZABETH; Summit HS; Summit, NJ; (3); Hosp Aide; Model UN; Pres Temple Yth Grp; Concert Band; Trs Mrchg Band; Yrbk Ed-Chief; Yrbk Stf; Stat Swmmng; Hon Roll; NHS; Bus.

WAGNER, JILL; Clearview Regional HS; Sewell, NJ; (3); 57/171; Rep SADD; Nwsp Ed-Chief; Rep Stu Cncl; Var Capt Fld Hcky; Var Trk; Track Tm Chmps 85; 1st SADD Chap 87; Phys Thrpy.

WAGNER, KATHLEEN; Cherry Hill West HS; Cherry Hill, NJ; (4); PAVAS; Spanish Clb; Capt Color Guard; Hon Roll; NHS; Awd Excptnl Svc Mrchng Band 86-87; Hnrb Mntn Garden St Schlrs Pgm 86; U Of MA; Math.

WAGNER, KRISTINE; Middletown HS South; Middletown, NJ; (4); 140/450; Church Yth Grp; Cmnty Wkr; Dance Clb; Drama Clb; Hosp Aide; Ski Clb; Teachers Aide; Thesps; Acpl Chr; Chorus; Brookdale; Comm.

WAGNER, WENDY; The Hun School Of Princetn; Lawrenceville, NJ; (3); 25/110; CAP; VP French Clb; Stage Crew; Yrbk Stf; Stu Cncl; Var L Bsktbl; Var L Lcrss; Var L Socr; High Hon Roll; Hon Roll; Coachs Awd Vrsty Sccr 86-87; Pre-Med.

WAHBA, SYLVIA; St John Vianney HS; Old Bridge, NJ; (1); Church Yth Grp; Drill Tm; Mrchg Band; School Musical; VP Frsh Cls; Var Twrlr; High Hon Roll; Gld & White Awd Svrl Schl Actvts 87; Frnch II & Englsh Awds 87; Orthpdc Srgn.

WAHLGREN, PATRICIA; Mainsquan HS; Manasquan, NJ; (3); 34/226; Drama Clb; French Clb; Thesps; Acpl Chr; Mgr Chorus; School Musical; School Play; Stage Crew; Variety Show; Lit Mag.

WAHNER, KRISTIN; Cinnaminson HS; Cinnaminson, NJ; (2); German Clb; JA; Chorus; Concert Band; Jazz Band; Crs Cntry; Trk; Bus.

WAIN, KATIE; Newton HS; Newton, NJ; (2); 17/222; VP French Clb; Band; Concert Band; JV Fld Hcky; Var Sftbl; Elem Ed.

WAIN, TOMMY; Bridgewater-Raritan East HS; Bridgewater, NJ; (3); Var Bsbl; Var Ftbl.

WAITERS, KATRINA; Marylawn HS; Irvington, NJ; (4); Pres Latin Clb; Trs Math Clb; Pres Science Clb; Yrbk Ed-Chief; French Hon Soc; NHS; School Musical; Stu Cncl; Gold Mdl Summa Cum Laude Natl Latin Exam 85; French Stu Awd 86; Radcliffe Coll; Pol Sci.

WAJSZCZUK JR, JOSEPH F; Madison HS; Madison, NJ; (3); 3/211; Am Leg Boys St; Drm Mjr(t); School Musical; School Play; Lit Mag; NHS; High Hon Roll; Exploring; Science Clb; Band; NJ Govrs Schl Sci 87; NJ Young Plywrghts Festvl 87; NJ Govrnrs Awd Arts Ed 87.

WALDER, KATHLEEN; Riverside HS; Delanco, NJ; (3); Art Clb; Drama Clb; French Clb; School Play; Yrbk Stf; Stat Bsktbl; Var Fld Hcky; Score Keeper; Moore Coll Of Art; Intr Dsgn.

WALDER, TRACI E; Bordentown Regional HS; Bordentown, NJ; (3); Am Leg Aux Girls St; Jr Civitan Int; Pres SADD; School Musical; Pres Frsh Cls; Rep Stu Cncl; Var Bsktbl; Var Socr; Var Swmmng; NHS; Elks Outstndng Athletic Ldr Awd 87.

WALKER, BRET; Pitman HS; Pitman, NJ; (4); Dance Clb; 4-H; Band; Chorus; Church Choir; Concert Band; Jazz Band; Mrchg Band; Orch; John Phillip Sousa Natl H S Hnrs Band 87; Semper Fidelis Marine Band Awd 87; Dir Awd Music 87; Ithaca; Music.

WALKER, CHRISTINA; Plainfiled HS; Plainfield, NJ; (3); 52/362; FBLA; Band; Church Choir; Concert Band; Mrchg Band; High Hon Roll; Hon Roll; NHS; RCA Minorities In Engrng 84-85; Model Congress 86-87; Chem.

WALKER, DENISE; Teaneck HS; Teaneck, NJ; (2); Cmnty Wkr; Hosp Aide; Office Aide; SADD; Yrbk Stf; Trk; Hon Roll; Prfct Atten Awd; Rutgers U; Law.

WALKER, DONNA; Warren County Vo Tech; Hackettstown, NJ; (3); Church Yth Grp; Key Clb; Nwsp Stf; Stat Bsbl; Score Keeper; Sftbl; Hon Roll; Prfct Atten 85; Johnson & Wales; Chef.

WALKER, ERIKA; John F Kennedy HS; Willingboro, NJ; (3); Computer Clb; Dance Clb; Drama Clb; Hosp Aide; Band; Chorus; Church Choir; Color Guard; Concert Band; Mrchg Band; Cheney Univ Summer Prog 85; Engrng.

WALKER, HARVEY; Marist HS; Bayonne, NJ; (3); Aud/Vis; Camera Clb; Computer Clb; Office Aide; Mgr Bsbl; Mgr Bsktbll; Coach Actv; Mgr Ftbl; Mgr(s); Mgr Tennis; Vrsty Achvt Awd Bsktbll & Ftbll 86-87.

WALKER, JAMES; Northrn Burlngtn County Regnl HS; Juliustown, NJ; (4); Church Yth Grp; Drama Clb; School Musical; School Play; Variety Show; Rep Stu Cncl; Socr; Bst Actr Awd-Schlstc Drama Cmpttn 87; Pt Park Coll; Actr.

WALKER, JENNY; Secaucus HS; Secaucus, NJ; (3); Pres Key Clb; Math Clb; Mu Alpha Theta; Spanish Clb; Score Keeper; High Hon Roll; Hon Roll.

WALKER, KAREN; West Milford Twsp HS; W Milford, NJ; (3); 115/403; Dance Clb; Church Choir; Nwsp Rptr; Yrbk Rptr; Rptr Lit Mag; JV Sftbl; Jr NHS; Dancing Awds 79-86; Tchr.

WALKER, KENNETH; Essex Catholic Boys HS; East Orange, NJ; (4); Art Clb; Yrbk Stf; Im Bsktbl; Im Bowling; Im Fld Hcky; Im Sftbl; Hon Roll; Franklin Pierce Coll; Accntng.

WALKER, LISA; Glen Ridge HS; Glen Ridge, NJ; (3); Key Clb; Sec Frsh Cls; Sftbl; High Hon Roll; Math.

WALKER, NORMA; Dwight Morrow HS; Englewood, NJ; (3); Church Yth Grp; Hosp Aide; Office Aide; Teachers Aide; Church Choir; Color Guard; Hon Roll; Prfct Atten Awd; Rutgers U; Bus Admin.

WALKER, ROBERT G; Chatham Township HS; Chatham, NJ; (4); 11/140; Math Tm; Concert Band; Jazz Band; Pep Band; Var Bsbl; Var Socr; Gov Hon Prg Awd; Ntl Merit SF; Boy Scts; Key Clb; Grdn St Dstngshd Schlr 86; Congrssnl Schlr 86; Acdmc All Amer 85-86.

WALKER, ROBIN; Passaic County Tech; Paterson, NJ; (3); Girl Scts; Band; School Musical; School Play; VP Frsh Cls; Pres Soph Cls; Sec Stu Cncl; JV Sftbl; Var Trk; Var Vllybl; Howard U; Bus Mgmt.

WALKER, ROSALYN; Edgewood Reg SR HS; Sicklerville, NJ; (3); VP Church Yth Grp; Quiz Bowl; Band; Church Choir; Mrchg Band; Rutgers-Camdem; Accntnt.

WALKER, RUSSELL J; Memorial HS; Cedar Grove, NJ; (4); 6/123; Key Clb; Varsity Clb; Rep Stu Cncl; Bsbl; Im Bsktbl; Var L Ftbl; Im Swmmng; High Hon Roll; Hon Roll; NHS; HOBY Ldrshp Smnr 85; Phy Ed Awd 85-86; Bus Mgmt.

WALKER, SHANNON B; West Milford HS; West Milford, NJ; (3); Am Leg Boys St; Boys Clb Am; Church Yth Grp; Debate Tm; Model UN; VP Varsity Clb; Stu Cncl; L Bsbl; Capt L Bsktbl; L Ftbl; MVP Bsktbl 87; Eagle Sct; Pol Sci.

WALKER, TAMMY; Toms River North HS; Toms River, NJ; (4); 89/415; Hosp Aide; Q&S; Orch; School Musical; Nwsp Rptr; Lit Mag; Stu Cncl; Mgr(s); Yrbk Rptr; Nwsp Edtrls Edtr; Yrbk Clbs Actvts Edtr; All S Jrsy Rgnl Orch; Cedarcrest Coll; Comm.

WALKER, TIMOTHY; Franklin HS; Somerset, NJ; (3); Office Aide; Teachers Aide; Ftbl; Grambling ST U.

WALKER, TRACY; Edison Vo Tech HS; Elizabeth, NJ; (4); 25/110; Church Yth Grp; Cmnty Wkr; Computer Clb; Office Aide; VICA; Church Choir; School Musical; Sec Stu Cncl; Bsktbl; Bowling; Mst Outstndng Stu Plaque Art Performncy 87; JR Cls VP 87; Union Cnty Coll; Bus.

WALKES, WENDI; Cherry Hill HS West; Cherry Hill, NJ; (3); Rep Jr Cls; Rep Stu Cncl; Var Gym; JV Lcrss; Var Socr; Prtcptn City Wide Drug Awarness Pgm-Instr; Intl Bus.

WALKO, JOANNE; Linden HS; Linden, NJ; (4); 12/364; Church Yth Grp; Key Clb; Science Clb; Rep Frsh Cls; Rep Soph Cls; Rep Stu Cncl; Var Sftbl; Var Capt Tennis; High Hon Roll; Hon Roll; M B Levine Schlrshp Awd 87; PTA Schlrshp 87; Cook Coll; Sci.

WALKOW, ALAN N; Livingston HS; Livingston, NJ; (4); 20/425; Chess Clb; French Clb; Math Clb; Math Tm; Temple Yth Grp; Varsity Clb; Nwsp Rptr; Nwsp Stf; Socr; Wrstlng; NJ Dist Schlr 86; Sailing 2nd Intl JR Penguin Races 83; Rutgers Deans Smmr Schlr 86.

WALL, DAVID; Essex Catholic Boys HS; Newark, NJ; (3); Art Clb; Im Sftbl; Hon Roll; Engrng.

WALL, ERIK J; Delran HS; Delran, NJ; (3); 2/200; Am Leg Boys St; Church Yth Grp; Civic Clb; FCA; Math Tm; Q&S; Yrbk Ed-Chief; Rep Sr Cls; Var Golf; NHS; Prncpls Lst Acdmcs 85-87; Natl Merit Ltr; Engrng.

WALL, MARY BETH; Manchester Regional HS; Prospect Park, NJ; (3); GAA; Rep Soph Cls; Trs Jr Cls; Rep Stu Cncl; Var Capt Bsktbl; Var Crs Cntry; Capt Powder Puff Ftbl; Var Trk; Hon Roll; NHS; Bsktbl Mst Imprvd Plyr Awd 86; Tchr.

WALL, NITA; Morris Catholic HS; Parsippany, NJ; (3); 65/138; Girl Scts; Pep Clb; Spanish Clb; Nwsp Stf; Rep Frsh Cls; Rep Soph Cls; JV Bsktbl; JV Powder Puff Ftbl; Im Sftbl; JV Vllybl; Color Guard P A L Dist Champ; Marathons For St Jude Chldrns Hosp; Hands Across Amer; Public Rltns.

WALL, STEPHEN; Fair Lawn HS; Fair Lawn, NJ; (3); 14/350; Am Leg Boys St; Computer Clb; Drama Clb; Science Clb; School Play; Rep Stu Cncl; Bausch & Lomb Sci Awd; Hon Roll; NHS; Capt Var Boys Fencing.

WALLACE, ANNMARIE; Bound Brook HS; So Bound Brook, NJ; (4); VP Church Yth Grp; Trs Service Clb; Yrbk Stf; Stu Cncl; Cheerleading; Stat Wrstlng; Hon Roll; NHS; Spanish NHS; Twin Boro Comm Schlrshp 87; Roger Williams Coll; Arch.

WALLACE, CHERYL ANNE; Linden HS; Linden, NJ; (3); French Clb; Key Clb; Chorus; Drm Mjr(t); Jazz Band; Madrigals; Mrchg Band; School Musical; High Hon Roll; Bst Drm Majr 86-87; Schlrshp Shw Choir Camp 87.

WALLACE, CLINTON; Morristown HS; Morristown, NJ; (2); Aud/Vis; Boy Scts; Cmnty Wkr; Exploring; NAACP; Radio Clb; JV Crs Cntry; Trk; JV Wrstlng; Hstry.

WALLACE, COLLEEN; Lower Cape May Regional HS; N Cape May, NJ; (2); Varsity Clb; Band; Chorus; Church Choir; Concert Band; Mrchg Band; Rep Soph Cls; Var JV Bsktbl; JV Golf; Hon Roll.

WALLACE, MARCIA; Manchester Twp HS; Lakehurst, NJ; (3); Am Leg Aux Girls St; Science Clb; Color Guard; Sec Soph Cls; Score Keeper; Var Stat Socr; High Hon Roll; NHS; Spanish NHS; Voice Dem Awd; Chem Tech Chem Awd 87.

WALLACE, MARIE B; Lower Cape May Regional HS; North Cape May, NJ; (4); Am Leg Aux Girls St; Pres Church Yth Grp; VP Key Clb; Pres Spanish Clb; Varsity Clb; Band; Concert Band; Mrchg Band; School Musical; Nwsp Rptr; Acdmc Achvt Awd 86; Frgn Lang.

WALLACE, SEAN; West Windsor-Plainsboro HS; Princeton, NJ; (3); Ftbl; JV Wrstlng; Hon Roll; Won A Trip-Spain, Carrier Cntst 86; Hnr Carrier-Trntn Tms 86.

WALLACH, MICHAEL SCOTT; Cherry Hill H S West; Cherry Hill, NJ; (4); ROTC; Mgr Bsbl; Hnr Roll 84-85; JR AFROTC Golden Eagle Div 85-87; Med.

WALLACO, WALTER BERNARD; Weequahic HS; Newark, NJ; (4); 27/327; Boys Clb Am; Boy Scts; Church Yth Grp; Cmnty Wkr; Pres Soph Cls; Cit Awd; John Jay; Crmnl Jstc.

WALLING, JOHN; Middletown H S South; Red Bank, NJ; (2); German Clb; Band; Ftbl; Wt Lftg; Wrstlng; Hon Roll; Bus Mgmt.

WALP JR, CARL E; Manville HS; Manville, NJ; (3); 1/108; Aud/Vis; JV Var Bsktbl; Var Crs Cntry; Var Trk; High Hon Roll; Hon Roll; NHS; Rutgers Schlrs Prog 87; Rutgers U; Comp Sci.

WALP, THOMAS; Highland HS; Blackwood, NJ; (3); JV Bsktbl; Var Ftbl; JV Trk; Hon Roll; Archtct.

WALSH, ANDREW; Red Bank Regional HS; Little Silver, NJ; (3); Church Yth Grp; Ski Clb; Var Bsbl; Var Ftbl; Var Swmmng; Hon Roll; Math.

WALSH, BRYAN; Arthur L Johnson Regional HS; Clark, NJ; (3); Art Clb; Chess Clb; Hosp Aide; Science Clb; Stage Crew; Lit Mag; JV Trk; Hon Roll; Ntl Merit Ltr; 100 Hr Awd 86; 1st Pl Bwlng Trphy 85; Sci Leag Cert 86-87; Wrtng.

WALSH, CHRISTINE M; Sparta HS; Sparta, NJ; (4); Church Yth Grp; Key Clb; Yrbk Stf; Stu Cncl; Var Cheerleading; Hon Roll; Jrnlsm.

WALSH, COLLEN; Morris Catholic HS; Montville, NJ; (2); 64/167; Hosp Aide; Cheerleading; Var Sftbl; Hon Roll; Office Aide; Service Clb; Cit Awd; Nrsng.

WALSH, CYNDY; Toms River High School North; Toms River, NJ; (4); 72/412; Q&S; Band; Concert Band; Jazz Band; Mrchg Band; Tennis; Hon Roll; Intl Hnrary Soc For HS Jrnlsts 86; Wstrn MD; Psych.

WALSH, JOAN M; Acad Of The Holy Angels; Wyckoff, NJ; (4); 22/158; French Clb; Model UN; Mu Alpha Theta; Color Guard; Stage Crew; Nwsp Bus Mgr; Rep Stu Cncl; Acctng.

WALSH, KAREN; St John Vianney HS; Manalapan, NJ; (4); 155/252; Art Clb; Church Yth Grp; SADD; Stage Crew; Yrbk Stf; JV Cheerleading; Pom Pon; Powder Puff Ftbl; Channel 13 Stu Arts Fstvl Awd 86; Coll Of St Elizabeth; Art.

WALSH, KATHLEEN; Morris Catholic HS; Budd Lake, NJ; (3); 19/135; Dance Clb; German Clb; Math Clb; Natl Beta Clb; Pep Clb; Chorus; Rep Jr Cls; Socr; Trk; DAR Awd; Engl Grammar Awd 85; :Adv.

WALSH, KERRY; Morris Catholic HS; Denville, NJ; (1); 40/156; Church Yth Grp; Chorus; JV Bsktbl; Var L Socr; JV Sftbl; Prfct Atten Awd; Stu Athl Of Yr 87; Vrsty Soccer Lttr 86-87; UNC; Bus Adm.

WALSH, KEVIN; Palmyra HS; Palmyra, NJ; (1); Computer Clb; Office Aide; JV Var Bsbl; JV Bsktbl; High Hon Roll; Sci Awd,Rdng Awd & Comp Awd 86; Acadc Awds 86; Rutgers U; Bio.

WALSH, LAURA ANN; Hackettstown HS; Hackettstown, NJ; (4); 79/236; FBLA; Key Clb; Chorus; Drill Tm; Mrchg Band; High Hon Roll; Hon Roll; Hstrc Preservation.

WALSH, LIZ; Secaucus HS; Secaucus, NJ; (3); Key Clb; Varsity Clb; Band; Concert Band; Mrchg Band; School Play; Stage Crew; Yrbk Stf; Hon Roll; Bus.

WALSH, STACEY; Acad Of The Holy Angels; New Milford, NJ; (3); Church Yth Grp; Cmnty Wkr; Drama Clb; Hosp Aide; VP Model UN; Office Aide; Spanish Clb; Teachers Aide; Chorus; Church Choir; NY JR Srvc Awd 84 & 85; Semi-Fnlst NJ ST Miss Amer Co-Ed Pgnt 86; US Air Force Acad; Intl Rltns.

WALTER, CHRISTOPHER D; North Bergen HS; Guttenberg, NJ; (4); French Clb; SADD; Nwsp Stf; Rep Sr Cls; Stu Cncl; High Hon Roll; Gttnbrg Educ Assn Schlrshp 87; St Cncl Schlrshp 87; Stu Cncl Cert Rcgntn 84-86; U Of Notre Dame; Mrktng.

WALTER, ERIC; Millville HS; Millville, NJ; (3); 62/524; Am Leg Boys St; Church Yth Grp; FCA; Ski Clb; Church Choir; Bsbl; Bsktbl; Ftbl; Hon Roll; NHS; Chld Psych.

WALTER, KRISTIE; Hillsborough HS; Belle Mead, NJ; (3); 27/328; Church Yth Grp; Drama Clb; Hosp Aide; SADD; School Musical; School Play; Stat Socr; Hon Roll; NHS; Bus.

WALTER, NICHOLE; Paul VI HS; Blackwood, NJ; (4); 50/501; Drama Clb; French Clb; Camera Clb; School Musical; Variety Show; Pom Pon; Trk; Hon Roll; NHS; Bio-Pre-Med.

WALTER, RANDY S; Princeton Day Schl; Belle Mead, NJ; (4); Debate Tm; Sec Trs Drama Clb; Model UN; School Play; Stage Crew; Yrbk Bus Mgr; Var L Socr; Ntl Merit Ltr; Im Ice Hcky; JV Tennis; Schl Headmasters List 84-87; Drama Prz 87; Art Awd 87; Carnegie Mellon U; Archit.

WALTERS, ROBERTA; Manville HS; Manville, NJ; (4); Civic Clb; Church Choir; Sftbl; Hon Roll; Am Legion Aux Schlrshp 87; Fraternal Order Of Eagles Awd 87; Natl Jrnlsm Awd 86; Catawba Coll; Sports Med.

WALTMAN, SHEILA; Paulsboro HS; Bridgeport, NJ; (3); 10/190; Yrbk Ed-Chief; Wt Lftg; Hon Roll; NHS; Englsh Hnrs 84-86; Englsh Gftd & Tlntd 86-88; Brthrhd Asmbly Phtgrphr 87; Brkly Schl Of Bus; Accntng.

WALTON, JASON; Collingswood SR HS; Collingswood, NJ; (2); Office Aide; Capt Band; Capt Concert Band; Capt Jazz Band; Capt Mrchg Band; Capt Orch; School Musical; School Play; Stage Crew; Rep Frsh Cls; Pres Acdmd Ftnss Awd 85-86; Exemplr Awd 85-86.

WALTON, YOLANDA; Irvington HS; Irvington, NJ; (4); 17/500; Dance Clb; Drama Clb; Band; Concert Band; Jazz Band; Mrchg Band; School Musical; Trs Soph Cls; Pres Stu Cncl; Capt Cheerleading; Hampton U; Bus Adm.

WALTSAK, MARTIN; Brick Memorial HS; Bricktown, NJ; (3); 8/381; JV Ftbl; JV Trk; High Hon Roll; John Hopkins U; Med.

WALTZ, CHRISTOPHER; West Essex SR HS; N Caldwell, NJ; (4); 22/345; Math Tm; Jazz Band; Mrchg Band; School Musical; Symp Band; Socr; Hon Roll; NHS; Ntl Merit SF; St Schlr; Army Rsv Schlr/Athlt Awd 87; VA Tech; Engr.

WALZMAN, SHERI B; Bruriah HS For Girls; Edison, NJ; (3); Math Tm; Spanish Clb; Sec Temple Yth Grp; VP Soph Cls; NHS; NEDT Awd.

WAMPLER, PAUL; Westfield HS; Westfield, NJ; (4); Am Leg Boys St; Latin Clb; SADD; Acpl Chr; Chorus; Church Choir; School Musical; Rep Stu Cncl; Ftbl; Lcrss; Bstr Clb Schlrshp; Schlr Athl Yr; Bk Gold; Vocal Music Awd; Frgn Lang Frnsic Trnmt 1st Pl Drama, Frnch; Princeton U; Chem.

WAN, GENEVIEVE; East Brunswick HS; E Brunswick, NJ; (3); Camera Clb; Church Yth Grp; Computer Clb; French Clb; Varsity Clb; Concert Band; Nwsp Phtg; Nwsp Rptr; Tennis; Hon Roll; Bus.

WANAMAKER, PATRICIA; Eastern Christian HS; North Haledon, NJ; (3); 9/85; Cmnty Wkr; High Hon Roll; Hon Roll; NHS; MI ST U; Vet.

WANAMAKER, SHERI; Hoboken HS; Hoboken, NJ; (2); Aud/Vis; Exploring; Teachers Aide; Var Tennis; Hon Roll; NHS; Brdcstng.

WANDER, KENNY; Northern Valley Regional HS; Harrington Pk, NJ; (3); Ski Clb; Temple Yth Grp; Socr; Trk; Hon Roll; U Of VT; Bus.

WANG, HELEN B; Manalapan HS; Manalapan, NJ; (3); 44/426; Cmnty Wkr; Debate Tm; Math Tm; Science Clb; Mrchg Band; Yrbk Stf; Trk; NHS; Girl Scts; Drill Tm; Hnrs Cncrt-Piano 84 & 85; Chem Engnrng.

WANG, HOWARD T; West Windsor-Plainsboro HS; Plainsboro, NJ; (4); /280; Am Leg Boys St; Math Tm; Model UN; Service Clb; Spanish Clb; Orch; High Hon Roll; NHS; Val; R C Byrd Schlrshp 87; PTA Schlrshp 87; Garden St Dstngshd Schlr 86; Cornell U; Med.

WANG, JOHN; Ramapo HS; Franklin Lakes, NJ; (4); 10/333; Camp Fr Inc; Church Yth Grp; Computer Clb; Debate Tm; Science Clb; Spanish Clb; Mrchg Band; Symp Band; Nwsp Phtg; Nwsp Rptr; Cornell; Engr.

WANG, MARJORIE C; Summit HS; Summit, NJ; (4); 2/271; Cmnty Wkr; French Clb; Hosp Aide; Orch; School Play; Nwsp Phtg; Nwsp Rptr; Yrbk Phtg; Yrbk Stf; Lit Mag; Govnrs Schl Of Arts 86; Psych.

WANG, REYNOLD; Middle Township HS; Cape May Court, NJ; (3); 2/ 200; Key Clb; Math Tm; Science Clb; Var Tennis; High Hon Roll; NHS; Ntl Merit Ltr; 2nd Tm Cape Atlntc Leag All-Stars Tennis Dbls 87; 7th St Sci Leag-Physics 87; Elec Engr.

WANG, YI-REN; Ocean Township HS; Oakhurst, NJ; (4); 20/330; French Clb; Chorus; Nwsp Stf; JV Bsktbl; JV Tennis; NHS; Spartan Schlr Awd 84-87; Pres Acad Fit Awd 87; N J I T; Architecture.

WANGERIEN, BRIAN; Allentown HS; New Egypt, NJ; (3); 3/205; Am Leg Boys St; Math Clb; Math Tm; Pres Stu Cncl; Var Bsbl; JV Bsktbl; Var Ftbl; Im Wt Lftg; High Hon Roll; NHS; Outstndng Stu-Eco & Lit 86-87; Engrng.

WANNISKI, MATTHEW; Morristown Beard Schl; Convent Sta, NJ; (3); Varsity Clb; Yrbk Stf; Stat Bsktbl; JV Var Crs Cntry; Var Trk.

WAPLES, JOY; Teaneck HS; Teaneck, NJ; (4) Office Aide; SADD; Yrbk Stf; Stat Bsktbl; Hon Roll; Ntl Merit Ltr; U Of Miami; Jrnlsm.

WARBURTON, JOAN; Clearview Regional HS; Mantua, NJ; (3); Church Yth Grp; DECA; 4-H; Bsktbl; Fld Hcky; Prfct Atten Awd; Bus Mgmt.

WARD, BREWSTER; Kingsway Regional HS; Swedesboro, NJ; (2); Art Clb; Pep Clb; Varsity Clb; JV Bsktbl; Var Ftbl; Var Trk; Outstndng Track Perfrmr 87; Pennwood Track Clb Awd 87; Art.

WARD, KATHLEEN; Mount Saint Mary Acad; Scotch Plains, NJ; (1); 2/ 0; Drama Clb; Intnl Clb; Science Clb; School Musical; High Hon Roll; Wilmna Frieir Schlrshp Awd 86; Top Ten Awd 87.

WARD, MICHAEL; Brick Memorial HS; Brick, NJ; (3); English Clb; SADD; Varsity Clb; VP Jr Cls; JV Ftbl; JV Socr; Var Wrstlng; Aero Engrng.

WARD, RONDA; High Point Regional HS; La Fayette, NJ; (4); 10/221; Trs Church Yth Grp; Sec Spanish Clb; Church Choir; Jazz Band; Yrbk Stf; High Hon Roll; Sec NHS; Science Clb; All-Sussex Cnty Band 85; Messiah Coll; Elem Educt.

WARD, RUSSELL SCOTT; Randolph HS; Randolph, NJ; (4); Concert Band; Mrchg Band; Symp Band; Tennis; Fordham U; Polt Sci.

WARDELL, CHARLES; West Orange HS; W Orange, NJ; (4); 70/372; Church Yth Grp; Spanish Clb; Off Frsh Cls; Off Jr Cls; Hon Roll; Spanish NHS; Capt Ski Tm 86; Howard U; Finance.

WARDELL, ED; Vernon Twp HS; Highland Lks, NJ; (3); Church Yth Grp; Band; Concert Band; Jazz Band; Mrchg Band; Hon Roll; Dartmouth; Mchncl Engrng.

WARFLE, BOBBY; Bridgeton HS; Pt Norris, NJ; (2); JV Ftbl; Engr.

WARFLE, RENEE; Nikos Acad; Port Norris, NJ; (4); 1/7; Church Yth Grp; Chorus; Stage Crew; L Bsktbl; Im Sftbl; Var L Tennis; Im Vllybl; High Hon Roll; Val; Acad Hnrs Scholar Pensacola Christian Coll 87-89; Pensacola Chrstn Coll; Phys Ed.

WARHAFTIG, SETH; Cranford HS; Cranford, NJ; (3); 4/280; VP Chess Clb; Pres Math Clb; Math Tm; VP Science Clb; Spanish Clb; Teachers Aide; Band; Rep Frsh Cls; Rep Soph Cls; Rep Jr Cls; NJ Sci Leag 86; Aerontcl Engrng.

WARING, KIMBERLY; St Aloysius HS; Jersey City, NJ; (4); 27/109; FHA; Library Aide; Spanish Clb; School Play; Variety Show; Nwsp Rptr; Nwsp Sprt Ed; Yrbk Bus Mgr; Capt Var Crs Cntry; Cit Awd; Coll Schlrshp; St Peters Coll; Comms.

WARK, KIMBERLY; Lower Cape May Regional HS; Cold Springs, NJ; (3); Trs Church Yth Grp; Key Clb; Lit Mag; Law.

WARNER, LESLIE; Clearview Regional HS; Sewell, NJ; (3); 8/171; Pres Church Yth Grp; VP Band; Mrchg Band; School Musical; Var JV Sftbl; High Hon Roll; Hon Roll; NHS; JV Trk; All South Jersey Wind Ensmbl & Orchstr 86; All South Jersey Symphc Band All St Symphc Band 87; Sci.

WARNER JR, THOMAS F; Bishop Eustace Prep Schl; Pennsauken, NJ; (3); Camera Clb; Church Yth Grp; German Clb; Pep Clb; Ski Clb; SADD; Varsity Clb; Church Choir; School Musical; Nwsp Phtg; HOTEL/Motel Restaurant Mngmt.

WARNKEN, CHAD; Christian Brothers Acad; Pt Pleasant, NJ; (3); Rep Frsh Cls; Im Ftbl; Im Sftbl; Hon Roll; Bus.

WARR, STACEY M; Southern Regional HS; Manahawkin, NJ; (4); 1/384; Model UN; Sec Spanish Clb; Rep Sr Cls; Rep Stu Cncl; Var Bsbl; Var Cheerleading; NHS; Prfct Atten Awd; Pres Schlr; Val; Elks Schlrshp 87; Model UN Outstndng Dlgtn 86; Garden St Dstngshd Schlr Awd 87; Pace U; Accntng.

WARREN, CRYSTAL; Academic HS; Jersey City, NJ; (3); Church Yth Grp; Computer Clb; Sec Jr Cls; Cheerleading; Powder Puff Ftbl; JV Sftbl; Trk; Med.

WARREN, JEANETTE LYNN; Holy Family Acad; Bayonne, NJ; (2); 4/96; Speech Tm; Chorus; Orch; Rotary Ctznshp Awd 85; Honor Roll 84-85; Fine Arts 85; Jersey City ST Coll; Jrnlsm.

WARREN, MELISSA; Abraham Clark HS; Roselle, NJ; (4); 15/170; Cmnty Wkr; Hosp Aide; Science Clb; Chorus; Lit Mag; Rep Sr Cls; Rep Stu Cncl; Hon Roll; NHS; Acadc All Amer 86-87; Kean Coll Urban Schlrshp 87-88; Kean Coll; Physcl Thrpy.

WARREN, MICHAEL; Marist HS; Bayonne, NJ; (3); Trs Stu Cncl; Var Bsktbl; Ftbl; Hon Roll; Acctg.

WARREN-STOUT, SHIRELL; Asbury Park HS; Asbury Park, NJ; (3); 20/153; French Clb; NFL; Nwsp Rptr; Trk; Hon Roll; Prfct Atten Awd; Voice Dem Awd; Rutgers U; Bus.

WARRINGTON, MELISSA; Buena Regional HS; Newtonvlle, NJ; (4); Math Clb; School Play; Variety Show; Natl Sci Merit Awd 87; Stockton ST Coll; Intr Dsgn.

WASACZ, MARGARET; St Rose HS; Avon By The Sea, NJ; (4); 62/214; Science Clb; Ski Clb; Nwsp Stf; Yrbk Stf; Kean ST Coll; Educ.

WASHKO, AMY; John F Kennedy HS; Willingboro, NJ; (3); #10 In Class; Church Yth Grp; Civic Clb; Cmnty Wkr; Computer Clb; Dance Clb; Drama Clb; Intnl Clb; Library Aide; Office Aide; PAVAS; Intl Order Of Rainbow Girls In NJ Ritual Awd; Rochester Inst; Physical Therpy.

WASIK, KERRI L; Academy Of The Holy Angels; Englewood Cliffs, NJ; (3); Hosp Aide; Math Clb; Math Tm; Model UN; Mu Alpha Theta; Spanish Clb; Hon Roll; NHS; Maxima Cum Laude Natl Latin Ex 85; Math Hnr Soc 87; Pre-Med.

WASINDA, JOHN; Holy Cross HS; Burlington, NJ; (3); 14/414; Ski Clb; Trs Spanish Clb; Ed Nwsp Stf; Rep Stu Cncl; Var Swmmng; Hon Roll; NHS; Ntl Merit Ltr; HOBY Smnr 86; Pre Med.

WASKO, WILLIAM; Toms River H S East; Toms River, NJ; (3); 149/550; Wt Lftg; Wrstlng; Hon Roll; Media Wrkshp Semnr For TV Prod At UCLA Coll 87; TV Prod.

WASLIN, LORRAINE; Holy Spirit HS; Linwood, NJ; (3); 7/332; French Clb; Im Vllybl; High Hon Roll; Comptv Cymntsc ST & Rgnl/Medals 84-86; Med.

WASNER, CATHERINE; Essex Catholic Girls HS; Colonia, NJ; (4); 15/ 53; Boys Clb Am; FBLA; Hosp Aide; Library Aide; Science Clb; Ed Yrbk Stf; High Hon Roll; Hon Roll; Cittone Inst; Court Rprtng.

WASSEF, VENICE; South Brunswick HS; Kendall Pk, NJ; (2); Art Clb; Drama Clb; Mrchg Band; Swmmng; Law.

WASSERMAN, BRYAN; Watchung Hills Regional HS; Watchung, NJ; (3); Scholastic Bowl; Ski Clb; School Musical; Stage Crew; Yrbk Bus Mgr; Yrbk Phtg; Rep Frsh Cls; JV Crs Cntry; Var L Trk; Hon Roll; Bioengr.

WASSILY, MARY ROSE G; John F Kennedy HS; Willingboro, NJ; (3); 9/300; Church Yth Grp; Intnl Clb; Key Clb; Science Clb; Cit Awd; High Hon Roll; Hon Roll; NHS; Rutgers; Pharm.

WASTELL, CHARLOTTA; Bridgeton HS; Bridgeton, NJ; (4); 15/191; SADD; Yrbk Stf; Rep Frsh Cls; Rep Soph Cls; Capt Sftbl; Swmmng; Var Tennis; High Hon Roll; NHS; Cmnty Wkr; HOSA Cls Rp & Vp 83-87; Frst Aid Tm; N Moore Nrsng Schlrshp; CCMHA Awd; E D Meyers Athltc Awd; Nrs Aide; Fairleigh Dickinson U; Nrs.

WASZAK, JEANNINE M; St John Vianney HS; Hazlet, NJ; (4); 43/250; Var L Bsktbl; Im Ftbl; Var Powder Puff Ftbl; Im Sftbl; Im Vllybl; Hon Roll; Presdntl Physcl Ftnss Awd 86-87; Kings Coll; Hmn Rsrs Mgf.

WATERS, CRAIG; De Paul HS; Lincoln Pk, NJ; (3); 40/160; Ski Clb; Hon Roll; Outstndng Achvmnt Art 84; Comp Graphics.

WATERS, NICOLE C; Bloomfield HS; Bloomfield, NJ; (3); Am Leg Aux Girls St; Key Clb; Spanish Clb; Chorus; Color Guard; Nwsp Stf; Trs Frsh Cls; Rep Stu Cncl; Hon Roll; Ntl Merit Ltr; Psych.

WATKINS, BRYAN GERARD; Christian Brothers Acad; Howell, NJ; (2); 19/240; Cmnty Wkr; Dance Clb; Math Tm; Stage Crew; Nwsp Rptr; JV Bsbl; JV Bsktbl; High Hon Roll; NHS; Pocono Invtnl Bsktbl Camp MVP 86-87; Bsbl All Star 85-87; Sports Agent.

WATKINS, CYNTHIA; Bernards HS; Bernardsville, NJ; (3); 19/186; Q&S; Concert Band; Mgr Mrchg Band; VP Orch; School Musical; Nwsp Stf; Twrlr; NHS; Baton Twirling 87.

WATKINS, MARK; Millville SR HS; Millville, NJ; (3); 134/524; DECA; Bus Admin.

WATKINS, WILLIE; River Dell SR HS; River Edge, NJ; (2); Boy Scts; Chess Clb; JV Socr; George Mason; Accntng.

WATSON, CHARLES; Gloucester City HS; Brooklawn, NJ; (3); Math Clb; Spanish Clb; School Play; Var Bowling; Var Socr; Wt Lftg; Gov Hon Prg Awd; Drexel U; Engrng.

WATSON, ERIC; Sparta HS; Sparta, NJ; (2); Quiz Bowl; Law.

WATSON, JOENATHAN; Orange HS; Orange, NJ; (3); Church Yth Grp; Computer Clb; Drama Clb; Varsity Clb; Capt Band; Pres Church Choir; Concert Band; Mrchg Band; School Musical; School Play; MVP Band Awd 86-87; Wrstlng Awd 86-87; Air Frc Acad; Aviatn.

WATSON, MARY BETH; Holy Spirit HS; Margate, NJ; (3); 25/332; Spanish Clb; Pres Soph Cls; Rep Stu Cncl; High Hon Roll; Hon Roll; Cmmnctns.

WATSON, MATTHEW; Don Bosco Prep; Pearl River, NY; (3); Boy Scts; Dance Clb; Drama Clb; Pres Model UN; Science Clb; Chorus; School Musical; School Play; Stage Crew; Yrbk Stf; Pre Optmtry.

WATSON, TERESA; Oakcrest HS; Sweetwater, NJ; (4); 4-H; GAA; Hosp Aide; Pres Key Clb; JV Bsktbl; Var Capt Fld Hcky; Var Sftbl; Var Trk; 4-H Awd; Cook Coll.

WATSON, TIM; Paul VI HS; Laurel Springs, NJ; (3); 140/475; SADD; Variety Show; JV Bsbl; JV Wrstlng; Hon Roll; 2nd Hnrs Acad 86-87; Blackwood Kiwanis Bsbl Tm 1st Pl All Stars 85-87; U DE; Chem.

WATSON, TRACEY; Weequahic HS; Newark, NJ; (3); #9 In Class; Church Yth Grp; NHS; Rutgers U; Nrsng.

WATT, ANNA; Ewing HS; Ewing, NJ; (2); Church Yth Grp; Computer Clb; French Clb; JA; Political Wkr; Acpl Chr; Chorus; Lit Mag; Cheerleading; Hon Roll; Blair Acad Gftd Pgm-Spnsr John Hopkins U 85 & 86; Stu Of Mnth 85-86; Pratt; Grphc Dsgn.

WATTS, JOSEPH; Manchester Regional HS; N Haledon, NJ; (3); Boy Scts; Church Yth Grp; Band; Mrchg Band; Var Socr; Var Trk; Cit Awd; VFW Awd; Eagle Sct 85; Sci Fair-Hrbl Mntn-Physics 85; U Of NM; Poli Sci.

WAWRA, FEDOR; Secaucus Mid Sec Schl; Secaucus, NJ; (4); 9/162; Boy Scts; Pres Math Clb; Math Tm; Mu Alpha Theta; Service Clb; Varsity Clb; Band; Concert Band; Jazz Band; Mrchg Band; MA Inst Tech; Aerontcl Engrng.

WCISLO, KAROLYN; J P Steven HS; Edison, NJ; (3); Ski Clb; Band; Color Guard; Concert Band; Swmmng; Var Trk; Bio.

WEACHOCK, JACKIE; Linden HS; Linden, NJ; (3); FBLA; FHA; Mrchg Band; Hon Roll; NHS; Prfct Atten Awd; Katherine Gibbs Ldrshp Awd 87; Berkeley Schl Woodbirdge; Sec.

WEBB, CHUCK; Clearview Reg HS; Mullica Hill, NJ; (3); 51/171; SADD; Rep Stu Cncl; Coach Actv; Var Diving; JV Socr; Var Capt Swmmng; Brd Of Ed Swmmng Hnr 86-87; Pre-Med.

WEBB, DORIAN K; St Marys Hall-Doane Acad; Pemberton, NJ; (4); 3/ 18; Am Leg Aux Girls St; Debate Tm; Drama Clb; PAVAS; Yrbk Ed-Chief; Pres Soph Cls; VP Jr Cls; Pres Sr Cls; High Hon Roll; Ntl Merit Schol; Schltc Art Awds Wnnr Natl Lvl 84; Schltc Art Awds Wnnr Regnl Lvl 85 & 87; Dsgn Sculptre Mall 85; Yale U; Archit.

WEBB, HEATHER; Woodstown HS; Elmer, NJ; (4); 4/215; Dance Clb; Sec English Clb; Pres 4-H; Sec German Clb; Hosp Aide; Drill Tm; Mrchg Band; School Musical; Capt Fld Hcky; NHS; Josten Fdn Ldrshp Awd 87; Clarence Hitchner Jr Vlntr Awd 87; Pole Tavern Ruritan Schlrshp 87; Johns Hopkins U; Med.

WEBER, CARL D; New Milford HS; New Milford, NJ; (3); 20/142; Am Leg Boys St; Church Yth Grp; Spanish Clb; Yrbk Stf; Rep Stu Cncl; Bsbl; Bsktbl; Socr; Cit Awd; Hon Roll; Engrng.

WEBER, DANIEL; Atlantic Friends Schl; Bargaintown, NJ; (3); 1/20; Cmnty Wkr; Drama Clb; Letterman Clb; Library Aide; Ski Clb; Spanish Clb; Thesps; Varsity Clb; Chorus; School Play; Kathryn Reese Morgan Schlrshp 84-85; Headmstrs Awd Acad Exclnc 84-85; Headmstrs Awd Ousttndng Contrbtn; Vasser; Journalism.

WEBER, ERIC; Glen Rock HS; Glen Rock, NJ; (3); 6/145; Am Leg Boys St; Boy Scts; Capt Varsity Clb; Capt Var Socr; Capt Var Wrstlng; Cit Awd; High Hon Roll; Jr NHS; NHS; Latin Clb; 2nd Tm All Cnty Wrstlng 86; 3rd Tm All Cnty Wrstlng 87; All Leag Wrstlng 85-87; Bnkng.

WEBER, ERIKA; West Essex HS; No Caldwell, NJ; (3); AFS; Am Leg Aux Girls St; Hosp Aide; Spanish Clb; Temple Yth Grp; Stu Cncl; Tennis; High Hon Roll; NHS; Spanish NHS; Yale Bk Awd 87; Yale.

WEBER, JENNIFER; Cresskill HS; Cresskill, NJ; (2); 7/103; Ski Clb; Band; Concert Band; Mrchg Band; Stage Crew; Var L Trk; Hon Roll; NHS; Frgn Lang.

WEBER, PETER; Middletown High School South; Red Bank, NJ; (3); Tennis; High Hon Roll; Jr NHS; NHS; Outstndng Stdnt Awd 84-85; MVP Schl Tennis Tm; Wnnr Monmouth Coll Invtnl & All Monmouth Cnty Tennis; Bus.

WEBER, SUSAN; New Milford HS; New Milford, NJ; (4); 36/139; Church Yth Grp; Nwsp Rptr; Nwsp Stf; Yrbk Stf; Bsktbl; Sftbl; Vllybl; Cit Awd; Hon Roll; Salvation Army Schlrshp 87; Seton Hall U; Elem Educ.

WEBSTER, ARIC; Orange HS; Orange, NJ; (2); Boy Scts; Church Yth Grp; Church Choir; Ftbl; Trk; Wrstlng; Cit Awd; Opt Clb Awd; SAR Awd; VFW Awd; Eagle Scout 86; Amer Lgn Awd 86; UCLA; Engr.

WEBSTER, JOHN CLAY; Highland Park HS; Highland Park, NJ; (4); 13/132; Ski Clb; Thesps; Stage Crew; Lit Mag; JV Tennis; JV Trk; High Hon Roll; Hon Roll; NHS; Pres Schlr; Rutgers Coll; Comp Sci.

WEBSTER, LAWRENCE; Montville Township HS; Pine Brook, NJ; (3); 57/268; FBLA; Key Clb; Ski Clb; Stage Crew; Nwsp Rptr; Var Socr; Var Tennis; High Hon Roll; NHS; FBLA ST Ldrshp Conf 4th Pl Prlmntry Procedure.

WECK, DAVE; Madison HS; Madison, NJ; (3); 25/315; Ftbl; Wt Lftg; NHS.

WECKESSER, ROBERT; Marist HS; Bayonne, NJ; (3); Computer Clb; SADD; Y-Teens.

WECKLER, MICHAEL; Newton HS; Newton, NJ; (4); 9/215; VP German Clb; Stu Cncl; JV Var Socr; JV Tennis; JV Trk; Hon Roll; NHS; Prfct Atten Awd; Sci Lgu 83; Engr.

WEDEL, ANDREW; Andrew W Wedel HS; Pittstown, NJ; (3); 30/237; Varsity Clb; Stu Cncl; Bsbl; Trk; Hon Roll; Cvl Engrng.

WEEDON JR, DAVID E; Asbury Park HS; Asbury Park, NJ; (3); Key Clb.

WEEKS, JODI; Lower Cape May Regional HS; Villas, NJ; (2); Church Yth Grp; Stage Crew; Soph Cls; Coach Actv; Acctnt.

WEG, THOMAS; Msgr Donovans HS; Howell, NJ; (3); Cmnty Wkr; Exploring; SADD; Hon Roll; St Verronica Vincentian Cmmttee 86-87; Law Enfrcmt.

WEGNER, CANDACE; Ramapo HS; Wyckoff, NJ; (4); 47/326; Church Yth Grp; Teachers Aide; Hon Roll; NHS; Pres Schlr; Cnty Wrtng Cont 2nd Pl 87; Wyckoff PTO Schlrshp 87; Scl Stds Excell Awd 87; Wheaton Coll; Engl.

WEGRZYN, CELESTE; Roselle Park HS; Roselle Park, NJ; (4); 12/165; Am Leg Aux Girls St; Radio Clb; Service Clb; Spanish Clb; Co-Capt Color Guard; Mrchg Band; Twrlr; Hon Roll; NHS; MVP Band 86-87; Close-Up Dely WA DC 8 6; Yth Cnty Govt Day Dely 86; Rutgers U; Dent.

WEHNER, ASTRID; Immaculate Heart Acad; Ho-Ho-Kus, NJ; (2); Model UN; Spanish Clb; Chorus; Yrbk Phtg; JV Tennis; Hon Roll.

WEHNER, LAURA J; Westwood HS; Westwood, NJ; (4); 25/214; Chorus; Variety Show; VP Jr Cls; VP Stu Cncl; JV Bsktbl; French Hon Soc; NHS; Intl Thespn Soc 85-87; 3rd Pl NJ ST Poetry Readng Cntst-Kean Coll 87; Parents Music Grp Schlrshp 87; U Of DE; Mrktng.

WEHNER, SUSAN; Ocean City HS; Tuckahoe, NJ; (4); 43/273; VP Band; Mrchg Band; Orch; Symp Band; Nwsp Rptr; Nwsp Sprt Ed; Nwsp Stf; Capt Crs Cntry; Capt Trk; Hon Roll; Cape Atlantic Lge 1600m Relay All Star 85:400 In Cape May Cnty Champ 85-86; Engl.

WEHNKE, KIMBERLY; Henry Hudson Regional HS; Highlands, NJ; (2); Drama Clb; Band; Mrchg Band; School Musical; School Play; Bsktbl; Crs Cntry; Fld Hcky; Sftbl; Vllybl; Bus.

WEHRMAN, MARY; Paul VI HS; Turnersville, NJ; (4); 37/503; Church Yth Grp; French Clb; Math Clb; Capt Color Guard; French Hon Soc; Hon Roll; NHS; Pre-Med.

WEICKER, RAYMOND; Bayonne HS; Bayonne, NJ; (3); Chess Clb; French Clb; Math Tm; Nwsp Rptr; Yrbk Rptr; Rep Frsh Cls; Rep Soph Cls; Rep Stu Cncl; Var Tennis; High Hon Roll; Med.

WEIDMAN, JAY; Maple Shade HS; Maple Shade, NJ; (2); French Clb; Varsity Clb; Yrbk Stf; Rep Stu Cncl; JV Bsktbl; JV Ftbl; Var Golf; Im Wt Lftg; High Hon Roll; NHS; Acdmc All AM 86.

WEIGAND, KEVIN; Queen Of Peace HS; Rutherford, NJ; (3); 66/279; JV Ftbl; Wt Lftg; Hon Roll; Opt Clb Awd; Acctng.

WEIGAND, SANDRA; Toms River H S South; South Toms River, NJ; (3); 66/405; FBLA; Cheerleading; Cit Awd; High Hon Roll; Hon Roll; Miss Jr Amer NJ 87fawd Exclinc Schlrshp 84; Awd Jazz Dancing 82; Katherine Gibbs; Ex Sec.

WEIGEL, DANA; Piscataway HS; Piscataway, NJ; (4); 35/495; Camera Clb; Varsity Clb; Yrbk Phtg; Score Keeper; Socr; Sftbl; Hon Roll; NHS; Pres Schlr; Horse Show Ribbons 83-87; Parent/Teacher Organization Schlrshp 87; Capt Softball Tm 87; Alleghany Coll; Envrnmntl Sci.

WEIGEL, KIM; St James HS; Salem, NJ; (2); Dance Clb; English Clb; Math Clb; Yrbk Stf; Trs Frsh Cls; Trs Soph Cls; Var Bsktbl; Var Fld Hcky; High Hon Roll; Hon Roll.

WEIGHTMAN, GREG; Brick Township Memorial HS; Brick, NJ; (3); 80/360; Bowling; Socr; High Hon Roll; Hon Roll; Atlantic CC; Culnry Arts.

WEIL, SUZANNE; West Field HS; Westfield, NJ; (4); Cmnty Wkr; SADD; Temple Yth Grp; Chorus; Nwsp Bus Mgr; Nwsp Stf; Swmmng; Syracuse U; Psych.

WEILER, MOLLY; Bound Brook HS; Bound Brook, NJ; (4); Church Yth Grp; Hosp Aide; Trs Key Clb; Lit Mag; Sec Sr Cls; VP Sec Stu Cncl; Tennis; Trk; Twrlr; NHS; U Of Pittsburgh; Phys Thrpy.

WEINBERGER, BETH; Overbrook Regional SR HS; Lindenwold, NJ; (4); 41/343; Teachers Aide; Off Soph Cls; Stu Cncl; Var Capt Cheerleading; Mgr(s); Powder Puff Ftbl; Mgr Trk; Stat Wrstlng; Hon Roll; Stockton ST; Pre-Law.

WEINER, JILL; Lakeland Reg HS; Wanaque, NJ; (4); Math Clb; Ski Clb; SADD; Teachers Aide; Yrbk Stf; Rep Stu Cncl; Cheerleading; Gym; High Hon Roll; NHS; Cornell U.

WEINER, RANDY; Ridge HS; Basking Ridge, NJ; (2); 5/169; Ski Clb; Stage Crew; Nwsp Rptr; Nwsp Stf; Lit Mag; Var L Socr; Var L Trk; High Hon Roll; Spanish NHS; HOBY Fndtn Ldrshp Sem Fin 87; Jim Courters Annual Ldrshp Sem 87; Dartmouth; Jrnlsm.

WEINER, TAMMY; Ocean Township HS; Ocean, NJ; (3); 3/344; Pres French Clb; Service Clb; Acpl Chr; Drm Mjr(t); School Musical; Symp Band; Gov Hon Prg Awd; High Hon Roll; Pres NHS; Brnz Congress Awd 85; NJ All ST 87; Rgn II 86-87; All Shore Bands 85-87; All Shore Chorus 87.

WEINGARTNER, LAURA; Notre Dame HS; Hightstown, NJ; (3); 39/396; Stage Crew; Yrbk Stf; Stat Ftbl; High Hon Roll; Hon Roll; Excllnc-Amer Lit 86; Outstndng Achvt-Acctng 87; Outstndng Achvt-US Hist 87; Bus.

WEINSTEIN, KIERSTEN; Delaware Valley Regional HS; Milford, NJ; (3); 30/230; Am Leg Aux Girls St; Church Yth Grp; Cmnty Wkr; Hosp Aide; Intnl Clb; Key Clb; Office Aide; Varsity Clb; Score Keeper; Hon Roll.

WEINSTEIN, MAC; West Orange HS; W Orange, NJ; (3); Math Tm; Spanish Clb; Nwsp Ed-Chief; Nwsp Rptr; Nwsp Sprt Ed; Nwsp Stf; Lit Mag; Trs Frsh Cls; Var L Bsktbl; High Hon Roll; Comm.

WEINTRAUB, BEN; Franklin HS; Somerset, NJ; (3); Boy Scts; Math Tm; Im Crs Cntry; Gov Hon Prg Awd; High Hon Roll; Hon Roll; JETS Awd; NHS; Ntl Merit Ltr; Pres Elec Clb 86-87; Rutgers Schlr 86-87; FAA Licnsd Prvte Pilot 87; Engrng.

WEINTRAUB, MICHELLE; Hunterdon Central HS; Flemington, NJ; (3); 178/543; GAA; Pep Clb; Service Clb; Rep Frsh Cls; Rep Soph Cls; Rep Jr Cls; Stu Cncl; JV Socr; JV Trk; Hon Roll; Mgmt.

WEIR, KAYLENE; Garden State Acad; Teaneck, NJ; (4); Art Clb; Cmnty Wkr; Drama Clb; Spanish Clb; Teachers Aide; Chorus; School Play; Yrbk Stf; Var Gym; JV Var Score Keeper; Oakwood Coll; Bio.

WEIR, SCOTT; Jefferson Township HS; Oak Ridge, NJ; (4); 2/235; Math Tm; Science Clb; SADD; Varsity Clb; Chrmn Stu Cncl; Var Bsbl; Var Crs Cntry; Capt Wrstlng; High Hon Roll; NHS; Dstngshd Schlr 86-87; 3rd Pl Wrld Smbo Chmpshps 86; Schlr Athlte 86-87; Princeton U; Med.

WEISBECKER, CHRISTOPHER; Holy Spirit HS; Absecon, NJ; (2); 10/397; French Clb; Rep Soph Cls; Var Trk; Hon Roll.

WEISCHADLE, DAVID E; Mc Corristin HS; Trenton, NJ; (4); 6/249; Church Yth Grp; Political Wkr; Nwsp Rptr; Nwsp Stf; High Hon Roll; Hon Roll; NHS; Pres Schlr; Var L Golf; Cert For Plsm Physcs Prgm Prnctn U 86; Pres Acdmc Ftns Awd 87; Itln Amer Ntl Hall Of Fame Schlrshp 87; Pre-Med.

WEISCHADLE, DOUGLAS E; Mc Corristin HS; Trenton, NJ; (3); 12/260; Church Yth Grp; Political Wkr; Var L Golf; High Hon Roll; Hon Roll; Jr NHS; NHS; Cert Plasma Physics Prog Princeton U 86; Ntl Merit Sci Awd 87; Cum Laude Ntl Latin Exam 85; Aeronautics.

WEISER, JACQUELINE; Mt Olive HS; Budd Lake, NJ; (3); 6/314; Cmnty Wkr; DECA; Trs FBLA; Math Tm; Rep Jr Cls; Sec Sr Cls; Rep Stu Cncl; JV Bsktbl; High Hon Roll; Ntl Merit SF; Rensselaer Polytechnic Inst For Sci/Math; 4th Hnrs-ST FBLA Cmptn-Acctng II, 4th Rgn Acctng I; CPA.

WEISGERBER, JOHN; Morristown HS; Morristown, NJ; (2); 108/432; Band; Concert Band; Jazz Band; Mrchg Band; School Musical; School Play; Stage Crew; Spec Effects Make-Up.

WEISS, DANIELLE; Morris Knolls HS; Wharton, NJ; (3); 82/425; Pep Clb; Ski Clb; Temple Yth Grp; Sec Soph Cls; Rep Stu Cncl; Var Cheerleading; JV Tennis; High Hon Roll; Hon Roll.

WEISS, ERIK; Wayne Hills HS; Wayne, NJ; (3); 67/375; Ski Clb; Spanish Clb; Varsity Clb; Var Socr; Var Swmmng; Var Trk; Hon Roll; All NBIAL 1st Tm 87; Bus.

WEISS, HEATHER; Red Bank Regional HS; Little Silver, NJ; (3); 1/250; SADD; Ed Yrbk Sprt Ed; French Hon Soc; Var L High Hon Roll; NHS; Ntl Merit Ltr; Val; 1st Pl-Schl-NJ Math Leag 86 & 87; 1st Pl-Schl-Amercn HS Math Exam 87; Geo Wshngtn U Awd 87; Arch.

WEISS, HEIDI LYNN; Millville SR HS; Millville, NJ; (3); Church Yth Grp; Drama Clb; French Clb; GAA; School Musical; Nwsp Ed-Chief; Nwsp Phtg; Nwsp Rptr; Yrbk Stf; Pres Stu Cncl; Exch Stu Frnc Smmr 86; Hrshy Pk Dncr 87; 12 Yrs Of Dnc 86; Jrnlst.

WEISS, MARTIN; Middletown South HS; Red Bank, NJ; (4); 16/458; Boy Scts; Chess Clb; ROTC; Band; Mrchg Band; Symp Band; High Hon Roll; Hon Roll; NHS; Garden St Dist Schlr 87; MIT Cooper Union; Engrng.

WEISS, MICHAEL; Madison HS; Madison, NJ; (3); 23/217; VP FBLA; Spanish Clb; Jazz Band; Nwsp Ed-Chief; VP Frsh Cls; VP Soph Cls; Rep Jr Cls; Ftbl; High Hon Roll; Sec NHS; U Of WI Madison; Music.

WEISS, MICHELLE; Abraham Clark HS; Roselle, NJ; (4); Jacques Hodge Awd 87; Roselle-Roselle Pk Rotry Clb Awd 87; Citlone Inst; Crt Reprtng.

WEISS, WENDY; Washington Township HS; Grenloch, NJ; (4); Sec Art Clb; Church Yth Grp; Band; Color Guard; Concert Band; Art Awds 84-87; Art.

WEISSBEIN, DANIEL A; Bridgewater-Raritan HS East; Bridgewater, NJ; (4); 90/280; Pres Temple Yth Grp; Concert Band; Rep Stu Cncl; JV Var Ftbl; Wt Lftg; JV Wrstlng; High Hon Roll; Hon Roll; NHS; Prsdntl Acad Fitness Awd 87; George Washington U; Lbrl Arts.

WEISSENBERGER, LISA; Haddonfield Memorial HS; Haddonfield, NJ; (2); Church Yth Grp; Cmnty Wkr; Dance Clb; Intnl Clb; Latin Clb; Library Aide; Office Aide; Variety Show; JV Tennis; High Hon Roll; Princeton U; Psych.

WELCH, JENNIFER; Dover HS; Mine Hill, NJ; (2); Chorus; Trs Jr Cls; Var Crs Cntry; Var Trk; Hon Roll; Bonne Bell Cir Excel Crss Cntry 87; Peer Ldrshp Awd 87; Bio Awd 87.

WELCH, SUZIE; Neptune SR HS; Bricktown, NJ; (3); Church Yth Grp; Drama Clb; School Musical; Nwsp Phtg; Yrbk Phtg; Rep Frsh Cls; Trs Sr Cls; JV Fld Hcky; JV Var Mgr(s); Var Score Keeper; Millikin U Schlrshp 87; Rutgers; Intl Bus Affrs.

WELDING, KAREN; Cherry Hill West HS; Cherry Hill, NJ; (1); Church Yth Grp; Spanish Clb; SADD; Rep Frsh Cls; Mgr(s); Stat Socr; Hon Roll; Psych.

WELLER, JILL; Villa Victoria Acad; Churchville, PA; (1); Cmnty Wkr; Chorus; School Musical; School Play; Var Bsktbl; Var Socr; Hon Roll; Villa Vctria Acdmy Schlrshp 86-90; Ntl Sci Mrt Awd 86-87.

WELLER JR, RONALD; St Pius X Regional HS; Piscataway, NJ; (3); 16/80; Boy Scts; Church Yth Grp; Chorus; Madrigals; School Play; Pres Sr Cls; Pres Stu Cncl; Var L Bsbl; Var L Ftbl; NHS; Rogate 84-87; St Pius X Reg Hon Mtn Bio 85.

WELLS, CANDICE; Lakewood HS; Lakewood, NJ; (3); 15/330; English Clb; JCL; Sec Latin Clb; Spanish Clb; Variety Show; Rep Jr Cls; Hon Roll; Jr NHS; NHS; Spanish NHS; Miami U OH; Bio.

WELLS, JESSICA; Vail-Deane Schl; Millburn, NJ; (4); French Clb; Science Clb; Chorus; Nwsp Rptr; Nwsp Stf; Rutgers; Jrnlsm.

WELLS, LEONORE; Vernon Township HS; Vernon, NJ; (3); 24/274; French Clb; Girl Scts; Math Clb; Science Clb; Band; Concert Band; Mrchg Band; Jr NHS; NHS; Young Ctzns Awd 87.

WELLS, SCOTT; Ridge HS; Basking Ridge, NJ; (4); 11/200; Church Yth Grp; Cmnty Wkr; Quiz Bowl; Yrbk Phtg; NHS; Ntl Merit Ltr; Pres Schlr; Latin Clb; Science Clb; High Hon Roll; Marshall Hahn Engrng Schlrshp; Rhone Poulene Schlrshp; RPI Math & Sci Medal 11; VA Tech; Elec Engrng.

WELSH, BARBARA; Red Bank Regional HS; Little Silver, NJ; (4); 94/260; Church Yth Grp; Exploring; FHA; Color Guard; School Play; Stage Crew; Hon Roll; Prfct Atten Awd; Vrsty Ltr & SR Blanket For Band Front 87; Little Slvr Womens Clb Schlrshp 87; Red Bnk Assn Schlrsp 87; Atlantic Christian Coll; Bio.

WELSH, KRISTEN; Holy Spirit HS; Linwood, NJ; (3); 50/300; Girl Scts; Yrbk Stf; Sftbl; Hon Roll; Holy Spirit Grls Crew 85-88; Rutgers Boston U; Liberal Arts.

WELSH, MARGARET; Mary Help Of Christians Acad; Suffern, NY; (4); 23/80; Cmnty Wkr; Drama Clb; French Clb; JCL; Quiz Bowl; SADD; Nwsp Rptr; Yrbk Stf; Hon Roll; NHS; SR Ldrshp Retreat 86; Latin Hnr Scty 86-87; H S Math Lge 86-87; Lehigh U; Accntnt.

WELSH, MELINDA S; Hopatcong HS; Hopatcong, NJ; (4); 5/200; Drama Clb; School Musical; School Play; Stage Crew; Variety Show; VP Soph Cls; Cit Awd; DAR Awd; Pres NHS; Ski Clb; HOBY Ldrshp 85; Wmns Lg Scholar 87; Drama Clb Awd MVP 85-87; Boston U; Comm.

WELSH, MICHAEL P; Mater Dei HS; Highlands, NJ; (4); 30/150; Am Leg Boys St; Debate Tm; Drama Clb; Math Clb; Model UN; School Musical; Nwsp Rptr; Lit Mag; Pres Stu Cncl; Powder Puff Ftbl; U Of DE; Engr.

WELT, JODI; Morris Knolls HS; Morris Plains, NJ; (3); Science Clb; Ski Clb; Temple Yth Grp; Var Capt Swmmng; Dance Clb; Drama Clb; Nwsp Stf; Yrbk Stf; JV Var Score Keeper; Sports Nutritn.

WELTER, JOHN; Ocean Township HS; Ocean, NJ; (3); 39/349; Key Clb; Tennis; Ntl Merit Ltr; Sprtn Schlr 85-86; Brnz Cngrssnl Awd 87; Medcl Engrng.

WEN, KAITI; Sayreville War Memorial HS; Parlin, NJ; (4); Teachers Aide; VP Jr Cls; VP Stu Cncl; Socr; Vllybl; Stu Cncl Hnr 87; Amercs Hmcmng Queen Hnr NJ ST Fnlst 87; Southeastern Acad; Travel Agnt.

WENCE, RONALD L; Palmyra HS; Palmyra, NJ; (4); 15/120; Am Leg Boys St; Church Yth Grp; Cmnty Wkr; German Clb; Key Clb; SADD; Teachers Aide; Yrbk Phtg; Yrbk Rptr; Yrbk Stf; Kenny Pennahue & Cmtny Svc Schlrshps & Amer Lgn Awd 87; Elizabethtown Coll PA; Math.

WENDOLOWSKI, JOHN; Raritan HS; Hazlet, NJ; (3); 12/327; CAP; Trs French Clb; JA; Nwsp Stf; Swmmng; JV Tennis; High Hon Roll; Hon Roll; Jr NHS; NHS; Embry-Riddle; Cmmrcl Pilot.

WENDT, LAURIE; Jackson Memorial HS; Jackson, NJ; (4); 71/403; Art Clb; Ski Clb; SADD; Pres Frsh Cls; VP Soph Cls; VP Jr Cls; Pres Sr Cls; Rep Stu Cncl; Cheerleading; Fld Hcky; Natl Art Hnr Scty; Jackson Schlrshp Fund 87; Outstndg SR Awd 87; Philadelphia Art Inst; Intr Dsg.

WENGER, SCOTT; The Pennington Schl; Somerset, NJ; (3); Boy Scts; Church Yth Grp; Ski Clb; SADD; Church Choir; Rep Stu Cncl; Var Lcrss; JV Var Socr; Swmmng; Hon Roll; Hungarian-Am Athltc Clb Sprng & Smmr Sccr 87; Aero Engr.

WENMAN, DOUG; Northern Valley Reg HS; Harrington Pk, NJ; (3); 16/274; Boy Scts; Computer Clb; French Clb; Latin Clb; Ski Clb; Var Crs Cntry; JV Trk; High Hon Roll; NHS; Hon Roll; George Washington U Engrng Awd 87; Sci Wzrd Bio 84; MIT; Elec Engr.

WENTWORTH, CHRISTOPHER P; St Peters Prep; Belleville, NJ; (2); Boy Scts; Church Yth Grp; Cmnty Wkr; German Clb; NFL; JV Crs Cntry; Cit Awd; Hon Roll; Acad Schlrshp To Regis HS NY City 85-86; Hstrn.

WENTZELL, DEBORAH; Woodstown HS; Woodstown, NJ; (4); 40/215; Cmnty Wkr; Trs English Clb; Pres Hosp Aide; Spanish Clb; Nwsp Rptr; Ed Lit Mag; Rep Stu Cncl; Hon Roll; Spanish NHS; Cndy Strpr Of Yr 85; Rep Of Salem Hosp At Vlntrs Cnvntn 86; Glassboro ST Coll; Comm.

WENTZELL, VICKI; A P Schalick HS; Elmer, NJ; (4); 16/133; Art Clb; Church Yth Grp; JA; Ski Clb; Drill Tm; Var Cheerleading; Var Pom Pon; JV Sftbl; Hon Roll; Western KY U; Juvenile Offcr.

WEREMIJENKO, CHRISSY; Notre Dame HS; Trenton, NJ; (3); FBLA; Library Aide; High Hon Roll; Hon Roll; Awd Excllnc Span II 87; Bus Admin.

WERFEL, BETH; John P Stevens HS; Edison, NJ; (3); 128/450; Cmnty Wkr; Science Clb; SADD; Tennis; Bus.

WERLEY, RICHARD; Lenape Valley Regional HS; Andover, NJ; (3); FBLA; Var Ftbl; Var Golf; Var Tennis; High Hon Roll; Hon Roll; NHS; Spanish NHS; FBLA Regnl Comp 3rd Pl 87; Lenape Schlr Awd 87; U PA; Ins Agnt.

WERTH, KATHLEEN; Monsignor Donovan HS; Toms River, NJ; (3); 54/245; Church Yth Grp; Drama Clb; Hosp Aide; Service Clb; SADD; Thesps; Co-Capt Flag Corp; Stage Crew; NHS; Prfct Atten Awd.

WERTZ, KEVIN; Baptist HS; Williamstown, NJ; (3); 6/50; Church Yth Grp; Drama Clb; Chorus; School Play; VP Soph Cls; Score Keeper; High Hon Roll; Hon Roll; Bptst Hgh Hnr Scty 87; Bob Jones U.

WESCHER, LEONA; Kings Christian HS; Riverside, NJ; (2); 7/53; Church Yth Grp; Band; Var Cheerleading; High Hon Roll; Hon Roll; Wheaton Coll; Mth.

WESCOTT, JULIE; Bishop George Ahr St Thomas HS; Edison, NJ; (4); Pres Trs Exploring; ROTC; Capt Drill Tm; Stage Crew; Yrbk Phtg; Rep Sr Cls; DAR Awd; ROTC Dstngshd Cadet, Cndt, Apt, Apprnce 84-86:NRA Mrksmn, Shrpshtr, Bar 1, & 2 84-86; Phgtgrphr.

WESLEY, RYAN; Arthur L Johnson Regional HS; Clark, NJ; (4); 37/195; Computer Clb; JV Socr; Var Trk; NCTE Awd; U Scranton.

WESLEY, SUZANNE; Wayne Hills HS; Wayne, NJ; (3); 43/330; GAA; Math Clb; Spanish Clb; Nwsp Ed-Chief; Lit Mag; Hon Roll; NHS; Comm.

WEST, ANN MARIE; Wall HS; Wall Township, NJ; (3); 20/300; Key Cl Ski Clb; Spanish Clb; Nwsp Rptr; Yrbk Stf; Stat Crs Cntry; JV Fld Hck; L Var Trk; High Hon Roll; Hon Roll; Trck Mdls 2; Girls State; Newspape Edit-In-Chief; Track Capt; Law.

WEST, BETH; Southern Regional HS; Barnegat, NJ; (4); Trs Church Yt Grp; Library Aide; Spanish Clb; Hon Roll; Prfct Atten Awd; Schls Edu Assn Schlrshp 87; Ocean Cnty Coll; Elem Educ.

WEST, HOLLY J; West Milford HS; West Milford, NJ; (3); DECA French Clb; SADD; Concert Band; French Hon Soc; Fnlst DECA St Cor 87; 1st Pl J Casablancas Model Srch 87; Fhsn Merch.

WEST, JULIE; Paramus Catholic HS; New Milford, NJ; (3); Drama Cl Teachers Aide; School Play; Nwsp Stf; High Hon Roll; Hon Roll; NED Awd; Frnch Awd 85; Engl Awd 87; Scl Stud Awd 87; Elem Educ.

WEST, RICHARD; West Windsor-Plainsboro HS; Robbinsville, NJ; (3 Boy Scts; Trs Chess Clb; Computer Clb; Model UN; Hon Roll; Comp Sc

WEST, STEVEN; Florence Memorial HS; Florence, NJ; (3); Church Yt Grp; English Clb; Latin Clb; Letterman Clb; NAACP; Variety Show; Nws Rptr; Nwsp Sprt Ed; Nwsp Stf; Ftbl; All Cnty Ftbl 87; Econ.

WESTCOTT, DIANE; Salem HS; Salem, NJ; (3); Church Yth Gr Drama Clb; Exploring; 4-H; Hosp Aide; Math Clb; Spanish Clb; SADI Teachers Aide; Stage Crew; Crmnl Lawyer.

WESTENDORF, DEANE; Saint John Vianney HS; Colts Neck, NJ; (1 SADD; Thesps; Twrlr; Actress.

WESTON, SARAH; West Essex HS; N Caldwell, NJ; (3); Church Yt Grp; French Clb; Key Clb; Latin Clb; Library Aide; Band; Chorus; Concer Band; School Play; Lit Mag; Arch.

WESTON, VALERIE; Asbury Pk HS; Jackson, NJ; (3); French Clb; Ho Roll; Newbury Coll; Clnry Art.

WESTWARD, TODD; High Point Regional HS; Newton, NJ; (3); Bo Scts; Church Yth Grp; Teachers Aide; Nwsp Phtg; Socr; Var Trk; Boy Sc Eagle Awd 87.

WETMORE, ALLISON; Marine Acad Of Science & Tech; Leonard, NJ (3); Drama Clb; ROTC; Ski Clb; VP Spanish Clb; VP Soph Cls; Sec St Cncl; Hon Roll; NHS; Intl Frgn Lng Awd 86; Chem.

WETMORE, JAMES; Ridgewood HS; Ridgewood, NJ; (4); 1/442; Mat Clb; Math Tm; Quiz Bowl; Science Clb; JV Trk; High Hon Roll; NHS; N Merit Schol; Val; Harvard Bk Awd 86; Magna Cum Laude Awd Ntl Lati Exam 85-86; Stanford U.

WETZEL, PAMELA; Paul VI Regional HS; Passaic, NJ; (4); Ski Cl Spanish NHS; Wm Patterson ST Coll; Nrsg.

WEXLIN, HILLARY B; East Brunswick HS; East Brunswick, NJ; (4 VP Art Clb; Dance Clb; Rep Key Clb; Ski Clb; SADD; Concert Band; V Jazz Band; Variety Show; Lit Mag; Band; Indigo Awd 87; Parsons Sch Dsgn; Fash Dsgn.

WEYMAN, BETH; Northern Burlington HS; Wrightstown, NJ; (4); 32 280; Drama Clb; FFA; Nwsp Ed-Chief; Rep Frsh Cls; Rep Soph Cls; Re Sr Cls; Var Capt Bsktbl; Var L Fld Hcky; Var Capt Trk; Hon Roll; Sprt Athltc Awd 87; Montclair ST; Bus.

WHALEY JR, JAMES C; Camden HS; Camden, NJ; (4); 25/423; Band Concert Band; Drm & Bgl; Jazz Band; Mrchg Band; Orch; Hon Roll; Prfc Atten Awd; St Schlr; Glassboro ST Coll; Music.

WHALLEY, DIANA LYNN; Watchung Hills Regional HS; Gillette, NJ (3); Cmnty Wkr; Office Aide; Political Wkr; Rep Service Clb; Chorus; Ho Roll; Stu Of Mnth 84-85; Bus.

WHEATON, CHERYL; Bridgeton HS; Cedarville, NJ; (3); 9/254; Nws Sprt Ed; Sec Jr Cls; JV Var Sftbl; NHS; Girl Scts; Varsity Clb; Churc Choir; Nwsp Rptr; Yrbk Stf; JV Bsktbl; Excllnc Chem 87, Math 85 & 86 Ctznshp Awd 83 & 84; Rll Schlrshp Hghst Hnrs 85; Spllng Bee 2nd P 82-84.

WHEELER, LAUREN; Monsignor Donovan HS; Toms River, NJ; (3) 67/240; Nwsp Stf; Sec Rep Stu Cncl; Capt Cheerleading; Var Tennis Drama Clb; Service Clb; Ski Clb; SADD; Law.

WHEELER, MICHAEL; Ewing HS; Trenton, NJ; (2); Cmnty Wkr Computer Clb; Science Clb; Chorus; JV Trk; Hon Roll; Spnsh & Prblms O Mdrn Man Awds 86; Bio Awd 87; Tech Sci.

WHELAN, PETER; Morris Catholic HS; Denville, NJ; (4); 48/137; Pe Clb; Varsity Clb; Var Capt Socr; All-Amer Tri St Sccr 86-87; All-St 1st Tm 86-87; All-Cnfrnc 1st Tm 86-87; U Of Dayton; Accntng.

WHELAN, THERESA; Mt St Dominic Acad; West Orange, NJ; (3); 5/56 Church Yth Grp; Intnl Clb; Yrbk Stf; Stu Cncl; JV Bsktbl; VP Crs Cntry VP Sftbl; High Hon Roll; NHS; Achvt Awd 85; NJ All-ST Sftbl Prvt Sch 87.

WHICKER, DANA; Belvidere HS; Belvidere, NJ; (4); 18/121; Compute Clb; Library Aide; Lit Mag; Elks Awd; Ntl Merit SF; Comp Pgmmng.

WHILDON, TERESA; Millville SR HS; Millville, NJ; (3); 250/524 Church Yth Grp; DECA; Girl Scts; Hosp Aide; Band; Concert Band Mrchg Band; Variety Show; Hon Roll; Comp Tech.

WHISTEN, SCOTT; Secaucus HS; Secaucus, NJ; (3); Key Clb; Math Clb Mu Alpha Theta; Var Bsbl; JV Ftbl; Im Wt Lftg; High Hon Roll; Jr NHS Mu Alpha Theta Awd; NHS; UCLA; Engnrng.

WHITACRE, KIM; Notre Dame HS; Lawrenceville, NJ; (2); Cmnty Wkr VP L Crs Cntry; High Hon Roll; Spanish NHS; Phys Sci Awd 85-86; U O NC Chapel Hill; Law.

WHITAKER, AUDRA; Notre Dame HS; Yardville, NJ; (3); Red Cross Aide; SADD; Yrbk Stf; Lit Mag; Hon Roll; Cmmnctns.

WHITAKER, KATRINA SHIRESE; Franklin HS; Somerset, NJ; (3); Key Clb; SADD; Chorus; School Musical; Rep Frsh Cls; Rep Soph Cls; Rep Jr Cls; Rep Sr Cls; Rep Stu Cncl; JV Capt Fld Hcky; Medicine/Phys Ther

WHITAKER, LOSSIE; Arts HS; Newark, NJ; (4); Acpl Chr; Chorus; Church Choir; Off Jr Cls; Off Sr Cls; Stu Cncl; Bsktbl; Cheerleading; Trk; Cit Awd; Tri-Music Hnr Soc 86; Chamber Ensmbl 86-87; Prfct Atten Awd 84; Cmnty Prtcptn Awd 87; Sexon Hall U; Pediatrcn.

WHITE, ANDREW; Howell HS; Howell, NJ; (4); 4/354; Exploring; Math Clb; NFL; Scholastic Bowl; Var Ftbl; JV Trk; Im Wt Lftg; L Wrstlng NHS; 1st Pl Accntng I Cont 86; Treas-Natl Hnr Scty 86-87; Sociology Dept Awd 87; U Of S CA; Bus.

WHITE, CHERYL; Abraham Clark HS; Roselle, NJ; (4); GAA; Hosp Aide; Spanish Clb; Sec Jr Cls; Stu Cncl; Capt JV Cheerleading; Sftbl; Capt Var Trk; NJIT; Comp Sci.

WHITE, CHRIS; Dwight Morrow HS; Englewood, NJ; (3); #37 In Class, Latin Clb; Rep Frsh Cls; Rep Soph Cls; Rep Jr Cls; Var L Bsktbl; Hon Roll; Attndnc Awd 86-87; Sprtsmnshp Awd Bsktbl Smmr Leag 86; Vrsty Athl Awd 87; Cmmnctns.

WHITE, CLINT; Christian Brothers Acad; Oceanport, NJ; (4); 2/200; Cmnty Wkr; Computer Clb; Ski Clb; Jazz Band; Nwsp Rptr; Im Fld Hcky; Im Ftbl; High Hon Roll; Hon Roll; Embry-Riddle U; Aeronautcl Engr.

WHITE, DELORIS; Perth Amboy HS; Perth Amboy, NJ; (4); 39/388; Nwsp Stf; Yrbk Sprt Ed; Sr Cls; Var Capt Cheerleading; JV Sftbl; CC Awd; Hon Roll; Acadmc All Am 87; Montclair ST Coll; Bus Admin.

WHITE, DERREK; Manchester Regional HS; Haledon, NJ; (3); 2/160; Am Leg Boys St; Band; Math Tm; Science Clb; Ski Clb; Rep Stu Cncl; High Hon Roll; Hon Roll; NHS; Church Yth Grp; Captn Mens Epee Fencing 85-87; Bio.

WHITE, ELAINE; Franklin HS; Somerset, NJ; (1); Cmnty Wkr; FBLA; Hosp Aide; SADD; Hon Roll; Spanish NHS; NJ Bus Ed Assn 87; NJ Prfcncy Tst 86; Princeton U; Lawyr.

WHITE, ERICH; Union HS; Union, NJ; (3); Science Clb; Spanish Clb; Rep Soph Cls; Im Trk; Hon Roll; Jr NHS; NHS; Ntl Sci Olympiad Awd 87; Rutgers; Finance.

WHITE, GARY; Edgewood Regional HS; Atco, NJ; (3); 17/390; Church Yth Grp; JCL; Latin Clb; Nwsp Stf; Yrbk Stf; Rep Frsh Cls; Rep Jr Cls; Hon Roll; Jr NHS; Pres NHS; Selection Into Te LEAD Pgm In Bus 87; Engrng.

WHITE, HEATHER; Woodstown HS; Elmer, NJ; (4); 12/215; Drama Clb; French Clb; Spanish Clb; Band; Chorus; Church Choir; Mrchg Band; Sec Soph Cls; Stat Socr; NHS; Hood Coll.

WHITE, JANINE; Henry Hudson Regional HS; Highlands, NJ; (3); VICA; Nwsp Stf; JV Sftbl; Hon Roll; Fshn Mrchndsng.

WHITE, JONATHAN; Timothy Christian Schl; Millington, NJ; (4); 1/32; JV Socr; VP NHS; Grdn ST Dstngshd Schlr Awd; Comp Engrng.

WHITE, LA NISSIR; Hillside HS; Hillside, NJ; (3); Science Clb; Ski Clb; Y-Teens; Church Choir; Yrbk Stf; Rep Soph Cls; Trs Jr Cls; Sec Stu Cncl; Capt Cheerleading; Var Sftbl; Lehigh U; Brdct Jrnlst.

WHITE, LORI ANN; Paulsboro HS; Paulsboro, NJ; (3); Cmnty Wkr; English Clb; Flag Corp; Nwsp Stf; Yrbk Stf; Lit Mag; JV Var Sftbl; Var Trk; Prfct Atten Awd; Rutgers; Law.

WHITE, MICHAEL; Essex Catholic Boys HS; Orange, NJ; (3); Cmnty Wkr; Bsbl; Bsktbl; Ftbl; Sftbl; High Hon Roll; Hon Roll; 1st Hnr Roll 84-85; 2nd Hnrs 85-87; JV Ftbl MVP Ftbl Plyr Of Yr 86-87; Engrng.

WHITE, NICHOLAS; Vineland HS; Vineland, NJ; (3); 10/750; Exploring; Math Tm; Spanish Clb; Tennis; Trk; High Hon Roll; Hon Roll; Prfct Atten Awd; Math.

WHITE, PAUL; Hunterdon Central HS; Sergeantsville, NJ; (2); 86/478; Ski Clb; Var Ftbl; JV Lcrss; Jr NHS; Prfct Atten Awd; US Naval Acad; Bus.

WHITE, SHAWN; John F Kennedy HS; Avenel, NJ; (3); 88/235; Girl Scts; SADD; Yrbk Stf; Rep Frsh Cls; Rep Soph Cls; Rep Stu Cncl; Var Bowling; Var Trk; Hon Roll; Middlesex Cnty YABA JR Master Tourn 84-85; Rutgers; Comp Sci.

WHITE, STEPHANIE; Ocean Township HS; Asbury Park, NJ; (3); 71/344; French Clb; Var Fld Hcky; JV Sftbl; Var Swmmng; Science.

WHITE, SUZANNE L; Academy Of The Holy Angels; Oradell, NJ; (3); French Clb; Hosp Aide; Model UN; Mu Alpha Theta; Color Guard; Nwsp Rptr; Yrbk Stf; Hon Roll; Mu Alpha Theta Awd; Slvr Mdl Natl Latin Exam 85; Georgetown U; Intl Bus.

WHITEFLEET, KEVIN; Bergen Tech; Elmwood Park, NJ; (3); #2 In Class; Var Ftbl; Var Trk; Capt Wrstlng; High Hon Roll; Hon Roll; NHS.

WHITEHEAD, EMILIE; Livingston HS; Livingston, NJ; (3); 30/417; AFS; Church Yth Grp; French Clb; Leo Clb; Band; Concert Band; Mrchg Band; French Hon Soc; High Hon Roll; Jr NHS; JV & Vrsty Ltrs, Cert Cncrt, Mrchng Band 86-87; VA Weslyan; Bio.

WHITEHEAD, VANESSA; Kent Place Schl; Newark, NJ; (3); VP Church Yth Grp; Chorus; Madrigals; Nwsp Rptr; Rep Soph Cls; Rep Jr Cls; JV Vllybl; High Hon Roll; Top Stu Engrng Trphy Stevens Inst Of Tech 87; Natl Presdntl Physcl Ftns Awd 87; Engr.

WHITESEL, TODD; Morris Knolls HS; Randolph, NJ; (3); Debate Tm; JCL; Math Clb; Ski Clb; Lit Mag; High Hon Roll; ACM Awd North Jersey Rgnl Sci Fair 87; Sci.

WHITFIELD, LESLIE; University HS; Newark, NJ; (3); Exploring; JA; Leo Clb; Model UN; NAACP; Nwsp Stf; Bus.

WHITFIELD, WILLIAM J; Northern Burlington Regional HS; Wrightstown, NJ; (4); 6/235; Church Yth Grp; Math Tm; School Musical; Stu Cncl; JV Ftbl; JV Socr; Hon Roll; Pres NHS; Spanish NHS; St Schlr; Ntl Merit Schrlsh Pcorp Outstndng Negro Stu 86; Sci Comp Dept Awd 85-86; Trenton ST Coll; Mech Engr.

WHITING, JAMES; Ridge HS; Basking Ridge, NJ; (3); Boy Scts; Trs Church Yth Grp; Pep Clb; Ski Clb; Trs Jr Cls; Trs Sr Cls; L Im Coach Actv; JV Var Ftbl; Powder Puff Ftbl; Im Wt Lftg; Prom Prince 87; Bus.

WHITING, TERRI; Clayton HS; Clayton, NJ; (4); Church Yth Grp; Trs Key Clb; Teachers Aide; Drm Mjr(t); Mrchg Band; School Play; Yrbk Stf; Off Stu Cncl; Mgr(s); Capt Pom Pon; Gftd & Tlntd 83-87; Elem Ed.

WHITLEY, DIONNE; Abraham Clark HS; Roselle, NJ; (3); Church Choir; High Hon Roll; Church Yth Grp; FHA; Office Aide; Gym; Hon Roll; Rutgers U; Bus Adm.

WHITLOW, WYNSTON; Bridgeton SR HS; Bridgeton, NJ; (3); Church Yth Grp; Chorus; Church Choir; Pep Band; Bsktbl; Crs Cntry; Trk; NHS; Ntl Merit Schol; Berkeley; Engrng.

WHITMAN, LES; Burlington Township HS; Burlington, NJ; (3); 5/136; Am Leg Boys St; Chorus; Var Crs Cntry; Var Trk; Hon Roll; NHS; Olympcs Mnd 86-87; Lang Clb 85-87; Stu Fnds Accntnt 86-87; Accntng.

WHITNEY, ALEXANDER D; Jackson Memorial HS; Jackson, NJ; (3); 2/425; Science Clb; JV Bsbl; Capt L Crs Cntry; L Trk; High Hon Roll; NHS; NEDT Awd; Ivy League U; Bio Sci.

WHITONIS, THOMAS; Pt Pleasant Bch HS; Pt Pleasant, NJ; (3); Art Clb; Boy Scts; Camera Clb; CAP; Cmnty Wkr; ROTC; Hon Roll; Pres Phys Ftnss Awd 86-87; Engrng.

WHITSITT, DEANNA; Union Catholic Regional HS; Scotch Plains, NJ; (3); 25/317; Library Aide; Service Clb; Wrk Prt Tm Clrcl For Mc Donough Murray & Korn Cnslrs At Law; Prev Wrkd Sls Clrk; Georgetown U; Law.

WHITTAKER, KERRI; Wood-Ridge HS; Wood Ridge, NJ; (3); 13/90; Latin Clb; Office Aide; Science Clb; JV Cheerleading; Var Trk; High Hon Roll; Hon Roll; NHS; Dntl Hygntst.

WHITTLE, ROSLYN; Frank H Morrell HS; Irvington, NJ; (4); 1/500; Drama Clb; Ed Key Clb; Sec Latin Clb; Chorus; Capt Flag Corp; Rep Frsh Cls; Rep Soph Cls; Rep Jr Cls; Rep Sr Cls; Capt Sftbl; Douglass Coll; Biomed Engrng.

WHORLEY, APRIL; West Morris Mendham HS; Chester, NJ; (2); 2/280; Math Tm; Science Clb; Teachers Aide; Var L Gym; JV L Trk; High Hon Roll; Mst Imprvd Gymnst Awd 86; Engr.

WICELINSKI, THERESE; St John Vianney HS; Hazlet, NJ; (4); 1/251; Pres Intnl Clb; Math Tm; Twrlr; High Hon Roll; NHS; St Schlr; Val; Manhattan Coll Schlrshp 87-91; Manhattan Coll; Chem Engrng.

WICHLERMAN, JENNIFER D; Haddon Township HS; Westmont, NJ; (3); Am Leg Aux Girls St; Art Clb; Ski Clb; Nwsp Sprt Ed; Nwsp Stf; Rep Stu Cncl; JV Bsktbl; JV Tennis; Hon Roll; Drexel U; Psych.

WICHROWSKI, NICOLE; Edgewood Regional HS; Chesilhurst, NJ; (3); Pres French Clb; Quiz Bowl; VP SADD; Nwsp Rptr; Hon Roll; Jr NHS.

WICKHAM, ROBERT; Dwight-Englewood HS; Englewood, NJ; (4); Exploring; Math Clb; Math Tm; Nwsp Phtg; Yrbk Phtg; Hon Roll; Achvt Sci 87; Bergen Cnty Math Leag Cert Merit 86-87; Columbia U; Aero Engrng.

WICZYK, HILLAH; Dwight Morrow HS; Englewood Cliffs, NJ; (3); 9/312; Cmnty Wkr; Drama Clb; Latin Clb; Spanish Clb; Stage Crew; Yrbk Stf; Var Vllybl; High Hon Roll; Hon Roll; GAA; Law.

WIDTH JR, RICHARD R; Voorhees HS; Califon, NJ; (4); 95/277; Church Yth Grp; Drama Clb; Intnl Clb; Thesps; Off Lit Mag; Gov Hon Prg Awd; Hon Roll; English Clb; School Musical; School Play; Arts Rcgntn & Tlnt Srch Lvl III 87; NJ ST Gvrnrs Awd Arts Educ 87; NJ Yng Plywrgts Awd 87; Boston U; Thtre.

WIECENSKI, LYNN M; Teaneck HS; Teaneck, NJ; (4); 66/425; Capt Dance Clb; Hosp Aide; School Musical; Yrbk Stf; Stu Cncl; Capt Cheerleading; Mgr(s); Hon Roll; NHS; Douglass Coll; Spnsh.

WIECZOREK, CYNTHIA; Frank H Morrell HS; Irvington, NJ; (4); 26/450; Church Yth Grp; Capt Flag Corp; Stage Crew; Lit Mag; Sftbl; Swmmng; High Hon Roll; NHS; TAG 87; GSS 87; Kean Coll Of NJ; Psych.

WIEDEMANN, JODY; Pemberton Twp HS; Browns Mills, NJ; (4); 1/406; Hosp Aide; Stu Cncl; JV Capt Socr; Swmmng; High Hon Roll; Timer; Val; Grdn ST Dstngshd Schlr 87; Rtry Clb Schlrshp 87; Kenny Haug Mem Schlrshp 87; Trntn ST Coll; Pltcl Sci.

WIEGAND, KATHRYN; Cedar Ridge HS; Old Bridge, NJ; (3); 39/352; Cmnty Wkr; Var L Cheerleading; High Hon Roll; Hon Roll; NHS; Spanish NHS; Old Bridge Educ Assn Schlrshp 87; Arts & Crafts Achvt Awd 87; Cook Coll; Vet.

WIEGAND, WENDY; Pompton Lakes HS; Pompton Lakes, NJ; (4); 7/130; Math Tm; Teachers Aide; Chorus; Nwsp Stf; High Hon Roll; Sec NHS; Prfct Atten Awd; Church Yth Grp; Stage Crew; Hon Roll; Zonta Clb Mst Svc Hrs In HS 87; JR Engrng Tech Soc Teams Comp 87; Prew Acad Ftns Awd 87; Ramapo Coll NJ.

WIEHE, KURT; Bernards HS; Gladstone, NJ; (3); Band; Chorus; Drm Mjr(t); Mrchg Band; School Musical; Capt Socr; Var Wrstlng; Music Hall Of Fame 86; Bus.

WIELECHOWSKI, AIMEE; Wallkill Valley Regional HS; Franklin, NJ; (4); 10/160; Drama Clb; English Clb; FBLA; School Play; Nwsp Ed-Chief; Nwsp Rptr; Nwsp Stf; Ed Lit Mag; Rep Stu Cncl; Sftbl; NY U; Jrnlsm.

WIENER, ANDREW CRAIG; Ocean Township HS; Wayside, NJ; (4); 30/330; Pres Key Clb; Ski Clb; Spanish Clb; Stu Cncl; Ftbl; Lcrss; Trk; Wt Lftg; Hon Roll; NHS; Rutgers Coll; Psych.

WIENER, ELLEN; Bruriah HS; Staten Island, NY; (1); NHS; NEDT Awd; Regents Schlrshp 87.

WIENER, LIZABETH I; Ridgewood HS; Ridgewood, NJ; (4); 22/445; Pres NFL; Trs Temple Yth Grp; Off Color Guard; Mrchg Band; Variety Show; High Hon Roll; NHS; St Schlr; U Of VA; Physcs.

WIERCISZEWSKI, MARK; Secausus HS; Secaucus, NJ; (2); 5/131; Math Clb; Mu Alpha Theta; Spanish Clb; Band; Concert Band; Var Bsbl; Var Bsktbl; High Hon Roll; Hon Roll; Jr NHS; U Of VA; Finance.

WIESKE, CHRISTINA; Cherry Hill West HS; Cherry Hill, NJ; (3); Church Yth Grp; Sec Drama Clb; PAVAS; Sec Thesps; Chorus; Drm Mjr(t); School Musical; Symp Band; Spanish Clb; Concert Band; Olympic Conf SR Hnrs Band 86; Home & Schl Awd 85-87; Communications.

WIGDER, DAVID; Glen Rock HS; Glen Rock, NJ; (3); 17/145; Cmnty Wkr; Drama Clb; School Play; Var Bsbl; Var Bsktbl; NHS; Govrnr Schl NJ Publ Issues & Futr NJ 87; Boys ST 87; AFS Exch Stdnt Denmark 86; Intl Rel.

WIGGINS, TRACIE; Bayonne HS; Bayonne, NJ; (3); Church Yth Grp; FBLA; NAACP; Chorus; Color Guard; Socr; Twrlr; Hal Jacksons Tlntd Teen Hudson Cnty 4th Rnnr Up 87; Qn Angelic Bapt Chrch Nrses Unit 84-86; Ct Steno.

WIGGLESWORTH, JENNIFER; Oakcrest HS; Nesco, NJ; (3); 15/263; Dance Clb; Drama Clb; Hst NFL; Hst Thesps; Chorus; School Musical; School Play; Stage Crew; Variety Show; Hon Roll; 3 Thespian Stars For Earning 56 Pts 87; Engl.

WIKOFF, SALLY; Mt St Marys Acad; New Brunswick, NJ; (3); Camera Clb; Church Yth Grp; Math Clb; Stage Crew; Rep Soph Cls; JV Cheerleading; Im Diving; Im Swmmng; Hon Roll; Spanish NHS; Engrng.

WILBERT, CHARITY; North West Christian HS; Newton, NJ; (2); School Play; Yrbk Phtg; Yrbk Stf; Socr; High Hon Roll; Hon Roll; Engl.

WILBURN, BEN; West Windsor Plainsboro HS; Princeton Junct, NJ; (3); 1/300; Am Leg Boys St; Cmnty Wkr; Pres Math Tm; Model UN; High Hon Roll; NHS; Rutgers Schlr 86-87; 1st Annl Smnr 86-87; 1st Annl Smithsnn Sci Smr 84-85; Physcs.

WILCAUSKAS, SHERRI; West Morris Mendham HS; Chester, NJ; (4); 2/340; Chorus; Var L Mrchg Band; School Musical; School Play; Symp Band; Ed Lit Mag; Bausch & Lomb Sci Awd; NHS; Ntl Merit SF; Sal; Mem Of All-St Chrs 85; MT Holyoke; Chem.

WILCOX, JOHN; Holy Cross HS; Edgewater Pk, NJ; (3); Chess Clb; Computer Clb; Drama Clb; German Clb; Science Clb; SADD; Stage Crew; Lit Mag; Hon Roll; Glassboro ST Coll; Theatr.

WILCOX, JULIE; Monsignor Donovan HS; Howell, NJ; (3); 17/239; Drama Clb; German Clb; Math Tm; Hon Roll; NHS; ROTC; Comm.

WILDER, DORTHEA; Burlington Township HS; Burlington, NJ; (4); 17/103; Am Leg Aux Girls St; French Clb; Key Clb; Political Wkr; Varsity Clb; Nwsp Stf; Yrbk Stf; Sec Jr Cls; Pres Sr Cls; Stu Cncl; Brewer Awd Exmplry Char 86-87; Syracuse U; Comm.

WILDER, JACK; Ft Lee HS; Kingspoint, NY; (3); Office Aide; VP Frsh Cls; VP Soph Cls; Pres Jr Cls; Rep Stu Cncl; Pol Sci.

WILEY, JEFF; Trenton HS; Trenton, NJ; (3); Boys Clb Am; Boy Scts; Elec Engr.

WILGUS, JEFF; Pennsauhen HS; Pennsauken, NJ; (2); Spanish Clb; Chorus; School Play; Swing Chorus.

WILGUS, JIM; Biernarus HS; Gladstone, NJ; (4); PAVAS; Band; Concert Band; Drm Mjr(t); Jazz Band; Mrchg Band; Orch; School Musical; Symp Band; 1st Drmmr In NJ For 4 Yrs 84-87; Rutgers U; Music.

WILHELM, SCOTT; Phillipsburg HS; Phillipsburg, NJ; (3); 50/331; Cmnty Wkr; Pep Clb; Variety Show; VP Jr Cls; VP Sr Cls; Rep Stu Cncl; Im Wt Lftg; Hon Roll; Pre Law.

WILHELMS, MARK; Toms River HS South; Pine Bch, NJ; (3); 77/405; Pres Church Yth Grp; Nwsp Ed-Chief; VP Capt Crs Cntry; Var Capt Trk; MVP Crss Cntry & Trk 86-87; Hopwood Smmr Schlrshp Pgm-Lynthburg Coll 87; Alt Washington Wrkshp Smnr; Hstry.

WILKENS, LYNN; Red Bank Regional HS; Little Silver, NJ; (3); Church Yth Grp; Drama Clb; Acpl Chr; Orch; School Musical; School Play; Symp Band; Nwsp Rptr; French Hon Soc; NHS; Carnegie-Mellon U Pre-Coll Pgm Fine Arts-Drama Smmr, Alt Govnrs Schl Art NJ Piano, Cncrt Mstr 87.

WILKERSON, DOLLENA; Morristown HS; Morristown, NJ; (2); Church Yth Grp; Cmnty Wkr; Girl Scts; Teachers Aide; Church Choir; Vllybl; Prfct Atten Awd; Engr.

WILKERSON, TODD E; Mon Mouth Regional HS; Tinton Falls, NJ; (4); VP Church Yth Grp; Computer Clb; DECA; JV Ftbl; Civic Clb; Hon Roll; Brick Comp Sci Inst; Comp Tech.

WILKES, MICHELLE; Cherry Hill High School West; Cherry Hill, NJ; (3); 24/400; VP French Clb; Intnl Clb; JCL; Spanish Clb; Stage Crew; Yrbk Rptr; Off Stu Cncl; Swmmng; High Hon Roll; NHS; Intl Law.

WILKEY, HEATHER MARIE; St Marys HS; Rutherford, NJ; (3); Library Aide; Band; Chorus; School Play; Yrbk Stf; Trk; Hon Roll; NHS; Frnch & Englsh 85-87; Wrld Cltr 85; Pier Mnstry 87; Montclair ST Coll; Sci.

WILKINS, MARION; Edison HS; Edison, NJ; (4); 16/398; Art Clb; Pres Church Yth Grp; Girl Scts; Spanish Clb; Mrchg Band; Rep Stu Cncl; Var JV Bsktbl; Hon Roll; Sec NHS; Spanish NHS; PTSA Invlvmnt Stu Bdy Awd, Spnsh Awd Contnng Stdy Coll 87; Rutgers U; Intl Bnkng.

WILKINSON, MATT; Freehold Township HS; Freehold, NJ; (4); #11 In Class; JV Var Socr; Var L Trk; NHS; Pres Schlr; Bstn U; Physcl Thrpy.

WILL, PATRICIA; Wall HS; Belmar, NJ; (3); 6/320; Chess Clb; Church Yth Grp; German Clb; Band; Concert Band; Drm Mjr(t); Jazz Band; Mrchg Band; Orch; Symp Band.

WILLBUS, MICHELLE; Plainfield HS; Plainfield, NJ; (2); High Hon Roll.

WILLETTS, BETH; Toms River H S North; Toms River, NJ; (3); 19/434; Am Leg Aux Girls St; School Musical; School Play; Capt Pom Pon; NHS; Voice Dem Awd; Mst Outstndng Stu Lillian Dean Studio 86; Miss Prfrmng Arts 87; Lillian Dean Dnc Awd 87; Montclair; Cmnctns.

WILLEVER, KATHRYN; Belvidere HS; Phillipsburg, NJ; (3); Quiz Bowl; Varsity Clb; Rep Jr Cls; JV Var Bsktbl; Var JV Sftbl; Hon Roll; NHS; Cngrssnl Yth Ldrshp Cncl 86; Aviatn.

WILLEY, LINDA; Lincoln HS; Jersey City, NJ; (3).

WILLIAMS III, ALBERT; Cherry Hill H S West; Cherry Hill, NJ; (4); Spanish Clb; Teachers Aide; Nwsp Rptr; Ftbl; La Salle U; Cmmnctns.

WILLIAMS, ALISON; Ocean Township HS; Asbury Park, NJ; (3); 1/344; Cmnty Wkr; Sec Key Clb; Service Clb; Pres Spanish Clb; Trs Lit Mag; Cit Awd; High Hon Roll; NHS; Grls Ctznshp Inst Delg, Rutgert Schlr 87; Engrng.

WILLIAMS, AMY; Newton HS; Newton, NJ; (3); 29/200; Off Latin Clb; Math Tm; Scholastic Bowl; SADD; Flag Corp; Lit Mag; Rep Stu Cncl; Im Tennis; NHS; Ntl Merit Ltr; NJ Sci Tchrs Assn & Sprvsrs Assn ST Bio Essay 2nd Pl 85; Summa Cum Laude Awd Latin Clb Advsr 86-87; Pre-Med.

WILLIAMS, ANDREA; Lakewood HS; Lakewood, NJ; (3); Hon Roll; Prfct Atten Awd; Rtgrs U; Bus Adm.

WILLIAMS, ANTHONY; Christian Brothers Acad; Freehold, NJ; (3); Church Yth Grp; Band; Lit Mag; Hnrs; Greenville Coll; Music.

WILLIAMS, BEVERLY; Matawan Regional HS; Cliffwood, NJ; (3); Art Clb; Church Yth Grp; Dance Clb; Drama Clb; FBLA; NAACP; Chorus; Color Guard; School Musical; Nwsp Rptr; Douglas Coll; Art.

WILLIAMS, CHARLES; Essex County Vocational HS; Newark, NJ; (2); Computer Clb; FBLA; Teachers Aide; Stu Cncl; Mgr(s); Score Keeper; Cit Awd; Hon Roll; Prfct Atten Awd; Outstndng Awd; Most Accurate Awd; Montclair ST Coll; Account.

WILLIAMS, CHRISTINE; Our Lady Of Good Counsel HS; Newark, NJ; (3); 25/125; Church Yth Grp; Dance Clb; Office Aide; Pep Clb; Church Choir; Yrbk Stf; Prfct Atten Awd; Pre Law.

WILLIAMS, CLIFF; Dickerson HS; Jersey, NJ; (2); Art Clb; Computer Clb; Latin Clb; Science Clb; JV Bsktbl; Var Ftbl; Var Wt Lftg; Hon Roll; Prfct Atten Awd; Penn ST; Bus.

WILLIAMS, COREY; Essex Catholic Boys HS; Newark, NJ; (3); Boys Clb Am; Varsity Clb; Church Choir; Rep Stu Cncl; Var Capt Ftbl; Var Capt Trk; Var Capt Wt Lftg; Hon Roll; Prfct Atten Awd; Temple U; Accntng.

WILLIAMS, DALE L; Montclair HS; Montclair, NJ; (3); 10/520; Am Leg Boys St; Rep Stu Cncl; Var Bsbl; JV Bsktbl; High Hon Roll; Hon Roll; Jr NHS; NHS; Ntl Merit Ltr; Comp Engrng.

WILLIAMS, DANIEL; Highland Regional HS; Clementon, NJ; (2); SADD; Lit Mag; Score Keeper; Trk; High Hon Roll; Prfct Atten Awd; Crmnlgy.

WILLIAMS, DANIELLE; Maple Shade HS; Maple Shade, NJ; (2); French Clb; Key Clb; Varsity Clb; Rep Frsh Cls; Stu Cncl; Cheerleading; Socr; Yth Merit Awd 86; Penn ST; Bus.

WILLIAMS, DAWN; Ocean City HS; Marmora, NJ; (3); Drama Clb; French Clb; Sec Girl Scts; Latin Clb; SADD; Acpl Chr; Band; Chorus; Church Choir; Concert Band; Natl Schl Orchstra Awd; Arion Awd Music; Girl Sct Gld Awd; Music Ed.

WILLIAMS, DEBORAH E; Middle Township HS; Ocean View, NJ; (4); 18/228; Science Clb; Chorus; Mrchg Band; School Musical; Rep Stu Cncl; Var Fld Hcky; High Hon Roll; Hon Roll; NHS; Rotary Awd; Acad Pres Awd 87; Engl Awd 87; Best Flag 85-87; Elizabethtown Coll; Music Thrpy.

WILLIAMS, DENNIS P; Mc Corristin HS; Hamilton Square, NJ; (4); 31/265; Debate Tm; Quiz Bowl; School Play; Rep Jr Cls; Ftbl; High Hon Roll; Hon Roll; Jr NHS; NHS; Ntl Merit SF; MENSA Socty 85-86; Dean Schlrshp Rutgers U 86; Georgetwn U; Engrng.

WILLIAMS, DERON T; Notre Dame HS; Trenton, NJ; (3); 129/373; Sec Church Yth Grp; Sec Latin Clb; Office Aide; Sec Church Choir; Bio Outstndng Achvt 85-86; Hlth.

WILLIAMS, DONNA; West Side HS; Newark, NJ; (3); French Clb; Girl Scts; Quiz Bowl; Chorus; Church Choir; VP Stu Cncl; Crs Cntry; Timer; High Hon Roll; Hon Roll; VP Stu Cncl 86-87; Quiz Bwl JETS Comptn 86-87; High Hnr Rl 86-87; Kean Coll; Pre Law.

WILLIAMS, EVON; Clifford HS; East Orange, NJ; (3); 11/280; Am Leg Boys St; Boy Scts; Church Yth Grp; FCA; JA; Math Tm; Spanish Clb; Church Choir; Mrchg Band; Hon Roll; Mntclr Coll; Bus Mngmnt.

WILLIAMS, GREGORY; Saint Mary Of The Assomption HS; Hillside, NJ; (2); School Musical; School Play; Variety Show; Bowling; Sftbl; Tennis; Im Vllybl; Drama.

WILLIAMS, JENNY; Newton HS; Newton, NJ; (2); French Clb; Hosp Aide; Band; Concert Band; Flag Corp; Orch; Symp Band; Yrbk Bus Mgr; Yrbk Phtg; DAR Awd; 300 Hrs Vlntr Svc Candystrpr 87; Hnr Rl Wrld Hstry 85-86; Vrsty N Lttr Band Frnt Mrchng Braves 86; Lawyr.

WILLIAMS, JO ANNE; Piscataway HS; Piscataway, NJ; (4); 15/496; Dance Clb; Varsity Clb; School Play; Gym; High Hon Roll; Hon Roll; NHS; Dance Comptns Trphs 83-87; Corporate Schlr Schlrshp 87; Jersey City ST Coll; Acctng.

WILLIAMS, JOE; Vineland HS; Newfield, NJ; (2); 43/868; Computer Clb; Political Wkr; Hon Roll; Ltr Recgntn Partcptn Model Senate Hearings 86.

WILLIAMS, KAMILI; Immaculak Conception HS; East Orange, NJ; (4); 13/78; Dance Clb; Drama Clb; Pep Clb; School Play; Nwsp Stf; Yrbk Phtg; Howard U; Accntnt.

WILLIAMS, KAREN; Morristown HS; Morristown, NJ; (3); 236/450; Church Yth Grp; Chorus; Color Guard; Flag Corp; Hon Roll; Office Aide; Montclair ST U; Accntng.

WILLIAMS, KARENLYNN MARIANNE; Delran HS; Delran, NJ; (4); 11/188; Q&S; Yrbk Ed-Chief; Rep Jr Cls; Sec Stu Cncl; Var Capt Fld Hcky; Lcrss; Sftbl; High Hon Roll; NHS; Gov Tchng Schlrs Pgm 87; Princpls Awd Svc 87; No 1 Clb 87; Ursinus Coll; Math.

WILLIAMS, KEVIN; West Windsor Plainsboro HS; Princeton Junct, NJ; (3); Boy Scts; Mgr Color Guard; Concert Band; Jazz Band; Mrchg Band; VP Orch; School Musical; Bsbl; JV Ftbl; JV Tennis; Mst Imprvd Brass Plyr Yr 86-87; Advncd Lfsvng & Wtrsfty 86-87; Secy HS Mrchng Band 87-88; Med.

WILLIAMS, KIMBERLY; Cranford HS; Cranford, NJ; (3); 3/268; Church Yth Grp; JCL; Pres Latin Clb; Math Tm; Band; Orch; Sec Jr Cls; Var Gym; NHS; Ambssdr Hgh Obrn Yth Ldrshp Smnr 86; Past Wrthy Advsr Azure Assmbly #40 Order Rnbw Grls 86; Music.

WILLIAMS, KIMBERLY; Jackson Memorial HS; Jackson, NJ; (3); 39/465; Ski Clb; Band; Concert Band; Mrchg Band; Mgr Bsbl; High Hon Roll; Hon Roll; High Hnr Roll Cert 86-87; Zoology.

WILLIAMS, KYLE; Orange HS; Orange, NJ; (3); JV Bsktbl; Var Crs Cntry; Var Tennis; Hon Roll; NHS; Aerospc Engr.

WILLIAMS, LALITA; Highland HS; Clementon, NJ; (3); Church Yth Grp; Hon Roll; Rutgers; Elem Ed.

WILLIAMS, LESLEY E; Wardlaw-Hartridge Schl; Scotch Plains, NJ; (4); Key Clb; Ski Clb; SADD; Acpl Chr; Chorus; Stage Crew; Nwsp Stf; Yrbk Rptr; Yrbk Stf; Var Bsktbl; Garden ST Schlr 87; Princeton U.

WILLIAMS, LESLIE; Gloucester City JR-SR HS; Gloucester, NJ; (4); 7/149; Am Leg Aux Girls St; Pres VP FBLA; VP Pep Clb; Speech Tm; Chorus; School Musical; Nwsp Rptr; Yrbk Rptr; Pres Stu Cncl; Var Capt Cheerleading; Douglass Coll; Fnnc.

WILLIAMS, LORI; Suxxex County Voc Tech HS; Franklin, NJ; (3); Stage Crew; Bkng.

WILLIAMS, MICHELE; Jackson Memorial HS; Jackson, NJ; (3); 42/456; Art Clb; German Clb; Girl Scts; Nwsp Ed-Chief; Nwsp Rptr; Nwsp Stf; Lit Mag; Bowling; Trk; High Hon Roll; Seton Hall U; Jrnlsm.

WILLIAMS, MYRON; Eastside HS; Paterson, NJ; (3); Letterman Clb; Varsity Clb; Nwsp Stf; Stu Cncl; Ftbl; Trk; Hon Roll; NHS; Prfct Atten Awd; Pre-Med.

WILLIAMS, NAKESHA; Woodrow Wilson HS; Camden, NJ; (3); Church Yth Grp; Cmnty Wkr; Drama Clb; Church Choir; Yrbk Rptr; VP Soph Cls; Pres Jr Cls; NHS; Oratorical Cont Wnnr 87; Jrnlsm.

WILLIAMS, NANCY; Pitman HS; Pitman, NJ; (4); Church Yth Grp; Dance Clb; Drama Clb; Teachers Aide; Mgr Thesps; Chorus; Rep Jr Cls; Bsktbl; Fld Hcky; Mgr(s); Mgmt.

WILLIAMS, PATRICIA ANN; Rahway SR HS; Winfield Park, NJ; (4); Am Leg Aux Girls St; Rep Jr Cls; Rep Sr Cls; Church Yth Grp; Girl Scts; Hosp Aide; Letterman Clb; Color Guard; School Musical; Nwsp Ed-Chief.

WILLIAMS, RISA; Atlantic City HS; Atlantic City, NJ; (3); Cmnty Wkr; Dance Clb; Key Clb; Model UN; Office Aide; Political Wkr; VP Band; Concert Band; Drm Mjr(t); Mrchg Band; Mvp Band 85; Brown U; Pre-Law.

WILLIAMS, ROBERT; Orange HS; Orange, NJ; (3); Boy Scts; Church Yth Grp; Nwsp Rptr; Hon Roll; NHS; Amer Lgn; MD U; Bus Admin.

WILLIAMS, RONALD; Bloomfield HS; Bloomfield, NJ; (3); Am Leg Boys St; Cmnty Wkr; Nwsp Stf; Yrbk Stf; Rep Soph Cls; Pres Jr Cls; Pres Stu Cncl; Var Tennis; Hon Roll; Law.

WILLIAMS, SARAH; Mt St Dominic Acad; W Orange, NJ; (3); Church Yth Grp; Drama Clb; Service Clb; Chorus; School Musical; School Play; Nwsp Phtg; Lit Mag; Var L Crs Cntry.

WILLIAMS, SHALONDA; Linden HS; Linden, NJ; (3); Church Yth Grp; FBLA; FHA; Rep Jr Cls; Spellman U; Bus Mgmt.

WILLIAMS, SHAMAS; Holy Cross HS; Edgewater Pk, NJ; (3); Boy Scts; Chess Clb; Church Yth Grp; Science Clb; Stage Crew; JV Crs Cntry; Var Diving; Var Swmmng; Trk.

WILLIAMS, SHARON; Glen Ridge HS; Glen Ridge, NJ; (3); Church Yth Grp; Key Clb; Spanish Clb; Church Choir; JV Sftbl; Sftvll Awd 85-86; Bus.

WILLIAMS, SHAWN; Burlington Township HS; Burlington Townsh, NJ; (3); 25/150; Boy Scts; Chess Clb; Debate Tm; FCA; Model UN; Ski Clb; Spanish Clb; SADD; Varsity Clb; Var Bsbl; Ftbl Awds-Al-Cnty, Al-Area, Al-Subrbn, Plyr Wk 86-87; Bsktbl Awds-Al-St, Al S Jersey, Al-Cnty 86-87; Comp Sci.

WILLIAMS, SHIRELLE; Millville SR HS; Woodbine, NJ; (4); 58/417; Chorus; Church Choir; School Musical; Crs Cntry; GEMS Schlrshps 87; Cty PTA Awd 87; Fine & Applied Arts Dept Schlrshp 87; Glassboro St Coll; Art.

WILLIAMS, SONIA; Lincoln HS; Jersy City, NJ; (4); 6/219; Sec FHA; Library Aide; Church Choir; Sec Stu Cncl; Mgr Socr; Hon Roll; Jr NHS; NHS; Prfct Atten Awd; Acadmc Achvmnt Awd 86; Stu To Asst You 85-86; Hudson Cnty Socces Tm Mgr Of Yr 86; Jersey City ST Clg; Educ.

WILLIAMS, TARA; Our Lady Of Good Counsel HS; Newark, NJ; (3); 12/121; Church Yth Grp; Pep Clb; Science Clb; Church Choir; Rep Stu Cncl; Capt Var Cheerleading; NHS; Prfct Atten Awd; Acad All Amer 87; Temple U; Pre-Law.

WILLIAMS, TIFFANY I; South Plainfield HS; S Plainfield, NJ; (3); 8/300; Dance Clb; Spanish Clb; Varsity Clb; Var Capt Gym; Hon Roll; NHS; Spanish NHS; Rep Stu Cncl; Cmnty Wkr; Computer Clb; MIP Gymnstcs 85-86; Hnr Cert Sympsm Arts-Dance 86-87; Hnr Cert Brd Educ Cgntcs Team 85-86; Ind Engr.

WILLIAMS, TODD; South River HS; S River, NJ; (2); Boy Scts; Stage Crew; Soph Cls; Hon Roll; Musicn.

WILLIAMS, TRACY; Paulsboro HS; Paulsboro, NJ; (3); Church Yth Grp; Drama Clb; Library Aide; Speech Tm; School Play; Stage Crew; Rep Soph Cls; Trk; Hon Roll; Toastmstrs 84; Squash 84-85; Rutgers U; Soc Wrkr.

WILLIAMS, TRACYANN; Hillsborough HS; Neshanic Sta, NJ; (3); Art Clb; Drama Clb; Spanish Clb; School Musical; Rep Frsh Cls; Rep Soph Cls; Rep Stu Cncl; High Hon Roll; Hon Roll; Pltcl Sci.

WILLIAMS, VERONICA; Immaculate Conception HS; Englewood, NJ; (3); Drama Clb; Variety Show; Bsktbl; High Hon Roll; Hon Roll; NHS; Spanish NHS; NY U; Law.

WILLIAMS, VICTORIA; Bridgeton HS; Bridgeton, NJ; (3); 1/200; Ski Clb; Nwsp Stf; Yrbk Stf; Var Swmmng; Bausch & Lomb Sci Awd; Cit Awd; Gov Hon Prg Awd; High Hon Roll; NHS; Ntl Merit SF; Am Chem Soc 86-87; Rutgers U Distgshd Schlr 86-87; Rensselear Polytech Inst Math & Sci Awd 86-87; Bio.

WILLIAMS, XAVIER L; Mc Corvistin HS; Trenton, NJ; (3); JV Bsbl; Var Ftbl; JV Socr; Sci.

WILLIAMS, YASMINE; Perth Amboy HS; Perth Amboy, NJ; (3); Church Yth Grp; French Clb; Chorus; Church Choir; Madrigals; Variety Show; Stu Cncl; Trk; High Hon Roll; Annl Schlrs Awd 86-87; Miss Collegate Intrschlstc Awd 85; Howard Univ; Chld Psych.

WILLIAMSON, JAMES; Don Basco Prep; Waldwick, NJ; (3); Im Bsktbl; Im Ftbl; Rutgers; Bus Mngmt.

WILLIAMSON, JULIE; Lakewood HS; Lakewood, NJ; (3); 34/330; Cmnty Wkr; English Clb; French Clb; Girl Scts; Latin Clb; Mrchg Band; Lit Mag; Var L Tennis; French Hon Soc; Hon Roll; 10 Yr Pin For Grl Scts 86; Natl Merit Schlrshp Rfrrl Svc 87; Intl Jrnlsm.

WILLIAMSON, LESLIE; Paulsboro HS; Gibbstown, NJ; (3); Yrbk Stf; Fld Hcky; Sftbl; Hon Roll; Stat Bsktbl.

WILLIAMSON, PATRICIA D; Franklin HS; Somerset, NJ; (3); CAP; Hosp Aide; Intnl Clb; Yrbk Stf; Sec Jr Cls; Var L Trk; Hon Roll; Girl Scts; Rep Frsh Cls; Rep Soph Cls; Girl Scout Silver Awd 85; New Jersey ST Fdrtn Grls Ctznshp Inst Delegate 87; Engrng.

WILLIS, BETH; Bridgeton HS; Bridgeton, NJ; (3); Aud/Vis; GAA; Color Guard; Mrchg Band; Bsktbl; Gym; Socr; Sftbl; Art Clb; Camera Clb; Secr.

WILLISTON, SIOBHAN; Pinelands Regional HS; Tuckerton, NJ; (2); Band; Capt Drm Mjr(t); Nwsp Rptr; Stat Bsbl; JV Bsktbl; Mgr(s); Score Keeper; Var Capt Twrlr; Hon Roll; Opt Clb Awd; Harvard; Crmnl Justice.

WILLMAN, WILLIAM; Oakcrest HS; Mays Landing, NJ; (3); 20/242; Computer Clb; French Clb; Math Clb; Concert Band; Mrchg Band; Var Tennis; JV Wrstlng; Hon Roll; NHS; Natl Hnr Rl 86-87; Vrsty Schlr 85-88; ROTC; Comp Sci.

WILLS, DOUG; Gloucester Catholic HS; Turnersville, NJ; (3); Chess Clb; School Musical; School Play; Rep Stu Cncl; Var Bsbl; Var Ftbl; Var Swmmng; Var Wt Lftg; Var Wrstlng; Hon Roll; Dfnsv Bck Vrsty Ftbl Team 86; Physcl Ftns Awds 85-87; Law.

WILLSON, AMY; Holy Spirit HS; Mays Landing, NJ; (2); 7/397; Stage Crew; Yrbk Stf; Hon Roll.

WILSON, AMY; Egg Harbor Township HS; Mays Landing, NJ; (3); 8/309; Pres Key Clb; Model UN; Ski Clb; Spanish Clb; Teachers Aide; Yrbk Ed-Chief; Lit Mag; Var Cheerleading; Stat Crs Cntry; JV Sftbl; Schlstc Lttr Awd 84-87; Aeronautical.

WILSON, BARBARA; Lenape Valley Regional HS; Stanhope, NJ; (3); 29/235; Sftbl; VP L Tennis; VP L Trk; DAR Awd; High Hon Roll; Hon Roll; Pres Schlr; Kthrn Gibbs Ldrshp Awd 87; Bus.

WILSON, CINDY; Rahway HS; Rahway, NJ; (3); Church Yth Grp; Girl Scts; Hosp Aide; JA; Spanish Clb; Color Guard; Flag Corp; Nwsp Rptr; Nwsp Stf; Hon Roll; Cittone Inst; Court Stenogrphr.

WILSON, DANIELLE; Hamilton HS West; Trenton, NJ; (4); 47/347; Concert Band; Mrchg Band; Symp Band; JV Var Fld Hcky; JV Sftbl; Hon Roll; Std Of Wk 85; Rutgers U; Comp Sci.

WILSON, DEBRA; Southern Regional HS; Barnegat, NJ; (4); Civic Clb; Cmnty Wkr; Dance Clb; Girl Scts; Hosp Aide; Ski Clb; Spanish Clb; Rep Soph Cls; Rep Sr Cls; Pom Pon; Stockton ST; Bus Mgt.

WILSON, DENNIS; Absegami HS; Absecon, NJ; (4); Office Aide; Ski Clb; SADD; JV Ftbl; JV Trk; JV Wrstlng; Hon Roll.

WILSON, ERIC; St James Catholic HS; Pennsvile, NJ; (4); 14/69; Varsity Clb; Rep Frsh Cls; Var L Bsbl; Var L Ftbl; Wt Lftg; Cit Awd; Hon Roll; NHS; MVP & All Conf Ftbl 86; Prncpls Trphy 86-87.

WILSON, JACQUELINE; Orange HS; Orange, NJ; (3); FBLA; VP Church Choir; Color Guard; Trs Jr Cls; Rep Stu Cncl; Hon Roll; Ldrshp Awd Katherine Gibbs Schl 86; Bus.

WILSON, JANET; Edgewood Regional SR HS; Atco, NJ; (4); 10/310; Church Yth Grp; Cmnty Wkr; Latin Clb; Pep Clb; Political Wkr; Teachers Aide; High Hon Roll; Hon Roll; Jr NHS; NHS; Dstngshd Persn Awd 86-87; Drexel U; Comp Anlyst.

WILSON, JENNIFER; St Rose HS; Bricktown, NJ; (3); 27/250; Camera Clb; Cmnty Wkr; Drama Clb; Key Clb; Nwsp Rptr; Var Trk; French Hon Soc; NEDT Awd; Psych.

WILSON II, JOHN C; Pemberton HS II; Browns Mills, NJ; (3); 67/240; Am Leg Boys St; Boy Scts; Church Yth Grp; Teachers Aide; Church Choir; Jazz Band; Symp Band; Rep Stu Cncl; High Hon Roll; All Pacific Hnr Band-Seoul, S Korea 86; Trenton Yth Orch-Moscow USSR, Bill Bradleys Yng Ctzns Awd 87; NJ Inst Of Tech; Comp Engrng.

WILSON, JONATHAN D; The Kings Christian HS; Somerdale, NJ; (4); 9/23; Church Yth Grp; Varsity Clb; Pres Frsh Cls; Rep Soph Cls; Rep Jr Cls; Trs Sr Cls; Rep Stu Cncl; Var L Bsbl; JV L Bsktbl; Var Capt Socr; ACSI Dstngshd Stu 87; Gardner-Webb Coll; Bus Admin.

WILSON, KELLY; Burlington City HS; Burlington, NJ; (4); 16/191; Am Leg Aux Girls St; Key Clb; Office Aide; Rep Stu Cncl; JV Var Fld Hcky; Hon Roll; Kiwanis Awd; Presdntl Acadc Ftnss Awd 87; Burlington County Coll; Paralgl.

WILSON, KIM; Lower Cape May Regional HS; Villas, NJ; (3); 9/187; Art Clb; Camera Clb; High Hon Roll; Hon Roll; Jr NHS; Kiwanis Awd; NHS; Prfct Atten Awd; Natl Yth Phys Ftnss Pgm Marine Corps 85-86; Schlstc Art Awds Cert Merit 83; Parsons Of CA; Comrcl Art.

WILSON, LISA; Eastside HS; Paterson, NJ; (3); 18/500; Computer Clb; Dance Clb; Drama Clb; Nwsp Rptr; Rep Jr Cls; Var Tennis; High Hon Roll; Hon Roll; NHS; Ntl Merit Ltr; Amer U; Jrnlsm.

WILSON, LISA; Warren Co Vo Tech; Belvidere, NJ; (4); Key Clb; Library Aide; Office Aide; VICA; Yrbk Stf; Hon Roll; AAA Mrt Citatn Awd-Ntnl Schl Trffc Sfty Prog 83-84; Hnr Rll 84-86; Data Oprtr.

WILSON, MARIE; Morris Hills HS; Rockaway, NJ; (3); Chorus; School Musical; School Play; Variety Show; Piano Awd 88; Band Awd 88; Cnty Coll Of Morris; Music.

WILSON, MAUREEN P; Haddontownship HS; Oaklyn, NJ; (3); Church Yth Grp; Varsity Clb; Nwsp Rptr; Sec Jr Cls; Crs Cntry; Trk; Hon Roll; NHS; Rep Frsh Cls; Rep Soph Cls; Tripple Vrsty Ltr Awds 86-88; Phy Thrpy.

WILSON, MICHELLE; Eastside HS; Paterson, NJ; (4); 300/450; DECA; Chorus; Church Choir; Hon Roll; SC ST Coll; Bus Admn.

WILSON, NATALIE; Middletown South HS; Lincroft, NJ; (3); 4-H; Hosp Aide; Mrchg Band; Pep Band; Symp Band; Nwsp Rptr; Yrbk Stf; 4-H Awd; Hon Roll; Brnz Cngrssnl Awd 87; Brd Educ Cmmndtns 86 & 87.

WILSON, PAMELA; Eastern HS; Berlin, NJ; (3); 12/387; Pres Church Yth Grp; Intnl Clb; Color Guard; Lcrss; Var Trk; Hon Roll; NHS; Acad Awd Gld Mdln Frnch II; Gdnc Cnslr.

WILSON, ROBERT; Essex Catholic Boys HS; Irvington, NJ; (3); Im Bsktbl; Im Ftbl; Im Sftbl; Hon Roll; Rutgers U; Bus.

WINFREV, OMAR; University HS; Newark, NJ; (2); Camp Fr Inc; JA; Red Cross Aide; Chorus; Swing Chorus; Variety Show; Var Bsktbl; Hon Roll; Prfct Atten Awd; Sec Frsh Cls; Prjct Bus JR Achvt Otstndng Accmplshmnts 85-86; Thtr U Imgs Tech Pgm 86-87; Bsktbll Trphy Vrsty 85-87; U Of NC; Comp.

WINGERT, CHRISTOPHER; De Paul HS; W Milford, NJ; (3); 39/150; Aud/Vis; Var Tennis; High Hon Roll; Hon Roll; Elec Engr.

WINICKY, ERIC; North Hunterdon HS; Hampton, NJ; (3); 81/328; Quiz Bowl; Varsity Clb; Chorus; Madrigals; Im Badmtn; JV Ftbl; JV Golf; Var Wrstlng; Hon Roll; Poli Sci.

WINJE, CAROLYN; West Windsor Plainboro HS; Princeton Junct, NJ; (4); AFS; Hosp Aide; Service Clb; Yrbk Stf; Hon Roll; Church Yth Grp; Cmnty Wkr; German Clb; Key Clb; Band; U Of RI; German.

WINSICK, JODY; Secaucus HS; Secaucus, NJ; (4); OEA; Varsity Clb; Band; Chorus; Concert Band; Mrchg Band; High Hon Roll; Hon Roll; Cmndtn Rprts 84 & 87; Vrsty Ltrs 86 & 87; Band Sectn Ldr 86 & 87; Bergen CC; Bus Adm.

WINTER, CATHERINE; Summit HS; Summit, NJ; (4); 19/271; Varsity Clb; Sec Frsh Cls; VP Soph Cls; Off Stu Cncl; Cheerleading; Fld Hcky; Lcrss; Swmmng; High Hon Roll; NHS; MSP La Crosse 87; Mst Imprvd 86; Perry Root Schlrshp, Albert J Bartholomew Schlrshp 87; U Of PA.

WINTER, JENNIFER; Our Lady Of Good Counsel; Newark, NJ; (3); 4/122; NFL; Pep Clb; Rep Jr Cls; Pres Sr Cls; Hon Roll; NHS; Ntl Merit Ltr; Science Clb; Omega Psi Phi/Eta Pi Chats Essy Awd 86; Blmfld Coll Upwrd Bnd Pgm Essy Awd 87; Stanford U; Optmtry.

WINTER III, MILFORD; Toms River HS East; Toms River, NJ; (3); Debate Tm; Exploring; NFL; Speech Tm; School Musical; School Play; Rep Stu Cncl; Trk; Wt Lftg; Ntl Merit Ltr; Nuclear Rsrch.

WINTERBOTTOM, HEATHER; Absegami HS; Egg Harbor City, NJ; (3); 12/280; GAA; Science Clb; Sec Jr Cls; Sec Sr Cls; L Var Bsktbl; L Var Sftbl; L Var Tennis; High Hon Roll; Hon Roll; NHS; Physcl Thrpy.

WINTERS, KELLY; Madison Central HS; Old Bridge, NJ; (3); 109/365; Dance Clb; DECA; SADD; Hon Roll; Itln Natl Hnr Soc 85-87; Itln Clb 84-87; Eng Tchr.

WINTON, KELLEY; Central Regional HS; Bayville, NJ; (3); 20/300; Am Leg Aux Girls St; Library Aide; Ski Clb; Orch; Yrbk Stf; VP Stu Cncl; High Hon Roll; Hon Roll; NHS; Arch Engr.

WISBESKI, HENRY C; Bound Brook HS; South Bound Brook, NJ; (3); Am Leg Boys St; NFL; Concert Band; Drm & Bgl; Jazz Band; Mrchg Band; VP Jr Cls; Var L Socr; Var L Trk; NHS; Dmstc Extmprns Spkng Fnlst NJ 85-86; MVP Soccer 86-87.

WISE, KATHARINE; West Windsor Plainsboro HS; Princeton, NJ; (3); Model UN; Pres Church Choir; Orch; School Musical; School Play; Lit Mag; High Hon Roll; Hon Roll; Ntl Merit SF; Chrch Bach Choir Made Prfssnl Tapes Ntl Choristers Gld 85 & 88; Art.

WISE, LILY; Princeton Day Schl; Belle Mead, NJ; (3); Cmnty Wkr; Drama Clb; Girl Scts; Spanish Clb; Stage Crew; Stat Fld Hcky; Stat Sftbl; High Hon Roll; Hon Roll; Bio.

WISHART, KIMBERLY; Buena Regional HS; Milmay, NJ; (4); 11/181; Drama Clb; Jazz Band; Madrigals; Mrchg Band; Swing Chorus; Var Trk; Cit Awd; 4-H Awd; Gov Hon Prg Awd; NHS; All S Jrsy Chrs 82-87; Schlrshp-Cmnty Srv & Acdmc Excllnc 87; NJ Schl Of Arts 83-87; Glassboro ST Coll; Comms.

WISNIEWSKI, BRIAN; Sayreville War Memorial HS; Parlin, NJ; (3); Ski Clb; Band; Concert Band; Jazz Band; JV Bsbl; JV Bsktbl; Var Ftbl; Im Vllybl; Im Wt Lftg; Hon Roll; Comp Engrng.

WITHERS, MARTIN; Holy Spirit HS; Brigantine, NJ; (2); 33/397; French Clb; Science Clb; VP Soph Cls; Socr; Im Vllybl; Hon Roll.

WITHKA, TOM; Bishop Anr HS; Milltown, NJ; (4); Church Yth Grp; Orch; Im Bsbl; Im Bsktbl; Var L Ftbl; Im Socr; High Hon Roll; Ftbl Full Acdmc 4 Yrs; Villanova U; Bus.

WITHYCOMBE, VICKY; Middletown HS South; Lincroft, NJ; (2); Church Yth Grp; Church Choir; JV Trk; High Hon Roll; Hon Roll; Outstndng Frnch Stu; Whitman Coll; Math.

WITKOWSKI, KARI; Maple Shade HS; Maple Shade, NJ; (3); VP DECA; Rep FBLA; SADD; Band; Concert Band; Mrchg Band; Rep Stu Cncl; Cheerleading; Var Mgr(s); Gftd & Talented Pgm; Intr Dsgn.

WITT, MATT; Spotswood HS; Milltown, NJ; (3); Cmnty Wkr; Bsbl; Ftbl; Med Sci.

WLAZLO, PAUL; Middletown HS South; Middletown, NJ; (3); Camera Clb; Church Yth Grp; Exploring; School Musical; School Play; Stage Crew; Variety Show; Nwsp Rptr; Nwsp Stf; Yrbk Phtg; NY Inst Of Tech; Comnctns Arts.

WLAZLOWSKI, JUDITH; Notre Dame HS; Englishtown, NJ; (4); 72/327; FBLA; Chorus; Church Choir; Drill Tm; Mrchg Band; School Musical; Pom Pon; High Hon Roll; Hon Roll; Loyola Coll; Bus.

WLAZLOWSKI, KAREN; Notre Dame HS; Englishtown, NJ; (3); 70/373; FBLA; Ski Clb; Church Choir; Fld Hcky; JV Var Sftbl; Vllybl; Hon Roll; NHS; Vrsty Ltr 87; Ntl Bus Hnrs Soc 86-87; Pace U; Bus.

WLODARCZYK, STEPHEN; North Hunterdon Regional HS; Pittstown, NJ; (3); 89/346; Boy Scts; Church Yth Grp; Ski Clb; Socr; Hon Roll; Eagle Scout Awd 87; Engrng.

WNEK, CHRISTINA; Monsignor Donovan HS; Toms River, NJ; (3); Pep Clb; Ski Clb; Spanish Clb; SADD; Yrbk Stf; Capt Cheerleading; Sftbl; Tennis; Hon Roll; Law.

WODARCZYK, ANNMARIE; Gloucester Catholic HS; Westville, NJ; (3); 12/188; Crs Cntry; Var Swmmng; Trk; Hon Roll; NHS; All S Jersey Crss Cnty 86; Early Chldhd.

WOEHRLE, SCOTT; Newton HS; Newton, NJ; (2); Pres French Clb; Ski Clb; Band; Symp Band; JV Bsbl; JV Ftbl; Wt Lftg.

WOJCIECHOWSKI, TINA; Bayonne HS; Bayonne, NJ; (3); Church Yth Grp; Hosp Aide; School Musical; Crs Cntry; Sftbl; Trk; Wt Lftg; Hon Roll; Valmey Schl; Csmtlgy.

WOJCIK, CRAIG; Bordentown Regional HS; Fieldsboro, NJ; (3); 18/142; Drama Clb; Key Clb; Math Tm; Chorus; School Musical; School Play; Var Bsbl; Var Ftbl; Im Wt Lftg; Hon Roll.

WOJIE, SCOTT; Oratory Catholic Prep; Scotch Plains, NJ; (4); Computer Clb; Dance Clb; Math Clb; Math Tm; Service Clb; Ski Clb; Varsity Clb; Nwsp Rptr; Trs Frsh Cls; VP Soph Cls; Sccr Al-Cnty, Al-ST 86; Prjct Acclrtn-Calculs Seton Hall U; Bus.

WOJTON, PAM; John F Kennedy St HS; Iselin, NJ; (3); 159/249; FTA; GAA; Varsity Clb; Bsktbl; Socr; Sftbl; MI ST; Elem Ed.

WOJTOWICZ, ANNE; Watchung Hills Regional HS; Warren, NJ; (3); German Clb; Intnl Clb; Key Clb; SADD; Orch; High Hon Roll; Hon Roll; NHS; Med.

WOJTOWICZ, KAREN; Hamilton H S East; Allentown, NJ; (2); Trs AFS; Chorus; Drm Mjr(t); Mrchg Band; School Musical; Nwsp Rptr; Lit Mag; Rep Stu Cncl; Score Keeper; Hon Roll; Hugh O Brian Ldrsshp Trnng Conf.

WOLBERT, MICHAEL; Bridgeton HS; Newport, NJ; (2); Crs Cntry; Arch.

WOLCOTT, DEBBIE; Manasquar HS; Manasquan, NJ; (3); 59/239; Church Yth Grp; Spanish Clb; Band; Color Guard; Concert Band; Mrchg Band; Cheerleading; Fld Hcky; Socr; Hon Roll.

WOLCOTT, JANET; Central Regional HS; Bayville, NJ; (4); 43/243; Drama Clb; Library Aide; Acpl Chr; Chorus; Madrigals; School Musical; School Play; Stage Crew; High Hon Roll; NHS; Northern Lights Theatre Co 100 Tech & Craft 87 & 200 Outstndng 87; Ocean Cnty Coll; Theatre.

WOLERT, JUDITH; Madison Central HS; Old Bridge, NJ; (3); French Clb; Girl Scts; Hosp Aide; SADD; Yrbk Stf; JV Crs Cntry; JV Trk; Natl Italian Honor Soc; Italian Club Pres; Foreign Lang Awd; Foreign Lang.

WOLF, BARRY F; Pascack Hills HS; Woodcliff, NJ; (4); 4/243; Am Leg Boys St; Debate Tm; Model UN; Concert Band; NHS; Ntl Merit Ltr; Rotary Awd; St Schlr; AAAS Sci Photo Cntst Semifnlst 86; Rutgers U; Engrng.

WOLF, CHRISTOPHER; Fairlawn HS; Fair Lawn, NJ; (3); 56/342; JV Capt Bsbl; Im Bsktbl; JV Ftbl; Law.

WOLF, KAREN; Parsippany Hills HS; Parsippany, NJ; (3); Church Yth Grp; Key Clb; NFL; Thesps; School Musical; School Play; Lit Mag; Stat Bsktbl; Hon Roll; Cmmnctns.

WOLF, SIMON; Jewish Educational Ctr; West Orange, NJ; (3); 2/30; Aud/Vis; Chess Clb; Debate Tm; Math Tm; Scholastic Bowl; Science Clb; Varsity Clb; Nwsp Ed-Chief; Nwsp Rptr; Yrbk Stf; Natl Bible Contst Natl Fnslst 86; Sci Lg Bsd On Schl Acadmcs Placement 84-87; Math Lg Acadmcs Plcmnt.

WOLF, TRACY; Gloucester Catholic HS; Gloucester, NJ; (3); 5/190; Am Leg Aux Girls St; French Clb; Hosp Aide; Varsity Clb; JV Bsktbl; Var Fld Hcky; Trk; Cit Awd; French Hon Soc; High Hon Roll; Intl Frgn Lang Awd 85-86; Grls Ctznshp Inst-Dgls Coll 86-87; Thomas Jefferson U; Physcl Thrp.

WOLFE, KATHLEEN; Paramus Catholic Girls Rgnl HS; Hackensack, NJ; (3); Camera Clb; Hosp Aide; SADD; Prfct Atten Awd; Elect Engrng.

WOLFE, STEPHEN P; Whippany Park HS; Whippany, NJ; (2); 7/180; Am Leg Boys St; Boy Scts; Church Yth Grp; Exploring; FBLA; Scholastic Bowl; Socr; Tennis; High Hon Roll; Rotary Awd; Gen Engrng.

WOLFERSBERGER III, JOSEPH; Pt Pleasant Beach HS; Pt Pleasant Bch, NJ; (3); 13/109; Am Leg Boys St; Drama Clb; Varsity Clb; Acpl Chr; School Musical; Var L Ftbl; Var L Trk; Hon Roll; VP NHS; Church Yth Grp; Princpls Advsry Committee 84-87; NJ ST Sci Comptn Schl Rep 87; Biochem.

WOLFRAM, JUDITH; Paul VI HS; Haddon Township, NJ; (3); 4/480; Math Clb; Spanish Clb; Var L Tennis; Trk; Hon Roll; Jr NHS; Spanish NHS; Psych.

WOLPERT, BRIAN A; St Joseph Of Palisades HS; Union City, NJ; (3); JV Bsbl; JV Bsktbl; Im Vllybl; High Hon Roll; Hon Roll; Spanish NHS; Air Force Acad; Engnrng.

WOLSKO, KRISTIN; Lyndhurst HS; Lyndhurst, NJ; (3); 34/175; German Clb; Ski Clb; Chorus; Variety Show; Sec Soph Cls; Sec Jr Cls; Var Capt Cheerleading; Sftbl; Hon Roll; Katherine Gibbs Ldrshp Awd 87; Entertainment.

WOLT, ETHAN; Freehold Twp HS; Freehold, NJ; (3); 4/401; Temple Yth Grp; Rep Soph Cls; Rep Jr Cls; Var L Bsbl; Var L Bsktbl; Im Wt Lftg; NHS; Comp.

WONDERSEK, ELIZABETH KAYE; Pennsville Memorial HS; Pennsville, NJ; (3); Am Leg Aux Girls St; German Clb; Office Aide; Chorus; School Musical; School Play; JV Mgr Trk; NHS; Grmn Natl Hnr Soc; Trenton ST Coll; Pre Dntstry.

WONDRACK, JENNIFER; Paramus Catholic Girls Rgnl HS; Teaneck, NJ; (3); Church Yth Grp; Cmnty Wkr; Service Clb; Ski Clb; Madrigals; Ed Lit Mag; High Hon Roll; Hon Roll; NHS; NEDT Awd; Christian Svc Awd 86-87; Bus Mgmt.

WONG, CHRISTINE P; Cherokee HS; Mariton, NJ; (3); 60/494; Am Leg Aux Girls St; Debate Tm; Sec French Clb; SADD; Chorus; School Musical; Nwsp Stf; Yrbk Stf; Var Gym; Tennis; Mst Dedicated Gymnst; Cmnctns.

WONG, JENNY; John F Kennedy HS; Willingboro, NJ; (2); 75/359; Aud/Vis; Intnl Clb; JA; Stage Crew; Yrbk Stf; Ntl Merit Ltr; Ntl Merit Awd 86; FL U; Bus Mgmt.

WONG, LEE; St Peters HS; Kendall Park, NJ; (4); 22/89; Math Clb; Church Choir; Drm Mjr(t); School Musical; Yrbk Phtg; Lit Mag; Crs Cntry; Trk; NHS; Chess Clb; Physic Awd 87; Suny; Bio Sci.

WONG, LISANNE; Notre Dame HS; Plainsboro, NJ; (2); Art Clb; Service Clb; French Hon Soc; NHS; Awd Jr Vlntr 86-87; Awd Schlstc Achvt Art 87; 1st & 2nd Pl Art II Shw 87; Art.

WONG, MEI LIN; Monsignor Donovan HS; Jackson, NJ; (3); Hosp Aide; Ski Clb; Rep Stu Cncl; Var Socr; Var Capt Tennis; NHS; MVP Tennis Awd 86-87.

WONG, VANNESA T; The Pennington Schl; Pennington, NJ; (3); 5/82; VP Intnl Clb; JV Tennis; JV Vllybl; High Hon Roll; Hon Roll; NHS; Excllnc Soph Math 85-86; Excllnc Hnrs Chem 86-87.

WOOD, ASHLEY; Cherry Hill HS East; Cherryhill, NJ; (3); FHA; Latin Clb; SADD; Nwsp Rptr; Rep Stu Cncl; Var Cheerleading; Powder Puff Ftbl; Trk; FOP Rotary X-Mas Party Handicapped Chldrn 86; Schl Blood Drive 87; Latin Cum Laude Awd 86; Cmmnctns.

WOOD, BEN; Ramapo HS; Wyckoff, NJ; (3); Boy Scts; Trs Church Yth Grp; Math Tm; Scholastic Bowl; Jazz Band; Var Capt Socr; Trk; Hon Roll; Ski Clb; Symp Band; Achvmnt Awd Math-Geom 85; Achvmnt Awds Chem & German 86; Physcs Tm 87; Engrng.

WOOD, BRITON; Edgewood SR HS; Sicklerville, NJ; (2); Varsity Clb; JV Bsbl; Var L Socr; Prfct Attndc 85-86; Hnr Rll 85-86.

WOOD, MELISSA; Chathamborough HS; Chatham, NJ; (4); 8/96; Church Yth Grp; Cmnty Wkr; Latin Clb; Library Aide; Pep Clb; Spanish Clb; Variety Show; Yrbk Stf; Stat Var Bsktbl; Var Sftbl; Spn Lang Awd 87; Bell Awd Lang 85; Sci 86; U Wmn Orgnztnl Awd 87; Colgate U.

WOOD, SCOTT; Deptford HS; Deptford, NJ; (4); 25/276; Boy Scts; JV L Bowling; JV Var Socr; JV L Trk; Jr NHS; NHS; Eagle Scout Trp 62 Almonesson NJ 87; 1st Pl & Best Catgry Engrng Thomas Edison Sci Fair 87; Rutgers ST U; Elect Engrng.

WOOD, STACIE; Florence Township Memorial HS; Burlington, NJ; (3); Am Leg Aux Girls St; GAA; Girl Scts; Band; Chorus; Concert Band; Jazz Band; Variety Show; Cheerleading; Hon Roll; Principals List, US Hstry I & Spnsh III Cert Of Awds 87; Hstry.

WOODRING, SHAWN; Bound Brook HS; Bound Brook, NJ; (4); 6/131; Teachers Aide; Band; Concert Band; Mrchg Band; Hon Roll; Rotary Awd; Gld Dbl B Hnr Soc 87; Bnd Brk Educ Assoc Schlrshp 87; Trenton St Coll; Erly Chldhd Ed.

WOODRUFF, EDWARD; Pinelands Regional HS; Tuckertown, NJ; (4); Church Yth Grp; High Hon Roll; Hon Roll; NHS; High Score Militry Tsts 85; Passd Navy Nclr Tst 86; Sworn Into Nuclear Navy 86; Nuclear Navy.

WOODRUFF, FRANK; Phillipsburg HS; Alpha, NJ; (3); High Hon Roll; Hon Roll; Ntl Merit Ltr; Aerospc Engrng.

WOODRUFF, JAMES; Howell HS; Howell, NJ; (3); Boy Scts; JCL; Latin Clb; SADD; Socr; Hon Roll; Im Bowling; JV Wrstlng; Pres Phys Ftnss Awd 84.

WOODS, DANIELLE; Bloomfield SR HS; Bloomfield, NJ; (3); Art Clb; Church Yth Grp; Drama Clb; FBLA; Girl Scts; Chorus; Church Choir; School Musical; Yrbk Stf; Sec Sr Cls; Aiding Guidance Dept 85-86; Comp.

WOODS, GREGORY; Newton HS; Newton, NJ; (3); 21/200; Trs Church Yth Grp; French Clb; Latin Clb; Mgr Stage Crew; Trs Frsh Cls; VP Jr Cls; Rep Stu Cncl; Var Golf; JV Wrstlng; NHS; NJ ST AAA Postr Cntst-1st Pl 86; 1st Pl Novice Wrstlng Trnmt; Engrng.

WOODS, JACQUELINE; Oak Knoll HS; Chatham, NJ; (2); Debate Tm; Teachers Aide; Chorus; Yrbk Stf; Cornell U; Law.

WOODS, NANCY; Bridgewater-Raritan West HS; Bridgewater, NJ; (3); Hosp Aide; Spanish Clb; Rep Frsh Cls; Rep Soph Cls; Rep Jr Cls; Rep Stu Cncl; Var Capt Cheerleading; JV Sftbl; Hon Roll; NHS.

WOODSON, CARLA; Trenton Central HS; Trenton, NJ; (3); Debate Tm; Pres Exploring; Pres FBLA; Scholastic Bowl; Off Soph Cls; Cit Awd; High Hon Roll; Hon Roll; Ntl Merit Ltr; Prfct Atten Awd; Achvmnt Awds 80-87; Poetry Awd 85-86; U Of Chicago; Law.

WOODWARD, KIMBERLEY ANN; Lower Cape May Regional HS; N Cape May, NJ; (4); 5/233; Mgr Socr; Var JV Sftbl; High Hon Roll; NHS; Joseph Carley Schlrshp Fromdexel 87-92; Drexel U; Engnrng.

WOODWARD, RUSSELL; Cumberland Regional HS; Bridgeton, NJ; (3); Church Yth Grp; Computer Clb; Chorus; JV Bsbl; Hon Roll; Jr NHS; Comp Sci.

WOODWARD, SHERRY; Highland Regional HS; Erial, NJ; (3); French Clb; JV Fld Hcky; Im Sftbl; Cncrs Natl De Francais Cert Merit 86-87; Phys Thrpy.

WOODWARD, SUSAN; Middlesex HS; Middlesex, NJ; (3); French Clb; Ski Clb; Spanish Clb; SADD; Varsity Clb; Flag Corp; Yrbk Stf; Var L Cheerleading; Im Gym; Var L Tennis; Lang.

WOODWORTH, STEPHEN R; Northern Valley Reg; Old Tappan, NJ; (4); 1/281; AFS; Boy Scts; Drama Clb; Math Clb; Math Tm; Science Clb; Ski Clb; Band; Concert Band; Mrchg Band; NJ Govnrs Schl In Sci 86; Columbia Sci Hnrs Pgm 84-86; 1st Pl Bio NJ ST Sci Pay 84; Princeton; Chem Rsrch.

WOODY, ELIZABETH; Notre Dame HS; Lawrenceville, NJ; (3); 54/378; Art Clb; Church Yth Grp; Hosp Aide; Mrchg Band; Stage Crew; Rep Soph Cls; Pom Pon; Hon Roll; NHS; 1st Pl Youth Art Awd Greater Mercer Cnty Area 86; Ex Art Awd Advncd Art 87; Lawyer.

WOODY, MARY; Notre Dame HS; Lawrenceville, NJ; (2); 4/400; Art Clb; Church Yth Grp; Hosp Aide; Stage Crew; High Hon Roll; Hon Roll; Otstndng Achvt In Spnsh I & II 86-87; 1st,2nd & Hnrb Mntn Awds In Art Show 87; Piano Tchrs Fstvl 87; Nrsng.

WOOLDRIDGE, BECKY; Hackensack Christian Schl; Hackensack, NJ; (2); Church Yth Grp; Varsity Clb; Chorus; Concert Band; School Play; Sec Trs Stu Cncl; Cheerleading; Sftbl; High Hon Roll; NHS; Top Grds Cls 87; Christian Chrctr Awd 87; Outstndng Accmpnst Awd 86; Liberty U; Music.

WOOLFOLK, STACI; Mary Help Of Christians Acad; Paterson, NJ; (1); NAACP; SADD; Nwsp Stf; Off Frsh Cls; Stu Cncl; Hon Roll; Howard U; Law.

WOOLWICH, ALLISON; Long Branch HS; Long Branch, NJ; (3); #8 In Class; Concert Band; Mrchg Band; School Musical; Symp Band; Nwsp Rptr; Lit Mag; Rep Stu Cncl; Tennis; Twrlr; NHS; Vrsty Schlr Awd 85-86; Jrnlsm.

WORKINGER, LYNNE S; Verona HS; Verona, NJ; (4); 25/182; Drama Clb; French Clb; Chrmn Intnl Clb; Chrmn Radio Clb; Speech Tm; Concert Band; Jazz Band; School Musical; Swing Chorus; Symp Band; Govrns Schl Of Arts 86; Band Prnts Assoc Music Schlrshp 87; Stu Cncl Schlrshp 87; Mason Gross Schl Arts; Thtr.

WORMACK, COREY A; South Plainfield HS; South Plainfield, NJ; (4); 8/211; Am Leg Boys St; CAP; Math Tm; Varsity Clb; Band; Jazz Band; Mrchg Band; Symp Band; JV Crs Cntry; Var Capt Trk; Suprntndts Awd Athl Acad Fine Arts 87; USAF Acad 87; USAF Acad; Aero Engr.

WOROB, JEFFREY A; Wayne Valley HS; Wayne, NJ; (4); #42 In Class; Aud/Vis; Cmnty Wkr; Rep Frsh Cls; Rep Soph Cls; Rep Jr Cls; Trs Sr Cls; Rep Stu Cncl; High Hon Roll; Hon Roll; NHS.

WOROCH, CHRYSTIA; Mount Saint Dominic Acad; West Orange, NJ; (3); 26/56; Girl Scts; Ski Clb; School Musical; Nwsp Stf; Lit Mag; VP Jr Cls; Cheerleading; Trk; Hon Roll.

WORSHAM, MATTHEW; Penns Grove HS; Carneys Point, NJ; (3); Pres Latin Clb; Varsity Clb; Ftbl; Wrstlng; Marines.

WORSTELL, CHRISTINE; Brick Memorial HS; Lakewood, NJ; (3); 15/390; Math Tm; Office Aide; Trs Spanish Clb; Band; Concert Band; Capt Mrchg Band; NHS; Futures Unlmtd Conf 86; Engrng.

WORTH, KEVIN; Scotch Plains-Fanwood HS; Scotch Plains, NJ; (4); 13/329; Cmnty Wkr; Key Clb; Model UN; Ski Clb; Temple Yth Grp; JV Bsktbl; JV Socr; Var L Tennis; CC Awd; High Hon Roll; Suburban Cblvsn Schlrshp, UNICO 87; Lehigh U; Fnnc.

WORTHINGTON, SCOTT; Maple Shade HS; Maple Shade, NJ; (4); DECA; Varsity Clb; JV Bsbl; Var Capt Ftbl; Var Capt Wrstlng; Vrsty Wrstlg Capt 84-88; Vrsty Ftbl Capt 85-88; Vrsty Clb 87-88.

WOSTBROCK, RICHARD A; Midland Park HS; Midland Park, NJ; (3); 5/150; Scrkpr JV AFS; Am Leg Boys St; Boy Scts; Math Tm; Stage Crew; Stu Cncl; JV Socr; JV Trk; JV Wrstlng; High Hon Roll; Arch Engrng.

WOTTAWA, LARRAINE; Mt St Dominic Acad; Roseland, NJ; (3); 15/56; Church Yth Grp; Nwsp Rptr; Nwsp Sprt Ed; Yrbk Phtg; Lit Mag; JV Stat Bsktbl; Var L Socr; Var L Trk; High Hon Roll; Hon Roll; Comm.

WOZNEY, AARON; Waldwick HS; Waldwick, NJ; (3); 13/155; Art Clb; Boy Scts; SADD; JV Bsktbl; JV Var Socr; Capt Var Tennis; NHS; MVP Of Tennis Tm 86 & 87; Comm Art.

WOZNIAK, KRISTEN; West Essex Regional HS; Roseland, NJ; (3); Key Clb; Tennis; Hon Roll; NHS.

WOZUNK, BOBBIE NADINE; A P Schalick HS; Bridgeton, NJ; (4); Art Clb; Church Yth Grp; DECA; Var L Cheerleading; JV Fld Hcky; Var L Sftbl; Hon Roll; Bob Jones U; Int Decrtr.

WRAMAGE, GREGG; Wall HS; Wall, NJ; (3); 9/300; German Clb; Band; Concert Band; Jazz Band; Mrchg Band; Orch; Pep Band; Symp Band; High Hon Roll; NHS; Outstndng Frosh Bnd Stu 81-83; Mst Imprvd Bnd Stu 85-86; Hartford U Hnrbl Mntn Bnd Stu 85; Pro Mscn.

WRIEDE, STEPHANIE; Watchung Hills Regional HS; Warren, NJ; (3); 7/321; Spanish Clb; SADD; Var Swmmng; High Hon Roll; NHS; Spanish NHS; MVP Swmmng 87; All Area Swm Team 200 M & 250 Mdly Rly 85-87; US Olympc Fest West Team 87; Bus Mgnt.

WRIGHT, CANDICE N; Ewing HS; Lawrenceville, NJ; (2); Debate Tm; SADD; Varsity Clb; Gov Hon Prg Awd; NHS; Ntl Merit Schol; Sal; Church Yth Grp; Howard U; Law.

WRIGHT, CAROLYN; Marylawn Of The Oranges HS; East Orange, NJ; (3); 9/68; Pep Clb; Service Clb; Spanish Clb; Chorus; School Play; High Hon Roll; NEDT Awd; Spanish NHS; Chld Psych.

WRIGHT, CHERYL; Buena Regional HS; Landisville, NJ; (1); Ski Clb; Flag Corp; Rep Frsh Cls; Rep Stu Cncl; Hon Roll; USBEA 87; Montclair.

WRIGHT, CHRISTINE; Morris Knolls HS; Denville, NJ; (2); Cmnty Wkr; Yrbk Stf; JV Sftbl; Hon Roll; Bus.

WRIGHT, DAVARN; Eastside HS; Paterson, NJ; (3); 13/500; Church Yth Grp; FBLA; Key Clb; NAACP; School Play; Variety Show; Cit Awd; High Hon Roll; Hon Roll; NHS; Gftd & Tlntd Awd 85; Stu Of Mth 87; Elec Engr.

WRIGHT, HAVEL; Orange HS; Orange, NJ; (3); Boy Scts; Scholastic Bowl; Science Clb; Spanish Clb; SADD; Band; Orch; Var Bsbl; JV Bsktbl; Capt Bowling; Schlrshp Bsktbl Jersey City ST 87-88; Mst Vlbl Plyr Bsbl 86-87; Hnr Rl 86-87; Embry-Riddle; Aviation Spec.

WRIGHT, JOSHSHINA CYNTHIA; West Side HS; Newark, NJ; (3); Church Yth Grp; Sec VP Drama Clb; Library Aide; Sec Office Aide; PAVAS; Red Cross Aide; Teachers Aide; Band; Chorus; Concert Band; Law.

WRIGHT, JULIE; Kingsway Reg HS; Swedesboro, NJ; (2); JV Fld Hcky; JV Trk; Communications/Teaching.

WRIGHT, KELLY; Holy Spirit HS; Absecon, NJ; (3); 75/313; JV Fld Hcky; Hon Roll; NHS; Bus.

WRIGHT, LORI ANN; Allentown HS; Allentown, NJ; (4); 13/205; Am Leg Aux Girls St; Varsity Clb; Color Guard; Sec Soph Cls; Sec Jr Cls; Sec Sr Cls; Var Fld Hcky; Trk; Gov Hon Prg Awd; NHS; Engl Awd 87; Educ.

WRIGHT, THEODORE S; Asbury Park HS; Asbury Park, NJ; (4); 1/200; Key Clb; Var Trk; Cit Awd; High Hon Roll; Kiwanis Awd; NHS; St Schlr; Vrsty Schlr 84-86; Rtgrs Schlr 86; Rnsslr Mdl 86; Rutgers U; Med.

WRIGHT, THERESA; Millville SR HS; Millville, NJ; (3); DECA; FNA; Hosp Aide.

WRIGHT, THERESA A; Perth Amboy HS; Perth Amboy, NJ; (4); Art Clb; German Clb; Trs Mu Alpha Theta; Off Stu Cncl; Var Bsktbl; Hon Roll; NHS; Garden ST Dstngshd Schlr 87; Math.

WRIGHT, VICTORIA; John F Kennedy HS; Willingboro, NJ; (4); Intnl Clb; Keywanettes; Band; Chorus; Drm Mjr(t); Orch; Capt Twrlr; Hon Roll; SR Music Awd Orch 87; Caldwell Coll; Psych.

WRIGHT, WENDY A; Ocean City HS; Marmora, NJ; (3); 25/342; Scholastic Bowl; Trs SADD; Trs Chorus; Stu Cncl; JV Fld Hcky; NHS; Ntl Merit Ltr; West Point Smmr Session; Girls Ctznshp Inst; Rotary Yth Ldrshp Awd; Scndry Ed.

WROBEL, DANIELLE; Ewing HS; Trenton, NJ; (3); Cmnty Wkr; Drama Clb; JA; Political Wkr; School Play; Variety Show; Yrbk Stf; Hst Soph Cls; Hst Jr Cls; Var L Cheerleading; Brd Of Ed Cert Of Mrt 86; Bus.

WROBEL, TRICIA; Mt St Dominic Acad; West Orange, NJ; (3); Art Clb; Church Yth Grp; Ski Clb; Var VP Bsktbl; Var Socr; Var Sftbl.

WROBLEWSKI, MELISSA; Newton HS; Newton, NJ; (3); 10/200; Math Tm; Thesps; Pres Chorus; Madrigals; School Musical; School Play; Rep Stu Cncl; JV Trk; NHS; Drama Clb; NJ Gvrnrs Schl Of Arts 86-87; Med.

WROBLEWSKI, PATRICK; Summit HS; Summit, NJ; (3); 25/250; SADD; Band; Var Capt Bsktbl; JV L Tennis; High Hon Roll; Jr NHS; Bsktbl St Runner-Up In Elks Clb Freethrow Cntst 82; Capt On St Chmpn Frisbee Tm 87; Stanford; Musician.

WU, AMY; Eastern Regional HS; Vooorhees, NJ; (3); 26/387; Church Yth Grp; Hosp Aide; Intnl Clb; Yrbk Stf; NHS; Engl Awd 87; Rutgers; Phrmcy.

WU, EDWIN; Livingston HS; Livingston, NJ; (3); 38/417; Chess Clb; Computer Clb; Math Clb; Band; Mrchg Band; Var Swmmng; Gvrnrs Schl Of Arts 87; Engnrg.

WU, JENNIFER; Cherry Hill High Schl West; Cherry Hill, NJ; (4); JCL; Pres PAVAS; Jazz Band; Off Sr Cls; Lcrss; JP Sousa Awd; NHS; St Schlr; Color Guard; School Musical; Hall Fame 87; Bryn Mawr.

WU, YU-CHIN; Red Bank Regional HS; Red Bank, NJ; (3); Hon Roll; Outstndng Studnt Spec Catgries 86; Bus.

WUNG, PEARSON; Tenafly HS; Tenafly, NJ; (4); Computer Clb; Math Clb; Ntl Merit SF.

WURST, KAREN M; Toms Rivers HS East; Toms River, NJ; (4); 12/580; Pres French Clb; Yrbk Ed-Chief; Yrbk Stf; Lit Mag; JV Var Fld Hcky; High Hon Roll; NHS; Ntl Merit Ltr; NJ Distng Schlr 87; Rutgers Univ; Bio.

WURTENBERGER, JOHN; Paulsboro HS; Paulsboro, NJ; (3); 74/150; Nwsp Stf; Yrbk Stf; Lit Mag; Hon Roll.

WYCKOFF JR, JOHN; Randolph HS; Randolph, NJ; (3); Church Yth Grp; Var L Bsbl; Var L Bsktbl; JV Ftbl; Hon Roll; Bus Admn.

WYCKOFF, WILLIAM; Blair Acad; Belvidere, NJ; (3); Var Library Aide; Var Science Clb; Var Nwsp Stf; JV Crs Cntry; JV Trk; Wt Lftg; High Hon Roll; Alg, Hist & Bio Prize.

WYLIE, LATRELL; Mt St Dominic Acad; Irvington, NJ; (2); Dance Clb; Exploring; Chorus; Church Choir; Sec Cheerleading; Hon Roll; NHS; 1 Of 20 Fnlsts Miss Amrcn Coed Pgm, 1st Pl Tstmstrs Spch Cntst 86; Accptd Inroads Pre-Coll Cmpnnt 87; Dist Attny.

WYNER, YAEL; Columbia HS; Maplewood, NJ; (1); Math Tm; Ski Clb; Nwsp Stf; Yrbk Stf; Fld Hcky; VP Swmmng.

WYNN, JONATHAN; Essex Catholic Boys HS; Newark, NJ; (3); Boy Scts; Trs Church Yth Grp; Hosp Aide; SADD; Rep Soph Cls; Rep Jr Cls; Rep Sr Cls; Stu Cncl; Capt Ftbl; Capt Wt Lftg; Law Enfrcmnt.

WYNNE, STEVEN; Holy Spirit HS; Linwood, NJ; (4); 19/363; Computer Clb; Math Tm; Science Clb; School Play; Nwsp Rptr; Im Ftbl; Im Vllybl; NHS; St Schlr; GA Inst Of Tech; Aerspc Engr.

WYSOCKI, CAROLYN; Edgewood Regional SR HS; Sicklerville, NJ; (3); 34/400; Exploring; Library Aide; Red Cross Aide; Spanish Clb; Varsity Clb; Var Capt Cheerleading; Var Trk; Stat Wrstlng; Hon Roll; NHS; Gifted & Talented; Bus Admin.

WYSOCKI, CATHRYN; Union Catholic RHS HS; Rahway, NJ; (3); 10/308; Service Clb; Nwsp Stf; Rep Soph Cls; JV Bsktbl; L Crs Cntry; Mgr(s); JV Capt Sftbl; Var Vllybl; Hon Roll; NHS; US Nvl Acad; Mltry Off.

WYSOCKI, JENNIFER; Union Catholic Reg HS; Rahway, NJ; (3); 8/308; Office Aide; Science Clb; Rep Frsh Cls; Var Bsktbl; French Hon Soc; High Hon Roll; NHS; Ntl Merit Ltr; Wharton; Bus Admin.

XANTHACOS, ATHENA; Lakewood HS; Lakewood, NJ; (4); 37/294; French Clb; Key Clb; Office Aide; Color Guard; Mrchg Band; Stage Crew; Yrbk Stf; Lit Mag; Trs French Hon Soc; Hon Roll; NJ Natl Teen Pag Fin 86 & 87; Miss Amer Coed Pag Fin 87; Rutgers; Pre-Law.

YACULLO, DENISE; Bloomfield HS; Bloomfld, NJ; (4); 34/437; Key Clb; Rep Soph Cls; Rep Jr Cls; Sec Sr Cls; Rep Stu Cncl; Var Cheerleading; Var Pom Pon; Hon Roll; NHS; Trenton ST Coll.

YACYKEWYCH, ANDREW; Clifton HS; Clifton, NJ; (2); Am Leg Boys St; Boy Scts; Math Clb; Math Tm; Spanish Clb; Im Capt Socr; JV Tennis; Var Capt Vllybl; Gov Hon Prg Awd; Hon Roll; Engrng.

YAGHEN, FIRAS; Manchester Reg HS; Prospect Pk, NJ; (3); German Clb; Math Clb; Var Crs Cntry; Capt Wrstlng; Rutgers U; Arch.

YAGOZINSKI, STEVEN; Pope John HS; Lk Hopatcong, NJ; (4); Church Yth Grp; Computer Clb; Library Aide; SADD; Varsity Clb; Band; Concert Band; Mrchg Band; Bowling; High Hon Roll; Seton Hall U; Acctng.

YAGUEZ, OLGA; Voorhees HS; Hampton, NJ; (4); 32/277; Am Leg Aux Girls St; GAA; JA; Spanish Clb; Varsity Clb; Var Bsktbl; Capt Var Fld Hcky; Sftbl; Hon Roll; NHS; Franklin & Marshall Coll.

YAKOW, KELLY; Vineland HS; Vineland, NJ; (4); 16/736; Trs Key Clb; Pep Clb; VP Varsity Clb; Ed Yrbk Stf; Trs Jr Cls; Trs Sr Cls; Var Capt Cheerleading; High Hon Roll; Trs NHS; Spanish NHS; Chrldng Coachs Awd 86; Rutgers; Lawyer.

YALLOWITZ, LAURIE; Hightstown HS; E Windosr, NJ; (4); 21/422; AFS; Hosp Aide; Spanish Clb; Teachers Aide; Rep Soph Cls; Off Stu Cncl; Var Trk; High Hon Roll; Hon Roll; NHS; Pres Acadmc Ftns Awd 87; La Fayette Coll; Chem.

YALONG, FRANCES; Bayonne HS; New Brunswick, NJ; (4); 44/350; French Clb; Office Aide; Spanish Clb; Trk; Hon Roll; NHS; Prfct Atten Awd; Rutgers U; Actrl Sci.

YAMBAO, EDELWINA; W L Dicksinson HS; Jersey City, NJ; (4); Computer Clb; Q&S; Trs Science Clb; Flag Corp; Yrbk Sprt Ed; Lit Mag; Pom Pon; Twrlr; Co-Capt Vllybl; Trs NHS; Nrs.

YANG, ARLENE; Livingston HS; Livingston, NJ; (4); 13/420; Ed Key Clb; Model UN; Band; Stage Crew; Var Fld Hcky; Twrlr; NHS; Ntl Merit SF; Acad Mdln 87; Peggy Judge Mem Awd-Vsl Arts 87; MA Inst Of Tech.

YANG, JING; Neptune SR HS; Neptune, NJ; (4); 14/300; French Clb; Var Tennis; Elks Awd; High Hon Roll; Hon Roll; Prfct Atten Awd; Pres Acadmc Ftnss Awd 87; Omega Psi Phi 84; Douglass Coll.

YANG, KENNETH; Oratory Prep; Berkeley Hts, NJ; (3); 3/45; Chess Clb; Ski Clb; Var Tennis; Vllybl; High Hon Roll; NHS.

YANG, ROBERT; Immaculata HS; Flemington, NJ; (2); Hosp Aide; Intnl Clb; Math Clb; Math Tm; Science Clb; Band; Concert Band; Orch; Symp Band; JV Bsktbl; Excel Hnrs Alg Awd 85-86; Excel Music Thry Awd 86-87; Hnrb Mntn Math/Sci Leag 86-87; Med.

YANIK, LEE M; West Milford HS; Hewitt, NJ; (3); Am Leg Boys St; Model UN; Varsity Clb; Rep Frsh Cls; Rep Soph Cls; Rep Jr Cls; Rep Stu Cncl; Ftbl; Wrstlng; Hon Roll.

YANNERELLA, LISA; Burlington City HS; Edgewater Pk, NJ; (3); Key Clb; Nwsp Stf; Yrbk Stf; Sec Soph Cls; Sec Jr Cls; Rep Stu Cncl; Cheerleading; Hon Roll.

YANOFSKY, LISA; Brurian HS; Staten Isl, NY; (4); Service Clb; Chorus; School Musical; Stage Crew; Ed Yrbk Stf; Trs Frsh Cls; Trs Soph Cls; NEDT Awd; St Schlr; NY ST Regents Coll Schlrshp Awd 87; Stern Coll; Law.

YANOSEY, DENISE; Lyndhurst HS; Lyndhurst, NJ; (3); 12/172; Debate Tm; FNA; Key Clb; Color Guard; Nwsp Bus Mgr; Var Stat Mgr(s); Var Stat Score Keeper; Stat Timer; Stat Trk; JV Capt Vllybl; Rutgers U; Sci.

YAO, JOYCE; Morris Knolls HS; Denville, NJ; (3); Dance Clb; Hosp Aide; Ski Clb; Varsity Clb; Band; Var L Socr; L Trk; Hon Roll; Miss Teen Amercn Star 87; Teen Miss Best Model 87; Hotel Mgmt.

YAP, MARGARET; Kent Place Schl; Morris Plns, NJ; (2); Cmnty Wkr; French Clb; Nwsp Bus Mgr; Nwsp Stf.

YARBOROUGH, DANIEL; Plainfield HS; Plainfield, NJ; (3); 13/500; Science Clb; Pres VP Y-Teens; Church Choir; Var L Swmmng; Trs NHS; Church Yth Grp; Computer Clb; Trk; Hon Roll; Operation Enterprise Natl Starch & Chem Corp Schlr 87; Poltcl Sci.

YARIS, MELISSA; Florence Twp Memorial HS; Roebling, NJ; (4); 3/85; Am Leg Aux Girls St; Sec Church Yth Grp; Math Clb; Sec Stu Cncl; Var Capt Bsktbl; Var Capt Cheerleading; Hon Roll; VP NHS; Spanish NHS; Voice Dem Awd; Athltc Unsng Hero Awd 87; 1st Plc Vc Of Dmcrcy Essy Cntst Awd 87; Hmcmg Qn Awd 86; Trenton ST Coll; Poly Sci.

YARUSO, JOANNE; Bridgewater-Raritan H S West; Raritan, NJ; (4); 80/265; Am Leg Aux Girls St; Spanish Clb; Sftbl; Hon Roll; Pres Acadmc Ftns Awd 87; Somerset Cnty Coll.

YASIN, KAMILAH; University HS; Newark, NJ; (3); JA; Chorus; Lit Mag; Var Tennis; High Hon Roll; Hon Roll; NHS; Acctng.

YASUNAS, FRANK J; Hunterdon Central HS; Sergeantsville, NJ; (3); 183/543; Cmnty Wkr; Varsity Clb; JV Var Bsbl; JV Var Bsktbl; Coach Actv; Hon Roll; Prfct Atten Awd; All Tourn Plyr Bsktbl 86-87; No 1 Bsbl Tm NJ Grp IV 87; Natl Rifle Assn 87; Bus Adm.

YATES, KAREN; The Kings Christian Schl; Woodbury, NJ; (4); 4/23; Sec VP Church Yth Grp; FCA; Chorus; Church Choir; Var Bsktbl; Var Fld Hcky; High Hon Roll; Hon Roll; NHS; Bob Jones U; Math.

YATES, MICHAEL; Montville HS; Montville, NJ; (2); FBLA; Ski Clb; Temple Yth Grp; Golf; Socr; Hnr Roll 85-86/86-87; Bus.

YATES, TIMOTHY; Sparta HS; Sparta, NJ; (2); 59/268; Trs Church Yth Grp; SADD; Off Frsh Cls; Off Stu Cncl; JV Socr; Hon Roll; Elctrcl Engnrng.

YAVOR, THERESA; Sayreville War Memorial HS; S Amboy, NJ; (4); 61/363; Hosp Aide; Math Clb; Spanish Clb; SADD; Flag Corp; Stage Crew; Nwsp Rptr; Ed Nwsp Stf; Stat Bsktbl; NHS; Rutgers Coll.

YAYAC, CINDY; Monsignor Donovan HS; Jackson, NJ; (4); 2/221; Am Leg Aux Girls St; Church Yth Grp; Drama Clb; Pres Math Tm; Thesps; Yrbk Stf; High Hon Roll; Trs NHS; Ntl Merit Ltr; Sal; Garden ST Distgshd Schlr 87; U Of DE; Engrng.

YEARICKS, VALERIE; Lower Cape May Regional HS; Green Creek, NJ; (4); Band; Concert Band; Mrchg Band; School Musical; Philadelphia Coll; Fshn Merch.

YEARWOOD, VINCENT; St Mary HS; Jamesburg, NJ; (4); 3/128; Am Leg Boys St; Crs Cntry; Socr; Wrstlng; Gov Hon Prg Awd; High Hon Roll; NHS; Aud/Vis; Library Aide; Spanish NHS; Gftd & Tlntd Assn 84-86; NJ Natl Grd & NOPA Schlrshps 86-87; Harvard U; Econ.

YEATS, STANLEY; Middlesex HS; Middlesex, NJ; (2); Church Yth Grp; French Clb; Key Clb; JV Bsbl; JV Bsktbl; Hon Roll; Wharton; Acctnt.

YEDWAB, DENNIS N; Fairlawn HS; Fairlawn, NJ; (4); 8/327; Math Tm; Political Wkr; Temple Yth Grp; Rep Frsh Cls; Rep Soph Cls; Rep Jr Cls; Rep Sr Cls; High Hon Roll; Hon Roll; NHS; Brown Univ Book Awd 86; Northwestern; Political Sci.

YEE, ALVIN MING-CZECH; Randolph HS; Saratoga, CA; (4); 7/369; Computer Clb; Hosp Aide; Math Tm; Science Clb; Mrchg Band; Bowling; High Hon Roll; NHS; Ntl Merit Ltr; Spanish NHS; U Of CA Berkeley; Med.

YEE, FREDDY S; James J Ferris HS; Jersey City, NJ; (4); 17/277; Nwsp Stf; Yrbk Stf; Lit Mag; Gov Hon Prg Awd; Kiwanis Awd; NJ Govnrs Awd Art Ed 87; Pratt Inst Scholar 87; NJ Art Annual Fnlst Photo 87; Schl Vis Arts; Illus.

YEH, MIMI; Ridgewood HS; Ridgewood, NJ; (4); 16/442; Cmnty Wkr; Science Clb; Powder Puff Ftbl; High Hon Roll; NHS; Chorus; Yrbk Stf; Lit Mag; NJ Distngshd Schlr Gdn ST Schlr 86; Pres Acad Fit Awd 87; Natl Sci Olympd Awd Physics 86; Tufts U; Intl Mgmt.

YEH, PAMELA; Monsignor HS; Lakewood, NJ; (3); Art Clb; FBLA; Math Clb; Math Tm; SADD; Flag Corp; Hon Roll; NHS; Flags Athl Awd 86; Annual Music Audition Hnr 87.

YEN, JOHN; Dwight-Englewood Schl; Englewood, NJ; (3); Hosp Aide; JCL; Latin Clb; Library Aide; JV Var Ftbl; JV Var Lcrss; JV Var Tennis; JV Var Trk; JV Wrstlng; Jr NHS; Latin Awd Exclnce 85.

YEPEZ, HUMBERTO R; Union Catholic HS; Clark, NJ; (3); 8/317; Am Leg Boys St; Rep Stu Cncl; Capt Socr; Hon Roll; NHS; Spanish NHS; NJAATSP Natl Exam 2nd Pl; U Of VA; Bus.

YEPEZ, MARIA; Unin Catholic R HS; Clark, NJ; (4); Math Tm; Science Clb; Ski Clb; Rep Stu Cncl; Capt Cheerleading; Coach Actv; Capt VP Gym; French Hon Soc; High Hon Roll; NHS; Ntl Scndry Ed Cncls Acad All-Amer Awd 86; Med Dr.

YEREX, JENNIFER A; Montville Township HS; Towaco, NJ; (3); 34/276; Debate Tm; Drama Clb; Girl Scts; Key Clb; Model UN; Sec Trs NFL; Political Wkr; Chorus; School Musical; School Play; Amnsty Intl 86-87; Quixote Cntr 84-87; Ltn Amer Stdys.

YERKES, TAMMY; Warren County Vo-Technical HS; Washington, NJ; (4); Key Clb; VICA; Yrbk Stf; VP Frsh Cls; Mgr(s); Hon Roll; Csmtlgy.

YEROVI, JAMES; De Paul HS; Wayne, NJ; (4); 34/156; Ski Clb; Var JV Socr; L Trk; Hon Roll; Varsity Clb; Nwsp Rptr; JV Tennis; Vllybl; NJ Inst Of Tech; Elec Engrng.

YEROVI, KATHERINE; North Arlington HS; N Arlington, NJ; (3); 2/119; Sec Pres Camera Clb; Trs Spanish Clb; Varsity Clb; Sec Acpl Chr; Cheerleading; Trk; High Hon Roll; NHS; Sec Spanish NHS; Psycht.

YEWSHENKO, NATALIE L; Somerville HS; Somerville, NJ; (4); Art Clb; Church Yth Grp; Drama Clb; 4-H; Office Aide; Spanish Clb; Nwsp Stf; Yrbk Stf; Badmtn; Hon Roll; Teen Arts Fest-Somerset Cnty 86; Marymount Coll; Art.

YEYE, SYLVIA; St Patricks HS; Newark, NJ; (3); Cmnty Wkr; Hosp Aide; Office Aide; Science Clb; Church Choir; School Play; Nwsp Ed-Chief; Rep Jr Cls; Hon Roll; NHS; Hghst Grd Prsnl Typng Awd 86-87; Sci Sem Union Co Coll Awd 87; Chem Wrkshp Coll St Elizabeth Awd 86; Columbia U; Physcn.

YNAYA, DONNA; Toms River H S North; Toms River, NJ; (3); 6/459; VP Exploring; French Clb; Band; Concert Band; Jazz Band; Mrchg Band; School Musical; High Hon Roll; Ntl Merit Ltr; Rep Jr Cls; Natl Piano Plyng Audtns 85; Amer Music Schlrshp Assn 83; T Mariner Bnd Awd 85-86; Engrng.

YOELSON, MARA; Marlboro HS; Morganville, NJ; (4); School Musical; VP Symp Band; Coach Actv; JV Co-Capt Pom Pon; JETS Awd; NHS; Ntl Merit Ltr; Drama Clb; Science Clb; Mrchg Band; Grdn St Dstngshd Schlr 87; Emory U Schlrs Pgm Harvey W Cox Awd 87; Royal Acad Of Dncng 87; Emory U.

YOKA, JOHN; Kearny HS; Kearny, NJ; (3); Am Leg Boys St; Cmnty Wkr; Pres German Clb; Letterman Clb; JV Bsbl; Var Bowling; Ice Hcky; Sftbl; Vllybl; Seton Hall; Law.

YOKOYAMA, TAKASHI; Ft Lee HS; Fort Lee, NJ; (4); 1/208; Trs FBLA; Trs VICA; Stat Bsktbl; Var Bsktbl; Var Trk; NHS; Ntl Merit Ltr; Spanish NHS; Val; Broward Cnty Fair Drafting 1st & 2nd Pl 84; John Hopkins U.

YON, MYONG; Collingswood SR HS; Woodlynne, NJ; (3); Am Leg Aux Girls St; Chorus; Yrbk Stf; Mst Imprvd Awd 85; Arch.

YONGE, AMY; Shore Regional HS; Sea Bright, NJ; (3); Cmnty Wkr; Sec Debate Tm; French Clb; Science Clb; Ski Clb; Yrbk Ed-Chief; Rep Sr Cls; Var Fld Hcky; Var Socr; Sftbl; Cngrsnl Awd 87.

YONKER II, DONALD; Woodstown HS; Pedricktown, NJ; (3); Debate Tm; English Clb; Key Clb; Ski Clb; Spanish Clb; Var Bsbl; JV Bsktbl; Var Crs Cntry; Hon Roll; U DE; Commnctns.

YOO, JOHN; Cresskill HS; Cresskill, NJ; (3); Boys Clb Am; Boy Scts; Church Yth Grp; Ski Clb; Trs Soph Cls; VP Jr Cls; VP Sr Cls; Sec Stu Cncl; Var Bsbl; Bus.

YOON, ANNA; Cumberland Regional HS; Bridgeton, NJ; (3); 10/384; Intnl Clb; Hst JCL; Model UN; Varsity Clb; Chorus; Rep Stu Cncl; Var Tennis; High Hon Roll; Jr NHS; Church Yth Grp; Outstndg Achvt Piano 84-86; Natl Latin Exm Cum Laude 84; Edwin A Ivins Awd Acad Achvt 84; Pre-Med.

YOON, GENE; Scotch Plains Fanwood HS; Fanwood, NJ; (3); Aud/Vis; German Clb; Quiz Bowl; Rep Jr Cls; JV Golf; JV Socr; High Hon Roll; Prfct Atten Awd; German NHS.

YOON, LARRY; West Essex HS; Fairfield, NJ; (2); Computer Clb; Key Clb; Math Tm; Science Clb; Lit Mag; JV Crs Cntry; Var Tennis; Hon Roll; Engrng.

YORK, MAIIVAH; Eastside HS; Paterson, NJ; (3); JV Bsktbl; Early Chldhd Ed.

YOUMANS, MATT; Brick Memorial HS; Brick, NJ; (3); Computer Clb; English Clb; Library Aide; Office Aide; SADD; Varsity Clb; Var Capt Bsbl; JV Bsktbl; Var Coach Actv; Var Capt Wt Lftg; Division I Coll; Elec Engrng.

YOUNG, CAROLINE; The Dwight Englewood Schl; Alpine, NJ; (3); Cmnty Wkr; VP Pres Intnl Clb; Math Clb; Math Tm; Nwsp Rptr; Nwsp Stf; Crs Cntry; Hon Roll; Ntl Merit Ltr; Lggtt Schlr 84-88; NJ ST Mth Leag Chmpnshp 85-87; J Hopkins Awd Acadc Tlntd Yth 84-87; Lbrl Arts.

YOUNG, CHRIS; Madison HS; New Vernon, NJ; (3); Boy Scts; Church Yth Grp; Ski Clb; Spanish Clb; Nwsp Ed-Chief; Nwsp Phtg; JV Var Tennis; High Hon Roll; Spanish NHS; Eagl Sct 87; Votd Deacn 1st Pres Chch New Vernon 86; New Vernon 1st Ad Sqd Vlntr 87; Bus Mgmt.

YOUNG, CHRISTINE; Bayonne HS; Bayonne, NJ; (3); Orch; Var Bsktbl; Var Sftbl; Hon Roll; Comp Pgmr.

YOUNG, DANIEL; Edgewood SR HS; Berlin, NJ; (2); JV Ftbl; Var Trk; Var Wrstlng; Hon Roll; Mech Engr.

YOUNG, GANG; Elizabeth HS; Elizabeth, NJ; (3); Cornell U; Math.

YOUNG, KARIN; Morris Knolls HS; Denville, NJ; (4); 18/359; Pres Art Clb; Cmnty Wkr; German Clb; Service Clb; High Hon Roll; Hon Roll; NHS; Summa Awd Cert 83-86; Summa Awd Medallion-4 Yrs Acad Exclnce 87; Cmmrcl Art.

YOUNG, KELLI; Randolph HS; Randolph, NJ; (4); 11/360; Church Yth Grp; 4-H; Chorus; Jazz Band; Mrchg Band; Hon Roll; NHS; Spanish Clb; Concert Band; School Musical; Grls Ctznshp Inst H S Delg NJ ST Fed Wmns Clb 86; 4-H ST Wnnr Yth Dev Presntn & Fashn Revw Wnnr 86; U Of Scranton; Humn Resrcs.

YOUNG, KISHA; Marylawn Of The Oranges HS; Newark, NJ; (3); 12/70; Latin Clb; Spanish Clb; Chorus; High Hon Roll; NHS; Trs Spanish NHS; U Of Maryland; Pre-Medicine.

YOUNG, LEE J; Point Pleasant Boro HS; Pt Pleasant, NJ; (3); 3/250; Am Leg Boys St; Key Clb; Science Clb; Yrbk Stf; Hon Roll; NHS; Prfct Atten Awd; Hnr Outstndng Achvmt Sp 87; 37th Yr St Sci Day 87; Bus.

YOUNG, MARVIN; Bridgeton HS; Bridgeton, NJ; (2); Cmnty Wkr; FTA; Spanish Clb; SADD; Nwsp Ed-Chief; Nwsp Rptr; Nwsp Stf; Lit Mag; Cit Awd; Hon Roll; JTPA Smr Yth Prgm Bst Wrkr & Prfct Atndnc Awds; WA ST Coll; Surgery.

YOUNG, MICHELLE; Pitman HS; Pitman, NJ; (2); Office Aide; Chorus; Rep Frsh Cls; Rep Soph Cls; Stu Cncl; Stat Bsktbl; Var L Tennis; Im Vllybl; Hon Roll; All Tri-Cnty Conf Tnns Tm 86; Acad Hnrs Awd 86 & 87; Acctng.

YOUNG, ROBERT C; John F Kennedy HS; Willingboro, NJ; (3); 20/292; Am Leg Boys St; Var JV Ftbl; Var Trk; Hon Roll; NHS; Aerospace Engrng.

YOUNG, SCOTT; Newton HS; Hancock, NY; (3); Am Leg Boys St; Letterman Clb; Varsity Clb; Trs Soph Cls; Trs Jr Cls; Rep Stu Cncl; Bsktbl.

YOUNG, STEVEN; Holy Spirit HS; Northfield, NJ; (4); 7/363; Church Yth Grp; French Clb; High Hon Roll; Hon Roll; NHS; Mrktng.

YOUNG IV, THOMAS E; Gloucester City JR/Sr HS; Brooklawn, NJ; (3); Band; Chorus; Concert Band; Drm & Bgl; Jazz Band; Mrchg Band; Orch; School Musical; VP Soph Cls; VP Jr Cls; Berklee Coll Of Music; Musician.

YOUNGLOVE, CATHERINE; Holy Cross HS; Willingboro, NJ; (4); Spanish Clb; Trs Sr Cls; JV Mgr Bsktbl; JV Capt Sftbl; JC Awd; NHS; Govs Tchng Schlrs Schlrshp 85; Willingboros Outstndng Stu/Ctzn Awd 86; Theology Awd 87; Trenton ST Coll; Elem Ed.

YOUNKERS, CHRISTINA A; Toms River HS South; Toms River, NJ; (2); Drama Clb; Thesps; Mrchg Band; School Musical; Sec Jr Cls; Pom Pon; Church Yth Grp; Intnl Clb; Swmmng; Hon Roll; Mbr Of Intl Thispian Soc.

YOUNUS, ZAINAB N; Washington Township HS; Sewell, NJ; (4); 27/486; French Clb; Intnl Clb; Math Clb; Math Tm; Nwsp Ed-Chief; Hon Roll; NHS; PA JR Acad Sci Rsrch Comptn 2nd Pl; Montgomery Cnty Rsrch Comptn Hnrb Mntn; Hnr Grad; Glassboro ST Coll; Math.

YOUSSEF, OLIVER; Hudson Catholic HS; Jersey City, NJ; (3); 1/177; Pres Chess Clb; Church Yth Grp; Computer Clb; Capt Debate Tm; Math Clb; Science Clb; Church Choir; Nwsp Stf; Yrbk Stf; Im Vllybl; Hghst Genl Excllnc Awd 85-87; Deans Smmr Schlrshp-Rutgers U 87; Pres Citation For Acad Achvt 87; Pre-Med.

YOUSSEF, SUSAN; Franklin HS; Somerset, NJ; (2); Church Yth Grp; German Clb; Library Aide; Church Choir; Orch; JV Gym; JV Sftbl; Hon Roll; Rutgers U; Lawyer.

YOZZO, ANDREA; Delaware Valley Regional HS; Milford, NJ; (3); 63/208; Church Yth Grp; Sec Key Clb; Varsity Clb; Band; Concert Band; Mrchg Band; Pres Jr Cls; Cheerleading; Gym; Trk; Drug Awrnss Prog 86-87; Psych.

YSKAMP, BRETT; Essex Catholic Boys HS; Newark, NJ; (2); Art Clb; Nwsp Rptr; Var Wrstlng; Hon Roll.

YTKIN, ANDREA; Notre Dame HS; Trenton, NJ; (2); Aud/Vis; Drama Clb; Hosp Aide; Stage Crew; Hon Roll; Italian I Acdmc Awd 86; Italian II Exclncy Awd & Club 87; Speech Therapist.

YU, JACK; Franklin HS; Somerset, NJ; (3); Boy Scts; Trs Church Yth Grp; Math Tm; Concert Band; Jazz Band; Mrchg Band; Nwsp Rptr; Lit Mag; JV Tennis; NHS; Deans Smmr Schlr 87; Gov Schl Of The Arts 87; Amer Hstry & Govt Awd 86.

YU, LOK WAH LEWIS; Union Hill HS; Union City, NJ; (4); Computer Clb; Math Clb; Mu Alpha Theta; Nwsp Stf; Yrbk Stf; Stat Mgr(s); Cit Awd; Hon Roll; NHS; Prfct Atten Awd; Outstndng Svc 83-84; UCLA; Comp Sci.

YUHAS, JENNIFER A; Wayne Valley HS; Wayne, NJ; (3); Church Yth Grp; Intnl Clb; Service Clb; Stage Crew; Nwsp Stf; Yrbk Stf; High Hon Roll; Teen Arts Fest ST Level 85; Paramus Art Show Hnrb Mntn 87.

YUN, KYONGSOP; Cherry Hill West HS; Cherry Hill, NJ; (3); Art Clb; Aud/Vis; Teachers Aide; Nwsp Stf; Yrbk Stf; Im JV Bsktbl; Hon Roll; Spanish NHS; ST Spnsh I Cont 7th Pl 84-85; Philadelphia Coll Art; Art.

YUN, YONSU; Holy Rosary Acad; Jersey City, NJ; (3); Art Clb; Hosp Aide; Math Clb; Math Tm; Science Clb; Spanish Clb; Yrbk Stf; Hon Roll; Ntl Math Awd 85; Ntl Sci Merit Awd 85; Columbia U; Doc.

ZABAWA, KRISTEN; Manville HS; Manville, NJ; (3); 15/108; Church Yth Grp; Ed Yrbk Stf; Pres Sr Cls; Var Capt Cheerleading; Hon Roll; NHS; Office Aide; Pep Clb; Band; Chorus; JV Chrldng Awd 86; Tchr.

ZACHARENKO, KAROLYN; De Paul HS; Lincoln Pk, NJ; (3); 47/150; Am Leg Aux Girls St; Church Yth Grp; Ski Clb; Bsktbl; Fld Hcky; Sftbl; Hon Roll; Montclair ST Coll; Paralegal.

ZADIE, DONNA MARIA; Camden Catholic HS; Blackwood, NJ; (4); 43/280; French Clb; Spanish Clb; Sftbl; French Hon Soc; NHS; Spanish NHS; Rsmnt Coll.

ZADRSKI, ALAN; Bayonne HS; Bayonne, NJ; (4); Pres Science Clb; Varsity Clb; Var Coach Actv; JV Var Ftbl; Im Vllybl; JV Var Wt Lftg; JV Var Wrstlng; Hon Roll; NHS; Stdnt Athl Awd Vrsty Ftbl 86-87; Bus Adm.

ZAGRA, CHRISTINE; Phillipsburg HS; Phillipsburg, NJ; (3); Drama Clb; Thesps; Chorus; School Musical; School Play; Stage Crew; Var Cheerleading; Dnc Schlrshp Stanton Studio 83-84; NY Dnc Schlrshp 86.

ZAHAJKEWYCZ, ULANA; Cranford HS; Cranford, NJ; (3); #102 In Class; Art Clb; Camera Clb; Stage Crew; Lit Mag; NHS; Yth Emplymnt Srv Awd 87; 3rd Pl Elzbthtwn Gas Pstr Cntst 87; Art Piece-Hnrd ST Fnls, Art 87; Kean.

ZAHARIADES, CHRISTOPHER; Northern Valley Regional HS; Norwood, NJ; (4); 91/275; AFS; Boy Scts; Church Yth Grp; Rep Stu Cncl; Capt Var Socr; JV Wrstlng; Eagle Scout 85; Fordham Univ; Invstmnt Bnkng.

ZAHNER, DAN; Pequannock Twp HS; Pompton Plains, NJ; (3); 7/220; Pres Church Yth Grp; Exploring; Spanish Clb; Var Capt Ftbl; High Hon Roll; Hon Roll; VP NHS; Ntl Merit SF; VP Spanish NHS; Tutored Stu Alg 87; Elec Engrng.

ZAHORCAK, ALYSSA; Morris Catholic HS; Lk Hiawatha, NJ; (3); 14/35; Church Yth Grp; Drama Clb; French Clb; Latin Clb; Chorus; School Musical; School Play; JV Cheerleading; Gov Hon Prg Awd; Hon Roll; Marine Bio.

ZAIN, MICHAEL; Don Bosco Tech HS; Paterson, NJ; (2); 23/86; JV Socr; Hon Roll; Acctng.

ZAKHARY, RANDA; Ocean Township HS; Ocean, NJ; (3); 10/344; Dance Clb; Drama Clb; Sec French Clb; JCL; Latin Clb; Nwsp Ed-Chief; Yrbk Ed-Chief; Trs NHS; Ntl Merit Ltr; Opt Clb Awd; PA Jr Acad Sci-St Lvl Wnnr 84-86; Hugh O Brian Yth Smnr 86; Girls Citizenship Inst 87; Med.

ZAKRZEWSKI, WENDY; Sayreville War Memorial HS; S Amboy, NJ; (3); Drama Clb; Girl Scts; JA; Pep Clb; PAVAS; Spanish Clb; Thesps; Band; Chorus; Color Guard; Vocal Music Cncrt Chorus 85-87; Teen Arts Fstvl 86-87; Schl Actvts Sales Awd 87; Hofstra Rutgers; Pre-Dntstry.

ZALESKI, ERIKA; Union HS; Union, NJ; (4); 91/550; Rep Key Clb; Sec Spanish Clb; Concert Band; Drm Mjr(t); Jazz Band; Mrchg Band; Orch; Hon Roll; Jr NHS; Band; Prjct Acclrtn Hnrs Pgm-Stn Hll U-Psychlg Hgh Hnr Roll 87; Solo Drm Mjr Awd 86; Georg Mason U; Mrktng.

ZALETA, LISA; Hunterdon Central HS; Hopewell, NJ; (4); Sec Key Clb; Mrchg Band; Symp Band; Variety Show; Off Frsh Cls; Off Jr Cls; Off Sr Cls; Hon Roll; NHS; Messiah Coll; Psych.

ZALEWSKI, JANET; Nutley HS; Nutley, NJ; (3); AFS; Key Clb; Political Wkr; Service Clb; Nwsp Bus Mgr; Nwsp Rptr; Nwsp Stf; Stu Cncl; Bio.

ZAMBRANO, ANNA; Villa Victoria Acad; Titusville, NJ; (4); 3/30; Cmnty Wkr; Hosp Aide; Chorus; School Musical; Yrbk Stf; Lit Mag; Pres Soph Cls; Sec Stu Cncl; Bausch & Lomb Sci Awd; High Hon Roll; Grdn St Dstngshd Schlr 87; Hnrs Engl 87; Pres Acad Fit Awd 87; St Josephs U; Bio.

ZAMKOTOWICZ, CHRISTINE; Hillsborough Twp HS; Somerville, NJ; (4); 27/285; High Hon Roll; Hon Roll; NHS; Ntl Merit SF; NJ ST Dstngshd Schlr 86; Blair Smmr Acad For Gftd 84 & 85; Brown U Smmr Acad 86; Bio.

ZAMORA, HAYDEE; St Joseph Of The Palisades HS; North Bergen, NJ; (4); 3/130; Spanish Clb; Nwsp Stf; Nwsp Phtg; Lit Mag; Var Swmmng; Bausch & Lomb Sci Awd; Cit Awd; High Hon Roll; NHS; Girls Ctznshp Inst 86; Law.

ZAMOS, CINDY; Newton HS; Newton, NJ; (3); VP French Clb; GAA; Latin Clb; PAVAS; Varsity Clb; Acpl Chr; Madrigals; Sftbl; Swmmng; Gov Hon Prg Awd; MVP Sftbl 87; Intl Rltns.

ZAMPAGLIONE, MARIA; St James HS; Gibbstown, NJ; (2); VP Frsh Cls; JV Capt Cheerleading; Hon Roll.

ZANDOMENEGA, CARA; Bridgewater-Raritan HS East; Basking Ridge, NJ; (3); Church Yth Grp; Var Powder Puff Ftbl; Stat Socr; Stat Swmmng; Hon Roll; NHS.

ZANE, KEITH; Clearview Regional HS; Sewell, NJ; (3); Boy Scts; Church Yth Grp; Cmnty Wkr; Band; Church Choir; Concert Band; Jazz Band; Mrchg Band; Orch; Symp Band; All S Jersey Symphnc Band 87; Music.

ZANES, SUSAN; Egg Harbor Township HS; Scullville, NJ; (4); GAA; Key Clb; Teachers Aide; Mgr(s); Hon Roll; 2 Schltc Ltr Awds-Acadmc Achvt 84-86.

ZANETTI, AMY; West Essex Regional HS; Fairfield, NJ; (4); 55/345; Church Yth Grp; Chorus; Church Choir; Orch; JV Fld Hcky; Hon Roll; Fncng Team 83-87; Slct Grls Ensmbl 84-85; Magna Cum Laude On Natl Latin Exam 85; Albrght Coll.

ZANGARI, ANTONIA; Belleville HS; Belleville, NJ; (3); Drama Clb; Chorus; Color Guard; School Musical; School Play; Pres Frsh Cls; Pres Soph Cls; Pres Jr Cls; Pres Sr Cls; Stu Cncl; Cmnctns.

ZANNA, GERMAINE; Secaucus HS; Secaucus, NJ; (4); 31/157; Intnl Clb; Key Clb; Math Clb; Mu Alpha Theta; Band; Concert Band; Drm Mjr(t); Mrchg Band; Yrbk Ed-Chief; High Hon Roll; Fashion Inst Of Tech; Fshn Merc.

ZAPICO, ANTHONY; Kearny HS; Kearny, NJ; (4); 32/383; Am Leg Boys St; Latin Clb; Math Tm; Science Clb; Yrbk Ed-Chief; VP Jr Cls; VP Sr Cls; Tennis; Wrstlng; Hon Roll; Natl Hispanic Schlr Awds 86-87; Rutgers U; Med.

ZAPOTOCKY, CHRISTINE; Rahway HS; Rahway, NJ; (4); 2/231; Sec Church Yth Grp; Sec Girl Scts; Pres Key Clb; Nwsp Stf; Yrbk Stf; Pres Stu Cncl; Var Vllybl; Pres French Hon Soc; NHS; St Schlr.

ZAPPALA, DAVID; St James HS; Woodstown, NJ; (2); 15/150; JV Bsbl; JV Ftbl; Hon Roll.

ZAPPOLA, DONNA; Paulsboro HS; Gibbstown, NJ; (4); 30/130; Church Yth Grp; School Musical; School Play; Variety Show; Capt Sftbl; Capt Tennis; Hon Roll; Gdnc Awd 87; Red Blt Krt 87; Eastern Coll St Davids; Med.

ZARBATANY, MATTHEW; Phillipsburg HS; Phillipsburg, NJ; (3); 19/315; Capt Scholastic Bowl; Ski Clb; Nwsp Ed-Chief; Ed Lit Mag; JV Socr; Var Trk; High Hon Roll; VP NHS; Ntl Merit SF; 2yrs Olympics Of The Mind Team Captain 85-87; 3 Olympics Of Mind RFCA; 1 In State Comp 85-87; Aerospace Engrg.

ZARETSKI, PATRICK; Dwight-Englewood Schl; Haledon, NJ; (3); Boy Scts; Nwsp Rptr; Nwsp Stf; Sec Jr Cls; VP Ice Hcky; Hon Roll; Comm Shlr Full Tuition-Dwight-Englewood 84-88; 1st Pl Schlrshp Awd-Don Bosco Prep Ramsey 84; Wrtr.

ZAROUNI, ALICIA; Middletown High School South; Middletown, NJ; (4); 19/450; Math Clb; Capt Math Tm; Var Capt Fld Hcky; Var Socr; Var Sftbl; Var Trk; French Hon Soc; High Hon Roll; Pres NHS; Garden ST Schlr 86; Acctng.

ZARRA, JENNIFER; Belleville HS; Belleville, NJ; (3); 14/401; Drm Mjr(t); Mrchg Band; High Hon Roll; NHS; Band; Jazz Band; Hon Roll; Italn Am Essy Cont 2nd Pl 86; JR Wmns Clb Poetry Cont 2nd Pl 86; Phrmcy.

ZASADZINSKI, REGINA; Whippany Park HS; Whippamy, NJ; (3); 64/185; 4-H; Hosp Aide; Concert Band; Jazz Band; Mrchg Band; School Musical; School Play; Stage Crew; Dnfth Awd; 4-H Awd; Music Commndtn 86; 4-H CWF Delegate 86; Art.

ZATKOS, JOHN; Wallington HS; Wallington, NJ; (2); Chess Clb; Science Clb; Varsity Clb; Trs Jr Cls; Var Bsbl; Var Ftbl; Wt Lftg; Hon Roll; Seton Hall; Sci.

ZATZARINY, EDDIE; Vineland HS; Vineland, NJ; (1); Band; Concert Band; Jazz Band; Hon Roll; Berkey U; Music Educ.

ZAUNCZKOWSKI, DIANE; St Mary HS; Wallington, NJ; (3); Office Aide; Ski Clb; Varsity Clb; Stage Crew; Yrbk Bus Mgr; Yrbk Stf; Sftbl.

ZAVADA, KARIN; Pequannock Township HS; Pequannock, NJ; (3); 62/210; Office Aide; Trs Frsh Cls; Bsktbl; Mat Maids; Stat Sftbl; Teen Arts Fstvl 86; Spch Ther.

ZAVADA, MICHELE; West Milford Township HS; West Milford, NJ; (2); 1/400; Church Yth Grp; Debate Tm; Math Tm; Science Clb; Ski Clb; SADD; Opt Clb Awd; Scholastic Bowl; Teachers Aide; High Hon Roll; Ranatra Fusca Crtvty Awd NJOM 87; 1st Pl Spanish Poetry Rdng Cntst 86; Pre-Med.

ZAVADIL, AMY; Verona HS; Verona, NJ; (3); Band; Concert Band; Mrchg Band; Hon Roll; Jmp Rope For Heart-Co-Chrpsn 85-87; Grls ST Alt 87; U Of West FL; Bus.

ZAVALA, FRED; St Joseph Regional HS; Westwood, NJ; (3); JV Trk; Hon Roll; Spanish NHS; Med.

ZAWACKI, ANDREW; Calvary Acad; Lakehurst, NJ; (3); 1/7; Chorus; VP Jr Cls; Pres Stu Cncl; Bsbl; Bsktbl; Socr; Cit Awd; Hon Roll; Church Yth Grp; German Awd 86-87; Hon Stu 87; Mst Likely To Succeed 86-87; Kings Coll; Accntng.

ZAWISTOWSKI, MARSHA; Sayreville War Memorial HS; Parlin, NJ; (2); Church Yth Grp; Spanish Clb; SADD; Drill Tm; Mrchg Band; Rep Frsh Cls; Rep Soph Cls; Rep Stu Cncl; Hon Roll; Presdntl Acadmc Ftns Awd 85-86; Medicine.

ZDANOWICZ, RICHARD; St Joseph Regional HS; Dumont, NJ; (3); 90/240; Boy Scts; Cmnty Wkr; Hosp Aide; Ftbl; Trk; High Hon Roll; Hon Roll; Spanish NHS; Aerosp Engrng.

ZDOROVYAK, IGOR; Passaic HS; Passaic, NJ; (4); Chess Clb; Computer Clb; Debate Tm; Intnl Clb; Math Clb; Model UN; Science Clb; Lit Mag; Hon Roll; NHS; Cert Appointmnt Offce Fire Dirctr 87; Cert Recogntn Partptcn Mock Trial Team 87; Acad Decathlon 87; Fairleigh Dickinson U; Comp Sci.

ZEBROWSKI, DAVID; Manalapan HS; Englishtown, NJ; (3); 122/484; Varsity Clb; Off Soph Cls; Im Bsbl; Capt Var Bsktbl; Im Ftbl; Var Golf; Var Socr; U DE; Comp.

ZEIGLER, JOHN M; Moorestown HS; Moorestown, NJ; (3); Am Leg Boys St; French Clb; Latin Clb; Varsity Clb; JV Bsbl; Var Socr; Var Wrstlng; Hon Roll; 2nd Tm All Star Wrstlng 85-86.

ZEIGLER, PENNY; Cumberland Christian HS; Williamstown, NJ; (3); Church Yth Grp; Chorus; VP Frsh Cls; Trs Jr Cls; Var Bsktbl; Var Fld Hcky; Sftbl; Hon Roll; Scripturte Mastry; Cedarville Coll; Phys Ed.

ZEISER, LAWRENCE; Highland Regional HS; Erial, NJ; (3); High Hon Roll; Hon Roll; Mck Trl 86-87; Sci Tm Bio-Chem 85-87; Wrld Affrs Cncl 86-87; Drexel U; Engnrng.

ZELAYA, KARLA; Ferris HS; Jersey City, NJ; (3); Prfct Atten Awd; Nrsng.

ZELINSKI, PAMELA; Holy Spirit HS; Marmora, NJ; (4); 38/363; Exploring; Nwsp Rptr; Nwsp Sprt Ed; Nwsp Stf; Hon Roll; NHS; Varsty Rowing 83-87; Jrnlsm.

ZELLEY, CHRISTINE; Washington Township HS; Sewell, NJ; (3); Church Yth Grp; German Clb; Hon Roll; NHS; Office Aide; Stage Crew; Air Force; Accntnt.

ZELLMAN, PATSY; Belvidere HS; Phillipsburg, NJ; (4); Varsity Clb; Nwsp Stf; Yrbk Stf; Capt Bsktbl; Var Fld Hcky; Var Sftbl; Hon Roll; Prfct Atten Awd; Northampton Cnty Area CC; Fhsn.

ZEMAITAITIS, DIANE; Woodstown HS; Elmer, NJ; (4); English Clb; Spanish Clb; SADD; Concert Band; Mrchg Band; Nwsp Stf; Lit Mag; Socr; Trk; Hon Roll; Radford U; Engl.

ZEMAITIS, GARY; John P Stevens HS; Edison, NJ; (3); Computer Clb; Bsbl.

ZEMIETRA, EVA M; Kearny HS; Kearny, NJ; (3); Sec German Clb; Ski Clb; Yrbk Bus Mgr; Yrbk Stf; Rep Jr Cls; Rep Sr Cls; JV Cheerleading; Coach Actv; JV Var Sftbl; Hon Roll; Delta Epsilon Phi German Hnr Scty 87; Awd Miss Co-Ed Pageant 86; Intl Lawyer.

ZENGEL, ROBYN; Toms River High School North; Toms River, NJ; (3); Pres FBLA; Hon Roll; NHS; 7th Pl FBLA Natl Conf Clerk Typist II 87; Bd Of Educ Cert Of Merit 87; K Gibbs Bus Ldrshp Awd 87; Bus Admn.

ZERBE, GEOFF; Ridge HS; Basking Ridge, NJ; (4); 27/207; French Clb; German Clb; Mu Alpha Theta; Y-Teens; Nwsp Phtg; Yrbk Phtg; Yrbk Stf; Hon Roll; Ntl Merit Ltr; GA Tech; Chem.

ZETO, JENNIFER; Middletown High School South; Lincroft, NJ; (4); 42/450; Cmnty Wkr; Flag Corp; Fld Hcky; Sftbl; Hon Roll; Stat Bsktbl; Var Bsktbl; Accntng.

ZETTLER, DANIEL; Paramus HS; Paramus, NJ; (3); Boy Scts; VP Temple Yth Grp; VP Band; Concert Band; Drm Mjr(t); Mrchg Band; Orch; School Musical; NHS; Ntl Hebrew Hmr Soc; Ntl Hebrew Cltr Cncl Awd; Nertamid Awd Boy Scouts; Engr.

ZGURZYNSKI, JOHN; Delaware Valley Regional HS; Frenchtown, NJ; (2); Boy Scts; VP Church Yth Grp; Cmnty Wkr; 4-H; JV Bsbl; JV Bsktbl; JV Crs Cntry; Im Tennis; High Hon Roll; Natl Cngrssnl Schlr Natl Yth Ldrs Cnfrnc 87; Ivy League; Bus.

ZICCHINO, HELEYNE; St Marys HS; Carlstadt, NJ; (4); 12/75; Yrbk Stf; Var Stat Bsbl; Var Sftbl; JV Vllybl; NHS; Stu Agnst Substncs; St Elizabeth Coll; Psych.

ZICKER, DONNA; Parsippany HS; Lake Hiawatha, NJ; (3); Computer Clb; Hst FBLA; Girl Scts; Hosp Aide; Spanish Clb; Stage Crew; Yrbk Stf; Sftbl; High Hon Roll; Hon Roll; FBLA Compttn Clrk Typst II 4th Pl 86; FBLA Compttn Wrd Prcssng 3rd Pl 87; Cndy Strpr 232 Hrs 84-86; Chem.

ZIEGLER, DOROTHY; West Deptford HS; Woodbury, NJ; (4); #41 In Class; Ski Clb; Varsity Clb; Im Bsktbl; Var Powder Puff Ftbl; Var Sftbl; Var Tennis; Hon Roll; NHS; Glassboro ST Coll; Elem Ed.

ZIEGLER, ERIC; Gloucester County Christian Schl; Sicklerville, NJ; (3); 5/23; Church Yth Grp; Chorus; Church Choir; VP Soph Cls; Sec Jr Cls; Var Socr; Var Trk; Hon Roll; Prfct Atten Awd; Med.

ZIEGLER, WILLIAM; Friends Schl; Turnersville, NJ; (3); Var Capt Bsktbl; Var Socr; Engr.

ZIEGLER, WILLIAM; Oratory Catholic Prep; Madison, NJ; (3); 7/45; Library Aide; Math Clb; Math Tm; Science Clb; Service Clb; Nwsp Stf; Var Bsktbl; Im Ftbl; Im Vllybl; High Hon Roll; Alg, Relgn Awds 85; Hstry Awd 85 & 86; Hstry.

ZIELINSKI, DOREEN; Woodbridge HS; Woodbridge, NJ; (3); 35/350; Church Yth Grp; Cmnty Wkr; Spanish Clb; Chorus; Nwsp Stf; Hon Roll; NHS; Spanish NHS.

ZIEMANN, BRITA; High Point Regional HS; Newton, NJ; (3); 20/234; Church Yth Grp; Cmnty Wkr; VP German Clb; Girl Scts; Drill Tm; School Musical; High Hon Roll; Hon Roll; NHS; Chem.

ZIEMBA, LAWRENCE S; Southern Regional HS; Barnegat, NJ; (4); 125/391; Church Yth Grp; Nwsp Bus Mgr; Nwsp Rptr; Yrbk Rptr; Yrbk Stf; Rep Frsh Cls; Rep Soph Cls; Off Jr Cls; Off Sr Cls; Stu Cncl; Gov NJ Phys Fit Awd 87; Times-Beacon Scholar Jrnlsm 87; Dolph Cranmer Awd Ath Yr 87; Allegheny Coll; Cmmnctns.

ZIEMINSKI, RICHARD; Fairlawn HS; Fair Lawn, NJ; (3); Computer Clb; Hon Roll; Elec Engr.

ZIER, LESLIE; Hamilton High School West; Yardville, NJ; (4); 63/474; Key Clb; SADD; Band; Concert Band; Mrchg Band; Symp Band; Off Stu Cncl; JV Sftbl; Mercer Co CC; Bus Admn.

ZIEROLD, KIRSTEN; Lakewood HS; Lakewood, NJ; (3); Church Yth Grp; FBLA; German Clb; Band; Color Guard; Mrchg Band; Cit Awd; Hon Roll; NHS; Med.

ZILAI, MARK; St Rose HS; Brielle, NJ; (4); 29/207; Var L Socr; Var L Tennis; Hon Roll; NHS; Shore Area Slct Socr Tm 85-86; Shore Boys Clb Premier Sccr Tm 83-87; MVP-HS Tnns Tm 87; U Of DE.

ZILAVY, SHARLENE; Vineland HS; Vineland, NJ; (3); Art Clb; Spanish Clb; Hon Roll; Art Recgntn Cert 86; Art Fld.

ZILINEK, LAURA SUE; Clifton HS; Clifton, NJ; (3); Am Leg Aux Girls St; Cmnty Wkr; Key Clb; SADD; Chorus; Var Mgr(s); Hon Roll; Psych.

ZILLES, MICHELLE; Emerson JR SR HS; Emerson, NJ; (2); Aud/Vis; Church Yth Grp; Cmnty Wkr; Drama Clb; English Clb; PAVAS; Spanish Clb; SADD; Thesps; Chorus; Fnlst 87 Talent Expo Grdn St Cltrl Showcase Of Stars 87; Most Proffssnl Act II Theater 86; Harvard.

ZIMA, KAREN; Brockport HS; Churchville, NY; (4); 29/335; Trs Church Yth Grp; French Clb; Rep Soph Cls; Var Capt Swmmng; High Hon Roll; NHS; Frnch II Awd 85; Frnch Hnr Soc Prize 87; Potsdam Coll; Frgn Lang.

ZIMAROWSKI, PAUL; John F Kennedy HS; Willingboro, NJ; (3); Boy Scts; Yrbk Stf; Diving; Mgr Fld Hcky; Var Swmmng; Hon Roll; Cert Of Hnr-American Cancer Soc 85; Art Inst Of Phila; Cmmrcl Art.

ZIMMER, BEN; Hunterdon Central HS; Flemington, NJ; (3); 13/557; Drama Clb; Latin Clb; Quiz Bowl; Scholastic Bowl; Sec Thesps; School Musical; School Play; Stage Crew; Nwsp Rptr; Pedicurist.

ZIMMER, KAREN; Toms River HS South; Toms River, NJ; (2); SADD; JV Fld Hcky; Stat Mgr(s); Var L Trk; Hon Roll; Dntl Hygenist.

ZIMMERMAN, ADAM; Ocean Township HS; Ocean, NJ; (3); 64/344; Key Clb; Ski Clb; JV Ftbl; Im Wt Lftg; Var L Wrstlng; Rutgers; Med.

ZIMMERMAN, ANDREA; Higland Regional HS; Sicklerville, NJ; (3); Church Yth Grp; GAA; Spanish Clb; Var Bsktbl; Var Capt Socr; JV Var Sftbl; Science Clb; Inducted Girst Interact 86; Hnr Mntn Girls Soccer 86; Elem Ed.

ZIMMERMAN, BRIAN M; Middletown South HS; Middletown, NJ; (4); 75/452; Boy Scts; Chess Clb; Thesps; School Musical; School Play; Nwsp Rptr; Lit Mag; L Crs Cntry; L Trk; Ntl Merit SF.

ZIMMERMAN, JON P; South Brunswick HS; Kendall Park, NJ; (4); 6/254; Math Tm; Mu Alpha Theta; Political Wkr; Trs Temple Yth Grp; Capt Crs Cntry; Var Trk; Mu Alpha Theta Awd; NHS; Ntl Merit SF; Spanish NHS; Garden ST Distngshd Schlr; NJ Gov Schl Sci.

ZIMMERMAN, KAREN; Abraham Clark HS; Roselle, NJ; (2); Dance Clb; GAA; Latin Clb; Ski Clb; Band; Color Guard; Cheerleading; Gym; Sftbl; Hon Roll; Miss Soph 86-87; Natl Dance Awds 84-87; Rutgers Med Schl; Nrs.

ZIMMERMAN, SARAH; Kent Place HS; Warren, NJ; (2); Cmnty Wkr; French Clb; Model UN; Chorus; Orch; Lit Mag; Var Jr Cls; Temple Yth Grp; Accdptnc NJ Yth Symphony & Teen Arts Fstvl Cnty Lvl 87; Accptnc Parsons Schl Design Smmr Prg 87; U Of VA; Art.

ZIMMERMAN, SARAH; Kent Place Schl; Mountain Lakes, NJ; (3); 1/58; Rep GAA; Key Clb; Rep Model UN; Ski Clb; Pres VP Temple Yth Grp; Chorus; Madrigals; Mgr Nwsp Stf; Lit Mag; Rep Frsh Cls; Social Wrk.

ZIMMERMANN, CRAIG; Morris HS; Hackettstown, NJ; (3); 110/265; Church Yth Grp; French Clb; JA; Office Aide; Bsbl; JV Crs Cntry; Hon Roll; NC ST; Arch.

ZIMMERMANN, HEIDI; Cherry Hill HS West; Cherry Hill, NJ; (3); Am Leg Aux Girls St; PAVAS; Chorus; School Musical; Variety Show; Nwsp Stf; Yrbk Stf; Var JV Socr; Hon Roll; NHS.

ZIMMERMANN, THOMAS; St Peters Prep; N Arlington, NJ; (4); 19/196; Math Tm; Stage Crew; Im Ftbl; VP L Trk; Hon Roll; NHS; Excllnc In Comp Sci Gld Mdl; St Peters Coll; Bus.

ZINDELL, CATHY; Montville Township HS; Pine Brook, NJ; (3); 69/300; FBLA; Key Clb; Model UN; Ski Clb; Varsity Clb; Stu Cncl; Cheerleading; JV L Fld Hcky; Powder Puff Ftbl; L Var Sftbl; American Hlth Care Assn Cert 87; Project Link-Up 87; Bus.

ZINN, CAROLYN; Vineland HS; Vineland, NJ; (3); Var Sftbl; Var L Tennis; 2nd Pl Tempra Painting Stu Art Exhbt 87; Advrtsng.

ZIOLKOWSKI, KRISTIN; Notre Dame HS; Trenton, NJ; (3); Dance Clb; Chorus; Capt Color Guard; School Musical; School Play; Hon Roll; NHS; Spanish NHS; U Of DE; Psych.

ZIPFEL, STACEY; Holy Spirit HS; Brigantine, NJ; (2); 1/397; Spanish Clb; Nwsp Rptr; High Hon Roll; Hon Roll.

ZIRVI, MONIB; Fairlawn HS; Fair Lawn, NJ; (2); 1/340; Computer Clb; Pres Math Clb; Pres Math Tm; Science Clb; High Hon Roll; Hon Roll; NJIT Comp Olympcs Schlrshp 85-86; FDU Comp Cntst Awd 86-87; Chem Leag-3rd NJ 86-87; Comp Sci.

ZISA, LILIANA; Immaculate Conception HS; Elmwood Park, NJ; (2); 3/89; Spanish Clb; Nwsp Stf; Yrbk Stf; Rep Soph Cls; Var JV Mgr(s); JV Vllybl; Hon Roll; Natl Army Rsrv Essy Cntst Hon Ment Awd 85-86; Archtct.

ZISS, LAUREN; Manalapan HS; Manalapan, NJ; (3); 21/439; Drama Clb; SADD; Temple Yth Grp; Thesps; Chorus; School Musical; School Play; Gym; JV Trk; NHS; Cert Of Hnr Outstndng Achvmnt Geometry 86; Cinematography.

ZITA, DAVID; Immaculate Conception HS; Belleville, NJ; (2); Aud/Vis; Church Yth Grp; Chorus; High Hon Roll; Otolaryngology.

ZITO, LISA ANN; Cranford HS; Cranford, NJ; (2); Church Yth Grp; Cmnty Wkr; Hosp Aide; Library Aide; SADD; JV Bsktbl; Cheerleading; Im Sftbl; Im Var Vllybl; Im Wt Lftg; Montclair ST; Soclgy.

ZITTEL, KIM; Park Ridge HS; Park Ridge, NJ; (3); 54/108; Church Yth Grp; Cmnty Wkr; GAA; PAVAS; Varsity Clb; Band; Chorus; Church Choir; Concert Band; Mrchg Band.

ZIZWAREK, MICHELLE; Jackson Memorial HS; Jackson, NJ; (4); 57/390; Drama Clb; Hosp Aide; School Musical; School Play; Var Stat Mgr(s); Mgr Wrstlng; High Hon Roll; Hon Roll; Hgh Hnr Rl 86-87; Ocean County Coll; Nrsng.

ZOCKS, ADAM; Livingston HS; Livingston, NJ; (4); 31/420; Key Clb; Band; Concert Band; Mrchg Band; School Musical; Bsktbl; Var Capt Trk; Hon Roll; Jr NHS; NHS; Home & Schl Assn Bnd Awd; MVP Trck; William & Mary Coll.

ZOINO, CINDY; Belleville HS; Belleville, NJ; (3); Church Yth Grp; Cmnty Wkr; Spanish Clb; Band; Chorus; Concert Band; Jazz Band; Mrchg Band; Orch; Rep Jr Cls; Psych.

ZOIS, ELEFTHERIA; Immaculate Conception HS; Lodi, NJ; (2); Sec Church Yth Grp; SADD; Stage Crew; JV Var Vllybl; Hon Roll; NEDT Awd; Medicine.

ZOLAND, ROBERT; John P Stevens HS; Edison, NJ; (3); 44/457; Debate Tm; Model UN; VP Temple Yth Grp; Thesps; School Musical; School Play; Stage Crew; Variety Show; Nwsp Stf; Hon Roll; Overall Commtmnt To Theater 86; Hghst Hnr For Securty Cncl In Model UN 86; Outstndng Delgtn 86.

ZOLANDZ, JOSEPH J; Manville HS; Manville, NJ; (4); #1 In Class; Aud/Vis; Ed Yrbk Stf; High Hon Roll; NHS; Ntl Merit SF; St Schlr; Rutgers Pres Scholar 86; Rutgers U; Comp Sci.

ZOLL, MARY; Palmyra HS; Palmyra, NJ; (3); 1/120; VP Church Yth Grp; Key Clb; SADD; School Play; Trs Frsh Cls; Trs Soph Cls; Trs Jr Cls; Trs Sr Cls; Trs Stu Cncl; JV Capt Fld Hcky; Girls Citiz Inst 87; HOB Ldrshp Smnrs 86.

ZONERAICH, NATHANIEL; Jonathan Dayton Regional HS; Springfield, NJ; (3); 3/252; Am Leg Boys St; Trs Latin Clb; Red Cross Aide; Spanish Clb; Temple Yth Grp; Yrbk Bus Mgr; Trs Stu Cncl; Var Tennis; NHS; Ntl Merit SF; Latin Magna Cum Laude Awd 85-86; Med.

ZORN, ALLISON; Southern Regional HS; Haven Bch, NJ; (3); Off Frsh Cls; Off Soph Cls; Off Jr Cls; Stu Cncl; JV Gym; Engl.

ZORN, JENNIFER; Notre Dame HS; Trenton, NJ; (3); 28/373; Red Cross Aide; Service Clb; Hon Roll; Jr NHS; NHS; Criminal Psychology.

ZOROWITZ, STACEY; Hightstown HS; East Windsor, NJ; (3); FBLA; SADD; Rep Stu Cncl; JV Fld Hcky; High Hon Roll; Hon Roll; Bus.

ZOZZARO, JOHN; Fair Lawn HS; Toms River, NJ; (3); Church Yth Grp; Ski Clb; Band; Concert Band; Jazz Band; Mrchg Band; School Musical; High Hon Roll; Chorus; Chiroprctc.

ZSARKO, JENNIFER; Boonton HS; Boonton, NJ; (2); JV Var Bsktbl; JV Var Trk; Hon Roll; Glassboro ST Coll; Hstry.

ZSILAVETZ, CHRISTINE; Southern Regional HS; Manahawkin, NJ; (3); 11/435; Ski Clb; Spanish Clb; Varsity Clb; Im JV Bsktbl; Var L Socr; Stat Sftbl; Hon Roll; NHS; Spanish NHS; JV Crs Cntry; Pres Acad Fit Awd 84; Hopwood Schlrs Prgm Lynchburg Coll Basic A 87; Gateway Prgm Middlesex Cnty Coll; Comp Sci.

ZSOREY, MICHAEL D; Sayreville War Memorial HS; Parlin, NJ; (3); Aud/Vis; Spanish Clb; Stage Crew; Pres Schlr; Rutgers U; Engrng.

ZUBRZYCKI, JEANENE; Burlington Twp HS; Burlington Twp, NJ; (3); 6/135; Am Leg Aux Girls St; Church Yth Grp; French Clb; Hosp Aide; VP Key Clb; Ski Clb; VP Varsity Clb; Chorus; Hon Roll; NHS.

ZUCCA, LOUISE ERNESTINE; Lacey HS; Forked River, NJ; (4); 2/276; Math Tm; Science Clb; Band; Chorus; Church Choir; Concert Band; Jazz Band; Orch; Nwsp Phtg; Nwsp Stf; Math Medal, Frnch Medal, Garden ST Dstngshd Schlr 86-87; Westminster Choir Coll; Music.

ZUCCARO, ROSEMARIE; Paramus Catholic Girls Regionl HS; Garfield, NJ; (2); Dance Clb; Spanish Clb; Nwsp Stf; Lit Mag; Hon Roll; Comm.

ZUIDEMA, DAVID; Eastern Christian HS; N Haledon, NJ; (4); 3/80; Cmnty Wkr; Drama Clb; Concert Band; Jazz Band; Ed Nwsp Phtg; JV Var Crs Cntry; Var Trk; NHS; Pres Schlr; Church Yth Grp; NJIT Faculty Schlr 87; Estrn Christian HS Sprtsmnshp Awd 84-87; Estrn Christian Ded Awd 87; Ftns Awd; NJ Inst Of Tech; Elec Engr.

ZUKAUSKAS, LORETTA; Buena Regional HS; Collings Lakes, NJ; (4); 18/180; Hon Roll; Hnrb Mntn Kthrn Gibbs Ldrshp Awd For Ftr Scrtrys 86; Ntl Scl Stdys Olympiad Awd 83; Kthrn Gibbs Schl; Wrd Prcsng.

ZUKERMAN, ITAI; Fair Lawn HS; Fair Lawn, NJ; (4); Pres Computer Clb; Math Clb; Math Tm; Science Clb; Hon Roll; Ntl Merit SF; Ltr In Vrsty Fnsng 86; CA Inst Of Tech; Jrnymn.

ZUKOWSKI, GREGORY A; De Paul HS; Wayne, NJ; (4); 18/150; Am Leg Boys St; JCL; Ski Clb; School Musical; School Play; Variety Show; Yrbk Stf; PA ST U.

ZULLA, CHRISTINE; Notre Dame HS; Trenton, NJ; (3); Yrbk Rptr; Yrbk Stf; JV Ftbl; Jrnlsm.

ZUMPANO, JENNIFER; Mainland Regional HS; Northfield, NJ; (4); 38/241; Church Yth Grp; Computer Clb; Exploring; Intnl Clb; Stockton ST Coll; Compu Sci.

ZUNIGA, ALEXANDER; A L Johnson Reg HS; Clark, NJ; (4); 18/197; Art Clb; French Clb; Key Clb; Var Socr; Var Trk; French Hon Soc; Hon Roll; Crestmont Fed Calndr Cntst Schlrshp 87; Cook Coll; Pre-Med.

ZUPKO, CHRISTINE; Gateway Regional HS; Wenonah, NJ; (3); 17/200; Am Leg Aux Girls St; Sec Key Clb; Latin Clb; Science Clb; Varsity Clb; Sec Frsh Cls; Trs Soph Cls; Rep Stu Cncl; Capt Cheerleading; Stat Wrstlng; Fang Dsgn.

ZUPKO, ROGER; Perth Amboy HS; Perth Amboy, NJ; (3); German Clb; Model UN; ROTC; Science Clb; Stage Crew; Nwsp Ed-Chief; Nwsp Rptr; Cit Awd; NJROTC Ddln Fndtn Awd 87; Mnmth Coll; Mltry Ofcr.

ZUZA, VALERIE; Kearny HS; Kearny, NJ; (1); Hosp Aide; Color Guard; Rep Frsh Cls; Rep Stu Cncl; Rutgers New Brunswick; Med.

ZVARA, LAURA; Union Catholic RHS; Scotch Plains, NJ; (4); 14/297; French Clb; Latin Clb; Ski Clb; Yrbk Phtg; Yrbk Stf; French Hon Soc; High Hon Roll; NHS; Garden ST Dstngshd Schlr 86-87; Natl Mrt Cmmnd Stu 86-87; Engr.

PENNSYLVANIA

ABADILLA, ANGELA; Ambridge Area HS; Baden, PA; (4); 98/265; Hosp Aide; Band; Concert Band; Jazz Band; Mrchg Band; Pep Band; School Musical; Crs Cntry; Trk; Lion Awd; Vin Vincent Pisano Schlrshp Awd 87; Band Schlrshp Awd 87; Semper Fidelis Awd Mscl Ex 87; WV U; Music Ed.

ABATE, GEORGE; Quaker Valley SR HS; Sewickley, PA; (2); Concert Band; School Play; Nwsp Stf; Lit Mag; JV Bsbl; Cit Awd; High Hon Roll; Prfct Atten Awd; Pres Schlr; Mrchg Band; Amer Lgn Cert Of Schl Awd 85.

ABBOTT, BRUCE; Dunmore HS; Dunmore, PA; (3); 7/148; French Clb; Spanish Clb; Chorus; Nwsp Rptr; Nwsp Stf; Yrbk Rptr; Yrbk Stf; High Hon Roll; NHS; Voice Dem Awd; Marywood Coll; Comm.

ABBOTT, CHERYL; Chambersburg Area SR HS; Chambersburg, PA; (2); French Clb; Hon Roll; Shippensburg U; Accntng.

ABBOTT, JOSEPHINE; Turkeyfoot Valley Area HS; Confluence, PA; (4); 1/57; Drama Clb; Q&S; Chorus; Capt Color Guard; Nwsp Sprt Ed; Yrbk Stf; Co-Capt Cheerleading; High Hon Roll; Lion Awd; Trs NHS; Spnsh I Awd 84-85; Typng I & Ii Awd 84-86; Prep Eng Awd 84-85; Spec Educ.

ABBOTT, KRISTEN; Uniontown HS; Smock, PA; (4); French Clb; Letterman Clb; SADD; Yrbk Stf; VP Frsh Cls; JV Bsktbl; Var L Sftbl; Var L Tennis; French Hon Soc; High Hon Roll; PA ST; Psych.

ABDEL-MASSIH, SALLY; Beaver JR SR HS; Beaver, PA; (4); 29/200; Church Yth Grp; Spanish Clb; SADD; High Hon Roll; Hon Roll; Mgmt Info Sys.

ABDULLAH, CRYSTAL; West Philadelphia HS; Phila, PA; (2); High Hon Roll; Hon Roll; Spanish NHS; Sclgy.

ABEL, RANDY J; Mohawk HS; Bessemer, PA; (3); Church Yth Grp; Drama Clb; French Clb; Band; Chorus; Church Choir; Concert Band; Jazz Band; Mrchg Band; Pep Band; Penn St U; Photo.

ABELEDA, MARIA; Cedar Crest HS; Lebanon, PA; (4); 5/312; French Clb; Pep Clb; Orch; School Musical; Cit Awd; High Hon Roll; Hon Roll; NHS; Rotary Awd; Presdntl Acad Fit Awd 87; Most Outstndng Strng Plyr Orch 84-87; Booster Club Schlrshp 83-87; U PA; Med.

ABNETT, WADE; Mechanicsburg HS; Mechanicsburg, PA; (3); 76/338; Boy Scts; Church Yth Grp; Ski Clb; Trk; High Hon Roll; Hon Roll; SOC Sci.

ABNEY, JONAS V; Central HS; Philadelphia, PA; (3); Church Yth Grp; Cmnty Wkr; Debate Tm; French Clb; Intnl Clb; Model UN; Office Aide; Socr; Wrstlng; Hon Roll; 2nd Pl Phila Elctrc Co Debate Enrgy 87.

ABPLANALP, DENNIS; Warren Area HS; Warren, PA; (3); Church Yth Grp; French Clb; Ski Clb; Church Choir; High Hon Roll; Hon Roll; Slvr B Awd 85; PA ST U; Engr.

ABRAHAM, COLLEEN; Vincentian HS; Wexford, PA; (3); 14/73; Hosp Aide; JA; NFL; Service Clb; Spanish Clb; Band; Chorus; Rep Jr Cls; NHS; Ntl Engl Merit Awd 86; Ntl Stu Cncl Awd 86; Psychlgy.

ABRAHAM, JAMES; Vincentian HS; Wexford, PA; (2); Boy Scts; Rep Soph Cls; High Hon Roll; Carnegie Museum Natural Hist Sci Awd 86; Hgh GPA Bio, Eng MWCIC 86; Bio.

ABRAHAM, JENNIFER; Fairchance-Georges HS; Fairchance, PA; (3); Church Yth Grp; Library Aide; Spanish Clb; Yrbk Stf; High Hon Roll; Hon Roll; Pres Schlr; WVU.

ABRAHAM, JOSEPH; New Castle SR HS; New Castle, PA; (3); 9/290; Church Yth Grp; Cmnty Wkr; Letterman Clb; Math Tm; NFL; Spanish Clb; Varsity Clb; Nwsp Rptr; Var Tennis; High Hon Roll; Engrng.

ABRAHAM, MANJU; Pennsbury HS; Yardley, PA; (3); Church Yth Grp; French Clb; Church Choir; Yrbk Stf; Hon Roll; Stu Of Month 85 & 86; Presdntl Acad Ftnss Awd 86; Pre-Med.

ABRAMOWICH, PATRICK; Shanksville-Stonycreek HS; Stoystown, PA; (4); 1/37; Pres Chess Clb; Capt Scholastic Bowl; School Play; Yrbk Ed-Chief; VP Sr Cls; VP Stu Cncl; Var L Bsbl; Var L Bsktbl; VP NHS; Val; Ntl Rural Elctrc Yth Tour 86; Hugh O Brien Yth Ldrshp Smnr 85; Amer Lgn Essay Cntst Wnr 85; Frkln Coll; Lawyer.

ABRAMS, AUDREY; Bensalem HS; Bensalem, PA; (2); Spanish Clb; SADD; Var Swmmng; JV Tennis; Gymnstcs Awd 84; Swmmng Awd 87; U Of PA; Law.

ABRAMS, DEBORAH; Marple Newtown HS; Broomall, PA; (3); 4/323; Girl Scts; Service Clb; Temple Yth Grp; Nwsp Stf; Yrbk Stf; Rep Stu Cncl; Mgr(s); High Hon Roll; NHS.

ABRAMS, JUDY; Northern Cambria HS; Spangler, PA; (3); French Clb; Band; Concert Band; Jazz Band; Mrchg Band; JV Vllybl; Amer Musical Fndtn Band Hnres 87; JR All Amer Hall Of Fame Band Hnrs 87; Cert Of Merit/Cert Achvt.

ABRAMS, MICHAEL; State College HS; State College, PA; (2); Band; Concert Band; Nwsp Stf; Yrbk Phtg; Yrbk Stf; Hon Roll; Intrvw For Govs Schl 87; Wrtng.

ABRAMS, SHANNON; Northern Cambria HS; Spangler, PA; (3); Drama Clb; FHA; Ski Clb; Teachers Aide; Chorus; Variety Show; Yrbk Stf; Sec Jr Cls; Var Cheerleading; Ntl Merit SF; Fshn.

ABRAMS, STACI; Plymouth Whitemarsh HS; Lafayette Hill, PA; (3); 25/390; Office Aide; Off Jr Cls; Vllybl; High Hon Roll.

ABRAMS, SUSAN; Wyoming Valley West HS; Kingston, PA; (2); 5/437; Key Clb; Pres Latin Clb; Nwsp Stf; Mgr Swmmng; Tennis; Cit Awd; High Hon Roll; NHS; NEDT Awd; Hstry Day Fair 3rd Pl 87; Kingston Rtry 1st Pl Peace Ltr 86; Ltn II; Hghst Cls Avg 86; Tchng.

ABRAMSON, BECKY; Wilmington Area HS; Pulaski, PA; (3); Drama Clb; French Clb; Variety Show; Hon Roll; Accntng.

ABRETSKE, BRENDA; Springdale HS; Harwick, PA; (3); Cmnty Wkr; Exploring; Acpl Chr; Chorus; School Musical; Nwsp Rptr; High Hon Roll; Hon Roll; NHS; Hgh Hnr Awd 85-86; Spnsh Diploma Merit 86; Engl.

ABREU, TABATHA; Garden Spot HS; E Earl, PA; (2); 30/226; Chorus; Rep Jr Cls; Cheerleading; Mgr(s); Score Keeper; Tennis; Trk; High Hon Roll; Hon Roll; Bus.

ABROMOVAGE, HEATHER; Wyoming Area SR HS; Wyoming, PA; (3); Key Clb; Ski Clb; Spanish Clb; Chorus; Sec Frsh Cls; Sec Jr Cls; Sec Sr Cls; Var Trk; Fshn Merch.

ABUK, ROY; Valley Forge Military Acad; Kinnelon, NJ; (3); Computer Clb; ROTC; Drill Tm; VP Frsh Cls; Rep Stu Cncl; Im Wt Lftg; Var Wrstlng; High Hon Roll; Hon Roll; Val; ROTC Awd Merit 85; Acdmc Excllnc Schlrshp 85-88; Hnr Course Scheduling 85-88; Penn ST; Political Sci.

ACCARDI, DANA; Pequea Valley HS; Ronks, PA; (3); Dance Clb; FBLA; Chorus; High Hon Roll; Hon Roll; NHS; Acctng.

ACCIAI, JOANN; Lackawanna Trl HS; Factoryville, PA; (4); 1/86; Scholastic Bowl; Yrbk Phtg; Rep Badmtn; Bausch & Lomb Sci Awd; NHS; Val; U Of PA; Biochem.

ACCULTO, LORI; Dunmore HS; Dunmore, PA; (3); 10/147; Drama Clb; French Clb; Ski Clb; Spanish Clb; School Play; Yrbk Stf; Capt Cheerleading; Var Trk; High Hon Roll; NHS; Pharmacy.

ACHENNE, NICOLE; Burrell HS; Lower Burrell, PA; (3); French Clb; JA; Chorus; Co-Capt Color Guard; High Hon Roll; Hon Roll; Jr NHS.

ACHEY, CHARLEEN; Bensalem HS; Bensalem, PA; (2); Church Yth Grp; Key Clb; Band; Concert Band; Mrchg Band; Stage Crew; Stu Cncl; High Hon Roll; NHS; Engrng.

ACHTER, HANS; Cowanesque Valley HS; Westfield, PA; (3); 5/80; Chess Clb; High Hon Roll; NHS; Pres Schlr; Cv Schlstc Achiev Awd 84-86.

ACHUFF, JIM; Upper Darby HS; Primos, PA; (3); 21/600; Boy Scts; Church Choir; Concert Band; Jazz Band; Orch; Lit Mag; JV L Bowling; Var Capt Swmmng; High Hon Roll; VA Polytech Inst; Aero Engrng.

ACKARD, DIANN M; State College Area SR HS; State College, PA; (4) 41/541; Sec French Clb; Acpl Chr; Pres Concert Band; Jazz Band; Orch Swing Chorus; Nwsp Stf; Hon Roll; NHS; NEDT Awd; Hege Awd Outstndng Mscnshp 87; U Of MN; Psych.

ACKER, BRETT; Council Rock HS; Churchville, PA; (3); Var Socr; Cit Awd; High Hon Roll; Hon Roll; NHS; Hghst German Avg Awd 87 American U; Intl Stds.

ACKER, KELLI; Central Cambria HS; Ebensburg, PA; (3); #1 In Class Dance Clb; 4-H; NFL; Ski Clb; Concert Band; Drm Mjr(t); Mrchg Band Stu Cncl; Cheerleading; High Hon Roll; Mst Outstndng Chrldr 85; Bst Drm Major 86; Dance Awd 84, 85 & 86; Penn ST; Bus.

ACKERMAN, CHERYL; S Williamsport Area SR HS; S Williamsport PA; (3); 1/111; Letterman Clb; Pep Clb; VP Soph Cls; Stu Cncl; Var Capt Cheerleading; Var L Trk; Cit Awd; High Hon Roll; Jr NHS; NHS; Amer Lgn Aux Awd 85-86; Math.

ACKERMAN, CHRISTINE; Abington Heights HS; Clarks Summit, PA (4); 16/260; Sec 4-H; Orch; School Musical; Symp Band; 4-H Awd; Hon Roll; NHS; 4 Dist & 2 Rgnl Orch Fest 83-87; 3 County, 2 Dist 1 St 4-H Comp Equestrian 84-86; PA ST U; Chem Engrng.

ACKERMAN, CHRISTINE N; St Huberts HS; Philadelphia, PA; (4) 112/364; Hosp Aide; Spanish Clb; Yrbk Stf; Cheerleading; Gym; Hon Roll Frankford Nursing Schl; Nrsng.

ACKERMAN, PETER; Danville Area HS; Danville, PA; (2); Rep Stu Cncl; L Ftbl; L Wrstlng; High Hon Roll; Pre Law.

ACKERMAN, R CHRISTIAN; Danville Area HS; Danville, PA; (4); Pres Sr Cls; Capt Wrstlng; Nwsp Stf; Yrbk Sprt Ed; Rep Soph Cls; Rep Jr Cls Socr; Hon Roll; Walter Mensch Schlr/Athlt Awd 87; P & D Schooley Schlrshp Awd-Outstndng Wrstlr 87; US Military Acad.

ACKINCLOSE, LORI; Frazier HS; Fayette City, PA; (4); 2/130; FNA Hon Roll; NHS; Sal; Schlrshp-Ntl Hnr Soc 87; Top Ten Stu 87; Presdntl Ftnss Awd 87; Penn ST U.

ACKINCLOSE, TIM; Frazier HS; Fayette City, PA; (4); Nwsp Rptr Bsktbl; DAR Awd; High Hon Roll; Acad All Amer 86-87; Mst Lkly To Succeed 87; CA U Of PA; Hstry Tchr.

ACKLEY, ANNE; Danville SR HS; Danville, PA; (3); Church Yth Grp Drama Clb; French Clb; Intnl Clb; Hst Pres Key Clb; School Play; Stage Crew; Yrbk Stf; JV Trk; Comp.

ACKLIN II, TIMOTHY PATRICK; Central Catholic HS; Pittsburgh PA; (3); 17/260; Trs Church Yth Grp; Cmnty Wkr; Letterman Clb; Ski Clb JV Bsbl; Var L Ice Hcky; French Hon Soc; High Hon Roll; NHS; Acdmc Cert Excllnc Awd 85-87; Cmmnctns.

ACORD, TRACY; Plum HS; Pittsburgh, PA; (3); 22/410; Drill Tm; JV Bsktbl; JV Vllybl; High Hon Roll; NHS; Hgh Math Awd; Tele Cmnctns.

ACOSTA, FELIX; The Christian Acad; Chester, PA; (4); Church Yth Grp; Debate Tm; Acpl Chr; Chorus; Pres Stu Cncl; Crs Cntry; Trk; Hon Roll; Seton Hall U; Hstry.

ACQUAROLO, MICHAEL; St John Neumann HS; Philadelphia, PA (4); 9/335; Computer Clb; French Clb; Latin Clb; Math Clb; Rep Stu Cncl Bsbl; Var L Bowling; French Hon Soc; High Hon Roll; Hon Roll; Schlrshp Awd 87; Temple U; Brdcstr.

ACRI, DEBRA; Hazelton HS; Hazleton, PA; (3); 23/450; Hosp Aide Office Aide; Pep Clb; Ski Clb; Thesps; Chorus; Nwsp Stf; Cheerleading Tennis; High Hon Roll; U Of Scranton; Phys Thrpy.

ADAIR, JENNIFER; General Mc Lane HS; Edinboro, PA; (4); 12/182 Model UN; Teachers Aide; Jazz Band; Capt Mrchg Band; Symp Band Hon Roll; JP Sousa Awd; NHS; Norman Schrivers Awd 87; Gen Mc Lane Educ Assoc Awd 87; Dorothy Clifford Awd 87; Edinboro U; Scndry Ed.

ADAIR, JOHN; Valley Forge Military Acad; Baltimore, MD; (4); Boy Scts; Computer Clb; Letterman Clb; Varsity Clb; Chorus; Church Choir Nwsp Stf; Pres Frsh Cls; God Cntry Awd; High Hon Roll; Cum Laude Hnr Grad 87; Exprmnt Intl Lvng Switzerland 85; Natl Yth Ldrshp Cnfrnc 87 Naval Acad; Nautcl Engnrng.

ADAIR, ROY S; Greensburg Salem SR HS; Greensburg, PA; (3); 58/302 FFA; Chorus; Bsktbl; Trk; Grnhd Awd 86-87; Penn ST; Ldscp Dsgnr.

ADAM, GINA; Oley Valley HS; Fleetwood, PA; (3); 11/138; Drama Clb JA; Library Aide; Pep Clb; Chorus; School Musical; Nwsp Rptr; Nwsp Stf Yrbk Stf; Var L Trk.

ADAM, JAMIE; Hamburg Area HS; Hamburg, PA; (3); Latin Clb Bausch & Lomb Sci Awd; Cit Awd; High Hon Roll; NHS; Pres Acad Ftns Awd 84-85; Acad Ltr Awd-Chem 85-86; Acad Ltr Awd-Alg III, Trig 86-87 Pre-Med.

ADAMCHIK, TRACY; Hempfield SR HS; Greensburg, PA; (3); Art Clb Church Yth Grp; VP 4-H; Hosp Aide; Band; Chorus; Church Choir Concert Band; Mrchg Band; 4-H Awd; Ribbns Shwg Hrse 84-87; Elem Ed.

ADAMEK, MICHAEL; Northern York County HS; Dillsburg, PA; (4) 105/229; Church Yth Grp; DECA; Varsity Clb; Coach Actv; Ftbl; Wrstlng Mr Crgs Awd 87; Harrisburg Area CC; CPA.

ADAMETZ, KAREN JEAN; Richland HS; Wexford, PA; (4); 43/183 Chorus; School Musical; School Play; Sec Swing Chorus; Variety Show Var Capt Cheerleading; Powder Puff Ftbl; High Hon Roll; Hon Roll Library Aide; Floyd Johnson Schlrshp 87; Slippery Rock U; Acctnt.

ADAMO, ANTHONY; Tunkahannock Area HS; Tunkhannock, PA; (4); 4/280; Pres Church Yth Grp; Key Clb; Trs Letterman Clb; Band; Pres Stu Cncl; Capt Var Crs Cntry; JV Var Trk; Gov Hon Prg Awd; Kiwanis Awd NHS; Natl Cncl Yth Ldrshp 86; Grad PA Gov Schl Of Agri 86; Dist II Trck & Fld Rec 83-85; U Of PA; Chem Engrng.

ADAMROVICH, DOUGLAS; Mt Pleasant Area HS; Mount Pleasant PA; (4); 85/250; German Clb; Capt Bsbl; Capt Ftbl; Wt Lftg; Hon Roll; All Dist Frst Tm Ftbll 86 & 87; Pittsburh Pst Gztt & Prs Ftbl 87; IN U; Hlth Ed.

ADAMS, AMY; Lackawanna Trail HS; Factoryville, PA; (3); Debate Tm Girl Scts; Hosp Aide; Var Crs Cntry; JV Var Fld Hcky; Var Sftbl; Twrlr Hon Roll; NHS; Rotary Awd; Intl Studies.

ADAMS, ASHLEY; Fairview HS; Fairview, PA; (3); Church Yth Grp Pres French Clb; Model UN; Q&S; Nwsp Ed-Chief; Yrbk Stf; Var L Socr Hon Roll; NHS; Ski Clb; Erie Philharmonic Youth Orchestra 85-86 Communications.

ADAMS, BERTHAJO; Sullivan County HS; Dushore, PA; (3); Church Yth Grp; Ski Clb; Flag Corp; School Play; Bsktbl; Crs Cntry; Sftbl; Vllybl NHS; Rotary Awd.

ADAMS, BETH; Moon SR HS; Coraopolis, PA; (3); French Clb; JA; Stage Crew; Yrbk Stf; High Hon Roll; Acadmc Achvt Ltr 84-85; Pilot.

ADAMS, BETH ANN; Dallas SR HS; Dallas, PA; (4); 8/248; Drama Clb Chorus; Pres Madrigals; School Musical; Nwsp Rptr; JV Cheerleading; Var Fld Hcky; NHS; Pres Schlr.

ADAMS, BRADFORD; Altoona Area HS; Altoona, PA; (4); 95/750 English Clb; JA; Ski Clb; Spanish Clb; Im Bsktbl; Im Ftbl; Im Vllybl Chess Clb; Lit Mag; Im Badmtn; Comp Scholar Du Quesne U 87; PA Tchrs Engl Essay Cont 87; Du Quesne U; Jrnlsm.

ADAMS, BRIAN; Connellsville SR HS; Connellsville, PA; (3); Church Yth Grp; Radio Clb; Off Stu Cncl; JV Wrstlng; Hon Roll; Vo-Tech Schl Parlimentarian 85-87; Penn ST; Law.

ADAMS, CARIANNE; Bishop Guilfoyle HS; Altoona, PA; (3); Spanish Clb; SADD; Chorus; Church Choir; Variety Show; Yrbk Stf; Im Bsktbl; JV Capt Cheerleading; Cit Awd; High Hon Roll; Bio.

ADAMS, CAROLYN; St Basil Acad; Huntingdon Vly, PA; (3); 10/83; Cmnty Wkr; Drama Clb; French Clb; GAA; Off Frsh Cls; Pres Soph Cls; JV Capt Bsktbl; Var Socr; Hon Roll; Penn ST; Bus.

ADAMS, CARRIE; Gettysburg SR HS; Gettysburg, PA; (4); FCA; Teachers Aide; Rep Frsh Cls; VP Sr Cls; Stat Bsktbl; Var Capt Fld Hcky; High Hon Roll; Hon Roll; Exch Stu Mnth; Gettysburg Area Ed Assn Scholar; Messiah Coll; Elem Ed.

ADAMS, CHARLAINE; Keystone HS; Shippenville, PA; (4); Church Yth Grp; DECA; Office Aide; Chorus; High Hon Roll; Hon Roll; Prfct Atten Awd; DECA 2nd Pl Mock Dist 86-87; Hstry Awd 83-84; Prncpls Lst 86-87; Clarion U; Wk Chldrn.

ADAMS, CHRIS; Central Catholic HS; Fleetwood, PA; (3); Church Yth Grp; German Clb; Letterman Clb; Ski Clb; Varsity Clb; Chorus; School Play; Var Bsbl; Var Ftbl; Hon Roll; Athlete Of Week Awd 86; All County Schlstc Ftbll Awd 86; U Of SC; Mktg.

ADAMS, CHRISTOPHER M; Chambersburg Area SR HS; Fayetteville, PA; (4); Off JCL; Sec NFL; Sec Speech Tm; Chorus; Lit Mag; Hon Roll; Ntl Merit SF; Haverford Coll; Cllscs Prof.

ADAMS, DAN; Trinity Area HS; Washington, PA; (3); 40/402; Pep Clb; Spanish Clb; School Play; Var Bsbl; Var Golf; Hon Roll; All Dist Bsbl Tm Ptchr 87.

ADAMS, DEAN; Cumberland Valley HS; Camp Hill, PA; (3); 32/597; Acpl Chr; Chorus; Orch; School Musical; School Play; Swing Chorus; Variety Show; Crs Cntry; Hon Roll; NHS; Pre-Med.

ADAMS, ERICA; Phila H S For Girls; Philadelphia, PA; (3); Boy Scts; Camp Fr Inc; Teachers Aide; Varsity Clb; Stu Cncl; Crs Cntry; Trk; Law.

ADAMS, GREGORY; Tunkhannock Area HS; Mehoopany, PA; (4); 63/265; Exploring; 4-H; FFA; Office Aide; Varsity Clb; JV Wrstlng; 4-H Awd; High Hon Roll; PAFC 2 Yr Schlr; Wldlfe Tech.

ADAMS, HOLLY; Central SR HS; York, PA; (3); Ski Clb; Varsity Clb; Rep Frsh Cls; Rep Soph Cls; Rep Jr Cls; Rep Stu Cncl; Capt Var Crs Cntry; Capt Var Trk; Engrng.

ADAMS, HOLLY; German SR HS; Leckrone, PA; (4); 23/85; Hosp Aide; Library Aide; Band; Concert Band; Mrchg Band; Yrbk Stf; Sec Soph Cls; Sec Jr Cls; Hon Roll; Waynesburg Coll; Nrsng.

ADAMS, JAMES; Everett HS; Clearville, PA; (3); FFA; VICA; Prfct Atten Awd.

ADAMS, JENNIFER; Chambersburg Area SR HS; Fayetteville, PA; (2); 41/735; Hst JCL; Chorus; Orch; Off Soph Cls; JV Cheerleading; Hon Roll.

ADAMS, JILL; Wyoming Valley West HS; Kingston, PA; (3); 40/350; Cmnty Wkr; French Clb; Pep Clb; Radio Clb; Ski Clb; Rep Stu Cncl; JV Var Cheerleading; Cit Awd; Hon Roll; NHS; Elem Ed.

ADAMS, JODI; Hamburg Area HS; Shoemakersville, PA; (4); 58/150; Library Aide; Spanish Clb; SADD; Hon Roll; Kutztown U; Elem Educ.

ADAMS, JOE; Central HS; E Freedom, PA; (3); Ski Clb; Varsity Clb; Chorus; Im Bsktbl; Var Ftbl; L Trk; High Hon Roll; Hon Roll; NHS; PA ST U; Software Engr.

ADAMS, JOHN; Central HS; Scranton, PA; (3); 40/350; Ski Clb; JV Bsbl; Comp Sci.

ADAMS, KAREN; Mechanicsburg SR HS; Shiremanstown, PA; (3); 33/352; FFA; Chorus; Sftbl; Hon Roll; 1st Pl Amer Rose Scty Art Arrang 87; Stu Qrtr Alg I 85-86; Stu Qrtr Geometry 86-87; Florist.

ADAMS, KATHY; Hamburg Area HS; Shoemakersvl, PA; (3); French Clb; Latin Clb; Ski Clb; SADD; Band; Hon Roll; Lebanan Vlly Coll; Bio.

ADAMS, KELLI; Moniteau HS; Harrisville, PA; (3); 16/136; Drama Clb; Exploring; Spanish Clb; SADD; Nwsp Stf; Lit Mag; Var L Trk; Var L Vllybl; Hon Roll; NHS; Photo.

ADAMS, KELLY; Portage Area HS; Portage, PA; (3); 26/112; Varsity Clb; Capt Color Guard; Sec Soph Cls; Stu Cncl; Var L Bsktbl; Twrlr; Hon Roll; Dent Asst.

ADAMS, KIP; Cowanesque Valley HS; Knoxville, PA; (3); #2 In Class; Letterman Clb; School Musical; Yrbk Phtg; Stu Cncl; Bsktbl; Ftbl; High Hon Roll; Hon Roll; NHS; Pres Schlr; Lnora B Clrk-Hstry-Awd 83; Presdntl Acadmc Physcl Ftnss Awd 85; Acadmc FFH Awd 84; Penn ST; Wldlf Sci.

ADAMS, MARSHA; Northwestern SR HS; Albion, PA; (3); Band; Concert Band; Mrchg Band; Pep Band; Cheerleading; Powder Puff Ftbl; Trk; Sales Mgmt.

ADAMS, MIKE; Athens Area HS; Milan, PA; (3); Art Clb; Bsbl; Bsktbl; Ftbl; Trk.

ADAMS, MONICA; Northwestern HS; Albion, PA; (2); 15/167; Library Aide; Color Guard; Drill Tm; Mrchg Band; Yrbk Stf; Sec Jr Cls; Var Trk; Hon Roll; Law.

ADAMS, PAM; Upper Dauphin HS; Lykens, PA; (4); 18/111; Pres Church Yth Grp; Soroptimist; Band; Chorus; Drm Mjr(t); Yrbk Bus Mgr; Pres Stu Cncl; VFW Awd; Drunk Driving Slogan Wnnr 85; Order Eastern Star Awd, Miss Christian Seal 87; U WV; Pol Sci.

ADAMS, PATRICIA; Dallas HS; Dallas, PA; (3); Church Yth Grp; Cmnty Wkr; Drama Clb; Hosp Aide; Chorus; Church Choir; Drill Tm; School Musical; School Play; Nwsp Stf; Bloomsburg U; Chld Devlpmt.

ADAMS, PATRICK; Bethlehem Catholic HS; Bethlehem, PA; (3); 19/203; Pres Stu Cncl; Var L Bsbl; Var L Ftbl; Var L Wrstlng; High Hon Roll; Trs NHS; Ntl Merit Ltr; Med.

ADAMS, RACHEL; Penn Trafford HS; Trafford, PA; (3); AFS; Church Yth Grp; Drama Clb; Hosp Aide; JCL; Acpl Chr; Band; Drm Mjr(t); Mrchg Band; Orch; All ST Band 87; Genetic Engrng.

ADAMS, RICHARD; Strong Vincent HS; Erie, PA; (4); 20/160; Var L Bsbl; Var L Bsktbl; Hon Roll; NHS; Penn ST Behrend; Bus.

ADAMS, SCOTT; Elizabethtown Area HS; Elizabethtown, PA; (3); 19/250; Varsity Clb; Var JV Bsbl; Var JV Bsktbl; Hon Roll; NHS; Bus.

ADAMS, SCOTT; Hempfield HS; Lancaster, PA; (4); 5/418; Rep Church Yth Grp; Church Choir; Mrchg Band; Hon Roll; NHS; Ntl Merit Ltr; Pres Schlr; Armstrong World Industries Schlrshp 87; Univ Schlrshp-VA Tech 87; 2nd Pl Physics Sci Fair 87; VA Polytech Inst; Architecture.

ADAMS, SHARI; Warren Area HS; Warren, PA; (4); 10/270; Acpl Chr; Band; Concert Band; Mrchg Band; Orch; School Musical; Cit Awd; High Hon Roll; NHS; Pres Schlr; Phlml Msc Schlrshp 87; Ntl Hstry Day Rgnl & ST Lvl 82-87; Msc Bstr Awd & Schlrshp 87; U Rchmnd; Chmstry.

ADAMS, STACEY; Somerset SR HS; Somerset, PA; (4); 28/234; English Clb; French Clb; Q&S; Varsity Clb; Variety Show; Yrbk Stf; Cheerleading; High Hon Roll; Hon Roll; NHS; Penn ST U; Lbrl Arts.

ADAMS, STACY; Elizabeth Forward SR HS; Elizabeth, PA; (2); Church Yth Grp; Drama Clb; French Clb; Girl Scts; Chorus; Church Choir; Yrbk Rptr; JV Sftbl; Var Swmmng; JV Vllybl; Duke U; Pblc Rltns.

ADAMS, TAMMY; Canon Mc Millan HS; Strabane, PA; (4); 20/357; French Clb; Ski Clb; Flag Corp; Im Vllybl; High Hon Roll; Ntl Merit Ltr; U Of Pittsburgh Merit Schlrshp 87; U Of Pittsburgh.

ADAMS, TAMMY; Danville SR HS; Danville, PA; (1); Church Yth Grp; Chorus; School Musical; Hon Roll; Vet.

ADAMS, TANYA; Carmichaels Area HS; Carmichaels, PA; (1); 9/130; DAR Awd; Jr NHS; Prsdntl Acdmc Ftnss Awd 86-87; Penn ST; Law.

ADAMS, TIMOTHY; North Hills HS; Pittsburgh, PA; (4); 7/467; Church Yth Grp; German Clb; Key Clb; Ski Clb; Rep Frsh Cls; JV Bsktbl; Var Tennis; High Hon Roll; NHS; Finance.

ADAMS, TYRESE; Harrisburg HS; Harrisburg, PA; (3); 11/297; Church Yth Grp; Girl Scts; Speech Tm; Band; Chorus; Church Choir; Concert Band; Jazz Band; Mrchg Band; Orch; Psych.

ADAMSKI, MICHAEL; Father Judge HS; Philadelphia, PA; (3); 3/402; Nwsp Sprt Ed; Nwsp Stf; Yrbk Phtg; Yrbk Stf; Lit Mag; DAR Awd; NHS; Cmnty Wkr; German Clb; Nwsp Rptr; Temple; Corp Law.

ADAMSON, C SCOTT; Waynesburg Central HS; Brave, PA; (3); 1/210; Church Yth Grp; 4-H; Letterman Clb; Var Wrstlng; French Hon Soc; High Hon Roll; NHS; French Clb; Bsbl; Var L Crs Cntry; Sci Awd, Frnch I Awd, Cvc Awd 85; Wrld Cltr Awd, Frnch Ii Awd 86; Eng Awd, Chem Awd, Frnch Iii Awd 87; Chem.

ADAMSON, KAREN; Springdale HS; Cheswick, PA; (3); 14/136; Church Yth Grp; GAA; Trs Spanish Clb; Capt Color Guard; Pres Jr Cls; Var JV Sftbl; High Hon Roll; Hon Roll; NHS; Band; Outstndng Clsrm Prfrmnc Awd Geom 85-86, Alg II 86-87; Maps Cert Achvt U Pittsbrgh 85-86; Hmcmng Rep; Math.

ADAMSON, SCOTT; Waynesburg Central HS; Brave, PA; (3); 1/200; Crs Cntry; Wrstlng; Cit Awd; Dnfth Awd; French Hon Soc; High Hon Roll; NEDT Awd; 4-H; French Clb; Letterman Clb; Frnch Clb, Sci, Phy Ftns Awds 84-85; Frnch II, Bio, Wrld Cltrs Awds NEDT 85-86; Phrmcy.

ADDEO, MARK; Ridgeway Area HS; Ridgway, PA; (4); 8/105; Ski Clb; Pres Jr Cls; Bsbl; Ftbl; High Hon Roll; Schlr Athlt Awd 86; Penn ST; Engrng.

ADDIS, JOHN; Bradford Area HS; Derrick City, PA; (4); Am Leg Boys St; Key Clb; Ski Clb; L Capt Ftbl; L Trk; Wt Lftg; L Capt Wrstlng; High Hon Roll; Hon Roll; N W Conf All Star Dist IX All Star Ftbl 87; Dist IX Hvywght Chmpn Wrstlng 87; Cornell U; Law.

ADE, DOUG; Loyalsock Township HS; Montoursville, PA; (3); 30/108; French Clb; Key Clb; Letterman Clb; Varsity Clb; Bsktbl; Coach Actv; Golf.

ADELMAN, LAURIE; Mercyhurst Prep Schl; Erie, PA; (3); Church Yth Grp; Yrbk Rptr; Yrbk Stf; Rep Soph Cls; Rep Stu Cncl; Teen Action Clb 84-87; Vlntr Tchr Church Catechism 85-87; Schl Intermurls 84-87; Bus Adm.

ADELMAN, MITCHELL; HS For Engineering & Science; Phila, PA; (3); 25/350; Fld Hcky; Hon Roll; NHS; Alpha Delta Kappa La Gamma Chaptr Wrtng Portfolio Comptn 87; WCAU-AMS Radio Classics Theater Comptn; Engrng.

ADELSTEIN, SHARON; Upper Dublin SR HS; Ft Washington, PA; (3); 68/283; Temple Yth Grp; Band; Concert Band; Mrchg Band; Orch; School Musical; Lit Mag; Hon Roll; Gratz Hebrew HS Scholar 86; Amer Music Abrd HI 86.

ADER, MARGIE; Pennsbury HS; Yardley, PA; (4); 19/777; Intnl Clb; Service Clb; Teachers Aide; Pres Temple Yth Grp; Chorus; JC Awd; NHS; Cmnty Wkr; SADD; School Musical; YWCA Teen Recognition Awd 87; Pennsbury Schlrshp Awd 87; Pres Acad Fit Awd 87; Bucknell U; Teaching.

ADEY, STUART; Cedar Crest HS; Rexmont, PA; (2); 129/337; Am Leg Boys St; Church Yth Grp; Drama Clb; Letterman Clb; Pep Clb; Spanish Clb; Varsity Clb; School Musical; School Play; Variety Show; AZ ST; Tchr Ed.

ADLESIC, DIANA; Shaler Area HS; Allison Pk, PA; (3); 83/486; Church Yth Grp; Hosp Aide; Ski Clb; SADD; Stat Socr; Educ.

ADOMAITIS, MICHELLE; Cedar Crest HS; Lebanon, PA; (3); Library Aide; Office Aide; Spanish Clb; Teachers Aide; Chorus; Rep Stu Cncl; Im Swmmng; Im Trk; Im Wt Lftg; Cert Merit Creatv Wrtng 87.

ADOMAITIS, TERI; Seneca Valley SR HS; Zelienople, PA; (4); Office Aide; SADD; Thesps; Color Guard; School Musical; School Play; Lit Mag; Hon Roll; Ins.

ADOMITIS, MELISSA; Wyoming Area HS; W Wyoming, PA; (4); 34/250; Drama Clb; French Clb; Key Clb; Nwsp Stf; Crs Cntry; High Hon Roll; Hon Roll; NHS; Robert Capin Memrl Acctg Schlrshp 87; Deans Schlrshp 87; Wilkes Coll; Acctg.

ADOMSHICK, PAUL; Penn-Trafford HS; Trafford, PA; (4); 5/340; Trs JCL; Trs Latin Clb; Band; Concert Band; Jazz Band; Mrchg Band; School Musical; High Hon Roll; NHS; Ntl Merit Ltr; Prsdntl Acdmc Ftnss Awd 87; Outstndng Cmptr Stu Of Yr 87; Pnn Trffrd Hi-Q Tm Mbr 87; PA ST U; Mech Engnrng.

ADZENTOIVICH, ERNEST J; Mahanoy Area HS; New Boston, PA; (4); 1/110; VP Aud/Vis; Ski Clb; Spanish Clb; Jazz Band; School Play; L Ftbl; Wrstlng; Hon Roll; NHS; Val; Rotry Schlrshp 87; Berklee Coll; Music.

AESCHBACH, DAWN; Dallas HS; Trucksville, PA; (3); Aud/Vis; German Clb; Band; Chorus; JV Cheerleading; Hon Roll; Bus.

AFFLECK, JOHN R; North Allegheny SR HS; Bradford Woods, PA; (2); 41/630; Boy Scts; Church Yth Grp; Mrchg Band; God Cntry Awd.

AFFLERBACH, MICHAEL; Quakertow Community HS; Quakertown, PA; (2); 43/325; Boy Scts; Ftbl; Trk; Wt Lftg; High Hon Roll; Hon Roll; Elec Engr.

AFFLERBACH, PETER; Parkland SR HS; Allentown, PA; (2); Key Clb; School Play; Stu Cncl; Socr; Swmmng; Tennis; Hon Roll; NHS; Pres Acad Ftns Awd 85; Bus Admin.

AFLALO, SHAWN; William Allen HS; Allentown, PA; (3); 155/659; Leo Clb; Ski Clb; Yrbk Stf; Hon Roll; Martin Goldman Fellowship Awd 86-87; Accntnt.

AFONSO, ALBERT; St John Neumann HS; Philadelphia, PA; (3); 25/359; Chorus; Socr; Swmmng; Tennis; Hon Roll; NHS; Drexel; Bus.

AFTON, DAVID; Brookville Area HS; Brookville, PA; (3); Boy Scts; Chess Clb; German Clb; ROTC; Ski Clb; Ftbl; Law.

AGAMEDI, MARY KATHRYN; Belle Vernon Area HS; Smithton, PA; (3); Debate Tm; Library Aide; Model UN; NFL; Pep Clb; Ed Nwsp Rptr; Yrbk Rptr; L Swmmng; High Hon Roll; NHS; Dgr Of Exc In Ntl Frnscs Lg 87; 4th Pl Wmns Clb ST Wrtng Cntst 87; Seton Hl Coll Grnbrg; Englsh.

AGARWAL, AJAY; Fox Chapel Area HS; Pittsburgh, PA; (4); 1/320; Math Tm; Ski Clb; Orch; Nwsp Stf; Var Tennis; NHS; Ntl Merit SF; Grand Prz Wnnr Essy Contst 86; 2nd Pl & Wnnr Schlrshp At U Of Pittsburgh Provost Day 86; Engineering.

AGERS, SIAN; The Christian Acad; Wilmington, DE; (3); 3/70; Acpl Chr; Chorus; School Play; Sec Stu Cncl; Var JV Cheerleading; Tennis; High Hon Roll; NHS; Church Yth Grp; Drama Clb; Chem Awd 86; Eurpn Hstry Awd 85; Stwrdshp Awd 86-87; Law.

AGLE, GRANT; Upland Country Day Schl; West Chester, PA; (1); 3/20; Computer Clb; Science Clb; Ski Clb; Spanish Clb; School Play; Stage Crew; Variety Show; Var Ice Hcky; Var Lcrss; Var Socr; Malvern Prep; Finance.

AGOLINO, JOSEPH; Wyoming Area HS; W Pittston, PA; (3); 85/250; Band; Concert Band; Mrchg Band; Bowling; U Of Scranton; Accntng.

AGOSTINO, JOHN; Lower Dauphin HS; Hummelstown, PA; (3); Chorus; Wrstlng; Hon Roll.

AGOSTINO, MARK; Lower Dauphin HS; Hummlestown, PA; (3); Chorus; Ftbl; Hon Roll.

AGUILAR, CRIS; Central HS; Philadelphia, PA; (2); Political Wkr; Chorus; Jazz Band; Mrchg Band; Orch; Hon Roll.

AGUILERA, BRIAN; Bishop Mc Cort HS; Johnstown, PA; (3); Mu Alpha Theta; Ski Clb; Var L Swmmng; Var Tennis; High Hon Roll; Mu Alpha Theta Awd; Pre Med.

AHEARN, MATTHEW; Daniel Bonne Area HS; Birdsboro, PA; (2); 13/166; Church Yth Grp; French Clb; Pres Soph Cls; Var Bsbl; Var Ftbl; Wrstlng; Hon Roll; Hstry Ed.

AHEIMER, MARIE ELENA; Council Rock HS; Newtown, PA; (3); #192 In Class; Key Clb; SADD; Var Bsktbl; Var Trk; Im Vllybl; Hon Roll; Grls 1st Tm Suburban I-Javelin 87; Engrng.

AHENGER, JENNIFER; Warren Area HS; Waren, PA; (3); 9/287; Art Clb; Varsity Clb; Acpl Chr; L Bsktbl; Sftbl; JV Swmmng; High Hon Roll; Hon Roll; Jr NHS; NHS; Silver B Awd 84-85; Penn ST; Med Tech.

AHERN, BRIDGET; Archbishop Carroll HS; Bryn Mawr, PA; (3); Church Yth Grp; VP Frsh Cls; Off Soph Cls; Off Jr Cls; JV Bsktbl; JV Fld Hcky; JV Sftbl; Var L Tennis; High Hon Roll; Hon Roll; All Cthlc Awd-Phila Cathlc Lge Tnns; MVP-PHILA Chthlc Lge Tnns; Mgmt.

AHLBORN, GEORGE; Mt Pleasant Area HS; Mt Pleasant, PA; (3); VICA.

AHLUM, DENISE; Wilmington Area HS; New Wilmington, PA; (3); 22/114; Sec FBLA; Band; Concert Band; Mrchg Band; Im Powder Puff Ftbl; VP Trk; Hon Roll; PA Free Entrprs Wk Schlrshp 87; 1st Pl-Imprmptu Spkg Rgn II, 10th Pl St 87; Slippery Rock U; Acctg.

AHN, MAX; North Alleghany SR HS; Gibsonia, PA; (4); 8/642; Drama Clb; Thesps; School Musical; School Play; Yrbk Ed-Chief; Var L Trk; High Hon Roll; Jr NHS; NHS; Ntl Merit SF; $12500 Carnegie Malon U Schlrshp 86; PA Higher Educ Asstnc Agency Cert Of Merit 86; Pre Med.

AHNER, BRADLEY; Lehighton Area HS; Lehighton, PA; (3); #36 In Class; VICA; Var Ftbl; High Hon Roll; Hon Roll; Pres Phys Ftns 85-87; Lincoln Tech; Elec Tech.

AHOLA, KRISTEN; Coatesville Area HS; Thorndale, PA; (3); 81/530; Church Yth Grp; Leo Clb; Ski Clb; Spanish Clb; Chorus; School Musical; Soph Cls; Jr Cls; Cheerleading; Hon Roll; Vrsty Chrldg Ltr 87.

AHRENS, APRIL; Mc Guffey HS; Washington, PA; (3); Church Yth Grp; Pep Clb; Spanish Clb; Band; Mrchg Band; Hon Roll; Liberty U; Med.

AHRENS, JESSICA M; Jersey Shore Area SR HS; Jersey Shore, PA; (4); 8/240; Pres Church Yth Grp; Letterman Clb; Varsity Clb; Jazz Band; Capt Trk; High Hon Roll; JP Sousa Awd; NHS; French Clb; Band; Dist & Rgnl Choir 85; Dist & Rgnl Band 87; IN U PA; Frnch.

AICHER, JED; Wilson Area HS; Easton, PA; (2); 3/156; Drama Clb; Band; Chorus; Jazz Band; Madrigals; Orch; School Musical; Pres Soph Cls; Crs Cntry; High Hon Roll; Regional Bnd, District Bnd 86-87; Regional Chorus, Dist Chorus 86-87; Dist Orchestra; Performing Arts.

AIELLO, FRANK; Freeland HS; Freeland, PA; (3); Computer Clb; Pep Clb; Band; Concert Band; Mrchg Band; Yrbk Stf; Stu Cncl; Hon Roll; Comp Sci.

AIELLO, JAMES; West Hazleton HS; W Hazleton, PA; (4); 83/221; Capt Scholastic Bowl; Spanish Clb; Var JV Bowling; PA ST U; Microcomp Tech.

AIELLO, RONALD C; Monessen JR SR HS; Monessen, PA; (3); French Clb; High Hon Roll; Hon Roll; Crmnlgy.

AIKEN, DAVE; Moon SR HS; Coraopolis, PA; (3); 66/304; Hon Roll; Embry-Riddle; Cmmrcl Pilot.

AIKEY, BONNIE; Milton SR HS; White Deer, PA; (2); FBLA; Girl Scts; Library Aide; Spanish Clb; 2nd Pl Rgnl Bus Math 87; Sec.

AIKEY, LAURA; Westmont Hilltop HS; Johnstown, PA; (4); 20/158; Concert Band; Mrchg Band; Vllybl; High Hon Roll; NHS; Band Boosters Awd 87; IUP Honors Band 85-87; Regional Band 86-87; IN U Of PA; Frnch Ed.

AIKEY, WADE; Stroudsburg HS; Stroudsburg, PA; (2); 60/300; Church Yth Grp; Cmnty Wkr; Var Ftbl; Hon Roll; Penn ST U; Forestry.

AILES, REBECCA; Strath Haven HS; Morton, PA; (3); Camera Clb; Church Yth Grp; Teachers Aide; Chorus; Color Guard; Nrsng.

AINSLEY, MARCIA; Connellsville SR HS; Normalville, PA; (4); Camera Clb; Church Yth Grp; Girl Scts; Ski Clb; Band; Concert Band; Jazz Band; Mrchg Band; High Hon Roll; Hon Roll; PA ST; Anml Sci.

AINSWORTH, TRACY; Notre Dame Acad; Bryn Mawr, PA; (3); 1/80; FCA; Yrbk Phtg; Lit Mag; Pres Jr Cls; Pres Stu Cncl; JV Capt Bsktbl; Var Lcrss; Var Capt Socr; Var Tennis; High Hon Roll; Ntl Frnch Cntst Hnbl Mntn 85-86; Harcum JC Art Cntst 2nd Prz 87; Arch.

AIRESMAN, RENEE; Somerset Area SR HS; Somerset, PA; (3); 9/228; VP Church Yth Grp; English Clb; French Clb; Office Aide; Church Choir; High Hon Roll; Hon Roll; NHS; Charles Scribner Mem Art Awd 85; 2 Acdmc Awds & Let 85-87; Shippensburg U; Scl Wrk.

AITKEN, KIP; Mt Lebanon HS; Pittsburgh, PA; (4); 120/530; Science Clb; SADD; School Musical; School Play; Stage Crew; Pres Stu Cncl; Pres Schlr; St Schlr; Aud/Vis; Latin Clb; Schlrshp Wbsh Coll 86-87; Wabash Coll; Med.

AITKEN, MARYELLEN; Tunkhannock Area HS; Mehoopany, PA; (3); 28/325; Church Yth Grp; Cmnty Wkr; Letterman Clb; SADD; Varsity Clb; Trs Frsh Cls; Sec Soph Cls; Trs Jr Cls; Capt Bsktbl; Sftbl; U Of Scranton; Fshn Mrchndsng.

AIZUPITIS, VARIS R; Westtown Schl; W Chester, PA; (4); School Play; Socr; Ntl Merit Schol; Cngrss-Bunderstag Yth Exch Schlrshps 85-86; Telluride Assoc Summer Pgm 86; U Of Chicago; Math.

AKER, HEATHER; Harry S Truman HS; Bristol, PA; (3); Church Yth Grp; Office Aide; SADD; Jazz Band; Rep Stu Cncl; Fld Hcky; Mgr(s); Score Keeper; Hon Roll; Prfct Atten Awd; Law.

AKERS, TRACY; Trinity HS; Camp Hill, PA; (3); 25/150; Drama Clb; Model UN; Varsity Clb; Rep Stu Cncl; Var Cheerleading; Hon Roll; Prelaw.

AKHTAR, SAADIA R; Schenley HS; Pittsburgh, PA; (4); 1/188; Math Tm; School Musical; Ed Yrbk Stf; Off Jr Cls; Off Sr Cls; Mgr Swmmng; Cit Awd; High Hon Roll; NHS; Prfct Atten Awd.

AKINS, AMY; Leechburg HS; Leechburg, PA; (2); SADD; Concert Band; Mrchg Band; High Hon Roll; Hon Roll; Med Tech.

ALAMPI, MICHAEL; Bangor Area HS; Bangor, PA; (4); 10/170; Leo Clb; Office Aide; Yrbk Stf; Rep Stu Cncl; Var L Bsktbl; Capt Var Golf; High Hon Roll; Hon Roll; Jr NHS; Sec NHS; IN U Of PA; Econ.

ALAN, WAGNER; Blairsville SR HS; Blairsville, PA; (4); 44/123; Boy Scts; Rep Church Yth Grp; Rptr FFA; Hon Roll; Eagle Sct 85; Brotherhd Yth Ordr Arrow 86; Yth Blairsville Civl War Trvlng Sqd 86-87; IN U Of PA; Indstrl Engr.

ALBA, MICHAEL; Father Judge HS; Philadelphia, PA; (3); 19/403; Church Yth Grp; Yrbk Rptr; Rep Soph Cls; Rep Jr Cls; Sec Sr Cls; Stu Cncl; Stat Bsktbl; Ftbl; Score Keeper; High Hon Roll; Optimist Club Awd 82-83; Capt Tm Sports 83-81 & 83-84; Oceanogrphy.

ALBA, PATRICK; Wyo Area HS; Wyoming, PA; (4); 50/720; Church Yth Grp; Cmnty Wkr; Math Clb; Ski Clb; SADD; Band; Concert Band; Jazz Band; Mrchg Band; Orch; Penn ST; Ceramic Engr.

ALBA JR, ROBERT; Reading HS; Reading, PA; (4); 30/574; Chess Clb; Quiz Bowl; Hon Roll; NHS; NY U; French.

ALBANESE, ANDREA; Mifflinburg HS; Mifflinburg, PA; (3); French Clb; Sec VP Key Clb; Spanish Clb; Mrchg Band; Trs Frsh Cls; Stu Cncl; JV L Fld Hcky; Mgr Trk; High Hon Roll; Hon Roll; Essay Awd 1st ST & 2nd Natls 85; Physcl Thrpy.

ALBANO, DINA; Immaculate Conception HS; Washington, PA; (3); 4/38; Yrbk Stf; Trs Frsh Cls; Var L Bsktbl; Var L Sftbl; Var L Vllybl; High Hon Roll; NHS; Rotary Awd; Bio.

ALBANO, MARYBETH; Kennard Dale HS; Felton, PA; (2); Art Clb; Sec Church Yth Grp; Drama Clb; Band; Church Choir; Concert Band; Mrchg Band; Co-Capt Cheerleading; Trk; Teacher.

ALBANO, ROBERT; St John Newmann HS; Philadelphia, PA; (3); 86/352; Hon Roll; Acdmc Hnr Awd 87; 2nd Hnrs 85-86 & 84-85; Chef.

ALBAUGH, MATTHEW; Reynolds HS; Greenville, PA; (3); 14/160; Latin Clb; Band; Jazz Band; Mrchg Band; Stage Crew; JV Wrstlng; Hon Roll; NHS; Acad All Amer 86; Butler County CC; Arch Tech.

ALBEE, MARK; Carlisle HS; Carlisle, PA; (3); Church Yth Grp; Ski Clb; Church Choir; Im Socr; Var Swmmng; Var Tennis; Hist.

ALBERS, ROBERT; Corry Area HS; Corry, PA; (3); JV Bsktbl; JV L Ftbl; Var L Trk; High Hon Roll; Hon Roll; German Hnr Soc 85-86; Electrncs.

ALBERT, ALICIA; Grace Christian Schl; Lebanon, PA; (3); 3/22; Church Yth Grp; Cmnty Wkr; Hosp Aide; School Play; Cheerleading; Fld Hcky; Sftbl; Trk; Hon Roll; Vet Med.

ALBERT, BRIDGET; Johnstown HS; Johnstown, PA; (3); French Clb; Pep Clb; Ski Clb; Chorus; Church Choir; Capt Color Guard; Orch; Rep Jr Cls; Rep Stu Cncl; Hon Roll; Phrmcy.

ALBERT, DANETTE; Hamburg Area HS; Hamburg, PA; (4); 24/141; Sec VP Chess Clb; French Clb; German Clb; Library Aide; Ski Clb; Chorus; Variety Show; Hon Roll; NHS; Acdmc Ltr Hstry 85-87; Penn ST U; Mech Engr.

ALBERT, JAN; E Stroudsburg HS; Marshalls Creek, PA; (1); 17/240; Model UN; Band; Church Choir; Concert Band; Flag Corp; Mrchg Band; Pep Band; School Musical; Penn ST U.

ALBERT, JOHN; Spring-Ford HS; Collegeville, PA; (3); Boy Scts; Cmnty Wkr; Drama Clb; Math Clb; Spanish Clb; Nwsp Rptr; Nwsp Stf; Crs Cntry; Trk; Prfct Atten Awd.

ALBERT, JUDITH; Northern SR HS; Dillsburg, PA; (4); 20/200; Church Yth Grp; French Clb; Hosp Aide; Chorus; Church Choir; Hon Roll; Yrk Cnty Wmns Clb Awd 87; Grtr Hrrsbrg Fndtn Awd 87; Lancaster Schl Of Nrsng; Nrsng.

ALBERT, JUNE; Northwester SR HS; Albion, PA; (3); 3/165; Computer Clb; 4-H; Model UN; Rep Soph Cls; Rep Jr Cls; Rep Computer Clb; Rep Stu Cncl; Var Trk; 4-H Awd; High Hon Roll; Psych.

ALBERT, KATHLEEN; Tunkhannock Area HS; Dalton, PA; (2); 35/230; Key Clb; Ski Clb; Spanish Clb; Flag Corp; Mrchg Band; School Musical; School Play; Mgr(s); Hon Roll; Cmnty Wkr; Dist IX Chorus 2nd Pl 86; Med.

ALBERT, MELISSA; Westmont Hilltop HS; Johnstown, PA; (2); French Clb; GAA; Key Clb; Letterman Clb; VP Pep Clb; School Musical; Rep Jr Cls; JV Bsktbl; Var L Sftbl; High Hon Roll; Med.

ALBERT, MYRNA; Northern SR HS; Dillsburg, PA; (4); 3/200; French Hon Soc; High Hon Roll; Hon Roll; Boyd Schl; Travel.

ALBERTA, ROBERT; Valley HS; New Kensington, PA; (3); 85/225; Drama Clb; Science Clb; Varsity Clb; Concert Band; Mrchg Band; School Play; Var Capt Golf; Hon Roll; IN U Of PA; Scndry Educ.

ALBERTER, CHRISTINE; Windber Area HS; Windber, PA; (3); Drama Clb; Sec Girl Scts; JA; Band; Jazz Band; Mrchg Band; School Play; Yrbk Stf; Rep Jr Cls; High Hon Roll; Nrsng.

ALBERTINI, KATHRYN; Danville HS; Danville, PA; (2); 10/175; Church Yth Grp; Key Clb; Trs Soph Cls; Var Cheerleading; Tennis; Trk; Cert Outstndng Perfrmnc Natl Latin Exam 87.

ALBERTSON, BRENDA; Danville SR HS; Danville, PA; (1); Church Yth Grp; Hosp Aide; Chorus; Color Guard; Flag Corp; Hon Roll; Pres Acad Ftns Awd 86-87; Vet-Med.

ALBERTSON, BRENT; Danville SR HS; Danville, PA; (2); Bsbl; Bsktbl; Ftbl; High Hon Roll.

ALBERTSON, LANCE; Milton Area HS; Milton, PA; (3); Pres Letterman Clb; SADD; Pres Varsity Clb; Trs Chorus; Variety Show; Var L Bsbl; Var L Ftbl; Im Vllybl; Hon Roll; Sec Frsh Cls; Mansfield; Fish Culture.

ALBRECHT, DEBBIE; Mt Penn HS; Reading, PA; (3); FBLA; GAA; Y-Teens; Yrbk Stf; Var L Bsktbl; Var L Fld Hcky; Mgr(s); Var L Sftbl; Hon Roll; Jr NHS; Amer Lgn Schl Awd 85; Mst Imprvd Bsktbl 87; Bus.

ALBRECHT, LORI; James M Coughlin HS; Wilkes-Barre, PA; (4); 6/324; Exploring; Yrbk Ed-Chief; Yrbk Stf; High Hon Roll; Hon Roll; Dance Clb; Lion Awd; NHS; Moreau Schlrshp 87-91; Cong Yth Ldrshp Cncl Schlr 87; Kings Coll.

ALBRECHT, PHILLIP J; Montoursville HS; Montoursville, PA; (4); 11/174; Debate Tm; Letterman Clb; Ski Clb; Varsity Clb; Off Stu Cncl; Bsbl; Ftbl; Ice Hcky; Wrstlng; Pres Schlr; PA ST U; Psychological Med.

ALBRECHT, WENDY; Mr Penn JR/SR HS; Reading, PA; (2); FBLA; Y-Teens; Drill Tm; Var L Bowling; Var JV Fld Hcky; Var L Sftbl; Secr.

ALBRIGHT III, CLARK N; Connellsville SR HS; Mill Run, PA; (3); Computer Clb; VICA; Rep Stu Cncl; JV Wrstlng; Hon Roll.

ALBRIGHT, DAVID; Central HS; Martinsburg, PA; (3); 44/190; Teachers Aide; Yrbk Stf; Hon Roll; Bus Mgmt.

ALBRIGHT, DAWN; Altoona Area HS; Altoona, PA; (4); Science Clb; Ski Clb; Spanish Clb; Var Cheerleading; Jr NHS; Penn ST U; Educ.

ALBRIGHT, EUGENE; Elizabeth Forward HS; Bunola, PA; (3); Chess Clb; French Clb.

ALBRIGHT, INGRID; West Perry SR HS; Landisburg, PA; (2); Church Yth Grp; FBLA; Office Aide; Hon Roll.

ALBRIGHT, KATHERINE; Jenkintown HS; Jenkintown, PA; (3); 3/37; Band; School Musical; Mgr Stage Crew; Nwsp Stf; Yrbk Stf; Sec Jr Cls; Var Fld Hcky; NHS; Ntl Merit Ltr; Spanish NHS; 1st Pl-Schl Sci Fair 86.

ALBRIGHT, LISA; Connellsville SR HS; White, PA; (3); Church Yth Grp; Pres VICA; Pres Chorus; Church Choir; Nwsp Stf; Pres Soph Cls; Trs Jr Cls; Pres Trs Stu Cncl; Pres Hon Roll; NHS; VICA-LDRSHP Awd 86; Dir List Awd 87; Pittsburgh Beauty Acad; Csmtlgy.

ALBRIGHT, SHANE R; Cumberland Valley HS; Mechanicsburg, PA; (3); 2/518; German Clb; VP Key Clb; Model UN; NHS; Ntl Merit SF; Latin Clb; Math Tm; Quiz Bowl; Ski Clb; Hon Roll; PA Gvrnr Schl Sci 86; Hnbl Mntn Schlstcs Wrtg Comptns; Stanford; Bio Sci.

ALBRIGHT, THERESA; Mechanicsburg Area SR HS; Mechanicsburg, PA; (2); 3/309; Church Yth Grp; Speech Tm; Band; Concert Band; Stage Crew; Symp Band; Var L Cheerleading; High Hon Roll; NHS; Mltry Srvc.

ALBUS, GEORGIANNE; Bishop Mc Devitt HS; Grantville, PA; (3); 116/200; Art Clb; Spanish Clb; Nwsppr Educ Cert Recog 87; HACC; Police Sci.

ALBUS, PATRICK; Liberty HS; Bethlehem, PA; (3); 52/429; VP Stu Cncl; JV Bsbl; Var Ftbl; Hon Roll; Sprts Med.

ALCARAZ, LORI; Shenandoah Valley HS; Shenandoah, PA; (4); 41/103; Computer Clb; FBLA; Stage Crew; Score Keeper; Sftbl; A P Damato Medal Of Hnr Legion Post Awd 87; Schuylkill Bus Inst; Med Sec.

ALCENDOR, VINNAE; Steelton-Highspire HS; Steelton, PA; (4); 35/96; Church Yth Grp; Computer Clb; Library Aide; Pep Clb; Spanish Clb; Speech Tm; Yrbk Stf; Cit Awd; Schlrshp Omnia Bona, Schlrshp Wmn Howrd Day Cmtry, JR Ctznshp Schlrshp Lawyr Auxllry 87; HACC; Brdcst Engrng.

ALCORN, DIANE; Punxsutawney HS; Mayport, PA; (4); 41/245; FBLA; Hon Roll; Dubois Bus Coll; Mdcl Secy.

ALDERFER, AIMEE; Lower Moreland HS; Huntingdon Valley, PA; (4); 22/201; Church Yth Grp; Drama Clb; French Clb; Chorus; Rep Frsh Cls; Rep Soph Cls; Rep Jr Cls; Rep Stu Cncl; Capt Tennis; Var Trk; U Of Richmond.

ALDERFER, TIFFANY; Souderton Area HS; Harleysville, PA; (4); Church Yth Grp; School Musical; Trs Frsh Cls; Rep Sr Cls; Rep Stu Cncl; JV Sftbl; Hon Roll; Rep Soph Cls; Rep Jr Cls; Jr NHS; Svc Awd 84; Messiah Coll; Nrsng.

ALDERSON, LARRY; Northeast Bradford HS; Lerayville, PA; (4); 5/73; Computer Clb; Quiz Bowl; Scholastic Bowl; Pres Soph Cls; Pres Jr Cls; Pres Sr Cls; Cit Awd; High Hon Roll; NHS; Pres Schlr; Acdmc Ftns Awd 87; 69th Pl IUP Physics Tst 87; Farmng.

ALDINGER, DREW; W B Saul HS; Philadelphia, PA; (2); Debate Tm; FFA; Hosp Aide; Im Golf; Im Tennis; Hon Roll; NHS; Church Yth Grp; Computer Clb; Exploring; Outstndng Soph Awd 87; Schlrshp PA ST FFA Week 86-87; Schlrshp PAFC Summer Inst 87; PA ST U; Food Insp Agent.

ALDOUS JR, THOMAS; Hershey HS; Palmyra, PA; (3); 9/209; Church Yth Grp; Chorus; Madrigals; School Musical; School Play; Variety Show; NHS; Spanish NHS.

ALDRICH, KEANE; Tunkhannock Area HS; Dalton, PA; (3); Spanish Clb; Im Bowling; Im Ftbl; Var Socr; Var Trk; High Hon Roll; Hon Roll; NHS; Ntl Merit Ltr; Elctrcl Engrng.

ALDRICH, KIMBERLY; Monessen SR HS; Monessen, PA; (3); Aud/Vis; FBLA; JA; Church Choir; Rep Soph Cls; Capt Cheerleading; Hon Roll; USCA Natl Champ Top 10 Chrldr 85; Miss Mon Vly OIC Beauty Pgnt 85.

ALEPRETE, MICHAEL; Plum HS; Pittsburgh, PA; (2); Chess Clb; Im Socr.

ALESSANDRINI, SUE; Methacton HS; Norristown, PA; (4); Exploring; Hon Roll; Adubin Womens Clb Awd 87; Moore Art Coll; Art.

ALEXANDER, AMY; Neshannock HS; New Castle, PA; (3); 3/102; VP Church Yth Grp; Pres Exploring; Yrbk Sprt Ed; Rep Stu Cncl; Var Capt Bsktbl; Var Tennis; Var Trk; High Hon Roll; Trs NHS; NEDT Awd; PA ST.

ALEXANDER, CLIFFORD; Northern Lebanon HS; Jonestown, PA; (3); 52/200; Boy Scts; Band; Concert Band; Mrchg Band; Pep Band; Off Sr Cls; Bowling; Tennis; Cit Awd; Eagle Sct Awd 86; Brnz Palm 86; PA Band Stu Awd MIP Band 86; USN; Mltry.

ALEXANDER, DAWN; Halifax Area HS; Halifax, PA; (4); Church Yth Grp; Drama Clb; FBLA; Sec FFA; VP SADD; Band; Chorus; Variety Show; Temple U; Psych.

ALEXANDER, JENNIFER; Tunkhannock Area HS; Tunkhannock, PA; (2); #3 In Class; French Clb; Letterman Clb; Concert Band; Jazz Band; Mrchg Band; Var L Trk; Var L Vllybl; Im Wrstlng; Cit Awd; Hon Roll; Keystone Gms Brnz Medl Shot Put 86; Schl Recrd Trck Discus 86; AAU JR Olmpc Regn I Slvr Discus 86.

ALEXANDER, PETE; West Branch HS; Karthaus, PA; (3); Boy Scts; Varsity Clb; VICA; JV Bsbl; Elec.

ALEXANDER, S SHANE; Butler Area SR HS; Butler, PA; (4); Art Clb; Spanish Clb; Band; Mrchg Band; Variety Show; Socr; Vllybl; Wrstlng; Kings Ct 87; IN U Of PA; Intl Bus.

ALEXANDER, SUZANNE; Hopewell HS; Aliquippa, PA; (3); Art Clb; Sec Church Yth Grp; Exploring; French Clb; Chorus; Yrbk Stf; VP Stu Cncl; Var Capt Cheerleading; Powder Puff Ftbl; Trk.

ALEXANDER, TIMOTHY; Cumberland Valley HS; Carlisle, PA; (3); 67/610; JV Swmmng; Hon Roll; 2nd Pl Keystoners Poetry Cntst 87; Cert Of Achvmnt For Excllnc In Frnch 87; Tchng Sci.

ALEXANDER, TODD; Mercer Area JR SR HS; Mercer, PA; (3); Church Yth Grp; Computer Clb; Nwsp Stf; Yrbk Stf; Trk; High Hon Roll; NHS; Prfct Atten Awd; Ottaway Nwspr Carrier Schlrshp 85.

ALEXANDER, WENDY; Towanda Area HS; Towanda, PA; (4); 3/139; Am Leg Aux Girls St; Science Clb; Yrbk Stf; Sec Jr Cls; Sec Sr Cls; Elks Awd; High Hon Roll; NHS; Joseph G Pratt Schlrshp Awd 87; Morris Schlrshp 87; Jean L Holcombe Awd 87; Devry Inst Technlgy; Elec Engrn.

ALFANO, KELLY; Pittston Area HS; Pittston, PA; (3); #66 In Class; Drama Clb; FNA; Key Clb; Ski Clb; Chorus; Capt Twrlr; Hon Roll; CMC; Nrsng.

ALFERA, RACHELLE; Kennedy Christian HS; Sharpsville, PA; (3); 18/97; Church Yth Grp; Spanish Clb; L Cheerleading; High Hon Roll; Hon Roll; Christian Ldrshp Inst Awd 86; Phrmcy.

ALFERY, PETER; Greensburg Central Catholic HS; Youngwood, PA; (2); 73/230; Ski Clb; Socr; Hon Roll; Accntng.

ALFONSO, EMMANUEL; Quigley HS; Sewickley, PA; (2); 8/88; Math Tm; Im Bsktbl; L Golf; L Tennis; Hon Roll; Mensa Stu 86.

ALFRED, DARRIN; Carlynton HS; Carnegie, PA; (3); Boys Clb Am; Boy Scts; Computer Clb; JA; Political Wkr; Flag Corp; Score Keeper; Socr; Hon Roll; Ltrmns Jckt 87; Bus.

ALGAR, DANIEL; Tunkhannock HS; Tunkhannock, PA; (4); Letterman Clb; Science Clb; Ski Clb; Varsity Clb; Crs Cntry; Ftbl; Trk; Wt Lftg; Hon Roll; NHS; PA ST; Engrng.

ALI, KEESHA; Philadelphia H S For Girls; Philadelphia, PA; (3); 72/409; Boys Clb Am; Sec Intnl Clb; JA; Service Clb; Spanish Clb; Teachers Aide; Rep Soph Cls; Rep Jr Cls; Spanish NHS; Meritorious Awd 85-87; Bio/Pedtrcn.

ALI, MAHBUBUL A; Annville-Cleona HS; Annville, PA; (3); Boys Clb Am; Math Tm; Varsity Clb; Band; Var Crs Cntry; Var Socr; Var Trk; Hon Roll; NHS; Prfct Atten Awd; Bloomsburg U; Aerosp Engr.

ALINDOGAN, DAFFODEL; Blue Mountain Acad; Philadelphia, PA; (3); Computer Clb; Teachers Aide; Band; Concert Band; Nwsp Rptr; Yrbk Stf; Trs Soph Cls; High Hon Roll; Prfct Atten Awd; Blue Mountain Acadmy Extra Curricly Actvty Ltr 85-86; Acadmc Standards Awd 85-86; Harvard U; Med.

ALISESKY, MARK; Bethel Park HS; Bethel Park, PA; (4); 34/519; Band; Concert Band; Jazz Band; Mrchg Band; Orch; School Musical; School Play; Symp Band; Variety Show; High Hon Roll; Penn ST U; Engrng.

ALLAR, SUSAN; Pine Grove Area HS; Tremont, PA; (3); Am Leg Aux Girls St; SADD; Yrbk Stf; Lit Mag; JV Bsktbl; Mrktng.

ALLEBACH, KATHY; Souderton Area HS; Souderton, PA; (3); Church Yth Grp; Teachers Aide; Var Lcrss; Var Swmmng; Var Tennis; Buy-Mnt Mdgt Ftbl Leag-All Schlstc Tm 84; Leisr Manag.

ALLEGAR, BILLIE; Benton Area JR SR HS; Benton, PA; (2); Drama Clb; Keywanettes; Band; Chorus; Concert Band; Mrchg Band; School Musical; Nwsp Rptr; Nwsp Stf; Hon Roll; Bloomsburg U; Engl Tchr.

ALLEMAN, FRANCES; Moshannon Valley HS; Glen Hope, PA; (4); 8/120; Church Yth Grp; Red Cross Aide; SADD; Church Choir; High Hon Roll; Hon Roll; NHS; Pres Acad Ftnss Awd 87; Dubois Bus Coll; Acctg.

ALLEN, AMY; Northwestern HS; Girard, PA; (3); 7/167; Model UN; Chorus; Trs Church Choir; Madrigals; Var Capt Bsktbl; Powder Puff Ftbl; Trk; Hon Roll; NHS; Occptnl Thrpy.

ALLEN, AMY; W Middlesex HS; New Wilmington, PA; (4); Band; Mrchg Band; Stu Cncl; Var Bsktbl; Trk; Var Vllybl; Bsktbl MVP, 1st Tm All Cnty, Hnbl Mntn 83-86; Vllybl 1st Tm 84-85; Hnrs 85-86.

ALLEN, BOICE; Clairton JR SR HS; Clairton, PA; (3); Band; Chorus; Church Choir; Concert Band; Drm Mjr(t); Mrchg Band; VP Jr Cls; High Hon Roll; Hon Roll; Med.

ALLEN, CHARINA; Chester HS; Chester Twp, PA; (3); 34/458; Church Yth Grp; French Clb; Key Clb; Temple Yth Grp; Band; Chorus; Church Choir; Concert Band; Nwsp Stf; Mgr(s); Hampton U; Mdcl.

ALLEN, CHARISSE; Cheltenham HS; Lamott, PA; (2); Chorus; Math.

ALLEN, DANIELLE; Taylor Allderdice HS; Pittsburgh, PA; (3); Sec JA; VP Jr Cls; Hon Roll; Psych.

ALLEN, DAREN T; Seneca HS; Union City, PA; (3); Band; Concert Band; Mrchg Band; Var Bsktbl; Var Crs Cntry; Hon Roll; JV Bsktbl MVP 86-87; IN U Of PA; Crimnlgy.

ALLEN, HEATHER ELIZABETH; Delaware County Christian Schl; Newtown Sq, PA; (4); Drama Clb; Math Tm; Band; Rep Sr Cls; Var Stat Bsktbl; Var Sftbl; Var Trk; High Hon Roll; NHS; School Play; Prsdntl Acdmc Ftnss Awd 87; Houghton Coll.

ALLEN, JAMES; Central Dauphin HS; Harrisburg, PA; (3); 88/375; CAP; JV Ftbl; Var Capt Trk; Im Vllybl; Wt Lftg; Hon Roll; Jr NHS; Air Force; Plot.

ALLEN, JAN; Belle Vernon Area HS; Belle Vernon, PA; (3); Aud/Vis; Church Yth Grp; Girl Scts; NFL; Pep Clb; Band; Stage Crew; High Hon Roll; NHS; Frnch Stu Of Mon & 3rd Pl-Intrschlstc Frnch Comp 86; Wrthy Advsr-Belle Vrnon Rnbow Grls 86.

ALLEN, JENNI; Parkland HS; Coplay, PA; (4); Sec Latin Clb; Q&S; Yrbk Sprt Ed; Sec Frsh Cls; Off Stu Cncl; Capt Cheerleading; JV Sftbl; Var Vllybl; Hon Roll; Savng Drowng Grl Rcgntn-Lfguard 87; U Of DE; Genetic Engrng.

ALLEN, KELLY; Penn Hills SR HS; Verona, PA; (3); French Clb; Hon Roll.

ALLEN, KENNETH; William Tennent HS; Warminster, PA; (4); 5/560; Key Clb; Math Tm; SADD; Temple Yth Grp; Var Capt Crs Cntry; Var Trk; High Hon Roll; Hon Roll; Jr NHS; NHS; Betz Lbrtrs, Outstndng Achvt-Math & Sci 87; Ntl Soc Prfssnl Engnrs, Outstndng Achvt 87; Northwestern U; Engnrng.

ALLEN, KENNETH C; High Schl Of Engineering & Sci; Philadelphia, PA; (1); Chess Clb; Hon Roll; NHS; Ntl Merit SF; Prfct Atten Awd; Early Admssn U Of PA 86; U Of PA; Sys Engrng.

ALLEN, KERI JO; Northeast Bradford HS; Rome, PA; (4); Varsity Clb; Capt Drm Mjr(t); VP Jr Cls; Sec Stu Cncl; Cheerleading; Var Crs Cntry; Twrlr; High Hon Roll; Hon Roll; NHS; Slvr Schlr Plaq 83-86; Mansfield U; Nrsng.

ALLEN, KEVIN; La Salle College HS; Hatboro, PA; (3); 10/230; Church Yth Grp; Pep Clb; Rep Frsh Cls; Rep Soph Cls; Rep Jr Cls; Rep Sr Cls; Rep Stu Cncl; Im Bsbl; Im Bsktbl; Capt Var Ftbl; Hghst Hnrs Frnch, Engl, & Rlgn 84-87; &rtl Schlrhsp La Salle Coll HS 84; Acadmc Lttrmn 84-87; Business.

ALLEN, LARON; Jules E Mastbaum HS; Philadelphia, PA; (3); Boy Scts; Church Yth Grp; Cmnty Wkr; Computer Clb; Library Aide; Math Tm; Office Aide; Temple Yth Grp; School Musical; Penn ST-LINCOLN; Elec Engr.

ALLEN, LISA; Cedar Cliff HS; New Cumberland, PA; (2); 50/288; Church Yth Grp; FCA; Key Clb; Pep Clb; Stu Cncl; Var Capt Cheerleading; Sftbl; Hon Roll; Prfct Atten Awd; Spanish NHS; Psychlgy.

ALLEN, LONNIE; Marple Newtown SR HS; Broomall, PA; (3); 2/322; Hosp Aide; Math Clb; SADD; Chorus; Orch; Rep Stu Cncl; High Hon Roll; Hon Roll; NHS; French Clb; 1st Pl Rgnl & 3rd Pl ST-HSTRY Day 85; Med.

ALLEN, LYNN MARIE; Cardinal Dougherty HS; Philadelphia, PA; (4); 155/695; Cmnty Wkr; Hosp Aide; Service Clb; Rep Stu Cncl; Prfct Atten Awd; Immaculata Coll; Dietcs.

ALLEN, MICHELE; Tech Memorial HS; Erie, PA; (3); Drama Clb; Chorus; School Play; Variety Show; Yrbk Stf; Hon Roll; Accntng.

ALLEN, MOLLY; Boiling Springs HS; Carlisle, PA; (2); GAA; Ski Clb; Varsity Clb; Chorus; School Play; Stage Crew; Trs Frsh Cls; Pres Soph Cls; Stu Cncl; Capt Fld Hcky; HOBY 87.

ALLEN, RALPH; Germantown Acad; Philadelphia, PA; (4); Orch; Crs Cntry; Trk; High Hon Roll; Ntl Merit Ltr; Prfrmng Musician Awd 86 & 87; Wnnr Cncrto Solo Cmptn 80; Juillard Pre-Coll 82-87; Yale; Music.

LLEN, RONDA; Jefferson-Morgan HS; Jefferson, PA; (4); 12/97; Art llb; Aud/Vis; Church Yth Grp; French Clb; Library Aide; Office Aide; 'arsity Clb; Chorus; Nwsp Rptr; Nwsp Stf; Waynesburg Coll; Jrnlsm.

LLEN, SHANNAN; West Catholic Girls HS; Philadelphia, PA; (3); rama Clb; Concert Band; Orch; Hon Roll; Prfct Atten Awd; Temple U; mmnctns.

LLEN, THEODORE; Blue Mountain Acad; Amityville, NY; (3); 'horus; Church Choir; Rep Stu Cncl; Var Bsktbl; Capt Wt Lftg; Hon Roll; usiness Mgmt.

LLEN, YVETTE; Pennridge HS; Telford, PA; (2); FHA; Girl Scts; ADD; Color Guard; Trk; Hon Roll; Jan Nagy Modlng & Fnshg Schl Achvt wd 87; Le High Vly Coll; Modlng.

LLENBAUGH, ROXANA; Tunkhannock Area HS; Tunkhannock, PA; 3); 41/320; Drama Clb; Spanish Clb; Stage Crew; Nwsp Bus Mgr; Nwsp ptr; Nwsp Stf; Hon Roll; Busnss Mgmt.

LLER, JIM; Burgettstown JR SR HS; Burgettstown, PA; (3); French 'lb; Ski Clb; Band; L Var Bsbl; L Var Ftbl; Im Wt Lftg; Phys Ther.

LLERSMA, MIRIAM; Schenley HS; Pittsburgh, PA; (4); 1/188; Church 'th Grp; Sec Intnl Clb; JA; Math Tm; Scholastic Bowl; School Musical; o-Capt Var Swmmng; Mgr Tennis; High Hon Roll; VP NHS; Symp Essay ntst Fnlst 86; PHEAA Cert Of Merit 86; Schlrshp Lttr Hnr Roll 86; Lib rts.

LLESCH, CYNTHIA; Panther Valley HS; Coaldale, PA; (3); 21/132; irl Scts; ROTC; VICA; Chorus; School Play; Cheerleading; High Hon oll; Hon Roll; Csmtlgy.

LLIS JR, ANDREW P B; York Suburban HS; York, PA; (3); 40/180; rama Clb; Chorus; Concert Band; Mrchg Band; School Musical; School lay; Nwsp Stf; Yrbk Stf; Off Sr Cls; Hon Roll; Advrtsng.

LLISON, ANDREA; Chambersburg Area SR HS; Chambersburg, PA; 2); Sec Church Yth Grp; Trs 4-H; French Clb; Pep Clb; Band; Chorus; ep Soph Cls; Var Capt Cheerleading; Capt Vllybl; High Hon Roll.

LLISON, ANDREW; Loyalsock Township HS; Montoursville, PA; (3); oy Scts; Church Yth Grp; German Clb; Key Clb; Model UN; Ski Clb; chool Play; Var Socr; Var Tennis; High Hon Roll; Arch Engrng.

LLISON, BRAD; Chestnut Ridge S HS; New Paris, PA; (3); 14/137; hurch Yth Grp; Cmnty Wkr; FBLA; Off Jr Cls; Var L Bsbl; Var JV Ftbl; n Wt Lftg; Hon Roll; NHS; Voice Dem Awd; Pre-Law.

LLISON, CARYN; Central Dauphin HS; Harrisburg, PA; (2); Church 'th Grp; French Clb; Chorus; Stage Crew; Rep Frsh Cls; Rep Soph Cls; JV sktbl; Var Trk; French Hon Soc; Penn Jr Acad Of Sci 2nd Pl 85-86; U Of C; Indstrl Psych.

LLISON, DALLAS; Chestnut Ridge SR HS; Alum Bank, PA; (3); hurch Yth Grp; FCA; Bsktbl; High Hon Roll; Hon Roll; Acad Letter 6-87; Engr.

LLISON, JEANNINE; Lansdale Catholic HS; Lansdale, PA; (3); VP amera Clb; Exploring; Hosp Aide; Office Aide; Chorus; High Hon Roll; on Roll; Villanova U; Paralgl.

LLISON, KAREN L; Central HS; Roaring Spring, PA; (4); Pres 4-H; res FTA; GAA; Girl Scts; Hosp Aide; Speech Tm; Rep Stu Cncl; 4-H wd; High Hon Roll; NHS; Soph Ambssdr Hugh O Brien Yth Ldrshp mnr 85; PA JR Acad Of Sci 86; Hldy Bwl Yth Bwlng Leag Champ 86; lessiah Coll; Bio-Chem.

LLISON, KATHIE; Carbondale Area JR SR HS; Carbondale, PA; (4); 'rench Clb; FHA; Ski Clb; Lackawana JC; Med Secr.

LLISON, KEITH; HS Of Engineering & Science; Philadelphia, PA; (3); 8/241; Math Clb; Red Cross Aide; SADD; Varsity Clb; School Musical; tage Crew; Rep Stu Cncl; Im Ftbl; Var Socr; Im Sftbl; Schlrshp Temple J 87; Temple U; ; Physcs.

LLISON, LIANE; Kiski Area HS; Apollo, PA; (3); 5/352; Cmnty Wkr; -H; Ed Spanish Clb; Band; Jazz Band; Pep Band; Symp Band; High Hon oll; NHS; Sprts Med.

LLISON, MELISSA L; Windber Area HS; Windber, PA; (3); FTA; ibrary Aide; Pep Clb; Spanish Clb; Var L Sftbl; Hon Roll; Wrkng Wth hldrn.

LLISON, MICHAEL; Central York HS; York, PA; (3); 3/250; Ski Clb; 'arsity Clb; Var Bsbl; JV Bsktbl; Cit Awd; High Hon Roll; NHS; Ntl lerit Ltr; Sci Olympiad Comptn 85-86; Engrng.

LLISON, MIKE; Mt Pleasant Area HS; Mt Pleasant, PA; (3); 13/250; 'P Church Yth Grp; Church Choir; Stage Crew; Im Bsktbl; Im Vllybl; ligh Hon Roll; Hon Roll; NHS; Math Tchr.

LLMAN, MICHAEL; Millersburg Area HS; Millersburg, PA; (3); 6/72; 'arsity Clb; Var L Bsbl; Var L Ftbl; Wt Lftg; High Hon Roll; Hon Roll; IEDT Awd.

LLOTT, GEORGE T; Chartiers Valley HS; Carnegie, PA; (3); JV Var sbl; Var Ftbl; JV Wrstlng; Phy Educ.

LLOWAY, DEBRA; Garnet Valley HS; Boothwyn, PA; (2); Spanish lb; Stu Cncl; Crs Cntry; Fld Hcky; Swmmng; Hon Roll; Awds For Swmng 7; Acad Exc 85-86; Top Stu Spnsh Awd 85-86; Med.

LLSHOUSE, DAVID W; Dubois Area SR HS; Du Bois, PA; (3); Chess lb; German Clb; Varsity Clb; Band; Concert Band; Mrchg Band; JV Var sktbl; Hon Roll; Arch.

LLSHOUSE, DEAN; Greencastle Antrim HS; Greencastle, PA; (3); lon Roll.

LLSHOUSE, JESSICA; Ringgold SR HS; Donora, PA; (4); 56/209; rama Clb; Pres JA; Library Aide; SADD; School Musical; School Play; 'ariety Show; Sftbl; Hon Roll; Prfct Atten Awd; Math, Sci Hnr Soc; CA U A; Math.

LLSHOUSE, LYNNANNE; Muncy HS; Muncy, PA; (4); 1/76; French lb; Letterman Clb; Spanish Clb; Varsity Clb; Yrbk Bus Mgr; Var L Sftbl; lon Roll; NHS; Ntl Merit SF; Pep Clb; Acad All Amer 86; OAS 86; Local otary Stu Of The Mnth 86; PA ST U; Bus Admin.

LLSHOUSE, SHAWN; Johnstown Christian Schl; Johnstown, PA; (2); hess Clb; Church Yth Grp; Drama Clb; Ski Clb; Chorus; Pres Frsh Cls; 'res Soph Cls; JV Bsktbl; Var JV Socr; Hon Roll.

LLWEIN, JOHN; Annville Cleona HS; Annville, PA; (4); German Clb; tage Crew; Bsktbl; Crs Cntry; Socr; Trk; Wt Lftg; IN U Of PA; Bus.

LLWEIN, JULIA E; Cedar Crest HS; Lebanon, PA; (3); 132/342; hurch Yth Grp; Trs Drama Clb; SADD; Chorus; Orch; School Musical; heerleading; Hon Roll; French Clb; Pep Clb; Regnl Orchestra 86; Dist rchestra 84-86; Harrisburg Yth Symphony 84-87; Music Thrpst.

LMADY, KEITH; Canon Mc Millan JHS At Cecil; Mc Donald, PA; (1); hurch Yth Grp; Debate Tm; French Clb; Variety Show; VP Frsh Cls; Off tu Cncl; L Bsktbl; Capt L Ftbl; Capt L Trk; Wt Lftg; Elem Acadmc Awd 3-84; Outstndng Trck & Fld Prfrmr 85-86; Sci Tchr.

LMES, DAWN E; Carlisle SR HS; Carlisle, PA; (3); 25/458; Am Leg Aux irls St; Church Yth Grp; Pep Clb; Flag Corp; Hon Roll; Sec NHS; HOBY 6; Lebanon Vly Coll Yth Schlrs Inst German 87; Intl Stds.

ALMOND, SCOTT; Morrisville HS; Morrisville, PA; (4); 1/94; Scholastic Bowl; Yrbk Ed-Chief; Off Stu Cncl; High Hon Roll; NHS; Pres Schlr; Val; Xchng Clb Of Levttwn Stu Of Mnth 87; E Hawkins Math Awd 87; Stanford Coll; Engrng.

ALMONEY, LADORA; Central York SR HS; York, PA; (2); Pres Sec Church Yth Grp; Chorus; Church Choir; Orch; School Musical; School Play; Hon Roll; Ricks Coll; Int Dsgn.

ALMQUIST, KARIN; Henderson HS; West Chester, PA; (3); 3/375; Church Yth Grp; Pres Intnl Clb; JCL; Church Choir; Ed Lit Mag; JV L Vllybl; French Hon Soc; Gov Hon Prg Awd; High Hon Roll; NHS; PA Govnr Schl Intnl Rltns 87; Temple U Future Stdy Smmr Pgm Gftd HS Stu 86.

ALOE, LISA; Ambridge Area HS; Ambridge, PA; (3); Church Yth Grp; Hosp Aide; Library Aide; Pep Clb; Band; Mrchg Band; Symp Band; Off Jr Cls; Stu Cncl; Cheerleading; ISLI-STU Ldrshp 87; Japanese Clb 86-87; Fshn Merch.

ALOIA, MICHELE; Trinity SR HS; Washington, PA; (3); 4-H; French Clb; Hosp Aide; Key Clb; Y-Teens; Chorus; Hon Roll; U Of Pittsburgh; Psych.

ALOISI, MARCO J; Father Judge HS; Philadelphia, PA; (3); 94/402; Am Leg Boys St; Church Yth Grp; Cmnty Wkr; JV Var Bsbl; Im Bsktbl; JV Ftbl; Hon Roll; Hnrs Religion Cls 86-87.

ALSDORF, JARED; Corry Area HS; Spartansburg, PA; (2); Church Yth Grp; 4-H; Ski Clb; Band; Concert Band; Mrchg Band; Pep Band; JV Capt Bsktbl; Var Crs Cntry; Var L Trk.

ALSPACH, ALEX D; Wilmington Area HS; New Wilmington, PA; (2); Spanish Clb; Concert Band; Drm Mjr(t); Mrchg Band; Pep Band; Nwsp Phtg; Nwsp Rptr; Nwsp Stf; Im Golf; Socr; Telecomms.

ALSPACH, JENNIFER; Middletown Area HS; Middletown, PA; (4); 16/180; Church Yth Grp; Color Guard; Yrbk Phtg; Yrbk Stf; Stu Cncl; Stat Bsktbl; Hon Roll; Jr NHS; NHS; Rotary Awd; Retail Cmmtte Awd 87; H K Alwine Schlrshp 87; West Chester ST U; Bus.

ALSTON, KIMBERLY; Engineering & Sci HS; Phila, PA; (3); Church Yth Grp; Drama Clb; Office Aide; Church Choir; Yrbk Stf; Richard & Anna Donahue Schlrshp Fr Outstndng Schlstc Achvt 86; Med.

ALSTON, MARGARET ETTA; Chester HS; Chester, PA; (3); Church Yth Grp; Hosp Aide; Model UN; Temple Yth Grp; Band; Chorus; Church Choir; Color Guard; Bsktbl; Prfct Atten Awd.

ALSTON, TRACEY; Bishop Mc Davitt HS; Philadelphia, PA; (3); 140/349; Computer Clb; Dance Clb; Latin Clb; Spanish Clb; Variety Show; Bowling; Vllybl; Cit Awd; Hon Roll; Charles Ellis Schlrshp 84-88; Lawyer.

ALT, CATHY; Bedford HS; Bedford, PA; (3); 39/204; VP Exploring; SADD; Band; Concert Band; Flag Corp; Mrchg Band; School Musical; Trs Frsh Cls; Stu Cncl; Trk; AL; Lawyer.

ALT, KIM; Franklin HS; Franklin, PA; (2); Var Swmmng; Hon Roll.

ALTARES, RACHEL; Quigley HS; Coraopolis, PA; (3); 28/80; Hnr Roll 83-84; Legal Asst.

ALTAVILLA, LISA; Hanover Area JR SR HS; Wilkes Barre, PA; (3); 7/194; Key Clb; Ski Clb; Drill Tm; School Musical; School Play; Yrbk Stf; Trs Stu Cncl; High Hon Roll; NHS; NEDT Awd; Accptd Natl Yth Salute 86-87; Commnctns.

ALTAVILLA, NANCY; Hazleton HS; Hazleton, PA; (3); 80/430; FBLA; Office Aide; Pep Clb; Stu Cncl; Capt Cheerleading; Hon Roll.

ALTEMARE JR, CLIFFORD D; Mon Valley Catholic HS; Monongahela, PA; (3); 5/99; Letterman Clb; Spanish Clb; Var Bsbl; Var Bsktbl; L Ftbl; Rep Wt Lftg; High Hon Roll; NHS; Spanish NHS; Bst Def Ftbl Plyr 86-87; Engrng.

ALTEMOSE, JEFF; Pen Argyl Area HS; Windgap, PA; (4); 40/117; Pep Clb; Ski Clb; Bsbl; Bsktbl; Ftbl; Wt Lftg; T Wilson Mem Awd Mst Enthstc Bsbl 87; Knight Day 1st Tm Colonial Lgue 87; All Area Hnbl Mntn Ftbl 87; Moravian Coll; Ind Psych.

ALTEMOSE, RODNEY; Nazareth SR HS; Nazareth, PA; (3); 59/275; Art Clb; Key Clb; Teachers Aide; Band; Concert Band; Drm & Bgl; Jazz Band; Mrchg Band; Pep Band; School Musical; US Collegiate Wind Bands 85-86 & 86-87; Acad All Amer 86-87; JR All Amer Hall Fame Band Hnrs 86; Crimnl Law.

ALTERI, DENISE; Sayre Area HS; S Waverly, PA; (4); 4/107; French Clb; Spanish Clb; Nwsp Stf; Yrbk Stf; Rep Soph Cls; High Hon Roll; Hon Roll; NHS; Almni Assn Engl Awd, Sayre Rtry Awd Bkkpng, Marleah Jrdn Crnll Meml Awd 87; Central PA Bus; Paralgl.

ALTHOFF, DAVID; Dover Area HS; Dover, PA; (3); 41/246; Pres Church Yth Grp; JV Var Bsbl; Hon Roll; Bio-Med.

ALTHOUSE, JED; Warwick HS; Lititz, PA; (2); 3/327; Church Yth Grp; Computer Clb; Varsity Clb; Var JV Bsktbl; Var Crs Cntry; Var Score Keeper; Var Trk; High Hon Roll; Am Lgn Ctznshp Awd 85; Sci Schlr 85.

ALTIER JR, FRNAK; Jeannette SR HS; Jeannette, PA; (2); 5/130; French Clb; Ski Clb; Trs Frsh Cls; Trs Soph Cls; Var JV Bsktbl; Var L Golf; High Hon Roll; Westmoreland Intermediate Unit 86; Bio.

ALTIER, MARCI; Greensburg Salem SR HS; Greensburg, PA; (2); 14/302; Church Yth Grp; Sec German Clb; Chorus; Yrbk Stf; Twrlr; Cit Awd; High Hon Roll; Jr NHS.

ALTIERI, KIMBERLY; Canon Mc Millan SR HS; Cecil, PA; (3); 1/376; Band; Church Choir; Capt Flag Corp; School Musical; High Hon Roll; NEDT Awd; Pres Schlr; Acad All-Amer 84-85; Nclr Engrng.

ALTLAND, BRIAN; West York Area SR HS; York, PA; (2); 10/212; Drama Clb; JA; Ski Clb; Spanish Clb; Yrbk Stf; Off Stu Cncl; Vllybl; High Hon Roll; Ldrshp Cmmndtn 86-87; Hgh Obrn Yth Ambsdr 87; Engrng.

ALTLAND, MICHAEL; Christian School Of York; York, PA; (3); Church Yth Grp; Spanish Clb; Varsity Clb; Band; Chorus; Concert Band; School Play; Var Bsktbl; Var Socr; Var Trk; Lancaster Bible Coll.

ALTLAND, SALLY; Susquehannock HS; Glen Rock, PA; (3); 4-H; GAA; SADD; Teachers Aide; Yrbk Stf; Var Trk; Eng Equitation 1st Pl 84-85.

ALTMAN, ANITA; Keystone JR Sr HS; Knox, PA; (3); Model UN; Pres SADD; Varsity Clb; School Musical; School Play; Pres Frsh Cls; Pres Soph Cls; Rep Stu Cncl; Capt Cheerleading; High Hon Roll; WV U; Poltcl Sci.

ALTMAN, BRIAN; Fort Le Boeuf HS; Erie, PA; (2); Art Clb; Boy Scts; Band; Concert Band; Jazz Band; Mrchg Band; Pep Band; School Musical; Nwsp Stf; High Hon Roll.

ALTMAN, DAVID; Shenango HS; New Castle, PA; (4); 22/112; Art Clb; Aud/Vis; Church Yth Grp; Y-Teens; Nwsp Phtg; Nwsp Rptr; Yrbk Phtg; Wt Lftg; NHS; Rotary Awd; Gannon U; Pre Med.

ALTMAN, LELAND; Neshannock HS; Neshannock, PA; (3); 45/114; Church Yth Grp; Drama Clb; Chorus; School Musical; School Play; Nwsp Rptr; Yrbk Phtg; Yrbk Stf; Var Bsbl; Im Vllybl; Hnr & Dist Choirs 85-86; Regl Choir 86; Music Prfrmnc.

ALTMAN, MATTHEW T; Cowanesque Valley HS; Westfield, PA; (2); 4/84; Boy Scts; Pres Soph Cls; JV L Bsktbl; Var L Ftbl; Im Golf; Var Tennis; Hon Roll; HOBY 87; Naval Acad-Annapolis MD.

ALTMANN, KYRSTEN; Dunmore HS; Dunmore, PA; (3); 2/149; Drama Clb; Letterman Clb; Scholastic Bowl; Science Clb; Spanish Clb; School Play; Nwsp Ed-Chief; Yrbk Stf; Var Cheerleading; High Hon Roll; Med.

ALTMILLER, COOPER; Lakeland JR SR HS; Clarks Summit, PA; (4); 4/147; Computer Clb; French Clb; Capt Crs Cntry; JV Ice Hcky; Var Trk; Hon Roll; Trs NHS; Prfct Atten Awd; Acad Schlrshp 87; Susquehanna U; Comp Sci.

ALTO, SHELBY; Monongahela Catholic HS; Scenery Hill, PA; (4); 29/75; Church Yth Grp; Cmnty Wkr; Girl Scts; Spanish Clb; Chorus; Powder Puff Ftbl; Hon Roll; Wheeling Coll; Nrsng.

ALTON, JAMES; Harrisburg HS; Harrisburg, PA; (3); Church Yth Grp; Cmnty Wkr; Chorus; Orch; Rep Jr Cls; Swmmng; Trk; Wt Lftg; Hon Roll; Prfct Atten Awd; Morehouse U; Med.

ALU, NICOLE; Wyoming Area SR HS; Exeter, PA; (3); Church Yth Grp; VP French Clb; Key Clb; Band; Concert Band; Mrchg Band; Pres Frsh Cls; Pres Stu Cncl; High Hon Roll; NHS; Acclrtd Sci & Engl Pgms; Sci.

ALUNNI, PARIS; Dunmore HS; Dunmore, PA; (3); 18/147; Boy Scts; Stage Crew; Capt Var Ftbl; High Hon Roll; NHS; Eagle Scout Bronze & Gold Palms; Engrng.

ALVAREZ, LAURIE; Mon Valley Catholic HS; Donora, PA; (4); Pres FBLA; Pep Clb; Ski Clb; Chorus; Church Choir; Variety Show; Stu Cncl; Hon Roll; Rotary Awd; Donora Rotary Awd Outstndng Svc & Ldrshp 87; IN U Of PA; Pre-Law.

ALVIAR, TONY; Uniontown Area SR HS; Ohiopyle, PA; (2); Computer Clb; Spanish Clb; Teachers Aide; VP Frsh Cls; High Hon Roll; Hon Roll; JV Amer Comp Sci Leag 85-86; V Amer Comp Sci Leag 86-87; Tchng.

ALWARD, ALICIA; General Mc Lane HS; Edinboro, PA; (3); 1/225; Church Yth Grp; Church Choir; Concert Band; Flag Corp; Jazz Band; Pep Band; High Hon Roll; NHS.

ALWINE, MARCY; Highlands SR HS; Brackenridge, PA; (4); 38/276; Church Yth Grp; Exploring; SADD; Stage Crew; Yrbk Stf; Soph Cls; Jr Cls; Sr Cls; Vllybl; NHS; Gold Awds 86-87; Brown Awds 84-86; Oakbridge Acad; Lab Tech.

ALWINE, STEVE; Vo Tech Schl; York, PA; (2); Chess Clb; Church Yth Grp; VICA; PA ST; Engrng.

ALWORTH, GLYNIS; Sateway SR HS; Monroeville, PA; (4); Dance Clb; Off NFL; PAVAS; Chorus; School Play; Nwsp Bus Mgr; Nwsp Rptr; Nwsp Stf; Ed Lit Mag; High Hon Roll; Forensics Awd; Deans Comptn Awd; East Stroudsburg U; English.

AMALONG, CATHY; Shenango JR SR HS; New Castle, PA; (4); 2/112; Varsity Clb; Gym; Trk; Vllybl; Hon Roll; NHS; Sal; Acad Games; Pre-Vet Med.

AMARAL, SANDRA G; Saucon Valley SR HS; Hellerton, PA; (3); 5/156; Am Leg Aux Girls St; Art Clb; Sec Church Yth Grp; Sec French Clb; Model UN; Ski Clb; Nwsp Stf; JV Var Fld Hcky; High Hon Roll; NHS; Prsdntl Acdmc Fitness Awd 85.

AMATI, LEE; Ringgold HS; Monongahela, PA; (3); Ftbl; Wt Lftg; Math & Sci Hnr Scty 86-87; Hnr Roll 85-86; Penn ST U; Engrng.

AMATO, ALFRED J; Archbishop Ryan HS For Boys; Philadelphia, PA; (2); 22/354; Computer Clb; Political Wkr; Prin Awd 85-86; Drexel U.

AMATO, DENNIS M; Archbishop Ryan H S For Boys; Philadelphia, PA; (3); 1/437; Red Cross Aide; Spanish Clb; Concert Band; Yrbk Stf; Var JV Bsbl; High Hon Roll; Hon Roll; NHS; Theol Awd 86; Dstngshd Hnrs Awd 86; Bsbl Awd 86; Penn ST; Comm.

AMATO, JONNA; Big Spring SR HS; Newville, PA; (4); 44/187; FBLA; Chorus; School Play; Rep Stu Cncl; Gym; Hon Roll; Stu Cncl Awd 87; Fairleigh Dickinson U; Dance.

AMATO, ROCCO; St John Neumann HS; Philadelphia, PA; (2); Teachers Aide; Varsity Clb; Var L Ftbl; Wt Lftg; Archtct.

AMBOOKEN, MARY JANE; Meadville HS; Meadville, PA; (3); 129/363; Church Yth Grp; French Clb; Key Clb; Science Clb; SADD; Varsity Clb; JV VP Cheerleading; Var Trk; Hon Roll; Advncd Dnc Awds 84-86; Phy.

AMBRO, STEFANIE; Northwestern HS; Cranesville, PA; (3); 14/145; Art Clb; Chorus; Yrbk Stf; Hon Roll; Lttr Acdmc Achvmnt 87; Penn ST Behrend; Bus Admin.

AMBROSE, CINDY; Crestwood HS; Mountaintop, PA; (4); Sec VP Church Yth Grp; Civic Clb; Key Clb; Math Tm; NFL; Spanish Clb; High Hon Roll; NHS; Pres Schlr; Bloomsburg U Of PA.

AMBROSE, DANIELE; Hempfield HS; New Stanton, PA; (2); French Clb; Hosp Aide; Pep Clb; Ski Clb; Chorus; School Musical; Nwsp Stf; JV Vllybl; High Hon Roll; Dance Clb; U VA; Engl Novlst.

AMBROSE, TRACY; Charleroi Area JR-SR HS; Charleroi, PA; (4); 24/162; Church Yth Grp; Sec French Clb; Science Clb; Capt Drm Mjr(t); Mrchg Band; School Musical; Symp Band; Nwsp Rptr; Nwsp Sprt Ed; Yrbk Stf; Am Leg Scholar 87; Band Booster Scholar 87; Pres Acad Fit Awd 87; PA ST U; Math.

AMENT, DOUG; Kiski Area HS; Apollo, PA; (3); Teachers Aide; Band; Mrchg Band; JV Bsktbl; Mgr(s); JV Var Trk; Hon Roll; Prfct Atten Awd.

AMENT, SHERRI; Kiski Area HS; Leechburg, PA; (4); Church Yth Grp; Office Aide; Band; Color Guard; High Hon Roll; Acdmc Ltr; Penn ST; Nrsg.

AMENTA, MICHAEL; Cathedral Preparatory Schl; Girard, PA; (3); 14/193; Im Bsktbl; High Hon Roll; Hon Roll; NHS; Teenage Action Clb 86-7; Italian Clb 84-6; Notre Dame; Bus.

AMES, MARYBETH; Abington Hts HS; Clarks Summit, PA; (3); 7/289; Ski Clb; Chorus; Concert Band; Mrchg Band; Orch; School Musical; Lit Mag; Trs Soph Cls; Trk; Hon Roll; Natl Ltn Exm Slv Mdl 85-86; Amercn Chem Soc Fest 1st Pl 86; Dist & Rgnl St Chorus 87; Bus Admin.

AMES III, RALPH G; Northern Chester County Tech Schl; Elverson, PA; (3); Stage Crew; Nwsp Stf; Trs Jr Cls; Hon Roll; NHS; Comp Svc Tech.

AMICK, CHRISTY L; Chambersburg Area SR HS; Newburg, PA; (3); 24/697; French Clb; Nwsp Ed-Chief; Nwsp Phtg; Nwsp Rptr; Nwsp Stf; JV Crs Cntry; High Hon Roll; Hon Roll; Specl Ed.

AMICK, WADE; Elizabethtown Area HS; Elizabethtown, PA; (3); Church Yth Grp; Ski Clb; Band; Concert Band; Jazz Band; Mrchg Band; Orch; Pep Band; JV Socr; Var Tennis; Engrng.

AMMANN, TYNYA; Fleetwood Area HS; Kutztown, PA; (3); Ski Clb; Band; JV Var Cheerleading; JV Fld Hcky; JV Var Trk; Hon Roll; Fshn Merch.

AMMER, JAY; North Catholic HS; Pgh, PA; (3); Church Yth Grp; Im Bsktbl; Hon Roll.

AMMERMAN, JUDY; Sayre Area HS; Athens, PA; (4); 10/113; French Clb; Band; Chorus; Concert Band; Jazz Band; Mrchg Band; Pep Band; High Hon Roll; Hon Roll; Prfct Atten Awd; Dist Band & Chrs; Merit Instrmntl Awd; Simphler Fidelis Musical Excel Awd; Temple U; Music.

AMMON, WENDY; Pequea Valley HS; Gap, PA; (3); 24/142; GAA; Varsity Clb; Chorus; Capt Bsktbl; Capt Fld Hcky; Hon Roll; NHS; Athlete Wk 86; Stu Mnth 87; Outstndng Achvt Awd 87; Jrnlsm.

AMODIE, LARRY; New Castle SR HS; New Castle, PA; (2); Band; Yrbk Stf; Golf; Hon Roll.

AMON, STEPHANIE; Fort Boeuf HS; Waterford, PA; (4); Church Yth Grp; Dance Clb; Var JV Cheerleading; Hon Roll; Erie Bus Center; Bus Mgmt Sls.

AMOROSO, KARLA; Mon Valley Catholic HS; Monongahela, PA; (3); FBLA; Hosp Aide; Spanish Clb; Yrbk Phtg; Yrbk Stf; Var JV Cheerleading; Im Powder Puff Ftbl; Stat Vllybl; Hon Roll; Spanish NHS; U Pittsburgh; Phys Ther.

AMOS, ALEX; Lower Moreland HS; Huntingdon Valley, PA; (2); Church Yth Grp; FBLA; German Clb; Science Clb; Stage Crew; JV Socr; Wt Lftg; VP Wrstlng; Cit Awd; Hon Roll; U Of PA; Bus Admin.

AMOS, LORI; Conneaut Lake HS; Conneaut Lake, PA; (4); 20/80; JA; Spanish Clb; Mrchg Band; Var Sftbl; Hon Roll; Clarion U PA; Sec Ed.

AMOW, MIKE; Pleasant Valley HS; Saylorsburg, PA; (2); Math Tm; Pres Frsh Cls; Pres Soph Cls; Var Bsbl; JV Bsktbl; Ftbl; Hon Roll; NHS; Law.

AMRHEIN, JENNIFER; Bishop Conwell HS; Levittown, PA; (3); 37/277; Church Yth Grp; Dance Clb; French Clb; PAVAS; School Musical; School Play; Nwsp Rptr; JV Capt Cheerleading; Prfct Atten Awd; Shippensburg U; Comm.

AMSLER, VALERIE; Cranberry Area HS; Venus, PA; (2); Sec Church Yth Grp; French Clb; Pep Clb; Teachers Aide; Chorus; Church Choir; Orch; Stat Trk; Hon Roll.

ANANEA, NORHALA; Villa Maria Acad; Erie, PA; (3); Pres Exploring; PAVAS; Spanish Clb; SADD; School Play; Im Bowling; High Hon Roll; NHS; Vlntr Svc Awd 85-86; Intl Bus.

ANCHORS, JANET; Mt Lebanon SR HS; Pittsburgh, PA; (4); Church Yth Grp; Dance Clb; French Clb; Pep Clb; Ski Clb; SADD; Acpl Chr; Band; Chorus; Church Choir; IN U Of PA; Journalism.

ANDEREGG, MARIA; Faith Community Christian Schl; Pittsburgh, PA; (4); 3/29; Church Yth Grp; Teachers Aide; Nwsp Bus Mgr; Yrbk Bus Mgr; Rep Sr Cls; Stu Cncl; High Hon Roll; NHS; Chmstry Awd 85; U Of Pittsburgh; Elec Engnrng.

ANDERMAN, KIMBERLY; East HS; Thornton, PA; (3); 32/455; Church Yth Grp; Church Choir; Orch; Lit Mag; JV Capt Cheerleading; French Hon Soc; Hon Roll; Law.

ANDERS, KIMBERLY; Ringgold HS; Monongahela, PA; (4); 23/300; Am Leg Aux Girls St; Church Yth Grp; Rep Frsh Cls; Hon Roll; NHS; Neal Marcus Schlrshp 87; California U Of PA; Educ.

ANDERS, LES J; North Penn HS; Lansdale, PA; (4); 100/700; Acpl Chr; Band; Chorus; Church Choir; Concert Band; Jazz Band; Madrigals; Mrchg Band; School Musical; Swing Chorus; Natl Merit Spec Scholar Lees & Northrup Co 87; Soc Dstngshd Amer H S Stu 86; John Phillip Sousa Awd 87; Temple U; Music Prfrmnce.

ANDERS, NEIL; South Western HS; Spring Grove, PA; (3); 54/233; Church Yth Grp; Varsity Clb; JV Var Bsbl; Im Bsktbl; JV Var Ftbl; Hon Roll; Wldlf Mgmt.

ANDERSON, ALAN; Jamestown Area JR-SR HS; Jamestown, PA; (3); 4/63; Drama Clb; Pres French Clb; Service Clb; Varsity Clb; Band; Chorus; School Play; Im JV Bsktbl; Var Im Golf; NHS; Hnr Chorus 85-86; Dist Chorus 87; Aero Engr.

ANDERSON, AMY; Butler SR HS; Butler, PA; (3); Church Yth Grp; Drama Clb; Hosp Aide; Thesps; Chorus; School Play; Stage Crew; Variety Show; Var Bsktbl; Jr NHS; Communctns.

ANDERSON, AMY; Upper Dublin HS; Maple Glen, PA; (3); 42/300; Church Yth Grp; FBLA; Intnl Clb; Color Guard; Mrchg Band; Nwsp Stf; Lit Mag; Hon Roll; NHS; Engl Ed.

ANDERSON, ANGELA; Riverview HS; Oakmont, PA; (2); Cmnty Wkr; French Clb; Key Clb; Band; Concert Band; Mrchg Band; Stat Bsktbl; Hon Roll; Bsktbl Ltr Ststcn 87; Bus.

ANDERSON, AUDREY; Upper Dublin HS; N Hills, PA; (3); 87/295; Church Yth Grp; Band; Concert Band; Jazz Band; Mrchg Band; Orch; Pep Band; Symp Band; Hon Roll; Cavalcade Bands St Chmpns 84 & 86; Amer Music Abrd 86; Engrng.

ANDERSON, BETH; Dover Area HS; Dover, PA; (3); 13/314; Church Yth Grp; Varsity Clb; Acpl Chr; School Musical; Rep Soph Cls; Var Capt Fld Hcky; Var L Trk; Hon Roll; NHS; Vlntr Mssnry Wrk Mexic 85-86; Frnch Awd Acadmc Excllnc 85-86; Art.

ANDERSON, BRIDGETTE; Phil-Mont Christian Acad; Warminster, PA; (1); Church Yth Grp; Library Aide; Band; School Play; Stu Cncl; High Hon Roll; MIT; Aerospace Engineering.

ANDERSON, CHRISTINE; South Park HS; Library, PA; (4); 30/203; Drama Clb; Exploring; Political Wkr; Thesps; Chorus; School Play; Stage Crew; Gov Hon Prg Awd; High Hon Roll; NEDT Awd; Cert Merit PA Hghr Ed Assn 86; Allegheny Coll; Lawyer.

ANDERSON, DAWN; Central Dauphin East HS; Harrisburg, PA; (4); 4/244; Acpl Chr; Sec Chorus; Flag Corp; School Musical; School Play; Rep Jr Cls; Rep Sr Cls; NHS; Ntl Merit Ltr; Pres Schlr; John Hall Fndtn Schlrshp 87-88; Lns Clb Awd 87; Harrisburg Are Comm Coll; Bio.

ANDERSON, DAWN; Hazleton HS; Drums, PA; (3); 125/420; Girl Scts; Band; Concert Band; Mrchg Band; Var L Swmmng; Hon Roll.

ANDERSON, DEREK; West Allegheny SR HS; Coraopolis, PA; (3); Computer Clb.

ANDERSON, DOREEN; Villa Maria Acad; Erie, PA; (4); 56/127; Diving; Edinboro U; Elem Ed.

ANDERSON, GEORGE; Curwensville Area HS; Curwensville, PA; (3); Letterman Clb; Stage Crew; Var L Bsbl; Var L Ftbl; Var L Golf; Wt Lftg; Wrstlng; Hon Roll; Lock Haven; Athletic.

ANDERSON, HEATHER; Lakeview HS; Mercer, PA; (2); Drama Clb; Band; Chorus; Concert Band; Mrchg Band; Dstngshd Exprt Mrksmn 85; J Casablancas Mdlng Crs 85; Spnsh Exllnc Awd 87; Med.

ANDERSON, HOLLY; St Paul Cathedral HS; Pittsburgh, PA; (4); 18/56; Camera Clb; Boys Clb Am; Dance Clb; Drama Clb; FBLA; Intnl Clb; Political Wkr; Science Clb; Nwsp Stf; Hon Roll; Typng Awd 86-87; HS Gst Pgm 85-86; U Of Pittsburgh; Eng.

ANDERSON, ISIAH; Scotland School Or Vet Child; Philadelphia, PA; (3); ROTC; Varsity Clb; Band; Concert Band; Drill Tm; Mrchg Band; Pres Jr Cls; Pres Sr Cls; Rep Stu Cncl; Var L Bsktbl; Noncmmssnd Ofcr Ldrshp Awd 87; Valley Forge Mltry Acad; Bus.

ANDERSON, JANET; Mercer Area HS; Sharpsville, PA; (3); Trk; Hon Roll; Bus Ed.

ANDERSON, JASON; West Mifflin Area HS; West Mifflin, PA; (3); 8/301; High Hon Roll; NHS.

ANDERSON, JEFF; Tidioute Area HS; Tidioute, PA; (3); 3/22; Debate Tm; JA; SADD; Varsity Clb; Band; Concert Band; Yrbk Stf; High Hon Roll; Hon Roll; NHS; Yth Ldrshp Awd 86; Cnsrvtn Awd 86; Penn ST; Phys Sci.

ANDERSON, JEREMY; Tunkhannock Area HS; Tunkhannock, PA; (4); Spanish Clb; JV Bsbl; Var L Bsktbl; Var Capt Socr; Var Trk; Hon Roll; NHS; Band; Concert Band; Villanova U; Acctg.

ANDERSON, JILL; Central HS; Philadelphia, PA; (2); Dance Clb; Chorus; Variety Show; Hon Roll; Law.

ANDERSON, JODY; Freeport HS; Freeport, PA; (2); Office Aide; Band; Concert Band; Mrchg Band; Symp Band; Pres Schlr; Nrsng.

ANDERSON, JULIE; Cambridge Springs Joint HS; Cambridge Spgs, PA; (2); 8/99; Pep Clb; Spanish Clb; SADD; Chorus; Church Choir; Stu Cncl; JV Cheerleading; NHS; Mrn Bio.

ANDERSON, JULIE; Columbia Montour Area Vo Tech; Bloomsburg, PA; (3); Cmnty Wkr; Mrchg Band; Nwsp Rptr; Tchg.

ANDERSON, JULIE; Harbor Creek HS; Erie, PA; (3); Computer Clb; Exploring; Hosp Aide; Office Aide; Science Clb; Bowling; Hon Roll; Comm.

ANDERSON, KELLY KRISTIN; Nazareth Acad; Holland, PA; (3); 18/125; Church Yth Grp; Co-Capt Dance Clb; Hosp Aide; Math Clb; Service Clb; School Musical; Nwsp Rptr; Var Cheerleading; Fld Hcky; Hon Roll; Archdiocesan Scholars Program Finalist 87; La Salle U; Bus Law.

ANDERSON, KEVIN; Central Fulton HS; Needmore, PA; (3); Church Yth Grp; 4-H; FFA; Band; Church Choir; Stage Crew; Yrbk Stf; 4-H Awd; Gov Hon Prg Awd; Hon Roll; Ag Mchncs 86-87; Cert Of Rcgntn PA & NJ REA Tour Wash DC 87; FFA Beef Awd 85-86; Penn ST U.

ANDERSON, KRISTEN; Warren Area HS; Warren, PA; (3); Pres Church Yth Grp; Spanish Clb; Acpl Chr; Chorus; Jazz Band; Mrchg Band; Orch; School Musical; Hon Roll; Jr NHS; Jr Philomel Clb 86-87; Soc Wrk.

ANDERSON, KRISTIE; E Allegheny HS; North Versailles, PA; (3); Dance Clb; Chorus; School Musical; Nwsp Rptr; Nwsp Stf; Hon Roll; NHS; Dance Masters Of PA 3rd Pl 85 & 2nd 86 & 87; U Of Pittsburgh; Law.

ANDERSON, LENNI; California Area SR HS; California, PA; (4); Drama Clb; Pres VP FBLA; VP FNA; Pep Clb; Ski Clb; Teachers Aide; Band; Concert Band; School Play; Yrbk Stf; CA U PA.

ANDERSON, LISA; Connellsville SR HS; Connellsville, PA; (4); Church Yth Grp; Girl Scts; SADD; Hon Roll; Upward Bound Mst Imprvd Rdng 84; Upward Bound Prfct Atten 87; Upward Bound Bridge 88; Little CA U; Library Sci.

ANDERSON, LISA M; Gwynedd Mercy Acad; Ft Washington, PA; (2); Rep Frsh Cls; Rep Soph Cls; Pres Jr Cls; Bsktbl; JV Fld Hcky; JV Var Lcrss; Swmmng; High Hon Roll; Lat Frnch & Alg Cert Awd; Frnch Cert Awd.

ANDERSON, MARY E; Christian Schl Of York; Red Lion, PA; (4); Church Yth Grp; Library Aide; Band; Chorus; Church Choir; School Musical; Nwsp Stf; Cit Awd; High Hon Roll; Hon Roll; 2nd Pl-Sci Fair Rgnl 85; Jrnlsm Awd-York Co Hndcppd-1st Pl 86; Music.

ANDERSON, MELINDA L; Crestwood HS; Mountaintop, PA; (3); 28/198; Ski Clb; VP Jr Cls; VP Sr Cls; Rep Sec Stu Cncl; Var Capt Fld Hcky; High Hon Roll; Fld Hcky Awds/Champs, Conf All Stars; AMA, NAA & FAI Mbr, AMA Natl Champ 84-87; Ski Instr 86-87; Engrng.

ANDERSON, MICHAEL; Burgettstown Area JR SR HS; Burgettstown, PA; (3); Cmnty Wkr; Ski Clb; Var L Bsbl; JV Bsktbl; L Capt Ftbl; Var L Golf; Hon Roll; NHS; Hanover Vol JR Fire Dept-Chief & Asst Chief 85-87; Penn ST; Engrng.

ANDERSON, NICOLE; Franklin Learning Ctr; Philadelphia, PA; (3); Band; Bsktbl; Vllybl; Hon Roll; Jr NHS; Var Ltr Bkstbl, Vllybl 87; Eng 10 86; Obstrcn.

ANDERSON, NICOLE LYNN; Palmyra Area SR HS; Palmyra, PA; (3); Church Yth Grp; Drama Clb; French Clb; Hosp Aide; SADD; Church Choir; School Musical; School Play; Tennis; Hon Roll; Penn ST U; Commnctns.

ANDERSON, PAMELA; Brookville Area HS; Brookville, PA; (3); 8/178; Dance Clb; French Clb; Key Clb; SADD; Varsity Clb; School Musical; Var L Cheerleading; Var Diving; Hon Roll; Jr NHS; PA Free Entrps Wk 86; Ntl Hstry & Govt Awd 85.

ANDERSON, PAMELA; Homer Center JR SR HS; Indiana, PA; (3); VP Church Yth Grp; French Clb; Varsity Clb; Color Guard; Concert Band; Flag Corp; Stat Bsktbl; Var Sftbl; Hon Roll; Jr NHS; 3 Vrsty Ltrs Sftbl 86-87; IN U Of PA; Mngmt.

ANDERSON, PAUL; Belle Vernon Area HS; Fayette City, PA; (3); Art Clb; Church Yth Grp; Ski Clb; Sec Soph Cls; Sec Jr Cls; Stu Cncl; Var Ftbl; Var Trk; Wt Lftg; Var Wrstlng; Penn ST U; Med.

ANDERSON, RACHEL; Chambersburg Area SR HS; Chambersburg, PA; (3); 50/650; Girl Scts; Sec JCL; Red Cross Aide; Band; Chorus; Yrbk Stf; Rep Stu Cncl; L Mgr(s); Hon Roll; Natl Latin Awd-Magna Cum Laude 84-85.

ANDERSON, RENEE; Ringgold HS; Donora, PA; (3); 17/350; FTA; Hosp Aide; Math Clb; Science Clb; Ski Clb; Spanish Clb; Mgr(s); Hon Roll; NHS; Interact Clb; Outdoor Ed Clb; U Of Pittsburgh; Pharmacy.

ANDERSON, RHONDA; Northwestern HS; Girard, PA; (3); 21/148; Church Yth Grp; Computer Clb; Girl Scts; Pep Clb; Spanish Clb; Flag Corp; Nwsp Stf; Yrbk Stf; Cheerleading; Powder Puff Ftbl; Achvt Awd Math 85; Fshn Mrchndsng Mgmnt.

ANDERSON, SARA; Trinity HS; Washington, PA; (3); #2 In Class; Am Leg Aux Girls St; VP German Clb; Yrbk Sprt Ed; Pres Stu Cncl; Co-Capt Swmmng; Trk; Vllybl; High Hon Roll; Hst NHS; Rotary Awd.

ANDERSON, SCOTT; West Perry HS; New Bloomfield, PA; (2); 9/229; Church Yth Grp; Spanish Clb; Concert Band; Sec Stu Cncl; JV Bsbl; JV Ftbl; Wt Lftg; Wrstlng; High Hon Roll; Hon Roll; US Naval Acad; Mrn Blgy.

ANDERSON, SHARON; Lincoln HS; Ellwood City, PA; (4); 7/165; AFS; Church Yth Grp; Ski Clb; Spanish Clb; SADD; Chorus; School Musical; Powder Puff Ftbl; High Hon Roll; NHS; INCO Schlrshp 87; Top 10 Grad 87; Grove City Coll; Elem Ed.

ANDERSON, SHELLY; Williams Valley JR- SR HS; Wiconisco, PA; (3); Pres VP Church Yth Grp; Dance Clb; Drama Clb; Girl Scts; Math Clb; Pep Clb; Spanish Clb; Chorus; Church Choir; Rep Stu Cncl; Sunday Schl Perfect Atten Awd 85-86; Empire Beauty Schl; Cosmet.

ANDERSON, STACY; Connellsville SR HS; Connellsville, PA; (2); 88/550; Office Aide; JV Swmmng; Hon Roll; Prfct Atten Awd; Ped Nurse.

ANDERSON, STEPHANIE; Brockway HS; Falls Creek, PA; (3); VP Church Yth Grp; Drama Clb; Exploring; Thesps; Band; Concert Band; Capt Drill Tm; Mrchg Band; Ed Yrbk Stf; Cit Awd; Schlrshp Lck Hvn Free Entrprs Wk 87; Accptd-Rvrvw Smmr Acad-Math 87; Brckwys Undftd Mck Trl Tm Mbr 87; Lock Haven; Math.

ANDERSON, STEVE; Frazier HS; Perryopolis, PA; (3); Boy Scts; NHS; Chem Engr.

ANDERSON, TERESA; West Greene HS; Aleppo, PA; (3); 15/105; T
Varsity Clb; Pres Band; Drm Mjr(t); Trs Frsh Cls; Trs Soph Cls; Trs J
Cls; Pres Sr Cls; Rep Stu Cncl; Coach Actv; Capt Sftbl; Most Outstnd
Muscn 85; Acad Excllnc Awds 85 & 86; 3H Valley Medical; Rad Tech.

ANDERSON, TIFFANY; Connellsville Area HS; Connellsville, PA; (3
Church Yth Grp; Teachers Aide; Chorus; Nwsp Rptr; VP Frsh Cls; Re
Soph Cls; Rep Jr Cls; Cheerleading; Sftbl; Capt Vllybl; MVP Vllybl 8
KCEA 1st Pl Ptry 84; KCEA 1st Pl Ensmbl 86; Jrnlsm.

ANDERSON, TODD MICHAEL; Milton Area SR HS; Milton, PA; (2
3/254; Church Yth Grp; Key Clb; Varsity Clb; Rep Frsh Cls; Crs Cntry; W
Lftg; Wrstlng; High Hon Roll; Hon Roll; Pres Schlr; Med.

ANDERSON, TRACI; Penn Trafford HS; Harrison City, PA; (4); JC
Latin Clb; Math Clb; Service Clb; Capt Color Guard; Mrchg Band; L
Mag; High Hon Roll; NHS; Prfct Atten Awd; Mnfctrers Hnovr Qrtr Cntr
Clb & Penn Trffrd Educ Assn Schlrshps 87; Grove City Coll; Elem Edu

ANDERSON, TRACY; Carlisle SR HS; Carlisle, PA; (3); 47/467; Art Cl
Hosp Aide; JA; Math Clb; Cheerleading; Hon Roll; Prfct Atten Awd; A
Hnr Soc Awd 86-87; Elem Ed.

ANDERSON, TRACY; Rocky Grove HS; Franklin, PA; (3); 10/81; Hos
Aide; Chorus; School Musical; Wt Lftg; Hon Roll; Acad Excllnc Awd 85-8
Cert Of Appreciation Stu Senate Sec Treas 87; Most Volunteered Hrs I
Wk 85-86; Bradford Schl Of Bus; Rtl Mgmnt.

ANDERSON, TREENA; Daniel Boone SR HS; Douglasville, PA; (3); 2
172; French Clb; German Clb; Mrchg Band; Var Cheerleading; Var Tr
Twrlr; Hon Roll; Penn ST; Pre-School Education.

ANDERSON, VICKI; Western Beaver HS; Midland, PA; (3); Dance Cl
FHA; Girl Scts; Pep Clb; SADD; Chorus; Nwsp Stf; Yrbk Stf; Pres Sop
Cls; Stu Cncl; Robert Morris; Accntng.

ANDERSON, VICTORIA C; Mount St Joseph Acad; Philadelphia, P
(4); French Clb; Latin Clb; VP Soph Cls; Pres Jr Cls; Pres Sr Cls; Templ
Pres Awd 87; Tyler Schl Of Art; Tchng.

ANDERSON, WENDY; Hempfield HS; Greensburg, PA; (4); Art Cl
Cmnty Wkr; Dance Clb; Ski Clb; Spanish Clb; VICA; School Play; Sftb
Vllybl; Hon Roll; Pittsburgh Beauty Acad; Cosmet.

ANDERSON, WENDY; Sheffield Area HS; Sheffield, PA; (4); Dram
Clb; FHA; Pres Library Aide; SADD; Varsity Clb; Color Guard; Nwsp St
Stu Cncl; Cheerleading; Sftbl; Warren Vo-Tech Schl; Sec.

ANDERSON, WILL; Central Catholic HS; Pittsburgh, PA; (2); Comput
Clb; Pepperdine; Radio.

ANDERSSON, J KRIS; North Allegheny HS; Wexford, PA; (3); 275/64
Thesps; Church Yth Grp; Drama Clb; School Musical; School Play; Variet
Show; Lit Mag; Gov Hon Prg Awd; Amer Lgn Essy Cont, HS Excllr
Wrtng Awd 87; PA Govs Schl Arts Schlrshp 86; Carnegie Mellon
Comms.

ANDES, JENNIFER; Donville SR HS; Danville, PA; (4); Cmnty Wk
Latin Clb; Chorus; Color Guard; School Musical; Mat Maids; High Ho
Roll; Hon Roll; Stu Of Mnth Home Ec 87; Lock Haven U; Radlgy.

ANDO, CASSANDRA; Bishop Neumann HS; Montoursville, PA; (3);
40; FBLA; Office Aide; Pep Clb; SADD; Yrbk Rptr; Yrbk Stf; Sec Frsh Cl
Pres Soph Cls; Pres Jr Cls; Pres Stu Cncl; Kings Coll Spanish Exm Hnr
Mntn 86; Heidelburg Coll Smmr Stdy Madrid, Spain 87; Intl Law.

ANDRACA, PATRICIA; Cardinal O Hara HS; Broomall, PA; (4); 5/77
Dance Clb; Math Tm; School Musical; Stu Cncl; Cheerleading; High Ho
Roll; Lion Awd; NHS; Ntl Merit Ltr; Pres Schlr; St Josephs Brd Of D
Schlrshp 87; Widener U Prsdntl & Emerson Electric Co B A Purce
Schlrshps 87; St Josephs U; Comp Sci.

ANDRAE, REBECKA; Jeannette SR HS; Jeannette, PA; (4); Churc
Yth Grp; CAP; Hosp Aide; SADD; Band; Chorus; Church Choir; Mrch
Band; Rep Stu Cncl; Hon Roll; Music Hnr Awd 83-84; Central PA Bu
Schl; Travel.

ANDREAS, DIANA; Hazleton HS; Hazleton, PA; (3); 35/445; Churc
Yth Grp; Drama Clb; Color Guard; Flag Corp; Hon Roll; Kings Col
Physcns Asst.

ANDREAS, SEAN; Big Beaver Falls SR HS; Beaver Falls, PA; (3); 1
175; Church Yth Grp; Varsity Clb; Var Bsbl; Var Ftbl; High Hon Ro
NHS; Rotary Awd; Stdnt Athl Ftbl 85-87; Engrng.

ANDREASSI, JASON; Moniteau HS; Boyers, PA; (3); Church Yth Gr
Cmnty Wkr; Spanish Clb; Band; Trs Jr Cls.

ANDRES, DANA; W Mifflin Area HS; West Mifflin, PA; (2); Art Cl
Chess Clb; Drama Clb; Exploring; German Clb; Band; Concert Ban
Mrchg Band; Orch; Nwsp Rptr; U Of Pittsburgh; Music.

ANDRESKI, JEFFREY; North Pocano HS; Lake Ariel, PA; (3); 23/24
Church Yth Grp; Debate Tm; VP JA; Ski Clb; Band; Orch; Bsbl; High Ho
Roll; Hon Roll; Outstndng Young Entreprenr 86-87; JA 1st Pl VP Mktr
86-87; Engrng.

ANDREUZZI, DAVID; West Hazleton HS; Tresckow, PA; (3); 98/22
Church Yth Grp; Letterman Clb; School Play; Rep Stu Cncl; Ftb
Wrstlng; MVP Ftbll & Wrstlng 85; Mr 3-D Awd 84-85; Penn ST
Engrng.

ANDREW, JOSEPH; Linesville HS; Espyville, PA; (2); Church Yth Gr
4-H; FFA; 4-H Awd; PA ST; Agri.

ANDREWS, AMY; Penns Valley Area HS; Centre Hall, PA; (3); 1/15
French Clb; Band; School Musical; Nwsp Ed-Chief; Ed Yrbk Stf; Trs St
Cncl; Var Cheerleading; Var Trk; High Hon Roll; NHS; Altnt Govs Sc
Intl Study 87; Engl.

ANDREWS, AMY; Ringgold HS; Monongahela, PA; (4); Drama Cl
FNA; Hosp Aide; JA; Chorus; Church Choir; School Musical; Variet
Show; Stu Cncl; Vllybl; U W VA; Music.

ANDREWS, JENNIFER; Trinity HS; Washington, PA; (4); French Cl
Math Clb; Math Tm; Pep Clb; Ski Clb; Jazz Band; Im Swmmng; Im Vllyb
High Hon Roll; Purdue U; Engrng.

ANDREWS JR, JOHN F; St Pius X HS; Phoenixville, PA; (4); 7/18
Debate Tm; Pres JA; Spanish Clb; Capt Ftbl; Trk; Hon Roll; NEDT Aw
Natl Merit Awd Physics & Chem 87; West Point; Elec Engrng.

ANDREWS, JOY; Garden Spot HS; New Holland, PA; (4); JA; Nws
Rptr; Nwsp Sprt Ed; Nwsp Stf; Trs Frsh Cls; Trs Soph Cls; Trs Jr Cls; T
Sr Cls; JV Var Fld Hcky; Powder Puff Ftbl; A Baker Fund 87; Dean J
Fshn Mrchndsng.

ANDREWS, KAREN; Jim Thorpe SR HS; Jim Thorpe, PA; (2); Choru
JV Cheerleading; Hon Roll; Peer Helper 85-87; Lock Haven; Elem Tchr

ANDREWS, KELLY J; Upper Dublin HS; Ambler, PA; (4); 1/307; Nws
Rptr; Yrbk Ed-Chief; Lit Mag; NCTE Awd; VP NHS; Ntl Merit SF; Prf
Atten Awd; Val; Schlstc Wrtng Awds Hnrbl Ment 85; Am Assoc Tchrs Sp
85; Stu Wk; Jrnlsm.

ANDREWS, KIMBERLY M; David B Oliver HS; Pittsburgh, PA; (4);
238; Exploring; Library Aide; Red Cross Aide; Band; Church Choi
Concert Band; Mrchg Band; Crs Cntry; High Hon Roll; NHS; U D
Pre-Med.

ANDREWS, MELISSA; South Allegheny JR-SR HS; Glassport, PA; (2); French Clb; Library Aide; Y-Teens; Yrbk Stf; Rep Stu Cncl; L Trk; High Hon Roll; Hon Roll; WV; Pharm.

ANDREWS, MICHELLE; Fleetwood Area HS; Fleetwood, PA; (3); Band; Concert Band; Mrchg Band; JV Var Cheerleading; Stat Fld Hcky; Mgr(s); Hon Roll; Jr NHS; NHS; Law.

ANDREWS, NICOLE; J M Coughlin HS; Wilkes Barre, PA; (3); 20/362; GAA; Math Clb; Band; Concert Band; Jazz Band; Mrchg Band; Orch; Trs Jr Cls; Trs Sr Cls; Var L Sftbl; Phrmcy.

ANDREWS, PAUL R; C B HS West; New Britain, PA; (3); 86/481; CAP; Science Clb; Hon Roll; Air Force.

ANDREWS JR, ROBERT E; The Christian Acad; Claymont, DE; (3); Church Yth Grp; Acpl Chr; Chorus; Stu Cncl; JV Var Bsbl; Im Bsktbl; JV Var Socr; Im Vllybl; Hon Roll; NHS; Exmplry Stu Ldr Awd 87; U Of DE; Phy Sci.

ANDREWS, WILLIAM V; Geo Wash Carver HS Engrng And Sci; Philadelphia, PA; (4); Im Bsktbl; Im Ftbl; Drexel U; Elec Engr.

ANDREZZE, MARINA; Berwick Area SR HS; Berwick, PA; (4); Capt Dance Clb; Sec FBLA; Library Aide; Elks Awd; NHS; Bloomsburg U; Bus Educ.

ANDRIEVK, JEFF D; Bethlehem Ctr; Marianna, PA; (3); 1/150; Am Leg Boys St; Ski Clb; Spanish Clb; Rep Jr Cls; Rep Stu Cncl; High Hon Roll; NHS; Schl Board Stu Rep 86-88; Phys Therapist.

ANDRIS, KATHLEEN; Cardinal Dougherty HS; Philadelphia, PA; (3); 33/670; Latin Clb; Service Clb; Nwsp Stf; Rep Frsh Cls; Rep Soph Cls; Rep Jr Cls; Pres Sr Cls; Stu Cncl; Bsktbl; Fld Hcky; Hnbl Mntn All Cathlc Fld Hcky 86-87; SR Clss Pres 87-88; Cmnctns.

ANDRUKAITIS, LAURA; West Scranton HS; Scranton, PA; (4); 15/250; Boys Clb Am; Dance Clb; Letterman Clb; Red Cross Aide; Spanish Clb; Yrbk Stf; Stu Cncl; Cheerleading; Trk; NHS; U Of Scrntn Pres III Schlrshp 87; Stu Tchrs Schlrshp 87; U Of Scranton; Pre-Med.

ANDRUS, ERIK; Lake-Lehman HS; Dallas, PA; (1); Hon Roll; Jr NHS; NHS.

ANDRUSKY, MARTINA; Sharon SR HS; Sharon, PA; (3); #41 In Class; French Clb; Y-Teens; Mst Imprvd Stu Accntng II 87; Shenango Vly Schl Of Bus; Acctg.

ANDY, ANGELA; Immaculate Conception HS; Washington, PA; (3); 8/40; VP Jr Cls; Stat Bsbl; Var L Cheerleading; Var Mgr(s); Hon Roll; NHS.

ANGELELLI, JOSEPH J; Bethel Park SR HS; Bethel Park, PA; (3); 76/554; Am Leg Boys St; Church Yth Grp; Trs Sr Cls; Stu Cncl; Var Ftbl; Var L Wrstlng; Bio.

ANGELES, CARLOS; Hazleton HS; Hazleton, PA; (2); Scholastic Bowl; Yrbk Stf; Stu Cncl; Hon Roll; Pres Schlr; French Clb; Bowling; PA ST U; Psych.

ANGELLO JR, MICHAEL J; Ford City HS; Ford City, PA; (3); 12/160; Trs Key Clb; Spanish Clb; Trs Chorus; Yrbk Bus Mgr; Yrbk Ed-Chief; Rep Frsh Cls; Rep Stu Cncl; High Hon Roll; NHS; U Of Pittsburgh; Pre-Med.

ANGELLO, TONI M; Northampton SR HS; Northampton, PA; (4); Church Yth Grp; Leo Clb; SADD; Yrbk Ed-Chief; Var Powder Puff Ftbl; Var L Socr; Var L Swmmng; Var L Trk; Im Sec Wt Lftg; Hon Roll; Exchng Stu Venezuela 85-86; BPW Nov Grl Of Mnth 86; Psych.

ANGELO, JEANINE; Southern Columbia Area HS; Catawissa, PA; (3); 13/104; Key Clb; Ski Clb; Varsity Clb; Rep Stu Cncl; Var Capt Cheerleading; Hon Roll; NHS; Span.

ANGELO, KIMBERLY; Bishop Hafey HS; Hazleton, PA; (3); Pres Church Yth Grp; Drama Clb; 4-H; Ski Clb; Spanish Clb; Thesps; School Play; Yrbk Stf; Stu Cncl; Trk.

ANGELO, PHILIP; Downingtown SR HS; Downingtown, PA; (4); 20/551; Pres French Clb; Intnl Clb; JA; Math Tm; Acpl Chr; School Musical; Nwsp Stf; Var Ftbl; Capt Vllybl; NHS; High Hnr Roll 84-87; Ntl Mrt Ltr 86; Ntl Educ Dvlpmnt Tst Awd 84-85; Aerospc Engnrng.

ANGELO, SAMUEL R; Frazier HS; Perryopolis, PA; (3); Var Wt Lftg; High Hon Roll; Hon Roll; NHS; Penn ST.

ANGELUCCI, CHRISTOPHER B; St Josephs Prep; Philadelphia, PA; (4); Yrbk Stf; Off Lit Mag; Philadelphia Coll Of Art.

ANGIOLELLI, VINCIE; Shenango Area HS; New Castle, PA; (4); 5/111; Hosp Aide; Jazz Band; Mrchg Band; Pep Band; Rep Stu Cncl; Cit Awd; DAR Awd; Pres NHS; Gannon U; Pre Med.

ANGLE, ALEXANDRA; Danville Area HS; Danville, PA; (2); 42/159; Drama Clb; NFL; Ski Clb; Band; School Play; JV Fld Hcky; Var Mat Maids; French Hon Soc; Hon Roll; Psych.

ANGOVE, SCOTT; Eisenhower JR- SR HS; Russell, PA; (3); Pres Aud/Vis; Boy Scts; Pres Church Yth Grp; Acpl Chr; Chorus; Church Choir; Golf; High Hon Roll; Pres NHS; Grove City Coll; Engrng.

ANGST, ROBERT; Pottsville Area HS; Pottsville, PA; (2); Chorus; Wrstlng; V Wrstlng Coachs Awd 86; Lawyr.

ANISCHENKO, TRACY; Chestnut Ridge HS; Schellsburg, PA; (3); 12/147; Church Yth Grp; Library Aide; SADD; Church Choir; Ed Lit Mag; Var Trk; Prfct Atten Awd; Camera Clb; Chess Clb; Speech Tm; Miss TEEN Pagnt Contstnt 87; Rurral Electric Trip Recip DC 87; Tchr.

ANKNEY, CHRISTY; Jefferson-Morgan HS; Mather, PA; (4); 19/100; Am Leg Aux Girls St; Nwsp Rptr; Yrbk Stf; Rep Civic Clb; VP Soph Cls; Rep Jr Cls; Var Capt Cheerleading; High Hon Roll; Hon Roll; CA U Of PA; Socl Wrk.

ANKNEY, MONNA; Oxford Area HS; Oxford, PA; (3); 1/197; Sec FBLA; Color Guard; Nwsp Stf; High Hon Roll; NHS; Shrthnd I, Typng II & Bkkpng I Awds 86-87; Sec.

ANLAUF, ROBIN; Conneaut Valley HS; Conneautville, PA; (2); Church Yth Grp; Pep Clb; Science Clb; Spanish Clb; Bsktbl; Score Keeper; Sftbl; Vllybl; High Hon Roll; NHS.

ANNA, KATHY; Vincentian HS; Allison Park, PA; (4); Pres JA; NFL; Nwsp Bus Mgr; Ed Yrbk Stf; Pres Frsh Cls; Pres Soph Cls; Pres Jr Cls; Pres Sr Cls; Var Capt Fld Hcky; NHS; Hugh O Brian Yth Ldrshp Smnr 84; PA Free Entrprs Week CEO 86; Corp Law.

ANNA, SHAREN; Vincentian HS; Allison Park, PA; (2); JA; Pres Frsh Cls; JV Fld Hcky; Hon Roll.

ANNACARTO, ANGELO; Technical HS; Scranton, PA; (3); Ski Clb; Yrbk Stf.

ANNO, PETER; Seneca Valley SR HS; Harmony, PA; (3); 10/331; Church Yth Grp; VP JA; Math Tm; Ski Clb; Var L Crs Cntry; Var Trk; High Hon Roll; Hon Roll; NHS; Prfct Atten Awd; USAF Acad; Aerontcl Sci.

ANSARI, BUSHRA; Lincoln HS; Zelienople, PA; (3); VP Camera Clb; Debate Tm; French Clb; Quiz Bowl; JV Bsktbl; High Hon Roll; Hon Roll; Qz Bwl Awd 2nd Pl 85-86; Physcs.

ANSARI, NENA A; Westinghouse HS; Pittsburgh, PA; (4); 16/190; Library Aide; Chorus; School Play; Sec NHS; Med.

ANSBACH, MELISSA; Mahanoy Area HS; Mahanoy City, PA; (3); French Clb; Flag Corp; Variety Show; Sftbl; Hon Roll; NHS.

ANSELL, BRADLEY; Rockwood Area HS; Rockwood, PA; (2); Computer Clb; Band; Concert Band; Bsktbl; Crs Cntry; Trk; High Hon Roll.

ANSELL, PATTI; Connellsville SR HS; Vanderbilt, PA; (2); 76/566; Sec Church Yth Grp; Band; Chorus; School Musical; Yrbk Phtg; Sec Stu Cncl; Capt L Cheerleading; High Hon Roll; Jr NHS; Prfct Atten Awd; Mst Schl Sprt; Outstndng Trk Mgr; CA U PA; Psych.

ANSPACH, SCOTT; Nothern Lebanon JR SR HS; Palmyra, PA; (4); VP Church Yth Grp; Pres Science Clb; School Play; Im Powder Puff Ftbl; Var Trk; Im Wt Lftg; Lion Awd; Stu Mth 87; Pres Ecology Clb 86; Milersville U; Erth Sci.

ANSWINI, DOMINICK; Wyoming Area HS; West Wyoming, PA; (4); 32/240; Church Yth Grp; Drama Clb; Key Clb; Math Clb; Ski Clb; Concert Band; Jazz Band; VP Mrchg Band; High Hon Roll; NHS; Dstrct Band 85-86; Rgnl Band Amer Hstry Awd 86; Dstrct Band Dstrct Orch 87; Liberal Arts.

ANSWINI, GEOFFREY; William Allen HS; Allentown, PA; (4); 41/550; Church Yth Grp; Pres Intnl Clb; JA; Letterman Clb; Varsity Clb; Yrbk Stf; Capt Swmmng; High Hon Roll; Jr NHS; NHS; NISCA All Amer Swmng 86-87; Swmmr Of Yr Allen HS 85-87; Var Awds Swmmng 87; Auburn U; Pre-Med.

ANTALL, DAVID; Wyoming Valley West HS; Swoyersville, PA; (3); 30/420; Science Clb; Im Bsktbl; Im Vllybl; High Hon Roll; Hon Roll; NHS; Prfct Atten Awd; Intl Frgn Lang Awd 85-86; Hon Mntn Kings Coll Spnsh Exam 85-86; Frgn Lang Achvt Awd 86-87.

ANTEL, AMY E; West Allegheny HS; Mc Donald, PA; (4); Hosp Aide; Office Aide; Spanish Clb; SADD; Color Guard; Flag Corp; Yrbk Phtg; Yrbk Rptr; Lit Mag; Stu Cncl; Flag Corp Capt 86-87; Winter Guard 85-86; Teen Inst Clb 85-86; Carlow Coll; Physcl Thrpy.

ANTELL, JENNIFER LYNN; Villa Maria Acad; Havertown, PA; (3); Rep Stu Cncl; Bsktbl; Capt JV Cheerleading; Var JV Lcrss; Hon Roll; Spanish NHS; 1st Hnrs 85-87; 2nd Hnrs 85 & 87.

ANTHONY, CRIS; Kittanning SR HS; Worthington, PA; (4); SADD; Band; Chorus; Sec Stu Cncl; JV Capt Cheerleading; Vllybl; Hon Roll; Chrstms Court 87; Prom Court 87; Butler CC; Archit Drftg.

ANTHONY, GARNETT; Germantown HS; Philadelphia, PA; (3); Sec Church Yth Grp; Cmnty Wkr; Debate Tm; Service Clb; Teachers Aide; Hon Roll; Jr NHS; Teen Talk Hotline Awd 86-87; Germantown Mag Stff, Net Clases-Acdmc Cls 84-87; Chem Engr.

ANTHONY, JENNIFER; Bishop Shanahan HS; Kennett Sq, PA; (4); 78/215; Church Yth Grp; Cmnty Wkr; Chorus; Madrigals; School Play; Yrbk Stf; Socr; Shippensburg U.

ANTHONY, LYNN; St Marys Area HS; St Marys, PA; (2); 78/312; Concert Band; Mrchg Band; Capt Co-Capt Twrlr; Hon Roll; Comp Prgmr.

ANTHONY, MARK; Ford City HS; Ford City, PA; (3); 14/162; Rep Sr Cls; Rep Stu Cncl; Var L Crs Cntry; High Hon Roll; NHS; Engrng.

ANTHONY, MISSI; Highlands HS; Tarentum, PA; (3); 9/329; French Clb; Intnl Clb; Soph Cls; Jr Cls; Hon Roll; Jr NHS; NHS; Gld Awds 85-87; U Of Pittsburgh; Obstetrcn.

ANTHONY, RAY; Northampton SR HS; Northampton, PA; (4); AFS; Boy Scts; Cmnty Wkr; Exploring; Stage Crew; Stu Cncl; Hon Roll; Pres Emergency Rspnse Tm 87; Trnr For Fall Sports 86-87; Emrgncy Med.

ANTHONY JR, WILLIAM H; Altoona Area HS; Altoona, PA; (3); Art Clb; Computer Clb; Ski Clb; Spanish Clb; JV Ftbl; Var Socr; Var Tennis; High Hon Roll; Hon Roll.

ANTIMARY, MICHAEL J; Springdale HS; Cheswick, PA; (3); Trs Computer Clb; Comp Pgmng.

ANTINNES, MARCY LYN; Abington Heights HS; Clarks Summit, PA; (1); 57/269; Dance Clb; Hosp Aide; Ski Clb; SADD; Chorus; Orch; School Play; JV Cheerleading; Hon Roll; Spanish NHS; Acad Honor Spnsh Awd 87; Comm Art.

ANTOINE, TRAVIS; Western Wayne HS; Lake Ariel, PA; (2); Boy Scts; Band; Concert Band; Jazz Band; Mrchg Band; School Musical; School Play; JV Bsbl; JV Bsktbl; Var Socr; Music.

ANTON, YVONNE; Ringgold HS; Donora, PA; (3); Library Aide; Office Aide; Spanish Clb; Teachers Aide; Nwsp Stf; Yrbk Stf; Hon Roll; Prfct Atten Awd; MYEA 84-86; Robert Morris U; Bus.

ANTONETTI, MICHAEL; Burgettstown Area HS; Burgettstown, PA; (4); 8/140; Ski Clb; Yrbk Phtg; Yrbk Stf; High Hon Roll; NHS; Ind Arts Awd 87; Presdntl Ftns Awd 87; U Pittsburgh; Engrng.

ANTONIK, MARK; Westmont HS; Johnstown, PA; (3); 85/200; Art Clb; Church Yth Grp; Spanish Clb; Bsbl; Ftbl; Wt Lftg; Wrstlng; Outstndng Wrstlr Awd 6th PA ST Champshp 86-87; Mst Falls Awd Wrstlg & Rnkd 1 AA St Of PA 85-87; Comm Real Est.

ANTONINI, MICHELLE; Hopewell HS; Aliquippa, PA; (4); 45/246; Trs Computer Clb; Yrbk Phtg; Yrbk Stf; Trs Soph Cls; Var Capt Bsktbl; Im Capt Powder Puff Ftbl; Var Sftbl; Var Capt Vllybl; High Hon Roll; NHS; Raccoon PTA Scholar 87; Schlr Ath Awd 86-87; Sftbl Ltr 87; 3 Sport Ltr Wnnr 87; Davis & Elkins Coll; Comp Sci.

ANTONINI, MICHELLE; Immaculate Conception HS; Washington, PA; (3); JA; Yrbk Stf; Cheerleading; Pom Pon; PA ST; Crmnl Jstc.

ANTONUCCI, TONI; Freeport SR HS; Sarver, PA; (3); Nwsp Ed-Chief; Nwsp Stf; Yrbk Stf; Vllybl; Hon Roll; Stu Mnth 84-85; Svc Awd 85-87; Crmnlgy.

ANTOSH, JOSEPH J; North Pacono HS; Moscow, PA; (4); 9/250; Golf; High Hon Roll; NHS; Pres Schlr; U Of Scranton; Comp Sci.

ANTOUN, VANESSA; Chambersburg Area SR HS; Chambersburg, PA; (3); #3 In Class; AFS; 4-H; Spanish Clb; Band; Concert Band; Mrchg Band; Nwsp Rptr; High Hon Roll; Law.

ANTUNES, ANABELA; Phila HS For Girls; Philadelphia, PA; (3); Teachers Aide; Hon Roll.

ANWEILER JR, JAMES C; Churchill HS; East Pittsburgh, PA; (4); Boy Scts; Church Yth Grp; Pep Clb; Ski Clb; Varsity Clb; Acpl Chr; Chorus; Stage Crew; Bsbl; Bsktbl; IUP; Bus.

ANWEILER, JENNIFER; Churchill HS; East Pittsburgh, PA; (2); Art Clb; Church Yth Grp; Sec Soph Cls; JV Bsktbl; Var Cheerleading; Var Sftbl; JV Vllybl; Gov Hon Prg Awd; Hon Roll; Crt 86; HS Banner Cmptn 87; Cnslng.

ANZALONE, ANTHONY C; Lancaster Catholic HS; Lititz, PA; (3); Art Clb; Boy Scts; Church Yth Grp; Cmnty Wkr; Drama Clb; French Clb; PAVAS; School Play; JV Trk; Cit Awd; Millersville U; Art.

ANZUR, SUZANNE; Yough HS; Herminie, PA; (4); 8/250; 4-H; Office Aide; Ski Clb; Band; Concert Band; Mrchg Band; Nwsp Rptr; Rep Frsh Cls; VP Soph Cls; Pres Jr Cls; U Cincinnati; Engrng.

APFELBAUM, MELISSA; William Allen HS; Allentown, PA; (3); Art Clb; Intnl Clb; Ski Clb; SADD; Lit Mag; Trk; High Hon Roll; Hon Roll; NHS; Ntl Merit Ltr; Gold Key Schlstc Art Awd 86; NE PA Downhill Ski Racing 2nd Pl 87; Renovation Arch.

APGAR, ANDERS; Manheim Township HS; Lancaster, PA; (4); 5/337; JA; Var L Bsbl; Var L Wrstlng; High Hon Roll; NHS; Sal; Coach Actv; J A Salesman Of Yr-Entrepreaner Or Yr 86-87; A A U Wrestling Schlrshp 87; Traffic Club Schlrshp 87; Wesleyan U Middletown; Medicine.

APICELLA, ANNE-MARIE; W Philadelphia Catholic Girls HS; Philadelphia, PA; (3); 25/250; Girl Scts; Hosp Aide; Office Aide; Scholastic Bowl; Variety Show; Lit Mag; Rep Frsh Cls; Rep Soph Cls; Rep Jr Cls; VP Stu Cncl; Amer Lgn Awd 84; Outstndng Svc 87; Temple U; Phys Thrpst.

APOLLO, ROB; Shamokin Area HS; Shamokin, PA; (3); 12/223; Pres Drama Clb; Pep Clb; Science Clb; Speech Tm; Varsity Clb; School Play; Var Ftbl; Var Trk; High Hon Roll; Hon Roll.

APOSHIAN, ARA; Bellwood-Antis HS; Tyrone, PA; (3); 6/115; Varsity Clb; Var L Wrstlng; High Hon Roll; Prfct Atten Awd; PA ST U; Chmcl Engr.

APPELBAUM, LAUREN; Central HS; Philadelphia, PA; (4); 16/340; Concert Band; Mrchg Band; Orch; Yrbk Stf; NHS; Barnwell Hnrs; Jefferson Bk Awd From U Of VA; Brain Science.

APPLE, CHRYSTI; East Juniata HS; Millerstown, PA; (4); 8/82; Concert Band; Mrchg Band; Ed Yrbk Stf; Var L Fld Hcky; Var Capt Sftbl; High Hon Roll; NHS; Chess Clb; Band; Pep Band; Modern Music Masters 84-87; Outstndng Sftbl Plyr Awd 86 & Hockey Plyr 87; Millersville U; Jrnlsm.

APPLEBY, JANICE; East Pennsboro HS; Camp Hill, PA; (3); 8/196; Church Yth Grp; Sec Spanish Clb; Chorus; Concert Band; Mrchg Band; School Musical; Stu Cncl; Var Swmmng; Trk; NHS; 1st Pl Essay Cont Leader Nrsg Home 87; Comm.

APPLEGATE, DOMINICA; Bradford HS; Bradford, PA; (3); Ski Clb; SADD; Rep Stu Cncl; Var Bsktbl; Var Crs Cntry; JV Gym; Sftbl; Var Trk; JV Vllybl; Hon Roll; James Manners Outstndg Athlt Trck Awd 87; Co MVP Bsktbl 87; MVP Trck 87; Phy Ed.

APPLEMAN, TODD; Abraham Lincoln HS; Philadelphia, PA; (3); VP Trs Church Yth Grp; Letterman Clb; Church Choir; Variety Show; Im Socr; Var L Trk; Hon Roll; PA ST U; Hotel.

APPLEY, MARY FRANCES; Conemaugh Valley JR SR HS; Parkhill, PA; (4); 1/121; Am Leg Aux Girls St; French Clb; Speech Tm; Nwsp Rptr; Yrbk Ed-Chief; Stu Cncl; Capt Twrlr; DAR Awd; Pres NHS; Val; Girl Of Mnth 87; Hgh Math, Engl & Lang Awds 87; Milan Gjurich Schlrshp Awd 87; PA ST U; Trnsltr.

APPMAN, KELLY; Wilson Christian Acad; N Versailles, PA; (3); Church Yth Grp; Hosp Aide; Chorus; Yrbk Stf; Var L Bsktbl; Var Cheerleading; Sftbl; Vllybl; Sci Fair Awd 84 & 85; Pitt; Physcl Thrpy.

APPNEL, LORI; Pittston Area HS; Avoca, PA; (3); 66/320; Drama Clb; Key Clb; Science Clb; Chorus; School Musical; Diving; Swmmng; Trk; Schl Hi Jmp Rec 86; Dist Trck Meet Slvr Mdlst 86.

ARANGO, LUZ; Coatesville SR HS; Coatesville, PA; (3); Ski Clb; Chorus; Rep Soph Cls; Stu Cncl; Hon Roll; NHS; Millersville U; Genetics.

ARBITTIER, JENNIFER; Abington SR HS; Elkins Pk, PA; (3); 6/502; Key Clb; Chorus; Madrigals; School Musical; Nwsp Stf; Yrbk Stf; Stu Cncl; High Hon Roll; NHS; Ntl Merit SF; News Bureau Awd 87; Bst Musicn Awd 85; Frnch Awd 85; Law.

ARBOGAST, LISA; Shamokin Area HS; Sunbury, PA; (3); 50/200; Sec Church Yth Grp; FHA; FNA; German Clb; Girl Scts; Hosp Aide; Office Aide; SADD; Church Choir; Hon Roll; Cedar Crest; Nrsng.

ARBOGAST, SHERRY; Shamokin Area HS; Sunbury, PA; (3); Church Yth Grp; German Clb; Office Aide; SADD; Band; Concert Band; Mrchg Band; Orch; Hon Roll; Pep Clb; Psych.

ARCHER, ANDREW; Hempfield HS; Lancaster, PA; (3); 2/420; Am Leg Boys St; Quiz Bowl; Chorus; Orch; School Musical; School Play; Nwsp Ed-Chief; Nwsp Sprt Ed; JV Var Socr; Im Vllybl; Hugh O Brien Cntrl PA Yth Ldrshp Conf 86; Rsrch Intrnshp Chem 87; Engrng.

ARCHER, BRETT; Mc Guffey HS; Claysville, PA; (3); French Clb; Y-Teens; Var L Bsbl; Var L Bsktbl; Var L Ftbl; Wt Lftg; Hon Roll.

ARCHER, DENELLE T; Living Word Acad; Lancaster, PA; (3); Church Yth Grp; Cmnty Wkr; Rep Stu Cncl; Var Fld Hcky; Trk; Prfct Atten Awd; Chrctr Hnr Roll 85-86; YWCA Cnslr Of Yr Awd 85-86; Oral Roberts U; Bus Admin.

ARCHER, MICHAEL; Moshannon Valley HS; Houtzdale, PA; (3); 9/116; Church Yth Grp; Exploring; Ski Clb; Church Choir; Concert Band; Mrchg Band; Pep Band; School Play; High Hon Roll; Hon Roll; Phrmctcs.

ARCHER, OLIVER B J; Blue Mountain Acad; Brooklyn, NY; (4); Church Yth Grp; Chorus; Church Choir; School Musical; School Play; Variety Show; Off Sr Cls; Var Im Bsktbl; Var Gym; Ntl Merit Schol; Andrews U; Avtn Rpr.

ARCHER, STEPHANIE; Moshannon Valley JR SR HS; Houtzdale, PA; (3); 3/112; Cmnty Wkr; VP Spanish Clb; Pres SADD; Band; Sec Chorus; Stat Bsktbl; Twrlr; High Hon Roll; NHS; Ntl Merit Ltr; Physcn.

ARCHIE, KEITA; Springside Schl; Philadelphia, PA; (3); Dance Clb; Drama Clb; Girl Scts; Hosp Aide; Orch; School Play; Variety Show; Pres Civic Clb; JV Bsktbl; JV Fld Hcky; Instrmntl/Violin Awd 86; Opertn Undrstndng 87; Mayors Yth Advsry Cmmssn 86-87; Spelman Coll; Attrny.

ARCHIE, TIFFENIA; Reading SR HS; Reading, PA; (3); 11/710; Sec Key Clb; Quiz Bowl; VP SADD; Yrbk Ed-Chief; Hon Roll; Sec Jr NHS; NHS; Am Leg Schlr Awd 85; Kutztown U; Psych.

ARCURI, JOSEPH; West Scranton SR HS; Scranton, PA; (2); 1/270; Rep Church Yth Grp; Latin Clb; Letterman Clb; Pres Orch; JV Var Ftbl; Var Swmmng; High Hon Roll; Jr NHS; 1st Chair 1st Violin Dit 9 Orchestra 87.

ARDINI, LEE A; Central Cambria HS; Nanty-Glo, PA; (4); 11/210; VP Key Clb; Science Clb; Distngshd Amer Stu 85; Med Tech.

ARDITO, ALEC; Burrell HS; Lower Burrell, PA; (3); 21/176; Exploring; French Clb; Var Capt Bsktbl; L Var Golf; Var L Trk; Hon Roll; Rotary Awd; Bst Defnsve Plyr Wstmnstr Bsktbl Camp 86; MVP Bsktbl 86.

ARDIZZI, JOSEPH; Cardinal O Hara HS; Havertown, PA; (3); 56/710; Pres VP Church Yth Grp; Scholastic Bowl; Spanish Clb; Rep Sr Cls; Rep Stu Cncl; Im Bsktbl; Hon Roll; Ntl Merit Ltr; DE Cnty Sci Fair 2nd Pl; De Vly Sci Fair Hon Mntn; Mgmt.

ARDREY, JACQUELINE; Bensalem HS; Bensalem, PA; (4); 36/499; French Clb; Chorus; Capt Color Guard; Mrchg Band; Rep Frsh Cls; Rep Soph Cls; Fld Hcky; Capt Sftbl; High Hon Roll; Hon Roll; Outstndng Sr Awd 87; Presdntl Acad Ftnss Awd 87; Rider Coll Fornsc Lang Trnmnt 86; Penn ST U; Elem Educ.

ARENA, CARY A; Pittston Area HS; Pittston, PA; (3); Swmmng; Trk; High Hon Roll; Hon Roll; Jr NHS; NHS; Drama Clb; FNA; Science Clb; Ski Clb; 2nd Rnnr Up In Beauty Pgnt; Med.

ARENDT, SUSAN; Marple-Newtown SR HS; Newtown Square, PA; (3); Drama Clb; School Play; NCTE Wrtng Compttn Prtcptn 87; Penn ST U/ Penn Cncl Tchrs Engl Essy Cont Prtcptn 85; Comms.

ARGOT JR, ROBERT G; Pleasant Valley HS; Saylorsburg, PA; (4); 2/ 198; Capt Scholastic Bowl; Yrbk Rptr; Capt Golf; Elks Awd; Kiwanis Awd; Trs NHS; Ntl Merit Ltr; Sal; Boy Scts; Drama Clb; Eagle Scout 85; PA ST U; Sci.

ARISTA, KAREN S; Tyrone Area HS; Warriors Mark, PA; (3); Key Clb; Spanish Clb; Chorus; Church Choir; High Hon Roll; Hon Roll; Mst Outstndng Engl & Spnsh Awd 86-87; Penn ST U; Law.

ARIZINI, DAVID; Archbishop Carroll HS; Wayne, PA; (3); 28/386; Ski Clb; Nwsp Phtg; Var Golf; Score Keeper; Tennis; High Hon Roll; Hon Roll; NHS; Intrmrls 85-88; Bus.

ARMAGOST, STACY; Clarion-Limestone HS; Corsica, PA; (3); FFA; SADD; Varsity Clb; Chorus; VP Soph Cls; VP Jr Cls; VP Sr Cls; Rep Stu Cncl; L Var Bsktbl; VP L Cheerleading; Bus.

ARMBRUST, MICHELLE; Penn Trafford HS; Irwin, PA; (2); 30/300; Band; Chorus; Concert Band; Mrchg Band; JV Bsktbl; JV Trk; JV Vllybl; High Hon Roll; Hon Roll; E Div US JR Olympic Vllybl 87.

ARMBRUSTER, DAVID; Upper Dublin HS; Dresher, PA; (3); 30/295; Church Yth Grp; SADD; Varsity Clb; Var L Trk; NHS; Ntl Merit Ltr; Gold Medal, ACL NJCL Natl Latin Exam 87.

ARMER, JODI; Solanco HS; Quarryville, PA; (3); FBLA; Trs Frsh Cls; Trs Soph Cls; Trs Jr Cls; Trs Sr Cls; Rep Stu Cncl; Mgr(s); Powder Puff Ftbl; Hon Roll; Spanish Clb; Bus.

ARMIGER, CANDY; Kennard-Dale HS; Delta, PA; (2); Ski Clb; Chorus; Hon Roll.

ARMINAS, LARA; Geibel HS; Uniontown, PA; (3); Drama Clb; SADD; Pres Jr Cls; Pres Sr Cls; French Hon Soc; High Hon Roll; VP NHS; Dance Clb; French Clb; Library Aide; Hmcmng Attendnt 86-87; Pres Phys Ftnss Awd; Many Dance Awds, Schlrshps; Educ.

ARMITAGE, RUTH ANN; West Middlesex HS; Mercer, PA; (2); Library Aide; Spanish Clb; SADD; Chorus; Church Choir; High Hon Roll; Jr NHS; NHS; Thiel Coll; Chemstry.

ARMITAGE, VICKI; Wyalusing Valley HS; Wyalusing, PA; (4); 13/132; Letterman Clb; Ski Clb; Spanish Clb; Mrchg Band; Var L Cheerleading; Var L Twrlr; Sr Hmcmng Ct 86; Penn St University Park; Spnsh.

ARMOLD, MELISSIA; Donegal HS; Marietta, PA; (4); 17/168; Spanish Clb; Pres Stu Cncl; Cheerleading; Sftbl; Hon Roll; Ntl Merit Ltr; Spanish NHS; Pres Acad Ftns Awd 86-87; Acad All Amer 87; U Of Pittsburgh; Phrmcy.

ARMON, LORI ELLEN; Bensalem HS; Bensalem, PA; (4); 5/520; Debate Tm; Drama Clb; School Play; Nwsp Stf; VP Sr Cls; Stu Cncl; High Hon Roll; VP NHS; Syracuse U; Cmmnctns.

ARMOUR, TIMOTHY; Trinity HS; Washington, PA; (3); 88/405; Letterman Clb; Office Aide; Pep Clb; L Bsktbl; L Ftbl; Wt Lftg; Hon Roll.

ARMSTRONG, CLARENCE; Chichester HS; Aston, PA; (3); 69/297; Spanish Clb; VP Sr Cls; Bsbl; Bsktbl; Jr NHS; Prfct Atten Awd; Spanish NHS; All-Leag, All Cnty Bsktbll 85-87; Acad All-Amer 87-88; Engnrng.

ARMSTRONG, COREY; Chester HS; Chester, PA; (3); German Clb; JV Bsktbl; Hon Roll; Philadelphia Coll Art; Comm Art.

ARMSTRONG, ERIK; Lampeter Strasburg HS; Refton, PA; (3); Church Yth Grp; FFA; Varsity Clb; Band; Concert Band; Mrchg Band; JV Var Ftbl; JV Socr; Var L Trk; Voice Dem Awd; PA ST U; Mech Engr.

ARMSTRONG, JUDITH; Lower Dauphin HS; Hershey, PA; (3); Church Yth Grp; Cmnty Wkr; Ski Clb; Thesps; Var Crs Cntry; Brandywine Coll; Fshn Merch.

ARMSTRONG, MICHELE; Unionville HS; Chadds Ford, PA; (4); Band; Orch; School Musical; Stat Ftbl; Stat Lcrss; Var Mgr(s); Var Score Keeper; Stat Wrstlng; Hon Roll; NHS; West Chester U; Athl Trng.

ARMSTRONG, NICHOLE; Beaver Falls HS; Beaver Falls, PA; (3); 69/ 177; Aud/Vis; Dance Clb; Library Aide; NAACP; Office Aide; SADD; Teachers Aide; Nwsp Phtg; Yrbk Phtg; Stu Cncl; Bradford Bus Schl; Retail Mgmt.

ARMSTRONG, NORA; Northern HS; Wellsville, PA; (4); Band; Hon Roll; Misericordia Coll; Elem Ed.

ARMSTRONG, RICKY; Pocono Mt SR HS; Stroudsburg, PA; (3); 80/ 330; Dance Clb; School Musical; Stage Crew; Variety Show; Stu Cncl; Gym; Hon Roll; Merit Schlrshp-Bllt, Ntl Acad Arts IL 84-86; Merit Schlrshp-Jzz, Gs Giordana Jazz Ctr, IL 85-87; Sprts Med.

ARMSTRONG, SANDRA; Lower Merion HS; Merion, PA; (3); Drama Clb; German Clb; Chorus; Orch; School Musical; School Play; Variety Show; Hon Roll; Sci.

ARNDT, JASON; Bermadian Springs HS; Dillsburg, PA; (2); FFA; Star Frmr Awd, Chptr Frmr Degree, & STS Cont 1st Pl Pleasure Horse 86-87; Anml Sci.

ARNESE, LAURIE; Carbondale Are JR SR HS; Carbondale, PA; (3); JA; Ski Clb; Spanish Clb; Co-Capt Color Guard; High Hon Roll; NHS.

ARNHOLT, CHRISTOPHER; Quakertown Community HS; Quakertown, PA; (1); Art Clb; Jazz Band; Hon Roll; Art.

ARNOLD, ANGIE; South Williamsport HS; S Williamsport, PA; (4); 16/ 140; Pres French Clb; Yrbk Stf; Rep Stu Cncl; Hon Roll; Natl Frnch Cmptn 84; U Of Pittsburgh; Physcl Thrpy.

ARNOLD, BRUCE C; Central Bucks HS East; Buckingham, PA; (3); Am Leg Boys St; Boy Scts; Church Yth Grp; Ski Clb; Stu Cncl; Ftbl; Trk; Wt Lftg; Cit Awd; High Hon Roll; Eagl Sct 87; Cornell U; Arch.

ARNOLD, COLLEEN; Kennedy Christian HS; Eden, GA; (2); 60/90; French Clb; Ski Clb; JV Bsktbl; Var Mat Maids; Trk; Im Vllybl; Hon Roll; St Leos; Elem Schl Tchr.

ARNOLD, DAWN; Tunkhannock Area HS; Tunkhannock, PA; (3); 31/ 330; Art Clb; Rep Frsh Cls; Rep Soph Cls; Rep Jr Cls; High Hon Roll; Hon Roll; Fshn Dsgnr.

ARNOLD, JOE; Shenango HS; New Castle, PA; (3); 16/122; Church Yth Grp; Mgr Stage Crew; VP Sr Cls; Im Bsktbl; Var JV Ftbl; Var Tennis; Bus Admin.

ARNOLD, KAREN; Emmaus HS; Emmaus, PA; (2); Cmnty Wkr; Math Tm; Yrbk Stf; High Hon Roll; Jr NHS; Acctng.

ARNOLD, KEVIN; Salisbury HS; Allentown, PA; (3); Church Yth Grp; Hon Roll; Prfct Atten Awd; Acctng.

ARNOLD, KRISTEN; Cedar Crest HS; Lebanon, PA; (4); VP French Clb; VP Key Clb; Pep Clb; Yrbk Ed-Chief; Lit Mag; Socr; Im Vllybl; High Hon Roll; Hon Roll; NHS; American U.

ARNOLD, LAURIE LYNN; Lower Merion HS; Narberth, PA; (4); 36/ 374; French Clb; Ski Clb; VP Orch; French Hon Soc; High Hon Roll; Hon Roll; NHS; Orchestral Awd 87; Joseph Carmitchell Music Awd 87; Lower Merion Scholar Fund 87; Sthrn Methodist U; Music Perf.

ARNOLD, LISA; Trinity Christian Schl; Pittsburgh, PA; (4); 5/13; Yrbk Ed-Chief; VP Sr Cls; VP Stu Cncl; JV Var Bsktbl; High Hon Roll; NHS; Ntl Merit Ltr; Church Clb; JA; Natl Achvt Semi Fnlst 86; Art Awd, Engl Awd 85-86; PA ST U; Engrng.

ARNOLD, LORI; Tyrone JR/Sr HS; Tyrone, PA; (4); Key Clb; VP Spanish Clb; Pres SADD; Varsity Clb; VP Band; Chorus; Capt Bsktbl; Powder Puff Ftbl; High Hon Roll; JC Awd; M Gunter Kahour Schlrshp 87; Nate Levine Outstndng Fml Athlt Awd 87; Rays Riverside Grls Bsktbl Awd 87; Indiana U; Bus.

ARNOLD, LOUIS; Shenango JR/SR HS; New Castle, PA; (4); 1/113; Church Yth Grp; Computer Clb; Rep Stu Cncl; Im Bsktbl; Var L Tennis; Im Vllybl; Cit Awd; NHS; Elec Engrng.

ARNOLD, MATTHEW; Cedar Crest HS; Lebanon, PA; (2); Boy Scts; Camera Clb; Church Yth Grp; 4-H; German Clb; Pep Clb; Red Cross Aide; SADD; Chorus; Stage Crew; Lab Work.

ARNOLD, MICHAEL; Tyrone Area HS; Tyrone, PA; (3); 77/209; Boy Scts; Varsity Clb; Band; Concert Band; Jazz Band; Mrchg Band; Pep Band; Var L Bsktbl; Var L Trk; Im Vllybl.

ARNOLD, SONJA; Phila H S For Girls; Philadelphia, PA; (2); Church Yth Grp; Teachers Aide; Church Choir; Trs Soph Cls; Im Bsktbl; Im Fld Hcky; Im Lcrss; Im Mgr(s); Im Sftbl; Im Swmmng; Amer Legion Cert 83; Ctznshp Cert 83; Stu Cncl Cert 83; Hampton Inst; Nrsng.

ARNOLD, STEVE; Meadville Area SR HS; Meadville, PA; (2); French Clb; Ski Clb; Swmmng; High Hon Roll; Hon Roll; Invstmnt Banker.

ARNOLD, THOMAS; Hampton HS; Gibsonia, PA; (3); Chorus; School Musical; School Play; Hon Roll; Accntng.

ARNOLD, TODD; Daniel Boone HS; Douglassville, PA; (3); Scholastic Bowl; JV Bsbl; Var Bowling; JV Wrstlng; PENN ST U.

ARNOLDIN, JOSEPH B; Upper Perkiomen HS; Palm, PA; (3); 3/250; Stu Cncl; Var L Socr; JV Tennis; High Hon Roll; Outstndng Achvt Physcs 87; PAC 8 All Conf Tm Hon Mntn Sccr 86; Astrphysst.

ARNOUT, AMY M; Nativity BVM HS; St Clair, PA; (2); 4/80; NFL; Drm Mjr(t); Variety Show; Bsktbl; High Hon Roll; NHS; Prfct Atten Awd; Pen JR Acad Sci Rgnl & ST 86-87; Acad All Amer Schlr Prog 86-87; Hugh O Brian Ldrshp Smnr 86-87; Med.

ARNOUT, ERIC R; Nativity BVM HS; St Clair, PA; (4); 2/93; Church Yth Grp; Cmnty Wkr; NFL; Science Clb; Chorus; Pres Concert Band; Pres Mrchg Band; Variety Show; Sr Cls; DAR Awd; PA Jnr Acad Sci-3rd, 1st & 1st Pl 85, 86, 87; Cptl Area Sci Fair 3rd, 3rd & 2nd Pl 84, 85, 87; St Chrls Borromeo Smnry; Thlgy.

AROCA-BISQUERT, FUENSANTA; Purchase Line HS; Spain; (4); Drama Clb; Pep Clb; Spanish Clb; Stage Crew; Stu Cncl; Var Bsbl; High Hon Roll; NHS; Consrvtrio Art Madrid; Frgn Svc.

AROCHO, MIGUEL; Harrisburg HS; Harrisburg, PA; (3); Apex Tech; Auto Mech.

ARONSON, KIM; Pennsbury HS; Yardley, PA; (4); 170/770; Cmnty Wkr; Red Cross Aide; Spanish Clb; Temple Yth Grp; Yrbk Stf; Hon Roll; E Stroudsburg U; Elec Educ.

ARONSON, MICHELLE; Susquehanna Township HS; Harrisburg, PA; (3); Ski Clb; Varsity Clb; Chorus; Yrbk Stf; Rep Jr Cls; Rep Sr Cls; Rep Stu Cncl; Mgr(s); Var Swmmng.

AROST, SYLVIA; Council Rock HS; Richboro, PA; (2); Art Clb; FBLA; Spanish Clb; Temple Yth Grp; Powder Puff Ftbl; Med.

ARP, JESICA; The Baptist HS; Clarkssummit, PA; (3); 2/12; Church Yth Grp; Sec Chorus; Stu Cncl; Var Capt Bsktbl; Var Capt Cheerleading; Var L Socr; Hon Roll; Pres Phsycl Ftnss Awd 86-87; Baptist Bible Coll.

ARPA, VINCENT C; Archbishop Carroll HS; Wayne, PA; (3); Var Trk; Chem Awd 87; Comp Sci.

ARPINO, MICHELE; Bishop Carroll HS; Portage, PA; (4); 30/107; Drama Clb; PAVAS; Ski Clb; SADD; Rep Frsh Cls; Trs Jr Cls; Trs Sr Cls; Rep Stu Cncl; Var Bsktbl; Im Bowling; Spts Med.

ARQUILLO, MARIA; Charleroi Area HS; Charleroi, PA; (4); 10/162; French Clb; VP Band; Concert Band; Drm Mjr(t); Jazz Band; Mrchg Band; Symp Band; Bsktbl; Hon Roll; CA U; Clncl Psych.

ARRIGO, CHUCK; Carlynton HS; Pittsburgh, PA; (4); 3/172; German Clb; High Hon Roll; VP NHS; Pres Schlr; PA ST U; Aero Engr.

ARRIGO, PHILIP; Penn Hills HS; Pittsburgh, PA; (4); 106/616; Drama Clb; French Clb; Science Clb; School Play; Stu Cncl; U Of Pittsburgh; Bus Admin.

ARRINGTON, NICOLE; Perry Traditional Acad; Pittsburgh, PA; (3); Church Choir; Cit Awd; High Hon Roll; Hon Roll; Jr NHS; Pittsburgh U; Pdctrcs.

ARRIOLA, MARTIN; Cedar Cliff HS; Mechanicsburg, PA; (3); 58/304; Church Yth Grp; German Clb; SADD; Church Choir; Pres Frsh Cls; Pres Soph Cls; Pres Jr Cls; Var Ftbl; JV Wrstlng; High Hon Roll; Natl Hnr Soc Cert Of Achvt 86; US Air Force Acad; Comp Engr.

ARROW, AMY; Lancaster Country Day HS; Lancaster, PA; (2); GAA; Yrbk Phtg; Yrbk Stf; Rep Frsh Cls; Rep Stu Cncl; Var JV Bsktbl; Stat Sftbl; High Hon Roll; Hon Roll; PA All St Piano Concert, Schlstc Art Awds, Cert Merit, Magna Cum Laude Natl Latin Exam 86; Engl.

ARROWSMITH, HELEN; Solanco HS; Peach Bottom, PA; (3); Sec 4-H; Girl Scts; Ski Clb; Varsity Clb; Band; VP Stu Cncl; Var L Bsktbl; Var Capt Fld Hcky; Trk; 4-H Awd; Most Imprvd Fld Hockey 86; Master Fitter Awd 4-H 86; Am Jersey Cattle Clb JR Div Production Awd 85; Penn ST; BSN.

ARTELLO, DEBBIE; Villa Maria Acad; Girard, PA; (3); Pres Art Clb; Church Yth Grp; Model UN; PAVAS; SADD; High Hon Roll; Gvrns Schl For The Arts 86-87; Tresa Burns Schlrshp For Art 85-87; Art.

ARTERS JR, JOHN; Downingtown SR HS; Lyndell, PA; (3); Church Yth Grp; VICA; Im Bowling; Im Vllybl; Hon Roll; Auto Mech.

ARTH, BRIAN; Clarion Area HS; Clarion, PA; (4); Band; Chorus; Concert Band; Jazz Band; School Musical; Var L Ftbl; Var L Trk; Clarion U Of PA.

ARTHUR, AMY; Kennard-Dale HS; Fawn Grove, PA; (3); 8/165; VP Band; Concert Band; Orch; Ed Nwsp Stf; Yrbk Stf; Im Var Socr; Dnfth Awd; Hon Roll; NHS; NEDT Awd; PMEA Lwr Dstrct 7 Bnd 86-87; Stu Of Mnth 87.

ARTHUR, CHRISTINE; Susquehanna Community HS; Lanesboro, PA; (4); 14/84; Church Yth Grp; Ski Clb; Yrbk Stf; Capt Cheerleading; Powder Puff Ftbl; Bloomsburg U; Psychology.

ARTHUR, KRIS; Mechanicsburg SR HS; Mechanicsburg, PA; (2); 102/ 309; Socr; Rep Frsh Cls; Mgr(s); Mgr Vllybl; Mgr Wrstlng; Hon Roll; Marine Bio.

ARTIGIANI, TABETHA; Lancaster Catholic HS; Lancaster, PA; (3); Intnl Clb; NFL; Cum Laude Awd Ntl Ltn Exam 87; 4th Pl Susquehanna Dist Frnch I Exam 85; Intl Affrs.

ARTMAN, NANCY; Meadville Area SR HS; Meadville, PA; (3); French Clb; Nwsp Rptr; Yrbk Stf; Trs Frsh Cls; Off Soph Cls; Trs Jr Cls; Off Sr Cls; Stu Cncl; Hon Roll.

ARTMAN, RHONDA; Commodore Perry HS; Hadley, PA; (3); Trs Church Yth Grp; FTA; Chorus; Cheerleading; Hon Roll.

ARTZ, SANDRA; Tri-Valley HS; Spring Glen, PA; (3); Spanish Clb; Band; Concert Band; Mrchg Band; Yrbk Stf; JV Bsktbl; Var L Sftbl; Hon Roll; NEDT Awd; Med.

ARTZ, SHAIN; Williams Valley HS; Williamstown, PA; (4); 23/110; Computer Clb; Teachers Aide; Chorus; Church Choir; Color Guard; School Play; Yrbk Stf; Stu Cncl; Cheerleading; Coach Actv; Miss Christmas Seal 86; John Hall Scholar 87; Mary Margaret Nestor Fndtn Scholar 87; Harrisburg Area CC; Data Proc.

ARTZ, TRACEY; Tri-Valley HS; Hegins, PA; (3); 16/76; Art Clb; FBLA; Hosp Aide; Yrbk Stf; Pres Jr Cls; Stat Bsbl; Cheerleading; Stat Vllybl; Hon Roll; NHS; Med.

ARUSKEVICIUS, ANDY; Marion Center HS; Ernest, PA; (4); Church Yth Grp; Stat Bsbl; JV Var Trk; Wrstlng; Hon Roll; Hnrs Cord Grad 87; PA ST; Nuclr Engr.

ARUSKEVICIUS, BRIAN; Marion Center HS; Ernest, PA; (3); Church Yth Grp; JV Trk; NHS; Penn ST; Engrng.

ARVAY, JILL; Freeport HS; Freeport, PA; (3); 13/213; English Clb; Girl Scts; Office Aide; Concert Band; Mrchg Band; Pep Band; Yrbk Stf; Rep Stu Cncl; Stat Bsktbl; Trk; Pre Med.

ASBURY, ANSON; Warren Area HS; Pittsfield, PA; (3); Debate Tm; Math Tm; Political Wkr; Stu Cncl; Bsktbl; Ftbl; Tennis; Trk; Hon Roll; Ntl Merit Ltr; PA Free Entrprs Wk; Undefeated Debate Clb Awd; Outstndng Hstry Stu Awd; Georgetown U; Poli Sci.

ASBURY, DAVID; Mechanicsbury Area SR HS; Mechanicsburg, PA; (3); Church Yth Grp; Debate Tm; Band; Church Choir; Concert Band; Mrchg Band; Symp Band; Hon Roll; Pres Schlr.

ASCANI, DANIELLE; Trinity HS; Shiremanstown, PA; (3); 39/138; Drama Clb; Model UN; Spanish Clb; Band; Concert Band; Drill Tm; Mrchg Band; Yrbk Stf; High Hon Roll; Hon Roll; True Value Hrdwr Ldrshp & Bethany Vlg Dstngshd Vlntr Awds 85-87.

ASCH, ERIC; Lakeland HS; Olyphant, PA; (3); 7/150; Scholastic Bowl; Rep Stu Cncl; Var Golf; Var Trk; Wt Lftg; Hon Roll; NHS; Ntl Merit SF; Nclr Engr.

ASCHE, JIM; Butler Intermediate HS; Butler, PA; (2); High Hon Roll; Jr NHS; Schlstc Let Awd 87; Penn ST U; Engrng.

ASH, ROBERT; Milton Hershy Schl; Hershy, PA; (4); 1/135; Nwsp Rptr; Nwsp Sprt Ed; Bausch & Lomb Sci Awd; NHS; Ntl Merit SF; Val; JV Bsbl; Stat Ftbl; Stat Socr; Military Offcr.

ASHARI, ASLINDA; Schenley HS; Pittsburgh, PA; (4); 4/188; Cit Awd; High Hon Roll; NHS; Prfct Atten Awd; Bus Admin.

ASHBAUGH, LISA; Littlestown HS; Littlestown, PA; (3); Varsity Clb; Yrbk Stf; Crs Cntry; Fld Hcky; Trk.

ASHBAUGH, MARCY; Saltsburg JR-SR HS; Saltsburg, PA; (4); Camera Clb; Office Aide; Sec Varsity Clb; Yrbk Stf; VP Frsh Cls; Sec Soph Cls; VP Jr Cls; VP Sr Cls; Bsktbl; Var Vllybl; Oakbridge Acad; Mdl Asst.

ASHBERRY, ERIC; Halifax Area HS; Halifax, PA; (4); Drama Clb; Varsity Clb; Chorus; School Musical; School Play; Variety Show; Rep Stu Cncl; Var Bsbl; JV Var Ftbl; Church Yth Grp; Dist Chorus 85-86; Frostburg ST; Bio.

ASHBROOK, ANNE; Cardinal O Hara HS; Woodlyn, PA; (3); 318/710; School Musical; Yrbk Stf; Hon Roll; Fash Merch.

ASHBURN, DOYLE; Carlisle SR HS; Carlisle, PA; (3); 101/454; Church Yth Grp; Var L Ftbl; Var L Wrstlng; Hon Roll; Prfct Atten Awd; CASAC Slvr Mdl Chem 86; CASAC Gld Mdl Biol II 87; Sci.

ASHBY, MATTHEW; Kiski Area HS; Leechburg, PA; (4); 18/351; SADD; Varsity Clb; Chorus; Yrbk Sprt Ed; Yrbk Stf; Rep Stu Cncl; Var L Crs Cntry; Var L Trk; High Hon Roll; NHS; Vndrgrft Lions Clb Boy Of Mon 86; Acdmc Ltrs 84, 85 & 86; VP Ntl Hnr Soc 86-87; Indiana U Of PA.

ASHCRAFT JR, TERRY; Charleroi Area JR/Sr HS; Charleroi, PA; (3); Rep VICA; Ftbl; Prfct Atten Awd; Auto Bdy Repair.

ASHCROFT, JAMES; South Side HS; Hookstown, PA; (3); 5/140; Am Leg Boys St; FBLA; VP Soph Cls; Var L Bsbl; Var L Bsktbl; Var L Ftbl; High Hon Roll; Hon Roll; NHS; 2nd Tm All-Conf Bsbl 86 & 87; Prom Ct 87.

ASHFORD, NINA; Freedom HS; Emmaus, PA; (4); 26/465; Drama Clb; French Clb; Science Clb; Ski Clb; SADD; School Play; Nwsp Stf; Rep Jr Cls; Rep Stu Cncl; French Hon Soc; 2nd Pl Sci Fair 84; Rep Johns Hopkins U Open House 83; Lenoir-Rhyne Coll; Psych.

ASHOFF, REBECCA S; Steel Valley HS; Munhall, PA; (4); 1/207; Church Yth Grp; Varsity Clb; Var Swmmng; Var Tennis; High Hon Roll; Hon Roll; NHS; JR Marshall 86; Intl Bus.

ASHTON, KIRK; Meadville SR HS; Meadville, PA; (4); Trs Church Yth Grp; Rep SADD; Varsity Clb; JV Capt Ftbl; Var Trk; Wt Lftg; JV Wrstlng; Ofnsv Plyr Yr Ftbl, NW Cnfrnc 1st Tm Ofnsv & Defnsv Ftbl 85-86; Schlrshp Edinboro U 87; Edinboro U; Educ.

ASIELLO, DOUGLAS; Carlisle SR HS; APO, NY; (3); 1/450; Exploring; Ski Clb; Stat Bsktbl; Var Socr; Var Trk; Gov Hon Prg Awd; High Hon Roll; NHS; Ntl Merit SF; Hnry Mntn St Sci Fair In GA 85-86; Pol Sci.

ASK, KRISTEN; William Allen HS; Allentown, PA; (3); Art Clb; Church Yth Grp; Sec German Clb; Service Clb; Ski Clb; SADD; Chorus; Yrbk Stf; Gym; Mgr(s); Interior Dsgn.

ASKEW, AMY; Tunkhannock Area HS; Tunkhannock, PA; (2); 47/320; SADD; High Hon Roll; Cmptr Awds 86; Bus Coll; Prlgl Asst.

ASKEW, CARLA; Gateway HS; Monroeville, PA; (4); Ski Clb; Rep Frsh Cls; Trs Soph Cls; Rep Jr Cls; Rep Sr Cls; JV Var Cheerleading; U Of Pittsburgh; Info Sci.

ASKEY, MELISSA; Mechanicsburg SR HS; Mechanicsburg, PA; (4); Pres Church Yth Grp; Chorus; Church Choir; Mrchg Band; Orch; Symp Band; High Hon Roll; NHS; Ntl Merit Ltr; Pres Schlr; Lebanon Valley Coll; Actrl Sci.

ASKINS, WENDY; Marion Center HS; Home, PA; (3); Latin Clb; Office Aide; Varsity Clb; JV Var Bsktbl; JV Var Crs Cntry; JV Var Trk; Clarion; Psych.

ASMAN, DAWN; Northeast Bradford HS; Rome, PA; (4); 10/88; Sec Art Clb; Camera Clb; FHA; SADD; Yrbk Stf; Sec Stu Cncl; Var Capt Socr; Var Capt Vllybl; High Hon Roll; Hon Roll; Ursinus Coll; Intr Dsgn.

ASPEY, SUSAN; Carmichaels Area JR HS; Carmichaels, PA; (1); 23/130; Church Yth Grp; 4-H; Band; Concert Band; Mrchg Band; Pep Band; Nwsp Rptr; Nwsp Stf; 4-H Awd; Hon Roll; PA St Farm Show 86; Civic Clb Gen Sewng 87; U Of MD; Neurosrgry.

ASPINALL, SUSAN ELAINE; Bethel Park SR HS; Bethel Park, PA; (4); 48/498; French Clb; FBLA; Sec Mrchg Band; Sec Symp Band; Off Frsh Cls; Off Jr Cls; Mat Maids; Sftbl; NHS; Pres Schlr; Clarion U; Secdry Ed.

ASSAD, CHRISTA; Riverview HS; Oakmont, PA; (3); 1/114; French Clb; Pres Band; VP Jr Cls; Off Stu Cncl; Var Bsktbl; Var Trk; Var Vllybl; High Hon Roll; NHS; NEDT Awd; HOBY Ldrshp Awd 86; Penn St U; Math.

ASSAL, MARIE; Allentown Central Catholic HS; Breiningsville, PA; (4); 5/214; Church Yth Grp; JA; Math Clb; Q&S; Lit Mag; High Hon Roll; Hon Roll; Ntl Merit Schol; Scty Wmn Engrs Merit Math, Sci; Phil Coll Phrmcy, Sci Schlrshp; PA Auto Assn Schl; Army.

ASSELTA, ROCCO; Plum SR HS; Pittsburgh, PA; (3); Drama Clb; SADD; Chorus; School Musical; School Play; Yrbk Stf; Pres Soph Cls; Pres Jr Cls; Bsbl; Ftbl; Cmmnctns.

ASSID, NIKKI; Union Area HS; New Castle, PA; (3); 12/70; Drama Clb; French Clb; Pep Clb; Chorus; Madrigals; School Musical; School Play; Yrbk Stf; Sec Soph Cls; Sec Jr Cls; Homecoming Court 85-87; Teenette Court 85-87.

ASSISE, MICHAEL; Northe Dame HS; Easton, PA; (3); Church Yth Grp; Office Aide; Ski Clb; JV Bsbl; JV Bsktbl; Var Ftbl; Var Trk; Var Wt Lftg; Outstndng Effrt Accntng Awd 87; Ntl Chmp Drug Free Pwr Lftng 87; Accntng.

ASTLE, SARA; Montrose Area HS; Montrose, PA; (3); French Clb; Latin Clb; Chorus; Nwsp Rptr; Var Crs Cntry; NHS; Ntl Merit Ltr; Most Dedicated Girl Crs Cntry 85; Psychiatry.

ASTLE, TAMMY; Ringgold HS; Monongahela, PA; (4); 27/309; Hosp Aide; Varsity Clb; Vllybl; Hon Roll; NHS; US Army Rsrv Schlr Athl Awd 87; WPIAL Vllybl All Star 2nd Team 86; U Pittsburgh; Phys Ther.

ASTLEY, AUTUMN; Hempfield SR HS; Youngwood, PA; (4); 17/693; Church Yth Grp; Trs Spanish Clb; High Hon Roll; NHS; Pres Schlr; Sec Spanish NHS; Best Bio Stu 87; 1st Pl Spnsh Prose-Humanities Day 87; 2nd Pl Spnsh Mscl Prsntn 87; Concord Coll; Bio Rsrch.

ASTOLFI, ERIN; Crestwood JR SR HS; Mountaintop, PA; (4); Q&S; SADD; Pres Y-Teens; Chorus; School Musical; Nwsp Ed-Chief; Nwsp Stf; JV Socr; Var L Trk; High Hon Roll; Semi Fnlst Gov Schl For The Arts 86; Ntl JR Olymps Comptr 85; Schl Mascot 86-87; Kutztown U PA; Art.

ASTORINO, HOLLY; Franklin HS; Franklin, PA; (4); 1/250; French Clb; Radio Clb; Pres Stage Crew; Rep Jr Cls; Rep Sr Cls; Bausch & Lomb Sci Awd; DAR Awd; High Hon Roll; Kiwanis Awd; NHS; Gannon U; Family Med.

ATCHESON, DEBORAH; Bethlehem Ctr; Fredericktown, PA; (3); Cmnty Wkr; FBLA; Spanish Clb; Bus Admin.

ATCHISON, JENNIFER; Plum SR HS; Pittsburgh, PA; (2); 40/410; Cmnty Wkr; FBLA; SADD; Varsity Clb; Yrbk Stf; Chorus; Var Sftbl; JV Vllybl; Hon Roll; Presdntl Acadc Ftns Awd 86; Exec Secr.

ATER, TRACEY; Montour HS; Pittsburgh, PA; (2); 4-H; German Clb; Swmmng; Hon Roll; Francis Marian Coll; Engl.

ATHANASION, CONSTANCE; St Francis Acad; Bethelehem, PA; (4); 2/21; Church Yth Grp; Dance Clb; Office Aide; Chorus; Church Choir; School Musical; School Play; Variety Show; Nwsp Stf; Rep Soph Cls; Intl Facility Mgmt Awd 87; Northampton CC; Intr Desgn.

ATHEY, LISA; Pine Grove Area HS; Tremont, PA; (3); 23/110; Rep Varsity Clb; Rep Frsh Cls; Rep Sec Soph Cls; Hst Sr Cls; Rep Stu Cncl; JV Bsktbl; Im Powder Puff Ftbl; Im JV Sftbl; Var JV Vllybl; Hon Roll.

ATHILL, MONICA; Sister Clara Muhammad HS; Philadelphia, PA; (1); 1/23; Computer Clb; Girl Scts; Temple Yth Grp; School Play; Hon Roll; Columbia U; Pre-Med.

ATIYEH, SHANNON; William Allen HS; Allentown, PA; (2); Art Clb; Drama Clb; Pres Leo Clb; School Play; Nwsp Rptr; Ed Yrbk Stf; Sec Sr Cls; Sec Stu Cncl; Lion Awd; Opt Clb Awd; Strs Of Tmrrw Lions Clb-1st Pl 85, 2nd Pl 87; Allntwn Schl Dist Ortrcl Cont Chmp 86-87; Thtr Arts.

ATKIN, ROBERT; Fox Chapel HS; Pittsburgh, PA; (4); 10/322; Chess Clb; Computer Clb; Key Clb; Quiz Bowl; Ski Clb; Socr; High Hon Roll; NHS; Ntl Merit Ltr; Pres Schlr; Wstnghs Sci Hnrs Inst-3rd Pl 87; Comp Cntst-Wstmnstr Coll 86 & 87; Rdmn Schlr-U VA 87; Princeton U; Engrng.

ATKINS, ANGELA LYNN; Donegal HS; Maytown, PA; (4); Am Leg Aux Girls St; Pres FBLA; Pep Clb; Powder Puff Ftbl; JV Trk; Rotary Awd; Rtry Ldrshp Conf 86; Xenophile Banq Cmte; Mc Connell Schl; Trvl.

ATKINS, RICHARD; Meadville Area SR HS; Meadville, PA; (2); Im Badmtn; JV Wrstlng; Hon Roll; JV Wrstlng Coaches Awd 86-87.

ATKINS, SHARON M; Canevin Catholic HS; Pittsburgh, PA; (4); 2/175; Exploring; FBLA; Office Aide; Yrbk Ed-Chief; High Hon Roll; NHS; Ntl Merit Ltr; Prfct Atten Awd; Rotary Awd; Sal; Penn ST Excllnc Schlrshp 86-87; U Of Dayton Pres Schlrshp 86-87; Pttsbrgh Rgnl Schl Sci & Engnrng Fr; PA ST U; Engnrng.

ATKINSON, CODEE; Marion Center HS; Smicksburg, PA; (4); FBLA; FNA; Intnl Clb; Library Aide; Pep Clb; SADD; Teachers Aide; Var Score Keeper; JV Trk; High Hon Roll; Ricks Coll; Bus.

ATKINSON, SONYA; Center HS; Aliquippa, PA; (2); Church Yth Grp; Cmnty Wkr; German Clb; Yrbk Stf; JV Bsktbl; Hon Roll; Stu Art Awd 87.

ATTARDO, CHARLES A; Crestwood HS; Mountaintop, PA; (4); 22/220; Cmnty Wkr; Science Clb; Ski Clb; Sr Cls; Stu Cncl; Bsbl; Capt Socr; Capt Vllybl; High Hon Roll; NHS; Bd Of Educ Awd 87; PA ST U; Marine Sci.

ATTICKS, BILL; Central Dauphin HS; Harrisburg, PA; (2); 47/350; Hon Roll; Jr NHS; Villanova U; Stckbrkr Invstr.

ATWATER, JASON D; Reading SR HS; Reading, PA; (3); 13/710; Key Clb; Quiz Bowl; VP SADD; Pres Stu Cncl; Hon Roll; Pres NHS; Ntl Merit SF; JA; Chorus; Acadc All Am 87; Hgh Stpr Smmr Stu 87; Carnegie-Mellon; Engr.

ATWATER, LEROY; William Penn SR HS; York, PA; (3); Rep Frsh Cls; Sec Soph Cls; Pres Jr Cls; Stat Bsktbl; Var JV Ftbl; Hon Roll; U Of Penn ST; Comp Sci.

ATWELL, HOLLY; Sheffield JR-SR HS; Clarendon, PA; (4); 18/84; Drama Clb; French Clb; Letterman Clb; SADD; Varsity Clb; Chorus; Color Guard; Nwsp Ed-Chief; Bsktbl; Trk; Ltr Bsktbl & Trck 87; Indiana U Of PA; Theatre Arts.

AUDENRIED, LORIE; Nazareth SR HS; Nazareth, PA; (3); Drama Clb; Band; Concert Band; Mrchg Band; School Musical; School Play; Nwsp Stf; Hon Roll; Jrnlsm.

AUDRA, DAVIS; Crestwood HS; Wopwallopen, PA; (4); Computer Clb; VP 4-H; FBLA; Teachers Aide; VICA; Color Guard; 4-H Awd; High Hon Roll; Hon Roll; Pres Schlr; JR Acdmy Sci-Rgnl & ST Wnnr 87; Outstndng Shp SR & Prjct Awd 87; Scintfc Data Prcssng Awd 87; Marywood Coll; Infrmtn Systms.

AUEN, BRIAN; Jeannette HS; Jeannette, PA; (2); Church Yth Grp; Ski Clb; Spanish Clb; Band; Wrstlng; Hon Roll; Engr.

AUER, CINDY; Connellsville SR HS; Mount Pleasant, PA; (3); Hst Church Yth Grp; SADD; Hon Roll.

AUER, TIM; Connellsville SR HS; Mt Pleasant, PA; (4); 44/530; Boy Scts; Library Aide; High Hon Roll; NHS; Westmoreland County CC; Elctrn.

AUERBACH, ELISE M; Springfield Twnshp HS; Erdenheim, PA; (4); 7/129; Capt Pres Thesps; Concert Band; Jazz Band; Mrchg Band; School Musical; School Play; Rep Stu Cncl; Lcrss; Gov Hon Prg Awd; High Hon Roll; Soph Bk Awds 85; Yng Mscns Series 84-85; Haddonfield Symphony Cmpttn 84-86; Temple U; Piano.

AUGHINBAUGH, JAMES; Greensburg Central Catholic HS; Greensburg, PA; (3); Church Yth Grp; Math Clb; Science Clb; Spanish Clb; Bsbl; Bsktbl; Ftbl; Socr; Sftbl; Wt Lftg; Arch.

AUGUSTINE, LAUREN; Penn Trafford HS; Trafford, PA; (2); JCL; Latin Clb; Band; Concert Band; Mrchg Band; School Musical; Symp Band; Hon Roll; 2nd Pl Art Awd PA Ltn Cnvntn 86; 1st Chair Flute-Westmoreld Cnty Band 86; Asst Flute Sec Ldr 86; Bus.

AUGUSTINE, RITA M; Mount Saint Joseph Acad; Huntingdon Val, PA; (4); Pres Drama Clb; Pres Chorus; School Musical; High Hon Roll; NHS; Ntl Merit Ltr; Spanish NHS; Latin Clb; Spanish Clb; NEDT Awd; Eugene Du Pont Mem Scholar U DE 87; Best Of The Class Channel 6 87; Brown U Book Awd 86; U DE; Bus.

AUGUSTINE, SCOTT; Fort Cherry JR SR HS; Midway, PA; (3); Aud/Vis; Drama Clb; Math Clb; Science Clb; Spanish Clb; Varsity Clb; School Play; Var L Tennis; Hon Roll; Gftd & Tlntd Prog 81; Hmnts Symposium 86; Mech Engnr.

AUGUSTINE, SHAUNA; Greenville SR HS; Greenville, PA; (1); 11/160; French Clb; Library Aide; Chorus; Var Cheerleading; Hon Roll; Law.

AUGUSTUS, FAITH; Allentown Central Catholic HS; Allentown, PA; (4); Church Yth Grp; Drama Clb; Pres VP Intnl Clb; Math Clb; Speech Tm; Teachers Aide; Capt Band; Chorus; Color Guard; School Musical; Hugh O Brien Ldrshp Awd 84; Princpls Awd 86; Sura Clb Sprt Awd 87; Marywood Coll; Physcl Thrpst.

AUGUSTUS, JOSEPH; Allentown Central Catholic HS; Allentown, PA; (3); Church Yth Grp; Ski Clb; Trs Jr Cls; Trs Sr Cls; Bsbl; Bsktbl; Ftbl; Wt Lftg; Wrstlng; Rotary Awd; Rotry Intl Cmp Neidig Ldrshp Cmp 87.

AUKBURG, BRETT; Lower Marion HS; Cynwyd, PA; (3); Intnl Clb; Jazz Band; Orch; Hon Roll; Ntl Merit Ltr; Arch Engnrng.

AULD, ALLISON; St Maria Goretti HS; Philadelphia, PA; (3); 14/350; Drama Clb; SADD; Thesps; Orch; School Musical; Stage Crew; Nwsp Rptr; Yrbk Rptr; Lit Mag; NHS; Wnr Poetry Cont; Wnr Catholc Tchrs Assn Essay Cont; Diocesn Schlrs Prog; Tchr.

AULT, PATRICIA; Trinity HS; Washington, PA; (3); 113/322; German Clb; Pep Clb; High Hon Roll; Hon Roll; Phys Thrpy.

AULTMAN, LESLIE; Carmichaels Area HS; Carmichaels, PA; (2); French Clb; Nwsp Stf; DAR Awd; High Hon Roll; Jr NHS; NCTE Awd; Prfct Atten Awd; Pres Schlr; Acdmc All Am 86-87.

AULTZ, THOMAS; Somerset Area HS; Sipesville, PA; (3); 77/217; Band; Jazz Band; Mrchg Band; Pep Band; Var Tennis.

AUMACK, SHERRY; Blue Mountain Acad; Hamburg, PA; (4); Chorus; School Musical; VP Frsh Cls; VP Jr Cls; Stu Cncl; Bsktbl; Gym; Vllybl; Wt Lftg; Hon Roll; Acad Schlrshp To Columbia Union Coll 87; Mscl Grp Schlrshp To Columbia Union Coll 87; Columbia Union Coll; Offc Adm.

AUMAN, ALAN; Conrad Welser HS; Womelsdorf, PA; (3); 40/179; Boy Scts; JCL; Key Clb; Band; Concert Band; Jazz Band; Mrchg Band; Pep Band; Bowling; Hon Roll; Rtl Awd Dmly 87; Egl Sct 1 Plm Mrt Bdgs 85; Millersville U;CPA.

AUMAN, KRISTIE; St Marys Area HS; St Marys, PA; (2); Hosp Aide; Color Guard; Twrlr; Mdlng.

AUMAN, SUSAN; Cedar Crest HS; Lebanon, PA; (3); 27/328; Art Clb; Church Yth Grp; FTA; Latin Clb; Spanish Clb; SADD; Bsktbl; Tennis; Hon Roll; NHS.

AUMAN, TERESA; W Middlesex Area HS; West Middlesex, PA; (2); Spanish Clb; Band; Concert Band; Mrchg Band; High Hon Roll; Hon Roll; Jr NHS; Stu Achvrs Awd 87.

AUMEN, MARK; Hanover HS; Hanover, PA; (3); Boy Scts; Chess Clb; Church Yth Grp; School Play; Mgr(s); Tennis; Trk; Hon Roll; Finance.

AUNGST, STACY; Ephrata SR HS; Hopeland, PA; (4); 76/253; Church Yth Grp; Cmnty Wkr; Chorus; Church Choir; School Musical; Variety Show; Fld Hcky; Hon Roll; Gregg Typing Awd 85-86; TX Lutheran Coll; Soc Wrk.

AUNKST, KAREN; Montgomery Area JR SR HS; Montgomery, PA; (4); Pres FHA; Letterman Clb; Varsity Clb; Chorus; Flag Corp; Bsktbl; Bowling; Trk; Ertel Hme Ecnmcs Awd 87; Mid Penn Bsktbl Chmpnshp 86-87; Lock Haven U Of PA; Elem Tchng.

AURAND, MICHELE; Hazleton HS; Drums, PA; (3); #1 In Class; Scholastic Bowl; Var L Swmmng; French Hon Soc; High Hon Roll; Lion Awd; 1st Awd-Tlrtn & Hood Essy Cntst 87; Schlrshp-Penn ST Smmr Intnsv Lang Inst 87.

AUREDNIK, DENISE; Moon SR HS; Coraopolis, PA; (3); DECA; Hon Roll; Rsrvtnst.

AUSTIN, LINDA M; Shikellamy HS; Sunbury, PA; (2); 31/360; Church Yth Grp; German Clb; SADD; Chorus; Rep Frsh Cls; Rep Soph Cls; Cheerleading; Hon Roll; Cert Of Reocognition-Brd Of Educ/Dist Chorus 87; Bus Mgmt.

AUSTIN, PATTI; Wyoming Valley West HS; Kingston, PA; (3); 11/419; Cmnty Wkr; Key Clb; Radio Clb; Off Stu Cncl; Mgr(s); Cit Awd; High Hon Roll; NHS; NEDT Awd; ST Hstry Day Wnnr 86 & 87; Georgetown U; Med.

AUSTIN, PAUL; Governor Mifflin HS; Shillington, PA; (4); 8/260; Stage Crew; Im Bsktbl; Var Capt Ftbl; Var Capt Trk; Wt Lftg; Var Capt Wrstlng; Hon Roll; Lion Awd; NHS; Pres Schlr; Buckwell U; Mech Engrng.

AUSTIN, RONALD; Western Beaver JR SR HS; Industry, PA; (3); 12/110; Am Leg Boys St; Chorus; Ftbl; Trk; Hon Roll; NHS; Amer Legion Awd 84.

AUSTIN JR, ROY; State College Area SR HS; State College, PA; (4); Debate Tm; Nwsp Ed-Chief; Yrbk Sprt Ed; JV Var Socr; Cit Awd; Ntl Merit Ltr; Intnl Clb; Library Aide; Model UN; Quiz Bowl; PA Govrnrs Schl Intl Stdys 85; Ntl Merit Schlrshp Outstndng Negro Stu 87; Yale U; Law.

AUSTRA, TAMMY; Wyoming Valley West HS; Larksville, PA; (2); French Clb; Key Clb; SADD; JV Var Cheerleading; Var Trk; High Hon Roll; Hon Roll; NHS; NEDT Awd; Engrng.

AUTEN, ANNE; Springside Schl; Philadelphia, PA; (3); Nwsp Ed-Chief; Yrbk Phtg; Lit Mag; Var Jr Cls; Im Fld Hcky; Hon Roll; Ntl Merit Ltr; Amer Chem Scty Awd 86; U PA Book Awd 87; Mount Holyoke Book Awd 87; Cum Laude 87.

AUTREY, SHAUN; Elizabethtown Area HS; Elizabethtown, PA; (3); 33/224; Var L Crs Cntry; Im Ftbl; Var L Trk; Bio.

AUTREY, TARA; Bethlehem Catholic HS; Bethlehem, PA; (3); 52/200; Varsity Clb; Var L Bsktbl; Var L Vllybl; Hon Roll; E Penn League All Star Vllybl 86.

AVERBUKH, IRINA; High School Of Engineering & Science; Philadelphia, PA; (3); 2/241; JA; Math Clb; Math Tm; Science Clb; Temple Yth Grp; Concert Band; Yrbk Stf; Off Jr Cls; Im Tennis; High Hon Roll; Business.

AVERDUNK, HOLGER; Coatesville Area SR HS; Thorndale, PA; (3); Ski Clb; Trk; Chem Biol.

AVERETT, TANYA; Oxford Area HS; Lincoln Univers, PA; (3); 33/194; FBLA; Varsity Clb; Var Bsktbl; Var Trk; JV Var Vllybl; Hon Roll; Rotary Awd; Rotry Intl Exchng Stu Brzl 86-87; Acdmc Excllnc Awd Wrld Cltres & Spnsh II 86; Pres Phys Ftns Awd; Intl Affairs.

AVERY JR, GERALD; Plymouth-Whitemarsh HS; Conshohocken, PA; (3); 152/356; Church Yth Grp; French Clb; SADD; Chorus; Church Choir; Concert Band; Mrchg Band; School Musical; School Play; Nwsp Phtg; Eckerd Coll; Biochem.

AVERY, JOEL; Blue Mountain Acad; Secane, PA; (4); Aud/Vis; Quiz Bowl; School Play; Nwsp Phtg; Yrbk Phtg; Yrbk Rptr; Off Soph Cls; Pres Jr Cls; Pres Sr Cls; Rep Stu Cncl; Andrews U; Arch.

AVERY, MICHELLE A; Little Flower HS; Philadelphia, PA; (4); Dance Clb; French Clb; Model UN; Swmmng; Prfct Atten Awd; Perf Attndnc Awd 83-87; 2nd Hnrs 85; Awd For Hghst Avg In Geo 86; Hahnemann U; Dctr.

AVERY, PAM; Connellsville Area SR HS; Connellsville, PA; (3); Temple Yth Grp; VICA; Band; Color Guard; Concert Band; Flag Corp; Symp Band; Uniontown Laurel Bus Inst; Bnkg.

AVEY, LORI; Waynesboro SR HS; Waynesboro, PA; (3); JCL; Chorus; Concert Band; Drm Mjr(t); Mrchg Band; Yrbk Stf; Hon Roll; Computer Clb; Cnty Band & Band Awd 85; 1st Rnnr Up-Beauty & 3rd Rnnr Up-Mdlng Miss Hemsphr Pgnt-Cnty Levl 86; Comp Sci.

AVILES, PRICILA; Tech Memorial HS; Erie, PA; (3); 9/311; Red Cross Aide; SADD; VICA; Hon Roll; NHS; Spec Cmmndtn Awd Acad Excllnce, Dist VICA Comp 3rd Pl Nurs Asst 87.

AVILLION, AMY; Hazleton SR HS; Hazleton, PA; (3); 36/488; FBLA; Hosp Aide; Spanish Clb; Nwsp Ed-Chief; Yrbk Stf; Off Stu Cncl; L Trk; Hon Roll; Intl Frgn Lng Awd 86-87; Pres Acad Ftnss Awd 85; Indvdul Cllctv Awds Jrnlsm 85; Spch Pthlgy.

AVILLION, JIM; Hazleton HS; Hazleton, PA; (3); 107/445; Office Aide; Scholastic Bowl; Spanish Clb; SADD; Im Bsktbl; Var L Trk; Im Vllybl; Hon Roll; Penn ST.

AVILLION, LORI; Hazleton HS; Mc Adoo, PA; (3); 122/435; Dance Clb; Girl Scts; Leo Clb; Library Aide; Office Aide; Pep Clb; Ski Clb; Spanish Clb; Chorus; School Play; Hnrs For Grades & High Avg 85-87.

AVOLIO, RITA; Jeannette SR HS; Jeannette, PA; (3); 36/134; FBLA; Office Aide; Spanish Clb; Nwsp Rptr; Trs Nwsp Stf; Rep Stu Cncl; Capt Sftbl; Tennis; Ette-Kette Clb 86-88; Membr Of Italian Sons & Dghtrs Of Amer 87; Penn ST; Acctng.

AVVISATO, KELLY; Pittston Area SR HS; Duryea, PA; (3); FNA; Key Clb; Drill Tm; Sec Jr Cls; Swmmng; High Hon Roll; NHS; Acadmc Al-Amercn 86; Phrmcst.

AVVISATO, KRISTIN; Pittston Area SR HS; Duryea, PA; (3); 23/360; FNA; Key Clb; Drill Tm; Swmmng; Trk; High Hon Roll; Hon Roll; NHS; Srgcl Nrs.

AVVISATO, PRISCILLA; Pittston Area HS; Avoca, PA; (3); Chorus; Stu Cncl.

AVVISATO, SHARON; Old Forge HS; Old Forge, PA; (3); Drama Clb; Ski Clb; Bsktbl; Crs Cntry; Gym; Gov Hon Prg Awd; High Hon Roll; NHS; PA ST U; Engrng.

AWAD, MICHAEL; Danville HS; Danville, PA; (2); 7/160; Computer Clb; NFL; Ski Clb; Hst Frsh Cls; JV Socr; JV Trk; Boy Scts; Church Yth Grp; Drama Clb; Key Clb; Hugh O Brien Youth Fndtn Cntrl PA Ambsdr Intl Ldrshp Smnr ILS 87; PA Govnrs Schl Intl Stds 87; Dickinson Coll; Intl Stds.

AXE, BRIAN; Ridley SR HS; Secane, PA; (3); 9/423; Cmnty Wkr; Dance Clb; French Clb; Math Clb; SADD; JV Var Socr; Sftbl; High Hon Roll; Hon Roll; NHS; Pres Acad Ftnss Awd 84-85; Ctr Chmpn Of Coca-Cola Ntl JR Bwlng Chmp 85-86; Bst JV Offnsv Plyr Sccr; Hofstra; Comp Sci.

AXELROD, BILL; Upper Dublin HS; Dresher, PA; (2); 67/260; Drama Clb; SADD; Chorus; School Musical; JV Swmmng.

AXIBAL, ELDA; Pine Forge Acad; Jersey City, NJ; (3); Pep Clb; Church Choir; Im Bsktbl; Cheerleading; Cit Awd; High Hon Roll; Hon Roll; Photo Awd 86-87.

AYATI, MARJUN; Abington SR HS; Jenkintown, PA; (4); 54/486; Art Clb; Ski Clb; Tennis; Cit Awd; Hon Roll; Schlrshp Beaver Coll 87; Pres Acad Ftns Awd 87; Beaver Coll; Med.

AYERS, CHERIE; Central Cambria HS; Mineral Pt, PA; (3); #21 In Class; Library Aide; NFL; Nwsp Stf; Yrbk Stf; Stu Cncl; Acclrtd Clsses 84-87; Penn ST U; Law.

AYERS, DENISE; Lancaster Christian HS; Lancaster, PA; (1); Church Yth Grp; Yrbk Stf; Sec Frsh Cls; Hon Roll; Cmmnctns.

AYERS, MARY; Oswayo Valley JR SR HS; Shinglehouse, PA; (3); French Clb; Hosp Aide; Band; Chorus; Church Choir; Stat Bsktbl; JV Vllybl; High Hon Roll; Hon Roll; NHS; Nrsng.

AYERS, MELINDA; Lawrence County Vo-Tech; New Castle, PA; (3); Church Yth Grp; Computer Clb; VICA; Nrsng.

AYERS, MICHELE; Franklin Learning Cntr; Philadelphia, PA; (3); Church Yth Grp; Library Aide; Office Aide; Red Cross Aide; Chorus; Church Choir; Trs Soph Cls; Trs Jr Cls; High Hon Roll; Prfct Atten Awd; Cert Acdmc Excllnc 86-87; Howard U; Phy.

AYERS, SABRINA; Central HS; Martinsburg, PA; (3); 9/185; Church Yth Grp; FTA; Yrbk Stf; High Hon Roll; Hon Roll; NHS; HOBY Ldrshp Smnr 85-86; Spnsh.

AYERS, STEPHANIE; Albert Gallatin SR HS; Point Marion, PA; (4); 3/133; Pres Church Yth Grp; Math Tm; Band; Mrchg Band; Yrbk Ed-Chief; Stu Cncl; Score Keeper; Twrlr; DAR Awd; High Hon Roll; Acadmc All Amer 86; Hmcmng Queen 86-87; Exchg Clb Awd, Progrs Clb Awd 87; Johnson Bible Coll; Media Comm.

AYERS, TANYA; Oswayo Valley JR & SR HS; Shinglehouse, PA; (3); Church Yth Grp; Library Aide; Office Aide; Varsity Clb; Chorus; Church Choir; Color Guard; School Musical; Secy Sci.

AYLESOWRTH, SCOTT; Lackawanna Trail HS; Nicholson, PA; (3); Rep Frsh Cls; Coach Actv; Var L Ftbl; Var L Wrstlng; Hon Roll; Aerontcl Engr.

AYMONG, NICOLE; Mercyhurst Prep HS; Erie, PA; (4); 51/158; Cmnty Wkr; Debate Tm; VP Sec Drama Clb; Exploring; French Clb; Model UN; Thesps; School Musical; School Play; Stage Crew; Wolves Clb $1000 Awd 87; Cnsrvtn Dist $400 Awd 87; Miss PA Cntstnt 86; Slippery Rock U; Poli Sci.

AYOOB, RACHEL; St Francis Acad; Pittsburgh, PA; (3); 5/50; Church Yth Grp; Drama Clb; VP JA; Pep Clb; SADD; Stage Crew; Nwsp Rptr; Yrbk Stf; Powder Puff Ftbl; Vllybl.

AYOTTE, CHRIS; Oil City SR HS; Oil City, PA; (3); Chess Clb; Computer Clb; Varsity Clb; Im Socr; Im Tennis; Var L Trk; Im Vllybl; Im Wrstlng; High Hon Roll; Hon Roll; Engrng.

AYRES, JAMES; Strath Haven HS; Swarthmore, PA; (3); Band; Jazz Band; Variety Show; Rep Stu Cncl; Var Lcrss; Hon Roll; Music.

AYUYANG, RAOUL Q; North Catholic HS; Glenshaw, PA; (3); 7/285; Art Clb; Ski Clb; Spanish Clb; School Musical; Rep Soph Cls; Rep Jr Cls; Hon Roll; NHS; Archtctr.

AZAR, NATALIE; York Suburban SR HS; York, PA; (3); Varsity Clb; Yrbk Stf; Var L Tennis; High Hon Roll; Hon Roll; Jr NHS; NHS; JR Miss Fnlst 87; #1 All Str Dbls Tm 85-87; ST Mbr Natl Piano Gld Adtns 83-86; U Of PA; Med.

AZAR, RODMAN; Tunkhannock Area HS; Tunkhannock, PA; (2); 3/340; Letterman Clb; Spanish Clb; Concert Band; Mrchg Band; Pres Soph Cls; Rep Stu Cncl; Var Ftbl; Var Trk; Var Wrstlng; Hon Roll; Bucknell U; Bus Adm.

AZBILL, LESLIE; Downingtown SR HS; Downingtown, PA; (3); 51/648; Pres Church Yth Grp; GAA; Spanish Clb; Teachers Aide; Chorus; Swing Chorus; Rep Frsh Cls; Rep Jr Cls; Var Capt Cheerleading; Trk; Pre-Law.

AZEN, AL; East Pennsboro Area HS; Mechanicsburg, PA; (3); Model UN; Ski Clb; Spanish Clb; JV Capt Socr; High Hon Roll; Psych.

AZINGER, TIM; Kiski Area HS; Saltsburg, PA; (4); Key Clb; Math Clb; Math Tm; Science Clb; SADD; Nwsp Rptr; Var Ftbl; Wt Lftg; High Hon Roll; Hon Roll; Rotry Schlrshp Awd 83-84; U Of Pittsburgh; Comms.

AZIZ, MAISHA; Sister Clara Muhammad HS; Lawnside, NJ; (1); 2/25; Girl Scts; Red Cross Aide; Trk; U Of Penn; Lawyer.

BAACK, KAREN; Upper Dublin HS; Maple Glen, PA; (4); Church Yth Grp; Cmnty Wkr; FBLA; Intnl Clb; JA; SADD; Yrbk Stf; Lcrss; Bloomsburg U; Bus Admin.

BAAS, WILLIAM; The Hill Schl; Elverson, PA; (4); Model UN; Im Mgr Gym; Im Mgr Socr; Im Mgr Tennis; DAR Awd; High Hon Roll; Navy ROTC 4 Yr Schlrshp 87; USN Sea Cadet Of Yr Awd 87; PA Hghr Educ Cert Of Merit 87; U Of PA; Nvl Ofcr.

BAATZ, MATTHEW; William Allen HS; Allentown, PA; (3); Boy Scts; Church Yth Grp; Engrng.

BABB, ANGELA; Fannett-Metal HS; Willow Hill, PA; (3); Varsity Clb; Band; Chorus; Nwsp Rptr; Bsktbl; Cheerleading; Socr; Sftbl; Hon Roll; NHS; Hnrb Mntn PO Bsktbl All Star 85-86; Bsktbl All Star Team Lions Clb Tourn 86; Pre Med.

BABCO, PATTI; Purchase Line HS; Gipsy, PA; (3); 8/98; Pres FBLA; Trs Pep Clb; SADD; Nwsp Stf; Stu Cncl; Cheerleading; Hon Roll; NHS; Future Bus Ldrs Of Amer Rgn III Reprtr 87-88; Bus.

BABCOCK, GWEN D; Penn Hills SR HS; Pittsburgh, PA; (4); 1/616; Church Yth Grp; German Clb; Ed Lit Mag; High Hon Roll; NHS; Ntl Merit SF; VIP Awd 86; U Of Pittsburgh Math Cont Wnnr 86; Bio.

BABCOCK, STACIE; Bedford HS; Bedford, PA; (3); Art Clb; Band; Chorus; Flag Corp; Score Keeper; Trk; Csmtlgy.

BABETSKI, LINDA; Lake-Lehman SR HS; Dallas, PA; (4); 2/154; Church Yth Grp; Ski Clb; Band; Yrbk Stf; L Golf; Tennis; High Hon Roll; Lion Awd; NHS; Sal; Pres Schlrshp 87-88; Local Wmns Club Awd 87; Wmns Club Acad Schlrshp 87; Fitchburg ST Coll; Med Tech.

BABIARZ, MARY ROSE; Old Forge HS; Old Forge, PA; (4); Drill Tm; Yrbk Stf; Hon Roll; Spanish NHS; Typg Awd 86; Span Awd 85; Coll Misericordia; Occ Ther.

BABIC, NICHOLAS; Council Rock HS; Newtown, PA; (3); 128/908; Ftbl; Wt Lftg; NHS; Engnrng.

BABIN, JENNIFER; North Hills HS; Pittsburgh, PA; (3); 67/489; Acpl Chr; Chorus; JV Vllybl; High Hon Roll; Hon Roll; Ntl Merit Ltr; U Of Pittsburgh; Mktg.

BABINCHAK, JOHN; Shenandoah Valley HS; Shenandoah, PA; (4); 4/107; Debate Tm; Pep Clb; Ski Clb; Nwsp Sprt Ed; Yrbk Stf; Pres Frsh Cls; Pres Soph Cls; VP Jr Cls; Trs Sr Cls; Stu Cncl; Stud Of Mnth 86; Hnr Rll 84-87; Bloomsburg Univ; Bus Mgmt.

BABINSACK, STEFANIE; Highlands SR HS; Natrona, PA; (3); 57/311; Hosp Aide; Intnl Clb; Office Aide; Chorus; Concert Band; Rep Mrchg Band; Bsktbl; Trk; High Hon Roll; Jr NHS; Poli Sci.

BABST, MICHAEL STEPHEN; Archbishop Wood HS For Boys; Holland, PA; (4); 2/277; Trk; High Hon Roll; NHS; Gibbons Hlf Tuitn Scholar Catholic U Amer 87; Adv Plcmnt Physics Awd 87; Bucks Cnty Sci Fair 2nd & 3rd; Lehigh U; Engrng.

BABU, SINDHU; Exeter SR HS; Birdsboro, PA; (3); Church Yth Grp; Dance Clb; Drama Clb; Intnl Clb; Latin Clb; Letterman Clb; Office Aide; Spanish Clb; Varsity Clb; VP Y-Teens; U Of PA; Humanities.

BABULA, ANGELA; West Hazelton JR/Sr HS; Sugarloaf, PA; (2); Ski Clb; Spanish Clb; Vllybl; Hon Roll.

BABULA, JAMES; Hazleton HS; Lattimer, PA; (3); 61/450; Boy Scts; Teachers Aide; JV Bsbl; Im Bsktbl; Var Crs Cntry; Hon Roll; Rotary Awd; PA JR Acad Sci 1st Pl Rgnls 86; Frgn Lang Orgnztn 86-87; Hlth Career Clb 86-87.

BACCARI, ROBERT; Abington SR HS; Huntingdon Valley, PA; (3); Latin Clb; Bsktbl; Ftbl; High Hon Roll; Hon Roll; NHS; Penn ST; Bus.

BACCHUS, ROZANNA; Girls HS; Philadelphia, PA; (2); Computer Clb; Cit Awd; High Hon Roll; Hon Roll; Ntl Merit Ltr; Prfct Atten Awd; Spanish NHS; Optometry.

BACCO, CHRISTINE; Ringgold HS; Monongahela, PA; (4); 60/326; Teachers Aide; Nwsp Stf; Mgr(s); Timer; Hon Roll; U Of Pittsburgh-Grnsbg; Cmmnctn.

BACCO, TRACY; Yough SR HS; West Newton, PA; (3); Church Yth Grp; Computer Clb; French Clb; Office Aide; Pep Clb; Science Clb; Ski Clb; Band; Chorus; Mrchg Band; Accntnt.

BACH, CATHLEEN; Spring-Ford HS; Royersford, PA; (2); 108/289; Church Yth Grp; French Clb; SADD; Band; Church Choir; Concert Band; Mrchg Band; Yrbk Stf; JV Sftbl; Law.

BACHER, JOY; New Hope-Solebury HS; New Hope, PA; (4); 1/79; Art Clb; Math Tm; Var Capt Bsktbl; JV Fld Hcky; Var Capt Tennis; Var Capt Twrlr; High Hon Roll; NHS; Ntl Merit Schol; Val; Natl Phy Ed Awd 86-87; Spnsh Awd 84.

BACHERT, SHARON; Mt Calvary HS; Elizabethtown, PA; (3); 5/23; Sec Church Yth Grp; Church Choir; School Play; Bsktbl; Fld Hcky; Sftbl; Trk; Cit Awd; Hon Roll; NHS; Var Ath Yr Awd 85-86; CCAC All Conf Bsktbl Tm 85-86; Coaches Awd 86; Phys Ed.

BACHMAN, CHRISTINE R; Warrior Run HS; Watsontown, PA; (3); 10/200; Am Leg Aux Girls St; Aud/Vis; Trs Church Yth Grp; Spanish Clb; Chorus; Ed Nwsp Ed-Chief; High Hon Roll; Hon Roll; Sec NHS; Spnsh Awd; Pre Med.

BACHMAN, CRISTEN; Freedom SR HS; Bethlehem, PA; (4); 119/446; Cmnty Wkr; Political Wkr; Nwsp Stf; Hon Roll; Arch.

BACHMAN JR, THOMAS C; Tunkhannock Area HS; Falls, PA; (3); 29/320; Church Yth Grp; Ski Clb; Hon Roll; NHS; Ntl Merit Ltr; Wallops Island Marine Sci Pre Coll Cert 85-87; Mock Trial Part Cmmndtn 87; Aerontcs.

BACHOUCHIN, MATTHEW; Bishop Mc Cort HS; Johnstown, PA; (3); French Clb; JV Ftbl; High Hon Roll; Hon Roll; NHS; Duquesne; Comp Sci.

BACHSTEIN, SHANIN; Lehigh Christian Acad; Stewartsville, NJ; (3); 2/14; Church Yth Grp; FCA; Spanish Clb; Sec Soph Cls; L Capt Bsktbl; Capt L Sftbl; Var L Vllybl; Hon Roll; Ntl Merit Schol; MVP Sftbl 85-87; MVP Bsktbl 85-87; Outstndng Acadc Excel Awd 85-87; Phy Ed.

BACHTLE, BRETT M; Wallenpaupack Area HS; Newfoundland, PA; (4); 2/160; Am Leg Boys St; Scholastic Bowl; VP Jr Cls; Var Capt Bsktbl; Var Capt Ftbl; Var Trk; Bausch & Lomb Sci Awd; Trs NHS; Air Force Acad.

BACHURA, DEBBIE; Butler SR HS; Butler, PA; (4); 58/755; Cmnty Wkr; Exploring; Office Aide; Teachers Aide; Yrbk Stf; Jr NHS; Geneva Coll; Elem Educ.

BACKHUAS, FRED; Neshaminy HS; Langhorne, PA; (3); Art Clb; Church Yth Grp; Ski Clb; Bsbl; Bsktbl; Ftbl; Vllybl; Wt Lftg; Hon Roll; Prfct Atten Awd.

BACKOS, MARCIE; Brownsville Area HS; Brownsville, PA; (3); 5/200; Sec VP Hosp Aide; Math Tm; SADD; Band; Drill Tm; High Hon Roll; NHS; Phrmcy.

BACKOS, TRACY; Brownsville Area HS; Brownsville, PA; (3); 5/230; Pres Hosp Aide; Math Clb; Math Tm; Office Aide; SADD; Mrchg Band; Cit Awd; High Hon Roll; Pres NHS; Pres Ntl Hnr Scty 87-88; WV U; Pre-Med.

BACON, JOEL; Conrad Weiser HS; Robesonia, PA; (3); 44/179; Church Yth Grp; Spanish Clb; Hon Roll; Lion Awd; Tennis Awd-Mst Imprvd & Mst Outstndng 85 & 87; Wheaton Coll; Bio.

BACON, KIMBERLY; Farrell HS; Farrell, PA; (2); Church Yth Grp; French Clb; Letterman Clb; Library Aide; Teachers Aide; Church Choir; Var Capt Cheerleading; Var Trk; NHS; Nrs.

BACON, PAUL ERIC; Greenville HS; Greenville, PA; (4); 7/125; Boy Scts; Cmnty Wkr; German Clb; Library Aide; NHS; Earlham.

BACZEWSKI, GARY; Hopewell SR HS; Aliquippa, PA; (4); 50/254; Chess Clb; VP Exploring; Trs German Clb; Band; Chorus; School Musical; School Play; Hon Roll; Slippery Rock U; Marn Bio.

BADAMO, LEESA; North Allegheny SR HS; Pittsburgh, PA; (3); Church Yth Grp; Cmnty Wkr; German Clb; Hosp Aide; JA; Lit Mag; Rep Frsh Cls; Vllybl; Cert Of Merit Intro Acct I Hghst Clss Avg 86-87; Cert Of Profcncy Century 21 Acctng 86-87; IUP; Spcl Ed.

BADDORF, ROBERT; Northern York HS; Dillsburg, PA; (3); 21/250; Church Yth Grp; Band; Concert Band; Mrchg Band; School Musical; Stage Crew; High Hon Roll; Messiah Coll; Engrng.

BADEN, AMANDA; Cumberland Valley HS; Camp Hill, PA; (4); Art Clb; Key Clb; Model UN; Nwsp Rptr; High Hon Roll; Hon Roll; NHS; Cmnty Wkr; German Clb; Ski Clb; Hall Fndtn Scholar 87; PA ST U; Arch Engr.

BADEN, CANDICE; W Scranton SR HS; Scranton, PA; (2); 26/268; Letterman Clb; Red Cross Aide; Spanish Clb; Speech Tm; Thesps; Rep Stu Cncl; JV Cheerleading; Var Trk; Hon Roll; Jr NHS; Law.

BADINGER, JILL MARIE; Schuylkill Valley HS; Reading, PA; (4); 7/132; German Clb; Spanish Clb; Concert Band; Nwsp Rptr; Nwsp Stf; Yrbk Rptr; Yrbk Stf; Bsktbl; Fld Hcky; Sftbl; Elizabethtown Coll Acadmc Schlrshp 87; $250 M Silverman Mem Awd 87; $150 Wm E Spaty Comptv Sprt Awd 87; Elizabethtown Coll; Psych.

BADINGER, KAREN; Daniel Boone HS; Birdsboro, PA; (4); 53/162; Varsity Clb; Drill Tm; Capt Cheerleading; Hon Roll; Yth Educ Assn Pres 85-87; Bus Mgmt.

BADORF, SUSAN; Warwick HS; Lititz, PA; (2); 10/325; Computer Clb; Teachers Aide; Yrbk Stf; Trk; High Hon Roll.

BAER, CINDY LEE; Mechanicsburg SR HS; Mechanicsburg, PA; (3); 18/338; Band; Mrchg Band; Orch; Symp Band; Stu Cncl; JV Var Bsktbl; Trk; High Hon Roll; Hon Roll; NHS; Air Force; Socl Wrk.

BAER, JEFF; Scranton Tech; Scranton, PA; (4); Letterman Clb; Capt Swmmng.

BAER, LISA; Beaver Area JR SR HS; Beaver, PA; (4); Office Aide; SADD; Teachers Aide; Powder Puff Ftbl; High Hon Roll; Hon Roll; Acdmc Awd 85-87; Outstndng Distrbtv Ed Stu Yr 86-87; Trvl.

BAER, MICHELLE; Newport HS; Duncannon, PA; (2); 9/117; German Clb; Band; Concert Band; Jazz Band; Mrchg Band; Pep Band; JV Sftbl; Hon Roll; Prfct Atten Awd; Im Mat Maids; West Chester U; Music.

BAFILE, LOUIS; Windber Area HS; Windber, PA; (3); French Clb; JA; Nwsp Ed-Chief; Nwsp Stf; High Hon Roll; Hon Roll; NHS; U Of Pittsburgh Johnstwn; Comp.

BAGAMERY, JONATHAN; Beaver Area HS; Beaver, PA; (4); Boy Scts; JCL; Q&S; Nwsp Stf; Lit Mag; High Hon Roll; Hon Roll; E M Cassidy Mem Awd For Exc In Englsh 87; Crtnst.

BAGAY, LISA; Ringgold HS; Monongahela, PA; (3); Drama Clb; Science Clb; Color Guard; School Musical; Variety Show; Hon Roll; Sec NHS; GEAR Ringgold; Pre-Law.

BAGWELL, JASON; Quaker Valley SR HS; Sewickley, PA; (2); Church Yth Grp; Cmnty Wkr; Debate Tm; French Clb; Key Clb; Red Cross Aide; Nwsp Stf; Rep Stu Cncl; Trk; Wrstlng; US Military Acad; Cvl Engrng.

BAGWELL, JENNIFER; Avon Grove HS; West Grove, PA; (3); 16/214; VP Church Yth Grp; Pres 4-H; Hosp Aide; Red Cross Aide; School Play; Nwsp Rptr; Yrbk Stf; Im Mgr Wt Lftg; Stat Wrstlng; Frnch Awd 85 & 87; Engl & Gen Bus Awd 85-86; Acctng Awd 87; Pre-Med.

BAHARA, ROBBIE; Scranton Prep; Moscow, PA; (4); Church Yth Grp; Letterman Clb; Ski Clb; SADD; Varsity Clb; Var Bsbl; Var Capt Ftbl; Var Wt Lftg; Cit Awd; Dec Alumnus Awd 87; Dist Champnshp Bsbl Tm 86; U Scranton; Bus.

BAHL, COLLEEN; Hanover HS; Hanover, PA; (3); Ski Clb; Varsity Clb; Concert Band; Mrchg Band; Variety Show; Rep Frsh Cls; Var L Bsktbl; Var L Vllybl; Hon Roll; Prfct Atten Awd; Acctnt.

BAHM, MICHELLE; Seneca HS; North East, PA; (3); 24/150; Dance Cl Library Aide; Pep Clb; Drill Tm; School Musical; Var JV Cheerleadin Hon Roll; Dentstry.

BAHN, DANIEL; Bermudian Springs HS; E Berlin, PA; (3); Church Y Grp; Band; Concert Band; Jazz Band; Mrchg Band; Hon Roll; Dickinso Law Schl; Lwyr.

BAHR, JENNIFER S; Mercer HS; Sharon, PA; (3); 4-H; German Cl Band; Concert Band; Jazz Band; Mrchg Band; School Play; Rep Stu Cn L Bsktbl; L Trk; Psych.

BAHR, NICOLE; Mercer Area JR-SR HS; Sharon, PA; (1); NFL; Spee Tm; Concert Band; Jazz Band; Mrchg Band; Pep Band; Stu Cncl; Bskt Trk; Hon Roll; 1st Pl Talent Shw 86; PA Frstry Depts 100th Anniv 4 Essay 86.

BAHURIAK, DAVID; Fairchance-Georges HS; Smithfield, PA; (Church Yth Grp; Computer Clb; Ski Clb; VP Frsh Cls; Trs Soph Cls; T Jr Cls; Ftbl; Wt Lftg; Wrstlng; High Hon Roll; Acad Ftns Awd 86; Psyc

BAIGIS, JOSEPH; Montrose Area HS; Montrose, PA; (4); 9/165; Lat Clb; Scholastic Bowl; Ski Clb; JV Bsktbl; High Hon Roll; NHS; Presdr Acdmc Awd, Schlrshp Bwl 87; Penn ST-HAZLETON; Engrng.

BAILEY, AMANDA; Meadville Area SR HS; Meadville, PA; (2); Chur Yth Grp; French Clb; Varsity Clb; Nwsp Stf; Pres Soph Cls; Stu Cncl; V L Swmmng; High Hon Roll; Hon Roll; All Amer Swmmng 200 Yr Medl Relay 86-87; ST Rcrd Hldr 200 Y R Medley Relay 87.

BAILEY, CHRISTOPHER; Bensalem SR HS; Bensalem, PA; (Science Clb; Band; Rep Stu Cncl; Bsbl; JV Socr; Var Swmmng; CC Aw Most Imprvd Soccer Plyr 86-87; Awd For Excllnc Natl Sci Olympi 86-87; PA ST; Chem.

BAILEY, COREY; Warren Area HS; Warren, PA; (3); French Clb; Ac Chr; Chorus; School Musical; Hon Roll; Comp Sci.

BAILEY, DENISE; Du Bois Area HS; Dubois, PA; (2); 45/420; Ban Chorus; Concert Band; Mrchg Band; School Musical; Hon Roll; Pres Aca Ftns Awd 85; Nrth Str Sccr Leag-Chmpns 80-86; Dynmcs-Shw Chr 86-8 Clarion Coll; Elem Educ.

BAILEY, ERIC; S Williamsport Area JR SR HS; S Williamsport, PA; (3 26/111; Rep Stu Cncl; Badmtn; JV Bsktbl; JV Ftbl; JV Golf; Vllybl; W Lftg; Bio.

BAILEY, GEOFFREY; Haverford HS; Ardmore, PA; (3); 52/450; Chur Yth Grp; German Clb; Ski Clb; Rep Frsh Cls; Rep Stu Cncl; JV Bsbl; V JV Wrstlng; Hon Roll; UCLA; Pre-Law.

BAILEY, GREGORY M; Meadville Area SR HS; Meadville, PA; (4 Church Yth Grp; Key Clb; Science Clb; Varsity Clb; L Var Ftbl; Capt Swmmng; Trk; High Hon Roll; Hon Roll; Levinson Awd 87; 100 Yd Brea Stroke Rcrd 87; The Coll Of Wooster.

BAILEY, HEATHER; Carlynton JR SR HS; Carnegie, PA; (3); Chur Yth Grp; Dance Clb; Drama Clb; Variety Show; Rep Stu Cncl; Powd Puff Ftbl; Cit Awd; High Hon Roll; Jr NHS; NHS; HOBY W PA Ldrsh Smnr Ambssdr 86; Thtr Arts.

BAILEY, JAMES; Central Catholic HS; Munhall, PA; (2); 73/33 Duquesne U.

BAILEY, JEROME; Edward Bole Tech HS; Philadelphia, PA; (3); Bo Clb Am; Camera Clb; Drama Clb; Stage Crew; Variety Show; Bsbl; Bskt Bowling; Ftbl; Sftbl; Comms.

BAILEY, JESSICA; Franklin Learning Ctr; Philadelphia, PA; (4 Exploring; Red Cross Aide; Science Clb; Spanish Clb; Yrbk Ed-Chief; Yr Phtg; Yrbk Stf; Sec Soph Cls; Sec Jr Cls; Rep Stu Cncl; Humanitari Awd-Juvnl Diabeties 85; Spcl Olympcs Chrmn Awd 86; Delgt-St HOS Conf 86; Temple U; Hosp Adm.

BAILEY, JODI; Peters Township HS; Venetia, PA; (2); Church Yth Gr Intnl Clb; Service Clb; Mrchg Band; Sftbl; Grand Lecturer Dist No 15 S Of PA 87; Intl Order Of Rainbow Girls; Business.

BAILEY, JOHN; Penn-Trafford HS; Jeannette, PA; (3); Chess Clb; T JCL; Capt Quiz Bowl; School Musical; School Play; High Hon Roll; NH PA JR Clsscl Lg Parlmntrn 87-88; Amer Invit Math Exam 87.

BAILEY, KATHLEEN; Neshaminy HS; Langhorne, PA; (3); 19/72 SADD; Band; Stu Cncl; JV Var Fld Hcky; Socr; Sftbl; Trk; High Hon Ro Hon Roll; Sec NHS; All Area & Golden 18 Bucks Cnty Soccr 85-87; All S & Inter-Cnty Soccr 85-86; 1st All Area Fld Hcky; PA ST; Ed.

BAILEY, KIM; Towanda Area HS; Towanda, PA; (3); 16/140; Chur Yth Grp; 4-H; FBLA; Library Aide; Spanish Clb; Church Choir; Hon Ro Business.

BAILEY, KRISTA; Philipsburg-Osceola SR HS; Philipsburg, PA; (4); 1 243; FCA; Sec Letterman Clb; Ski Clb; Varsity Clb; Yrbk Stf; Stat Bsk Var Bsktbl; Var JV Cheerleading; Var Vllybl; Hon Roll; NEDT Awd 8 Outstndg SR Chrldr 87; SR Chrldr Schlr Awd 87; Indiana U Of P Chldhd Ed.

BAILEY, LISA; Tyrone Area HS; Tyrone, PA; (4); Pres FBLA; Libra Aide; Spanish Clb; SADD; Chorus; Im Vllybl; High Hon Roll; Hon Ro NHS; Prfct Atten Awd; Penn ST U; Bus Admin.

BAILEY, LORI; Dover HS; Dover, PA; (3); 104/376; Band; Choru Concert Band; Mrchg Band; York Coll; Law.

BAILEY, MICHELLE; Burgettstown JR SR HS; Langeloth, PA; (Drama Clb; French Clb; Speech Tm; Chorus; School Musical; School Pla Variety Show; Hon Roll.

BAILEY, MICHELLE; South Side Area HS; Georgetown, PA; (3); S Varsity Clb; Band; Nwsp Stf; Pres Frsh Cls; Pres Soph Cls; Rep Stu Cnc Var JV Bsktbl; Var JV Cheerleading; Var Sftbl; Hon Roll.

BAILEY, SHARON A; Tyrone Area HS; Tyrone, PA; (4); DECA; Pe Clb; Chorus; Powder Puff Ftbl; Retail.

BAILEY, SHERI; Harry S Truman HS; Levittown, PA; (3); Aud/Vi SADD; Band; Stage Crew; Cheerleading; Fld Hcky; Trk; NHS.

BAILEY, TAMEKA M; Edward Bok AVT HS; Philadelphia, PA; (DECA; FBLA; Varsity Clb; Church Choir; Nwsp Rptr; Yrbk Stf; J Bsktbl; Var Trk; Var Vllybl; Cit Awd; Ft Lauderdale Coll; Bus Law.

BAILEY, TOM; Wilmington Area HS; New Wilmington, PA; (2 Computer Clb; Nwsp Stf; Im Bsbl; Hon Roll; Elec.

BAILEY, TRACY; Philipsburg-Osceola SR HS; Philipsburg, PA; (4); 5 234; Letterman Clb; Ski Clb; SADD; Flag Corp; Yrbk Stf; Rep Sr Cls; Re Stu Cncl; Stat Bsktbl; Var L Cheerleading; Var Sftbl; Duquesne U; Pharm

BAILEY, WENDY; West Scranton HS; Scranton, PA; (2); 13/200; S Church Yth Grp; Dance Clb; FNA; Spanish Clb; Orch; Var Pom Pon; Ho Roll; Jr NHS; Law.

BAILOR, RACHEL; Curwensville Area HS; Curwensville, PA; (3 Drama Clb; Hosp Aide; Band; Concert Band; Pep Band; Yrbk Stf; St Cncl; Hon Roll; Oyal Order Of The Moose Just Say No Cnvtn 87; Unil Rurul Elect Yth Tour 87.

BAILY, RONALD; Waynesburg Central HS; Waynesburg, PA; (3); 1/24 Spanish Clb; Trs Frsh Cls; Trs Soph Cls; Capt L Bsbl; Capt L Bsktbl; Ca L Socr; High Hon Roll; NHS; NEDT Awd; Spanish NHS.

BAINBRIDGE, CHRISTINE; Ft Le Boeuf HS; Waterford, PA; (2); Dance Clb; Drill Tm; School Musical; High Hon Roll; Engl.

BAINE, KRISTIN; Archbishop Carroll HS; Audubon, PA; (3); 104/369; Art Clb; JV Trk; Genetcs.

BAIR, AMY; Carmichaels Area HS; Rices Landing, PA; (3); 9/115; Drama Clb; Ski Clb; Spanish Clb; Band; Chorus; Pres Frsh Cls; Stu Cncl; Var Cheerleading; High Hon Roll; NHS; Standing Comm 86-87; Spnsh Awd 86; Schl Plays; Comm.

BAIR, ANGEL; Greater Works Acad; North Huntington, PA; (3); 1/44; Church Yth Grp; Ski Clb; Stage Crew; Stu Cncl; L Var Bsktbl; L Var Sftbl; Var Vllybl; High Hon Roll; NHS; All Star Bsktbl Tourn York PA 86; All Star Bsktbl Leg 86-87; All Str Vllybl Tourn 87.

BAIR, BRIAN; West Mifflin Area HS; W Mifflin, PA; (3); 14/250; Church Yth Grp; Band; Yrbk Stf; Sec Jr Cls; Ftbl; High Hon Roll; Hon Roll; NHS; VFW Awd; Voice Dem Awd; PTA Ltrtr Awd 87; Capt OH Rvr Vly Bible Bowl Chmpns 85-87; Opthlmlgy.

BAIR, CONNIE; South Western HS; Hanover, PA; (3); 32/233; Church Yth Grp; Girl Scts; Church Choir; Concert Band; Mrchg Band; Pep Band; School Musical; Symp Band; Mst Imprvd Muscn Awd 84; NEDT Awd 84; Interior Designer.

BAIR, LAURIE; Northeastern SR HS; Manchester, PA; (3); 32/236; Art Clb; Church Yth Grp; Chorus; Var Cheerleading; Trk; Hon Roll; Nrsng.

BAIR, SERENA M; Mt Pleasant Area SR HS; Norvelt, PA; (3); French Clb; PAVAS; Concert Band; Mrchg Band; Nwsp Rptr; Var L Swmmng; High Hon Roll; Hon Roll; U Of Pittsburgh; Occ Therapy.

BAIRD, KAREN; Unionville HS; Unionville, PA; (4); 43/316; Pres Sec Church Yth Grp; French Clb; Flag Corp; Yrbk Stf; Powder Puff Ftbl; Gov Hon Prg Awd; High Hon Roll; Hon Roll; NHS; Prsdntl Clssrm; VA Tech; Engnrng.

BAIREN JR, JOHN; Burgettstown JR SR HS; Bulger, PA; (3); 12/140; French Clb; Ftbl; Vllybl; High Hon Roll; Hon Roll; Jr NHS; High Hnr Awd 86-87; Elec Engr.

BAJURA, KEITH; West Mifflin Area HS; Pittsburgh, PA; (4); 3/328; Boy Scts; Math Tm; Quiz Bowl; Scholastic Bowl; Orch; School Play; High Hon Roll; NHS; Pres Schlr; Natl Schl Orch Awd 87; Natl Honor Scty 87; PTSA Cltrl Arts Awd Music 87; Carnegie Mellon U; Music.

BAKER, ADRIENNE; Emmaus HS; Allentown, PA; (4); Church Yth Grp; Cmnty Wkr; Key Clb; Political Wkr; Spanish Clb; Stu Cncl; Capt Bsktbl; Safe Rides 86-87; Boston Coll; Comm.

BAKER, CAROL; Waynesboro Area SR HS; Waynesboro, PA; (4); Ski Clb; Church Choir; Yrbk Stf; Cit Awd; High Hon Roll; Hon Roll; Prfct Atten Awd; Rbrt E Arthr Mem Awd 87; PA ST U; Comp Sci.

BAKER, CHERI; North Clarion HS; Lucinda, PA; (4); FHA; Pep Clb; SADD; VICA; Color Guard; Yrbk Stf; Var Mgr(s); Var Vllybl; Hon Roll; VICA Comptn 3rd Pl Cake Decrtng 87; Dir List 87.

BAKER, CHERYL; Baldwin HS; Pittsburgh, PA; (3); 160/477; Art Clb; Diving; Swmmng; Church Yth Grp; Church Choir; Hon Roll; Art Hnr Scty 85-87; Young Athletes Exhibit Seton Hill Coll 86.

BAKER, CLARKE; Peters Twp HS; Mcmurray, PA; (2); SADD; Thesps; Band; Concert Band; Jazz Band; Mrchg Band; School Musical; School Play; Church Yth Grp; Prfct Atten-Mrchng Band 86-87; Drl Dwn Mrchng Band-2nd Pl 86-87; Penn ST U; Bus Admin.

BAKER, DANIEL S; Big Spring HS; Carlisle, PA; (4); 5/181; Hon Roll; Lion Awd; Ntl Merit Schol; Pres Schlr; Capt Socr; Pres Phys Fit Awd 86-87; PHEAA Cert Merit 86-87; Penn ST; Engrng.

BAKER, DIANE; York Suburban SR HS; York, PA; (3); 1/177; Church Yth Grp; Chorus; Nwsp Rptr; Sec Nwsp Stf; Yrbk Ed-Chief; Bausch & Lomb Sci Awd; High Hon Roll; Pres NHS; Yrbk Rptr; Rensselaer Sci, Mth Awd 87; Top Stu 85-86; Jrnlsm Awd Outstndng Svc Schl Nwsp 87; U DE; Bus Fin.

BAKER, ERIC; Kennard-Dale HS; Delta, PA; (3); 15/187; Boy Scts; German Clb; Ski Clb; Crs Cntry; Socr; Trk; Hon Roll; NHS; Engrng.

BAKER, GENA; Peters Township HS; Mcmurray, PA; (3); Thesps; Lit Mag; Bsktbl; Psych.

BAKER, GLORIA; Red Land HS; New Cumberland, PA; (4); 5/255; Quiz Bowl; School Play; Stu Cncl; Tennis; Bausch & Lomb Sci Awd; NHS; Spanish NHS; Dickinson Coll Smmr Acad Schlrshp 86; Ntl Merit Cmmndtn 87; 1st Pl Shoppensburg U Sprng Lang Cntst 87; U Of PA; Engrng.

BAKER, GUY; Jefferson Morgan JR-SR HS; Waynesburg, PA; (3); Art Clb; Church Yth Grp; Drama Clb; Quiz Bowl; School Play; Ftbl; Trk; IN ST U; Physcs.

BAKER II, JAMES L; Harrisburg HS; Harrisburg, PA; (2); 85/375; Bsbl; JV Ftbl; Trk; U MI; Bus Adm.

BAKER, JANET; Carmichaels Area HS; Carmichaels, PA; (3); 3/112; Pep Clb; Spanish Clb; Church Choir; Color Guard; Gov Hon Prg Awd; High Hon Roll; NHS; Engl & Spnsh Awd 86; Pres Church Yth Grp 86-87; Engl.

BAKER, JEAN; Archbishop Carroll HS; Paoli, PA; (3); 25/376; Science Clb; School Musical; Cheerleading; High Hon Roll; Hon Roll; NHS; Alg Awd 84-85; Diocesan Schlr 86-87; Architecture.

BAKER, JEFFREY; Moon Area HS; Coraopolis, PA; (3); 4/306; German Clb; Rep Frsh Cls; Rep Jr Cls; JV Bsktbl; Var L Ftbl; Var L Trk; Bausch & Lomb Sci Awd; High Hon Roll; NHS; Ntl Merit Ltr; Engrng.

BAKER, JEFFREY S; Mifflinburg Area HS; Lewisburg, PA; (4); 66/154; Drama Clb; Chorus; School Musical; School Play; Yrbk Stf; High Hon Roll; HOBY Fndtn Ldrshp Seminar 85; PA ST Parlimentary 1st Pl Tm 86; Antonelli Inst Of Art & Photo.

BAKER, JENNIFER; Mechanicsburg Area SR HS; Mechanicsburg, PA; (4); 29/303; Color Guard; High Hon Roll; Hon Roll; NHS; Pres Schlr; Faclty Schlrshp Awd 87; Halloween Parade Qn 86; Millersvl U; Elem Ed.

BAKER, KAREN; Emmaus HS; Emmaus, PA; (4); 143/469; Church Yth Grp; Key Clb; Chorus; Church Choir; School Musical; School Play; Nwsp Stf; Mgr Vllybl; Hon Roll; Voice Of Demcrcy Essy Cont Fnlst 86-87; Penn ST U; Microbio.

BAKER, KELLI; Monaca JR-SR HS; Monaca, PA; (3); Church Yth Grp; French Clb; Office Aide; Pep Clb; Red Cross Aide; Spanish Clb; Band; Concert Band; Mrchg Band; Pep Band; Bradford Schl Of Bus; Lgl Sec.

BAKER, KENNETH; Kiski Area HS; Apollo, PA; (3); Computer Clb; French Clb; Math Tm; Spanish Clb; Nwsp Stf; High Hon Roll; Hon Roll; NHS; Pres Schlr; Rotary Awd; Acadmc Ltr 86 & 87; Rotary Yth Ldrshp Cnfrnc 87.

BAKER, KEVIN; Bishop Hoban HS; Mountaintop, PA; (3); 13/300; Art Clb; Aud/Vis; Boy Scts; Camera Clb; Chess Clb; Church Yth Grp; CAP; Computer Clb; Drama Clb; English Clb; Arntcl Engrng.

BAKER, KEVIN; Ford City JR SR HS; Ford City, PA; (3); 9/160; Chess Clb; Cmnty Wkr; Key Clb; Trs Spanish Clb; Yrbk Stf; High Hon Roll; Hon Roll; NHS; Mentorship Proj 86; PA JR Acad Sci 2nd Pl 85-86; Accltd Acad Crs 85-87; Penn ST U; Engr.

BAKER, LISA; Tussey Mountain HS; Saxton, PA; (4); 7/116; Ski Clb; Lib Band; Mrchg Band; Yrbk Stf; Sec Sr Cls; Stu Cncl; Trk; Hon Roll; NHS; Shippensburg U; Educ.

BAKER, LORI; Slippery Rock Area HS; Portersville, PA; (4); 11/178; German Clb; Mrchg Band; Rep Stu Cncl; Elks Awd; High Hon Roll; Jr NHS; NHS; Ntl Merit SF; Pres Schlr; Rifle Vrsty Ltr, Bar & Shrpshtr Medal 86-87; U Of Pittsburgh; Math.

BAKER, LORNA; Nazareth Area SR HS; Nazareth, PA; (3); 161/262; Drama Clb; Key Clb; Stage Crew; Nwsp Phtg; Schtlc Art Awds 85 & 86; Graphic Arts.

BAKER, MARCY; Bensalem HS; Bensalem, PA; (2); Socr; Hon Roll; Sci.

BAKER, MARK A; Garden Spot HS; New Holland, PA; (4); 95/205; Church Yth Grp; Pres VP Drama Clb; Chorus; School Musical; School Play; Stage Crew; PA Govs Schl For Arts 86; Drama Clb-Spcl Svc Awd 87; Drama Clb-Best Spprtng Actr 87; Theatre Mgmt.

BAKER, MICHELLE; Newport HS; Newport, PA; (3); 28/126; Varsity Clb; Yrbk Stf; Trs Frsh Cls; Pres Stu Cncl; JV Var Cheerleading; Im Wt Lftg; Hon Roll; Pltcl Sci.

BAKER, NATALIE; Monogahela Valley Catholic HS; Charleroi, PA; (3); Spanish Clb; Varsity Clb; Band; Var Bsktbl; Sftbl; Hon Roll; Spanish NHS.

BAKER, NICOLE; Danville Area HS; Riverside, PA; (1); Church Yth Grp; Hosp Aide; Chorus; Church Choir; JV Fld Hcky; Hon Roll; Pres Fit Awd 87.

BAKER, PAUL; Butler SR HS; Butler, PA; (3); Boy Scts; Mrchg Band; L Var Trk; Cit Awd; High Hon Roll; Hon Roll; Jr NHS; Prfct Atten Awd; Band; Orch; Eagle Sct 85; Vrsty Rfl Tm, Lttrd, Hgh Av, & MVP Awd 87; Engrng.

BAKER, PAULA; Beaver JR SR HS; Beaver, PA; (2); German Clb; Hosp Aide; Band; Concert Band; Mrchg Band; JV Bsktbl; Socr; Var L Sftbl; JV Tennis; Hon Roll; Pre-Law.

BAKER, RAY; Kiski Area HS; Leechburg, PA; (4); Aud/Vis; Science Clb; Chorus; Mrchg Band; School Play; Stage Crew; Nwsp Rptr; Trk; Wrstlng; Hon Roll; Pasavant Schlrshp 87; Cnty Chorus 84 & 87; Wrstlng WPIAL Champn 84; Thiel; Elec Engrng.

BAKER, REBECCA; Seneca Valley HS; Harmony, PA; (3); Exploring; JV Sftbl; Var Trk; Hon Roll; Schlstc Awd Acadc Achvt 86-87; Psych.

BAKER, REGINA; Cambria Heights SR HS; Carrolltown, PA; (3); 16/206; Q&S; Concert Band; Mrchg Band; Nwsp Rptr; Nwsp Stf; Hon Roll; NCTE Awd; NHS; NEDT Awd; Am Leg Aux Girls St.

BAKER, ROBIN; Rockwood Area HS; Markleton, PA; (3); Church Yth Grp; Hosp Aide; NFL; Speech Tm; Band; Chorus; Church Choir; Concert Band; Mrchg Band; School Play; Phy Therapy.

BAKER, SAM; Western Beaver HS; Darlington, PA; (3); Bsbl; Bowling; Athl Month 87; Accntng.

BAKER, SHARON; Brookville Area HS; Brookville, PA; (3); VP Church Yth Grp; Sec Varsity Clb; Var JV Bsktbl; Coach Actv; Sftbl; NHS; Law.

BAKER, SHARON; Highlands HS; Natrona Heights, PA; (3); Hosp Aide; Band; Chorus; High Hon Roll; Jr NHS; NHS; Ntl Merit Ltr; Church Yth Grp; Cmnty Wkr; Acdmc All Amer 86; Ntl Ldrshp Svc Awd 87; U Of Pittsburgh; Pharm.

BAKER, SONDRA JO; Martinsburg Central HS; Roaring Spring, PA; (4); Drama Clb; VP FTA; JA; Sec Band; Sec Chorus; Stage Crew; Nwsp Stf; Yrbk Stf; Bsktbl; Hon Roll; IN U; Med Tech.

BAKER, STACEY; Sun Valley SR HS; Aston, PA; (4); 3/312; SADD; VP Band; Concert Band; Mrchg Band; Variety Show; Yrbk Stf; Capt Var Tennis; DAR Awd; High Hon Roll; Pres NHS; Cert Of Merit 86.

BAKER, SUSANNE; Huntingdon Area HS; Allensville, PA; (2); Pres Church Yth Grp; Key Clb; Ski Clb; Chorus; VP Frsh Cls; VP Soph Cls; Rep Stu Cncl; Var L Fld Hcky; Hon Roll; JV Trk; Hmrm Rep 85-87; Supr Perf On Natl Ed Dev Test 86.

BAKER, TAMMY; Elderton JR/Sr HS; Ford City, PA; (3); Intnl Clb; Spanish Clb; Band; Drill Tm; Mrchg Band; Yrbk Stf; High Hon Roll; Hon Roll; NHS.

BAKER, TAMMY K; Waynesboro Area HS; Waynesboro, PA; (3); Church Yth Grp; Color Guard; Mrchg Band; Cheerleading; Bus.

BAKER, TANYA; Hanover SR HS; Hanover, PA; (3); Band; Chorus; Drm Mjr(t); Orch; School Musical; Trs Jr Cls; Capt JV Bsktbl; Var L Trk; Hon Roll; NEDT Awd.

BAKER, TERESA; Du Bois Area HS; Dubois, PA; (4); 45/278; Bowling; Exploring; Intnl Clb; Pep Clb; Teachers Aide; Chorus; School Musical; Nwsp Bus Mgr; Nwsp Rptr; Nwsp Stf; US Mrn Corps; Law.

BALAITY, MELISSA; Bensalem HS; Trevose, PA; (2); Key Clb; School Musical; Nwsp Rptr; Hon Roll; Cmmnctns.

BALAKONIS, PAULA; Central Dauphin HS; Harrisburg, PA; (4); 43/387; Church Yth Grp; Key Clb; Varsity Clb; Rep Stu Cncl; Var Capt Bsktbl; Coach Actv; Var Capt Sftbl; Im Capt Vllybl; Hon Roll; Lion Awd; US Army Rsrv Schlr Athlt Awd 87; Lingle-George Athltc Awd & Schlrsp Awd Mst Outstndg Fml 87; Mt ST Marys Coll; Chem.

BALANDOVICH, AMIE; Abington HS; Phila, PA; (4); 5/486; Intnl Clb; Off Sr Cls; Socr; High Hon Roll; VP Jr NHS; NHS; Pres Schlr; USAF Recruiting Svc Math/Sci Awd, Messinger Sci Awd,NHS Schlrshp 87; Cornell U; Vet.

BALAS, CHERI; Panther Valley HS; Nesquehoning, PA; (2); 37/120; Church Yth Grp; Speech Tm; Flag Corp; Nwsp Stf; Im Cheerleading; Var Trk; JV Vllybl; Hon Roll; PA ST Coll; Sec.

BALAS, WENDY A; Central Bucks East HS; Buckingham, PA; (3); 12/483; Am Leg Aux Girls St; Yrbk Bus Mgr; JV Var Cheerleading; Trk; High Hon Roll; Hon Roll; Sec Jr NHS; NHS; Pres Schlr; Stu Art Gallery Awd 85; Guest Spkr Amer Lgn Aux Cnvntn 87.

BALASCIO, KIMBERLEY; Mid Valley HS; Dickson, PA; (4); VICA; High Hon Roll; Hon Roll; Lion Awd; Pres Schlr; Sal; Tchrs Schlrshp To Bradford Beauty Acad 87-88; Beadford Beauty Acad; Csmtlgy.

BALATGEK, STEVEN; Hamburg Area JR/Sr HS; Shoemakersville, PA; (3); Rep Soph Cls; Rep Stu Cncl; Var L Bsbl; JV Capt Bsktbl; JV Capt Socr; Hon Roll; Schl Spirit Awd 86; Muhlenberg Coll; Hist.

BALAWAJDER, KATHLEEN; Penn-Trafford HS; Irwin, PA; (3); 6/296; French Clb; FHA; Band; Concert Band; Mrchg Band; Symp Band; Nwsp Phtg; Nwsp Stf; High Hon Roll; NHS; Nwspaper Co-Editor-In-Chief 87-88; Ceramic Engrng.

BALBACH, ANGIE; Hampton HS; Wildwood, PA; (1); French Clb; Color Guard; Mrchg Band; Orch; Symp Band; Nwsp Stf; High Hon Roll; Church Yth Grp; Band; PA ST U/PA Cncl Of Tchrs Engl Essy Cntst 86-87; Sorbonne U Paris Frnc; Frnch.

BALBERCHAK, LUCAS FRANCIS; Bishop O Reilly HS; Forty Fort, PA; (3); Rep Frsh Cls; Pres Stu Cncl; JV Var Bsktbl; Var Crs Cntry; Wt Lftg; High Hon Roll; Hon Roll; Jr NHS; NHS; Ntl Merit Ltr; Highst GPA Avg Chem, Engl III,Relgn III,Amer Hstry III, Acctng I, Math 86-87; Acctng.

BALCEREK, KIMBERLY; Southmoreland SR HS; Mt Pleasant, PA; (3); 11/224; Drama Clb; French Clb; Letterman Clb; Math Clb; Pep Clb; Color Guard; Stage Crew; Im Powder Puff Ftbl; Var Sftbl; French Hon Soc; Elem Ed.

BALCH, MAGGIE; Canon Mc Millan HS; Canonsburg, PA; (4); French Clb; Office Aide; Yrbk Stf; L Tennis; High Hon Roll; Hon Roll; Pres Campus Life,Pres SAAD 87; PA Anncr 84-87; Outstndg Camper 86-87; Camp Cnslr 87; Penn ST ; Elem Ed.

BALCHUNE, LISA; Pittston Area HS; Duryea, PA; (2); 30/328; High Hon Roll; NHS.

BALCITA, JUDITH JOYCE GUEVARA; Burrell HS; Lower Burrell, PA; (3); Chorus; Nwsp Rptr; Yrbk Ed-Chief; Sec Stu Cncl; Var JV Cheerleading; L Trk; French Hon Soc; NHS; French Clb; School Play; Estrn Chrldrs Assn Super Rbbn 86; Schltc Achvt Ltr B 86; 1st Pl Hghts Plz Merchnts Assn Chrldng 86; Psych.

BALDASSANO, GUS; Methacton HS; Eagleville, PA; (3); 130/381; Boy Scts; Church Yth Grp; Cmnty Wkr; JA; Leo Clb; Office Aide; Red Cross Aide; SADD; Nwsp Rptr; Yrbk Rptr; Bus Admin.

BALDAUF, E MICHAEL; Ringgold HS; Finleyville, PA; (4); 7/360; Band; Drm Mjr(t); Nwsp Bus Mgr; Yrbk Bus Mgr; High Hon Roll; NHS; Church Yth Grp; Math Clb; Science Clb; Ski Clb; Ambass HOBY Sem 86; Rep Intl Order Odd Fllws U N Pilgrimage 86; Cnty Band 85-87, Dist Band 86-87; Carnegie Mellon U; Engrng.

BALDERSON, JEFF; Hopewell SR HS; Aliquippa, PA; (4); 9/245; Church Yth Grp; Latin Clb; Yrbk Phtg; Yrbk Stf; Rep Frsh Cls; Rep Soph Cls; Rep Jr Cls; VP Sr Cls; Rep Stu Cncl; Capt Socr; Lions Clb Boy Of Month; Beaver Cnty Times Schlrshp; KDKA-TV Extra Effrt Awd; WV U; Journlsm.

BALDESARI, KENNETH; Hazleton HS; Hazleton, PA; (3); 169/455; Ski Clb; Stu Cncl; Ftbl; Wt Lftg; Wrstlng; Hon Roll; Htl Mgmt.

BALDONIERI, KEN; Gr Latrobe SR HS; Latrobe, PA; (3); 33/373; Letterman Clb; Ski Clb; Varsity Clb; Capt L Socr; High Hon Roll; Comp Engrng.

BALDRIDGE, NANCY; Fox Chapel Area HS; Pittsburgh, PA; (3); 1/361; Ski Clb; Concert Band; Mrchg Band; School Musical; Yrbk Stf; Trs Frsh Cls; Var Crs Cntry; High Hon Roll; NHS; Key Clb; PITT Hnrs Convocation Awd U Of Pittsburgh 87; Bio-Psych.

BALDRIDGE, PATRICIA; Fox Chapel Area HS; Pittsburgh, PA; (3); Church Yth Grp; Key Clb; Ski Clb; Concert Band; Lib Mrchg Band; School Musical; Yrbk Stf; Rep Frsh Cls; High Hon Roll; NHS; Summa Cum Laude Ntl Ltn Exm 87; Pitt U Hnrs Cnvctn 87.

BALDWIN, APRIL; Susquehanna Community HS; Susquehanna, PA; (3); Band; Concert Band; Mrchg Band; Stat Bsktbl; Capt Cheerleading; Capt Twrlr; JV Var Vllybl; Soc Wrk.

BALDWIN, BENJAMIN; Cumberland Valley HS; Mechanicsburg, PA; (3); 95/630; Boys Clb Am; Hon Roll; Schlstc Arts Regl Awd 86; Jung Sim Do Korean Karate Black Belt 86; Engrng.

BALDWIN, DAVID; Lincoln HS; Ellwood City, PA; (2); Computer Clb; Math Clb; Red Cross Aide; Chorus; Ftbl; Swmmng; Wt Lftg; Wrstlng; High Hon Roll; Hon Roll; ROTC; Chem Engr.

BALDWIN, DAWN E; Bellwood-Antis HS; Bellwood, PA; (2); Library Aide; Ski Clb; SADD; Chorus; JV Fld Hcky; L Trk; Hon Roll; Acad All-Amer Schlr 86; Marine Bio.

BALDWIN, HOLLY; California Area SR HS; California, PA; (4); Drama Clb; FBLA; FNA; Ski Clb; Mrchg Band; School Play; Twrlr; U Of PA California; Bus Admin.

BALDWIN, JAMES; Linesville HS; Linesville, PA; (3); 3/98; Pres Drama Clb; Concert Band; Jazz Band; VP Mrchg Band; Pep Band; Nwsp Stf; Yrbk Stf; Sec Jr Cls; High Hon Roll; Pres NHS; Tenor Sax Plyr At PMEA ST Music Fstvl In Phil 87; Greenville Symphony Orch & Mercer Comm 87; Bio.

BALDWIN, JILL; Ringgold HS; Donora, PA; (2); Church Yth Grp; Cmnty Wkr; Girl Scts; Red Cross Aide; Socr; Hon Roll; Prfct Atten Awd; CA U Of PA; Comp Pgmmr.

BALDWIN, LISA; Red Lion Area SR HS; Brogue, PA; (2); 56/344; Library Aide; Hon Roll; Bus.

BALE, HOPE; Freeport Area HS; Sarver, PA; (4); 1/170; Church Yth Grp; Drama Clb; Chorus; School Musical; Yrbk Stf; Rep Stu Cncl; Capt Cheerleading; Var Trk; High Hon Roll; Ntl Merit Ltr; Prncpls Awd Acadc Excllnc 87; Schl Brd Stu Awd 87; Stu Govt Ofcr Of Yr Awd 87; Duke U; Corp Law.

BALENOVICH, RENEA; Yough SR HS; W Newton, PA; (3); Sec Church Yth Grp; Office Aide; Spanish Clb; Sec Chorus; Ed Nwsp Stf; Yrbk Stf; Powder Puff Ftbl; Trk; Twrlr; Hon Roll; Pres Phy Ftnss Awd 85; PA ST U; Bus Admn.

BALES, PATRICIA; Jenkintown HS; Jenkintown, PA; (3); 7/40; Church Yth Grp; Pep Clb; Varsity Clb; School Play; Nwsp Phtg; Yrbk Phtg; Cheerleading; Fld Hcky; Lcrss; French Hon Soc; Lib Arts.

BALESTRIERI, CHRISTINA; Vincentian HS; Pittsburgh, PA; (3); 5/73; Service Clb; School Musical; Nwsp Stf; High Hon Roll; Hon Roll; U Of Pittsburgh; Phrmcy.

BALINT, SCOTT; Central Catholic HS; Pittsburgh, PA; (2); 69/280; Church Yth Grp; Sec JA; SADD; Chorus; Church Choir; Var Trk; Hon Roll; Carnegie Mellon U; Elec Engr.

BALISTRIERI, LESLIE; Shaler Area Sr HS; Pittsburgh, PA; (3); 88/493; Ski Clb; Yrbk Phtg; Yrbk Stf; Hon Roll; Law.

BALL, BRANDON; Brownsville Area HS; Brownsville, PA; (3); 10/207; Drama Clb; Ski Clb; SADD; School Musical; Stage Crew; Nwsp Rptr; Stat Ftbl; L Trk; L Wrstlng; High Hon Roll; Med.

BALL, JAMES; Valley Forge Military Acad; Bondville, VT; (3); 27/144; Debate Tm; ROTC; Nwsp Rptr; Im Ftbl; JV Lcrss; Im Socr; JV Swmmng; JV Wrstlng; Hon Roll; Jr NHS; U Of VT; Pre-Law.

BALL, JASON; Meadville Area SR HS; Meadville, PA; (2); Church Yth Grp; Cmnty Wkr; JCL; Latin Clb; Ski Clb; Bsbl; JV Ftbl; High Hon Roll; Hon Roll; Prfct Atten Awd; Aerospc.

BALL, JENNIFER; Central SR HS; York, PA; (3); Trs Church Yth Grp; French Clb; German Clb; Chorus; Color Guard; Flag Corp; School Musical; Fld Hcky; Hon Roll; Jrnlsm.

BALL, JONATHAN; Henderson HS; West Chester, PA; (2); Church Yth Grp; Computer Clb; SADD; Church Choir; Rep Nazarene Yth Cngrs 87; Comp Sci.

BALL, MICHELLE; Kiski Area HS; Leechburg, PA; (3); FBLA; Library Aide; Teachers Aide; Hon Roll; Bradford Schl Bus; Lgl Secr.

BALLANTINE, THOMAS T; Palmyra Area HS; Palmyra, PA; (3); Am Leg Boys St; Boy Scts; Band; Drm Mjr(t); Jazz Band; Stu Cncl; Var Crs Cntry; Var Swmmng; Var Trk; NHS.

BALLARINO, ALISSA; Council Rock HS; Richboro, PA; (3); Rep Stu Cncl; JV Sftbl; Var Vllybl; Hon Roll; Ind Arts Awd 86-87; Cert Awd Vrsty Vlybl Team 84; Vrsty Ltr Vlybl 84; Arts.

BALLAS, AMY; Mercyhurst Prep HS; Erie, PA; (3); Ski Clb; Nwsp Phtg; Nwsp Rptr; Yrbk Stf; Sftbl; Hon Roll; Gannon U; Bus Mngt.

BALLAS JR, EDWARD J; Penns Manor HS; Alverda, PA; (3); Chess Clb; Church Yth Grp; Trk; NEDT Awd; Chem Engr.

BALLAY, KIMBERLY; Nazareth Acad; Philadelphia, PA; (4); Spanish Clb; Pres Chorus; Church Choir; Jazz Band; School Musical; School Play; Variety Show; Rep Stu Cncl; Hon Roll; 4 Yr Awd-Glee Clb 87; 4 Yr Awd-Hnr Chrl Pres 87; 2 Yr Awd-Chrch Choir & Hndbll Chr 87; Temple U; Educ.

BALLICK, MICHELE; West Hazleton HS; Tresckow, PA; (3); 46/221; French Clb; Yrbk Stf; Stu Cncl; Bsktbl; Cheerleading; Trk; Hon Roll; NHS; MVP-BSKTBL 84-85; Natl Hnr Soc 87-88; Physcl Thrpy.

BALLIET, ANTOINETTE; Northampton Area SR HS; Walnutport, PA; (3); Rptr DECA; Rep Frsh Cls; JV Cheerleading; Powder Puff Ftbl; Var Trk; Bus Admin.

BALLIET, CHRISTINE; Northampton Area HS; Treichlers, PA; (2); Drama Clb; Vllybl; Hon Roll; Med.

BALLIET, JAMIE; Palmerton Area HS; Palmerton, PA; (3); 6/173; Church Yth Grp; Nwsp Phtg; Nwsp Rptr; Yrbk Phtg; Off Stu Cncl; Var Bsktbl; Hon Roll; NHS; Acdmc Awd Grmn I, II & III 85-87; Acdmc Awd Wrld Cltres 87; Comms.

BALLIET, LISA; Hazleton SR HS; Drums, PA; (4); 54/385; Church Yth Grp; French Clb; FBLA; Hosp Aide; SADD; Nwsp Stf; Yrbk Stf; JV Var Cheerleading; Hon Roll; NHS; Geisinger Nrsng Schl; Nrsng.

BALLIET, TARYN; Leighton Area HS; Lehighton, PA; (3); Church Yth Grp; FBLA; SADD; FBLA-RGNL Secy, Chptr Jr Pres 86-87; FBLA-RGNL Pres, Chptr Pres 87-88; Bus Ed.

BALMER, KIM; Ephrata HS; Stevens, PA; (3); Pep Clb; Yrbk Rptr; Yrbk Stf; Rep Soph Cls; Rep Jr Cls; Var Cheerleading; Var Powder Puff Ftbl.

BALOG, JAMES; Conemaugh Valley HS; Johnstown, PA; (4); 2/121; Yrbk Stf; Cit Awd; High Hon Roll; Jr NHS; Lion Awd; NHS; Sal; Schlrshps-Franklin Alumni, Heffley Merit 87; Exchng Clb Stu Mnth March 87; U Of Pittsburgh; Chem.

BALOG, JEFFREY; Highlands SR HS; Natrona, PA; (4); 56/276; Key Clb; Trs Concert Band; Trs Mrchg Band; Rep Jr Cls; Rep Sr Cls; Rep Stu Cncl; JV Var Bsbl; Hon Roll; Ntl Merit Ltr; John & Mary Mc Ginley Schlrshp Fund 87; Home Cmng Ct 86; Clarion U Of PA; Bus Admin.

BALOUGH, PAMELA; Central Cambria HS; Ebensburg, PA; (3); 23/180; Art Clb; Church Yth Grp; Sec 4-H; FBLA; JA; Swmmng; 4-H Awd; Hon Roll; Swimming Ltrmn & Job Interview-Dist FBLA 3rd Pl 87; Equine Stds.

BALOURIS, MARIA; Northgate JR SR HS; Pittsburgh, PA; (3); Sec Church Yth Grp; Debate Tm; Math Tm; SADD; Church Choir; Rep Frsh Cls; Rep Soph Cls; Pres Jr Cls; Var Bsktbl; Var Sftbl; HOBY Ambssdr 86; Smmr Sftbl All Star 84; Cty & Suburbn Life Grl Athltc 86; Med.

BALPH, JENNIFER; Beaver Falls SR HS; Beaver Falls, PA; (3); 55/155; Am Leg Aux Girls St; Art Clb; Drama Clb; Spanish Clb; Thesps; School Musical; School Play; Stage Crew; Hon Roll; Beaver County CC; Accntng.

BALSAM, ILYSE; Bensalem HS; Bensalem, PA; (3); Key Clb; Varsity Clb; Var Socr; NHS; Drama Clb; Temple Yth Grp; Rep Stu Cncl; Stat Mgr(s); Var Tennis; Var Trk; U MD; Phy Thrpy.

BALSBAUGH, AMY; Central Dauphin HS; Harrisburg, PA; (4); 12/380; Church Yth Grp; Key Clb; Chorus; Swing Chorus; Yrbk Stf; Stu Cncl; Crs Cntry; Swmmng; Vllybl; High Hon Roll; Lafayette Coll; Intl Affrs.

BALTA, BRIAN; Immaculate Conception HS; Washington, PA; (3); 10/38; Art Clb; Church Yth Grp; JA; Ski Clb; Chorus; Yrbk Phtg; Yrbk Stf; VP Sr Cls; Bsbl; JV Bsktbl; U Of Chicago; Economics.

BALTER, KIM; Saint Benedict Acad; Erie, PA; (3); Yrbk Phtg; Yrbk Stf; Rep Stu Cncl; Var Sftbl; Hnr Mntn Edinboro U Art Dept 87; PA Jr Acad Sci 2nd Pl 85; PA Schl Press Assn 2nd Pl 87; Crmnl Jstc.

BALTHASER, KRISTIN; Greenwood HS; Millerwtown, PA; (1); Trs Church Yth Grp; VP 4-H; Band; Chorus; Concert Band; Mrchg Band; JV Bsktbl; JV Fld Hcky; Trk; Hon Roll.

BALTHASER, TAMMY; Hamburg Area HS; Bernville, PA; (3); 18/170; 4-H; Pres FFA; SADD; Yrbk Stf; Pres Sr Cls; Var Fld Hcky; Var Trk; 4-H Awd; Hon Roll; NHS; Ms Teen PA 2nd Rnr-Up 87; PA FFA Ind Pl Extmprneous Pblc Spkr 87; 4-H PA Keystn Awds Wnr 86; Genetics.

BALTOSSER, AMY; Bellefonte Area SR HS; Pleasant Gap, PA; (3); Pres Church Yth Grp; Girl Scts; SADD; Band; Chorus; Concert Band; Mrchg Band; Rep Frsh Cls; Rep Soph Cls; Hon Roll; South Hills Bus Schl; Bus.

BALTOSSER, MICHAEL; Susquenita HS; Marysville, PA; (3); Art Clb; English Clb; Spanish Clb; Band; Gov Hon Prg Awd; High Hon Roll; Hon Roll; NCTE Awd; NEDT Awd; Mechanical Engr.

BALTZER, BRENDA; Greater Johnstown SR HS; Johnstown, PA; (4); 16/306; French Clb; NFL; Chorus; Concert Band; Jazz Band; Mrchg Band; Orch; Rep Sr Cls; Hon Roll; NHS; Comp Systems Insti; Prlgl.

BAMBERGER, TODD; West York Area HS; York, PA; (3); 15/185; Boy Scts; Church Yth Grp; Concert Band; Jazz Band; Mrchg Band; Hon Roll; Envrmntl Biol.

BAMBLING, GARTH; Central York SR HS; York, PA; (3); 85/265; Cmnty Wkr; VP Exploring; Capt Science Clb; Hon Roll; Schlrshp Cnsrvtn Ldrshp Schl 86; Bio Sci.

BAMFORD, HOLLY; Dunmore HS; Dunmore, PA; (2); 13/160; Cmnty Wkr; French Clb; GAA; JA; Letterman Clb; Ski Clb; Spanish Clb; Chorus; Sec Frsh Cls; Bsktbl; All Star Trck Tm 86; Hnrbl Mntn Bsktbl 87; Bus.

BAMFORD, SUSAN; Ringgold HS; Donora, PA; (4); 31/343; Concert Band; Mrchg Band; School Play; Nwsp Stf; Yrbk Stf; Hon Roll; NHS; Hnr Crds 87; Bradford; Exec Sec.

BAMFORD, TRACEY; Shamokin Area HS; Shamokin, PA; (3); 11/223; Art Clb; Camera Clb; Debate Tm; Drama Clb; German Clb; VP Key Clb; Pep Clb; Radio Clb; Science Clb; Speech Tm; Pre-Med.

BAN, RACHEL ELIZABETH; Pennsbury HS; Yardley, PA; (3); Church Yth Grp; German Clb; Red Cross Aide; Concert Band; Mrchg Band; Nwsp Stf; Yrbk Stf; Hon Roll; NHS; Accounting.

BANDALO, COURTNEY A; Monongayela Valley Catholic HS; Donora, PA; (3); Camp Fr Inc; Church Yth Grp; Ski Clb; Varsity Clb; Im Powder Puff Ftbl; Var Socr; Var L Vllybl; Sec French Hon Soc; Hon Roll; NHS; U Pittsburgh; Law.

BANDHOLZ, BILL; Nativity B V M HS; Orwigsburg, PA; (3); Boy Scts; Chess Clb; Var Crs Cntry; JV Ftbl; Var Trk; Hon Roll; 1st Pl Sci Fair 87; Armd Svc.

BANDISH II, DENNIS M; Valley Forge Military Acad; Moorestown, NJ; (2); Varsity Clb; Bsbl; Bsktbl; Ftbl; Hon Roll; Schlrshp Ftbl & Bsbl, Acdmcs,Schlrshp 87-88; Invstmnt Bnkr.

BANE, CHRISTOPHER D; Nativity B V M HS; Orwigsburg, PA; (1); 2/94; French Clb; Ftbl; Trk; High Hon Roll; Amer Chem Soc Merit Awd 87; PA Jr Acad Sci St Mtng 1st Awd 87; Capita Sci & Engrg Fair 1st Pl 87.

BANE, KIMBERLY A; Nativity B V M HS; Orwigsburg, PA; (3); 4/86; Band; Nwsp Rptr; Crs Cntry; High Hon Roll; NHS; French Clb; Hosp Aide; Concert Band; Yrbk Stf; Rep Jr Cls; 1st Pl Zoology-Capitol Area Sci & Engrng Fair 87; 1st Pl PA Jr Acad Sci 86.

BANE, STEPHANIE; Mc Guffey HS; Claysville, PA; (4); Church Yth Grp; French Clb; Sftbl; Tennis; Poetry Pblshd 87; Case Wstrn Rsrv U; Jrnlsm.

BANERJEE, RINI; The Ellis Schl; Pittsburgh, PA; (4); 1/35; Dance Clb; Temple Yth Grp; Chorus; Madrigals; VP Frsh Cls; Sec Sr Cls; Cit Awd; French Hon Soc; High Hon Roll; Ntl Merit SF; Virginia P Stvnsn Awd Amrcn Hstry 86; U Of Pttsbrgh Prvst Schlrshp Frnch 86; Wrld Affrs Cncl 86.

BANES, BRENDA; Central Bucks West HS; Doylestown, PA; (3); 180/400; Church Yth Grp; Band; Concert Band; Rep Stu Cncl; Lcrss; Mgr(s); Score Keeper; Socr; Wt Lftg; Hon Roll; Maine Line Models 87; Southeastern Acad; Trvl.

BANEY, LEANN; Juniata HS; Mifflintown, PA; (3); 1/200; Church Yth Grp; SADD; Varsity Clb; Concert Band; Mrchg Band; Mgr Stage Crew; Yrbk Stf; Capt Cheerleading; High Hon Roll; NHS; PA ST U; Acctng.

BANEY, RAENETTE; Bellefonte Area HS; Bellefonte, PA; (3); 33/250; Church Yth Grp; GAA; Pep Clb; Varsity Clb; Chorus; Rep Stu Cncl; JV Cheerleading; Var Trk; Hon Roll; Untd Wesleyan Coll; Med Mssns.

BANEY, RENEE; Juniata HS; Pt Royal, PA; (3); Church Yth Grp; Drama Clb; SADD; Varsity Clb; Mrchg Band; Nwsp Stf; Yrbk Stf; Stat Trk; Hon Roll; NHS; Paralgl.

BANEY, TODD; Bellwood-Antis HS; Tyrone, PA; (3); 8/115; Varsity Clb; Chorus; School Musical; Chrmn Jr Cls; Rep Stu Cncl; Var L Ftbl; Var L Wrstlng; Hon Roll; NHS; HOBY Fndtn Alumni 86; Acad All Amer 85-87.

BANH, MINH; J P Mc Caskey HS; Lancaster, PA; (3); Boy Scts; Computer Clb; Exploring; Math Clb; Math Tm; Science Clb; Teachers Aide; Yrbk Ed-Chief; Yrbk Phtg; Yrbk Rptr; ST Rep Young Day Govt 87; Schl Brd Young Day Govt 87; Northwestern U; Phys Thrpy.

BANICK, RICHARD; Dunmore HS; Dunmore, PA; (3); 56/152; Boy Scts; Computer Clb; Trs Band; Trs Concert Band; Trs Mrchg Band; Nwsp Phtg; Yrbk Phtg.

BANICKY, LISA; Middletown Area HS; Middletown, PA; (3); 22/193; Church Yth Grp; VP FCA; Library Aide; Band; Chorus; Church Choir; Concert Band; Drm & Bgl; Mrchg Band; Nwsp Rptr.

BANIECKI, MARY L; Carmichaels Area JR-SR HS; Carmichaels, PA; (1); 5/130; Band; Concert Band; School Play; Nwsp Stf; Sftbl; DAR Awd; High Hon Roll; JC Awd; Jr NHS; Pres Schlr; Pres Acdmc Fit Awd 86-87; Athltc Awd 86-87; Band, Nwspr Staff Hnry Cert 86-87.

BANKERT, AMY; Kennard-Dale HS; Stewartstown, PA; (3); 52/165; Chorus; School Musical; L Mgr(s); JV Stat Vllybl; Hon Roll; Mc Donalds Crw Prsn Of Mnth 87; Cntrl Penn Bus Schl; Acctng.

BANKERT, SHERRY; Spring Grove Area SR HS; Spg Grove, PA; (4); 13/274; Camera Clb; Yrbk Stf; Var L Bsktbl; CC Awd; High Hon Roll; Hon Roll; NHS; Pres Fit Awd 87; Spring Grove Womns Clb Schlrshp 87; Yorktown Chptr ABWA Schlrshp 87; Shippensburg U; Finc.

BANKES, MARGARET; Danville SR HS; Danville, PA; (4); Art Clb; Hosp Aide; Latin Clb; Band; Color Guard; Hon Roll; Home Ec Awd Highest GPA 87.

BANKS, NICOLE; William Penn SR HS; York, PA; (3); 53/383; VP JA; Color Guard; Mrchg Band; Trs Frsh Cls; Trs Soph Cls; Trs Jr Cls; Rep Stu Cncl; JV Bsktbl; NHS; Stu Of Mnth 87; Upwrd Bnd 86; Accntnt.

BANKS, PATRICIA; Harry S Truman HS; Croydon, PA; (4); 100/634; High Hon Roll; Hon Roll; Temple U; Acctg.

BANKS, TAMMY; Forest Hills SR HS; Salix, PA; (4); Church Yth Grp; FBLA; Teachers Aide; VP Y-Teens; Band; Sec Chorus; Church Choir; Concert Band; Mrchg Band; High Hon Roll; Ntl Jr Hnr Soc 84; Bob Jones U; Accntng.

BANNER, PAUL; Venango Christian HS; Fryburg, PA; (4); 9/36; SADD; VP Stu Cncl; Var Bsbl; Var Capt Ftbl; High Hon Roll; NHS; NEDT Awd; Boy Scts; 4-H; SADD; US Army Rsrv Schlr Athlt Awd 87; Presdntl Acadc Ftnss Awd 87; Acadc All Am 87; Penn ST U; Mechncl Engrng.

BANNISTER, ALLYSON; Academy HS; Erie, PA; (3); 23/226; Church Yth Grp; Girl Scts; Band; Concert Band; Mrchg Band; Pep Band; Hon Roll; NHS; Bus.

BANOGON, FRANCISCO; Bishop Mc Devitt HS; Harrisburg, PA; (3); 52/216; Art Clb; Key Clb; Office Aide; Service Clb; Ski Clb; Band; Concert Band; Drm & Bgl; Jazz Band; Rep Frsh Cls; Inter Dsgn.

BANZHOF, ABIGAIL; Parkland SR HS; Allentown, PA; (3); 78/481; Computer Clb; Dance Clb; Math Clb; Ski Clb; SADD; Y-Teens; Chorus; Concert Band; Mrchg Band; School Play.

BARABAS, MATT; Westmont Hilltop HS; Johnstown, PA; (2); Church Yth Grp; Civic Clb; Ski Clb; Concert Band; Jazz Band; Mrchg Band; Rep Stu Cncl; Cit Awd; Hon Roll; Lion Awd; Amrcn Lgn Awd 85; Case Western; Dntstry.

BARACH, JENNY; Gettysburg HS; New Oxford, PA; (4); Pep Clb; Spanish Clb; Nwsp Rptr; Nwsp Stf; Capt Cheerleading; Vllybl; High Hon Roll; Hon Roll; NHS; Dickinson Coll; Bio.

BARACKMAN, CHRISTOPHER; Greater Latrobe HS; Latrobe, PA; (3); Boy Scts; Church Yth Grp; German Clb; Ski Clb; Band; Pres Concert Band; Pres Mrchg Band; High Hon Roll; High Hnrs 86-87.

BARAKAT, LABIBA; L E Dieruff HS; Allentown, PA; (3); Church Yth Grp; Dance Clb; Ski Clb; Rep Stu Cncl; Var Mgr(s); Vllybl; Hon Roll.

BARAN, CHRISTINE; G A R Memorial HS; Wilkes-Barre, PA; (3); 1/152; Key Clb; Library Aide; Band; Chorus; Concert Band; Mrchg Band; Pep Band; Symp Band; High Hon Roll; Hon Roll; Pre Med.

BARAN, MICHAEL; Allentown Central Catholic HS; Whitehall, PA; (3); Church Yth Grp; Math Tm; Pres Stu Cncl; JV Bsktbl; JV Crs Cntry; High Hon Roll; NHS; 2nd Pl Rgnl PA JR Acad Of Sci 85-86; US Achvt Acad Ntl Sci Merit Awd 85; Acctng.

BARAN, RITA; Bishop Hafey HS; Beaver Mdws, PA; (3); 27/114; Pres Church Yth Grp; French Clb; Y-Teens; Var Capt Bsktbl; Var Sftbl; Hon Roll; Sftbl Cert Of Merit 84-87; Psych.

BARAN, SHAR; Corry Area HS; Columbus, PA; (3); French Clb; Library Aide; Rep Sr Cls; JV Var Vllybl; Hon Roll; Intr Dcrtr.

BARAN, SUSAN; Monessen JR & SR HS; Monessen, PA; (3); Sec Band; Concert Band; Drm Mjr(t); Jazz Band; Mrchg Band; Stage Crew; Nwsp Rptr; Stu Cncl; High Hon Roll; Hon Roll; Psych.

BARANIENICZ, WALTER; Northeast Catholic HS; Philadelphia, PA; (4); 11/369; Yrbk Rptr; Im Bsktbl; Im Vllybl; Hon Roll; NHS; PA ST U; Bus Admin.

BARANOWSKI, JOS; Archbishop John Carroll HS; Havertown, PA; (3); 168/396; Rep Soph Cls; Rep Stu Cncl; JV Bsktbl; Var Lcrss; Hon Roll; West Chester; Accntng.

BARBALINARDO, FRANCO; St John Neumann HS; Philadelphia, PA; (2); 4/351; English Clb; Latin Clb; Math Clb; High Hon Roll; Hon Roll; Jr NHS; Cert Of Honor 87; Penn ST; Med.

BARBEE, BRIAN; Aliquippa SR HS; Aliquippa, PA; (3); Church Yth Grp; NAACP; Var Ftbl; Var Wt Lftg; Cmmnctns.

BARBEE, ERROL; Jules E Mastbaum Area Vo Tech; Philadelphia, PA; (3); Boy Scts; Varsity Clb; VICA; Stage Crew; Bowling; Ftbl; Trk; High Hon Roll; Hon Roll; Elec Engr.

BARBELLA, JOSEPH; St John Neumann HS; Philadelphia, PA; (3); 126/349; Var Bowling; All Cthlc Bwlng Tm, MVP Bwlng Tm, & Hghst Av Bwlng Tm 86-87; Phila Schl Phrmcy; Phrmcst.

BARBEN, SHANNON; Mount Union Area HS; Mc Veytown, PA; (3); 10/152; Church Yth Grp; Drama Clb; Concert Band; Co-Capt Flag Corp; Hon Roll; NHS; Comp.

BARBER, DENISE; Everett Christian Acad; Crystal Spring, PA; (2); 1/5; Church Yth Grp; Band; Chorus; Church Choir; Concert Band; Sec Stu Cncl; Var Bsktbl; Var Cheerleading; Var Vllybl; Hon Roll.

BARBER, DOUG; Butler SR HS; Butler, PA; (2); Church Yth Grp; Bsktbl; JV Ftbl; JV Trk; JV Wt Lftg; Hon Roll.

BARBER, JEAN; Lake Lehman SR HS; Hunlock Creek, PA; (2); Ski Clb; SADD; VP Soph Cls; Stat Mgr(s); Stat Score Keeper; Var L Trk; High Hon Roll; Hon Roll; Jr NHS; NHS; Vet.

BARBER, KATHY; Mifflinburg Area HS; Mifflinburg, PA; (1); Church Yth Grp; FBLA; FHA; Church Choir; High Hon Roll; Hon Roll; NHS; 4-H; 4-H Awd; Sec.

BARBER, RICHARD; Mercer Area JR SR HS; Mercer, PA; (4); 13/140; Church Yth Grp; SADD; Band; Concert Band; Jazz Band; Mrchg Band; Pep Band; Stage Crew; Nwsp Stf; Yrbk Stf; U S Marine Corps.

BARBER, SUZANNE; Brockway HS; Brockway, PA; (3); 24/105; Art Clb; Exploring; Girl Scts; Yrbk Stf; Penn ST; Cvl Engrng.

BARBERI, DAVID; B Reed Henderson SR HS; Exton, PA; (3); 79/370; Camera Clb; Cmnty Wkr; Debate Tm; Intnl Clb; Science Clb; Stage Crew; Nwsp Phtg; Yrbk Phtg; Lit Mag; Hon Roll; Schlstc Art Awds Natl Merit Photogrphy 87; PA Gvrnrs Schl Arts Semi Fnlst 87; NYU; Photogrphy.

BARBERIO, CARLA; Jeannette SR HS; Jeannette, PA; (2); French Clb; Spanish Clb; IN U Of PA; Acctg.

BARBERIO, GREG; Lincoln HS; Ellwood City, PA; (3); VP Spanish Clb; SADD; Yrbk Stf; L Bsbl; Bowling; L Ftbl; Hon Roll; Psych.

BARBERIO, LYNN; Jeannette SR HS; Jeannette, PA; (2); #45 In Class; Spanish Clb; Rep Frsh Cls; U Of Pitt; Teaching.

BARBERY, KENDRA; Southmoreland HS; Scottdale, PA; (4); French Clb; Math Clb; Chorus; Concert Band; Mrchg Band; Nwsp Stf; Lit Mag; French Hon Soc; Trs NHS; Church Yth Grp; Carnegio Mellon U; Psych.

BARBIERI, CHRISTINE; Bensalem HS; Bensalem, PA; (2); Key Clb; Office Aide; Teachers Aide; Rep Soph Cls; Var Tennis; JV Trk; High Hon Roll; NHS.

BARBIERI, DONNA; Dawningtown SR HS; Exton, PA; (3); GAA; Ski Clb; Spanish Clb; Diving; Lcrss; Trk; NHS; NEDT Awd; Lang.

BARBIN, TRACEY; Canon Mc Millan HS; Cecil, PA; (3); 98/367; Drama Clb; SADD; Thesps; School Musical; School Play; Yrbk Stf; JV Cheerleading; Im Vllybl; Hon Roll; Spanish NHS; Pres Acad Fit Awd 85; Penn ST U; Elem Ed.

BARBOSA, ADRIANNE; Palmerton Area HS; Palmerton, PA; (3); Yrbk Stf; Pres Frsh Cls; Stu Cncl; JV Bsktbl; Var Crs Cntry; Var Trk.

BARBOUNIS, CONSTANTINE; Parkland HS; Allentown, PA; (3); 62/481; Pres Church Yth Grp; Exploring; Band; Chorus; Yrbk Phtg; Var JV Bsktbl; Var L Socr; Var L Trk; High Hon Roll; Hon Roll; Pre-Med.

BARBOUR, KEVIN; Elizabethtown Area HS; Elizabethtown, PA; (3); 8/228; Church Yth Grp; Band; Chorus; Jazz Band; Orch; Var Socr; Var Tennis; JV Var Wrstlng; NHS; Grove City; Elec Engrng.

BARBOUR, RENEE; John Harris HS; Harrisburg, PA; (3); Band; Chorus; Church Choir; Drill Tm; Hon Roll; Prfct Atten Awd; VP Peer Counslrs 85-87; Harrisburg Arts Magnet Schl Theatre 85-87; Schl Gospel Choir 86-87; Public Rltns.

BARCLAY, DEBRA; Connellsville Area HS; Mt Pleasant, PA; (4); 3/500; Trs Church Yth Grp; Office Aide; Trs SADD; Band; Capt Color Guard; Mrchg Band; Rep Stu Cncl; French Hon Soc; High Hon Roll; NHS; U Of Pittsburgh; Pre Med.

BARCLAY, JANICE E; Creative & Performing Arts HS; Philadelphia, PA; (4); 18/123; Church Yth Grp; Girl Scts; Library Aide; Teachers Aide; Chorus; School Musical; Stage Crew; Rep Frsh Cls; Rep Soph Cls; Rep Jr Cls; W Chester U; Elem Ed.

BARCLAY, ROBERT; Moniteau HS; Parker, PA; (4); #4 In Class; Drama Clb; Spanish Clb; Chorus; L Bsktbl; L Ftbl; Capt L Trk; Pres Schlr; Boy Scts; Varsity Clb; Variety Show; Luciano Plesakov Awd 87; Outstndg Stu 87; Lttl 12 Ftbl Schlrshp 87; Grove City Coll; Elec Engrng.

BARCUS, CHRISTA; B Reed Henderson HS; West Chester, PA; (3); 11/377; Church Yth Grp; French Clb; Ski Clb; Lit Mag; Var Cheerleading; Lcrss; French Hon Soc; Hon Roll; Psych.

BARCZAK, LESLIE; Westmont Hilltop HS; Johnstown, PA; (3); #7 In Class; VP Art Clb; French Clb; Pep Clb; Ski Clb; Yrbk Phtg; Yrbk Stf; JV Bsktbl; Var Sftbl; Var Tennis; High Hon Roll; YEA Hnrs 86-87.

BARCZYK, ANITA; Yough SR HS; Ruffsdale, PA; (3); 99/280; Church Yth Grp; Cmnty Wkr; French Clb; Pep Clb; Ski Clb; SADD; Chorus; Cheerleading; Mgr(s); Powder Puff Ftbl; Natl Eng Merit Awd 86-87; Phy Thrpy.

BARD, CYNTHIA; Ambridge Area HS; Ambridge, PA; (4); Office Aide; Pep Clb; Spanish Clb; Off Frsh Cls; Off Soph Cls; Off Jr Cls; Off Sr Cls; Mgr Wrstlng; Hon Roll; Slippery Rock U; Secndry Ed.

BARD, WILLIAM; Solanco HS; Kirkwood, PA; (2); 2/400; Rep Soph Cls; Im Bsktbl; JV Crs Cntry; JV Trk; High Hon Roll; Hon Roll; NHS.

BARDASH, LINDA; Shenango Area HS; New Castle, PA; (3); 22/125; French Clb; Chorus; Jazz Band; Mrchg Band; Sec Soph Cls; Sec Jr Cls; Sec Sr Cls; Rep Stu Cncl; JV Var Bsktbl; Tlntd/Gftd Stus Pgm 87; Ed.

BARE, JENNIFER; Henderson HS; W Chester, PA; (3); JV Var Cheerleading; Mgr Fld Hcky; Hon Roll; Spanish NHS.

BAREFOOT, DENA K; Franklin Regionall HS; Murrysville, PA; (3); AFS; Rep JA; Ski Clb; SADD; Ed Nwsp Stf; Tennis; High Hon Roll; Amrcn Lgn Awd 83; Achvr Yr-JR Achvt, Schlrshp PA Free Entrprse Wk 86; Westminster; Bus.

AREFOOT, RUSSELL; Duquesne HS; Duquesne, PA; (3); 4/96; French lb; Band; Concert Band; Jazz Band; Mrchg Band; Nwsp Ed-Chief; Yrbk tf; Pres Jr Cls; VP Stu Cncl; VP NHS.

AREFOOT, TRACY; Chestnut Ridge HS; Alum Bank, PA; (4); 30/129; rs FHA; Chorus; Church Choir; Variety Show; Hon Roll; CA U; Med ech.

ARGER, CRYSTAL; Freeport SR HS; Sarver, PA; (3); 31/216; FBLA; Irchg Band; Trk; Twrlr; Hon Roll; Nrsng.

ARGER, DAVE; Grader Johnstown Vo-Tech; Osterburg, PA; (3); Boy cts; VICA; Cit Awd; Mchnc.

ARGER, LYDI; Union HS; Rimersburg, PA; (2); 1/74; Sec Church Yth rp; FCA; SADD; Band; Chorus; Concert Band; Mrchg Band; JV Bsktbl; V Trk; JV Vllybl; Pharm.

ARGER, OLEVA; Union HS; Rimersburg, PA; (2); VP Church Yth Grp; ADD; Color Guard; Nwsp Stf; VP Soph Cls; Trk; Twrlr; Vllybl; Hon Roll; HS; Educ.

ARGER, PATRICIA; Karns City HS; Fenelton, PA; (3); FHA; Library ide; Chorus; Ntl Merit Ltr; Du Boise Bus Coll; Med Sec.

ARGER, RICHARD; Karns City Area HS; Chicora, PA; (3); 15/100; hurch Yth Grp; Exploring; Spanish Clb; Chorus; JV Bsktbl; Var L Golf; ar L Trk; Hon Roll; NHS; Qlfd & Cmpltd-Dist Trk & Fld Chmpnshps 87; eronaut Engrng.

ARGO, CATHERINE; Dauphin County Tech Schl; Harrisburg, PA; (3); ud/Vis; FNA; Girl Scts; Hosp Aide; VICA; Chorus.

ARHITE, VERONICA E; Sheffield HS; Warren, PA; (4); 6/78; Sec hurch Yth Grp; FHA; Sec Band; School Play; Capt Bsktbl; Cit Awd; High on Roll; NHS; SADD; Teachers Aide; HS Stu Yr 87; Gst Pg PA Hs Rep 5; IN U P A; Chld Dvlpmnt.

ARINGER, STEFANIE S; Quakertown HS; Quakertown, PA; (3); Am eg Aux Girls St; Church Yth Grp; SADD; Chorus; Church Choir; Color uard; Mrchg Band; School Musical; Variety Show; Rep Jr Cls; Amer Lgn chl Awd 85; Psych.

ARKDOLL, MICHAEL; Waynesboro Area SR HS; Waynesboro, PA; 4); Im Bowling; JV Ftbl; Im Tennis; Im Vllybl; Hon Roll; PA ST U, Mt lto; Lbrl Arts.

ARKDOLL, TY; Waynesboro Area SR HS; Waynesboro, PA; (4); 2/365; res Chess Clb; Pres Church Yth Grp; Trs JCL; Band; Chorus; Concert and; Jazz Band; School Musical; Swing Chorus; Cit Awd; WAEA chlrshp 87; Landis Schlrshp 87; Sthrn Engrng Sco Schlrshp; Penn ST; lec Engrng.

ARKER, CARL; Coatesville HS; Coatesville, PA; (3); 54/517; Spanish lb; Var Ftbl; Var Trk; Im Wt Lftg; Hon Roll; NHS.

ARKER, CHRIS; Franklin Regional HS; Murrysville, PA; (3); Art Clb; rench Clb; JA; Ski Clb; Nwsp Stf; Bsktbl; Hon Roll; NHS; Dickinson oll; Arch.

ARKER, COLLEEN; West Mifflin Area HS; W Mifflin, PA; (4); #96 In lass; Drama Clb; Thesps; School Play; Score Keeper; High Hon Roll; Hon oll; Penn ST U; Comm.

ARKER, GIDGET; Fort Le Boeuf HS; Waterford, PA; (2); Ski Clb; panish Clb; School Musical; Stage Crew; Yrbk Stf; High Hon Roll; Law nforcement.

ARKER, HEATHER; Fort Le Boeuf HS; Waterford, PA; (3); Art Clb; ki Clb; Stage Crew; High Hon Roll; Law Enfrcmnt.

ARKER, JARED; Elizabeth-Forward HS; Monongahela, PA; (3); Chess lb; Computer Clb; Nwsp Rptr; Sftbl; Ntl Merit SF; Acdmc All-Amer 87; us Law.

ARKER, JENNY; Garden Spot HS; Narvon, PA; (2); 14/226; Church th Grp; Band; Chorus; Church Choir; Concert Band; Mrchg Band; Rep oph Cls; Var Sftbl; High Hon Roll; Hon Roll; Bus.

ARKER, THOMAS; Solanco HS; Kirkwood, PA; (3); Chess Clb; Pres hurch Yth Grp; German Clb; High Hon Roll; Hon Roll; NHS; Sci Solanco chlr 84-85; Sci Cert Of Awd 84-85; Wstrn Cvlztns Cert Of Awd 85-86; eronautics.

ARKLEY, JENNIFER; Knoch HS; Butler, PA; (3); Church Yth Grp; ep Clb; SADD; Chorus; School Musical; Yrbk Stf; Sec Frsh Cls; Sec Soph ls; Sec Jr Cls; Rep Stu Cncl; Cmnctns.

ARKLEY, SHANNAN F; David B Oliver HS; Pittsburgh, PA; (2); Hosp ide; Nwsp Rptr; Rep Soph Cls; Stu Cncl; Vllybl; DAR Awd; Hon Roll; lasonic Awd; Pres Schlr; U Pittsburgh.

ARKMAN, CHRISTIE; Everett Area HS; Everett, PA; (3); Sec Church th Grp; Drama Clb; Office Aide; Spanish Clb; Band; Church Choir; oncert Band; Mrchg Band; Pep Band; Stat Trk; Bedford County Band 7; Shippensburg U; Elem Eductn.

ARKMAN, RENO; Rockwood Area HS; Rockwood, PA; (2); 30/128; oy Scts; Chess Clb; Church Yth Grp; Computer Clb; 4-H; Spanish Clb; hurch Choir; Sec Frsh Cls; Stu Cncl; Var Bsbl; IN U Of PA; Sci.

ARKOVIC, LEA; Center HS; Aliquippa, PA; (2); Camera Clb; xploring; Latin Clb; Scholastic Bowl; Trs Frsh Cls; Rep Stu Cncl; High on Roll; Hon Roll; Latin Cum Laude Awd 87; Med Field.

ARKOVIC, LORI; Center Area HS; Aliquippa, PA; (3); Exploring; atin Clb; Office Aide; Scholastic Bowl; Sec Jr Cls; Sec Sr Cls; Rep Stu ncl; Bowling; Hon Roll; NHS; Latin Cum Laude Awd 87; Pre Med.

ARKUS, JOSEPH; Hazleton HS; Hazleton, PA; (3); 91/438; Var Bsbl; igh Hon Roll; Penn ST U; Nclr Engrng.

ARLAMAS, CONSTANCE; Ambridge Area HS; Ambridge, PA; (4); 14/ 35; Pres Church Yth Grp; JA; Sec Red Cross Aide; Spanish Clb; Band; Off r Cls; Off Sr Cls; Wrstlng; High Hon Roll; NHS; AHEPA Schlrshp; Penn T U.

ARLETTA, FRANK; Hazleton HS; Hazleton, PA; (3); 19/450; Math m; Quiz Bowl; Yrbk Stf; Rep Stu Cncl; Hon Roll; Ntl Merit SF; Acad All mer 87; Engrng.

ARLEY, NITA; Christian School Of York; Dallastown, PA; (2); Yrbk us Mgr; JV Bsktbl; Var Sftbl; Hon Roll; Bus Admin.

ARLOW, DANIELLE; Northern Lehigh HS; Slatington, PA; (3); 6/166; ebate Tm; Hosp Aide; Ski Clb; School Musical; Variety Show; Yrbk Stf; tu Cncl; Cheerleading; High Hon Roll; NHS; Phys Thrpy.

ARLOW, JEFF; Harry S Truman HS; Levittown, PA; (3); FBLA; JA; panish Clb; Bsktbl; Trk; Wt Lftg; Bsktbl.

ARLOW, JENNIFER; Haverford HS; Havertown, PA; (3); 20/450; Drill m; Ed Nwsp Stf; Ed Lit Mag; Hon Roll; NHS; Pen & Ink Awd 86.

ARLOW, JILL; Mc Keesport Area HS; Dravosburg, PA; (2); Cmnty Vkr; Office Aide; Mrchg Band; Symp Band; Off Frsh Cls; Stu Cncl; High on Roll; Yearly Hnr Rl 85-86 & 86-87; Law.

ARLOW, WILLIAM; Turkeyfoot Valley HS; Addison, PA; (3); Boy cts; Ski Clb; Band; Concert Band; Jazz Band; Mrchg Band; School Play; ep Stu Cncl; High Hon Roll; HOBY Yth Ldrshp Smnr 85-86; Computer 'rade Schl; Comp Oper.

BARMOY, JOY; Meyersdale Area HS; Meyersdale, PA; (3); French Clb; Band; Chorus; Church Choir; Concert Band; Drm Mjr(t); Mrchg Band; School Musical; Yrbk Stf; Stat Vllybl; Elem Educ.

BARNA, JANET; Waynesburg HS; Waynesburg, PA; (3); French Clb; Ski Clb; Mat Maids; Hon Roll; Natl Sci Merit Awd 83-84; Pres Clb Awd.

BARNA, KIM; Tunkhannock Area HS; Tunkhannock, PA; (3); VP Church Yth Grp; Ski Clb; Rep Civic Clb; Rep Soph Cls; Rep Jr Cls; Rep Sr Cls; JV Bsktbl; Hon Roll.

BARNA, ROBERT; Hazleton HS; Drums, PA; (3); Boy Scts; Drama Clb; Ski Clb; Hon Roll; Wrld Cnsrvtn Awd 86; Penn ST U; Aerospce Engrng.

BARNARD, PATRICIA; W Philadelphia Catholic Girls HS; Philadelphia, PA; (3); 13/246; Church Yth Grp; Spanish Clb; Nwsp Rptr; High Hon Roll; Hon Roll; Penn ST U; Jrnlsm.

BARNASEVITCH, MARY; Hazleton HS; Beaver Mdws, PA; (2); French Clb; Scholastic Bowl; Chorus; Yrbk Stf; JV Bowling; French Hon Soc; Hon Roll; Pres Acdmc Fit Awd 86; Amer Legion Auxlry Awd 86; PA ST U; Merchndsng.

BARNDT, BETH; Somerset Area SR HS; Somerset, PA; (3); 51/239; Church Yth Grp; English Clb; German Clb; Letterman Clb; Office Aide; Red Cross Aide; Pres SADD; Varsity Clb; Chorus; Church Choir; Lock Haven U; Hlth Sci.

BARNDT, ROBERT; Somerset Area SR HS; Friedens, PA; (3); 1/235; Art Clb; English Clb; German Clb; Band; Chorus; Concert Band; Jazz Band; Mrchg Band; Orch; Pep Band; 1st Pl Awd Gnnon Univ Ptry Cntst 87; Bus.

BARNDT, TRACY; Windber Area HS; Windber, PA; (3); 59/128; Art Clb; Pres Church Yth Grp; FTA; Math Clb; Sec Trs Spanish Clb; Pres Jhnstwn Dist Cncl Yth Mnstries 86-87; Cnslng.

BARNER, JODY; Sheffield Area JR-SR HS; Sheffield, PA; (4); 8/76; SADD; Varsity Clb; Sec Jr Cls; VP Stu Cncl; Var L Cheerleading; Var L Vllybl; High Hon Roll; Sec NHS; VFW Awd; Voice Dem Awd; T C A C All Star Vllybl Tm Hon Mntn 86-87; Big 30 Charity Classic Chrldr 86-87; Hnr Grad 86-87; PA ST U; Secndry Sci Educ.

BARNER, SHERRI; Emmaus HS; Emmaus, PA; (4); 137/450; Church Yth Grp; Latin Clb; Varsity Clb; Chorus; Sec Frsh Cls; Rep Sr Cls; Rep Stu Cncl; Var L Sftbl; Gold Awd Awd To 2 Time Vrsty Lttr In Same Sport 87; Shippensburg U; Govt.

BARNER, TAMMY; Jersey Shore Area SR HS; Jersey Shore, PA; (4); 1/ 240; German Clb; Service Clb; Varsity Clb; Rep Soph Cls; Rep Stu Cncl; Var Sftbl; Bausch & Lomb Sci Awd; Hon Roll; NHS; Val; Elizabethtown Coll; Teaching.

BARNES, AMY; Greensboro Central Catholic HS; W Newton, PA; (3); Church Yth Grp; Capt Civic Clb; Drama Clb; Pep Clb; Ski Clb; Band; Chorus; Concert Band; Mrchg Band; Pep Band; U Pittsburgh; Nrsng.

BARNES, CHARLES; Claysburg-Kimmel HS; Portage, PA; (4); 4/50; Yrbk Sprt Ed; Pres Frsh Cls; Pres Soph Cls; Pres Jr Cls; Pres Sr Cls; Sec Trs Stu Cncl; Bsbl; Ftbl; Hon Roll; NHS; PA ST U; Aerospc Engrng.

BARNES, CHRISTOPHER N; Clearfield SR HS; Clearfield, PA; (4); Key Clb; Bsbl; Capt Bsktbl; Cit Awd; Hon Roll; Bill Kruckenberg Bsktbl Awd Meml 87; MVP Bsktbl 87; Dist IX AAAA All-Star Awd 87; IUP; Bus Adm.

BARNES, CRAIG; Greencastle Antrim HS; Greencastle, PA; (3); Var Bsbl; Var Bsktbl; Im Coach Actv; Var Ftbl; Var Wt Lftg; Prfct Atten Awd; Defensive Back Awd Ftbl 85-86; Offensive Back Awd Ftbl 86-87; Phys Ed.

BARNES JR, DONALD W; Peters Township HS; Mcmurray, PA; (4); 79/242; JA; School Play; Stage Crew; Beta Awd Acadc Achvt 84-85; U Of Pittsburgh; Engrng.

BARNES, HEATHER; Valley HS; New Kensington, PA; (3); 53/216; Math Tm; Pep Clb; Ski Clb; Varsity Clb; JV Bsktbl; Capt JV Cheerleading; Var JV Tennis; Hon Roll; U Of CO Boulder; Engrng.

BARNES, J SCOTT; Octorara Area HS; Parkesburg, PA; (4); 2/163; Radio Clb; Scholastic Bowl; Band; Mrchg Band; School Musical; Stage Crew; Nwsp Ed-Chief; High Hon Roll; Sal; Aud/Vis; Pres Acdmc Ftnss Awd, Pllsbry Co Schlrshp, & Natl Soc Prfssnl Engrs Schlrshp 87; U Rochester; Elec Engrng.

BARNES, LISA; St Clair Area HS; Pottsville, PA; (4); 20/76; Drama Clb; Ski Clb; SADD; Varsity Clb; Variety Show; Capt Var Bsktbl; Capt Trk; Capt JV Vllybl; High Hon Roll; Hon Roll; Bloomsburg U; Acctng.

BARNES, PAMELA; Notre Dame HS; Easton, PA; (3); Church Yth Grp; Cmnty Wkr; French Clb; Office Aide; Chorus; Church Choir; Flag Corp; School Play; Stage Crew; Pom Pon; Lab Tech.

BARNES JR, PAUL Z; Carlisle SR HS; Burke, VA; (4); 64/382; FCA; Band; Concert Band; Drm Mjr(t); Mrchg Band; School Musical; Symp Band; Var Crs Cntry; JV Bsbl; Hon Roll; Outstndng Musicn 86; Carlisle Brrcks Acdmc Achvt Awd 87; FL ST U; Comp Sci.

BARNES, RENEE; Canon Mc Millan HS; Eighty Four, PA; (4); 50/357; Chess Clb; Hosp Aide; Office Aide; Spanish Clb; SADD; Yrbk Stf; Im Badmtn; High Hon Roll; Hon Roll; NHS; Prsdntl Acdmc Ftnss Awd 87; Westminster Coll.

BARNES, RHONDA; Mohawk JR SR HS; New Galilee, PA; (4); Pres VP FHA; Concert Band; Mrchg Band; School Play; Stat Bsktbl; Powder Puff Ftbl; Stat Trk; VP NHS; Rtry Exch Stu To Germany 86; PA ST; Micro Bio.

BARNES, ROXANNE; Conemaugh Township HS; Johnstown, PA; (4); 18/101; Church Yth Grp; Office Aide; Pep Clb; Nwsp Rptr; Nwsp Stf; Yrbk Stf; Rep Stu Cncl; Var L Bsktbl; L Sftbl; Hon Roll; IN U Of PA; Acctng.

BARNES, SARAH; Susquehanna Community HS; Susquehanna, PA; (3); Band; Chorus; Concert Band; School Play; Stage Crew; US Natl Ldrshp Mrt Awd 86; USAA Natl Awd Blgy 85; Hstry.

BARNES, TRINA; Chester HS; Chester, PA; (3); Library Aide; Spanish Clb; Church Choir; Trk.

BARNETT, AMY; Central Dauphin HS; Harrisburg, PA; (3); Var L Cheerleading; Var L Gym; Var L Trk; Im Vllybl; Hon Roll; Jr NHS.

BARNETT, CHASTIDY; Connellsville Area SR HS; Mt Pleasant, PA; (2); Church Yth Grp; DECA; Library Aide; Office Aide; Rep Frsh Cls; Mgr(s); Hon Roll; Daily Courier Spelling Bee Rnnr-Up 85-86; Art Inst; Fashion Des-Mgr.

BARNETT, CHRISTINE; William Allen HS; Allentown, PA; (3); Latin Clb; Yrbk Stf; JV Sftbl; Hon Roll; NHS; Spelling Bee Fnlst 85-86; Moravian Coll; Bus Educ.

BARNETT, JOHN; Center Area HS; Monaca, PA; (2); ROTC; Spanish Clb; Varsity Clb; Var L Crs Cntry; Var L Socr; Im Tennis; Var L Trk; Hon Roll; Span Merit Awd 86; Slippery Rock Comptn Forgn Lang 86; Bus Admin.

BARNETT JR, JOHN; Spring-Ford HS; Schwenksville, PA; (3); 16/256; Boy Scts; German Clb; Band; Concert Band; Var JV Ftbl; Hon Roll; NHS; Writer Of Yr 85; Juniata Coll; Rsrch Bio.

BARNETT, JUDY; Reading SR HS; Reading, PA; (4); 62/579; Aud/Vis; Church Yth Grp; Hosp Aide; Chorus; JV L Bsktbl; Var L Tennis; Vllybl; Vet Med.

BARNETT, MAURICE S; Westinghouse HS; Pittsburgh, PA; (4); #4 In Class; Aud/Vis; Drama Clb; Exploring; JA; Quiz Bowl; Science Clb; Teachers Aide; VICA; School Play; Stage Crew; HBCIA Awd Otstndng Stud 87; GKS Poetry Awd 87; Drftng Awd VICA 87; Tuskegee Univ; Elec Eng.

BARNETT, SUZANNE; Upper Dublin HS; Glenside, PA; (3); Intnl Clb; Office Aide; Temple Yth Grp; Varsity Clb; Rep Frsh Cls; Rep Stu Cncl; Var L Diving; Montgomery Cnty Sci Rsrch Comptn 1st Hnrb Mntn 85; PA JR Acad Sci 2nd Pl 85; Child Psych.

BARNETTE, ANDREW; Portersville Christian Schl; Evans City, PA; (3); Quiz Bowl; Speech Tm; Variety Show; Yrbk Phtg; Yrbk Rptr; Hon Roll; NHS; U Of Pittsburgh; Poli Sci.

BARNEY, TIFFANY; West Greene SR HS; W Finley, PA; (2); French Clb; Science Clb; Ski Clb; Stat Sftbl; Elem Ed.

BARNFATHER, ERIC; Shady Side Acad; Pittsburgh, PA; (4); Aud/Vis; PAVAS; Thesps; School Play; Stage Crew; Variety Show; Ed Lit Mag; Trk; Wt Lftg; Hon Roll; Gargoyle Club Awd 86; E Bruce Hill Jr Mem Prz 87; Sargon Scty 87; Westminster Coll; Theatre.

BARNHART, BETH; Chapel Christian HS; New Stanton, PA; (3); Church Yth Grp; Ski Clb; Ed Yrbk Stf; Var Cheerleading; High Hon Roll; Hon Roll; California U Of PA.

BARNHART, DAWN; Southern Fulton HS; Needmore, PA; (3); Hosp Aide; ROTC; Hon Roll; Awds Beauty Shcl; Bus.

BARNHART, DE ANN; Annville-Cleona HS; Annville, PA; (4); 19/120; VP 4-H; SADD; Band; Chorus; Mrchg Band; Yrbk Bus Mgr; NHS; Ntl Merit Ltr; NEDT Awd; Suny At Delhi; Vet Sci Tech.

BARNHART, JODY; Moniteau HS; Chicora, PA; (3); 30/120; FHA; Nwsp Rptr; Yrbk Stf; Var Capt Cheerleading; Hon Roll; Med Asstnt.

BARNHART, LORI; Mt Pleasant Area SR HS; Mt Pleasant, PA; (3); Church Yth Grp; German Clb; Bus Stu Mnth 87.

BARNHART, MARCY; Northern Lebanon HS; Palmyra, PA; (3); 17/ 213; Church Yth Grp; VP 4-H; VP FFA; Chorus; Church Choir; Trk; 4-H Awd; Hon Roll; NHS; Susan Heilinger Memrl Awd 84; Resrve Grd Chmpn Shwmn 86.

BARNHART, STEVE; Annville-Cleona HS; Cleona, PA; (3); Math Tm; Varsity Clb; Var JV Bsktbl; Var JV Crs Cntry; Var L Trk; Jr NHS; NHS; Penn ST U; Comp Sci.

BARNHART, SUSAN; Jersey Shore Area SR HS; Jersey Shore, PA; (4); French Clb; FBLA; Lock Haven U; 2nd Educ.

BARNINGER, CYNTHIA; E Pennsboro HS; Enola, PA; (2); Spanish Clb; Chorus; Yrbk Phtg; Hon Roll; Pre-Med.

BARNISH, GREIG; Huntingdon Area HS; Huntingdon, PA; (3); Am Leg Boys St; Boy Scts; Computer Clb; 4-H; Rep Frsh Cls; Rep Soph Cls; Hon Roll; Penn ST U; Pre Law.

BARNISH, JAMES E; Jefferson Morgan JR SR HS; Waynesburg, PA; (3); 10/89; Ski Clb; Stage Crew; Yrbk Stf; Rep Sr Cls; Bsbl; Ftbl; Hon Roll; Amer Leg PA St Police Yth Wk Rep 87; U S Air Force.

BARON, DAWN; Unionville HS; West Chester, PA; (4); 118/316; Fld Hcky; Hon Roll; Jr NHS; Philadelphia Coll; Intrior Dsgn.

BARON, JANE; Mc Guffey HS; Washington, PA; (4); 2/203; Church Yth Grp; German Clb; Model UN; Political Wkr; Var Capt Tennis; High Hon Roll; NHS; Sal; Mobay/Bayer Exch Prgm; Ntl Yng Ldrs Conf; Intl Law.

BARON, JOHN; Brownsville Area HS; New Salem, PA; (3); 6/200; Library Aide; Office Aide; Ski Clb; Nwsp Phtg; Nwsp Stf; Hon Roll; NHS; Rotary Awd; U Ptsbrgh.

BARON, MICHAEL; Cathedral Prep Schl; Erie, PA; (3); 36/200; Model UN; Service Clb; Bsktbl; Socr; Vllybl; High Hon Roll; Hon Roll; PA ST U; Mech Engrng.

BARON, TIM; New Castle HS; New Castle, PA; (3); 40/250; French Clb; Temple Yth Grp; Band; School Play; Bsbl; Bowling; Crs Cntry; Golf; Business.

BARONA, LIBERKYS; Central Catholic HS; Allentown, PA; (3); 44/236; Flag Corp; Bsktbl; Bus.

BARONAS, MARGARET; Peabody HS; Pittsburgh, PA; (4); 26/292; Ski Clb; Pres Spanish Clb; Band; Concert Band; Jazz Band; Mrchg Band; Cheerleading; Tennis; High Hon Roll; Hon Roll; All City Band 84-85; PA ST U; Liberal Arts.

BARONI, LAURA; North Catholic HS; Pittsburgh, PA; (3); French Clb; Med.

BARONI, MICHAEL; Homer Ctr HS; Indiana, PA; (3); 22/120; French Clb; Library Aide; Ski Clb; Band; Concert Band; Jazz Band; Mrchg Band; School Musical; Bsbl; Bsktbl; Duquesne; Phrmcy.

BARR, BRIAN; Boyertown Area HS; Bechtelsville, PA; (4); 38/429; Trs Church Yth Grp; SADD; Band; Jazz Band; Mrchg Band; Trk; Hon Roll; Prfct Atten Awd; Pres Acdmc Fit Awd 87; Drexel U; Chem Engrng.

BARR, BRIAN; Warren Area HS; Warren, PA; (3); Church Yth Grp; Cmnty Wkr; French Clb; Service Clb; Chorus; JV Bsktbl; Hon Roll; Golden Dragon Awd 87; Engrng.

BARR, CYNTHIA; Schuylkill Haven HS; Auburn, PA; (2); 13/104; FFA; Teachers Aide; L Drill Tm; VP Crs Cntry; VP Trk; High Hon Roll; Hon Roll; Crss Cntry Al-Star Tm 85; Flrl Dsgnr.

BARR, ERIC; South Side Area HS; Georgetown, PA; (3); Church Yth Grp; Computer Clb; Ski Clb; Trk; Hon Roll; Hnrs Clb 84-87; Karate Green Belt 87; Comp Pgmmng.

BARR, MELISSA; Penn Hills SR HS; Penn Hills, PA; (3); Office Aide; Ski Clb; VP Spanish Clb; Jr Cls; Sr Cls; Stu Cncl; Hon Roll; Nrsg.

BARR, MICHAEL; Central SR HS; York, PA; (3); Political Wkr; Nwsp Rptr; Nwsp Stf; Hstry.

BARR, MICHAEL; Hopewell Area HS; Aliquippa, PA; (2); Chorus; School Musical; Variety Show; Nwsp Stf; Trs Frsh Cls; Rep Soph Cls; Var L Ftbl; Wt Lftg; High Hon Roll; Citation Hse Rep Art 87.

BARR, ROSE; Curwensville Area HS; Curwensville, PA; (3); Church Yth Grp; Ski Clb; Chorus; Color Guard; Nwsp Rptr; High Hon Roll; NHS; Acad All-Amer 87.

BARR, SARAH; Grove City HS; Grove City, PA; (3); Sec Drama Clb; School Play; Yrbk Stf; Sec Frsh Cls; Sec Soph Cls; Sec Jr Cls; Sec Sr Cls; Sec Stu Cncl; Var L Bsktbl; Capt Cheerleading; Sharon Genl Hosp/Nrsg; Nrsg.

BARR, SHERRIE; Rochester Area HS; New Brighton, PA; (3); Rep Church Yth Grp; French Clb; Ski Clb; Nwsp Stf; Sec Stu Cncl; Powder Puff Ftbl; Var L Tennis; Var L Trk; High Hon Roll; Hon Roll; Presdntl Acadc Ftns Pgm 85; Acadc All Star-Beaver Cnty Times 85-86; Hmcmng Court 86-87.

BARR, STACY; Seton La Salle HS; Pittsburgh, PA; (2); Church Yth Grp; Dance Clb; Hosp Aide; Spanish Clb; Hon Roll; U Pittsburgh.

BARR, TAMMALA J; Oil City SR HS; Rouseville, PA; (3); 57/218; AFS; Chorus; Nwsp Stf; Yrbk Stf.

BARR, TINA; Tyrone Aera HS; Tyrone, PA; (4); 8/184; Pres Spanish Clb; High Hon Roll; Hon Roll; NHS; Outstndng Food Svc Awd, Bus & Prof Wmns Club Schlrshp & Rotry Club Voc Awd 87; Penn ST; Dietetics.

BARRALL, DEANNA; Louis E Dieruff HS; Allentown, PA; (3); JA; Yrbk Phtg; Yrbk Rptr; Yrbk Stf; Allentown Schl District Spelling Bee Fnlst & Troika Hnr Soc Cert 87; Lehigh Cnty Cmnty Coll; Comms.

BARRETT, ALICE; Curwensville Area HS; Curwensville, PA; (3); Drama Clb; Ski Clb; Nwsp Stf; Yrbk Phtg; Cheerleading; Gym; Hon Roll.

BARRETT, DEBORAH L; Curwensville Area HS; Curwensville, PA; (3); Ski Clb; Chorus; Yrbk Stf; Im Bsktbl; Vllybl; High Hon Roll; NHS; Acad All Amer 87; Nrsg.

BARRETT, ELLEN; Center Area HS; Monaca, PA; (3); 30/136; German Clb; Sec Band; Chorus; Concert Band; Capt Drill Tm; Jazz Band; School Musical; Sec Soph Cls; Stu Cncl; NHS; 3rd Pl Germ Slippery Rock U Forgn Lang Comptn 87; Germ Awd 4.0 Aver 87; Comm.

BARRETT, ERIN; Bellefonte SR HS; Bellefonte, PA; (3); 51/211; Band; Concert Band; Mrchg Band; Off Soph Cls; Off Jr Cls; Hon Roll; Dist & Rgnl Band 87; Brass Choir 85-87; Int Dsgn.

BARRETT, ERIN; Sacred Heart HS; Munhall, PA; (4); 13/136; Drama Clb; Scholastic Bowl; Spanish Clb; School Musical; School Play; Stage Crew; High Hon Roll; NHS; Pres Schlr; Hosp Aide; Wstnghs Sci Hnrs Inst 87; AM Values Schlrshp 87-88; Prsdntl Acdmc Ftnss Awd 87; John Carroll U; Apsychlgy.

BARRETT, JENNIFER; West Scranton SR HS; Scranton, PA; (2); FNA; Var JV Cheerleading; Var Sftbl.

BARRETT, JOHN; Brookville Area HS; Brookville, PA; (3); 76/216; Boy Scts; Drama Clb; German Clb; Varsity Clb; Band; L Var Swmmng; Var Trk; Concert Band; Jazz Band; Mrchg Band; PMEA Dist 3 Bnd 86-87; Clarion U; Ed.

BARRETT, KIM; Pine Forge Acad; Durham, NC; (4); 10/79; Church Yth Grp; Pep Clb; Chorus; Nwsp Ed-Chief; Pres Stu Cncl; High Hon Roll; Hon Roll; NHS; Mst Lkly To Succeed 87; Oakwood Coll; Cmmnctns.

BARRETT, KRISTIN; Greensburg Central Catholic HS; Greensburg, PA; (3); Chorus; School Musical; School Play; Yrbk Stf; Rep Frsh Cls; Rep Jr Cls; High Hon Roll; NHS; Spcl Educ.

BARRETT, LEAH; Hazleton HS; Hazleton, PA; (2); Church Yth Grp; Drama Clb; Chorus; Nwsp Ed-Chief; Yrbk Stf; Bsktbl; JV Var Trk; Hon Roll; Pres Acad Ftnss Awd, Hnrb Mntn King Coll Spnsh Contest & Salvation Army Essay Contest 1st Pl 86.

BARRETT, MATTHEW; Ringgold HS; Finleyville, PA; (4); Church Yth Grp; Computer Clb; Office Aide; Science Clb; Ski Clb; Varsity Clb; Bsktbl; Ftbl; Golf; Hon Roll; Ntl Math,Sci Hnr Soc 84-87; U Pittsburgh; Bus Adm.

BARRETT, RAYMOND; West Catholic Boys HS; Philadelphia, PA; (3); 57/249; Stage Crew; Nwsp Phtg; Yrbk Phtg; Bowling; Wrstlng; Hnr Rl 86-87; Prfct Condct 84-87; Drexel U; Arch.

BARRETT, THERESE; Archbishop John Carroll HS; Berwyn, PA; (3); 69/376; Cmnty Wkr; Nwsp Stf; Yrbk Stf; Spanish NHS; Drexel U; Intr Dsgn.

BARRETT, TONI; Curwensville Area HS; Grampian, PA; (3); VP DECA; French Clb.

BARRICK, REBECCA; Newport HS; Newport, PA; (4); 19/89; FBLA; FTA; Flag Corp; Mrchg Band; Yrbk Stf; Hon Roll; Hrrisburg Area CC; Bus Adm.

BARRINEAU, TRACY LYNN; Greencastle-Antrim HS; Greencastle, PA; (4); 18/172; Teachers Aide; Flag Corp; Mrchg Band; Nwsp Stf; Yrbk Sprt Ed; Stu Cncl; High Hon Roll; NHS; Prfct Atten Awd; Alumni Awd,HBC Schlrshp 87; Cmmnty Refuse Grant 87; Hagestown Bus Coll; Accntng.

BARRIS, ROBERT; Sharpsville HS; Sharpsville, PA; (3); 21/110; Camera Clb; German Clb; Library Aide; Political Wkr; Chorus; Ftbl; Wt Lftg; Acadc Achvt Awd 84-85; Aerdynmc Engrng.

BARRISH, ANDREW; Mapletown HS; Greensboro, PA; (4); 2/76; Cmnty Wkr; Letterman Clb; Ski Clb; Varsity Clb; Var Bsbl; JV Coach Actv; Var Capt Ftbl; Wt Lftg; DAR Awd; High Hon Roll; Hgh Hnrs 87; All Conf 87; Stu By Of Mnth; Waynesburg Coll; Bio.

BARRON, AMY; Mon Valley Catholic HS; Belle Vernon, PA; (3); 9/108; Cmnty Wkr; Ski Clb; Teachers Aide; Concert Band; Mrchg Band; Yrbk Stf; L Vllybl; French Hon Soc; High Hon Roll; NHS; Karate Achvt Tae Kwon Doe 87; U Of Pittsburgh; Phys Thrpy.

BARRON, DIANE; Elizabethtown Area HS; Elizabethtown, PA; (4); Drama Clb; 4-H; Sec Band; Concert Band; Mrchg Band; Orch; Bsktbl; Powder Puff Ftbl; Twrlr; 4-H Awd; Cnty Band; Millersville U; Elem Educ.

BARRON, GAIL; North Star HS; Stoystown, PA; (3); 7/133; Church Yth Grp; FCA; FBLA; Nwsp Stf; Yrbk Stf; Hon Roll; Stu Of Mnth-Aprl 87; Somerset Vo-Tech; Scrtrl.

BARRON, JEROME; Moh Valley Catholic HS; Belle Vernon, PA; (2); 9/90; Cmnty Wkr; Ski Clb; Concert Band; Mrchg Band; Yrbk Phtg; Yrbk Sprt Ed; High Hon Roll; NHS; Spanish NHS; HOBY Awd 87; Karate Tae Kwon Doe 87; Carnegio Mellon U; Psych.

BARRON, JOHN; Weatherly Area HS; White Haven, PA; (3); 2/50; Band; Mrchg Band; JV Bsktbl; JV Golf; Hon Roll; Phrmcy.

BARRON, LISA; Somerset Area HS; Somerset, PA; (3); 35/297; English Clb; German Clb; JA; Band; Concert Band; Mrchg Band; Pep Band; Yrbk Stf; High Hon Roll; Hon Roll; Schl Nom For Rural Elec Yth Tour 87; Clarion Univ; Acctg.

BARRON, MICHELLE; Conneaut Valley HS; Springboro, PA; (3); Trs Church Yth Grp; German Clb; Pep Clb; Ski Clb; Varsity Clb; Band; Chorus; Concert Band; Mrchg Band; Rep Jr Cls; IN U Of PA; Educ.

BARRONER, LYNN; Hollidaysburg Area HS; Hollidaysburg, PA; (3); Band; Flag Corp; Variety Show; Rep Stu Cncl; Vllybl; Vlntr Svc Awd Vets 84.

BARRY, GAYLE; Northgate JR/Sr HS; Pittsburgh, PA; (4); Church Yth Grp; SADD; Nwsp Stf; Yrbk Stf; Stu Cncl; Mgr(s); Score Keeper; Vllybl; Prfct Atten Awd; N Boroughs Dstngshd Yth Awd 86-87; Bus Adm.

BARRY, GLEN; Lower Moreland HS; Huntingdon Valley, PA; (4); 105/205; Var Capt Bsbl; Var Capt Bsktbl; Var L Socr; All League Soccer & Cptn In Bsbl & Bsktbl; Sbrbn Phldlpha Athlt Of Week; All Rnd Athlt 87; U DE; Lbrl Arts.

BARRY, MICHAEL; Lehighton Area HS; Lehighton, PA; (3); 1/250; Debate Tm; Scholastic Bowl; Varsity Clb; Chorus; Yrbk Sprt Ed; Var L Bsbl; Var L Bsktbl; High Hon Roll; NHS; Ntl Merit Ltr; Schltc Scrimmage Television Tm 85-87; Hgh Hnrs 84-87; Pres Fit Awd 87; Cornell; Bus.

BARRY, WILLIAM; Cathedral Prep Schl; Erie, PA; (3); 3/193; French Clb; Letterman Clb; Service Clb; Varsity Clb; Pres Soph Cls; Off Stu Cncl; L Ftbl; High Hon Roll; Ntl Merit Ltr; Engrng.

BARSH, LISA; Upper Dublin HS; Ambler, PA; (3); Intnl Clb; Office Aide; SADD; Temple Yth Grp; Varsity Clb; Chorus; Yrbk Stf; Var L Cheerleading; JV Tennis; Hon Roll; Phy Thrpy.

BARSHINGER, CHAD; Eastern York HS; E Prospect, PA; (2); #9 In Class; Band; Mrchg Band; Pres Soph Cls; JV Bsbl; Var Wrstlng; High Hon Roll; Crmnl Invstgtn.

BARSHINGER JR, RONALD E; Tulpehocken HS; Myerstown, PA; (4); Boy Scts; Pres Band; Concert Band; Mrchg Band; Pep Band; School Musical; School Play; Stage Crew; Yrbk Stf; Var Trk; Eagle Sct 87; Machnst.

BARSHINGER, TIMOTHY; Red Lion Area SR HS; York, PA; (3); 43/342; VP Church Yth Grp; Exploring; Latin Clb; Chorus; Church Choir; School Musical; School Play; Hon Roll; :Pediatrics.

BARSTOW, SUSAN; Cumberland Valley HS; Camp Hill, PA; (2); Church Yth Grp; Hosp Aide; Latin Clb; SADD; Band; Chorus; Concert Band; Mrchg Band; School Musical; Stage Crew; Phys Ther.

BARTASAVICH, DAVID; Lakeland HS; Jermyn, PA; (4); Var JV Bsbl; JV Bsktbl; Hon Roll; Pres Acad Ftnss Awd 87; US Bus Ed Awd 87; Penn ST U; Bus Admin.

BARTASHUMAS, KAREN; Wyoming Area SR HS; West Wyoming, PA; (3); 11/260; Church Yth Grp; Key Clb; Yrbk Bus Mgr; VP L Swmmng; High Hon Roll; NHS; Soc Studs Excllnce Awd 87; Engrng.

BARTASHUNAS, KAREN; Wyoming Area SR HS; W Wyoming, PA; (3); 11/260; Church Yth Grp; Key Clb; Yrbk Bus Mgr; VP L Swmmng; High Hon Roll; NHS; Soc Studs Excllnce Awd 87; Engrng.

BARTEL, EDWARD; Peters Township HS; Mc Murray, PA; (3); German Clb; Latin Clb; Library Aide; Science Clb; Ski Clb; Nwsp Phtg; Yrbk Phtg; JV Socr; Kiwanis Awd; U Of CO Boulder.

BARTELLO, AROS; Schenley HS; Pittsburgh, PA; (3); Art Clb; Boy Scts; Chess Clb; Church Yth Grp; Model UN; Ski Clb; Yrbk Stf; High Hon Roll; Hon Roll; CMU Pre-Coll Art 86-87.

BARTELLO, STEVEN H; Shikellamy HS; Sunbury, PA; (4); Bsbl; Bsktbl; Ftbl.

BARTELMO, DEBBIE; Bishop Shanahan HS; West Chester, PA; (3); Dance Clb; PAVAS; Service Clb; Chorus; School Musical; School Play; Off Frsh Cls; Off Soph Cls; Off Jr Cls; Cheerleading; Prof Dancer.

BARTELS, BRYAN; Cambridge Springs HS; Cambridge Springs, PA; (4); 8/104; Key Clb; Pep Clb; Spanish Clb; Yrbk Ed-Chief; Stu Cncl; NHS; GA Inst Tech; Aerospc Engr.

BARTHELEMY, MICHAEL; Immaculate Conception HS; Canonsburg, PA; (3); Computer Clb; JA; Math Tm; Ski Clb; Var L Golf; Var L Wrstlng; High Hon Roll; Hon Roll; Dale Carnegie Pblc Spkng Schlrshp JA, Grad Asst 87; Delg Natl JA Conf 87; Penn ST U; Aerospc Engr.

BARTHLOW, THOMAS E; Northern Lehigh HS; Neffs, PA; (4); 8/136; Am Leg Boys St; Pres Church Yth Grp; Scholastic Bowl; Rep Stu Cncl; Var Trk; Lion Awd; Pres NHS; Pres Schlr; SAR Awd; Band; OH Nrthrn U Deans Scholar 87; OH Nrthrn U; Phrmcst.

BARTHOLIC, MARK; Butler SR HS; Butler, PA; (3); 12/734; Church Yth Grp; VP Latin Clb; Var L Bsktbl; Var L Golf; Jr NHS; NHS; KDKA Extra Effrt Awd; Mark Bartholic Rcgntn Day.

BARTHOLOMAI, LISA; Connellsville SR HS; S Connellsvl, PA; (3); High Hon Roll; Hon Roll; Spanish NHS; Prim Ed.

BARTHOLOMEW, LESLIE; Spring-Ford SR HS; Royersford, PA; (4); 24/265; Church Yth Grp; Pres 4-H; Radio Clb; Pres Thesps; School Musical; Yrbk Phtg; Rep Stu Cncl; Tennis; Trk; Dnfth Awd; 4-H ST Awd 87; Pres Ldrshp Scholar 87; Hood; Nutrition.

BARTIS, SARAH; Peters Twp HS; Venetia, PA; (4); VP NFL; VP Spanish Clb; Sec Pres SADD; Sec Thesps; School Play; JV Vllybl; High Hon Roll; PTA Lit Awd; U Pittsburgh; Ed.

BARTKO, PAULA; Nazareth SR HS; Nazareth, PA; (3); Camera Clb; VP Sec Church Yth Grp; Drama Clb; Key Clb; Office Aide; SADD; School Play; Variety Show; Yrbk Stf; Hon Roll; Mktg.

BARTKUS, WENDY; Hazleton HS; Hazleton, PA; (2); Church Yth Grp; Drama Clb; Spanish Clb; Chorus; Color Guard; Flag Corp; Yrbk Stf; Capt Cheerleading; Hon Roll; Pres Schlr; 4th Pl Kings Coll Spnsh Cntst 86; Hnbl Mntn Kings Coll Spnsh Cntst 87; Med.

BARTLE, VICKI; Beaver Falls HS; Wampum, PA; (3); Am Leg Aux Girls St; French Clb; Yrbk Stf; High Hon Roll; NHS; Physcl Thrpy.

BARTLETT, JASON E; Cumberland Valley HS; Boiling Springs, PA; (3); Art Clb; French Clb; Key Clb; Rep Stu Cncl; JV Wrstlng; High Hon Roll; Hon Roll; Chorus; JV Trk; Frnch Cert Merit Awd 86; Penn ST U; Aero Engrng.

BARTLETT, MARK; Mt Lebanon HS; Pittsburgh, PA; (4); 8/521; Church Yth Grp; Var Bsbl; Im Bsktbl; High Hon Roll; Ntl Merit SF; Mt Lebanon PTA Schlrshp 87; Lehigh U; Cvl Engrng.

BARTLEY, ELAINE; Shenango HS; New Castle, PA; (4); Office Aide; Yrbk Stf; Hon Roll; NHS; Slippery Rock U; Med Ofc Mgt.

BARTLEY, PAUL E; Wyoming Seminary HS; Tunkhannock, PA; (4); Ski Clb; SADD; Varsity Clb; Pres Soph Cls; Var Ftbl; Var Swmmng; Var Tennis; JV Wrstlng; High Hon Roll; USC Scholar; USC; Bus.

BARTMESS, AARON; Chambersburg SR HS; Fayetteville, PA; (3); Church Yth Grp; Red Cross Aide; Spanish Clb; Church Choir; Orch; Symp Band; Hon Roll; Lebanon Valley; Music.

BARTNICK JR, CARL J; Crestwood HS; Mountaintop, PA; (4); Art Clb; Church Yth Grp; Science Clb; Rep Frsh Cls; Rep Soph Cls; Ftbl; Trk; Wt Lftg; Luzerne County CC; Med.

BARTO, BART; Ambridge Area HS; Freedom, PA; (3); Aud/Vis; Cmnty Wkr; German Clb; Letterman Clb; Library Aide; Pep Clb; Ski Clb; Band; Chorus; Var Vllybl; Robert Morris Coll; Pilot.

BARTOCK, KIM; Southmoreland SR HS; Scottdale, PA; (4); Church Yth Grp; FFA; Pep Clb; Flrl Dsgnr.

BARTOE, GREG; Karns City HS; Petrolia, PA; (3); FCA; L Ftbl; Trk; Hon Roll; NHS; Acdmc Lttr 87; York Coll Of PA; Arch.

BARTOE, MICHAEL T; Northwestern SR HS; Albion, PA; (4); 16/142; Trs Sr Cls; Stu Cncl; JV Bsbl; JV Crs Cntry; Var Ftbl; JV Trk; Var Wrstlng; Hon Roll; Army; Equp Rcrds Spclst.

BARTOLAC, DAVID; Ambridge Area HS; Ambridge, PA; (3); Am Leg Boys St; FCA; German Clb; JV Var Bsbl; JV Var Bsktbl; JV Var Ftbl; Hon Roll; Prfct Atten Awd; Acdmc Athl All Strs 86-87; Ftbl 1st Tm All Conf Defns 86-87; Phy Thrpy.

BARTOLACCI, PAULETTE; Notre Dame HS; Easton, PA; (4); 12/85; Yrbk Ed-Chief; Yrbk Stf; Trs Stu Cncl; Mgr Bsbl; Cheerleading; Mgr(s); High Hon Roll; Hon Roll; NHS; Chorus; Acadc Excel Achvt 86-87; Yrbk Awd 86-87; Ltrgcl Music Awd 86-87; St Josephs U; Educ.

BARTOLETTI, AMY; James M Coughlin HS; Wilkes Barre, PA; (3; Drama Clb; French Clb; Math Clb; School Play; VP Jr Cls; Ca Cheerleading; L Diving; High Hon Roll; NHS; NEDT Awd; 5th Pl Wilk Coll Math Cont 87; Marywood Math Cont Awd 86; Luzerne Cnty Sci Aw 85; Yale U; Actng.

BARTOLOWITS, DANIEL; North Catholic HS; Pittsburgh, PA; (3 Church Yth Grp; Sec German Clb; Ftbl; Hon Roll; 1st Pl Hockey CYO 8 Stu Mt Troy Vol Fire Dept 85-87; Acolyte Mst Holy Name C Hrch 84-8

BARTON, DANA; Penn Trafford HS; Claridge, PA; (2); Cmnty Wk FBLA; GAA; Hosp Aide; Political Wkr; SADD; Trs Soph Cls; Stu Cncl; J Bsktbl; JV Sftbl; Psych.

BARTON, DEB; Cedar Crest HS; Quentin, PA; (3); Church Yth Grp; Pe Clb; Spanish Clb; Church Choir; Symp Band; Cheerleading; Hon Roll; Di Band 86-87; Comm.

BARTON, RUTH; Central Dauphin HS; Harrisburg, PA; (4); 8/36 Chorus; Concert Band; Mrchg Band; School Musical; Hon Roll; NHS; N Merit Ltr; Messiah Coll; Frnch.

BARTON, SUZANNE M; Owen J Roberts HS; Elverson, PA; (3); 21/29 Church Yth Grp; JA; Church Choir; Mrchg Band; Symp Band; Rep St Cncl; Im Bsktbl; Hon Roll; NHS; VP PA Teens Life 86.

BARTON, TRACY; Penn-Trafford HS; Trafford, PA; (4); FBLA; SAD Var Capt Swmmng; Var Trk; IN U Of PA; Elem Ed.

BARTOW, SUSAN MARIE; Boyertown Area SR HS; Boyertown, P (4); 8/426; Chorus; School Play; Rep Stu Cncl; Var Co-Capt Bsktbl; V Co-Capt Fld Hcky; Var Co-Capt Sftbl; High Hon Roll; Trs NHS; Pr Schlr; Church Yth Grp; Outstndng Athl Amer 87; US Army Rsrv Na Schlr Athl Awd 87; G Marcella Wse Athl Awd 87; Cong Schlr 87; Itha Coll; Bio.

BARTUSH, ROSE; Nativity BVM HS; Pottsville, PA; (4); 16/10 Library Aide; Yrbk Stf; Rep Stu Cncl; Bsktbl; Var Capt Crs Cntry; Hi Hon Roll; VP NHS; Acdmc All AM Awd-Latin 84; Tulane U; El Engnrng.

BARTYNSKI, ROBERT L; Louis E Dieruff HS; Allentown, PA; (2); 340; Pres Soph Cls; Pres Jr Cls; Rep Stu Cncl; JV Bsbl; JV Var Frsh C Var L Socr; Hon Roll; Chorus; Allentown Cncl Of Yth 85-87; Allentow Schl Dist Splng Bee 5th Pl 87; Law.

BARWICK, MARY; Norte Dame HS; Stroudsburg, PA; (3); Scho Musical; School Play; Yrbk Stf; Sec Soph Cls; Var L Fld Hcky; Var L Gy Var L Sftbl; Hon Roll; Prfct Atten Awd; Sci.

BARYCKI, ANDREA MELISSA; Old Forge HS; Old Forge, PA; (4 Color Guard; Mrchg Band; Pom Pon; High Hon Roll; Hon Roll; NH Highest Bus Awd 87; Mech.

BARYCKI, JOSEPH; Old Forge HS; Old Forge, PA; (4); 1/104; Yrbk St VP Jr Cls; VP Sr Cls; Var Bsktbl; Var Capt Ftbl; Bausch & Lomb Sci Aw High Hon Roll; NHS; Ntl Merit Ltr; Bausch & Lomb Schlrshp 87; U Rochester; Pre-Med.

BARZANTI, LADA; Mapletown HS; Bobtown, PA; (4); 4/75; Mrc Band; Nwsp Ed-Chief; Nwsp Stf; Yrbk Bus Mgr; Yrbk Stf; Im Vllybl; Hig Hon Roll; Hon Roll; NHS; Waynesbrg Coll Hnr Schlr Schlrshp 8 Waynesburg Coll; Pre Law.

BASARA, JOYCE; Pine Grove Area HS; Pine Grove, PA; (2); Trs Chur Yth Grp; ROTC; Rep Frsh Cls; Rep Soph Cls; Im Vllybl; Sci & Bus Awds 87; Pres Physcl Ftns Awd 87; Med.

BASARAB, AIMEE; E L Meyers HS; Wilkes Barre, PA; (4); Dance Cl Key Clb; Red Cross Aide; Ski Clb; Chorus; Color Guard; Hon Roll; NHS; NHS; Spanish NHS; U Of Scranton; Mrktng.

BASEHORE, MELISSA; Bermudian Springs HS; E Berlin, PA; (3); 1 128; Girl Scts; Chorus; Madrigals; Yrbk Stf; Stu Cncl; Var L Bsktbl; V L Trk; Var L Vllybl; Hon Roll; Band; MVP Trk 87; Phys Ed Awd 87; M Vllybl 87.

BASH, LORIEL; Kiski Area HS; Apollo, PA; (2); Chorus; High Hon Ro Hon Roll; Acad Ltr 86-87; Bus.

BASHLINE, PATRICK J; Elderton JR-SR HS; Elderton, PA; (3); Pr Church Yth Grp; Band; Concert Band; Mrchg Band; Stage Crew; Stu Cn Vllybl; High Hon Roll; Hon Roll; NHS; IN U; Crmnlgy.

BASHORE, CATHI; Cedar Crest HS; Lebanon, PA; (2); 51/345; Germa Clb; Key Clb; Latin Clb; Pep Clb; SADD; Concert Band; Mrchg Band; P Band; Hon Roll; NHS; Hnrs Bnqt 86; Psych.

BASHORE, JENNIFER; Shamokin Area HS; Shamokin, PA; (2); 32/25 Hosp Aide; Office Aide; SADD; Concert Band; Jazz Band; Mrchg Ban Yrbk Stf; Trk; Hon Roll; Central PA Luthern Yth Convocation 86; Huma Resources.

BASHOUR, MARY JO; Brownsville Area HS; Republic, PA; (3); 24/20 Hosp Aide; Intnl Clb; Office Aide; Ski Clb; SADD; Nwsp Rptr; Nwsp S Mgr(s); Stat Sftbl; Hon Roll; Mdl Awd Amer Lgn Auxiliary 84; Slippe Rock; Pre Physcl Thrpy.

BASILE, ANDREW; The Hill Schl; Douglassville, PA; (4); Lcrss; Cmn Wkr; Ski Clb; Varsity Clb; Nwsp Phtg; Yrbk Phtg; VP Sr Cls; Rep S Cncl; Gym; Socr; U Of NC Chapel Hill.

BASILE, CARL; Shenango HS; New Castle, PA; (2); Aud/Vis; Ban Concert Band; Jazz Band; Mrchg Band; Pep Band; School Play; Sta Crew; Var Golf; Hon Roll; Cmmnctns.

BASILE, MARIA A; Downingtown SR HS; Downingtown, PA; (4); 7 523; St Josephs U Scholar 87; PHEAA Cert Merit 86; St Josephs Acctng.

BASILE, VICKI; Center Area HS; Aliquippa, PA; (3); 61/187; Hosp Aid Spanish Clb; Yrbk Stf; Bsktbl; Bowling; Powder Puff Ftbl; Sftbl; Hon Ro Penn ST; Sci.

BASINGER, DAWN; Jefferson-Morgan HS; Waynesburg, PA; (4); 9/9 Sec VP DECA; SADD; Varsity Clb; Rep VP VICA; Color Guard; Var Sftbl; High Hon Roll; Hon Roll.

BASINGER, MARGARET; Connellsville Area SR HS; Connellsville, P (2); Nwsp Rptr; Nwsp Stf; Yrbk Stf; Spanish NHS.

BASISTA, BRIAN; Freeland HS; Freeland, PA; (3).

BASISTA, CHRISTOPHER C; Highlands SR HS; Tarentum, PA; (3 Boys Clb Am; Boy Scts; Church Yth Grp; Computer Clb; DEC Exploring; Chorus; Im Bowling; Prfct Atten Awd; Duquesne; Law.

BASS, MICHAEL; Penn-Trafford HS; Levelgreen, PA; (2); 1/311; Chur Yth Grp; JCL; Latin Clb; Math Clb; JV Bsbl; JV Bsktbl; JV Var Ftbl; I Swmmng; High Hon Roll; Engrng.

BASS, MICHELE; Chichester HS; Marcus Hook, PA; (3); 52/293; GA SADD; Band; Church Choir; School Play; Stu Cncl; Var Cheerleading; V JV Fld Hcky; Var JV Lcrss; Hon Roll; Law.

BASSETT, LYNNETTE; Nativity BVM HS; Cumbola, PA; (2); 36/7 Chess Clb; Girl Scts; Library Aide; Office Aide; Psych.

BASSETT, WILLIAM; Valley HS; New Kensington, PA; (2); Pre-Law.

ASSETTI, JULIE; Bishop Mc Devitt HS; Philadelphia, PA; (4); 120/ 49; Hosp Aide; Spanish Clb; Nwsp Stf; Bus.

ASSO, CHRISTINE; Wm Allen HS; Allentown, PA; (4); Aud/Vis; ebate Tm; Drama Clb; Intnl Clb; Leo Clb; Chorus; Rep Stu Cncl; JV Fld cky; Hon Roll; PHEAA Cert Of Merit 86; :Bus Adm.

ASSO, REBECCA; Pen Argyl Area HS; Nazareth, PA; (3); 19/159; hurch Yth Grp; Drama Clb; Chorus; Color Guard; Capt Flag Corp; Mrchg and; Mgr Stage Crew; Yrbk Stf; Stu Cncl; High Hon Roll; Lang.

ASSO, STEVEN; Carlisle SR HS; Harker Heights, TX; (3); 137/454; oy Scts; Church Yth Grp; FBLA; Letterman Clb; Ski Clb; Spanish Clb; ep Frsh Cls; JV Ftbl; Var L Socr; Im Vllybl; Hnbl Mntn Essy US Cnstitn ; Aero Engr.

ASTA, ANGELA; Pittston Area HS; Pittston, PA; (3); Art Clb; Aud/ is; Key Clb; Letterman Clb; Ski Clb; Pres Frsh Cls; Pres Soph Cls; Pres Cls; Var Cheerleading.

ASTIAN, JENNIFER; Emmaus SR HS; Emmaus, PA; (4); Church Yth rp; Cmnty Wkr; GAA; Rep Soph Cls; Rep Jr Cls; Var L Sftbl; High Hon oll; Jr NHS; NHS; Ntl Merit Ltr; PA ST U; Arch Engr.

ASTIAN, MELISSA; Milton Area SR HS; New Columbia, PA; (2); ibrary Aide; Spanish Clb; Chorus; Color Guard; Mrchg Band; Hon Roll; xcell Scl Stds Awd 85-86; Pres Acad Ftns Awd 85-86.

ASTIEN, ANDREW; Fairfield Area HS; Fairfield, PA; (3); Computer lb; Spanish Clb; Var Crs Cntry; Hon Roll; Cmptr Sci.

ATAILLE, NATHALIE; Kennedy Christian HS; Sharon, PA; (3); 12/ ; Cmnty Wkr; French Clb; Ski Clb; Band; Church Choir; Concert Band; o-Capt Flag Corp; Mrchg Band; Yrbk Stf; Hon Roll; Grove City Coll; Bus gmt.

ATEMAN, FRAN; Merion Mercy Acad; Merion, PA; (4); 11/87; French lb; Rep Frsh Cls; Rep Soph Cls; Sec Jr Cls; Pres Stu Cncl; Mgr Bsktbl; apt Fld Hcky; Capt Tennis; NHS; Schlr Athlete 87; Boston Coll.

ATEMAN, JAMES; Hickory HS; Hermitage, PA; (2); Camera Clb; ebate Tm; Library Aide; NFL; Speech Tm; SADD; Chorus; Stage Crew; rbk Phtg; ST Sci Olympd 87; U Of Tampa; Mrn Bio.

ATEMAN, MIKE; Chichester HS; Boothwyn, PA; (3); 26/296; omputer Clb; French Clb; Varsity Clb; Var L Bsbl; Im Bsktbl; Var L Ftbl; n Vllybl; French Hon Soc; Hon Roll; NHS; 2nd Tm Al-Del-Val sbl-Ptchng 87; Alg Awd-Bst Stu 85; Comps.

ATEMAN, SANDY; Yough SR HS; Irwin, PA; (3); 69/237; Computer lb; French Clb; Pep Clb; Band; Concert Band; Hon Roll; Trvl-Toursm.

ATES, BEVERLY; Saltsburg JR SR HS; New Alexandria, PA; (2); 15/ ; SADD; Band; Concert Band; Mrchg Band; Nwsp Rptr; Stu Cncl; Sftbl; llybl; 4-H Awd; High Hon Roll; Penn ST U; Vet.

ATES, CINDY; Palmyra Area HS; Palmyra, PA; (4); Sec Trs Drama lb; Ski Clb; Chorus; Concert Band; Jazz Band; Mrchg Band; Pres Soph ls; Pres Jr Cls; Var Capt Fld Hcky; JP Sousa Awd; Outstndng Grl 84; dnt Yr Womns Clb 87; Amer Legn Schl Awd 87; Bloomsburg U; Psych.

ATES, JASON; Venango Christian HS; Oil City, PA; (3); Computer Clb; ADD; Rep Sr Cls; Hon Roll; Prfct Atten Awd; Bus Adm.

ATES, LAURENCE; Shamokin Area HS; Shamokin, PA; (3); 25/236; cience Clb; Sec VICA; Var L Bsbl; JV Bsktbl; Hon Roll; Wldlf Mgmt.

ATESON, TRACY; West York HS; York, PA; (3); Art Clb; Church Yth rp; JA; Yrbk Stf; Rep Frsh Cls; Im Bsktbl; Im Vllybl; Hon Roll; Acctng.

ATINICH, LIZANNE; Burgettstown JR SR HS; Burgettstown, PA; (3); m Leg Aux Girls St; Church Yth Grp; Drama Clb; Ski Clb; Band; Concert and; Mrchg Band; Pep Band; Symp Band; VP Soph Cls; Phys Thrpst.

ATORY, SUZANNE; Council Rock HS; Richboro, PA; (4); 90/850; hurch Yth Grp; Sec VP 4-H; Hosp Aide; Key Clb; Band; Church Choir; oncert Band; Mrchg Band; Orch; Symp Band; Ruth Keith Meml chlrshp 87; Northamptons Wmns Clb Schlrshp 87; Wilkes Col6; Psych.

ATOUYIOS, RENEE; Riverview HS; Verona, PA; (3); Church Yth Grp; rama Clb; Orch; Yrbk Phtg; Yrbk Stf; Hon Roll; Duquesne U Pittsburgh; mmnctns.

ATOVICH, TAMARA; Bishop Mc Cort HS; Johnstown, PA; (3); panish Clb; Concert Band; Mrchg Band; Vllybl; Cmnty Wkr; Band; Orch; ounty Band 84-85; Aero Engrng.

ATRLA, PAMELA; Aliquippa JR & SR HS; Aliquippa, PA; (4); Sec ECA; French Clb; Drill Tm; Pom Pon; Hon Roll; NHS; 5th Plc Dist 2 ECA Cnrnc Advrtsg 87; ICM Schl Of Bus; Med Offc Asst.

ATROSS, JONATHAN; Riverview HS; Oakmont, PA; (3); 13/113; xploring; Ski Clb; Band; Jazz Band; Var Ftbl; Var Trk; Var Capt rstlng; High Hon Roll; Hon Roll; NEDT Awd; Penn ST; Engrng.

ATTAGLIA, GINA; Brookville Area HS; Brookville, PA; (3); German lb; Key Clb; Pep Clb; Varsity Clb; Rep Jr Cls; Cheerleading; Trk; High on Roll; Jr NHS; NHS.

ATTAGLIA, STACY; Mc Dowell HS; Erie, PA; (2); Church Yth Grp; mnty Wkr; FHA; Library Aide; Office Aide; Teachers Aide; Dntl Hygnst.

ATTAGLINI, DANEEN; Brownsville Area HS; Republic, PA; (4); BLA; Office Aide; Hon Roll; Accntng.

ATTALINI, AARON; Aliquippa HS; W Aliquippa, PA; (2); Church Yth rp; Var Bsbl; JV Var Ftbl; JV Var Wt Lftg; Var L Wrstlng.

ATTE, ERICA; Churchill HS; Braddock, PA; (2); Church Yth Grp; rench Clb; JA; Acpl Chr; Chorus; Church Choir; School Musical; Off Stu ncl; High Hon Roll; Hon Roll; U Pittsburgh; Bus Admin.

ATTELLI, LORI A; West Mifflin Area HS; West Mifflin, PA; (4); 65/ 30; Church Yth Grp; Cmnty Wkr; Exploring; Girl Scts; Hosp Aide; cience Clb; Ski Clb; Vllybl; Hon Roll; Westinghouse Sci Hnrs Inst 87; enn ST; Pre-Med.

ATTISTA, MARY ANN; Central Cambria HS; Ebensburg, PA; (2); ath Clb; Science Clb; Chorus; Crs Cntry; Swmmng; Trk; Vllybl; Cit Awd; igh Hon Roll; Prfct Atten Awd; Engrng.

ATTLES, JOHN; Libert & Vetoch Prep; Bethlehem, PA; (2); 48/498; oy Scts; CAP; Rep Soph Cls; Hon Roll; MA Inst Of Tech; Elect Engr.

ATZ, MICHELLE; Tulpehocken HS; Bethel, PA; (2); Church Yth Grp; and; Church Choir; Concert Band; Mrchg Band; School Musical; Nwsp ptr; Dir Music Awd 85; Bus.

AU, DIADRA; Johns S Fine HS; Nanticoke, PA; (2); 3/243; NFL; peech Tm; Band; Chorus; Concert Band; Mrchg Band; Mgr(s); Score eeper; Sftbl; Timer.

AUDUIN, RACHEL; Avella Area JR SR HS; Avella, PA; (4); 13/50; Art lb; Camera Clb; Church Yth Grp; Key Clb; Math Tm; VP Band; Concert and; Mrchg Band; Yrbk Stf; Hon Roll; Cnty Band 86-87; PA ST.

AUER, AMY; Seneca Valley SR HS; Mars, PA; (2); Dance Clb; FTA; and; Color Guard; Symp Band; Var Pom Pon; High Hon Roll; Mellissa ang Most Outstndng Color Guard Awd 86-87; 1ST Yr Awd Schltc Achvt 6-87; Grove City Coll; Sci.

BAUER, ELIZABETH; Pottstown SR HS; Pottstown, PA; (3); 23/155; Key Clb; Rep Soph Cls; Rep Jr Cls; Rep Stu Cncl; Capt Twrlr; High Hon Roll; Hon Roll; NHS; $50.00 Bond For Essy On Jane Goodalll 85; Hnrb Mentn For Essy On Nclr Enrgy 86; Optmst Intl 87; Engl.

BAUER, JENNIFER; Upper Moreland HS; Hatboro, PA; (3); 109/275; Mrchg Band; School Musical; Stu Cncl; Dance Clb; Intr Dsgn.

BAUER, JOE; Oxford Area HS; Oxford, PA; (3); Aud/Vis; VICA; High Hon Roll; OH Diesel Inst; Diesel Mech.

BAUER, JULIE; Parkland HS; Schnecksville, PA; (3); Church Yth Grp; Math Tm; VP SADD; Thesps; Chorus; School Musical; Swing Chorus; High Hon Roll; NHS; Drama Clb; Dncng Majortts & Dance Line For Mrchng Band 83-85; Penn ST; Cmmnctns.

BAUER, KELLY; St Marys Area HS; St Marys, PA; (2); JV Bsktbl; JV Cheerleading; JV Score Keeper; Var Sftbl; Hon Roll.

BAUER, KELLY M; North Clarion HS; Lucinda, PA; (4); Trs French Clb; Trs SADD; Dnfth Awd; DAR Awd; Hon Roll; NHS; Drama Clb; Library Aide; Chorus; School Play; Schlrshp PA Gvrnrs Schl Arts-Dance 85; Schlrshp PA Free Entrprs Wk 86; Prsdntl Acdmc Ftnss Awd 87; IN U-Bloomington; Lbrl Arts.

BAUER, KEVIN; Elk County Christian HS; St Marys, PA; (3); 13/72; Boy Scts; Var JV Ftbl; Var Trk; Var JV Wrstlng; Hon Roll.

BAUER, KIMBERLY; High Point Baptist Acad; Glenmore, PA; (3); 3/ 32; Church Yth Grp; Hosp Aide; Sec Frsh Cls; Hon Roll; Amer Christian Hnr Soc 87; Nrsg.

BAUER, MARCIA; Clarion Area HS; Clarion, PA; (3); 1/96; French Clb; Yrbk Ed-Chief; Vllybl; High Hon Roll; Jr NHS; NHS; Ntl Merit SF; Prfct Atten Awd; PA Gov Schl Sci, Clarion U Smmer Acad, Acdmc All-Amer Awd 87; Chem Engrng.

BAUER, PATRICK; Elk County Christian HS; St Marys, PA; (4); 24/79; Boys Clb Am; Boy Scts; Ski Clb; JV Bsbl; JV Bsktbl; JV Ftbl; Hon Roll; Pres Schlr; Gannon U; Marine Bio.

BAUER, REBECCA; Northampton HS; Bath, PA; (3); Church Yth Grp; Drama Clb; Leo Clb; SADD; School Musical; School Play; Stage Crew; Variety Show; Hon Roll; Prelaw.

BAUER, RICHARD; Central Cambria HS; Mineral, PA; (3); 15/205; Boy Scts; Letterman Clb; Varsity Clb; Pres Jr Cls; Var L Bsbl; JV Ftbl; Mgr(s); Var L Wrstlng; High Hon Roll; Hon Roll; U Of Pittsburgh; Pre Dentstry.

BAUER, RUTH; Northampton Area School District; Northampton, PA; (4); 45/430; FBLA; Chorus; Chorus Let; Northampton CC; Photography.

BAUERSFELD, JENNIFER; The Ellis Schl; Pittsburgh, PA; (3); Dance Clb; Hosp Aide; SADD; Nwsp Stf; Yrbk Stf; JV Fld Hcky; Jane L Scarborough Art Awd 85; George Washington U; Psych.

BAUGH, ALYSON; Laurel Highlands HS; Lemont Furnace, PA; (2); Vllybl; High Hon Roll; Hon Roll; Penn St; Bus Adm.

BAUGHMAN, JAMES; Franklin HS; Polk, PA; (2); Art Clb; Computer Clb; 4-H; ROTC; Chorus; Hon Roll; Edingorough; Crtnst.

BAUGHMAN, NICOLE; Berlin Brothers Valley HS; Berlin, PA; (3); 20/ 90; Church Yth Grp; Pres French Clb; FBLA; SADD; School Play; Nwsp Rptr; Nwsp Stf; Rep Stu Cncl; French Hon Soc; Hon Roll; Hotel-Motel Mgmt.

BAUGHMAN, PAUL; Cameron County HS; Driftwood, PA; (2); German Clb; Yrbk Stf; Pres Jr Cls; Crs Cntry; Var Trk; Delta Epsilon Phi 86-87; Natl Sci Olympiad Bio 85-86.

BAUM, DEANNA; Northern Cambria HS; Barnesboro, PA; (3); Church Yth Grp; Girl Scts; Chorus; Church Choir; Color Guard; Nwsp Stf; Yrbk Stf; JV Var Score Keeper; Var L Vllybl; NHS; Hgh Hnr Rll 84-86; Hnr Rll 86-87; USAF.

BAUM, KATRINA; Eastern York HS; York, PA; (3); Drama Clb; GAA; Letterman Clb; SADD; Varsity Clb; Chorus; School Musical; School Play; Var L Cheerleading; JV Trk; Pres Phys Ftnss Awd 85-87; Beautcn.

BAUM, LEISL; Mechanicsburg SR HS; Mechanicsburg, PA; (3); 49/338; Trs Art Clb; Church Yth Grp; Pep Clb; Ski Clb; Church Choir; Stat Bsktbl; Var JV Fld Hcky; High Hon Roll; Hon Roll; Intr Design.

BAUM, MICHELLE; Spring Grove SR HS; Codorus, PA; (3); 3/302; Art Clb; Church Yth Grp; Drama Clb; School Play; High Hon Roll; NHS; Pres Acdmc Ftnss Awd 84-85; Chrch Constrymbr 87; Diplma Brr Grad Crmny 87; Poli Sci.

BAUM, SHERRY; Cumberland Valley HS; Camp Hill, PA; (3); Chorus; Flag Corp; Pom Pon; Bus Adm.

BAUMAN, ANDREA; Pittston Area HS; Duryea, PA; (3); 1/305; French Clb; Key Clb; Rep Math Clb; Chorus; L Drill Tm; School Play; High Hon Roll; Jr NHS; NHS; NEDT Awd; Acdmc All Am 86; Math Tchr.

BAUMAN, BEVIN; Hampton HS; Allison Park, PA; (3); #1 In Class; Latin Clb; NFL; SADD; Chorus; School Musical; Sec Stu Cncl; High Hon Roll; Rep Frsh Cls; Tennis; Spanish Clb; NATS 4th Pl Tri-ST 86; Frgn Affairs.

BAUMAN, BRIAN; Archbishop Wood HS For Boys; Warrington, PA; (2); 7/286; Church Yth Grp; German Clb; SADD; Im Bsktbl; JV Socr; Trk; High Hon Roll; NHS; Penn ST; Med.

BAUMAN, CINDY; Christopher Dock Mennonite HS; Souderton, PA; (4); Pres Church Yth Grp; Pres 4-H; Sec Trs Band; Jazz Band; Yrbk Phtg; Hon Roll; Prfct Atten Awd; Bluffton Coll; Spec Ed.

BAUMAN, CYNTHIA J; Christopher Dock Mennonite HS; Souderton, PA; (4); Pres Church Yth Grp; Pres 4-H; Sec Trs Concert Band; Jazz Band; Orch; School Play; Yrbk Phtg; 4-H Awd; Hon Roll; Prfct Atten Awd; Bluffton Coll; Spec Ed.

BAUMAN, SAMUEL; Lock Haven SR HS; Lock Haven, PA; (3); Boy Scts; Church Yth Grp; Key Clb; Chorus; Variety Show; L Ftbl; Im Socr; L Trk; Cit Awd; Hon Roll; Penn ST U.

BAUMANN, BRANT; Kennedy Christian HS; Hermitage, PA; (3); Nwsp Rptr; Nwsp Stf; Yrbk Rptr; Yrbk Stf; Wrstlng; High Hon Roll; Advrtsg.

BAUMANN, HEIDI; Ringgold HS; Finleyville, PA; (3); Office Aide; Chorus; Variety Show; Hon Roll; NHS; Sci & Math Hnrs Scty 86-87; U Of S CA; Comm.

BAUMBACH, ANGELA; Conestoga Valley HS; Leola, PA; (4); 26/246; Church Yth Grp; Cmnty Wkr; Dance Clb; Girl Scts; Hosp Aide; Capt Flag Corp; Rep Sr Cls; Var Cheerleading; Cit Awd; Hon Roll; Acdmc Schlrhsp 87; Kings Coll.

BAUMBARDNER, WILLIAM; Newport HS; Newport, PA; (3); Church Yth Grp; Yrbk Stf; Bsktbl; Ftbl; Hon Roll.

BAUMGRATZ, GREGORY; Fort Le Boeuf HS; Waterford, PA; (3); 6/ 207; Computer Clb; Debate Tm; School Musical; Stage Crew; Nwsp Rptr; Nwsp Stf; High Hon Roll; Hon Roll; NHS; Prfct Atten Awd; Gannon U; Engrng.

BAUMGRATZ, HEATHER; Du Bois Area HS; Sykesville, PA; (3); Art Clb; Camera Clb; Church Yth Grp; 4-H; GAA; Letterman Clb; Varsity Clb; Chorus; Stage Crew; Yrbk Phtg; MVP-BSKTBL Cmp-Clarion U Of PA 87; Nwspr Artcls-Cmnty Imprvmts 87; Nice Stu Awd 86; Law.

BAUMGRATZ, WILLIAM; Ft Leboeuf HS; Waterford, PA; (1); 10/202; Band; Concert Band; Jazz Band; Mrchg Band; Bsktbl; High Hon Roll; Acad All-Amrcn 86-87.

BAUN, TRACILYN; Arschbishop Prendergast HS; Upper Darby, PA; (3); 30/390; Intnl Clb; Office Aide; Ski Clb; Band; Yrbk Stf; Bsktbl; Hon Roll; NHS; Spanish Clb; Drill Tm; Diocesan Schlr 87; All-Star Bsktbl & Sftbl 86; Scranton U; Phy Thrpy.

BAUTTI, JOANN; Quigley HS; Midland, PA; (4); 12/99; Pres Girl Scts; Yrbk Ed-Chief; Powder Puff Ftbl; L Tennis; High Hon Roll; Jr NHS; NHS; Ntl Merit Ltr; Histry Awd 84; Gold Awd Grl Scts 86; Outstndng JR Yrbk Stf 86; Ursuline Coll; Fshn Mdse.

BAUTZ, AMY; Monongahela Valley Catholic HS; New Eagle, PA; (4); JA; Pep Clb; Ski Clb; Ed Yrbk Stf; Var Stat Bsktbl; Powder Puff Ftbl; Var Score Keeper; Stat Sftbl; Trs French Hon Soc; 1st Pl JR Clss Art Cntst 85-86; Ed.

BAXTER, BRENT; Danville HS; Danville, PA; (4); 46/200; Church Yth Grp; Computer Clb; Key Clb; Spanish Clb; Band; Var Ftbl; High Hon Roll; Hon Roll; Prfct Atten Awd; Susquehanna U; Accntng.

BAXTER, DANIEL V; Valley Forge Military Acad; Gretna, LA; (2); 2/7; Chess Clb; Office Aide; ROTC; Spanish Clb; Varsity Clb; Nwsp Sprt Ed; Nwsp Stf; Sec Soph Cls; JV Bsktbl; JV Socr; Cadet Mnth; Anthony Wayne Hnr Guard 85; Engl,Scl Stds Harvey Medals 85; Phy Trng Badge,ROTC Medal 86; Naval Acad; Engr.

BAXTER, JOHN; Brockway Area HS; Brockport, PA; (3); Art Clb; Church Yth Grp; Thesps; Varsity Clb; Band; Chorus; School Musical; Off Stu Cncl; Wt Lftg; Wrstlng; Mst Imprvd Wrstlr 86-87; Dist Chorus 86-87; IUG Smmr Acad Clarion U 86-87.

BAXTER, KIM; Fairview HS; Erie, PA; (3); Debate Tm; French Clb; Ski Clb; Nwsp Stf; Yrbk Stf; Lit Mag; Swmmng; Hon Roll; Ntl Merit Ltr.

BAXTER, MICHELLE; Central Dauphin HS; Harrisburg, PA; (3); Orch; Trk; High Hon Roll; Hon Roll; Jr NHS; Awd For Outstndgn Prfrmnc In Graphic Arts 86-87; Fine Art.

BAXTER, MICHELLE; Warren Area HS; Warren, PA; (3); Art Clb; Library Aide; Office Aide; Acpl Chr; Church Choir; Orch; School Musical; JV Bsktbl; NHS; Girl Scts; Eco-Mt Envrnmntl Educ Compttn Capt 83-88; Silver B Ctznshp Awd 83-84; Grove City Coll; Bio.

BAXTER, RONALD; Highlands SR HS; Tarentum, PA; (2); Aud/Vis; Computer Clb; Jr NHS; Brown Awd Semester Avg 3.0 86-87; Penn ST; Mech Engr.

BAYER, JASON; Hickory HS; Hermitage, PA; (2); Trs Latin Clb; Chorus; Yrbk Sprt Ed; Yrbk Stf; VP Soph Cls; JV L Bsktbl; Var L Crs Cntry; Var L Trk; Im Vllybl; Wt Lftg; Latn Hnr Soc 86-87.

BAYES, SHIELA; John Bartram HS; Philadelphia, PA; (4); 8/625; Church Yth Grp; Hosp Aide; Office Aide; Sec Church Choir; Rep Stu Cncl; Gym; Hon Roll; NHS; Stu Wk 86; Temple U; Psycht.

BAYLES, AUTUMN; Bethlehem Catholic HS; Nazareth, PA; (3); 15/202; Trs Key Clb; Trs SADD; Chorus; Stage Crew; Nwsp Stf; Yrbk Stf; Tennis; High Hon Roll; Hon Roll; NHS; Natl Lang Arts Olympd 85; Comp Engr.

BAYLIS, FRANCINE C; Chichester SR HS; Boothwyn, PA; (3); 16/300; Art Clb; SADD; JV Bsktbl; Var Fld Hcky; Var Lcrss; Score Keeper; Hon Roll; 1st Hnrs 85-87; U Of DE; Bus.

BAYLOR, ERIC; Keystone HS; Knox, PA; (3); VICA; Hon Roll; Contrctr.

BAYNARD, DION; Pine Forge Acad; Pine Forge, PA; (4); 14/80; Camera Clb; Ski Clb; Nwsp Stf; Stu Cncl; JV Bsktbl; Hon Roll; NHS; Oakwood Coll; Public Adm.

BAYNES, JOYA Z; Central SR HS; York, PA; (4); Boy Scts; Church Yth Grp; Exploring; JA; Teachers Aide; Variety Show; Nwsp Rptr; Nwsp Stf; VP Frsh Cls; Rep Stu Cncl; Pres York Cnty Law Explorers Post 86-87; Ethel M Lawd Career Awd 87; Law.

BAYUS, MICHAEL; Owen J Roberts HS; Elverson, PA; (3); Concert Band; Jazz Band; Mrchg Band; Symp Band; Yrbk Ed-Chief; Yrbk Stf; Hon Roll; NHS; Ed.

BE HANNA, CHRISTOPHER G; Norwin SR HS; N Huntingdon, PA; (4); 2/557; Letterman Clb; Math Clb; Math Tm; Chorus; Crs Cntry; Trk; High Hon Roll; Ntl Merit SF; Sal; RPI Math & Sci Mdl, Atl-Pac Math Leag Bk Awd 86; ASHME Profcncy Awd 85.

BEABES, SHANE; Indiana SR HS; Indiana, PA; (2); Stage Crew; High Hon Roll; Hon Roll; Jr NHS; Arch.

BEABOUT, LISA D; East Brady HS; Karns City, PA; (4); Cmnty Wkr; Capt Color Guard; Mrchg Band; Variety Show; Nwsp Rptr; Yrbk Stf; Rep Sr Cls; Powder Puff Ftbl; Hon Roll; U Of Pittsburgh; Psych.

BEABOUT, MELISSA; Hanover HS; Hanover, PA; (3); Science Clb; Ski Clb; Varsity Clb; School Play; Var Bsktbl; Var Fld Hcky; Pittsburgh U; Pharmacy.

BEACH, JEFF; Northern Bedford County HS; New Enterprise, PA; (3); Church Yth Grp; Math Clb; SADD; Varsity Clb; School Musical; JV Bsbl; JV Ftbl; Var Wt Lftg; L Var Wrstlng; Hon Roll; Physcl Educ.

BEACH, JEFFREY; Oil City SR HS; Oil City, PA; (3); 14/218; Aud/Vis; Computer Clb; German Clb; Hon Roll; Law.

BEACH, JENNIFER; Northern Bedford HS; New Enterprse, PA; (2); Church Yth Grp; FFA; Letterman Clb; Varsity Clb; Concert Band; Jazz Band; Mrchg Band; Var L Trk; JV Vllybl; 4-H; Gold Mdl FFA Swine Prodctn 86; Publc Spkng Awd 86; FFA Fndtn Awd 86; Comp Pgmmr.

BEACH, JOHN; Franklin HS; Polk, PA; (4); 3/212; Church Yth Grp; Spanish Clb; Varsity Clb; Band; Concert Band; L Ftbl; High Hon Roll; NHS; Pres Schlr; US Army Rsrv Ntl Schlr/Athlt Awd 86-87; Prsdntl Acdmc Ftnss Awd 86-87; Hlf-Hlmt Awd-Ftbl Achvt 86-87; OK ST U; Vet.

BEACH, KERRIE; Schuykill Haven Area HS; Sch Haven, PA; (2); 4/101; Rep Stu Cncl; High Hon Roll; German Clb; SADD; Chorus; Nwsp Rptr; VP Frsh Cls; Sec Soph Cls; Capt Cheerleading; Hon Roll; Acdmc Excllnc 87; HOBY Smnr 87.

BEACH, MARK; Fairview HS; Erie, PA; (4); 26/154; Church Yth Grp; Band; Church Choir; Concert Band; Jazz Band; Mrchg Band; NHS; French Clb; Library Aide; SR Dept Awd Frgn Lang 86-87; Latin Natl Hnr Scty 86-87; Instr Mag Musicianship Awd 86-87; IN U Of PA; Frnch.

BEACH, MELODY; Blair County Christian Schl; Hollidaysburg, PA; (3); 6/17; Church Yth Grp; Debate Tm; Nwsp Stf; Yrbk Bus Mgr; Yrbk Ed-Chief; Trs Soph Cls; Var Bsktbl; Capt Cheerleading; Var Sftbl; Var Trk; Bob Jones U; Bus.

BEACH, ROCHELLE; Minersville Area HS; Minersville, PA; (3); FBLA; Library Aide; Spanish Clb; Hon Roll; Acct.

BEACHELL, BETH; Northern Lebanon HS; Grantville, PA; (4); 6/166; Cmnty Wkr; Quiz Bowl; Mrchg Band; Nwsp Ed-Chief; Sec Jr Cls; Pres Stu Cncl; L Var Fld Hcky; Capt L Trk; DAR Awd; High Hon Roll; U PA; Peace Studs.

BEACHELL, JOSEPH; Mountain View Christian Schl; Hummelstown, PA; (4); 2/4; School Play; Yrbk Stf; Pres Jr Cls; Pres Sr Cls; Var Capt Bsktbl; Var Capt Socr; Var Capt Sftbl; Hon Roll; Sal; Bob Jones U; Bus.

BEACHEM, KELLY; Lincoln HS; Ellwood, PA; (4); 53/168; Camera Clb; Key Clb; Y-Teens; Chorus; Powder Puff Ftbl; Hon Roll; Slippery Rock U; Acctng.

BEACHY, MICHAEL; Mifflinburg Area HS; Mifflinburg, PA; (1); Church Yth Grp; FCA; FFA; German Clb; Vet.

BEAGHAN, ROBERT; Kennard-Dale HS; Stewartstown, PA; (2); Varsity Clb; VP JV Bsbl; JV Im Bsktbl; JV Im Ftbl; Wt Lftg; High Hon Roll.

BEALE, HEATHER; Johnstown Christian Schl; Boswell, PA; (1); #3 In Class; Church Yth Grp; Spanish Clb; Sec Frsh Cls; JV Cheerleading; Im Socr; Hon Roll; Penn ST U; Blgy.

BEALE, JACQUELINE; Freeport Area SR HS; Freeport, PA; (2); 22/202; Church Yth Grp; Band; Church Choir; Mrchg Band; Symp Band; Nwsp Bus Mgr; Nwsp Ed-Chief; Nwsp Stf; High Hon Roll; Clarion U; Translator.

BEALER, BERTRAM; Liberty HS; Bethlehem, PA; (3); Art Clb; Boy Scts; SADD; Crs Cntry; Trk; Bio.

BEAM, JACKIE; Ambridge Area HS; Ambridge, PA; (3); Church Yth Grp; Pep Clb; Red Cross Aide; VP Spanish Clb; SADD; Band; Pep Band; Off Jr Cls; Hon Roll; NHS; Robert Morris; Bus Admin.

BEAM, JESSE; Newport HS; Liverpool, PA; (4); 6/97; Chess Clb; Quiz Bowl; Stu Cncl; Hon Roll; Trs NHS; Ntl Merit Ltr; Prfct Atten Awd; Cmmnwlth PA Cert Merit 86; PA ST U; Engnrng.

BEAMENDERFER, CHRIS; Lampeter-Strasburg HS; Lancaster, PA; (4); 34/160; Church Yth Grp; Bsbl; Ftbl; Wt Lftg; Penn ST.

BEAMER, EMILY; Newport HS; Newport, PA; (1); Pep Clb; Chorus; Concert Band; Mrchg Band; School Musical; Swing Chorus; Rep Stu Cncl; JV Cheerleading; Wt Lftg; Hon Roll.

BEAMER, ROBIN LYNNE; Hempfield Area SR HS; Bovard, PA; (4); Sec Trs Church Yth Grp; Pres Library Aide; Sec Church Choir; Concert Band; Mrchg Band; Orch; High Hon Roll; Hon Roll; Jr NHS; NHS; Jeff Smalley Awd 87; Milligan Christian Coll; Psych.

BEAN, AMY; Forest City Regional HS; Pleasant Mount, PA; (4); 15/58; Letterman Clb; Trs Band; Concert Band; Mrchg Band; Nwsp Stf; Yrbk Stf; Sftbl; Vllybl; Hon Roll; U Scranton; Nrsng.

BEANS, REKISHIA; Coatesville Area SR HS; Coatesville, PA; (3); 36/517; French Clb; ROTC; Band; Hon Roll; NHS; Var Im Bsktbl; Var Im Socr; Daedalian AFJROTC Achvt Awd 87; Mltry Ordr Wrld Wars Mdl AFJROTC 86; Penn ST; Opthmlgst.

BEAR, JENNIFER MARIE; Warwick HS; Lititz, PA; (3); 73/267; Church Yth Grp; FBLA; JA; Flag Corp; Yrbk Stf; Mgr(s); Hon Roll.

BEAR, KIMBERLY; Big Spring HS; Newville, PA; (3); Sec Church Yth Grp; Girl Scts; Library Aide; Stage Crew; Hon Roll; Grl Sct Slvr Awd 87; 1st Hnrs Pin 85 87; Vlntr Svc Awd 86; Socl Wrk.

BEAR, SHARON; Cumberland Valley HS; Mechanicsburg, PA; (3); 54/591; Am Leg Aux Girls St; French Clb; JV Bsktbl; Var Crs Cntry; JV Fld Hcky; French Hon Soc; High Hon Roll; Jr NHS; NHS; NC U Chapel Hill; CPA.

BEAR, SHONDA; Parkland SR HS; Allentown, PA; (3); Key Clb; Library Aide; Ski Clb; Stu Cncl; Var Cheerleading; Im Wt Lftg; High Hon Roll; Hon Roll.

BEARD, MELISSA; Cocalico HS; Denver, PA; (3); 29/166; Sec Sr Cls; High Hon Roll; Hon Roll; Prfct Atten Awd; Church Yth Grp; Drama Clb; FBLA; Band; Church Choir; HOBY Ldrshp Sem 86; Law.

BEARD, PAUL; Bishop Guilfoyle HS; Altoona, PA; (3); Var L Bsktbl; Var L Ftbl.

BEARDSLEY, JOSEPH; Corry Area HS; Columbus, PA; (2); Dickinson; Atty.

BEARER, ANNMARIE; Northern Cambria HS; Spangler, PA; (3); Spanish Clb; Chorus; Color Guard; JV Var Bsktbl; Var Trk; High Hon Roll; Hon Roll; NHS; Spanish NHS; Elem Ed.

BEARER, SUE; Cambria Heights HS; Carrolltown, PA; (3); Art Clb; Drama Clb; Ski Clb; Spanish Clb; Band; Chorus; Concert Band; Drm Mjr(t); Mrchg Band; Yrbk Stf.

BEARLEY, JOYCE; Dallas HS; Shavertown, PA; (3); 40/230; AFS; Aud/Vis; Sec Church Yth Grp; Drama Clb; Girl Scts; Library Aide; Nwsp Stf; Mgr(s); Stat Trk; Hon Roll; Hstry.

BEARY, THERDSA; North Clarion JR SR HS; Shippenville, PA; (3); Chorus; Trk; Hon Roll.

BEASLEY, CANDICE; Westinghouse HS; Pittsburgh, PA; (3); Church Yth Grp; FHA; JA; Natl Beta Clb; Church Choir; Sec Soph Cls; High Hon Roll; Hon Roll; Natl Engl Merit Awd 85; U Of Pittsburgh; Accntng.

BEASLEY, LAURA; Gettysburg HS; Gettysburg, PA; (2); Office Aide; Varsity Clb; Band; Mrchg Band; JV Var Bsktbl; JV Fld Hcky; Var Sftbl; Var Trk; JV Vllybl; Health And Phys Educ.

BEASLEY, MIA; Penn Center Acad; Philadelphia, PA; (4); 8/50; Office Aide; Yrbk Stf; Pres Jr Cls; Rep Stu Cncl; Hon Roll; NHS; Svc, Ldrshp Awds 86; Carnegie Mellon; Mech Engr.

BEASLEY, MONA; William Penn SR HS; York, PA; (3); Dance Clb; Debate Tm; Exploring; Hon Roll; Temple U; Attny.

BEASOM, LISA ANN; Hempfield HS; Mt Joy, PA; (4); Varsity Clb; Capt Bsktbl; Fld Hcky; Sftbl; Hon Roll; NHS; U PA Clarion.

BEASTON, ROBIN; Fannett-Metal HS; Concord, PA; (3); 4-H; Band; Chorus; Mrchg Band; Yrbk Stf; Trs Soph Cls; 4-H Awd; Hon Roll; Most Prmsng Bus Stu 86; Sec.

BEASTON, SHERRY; West Perry SR HS; Landisburg, PA; (3); 71/283; Math Tm; Office Aide; Actuarial Sci.

BEATTY, ANGIE; Jamestown HS; Greenville, PA; (4); Drama Clb; Spanish Clb; SADD; Pres VICA; Variety Show; Csmtlgy Pres, Mercer Vo-Tech Pres & Outstndng Stu 87; Penn ST; Csmtlgy Tchr.

BEATTY, CHRISTINA; Susquehannock HS; New Freedom, PA; (2); 32/243; SADD; Chorus; Stage Crew; JV Sftbl; JV Vllybl; NHS; Psych.

BEATTY, DEBORAH S; Greater La Trobe SR HS; Latrobe, PA; (4); 3/405; Church Yth Grp; Chorus; High Hon Roll; NHS; Pres Scholar St Francis Coll 87; St Francis Coll; Physcn Asst.

BEATTY, HOLLY; Milton SR HS; Milton, PA; (2); Am Leg Aux Girls St; Church Yth Grp; Key Clb; Spanish Clb; Varsity Clb; Chorus; Cheerleading; Trk; Hon Roll; Prfct Atten Awd; Outstndng Chrldr Awd 86; 2 1st Pl Mdls In Trk 87; Williamsport Area CC.

BEATTY, LINDA; Marion Center Area HS; Home, PA; (3); 19/153; 4-H; Latin Clb; Science Clb; Band; Chorus; Concert Band; Mrchg Band; JV Swmmng; Hon Roll; Natl 4-H Cngrss & 4-H Conf; Phys Thrpy.

BEATTY, SHERRY; Du Bois Area HS; Luthersburg, PA; (3); 63/350; Church Yth Grp; Library Aide; Band; Church Choir; Concert Band; Mrchg Band; Hon Roll; Nice Kid Awd 85-86; Coronation Ct 86-87; Nursing.

BEATTY, TARA J; Norristown Area HS; Norristown, PA; (4); 50/417; Church Yth Grp; DECA; FCA; Key Clb; Mrchg Band; Yrbk Phtg; Yrbk Stf; Stu Cncl; Hon Roll; NHS; Bloomsburg U; Elem Ed.

BEATY, SUZANNE; Methacton SR HS; Collegeville, PA; (3); 90/400; FBLA; Office Aide; Chorus; Off Frsh Cls; Off Soph Cls; Off Jr Cls; Off Sr Cls; Var Sftbl; JV Trk; Hon Roll; Bus.

BEAUCHAMP, JON PAUL; St Pius X HS; Gilbertsville, PA; (2); Cmnty Wkr; Drama Clb; SADD; School Musical; School Play; Stage Crew; Nwsp Rptr; Nwsp Stf; Yrbk Rptr; Yrbk Sprt Ed; U Of Scranton; Orthpdc Srgry.

BEAUFORD, ANGEL; Big Beaver Falls Area HS; Beaver Falls, PA; (3); 11/177; Church Yth Grp; Science Clb; Spanish Clb; Band; Church Choir; Concert Band; Mrchg Band; Pep Band; High Hon Roll; NHS; SC ST Coll; Math.

BEAUMAN, DALE; Towanda HS; Wysox, PA; (3); Church Yth Grp; FFA; Frmr.

BEAUMONT, GREGG; West Allegheny SR HS; Oakdale, PA; (4); 36/205; Drama Clb; Pres Chorus; Pres Concert Band; Jazz Band; Pres Mrchg Band; Pep Band; School Play; Hon Roll; JP Sousa Awd; Ntl Merit Ltr; PMEA Dist 1 Hnrs Band, Rgn 1 All ST Band, & Dist 1 Chorus 87; PA ST U; Mech Engr.

BEAUMONT, PENNI; Marple-Newtown HS; Broomall, PA; (4); 14/326; Capt Debate Tm; Model UN; Red Cross Aide; SADD; Var L Trk; NHS; Ntl Merit Ltr; Pres Schlr; Amer Lgn Schl Awd 87; Sherborne Schl; Intl Stds.

BEAUREGARD, JOHN; Richland HS; Gibsonia, PA; (3); 39/151; Boy Scts; Church Yth Grp; Cmnty Wkr; Acpl Chr; Chorus; Church Choir; Coach Actv; Trk; High Hon Roll; Hon Roll; Bus.

BEAVEN, RACHEL; Wilmington Area HS; New Wilmington, PA; (4); Dance Clb; Drama Clb; French Clb; Band; Concert Band; Drill Tm; Flag Corp; Pep Band; School Play; Nwsp Stf; IN U PA; Engl.

BEAVER, CHRIS; Newport HS; Newport, PA; (3); 24/117; Varsity Clb; Stage Crew; Var L Bsbl; Var L Bsktbl; Var L Ftbl; Vllybl; Wt Lftg; Hon Roll; Prfct Atten Awd.

BEAVER, DANIEL; Bermudian Springs HS; E Berlin, PA; (3); 80/120; Band; Chorus; Church Choir; Concert Band; Madrigals; Mrchg Band; School Musical; School Play; Stage Crew; Swing Chorus.

BEAVER, ELIZABETH A; Hershey HS; Hershey, PA; (3); 1/205; Church Yth Grp; Chorus; Concert Band; Jazz Band; Mrchg Band; School Musical; JV Bsktbl; JV Fld Hcky; High Hon Roll; NHS.

BEAVER, JULIE; Greenwood HS; Millerstown, PA; (3); Leo Clb; Chorus; Concert Band; Mrchg Band; School Musical; Swing Chorus; Nwsp Ed-Chief; Hon Roll; NHS; Am Leg Schl Awd 84; Hlth Care Admin.

BEAVER, KAREN ELISABETH; East Pennsboro HS; Enola, PA; (4); 11/190; Church Yth Grp; Sec German Clb; Chorus; Concert Band; Drill Tm; Mrchg Band; School Musical; NHS; Science Clb; Band; Cvc Clb, Semper Fidelis Music & Panhellenic Awds 87; Dickinson Coll; Bio.

BEAVER, LEE ANN MARIE; Meadowbrook Christian HS; Milton, PA; (3); 3/15; Church Yth Grp; Pres Spanish Clb; Chorus; Yrbk Phtg; Socr; High Hon Roll; Prfct Atten Awd; Rotary Awd; Awds Engl & Character 85; Educ.

BEAVER, MELISSA; Milton SR HS; Milton, PA; (4); Hosp Aide; Service Clb; Spanish Clb; SADD; Band; Nwsp Rptr; Lit Mag; Bloomsburg U Of PA; Mass Cmnct.

BEAVERS, DEBORAH; Upper Moreland HS; Hatboro, PA; (4); 58/257; High Hon Roll; Hon Roll; George Marin Data Tech Awd 87; Bus.

BEAVERS, RANDY; North Pocono HS; Moscow, PA; (3); 27/231; JV Bsbl; Hon Roll; NHS; Penn St.

BEAVERSON, BRENDA; Spring Grove SR HS; Thomas Ville, PA; (3); 43/301; Church Yth Grp; Ski Clb; Band; Concert Band; Mrchg Band; Hon Roll; 200 Pt Pin; Indiana U Of PA; Nrsng.

BEBENEK, FRANCINE; Lourdes Regional HS; Shamokin, PA; (4); Drama Clb; Pep Clb; Spanish Clb; Band; Mrchg Band; Pep Band; School Play; Variety Show; Band Letter 87; Most Dedicated Majorette 87; May Crwng Ct 87; Hmcmng Ct 87; Bloomsburg U; Acctng.

BEBKO, ANTHONY; Cathedral Prep; Erie, PA; (4); 14/212; Church Yth Grp; French Clb; Model UN; Concert Band; Jazz Band; Mrchg Band; Im Vllybl; High Hon Roll; Pres Schlr; Penn ST U; Bio.

BEBKO, RENEE; Technical Memorial HS; Erie, PA; (4); 10/324; CAP; Girl Scts; Hosp Aide; Rep Frsh Cls; Trk; Hon Roll; NHS; Villa Maria; Nrsng.

BEBLO, DAN; Butler Entermediate HS; Butler, PA; (2); Church Yth Grp; JA; Spanish Clb; Im Bsktbl; Coach Actv; Im Ftbl; Mgr(s); Hon Roll; NHS; Bus Admin.

BECCARI, BETH; West Phila Catholic Girls HS; Philadelphia, PA; (3); 16/246; High Hon Roll; Hon Roll; Bus.

BECHAK, CHRISTINA A; North Allegheny HS; Pittsburgh, PA; (4); NFL; Speech Tm; Thesps; Chorus; School Musical; Symp Band; Nwsp Rptr; Ntl Merit SF; Quiz Bowl; Concert Band; Morning Anncmnts 86-87; Squish & The Revivals 86-87; Polit Sci.

BECK, AMY; Ambridge Area HS; Ambridge, PA; (3); FBLA; Pep Clb; Spanish Clb; Band; Concert Band; Mrchg Band; Pep Band; Symp Band; Jr Cls; Hon Roll; PA ST U; Comp Sci.

BECK, ANDREA; Central Columbia HS; Berwick, PA; (2); DECA; 4-H; 4-H Awd; Attnd ST DECA Conf In Lancaster PA 87; Bus.

BECK, ANDREW; Bangor Area HS; Ackermanville, PA; (3); Church Yth Grp; Drama Clb; Band; Church Choir; Concert Band; Drm Mjr(t); Jazz Band; Madrigals; Mrchg Band; Orch; Dist 10 Chorus 86-87; Regn 5 Chorus 86-87; PA ALL ST Chorus & Fred Warings US Chorus 87; Music Prfrmnc.

BECK, ANDY; Council Rock HS; Churchville, PA; (2); Hon Roll; La Salle U; Orthdntcs.

BECK, DANIELLE; Everett Area HS; Everett, PA; (3); 1/136; French Clb; GAA; Yrbk Stf; Stu Cncl; French Hon Soc; High Hon Roll; Prfct Atten Awd; Amer Lgn Aux Awd Most Outstndng Female 85; Outstndng Hist Stu 85; 2nd Pl Essay About Amer 85; Law.

BECK, FLOYD; St Marys Area HS; Saint Marys, PA; (4).

BECK, JEFFREY A; Daniel Boone HS; Douglassville, PA; (2); Boy Scts; Church Yth Grp; German Clb; Church Choir; Wrstlng; High Hon Roll.

BECK, JENNIFER; Council Rock HS; Newtown, PA; (3); Church Yth Grp; Letterman Clb; Ski Clb; Spanish Clb; JV Var Fld Hcky; Powder Puff Ftbl; Var Socr; JV Sftbl; Hon Roll.

BECK, JENNY; Brandywine Hgts HS; Fleetwood, PA; (3); Art C Church Yth Grp; School Play; Tennis; Vllybl; High Hon Roll; Hon Ro Prfct Atten Awd; Rotary Awd; Top Art Stu 85-87; Hnr Soc 86-8 Commercial Artist.

BECK, JUDY; Du Bois Area HS; Reynoldsville, PA; (3); Pres Church Y Grp; Chorus; Church Choir; School Musical; Swing Chorus; Sec Sr C Hon Roll; Dist III Chorus 86-87; Nrsng.

BECK, KAREN; Brandywine Heights HS; Topton, PA; (4); Girl Sc Hosp Aide; Sec Band; Concert Band; Jazz Band; Mrchg Band; Pep Ban Swmmng; High Hon Roll; County Band 86-87; Alvernia Coll; Pyscl Thrp

BECK, KARYN; Penncrest HS; Chester, PA; (4); 10/320; Intnl C School Play; Variety Show; Nwsp Bus Mgr; Ed Lit Mag; Var JV Bskt Stat Vllybl; High Hon Roll; NHS; Ntl Merit Ltr; Natl Spn Cont 1st Pl 8 Dist Spn Cont 1st Pl 87; Dist Frnch Cont 1st Pl 87; U PA.

BECK, KATHERINE; Palmerton Area HS; Bowmanstown, PA; (3); 1 173; Church Yth Grp; Debate Tm; Pres 4-H; Pep Clb; Yrbk Stf; Sec Fr Cls; Sec Soph Cls; Sec Jr Cls; Sec Sr Cls; Stu Cncl; PAHA St Merit Av 4-H 1st Pl 85; High Point Yr-End Awd Penn Jersey Horse Assoc 85-8 Pres Phys Ftns.

BECK, KELLY; Garden Spot HS; Narvon, PA; (3); 49/186; Pres Chur Yth Grp; Radio Clb; Church Choir; Nwsp Rptr; Yrbk Stf; Trs Soph C Trs Jr Cls; Pom Pon; JV Capt Sftbl; Hon Roll; Sftbl-Tm Spirit, Ldrs Awd 85-86; Intl Rltns.

BECK, KIMBERLY; Daniel Boone HS; Douglassville, PA; (3); 3/16 Pres Church Yth Grp; Pres Girl Scts; Service Clb; Band; Church Choi Concert Band; Mrchg Band; Yrbk Stf; High Hon Roll; NHS; Grl Scts Sl Awd 85; Nursing.

BECK, KRISTIE; Bishop Carroll HS; Portage, PA; (3); 2/128; Cmn Wkr; Drama Clb; Red Cross Aide; Ski Clb; Co-Capt Speech Tm; T SADD; Band; School Play; Rep Stu Cncl; NHS.

BECK, LANCE; Monessen SR HS; Monessen, PA; (3); JA; Model U Yrbk Stf; Rep Stu Cncl; Var L Bsktbl; Var L Ftbl; Var Wt Lftg; High Ho Roll; NHS; Acad All-American 84-86; Eastern A All-Star Tm 86; Sci Da 87; Chem Engrng.

BECK, LAURA; Belle Vernon Area HS; Belle Vernon, PA; (4); 34/27 Art Clb; Pep Clb; High Hon Roll; Hon Roll; NHS; Lang Awd 87; Californ U Of PA; Educ.

BECK, LORI; Hatboro Horsham HS; Hatboro, PA; (4); #2 In Class; Hos Aide; Fld Hcky; Lcrss; Powder Puff Ftbl; Hon Roll; NHS; Prfct Atte Awd; Pres Schlr; Sal; Outstndng Achvt Scholar Temple U 87; Temple Nrsng.

BECK, LYNN; Brandywine Heights HS; Fleetwood, PA; (3); #21 Class; Art Clb; Church Yth Grp; Library Aide; Spanish Clb; School Pla Stage Crew; Yrbk Stf; L Tennis; Hon Roll; Prfct Atten Awd; Lar Day-Alvernia Coll For Password 5th Pl & Art Clb Pres 87.

BECK, MICHELLE; York County Vo Tech; York, PA; (4); 41/408; VIC 1st Pl Open & Closng Tm VICA Sklls Olympcs 85-86; ASPERO Phys F Awd 85-86; Iles Scholar York Coll; York Coll PA.

BECK, NICHOLE; Moshannon Valley HS; Houtzdale, PA; (3); 1/11 Aud/Vis; Sec SADD; Acpl Chr; Sec Chorus; School Play; Ed Nws Ed-Chief; Bausch & Lomb Sci Awd; Chess Clb; Pres NHS; Spanish Cl Bausch & Lmb Sci 87; Chem.

BECK, PATRICIA ANN; Ambridge HS; Sewickley, PA; (4); 12/36 Church Yth Grp; Girl Scts; Red Cross Aide; NHS; German Clb; Pep Cl Off Frsh Cls; Off Soph Cls; Off Jr Cls; Off Sr Cls; Outstndng Accntr Stu-Den 3-HS Wlvs Clb 87; Grl Of Mnth-HS Bus & Prfssnl Wmns Clb 8 Robert Morris Coll; Accntng.

BECK, ROBERT; Nazareth Area SR HS; Wind Gap, PA; (3); 2/265; A Leg Boys St; Church Yth Grp; Math Tm; Var L Ftbl; Var Trk; Im Wt Lft High Hon Roll; NHS; Acadmc Achvt Awd; Gifted Pgm Activite Stockmarkt Lehigh U 85-87; Engineering.

BECK, SHARON; Harmony Area HS; Westover, PA; (4); 3/50; Teache Aide; Band; Concert Band; Mrchg Band; Yrbk Stf; Im Sftbl; Im Vllyb High Hon Roll; NHS; Prfct Atten Awd; IN U Pennsylvania; Pediatrics.

BECK, THUY; Eastern York HS; York, PA; (3); SADD; Band; Conce Band; Drm Mjr(t); Jazz Band; Mrchg Band; Var Capt Sftbl; DAR Aw High Hon Roll; Jr NHS; Pres Fit Awd 85-87; Ed.

BECKER, BRENT; Lampeter Strasburg HS; Strasburg, PA; (3); FBL Socr; Tennis; Wrstlng; Hon Roll; Millersville ST U.

BECKER, DANIEL; Lower Dauphin HS; Middletown, PA; (3); Churc Yth Grp; Var L Ftbl; Var Trk; Im Wt Lftg; Hon Roll; Comp Sci.

BECKER, DAWN; Steelton-Highspire HS; Steelton, PA; (3); NHS.

BECKER, JEFFREY; Spring Grove Area SR HS; Spring Grove, PA; (2 JV Ftbl; JV Trk; Var Wrstlng; High Hon Roll; Hon Roll; 90.3 GPA 86-8 U Of Miami; Marine Bio.

BECKER, JOHN E; Danville Area HS; Danville, PA; (3); Latin Cl NFL; Spanish Clb; Nwsp Rptr; Nwsp Stf; Yrbk Phtg; Yrbk Stf; Tenni Trk; NHS; Photo.

BECKER, JOSEPH; Aliquippa HS; Aliquippa, PA; (2); Var Ftbl; W Lftg; Hon Roll.

BECKER, JOSHUA B; Harriton HS; Villanova, PA; (4); Cmnty Wk Co-Capt Debate Tm; JA; VP Math Tm; Nwsp Ed-Chief; Hon Roll; NHS Ntl Merit SF; NFL; Political Wkr; Pol Sci.

BECKER, KYMBERLY; Mt Penn JR/SR HS; Mt Penn, PA; (3); Churc Yth Grp; FBLA; JA; Model UN; Y-Teens; Band; Concert Band; Mrch Band; Gvrnrs Awd 84-858; Accntng.

BECKER, MONA; Lampeter-Strasburg HS; Willow Street, PA; (2 Church Yth Grp; Hst FFA; Chorus; Church Choir; Yrbk Stf; Trk; Varsit Clb; Score Keeper; Timer; Hnrd Seminar Co-Ops High Tst Score 87 Church Quiz Tm Captn Awd 87; 2nd Yr Varsty Ltr Awd Trk 87; Georg Washington U; Sci.

BECKER, NOAH; Bensalem SR HS; Bensalem, PA; (3); Chess Cl Debate Tm; Math Clb; Math Tm; Scholastic Bowl; Science Clb; Speec Tm; JV Socr; JV Trk; High Hon Roll; St Chmpnshp Futur Prblm Slvg Tn 86-87; Amer Invtnl Math Exm 86-87; Econ.

BECKER, PATRICK; United HS; Armagh, PA; (4); 18/160; Church Yt Grp; Ski Clb; Stu Cncl; Ftbl; Trk; Wt Lftg; Hon Roll; NHS; Penn ST Univ Bus.

BECKER, SUSAN; Penn Wood HS; Lansdowne, PA; (4); 7/337; Churc Yth Grp; Teachers Aide; Chorus; Church Choir; School Musical; Yrbk Bu Mgr; Yrbk Ed-Chief; Rptr Lit Mag; VP NHS; Pres Schlr; West Chester PA; Scndry Ed.

BECKERLEG, KEIRSTEN; Mt Pleasant Area SR HS; Mt Pleasant, PA (4); 35/249; Church Yth Grp; Cmnty Wkr; Rep GAA; Girl Scts; Librar Aide; Spanish Clb; Color Guard; DAR Awd; Hon Roll; Prfct Atten Aw Slippery Rock U; Educ.

BECKINGER, CRAIG; Ringgold HS; Monongahela, PA; (3); Art Clb; Boy Scts; Science Clb; Spanish Clb; Trs Chorus; Rep Stu Cncl; JV Trk; Hon Roll; NHS; Sci & Math Hnr Soc, Prom Cmte, & Stu Actvties Cmte 86-87; Secondry Ed.

BECKLEY, ALLISON; Mifflinburg SR HS; Mifflinburg, PA; (1); Pres 4-H; French Clb; Chorus; Church Choir; Concert Band; Stage Crew; Capt Cheerleading; High Hon Roll; Hon Roll; Prfct Atten Awd.

BECKLEY, JOHNNENE; West Hazleton HS; W Hazleton, PA; (3); 49/250; Church Yth Grp; Office Aide; Pep Clb; Spanish Clb; Color Guard; Capt Flag Corp; Mrchg Band; Pep Band; Capt Twrlr; Hon Roll; Med Sec.

BECKMAN, HEATHER L; North Allegheny SR HS; Pittsburgh, PA; (4); 11/642; French Clb; NFL; Ski Clb; Thesps; Drill Tm; Mrchg Band; Symp Band; Trs Sr Cls; NHS; Ntl Merit SF; Med.

BECKMAN, JODI; South Williamsport SR HS; S Williamsport, PA; (3); Computer Clb; French Clb; Hosp Aide; Key Clb; Nwsp Rptr; High Hon Roll; NHS.

BECKMAN, RONALD; Bishop Neumann HS; Williamsport, PA; (3); Hosp Aide; SADD; Yrbk Bus Mgr; Yrbk Stf; Im Vllybl; High Hon Roll; Hon Roll; Prfct Atten Awd; Rotary Awd; Villanova U; Mech Engrng.

BECKWITH, AMY; Corry Area HS; Corry, PA; (2); Church Yth Grp; Drama Clb; Y-Teens; Band; Acpl Chr; Mrchg Band; Cheerleading; Hon Roll; Yrbk Stf; Stat Trk; Pre Med.

BECKWITH, KIMBERLY; Freeport SR HS; Sarver, PA; (2); Church Yth Grp; Chorus; High Hon Roll; Hon Roll; Prfct Atten Awd.

BECSE, SYLVIA TINA; Canon Mc Millan SR HS; Canonsburg, PA; (4); Ski Clb; Spanish Clb; Band; Yrbk Stf; Tennis; Trs Spanish NHS; La Salle U; Bus.

BEDDINGS, KAREN; Moon SR HS; Coraopolis, PA; (3); 20/330; Spanish Clb; Rep Stu Cncl; Socr; Vllybl; High Hon Roll; Hon Roll; NHS; Penn ST; Bus.

BEDEAUX, MARY; Brookville Area HS; Reynoldsville, PA; (3); German Clb; Pep Clb; Varsity Clb; Chorus; Orch; JV Bsktbl; Var Sftbl; Var Vllybl; Bradford; Med Secy.

BEDELL, HEATHER; Du Bois HS; Du Bois, PA; (3); Church Yth Grp; Dance Clb; Band; Chorus; Church Choir; Concert Band; Mrchg Band; Orch; School Musical; Symp Band; Music.

BEDELL, ROB; Faith Christian Schl; Bangor, PA; (3); 4/15; Church Yth Grp; Drama Clb; Church Choir; Var Socr; High Hon Roll; Hon Roll; Val; Princ Awd 80; Pilot USAF.

BEDFORD, MELISSA; Greater Nanticoke Area HS; Nanticoke, PA; (1); Hon Roll.

BEDFORD, MICHAEL; Tunkhannock Area HS; Mehoopany, PA; (3); 53/310; Art Clb; Boy Scts; Pres Church Yth Grp; SADD; Church Choir; Var Socr; JV Vllybl; Hon Roll; Yllw Belt Zen Budokai & Mst Imprvd Stu 87; Rossetti Mem Art Shw 87; PA Art Careers Wkshp 87; Pratt Inst; Fine Arts.

BEDFORD, RICHARD; Du Bois Area HS; Reynoldsville, PA; (3); 69/300; Varsity Clb; JV Bsbl; JV Wrstlng; Hon Roll; Aerosp Engr.

BEDICS, MARK; Central Catholic HS; Allentown, PA; (3); Church Yth Grp; Math Clb; JV Var Bsbl; JV Bsktbl; Var Golf; Hon Roll; E Penn Golf Trnmnt 3rd Pl 85; Bus Admn.

BEDILION, CYNDEE; Jefferson-Morgan JR-SR HS; Waynesburg, PA; (3); 11/100; Art Clb; Intnl Clb; Office Aide; Spanish Clb; Varsity Clb; Band; Sec Soph Cls; Var Bsktbl; High Hon Roll; Tchr.

BEDNAR, CHRIS; Marian HS; Tamaqua, PA; (3); 20/117; Bsbl; Bsktbl; Ftbl; Trk; High Hon Roll; Hon Roll; Acctg Awd 87; Allentwn Diocese Schlrshp Awd 85; Penn ST.

BEDNAR, JENNIFER; Nazareth SR HS; Wind Gap, PA; (3); 22/265; Art Clb; Camera Clb; Hon Roll; Kiwanis Awd; Cert Merit Schltc Photo Comptn 87; Semi Finlst Govrns Schl Of Arts 86-87; Photo.

BEDNAR, SHERRI; G A R Memorial HS; Wilkes-Barre, PA; (3); 24/152; German Clb; Key Clb; Band; Chorus; Concert Band; Mrchg Band; Orch; Rep Stu Cncl; Stat Bsktbl; Capt Fld Hcky; Wrkng W/Kids.

BEDNAR, THOMAS M; Charleroi Area JR-SR HS; North Charleroi, PA; (4); 19/165; Church Yth Grp; Science Clb; Ski Clb; Varsity Clb; Trk; Hon Roll; NHS; Acad All Amer 86-87; PA ST U; Mech Engrng.

BEDNARCZYK, JOHN; Carbondale Area HS; Simpson, PA; (3); 43/119; Boy Scts; Cmnty Wkr; Red Cross Aide; Ski Clb; Spanish Clb; Stage Crew; JV VP Ftbl; Hon Roll; Medicine.

BEDNAROVSKY, CRAIG E; Mc Keesport SR HS; White Oak, PA; (4); VP Church Yth Grp; NFL; Pep Clb; Scholastic Bowl; Nwsp Stf; Var L Bsktbl; Trk; Trs NHS; Rotary Awd; Pres Schlrshp 87; U Schlrshp 87; Pres Acad Ftns Awd 86-87; American U; Ecmncs.

BEDNER, KIMBERLY; Mohessen JR SR HS; Monessen, PA; (3); 15/108; Drama Clb; French Clb; Sec FTA; Key Clb; Library Aide; Teachers Aide; Trs Temple Yth Grp; Nwsp Rptr; High Hon Roll; Hon Roll; WV Wesleyan Coll; Bus Mgmt.

BEDWELL, WHITNEY; Oxford Area HS; Oxford, PA; (3); Church Yth Grp; Cmnty Wkr; FTA; JA; Chorus; Color Guard; Yrbk Stf; Fld Hcky; Trk; Hon Roll; D Carnegie Effctv Spkng Crs Schlrshp 85; JR Cls Rep 86-87; Anthrplgy.

BEDWICK, JENNIFER; E L Meyers HS; Wilkes-Barre, PA; (4); #8 In Class; Church Yth Grp; German Clb; Key Clb; SADD; Chorus; Yrbk Stf; VP Stu Cncl; L Fld Hcky; High Hon Roll; Jr NHS; Gwynedd Mercy; Nrsng.

BEDWICK, JOSEPH; Elmer L Meyers HS; Wilkes Barre, PA; (4); 5/160; SADD; Chorus; School Musical; Yrbk Stf; Crs Cntry; Trk; Jr NHS; NHS; NEDT Awd; Pres Schlr.

BEE, DAVE; Bensalem HS; Bensalem, PA; (3); Boys Clb Am; Wt Lftg; High Hon Roll; Hon Roll; Biochem.

BEE, JENNIFER; Greensburg Salem SR HS; Greensburg, PA; (2); 56/294; Off French Clb; Pep Clb; Ski Clb; Concert Band; Mrchg Band; Yrbk Stf; Stu Cncl; Gym; Twrlr; Hon Roll; Art Dsgnr.

BEE, MATTHEW; Greenville HS; Greenville, PA; (4); Spanish Clb; Ftbl; Trk; Cmnty Wkr; NHS; Grove City Coll; Bio Chem.

BEEBE, LORI; John Bartram HS; Philadelphia, PA; (4); 1/600; Dance Clb; Yrbk Stf; Trs Stu Cncl; JV Badmtn; JV Sftbl; High Hon Roll; Hon Roll; NHS; Stu Of Wk 86; Bst Stu 87; Acad All Star 85-87; Elem Ed.

BEEBE, WILLIAM C; Riverview HS; Oakmont, PA; (2); Varsity Clb; Var L Bsbl; Var L Bsktbl; Var L Ftbl; Cit Awd; Hon Roll; Pre-Law.

BEECH, BETH; Hopewell Area HS; Aliquippa, PA; (3); 57/270; Band; Concert Band; Mrchg Band; Hon Roll; MDA Smmr Camp VA 86-87; Med.

BEECHAY, LYNN; Bishop Hafey HS; Hazleton, PA; (3); 20/113; Key Clb; Math Clb; Service Clb; Ski Clb; Spanish Clb; Rep Stu Cncl; Var L Cheerleading; Var L Trk; Hghst Avg-Rlgn 85-86; Stu Cncl Ldrshp & Svc Awd 85-86; Villanova Coll; Psychlgy.

BEECHER, TAMARA; Solanco HS; Drumore, PA; (3); Church Yth Grp; Pep Clb; Ski Clb; Varsity Clb; Church Choir; Sec Jr Cls; Sec Sr Cls; Rep Stu Cncl; Var Capt Cheerleading; JV Var Sftbl; Most Imprvd Stu 86; Trvl Consltnt.

BEECHER, TRACEY; Cedar Cliff HS; Camp Hill, PA; (2); 45/286; High Hon Roll; Hon Roll; Magna Cum Laude In Natl Latin Exam 85-86; Latin Honor Soc 86-87; Teaching.

BEEDLE, ARI; Meadville SR HS; Meadville, PA; (3); 92/329; Aud/Vis; Church Yth Grp; Letterman Clb; Varsity Clb; Ftbl; Wrstlng; Sports Med.

BEEGHLEY, JAMES; Connellsville Area HS; S Connellsville, PA; (2); Boy Scts; Computer Clb; Library Aide; Capt Stage Crew; Off Stu Cncl; Swmmng; Wrstlng; High Hon Roll; Hon Roll; U Of Pittsburgh; Cmptr Prgmr.

BEEGLE, JODIE; Northern Bedford County HS; New Enterprise, PA; (4); 17/92; Trs FBLA; Office Aide; Color Guard; Yrbk Stf; Mgr Bsktbl; Hon Roll; Century 21 Accntng Awd 86; Rgnl FBLA Entreprnrshp II 1st Pl 87; Altoona Schl Commerce; Bus Mgmt.

BEELER, SUSAN; Bishop Gail Foyle HS; Altoona, PA; (3); SADD; U S Air Frc; Accntng.

BEENER, CHRISTY; North Star HS; Boswell, PA; (4); 2/130; Church Yth Grp; FCA; Capt Flag Corp; Yrbk Stf; Stu Cncl; Cit Awd; Hon Roll; Lion Awd; NHS; Englsh Awd 84; US Mth Awd 83; Ms Congeniality Mpl Prncss Cntst 86; Anderson-Braoddus Coll; Rad.

BEER, CHRISTINA; Greensbuyrg Central Catholic HS; Greensburg, PA; (4); Pep Clb; Ski Clb; Yrbk Stf; Lit Mag; Powder Puff Ftbl; Im Vllybl; Hon Roll; West VA U; Pre-Jrnlsm.

BEER, GREGORY; Freeport Area HS; Freeport, PA; (3); Psych.

BEERS, DAWN; Clarion Area HS; Clarion, PA; (4); Civic Clb; Cmnty Wkr; FBLA; FHA; SADD; Chorus; Yrbk Stf; Hon Roll; JC Awd; NHS; Clarion U PA; Ed.

BEERS, JEANETTE; Freedom HS; Bethlehem, PA; (4); 9/446; Spanish Clb; Chorus; High Hon Roll; NHS; Ntl Merit Schol; Natl Merit Scholar 87; Merit Scholar Cedar Crest Coll 87; Cedar Crest Coll; Genetic Engr.

BEERS, MICHELLE; Pleasant Valley HS; Brodheadsville, PA; (2); 24/243; Cmnty Wkr; Drama Clb; Math Clb; Teachers Aide; School Play; Lit Mag; Stat Trk; High Hon Roll; Hon Roll; Jr NHS; Bus Law.

BEERS, TARA; Pennsbury HS; Yardley, PA; (3); 8/770; Band; Concert Band; Jazz Band; Mrchg Band; Im Sftbl; Gov Hon Prg Awd; High Hon Roll; Hon Roll; NHS; Prfct Atten Awd; Bucks Cnty Sci Smnr 87; CTY-JOHNS Hopkins Pgm 84; PA Free Entrprs Wk 87; Sci.

BEERS, TREVOR; Du Bois Area HS; Reynoldsvl, PA; (2); Aud/Vis; Bsktbl; Ftbl; Trk; Wt Lftg; Wrstlng; Stu Of Week 85-86; Nice Kid Awd 86-87; Bio.

BEERY, RHONDA; Bellwood-Antis HS; Tyrone, PA; (2); Church Yth Grp; Chorus; Church Choir; Trk; Wt Lftg; Hon Roll; Prfct Atten Awd; Stdnt Wk, Cert Awd Spnsh I, Erth Sci, Alg I 86.

BEES, JEFFREY; Neshannock HS; New Castle, PA; (3); 13/102; Pres Sec Church Yth Grp; Library Aide; Scholastic Bowl; Nwsp Stf; JV Crs Cntry; Var Trk; Hon Roll; NHS; NEDT Awd; Prfct Atten Awd; Svc Awd 86-87; Presdntl Schlr 85-86; Hstry.

BEESON, STEPHANIE; Chapel Christian Schl; Vanderbilt, PA; (3); Church Yth Grp; Hosp Aide; Chorus; Stage Crew; Yrbk Stf; Bowling; Cheerleading; Hon Roll; Bio.

BEGGS, TIMOTHY R; Butler Area SR HS; Butler, PA; (3); Exploring; French Clb; Math Tm; SADD; Yrbk Stf; Var Crs Cntry; JV Socr; NHS; Penn ST U; Engrng.

BEGLEY, CAROL; St Huberts Catholic HS; Philadelphia, PA; (3); Church Yth Grp; Cmnty Wkr; Exploring; Hon Roll.

BEGLIN, ROBERT; Jefferson Morgan JR-SR HS; Clarksville, PA; (3); 22/70; Leo Clb; Spanish Clb; Varsity Clb; Yrbk Stf; Rep Frsh Cls; Pres Soph Cls; Pres Jr Cls; Rep Sr Cls; Var Bsbl; Var Ftbl; Wildlife Tech.

BEHANNA, STACI; Trinity HS; Washington, PA; (4); French Clb; Hosp Aide; Key Clb; Pep Clb; Ski Clb; Drill Tm; Hon Roll; Hmcmg Qn 86; May Day Ct 87; WV U; Nrsng.

BEHANNA, VICKI; Ringgold HS; Monohahela, PA; (4); 7/355; Ski Clb; Chorus; School Play; Off Frsh Cls; Var Cheerleading; Pom Pon; L Socr; Hon Roll; NHS; U Pittsburgh; Indstrl Engrg.

BEHE, JANEL; Central Cambria HS; Edensburg, PA; (3); 35/210; Trs Art Clb; Church Yth Grp; Band; Concert Band; Jazz Band; Mrchg Band; Pep Band; L Var Swmmng; Hon Roll; Prfct Atten Awd; Medicine.

BEHE, MICHAEL; Cambria Heights HS; Carrolltown, PA; (3); 42/182; Stage Crew; L Var Ftbl; L Var Swmmng; Var Trk; IN U Of PA; Tchng.

BEHLER, LORI; Lehighton Area HS; Lehighton, PA; (3); 37/250; Church Yth Grp; FBLA; SADD; Band; Color Guard; Concert Band; Drill Tm; Drm Mjr(t); Hon Roll; Prfct Atten Awd; X-Ray Tech.

BEHLER, ROBERT; Parkland SR HS; Schnecksville, PA; (2); JV Var Ftbl; Im Wt Lftg; Hon Roll; Med.

BEHLING, KAREN; Ringgold HS; Monongahela, PA; (4); 49/337; Drama Clb; FNA; Office Aide; SADD; Varsity Clb; School Musical; Stage Crew; Bsktbl; Capt Socr; Hon Roll; Interact Clb-Rotary Orgnztn Pres 86-7; Penn ST; Nrsng.

BEHR, BRIDGET; Mercyhurst Prep; Erie, PA; (3); 79/179; French Clb; Yrbk Phtg; Yrbk Stf; JV L Socr; JV L Stfbl; Hon Roll; Gannon U; Bus.

BEHRENS, DAYNA; Bishop Guilfoyle HS; Altoona, PA; (3); Church Yth Grp; GAA; Ski Clb; Band; Rep Stu Cncl; JV Cheerleading; Var Pom Pon; Bus.

BEHRLE, JOSEPH; Aliquippa JR-SR HS; Aliquippa, PA; (4); Pres Chess Clb; CAP; Computer Clb; French Clb; Teachers Aide; Yrbk Stf; JV Ftbl; Var Mgr(s); Hon Roll; Slippery Rock U; Law.

BEHUN, BILL; Council Rock HS; Washington Crssng, PA; (3); 43/908; Drama Clb; Concert Band; School Musical; School Play; Stage Crew; VP Frsh Cls; Pres Soph Cls; NHS; Cert Ltr Theatre 87; Theatre Ed.

BEICHNER, HEIDI; Keystone HS; Shippenville, PA; (2); Cmnty Wkr; 4-H; French Clb; SADD; Varsity Clb; L Trk; French Hon Soc; 4-H Awd; High Hon Roll; Prfct Atten Awd; Pharmacist.

BEIDELMAN, KAREN; Freedom HS; Bethlehem, PA; (4); 19/433; Sec Church Yth Grp; VP French Clb; Hosp Aide; Science Clb; Chorus; Church Choir; Hon Roll; NHS; Pres Schlr; Beaver Coll; Phys Thrpy.

BEIDLER, JOHN; Annville HS; Annville, PA; (4); Boy Scts; Acpl Chr; Chorus; School Musical; School Play; Ftbl; NHS; US Music Ambssdr 86; Air Force; Elect.

BEIER, TAMMY ANN; Shaier Area HS; Pittsburgh, PA; (4); 186/510; Church Yth Grp; Office Aide; Ski Clb; SADD; Variety Show; Nwsp Rptr; Bsktbl; Coach Actv; Var Vllybl; Hon Roll; Cortez Peters Typng Awd 87; All Str Tm Awd, Bst Off Plyr Vlybl 86-87; Robert Morris Coll; Bus.

BEIERLE, KARLA; Northeastern HS; York, PA; (2); Camera Clb; Church Yth Grp; JA; Chorus; Church Choir; Trk; Hon Roll; Shippensburg Sprg Lang Cntst 2nd Pl Spnsh Cmptn 87; Music Cmpstn.

BEIGH, JASON; Mechanicsburg Area SR HS; Mechanicsburg, PA; (3); 126/338; Church Yth Grp; Dance Clb; ROTC; Ski Clb; Band; Trk; Vllybl; Hon Roll; NHS; Natl Hnr Roll Yearbook 87; BFA Coll; Advertising.

BEIGHEY, ERIC L; New Brighton Area HS; New Brighton, PA; (4); 41/141; Computer Clb; DECA; High Hon Roll; Hon Roll; Lion Awd; De Vry Inst Of Tech; Elec Engr.

BEIGI, RICHARD; Fox Chapel SR HS; Pittsburgh, PA; (3); 50/350; Ski Clb; Var L Bsbl; Var L Ftbl; JV Trk; Wrstlng; High Hon Roll; NHS.

BEIL, CYNTHIA M; Saucon Valley SR HS; Hellertown, PA; (3); 1/156; Trs Exploring; Hosp Aide; Model UN; Red Cross Aide; Spanish Clb; Band; L Swmmng; High Hon Roll; Jr NHS; NHS.

BEILER, JOEL; Pequea Valley HS; New Holland, PA; (3); 23/144; Church Yth Grp; Acpl Chr; Chorus; Church Choir; Stage Crew; Var JV Bsktbl; Var L Tennis; Hon Roll; NHS; Estrn Nazarene Coll; Engrng.

BEILER, KEITH; Faith Mennonite HS; Paradise, PA; (4); 4/26; Pres Church Yth Grp; Math Tm; Pres Acpl Chr; Pres Frsh Cls; VP Stu Cncl; High Hon Roll; Frmg.

BEILER, MELISSA; Garden Spot HS; New Holland, PA; (2); Church Yth Grp; Chorus; Church Choir; School Musical; Stage Crew; High Hon Roll; Hon Roll; Bus.

BEILER, ROSITA; Faith Mennonite HS; Paradise, PA; (4); 5/27; Church Yth Grp; Library Aide; Teachers Aide; Acpl Chr; High Hon Roll; Hon Roll.

BEILSTEIN, DARREN; Hampton HS; Allison Park, PA; (3); JV Bsbl; Var Capt Swmmng; High Hon Roll; Hon Roll; NHS; Pre Med.

BEIMEL, RICK; St Marys Area HS; Kersey, PA; (4); Church Yth Grp; JA; L Golf; L Tennis; Trk; High Hon Roll; NHS; Penn ST U; Comp Engr.

BEISLER, JOHN; Mc Keesport Area HS; Mc Keesport, PA; (2); Bsktbl; JV L Bsktbl; Hon Roll; Prfct Atten Awd.

BEISLLINE, JENIFER; Daniel Boone HS; Birdsboro, PA; (3); 10/170; Trs Church Yth Grp; Church Choir; Var Sftbl; NHS; Comp Sci.

BEITZEL, CHRIS; Valley Forge Military Acad; Accident, MD; (3); Church Yth Grp; Trs 4-H; ROTC; Ski Clb; U MD; Econ.

BELAK, BRETT; Norwin HS; N Huntingdon, PA; (4); Church Yth Grp; Letterman Clb; Political Wkr; Ski Clb; SADD; Rep Stu Cncl; Swmmng; Kent ST U; Aero Flght Tech.

BELANSKY, PAMELA; North Hills HS; Pittsburgh, PA; (4); 3/467; Drama Clb; Exploring; JA; Ski Clb; L Tennis; High Hon Roll; NHS.

BELARDI, CHRISTINE; Somerset Area SR HS; Somerset, PA; (3); Computer Clb; FHA; Ski Clb; Varsity Clb; Nwsp Rptr; Nwsp Stf; Yrbk Stf; JV Cheerleading; Mat Maids; Hon Roll; Prm Cmmtee 86-87; Soph SR Cmmtee 85-86; Bus Admin.

BELARDINELLI, MARTINA; G A R Memorial HS; Wilkes-Bare, PA; (3); 27/154; Key Clb; Library Aide; Ski Clb; Chorus; Capt L Fld Hcky; Hon Roll; Jr NHS; NHS.

BELASKI, BOB; Riverside HS; Taylor, PA; (3); Art Clb; Boy Scts; JA; School Musical; Stage Crew; Variety Show; JV Var Ftbl; Wt Lftg; Hon Roll; Lbrl Arts.

BELCHER, JASON ALLAN; Thomas Jefferson HS; Pittsburgh, PA; (3); 4/269; AFS; Church Yth Grp; CAP; French Clb; Political Wkr; Crs Cntry; Trk; High Hon Roll; NHS; Rotary Awd; PA Mock Trial Comp 87; People People Stu Ambssdr 87; Air Force Acad; Pilot.

BELCIK, MARGARET; Farrell SR HS; Farrell, PA; (2); 7/90; Science Clb; Spanish Clb; Nwsp Rptr; Nwsp Sprt Ed; Nwsp Stf; Hon Roll; Hnr Rll 86-87; Hnr Soc 86-87; Duquesne U; Bio.

BELCULFINE, MARK; Hopewell HS; Aliquippa, PA; (3); 52/255; Church Yth Grp; Latin Clb; Bsbl; Bsktbl; High Hon Roll; US Naval Acad; Aerontcl Engrng.

BELDEN, HENRY S; Kiski HS; N Canton, OH; (4); Art Clb; Boy Scts; Camera Clb; French Clb; Variety Show; Nwsp Phtg; Nwsp Stf; Yrbk Phtg; Yrbk Stf; Im Ftbl; Rochester Inst Tech Schlrshp 87; Bortz Imprvmnt Awd 86; Rochester Inst Of Tech; Photo.

BELDOTT, ALEX; Vally Forge Milatary Acad; Ossining, NY; (3); Boy Scts; ROTC; Spanish Clb; Var Ftbl; Lcrss; Wt Lftg; Wrstlng; Eagle Sct; Naval Aviatn.

BELFI, ERIC; St John Neumann HS; Philadelphia, PA; (3); 51/360; High Hon Roll; Law Enfrcmnt.

BELFIELD, JOSEPH; Union HS; Sligo, PA; (3); Band; Chorus; Concert Band; Pep Band; School Musical; Art.

BELFIORE, GEORGE; St John Neumann HS; Philadelphia, PA; (3); 14/335; Math Tm; High Hon Roll; NHS; Drexel U; Comp Prgmr.

BELFORD, DAVE; Penns Manor JR SR HS; Clymer, PA; (3); Art Clb; Camera Clb; Pres 4-H; Chorus; 4-H Awd; Hon Roll; Outstndng SR Horse Awd 87; 1st Pl Equine Symposm Art Shw 86; Capt PA ST Horse Bowl Team 87; Vet Med.

BELFORD, DAVID; Phil-Mont Christian Acad; Philadelphia, PA; (4); Church Yth Grp; VP Sr Cls; Rep Stu Cncl; Var Capt Crs Cntry; Var Capt Trk; High Hon Roll; Hon Roll; Chorus; Stage Crew; Stat Bsktbl; Positive Christian Chrctr & Bhvr Awd Recognition 85-87; Stu Cncl Awd & Coaches Cup Awd At Grad 86-87; Temple U; Bus.

BELFORD, LYNETTE; Lock Haven HS; Lock Haven, PA; (3); Art Clb; Church Yth Grp; Cmnty Wkr; Drama Clb; Hosp Aide; Spanish Clb; SADD; School Play; Variety Show; Prfct Atten Awd; Thespn Hnrs; Spch Pathlgy.

BELIN, MARGARET; Clearfield Area HS; Clearfield, PA; (4); Rep Church Yth Grp; Ed Yrbk Stf; Sec Sr Cls; Stu Cncl; Var L Bsktbl; Var L Sftbl; L Trk; High Hon Roll; Hon Roll; NHS; Outstndg Stu Geometry & Wrld Cltrs 85,Alg II 84; St Marys Coll; Pre-Law.

BELITSKUS, DEAN; Valley HS; New Kensington, PA; (2); 10/175; Science Clb; Mrchg Band; Bsktbl; Ftbl; Wt Lftg; High Hon Roll; Amer Lgn Awd 85; Engrng.

BELL, APRIL; Juaniata HS; Mifflintown, PA; (3); Computer Clb; Drama Clb; FHA; SADD; Concert Band; Flag Corp; Mrchg Band; Yrbk Stf; Var Cheerleading; Hon Roll.

BELL, ASHLEY; Hempfield HS; Lancaster, PA; (4); Church Yth Grp; Dance Clb; Varsity Clb; Chorus; Church Choir; Stu Cncl; JV L Cheerleading; Var L Tennis; Spnsh Art Awd 84-85; U Of DE; Lbrl Arts.

BELL, BRIAN; Cumberland Valley HS; Boiling Spgs, PA; (4); 6/522; Drama Clb; Key Clb; Model UN; NFL; Quiz Bowl; Ski Clb; Spanish Clb; School Play; VP Stu Cncl; Kiwanis Awd; Stu Cncl Hnr Awd 87; Bst Prsnlty 87; Hnr Engl Awd 87; U Of Penn.

BELL, DENISE; Oley Valley HS; Oley, PA; (3); 1/142; Quiz Bowl; Chorus; School Musical; Nwsp Stf; Yrbk Ed-Chief; Yrbk Stf; High Hon Roll; NHS; JA; Nwsp Rptr; County Chorus; Maxima Cum Laude Natl Latin Exam; Elizabethtown Coll.

BELL, DIANE; Blairsville SR HS; Blairsville, PA; (4); Chess Clb; 4-H; Band; Concert Band; Mrchg Band; Sftbl; Wt Lftg; 4-H Awd; High Hon Roll.

BELL, HEATHER; Highlands SR HS; Tarentum, PA; (3); Office Aide; Chorus; Hon Roll; Jr NHS; Prfct Atten Awd; Schlstc Achvt Awd Brown Cert 85-87; Schlstc Achvt Awd Gold Cert 85-86; Crmnl Just.

BELL, J DAVID; Frankford HS; Philadelphia, PA; (3); Hosp Aide; ROTC; Color Guard; Off Drill Tm; DAR Awd; High Hon Roll; NHS; Prfct Atten Awd; SAR Awd; Voice Dem Awd; Battalion Cmmndr JROTC 86-87; Drill Exclnc Awd 85-87; PATHS Stu Writer 2nd Pl 87; Econ.

BELL, JAMES; Shenandoah Valley JR/Sr HS; Shenandoah, PA; (4); 21/107; Aud/Vis; Letterman Clb; Pep Clb; Ski Clb; Band; Nwsp Rptr; Nwsp Stf; Yrbk Rptr; Yrbk Sprt Ed; Yrbk Stf; Wilkes Coll; Cmmnctns.

BELL, JENNIFER; Elk Lake HS; Springville, PA; (1); French Clb; Red Cross Aide; SADD; Band; Mrchg Band; Stat Socr; Stat Wrstlng; Church Yth Grp; Ski Clb; Mgr(s).

BELL, JOHN; Elizabeth Forword HS; Elizabeth, PA; (3); Exploring; Blck Blt Tang Soo Do 79; Nuclr Engrng.

BELL, JOSHUA; Daniel Boone HS; Douglassville, PA; (3); School Play; Yrbk Stf; Lit Mag; Pres Jr Cls; Ftbl; Wrstlng; Ntl Merit Ltr; Opt Clb Awd.

BELL, JULIA; West Branch HS; Grassflat, PA; (2); Church Yth Grp; Drama Clb; Hosp Aide; Spanish Clb; SADD; Varsity Clb; Chorus; Church Choir; School Play; Stage Crew; Mt Alawshes; RN.

BELL, KIMBERLY; Upper Moreland SR HS; Willow Grove, PA; (3); 105/275; Nwsp Ed-Chief; Hon Roll; Jr NHS.

BELL, KRISTEN; Abington Heights HS; Clarks Summit, PA; (3); 18/292; Ski Clb; Orch; Rep Stu Cncl; Trk; Hon Roll; NHS; Marywood Orch 86-87; Rotary Exch Stu Schlrshp Music Camp.

BELL, LISA; Bishop Guilfoyle HS; Altoona, PA; (3); 17/145; Hosp Aide; Science Clb; Color Guard; High Hon Roll; Hon Roll.

BELL, LISA; Windber Area HS; Windber, PA; (3); Church Yth Grp; Sec French Clb; Chorus; Church Choir; Color Guard; Nwsp Stf; Hon Roll; NHS; Pres Acdmc Ftns Awd 84-85; Stu Of Mnth; Advrtsng.

BELL, MARK; Portersville Christian HS; Butler, PA; (4); 5/15; Church Yth Grp; Drama Clb; Chorus; Church Choir; Nwsp Phtg; Nwsp Stf; Yrbk Ed-Chief; Yrbk Phtg; Yrbk Stf; High Hon Roll; 6th Pl Yrbk Comptn 86; Grove City Coll; Engl Ed.

BELL, MICHAEL L; Conestoga Valley HS; Brownstown, PA; (4); 12/230; Nwsp Rptr; Lit Mag; Im Ice Hcky; Var Socr; Im Wt Lftg; High Hon Roll; Hon Roll; Pres Schlr; PA ST U; English.

BELL, MICHELE; Blue Mountain HS; Pottsville, PA; (3); SADD; Chorus; Mrchg Band; School Musical; School Play; Swing Chorus; Nwsp Rptr; Vllybl; High Hon Roll; Hon Roll; Cnty Chorus 86 & 87; Dist Chorus 87; Worthy Advisr Intl Order Rainbow Girls 87; CPA.

BELL, PAUL; Fort Cherry HS; Mc Donald, PA; (3); French Clb; Science Clb; Ski Clb; Chorus; Rep Stu Cncl; Audio Engrng.

BELL, REBECCA; St Hubert HS; Philadelphia, PA; (3); 113/368; Computer Clb; Hosp Aide; Office Aide; Spanish Clb; Teachers Aide; Rep Frsh Cls; Rep Soph Cls; Hon Roll; Temple; Scl Wrkr.

BELL, ROBIN; Carlisle SR HS; Carlisle, PA; (3); 139/454; Church Yth Grp; Church Choir; Variety Show; Hon Roll; Prfct Atten Awd; Dntl Hygiene.

BELL, SANDRA; Lenape Vocational-Technical HS; Chicora, PA; (4); Girl Scts; VICA; Band; Chorus; Concert Band; Mrchg Band; Pep Band; Yrbk Stf; Vllybl; High Hon Roll; Morgan Schlrshp Awd 87; U Of Pittsburg; Phrmcy.

BELL, THOMAS J; Mercersburg Acad; Boyce, VA; (4); 7/129; Art Clb; Computer Clb; PAVAS; Lit Mag; Capt Lcrss; Hon Roll; 1st Tm Regnl All Star Soccr 85, 2nd Tm 86; Natl Schltc Art Awd 85; Hartwick Coll; Bus.

BELL, TRACEY; Penn Hills SR HS; Pittsburgh, PA; (4); Hon Roll; Partl Schlrshp Monroevl Schl Bus 87; Exec Secy.

BELL, VICTORIA; Abraham Lincoln HS; Philadelphia, PA; (3); 34/550; Dance Clb; Var Badmtn; Hon Roll; Accntng.

BELLAS, MELISSA; Weatherly Area HS; Weatherly, PA; (4); 26/65; Am Leg Aux Girls St; Rptr 4-H; Trs FBLA; FHA; Office Aide; School Play; Nwsp Rptr; Sec Frsh Cls; Off Jr Cls; Off Sr Cls; Air Force; X-Ray Tech.

BELLAS, MIKE; Sharpsville Area SR HS; Greenville, PA; (3); NHS.

BELLES, THOMAS; James M Coughlin HS; Wilkes Barre, PA; (3); VP Sr Cls; Var Ftbl; Var L Wrstlng.

BELLETERI, CHRISTOPHER; Upper Merion Area HS; King Of Prussia, PA; (3); Trs Drama Clb; Math Tm; Chorus; School Musical; School Play; Mgr Stage Crew; Swing Chorus; Rep Stu Cncl; Trk; Vllybl; Comp Sci.

BELLI, RICHARD; Aliquippa HS; Aliquippa, PA; (4); 12/135; Boy Scts; Mrchg Band; High Hon Roll; Hon Roll; Lion Awd; NCTE Awd; NHS; Prfct Atten Awd; Acad Schlrshp 87; Eagle Scout Awd 86; Gannon U; Pre-Med.

BELLIS, JOSEPH; Butler Area SR HS; Butler, PA; (3); Im Ftbl; Hon Roll; Archtrl Engrng.

BELLOMO, ALAN J; Central Cambria HS; Ebensburg, PA; (2); Aud/Vis; FBLA; JA; Stage Crew; JV Ftbl; JV Wt Lftg; Hon Roll; 4-H; 4-H Yth Ldr 87; Ebensburg Yth Leag Coach 86; Vlntr Ebensburg Ctr 86-87; Poli Sci.

BELLOTTI, CURT; Kittanning SR HS; Worthington, PA; (2); High Hon Roll; Electrncs.

BELLSTEIN, DARREN; Hampton HS; Allison Park, PA; (3); Boy Scts; Red Cross Aide; JV Church Yth Grp; Capt L Swmmng; High Hon Roll; Hon Roll; NHS; Lehigh; Medicine.

BELLUCH, KENNETH S; Muhlenberg HS; Reading, PA; (3); #1 In Class; Exploring; Bsbl; Bsktbl; Ftbl; Tennis; Hon Roll; Mst Deservng Acad Stu 86-87; Outstndng Sci Awd 86-87; Elec Engrng.

BELONZI, BRIAN; Seneca Valley HS; Mars, PA; (3); Church Yth Grp; Cmnty Wkr; Ski Clb; Golf; Hon Roll; Music.

BELOTTI, ROB; Deleware Valley HS; Dingmans Ferry, PA; (3); German Clb; Ski Clb; Spanish Clb; Im Wt Lftg; Hon Roll; UCLA; Bus.

BELSER, JENNIFER; Bradford Area HS; Bradford, PA; (3); 57/302; Church Yth Grp; Pep Clb; Chorus; VP Stu Cncl; Cheerleading; Trk; Vllybl; Hon Roll; Jr NHS; Prfct Atten Awd; Sftbl Tm 1st Div & Lg 86; Bowling Rep Coca-Cola Jr 86-87; Lg Byllye Lanes.

BELSEY, MICHELE; Bishop Guilfoyle HS; Altoona, PA; (4); 9/123; Hosp Aide; Service Clb; Ski Clb; Speech Tm; Chorus; Yrbk Stf; Cheerleading; Tennis; High Hon Roll; Hon Roll; High Hnrs 83-86; Hnr Awds 83-86; Duquesne U; Phrmcy.

BELZ, AMY; Abraham Lincoln HS; Philadelphia, PA; (3); 24/530; Red Cross Aide; SADD; Varsity Clb; Nwsp Ed-Chief; Var Diving; JV Var Fld Hcky; Var Swmmng; Physcl Thrpy.

BELZ, COLLEEN; Gwynedd-Mercy Acad; Conshohocken, PA; (2); Hosp Aide; Service Clb; Chorus; School Musical; Variety Show; Im Bsktbl; JV Lcrss; Var Tennis.

BEMENT, TIMOTHY; Greater Latrobe SR HS; Latrobe, PA; (4); 14/405; Church Yth Grp; VP JA; Band; Pres Chorus; Jazz Band; Madrigals; Mrchg Band; School Musical; Variety Show; High Hon Roll; Frederick Chopin Awd 87; U Of Cincinnati; Intr Dsgn.

BEMISDERFER, DWIGHT; Greencastle Antrim HS; Greencastle, PA; (3); Drama Clb; Prfct Atten Awd; Voice Dem Awd; Commnctns.

BENAMATI, MICHELLE; Marion Center HS; Indiana, PA; (3); Band; Chorus; Orch; Intnl Clb; Var Cheerleading; Trk; High Hon Roll; NHS; Psychlgy.

BENAMATI JR, ROBERT; Bishop Carroll HS; Spangler, PA; (4); 11/112; Band; Concert Band; Pep Band; Stage Crew; Yrbk Sprt Ed; Bsbl; Im Bsktbl; Bowling; Crs Cntry; Penn St; Aerospace Engnrng.

BENARD, TRACIE; Canon-Mc Millan HS; Canonsburg, PA; (3); Ski Clb; Acpl Chr; VP Sec Chorus; Twrlr; Hon Roll; Wrtng.

BENCAK, RICHELLE; Lancaster Catholic HS; Conestoga, PA; (1); Church Yth Grp; Dance Clb; Thesps; Band; Concert Band; Mrchg Band; Pep Band; School Musical; Nwsp Stf; Hon Roll; Prfrmng Arts.

BENCHEK, TOM; Corry Area HS; Corry, PA; (2); Dance Clb; VP 4-H; FFA; Radio Clb; Ski Clb; SADD; 4-H Awd; Hon Roll; PA ST U; Elec Engr.

BENCIVENGO, DAVID; Kennedy Christian HS; Brookfield, OH; (3); 23/97; Exploring; Concert Band; Jazz Band; Mrchg Band; Trs Jr Cls; Hon Roll; Latin Clb; Science Clb; Band; PA JR Acad Sci 86; Natl Hnr Rll 87; Ed.

BENDER, CHERYL A; Nativity Blessed Virgin Mary HS; Pottsville, PA; (1); 4/94; Speech Tm; Nwsp Stf; Vllybl; High Hon Roll; Spanish NHS; Diocese Partial 1 Yr HS Schlrshp 86.

BENDER, CHRISTINE M; Nativity Blessed Virgin Mary HS; Pottsville, PA; (3); 8/86; Drill Tm; Nwsp Stf; Vllybl; Hon Roll; NHS.

BENDER, COREY; Pine Grove Area HS; Pine Grove, PA; (3); Boy Scts; Quiz Bowl; Math Awds Alg II, Advncd Math 86-87; Sci Awd-Bio I 85-86; Math.

BENDER, DENISE; Williams Valley JR SR HS; Tower City, PA; (3); Church Yth Grp; Chorus; Stage Crew; Sec Stu Cncl; Var Sftbl; Golden Bat Awd In Sftbl 86-87; Hotel Mgmt.

BENDER, DOUGLAS RAY; Chambersburg Area SR HS; Pleasant Hall, PA; (3); Camera Clb; Church Yth Grp; Computer Clb; SADD; Hon Roll; Embry-Riddle; Cmmrcl Pilot.

BENDER, ELIZABETH; Mt Alvernia HS; Pittsburgh, PA; (3); Church Yth Grp; Cmnty Wkr; Chorus; High Hon Roll; Hon Roll; NHS; Chem Awd 85-86; Spnsh Awd 86-87.

BENDER, GREG; Riverside HS; Beaver Falls, PA; (4); 42/180; Pres DECA; DECA Dist Food Mrktng 1st Pl 87; DECA 2nd Pl ST Comp 87; DECA Cert Excell Food Mrktng Natl Conf 87; Penn ST U; Bus Admin.

BENDER, JAMES; Cedar Crest HS; Lebanon, PA; (1); Sec Pres Boy Scts; German Clb; Score Keeper; Vllybl; PA ST U; Navy.

BENDER, JEANETTE; Ephrata SR HS; Ephrata, PA; (4); 3/253; Sec Church Yth Grp; Intnl Clb; Library Aide; Chorus; Nwsp Ed-Chief; Hon Roll; NHS; PHEAA Cert Of Merit 86; Jr League Outstndng Yth Volunteer & Menno Simmons Schlrshp 87; Easter Mennonite Coll; Arts.

BENDER, JENNIFER; Saltsburg JR SR HS; Saltsburg, PA; (1); 1/74; Church Yth Grp; Radio Clb; Concert Band; Mrchg Band; Stat Vllybl; High Hon Roll; Chld Psych.

BENDER, LORETTA; Salisbury-Elk Lick HS; Meyersdale, PA; (4); 2/21; Church Yth Grp; FHA; Nwsp Ed-Chief; Nwsp Rptr; Nwsp Stf; High Hon Roll; Hon Roll; Prfct Atten Awd; Acad All-Amer Awd 85; US Achvt Acad Awd 87; Wrk With Cldrn.

BENDER, LYNETTE; Salisbury-Elk Lick HS; Meyersdale, PA; (2); 4/40; FHA; Hon Roll; Prfct Atten Awd; Anl Math Exam Awd 87.

BENDER, LYNNETTE; New Covenant Acad; Morris Run, PA; (3); Church Yth Grp; Debate Tm; Drama Clb; Sec Pres 4-H; Ski Clb; Band; Chorus; School Play; Cheerleading; Swmmng; Nrsng.

BENDER, MELISSA; Blairsville SR HS; Blairsville, PA; (2); 25/118; Trs Church Yth Grp; Chorus; School Musical; VP Soph Cls; Stu Cncl; JV L Cheerleading; High Hon Roll; U Pittsburgh; Phys Thrpy.

BENDER, MICHELLE; Benton Area HS; Stillwater, PA; (3); Art Clb; Drama Clb; Girl Scts; Chorus; Nwsp Rptr; Stu Cncl; Var Cheerleading; Twrlr; High Hon Roll; NHS; Century 21 Typing Awd 86.

BENDER, MICHELLE; Penn Cambria HS; Loretto, PA; (3); Spanish Clb; SADD; Twrlr; Hon Roll; Penn ST U; Social Wrk.

BENDER, PAUL; Seton-La Salle HS; Pittsburgh, PA; (3); 115/245; Spanish Clb; Jazz Band; Orch; Bsbl; Capt Ftbl; Wt Lftg; Hon Roll; Acdmc All Amer 87; Pre Med.

BENDER, RANDY; Chichester HS; Marcus Hook, PA; (3); Art Clb; Lit Mag; Crs Cntry; Ftbl; Wrstlng; Prfct Atten Awd; Gld Key Phila Coll Of Arts Awd 87; Drexel U; Arch.

BENDER, STACIE; Marion Center HS; Marion Center, PA; (3); 8/153; Chess Clb; Latin Clb; Library Aide; SADD; Varsity Clb; Band; Concert Band; Mrchg Band; Orch; Crs Cntry; Hyscl Thrpst.

BENDER, TAMMY; Williamsport Area HS; Williamsport, PA; (4); 99/490; Hst FBLA; Hst VP FHA; Girl Scts; Hosp Aide; Hon Roll; Bus Dept Awd 86-87; Williamsport Area CC; Exec.

BENDER, TRICIA L; Northern Lebanon HS; Jonestown, PA; (1); Trs Church Yth Grp; Chorus; Color Guard; Flag Corp; Rep Frsh Cls; Rep Stu Cncl; Stat Bsbl; Var Cheerleading; Pom Pon; Prfct Atten Awd; Hrsbrg Area CC; Tourism.

BENEDETTO, CHRISTOPHER; Friends Select Schl; Philadelphia, PA; (4); Drama Clb; School Musical; School Play; Yrbk Stf; Hon Roll; Jnthn Levine Drama Awd 87; Ithaca Coll.

BENEDICK, RODNEY N; James Buchanan HS; Fort Loudon, PA; (4); 2/211; Band; Jazz Band; Stu Cncl; Var L Bsbl; Var L Bsktbl; Var L Socr; Elks Awd; High Hon Roll; NHS; Pres Schlr; Frnklin & Mrshl Coll; Pre-Med.

BENEDICT, JULIE; Canon Mc Millan HS; Cecil, PA; (3); French Clb; Varsity Clb; School Musical; Rep Stu Cncl; Var Capt Cheerleading; High Hon Roll; NHS.

BENEDICT, SHELLEY; Cambridge Springs HS; Cambridge Springs, PA; (3); Drama Clb; Key Clb; Pep Clb; SADD; Nwsp Rptr; Rep Stu Cncl; Capt Var Cheerleading; Var Twrlr; Var Stat Vllybl; Art Clb; Rep For Yth Town Cncl 85-86; Engl.

BENEDIX, BROOKE; Downingtown Joint SR HS; Exton, PA; (4); 48/551; GAA; Spanish Clb; Teachers Aide; VP Stu Cncl; Var Bsktbl; Var Fld Hcky; High Hon Roll; NHS; Outstndng Amer Stu Awd 87; Daisy Chain 86; Cmnctns.

BENEK, COLEEN; Blue Mountain HS; New Ringgold, PA; (2); 30/20 Drama Clb; Girl Scts; PAVAS; SADD; Chorus; School Musical; Nwsp St Trk; Hon Roll.

BENES, THOMAS B; Plum SR HS; Pittsburgh, PA; (3); Exploring; J Trk; Vllybl; Hon Roll; NHS; Sales Clb Awd 86; Clsrm Awds 86-87; PA S U; Engr.

BENFER, DREW; Marple-Newton SR HS; Broomall, PA; (2); 3/324; Pre Frsh Cls; Pres Soph Cls; Pres Jr Cls; Var Lcrss; Var Socr; Var Swmmn High Hon Roll; Ntl Hstry Day Dist, ST, Ntn 1st; Scotts Hi-Q Team; Engr

BENFIELD JR, DANIEL R; Quakertown Community HS Spinnerstown, PA; (2); 4/359; Church Yth Grp; Drama Clb; Chorus; Schoo Musical; School Play; Rep Stu Cncl; High Hon Roll; Hon Roll; Jr NHS Aud/Vis; Pres Acdmc Fit Awd 85-86; Stu Of Mnth Awd 85-86.

BENFORD, ERIC; Rockwood Area HS; Rockwood, PA; (3); Am Leg Boy St; 4-H; Yrbk Phtg; Yrbk Stf; Var Bsbl; Var Bsktbl; 4-H Awd.

BENFORD, SHELDON; Rockwood Area HS; Rockwood, PA; (4); 36/9 Boy Scts; FFA; Band; Concert Band; Drm Mjr(t); Mrchg Band; Var Bsbl; Capt Var Bsktbl; Hon Roll; Dairy Jdgng Awd 87; Rifle Clb Awd 87

BENINI, ANTHONY; Somerset SR HS; Sipesville, PA; (3); French Clb German Clb; SADD; Rep Stu Cncl; Socr; High Hon Roll; Hon Roll; Ai Force Acad.

BENINI, KRISTINA; Somerset Area HS; Sipesville, PA; (4); 55/34 English Clb; Q&S; Ski Clb; Soroptimist; Sec Spanish Clb; Varsity Clb; E Yrbk Stf; Chrmn Stu Cncl; Var L Socr; High Hon Roll; Hmcmng Attndn Bsktbl Crt Qn, Soroptmst Grl Mnth 86-87; Shadyside Hosp Schl; RN.

BENJAMIN, CHRISTOPHER; Danville Area HS; Danville, PA; (2) Latin Clb; Ski Clb; JV Bsbl; JV Golf; Wrstlng; High Hon Roll; Latin Hn Scty 87; Law.

BENKO, ANGELA S; Ephrata SR HS; Ephrata, PA; (4); 40/260; Pe Clb; Nwsp Phtg; Yrbk Phtg; Ed Yrbk Stf; VP Sr Cls; Stu Cncl; Va Cheerleading; JV Fld Hcky; Var Powder Puff Ftbl; Hon Roll; Tmple Pres Tourn-2nd Pl Photo 86; J Herry Hibshman Schlrshp-$4000 87; U O Pittsburgh; Pre Law.

BENKO, PATRICIA; Portage Area HS; Portage, PA; (4); 18/123; French Clb; Office Aide; Varsity Clb; Sec VP Stu Cncl; JV Var Bsbl; Var Capt Cheerleading; JV Var Score Keeper; Var Trk; High Hon Roll; Hon Roll Pres Phy Fit Awd 84-86; Soph Cls Homecoming 84-85; U Of PA Indiana Nrsng.

BENKO, RACHEL; Hempfield Area HS; Greensburg, PA; (3); GAA Latin Clb; Pep Clb; JV Var Bsktbl; High Hon Roll; Hon Roll; Trs Jr NHS Girls Bsktbl-2nd Tm All-Section & Hnr Mntn All Dist 86-87; Accntng.

BENKO, REBECCA; Portage Area HS; Portage, PA; (3); 8/115; French Clb; Ski Clb; Varsity Clb; VP Soph Cls; VP Jr Cls; Rep Dance Clb; High Hon Roll; Hon Roll; NHS; Prsdntl Physcl Ftnss Awd 85-86; Soph Clss Hmcmng Attndnt 85-86.

BENKO, RENE; Portage HS; Portage, PA; (3); French Clb; Ski Clb Band; Chorus; Concert Band; Jazz Band; Mrchg Band; Pep Band; Stage Crew; Hon Roll; Temple U; DR.

BENKO, RENEE; Ambridge Area HS; Ambridge, PA; (3); Pep Clb; Red Cross Aide; Band; Concert Band; Mrchg Band; Symp Band.

BENN, DIANE; Du Bois Area SR HS; Du Bois, PA; (3); Varsity Clb; Yrbk Ed-Chief; Yrbk Stf; Trk; Hon Roll; Commrcl Adv.

BENN, MELISSA; Wilson Christian Acad; Mckeesport, PA; (4); Church Yth Grp; Yrbk Ed-Chief; Yrbk Stf; Trs Sr Cls; Capt Bsktbl; Hon Roll; NHS; Penn ST U.

BENNAGE, JENNIFER; William Allen HS; Allentown, PA; (3); 88/660; Drama Clb; Intnl Clb; Latin Clb; Leo Clb; SADD; Stage Crew; Hon Roll; Jr NHS; Mary Alice Miller Mem Fund Schlrshp For Wk In Canada 87; Natl Latin Exam Hnbl Mntn 87; Law.

BENNER, CYNTHIA; Steelton-Highspire HS; Highspire, PA; (3); 9/102; Chess Clb; Girl Scts; Model UN; Band; Chorus; Church Choir; Concert Band; Jazz Band; Mrchg Band; School Musical; Clarkson; Aero Mech Engr.

BENNER, NICOLE; Pen Argyl HS; Nazareth, PA; (2); 13/128; Church Yth Grp; Drama Clb; Ski Clb; Band; Concert Band; Orch; Trs Soph Cls; Rep Stu Cncl; Cheerleading; Hon Roll; Med.

BENNETT, AMY; Tunkhannock HS; Tunkhannock, PA; (2); German Clb; JA; Science Clb; Ski Clb; Orch; Var Crs Cntry; JV Trk; High Hon Roll; Hon Roll; Hon Roll.

BENNETT, BETH L; Bishop Mccort HS; Armagh, PA; (3); Hosp Aide; Mu Alpha Theta; Chorus; Rep Stu Cncl; Var L Bsktbl; Jr NHS; NHS; 4-H; Library Aide; Ski Clb; Optometry.

BENNETT, BRIDGET; Dover Area HS; Dover, PA; (3); 40/260; Church Yth Grp; Intnl Clb; Spanish Clb; Varsity Clb; Band; Chorus; School Musical; Rep Jr Cls; JV Var Bsbl; Hon Roll; Comm.

BENNETT, DENNIS; Belle Vernon Area HS; Belle Vernon, PA; (3); JV L Ftbl; JV Vllybl; Cit Awd; Hon Roll; NHS; Prfct Atten Awd; Culinary Arts Inst Of PA; Chef.

BENNETT, DONNA; Susquehanna HS; Penbrook, PA; (3); Art Clb; Keywanettes; SADD; Drill Tm; Yrbk Stf; Tennis; Bus.

BENNETT, EDWARD J; Meadville Area SR HS; Meadville, PA; (4); 2/291; Church Yth Grp; French Clb; Science Clb; Var L Trk; High Hon Roll; Kiwanis Awd; Sal; Computer Clb; US Army Res Acad Athlete 86-87; Presdntl Acad Ftns Awd 86-87; Presdntl SR Mrt Physcl Ftnss Awd 84-87; Carnegie Mellon U; Physics.

BENNETT, ELIZABETH M; Strath Haven HS; Swarthmore, PA; (3); Acpl Chr; Chorus; Church Choir; School Musical; School Play; Rep Frsh Cls; Pres Soph Cls; Rep Stu Cncl; Swarthmore Coll Book Awd 87; Cls-Wide Essay Cntst 2 Time Wnnr 85-87; Psych.

BENNETT, GEORGE; Greenville HS; Greenville, PA; (3); 2/130; German Clb; VP Letterman Clb; VP Varsity Clb; Var L Bsktbl; Var L Crs Cntry; Var L Trk; NHS; Delta Epsilon Phi/German Natl Hnr Soc; Youngstown ST U Engl Fest.

BENNETT, JEAN; Forest City Regional HS; Herrick Center, PA; (3); Church Yth Grp; Dance Clb; 4-H; German Clb; Hosp Aide; Ski Clb; Church Choir; JV Trk; 4-H Awd; Hon Roll; Gregg Typing Awd 87; Hussian Schl Of Art; Commcl Art.

BENNETT, KYE; Engineering & Science HS; Philadelphia, PA; (3); 83/243; Boy Scts; Dance Clb; Exploring; Girl Scts; Teachers Aide; Church Choir; Cheerleading; Swmmng; Wt Lftg; Dntl Hygnst.

BENNETT, LISA; Montoursville HS; Montoursville, PA; (3); Spanish Clb; Varsity Clb; Off Jr Cls; Stu Cncl; Pom Pon; Powder Puff Ftbl; Sftbl; Tennis.

BENNETT, MARK; Milton Area HS; New Columbia, PA; (2); Boy Scts; Spanish Clb; Stu Cncl; JV Var Ftbl; Hon Roll; US Air Force; Comp Pgmr.

ENNETT, MATTHEW MAC GEORGE; The Haverford Schl; Paoli, A; (2); 8/73; Swmmng; Wrstlng; High Hon Roll; Church Yth Grp; French Clb; Varsity Clb; Chorus; Crs Cntry; Lcrss; Hon Roll; Maxima Cum Laude Natl Latin Fndntn 86-87; Princeton; Phys.

ENNETT, MICHAEL; Greater Johnstown Vo-Tech; Johnstown, PA; 3); JA; Varsity Clb; VP VICA; Var L Bsbl; JV Ftbl; Wt Lftg; Hon Roll; aw.

ENNETT, PEGGY; Waynesburg Central HS; Waynesburg, PA; (3); hurch Yth Grp; FHA; Pres Library Aide; Pep Clb; SADD; Nwsp Rptr; JV sktbl; Hon Roll; Elem Ed.

ENNETT, ROBERT A; Abington Heights HS; Clarks Summit, PA; (3); hurch Yth Grp; Ski Clb; Concert Band; Drm Mjr(t); Jazz Band; Mrchg and; Orch; School Musical; School Play; Var L Vllybl; U Scranton; Chem.

ENNETT, SCOTT; Ambridge Area HS; Baden, PA; (3); Exploring; Pep lb; VICA; JV Bsbl; Auto Mech.

ENNETT, SHELLEY; Fort Le Boeuf HS; Waterford, PA; (4); 10/168; amera Clb; Church Yth Grp; Computer Clb; Flag Corp; Mrchg Band; wsp Stf; Stat Trk; High Hon Roll; NHS; High Hnrs 87; PA ST; Elec ngrng.

ENNETT, TERRI; East Pennsboro Area HS; Enola, PA; (2); French lb; Ski Clb; Band; Concert Band; Mrchg Band; Yrbk Phtg; Rep Frsh Cls; st Soph Cls; Cheerleading; Tennis; Frnch I Acdmc Achvt 86-87; Earth pace I Acdmc Achvt 85-86; Outstndnt Chrlding Cert 85-86; PA ST U; cctg.

ENNETT, THOMAS; Methacton HS; Norristown, PA; (3); Boy Scts; hurch Yth Grp; VICA; Rep Stu Cncl; Hon Roll; Lndscp Arch.

ENNETT, TRICIA; York Catholic HS; Dallastown, PA; (4); 5/168; rench Clb; Chorus; Flag Corp; Stage Crew; Sec Stu Cncl; Stat Trk; High on Roll; NHS; Rotary Awd; Church Yth Grp; Mllrsvll U Srch For Excllnc chlrshp 87; Millersville U; Math.

ENNICOFF, CATHY L; Grace Christian Schl; Kempton, PA; (3); rama Clb; Office Aide; School Play; Yrbk Stf; Sec Jr Cls; Var heerleading; Hon Roll; Fruit Of The Spirit Awd 84-85; Psych.

ENNINGER, APRIL; Northampton SR HS; Bath, PA; (4); 30/350; FS; Aud/Vis; Exploring; SADD; Yrbk Stf; Stu Cncl; Tennis; Trk; High on Roll; NHS; Spec Olympcs Vlntr 85-86; Kutztown U; Speech mmnctns.

ENNINGER, SANDY; Elk Lake HS; Meshoppen, PA; (4); 18/94; hurch Yth Grp; Sec VICA; Chorus; Stu Cncl; JV Var Bsktbl; JV Var tbl; JV Var Vllybl; Hon Roll; Williamsport CC; Bus Mgt.

ENNIS, CHERYL; Upper Darby HS; Drexel Hill, PA; (4); Church Yth rp; French Clb; Girl Scts; Office Aide; Bowling; High Hon Roll; Hon Roll; rsdntl Acdmc Ftnss Awd 87; PA Coll Of Pharmacy & Sci.

ENO, CATHY; Trinity HS; Washington, PA; (4); French Clb; JA; Key lb; Pep Clb; Band; Concert Band; Mrchg Band; Pep Band; Prfct Atten wd; Slippery Rock U; Educ.

ENO, CHERIE; Trinity Area HS; Washington, PA; (3); Exploring; ath Clb; Math Tm; Band; Concert Band; Mrchg Band; Pep Band; Vllybl; rench Hon Soc; Hon Roll; Pssd Tstng Dtch Wltz Tango Ice Sktg 85; Sect hmps Bst Prcssn MBA 86; Frstry.

ENSAVAGE, TODD; Wyalusing Valley HS; Wyalusing, PA; (4); 23/135; y Scts; Computer Clb; Debate Tm; Ski Clb; Spanish Clb; Stat Bsktbl; s Cntry; Mgr(s); Hon Roll; Penn ST U; Elec Engr.

ENSE, VICTORIA; Windber Area HS; Windber, PA; (3); French Clb; irl Scts; Scholastic Bowl; Ski Clb; VP Speech Tm; Band; Concert Band; rchg Band; Nwsp Stf; Yrbk Stf; Grl Sct Slvr Awd 85; Grl Sct Ldrshp wd 86; PFEW Schlrshp 87; U Of DE; Aeromed Nrsng.

ENSINGER, KIM; Blue Mountain HS; Sch Haven, PA; (4); 3/215; Mu pha Theta; Chorus; Nwsp Rptr; Rep Stu Cncl; Capt Cheerleading; iving; Swmmng; Capt Trk; High Hon Roll; Hon Roll; Pres III 87-91; ocal No 13 Blrmkrs 87-91; U Of Scranton; Phys Thrpy.

ENSON, JANINE; Johnsonburg Area HS; Johnsonburg, PA; (4); Yrbk d-Chief; Hon Roll.

ENSON, JOSEPH; Jeanette SR HS; Jeannette, PA; (2); French Clb; ar Bsbl; US Naval Acad; Naval Offcr.

ENSON, JULIE; Nazareth SR HS; Nazareth, PA; (3); Church Yth Grp; mnty Wkr; Teachers Aide; Yrbk Stf; Rep Soph Cls; Rep Jr Cls; Rep Stu ncl; JV Tennis; Physical Therapist.

ENSON, RANDY; Butler HS; Butler, PA; (2); Socr.

ENSON, SUE; Palmyra Area HS; Palmyra, PA; (4); Dance Clb; Drama b; Trs French Clb; Chorus; Capt Color Guard; Trk; High Hon Roll; HS; Library Aide; Teachers Aide; Prsdntl Acdmc Fitness Awd; Natl nch Tchrs Cert Of Merit; IN U; Med.

ENTLER, KENNETH; Dunmore HS; Dunmore, PA; (3); 12/150; JV sbl; High Hon Roll; Jr NHS; Elec.

ENTON, BECKY; Blairsville SR HS; Blairsville, PA; (1); 35/118; hurch Yth Grp; SADD; Band; Concert Band; Mrchg Band; Math.

ENTON, DAVID; Mastawn HS; Philadelphia, PA; (2); Computer Clb; ibrary Aide; Varsity Clb; Off Jr Cls; Bsktbl; Cit Awd.

ENTON, JAMES; Hollidaysburg SR HS; Duncansville, PA; (2); Boy ts; Trs FFA; School Play; L Ftbl; L Wrstlng; High Hon Roll; Presdntl cadc Ftnss Awd 86; FFA Chptr Schlrshp Awd 86-87; Hghst Mth Avg Awd ; Engr.

ENTON, LYN; Hickory HS; Hermitage, PA; (4); 20/170; Art Clb; Pres rama Clb; VP Math Clb; Band; Chorus; School Play; Nwsp Rptr; wanis Awd; Ntl Merit Ltr; Voice Dem Awd; Amrcn Lgn Spch Cntst 84; arnegie-Mellon; Engnrng.

ENTON, SUZANNE; Hollidaysburg SR HS; Newry, PA; (3); German b; Orch; Im Vllybl; Tri-Cnty Orch Fest 84-85; Dist Orch Fest 87; PMEA usic Awd 87.

ENTZ, CHRIS; Minersville Area HS; Minersville, PA; (4); 5/117; Boy ts; Ski Clb; School Musical; School Play; Yrbk Stf; Var Bsbl; Var Bsktbl; ar Ftbl; Hon Roll; NHS; Ctzn Schlrshp Fndtn Am, Minersville Area chlrshp Fund, J Calderone Mem Schlrshp Awd 87; Bloomsburg U; ngrng.

ENTZEL, CARRIE; Spring Grove Area SR HS; Spring Grove, PA; (3); /351; Varsity Clb; VP Pres Stu Cncl; Var Capt Tennis; High Hon Roll; on Roll; NHS; Mixed Dbls ST Champ Tennis 86-87; Dist Sngls Champ nnis 86; Sngls & Dbls Champ 85-86; Accntng.

ENTZEL, DAVID; West York HS; York, PA; (3); 23/198; Stage Crew; Bowling; JV Vllybl; Hon Roll; VFW Awd; Voice Dem Awd; Vet.

ENTZEL, THOS; Carlisle SR HS; Carlisle, PA; (3); 102/467; Boy Scts; hess Clb; Church Yth Grp; Var Trk; Hon Roll; Physcl Sci.

ENYIK, DEBORAH; Haverford Township HS; Havertown, PA; (3); ench Clb; Ski Clb; JV Bsktbl; Capt Var Crs Cntry; Var Trk; High Hon ll; Hon Roll; NHS; U Of Pittsburgh; Phrmcy.

BENYO, TIMOTHY; Jim Thorpe HS; Jim Thorpe, PA; (3); Trs Stu Cncl; Var L Bsbl; JV Crs Cntry; JV Ftbl; Var L Wrstlng; Amercn Legn Awd 84; East Stroudsburg U; Hlth Educ.

BERAD, JENNIFER; Center HS; Monaca, PA; (2); Spanish Clb; Band; Jazz Band; Bsktbl; Powder Puff Ftbl; Var L Sftbl; High Hon Roll; Hon Roll; Westminster Hnrs Band 87; Beaver Cnty Hnrs Band 87; Engr.

BERARDI, ALAN; Valley View JR SR HS; Peckville, PA; (4); Computer Clb; Spanish Clb; JV Bsbl; Im Vllybl; PA ST U; Engrng.

BERARDI, LISA; Beaver JR-SR HS; Beaver, PA; (2); Spanish Clb; Capt JV Cheerleading; U Of Pittsburgh; Spts Med.

BERARDI, MICHAEL; Northeast Catholic HS; Philadelphia, PA; (3); 30/400; Church Yth Grp; Pres Jr Cls; Crs Cntry; Hon Roll; NHS; Jr Del Natl Hnr Soc 87; U PA; Med.

BERARDINELLI, BRIDGET; Trinity HS; Washington, PA; (2); German Clb; Yrbk Phtg; JV Bsktbl; Var Trk; High Hon Roll; Hon Roll; Penn ST; Med.

BERCHIN, CHRISTOPHER; W Mifflin Area HS; W Mifflin, PA; (3); 1/300; Band; Concert Band; Mrchg Band; JV Socr; JV Trk; Jr NHS; NHS; Ntl Merit Ltr; High Hon Roll; Natl Sci Olympd Awd 85; All Amer Hall Of Fame Band Hnrs 86; Gftd & Tlntd SR High Calcu 86; Penn ST; Elec.

BERCHOK, CATHY; Elizabeth Forward HS; Elizabeth, PA; (4); 10/293; Exploring; JV Bsktbl; Var Capt Diving; Var Capt Vllybl; High Hon Roll; NHS; Pres Schlr; Army Rsv Schlr Athlt Awd 87; Acadc All-Am 87; Distgshd Sci Stu Carnegie 87; Presdntl Acadc Ftns Awd 87; U Pittsburgh; Chem.

BERCKMILLER, BETH; Montour HS; Coraopolis, PA; (2); Boy Scts; Church Yth Grp; Girl Scts; SADD; Mrchg Band; Symp Band; Yrbk Stf; High Hon Roll; Acad Achvt Awd Hstry 86-87; PA ST; Elem Ed.

BERDAN, KRISTINA; Schenley HS; Bethesda, MD; (3); VP French Clb; Rep Frsh Cls; Rep Soph Cls; Cit Awd; French Hon Soc; High Hon Roll; NHS; Schlrshp Pittsburgh Ballet Theat Schl 86-87.

BERDAR, MICHAELEEN; West Mifflin Area HS; W Mifflin, PA; (2); Office Aide; Pep Clb; Ski Clb; Yrbk Stf; Mgr(s); Mat Maids; Score Keeper; High Hon Roll; Jr NHS; NHS; Law.

BERDELL, JENNIFER; Downingtown SR HS; Downingtown, PA; (3); Church Yth Grp; Dance Clb; Ski Clb; Spanish Clb; Concert Band; Mrchg Band; Yrbk Stf; Wnnr Frgn Lang Wk-Spnsh Postr Cntst 86; Bus.

BERDIS, JOE; Swissvale HS; Pittsburgh, PA; (4); 13/200; Boy Scts; French Clb; JA; Latin Clb; Band; Concert Band; Mrchg Band; Nwsp Stf; Im Bsktbl; Capt Bowling; Latin Awd 85; Grdtd Hgh Hnrs 87; Hofstra U; Engnrng.

BERES, KAREN E; Shippensburg Area SR HS; Shippensburg, PA; (4); 3/216; Church Yth Grp; Pres Girl Scts; Band; Chorus; Pres Orch; School Musical; Var L Fld Hcky; High Hon Roll; NCTE Awd; NHS; Music.

BERES, RACHEL E; St Paul Cathedral HS; Homestead, PA; (4); Political Wkr; VP Spanish Clb; Thesps; Nwsp Rptr; Lit Mag; NHS; Spanish NHS; HS Guest Stu 86-87; In Rds Intrn 87; Hghst Hnrs 86-87; Chatham Coll; Intl Bus.

BERES, SCOTT; Fort Le Boeuf HS; Waterford, PA; (2); FFA; Hon Roll; PA ST; Ag.

BERESH, MARK; Ringgold HS; Donora, PA; (1); Hon Roll; Engrng.

BERESKY, DEIDRE; North Allegheny SR HS; Allison Pk, PA; (3); 163/649; Library Aide; Var L Socr; Var L Tennis; NHS; Dstngshd Achvt Awd Bus Ed Acctg 87; TX A&M U.

BERESNYAK, FRANCINE; Marion Center HS; Home, PA; (4); FBLA; Latin Clb; SADD; Varsity Clb; Var Cheerleading; Hon Roll; Robert Morris Coll; Lgl Sec.

BEREZNAK, CHRISTOPHER; Bishop Hafey HS; Freeland, PA; (4); 11/127; VP German Clb; NFL; Quiz Bowl; Scholastic Bowl; Science Clb; Nwsp Ed-Chief; High Hon Roll; Hon Roll; NHS; Pres Schlr; Lebanon Vly Coll Yrth Schlrs Prgm 86; Dndl Mason Schlrshp In Sci 86; Wstnghs ST Sci Awd 86; U Scrntn; Genetics.

BEREZNAY, CHRIS; Belle Vernon Area HS; Belle Vernon, PA; (3); Ski Clb; Pres Jr Cls; Var Ftbl; Powder Puff Ftbl; Var Lftg; Hon Roll; Med.

BERG JR, EUGENE; Freedom HS; Bethlehem, PA; (3); 4/509; Boy Scts; Church Yth Grp; Exploring; Math Clb; Band; Yrbk Stf; High Hon Roll; NHS; Eagle Scout 86; Leg Band 87; Arch.

BERG, GRETCHEN; North Allegheny HS; Pittsburgh, PA; (2); 44/660; Church Yth Grp; NFL; Speech Tm; Chorus; School Musical; School Play; Nwsp Phtg; Nwsp Rptr; High Hon Roll; Jr NHS; Film Prodctn.

BERG, JULIE; Nazareth Acad; Philadelphia, PA; (3); Cmnty Wkr; Variety Show; Trs Frsh Cls; Im Vllybl; SCI.

BERG, KARLA; Hampton HS; Allison Park, PA; (3); 33/207; Sec Church Yth Grp; French Clb; JA; Ski Clb; Orch; Hon Roll; Ntl Merit Ltr; Rotary Awd; Exploring; Church Choir; Washington Wrkshps I 86; Cultural Exch To France 87; Vlntr At Chldrns Home 86-87.

BERGAMINO, JACQUELYN; Old Forge HS; Old Forge, PA; (4); 23/104; Sftbl; Hon Roll; NHS; Girl Scts; Spanish Clb; Spnsh Awd 84-85; Typng Awd 85-86; Misericordia; Nrsng.

BERGEMANN, MICHELE; Seneca HS; Erie, PA; (3); 11/163; French Clb; Band; Concert Band; Drm Mjr(t); Mrchg Band; Orch; School Musical; Hon Roll; NHS; Yrly Musicl Awds Mrchng, Cncrt Band; Cert Awds Orchstra; Presdntl Awd 87; Restaurnt Mgmt.

BERGEN, JOANN; Creative & Performing Arts HS; Philadelphiia, PA; (4); 56/124; JA; Yrbk Ed-Chief; Comp Progrmr.

BERGER, CHRISTOPHER; Bishop Guilfoyle HS; Altoona, PA; (3); Church Yth Grp; Var L Bsbl; Var L Bsktbl; Var L Ftbl; High Hon Roll.

BERGER, JOAN; A Central Catholic HS; Allentown, PA; (3); Church Yth Grp; Stat Mgr(s); Im Powder Puff Ftbl; Im Swmmng; L Var Vllybl; Cabrini; Pharm.

BERGER, JOSEPH; MMI Preparatory Schl; Conyngham, PA; (3); 2/38; Boy Scts; Church Yth Grp; Rep Stu Cncl; Capt Bowling; Var Crs Cntry; High Hon Roll; JETS Awd; NHS; Ntl Merit SF; NEDT Awd.

BERGER, KIRK; Pine Grove Area HS; Pine Grove, PA; (3); JV Wrstlng; Schuylkill Cnty Indstrl Arts Fair 1st Pl 85-86 & 86-87; Cabinet Mkr.

BERGER, MATTHEW; Hempfield HS; Landisville, PA; (2); 182/446; Key Clb; Var L Ftbl; Boy Scts; Church Yth Grp; Ski Clb; Rep Frsh Cls; God Cntry Awd; Hon Roll; Business.

BERGER, PATRICK; Fleetwood Area HS; Fleetwood, PA; (4); 3/107; Computer Clb; Math Clb; Pep Clb; Quiz Bowl; Band; Concert Band; Drm & Bgl; Jazz Band; Mrchg Band; Orch; MVP-GOLF 87; Penn ST U; Comp Sci.

BERGER, RUTH; Greater Johnstown SR HS; Johnstown, PA; (4); 20/314; Band; Sec Chorus; School Musical; School Play; Nwsp Rptr; Yrbk Rptr; Sec Stu Cncl; JV L Cheerleading; High Hon Roll; NHS; Dirs Choral Awd 87; U Of Pittsburgh-Johnstown; Law.

BERGER, STACEY; Ambridge Area HS; Ambridge, PA; (4); German Clb; JA; Pep Clb; Red Cross Aide; Chorus; Off Jr Cls; Robert Morris; Accntnt.

BERGER, STEVE; Punxsutawney Area HS; Punxsutawney, PA; (3); Math Tm; JV Bsktbl; Var Ftbl; Var Trk; High Hon Roll; Hon Roll; NHS; Embry Riddle; Aero Engrng.

BERGER, TRACY; Pleasant Valley HS; Saylorsburg, PA; (2); 7/243; Math Tm; Pep Clb; Teachers Aide; Cheerleading; Sftbl; High Hon Roll; Hon Roll; Jr NHS; Top 20 Stud In Fresh Clss 85-86; Zoolgst.

BERGER, TRICIA; Hempfield SR HS; Greensburg, PA; (3); Trs FNA; Pep Clb; VICA; Church Choir; Off Jr Cls; Hon Roll; Nrs Clb Cert 84-85; Culinary Arts Inst; Caterer.

BERGER, TRISHA; Palmerton Area HS; Palmerton, PA; (3); 9/173; Church Yth Grp; Chorus; School Musical; Yrbk Stf; Mgr(s); Twrlr; Hon Roll; CPA.

BERGERSTOCK, STEVE; Milton Area SR HS; Milton, PA; (4); Trs Church Yth Grp; Chorus; Concert Band; Drm Mjr(t); Mrchg Band; Var Cheerleading; Socr; Wt Lftg; JV Wrstlng; Elizabethtown Coll.

BERGEY, JASON; Upland Country Day Schl; Chadds Ford, PA; (1); 2/23; Church Yth Grp; Band; School Musical; School Play; Pres Stu Cncl; Capt Ice Hcky; Capt Lcrss; Capt Socr; NHS; Boy Acad Awd-Cls 86-87.

BERGEY, MELISSA; West Branch Area HS; Morrisdale, PA; (2); Drama Clb; Spanish Clb; SADD; Band; Chorus; Color Guard; Mrchg Band; Stage Crew; Cheerleading; WA DC Hnr & Awd Band 86; Jr High Cheerldng Awd 85-86; 1 Mile Running Awd 87; Acctnt.

BERGMAN, MICHELLE; Methacton HS; Audubon, PA; (3); Med.

BERGMANN, ALEX; Bermudian Springs HS; Gardners, PA; (1); FFA; Bsktbl; Ftbl; Wt Lftg.

BERGMANN, DOMINIQUE; Liberty HS; Bethlehem, PA; (3); 1/490; Church Yth Grp; Cmnty Wkr; Debate Tm; French Clb; Model UN; Political Wkr; Red Cross Aide; Thesps; School Musical; School Play; Mt Holyoke Almn Assn Ctznshp Awd 87; Govr Schl Sci Fnlst 86; Med Exmnr.

BERINTI, LORI; South Allegheny JR SR HS; Elizabeth, PA; (3); Trs French Clb; Band; Concert Band; Jazz Band; Capt Mrchg Band; Pep Band; Yrbk Stf; Trk; John Phillip Sousa Awd 84-85; Frnch Hon Soc 84-87; Chldhd Ed.

BERKEBILE, BRADLEY; Conemaugh Valley JR SR HS; Johnstown, PA; (4); 4/118; Am Leg Boys St; Drama Clb; French Clb; Pres VP JA; NFL; Band; School Play; High Hon Roll; NHS; Rotary Awd; Dale Carnegie Course Schlrshp JR Achvt 84-85; U Pittsburgh.

BERKEBILE, JAMES; Shade-Central City Schl; Cairnbrk, PA; (3); FBLA; Spanish Clb; Accntng Awd 86-87; Accntng.

BERKEBILE, SCOTT; Avon Grove HS; Landenberg, PA; (3); 10/210; Art Clb; Camera Clb; Church Yth Grp; Computer Clb; French Clb; Math Clb; Nwsp Phtg; Yrbk Phtg; Golf; Hon Roll; Physcs.

BERKEBILE, TRACY; North Star HS; Boswell, PA; (4); 20/135; Sec Teachers Aide; Varsity Clb; Yrbk Ed-Chief; Yrbk Stf; Sec Soph Cls; Sec Jr Cls; VP Sr Cls; Var L Bsktbl; Var L Vllybl; Hon Roll; Hmcmng Prncs 1st Rnr Up 86-87; Al-Trny, Al Cnty Vllybl 1st Tm 86-87; Stu Mth 86 & 87; Bradford Schl; Lgl Secy.

BERKEBILE, WALLACE; North Star HS; Stoystown, PA; (4); FCA; Varsity Clb; Yrbk Stf; Bsktbl; Cit Awd; Lion Awd; MVP Bsktbll Christmas Torun Team 86; All Tourn Team Snyders Undrclssmn 86; Ctznshp Awd; U Pittsburg Johnstown; Bus Mngt.

BERKENSTOCK, JENNIFER K; Nativity Blessed Virgin Mary HS; Schuylkill Haven, PA; (3); 9/86; School Play; Stage Crew; Yrbk Phtg; Yrbk Stf; Var Capt Bsktbl; Var Capt Vllybl; High Hon Roll; Hon Roll; Highest Achvt Latin I & II 85-86; 3rd Sci Fair 87; American U DC; Pol Sci.

BERKEY, ANDREW; Danville Area HS; Danville, PA; (3); 18/187; Var Bsktbl; NHS.

BERKEY, JONATHAN; Danville HS; Danville, PA; (4); Am Leg Boys St; L Capt Crs Cntry; L Trk; Hon Roll; NHS; Yng Amercn Awd 87; Gettysburg Coll; Hstry.

BERKEY, SUSIE; Chestnut Ridge HS; Fishertown, PA; (3); Church Yth Grp; GAA; SADD; Band; Var Bsktbl; Var Sftbl; Var Vllybl; NHS; WV U; Physical Thrpy.

BERKHEIMER, BRIAN P; Southwestern HS; Hanover, PA; (3); Church Yth Grp; Band; Concert Band; Jazz Band; Mrchg Band; School Musical; Stage Crew; Symp Band; Nwsp Stf; Hon Roll.

BERKHIMER, JAMES; Claysburg-Kimmel HS; Portage, PA; (3); German Clb; Varsity Clb; Pres Frsh Cls; Pres Soph Cls; Pres Jr Cls; Var Bsbl; Var Ftbl; High Hon Roll; NHS; Church Yth Grp; Forestry.

BERKOBEN, JAMES; Mechanicsburg Area HS; Mechanicsburg, PA; (2); 37/309; Cit Awd; High Hon Roll; Hon Roll.

BERKOVITZ, KELLI; Mon Valley Catholic HS; Belle Vernon, PA; (3); Yrbk Stf; Spanish NHS; Bus.

BERKOWITZ, BRIAN; Upper Dublin HS; Ft Washington, PA; (3); 8/309; Intnl Clb; Im Bsktbl; Var Tennis; Hon Roll; NHS.

BERKSHIRE, LANA; Fairchance-Georges HS; Fairchance, PA; (3); FHA; Spanish Clb; JV Var Bsktbl; High Hon Roll; Hon Roll; Jr NHS; NHS; Pres Schlr; Physcl Thrpy.

BERKSTRESSER, BRONWYN; Everett Christian Acad; Crystal Spring, PA; (1); Church Yth Grp; Chorus; Church Choir; Var Bsktbl; Var Vllybl; Acdmc RN.

BERKSTRESSER, SHAWN; Mc Connellsburg HS; Mcconnellsburg, PA; (4); 4/66; Spanish Clb; School Play; Trk; Engl,Math & Chem Awds 86; Engl,Physics & Adv Chem Awds 87; Penn ST U; Engr.

BERKUN, ELIZABETH; Taylor-Alderdile HS; Pittsburgh, PA; (3); JA; Latin Clb; Q&S; SADD; Temple Yth Grp; Nwsp Rptr; Nwsp Stf; Yrbk Stf; Lit Mag; U Pittsburgh Hnrs Convoctn HS Achvt 87; Spkr Lionist Orgnztn Amer Scholar Inner 86.

BERLOT, MELISSA; Bishop Hoban HS; Nanticoke, PA; (4); 3/226; Church Yth Grp; Cmnty Wkr; Dance Clb; French Clb; GAA; Political Wkr; Red Cross Aide; Variety Show; Pres Soph Cls; Sec Sr Cls; Yth Salute Catholic Dghtrs Of Amer 85-86; Poet Cont Natl Awd 85-86; 1st Rnr-Up Miss Bisohp Hoban Prom; U Scranton; Pre-Law.

BERLY, JENNIFER; Meadville Area SR HS; Meadville, PA; (3); 23/328; Church Yth Grp; French Clb; Latin Clb; School Play; Stage Crew; High Hon Roll; Hon Roll; Im Bowling; Travel.

BERMAN, KATHRYN; Upper Dublin SR HS; Dresher, PA; (3); English Clb; Science Clb; SADD; Teachers Aide; Temple Yth Grp; Band; Chorus; Concert Band; Mrchg Band; Nwsp Rptr; PA JR Acad Sci Ust Pl 86 & 87; Montgomery Cnty Sci Fair 1st Pl 86 & 87; Old Crow Assn Physics Awd 87; Creatv Wrtng.

BERMAN, LYLE; Lower Moreland HS; Huntingdon Vly, PA; (4); 31/203; Capt Chess Clb; Political Wkr; Pres Science Clb; Nwsp Ed-Chief; Nwsp Rptr; JV Trk; Pres Schlr; NY U; Educ.

BERNABEO, GREGORY; Marple Newtown SR HS; Newtown Square, PA; (2); 11/340; High Hon Roll; Hon Roll.

BERNARD, ANDREA; Twin Valley Area HS; Morgantown, PA; (3); 10/148; Am Leg Aux Girls St; Trs Varsity Clb; School Musical; Sec Frsh Cls; Sec Soph Cls; Sec Jr Cls; Var Capt Fld Hcky; Var Trk; Hon Roll; NHS; All Div Fld Hcky 87; ST Fnlst Am Lgn Essy Cntst 87; Keystone Girls ST Govt Cmp 87; Phys Thrpy.

BERNARD, ELISA; Nazareth Acad; Philadelphia, PA; (4); 45/120; Drama Clb; NFL; Chorus; School Musical; School Play; Nwsp Rptr; Hon Roll; Prfct Atten Awd; Itln Clb-Pres-Ldrshp Awd-Frgn Lang 84-87; Presdntl Clsrm-Wash DC 87; Awd-Outstndng Achvt-Music 87; Phila Coll/Txtls & Sci; Fshn Me.

BERNARD, GINA; Marion Center Area HS; Marion Center, PA; (3); Library Aide; Sec VICA; Trk; Wt Lftg; Hrse Trnr.

BERNARD, RHONDA MAIRE; Coatesville Area SR HS; Coatesville, PA; (4); French Clb; FBLA; SADD; Concert Band; Drm Mjr(t); Mrchg Band; Trs Yrbk Stf; Var Lcrss; Hon Roll; Instrmntl Music Dir Awd 87; Westchester U.

BERNARDI, ANGELA; Danville JR HS; Danville, PA; (1); 1/235; Church Yth Grp; Ski Clb; Pres Stu Cncl; Cheerleading; Im Gym; JV Tennis; JV Trk; High Hon Roll; Prfct Atten Awd; Pres Schlr; Key Club Awd 87; Fshn Coord.

BERNARDINI, PATRICIA; South Park HS; Pittsburgh, PA; (3); 15/225; VP Socr; High Hon Roll; Hon Roll.

BERNAT, CRISTA; Central Dauphin HS; Harrisburg, PA; (3); Key Clb; Nwsp Stf; Yrbk Stf; IN U; Fash Merch.

BERNBERG, SCOTT; Henderson HS; W Chester, PA; (2); 5/335; Ski Clb; Band; Chorus; Concert Band; Jazz Band; Mrchg Band; Orch; School Musical; Symp Band; Hon Roll; Sci.

BERND, KATHERINE; W Mifflin Area HS; Whitaker, PA; (3); Cmnty Wkr; Ski Clb; Church Choir; Nwsp Ed-Chief; Nwsp Rptr; Pres Jr Cls; Mat Maids; JV Vllybl; Jr NHS; NHS; PTSA Treas 87-88; Psyclgy.

BERND, RUSSELL; Greensburg Catholic HS; Greensburg, PA; (3); Church Yth Grp; Letterman Clb; Varsity Clb; Var L Ftbl; Var L Wrstlng; Hon Roll; Pre-Dntstry.

BERND, WENDY; Purchase Line HS; Cherry Tree, PA; (2); Church Yth Grp; Rep Pep Clb; Varsity Clb; Rep Stu Cncl; Cheerleading; Trk; Hon Roll; Prfct Atten Awd; Chosen For Appalachia Conf Track Tm 86-87; All Gazette Grls Track Tm 87.

BERNECKER, STACEY; William Allen HS; Allentown, PA; (3); 50/659; Church Yth Grp; Cmnty Wkr; Dance Clb; German Clb; Key Clb; Var Cheerleading; Hon Roll; Jr NHS; NHS; Ntl Merit Ltr; Mc Cormick Bk Awd Illustrations 87; Temple; Pharm.

BERNHARDT, ANNETTE; Lancaster Catholic HS; Mountville, PA; (3); 14/200; Drama Clb; Band; Chorus; School Musical; School Play; Var Cheerleading; Hon Roll; NHS; Church Yth Grp; Variety Show; Summer Theatre Inst 86; Theatre.

BERNHARDT, MELANA; Penn Manor HS; Willow St, PA; (3); Church Yth Grp; Exploring; French Clb; Spanish Clb; Teachers Aide; Chorus; Church Choir; Stage Crew; Vllybl; Hon Roll; Awd Rsng Mny For MS 85; Photo.

BERNHART, JOHN; Northwestern HS; New Tripoli, PA; (4); 3/170; Boy Scts; Scholastic Bowl; Band; School Play; Nwsp Ed-Chief; Yrbk Ed-Chief; Pres Stu Cncl; Pres Schlr; Church Yth Grp; Debate Tm; Presdntl Clsrm; Edtr Chf Undrgrnd Paper; U PA; Egyptlgy.

BERNICE, PATRICIA; Hickory HS; Sharpsville, PA; (3); Art Clb; Church Yth Grp; Drama Clb; Intnl Clb; Service Clb; Varsity Clb; Chorus; Yrbk Stf; JV Var Cheerleading; NHS; Edinboro U; Soc Wk.

BERNINI, MARK; Lourdes Regional HS; Mt Carmel, PA; (4); 22/90; Pres Key Clb; Yrbk Stf; Pres Frsh Cls; Rep Soph Cls; Rep Jr Cls; Pres Sr Cls; Im Bsktbl; Var Capt Golf; Hon Roll; Catholic Hgh Alumni Schlrshp 87; York Coll PA; Crmnl Jstc.

BERNOT, KATHLEEN; Blacklick Valley HS; Nanty-Glo, PA; (2); 1/105; Library Aide; Red Cross Aide; Speech Tm; Varsity Clb; Off Stu Cncl; JV Var Cheerleading; Gym; Var Trk; High Hon Roll; Girl Scts; Acad All Amer 85-6; Notre Dame; Pre-Med.

BERNOT, LAWRENCE; Blacklick Valley HS; Nanty-Glo, PA; (4); 2/96; Aud/Vis; German Clb; Red Cross Aide; Varsity Clb; Trk; High Hon Roll; Boy Scts; Church Yth Grp; Ski Clb; Acad All Amer 85-86; German Ntl Hnr Soc; Cert Of Merit Outstndng SAT Score 86; Pittsburgh; Pre-Med.

BERNOT, RANDY; Shaler Area HS; Allison Pk, PA; (3); 45/486; French Clb; Var JV Bsktbl; Var JV Socr; Trs French Hon Soc; High Hon Roll.

BERNSTEIN, ELIZABETH; Bishop Hafey HS; Conyngham, PA; (3); 28/115; Sec Church Yth Grp; Drama Clb; French Clb; FNA; Ski Clb; Y-Teens; Nwsp Rptr; Yrbk Stf; Lit Mag; Gov Hon Prg Awd; PA Govr Schl Alternate For Creative Writing 86.

BERNSTEIN, JULIE; Taylor Allderdice HS; Pittsburgh, PA; (3); Drama Clb; Chorus; Orch; Nwsp Ed-Chief; High Hon Roll; NHS; Ntl Merit SF; U Pittsbrgh Provost Day Cmptn Fnlst 87; Duquesnt U DUSPA Awd-Bst Nwspr 86 & 87; Psych.

BERNSTEIN, RACHEL; Cheltenham HS; Melrose Pk, PA; (4); 87/350; Chorus; School Musical; School Play; Capt Var Gym; Holden Awd 86-87; Acad Schlrshp To Textiles 87; Phila Coll Of Textiles; Fshn Ds.

BERRESFORD, CHRISTINA; Southmoreland SR HS; Scottdale, PA; (4); 2/229; French Clb; Sec Math Clb; French Hon Soc; Sec NHS; Ntl Merit Ltr; Sal; St Vincnt Coll Acdmc Schlrshp 87; 2nd Pl Const U Pittsbrgh Humnties Day 86; Cptn Knwldge Mstr Opn Comp; St Vincent Coll; Physcs Tchr.

BERRET, THOMAS; Central Catholic HS; Pittsburgh, PA; (3); 32/260; Im Bsktbl; Im Crs Cntry; Im Ftbl; Var Trk; Im Vllybl; Var Capt Wrstlng; Hon Roll; NHS; Ntl Merit Ltr; Cert Of Acad Excll PSAT 87.

BERRETTINI, SUSAN; Wyoming Valley West HS; Forty Fort, PA; (4); Key Clb; Nwsp Stf; Yrbk Stf; Pres Jr Cls; Pres Sr Cls; Cit Awd; Lion Awd; NHS; WY Vly W Fclty Awd 87; Presdntl Acad Ftnss Awd 87; Frty Frt Bus & Prfsshl Assoc Schlrshp Awd 87; Villanova U; Law.

BERRINGER, JODIE; Penns Manor HS; Strongstown, PA; (3); 7/95; Sec Church Yth Grp; Band; Concert Band; Flag Corp; Mrchg Band; Nwsp Rptr; Var L Vllybl; Hon Roll; NHS; NEDT Awd.

BERRY, CHRISTINE; West Scranton HS; Scranton, PA; (3); 17/260; Letterman Clb; Stu Cncl; L Tennis; Hon Roll.

BERRY, DWIGHT; Somerset Area SR HS; Somerset, PA; (3); 27/230; Am Leg Boys St; English Clb; Chorus; Yrbk Ed-Chief; Ftbl; High Hon Roll; Hon Roll; NHS; Prfct Atten Awd; Air Force Acad; Bus.

BERRY, GEORGIA; Lock Haven HS; Lock Haven, PA; (4); #42 In Class; Church Yth Grp; Spanish Clb; Chorus; Church Choir; School Play; Socr; High Hon Roll; Hon Roll.

BERRY, GREGORY; Tunkhannock Area HS; Tunkhannock, PA; (3); Key Clb; SADD; Var Bsktbl; Var Vllybl.

BERRY, JEAN ELLEN MARIE; Bethlehem Center HS; Marianna, PA; (4); 8/153; Church Yth Grp; Drama Clb; Pres 4-H; FBLA; Spanish Clb; Nwsp Rptr; Yrbk Stf; Mat Maids; Sec NHS; Acad All-Amer 85; Natl Ldrshp & Svc Awd 85; US Bus Ed Awd Acctng 84.

BERRY, JODI; Central Dauphin HS; Harrisburg, PA; (2); Stage Crew; Cheerleading; Hon Roll; Awd Prtcptn-PTA Art Shw 85-86; PA ST U; Nrsng.

BERRY, MARK; Altoona Area HS; Altoona, PA; (3); German Clb; Ski Clb; Spanish Clb; Drm & Bgl; Yrbk Stf; Var Bsbl; Var Socr; FL ST U; Criminology.

BERTA, TONI; Leechburg Area HS; Leechburg, PA; (2); Church Yth Grp; Drama Clb; Chorus; Color Guard; Hon Roll; IN U Of PA; Accntng.

BERTELE, LORIANN; Upper Darby HS; Upr Darby, PA; (3); Dance Clb; GAA; Girl Scts; Varsity Clb; Im Bsktbl; Var French Clb; Trk; Hon Roll; Harcum JC; Phy Thrpst Asst.

BERTELLI, ANTHONY; Sharon HS; Sharon, PA; (3); 4/181; French Clb; Chorus; Orch; Rep Stu Cncl; Var Golf; High Hon Roll; Hon Roll; Govt.

BERTI, LOIS; Wyoming Valley West HS; Swoyersville, PA; (4); 35/354; Church Yth Grp; Key Clb; Fld Hcky; Sftbl; High Hon Roll; NHS; Philadelphia Coll; Phrmcy.

BERTOLDI, ALISSA; West Hazleton HS; Weston, PA; (3); 30/220; Church Yth Grp; French Clb; Ski Clb; Thesps; Var L Trk; Pres Acdmc Fit Awd 85; Natl Frnch Cntst 6th Pl 85; Marn Bio.

BERTOTY, SHARYN; Mc Keesport Area HS; Mckeesport, PA; (3); 50/450; Office Aide; Acpl Chr; Color Guard; Orch; School Musical; Stage Crew; Nwsp Phtg; Stu Cncl; Hon Roll; Prfct Atten Awd; CA U PA; Scndry Ed.

BERTRAM, TAMMY; Frazier HS; Perryopolis, PA; (4); 1/130; Drama Clb; Nwsp Ed-Chief; Pres Stu Cncl; Capt Powder Puff Ftbl; DAR Awd; High Hon Roll; Lion Awd; NHS; Pres Schlr; Val; U Of Pittsburgh Schlr, Sons Of Italy Schlrshp 87; Outstndng Srvc Awd Drama 86; U Of Pittsburgh; Cvl Engrng.

BERTSCH, DAVE; Kutztown Area HS; Kempton, PA; (4); Cmnty Wkr; Variety Show; Im Vllybl; High Hon Roll; Grimley Trust Schlrshp 87; Peter Fasig Mem Schlrshp 87; Millersville U; Chem Engrng.

BERTY, AMY; Canon Mc Millan SR HS; Canonsburg, PA; (3); Church Yth Grp; Exploring; FBLA; Mgr(s); Score Keeper; Im Vllybl; High Hon Roll; Hon Roll; Intramural Racquetball Awd 86; Med Sec.

BERUBE, HEATHER SUZANNE; St College Area Intermediate HS; State College, PA; (1); 88/476; Camera Clb; Service Clb; Teachers Aide; Im Sftbl; Hon Roll; Cert Merit Spn; Jrnlsm.

BERZINSKY, CLARISSA; Greater Johnstown HS; Johnstown, PA; (4); 42/300; Exploring; Intnl Clb; JA; Key Clb; Political Wkr; Ed Nwsp Stf; Yrbk Stf; High Hon Roll; Hon Roll; NHS; Bsktbl Awd 86; Hnr Awd-Grad 87; Hnr Cord/Lttr 87; Navy; Comp.

BESECKER, JESSICA; Hanover SR HS; Hanover, PA; (3); 2/126; Varsity Clb; Band; Chorus; Concert Band; Mrchg Band; Orch; Rep Stu Cncl; Var Tennis; Bausch & Lomb Sci Awd; High Hon Roll; Bio.

BESECKER, MICHELLE; Waynesboro Area SR HS; Waynesboro, PA; (4); Church Yth Grp; FBLA; Spanish Clb; Rep Frsh Cls; Rep Soph Cls; Rep Jr Cls; L Fld Hcky; High Hon Roll; VP NHS; Coll Club Schlrshp; Shippensburg U; Acct.

BESECKER, NICOLE; Pocono Mountain HS; Scotrun, PA; (3); 46/325; Pep Clb; SADD; Concert Band; Mrchg Band; Rep Frsh Cls; Rep Soph Cls; Rep Jr Cls; Stat Bsbl; Var JV Cheerleading; Hon Roll; Scl Actvts Co-Chrprsn; Day Care.

BESHGETOORIAN, ELLEN J; Lower Moreland HS; Huntingdon Valy, PA; (4); Church Yth Grp; Drama Clb; Key Clb; Office Aide; SADD; Band; Chorus; Concert Band; Mrchg Band; Orch; Cmnty Music Schl Schlrshp 85-87; Shenandoah Coll; Music Thrpy.

BESS, JOANNE; Cowanesque Valley HS; Knoxville, PA; (3); Church Yth Grp; French Clb; SADD; School Musical; Yrbk Stf; Mgr(s); Hon Roll; Acadc 86 Vrsty Cert 87; JV Ltr 85; Jrnlsm.

BEST, BARBARA; Chartiers Valley HS; Presto, PA; (4); 13/299; Church Yth Grp; Cmnty Wkr; Dance Clb; Ski Clb; Drill Tm; School Musical; School Play; Yrbk Stf; Pom Pon; High Hon Roll; Sprls Gftd Pgm 83-87; PA ST U; Accntng.

BEST, DONNA; Mc Keesport Area HS; White Oak, PA; (3); 71/410; AFS; Pep Clb; Orch; School Musical; Yrbk Stf; Powder Puff Ftbl; U Of Pittsburgh; Medical Tech.

BEST, JAMIE; Curwensville Area HS; Clearfield, PA; (3); French Clb; Chorus; Color Guard; Nwsp Rptr; Yrbk Stf; Trs Frsh Cls; Sec Jr Cls; Sec Stu Cncl; 2nd Rnnr Up-Crwnsvl Fire Qn 87; Wrstlrtts 87.

BEST, MARGUERITE A; Lancaster Catholic HS; Lancaster, PA; (3); 34/190; Church Yth Grp; Pep Clb; Service Clb; Speech Tm; Varsity Clb; Drill Tm; Stat Mgr Bsktbl; JV Cheerleading; Coach Actv; Hon Roll; Chrstn Moralty Crs Hgh Avg 86; Pre Law.

BEST, PEGGY; Seneca HS; Union City, PA; (3); 53/150; Trs FBLA; Var JV Cheerleading; Hon Roll; Acctng I 4th Pl-Rgnl Ldrshp Cnfrnc 86; Acctng II 2nd Pl-Rgnl Ldrshp Cnfrnc 87; Chld Dvlpmnt.

BESTER, ALISHA; Lawrence County Area Vo Tech; New Castle, PA; (3); 2/296; NAACP; Pep Clb; SADD; VICA; Nwsp Stf; High Hon Roll; Hon Roll; Voctnl Awd Excllnce 86-87; Govt Awd 86; Bradford; Comp Engrng.

BESTRYCKI, JAMES; Scranton Technical HS; Scranton, PA; (2); Church Yth Grp; Johnson Tech Inst; Auto Tech.

BETHEA, DAVID; Mastbaum Area Vocational HS; Philadelphia, PA; (2); Elctrncs.

BETHEA, TIA; Germantown HS; Philadelphia, PA; (3); FBLA; JA; Cit Awd; Gov Hon Prg Awd; High Hon Roll; Jr NHS; NHS; Opt Clb Awd; LAW.

BETHEL, WILLIAM; West Catholic Boys HS; Philadelphia, PA; (2); 23/249; Cmnty Wkr; JV Bsbl; Stat Bsktbl; Hon Roll; NHS; Drexel; Acctnt.

BETKER, FAITHA; Turkey Foot Valley Area HS; Confluence, PA; (3); Library Aide; Nwsp Stf; Sftbl; High Hon Roll; Engl Awd 85-86; Gov Energy Asstnce Awd 86-87; Bus.

BETSA, VIRGINIA; Marion Center HS; Home, PA; (3); 22/172; Chess Clb; French Clb; Intnl Clb; SADD; Varsity Clb; Band; Bsktbl; Trk; Vllybl; Wt Lftg; PA ST Police Acad.

BETTA, SANTINA; Somerset Area HS; Somerset, PA; (4); Sec French Clb; Pres FHA; Varsity Clb; Stage Crew; Yrbk Stf; Stu Cncl; Var L Cheerleading; Var L Socr; Ftbl Ct Atten 87; Wrstlng Queen 87; Shippensburg U.

BETTEN, ALAN R; Central Catholic HS; Pittsburgh, PA; (3); 42/260; Teachers Aide; Var Bowling; High Hon Roll; Hon Roll; NHS; PA ST; Arch.

BETTING, JONATHAN; Greenwood HS; Liverpool, PA; (1); FFA; Band; Concert Band; Mrchg Band; Ftbl; Trk; FFA Star Greenhand 86-87.

BETTOLE, GINA; Cardinal Ohara HS; Morton, PA; (3); 47/710; Cm Wkr; French Clb; SADD; School Play; Off Stu Cncl; French Hon Soc; H Roll; Church Yth Grp; Office Aide; School Musical; Cardinal Ohara Fair 85-87; DE Vly Sci Fair 87; Prncpls Awd Acadmc Excllnc 85-87.

BETTOR, LESLIE; Kiski Area HS; New Kensington, PA; (4); Off Aide; Band; Concert Band; Mrchg Band; Mgr Trk; High Hon Roll; H Roll; Louise S Mc Clintic Schl Nrsng.

BETTS, CRAIG; Christian School Of York; Camp Hill, PA; (4); 20/ Chorus; Concert Band; Orch; School Play; Rep Stu Cncl; Var Mgr(s); H Roll; Ntl Merit Ltr; Stu Cncl Schlrshp Awd, Assn Chrstn Schls I Dstngshd Chrstn Stu, Awds Choir & Band 86-87; Messian Coll; Music I

BETTS, DONALD; Delaware County Christian Schl; Radnor, PA; (4); Var Bsktbl; Var L Crs Cntry; High Hon Roll; Hon Roll; Clemson U.

BETTS, MICHELLE; Warren Area HS; Warren, PA; (3); Church Y Grp; Acpl Chr; Concert Band; Madrigals; Mrchg Band; School Music Trk; Wt Lftg; High Hon Roll; Jr NHS; Warren Area HS Golden Drag Awd 87; Bus Admin.

BETTS, TAMMY; Punxsutawney Area HS; Walston, PA; (4); 28/ Aud/Vis; FBLA; Variety Show; Hon Roll; Top Acctg Stu 87; Mary A Irvin Schlrshp Fndtn 87; Margaret C Boles Mem Schlrshp Fndtn 87; Bois Bus Coll; Med Sec.

BETTWY, CATHY; Bishop Guilfoyle HS; Altoona, PA; (3); 7/1 Church Yth Grp; SADD; Band; High Hon Roll; Hon Roll; Penn S Rehbltatn.

BETZ, CHRISTOPHER; Danville JR HS; Washingtonville, PA; (1); Clb; Rep Frsh Cls; JV Ftbl; JV Trk; High Hon Roll; Pres Schlr; Presd Acad Fitness Awd 87; Spnsh Awd 87; Ind Arts Awd 87; US Air Force Ac

BETZ, CINDY; Philadelphia Montgomery Christ Acad; Philadelphia, P (3); Art Clb; FCA; Church Yth Grp; Yrbk Stf; Var Bsktbl; Var Gym; Sftbl; Var Trk; High Hon Roll; Hon Roll; Design.

BETZ, DAWN; Crestwood HS; Mountaintop, PA; (1); Church Yth G Ski Clb; Church Choir; School Play; Stage Crew; JV Cheerleading; Gy Trk; Awd Exclnc Chrldng 87; Wilkes Coll; Pre-Law.

BETZ, HEATHER; Philadelphia Montgomery Chrstn Ac Philadelphia, PA; (1); Church Yth Grp; School Play; JV Bsktbl; JV F Hcky; High Hon Roll.

BETZ, HEIDI; Donegal HS; Mount Joy, PA; (4); 44/164; Church Yth G School Play; Stage Crew; Variety Show; Yrbk Ed-Chief; Off Frsh Cls; Soph Cls; Stu Cncl; Fld Hcky; Trk; Donegal Ed Assoc Schlrshp 87; Ro Intl Ldrshp Conf 86; Teen Wk Lancaster New Era Stu Mnth 87; WV Pharm.

BETZ, KARINA; Trinity HS; Mechanicsburg, PA; (2); French Clb; Bsktbl; L Vllybl; Pep Clb; School Play; Hon Roll; Cert Merit Schltc Wr Awd Short Story 86; Psych.

BETZ, LISA; Central Dauphin HS; Harrisburg, PA; (2); Church Yth G Civic Clb; JV L Bsktbl; Var Sftbl; Hon Roll.

BETZ, MIKE; Center HS; Aliquippa, PA; (3); 20/185; Am Leg Boys St; Bsktbl; Im Bowling; High Hon Roll; Hon Roll; Prfct Atten Awd; 4.0 A Awd Ger 87; Engrng.

BEUGLESS, REBECCA; Henderson HS; W Chester, PA; (3); Chu Yth Grp; JCL; Capt Cheerleading; Hon Roll.

BEVACQUA, MELISSA; West Mifflin Area HS; W Mifflin, PA; (Exploring; Band; Concert Band; Mrchg Band; Yrbk Stf; High Hon R Hon Roll; NHS; Pres Schlr; U Of Pittsburgh; Occptnl Thrpy.

BEVAN, CYNTHIA; Bensalem SR HS; Bensalem, PA; (3); Church Y Grp; Drama Clb; French Clb; Color Guard; Mrchg Band; School Music School Play; Stat Bsbl; Cheerleading; Stat Fld Hcky.

BEVARD, TRISHA; South Western HS; Hanover, PA; (2); Var C Cheerleading; Pres Phsical Fitness Awd 86-87; Teacher.

BEVENRNO, JILL; Warren Area HS; Warren, PA; (3); 12/272; Ski C Varsity Clb; Acpl Chr; Pres Frsh Cls; Pres Soph Cls; Pres Sr Cls; VP Cncl; Sftbl; Vllybl; NHS; Amer Lgn Auxlry PA 85; Vrstyltr Grls Vly Sftbl 86; Penn ST U; Bus Admin.

BEVERIDGE, ALISON; St Marys Area HS; Kersey, PA; (3); Exploring; Ski Clb; Var Capt Cheerleading; Hon Roll; Nurs.

BEVERIDGE, AMY; West Middlesex HS; West Middlesex, PA; (Dance Clb; Spanish Clb; Hon Roll; Pres Schlr; Fashion Inst Of Pgh; F Dsgn.

BEVERIDGE, DOUGLAS; Cathedral Prep Schl; Erie, PA; (3); 11/ Church Yth Grp; Civic Clb; German Clb; Im Bsktbl; Im Vllybl; High H Roll; Ntl Merit Ltr.

BEVERIDGE, GREG; Meadville HS; Meadville, PA; (3); Cmnty W Computer Clb; FCA; Letterman Clb; SADD; Frsh Cls; Soph Cls; Stu Cr Crs Cntry; Trk; Mercyhurst Coll; Crmnl Justc.

BEVERIDGE, SCOTT; Carrick HS; Pittsburgh, PA; (3); Ski Clb; Sch Musical; School Play; Stage Crew; JV Ftbl; Golf; High Hon Roll; Pr Atten Awd; Ltrd Cty Chmpnshp Glf Tm 86; Penn ST; Elec Engrng.

BEVERLY, NYCOLE; West Catholic For Girls HS; Philadelphia, P (3); 69/296; Library Aide; NAACP; Pres Spanish Clb; Teachers Aide; H Roll; Hghst Grd Avg In Wstrn Cvlztn 84-85; Hghst Grd Avg In Bio 85- Penn ST; Pdtrcs Nrs.

BEVEVINO, JENNIFER; Wyoming Valley West HS; Forty Fort, P (3); 9/419; Church Yth Grp; Key Clb; Pep Clb; Rep Stu Cncl; Cheerleading; Var L Fld Hcky; Var L Sftbl; Cit Awd; High Hon Roll; NHS; Natl Cncl Yth Ldrshp 87; Pre Med.

BEVEVINO, ROSS; Immaculate Conception HS; Canonsburg, PA; (2); 37; Math Tm; Pep Clb; Yrbk Stf; VP Stu Cncl; Var Bsbl; JV Bskt Tennis; Cit Awd; DAR Awd; High Hon Roll; Princeton; Law.

BEVILACQUA, ALICIA M; Archbishop Prendergast HS; Yeadon, P (4); 23/325; Art Clb; Office Aide; Orch; Hon Roll; Jr NHS; Gold Meda Achvt 87; Art Awd 85-86; Arts Recognition & Talent Search-Hnrb Mr 87; Drexel U; Intr Dsgn.

BEVILACQUA, ANN MARIE; West Scranton HS; Dunmore, PA; (35/243; Spanish Clb; Nwsp Stf; Yrbk Stf; Rep Stu Cncl; Pom Pon; H Hon Roll; Jr NHS; NHS; Empire Beauty Schl; Csmtlgy.

BEVINGTON, BONITA JANE; Beaver Area SR HS; Beaver, PA; (Church Yth Grp; Sec French Clb; Hosp Aide; Orch; Symp Band; Powd Puff Ftbl; Trk; High Hon Roll; Bible Qzzr Of Yr 85 & 87; Hnry Achvm Awd 86-87; Gannon U Erie PA; Engrng.

BEWAK, DAVID; Bishop Mc Cort HS; Johnstown, PA; (3); Elec Tec

BEWLEY, JOHN; Avon Grove HS; West Grove, PA; (3); Stage Crew; Lftg; Hon Roll; Chem Awd 86-87; Mgmnt.

BEWLEY, KEVIN; Henderson HS; West Chester, PA; (2); 6/335; B Scts; French Clb; Ski Clb; Var Lcrss; JV Socr; French Hon Soc; Hon R Acctng.

BEY, AMBER ARNOLD; Schenley HS Teachers Ctr; Pittsburgh, PA; (3); Camera Clb; German Clb; Var Trk; Wt Lftg; High Hon Roll; NHS; Prfct Atten Awd; Gftd & Tlntd Ed Prog 85; Brd Of Ed Dist Achvt Awd 85; Cert GATE Conf & Expstn 85; U Of CA; Bio Sci.

BEY, DAWN; Mastbaum AVTS; Philadelphia, PA; (3); FBLA; Trs Jr Cls; Ntl Merit Schol; Prfct Atten 86-87; Bus Admin.

BEY, RASHEEDA; Sis Clara Muhammad Schl; Philadelphia, PA; (2); Science Clb; Teachers Aide; Cit Awd; Princeton U; Management.

BEYER, BECKY; Seneca Valley HS; Mars, PA; (2); Art Clb; Aud/Vis; Church Yth Grp; Math Tm; Chorus; Pep Band; Nwsp Rptr; Lit Mag; Twrlr; Hon Roll; Scndry Ed.

BEYER, GWYNN; Southern Columbia HS; Elysburg, PA; (3); Church Yth Grp; Band; Concert Band; Drill Tm; Drm Mjr(t); Jazz Band; Mrchg Band; Pep Band; School Play; Nwsp Ed-Chief; Creative Wrtng Awd 85; Cnty Band 87; Spec Educ.

BEYER, JEFFREY; Constoga SR HS; Paoli, PA; (2); Cmnty Wkr; German Clb; Intnl Clb; Varsity Clb; Var Socr; Business Mgmt.

BEYER, MARK; Phoenixville Area HS; Phoenixville, PA; (3); SADD; Band; Nwsp Stf; Yrbk Stf; NHS.

BEYER, PETER; Danville SR HS; Danville, PA; (1); Church Yth Grp; Ski Clb; JV Crs Cntry; JV Trk; High Hon Roll; Pres Schlr; Wheaton Coll.

BEYER, SUE ANNE; Danville SR HS; Danville, PA; (4); 5/202; Church Yth Grp; Drama Clb; French Clb; Church Choir; School Musical; High Hon Roll; NHS; Ntl Merit SF; Engl.

BEYNON, BRIDGET; Lackawanna Trail HS; Factoryville, PA; (4); 9/86; Church Yth Grp; Ski Clb; Chorus; Yrbk Stf; Stu Cncl; Bsktbl; Sftbl; Hon Roll; NHS; Pres Schlr; Schlr Athl Awd 87; La Salle U; Cmmnctns.

BEYRENT, JOHN; Abington Heights HS; Clarks Summit, PA; (3); Lit Mag; Var JV Bsbl; JV Bsktbl; Var JV Ftbl; Wt Lftg; Hnrbl Mntn All Schlstc-Ftbl 86; 16 Yr Old All Star Babe Ruth League-Bsbl 87; Bus.

BEZEK, WILLIAM; Central Cambria HS; Johnstown, PA; (4); 8/214; Boy Scts; Computer Clb; Wt Lftg; High Hon Roll; Hon Roll; Eagle Scout Awd 84; U Of Pittsburgh; Elec Engrng.

BEZSYLKO, JOHN-CHRISTOPHER; Bishop Dc Devitt HS; Harrisburg, PA; (4); 13/190; Rep Frsh Cls; VP Soph Cls; Pres Sr Cls; Pres Stu Cncl; Var Bsbl; Capt Ftbl; Hon Roll; Jr NHS; VP NHS; Yth & Govt Pres 86-87; Bus Mgmt.

BHAN, ROMAL; Abington Heights HS; Clarks Green, PA; (3); Science Clb; Yrbk Rptr; Yrbk Stf; Tennis; Hon Roll; NHS; Rotary Awd; Tnns-Ltrmn 86; Med.

BHAVANANDAN, SATHY V; Hershey HS; Hershey, PA; (2); 1/200; Aud/Vis; Camera Clb; Rep Soph Cls; High Hon Roll; Med.

BIAGETTI, LISA; Seton-La Salle HS; Pittsburgh, PA; (4); 48/270; Cmnty Wkr; Ski Clb; Color Guard; Drill Tm; Nwsp Bus Mgr; Nwsp Stf; Pom Pon; Stat Sftbl; High Hon Roll; Hon Roll; Duquesne U; Elem Ed.

BIALEK, KIMBERLY S; Southmoreland HS; Scottdale, PA; (4); VP Church Yth Grp; French Clb; Math Clb; Pep Clb; Ski Clb; VP Band; VP Concert Band; VP Mrchg Band; French Hon Soc; Pres Acad Ftnss Awd 87; Schlrshp Awd 87; Marine Fidelis Awd 87; West Penn Hosp Schl; Nrsng.

BIALON, AARON; Mon Valley Catholic HS; Belle Vernon, PA; (3); Var L Ftbl; JV Mgr(s); Im Wt Lftg; Pre-Law.

BIALON, MARY; Ringgold HS; Monongahela, PA; (3); Drama Clb; Office Aide; SADD; Trs Chorus; School Musical; School Play; Swing Chorus; Variety Show; Nwsp Ed-Chief; Yrbk Ed-Chief; Lbry Awd 86; Jrnlsm Hnr/Awd 87; Jrnlsm.

BIALOWAS, RENEE; Center HS; Aliquippa, PA; (3); 24/190; Church Yth Grp; Exploring; Spanish Clb; Stu Cncl; Pom Pon; High Hon Roll; Hon Roll; Hosp Aide; Scholastic Bowl; Phrmcy.

BIANCO, TAMI; Conemaugh Township HS; Johnstown, PA; (3); VP French Clb; JA; NFL; Spanish Clb; Band; French Hon Soc.

BIANCULLI, RONALD; St John Neumann HS; Philadelphia, PA; (2); 38/351; Im Bsktbl; Cert For Making Hnrs 86-87.

BIANCULLI, STEVEN; Seneca Valley HS; Mars, PA; (4); Boys Clb Am; Church Yth Grp; High Hon Roll; Hon Roll; Merit Schlrshp; Engr Alumni Hnrs Schlrshp 87; U Of Pittsburgh; Engr.

BIANCUZZO, STEVEN P; Moshannon Valley HS; Houtzdale, PA; (3); 3/150; Boy Scts; Wrstlng; High Hon Roll; Military.

BIAS, BROOKE; Western Beaver HS; Industry, PA; (3); Church Yth Grp; FHA; Chorus; Church Choir; JV Var Vllybl; High Hon Roll; Hon Roll; Trvl.

BIBLE, ROBERT; Aliquippa JR SR HS; Aliquippa, PA; (3); Var L Bsbl; Var JV Ftbl; High Hon Roll; Naval Acad; Elec Engrng.

BIBUS, CHRIS; Hamburg Area HS; Hamburg, PA; (4); 23/146; Church Yth Grp; German Clb; Ski Clb; Soph Cls; Bsbl; Ftbl; High Hon Roll; Hon Roll; Vrsty Ltr Ftbl & Bsbl; Loch Haven U; Elec Engrng.

BICKEL, BETH; Altoona Area HS; Altoona, PA; (4); 131/718; Drama Clb; French Clb; Pres Key Clb; Ski Clb; SADD; Capt Color Guard; Concert Band; Orch; Lit Mag; Stu Cncl; SE Acad; Travel.

BICKEL, DAVID; Hopewell SR HS; Aliquippa, PA; (3); 35/295; 4-H Awd; High Hon Roll; Hon Roll; NHS; L F Blancy Consrvatn Awd; PA ST; Architecture.

BICKEL, PAUL; Parkland HS; Allentown, PA; (4); 46/428; Boy Scts; Church Yth Grp; VP Band; Jazz Band; School Musical; JP Sousa Awd; NHS; Math Tm; Concert Band; Mrchg Band; Slctd PA Yth Hnrs Cncrt Band & AM Music Abrd Europe Tour 87; Spcl Ldrshp Awd-Band 87; Massiah Coll; Engnrng.

BICKERSTAFF, DAWN; Beaver Area SR HS; Beaver, PA; (2); Church Yth Grp; French Clb; JCL; Key Clb; Latin Clb; Pep Clb; Chorus; Church Choir; School Musical; Nwsp Rptr; Super Rnking, Vocal Music-Chrch Cmpttn, Dist & Ntl Lvls 86; Nrsng.

BICKERT, TODD; Pen Argyl Area HS; Nazareth, PA; (3); Church Yth Grp; Trs Drama Clb; FBLA; Trs PAVAS; Rep SADD; Chorus; School Musical; School Play; Stage Crew; Nwsp Phtg; Broadcasting.

BICKERTON, ROBERT; Center HS; Monaca, PA; (3); Am Leg Boys St; Spanish Clb; Stu Cncl; Var L Bsbl; Bsktbl; Ftbl; Var Golf; Hon Roll; NHS; Cmmnctns.

BICKFORD, ROD; Albert Gallatin HS; Masontown, PA; (4); Band; Concert Band; Drm Mjr(t); Mrchg Band; Trs Soph Cls; Trs Jr Cls; Trs Sr Cls; Off Stu Cncl; Score Keeper; Wrstlng; US Natl Ldrshp Awd 85-86; Waynesburg U; Accntng.

BICKHART, JANET; Ephrata SR HS; Ephrata, PA; (4); 13/257; Church Yth Grp; Exploring; Hosp Aide; Library Aide; Red Cross Aide; Teachers Aide; Mrchg Band; Hon Roll; NHS; Gold Key Art Awd 84-85; Hibshman Schlrshp 87; Wolfe Schlrshp 87; Geisinger Med Ctr; Rad Tech.

BICKLEY, BRIAN ALAN; Germantown HS; Philadelphia, PA; (2); 10/25; Cit Awd; Hon Roll; Prfct Atten Awd; Cert Merit Frnch 86; PA ST; Comp Sci.

BICKSLER, GARY; Tulpehocken HS; Richland, PA; (4); 13/115; VP 4-H; Pres FFA; Var Bsbl; 4-H Awd; Hon Roll; NHS; Gov Schl Agri 86; Charles Ohlinger Schlrshp 87; Keystone Frmr Degree 87; FFA Star Greenhand Awd 84; Penn ST; Dairy Sci.

BIDDLE, EILEEN; Tyrone Area HS; Warriors Mark, PA; (3); Church Yth Grp; French Clb; FBLA; Library Aide; SADD; Hon Roll; Accntnt.

BIDDLE, PAUL; Beaver Area HS; Beaver, PA; (2); Computer Clb; German Clb; L Socr; High Hon Roll; Comp Engrng.

BIDDLE, TRACY; Red Land HS; New Cumberland, PA; (3); 35/306; Sec Camera Clb; Pres Church Yth Grp; Model UN; Spanish Clb; Orch; Symp Band; Var Trk; Im Vllybl; Hon Roll; Spanish NHS; Intl Bus.

BIDELSPACH, JILL; Southern Columbia Area HS; Elysburg, PA; (4); 24/77; Ski Clb; School Play; Pres Frsh Cls; Pres Soph Cls; Pres Stu Cncl; JV Cheerleading; JV Trk; Prm Qn; CMBA Awd; Ralpho Twsp Wmns Clb Awd; York Coll PA; Intl Studies.

BIDLACK, BENJAMIN; Fox Chapel HS; Wexford, PA; (3); 40/345; Boy Scts; Cmnty Wkr; French Clb; Band; Concert Band; Jazz Band; Mrchg Band; Pep Band; School Play; L Wrstlng; Ntl Hnr Soc 87-89; Hgh Hnr Rll 84-87; Mgna Cum Laudi Ltn Awd 87; Bio.

BIDWELL, HOLLY; North Pocono HS; Moscow, PA; (4); 7/240; Ski Clb; Yrbk Stf; Rep Frsh Cls; Var Capt Crs Cntry; Var Capt Trk; High Hon Roll; NHS; Pres Schlr; H Loren Clements Schlrshp 87; Ath Of Wk Awd 86; PA ST U; Pre-Med.

BIDWELL, KEVIN; Warren Area HS; Warren, PA; (3); Sec French Clb; Ski Clb; JV Bsbl; Var Bsktbl; JV Ftbl; Im Tennis; Trk; High Hon Roll; Hon Roll; Slvr B Awd 85; Arch.

BIEBER, BECKY; Burgettstown Area JR-SR HS; Pittsburgh, PA; (4); 21/138; Pres Trs Science Clb; Sec Trs Band; Drm Mjr(t); Mrchg Band; Symp Band; Trs Stu Cncl; Hon Roll; NHS; Pres Schlr; PMEA Hnrs Band 86-87; Natl Arion Awd Band 87; Our Lady Lordes Scholar 87; Duquesne U; Music Ed.

BIEBER, TANYA; William Allen HS; Allentown, PA; (2); German Clb; JA; Ski Clb; VP SADD; Nwsp Stf; Lit Mag; Hon Roll; Jr NHS.

BIEDA, KELLY; Red Lion SR HS; Felton, PA; (3); 7/342; Varsity Clb; Yrbk Stf; VP Soph Cls; Rep Stu Cncl; Var L Bsktbl; Capt Var Crs Cntry; L Var Trk; High Hon Roll; NHS; Natl Rural Elect Assn Yth Tour 87; Lebanon Vly Chem Yth Schlrs Pgm 87; Hnrs Natl Assn Biol Tchrs 87; Chem.

BIEGA, DOUG; Center Area HS; Monaca, PA; (2); Spanish Clb; JV Bsktbl; Coach Actv; Var Golf; Var Trk; Hon Roll; UNC Chapel Hill; Phrmcst.

BIELAUS, SUSAN; Pennsbury HS; Yardley, PA; (3); 40/800; French Clb; Letterman Clb; Concert Band; Mrchg Band; Yrbk Stf; Var Crs Cntry; Var Trk; Im Vllybl; Hon Roll; NHS; Bio.

BIELSKI, GARY; Ringgold HS; New Eagle, PA; (3); Yrbk Phtg; Yrbk Rptr; Yrbk Sprt Ed; Yrbk Stf; Hon Roll; 2nd Pl PTSA Rflctns 86; Rgnl Sci Olympd Clairion U 87; Penn St; Chem Engr.

BIENIEK, JANET; Bishop Guilfoyle HS; Altoona, PA; (4); 3/123; Chorus; Var L Vllybl; High Hon Roll; PA ST U; Scndry Ed.

BIENKO, CHRIS; Central Catholic HS; Oakmont, PA; (2); 37/303; Pep Clb; Im Ftbl; Hon Roll; U Of Pittsburgh; Med.

BIER, PATRICK J; Apollo-Ridge SR HS; North Apollo, PA; (4); 3/167; German Clb; Band; Concert Band; Mrchg Band; Pep Band; School Play; Lit Mag; JP Sousa Awd; Lion Awd; NHS; Boy Mnth Apollo Lions 86-87; Boy Yr Apollo Lions 87; Gannon U; Chem Engrng.

BIERER, LISA; Waynesburg Central HS; Waynesburg, PA; (3); Church Yth Grp; Hosp Aide; Spanish Clb; Band; Concert Band; Mrchg Band; Var Trk; JV Vllybl; Hon Roll; Prfct Atten Awd; Pre-Elem Dsgn.

BIERER, MELISSA; Connellsville HS; Connellsville, PA; (3); Sec Art Clb; 4-H; Library Aide; Office Aide; Chorus; Stage Crew; French Hon Soc; High Hon Roll; NHS; WV U; Math.

BIERNACKI, KAREN; Immoculate Conception HS; Amity, PA; (3); 1/38; Im Coach Actv; JV Score Keeper; Var Sftbl; Var Vllybl; High Hon Roll; NHS; Frnch, Ltn, US Hstry Acadc Excel Awds 86-87; Vet.

BIERNESSER, DARLENE; Fox Chapel Area HS; Pittsburgh, PA; (4); Church Yth Grp; GAA; Office Aide; Stu Cncl; Capt Powder Puff Ftbl; Capt L Socr; Vllybl; Hon Roll; Rgnl All Amer 86; WPIAL Coachs All Str Tm 86; Parae Chmpns Outstndn Wmn Athl 87; Bethany Coll.

BIESECKER, PAULA; Middletown Area HS; Middletown, PA; (3); 2/209; Varsity Clb; Trs Frsh Cls; Trs Soph Cls; Trs Jr Cls; Rep Stu Cncl; JV Bsktbl; Ftbl; JV Sftbl; High Hon Roll; Hon Roll; Sports.

BIESER, ERNIE; Cowanewque Valley HS; Middlebury Cntr, PA; (3); Boy Scts; Drama Clb; FFA; Letterman Clb; School Play; Stu Cncl; Bsbl; Capt Ftbl; Hon Roll; NHS; Eagle Sct 86.

BIESINGER, JAMES; Claysburg-Kinnel HS; Claysburg, PA; (2); 9/97; Ski Clb; Spanish Clb; Concert Band; School Musical; Stage Crew; VP Soph Cls; Im Bsktbl; JV Ftbl; VFW Awd; Naval Acad-Annapolis; Aerontcs.

BIETSCH, RYAN; Shippensburg Area SR HS; Shippensburg, PA; (3); 62/263; Boy Scts; Varsity Clb; Var L Bsbl; JV L Bsktbl; Var L Ftbl; Im Wt Lftg; Slctd Mid-Penn Conf All Star Ftbl Tm 86; Pol Sci.

BIEVENOUR, MICHELLE; Dover Area HS; Dover, PA; (3); VP JA; Library Aide; Chorus; Yrbk Stf; Hon Roll; Rotary Awd; Schlrshp JR Achvmnt 87; Rgnl JR Achvmnt Fnlst 87; York Coll; Crmnlgy.

BIEVENOUR, PATRICIA; York Catholic HS; York, PA; (2); JA; Pep Clb; Art Clb; SADD; Socr; Sftbl.

BIGGANS, MARY; West Branch HS; Grassflat, PA; (2); Spanish Clb; Band; Chorus; Concert Band; Mrchg Band; Off Frsh Cls; Off Soph Cls; Hon Roll.

BIGGINS, KIMBERLY; Gettysburg HS; Mcknightstown, PA; (2); Pep Clb; Varsity Clb; Var L Cheerleading; Shippensburg U; Accntng.

BIGGS, COLLEEN; Allentown Central Catholic HS; Allentown, PA; (4); 8/204; Exploring; Hosp Aide; Pep Clb; Service Clb; Band; Concert Band; Mrchg Band; Pep Band; High Hon Roll; NHS; Exchng Clb Salute To Schlrs 87; Air Prod Cert Of Merit Sci 87; Gwynedd-Mercy; Nrsng.

BIGGS, JENNIFER; Central Catholic HS; Allentown, PA; (3); 63/233; Hosp Aide; Band; Chorus; Church Choir; Concert Band; Mrchg Band; Pep Band; School Play; Hon Roll; Church Yth Grp; Schl Half Scholar 84-85; 3rd Prz PA JR Acad Sci 84-85; Natl Ldrshp Svc Awd 85-86; Nrsng.

BIGGS, SUSAN; Plum SR HS; Pittsburgh, PA; (3); Church Yth Grp; French Clb; Hosp Aide; Color Guard; Stat Trk; Commnctns.

BIGLEY, JILL; Yough SR HS; Smithton, PA; (3); Office Aide; Pep Clb; Spanish Clb; Thesps; Band; Chorus; Off Stu Cncl; Var L Bsktbl; Powder Puff Ftbl; Vllybl; Physcl Educ.

BILAFER, ELIZABETH A; Eisenhower HS; Russell, PA; (3); Church Yth Grp; Chorus; Sec Frsh Cls; Rep Stu Cncl; Var Capt Cheerleading; Var Trk; High Hon Roll; Sec Pres Jr NHS; Pres NHS; Bus Mgmt.

BILBAY, TAMMY; Lock Haven SR HS; Lock Haven, PA; (3); FBLA; Band; Color Guard; Accntnt.

BILBEE, GINA; Lansdale Catholic HS; Hatfield, PA; (3); Cmnty Wkr; Dance Clb; Rep Soph Cls; Rep Jr Cls; Rep Sr Cls; Stu Cncl; Fld Hcky.

BILETNIKOFF II, EPHRIAM; Cathedral Prep Schl; Erie, PA; (4); 121/212; Var Ftbl; Penn ST U; Engnrng.

BILGER, DANIEL; Governor Mifflin HS; Shillington, PA; (3); Chess Clb; Acpl Chr; Chorus; School Musical; Var Crs Cntry; Var Trk; Hon Roll; U Of Miami; Oceangrphy.

BILGER, KIM; Westmont Hilltop SR HS; Johnstown, PA; (2); Church Yth Grp; Drama Clb; Chorus; Church Choir; School Musical; Cheerleading; Score Keeper; Vllybl; Wt Lftg; Le Tourneau; Nrs.

BILGER, LISA; Solanco HS; Christiana, PA; (4); SADD; Color Guard; Flag Corp; School Musical; Stu Cncl; Powder Puff Ftbl; Hon Roll; Prfct Atten Awd; Gold Key Awd-Artistic Achvt 87; Lancaster Gen Hosp; Nrsng.

BILKER, LORI; Marple Newtown SR HS; Broomall, PA; (2); 14/324; JV Mu Alpha Theta; Spanish Clb; Yrbk Stf; Rep Stu Cncl; JV Bsktbl; JV Lcrss; Hon Roll; Rotary Awd; Hstry Day Awd 86; Cnstnl Pstr Awd 87; Biomed Engrng.

BILL, DARRIC; South Allegheny HS; Mckeesport, PA; (3); 12/165; Am Leg Boys St; Boy Scts; French Clb; Lib Chorus; School Musical; School Play; God Cntry Awd; Hon Roll; NHS; Prfct Atten Awd; Eagle Scout 84; Brthrhd Rnk Order Arrow 82; Basic Rescuer Med Expl 84; PA ST U.

BILLARD, JOHN; Wallenpaupack Area HS; Hawley, PA; (4); 19/148; Quiz Bowl; Science Clb; Ski Clb; Varsity Clb; School Musical; School Play; Stu Cncl; Capt Socr; Capt Tennis; Pres NHS; NROTC Marine Corp Option 4 Yr Schlrshp 87-91; Stu Of Month 87; Schlr Of Week 87; Ithaca Coll; Pol Sci.

BILLE, TODD; Elk County Christian HS; St Marys, PA; (3); 14/72; Var JV Ftbl; Var Golf; High Hon Roll; Hon Roll; NHS; Honor Roll; Natl Hnr Roll 86-87; Penn ST; Chem Engrng.

BILLER, ALLISON; Mt Pleasant Area SR JR HS; Mt Pleasant, PA; (2); German Clb; Pep Clb; Ski Clb; Band; Color Guard; Rep Stu Cncl; Hon Roll; Chem Engrng.

BILLER, THOMAS; Bishop Carroll HS; Ebensburg, PA; (3); 26/135; Church Yth Grp; Pep Clb; Ski Clb; Spanish Clb; SADD; VP Frsh Cls; Var JV Bsbl; Var Capt Ftbl; Wt Lftg; Hon Roll; Bus.

BILLET, CHRIS; Danville SR HS; Danville, PA; (1); JV Crs Cntry; JV Trk; Hghst GPA Sci & Scl Stds 87; Pres Acad Ftns Awd 87; Bus.

BILLET, KEITH; York County Vocational Tech Schl; York, PA; (3); Church Yth Grp; VICA; Military; Cmmrcl Art.

BILLET, MELISSA; Conestoga SR HS; Devon, PA; (2); Sec Frsh Cls; Rep Soph Cls; Trs Stu Cncl; Capt Bsktbl; JV Fld Hcky; JV Capt Lcrss; Hon Roll; Prfct Atten Awd; Pres Schlr; Chorus; Prtcpnt PA ST U/PA Cncl Tchrs Engl Essy Cont, Athl Yr 85-86.

BILLEY, ELISA E; Hempfield SR HS; New Stanton, PA; (4); 4/676; Pres AFS; Drama Clb; NFL; School Musical; School Play; Trs Stu Cncl; VP French Hon Soc; NHS; Sec Latin Clb; Ski Clb; PA Gov Schl Arts 86; JR Mndlsshn Chr 87; 1st Pl Carnegie Awds 87; Carnegie Mellon U; Music.

BILLGER, JESSICA; Newport HS; Newport, PA; (1); Am Leg Aux Girls St; School Musical; Swing Chorus; Rep Stu Cncl; JV Bsktbl; JV Fld Hcky; JV Sftbl; Wt Lftg; High Hon Roll; Hnbl Mntn At Dcknsn Coll Sci Fair 87; Fld Hcky Play Day Allstar 1st Tm Link 86; Hmcmng Atten 86.

BILLINGSLEY, LISA; Franklin HS; Franklin, PA; (2); 7/243; German Clb; SADD; Band; Concert Band; Mrchg Band; Rep Soph Cls.

BILLISITS, JODY; Frazier HS; Perryopolis, PA; (3); Rep Jr Cls; Vllybl; High Hon Roll; Hon Roll; Jr NHS; NHS; IN U; Accntng.

BILLMAN, GREGORY J; Greensburg Central Catholic HS; Jeannette, PA; (2); 1/230; Teachers Aide; JV Bsktbl; L Crs Cntry; Im Score Keeper; High Hon Roll; Pediatrcn.

BILLONI, PHILIP; Hempfield HS; Lancaster, PA; (3); 60/430; Boy Scts; Trs JA; Trs Science Clb; Ski Clb; Band; Mrchg Band; School Play; Stu Cncl; High Hon Roll; Hon Roll; Biochmstry.

BILLOW, SARAH; Upper Dauphin Area HS; Elizabethville, PA; (4); 9/108; Church Yth Grp; Chorus; Church Choir; School Musical; School Play; VP Soph Cls; VP Jr Cls; Sftbl; Hon Roll; NHS; Vocal Music Awd; Prsdntl Ftnss Awd; Physcl Ftnss Awd; Eastern Coll; Sec Educ.

BILOTTA, TONYA; Pius X HS; Roseto, PA; (3); Church Yth Grp; Drama Clb; GAA; Library Aide; Pep Clb; Spanish Clb; Church Choir; School Musical; Lit Mag; JV Sftbl; Empire Beauty Schl.

BILOTTI, DEANA; Frankford HS; Philadelphia, PA; (3); 23/639; Cmnty Wkr; FBLA; Girl Scts; Pep Clb; Rep Stu Cncl; Stat Bsbl; Mgr(s); Im Socr; Im Sftbl; Hon Roll; Bus.

BILSKI, ERICA; Central Catholic HS; Reading, PA; (4); German Clb; Pep Clb; Mrchg Band; Stage Crew; Variety Show; NHS; Prfct Atten Awd; Hosp Aide; Twrlr; Bst Wrk In German Awd 83-87; Hghst Acad Stu In Mt Penn & Exeter Area 87; Pres Acad Fit Awd 87; Hahnemann Univ; Nrsng.

BILSKI, JOHN; GAR Memorial HS; Wilkes-Barre, PA; (3); 15/152; Church Yth Grp; French Clb; Chorus; Stage Crew; Rep Stu Cncl; Var Ftbl; Var L Trk; Im Wt Lftg; High Hon Roll; Hon Roll; Lzrn Cnty Sci Tchrs Assoc Outstndng Sci Stu Awd 85; Med Tech.

BILTCLIFF, TIMOTHY A; Kutztown Area HS; Kutztown, PA; (3); Quiz Bowl; Band; High Hon Roll; NHS.

BIMLE, LISA; Portage Area HS; Portage, PA; (3); Ski Clb; Flag Corp; Mrchg Band; Hon Roll; Pres Fit Awd 85 & 87; UPJ; Acctng.

BINCKLEY JR, THOMAS L; Jenkintown HS; Jenkintown, PA; (4); 6/43; Varsity Clb; Yrbk Stf; Var Badmtn; Var Bsktbl; Var Ftbl; Hon Roll; NHS; Spanish NHS; Med.

BINGAMAN, AUDRA; Newport HS; Newport, PA; (3); Art Clb; Pep Clb; Spanish Clb; Band; Concert Band; Jazz Band; Mrchg Band; School Play; Mgr Bsktbl; Hon Roll; Tri-M Music Hnr Soc 86; Schlstc Art Awd 85; Perry Co Band 87; Spnsh.

BINGAMAN, BRIAN; Souderton Arfa HS; Salfordville, PA; (3); Boy Scts; School Musical; School Play; Nwsp Rptr; Off Jr Cls; Stu Cncl; Hon Roll.

BINGAMAN, CONNIE; Greencastle Antrim HS; Greencastle, PA; (4); FFA; VICA; IBM Prntg Press Oper.

BINGAMAN, DAWN; Elizabethtown Area HS; Elizabethtown, PA; (3); 22/261; Church Yth Grp; School Play; Fld Hcky; Sftbl; Vllybl; Hon Roll; NHS; Rch Am-Grp Agnst Drgs 86-87; Soc Wrk.

BINGAMAN, DEBBIE; Millersburg Area HS; Millersburg, PA; (3); Church Yth Grp; French Clb; Spanish Clb; Chorus; Var Powder Puff Ftbl; JV Sftbl; Hon Roll; NEDT Awd; Fgn Lang.

BINGAMAN, MICHAEL; Cumberland Valley HS; Camp Hill, PA; (3); 149/582; Church Yth Grp; L Swmmng; Hnrb Mntn JR Natl Water Polo 86; Dist III Medlye Relay Chmps 86; JR Natl Qlfr; All Amercn 400 Relay; Math.

BINGAMAN, SHERRI; Purchase Line HS; Arcadia, PA; (3); FBLA; SADD; Pep Clb; JV Cheerleading; Hon Roll; FL Coll; Nrsng.

BINGHAM, SUSANNE; North Allegheny HS; Wexford, PA; (2); Rep Stu Cncl; Cmmnctns.

BIONDI, KIMBERLY; Quarer Valley SR HS; Leetsdale, PA; (2); Debate Tm; Drama Clb; French Clb; Key Clb; Q&S; Thesps; School Play; Nwsp Stf; Lit Mag; Stu Cncl; Acting.

BIRCH, CHRISTINE; Trinity HS; Washington, PA; (3); French Clb; Band; Concert Band; Mrchg Band; Lit Mag; Cert Of Ed Dev Natl 87; W VA U; Jrnlsm.

BIRCH, MARIETTE; Homer-Center HS; Homer City, PA; (4); Dance Clb; French Clb; Chorus; School Play; Nwsp Rptr; Yrbk Rptr; Rep Stu Cncl; Cheerleading; Stat Trk; Hon Roll; Amer Extrdrs Cncl Schlrshp 87; Indiana U Of PA; Psychlgy.

BIRCHER, CATHY; Fairchance-Georges SR HS; Fairchance, PA; (3); Spanish Clb; Band; Drill Tm.

BIRCKBICHLER, EDWARD; Wilmington Area HS; Volant, PA; (2); Church Yth Grp; Computer Clb; Radio Clb; Hon Roll; Med.

BIRD, BRIAN; Danville HS; Danville, PA; (4); Church Yth Grp; 4-H; Pres FFA; Sftbl; 4-H Awd; Kystone & Chptr Farmr 86; Deklb Awd 87.

BIRD, DEBORAH; Mercer JR SR HS; Mercer, PA; (3); VP Dance Clb; Rep Ski Clb; Drill Tm; School Play; Nwsp Stf; Yrbk Stf; Trs Jr Cls; Rep Stu Cncl; JV Cheerleading; Var Trk; Stu Sec-Athltcs Dir; Coach-Pee Wee & Mdgt Ftbl Chrldrs; Accntng.

BIRD, JESSIE; Philadelphia Montgomery Chrstn Acad; Wyndmoor, PA; (1); JV Trk; High Hon Roll; Hortcltr.

BIRD, JONATHAN; Phil-Mont Christian Acad; Wyndmoor, PA; (3); Chess Clb; Church Yth Grp; Math Tm; Chorus; Var L Crs Cntry; Var L Trk; Hon Roll; NHS; Ntl Merit SF; Slvr Mdlst In Mid Atlantc Music Comp 85-86; 3rd Pl In Lge Cross-Cntry Champshp 86-87; West Point; Bio Engr.

BIRD, MICHELLE; Western Wayne HS; Moscow, PA; (3); Church Yth Grp; Band; Drm Mjr(t); Mrchg Band; JV Bsktbl; Score Keeper; Sftbl; Twrlr; Hon Roll.

BIRES, MAUREEN; Hopewell SR HS; Aliquippa, PA; (3); 27/255; Art Clb; Math Clb; Spanish Clb; Rep Stu Cncl; Powder Puff Ftbl; Trk; High Hon Roll; NHS; Trk Ltr 85-87.

BIRES, MELISSA; Hopewell SR HS; Aliquippa, PA; (4); 3/245; Church Yth Grp; Latin Clb; Chorus; Concert Band; Mrchg Band; School Musical; Sec Jr Cls; Sec Sr Cls; Bowling; Pres NHS; Fld Cmmndng Trphy 86; Cert Of Merit-Fld Cmmndng 85-86; Duquesne U; Educ.

BIRGE, WENDY; Beaver Area JR/Sr HS; Bridgewater, PA; (4); FBLA; Girl Scts; Library Aide; Office Aide; Church Choir; School Play; Stage Crew; Powder Puff Ftbl; Hon Roll; 2nd Pl Awd For FBLA Rgnl Cmptn 86; Comp Sci.

BIRGEL, KARIN; George Washington HS; Philadelphia, PA; (3); 167/937; Trs Church Yth Grp; Drama Clb; German Clb; Hosp Aide; NFL; Office Aide; SADD; Church Choir; Stage Crew; Yrbk Phtg; AARG Awds German 2-4 84-86; Psych.

BIRINGER, MICHELE; Fort Cherry HS; Hickory, PA; (4); 6/112; Church Yth Grp; Computer Clb; Math Clb; Spanish Clb; Drill Tm; Nwsp Rptr; Nwsp Stf; Jr NHS; NHS; TX A&m Galveston; Mrn Bio.

BIRKETT, SUSAN; Central York SR HS; York, PA; (4); Trs Varsity Clb; School Musical; Nwsp Stf; Yrbk Stf; Rep Stu Cncl; Co-Capt Cheerleading; Coach Actv; Vllybl; High Hon Roll; Hon Roll; Ted Berkheimer Awd 87; Stu Cncl Svc Awd 87; Towson ST U; Bus Admin.

BIRKOFER, JANE; Cardinal O Hara HS; Brookhaven, PA; (3); 9/710; Church Yth Grp; Cmnty Wkr; Office Aide; Spanish Clb; Nwsp Stf; Yrbk Stf; Cheerleading; VP NHS; Spanish NHS; Acdmc Convctn 85-87; VP 87-88.

BIRKOS, STEVE; Riverview HS; Verona, PA; (2); Yrbk Stf; L Tennis; High Hon Roll; Clemson; Biochem.

BIRMINGHAM, RAYMOND; Mc Keesport Area HS; Mc Keesport, PA; (3); German Clb; High Hon Roll; Hon Roll; Aerospace Engnrng.

BISBEE, DANIELLE; Tunkhannock Area HS; Tunkhannock, PA; (2); 36/330; Pep Clb; Spanish Clb; Bsktbl; Var Cheerleading; Sftbl; Var Tennis; Hon Roll.

BISCARDI, JOSEPH; Charleoi Area HS; Charleroi, PA; (3); 3/180; Pres French Clb; Science Clb; Ski Clb; Rep SADD; Varsity Clb; Nwsp Stf; Yrbk Stf; Rep Soph Cls; Rep Jr Cls; Rep Sr Cls; Elec Engnrg.

BISCHOF, JENNIFER; Lower Dauphin HS; Hummelstown, PA; (3); 44/276; Trs Church Yth Grp; Dance Clb; Hosp Aide; Hon Roll; Booster Club; Communications.

BISCONTINI, LAURA; J M Coughlin HS; Wilkes Barre, PA; (3); Ski Clb; SADD; Drill Tm; Stat Bsktbl; Mgr(s); Hon Roll; Spn Cert Kings Coll 84-85; Bloomsburg U; Elem Ed.

BISCOTTO, LYNN; Pittston Area SR HS; Pittston, PA; (2); SADD; Teachers Aide; Hon Roll; Chld Psych.

BISEL, CHERI; Cowanesque Valley HS; Westfield, PA; (3); FFA; Letterman Clb; Soph Cls; Jr Cls; Stu Cncl; Bsktbl; Sftbl; Vllybl; NHS; Cnty Frmrs Dgre FFA 86; Schlr Athlt Awd 85-86; Penn ST; Anml Hsbndry.

BISH, CORY; Ambridge Area HS; Ambridge, PA; (2); Church Yth Grp; Hon Roll; Penn ST U; Comm Pilot.

BISH, MELANIE; Clarion Area HS; Shippenville, PA; (4); SADD; Mrchg Band; School Musical; Swing Chorus; Yrbk Stf; Stat Bsktbl; Twrlr; Hon Roll; Pres Schlr; Pep Clb; Amer Lgn Essay Cont Wnnr 86; Penn ST U; Comms.

BISHOP, AMY; Lakeland HS; Olyphant, PA; (3); 45/134; Art Clb; Var L Trk; Hon Roll; Art.

BISHOP, CHARLES; Mechanicsburg HS; Mechanicsburg, PA; (2); 144/309; Church Yth Grp; Intnl Clb; Service Clb; Chorus; Pres Frsh Cls; Pres Soph Cls; Rep Stu Cncl; JV Capt Bsbl; Capt JV Bsktbl; Capt Ftbl; Ed.

BISHOP, CHRISTINA L; Norristown Area HS; Norristown, PA; (4); 55/478; Cmnty Wkr; Pres VICA; Trs Soph Cls; VP Jr Cls; Pres Sr Cls; Pres Stu Cncl; High Hon Roll; NHS; ST VP-VCTNL Indstrl Clbs Of Amer 86-87; Temple U; Htl-Rest Mngt.

BISHOP, DAVID; Seton La Salle Regional HS; Pittsburgh, PA; (4); 29/270; Dance Clb; Drama Clb; FBLA; Pep Clb; SADD; Variety Show; Yrbk Rptr; Yrbk Stf; Off Sr Cls; Im Bsktbl; Clarion U Of PA; Acctng.

BISHOP, LYNN; Greensburg Central Catholic HS; Jeannette, PA; (2); Cmnty Wkr; Ski Clb; Rep Soph Cls; JV Cheerleading; JV Pom Pon; Swmmng; Tennis; Cit Awd; High Hon Roll; Hon Roll.

BISHOP, MATTHEW S; Karns City HS; Petrolia, PA; (4); Church Yth Grp; Band; Var Bsktbl; Var Ftbl; Var Trk; Hon Roll; NHS; Pres Schlr; Clarion U; Fin.

BISHOP, TODD; Moshannon Valley Christian Acad; Coalport, PA; (4); 2/5; Pres Church Yth Grp; Drama Clb; Spanish Clb; Yrbk Stf; Pres Stu Cncl; Var Capt Bsktbl; Var Capt Socr; Cit Awd; Hon Roll; Prncpsl Awd Top Stu Schl 85; Supv Awd Top Stu Cls 85; Accntng.

BISHOP, TRIS; Elizabethtown Area HS; Rheems, PA; (3); 52/278; Drama Clb; German Clb; Teachers Aide; Thesps; Fld Hcky; Powder Puff Ftbl.

BISKING, TRIXIE; Lancaster Catholic HS; Lancaster, PA; (4); 17/190; Art Clb; Varsity Clb; Capt L Bsktbl; Mgr Ftbl; Mgr(s); Im Sftbl; Var Trk; Hon Roll; NHS; Prsdntl Acad Fitness Awd 87; Volunteer Of Yr Lancashire Hall 87; U Of Pittsburgh; Sprts Med.

BISKUP, KATHLEEN; Center Area HS; Monaca, PA; (2); Cmnty Wkr; Hosp Aide; Spanish Clb; Stu Cncl; JV Bsktbl; Bowling; Powder Puff Ftbl; High Hon Roll; Hon Roll.

BISSETT, SHELIA; Ft Cherry HS; Hickory, PA; (3); 20/145; Pres 4-H; Math Clb; Science Clb; Ski Clb; Spanish Clb; 4-H Awd; High Hon Roll; Hon Roll; Penn ST; Engrng.

BISTLINE, MELINDA; Donegal HS; Mount Joy, PA; (4); 5/164; Church Yth Grp; VP Chorus; School Play; Yrbk Ed-Chief; Trk; Hon Roll; NHS; VFW Awd; Voice Dem Awd; Pres Schlrshp 87; Donegal Educ Assn Schlrshp 87; Thomas D Mc Coy Ptrtsm Awd 87; Bridgewater Coll; Educ.

BISTRICHAN, DANIELLE; Hanover Area JR SR HS; Wilkes Barre, PA; (3); 8/154; Cmnty Wkr; Hosp Aide; Chorus; Church Choir; High Hon Roll; Jr NHS; NHS; NEDT Awd; Wilkes Coll; Pre-Vet.

BITER, ROB; Bishop Carroll HS; Cresson, PA; (3); 8/128; VP JA; Pres NFL; SADD; Yrbk Ed-Chief; Pres Frsh Cls; Rep Jr Cls; Var L Trk; Trs NHS; Church Yth Grp; Cmnty Wkr; Hugh O Brian Yth Fndtn ST & Intl Amb 85-86; 1st Pl ST JR Acad Of Sci Comp 85-86; Med.

BITLER, REAGAN; Hughesville JR-SR HS; Hughesville, PA; (3); 13/145; Pres Church Yth Grp; VP 4-H; FTA; Yrbk Rptr; Yrbk Stf; Rep Soph Cls; Rep Jr Cls; Socr; 4-H Awd; Hon Roll; Rep Susqhanns Wrkshp Bus 87; Secndry Ed.

BITNER, ELIZABETH A; Souderton Area HS; Harleysville, PA; (4); 9/375; Church Yth Grp; Ed Nwsp Stf; Ed Lit Mag; Cit Awd; High Hon Roll; Jr NHS; NCTE Awd; NHS; Ntl Merit SF; Rotary Awd; Cnty Sci Fair 1st Pl Zoology; Engl Awd; Frnch Awd; Psych.

BITNER, KRISTA; Donegal HS; Mount Joy, PA; (3); 12/175; Color Guard; Yrbk Stf; Rep Stu Cncl; Cheerleading; Hon Roll; NHS; Crs Cntry; Radiologic Tech.

BITNER, MIKE; Sauderton HS; Haleysville, PA; (3); Church Yth Grp; Socr; Trk; Math.

BITNER, STEVE; Greencastle Antrim HS; Greencastle, PA; (3); 4/167; Church Yth Grp; Computer Clb; JV Bsktbl; Wt Lftg; High Hon Roll; Hon Roll; VP NHS; Prfct Atten Awd; Acadc Achvt Awd 86-87; Mth Cont Awd 86-87; Bus.

BITNER, VANESSA; Big Spring HS; Newville, PA; (2); GAA; Band; Concert Band; Mrchg Band; VP Jr Cls; Mgr(s); Trk; Stat Wrstlng; High Hon Roll; U Of DE; Med.

BITSKO, ROSLYN; Conemaugh Valley HS; Conemaugh, PA; (4); 12/119; Drama Clb; Office Aide; Pep Clb; Yrbk Stf; Var Cheerleading; Hon Roll; NHS; Prom Comm Chrmn 86; IN U Of PA; Resp Thrpy.

BITTINBGER, JOEANNE L; Salisbury Elk-Lick HS; Meyersdale, PA; (3); Am Leg Aux Girls St; Art Clb; Rptr FFA; Red Cross Aide; School Play; Nwsp Stf; Yrbk Ed-Chief; Yrbk Stf; Sec Jr Cls; Hon Roll; Clarion U; Spch Pthlgy.

BITTINGER, JOANNE; Salisbury Elk Lick HS; Meyersdale, PA; (3); Am Leg Aux Girls St; Art Clb; Rptr FFA; Red Cross Aide; School Play; Nwsp Stf; Ed Yrbk Stf; Sec Jr Cls; High Hon Roll; 2nd Amrcn Lgn Essy Cont 87; Clarion U; Spch Pathlgy.

BITTLE, LEE ANN; Elizabeth Forward HS; Elizabeth, PA; (2); Im Bsktbl; Var L Vllybl; Hon Roll.

BITTLEBRUN, MELANY; Bethlehem Center SR HS; Richeyville, PA; (2); Church Yth Grp; Mgr(s); Im Vllybl; High Hon Roll; Hon Roll; 3rd Pl Engl Writing Cont 86; Art.

BITTLER, ROBERT; Mercer HS; Mercer, PA; (2); Var Bsktbl; Var Crs Cntry; Var Trk; Hon Roll; Ecolgy Tm 85-87.

BITTLER, RONALD; Mercer HS; Mercer, PA; (2); Chess Clb; Stu Cncl; Var Bsktbl; Var Crs Cntry; Var Trk; Hon Roll; Eco Tm Dist Champs 85-87.

BITTMAN, KEVIN; Council Rock HS; Newtown, PA; (3); 72/908; Cmnty Wkr; Temple Yth Grp; Band; Concert Band; Jazz Band; Mrchg Band; Variety Show; Lit Mag; Socr; Hon Roll; Elec Engrng.

BITTNER, CHRISTINE; Meyersdale Area HS; Meyersdale, PA; (4); Trs Church Yth Grp; French Clb; Letterman Clb; Varsity Clb; Band; Concert Band; Mrchg Band; L Sftbl; NHS; Pres Physcl Ftns Awd 81-87; Conemough Vly Mem Schl Of Nrs.

BITTNER, DEE; Danville HS; Danville, PA; (2); 4-H; Band; Concert Band; Mrchg Band; Lake Erie Coll; Equestrian.

BITTNER, GINA; Northwestern Lehigh HS; Germansville, PA; (3); 2/160; Sec 4-H; Pres Sec Chorus; Church Choir; School Musical; Nwsp Rptr; Rep Jr Cls; NHS; Debate Tm; Band; Mrchg Band; Cnty Dist & Regnl Chorus 85-87; Hugh O Brian Ldrshp Sem Rep 86; Altrnt Govs Schl For Arts 86.

BITTNER, ROY; Berlin-Brothersvalley HS; Meyersdale, PA; (4); 17/81; Chess Clb; Pres Trs 4-H; French Clb; FFA; School Play; Yrbk Stf; JV Wrstlng; 4-H Awd; Hon Roll; Lion Awd; Sterner Schlrshp 87; U Of Pittsburgh; Comp Sci.

BITTNER, SCOTT; North Star HS; Boswell, PA; (3); Cmnty Wkr; FCA; Letterman Clb; Varsity Clb; Pres Soph Cls; Ftbl; Wt Lftg; L Wrstlng; Cit Awd; Hon Roll; Stdnt Mnth; IUP; Lwyr.

BITTNER, SCOTT; Southern Columbia HS; Catawissa, PA; (4); 40/72; Art Clb; Computer Clb; Letterman Clb; Varsity Clb; Coach Actv; Capt L Ftbl; Var L Trk; Wt Lftg; Var L Wrstlng; Wrestling-Geo Gold Awd 87; Wrstlng St Title Wrstlng Tm 84-85; Kutztown U; Bus Admin.

BITTNER, STEPHANIE; Abraham Lincoln HS; Philadelphia, PA; (3); 18/400; Church Yth Grp; Red Cross Aide; Service Clb; Sec Stu Cncl; Hon Roll; 3rd Pl Bus Edctrs Assn Typng Comptn 87; Bus Mgmt.

BITZEL, GERALD; Northeastern SR HS; Mt Wolf, PA; (3); Church Yth Grp; Computer Clb; Drama Clb; Pres VP FBLA; Vllybl; Hon Roll; Voice Dem Awd; 3rd Pl Voice Demcrcy 85-86; Aviation.

BITZER, BECKY; Donegal HS; Mount Joy, PA; (2); Church Yth Grp; Band; Concert Band; Jazz Band; Mrchg Band; Nwsp Rptr; Nwsp Stf; Tennis; Band Awd 85-87; Nwspr Awd 86-87.

BIVENS, JENNIFER; Meadville Area SR HS; Meadville, PA; (2); JCL; Pres Latin Clb; VP Ski Clb; Trk; Hon Roll; Psychlgy.

BIXEL, KENNETH; Chambersburg Area SR HS; Chambersburg, PA; (3); Church Yth Grp; Cmnty Wkr; Pres 4-H; Band; JV Ftbl; 4-H Awd; Hon Roll; Vet Med.

BIXLER, APRIL; Central Dauphin HS; Harrisburg, PA; (3); 56/370; Chorus; Yrbk Stf; Stat Swmmng; Im Vllybl; Hon Roll; Jr NHS; NHS; Pres Acdmc Ftnss Awd 85; Elem Educ.

BIXLER, DARLENE; Center HS; Aliquippa, PA; (3); Spanish Clb; Sec Trs Frsh Cls; VP Soph Cls; VP Jr Cls; VP Sr Cls; Mgr Bsbl; Bowling; Mgr Powder Puff Ftbl; Twrlr; Hon Roll; Bus Mgnt.

BIXLER, PATTI; Annville-Cleona HS; Annville, PA; (3); 19/127; French Clb; Chorus; Nwsp Stf; Yrbk Stf; Hon Roll; Jr NHS; NHS; Millersville U; Spec Ed.

BJES, TIFFANY; North Star HS; Boswell, PA; (4); 32/136; Band; Yrbk Bus Mgr; Pres Soph Cls; Pres Jr Cls; Pres Sr Cls; JV Cheerleading; Sec Mat Maids; Hon Roll; Lion Awd; Mple Prncss, 1st Rnnr Up 87; Hmcmng Ct 87; Drvrs Educ Awd 87; Cambria-Rowe; Bus Admin.

BJORNSON, KRISTEN; Lampeter Strasburg HS; Lancaster, PA; (4); 5/146; Hst AFS; FBLA; Band; School Musical; Yrbk Stf; Trk; Sec NHS; Pres Schlr; U S Ldrshp Awd 87; Sci Fair Wnnr City/Cnty 1st Chem 86; Schl Ed Assoc Schlrshp 87; PA ST U; Scl Wrk.

BLAC, KLYNANNE; Bishop Mc Cort HS; Johnstown, PA; (3); 9/155; Latin Clb; Mu Alpha Theta; Ski Clb; Band; Chorus; Church Choir; Concert Band; Mrchg Band; Orch; Yrbk Stf; Duquesne U; Phrmcy.

BLACK, BELINDA; Cambridge Springs HS; Cambridge Spgs, PA; (2); 5/105; Pep Clb; Sec Spanish Clb; Rep Stu Cncl; JV Var Cheerleading; Hon Roll; NHS; Amercn Achvt-Physcl Ftns 86 & 87; Elem Schl Tchr.

BLACK, CHRISTINE; Eastern York HS; Windsor, PA; (3); SADD; Hon Roll.

BLACK, CHRISTOPHER; Cambridge Springs HS; Cambridge Spg, PA; (3); Pep Clb; Spanish Clb; Var Bsktbl; Hon Roll; Bus Mgmt.

BLACK, CHRISTOPHER J; Peters Township HS; Mc Murray, PA; (3); 26/236; Varsity Clb; Yrbk Stf; Rep Jr Cls; Var Wrstlng; Bus.

BLACK, DEBORAH; Coudersport Area JR SR HS; Coudersport, PA; (4); 13/90; Sec FTA; Teachers Aide; Varsity Clb; Drm Mjr(t); Sec Sr Cls; NHS; Trs French Clb; Chorus; Nwsp Stf; Yrbk Stf; HS Educ Assoc Schlrshp 87; Prsnl Dvlpmnt Awd 85; 1st Rnr Up Maple Swthrt Cntst 86; Clarion U Of PA; Elem Educ.

BLACK, HEATHER; Center HS; Aliquippa, PA; (3); 13/186; Cmnty Wkr; Drama Clb; Spanish Clb; Chorus; School Musical; Nwsp Stf; Yrbk Stf; VP Stu Cncl; Hon Roll; NHS; Stu Of Week 87; Hnrb Mntn Spanish Verbs Tst 87; Schlrshp Perform Sound Of Amer Hnrs Chorus 87; Bus.

BLACK JR, JAMES THOMAS; Bishop Mc Cort HS; Johnstown, PA; (2); Art Clb; Church Yth Grp; French Clb; Golf; Cit Awd; Hon Roll.

BLACK, JENNIFER; Nazareth Acad; Philadelphia, PA; (3); Church Yth Grp; German Clb; Hosp Aide; Pep Clb; Red Cross Aide; Service Clb; VP Soph Cls; Pres Jr Cls; Var Fld Hcky; Im Vllybl; Hnr Cert Of Merit 85-87; Awd 151 Hrs Of Vlntr Svc Nazareth Hosp 86; Sprts Awd 86 & 87.

BLACK, JIM; Charleroi Area JR SR HS; N Charleroi, PA; (3); Spanish Clb; Bowling; Hon Roll; Penn ST U; Jrnlsm.

BLACK, JULIE; York Catholic HS; York, PA; (3); Church Yth Grp; Cmnty Wkr; Hosp Aide; Spanish Clb; Varsity Clb; Rep Frsh Cls; Var Capt Cheerleading; Coach Actv; Stat Mgr(s); High Hon Roll; PMTA Lcl & St Conf Wnnr 83-86; Med.

BLACK, KATHY; Liberty JR SR HS; Liberty, PA; (4); 11/45; Church Yth Grp; Pres Sec 4-H; FHA; German Clb; JV Bsktbl; Var Trk; JV Var Vllybl; 4-H Awd; Bloomsburg U; Spch Path.

BLACK, LARRY; Windber Area HS; Windber, PA; (3); 20/128; Pres Church Yth Grp; Math Tm; Spanish Clb; Band; Church Choir; Rep Frsh Cls; Trs Stu Cncl; High Hon Roll; Hon Roll; Sec Trs NHS; Stu Of Mnth Awd 85-87; Arch Engr.

BLACK, LORI; Plum SR HS; Pittsburgh, PA; (3); French Clb; VP FTA; Band; Mrchg Band; Stage Crew; Nwsp Stf; Trk; Hon Roll; Schlrshp-Carnegie Mellons Pre-Coll Art Classes 85; Fine Arts.

BLACK, MAURICE; George Washington Carver HS Eng/Sci; Philadelphia, PA; (3); VP Church Yth Grp; Quiz Bowl; Im Ftbl; Cit Awd; Phila Archdiocesan Catholic Youth Orgnztn Prs 87-88; Electrcl Engrng.

BLACK, MELISSA; Portage Area HS; Portage, PA; (4); Am Leg Aux Girls St; Aud/Vis; Computer Clb; German Clb; Band; Sec Chorus; Concert Band; Jazz Band; Mrchg Band; Pep Band; IUP; Airline Stewardess.

BLACK, RACHAEL; Highlands SR HS; Brackenridge, PA; (3); Library Aide; Office Aide; Pep Clb; Nwsp Rptr; Nwsp Stf; Tennis; Hon Roll; Poly Sci.

BLACK, RODERICK S; Hollidaysburg Area SR HS; Duncansville, PA; (3); 35/371; Science Clb; VP Spanish Clb.

BLACK, SHARI; Everett Area HS; Everett, PA; (4); 4/107; Band; Chorus; Concert Band; Jazz Band; Mrchg Band; Pep Band; Variety Show; Hon Roll; JP Sousa Awd; NHS; All Estrn Band-Bltmr MD 87; IN U Of PA Hnrs Band 84-86; Indiana U Of PA; Music.

BLACK, STACEY; Forbes Road HS; Hustontown, PA; (3); Sec FFA; Varsity Clb; Sec Frsh Cls; Rep Soph Cls; Rep Jr Cls; Stu Cncl; JV Bsktbl; L Cheerleading; L Fld Hcky.

BLACK, TERRI; Biglerville HS; Bendersville, PA; (3); #22 In Class; Art Clb; Mrchg Band; Fld Hcky; Twrlr; Hon Roll; Marine Bio.

BLACKBURN, GINA; Hollidaysburg Area SR HS; Hollidaysburg, PA; (4); 13/345; Sec Trs 4-H; Trs French Clb; JA; Nwsp Stf; Im Vllybl; Cit Awd; High Hon Roll; Kiwanis Awd; NHS; Ntl Merit Schol; Penn ST U; Nrsng.

BLACKBURN, THOMAS; Highlands SR HS; Natrona Hts, PA; (3); Rep Soph Cls; Rep Jr Cls; Var JV Ftbl; Swmmng; Hon Roll; Jr NHS; NHS; Prfct Atten Awd.

BLACKEDGE, DIANE; Benton Area JR SR HS; Shickshinny, PA; (4); 1/49; Cmnty Wkr; Drama Clb; FTA; GAA; Hosp Aide; Keywanettes; Red Cross Aide; School Musical; School Play; Yrbk Stf; Benton Alumni Schlrshp 87; Clmbia Cnty Frmrs Natl Bnk Schlrshp 87; UPIU Schlrshp 87; PA ST U; Jvnl Cnslng.

BLACKLEDGE, DAVID; Benton JR-SR HS; Shickshinny, PA; (2); Chorus; JV Bsktbl.

BLACKLEDGE, DIANE M; Benton Area JR/Sr HS; Shickshinny, PA; (4); 1/41; Drama Clb; FTA; Hosp Aide; Keywanettes; Red Cross Aide; School Musical; School Play; Yrbk Stf; VP Frsh Cls; VP Soph Cls; Columbia Cnty Farmers Natl Bank Scholar 87; United Paperwrkrs Intl Union Scholar 87; Benton Alumni Sch; PA ST U; Socl Wrk.

BLACKMAN, SHELLEY; Sayre Area HS; Sayre, PA; (3); Spanish Clb; Chorus; Concert Band; Mrchg Band; School Play; Nwsp Rptr; JV Vllybl; High Hon Roll; NHS; Intl Stds.

BLACKMON, ROBERT; Taylor Allderdice HS; Pittsburgh, PA; (1); Church Yth Grp; Political Wkr; Ski Clb; JC Awd; Jr NHS.

BLACKMON, THEODORE; Taylor-Anderdice HS; Pittsburgh, PA; (3); Var Bsktbl; Im Ftbl; High Hon Roll; Jr NHS.

BLACKSTOCK, KEVIN; Bishop Mc Devitt HS; Philadelphia, PA; (3); Var Ftbl; Var Trk; Hampton; Acctg.

BLACKSTON, KIMBERLY; St Paul Cathedral HS; Pittsburgh, PA; (3); Spanish Clb; Y-Teens; Nwsp Stf; Trs Jr Cls; VP Stu Cncl; Hon Roll; Prfct Atten Awd; Carnegie Mellon U Natl Hstry Day Awd 1st Pl 87; Pittsburgh Prss Ftr Artcl-Sci Rsrch Pgm 86; U Of Pittsburgh; Opthamlgy.

BLACKWELL, GENEVIEVE; Chichester HS; Aston, PA; (3); Church Yth Grp; Band; Chorus; Concert Band; Capt Drill Tm; Sec Sr Cls; Fld Hcky; Mgr(s); Hon Roll; VP NHS; Elec Engrng.

BLADEL, LIZ; Carolynton HS; Pittsburgh, PA; (4); 9/172; German Clb; Yrbk Stf; Trs Stu Cncl; Var Capt Bsktbl; Cheerleading; Capt Powder Puff Ftbl; Dnfth Awd; High Hon Roll; Hon Roll; NHS; K Of C St Free Throw Champ 84; Presdntl Acad Ftnss Awd 87; Penn ST; Educ.

BLAICH, MARY; Cardinal Dougherty HS; Philadelphia, PA; (3); 176/670; Cmnty Wkr; Bowling; Bus.

BLAIN, ROBERT; Pine Grove Area HS; Pine Grove, PA; (4); Pres 4-H; Elec Tech.

BLAINE, JONATHAN; Cranberry HS; Seneca, PA; (3); CAP; Computer Clb; French Clb; Science Clb; Ski Clb; Hon Roll; NHS; Clarion U; Comp Pgmng.

BLAINE, KELLY; Newport JR/Sr HS; Newport, PA; (3); Yrbk Stf; Ftbl; Mgr(s); Wrstlng; Hon Roll; V P 86; Studnt Cncl 86-87; Hotel Mngt.

BLAINE, RICHELLE; E L Meyers HS; Wiles Barre, PA; (4); 10/180; Key Clb; Yrbk Stf; Rep Stu Cncl; Var L Sftbl; Var L Vllybl; Hon Roll; NHS; NEMA 86-87; Med.

BLAIR, AMY; Weatherly Area HS; Weatherly, PA; (3); 6/60; FBLA; Girl Scts; Ski Clb; Band; Concert Band; Flag Corp; Nwsp Rptr; Var JV Bsktbl; Var JV Golf; Hon Roll; Bus.

BLAIR, ANN MARIE S; Calvary Christian Acad; Mt Union, PA; (4); 1/8; Church Yth Grp; Office Aide; Pep Clb; Political Wkr; Chorus; School Play; Var Bsktbl; Var Socr; Hon Roll; Val; Hghst Acad Avrg 85-86; Sprtsmnshp Awd-Bsktbl 86-87; Most Improved-Vlybl 84-85.

BLAIR, DANIELLE; Conneaut Lake HS; Conneaut Lake, PA; (3); Spanish Clb; Chorus; Nwsp Rptr; Nwsp Stf; Var JV Cheerleading; Gym; Hon Roll.

BLAIR, JANET; Ridley HS; Folsom, PA; (3); 55/436; Church Yth Grp; Cmnty Wkr; Computer Clb; French Clb; GAA; Office Aide; Ski Clb; Varsity Clb; Chorus; Bsktbl; Tchr.

BLAIR, KELLY; Jeannette SR HS; Jeannette, PA; (2); Church Yth Grp; Drama Clb; Spanish Clb; Sec Band; Chorus; Color Guard; Concert Band; Jazz Band; Mrchg Band; Hon Roll; JR Mendelssohn Choir Pittsbrgh PA 87; Cnty Chorus 86-87; Clr Grd Co-Capt 87-88; Jvnl Prbtn Offcr.

BLAIR, KIMBERLY; Cranberry HS; Seneca, PA; (2); 9/140; Church Yth Grp; Hosp Aide; Off Science Clb; Spanish Clb; SADD; Teachers Aide; Hon Roll; Law.

BLAIR, KRISTIN; Ringgold HS; Donora, PA; (3); #23 In Class; Drama Clb; School Musical; School Play; Stage Crew; High Hon Roll; Hon Roll; NHS; Math/Sci Hnr Soc 86-87; Donora Goldn JR Tamburzitzns 83-87; Bus.

BLAIR, KRISTY; Warren Area HS; Warren, PA; (3); Cmnty Wkr; French Clb; Ski Clb; SADD; Concert Band; Yrbk Stf; Im Tennis; Hon Roll; Silver B Citznshp Awd 84; Math.

BLAIR, MELISSA; Harbor Creek HS; Erie, PA; (3); #8 In Class; Variety Show; Hon Roll.

BLAIR, PAUL; Knoch JR SR HS; Butler, PA; (2); FFA; Chorus; Church Choir; Madrigals; Vllybl; Hon Roll; Chptr Frmr Awd FFA 87; Penn ST U; Ag.

BLAIR, REBECCA; Mt Union Area HS; Mt Union, PA; (4); 17/172; Sec Church Yth Grp; French Clb; FBLA; Concert Band; Jazz Band; Mrchg Band; Trs Sr Cls; High Hon Roll; NHS; GAA; Rcvd Nrsg Schlrshp Socty 87; Reisinger Med Ctr Schl Nrsg.

BLAIR, SUSAN; Lincoln HS; Ellwood City, PA; (3); 15/162; French Clb; Ski Clb; Cheerleading; Hon Roll; NHS; NEDT Awd; Bus.

BLAIR, TAMMIE; Purchase Line HS; Hillsdale, PA; (2); 17/150; Church Yth Grp; Letterman Clb; Pep Clb; Scholastic Bowl; Spanish Clb; SADD; Varsity Clb; Band; Concert Band; Pep Band; West Point; Pre Med.

BLAISDELL, TRICIA A; Bradford Area HS; Lewis Run, PA; (4); Pres DECA; Am Leg Boys St; Sec Chorus; Vllybl; Hon Roll; 1st Pl DECA Cmpttn-Food Mrktng 86; Olean Bus Inst; Bus Admin.

BLAISURE, CHARLENE; Elk Lake HS; Meshoppen, PA; (4); 9/94; Art Clb; Drama Clb; French Clb; Ski Clb; SADD; Chorus; School Musical; School Play; Tyler Memrl Schlrshp 87; U Of Miami; Phy Thrpy.

BLAISURE, JASON; Tunkhannock Area HS; Mehoopany, PA; (1); Ski Clb; JV Socr; JV Tennis; Hon Roll; Embry-Riddle; Aerntcl Engr.

BLAKE, EDWIN; Hollidaysbyurg SR HS; Hollidaysburg, PA; (3); Band; Concert Band; Jazz Band; Mrchg Band; Golf; Ind Arts.

BLAKE, LIZ; Waynesburg Central HS; Spraggs, PA; (4); DECA; VICA; Hon Roll; Distrbtv Educ Clbs Amer Pres 86.

BLAKE-JONES, RUARRI; Philadelphia HS For Girls; Philadelphia, PA; (2); Library Aide; Office Aide; Service Clb; Trk; Pres Schlr; Prsdntl Acdmc Ftnss Awd; Georgetown U; Bus Admin.

BLAKELY, ANNE; The Agnes Irwin Schl; Radnor, PA; (3); Nwsp Rptr; Var Bsktbl; Var Fld Hcky; Var Lcrss; High Hon Roll; Comp Sci Awd 86; Brown Bk Awd 87; Math Cont Wnnr 87.

BLALOCK, MARSHALL; Chester HS; Chester, PA; (4); 8/398; Band; Chorus; Church Choir; Concert Band; Mrchg Band; School Musical; Dnfth Awd; Jr NHS; NHS; Rotary Awd; Kim Hixson Mem Awd 84-85; Harry Hoosier Annl Blck Laypersons Awd 86; Lttr Of Excel Acad 86; Temple U; Cmptr Sci.

BLANARIK, CARYN; Ambridge HS; Baden, PA; (2); Trs Church Yth Grp; Latin Clb; Pep Clb; Chorus; Nwsp Rptr; Nwsp Stf; Hon Roll; Jrnlsm.

BLANCH, MICHELINE; Bishop Mc Devitt HS; Highspire, PA; (4); FBLA; Science Clb; Yrbk Phtg; Rep Jr Cls; Stu Cncl; Sftbl; High Hon Roll; Hon Roll; NHS; Ntl Merit Ltr; PA ST U; Aero Sp Engr.

BLANCHARD, GABRIELLE; Meadville SR HS; Meadville, PA; (4); 52/306; Service Clb; Band; Hon Roll; Hnr Soc 86-87; Mercyhurst Coll; Accntng.

BLANCHARD, ROBIN; Bald Eagle Nittany HS; Mill Hall, PA; (2); 1/136; Spanish Clb; Chorus; Concert Band; Drm Mjr(t); Madrigals; School Musical; Twrlr; High Hon Roll; Hon Roll; NHS.

BLANCHE, CAMILLE; Spring-Ford HS; Royersford, PA; (3); 52/256; Girl Scts; Spanish Clb; SADD; School Musical; School Play; Var L Bsktbl; Stat Crs Cntry; Score Keeper; Var L Sftbl; Hon Roll; Bus Adm.

BLANCHETTE, JOHN; Notre Dame HS; E Stroudsburg, PA; (4); 5/43; Cmnty Wkr; Math Tm; Red Cross Aide; Capt Scholastic Bowl; Teachers Aide; Stage Crew; Nwsp Rptr; Trs Sr Cls; Rep Stu Cncl; L Bsktbl; Rendselaer Polytech Inst Schlrshp 87; R K R Hess Architecture Schlrshp 87; Pres Acadmc Ftns Awd 87; Rensdelaer Polytech Inst; Arch.

BLANCO, CHRISTINA; Central Bucks East HS; Mechanicsville, PA; (3); Art Clb; Acpl Chr; Chorus; Yrbk Stf; Lit Mag; Hon Roll; Strdy Classes-Fshn Inst Tech-Gr A 87, Tylr Schl Art-Jwlry Dsgn-Gr A 86-87; Moore Coll Art-Fshn Cert; Fashion Inst Of Tech; Fshn Dsgn.

BLANCO, KAREN; Canon Mc Millan SR HS; Cecil, PA; (3); French Clb; Drill Tm; School Musical; Stu Cncl; Bsktbl; Cheerleading; Trk; Hon Roll; Dnc Instrctr.

BLANCO, THERESA; Central Bucks High School East; Mechanicsville, PA; (4); Band; Concert Band; Jazz Band; Mrchg Band; School Musical; Symp Band; Nwsp Ed-Chief; Nwsp Rptr; High Hon Roll; Hon Roll; Natl Hispanic Schlrshp Semi-Fnlst 86-87; Excllnc In Jrnlsm Awd 86; American U; Jrnlsm.

BLAND, DEEDRA; West Greene HS; Wind Ridge, PA; (3); French Clb; Chorus; Nwsp Rptr; Nwsp Stf; JV Bsktbl; Hon Roll.

BLAND, DENISE; West Greene HS; Wind Ridge, PA; (2); Art Clb; French Clb; Intnl Clb; Science Clb; JV Var Sftbl; Hon Roll.

BLAND, SANDY; Waynesburg Central HS; Waynesburg, PA; (3); Church Yth Grp; 4-H; Natl Beta Clb; Office Aide; Spanish Clb; Var JV Bsktbl; 4-H Awd; High Hon Roll; Hon Roll; Prfct Atten Awd; Outstndng Englsh Stu Of Yr 87; Bus.

BLANEY, DIANNE; St Hubert HS; Philadelphia, PA; (3); 136/421; Dance Clb; School Musical; School Play; Mdrn Dance.

BLANK, LISA; Pequea Valley HS; Gap, PA; (3); AFS; Church Yth Grp; FBLA; Chorus; Yrbk Stf; Hon Roll; NHS.

BLANK, MARY HARTMAN; Lincoln HS; Ellwood City, PA; (3); 12/162; Y-Teens; Band; Concert Band; Jazz Band; Mrchg Band; School Musical; School Play; Rep Jr Cls; Rep Stu Cncl; NHS; Amer Lgn Awd 83-84; Outstndng Schlsct Achvt Awd 87.

BLANKLEY, ANGELA; Everett Area HS; Everett, PA; (4); 1/105; Church Yth Grp; Pres 4-H; Spanish Clb; Sec Band; Yrbk Ed-Chief; Stu Cncl; Bausch & Lomb Sci Awd; High Hon Roll; NHS; Spanish NHS; Ntl Awd Amer Qutrhrse Assn 86; Penn ST; Elem Ed.

BLANNETT JR, ALBERT P; Hanover Area JR-SR HS; Ashley, PA; (4); Pres Church Yth Grp; Ski Clb; Band; Concert Band; Jazz Band; Pres Mrchg Band; Pep Band; JP Sousa Awd; Rcvd Cngrssnl Citation-For Sousa Hnrs Band 87.

BLANNETT, JOSEPH; Wyoming Valley West HS; Kingston, PA; (3); 12/402; Yrbk Stf; Rep Stu Cncl; Bsktbl; Ftbl; Trk; Cit Awd; High Hon Roll; NHS; Pep Clb; Nwsp Stf; Comp Sci.

BLASCO, MARY; Jeannette SR HS; Jeannette, PA; (3); Trs Band; Concert Band; Mrchg Band; Symp Band; Trs Frsh Cls; Trs Soph Cls; JV Var Bsktbl; Sec Sftbl; Hon Roll; Accntng.

BLASE, MARY; Bishop Neumann HS; Williamsport, PA; (3); Church Yth Grp; Sec FBLA; Spanish Clb; SADD; Chorus; Stage Crew; Var Bsktbl; Var Sftbl; Im Vllybl; Hon Roll; Typing I Merit Awd 87; Med.

BLASHAK-TOMPKINS, STACEY; Shenango HS; New Castle, PA; (2); Letterman Clb; Library Aide; Office Aide; Spanish Clb; Teachers Aide; Band; Flag Corp; Var Bsktbl; Sftbl; Hon Roll; Naval Acad; Med.

BLASIAK, WENDY; Bishop Hafey HS; Drums, PA; (3); Red Cross Aide; Y-Teens; JV Var Bsktbl; Hon Roll; Pre Med.

BLASICK, JEN; Danville SR HS; Riverside, PA; (2); Computer Clb; Dance Clb; Letterman Clb; Spanish Clb; L Trk; Hon Roll; 2nd Pl Sci Fair; Athltc Trnr; Sci.

BLASKO, STEPHANIE L; M M I Prep; Freeland, PA; (3); Church Yth Grp; Cmnty Wkr; Pep Clb; Varsity Clb; Var L Bowling; Var L Cheerleading; Var L Crs Cntry; Var L Sftbl; Hon Roll; 1st Pl Spnsh Awd-Blmsburg Coll 84-85; All Arnd Female Athl 85-86; In Top 90th Prcntl Of NEDTS 84-86; Psychlgy.

BLASLAK, WENDY; Bishop Hatey HS; Drums, PA; (3); Library Aide; Y-Teens; JV Var Bsktbl.

BLASS, TIMOTHY; Danville SR HS; Danville, PA; (2); 13/160; Computer Clb; Debate Tm; L Tennis; Wharton Schl Of Bus; Bus Adm.

BLATHER, GRETTA; Central York HS; York, PA; (3); Pres 4-H; SADD; Varsity Clb; Yrbk Phtg; Yrbk Sprt Ed; Var L Tennis; Rotary Awd; Won Eastern Natl Hippology Tm Tournmnt 87; Show Amer Qurtr Horses 85-87; Bio Chem.

BLATT, CARYN; South Park HS; Tampa, FL; (2); Cmnty Wkr; Office Aide; Teachers Aide; Mrchg Band; Rep Frsh Cls; Rep Soph Cls; Rep Stu Cncl; JV Var Mgr(s); JV Var Score Keeper; JV Sftbl; Comm.

BLATT, JODI; Purchase Line HS; Glen Campbell, PA; (2); Church Yth Grp; FBLA; FHA; Library Aide; Pep Clb; Red Cross Aide; SADD; Vllybl; High Hon Roll; Hon Roll; Psych.

BLATT, MICHELLE; Grace Christian Schl; Richland, PA; (3); 1/21; Church Yth Grp; Drama Clb; School Play; Pres Frsh Cls; Pres Soph Cls; JV Var Fld Hcky; JV Var Trk; JV Var High Hon Roll; Art Clb; Frt Sprt Awd 82-83; Joshua Awd 85-86; Baranbas Awd Sftbl 84-85.

BLATTENBERGER, KELLY; United HS; New Florence, PA; (3); Art Clb; Camera Clb; Ski Clb; Band; Chorus; Nwsp Stf; Yrbk Stf; Rep Stu Cncl; Hon Roll; Prfct Atten Awd; Penn ST U; Archtcture.

BLATTENBERGER, SAMANTHA; Blairsville SR HS; Black Lick, PA; (3); SADD; Sec Soph Cls; Sec Jr Cls; Sec Sr Cls; Stu Cncl; Cheerleading; High Hon Roll; Hon Roll; Elem Ed.

BLAU, BRIAN; Neshannock HS; New Castle, PA; (2); Trs Temple Yth Grp; Bsktbl; Score Keeper; Hon Roll; Pres Acdmc Ftns Awd 86; NADT Awd 86; UCLA.

BLAUCH, BRIAN; Northern Lebanon HS; Jonestown, PA; (4); 10/160; Church Yth Grp; Band; Concert Band; Mrchg Band; Pep Band; School Musical; School Play; Symp Band; Hon Roll; JP Sousa Awd; PA Regn 5 Band 85-87; PA All ST Band 87; John Philip Sousa Natl Hgh Schl Hnrs Band 87; Music Prfrmnc.

BLAUSER, DEANNA; Fellowship Christian Acad; Parker, PA; (4); Church Yth Grp; Spanish Clb; Church Choir; Color Guard; Score Keeper; High Hon Roll; Hon Roll; Cert Tchr Trng Child Evnglsm Fllwshp 86; ICM Schl Bus; Accntng Mgmt.

BLAUSER, DIONIS; Hickory HS; Hermitage, PA; (3); Church Yth Grp; French Clb; Girl Scts; Sec NFL; Office Aide; Orch; Nwsp Stf; Ntl Merit Ltr; Voice Dem Awd.

BLAZE, CLIFFORD; Big Spring HS; Newville, PA; (3); 31/258; Ski Clb; Band; Var L Socr; Var L Swmmng; Hon Roll; NHS.

BLAZESEWSKI, STEPHEN; Coughlin HS; Wilkes Barre, PA; (3); 18/374; Stage Crew; Var L Ftbl; Im Wt Lftg; Var L Wrstlng; High Hon Roll; NHS; Engrng.

BLAZIC, TRISHA; Neshannock HS; New Castle, PA; (3); Church Yth Grp; Drama Clb; Library Aide; Church Choir; Flag Corp; School Play; Ski Clb; Nwsp Sprt Ed; JV Cheerleading; Hon Roll; Srv Awd; Hnr Awd; Msnry.

BLEAKNEY, BRYAN; Hickory HS; Hermitage, PA; (3); Church Yth Grp; Drama Clb; German Clb; Letterman Clb; Varsity Clb; Band; Chorus; Church Choir; Mrchg Band; Orch; Elec Engrng.

BLEMLER, MARK; Boiling Springs HS; Boiling Spgs, PA; (3); 8/123; Drama Clb; Thesps; School Play; Yrbk Sprt Ed; Yrbk Stf; Drama.

BLENKO, JAMES C; Episcopal Acad; Haverford, PA; (4); Sec Debate Tm; Pres Chorus; Church Choir; School Musical; Ed Nwsp Stf; Var Crs Cntry; Var Trk; Ntl Merit SF; Harvard Clb Prz 86.

BLESSMAN, JENNIFER; Neshaminy HS; Langhorne, PA; (3); 37/799; Church Yth Grp; Band; Chorus; Jazz Band; Mrchg Band; Orch; JV Fld Hcky; JV Socr; Var Sftbl; Var Swmmng; NASA Space Camp 84; Natl Piano Auditions 84; Drexel U; Intl Banking.

BLETT, STEPHEN; Shikellamy SR HS; Northumberland, PA; (3); 130/350; Church Yth Grp; FCA; Rep Stu Cncl; Var Bsbl; JV Bsktbl; JV Bowling; Var Ftbl; Bloomsburg; Pre-Med.

BLEVINS, LESA; Twin Valley HS; Morgantown, PA; (4); 49/124; FBLA; Pres JA; Spanish Clb; Chorus; Capt Flag Corp; School Musical; Stage Crew; Trs Frsh Cls; Trs Soph Cls; Dstngshd Sales Mktng Awd 87; Kutztown U; Bus Admin.

BLEVINS, TRICIA; Penn Manor HS; Lancaster, PA; (4); 26/318; Trs Varsity Clb; Pres Jr Cls; Stu Cncl; Fld Hcky; Powder Puff Ftbl; Trk; Hon Roll; NHS; Rotary Awd; Ditlow Awd 87; Bvr Coll Schlrshp 87; Beaver Coll; Sci.

BLEYER, LEE A; Mt Penn HS; Mt Penn, PA; (4); 10/70; Chess Clb; Sec German Clb; Quiz Bowl; Science Clb; Concert Band; Mrchg Band; Yrbk Stf; High Hon Roll; Hon Roll; Ntl Merit SF; Hist Merit Awd; Frgn Lang Merit Awd; Sci Merit Awd; Penn ST U; Psych.

BLICHA, JOHN M; Canon Mc Millan SR HS; Eighty Four, PA; (4); 90/371; French Clb; Ski Clb; Var L Bsbl; Var L Golf; Hon Roll; 1st Awd Frnch Dctn CA U Of PA 86; IN U Of PA; Bus.

BLIMLINE, MICHAEL; Cocalico HS; Reinholds, PA; (3); 49/180; Church Yth Grp; L Tennis; JV Wrstlng; Hon Roll; Outstndng Wrstlr Awd 85; Bio Rsrch.

BLINER, JERRY; Belle Vernon Area HS; Webster, PA; (4); 137/267; Chess Clb; Computer Clb; Spanish Clb; Ftbl; Hon Roll; Frgn Lang Comptn 85-86; ROTC; Psych.

BLISS, DEBORAH; Huntingdon Area HS; Hesston, PA; (4); GAA; Band; Chorus; Concert Band; Mrchg Band; Hon Roll; NHS; Pres Acdmc Fit Awd 87; Penn ST U; Acctg.

BLISS, SARA; Johnsonburg Area HS; Johnsonburg, PA; (3); Camera Clb; Teachers Aide; Yrbk Stf; Stat Bsktbl; JV Capt Vllybl; Bus.

BLISS, SUSAN; Huntingdon Area HS; Hesston, PA; (2); 24/200; Church Yth Grp; GAA; Band; Concert Band; Mrchg Band; JV Bsktbl; JV Var Sftbl; Hon Roll.

BLITHE, TRACY; Interboro HS; Glenolden, PA; (3); Art Clb; Sec Drama Clb; Trs French Clb; Capt Flag Corp; Nwsp Rptr; Ed Yrbk Stf; Chrmn Stu Cncl; Hon Roll; Jr NHS; NHS; Exchange Stu France 86; Home & Schl Assn Ctznshp Awd 86; Brdcstng.

BLOB, RICHARD; Upper Merion Area HS; King Of Prussia, PA; (3); 1/290; Pres Drama Clb; Trs German Clb; Chorus; Trs Stu Cncl; Crs Cntry; Trk; Bausch & Lomb Sci Awd; NHS; Ntl Merit Ltr; Math Tm; Schlr Wk Johns Hopkins U Ctr Talented Yth 86; PA Govnrs Schl Sci 87; Exch Clb Stu Recog Awd 87; Intl Stud.

BLOCH, JONATHAN; Parkland HS; Allentown, PA; (4); 51/460; Computer Clb; Math Clb; Math Tm; Im Bsktbl; High Hon Roll; Hon Roll; Math & Verbal Tlnt Search 82; Allentown AZA VP 86-87; U Of Pittsburgh; Bus.

BLOCH, SUSAN; Highlands HS; Brackenridge, PA; (3); Girl Scts; Rep Jr Cls; Rep Stu Cncl; Cheerleading; Trk; High Hon Roll; NHS; Church Yth Grp; Hosp Aide; Intnl Clb; HOBY Ldrshp Awd 86; GS Gold Ldrshp Awd 86; Religious Scouting Awds 85-87.

BLODGETT, DIANE; Everett Area HS; Severna Park, MD; (4); 2/105; Hst French Clb; Chorus; School Musical; Off Stu Cncl; Sec French Hon Soc; High Hon Roll; Hon Roll; VP NHS; Pres Schlr; Sal.

BLODGETT, STACEY; Canon Mc-Millian SR HS; Canonsburg, PA; (4); Exploring; Latin Clb; Office Aide; Pep Clb; Ski Clb; Varsity Clb; Yrbk Stf; Var Sftbl; High Hon Roll; Hon Roll; Phila Coll Pharm/Sci; Bio.

BLONDET, ANTONIO K; East Stroudsburg HS; East Stroudsburg, PA; (4); 12/200; Chess Clb; Key Clb; Teachers Aide; Band; Concert Band; Mrchg Band; High Hon Roll; NHS; Pep Band; Prfct Atten Awd; Ntl Achvt Fnlst Schlrshp 87; Coordntr Ntl Hnr Soc Tutorng Pgm 86-87; Carnegie Mellon; Chem.

BLONSKI, RON; Beaver JR SR HS; Beaver, PA; (2); Spanish Clb; JV Ftbl; Wt Lftg; High Hon Roll; Hon Roll; Air Force Acad; Wldng Engr.

BLOOM, CHRISTIE; Connellsville Area SR HS; Connellsville, PA; (3); Church Yth Grp; Y-Teens; Band; Chorus; Church Choir; Symp Band; Rep Frsh Cls; Trs Jr Cls; JV Trk; Hon Roll; Physcl Thrpst.

BLOOM, COLLETTE; South Western HS; Spring Grove, PA; (3); 47/233; Key Clb; Varsity Clb; Band; Concert Band; JV Var Cheerleading; Hon Roll; Penn ST.

BLOOM, KERRI L; Liberty JR-SR HS; Liberty, PA; (3); Trs Church Yth Grp; Pres FHA; Trs German Clb; Band; Chorus; School Musical; Yrbk Stf; Rep Stu Cncl; Co-Capt Cheerleading; Hon Roll; HOBY Rep 86; Dstrct Chorus 85; Hotel Mngmnt.

BLOOM, KRISTY; Chestnut Ridge SR HS; Alum Bank, PA; (3); Dance Clb; SADD; High Hon Roll; NHS; Cmrcl Art.

BLOOM, SHARI; Curwensville Area HS; Curwensville, PA; (3); Drama Clb; French Clb; Hosp Aide; Ski Clb; Chorus; Concert Band; Mrchg Band; Var Sftbl; Var Vllybl.

BLOOMBERG, TRACY; Steel Valley HS; Munhall, PA; (3); 40/212; Color Guard; Nwsp Stf; Var L Bsktbl; Var Capt Sftbl; MVP-FST Ptch Sftbl 87; Elem Ed.

BLOOMER, BRIAN; Mastbaum AVT; Philadelphia, PA; (3); Boy Scts; Church Yth Grp; VICA; Stage Crew; JV Var Bsbl; JV Var Socr; Hon Roll; Prfct Atten Awd.

BLOSE, ELIZABETH; Freeport Area SR HS; Freeport, PA; (3); 26/200; Church Yth Grp; School Musical; Stat Bsktbl; Hon Roll; Intr Dsgn.

BLOSE, MICKI; Brookville Area HS; Sigel, PA; (3); Hst Art Clb; FHA; German Clb; Hosp Aide; VP Library Aide; Band; Hon Roll; Rcgntn Outstndng Voluntary Svc Brookville Hosp Cert Of Apprctn 87; Air Force; Trvl Agnt.

BLOSE, RICHARD; Du Bois Area HS; Reynoldsville, PA; (3); 35/330; Church Yth Grp; Cmnty Wkr; Bowling; Sftbl; Trk; Wt Lftg; Hon Roll; Good Kid Awd 85-86; Penn St.

BLOSSER, ELIZABETH; Harbor Creek HS; Erie, PA; (3); 8/215; Church Yth Grp; Girl Scts; Model UN; Concert Band; Mrchg Band; Yrbk Phtg; Rep Stu Cncl; Var L Swmmng; Hon Roll; NHS; NACEL Exchng Pgm 87; US Achvt Acad 87; Rep Lk Erie Prsbytry Pcmkng Smnr 87; Lang.

BLOTZER, ANDREA; Clarion-Limestone HS; Summerville, PA; (3); 10/86; Spanish Clb; SADD; Chorus; Var JV Cheerleading; Hon Roll; NHS; Prfct Atten Awd; Early Chldhd Ed.

BLOUCH, TIMOTHY; Northern Lebanan HS; Jonestown, PA; (3); Boy Scts; Chess Clb; Church Yth Grp; Model UN; Band; Chorus; Church Choir; Concert Band; Mrchg Band; Pep Band; Outstndng Profcncy Amer Hist 87; Eagle Scout Awd 87; Hnr Del Model UN 87; Govt.

BLOUGH, JANICE; Shade-Central HS; Hooversville, PA; (3); 7/76; Sec Trs Church Yth Grp; Hosp Aide; Spanish Clb; VP Church Choir; Stat Vllybl; Hon Roll; Sec NHS; Pre-Dental.

BLOUNT, RAYMOND; Fort Le Boeof HS; Waterford, PA; (3); 58/224; Boy Scts; Computer Clb; Exploring; Yrbk Stf; Hon Roll; Wrld Conservation Awd 86; Biology.

BLOUNT, SHANI; St Pius X HS; Phoenixville, PA; (1); Church Yth Grp; Drama Clb; NFL; Chorus; Church Choir; School Musical; JV Bsktbl; JV Sftbl; Var Trk; Hon Roll; Cmmnctns.

BLOUSE, TAMMY; Red Lion Area SR HS; Wrightsville, PA; (3); 17/375; SADD; Yrbk Stf; Trs Sr Cls; Var Mgr(s); Var Tennis; Stat Trk; High Hon Roll; Hon Roll; NHS; Latin Clb; Ltn Hnr Scty 86; Scndry Ed.

BLOW, SHANNON; Wyalusing Valley JR SR HS; Wyalusing, PA; (4); 12/132; Sec Church Yth Grp; Cmnty Wkr; Debate Tm; Drama Clb; 4-H; Ski Clb; Sec Spanish Clb; SADD; Chorus; School Musical; JR Miss Fnlst 87; 2nd Rnnr Up Schlstc Achvt Awd In Miss Teen 86; Lehigh Cnty CC; Comp Sci.

BLUBAUGH, MELISSA; Turkeyfoot Valley Area HS; Addison, PA; (4); 2/57; Q&S; Band; Yrbk Stf; Sec Frsh Cls; Sec Soph Cls; Sec Jr Cls; Stat Bsktbl; High Hon Roll; Lion Awd; Schlrshp St Vincent Coll 86; St Vincent Coll.

BLUE, KATHY; Danville SR HS; Danville, PA; (3); 4-H; French Clb; Yrbk Phtg; Yrbk Stf; Crs Cntry; Fld Hcky; Trk; Photo.

BLUE, TROY; Danville Area HS; Danville, PA; (3); 34/212; Spanish Clb; Var Trk; Hon Roll; NHS; PA ST U; Engr.

BLUEMLE, AMY; The Agnes Irwin Schl; Rosemont, PA; (3); Art Clb; Debate Tm; Hosp Aide; Chorus; Pres Orch; Nwsp Stf; Cit Awd; High Hon Roll; Bsktbl; Crs Cntry; Composer Sngwrtr Cpy Wrttn Work 87; Violinist Of DE Cnty Yth Orch 82-88; English.

BLUM, JAMIE; Fort Le Boeuf HS; Waterford, PA; (2); Spanish Clb; Nwsp Rptr; Nwsp Stf; Hon Roll; Acctnt.

BLUM, MARK; Central HS; York, PA; (2); Varsity Clb; Bsktbl; Socr; Vllybl; Hon Roll.

BLUM, TIM; Fort Le Boeuf HS; Waterford, PA; (3); Ski Clb; Band; Concert Band; Jazz Band; Mrchg Band; Pep Band; School Musical; Stage Crew; Trk; Hon Roll; Archtcr.

BLUMBERG, JILL; Harriton HS; Villanova, PA; (3); Yrbk Ed-Chief; JV Fld Hcky; Var Lcrss; Hon Roll; Pres NHS; Cmnty Wkr; French Clb; Pep Clb; SADD; Var Tennis.

BLUMENTHAL, CARL; South Western HS; Hanover, PA; (3); Church Yth Grp; Concert Band; Mrchg Band; Pep Band; JV Ftbl; JV Tennis; High Hon Roll; Hon Roll; Prfct Atten Awd; U Of Miami; Engl.

BLUMENTHAL, ERIKA; Central HS; Glenside, PA; (3); 6/538; Church Yth Grp; Office Aide; Lit Mag; Sec Jr Cls; Sec Sr Cls; High Hon Roll; Cert Merit Germn Soc PA 85-86; PA Govrnrs Schl Intl Studs Schlrshp, Intnsve Lang Inst Schlrshp 87; La Salle U; German.

BLYMIER, RITCH; South Western HS; Hanover, PA; (3); 40/230; Church Yth Grp; FCA; JA; Pres Varsity Clb; Jazz Band; Symp Band; Yrbk Stf; Var L Bsktbl; Var L Trk; Hon Roll; Pres Ftns Awd 86-87; Liberty U; Crss Cultural Mssns.

BLYSHAK, NANCY; Elizabeth Forward HS; Monongahela, PA; (3); 90/330; 4-H; Pep Clb; Yrbk Stf; Trs Soph Cls; Rep Jr Cls; Var Cheerleading; Mat Maids; Hon Roll; Dietry Sci.

BLYSTONE, BETSY; Connellsville Area SR HS; White, PA; (3); 33/480; Exploring; Hosp Aide; Office Aide; High Hon Roll; NHS; Spanish NHS; Jrnlsm.

BLYSTONE, JENNIFER; Kiski Area HS; Apollo, PA; (4); Computer Clb; Math Clb; Math Tm; Spanish Clb; Band; Mrchg Band; Symp Band; Rep Frsh Cls; Trk; Hon Roll; Penn ST U; Engr.

BLYSTONE, RAY; Elderton JR SR HS; Spring Church, PA; (3); 4-H; Spanish Clb; Varsity Clb; Band; Concert Band; Mrchg Band; Var Capt Bsbl; Var Capt Bsktbl; Var Socr; Wt Lftg; Toxolgy.

BLYTHE, D JENNIFER; Chartiers Valley SR HS; Heidelberg, PA; (3); Church Yth Grp; DECA; Girl Scts; Hosp Aide; Library Aide; Office Aide; Y-Teens; Acpl Chr; Spring Chorus; Rep Stu Cncl; Exec Women Intl Bus Career Dvlpmnt Prgm 87; Dir List Of Hnr Stu & Outstndg Mktng I Stu 87; Robert Morris Coll; Mktng.

BOAL, KIMBERLY; Ringgold HS; Finleyville, PA; (3); Ski Clb; Spanish Clb; SADD; Teachers Aide; Color Guard; Mgr(s); Score Keeper; Timer; Sci & Math Hnr Socty 86-87; Pitt U; Phrmcy.

BOBACK, AARON; Ford City HS; Ford City, PA; (3); 21/160; Spanish Clb; High Hon Roll; NHS.

BOBAK, JUSTIN; Northern Cambria HS; Barnesboro, PA; (3); 1/152; French Clb; Var Trk; High Hon Roll; NHS; Ntl Merit Ltr; Penn ST U; Elec Engr.

BOBAN, ALLYSON; Conneaut Valley HS; Conneautville, PA; (3); FFA; Ski Clb; Chorus; Stat Bsktbl; Mgr(s); Score Keeper; Sftbl; Vllybl; Bus.

BOBBIE, CHRIS; W Middlesex HS; Mercer, PA; (3); 8/104; Library Aide; Spanish Clb; Chorus; High Hon Roll; Hon Roll; NHS; Pres Acad Ftnss Awd 85; Elem Ed.

BOBBY, VICKI; Cambria Heights HS; Patton, PA; (3); 49/182; Church Yth Grp; Soroptimist; Chorus; Yrbk Stf; Var L Cheerleading; Var L Swmmng; JV Vllybl; Elem Ed.

BOBECK, LINDA; West Side Tech; Edwardsville, PA; (3); Key Clb; Letterman Clb; Chorus; Yrbk Stf; Pres Soph Cls; VP Jr Cls; Bsktbl; High Hon Roll; Hon Roll; School Musical.

BOBETICH, MICHELE; Altoona Area HS; Altoona, PA; (3); 59/700; French Clb; Stu Cncl; Pom Pon; Penn ST; Math.

BOBEY, HOLLY; Hazleton SR HS; Hazleton, PA; (2); FNA; Spanish Clb; Nwsp Rptr; Yrbk Stf; Drama Clb; Pep Clb; Chorus; Score Keeper; Hon Roll; Keystone Awd 86; Reading Hosp Schl Nrsng.

BOBEY, ROXANN; West Hazleton HS; W Hazleton, PA; (2); FBLA; FTA; Ski Clb; Spanish Clb; SADD; Thesps; Band; Chorus; Color Guard; Mrchg Band.

BOBINETS, JAMIE; Home Center JR SR HS; Homer City, PA; (4); Service Clb; Varsity Clb; Band; Mrchg Band; Score Keeper; Capt Twrlr; Vllybl; Hon Roll; Jr NHS; NHS; Band Booster Scholar 87; Lock Haven U; Spts Med.

BOBKOWSKI, MARY ANN; Wyoming Valley West HS; Kingston, PA; (4); 33/390; Pres Church Yth Grp; Key Clb; Science Clb; Hon Roll; NHS; Prfct Atten Awd; Amrcn Bus Wmns Schlrshp 87; Upwrd Bnd Schlrshp 87; Wlks Coll Upwrd Bnd Svc Pgm Awd 87; Wilkes Coll; Bus Admin.

BOBOIGE, FRED; Punxsutawney HS; Punxsutawney, PA; (2); Church Yth Grp; High Hon Roll; Hon Roll; Clarion Upward Bound Pgm 86-87; Clarian U; Law.

BOBON, SHANAN; Oxford Area HS; Cochranville, PA; (3); FBLA; SADD; Chorus; Var Bsktbl; Var Sftbl; Var Capt Vllybl; Hon Roll; Sftbl All League Team 87; Pres Councl Phy Fitns 85-87.

BOBRO, DARLENE; Sto Rox SR HS; Mckees Rocks, PA; (3); 96/180; Church Yth Grp; Dance Clb; Girl Scts; VP JA; Office Aide; Band; Chorus; Church Choir; Nwsp Rptr; Yrbk Stf; Hnr Roll 86-87; Penn ST U; Vet.

BOBROWSKY, BRYAN; Cardinal Brennan HS; Shenandoah, PA; (3); 10/60; Chess Clb; German Clb; School Musical; Ftbl; Vllybl; Wt Lftg; High Hon Roll; Hon Roll; NHS; Prfct Atten Awd; Cert Hnr Outstndng Achvt Engl III 87; Cert Hnr Outstndng Achvt Thlgy II 86; Natl Hnr Soc Pres 87-88; US Naval Acad.

BOCCHINFUSO, DIANE; St Hubert HS For Girls; Philadelphia, PA; (3); 2/446; Hosp Aide; Math Tm; Off Stu Cncl; Swmmng; Vllybl; High Hon Roll; Hon Roll; NHS; Prfct Atten Awd; All-Cath Swmmg Hnrs 86-87; Italn Awd 85-87; Widener U; Nrsg.

BOCHAK, ELEANOR V; Ambridge Area HS; Ambridge, PA; (3); Church Yth Grp; GAA; Pep Clb; Red Cross Aide; SADD; Band; Concert Band; Mrchg Band; Symp Band; Hon Roll.

BOCHICCHIO, NIKKI; Panther Valley HS; Nesquehoning, PA; (1); 40/129; Ski Clb; JV Cheerleading; Hon Roll.

BOCK, JIM; Central Dauphin HS; Harrisburg, PA; (3); 73/369; Var Ftbl; JV Socr; Var Trk; Im Vllybl; Hon Roll; Jr NHS; Sphmr Trk Awd 86; 3rd Pl Dist III Trk 87; Geology.

BOCK, JODIE; Fleetwood Area HS; Kutztown, PA; (3); Church Yth Grp; German Clb; Ski Clb; Rep Jr Cls; Gym; Capt Var Sftbl; Tennis; High Hon Roll; Hon Roll; Jr NHS; Fleetwood Schlr 86-87; Arch.

BOCK, KAREN; Brandywine Heights HS; Mertztown, PA; (2); Church Yth Grp; Hosp Aide; Band; Concert Band; Mrchg Band; Bsktbl; Nrsng.

BOCK, LORI; West Branch Area HS; Morrisdale, PA; (2); Spanish Clb; SADD; Chorus; Concert Band; Mrchg Band; Orch; Yrbk Stf; Hon Roll; Accntnt.

BOCK, LYNNETTE; Philipsburg-Osceola Area SR HS; Philipsburg, PA; (4); 1/227; Band; Yrbk Stf; Bsktbl; Hon Roll; NHS; Val; Jdg Rchrd M Shrp Mem Awd 87; Prsdntl Acdmc Ftnss Awd 87; U Of Pittsburgh; Med.

BOCK, WENDY; Bethel Park SR HS; Bethel Park, PA; (4); 70/502; Church Yth Grp; FBLA; Sec Mrchg Band; Sec Symp Band; Mat Maids; High Hon Roll; Pres Schlr; Westminster Coll; Acctng.

BOCKIUS, CATHERINE; Upper Dublin HS; Oreland, PA; (3); 12/301; Hosp Aide; Intnl Clb; Office Aide; SADD; Yrbk Stf; JV Fld Hcky; JV Lcrss; Hon Roll; NHS; Ed.

BOCKNACK, BRIAN; Council Rock HS; Holland, PA; (4); 8/848; JCL; Trs Latin Clb; Spanish Clb; Lit Mag; High Hon Roll; Jr NHS; NHS; Ntl Merit SF; Penn ST Acdmc Exclinc Schlrshp 87; Betz Lab Schlrshp 87; Penn ST U; Chem Engrng.

BOCSY, ERIN; North Star HS; Boswell, PA; (4); 8/130; Church Yth Grp; FCA; 4-H; Color Guard; School Play; Yrbk Stf; Chrmn Stu Cncl; Var Vllybl; Hon Roll; Trs NHS; Assoc Schls Inc; Trsm.

BODAI, TAMME; Wilson Area HS; Easton, PA; (3); 19/169; Church Choir; Var Bsktbl; Var Fld Hcky; Var Sftbl; Hon Roll; Bio.

BODAMER, D LYNNE; Warren County Christian HS; Titusville, PA; (4); 2/7; Church Yth Grp; Chorus; School Musical; Yrbk Stf; VP Pres Stu Cncl; Bsktbl; Sftbl; Vllybl; Sal; MVP Vllybl 86; MVP Bsktbl & Sftbl 87; Messiah Coll; Elem Educ.

BODANI, FRANK C; Susquehannock HS; Glen Rock, PA; (4); 25/214; Am Leg Boys St; Orch; Nwsp Sprt Ed; Var L Bsbl; Hon Roll; NHS; Church Yth Grp; SADD; Bsktbl; Tennis; Dist Rgnl & St Orchstr 87; Mbr York Symphny Orchstr 86 & 87; Pres Acadc Ftns Awd 87; Crtv Wrtng Awds; Duquesne U Pittsburgh; Jrnlsm.

BODE, ANNE-MARIE; Western Wayne HS; Hamlin, PA; (3); 57/200; Drama Clb; French Clb; Nwsp Rptr; Nwsp Stf; Lit Mag; VP Soph Cls; Rep Stu Cncl; Var Cheerleading; Score Keeper; Hon Roll; Elks Yth Day 84-86; Columbia U; Engl.

BODEN, JENNIFER S; Elizabeth Forward HS; Monongahela, PA; (3); Camera Clb; 4-H; Pres JA; Letterman Clb; Pep Clb; Chorus; Var L Vllybl; 4-H Awd; Hon Roll; Cert Of Offcrs Trnng Course 87; Cert Of Part In R Morris Schlrshp Test 87; Apprec Cert 85; IN U Of PA; Tech Wrtng.

BODENSCHATZ, WENDY; Forest Hills HS; Summerhill, PA; (4); 138/154; Pres Drama Clb; Pres NFL; Pres Thesps; Chorus; Nwsp Ed-Chief; Cmnty Wkr; Church Choir; School Musical; School Play; Stu Cncl; Fornscs Awd 87; Outstndng Stu 87; Somerset JR Miss Fnlst 87; Slippery Rock U; TV Comm.

BODES, KIMBERLY; Salisbury Elk-Lick HS; Meyersdale, PA; (2); Art Clb; Concert Band; Mrchg Band; Pres Soph Cls; Var JV Cheerleading; Cit Awd; Hon Roll.

BODINE, HEATHER; Unionville HS; Kennett Square, PA; (4); 31/316; Church Yth Grp; Chorus; Concert Band; Capt Flag Corp; Orch; School Musical; NHS; Mitrani Scholar 87; Bloomsburg Schlrs Prgm; Instrmntl Music Awd 85; Bloomsburg U; Hstry.

BODNAR, MICHON; St Paul Cathedral HS; Pittsburgh, PA; (3); French Clb; Color Guard; Nwsp Rptr; Yrbk Stf; Cheerleading; Gym; Swmmng; PA ST; Jrnlsm.

BODOSKY, MICHELLE; Portage Area HS; Portage, PA; (3); Chorus; Var Trk; Grls Ensmbl 86-88; Legl Secy.

BODUCH, SCOTT; Quaker Valley HS; Sewickley, PA; (2); Bsktbl; Ftbl; Trk; Hon Roll; Pittsburgh Tech Inst; Drftng.

BODURA, PAUL; Steel Valley HS; Munhall, PA; (3); Band; Concert Band; Mrchg Band; Hon Roll; Physics.

BODZIO, DEBBIE; Hanover Area JR SR HS; Wilkes Barre, PA; (3); Exploring; Mrchg Band; Twrlr; NHS; Pharmacy.

BOEDEKER, MARY; Wyoming Area HS; Wyoming, PA; (3); 56/256; Sec 4-H; German Clb; Library Aide; Scholastic Bowl; Hst SADD; Band; Concert Band; Mrchg Band; Pep Band; 4-H Awd; Acad Exclnc German II 85-86; Acad Exclnc German III 86-87; Wilkes Coll; Nrsng.

BOEDEWIG, MICHAEL; Archbishop Wood For Boys; Warminster, PA; (3); 1/241; Math Tm; SADD; Nwsp Rptr; Yrbk Rptr; Rep Soph Cls; Rep Jr Cls; High Hon Roll; Pres NHS; Ntl Merit SF; Var Highest GPA Awds 84-87.

BOEHM, DEBORAH J; Freedom HS; Easton, PA; (4); 130/433; Art Clb; Church Yth Grp; German Clb; Pep Clb; Mgr(s); JV Sftbl; Hon Roll; NCACC; Design Technlgy.

BOEHM, LYNDA; Hampton HS; Gibsonia, PA; (4); Band; Concert Band; Mrchg Band; Pep Band; Powder Puff Ftbl; Mgr Socr; High Hon Roll; Hon Roll; NHS; IN U Of PA; Accntng.

BOEHMER, LISA; West Hazleton HS; Weston, PA; (4); 47/225; French Clb; FBLA; FTA; Office Aide; Flag Corp; Hon Roll; NHS; 3rd Pl FBLA Regnl & 8th Pl ST Acctg I-II 86; Troph Hghst Avg 100 Pct Acctg I 86; Bloomsburg U; Acctg.

BOEHMIG, CINDY; Knoch HS; Butler, PA; (4); 3/243; FHA; Band; Concert Band; Mrchg Band; School Musical; Stage Crew; High Hon Roll; NHS; Pres Schlr; PA ST U; Mech Engrng.

BOEHMKE, SANDRA; Saint Hubert Cath HS For Girls; Philadelphia, PA; (4); 34/364; Cmnty Wkr; Pres Exploring; Office Aide; Capt Bsktbl; Coach Actv; Prfct Atten Awd; Dean Schlrshp E Stroudsburg U 87; Pres Acad Ftns Awd 87; E Stroudsburg U; Hosp Mgmt.

BOEHNE, LISA F; The Baldwin Schl; Devon, PA; (4); Church Yth Grp; Drama Clb; Latin Clb; PAVAS; Thesps; Jazz Band; School Play; Stage Crew; Nwsp Stf; Tennis; Cornelia Otis Skinner Awd 87; Richmond Lattimore Vergil Prz 87; Excllnc In Drama 84-86; Mt Holyoke Coll; Clsscs.

BOELKY, KATIE; Beaver Area JR/Sr HS; Beaver, PA; (2); Spanish Clb; Stage Crew; Rep Stu Cncl; Hon Roll; Advertising.

BOERNER, DOROTHEA; Harry S Truman HS; Croydon, PA; (4); 8/592; Girl Scts; VICA; Hon Roll; NHS; Prfct Atten Awd; Pres Schlr; Distingshd Stu Awd 87; Photography Cls Foreman 86-87; Philadelphia Coll Of Arts; Phtg.

BOERSTLER, BRAD; Westmont Hilltop HS; Johnstown, PA; (3); Church Yth Grp; Golf; High Hon Roll; NHS; U Of Pittsburgh.

BOESHORE, KRISTEN; Annville-Cleona HS; Annville, PA; (3); 1/140; Acpl Chr; Band; Chorus; Concert Band; Jazz Band; Madrigals; Mrchg Band; Pep Band; School Musical; Hon Roll; Wdmn Of Wrld Hstry Awd 86; Lebanon Cnty Hstry Awd 85; Lebanon Vly Coll; Chmstry.

BOETH, JACK; West Scranton HS; Scranton, PA; (4); 10/242; Drama Clb; NFL; Scholastic Bowl; Ski Clb; Spanish Clb; Speech Tm; Pres Thesps; School Musical; School Play; NHS; Rotary Ldrshp Schlrshp 85; Philadelphia Coll; Pharm.

BOFFA, CAROLYN; Nazareth Acad; Philadelphia, PA; (4); Art Clb; Dance Clb; Drama Clb; French Clb; Pep Clb; Service Clb; Spanish Clb; Stage Crew; Gym; Tennis; Fnlst-Miss Grtr N E Pgnt 86; Penn ST; Nrsg.

BOFINGER, MARC; Northeast Catholic HS; Philadelphia, PA; (4); 46/362; Boys Clb Am; Boy Scts; Chess Clb; Office Aide; Service Clb; Varsity Clb; Yrbk Stf; Rep Jr Cls; Rep Sr Cls; Union League Of Phldlpha Awd 85; Ntl Hnr Scty Srv Awd 85-87; Law.

BOGACKI, JEFFREY; Du Bois Area HS; Reynoldsville, PA; (3); 6/329; Off Stu Cncl; Im Vllybl; Hon Roll; NHS; Optmtry.

BOGACZYK, LUANN; Williamson HS; Tioga, PA; (2); Church Yth Grp; Computer Clb; Math Clb; Pres Spanish Clb; SADD; JV Bsktbl; Cit Awd; High Hon Roll; NHS; Math.

BOGAN, NICOLE; Freeport Area SR HS; Freeport, PA; (3); Exploring; Trs OEA; Rep Frsh Cls; Hon Roll; Oakbridge Acad; Cmmrcl Art.

BOGAR, BILL; Immaculate Conception HS; Avella, PA; (3); 6/38; Bsbl; Bsktbl; Hon Roll; NHS; Wrld Hstry & US Hstry Awd 85-86 & 86-87; Hlth & Frnch III Awd 86-87.

BOGART, DOUG; Danville HS; Danville, PA; (3); Boy Scts; Church Yth Grp; Cmnty Wkr; FFA; Star Chapter Farmer 86; Ag Mech Silver Mdlst At Penn St 85.

BOGATIUK, SUZANNE; Cardinal Dougherty HS; Philadelphia, PA; (3); 22/670; Church Yth Grp; Cmnty Wkr; Hosp Aide; Service Clb; Mgr Stage Crew; Hon Roll; NHS; Prfct Atten Awd; Natl Ldrshp & Svc Awds 87 Psych.

BOGATS, JENNIFER; Carlynton HS; Carnegie, PA; (3); Church Yth Grp; FBLA; JA; Ski Clb; Spanish Clb; Rep Jr Cls; Powder Puff Ftbl; Trk; Vllybl; Am Lgn Aux Awd 83-84; Math.

BOGDAN, JAMES; Trinity HS; Camp Hill, PA; (2); Jazz Band; Socr; Aviation.

BOGDAN, KRISTIN; Cheltonham HS; Glenside, PA; (4); 154/365; Church Yth Grp; Var Lcrss; Var Socr; JV Trk; Wst Chstr; Scl Wrk.

BOGDANOFF, HEATHER; Strath Haven HS; Media, PA; (3); Spanish Clb; School Musical; Ed Yrbk Phtg; Rep Stu Cncl; Cheerleading; Hon Roll; Intnl Clb; Teachers Aide; Temple Yth Grp; Nwsp Stf; Var Arts Ltr/Awd, Confermation Cls Awds 85-86.

BOGDANOVICH, KENNETH C; Central HS; Scranton, PA; (4); 36/300; High Hon Roll; NHS; Presdntl Schlrshp 87-88; U Scranton; Med.

BOGDON, MICHAEL; Wyoming Valley West HS; Plymouth, PA; (3); Band; Concert Band; Jazz Band; Mrchg Band; Orch; Pep Band; School Musical; Hon Roll; Ntl Merit Ltr; Vet Day Svc With Vets For Memorial Day 85-86; Music.

BOGERT, PAM; Emmaus SR HS; Wescosville, PA; (3); Exploring; Key Clb; Ski Clb; High Hon Roll; Hon Roll; Jr NHS; NHS; 1st Prz Photo Tr Cnty Indstrl Fair 85; Eyer JR HS Awd 84-85; Presdntl Acad Fit Awd 85; Photo.

BOGGESS, SHARON; Peabody HS; Pittsburgh, PA; (4); 17/300; Yrbk Stf; Pres Frsh Cls; Pres Jr Cls; Pres Sr Cls; Var Sftbl; Cit Awd; NHS; JR Clss Soc Chrmn 85-86; SR Clss VP 86-87; Acadmc All Am 85-86; Slippery Rock U; Pre-Law.

BOGGESS, TERESA; South Side HS; Hookstown, PA; (3); Church Yth Grp; Teachers Aide; Varsity Clb; Band; Mrchg Band; Pep Band; Stu Cncl; Stat Trk; Hon Roll; Child Dvlpmnt.

BOGGS, BILL; South Side HS; Hookstown, PA; (3); 12/150; VP Jr Cls; Var Bsktbl; Var Ftbl; NHS; PA ST; Engr.

BOGGS, BRADLEY; Beaver Area HS; Beaver, PA; (3); Aud/Vis; German Clb; Ski Clb; Bsktbl; Var L Swmmng; High Hon Roll; Hon Roll; Pre-Coll Pgm Fine Art CMU Schlrshp 87; Carnegie-Mellon U; Indstrl Mgmt.

BOGGS, JOHN; Butler SR HS; Butler, PA; (2); German Clb; Latin Clb; Band; Mrchg Band; Rep Stu Cncl; Gym; Socr; Hon Roll; UCLA; Arch.

BOGGS, LEAH; St Maria Goretti HS; Philadelphia, PA; (3); 30/350; Cmnty Wkr; Exploring; Math Clb; Math Tm; Spanish Clb; Teachers Aide; Orch; School Musical; Hon Roll; Prfct Atten Awd; Rlgn Awd 85-86; Math Awd 86-87; Notre Dame; Arch Engr.

BOGNER, MICHELLE; Lebanon HS; Lebanon, PA; (4); 50/285; Latin Clb; Ski Clb; Teachers Aide; Varsity Clb; Var L Fld Hcky; Var Mgr(s); Var Capt Sftbl; Hon Roll; Millersville U; Acctng.

BOGOVICH, MARK; Shikellamy HS; Northumberland, PA; (4); 22/301; Am Leg Boys St; VP Jr Cls; Pres Stu Cncl; Var Ftbl; Wt Lftg; Var Wrstlng; Hon Roll; Cmnty Wkr; Kiwanis Awd; Young Amer Awd 86; Math.

BOGUSH, STEPHEN; Southern Columbia Area HS; Elysburg, PA; (4); 1/77; Ski Clb; Yrbk Phtg; VP Soph Cls; Rep Stu Cncl; Var Bsbl; JV Bsktbl; High Hon Roll; Pres NHS; Pres Schlr; Val; Jacques H Mitrani Fndtn Med Schlrshp 87; Penn ST U; Pre-Med.

BOGUSZ, SCOTT; Plum SR HS; Pittsburgh, PA; (3); 30/410; Church Yth Grp; Varsity Clb; L Var Bsbl; Var JV Bsktbl; Trk; High Hon Roll; NHS; Prfct Atten Awd.

BOHAN, BRIAN; Charles Boehn HS; Yardley, PA; (2); Cmnty Wkr; Political Wkr; L Bsbl; L Bsktbl; L Ftbl.

BOHART, LINDA; Liberty JR SR HS; Liberty, PA; (2); FHA; German Clb; Chorus; Rep Stu Cncl; JV Var Bsktbl; Var L Crs Cntry; Var Sftbl; Var L Trk; Var L Vllybl; Rep Frsh Cls; MVP Sftbl 86; Allstars Teen Leag Sftbl 86; 1st Pl Canoe Tilt 86; Jrnlsm.

BOHEEN, ERICA; Central Bucks High Schl East; Doylestown, PA; (4); 2/452; School Musical; School Play; Yrbk Ed-Chief; Var L Swmmng; Bausch & Lomb Sci Awd; High Hon Roll; Jr NHS; NHS; Pres Schlr; Sal; Outstndng Stu Schlrshp 87; Shippensburg U; Chem.

BOHIZIC, RENEE; Union HS; New Castle, PA; (4); 18/66; French Clb; Office Aide; Pep Clb; Band; Concert Band; Yrbk Stf; Co-Capt Twrlr; Hon Roll; VP NHS; Natl Sci Awd Wnnr 87; IN U Of PA; Psych.

BOHLANDER, JACKIE; Yough HS; W Newton, PA; (3); French Clb; Library Aide; Office Aide; Pep Clb; Spanish Clb; Band; Chorus; Mrchg Band; Yrbk Stf; Nrsng.

BOHLMAN, KELLY; Palisades HS; Revere, PA; (3); 5/196; Pres VP Church Yth Grp; Chrmn German Clb; Church Choir; VP Jr Cls; Sec Stu Cncl; Var Fld Hcky; Var Trk; High Hon Roll; Hon Roll; NHS; HOBY Ldrshp Semnr Rep 85; Pre-Mdcn.

BOHN, CHRISTINE; Avon Grove HS; Chatham, PA; (3); 74/210; Var Cheerleading; Engl Awd 85; Goldey Beacom Coll; Bus.

BOHN, MIKE; Daniel Boone JR SR HS; Douglassville, PA; (2); German Clb; Var Bsbl; Bio-Chem Fld.

BOHR, ANDREW C; Northeastern HS; Manchester, PA; (4); Church Yth Grp; Ski Clb; Pres Band; Chorus; Church Choir; Concert Band; Jazz Band; Mrchg Band; Orch; Pep Band; Semper Fidelis Awd 87; Natl Schl Orchstra Awd 87; Towson ST U; Finance.

BOHRER, MATTHEW; Hempfield HS; Lancaster, PA; (3); JA; Chorus; Church Choir; School Musical; School Play; Variety Show; Rep Soph Cls; Rep Jr Cls; Rep Stu Cncl; JV Var Socr; Pol Sci.

BOJALAD, FRANK; Central Christian HS; Du Bois, PA; (3); 31/170; Computer Clb; Swmmng; Penn ST U; Engrng.

BOJANOWSKI, CAROL ANN; Philadelphia High School For Girls; Philadelphia, PA; (4); 19/340; Service Clb; Nwsp Sprt Ed; Rep Jr Cls; Stu Cncl; Crs Cntry; Sftbl; Swmmng; Hon Roll; NHS; Spanish NHS; Mellie Matern Awd Alumnae Assn 87; Summa Cum Laude 87; Temple U; Pharm.

BOJARSKI, JAMES; Cathedral Preparatory Schl; Erie, PA; (3); 54/193; German Clb; Im Bsktbl; Im Vllybl.

BOKANOVICH, PHILIP; Trinity HS; Washington, PA; (3); 93/433; Bsktbl; Golf; Hon Roll.

BOLAM, JANEL; Waynesburg Central HS; Brave, PA; (3); Hosp Aide; Natl Beta Clb; Office Aide; Spanish Clb; High Hon Roll; Hon Roll; NHS; Spanish NHS.

BOLAND, BETH; Gwynedd-Mercy Acad; Ambler, PA; (2); Var Cheerleading; JV Crs Cntry; JV Fld Hcky; JV Lcrss; JV Score Keeper; JV Timer; JV Trk; JV Vllybl; Hon Roll; Spnsh Awd 86-87; Honors 86-87; Marine Bio.

BOLCAROVIC, ROBERT; Tunkhannock Area HS; Tunkhannock, PA; (4); Band; Concert Band; Mrchg Band; Hon Roll; Penn ST; Elec Engr.

BOLCAVAGE, SUE; Valley View JR SR HS; Archbald, PA; (3); Church Yth Grp; French Clb; Hosp Aide; Latin Clb; Stu Cncl; Bsktbl; Hon Roll; Natl Hnr Soc 86.

BOLDEN, DAMON; Engineering & Science HS; Philadelphia, PA; (3); 114/241; Boys Clb Am; Church Yth Grp; Variety Show; Yrbk Rptr; Pre-Med.

BOLDEN, JEFFREY; Harreton HS; Gladwyne, PA; (3); Chess Clb; Computer Clb; Capt Debate Tm; Math Clb; Political Wkr; Speech Tm; Stage Crew; Ed Nwsp Stf; Hon Roll; Yth Govt; Comp Pgms & Repair Skills; Hist.

BOLE, REBECCA; Williamsport HS; Cogan Station, PA; (1); VP Church Yth Grp; French Clb; Chorus; Church Choir; Concert Band; Off Frsh Cls; High Hon Roll; Hon Roll; Flght Attndnt.

BOLEWITZ, AMY; Highlands HS; Natrona Hgts, PA; (3); Hst Church Yth Grp; Hosp Aide; Color Guard; Drill Tm; Var Bsktbl; Hon Roll; Pres Schlr; Humn Rel.

BOLGIANO, CAROLYN; Hempfield HS; Lancaster, PA; (4); Drama Clb; Exploring; Hosp Aide; Red Cross Aide; Science Clb; School Play; Nwsp Rptr; Crs Cntry; High Hon Roll; Hon Roll; U Of MD College Pk; Phys Thrpy.

BOLICH, EDWARD; Nativity BVM HS; Pottsville, PA; (3); Chess Clb; Church Yth Grp; PAVAS; Thesps; Trk; Wt Lftg; High Hon Roll; Hon Roll; Voice Dem Awd; Sci Fair 3rd Pl 86-87; Theatre Arts.

BOLIND, KERRY J; West Allegheny HS; Clinton, PA; (3); 10/200; Church Yth Grp; 4-H; Hosp Aide; Model UN; Spanish Clb; Chorus; Color Guard; Mrchg Band; High Hon Roll; NHS; Span Merit 4.0 Aver 85-87; Hnr Roll Awds 85-87; Med.

BOLINGER, KELLI; Northern Cambria HS; Nicktown, PA; (4); Church Yth Grp; VP Concert Band; VP Mrchg Band; Trk; DAR Awd; High Hon Roll; NHS; Spanish NHS; Grove City Coll; Chrstn Mnstrs.

BOLIVER, KIMBERLY; Richland HS; Gibsonia, PA; (2); Chorus; Color Guard; Mrchg Band; Nwsp Stf; Hon Roll; Sec.

BOLK, KRISTEN; Yough HS; Yukon, PA; (3); 12/249; Pep Clb; Service Clb; Ski Clb; Spanish Clb; Chorus; Concert Band; Mrchg Band; NHS; Phrmcy.

BOLKOVAC, ALBERT J; Northgate JR SR HS; Pittsburgh, PA; (4); 23/143; Am Leg Boys St; Camera Clb; Math Tm; SADD; Var L Ftbl; Var L Trk; Cit Awd; Hon Roll; Prfct Atten Awd; Westinghouse Sci Hnrs Inst 86-87; Penn ST; Aerospc Engrng.

BOLLAG, JUDY; State College Area HS; State College, PA; (4); 23/563; Trs Service Clb; Concert Band; Mrchg Band; Rep Soph Cls; Rep Jr Cls; VP Sr Cls; Cit Awd; High Hon Roll; NEDT Awd; Cls Of 86 Spirit Awd 87; Penn ST; Bus Admin.

BOLLENDORF, P ALEXANDER; Salisbury HS; Allentown, PA; (3); Boy Scts; Debate Tm; Scholastic Bowl; Thesps; Rep Soph Cls; Sec Stu Cncl; Var Crs Cntry; Var Trk; Var Wrstlng; Hon Roll; Track MVP 87; Pre-Med.

BOLLINGER, AMY; Boiling Springs HS; Boiling Spgs, PA; (3); 5/140; Chorus; School Play; Yrbk Stf; Rep Stu Cncl; Stat JV Fld Hcky; JV Swmmng; High Hon Roll; Hon Roll; NHS; Schlstc Wrtng Awd-Gold Key 87; Scl Psyhlgst.

BOLLINGER, BECKY J; Mechanicsburg SR HS; Mechanicsburg, PA; (4); 50/303; Band; Concert Band; Mrchg Band; Symp Band; Stat Bsbl; Stat Bsktbl; High Hon Roll; Hon Roll; Hmcmng & Prm Qn 86-87; Bloomsburg U; Cmmnctns.

BOLLINGER, BONNIE; Richland HS; Gibsonia, PA; (4); 20/185; Sec Church Yth Grp; Hosp Aide; Pres NFL; Band; Chorus; School Musical; Swing Chorus; Var L Cheerleading; Var L Trk; NHS; Trck & Frnscs Ltrs 84-87; Capital U; TV Brdcstng.

BOLLINGER, CAROL; Warwick HS; Lititz, PA; (3); #5 In Class; Church Yth Grp; 4-H; Library Aide; High Hon Roll; NHS; Schlr Awd For Spnsh 87; Cmmnctns.

BOLLINGER, DENISE; Huntingdon Area HS; Mill Creek, PA; (3); 15/224; DECA; Pres VP 4-H; Sec FFA; JV Sftbl; 4-H Awd; Hon Roll; NHS; Rotary Awd; Penn ST; Frstry.

BOLLINGER, DENISE; Jeannette SR HS; Jeannette, PA; (2); Art Clb; French Clb; Ski Clb; Color Guard; Concert Band; French Hon Soc; Hon Roll.

BOLLINGER, JENNIFER; Dover Area HS; Dover, PA; (3); Church Yth Grp; Varsity Clb; Chorus; Yrbk Stf; Fld Hcky; Trk; Hon Roll; Slippery Rock; Physical Ed.

BOLLINGER, JENNIFER; Shikellamy HS; Northumberland, PA; (4); 39/301; French Clb; Band; Church Choir; Concert Band; Drill Tm; Mrchg Band; Orch; Yrbk Stf; Stu Cncl; French Hon Soc; Dist Band 85 & 87; Susquehanna Valley Band 85-87; Educ Assoc Awd 7; Bloomsburg U; Educ.

BOLLMAN, KRISTA; Everett Area HS; Everett, PA; (2); Drama Clb; VP 4-H; French Clb; Varsity Clb; Band; Off Stu Cncl; Var L Socr; Var L Trk; 4-H Awd; High Hon Roll.

BOLOGNA, ANTHONY; St John Neumann HS; Philadelphia, PA; (2); 46/354; Boy Scts; Exploring; School Musical; School Play; Stage Crew; JV Var Bsbl; JV Ftbl; Hon Roll; La Salle; CPA.

BOLT, ANNE; New Covenant Acad; Mainesburg, PA; (1); Church Yth Grp; 4-H; Ski Clb; Chorus; Socr; 4-H Awd; Messiah Coll; Math.

BOLTON, KRIS; Greenwood HS; Millerstown, PA; (3); GAA; Chorus; School Musical; Sec Soph Cls; Sec Jr Cls; JV Bsktbl; JV Var Fld Hcky; Mgr(s); Trk; Hon Roll; Central PA Bus Schl; Paralgl.

BOLTZ, CHRIS; Mt Penn HS; Reading, PA; (2); 36/58; Boy Scts; Exploring; Im Coach Actv; Var L Ftbl; Wt Lftg; Prfct Atten Awd; Hnrb Mntn Sci Fair 83; Coaching Awd PA-ALSACE Little Lg 85; Var Ltr 86; PA ST; Bus Mgmt.

BOLTZ, MARIANNE; Pine Grove Area HS; Tremont, PA; (3); 1/115; Am Leg Aux Girls St; Quiz Bowl; SADD; Concert Band; Drm Mjr(t); Yrbk Ed-Chief; Off Stu Cncl; Hon Roll; Sec NHS; Church Yth Grp; Hugh O Brien Yth Fndtn Ldrsh Smnr 86.

BOLZE, JILL; West Perry HS; Landisburg, PA; (4); Varsity Clb; VP Frsh Cls; Trs Jr Cls; Rep Sr Cls; Off Stu Cncl; Stat Bsktbl; Stat Socr; L Trk; Church Yth Grp; Spanish Clb; Qlfd Dist Lng & Triple Jump Trk 86-87; Homecoming 2nd Rnr-Up 87; Shippensburg U; Chldhd Ed.

BOMAR, SHAWN A; East Allegheny HS; North Versailles, PA; (4); 90/215; Boy Scts; Letterman Clb; Ski Clb; Pres Spanish Clb; Rep Frsh Cls; Rep Soph Cls; Pres Jr Cls; Pres Sr Cls; Rep Stu Cncl; Capt Var Bsktbl; All Star Allegheny Conf Ftbll 86; WPIL Track Fnlst 1600 Meter Relay 85; Engr.

BOMBALSKI, JAMIE; Highlands HS; Natrona Hgts, PA; (3); Church Yth Grp; Hosp Aide; Intnl Clb; Office Aide; SADD; VP Drill Tm; Rep Stu Cncl; Var Swmmng; Jr NHS; Schlstc Achvt Awd 84-85 & 86-87; Pitt; Nursing.

BOMBERGER, ANGELA M; Cedar Cliff HS; Camp Hill, PA; (2); 89/287; Spanish Clb; Flag Corp; JV Trk; Hon Roll; Prfct Atten Awd; Acadc Excllnc Awd Bio I 87; Mid Penn Conf Div I Chmpnshp Trk 87; Penn ST U; Jrnlsm.

BOMBERGER, HEATHER; Northern SR HS; Dillsburg, PA; (4); 13/200; Model UN; Political Wkr; Pres Sec Speech Tm; Band; Chorus; Drm Mjr(t); School Musical; Nwsp Ed-Chief; French Hon Soc; High Hon Roll; Semester Intrnshp St Rep Bruce I Smith 87; Tied St Champion At PHSSL St Comp Poetry 87; St Chorus 87; WV Wesleyan Coll; Intl Studies.

BOMBERGER, MARCIE; Northern HS; Dillsburg, PA; (3); 12/248; Church Yth Grp; Girl Scts; NFL; Band; Rep Soph Cls; Rep Jr Cls; Var L Fld Hcky; High Hon Roll; NHS; Debate Tm; Exec Wmns Intl Bus Cr Schlrshp Pgm 86-87; York JR Miss Schlrshp Pgm 86-87; Bus Admin.

BOMGARDNER, BUFFY; Donegal HS; Mount Joy, PA; (2); Concert Band; Mrchg Band; Nwsp Stf; Yrbk Stf; Pres Frsh Cls; Rep Stu Cncl; Var Fld Hcky; Stat Mgr(s); JV Sftbl; Hon Roll; Psych.

BOMGARDNER, KYNEL DENISE; Northern Lebanon HS; Ono, PA; (2); Church Yth Grp; FCA; Trs Rptr 4-H; Band; Concert Band; 4-H Awd; Hon Roll; Jr NHS; NHS; Prfct Atten Awd; Vrsty Ltr In Trck 86 & 87; Lncstr Bible Coll; Bible.

BONACCI, BETH; Bishop Hafey HS; Oneida, PA; (4); French Clb; Trs Ski Clb; Trs Y-Teens; School Play; Trs Jr Cls; Stu Cncl; Cheerleading; Hon Roll; Orch; Yrbk Stf; Northeastern U; Brdcstng.

BONACCI, VALERIE; Carbondale Area JR SR HS; Carbondale, PA; (3); 7/138; Church Yth Grp; English Clb; German Clb; JA; Church Choir; Yrbk Stf; High Hon Roll; NHS; Ltry Awd 86; Nvlst.

BONACUSE, JENNIFER; Ephrata SR HS; Akron, PA; (3); Mgr(s); Powder Puff Ftbl; Score Keeper; Swmmng; Timer; Hon Roll; Fashn Mrchndsng.

BONADIO, JOSEPH; Connellsville Area SR HS; Vanderbilt, PA; (2); Am Leg Boys St; Church Yth Grp; Office Aide; Pep Clb; Science Clb; Varsity Clb; VP Frsh Cls; JV Var Bsbl; Ftbl; JV Wt Lftg; Awd All ST Tm 87.

BONADIO, KIMBERLY; Somerset Area HS; Somerset, PA; (3); Dance Clb; English Clb; French Clb; Ski Clb; SADD; Chorus; Orch; Off Stu Cncl; Hon Roll; NHS.

BONANNI, MARC; Easton Area HS; Easton, PA; (4); 59/447; Drama Clb; Teachers Aide; Band; Jazz Band; Orch; Pres Soph Cls; Pres Jr Cls; Pres Sr Cls; Easton Area Educ Assoc Awd & Cole-Auld Palmer PTA Schlrshp 87; Temple U; Eng.

BONANTI, MARGARET; Fort Le Boeuf HS; Erie, PA; (3); 10/212; Gannon U; Law.

BONAROTI, JENNIFER; Plum SR HS; Pittsburgh, PA; (3); Camera Clb; Cmnty Wkr; French Clb; FHA; Chorus; Hon Roll; ASETS 86-87; Awds Hnrs Engl III & World Cults 86-87; U Pittsburgh; Psych.

BONARRIGO, LIANE; Blairsville SR HS; Blairsville, PA; (4); Church Yth Grp; Drama Clb; Hosp Aide; Ski Clb; Band; Church Choir; Color Guard; Concert Band; School Musical; Yrbk Bus Mgr; PA ST U; Pre Med.

BONASKIEWICH, BECKY; Northampton HS; Walnutport, PA; (3); Drama Clb; Thesps; High Hon Roll; Hon Roll; Theatre Arts.

BONAVENTURA, CLIFFORD; Methacton HS; Phoenixville, PA; (3); 12/381; Boy Scts; Math Tm; Ski Clb; JV L Trk; High Hon Roll; NHS; Penn ST; Electrnc Engrng.

BONAVINA, SANDRA; Hanover Area JR-SR HS; Wilkes Barre, PA; (3); Chorus; Bsktbl; Crs Cntry; Swmmng; Trk; Vllybl; High Hon Roll; Hon Roll; Jr NHS; NHS; Dist Chmp Trck Javelin 85 & 86; Yth Solute 86-87; Offcl Lf Grd CPR Cert 86-87; Comp.

BONAVITA, MICHAEL; Central Catholic HS; Pittsburgh, PA; (3); 61/320; VP JA; Band; Jazz Band; Rep Soph Cls; Rep Jr Cls; Var Bsbl; Var Ftbl; Hon Roll; NHS; Ldrshp Wrkshp 85.

BONAWAITZ, DANIEL; Lower Dauphin HS; Grantville, PA; (3); 85/312; Var Bsbl; Swmmng; Economics.

BOND, AMY; Venango Christian HS; Clarion, PA; (3); Chrmn Model UN; Nwsp Stf; Yrbk Stf; Pres Soph Cls; Sec Sr Cls; Rep Stu Cncl; Var Cheerleading; Hon Roll; Pres Trs NHS; Natl Educ Dvlpmnt Tst-Hghst Clss Scr Awd 86; Lbrl Arts.

BOND, KIMBERLY; Wyoming Area HS; Pittston, PA; (3); Art Clb; German Clb; Key Clb; Pres VP SADD; Color Guard; Pre-Law.

BOND, TARA; Grace Christian Schl; Wernersville, PA; (2); Church Yth Grp; Computer Clb; Drama Clb; Pep Clb; Spanish Clb; Chorus; School Play; Yrbk Stf; Trs Soph Cls; Var Cheerleading; Engl Awd 87; Imprvmnt Awd Hockey 87; Imprvmnt Awd Chrldng 87; Dntstry.

BONDE, LISA; Belle Vernon Area HS; Belle Vernon, PA; (4); 15/275; Hosp Aide; Ski Clb; Variety Show; Nwsp Rptr; Yrbk Stf; Pres Soph Cls; VP Jr Cls; VP Sr Cls; Capt Cheerleading; Cit Awd; U Pittsburgh; Phy Thrpy.

BONDI, GREG; St Pius X HS; Collegeville, PA; (1); 11/146; 4-H; Band; School Play; High Hon Roll; Hon Roll; Acad 1st Hnrs 86-87; Acad Awd Outstndg Perf Sci 86-87; Sci.

BONE, LISA; Jeannette SR HS; Jeannette, PA; (3); 47/124; NAACP; VICA; VP Band; Color Guard; Concert Band; Drm & Bgl; Jazz Band; Mrchg Band; Symp Band; VP Frsh Cls; Stu Chrs 85; Stu Yr 85; Bus.

BONEBREAK, LISA; Newport HS; Newport, PA; (3); 39/120; Chorus; School Musical; School Play; Hst Frsh Cls; Rep Stu Cncl; Fld Hcky; Voice Dem Awd; Church Yth Grp; Cnty Chorus & Hnrb Mntn To All-Stars At Mid Atlantic Field Hockey Camp 87; Pblc Rltns.

BONELLI, MICHELLE; Parkland SR HS; Allentown, PA; (3); 191/481; Drama Clb; Exploring; Girl Scts; Band; Concert Band; School Musical; School Play; Stage Crew; Yrbk Phtg; Stu Cncl; Slvr Awd Grl Scts 85; Entrprnr.

BONENBERGER JR, KENNETH J; Bishop Egan HS; Levittown, PA; (4); 8/214; Pres German Clb; Q&S; Yrbk Ed-Chief; Var Capt Crs Cntry; Var Capt Trk; Lion Awd; NHS; Prfct Atten Awd; Tom Juno Schlr Athl Awd 86-87; All Cthlc All Area Crss Cntry; MVP Crss Cntry Trk Teams; Haverford Coll; Pre Med.

BONENBERGER, LAURA; William Allen HS; Allentown, PA; (2); 79/634; Band; Concert Band; Mrchg Band; Orch; Hon Roll; Jr NHS; Raub Mdl Schl Stu Of Mnth Awd 83-84; Raub Mdl Schl Music Awd Band & Orch 85; Dist Orch 84-87; Tri M 86; West Cheter U; Music Educ.

BONENBERGER, REGINA; Wm Allen HS; Allentown, PA; (4); 90/541; Sec Latin Clb; Band; Concert Band; Mrchg Band; Sec Orch; Hon Roll; Jr NHS; NHS; Phila Clsscl Soc Cert Merit 87; Summo Cum Hnr Schlrshp Awd 85-86; HS Schlrshp 87; Semper Fidelis Awd; Allentown Coll; Acctng.

BONETTI, ANN MARIE; Danville Area SR HS; Danville, PA; (3); 20/187; Ski Clb; Spanish Clb; Yrbk Stf; Bsktbl; Fld Hcky; Sftbl; High Hon Roll; NHS; Premed.

BONEY, MICHELLE; Mifflinburg Area HS; Mifflinburg, PA; (1); FHA; Band; Concert Band; Mrchg Band; JV Fld Hcky; JV Sftbl; Hon Roll; Cmmrcl Artst.

BONI, DAVE; Buryettstown JR/Sr HS; Bulger, PA; (3); Sec French Clb; Chorus; Sec Trs Frsh Cls; Sec Trs Soph Cls; Sec Trs Jr Cls; High Hon Roll; Hon Roll; Jr NHS; NHS; Engr.

BONI, ERIC N; Peters Township HS; Mc Murray, PA; (4); 30/242; VP Computer Clb; FBLA; Science Clb; JV Bsbl; Hon Roll; Ntl Merit SF; Prfct Atten Awd; Amer Comp Sci League Wnr 83-84; Bus.

BONIGER, JULIE; Villa Maria Acad; Erie, PA; (3); Dance Clb; PAVAS; Q&S; Spanish Clb; SADD; School Musical; School Play; Nwsp Rptr; High Hon Roll; NHS; Law.

BONITA, JOHN A; James M Coughlin HS; Plains, PA; (4); 50/324; Band; Var L Trk; Var L Wrstlng; Jr NHS; NHS; Franklin.

BONITO, VALERIE; Phila HS For Girls; Philadelphia, PA; (2); Lit Mag; Sftbl; Hon Roll; Sci.

BONNELL, RENEE; Fort Le Boeuf HS; Erie, PA; (3); 1/222; Dance Clb; Model UN; Chorus; Yrbk Ed-Chief; Yrbk Phtg; Rep Jr Cls; JV Var Cheerleading; NHS; Camera Clb; French Clb; Altrnt PA Govs Schl Intl Study 87; Zonta Clb Amelia Earhart Awd 87.

BONNER, ANN; Mid-Valley Secondary Center; Dickson City, PA; (3); Library Aide; Rep Stu Cncl; Hon Roll; 1st Pl Litr Locl Lvl PTSA Reflctns Cont 87; HOSA; Early Chldhd Ed.

BONNER, CAROLE; Bishop Hafey HS; Beaver Brook, PA; (3); Art Clb; Church Yth Grp; 4-H; Library Aide; PAVAS; Orch; Bsktbl; Mgr(s); Score Keeper; Sftbl; Outstndng 4-H Vlntr 86; Outstndng Mssn Cllctr 84; Outstndng Catholc Yth 87; Manhattan; Phys Thrpst.

BONNER, MARTIN; Bishop Neumann HS; S Williamsport, PA; (2); 23/52; Cmnty Wkr; Dance Clb; Pep Clb; Ski Clb; Spanish Clb; SADD; Rep Frsh Cls; Stu Cncl; L Bsbl; L Bsktbl; Law.

BONNER, ROBERT A; Archbishop Ryan Boys HS; Philadelphia, PA; (2); Computer Clb; High Hon Roll; Prncpls Awd 86-87; Comm.

BONNER, SAM; Jim Thorpe Area HS; Jim Thorpe, PA; (2); 16/95; Chorus; Bsktbl; JV Ftbl; Wt Lftg; Hon Roll; Treas Peer Cnslr; Zoolgst.

BONNER, SHAWN; Carver H S Engineering & Science; Philadelphia, PA; (3); 65/241; Church Yth Grp; Cmnty Wkr; Cit Awd; Drexel U; Arch Engrng.

BONNER, TRACY; West Catholic For Girls HS; Philadelphia, PA; (3); 96/246; Varsity Clb; Band; Church Choir; Concert Band; Jazz Band; Orch; Rep Jr Cls; Var JV Bsktbl; JV Gym; Stat Score Keeper; Hahnemann U; Ped Nurse.

BONNICI, MARK S; William Allen HS; Allentown, PA; (4); Boy Scts; Band; Chorus; Concert Band; Jazz Band; Mrchg Band; Pep Band; Bowling; Slippery Rock U.

BONO, BARTHOLOMEW R; Wyomissing Area HS; Wyomissing, PA; (4); 8/102; VP Exploring; French Clb; Band; Jazz Band; Var Trk; Ntl Merit SF; Model UN; Concert Band; Drm Mjr(t); Mrchg Band; Pa All-St Bnd 85-86.

BONO, WENDY; Kittanning HS; Worthington, PA; (3); Drill Tm; Rep Sr Cls; Var JV Tennis; IUP.

BONSER, AMY; Hazelton HS; Hazleton, PA; (2); 1/300; Church Yth Grp; Pep Clb; Scholastic Bowl; Ski Clb; Church Choir; Nwsp Stf; Cit Awd; High Hon Roll; Pres Schlr; Ed Yrbk Ed-Chief; Amrcn Lgn Frst Plc Awd 86; Kings Coll Spnsh Cntst Wnr 86; Math.

BONUS JR, ROBERT; Washington HS; Washington, PA; (2); 18/185; Key Clb; Ski Clb; Spanish Clb; Varsity Clb; School Play; Stage Crew; Rep Stu Cncl; JV Bsbl; JV Var Ftbl; Var Tennis; Nuclr Engrng.

BONYUN, SANDY; George Washington HS; Philadelphia, PA; (3); DECA; FBLA; Library Aide; Teachers Aide; Dstrbtv Ed Clbs Of Amer 85-87; Holy Family; Bus Mngmnt.

BOOK, BONNIE; Neshannock HS; New Castle, PA; (3); 17/112; Church Yth Grp; NFL; Ski Clb; Chorus; Drill Tm; School Musical; Nwsp Stf; Hon Roll; NEDT Awd; Forensics Awd 85-86; Hnr Awd 86-87; Presdntl Acad Fitness Awd 85; Psychlgy.

BOOK, DOUG PARKER; Palisades HS; Pipersville, PA; (4); 1/179; Band; High Hon Roll; JP Sousa Awd; Val; Scholastic Bowl; Concert Band; Mrchg Band; Orch; School Musical; Nwsp Rptr; PA Dist Band-Orchestra ST Band 86-87; Bulbs Co Sci Acad 86; Chem Awd 87; UCSD; Mat.

BOOK, GARTH; West Hazleton HS; Sugarloaf, PA; (3); Church Yth Grp; FBLA; Ski Clb; SADD; Var Bsktbl; Var Ftbl; Im Vllybl; Penn ST U; Arch.

BOOK, LISA; Annville-Cleona HS; Annville, PA; (4); Sec Church Yth Grp; FBLA; Hosp Aide; Chorus; Mrchg Band; School Musical; School Play; Trk; NHS; NEDT Awd; Penn ST U; Nrsng.

BOOKBINDER, KARIN; Creative & Performing Arts HS; Philadelphia, PA; (3); Dance Clb; Office Aide; School Musical; Variety Show; High Hon Roll; NHS; Schlrshp Training Prog Dance Comp 84; NYU; Dance.

BOOKER, MARLA; West Catholic High For Girls HS; Philadelphia, PA; (3); Church Yth Grp; Cmnty Wkr; FCA; Chorus; Church Choir; Orch; Rep Sr Cls; JR Svc Awd 87; Hnr Biblical Knowldge & Comprhnsn 84; Hnr Free Libr Phila Reading Pgm 84; Cabrini Coll; Psych.

BOOKER III, ROBERT S; Engineering & Science HS; Philadelphia, PA; (4); 5/190; Computer Clb; High Hon Roll; Hon Roll; NHS; Ntl Merit Schol; Prfct Atten Awd; Delta Sigma Theta Schlrshp 86; Natl Soc Of Pro Engrs 86; Omin Essay Awd 85; MA Inst Of Tech; Bio Med Engr.

BOOKHAMMER, DANIEL; Williamsburg HS; Williamsburg, PA; (3); Letterman Clb; Varsity Clb; Rep Frsh Cls; Bsbl; Ftbl; Wt Lftg; Hon Roll; NHS.

BOOKS, RONALD; Hampton HS; Gibsonia, PA; (3); Ski Clb; Spanish Clb; Var L Bsbl; Im JV Bsktbl; Im Bowling; Im Ftbl; Im Socr; Hon Roll; Engrng.

BOONE, LEANN; Connellsville SR HS; Connellsville, PA; (3); Art Clb; Office Aide; Pep Clb; Drill Tm; Nwsp Rptr; Nwsp Stf; Sec Soph Cls; High Hon Roll; Pittsburgh Beauty Acad.

BOONE, SUSAN LYNN; Canon Mc Millan HS; Washington, PA; (4); Exploring; 4-H; Office Aide; Ski Clb; SADD; Yrbk Stf; JV Swmmng; Natl Young Ldrs Conf 87; CA U PA.

BOORE, JAMES; William Allen HS; Allentown, PA; (3); Leo Clb; Band; Concert Band; Drm Mjr(t); Jazz Band; Mrchg Band; Orch; Pep Band; Splling Bee Fnlst 87; Embry Riddle; Aerospc Engrng.

BOORNAZIAN, LORI; Lower Merion HS; Ardmore, PA; (3); Intnl Clb; Service Clb; Spanish Clb; SADD; Yrbk Stf; High Hon Roll; Ntl Merit SF; Spanish NHS; Intl Bus.

BOORNAZIAN, MICHELE; Penn Wood HS; Lansdowne, PA; (4); Band; Concert Band; Mrchg Band; JV Fld Hcky; JV Tennis; NHS; Home & Schl Assn 87; Millersville U; Bio.

BOOSE, DAVID; Central York SR HS; York, PA; (2); VP Church Yth Grp; Hon Roll.

BOOSE, ELIZABETH; Central York SR HS; York, PA; (4); 45/203; Trs Church Yth Grp; Band; Concert Band; Symp Band; Hon Roll; Literature.

BOOSE II, GEORGE; West Perry SR HS; Loysville, PA; (3); 7/232; Boy Scts; Pres Church Yth Grp; Var L Socr; Var JV Wrstlng; God Cntry Awd; High Hon Roll; Hon Roll; NHS; Vigil Hnr 86; PA ST U; Elec Engrng.

BOOSE, MARILEE; Garden Spot HS; New Holland, PA; (2); 20/226; Pres Church Yth Grp; Trs 4-H; Sec VICA; Chorus; Church Choir; Concert Band; Flag Corp; Mrchg Band; Sftbl; Tennis; Hnr Roll 85-87; Arch.

BOOTERBAUGH, MARY K; Penn Cambria HS; Cresson, PA; (4); 4/196; Drama Clb; Ski Clb; Chorus; Yrbk Stf; Sec Frsh Cls; JV Cheerleading; Var Vllybl; High Hon Roll; Hon Roll; Sec NHS; Pitt; Pharm.

BOOTH, ANGELA; Southern Fulton HS; Warfordsburg, PA; (3); FBLA; FHA; Library Aide; Band; Nwsp Phtg; Nwsp Stf; JV Cheerleading; Hon Roll; 1st Pl FBLA Rgnls In Bus Math 86.

BOOTH, CHRISTINE; Montour HS; Coraopolis, PA; (2); SADD; Yrbk Stf; High Hon Roll; Hon Roll; Acad Achvt Awd 87.

BOOTH, JEFFREY; Hershey HS; Hershey, PA; (3); 51/204; Computer Clb; Quiz Bowl; Science Clb; Nwsp Phtg; Var Crs Cntry; Stat Mgr(s); JV Socr; Im Vllybl; High Hon Roll; Hon Roll; ST Sci Olympd Chmpns-Slvr ST Sci Bwl, Brnz-Ntl Sci Bwl 85; ST Sci Olympd Chmpns 86; Engrng.

BOOTH, MARIA; Galeton Area JR SR HS; Galeton, PA; (3); 1/40; VP French Clb; Band; Yrbk Stf; Sec Soph Cls; VP Jr Cls; Trs Stu Cncl; Var Bsktbl; Var Tennis; Hon Roll; NHS; Intl Bus.

BOOTH, MARY; Saltsburg JR/Sr HS; Saltsburg, PA; (2); 22/96; SADD; Chorus; Rep Stu Cncl; Stat Bsktbl; Hon Roll; Acad Of Med Arts & Bus; Bus.

BOOTH, MICHELLE; Galeton Area JR SR HS; St Galeton, PA; (3); 1/38; VP French Clb; Chorus; Yrbk Stf; Sec Soph Cls; VP Jr Cls; Trs Stu Cncl; JV Bsktbl; Tennis; Stat Trk; NHS; Intl Busi.

BOOTH, TRACY; Wyoming Valley West HS; Edwardsville, PA; (3); Spanish Clb; Chorus; L Crs Cntry; Trk; Hon Roll; OH Test Schltc Achvt Algebra Cert 85; Cert Of Achvt Natl Hstry Day 86.

BOOTHMAN, DEANA; St Hubert HS For Girls; Philadelphia, PA; (3); 14/421; Aud/Vis; Church Yth Grp; Cmnty Wkr; Math Tm; Spanish Clb; Teachers Aide; Chorus; Hon Roll; NHS; Opt Clb Awd; Sec Comm Svc Corps 88; Spanish Awd 87; Occu Ther.

BOOTZ, GERRY; Sharpsville HS; Sharpsville, PA; (3); Camera Clb; Chess Clb; German Clb; Chorus; Var Bsktbl; NHS; Grove City Coll; Comp Sci.

BOOZ, KIMBERLY J; Norristown Area HS; Norristown, PA; (3); 32/520; Church Yth Grp; GAA; Letterman Clb; Yrbk Rptr; Off Jr Cls; Off Stu Cncl; Fld Hcky; Sftbl; High Hon Roll; NHS; Med.

BOOZER, KELLIE; Elizabethtown HS; Elizabethtown, PA; (4); 78/223; Pres Church Yth Grp; Dance Clb; Band; Chorus; Orch; School Musical; Capt Crs Cntry; Capt Trk; Mgr Wrstlng; Track Scholar Millersville U 87-88; Millersville U; Cmmnctn.

BOOZER, NYCOLE; Shanksville-Stony Creek HS; Shanksville, PA; (3); 3/34; Ski Clb; Yrbk Stf; VP Soph Cls; VP Jr Cls; Off Stu Cncl; Var L Bsktbl; Var L Vllybl; Hon Roll; NHS; Spanish NHS.

BORAN, KAREN M; Nativity B U M HS; Pottsville, PA; (3); 7/86; School Play; Nwsp Stf; JV Bsktbl; Var L Sftbl; Var L Vllybl; High Hon Roll; Hon Roll; NHS; Prfct Atten Awd.

BORAWSKI, KATHY; Villa Maria Acad; Erie, PA; (3); 3/157; Church Yth Grp; Science Clb; SADD; Chorus; Church Choir; School Musical; Variety Show; Rep Stu Cncl; Im Bsktbl; High Hon Roll.

BORCHICK, MARIE; Hazleton SR HS; Hazleton, PA; (3); Pep Clb; VICA; Chorus; Hon Roll; Cosmetics Rsrch.

BORCICH, ROBERT; Archbishop Ryan Boys HS; Philadelphia, PA; (2); 70/349; NHS; Bus.

BORDAS, TONYA; Connellsville SR HS; Dickerson Run, PA; (4); FTA; Math Clb; Radio Clb; Red Cross Aide; Science Clb; SADD; VICA; Y-Teens; Hon Roll; Prfct Atten Awd; Outstndng Stu Yr Csmtlgy 87; Pittsbrgh Beau Acad Schlrshp 87; Dirctrs Lst 85-87; Pittsbrgh Beaut Acad; Tchr.

BORDEN, LESLIE; Mid Valley HS; Dickson City, PA; (3); Art Clb; Camera Clb; Drama Clb; Ski Clb; School Play; Stage Crew; Nwsp Rptr; Nwsp Stf; Yrbk Ed-Chief; Yrbk Stf; Nrsg.

BORDEN, SHELDON T; S R U HS; Gillett, PA; (4); Pres Art Clb; Varsity Clb; Bsbl; Bsktbl; Socr; Trs Trk; Wrstlng; Letterman Clb; Red Cross Aide; Mgr(s); Schlstc Art Awd 83 & 85; Joyce Hewitt Beck Memrl & Doug Bolster Memrl Awd 87; Edinboro U; Fine Arts.

BORDERS, MONIQUE; Vo Tech Of Lawrence Co HS; New Castle, PA; (2); Drama Clb; SADD; VICA; School Play; Voc Aw: Excllnc 87; U Of CA; Federal Lawyer.

BORDNER, PAM; Waynesboro Area SR HS; Waynesboro, PA; (3); Chorus; Yrbk Phtg; Yrbk Stf; Var Fld Hcky; Hon Roll.

BORDNER, ROBYN; Danville SR HS; Danville, PA; (2); 4-H; Spanish Clb; Bus.

BOREK JR, THOMAS; Connellsville Area SR HS; Connellsville, PA; (3); Band; Concert Band; Mrchg Band; Stage Crew; High Hon Roll; Hon Roll; Fish & Game Clb; Molinaro Marchng Band Local.

BORELLA, ROBERT J; Archbishop Ryan HS; Philadelphia, PA; (3); 9/414; French Clb; Im Bsktbl; High Hon Roll; Hon Roll.

BORELLI, NATOLI; Victor Christian Acad; Fleetwood, PA; (2); Acpl Chr; School Musical; Cheerleading; Vllybl.

BORETTI, JOHN; Tunkhannock Area HS; Tunkhannock, PA; (4); 14/270; Spanish Clb; Im Bsbl; Var Capt Bsktbl; Var L Golf; Hon Roll; Physcs Clb 86-87.

BORETTI, MATTHEW; Tunkhannock Area HS; Tunkhannock, PA; (2); Church Yth Grp; Spanish Clb; JV Bsktbl; Var Socr; Var Tennis; Hon Roll; Boston Coll.

BORGEL, SUZANNE; Dover HS; Dover, PA; (3); French Clb; Ski Clb; Hon Roll; NHS; Bio.

BORGER, ANNETTE; Pleasant Valley HS; Kunkletown, PA; (3); 2/232; Math Tm; SADD; Mrchg Band; Lit Mag; JV Var Bsktbl; JV Var Fld Hcky; Var Trk; High Hon Roll; Varsity Clb; Concert Band; Stu Mnth 85; Med.

BORGER, JASON; Northhampton SR HS; Northampton, PA; (2); Boy Scts; JV Bsbl; Mgr(s); Hon Roll; Crmnl Invstgtn.

BORGHETTI, ERNEST; Neshannock HS; New Castle, PA; (3); 23/104; Var Bsktbl; Var Ftbl; Jrnlsm.

BORGHISE, JODI; Little Flower HS; Philadelphia, PA; (3); Cmnty Wkr; Dance Clb; Office Aide; Amer Legn Merit & Achvt Awds 84; Dnc.

BORING, ALISON; Butler SR HS; Butler, PA; (2); Drama Clb; Thesps; Chorus; Jazz Band; School Play; French Clb; Drill Tm; Pom Pon; Music.

BORING, DAVID; Penn Trafford HS; Trafford, PA; (2); Band; Concert Band; Mrchg Band; Pep Band; Hon Roll.

BORING, DONALD; United HS; New Florence, PA; (3); 1/152; Camera Clb; Chess Clb; Mu Alpha Theta; Ski Clb; VP Band; VP Mrchg Band; Var L Trk; JV Wrstlng; High Hon Roll; NHS; Engr.

BORING, DONNA; Penns Manor HS; Strongstown, PA; (3); 42/97; FBLA; Pres VP FHA; Library Aide; SADD; Var Cheerleading; JV Vllybl.

BORING, SHANNON; Spring-Ford SR HS; Schwenksville, PA; (2); 36/289; Drama Clb; French Clb; Radio Clb; Band; Concert Band; Mrchg Band; Yrbk Stf; Hon Roll; Commnctns.

BORINO, LISA; Wilson Christian Acad; Belle Vernon, PA; (3); Church Yth Grp; Spanish Clb; Teachers Aide; Yrbk Stf; Sec Sr Cls; Sec Stu Cncl; Vllybl; Hon Roll; Acdmc All-Amrcn Engl III 86-87; Secr.

BORJA, MICHAEL; Butler SR HS; Butler, PA; (3); French Clb; Band; Concert Band; Mrchg Band; School Musical; Symp Band; Variety Show; Yrbk Phtg; Yrbk Stf; Trs Soph Cls; Boston U; Biomed Engrng.

BORK, JUDY; Shaler Area HS; Pittsburgh, PA; (3); 82/490; Church Yth Grp; Hosp Aide; Pep Clb; SADD; Yrbk Stf; Capt L Crs Cntry; L Var Swmmng; L Var Trk; High Hon Roll; Hon Roll; Phys Thrpy.

BORKOWSKI, KEVIN; Ringgold HS; Donora, PA; (3); 28/372; Math Clb; Science Clb; L Crs Cntry; Var Trk; Hon Roll; NHS; Mech Engnrng.

BORKOWSKI, TERRY; Highlands HS; Tarentum, PA; (3); Spanish Clb; JV Var Bsktbl; Var L Ftbl; Var Trk; Bio.

BORN, SHANNON E; Solanco HS; Gulf Breeze, FL; (3); Drama Clb; Chorus; School Musical; School Play; Nwsp Stf; High Hon Roll; Hon Roll; NHS; Wwf; Bus Adm.

BORNEISEN, JENNIFER; West Hazleton HS; Jeanesville, PA; (2); French Clb; Pep Clb; SADD; Band; Mrchg Band; Nwsp Stf; Yrbk Stf; Trk.

BORNER, DAWN; North Hills HS; Pittsburgh, PA; (3); Exploring; Office Aide; Ski Clb; Color Guard; Mrchg Band; Frsh Cls; Mgr(s); High Hon Roll; Hon Roll; NHS; Engnrng.

BORNER, JAMES; Delaare Valley HS; Milford, PA; (3); 7/150; Hon Roll; Polt Sci.

BOROCH, BLAIR; Upper Merion HS; King Of Prussia, PA; (3); 11/308; Math Tm; Spanish Clb; Concert Band; Crs Cntry; Tennis; High Hon Roll; NHS; Natl Electrochem Soc Awd 2nd Prz 85; Natl Sci Olympd Awd Dstnctn 86; Montgmry Co Sci Rsrch Hnrbl Mntn; Duke U; Lbrl Arts.

BOROCHOVITZ, RAELENE; Taylor Allderdice HS; Pittsburgh, PA; (2); Chess Clb; Debate Tm; Hosp Aide; Temple Yth Grp; Rep Stu Cncl; Swmmng; High Hon Roll; NHS; Lead Role-Lry Wllms-Mscl Oklhma 87; Achvd Lvl Grn Blt Wth Brwn Strp-Kngs Krte Acad 87; Psychlgy.

BORODATY, GREGORY; Ringgold HS; Charleroi, PA; (4); 1/347; Quiz Bowl; Ski Clb; Stu Cncl; Golf; High Hon Roll; VP NHS; Ntl Merit Ltr; Rennselaer Poly Inst; Engrng.

BOROSKY, GREG; Carbondale Area HS; Carbondale, PA; (3); Ski Clb; Spanish Clb; Var JV Bsbl; Var JV Bsktbl; JV Ftbl; Var JV Golf; Radiology.

BOROSKY, PATRICIA; Carbondale Area HS; Simpson, PA; (4); 2/139; Computer Clb; FBLA; Science Clb; Varsity Clb; Yrbk Bus Mgr; Yrbk Phtg; Bsktbl; Crs Cntry; Trk; Vllybl; Free Enterprise Wk Lock Haven U Schlrshp 86.

BOROUGHS, HOWARD; Milton Hershey Schl; Hershey, PA; (4); 2/130; Pres Boy Scts; Pres Exploring; Nwsp Stf; Lit Mag; Stu Cncl; Ftbl; Capt Wrstlng; High Hon Roll; Pres NHS; Rotary Awd; Stu Ldrshp Scty Pres 87; Aero Engr.

BOROWICZ, BETH; Mercer JR SR HS; Mercer, PA; (1); Chorus; JV Bsktbl; Var Trk; Var Vllybl; Hon Roll.

BORRELLI, MELINDA; New Castle SR HS; New Castle, PA; (3); 30/280; Church Yth Grp; Dance Clb; Exploring; Math Tm; Spanish Clb; SADD; Variety Show; Yrbk Stf; Rep Frsh Cls; Stu Cncl; Sci.

BORRELLI, SHERI; Valley HS; New Kensington, PA; (3); 40/240; Ski Clb; Spanish Clb; Varsity Clb; Chorus; Rep Stu Cncl; Var Cheerleading; Var Tennis; Var Trk; High Hon Roll; Hon Roll; MV Cheerldr Awd 85 Girls Tennis Section Doubles Chmpn & Prsdntl Phys Fitness Awd 87.

BORRONI, JEFF; Big Beaver Falls Area HS; Koppel, PA; (3); 6/170; Cmnty Wkr; French Clb; VP Soph Cls; Var L Bsbl; Var L Ftbl; High Hon Roll; Yrbk Stf; French Stu Mnth 85; Def Capt Ftbl Tm 84.

BORSCH, PAM; Strath Haven HS; Morton, PA; (3); Church Yth Grp; Cmnty Wkr; GAA; Red Cross Aide; Yrbk Sprt Ed; Yrbk Stf; Stu Cncl; Bsktbl; Fld Hcky; Sftbl; Capt Of Varsity Sftbl Tm 87-88; MVP Field Hockey 84; Htl Mgmt.

BORTMAS, DENISE; Butler SR HS; East Butler, PA; (3); Church Yth Grp; FBLA; German Clb; JA; Church Choir; Concert Band; Mrchg Band; Yrbk Stf; High Hon Roll; NHS; Bus.

BORTNER, ANGELA S; Spring Grove SR HS; Codorus, PA; (3); Church Yth Grp; Chorus; Color Guard; School Musical; Nwsp Stf; Stu Cncl; Cheerleading; Powder Puff Ftbl; Trk; Hon Roll.

BORTNER, MELINDA; Hanover HS; Hanover, PA; (2); Cmnty Wkr; Sec Band; School Play; Pres Frsh Cls; Pres Soph Cls; Pres Jr Cls; Pres Sr Cls; Rep Stu Cncl; Capt Cheerleading; Gov Hon Prg Awd; Bus.

BORTZ, CANDY; Brandywine Heights Area HS; Kutztown, PA; (2); Library Aide; Color Guard; JV Sftbl.

BORTZ, KATHLEEN; Northeastern HS; Manchester, PA; (3); 9/195; Church Yth Grp; Acpl Chr; Chorus; Church Choir; Stat Socr; High Hon Roll; Hon Roll; NHS; Dist And Regnl Chorus 87; Penn ST; Comm.

BORTZ, LISA; Hickory HS; Hermitage, PA; (2); 29/202; Church Yth Grp; Hosp Aide; Latin Clb; Chorus; Concert Band; Mrchg Band; Orch; Rep Stu Cncl; Stat Bsktbl; JV Var Cheerleading; Ntl Latin Hnr Scty 85-86; Gannon U; Med.

BORTZ, MICHELLE; Hempfield HS; Columbia, PA; (3); Teachers Aide; Chorus; School Musical; Nwsp Rptr; High Hon Roll; Hon Roll; Cmmrcl Pilot.

BORTZFIELD, TRICIA; Lampeter Strasburg HS; Lancaster, PA; (4); 36/158; Art Clb; Thesps; Varsity Clb; School Musical; Var Bsktbl; Var Fld Hcky; Var Sftbl; Hon Roll; Acpl Chr; Band; Art Awd 87; Schltc Art Awds 86-87; Millersville U; Art Ed.

BORUCH JR, PAUL; Northampton Area SR HS; Danielsville, PA; (2); Band; Concert Band; Drm Mjr(t); Jazz Band; Mrchg Band; Orch; Symp Band; Bsbl; Bsktbl; Hon Roll.

BORUM, SANDY; Coughlin HS; Wilkes Barre, PA; (3); #141 In Class; German Clb; Pres Band; Chorus; Concert Band; Jazz Band; Mrchg Band; Orch; School Musical; JV Sftbl; JV Vllybl; Mst Outstndng Music Awd; Mst Outstndng Trumpet Plyr/Stage Band Fest; Music.

BORYS, SEAN; Lake-Lehman SR HS; Hunlock Crk, PA; (2); JV Trk; Hon Roll; Jr NHS; NEDT Awd; Gftd Pgm 86; Villanova U; Jrnlsm.

BORYSCHUK, SCOTT J; William Tennent HS; Warminster, PA; (4); 36/560; Boy Scts; Church Yth Grp; Concert Band; Mrchg Band; Orch; Im Mgr Socr; Var Swmmng; High Hon Roll; NHS; Martin Luther King Scholar; Marlyn Moyer Jr Scholar; Estrn Nazarene Coll; Chem.

BORZILLO, KEITH; Owen J Roberts HS; Parkerford, PA; (4); 37/271; SADD; Var L Ftbl; Im Vllybl; Im Wt Lftg; High Hon Roll; Hon Roll; PA ST; Bus Adm.

BORZOK, MICHELLE; Cardinal Brennan HS; Frackville, PA; (3); 15/58; Church Choir; Nwsp Stf; Var JV Bsktbl; Var L Sftbl; Prfct Atten Awd; Awd For Being Slctd To All-Star Tm For Sftbl 86; Bus Admn.

BOSAK, STEPHEN; Punxsutawney Area HS; Delancey, PA; (4); Varsity Clb; Var L Ftbl; PA ST U; Elec Engrng.

BOSE, ANIRUDDHA M; Lower Merion HS; Wynnewood, PA; (3); Boy Scts; Band; Concert Band; Mrchg Band; Symp Band; Nwsp Rptr; Nwsp Stf; Yrbk Rptr; Yrbk Stf; Trs Frsh Cls.

BOSE, MEENEKSHI; Winchester-Thurston HS; State College, PA; (4); French Clb; Intnl Clb; Service Clb; SADD; Stage Crew; Nwsp Rptr; Ed Nwsp Stf; Lit Mag; Sec Trs Frsh Cls; Sec Trs Jr Cls; Smith Coll Bk Awd 86; Jrnlsm Awd 86; Lit Mag Awd 84; Penn ST U; Frgn Svc.

BOSETTI, HEATHER; Moon Area SR HS; Coraopolis, PA; (4); Church Yth Grp; Acpl Chr; Chorus; Flag Corp; Stu Cncl; JV Sftbl; High Hon Roll; NHS; PA ST U; Bio.

BOSETTI, NORMAN; Yough SR HS; Smithton, PA; (4); Im Badmtn; Var Ice Hcky; Im Vllybl; Hon Roll; Penn ST Mc Keesport; Bio-Med.

BOSIN, KELLY; Leechburg Area HS; Leechburg, PA; (2); 16/95; Band; Concert Band; Mrchg Band; Pep Band; Yrbk Stf; Var Twrlr; Phrmcy.

BOSLET, LEAH; Bishop Guilfoyle HS; Altoona, PA; (4); 8/123; Cmnty Wkr; Sec Science Clb; Ski Clb; SADD; Yrbk Stf; Sec Stu Cncl; JV Cheerleading; Var Capt Vllybl; High Hon Roll; Hon Roll.

BOSLEY, WILL; Elizabethtown Area HS; Elizabethtown, PA; (2); Thesps; Band; Chorus; Concert Band; Jazz Band; Mrchg Band; Orch; School Musical; School Play; Stage Crew; Elec Engrng.

BOSNJAK, MICHELLE; Steelton Highspire HS; Highspire, PA; (3); 8/102; Girl Scts; Quiz Bowl; VP Spanish Clb; Drill Tm; Yrbk Sprt Ed; Yrbk Stf; Var Sftbl; Var Twrlr; Hon Roll; NHS; 2nd Pl Statue Of Liberty Cntst 85-86; Harrisburg Area CC; Elem Educ.

BOSS, SUSAN; Penn Hills HS; Pittsburgh, PA; (4); 1/616; Drama Clb; German Clb; Girl Scts; Letterman Clb; Nwsp Stf; Stu Cncl; Bsktbl; Crs Cntry; Sftbl; Trk; Crs Cntry Ltr 83 & 85-86; St Vincent Acad Scholar 86; Gannon U Acad Scholar 86; St Vincent Coll; Pre-Med.

BOSSARD, SHERRI; Maplewood HS; Townville, PA; (3); Church Yth Grp; Girl Scts; Hosp Aide; Band; Church Choir; Concert Band; Sec.

BOSSARD, SUE; Conneaut Lake HS; Conneaut Lake, PA; (3); School Play; Nwsp Sprt Ed; Yrbk Stf; Var Bsktbl; Var Sftbl; JV Vllybl; Drama Clb; GAA; Spanish Clb; JV Cheerleading; Elem Educ.

BOSSERMAN, BRIAN MICHAEL; Peters Township HS; Bridgeville, PA; (3); 70/265; Cmnty Wkr; Intnl Clb; Key Clb; SADD; Varsity Clb; Yrbk Stf; Capt Swmmng; Natl Swm Mts-Orlndo FL 86; All ST & ST Top 10 Awds-200 Mdly Rly 87; All Amer Cnsdrtn 87; Cornell U; Intl Bus.

BOSSERT, BARBARA; Quakertown SR HS; Milford Sq, PA; (3); 21/310; Art Clb; Var Mgr(s); JV Sftbl; JV Vllybl; High Hon Roll; Hon Roll.

BOSSERT, LORI; St Pauls Cathedral HS; Penn Hills, PA; (3); Drama Clb; French Clb; Library Aide; Red Cross Aide; Teachers Aide; Chorus; School Musical; School Play; Nwsp Ed-Chief; Cmnty Wkr; Outstndg Stu Music Supr Prfrmnc PSAT 87; Jr Achvmnt Dist Sec Of Yrr 86; Natl Hist Day Awd Of Excel 87; Erly Chldhd Ed.

BOST, DEBORAH; West Mifflin HS; W Mifflin, PA; (3); Hosp Aide; Ski Clb; Teachers Aide; Band; Jazz Band; Mrchg Band; VP L Sftbl; Im Vllybl; Sawyer Schl; Airline Reservtnst.

BOST, JONETTE; West Mifflin Area HS; W Mifflin, PA; (3); 11/318; Art Clb; Teachers Aide; Color Guard; Nwsp Stf; Yrbk Ed-Chief; Sec Soph Cls; Off Jr Cls; High Hon Roll; Jr NHS; NHS; Phys Thrpy.

BOSTANY, LISA; Pocono Central Catholic HS; Mt Pocono, PA; (4); 2/25; Art Clb; Pep Clb; Sec Service Clb; Ski Clb; Spanish Clb; Chorus; School Musical; School Play; Ed Yrbk Stf; Sec Jr Cls; Sci Hnr Awd 84-86; Excllnce Spnsh & Spllng Awd 84-86; Psych.

BOSTIAN, APRIL; Danville Ssr HS; Danville, PA; (3); Drama Clb; Office Aide; Red Cross Aide; Chorus; Color Guard; School Musical; Var Shrthnd Awds 86-87; Bank Teller.

BOSTIC, JEFF; York Catholic HS; York, PA; (2); 33/125; Ski Clb; Crs Cntry; Trk; Accntng.

BOSTICK, ROBYNE; Trinity HS; Mechanicsburg, PA; (2); French Clb; Bsktbl; Stat Ftbl; Trk; Vllybl; Hon Roll; Sprts Med.

BOSTJANCIC, SCOTT; Canon Mc Millan HS; Eighty Four, PA; (4); Latin Clb; Ski Clb; Band; Concert Band; Jazz Band; Mrchg Band; Pep Band; Golf; Var L Tennis; Trk; PA ST U; Ceramic Engrng.

BOSTON, CHRISTOPHER; Devon Prep; West Chester, PA; (1); Aud/Vis; Church Yth Grp; Spanish Clb; Chorus; School Musical; Stage Crew; Nwsp Rptr; JV Bsbl; JV Socr; Hon Roll; Acad Schlrshp To Devon Prep Schl 86; Prsdntl Acad Schlr Awds.

BOSTWICK, MICHEAL; Sayre Area HS; Athens, PA; (3); Band; Bsbl; Var Bsktbl; JV Ftbl; Hon Roll; Cert Of Merit For Schltcs Art 86-87; Msc.

BOTDORF, RHONDA; West Snyder HS; Mcclure, PA; (4); 4/90; Chorus; Drm Mjr(t); School Musical; Sec Sr Cls; Sec Stu Cncl; Capt L Bsktbl; Capt L Fld Hcky; L Var Sftbl; DAR Awd; NHS; Natl Schl Choral Awd, Drama Awd & Prsdntl Acdmc Fitness Awd 87; Penn ST U; Elem Educ.

BOTE, ROBERT; Donegal HS; Maytown, PA; (3); Boy Scts; JV Socr; JV Tennis; MI U; Naval Arch.

BOTT, CHARLES; Jim Thorpe SR HS; Jim Thorpe, PA; (3); Scholastic Bowl; Nwsp Ed-Chief; Nwsp Rptr; High Hon Roll; NHS; Acdmc All Amer 86.

BOTT, PETER; Jim Thorpe HS; Jim Thorpe, PA; (2); Band; High Hon Roll; Hon Roll; Comp Pgmmng.

BOTTE, MICHAEL; Western Beaver HS; Industry, PA; (3); Church Yth Grp; Cmnty Wkr; Letterman Clb; Varsity Clb; Chorus; Var L Bsbl; Var L Bsktbl; High Hon Roll; Hon Roll; NHS; Penn ST U; Chem Engrng.

BOTTIGER, JASON; Shi Kellamy HS; Sunbury, PA; (4); 38/300; VP Sr Cls; Rep Stu Cncl; Var Wrstlng; Hon Roll; Var Bsbl; Ed.

BOTTJER, GREG; Parkland HS; Orefield, PA; (2); Bsktbl; Golf; High Hon Roll; Hon Roll; Prfct Atten Awd; Prsdntl Acdmc Achvt Awd 86; Cmmnctn.

BOTTS, CRISTINA; Mifflinburg Area HS; Lewisburg, PA; (4); Art Clb; Church Yth Grp; French Clb; Chorus; L Trk; VP 4-H Awd; Hon Roll; Prfct Atten Awd; Tri-Hi-Y Hnr 87; Slippery Rock U; Elem Ed.

BOTTS, RANDY; Boyertown Area SR HS; Boyertown, PA; (4); 25/429; Church Yth Grp; Var Golf; Var Tennis; High Hon Roll; Pres Schlrshp; Widener U; Hotel Mngmnt.

BOTYRIUS, ERIC; Wyoming Area HS; Wyoming, PA; (3); Key Clb; Spanish Clb; JV Bsktbl; JV Ftbl; Var Vllybl.

BOTYRIUS, TONY; Wyoming Area HS; Wyoming, PA; (4); 1/249; Boy Scts; German Clb; Key Clb; Science Clb; Rep Stu Cncl; High Hon Roll; NCTE Awd; Pres NHS; Val; Congrssnl Yth Ldrshp Cncl Stu 87; Bucknell; Bio.

BOUCH, KATHERINE; Lower Pauphin HS; Hummelstown, PA; (2); Ski Clb; VP Frsh Cls; VP Soph Cls; Var Fld Hcky; Var Sftbl; Hon Roll; Natl Art Hnr Scty 86-87.

BOUCH, LISA-JEAN; Highlands SR HS; Natrona Heights, PA; (3); Library Aide; Office Aide; Band; Mrchg Band; Pep Band; Hon Roll; Law.

BOUCHARD, SARAH; Hanover SR HS; Hanover, PA; (3); Church Yth Grp; Hosp Aide; Band; Chorus; Mrchg Band; School Musical; School Play; Swing Chorus; Variety Show; Sec Soph Cls; Dist Chorus 86; Intl Stu.

BOUCHER, SHERRY; Rockwood Area HS; Rockwood, PA; (4); 10/95; VP Sec Church Yth Grp; Spanish Clb; Yrbk Stf; Sec Frsh Cls; Var Sftbl; Var Capt Vllybl; High Hon Roll; Hon Roll; NHS; Penn ST; Pre-Vet.

BOUDEMAN, HENRY; Hughesville HS; Unityville, PA; (3); Hon Roll; Williamsport Area CC; Auto Mec.

BOUDMAN, EDWARD; Danville SR HS; Danville, PA; (2); Church Yth Grp; Drama Clb; Ski Clb; Band; Jazz Band; Mrchg Band; Pep Band; School Musical; Stage Crew; JV Socr.

BOUDREAUX, RACHEL; Chichester HS; Aston, PA; (3); Church Yth Grp; Office Aide; Red Cross Aide; SADD; VP Soph Cls; VP Jr Cls; Rep Stu Cncl; Var Capt Crs Cntry; Var Capt Trk; Var L Vllybl; Sprtmnshp Awd 84 & 87; Educ.

BOUGHTON, PATRICIA; Cardinal Dougherty HS; Philadelphia, PA; (2); Comp Sci.

BOUIKIDIS, EUGENIA; Upper Darby HS; Upper Darby, PA; (3); Art Clb; Church Yth Grp; Dance Clb; Debate Tm; GAA; Capt Bsktbl; Coach Actv; Lcrss; Score Keeper; Sftbl; Hellenic Olympics 86-87; Tm Capt Vllybll, Bsktbl, Lacross 84-85; Phila Schl Of Arts; Intr Dcrtr.

BOULER, RON; Ambridge Area HS; Ambridge, PA; (3); FBLA; JA; NAACP; SADD; Cit Awd; NHS; Ntl Merit Schol; Pres Schlr; Acctng.

BOULTON, KRISTA; Moshannon Valley HS; Houtzdale, PA; (4); 17/120; Hosp Aide; Varsity Clb; Band; Yrbk Stf; Capt Cheerleading; Stat Wrstlng; Girl Scts; Letterman Clb; Jazz Band; Mrchg Band; Slipper Rock Univ.

BOUNDS, DEBORAH; Quigley HS; Beaver Falls, PA; (4); 2/98; Math Tm; SADD; Band; Church Choir; Mrchg Band; Symp Band; High Hon Roll; NHS; Ntl Merit Ltr; Sal; Baden Lions Clb Stu Of Math 86; Ganon U Merit Awd-Sci/Math 85; Biochem.

BOURG, MICHELLE; Canon Mc Millan HS; Muse, PA; (4); 19/355; Church Yth Grp; French Clb; Office Aide; Band; Color Guard; Concert Band; Mrchg Band; High Hon Roll; NHS; Amer Lgn Awd 84; Clarion U Of PA; Soclgy.

BOURNE, MICHELLE; Carlisle HS; Clifton, VA; (3); 104/455; Church Yth Grp; German Clb; Ski Clb; SADD; Var Sftbl; High Hon Roll; Hon Roll; Prfct Atten Awd; Bus Admin.

BOUSUM JR, JOHN V; Downingtown HS; Downingtown, PA; (4); Letterman Clb; Ski Clb; Spanish Clb; Varsity Clb; Nwsp Sprt Ed; Yrbk Stf; Rep Frsh Cls; Rep Soph Cls; Rep Jr Cls; Rep Sr Cls; Bucknell U; Eng.

BOUTILLER, GEORGE; Bellwood Antis HS; Tyrone, PA; (3); 46/115; FFA; Aud/Vis; Boy Scts; Church Yth Grp; Computer Clb; Debate Tm; Drama Clb; Intnl Clb; Library Aide; Political Wkr.

BOUTSELIS, GEORGE RICHARD; Schuykill Haven Area HS; Sch Haven, PA; (2); 9/104; VICA; Chorus; School Play; JV Ftbl; JV Wt Lftg; JV Wrstlng; High Hon Roll; Hon Roll; Air Force; Electrncs.

BOUVIER, MARIA; Henderson HS; Thornton, PA; (3); JV Sftbl; JV Vllybl; Hon Roll; Spanish NHS; Franklin Morris Acad; Flgt Attn.

BOVA, KELLY; Warren Area HS; N Warren, PA; (3); Church Yth Grp; German Clb; Hosp Aide; Band; Chorus; Concert Band; Mrchg Band; Orch; Hon Roll; Nrsg.

BOVA, LISA; Laural Highlands HS; Uniontown, PA; (3); Color Guard; School Play; Variety Show; Var Swmmng; Hon Roll; 3rd Pl ST PA JR Acad Sci 84; Fshn Merch.

BOWANKO, JOE; J M Coughlin HS; Hudson, PA; (4); Bsbl; Ftbl; Hon Roll; Penn ST U; Engrng.

BOWDEN, BRADLEY; Belle Vernon HS; Belle Vernon, PA; (3); Cmnty Wkr; Ski Clb; Band; Concert Band; Nwsp Sprt Ed; Rep Frsh Cls; Var L Bsbl; Var L Ftbl; High Hon Roll; Prfct Atten Awd; 1st Tm All Sectn Shrtstp 86&87.

BOWDERS, JENNIFER; West York Area HS; York, PA; (4); FCA; Varsity Clb; Yrbk Rptr; Yrbk Sprt Ed; Yrbk Stf; Rep Frsh Cls; Trs Jr Cls; Rep Stu Cncl; Var L Bsktbl; Var L Fld Hcky; 2 Yr All Cnfrnce Tms Bsktbl & Sftbl 84-86; WV U; Pol Sci.

BOWEN, BRIAN; Notre Dame HS; Effort, PA; (3); Am Leg Boys St; Boy Scts; Stage Crew; JV Var Bsbl; Gvrnrs Enrgy Awd 86; Embry-Riddle Aeronctcl U; Pilot.

BOWEN, CHRISTOPHER P; Red Land HS; Etters, PA; (3); 32/306; Am Leg Boys St; Church Yth Grp; Ski Clb; Rep Soph Cls; Rep Sr Cls; Rep Stu Cncl; Im Bowling; Var Socr; Var Trk; Im Vllybl; Engrng.

BOWEN, LESLIE; Juniata HS; Port Royal, PA; (4); Pres 4-H; VP FFA; SADD; Band; School Musical; Var JV Fld Hcky; 4-H Awd; Gov Hon Prg Awd; Hon Roll; NHS; Allen L & Richard H Baker Mem 4-H Schlrshp 87; De Kalb Ag Achvmnt Awd 87; FFA Kystne Deg 87; Penn ST U; Anml Biosci.

BOWEN, LYNN; Beaver Area HS; Beaver, PA; (4); 27/200; Cmnty Wkr; French Clb; Pres Key Clb; Ski Clb; Pres Trs Stu Cncl; Kiwanis Awd; NHS; Hosp Aide; JA; JCL; Mdrn Miss Pgnt 86; Acad Awde 85; Kiwanis Schlrshp $500 87; American U; Intl Bus.

BOWEN, MIKE; N Pocono HS; Moscow, PA; (3); 29/231; French Clb; Var Capt Bsbl; Var Ftbl; Im Wt Lftg; Hon Roll; NHS; Prfct Atten Awd; Babe Ruth Bsebl All Star 85-86.

BOWEN, ROB; Towanda Area HS; Towanda, PA; (3); Crs Cntry; Accntng.

BOWEN, SHERRI; Wellsboro SR HS; Wellsboro, PA; (4); 16/130; Pep Clb; VP Sr Cls; Capt Var Bsktbl; Capt Var Trk; Capt Var Vllybl; Hon Roll; NHS; Pckr Fndtn Schlrshp 87; Athltc Of Yr 87; Lock Haven U; Hlth Educ.

BOWER, BILLIE; Lock Haven SR HS; Flemington, PA; (3); FHA; Spanish Clb; SADD; Nwsp Stf; Yrbk Stf; Prfct Atten Awd; Jstns NE Smmr Yrbk Wrkshp 87.

BOWER, CHERYL; Bedford HS; Buffalo Mills, PA; (4); 6/176; Church Yth Grp; Cmnty Wkr; Science Clb; SADD; High Hon Roll; NHS; Prfct Atten Awd; Ntl Sci Mrt Awd 86; Cert Of Prfcncy In Busi 84.

BOWER, GEOFFREY C; Solanco HS; Nottingham, PA; (4); 1/230; Chess Clb; Church Yth Grp; Trs German Clb; Science Clb; Nwsp Rptr; Lit Mag; High Hon Roll; NHS; Ntl Merit SF; Gnrl Sci Awd At Lane Cnty Sci Fair 86; Harrisburg Area Cmnty Clg Comp Problem Slvng Cntst 85; Math.

BOWER, STACIE; Danville HS; Danville, PA; (2); 2/150; Sec Church Yth Grp; Pres VP 4-H; Hosp Aide; Color Guard; Concert Band; JV Fld Hcky; High Hon Roll.

BOWER, TOBY; Brandywine Heights HS; Mertztown, PA; (2); Mrchg Band; School Play; Stu Cncl; Culinry Art.

BOWERMAN, JOHN; Williams Valley HS; Williamstown, PA; (3); Aud/Vis; Quiz Bowl; Chorus; Mrchg Band; School Musical; VP Stu Cncl; JV Ftbl; High Hon Roll; Hon Roll; Mst Spirtd Stdnt 86-87; Cmmnctns.

BOWERS, ABBEY; Conrad Weiser HS; Robesonia, PA; (2); 83/165; Church Yth Grp; Drama Clb; JCL; Key Clb; Chorus; Color Guard; Mrchg Band; School Musical; Nwsp Stf; Lit Mag; Jrnlsm.

BOWERS, CAROL; Butler SR HS; Butler, PA; (4); 94/754; Church Yth Grp; DECA; FBLA; Office Aide; SADD; Church Choir; FBLA 1st Pl Prlmntry Proc Regnls 87; Med Secy.

BOWERS, CORI; Cheltenham HS; Wyncote, PA; (4); SADD; Var Capt Gym; Hon Roll; Art Cmmtte; East Stroudsburg U.

BOWERS, DOUGLAS; Punxsutawney Area HS; Punxsutawney, PA; (4); 33/245; French Clb; Math Tm; Science Clb; Ftbl; Hon Roll; PA ST Dean Awd 87; PA ST Scholar 87; PA ST U; Meteorlgy.

BOWERS, GERALYN; Cardinal Dougherty HS; Philadelphia, PA; (3); 26/676; Latin Clb; Math Clb; NHS; Profcncy Awd Alg I 84-85; Cert For 1st Hnrs 85-8m.

BOWERS, HEATHER; Minersville Area HS; Minersville, PA; (4); 4/112; Church Yth Grp; Pres French Clb; Hosp Aide; Pep Clb; Ski Clb; SADD; Band; Color Guard; Nwsp Rptr; Yrbk Ed-Chief; Schlstc Achvmnt Awd 84-87; Frnch Awd 84-87; Alld Hlth Schlrshp 87; Bloomsburg U; Med Tech.

BOWERS, JENNIFER; Littlestown SR HS; Littlestown, PA; (4); 12/120; Drama Clb; Speech Tm; Band; Chorus; Church Choir; School Play; Sec Stu Cncl; Vllybl; Hon Roll; Dist Chrs 86-87; Dist Bnd 86-87; Regnl Bnd 86; Amer U; Govt.

BOWERS, JULIE A; Academy HS; Erie, PA; (4); 73/197; Art Inst Pittsburgh; Visual Cmm.

BOWERS, KRISTI LYNN; Saltsburg JR SR HS; Clarksburg, PA; (3); Church Yth Grp; 4-H; Hosp Aide; VICA; Hon Roll; HOSA Opng & Clsng Tm 3rd Pl 87; Gld Mdl In Gymnstcs 85; IUP Med; Ansthslgst.

BOWERS, MELANIE; Canon Mc Millan HS; Eighty Four, PA; (3); 12/367; Hon Roll; U Pittsburgh.

BOWERS, SHAUNNA; Spring Grove SR HS; York, PA; (3); Girl Scts; SADD; JV Var Fld Hcky; Hon Roll; Bus.

BOWERS, STACY; Newport JR SR HS; Duncannon, PA; (4); 2/95; Quiz Bowl; Gym; High Hon Roll; NHS; PA ST U; Psych.

BOWERS, TIM; Conanesquw Valley HS; Westfield, PA; (4); Varsity Clb; Band; Concert Band; Mrchg Band; Bsktbl; Ftbl; Hon Roll; US Army Reservce Schlr Ath Awd 86; Tri Cnty Ftbl All Star Awd 86-87; CB Schlr Ath Awd 86-87; MVP Ftb; Lock Haven U; Phy Educ.

BOWERS, TRACY; Newport HS; Duncannon, PA; (4); 1/95; Quiz Bowl; Gym; Trk; High Hon Roll; NHS; Hghst Erth Sci Stu-$50 Svngs Bnd 84; PA ST U; Pre-Med.

BOWERS, TROY; Dower Area HS; Dover, PA; (3); 125/263; Church Yth Grp; Varsity Clb; Rep Frsh Cls; Rep Soph Cls; Rep Jr Cls; Var Socr; Var Swmmng; Var Tennis; Var Trk; Wnnr & Rcrdhldr 16-18 Age Grp 3rd Annual Chmbrsbrg Biathln 86; Wnnr & Rcrdhldr 4th Annual Biathln 87; Radio/TV Brdcstng.

BOWERS, WENDY; Bermudian Springs HS; E Berlin, PA; (3); Am Leg Aux Girls St; FNA; Yrbk Stf; Var L Trk; JV Vllybl; Bio.

BOWERSOX, JULIANNE; Chichester HS; Linwood, PA; (3); 7/293; SADD; Mrchg Band; School Musical; Nwsp Stf; Capt JV Lcrss; Twrlr; Hon Roll; NHS; Pres Schlr; Spanish NHS; BSN.

BOWES, JASON; Montour Area HS; Pittsburgh, PA; (2); SADD; Rep Stu Cncl; JV Ftbl; Hon Roll; Wt Lftg; GATE 86-87; Law.

BOWIE, TASHA; Olney HS; Philadelphia, PA; (3); 112/712; Var Bsktbl; Var Crs Cntry; Var Fld Hcky; Trk; 1st Tm Pblc Field Hcky 87; 5th Pl City Intered 4x100 86; W Chester Coll; Psychology.

BOWKER, MELINDA; Trinity HS; Mechanicsburg, PA; (3); 1/138; Yrbk Bus Mgr; Pres Soph Cls; Pres Jr Cls; Pres Sr Cls; JV Crs Cntry; High Hon Roll; NHS; JV Trk; Hnrbl Mntn, 2nd Pl Dcknsn Coll Sci Fair 84-86; Gld Key Lit Awd 84-85; FORCE VP 87-88.

BOWLER, JANET; Saint Clair Area HS; St Clair, PA; (4); 1/77; VP Drama Clb; Mu Alpha Theta; Pres Band; Nwsp Ed-Chief; Bausch & Lomb Sci Awd; Dnfth Awd; High Hon Roll; Sec NHS; Val; Voice Dem Awd; Natl HS Math Exam Awd 87; Pres Scholar Elizabethtown Coll HOBY Fndtn 87; Am Leg Ctznshp Awd 87; Elizabethtown Coll; Bio.

BOWLEY, KAREN; Clairon-Limestone HS; Brookville, PA; (3); Church Yth Grp; DECA; French Clb; Socr; 4th Pl DECA Dist Comptns 86; 2nd Pl Mock DECA Dists Comptns 86; 3rd Pl Mock DECA Dists Comptns 85; Bus.

BOWMAN, AMY; Seneca Valley HS; Callery, PA; (4); 9/347; Sec Ski Clb; Varsity Clb; Chorus; Var L Crs Cntry; Var L Trk; Sec Church Yth Grp; School Musical; Nwsp Rptr; Hon Roll; 3 Yr Schlstc Awd 87; Mst Outstndng Crss Country Awd 86; Dickinson Coll; Pre-Law.

BOWMAN, AUDREY; Tri-Valley HS; Valley View, PA; (2); 4/85; Sec Church Yth Grp; Off Drama Clb; Quiz Bowl; Band; Chorus; Concert Band; Jazz Band; Mrchg Band; School Musical; Var L Bsktbl.

BOWMAN, BETH; St Marys Area HS; Benezett, PA; (4); Drama Clb; Exploring; Hon Roll; Williamsport Area CC; Nrsng.

BOWMAN, COREY; Hughesville HS; Muncy, PA; (3); Church Yth Grp; Ski Clb; Spanish Clb; Varsity Clb; Church Choir; Sftbl; JV Swmmng; Tennis; Trk; Im Vllybl; Lttr Awd 86-87; Millersville U; German.

BOWMAN, DENISE; Halifax Area HS; Halifax, PA; (4); VP FHA; Chorus; Yrbk Sprt Ed; VP Jr Cls; Pres Sr Cls; Pres Stu Cncl; DAR Awd; Lion Awd; Camera Clb; Church Yth Grp; Hmcmng Queen 87; Halloween Queen 87.

BOWMAN, DONALD; Cedar Crest HS; Lebanon, PA; (4); 13/308; French Clb; FBLA; Pep Clb; Hon Roll; NHS; Ntl Merit Ltr; Penn ST U Acdmc Excllnc Schlrshp 87; Penn ST U; Fnnc.

BOWMAN, EMILY; Methacton SR HS; Collegeville, PA; (2); 47/307; Church Yth Grp; Cmnty Wkr; Orch; Stage Crew; Var Bsktbl; JV Sftbl; Hon Roll; Art.

BOWMAN, ERIK; Lehighton Area HS; Lehighton, PA; (3); 16/250; Scholastic Bowl; Chorus; Yrbk Sprt Ed; Rep Stu Cncl; Var Ftbl; Var Trk; Hon Roll; USAF Acad; Engrng.

BOWMAN, HEATHER; Hershey HS; Hershey, PA; (3); 70/200; Hosp Aide; Color Guard; Rep Soph Cls; Var Cheerleading; High Hon Roll; Hon Roll; Phys Ftnss Awd 85; Hershey Med Ctr; Rad Tech.

BOWMAN, KELLY; Hershey HS; Hershey, PA; (2); 39/196; Hosp Aide; Band; Mrchg Band; Rep Frsh Cls; JV Cheerleading; High Hon Roll; Hon Roll; Milton S Hershey Med Schl-Rad.

BOWMAN, KIMBERLY A; Strath Haven HS; Swarthmore, PA; (4); VP German Clb; Ski Clb; Nwsp Phtg; JV VP Tennis; Ntl Merit SF; Schlrshp Moore Coll Arts 86.

BOWMAN, LAURA C; Central HS; York, PA; (4); 28/203; Pres Church Yth Grp; Girl Scts; VP JA; Varsity Clb; Chorus; Nwsp Rptr; Yrbk Rptr; Capt L Fld Hcky; Hon Roll; Opt Clb Awd; Shippensburg U; Bus.

BOWMAN, LETITIA; Everett Area HS; Everett, PA; (4); 7/105; Spanish Clb; Capt Color Guard; Pres Stu Cncl; Hon Roll; NHS; Spanish NHS; Prncpls Awd 87; Cntrl PA Bus Schl; Acctng.

BOWMAN, MARY; Glendale HS; Coalport, PA; (4); 17/95; Science Clb; VP Band; VP Mrchg Band; Yrbk Phtg; Yrbk Stf; Hon Roll; NHS; Bus, Prfssnl Wmn Awd 87; Penn ST; Comp Sci.

BOWMAN, MARY A; South Fayette HS; Mc Donald, PA; (4); 13/72; Ski Clb; Band; Mrchg Band; Orch; Pep Band; Hon Roll; U Of Pittsburgh; Mdcl Technlgy.

BOWMAN, MATTHEW; Cedar Crest HS; Lebanon, PA; (2); 19/345; German Clb; Band; Concert Band; Jazz Band; Orch; School Musical; Symp Band; Mrchg Band; Hon Roll; All ST Jazz Band 87; Lebanon Vly Coll Jazz Band 86-87; Lebanon Vly Coll Symph Orch; Berkleey Schl Music; Music Perf.

BOWMAN, MICHAELENE; James M Coughlin HS; Wilkes-Barre, PA; (3); Hosp Aide; Yrbk Stf; Hon Roll; Jr NHS; NHS; Psych.

BOWMAN, MICHELLE; Mahanoy Area HS; Mahanoy City, PA; (3); French Clb; Church Choir; School Play; Variety Show; Yrbk Stf; Bsktbl; Cheerleading; Gym; Sftbl; Swmmng; VICA Sec 87; Mech Engrng.

BOWMAN, ROBERT; Benton Area JR SR HS; Benton, PA; (3); Var Bsbl; Var Bsktbl; Var Socr; NHS; Columbia Co Lg All Strs 86-87.

BOWMAN, TYANN; Venango Christian HS; Reno, PA; (3); 2/36; Hosp Aide; Model UN; Spanish Clb; Yrbk Stf; Sec Trs Frsh Cls; Sec Trs Jr Cls; Trs Stu Cncl; Var Cheerleading; High Hon Roll; Trs NHS; Homcmng Ct; Pa Free Entrprs Wk; Law.

BOWMASTER, ERIC; Biglerville HS; Biglerville, PA; (2); 22/105; Rep Soph Cls; Trs Jr Cls; JV Bsbl; JV Bsktbl; Hon Roll; Jr NHS; NHS.

BOWMASTER, MICHAEL; Biglerville HS; Biglerville, PA; (4); 2/78; Yrbk Ed-Chief; Trs Soph Cls; Trs Jr Cls; Trs Sr Cls; High Hon Roll; NHS; Sal; Varsity Clb; Yrbk Stf; April Stu Of Month, Schl Brd Schlr & Jeffrey Craig Bosserman Math Awd 87; Kings Coll; Comp Sci.

BOWMER, DEREK; Scotland Schl; Philadelphia, PA; (4); ROTC; Varsity Clb; Band; Concert Band; Mrchg Band; Symp Band; Var L Bsbl; Var L Bsktbl; Var L Ftbl; Hon Roll; 1st Tm Ftbl All Str-Lnbckr 86-87; Outstndng Vctnl Stu, Cthlc War Vtrns 87; Johnson & Wales Coll; Clnry Art.

BOWSER, BRIAN; Carmichaels Area HS; Riceslanding, PA; (4); Ftbl; Lion Awd; Pep Clb; Teachers Aide; Stage Crew; Coach Actv.

BOWSER, GREGORY H; Bedford HS; Manns Choice, PA; (3); Church Yth Grp; Teachers Aide; Bsbl; Bsktbl; Ftbl; Mgr(s); Socr; Sftbl; Hon Roll; Score Keeper; US Cst Grd Trng Ctr Grad 87; VA ST; Fr Fghtr.

BOWSER, JAMIE; Freeport SR HS; Sarver, PA; (3); 7/240; Church Yth Grp; School Play; Sftbl; Var JV Vllybl; High Hon Roll; Indiana St; Psych.

BOWSER, JENNIFER; Butler Intermediate HS; Butler, PA; (2); Church Yth Grp; French Clb; Girl Scts; Y-Teens; Orch; Yrbk Phtg; Yrbk Stf; Rep Frsh Cls; Rep Soph Cls; Rep Stu Cncl; Dstrct & Rgnl Orchestra Fstvl & Gold Ldrshp Awd In Girl Scouts 87; Kent; Math.

BOWSER, KRISTEN; Kittaning SR HS; Worthington, PA; (3); 27/226; Pres Church Yth Grp; Hosp Aide; Church Choir; Rep Soph Cls; Rep Jr Cls; Rep Sr Cls; High Hon Roll; Sec NHS; Accntng.

BOWSER, LAVERNE; Connellsville Area SR HS; Millrun, PA; (4); Art Clb; VP Church Yth Grp; Exploring; Sec 4-H; Office Aide; Church Choir; Variety Show; Nwsp Stf; Cit Awd; 4-H Awd; Laurel Bus Inst; Med Secy.

BOWSER, LISA; Ford City HS; Ford City, PA; (3); 1/163; Church Yth Grp; Sec Key Clb; Concert Band; Drm Mjr(t); Yrbk Stf; Rep Frsh Cls; Rep Stu Cncl; Capt Twrlr; High Hon Roll; NHS.

BOWSER, MARCY; Moniteau JR SR HS; Parker, PA; (3); 20/167; Band; Concert Band; Mrchg Band; Orch; Stage Crew; Hon Roll; JR All Amer Hall Fame Band Hnrs 87; Pre-Law.

BOWSER, MELISSA; Highlands HS; Tarentum, PA; (4); 30/288; Office Aide; Varsity Clb; Off Frsh Cls; Off Soph Cls; Off Jr Cls; Rep Sr Cls; Rep Stu Cncl; Capt Gym; Hon Roll; NHS; PA ST U; Psychlgy.

BOWSER, MICHELLE; Windber Area HS; Windber, PA; (3); Pres Sec Church Yth Grp; JA; Speech Tm; Chorus; Church Choir; Var Sftbl; Hon Roll; NHS; Pres Schlr; Stu Mnth 84-87; Forestry.

BOWSER, MIKE; Chestnut Ridge SR HS; Alum Bank, PA; (4); Nwsp Phtg; Nwsp Stf; Var Bsktbl; High Hon Roll; Hon Roll; NHS; Prfct Atten Awd; Pres Schlr; Lions Tale Jrnlstc Awd 87; Pres Acad Ftns Awd 87; Lions Tale Outstndg Staffer 85-86; Drftsmn.

BOWSER, RONDA; Butler Intermediate HS; Butler, PA; (2); Art Clb; Church Yth Grp; GAA; Var Socr; Var Trk; Prfct Atten Awd; Cnslng.

BOWSER, TODD; Annville-Cleona HS; Lebanon, PA; (3); 12/108; Church Yth Grp; Model UN; Varsity Clb; Acpl Chr; Band; Chorus; Church Choir; Concert Band; Jazz Band; Madrigals; Dist & Regnl Chrs 86-87; Dist Band 85-86; Outstndg Musician Cls 85-86; Franklin & Marshall U; Biol.

BOWSER, TRACY; Punxsutawney Area SR HS; Punxsutawney, PA; (3); FBLA; Band; Mrchg Band; Stat Bsktbl; Hon Roll; Stenographer Rgnl FBLA Cmpttn 4th Pl 87.

BOYCE, CARRIE; Western Beaver HS; Ohioville, PA; (2); Chess Clb; Church Yth Grp; Computer Clb; French Clb; High Hon Roll; Hon Roll; Prfct Atten Awd; Won Pirate Tckts To Gaem For Straight A' 87; Accntng.

BOYCE, MARIANNE; Council Rock HS; Churchville, PA; (3); 356/908; Church Yth Grp; 4-H; Chorus; Church Choir; School Musical; School Play; Swing Chorus; Variety Show; 4-H Awd; VA Rvw Swng Choir Supr Rnkng 86; Acmpnst Schl Choir 85-87; Msc Tchr.

BOYCE, STEVE; Ringgold HS; Monongahela, PA; (3); Science Clb; Spanish Clb; Var Crs Cntry; Var Trk; Hon Roll; Aero Engr.

BOYD, ALBERT; Reading HS; Reading, PA; (4); Church Yth Grp; Stage Crew; Var Bowling; Socr; Trk; Capt Wrstlng; Hon Roll; Northwest Svc Awd 84; Outstndng Track Awd 84; City Champn-Wrestlng 84; U Of Miami; Marine Bio.

BOYD, ARETHA; West Alleghney HS; Pittsburgh, PA; (3); JA; Church Choir; Hon Roll; Bradford Bus Schl; Acctnt.

BOYD, BRAD; Reynolds HS; Transfer, PA; (3); 4/150; Church Yth Grp; Latin Clb; Letterman Clb; Varsity Clb; Chorus; Church Choir; Off Sr Cls; Ftbl; Trk; Wrstlng; Amer Lgn Awd 84-85; Engrng Achvt Awd 85-87; Physcl Thrpst.

BOYD, CHARLES; Tyrone Area HS; Tyrone, PA; (3); High Hon Roll; Hon Roll; Bst Elec Stu 85-86; Elec Engr.

BOYD, DONALD; Elizabeth Forward HS; Mc Keesport, PA; (2); Letterman Clb; Var L Crs Cntry; Var L Swmmng; Var L Trk; High Hon Roll; Hon Roll; NHS; NISCA St Swmmng Awd 86; All St Swmmng Tm, Swmmng Coaches Assn 86 & 87; Pdtrcn.

BOYD, HEATHER; Elizabeth Forward HS; Mckeesport, PA; (2); Library Aide; Chorus; Yrbk Stf; Sec Frsh Cls; Sec Soph Cls; Rep Stu Cncl; Co-Capt Cheerleading; PA ST; Nrsng.

BOYD, JAYNELL; Penn Hills SR HS; Penn Hills, PA; (3); Church Yth Grp; Exploring; Girl Scts; Hosp Aide; Band; Concert Band; Mrchg Band; Stat Bsktbl; Mgr(s); Prfct Atten Awd; Comp Sci.

BOYD, JENNIFER; Meadville Area SR HS; Meadville, PA; (4); 20/305; Dance Clb; Science Clb; Service Clb; Varsity Clb; Rep Frsh Cls; Rep Soph Cls; Rep Jr Cls; Rep Sr Cls; Rep Stu Cncl; Golf; US Stud Cncl Awd 86.

BOYD, KATHERINE; State Clg Area Intermediate HS; State College, PA; (2); 90/553; Ski Clb; Orch; Rep Frsh Cls; Rep Stu Cncl; Im Powder Puff Ftbl; Sftbl; L JV Trk; High Hon Roll; Track/Field Dist 800 Meter Champ 85-86; Intermediate Symphony Orch-1st Chair Cellist 86; Penn ST U; Perfrmng Arts.

BOYD, LARRY; Garnet Valley HS; Glen Mills, PA; (3); German Clb; Ski Clb; Trk; High Hon Roll; Hon Roll; Chem Engrng.

BOYD, LAURIE JO; Belle Vernon Area HS; Belle Vernon, PA; (3); Band; Concert Band; Mrchg Band; Yrbk Stf; Hon Roll; Lion Awd; 1st Pl Poetry Crtv Crft Crnvl 85.

BOYD, MARK; Penn Manor HS; Conestoga, PA; (3); #25 In Class; Church Yth Grp; Ski Clb; Bsktbl; Vllybl; Hon Roll; PA ST; Engrng.

BOYD, NOELLE; North Star HS; Stoystown, PA; (3); 17/141; AFS; Church Yth Grp; FCA; Hosp Aide; Mu Alpha Theta; Ski Clb; Band; Rep Stu Cncl; Stat Score Keeper; Var L Vllybl; 1st Tm Somerset All-Cnty Vllybll Tm 86; Busi.

BOYD, RHONDA; Philadelphia Girls; Philadelphia, PA; (3); 6/405; Church Yth Grp; Intnl Clb; Office Aide; Radio Clb; Variety Show; High Hon Roll; Spanish NHS; Natl Span Cont Immaculata Coll & SE PA Chaptr 87; Bailey Williams Mem Hnr Key Awd 85-86; Med.

BOYD, STEPHEN; Burrell HS; Lower Burrell, PA; (3); Nwsp Rptr; Nwsp Stf; Var Trk; Hon Roll; Comm.

BOYD, THOMAS; Duquesne HS; Duquesne, PA; (3); High Hon Roll; Jr NHS; NHS; Ntl Merit Ltr; Pittsburgh Inst Of Aern; Engrng.

BOYD, TIMOTHY S; Waynesburg Central HS; Waynesburg, PA; (3); Drama Clb; French Clb; Ski Clb; Nwsp Stf; Rep Stu Cncl; Var L Socr; Var L Trk; Var L Wrstlng; Hon Roll.

BOYER III, ALEX; Dayton HS; New Bethlehem, PA; (3); 15/54; Chess Clb; Computer Clb; 4-H; Variety Show; 4-H Awd; Hon Roll; JC Awd; PA ST; Drftng & Dsgn.

BOYER, ANDREA; Central Dauphin East HS; Harrisburg, PA; (4); Pres Sec Church Yth Grp; SADD; Church Choir; Orch; School Musical; School Play; Stu Cncl; JV Trk; Hon Roll; Hon Roll; Carnegie Mellon U; Humanities.

BOYER, APRIL; Hopewell SR HS; Aliquippa, PA; (2); 10/270; Church Yth Grp; Exploring; Pep Clb; Spanish Clb; School Play; Nwsp Stf; Yrbk Stf; Var Im Swmmng; High Hon Roll; Pre Law.

BOYER, DOUG; Schuylkill Haven HS; Auburn, PA; (2); 24/104; Church Yth Grp; FCA; Spanish Clb; Var Bsktbl; Wt Lftg; Hon Roll.

BOYER, JEFF; Berlin Brothersvalley HS; Berlin, PA; (2); Boy Scts; Chess Clb; 4-H; Ski Clb; Spanish Clb; Varsity Clb; Bsbl; Bsktbl; Ftbl; Wt Lftg.

BOYER, JULIE; Mohawk HS; Bessemer, PA; (4); 8/137; French Clb; FBLA; Chorus; Drill Tm; Flag Corp; School Musical; School Play; Stat Trk; High Hon Roll; Hon Roll; U Of Pittsburgh; Pre-Med.

BOYER, KATHY JO; Quigley HS; Baden, PA; (3); Church Yth Grp; Math Tm; VP Pep Clb; Church Choir; Stat Bsbl; Var Powder Puff Ftbl; JV Vllybl; Hon Roll; Cortez Peters Chmpnshp Typng Awd 86; Phtsical Therapist.

BOYER, KELLY RHONDA; Pine Grove Area HS; Pine Grove, PA; (4); Am Leg Aux Girls St; Sec Frsh Cls; Sec Soph Cls; Sec Jr Cls; Sec Sr Cls; Sec Stu Cncl; Var JV Bsktbl; Var JV Vllybl; Varsity Clb; Flag Corp; SR Mnth 86; Comp Tech.

BOYER, KIM; Millersburg Area HS; Millersburg, PA; (3); 4-H; Band; Concert Band; Mrchg Band; Nwsp Stf; Yrbk Stf; Sftbl; 4-H Awd; Hon Roll; Central PA Bus Schl; Steno.

BOYER, LAURA; Coatesville Area SR HS; Coatesville, PA; (3); 59/517; Drama Clb; French Clb; Library Aide; SADD; Var L Cheerleading; High Hon Roll; Hon Roll; Psych.

BOYER, LEROY; Schuylkill Haven HS; Schuylkill Haven, PA; (3); 2/103; Boy Scts; Chess Clb; Spanish Clb; Nwsp Sprt Ed; Var JV Bsbl; Var Wrstlng; Comm.

BOYER, MATTHEW; Conrad Weiser HS; Robesonia, PA; (4); 46/184; Boy Scts; Church Yth Grp; Library Aide; Bsbl; Bsktbl; Socr; Vllybl; Hon Roll; Shippensburg U; Bus Admin.

BOYER, MICHELE; West York Area HS; York, PA; (4); 14/195; Pres Church Yth Grp; Drama Clb; French Clb; Band; Chorus; Jazz Band; School Play; Rep Stu Cncl; Stat Vllybl; NHS; Bsc Fndmntls Firefghtng Awd; PTO Elem Schlrshp, Schlrs In Educ Schlrshp; Shippensburg U; Math Educ.

BOYER, MICHELLE; Elizabethtown Area HS; Elizabethtown, PA; (3); 49/259; Church Yth Grp; VP Girl Scts; Concert Band; Mrchg Band; Orch; Pep Band; JV Fld Hcky; Im Powder Puff Ftbl; Ski Clb; Challenge Of Being Grl Scout 86; Envrn Sci.

BOYER, NATALIE; West Perry HS; New Bloomfield, PA; (3); 71/250; Pep Clb; Spanish Clb; Varsity Clb; Pep Band; Sec Frsh Cls; Rep Stu Cncl; Capt L Cheerleading; Im Gym; Var Trk; Im Vllybl; ICF Cnslr 87; Trvl.

BOYER, STEPHEN; Lewistown Area HS; Lewistown, PA; (2); French Clb; Var Bsbl; JV Crs Cntry; Im Wt Lftg; High Hon Roll; NHS.

BOYER, TROY; Cocalico HS; Denver, PA; (3); 14/168; Sec Church Yth Grp; Rep Stu Cncl; VP L Bsbl; Stat Bsktbl; VP Ftbl; High Hon Roll; Prfct Atten Awd; Communications.

BOYER, WENDY; Bermudian Springs HS; York Spgs, PA; (3); 11/125; Cmnty Wkr; GAA; SADD; Varsity Clb; Band; Chorus; Concert Band; Jazz Band; Mrchg Band; School Musical; Marine Phys Fitness Awd 87; Accntng.

BOYER, YVONNE M; Schuylkill Haven Area School Dist; Schuylkill Haven, PA; (3); 17/85; Am Leg Aux Girls St; Church Yth Grp; FNA; Library Aide; Pep Clb; Drill Tm; Nwsp Stf; Yrbk Phtg; Sec Sr Cls; Var JV Sftbl; Antonelli Inst Of Art; Phtgrphr.

BOYESEN, MARGIT; Freeport SR HS; Freeport, PA; (2); Art Clb; Sec Church Yth Grp; Chorus; Concert Band; Diving; Gym; High Hon Roll; Hon Roll; Legsltv Schl Art Exhibit Paintng 87; Art Schlrshp IUP Smmr Hppng 87; ST Fnlst Miss Amer Co-Ed Pgnt; Chem.

BOYKO, PATTIE; Mid-Valley HS; Dickson, PA; (3); Computer Clb; JA; Drill Tm; Crs Cntry; Sftbl; Vllybl; High Hon Roll; NHS; Dentl Hygne.

BOYLE, BRENDA; Wilmington Area HS; New Wilmington, PA; (4); Key Clb; Latin Clb; Office Aide; Pres Spanish Clb; Powder Puff Ftbl; Hon Roll; NHS; Cum Laude Natl Latin Exam Hnr 87; Pres Acadmc Ftns Awd 87; Acadmc Achvt Awd 85; IN U Of PA.

BOYLE, CATHERINE; Burrell SR HS; Lower Burrell, PA; (3); Church Yth Grp; Cmnty Wkr; Band; School Play; Nwsp Stf; Sec Soph Cls; L Swmmng; L Trk; High Hon Roll; NHS; Acadc Ltr 85-87; Mid-Estrn US Al-Star Band 85-87; Alle-Kiski Al-Star Band 86.

BOYLE, CHRISTINE; Mc Keesport HS; Mckeesport, PA; (3); 5/433; VP Church Yth Grp; Hosp Aide; Pep Clb; JV Var Bsktbl; Capt Powder Puff Ftbl; Var Sftbl; JV Vllybl; High Hon Roll; Sec NHS; Prfct Atten Awd; PA ST.

BOYLE, CYNTHIA; Cardinal O Hara HS; Swarthmore, PA; (3); 174/710; Cmnty Wkr; Hon Roll; Prfct Atten Awd; Photo Jrnlst.

BOYLE, DAVID; Butler HS; Butler, PA; (2); ROTC; Color Guard; Drill Tm; Hon Roll; Penn St U; Sci.

BOYLE, JOANNE; Lake-Lehman HS; Dallas, PA; (3); 33/235; Sec 4-H; Band; Rep Jr Cls; Stat Bsktbl; Var L Fld Hcky; JV Sftbl; 4-H Awd; Hon Roll; Jr NHS; Pharmacy.

BOYLE, KATHLEEN; Archbishop Ryan Girls HS; Phila, PA; (3); Cmnty Wkr; Latin Clb; JV Fld Hcky; Trk; Frsh Cls; Cum Laudae Awd 87; Law.

BOYLE, KELLY; Allentown Central Catholic HS; Allentown, PA; (4); Chorus; Color Guard; High Hon Roll; Hon Roll; JR Prom Cmmtte 86; SR Prom Cmmtte 87; Allentwn Coll; Bio.

BOYLE, MATTHEW; Central Catholic HS; Pittsburgh, PA; (3); 3/275; Church Yth Grp; Chorus; Var L Crs Cntry; Im Ftbl; Var L Trk; High Hon Roll; NHS; Cert Schlstc Excllnc-Grmn II & III 86 & 87; Invtn U Of Pttsbrgh Hnrs Cnvctn Day 87; Engnrng.

BOYLE, MICHELLE; Ringgold HS; Finleyville, PA; (3); Varsity Clb; Off Stu Cncl; Var L Bsktbl; Sftbl; Var L Trk; Var L Vllybl; High Hon Roll; Acadmc All Amercn Mth & Sci Hnr Scty Co Chrmn 85-86 & 86-87; Engrng.

BOYLE, PATRICK; North Catholic HS; Philadelphia, PA; (2); 26/365; Church Yth Grp; Stage Crew; Mgr(s); Score Keeper; Trk; Hon Roll; NHS; Acctng.

BOYLE, RICH; Mid Valley Secondary Center; Dickson City, PA; (4); Rep Stu Cncl; Im Bsktbl; Pres Schlrshp U Scanton 87-88; U Of Scranton; Bus.

BOYLER, ANNA; Chambersburg Area SR HS; Chambersburg, PA; (2); Chorus; Symp Band; Chess Clb; Church Yth Grp; French Clb; Red Cross Aide; Ski Clb; Church Choir; Orch; Hon Roll.

BOYLES, HEATHER E; Montoursville Area HS; Montoursville, PA; (3); 3/185; Am Leg Aux Girls St; Trs German Clb; Trs Key Clb; Concert Band; Mrchg Band; School Musical; Mgr(s); Hon Roll; Sec NHS; Trs Church Yth Grp; Grmn Hnr Soc; Lycmng Untd Way Yth Alloctn Grp; Intl Rltns.

BOYLES, LISA; Tyrone Area HS; Pt Matilda, PA; (2); Science Clb; SADD; Chorus; Off Lit Mag; Hon Roll; Penn ST; Jrnlsm.

BOYLES, SHELLEY; Neshanock HS; Neshannock, PA; (3); 27/102; Church Yth Grp; Hosp Aide; Band; Concert Band; Mrchg Band; Nwsp Phtg; Presdntl Acadc Ftns Awd 85; Youngstown ST U Enlg Fstvl Bk Quiz 85; Svc Awd 85; Psych.

BOZUNG, JENNIFER; Bloomsburg HS; Bloomsburg, PA; (3); 22/122; Church Yth Grp; Drama Clb; Pep Clb; Church Choir; Varsity Clb; School Musical; Rep Stu Cncl; Bsktbl; Cheerleading; Powder Puff Ftbl.

BOZZARELLI, ALBERT; Kiski Area SR HS; Avonmore, PA; (4); Triangle Tech; Cadd Drftng.

BRAATZ, KEN; Plymouth-Whitemarsh HS; Lafayette Hill, PA; (3); Boy Scts; VICA; High Hon Roll; Hon Roll; Montgomery CC; Electrician.

BRABAZON, DANIELLE; Central Bucks HS West; Doylestown, PA; (4); 7/487; FBLA; Pres Intnl Clb; Sec Yrbk Sprt Ed; Rep Stu Cncl; Capt Trk; Vllybl; High Hon Roll; NHS; Prfct Atten Awd; Betz Labrtry Schlrshp 87; U Of Scrantn; Biochem.

BRACCI, LUCI; Ambridge Area HS; Ambridge, PA; (2); Church Yth Grp; Drill Tm; Im Var Cheerleading; Pom Pon; Hon Roll; Bradford Bus Schl; Exec Sec.

BRACE, CALVIN; Elk Lake HS; Montrose, PA; (2); Church Yth Grp; FCA; Spanish Clb; SADD; Band; Mrchg Band; Var Bsbl; Elem Math Tchr.

BRACE, PATTIE; E L Meyers HS; Wilkes Bare, PA; (4); Camera Clb; FTA; Ski Clb; Band; Chorus; Color Guard; Concert Band; Mrchg Band; Yrbk Stf; Mgr(s); Misericordia Coll; Elem Ed.

BRACEY, MICHAEL; Scranton Central HS; Scranton, PA; (3); Aud/Vis; French Clb; SADD; Lit Mag; Trk; Govs Cmte On Employment Of Handicapped Essay Awd & Army Rsrv Natl Essay Contest Awd 87; U Of Scranton; Jrnlsm.

BRACEY, NICCOLE; Frankford HS; Philadelphia, PA; (3); #11 In Class; Teachers Aide; Nwsp Stf; Yrbk Stf; Rep Stu Cncl; Hon Roll; Pres Schlr; Acctg.

BRACHER, KRISTY; Salisbury SR HS; Allentown, PA; (3); 20/165; Sec Drama Clb; Scholastic Bowl; School Play; Stage Crew; Nwsp Ed-Chief; Nwsp Rptr; Nwsp Stf; High Hon Roll; Hon Roll; Hofstra U; Grphc Dsgn.

BRACKEN, PATTY; Northern Cambria HS; Barnesboro, PA; (3); 33/152; Cmnty Wkr; Sec Drama Clb; Hosp Aide; Sec NFL; Chorus; School Play; Twrlr; High Hon Roll; Hon Roll; NHS; ST History Day 86; Dist History Day 1st Pl Perfrmnc 86; US Air Force; Pre Med.

BRACKEN, SAMOYA; Harrisburg High John Harris Campus; Harrisburg, PA; (2); 47/356; Church Yth Grp; Cmnty Wkr; Band; Concert Band; Jazz Band; Orch; Hon Roll; Prfct Atten Awd; Natl Hnr Rl 86-87; Stu Art Month Recgntn & Display 86; Crimnl Justc.

BRADAC, DOUGLAS; North Hills HS; Pittsburgh, PA; (4); 33/467; Exploring; Key Clb; Ski Clb; Rep Jr Cls; L Bsbl; Var Capt Bsktbl; L Swmmng; High Hon Roll; NHS.

BRADBURY, NOELLE; Mahanoy Area HS; Mahanoy City, PA; (4); 18/110; Drama Clb; Hosp Aide; Ski Clb; Spanish Clb; Sec Band; Chorus; Church Choir; Concert Band; Jazz Band; Mrchg Band; Helen L Ruth Schlrshp 87; Harold C Buzza Music Schlrshp 87; Geisinger Nursing Schl; Nrsng.

BRADBURY, RUTH; Hopewell HS; Aliquippa, PA; (4); 29/260; VP Church Yth Grp; Pres Spanish Clb; Band; Chorus; Capt Trk; L Vllybl; High Hon Roll; NHS; Pres Schlr; Geneva Schlr Awd 87; Geneva Coll; Spch Pthlgy.

BRADDOCK, LORETTA; Waynesburg Central HS; Carmichaels, PA; (4); Spanish Clb; JV Bsktbl; Var Sftbl; JV Var Vllybl; Hon Roll; Spanish II & III Awds 85 & 86; Waynesburg Coll.

BRADFORD, MARY; St Huberts HS; Philadelphia, PA; (4); 192/364; Art Clb; Aud/Vis; Camp Fr Inc; Service Clb; Chorus; School Musical; Lit Mag; Rep Sr Cls; Church Yth Grp; Office Aide; Marywood Coll Grant 87-88; Marywood Coll; Lib Art.

BRADLAW, APRIL; Southmoreland SR HS; Connellsville, PA; (3); Pep Clb; Teachers Aide; Chorus.

BRADLEY, BETH; Bishop Carroll HS; Loretto, PA; (3); Drama Clb; Pep Clb; Ski Clb; SADD; School Play; Stage Crew; Stat Bsktbl; L Trk; Var L Vllybl; St Francis Coll; Elem Educ.

BRADLEY, CHRISTINE; Haverford SR HS; Havertown, PA; (3); 33/423; Ski Clb; Nwsp Phtg; Yrbk Stf; Var Bsktbl; Var Fld Hcky; Var Sftbl; Hon Roll; NHS; Schlr-Athl Awd & Amer Lgn Auxilary 85; Chem.

BRADLEY, CHRISTY; Plum SR HS; New Kensington, PA; (3); Band; Mrchg Band; Hon Roll; Prfct Atten Awd.

BRADLEY, KATHLEEN; Philipsburg-Osceola SR HS; Philipsburg, PA; (4); 25/239; Art Clb; Church Yth Grp; Letterman Clb; Pep Clb; Ski Clb; SADD; School Musical; School Play; Nwsp Rptr; Off Frsh Cls; U S Mrn Corps Dstngshd Athlt Awd 87; Juniata Coll; Scndry Educ.

BRADLEY, KELLY; Schuylkill Haven Area HS; Shylkl Haven, PA; (3); Computer Clb; FNA; Science Clb; Spanish Clb; SADD; Yrbk Phtg; Hon Roll; Penn ST; Pre Med.

BRADLEY, LEANNE; Moon SR HS; Maryville, TN; (4); 76/305; Pep Clb; SADD; Band; Concert Band; Mrchg Band; Pep Band; Symp Band; Variety Show; Hiwassee Coll; Bus.

BRADLEY, LEWIS; Blue Mountain HS; Orwigsburg, PA; (3); 1/210; Chorus; Nwsp Stf; Yrbk Stf; JV Bsbl; JV Golf; Trk; High Hon Roll; Cert Of Mrt French 85; Sthrn Div Golf Champ 86; Dist Hnr Rll 84-87; USMA-W PT; Med.

BRADLEY, MELANIE; Quaker Valley HS; Sewickley, PA; (1); 1/154; Church Yth Grp; Office Aide; Band; Church Choir; Concert Band; Mrchg Band; Rep Stu Cncl; High Hon Roll; Prsdnts Acdmc Ftnss Awd 87; Sclstc Awd 87.

BRADLEY, RENEE; Blue Mountain HS; Pottsville, PA; (4); 5/218; VP Church Yth Grp; Girl Scts; Nwsp Rptr; Var L Swmmng; Mu Alpha Theta Awd; NHS; Pres Schlr; Exploring; Mu Alpha Theta; Chorus; Natl Sci Olympd Awd Bio 85; Latin Hon Soc 85-87; WAEB Radio/Lehigh Vly Bk Schlrshp 86; Frankln & Marshll Coll; Pre-Med.

BRADLEY, ROBERT; Stroudsburg HS; Stroudsburg, PA; (2); Spanish Clb; Ftbl; Socr; Trk; Hon Roll.

BRADLEY, TIMOTHY; Our Lady Of Lourdes Regional HS; Shamokin, PA; (3); 19/88; Key Clb; SADD; Varsity Clb; Variety Show; Pres Soph Cls; Pres Sr Cls; Rep Stu Cncl; Im Bsktbl; Var Ftbl; Hon Roll; Lifelns Essy Cntst-Spcl Mntn 87; Mech Engrng.

BRADLEY, WILLIAM; Father Judge HS; Philadelphia, PA; (3); 88/402; Letterman Clb; JV Socr; Hon Roll; Aerosp Engrng.

BRADMON, TARA L; Laurel Highlands HS; Uniontown, PA; (4); Dance Clb; Hosp Aide; Office Aide; Ski Clb; Var Co-Capt Cheerleading; Hon Roll; Penn ST U; Phys Thrpy.

BRADNICK, MELISSA; Forbes Road JR-SR HS; Hustontown, PA; (3); French Clb; FFA; FHA; Chorus; Yrbk Stf; NHS; Phys Thrpy.

BRADSHAW, BETH; Quigley HS; Midland, PA; (3); 30/88; Spanish Clb; Chorus; Capt Cheerleading; Powder Puff Ftbl; L Trk; MVP Girls Track 87; U Of NC; Comp.

BRADSHAW, JENNY; Souderton HS; Telford, PA; (4); Aud/Vis; 4-H; Nwsp Rptr; Var Capt Fld Hcky; Var Capt Trk; Cit Awd; 4-H Awd; JC Awd; Kiwanis Awd; Church Yth Grp; Athlt Yr 87; Grl Mnth 86; Otstndng Athlt 85; Amer Lgn Awd 85; East Stroudsburg; Physcl Ed.

BRADY, BRIAN; Mc Connellsburg HS; Big Cove Tnry, PA; (2); Chess Clb; Church Yth Grp; 4-H; 4-H Awd; High Hon Roll; Hon Roll; Jr NHS; NHS; Ag Sci.

BRADY, BRYAN; Danville Area SR HS; Danville, PA; (3); French Clb; Yrbk Stf; Im Bsbl; Im Bsktbl; Capt Ftbl; Im Socr; L Trk; US Military Acad; Mgmt.

BRADY, CAROL; Trinity HS; Mechanicsburg, PA; (3); Cmnty Wkr; Girl Scts; Hosp Aide; Pep Clb; Ski Clb; Crs Cntry; Trk; Bus Mgt.

BRADY, CARRIE; Brownsville Area HS; Brownsville, PA; (3); Office Aide; SADD; Hon Roll.

BRADY, COREEN; Saltsburg JR-SR HS; Saltsburg, PA; (4); 21/89; Varsity Clb; Flag Corp; Capt L Bsktbl; Sftbl; Capt L Vllybl; Hon Roll; NHS; School Musical; Powder Puff Ftbl; IN Cnty Plyr Of Yr-Vllybl 86; Vngrd Clssc Tourn All Str-Bsktbl 86-87; Aplchn Conf Plyr Of Yr-Sftbl 87; WCCC; Nrsng.

BRADY, DIANA; Connellsville SR HS; Connellsville, PA; (2); Church Yth Grp; Teachers Aide; Y-Teens; Chorus; Church Choir; Yrbk Stf; Hon Roll; Frnch Awd; Hgh Schl Cnslr.

BRADY, DIANE MARIE; Lansdale Catholic HS; Furlong, PA; (4); 9/218; VP Church Yth Grp; Drama Clb; Math Clb; Model UN; Sec SADD; Chorus; School Musical; High Hon Roll; NHS; Pres Schlr; Phldphia Ntl Bank Awd 87; Art Awd-Mst Crtv & Dctd Stu 87; Chmstry Awd 85; La Salle U; Pltcl Sci.

BRADY, DONNA M; Lansdale Catholic HS; Furlong, PA; (4); 10/218; Sec Church Yth Grp; Cmnty Wkr; Drama Clb; Sec SADD; Pres VP Chorus; School Musical; School Play; Rep Soph Cls; High Hon Roll; NHS; La Salle U Christian Bros Full Acdmc Schlrshp 4 Yrs; Cathlc Natl Trng Inst Ldrshp & Svc Levl II 86; La Salle U; Med.

BRADY, ERIN GAREY; Lake-Lehman HS; Lehman, PA; (2); #3 In Class; Letterman Clb; Ski Clb; Rep Stu Cncl; JV Bsktbl; JV Fld Hcky; L Trk; High Hon Roll; Jr NHS; Med.

BRADY, HEATHER; Governor Mifflin SR HS; Shillington, PA; (3); Flag Corp; Orch; Yrbk Stf; Pres Frsh Cls; Rep Soph Cls; Pres Jr Cls; Pres Sr Cls; Pres Stu Cncl; Var Fld Hcky; Var Swmmng.

BRADY, KIMBERLY; Greensburg Central Catholic HS; Irwin, PA; (3); French Clb; Girl Scts; Letterman Clb; Varsity Clb; Var L Bsktbl; Var L Crs Cntry; Powder Puff Ftbl; Var L Trk; Wt Lftg; Hon Roll; ACCTNG.

BRADY, LISA; Elizabeth Forward HS; Boston, PA; (3); Boy Scts; Trs Church Yth Grp; Trs Girl Scts; Band; Concert Band; Mrchg Band; Im Mgr Swmmng; Hon Roll; Acctng.

BRADY, SARAH; Lock Haven SR HS; Lock Haven, PA; (3); Sec Church Yth Grp; French Clb; FHA; Library Aide; Flag Corp; Lock Haven U; Elem Ed.

BRADY, SCOTT; West Catholic HS For Boys; Philadelphia, PA; (3); 91/244; Cmnty Wkr; Im Bsbl; Im Bsktbl; Im Ice Hcky; Var L Socr; Cit Awd; Hon Roll; Cty Athltc Assn Wayne Gretsky Hghst Scorer 86; Cty Athltc Assn Bill Barber Comp Plyr Awd 86; U MN; Bus.

BRADY, TIM; Riverview HS; Verona, PA; (3); 30/120; Varsity Clb; Capt Crs Cntry; Capt Trk; Capt Wrstlng; Hon Roll; NEDT Awd.

BRAGG, LISA; Millville Area HS; Millville, PA; (4); 3/73; Pres FBLA; Library Aide; Office Aide; SADD; High Hon Roll; NHS; Jr Wmns Clb & WACC Schlrshps 87; Bus Wrk Stdy, Cmrc & Schl Prsnl Achvt Awds 87; Wlmsprt Area CC; Accntng.

BRAHEEM, MICHAEL ROBERT; Burgettstown JR SR HS; Burgettstown, PA; (3); VP French Clb; Ski Clb; Chorus; Variety Show; JV Var Stu Cncl; JV Var Bsktbl; Var Ftbl; Tennis; Im Wt Lftg; Hon Roll; Pre-Law.

BRAHO, DIANNE; Sharon HS; Sharon, PA; (3); 17/188; Church Yth Grp; French Clb; Yrbk Stf; JV Crs Cntry; JV Trk; Hon Roll; Psych.

BRAIDO III, JOSEPH; Easton Area HS; Easton, PA; (4); #27 In Class; Pres Frsh Cls; VP Soph Cls; VP Jr Cls; VP Sr Cls; JV Var Bsbl; JV Var Bsktbl; Hon Roll; Lion Awd; NHS; Prfct Atten Awd; Schlmns Assoc Schlrshp 87; Brad Weaver Mem Schlrshp, Sales & Mktg Execs Schlrshp 87; Penn ST U; Mktg.

BRAIM, NANCY; Abington HS; Abington, PA; (4); 134/486; Girl Scts; Hosp Aide; Teachers Aide; Band; Church Choir; Concert Band; Mrchg Band; Stage Crew; Yrbk Stf; Off Sr Cls; Millersville U PA; Elem Ed.

BRAIN, TRACY; Seneca Valley HS; Harmony, PA; (3); 8/400; Church Yth Grp; Varsity Clb; Var L Bsktbl; Var L Trk; Lion Awd; NHS; GAA; Band; Symp Band; Yth Undrstndng Intl Exchng Cert Merit; HOBY Rep; Rotry Yth Ldrshp Awds Rep; Elem Ed.

BRAMBLE, LAURA; Harry S Truman HS; Fairless Hills, PA; (3); Sec Debate Tm; Drama Clb; NFL; Sec Speech Tm; Chorus; School Play; Hon Roll; Thtr.

BRAMBLEY, LYNNE ANN; Everett Christian Acad; Breezewood, PA; (4); Sec Church Yth Grp; Sec 4-H; Sec VICA; Church Choir; Concert Band; VP Jr Cls; VP Sr Cls; Pres Stu Cncl; Var L Bsktbl; Var Vllybl; Penn State,Scndry Mth.

BRAMHALL, RONALD; Yough HS; Irwin, PA; (3); Cmnty Wkr; Computer Clb; Ski Clb; Nwsp Stf; Lit Mag; Trk; Wrstlng; 4-H Awd; High Hon Roll; Hon Roll; 2nd Pl Poetry-Pittsburgh U Humanities Day 87; Hnrry Grn Beret 12th Spcl Frcs Grp 84; IN U-PA; Mltry Jrnlsm.

BRAMLETTE, JENNIFER PAGE; Carlisle SR HS; Ft Belvoir Dr, VA; (4); 6/386; Church Yth Grp; FBLA; Pres Key Clb; Chorus; School Musical; Rep Soph Cls; Rep Jr Cls; Rep Sr Cls; Stu Cncl; JV Crs Cntry; Ger Hnr Soc; WA & Lee U; Lang.

BRANAGAN, BETH; Montour HS; Corapolis, PA; (4); 69/300; Aud/Vis; Cmnty Wkr; Hosp Aide; JA; Band; Concert Band; Mrchg Band; Hon Roll; Pres Acadc Ftns Awd 87; U Pittsburgh; Pre-Med.

BRANAM, SUSAN; Shanksville Stonycreek HS; Friedens, PA; (4); 6/37; Chorus; Church Choir; Capt Stat Bsktbl; JV Cheerleading; L Vllybl; Hon Roll; Prfct Atten Awd; Spanish NHS; Intl Frgn Lang Awd.

BRANAS, JEFFREY; Pittston Area HS; Duryea, PA; (2); SADD; Var Trk.

BRANCH, BARBARA; Elizabethtown Area HS; Elizabethtown, PA; (3); Church Yth Grp; German Clb; Library Aide; Vo-Tech; Data Processing.

BRAND, CHERI; West Forest HS; Tionesta, PA; (1); 1/42; Swing Chorus; Bausch & Lomb Sci Awd; DAR Awd; Pres Schlr; Val; Model UN; Chorus; School Play; H C Seigworth Awd 87; Fulton Awd 87; Rcvd Cert Of Outstndng Achiev In Chem From Amer Chem Scty 87; IN Univ Of PA; Chem.

BRAND, MELISSA; Chambersburg Area SR HS; Fayetteville, PA; (4); 32/600; Church Yth Grp; Cmnty Wkr; English Clb; JCL; Sec Band; Trs Chorus; Lit Mag; NCTE Awd; VP NHS; 8th Pl Dist Chorus 86-87; Lib Arts.

BRAND, STUART; Lowr Moreland HS; Huntingdon Valley, PA; (3); Debate Tm; Science Clb; Lit Mag; JV Crs Cntry; JV Crs Cntry; JV Trk; Timer; Asian Cultures Semnr 87; Librl Arts.

BRANDAU, LORRI; Wilson Area HS; Easten, PA; (3); 35/169; Ski Clb; Nwsp Bus Mgr; Nwsp Phtg; Nwsp Stf; Sec Soph Cls; Sec Jr Cls; Var L Crs Cntry; Var L Trk; X-Cntry Leag Champ 86; PA Jersey Horseshow Assn Grand Champ 86; Track ST Fnlst 86; X-Cntry Dist Champ; Communications.

BRANDON, LISA; Knoch HS; Cabot, PA; (3); GAA; JA; Chorus; Madrigals; School Musical; Coach Actv; Var L Vllybl; High Hon Roll; Hon Roll; NHS; Clarion U; Comm.

BRANDON, SEAN; Butler SR HS; Butler, PA; (3); Boy Scts; Exploring; Var L Ftbl; Var Trk; NHS; Mech Engr.

BRANDT, ARTHUR; Akibu Hebrew Acad; Philadelphia, PA; (4); Camera Clb; Computer Clb; Science Clb; Service Clb; Nwsp Rptr; Yrbk Phtg; Lit Mag; VP Jr Cls; Stu Cncl; Var Socr; Sigma Al&ha Rho Omega Chpt Treas 86; Sigma Alph Rho Omega Chpt Stu At Large 87; American U; Pre-Law.

BRANDT, DENA S; Boiling Springs JR SR HS; Gardners, PA; (3); Art Clb; Nwsp Stf; JV Bsktbl; Stat Fld Hcky; Var JV Mgr(s); Timer; Stat Trk; Hon Roll.

BRANDT, JENIFER; Sharpsville Area HS; Sharpsville, PA; (4); 25/120; Art Clb; Drama Clb; Spanish Clb; Thesps; School Play; L Cheerleading; Wt Lftg; High Hon Roll; Hon Roll; NHS; Acad Achvt Awd 85-87; Hnrs Bio & Sci 86-87; Edinboro U; Cmmrcl Art.

BRANDT, KENTON D; Churchill HS; Pittsburgh, PA; (4); 56/190; Am Leg Boys St; Pres Exploring; Ski Clb; Ftbl; Capt Socr; Capt Trk; Hon Roll; US Army Rsrv Natl Schlrs/Athl Awd, 6th Pl Western PA ST 400 M Dash 87; Keystone ST Trk 3rd Pl 86; VA Tech; Bus.

BRANDT, MICHELLE; Palmyra HS; Palmyra, PA; (4); French Clb; Pep Clb; Varsity Clb; Chorus; Color Guard; Rep Jr Cls; Rep Sr Cls; Stu Cncl; Capt Cheerleading; Swmmng; Harrisburg Area CC; Psych.

BRANDT, STEPHANIE; Northern Lebanon HS; Jonestown, PA; (2); Church Yth Grp; Pep Clb; Cheerleading; Coach Actv; Hon Roll.

BRANDT, SUZANNE; Central Dauphin East HS; Harrisburg, PA; (4); 9/237; Church Yth Grp; Cmnty Wkr; Chorus; Concert Band; Yrbk Stf; Twrlr; Hon Roll; NHS; Ntl Merit Ltr; Messiah Coll; Nrs.

BRANE, CHERI; Bishop Shanahan HS; W Chester, PA; (4); 4/215; Teachers Aide; Nwsp Ed-Chief; Nwsp Stf; High Hon Roll; NHS; Prfct Atten Awd; Pres Acad Fit Awd; Elizabethtown Pres Scholar; Hghst Avg Biol Frnch Theol & Engl; Elizabethtown Coll; Acctg.

BRANGO, MICHAEL; Phoenixville Area HS; Phoenixville, PA; (3); Key Clb; Yrbk Stf; Off Jr Cls; Off Sr Cls; Stu Cncl; JV Bsbl; Var Golf; Var Trk; Cit Awd; Hon Roll; Bus.

BRANHAM, GREGORY; Pine Forge Acad; Adrian, GA; (3); Band; Church Choir; Bowling; Swmmng; Cit Awd; Hon Roll; Fine Arts Schlrshp 87; Tlnt & Fshn Pagnt Wnnr 87; Oakwood Coll; Physcn.

BRANIFF, ANDREW; Peters Township HS; Venetia, PA; (2); Intnl Clb; Rep Key Clb; NFL; Spanish Clb; Thesps; School Play; Ftbl; Tennis; High Hon Roll; VFW Awd.

BRANNAN, JEFFREY; Carlynton HS; Carnegie, PA; (3); Boys Clb Am; Church Yth Grp; Letterman Clb; Var L Bsbl; CPA.

BRANNAN, TERRI; Lewistown HS; Lewistown, PA; (3); Sec AFS; VP Boy Scts; Church Yth Grp; Civic Clb; French Clb; Hosp Aide; Key Clb; Pep Clb; Ski Clb; Hon Roll; People To People HS Stu Ambsdr Pgm N Europe 87; Bus.

BRANNING, TODD; Butler SR HS; Butler, PA; (3); Church Yth Grp; Spanish Clb; Yrbk Stf; JV Bsbl; Im Ftbl; Hon Roll; Gld Awd 87; Bus.

BRANOWITZER, MELISSA; Hopewell HS; Aliquippa, PA; (2); Church Yth Grp; Cmnty Wkr; French Clb; Hosp Aide; Pep Clb; High Hon Roll; Hon Roll.

BRANSTETTER, ERIN; Tyrone Area HS; Tyrone, PA; (3); 4-H; Trs FFA; Hon Roll; Grnd Chmpn PA ST FFA Holstein Shw 85; Treasr Huntingdn Co JR Holstein Clb 87; Dairy Frmng.

BRANSTETTER, TERRY; Tyrone Area HS; Tyrone, PA; (4); 4/180; 4-H; French Clb; Yrbk Stf; Var Crs Cntry; 4-H Awd; High Hon Roll; NHS; Pres Schlr; Marine Optn NROTC Schlrshp 87; GA Inst Of Tech; Engrng.

BRANT, EDWARD; Warren Area HS; Warren, PA; (3); Boy Scts; Church Yth Grp; Cmnty Wkr; Acpl Chr; Chorus; Swmmng.

BRANT, GRETCHEN; Shippensburg Area SR HS; York, PA; (3); 3/250; Church Yth Grp; Chorus; Stage Crew; Yrbk Stf; Score Keeper; High Hon Roll; NHS; Spanish NHS; Natl Spnsh Exam, Spnsh II 1st Pl & Spnsh Listening Comprehension Test Spnsh II 2nd Pl 86; Special Educ.

BRANT, HEATHER; Big Spring HS; Carlisle, PA; (2); Art Clb; Church Yth Grp; Debate Tm; Band; Color Guard; Concert Band; Mrchg Band; Sec Jr Cls; Stu Cncl; Hon Roll; Swm Tm Mngr Tmr Awd 86-87; Hmcmng Crt Rep 86-87; Spnsh Clb 85-87; Shippensburg U; Elem Tchng.

BRANTNER, KELLY; Rochester Area HS; Rochester, PA; (3); 13/106; Pep Clb; Service Clb; Ski Clb; Yrbk Phtg; Yrbk Stf; Trs Sr Cls; Var L Bsktbl; Powder Puff Ftbl; Var L Trk; High Hon Roll; Pre-Med.

BRANTNER, MICHELE; Oxford Area HS; Oxford, PA; (4); French Clb; Sec FFA; Hosp Aide; Ski Clb; Speech Tm; Color Guard; Mat Maids; Sftbl; Hon Roll; Midway Coll; Nrsng.

BRASCO, SUZANNE; Jeannette SR HS; Jeannette, PA; (3); 25/130; Spanish Clb; Nwsp Stf; Var Capt Cheerleading; Hon Roll; Ette Kette Clb Pres 87-88; Elctrcl Engrng.

BRASINGTON, JENNIFER; Warren Area HS; Warren, PA; (3); Acpl Chr; Chorus; Orch; School Musical; Var L Swmmng; Hon Roll; Kylander Mem Awd Swmmng 87; Hgh Pt Awd Swmmng 85-87.

BRASINGTON, MARTY; Warren Area HS; Warren, PA; (4); Spanish Clb; Band; Concert Band; Jazz Band; Mrchg Band; Orch; School Musical; JV Ftbl; Hon Roll; Jr NHS; Outstndng Instrmntalst Awd 86; Slvr B Awd 84; Berklee Coll Music; Music Prfmc.

BRASSELL, DIANE; Nazareth Acad; Bensalem, PA; (3); Debate Tm; Pres NFL; Service Clb; Spanish Clb; Speech Tm; Ed Lit Mag; High Hon Roll; Hon Roll; Pres NHS; Philadelphia Diocesan Schlr 87; Bus.

BRASWELL, BROOKE; Clairton HS; Clairton, PA; (3); 6/101; Church Yth Grp; JA; VP NAACP; Nwsp Stf; Off Stu Cncl; Bsktbl; Sftbl; High Hon Roll; NHS; Engrng.

BRATCHER, BEVERLY; Cardinal O Hara HS; Media, PA; (4); 275/776; Cmnty Wkr; French Clb; FNA; Hosp Aide; Pres NAACP; Office Aide; SADD; Teachers Aide; JV L Vllybl; Duquesne U; Nrsng.

BRATCHER, YVONNE; Cardinal O Hara HS; Media, PA; (1); 280/702; Cmnty Wkr; Library Aide; VP NAACP; Bsktbl; Bus Managmnt.

BRATE, CHRISTINE ELIZABETH; Central Bucks H S East; Doylestown, PA; (4); Chess Clb; Chorus; Stu Cncl; Var Swmmng; Im Vllybl; Hon Roll; Rotary Awd; Rtry Intl Exchng Stu Venezuela 84-85; Amrcs Outstndg HS Stu Names & Faces 83-84; Mst Prmsng 83-84; Temple U; Phlsphy.

BRATIS, PERRY; Council Rock HS; Richboro, PA; (4); 32/860; Chess Clb; Math Tm; Quiz Bowl; Scholastic Bowl; Band; Tennis; NHS; Ntl Merit Ltr; Aon Corp Schlrshp 87-88; Penn ST; Engr.

BRATIS, RON; Council Rock HS; Richboro, PA; (2); Acpl Chr; Chorus; Swing Chorus; Hon Roll; Snd Engrng.

BRATT, KELLY; Iroquois HS; Erie, PA; (4); 1/126; Letterman Clb; Model UN; Concert Band; Drm Mjr(t); Jazz Band; Mrchg Band; Pep Band; Ed Yrbk Stf; Swmmng; Wt Lftg; GE Star Awd 86-87; Penn ST Acadmc Exclnc Awd 86-87; Athltc Ldrshp Awd 86-87; Penn ST U; Physcl Thrpy.

BRATTON, AMY; Cumberland Valley HS; Camp Hill, PA; (4); 11/598; German Clb; Hosp Aide; Key Clb; Varsity Clb; Stu Cncl; Var Swmmng; Var Capt Tennis; High Hon Roll; NHS; PA JR Acad Sci 2nd Awd, Acclds Wrtng Awd 87.

BRATTON, DARLA; Greenwood HS; Millerstown, PA; (3); 18/72; 4-H; FTA; Teachers Aide; Band; Chorus; Concert Band; Mrchg Band; School Musical; Pres Jr Cls; Var Bsktbl; All-Star Field Hcky Team 85-86; Penn ST; Elem Edu.

BRAUCHLE, KIMBERLY; Allentown Central Catholic HS; Allentown, PA; (4); 14/208; Pres Exploring; Key Clb; Rep Chorus; Capt Drill Tm; Capt Flag Corp; School Musical; High Hon Roll; Hon Roll; NHS; Math Clb; Congrsnl Yth Ldrshp Coun 87; 3rd Pl JR Acad Sci PA 85; Drexel U; Acctng.

BRAUN, DONNA; Cardinal Dougherty HS; Philadelphia, PA; (3); 14/670; Church Yth Grp; Cmnty Wkr; Latin Clb; Yrbk Stf; High Hon Roll; NHS; Temple U; Elem Ed.

BRAUN, DOUGLAS; Woodland Hills HS; East Pittsburgh, PA; (3); Im Trk; High Hon Roll; Hon Roll; NHS; Penn ST; Elec Engr.

BRAUN, JEFFREY; General Mc Lane HS; Mckean, PA; (4); 3/188; Chess Clb; French Clb; Band; Concert Band; Mrchg Band; High Hon Roll; Hon Roll; NHS; 1st Pl Comp Prgrmng Cntst Erie Cnty 87; SR Soc Studies Awd 87, R Comp Awd 87; Edinboro U; Pre Law.

BRAUN, MARY LYNN; St Marys Area HS; St Marys, PA; (4); 19/302; Trs Frsh Cls; Trs Soph Cls; Trs Jr Cls; Trs Sr Cls; Var Bsktbl; Var Sftbl; High Hon Roll; NHS; Full Tuition Schlrshp Triangl Tech-Du Buis, PA 87; Triangle Tech; Arch Drftng.

BRAUN, MICHAEL; Lower Moreland HS; Huntingdon Valley, PA; (3); Debate Tm; German Clb; Model UN; Political Wkr; Concert Band; Orch; School Musical; Rep Stu Cncl; High Hon Roll; NHS; Intl Law.

BRAUN, TIMOTHY; Susquehanna Community HS; Susquehanna, PA; (4); 7/84; Math Tm; Ski Clb; Nwsp Stf; Var Trk; Hon Roll; Penn ST U; Comp Sci.

BRAUND, JAY; Troy SR HS; Troy, PA; (3); 30/180; Art Clb; Church Yth Grp; Computer Clb; 4-H; Band; Mrchg Band; Trk; 4-H Awd; PA ST; Ecnmcs.

BRAUNGARD, NANCY; Pequea Valley HS; Ronks, PA; (3); Pep Clb; Varsity Clb; Band; Chorus; Concert Band; Mrchg Band; Cheerleading; Sftbl; Hon Roll; Prfct Atten Awd; Outstndng Wrstlng Chrlder 87; Gym Hnr Rl 87.

BRAUNSTEIN, ELLEN; Bensalem SR HS; Bensalem, PA; (3); Drama Clb; French Clb; JV Trk; NHS; Penn ST U; Bus Admin.

BRAUNSTEIN, NEIL; Conestoga HS; Berwyn, PA; (2); AFS; Band; Concert Band; Jazz Band; Mrchg Band; Trk; Hon Roll.

BRAVIN, KATHLEEN; Altoona Area HS; Altoona, PA; (4); 23/718; German Clb; PAVAS; SADD; Chorus; Stage Crew; Lit Mag; Off Sr Cls; Crs Cntry; Trk; NHS; St Vincent Coll Acad Schlrshp 87; Bia A Bstr Awd Ldrshp & Imprvmnt Crss Cntry 86; St Vincent Coll; Scndry Ed.

BRAWDY, CHRISTINE; Keystone Oaks HS; Brunswick, ME; (4); Camera Clb; Drama Clb; Exploring; Vllybl; Schlrshp Booker/Mc Kenny Trst Fnd 87; IN U Engrng; Arch.

BRAWLEY, SANDRA; Bishop Carroll HS; Carrolltown, PA; (3); 12/128; Pep Clb; Spanish Clb; Chorus; Sec Frsh Cls; Trk; Vllybl; Hon Roll; NHS; Ntl Merit Ltr; Natl Sci Merit Awd 85-86.

BRAWLEY, TONY; Bishop Carroll HS; Carrolltown, PA; (4); 14/107; Ski Clb; Chorus; Stage Crew; Hon Roll; Embry-Riddle; Airline Pilot.

BRAXTON, JAMIE; Connellsville Area HS; Vanderbilt, PA; (1); 15/200; Hosp Aide; Nwsp Ed-Chief; Yrbk Stf; Stu Cncl; Stat L Bsktbl; JV Vllybl; French Hon Soc; Hon Roll; Pres Jr NHS; Prfct Atten Awd; Achiev In Sci 87.

BRAY, JEANNINE D; Creative And Performing Arts; Philadelphia, PA; (3); 16/140; Spanish Clb; Church Choir; Nwsp Phtg; Nwsp Rptr; Nwsp Stf; Lit Mag; Rep Soph Cls; Im Crs Cntry; Im Wt Lftg; Hon Roll; R Stuart Ruach-Amer Philsphcl Socty Awd 86; TMOT Awd 86; Temple U; Jrnlsm.

BRAY, LAMEIERTHA; Mc Keesport SR HS; Mc Keesport, PA; (3); 93/410; AFS; Cmnty Wkr; DECA; Exploring; Hosp Aide; Drill Tm; Drm Mjr(t); Nwsp Stf; L Trk; Elks Awd; St Vincent Coll; Bus Adm.

BRAY, LORA; Mc Keesport SR HS; Mckeesport, PA; (4); 20/350; AFS; Hosp Aide; Capt Drm Mjr(t); Pres Orch; Nwsp Rptr; Powder Puff Ftbl; High Hon Roll; NHS; Pres Schlr; Rotary Awd; Ntl Schl Orchstra Assc Awd 87; PMEA Hnrs Orchstra 87; Blly Chrs Mem Schlrhsp Awd 87; U Of Pittsburgh; Med.

BRAY, RICHARD B; Valley View JR SR HS; Peckville, PA; (3); Church Yth Grp; SADD; Church Choir; VP Jr Cls; Rep Stu Cncl; Var Bsbl; Var Bsktbl; Var Ftbl; Hon Roll; All Schlstc Offnsv, Dfnsv 86-87; All Schlstc Bsktbl 85-86; Finance.

BRAZZO, ALLISON; M M I Prepartory Schl; Hazleton, PA; (4); Church Yth Grp; SADD; Yrbk Stf; VP Frsh Cls; Off Soph Cls; Off Jr Cls; Off Sr Cls; Pres Stu Cncl; Bowling; Sftbl; PA JR Acad Of Sci 1st & 2nd Plc Rgnl & ST Lvls 83-86; NEDT Awd 84-85; Grmn Ntl Hnr Soc 85-87; Law.

BREAKEY, MATTHEW; Trinity Christian HS; Trafford, PA; (4); 3/13; VP Jr Cls; Rep Stu Cncl; Var L Bsktbl; High Hon Roll; Hon Roll; Jr NHS; NHS; NEDT Awd; Radio Clb; Humanities Awd 87; Pres Acadmc Ftns Awd 87; Penn ST; Arch.

BREAULT, ANDY; Elizabethtown HS; Elizabethtown, PA; (3); 109/259; JV Bsbl; Var Bsktbl; Capt Var Ftbl; Var Trk; Outstndng Ftbl Plyr 86; William T Frantz Mrl Awd 86; Athlt Week 86; Elizabethtown Lions Clb Awd 86.

BRECHBIEL, JAY; Greencastle-Antrim HS; Greencastle, PA; (4); 8/174; JV Bsktbl; Im Sftbl; Hon Roll; NHS; VFW Awd; Amer Lgn Schlrshp; Wyanesboro Area Hosp Schlrshp; PA ST U; Pre Med.

BRECHBIEL, LESLEY A; Waynesboro Area SR HS; Waynesboro, PA; (4); 4/383; Art Clb; Camera Clb; Cmnty Wkr; Chorus; Im Sftbl; High Hon Roll; NHS; Reserve Wrld Champ Ntal Reining Horse Assn 86; Yth AQHA Champ 84; Treas Keystone Jr Qrtr Horse 84; Intl Bus.

BRECHT, ERIK M; Coatesville Area SR HS; Coatesville, PA; (4); 75/480; Boy Scts; Cmnty Wkr; Capt Exploring; Ski Clb; SADD; Varsity Clb; Acpl Chr; School Musical; Stage Crew; Nwsp Rptr; York Coll Of PA; Nrsng.

BRECK, MICHAEL; Dubois Area HS; Dubois, PA; (3); 24/364; Boy Scts; Varsity Clb; Var L Swmmng; Vllybl; Hon Roll; Engr.

BRECKER, LISA; Our Lady Of Lourdes Regional HS; Kulpmont, PA; (3); 5/89; Cmnty Wkr; Drama Clb; French Clb; Pep Clb; Radio Clb; Yrbk Sprt Ed; Yrbk Stf; Cheerleading; French Hon Soc; Hon Roll; Acdmc All Amer Schlr Awd 86; Nrsng.

BREDBENNER, AMY; Hazelton HS; Hazleton, PA; (2); Drama Clb; Pep Clb; Chorus; Nwsp Stf; Yrbk Ed-Chief; Var L Crs Cntry; Var L Trk; Hon Roll; Im Vllybl; Prsdntl Acdmc Fitness Awd & Kings Coll Spnsh Test Hnrb Mntn 86.

BREDBENNER, DEBBIE; Hazleton HS; Hazleton, PA; (3); 93/468; Spanish Clb; Var L Bsktbl; Var Crs Cntry; Var L Sftbl; Hon Roll; Sundy Papr 1st Tm Bsktbl, Stndrd Spkr 2nd Tm Bsktbl 86-87.

BREEN, COLLEEN; Archbishop Carroll HS; Havertown, PA; (3); 64/364; Church Yth Grp; Cmnty Wkr; Hosp Aide; Service Clb; Im Ftbl; Var Swmmng; Var Trk; Hon Roll; Latin Awd, Hstry Awd 86; Medcl Prfssn.

BREEN, JENNIFER; Lock Haven SR HS; Lock Haven, PA; (1); Church Yth Grp; Hosp Aide; Rep Frsh Cls; Tennis; High Hon Roll; Hon Roll; Pres Schlr; Pres Acdmc Fit Awd 87; Natl USTA Awd 87; Med.

BREENE, JOHN E; Oil City Area SR HS; Oil City, PA; (4); 21/233; Lib Computer Clb; Varsity Clb; School Play; L Var Crs Cntry; Var L Trk; NHS; Pres Schlr; Rotary Awd; Math Tm; Hon Roll; Pres Phys Ftnss Awd; Natl Merit Awd Phys Ftnss; Leadr Corps; Grove City Coll; Elec Engrng.

BREHM, DARLA; North Star HS; Hooversville, PA; (4); 15/130; Church Yth Grp; FCA; French Clb; Nwsp Stf; Yrbk Stf; Hon Roll; Hm Ecs Awd 87.

BREHM, MIKE; South Western HS; Hanover, PA; (2); Band; Concert Band; Mrchg Band; Pep Band; Symp Band; JV Trk; Genetic Engr.

BREHM, ROBIN; Windber Area HS; Windber, PA; (4); Church Yth Grp; 4-H; Library Aide; Cit Awd; Hon Roll; Hm Ec Awd 86-87; Conemaugh Vly Memrl Hosp; RN.

BREHM, TRACEY; West Mifflin Area HS; Pittsburgh, PA; (2); Cheerleading; Hon Roll; NHS; Slippery Rock U; Socl Wrk.

BREIDEGAM, DENISE; Lehighton Area HS; Lehighton, PA; (3); Debate Tm; Sec FHA; SADD; Chorus; Nwsp Phtg; Nwsp Rptr; Nwsp Stf; Var L Trk; Hugh O Brian Ldrshp Awd 86; Worthy Advisor Gnoden Huetten Rainbow Assmbly 87; Jrnlsm.

BREIDIGAM, DARIN; Brandywine Heights Area HS; Mertztown, PA; (4); 6/121; Boy Scts; Co-Capt Quiz Bowl; Band; Jazz Band; Var Bsktbl; Var L Socr; Var L Tennis; High Hon Roll; NHS; Pres Schlr; PA ST U; Aerospc Engrng.

BREIDINGER, PAULETTE; Rocky Grove HS; Cooperstown, PA; (4); 8/89; Dance Clb; Drama Clb; Chorus; School Play; Yrbk Phtg; JV Var Pom Pon; Var Sftbl; High Hon Roll; Hon Roll; NHS; Future Prblm Slvng Pgm 84-87; Penn ST U; Nrsng.

BREINDEL, ERIC; St Marys Area HS; St Marys, PA; (3); Church Yth Grp; JV Ftbl; JV Wt Lftg; Conservation Ldrshp Awd 87.

BREINDEL, GLENN; Ford City HS; Ford City, PA; (3); 17/170; Boy Scts; Trs Spanish Clb; Chorus; Variety Show; Yrbk Phtg; Stu Cncl; Bsktbl; Golf; Trk; Wt Lftg; HOBY Outstndng Stu Awd 85-86; PA JR Acad Sci 1st Pl ST Lev Comp Sci 85; PA ST; Math.

BREINER, MARSHA L; Tamaqua Area SR HS; Andreas, PA; (3); Cmnty Wkr; 4-H; FFA; 4-H Awd; High Hon Roll; Hon Roll; Agri.

BREITENBACH, HEATHER; Mount Alvernia HS; Pittsburgh, PA; (3); Computer Clb; Drama Clb; French Clb; Chorus; School Play; Nwsp Rptr; Trs Soph Cls; Rep Stu Cncl; High Hon Roll; Hon Roll; Law.

BREITENBACH, KRISTINE; Methacton SR HS; Collegeville, PA; (3); 32/381; Key Clb; Red Cross Aide; Chorus; Orch; Yrbk Sprt Ed; Off Sr Cls; Var JV Tennis; High Hon Roll; Acad Achvmnt Awd 86-87; Acad Fitness Awd 84-85; Hlth Prof.

BREITENSTEIN, BRETT; Moon SR HS; Coraopolis, PA; (4); JA; Band; Jazz Band; Mrchg Band; Pep Band; Symp Band; Ntl Merit SF; Army Rsrvs 86; U Of Pittsburgh; Crmnlgy.

BREITENSTEIN, LYNN; Richland SR HS; Gibsonia, PA; (3); 2/151; Band; Concert Band; Drm Mjr(t); Mrchg Band; Var Crs Cntry; Im Powder Puff Ftbl; Var Trk; Hon Roll.

BREITFELD, MICHELE; Louis E Dieruff HS; Allentown, PA; (2); German Clb; Stu Cncl; Stat Fld Hcky; Gym; Mgr(s); Score Keeper; Sftbl; Hon Roll; Prfct Atten Awd.

BREITFELDER, RINA; Cambridge Springs Joint HS; Cambridge Spgs, PA; (2); 42/99; Pep Clb; SADD; Variety Show; Rep Stu Cncl; Var L Cheerleading; L Pom Pon; JV Sftbl; Var L Vllybl; Fshn.

BRELSFORD, DAVID R; Meyers HS; Wilkes Barre, PA; (4); German Clb; Luzerne County Coll; Elec Engr.

BREMS, BRYAN; Exeter HS; Reading, PA; (4); 25/210; VP Church Yth Grp; VP Drama Clb; JV Golf; JV Var Tennis; Chorus; Church Choir; School Musical; School Play; High Hon Roll; Jr NHS; Cmpr Of Yr, Lthrn Smmr Music Camp 85; Webster U; Musical Theater.

BRENDEL, MICHELLE; Conrad Weiser HS; Robesonia, PA; (3); 70/179; Band; Chorus; Concert Band; Jazz Band; School Musical; Yrbk Stf; Hon Roll; Secdry Ed.

BRENDLE, STEVEN T; Governor Mifflin HS; Mohnton, PA; (3); 12/315; Church Yth Grp; Band; Chorus; Concert Band; Jazz Band; Mrchg Band; Orch; School Musical; High Hon Roll; Jr NHS; Unified Achvt Awd 87; PA ST U; Microbio.

BRENDLINGER, AMY; United HS; Seward, PA; (3); 5/147; Trs Church Yth Grp; Drama Clb; Band; Concert Band; Mrchg Band; Var L Vllybl; Hon Roll; NHS; Spanish Clb; Jr NHS; Cnty Band 85-87; Dist Band 87; IN Gazetts All Cnty Vlybl Tm 86; Nrsng.

BRENEMAN, DOUG; Spring Grove HS; Dover, PA; (3); Pres Church Yth Grp; Band; Concert Band; Jazz Band; JV Bsktbl; Var Ftbl; Trk; Hon Roll; Bus Admin.

BRENEMAN, PAMELA; Donegal HS; Mount Joy, PA; (4); 55/155; VP Church Yth Grp; Drama Clb; Library Aide; Chorus; School Play; Stage Crew; Nwsp Stf; Farm & Hme Fndtn Schlrshp-$1000 87; Messiah Coll; Erly Chldhd Educ.

BRENFLECK, BRIAN; Emmaus HS; Macungie, PA; (3); 63/548; German Clb; Key Clb; Pres Band; Concert Band; Jazz Band; Mrchg Band; Hon Roll; Jr NHS; NHS; Prfct Atten Awd; PMEA Dist X Band 86-87; PMEA Rgn IV ST Band, Lehigh Cnty Band 87.

BRENIZE, BRETT A; Shippensburg Area HS; Newburg, PA; (2); Boy Scts; Church Yth Grp; School Play; Pres Soph Cls; Stu Cncl; JV Ftbl; JV Wrstlng; High Hon Roll; Spanish NHS; Penn ST U; Aero Engrng.

BRENNAN, ANNE; Biglerville HS; Gardners, PA; (2); 19/109; Library Aide; Spanish Clb; Chorus; Jr NHS.

BRENNAN, ARTHUR; Chartiers Valley HS; Bridgeville, PA; (3); Pres Church Yth Grp; Varsity Clb; Rep Stu Cncl; Var Bsbl; Var L Bsktbl; Capt Var Golf; NHS; Pre-Law.

BRENNAN, BERNARD; Father Judge HS; Philadelphia, PA; (3); 11/402; Var Golf; 1st Hnrs 84-85; 2nd Hnrs 85-87; Arch.

BRENNAN, EILEEN; St Huberts High For Girls; Philadelphia, PA; (3); 80/462; Aud/Vis; Drama Clb; Chorus; School Musical; School Play; Socr; Trk; High Hon Roll; Hghst Acdmc Achvt-Rltd Arts & Cthlc Dghtrs-Amer Awd 2nd Pl Pstr Cntst 86; Awd-Mrt-Enrgy Pstr Cntst 85; Comms.

BRENNAN, GARY; Tunkhannock HS; Tunkhannock, PA; (3); German Clb; Letterman Clb; Ski Clb; Bsbl; Ftbl; Wt Lftg; Hon Roll; Rng Cmmtte 85; Strng Cmmtte 86-87; Engrng.

BRENNAN, JENNIFER M; Nativity BVM HS; Pottsville, PA; (1); 5/95; Drama Clb; Girl Scts; Hosp Aide; Nwsp Rptr; High Hon Roll; Schlstc Achvt Awd 87; Engrng.

BRENNAN, JOHN; Nativity BVM; Pottsville, PA; (3); 45/87; Computer Clb; Exploring; Ski Clb; JV L Bsbl; JV L Bsktbl; L Ftbl; Var L Trk; Wt Lftg; Hon Roll; Highest Aver Hlth Cert 86-87.

BRENNAN, MARTIN; Central Catholic HS; Monroeville, PA; (3); Pres Church Yth Grp; JA; Pep Clb; Chorus; Pres Frsh Cls; Pres Soph Cls; VP Stu Cncl; Capt Socr; Var Swmmng; High Hon Roll; Le Salleon Ldrshp Trng 87.

BRENNAN, MELISSA; Nativity BVM HS; Pottsville, PA; (1); 3/95; Math Clb; Nwsp Stf; Vllybl; High Hon Roll; Acad All Amer 86-87; Intl Frgn Lang Awd 86-87.

BRENNAN, PAMELA; Lewisburg Area HS; Lewisburg, PA; (4); Church Yth Grp; Sec Exploring; German Clb; SADD; Mrchg Band; School Musical; Stage Crew; Nwsp Rptr; Var Crs Cntry; JV Fld Hcky; Chsn Stu Ldrshp Nwspr 87; Kings Coll; Cmmnctns.

BRENNAN, SHANNON; Nativity B V M HS; St Clair, PA; (3); 28/96; Debate Tm; Ski Clb; Stage Crew; Rep Stu Cncl; JV Cheerleading; Cit Awd; High Hon Roll; Hon Roll.

BRENNAN, THERESA; Liberty HS; Bethlehem, PA; (2); 40/507; School Play; Hon Roll.

BRENNEMAN, AMY; York Catholic HS; York, PA; (2); 10/147; Hosp Aide; Pep Clb; Spanish Clb; Varsity Clb; Chorus; School Musical; Var JV Cheerleading; JV Trk; High Hon Roll; Hon Roll; Spch Fest Semifnlst 86-87; Psych.

BRENNEMAN, DANIELLE; Red Lion Area SR HS; Red Lion, PA; (3); 18/342; Church Yth Grp; Varsity Clb; Pres Sr Cls; Stu Cncl; Var L Swmmng; Var Trk; Hon Roll; Tutor 85-86; Aquatic Stu Ldr 85-87; Dlgt PA State Brds Assoc ST Cnfrnc 85; Bauder Fshn Coll; Fshn Mrchndsr.

BRENNEMAN, DAWN; Frankford HS; Philadelphia, PA; (4); 78/395; Church Yth Grp; Red Cross Aide; Var Badmtn; Mgr(s); Stat Sftbl; Hon Roll; Mark W Murphy Mem Awd 87; Dr Benjamin Chandlee Mem Grnt Awd 87; Voctnl Hnr Soc Swenson Sklls Ctr 86-87; Manor JC; Med Lab Tech.

BRENNEMAN, ELAINE; Freeport Area HS; Freeport, PA; (3); Church Yth Grp; Drama Clb; School Play; Nwsp Ed-Chief; Nwsp Phtg; Nwsp Rptr; Sftbl; Capt Vllybl; High Hon Roll; Hon Roll; Harmarville Rehab Ctr Vol Awd 86-87; Physcl Thrpy.

BRENNEMAN, JILL; Mechanicsburg Area SR HS; Mechanicsburg, PA; (3); 120/338; Key Clb; Pep Clb; Ski Clb; Teachers Aide; Var L Cheerleading; JV Trk; Hon Roll; Natl Art Hnr Soc 87.

BRENNEMAN, MICHAEL; Hampton HS; Allison Park, PA; (3); 1/200; Chess Clb; Quiz Bowl; Band; Symp Band; High Hon Roll.

BRENNEMAN, TANA; Christian Schl Of York; Glen Rock, PA; (4); Church Yth Grp; Chorus; Church Choir; Orch; School Play; Yrbk Stf; Var Bsktbl; Hon Roll; Presdntl Acadmc Ftns Awd 87; Sbjct Awd-Life Sci 87; Messiah Coll; Mdcl Tech.

BRENNER, DALE; Wilmington Area HS; New Castle, PA; (2); Exploring; Radio Clb; Nwsp Rptr; Nwsp Stf; Stu Cncl; Im Var Ftbl; JV Var Wt Lftg; Hon Roll; Currently On-Air Personality WKST-AM/MFEM-FM New Castle 87 Also WWNW-FM New Wilmington 86; Bus Law.

BRENNER, ELAINE K; Grove City SR HS; Grove City, PA; (4); 9/193; Girl Scts; Library Aide; Office Aide; Teachers Aide; Band; Concert Band; Jazz Band; Mrchg Band; Pep Band; Var L Bsktbl; Natl Hstry Day ST Fin 84-87; Natl Hstry Day Natl Fin 86; Girl Scout Gold Awd 84; Grove City Coll; Pre-Med.

BRENNER, ERIC; Mohawk HS; New Castle, PA; (4); 25/132; Church Yth Grp; L Ftbl; L Trk; Ntl Merit Ltr; Frgn Lang Awd 84; Youngstown ST U.

BRENNER, JANE; Northeastern HS; Mt Wolf, PA; (3); 18/190; Church Yth Grp; Trs Band; Concert Band; Jazz Band; Mrchg Band; Orch; School Musical; VP Frsh Cls; Rep Soph Cls; Rep Jr Cls; Real Estate.

BRENNER, TERENCE; Central Catholic HS; Reading, PA; (4); 32/122; Letterman Clb; Varsity Clb; JV Bsktbl; Var Capt Ftbl; Var L Trk; Hon Roll; Ftbl Coaches Awd 86; All Berks Acad Ftbl 86; Drexel U; Comm.

BRERETON, JOSEPH; Archbishop Wood Hs For Boys; Holland, PA; (3); 6/254; Math Tm; Political Wkr; Service Clb; SADD; Yrbk Bus Mgr; Var Tennis; High Hon Roll; NHS; 1st Bucks Cnty Sci Fair 86 & 87; Hnrble Mntn Sci Fair 85; Bus.

BRESLER, JODIE; Fleetwood HS; Fleetwood, PA; (3); 20/115; Church Yth Grp; Band; Mrchg Band; L Bsktbl; L Var Fld Hcky; JV Sftbl; Hon Roll; HOBY Ldrshp Smnr 86; Scndry Ed.

BRESLIN, MARY; Cardinal O Hara HS; Havertown, PA; (4); 220/771; FNA; Hosp Aide; School Play; Rep Sr Cls; Hon Roll; Church Yth Grp; Office Aide; Teachers Aide; Chorus; Rep Soph Cls; Hahemann U; Nrsng.

BRESLIN, PATRICIA; Archbishop Carroll HS; Berwyn, PA; (3); 40/376; Intnl Clb; Service Clb; School Musical; Yrbk Phtg; Yrbk Sprt Ed; Yrbk Stf; Var L Cheerleading; Im Ftbl; Hon Roll; NHS; Commnctns Bus Admn.

BRESLIN, PATRICIA; St Hubert HS; Philadelphia, PA; (3); 30/421; Office Aide; Hon Roll; Prfct Atten Awd; Coach Of Chrldng For Local Boys Clb 84; Lgl Sec.

BRESNER, JAMES; Penn-Trafford HS; Irwin, PA; (3); 20/300; Art Clb; Exploring; Spanish Clb; Varsity Clb; Yrbk Stf; L Swmmng; Trk; High Hon Roll; Hon Roll.

BRESSI, JOSEPH; Shamokin Area HS; Shamokin, PA; (3); 19/240; Art Clb; German Clb; Science Clb; Varsity Clb; Sec Frsh Cls; Sec Soph Cls; Sec Jr Cls; Pres Stu Cncl; Capt Bsktbl; Capt Trk; Engrng.

BRESSIER, CYNTHIA; Lock Haven HS; Castanea, PA; (3); Spanish Clb; SADD; Band; Concert Band; Mrchg Band; Orch; Pep Band; Nwsp Stf; Yrbk Stf; Church Yth Grp; Dist Orchestra 86-87; County Band 86-87; Outstndng Band Mbr 84-85; Elem Ed.

BRESSLER, SCOTT; Johnsonburg Area HS; Johnsonburg, PA; (4); 2/65; Church Yth Grp; Cmnty Wkr; Pres Frsh Cls; Pres Jr Cls; Pres Sr Cls; Bsbl; Bsktbl; Tennis; Hon Roll; NHS; Penn ST U.

BRESSLER, TRACIE; Big Spring HS; Carlisle, PA; (3); 8/263; Church Yth Grp; Girl Scts; Teachers Aide; Chorus; School Musical; Stage Crew; Nwsp Rptr; Lit Mag; Stu Cncl; High Hon Roll; Notre Dame U; Psych.

BRESTENSKY, RENEE; Freeport Area SR HS; Freeport, PA; (3); Library Aide; Office Aide; VP Frsh Cls; Sec Stu Cncl; Stat Bsktbl; JV Cheerleading; L Trk; Hon Roll; Phrmcy.

BRETT, ANNE E; Bishop Mc Cort HS; Johnstown, PA; (4); 21/135; French Clb; Girl Scts; Latin Clb; NFL; Pep Clb; VP Speech Tm; Chorus; Nwsp Rptr; High Hon Roll; Hon Roll; Johnstown Exchange Clbs Stu Of Month Awd 87; PA ST U.

BRETT, CORINNE; Bethlehem Catholic HS; Bethlehem, PA; (4); 86/190; Key Clb; Ski Clb; Yrbk Stf; Stat Bsbl; Powder Puff Ftbl; Hon Roll; Bloomsburg U; Bus.

BRETTON, PHILIP; Neshannock HS; Neshannock, PA; (3); Speech Tm; Band; Chorus; Concert Band; Jazz Band; Mrchg Band; Pep Band; School Musical; Var Tennis; Cit Awd; Amer Legn Ortorcl Cont 85-87; Geneva Coll Forensics Tourn 86; B Nai Brith Yth Grp Regnl Pres 85-86; Music.

BREUER, KEITH E; Riverside HS; Ellwood City, PA; (4); Sec Computer Clb; Jazz Band; Mrchg Band; U Of Pittsburgh; Elec Engr.

BREWER, DAWN MARIE; Pennsbury HS; Yardley, PA; (4); 34/777; VP Church Yth Grp; French Clb; Service Clb; Band; Church Choir; Mrchg Band; Hon Roll; NHS; Pres Schlr; Acad Schlrshp-Elizabethtown 87; Presdntl Acad Fitness Awd 87; Schlrshp From HS 87; Elizabethtown; Occupatnl Thrpy.

BREWER, JAMES; Cedar Crest HS; Lebanon, PA; (3); Math Tm; Pep Clb; Quiz Bowl; Pep Band; Nwsp Rptr; Gov Hon Prg Awd; High Hon Roll; NHS; Ntl Merit SF; German Clb; Bstr Clb Hnr Awd 87; U Of PA; Bus Mgmt.

BREWER, JAMES; Manheim Central HS; Manheim, PA; (2); Boy Scts; Church Yth Grp; JV Trk; Hon Roll; Millersville U; Comp.

BREWER, KELLEY; Purchase Line HS; Cherry Tree, PA; (4); FHA; Pep Clb; Teachers Aide; Chorus; Church Choir; Color Guard; Drill Tm; Mrchg Band; Sftbl; Hon Roll; IN County Bankers Assn Schlrshp 87; Du Bois Bus Clb; Legal Secy.

BREWER, KELLY; Bangor SR HS; Bangor, PA; (2); Computer Clb; Girl Scts; Spanish Clb; Varsity Clb; VP Frsh Cls; VP Stu Cncl; Cheerleading; Trk.

BREWER, MARGIE; Penn Center Acad; Philadelphia, PA; (3); Art Clb; Debate Tm; Drama Clb; Band; Chorus; School Play; High Hon Roll; Hon Roll; Colombia U-New York; Law.

BREZEALE, CHRISTINA; Grace Christian Schl; Sinking Spring, PA; (4); 1/20; Church Yth Grp; Chorus; Orch; School Play; Ntl Merit SF; Val; Hosp Aide; Teachers Aide; Church Choir; Dist 7 Orch-12th Stndg In Violin 86; Chmbr Ensmbl/Concert Chr Tour 86-87; Soc Dstngshd Chrstn Stu 85-6; Messiah Coll; Music.

BREZINA, KAREN; Allentown Central Catholic HS; Allentown, PA; (3); Church Yth Grp; Key Clb; Spanish Clb; Band; Concert Band; Mrchg Band; Hon Roll; 1st Pl Regnl & 2nd Pl ST Comptn PA Jr Acad Of Sci 85-86.

BREZLER, CHRISTOPHER; Carlisle HS; Carlisle, PA; (3); 171/468; Church Yth Grp; Latin Clb; Hon Roll; Var L Crs Cntry; Var L Trk; US Cyclng Fedrtn 85-86; Hurnsburg Bike Clb 86-87; Calise 1000 Mle Runng Clb 86-87; Shippensburg; Bus.

BREZSKI, RICH; St Pius X HS; Collegeville, PA; (1); 30/146; Ski Clb; Capt Bsktbl; Capt Ftbl; Bus Mgmt.

BRICKELL, ALLISON; Purchase Line HS; Clymer, PA; (2); Church Yth Grp; 4-H; Pep Clb; Spanish Clb; Chorus; Stu Cncl; Var Cheerleading; JV Var Vllybl; 4-H Awd; Hon Roll; IN U; Heatlh.

BRICKER, ANNE; Fairview HS; Erie, PA; (3); 11/148; Church Yth Grp; Cmnty Wkr; French Clb; Model UN; Science Clb; Ski Clb; JV Crs Cntry; Stat Swmmng; Hon Roll; NHS.

BRICKLEY, JENNIFER; Upper Merion Area HS; King Of Prussia, PA; (3); Church Yth Grp; Cmnty Wkr; Drama Clb; SADD; Chorus; School Musical; Nwsp Rptr; Pres Stu Cncl; Stu Recog Awd-Exch Clb 87; Cmmnctns.

BRICKLIN, ALISA; Upper Merion Area HS; Wayne, PA; (3); French Clb; Library Aide; Rep Soph Cls; Fld Hcky; Lcrss; Most Valuble Offnse Fld Hckey 84-85; Psych.

BRIDDES, DONNA; Upper Darby HS; Upr Darby, PA; (4); 42/590; Cmnty Wkr; Exploring; Library Aide; Office Aide; SADD; Mgr(s); High Hon Roll; Hon Roll; Pres Schlr; VFW Awd; Princ Schlrshp 87; Home & Schl Assn Schlrshp 87; Var Ltr Swmmng 87; West Chester U; Psych.

BRIDENBAUGH, ALINA; Lock Haven HS; Lock Haven, PA; (3); 41/250; Church Yth Grp; Service Clb; Spanish Clb; VP SADD; Chorus; School Play; Variety Show; Im Socr; Var Swmmng; Hon Roll; Penn ST; Chld Psych.

BRIDGE, DANIELLE; Cranberry Area HS; Oil City, PA; (2); Church Yth Grp; French Clb; Science Clb; SADD; Varsity Clb; Nwsp Stf; Var Bsktbl; Var L Crs Cntry; Var L Trk; Hon Roll; U Of Pittsburgh; Ntrtn.

BRIDGE, DEBRA; Lancaster Catholic HS; New Holland, PA; (3); Bsktbl; Crs Cntry; Score Keeper; Trk; Acdmc Achvt Awd-Clthng Cnst 87.

BRIDGES, RENEE; Chartiers Valley HS; Pittsburgh, PA; (3); Pep Clb; Spanish Clb; Nwsp Rptr; Ed Nwsp Stf; Yrbk Stf; Cmnctns.

BRIDY, ANDREA; Upper Darby SR HS; Upper Darby, PA; (4); Camp Fr Inc; French Clb; Crs Cntry; Gym; Trk; High Hon Roll; Hon Roll; Phila Coll Phrmcy & Sci; Phrmcy.

BRIEL II, JAMES L; Mahanoy Area HS; Mahanoy City, PA; (4); 6/111; Letterman Clb; Ski Clb; Teachers Aide; Chorus; Concert Band; Jazz Band; Mrchg Band; Pep Band; School Play; Variety Show; Rep PA Congrssnl Yth Ldrshp Cncl 87; Navy; Nuclear Engr.

BRIGANDI, LAURIE; Ridley SR HS; Folsom, PA; (2); 12/434; Church Yth Grp; Drama Clb; Girl Scts; Band; Chorus; School Musical; Var Bsktbl; JV Lcrss; Capt Vllybl; High Hon Roll.

BRIGGS, CHARLES; Western Wayne HS; Sterling, PA; (2); Trs FBLA; Spanish Clb; Im Var Socr; Hon Roll; Rep NHS; JV Bsktbl; Hon Ment All Star Soccer 86; 3rd Pl ST Ldrshp Conf FBLA Bus Math 87; Regnl FBLA Treas 87-88; Villanova; Intl Bkng.

BRIGGS, GLENN; Southern Fulton HS; Needmore, PA; (3); Chess Clb; FFA; Rep Stu Cncl; Var JV Bsbl; Bsktbl; L Mgr(s); Hon Roll; Cnty Ftbl 3rd Pl Trphy 84; Trck Drvng.

BRIGGS, GWEN; John Pierson Mc Caskey HS; Lancaster, PA; (4); 25/450; Cheerleading; Trk; Hon Roll; Spanish NHS; Natl Hrtg Awd For Essay Cont 84; Shippensburg U; Ofc Admn.

BRIGGS, JENNIFER; Cambridge Springs HS; Cambridge Spgs, PA; (2); French Clb; Hosp Aide; Pep Clb; SADD; School Play; Stage Crew; Variety Show; Stu Cncl; Var L Bsktbl; Score Keeper; Smmr Sftbl Leag Co-MVP 86; Villa Maria; Dntl Hygnst.

BRIGGS, PAULA; Yough HS; Smithton, PA; (3); Computer Clb; French Clb; Library Aide; Office Aide; Chorus; Hon Roll; Med.

BRIGGS, REBECCA; John S Fine HS; Wapwallopen, PA; (2); 32/243; Chorus; NEDT Awd; Elec Engr.

BRIGGS, STACY; Harry S Truman HS; Fairless Hills, PA; (4); Church Yth Grp; Girl Scts; Teachers Aide; VICA; Bsktbl; Hon Roll; Ntl Merit Ltr; Hnr Awd For Sngl Mthrs 86; Chld Home & Cmnty Awd Prenatal Awd 87; Nrsng.

BRIGGS, TAMMY; Ft Cherry HS; Hickory, PA; (4); 10/109; Church Yth Grp; Sec Math Clb; Trs Chorus; L Bsktbl; L Sftbl; L Vllybl; Cit Awd; High Hon Roll; NHS; Outstndg Athl 86-87; Grove City Coll; Accntng.

BRIGHT, CHRISTY; Nazareth Acad; Phila, PA; (3); Cmnty Wkr; French Clb; Mgr GAA; Chorus; School Play; Variety Show; Yrbk Rptr; Yrbk Stf; Stat Bsktbl; Stat Fld Hcky; Comm.

BRIGHT, KAREN; South Side HS; Hookstown, PA; (3); 9/135; Church Yth Grp; Exploring; 4-H; Rep Stu Cncl; Powder Puff Ftbl; High Hon Roll; Hon Roll; NHS; Wnnr Amer Legn Auxlry Essy Cntst 87; Law.

BRIGHT, KENNETH; Conrad Weiser HS; Robesonia, PA; (2); 59/163; Church Yth Grp; Drama Clb; JCL; Latin Clb; Mgr Chorus; School Musical; School Play; JV Bsbl; JV Bsktbl; JV Socr; PA ST.

BRIGHT, MICHELLE; Nativity BVM; Orwigsburg, PA; (4); 40/93; Library Aide; Capt Var Bsktbl; Var Sftbl; Capt Var Vllybl; Prsdntl Phy Ftnss Awd 86-87; Air Force; Admin.

BRIGHT, RICHARD; Western Beaver HS; Beaver, PA; (3); Church Yth Grp; Computer Clb; Drama Clb; French Clb; School Play; JV Bsktbl; Comp Sci.

BRIGHT, SCOTT; Shaler Area School District; Glenshaw, PA; (2); 111/514; Band; Concert Band; Mrchg Band; Pep Band; Symp Band; High Hon Roll; Hon Roll; Prfct Atten Awd; Law Enfrcmnt.

BRIGHTBILL, JODI; Palmyra Area HS; Palmyra, PA; (4); 89/196; Church Yth Grp; VP SADD; Band; Chorus; Concert Band; Mrchg Band; Trk; Twrlr; Hon Roll; Central PA Bus Schl; Med Secr.

BRIGHTER, VIRGINIA; St Hubert HS; Philadelphia, PA; (3); 109/421; Cmnty Wkr; Hosp Aide; Office Aide; Service Clb; Btty Crckr Awd; Hon Roll; Off Aid Hnr 86-87; Med Asst.

BRIGHTON, KELLY; Connellsville SR HS; Indian Head, PA; (2); 62/580; Pres Church Yth Grp; Teachers Aide; Chorus; Church Choir; Flag Corp; Mrchg Band; School Musical; Stage Crew; Rep Frsh Cls; Rep Stu Cncl; Alt-PA St Lang Inst Schlrshp 87; Archeology.

BRILLA, MELISSA; Nativity BVM HS; Minersville, PA; (3); Art Clb; Ftbl; Physcl Thrpst.

BRILLMAN, MARY BETH; New Ho Pe-Solebury JRSR HS; Solebury, PA; (4); 7/78; Art Clb; Church Yth Grp; FBLA; Band; Chorus; Mrchg Band; Orch; Pep Band; School Musical; Bsktbl; Shrthnd Awd Trnscrptn 85-86; Free Entrprs Wk 86; Temple U; Accntng.

BRIM, BETH; Portersville Christian HS; Mars, PA; (3); 4/10; Church Yth Grp; Church Choir; Hnrl Roll 85-86; Natl Merit Awd 85-86; Speech Tm 85-86; Secretary.

BRIMMER, JASON; Cedar Crest HS; Lebanon, PA; (1); 18/350; Church Yth Grp; German Clb; Pep Clb; Concert Band; Orch; School Musical; School Play; Stage Crew; Hon Roll; Pblc Svc.

BRIMNER, AMY; Burgettstown JR SR HS; Burgettstown, PA; (4); 40/138; Ski Clb; Band; Jazz Band; School Play; Symp Band; Variety Show; Stu Cncl; Tennis; Hon Roll; Band Hnr 86-87; WV Northrn Brnch; Accntng.

BRINDISI, MICHAEL; Kennedy Christian HS; Farrell, PA; (3); 35/97; JV Bsktbl; Youngstown St; Law.

BRINDZA, TRACEY; Wilmington Area HS; New Wilmington, PA; (3); Church Yth Grp; Dance Clb; Trs FBLA; Hosp Aide; Library Aide; Office Aide; Band; Drill Tm; Variety Show; Powder Puff Ftbl; Duquesne U; Phrmcy.

BRINER, HEATHER; West Perry SR HS; New Bloomfield, PA; (4); 34/184; Spanish Clb; Teachers Aide; Sec Varsity Clb; Capt Color Guard; Yrbk Stf; Pres Frsh Cls; Pres Soph Cls; Rep Sec Stu Cncl; Stat Bsktbl; Trk; Juniata Coll; Bus Adm.

BRININGER, MICHELLE; Lewisburg Area HS; Winfield, PA; (3); Church Yth Grp; VP FHA; JV Bsktbl; Mgr Ftbl; JV Var Sftbl; Hon Roll; Geisinger Med Schl; Nrs.

BRINK, LUANN; Saltsburg JRSR HS; Saltsburg, PA; (1); 1/74; Church Yth Grp; Radio Clb; Band; Concert Band; Mrchg Band; Sftbl; Vllybl; High Hon Roll; Spanish NHS; Notre Dame; Pedtrcn.

BRINK, MELINDA; Dunmore HS; Dunmore, PA; (4); 27/143; Church Yth Grp; Exploring; French Clb; Hosp Aide; Sec JA; Band; Chorus; Hon Roll; Yth Undrstndng Intl Exchn Schlrshp 85; E Defazio Frgn Lang Awd 87; Passvnt Rcgntn Awd 87; Thiel Coll; Poltcl Sci.

BRINSER, JEFFREY; Elizabethtown HS; Mt Joy, PA; (3); Am Leg Boys St; Church Yth Grp; Pres Thesps; Sec Band; Concert Band; Jazz Band; Mrchg Band; School Musical; School Play; Wrstlng; Penn ST; Engrng.

BRINSER, TIFFANY A; Lower Dauphin HS; Hummelstown, PA; (4); Pres Debate Tm; Model UN; VP Thesps; Nwsp Stf; Hon Roll; NHS; Ntl Merit Ltr; Drexel U Pres Schlrshp 87; Pres Acdmc Ftnss Awd 87; Karate, Tae Kwon Do 84-87; Drexel U; Chem.

BRINSON, DIANA; Parkland HS; Allentown, PA; (3); Church Yth Grp; Drama Clb; VP Exploring; Key Clb; Leo Clb; Stage Crew; Lamaze Coach 86; Asst, Vet Oprtns 85-87; Red Crss Cert-Babysttng 87; Vet.

BRINTON, TIMOTHY; Solanco HS; Peach Bottom, PA; (2); Church Yth Grp; CAP; JV Bsktbl; JV Socr.

BRINTZENHOFF, KELLY; Oley Valley HS; Oley, PA; (3); Computer Clb; FBLA; Library Aide; Pep Clb; Nwsp Stf; Mgr(s); Prfct Atten Awd; Data Processor.

BRION, JANELLE; Liberty JR/Sr HS; Liberty, PA; (3); Sec Church Yth Grp; Sec Trs FHA; German Clb; Yrbk Ed-Chief; Sec Stu Cncl; Var Cheerleading; JV Var Vllybl; Stat Wrstlng; Hon Roll; NHS; Sec Educ.

BRISBANE, THOMAS P; Jim Thorpe HS; Jim Thorpe, PA; (2); Boy Scts; Church Yth Grp; Computer Clb; German Clb; Letterman Clb; Ski Clb; Varsity Clb; God Cntry Awd; L Wrstlng; Chem Engr.

BRISBOIS, JAMES; Phoenixville Area HS; Phoenixville, PA; (2); Camera Clb; Computer Clb; Pep Clb; School Play; Stu Cncl; Trk; Cit Awd; Hon Roll; Prfct Atten Awd; U Of VA; Bio.

BRISKAR, STEFANIE; Clearfield HS; Clearfield, PA; (1); Church Yth Grp; French Clb; Band; Chorus; Church Choir; Concert Band; Mrchg Band; Orch; Cheerleading; Crs Cntry; Penn St U; Psych.

BRISKEY, SHAWN; Meyersdale Area HS; Meyersdale, PA; (3); Spanish Clb; Hon Roll; NHS; Intl Frgn Lang Awd 85-86; Hstry.

BRISLIN, EDW; James M Coughlin HS; Wilkes Barre, PA; (3); Church Yth Grp; Math Clb; Ski Clb; Nwsp Rptr; Nwsp Stf; L Trk; High Hon Roll; Jr NHS; NHS; NEDT Awd; WY Vlly Yth Salute 87; WY Vlly Schlstc Art Awd 85.

BRISTOW, SHARMAINE; West Mifflin Area HS; W Mifflin, PA; (2); Drama Clb; Girl Scts; JA; Pep Clb; Chorus; Church Choir; School Play; Nwsp Stf; Yrbk Stf; Pres Stu Cncl; Lawyer.

BRITCHER, COREY; Newport HS; Newport, PA; (3); Church Yth Grp; Church Choir; Var Ftbl; Wt Lftg; Hon Roll; Army.

BRITCHER, MICHELLE; Newport HS; Newport, PA; (3); 5/117; Chorus; School Musical; School Play; VP Frsh Cls; JV Fld Hcky; High Hon Roll; Hon Roll; NHS; Off Stu Cncl; JV Sftbl; Tri M; Law.

BRITT, TAMMI; Penn Hills SR HS; Verona, PA; (3); JA; Spanish Clb; Stu Cncl; Bsktbl; Trk; High Hon Roll; Hon Roll; Acad Achvt Frgn Lang 85-86; Acad Achvt Bus 86; Acad Achvt Reading 85; Nrsng.

BRITTAIN, CHRISTINA; Benton Area JR-SR HS; Stillwater, PA; (4); 14/48; Girl Scts; Band; Chorus; Concert Band; Mrchg Band; School Musical; School Play; JV Var Fld Hcky; NHS; FTA; Soda Schlrshp; IN U Of Penn; Pre Med.

BRITTEN, GLORIA; Bensalem HS; Trevose, PA; (3); Church Yth Grp; ROTC; Band; Church Choir; Concert Band; Mrchg Band; Rep Jr Cls; Cit Awd; DAR Awd; Prfct Atten Awd; Dstngshd Svc Awd-Marine Corps League ROTC 86; Outstndng Cadet-Marine Corps ROTC 86; Xavier U; Bus.

BRITTON, CRAIG; Oley Valley HS; Bovertown, PA; (3); FFA; Varsity Clb; Var Wrstlng; Hon Roll; Pres FFA 87-88; Phys Ther.

BRITTON, DOUGLAS G; Norristown Area HS; Norristown, PA; (4); 39/478; Key Clb; Math Clb; SADD; School Play; Nwsp Stf; Stu Cncl; JV Var Ftbl; Hon Roll; Ntl Merit Ltr; Outstndng Awd Hlth & Phys Ed 86; Elec Engr.

BRITTON, MONIQUE; Phila H S For Girls; Philadelphia, PA; (4); Church Yth Grp; Drama Clb; Exploring; 4-H; Girl Scts; Intnl Clb; Library Aide; Model UN; Office Aide; Service Clb; Cum Laude; Merit Schlrshp; Widener U; Cvl Engrng.

BRITTON, URSELA; Berks Christian Schl; W Reading, PA; (3); 4/22; Chorus; School Musical; School Play; Yrbk Stf; Var L Trk; Hon Roll; MVP Trck 87; Messiah; Child Psych.

BRITZ, CHRISTINE; Central Bucks West HS; New Britain, PA; (4); 23/479; Computer Clb; FBLA; Intnl Clb; Ed Lit Mag; Crs Cntry; Lcrss; High Hon Roll; Hon Roll; Schlrshp Lebanon Vllys Yth Schlrs Prg Chem 85-86; Schlrshp Moore Coll Art 85-86; Bloomsburg U; Bus Mngmnt.

BRNICH, JOSHUA; Bensalem HS; Bensalem, PA; (3); French Clb; Bsktbl; Wt Lftg; Bus Adm.

BRNIK, ANGELA; West Branch Area HS; Grassflat, PA; (3); 26/126; Drama Clb; SADD; Hon Roll; Accntng.

BRNIK, BRIAN; West Branch JR/Sr HS; Grassflat, PA; (2); SADD; Varsity Clb; JV Var Ftbl; Wt Lftg; Elec Engr.

BRO, DANNY; Cardinal Brennan HS; Shenandoah, PA; (3); 22/58; Var L Bsktbl; Im Vllybl; Hon Roll; Prfct Atten Awd; Algbr II & Englsh Acadmc Awd 86-87; Bio & Gemtry Acadmc Awd 85-86; Engr.

BROCATO, TINA; Churchill HS; Pittsburgh, PA; (2); 44/222; Church Yth Grp; Stu Cncl; Mgr(s); Hon Roll; Smmnr Wrkshp Pittsburgh Renaissance Yth Ballet Schlrshp 87; Vlntr Eye & Ear Hosp 86-87; Physcl Thrpst.

BROCIONS, ERIC; Purchase Line HS; Dixonville, PA; (3); 29/109; Letterman Clb; Scholastic Bowl; Varsity Clb; Nwsp Phtg; Nwsp Sprt Ed; VP Frsh Cls; Rep Stu Cncl; Var L Bsktbl; Var L Ftbl; Var L Trk; Sthrn Alleganies Off MVP Ftbl 87; IN U PA; Acctng.

BROCIOUS, BRENDA; Fairview HS; Fairview, PA; (4); 78/156; French Clb; Intnl Clb; Library Aide; Ski Clb; Teachers Aide; Drill Tm; Nwsp Rptr; Nwsp Stf; Cheerleading; Socr; Indiana U Of PA; Bus Admin.

BROCKMANN, NICOLE; Gateway SR HS; Monroeville, PA; (3); Math Clb; Orch; High Hon Roll; NHS; Ntl Merit Ltr; Dist Regnl PA All-State Orchstra 86-87; Music.

BROCKMYER, TERRIE; Ft Cherry JR SR HS; Mc Donald, PA; (3); Church Yth Grp; Science Clb; Ski Clb; Varsity Clb; Chorus; Bsktbl; Sftbl; Vllybl; High Hon Roll; Spanish Clb; Marine Phys Ftnss Tm Vrsty Lttr 85-88; X-Ray Tech.

BROCKWAY, BRIAN; Reynolds HS; Greenville, PA; (3); 2/152; Latin Clb; Trk; Hon Roll; NHS; Acad All Amer Awd 85; Ntl Ldrshp & Srv Awd 86; PA Free Entrprs Wk Schlrshp 87; Med.

BRODAK, JOE; Carmichaels Area HS; Carmichaels, PA; (3); 9/112; Spanish Clb; Yrbk Rptr; JV Ftbl; High Hon Roll; NHS; Physics.

BRODBECK, BETHEL; Dover Area HS; Dover, PA; (4); 16/237; Pres 4-H; Chorus; Yrbk Bus Mgr; Yrbk Stf; Rep Stu Cncl; Var L Bsktbl; Var L Vllybl; 4-H Awd; High Hon Roll; NHS; PA ST U; Bus Admn.

BRODBECK, DUANE; Parkland SR HS; Neffs, PA; (2); Chess Clb; Library Aide; Penn ST; Air Force.

BRODERIC, DAVID; Lebanon Catholic HS; Cornwall, PA; (3); 6/72; Chess Clb; Debate Tm; German Clb; Science Clb; School Play; Nwsp Ed-Chief; Nwsp Rptr; Trs Stu Cncl; Golf; Hon Roll; Bus Adm.

BRODERICK, JANE; Pocono Mountain HS; Pocono Summit, PA; (2); 82/350; Church Yth Grp; Pep Clb; L Chorus; Mrchg Band; JV L Bsktbl; JV L Sftbl; Hon Roll; Prfct Atten Awd.

BRODEUR, ERIC; Lansdale Catholic HS; Quakertown, PA; (3); Computer Clb; Lit Mag; JV Crs Cntry; JV Trk; Penn ST U; Comp Sci.

BRODISCH, CHRISTINE S; Greenwood HS; Millerstown, PA; (3); Church Yth Grp; Rep Varsity Clb; Capt Flag Corp; VP Jr Cls; JV Var Fld Hcky; L Trk; High Hon Roll; Hon Roll; NHS; Sec FTA; Cptl Area Stu Forum Rep Grnwod HS 86-87; WV U; Pre-Med.

BRODNICK, JASON; Penn Wood HS; Yeadon, PA; (3); 81/350; Art Clb; FBLA; Math Tm; Chorus; Rep Stu Cncl; Hon Roll; Outstndg Art Achvt Awd 85-87; Most Outstndg Art Stud Awd 85-86; Art Show Rbbns 85-87; Philadelphia Coll Art; Visual.

BRODOSKI, DONNA; Northern Lehigh HS; Walnutport, PA; (3); 2/166; Chorus; Sec Concert Band; Drm Mjr(t); Sec Mrchg Band; Pep Band; Nwsp Rptr; NHS; Hosp Aide; Band; Jazz Band; Hugh O Brian Yth Fndtn Ldrshp Smnr 86; Lions Clb Yth Ldrshp Smnr 87; Prncpls List 84-87; Comp Sys Anlyst.

BRODOVICZ, STEPHEN; Middletown Area HS; Middletown, PA; (4); 10/170; Am Leg Boys St; Church Yth Grp; Key Clb; Band; Cit Awd; NHS; Pres Schlr; Rotary Awd; Voice Dem Awd; Lehigh U.

BRODSKY, AILEEN F; George Washington HS; Philadelphia, PA; (4); 104/725; Cmnty Wkr; Library Aide; Office Aide; SADD; Y-Teens; Yrbk Stf; Rep Soph Cls; Rep Jr Cls; Rep Sr Cls; Hon Roll; Bst Wrld Prcssng Stu 87; Penn ST U; Hotel Mgmnt.

BRODSKY, GEEIA; South Fayette HS; Bridgeville, PA; (3); Drama Clb; Key Clb; Chorus; School Play; Nwsp Rptr; Nwsp Stf; JV Bsktbl; High Hon Roll; Hon Roll; NHS; S Hls Area Dist Addn Awd Stu Excllnc 86; Jrnlsm.

BRODSKY, JONATHAN; Upper Dublin HS; Dresher, PA; (3); 2/283; School Musical; Nwsp Ed-Chief; VP Frsh Cls; Pres Soph Cls; Pres Jr Cls; Pres Sr Cls; Stu Cncl; Bsbl; Bsktbl; High Hon Roll.

BRODT, DALE; William Allen HS; Allentown, PA; (2); Church Yth Grp; Band; Chorus; Jazz Band; Mrchg Band; Photo.

BRODY, MICHAEL; Cheltenham HS; Elkins Pk, PA; (4); 2/365; Yrbk Sprt Ed; Var Capt Ice Hcky; JV Sftbl; High Hon Roll; NHS; Pres Schlr; 1st Representing HS PA Statewide Mock-Trl Comptn Pres Classroom Young Amers; U PA; Med.

BROFEE, KIM; Greenwood HS; Millerstown, PA; (3); Rep Chorus; JV Var Bsktbl; JV Var Fld Hcky; High Hon Roll; Hon Roll; NHS; Amer Horse Show Assn; Cntrl Pa Jr Hunter Circuit; Pfoutz Vly Untd Mthdst Chrch; Phys Thrpy.

BROFEE, MINDY; Greenwood HS; Millerstown, PA; (1); Church Yth Grp; GAA; Chorus; School Musical; Bsktbl; Fld Hcky; Trk; Hon Roll; Elem Ed.

BROGAN, BETH; Cardinal O Hara HS; Swarthmore, PA; (4); 235/771; JA; Rep Band; Concert Band; Mrchg Band; School Musical; Stage Crew; Yrbk Stf; Lit Mag; Hon Roll; Prfct Atten Awd; Oustndg Achvt Bio 84-85; Music Awd Hrnbl Mntn 86-87; Jesuit Grant St Josephs U 87-88; St Josephs U; Engl.

BROGAN, COLLEEN; Wyoming Valley West HS; Larksville, PA; (2); Red Cross Aide; Mrchg Band; Rep Stu Cncl; Twrlr; Im Vllybl; High Hon Roll; Hon Roll; NHS; U PA; Sci.

BROGAN, MIKE; Wyoming Area HS; Exeter, PA; (3); Spanish Clb; Rep Stu Cncl; Var Bsbl; Hon Roll; Engr.

BROGAN, PAMELA; Big Spring HS; Newville, PA; (2); Chorus; School Musical; Stage Crew; High Hon Roll; Hon Roll; NHS; County Chorus 85-86; Theatrcl Arts.

BROGAN, SEAN; Archbishop Carroll HS; Bala Cynwyd, PA; (3); 61/376; Var Capt Lcrss; JV Socr; Hon Roll.

BROGGI, RORI; Mon Valley Catholic HS; Monongahelan, PA; (3); Ski Clb; Spanish Clb; Nwsp Stf; Yrbk Stf; Stat Bsktbl; Spnsh Hnr Scty; Mission Clb Offcr; Bus.

BROGLEY, BRUCE; Montour HS; Coraopolis, PA; (2); Im Ftbl; High Hon Roll; Hon Roll; Dean Tech; Elec Tech.

BROGLEY, KIMBERLY; Haverford HS; Drexel Hill, PA; (3); Library Aide; Office Aide; Spanish Clb; School Play; Bsktbl; Cheerleading; Fld Hcky; Lcrss; Sftbl; Hon Roll; Pres Physcl Ftns Awd 86.

BROGLIO, MICHAEL; Leechburg Area HS; Leechburg, PA; (3); Band; Mrchg Band; Pep Band; Penn ST; Elec Engrng.

BROJACK, LORI; Lakeland HS; Olyphant, PA; (3); 3/144; VP Sec Church Yth Grp; FHA; SADD; Band; Nwsp Stf; Var Cheerleading; Var Vllybl; High Hon Roll; NHS; Semi-Fnlst Miss Amer Co-Ed Pgnt 87; Mem Of Yng Comm Ldrs Of Amer 86; Penn ST Univ; Crmnl Jstc.

BROKER, MARSHA; Penn Trafford HS; Harrison City, PA; (3); Church Yth Grp; FBLA; Girl Scts; Office Aide; Bus.

BROKUS, AMY; Mt Carmel Area JR SR HS; Mt Carmel, PA; (2); Key Clb; Latin Clb; Pep Clb; Band; Concert Band; Mrchg Band; Rep Frsh Cls; Rep Soph Cls; Trk; Hon Roll.

BROMAN, TREVOR; West Mifflin Area HS; W Mifflin, PA; (3); Var Bsktbl; Var Trk; High Hon Roll; Jr NHS; NHS; Med.

BROMBERG, ROBERT; Lock Haven SR HS; Lock Haven, PA; (4); Aud/Vis; Boy Scts; Computer Clb; French Clb; SADD; Temple Yth Grp; Nwsp Stf; Rep Stu Cncl; JV Socr; L Trk; PA ST; Bus.

BROMFIELD, PAMELA; Downingtown SR HS; Exton, PA; (4); 50/563; French Clb; GAA; Orch; Nwsp Stf; Tennis; High Hon Roll; NHS; Outstndng Amercn Stu 87; Chstr Cnty JR Miss Fnlst 86; Fairfield U Of CT; Pre Law.

BROMLEY, JENNIFER; New Castle SR HS; New Castle, PA; (3); Church Yth Grp; French Clb; Hosp Aide; Pep Clb; SADD; Chorus; Rep Frsh Cls; Rep Soph Cls; Rep Jr Cls; Stu Cncl.

BRONISZEWSKI, SHANNON; Our Lady Of The Sacred Heart HS; Mc Kees Rocks, PA; (4); 19/57; Chorus; Church Choir; School Musical; School Play; Merry Hosp Schl Of Nrsng.

BRONNER, SHAWNNA; Downingtown HS; Exton, PA; (3); 84/741; French Clb; GAA; Ski Clb; Chorus; Var Cheerleading; Hon Roll.

BRONOWICZ, SHARON; Shaler Area SR HS; Pittsburgh, PA; (4); 134/509; Office Aide; Ski Clb; Var Capt Cheerleading; Stat Ftbl; Var L Trk; High Hon Roll; Hon Roll; Sawyer Schl; Bus.

BRONSTEIN, JOHN; Cedar Crest HS; Lebanon, PA; (3); #43 In Class; Latin Clb; Quiz Bowl; Nwsp Sprt Ed; Bowling; Var L Socr; Var L Swmmng; Var Trk; Im Vllybl; NHS; Ntl Merit Ltr; Econ.

BRONSTEIN, STACEY; State College Intermediate HS; State College, PA; (2); Drama Clb; Spanish Clb; Chorus; School Musical; School Play; Im Vllybl; Hon Roll; Otstndng Excllnc In Wrld Cultures 87; Imprvd Exllnc Algebra 87; Highest Grd In Spnsh III Class 87; PA ST U; Interprtng.

BROOKE, JENNIFER; Bishop Conwell HS; Yardley, PA; (4); 8/263; Art Clb; Church Yth Grp; French Clb; Latin Clb; Math Tm; SADD; Nwsp Stf; Yrbk Stf; Lit Mag; Rep Sr Cls; Intl Sci & Engrng Fair 87; Moore Coll Of Art Schlrsh& Drwng Instrctn 86; Knights Of Columbus Cncl 7515; Drexel U; Design & Merch.

BROOKER, MICHELLE; North Allegheny HS; Wexford, PA; (4); Variety Show; Sec Frsh Cls; Sec Soph Cls; Sec Stu Cncl; Cheerleading; Powder Puff Ftbl; Kent ST U; Nrsng.

BROOKHART, MELISSA; Greenwood HS; Millerstown, PA; (4); 10/62; GAA; Sec Chorus; Drill Tm; School Musical; Swing Chorus; Yrbk Stf; Fld Hcky; Trk; 4-H Awd; NHS; Phy Thrpy.

BROOKINS, RACHEL; Schenley HS; Pittsburgh, PA; (3); Cmnty Wkr; OEA; Sec Jr Cls; Rep Stu Cncl; Pom Pon; Wt Lftg; Cit Awd; High Hon Roll; Hon Roll; Prfct Atten Awd; Robert Morris; Bus.

BROOKMAN, LORI; Trinity HS; Washington, PA; (3); Drama Clb; Key Clb; Office Aide; Pep Clb; Ski Clb; Spanish Clb; Speech Tm; SADD; School Play; Nwsp Stf; Nursing.

BROOKS, DAVID; Engineering & Science HS; Philadelphia, PA; (3); 24/193; Computer Clb; Hon Roll; NHS; White-Wllms Schlrshp 87-88; Drexel U; Comp Sci.

BROOKS, DEBRA L; Shaler SR HS; Pittsburgh, PA; (4); 145/509; Pep Clb; Ski Clb; Robert Morris Coll; Accntng.

BROOKS, GREGORY A; Kaoch JR SR HS; Saxanburg, PA; (4); 15/247; Concert Band; Madrigals; Mrchg Band; Pep Band; School Musical; NHS; Ntl Merit SF; Duquesne U; Music Ed.

BROOKS, HOLLY L; Beaver Falls HS; Beaver Falls, PA; (4); 5/172; VP Art Clb; Pres Aud/Vis; Q&S; Service Clb; Band; Nwsp Stf; Yrbk Stf; Sftbl; High Hon Roll; NHS; Bus & Prof Womens Club Girlf Mnth Nov 86; ST Fnlst Miss Amer Coed 86; La Roche Schlrshp 87; La Roche Coll; Grphc Dsgn.

BROOKS, JAMIE; Mt Union Area HS; Mt Union, PA; (4); 31/167; Art Clb; GAA; Hosp Aide; JV Bsktbl; Im Bowling; Var Socr; Var Sftbl; Hon Roll; Fytvl Tech; Drftng.

BROOKS, JO ELLEN; Chambersburg Area SR HS; Chambersburg, PA; (4); 56/552; Sec FTA; Pres Spanish Clb; Pres Teachers Aide; Chorus; Orch; Hon Roll; PA ST Chorus 87; Edwin Sponsellr Schlrshp 87; Christa Mc Cauliffe Schlrshp 87; Slippery Rock U; Elem Ed.

BROOKS, JULIE; Benton HS; Stillwater, PA; (3); Art Clb; Keywanettes; Ski Clb; Band; Chorus; Mrchg Band; Cheerleading; Sftbl; High Hon Roll; Rotary Awd; Rotary Intl Yth Exchng Rep Grmny 86-87; Hugh O Brien Yth Ldrshp Cnfrnc 86; Dist, Rgnl Bands 86; Lwyr.

BROOKS, LEONARD; Bishop Mc Devitt HS; Philadelphia, PA; (3); 148/349; Boy Scts; Spanish Clb; Teachers Aide; Im Bsktbl; Ftbl; Temple; Acctng.

BROOKS, NICOLE; Pine Forge Acad; Los Angeles, CA; (4); 13/79; Mgr Church Yth Grp; Mgr Ski Clb; Sec Chorus; Mgr Church Choir; Yrbk Bus Mgr; Sec Badmtn; Hon Roll; NHS; Loyola Mrymnt U; Gnyclgst.

BROOKS, RANA; Connellsville Area SR HS; Connellsville, PA; (3); 40/560; Office Aide; Band; Concert Band; Mrchg Band; High Hon Roll; Hon Roll; Jr NHS; NHS; Resprtry Thrpy.

BROOKS, RENEE; Bellefonte HS; Bellefonte, PA; (3); 25/211; Church Yth Grp; French Clb; SADD; Church Choir; Concert Band; Mrchg Band; Pep Band; High Hon Roll; Hon Roll; Pep Clb; Natl Hnr Roll 86-87.

BROOKS, ROD; Jersey Shore Area SR HS; Jersey Shore, PA; (4); 4-H; FFA; Ski Clb; Hon Roll; Lycoming Cnty Sml Gas Engs Awd 86-87; Forestry.

BROOKS, TIMOTHY; Tunkhannock HS; Tunkhannock, PA; (3); 48/330; Ski Clb; JV Crs Cntry; JV Wrstlng; Hon Roll; Crmnl Sci.

BROOKS, TINA; Canon Mc Millan HS; Canonsburg, PA; (3); 43/349; Church Yth Grp; French Clb; Teachers Aide; Bsktbl; Mgr(s); Score Keeper; High Hon Roll; Hon Roll; Prfct Atten Awd; Cert Of Prtctn CA U 86; Intl Bus Coll; Frgn Lang.

BROOKS, TRACY; Ringgold HS; New Eagle, PA; (3); Hosp Aide; Math Clb; Scholastic Bowl; Science Clb; L Mgr Trk; High Hon Roll; NHS; Ski Clb; Chorus; Del UN Pilgrimage Yth 87; Math/Sic Hnr Soc Exec Bd 87-88; Doc.

BROOKS, TROY; Corry Area HS; Corry, PA; (4); 5/192; Var Capt Bsktbl; Var Golf; High Hon Roll; Hon Roll; Pres Schlr; Acdmc Awd Physics 87; UC Curtis Schlrshp 87; Fisher-Allen Schlrshp 87; V E & Betty Philips Schlrshp 87; Thiel Coll; Comp Engrng.

BROOKSHIRE, AMY; Central York SR HS; York, PA; (3); 57/248; Church Yth Grp; Ski Clb; Band; Mrchg Band; Yrbk Stf; Rep Frsh Cls; Rep Sr Cls; Rep Stu Cncl; JV Var Mgr(s); Hon Roll; Indiana U Of PA; Med Tech.

BROOMES, GENEVIEVE; Lutheran HS; Philadelphia, PA; (3); 3/11; Church Yth Grp; Debate Tm; Hosp Aide; Office Aide; Quiz Bowl; Church Choir; Drill Tm; Trk; High Hon Roll; Hon Roll; Charles E Ellis Grnt & Schlrshp Fund 87; Med.

BROSCIOUS, JOE; Southern Comubia Area HS; Shamokin, PA; (3); Cmnty Wkr; Computer Clb; Teachers Aide; JV Bsktbl; Var Ftbl; Im Sftbl; Var Wt Lftg; Voice Dem Awd; Schlrshp Awd Alg 85; Bus Admin.

BROSCIOUS, KELLIE; Clearfield Area HS; Clearfield, PA; (4); French Clb; Yrbk Stf; VP Frsh Cls; VP Soph Cls; Bsktbl; Bowling; Sftbl; NHS; NEDT Awd; Pres Schlr; Hghst Sngl Bowling Trphy 87; Duquesne U; Phrmcy.

BROSIUS, AMY; Keystone JR SR HS; Knox, PA; (3); #1 In Class; Church Yth Grp; 4-H; French Clb; FBLA; Pep Clb; Varsity Clb; Chorus; School Musical; Nwsp Stf; Yrbk Stf; Prncpls Lst 85-87; Bus Awd 85; Northeastrn Christian JC; Econ.

BROSIUS, ANGELA; Nazareth Acad; Feasterville, PA; (4); Rep Cmnty Wkr; German Clb; Lit Mag; Bowling; Cheerleading; OH Wesleyan U; Econ Mgmt.

BROSIUS, CHRISTIE; Mifflinburg Area HS; Mifflinburg, PA; (2); Church Yth Grp; French Clb; JV Bsktbl; JV Sftbl; High Hon Roll; NHS; Cand PA JR Sci & Math Symposium 86.

BROSIUS, ERIC; Purchase Line HS; Dixonville, PA; (3); 20/118; Letterman Clb; Chorus; Nwsp Phtg; Nwsp Rptr; Nwsp Sprt Ed; VP Frsh Cls; Var L Bsktbl; Var L Ftbl; Var L Trk; Hon Roll; Sthrn Allganies Offnsv MVP Ftbl 86; IN U Of PA; Accntng.

BROSIUS, STEVE; Calvary Baptist Christian Schl; Lancaster, PA; (3); 3/12; Church Yth Grp; Pep Clb; Band; Chorus; Yrbk Stf; VP Bsktbl; Score Keeper; VP Socr; Hon Roll; Prfct Atten Awd; Conestoga Christian Athlt Lgu Soccer All Lgu Tm 85-86; Maranatha Baptist Bible Coll.

BROTHERS, KIMBERLY; Keystone HS; Emlenton, PA; (3); 12/144; Band; Chorus; Jazz Band; Mrchg Band; Pep Band; Nwsp Stf; Yrbk Bus Mgr; Hon Roll; NHS; Clarion U Of PA; Accntng.

BROTT, AARON; Williamson HS; Tioga, PA; (3); 1/96; Boy Scts; Jazz Band; Yrbk Stf; Pres Soph Cls; Pres Jr Cls; Capt Socr; Wrstlng; Cit Awd; High Hon Roll; NHS; Chem Awd 87; Amer Govt Awd 87; Amer Hist Awd 86; Penn ST U; Chem.

BROUGH, AIMEE; Lincoln HS; Ellwood City, PA; (4); 8/169; French Clb; Y-Teens; Chorus; Stu Cncl; Powder Puff Ftbl; French Hon Soc; High Hon Roll; Hon Roll; NHS; NEDT Awd; IUP; Political Sci.

BROUGHER, CHRISTINE; Penn-Trafford HS; Irwin, PA; (3); Office Aide; Sec Band; Chorus; Concert Band; Drm Mjr(t); Mrchg Band; High Hon Roll; Hon Roll; Hnr Wrkng Ovr 100 Hrs Vlntr Wrk 86; Nrsng.

BROUGHER, JENNIFER; North Star HS; Boswell, PA; (3); 21/137; Varsity Clb; Yrbk Stf; Sec Soph Cls; Pres Jr Cls; Stu Cncl; Cheerleading; Hon Roll; FCA; Ski Clb; Booster Club Stu Of Mnth 86; Fnlsts For Somerset/Cambria Cnty JR Miss 87; Barbizon Mdlng Schl 85; Cmmnctns.

BROUGHER, MELISSA; Rockwood Area HS; Markleton, PA; (2); 35/107; Sec Church Yth Grp; Computer Clb; 4-H; Girl Scts; Band; Chorus; Church Choir; Concert Band; Mrchg Band; High Hon Roll.

BROUSE, JAMES; Garden Spot HS; E Earl, PA; (2); 30/226; Church Yth Grp; Band; Chorus; Concert Band; Var Ftbl; JV Trk; Im Wt Lftg; JV Wrstlng; High Hon Roll; NHS; Art.

BROVERMAN, SUZANNE; Marple Newtown SR HS; Newtown Square, PA; (3); Cmnty Wkr; Color Guard; Flag Corp; School Play; Nwsp Rptr; Lit Mag; Twrlr; Engl.

BROVEY, ALLISON; East Stroudsburg HS; East Stroudsburg, PA; (3); 4/250; Sec Cmnty Wkr; FBLA; Girl Scts; Rep Model UN; Swing Chorus; Nwsp Rptr; Sec Stu Cncl; Co-Capt Tennis; High Hon Roll; NHS; Girl Scout Gold Awd 87; Acad Scholar Awd; Monroe Cnty Spelling Bee Fin 87; PA ST; Cmmnctns.

BROVEY, JENNIFER; East Stroudsburg HS; East Stroudsburg, PA; (3); 6/240; Church Yth Grp; FBLA; Girl Scts; Hosp Aide; Math Clb; Model UN; Band; Chorus; Church Choir; Mrchg Band; ACAD Crrclum Awds Hstry Eng Phy Ed; US Achvmnt Acad Awd; Reg Bus Ldrshp; Penn ST U; Cmmnctns.

BROWDER, KARYN; Meadville Area SR HS; Meadville, PA; (4); Spanish Clb; SADD; Stage Crew; Yrbk Ed-Chief; Yrbk Stf; Var L Trk; High Hon Roll; Prfct Atten Awd; Concert Band; Hon Roll; Schlstc Hnr Soc 87; Pres Physcl Ftnss Awd 85 & 86; Gftd Pgm 83-86; Intl Bus.

BROWER, AMY; Marple-Newtown HS; Broomall, PA; (4); 113/340; Church Yth Grp; Civic Clb; Girl Scts; Office Aide; Church Choir; Stu Cncl; Bsbl; Bsktbl; Mgr(s); Score Keeper; Keystone Business Schl; Bus.

BROWER, SHANE; Bald Eagle Area HS; Howard, PA; (4); 1/184; Varsity Clb; Capt Var Ftbl; Var L Trk; NHS; Ntl Merit Ltr; Val; ASAAC 87; AAPT Outstndng Physcs Stu Yr 86; Natl Sci Olympd Bio 85; Bucknell U; Physcs.

BROWN, ALISON; Mc Dowell HS; Erie, PA; (2); 91/629; Rep Frsh Cls; Rep Soph Cls; Rep Stu Cncl; JV Var Bsktbl; Hon Roll; Music Schlrshp 86; Bsktbl Tm MVP 87; Dist Wnnr Natl Piano Plyng Audtns 80-86; Penn ST U; Acctng.

BROWN, AMY; West Middlesex HS; West Middlesex, PA; (2); Church Yth Grp; VP French Clb; Chorus; Var Cheerleading; Mgr(s); Stat Trk; Im Vllybl; Hon Roll; Poltcl Sci.

BROWN, ANDRE; John Harris HS; Harrisburg, PA; (2); Yrbk Phtg; Yrbk Stf; Rep Soph Cls; Var JV Ftbl; Var Trk; Hon Roll; Prfct Atten Awd; Bus Admin.

BROWN, ANISSA; Lincoln HS; Philadelphia, PA; (3); Drama Clb; FBLA; Spanish Clb; School Play; Pom Pon; Vllybl; Dickinson U; Bus.

BROWN, ANITA; Salisbury Elk-Lick HS; Salisbury, PA; (3); School Play; Nwsp Bus Mgr; Yrbk Stf; Var Capt Bsktbl; Score Keeper; Sftbl; Hon Roll; Prfct Atten Awd; Amer Leg Schl Awd 83-84.

BROWN, ANNA; North Penn HS; North Wales, PA; (4); 43/699; Hst Jr Cls; Hst Sr Cls; Rep Stu Cncl; Var Cheerleading; Var Lcrss; High Hon Roll; Hon Roll; NHS; All Lg 1st Tm La Crosse 86-87; Outstndg Steering Comm 86-87; Penn ST; Comm.

BROWN, AUDREY; Halifax HS; Halifax, PA; (4); 5/99; FBLA; Pres FHA; Nwsp Ed-Chief; Var Capt Cheerleading; High Hon Roll; Trs NHS; FHA St Offr; Sec Awd; Cmnty Svc Awd; Clrcl.

BROWN, BARBARA; William Allen HS; Allentown, PA; (4); 65/560; Band; Concert Band; Jazz Band; Mrchg Band; Orch; School Musical; Hon Roll; NHS; Natl Hnr Soc Awd-Schlrshp 87; Womans Clb Schlrshp 87; Summa Cum Honore-Natl Hnr Soc 86; Muhlonberg Coll; Russian Stds.

BROWN, BELINDA; Valley View JR SR HS; Peckville, PA; (2); Ski Clb; Spanish Clb; School Musical; Variety Show; Gym; Swmmng; Tennis; Trk; Vllybl; High Hon Roll; Amer Allnc Hlth & Phys Ed 86-87; Pres Physcl Ftns Awd 86-87.

BROWN, CHAD; Coatesville Area SR HS; Coatesville, PA; (3); 103/517; ROTC; JV Socr; Im Vllybl; Hon Roll; Engrng.

BROWN, CYNTHIA; Phila High School For Girls; Philadelphia, PA; (4); 31/395; Cmnty Wkr; 4-H; Sec Band; Sec Mrchg Band; Sec Orch; Pres Jr Cls; Rep Stu Cncl; Cit Awd; Hon Roll; Phila Clsscl Scty Awds 84-87; Natl Achvt Schlrshp Commended Stu 87; Cornell Natl Schlr 87; Cornell U; Med.

BROWN, DAVID; Ephrata SR HS; Ephrata, PA; (4); 31/253; Chess Clb; Computer Clb; Math Tm; Quiz Bowl; Scholastic Bowl; Science Clb; Hon Roll; NHS; Hibshman Schlrshp 87; Clarkson U Trustees Schlrshp 87; Wolf Schlrshp 87; Clarkson U; Physics.

BROWN, DAVID; Saint Marys Area HS; St Marys, PA; (4); 2/276; Math Tm; Swmmng; Bausch & Lomb Sci Awd; NHS; Ntl Merit Schol; Pres Schlr; Sal; PA Gvrnrs Schl For The Sci-Grad 86; Attnded Jhns Hpkins Cty Pgm 82 & 83; Stckpl Corp Merit Schlrshp; Cornell U; Physcs.

BROWN, DAVID B; John Piersol Mc Caskey HS; Lancaster, PA; (4); 9/450; VP AFS; Capt Debate Tm; Exploring; NFL; Quiz Bowl; Ed Lit Mag; NCTE Awd; NHS; Ntl Merit SF; Lancaster Exchng Clb Stu Of The Mnth For Oct 86; Yale U; Pol Sci.

BROWN, DAWN; Penn-Trafford HS; Jeannette, PA; (4); Drama Clb; FBLA; Hosp Aide; Spanish Clb; Sftbl; High Hon Roll; Hon Roll; Westmoreland CC; Child Care.

BROWN, DEBBIE; Du Bois Area HS; Dubois, PA; (3); 4/360; Letterman Clb; Yrbk Stf; Rep Stu Cncl; Var L Tennis; High Hon Roll; Hst NHS; Mst Imprvd Plyr Ten 87; Spn Merit Diploma 85; PA Just Say No To Drugs Moose Stu Congress 87; PA ST U; Finance.

BROWN, DEBORAH; West Mifflin Area HS; West Mifflin, PA; (3); Church Yth Grp; Cmnty Wkr; Pep Clb; Nwsp Stf; Hon Roll; Cultural Arts Contest 85; Advanced Engl Hnrs Pgm; Law.

BROWN, DREAMA; Shalom Christian Acad; Chambersburg, PA; (3); AFS; Pres Church Yth Grp; Cmnty Wkr; Ski Clb; Acpl Chr; Chorus; JV Swmmng; Ec.

BROWN, EILEEN; Dunmore HS; Dunmore, PA; (3); 5/150; Church Yth Grp; Computer Clb; FBLA; Letterman Clb; Spanish Clb; Chorus; Yrbk Sprt Ed; Var L Bsktbl; Var L Sftbl; Var L Tennis; Sci Olympics ST Comp 87.

BROWN, ELI; Taylor Allderdice HS; Pittsburgh, PA; (2); Drama Clb; Hosp Aide; Nwsp Rptr; Nwsp Stf; High Hon Roll; NHS; Acad Ltr 85-86; Cmmnctns.

BROWN, ELSBETH; Harriton HS; Gladwyne, PA; (3); JV Fld Hcky; JV Swmmng.

BROWN, ERIC D; North Penn SR HS; N Wales, PA; (4); 40/655; Ski Clb; JV Bsbl; Var L Socr; NHS; St Schlr; Aud/Vis; Church Yth Grp; Math Clb; Radio Clb; Rep Frsh Cls; Air Force ROTC 4-Yr Schlrshp, Gannett Inc 4-Yr Schlrshp 87; North Penn Hnr Awds 85-87; Lehigh U; Elec Engrng.

BROWN, ERICA; Burgettstown JR SR HS; Burgettstown, PA; (3); French Clb; Science Clb; Ski Clb; Color Guard; Drill Tm; Sec Stu Cncl; Gym; High Hon Roll; Hon Roll; NHS; Med.

BROWN, ERIK; South Western HS; Hanover, PA; (2); Church Yth Grp; Band; Concert Band; Mrchg Band; Pep Band; School Musical; York Coll; Bus.

BROWN, ERRIKA; Strawberry Mansion/Bensalem HS; Phila, PA; (3); Cmnty Wkr; Dance Clb; Chorus; Var JV Cheerleading; JV Pom Pon; Hon Roll; Csmtlgst.

BROWN, GEOFFREY; Punxsutawney Area HS; Punxsutawney, PA; (3); Boy Scts; Church Yth Grp; Spanish Clb; Yrbk Stf; Golf; Pre Law.

BROWN, GLEN; Cambridge Springs HS; Cambridge Springs, PA; (4); 1 104; Scholastic Bowl; Var L Bsbl; Var Capt Bsktbl; Var Capt Ftbl; Va Capt Vllybl; Elks Awd; Hon Roll; JETS Awd; NHS; Prfct Atten Awd Presdntl Acadmc Ftns Awd 86-87; Hghst Achvt-Math, Hlth Phy Ed, Frncl & Scl Stds 87; U S Military Acad; Chmcl Engrng.

BROWN, HARRY J; Nativity BVM HS; Schuylkill Haven, PA; (1); 9/96 Church Yth Grp; Spanish Clb; Ftbl; Trk; Hon Roll; NHS; Pres Schlr; 1s Pl CYO Short Stry Fantasy 85; 1st Pl CYO Short Stry Mystry & Humo 86; 2nd Pl Capital Sci & Engr.

BROWN, J TODD; Pequea Valley HS; Gap, PA; (4); 1/109; Pres AFS Pres Drama Clb; Office Aide; VP Band; Chorus; Church Choir; Concer Band; Drill Tm; Jazz Band; Madrigals; ST Band & All E Band Bassoon Super Rtng PA Fedrtn Of Music Clbs Piano; SICO Schlrshp; Millersvill U; Music.

BROWN JR, JAMES; Abington Heights HS; Clarks Summit, PA; (3); 21 270; High Hon Roll; NHS; Var Ltr Rfle Tm 85-87; Envrnmntl Engrng.

BROWN, JANET; Parkland HS; Orefield, PA; (2); Church Yth Grp; JA Letterman Clb; Y-Teens; Church Choir; School Musical; Stu Cncl; Gym JV Var Vllybl; Hon Roll; Grad Dale Carnegie Publc Spkng & Human Rltn 87; Physcl Ftns Team 87; YWCA Gymnstc Team 84-87; Physcl Thrpst.

BROWN, JASON; Cedar Crest HS; Lebanon, PA; (3); Art Clb; French Clb; SADD; Vllybl; Hon Roll; Ntl Merit Ltr; Schlstc Art Awd 86; Cmrc Art.

BROWN, JASON; Central Catholic HS; Oakmont, PA; (3); 61/253 French Clb; Socr; French Hon Soc; Hon Roll; NHS.

BROWN, JASON; Downingtown HS; Exton, PA; (3); Church Yth Grp Letterman Clb; Library Aide; Pep Clb; SADD; Varsity Clb; Nwsp Stf Yrbk Stf; Var L Golf; Hon Roll; Mst Imprvd Stu 84-85; Mst Schl Spr 84-86; Cmmnctns.

BROWN, JASON; G Washington Carver Hs For Eng/Sci; Philadelphia PA; (3); Trs Church Yth Grp; Computer Clb; PA Jr Acad Of Sci; Ame Fndtn For Negro Affrs; Treas Of Yth Dept-Faith Chapel COGIC; Drexe U; Comp Engr.

BROWN, JENNIFER; Bishop Hafey HS; Hazleton, PA; (4); 2/126 German Clb; Math Clb; Ed Yrbk Stf; Rep Stu Cncl; Bsktbl; Bowling; Hig Hon Roll; NHS; PA ST U; Sci.

BROWN, JENNIFER; Tunkhannock Area HS; Tunkhannock, PA; (2) 32/330; German Clb; Band; Chorus; Concert Band; Co-Capt Twrlr; High Hon Roll; Hon Roll; NHS; Office Aide; Acpl Chr; Prsdntl Acdmc Ftns Awd 85; Atlntc-Pcfc Math Lg 1st Plc 85; PA Math Lg 1st Plc 85.

BROWN, JENNIFER; Western Wayne HS; Lk Ariel, PA; (4); 3/140 Yrbk Stf; Sec Pres Stu Cncl; Socr; Sftbl; Tennis; High Hon Roll; NHS Pres Schlr; Schlr Yr 86-87; Stu Mnth 86-87; St Lawrence U; Math.

BROWN, JODI; Trinity HS; Mechanicsburg, PA; (3); Model UN; Pe Clb; Ski Clb; Spanish Clb; Capt Drill Tm; Drm Mjr(t); Mrchg Band; Yrbk Stf; Var Crs Cntry; High Hon Roll; Arch.

BROWN, JOHN; Conneaut Valley HS; Springboro, PA; (3); Hon Roll Mech Drftng.

BROWN, JOHN; Susquehanna Community HS; Susquehanna, PA; (2) Band; Concert Band; Mrchg Band; Ftbl; Vllybl; Hon Roll.

BROWN, JULIA; Fairview HS; Fairview, PA; (3); 1/162; Trs French Clb Ski Clb; Varsity Clb; Trs Frsh Cls; Trs Soph Cls; Trs Jr Cls; Rep Sr Cls Var Swmmng; NHS; Stu Cncl; Amelia Earhart Ldrshp Awd 87.

BROWN, KAREN; Avon Grove HS; Landenberg, PA; (3); 9/210; Tr FNA; Hosp Aide; Concert Band; Jazz Band; Mrchg Band; School Musical Lit Mag; Var JV Vllybl; High Hon Roll; NHS; Bio.

BROWN, KAREN; Dunmore HS; Dunmore, PA; (4); 4/143; Church Yth Grp; Ski Clb; Yrbk Stf; Co-Capt Swmmng; High Hon Roll; Jr NHS; NHS Penn ST; Bus.

BROWN, KAREN; Interboro HS; Norwood, PA; (3); Scrkpr AFS; JCL Key Clb; Latin Clb; Yrbk Stf; Sec Jr Cls; Fld Hcky; Hon Roll; Jr NHS; Rep NHS; Bus.

BROWN, KAREN; South Phila High Mohratn; Philadelphia, PA; (4); 88/489; Dance Clb; Cheerleading; Sftbl; Spanish NHS; U Of Pittsburgh Liberal Arts.

BROWN, KARIN; Spring-Ford SR HS; Phoenixville, PA; (3); Sec Church Yth Grp; Spanish Clb; Band; Church Choir; Concert Band; Mrchg Band; Yrbk Stf; Var Sftbl; Tennis; Hon Roll; Radiolgy.

BROWN, KATHLEEN L; Donegal HS; Mount Joy, PA; (3); 73/177; FBLA; Color Guard; Cheerleading; Tennis.

BROWN, KATHRYN; Cranberry HS; Seneca, PA; (2); Church Yth Grp; Science Clb; Spanish Clb; Y-Teens; Church Choir; Trk; Hon Roll; Med.

BROWN, KATHY JO; Shenango JR SR HS; New Castle, PA; (3); 1/125; French Clb; Speech Tm; Jazz Band; Nwsp Rptr; Capt Twrlr; High Hon Roll; NHS; Nwsp Stf; Hon Roll; Semi Fnlst PA Gvrnrs Schl Intl Stds; Hugh Obrien Rep; Amrcn Lgn Oratrcl Cntst Wnnr Lawrence Co.

BROWN, KEITH; Canon-Mc Millan SR HS; Muse, PA; (4); Church Yth Grp; Band; Chorus; Church Choir; Concert Band; Jazz Band; Mrchg Band; Pep Band; School Musical; School Play; L Armstrong Jzz Awd 87; Cdr Pt Msc Park Outstndng Soloist 87; Shnndh Cnsvtry & Cdr Pt Msc Schlrshp 87; Shenandoah Coll; Jazz.

BROWN, KELLI; Greater Works Acad; North Versailles, PA; (4); 2/32; Church Yth Grp; Ed Yrbk Ed-Chief; Var Co-Capt Cheerleading; Vllybl High Hon Roll; Sal; Pres Phys Fit Awd; Outstndg Achvt Biol; Penn ST U.

BROWN, KELLY; Dallas SR HS; Dallas, PA; (3); Art Clb; Library Aide Yrbk Stf; VP Jr Cls; Rep Stu Cncl; Mgr(s); Score Keeper; Hon Roll; Psych.

BROWN, KELLY; Monessen HS; Monessen, PA; (3); 16/120; Chorus; High Hon Roll; Hon Roll; NHS; Church Yth Grp; French Clb; Hosp Aide Nwsp Rptr; Nwsp Stf; Yrbk Stf; Cnty & Dist Chorus 84-87; Music Engrng Tech.

BROWN, KENNETH; Annville Cleona HS; Annville, PA; (3); Boy Scts; Model UN; Speech Tm; Varsity Clb; Mrchg Band; Stu Cncl; Var Socr; Jr NHS; NHS; Opt Clb Awd; Intl Rel.

BROWN, KERRY; Connelsville SR HS; Vanderbilt, PA; (3); Church Yth Grp; DECA; GAA; Office Aide; VICA; Chorus; Church Choir; Crs Cntry Trk; Hon Roll.

BROWN, KEVIN; Archbishop Ryan For Boys HS; Philadelphia, PA; (2) 74/349; Boy Scts; Computer Clb; Red Cross Aide; Hon Roll; Amer Lgn Awd Sctng 85 & 86; Temple U-Philadelphia; Arch.

BROWN, KIMBERLY D; Harrisburg HS; Harrisburg, PA; (4); 1/101; JA VICA; Chorus; High Hon Roll; Hon Roll; Jr NHS; NHS; Val; Deans List Harrisburg Area CC 86 & 87; Hall Fndtn Educating Yth For The Future 87; Natl Merit Scholar; Child Care.

BROWN, KRISTI; Waynesburg Central HS; Waynesburg, PA; (3); Church Yth Grp; Dance Clb; Spanish Clb; Yrbk Bus Mgr; Yrbk Ed-Chief; Yrbk Sprt Ed; Yrbk Stf; High Hon Roll; NHS; NEDT Awd; Actg.

BROWN, KRISTINA; Downingtown SR HS; Glenmoore, PA; (3); Intnl Clb; Pep Clb; Ski Clb; Spanish Clb; SADD; Yrbk Stf; Off Jr Cls; Off Stu Cncl; Im Tennis; Im Vllybl; Psych.

BROWN, KRISTY LEE; Riverside JR SR HS; Moosic, PA; (3); 47/137; Art Clb; Church Yth Grp; FBLA; Band; Hon Roll; Ntl Piano Plyng Adtn Awd 85 & 86; Gregg Typng Awd 87; Marywood Coll; Bus Admin.

BROWN, LANCE C; Mc Keesport Area HS; Mckeesport, PA; (3); 79/410; Exploring; German Clb; Acpl Chr; Chorus; Var L Bsktbl; Var L Trk; Hon Roll; Prfct Atten Awd; Scott C O Neil Mem Sprtsmnshp Awd 86.

BROWN III, LEONARD G; Solanco HS; Kirkwood, PA; (4); Trs VP 4-H; Teachers Aide; School Musical; Pres Stu Cncl; Var L Socr; Var L Trk; DAR Awd; Hon Roll; Opt Clb Awd; Rotary Awd; Outstndg SR Awd 87; Outstndg Soccer Plyr 87; US Military Acad; Pre-Law.

BROWN, LISA; Bishop Guilfoyle HS; Altoona, PA; (3); Church Yth Grp; Cmnty Wkr; Red Cross Aide; Teachers Aide; Yrbk Stf; Altoona Area Schl Cmmrc; Accntg.

BROWN, LORETTA; Philadelphia H S For Girls; Philadelphia, PA; (2); Library Aide; Teachers Aide; High Hon Roll; Jr NHS; Prnctn U; Pre-Med.

BROWN, LOUANN; Connellsville SR HS; White, PA; (3); 42/500; Church Yth Grp; Office Aide; Chorus; Church Choir; Jazz Band; School Musical; Symp Band; Yrbk Stf; High Hon Roll; NHS; Socl Wrkr.

BROWN, LUKE; Phil-Mont Christian Acad; Maple Glen, PA; (2); Church Yth Grp; Var Crs Cntry; JV Trk; High Hon Roll; Hon Roll.

BROWN, LYNNISE; New Castle HS; New Castle, PA; (4); 46/232; French Clb; Drill Tm; Capt Trk; Pres Schlr; Pres Acad Fit Awd 87; WPIAL 400 M Champ Recrd Holder 85-87; Air Force; Bus Adm.

BROWN, MARCELLE; Blairsville SR HS; Blairsville, PA; (1); Chess Clb; Girl Scts; Concert Band; Mrchg Band; Sftbl; High Hon Roll; Pres Schlr; Gftd Stu; Law.

BROWN, MARY; Montoursville HS; Montoursville, PA; (4); 67/174; German Clb; Letterman Clb; Ski Clb; Band; Color Guard; Mrchg Band; JV Var Cheerleading; Powder Puff Ftbl; Trk; IN U PA; Pltcl Sci.

BROWN, MARY; Myerstown Grace Christian HS; Myerstown, PA; (2); Church Yth Grp; Church Choir; Sec Frsh Cls; Var JV Fld Hcky; Var Sftbl; JV Trk; High Hon Roll; Hon Roll; Nrsg.

BROWN, MARY ANN; Northeast Bradford JR SR HS; Leraysville, PA; (3); Church Yth Grp; FHA; German Clb; Chorus; Hon Roll; Prfct Atten Awd; ASETS Awd 87; Mansfield U; Elem Educ.

BROWN, MELINDA; Pine Grove Area HS; Pine Grove, PA; (3); Am Leg Aux Girls St; Church Yth Grp; GAA; ROTC; SADD; Varsity Clb; Band; Chorus; Church Choir; Concert Band; 1st Team Bsktbl & 2nd Team Sftbl 86-87; 2nd Team Bsktbl 85-86; Sci.

BROWN, MELINDA; Red Lion Area SR HS; Felton, PA; (3); 69/375; 4-H; JV Vllybl; 4-H Awd; Hon Roll; Outstndng Spnsh Stu Awd 87; Karate Awd 85.

BROWN, MELISSA; Connellsville SR HS; Acme, PA; (4); 70/520; Camera Clb; 4-H; Pep Clb; Thesps; Band; Stage Crew; French Hon Soc; High Hon Roll; NHS; Point Park; Bus.

BROWN, MELISSA S; Governor Mifflin HS; Shillington, PA; (3); 57/336; Church Yth Grp; English Clb; Chorus; Concert Band; Mrchg Band; JV Var Fld Hcky; Var Swmmng; JV Trk; High Hon Roll; Hon Roll; Bio Chmstry.

BROWN, MICHAEL; Garden Spot HS; Terre Hill, PA; (2); 17/226; German Clb; Stage Crew; High Hon Roll; Hon Roll; Jr NHS; NHS; Sales Mrktng.

BROWN, MICHELE; Donegal HS; Mount Joy, PA; (3); Band; School Play; Nwsp Rptr; Rep Frsh Cls; Rep Soph Cls; Rep Jr Cls; Rep Stu Cncl; JV Var Cheerleading; Im Powder Puff Ftbl; Stat Trk; Lebanon Vly Coll Hnrs Band 86 & 87; Stu Rptr Campus Chronicle 87; Advrtsng.

BROWN, MICHELLE; Saltsburg JR-SR HS; Saltsburg, PA; (3); 6/66; SADD; Varsity Clb; Flag Corp; Yrbk Stf; Bsktbl; Powder Puff Ftbl; Sftbl; Vllybl; High Hon Roll; NHS.

BROWN, MIKE; Clarion Area HS; New Bethlehem, PA; (4); 4-H; Var Ftbl; Var L Trk; Wt Lftg; Prfct Atten Awd; All Conf 1st Tm Ftbl 87; St Francis.

BROWN, MONICA; Hatboro-Horsham HS; Hatboro, PA; (3); Church Yth Grp; Pep Clb; Red Cross Aide; Ski Clb; SADD; Lcrss; Powder Puff Ftbl; Vllybl; Jacksonville U; Marine Bio.

BROWN, NICOLE D; Penncrest HS; Media, PA; (4); Church Yth Grp; Hosp Aide; NAACP; Pep Clb; SADD; Variety Show; Bsktbl; Fld Hcky; Trk; Pre-Med.

BROWN II, NILES K; HS Engineering & Science; Philadelphia, PA; (4); 28/210; Boy Scts; Chess Clb; Im Ftbl; Hon Roll; NHS; Schlrshp Phillips Exeter,Penn ST,Phila Coll 85-87; FL A & M U; Acctng.

BROWN, OWEN; Downingtown HS; Downingtown, PA; (3); 104/648; Letterman Clb; Ski Clb; Pres Stu Cncl; Var Bsbl; Var Capt Socr; High Hon Roll; Hon Roll; NHS; Spanish Clb; Teachers Aide; Sccr 1st Tm All Ches-Mont 86; Pres Acdmc Ftnss Awds Pgm 84-85; Bus.

BROWN, PAM; South Western HS; Hanover, PA; (3); Computer Clb; Dance Clb; Drama Clb; French Clb; FTA; SADD; Teachers Aide; Comp Prgmmr.

BROWN, PATRICK; Shenango JR SR HS; New Castle, PA; (3); 6/125; Church Yth Grp; Letterman Clb; JV Var Bsktbl; Var L Ftbl; L Var Trk; Wt Lftg; Cit Awd; High Hon Roll; Hon Roll; NHS.

BROWN, PAULA LOUISE; Highlands HS; Natrona, PA; (3); Am Leg Aux Girls St; Church Yth Grp; Dance Clb; Girl Scts; Hosp Aide; Intnl Clb; JA; Stat Bsktbl; Jr NHS; Exploring; 3 Gld Awd 3.6-4.0 GPA; 5 Brwn Awd 3.0-3.59 GPA; Slvr Ldrshp Awd 84-85; PA ST U; Accntng.

BROWN, PENNY; Chestnut Ridge SR HS; New Paris, PA; (3); 23/143; SADD; Chorus; Church Choir; Hon Roll; NHS; Med.

BROWN, RACHEL; Warrior Run HS; Turbotville, PA; (4); 7/139; AFS; Trs Church Yth Grp; Trs 4-H; Spanish Clb; Nwsp Stf; Ed Yrbk Stf; NHS; Chrstn Ldrshp Achvt Awd 87; Jrnlsm Awd 87; Med Schlrshp Awd 87; Beaver Coll; Phys Ther.

BROWN, RAQUEL; Lincoln HS; Ellwood City, PA; (3); #69 In Class; AFS; German Clb; Office Aide; SADD; Temple Yth Grp; Y-Teens; Powder Puff Ftbl; Bus Mgmt.

BROWN, RAY; Connellsville Area HS; Connellsville, PA; (3); Church Yth Grp; Pres Service Clb; Jazz Band; Mrchg Band; School Musical; School Play; Stage Crew; Symp Band; Stu Cncl; Prfct Atten Awd; California U PA.

BROWN, REGINA; Palmerton HS; Kunkletown, PA; (3); 4-H; Hon Roll; Awd Folk Poetry.

BROWN, RICHARD; Olney HS; Philadelphia, PA; (4); Cmnty Wkr; Drama Clb; FBLA; Band; Church Choir; Trs Soph Cls; Sec Sr Cls; Prfct Atten Awd; Awd Charity Fund Raiser 82 & 85-87; CC; Acct.

BROWN JR, RICHARD M; Milton HS; Milton, PA; (2); Latin Clb; Nwsp Rptr; Nwsp Stf; Lit Mag; Im Bsbl; JV Ftbl; JV Trk; Im Wt Lftg; Milton Stdnt Totl Fit Brnz Plus Levl 86-87; PA ST U; Acctg.

BROWN JR, RICHARD S; Moon HS; Coraopolis, PA; (3); Cmnty Wkr; Sec Exploring; VP Trs JA; Ski Clb; Rep Frsh Cls; Im Bsktbl; Im Coach Actv; Var L Crs Cntry; Var L Trk; Var L Wrstlng; WPIAL Crss Cntry Champs 85 & 86; Solo Cert Priv Pilot License 86; Numerou Trphs & Mdls 85-87; Aerospace Engrng.

BROWN, ROB; Mercer JR SR HS; Mercer, PA; (3); Art Clb; Aud/Vis; Spanish Clb; L Bsbl; Capt Golf; High Hon Roll; Hon Roll; NHS.

BROWN, ROBERT; Dunmore HS; Dunmore, PA; (3); 31/156; Drama Clb; Letterman Clb; School Play; Nwsp Stf; Bsbl; Ftbl; Wt Lftg; High Hon Roll; Jr NHS; Kiwanis Awd; Aerospace.

BROWN, ROBERT; Elk Lake HS; Montrose, PA; (3); 4-H; French Clb; Ski Clb; SADD; Chorus; Concert Band; Yrbk Phtg; Var Tennis; Hon Roll; Stu Mnth 86.

BROWN, ROHAN; Martin L King HS; Philadelphia, PA; (2); Computer Clb; Math Clb; Math Tm; Teachers Aide; Stage Crew; Nwsp Rptr; Nwsp Stf; Yrbk Rptr; Yrbk Stf; High Hon Roll; Cert For Achvt Math; Excllnce In Social Studies, Readng, Math, Sci, Physcl Educ, Bus Educ & Sci 86; Comp Progrmmr.

BROWN, RUTH; York Catholic HS; York, PA; (2); Church Yth Grp; Library Aide; Chorus; Var JV Bsktbl; Var JV Trk; Var JV Vllybl; High Hon Roll; NHS; Rsrch.

BROWN, SARAH; Phil-Mont Christian Acad; Maple Glen, PA; (1); Church Yth Grp; Church Choir; Trs Frsh Cls; JV Sftbl; High Hon Roll.

BROWN, SHAMAINE; West Catholic Girls HS; Philadelphia, PA; (3); 27/246; Church Yth Grp; Rep Library Aide; Band; Chorus; Rep Stu Cncl; High Hon Roll; Hon Roll; Exmplry Stu Awd 87; Comp Sci.

BROWN, SHARI; Maplewood HS; Guys Mills, PA; (3); VP Church Yth Grp; VP Leo Clb; Pep Clb; SADD; Color Guard; Concert Band; Pep Band; Ed Nwsp Stf; Ed Yrbk Stf; Rep Stu Cncl; Accounting.

BROWN, SHAWN; Martin Luther King HS; Philadelphia, PA; (4); FBLA; Office Aide; OEA; Teachers Aide; Stage Crew; Nwsp Rptr; Bsktbl; Ftbl; Vllybl; Hon Roll; Recgtn Awds Summer Pgm Lincoln U 86; Cert Apprctn 87; Lincoln U; Bus Adm.

BROWN, SHELLEY; Northeast Bradford HS; Rome, PA; (4); 19/73; Computer Clb; 4-H; Sec Pres FHA; Hosp Aide; SADD; Nwsp Stf; Mgr Wrstlng; High Hon Roll; Orwell Grange Awd 87; Alt Dairy Princess 86; Penn ST U; Nrsng.

BROWN, STACEY; Pottstown SR HS; Pottstown, PA; (3); 22/155; Pres Church Yth Grp; JA; Pres Key Clb; Pep Clb; Sec Service Clb; Flag Corp; Yrbk Stf; VP Frsh Cls; VP Soph Cls; VP Jr Cls; PA ST; Pedtrcn.

BROWN, STACEY; Warwick HS; Lititz, PA; (2); 70/324; Exploring; Chorus; School Musical; Nwsp Rptr; Nwsp Stf; Yrbk Rptr; Yrbk Stf; Var Mgr(s); Vllybl; Hon Roll.

BROWN, STEPHANIE; Cumberland Valley HS; Camp Hill, PA; (3); FBLA; Latin Clb; SADD; Var Fld Hcky; Hon Roll; Latin Fest Awd 87; Financng.

BROWN, STEPHANIE; W B Saul HS; Philadelphia, PA; (4); 37/143; Pres Boy Scts; Sec Church Yth Grp; Cmnty Wkr; Computer Clb; Debate Tm; FFA; Pres Girl Scts; Chorus; Orch; Political Wkr; NAI Summr Flight Acad Scholar 86; US Rep Intl Experience 85; Phila Rep White House Lunchn 84; WVU; Math.

BROWN, SUSAN; Bellwood-Antis HS; Tyrone, PA; (2); Church Yth Grp; Band; Concert Band; Jazz Band; Mrchg Band; Fld Hcky; PA ST U; Law.

BROWN, TAMARA; Solebury Prep Schl; Trenton, NJ; (3); Church Yth Grp; Cmnty Wkr; Dance Clb; Spanish Clb; School Play; Nwsp Phtg; Yrbk Phtg; Yrbk Stf; Var L Bsktbl; Var Lcrss; Pre-Law.

BROWN, TAMMY; Elizabeth Forward HS; Elizabeth, PA; (3); Camera Clb; Church Yth Grp; Drama Clb; Exploring; Pep Clb; Acpl Chr; Orch; Capt Cheerleading; Crs Cntry; 1st Runner Up Spch Comptn & Fnlst Miss Metro Pitt Natl Teen 86; Prom Ct 87; JR HS Orch Fest Awd 85; Drafting.

BROWN, TINA; Plymouth Whitemarsh HS; Lafayette Hill, PA; (3); DECA; Spanish Clb; Yrbk Stf; Rep Soph Cls; Capt Cheerleading; Capt Pom Pon; Powder Puff Ftbl; Hon Roll; Med.

BROWN, TRACI; Waynesburg Central HS; Waynesburg, PA; (3); French Clb; Pep Clb; Rep Stu Cncl; Var Capt Cheerleading; Im Coach Actv; High Hon Roll; Hon Roll; Prfct Atten Awd; Nwsp Stf; Natl Sci Awd 84; Chrldng Awd 84; Pres Phys Fit Awd 84; Waynesburg Coll; Nrsng.

BROWN, TRICIA; Ephrata HS; Ephrata, PA; (3); 41/287; VP Frsh Cls; Var Bsktbl; Var Mgr(s); Var Sftbl; Hon Roll; Math.

BROWN, TRICIA; Faith Community Christian Schl; Pittsburgh, PA; (2); 5/40; Dance Clb; Drama Clb; French Clb; Ski Clb; School Play; Nwsp Ed-Chief; Yrbk Stf; Sec Frsh Cls; High Hon Roll; Hon Roll; Carnegie Mellon U; Arch.

BROWN, VIRGINIA GRACE; Elizabeth Forward HS; Elizabeth, PA; (3); 44/356; GAA; Library Aide; Teachers Aide; Nwsp Stf; Yrbk Stf; Mgr(s); JV Stat Sftbl; High Hon Roll; Hon Roll; Timer; 2nd Pl Wmns Assn Art Contst 87; 4th Pl & Hnrble Mntn In PTA Art Cntst 85; PA ST; Chem.

BROWN, WILLIAM; Canon Mc Millan HS; Mc Donald, PA; (2); Fld Hcky; JV Socr; Wrstlng; Hon Roll.

BROWN, WILLIAM; Cedar Crest HS; Lebanon, PA; (1); Boy Scts; German Clb; Pep Clb; SADD; Swmmng; Hon Roll; Sci.

BROWNAWELL, ROBERT; York County Vo-Tech; Mt Wolf, PA; (3); Boy Scts; Exploring; VICA; Hon Roll.

BROWNE, STACY; Connellsville Area SR HS; Connellsville, PA; (3); Am Leg Aux Girls St; Pep Clb; SADD; School Play; Nwsp Stf; Rep Frsh Cls; Sec Trs Jr Cls; Mgr(s); Var Trk; Readrs Dgst Fndtn Schlrshp 87; Advrtsng.

BROWNFIELD JR, CHARLES; South Meadow SR HS; Scottdale, PA; (2); 3/223; Church Yth Grp; JCL; Latin Clb; Nwsp Rptr; Nwsp Stf; Lit Mag; Var Socr; Var Swmmng; Math.

BROWNFIELD, KELLY; Valley HS; Arnold, PA; (3); Church Yth Grp; French Clb; Girl Scts; Chorus; Church Choir; Yrbk Stf; Chorus-Acompany The Concert Chorus On Piano Awd 85-86.

BROWNFIELD, SHAWNNE; Duquesne SR HS; Duquesne, PA; (3); 9/96; Office Aide; Y-Teens; Drill Tm; Nwsp Stf; Yrbk Stf; Score Keeper; NHS; Howard Univ; Accntng.

BROWNING, SCOTT; Saint Pius X HS; Pottstown, PA; (4); 38/148; JA; Science Clb; Concert Band; Im Bowling; Var L Ftbl; Var L Tennis; Hon Roll; NHS; Prfct Atten Awd; PA ST U; Elctrcl Engrng.

BROWNING, TODD; Shanksville-Stonycreek HS; Stoystown, PA; (4); 2/34; Am Leg Boys St; Boy Scts; VP Chess Clb; Band; Concert Band; Mrchg Band; School Play; Nwsp Rptr; NHS; Sal; Rochester Inst Of Tech; Chem.

BROWNLEE, CHARLES; Salisbury Elk-Lick HS; Salisbury, PA; (3); 8/30; Church Yth Grp; 4-H; FFA; Nwsp Rptr; Nwsp Stf; Yrbk Phtg; VP Jr Cls; Var Bsktbl; JV Cheerleading; Var Capt Socr; Slctd To Bi-ST Sccr All-Stars 86-87; Lock Haven U; Comp Sci.

BROWNLEE, KATHERINE; Taylor Allderdice HS; Pittsburgh, PA; (2); Model UN; Ski Clb; Nwsp Rptr; Nwsp Sprt Ed; High Hon Roll; NHS; AFS; Jr NHS; Med.

BROWNLEE, SHERRILL; Garden Spot HS; New Holland, PA; (4); Church Yth Grp; Drama Clb; Girl Scts; Hosp Aide; Stage Crew; Bsktbl; Mgr(s); Powder Puff Ftbl; Hon Roll; Shclstcs Gold Key Art 87; Messiah Coll; Erly Chldhd Ed.

BROWNLEE, WESTON; Salisbury Elk-Lick HS; Salisbury, PA; (3); Art Clb; 4-H; FFA; School Play; Nwsp Rptr; Nwsp Stf; VP Jr Cls; Var Bsktbl; Var Capt Socr; Hon Roll; Chem.

BROYLES, CHARLES J; Central Dauphin HS; Harrisburg, PA; (3); Church Yth Grp; Cmnty Wkr; Drama Clb; Pep Clb; Red Cross Aide; Chorus; School Musical; School Play; Stage Crew; Var L Swmmng; Comm.

BROZEK, JENNIFER; Waynesboro SR HS; Livermore, CA; (3); Cmnty Wkr; Hosp Aide; Library Aide; Spanish Clb; Chorus; Fld Hcky; Cit Awd; High Hon Roll; Hon Roll; Otstndng Acad Achvmnt 86; Pres Acad Ftnss Awd 86; Engr.

BROZENA, LEE; Hanover Area JR SR HS; Wilkes Barre, PA; (3); Var Bsbl; Var Bsktbl; Var Crs Cntry; L Trk.

BRUBACKER, DAVID; Grace Christian HS; Bethel, PA; (2); 4/20; Var L Bsbl; Mgr Bsktbl; Hon Roll; Penn St; Aero Engr.

BRUBAKER, ALEX S; Manheim Twp HS; Lancaster, PA; (4); 4/325; Church Yth Grp; Quiz Bowl; Var L Socr; High Hon Roll; NHS; James Hale Steinman Schlrshp; Math Awd; Sci Awd, Grmn Awd; U Of PA; Engrng.

BRUBAKER, CHRISTINA; Middleburg HS; Kreamer, PA; (3); SADD; JV Var Sftbl; Hon Roll; NHS; Vrsty Ltr 86-87; Cert Of Schlstc Achvt 85-87; Athltc Cert 85-86; Acctng.

BRUBAKER, JULIA; Catasauqua HS; Catasauqua, PA; (4); 12/127; Church Yth Grp; Church Choir; Stu Cncl; Stat Fld Hcky; Hon Roll; NHS; U Of Richmond; Bus.

BRUBAKER, KEVIN; Williamsburg HS; Williamsburg, PA; (3); VICA; School Play; Stage Crew; Prfct Atten Awd; Prfct Attndnc 85-86; Industrial Electrician.

BRUBAKER, LAUREN; Monongahela Valley Catholic HS; Monongahelan, PA; (3); Church Yth Grp; FBLA; Library Aide; Ski Clb; Chorus; School Musical; Nwsp Stf; Yrbk Stf; JV Bsktbl; Im Vllybl; FBLA 3rd Pl Bus Grphcs Tm Rgnl Ldrshp Conf 87; Lock Haven U Of PA; Recrtn.

BRUBAKER, LISA; Ephrata SR HS; Ephrata, PA; (4); Church Yth Grp; FBLA; Spanish Clb; Chorus; Church Choir; Var Tennis; 4-H Awd; High Hon Roll; NHS; 4-H; Outstndng Bus Stu 87.

BRUBAKER, LISA; Lancaster Mennonite HS; Mechanicsburg, PA; (3); Church Yth Grp; Library Aide; Band; Chorus; Church Choir; Vllybl; High Hon Roll; Hon Roll; NHS; Scl Wrk.

BRUBAKER, RON; Hughesville HS; Muncy, PA; (4); 5/139; Rep Stu Cncl; Hon Roll; NHS; Aero Engr.

BRUBAKER, ROY; Lancaster Mennonite HS; Mifflintown, PA; (3); Service Clb; Teachers Aide; Chorus; VP Jr Cls; Hon Roll; VP NHS; Ntl Merit Ltr; Rotary Awd; Chess Clb; Acpl Chr; Ebveneezer Awd 87; Cert Of Merit 85-87; Tri-M 85-86; U Of SC; Marine Bio.

BRUCHOK, BART; Southern Lehigh HS; Center Valley, PA; (4); 8/230; Exploring; Varsity Clb; Jazz Band; Stu Cncl; Ftbl; Golf; Vllybl; Wt Lftg; High Hon Roll; NHS; Nvl Acad & West Pt 86; US Nvl Acad; Elctrcl Engr.

BRUCK, BETH; Hyndman Middle SR HS; Hyndman, PA; (4); 3/40; Church Yth Grp; Drama Clb; Girl Scts; JA; Library Aide; Pep Clb; Ski Clb; Soroptimist; Spanish Clb; Teachers Aide; Frostburg ST Coll; Elem Educ.

BRUCKER, JENNIFER; Valley HS; New Kensington, PA; (2); French Clb; Office Aide; Var JV Sftbl; JV Vllybl; High Hon Roll; Hon Roll; Best All Around JV Vllybl Plyr 84; Pres Acad Awd 85; Hnrb Mntn Awd Anti-Litter Poster Cont 85; PA ST U; Acctng.

BRUCKER, LAURIE; Central Bucks West HS; Chalfont, PA; (3); Var Bsktbl; Var JV Sftbl; Var Drama Clb; Co-Capt Var Tennis; Hon Roll; Tnns-2nd All-Conf Tm & Mst Imprvd Trophy In Tnns 86-87; Elem Educ.

BRUCKER, MICHELE; Shaler Area SR HS; Pittsburgh, PA; (2); 234/514; Ski Clb; Var Cheerleading; Var Trk; Hon Roll.

BRUCKNO, GREGG; Abraham Lincoln HS; Philadelphia, PA; (3); 7/580; Pres Church Yth Grp; Nwsp Ed-Chief; Pres Soph Cls; JV Socr; Var Tennis; NHS; Opt Clb Awd; Spanish Clb; Varsity Clb; Nwsp Stf; 13 Wnng Awds Essay Cntst; 8 1st Pl Essay Cntst; Cmnctns.

BRUDNICKI, BRENDA; Southern Columbia Area HS; Elysburg, PA; (3); Drama Clb; Exploring; Key Clb; Chorus; School Play; Im Socr; Im Sftbl; Im Swmmng; Im Vllybl; Hon Roll; Air Force Acad; Pilot.

BRUECKEN, CARL; North Catholic HS; Pittsburgh, PA; (2); 4/234; Church Yth Grp; Debate Tm; JA; NFL; Hon Roll; NEDT Awd; Natl Sci Olympd 86; Natl Fornsc Leag Degr Merit 86, Degr Hnr 87.

BRUMBAUGH, JOSEPH; Altoona Area HS; Altoona, PA; (3); Var Bsktbl; Bsktbl Awds; Altoona Mirror Plyr Of Yr 86-87; Mid Alleghenies Conf 86-87; Hnrb Mntn Consenus Bsktbl Tm; Bus Admin.

BRUMBAUGH, PAM; Central HS; E Freedom, PA; (4); 19/190; Church Yth Grp; GAA; JA; Chorus; Church Choir; Sftbl; Hon Roll; U Of Pittsburgh; Pharm.

BRUMBAUGH, SUSAN; East Pennsboro HS; Camp Hill, PA; (3); German Clb; GAA; Ski Clb; Band; Chorus; School Musical; Stu Cncl; Swmmng; Trk; NHS; Priv Invstgtr.

BRUMFIELD, BETSY; Seneca Valley HS; Mars, PA; (3); Church Yth Grp; Church Choir; High Hon Roll; Hon Roll; Bus.

BRUMMETT, MELISSA; Northern York County HS; Wellsville, PA; (3); 68/243; Church Yth Grp; Computer Clb; Yrbk Stf; Cit Awd; High Hon Roll; Hon Roll; Comp.

BRUNDIN, KEITH; Quakertown HS; Quakertown, PA; (3); Var Vllybl; Engrng.

BRUNER, DAVID; Connellsville Area SR HS; Champion, PA; (4); 90/521; Pres Church Yth Grp; Ftbl; Hon Roll; NHS; U Pittsburgh.

BRUNER, PAMELA; Jim Thorpe HS; Jim Thorpe, PA; (2); Chorus; Drill Tm; Nwsp Stf; Sec Soph Cls; Var Cheerleading; Capt Twrlr; JV Vllybl; High Hon Roll; Hon Roll; NHS; EXEC Sec.

BRUNER, RONALD; Steel Valley HS; Munhall, PA; (3); High Hon Roll; Hon Roll; NHS; Prfct Atten Awd; Meteorologist.

BRUNETTI, KENNETH; West Catholic High For Boys; Philadelphia, PA; (4); 18/265; Var Capt Ftbl; Hon Roll; NHS; Pres Schlr; All-Catholic Ftbl 87; Presdntl Acad Fitness Awd 87; Christian Bros & Supplmntl Grants 87; La Salle U; Accntng.

BRUNGESS, BARBARA; Owen J Roberts HS; Spring City, PA; (4); 25/270; Church Yth Grp; Church Choir; Hon Roll; NHS; Grmn Awd 86-87; Ursinus Coll; Pre-Med.

BRUNGESS, REBECCA; Owen J Roberts HS; Spring City, PA; (3); Church Yth Grp; Cmnty Wkr; Letterman Clb; Church Choir; Capt Mrchg Band; JV Var Sftbl; Im Vllybl; Hon Roll; Trng & Rdng Horses Won Rbns 84; Art Merit Awd 84-86; Art,Math Tchr.

BRUNI, TONI; Parkland SR HS; Allentown, PA; (3); 91/481; Library Aide; Teachers Aide; Drm Mjr(t); Swmmng; Hon Roll; Prfct Atten Awd; Med Sec.

BRUNNER, BONITA; Southern Huntingdon HS; Mapleton Depot, PA; (3); 3/154; Girl Scts; SADD; Band; Chorus; Church Choir; Concert Band; Jazz Band; Mrchg Band; NHS; Church Yth Grp; Gold Awd Hghst Girl Scouts 87; God & Church Awd 86; Comp.

BRUNNER, BRIGITTA; Parkland HS; Allentown, PA; (2); 64/462; Church Yth Grp; Exploring; Math Clb; Service Clb; Stu Cncl; Hon Roll; Pres Acdmc Fitness Awd Pgm 85-86; Bio.

BRUNNER, CHRIS; Jersey Shore HS; Jersey Shore, PA; (3); Computer Clb; FBLA; Service Clb; Varsity Clb; Var L Bsbl; Var L Wrstlng; Bus Admin.

BRUNNER, DOUG; St Marys Area HS; Saint Marys, PA; (4); JV Bsbl; Im Bsktbl; Var L Tennis; Hon Roll; NHS; U Of Pittsburgh; Sci.

BRUNNER, GEOFF; Pocono Mountain HS; Tannersville, PA; (4); 17/329; Boy Scts; Var Bsbl; Var Crs Cntry; Var Ftbl; Var Wrstlng; Hon Roll; Schlr Ath 86-87; Multiple Schlerosis Rep DE Vly Chptr 86-87; Athlete Wk 85-86; U DE; Pol Sci.

BRUNNER, MARC; Seneca Valley HS; Mars, PA; (3); 50/460; Ski Clb; Kent ST U; Aero Engr.

BRUNNER, MICHELE; Louis E Dieruff HS; Allentown, PA; (3); 28/350; Var Capt Cheerleading; Hon Roll; Jr NHS.

BRUNO, ANGELA; Shady Side Acad; Pittsburgh, PA; (3); Letterman Clb; Yrbk Stf; Var Bsktbl; Var Mgr(s); JV Sftbl; Var Capt Tennis; Trk; Hon Roll; Medlln Ball 100 Hr Vlntr Wrk 87.

BRUNO, BRAD; Norwin HS; N Huntingdon, PA; (4); 208/598; Church Yth Grp; Cmnty Wkr; Dance Clb; DECA; Letterman Clb; SADD; Variety Show; Bsktbl; Trk; DECA Mrktng Awd Rgnl Div 87; Westmoreland Cnty Coachs Awd 87; WPIAL Awd 87; Robert Morris Coll; Bus Admin.

BRUNO, DANIEL; Middleburg HS; Middleburg, PA; (3); 1/138; Drama Clb; SADD; School Play; Bausch & Lomb Sci Awd; High Hon Roll; NHS; Prfct Atten Awd; Woodmen Of Wrld Life Ins Soc Awd Outstndng Amer Hstry 86; Bio Yth Schlrs Inst 87; Pa Free Entprs Wk 87; Pre-Med.

BRUNO, FRANK; Camevim HS; Pittsburgh, PA; (3); Hon Roll; Robert Morris Coll; Acctg.

BRUNO, GINA; General Mc Lane HS; Edinboro, PA; (4); German Clb; Teachers Aide; Trs Jr Cls; Off Stu Cncl; Stat Bsktbl; Sftbl; NHS; Pres Schlr; Acdmc Schlrshp 87-88; Westminster Coll; Bio.

BRUNO, JAMES; Bishop Mc Devitt HS; Harrisburg, PA; (3); 90/247; FBLA; Service Clb; Varsity Clb; Band; Nwsp Rptr; Rep Frsh Cls; Pres Soph Cls; Stu Cncl; Var Bsbl; Var JV Bsktbl; Penn ST; Bus Mgmt.

BRUNO, JEANNINE M; Somerset Area SR HS; Friedens, PA; (4); 1/239; Am Leg Aux Girls St; JA; Q&S; Speech Tm; Rep Stu Cncl; DAR Awd; NHS; Ntl Merit SF; English Clb; German Clb; Congress Bundestag Schlrshp 86; Hugh O Brian Yth Fndtn Awd 84; American U; Intl Rel.

BRUNO, JENIFIR; Wyoming Area HS; West Pittston, PA; (3); 24/250; Drama Clb; Key Clb; Ski Clb; Spanish Clb; Nwsp Stf; Yrbk Stf; Rep Stu Cncl; Var L Sftbl; High Hon Roll; NHS; Pre Med.

BRUNO, MARGARET; Archbishop Prendergast HS; Upper Darby, PA; (3); 100/365; Sec Church Yth Grp; Y-Teens; Acpl Chr; Chorus; Variety Show; Off Frsh Cls; Off Jr Cls; Stu Cncl; Crs Cntry; Trk; Acad Excllnce Awd Home Ed 87; West Chester ST U; Chldhd Ed.

BRUNO, MARK; Union Area HS; Edinburg, PA; (4); 2/67; Church Yth Grp; Pep Clb; L Bsbl; L Ftbl; High Hon Roll; Hon Roll; Lion Awd; Pres NHS; Sal; Slippery Rock U; Psych.

BRUNO, ROBERT JOHN; Crestwood HS; Mountaintop, PA; (3); Church Yth Grp; Computer Clb; Band; Concert Band; Mrchg Band; Trk; Wt Lftg; Wrstlng; High Hon Roll; Hon Roll; Kings Coll; Comp Sci.

BRUNO, STEPHEN; Trinity HS; Washington, PA; (3); French Clb; Ski Clb; Var L Ftbl; JV Tennis; Var L Wrstlng; Hon Roll; U Pittsburgh; Engr.

BRUNS, JENNY; Notre Dame HS; E Stroudsburg, PA; (3); Hosp Aide; Library Aide; JV Var Bsktbl; JV Fld Hcky; Stat Mgr(s); JV Capt Socr; Var Sftbl; Hon Roll; MVP Sftbl 87; MVP Sccr 84; Nrsg.

BRUNS, NED; North Allegheny HS; Pittsburgh, PA; (2); 22/633; Boy Scts; Var Bsbl; Var L Ftbl; High Hon Roll; Hon Roll; Jr NHS; Pre Med.

BRUNSON, SCOTT; Penn-Trafford HS; Trafford, PA; (3); Spanish Clb; SADD; Varsity Clb; Ftbl; Trk; Wt Lftg; Military.

BRUNT, DOUGLAS; Haverford Schl; Newtown Sq, PA; (2); Exploring; Office Aide; Bsbl; Ftbl; Wt Lftg; High Hon Roll.

BRUNTON, REBECCA; Hopewell SR HS; Aliquippa, PA; (3); 42/249; 4-H; Latin Clb; Chorus; Powder Puff Ftbl; Var L Vllybl; 4-H Awd; Hon Roll; NHS.

BRUSH, LINDA; Crestwood HS; Mountaintop, PA; (4); 1/217; FBLA; Math Clb; Science Clb; Bausch & Lomb Sci Awd; High Hon Roll; Mu Alpha Theta Awd; NHS; NEDT Awd; Luzerne Cnty Sci Tchrs Assoc Awd 87; PA JR Sci & Hmnts Symps 86; Pres Acad Ftns Awd 87; Bloomsburg U; Math.

BRUTOUT, LISA; Beaver Valley Christian Acad; Freedom, PA; (4); 3/14; Church Yth Grp; Chorus; Cheerleading; Sftbl; Trk; Hon Roll; NHS; PA ST U; Adlscnt Psych.

BRUWELHEIDE, LISA; Seneca Valley SR HS; Mars, PA; (3); Art Clb; Church Yth Grp; Ski Clb; Rep Frsh Cls; U Of Pittsburgh; Dntl Hygn.

BRUZDA, MARY; Saltsburg JR SR HS; Saltsburg, PA; (2); 10/97; Color Guard; Mrchg Band; Vllybl; High Hon Roll; Hon Roll; Pres Acdmc Ftnss Awd 86; Nrsng.

BRUZIO, CYNTHIA ELIZABETH; Quaker Valley JR HS; Sewickley, PA; (1); Church Yth Grp; Dance Clb; Y-Teens; School Musical; Gym; JV Socr; Hon Roll; Bus.

BRYAN, BERNADETTE; Upper Moreland SR HS; Willow Grove, PA; (3); 78/275; Art Clb; Boy Scts; Cmnty Wkr; SADD; VICA; School Musical; Stage Crew; Nwsp Stf; Yrbk Stf; Lit Mag; Cmmrcl Art.

BRYAN, FEDDOCK; Crestwood HS; Mountaintop, PA; (4); 68/250; Boy Scts; SADD; Band; Concert Band; Mrchg Band; L Capt Bsktbl; JV Ftbl; Var JV Golf; Im Score Keeper; Im JV Trk; Penn ST; Crmnl Jstc.

BRYAN, KATHY; Great Valley HS; Malvern, PA; (3); 11/267; Church Yth Grp; Spanish Clb; Rep SADD; Varsity Clb; Yrbk Stf; Var Trs Cheerleading; High Hon Roll; NHS; Mst Dedctd Chrldr 85 & 86; Educ.

BRYAN, MICHELLE LYNN; Oil City SR HS; Oil City, PA; (3); 3/230; AFS; French Clb; Hosp Aide; Acpl Chr; Chorus; School Musical; Yrbk Stf; Off Stu Cncl; High Hon Roll; Prfct Atten Awd; Natl Ldrshp & Schlrshp Awd NLSA 86-87; Clarion U Of PA; Nursing.

BRYAN, RACHELE; James M Coughlin HS; Wilkes Barre, PA; (3); 85/362; FBLA; Var Co-Capt Fld Hcky; Sftbl; Hon Roll; PENN ST U; Htl Rsrtnt Mgmt.

BRYAN, TAMMY; Curwensville HS; Grampian, PA; (3); Debate Tm; Drama Clb; French Clb; Band; Chorus; Color Guard; Concert Band; Mrchg Band; Pep Band; Hon Roll; Secy.

BRYANT, DEVON; West Philadelphia HS; Philadelphia, PA; (3); Boy Scts; Church Yth Grp; Church Choir; Ftbl; Var Gym; Swmmng; Var Trk; High Hon Roll; Mit; Elec Engr.

BRYANT, RICHANN; Bethel Park HS; Bethel Pk, PA; (4); VP Church Yth Grp; Exploring; FHA; Intnl Clb; School Musical; Tennis; PA ST.

BRYANT, WILLIAM T; Fairview HS; Fairview, PA; (3); Boy Scts; Church Yth Grp; Computer Clb; Letterman Clb; Varsity Clb; Band; Chorus; Concert Band; Jazz Band; Mrchg Band.

BRYCHIK, MELISSA; Quigley HS; Beaver, PA; (3); Drama Clb; Chorus; Yrbk Stf; Stat Bsbl; JV Capt Cheerleading; Trk; Yrbk Svc Awd 86-87; Comp Appletns Awd 87; Comp Sci.

BRYLA, DAMIAN; Lakeland HS; Olyphant, PA; (3); Boy Scts; Nwsp Stf; Var Ftbl; Var Trk; Im Wt Lftg; Hon Roll; Spcl Olympics Coach 87; Eagle Scout 85; Med Tech.

BRYLA, ERIC; Lakeland JR SR HS; Olphant, PA; (4); 14/147; Chess Clb; Drama Clb; Stage Crew; Stage Crew; Nwsp Ed-Chief; Nwsp Phtg; Var Capt Golf; Im Vllybl; Hon Roll; VP NHS; Edtrs Awd 87; Presdntl Schlrshp 87; U Scranton; Mech Engrng.

BRYNER, DOUGLAS; Southmoreland HS; Connellsville, PA; (3); 7/150; Church Yth Grp; Latin Clb; Var Ftbl; High Hon Roll; Mech Engr.

BRYNER, LAURA; Yough SR HS; W Newton, PA; (3); 25/249; Ski Clb; Spanish Clb; Acpl Chr; VP Chorus; Concert Band; Pres Mrchg Band; Yrbk Phtg; Powder Puff Ftbl; Hon Roll; NHS; Phrmcy.

BRYSON, DAWN; Beaver Valley Christian Acad; Beaver, PA; (3); 3/10; Debate Tm; Exploring; Scholastic Bowl; Band; Chorus; School Musical; Sec Jr Cls; L Var Bsktbl; Pres Schlr; Voice Dem Awd; Law.

BRYSON, PATRICK; Mc Guffey HS; Washington, PA; (4); 39/199; Trs VP French Clb; Pep Clb; Pres Ski Clb; Varsity Clb; L Trk; Edinboro U; Acctng.

BRYTUS, ROBIN; Mon Valley Catholic HS; Finleyville, PA; (3); Computer Clb; Spanish Clb; Nwsp Stf; Hon Roll; NHS; Spanish NHS; Bus Mgmt.

BRZEGOWSKI, DAVID; Carbondale Area JR SR HS; Carbondale, PA; (2); Spanish Clb; Im Bsbl; Im Wt Lftg; Hon Roll; Drug & Alcohol Abuse Essay Awd 86; Bus.

BRZEZINSKI, MELISSA; Oil City Area SR HS; Oil City, PA; (3); 23/218; Color Guard; Stu Cncl; Chrpctr.

BRZYSKI JR, ROBERT; Archbishop Ryan HS; Philadelphia, PA; (2); 120/349; Ftbl; Trk; Hnrs Cnvctn Mdrn Wrld 87; Wrld Affrs Cncl 87; Med.

BUBACZ, ERIC; Donegal HS; Mount Joy, PA; (2); Chess Clb; Church Yth Grp; Band; Concert Band; Jazz Band; Mrchg Band; Pep Band; Hon Roll; Perfrmnc Music.

BUBASH, AMY; Moon SR HS; Coraopolis, PA; (3); 40/306; Var L Sftbl; Band; Prfct Atten Awd; U VT; Ag Econ.

BUBASH, CHRIS; Moon Area SR HS; Coraopolis, PA; (4); Exploring; Spanish Clb; Mrchg Band; Symp Band; High Hon Roll; Hon Roll; Jr NHS; NHS; Prfct Atten Awd; JA; 4 Yr Acdmc Schlrshp 87; Northwestern; Elec Engnrng.

BUBB, MARCEY; Lincoln HS; Ellwood City, PA; (4); 70/170; VP Church Yth Grp; Letterman Clb; Ski Clb; Spanish Clb; Y-Teens; Color Guard; Flag Corp; Mrchg Band; School Musical; Bowling; Pittsburgh Tecn Inst; CADD.

BUBB, MITCH; Susquehannock HS; Glen Rock, PA; (3); 46/194; Church Yth Grp; Computer Clb; Ski Clb; Teachers Aide; Yrbk Stf; Bsktbl; Vllybl; Hon Roll; Accntng.

BUBNIS, JOHN; Cardinal Brennan HS; Ashland, PA; (4); 20/58; Var JV Ftbl; Im Vllybl; Hon Roll; English Awd 86; Med.

BUBONIC, EILEEN; Hopewell SR HS; Aliquippa, PA; (1); Church Yth Grp; French Clb; Latin Clb; Library Aide; Flag Corp; Mrchg Band; High Hon Roll; 1st Pl Frgn Lang Comptn Slippery Rock U 87.

BUCCI, KAREN; Emmaus HS; Wescosville, PA; (4); Drama Clb; Key Clb; Chorus; School Musical; School Play; Lit Mag; High Hon Roll; NHS; Prfct Atten Awd; Pres Schlr; Gen Beary Crtvty Engl Awd, Templ U Prsdnts Schlrshp Awd 87; Temple U.

BUCCI, LORI; Blacklick Valley HS; Belsano, PA; (4); 21/91; Church Yth Grp; 4-H; Girl Scts; Ski Clb; Speech Tm; Varsity Clb; Stu Cncl; Cheerleading; Hon Roll; W Penn Schl Of Nrsg; RN.

BUCCI, MARIANNA; Montour HS; Coraopolis, PA; (3); Church Yth Grp; SADD; Chorus; Off Frsh Cls; Trk; High Hon Roll; Hon Roll; NHS; Prfct Atten Awd; Duquesne U; Sec Tchng.

BUCCI, NICK; Avella Area JR SR HS; Avella, PA; (3); Computer Clb; Math Tm; Pres Band; Pres Jazz Band; Pres Mrchg Band; Pres Symp Band; High Hon Roll; Ntl Merit Ltr; Pres Schlr; Science Clb; 1st Pl Avella 87 Sci Fair Hologram Prod 87; Gifted & Tlntd Engl II 87; Physics.

BUCCITELLI, DIANE E; Freedom Area HS; Conway, PA; (4); 46/163; Art Clb; Camera Clb; DECA; Pep Clb; Spanish Clb; Drill Tm; Pres Frsh Cls; Pres Soph Cls; Pres Jr Cls; Pres Sr Cls; 7th Pl St-Adv-DECA Comptn, Dist Trphy-Adv DECA Comptn 87; CCBC; Crim Just.

BUCHANAN, ALYSSA; Archbishop Ryan Girls; Phila, PA; (3); Cmnty Wkr; French Clb; Intnl Clb; Stage Crew; Coll Of Sci; Sci.

BUCHANAN, ANDREA; Waynesburg Central HS; Waynesburg, PA; (3); 12/210; Pres Sec Church Yth Grp; VP French Clb; Letterman Clb; Var Capt Bsktbl; Var L Trk; Var L Vllybl; High Hon Roll; NHS; Voice Dem Awd; AFS; MVP Trk 87; 17 Teen Brd Mdl 85-87; Doctor.

BUCHANAN, ANDREW W; Downingtown Area HS; Downingtown, PA; (3); Computer Clb; Model UN; Var Trk; High Hon Roll; NHS; Ntl Merit Schol; Aero Engrng.

BUCHANAN, DEANNA; Susquehannock HS; Glen Rock, PA; (3); 75/194; Teachers Aide; Chorus; Prfct Atten Awd; Bus.

BUCHANAN JR, JAMES; Lawrence County Area Vo Tech; Edinburg, PA; (3); Church Yth Grp; French Clb; Math Tm; VICA; Wt Lftg; Hon Roll; Hnr Awd Outstndng Achvt Acdmc Voc Educ 87; Penn ST; Engrng.

BUCHANAN, JENNIFER; Purchase Line HS; Commodore, PA; (2); 7/158; Intnl Clb; Church Choir; Drm Mjr(t); Pep Band; Nwsp Rptr; 4-H Awd; High Hon Roll; NEDT Awd; 4-H; Band; Acad All Amer 87; Cnty, Dist, Reg Bnds 87; IN U Of PA; Music Ed.

BUCHANAN, KATHLEEN M; Gwynedd Mercy Acad; Hatboro, PA; (4); 6/102; Church Yth Grp; Cmnty Wkr; Hosp Aide; Service Clb; SADD; Nwsp Stf; High Hon Roll; Hon Roll; Sec NHS; James J Kerrigan Mem Scholar 87; La Salle U; Bio.

BUCHANAN, RENAE; Sharon HS; Sharon, PA; (3); Hosp Aide; Sftbl; Allegheny CC; Retail Mgmt.

BUCHEIT, JENNIFER; Coudersport JR SR HS; Coudersport, PA; (3); Church Yth Grp; Band; Chorus; Concert Band; Mrchg Band; Nwsp Stf; Yrbk Stf; Bsktbl; Vllybl; Hon Roll.

BUCHER, ANDY; Council Rock HS; Richboro, PA; (3); Teachers Aide; Off Frsh Cls; Off Soph Cls; Bsktbl; Wrstlng; Hon Roll; Prfct Atten Awd; Law.

BUCHER, JENNIFER; St Cyril Acad; Milton, PA; (4); Hosp Aide; Sec Sr Cls; Hst Stu Cncl; JV Var Cheerleading; Hon Roll; Pres Boy Scts; Teachers Aide; Varsity Clb; Chorus.

BUCHER, KATHRYN; Elk County Christian HS; St Marys, PA; (2); Am Leg Aux Girls St; Chorus; Church Choir; Bowling; Score Keeper; Trk; CC Awd; High Hon Roll; Hon Roll; NHS; Phys Thrpst.

BUCHER, STEFANIE; Annville Cleona HS; Cleona, PA; (4); 23/112; Aud/Vis; SADD; Varsity Clb; Chorus; Bsktbl; Fld Hcky; Score Keeper; Trk; Kiwanis Awd; NHS; Dstngshd Am HS Studs Soc 86-87; Rtry Clbgirl 87-88; E Stroudsburg U.

BUCHHEIM, CHRISTINE; Nazareth Acad; Philadelphia, PA; (3); Church Yth Grp; NFL; Spanish Clb; Chorus; Church Choir; School Musical; Swing Chorus; Var Cheerleading; JV Sftbl; Im Vllybl; Diocesan Schlr Fnlst 87; Ed.

BUCHINSKI, DENNIS; Western Wayne HS; Waymart, PA; (3); JV Bsbl; Var JV Ftbl; Im Wt Lftg; Hon Roll; Penn St; Engrng.

BUCHINSKI, PAMELA; Our Lady Of Lourdes HS; Kulpmont, PA; (3); 10/89; Pep Clb; Radio Clb; Spanish Clb; Yrbk Stf; JV Capt Cheerleading.

BUCHINSKY, LISA; Saltsburg JR SR HS; Nw Alexandria, PA; (2); 25/89; Band; Concert Band; Mrchg Band; School Musical; Vllybl; Hon Roll; Flght Attndnt.

BUCHLER, ROBERT H; Neshaminy HS; Trevose, PA; (4); 14/730; Var Socr; High Hon Roll; James P Smith Memrl Schlrshp 87; Stdnt Mnth 87; Drexel U; Chem Engrng.

BUCHMAN, ANDREW; Westmont Hilltop HS; Johnstown, PA; (4); 5/158; Art Clb; Pres Temple Yth Grp; School Play; Stage Crew; Drama Clb; U PA; Bio-Chem.

BUCHTA, CHRISTINE; Sun Valley HS; Brookhaven, PA; (4); 16/310; Church Yth Grp; Red Cross Aide; SADD; Concert Band; Mrchg Band; School Musical; Symp Band; Variety Show; NHS; Drama Clb; Drexel U; Engrng.

BUCHTER, APRIL; St Huberts High School For Girls; Philadelphia, PA; (3); GAA; Hon Roll; Penn ST U.

BUCHTER, CINDY; Ephrata SR HS; Ephrata, PA; (4); 79/254; JV Var Sftbl; Hon Roll; Sftbl Vrsty Ltr 86-87; Dist III PIAA Sftbl Mdl Awd; Millersville; Acctng.

BUCHTER, COLLEEN; Cocalico HS; Stevens, PA; (3); 8/168; GAA; Teachers Aide; Bsktbl; Var L Fld Hcky; High Hon Roll; Hon Roll; NHS; Ldrshp Awd 86-87; Bloomsburg U; Nurse.

BUCK, ANGELA; Clearfield Area HS; Woodlands, PA; (4); Trs FBLA; Key Clb; Office Aide; Spanish Clb; Mat Maids; High Hon Roll; Hon Roll; NHS; Bookkeeping Awd 87; Bus.

BUCK, CRAIG; Conneaut Lake HS; Conneault Lake, PA; (3); Letterman Clb; Math Clb; Science Clb; Spanish Clb; SADD; Stu Cncl; L Bsbl; L Bsktbl; L Crs Cntry; Im Vllybl; Prm Attendt, Chrmn; Engrng.

BUCK, EILEEN S; Friends Select Schl; Philadelphia, PA; (4); Church Yth Grp; Drama Clb; Model UN; PAVAS; Band; Chorus; Church Choir; Orch; Yrbk Stf; Hon Roll; Natl Fndtn Advncmnt Arts, & Hon Mntn Arts Recog & Tlnt Srch 86; San Francisco Cnsrvtry Music 84-85; Curtis Inst Music; Piano.

BUCK, GENEVRA; Lower Dauphin HS; Elizabethtown, PA; (3); Hosp Aide; Hon Roll; Ed.

BUCK, JANELLE; Cocalico SR HS; Adamstown, PA; (1); Chrmn Church Yth Grp; Pep Clb; JV Cheerleading; Hon Roll; Phys Ther.

BUCK, JENIFER; Danville SR HS; Danville, PA; (3); 8/187; Church Yth Grp; Latin Clb; Rep Frsh Cls; JV Bsktbl; JV Sftbl; God Cntry Awd; High Hon Roll; NHS; Prfct Atten Awd; Natl Latin Honor Scty 87; Accntng.

BUCK, LA CHELLE; Harrisburg HS; Harrisburg, PA; (3); 2/165; Political Wkr; Chorus; Hon Roll; Comp Sci.

BUCK, MICHAEL; Danville SR HS; Danville, PA; (1); High Hon Roll; JV Bsbl; JV Ftbl; Amer Legn Aux Awd; Phy Ed Awd; Pres Acdmc Fit Awd.

BUCK, SANDY; Purchase Line HS; Mahaffey, PA; (2); Band; Mrchg Band; Trk.

BUCK, SHERRY; Curwensville Area HS; Curwensville, PA; (4); Hst FBLA; Hon Roll; Acdmc All Amer 84-87; Du Bois Bus Coll Half Tuition Schlrshps 86-87; Du Bois Bus Coll; Accntng.

BUCK, TERRI; Central Bucks H S West; New Britain, PA; (4); 2/473; Church Yth Grp; FCA; Hosp Aide; Acpl Chr; Rep Stu Cncl; Var Capt Fld Hcky; High Hon Roll; VP NHS; Ntl Merit SF; Sal; UNC Chapel Hill; Phys Thrpy.

BUCKALEW, NEILLY ANN; North Allegheny SR HS; Wexford, PA; (4); Art Clb; Church Yth Grp; Exploring; French Clb; Science Clb; Ski Clb; Rep Frsh Cls; Rep Soph Cls; Rep Jr Cls; Diving; Maer Scholar Dartmouth 87; Dstngshd Achvr NASH 87; Pre-Coll Art Cls Carnegie Mellon 87; Dartmouth; Phys Ther.

BUCKEL, JEFFREY A; Northgate JR SR HS; Pittsburgh, PA; (4); 53/141; Church Yth Grp; SADD; Var L Bsbl; Var-L Ftbl; Var Wt Lftg; Hon Roll; Pres Phys Ftnss Awd 86-87; Phys Educ Dept Awd 87; US Marine Corps; Law Enfrcmnt.

BUCKEL, ROBERT; Cathedral Prep; Erie, PA; (3); 8/193; Im Bsktbl.

BUCKHOLT, DAN; Langley HS; Pittsburgh, PA; (4); 20/265; JA; Office Aide; Var L Ftbl; High Hon Roll; Jr NHS; WV Wesleyan Coll Schlrshp 87; Waynesburg Coll Hnr Schlrshp 87; WV Wesleyan Coll Hnrs Schlrshp 87; WV Wesleyan Coll; Bus Admin.

BUCKLAND, ANDREW; Beaver JR SR HS; Beaver, PA; (3); Chess Clb; JCL; Latin Clb; Stage Crew; Yrbk Stf; Socr; Dir, Edtr Video Yrbk 87-88; Filmmkng.

BUCKLEN, MATTHEW; Spring Grove Area SR HS; Spring Grove, PA; (3); Boys Clb Am; Boy Scts; Band; Boy Scts; Mrchg Band; Orch; School Musical; School Play; Am Lgn Acadc Awd 84; Lehigh U; Bus,Elec Engr.

BUCKLEY, DOYLE ADAM; Red Lion SR HS; Felton, PA; (3); 75/378; Computer Clb; English Clb; JA; Mgr Ftbl; Tennis; High Hon Roll; Hon Roll; John Hopkins Tlnt Srch 83; Aerosp Sci.

BUCKLEY, JAMES; Middletown Area HS; Middletown, PA; (3); 6/195; Band; Chorus; Drm Mjr(t); Jazz Band; Mrchg Band; Pep Band; School Musical; School Play; Swing Chorus; Hon Roll; Ostndng Bnd Mbr Awd 84; Bio-Chem.

BUCKLEY, LORI; Danville HS; Danville, PA; (1); Ski Clb; JV Cheerleading; JV Gym; High Hon Roll; Bus.

BUCKLEY, MARY ANN; Blue Mountain Acad; Fort Salonga, NY; (3); Computer Clb; Church Choir; Concert Band; Am Leg Boys St; Im Crs Cntry; Im Vllybl; Hon Roll; Physics.

BUCKLEY, PAMELA; Moniteau HS; West Sunbury, PA; (3); 1/136; Drama Clb; Trs Spanish Clb; SADD; Capt Drill Tm; School Play; Lit Mag; High Hon Roll; NHS; Slippery Rock U Frgn Lang Cmptn 86; Slippery Rock U Spnsh Vcblry Vrbs 87; Carnegie Mellon U; Chem Engr.

BUCKMAN, DARLENE; Pennridge HS; Perkasie, PA; (4); 14/396; Pres AFS; Pres 4-H; Var Vllybl; Dnfth Awd; 4-H Awd; High Hon Roll; JC Awd; Sec NHS; Pres Schlr; Outstndng Chem Stu & Peer Counselor 87; U Of Pittsburgh; Chem Engrng.

BUCKNER, ADRIENNE; Wilkinsburg JR/Sr HS; Pittsburgh, PA; (4); Trs Spanish Clb; Mrchg Band; Yrbk Stf; Cheerleading; Hon Roll; Jr NHS; Natl Achvt Schlrshp For Outstndng Negro Stu 87; Rcvd Schlrshp Howard U 87; Howard U; Accntng.

BUCKWALTER, JOHN D; Manheim Central HS; Lititz, PA; (3); 20/245; Am Leg Boys St; Trs Church Yth Grp; Drama Clb; 4-H; School Musical; Yrbk Stf; Var JV Bsktbl; Hon Roll; NHS; Vlntr Awds-Smmr Vlntr Wrk 85 & 86; Penn ST U; Elctrcl Engr.

BUCKWALTER, KIMBERLY; William Allen HS; Allentown, PA; (2); Band; Concert Band; Mrchg Band; Pep Band; Hon Roll.

BUCKWALTER, PATRICK; Living Word Acad; Lancaster, PA; (3); Church Yth Grp; Pep Clb; Socr; Trk; Hon Roll.

BUCKWALTER JR, TERRY E; Wilmington Area HS; New Wilmington, PA; (3); 1/115; Drama Clb; Latin Clb; Office Aide; School Play; Stage Crew; High Hon Roll; Hon Roll; Gd Ctznshp Awd 85; Acdmc Achvmnt Awds 84-86; Allegheny Coll; Bio.

BUCYNSKI, KIRK; Huntingdon Area HS; Huntingdon, PA; (4); 10/234; Church Yth Grp; Var L Bsbl; Var L Bsktbl; High Hon Roll; NHS; Schlrshp Engrng Pitt; Army Rsrve Schlr Athlte Awd; Outstndng Phys Sci Stu Awd; U Of Pittsburgh; Engrng.

BUCZYNSKI, DEANNA M; Freedom Area SR HS; Freedom, PA; (2); French Clb; Trs German Clb; SADD; Band; Yrbk Ed-Chief; L Cheerleading; Var L Vllybl; Stat Wrstlng; High Hon Roll; 3rd Pl Frnch Oral Cmprhnsn Lang Cmptn 87; Achvt Awd Bio 87; Achvt Awd Scl Studies & Sci 86; Intrprtr.

BUDACKI, STEPHANIE; New Brighton Area HS; New Brighton, PA; (4); 14/141; Chorus; Concert Band; Mrchg Band; Yrbk Stf; Sec Soph Cls; Pres Jr Cls; Trs Sr Cls; Rep Stu Cncl; High Hon Roll; Hon Roll; Pres Acdmc Fit Awds Prg 87; Stu Of Wk Awd 83; Westminster Hon Band 84; Indiana U Of PA; Elem Ed.

BUDAY, GRETCHEN; Villa Maria HS; Poland, OH; (4); Chorus; School Musical; Stu Cncl; NHS; Spanish NHS; Schlrshpyngstwn ST U Dana Schl Music 87-91; Yngstwn ST Philhrmnc Piano Comptn 84-87; Natl Glds Msc87; Youngstown ST U; Piano Perf.

BUDAY, KIMBERLY; Highlands SR HS; Natrona Hgts, PA; (3); Art Clb; Camera Clb; Church Yth Grp; FNA; Off JA; Library Aide; Office Aide; Band; Chorus; School Musical; Pres Acadmc Achvt Awd 84-85; Schlstc Achvt Gld Cert 85; Schlstc Achvt Brown Cert Awd 85-87; Air Force; Aeronautics.

BUDD, ERIC; Bangor SR HS; Mt Bethel, PA; (2); Camera Clb; Computer Clb; JV Tennis; High Hon Roll; Hon Roll; Jr NHS; Outstndng Bio Stu 87; 3rd Pl Sci Fair 86.

BUDGE, DEBRA; St Hubert Catholic HS; Philadelphia, PA; (3); 189/421; Cmnty Wkr; FNA; Hosp Aide; Office Aide; Pep Clb; Red Cross Aide; Speech Tm; Chorus; Variety Show; Cheerleading; Hnr Rl 85; Pre Med.

BUDGE, KELLIE; St Basil Acad; Philadelphia, PA; (4); 1/97; Drama Clb; English Clb; German Clb; Latin Clb; Math Clb; Scholastic Bowl; Orch; High Hon Roll; Natl Eng Mrt Awd 85-86; Lang Awd .atin 86; Boston Coll; Educ.

BUDWAY, MATTHEW; Keystone Oaks HS; Pittsburgh, PA; (3); 1/252; Political Wkr; Radio Clb; Nwsp Rptr; Stu Cncl; Tennis; Gov Hon Prg Awd; NHS; Rotary Awd; Voice Dem Awd; Art Clb; Prsdntl Clssrm Schlrshp-Wshngtn DC 87; U For Yng Amrcns Schlrshp-Chthm Coll 86; Archlgy Appr Schlrshp; Brown U; Ophthlmlgy.

BUDZBANOWSKI, LISA; Meadville Area SR HS; Meadville, PA; (4); 72/306; Church Yth Grp; Dance Clb; JV Var Bsktbl; JV Vllybl; Hon Roll; U Of Pittsburgh; Phrmcy.

BUDZINSKI, AMY; Lakeland JR SR HS; Olyphant, PA; (3); Church Yth Grp; FHA; Girl Scts; Band; Concert Band; Mrchg Band; School Musical; Nwsp Stf; High Hon Roll; Hon Roll; Chem.

BUEHLER, CHRISTINE M; Cedar Crest HS; Lebanon, PA; (4); French Clb; Pep Clb; SADD; Pres Frsh Cls; Pres Soph Cls; Pres Jr Cls; Pres Sr Cls; Cheerleading; Trk; Hon Roll; Shpnsbrg U; Law.

BUEHNER, PATRICIA; Little Flower HS; Philadelphia, PA; (3); 52/322; Church Yth Grp; Nwsp Stf; Rep Jr Cls; Pres Sr Cls; Var Bsktbl; JV Fld Hcky; JV Capt Sftbl; High Hon Roll; Prfct Atten Awd; Vrsty Bsktbl Lttr; JV Pins Sftbl & Fld Hcky; Awd Stenogrphr Cont; Typng Awd; Temple U; Law Enfrcmnt.

BUEHRLE, DAVID C; Delone Catholic HS; Hanover, PA; (3); Boy Scts; Cmnty Wkr; Computer Clb; Service Clb; God Cntry Awd; Hon Roll; Drama Clb; Exploring; German Clb; JA; Drew; Physcs.

BUELA, CASSANDRA; Bishop Mc Devitt HS; Elizabethtown, PA; (3); 34/214; Band; Concert Band; Drill Tm; Mrchg Band; Yrbk Stf; High Hon Roll; Hon Roll; Bus Admin.

BUERKLE, LAURA L; John A Brashear HS; Pittsburgh, PA; (4); 8/373; Drama Clb; Hosp Aide; JA; Math Clb; Pep Clb; Ski Clb; Varsity Clb; Color Guard; School Play; Nwsp Stf; Gannon U; Physcn Asst.

BUFALINI, CAROL; Ambridge HS; Ambridge, PA; (4); Church Yth Grp; German Clb; Girl Scts; Pep Clb; SADD; Band; Rep Jr Cls; Rep Sr Cls; JV Bsktbl; Var Trk; Vllybl Team PIAA Champ; IN U.

BUFALINI, DIANE; Hopewell HS; Aliquippa, PA; (4); 90/246; Church Yth Grp; Sec FBLA; Spanish Clb; Band; Chorus; Yrbk Phtg; Stu Cncl; Cheerleading; Powder Puff Ftbl; Trk; Future Secretaries Of Amer Schlrshp 87; Robert Morris Coll; Admin Mgmnt.

BUFALINI, DIANNE; Ambridge Area HS; Ambridge, PA; (4); 112/365; German Clb; Pep Clb; Spanish Clb; Band; Concert Band; Mrchg Band; Off Jr Cls; Off Sr Cls; Stu Cncl; Hon Roll; Edinboro U Of PA; Spcl Ed.

BUFALINI, REBECCA; Ambridge Area HS; Ambridge, PA; (3); Pep Clb; Spanish Clb; Lib Band; Concert Band; Mrchg Band; Frsh Cls; Soph Cls; Jr Cls; JV L Vllybl; Hon Roll; USUBA JR Olympcs 87; Nrsng.

BUFANO, KELLY; Reading HS; Reading, PA; (3); 33/800; Pres German Clb; Chorus; Vllybl; Hon Roll; NHS; Reading Hosp Schl Nrsng; Nrs.

BUFFALO, SHAWN; Saltsburg JR SR HS; Clarksburg, PA; (1); Church Yth Grp; Off Frsh Cls; Bsktbl; Trk; High Hon Roll; Engr.

BUFFALOE, BRIDGET; Bishop Conwell HS; Fairless Hills, PA; (3); 13/300; Art Clb; PAVAS; Nwsp Rptr; Nwsp Stf; Yrbk Stf; Var Capt Cheerleading; Var L Trk; Hon Roll; NHS; Outstndng Achvt Art 85-86; Scholar Moore Coll Art 86-87; 2nd Pl Phila Elect Co Enrgy Cons Poster Cont; Apprl Dsgn.

BUFFINGTON, FRANK; Center HS; Monaca, PA; (2); German Clb; Letterman Clb; Varsity Clb; Chorus; Swing Chorus; Bsbl; Bsktbl; Coach Actv; Ftbl; Wt Lftg; Mst Imprvd Stu In Grmn 86-87; Hnrbl Mntn For Kicking In Ftbl 86; Schlr Athlte In Bsbl 87; Engrng.

BUFFINGTON, PATRICIA; Upper Dauphin Areea HS; Elizabethville, PA; (3); 8/115; VP Church Yth Grp; GAA; Varsity Clb; Chorus; Mrchg Band; Rptr Stu Cncl; Var Bsktbl; Var Sftbl; NHS; Hgh Math Awd 84-85; Math.

BUFFINGTON, TRAVIS; Waynesboro Area SR HS; Waynesboro, PA; (4); Chess Clb; VP JCL; School Play; Trs Jr Cls; Crs Cntry; Trk; Capt Wrstlng; Mst Schl Sprt 87; Mst Outstndng Wrstlr 87; West Chester U.

BUFFLAP, JENNIFER; Spring Grove SR HS; Seven Valleys, PA; (3); 26/308; Church Yth Grp; Chorus; Concert Band; Jazz Band; Mrchg Band; Orch; JV Tennis; Hon Roll; NHS; 300 Pt Pin.

BUGAJSKI, CHERI L; East Allegeny HS; East Mckeesport, PA; (4); 3/217; Pres German Clb; Girl Scts; Sec Soph Cls; Pres Stu Cncl; Capt Bsktbl; Capt Cheerleading; High Hon Roll; Pres NHS; Opt Clb Awd; Prfct Atten Awd; Mdl Hnr Schlrshp 87; Washngtn-Jefferson; Biomed Engr.

BUGASH, ANDREA; Red Lion Area SR HS; Red Lion, PA; (4); 30/372; VP Church Yth Grp; Mrchg Band; Symp Band; Nwsp Rptr; High Hon Roll; Hon Roll; NHS; Mdrn Music Mstrs Hnr Soc 86-87; Dist Rgnl & All-ST Bnds; All-Amer Yth Hnr Mscns; Elizabethtown Coll.

BUGAY, ROBERT; Purchase Line HS; Commodore, PA; (1); FFA; SADD; Hon Roll; Dew Castl Schl Trades; Electrnc.

BUGDA, JAMES; Hazleton HS; Hazleton, PA; (4); 22/388; French Clb; VP Sr Cls; L Crs Cntry; L Trk; Elks Awd; French Hon Soc; NHS; Teenager Of Month 86; Pres Acdmc Fit Awd 87; Awd For Outstndg Serv Schl & Cmmnty; U Of Scranton; Ecnmcs.

BUGDEN, JANE; Ridgway Area HS; Ridgway, PA; (4); 1/105; Ski Clb; Nwsp Stf; Yrbk Stf; Sec Stu Cncl; Capt Cheerleading; L Tennis; High Hon Roll; NHS; Allegheny Coll; Math.

BUGGY, SEAN; Cardinal O Hara HS; Drexel Hill, PA; (3); 167/715; Church Yth Grp; Nwsp Stf; Yrbk Stf; Im Bsktbl; Var Bowling; Cert Top 10 Pct Cls 86; 2nd Hnrs 86.

BUGLIA, MELISSA; Newport HS; Newport, PA; (3); 50/115; Church Yth Grp; Pres VP FBLA; FTA; Spanish Clb; Cheerleading; Fld Hcky; Hon Roll; Most Outsndng JR Bus Stu Awd 86-87; Hansburg CC; Elem Schl Tchng.

BUGULISKIS, LINDA; Nazareth Acad; S Hampton, PA; (3); 13/125; Church Yth Grp; French Clb; Band; Jazz Band; Orch; School Musical; School Play; Hon Roll; La Salle U; Psych.

BUI, YUNG; Springdale HS; Springdale, PA; (3); Rep Acpl Chr; Chorus; Cheerleading; JV Sftbl; Capt Vllybl; Outstndng Clsrm Perfrmnce Spanish,Gym 85-87; Hnr Roll 85-86; Pitt; Dental Hygenist.

BUIGE, JACQUELYN; Blacklick Valley HS; Nanty-Glo, PA; (3); 15/100; NFL; Ski Clb; Speech Tm; Varsity Clb; VP Stu Cncl; Capt Var Cheerleading; Trk; Hon Roll; NHS; Pres Schlr; Dist VI Duo Intrpttn Champ 86.

BUKA, STEPHANIE; Richland HS; Wexford, PA; (3); Chorus; High Hon Roll; Hon Roll; 1st Pl Solo Danc Awd-Tlnt Show 86; Prfrmd W/Pittsburgh Ballet Theatr 80-87; Gymstcs Rbbns 75-80; Danc.

BUKATA, KRISTEN; Villa Maria Acad; Blue Bell, PA; (3); 53/98; Church Yth Grp; Cmnty Wkr; Girl Scts; Hosp Aide; Library Aide; Rep Frsh Cls; Rep Jr Cls; Rep Sr Cls; Rep Stu Cncl; Var Sftbl; MVP Awd Sftbl 85; Phys Ther.

BUKOVINSKY, LISA MARIE; Kennedy Christian HS; Farrell, PA; (2); 18/96; Hosp Aide; Latin Clb; Library Aide; Hon Roll; U Pittsburgh Temple U; Dentist.

BUKOWKSI, KRISTEN; Mt Penn HS; Reading, PA; (3); 6/78; Aud/Vis; Computer Clb; Science Clb; Stage Crew; Var Bsktbl; Var Sftbl; Jr NHS; All Div I Sftbl Tm 87; Mech Engr.

BUKOWSKI, JOHN F; Bethel Park SR HS; Bethel Park, PA; (4); 9/519; Pres Math Clb; Capt Math Tm; Pres Science Clb; Jazz Band; Orch; Variety Show; Stu Cncl; NHS; Ntl Merit SF; Rotary Awd; Amer Hs Math Exam Bronze Medal 86; Math.

BULA, JACQUELYN; Villa Maria Acad; Erie, PA; (4); Ski Clb; Spanish Clb; Hon Roll; John Carrol U; Acctng.

BULAS, BOB; Bishop Mc Cort HS; Johnstown, PA; (3); 76/179; Computer Clb; French Clb; JA; Letterman Clb; Ski Clb; SADD; Chorus; Nwsp Rptr; Nwsp Stf; Pres Frsh Cls; Acctng.

BULER, DAVID; Spring-Ford HS; Royersford, PA; (2); 39/289; Library Aide; Hon Roll; Sectn Wrtr Of Yr 85-86; Minister.

BULL, ERIN; York Catholic HS; New Freedom, PA; (3); 2/165; Hosp Aide; Concert Band; Mrchg Band; School Musical; School Play; Nwsp Bus Mgr; Yrbk Phtg; High Hon Roll; NHS; Opt Clb Awd; Exch Stu To Germany 87; York Yth Symphny 85; 100 Hr Svc Pin-York Hosp 87; Biochem.

BULL, FRIN; York Catholic HS; New Freedom, PA; (3); 2/160; Hosp Aide; Concert Band; Mrchg Band; School Musical; School Play; Nwsp Bus Mgr; Nwsp Phtg; Yrbk Phtg; NCTE Awd; NHS; Yth Debates On Energy Hnrble Mntn Cert 85; Awd Holding Ninety Pct Avg Or Better For 3 Yrs 87; Biology.

BULLA, THEODORE; Perry Traditional Acad; Pittsburgh, PA; (4); 1/120; High Hon Roll; NHS; Val; Michael A Wolak Awd Outstndng SR, Awd For Outstndng Achvt Math 87; U Of Pittsburgh; Elec Engrng.

BULLER, CHRISTINE R; Conestoga Valley HS; Lancaster, PA; (4); Dance Clb; Library Aide; Office Aide; Teachers Aide; Variety Show; Hon Roll; Stu Of Mon 87; Outstndng Bus Stu Awd 87; AMS Stu Of Mon 87; Millersville U; Bus Admin.

BULLER, MIKE; Donegal HS; Mt Joy, PA; (3); JV Var Bsktbl; JV Bsktbl Capt 86-87.

BULLIED, ELANA; Frazier HS; Perryopolis, PA; (3); 90/180; Cmnty Wkr; FHA; FNA; Spanish Clb; SADD; Teachers Aide; Hon Roll; Upward Bnd Prog 84-88; Outstndng Catechist Awd 85; Best Geo Stu Awd-CA U Of PA 87; U Of Pittsburgh; Hlth Prfssn.

BULLOCK, EDWARD; Northern HS; Wellsville, PA; (3); Band; Concert Band; Mrchg Band; Var Trk; High Hon Roll; NEDT Awd; Cert Of Hnr In Sci 85; Cert Of Merit In Algbr II 87; Dstngshd Hnr Ltr 86-87; Arspc Engr.

BULLOCK, JOSEPH; Tunkhanneck Area HS; Tunkhannock, PA; (4); 40/267; Letterman Clb; Spanish Clb; Varsity Clb; JV Bsbl; Var JV Ftbl; Wt Lftg; Mansfield U Of PA; Crmnl Just.

BULLOCK, NICOLE ALEXANDRA; Gwynedd-Mercy Acad; Norristown, PA; (2); Dance Clb; Drama Clb; Chorus; School Musical; Nwsp Rptr; Yrbk Stf; Rep Soph Cls; Rep Jr Cls; Rep Stu Cncl; Lcrss; Awds Excllnc Bio, Hnrs Eng, Lat II 86-87; Awds Excllnc Wrld Hstry, Eng, Lat I 85-86.

BUMBARGER, SHERRI; Westbranch JR SR HS; Morrisdale, PA; (3); 8/120; Drama Clb; Office Aide; Science Clb; SADD; Chorus; Socr; Hon Roll; NHS.

BUMBARGER, VIRGINIA; Curwensville Area HS; Curwensville, PA; (3); Drama Clb; French Clb; VICA; Chorus; High Hon Roll; NHS; Acad All Amercn 86-87; NSMA 85-86; Bus.

BUMBULSKY, APRIL; Hazleton HS; Mcadoo, PA; (2); Office Aide; Pep Clb; Cheerleading; Gym; USCA Natl Champs 86; NCA Natl Champs 87; Acdmc Hnrs 86-87; Mgmt.

BUMEDER, LYNNANN; Lansdale Catholic HS; Sellersville, PA; (3); 31/232; Chorus; Church Choir; Hon Roll; Prsdntl Acad Fitness Awd 86-87; Chld Care.

BUMGARDNER, DOUGLAS; New Castle HS; New Castle, PA; (3); 8/403; Boy Scts; Ski Clb; SADD; Varsity Clb; Jazz Band; Yrbk Stf; Var Crs Cntry; High Hon Roll; Hon Roll; NHS; News Carrier Of Yr 86; Engrng.

BUNCHALK, LORI; Hazleton HS; Hazleton, PA; (3); FBLA; Office Aide; Thesps; Band; Mrchg Band; Yrbk Stf; Sec Stu Cncl; PA ST; Accntng.

BUNDRIGE, DARRYL; Gateway SR HS; Monroeville, PA; (3); NFL; PAVAS; Pres Chorus; SADD; Off Frsh Cls; Pres Soph Cls; Pres Jr Cls; VP Sr Cls; Stu Cncl; Hon Roll; HOBY Fndtn Awd 86; Rotary Yth Ldrshp 87; TV Brdcstr.

BUNDY, CAROLYN A; Chambersburg Area SR HS; Chambersburg, PA; (3); 137/697; Art Clb; Chorus; Church Choir; Concert Band; Mrchg Band; Rep Stu Cncl; Var L Tennis; Hon Roll; Finlst Mid-Penn Tns Tournmnt 86; Choiristers 86; Hist Club 86; U NC; Hist.

BUNEVICIUS, SUSAN; Scranton Central HS; Scranton, PA; (2); Am Leg Aux Girls St; Church Yth Grp; French Clb; NFL; Pep Clb; Speech Tm; Thesps; Cheerleading; Twrlr; Hon Roll; CFLS 1st Pl Oratorical Decl 86-87; PA ST; Hotel Mgmt.

BUNGARD, TERRY; Mt Pleasant SR HS; Mt Pleasant, PA; (2); VICA; Stage Crew; Ftbl; Wt Lftg; Hon Roll; Law Enfrcmnt.

BUNGE, JENNIFER L; Shippensburg SR HS; Shippensburg, PA; (3); 6/258; Am Leg Aux Girls St; Cmnty Wkr; Band; School Musical; High Hon Roll; NHS; Church Yth Grp; Girl Scts; Spanish Clb; Girl Scout Slvr Awd 87; Schlstc Wrtng Cert Of Mrt 86; Cumberland Cnty Orch 87; Mary Washington; Hstrc Prsrvtn.

BUNGE, KELLY; Southern Columbia Area HS; Catawissa, PA; (3); 19/107; Computer Clb; Key Clb; Fld Hcky; Sftbl; Hon Roll; NHS; IN U Of PA; Spch Thrpy.

BUNK, ERIC; Windber Area HS; Windber, PA; (3); French Clb; High Hon Roll; Hon Roll; NHS; PA Free Enterprise Wk 87; IN U Of PA.

BUNK, GREG; West Hazleton HS; W Hazelton, PA; (3); 7/220; Church Yth Grp; French Clb; Var Crs Cntry; Var Tennis; Var Trk; High Hon Roll; Penn ST U; Mtrlgy.

BUNN, ALICIA; Pine Forge Acad; Scotch Plains, NJ; (3); Church Choir; Trs Soph Cls; Swmmng; Vllybl; Cit Awd; High Hon Roll; Hon Roll; Prfct Atten Awd; Rutgers U.

BUNN, FRANK; Bishop Mc Devitt HS; Harrisburg, PA; (4); 25/190; Drama Clb; Band; Chorus; Concert Band; Mrchg Band; School Musical; School Play; Hon Roll; NHS; Boy Scts; Psych.

BUNN, KAREN; Greater Johnstown HS; Johnstown, PA; (4); 25/297; Ski Clb; Spanish Clb; SADD; Color Guard; Variety Show; Off Jr Cls; Stu Cncl; L Trk; Hon Roll; NHS; Wmns Clb Schlrshp 87; Almn Schlrshp 87; Pssvnt Schlrshp 87; Thiel Coll; Nrsng.

BUNSO, SAMANTHA; Jim Thorpe Area HS; Jim Thorpe, PA; (2); Band; Trs Soph Cls; Stu Cncl; Var Cheerleading; High Hon Roll; Hon Roll; NHS; HOBY 87; Acad All Amer 86 & 87; US Chrldr Achvt Awd 86; Med.

BUNTING, JOHN F; Upper Darby SR HS; Drexel Hill, PA; (3); Cmnty Wkr; Var JV Trk; Hon Roll; Penn ST U; Bus Mgmt.

BUONANNO, ANTHONY J; Great Valley HS; Malvern, PA; (3); Pres FBLA; Science Clb; Capt Var Ftbl; Var L Trk; Dnfth Awd; High Hon Roll; NHS; Outstndng Thrower Trk 87; Am Legion Schl Awd 87; FBLA Comp-9th Reg, 7th ST, 10th 1st Reg 13th ST; PA U; Accntng.

BUONO, BOB; Bishop Shanahan HS; W Chester, PA; (3); Drexel U; Bus Mgmt.

BUPP, DAVID; Bermudian Springs HS; Gardners, PA; (3); Yrbk Stf; Hon Roll; Stdnt Yr 84-85; Hghst Avg Hstry, Spnsh, Bio, Geom, Engl 85-86; Air Force; Elctrncs.

BUPP, JENNIFER; Tyrone Area HS; Tyrone, PA; (3); Band; Yrbk Stf; Var JV Sftbl; U S Air Frc.

BUR, LAUREN; Abiongton SR HS; Abington, PA; (3); 31/502; Dance Clb; Hosp Aide; Latin Clb; Office Aide; SADD; Band; Chorus; Concert Band; Orch; School Musical; Clncl Chsl Psych.

BURAKS, KEVIN; Upper Dublin HS; Maple Glen, PA; (4); 53/320; Debate Tm; SADD; Varsity Clb; Yrbk Stf; Rep Stu Cncl; Var Capt Socr; Hon Roll; NHS; Pres Schlr; Im Bsktbl; 1st Tm Al-Subrbn Sccr Tm 86; Haverford Coll; Pre-Med.

BURANOVSKY, LYNNE; Sto-Rox SR HS; Mc Kees Rocks, PA; (2); Church Yth Grp; Chorus; Yrbk Stf; Hon Roll; Art.

BURATTY, MATT; Berlin Brothersvalley HS; Berlin, PA; (2); JV Ftbl; Cit Awd; Hon Roll; Spnsh Cltrl Awd 85.

BURAU, KEVIN; Big Beaver Falls Area HS; Beaver Falls, PA; (3); 34/170; JV Bsbl; Var Score Keeper; Hon Roll; Prfct Atten Awd.

BURBA, CHRISTINE; Purchase Line JR SR HS; Arcadia, PA; (4); Spanish Clb; SADD; Chorus; Church Choir; Concert Band; Mrchg Band; JV Sftbl; High Hon Roll; Hon Roll; NHS; IN U; Engl Ed.

BURBA, WILLIAM; Purchase Line HS; Glen Campbell, PA; (2); FFA; Hon Roll; FFACA Av Schlrshp Awd 87; Tchr.

BURCH, DAWN E; Plumstead Christian HS; Perkasie, PA; (3); Art Clb; Hosp Aide; Pep Clb; JV Cheerleading; Stat Socr; JV Sftbl; Hon Roll; Prfct Atten Awd; Art Merit Prjct 87; Psych.

BURCH, HAROLD; Washington HS; Washington, PA; (2); French Clb; Letterman Clb; Yrbk Stf; Pres Frsh Cls; VP Soph Cls; Var L Crs Cntry; Capt Var Trk; Wt Lftg; Hon Roll; Washinton Guardian Angels Co-Pres 87; Pepperdine U; Cardlgst.

BURCH, KARL; Newport HS; Newport, PA; (1); Art Clb; Boy Scts; Computer Clb; German Clb; SADD; Off Frsh Cls; Im Bsbl; Im Bsktbl; Hon Roll; Capital Area Sci Fair 2nd Pl 87; PA ST U; Arch.

BURCH, LISA; Blacklick Valley HS; Nanty Glo, PA; (4); Art Clb; Camera Clb; Church Yth Grp; Debate Tm; Drama Clb; NFL; Ski Clb; Speech Tm; Varsity Clb; Chorus; Dstngshd Ldr 86-87; Conemaugh Vly Memorial; Nrsng.

BURCHALK, LORI; Hazleton HS; Hazleton, PA; (3); Drama Clb; FBLA; Office Aide; Band; Mrchg Band; Yrbk Rptr; Cheerleading; Acctng.

BURCHARDT, CHRISTINE; North Pecono HS; Moscow, PA; (3); Aud/Vis; Cmnty Wkr; French Clb; Letterman Clb; Service Clb; Ski Clb; Tennis; Trk; High Hon Roll; NHS; U Of Scranton; Pre Med.

BURCHERI, STEVEN JOSEPH; Lakeland JR/Sr HS; Clarks Summit, PA; (3); 10/136; Sec Church Yth Grp; JA; SADD; Concert Band; Mrchg Band; School Musical; Variety Show; Rep JV Stu Cncl; High Hon Roll; NHS; Law.

BURCHETT, ANGELA; Hanover SR HS; Hanover, PA; (3); Bus Admin.

BURCHETT, CATHY; Red Lion SR HS; Airville, PA; (3); 36/342; Latin Clb; Hon Roll.

BURCHETT, NICA; Trinity HS; Washington, PA; (4); VP Church Yth Grp; Girl Scts; Key Clb; Library Aide; Pep Clb; Flag Corp; Mrchg Band; GS Gold Awd 87; WV U; Psychology.

BURCKHARDT, DOLORES; Saint Hubert HS; Philadelphia, PA; (3); Camera Clb; Dance Clb; Drama Clb; FNA; Girl Scts; Spanish Clb; School Musical; School Play; Capt Bowling; JV Cheerleading; Mdcl Technlgst.

BURD, CLIFFORD; Pius X HS; Bangor, PA; (3); Pep Clb; Varsity Clb; Stage Crew; Trs Sr Cls; Trs Stu Cncl; Var Bsbl; JV Var Bsktbl; MVP Varsity Basebll 86 & 87; Bus Economics.

BURDEN, TERENCE A; West York Area SR HS; York, PA; (2); Church Yth Grp; Varsity Clb; Church Choir; Bsktbl; Ftbl; Trk; High Hon Roll; Hon Roll; Prfct Atten Awd; Natl Piano Plyng Audtns 86-87; Reg Fnlst AAU/USA JR Olympcs Trck 86; HS Acdmc Awds 86-87; Med.

BURDETT, LAURIE; Pittston Area HS; Pittston, PA; (4); 17/365; VP Aud/Vis; Sec Chorus; Sec Concert Band; Sec Mrchg Band; Nwsp Rptr; Hon Roll; NHS; Mansfield; Music Educ.

BURDETTE, TRICIA; Dallas SR HS; Trucksville, PA; (3); 25/212; Ski Clb; Mrchg Band; School Play; Rep Soph Cls; Rep Stu Cncl; JV Cheerleading; Hon Roll; PA ST; Engrng.

BURDGE, DAVID; Norristown Area HS; Norristown, PA; (3); 24/491; Key Clb; Stu Cncl; JV Bsbl; Var Tennis; High Hon Roll; Hon Roll; U Stanford; Bus Adm.

BURDICK, BRENDA; Northern Potter HS; Genesee, PA; (3); 9/68; Ski Clb; Nwsp Rptr; Yrbk Stf; Hon Roll; Trvl Agnt.

BURDICK, JAIME; Moravian Acad; Monroeville, PA; (4); Key Clb; Chorus; School Musical; VP Sr Cls; Rep Stu Cncl; JV Bsktbl; Capt Var Lcrss; Cit Awd; High Hon Roll; Hon Roll; Cum Laude Soc 85-87; Holk Awd Englsh 87; William Poster Awd Englsh 86; Bucknell U.

BUREK, KIM; Springdale HS; Cheswick, PA; (3); Church Yth Grp; German Clb; Bsktbl; Sftbl; High Hon Roll; Hon Roll; NHS; Hgh Hnr Awd 86-87; Elem Tchr.

BURES, JEFFREY; Freeport Area HS; Sarver, PA; (2); Band; Concert Band; Jazz Band; Mrchg Band; Pep Band; Stage Crew; Symp Band; Yrbk Stf; Hon Roll.

BURGAN, TAMMY; Greater Johnstown HS; Johnstown, PA; (4); 47/293; Pres Church Yth Grp; JA; Pep Clb; Spanish Clb; SADD; Y-Teens; Capt L Bsktbl; Var L Sftbl; Hon Roll; Pres Ftnss Awd 85-86; Alld Artsts Jr Art Show-2nd Pl 85; Air Force; Electrncs.

BURGARD, BRENT; Solonco HS; Quarryville, PA; (2); Church Yth Grp; Capt Band; Chorus; Concert Band; Jazz Band; Capt Mrchg Band; JV Bsbl; JV Socr; JV Trk; Cnty Band 87; Outstndng In Band 87; Engrng.

BURGARD, KARA; Woodland Hills HS; East Pittsburgh, PA; (2); Art Clb; Church Yth Grp; German Clb; Letterman Clb; Ski Clb; Trs Frsh Cls; Trs Soph Cls; Trs Jr Cls; Hst Stu Cncl; Var Crs Cntry; MVP Cross Cntry 85-86; Rookie Yr Swmmng 85; Phy Thrpy.

BURGARD, KRISTIN; Churchill HS; E Pittsburgh, PA; (4); 1/200; Ski Clb; Pres Jr Cls; Pres Sr Cls; Trs Stu Cncl; Capt Crs Cntry; Swmmng; Capt Trk; High Hon Roll; Kiwanis Awd; Rotary Awd; St Fnls Crss Cntry; Schlr Athltc; Carnegie Mellon; Bio.

BURGBACHER, DAVID; Westmont Hilltop HS; Johnstown, PA; (4); 5/160; Boy Scts; Church Yth Grp; Ski Clb; JV Var Ftbl; Var L Trk; High Hon Roll; NHS; Exchng Clb Stu Mnth March, Top Ten Grad Cls 87; Carnegie-Mellon U; Biomed Engr.

BURGE, CHARLES; Chambersburg Area SR HS; Chambersburg, PA; (3); 148/697; Church Yth Grp; Trk; Hon Roll; Spanish Awd 86-87.

BURGE, JODI; Carmichaels Area HS; Carmichaels, PA; (3); 10/180; Library Aide; Ski Clb; Varsity Clb; Stu Cncl; Cheerleading; DAR Awd; High Hon Roll; NHS; Pres Schlr; Miss Rain Day 84; Albert Gallatin Regatta Qn 87; U Of Pittsburgh; Comm.

BURGER, BOB; Hampton HS; Allison Park, PA; (3); Spanish Clb; Var L Socr; Var Trk; High Hon Roll; NHS.

BURGER, CAROL; West Hazleton HS; Sugarloaf, PA; (4); 21/224; French Clb; Off Ski Clb; SADD; Varsity Clb; Nwsp Stf; Yrbk Stf; Stu Cncl; Im Mgr Bsktbl; JV Var Cheerleading; Hon Roll; Natl Frnch Cntst 1st Pl 84; Penn ST U; Microbio.

BURGER, LORI; Upper Dauphin Area HS; Lykens, PA; (3); 3/120; German Clb; Varsity Clb; Band; Chorus; Concert Band; Jazz Band; Mrchg Band; JV Sftbl; L Trk; Hon Roll; Ger Awd 86 & 87; Spts Med.

BURGER, MARGGIE; West Middlesex HS; W Middlesex, PA; (4); Church Yth Grp; Office Aide; Spanish Clb; Band; Chorus; Church Choir; Mrchg Band; Stu Cncl; WV U; Phys Thrpy.

BURGER, MATTHEW F; Fox Chapel Area HS; Pittsburgh, PA; (4); 29/322; Key Clb; Ski Clb; Chorus; Madrigals; Nwsp Stf; Stu Cncl; Bsktbl; Socr; Tennis; High Hon Roll; Ldrshp Awd 85; Madrigal Chrs Gold Mdlst 86; Lat Awd 86; Engl Awd 85; Politcs.

BURGER, MICHELE; Cambridge HS; Cambridge Spg, PA; (3); #3 In Class; Church Yth Grp; Exploring; Spanish Clb; SADD; JV Bsktbl; Var Sftbl; High Hon Roll; JETS Awd; Psych.

BURGER, RICHARD; Belle Vernon Area HS; Belle Vernon, PA; (3); Golf; Im Vllybl; High Hon Roll; NHS; Pitt U; Med.

BURGESON, KIRK; St Marys Area HS; St Marys, PA; (2); Boy Scts; Ftbl; Trk; Wt Lftg; Penn ST; Bus.

BURGESS, BETSY; Souderton Area HS; Harleysville, PA; (4); 15/365; Hosp Aide; Concert Band; Mrchg Band; Yrbk Stf; Ntl Merit SF; DAR Awd; High Hon Roll; NHS; Pres Schlr; Rotary Awd; Juniata Coll; Physical Therapy.

BURGESS, CHRISTOPHER J; Bethel Park SR HS; Bethel Pk, PA; (4); Pres Church Yth Grp; German Clb; Band; Concert Band; Mrchg Band; Wrstlng; U Of Pittsburgh; Intl Bus.

BURGESS, DEANNA; Shikellamy HS; Sunbury, PA; (4); Church Yth Grp; French Clb; SADD; Yrbk Stf; Cedar Crest Coll; Bus Admin.

BURGESS, FLOYD; Central Christian HS; Hyde, PA; (4); Sec Trs Church Yth Grp; VP FBLA; Radio Clb; Nwsp Stf; FBLA 1st Pl Job Intrvw 85-86; FBLA 2nd Pl Mr FBLA 86-87; Du Bois Bus Coll.

BURGESS, JASON L; Navity Bvm HS; Pottsville, PA; (1); 6/94; Latin Clb; Rep Frsh Cls; Bsktbl; Crs Cntry; Vllybl; High Hon Roll; Doctor.

BURGESS, JENNY; Elk Lake HS; Meshoppen, PA; (2); Church Yth Grp; 4-H; Library Aide; SADD; Band; Mrchg Band; Stage Crew; Rep Stu Cncl; JV Bsktbl; Hon Roll; Doctor.

BURGET, KELLI; Avon Grove HS; Landenberg, PA; (3); 1/215; Church Yth Grp; Service Clb; SADD; Scholastic Bowl; Mrchg Band; Nwsp Stf; JV Vllybl; Trs NHS; Dist & Rgnl Band 87; Aerosp Engrng.

BURGHARDT III, KARL F; Palisades HS; Coopersburg, PA; (4); 3/159; AFS; Scholastic Bowl; High Hon Roll; Hon Roll; Jr NHS; NHS; Ntl Merit Ltr; Prfct Atten Awd; Pres Schlr; Spnsh Awd & Russel Stever Data Prcssng Awd 87; Lehigh U; Comp Engrng.

BURGOS, MARIO; Friends Select Schl; Cherry Hill, NJ; (4); Temple Yth Grp; School Musical; School Play; Stage Crew; Nwsp Stf; Yrbk Stf; JV Socr; Ntl Merit SF; 2nd Dan Black Belt Karate 85; Karateinstrctr 87; Lawyer.

BURGOS, RAFAEL; Tech Memorial HS; Erie, PA; (3); 30/320; Spanish Clb; Im Bsbl; Im Ftbl; Var Wrstlng; FL; US Marshall.

BURGOYNE, AMY; Gwynedd Mercy Acad; Warrington, PA; (2); Church Yth Grp; Cmnty Wkr; Drama Clb; Hosp Aide; SADD; Chorus; School Musical; JV Fld Hcky; JV Lcrss; Var High Hon Roll; Schlrshp PA Free Entrprs Wk 87; Acadc Awd Lat, Eng, Wrls Hstry 86; Acadc Awd Frnch 86-87; Physcl Thrpy.

BURGUM, STACY; Hempfield HS; Lancaster, PA; (4); 1/418; Camera Clb; Church Yth Grp; Debate Tm; Exploring; Quiz Bowl; Service Clb; Nwsp Stf; Im Mgr(s); Im Powder Puff Ftbl; Im Vllybl; Armstrng Wrld Indstrs Schlrshp, Hempfld Ed Assn Awd, Jamesway Valdctrn Awd, W E Druckenbrod Memrl 87; Coll William & Mary; Intl Bus.

BURKE, ANNE E; Bishop Mcdevitt HS; Glenside, PA; (4); 2/356; Church Yth Grp; Debate Tm; Capt Drill Tm; Stage Crew; Nwsp Ed-Chief; High Hon Roll; NCTE Awd; VP NHS; Ntl Merit SF; Intnl Clb; Sci Fair Awd; Amrcn HS Math Exam Awd; Acad Profcncy Awds Math, Englsh, Latin, Sic, Hstry; Chemstry.

BURKE, BRIAN; Keystone Oaks HS; Pittsburgh, PA; (3); Am Leg Boys St; PAVAS; Political Wkr; Scholastic Bowl; Chorus; High Hon Roll; NHS; Rotary Awd; Val; Boy Scts.

BURKE, DENNIS; Abington Heights HS; Clarks Summit, PA; (3); 84/292; Church Yth Grp; Hon Roll; Rifle Tm Vrsty Ltr 86-87; Envrnmntl Stdy.

BURKE, ERIN; Wyoming Area HS; West Pittston, PA; (3); French Clb; Var Trk; Var Im Vllybl; U Of Pittsburgh; Spch Pthlgy.

BURKE, HEIDI; Garnetvalley HS; Boothwyn, PA; (2); Key Clb; Spanish Clb; Varsity Clb; Rep Jr Cls; Rep Stu Cncl; Var L Bsktbl; Var L Sftbl; Hon Roll; Spn Acad Awd 86-87; Peer Cnslng 87; Bus.

BURKE, LEONARD; Dunmore HS; Dunmore, PA; (3); 14/150; Drama Clb; Letterman Clb; Pres Frsh Cls; Pres Soph Cls; Pres Pres Sr Cls; Var Capt Ftbl; Trk; High Hon Roll; NHS; JV Bsbl; U Of Scranton.

BURKE, LISA; Westmont Hilltop HS; Johnstown, PA; (2); Church Yth Grp; French Clb; Key Clb; Math Clb; Pep Clb; Band; Concert Band; Jazz Band; Mrchg Band; Yrbk Stf.

BURKE, LORI; Mc Caskey HS; Lancaster, PA; (4); Teachers Aide; Variety Show; Var Cheerleading; Var Powder Puff Ftbl; JV Trk; Hon Roll; Empire Beauty Schl; Own Bus.

BURKE, MARK; Tussey Mountain HS; Saxton, PA; (4); 16/116; Drama Clb; SADD; Band; Chorus; Church Choir; Concert Band; Drill Tm; Jazz Band; Mrchg Band; Pep Band; All St Band 86 & 87; Pres Acad Ftnss Awd 87; Mansfield U; Music Educ.

BURKE, MELISSA; Oxford Area HS; Nottingham, PA; (2); 22/162; Church Yth Grp; JV Trk; Twrlr; Hon Roll; RN.

BURKE, MICHELE; Marian Catholic HS; Mahanoy City, PA; (4); Church Yth Grp; SADD; Band; Chorus; Church Choir; Concert Band; Jazz Band; Mrchg Band; Pep Band; School Play; Pottsville Hosp Schl; RN.

BURKE, PATRICIA; North Schuylkill JR SR HS; Ringtown, PA; (3); 18/210; Yrbk Stf; Rep Jr Cls; Rep Stu Cncl; Var JV Cheerleading; Hon Roll; Pre Law.

BURKE, RICHARD; St Marys Area HS; Weedville, PA; (4); Penn ST U.

BURKE, SEAN; Lewistown HS; Lewistown, PA; (2); Church Yth Grp; French Clb; Score Keeper; High Hon Roll; NHS; NHS 87; Juniata Coll; Sci.

BURKE, SHANNON; Upper St Clair HS; Pittsburgh, PA; (3); 80/420; Sec Art Clb; NFL; Speech Tm; High Hon Roll; NHS; Bst Novce Intrprtn 85; 4th Pl Stndrs Oratry 85; Art Hnr Awd 86; Trinty Coll Music 1st & 2nd Hnrs 87; Elem Ed.

BURKE, SHEILA; Lakeland HS; Clarks Summit, PA; (4); VP FHA; Pep Clb; Yrbk Stf; Cheerleading; Hon Roll; VP Fut Hmmkrs Amer 86-87; Hmcmng Prncs; Penn ST U; Admin Of Justc.

BURKE, SHEILA; Vincentian HS; Pittsburgh, PA; (2); Church Yth Grp; Service Clb; Sec Frsh Cls; VP Soph Cls; JV Capt Bsktbl; L Fld Hcky; Golf; Sftbl; Hon Roll; Pres Schlr.

BURKE, TRACIE; Northeast Prep HS; Philadelphia, PA; (3); Camp Fr Inc; Church Yth Grp; Mrchg Band; School Play; Crs Cntry; Mdcl Fld.

BURKE, WENDY; Eastern York HS; Hellam, PA; (3); 69/177; SADD; Varsity Clb; Yrbk Stf; Im Bowling; Var Capt Cheerleading; Hon Roll; Prsdntl Fitness Awd 86-87; Arch.

BURKE, WENDY; Ephrata SR HS; Ephrata, PA; (4); 42/243; Art Clb; Church Yth Grp; German Clb; Trs Girl Scts; Intnl Clb; Pep Clb; JV Cheerleading; JV Fld Hcky; JV Var Powder Puff Ftbl; Hon Roll; Honor Grad 87; Hammon Mem Schlrshp 87; Outstndg Swmmng Instr 84; Kutztown U; Art Ed.

BURKELL, STEPHANIE; Academy HS; Erie, PA; (3); 23/230; Capt Dance Clb; Church Yth Grp; Capt Drill Tm; Mrchg Band; Variety Show; Vllybl; Hon Roll.

BURKEPILE, ANGEL; Big Spring HS; Carlisle, PA; (2); Pres Church Yth Grp; Sec 4-H; Band; Concert Band; Jazz Band; Mrchg Band; Yrbk Stf; 4-H Awd; Hon Roll; NHS; Amer Msc Fndtn Outstndng Mscn 87; Intrntl Frgn Lnge Awd-Frnch 87; Assc Amer Des Prfsrs Frnch Hnrs 87; PA ST U; Frgn Lngues.

BURKERT, DEBBIE; Butler SR HS; Renfrew, PA; (3); Church Yth Grp; VP JA; Chorus; Church Choir; Orch; School Musical; Swing Chorus; Hon Roll; Elem Educ.

BURKET, HOPE; Tyrone Area HS; Tyrone, PA; (2); Sec VP 4-H; FBLA; Ski Clb; SADD; Varsity Clb; Stage Crew; Off Stu Cncl; Var Bsktbl; JV Bsktbl; Var Crs Cntry; Outstndng Math Stu 87; CPA.

BURKETT, FLEUR; Punxsutawney Area HS; Punxsutawney, PA; (2); Church Yth Grp; FBLA; Spanish Clb; Yrbk Stf; Hon Roll; Med.

BURKETT, RICHARD J; Kiski Area HS; Apollo, PA; (4); 3/351; Pres Math Tm; Spanish Clb; Elks Awd; High Hon Roll; NHS; Ntl Merit Ltr; Pres Schlr; Gannett Nwspr Carrier Schlrshp 87; Vlntr Coach Elem Ftbl & Scr 85-86 & 86-87; Tp Scr Strongland Mth Lg; Yale U; Engrng.

BURKETT, ROCHELLE; Punxsutawney Area SR HS; Punxsutawney, PA; (3); FBLA; Math Tm; Spanish Clb; Yrbk Stf; High Hon Roll; NHS; Minister.

BURKETT, SCOTT; Greensburg-Salem SR HS; Greensburg, PA; (4); Aud/Vis; Church Yth Grp; French Clb; Wrstlng; High Hon Roll; Hon Roll; Jr NHS; Pharm.

BURKETT, SUSAN; Portage Area HS; Portage, PA; (4); 7/118; Church Yth Grp; Varsity Clb; Trs Band; Chorus; Concert Band; Jazz Band; Mrchg Band; Var Bsktbl; Hon Roll; NHS; Pitt U; Pharm.

BURKETT, SUSAN; Yough HS; W Newton, PA; (3); Church Yth Grp; VP Cmnty Wkr; Debate Tm; Drama Clb; French Clb; Library Aide; Band; Chorus; Church Choir; Yrbk Stf; Natl Engl Merit Awd 87; Poltcl Sci.

BURKETT JR, VAUGHN; Middletown Area HS; Middletown, PA; (3); 15/193; Var L Ftbl; Var L Trk; Im Wt Lftg; High Hon Roll; Hon Roll; Biochem.

BURKEY, ADAM; Amethacton HS; Lansdale, PA; (3); 6/381; Computer Clb; Math Tm; Scholastic Bowl; Science Clb; Lit Mag; Var Crs Cntry; High Hon Roll; NHS; Boy Scts; Debate Tm; Pre Med.

BURKEY, JESSICA; Yough SR HS; Ruffsdale, PA; (3); Cmnty Wkr; Sec Computer Clb; Office Aide; Nwsp Ed-Chief; Nwsp Rptr; Rep Sr Cls; Powder Puff Ftbl; Tennis; NHS; Drama Clb; Various Jrnlsm Achvt Awds 86-88; Seton Hill Coll; Cmmnctns.

BURKEY, KIRSTEN; Bishop Carroll HS; Loretto, PA; (3); 4/128; Drama Clb; NFL; Ski Clb; SADD; School Play; Stage Crew; High Hon Roll; Hon Roll; NHS.

BURKEY, REBECCA; Governor Mifflin SR HS; Mohnton, PA; (3); Q&S; Chorus; Nwsp Sprt Ed; Yrbk Stf; Trs Jr Cls; Cheerleading; Fld Hcky; Trk; Hon Roll; Rep Frsh Cls; Unified Achvt Awd 85-86.

BURKHARDT, DEBBIE; North Clarion JR/Sr HS; Lucinda, PA; (4); Spanish Clb; Chorus; Nwsp Rptr; Nwsp Stf; Yrbk Stf; Sec Bsktbl; Score Keeper; Hon Roll; Prfct Atten Awd.

BURKHARDT, DIANE; Northwestern HS; Fogelsville, PA; (4); 1/160; Debate Tm; Chorus; School Musical; School Play; Stage Crew; Nwsp Rptr; Nwsp Stf; Cit Awd; High Hon Roll; NHS; Hnrs Lng Mth Frnch Eng Physics Blgy Dbt Nwspr NEDT; Messiah Coll; Math Ed.

BURKHARDT, IRENE; United HS; Vintondale, PA; (4); 23/158; Ski Clb; Stat Bsktbl; Var Sftbl; Var Vllybl; Hon Roll; NHS; V Lttr Vllybl & Sftbl 86 & 87; Hnr Roll 84-87; U Of Pittsburgh; Elem Educ.

BURKHARDT, KIM M; Bethlehem Catholic HS; Bethlehem, PA; (3); 9/202; Key Clb; Ski Clb; SADD; Chorus; Pres Frsh Cls; Var Capt Bsktbl; L Mgr(s); High Hon Roll; NHS; Church Yth Grp; PA JR Acad Sci ST Mt 1st Pl 85; Beth Anne Mather Mem Schlrshp 86; Pre-Med.

BURKHARDT, MARCI; Cranberry HS; Franklin, PA; (2); Church Yth Grp; FBLA; Pep Clb; Political Wkr; Spanish Clb; Stat Wrstlng; FBLA Rgnls Bus Math 3rd Pl 86-87; Bus Admin.

BURKHART, ANNETTE; Cambria Heights HS; Carrolltown, PA; (3); Chorus; Concert Band; Mrchg Band; Stage Crew; Yrbk Stf; Capt Timer; Var Trk; JV Vllybl; FHA; Yrbk Staff Cert 86-87; Stage Crew Cert 86-87; Elem Ed.

BURKHART, JILL; Corry Area HS; Corry, PA; (2); Church Yth Grp; Off Soph Cls; Stu Cncl; JV Bsktbl; JV Capt Cheerleading; Tchng.

BURKHART, VALARIE; Hickory HS; Hermitage, PA; (3); 23/180; Drama Clb; Chorus; Madrigals; School Musical; School Play; Yrbk Bus Mgr; Yrbk Ed-Chief; Yrbk Phtg; NHS; Clarion U PA; Elem Ed.

BURKHODER, KELLY; Lockhaven SR HS; Lock Haven, PA; (3); Art Clb; FBLA; FHA; Hosp Aide; Spanish Clb; SADD; Yrbk Phtg; Yrbk Stf; Hon Roll; 1st Rnnr Up Flaming Floliege Fest 87.

BURKHOLDER, AMY; Connellsville Area SR HS; Connellsville, PA; (2); 113/500; Church Yth Grp; Office Aide; Pep Clb; Band; Concert Band; Mrchg Band; Orch; Pep Band; School Musical; School Play; Bus Admin.

BURKHOLDER, DON; Ringgold HS; Finleyville, PA; (3); Boy Scts; Church Yth Grp; Office Aide; Quiz Bowl; Teachers Aide; JV Bsbl; Var Bsktbl; JV Ftbl; Trk; Wt Lftg; Sci Math Hnr Soc 86-87; U Of Pittsburgh; Law Enfrcmnt.

BURKHOLDER, ERIC S; Chambersburg Area SR HS; Chambersburg, PA; (3); 69/695; Am Leg Boys St; Boy Scts; German Clb; Chorus; Orch; JV Ftbl; L Swmmng; Var Tennis; Var Trk; Eagle Scout Awd 87; US Naval Acad; Engr.

BURKHOLDER, KELLY; Montgomery Area HS; Muncy, PA; (4); 14/62; VP Church Yth Grp; Sec Band; Ed Yrbk Phtg; Trs Sr Cls; Pres VP Stu Cncl; DAR Awd; Lion Awd; 4-H; French Clb; Amer Lgn Awd 87; Outstndng Citiz Awd 87; Bloomsburg U; Spch Thrpy.

BURKHOLTZ, WENDY; Northern Lebanon HS; Fredericksburg, PA; (3); 1/212; Pres VP Church Yth Grp; Band; Church Choir; Concert Band; Mrchg Band; School Play; Rep Stu Cncl; High Hon Roll; NHS; Elem Schl Tchr.

BURKLEY, RICHARD CRAIG; Penns Manor HS; Penn Run, PA; (3); Boy Scts; Church Yth Grp; Pres Varsity Clb; Band; Concert Band; Jazz Band; Mrchg Band; Pep Band; JV Bsktbl; JV Var Ftbl; Eagle Scout Awd 86; 1 Bronze Palm 86; Oceanography.

BURKMAN, JAMES M; Swissvale HS; Pittsburgh, PA; (3); 1/185; Am Leg Boys St; Q&S; Pres Soph Cls; Pres Jr Cls; Pres Stu Cncl; Stat Ftbl; Var Golf; DAR Awd; High Hon Roll; NHS; Harvard Prize Book 87; Rensselaer Awd 87; PA JR Acad Of Sci 85-87.

BURKS, CARMEN; New Brighton Area HS; New Brighton, PA; (4); 36/141; Art Clb; Drama Clb; Nwsp Stf; Yrbk Stf; Trk; High Hon Roll; IFLA 87; Howard U; Intl Bus.

BURLEIGH, JILLANE H; New Covenant Acad; Mansfield, PA; (1); 1/7; Church Yth Grp; Library Aide; Ski Clb; Band; Chorus; JV Bsktbl; JV Socr; JV Swmmng; JV Trk; Math Talnt Srch 86; PA ST U; Med Resrch.

BURLEY, ALICIA; Franklin HS; Franklin, PA; (4); 72/200; French Clb; Spanish Clb; Hon Roll; Prfct Atten Awd; Ruth Hill Schlrshp 87; Pell Grant & PHEEA Grant 87; Courtesy Clb & B & B Plyer 87; Mt Vernon Coll; Intr Dsgn.

BURLEY, CHRISTIAN; Penns Manor HS; Barnesboro, PA; (4); 12/100; Varsity Clb; Band; Concert Band; Pep Band; Ftbl; Hon Roll; NHS; Appalachn Conf Band Ftbl 87; Penn ST Altoona; Assoc Sci.

BURLING, ERIC; Marple Newtown SR HS; Newtown Square, PA; (3); Church Yth Grp; German Clb; Ski Clb; SADD; Varsity Clb; JV Bsbl; Var Bsktbl; Im Ice Hcky; Var Socr; Hon Roll; PA Keystone Games Team Soccer 87; Cnty Select Team Soccer 87; Engr.

BURLINGAME, KRISTA; S R U HS; Gillett, PA; (2); 2/61; Drama Clb; School Play; Cit Awd; Hon Roll; NHS; Prfct Atten Awd; Elem Ed.

BURMEISTER, DAVE; Glendale JR SR HS; Coalport, PA; (3); 9/86; Science Clb; Varsity Clb; Pres Frsh Cls; Pres Soph Cls; Pres Jr Cls; Rep Stu Cncl; L Var Bsbl; Capt L Bsktbl; Im Mgr Coach Actv; L Ftbl; Moshannon Valley Bsktbl All Star 85-86; Phy Thrpy.

BURMEISTER, MICHELLE; Susquehanna Community HS; Thompson, PA; (2); Sec SADD; Color Guard; Mrchg Band; Variety Show; Nwsp Stf; Lit Mag; Var Cheerleading; JV Vllybl; Deaf Instrctr.

BURN, JONATHAN; Gettysburg SR HS; York, PA; (2); Church Yth Grp; Drama Clb; Model UN; Office Aide; Trs Yrbk Stf; Rep Soph Cls; Off Stu Cncl; Im Lcrss; JV Socr; High Hon Roll.

BURNARD JR, WARREN W; Northern Lehigh HS; Walnutport, PA; (1); 3/185; Math Tm; SADD; Concert Band; Jazz Band; Mrchg Band; Im Bsbl; JV Trk; Im Vllybl; High Hon Roll; Prfct Atten Awd; Prsdntl Acdmc Fitness Awd 87.

BURNELL, MARCUS; Bald Eagle Nittany HS; Mill Hall, PA; (3); Var Ftbl; Coll Boca Raton; Aviatn Mngmnt.

BURNETT, DAVE; Baldwin HS; Pittsburgh, PA; (3); 130/490; Art Clb; Math Clb; Varsity Clb; Rep Frsh Cls; Rep Soph Cls; Var L Socr; Var L Trk; Engrng.

BURNETT, LACHELLE; Coatesville Area SR HS; Coastesville, PA; (4); 141/500; Band; Chorus; Concert Band; Mrchg Band; Rep Frsh Cls; Rep Soph Cls; Rep Jr Cls; Rep Sr Cls; Rep Stu Cncl; JV Var Cheerleading; Mlrsvl U Brd Of Gvnrs Schlrshp 87; E E Blevins Mem Awd 87; Mlrsvil U; Bud Adm.

BURNETT, STEVE; Central Catholic HS; Pittsburgh, PA; (3); 96/320; Church Yth Grp; NAACP; Service Clb; Band; Chorus; Concert Band; Jazz Band; Mrchg Band; Orch; Var L Bsktbl; Comm.

BURNETTE, DONNIE; Kennedy Christian HS; Hermitage, PA; (2); 40/96; Boy Scts; Ski Clb; Spanish Clb; Trk; Natl Educ Dev Test Awd 86.

BURNHAM, WILLIAM; Central Catholic HS; Pittsburgh, PA; (2); Drama Clb; Pep Clb; Political Wkr; Ski Clb; Chorus; School Musical; School Play; Stage Crew; Nwsp Stf; Im Fld Hcky.

BURNLEY, JEFFREY L; Upper Moreland HS; Hatboro, PA; (4); 83/254; Boy Scts; Church Yth Grp; Band; Church Choir; Concert Band; Drm Mjr(t); Jazz Band; Mrchg Band; School Musical; Symp Band; Cavalcade Bands Schlrshp 87; Band Dir Awd 87; Yth Ldrshp Am Awd 85; West Chester U; Bus.

BURNS, ELLEN E; North Allegheny HS; Pittsburgh, PA; (4); 14/660; Red Cross Aide; Lit Mag; Socr; Sftbl; High Hon Roll; Jr NHS; NHS; Ntl Merit Ltr; Prfct Atten Awd; Schlrshp Awd 87; Spnsh, Bio Orgnc Chem Hnr Awd 86-87; Coll Of William & Mary; Bio.

BURNS, JAMES; Lakeland JR-SR HS; Carbondale, PA; (4); Art Clb; French Clb; Library Aide; SADD; Stage Crew; Hon Roll; Pres Acad Ftns Awd 87; Pres Schlrshp 87-88; U OH Scrntn; Bus Mngmnt.

BURNS, KAREN; Neshannock HS; New Castle, PA; (3); 5/120; Concert Band; Jazz Band; Mrchg Band; School Musical; School Play; Nwsp Stf; Hon Roll; NHS; Pres Schlr; Math Clb; Flute Ensemble 87; French Comp 87; Yth Against Cancer 87.

BURNS, KATHY A; Central HS; Scranton, PA; (4); 2/306; French Clb; Hosp Aide; JA; Yrbk Ed-Chief; French Hon Soc; Gov Hon Prg Awd; High Hon Roll; Jr NHS; Ntl Merit SF; St Schlr; 1st Pl Ltrary Comp Rgnl PTA Spnsrd 85; 4th Pl Art Comp Rgnl Schls 84; Gvrnrs Schl Schlrshp 86; Pre-Med.

BURNS, KEVIN; Meadville Area SR HS; Meadville, PA; (2); 25/300; JV Golf; JV Ice Hcky; High Hon Roll; Hon Roll; Spanish NHS; Penn ST; Comp.

BURNS, LEAH; Northern HS; Dillsburg, PA; (4); 38/200; Church Yth Grp; Cmnty Wkr; Chorus; Concert Band; Mrchg Band; School Musical; Yrbk Phtg; Yrbk Stf; Fld Hcky; Hon Roll; Union U Act Awd 87; Union U; Radio Cmmnctns.

BURNS, LISA; Mc Keesport Area HS; Mc Keesport, PA; (2); AFS; German Clb; NFL; Co-Capt Drm & Bgl; Rep Stu Cncl; Var Trk; Var JV Vllybl; High Hon Roll; Hon Roll; Prfct Atten Awd; Outstndng Stu Bio I 87; Natl Acdmc Games Qualifier 85-86; Frgn Affrs.

BURNS, MARK A; Council Rock HS; Newtown, PA; (3); 99/908; Boy Scts; Hon Roll; NHS.

BURNS, MARLENE; Bensalem HS; Bensalem, PA; (3); Key Clb; SADD; Nwsp Stf; Fld Hcky; CC Awd; High Hon Roll; Hon Roll; NHS; Bob Jones U; Bus Mgmnt.

BURNS, MARY ANN; Hazleton HS; Hazleton, PA; (3); 9/465; Leo Clb; Pep Clb; Red Cross Aide; Ski Clb; Spanish Clb; Pres Acad Ftns Awd 85; Pharm.

BURNS, ROBERT; Cambridge Springs HS; Conneautville, PA; (4); 2/104; Pres VP Church Yth Grp; Spanish Clb; Church Choir; Stu Cncl; Hon Roll; Ntl Merit Ltr; Pres Schlr; Sal; Deans Schlrshp Messiah Coll 87-88; Hi Q Tm 86; Hnrs Engl 12 Clss 86-87; Messiah Coll; Rado.

BURNS, SARAH; North Allegheny HS; Pittsburgh, PA; (3); Pres AFS; Cmnty Wkr; Drama Clb; Exploring; JA; Thesps; VP Y-Teens; School Play; Nwsp Rptr; VP Jr Cls; Bus Cmpstn Awd 85; Hnrb Mntn Sci Fair 84.

BURNS, SARAH; Pequea Valley HS; Kinzers, PA; (3); Church Yth Grp; Acpl Chr; VP Band; Chorus; Church Choir; Concert Band; School Musical; Hon Roll; NHS; Mrchg Band; Cnty, Dist & Rgnl Chrs 86 & 87; Hnr Cmpr, Cmp Tpwngo 86; Scl Wrk.

BURNS, SEAN; West Snyder HS; Beavertown, PA; (3); 3/95; Am Leg Boys St; Chess Clb; Varsity Clb; Band; Concert Band; Jazz Band; Mrchg Band; School Musical; Rep Jr Cls; Rep Sr Cls; PA Kystn Boys ST 87; Ntl Yth Ldrshp Wk In Wshngtn DC 86; MVP Glf Team 86; PA ST; Nclr Engrng.

BURNS, SUSAN; Penn Trafford HS; Irwin, PA; (4); Hosp Aide; JCL; Latin Clb; VICA; High Hon Roll; Hon Roll; Debrah Hope Gale Tuition Scholar Median Schl 87; Median Schl Hlth; Med Asst.

BURNS, TOM; Pennsbury HS; Fairless Hills, PA; (4); 350/800; German Clb; JV Bsbl; Var L Ftbl; JV Wrstlng; Ftbl Schlrshp To Millersville U 87; Bud Means Mem Awd; Millersville U; Pltcl Law.

BURNS, TRACEY; James M Cooghlin HS; Wilkes Barre, PA; (4); 39/340; Aud/Vis; Church Yth Grp; FBLA; Ski Clb; Pres SADD; Nwsp Stf; Yrbk Ed-Chief; Yrbk Stf; Pres Jr Cls; High Hon Roll; Pres Schlrshp U Of Scranton 87; FBLA ST Compt 2nd Pl Pblc Spkng 87; Natl Cncl On Yth Ldrshp 86; U Of Scranton; Pre Law.

BURNS, WILLIAM T; Norristown Area HS; E Norristown, PA; (4); 14/478; Intnl Clb; Math Clb; Hon Roll; Prfct Atten Awd; Accntng.

BURPRICH, THOMAS; Hickory HS; Hermitage, PA; (3); 1/180; German Clb; Math Clb; Chorus; Nwsp Rptr; Nwsp Stf; Var Capt Bsktbl; Wt Lftg; Jr NHS; NHS; Comp Sci.

BURR, R WILLIAM; Keystone Oaks HS; Castle Shannon, PA; (4); 63/268; Nwsp Bus Mgr; Nwsp Ed-Chief; Nwsp Rptr; Rep Sr Cls; Rep Stu Cncl; Bowling; Hon Roll; Vtd Prom Kng Sr Cls Prm 87; Mstr Of Ceremnys Vrsty Shw 86 & 87; Bethany Coll; Cmmnctns.

BURRELL, BETH; Hempfield SR HS; Irwin, PA; (4); 195/664; FBLA; Pep Clb; Ski Clb; Teachers Aide; Cheerleading; Hon Roll.

BURRELL, THOMAS; Mountain View JR/Sr HS; Union Dale, PA; (3); Boy Scts; Exploring; 4-H; Band; Chorus; Concert Band; Mrchg Band; Orch; Nwsp Rptr; Nwsp Stf; Crimnl Justc.

BURRELL, TIASHA; West Philadelphia Catholic HS For Girl; Philadelphia, PA; (3); 79/249; Church Yth Grp; Pres Spanish Clb; Concert Band; Hon Roll; Hon Roll 85-87; Acad Achvmnt Awd Engl III 87, Math 85; Comp Sci.

BURRIS, JANIE; Bellefonte Area HS; Bellefonte, PA; (4); 27/237; Sec Church Yth Grp; Rep SADD; Church Choir; Nwsp Rptr; Rep Frsh Cls; Rep Soph Cls; Rep Jr Cls; Rep Sr Cls; Var Cheerleading; Co-Capt Twrlr; Charles P M, Eliz T Smith To Penn ST U 87; KIDA Majrette Schlrshp 87; Acadmc, Genl Excllnc Schlrshp; Penn ST U; Comm.

BURRIS, JENNIFER; State Coll Area Intermediate HS; State College, PA; (1); 80/476; Ski Clb; Powder Puff Ftbl; Sftbl; Trk; Wt Lftg; Hon Roll; Hon Mention-Poetry Cont 86-87; PA ST U; Teaching.

BURRIS, WADE; Freeport SR HS; Freeport, PA; (2); Church Yth Grp; Chorus; School Musical; Swing Chorus; Hon Roll; Frstry.

BURROUGHS, CHRIS ANN; Mountain View JR SR HS; Harford, PA; (2); Hon Roll; Bus.

BURROWS, PAMELA M; Germantown Friends HS; Philadelphia, PA; (4); Cmnty Wkr; Stage Crew; Im Crs Cntry; Im Tennis; Ntl Merit SF.

BURROWS, STEPHEN; Peabody HS; Pittsburgh, PA; (4); 18/292; Spanish Clb; Trs Frsh Cls; Im JV Vllybl; Hon Roll; NHS; Ntl Merit SF; FL A&M; Elec Engrng.

BURRUANO, ANGEL; North Pocono HS; Moscow, PA; (2); 30/256; Drama Clb; Spanish Clb; Varsity Clb; Sec Stu Cncl; Var Cheerleading; Hon Roll; NHS; Comm.

BURSK, NORABETH; Neshaminy HS; Langhorne, PA; (3); 15/788; Church Yth Grp; Hosp Aide; Band; Chorus; Orch; Swmmng; High Hon Roll; Hon Roll; NHS; Vrsty Ltr Awd Swmmg 86-87; Swmtm Spirit Awd 86-87; Penn ST; Elem Educ.

BURSON, KATHY; Mount Carmel Area JR SR HS; Kulpmont, PA; (3); 10/130; Spanish Clb; Band; Concert Band; Mrchg Band; Nwsp Stf; Hon Roll; Jr NHS; NHS; IN U Of PA; Market Rsrch Anal.

BURSTEIN, ANDREW; Lower Moreland HS; Huntingdon Valley, PA; (4); Cmnty Wkr; Debate Tm; FBLA; Key Clb; Science Clb; Sec Soph Cls; Rep Stu Cncl; Tennis; Wrstlng; Hugh O Brian Ldrshp Awd 85; Bus Law Cntst 87; George Washington U; Bus Admin.

BURT, LAURIE J; Norristown Area HS; Norristown, PA; (4); 30/478; Church Yth Grp; DECA; Drama Clb; Key Clb; Band; Chorus; Rep Sr Cls; Capt Var Fld Hcky; Var Lcrss; Sec NHS; Hnr Rll; Physcl Ftnss Awd 84; West Chester Drm Cmptn 85-86; Allentown Coll; Actng.

BURT, ROBIN N; J R Masterman HS; Philadelphia, PA; (4); 18/28; Art Clb; Dance Clb; Orch; School Musical; Nwsp Ed-Chief; Nwsp Rptr; Vllybl; Ntl Merit Schol; Georgetown U; Intl Affairs.

BURTI, MICHELE; Central SR HS; York, PA; (3); Church Yth Grp; Ski Clb; Speech Tm; Varsity Clb; Yrbk Stf; Var Bsktbl; Var Tennis; Var Trk; Hon Roll; Sls Mktng.

BURTNETT, BRYAN; Everett Area HS; Everett, PA; (2); 36/150; Computer Clb; Band; Concert Band; Mrchg Band; Pep Band; Hon Roll; Comp Pgmmr.

BURTON, DARLENE; Curwensville Area HS; Curwensville, PA; (4); 12/114; French Clb; Hosp Aide; Im Bsktbl; Im Socr; Im Vllybl; High Hon Roll; Hon Roll; NHS; Upwrd Bnd; IN U Of PA; Educ.

BURTON, KIMBERLY; Tunkhannock Area HS; Dalton, PA; (3); Art Clb; Ski Clb; Band; Concert Band; Mrchg Band; Yrbk Stf; Var Diving; Hon Roll; Mst Imprvd Stu Yr 86-87; Clarion U; Physcl Thrpy.

BURTON, LORI; Philipsburg-Osceola SR HS; Philipsburg, PA; (4); 27/237; Ski Clb; Yrbk Sprt Ed; Yrbk Stf; Hon Roll; NHS; C PA Schl Nrsng; Nrsng.

BURTON, ROBERT; Riverview HS; Oakmont, PA; (3); 22/110; Sec Key Clb; JV Wrstlng; NEDT Awd; Engrng.

BURY, TERESA; Oley Valley HS; Fleetwood, PA; (3); 60/165; SADD; Var Bsktbl; Var Sftbl; JV Trk; Var Vllybl; Chiropractic Specialist.

BURYCHKA, HEATHER; Boyertown Area HS; Perkiomenville, PA; (4); 9/429; Church Yth Grp; Pres Pep Clb; SADD; Drill Tm; Nwsp Stf; VP Stu Cncl; High Hon Roll; Pres NHS; Clark U; Modrn Frgn Lang.

BUSCH, DAVID; Seneca Valley SR HS; Mars, PA; (3); Aud/Vis; Exploring; High Hon Roll; Comp Sci.

BUSCH, DAVID; West Mifflin Area HS; W Mifflin, PA; (3); 23/330; Key Clb; Letterman Clb; Ski Clb; Var Ftbl; Wt Lftg; Var Wrstlng; Hon Roll; NHS; Vrsty Lttr Ftbl 86; Penn ST; Bus.

BUSCH, DAVID R; New Brighton Area HS; New Brighton, PA; (3); 3/168; Am Leg Boys St; Yrbk Sprt Ed; VP Soph Cls; Pres Jr Cls; Pres Sr Cls; Rep Stu Cncl; Var L Bsbl; High Hon Roll; Var L Mgr(s); HOBY Ldrshp Seminar.

BUSCH, JUDITH A; Ringold HS; Finleyville, PA; (3); Dance Clb; GAA; Hosp Aide; Spanish Clb; Speech Tm; Chorus; Drill Tm; Mrchg Band; Variety Show; Var L Twrlr; Ed.

BUSER, TAMMY; Eastern York JR SR HS; York, PA; (3); 41/177; Sec Pres 4-H; Rptr Pres FFA; SADD; Hon Roll; Agrnmy Cntst FFA Wk Penn ST 2nd Pl 87; White Rose Degr 86; Penn ST; Agrnmy.

BUSFIELD, MELANIE; Bensalem HS; Bensalem, PA; (2); JV Socr; JV Tennis; NHS.

BUSH, ANDREW; Danville HS; Washingtonvl, PA; (2); Ski Clb; JV Socr; Var Tennis; High Hon Roll; NEDT Awd.

BUSH JR, CLARK; Elk Lake HS; Springville, PA; (1); French Clb; Band; Chorus; Jazz Band; School Musical; Variety Show; Stu Cncl; Trk; Wrstlng.

BUSH, DARLENE; St Benedict Acad; Erie, PA; (3); 12/53; Hosp Aide; Hon Roll; NHS; Bio.

BUSH, GARY; Windber Area HS; Windber, PA; (4); Am Leg Boys St; Boy Scts; Drama Clb; JA; Prfct Atten Awd; Natl Sci Merit Awd 87; Eagle Scout Awd 87; Amer Lgn Good Ctznshp Citation 87; Stu Of Mnth 87; Penn ST; Commnctns.

BUSH, JAMES; Lourdes Regional HS; Atlas, PA; (3); 29/88; Camera Clb; Drama Clb; Key Clb; Letterman Clb; Ski Clb; Pres SADD; Varsity Clb; Bsbl; Ftbl; Comm.

BUSH, JAMIE; Tidioute HS; Tidioute, PA; (2); Chess Clb; Chorus; Military.

BUSH, KIMBERLEY; Youngsville HS; Youngsville, PA; (4); 2/96; Church Yth Grp; Art Clb; Spanish Clb; Chorus; Mrchg Band; Nwsp Rptr; Lit Mag; High Hon Roll; NHS; Clarion U Of PA; Commctns.

BUSH, KRISTEN; Kiski Area HS; Apollo, PA; (4); Debate Tm; Spanish Clb; SADD; Color Guard; Concert Band; Mrchg Band; Var Trk; High Hon Roll; NHS; Girl Of Mnth From Vandergrift Bus & Prfssnl Womens Clb 87; Westminster Coll; Elem Educ.

BUSH, MICHELLE L; Sewickley Acad; Pittsburgh, PA; (4); 1/64; Sec French Clb; NFL; Capt Speech Tm; Nwsp Ed-Chief; Pres Jr Cls; Bausch & Lomb Sci Awd; Gov Hon Prg Awd; High Hon Roll; Ntl Merit SF; Computer Clb; Alumni Awd Outstndng Grad 84; Brown U Bk Awd 86; PA JR Acad Sci 1st Pl Awd 85-86; Physcs.

BUSH, RICKI; Dubois Area SR HS; Du Bois, PA; (3); Hon Roll.

BUSH, ROBERT; Stroudsburg HS; East Stroudsburg, PA; (3); 8/280; Scholastic Bowl; Science Clb; Concert Band; Mrchg Band; School Musical; High Hon Roll; NHS; Ntl Merit Ltr; Math Tm; Penn ST Smmr Intnsv Lang Inst 87; 6th Pl Monroe Cnty Spellg Cntst 87; Geolgy.

BUSH, STACEY; Lincoln HS; Ellwood City, PA; (3); French Clb; Hosp Aide; Key Clb; Office Aide; SADD; Y-Teens; Drill Tm; Mrchg Band; Legl Sec.

BUSHMAN, MICHAEL T; Holy Ghost Prep; Philadelphia, PA; (3); Boy Scts; Debate Tm; NFL; ROTC; Yrbk Stf; Sec Sr Cls; Stu Cncl; Bsbl; Hon Roll; Union Leag Awd Good Ctznshp 85; Keystone Boys ST Outstndg Svc 86; Villanova; Bus.

BUSHNER, JOSEPH A; William Allen HS; Allentown, PA; (4); 95/559; Key Clb; Model UN; ROTC; Thesps; VP Sr Cls; Rep Stu Cncl; Var L Ftbl; Hon Roll; Amer Legn Schlstc Excllnc Awd 86; 1st Pl Forencis Comp JR High 83; Hnrbl Mntn Coffee Achvrs Awd 86; Engr.

BUSHONG, JUDY; Solanco SR HS; Quarryville, PA; (4); Church Yth Grp; Band; Concert Band; Jazz Band; Mrchg Band; School Musical; Var Bsktbl; Var Fld Hcky; Var Sftbl; Var Trk; All Arnd Girl Athl 87; Cls Awd 87; Lancaster-Lebanon Leag Bsktbl All Star 87; Kutztown U; Crmnl Justc.

BUSHONG, NANETTE; Hempfield HS; Columbia, PA; (3); Pres Church Yth Grp; Pres 4-H; Chorus; Fld Hcky; Powder Puff Ftbl; 4-H Awd; Hon Roll; Cnty Dairy Prncss 87-88; Early Chldhd Educ.

BUSHWACK, JENNIFER; Greater Latrobe HS; Greensburg, PA; (1); Church Yth Grp; 4-H; Scholastic Bowl; Teachers Aide; Chorus; Church Choir; JV Trk; 4-H Awd; High Hon Roll; Hon Roll; Choral Instrctr.

BUSS, BRENT; Fleetwood Area HS; Fleetwood, PA; (3); 2/110; Ski Clb; Band; Concert Band; Mrchg Band; Var L Bsktbl; Var L Socr; Var L Tennis; Hon Roll; NHS; All Cntry Soccr Tm 85-86; All State Soccr Tm 86; Engr.

BUSSARD, AMY; Penn Trafford HS; Penn, PA; (2); FBLA; Hosp Aide; JCL; Latin Clb; SADD; Yrbk Stf; Capt Jr Cls; Im Bsktbl; JV Im Sftbl; High Hon Roll; Med.

BUSSARD, JOHNNA; Everett Area HS; Everett, PA; (3); Pres 4-H; FFA; GAA; SADD; VICA; Trk; 4-H Awd; Hon Roll.

BUSSARD, SABRENA; Northern Bedford HS; New Enterprise, PA; (3); Church Yth Grp; Spanish Clb; Color Guard; Hon Roll; Wheelock Coll; Chld-Life Spclst.

BUSSE, CLAIRE; Sacred Heart HS; Pittsburgh, PA; (4); Drama Clb; French Clb; Q&S; Band; Chorus; Mrchg Band; Nwsp Stf; High Hon Roll; NHS; Pres Schlr; Wellesley Coll.

BUSSELL, LINDA; Lampeter Strasburg HS; Lampeter, PA; (3); Band; Concert Band; Mrchg Band; JV Bsktbl; Var JV Fld Hcky; Var JV Sftbl; NHS.

BUSSOM, TRACY; Hughesville HS; Picture Rocks, PA; (4); Church Yth Grp; Ski Clb; Varsity Clb; Chorus; Rep Soph Cls; Rep Stu Cncl; L Tennis; Hon Roll; NHS; Grn & Wht Ad 84; HS Alumni Awd 87; Blmsbrg U; Bus Adm.

BUSTARD, MICHELE A; Bensalem HS; Oakford, PA; (4); Pres FFA; Teachers Aide; Stu Cncl; JV Var Fld Hcky; JV Sftbl; Im Tennis; Im Vllybl; Hon Roll; Elvamay Schl Flrl Dsgn; Flrst.

BUSTI, STEVEN; Wallenpaupack Area HS; Hawley, PA; (3); 15/157; Am Leg Boys St; Socr; Var L Trk; High Hon Roll; Jr NHS; NHS; Rotary Awd; 1st Pl ST Postr Cntst Penn Assoc Cnsrtn 83; Bst Shw Pke Cnty Arts Cncl Yng Visl Arts Comptn 87; Comm Artst.

BUSZA, TODD; Ridley HS; Morton, PA; (3); 29/453; Bsbl; Bsktbl; Ftbl; Lcrss; Hon Roll; Engrng.

BUTCH, ROBERT J; Archbishop Ryan HS For Boys; Philadelphia, PA; (4); 25/425; Church Yth Grp; Civic Clb; Varsity Clb; Nwsp Stf; Yrbk Stf; Var JV Fld Hcky; Var JV Ftbl; Var Sftbl; All Am Awd 86-87; Principals Awd 86; Math Awd 84 & 85; Hstry Awd 85; Swarthmore Coll; Mech Engrng.

BUTCH JR, RONALD; Mohawk HS; Edinburg, PA; (4); 5/135; Boy Scts; Church Yth Grp; Latin Clb; Band; Concert Band; Mrchg Band; Pep Band; School Play; Trs Jr Cls; Stu Cncl; Dr R Joseph Mem Schlstc Achvmnt Awd 87; Penn ST U; Engr.

BUTCHER, CAROLYN; Wyoming Valley West HS; Plymouth, PA; (4); 5/393; Sec Church Yth Grp; Nwsp Stf; Yrbk Ed-Chief; Lit Mag; Rep Stu Cncl; Cit Awd; NHS; Key Clb; Pep Clb; Red Cross Aide; HOBY Ldrshp Awd; Plymth Rtry Wrld Undrstndng Awd; Wstside JR Wmns Clb Schlrshp Awd; Bloomsbrg U; Mgmt.

BUTCHER, KEITH; Church Farm Schl; Orange, VA; (3); Drama Clb; German Clb; Latin Clb; Math Clb; Cmnty Wkr; JV Socr; Sftbl; JV Wrstlng; Hon Roll; Bus.

BUTCHER, SUZANNE; Penn Trafford HS; Claridge, PA; (2); FBLA; German Clb; Girl Scts; Ski Clb; Nwsp Rptr; Gym; Sftbl; Tennis; Trk; Hon Roll; PA ST U.

BUTCHKO, JEAN; Bishop O Reilly HS; Swoyersville, PA; (4); 4/120; Debate Tm; Acpl Chr; Chorus; School Play; Nwsp Rptr; Yrbk Stf; Var Cheerleading; High Hon Roll; NHS; Acadmc All Amercn 84; Ntl Sci Merit Awd Wnnr 85; Intl Chrldng Fndtn Spirt Awd 84; Comm.

BUTCHKO, TINA; Pittston Area; Pittston, PA; (4); 18/360; Computer Clb; Exploring; FBLA; Key Clb; Math Clb; Science Clb; Score Keeper; Var Swmmng; Capt Vllybl; High Hon Roll; Penn ST; Math.

BUTCHKO, TOM; Wyoming Area HS; Exeter, PA; (3); 48/250; Key Clb; Spanish Clb; Bsbl; Hon Roll; Rotry Intl Ldrshp Camp 85-86; Bus Admin.

BUTCHKOSKI, BRENDA; Saltsburg JR SR HS; Clarksburg, PA; (2); 17/97; Church Yth Grp; Drama Clb; FTA; Sec Soph Cls; Bsktbl; Sftbl; Vllybl; High Hon Roll; Pres Acad Fit Awd 85-86; IN U PA; Psych.

BUTENSKY, LEE ANN; Minersville Area HS; Branch Dale, PA; (3); 22/105; FBLA; Spanish Clb; Yrbk Stf; Hon Roll; Jr NHS; Med Sec.

BUTERBAUGH, BETH; Punsutawney Area HS; Big Run, PA; (4); 36/245; Church Yth Grp; Drama Clb; Teachers Aide; Varsity Clb; Church Choir; Variety Show; Nwsp Ed-Chief; Nwsp Phtg; Nwsp Rptr; Nwsp Stf; CA Coll; Theatre.

BUTERBAUGH, LIANNE; Fannett-Metal HS; Ft Loudon, PA; (3); Drama Clb; VICA; Band; Chorus; Concert Band; Sec Frsh Cls; Sec Jr Cls; Hon Roll; NHS; Comp Oper.

BUTERBAUGH, ROBERT; Purchase Line HS; Commodore, PA; (3); FBLA; School Play; Hon Roll; Bus.

BUTERBAUGH, SCOTT; Seneca Valley HS; Mars, PA; (3); Boy Scts; Church Yth Grp; Chorus; Jazz Band; Madrigals; Mrchg Band; Symp Band; Tnor Schl Brbrshp Qrtet 86, 87 & 88; PA ST Lgsltv Schl Art Exhbt 87.

BUTERBAUGH, TRENT; Saltsburg JR SR HS; Saltsburg, PA; (3); Camera Clb; Radio Clb; Speech Tm; Stage Crew; Nwsp Stf; VP Jr Cls; Stu Cncl; Bsktbl; High Hon Roll; NHS; Nurse Asst.

BUTINA, DARINDA; Trinity HS; New Cumberland, PA; (3); 46/138; Pres Church Yth Grp; Pep Clb; Ski Clb; Spanish Clb; Variety Show; Capt Cheerleading; Hon Roll; Psych.

BUTKO, CHRISANNE; Steel Valley HS; Munhall, PA; (3); Church Yth Grp; Exploring; Tennis; High Hon Roll; NHS.

BUTLER, ANITA; Engineering & Science HS; Phila, PA; (3); Boys Clb Am; Boy Scts; Computer Clb; 4-H; French Clb; FTA; Hosp Aide; Library Aide; Office Aide; Pep Clb; Hampton U; Bus Admin.

BUTLER, BRADLEY; Bethal Park SR HS; Bethel Park, PA; (4); Sec Pres Boy Scts; Church Yth Grp; German Clb; Mrchg Band; Orch; Symp Band; Sr Cls; Stu Cncl; High Hon Roll; NHS; Egl Sct Awd BSA 84; Pres Acad Ftns Awds Pgm 86-87; U Of MI; Aero Engr.

BUTLER, DEREK; Aliquippa HS; Aliquippa, PA; (2); Chess Clb; Debate Tm; Spanish Clb; Concert Band; Jazz Band; Mrchg Band; Pep Band; Cit Awd; High Hon Roll; Hon Roll; Nvl Acad.

BUTLER, EVELYN DORINDA; Oxford HS; Oxford, PA; (3); 41/194; Sec Church Yth Grp; Chorus; Church Choir; Orch; Stage Crew; Nwsp Rptr; JV Var Trk; Capt Twrlr; Hon Roll; NHS; Bus.

BUTLER, FRANK-KEY; John Harris HS; Harrisburg, PA; (4); 39/233; Boy Scts; Church Yth Grp; Cmnty Wkr; 4-H; VP Stu Cncl; Tennis; Trk; Sec Hon Roll; I Dare You Awd 87; Millersville U John Hall Schlrshp 87; Millersville U; Arch.

BUTLER, JEFF; Greensburg Central Catholic HS; Greensburg, PA; (4); 41/220; Church Yth Grp; Ski Clb; Im Bsktbl; Im Sftbl; Im Vllybl; Var Wrstlng; WV U; Pre-Dentistry.

BUTLER, JEFF; Mt Pleasant Area HS; Mt Pleasant, PA; (4); Red Cross Aide; Ski Clb; Stat Coach Actv; L Ftbl; Var Trk; Im Wt Lftg; High Hon Roll; Hon Roll; Hstry Tchr.

BUTLER, KRISTINE M; Cardinal O Hara HS; Havertown, PA; (4); #10 In Class; Spanish Clb; SADD; School Musical; Nwsp Ed-Chief; Yrbk Rptr; Lit Mag; Hon Roll; Lion Awd; NHS; Spanish NHS; Anna M Vincent Schlrshp, Prsdntl Acdmc Ftnss Awd 87; U Of PA; Spnsh.

BUTLER, LORETTA; Bishop Kenrick HS; Norristown, PA; (4); 24/285; Cmnty Wkr; Service Clb; Nwsp Rptr; Sec Stu Cncl; Powder Puff Ftbl; Hon Roll; NHS; Rep Frsh Cls; Rep Soph Cls; Rep Jr Cls; Hmcmng Queen; U Of Scranton; Engl.

BUTLER, LORI; Coatesville Area SR HS; Coatesville, PA; (3); 24/512; Sec Church Yth Grp; Leo Clb; Ski Clb; Band; Chorus; Yrbk Ed-Chief; Frsh Cls; Soph Cls; Jr Cls; High Hon Roll.

BUTLER, MELODIE; Jefferson-Morgan JR SR HS; Waynesburg, PA; (4); 4/96; French Clb; Chorus; Color Guard; School Play; Stat Bsktbl; Pres NHS; NEDT Awd; Voice Dem Awd; Ltn Awd 86; Intrct Clb 85-87; E Nazerene Coll.

BUTLER, MICHELE; Cecilian Acad; Philadelphia, PA; (3); Cmnty Wkr; Office Aide; School Play; Stage Crew; Var Mgr(s); Var Score Keeper; Art Clb; Church Yth Grp; Dance Clb; Hosp Aide; Phys Thrpy.

BUTLER, MICHELLE L; Punxsutawney Area HS; Punxsutawney, PA; (3); Am Leg Aux Girls St; Math Tm; SADD; Hon Roll; Bio.

BUTLER, PENNY S; North East HS; North East, PA; (3); Am Leg Aux Girls St; Pres Church Yth Grp; Letterman Clb; Church Choir; Yrbk Phtg; Yrbk Stf; Var L Keywanettes; Var Trk; Var Vllybl; Hon Roll; Arch.

BUTLER, PHIL; Carlynton SR HS; Pittsburgh, PA; (4); Computer Clb; Rep Stu Cncl; Var L Bowling; Var Ftbl; Var L Trk; Im Capt Vllybl; High Hon Roll; Omega Psi Phi Schlrshp 87; Anml Bhvr Intrnshp U 86; Blck Achvrs Awd Penn ST U 87; Penn ST U; Vet Sci.

BUTLER, TODD; Emmaus HS; Macungie, PA; (3); 5/530; Church Yth Grp; Trs Sec German Clb; VP JA; Sec Model UN; Scholastic Bowl; School Musical; Hst Jr Cls; L Crs Cntry; High Hon Roll; Ntl Merit Ltr; Georgetown-U Of PA; Int Rltns.

BUTO, JAMES; Cathedral Prep Schl; Mc Kean, PA; (3); 93/197; Church Yth Grp; Cmnty Wkr; Debate Tm; Spanish Clb; Im Bsktbl; Im Vllybl; Bus Mgmt.

BUTRIE, MATTHEW; Marian HS; Lansford, PA; (4); 2/109; Chess Clb; Math Clb; Scholastic Bowl; French Hon Soc; High Hon Roll; NHS; Ntl Merit Ltr; Sal; Duquesne U; Theology.

BUTSON, RANDY J; Warwick HS; Lititz, PA; (3); 36/300; Am Leg Boys St; Pres JA; Math Clb; Spanish Clb; Variety Show; Pres Soph Cls; Pres Sr Cls; Vllybl; High Hon Roll; NHS; Temple U; Bus.

BUTTACAVOLI, MICHELLE; Council Rock HS; Holland, PA; (2); Drama Clb; School Musical; School Play; Stage Crew; Hon Roll; Prfct Atten Awd; Marine Bio.

BUTTERMORE, DEBORAH; Dubois Area HS; Dubois, PA; (3); 13/300; Ski Clb; SADD; Varsity Clb; Nwsp Stf; L Sftbl; VP Capt Vllybl; High Hon Roll; Hon Roll; NHS; Pres Stu Cncl; Sci.

BUTTERY, TAMARA; Punxsutawney Area SR HS; Punxsutawney, PA; (4); 76/245; French Clb; Variety Show; Var L Tennis; IN U Of PA; Psych.

BUTTON, CHRISTINE; Bellefonte SR HS; Bellefonte, PA; (3); Csmtlgst.

BUTTON, KATHRYN; Lock Haven SR HS; Lock Haven, PA; (3); Art Clb; Cmnty Wkr; FHA; German Clb; Intnl Clb; Science Clb; SADD; Hon Roll; NHS; Prfct Atten Awd; FHA Stu Yr 84-85; Child Psych.

BUTTS, BLYTHE; Tamaqua Area HS; Nesquehoning, PA; (3); Church Yth Grp; Cmnty Wkr; Pep Clb; Service Clb; Mgr(s); Swmmng; French Hon Soc; Hon Roll.

BUTTS, DARRON; Mcconnellsburg HS; Mcconnellsburg, PA; (4); 13/68; FFA; Yrbk Stf; Bsbl; NHS; Frank Gannett Nwspr Carr Schlshp 87; Natl Hnr Soc Trea; Shippensburg U.

BUTTS, DAWN A; Great Valley HS; Paoli, PA; (3); Church Yth Grp; FBLA; Varsity Clb; Var Cheerleading; Var Gym; Mgr(s); Var Trk; Hon Roll; Acctng.

BUTTS, JENNIFER; Mc Keesport Area HS; Dravosburg, PA; (2); AFS; GAA; Pep Clb; Hon Roll; Frgn Lang.

BUTZ, CHRIS; William Allen HS; Allentown, PA; (3); Rep Frsh Cls; Rep Soph Cls; Rep Jr Cls; Im Powder Puff Ftbl; Gifted Prog 84-86; Acctg.

BUTZ, JENNY; Chambersburg Area SR HS; Chambersburg, PA; (2); Church Yth Grp; JCL; Latin Clb; Ski Clb; Trs Chorus; Sftbl; Trk; Hon Roll; U Of Pittsburgh; Pharm.

BUTZER, PAMELA; Ephrata HS; Akron, PA; (4); 1/247; Church Yth Grp; Cmnty Wkr; Teachers Aide; Concert Band; Mrchg Band; Bausch & Lomb Sci Awd; Hon Roll; NHS; Ntl Merit SF; Val; PA ST U; Nrsng.

BUXBAUM, AMY M; Ferndale Area HS; Johnstown, PA; (3); 1/82; Am Leg Aux Girls St; Church Yth Grp; Computer Clb; Leo Clb; SADD; Varsity Clb; Yrbk Phtg; Var Bsktbl; Sftbl; Vllybl; Finance.

BUYNACK, KATHLEEN; Bishop Carroll HS; Ebensburg, PA; (3); Drama Clb; Spanish Clb; SADD; Chorus; Stage Crew; Trk; Paralegal Stud.

BUYNAK, SONYA; Philipsburg-Osceola SR HS; Osceola Mills, PA; (4); 7/234; Art Clb; Library Aide; Office Aide; Teachers Aide; Stage Crew; Yrbk Stf; Hon Roll; NHS; NEDT Awd; Pres Acdmc Ftns Awd 87; Psychlgy.

BUZARD, BRENDA; Fort Le Boeuf HS; Waterford, PA; (4); 13/167; Dance Clb; Band; Concert Band; Co-Capt Drill Tm; Mrchg Band; Cheerleading; Gym; High Hon Roll; Pres Schlr; Church Yth Grp; Ntl Hstry & Gvrnmnt Awd 85 & 86; Prsdntl Acdmc Ftnss Awd 87; Ft Lebf Stu Cncl Schlrshp 87; Indiana U Of PA; Crmnlgy.

BUZARD, FRED; Keystone HS; Knox, PA; (3); Var Ftbl; Farmer.

BUZZANCA, MELISSA; Gwynedd Mercy Acad; Warminster, PA; (4); 4/102; Cmnty Wkr; Service Clb; SADD; Stage Crew; Nwsp Stf; JV Fld Hcky; JV Sftbl; Trs NHS; Gold Grad Mdl Math & Spnsh 87; Georgetown U; Lang.

BUZZARD, SCOTT; Pen Argyl HS; Windgap, PA; (4); 7/113; Am Leg Boys St; Ski Clb; Bsbl; Ftbl; Dnfth Awd; Hon Roll; James R Charron Memorial, Pen Argyla Natl Bank & Prsdntl Acdmc Fitness Awds 87; Wake Forest U; Bus.

BUZZARD, STACEY; Garden Spot HS; New Holland, PA; (2); 90/226; Church Yth Grp; Chorus; Orch; School Musical; Stage Crew; JV Stat Trk; Drama Clb; 4-H; Stat Bsktbl; Mgr(s); Trinty Coll Music Exam Lvl 2 Merit Awd 86; Trinty Coll Music Exam Lvl 4 Merit Awd 87; Hghst Grd Pt Awd; Elem Ed Music.

BUZZELLA, LYNN; Penncambria HS; Gallitzin, PA; (4); 9/199; Camera Clb; Drama Clb; Spanish Clb; SADD; Nwsp Stf; Yrbk Stf; Rep Stu Cncl; Hon Roll; NHS; Bus.

BUZZELLI, MLISA; Scranton Central HS; Scranton, PA; (3); 35/300; Art Clb; Pep Clb; Spanish Clb; Orch; Rep Stu Cncl; Cheerleading; Hon Roll; NHS; YVA; Med.

BUZZELLI, TRICIA; Connellsville Area HS; Dunbar, PA; (1); Art Clb; Church Yth Grp; Hon Roll.

BYARD, JENNIFER L; Lancaster Catholic HS; Columbia, PA; (3); 44/200; Church Yth Grp; Girl Scts; Pep Clb; Varsity Clb; Chorus; Church Choir; Stage Crew; Cheerleading; Sftbl; DAR Awd; Law.

BYARS, APRIL; Scotland Sch For Vet Children; Sicklerville, NJ; (3); Art Clb; ROTC; Band; Concert Band; Drm Mjr(t); Mrchg Band; Pep Band; School Play; Symp Band; Pres Soph Cls; Musicnshp Awd; VA ST U; Psych.

BYDAIRK, MIKE; Athens HS; Sayre, PA; (3); French Clb; Hosp Aide; Speech Tm; Nwsp Rptr; Drma.

BYERLEY, WILLIAM; Spring-Ford HS; Phoenixville, PA; (3); 29/290; Sec Church Yth Grp; Pres German Clb; Pres Band; Concert Band; Jazz Band; JV Bsbl; Var Ftbl; Wt Lftg; Hon Roll; Bus.

BYERLY, DIANNE; Elizabethtown Area HS; Elizabethtown, PA; (2); 7/309; Church Yth Grp; Rep Stu Cncl; Var Crs Cntry; Var Trk; NHS; Psychlgy.

BYERS, DARLENE; Purchase Line HS; Mahaffey, PA; (4); Cmnty Wkr; School Play; Sftbl; Vllybl; Hon Roll; Mount Ida Coll; Vet.

BYERS, JAMES; Belle Vernon Area HS; Belle Vernon, PA; (3); Boy Scts; Cmnty Wkr; Hosp Aide; Ski Clb; Stage Crew; Variety Show; Nwsp Rptr; Gov Hon Prg Awd; Govrs Schl Prfrmng Arts 86; Music.

BYERS, JEFF; Gateway SR HS; Monroeville, PA; (3); Church Yth Grp; Exploring; Var Swmmng; Ntl Merit Ltr; Engrng.

BYERS, JUDITH; Chambersburg Area SR HS; Chambersburg, PA; (3); Church Yth Grp; German Clb; SADD; Band; Chorus; Church Choir; Concert Band; Mrchg Band; Hgh Hnr Rll 85; Soc Dstngshd Am HS Stu 86; Phys Ther.

BYERS, KELLIE; South Allegheny HS; Mckeesport, PA; (3); Library Aide; Y-Teens; Bsktbl; Capt Powder Puff Ftbl; Sftbl; Tennis; Hon Roll; Jr NHS; NHS.

BYERS, STEPHANIE; Milton Area SR HS; Milton, PA; (3); VP Camera Clb; Pres Key Clb; Pres Service Clb; Hst Varsity Clb; Band; Nwsp Phtg; Var Bsktbl; Im Powder Puff Ftbl; Var Sftbl; Im Cmnty Wkr; Sprts Med.

BYERS, TERI; Mc Guffey HS; Avella, PA; (4); 60/205; DECA; Pres 4-H; Girl Scts; Pep Clb; Teachers Aide; Band; Church Choir; 4-H Awd; High Hon Roll; Hon Roll.

BYES, WILLIE; Technical Memorial HS; Erie, PA; (3); 59/289; Camera Clb; Church Yth Grp; Cmnty Wkr; 4-H; Library Aide; Office Aide; Teachers Aide; School Play; Variety Show; Nwsp Stf; JV Football Capt 86; Student Council VP 82; Machinist.

BYKOWSKI, REGINA THERESA; Laurel Highlands HS; Hopwood, PA; (4); 3/310; JA; Math Tm; Ski Clb; Yrbk Stf; Cheerleading; CC Awd; High Hon Roll; Jr NHS; NHS; Miami U; Intl Studies.

BYLER, NADINE L; Lower Dauphin HS; Hershey, PA; (4); 23/234; Church Yth Grp; JV Capt Bsktbl; Var JV Fld Hcky; High Hon Roll; Prfct Atten Awd; Ldrshp Schlrshp 87; Outstndng Hm Ec Awd 87; Phila Coll Bible; Elem Ed.

BYLER, SUANN; Shenango HS; New Castle, PA; (3); 26/125; Church Yth Grp; Hosp Aide; Trs Band; Concert Band; Jazz Band; Mrchg Band; Pep Band.

BYNUM, REGINA; John Bartram HS; Philadelphia, PA; (3); #2 In Class; Office Aide; Teachers Aide; Wt Lftg; High Hon Roll; Hon Roll; Jr NHS; NHS; Prfct Atten Awd; Acad All ST, Zukin Fdtn Awd Wrtng 86; Hghst Aver Frnch 85; Wharton; Acctnt.

BYRAM, TARA; Crestwood HS; Mountaintop, PA; (3); 55/198; Math Clb; Ski Clb; Rep Stu Cncl; Var Cheerleading; Var Trk; Hon Roll; PA Jnr Acad Of Math 86.

BYRD, JAMES; Mc Keesport HS; Mckeesport, PA; (4); Boys Clb Am; JV Ftbl; Wt Lftg; Hon Roll; Sir Thomas J Lipton Bys Clb Sprtsmnshp Awd 86; Pittsburgh Barber Schl; Barber.

BYRD, MATT; Hempfield HS; Lancaster, PA; (2); Church Yth Grp; JV Socr; Hon Roll; Sci.

BYRNE, JIM; Greenwood HS; Millerstown, PA; (3); VP Chorus; School Musical; Off Stu Cncl; JV Var Bsktbl; JV Var Socr; Var Trk; Hon Roll; NHS; Tri-M 86-88; Crmnl Jstc.

BYRNE, JULIA S; Mt Lebanon HS; Pittsburgh, PA; (3); 8/537; Church Yth Grp; Service Clb; Ski Clb; Mrchg Band; Symp Band; Lit Mag; High Hon Roll; Ntl Merit SF; Carnegie Mellon U Pre-Coll Art Schlrshps 85-86; Carnegie Museum Art Schlrshp 84; Eng.

BYRNE, JULIE; Bishop Carroll HS; Ebensburg, PA; (4); 15/107; Pep Clb; Spanish Clb; SADD; Rep Soph Cls; Capt L Bsktbl; L Trk; Hon Roll; Phy Thrpy.

BYRNE, KELLIE; Nazareth Acad; Philadelphia, PA; (3); Church Yth Grp; Sec Math Clb; Spanish Clb; 2nd Hnrs For 1st Sem 86-87; Perfect Attendance 84-87; Engr.

BYRNE, MICHAEL; Devon Preparatory Schl; Havertown, PA; (3); Camera Clb; Pres Chess Clb; Computer Clb; Nwsp Rptr; Nwsp Stf; High Hon Roll; Grmn Awd 85; Bio Awd 86; Bio.

BYRNE, PAUL; Seton-La Salle HS; Pittsburgh, PA; (3); 12/249; Church Yth Grp; Math Tm; Science Clb; Ski Clb; Im Ftbl; Var Socr; Var Trk; Var Wrstlng; High Hon Roll; NHS; Am Chem Soc Spec Rcgntn Awd 85-86; All A Awd 85-86; Acad Achvt Acad Chem I & Poetry/Drama 85-86; Chem.

BYRNE, STEPHANIE; Cardinal O Hara HS; Springfield, PA; (3); 6/710; Church Yth Grp; Dance Clb; French Clb; Pres Service Clb; SADD; School Play; French Hon Soc; High Hon Roll; NHS; Principals Awd Wrld Cult European Hstry Frnch II III & Engl III 85-87; Sci Fair Awds 85-86; Intl Rel.

BYRNES, CHRISTOPHER S; Beaver Area JR SR HS; Beaver, PA; (2); 10/240; Church Yth Grp; German Clb; Var L Socr; Var Trk; High Hon Roll; Honor Awd Acad Awds Rcgntn 87; Outstdng News Carrier Of Yr Beaver Co Ntl Assoc Of US Soccer Fed 87; Law.

BZDAK, PATRICK; Milton Area HS; New Columbia, PA; (2); Crs Cntry; Wt Lftg; Wrstlng.

CABE, ERICH; Somerset Area HS; Somerset, PA; (3); 10/230; English Clb; German Clb; JA; Letterman Clb; Mu Alpha Theta; Ski Clb; Spanish Clb; Varsity Clb; Var L Socr; High Hon Roll; Physcl Ftns Awd.

CABILI, MARIA; Penn Hills SR HS; Pittsburgh, PA; (4); 50/616; Exploring; German Clb; NHS; Tutrng Cert, S E O G Grnt, ST Grnt, Pell Grnt 87; Smmr Yth Grp Cert 86; Pitt U; Pre Med.

CABLE, JEANNETTE; Conemaugh Twp Area HS; Hollsopple, PA; (3); Church Yth Grp; Drama Clb; Band; Concert Band; Jazz Band; Mrchg Band; School Musical; School Play; Speech Tm; Occptnl Thrpst.

CABLE, JONATHAN D; Eisenhower HS; Russell, PA; (3); Church Yth Grp; JV Bsktbl; Var L Golf; Hon Roll.

CABLE, LAURA; Conemaugh Township HS; Boswell, PA; (3); 11/122; Sec Trs Church Yth Grp; Trs 4-H; Hosp Aide; Band; Concert Band; Mrchg Band; School Musical; Stage Crew; Hon Roll; NHS.

CABUNGCAL, CATHERINE ROY; St Basil Acad; Cheltenham, PA; (4); #8 In Class; French Clb; Math Clb; Orch; Variety Show; Socr; Hon Roll; Cert Efft & Achvt Frnch 86; Piano Talnt Wnnr 86.

CADDICK, JEFF; Hatboro-Horsham HS; Ambler, PA; (3); Church Yth Grp; Chorus; Church Choir; God Cntry Awd; Boy Scts; Chess Clb; Library Aide; Stage Crew; Lit Mag; Educ.

CADE, MICHAEL; Interboro HS; Glenolden, PA; (4); Drama Clb; Pres VP German Clb; School Play; Stage Crew; Yrbk Stf; Hon Roll; Jr NHS; NHS; Rotary Awd; Engl Key 87; Pres Acad Fit Awd 87; Temple U; Acctg.

CADEK, PETER; Gateway SR HS; Monroeville, PA; (3); Ski Clb; JV L Ftbl; Var L Swmmng; Hon Roll; SGA 86-87.

CADORI, LISA; St Marys Area HS; Byrnedale, PA; (3); 37/288; Church Yth Grp; Cmnty Wkr; Office Aide; Stat Trk; High Hon Roll; Hon Roll; PA ST U; Journlsm.

CADWELL, KAJSA; Springside Schl; Glenside, PA; (3); Drama Clb; Girl Scts; Chorus; School Play; Stage Crew; Yrbk Stf; Cit Awd; Hon Roll; Acpl Chr; Madrigals; Grl Sct Gld Awd 87; Doane Awd 86.

CADY, MELISA; Fort Le Boeut HS; Waterford, PA; (3); 62/236; Bsktbl; Sftbl; Hon Roll; Hnrb Mntn For Sftbl 87.

CADY, SHERILYN; Towanda Area HS; Towanda, PA; (4); 8/142; Church Yth Grp; Sec SADD; Band; Yrbk Stf; Var Capt Cheerleading; Pom Pon; NHS; Model UN; Rep Stu Cncl; School Play; PA Outstndng Stu & PA Rep NRECA Yth Cnsltng Brd, & Rnbw Grls ST Offcr & Grnd Crss Clr Awd 86-87; Ithaca Coll; Telecomm.

CAFAZZO, KATHLEEN R; Lakeland HS; Mayfield, PA; (3); 8/139; Nwsp Stf; Rep Stu Cncl; L Var Bsktbl; L Var Sftbl; High Hon Roll; Hon Roll; NHS; Ntl Merit Schol; Prfct Atten Awd; Pres Phys Fit Awd 85-87; Leag/Cnty All Star Tms Sftbl 87; Penn ST; Recrtn.

CAFEO, DAVID S; Penn Cambria HS; Cassandra, PA; (3); SADD; Nwsp Ed-Chief; Wrstlng; Hon Roll; Schltc Jrnlst Awd 86-87; ITEA Recgntn Awd 86-87; Otterbein Coll; Jrnlsm.

CAFFREY, TRISHA; Pen Argyl HS; Pen Argyl, PA; (2); 49/127; VP Church Yth Grp; Hosp Aide; Leo Clb; Ski Clb; Chorus; Drill Tm; Nwsp Rptr; Yrbk Stf; Var Cheerleading; Mgr(s); East Stroudsburg Coll; Nrsng.

CAGLIUSO, ANTHONY J; Center HS; Monaca, PA; (4); 7/186; Spanish Clb; Im Bsbl; Im Bsktbl; High Hon Roll; Hon Roll; NHS; PA St Exec Ofcrs Schlrshp 87; Outstndg Spanish Student Awd 84-85; PA ST U; Acctng.

CAGNI, BERTHA ANNE; Peters Township HS; Mc Murray, PA; (4); Church Yth Grp; Thesps; Hon Roll; Pres Schlr; CA U Of PA; Elem Ed.

CAHILL, CHRISTINE; Nativity Bvm HS; Orwigsburg, PA; (3); Church Yth Grp; Pres French Clb; SADD; Church Choir; Nwsp Phtg; Off Frsh Cls; Off Soph Cls; Off Jr Cls; Pres Stu Cncl; Capt Bsktbl; All Regnl 2nd Bsemn 86-87; Sci Fair Hon Ment 84-85; Polt Sci.

CAHILL, COLLEEN; Little Flower Catholic HS For Girls; Philadelphia, PA; (3); Hosp Aide; Service Clb; Hon Roll; Prfct Atten Awd; Phrmcy.

CAHILL, JACQUELINE; The Solebury Schl; Newtown, PA; (2); Var L Lcrss; Var L Socr; High Hon Roll; Hon Roll; French Awd One Of Best Stu 86-87; Ceramics Awd Most Creative St 86-87; Bus.

CAHILLY, JASON; Carlisle SR HS; Carlisle, PA; (3); JA; Spanish Clb; Capt Crs Cntry; Capt Trk; High Hon Roll; NHS; Prfct Atten Awd; Reiff-Lhmn Trck Awd 87; Law.

CAIARELLI, GENA; Gateway SR HS; Monroeville, PA; (2); Cmnty Wkr; Variety Show; Rep Jr Cls; Stu Cncl; High Hon Roll; Hon Roll; Prfct Atten Awd; IUP Westland; Jrnlsm.

CAIAZZO, JUSTINE; Pius X HS; Bangor, PA; (4); 5/38; Dance Clb; Pep Clb; School Musical; Nwsp Stf; Yrbk Ed-Chief; Rep Jr Cls; Rep Sr Cls; Var Cheerleading; Var Sftbl; Hon Roll; Allentown Bus Schl; Fash Merch.

CAIMANO, PAUL; New Castle SR HS; New Castle, PA; (3); 3/316; Church Yth Grp; Exploring; Math Tm; Spanish Clb; Chorus; JV Var Bsktbl; High Hon Roll; Pre-Med.

CAIMI, STEVE; St John Newmann HS; Philadelphia, PA; (2); 20/351; Latin Clb; Hon Roll; Bus.

CAIN, LESLIE; South Side Beaver HS; Georgetown, PA; (3); Exploring; Varsity Clb; Chorus; Rep Jr Cls; Rep Stu Cncl; Var L Mgr(s); Var Powder Puff Ftbl; Var L Sftbl; Var JV Vllybl; Hon Roll; Elect Engr.

CAIN, MARTHA; Kiski Area HS; Apollo, PA; (4); Aud/Vis; Science Clb; SADD; Band; Chorus; Mrchg Band; Stage Crew; Nwsp Ed-Chief; Nwsp Rptr; High Hon Roll; Ithaca Coll; TV Radio.

CAIONE, RYAN; Beaver Area HS; Beaver, PA; (2); Art Clb; Chess Clb; Church Yth Grp; German Clb; Yrbk Stf; Lit Mag.

PENNSYLVANIA CAMPBELL 173

CAIRD, KRISTIN; Elizabeth Forward SR HS; Elizabeth, PA; (3); Yrbk Sprt Ed; Yrbk Stf; JV Trk; Var Capt Vllybl; High Hon Roll; NHS; Prfct Atten Awd; Pres Schlr.

CAIRNS, BRIAN A; Mon Valley Catholic HS; Donora, PA; (4); 1/76; Concert Band; Mrchg Band; School Play; Yrbk Ed-Chief; Yrbk Sprt Ed; Stu Cncl; Bausch & Lomb Sci Awd; French Hon Soc; NHS; Val; Pa Gvrnr Schl Of Sci 86; St Vincent Coll Chllng Prgm Pres Schlrshp 85; Engrng.

CAIRNS, MISSY; Fort Cherry HS; Mc Donald, PA; (3); Computer Clb; Math Clb; Science Clb; Ski Clb; Spanish Clb; Varsity Clb; Chorus; JV Var Bsktbl; JV Var Vllybl; Hon Roll.

CAITO, MAUREEN; St Paul Cathedral HS; Pittsburgh, PA; (3); 2/53; Chorus; Stage Crew; Nwsp Rptr; Yrbk Stf; Var JV Vllybl; French Hon Soc; High Hon Roll; NHS; NEDT Awd; French Clb; Bio.

CALABRESE, CHRISTINE; Pittston Area SR HS; Pittston, PA; (4); 11/350; Computer Clb; Dance Clb; Key Clb; Math Clb; Science Clb; Ski Clb; L Var Trk; High Hon Roll; NHS; Penn St U; Comp Sci.

CALABRESE, JOANNE; Merion Mercy Acad; Phila, PA; (4); Hosp Aide; Science Clb; Spanish Clb; Im Bsktbl; Sftbl; Im Vllybl; High Hon Roll; NHS; Spanish NHS; U Of Scranton Pres Schlrshp 87; Spnsh Awd 87; U Of Scranton; Pre-Med.

CALABRESE, LAUREN; Shenango Jr-Sr HS; New Castle, PA; (3); Library Aide; Office Aide; Drill Tm; VP Frsh Cls; VP Soph Cls; VP Jr Cls; Rep Stu Cncl; Cheerleading; Trk; Vllybl; Yth Against Cancer; Natl Sci Mrt Awd Biology I; Bus.

CALABRESE, PAULA; Ft Le Boeuf HS; Erie, PA; (3); Church Yth Grp; French Clb; Nwsp Stf; Yrbk Stf; Trs Rep Stu Cncl; JV Cheerleading; JV Trk; Im Vllybl; Hon Roll; Chld Psych.

CALABRESE, SAM; Pittston Area HS; Pittston, PA; (3); 18/365; Computer Clb; Drama Clb; Math Clb; Science Clb; Chorus; School Musical; School Play; Swing Chorus; High Hon Roll; Hon Roll; Albany Coll Of Pharm; Pharmacy.

CALABRETTA, MARIO; Bishop Kenrick HS; Norristown, PA; (4); 4/287; Church Yth Grp; Math Tm; Science Clb; Varsity Clb; Socr; Hon Roll; NHS; Ntl Merit Ltr; Math Clb; Ftbl; Yth Yr Awd Exch Club Norristown 86; PA Hghr Educ Asst Agncy Cert Merit 86; PA ST U; Mech Engr.

CALABRO, DAVID; Canon-Mc Millan HS; Canonsburg, PA; (3); Stage Crew; Rep Soph Cls; Rep Jr Cls; Rep Sr Cls; Rep Stu Cncl; Golf; Trk; Wt Lftg; Wrstlng; Bus.

CALABRO, DAVID; Immaculate Conception HS; Washington, PA; (3); 5/48; Math Tm; Ski Clb; Nwsp Rptr; Yrbk Phtg; Yrbk Rptr; Rep Sr Cls; Stu Cncl; JV Gym; Var Wrstlng; High Hon Roll; Alg III Acad 85-86; US Hstry & Hlth Acad 86-87.

CALABRO, FRANCINE R; Canon Mc Millan HS; Canonsburg, PA; (4); FBLA; Office Aide; Hon Roll; Bradford Bus Schl; Word Proc.

CALAFUT, MARIA; Sacred Heart HS; Carbondale, PA; (4); Church Yth Grp; French Clb; School Play; Yrbk Rptr; Rep Soph Cls; Sec VP Stu Cncl; Cit Awd; High Hon Roll; Trs NHS; US Stu Cncl Awd, Acdmc All-Amrcn Awd 86; Marywood Coll; Elem Educ.

CALAMAN, GREGORY; Sullivan Cnty HS; Dushore, PA; (4); 1/83; Pres Concert Band; Madrigals; Crs Cntry; JP Sousa Awd; VP NHS; Ntl Merit Ltr; Val; 4-H; Key Clb; Acpl Chr; Army, Navy, Air Force & ROTC Schlrshps 87; Naval Air Force Acdmc Appt 87; Sen Madigan Ctznshp Awd 87; U S Naval Acad; Aerospace Engrn.

CALARIE, NATALIE; Indiana SR HS; Indiana, PA; (3); Sec Church Yth Grp; Key Clb; Red Cross Aide; Acpl Chr; Orch; School Musical; School Play; Yrbk Stf; Capt Cheerleading; Hon Roll; Law.

CALCUTTA, JENNIFER; Montour HS; Pittsburgh, PA; (3); Church Yth Grp; Drama Clb; Exploring; SADD; Nwsp Stf; Yrbk Stf; Hon Roll; Rutgers U.

CALDERARO, BILLY; Oxford Area HS; Oxford, PA; (3); 31/197; Yrbk Bus Mgr; Pres Frsh Cls; Pres Soph Cls; Pres Jr Cls; Pres Sr Cls; Bsktbl; Socr; Tennis; High Hon Roll; Hon Roll; Prom King; Blood Drive.

CALDERONE, GINO; Ambridge HS; Baden, PA; (3); FCA; SADD; Thesps; School Musical; Variety Show; Rep Jr Cls; Var Ftbl; Wt Lftg; High Hon Roll; Hon Roll; PA ST U; Indstrl Engrng.

CALDERONE, KATE; Nativity BVM HS; Minersville, PA; (3); Church Yth Grp; Cmnty Wkr; Hosp Aide; Political Wkr; Chorus; Church Choir; Cheerleading; Diocesan Choir 86; Schuylkill County Chorus 87.

CALDWELL, ALAN; Jeannette SR HS; Jeannette, PA; (2); Boy Scts; Eagle Scout 86; Elec Engr.

CALDWELL, DEBBIE; Upper Moreland HS; Hatboro, PA; (4); 30/254; Capt Bsktbl; Sftbl; Tennis; High Hon Roll; NHS; Robert Alexander Mem Awd 87; Charles J Ritinski Mem Awd 87; Babe Ruth Awd 87; Shippensburg U; Bus.

CALDWELL, DERRICK; Reading HS; Reading, PA; (3); 245/819; Wrstlng; Bus.

CALDWELL, GREGORY A; Butler Area SR HS; Butler, PA; (3); Aud/Vis; Church Yth Grp; Spanish Clb; Stage Crew; Yrbk Stf; Var Bsbl; Score Keeper; Hon Roll; Jr NHS; Acad Achvt Awd 86-87; Gannon U; Optmtry.

CALDWELL, JANIS; Cowanesque Valley HS; Westfield, PA; (3); 8/83; Art Clb; Church Yth Grp; Computer Clb; Acpl Chr; Chorus; School Musical; Yrbk Stf; CC Awd; Hon Roll; NHS; Xmas Wndw Pntng Cntst 3rd Pl 86; Penn ST U; Art.

CALDWELL, JOANN; Cambridge Springs HS; Saegertown, PA; (4); Pep Clb; SADD; VP Sec Chorus; Capt Color Guard; Stage Crew; Hon Roll; Ntl Chorle Awd 87; Sectrl.

CALDWELL, JOHN; South Park HS; Library, PA; (3); 6/229; L Crs Cntry; JV Socr; L Trk; High Hon Roll; NEDT Awd; Wstrn PA Intrschlstc Athltc Lg AA X-Cntry Tm Chmps 85&86; Cornell; Med.

CALDWELL, KRISTIE; Jenkintown HS; Jenkintown, PA; (2); Chorus; School Musical; Stat Bsktbl; Var Cheerleading; JV Fld Hcky; Stat Ftbl; Var Lcrss.

CALDWELL, LYNN; Council Rock HS; Richboro, PA; (3); 11/908; Church Yth Grp; Jazz Band; Mrchg Band; Pep Band; Symp Band; Im Vllybl; Hon Roll; NHS; Grove City Coll; Aerospace Engr.

CALDWELL, MELISSA; Donegal HS; Maytown, PA; (2); Varsity Clb; Chorus; Color Guard; Flag Corp; Mrchg Band; Ed Frsh Cls; Stu Cncl; Cheerleading; Trk; Hon Roll; Presdntl Physcl Ftnss Awd 85-86; Corp Law.

CALDWELL, MELISSA; Newport JRSR HS; Newport, PA; (3); 12/120; Church Yth Grp; Church Choir; School Play; Im Vllybl; Hon Roll; Achvmnt Awd 85; Dstnctn Awd Natl Lang Arts 85.

CALDWELL, RUSSELL; Waynesburg Central HS; Waynesburg, PA; (4); 31/180; Church Yth Grp; Spanish Clb; Band; Orch; Hgh Hnr Roll 85-87; Acadc Achvt-Advrsty 85; Past Mstr Cnclr Ordr Demolay 85-86; Art Inst Of Pgh; Intr Dsgn.

CALEN, MELISSA; Lincoln HS; Ellwood City, PA; (3); Hosp Aide; Latin Clb; Y-Teens; Band; Concert Band; Mrchg Band; Powder Puff Ftbl; High Hon Roll; Hon Roll; RN.

CALHOUN, ROXANNE; Blue Mountain Acad; Smethport, PA; (2); Teachers Aide; Bsktbl; Vllybl; High Hon Roll; 3 Hrn Rll Tmns In Typng 86; Andrews U; Pre-Calculus.

CALIBEO, NICOLE; Cocalico SR HS; Denver, PA; (4); 12/174; FBLA; Hosp Aide; VP Stu Cncl; Var JV Cheerleading; Im Fld Hcky; Var JV Sftbl; Im Trk; High Hon Roll; Typng Awd 87; Marywood Coll; Comm.

CALIFORNIA, JOHN; Kiski Area HS; Vandergrift, PA; (4); Computer Clb; Stage Crew; Ftbl; Hon Roll; U Of Pittsburgh; Comp Sci.

CALKINS, DENNIS; Cowanesque Valley HS; Westfield, PA; (4); Boy Scts; Church Yth Grp; French Clb; Letterman Clb; SADD; Chorus; School Musical; Stat Bsktbl; Hon Roll; Mansfield U; Bus Admin.

CALLA, KIMBERLY; Central Christian HS; Dubois, PA; (3); Hosp Aide; Sec Pep Clb; Chorus; Nwsp Stf; Yrbk Stf; Sec Soph Cls; Rep Stu Cncl; NHS.

CALLAGHAN, MARYANNE; Center Area HS; Monaca, PA; (4); 54/186; Latin Clb; Letterman Clb; Spanish Clb; Varsity Clb; Nwsp Rptr; Nwsp Stf; Powder Puff Ftbl; Var Capt Trk; Var Capt Vllybl; Cit Awd; Seton Hill Coll.

CALLAGHAN, THOMAS; Center Area HS; Monaca, PA; (2); Church Yth Grp; Cmnty Wkr; German Clb; Latin Clb; Varsity Clb; Yrbk Bus Mgr; Yrbk Stf; VP Soph Cls; Var L Bsbl; Var Bsktbl; HOBY 87; Ftbl Hon Mntn All Sctn Lnbckr 86; Bvr Cnty Colt Leag All Star Team 87; Notre Dame; Law.

CALLAHAN, BILL; Our Lady Of Lourdes HS; Shamokin, PA; (4); Cmnty Wkr; Key Clb; Pep Clb; Political Wkr; Varsity Clb; Rep Frsh Cls; Pres Jr Cls; Pres Stu Cncl; L Capt Bsbl; Capt Bsktbl; Susquehanna U; Math Tchr.

CALLAHAN, GARY; Northeast Catholic HS; Philadelphia, PA; (2); 54/363; Rstrnt Mngmnt.

CALLAHAN, MAUREEN; West Middlesex HS; New Wilmington, PA; (4); 12/92; Library Aide; Spanish Clb; Chorus; Var Capt Cheerleading; Hon Roll; Spanish NHS; Natl Sci Merit Awd 84; Ldrshp Awd 87; Sharon Genl Schl Of Nrsg; RN.

CALLAHAN, SUSAN; Spring Grove Area SR HS; Spring Grove, PA; (4); 4/275; Pres Church Yth Grp; Drama Clb; Chorus; Church Choir; School Musical; School Play; High Hon Roll; Jr NHS; NHS; Stu Of Mnth 86; Gftd Sci & Math Stu Smmr Prog 86; US AF Memrl Awd 87; Lehigh U; Engrng Physcs.

CALLANDER, MARY; Allegheny-Clarion Valley HS; Parker, PA; (4); 2/97; Sec Varsity Clb; Sec Stu Cncl; Var Capt Cheerleading; Var L Trk; Cit Awd; High Hon Roll; NHS; Sal; Army Schlr Athl Awd 87; Acad Athl Awd 87; Clarion U; Elem Educ.

CALLAWAY, ROBERT RYAN; Belle Vernon Area HS; Belle Vernon, PA; (3); Church Yth Grp; Ski Clb; SADD; VICA; Sec Jr Cls; JV Golf; L Mgr(s); JV Powder Puff Ftbl; Im Sftbl; Im Vllybl; Triangle Tech; Const Wrk.

CALLIHAN, BETH; Karns City Area HS; Chicora, PA; (4); 6/116; Church Yth Grp; Exploring; Band; Stage Crew; Hon Roll; NHS; Pres Schlr; St Schlr; Camera Clb; Concert Band; 1st Pl ST Awd-PA JR Acad Of Sci 86 & 87; Pres-Ntl Hnr Soc 86-87; SR All Amercn Band Hall/Fame 86; Westminster Coll; Chem.

CALLIHAN, DARREN; Karns City HS; Chicora, PA; (3); Boy Scts; Church Yth Grp; Bsktbl; Ftbl; Sftbl; Trk; U Of Pittsburgh; Sls.

CALLIHAN, JON; Johnstown Christian HS; Windber, PA; (4); 3/20; Church Yth Grp; Drama Clb; Chorus; Yrbk Stf; Pres Sr Cls; Var Bsbl; Var Bsktbl; Hon Roll; U PTSBRGH; Comp Sci.

CALLWOOD, JOYCELYN MONICE; Harrisburg HS; St John, PR; (4); 20/225; Dance Clb; 4-H; Leo Clb; CC Awd; High Hon Roll; Hon Roll; NHS; Princ Awd, Supts Awd & Pres Acdmc Ftnss Awd Pgm 87; Morris Coll; Secondary Educ.

CALLY, STEVEN J; Sun Valley HS; Brookhaven, PA; (4); 14/308; Intnl Clb; Var L Socr; JV L Swmmng; High Hon Roll; Lion Awd; NHS; Prfct Atten Awd; School Play; Stage Crew; Trk; PA ST Schlrs Awd & Scholar 87; PHEAA Cert Merit SAT Scores 87; Del Val Ath Assn Sportsmnshp Awd 87; PA ST U; Moleclr/Cell Bio.

CALNAN, DANIELLE; Donegal HS; Mount Joy, PA; (3); 52/176; Church Yth Grp; Drama Clb; FBLA; Pep Clb; Color Guard; Nwsp Stf; Yrbk Stf; Hon Roll; Natl Hstry Govt Awd 85; 2nd Pl Data Prcssng Cncpts FBLA Rgnls 86-87; Hlth Fld.

CALOMINO, MARK; Dunmore HS; Dunmore, PA; (3); 34/160; French Clb; FBLA; Var JV Bsbl; JV Bsktbl; Sprtsmnshp Awd-Shautz Tnr League 85; Accntng.

CALORE, TRACY; Parkland HS; Orefield, PA; (3); 21/491; SADD; High Hon Roll; NHS; USA Ntl Gymnstc Tm 83-87; USA Wrld Games Tm 85; Pblc Rltns.

CALPIN, SHARON; West Scranton HS; Scranton, PA; (3); 7/264; Orch; Hon Roll; Jr NHS; NHS; Acad All Amrcn; Vet Sci.

CALTAGARONE, JACQUELINE; Brookville Area HS; Sigel, PA; (3); Art Clb; VP Sec French Clb; Key Clb; Pep Clb; Varsity Clb; Pres Frsh Cls; Capt Sftbl; Var Vllybl; Jr NHS; Art Awds 85-86; Pittsburgh U; Phrmcy.

CALTAGIRONE, CHRIS; Conrad Weiser HS; Robesonia, PA; (3); 35/179; Drama Clb; FBLA; Golf; Tennis; Hon Roll; Cert Apprctn Local Polce 85; Theatre Arts.

CALVE, ROBERT; Mohawk JR-SR HS; Hillsville, PA; (3); 39/136; Latin Clb; Band; Concert Band; Mrchg Band; Pep Band; School Musical; School Play; Var Ftbl; Mgr(s); Powder Puff Ftbl; Penn ST U; Engr.

CALVERT, KANDICE; Conneaut Lake Area HS; Hartsown, PA; (3); Church Yth Grp; 4-H; Pep Clb; Spanish Clb; Concert Band; Mrchg Band; Var JV Bsktbl; Mgr(s); Mgr Sftbl; 4-H Awd; Drftng.

CALVERT, MICHELLE; Kennedy Christian HS; Hermitage, PA; (3); 46/98; Cmnty Wkr; Pep Clb; Spanish Clb; Mrchg Band; Sec Jr Cls; Sec Stu Cncl; Tennis; Hon Roll; Hmcmng Attndt 86-87; Kent ST U; Fshn Merch.

CALVEY, ELIZABETH; Shaler Area HS; Pittsburgh, PA; (3); 128/486; Drill Tm; Yrbk Bus Mgr; L Pom Pon; Hon Roll; Acctng.

CAMARATTA, FRANK; North Catholic HS; Philadelphia, PA; (2); 91/363; Cmnty Wkr; Hon Roll; Karate Champnshp Fnls 1st Pl 86; Temple U; Physcl Thrpst.

CAMARDA, ANTOINETTE; Sholer Area SR HS; Pittsburgh, PA; (4); 48/510; Exploring; JA; Band; Church Choir; Mrchg Band; School Musical; Symp Band; Ed Yrbk Rptr; Hon Roll; U Pittsburgh; Phys Ther.

CAMBERG, JENNIFER; Altoona Area HS; Altoona, PA; (4); 17/718; Cmnty Wkr; Spanish Clb; Jazz Band; Mrchg Band; Orch; Lit Mag; Swmmng; Twrlr; Jr NHS; NEDT Awd; Pres Physcl Fitns Awd; Brdcst Jrnlsm.

CAMBRUZZI, RITA; Yough SR HS; Ruffsdale, PA; (4); 19/235; Computer Clb; Drama Clb; 4-H; French Clb; SADD; Chorus; School Play; Variety Show; Nwsp Stf; Yrbk Stf; Thiel Acad Awd, Hugh O Brian Ldrshp Awd 87; Bst All Around Stu 87; Schl Bd Rep 85-87; Thiel Coll; Cmmnctns.

CAMERON, ANDY; Greenwood HS; Millerstown, PA; (3); Varsity Clb; VP Stu Cncl; Var Bsbl; Var Bsktbl; Var Socr; High Hon Roll; Hon Roll; NHS.

CAMERON, BETH; Steel Valley HS; West Homestead, PA; (4); 30/201; Pres Church Yth Grp; Varsity Clb; Band; Concert Band; Off Jr Cls; Trs Sr Cls; Score Keeper; Var L Swmmng; Hon Roll; NHS; Hmcmng Qn 86; Ed.

CAMERON, DANIEL; Greenwood HS; Millerwtown, PA; (1); Church Yth Grp; Pres Frsh Cls; JV Bsbl; JV Bsktbl; JV Socr; Cit Awd; High Hon Roll; Amer Leg Awd Outstndng Boy 86; Math.

CAMERON, JAMIE; Central Cambria HS; Ebensburg, PA; (4); 5/209; French Clb; FBLA; Library Aide; Score Keeper; Sftbl; High Hon Roll; Hon Roll; Penn ST; Bus Anlysis.

CAMERON, LISA; Wyoming Seminary College Prep; Wyoming, PA; (2); Letterman Clb; Varsity Clb; Chorus; Var L Bsktbl; Var L Fld Hcky; Var L Sftbl; High Hon Roll; NEDT Awd; Prfct Atten Awd; MVP Grls Bsktbl 86-87; Semifnlst Gvrnrs Schl For Arts 87; Gld Kys Schlstc Art Awd 86&87; Oceangrphy.

CAMERON, LYNNE; Milton Area SR HS; Milton, PA; (2); Intnl Clb; Spanish Clb; Chorus; Color Guard; Mrchg Band; Rep Stu Cncl; Trk; Twrlr; Hon Roll; Prfct Atten Awd; Pres Acad Ftns Awd 85.

CAMERON, MELISSA; Clairton HS; Clairton, PA; (3); High Hon Roll; NHS; Penn St.

CAMILLI, KEITH; Hershey SR HS; Hummelstown, PA; (3); 14/210; Boy Scts; Var Crs Cntry; Var Swmmng; JV Trk; God Cntry Awd; High Hon Roll; NHS; Ntl Merit Ltr; Opt Clb Awd; Voice Dem Awd; Sci Olympiad Tm 2 Time Natl Fnlsts 85-86/86-87; Quiz Bowl Rgnl Comp 86-87.

CAMMAUF, SUANNE; Cocalico HS; Denver, PA; (1); 40/180; Pres Frsh Cls; Rep Stu Cncl; Im Badmtn; Var L Cheerleading; Fld Hcky; Im Socr; Im Vllybl; Hon Roll; Kutztown U; Danc.

CAMP, JAMES; Cathedral Prep; Erie, PA; (3); 44/191; Letterman Clb; Var L Bsktbl; Var L Trk; Var Vllybl; Hon Roll; Tng Actn Clb; Actn Clb Brd Pblc Rltns Ofc.

CAMP, JEAN; Leechburg Area HS; Leechburg, PA; (4); 4/82; Church Yth Grp; Library Aide; Chorus; Yrbk Stf; High Hon Roll; Hon Roll; NHS; Pres Acadmc Ftns Awd 87; Hnr Stu 87; IN U Of PA; Acctng.

CAMP, JOEL; Pelers Township HS; Venelia, PA; (3); Church Yth Grp; Pres German Clb; Political Wkr; Acpl Chr; Chorus; Concert Band; Jazz Band; Variety Show; Nwsp Stf; VP Frsh Cls; Arch.

CAMP, LISA; St Benedict Acad; Erie, PA; (4); 9/60; Q&S; Quiz Bowl; Yrbk Stf; Lit Mag; Stu Cncl; Var Bsktbl; Var Tennis; Hon Roll; NHS; Pres Schlr; Hugh Obrien Yth Ldrshp Smnr; PA Schl Prss Awd; Egan Hnrs Schlrshp; Mercyhurst Coll; Sprts Med.

CAMP, ROZ; West Snyder HS; Beavertown, PA; (3); 4/85; Varsity Clb; Pres Band; Jazz Band; School Musical; Pres Jr Cls; Var Bsktbl; Var Fld Hcky; Var Sftbl; NHS; NEDT Awd; Sprts Med.

CAMPAGNA, JEANINE; Penn Cambria HS; Lilly, PA; (3); 7/216; SADD; Frsh Cls; Bsktbl; NHS; ST Free Thrw Champn 85; Tri Cnty All Strs 86-87; Pres Physcl Ftnss Awds 84-87; Archtctr.

CAMPAGNA, SHERRY; Penn Cambria HS; Cresson, PA; (3); Camera Clb; Drama Clb; Speech Tm; SADD; VP Jr Cls; High Hon Roll; Intl Forgn Lang Awd Wnnr 86-87; Presdntl Physcl Fitness Awd 85-87; PA ST U; Nurse Anesthetist.

CAMPBELL, AMY; Donegal HS; Mt Joy, PA; (3); 11/174; Band; Color Guard; School Play; Nwsp Rptr; Hst Sr Cls; Sec Stu Cncl; JV Cheerleading; Hon Roll; NHS; Spanish NHS; Cmmnctns.

CAMPBELL, ANDRE J W; Pine Forge Acad; S Orange, NJ; (1); 3/45; Church Yth Grp; Library Aide; Math Tm; Ski Clb; Acpl Chr; Band; Color Guard; Capt Drill Tm; Capt Drm & Bgl; VP Frsh Cls; Schlrshp Pine Frg Acad 86; Acdmc Achvmnt Awd 86; Hnr Rll Cert; Oakwood Coll; Law.

CAMPBELL, ANNE; Butler Intermediate HS; Butler, PA; (2); Church Yth Grp; Drama Clb; French Clb; German Clb; Mrchg Band; Var L Crs Cntry; Var Trk; Hon Roll; Pres Jr NHS; Math Tm; Acad Lttr For JR Natl Hnr Scty 87.

CAMPBELL, BILL; Avella JR-SR HS; Avella, PA; (2); ROTC; Drill Tm; Var L Ftbl; Trk; Wt Lftg; Hon Roll; Prfct Atten Awd; Computer Clb; 4-H; Phys Fit Awd 85-87; Rifle Tm 85-86; JROTC 85-86.

CAMPBELL, BRIAN; Ft Cherry HS; Bulger, PA; (2); Church Yth Grp; High Hon Roll; Hon Roll; Computers.

CAMPBELL, CATHLEEN; Steel Valley HS; Munhall, PA; (3); VP Key Clb; Latin Clb; Band; Mrchg Band; Yrbk Stf; Sec Frsh Cls; High Hon Roll; Hon Roll; NHS; Grphc Arts.

CAMPBELL, CHRISTINE; Bellwood-Antis JR SR HS; Tyrone, PA; (2); SADD; Band; Chorus; Concert Band; Jazz Band; Mrchg Band; Pep Band; School Musical; Symp Band; Sci Day Juniata Coll 86; Sci Stu Top 10 84-86; Awd Span I, Eng & Sci 85-86; Juniata Coll; Psych.

CAMPBELL, CHRISTINE; Sharpsville Area HS; Sharpsville, PA; (3); Camera Clb; Sec Trs Chess Clb; Math Clb; Ski Clb; Chorus; Drill Tm; School Musical; Nwsp Ed-Chief; Yrbk Stf; Rep Soph Cls; Dist, Rgnl Chorus 87; Smmr Acad Perfrmng Arts 87; Jrnlsm.

CAMPBELL, CRYSTAL; Chester HS; Chester, PA; (2); Key Clb; Chorus; Hon Roll; Awd Math Outstndng Achvt 87; Awd Acdmc Achvt & Persnl Grwth 87; Indstrl Engrng.

CAMPBELL, DAVID R; Berwick Area HS; Berwick, PA; (4); 6/200; Boys Clb Am; Rep Stu Cncl; Capt Var Ftbl; L Var Trk; Hon Roll; Jr NHS; NHS; Ntl Merit SF; Lbrl Arts.

CAMPBELL, DEBORAH; William Penn HS; York, PA; (3); 29/374; Mrchg Band; School Play; Stage Crew; Variety Show; Nwsp Stf; Yrbk Stf; VP Stu Cncl; Var JV Bsktbl; JV L Trk; Hon Roll; 2nd Pl Mdl Dist Bsktbl, & Stu Mnth Awd 86-87; IN U PA; Brdcst Jrnlsm.

CAMPBELL, DENISE; Chester HS; Chester, PA; (3); Teachers Aide; Hon Roll; Sci Awd 86; Comp Oprtr.

CAMPBELL, DONALD H; Mt Pleasant Area HS; Acme, PA; (3); Boy Scts; Pres Church Yth Grp; German Clb; L Var Bsbl; JV Var Ftbl; Hon Roll; Comp Sci.

CAMPBELL, DOREEN K; Bradford Area HS; Derrick City, PA; (3); AFS; Drama Clb; Yrbk Stf; Crs Cntry; Trk; Prfct Atten Awd; PA Free Entrprs Wk 87; Trvl.

CAMPBELL, DWIN; Dallas SR HS; Dallas, PA; (3); Band; Concert Band; Drm Mjr(t); Mrchg Band; School Musical; Hon Roll; JP Sousa Awd; NHS; PMEA Dist IX Band 87, Rgn IV Band 87; Ithaca Coll; Music.

CAMPBELL, ED; Abraham Lincoln HS; Philadelphia, PA; (3); 15/540; Pres Church Yth Grp; Spanish Clb; Speech Tm; Nwsp Sprt Ed; Rptr Frsh Cls; Rptr Soph Cls; Jr Cls; JV Capt Bsbl; JV Bsktbl; JV Var Socr; Mntlly Gftd Pgm; Colonl PHLDLPHIA Hstrcl Soc Essy Fnlst 86.

CAMPBELL, ELIZABETH; South Williamsport Area HS; S Williamsport, PA; (4); 1/140; Pres Key Clb; Sec Concert Band; Sec Mrchg Band; Rep Stu Cncl; JETS Awd; High Hon Roll; NHS; Val; Var Tennis; Var Trk; Amer Legion Aux Awd; Provost Schlrshp; Dist & Regnl Orch; U Of Pittsburgh; Bio-Chem.

CAMPBELL, GWENDOLYN M; The Agnes Irwin Schl; Strafford, PA; (4); Pres Debate Tm; Nwsp Bus Mgr; Yrbk Phtg; VP Sr Cls; Pres Stu Cncl; Capt Fld Hcky; High Hon Roll; Ntl Merit SF; Camera Clb; Cmnty Wkr; Havard Clb Phila Prz Bk 86; Top Schlr Awd Psych Clss Brown U Smmr Acad Crrnt Evnts Clb Pres 86.

CAMPBELL, HEATHER; Catasauqua HS; Catasauqua, PA; (3); Ski Clb; Yrbk Stf; Stu Cncl; Var Capt Cheerleading; Powder Puff Ftbl; Trk.

CAMPBELL, HEATHER; Lincoln HS; Ellwood City, PA; (3); 103/168; AFS; Camera Clb; Church Yth Grp; French Clb; Girl Scts; Y-Teens; Im Powder Puff Ftbl; Stat Trk; Hon Roll; Bus Admin.

CAMPBELL, JAMES; Glendale JR SR HS; Coalport, PA; (3); 3/73; Church Yth Grp; Cmnty Wkr; Science Clb; Yrbk Bus Mgr; Yrbk Stf; VP Soph Cls; Wt Lftg; DAR Awd; High Hon Roll; NHS.

CAMPBELL, JEFF; Canon-Mc Millan SR HS; Canonsburg, PA; (3); 54/349; Boy Scts; Pres Exploring; Ski Clb; Yrbk Phtg; Var L Golf; Var L Trk; Hon Roll; Ad Altare Dei Awd 87; Pilot.

CAMPBELL, JEFFREY; Punxsutawney Area HS; Punxsutawney, PA; (3); Varsity Clb; JV Bsbl; Var L Golf; Hon Roll; Mst Imprvd JR Glfr 86; Engrng.

CAMPBELL, JENNIFER; Ringgold HS; Donora, PA; (4); 10/290; School Musical; Hon Roll; Rotary Awd; Duffs Bus Inst; Exec Sec.

CAMPBELL, JENNIFER; Riverside HS; Beaver Falls, PA; (2); FHA; Pep Clb; Pres Chorus; Color Guard; Concert Band; Drill Tm; Mrchg Band; School Musical; Trk; Hon Roll; Pittsburgh Coll; Physcl Thrpy.

CAMPBELL II, JOHN; Mercer Area JR SR HS; Mercer, PA; (3); VP Church Yth Grp; SADD; School Play; Trs Soph Cls; Var Trk; Hon Roll; Prfct Atten Awd; Bus Adm.

CAMPBELL, KARNICE; Pine Forge Acad; Chapel Hill, NC; (4); 8/82; Drill Tm; VP Sr Cls; Cheerleading; NHS; Drill Tm; Rep Jr Cls; L Swmmng; Im Vllybl; High Hon Roll; Yng Comm Ldrs Of Amer; U Of NC; Acctng.

CAMPBELL, KEELY; Ridgway Area HS; Johnsonburg, PA; (4); 1/107; Ski Clb; Pres Frsh Cls; Pres Soph Cls; JV Cheerleading; Im JV Vllybl; High Hon Roll; Jr NHS; NHS; Val; PA ST U; Mlclr & Cll Bio.

CAMPBELL, KELLY; Karns City HS; Petrolia, PA; (3); Church Yth Grp; Spanish Clb; SADD; Stage Crew; Yrbk Stf; Cheerleading; Hon Roll; Timer; Pres Schlr; Rotary Awd; Pltcl Sci.

CAMPBELL, KEVIN; Haverford SR HS; Havertown, PA; (1); Ski Clb; Bsktbl; Var Socr; Im Wt Lftg; Hon Roll.

CAMPBELL, KIM; Elizabeth Forward HS; Elizabeth, PA; (2); Church Yth Grp; Exploring; French Clb; Drm Mjr(t); High Hon Roll; Hon Roll; Psych.

CAMPBELL, KIMBERLEE; Chichester SR HS; Linwood, PA; (3); 16/296; French Clb; SADD; Band; Chorus; Concert Band; Mrchg Band; School Musical; School Play; Lit Mag; Capt Twrlr; West Chester U; Music Educ.

CAMPBELL, KRISTIE; Connelsville Area SR HS; Normalville, PA; (3); Trs Church Yth Grp; Sec FHA; Band; Concert Band; Mrchg Band; Hon Roll.

CAMPBELL, MARK; Exeter Twp SR HS; Reading, PA; (4); 26/215; Capt Pres Key Clb; Varsity Clb; Rep Stu Cncl; Var Capt Ftbl; Var L Trk; High Hon Roll; Jr NHS; NHS; All Cnty, IC Leag, 1st Tm, Def Bck Ftbl, Trck 3 PA Dist, Hmcmnt Crt 86; Bus Admn.

CAMPBELL, MARY ELLEN; Bishop Kenrick HS; Norristown, PA; (4); 101/287; Church Yth Grp; Cmnty Wkr; Hosp Aide; Office Aide; Spanish Clb; JV Crs Cntry; Hon Roll; Prfct Atten Awd; Cash Awd Christian Chrctr & Loyalty 87; Montgomery County CC; Nrsng.

CAMPBELL, MEGAN; W Middlesex HS; Pulaski, PA; (4); 5/92; French Clb; Band; Chorus; Variety Show; Nwsp Stf; Ed Yrbk Ed-Chief; Sec Sr Cls; Pres Stu Cncl; Trk; Vllybl; Pre Laws.

CAMPBELL, MELISSA; Freeport HS; Sarver, PA; (3); Church Yth Grp; Chorus; Church Choir; School Musical; Hon Roll.

CAMPBELL, MONICA; Oxford Area HS; Nottingham, PA; (3); Church Yth Grp; Band; Chorus; Church Choir; Color Guard; Flag Corp; Mrchg Band; Nwsp Phtg; Nwsp Rptr; Twrlr; Hnr Rll 84-86; Twrlng 87-88; Chrs 86-88; Trvl.

CAMPBELL, NICOLE; Seneca Valley SR HS; Mars, PA; (2); Art Clb; Pitt U; Acctnt.

CAMPBELL, RICHARD; Danville HS; Danville, PA; (3).

CAMPBELL JR, RICHARD LEE; Saltsburg SR HS; Saltsburg, PA; (2); Bsktbl; Comp Prog.

CAMPBELL, SCOTT; Laurel Highlands HS; Hopwood, PA; (4); JA; Science Clb; Hon Roll; JETS Awd; Ntl Merit Ltr; NEDT Awd; PA JR Acad Sci ST 85 & 87; Boston U; Comp Engr.

CAMPBELL, SCOTT; Marion Center Area HS; Indiana, PA; (3); 21/149; Var Bsbl; High Hon Roll; Hon Roll; Engrng.

CAMPBELL, SHANON; South Western HS; Hanover, PA; (2); Key Clb; Varsity Clb; Chorus; Nwsp Stf; Golf; Swmmng.

CAMPBELL, SHERI LYNN; West Mifflin Area HS; West Mifflin, PA; (4); Hosp Aide; Pres Science Clb; Sec Band; Sec Concert Band; Sec Mrchg Band; Pres Orch; Pep Band; Var Mat Maids; Stat Wrstlng; Hon Roll; Edinboro U Of PA; Nursing.

CAMPBELL, SUSAN; Greensburg Salem SR HS; Delmont, PA; (3); Art Clb; Pep Clb; Ski Clb; Spanish Clb; VICA; Band; Im Cheerleading; Im Sftbl; Im Twrlr; Hon Roll; Westmoreland CC; Interior Dsgn.

CAMPBELL, TIMOTHY; Archbishop Wood HS; Churchville, PA; (4); 60/270; Library Aide; Nwsp Stf; Bowling; Penn ST U; Bio.

CAMPBELL, TIMOTHY; Williamsburg Community HS; Williamsburg, PA; (4); 2/69; Trs Church Yth Grp; Letterman Clb; Varsity Clb; Nwsp Ed-Chief; Yrbk Stf; Trs Sr Cls; Stu Cncl; Bsbl; Ftbl; Bausch & Lomb Sci Awd; Babe Ruth Sprtsmnshp Awd 87; Stu Athltc Awd 87; Micro Age Math Awd 87; Penn ST U; Arch.

CAMPBELL, TRACEY; Archbishop Carroll HS; Philadelphia, PA; (3); 198/375; Girl Scts; Intnl Clb; Library Aide; SADD; Variety Show; Rep Frsh Cls; Sec Jr Cls; Prfct Atten Awd; Minority Affairs Awd 87; NC-FAYETTEVILLE U; Bio.

CAMPBELL, VALERIE; Waynesburg Central HS; Mt Morris, PA; (3); Spanish Clb; Chorus; Church Choir; Hon Roll; NHS; Frederic Chopin Piano Awd.

CAMPBELL, WILLIAM; Abraham Lincoln HS; Philadelphia, PA; (3); Cmnty Wkr; Office Aide; Nwsp Rptr; Nwsp Sprt Ed; Lit Mag; Off Stu Cncl; JV Var Bsbl; JV Var Ftbl; Cmmnctns.

CAMPBELL, YOLANDA M; Harry S Truman HS; Levittown, PA; (3); Art Clb; Girl Scts; Speech Tm; School Play; Bsktbl; Swmmng; Trk; Hon Roll; Law.

CAMPER, THOMAS; Chester HS; Chester, PA; (3); 40/428; French Clb; Jazz Band; Mrchg Band; Stat Bsktbl; JV Ftbl; Var Trk; High Hon Roll; Jr NHS; Prfct Atten Awd; Rotry Intl Tomrrws Ldrshp Conf 87; Accntng.

CAMPHIRE, CHRIS; Pennsbury HS; Morrisville, PA; (3); Church Yth Grp; Bsbl; Im Ftbl; Intl Studs.

CAMPION, ELIZABETH S; Harriton HS; Villanova, PA; (3); VP Service Clb; Yrbk Stf; Pres Soph Cls; Sec Stu Cncl; Var Cheerleading; JV Capt Fld Hcky; Var Capt Lcrss; High Hon Roll; NHS; Cmnty Wkr; Principals Awd 87.

CAMPOLI, WENDI; New Castle SR HS; New Castle, PA; (4); 23/228; AFS; Exploring; Library Aide; Office Aide; Spanish Clb; High Hon Roll; Hon Roll; NHS; Pres Schlr; Soc Studs Dept Awd 87; Acad Gen Scholar Westminster Coll 87; Westminster Coll; Pre-Law.

CAMPOMIZZI, STEPHANIE; Cardinal Brennan HS; Ashland, PA; (3); Band; Chorus; Concert Band; Mrchg Band; School Musical; Yrbk Stf; Capt Var Cheerleading; Pre Elem Ed.

CANAVAN, HILARY; Academy Of Notre Dame; Lafayette Hill, PA; (3); 20/76; Art Clb; Pres Camera Clb; Service Clb; Yrbk Phtg; Yrbk Stf; Tennis; Hon Roll; Philadelphia Archdcsn Schlr 87-88; Moore Coll Schlrshp 86-88; Gold Key Awd Philadelphia Coll Of Art 87; Photgrphy.

CANAVAN, JEFFREY; Somerset Area HS; Somerset, PA; (3); 44/220; Boy Scts; Church Yth Grp; Computer Clb; English Clb; German Clb; Ski Clb; Band; Concert Band; Mrchg Band; Yrbk Stf; Eagle Scout Awd 85; Cert Accmplshmnt Proj Bus J A 85; Band Ltr 86; Order Of Arrow 82-87; Penn ST U; Bus.

CANAVAN, JENNIFER; Methacton HS; Lansdale, PA; (3); 64/381; Church Yth Grp; Office Aide; Red Cross Aide; Var Lcrss; Var Swmmng; High Hon Roll; Mst Vlble Swmmr, Acad Awd For Dist Hnrs 86 & 87; Elem Ed.

CANAVAN, JOHN; Cathedral Prep; Erie, PA; (3); 92/194; Church Yth Grp; Letterman Clb; Stu Cncl; Var L Wrstlng; Crimnl Justc.

CANAVAN, MARIA; Cardinal Brennan HS; Frackville, PA; (3); 12/58; Chorus; Rep Stu Cncl; Var Sftbl; Capt Twrlr; Hon Roll; Sec NHS; Church Yth Grp; German Clb; Ski Clb; School Musical; Schlrshp 84-85; Pharm.

CANCEL, JEN; Pennsbury HS; Fairless Hls, PA; (3); Art Clb; Y-Teens; Nwsp Rptr; Yrbk Ed-Chief; Lit Mag; Rep Frsh Cls; Rep Soph Cls; Rep Stu Cncl; JV Cheerleading; JV Var Sftbl; Scl Wrk.

CANDELA, DANIEL; North Allegheny SR HS; Pittsburgh, PA; (3); 109/649; Boy Scts; Var L Swmmng; Cit Awd; God Cntry Awd; Hon Roll; VFW Awd; Egl Sct 85; Sci.

CANE, CATHY JO; Rockwood Area HS; Somerset, PA; (2); Sec FBLA; Office Aide; Chorus; High Hon Roll; Hon Roll; Awd Highest Grade In Section 85-86; Bus.

CANFIELD, JENNIFER; Tunkhannock Area HS; Tunkhannock, PA; (3); 50/365; Drama Clb; German Clb; Band; Church Choir; Concert Band; Jazz Band; Mrchg Band; Pep Band; School Musical; School Play; PA Music Educ Assoc Wnnr 81; Hstrns Clb 86; Dist Band 85-86; Music Ed.

CANFIELD JR, JOSEPH; Bishop Mc Devitt HS; Harrisburg, PA; (3); 6/226; VP FBLA; Capt Golf; NHS; Ntl Merit Ltr; Computer Clb; Ski Clb; Yrbk Sprt Ed; Var Tennis; Hon Roll; Key Stone Boys ST 87; Accntng.

CANFIELD, JUDY; Susquehanna Community HS; Susquehanna, PA; (3); Band; Concert Band; Rep Stu Cncl; Stat Crs Cntry; Powder Puff Ftbl; Sftbl; Capt Co-Capt Vllybl; Phy Thrpy.

CANFIELD, STEPHEN; Oswayo Valley HS; Shinglehouse, PA; (3); 1/75; Boy Scts; Church Yth Grp; Band; Mrchg Band; Var Wrstlng; High Hon Roll; NHS; Mechncl Engrng.

CANJAR, JENNIFER; Morrisville HS; Morrisville, PA; (3); 6/90; FBLA; Sec Frsh Cls; Sec Soph Cls; Sec Jr Cls; High Hon Roll; Hon Roll; NHS; Bus Law ST Fnls 87; DE Vly Coll; Chem.

CANN, RHONDA; Purchase Line HS; Cherry Tree, PA; (3); 20/156; FBLA; Mrchg Band; Nwsp Stf; Trk; Capt Twrlr; Wt Lftg; Hon Roll; Bus Mngr.

CANN, TONYA; Purchase Line HS; Cherry Tree, PA; (3); #8 In Class; Mrchg Band; Nwsp Ed-Chief; Nwsp Stf; Hon Roll; NHS; Journlsm.

CANNARSA, MICHELLE R; Hollidaysburg Area Schl; Duncansville, PA; (3); 2/385; Drama Clb; Science Clb; Ski Clb; Band; Chorus; Orch; Swing Chorus; Lit Mag; High Hon Roll; NHS; Intensv Lang Inst Scholar PA ST U 87; PA ST Band Fest 87; American U; Lang.

CANNELLA, JEREMY C; Downingtown SR HS; West Chester, PA; (4); 38/560; Chorus; Concert Band; Mrchg Band; School Musical; Swing Chorus; Symp Band; Nwsp Stf; Bowling; Ntl Merit SF; Hon Roll; 3 Yr Bnd Pn 86-87; 2 Yr Bnd Lttr 85-86; Bus Admn.

CANNEY, CATHLEEN; Lansdale Catholic HS; Lansdale, PA; (3); 41/225; Cmnty Wkr; Drama Clb; SADD; Church Choir; School Musical; Stage Crew; Lit Mag; Hon Roll; Prfct Atten Awd; Hrnable Mntn Wrld Ptry Cntst Ctgry Grt Amer 87; Gldn Globe Awd Ptry 87; Pediatrics.

CANNON, AMY; Hopewell HS; Aliquippa, PA; (3); 30/255; Pres Church Yth Grp; Dance Clb; Drama Clb; German Clb; Spanish Clb; VP Thesps; School Musical; School Play; Variety Show; NHS; Special Education.

CANNON, AMY; Trinity HS; Camp Hill, PA; (3); 25/150; Church Yth Grp; Cmnty Wkr; Model UN; Ski Clb; Spanish Clb; Yrbk Stf; Sr Cls; JV Crs Cntry; Hon Roll; Pep Clb; PAL; Piano Cmptn Harrisburg Arts Fest 4th Pl 85; Bus.

CANNON JR, DONALD; Dover Area HS; Dover, PA; (3); Band; Concert Band; Mrchg Band; Symp Band; Ed Yrbk Stf; High Hon Roll; Hon Roll; Stu Tutor 87; Engrng.

CANNON, ROBERT J; Bishop Hafey HS; Hazleton, PA; (2); 29/106; JA; Ski Clb; Var Bsktbl; Im Crs Cntry; Im Trk; Wt Lftg; Hon Roll; U Of Scranton; Psych.

CANNON, SUSAN; Norwin SR HS; Westmoreland City, PA; (3); Church Yth Grp; DECA; FBLA; Library Aide; Teachers Aide; Sec Stu Cncl; Powder Puff Ftbl; Hon Roll; NHS; 5th Pl Finance & Crdt 87; ST Cmptn Finance & Crdt 87; Secy DECA Clb 86-87; Westmoreland CC; Mrktng.

CANNONIE, PATRICK; Penn Cambria HS; Lilly, PA; (3); JV Var Ftbl; Hon Roll; IN U Of PA; Bus.

CANOSA, HANS; Blue Mountain Acad; Hamburg, PA; (3); 1/66; Band; Chorus; Nwsp Ed-Chief; Nwsp Rptr; Ed Nwsp Stf; Off Frsh Cls; Pres Soph Cls; High Hon Roll; Val; Harvard Schl Of Bus; Bus Admin.

CANOSA, HEIDI; Blue Mountain Acad; Hamburg, PA; (1); Band; Gym; High Hon Roll; Vet.

CANOVA, DEREK; Penns Valley Area HS; Spring Mills, PA; (3); 8/150; Boy Scts; Ski Clb; Sec Varsity Clb; Var L Ftbl; JV L Trk; Dnfth Awd; High Hon Roll; Hon Roll; Pres Schlr; PA ST.

CANTALUPO, PAUL; Northern Cambria HS; Barnesboro, PA; (3); 1/152; Computer Clb; Debate Tm; Speech Tm; Nwsp Sprt Ed; Nwsp Stf; Var Trk; High Hon Roll; NHS; Natl Hstry Day-Lcl, Dist & ST 86.

CANTALUPO, SCOT; Littlestown HS; Littlestown, PA; (2); 4-H; FFA; VICA; Stage Crew; Trk; Hon Roll; Technlgy Arts.

CANTERINI, DAMIAN; James M Coughlin HS; Wilkes Barre, PA; (3); 6/374; Band; Concert Band; Mrchg Band; High Hon Roll; Hon Roll; NHS; NEDT Awd.

CANTERNA, KIERSTEN; Trinity HS; Washington, PA; (2); Ski Clb; Swmmng; Trk; Vllybl.

CANTEY, VERNETTA; Strawberry Mansion HS; Phila, PA; (3); 1/120; Rep Stu Cncl; High Hon Roll; NHS; Temple; Psych.

CANTOLINA, ANGELINA; West Branch Area HS; Morrisdale, PA; (3); 5/118; Science Clb; Spanish Clb; Chorus; Color Guard; Mrchg Band; School Play; Stage Crew; Hon Roll; Cert Of Merit For Outstndng Accmplshmnt In Russian I 86; Engl.

CANTOLINA, MICHAEL; West Branch Area HS; Morrisdale, PA; (2); Science Clb; JV Ftbl; JV Var Wt Lftg; Hon Roll; Prfct Atten Awd; PA ST U; Elec Engr.

CANTOLINA, PATRICIA; West Branch Area HS; Morrisdale, PA; (3); Drama Clb; Hosp Aide; Library Aide; SADD; Band; Chorus; Concert Band; Mrchg Band; Stage Crew; Penn ST; Counselor.

CANTONE, AUDRA; Allentown Central Catholic HS; Macungie, PA; (4); 13/208; Intnl Clb; Pep Clb; High Hon Roll; Hon Roll; NHS; 1st Pl PA JR Acad Of Sci; Lehigh U; Bhvrl Bio.

CANTRILL, CHRISTINA; Philadelphia HS For Girls; Philadelphia, PA; (3); 17/405; Teachers Aide; Orch; School Musical; Variety Show; Var JV Fld Hcky; Im Lcrss; Var JV Sftbl; High Hon Roll; Ellis Scholar Intl Vistors Pgm 87.

CANTWELL, BRYAN; Father Judge HS; Philadelphia, PA; (3); 66/409; Band; Concert Band; Drm & Bgl; Jazz Band; Mrchg Band; Symp Band; Temple; Comp Tech.

CANTWELL, DAVID C; Owen J Roberts HS; Phoenixville, PA; (3); 15/300; Boy Scts; Church Yth Grp; Rep Key Clb; Band; Concert Band; Mrchg Band; School Musical; School Play; Yrbk Stf; Bsktbl; Ldrshp Conf 86; Amnesty Intl 86; Med.

CANTWELL, SUZANNE E; St Basil Acad; Philadelphia, PA; (4); Dance Clb; Drama Clb; French Clb; Sec FBLA; PAVAS; Spanish Clb; SADD; Chorus; School Play; Variety Show; Temple U Grant 87; Engl Awd 83; Temple U; Dance.

CANUSO, DONALD J; Archbishop Ryan HS For Boys; Philadelphia, PA; (3); 18/419; Hon Roll; Hnr Theology; Hnr In English 86.

CANZANO, KRIS; Wm Allen HS; Allentown, PA; (3); Letterman Clb; Ski Clb; Varsity Clb; Var Gym; Stat Mgr(s); Var Capt Vllybl; Im Wt Lftg; Hon Roll; Mc Cormick Book Awd 87; Ldrs Clb Pres 87-88; Comm.

CAO, PHUONG; Waynesboro SR HS; Waynesboro, PA; (3); 18/396; Chess Clb; Library Aide; Band; Bowling; Var Socr; Cit Awd; High Hon Roll; Hon Roll; NHS; Pres Schlr; Pres Acdmc Awd 85; Penn ST; Elctrc Engrng.

CAP, ANDREW; Notre Dame HS; Easton, PA; (3); 4/96; Boy Scts; Scholastic Bowl; Band; School Musical; School Play; Tennis; Hon Roll; NHS; Ntl Merit SF.

CAPAN, DONNA; Uniontown SR HS; Vanderbilt, PA; (3); Office Aide; Spanish Clb; Teachers Aide; Bsktbl; Ftbl; Hon Roll.

CAPAN, DOROTHY; Union City HS; Union City, PA; (3); 5/120; Pres Varsity Clb; Powder Puff Ftbl; High Hon Roll; NHS; Pres Schlr; Var JV Bsktbl; Var L Cheerleading; Var L Crs Cntry; Var L Trk; Prsdntl Phys Ftns Awd All-County Cross Country Busy Bear Awd; Med Doctor.

CAPASSO, CINDA; Hempfield Area SR HS; Greensburg, PA; (4); 210/693; Pep Clb; SADD; Varsity Clb; VP VICA; Yrbk Phtg; Yrbk Stf; Var JV Cheerleading; High Hon Roll; Csmtlgy.

CAPASSO, WENDY; Hempfield Area SR HS; Irwin, PA; (2); Pep Clb; Spanish Clb; Band; Concert Band; Mrchg Band; Rep Stu Cncl; Var Vllybl; Cit Awd; Hon Roll; Jr NHS; Tchr.

CAPATOSTI, JENNIFER; Brownsville Area HS; Brownsville, PA; (4); 37/200; Drama Clb; Office Aide; Ski Clb; SADD; Flag Corp; Mrchg Band; Yrbk Bus Mgr; Yrbk Stf; Stat Trk; Hon Roll; CA U Of PA.

CAPECCI, MICHAEL E; Mt Lebanon HS; Pittsburgh, PA; (4); Camera Clb; Dance Clb; Pres Debate Tm; Drama Clb; English Clb; Pres NFL; PAVAS; Speech Tm; School Musical; School Play; Lvl III Awd Arts Rcgntn 86-87; Zonta Clb Prfrmng Arts Awd 86-87; PA ST Chmp PHSSL Frnscs 85-86; NY U; Drmtc Arts.

CAPECE, DENA; New Castle SR HS; New Castle, PA; (3); Office Aide; Drill Tm; Vllybl; Hon Roll; Italian Clb; Elem Ed.

CAPELLI, ANGELIA; Blacklick Valley HS; Nanty Glo, PA; (4); 13/91; Art Clb; Camera Clb; 4-H; High Hon Roll; Hon Roll; NHS; Acad All Amer 86; Robert Morris Coll; Actg.

CAPELLO, CHRISTA; Trinity HS; Camp Hill, PA; (2); 8/140; Drama Clb; Exploring; French Clb; Model UN; NFL; Pep Clb; School Play; High Hon Roll; Schlrshp Intnsv Lang Inst Penn ST U 87; Intl Rltns.

CAPERS JR, LARRY C; Abraham Lincoln HS; Philadelphia, PA; (3); JV Bsktbl; Hon Roll; Elec Engr.

CAPETILLO, NELSON; Roman Catholic HS; Philadelphia, PA; (4); 18/130; Boy Scts; Church Yth Grp; Computer Clb; Office Aide; Hon Roll; NHS; Prfct Atten Awd; 4 Yr Schlrshp Rmn Cthlc 83-87; 4 Yr Schlrshp Wstchstr U 87; West Chester U; Engnrng.

CAPEZZUTI, CHERYL; Hampton HS; Gibsonia, PA; (3); Church Yth Grp; Spanish Clb; Rep Jr Cls; Rep Stu Cncl; Capt Powder Puff Ftbl; Var L Swmmng; Var L Vllybl; High Hon Roll; NHS; Most Imprvd Swmmr 85; Penn ST; Archtctr.

CAPIROSE, LISA; Pennsbury SR HS; Levittown, PA; (4); 11/771; Cmnty Wkr; Math Tm; Spanish Clb; Cit Awd; Hon Roll; NHS; Pres Acad Fitness Awd; Achvmnt Awd Of Acad Excllnc; Bucknell U; Psycht.

CAPIZZI, JACKIE; North Catholic HS; Pittsburgh, PA; (3); 32/275; Spanish Clb; Trs Frsh Cls; Capt Bsktbl; High Hon Roll; Hon Roll; NHS; Bus.

CAPLAN, IRA; Chartiers Valley HS; Pittsburgh, PA; (3); Ski Clb; Temple Yth Grp; Varsity Clb; School Musical; Nwsp Rptr; Bsktbl; Var Swmmng; NHS.

CAPLINGER, JILL; Center Area HS; Monaca, PA; (3); 43/186; Sec Church Yth Grp; Girl Scts; Latin Clb; Band; Rep Stu Cncl; Hon Roll; NHS.

CAPOBIANCO, DENA; Norte Dame HS; Martins Creek, PA; (4); 3/86; Dance Clb; Pep Clb; Yrbk Stf; Crs Cntry; Mgr(s); Trk; French Hon Soc; High Hon Roll; NHS; Spirit JR Miss Northampton Cnty, Jr Miss Pgnt ST Fnlst Miss Natl Teenager Pgnt 87; Lafayette Coll; Bio.

'APOBRES, KIMBERLY; Immaculate Conception HS; Washington, 'A; (4); Rep Stu Cncl; Stat Bsbl; Var L Cheerleading; Hon Roll; Vashington & Jefferson Coll; Dr.

'APOCCI, CHRISTOPHER; Saint John Neumann HS; Philadelphia, 'A; (3); 87/354; Am Leg Boys St; Chorus; Bus.

'APONE, CHRISTINE MARIE; Mahonoy Area HS; Mahanoy City, 'A; (4); Pres DECA; School Play; Var Sftbl; High Hon Roll; Bus Mgmnt.

'APONE, DAWN; Valley HS; Arnold, PA; (2); Ski Clb; Spanish Clb; 'arsity Clb; Chorus; Rep Soph Cls; Cheerleading; Gym; Lawyr.

'APONIGRO, CHRISTINE; Bangor SR HS; Roseto, PA; (3); 21/205; 'omputer Clb; Pep Clb; Scholastic Bowl; Nwsp Stf; Lit Mag; Bsktbl; Fld Icky; Sftbl; High Hon Roll; Pres NHS; Mrn Bio.

'APORALE, SHERRY; Harry S Truman HS; Levittown, PA; (3); Pep 'lb; SADD; Rep Sr Cls; Rep Stu Cncl; JV Cheerleading; Var Mgr(s); Stage 'rew; Yrbk Stf; Score Keeper; Ski Club 87-88; Guidance Cnlsr 86-88; Adv.

'APORALE, VINCENT; St John Neumann HS; Philadelphia, PA; (3); 6/350; Church Yth Grp; Im Bsktbl; High Hon Roll; Hon Roll; NHS; Cert st Hnrs & Being In Ntl Hnr Soc 87; Acctnt.

'APOZZI, PATTY; Penn Trafford HS; Jeannette, PA; (3); 77/301; Hosp ide; Office Aide; SADD; Pres Frsh Cls; Pres Soph Cls; Pres Jr Cls; Sftbl; ligh Hon Roll; Hon Roll; Lion Awd.

'APOZZOLI, KRISTA; Brownsville Area HS; Republic, PA; (3); Church 'th Grp; Ski Clb; SADD; Chorus; Stu Cncl; Var Bsktbl; Mgr(s); Hon Roll; 'A U; Journlsm.

'APP, CYNTHIA; Bethel Park SR HS; Bethel Park, PA; (4); 5/502; 'hurch Yth Grp; Science Clb; Var L Bsktbl; Var L Sftbl; Var L Vllybl; ligh Hon Roll; NHS; Ntl Merit SF; Pres Acad Ftns,US AF Svc Math & 'ci Awds87; YMCA Westerns PA Schlr Athlts 87; WV Wesleyan Coll; 'hyscs.

'APP, SANDRA; Bethel Park SR HS; Bethel Park, PA; (4); 5/502; 'hurch Yth Grp; Science Clb; L Var Bsktbl; L Var Sftbl; L Var Vllybl; ligh Hon Roll; Lion Awd; NHS; Ntl Merit Ltr; Pres Acadc Ftns Awd 87; 'S AF Rcrtng Svc Math & Sci Awd 87; YMCA Westrn PA Schlr Athlts 87; V VA Wesleyan Coll; Chem.

'APPAREL, SCOTT; Parkland HS; Allentown, PA; (2); 146/476; Chess 'lb; JV Bsbl; Im Bsktbl; Math.

'APPELL, DONNA; Hampton HS; Allison Pk, PA; (4); Drill Tm; L Pom 'on; Band; Hon Roll; Slippery Rock U; Cmmnctns.

'APPELLI, HEATHER; Charleroi Area JR-SR HS; N Charleroi, PA; 3); Sec Jr Cls; Psychlgy.

'APPER, BETSY; C A S HS; Coatesville, PA; (2); Cheerleading; Trk; Ion Roll.

'APPIELLO, ANNEMARIE; Morrisville HS; Morrisville, PA; (3); 12/ 2; High Hon Roll; Hon Roll; Attitd & Svc Awd-Grmn III 86-87; Attitd Awd-Alg II 86-87; Achvt & Attitd Awd-Acadc Engrng II 86-87.

'APUANO, SHEILA; Bethlehem Catholic HS; Fountain Hill, PA; (4); 'hurch Yth Grp; Hosp Aide; Library Aide; Office Aide; Fld Hcky; Hon Roll; Northampton Coll; Htl Mgmt.

'APUTO, CRAIG; Mc Keesport SR HS; Mckeesport, PA; (4); 7/342; Math Tm; Pep Clb; Scholastic Bowl; Nwsp Rptr; Capt L Ftbl; Capt Wrstlng; High Hon Roll; NHS; Rotary Awd; Richard Gergley Mem Fund Wrstlng 87; Goodman Sprtmshp Awd Ftbl 86-87; Pittsburgh Press Al Star Achvt; Carnegie Mellon U; Chem Engrng.

'APUTO, JENNIFER; Bethlehem Center HS; Brownsville, PA; (4); 5/ 157; Drama Clb; JA; Yrbk Ed-Chief; Pres Stu Cncl; High Hon Roll; VFW Awd; NHS; Yth Trffc Sfty Cncl; Gftd Pgm; Mrchng Band Anner; OH Northern U; Phrmcy.

'APUTO, LYNN; Mc Keesport Area HS; Mckeesport, PA; (3); 24/410; French Clb; Hosp Aide; Chorus; Nwsp Stf; JV Var Cheerleading; JV Powder Puff Ftbl; Stat Wrstlng; High Hon Roll; NHS; Varsity Ltr Chrldng 86-87; Bus Admin.

'APWELL, BRENDA LYN; Tunkhannock Area HS; Dalton, PA; (4); 33/270; French Clb; Office Aide; Science Clb; Var Stat Fld Hcky; Hon Roll; NHS; Ntl Merit Ltr; Pres Acdmc Ftns Awd 86-87; PA ST U; Lbrl Arts.

CARACCIOLO, JOHN; Altoona Area HS; Altoona, PA; (4); 22/718; Q&S; Spanish Clb; Band; Concert Band; Mrchg Band; Orch; Pep Band; Ed Yrbk Stf; Hon Roll; NHS; Strght 5s Awds In Engl Soc Stud & Sci 84; Penn ST U; Educ.

CARATHERS, CHRISTY L; Bentworth HS; Bentleyville, PA; (4); 25/ 126; Pres Art Clb; Varsity Clb; Sec Band; School Play; Yrbk Stf; Stu Cncl; Hon Roll; Pres Schlr; Old Trls Stu Mnth Awd Art, 3rd WA Cnty Art Comptn 87; Pittsburgh Art Inst; Cmrcl Art.

CARAVELLA, LISA M; Freeland HS; White Haven, PA; (4); FBLA; Pep Clb; Chorus; School Play; Bsktbl; Capt Var Cheerleading; Sftbl; Vllybl; FBLA Hghst Ofc Pract Avg 87.

CARBAUGH, ANN; Chambersburg Area SR HS; Chambersburg, PA; (2); Computer Clb; Drama Clb; German Clb; Rep Frsh Cls; Rep Soph Cls; Stu Cncl; Hon Roll; Bus Secy.

CARBAUGH, JACK; Steel Valley SR HS; W Homestead, PA; (3); Nwsp Stf; Carnegie Mellon U; Comp Sci.

CARBAUGH, MARIANNE E; James Buchanan HS; Mercersburg, PA; (3); 11/250; VP AFS; French Clb; Ski Clb; SADD; Chorus; Variety Show; Rep Stu Cncl; Hon Roll; NHS; Accmpanst For Chorus 85-86; U Of Pittsburgh; Pre-Law.

CARBAUGH, MICHELE A; Mc Connellsburg HS; Mcconnellsburg, PA; (3); 3/65; Am Leg Aux Girls St; VP Band; Chorus; Drm Mjr(t); Yrbk Ed-Chief; High Hon Roll; Sec Jr NHS; NHS; Art Clb; 4-H; PMEA Dist 4 Band 86-87; Instrmnt Awd 87; Med.

CARBAUGH, SHEILA; Cranberry Area HS; Seneca, PA; (3); 12/147; Trs Church Yth Grp; FBLA; FHA; SADD; Teachers Aide; High Hon Roll; Hon Roll; Prfct Atten Awd; Erly Chldhd Dvlpmnt.

CARBAUGH, TERESA; Oil City HS; Cooperstown, PA; (3); 49/192; Debate Tm; French Clb; Office Aide; Variety Show; JV Capt Cheerleading; Score Keeper; Trk; Wt Lftg; Hon Roll; NHS; Penn ST; Psych.

CARBO, NATALIE; Fairview HS; Fairview, PA; (4); French Clb; Yrbk Stf; Pres Jr Cls; Pres Sr Cls; Off Stu Cncl; Capt JV Cheerleading; Capt Socr; Hon Roll; NHS; Gftd Pgm; WV U; Bus.

CARD, SHAWNA; Northwestern SR HS; Albion, PA; (4); 6/145; VP Drama Clb; Thesps; Color Guard; School Musical; Cheerleading; Hon Roll; Church Yth Grp; Red Cross Aide; Band; Chorus; Extra Ordnry Stu Of Amer 86-87; Dist Chorus & Regnl Chorus; St Vincent Schl; Nrsng.

CARDAMONE, ANGELA M; Kennedy Christian HS; Sharon, PA; (3); 10/97; French Clb; Hosp Aide; Sec Frsh Cls; Stu Cncl; Capt Cheerleading; High Hon Roll; Rtry Yth Ldrshp Awds 87; Gebtc Rsrch.

CARDELL, DIANE; Interboro HS; Glenolden, PA; (4); Intnl Clb; Key Clb; Sec Spanish Clb; Varsity Clb; Rep Soph Cls; Rep Jr Cls; Rep Sr Cls; Var L Fld Hcky; Im Sftbl; Im Vllybl; All Del Val Fld Hcky Hnbl Mntn 85; Temple U; Acctg.

CARDELLO, CHRIS; Pleasant Valley HS; Tannersville, PA; (3); 21/225; German Clb; Pep Clb; SADD; Yrbk Sprt Ed; Lit Mag; Rep Stu Cncl; Stat Trk; High Hon Roll; Hon Roll; Jr NHS; Bloomsburg U; Secndry Ed.

CARDIFF, BILL; Penn Trafford HS; Level Green, PA; (3); JCL; High Hon Roll; NHS; Black Belt 1st Degree 86; Military.

CARDILLO, LISA; Wyoming Valley West HS; Forty Fort, PA; (4); Key Clb; Flag Corp; Jazz Band; Nwsp Phtg; Yrbk Phtg; Lit Mag; Cit Awd; High Hon Roll; NHS; NEDT Awd; Bloomsburg U.

CARDINALE, JOSEPH; Emmaus HS; Emmaus, PA; (4); 4/475; Boy Scts; Church Yth Grp; VP Key Clb; Model UN; Scholastic Bowl; Varsity Clb; Band; Concert Band; Mrchg Band; Orch; Excllnc Scl Stds 87; RIT; Engrng.

CARDONE, KRISTEN; Notre Dame Acad; Bryn Mawr, PA; (4); Church Yth Grp; Cmnty Wkr; Intnl Clb; Nwsp Sprt Ed; Yrbk Stf; Var Fld Hcky; Var Lcrss; Var Trk; Hon Roll; Ntl Merit Ltr; Holy Cross Coll.

CARDONI, GINA; James M Coughlin HS; Laflin, PA; (4); Math Clb; VP SADD; Var L Fld Hcky; Sftbl; Var Capt Swmmng; High Hon Roll; Hon Roll; Jr NHS; NHS; Hgh Obrn Smnr Rep 84; Geo Washngtn U; Bus.

CARDONI, JEFF; Coughlin HS; Plains, PA; (3); 30/375; JA; Letterman Clb; Math Clb; Ski Clb; Varsity Clb; Band; Jazz Band; Variety Show; JV Bsktbl; Var Ftbl; Acdmc All Amer 87; Engrng.

CARDUCCI, DOREEN; Chichester SR HS; Boothwyn, PA; (3); 4/296; Sec Church Yth Grp; Sec Drama Clb; VP SADD; VP Band; Chorus; Capt Flag Corp; Mrchg Band; School Play; Jr NHS; Spanish NHS; Spnsh Awd Hghst Avg 85; Ntl Hnr Soc 86; Pns Chorus & Band 87; Penn ST; Bio.

CARDWELL, JEFFREY; Walter Biddle Saul HS; Philadelphia, PA; (3); JV Bsbl; Capt Bsktbl; Capt Ftbl; Amer Leg Schl Awd 84; Achvt Awd Outstndng Perf Flower Show 87; Citznshp Awd 84; Temple; Landscape Design.

CARELLE, JOANN; Homer Center HS; Homer City, PA; (3); 3/117; Sec French Clb; Library Aide; SADD; Varsity Clb; Concert Band; Mrchg Band; Nwsp Stf; JV Var Sftbl; Trk; NHS; Law.

CARETTI, DENA; Meadville Area SR HS; Meadville, PA; (3); 72/362; French Clb; Ski Clb; High Hon Roll; Hon Roll; Pharmacy.

CAREY, JENNIFER; Central HS; Philadelphia, PA; (2); Mgr Gym; Var Trk; JV Vllybl.

CAREY, JENNIFER; Maplewood HS; Townville, PA; (3); #81 In Class; French Clb; Pep Clb; SADD; Nwsp Ed-Chief; Rep Stu Cncl; JV Sftbl; Archlgy.

CAREY, KATHLEEN; St Huberts HS; Philadelphia, PA; (3); French Clb; Girl Scts; Sftbl; Hon Roll; Holy Family Coll; Crmnl Jstc.

CAREY, KEVIN; Lake Lehman HS; Harveys Lake, PA; (3); 7/219; Pres Church Yth Grp; JV Bsbl; VP Ftbl; High Hon Roll; Hon Roll; Jr NHS; NHS; NEDT Awd; Pre-Med.

CAREY, KRISTIN; Washington HS; Washington, PA; (2); Letterman Clb; Band; Jazz Band; Mrchg Band; Orch; Trk; High Hon Roll; Hon Roll; Cmps Life 85-87; Rfle Tm 85-87.

CAREY, PATRICIA; Pittston Area SR HS; Pittston, PA; (3); 17/344; French Clb; FNA; Key Clb; Math Clb; Band; Chorus; Cit Awd; Hon Roll; NHS.

CAREY, STEPHEN; Cardinal O Hara HS; Glenolden, PA; (3); 89/782; German Clb; JV Crs Cntry; Var Trk; High Hon Roll; Hon Roll; NHS.

CAREY, VALERIE; Seneca HS; Wattsburg, PA; (4); Hon Roll; Ntl Merit Ltr; Prfct Atten Awd; Mt Union Acdmc Schrshp & PTSU Schlrshp 87; Mt Union Coll; Sports Med.

CARFREY, KARA L; Upper Merion Area HS; Gulph Mills, PA; (2); 54/ 320; SADD; Trs Frsh Cls; Trs Soph Cls; Trs Jr Cls; Var Cheerleading; Capt Lcrss; JV Tennis; Hon Roll; Mst Sprtd Chrldr 87; Cmnctns.

CARGANILLA, CATHERINE; Bishop Conwell HS; Bensalem, PA; (3); 10/277; Trs French Clb; Latin Clb; Library Aide; Scholastic Bowl; Sec Service Clb; Nwsp Stf; Im Bsktbl; Hon Roll; NHS; Prfct Atten Awd; Hon Mntn Frnch; Cert Merit Natl Frnch Cont; Accntng.

CARGNONI, GINA; Canon Mc Millan SR HS; Canonsburg, PA; (3); 46/ 380; Varsity Clb; VP L Sftbl; VP L Swmmng; Hon Roll; Mst Cooprtv Swm Tm Mdl 85-86; Hghst Base Prcntg Sftbl Trphy 86-87.

CARIFO, NICHOLAS; Center Area HS; Aliquippa, PA; (3); Aud/Vis; Spanish Clb; SADD; Variety Show; Hon Roll; USMC Awd 85; 2nd Pl Wnnr JR Mgcns Stg Cont 87; Penn ST U; Cmmnctns.

CARINO, LORI; Bishop Mc Cort HS; Johnstown, PA; (3); Pep Clb; Chorus; High Hon Roll; Hon Roll; NHS; Central Penn Bus Schl; Lgl Sec.

CARISTO, ANTHONY M; St John Neumann HS; Philadelphia, PA; (3); 8/352; Aud/Vis; Computer Clb; French Clb; Library Aide; Office Aide; Q&S; Teachers Aide; Im Bsktbl; High Hon Roll; Hon Roll; Irish Amer Soc Essay Cont 86-87; U PA; Pre-Med.

CARISTO, GINA; STO-ROX HS; Mckees Rocks, PA; (2); Band; Chorus; Concert Band; Mrchg Band; Yrbk Stf; Journlsm.

CARKHUFF, ELAINA C; Northeastern SR HS; Mt Wolf, PA; (3); Band; Chorus; Concert Band; Mrchg Band; Orch; Yrbk Stf; Fld Hcky; Hon Roll; NHS; Exploring; HOBY Awd 86; Law.

CARL, ALICE; Tri-Valley HS; Hegins, PA; (3); 23/78; Art Clb; Church Yth Grp; Drama Clb; VP FBLA; Girl Scts; Boys Clb Am; Color Guard; School Play; Yrbk Stf; Co-Capt Cheerleading.

CARL, BETH; Tri Valley HS; Hegina, PA; (3); FBLA; Hosp Aide; Teachers Aide; Stu Cncl; 4-H; Girl Scts; VICA; Band; Mrchg Band; Candy Strppng Awd 84; Bus.

CARL, BRIAN; Tri-Valley HS; Valley View, PA; (3); 4/76; Pres Church Yth Grp; Cmnty Wkr; Rep SADD; Var Bsbl; Var Bsktbl; Var Ftbl; High Hon Roll; Hon Roll; NHS; Cntntl Mth Leag Awd & Mdl 85; Stu Chmpnshp Ftbl Tm 86; Wilkes; Optmtry.

CARL, CHRISTOPHER; Steelton-Highspire HS; Steelton, PA; (3); 1/ 112; Pres Church Yth Grp; Quiz Bowl; Band; Concert Band; Drm Mjr(t); Mrchg Band; School Musical; Stage Crew; Yrbk Sprt Ed; High Hon Roll; Drum Mjr Marchng Band; Stage Mgr Schl Muscl; Yr Bk Sports Editor; Temple U; Sports Jrnlsm.

CARL, CINDY L; William Allen HS; Allentown, PA; (3); Church Yth Grp; Exploring; FBLA; Girl Scts; JA; Hon Roll; Jr NHS; Prfct Atten Awd; FBLA Regn 21 Acctnt II 3rd Pl 86-87; Bloomsburg U; Acctnt.

CARL, DANNY; Williams Valley HS; Muir, PA; (3); 4/90; Aud/Vis; Pep Clb; Chorus; Stu Cncl; JV Bsktbl; High Hon Roll; NHS; Air Force; Aerospace Engr.

CARL, DOUGLAS E; Millersburg Area HS; Millersburg, PA; (2); Church Yth Grp; Ski Clb; JV L Bsbl; JV L Bsktbl; JV L Ftbl; Wt Lftg; Hon Roll; Cvl Engrng.

CARL, KATHERINE; Central Dauphin HS; Harrisburg, PA; (4); Church Yth Grp; Band; Chorus; School Musical; School Play; Hon Roll; Jr NHS; NHS; Jazz Band; Orch; Pres Acad Fit Awd 87; Scholar Amer Bus Wmns Assn 87; Oberlin Coll; Lib Arts.

CARL, MANDY; Williams Valley HS; Wiconisco, PA; (1); Band; Chorus; Mrchg Band; JV Bsktbl; Tempel; Physcl Thrpst.

CARL, SCOTT; Elizabethtown Area HS; Elizabethtown, PA; (4); 30/230; Computer Clb; Teachers Aide; Wt Lftg; Wrstlng; Hon Roll; Vrsty Ltrs; U Of Pittsburgh; Engrng.

CARL, VALERIE; Tri-Valley HS; Valley View, PA; (4); Church Yth Grp; Quiz Bowl; Concert Band; Mrchg Band; Yrbk Ed-Chief; Rep Stu Cncl; Hon Roll; Pres NHS; Ntl Merit SF; NEDT Awd; Century III Ldrshp HS Rep 86-87; Rotary Stu Month 86-87; Most Likely Succeed SR Cls 86-87; Bucknell U; Bus.

CARLIER, CURT; Salisbury HS; Allentown, PA; (3); Computer Clb; Key Clb; Teachers Aide; Stat Bsktbl; High Hon Roll; Hon Roll; NHS; Prfct Atten Awd; Radiology.

CARLIN, GREG; South Park HS; Library, PA; (3); JA; Var Crs Cntry; Var L Timer; High Hon Roll; NHS; Ntl Merit Ltr; Engnrng.

CARLIN, JENNI; Sayre Area HS; Sayre, PA; (3); Church Yth Grp; FNA; Library Aide; Pep Clb; VICA; Band; Chorus; Concert Band; Yrbk Stf; Im Swmmng; Occptnl Thrpst.

CARLIN, JENNIFER; Saint Hubert HS; Philadelphia, PA; (3); 112/421; Var Crs Cntry; Var Trk.

CARLINO, CHRIS; Central Bucks HS East; Furlong, PA; (3); Camera Clb; Exploring; Badmtn; Var Crs Cntry; Swmmng; Var Trk; Vllybl; Hon Roll; Kiwanis Awd; Photo.

CARLISLE, JOE; Mc Guffey HS; Washington, PA; (3); 12/240; French Clb; Trs Jr Cls; Bsktbl; L Ftbl; L Trk; Wt Lftg; High Hon Roll; VP NHS; US Naval Acad; Physcs.

CARLL, CYNTHIA; Oswayo Valley HS; Coudersport, PA; (3); Church Yth Grp; French Clb; Library Aide; Varsity Clb; Stat Bsktbl; Im Vllybl; High Hon Roll; Hon Roll; NHS; Accntng.

CARLO, GRETCHEN; Beaver Area SR HS; Beaver, PA; (2); Church Yth Grp; Cmnty Wkr; FCA; Drill Tm; Mrchg Band; School Musical; Rep Soph Cls; High Hon Roll; French Clb; Pep Clb; Schltc Achvt Awd 87; Vol Tutor 86 & 87; Chld Psych.

CARLSON, CHRISTINE A; East Stroudsburg HS; East Stroudsburg, PA; (3); #36 In Class; Am Leg Aux Girls St; Pres Art Clb; Church Yth Grp; Trs French Clb; Trs German Clb; Math Tm; Model UN; ROTC; Trs Spanish Clb; Chorus; Cornell U; Pre-Med.

CARLSON, CLARE; General Mc Lane HS; Edinboro, PA; (4); 19/187; Church Yth Grp; French Clb; Im Wt Lftg; Hon Roll; Wthrspoon Schlrshp 86; Acadc Ftns Awd 87; Deans List 86; Edinboro U Of PA; Mdcl Tech.

CARLSON, DEBRA L; Washington HS; Washington, PA; (3); Drama Clb; French Clb; Key Clb; Letterman Clb; Ski Clb; Cheerleading; Tennis; High Hon Roll; Hon Roll; Phrmcy.

CARLSON, JENNIFER; Quakertown HS; Quakertown, PA; (2); 1/345; SADD; Varsity Clb; Off Soph Cls; Rep Stu Cncl; Var Capt Bsktbl; Coach Actv; Var L Fld Hcky; Sftbl; High Hon Roll; NHS; Psychology.

CARLSON, JOHN; Brockway Area HS; Brockway, PA; (3); #3 In Class; Cmnty Wkr; Exploring; Varsity Clb; Mgr Ftbl; Wt Lftg; Var Capt Wrstlng; Hon Roll; NHS.

CARLSON, JOHN A; Eisenhower HS; Sugar Grove, PA; (1); Church Yth Grp; Speech Tm; Y-Teens; Bsktbl; Ftbl; Wt Lftg; High Hon Roll; Jr NHS; Penn ST; Physicst.

CARLSON, KATHRYN; Cowanesque Valley HS; Westfield, PA; (4); Church Yth Grp; French Clb; Letterman Clb; Band; Chorus; School Musical; Trs Frsh Cls; Trs Soph Cls; Trs Jr Cls; Trs Sr Cls; Schlr Athl; William L Clark Frnch Awd 86; Intl Bus.

CARLSON, KIM; Manhiem Twp HS; Lancaster, PA; (2); Ski Clb; Sec Frsh Cls; Cheerleading; High Hon Roll; Hon Roll.

CARLSON, LINDA; Jenkintown HS; Jenkintown, PA; (2); Drama Clb; French Clb; NFL; Q&S; Speech Tm; Band; Chorus; Concert Band; Mrchg Band; School Musical; 1st Pl Dist Spch; 2nd Pl JV Poetry; North Park Coll; Tchr.

CARLSON, MATTHEW; Warren Area HS; Warren, PA; (3); German Clb; Acpl Chr; Band; Chorus; Concert Band; Jazz Band; Madrigals; Mrchg Band; Orch; School Musical; Dist & Regnl Band 86-87; Dist Jazz Band 86-87; Dist & Regnl Choir.

CARLSON, RENA; Upper Merion HS; King Of Prussia, PA; (4); 92/290; Sec-Pan Amercn Clb 86-87; Bus.

CARLSON, SEAN; Strong Vincent HS; Erie, PA; (3); 6/191; Letterman Clb; Stage Crew; VP Jr Cls; VP Sr Cls; Bsbl; Capt Ftbl; Trk; Wt Lftg; Wrstlng; High Hon Roll; 2nd Tm All Metro Dfnsv Tackle 86; Pre Dentl.

CARLSON, WENDY; Sheffield Area JR SR HS; Sheffield, PA; (4); 5/71; Drama Clb; FHA; SADD; Trs Chorus; Co-Capt Color Guard; Mrchg Band; School Play; Yrbk Phtg; Ed Yrbk Stf; Stat Trk; Hnr Stu 87; Schlstc Awd; Edinboro U; Mntl/Phys Hndicp Ed.

CARLTON, KAREN; Fort Cherry HS; Midway, PA; (3); Computer Clb; French Clb; Math Clb; Science Clb; Ski Clb; Chorus; Tennis; Twrlr; High Hon Roll; NHS; Duquesne U; Pharmacy.

CARLUCCI, AMY; Carlisle SR HS; Carlisle, PA; (3); 74/476; Church Yth Grp; Cmnty Wkr; Mrchg Band; Nwsp Stf; Capt Swmmng; High Hon Roll; Hon Roll; MVP Swim 86; Mst Outstndng Swimmr 86-87; Natl YMCA Champnshp Qlfr Co-Capt 86-87; Med.

CARMACK, WILLIAM; Valley Forge Military Acad; Washington, DC; (3); 25/150; ROTC; Ski Clb; Spanish Clb; Yrbk Rptr; Yrbk Stf; Bsktbl; Diving; Socr; Sftbl; Tennis; Hnr Guard 87; U Of VA; Frgn Plcy.

CARMAN, CHRISTINE; Canevin Catholic HS; Pittsburgh, PA; (3); 69/ 190; Cmnty Wkr; Dance Clb; FBLA; Ski Clb; Spanish Clb; Cheerleading; Coach Actv; Gym; Powder Puff Ftbl; Hon Roll; High Achvt & Dedication-Gymnastics 86; Bradford Schl; Bus.

CARMAN, STACEY RICHELLE; Athens HS; Sayre, PA; (3); 7/119; Am Leg Aux Girls St; Church Yth Grp; Sec 4-H; Ski Clb; Chorus; Concert Band; Mrchg Band; Orch; Hon Roll; Mdcl Career.

CARNACK JR, DANIEL E; Connellsville Area SR HS; Dunbar, PA; (4); 49/500; Pres FTA; Pres German Clb; School Musical; School Play; Stage Crew; Trk; Jr NHS; NHS; Voice Dem Awd; German Hnr Soc; Salisbury St Coll; History.

CARNAHAN, CHRISTINE; Conemaugh Township Area HS; Johnstown, PA; (3); 3/121; Nwsp Sprt Ed; Trs Frsh Cls; Trs Soph Cls; Pres Stu Cncl; Var Bsktbl; Im Socr; Var Trk; Var Vllybl; Hon Roll; NHS; Hnrb Mntn All-Cnty Vllybl Tm, 6th Pl Dist Trck Mt, Rotry Yth Ldrshp Awd 86-87; Pitt; Phrmcy.

CARNAHAN, DAVID; Beth-Center HS; Millsboro, PA; (3); 3/146; Church Yth Grp; Spanish Clb; Band; Concert Band; Mrchg Band; High Hon Roll; Hon Roll; NHS; Sci.

CARNAHAN, MICHAEL; Elizabeth-Forward SR HS; Mc Keesport, PA; (3); 119/330; Pres Leo Clb; Pres SADD; Concert Band; Jazz Band; Pres Mrchg Band; Pep Band; Lion Awd; Cmnty Wkr; Pep Clb; Band; Cert Intl Leo Forum Taiwan 87; Citatn Excllnc Bands Amer 84-86; George Washington U; Pol Sci.

CARNATHAN, CHRISTINE; Penn Trafford HS; Claridge, PA; (3); FBLA; Spanish Clb; SADD; High Hon Roll; Hon Roll.

CARNATHAN, JOHN; Jeannette SR HS; Jeannette, PA; (3); Cmnty Wkr; French Clb; Spanish Clb; L Var Bsbl; L Var Bsktbl; High Hon Roll; Hon Roll; NHS; Pre Med.

CARNATHAN, KAREY; Penn Trafford HS; Claridge, PA; (3); Drama Clb; SADD; Bus Mgmt.

CARNER, ERRIN; Cranberry Area HS; Seneca, PA; (3); 14/140; Pres Church Yth Grp; VP Science Clb; Band; Chorus; Concert Band; Jazz Band; Pep Band; School Musical; Swing Chorus; Rep Stu Cncl; PA ST U; Ecnmcs.

CARNER, HEIDI; Fairview HS; Fairview, PA; (4); 16/154; Drama Clb; French Clb; Ski Clb; VP Chorus; Symp Band; School Musical; Trk; Vllybl; High Hon Roll; Acad Achvt Awds 84-85; Fnlst In Gvrnrs Schl Of Arts; Occptnl Thrpy.

CARNES, PAUL; Middletown Area HS; Middletown, PA; (3); Am Leg Boys St; Boy Scts; Pres Band; Jazz Band; School Musical; School Play; Swing Chorus; Bsbl; Chorus; Concert Band; Eagle Scout Awd 87; Ad Altare DEI 85; Pharm.

CARNEY, DANIEL; Penn Cambria SR HS; Gallitzin, PA; (3); 4/215; Wt Lftg; Var Wrstlng; High Hon Roll; Hon Roll; NHS; Vet.

CARNEY, DOYLE; United JR SR HS; Seward, PA; (4); 3/155; Camera Clb; Church Yth Grp; Mu Alpha Theta; Ski Clb; Yrbk Phtg; Stat Bsktbl; Hon Roll; Jr NHS; Pres NHS; Prfct Attndnc Awd 81-85; PA St U; Cmptr Sci.

CARNEY, KATHRYN M; Altoona Area HS; Altoona, PA; (3); Church Yth Grp; VICA; Stage Crew; Hon Roll; Pittsburgh Art Inst; Cosmetolgy.

CARNEY, MARK; Allderdice HS; Pittsburgh, PA; (3); JA; Political Wkr; Band; Concert Band; Mrchg Band; Pep Band; Nwsp Sprt Ed; Var Socr; High Hon Roll.

CARNIELLO, SEAN; Waynesboro SR HS; Waynesboro, PA; (4); 105/400; Intnl Clb; Ski Clb; Chorus; School Musical; Swing Chorus; Yrbk Stf; Rep Soph Cls; VP Stu Cncl; Ntl Piano Playing Auditions 86; Chopin Paino Awd 87; Pastoral Musician 86; Shenandoah Consvrtry; Music.

CARNS, DARREN; United HS; Armagh, PA; (4); 2/156; Pres Church Yth Grp; Math Clb; Mu Alpha Theta; Chorus; Church Choir; School Musical; Pres Sr Cls; L Bsktbl; L Trk; DAR Awd; IUP Mentorship Pgm 86; Juniata; Chemical Engr.

CARO, CHANDA; Aliquippa HS; Aliquippa, PA; (2); Church Yth Grp; French Clb; School Play; Sftbl; Hon Roll; U Of Pittsburgh.

CAROMANO, CATHLEEN; Cardinal O Hara HS; Havertown, PA; (2); 138/647; Church Yth Grp; Cmnty Wkr; Hon Roll; Accntng.

CARONE, TIM; Venango Christian HS; Oil City, PA; (3); 11/35; Rep Soph Cls; JV Bsbl; Capt Bsktbl; JV Var Ftbl; Var Golf; NHS; Mercyhurst Coll Erie PA; Finc.

CAROSELLI, JOSEPH; Cardional O Hara HS; Springfield, PA; (4); 1/771; Chess Clb; French Clb; Math Tm; Office Aide; Quiz Bowl; Nwsp Stf; French Hon Soc; Gov Hon Prg Awd; High Hon Roll; Lion Awd; Mc Cabe Schlrs Awd 87; Rensallaer Schlrshp Awd 87; Carnegie-Mellon Ntl Merit Schlrshp Awd 87; CA Inst Tech; Math.

CAROTHERS, JENNIFER; W Allegheny HS; Coraopolis, PA; (3); JA; Library Aide; Spanish Clb; Chorus; Rep Stu Cncl; Var Bsktbl; Var Crs Cntry; Var Capt Powder Puff Ftbl; Score Keeper; JV Var Sftbl; Sheredan Stow Pitch Sftbll Tourn MVP 86; Sr Girls Slow Pitch All Star Team 86-87.

CAROTHERS, KELLY DYVONNE; Pottstown SR HS; Pottstown, PA; (3); Key Clb; Latin Clb; Nwsp Stf; Stu Cncl; Cheerleading; Fld Hcky; Lcrss; High Hon Roll; Hon Roll; NHS; Bio.

CAROTHERS, SHARON; Upper Darby HS; Lansdowne, PA; (3); 52/598; Chorus; Pres Frsh Cls; Pres Soph Cls; VP Jr Cls; Rep Stu Cncl; JV Bsktbl; JV Fld Hcky; JV Lcrss; High Hon Roll; Hon Roll; Schl Rep Ldrshp Conf GE Twn Mtng Tmrrw 86-87; Htl Mgr.

CARPENTER, ANGELA R; Littlestown SR HS; Littlestown, PA; (3); Letterman Clb; Pep Clb; Varsity Clb; Band; Chorus; Color Guard; Drm Mjr(t); Mrchg Band; L Var Cheerleading; Im Fld Hcky; Trvl.

CARPENTER, CHARLES; Wyoming Valley West HS; Forty Fort, PA; (4); Math Tm; Var Socr; Var L Tennis; High Hon Roll; Hon Roll; NHS; Pres Schlr; PA ST U; Engrng.

CARPENTER, CHRIS; Hyndman HS; Buffalo Mls, PA; (4); 11/39; Ski Clb; Varsity Clb; Nwsp Phtg; Nwsp Rptr; Cit Awd; Hon Roll; Lion Awd; Prfct Atten Awd; VFW Awd; Voice Dem Awd; Prncpls Awd; Cntry Clb Mall Retail Mngmnt Schlrshp 87; Allegany CC; Retail Mngmnt.

CARPENTER, KELLI; Cedar Crest HS; Cornwall, PA; (3); Camera Clb; French Clb; Letterman Clb; Pep Clb; Science Clb; Varsity Clb; Band; Yrbk Phtg; Yrbk Stf; Rep Soph Cls.

CARPENTER, KENDRA; Everett Area HS; Breezewood, PA; (3); 9/136; Varsity Clb; Band; Chorus; Sec Frsh Cls; Trs Sr Cls; Rep Stu Cncl; Tennis; Trk; Twrlr; French Hon Soc; Educ.

CARPENTER, MARK J; Slippery Rock Area HS; Slippery Rock, PA; (4); 1/170; VP Church Yth Grp; JCL; Math Tm; Nwsp Rptr; Ed Lit Mag; High Hon Roll; Trs NHS; Ntl Merit SF; Val; Elks Awd; Rotary Yuth Ldrshp Awds; Princeton U; Math.

CARPENTER, ROBERT; HS For Engineering And Science; Philladelphia, PA; (4); 8/207; Chess Clb; Pres Church Yth Grp; Computer Clb; Math Tm; Church Choir; Nwsp Rptr; Yrbk Stf; Rep Stu Cncl; Im Vllybl; High Hon Roll; Early Admission Temple U Scholar 86-87; Lebanon Vly Coll; Audio Tech.

CARPENTER, TIFFANY; West Greene HS; Wind Ridge, PA; (2); Cmnty Wkr; FTA; Science Clb; Yrbk Stf; VP Frsh Cls; VP Soph Cls; Rep Stu Cncl; Stat Ftbl; Stat Wrstlng; Hon Roll; Sphmr Prm Attndnt 87; Pjas 2dn Pl Awd 87; Waynesburg Coll; Nrsng.

CARPENTER, TRICIA; Oswayo Valley HS; Shinglehouse, PA; (3); Ski Clb; Varsity Clb; Bsktbl; Crs Cntry; Trk; French Clb; Library Aide; Color Guard; Yrbk Stf; Hon Roll; Flght Atten.

CARPER, MARK; Somerset SR HS; Somerset, PA; (4); 41/240; English Clb; VP JA; Math Clb; Mu Alpha Theta; Varsity Clb; Nwsp Stf; Var Crs Cntry; Var L Socr; Var L Trk; Hon Roll; PHEAA Cert Of Merit For SAT Scores 86; Penn ST; Engnrng.

CARPIN, TRACEY; St Marys Area HS; Weedville, PA; (4); 9/280; Cmnty Wkr; Teachers Aide; Pres Yrbk Ed-Chief; Hon Roll; Kiwanis Awd; NHS; Daemen Coll Dean Schlrshp 87; Daemen Coll Dept Schlrshp 87; Womens Club Schlrshp 87; Daemen Coll; Phy Thrpy.

CARPINELLA, MICHAEL; St John Neumann HS; Philadelphia, PA; (2); Church Yth Grp; Dance Clb; JV Bsbl; Hon Roll; Prfct Atten Awd; La Salle.

CARPINELLO, JOYCE M; St Huberts HS; Philadelphia, PA; (3); 55/421; Hon Roll; Acdmc Decathln 85; Cert Acdmc Merit Accntng I 87; Accntng.

CARR, BARBARA; Archbishop Prendergast HS; Upper Darby, PA; (4); 2/324; Church Yth Grp; Intnl Clb; Service Clb; Stage Crew; Im Vllybl; High Hon Roll; NHS; Ntl Merit Schol; Opt Clb Awd; Sec Spanish NHS; Outstndg Achvmnt Schlrshp 87; Schlrshp NYU 87; Various Archbishop Prendergast Acad Awds 84-87; Temple U; Cmmnctns.

CARR, BRENDA; Danville SR HS; Danville, PA; (2); Chorus; Color Guard; High Hon Roll; Hon Roll; Pres Schlr; Bloomsburg U; Vet.

CARR, CAROL; Harry S Truman HS; Levittown, PA; (4); Art Clb; SADD; Hon Roll; NHS; Moore Coll Art Schlrshp 86; Bucks Cnty Schls Smmr Art Acad Schlrshp 85; Temple U.

CARR, DIANA; West Branch Area HS; Morrisdale, PA; (3); #6 In Class; Drama Clb; 4-H; Science Clb; Spanish Clb; SADD; Band; Chorus; Church Choir; Concert Band; Mrchg Band; Music.

CARR, ELIZABETH; Wilmington Area HS; Volant, PA; (3); Spanish Clb; Nwsp Stf; Stu Cncl; Var Cheerleading; Hon Roll.

CARR, GENEVA; Coatesville Area HS; Coatesville, PA; (3); Church Yth Grp; Trs FBLA; Var Fld Hcky; Hon Roll; Bsktbl Prfct Atten 84-85; Secr.

CARR, KARA; Emmaus HS; Wescusville, PA; (3); Keywanettes; Latin Clb; JV Trk; Yth Cnsl For St Thomas More Chrch 87; Lbry Sci.

CARR, LISA ANN; Nazareth Academy HS; Phila, PA; (3); 62/124; Church Yth Grp; GAA; Hosp Aide; Pep Clb; Red Cross Aide; Spanish Clb; Trs Jr Cls; Var Fld Hcky; Vllybl; Bio.

CARR, RENEE; Central Christian HS; Du Bois, PA; (2); Pep Clb; Ski Clb; Varsity Clb; Chorus; Sec Soph Cls; Var Cheerleading; Hon Roll; Psych.

CARR, ROBERT; Cathedral Prep; Erie, PA; (2); 185/238; Im Bsktbl; Var L Ftbl; Im Swmmng; Var L Trk; OK ST; Pro Ftbl.

CARR, ROBERT ALAN; St Marys Area HS; Saint Marys, PA; (4); 3/276; Boys Clb Am; Var L Bsbl; Bsktbl; JV L Ftbl; Var Trk; DAR Awd; Hon Roll; NHS; Outstndng Male Sr 87; Elk-Cameron Cnty Med Aux Awd 87; Penn ST U.

CARR, STEVEN T; Norristown Area HS; Norristown, PA; (3); 21/491; Civic Clb; Ski Clb; Rep Jr Cls.

CARRERA JR, JOSE LUIS; Mastbaum ANTS; Philadelphia, PA; (4); FBLA; Chorus; Concert Band; Jazz Band; Orch; Yrbk Stf; Stu Cncl; Crs Cntry; Trk; Prfct Atten Awd; PA ST U; CPA.

CARRERO, KAREN; Creative & Performing Arts HS; Philadelphia, PA; (2); Church Yth Grp; Drama Clb; School Musical; School Play; Variety Show; Rep Frsh Cls; Rep Stu Cncl; 1 Yr Dnc Schlrshp, 1st Pl Phila Dnc Cr 87-88; Harvard U; Bus Law.

CARRIER, MICHAEL; Brookville Area HS; Brookville, PA; (3); Boy Scts; Church Yth Grp; SADD; Hon Roll; PA ST U; Electrncs Engnr.

CARRIER, REBECCA; Ridgway Area HS; Ridgway, PA; (4); 5/105; Sec Trs Church Yth Grp; FNA; Church Choir; Yrbk Stf; Trk; High Hon Roll; Hon Roll; NHS; Pres Schlr; Waynesburg Coll; Nrsng.

CARRIGLITTO, JIM; Blue Mountain HS; Rew Ringgold, PA; (4); 26/227; Drama Clb; School Musical; School Play; Stage Crew; Nwsp Rptr; Nwsp Sprt Ed; Lit Mag; Stat Bsbl; Hon Roll; NEDT Awd; Jrnlsm.

CARRINGTON, PENNY; Central HS; Philadelphia, PA; (3); Math Clb; School Musical; Stage Crew; Trk; Hon Roll; U Of PA; Bus.

CARRION, SANDRA; Engineering & Science HS; Philadelphia, PA; (3); 55/241; Cmnty Wkr; Rep Frsh Cls; Rep Jr Cls; Hon Roll.

CARROLL, ANN; Fox Chapel Area HS; Pittsburgh, PA; (3); Hosp Aide; Library Aide; Acpl Chr; Chorus; School Musical; High Hon Roll; Hon Roll; 250 Hrs Vlntr Wrk Locl Libry 84-86; Prop Asst Sprng Musicl 85-86; Psych.

CARROLL, DEBBIE; Elizabeth Forward HS; Greenock, PA; (4); 37/297; Art Clb; Chess Clb; Computer Clb; Exploring; GAA; Latin Clb; Letterman Clb; Ski Clb; Spanish Clb; Varsity Clb; Yng Cmmnty Ldr Amer 86-87; Western PA Inds Arts Fair 84; Phys Fit Awd 84-86; Duquesne U; Phrmcy.

CARROLL, MARYANN; Burgettstown JR SR HS; Burgettstown, PA; (3); French Clb; Ski Clb; Mrchg Band; Yrbk Stf; Comm.

CARROLL, MICHAEL A; East HS; West Chester, PA; (4); 47/422; Church Yth Grp; Band; Variety Show; Nwsp Rptr; Lit Mag; Sec Frsh Cls; Rep Stu Cncl; Stat Bsktbl; JV Crs Cntry; Hon Roll; Natl Achvt Awd 87; Cornell U; Arch.

CARROLL, SUSAN; East HS; Thornton, PA; (3); 7/476; Church Yth Grp; Var L Vllybl; Hon Roll; NHS; Spanish NHS; Acad Achvt Awd W Chester Area Schl Dist 87; Dist Wnnr Intermed Cls Natl Piano Aud Amer Coll Musicns.

CARROTO, CHRISTIN; Mon Valley Catholic HS; Monessen, PA; (3); Church Yth Grp; JA; Spanish Clb; Drill Tm; Nwsp Ed-Chief; Yrbk Ed-Chief; Mgr(s); Stat Sftbl; Hon Roll; Spanish NHS; Seton Hill Coll; Engl.

CARROZZA, THOMAS; Wissahickon HS; Ambler, PA; (3); DECA; Key Clb; Library Aide; Ski Clb; Lit Mag; Coach Actv; Lcrss; Socr; Wt Lftg; Pre-Law.

CARRUTHERS, BRAD; Homer Center JR SR HS; Homer City, PA; (3); 27/114; Boy Scts; Pep Clb; Ski Clb; Varsity Clb; Chorus; Stage Crew; JV Var Ftbl; Var Trk; Prncpls Advsry Cncl 85-86 & 86-87; Indiana U Of PA; Crmnlgy.

CARSON, ALBERT; Rocky Grove HS; Franklin, PA; (4); Aud/Vis; Chess Clb; 4-H; Band; Concert Band; Jazz Band; Pep Band; Stage Crew; 4-H Awd; Hon Roll; Outstndg 4-Her 85; Clarion U; Crmnlgy.

CARSON, ELEANOR B; Franklin Regional SR HS; Murrysville, PA; (4); 1/338; Pres AFS; French Clb; Math Tm; School Musical; School Play; Trs Jr Cls; Sec Sr Cls; Var L Diving; NHS; Ntl Merit SF; Wms Coll; Genetics.

CARSON, GREGORY; Bristol HS; Bristol, PA; (3); Scholastic Bowl; Hon Roll; Bucks Cnty Sci Seminar 86-87; Stu Of Month; Chem Engrng.

CARSON, GREGORY; Huntingdon Area HS; Huntingdon, PA; (4); 20/234; Pres Band; Pres Concert Band; Pres Mrchg Band; Teachers Aide; High Hon Roll; NHS; U Pittsburgh; Chem.

CARSON, JEFF; Rocky Grove HS; Franklin, PA; (3); 17/80; Church Yth Grp; Band; School Musical; Bsktbl.

CARSON, LARA M; Radnor HS; Wayne, PA; (4); 3/298; VP Church Yth Grp; Cmnty Wkr; Drama Clb; GAA; Math Clb; Math Tm; Service Clb; Soroptimist; Chorus; Church Choir; Georgetown U; Med.

CARSON, ROBERT; Girard College; Philadelphia, PA; (3); Boy Scts; Chess Clb; Exploring; Ski Clb; JV Bsktbl; Tennis; Hon Roll; Temple; Cmmnctns.

CARSON, SEAN; Garnet Valley HS; Glen Mills, PA; (2); 1/170; Church Yth Grp; German Clb; Intnl Clb; Model UN; Rep Stu Cncl; JV Socr; Var Trk; High Hon Roll; Stanford U.

CARSON, TAMMY; Central Dauphin HS; Harrisburg, PA; (3); 84/389 Ski Clb; Band; Chorus; Concert Band; Mrchg Band; School Musical; Of Stu Cncl; Swmmng; Trk; Hon Roll; Comp Pgmmg.

CARSON JR, WILLIAM M; William Allen HS; Allentown, PA; (3); 23 619; VP Church Yth Grp; Trs Exploring; VP German Clb; Orch; Hon Roll Pres NHS; Ntl Merit Ltr; Opt Clb Awd; Chorus; Church Choir; Natl Hn Soc Hnr Cum Laud Awd 87; Mntlly Gftd Pgm 87-88; Aerospce Engrng.

CARTAFALSA, LISA; St Hubert HS; Philadelphia, PA; (3); Drama Clb SADD; Chorus; Frsh Cls; Jr Cls; Stu Cncl; JV Fld Hcky; High Hon Roll Hon Roll; NHS; Drama Awd 86; Stdnts Agnst Drnk Drvg SADD 86-87 Itln Clss Awd 86-87; Pol Sci.

CARTER, ADUANNE; John Harris HS; Harrisburg, PA; (2); 16/500 Boys Clb Am; Boy Scts; Hon Roll; Ntl Hnr Roll 87; PA ST U; Bio.

CARTER, BRITT; Eisenhower HS; Russell, PA; (4); 1/116; Band; Rep Stu Cncl; Capt Var Cheerleading; Capt Var Sftbl; DAR Awd; High Hon Roll; JETS Awd; Sec NHS; Val; Presdntl Acadc Ftns Awd 87; PA York Am Chem Soc Awd 87; Army Acadc Athlt 87; Lehigh U; Engr.

CARTER, CHRIS; St Josephs Prep Schl; Moorestown, NJ; (4); Pep Clb Spanish Clb; Varsity Clb; Yrbk Sprt Ed; Var Ftbl; Var Tennis; Wt Lftg Vrsty Crew Tm 86-87; Boston U; Bus Mngmt.

CARTER, DELVIE; West Catholic For Boys; Philadelphia, PA; (2) Bsktbl; Crs Cntry; Ftbl; Conduct Good Awd 86-87.

CARTER, GEORGE; Central Catholic HS; Pittsburgh, PA; (2); Chess Clb; Latin Clb; NAACP; JV Crs Cntry; Hon Roll; Latin Hnr Scty 87 Brown U; Pre-Med.

CARTER, JACK; Wyomissing Area HS; Wyomissing, PA; (4); 10/101 Boy Scts; Pres JA; Pres JCL; High Hon Roll; Church Yth Grp; Computer Clb; Drama Clb; Trs French Clb; German Clb; Pres Latin Clb; Svc Actvts Awd 86; PA ST U; Engrng.

CARTER, JENNIFER; West York Area HS; York, PA; (2); Church Yth Grp; Varsity Clb; Chorus; School Play; Rep Stu Cncl; Var L Trk; JV L Vllybl; High Hon Roll; German Clb; Church Choir; Modern Music Masters 87; Math.

CARTER, KISHA; Flisg Gratz HS; Philadelphia, PA; (4); Tennis; Trk; Ruth Hayfe Schlshps 87; Shippensburg; Pol Sci.

CARTER, LORETTA; Philadelphia HS For Girls; Philadelphia, PA; (3); 38/405; Math Clb; Office Aide; Service Clb; Teachers Aide; Drill Tm; Stage Crew; High Hon Roll; Hon Roll; NHS; Prfct Atten Awd; Italian Natl Honor Soc 86; Comp Sci.

CARTER, TAWANDA R; Oliver HS; Pittsburgh, PA; (3); Computer Clb; JA; Mu Alpha Theta; Science Clb; Drill Tm; Mrchg Band; Pres Frsh Cls; Pres Soph Cls; Var Bsbl; Var Bsktbl; Penn ST; Engrng.

CARTER, THEODORE; Greater Johnstown HS; Johnstown, PA; (3), NAACP; Var Ftbl; Psych.

CARTER, TILLARY; Boyertown Area SR HS; Boyertown, PA; (4); SADD; Teachers Aide; Nwsp Ed-Chief; Yrbk Stf; Score Keeper; Trk; Cit Awd; Hon Roll; Prfct Atten Awd; Grad Hnrs 87; Stanley G Flagg Schlrshp Awd-2nd Pl 87; Temple U; Cmmnctns.

CARTHORN, CHARLES; Farrell Area HS; Farrell, PA; (3); 19/95; Science Clb; Engrng.

CARTWRIGHT, DONNA; Calvary Baptist Acad; Norwood, PA; (4); 2/9; Church Yth Grp; Cmnty Wkr; Teachers Aide; Chorus; School Musical, School Play; Trs Sr Cls; Var L Bsktbl; High Hon Roll; Sal; Sprtsmnshp Awd In Grls Bsktbl 83-87; Piano Solo 1st & 2nd Pl 84-87; Pastors Awd 85-87; Liberty U; Elem Educ.

CARTWRIGHT, JEANNETTE; Abraham Lincoln HS; Philadelphia, PA; (3); #6 In Class; Pres Debate Tm; Girl Scts; ROTC; Madrigals; Ed Lit Mag; Rep Stu Cncl; Cit Awd; High Hon Roll; Hon Roll; Trs NHS; Air Force Assn Awd-Ldrshp & Schlrshp 87; Knights Of Pythius Ortrcl Awd-1st Pl St; Dist Ortrcl Cont 3rd; Acctg.

CARTWRIGHT, LISA; Du Bois HS; Brockway, PA; (3); Pep Clb; Nwsp Stf; Yrbk Stf; Pres Frsh Cls; Rep Stu Cncl; Var L Socr; High Hon Roll; Hon Roll; Sec Trs NHS; Essay Cont 1st Pl 86.

CARTWRIGHT, MEGHAN; Greenville HS; Greenville, PA; (4); 18/130; French Clb; Latin Clb; Letterman Clb; Varsity Clb; School Play; Yrbk Stf; Var L Crs Cntry; Var L Trk; Voice Dem Awd; 2dn Pl Impromtu Wrtng Cont YSU Engl Fest 84; ST Mdlst PIAA Cross Cntry 17th Pl 86; Pre Med.

CARTWRIGHT, STACY; Beaver Falls SR HS; Koppel, PA; (3); 19/174; Trs Pres Service Clb; Spanish Clb; Co-Capt Drill Tm; VP Sr Cls; Rep Stu Cncl; Var Sftbl; High Hon Roll; NHS; Med.

CARUANO, ROBERT M; Nativity B V M HS; Pottsville, PA; (2); 3/80; Trs Church Yth Grp; Exploring; Speech Tm; Sec Band; Variety Show; Pres Soph Cls; High Hon Roll; Acad All Armcn Awd 87; JR All Armcn Hall Fm Bnd Hnrs 87; PA JR Acad Of Sci Awd 87; Med.

CARULLI, MARCO; West Catholic Boys HS; Philadelphia, PA; (3); 21/247; Boy Scts; Church Yth Grp; CAP; High Hon Roll; Hon Roll; Prfct Atten Awd; St Josephs; Bnkng.

CARUSO, ANDY; Archbishop Wood HS For Boys; Willow Grove, PA; (2); 51/254; German Clb; SADD; Var Socr; Im Vllybl; Hon Roll; Amateur Athletic Union Of US; U Of IN; Sports Med.

CARUSO, BECCA; Penn-Trafford HS; Irwin, PA; (4); SADD; Varsity Clb; Stage Crew; Var Crs Cntry; Var Trk; Var Vllybl; NHS; CAP; Law.

CARUSO, CLARISSA; Nazareth Acad; Philadelphia, PA; (3); School Play; Stage Crew; Variety Show; Sec Frsh Cls; Peirce JC; Court Stenog.

CARUSO, DIANA; Saint Maria Goretti HS; Philadelphia, PA; (4); 94/384; Cmnty Wkr; Hosp Aide; Chorus; School Musical; School Play; Swing Chorus; Hon Roll; Ntl Merit Schol; Prfct Atten Awd; Pres Schlr; Pres Acad Ftnss Awd 87; Itln Hnrbl Mntn 85; Hahnemann U; RN.

CARUSO, JOHN; Tunkhannock HS; Tunkhannock, PA; (3); 40/320; Key Clb; Yrbk Stf; Trk; Hon Roll; U Of PA.

CARUSO, KRISTEN; Cardinal O Hara HS; Holmes, PA; (3); 166/715; Church Yth Grp; High Hon Roll; Hon Roll; Prfct Atten Awd; Lab Tech.

CARUSO, ROCHELLE; Upper Darby HS; Upr Darby, PA; (3); Cmnty Wkr; Hosp Aide; Office Aide; Teachers Aide; Stage Crew; Ed Yrbk Stf; Ed Lit Mag; High Hon Roll; Hon Roll; Jr NHS; Trauma Surgeon.

CARUSO, STACEY; Carmichaels Area JR SR HS; Carmichaels, PA; (3); 16/115; Pep Clb; Ski Clb; Sec Spanish Clb; Band; Concert Band; Mrchg Band; Pep Band; High Hon Roll; Hon Roll; PA Jr Acad Sci 1st Rgnl 86; PA Jr Acad Sci 2nd St 86; Gftd Pgm; WV U; Phrmcy.

CARUSO, TONIA; Sacred Heart HS; Pittsburgh, PA; (3); Cmnty Wkr; Service Clb; Spanish Clb; Nwsp Stf; Rep Frsh Cls; VP Soph Cls; Sec Stu Cncl; Hon Roll; NHS; Outstndg Stud 85-86; U Of Pittsburgh.

CARUTHERS, CHRIS; Elizabeth Forward HS; Elizabeth, PA; (3); AFS; French Clb; JA; Pep Clb; Sftbl; Var Trk; Var JV Vllybl; Hon Roll; Bus.

CARVALHO, JOSE; G W C Career HS Engineering & Science; Philadelphia, PA; (3); 7/241; Capt Debate Tm; VP Soph Cls; Pres Stu Cncl; Cit Awd; NHS; Prfct Atten Awd; Sen Yuth Pgm PA Rep 87; Prime Pgm 84-87; U &A; Arch Engrng.

RVER, CHANTEL; Hickory HS; Hermitage, PA; (3); Church Yth p; Hosp Aide; Service Clb; Chorus; NHS; Drama Clb; German Clb; ice Aide; Psych.

RVER, RAMI; Villa Maria Acad; Erie, PA; (3); PAVAS; Science Clb; anish Clb; SADD; Var Capt Cheerleading; Trk; Hon Roll; Acctng.

RVIN, AMY; Sasquehanna Community HS; Susquehanna, PA; (4); n Roll.

RY, TAMI; Seneca Valley HS; Mars, PA; (3); 77/371; Color Guard.

S SELLE, MALCOLM W; Southern Lehigh HS; Coopersburg, PA; (4); 30; SADD; Orch; School Musical; Yrbk Stf; Stu Cncl; Socr; Trk; High n Roll; Pres NHS; Ntl Merit SF; Physcs & Chmstry Awds 85 & 86; Ntl tn Awd 85; Semi Fnlst Ntl Achvt Schlrshp Prgrm 86; MIT; Engr.

SAL, CATHY; Western Wayne HS; Lake Ariel, PA; (2); Church Yth p; Cmnty Wkr; Spanish Clb; Chorus; Church Choir; School Musical; hool Play; Hon Roll; Prfct Atten Awd.

SALANDRA, STACI; Neshannock HS; New Castle, PA; (4); Office le; Teachers Aide; Mrchg Band; School Play; Nwsp Stf; Yrbk Bus Mgr; Jr Cls; Sec Sr Cls; Stu Cncl; Twrlr; Westminster Coll; Elem Educ.

SALNOVA, LUCIANNE; Villa Maria Acad; Springfield, PA; (3); 27/ Library Aide; Im Bsktbl; Im Fld Hcky; Hon Roll; Perfect Atten 85-86; try.

SANAVE, JOHN; Altoona Area HS; Altoona, PA; (2); Boy Scts; ence Clb; Ski Clb; High Hon Roll; Jr NHS; NEDT Awd; Pres Schlr; chtre.

SCIANI, MARC; Belle Vernon Area HS; Belle Vernon, PA; (4); 12/ ; Church Yth Grp; Ski Clb; Variety Show; Yrbk Stf; Bsktbl; Ftbl; Pom n; Wt Lftg; NHS; PA ST U; Mech Engnrng.

SCIO, ANTHONY; Mc Dowell HS; Erie, PA; (2); 190/639; Ski Clb; Stu cl; Hon Roll; Penn ST; Bus.

SE, BRADLEY L; Northern Lebanon HS; Myerstown, PA; (3); 27/213; rsity Clb; Chorus; Concert Band; Drm & Bgl; Mrchg Band; School sical; Swing Chorus; Var Bsktbl; Var L Crs Cntry; NHS; Woodmen Of e Wrld Life Ins Soc For Am Hist 85; HOBY Rep 86; Dist Band 87.

SE, CHRIS; Millville HS; Millville, PA; (4); 3/71; Yrbk Sprt Ed; Yrbk ; Sec Soph Cls; Var Fld Hcky; Var Sftbl; High Hon Roll; Hon Roll; IS; Sal; Bloomsburg U; Scndry Math Educ.

SELLA, GEORGE; Montoursville AREA HS; Montoursville, PA; (3); ; Hon Roll; Bio.

SELLA, VINCE; Old Forge HS; Old Forge, PA; (3); Var Bsktbl; Stat ore Keeper; Jr NHS.

SEY, ANGELA; Butler Area SR HS; Butler, PA; (4); 133/730; Church h Grp; French Clb; JA; Latin Clb; Math Tm; SADD; Nwsp Phtg; Nwsp tr; Nwsp Stf; Hon Roll.

SEY, CATHERINE; Upper Darby HS; Drexel Hill, PA; (3); Cmnty kr; Exploring; FTA; JA; Political Wkr; Red Cross Aide; SADD; Teachers le; VICA; Hon Roll; Tchr Of Yr Awd 85-86; Undergrad Of Yr 86-87; Dr nald Padula Awd DCCC 86-87; Educ.

SEY, KENNETH S; Carlisle SR HS; Carlisle, PA; (4); 6/400; Church h Grp; Drama Clb; Model UN; Ski Clb; Yrbk Phtg; Yrbk Stf; Rep Frsh s; Pres Soph Cls; Pres Jr Cls; Pres Sr Cls; Crlsl Areas Fnst Stu Awd 86; hlt Of Wk Awd 85; U Miami; Ocngrphy.

SEY, KERI; Bellefonte HS; Bellefonte, PA; (4); 2/237; Drama Clb; Sec nch Clb; Flag Corp; DAR Awd; French Hon Soc; High Hon Roll; NCTE vd; Pres NHS; Pres Schlr; Sal; Centre Daily Times Schlrshp 87; PA ST & PA Cncl Of Tchrs Engl Essy Fnlst 87; Dickinson Coll; Pol Sci.

SEY, KEVIN; Carlisle SR HS; Carlisle, PA; (4); Art Clb; Model UN; i Clb; Lit Mag; Sec Soph Cls; JV Socr; High Hon Roll; Hon Roll; NHS; fts U; Physcs.

SEY, LESLIE; Schenley HS; Pittsburgh, PA; (3); German Clb; Math ; NAACP; Chorus; Variety Show; High Hon Roll; Hon Roll; NHS; Prfct ten Awd; Pace U; Acctg.

SEY, MARY BETH; Nazareth Acad; Philadelphia, PA; (3); VP Frsh s; Pres Soph Cls; Rep Stu Cncl; Capt Cheerleading; Advertising.

SEY, MICHELE LYN; Knoch HS; Saxonburg, PA; (3); 1/227; AFS; nl Clb; School Play; VP Jr Cls; Church Yth Grp; Dance Clb; Teachers le; High Hon Roll; NHS.

SEY, THERESA; Nazareth Acad; Philadelphia, PA; (3); Cmnty Wkr; nch Clb; NFL; Yrbk Stf; Hon Roll; NHS; Temple U; Real Est.

SEY, TIFFANY; Bishop Carroll HS; Summerhill, PA; (3); 23/123; ama Clb; NFL; Spanish Clb; Speech Tm; SADD; Band; Concert Band; rchg Band; School Play; Stage Crew; Frnsc Lttr 87; Media Cmmnctns.

SHDOLLAR, CHARLES; Carrick HS; Pittsburgh, PA; (3); 86/391; p Frsh Cls; Rep Soph Cls; Var L Crs Cntry; Var L Trk; Im Vllybl; High on Roll; Hon Roll; Acad Lttr 85; Indoor Trk 86-87; Engl.

SILLI, JEFF; Peters Township HS; Mcmurray, PA; (2); Trs Frsh Cls; l; Golf; Wt Lftg; Hon Roll; Bus.

SKIE, STEPHEN; Tuplehocken HS; Myerstown, PA; (4); 7/115; anish Clb; Band; Concert Band; Mrchg Band; Pres Sr Cls; L Bsktbl; L lf; L Tennis; Hon Roll; Lion Awd; Allegheny Coll; Hstry.

SLER, LISA; Warren Area HS; Warren, PA; (3); Church Yth Grp; rman Clb; Acpl Chr; Church Choir; Madrigals; Mrchg Band; School usical; High Hon Roll; Jr NHS; NHS; PA Music Educ Assn Dist II Chrs PMEA Rgnl II Chrs 87; Eastern Nazarene Coll; Eng Lit.

SO, CHRIS; Notre Dame HS; Stroudsburg, PA; (4); 15/42; Radio Clb; rsity Clb; School Musical; School Play; Stage Crew; Nwsp Rptr; Trs ph Cls; Trs Jr Cls; JV Bsbl; Var L Bsktbl; 4th Pl SR Div Russell C ghs Splng Bee 87; Semifnlst Russell C Hughes Splng Bee 82-86; mple; Architect.

SON, DAWN L; Philadelphia HS For Girls; Philadelphia, PA; (1); urch Yth Grp; Dance Clb; Church Choir; Off Frsh Cls; Val; Pres Acadc hvt Awd 85-86; Cert Rcgntn Rsrch 85-86; Spirit Hlpng Others Awd -86; Spellman Coll; Chem.

SPER, BETTY ANN; Burgettstown JR SR HS; Burgettstown, PA; ; Drama Clb; French Clb; Library Aide; Science Clb; SADD; Chorus; urch Choir; School Musical; School Play; Variety Show; Eagle Scholar & J 87-88; Libr Essay Wnnr 86; Diploma Merit 87; Washington & fferson; Law.

SPER, DAVID; Father Judge HS; Philadelphia, PA; (3); 23/403; ench Clb; Letterman Clb; Red Cross Aide; Var Swmmng; Hon Roll; ocesan Schlr 87; Mech Engr.

SPER, KELLY; West Hazleton HS; West Hazleton, PA; (4); 11/247; ance Clb; Letterman Clb; Pep Clb; Ski Clb; Varsity Clb; Var L eerleading; Tennis; Trk; NHS; Penn ST U; Pharmcy.

SPER, SCOTT; Holy Ghost Prep; Bensalem, PA; (4); Math Tm; Nwsp tg; Yrbk Phtg; JV Crs Cntry; Var Trk; Bausch & Lomb Sci Awd; CC d; NHS; Drexel U; Elec Engrng.

CASPER, THERESA; HS For The Creative & Perf Arts; Philadelphia, PA; (4); 10/126; Chorus; Church Choir; School Musical; School Play; High Hon Roll; Prfct Atten Awd; Var L Vllybl; Im Sftbl; Var Bsktbl; Chrmn Rep Stu Cncl; Bucknell U; Voice Perfrmnc.

CASPER, TRENT; Aliquippa HS; Aliquippa, PA; (3); Exploring; French Clb; Yrbk Sprt Ed; Bsbl; Var JV Bsktbl; Hon Roll; Sprts Med.

CASSANO, CHRISTINA; Bishop Kenrick HS; Norrisotwn, PA; (4); 43/ 287; Dance Clb; Ski Clb; Rep Soph Cls; Rep Jr Cls; Rep Sr Cls; Rep Stu Cncl; Var Cheerleading; Powder Puff Ftbl; High Hon Roll; Hon Roll; Prfct Atten 83-87; Montgomery Cnty CC; Nrsng.

CASSEL, JACQUELINE MARYON; Lower Dauphin HS; Hummelstown, PA; (4); 21/236; Church Yth Grp; GAA; Bsktbl; Var JV Fld Hcky; Var JV Sftbl; Hon Roll; Kiwanis Awd; NHS; Charlotte Newton Sheppard Scholar; Robert Byrd Scholar; Harcum JC; Anim Hlth Tech.

CASSEL, JENNIFER; Emmaus HS; Macungie, PA; (2); Church Yth Grp; Chorus; School Musical; Mgr Trk; Hon Roll; Stu Of Mnth 85-86.

CASSEL, REBECCA; Central Dauphin HS; Harrisburg, PA; (4); Chorus; Yrbk Stf; Im Vllybl; Hon Roll; F Alexander Mem Awd 87; SICO Fndtn Schlrshp 87; Kutztown U; Bus Mgmt.

CASSEL, TRACY; Boyertown SR HS; Bechtelsville, PA; (2); Dance Clb; Spanish Clb; School Play; Yrbk Rptr; Fld Hcky; Lcrss; Sftbl; NHS; English Clb; Teachers Aide; Food Prep.

CASSELBERRRY, ELAINE; Mount Alvernia HS; Pittsburgh, PA; (3); 6/54; Teachers Aide; Chorus; Stage Crew; Nwsp Rptr; Nwsp Stf; Yrbk Rptr; Lit Mag; Sftbl; Hon Roll; Sec NHS; Specl Awd/Hnrs Pins US Hstry & Rlgn; Lttrs & Hnrs Pins Hnr Rll; Phrmcy.

CASSIDY, COLLEEN; Hollidaysburg Area SR HS; Hollidaysburg, PA; (3); Hosp Aide; Latin Clb; Office Aide; Band; Color Guard; Flag Corp; Variety Show; Yrbk Stf; Hon Roll; US Navy; Data Prcsr.

CASSIDY, DEANA; Purchase Line HS; Hillsdale, PA; (4); Concert Band; Sec Jr Cls; Sec Stu Cncl; Var Cheerleading; High Hon Roll; Hon Roll; NHS; Purch Line Ed Assoc Schlrshp 87; IN Cnty Cnslrs Assoc Schlrshp 87; IN Univ Of PA; Elem Ed.

CASSIDY, NICOLE; Purchase Line HS; Hillsdale, PA; (2); Pep Clb; Spanish Clb; SADD; Trs Frsh Cls; Stu Cncl; Var JV Bsktbl; JV Sftbl; Stat Trk; High Hon Roll; Hon Roll.

CASSLER, REGINA; Shade Central City HS; Central City, PA; (3); Church Yth Grp; FBLA; Ski Clb; Spanish Clb; Band; Chorus; Church Choir; Mrchg Band; Bsktbl; Mgr(s); Penn ST; Ag.

CASTAGNA, CARLA; Garden Spot HS; New Holland, PA; (2); Pres Church Yth Grp; Chorus; Concert Band; Mrchg Band; VP Jr Cls; JV Var Bsktbl; Var Cheerleading; Var Sftbl; Hon Roll; Girl Scts; Bsktbl Awd MIP 86-87; Bus.

CASTANO, APRIL; Coudersport JR/Sr HS; Coudersport, PA; (3); 7/90; Sec Drama Clb; Varsity Clb; Band; School Play; Yrbk Stf; Rep Stu Cncl; Var L Cheerleading; Trk; NHS; Hon Roll; PTA Acad Ltr 87; Theatre Arts.

CASTEEL, KAREN; Bedford HS; Bedford, PA; (3); Church Yth Grp; FCA; SADD; Chorus; School Musical; School Play; Variety Show; Chess Clb; Yrbk Rptr; Yrbk Stf; Outstndng Achvt For Typng II & Shrthdn I 87; Lgl Secr.

CASTEEL, RONALD B; Eisenhower HS; Russell, PA; (3); Boy Scts; VP Leo Clb; Var L Trk; JV Wrstlng; Jr NHS; NHS; Engr.

CASTELLANI, MARCY; Liberty HS; Bethlehem, PA; (3); 108/450; Church Yth Grp; Red Cross Aide; Chorus; Rep Stu Cncl; Cheerleading; Phys Thrpy.

CASTELLANO, NADINE; Scranton Central HS; Scranton, PA; (3); French Clb; JA; Pep Clb; Band; Concert Band; Mrchg Band; Stat Ftbl; Pom Pon; Hon Roll; Math.

CASTELLUCI, TONY; Mon Tour HS; Mckees Rocks, PA; (3); Cmnty Wkr; French Clb; Pep Clb; Varsity Clb; Band; Concert Band; Mrchg Band; Pep Band; Symp Band; Yrbk Stf; Bsktbl & Bsbl Awds; Duquesne; Sprts Med.

CASTERLINE, ARLENE; Bishop O Reilly HS; Dallas, PA; (3); 12/112; Church Yth Grp; VP Spanish Clb; Capt Cheerleading; Pom Pon; Hon Roll; NHS; Spanish NHS; All Amer Schlr; Yth Salute 87; Hghst Avg Bio 86-87; Elem Ed.

CASTERLINE, CHERYL; Hanover Area HS; Wilkes Barre, PA; (3); 6/ 194; High Hon Roll; Jr NHS; NHS; Bio.

CASTMAN, J RICHARD; Central Catholic HS; Pittsburgh, PA; (3); 52/ 296; JA; Yrbk Stf; Hon Roll; Cnslr Asst U Of Pittsburg Maps Prog 86-87; Mth.

CASTO, DEBORAH; New Covenant Acad; Mansfield, PA; (2); 1/5; Church Yth Grp; Drama Clb; Yrbk Stf; Rep Stu Cncl; Var Bsktbl; Var Socr; Var Sftbl; High Hon Roll; Debate Tm; Pres Physcl Ftns Awd 85-86; HOBY Ldrshp Sem 86-87; Cty Chorus; Azusa Pacific; Soclgy.

CASTO, STEVEN; New Covenant Acad; Mansfield, PA; (4); 1/3; Chess Clb; Church Yth Grp; Debate Tm; Drama Clb; Ski Clb; Chorus; School Play; Stage Crew; Yrbk Sprt Ed; Yrbk Stf; CO Chorus; W Point Military Acad; Engnrng.

CASTRONOVA, MARGARET LOUISE; Blue Ridge HS; Susquehanna, PA; (4); 12/94; Pep Clb; Band; Trs Chorus; Concert Band; Mrchg Band; School Musical; Variety Show; Stu Cncl; Mgr(s); Stat Vllybl; U Of Pittsburgh; Pharm.

CASURRA, LYNDA; Germantown HS; Philadelphia, PA; (3); Church Yth Grp; VP Frsh Cls; Rep Soph Cls; Rep Jr Cls; Cit Awd; Hon Roll; NHS; Val; Penn ST U; Pre-Med.

CASWELL, COURTNEY; State College Area SR HS; State College, PA; (2); Dance Clb; Ski Clb; Spanish Clb; SADD; School Musical; Rep Soph Cls; JV Cheerleading; JV Powder Puff Ftbl; Hon Roll; Church Yth Grp; Acdmc Excllnc Alg I; Sente Awd; PA ST U; Bus.

CASWELL, DENISE; Pocono Mountain HS; Stroudsburg, PA; (2); Pres 4-H; Pep Clb; SADD; Chorus; High Hon Roll; Hon Roll; Intl Frgn Lang Awd Spnsh 86; Spnsh.

CATALANO, ANGELO; Jeannette HS; Jeannette, PA; (3); 18/124; Am Leg Boys St; CAP; Ski Clb; Spanish Clb; Trs Stu Cncl; Var L Bsbl; Var L Ftbl; High Hon Roll; JC Awd; Trs NHS; Lions Clb Yth Sem Recpnt 87; Hnrb Mntn For All Star Tm In Ftbl 85; US Naval Acad; Aerontcl Engrng.

CATALDI, MARK; Hatboro-Horsham HS; Hatboro, PA; (3); Rep Stu Cncl; Var Bsktbl; Capt Socr; High Hon Roll; NHS; Geom, Spnsh II, Hlth, Bio Awds 85-86; All Bux-Mnt Leag, All Area Hon Mtn Bsktbl 85-86.

CATALDO, LORI; Jeannette HS; Jeannette, PA; (2); 3/119; Drama Clb; French Clb; Ski Clb; Spanish Clb; Tennis; High Hon Roll; Penn St; Engrng.

CATALINA, GABRIEL; Elizabeth Forward HS; Elizabeth, PA; (3); Church Yth Grp; Leo Clb; Rep Frsh Cls; Var L Bsbl; Var L Ftbl; High Hon Roll; Hon Roll; Lion Awd; NHS; Rotary Awd; Yth Ldrshp Conf 87; Engr.

CATALONE, GWENN; St Marys Area HS; St Marys, PA; (3); 17/269; Rep Stu Cncl; Hon Roll; IN U PA; Accntng.

CATANZARITO, JOHN; Dubois Area HS; Dubois, PA; (3); 60/375; Letterman Clb; Varsity Clb; Stu Cncl; Var L Ftbl; Var L Trk; Var L Wrstlng; Hon Roll; Outstndng JV Wrestler 85-86; Jr Olympic Track 86; Edinboro U; Accntng.

CATARELLI, TARA; Elizabethtown Area HS; Elizabethtown, PA; (2); Trs Girl Scts; Var Sftbl; NHS; Francis Hesselbein Awd Grl Scts 85; PA ST U; Pilot In USAF.

CATENA, TONI; Windber Area HS; Windber, PA; (3); 64/128; Pres Church Yth Grp; 4-H; Girl Scts; Hosp Aide; Math Clb; Spanish Clb; Band; Church Choir; Concert Band; Mrchg Band; Nrsng.

CATERINA, LORI; Quaker Valley HS; Sewickley, PA; (4); 10/157; Sec German Clb; Math Tm; Chorus; School Musical; Nwsp Rptr; Yrbk Ed-Chief; High Hon Roll; NHS; Pres Schlr; German Natl Hnr Scty-Delta Epsilon Phi 86-87; Leistungskunde Fur Deutsch 84-87; PA ST U; Biochem.

CATERINO, LYNN; West Mifflin Area HS; W Mifflin, PA; (3); GAA; Letterman Clb; Pep Clb; Ski Clb; Varsity Clb; Stu Cncl; Cheerleading; Powder Puff Ftbl; Hon Roll; U Pittsburgh; Comm.

CATES, DENISE MARIE; Kiski Area HS; New Kensington, PA; (4); Drama Clb; Math Tm; Pep Clb; Radio Clb; Varsity Clb; Band; Color Guard; School Musical; Var L Diving; 4-H Awd; ADJAC Conv JA 85; PA ST U; Arch.

CATHERMAN, DANA; Hillside Christian Acad; Mifflinburg, PA; (2); Church Yth Grp; Library Aide; Church Choir; Yrbk Stf; Cheerleading; Sftbl; Vllybl; Hon Roll; Prfct Atten Awd.

CATON, DAWN; Berlin Brothersvalley HS; Berlin, PA; (3); Church Yth Grp; Sec 4-H; FBLA; GAA; Pep Clb; Spanish Clb; SADD; Var Bsktbl; Var Sftbl; Var Vllybl; CPA.

CATTAU, KRISTOPHER; Kiski Area HS; Vandergrift, PA; (3); Boy Scts; Church Yth Grp; Concert Band; Jazz Band; Mrchg Band; Pep Band; Symp Band; Trk; Drexel U; Arch.

CATTELL, KENYAN; State College Area Intermediat HS; Pine Grove Mills, PA; (1); 178/476; Library Aide; Office Aide; Spanish Clb; Teachers Aide; Stage Crew; JV Crs Cntry; Var Powder Puff Ftbl; JV Score Keeper; JV Var Trk; Prfct Atten Awd; Intl Bus.

CATTOLICO, MARY; Bishop Conwell HS; Bensalem, PA; (3); 65/277; GAA; Spanish Clb; JV Sftbl; 1st Pl Rgnls, 3rd Pl ST-PA JR Acad Of Sci 86; Cert Of Merit-Spnsh 87; Marymount U; Brdcstr.

CAUDILL, TIMOTHY; Ringgold HS; Monongahela, PA; (2); Church Yth Grp; Rep Stu Cncl; Stat Bsktbl; JV Ftbl; JV Tennis; High Hon Roll; NHS; 1st Pl Lit PTSA Cultural Arts Cont 85; Pre-Med.

CAUFMAN, JULIE; Greencastle-Antrim HS; Chambersburg, PA; (3); Sec Church Yth Grp; Sec 4-H; Band; Chorus; Church Choir; Concert Band; Mrchg Band; Hnrb Mntn Sci Fair 86-87; Most Imprvd Percussion 87; Nagerstown Bus Coll; Sec.

CAUGHEY, DANIEL; Pennsbury HS; Yardley, PA; (3); Ski Clb; Var Socr; JV Vllybl; Hon Roll; Advtg.

CAUL, ASHLEE; Ambridge Area HS; Ambridge, PA; (3); Quiz Bowl; Yrbk Stf; Pres Stu Cncl; L Trk; High Hon Roll; NHS; Church Yth Grp; French Clb; Pep Clb; Off Soph Cls; Flmmkng.

CAULFIELD, KATHY; Sun Valley HS; Aston, PA; (3); 72/270; Drama Clb; Pres Leo Clb; SADD; Color Guard; Mrchg Band; School Musical; School Play; Variety Show; Nwsp Stf; Yrbk Stf; Millersville; Bus.

CAULFIELD, PATRICK; Shenandoah Valley HS; Shenandoah, PA; (4); 2/103; Yrbk Sprt Ed; VP Frsh Cls; VP Soph Cls; Stu Cncl; Bsktbl; Ftbl; High Hon Roll; Hon Roll; Pres NHS; Sal; Hghst Avg Male Stu; Villanova U; Cvl Engr.

CAULLER, LISA; Coatesville Area SR HS; Coatesville, PA; (3); 11/509; German Clb; Orch; Hon Roll; Vet Med.

CAURVINA, KAREN; Portage Area HS; Portage, PA; (3); Cmnty Wkr; German Clb; Hosp Aide; Library Aide; Ski Clb; Speech Tm; Chorus; Concert Band; Jazz Band; Trs Mrchg Band; Psych.

CAUSAK, KEVIN; Methacton HS; Eagleville, PA; (3); Var L Ice Hcky; Bio.

CAUVEL, MARY; Otto-Eldred HS; Derrick City, PA; (4); 3/79; Band; Concert Band; Drm Mjr(t); Mrchg Band; Ed Yrbk Stf; High Hon Roll; Hon Roll; JP Sousa Awd; NHS; Ntl Merit Ltr; Pres Schlrshp 87; Dist II Band 87; Regnl II ST Band 87; Alfred U; Nrsng.

CAVA, F J; Mt Lebanon HS; Pittsburgh, PA; (3); Am Leg Boys St; Boy Scts; Church Yth Grp; VP Exploring; Latin Clb; Band; JV Trk; God Cntry Awd; Hon Roll; Chess Clb; Eagle Sct 86; Dr.

CAVACINI, BETH; Upper Darby HS; Upper Darby, PA; (3); 188/560; French Clb; Office Aide; SADD; School Musical; Yrbk Stf; Var Fld Hcky; JV Stat Lcrss; Mgr(s); Hon Roll; Prfct Atten Awd; Law.

CAVADA, NICOLE; Jeannette SR HS; Jeannette, PA; (3); Sec French Clb; Ski Clb; Bsktbl; Sftbl; High Hon Roll; NHS.

CAVALIER, CHRISTINE; Pocono Central Catholic HS; Tobyhanna, PA; (3); 10/33; Pres Church Yth Grp; Latin Clb; Service Clb; Chorus; Var L Cheerleading; U Of Pittsburgh:Psychlgy.

CAVALIER, JOE; Central Cambria HS; Ebensburg, PA; (3); 4/210; Rep Stu Cncl; L Var Bsbl; L Var Bsktbl; L Var Golf; High Hon Roll; Hon Roll; U Of Pittsburgh; Dentstry.

CAVALIER, ROBIN; Connellsville HS; Connellsville, PA; (3); Drama Clb; Girl Scts; Chorus; School Musical; VP Frsh Cls; Off Soph Cls; Pres Jr Cls; Off Sr Cls; Rep Stu Cncl; Cheerleading; Rep Winter Sprts Ct 85-86; Cmmnty Yth Theatre-Perf Arts Grp 83-87.

CAVALLARO JR, EDWARD B; St John Neumann HS; Philadelphia, PA; (3); 23/350; Letterman Clb; Varsity Clb; Var L Bowling; Var L Socr; High Hon Roll; Hon Roll; Optmtry.

CAVALLO, FERNANDO F; Archbishop Ryan For Boys; Philadelphia, PA; (2); 32/351; Church Yth Grp; Spanish Clb; School Play; Rep Frsh Cls; Rep Soph Cls; Coach Actv; Var Trk; High Hon Roll; Hon Roll; Prfct Atten Awd; Temple; Elec Engr.

CAVANAUGH, GERALD; Gar Memorial JR SR HS; Wilkes-Barre Twp, PA; (3); 4/147; Exploring; Chorus; Concert Band; Jazz Band; Mrchg Band; Orch; Capt Golf; Trk; NHS; Rotary Awd; Med.

CAVANAUGH, TIMOTHY; Southmoreland HS; Scottdale, PA; (4); 15/ 222; Pres Church Yth Grp; German Clb; Latin Clb; Math Clb; Nwsp Stf; Im Bsktbl; Var Tennis; Pres Schlr; EMC Pres Schlrshp 87; Estrn Mennonite Coll; Comp Sci.

CAVE, HANNAH; Tyrone Area HS; Tyrone, PA; (2); French Clb; Key Clb; PAVAS; Teachers Aide; School Musical; School Play; Stage Crew; Hon Roll; Achvt Awd Wrtng 87; PSU; Independent Film Maker.

CAVICCHIO, JOHN; Greensburg Salem HS; Delmont, PA; (2); 2/294; Church Yth Grp; French Clb; Model UN; NFL; Ski Clb; Concert Band; Nwsp Sprt Ed; JV Bsktbl; JV Ftbl; Jr NHS; Outstndng Acad Achvt Awd 86; Qlfd For Ntl Spch Trnmnt In Dbt 87.

CAVIRIS, MIKE; Monessen HS; Monessen, PA; (3); 17/110; Church Yth Grp; JA; Letterman Clb; Ski Clb; Yrbk Sprt Ed; Im Bsktbl; Im Ftbl; Im Wt Lftg; High Hon Roll; Hon Roll; Bucknell; Psych.

CAVISTON, CHRSTINE MARIE; Cardinal Dougherty HS; Cheltenham, PA; (4); 5/98; Church Yth Grp; Cmnty Wkr; Hosp Aide; Latin Clb; Nwsp Rptr; NHS; Prfct Atten Awd; U PA Grant 86-87; Full Scholar Cabrini Coll; Prof Awd Math Anal/Trig 86-87; Villanova; Nrsg.

CAWLEY, DONNA; Pittston Area HS; Avoca, PA; (4); 1/365; Art Clb; Aud/Vis; Drama Clb; Sec French Clb; Key Clb; Math Clb; Science Clb; SADD; Yrbk Stf; High Hon Roll.

CAWLEY, TOM; Indiana Area SR HS; Indiana, PA; (3); 9/326; Debate Tm; Yrbk Stf; High Hon Roll; NEDT Awd; Prfct Atten Awd.

CAYLOR, JESSICA; Highlands HS; Natrona Hgts, PA; (3); Intnl Clb; JA; Nwsp Bus Mgr; Nwsp Stf; Rep Frsh Cls; Rep Soph Cls; Tennis; Hon Roll; Jr NHS; Sec NHS; Pol Sci.

CAZZILLE, CHARYL; Scott/Cashs HS; Coatesville, PA; (3); 43/509; Church Yth Grp; Ski Clb; Spanish Clb; Acpl Chr; Chorus; Church Choir; High Hon Roll; Hon Roll; Jr NHS; NEDT Awd; Prfct Attndnc 84-85; Scott Sngrs 84-86; Penn ST U; Med.

CEASE, THOMAS; Honesdale HS; Beach Lake, PA; (3); Penn ST; Arch.

CEASER, DIANA; Crestwood HS; Wapwallopen, PA; (1); Church Yth Grp; SADD; Sec Frsh Cls; Sec Soph Cls; Stu Cncl; Var L Cheerleading; High Hon Roll; Jr NHS; NEDT Awd; Letterman Clb; Math & Verbal Talent Srch 85; 2nd Pl Math League Cont In PA 86; U Of AZ; Psych.

CEBULA, STANLEY; Pittston Area SR HS; Pittston, PA; (2); JA; Key Clb; ROTC; Army.

CEBULA, SUSAN; North Star HS; Boswell, PA; (2); 9/135; FCA; Color Guard; Nwsp Stf; Pres Jr Cls; Stu Cncl; Stat Bsktbl; Mat Maids; Hon Roll; Engl Currclm Awd 86-87; Stdnt Mnth Awd 86-87; Comm Artst.

CECCARELLI, GARY; Aliquippa JR SR HS; Aliquippa, PA; (3); Church Yth Grp; Var L Bsbl; High Hon Roll; Hon Roll; Chrch Yth Grp 85-87; Bsbl Vrsty Ltr 85 & 87; Hgh Hnr Roll 87; IN U PA; Bus.

CECCO, COLEEN; St Cyril Acad; Numidia, PA; (2); Cmnty Wkr; Drama Clb; French Clb; Key Clb; School Play; Sec Frsh Cls; Sec Soph Cls.

CECERE JR, RALPH J; Swissvale HS; Swissvale, PA; (3); Am Leg Boys St; French Clb; Q&S; Varsity Clb; School Musical; Nwsp Sprt Ed; Rep Frsh Cls; Rep Soph Cls; Rep Jr Cls; Rep Stu Cncl; Elec Engrng.

CECIL, CHRISTOPHER; Boiling Springs JR SR HS; Boiling Spgs, PA; (2); Nwsp Stf; JV Var Socr; Var L Trk; Div Chmpn & 2nd Pl Grnd Chmpn Sci Fair 86.

CECIL, LISA; Bethlehem Center HS; Marianna, PA; (3); Computer Clb; Dance Clb; Spanish Clb; Band; Concert Band; Mrchg Band; Hon Roll; Campus Life 85-87; Jrnlsm.

CEKLOSKY JR, JOSEPH F; Wyoming Valley West HS; Kingston, PA; (4); Chess Clb; Computer Clb; JETS Awd; NHS; Prfct Atten Awd; Pres Schlr; Deans Schlrshp Wilkes Coll 87; Wilkes Coll; Comp Sci.

CEKLOSKY, LEIGH ANN; Wyoming Valley West HS; Kingston, PA; (2); Key Clb; Latin Clb; Hon Roll; NHS; Prfct Atten Awd; Natl Piano Adtns.

CEKOLA, AMY; Mc Guffey HS; Washington, PA; (3); 9/245; German Clb; Girl Scts; Pep Clb; Acpl Chr; Chorus; School Musical; Stage Crew; High Hon Roll; Hon Roll; NHS; Washington & Jefferson; Med.

CEKORIC, RICH; Ambridge HS; S Heights, PA; (2); Wt Lftg; Hon Roll; Archtctr.

CELECZ, JOY; Pennsbury HS; Fairless Hls, PA; (3); French Clb; Rep Frsh Cls; Rep Stu Cncl; JV L Sftbl; Im Wt Lftg; Physcl Ftns Awd Cert; Physcl Ftns Awd Patch; Hstry.

CELL, PAUL; Council Rock HS; Richboro, PA; (3); Aud/Vis; Church Yth Grp; Hon Roll; Prfct Atten Awd.

CELLINE, GINA; St Benedict Acad; Erie, PA; (3); 5/53; Model UN; Office Aide; Spanish Clb; Rep Trs Stu Cncl; Var Cheerleading; Var Socr; Hon Roll; VP NHS; Elem Ed.

CELLINI, DEENA; Strath Haven HS; Wallingford, PA; (4); Library Aide; PAVAS; Red Cross Aide; Teachers Aide; Capt Color Guard; School Musical; Variety Show; Hon Roll; Rep Stu Cncl; Vrsty Arts Awd SHHS 86-87; Outstndng Svc Dncln 86-87; Temple U; Comm.

CELONA, MARION; John Bartram HS; Philadelphia, PA; (4); 3/625; GAA; Yrbk Stf; VP Stu Cncl; Capt Fld Hcky; Capt Gym; L Sftbl; Hst DAR Awd; Sec NHS; Stu Of Wk 86; All Pblc Star Tm Fld Hcky 86; MVP Gymnstc Tm 86; Ursinus Coll; Intl Rltns.

CENSURATO, LAURA; Acad Of Notre Dame De Namur; King Of Prussia, PA; (4); Church Yth Grp; Hosp Aide; Chorus; Orch; School Play; Yrbk Stf; Hon Roll; PJAS Sci Comp Rgnls 1st & St 2nd 84; Tri-Cnty Music Comp 1st Pl 85; Prexel U Music Comp 1st Pl 84; Nrsng.

CENTIOLE, KATHLEEN; Cardinal Brennan HS; Girardville, PA; (4); 4/50; Church Yth Grp; Debate Tm; Office Aide; Nwsp Stf; Yrbk Ed-Chief; Stu Cncl; Cheerleading; Hon Roll; NHS; Spanish NHS; Miss Xmas Seal Schuylkill Cnty 86-87; Natl Achvt Acad 85-87; Millersville U; Communications.

CEPEC, JOSEPH; Gateway HS; Pitcairn, PA; (3); Church Yth Grp; Civic Clb; Computer Clb; French Clb; German Clb; Science Clb; High Hon Roll; Hon Roll.

CEPEK, ERIC; North Star HS; Hooversville, PA; (2); FCA; Stage Crew; Wt Lftg; Prfct Atten Awd.

CEPPARULO, JACQUELINE; West Catholic Girls HS; Philadelphia, PA; (3); 101/246; Teachers Aide; Nwsp Stf; Activities Rep; Guidance Rep; Italian Club; Temple U; Bus Mgmt.

CERA, MICHAEL; Hazelton HS; Hazleton, PA; (3); 38/438; L Bsbl; Var Bsktbl; High Hon Roll; Lehigh U; Civil Engrng.

CERATO, MELISSA; Plymouth Whitemarsh HS; Norristown, PA; (4); Aud/Vis; Pres FTA; Girl Scts; Hosp Aide; Office Aide; Drill Tm; Bsktbl; Cheerleading; Powder Puff Ftbl; Trk; Lankenau Hostp Schl Of Nrsng.

CERCEO, JENNIFER; Cardinal O Hara HS; Drexel Hl, PA; (3); Dance Clb; Office Aide; Pep Clb; Speech Tm; Varsity Clb; Nwsp Phtg; Yrbk Phtg; JV Cheerleading; Im Gym; Var Vllybl; JV & Var Vllybl 84-88; Chrldr 84-86; Dnc Clb 84-86; Phila Schl Textiles & Sci; Fshn.

CERCONE, LISA; Aliquippa HS; Aliquippa, PA; (2); Hon Roll; Cert Of Mrt For 1st Yr Algebra Cntst 85-86.

CERESINI, SCOTT; Cedar Crest HS; Lebanon, PA; (3); 51/350; Pep Clb; Im Bsbl; Im Fld Hcky; DAR Awd; Hon Roll; Bus.

CEREZO, SHAWN; Fort Cherry JR-SR HS; Bulger, PA; (3); Drama Clb; Science Clb; Ski Clb; Spanish Clb; L Thesps; Band; Chorus; Mrchg Band; School Play; Stage Crew; Navy; Nuclear Engr.

CERIFKO, THOMAS; Hanover HS; Hanover, PA; (3); Chess Clb; Var Bsbl; JV Bsktbl; JV Ftbl; Hon Roll; Accntng.

CERMAK, ELIZABETH MARIE; Ringgold HS; Donora, PA; (4); 174/343; Red Cross Aide; SADD; Hon Roll; SR Activities Commtte 86-87; JR Prom Cmmtte 85-86; CA U Of PA; Soc Wrk.

CERNICKY, LAURA; Valley HS; Arnold, PA; (2); Art Clb; Church Yth Grp; French Clb; Key Clb; Office Aide; SADD; Chorus; Var Cheerleading; Var Trk; Cit Awd; Amrcn Lgn Awd 85-86; Physcn.

CERNIGLIA, TIM; Wyalusing Valley HS; Wyalusing, PA; (3); 7/145; Library Aide; Spanish Clb; SADD; Teachers Aide; Stage Crew; Rep Stu Cncl; Stat Bsktbl; High Hon Roll; US Air Force; Sci.

CERNUTO JR, TERENCE F; Greensburg Central Catholic HS; Mt Pleasant, PA; (2); Band; Chorus; Mrchg Band; School Musical; School Play; Variety Show; Rep Stu Cncl; Ftbl; High Hon Roll; Teachers Aide; Youth Ministry Steering Comm 85-87; Westmoreland Intermediate Unit Stu Forum 86-87; Humanities Day.

CERRA, ADRIANNE; Pocono Mountain SR HS; Cresco, PA; (3); JA; Var L Cheerleading; Var L Fld Hcky; Im Gym; Var Powder Puff Ftbl; Var Trk; Hon Roll; Penn ST.

CERRA, CRAIG; Warren Area HS; Warren, PA; (3); Boy Scts; Church Yth Grp; Band; Concert Band; Jazz Band; Mrchg Band; Orch; Trk; God Cntry Awd; Boy Scts; Mrchng Band; Trk; Chemcl Engrng.

CERRA, ELENA; Valley View HS; Archbald, PA; (4); FBLA; Latin Clb; Spanish Clb; Nwsp Bus Mgr; Yrbk Bus Mgr; Trk; Vllybl; Hon Roll; Prfct Atten Awd; Vlly Vw Yrbk Awd Otstndng Svc 87; Vlly Vw Pnt Stf Awd 87; PA ST.

CERRA, KIM; Carbondale Area JR SR HS; Carbondale, PA; (3); 13/119; Art Clb; Spanish Clb; Chorus; High Hon Roll; Church Yth Grp; Italian Clb 86-87; Antonelli Inst; Cmmrcl Art.

CERRA, MICHAEL; Steel Valley HS; Munhall, PA; (3); 28/226; Nwsp Rptr; Var Golf; NHS; Penn St U; Agrnmy.

CERVELLERO, FRANCIS J; Father Judge HS; Philadelphia, PA; (3); 57/403; Letterman Clb; Varsity Clb; JV Var Bsktbl; Hon Roll; Chem.

CERVENAK, JAMES; Moshannon Valley JR SR HS; Morann, PA; (3); VICA; Nwsp Rptr; Var L Bsbl; JV Bsktbl; Hon Roll; Data Proc.

CERVONE, ROBERT S; Meadville Area SR HS; Meadville, PA; (4); 59/344; 4-H; Political Wkr; Quiz Bowl; Ski Clb; Variety Show; Coach Actv; Capt Ftbl; Wt Lftg; JV Wrstlng; 4-H Awd; Rcrd Hldr Bench Press 86-87; All Conf Ftbl 86-87; Weightlftng Awd 86-87; Brown U; Psych.

CESARE, MARIA; Riverside JR SR HS; Moosic, PA; (3); Girl Scts; Ski Clb; Im Bsktbl; Score Keeper; Stat Trk; Im Vllybl; Pres Schlr; Presdntl Acad Fit Awd; Duke; Acctng.

CESARE, SCOTT; Ford City JR SR HS; Cadogan, PA; (3); 26/160; Chorus; Church Choir; Yrbk Sprt Ed; Rep Frsh Cls; Rep Soph Cls; Rep Jr Cls; Rep Sr Cls; Rep Stu Cncl; High Hon Roll; NHS; Cnty, Dist Chorus 87; Bio.

CESARINI, CARRIE; Bishop O Hara HS; Peckville, PA; (4); 12/115; Church Yth Grp; Computer Clb; Dance Clb; Exploring; French Clb; Chorus; School Play; Sec Stu Cncl; Sftbl; High Hon Roll; U Of Scranton; Chem.

CESARINI, RICK; Valley View HS; Peckville, PA; (1); Church Yth Grp; Latin Clb; Bsbl; Vllybl; Hon Roll; Engrng.

CESARIO, STACY; Connellsville Area SR HS; Mt Pleasant, PA; (3); Library Aide; SADD; High Hon Roll; NHS; Bus.

CESOVSKI, KAREN; Charleroi Area HS; Charleroi, PA; (3); Church Yth Grp; FBLA; Hosp Aide; Library Aide; Band; Concert Band; Mrchg Band; Nwsp Ed-Chief; Nwsp Rptr; Nwsp Sprt Ed.

CESSNA, JENNIFER; Purchase Line HS; Glen Campbell, PA; (2); Band; Mrchg Band; Nwsp Phtg; High Hon Roll; Natl Engl Merit Awd; Acad All Amer; Intl Frgn Lang Awd.

CESSNA, JULIE; Meyersdale Area HS; Wellersburg, PA; (4); 10/116; Pres French Clb; Q&S; Band; Nwsp Ed-Chief; Stu Cncl; Stat Bsbl; Bsktbl; Vllybl; Hon Roll; NHS; CA U; Teaching.

CESSNA, MICHAEL; Punxsutowney Area HS; Punxsatawney, PA; (3); Im Bsktbl; JV Ftbl; Im Vllybl.

CESSNA, ROBERT; Connellsville HS; Connellsville, PA; (1); Boy Scts; Capt Wrstlng; High Hon Roll; Jr NHS.

CESSNA, TODD A; Bedford HS; Bedford, PA; (4); 52/175; Church Yth Grp; FCA; Ski Clb; SADD; Pres Chorus; Church Choir; School Musical; Im Bowling; L Var Ftbl; L Var Trk; Penn ST Altoona; Bus.

CHA, SUSAN; Boyertown Area SR HS; Boyertown, PA; (4); 16/426; Chorus; School Play; Soph Cls; Jr Cls; Sr Cls; High Hon Roll; NHS; Pres Schlr; Church Yth Grp; Library Aide; Freedom Fndtn 87; Berks Cnty Stu Forum 86-87; Pennsylvania ST U; Engr.

CHAAPEL, KIMBERLY A; Troy HS; Troy, PA; (3); 14/175; Am Leg Aux Girls St; Church Yth Grp; Band; Church Choir; Concert Band; Drm Mjr(t); Mrchg Band; Pres Frsh Cls; Var JV Mgr(s); NHS; Bus.

CHACK, TINA; Oxford Area HS; Oxford, PA; (3); Sec Trs Exploring; FFA; Girl Scts; Slvr Awd-Grl Scts 85; Grnhd Dgree FFA 85; Chptr Dgree FFA 86; Ag.

CHADDHA, ANIL; Richland HS; Gibsonia, PA; (3); Boy Scts; Co-Capt Debate Tm; Quiz Bowl; Speech Tm; Chorus; JV L Bsktbl; Var L Trk; High Hon Roll; NHS; Spkr House-Adwin Schlr Cngrs 86; Law.

CHADISH, BRENDA; Moon SR HS; Coraopolis, PA; (3); VP JA; Var Vllybl; High Hon Roll; NHS; Prfct Atten Awd; JR Achvt Top Seller Awd 86-87; Sales Clb Awd 86-87.

CHADWICK, DEBORAH; Hatboro-Horsham HS; Horsham, PA; (3); Church Yth Grp; Girl Scts; Band; Concert Band; Mrchg Band; JV Fld Hcky; JV Lcrss; Var Powder Puff Ftbl; Var Swmmng; Hon Roll; Nrsng.

CHADWICK, MELISSA; Mc Guffey HS; Washington, PA; (4); 7/196; Math Clb; Trs French Clb; Pep Clb; Chorus; School Musical; Yrbk Stf; Trk; Vllybl; Sec NHS; Acad All Amer 86-87; Pres Acad Fit Awd 87; Stu Recog 83-87; Wheeling Coll; Nrsg.

CHADWICK, WINIFRED; Saint Huberts HS; Philadelphia, PA; (3); 340/423; Church Yth Grp; Cmnty Wkr; Hosp Aide; Teachers Aide; School Play; Bsktbl; Sftbl; Prfct Atten Awd; Family & Child Devlpmnt.

CHAKEY, CARRIE; Elizabeth Forward SR HS; Elizabeth, PA; (3); 70/371; Cmnty Wkr; French Clb; JA; Pep Clb; Chorus; Church Choir; School Musical; School Play; Var Cheerleading; Hon Roll; Chorus Top 7 Soloist Assmbly 86; U Of Pittsburgh; Intl Pre-Law.

CHAKLOS, JODY; Nativity BVM HS; Port Carbon, PA; (2); 39/78; Aud/Vis; Rep Frsh Cls; Stat Bsktbl; Astrnmy.

CHAKMAKLIAN, M NINA; West Chester East HS; W Chester, PA; (4); 44/411; Pres Church Yth Grp; Debate Tm; Drama Clb; Exploring; FBLA; Intnl Clb; JA; Pep Clb; Spanish Clb; Nwsp Stf; Villanova U; Chem Engr.

CHALMERS, WENDY S; Lewisburg Area HS; Lewisburg, PA; (4); School Play; Ed Yrbk Ed-Chief; JV Score Keeper; Spanish Clb; Art Dept Faculty Awd; Natl Art Honor Scty Vice Pres; 1st Pl Portfolio Wnnr Dist Art Show; Cmmnty Awd; Cazenovia Coll; Adv Design.

CHALUPA, ROBERT; Aliquippa HS; Aliquippa, PA; (2); Chess (Pres Computer Clb; Concert Band.

CHAMBERLAIN, KATRINA; Everett Area HS; Everett, PA; Church Yth Grp; Pres GAA; Varsity Clb; Drm Mjr(t); Jazz Band; Band; Yrbk Stf; Stu Cncl; Bsktbl; Coach Actv.

CHAMBERLAIN, SHAWN; Oxford Area HS; Oxford, PA; (3); 65/ Sec Church Yth Grp; FFA; Hon Roll; FFA-CHAPTER Svc Awd Parliamentary Procedure Awd 87; Elem Educ.

CHAMBERS, BRENDA; Punxsutawney Area HS; Smicksburg, PA; FBLA; Math Tm; Varsity Clb; JV Var Bsktbl; JV Var Vllybl; Hon R VFW Awd; Acctg.

CHAMBERS, ERIC; Western Beaver HS; Midland, PA; (3); Chess Cl Trk; High Hon Roll; Hon Roll; NHS; Elec Engr.

CHAMBERS, ROXANA; Blue Mountain Acad; Philadelphia, PA; Art Clb; Church Yth Grp; Drama Clb; Girl Scts; Spanish Clb; Chu Choir; Drill Tm; School Play; Oakwood Coll; Med.

CHAMBLISS, EDEN; Center HS; Monaca, PA; (2); Church Yth G German Clb; Band; Flag Corp; Mrchg Band; Yrbk Stf; JV Cheerleadi Im Coach Actv; Var Powder Puff Ftbl; High Hon Roll.

CHAMPEN, APRIL; Pine Forge Acad; Brooklyn, NY; (3); Church Grp; Chorus; Drill Tm; Howard A Golden Awd; NAPA ST Coll; Dentist

CHAMPION, CHRISTIE; Leechburg Erea HS; Leechburg, PA; Church Yth Grp; Intnl Clb; Chorus; Yrbk Stf; Cheerleading; Prfct At Awd; Russian Lang.

CHAMPION, RICHARD; East Allegheny HS; North Versailles, PA; Pres VP Church Yth Grp; French Clb; Capt Quiz Bowl; High Hon R NHS; Inlt Final Bible Quiz Schlrhsp 86; Western PA Final Bible Q Schlrshp 85-086; U Pittsburgh; Pre Med.

CHAMPNESS, JENNIFER; Central York SR HS; York, PA; (3); 35/ French Clb; Ski Clb; Varsity Clb; Nwsp Stf; Yrbk Stf; Mgr(s); Trk; Vll High Hon Roll; Hon Roll; Rflctns Cont Wnnr Lit, All-Trnmt Tms-Vll 86-87; Engrng.

CHAN, JOHN; Roman Catholic HS; Philadelphia, PA; (3); 5/121; B Scts; FBLA; NHS; Yth & Amer Pol Sys Achvt Awd 87; Phila Job Inc Awd 86; Crmnl Just.

CHANDLER, DENISE; Susquehannock HS; Glen Rock, PA; (2); 69/ 4-H; Girl Scts; Bsktbl; Var JV Fld Hcky; Var JV Trk; 4-H Awd; Sci.

CHANDLER, JODI; Northern Lehigh HS; Slatington, PA; (3); 30/1 Debate Tm; Chorus; Church Choir; Concert Band; Jazz Band; Nwsp Rp Var L Fld Hcky; Var L Trk; High Hon Roll; Hon Roll; Studnt Of Mnth Bloomsburg; Sci.

CHANDLER, MICHELLE C; Wilson HS; Sinking Spring, PA; (4); 298; Drama Clb; French Clb; Spanish Clb; Varsity Clb; Ed Lit Mag; C Bowling; Var L Fld Hcky; High Hon Roll; NHS; Ntl Merit Ltr; 2nd Pl N Spnsh Exam 87; 4th Pl Natl Frnch Exam 86; Mdrn Lang Awd 87; Dickr Coll; Intl Stds.

CHANDLER, RAPHAEL; Hallahan Catholic High For Gi Philadelphia, PA; (2); Art Clb; Church Yth Grp; Cmnty Wkr; Dance C English Clb; Girl Scts; Hosp Aide; Office Aide; Pep Clb; Teachers Ai Med.

CHANEY, DOREEN; Salisbury-Elk Lick HS; Salisbury, PA; (3); 5/ Pres Church Yth Grp; Band; Chorus; School Play; Nwsp Ed-Chief; Y Stf; Im Stat Bsktbl; Im Socr; JV Sftbl; Hon Roll; Elem Educ.

CHANEY, KIMBERLY; William Allen HS; Allentown, PA; (4); Chu Yth Grp; Girl Scts; Hosp Aide; Intnl Clb; Spanish Clb; Chorus; Off Fr Cls; Off Soph Cls; Off Jr Cls; Off Sr Cls; Oratorical Cntst Fnlst 85; Hr Vocal Soloist 87; Cedar Crest Coll; Nrsng.

CHANEY, YOSHIMI; Philadelphia HS For Girls; Philadelphia, PA; (Library Aide; Math Clb; Office Aide; Teachers Aide; Yrbk Stf; Cit Av Hon Roll; Sal; Schl Dist Phila Acadcs Plus Hnr Awd 86; Cert Of Me Summa Cum Laude Phila Clsscl Soc 85.

CHANG, ERIC; Methacton HS; Audubon, PA; (3); 38/381; Math T Chorus; Concert Band; Jazz Band; Pres Frsh Cls; Pres Soph Cls; Pres Cls; Rep Stu Cncl; JV Crs Cntry; JV Trk; Psych.

CHANG, FONDA; Charleroi Area JR SR HS; Charleroi, PA; (4); 8/1 French Clb; SADD; Chorus; School Musical; Ed Nwsp Stf; Pres Stu Cn Cheerleading; Trk; High Hon Roll; Hon Roll; PA ST U; Arch Engrng.

CHANG, HOTAE; Southern Lehigh HS; Coopersburg, PA; (4); Chess C Pres JA; Math Clb; Mgr Scholastic Bowl; Science Clb; Varsity Clb; Nw Bus Mgr; Yrbk Stf; Var Tennis; Trs NHS.

CHANG, JOHN V; Pheonixville Area HS; Phoenix, AZ; (3); SAD Varsity Clb; Pres Soph Cls; VP Stu Cncl; Var L Socr; Pres Jr NHS; NH Key Clb; Pep Clb; Spanish Clb; Prsdnt Hugh Obrn Yth Fnd Alumni-EPA 87; Prsdntl Clssrm Ldrshp Smnr 87; Air Force Acad; Me

CHANG, LINDA; Philadelphia H S For Girls; Philadelphia, PA; (3); 405; Library Aide; Hon Roll; Bailey Wms Memrl Key 85-86; U Of P Clncl Psychology.

CHANG, MICHAEL; Cumberland Valley HS; Mechanicsburg, PA; (3); 548; Lit Mag; Var L Socr; JV Trk; High Hon Roll; Hon Roll; NHS; V Dickinsen Coll Summer Pgm Schlrshps 87; Harrisburg Area CC Journal 87; MA Inst Of Tech.

CHANG, PEARL C; The Baldwin Schl; Wynnewood, PA; (4); Math T Chorus; Trs Frsh Cls; Rep Stu Cncl; JV Capt Fld Hcky; JV Capt Lcrss; Merit SF; Model UN; Science Clb; Intnl Clb; Harvard Prz Bk Awd 86; Govrnrs Schl Sci 85; Natl Latn Exm Wnr-Gold, Slvr Mdls 84-85 & 86.

CHANG, YUNSOOK; Philadelphia HS For Girls; Philadelphia, PA; (Church Yth Grp; Orch; School Musical; Nwsp Ed-Chief; Yrbk Ed-Chi Bowling; Cit Awd; French Hon Soc; Gov Hon Prg Awd; High Hon Roll; Mayors Schlrshp 87; U PA; Pre Law.

CHAPIN, LORI; Butler SR HS; Butler, PA; (3); Drama Clb; Spanish C Chorus; Concert Band; School Play; Swing Chorus; Stu C Cheerleading; Swmmng; Hon Roll; Acdmc Achvt Awd 86-87; Phys Thr

CHAPIN, TOM; Bedford HS; Bedford, PA; (3); Computer Clb; Ski C JV Bsktbl; Var JV Ftbl; JV Trk; Hon Roll; Devry Inst-OH; Comp Arch

CHAPLAIN, SCOTT; Tech Memorial HS; Erie, PA; (3); 90/330; Var Ca Tennis; Ldrshp Conf 87; Athltc Hnr Soc 87; Law Enfrcmnt.

CHAPLIK, MARK; Carlynton HS; Pittsburgh, PA; (4); 7/168; Bar Concert Band; Mrchg Band; Pep Band; Symp Band; High Hon Roll; H Roll; NHS; Carnegie Mellon U; Engrng.

CHAPLIN, STACEY; Owen J Roberts HS; Pottstown, PA; (4); 7/2 Letterman Clb; VP Sr Cls; Rep Stu Cncl; Var Bsktbl; Var Capt Fld Hc Var Lcrss; DAR Awd; Hon Roll; NHS; Rep Frsh Cls; All Leag 1st Tm Hocky 86; Bus.

CHAPMAN, CHRISTINE; West Scranton HS; Scranton, PA; (3); Au Vis; Church Yth Grp; Drama Clb; FNA; Ski Clb; Thesps; Mgr Stage Cre Hon Roll; NHS; Med Tech.

CHAPMAN, CRAIG; Elizabethtown Area HS; Elizabethtown, PA; (3); 36/259; Rep Frsh Cls; Rep Soph Cls; Trs Jr Cls; Rep Trs Stu Cncl; Var JV Socr; Amer Wilderness Schl 87; Conservationldrshp Schl 85; Wmns Insur League Of Lancaster 86; Penn ST U; Forestry.

CHAPMAN, CURTIS; Tri-Valley SR HS; Uniontown, PA; (3); Hst Jr Cls; High Hon Roll; Hon Roll; NHS; WV U; Pre-Dental Med.

CHAPMAN, CYNTHIA; Western Beaver HS; Industry, PA; (3); Pres FHA; SADD; Band; Concert Band; Mrchg Band; Symp Band; Nwsp Rptr; Nwsp Stf; Cit Awd; NHS; Semi-Fnlst Govr Schl In Crtv Wrtng 87; Chptr Of Yr For Future Hmmkrs Of Amer 86; Ed.

CHAPMAN, JENNY; Moon SR HS; Coraopolis, PA; (3); 31/306; JA; Mrchg Band; Pep Band; Symp Band; Stu Cncl; High Hon Roll; Hon Roll; NHS; Ntl Merit Ltr; Band; Tri-M Music Hnr Scty 85-87; Top Fnlst In Natl Lang Arts Olympiad 85; Engr.

CHAPMAN, JESSICA; Indiana Area SR HS; Indiana, PA; (4); Debate Tm; Model UN; NFL; Speech Tm; School Musical; School Play; Crs Cntry; Rgnl Wnnr Extemporaneous Spkng In West PA 87; IN Univ Of PA; Poltcl Sci.

CHAPMAN, KIMBERLY; Frankford HS; Philadelphia, PA; (3); Acpl Chr; Band; Concert Band; Jazz Band; Mrchg Band; Orch; Pep Band; School Musical; School Play; Nwsp Rptr; Lttr Band 86-87; Comm.

CHAPMAN, LORIE; Lehigh Christian Acad; Allentown, PA; (3); Church Yth Grp; Dance Clb; Pep Clb; Church Choir; Var Bsktbl; Var Crs Cntry; Hon Roll; NHS; Engl Acad Awd 86; Chrstn Attitude Bsktbl Acad Awd 86-87; Psych.

CHAPMAN, MELISSA; Seneca HS; Waterford, PA; (4); 27/153; VP 4-H; Pres Pep Clb; Band; Concert Band; Mrchg Band; Orch; Yrbk Stf; Pres Trs Stu Cncl; NHS; SAR Awd; HOBY Awd 85; Stu Choice Spkr Cls 87; Mercyhurst Coll; Hotl Mngmt.

CHAPMAN, RANDY; West Scranton SR HS; Scranton, PA; (3); Spanish Clb; JV Wrstlng; Hon Roll; Bus Admin.

CHAPMAN, TRICIA; Newport HS; Newport, PA; (1); Chorus; VP Frsh Cls; Rep Stu Cncl; JV Bsktbl; JV Fld Hcky; JV Sftbl; High Hon Roll; Prfct Atten Awd; Penn ST U.

CHAPMAN, WILLIAM; Lincoln HS; Ellwood City, PA; (4); Rep Stu Cncl; Var Capt Bsbl; Var Capt Ftbl; Hon Roll; SAR Awd; Thiel Coll; Educ.

CHAPPELL, CYNTHIA; Richland HS; Gibsonia, PA; (4); 15/187; Band; Chorus; School Musical; Variety Show; Var L Cheerleading; Var L Tennis; Var L Trk; High Hon Roll; NHS; French Clb; U S Army Rsrvs Natl Schlr/ Athlt Awd 87; Allegheny Coll.

CHAPPELL, SHAWN; Lincoln HS; Ellwood City, PA; (4); 57/165; AFS; Spanish Clb; SADD; Y-Teens; Chorus; Nwsp Bus Mgr; Nwsp Rptr; Nwsp Stf; Yrbk Bus Mgr; JV Cheerleading; Accntng Cert; Bus Clb.

CHAPPELL, TIFFANY; Morrisville HS; Morrisville, PA; (3); 34/86; Chorus; School Play; Rep Frsh Cls; Rep Soph Cls; Sec Jr Cls; Pres Sr Cls; Var Bsktbl; Var Fld Hcky; MVP Bsktbl, Fld Hockey 86; Psych.

CHAPPIE, LEANNA; Greater Johnstown HS; Johnstown, PA; (4); 98/ 277; Hosp Aide; Ski Clb; Spanish Clb; Y-Teens; Nwsp Rptr; Nwsp Stf; Yrbk Stf; Edinboro U; Nrsng.

CHAPPLE, DAVID; Coughlin HS; Wilkes Barre, PA; (4); VP Church Yth Grp; Math Clb; Math Tm; Band; Church Choir; Concert Band; Mrchg Band; Golf; Hon Roll; NHS; Acdmc Pres Schlrshp Awd 86-87; Wilkes Coll; Arch Engrng.

CHAPUT JR, BERNARD R; Fr Judge HS; Philadelphia, PA; (4); 156/ 350; Latin Clb; Var L Socr; Prfct Atten Awd; Allentown Coll; Bus Adm.

CHARITON, DEBBIE; E L Meyers HS; Wilkes-Barre, PA; (4); 4/140; SADD; Temple Yth Grp; Nwsp Rptr; Nwsp Stf; Yrbk Bus Mgr; Yrbk Stf; High Hon Roll; NHS; NEDT Awd; Spanish NHS; JR Hnr Socty 83-85; ST Hnr Socty 85-87; Spnsh Hnr Socty 84-87; Brandeis U; Engl.

CHARLES, STACEY; Beaver Area HS; Beaver, PA; (3); 1/230; Church Yth Grp; French Clb; Chorus; Var Tennis; High Hon Roll; Pres NHS; Schlstc Schvt Awd 86 & 87; Hndbll Hnr Awd 87; Ltr Vrsty Tnns 87 & 88; Home Econ.

CHARLES, TANYA; Biglerville HS; Biglerville, PA; (2); 34/114; Church Yth Grp; Varsity Clb; School Play; Yrbk Stf; Var L Cheerleading; Gym; Wt Lftg; Jr NHS; NHS; Spanish Clb; Fshn Dsgnr.

CHARLIER, JODI; Burgettstown Area JR SR HS; Bulger, PA; (3); Library Aide; Ski Clb; Spanish Clb; Rep Band; Church Choir; Color Guard; Co-Capt Drill Tm; School Musical; Jr NHS; NHS; Pre-Med.

CHARLIER, REBECCA A; Burgettstown Area JR SR HS; Bulger, PA; (2); Church Yth Grp; Ski Clb; Spanish Clb; Chorus; Mrchg Band; Pep Band; Symp Band; Twrlr; High Hon Roll; Jr NHS.

CHARLTON, HENRY; Trinity HS; Camp Hill, PA; (3); 20/145; Boy Scts; Debate Tm; Ski Clb; Trs Spanish Clb; School Musical; School Play; Pres Stu Cncl; Bsktbl; Ftbl; Trk; Frfld U; Law.

CHARLTON, TRACEY; Little Flower HS; Philadelphia, PA; (2); Library Aide; Teachers Aide.

CHARNOCK, JULIE; West Chester East HS; West Chester, PA; (3); FBLA; Hosp Aide; JCL; Pep Clb; SADD; Stu Cncl; Swmmng; Hon Roll; Instrl Rltns.

CHARRON, PHILIP; Marple Newtown SR HS; Newtown Square, PA; (3); 46/320; Drama Clb; School Play; Stage Crew; Yrbk Phtg; Hon Roll; Cmnctns.

CHART, DAVE; General Mclane HS; Edinboro, PA; (3); 39/226; Chess Clb; Pres Computer Clb; Band; Jazz Band; Mrchg Band; Pep Band; Rep Stu Cncl; Stat Bsktbl; Hon Roll; NHS; Engrng.

CHARTIER, MARY; Cardinal O Hara HS; Ridley Park, PA; (3); 72/710; Band; Concert Band; Mrchg Band; Var Trk; Hon Roll; NHS; French Clb; FNA; Prncpls Awd Acadc Excel 86-87; Hmrm Rep 84-85; Cmnty Svc Corps Sntr 86-87; Lbrl Arts.

CHARYTON, CHRISTINE; Council Rock HS; Churchville, PA; (3); 105/ 898; Debate Tm; Drama Clb; Intnl Clb; Spanish Clb; Yrbk Stf; Crs Cntry; Trk; Hon Roll; Church Yth Grp; School Musical; Equestrian Compttn Prtcpnt 85-88; Sci.

CHASE, SUE; West Scranton HS; Scranton, PA; (2); 11/250; Church Yth Grp; Hosp Aide; Spanish Clb; Orch; Pom Pon; High Hon Roll; Hon Roll; Jr NHS; U Scranton; Comp Tech.

CHASE, SUZANNE; Nazareth Acad; Philadelphia, PA; (3); 21/125; Red Cross Aide; Spanish Clb; Varsity Clb; Sec Soph Cls; Sec Jr Cls; Bsktbl; Fld Hcky; Im Vllybl; Hon Roll; Cndt Archdiocesan Schlr Prgrm 87; Finance.

CHATMAN, SHAUN; Norristown HS; Norristown, PA; (3); VICA; Chorus; Nwsp Phtg; Bsktbl; Ftbl; Hon Roll; Coll Ltrs 87; Grphcs Arts.

CHAU, HOA; Carver HSES; Philadelphia, PA; (3); School Musical; Stage Crew; Yrbk Phtg; Im Badmtn; Im Tennis; NHS; Comp Engr.

CHAU, PHING; Philadelphia HS For Girls; Philadelphia, PA; (4); 72/365; Teachers Aide; Bowling; Hon Roll; Distngsh & Mrtrs Hnrs; U Of Pittsburg; Pharm.

CHAUDHRY, IFTIKHAR; Central HS; Philadelphia, PA; (4); 1/350; AFS; French Clb; Intnl Clb; Math Tm; Nwsp Stf; High Hon Roll; Ntl Merit Ltr; PA Sci Cncl Awd 87; Penn ST; Med.

CHAUDHRY, IJAZ; Central HS; Philadelphia, PA; (2); Chess Clb; Debate Tm; French Clb; Intnl Clb; Model UN; Office Aide; Speech Tm; Cit Awd; French Hon Soc; NHS; Med.

CHAUDRY, RABIA; Gateway SR HS; Monroeville, PA; (3); 40/500; Hosp Aide; Science Clb; Ski Clb; Tennis; Hon Roll; Med.

CHEATLE, SABINA; St Marys Area HS; Saint Marys, PA; (4); Boys Clb Am; Church Yth Grp; Cmnty Wkr; Dance Clb; German Clb; Girl Scts; Pep Clb; Yrbk Stf; High Hon Roll; Hon Roll; Fastest Typist 84-85; US Air Force; Accntng.

CHECCHIA, JANESA; Nazareth Acad; Philadelphia, PA; (3); 25/125; Drama Clb; French Clb; Red Cross Aide; Color Guard; Mrchg Band; Stage Crew; Prfct Atten Awd; Admtnc To Natl Hnr Roll Yrbk 86-87; Awd Of Rcgntn Fr Judge Mrchng Bnd 84-85; Corp Law.

CHECCHIO, CELESTE; Cardinal O Hara HS; Ridley Park, PA; (3); 123/ 710; JA; Spanish Clb; Lit Mag; Hon Roll; Marine Bio.

CHECHO, PAULA; West Scranton HS; Scranton, PA; (2); Spanish Clb; Off Jr Cls; Pom Pon; Hon Roll; Jr NHS.

CHECK, SHANNON; Uniontown Area HS; Uniontown, PA; (3); 5/318; Letterman Clb; Math Tm; Ski Clb; Trs Stu Cncl; Capt Cheerleading; CC Awd; Pres French Hon Soc; High Hon Roll; NHS; Prfct Atten Awd; Intl Forgn Lang Awd-Frnch 87; Intl Day CA U-3rd Pl Frnch 85 & 86; Arch.

CHECKER, DAVID; Lower Merion HS; Bala Cynwyd, PA; (3); Rep Jr Cls; Pres Stu Agnst Smkng Cmmttee; Penn ST; Law.

CHECKET, WILLIAM J; Northern Lebanon HS; Jonestown, PA; (3); 31/ 212; Drama Clb; Band; Chorus; School Musical; School Play; Swing Chorus; Nwsp Rptr; NHS; Church Yth Grp; Model UN; People To People HS St Ambsdrs 85; Psych.

CHECKOFF, JAIME; Lower Moreland HS; Huntingdon Valley, PA; (3); FBLA; Math Clb; Ski Clb; Bsktbl; Sftbl; Tennis; Hon Roll.

CHEESEMAN, JENNIFER; Elizabeth Foward HS; Elizabeth, PA; (2); French Clb; Sec Chorus; JV Bsktbl; Var Crs Cntry; JV Trk; Hon Roll; Schl Tchr.

CHELEN, DANIEL; Greensburg-Salem HS; New Alexandria, PA; (2); 23/305; Church Yth Grp; French Clb; NFL; Rep Stu Cncl; Var Trk; Var Wrstlng; High Hon Roll; Hon Roll; Sec Jr NHS; Ftnss Team 86-87; Air Force Acad; Engrng.

CHELKO, MICHELLE; Valley HS; New Kensington, PA; (3); AFS; VP Spanish Clb; Band; Chorus; Concert Band; Drm & Bgl; Mrchg Band; High Hon Roll; Hon Roll; Prfct Atten Awd; Stu Of The Mnth 85-86.

CHEN, ANNA; Lower Moreland HS; Huntingdon Valley, PA; (4); 1/201; Church Yth Grp; Math Tm; SADD; Teachers Aide; Orch; Ed Lit Mag; JV Var Trk; High Hon Roll; Hst NHS; Ntl Merit SF; Pre-Med.

CHEN, EUGENE; Exeter Twp HS; Reading, PA; (4); 13/213; Drama Clb; Quiz Bowl; Speech Tm; Chorus; Orch; School Musical; Variety Show; Yrbk Ed-Chief; Lit Mag; Dnfth Awd; Govrnr Schl Arts 85.

CHEN, GEORGE C; Wyomissing Area HS; Wyomissing, PA; (4); 1/103; JCL; Scholastic Bowl; L Spanish Clb; School Musical; Yrbk Ed-Chief; Chrmn Stu Cncl; Var L Trk; Bausch & Lomb Sci Awd; Gov Hon Prg Awd; NHS; Top Math Stu 9th-11th Grd; Ntl Latn Exm Magna Cum Laude 11th; Engr.

CHEN, HENRY I; Marple Newtown SR HS; Broomall, PA; (3); 5/322; Capt Math Tm; Scholastic Bowl; Service Clb; Trs SADD; Chorus; High Hon Roll; NHS; Math Clb; Mu Alpha Theta; Nwsp Stf; Rnslr Math & Sci Awd 87; Amrcn Chem Scty Ad 86; Hrn Rll Amrcn HS Math Exam 87; Pre-Med.

CHEN, HERALD; Butler SR HS; Butler, PA; (3); 12/755; Debate Tm; Latin Clb; NFL; SADD; School Musical; Yrbk Ed-Chief; Trs Sr Cls; Stu Cncl; Tennis; NHS; PA Gov Schl Sci 87; Pres Clsrm 87; Acad Sci 87.

CHEN, HSIAO-MING; Lansdale Catholic HS; Lansdale, PA; (3); 23/223; Church Yth Grp; Intnl Clb; Band; Chorus; Orch; Pep Band; Hon Roll; CESHY Smmr Schl Music Schlrshp Cello 85; Cello Solo N PA Symphny Orchstr 86; Mdrn Chem Awd 86-87; Nrse.

CHEN, JACK; Beaver Area HS; Beaver, PA; (3); 37/215; Drama Clb; Math Tm; Speech Tm; School Musical; School Play; Variety Show; JV Ftbl; Stat Var Swmmng; Var Trk; High Hon Roll; Volunteer Tutor 87; 2nd Pl Schl Speech Cntst 85; 2nd Pl Cnty, 7th Pl St Math Comp 85; U Of Pittsburgh; Acctng.

CHEN, JULIA; Altoona Area HS; Altoona, PA; (3); Drama Clb; Hosp Aide; Science Clb; Spanish Clb; SADD; Chorus; Concert Band; Tennis; High Hon Roll; Hon Roll; K-Pin Acad Awd-4.0 GPA 85; Band, Orch & Chrl Awd 85; Pres Acad Ftnss Awd 85; U Of PA; Bio.

CHEN, KATHERINE; Hatboro-Horsham SR HS; Dresher, PA; (3); Intnl Clb; Key Clb; Library Aide; SADD; JV Lcrss; Hon Roll; NHS; Engrng.

CHEN, TINA; Lower Moreland HS; Huntingdon Valley, PA; (2); Church Yth Grp; Cmnty Wkr; German Clb; Key Clb; Science Clb; SADD; Teachers Aide; Cit Awd; High Hon Roll; Prfct Atten Awd; U Of PA.

CHENEVEY, STEVE; Wilmington Area HS; New Wilmington, PA; (4); 6/112; Drama Clb; Jazz Band; Mrchg Band; Stage Crew; Var Capt Crs Cntry; Var L Trk; High Hon Roll; Hon Roll; NHS; X-Cntry MIP 84; Kent ST U; Telecmmnctns.

CHENEY, TRACY; Pocono Christian Schl; Stroudsburg, PA; (4); 2/5; Church Yth Grp; Chorus; Nwsp Stf; Yrbk Stf; Bsktbl; Cheerleading; High Hon Roll; Hon Roll; Sal; Church Choir; Prsdntl Schlrshp 87; Keystone JC; Lbrl Arts.

CHENG, KAREN; Louis E Dieruff HS; Allentown, PA; (4); 3/338; Science Clb; Chorus; Orch; Nwsp Rptr; Rep Soph Cls; Var L Tennis; Hon Roll; Lion Awd; Sec NHS; Ntl Merit SF; Mary Alice Miller Awd 84; Hstry Day 3rd Pl 85; 8 Wk Wrk Schlrshp Prog Lehigh U 86; Penn ST; Engrng.

CHENOT, FREDERICK; Montour HS; Pittsburgh, PA; (4); 19/302; Band; Chorus; Concert Band; Jazz Band; Mrchg Band; Pep Band; School Musical; JV Trk; High Hon Roll; NHS; Allegheny Comptve Exam Schlrshp 87; Allegheny Schlr 87; Allegheny Coll; Pre Med.

CHEPALONIS, LORI; Wyoming Area HS; Exeter, PA; (3); 47/250; Art Clb; Key Clb; Spanish Clb; Hon Roll; X-Ray Tech.

CHEPLIC, LORI; Ringgold HS; Finleyville, PA; (3); 9/372; Concert Band; Mrchg Band; Var JV Bsktbl; Var L Crs Cntry; Var L Trk; High Hon Roll; Sci & Math Hnr Scty 86; Med.

CHEPLICK, DENNIS R; Marian HS; Nesquehoning, PA; (4); 25/110; Chess Clb; Math Clb; School Play; Nwsp Sprt Ed; Nwsp Stf; Tennis; Hon Roll; Rotary Awd; Johnson & Wales Coll; Clnry Art.

CHEREPKO, TARA; Elizabeth-Forward HS; Elizabeth, PA; (3); Aud/ Vis; Cmnty Wkr; Dance Clb; French Clb; Band; Drill Tm; Twrlr; High Hon Roll; Hon Roll; NHS; PA ST; Engr.

CHERINCHAK, SHIRLEY; Carbondale Area HS; Simpson, PA; (3); 11/ 150; Art Clb; JA; Spanish Clb; Fld Hcky; High Hon Roll; NHS; Psych.

CHERNESKY, RITA; Shenandoah Valley JR SR HS; Shenandoah, PA; (4); 18/102; Library Aide; Pep Clb; Chorus; Color Guard; Nwsp Stf; Yrbk Sprt Ed; Var Trk; JV L Vllybl; Upward Bound Prog Bloomsburg U 85; Hotel Mgmt.

CHERNOUSKAS, CAROL; Pittston Area SR HS; Pittston, PA; (4); Key Clb; Science Clb; SADD; Yrbk Stf; Sec Jr Cls; High Hon Roll; NHS; Ntl Merit SF; Blgy.

CHERNOUSKAS, JEROME; Pittstown Area SR HS; Pittston, PA; (3); Church Yth Grp; Im Sftbl; Hon Roll.

CHEROK, TAMARA; Sacred Heart HS; Pittsburgh, PA; (3); 2/133; Hosp Aide; Spanish Clb; Chorus; Capt Cheerleading; Crs Cntry; Trk; High Hon Roll; Sci Awd-PJAS 1st Awd Rgnl 2nd Awd ST 85-86; Trk Coachs Awd For Sprntng 86-87; Hnrd At U Of Pgh 86-87; Bio Sci.

CHERRY, KEN; Bellwood-Antis HS; Tyrone, PA; (4); 37/110; Church Yth Grp; Trs French Clb; Key Clb; Chorus; Church Choir; School Musical; Swing Chorus; Variety Show; Trs Sr Cls; Hon Roll; Comp, Music Awds 86-87; Slippery Rock U; Elem Educ.

CHESLA, MATTHEW; Lawsdale Catholic HS; North Wales, PA; (3); SADD; Nwsp Rptr; Yrbk Stf; Pres Jr Cls; Sec Stu Cncl; Var L Bsbl; Var L Ftbl; Dnfth Awd; Art Illstrtn.

CHESNEY, DEAN; Shamokin Area HS; Shamokin, PA; (3); 55/223; Chess Clb; German Clb; Science Clb; JV Bsktbl; Var Golf; Hon Roll; Pre Med.

CHESNUTT, DANA; Ford City HS; Cadogan, PA; (3); Church Yth Grp; Key Clb; Spanish Clb; Band; Drm Mjr(t); Stu Cncl; Cheerleading; Sftbl; Hon Roll; NHS; Psychology.

CHESONIS, DERRICK; Shenandoah Valley HS; Shenandoah, PA; (4); 17/105; Cmnty Wkr; School Play; Stage Crew; JV Var Ftbl; Var Trk; JV Wrstlng; Hon Roll; Lincoln Tech Inst; Elec Tech.

CHESS, BART; Fairchance Georges SR HS; Smithfield, PA; (3); Wrstlng; Hon Roll; Jr NHS; NHS; Temple; Med.

CHESS, KATHY; Carmichaels SR HS; Carmichaels, PA; (3); 9/112; Pep Clb; Spanish Clb; Band; Concert Band; Mrchg Band; Trs Stu Cncl; Var Sftbl; Hon Roll; Psychlgy.

CHESTER, CARRIE; Ambridge Area HS; Freedom, PA; (3); French Clb; Pep Clb; Red Cross Aide; Yrbk Ed-Chief; Ed Yrbk Stf; Off Soph Cls; Off Jr Cls; High Hon Roll; NHS; Cmmtte Prvntn Drugs & Alcohol 86-87.

CHESTNEY, KIMBERLY; Manheim Central HS; Manheim, PA; (3); 72/ 464; Art Clb; Dance Clb; Drama Clb; French Clb; Hosp Aide; Chorus; Sec Soph Cls; JV Capt Cheerleading; High Hon Roll; Hon Roll; US Constitution Essay Awd-YWCA 87; Jrnlsm.

CHESTNUT, BETH; Ford City HS; Manorville, PA; (4); Spanish Clb; Chorus; School Musical; Rep Frsh Cls; Rep Soph Cls; Rep Jr Cls; Rep Sr Cls; Rep Stu Cncl; Var JV Cheerleading; Vllybl; New Kensington Commercial Schl.

CHESTNUT, KRISTINE; Hickory HS; Hermitage, PA; (4); 22/170; Church Yth Grp; Drama Clb; Service Clb; Chorus; Nwsp Rptr; Sec Soph Cls; Sec Jr Cls; Var L Cheerleading; Vllybl; NHS; Chrldng Acdmc Awd 85&86; Spnsh Hnr Soc 84-87; Grove City Coll; Bus.

CHEU, JENNIFER B K; East Stroudsburg Area HS; East Stroudsburg, PA; (3); 3/245; Am Leg Aux Girls St; Church Yth Grp; Intnl Clb; Model UN; Chorus; Trk; High Hon Roll; Hon Roll; NHS; School Musical; Acad Hnrs Awd Top 25 Stu; JR Miss Pag; Miss Teen Amer Pag; Elem Ed.

CHEUVRONT, LANCE; Aliquippa HS; Aliquippa, PA; (4); VP Chess Clb; Band; Pep Band; Wrstlng; Hon Roll; Marines; Military.

CHEWNING, ROBIN; Daniel Boone HS; Douglassville, PA; (3); 75/167; Debate Tm; French Clb; Model UN; SADD; Nwsp Stf; Yrbk Stf; Lit Mag; Off Frsh Cls; Off Soph Cls; Off Jr Cls; Temple U; NROTC.

CHHOUR, LORNG; Olney HS; Philadelphia, PA; (1); 19/701; Computer Clb; Math Clb; Office Aide; Yrbk Stf; Stu Cncl; High Hon Roll; Hon Roll; Jr NHS; NHS; Hnr Rl Awd 84-86; Beaver Coll; Comp Sci.

CHI, HERB; Williamsport Area HS; Williamsport, PA; (3); Math Tm; Off Jr Cls; Trk; Amer Chem Soc Chem I Exam Ust Pl 85-86.

CHI, IDA; Plymouth Whitemarsh HS; Plymouth Mtg, PA; (3); 15/350; Art Clb; Chess Clb; Chorus; Drill Tm; Nwsp Stf; Lit Mag; Trk; High Hon Roll; NCTE Awd; NHS; Wharton Schl; Bus.

CHI, KATHY; Lower Moreland HS; Huntingdon Valley, PA; (2); Church Yth Grp; Acpl Chr; Rep Stu Cncl; JV Cheerleading; JV Lcrss; Tennis; Hon Roll; Music Schlrshp Jenkintown Music Schl.

CHIAMPI, ROSLYN; Wyoming Area SR HS; West Pittston, PA; (3); French Clb; Ski Clb; Band; Concert Band; Mrchg Band; NC-CHAPEL Hill; Podiatry.

CHIANG, JASON; Hazleton HS; Hazleton, PA; (2); Leo Clb; Scholastic Bowl; Spanish Clb; Nwsp Stf; Pres Stu Cncl; L Tennis; High Hon Roll; Prfct Atten Awd; Pres Schlr; Rotary Awd.

CHIANG, MARIA; Hazetlton HS; Hazleton, PA; (3); 20/436; Drama Clb; VP FBLA; Leo Clb; Nwsp Stf; Var L Bowling; Hon Roll; NHS; Prfct Atten Awd; Voice Dem Awd; Kline Essay Awd 87; Kings Coll Spnsh Cont 2nd & 3rd Pl 85 & 87; Amer Lgn Awd Rnnr Up 85; Penn ST; Intl Stds.

CHIAO, ALICE; Gateway SR HS; Monroeville, PA; (3); 48/450; Church Yth Grp; VP NFL; Chorus; Lit Mag; Off Frsh Cls; Off Soph Cls; Off Jr Cls; Im Vllybl; Hon Roll; Schlrshp Intnsv Lang Prg 87; Prsdng Ofc Stu Cngrs Natl Frnsc Lge Fnls 87; Presdng Ofc Senate 87.

CHIAPPINI, KRISTIN; Moniteau JR SR HS; Chicora, PA; (3); 27/130; Church Yth Grp; 4-H; FHA; Spanish Clb; Chorus; Yrbk Stf; Cheerleading; Tchr.

CHICHY, STACY; Purchase Line HS; Commodore, PA; (2); French Clb; Nwsp Phtg; Nwsp Rptr; Stu Cncl; Stat Trk; High Hon Roll; Acad All Amercn 85-87; Hnrs Span Stu 86-87; Anesthesiologist.

CHICOLA, TINA; St Marys Area HS; St Marys, PA; (3); Cheerleading; Pom Pon; Prfct Atten Awd.

CHIEN, JENNIFER; Plymouth Whitemarsh SR HS; Plymouth Mtg, PA; (4); 18/240; Cmnty Wkr; Hosp Aide; Mu Alpha Theta; Chorus; Variety Show; Lit Mag; Var Stu Cncl; Stat Fld Hcky; Stat Lcrss; Var High Hon Roll; U Of PA.

CHIEN, PEG; Scranton Prep; Clarks Summit, PA; (1); 16/176; Art Clb; Dance Clb; Lit Mag; Cheerleading; High Hon Roll; Pres Schlr; PA Jr Acad Of Sci 1st Pl 86.

CHIK, WILSON; Upper Darby HS; Upr Darby, PA; (3); Intnl Clb; Spanish Clb; Chorus; Rep Soph Cls; Var Crs Cntry; Var Trk; High Hon Roll; Hon Roll; Jr NHS; Engl Awd 87; Wrkshp Chem 87; East Coast Chmp Trk Arco J Owens Gms 85; Math.

CHILDS, DENISE; Connellsville Area HS; Connellsville, PA; (4); 51/520; Pres Art Clb; Camera Clb; Office Aide; Ski Clb; Sftbl; Cit Awd; High Hon Roll; Algbr Awd; Indian U Of PA.

CHILDS, MARSHA; Montgomery Area HS; Montgomery, PA; (3); 5/86; French Clb; Thesps; Band; Chorus; Concert Band; Mrchg Band; Yrbk Stf; Var Stu Cncl; NHS; High Hon Roll; Dist 8 Region 4 Chorus PMEA 87; Dist 8 Band PMEA 1st Alt 87; Education.

CHILLE, MARIA; Bellwood-Antis HS; Bellwood, PA; (2); Church Yth Grp; Chorus; Concert Band; School Musical; Rep Soph Cls; Off Stu Cncl; JV Fld Hcky; Var Trk; Hon Roll; Stu Of The Wk 86; St Francis PA; Pre Dntl.

CHILLEMI, CAROLYN; Cardinol O Hara HS; Media, PA; (2); Church Yth Grp; Cmnty Wkr; Drama Clb; Spanish Clb; School Musical; School Play; Hon Roll; Engl Schlstc Awd 87; Med.

CHILSON, CLAY; Millersburg Area HS; Millersburg, PA; (3); Spanish Clb; Band; Concert Band; Bsbl; Wrstlng; Cit Awd; High Hon Roll; VP Frsh Cls; VP Soph Cls; Pres Jr Cls.

CHILSON, JOHN; Millersburg HS; Millersburg, PA; (4); 5/83; Am Leg Boys St; Trs Spanish Clb; Pres Stu Cncl; Var L Wrstlng; DAR Awd; NCTE Awd; NHS; Boy Scts; Church Yth Grp; Letterman Clb; Stu Forum Rep Sec; Acad All Amer; U Of PA; Pre Law.

CHIMOCK, RAYMOND; Wyoming Valley West HS; Swoyersville, PA; (3); Chess Clb; Church Yth Grp; Bsbl; JV Bsktbl; Bowling; JV Var Vllybl; Wt Lftg; Hon Roll.

CHINA, MELANI; Harrisburg HS; Harrisburg, PA; (3); 29/150; Church Yth Grp; Cmnty Wkr; FBLA; Pep Clb; Church Choir; Mrchg Band; Yrbk Stf; Stu Cncl; Cit Awd; Hon Roll; Bus Mngmnt.

CHINCOLA, JOHN B; Freeland HS; Freeland, PA; (2); Church Yth Grp; Cmnty Wkr; SADD; VP Frsh Cls; Off Stu Cncl; L Var Golf; Engrng.

CHING, EILEEN; Hatboro Horsham SR HS; Horsham, PA; (3); Key Clb; Library Aide; SADD; Lit Mag; Sec Jr Cls; JV Lcrss; Cit Awd; High Hon Roll; NHS; Prfct Atten Awd; Med.

CHING, PORCHHAY; U C HS; Philadelphia, PA; (4); Intnl Clb; NHS; Prfct Atten Awd; Pert Atten Awd 83; Drexel U; Arch Engr.

CHINTELLA, LEIGH; Hickory SR HS; Hermitage, PA; (3); Church Yth Grp; DECA; German Clb; Band; Concert Band; Mrchg Band; Pep Band; Youngstown ST U; Engrng.

CHIOCCA, ROBERT; Peters Twp HS; Venetia, PA; (4); Var L Socr; Var L Wrstlng; U Of SC; Accntng.

CHIORAZZI, CATHERINE; St Hubert HS; Philadelphia, PA; (4); 20/364; Church Yth Grp; Orch; Coach Actv; Co-Capt Swmmng; High Hon Roll; Hon Roll; NHS; Prfct Atten Awd; Prsdntl Acdmc Ftnss Awd, Stu Mnth 87; La Salle U; Bus.

CHIPELESKI, DARYL; West Hazleton HS; Drums, PA; (2); 26/250; Church Yth Grp; Exploring; Letterman Clb; Service Clb; Spanish Clb; Varsity Clb; Var Crs Cntry; Var Wrstlng; High Hon Roll; Hon Roll; Penn ST U; Frst Rngr.

CHIPOLETTI, KARA; Valley HS; Arnold, PA; (3); 13/127; Art Clb; Office Aide; SADD; Chorus; Color Guard; Swing Chorus; Yrbk Stf; Mgr(s); High Hon Roll; NHS; ST Fin Miss Natl PA Teen 87; Carlow Coll; Bus Mgmt.

CHIPPICH, MICHELE; Mount Alvernia HS; Pittsburgh, PA; (3); 1/54; VP JA; Library Aide; Red Cross Aide; Teachers Aide; Chorus; Nwsp Stf; Yrbk Stf; JV Var Cheerleading; High Hon Roll; Hon Roll; John Neumann Schlrshp Awd 87; Computer Summer Camp 86.

CHIRDON, MICHELE; Penn Cambria HS; Ashville, PA; (4); 20/200; Ski Clb; Pres Frsh Cls; Rep Soph Cls; Rep Jr Cls; Trs Sr Cls; Rep Stu Cncl; Sftbl; High Hon Roll; Hon Roll; NHS; Presdntl Phys Fitness Awd; U Of Pittsburgh; Phys Therapy.

CHIRIELEISON, KELLY; Plum SR HS; Pittsburgh, PA; (4); 41/400; Church Yth Grp; SADD; Varsity Clb; Band; Nwsp Stf; Yrbk Stf; Trk; High Hon Roll; Hon Roll; NHS; Cltrl Arts Cntst Hnrb Mntn 86; Humerous Clsrm Awds 83-87; U Of Pittsburgh; Pharmcy.

CHISEK, JOE; Forest City Regional HS; Browndale, PA; (3); #15 In Class; German Clb; Letterman Clb; Nwsp Stf; Rep Stu Cncl; Capt Crs Cntry; Hon Roll; NHS; Pres NEIU Stu Forum No 19 87-88; Gifted Prog.

CHISHKO, AMY; Jeannette SR HS; Jeannette, PA; (2); 32/125; Art Clb; Drama Clb; French Clb; Ski Clb; Spanish Clb; Yrbk Phtg; Yrbk Stf; IN U Of PA; Fshn Dsgn.

CHITESTER, MICHELLE; Coudersport Area JR-SR HS; Coudersport, PA; (3); Church Yth Grp; Drama Clb; Chorus; Var JV Mgr(s); Powder Puff Ftbl; Var Vllybl; Hon Roll; Acadc Ltr 86-87; Law.

CHIU, PEGGY; Taylor Allderdice HS; Pittsburgh, PA; (3); Speech Tm; High Hon Roll; Ntl Merit Ltr; Penn ST Smmr Frgn Lang Inst Schlrshp 87; Gld Mdl Rssn Olympd Wrttn Cmpstns 87; Brnz Mdl Pushkin Inst.

CHIZEK, CHRISTINE A; Central Bucks East HS; Doylestown, PA; (4); Hosp Aide; Mrchg Band; Yrbk Phtg; JV Var Fld Hcky; Score Keeper; U Of Pittsburgh; Nrsng.

CHIZMAR, DEBORAH; Penn Trafford HS; Jeannette, PA; (4); Church Yth Grp; Sec Trs Drama Clb; Exploring; Hosp Aide; VP JA; Pres Chorus; Swing Chorus; Variety Show; High Hon Roll; Hon Roll; Hnrs Grad 84; Tri-St PVA Schlrshp 87; Shadyside Nrsng Sch; Psycht Nrs.

CHIZMAR, KATRINA; Center HS; Aliquippa, PA; (4); 8/186; Am Leg Aux Girls St; Sec German Clb; Varsity Clb; School Musical; Nwsp Rptr; Yrbk Stf; Sec Stu Cncl; Capt Cheerleading; High Hon Roll; NHS; Ctr Cvc Wmns Clb Grl Mnth-Feb, Grtr Aliquippa Area Chmbr Cmmrc Awd, HS Hall Fame Mst Lkly Sccd 87; Carnegie-Mellon U; Indus Mgmt.

CHIZMAR, MELISSA; Washington HS; Washington, PA; (2); Hosp Aide; Key Clb; Spanish Clb; Band; Mrchg Band; Orch; Symp Band; Rep Stu Cncl; Var Trk; Var Twrlr; Pre Med.

CHMIEL, LESLIE JANE; Spring Grove SR HS; Spring Grove, PA; (3); Church Yth Grp; SADD; Chorus; Church Choir; Hon Roll; NHS; Art Clb; Pres Acdmc Ftnss Awd 84-85; Schlstc Achvt Awd 100 Point Pin; Schlstc Achvt Awd 200 Point Pin; Art.

CHMIELEWSKI, CAROL A; Peabody HS; Pittsburgh, PA; (4); 84/293; DECA; Yrbk Stf; Prfct Atten Awd; Prfct Atten Awd; DECA Awd; Peabody P; Robert Morris Coll; Bus Adm.

CHMIELEWSKI, DIANE; Norristown Area HS; Norristown, PA; (4); 50/450; Drama Clb; FCA; VP FBLA; Key Clb; Nwsp Ed-Chief; Yrbk Stf; Pres Stu Cncl; Cheerleading; Diving; NHS; 4 Chplns Jr Lgn Hon Mbrshp 86; Fnlst Cnty Jr Miss Prg 86; 1st Rgn & 3rd St Prlmntry Prcdr Tm 86; Poli Sci.

CHMIELEWSKI, LINDA; Bishop Hannan HS; Taylor, PA; (4); French Clb; Yrbk Stf; Bowling; Hon Roll; NHS; Jrnlsm Awd 87; Typing Awd 87; White Hnr Cord 87; Marywood Coll; Med Technlgy.

CHMIELEWSKI, LORI; West Scranton HS; Scranton, PA; (4); 15/274; Civic Clb; French Clb; Ski Clb; Spanish Clb; Yrbk Stf; Cheerleading; French Hon Soc; High Hon Roll; Jr NHS; NHS; U Of Scranton; Educ.

CHNUPA, AMY; Clearfield HS; Clearfield, PA; (1); Cheerleading; Hon Roll.

CHNUPA, KEITH; Clearfield Area HS; Clearfield, PA; (4); 35/290; Var Wt Lftg; Var Wrstlng; Hon Roll; 3rd Pl Natl Bnch Prssng Cntst Teenage Div 86; Slippery Rock U; Comp Sci.

CHOCOLAS, DENISE; Nazleton HS; Hazleton, PA; (4); 78/392; Pres Trs FBLA; JV VP Cheerleading; Sftbl; Swmmng; Hon Roll; Allentown Bus Schl; Lgl Asst.

CHOFFEL, CHERYL; Meadville Area SR HS; Meadville, PA; (3); Church Yth Grp; Hon Roll; Prfct Atten Awd; Business.

CHOI, BRIAN; Meadville Area SR HS; Meadville, PA; (2); Church Yth Grp; JA; Pres Ski Clb; Concert Band; Pep Band; Tennis; High Hon Roll; Hon Roll; Prfct Atten Awd.

CHOI, MINDY; Cardinal O Hara HS; Newtown Square, PA; (3); 48/715; Spanish Clb; SADD; Vllybl; Hon Roll; NHS; Church Yth Grp; Flag Corp; Yrbk Stf; Latin I Awd 87; Acad Excllnce Awd 85-87; Opthmlgst.

CHOI, NARI; Plymouth Whitemarsh HS; Plymouth Mtg, PA; (4); Model UN; Nwsp Rptr; Nwsp Stf; Ed Lit Mag; Hon Roll; NHS; Ntl Merit Ltr; Engl.

CHOI, SONIA; Meadville Area SR HS; Meadville, PA; (4); Church Yth Grp; Key Clb; Ski Clb; Yrbk Stf; Var Tennis; Hon Roll; Prfct Atten Awd; Rgstr Admin.

CHOI, UN JUNG; Plymouth Whitemarsh HS; Conshohocken, PA; (4); 9/328; Trs Church Yth Grp; Mu Alpha Theta; Drill Tm; Lit Mag; Sec Rep Stu Cncl; Trk; Vllybl; High Hon Roll; VP Pres NHS; Pres Schlr; Dr Kenneth Wilkinson Mem Schlrshp 87; VP & Pres Korean Club 85-87; Summa Cum Laude 83-87; U Of PA; Law.

CHOI, YOUNG; Wissahickow SR HS; Norristown, PA; (4); 15/287; Church Yth Grp; FBLA; Concert Band; Jazz Band; Mrchg Band; JV Ftbl; JV Tennis; Var Trk; High Hon Roll; Hon Roll; Natl Sci Olympd Awd Chem 85-86; Natl Cncl Suprvsrs Math, 1st Rgn 20 Clrk Typst Awd 86-87; PA ST U; Nutrtn.

CHOJNACKI, PAMELA; Hickory HS; Hermitage, PA; (2); 22/201; Computer Clb; Drama Clb; Exploring; French Clb; NFL; Office Aide; School Musical; Sftbl; Hon Roll; Forensics-PHSSL Dist 1-1st Pl Grls Extemp Spkng 87; Comp Sci.

CHOKEY, JAMES A; Bethel Park HS; Bethel Park, PA; (4); German Clb; Math Tm; Science Clb; Jazz Band; Trs Mrchg Band; Orch; Symp Band; High Hon Roll; NHS; Ntl Merit SF; Johns Hpkns Ctr Tlntd Yth 83-84.

CHOPP, DANIELLE; Yough SR HS; West Newton, PA; (3); French Clb; Ski Clb; SADD; Chorus; Nwsp Rptr; Yrbk Ed-Chief; Rep Frsh Cls; Stu Cncl; Var Capt Cheerleading; Powder Puff Ftbl; Comm.

CHOPP, KIMBERLY; Yough HS; Smithton, PA; (3); Ski Clb; Varsity Clb; Yrbk Stf; Rep Frsh Cls; Sec Soph Cls; Sec Jr Cls; Var Cheerleading; High Hon Roll; Hon Roll; NHS; Spec Plympcs Bdy 87; Acctng.

CHOPRA, GITANJALI; Ridley SR HS; Ridley Pk, PA; (3); 5/423; Hosp Aide; Mu Alpha Theta; High Hon Roll; Nrlgst.

CHOROSZEWSKI, JEFF; Ambridge Area HS; Ambridge, PA; (3); Pep Clb; Bsktbl; Ftbl; Trk; Wt Lftg; Pre-Med.

CHOU, TOM; Spring-Ford HS; Royersford, PA; (2); 6/289; Art Clb; French Clb; Library Aide; Math Clb; Var L Tennis; Im Vllybl; Hon Roll; NHS; Ntl Math Leag-Alg I Schl Wnnr 87; Microcomptr Tm-Co Capt 2nd Tm 87; Carnegie Mellon U; Comp Sci.

CHOW, NAOMI; Pequea Valley HS; Paradise, PA; (3); 21/138; Church Yth Grp; GAA; Chorus; School Musical; Stage Crew; Yrbk Stf; Var L Bsktbl; Hon Roll; NHS; Natl Lang Art Olympd 84-85; Fld Day Mdls & Rbbns 84-87; Phys Ed 100 Prcnt & Atten 85-86; Jrnlsm.

CHRISMER, LISA; York Catholic HS; York, PA; (3); Sec Church Yth Grp; Cmnty Wkr; French Clb; GAA; Hosp Aide; Latin Clb; Pep Clb; Service Clb; Ski Clb; Chorus; Hugh O Brien Natl Ldrshp Seminar Awd; Alpha Core Team Awd; Psych.

CHRIST, DAVID; Carlynton JR SR HS; Pittsburgh, PA; (2); Church Yth Grp; Ski Clb; VP Spanish Clb; Var L Socr; Marine Bio.

CHRISTENSEN, P NIELS; Devon Preparatory Schl; Broomall, PA; (2); 4/32; Boy Scts; Math Tm; Ski Clb; JV Bsktbl; Im Ftbl; JV Socr; JV Tennis; High Hon Roll; Notre Dame; Mech Engrng.

CHRISTENSON, STACY; Seneca Valley HS; Harmony, PA; (4); 10/356; Church Yth Grp; JA; Teachers Aide; Thesps; Stage Crew; High Hon Roll; Gannon U Acdmc Schlrshp 87; Gannon U; Intl Bus.

CHRISTIAN, DARREN; Dubois Area HS; Dubois, PA; (3); 10/320; Var Bsbl; Var Bsktbl; Hon Roll; NHS.

CHRISTIAN, LAURA; Upper Marion Area HS; King Of Prussia, PA; (3); 1/330; Church Yth Grp; Math Tm; Science Clb; Concert Band; Mrchg Band; Yrbk Stf; JV Sftbl; Var Capt Swmmng; Hon Roll; NHS; 1st Pl Sci Olympd Phys Sci 85; 2nd Pl Sci Olympd Chem 87; Cert Merit Hnr Sci & Math Soc Wmn Engrs 87; Med.

CHRISTIAN, PATTI; Stroudsburg HS; Stroudsburg, PA; (3); 20/256; Spanish Clb; Yrbk Stf; Trs Frsh Cls; Trs Soph Cls; Trs Jr Cls; JV Var Fld Hcky; Var L Sftbl; Var Capt Swmmng; High Hon Roll; NHS; MVP Swmmg 86-87; Tp 10 Pct Of Clss 84-87; Prsdntl Ftnss Awd 85-87; Arch.

CHRISTIAN, PAUL; Notre Dame HS; Stroudsburg, PA; (3); 5/50; Stage Crew; Yrbk Stf; Trs Jr Cls; JV Var Bsktbl; Im Vllybl; Hon Roll; NHS; Varsity Clb; JV Bsbl; Prfct Atten Awd; Comp Sci Awd, & Mech Drwng Awd 86-87; Phys Sci Awd 84-85; Arch.

CHRISTIAN, SHANON; St Josephs HS; Middletown, PA; (4); 2/19; Dnfth Awd; Hon Roll; Sal; Alvernia Coll; Scl Wrk.

CHRISTIAN, VERLENE; Valley HS; New Kensington, PA; (3); JA; Ski Clb; Band; Chorus; Church Choir; High Hon Roll; NHS; Acdmc All AM 87; Elem Ed.

CHRISTIANA, RICHARD; Our Lady Of Lourdes Regional HS; Shamokin, PA; (3); 51/89; Boy Scts; Ftbl; Prfct Atten Awd; Engrng Fld.

CHRISTIE, ANDREA; North Allegheny SDR HS; Pittsburgh, PA; (3); Art Clb; VICA; Yrbk Stf; Var Trk; Advertising.

CHRISTIE, CRAIG; Central Bucks West HS; Chalfont, PA; (4); Concert Band; Jazz Band; Var Socr; Var Swmmng; JV Tennis; High Hon Roll; Hon Roll; Kingsbury Awd 86; DVRA Invtnl 86; Otstndng Fresh Swmmr 84; Bucknell U; Law.

CHRISTIE, HEATHER; Oley Valley HS; Oley, PA; (3); 23/153; Art Clb; Church Yth Grp; Variety Show; Nwsp Rptr; Trs Soph Cls; Trs Jr Cls; Rep Stu Cncl; Cheerleading; Capt Coach Actv; Pom Pon; All-Amer Chrldr Semi-Finalist 85; Teen Mag Semi-Finalist-Mledl Search 85; Schl Bd 86-87.

CHRISTINE, KAREN; Freedom HS; Bethlehem, PA; (4); 65/433; DECA; FBLA; VP Soph Cls; Pres Jr Cls; Pres Sr Cls; Rep VP Stu Cncl; Var Capt Bsktbl; Mgr(s); Capt Powder Puff Ftbl; Cit Awd; Amer Bus Wmn Assn 87; Rose Gan Memrl Awd 87; Trvlrs Prtctv Assn Amer 87; Patriot Awd 87; Shppnsburg U; Acctng.

CHRISTINI, DAVID; Towanda Area HS; Towanda, PA; (4); 1/138; Am Leg Boys St; Boy Scts; Band; School Play; Trs Stu Cncl; Bsktbl; Bausch & Lomb Sci Awd; NHS; Val; Penn ST U Schlr 87; Penn ST U; Comp Engrng.

CHRISTLEY, DEANNA; Butler Intermediate HS; Butler, PA; (2) Cmnty Wkr; FBLA; Office Aide; Teachers Aide; Hon Roll; Bus Manag.

CHRISTMAN, CONNIE; Hamburg Area HS; Hamburg, PA; (3); VI Church Yth Grp; German Clb; Hosp Aide; Trs Latin Clb; Band; Nwsp Ed-Chief; Off Jr Cls; JV Capt Cheerleading; Gym; Trk; Reading Hosp Schl; Nrsng.

CHRISTMAN, JANE; Hershey SR HS; Hummelstown, PA; (4); Ski Clb; Spanish Clb; Teachers Aide; Band; Chorus; Variety Show; High Hon Roll; Hon Roll; Spanish NHS; Harrisburg Area CC; Hmn Svcs.

CHRISTMAN, JASON; Stroudsburg HS; E Stroudsburg, PA; (3); 5/320; Ski Clb; Varsity Clb; Var Swmmng; Var Trk; High Hon Roll; Rotary Awd; Annl Natl Math Exmntn Awd 87; Rtry Ldrs Cmp Schlrshp 87; PA JR Acad Sci 87; Princeton; Engrng.

CHRISTMAN, JAY; Downingtown HS; Glen Moore, PA; (3); 61/641; Letterman Clb; JV Ftbl; Im Lcrss; Var Trk; Im Wt Lftg; JV Wrstlng; High Hon Roll; NHS; NEDT Awd; Engrng.

CHRISTMAN, JODI; Plymouth-Whitemarsh HS; Flourtown, PA; (3); 146/356; Aud/Vis; Radio Clb; Nwsp Stf; Off Jr Cls; Capt Fld Hcky; JV Lcrss; Im Powder Puff Ftbl; JV Trk; Jr NHS; Comm.

CHRISTMAN, KELLY; Hamburg Area HS; Hamburg, PA; (3); Church Yth Grp; Sec German Clb; SADD; Band; Rep Stu Cncl; Cheerleading; Fld Hcky; Trk; Hon Roll; Acad Lttr Awd Grmn 86; Psych.

CHRISTMAN, TRACY; Connellsville SR HS; Normalville, PA; (3); VICA; Chorus; Trs Frsh Cls; Pres Soph Cls; JV Swmmng; JV Tennis; Vlybl Awd 87; Vica Frmn 87; Tri Hi Y Clb 86; Pgh Beauty Acad; Csmtlgy.

CHRISTMAS, KATINA SIMONE; Coastesville HS; Coatesville, PA; (3); 70/580; Drama Clb; Pres Sr Cls; Church Yth Grp; Spanish Clb; SADD; Band; Chorus; Church Choir; Mrchg Band; School Musical; Best Actress 87; Pres Acad Ftns Awd 86; NEDT Top 10% Awd 86; Med.

CHRISTNER, BRENT; Connellsville Area SR HS; Connellsvl, PA; (3); 52/600; Church Yth Grp; Ski Clb; Band; Chorus; Church Choir; Jazz Band; Nwsp Phtg; Yrbk Phtg; High Hon Roll; NHS; Outstndng Comp Prjct 87; Westminster; Pre Med.

CHRISTNER, DIANE; Mt Pleasant Area HS; Mt Pleasant, PA; (3); 11/250; Exploring; French Clb; GAA; Band; Concert Band; Jazz Band; Mrchg Band; High Hon Roll; NHS; Church Yth Grp; Pre-Law.

CHRISTON, WILLIAM; Rochester JR-SR HS; Rochester, PA; (3); Church Yth Grp; Cmnty Wkr; Computer Clb; French Clb; FBLA; Math Clb; Science Clb; Teachers Aide; Band; Stage Crew; Comp Ltrcy Awd 85; Edinboro ST U; Bus.

CHRISTOPHER, DENISE; Boiling Springs HS; Boiling Spgs, PA; (3); 23/125; Ski Clb; VP Frsh Cls; VP Soph Cls; VP Jr Cls; JV Bsktbl; Capt Var Fld Hcky; Capt Sftbl; Hon Roll; NHS; Carlsle Sci Fair 3rd Pl 85; Carlsl Sci Fair Hnrbl Mntn 87; All Stars Sftbl 86; Fin/Real Est.

CHRISTOPHER, LISA; Hazleton SR HS; Hazleton, PA; (3); 4/445; Drama Clb; Hosp Aide; Sec Leo Clb; Scholastic Bowl; Chorus; Nwsp Ed-Chief; Yrbk Stf; Tennis; Bausch & Lomb Sci Awd; High Hon Roll; Kings Coll Span Awd 85 & 87; Pres Acad Ftns Awd 85; Bio.

CHRISTOPHER, VICTOR; Center HS; Monaca, PA; (3); 21/186; Am Leg Boys St; Trs Latin Clb; Varsity Clb; Stu Cncl; JV Bsbl; Im Bsktbl; Var L Crs Cntry; Var L Trk; High Hon Roll; Hon Roll; U Of Pittsburgh; Dntl

CHRISTOU, CHRISTOS; Upper Darby HS; Drexel Hill, PA; (3); Church Yth Grp; Capt Socr; Hon Roll; United Soc Of Lesvos Outstndng Acmplshmnts Learng Greek Lang 85-86.

CHRISTY, KELLY; Freeport SR HS; Sarver, PA; (3); Chorus; School Musical; Yrbk Stf; JV Bsktbl; Var Capt Sftbl; Swmmng; Var Capt Vllybl; Hon Roll; Stu Of Crng Mlln Prep Schl Of Music 83-87; Wstmrlnd Cnty Cmnty Coll Vllybl Cmp MVP 87; Temple U; Crmnlgy.

CHRISTY, LISA; Penn Cambria HS; Gallitzin, PA; (2); 2/215; Drama Clb; Spanish Clb; SADD; Teachers Aide; Band; Chorus; Concert Band; Mrchg Band; Stu Cncl; Mgr Schls St Srvc Awd 85-86; Pres Acad Ftns Awd 86; Princeton; Bus Admn.

CHRISTY, NORA; Peabody HS; Pittsburgh, PA; (4); 3/292; French Clb; Ski Clb; L Swmmng; L Tennis; French Hon Soc; NHS; Off Stu Cncl; Yrbk Rptr; Yrbk Stf; Hnr Rl 82-87.

CHRONISTER, M SHANE; Tyrone Area HS; Tyrone, PA; (4); Boy Scts; Varsity Clb; Chorus; Var Ftbl; Var Wrstlng; God Cntry Awd; Prfct Atten Awd; Wrstlng Sprtsmnshp Awd, James Anderson Awd Athltc Pgm; Ruth-Don-Sam Kimberling SR Wrstlng Awd 87; Us Marine Corp.

CHRONOWSKI, KIMBERLEY; Tunkhannock HS; Factoryville, PA; (4); 35/270; Office Aide; Sec Science Clb; Spanish Clb; Rep Sr Cls; Fld Hcky; Mgr(s); Score Keeper; Hon Roll; NHS; Kings Coll.

CHRONOWSKI, RONALD; North Star HS; Stoystown, PA; (3); 10/141; Church Yth Grp; FCA; Mu Alpha Theta; Teachers Aide; Score Keeper; Timer; Trk; Hon Roll; Brdcstng.

CHRYST, REBECCA ANNE; Allentown Central Catholic HS; Allentown, PA; (3); 59/241; JA; Key Clb; Library Aide; Yrbk Stf; Stat Bsktbl; Crs Cntry; Capt Twrlr; Wt Lftg; High Hon Roll; Hon Roll; U S Navy.

CHRZANOWSKI, PATRICK; Cathedral Preparatory Schl; Erie, PA; (3); 49/200; Spanish Clb; Y-Teens; Nwsp Phtg; Yrbk Phtg; L JV Bsktbl; L Var Ftbl; JV Var Wt Lftg; DAR Awd; Hon Roll; Metro Ftbl Chmpnshp Troph 86; Dist 10 Ftbl Champshp Plq 86; Psych.

CHU, SIAO MEI; Lock Haven HS; Lock Haven, PA; (4); 6/243; Trs Model UN; Sec SADD; Sec Soph Cls; Off Jr Cls; Rep Sr Cls; Stat Bsktbl; JV Cheerleading; JV Socr; High Hon Roll; Sec NHS; Frnch Clb Awd; Advncd Bio Awd 87; Penn ST; Bio.

CHUBA, KELLIE; Valley HS; Arnold, PA; (4); 16/186; Varsity Clb; Chorus; Color Guard; Rep Stu Cncl; Trk; Capt Vllybl; High Hon Roll; Hon Roll; NHS; Pres Schlr; Edinboro U Of PA; Psych.

CHUBA, LEE ANN; Butler Intermediate HS; Butler, PA; (2); Cmnty Wkr; French Clb; SADD; Drill Tm; Mrchg Band; Var JV Pom Pon; Hon Roll; Jr NHS; Acadc Ltr Jr Ntl Hnr Soc 87; Elem Ed.

CHUBB, CONNIE; Quakertown HS; Quakertown, PA; (3); 71/315; Band; Concert Band; Jazz Band; Mrchg Band; Lankenau Schl Of Nursing; Nrsng.

CHUDEREWICZ, CARA; Serra Catholic HS; Elizabeth, PA; (3); 5/150; NFL; Pres Speech Tm; School Play; JV Bsktbl; Pres French Hon Soc; NHS; Drama Clb; French Clb; High Hon Roll; Hon Roll; Biol.

CHUDEREWICZ, LISA; Perry Traditional Acad; Pittsburgh, PA; (3); 26/189; Red Cross Aide; Drill Tm; School Musical; School Play; Stage Crew; Cheerleading; High Hon Roll; Hon Roll; NHS; Prfct Atten Awd; Essay Wnnr 87; Outstndng Tnns 85-87; Penn ST; Dancng.

CHUDOVAN, JOHN; Gettysburg SR HS; Gettysburg, PA; (2); Quiz Bowl; Band; Concert Band; Drm Mjr(t); Jazz Band; Mrchg Band; Pep Band; High Hon Roll; Cnty Envir Olympics Tm 86-87; ST Envir Olympics Tm 86-87; Penn ST U; Architecture.

CHUFF, LISA; Riverside HS; Taylor, PA; (3); 29/146; Yrbk Stf; VP Stu Cncl; Hon Roll; Pres Schlr; Cmmnctns.

CHUKLOCHAK, MICHAEL; Bishop Mc Cort HS; Johnstown, PA; (4); JA; Math Tm; Mu Alpha Theta; Spanish Clb; Band; Concert Band; Mrchg Band; Orch; JV Var Vllybl; Hon Roll; U Of Pittsburg At Johnstown.

CHULACK, CAROLINE; Plum SR HS; Pittsburgh, PA; (3); Art Clb; Cmnty Wkr; French Clb; Service Clb; Stage Crew; Bsktbl; Socr; Hon Roll; Girls Ldrs Assn Outstndng Svc Awd 86; Psych.

CHUMARD, MARCY; Western Wayne HS; Lake Ariel, PA; (3); Aud/Vis; Camera Clb; Church Yth Grp; Hosp Aide; SADD; Nwsp Phtg; Yrbk Phtg; Yrbk Rptr; Yrbk Stf; Lit Mag; Photo.

CHUNG, ANTHONY; Interboro HS; Glenolden, PA; (4); 2/300; Latin Clb; Ftbl; Trk; Vllybl; Wt Lftg; High Hon Roll; Ntl Merit Ltr; Sal; Acad All-Am 86-87; U Of PA; Bio/Nat Science.

CHUNG, ELIZABETH; Philadelphia H S For Girls; Philadelphia, PA; (3); 24/40; Church Yth Grp; Intnl Clb; Vllybl; Hon Roll; Pschtry.

CHUNG, LISA; Neshaminy HS; Penndel, PA; (4); 11/680; Spanish Clb; Band; Mrchg Band; Orch; Nwsp Stf; High Hon Roll; NHS; Hnr Awd For Ctznshp,Schlrshp & Attndnc 87; Sclstc Hnrs In Engl & Spnsh 87; U Of PA; Law.

CHUNG, LIZZ; Bethlehem Catholic HS; Bethlehem, PA; (4); 1/195; Key Clb; Political Wkr; SADD; Nwsp Ed-Chief; Capt Crs Cntry; Im Fld Hcky; Im Socr; NHS; Ntl Merit SF; Val; Soc Wmn Engrs Hghst Hnr 87; Dartmouth Book Awd 86; Dartmouth Coll.

CHUNG, THAI; Central HS; Philadelphia, PA; (2); Var Gym; Var Trk; Awd Trck-Polevault 87; Drexel; Arch.

CHUNG, WILLIAM; Cathedral Prep Schl; Erie, PA; (4); 22/212; Pep Clb; Ski Clb; Var L Socr; Var L Trk; Im Vllybl; Hon Roll; Case Wstrn Rsrv U; Pre-Dntstry.

CHUPKA, PAUL; Ambridge HS; Ambridge, PA; (4); 37/265; Am Leg Boys St; German Clb; Pep Clb; Color Guard; Jazz Band; Mrchg Band; Orch; Pep Band; Hon Roll; Lion Awd; Ambidge Wolves Clb Schlrshp 87; Duquesne U; Pre-Med.

CHUPP, KRISTIN J; Garden Spot HS; New Holland, PA; (2); Civic Clb; Pres Rptr 4-H; Pres FFA; Band; Mrchg Band; High Hon Roll; Hon Roll; NHS; FFA Star Greenhnd, Greenhnd Degree & Chaptr Degree 86; Vet.

CHURA, CHERYL; Purchase Line HS; Burnside, PA; (2); FBLA; Pep Clb; PAVAS; Spanish Clb; Chorus; Church Choir; Bsktbl; Vllybl; Prfct Atten Awd; PTA Cultural Arts 87; IN Cnty Cncl PTA Visual Arts 87; Acad Bus.

CHURCH, SCOTT; Waynesburg Central HS; Waynesburg, PA; (3); French Clb; Socr; Hon Roll; WV U; Psych.

CHURCHMAN, JAMES A; Reading HS; Reading, PA; (3); 57/709; Boys Clb Am; Key Clb; Math Tm; Yrbk Stf; Hon Roll; Jr NHS; Comp Sci.

CHURELLA, MARY; Cambria Heights HS; Datton, PA; (3); Church Yth Grp; Girl Scts; Pep Clb; Ski Clb; Varsity Clb; Nwsp Rptr; Nwsp Stf; Yrbk Stf; Cheerleading; Vllybl; Med Sec.

CHUZIE, STEPHANIE; Seneca HS; Erie, PA; (3); Church Yth Grp; Drama Clb; Exploring; JA; Yrbk Stf; Score Keeper; JV Var Sftbl; JV Vllybl; High Hon Roll; Hon Roll; Cert Of Schlrshp 86-87; Mst Prmsng In Vlybl 85-86; IUP; Mrktng.

CHYTIL, BRIAN; Canon Mc Millan HS; Canonsburg, PA; (4); Washington Coll; Chmst.

CIABATTONI, DAVID; Exeter Twp HS; Reading, PA; (4); 81/214; Key Clb; Trs Band; School Musical; Ftbl; Vllybl; Kiwanis Awd; Drama Clb; Bsbl; Trvlrs Protctn Assn/Ctznshp/Altrsm 87; Hmecmng King 87; Bloomsburg U; Scndry Hstry Educ.

CIACCIO, JOHN; St John Neumann HS; Philadelphia, PA; (2); 70/367; Naval Acad; Mltry.

CIAMACCO, ANTONELLA; Central Catholic HS; Allentown, PA; (3); JA; Math Tm; Pep Clb; Chorus; School Play; Rep Frsh Cls; Rep Soph Cls; JV Var Bsktbl; High Hon Roll; NHS.

CIAN, TODD; Dubois Area HS; Penfield, PA; (4); Aud/Vis; Boy Scts; Camera Clb; Chorus; Nwsp Stf; Yrbk Stf; Bsktbl; Ftbl; Mgr(s); Hon Roll; DAHS Nice Kid Awd 87; PA ST U; Frnch Educ.

CIANCI, MICHELE; West Scranton HS; Scranton, PA; (2); Spanish Clb; Orch; Co-Capt Pom Pon; Hon Roll; NHS.

CIANFLONE, CINDI; Carbondale Area HS; Carbondale, PA; (4); 7/156; Computer Clb; Yrbk Ed-Chief; High Hon Roll; VP NHS; Wilkes Coll; Engr.

CIARAMELLA, TERRI; Geibel HS; Masontown, PA; (4); 5/88; Drama Clb; French Clb; Pep Clb; School Musical; Stage Crew; DAR Awd; French Hon Soc; High Hon Roll; NHS; Prfct Atten Awd; PA JR Acad Sci 1st Pl Rgnl, 1st Pl ST 84; Duquesne Acdmc Schlrshp 87; Duquesne; Phrmcy.

CIARDI, LORI; Sayre Area HS; Sayre, PA; (3); Sec SADD; Band; Chorus; Concert Band; Mrchg Band; Pep Band; School Play; Swing Chorus; High Hon Roll; Hon Roll; Phrmcy.

CIARIMBOLI, BETSY; Greensburg Central Catholic HS; Greensburg, PA; (3); 7/231; Exploring; Pep Clb; Ski Clb; Yrbk Stf; Var Capt Cheerleading; Var Powder Puff Ftbl; High Hon Roll; NHS; Pre Med.

CIARLARIELLO, HOLLY; Seneca Valley HS; Evans City, PA; (4); Aud/Vis; Church Yth Grp; Hosp Aide; Ski Clb; Thesps; Band; Mrchg Band; School Play; Hon Roll; U Of Pittsburgh; Law.

CICCHINO, STEVE; Canevin HS; Pittsburgh, PA; (3); 32/192; Church Yth Grp; Letterman Clb; Varsity Clb; Rep Civic Clb; Var Bsbl; Var Ftbl; Hon Roll; Allegheny Coll; Bio.

CICCOLI, DENNIS; Norristown HS; Norristown, PA; (3); VICA; Cit Awd; Hon Roll; Montgomery CC; Hotel Mgmnt.

CICCONE, DONNA; Villa Maria HS; Poland, OH; (4); Key Clb; Pep Clb; Ski Clb; Band; Pep Band; Bsktbl; Cheerleading; Vllybl; Hon Roll; NHS; Youngstown ST U; Educ.

CICCOZZI, JILL; Center HS; Monaca, PA; (4); Drama Clb; SADD; Varsity Clb; Chorus; Swing Chorus; Nwsp Rptr; Pres Jr Cls; Trk; Vllybl; Pres Stu Forum Beaver Cnty 86-87; Actng.

CICERINI, GARY; Scranton Prep; Dunmore, PA; (2); Church Yth Grp; Cmnty Wkr; Political Wkr; Teachers Aide; Nwsp Stf; Stat Bsktbl; JV Crs Cntry; JV Wrstlng; Hon Roll; U Of Scranton; Gen Med.

CICERO, KAREN; Notre Dame HS; Easton, PA; (4); Church Yth Grp; Hosp Aide; Nwsp Ed-Chief; French Hon Soc; High Hon Roll; NHS; Spanish NHS; Pres Acad Ftnss Awd 87; Acad All Amer 87; Marist Coll; Cmmnctns.

CICERO, KATHLEEN; Pleasant Valley HS; Kresgeville, PA; (4); Church Yth Grp; German Clb; Girl Scts; Q&S; Ski Clb; SADD; Band; Concert Band; Drm Mjr(t); Mrchg Band; IN Univ PA; Pre Med.

CICHOWICZ, JEAN; Our Lady Of The Sacred Heart; Pittsburgh, PA; (4); 2/57; School Play; High Hon Roll; Hon Roll; NHS; Pres Schlr; Sal; Hghst Hnr Psych, Soclgy, Advncd Plcmnt Englsh, Chrstn Lifestyles 87; WV U; Exercise Physiology.

CICILIONI, LAURA; Bixhop O Hara HS; Dickson City, PA; (4); 10/115; French Clb; Latin Clb; Scholastic Bowl; Stage Crew; High Hon Roll; Hon Roll; NHS; Ntl Merit Ltr; Pres Schlrshp U Of Scranton 87; Schl Math Exam Awd 87; Pres Acdmc Fit Awd 87; U Of Scranton; Nrsng.

CICOTELLO, THOMAS; Bishop Carroll HS; Ebensburg, PA; (3); 10/128; Church Yth Grp; Computer Clb; 4-H; Var Bsktbl; Var L Ftbl; 4-H Awd; Hon Roll; Catholic Dghtrs Of Amer Poetry Cntst Wnnr 85; Natl Sci Merit Awd 85; Acad All Amer 86; Bus.

CIEPLINSKI, HENRY; Saint John Newmann HS; Philadelphia, PA; (3); Hon Roll; St Joseph U.

CIEPLINSKI, MATTHEW; St John Neumann HS; Philadelphia, PA; (3); 20/351; Math Clb; Band; Mrchg Band; Prfct Atten Awd.

CIESIELSKI, LEN; Sun Valley HS; Aston, PA; (3); Boy Scts; Church Yth Grp; FCA; Var L Ftbl; Var L Trk; Var Wt Lftg; JV Wrstlng; Hon Roll; Sports Med.

CIESIELSKI, MATTHEW; Burrell SR HS; Lower Burrell, PA; (3); AFS; Church Yth Grp; Spanish Clb; Band; Concert Band; Jazz Band; Mrchg Band; Pep Band; Tennis; High Hon Roll; Mid East All Str Bnd 84-88; Alle Kiski Hnrs Bnd 85-88; Arch.

CIESZYNSKI, SHERYL; St Paul Cathedral HS; Pittsburgh, PA; (3); 17/53; Girl Scts; JA; Spanish Clb; Yrbk Stf; Hon Roll; NHS; NEDT Awd; Carnegie Mellon U Hstry Day-3rd Pl 87; Spnsh Awds-I, II, III 84-87; Frgn Lang.

CIMINO, ANTHONY; Cathedral Prep; Erie, PA; (3); 110/196; Letterman Clb; Ski Clb; Varsity Clb; Rep Frsh Cls; Off Stu Cncl; Var Socr; Bus.

CIMINO, ELAINE; Cumberland Valley HS; Camp Hill, PA; (4); 23/519; Key Clb; Ski Clb; Spanish Clb; Band; Mrchg Band; Symp Band; Rep Soph Cls; Score Keeper; High Hon Roll; Hon Roll; Engrng, Merit Schlrshps U Of Pgh 87; Outstndng HS Stu Awd Inst Indstrl Engrs 87; U Of Pgh; Indstrl Engrng.

CINA, ELENA; West Philadelphia Cthlc Girls HS; Philadelphia, PA; (3); Dance Clb; Library Aide; Math Clb; Yrbk Stf; Prfct Atten Awd; Phys Thrpst.

CINALLI, TIMOTHY; Archbishop Wood HS For Boys; Richboro, PA; (2); 5/257; Nwsp Stf; Var JV Bsbl; Im Bsktbl; High Hon Roll; NHS; Awd Hghst Avg Frnch Yr 86; Awd Hghst Avg Wrld Cltrs Yr 86.

CINDRIC, HEATHER; St Marys Area HS; St Marys, PA; (3); 23/288; Var L Cheerleading; Var Trk; Naval Acad; Research Engineerng.

CINDRICH, ELAINE; Center HS; Aliquippa, PA; (3); Library Aide; Office Aide; Spanish Clb; SADD; Hon Roll; Intl Bus.

CINDRICH, LESLIE; Mon Valley Catholic HS; Ellsworth, PA; (3); Dance Clb; Library Aide; Ski Clb; Band; Chorus; Flag Corp; Mrchg Band; Var Bowling; Var Powder Puff Ftbl; Stat Score Keeper; U Of Pittsburgh.

CINFICI, WILLIAM; Reading HS; Reading, PA; (4); 6/563; Pres Debate Tm; VP Model UN; Pres Quiz Bowl; High Hon Roll; NHS; Horatio Alger Awd; Gettysburg Coll; Hstry.

CINTI, TODD; Penn Trafford HS; Claridge, PA; (2); Ftbl; Wt Lftg; High Hon Roll; Hon Roll; Chiroprctr.

CINTRON, DENISE; Philadelphia HS For Girls; Philadelphia, PA; (3); Spanish Clb; Teachers Aide; Bus.

CIOCCA, VINCE; Blairsville-Saltsburg JR SR HS; Saltsburg, PA; (3); 1/66; Church Yth Grp; Varsity Clb; Stage Crew; Pres Soph Cls; Pres Jr Cls; Chrmn Stu Cncl; L Bsktbl; L Ftbl; Var Trk; Var Wt Lftg; Appalachian Conf Basketball All Stars 87.

CIOCCIO, MELISSA; Elizabeth Forward HS; Elizabeth, PA; (2); Church Yth Grp; Chorus; Yrbk Stf; JV Var Cheerleading; High Hon Roll; Hon Roll.

CIOCHETTO, DAVID S; Slippery Rock Area HS; Forestville, PA; (3); 6/206; Pres Church Yth Grp; Intnl Clb; Math Tm; Spanish Clb; Band; Stage Crew; Gov Hon Prg Awd; High Hon Roll; Hon Roll; Pres NHS; Rifl Tm Vrsty Ltr, Bar 84-88; Butler Cnty Cnsrvtn Schl 86.

CIOPPA, ROSEMARY; New Castle HS; New Castle, PA; (4); 1/253; Exploring; Hosp Aide; SADD; Chorus; Drill Tm; Stu Cncl; Var Trk; High Hon Roll; NHS; Achvt Awd In Italian 86; Slippery Rock; Ed.

CIOTTI, MICHAEL J; Nazareth Area SR HS; Nazareth, PA; (3); Art Clb; Math Tm; Ski Clb; Var Tennis; Wt Lftg; JV Wrstlng; Hon Roll; Arch.

CIPOLETTI, CHRIS; West Greene HS; Graysville, PA; (2); Letterman Clb; Varsity Clb; Rep Stu Cncl; Bsktbl; Ftbl; Wt Lftg; High Hon Roll; Hon Roll.

CIPOLLONE, TONY; Plum HS; Pittsburgh, PA; (3); 75/410; Off Church Yth Grp; Varsity Clb; Acpl Chr; Chorus; Variety Show; Var Ftbl; Var Wrstlng; Hon Roll; Bus.

CIPRICH, CHERYL; West Branch Area JR SR HS; Kylertown, PA; (2); Church Yth Grp; Drama Clb; Spanish Clb; SADD; Band; Church Choir; Concert Band; Mrchg Band; Stage Crew; Off Stu Cncl; Phyllis Triolo Cntrl PA Music Tchr Assoc Awd 86; Tchrs Awd Spnsh II 87; Bttrwrth Awd Band 87; Music.

CIRKA, KEN; Ambridge Area SR HS; Baden, PA; (2); Cmnty Wkr; Computer Clb; Exploring; Pep Clb; Spanish Clb; Band; Concert Band; Mrchg Band; Symp Band; Hon Roll; Pitt; Acdmc Dentstry.

CIRUCCI, CINDY; Elizabeth Forward HS; Elizabeth, PA; (2); Aud/Vis; Chess Clb; Church Yth Grp; Camp Fr Inc; French Clb; Pep Clb; Stage Crew; Ed Yrbk Stf; Stat Trk; Hon Roll; Pres Physcl Fit Awd 85; U Of Pittsburgh; Pharmacy.

CISEK JR, RICHARD J; Venango Christian HS; Cranberry, PA; (3); 1/35; Computer Clb; Latin Clb; Spanish Clb; SADD; Pres Stu Cncl; High Hon Roll; NHS; Prfct Atten Awd; Attnd Wrld Affrs Cncl Conf 85-86; Attnd 1st Yr Algbr Cntst 84-85; Elctrcl Engnrng.

CISNEY, AMBER; Dover Area HS; Dover, PA; (4); 33/205; Chorus; Concert Band; Jazz Band; Mrchg Band; Orch; School Musical; Mgr Trk; Hon Roll; NHS; Semper Fidelis Awd 87; U Of Pittsburg; Physics.

CISNEY, ROBERT; York Catholic HS; Dover, PA; (2); Med.

CISNEY, TERESA; Southern Huntingdon Co HS; Blairs Mills, PA; (3); 10/150; FHA; GAA; SADD; Varsity Clb; Flag Corp; Fld Hcky; Powder Puff Ftbl; Sftbl; Hon Roll; NEDT Awd; Natl Acadmc All Amer Awd-87; Lock Haven; Hlth.

CITRONE, MICHAEL; York Catholic HS; York, PA; (4); 30/171; FBLA; Latin Clb; Spanish Clb; Varsity Clb; Nwsp Bus Mgr; Var Golf; Var L Socr; Var L Wrstlng; Hon Roll; NHS; Hampden-Sydney Coll; Math Econ.

CIUCCI, RONALD; Hopewell HS; Aliquippa, PA; (3); 49/250; Church Yth Grp; Cmnty Wkr; Math Tm; Stage Crew; Im Bsktbl; Coach Actv; Wt Lftg; Ed.

CIUFFOLETTI, ERIC; Valley HS; Arnold, PA; (3); 40/235; Chess Clb; Ski Clb; Band; Concert Band; Mrchg Band; JV Bsbl.

CIVILETTI, PIA; Wyoming Area HS; Pittston, PA; (4); 76/250; FBLA; VP German Clb; Chorus; Variety Show; Capt Cheerleading; High Hon Roll; Gymnstc Awds 84-85; Chrldng Awd 84; Penn ST U; Sci.

CIVIS, KELLIE; Bishop Mc Cort HS; Johnstown, PA; (4); German Clb; Mu Alpha Theta; Pep Clb; Ski Clb; School Musical; High Hon Roll; U Of Pittsburgh; Comms.

CIZEK, DELIA D; Coudersport Area JR SR HS; Coudersport, PA; (3); Am Leg Aux Girls St; Church Yth Grp; 4-H; French Clb; Chorus; Color Guard; Bsktbl; Trk; Hon Roll; NHS; Accntng.

CLAAR, KRISTIN; Altoona Area HS; Altoona, PA; (3); 21/796; Computer Clb; French Clb; PAVAS; SADD; Variety Show; Var JV Sftbl; Hon Roll; NEDT Awd; Prfct Atten Awd; Pres Schlr; Hnrbl Mntn Law Day Essay Cont 86; Pre-Law.

CLAAR, LISA; Bedford HS; Bedford, PA; (3); Off FFA; Grnhnd 85; Chptr Frmr 86; Frm Mgr.

CLABAUGH, DENISE; Connellsville SR HS; Connellsville, PA; (2); Dance Clb; Pep Clb; Band; Chorus; Concert Band; Jazz Band; Pep Band; School Musical; School Play; Nwsp Sprt Ed; Med.

CLABORN, DOUGLAS; New Freedom Christian HS; Parkton, MD; (4); Debate Tm; Teachers Aide; Yrbk Phtg; Yrbk Rptr; Yrbk Stf; Im Bsktbl; Im Ftbl; Mgr(s); Score Keeper; Hon Roll; Sci Fair 84; Jorunlsm Awd 84; Art Awd 83; Bob Jones U; Advrtsmnt.

CLAIR, BRENDAN; Taylor Allderdice HS; Pittsburgh, PA; (3); Art Clb; Boys Clb Am; Boy Scts; Church Yth Grp; Cmnty Wkr; Computer Clb; Political Wkr; Yrbk Stf; JV Bsbl; JV Bsktbl; Duquesne U; Comp.

CLAMSER, MARYANNE; Tunkhannock Area HS; Tunkhannock, PA; (2); Art Clb; Concert Band; Mrchg Band; Stat Diving; Var Mgr(s); Stat Swmmng; Hon Roll.

CLANCY, JOHN; Archbishop Wood For Boys HS; Southampton, PA; (2); 90/254; Rep Frsh Cls; JV Bsbl; JV Ftbl; U Of DE; Bsbl Plyr.

CLANCY, SHAWN; Otro Eldred HS; Duke Center, PA; (3); Stage Crew; Hon Roll; Sci & Drftng II Awd 87.

CLAPPER, BEVERLY; Ridley HS; Eddystone, PA; (3); 77/428; Office Aide; Spanish Clb; Chorus; Flag Corp; Mrchg Band; Nwsp Stf; Hon Roll; Keystone Schl Of Bus; Sec.

CLAPPER, DOMENIC; Bishop Guilfoyle HS; Ashville, PA; (3); Church Yth Grp; Ftbl; Hon Roll; Engrng.

CLAPPER, HEIDI; Harry S Truman HS; Levittown, PA; (4); Church Yth Grp; Debate Tm; NFL; Speech Tm; Stage Crew; Nwsp Rptr; Nwsp Stf; High Hon Roll; Lock Haven U; Eng Educ.

CLAPSADDLE, MICHELE; Christian School Of York; Mt Wolf, PA; (3); Off Soph Cls; Bsktbl; Fld Hcky; Trk; Hon Roll; History Teacher.

CLARK, AMY; Corry Area JR-SR HS; Corry, PA; (3); Trs Church Yth Grp; Office Aide; Radio Clb; Spanish Clb; SADD; Chorus; Cmnctns.

CLARK, ANDREA; William Allen HS; Allentown, PA; (4); 29/518; Rep Church Yth Grp; Hosp Aide; Church Choir; Yrbk Bus Mgr; Yrbk Rptr; Lit Mag; Hon Roll; Jr NHS; NHS; Pres Schlr; Ashlnd Chmcls-Ashlnd Schlr 87; Grace Coll; Scndry Educ.

CLARK, ANGELA B; Mt Pleasant Area HS; Stahlstown, PA; (2); German Clb; Band; Concert Band; Mrchg Band; Var JV Bsktbl; Hon Roll; Bus Mgmt.

CLARK, BELINDA; Fairchance Georges HS; Fairchance, PA; (4); 6/140; Teachers Aide; Concert Band; Mrchg Band; Yrbk Stf; Hst Sr Cls; Capt Var Bsktbl; Sftbl; Hon Roll; Sal; Hghst Typg Avg 86-87; Typg & Wrd Proc Cert 87; Hmrm Treas.

CLARK, BILL; Chestnut Ridge HS; New Paris, PA; (3); Band; JV Bsbl; Wt Lftg; Air Force; Mechnc.

CLARK, BILL; Coughlin HS; Wlks Barr Twp, PA; (3); Church Yth Grp; Computer Clb; Bsbl; Hon Roll; Jr NHS; NHS; Kings Coll; Psych.

CLARK, BONNIE; Wallenpaupack Area HS; Hawley, PA; (3); 16/159; Church Yth Grp; Ski Clb; Chorus; Church Choir; Color Guard; School Musical; Cheerleading; Mgr(s); High Hon Roll; NHS; Schlr Wk 84-85; Poli Sci.

CLARK, BRETT A; North Allegheny HS; Allison Pk, PA; (4); 79/660; Aud/Vis; FBLA; German Clb; Lit Mag; Rep Stu Cncl; Var Swmmng; Hon Roll; Jr NHS; NHS; Purchsng Mgrs Assn Pgh Schlrshp 87; Vrsty Ltrmn Swmmng 84-87; All ST Swmmng Hnrbl Mntn 87; WA U St Louis; Intl Bus.

CLARK, CHAPIN N; Conestoga SR HS; Berwyn, PA; (4); 29/454; Service Clb; Band; Orch; Variety Show; Var L Tennis; Hon Roll; NCTE Awd; NHS; Ntl Merit Ltr; Sprtswrtr For Lcl Paper 85-87; High Frnch Awd 84; Englsh.

CLARK, CHRIS; Butler Area HS; Butler, PA; (3); Spanish Clb; School Musical; Rep Stu Cncl; Im Bsktbl; L Var Ftbl; L Var Trk; Jr NHS; Acdmc Achvt Awd 87; Ed Hartman Awd Trk 87; Pre Med.

CLARK, CHRISTOPHER; Montrose Area HS; Montrose, PA; (3); German Clb; Pltcl Sci.

CLARK, CLAUDIA; Upper Darby SR HS; Drexel Hill, PA; (3); 9/575; German Clb; Band; Concert Band; Drm Mjr(t); Jazz Band; Mrchg Band; Orch; School Musical; High Hon Roll; Hon Roll; Sctn Ldr Mrchng Band Trmpt Section; Nrsng.

CLARK, CYNTHIA; Christian School Of York; Mechanicsburg, PA; (4); 10/58; Band; Chorus; Orch; School Play; Stage Crew; Nwsp Rptr; Bsktbl; High Hon Roll; Pres Schlr; Assoc Chrstn Schls Int Distgshd Chrstn Stu 86-87; Acad All Star Awd 87; Talent Awd 87; Grace Coll; Crmnl Just.

CLARK, CYNTHIA; High School Of Engineering & Science; Philadelphia, PA; (3); CAP; Drill Tm; Flag Corp; Yrbk Stf; VP Jr Cls; Cheerleading; Fld Hcky; Sftbl; Bryn Mawr Coll Wndws Into Sci Smmr Res Pgm 86; 2nd Pl-Sci Fair Cmptn 84; U Of PA; Engrng.

CLARK, CYNTHIA; Waynesburg HS; Waynesburg, PA; (3); Dance Clb; French Clb; Natl Beta Clb; Ski Clb; Color Guard; Mrchg Band; Pep Band; Variety Show; Mat Maids; Twrlr; Lttr 86; Band Awds 85-87; CA U; Bus.

CLARK, DAVE; Fort Cherry HS; Midway, PA; (4); Computer Clb; Drama Clb; English Clb; Math Clb; Science Clb; Ski Clb; Varsity Clb; Chorus; Stage Crew; Var Bsbl; WV.

CLARK, DAVID; Pine Grove Area HS; Pine Grove, PA; (3); Comps.

CLARK, EDWARD; North Catholic HS; Pittsburgh, PA; (2); 62/332; Church Yth Grp; Cmnty Wkr; FCA; German Clb; L Var Ftbl; L Wt Lftg; DAR Awd.

CLARK, ELAINE; Faith Mennonite HS; Kinzers, PA; (4); 2/26; VP Church Yth Grp; Pres 4-H; Cmnty Wkr; Library Aide; Acpl Chr; Yrbk Ed-Chief; 4-H Awd; High Hon Roll; Pblc Spkg Awd 86.

CLARK, ELIZABETH; Everett Area HS; Everett, PA; (1); Church Yth Grp; Band; Chorus; Church Choir; Mrchg Band; VP Frsh Cls; Bsktbl; Hon Roll; Prfct Atten Awd; Stu Mnth 85; Am Leg Awd 86.

CLARK, ERIKA; Linden Hall HS; Brooklyn, NY; (1); Model UN; Politics.

CLARK, GABRIELE; Trinity HS; Mechanicsburg, PA; (3); 2/139; Church Yth Grp; Model UN; Spanish Clb; Nwsp Rptr; Rep Stu Cncl; JV Var Trk; JV Var Vllybl; High Hon Roll; Hon Roll; NHS; Schlstic Writing Awd 84-85; Public Relations.

CLARK, HEATHER; Montour SR HS; Pittsburgh, PA; (4); Girl Scts; JA; Nwsp Rptr; Nwsp Stf; Church Yth Grp; Hosp Aide; Radio Clb; High Hon Roll; Hon Roll; JR Achvt VP Fnanc 85-87; Intl Order Of Rainbw-Grls-Wrthy Advsr 87; Geneva Coll; Brdcst Comm.

CLARK, HOLLIE; Meadville HS; Meadville, PA; (3); 90/363; Church Yth Grp; Spanish Clb; Nwsp Stf; Off Stu Cncl; Hon Roll; Early Chldhd Dev.

CLARK, JANINE; West Hazleton HS; Tresckow, PA; (2); 17/224; Church Yth Grp; Scholastic Bowl; Chorus; Yrbk Stf; Pres Stu Cncl; JV Bsktbl; Capt Cheerleading; JV Tennis; Var Trk; Hon Roll; Phy Educ.

CLARK, JEFF; Moon SR HS; Coraopolis, PA; (3); 62/304; Church Yth Grp; Computer Clb; Pres JA; Band; School Musical; Rep Soph Cls; JV Bsbl; Hon Roll; Litrary Cmpstn Cntst-3rd Pl Awd 84; Natl Fdrtn Music Clbs-PA Jr Piano Cmptn-1st Pl 85.

CLARK, JEFFREY; Everett Area HS; Everett, PA; (3); Church Yth Grp; SADD; Yrbk Stf; Trs Stu Cncl; Ftbl; Trk; Wt Lftg; Wrstlng; ST Wrstlng Chmpnshp 6th, PIAA Rgnl & Dist 5 Wrstlng Chmp 87; VA Military Inst.

CLARK, JEFFREY W; Red Land HS; New Cumberland, PA; (3); 62/308; Am Leg Boys St; Math Clb; Varsity Clb; Nwsp Stf; Trs Sr Cls; JV Trk; Im Vllybl; Im Wt Lftg; Var L Wrstlng; Hon Roll; Sr Proj 87-88; Wallops Island 85-86; Math Tutor 86-87; ROTC; Elec Engr.

CLARK, JENNIE; Hollidaysburg Area SR HS; Duncansville, PA; (3); 32/385; Latin Clb; Ski Clb; Band; Mrchg Band; Stage Crew; Lit Mag; Crs Cntry; Hon Roll; Ntl Merit SF; Rotary Awd; Bnd Achvt Awd 86; Acad Hnr Awd 86; Red White & Blue Edtrl Awd 85; Archaeology.

CLARK, JENNIFER; Linden Hall HS; Downingtown, PA; (3); Church Yth Grp; Var Fld Hcky; Mgr(s); Im Powder Puff Ftbl; Im Tennis; Im Wt Lftg; Hon Roll; Engl.

CLARK, JENNIFER; Northern Lebanon HS; Lebanon, PA; (3); 12/210; Church Yth Grp; Varsity Clb; Chorus; Church Choir; School Musical; Var Bsktbl; Var Fld Hcky; Var Sftbl; Hon Roll; NHS; Part In Keystone ST Gms 86; Mem Of People To People HS Stud Ambssdr Assoc 84; Msc.

CLARK, JOE; West Hazleton HS; Tresckow, PA; (4); 27/217; Scholastic Bowl; Varsity Clb; VP Sr Cls; Off Stu Cncl; Bsktbl; Hon Roll; NHS; VFW Awd.

CLARK, KAREN; Shikellamy HS; Sunbury, PA; (3); 25/319; Hon Roll.

CLARK, KIMBERLY; Upper Darby HS; Drexel Hill, PA; (3); GAA; Varsity Clb; Stu Cncl; Bsktbl; Crs Cntry; JV Var Lcrss; Mgr(s); Score Keeper; High Hon Roll; Hon Roll; Penn ST; Med.

CLARK, KRISTEN; Villa Maria Acad; Newtown Sq, PA; (3); Hosp Aide; Library Aide; Office Aide; Yrbk Rptr; Yrbk Stf; Ed Lit Mag; Im Bsktbl; Im Bsktbl; Im Fld Hcky; Im Lcrss; Caftria Aid 84-87; Chldrn Mry Orgnztn 8 5-87; Accntng.

CLARK, KURT A; Boyertown JR High East; Obelisk, PA; (1); Art Clb; Boy Scts; German Clb; Letterman Clb; Rep Stu Cncl; Var Bsktbl; Var Ftbl; Im Socr; Var Trk; High Hon Roll; Lehigh U; Engrng.

CLARK, MARC R; Ligonier Valley HS; Ligonier, PA; (3); Cmnty Wkr; NFL; Scholastic Bowl; Science Clb; Stage Crew; Stu Cncl; Trk; Wrstlng; High Hon Roll; NHS; Exclnc Eng 86; JR High Lttrmn Wrstlng; US Naval Acad; Naval Archt.

CLARK, MARY; Central Columbia HS; Nescopeck, PA; (4); 13/170; DECA; Yrbk Stf; Var Tennis; Trs French Hon Soc; Hon Roll; Bloomsburg U; Spch Thrpy.

CLARK, MATTHEW B; Redland HS; Zionsville, PA; (3); 34/307; German Clb; Concert Band; Jazz Band; Sec Mrchg Band; Orch; School Musical; Sec Symp Band; Trk; Hon Roll; Band; Amer Music Abroad Hnr Band 86; Resrch With Dr Arthur Dunham Big Bend Natl Pk 84; Svc Acad; Nuclear Engr.

CLARK, MAUREEN; Chartiers Valley HS; Pittsburgh, PA; (3); GAA; Ski Clb; Drill Tm; Yrbk Sprt Ed; Yrbk Stf; Fld Hcky; Penn ST U; Bus.

CLARK, MELINDA J; Everett Area HS; Everett, PA; (3); Am Leg Aux Girls St; Sec SADD; VICA; Trk; Pres Schlr; Pres Heroism Awd 85; Cntrl Dist Vol Fireman Awd 85; Gvnrs Senate & Hse Of Rep Apprec Awd 85-87; Cntrl PA; Court Reptr.

CLARK, MELISSA; Northern Bedford County HS; Everett, PA; (4); Sec Art Clb; FBLA; SADD; Varsity Clb; Band; Mgr Bsktbl; Trk; Hon Roll; NHS; 1st Pl Rgnl FBLA Bus Grphcs Cmptn 87; Century 21 Exclnc In Accntng 86, In Advncd Accntng 87.

CLARK, MEREDITH; Exeter SR HS; Reading, PA; (3); 10/245; French Clb; Spanish Clb; Varsity Clb; Variety Show; Var Cheerleading; Var L Crs Cntry; Var L Trk; High Hon Roll; Jr NHS; NHS; Acdmc Ftns Awd 85.

CLARK, MICHAEL; Connellsville Area SR HS; Dunbar, PA; (3); 106/530; Pres Jr Cls; Var L Ftbl; Hon Roll; Rep Bsbl; Sprts Med.

CLARK, RACHEL; Elizabethtown Area HS; Elizabethtown, PA; (3); 18/224; Band; Jazz Band; NHS.

CLARK, REBECCA L; Downingtown Area HS; West Chester, PA; (4); Dance Clb; Trs GAA; Ski Clb; Spanish Clb; Chorus; Stu Cncl; Im Bowling; Im Coach Actv; Var Lcrss; Im Socr; Salisbury ST Coll; Bus.

CLARK, RICHARD; Brockway Area HS; Brockway, PA; (3); 11/110; Varsity Clb; Var L Bsbl; Var L Bsktbl; Var L Ftbl; Im Vllybl; Im Wt Lftg; DAR Awd; High Hon Roll; Cntry 21 Accntng Cer Prfcncy 87; Accntng.

CLARK, RICHARD; Tunkhannock Area HS; Tunkhannock, PA; (3); 10/365; Church Yth Grp; Computer Clb; Letterman Clb; Ftbl; Trk; Wt Lftg; Hon Roll; NHS; Outstndng Recvr-Ftbl Awd 86; All Schlstc Recvr 86; Chemcl Engrng.

CLARK, ROBERT; Southern Columbia Area HS; Elysburg, PA; (4); 5/77; Boy Scts; VP Band; Chorus; Jazz Band; Mrchg Band; JP Sousa Awd; NHS; Church Yth Grp; Ski Clb; Concert Band; Eagl Sct 87; Arion Band Awd 86; Ordr Arrw Rnk Brohd 86; Penn ST U; Chem Engrng.

CLARK, ROBERT W; Gettysburg SR HS; Gettysburg, PA; (4); Chess Clb; Computer Clb; Capt Quiz Bowl; Ntl Merit SF; Carnegio Mellon Schlrshp 87; Leukemia Soc Of Amer Spl-A-Thn Merit Cert 84; Engl.

CLARK, ROBERTA; Elizabeth Forward HS; Elizabeth, PA; (2); French Clb; Library Aide; High Hon Roll; HS Frnch Tchr.

CLARK, SEAN; Northeast Catholic HS; Philadelphia, PA; (2); Hon Roll; Bus Adm.

CLARK, SID; Everett Area HS; Everett, PA; (2); 26/150; Boy Scts; Church Yth Grp; Computer Clb; Drama Clb; 4-H; Varsity Clb; Band; Chorus; Concert Band; Jazz Band; PA ST U; Comp Sci.

CLARK, STEVE; Pocono Mountain HS; Gouldsboro, PA; (3); Boy Scts; Trs Church Yth Grp; Im Wt Lftg; Hon Roll; Lion Awd; Boy Scout Eagle Scout; Aerontcs Engrng.

CLARK, STEVEN; Christian School Of York; Mechanicsburg, PA; (2); Band; Chorus; Var Bsbl; Var Bsktbl; Hon Roll.

CLARK, SUZANNE; Spring-Ford HS; Royersford, PA; (3); French Clb; Pep Clb; Band; Color Guard; Concert Band; Yrbk Stf; L Cheerleading; JV Fld Hcky; L Trk; Comm.

CLARK, TINA; Du Bois Area SR HS; Reynoldsvl, PA; (2); Chorus; Color Guard; Hon Roll; Nice Kid Awd 86-87.

CLARK, TINA N; George HS; West Trenton, NJ; (4); Chorus; School Musical; VP Stu Cncl; Trk; Gov Hon Prg Awd; Hon Roll; Ntl Merit Schol; Studnts Assctd For Grtr Empthy & Prefect 86-87; Columbia U; Accntng.

CLARK, TODD R; Shikellamy HS; Sunbury, PA; (4); 70/300; Church Yth Grp; Chorus; Church Choir; JV Trk; JV Stat Wrstlng; Engrng.

CLARK, TOM; Carrick HS; Pittsburgh, PA; (3); 2/434; Church Yth Grp; SADD; School Play; Rep Stu Cncl; Var Ftbl; Wt Lftg; High Hon Roll; Prfct Atten Awd; Med.

CLARK, TRACEY; West Scranton HS; Scranton, PA; (4); 80/265; Sec Letterman Clb; Pep Clb; Varsity Clb; Nwsp Phtg; Nwsp Rptr; Yrbk Stf; Var Capt Bsktbl; Var Capt Tennis; Var L Trk; Excptnl Chldrns Aid Clb Treas; Hlth Career Clb.

CLARK, TRACY; Curwensville Area HS; Curwensville, PA; (3); Drama Clb; French Clb; FNA; Hosp Aide; Varsity Clb; VICA; Chorus; Color Guard; Vllybl; Hnr Rl; Data Prcssng.

CLARK, TRACY M; Harbor Creek HS; Erie, PA; (3); 14/219; Cmnty Wkr; Model UN; Capt Color Guard; High Hon Roll; Hon Roll; NHS; IN U PA; Accntng.

CLARK, TRINA; Everett Area HS; Everett, PA; (2); 24/142; Drama Clb; GAA; Spanish Clb; Varsity Clb; Chorus; Stage Crew; Var Cheerleading; Trk; Hon Roll.

CLARK, WANDA; West Branch Area HS; Philipsburg, PA; (3); Drama Clb; FCA; SADD; Color Guard; Flag Corp; Mrchg Band; JV Bsktbl; Hon Roll; Scty Dist Amer HS Stu 87; Acctng.

CLARK, WENDY; Northeast Bradford HS; Rome, PA; (4); 1/75; Trs Soph Cls; Trs Jr Cls; Trs Sr Cls; Var Gym; High Hon Roll; Pres NHS; Pres Schlr; Val; Amer Assoc U Women Schlrshp & Awd 87; Cnty Ntl Bank Acadmc Awd 87; Sutfin Funeral Chapel Awd 87; Bethel Coll.

CLARKE, CATHERINE M; Southwest HS; Hanover, PA; (3); AFS; Am Leg Aux Girls St; Girl Scts; Key Clb; Varsity Clb; Var Fld Hcky; Var Capt Trk; Lib Arts.

CLARKE, COLLEEN; Chester HS; Chester, PA; (2); Hosp Aide; Math Clb; Hon Roll; Keystone Bus Schl; Secy.

CLARKE, KELLEY N; West Mifflin Area HS; W Mifflin, PA; (3); #32 In Class; Chorus; Wt Lftg; High Hon Roll; Hon Roll; NHS; PA ST Agri Pgm Minority Stds Partcptn Awd 86; Carnegie Mellon; Law.

CLARKE, KIMBERLY; Notre Dame HS; Bethlehem, PA; (3); 5/96; Cmnty Wkr; Hosp Aide; Ski Clb; Yrbk Stf; Var Sftbl; Var Tennis; Im Vllybl; Hon Roll; Var Mgr(s); Prfct Atten Awd; Excel Trig & Engl II 86-87; PA ST; Engr.

CLATCH, SHARON; Hazleton HS; Hazleton, PA; (2); Church Yth Grp; FBLA; Office Aide; Pep Clb; Cheerleading; Gym; Hon Roll; Dntl Hygnst.

CLAUS, DEBBY; Hampton HS; Allison Pk, PA; (4); 19/248; Exploring; Office Aide; Sec Teachers Aide; Church Choir; Color Guard; Sec Bowling; High Hon Roll; Sec NHS; Robert Morris Hon Awd Schlrshp 87; Robert Morris; Accntng.

CLAUS, LINDA A; Hampton HS; Allison Park, PA; (3); Ski Clb; Rep Frsh Cls; Rep Soph Cls; VP Jr Cls; Rep Sr Cls; Rep Stu Cncl; Var L Cheerleading; Var L Sftbl; High Hon Roll; Hon Roll; Explrs Clb For Law 86-87; Mock Legal Trl Prcdngs 86-87; Grove City Stu Cncl Wrkshp 86.

CLAUS, TRACY; North Catholic HS; Pittsburgh, PA; (3); JA; Ski Clb; Stage Crew; Nwsp Phtg; Crs Cntry; Hon Roll; Med.

CLAUSER, GARY; Salisbury HS; Allentown, PA; (3); Key Clb; Math Clb; JV Capt Socr; Hon Roll; Lion Awd; Stanley Home Products Schlrshp 87.

CLAWSON, DANIEL; North Start HS; Boswell, PA; (4); 5/130; FCA; Quiz Bowl; Ski Clb; School Play; Pres Stu Cncl; JV Bsktbl; JV Golf; Hon Roll; Lion Awd; Bst Hstry Stu 84; Lions Sr Mnth 87; Stu Of Mnth 85; Pre-Law.

CLAY, BILLIE JO; Blairsville SR HS; Blairsville, PA; (1); Spanish Clb; High Hon Roll; Hon Roll; Mrshl U.

CLAY, SEAN; Moon Area SR HS; Coraopolis, PA; (3); 36/360; French Clb; Key Clb; Q&S; School Musical; School Play; Stage Crew; Nwsp Rptr; Nwsp Stf; Yrbk Rptr; Yrbk Sprt Ed; Drama.

CLAYBAUGH, JULIEANN; Charleroi Area HS; Monongahela, PA; (3); Spanish Clb; Rep SADD; Trs Varsity Clb; Nwsp Rptr; Rep Soph Cls; Rep Jr Cls; Stu Cncl; Bsktbl; Hon Roll; NHS; Phys Thrpy.

CLAYBERGER, ROBT; Shikellamy HS; Sunbury, PA; (3); Boy Scts; German Clb; SADD; Trk; God Cntry Awd; Army; Machnst.

CLAYCOMB, BUDDY; Claysburg Kimmel HS; Queen, PA; (2); 41/97; Church Yth Grp; 4-H; FFA; JV Var Ftbl; Wt Lftg; 4-H Awd; 4-H Best Trail Rider Of Club 86.

CLAYCOMB, LAURA; Claysburg Kimmel HS; Claysburgh, PA; (4); 3/52; Camera Clb; Church Yth Grp; Cmnty Wkr; Computer Clb; Sec VP German Clb; Hosp Aide; Library Aide; Sec Trs Band; Concert Band; Mrchg Band; Harcum JC; Physcl Thrpy Asst.

CLAYCOMB, MICHELE; Hollidaysburg Area SR HS; Hollidaysburg, PA; (3); French Clb; Political Wkr; Ski Clb; Pres SADD; Var Cheerleading; Var Trk; Im Vllybl; Child Psychology.

CLAYPOLE, HEIDI; Aliquippa JR SR HS; Aliquippa, PA; (3); 26/140; Drama Clb; French Clb; School Musical; School Play; Variety Show; Bsktbl; Cheerleading; Hon Roll; Jr NHS; NHS; Trphy Bst Sprtng Actrs 87; Pittsburgh Plyhse Smr Schlrshp Awd 87; Fnrl Dir.

CLAYPOOL, JENNIFER; Kittaning HS; Worthington, PA; (2); Church Yth Grp; Cmnty Wkr; Hosp Aide; Chorus; Church Choir; School Musical; School Play; Hon Roll; X-Ray Tech.

CLAYPOOL JR, PAUL E; Seneca Valley SR HS; Mars, PA; (2); Aud/Vis; Civic Clb; Band; Jazz Band; Mrchg Band; Pep Band; Stage Crew; Symp Band; Hon Roll; Concert Band; Prtcptn Awd Clarion U PA 83-86; Penn ST Coll; Geo Physcs.

CLAYPOOL, VALERIE; Kittanning SR HS; Worthington, PA; (3); 49/262; Duffs Bus Inst; Mdcl Sec.

CLAYPOOLE, LISA; Karns City JR SR HS; Parker, PA; (3); Library Aide; Yrbk Stf; Hon Roll; Prfct Atten Awd; Trvl.

CLAYPOOLE, MARTHA; Oxford Area HS; Oxford, PA; (3); 27/197; Trs Art Clb; FTA; High Hon Roll; Hon Roll.

CLAYPOOLE, MELANIE; Harbor Creek HS; Erie, PA; (4); 33/213; Church Yth Grp; Model UN; Drill Tm; Variety Show; Yrbk Stf; Pres VP Stu Cncl; Stat Sftbl; Cit Awd; NHS; Edinboro Univ; Elem Educ.

CLAYTON, DOUGLAS; Blairsville SR HS; Blairsville, PA; (1); 31/118; Computer Clb; Concert Band; Mrchg Band; Stage Crew; PA Jr Acad Of Sci Region 9 Comptn 1st Plc 87; PA Jr Acad Of Sci PA State Comptn 2nd Pl 87; IN U Of PA; Comp Sci.

CLAYTON JR, JAMES; The Christian Acad; Chester, PA; (3); Chorus; Yrbk Phtg; JV Var Bsktbl; Var L Trk; Im Vllybl; Phys Thrpy.

CLAYTON, JEFFREY; Neshannock HS; Neshannock, PA; (3); Churc Yth Grp; Band; Concert Band; Jazz Band; Mrchg Band; Orch; Pep Banc School Musical; Hon Roll; Prfct Atten Awd; Math.

CLAYTON, KIMBERLY A; Jeannette SR HS; Jeannette, PA; (4 Drama Clb; Spanish Clb; Band; Chorus; Concert Band; Drm Mjr(t); Mrch Band; Hon Roll; Kiwanis Awd; NHS; La Roche Coll; Grphc Dsgn.

CLAYTON, MARGARET; Jeannette SR HS; Jeannette, PA; (3); 15/148 Am Leg Aux Girls St; Rep Stu Cncl; High Hon Roll; Hon Roll; NHS Drama Clb; French Clb; Band; Mrchg Band; U S Senate Scholar Prgn 86-87.

CLEAFIELD, KATHRYN; Southwestern HS; Hanover, PA; (3); 4/219 Am Leg Aux Girls St; Key Clb; School Musical; Yrbk Stf; Trs Jr Cls; Tr Sr Cls; JV Var Fld Hcky; High Hon Roll; NHS; NEDT Awd; Lt Govr PA Dist Key Club 87-88; MBA.

CLEARFIELD, KATHRYN E; Southwestern HS; Hanoer, PA; (3); 11 233; Am Leg Aux Girls St; Key Clb; School Musical; Nwsp Stf; Trs Jr Cls Trs Sr Cls; JV Dance Clb; JV Trk; NHS; NEDT Awd; Bus.

CLEARY, CHARLES B; Mc Keesport SR HS; White Oak, PA; (4); Boy Scts; Church Yth Grp; Trs Acpl Chr; Band; Chorus; Church Choir; Concert Band; Jazz Band; Mrchg Band; Pep Band; Sci Fair 1st Pl Awd 83-84; Hnrs Band, Dist, Regn & St Band 86-87; John Phillip Sousa Awd 87; Penn ST Elec Engr.

CLEARY, EDWARD; Arch Bishop Carroll HS; Philadelphia, PA; (3) Bsbl; Bsktbl; Hon Roll; NHS.

CLEARY, JULIE; Red Lion Area SR HS; Red Lion, PA; (4); 14/365 Church Yth Grp; Church Choir; School Play; Yrbk Stf; Bsktbl; Capt Cheerleading; Vllybl; High Hon Roll; Pres Schlrshp From York Coll 87 York Coll; Mgnt.

CLEARY, MICHELE R; Minersville Area HS; Minersville, PA; (4); 24 114; Dance Clb; FBLA; Pep Clb; Red Cross Aide; Ski Clb; SADD; VF Chorus; School Musical; Variety Show; JV Cheerleading; Garland Gr 85-87; Hmcmng Queens Ct 85-86; IN U Of PA; Bus.

CLEAVER, LINDA; Interboro SR HS; Glenolden, PA; (4); JCL; Pres Key Clb; Latin Clb; Jr Cls; Sr Cls; Var Lcrss; Hon Roll; Kiwanis Awd; Rep NHS; Hnr Rll 83-87; Gwynedd Mercy Coll; Nrsng.

CLEAVER, LISA; Brandywine Heights HS; Barto, PA; (2); 15/155; Sec Church Yth Grp; Chorus; Church Choir; Color Guard; Drill Tm; Hon Roll NHS; Rotary Awd; Pres Acdmc Ftnss Awd 85-86; Amer Lgn Auxlry Dept PA Awd 85-86; Lgl Asst.

CLECK, SHAN; The Christian Schl Of York; Hanover, PA; (2); Church Yth Grp; Radio Clb; Chorus; Hnr Roll 84-85; Dist Attrny.

CLEET, CHRIS; Quakertown Comm SR HS; Quakertown, PA; (3); CAP Teachers Aide; Band; Jazz Band; School Play; JV Socr; High Hon Roll; J NHS; NHS; Pres Schlr.

CLEGG, MICHAEL; Central HS Of Phila; Philadelphia, PA; (2); Church Yth Grp; Hon Roll; Barnwell Honors 86; Accntng.

CLELAND, BRIGITTA; Taylor Allderdice HS; Pittsburgh, PA; (2) Drama Clb; Math Clb; Ski Clb; Chorus; Church Choir; High Hon Roll NHS; Vet.

CLEMANS, COREY; Downingtown HS; Downingtown, PA; (4); Drama Clb; French Clb; FTA; Intnl Clb; Model UN; Band; School Musical; School Play; Im Vllybl; Hon Roll; Penn ST; Language.

CLEMENIC, DANIELLE; East Allegheny HS; East Mckeesport, PA; (4) French Clb; Girl Scts; JA; Color Guard; Orch; Ed Yrbk Stf; Trs Stu Cncl Trk; NHS; Opt Clb Awd; US Army Rsrv Schlr Awd 87; Grove City Coll Mgmnt Inf Sys.

CLEMENS, JOSEPH L; Central HS; Philadelphia, PA; (3); 16/523; Art Clb; Cmnty Wkr; Teachers Aide; Cit Awd; Barnwell Hnr Soc 85-87 Finance.

CLEMENS, KENT M; Christopher Dock Mennonite HS; Souderton, PA (4); 1/105; Chorus; Rep Frsh Cls; Rep Soph Cls; VP Jr Cls; Var L Bsbl; Var L Bsktbl; Var L Socr; High Hon Roll; NHS; Ntl Merit SF.

CLEMENS, YOLONDA; Seneca Valley SR HS; Zelienople, PA; (3) Chorus; Color Guard; School Musical; Rep Frsh Cls; High Hon Roll; Hon Roll; NHS; Schlstc Awd 87; Vet.

CLEMENTE, JOAN; G A R Memorial HS; Wilkes-Barre, PA; (3); 29/152 FBLA; Office Aide; Band; Chorus; Concert Band; Drill Tm; Flag Corp Bsktbl; Hon Roll; NHS; Penn ST U; TV Brdcstng.

CLEMENTE, KIMBERLY; St Basil Acad; Philadelphia, PA; (4); 9/97 French Clb; Nwsp Stf; Yrbk Stf; JV Capt Cheerleading; Hon Roll; Ntl Merit Ltr; Natl Sci & Eng Merit Awd 87; Phy Thrpy.

CLEMENTS, DAVID; Chester HS; Brookhaven, PA; (4); VP Church Yth Grp; VP NAACP; Pep Clb; Science Clb; Chorus; Pres Church Choir School Musical; Nwsp Rptr; Nwsp Stf; Yrbk Stf; NAACP Yth Svc Awd 85 Germn Awd 87; Wilberforce U; Bus Admn.

CLEMENTS, DAWN; Nazareth Acad; Bensalem, PA; (3); Cmnty Wkr Spanish Clb; Lit Mag; Hon Roll; Engl Tchr.

CLEMENTS, KIA LA DAWN; Cardinal O Hara HS; Chester, PA; (3) 32/710; Church Yth Grp; Dance Clb; Pres Jr Cls; Pres Sr Cls; High Hon Roll; NHS; JA; Office Aide; School Play; Variety Show; Latin Awd 85 French Awd, Harrisburg Alt Rep Stu Yth Forum 87; Pre-Med.

CLEMENTS, TRACY; South Williamsport Area JR/Sr HS; S Williamsport, PA; (3); 9/98; Church Yth Grp; Trs Spanish Clb; Band Concert Band; Jazz Band; Mrchg Band; Symp Band; Yrbk Stf; NHS Psych.

CLEMINS, RONALD; Northeast Catholic HS; Philadelphia, PA; (3); 90/362; Hon Roll; Comp Prgmmr.

CLEMMER, VALERIE; Lancaster Christian Schl; Leola, PA; (3) Church Yth Grp; Hosp Aide; Chorus; Orch; Sec Soph Cls; Sec Jr Cls Cheerleading; High Hon Roll; Chrldng Trphy 85-86; Music.

CLEMSON, AMY; Tamaqua Area HS; Tamaqua, PA; (3); Church Yth Grp; Pep Clb; Science Clb; Sec Service Clb; Sec Rep Stu Cncl; JV Cheerleading; Var Trk; Var Vllybl; Sec French Hon Soc; High Hon Roll Outstndng Schltc Achvt Cert 85-86; Outstndng Ctzns Awd 86-87 Bloomsbrg U; Spcl Educ.

CLENDENIN, BRIAN; Octorara Area HS; Cochranville, PA; (3); 1/172 Library Aide; Quiz Bowl; Stage Crew; Nwsp Stf; Gov Hon Prg Awd; High Hon Roll; NHS; Bausch & Lomb Sci Awd; JETS Awd; Franklin & Marshall Coll Gftd Prg 85-86; Temple Summer Cllqm Temple Phila PA 86; Am Reg Mth Leg 86-87; Engr.

CLEVELAND, JULIE; Moniteau HS; Petrolia, PA; (3); Computer Clb Drama Clb; French Clb; SADD; VICA; Chorus; School Play; Crs Cntry Trk; Hon Roll; Cunary Inst-Pittsburg; Fd Mgmt.

CLEVER, MORGAN; General Mc Lane HS; Albuquerque, NM; (4); Aud/Vis; Chess Clb; Church Yth Grp; German Clb; Library Aide; Radio Clb Spanish Clb; Rep Stu Cncl; Stat Bsktbl; Im Bowling; Library Awd 86-87 U Of NM; Pre-Med.

.EVER, REBECCA; Steel Valley HS; Munhall, PA; (3); Jazz Band; wsp Stf; Ed Yrbk Stf; Var Tennis; Hon Roll; Brdcstng Comm.

.IESA, JACQUIE; Freeport Area HS; Freeport, PA; (3); FBLA; Office de; Chorus; Nwsp Stf; Yrbk Stf; Hon Roll; Carlow Coll; Nrsng.

.IFFORD, BRIAN; Monsignor Bonner HS; Lansdowne, PA; (4); 81/ 2; Art Clb; Cmnty Wkr; Office Aide; Red Cross Aide; Ski Clb; SADD; rsity Clb; Stage Crew; Var Crs Cntry; Var Ftbl; 1st & 2nd Tm All Cath Tm All Delco For Trck 87; 1700 Schlrshp To Textiles 87; Phila Coll Of x & Sci; Mgnmt.

.IFT, SUSAN; St Huberts HS; Philadelphia, PA; (3); 173/421; Church h Grp; Computer Clb; Dance Clb; Girl Scts; Stu Cncl; Cheerleading; bl; White Williams Scholar; Chrldng & Sftbl Trophies; Bus.

.INE, AMY; Northern HS; Dillsburg, PA; (3); Church Yth Grp; Cmnty kr; Chorus; Pres Color Guard; Drill Tm; Mrchg Band; Powder Puff Ftbl; cr; Pres Twrlr; Hon Roll; York Coll; Nrsng.

.INE, AUSTIN REED; Downingtown SR HS; Coatesville, PA; (3); 34/ 3; Chess Clb; Computer Clb; German Clb; Teachers Aide; High Hon ll; NHS; Prsdntl Acdmc Ftnss Awd 85.

.INE, BILLI; Lewistown Area SR HS; Lewistown, PA; (2); AFS; rman Clb; Yrbk Stf; High Hon Roll; Hon Roll; Data Prcssng.

.INE, JAMI; Johnsonburg HS; Johnsonburg, PA; (4); Church Yth Grp; rl Scts; Office Aide; Band; Concert Band; Mrchg Band; Nwsp Stf; Yrbk f; Trs Jr Cls; NHS; Elem Educ.

.INE, JEANNINE; Central York SR HS; York, PA; (3); 18/266; VP JA; i Clb; Speech Tm; School Musical; High Hon Roll; NHS; Ntl Merit SF; urch Yth Grp; Dance Clb; Intnl Clb; Pres Clssrm Wshngtn DC 87; mr Math Mnt Holyoke Coll 86; Intrnshp Arch/Engrn Frm 87; inceton U; Engrng.

.INE, JENNIFER L; Forbes Road HS; Waterfall, PA; (3); Varsity Clb; bk Stf; Pres Frsh Cls; VP Soph Cls; Pres Jr Cls; Rep Stu Cncl; Var L ktbl; NHS; Church Yth Grp; French Clb; Envrnmntl Olympcs-Cnty & Tms 85-87; Stu Forum 86-87; Envrnmntl Engrng.

.INE, JULI; Middletown Area HS; Middletown, PA; (4); FCA; Key Clb; l Hcky; Vllybl; Hon Roll; NHS; Acdmc All Amer 86; U Of Pittsburgh; ys Thrpy.

.INE, NICOLE; Biglerville HS; Gardners, PA; (4); Church Yth Grp; anish Clb; Varsity Clb; Yrbk Stf; Trs Sr Cls; Var Capt Fld Hcky; Sftbl; Awd; Hon Roll; Trostel Awd Ldrshp & Citznshp 87; Shippensburg U; ildhood Educ.

.INE, THERESA; Harbor Creek HS; Harborcreek, PA; (3); Band; ncert Band; Mrchg Band; Pep Band; School Play; Variety Show; Yrbk tg; Var L Swmmng; L Trk; Hon Roll; Gannon U PA; Radiology.

.INGER, DAMON; Brookville Area HS; Brookville, PA; (3); Yrbk Stf; ktbl; Ftbl; JV Wrstlng; IN Univ Of PA; Crmnlgy.

.INGER, DAWN; Keystone JR SR HS; Knox, PA; (3); 7/150; Sec Pep ; Nwsp Rptr; Yrbk Sprt Ed; Sec Stu Cncl; Bsktbl; Trk; Vllybl; Hon ll; NHS; Spnsh & Eng Awds 85; Acadmc All Amer 87; Pitt U; Psych.

.INGERMAN, CANDI; Everett Area HS; Clearville, PA; (2); 14/150; urch Yth Grp; Spanish Clb; Band; Concert Band; Mrchg Band; High n Roll; Hon Roll; Travel Agent.

INGERMAN, LISA A; Everett Area HS; Artemas, PA; (4); Church Grp; FBLA; Varsity Clb; Band; Nwsp Stf; Yrbk Stf; Off Stu Cncl; cr; 2nd Pl Bus Engl-FBLA Cmptn 87; Allegany CC; Comp Tech.

.INGERMAN, SANDRA; Southern Fulton HS; Warfordsburg, PA; 4-H; FHA; Nwsp Rptr; Score Keeper; Var Sftbl; Hon Roll; Psychlgst.

.INGERMAN, TAMALA; Everett Area HS; Everett, PA; (2); Church Grp; French Clb; Varsity Clb; Band; Mrchg Band; Trs Soph Cls; Var eerleading; Tennis; French Hon Soc; Dntl.

.INK, VICKY; Northeast Bradford HS; Le Raysville, PA; (4); Pres Sec I; FHA; Drill Tm; Sec Stu Cncl; 4-H Awd; Hon Roll; L B Hulsander em Awd 84; Susquehanna Cnty Invl Bus Ed Cont 3rd Pl 87; Bus Ed mpsm 4th Pl 87; Rcptnst.

.INTON, BARBARA; Pennsbury HS; Levittown, PA; (3); School Play; bk Stf; Hon Roll; Pres Schlr; Cmmrcl Art.

.INTON, KRISTIN; Du Bois Area HS; Dubois, PA; (3); Chorus; Hon ll; IN U Pennsylvania; Med Tech.

.INTON, SHERRA; Linden Hall HS; Lititz, PA; (2); 6/50; Cmnty Wkr; ama Clb; School Play; Stage Crew; Lit Mag; High Hon Roll; Stud Of e Mnth 86; Intl Rltns.

.IPPINGER, CARYL; Big Spring HS; Newville, PA; (4); Band; Color ard; Concert Band; Mrchg Band; Swmmng; Trk; Lion Awd; The nerican U.

.ISHAM, TORI; Quakertown Community HS; Quakertown, PA; (2); urch Yth Grp; Var Cheerleading; Var Pom Pon; Var Socr; Var Trk; Hon ll; Jr NHS; French Clb; ECA Cheering Champs 4th Runner-Up 87; Pres dmc Ftnss Awd & All Amer Talent Awds Dance 2nd Pl 86; Sci.

.OAK, NANCY; Dayton HS; Templeton, PA; (3); 2/52; Church Yth p; Hosp Aide; Pep Clb; Band; Chorus; Church Choir; Concert Band; chg Band; Pep Band; Stat Bsktbl.

.OCKER, CASI; Susquehannock HS; Shrewsbury, PA; (2); 20/243; 'S; Church Yth Grp; School Musical; Off Jr Cls; Rep Stu Cncl; Var eerleading; Hon Roll; Bus Admin.

.OHERTY, KELLEY; Steel Valley HS; Munhall, PA; (3); 9/217; urch Yth Grp; Cmnty Wkr; Rep Stu Cncl; Var Bsktbl; High Hon Roll; n Roll; NHS; Enlg Essay Awd 87; U Pittsburgh; Criminology.

.ONEY, SHANNON; Eastern HS; York, PA; (4); 5/150; Varsity Clb; bk Stf; VP Frsh Cls; VP Soph Cls; VP Jr Cls; VP Sr Cls; Var L eerleading; Var L Fld Hcky; High Hon Roll; NHS; U Of NC.

.ONTZ, TODD; Punxsutawney Area HS; Stump Creek, PA; (4); 108/ ; Band; Concert Band; Jazz Band; Mrchg Band; Orch; Pep Band; Hon ll; Louis Armstrong Jazz Awd 87; Mary Ann Irvin Fndtn Schlrshp 87; U Of PA; Music Ed.

.ORAN, KAREN; Cardinal O Hara HS; Secane, PA; (3); 55/710; Cmnty kr; Y-Teens; Var Crs Cntry; Var Capt Trk; Hon Roll; NHS; Spanish HS; Crs Cntry-All Cthlc, All Delco 85-86; Mvp 86; Tck-All Cthlc, All lco 85, 87; Phys Thrpy.

.OSE, HEATHER RAE; York Catholic HS; Dover, PA; (3); 13/154; ploring; FBLA; Pep Clb; Spanish Clb; Var Stat Bsktbl; Capt JV Vllybl; HS; What My Family Means To Me Essy Cntst 3rd Pl 86; Bio.

.OSE, LAURE; Dunmore HS; Dunmore, PA; (4); 49/150; Art Clb; nch Clb; Letterman Clb; Ski Clb; Y-Teens; Yrbk Bus Mgr; Yrbk Stf; r Diving; Var Sftbl; Var Tennis; MVP Sftbll Awd 85-86 & 86-87; tstndng Tnns Plyr Awd 85-86 & 86-87; Won All Str Sftbll Tm 86-87; Inst Of Pittsburgh; Cmmnctn.

.OSE, NICOLE; Claysburg-Kimmel HS; Claysburg, PA; (3); Church h Grp; 4-H; Model UN; PAVAS; Speech Tm; Band; Concert Band; -Capt Cheerleading; 4-H Awd; NHS; U Of Pittsburgh; Pre-Med.

CLOSSON, NATALIE; Bellwood-Antis HS; Bellwood, PA; (4); 5/115; Sec Varsity Clb; Band; School Play; Sec Jr Cls; Stu Cncl; Stat Bsktbl; Capt Fld Hcky; Trk; Hon Roll; NHS; Grl Of Mnth 86; PA ST U; Bus Admin.

CLOTHIER, AMANDA; Springside Schl; Philadelphia, PA; (3); Church Yth Grp; Cmnty Wkr; Stage Crew; Nwsp Stf; Fld Hcky; JV Lcrss; JV Var Tennis; Vllybl; Hon Roll; Bus.

CLOUD, NOELLE; Wm Allen HS; Doylestown, PA; (3); 25/659; Sec Church Yth Grp; Key Clb; SADD; Off Soph Cls; Off Jr Cls; Off Sr Cls; L Var Fld Hcky; Lcrss; Hon Roll; NHS; Intl Relations.

CLOUGH, MELISSA; Nazareth HS; Nazareth, PA; (3); German Clb; Band; Concert Band; Lib Mrchg Band; Vet Med.

CLOUGH, VICKIE; Upper Dauphin Area HS; Lykens, PA; (3); German Clb; Chorus; Sftbl; Hon Roll; Big Sistr 86-87; Bwlg Clb 86-87; Vet.

CLOUSE, AMY L; Butler Area SR HS; Butler, PA; (4); Trs Debate Tm; Pres Hosp Aide; NFL; SADD; Nwsp Ed-Chief; Yrbk Ed-Chief; PA Gov Schl Sci Schlrshp 86; Armco Fndtn Schlrshp 87; Jostens Ldrshp Fndtn Schlrshp 87; Northwestern U; Bio.

CLOUSER, CATHI; Central Dauphin HS; Harrisburg, PA; (3); Boy Scts; Chorus; School Musical; Stat Bsktbl; Mgr Ftbl; Im Vllybl; Hon Roll; Jr NHS; Yth Schlrs Prgm Chem Lebanon Vly Coll 87; Chem.

CLOUSER, JEFFREY; Boyertown SR HS; Bechtelsville, PA; (4); 47/429; Drama Clb; Chorus; Church Choir; Mrchg Band; School Musical; School Play; Swing Chorus; Cit Awd; DAR Awd; Hon Roll; Natl Schl Chrl Awd 87; E & H K Reitnaver Schlrshp 87; Cnty Dist & Rgnl Choruses 85-87; Millersville U; Elem Ed.

CLOUSER, MARIBETH; Twin Valley HS; Birdsboro, PA; (4); FBLA; Girl Scts; Spanish Clb; School Play; Lcrss; Hon Roll; Nice Prsn Awd 87; Acadmc Schlrshp 87; Spnsh Awd 87; West Chester U.

CLOUSER, MEGAN; Newport HS; Newport, PA; (4); 5/95; Band; Chorus; School Musical; Swing Chorus; Cheerleading; NHS; Opt Clb Awd; Jazz Band; Gym; High Hon Roll; Gold Key Awd-Centrl PA Schlstc Writing 87; Sound Of Amer Hnr Band-Chorus 85; Tri-M Clb Historian 86; Penn ST; Communctns.

CLOUSER III, RALPH C; Elizabethtown Area HS; Elizabethtown, PA; (4); Varsity Clb; Var Bsbl; Var Golf; Kiwanis Awd; Sectn II All Str Bsbl 86-87; Schl Rcrd Golf 87; Elizabethtown Coll; Math.

CLUCK, DAVE; East Pennsboro HS; Enola, PA; (3); 40/184; Church Yth Grp; French Clb; Band; Chorus; Concert Band; Jazz Band; Mrchg Band; Orch; Pep Band; School Musical; U Pittsburgh; Phrmcy.

CLUGH, BEVERLY; Big Spring HS; Newville, PA; (2); 10/283; Band; Chorus; Concert Band; Jazz Band; Mrchg Band; Orch; School Play; Fld Hcky; Hon Roll; Achvt Frgn Lang Awd 87; Dickinson Coll.

CLUGSTON, AIMEE; Chambersburg Area SR HS; Chambersburg, PA; (2); 138/735; Church Yth Grp; Drama Clb; French Clb; Library Aide; Office Aide; Ski Clb; Speech Tm; Yrbk Stf; Trk; Hon Roll; PA ST U; Poltcl Sci.

CLUKEY, JEFF; Mechanicsburg Area SR HS; Mechanicsburg, PA; (4); 45/303; Ski Clb; School Play; VP Soph Cls; VP Jr Cls; Rep Stu Cncl; JV Socr; Var Tennis; Hon Roll; Chess Clb; Im Golf; Stu Yth Forum Rep, Sec; Juniata Coll; Vet Med.

CLUTTER, CRYSTAL; Mc Guffey HS; Prosperity, PA; (3); VP Church Yth Grp; Pres 4-H; Ski Clb; Spanish Clb; Varsity Clb; Bsktbl; Gym; Trk; High Hon Roll; Hon Roll; Pres Acad Awd 84-85; Spec Achvt Awd 84-85; VA Commonwealth U; Dentst.

CLUTTER, JENNIFER; Mc Guffey HS; West Finley, PA; (3); Am Leg Aux Girls St; German Clb; Pep Clb; Chorus; School Play; Stage Crew; Powder Puff Ftbl; High Hon Roll; NHS; Outstndng Stu Awd 85-87; Phrmcy.

CLUTTER, LAWRENCE; Mc Guffey HS; Claysville, PA; (3); Church Yth Grp; Spanish Clb; Varsity Clb; Var L Crs Cntry; Var L Chess Clb; High Hon Roll; NHS; Computer Clb; Letterman Clb; Ski Clb; Stu Recgntn Awd 85 & 87; Outstndng Stu Awd 86.

CLUVER, JOHN; Marple Newtown Senior HS; Media, PA; (2); 2/325; Concert Band; Jazz Band; Mrchg Band; JV Bsktbl; JV Lcrss; JV Socr; JV Swmmng; High Hon Roll.

CMAR, RENEE L; Mc Keesport HS; White Oak, PA; (3); 22/550; Church Yth Grp; German Clb; Teachers Aide; Swmmng; Trk; Cit Awd; Hon Roll; Yrly Hnr Rl Awd 86-87; Am Lgn Awd 83-84; PA ST; Physcl Thrpy.

COAST, JANICE; Franklin Area HS; Harrisville, PA; (4); 12/208; Church Yth Grp; VP 4-H; Library Aide; Radio Clb; Spanish Clb; Capt Color Guard; School Musical; Off Jr Cls; Off Sr Cls; Stu Cncl.

COATES, JIM; Cathedral Prep HS; Erie, PA; (3); JV Ftbl; Im Hon Roll; Pblc Rltns.

COATES, STEPHEN; Norristown Area HS; Norristown, PA; (3); 27/491; Concert Band; Jazz Band; Orch; Hon Roll; Cellr Biogst.

COATES, SUZANNE; Steelton-Highspire HS; Steelton, PA; (4); 1/97; Trs Spanish Clb; School Musical; Yrbk Ed-Chief; Hst Sr Cls; Capt Cheerleading; NHS; Pres Schlr; Val; Library Aide; Pep Clb; Harrisburg Exchng Clb Stu Mth 87; John Hall Fndtn Schlrshp 87; Rensselaer Awd Math, Sci 86; Fshn Inst Of Tech; Fshn Mrchnds.

COBB, EUGENE; Ambridge Area HS; Ambridge, PA; (4); FCA; Pres French Clb; Pep Clb; SADD; Chorus; School Play; Off Sr Cls; Bsktbl; Ftbl; Socr; Schlrshp PA Free Entrprs Work Lock Hvn 86; Pittsburgh Post Gzette 1st Tm Kicker 86; Wagner Coll; Finance.

COBLE, MANDY KAY; Purchase Line HS; Clymer, PA; (2); FBLA; Pep Clb; Band; Chorus; Concert Band; Mrchg Band; Hon Roll; VP JP Sousa Awd; Bus.

COBLE, SCOTT; Elizabethtown Area HS; Elizabethtown, PA; (4); 5/224; Am Leg Boys St; Aud/Vis; Church Yth Grp; Computer Clb; VP Sr Cls; Stu Cncl; Cit Awd; DAR Awd; NHS; Pres Acadc Ftns Awd 87; Penn ST U; Aerospace Engr.

COBLENTZ, RHEA; E L Meyers HS; Wilkes Barre, PA; (2); 1/146; Temple Yth Grp; Chorus; Yrbk Stf; Var L Bsktbl; Tennis; High Hon Roll; NHS; NEDT Awd; Spanish NHS; JA; Penn ST U; Law.

COBURN, DENISE; Bishop Mc Devitt HS; Harrisburg, PA; (4); Office Aide; Service Clb; Spanish Clb; Color Guard; NHS; PA ST U; Bus Admin.

COCCAGNA, CAROL; West Phila Catholic Girls HS; Philadelphia, PA; (4); 20/233; Cmnty Wkr; French Clb; Library Aide; Math Tm; Nwsp Rptr; High Hon Roll; Hon Roll; Prfct Atten Awd; Pres Schlr; 1st Pl Phys Sci JR Div Of HS Sci Fair 84; Drexel U; Math.

COCCHINI, RICHARD; West Scranton HS; Scranton, PA; (3); Boys Clb Am; Letterman Clb; Ski Clb; Golf; Hon Roll; PA ST; Arch Engrng.

COCCI, TOM; Strath Haven HS; Wallingford, PA; (3); Spanish Clb; Coach Actv; JV Ftbl; JV Var Trk; High Hon Roll; Hon Roll.

COCCIOLONE, TABITHA; Avon Grove HS; Landenberg, PA; (3); Mgr(s); Sftbl; Hon Roll; Physcl Educ Awd 85; Gen Bus Awd 86; Accntngn Awd, MVP-SFTBL & Athl Of Wk-Sftbl 87; Bus Admin.

COCCO, LOUIS; Archbishop Ryan HS For Boys; Philadelphia, PA; (4); 80/450; Drama Clb; French Clb; Ski Clb; Rep Frsh Cls; Rep Soph Cls; Stu Cncl; Ftbl; Ice Hcky; PA ST U; Bus.

COCHRAN, BETH; Beaver Area SR HS; Beaver, PA; (2); Exploring; JA; Pep Clb; Trs Spanish Clb; JV Cheerleading; High Hon Roll; Hon Roll; Var Trk; Attndnc Awd Explrng Atty Clb 86-87; Sales Awd JA 86-87; 2nd Pl Awd Cls Fndraisng Prjct 86-87; Law.

COCHRAN, JULIE; Octorara HS; Parkesburg, PA; (3); 16/176; Art Clb; Sec Trs Exploring; Spanish Clb; Stage Crew; Trk; Vllybl; High Hon Roll; Hon Roll; NHS; Crmnl Jstce.

COCHRAN, KRIS; Freedom HS; Bethlehem, PA; (3); 89/509; Church Yth Grp; Drama Clb; French Clb; Science Clb; SADD; Ed Yrbk Stf; Im Socr; Im Swmmng; Hon Roll; Debate Tm.

COCHRAN, SHARON; Oil City SR HS; Oil City, PA; (3); #2 In Class; AFS; Cmnty Wkr; Debate Tm; Acpl Chr; Mrchg Band; School Musical; Nwsp Ed-Chief; Stu Cncl; High Hon Roll; NHS; Duquesne; Law.

COCO, ANDREW; Conrad Weiser HS; Robesonia, PA; (3); Church Yth Grp; FBLA; Latin Clb; Chorus; Church Choir; School Musical; School Play; Swing Chorus; Yrbk Stf; VP Trs Stu Cncl; Rotary Clb Ldrshp Smmr Pgm 87; Acctng.

CODDINGTON, SHERI; Hillside Christian Acad; Mifflinburg, PA; (2); Trs Church Yth Grp; Library Aide; Church Choir; Yrbk Stf; Sftbl; Vllybl; Hon Roll; School Musical; Most Imprvd Stu 87; Scripture Mem Awds 85-86&86-87; 2nd Pace Comp Awd 86-87; Sci.

CODDINGTON, W; Geibel HS; Uniontown, PA; (3); Church Yth Grp; Drama Clb; Pep Clb; Stage Crew; JV Bsktbl; Var L Crs Cntry; Hon Roll; Engrng.

CODE, AIMEE; Taylor Allderdice HS; Pittsburgh, PA; (2); Debate Tm; Crs Cntry; Trk; Hon Roll; Bio.

CODELUPPI, JILL; Elizabeth Forward HS; Elizabeth, PA; (4); 26/293; Pres Church Yth Grp; SADD; Pres Acpl Chr; Co-Capt Color Guard; Yrbk Ed-Chief; Sec Sr Cls; Stat Swmmng; Hon Roll; NHS; Cmpttv Schlrshp-Duquesne U 87; Ldrshp Awd PTSA 87; Intl Piano Rcrdng Cmptn Brnz Mdls 82-87; Duquesne U; Acctng.

CODER, HEIDI; Huntingdon Area HS; Huntingdon, PA; (3); 42/224; Church Yth Grp; Key Clb; Chorus; Church Choir; Concert Band; Yrbk Sprt Ed; Rep Frsh Cls; Var Cheerleading; JV Vllybl; Hon Roll; Engrng.

CODY, COLLEEN; Gwynedd-Mercy Acad; Warrington, PA; (2); Church Yth Grp; GAA; Service Clb; Stage Crew; Fld Hcky; Sftbl; Hon Roll; Ltn Frnch Wrld Hstry Engl Achiev Awds 85-86.

CODY, JANINE R; Coatesville Area HS; Coatesville, PA; (3); FBLA; Girl Scts; Hosp Aide; Library Aide; Chorus; JV Fld Hcky; JV Lcrss; Hon Roll; Church Yth Grp; Ypwrd Bnd-Trphy Chmstry & Tnns Cert 84-87; Med.

CODY, LORI; Center HS; Aliquippa, PA; (4); 33/186; Art Clb; SADD; Varsity Clb; Yrbk Stf; Stu Cncl; Mgr(s); Powder Puff Ftbl; L Trk; NHS; Pres Schlr; Stu Cncl Schlrshp 87; PTA Schlrshp 87; U Of OK; Psych.

CODY, SCOTT; Neshannock HS; New Castle, PA; (3); VP Camera Clb; Church Yth Grp; Cmnty Wkr; Exploring; Ski Clb; Speech Tm; Nwsp Rptr; Lit Mag; Var Tennis; Cit Awd; Frnsc Awd 86-87; Frnch Cont Awd 86.

CODY, SUSAN; Seneca Valley SR HS; Evans Cty, PA; (3); Church Yth Grp; Cmnty Wkr; Dance Clb; Drama Clb; Red Cross Aide; Ski Clb; VP Thesps; Chorus; Madrigals; School Musical; Cmmnctns.

COEYMAN, CHAD; Red Lion SR HS; Red Lion, PA; (3); 28/342; Latin Clb; Var Trk; Hon Roll; Latin Hnr Soc 85-86; Vet Med.

COFFER, NANCY; Vough SR HS; W Newton, PA; (3); 15/256; Computer Clb; French Clb; Math Clb; VP Soph Cls; Var L Cheerleading; Var Capt Powder Puff Ftbl; Var L Sftbl; High Hon Roll; Hon Roll; NHS; Sewickley Nrsng Schl; Nrsng.

COFFIN, DAWN RENEE; Northern Lehigh HS; Slatington, PA; (4); 11/ 136; Nwsp Bus Mgr; Nwsp Rptr; Nwsp Stf; Var Fld Hcky; Var Trk; NHS; Ernest Snyder Memrl Schlrshp 87; NLHS Jrnlsm Awd 87; Lehigh Cnty JR Miss Cntst 87; West Chester U; Cmmnctns.

COFFMAN, AMY; Montoursville Area HS; Montoursville, PA; (3); 33/ 187; Art Clb; Church Yth Grp; German Clb; Church Choir; Color Guard; Mrchg Band; Var Powder Puff Ftbl; Var Twrlr; Hon Roll; Bald Eagle Art League Awd 85 & 86; Est Cst Chmpnshp Twrlng Awd 86 & 87; Art Hstry.

COFFMAN, DANIEL; Du Bois Area HS; Reynoldsvle, PA; (3); Chess Clb; Hon Roll; Jrnlsm.

COFFMAN, JOHN; Beth Center; Fredericktown, PA; (3); Church Yth Grp; Spanish Clb; Varsity Clb; Band; Ftbl; Wt Lftg; Wrstlng; WVU; CPA.

COFFMAN, MEGAN; Carlisle HS; Carlisle, PA; (3); 62/467; Chorus; Color Guard; Mrchg Band; Yrbk Rptr; High Hon Roll; Hnrs Banquet 87; Educ.

COFFMAN, STEPHAN; Riverview HS; Oakmont, PA; (3); French Clb; Pres VP Key Clb; Orch; High Hon Roll; Pittsburgh Yth Symph Orch 85-87; Aberdeen Scotland Intl Yth Fstvl Orch 87; All Eastern Orch; U Rochester; Vet Med.

COFFMAN, TOM; Connellsville Area HS; Connellsville, PA; (3); Teachers Aide; VICA; Hon Roll; 4 Time Wnnr N Fayette Vo-Tech Dirs Lst Awd 85-86 & 85-87; Elec.

COGAN, JACOB K; Akiba Hebrew Acad; Bala Cynwyd, PA; (4); Debate Tm; French Clb; Nwsp Stf; Yrbk Bus Mgr; Trs Jr Cls; JV Crs Cntry; Var Capt Wrstlng; Ntl Merit SF; Mvp Wrestling Awd Schl 83-84.

COGER, FRANCES; West Groone Middle SR HS; Mt Morris, PA; (4); Art Clb; Aud/Vis; Church Yth Grp; Drama Clb; 4-H; Office Aide; Spanish Clb; Chorus; Church Choir; School Musical; Waynesburg Coll; Comm.

COGGINS, DONNA; Lakeland HS; Carbondale, PA; (3); Church Yth Grp; Dance Clb; French Clb; Yrbk Stf; Rep Stu Cncl; Hon Roll; Elem Ed.

COGLEY, CAREN; Taylor Allderdice HS; Pittsburgh, PA; (2); JA; Cheerleading; Sftbl; Vllybl; High Hon Roll; Bus Mgmt.

COGLEY, LINDA; Marion Center Area HS; Indiana, PA; (3); 5/169; Trs Latin Clb; Trs Q&S; SADD; Trs Varsity Clb; School Play; Yrbk Stf; Stat Crs Cntry; Trk; High Hon Roll; NHS; Penn St; Molecular.

COHEN, ADAM; Council Rock HS; Richboro, PA; (2); Im Bsktbl; Im Tennis; Hon Roll; Fall Danc Ct 86-87; Mock Constntl Cnvtn 86-87; Corp Atty.

COHEN, ALISON; Lower Merion HS; Bala Cynwyd, PA; (3); French Clb; VP Service Clb; Nwsp Rptr; Nwsp Stf; Yrbk Stf; Rep Frsh Cls; Rep Soph Cls; Rep Jr Cls; Rep Sr Cls; Stu Cncl; Rtry Ldrshp Trng Prog 87.

COHEN, BETH; Abington SR HS; Abington, PA; (4); 53/486; Co-Capt Debate Tm; Pres Intnl Clb; Temple Yth Grp; Nwsp Stf; Rep Frsh Cls; Rep Soph Cls; Rep Jr Cls; Rep Sr Cls; Rep Stu Cncl; Hon Roll; Stu Of Mnth 86; Prncpls Awd 87; Cnfrmtn Cls Awd For Schlrshp 85; U Of PA; Intl Law.

COHEN, BRETT-EVAN; Plymouth Whitemarsh HS; Flourtown, PA; (3); 17/356; Math Clb; Mu Alpha Theta; Temple Yth Grp; Nwsp Ed-Chief; Nwsp Sprt Ed; JV Bsktbl; Var Tennis; High Hon Roll; VP NHS; Nwsp Stf; People To People Stu Ambassador Prog 87.

COHEN, CHAD; Lower Moreland HS; Huntingdon Valley, PA; (3); Tennis; High Hon Roll; FBLA; Temple Yth Grp; Y-Teens; Hon Roll; Distngshd Hnr Rll 86; Outstndng Frnch Stu 86; Middle ST Tnns Assoc 84, 85, & 86; Med.

COHEN, JAN; Shady Side Acad; Pittsburgh, PA; (3); Dance Clb; Ski Clb; Nwsp Stf; Sec Frsh Cls; Sec Soph Cls; Var Capt Bsktbl; JV Fld Hcky; JV Lcrss; JV Tennis; Var Trk; 7th Pl Fren II Cont 84-85; Bsktbl MVP; La Crosse MVP; Bus.

COHEN, MICHAEL A; Norristown Area HS; Norristown, PA; (3); 11/524; Computer Clb; Math Clb; Temple Yth Grp; Nwsp Rptr; Lit Mag; Pres Stu Cncl; Hon Roll; NHS; Phys-Ed Awd 85-86; Bus.

COHEN, NANCY I; Friends Select Schl; Philadelphia, PA; (4); Drama Clb; Sec Temple Yth Grp; Chorus; Madrigals; School Musical; School Play; Nwsp Stf; Yrbk Stf; Lit Mag; Ntl Merit SF; Engl.

COHEN, RACHEL; Lower Moreland HS; Huntingdon Valley, PA; (2); Cmnty Wkr; Drama Clb; FBLA; Key Clb; Science Clb; SADD; Temple Yth Grp; Chorus; Madrigals; School Musical.

COHEN, ROBERT M; Upper Dublin HS; Dresher, PA; (4); 53/316; FBLA; JA; Temple Yth Grp; Rep Jr Cls; Im Bsktbl; JV Bowling; JV Golf; Var Tennis; Hon Roll; NHS; Abraham Heshel Hon Soc United Synagogue Yth 86; FBLA Sprng Regnl Cntst 3rd Pl Entrprshp II 87; Emory U; Bus Admin.

COHEN, ROBIN; Marple Newtown SR HS; Broomall, PA; (3); 99/330; Yrbk Stf; Stu Cncl; Hon Roll; Clncl Psyclgy.

COHICK, STEPHANIE; Shamokin Area HS; Shamokin, PA; (2); Church Yth Grp; Nwsp Stf; Hon Roll; Outstndg Engl Stu Awd 87; Creat Wrtg Awd 86; Bloomsburg U; Acctg.

COLABERDINO, PATRICIA; Nazareth Acad; Philadelphia, PA; (4); 1/121; Church Yth Grp; Debate Tm; Pres NFL; Pres Speech Tm; Nwsp Stf; Jr Cls; Sr Cls; High Hon Roll; Pres NHS; Val; Amer Legn ST Fnlst 87; Ntl Qualfr Spch 85-87; Mayrs Schlrshp 87; U Of PA; Hlth Care Adm.

COLACICCO, LYNDA; North Pocano HS; Moscow, PA; (3); Sec Church Yth Grp; FBLA; Hosp Aide; Band; Concert Band; Mrchg Band; Mgr(s); Trk; CPA.

COLADONATO, JOSEPH; Aliquippa JR SR HS; Aliquippa, PA; (4); 1/132; Pres Church Yth Grp; Drama Clb; Math Tm; Band; Var Ftbl; High Hon Roll; Pres Jr NHS; Lion Awd; Pres NHS; Val; U Of PA; Biology.

COLADONATO, LEA; Aliquippa HS; Aliquippa, PA; (3); Church Yth Grp; Drama Clb; Exploring; French Clb; School Musical; School Play; Stage Crew; Trs Jr Cls; Cheerleading; Hon Roll; Dentistry.

COLAIZZI, MAUREEN; Beaver Falls HS; Beaver Falls, PA; (3); 8/174; AFS; Art Clb; Aud/Vis; Q&S; Yrbk Sprt Ed; Co-Capt Bsktbl; Tennis; Capt Trk; High Hon Roll; NHS; All Amer Acad All Star 87; Natl Hnr Rl 87; Landscape Arch.

COLAIZZI, MERRITT; Ellis School; Glenshaw, PA; (3); Ski Clb; Yrbk Phtg; L Fld Hcky; Var L Lcrss; Im Vllybl; Hon Roll; Lib Arts.

COLANGELO IV, AUGUSTUS B; State College Area Intermediat HS; State College, PA; (1); Drama Clb; Ski Clb; Thesps; Band; Church Choir; Orch; School Musical; Yrbk Stf; Im Socr; Hon Roll; Chrch Chr Chosen To Sing In Rome, Italy 87; Herff Jones Yrbk Cmp Schlrshp 86 & 87; Cmnty Theatr 84-87; Med.

COLANTONI, JEFFREY; Our Lady Of The Sacred Heart HS; Mc Kees Rocks, PA; (3); Var Socr; Acadc Awd 87; Ltr-Socr 85-87; Pittsburgh Inst Of Aeronautics.

COLBERT, ERINN; Nazareth Acad HS; Philadelphia, PA; (3); Hosp Aide; Latin Clb; NFL; Trs Speech Tm; Band; Church Choir; Concert Band; Orch; School Musical; Psyc.

COLBERT, KRISTIN; Strath Haven HS; Media, PA; (4); Church Yth Grp; Office Aide; Teachers Aide; Band; Concert Band; Mrchg Band; Orch; Symp Band; Var Capt Bsktbl; Var Capt Vllybl; Bucknell; Bus Mgmt.

COLBURN, JACQUELYN; Old Forge HS; Old Forge, PA; (3); Concert Band; School Musical; School Play; High Hon Roll; NHS; Church Yth Grp; Drama Clb; Ski Clb; Thesps; Band; Gifted Prgm Comp, Earth Sci, Lang, Arts & Physics 85-87; Explrrs Grp Law 85; Cmmnctns.

COLCOMBE, SCOTT; Central Catholic HS; Pittsburgh, PA; (3); 55/320; Boys Clb Am; Church Yth Grp; JA; JV Var Bsbl; High Hon Roll; Hon Roll; NHS; Bus.

COLDEN, RICHARD; Cardinal O Hara HS; Clifton Hgts, PA; (3); 41/710; Church Yth Grp; Cmnty Wkr; Im Bsktbl; Im Bowling; Hon Roll; NHS; Acdmc Cnvctn 85, 86 & 87; Bus.

COLDSMITH, MICHELLE; Chambersburg Area SR HS; Shippensburg, PA; (2); Church Yth Grp; JCL; Latin Clb; Var L Fld Hcky; Hon Roll; Im Vllybl.

COLE, AMANDA; Great Valley SR HS; Frazer, PA; (3); 4-H; Latin Clb; Office Aide; Ski Clb; SADD; Pres Y-Teens; Chorus; Stu Cncl; Cheerleading; High Hon Roll; Blmngdls Teen Mdlng Bd 86-87.

COLE, AMY; Butler Area SR HS; Butler, PA; (4); 158/699; Pres Trs Church Yth Grp; Debate Tm; French Clb; Teachers Aide; Acpl Chr; Chorus; Chorus; Hon Roll; Grove City Coll; Intl Bus.

COLE, CHRIS; Elk Lake HS; Meshoppen, PA; (2); 12/110; 4-H; Ski Clb; Sec Frsh Cls; Sec Soph Cls; Var Bsktbl; Socr; Hon Roll.

COLE, CHRISTINE; Meadville Area SR HS; Conneaut Lake, PA; (4); 53/285; French Clb; Nwsp Rptr; Hon Roll; Prfct Atten Awd; Edinboro U; Pre-Law.

COLE, DAVE; Emmaus HS; Emmaus, PA; (4); 69/487; Band; Sec Jr Cls; Sec Sr Cls; JV Var Bsbl; Hon Roll; Hon Roll; Jr NHS; NHS; Pres Acad Fit Awd; VA Tech; Elec Engrng.

COLE, DEBORAH; Waynesburg Central HS; Prosperity, PA; (3); Church Yth Grp; Mu Alpha Theta; Natl Beta Clb; Color Guard; Mrchg Band; Variety Show; High Hon Roll; Hon Roll; Prfct Atten Awd; 1st Pl & Cert Merit Fred J Miller Clintic 87; Cruise Dir.

COLE II, DONALD J; Tunckhannock Area HS; Tunkhannock, PA; (4); 29/280; Chess Clb; Band; Concert Band; Jazz Band; Mrchg Band; Golf; NHS.

COLE, DOUGLAS; Pennsbury HS; Yardley, PA; (2); Computer Clb; Political Wkr; Var L Diving; Im Vllybl; Hon Roll; Engnrng.

COLE, JAY; Blue Mountain Acad; Coudersport, PA; (3); Computer Clb; Ski Clb; Band; Concert Band; Stage Crew; Trs Jr Cls; Capt Ftbl; Capt Sftbl; Vllybl; Wt Lftg; Columbia Union Coll.

COLE, JAY; Blue Mt Acad; Hamburg, PA; (3); Computer Clb; Ski Clb; Acpl Chr; Concert Band; Bsktbl; Ftbl; Capt Sftbl; Vllybl; Wt Lftg; High Hon Roll; Columbia Union Clg.

COLE, KERRY; Gettysburg HS; Gettysburg, PA; (2); Dance Clb; FNA; Model UN; SADD; Stu Cncl; Gym; Cit Awd; High Hon Roll; Hon Roll; NHS; Prsnl Bst Awd Militry Phys Ftns Test 87; Penn ST; Nrsng.

COLE, KEVIN; Susquehannock HS; New Freedom, PA; (2); 55/289; Debate Tm; Speech Tm; School Musical; School Play; Trk; Mock Trial Somp 85-86; Penn ST; Chem Engrng.

COLE, LISA; Bishop Guilfoyle HS; Altoona, PA; (4); German Clb; Yrbk Stf; Rep Stu Cncl; JV Var Bsktbl; High Hon Roll; Hon Roll; St Francis; Nrsng.

COLE, MATT; Mt Pleasant Area SR HS; Norvelt, PA; (2); JV Bsbl; JV Bsktbl; JV Ftbl; Hon Roll.

COLE, MEGGAN; Jeannette HS; Jeannette, PA; (2); Pres Church Yth Grp; Drama Clb; Spanish Clb; Band; Co-Capt Color Guard; Hon Roll; Hugh O Brian Yth Ldrshp Awd 87; Penn ST; Law.

COLE, MICHELLE; Riverside HS; Taylor, PA; (3); 30/120; Church Yth Grp; FBLA; Ski Clb; Drill Tm; Pom Pon; Trk; Hon Roll; 16th In St PA 100 Meter Dash 87; Undftd 100 Mtr Dash Dist 2 86-87; Phys Thrpst.

COLE, MIKE; Mt Pleasant Area SR HS; Norvelt, PA; (2); JV Bsbl; JV Bsktbl; JV Ftbl; Hon Roll.

COLE, NORMAN; Hughesville HS; Muncy, PA; (3); Church Yth Grp; Drama Clb; Band; Chorus; Madrigals; School Musical; School Play; Var JV Bsktbl; Cit Awd; NHS; Semi Fnlst Cong Bundestag Exchng Pgm 86; Dist Chorus 87; Hstry Tchr.

COLE, ROBERT; Pittston Area HS; Duryea, PA; (3); 22/320; Var English Clb.

COLE, RONALD; Reading SR HS; Reading, PA; (2); 70/800; Yrbk Stf; Lit Mag; Hon Roll; Jr NHS; Math.

COLE, SHARON; Middletown Area HS; Middletown, PA; (4); Key Clb; Model UN; Soroptimist; Nwsp Stf; Capt Gym; Hon Roll; Jr NHS; NHS; Rotary Awd; Acad A U Amrcn 86; PSU.

COLE, STEVEN; St Marys Area HS; St Marys, PA; (3); Var Ftbl; Trk; Hon Roll; Pittsburgh; Mortuary Sci.

COLE, SYLVIA; Snook HS; Philadelphia, PA; (2); Church Yth Grp; Civic Clb; 4-H; FHA; Church Choir; JV Var Bsktbl; Capt Coach Actv; Trk; 4-H Awd; Prfct Atten Awd; Air Force; Brdcst Jrnlst.

COLELLA, CANDACE; New Castle SR HS; New Castle, PA; (4); 13/232; AFS; Church Yth Grp; Exploring; Spanish Clb; Flag Corp; Off Sr Cls; Rep Stu Cncl; Hon Roll; NHS; Prfct Atten Awd.

COLELLA, RENEE; New Castle SR HS; New Castle, PA; (3); 24/293; Chorus; Drill Tm; Rep Stu Cncl; Hon Roll.

COLEMAN, APRIL; Mercy Vocational HS; Philadelphia, PA; (3); Drama Clb; School Play; Stage Crew; Yrbk Rptr; Yrbk Stf; Rep Frsh Cls; Rep Soph Cls; Rep Jr Cls; Hon Roll; Prfct Atten Awd; Hghst Grd-Literature 84-85.

COLEMAN, BRENDA; Oil City SR HS; Oil City, PA; (3); Art Clb; Library Aide; Acpl Chr; Chorus; Yrbk Stf; Rep Stu Cncl; Wt Lftg; Hon Roll; NHS; Librry Aide Certs; X-Ray Tech.

COLEMAN, CARLA; Mc Keesport SR HS; Mc Keesport, PA; (1); SADD; Chorus; Yrbk Stf; Var L Bsktbl; Var Sftbl; High Hon Roll; Hon Roll; Var Bsktbl Ltr 86-87; MVP Bsktbl; Am Legn Awd 84-85; Acdmc Achvt Awd 83-84; Baby Prfssnl.

COLEMAN, CHRISTOPHER; Pine Forge Acad; Long Island, NY; (3); Computer Clb; Science Clb; Varsity Clb; Band; Church Choir; Drill Tm; JV Bsktbl; Sftbl; Hon Roll; Howard U; Med Socl Wrk.

COLEMAN, CRYSTAL; Berlin Brothers Valley HS; Berlin, PA; (3); 22/106; Pres Church Yth Grp; VP 4-H; FBLA; GAA; Pep Clb; Spanish Clb; SADD; Band; Im Bsktbl; Var L Sftbl; Ldrshp Awd In Sports 86-87; MVP Of Vlybl Tm 86-87; 1st Tm All Cnty Vllybl Tm 86-87; U Of Pittsburgh; Elem Educ.

COLEMAN, DALE; Brookville Area HS; Summerville, PA; (3); 19/162; German Clb; Concert Band; Jazz Band; Mrchg Band; School Musical; Variety Show; Hon Roll; Jr NHS; NHS; Band; IU Hnrs Band 86; Clarion U Of PA; Spch Pthlgy.

COLEMAN, DIANE; Trinity HS; Washington, PA; (3); 57/402; Var Tennis; Hon Roll; Bus Admin.

COLEMAN, FELICIA; Fort Cherry JR SR HS; Bulger, PA; (3); Science Clb; Ski Clb; Varsity Clb; Capt Var Cheerleading; Wt Lftg; Hon Roll; Pres Chorus; Variety Show; 2 Ltrs Rcvd Vrsty Chrldg 86 & 87; Pres Chorus 85; Stu Of Yr Awd Dncng Schl Jazz 86; Sawyer Schl; Sec Sci.

COLEMAN, JOANN M; Central York SR HS; York, PA; (4); 7/203; Ski Clb; Band; Capt Flag Corp; Mrchg Band; Nwsp Stf; Yrbk Stf; Cheerleading; Lion Awd; NHS; Pres Schlr; Bloomsburg U; Diagnstc Imagng.

COLEMAN, KEVIN; Cardinal O Hara HS; Newtown Sq, PA; (3); 25/710; Var Ftbl; Im Wt Lftg; Hon Roll; Prfct Atten Awd; Acad Convocation Grades 9-11; Aerospace Engrng.

COLEMAN, KRYSTEE E; Meadville Area SR HS; Meadville, PA; (3); 97/350; Hosp Aide; Library Aide; SADD; Varsity Clb; School Play; Rep Stu Cncl; Cheerleading; Hon Roll; Med.

COLEMAN, LAURA; Bishop Guilfoyle HS; Queen, PA; (4); Cmnty Wkr; Library Aide; Office Aide; Red Cross Aide; Science Clb; Service Clb; SADD; Flag Corp; Rep Stu Cncl; Hon Roll; PA ST U.

COLEMAN, LEROY; Lehighton Area HS; Lehighton, PA; (4); 22/245; 4-H; Off Soph Cls; Off Jr Cls; Off Sr Cls; Off Stu Cncl; Var L Ftbl; Var L Trk; Var L Wrstlng; Top 10 Pct Grad Clss 87; 2nd 400 Rlay & 1600 Rlay 4th 85-86; 4th 400 Rlay Leag 87; Wilkes Coll; Engrng.

COLEMAN, MARYJO; Freeport Area HS; Sarver, PA; (2); Chorus; Drill Tm; Nwsp Stf; Vllybl; Hon Roll; Elem Ed.

COLEMAN, MICHAEL; Beaver Valley Christian Acad; Rochester, PA; (3); 2/10; Chorus; School Musical; Hon Roll; Ntl Merit Ltr; VFW Awd; Voice Dem Awd; Chess Clb; Church Yth Grp; Debate Tm; Pres Acdmc Ftnss Awd 85; Kystn ST Games Fnlst Bsktbl 87; Bsktbl Sctnl MVP 87; Bus Admin.

COLEMAN, MICHELLE MARIE; Technical Memorial HS; Erie, PA; (4); 30/324; Pres Church Yth Grp; Cmnty Wkr; Pres Church Choir; Color Guard; School Musical; School Play; Rep Jr Cls; Hon Roll; NHS; Acdmc Excllnc Awd 87; Hnr Awds Gannon U Upwrd Bnd Pgm 83-87; Coop Pgm IBM 87; PA ST, Behrend; Bus Admin.

COLEMAN, PATRICIA; Saint Cyril Acad; Bethesda, MD; (2); 3/10; Aud/Vis; Hosp Aide; Key Clb; Teachers Aide; Chorus; School Play; Trs Soph Cls; Bowling; Walk For Wrld Harvest 87; Natl Soc Stud Olympiad Hnry Distntn 87.

COLEMAN, RUTH; Clairton HS; Clairton, PA; (3); #25 In Class; Church Yth Grp; NAACP; SADD; Chorus; Nwsp Stf; Trs Jr Cls; Rep Stu Cncl; Var JV Cheerleading; CC Awd; Hon Roll; Prom Queen 87; Stu Ldrshp 87; Lawyer.

COLEMAN, SARAH; Warren County Christian Schl; Warren, PA; (4); 2/7; Church Yth Grp; 4-H; Chorus; Church Choir; School Musical; Yrbk Stf; Rep Stu Cncl; Var Cheerleading; Score Keeper; Eastern Nazarnene Coll; Bus Adm.

COLEMAN, TIMOTHY; Frankford HS; Philadelphia, PA; (3); Accntng.

COLEMAN, TOM; Beaver Falls HS; Beaver Falls, PA; (3); Spanish Clb; Pres Sr Cls; High Hon Roll; NHS; Ntl Merit Ltr; Penn ST U; Exrcs & Sprts Sci.

COLEMAN, TRACY; Central York SR HS; York, PA; (3); 49/266; Clb; Concert Band; Mrchg Band; Symp Band; Nwsp Stf; Yrbk Stf; Bsktbl; Sftbl; Vllybl; Hon Roll; Millersville U; Elem Ed.

COLES, DAWNA; Western Beaver HS; Midland, PA; (4); Church Grp; Sec FBLA; JA; Band; Color Guard; Nwsp Phtg; Sec Sr Cls; Bowl Drama Clb; Concert Band; Band Queen 86-87; US Bus Ed Awd 86; Se

COLES, KEN; Old Forge HS; Old Forge, PA; (4); Ski Clb; Bsbl; Bsk Crs Cntry; Ftbl; Socr; Air Force; Law Infrcmnt.

COLES, WADE; Salisbury HS; Allentown, PA; (3); Prfct Atten A Arch.

COLESON, BRIAN; Ephrata SR HS; Ephrata, PA; (4); 46/252; Con Band; Mrchg Band; Socr; Hon Roll; Pres Schlr; J Harry Hibshm Schlrshp Fund & Wolf Fndtn For Educ 87-91; Sci Press Outstn Graphic Art Stu 87; Rochester Inst Of Tech; Sci.

COLFLESH, BRENDA; Turkeyfoot Valley Area HS; Ursina, PA; SADD; JV Cheerleading; Gov Hon Prg Awd; High Hon Roll; Hon R Coach Actv.

COLFLESH, SHERRY; Shanksville Stonycreek HS; Berlin, PA; (4) 37; Church Yth Grp; Spanish Clb; Chorus; School Play; Nwsp Bus M Nwsp Stf; Hon Roll; Spanish NHS; Intl Forgn Lang Awd; TAP Clb; U Pitts; Comp Sci.

COLGAN, SCOTT; Burrell SR HS; Lower Burrell, PA; (3); French C Ftbl; Rtry Schlr Awd 86; Johnson Coll; Clnry Arts.

COLIGAN, KIM; Canon-Mc Millian Jr High At Cecil; Canonsburg, (1); Church Yth Grp; Office Aide; Chorus; High Hon Roll; Hon Roll.

COLISTRA, JOSEPH; Cumberland Valley HS; Mechanicsburg, PA; 69/600; Var L Ftbl; Var L Trk; Im Wt Lftg; Var Wrstlng; NHS; Ntl Hnr Scty 86-87.

COLIZZA, JOSEPH; Steel Valley HS; W Homestead, PA; (3); 7/2 Church Yth Grp; English Clb; Math Clb; Spanish Clb; Vllybl; High H Roll; Hon Roll; NHS.

COLL, KELLIE; Seton-La Salle HS; Pittsburgh, PA; (2); 3/250; Ski C Spanish Clb; Bsktbl; Sftbl; Vllybl; DAR Awd; High Hon Roll.

COLLAR, TODD; Freeport Area HS; Freeport, PA; (2); Cmnty Wkr; FTA; JA; Chorus; Swing Chorus; Nwsp Ed-Chief; Nwsp Rptr; Rep Cncl; Hon Roll; Pres Schlr; Real Est Agnt.

COLLDAY, DONALD; MMI Preparatory Schl; Mountaintop, PA; Chess Clb; Math Tm; Ski Clb; Variety Show; Var Bsbl; JV Bowling; Golf; Hon Roll; 1st Pl Luzern Cnty Math Cntst 87; 2nd Pl PA JR Acad ST 85 & 86; RPI; Aeronautical Engrng.

COLLEN, RACHAEL; Hazleton SR HS; Hazleton, PA; (3); Drama C SADD; Temple Yth Grp; Chorus; Nwsp Rptr; Nwsp Stf; Yrbk Stf; Sp Pathlgy.

COLLETTE, DAVID C; Lincoln HS; Portersville, PA; (2); Church Grp; Ski Clb; Spanish Clb; Band; Mrchg Band; High Hon Roll; Hon R Penn ST U; Engrng.

COLLIER, CASSIE; Dayton JR SR HS; Templeton, PA; (3); 13/52; Trs 4-H; Chorus; Color Guard; Mrchg Band; School Musical; VP Jr VP Stu Cncl; JV Var Bsktbl; L Sftbl; High Hon Roll; Penn ST; Law.

COLLIER, DIANE; Aliquippa HS; Aliquippa, PA; (3); Pres Church Grp; Band; Chorus; Church Choir; Concert Band; Pep Band; Symp Ba Var Bowling; Var Sftbl; Hon Roll; Duquesne; Law.

COLLIER, JENNIFER; Susquehanna Comm HS; Susquehanna, PA; Band; Concert Band; Mrchg Band; Psych.

COLLIER, LAUREL; Quakertown SR HS; Quakertown, PA; (2); Church Yth Grp; SADD; Chorus; School Play; Stat Bsktbl; Mgr(s); Tim Var Trk; Hon Roll; Jr NHS.

COLLIER, SHELLEY; Central HS Of Philadel; Philadelphia, PA; (Pres Church Yth Grp; Drama Clb; Church Choir; School Musical; Sch Play; Stage Crew; Variety Show; Pres Clsrm Young Amer 87; Dir Poi Thatrcl Hnrs 85-86; Psych.

COLLINASH, CHANA; Harmony Area HS; Westover, PA; (3); #12 Class; Cmnty Wkr; Letterman Clb; Teachers Aide; Band; Chorus; Conc Band; Mrchg Band; Nwsp Rptr; Hon Roll; French Clb; Prsdntl Acad F Awd 86; Elem Edu.

COLLINS, ANITA; Neshaminy HS; Parkland, PA; (4); 219/705; VP FF Color Guard; Mrchg Band; Fld Hcky; Gym; Mgr Sftbl; Hon Roll; 2nd Hrrsbrg ST Frm Shw 85-86; 1st Prz PA Hrtcltrl Soc 84; Elva May Flo Schl; Flrst.

COLLINS, BARRY; St John Neuman HS; Philadelphia, PA; (3); 142/3 Yrbk Stf; Hosp Aide; Church Choir; School Musical; Stage Crew; Im F Im Wrstlng.

COLLINS, CHARMANE; George Washington HS; Philadelphia, PA; (Var Bsktbl; Schlrshp To U Of PA On Sats 87-88; Temple; Pharm.

COLLINS, DARREN; Bishop Boyle HS; West Homestead, PA; (Exploring; Nwsp Stf; Sec Trs Frsh Cls; VP Soph Cls; Var JV Bsktbl; JV Vllybl; High Hon Roll; NHS; Prfct Atten Awd; PJAS 2nd & 3rd Aw Leaps Buhl Sci Ctr; Sci.

COLLINS, DAVID; Gateway SR HS; Monroeville, PA; (3); Church Grp; Pres Band; Concert Band; Jazz Band; Mrchg Band; Pep Band; F Jr Cls; Rep Sr Cls; Trs Rep Stu Cncl; Math.

COLLINS, DWIGHT; Cedar Crest HS; Lebanon, PA; (3); 93/342; Clb; Pep Clb; Spanish Clb; Nwsp Stf; JV Wrstlng; Hon Roll; Schlstc Awd Rgnl Fnlst 86; Aerospc.

COLLINS, HEATHER; Grace Christian Schl; Lebanon, PA; (Teachers Aide; Chorus; Church Choir; Nwsp Rptr; Nwsp Stf; Yrbk Ph Yrbk Stf; Cheerleading; High Hon Roll; Cert Merit Natl Amateur Cont Instrctn Schls MN 85-86; Art.

COLLINS, JEFF; Curwensville Area HS; Curwensville, PA; (3); Fren Clb; Var Golf; High Hon Roll; NHS; Acctng.

COLLINS, JONI; Eisenhower HS; Sugargrove, PA; (3); Band; Conc Band; Sec Trs Mrchg Band; Yrbk Stf; JV Bsktbl; JV Bowling; JV Sf High Hon Roll; Hon Roll; Gannon U; Radiologic Technlgy.

COLLINS, KATHY; Sayre Area HS; Waverly, NY; (3); Church Yth G SADD; Varsity Clb; Yrbk Sprt Ed; Spanish Clb; Band; Chorus; Mrc Band; Pep Band; Yrbk Stf; Presdntl Clsrm 87; HOBY Ldrshp Smnr PA Old Dominion U; Polit Sci.

COLLINS, KEVIN P; Riverside HS; Beaver Falls, PA; (2); Compu Clb; School Musical; Stage Crew; High Hon Roll; Hon Roll; Pittsburgh; Engrng.

COLLINS, KRIS; Acad Of The New Church; Charlotte, NC; (3); Fren Clb; Ed Yrbk Phtg; Trs Sr Cls; Rep Stu Cncl; Tennis; Vllybl; Jr NHS; P Sci.

COLLINS, LENORA; Belle Vernon Area HS; West Newton, PA; (4); 267; NFL; Band; Nwsp Rptr; Nwsp Stf; High Hon Roll; NHS; Pres Sch VFW Awd; Voice Dem Awd; St Vincent Coll; Math.

COLLINS, MARY E; Bishop Hoban HS; Wilkes Barre, PA; (4); 27/220; FBLA; Hosp Aide; Latin Clb; Math Clb; Mu Alpha Theta; Ski Clb; Chorus; Var Capt Cheerleading; Hon Roll; NHS; U Of Scranton; Accntng.

COLLINS, MICHAEL J; Riverside HS; Beaver Falls, PA; (4); Computer Clb; Concert Band; Jazz Band; Mrchg Band; NHS; Ntl Merit Ltr; Pres Schlr; School Musical; Symp Band; High Hon Roll; Provost Schlrshp U Of Pittsburgh 87; High Hnrs Schlrshp; Schl Of Engrng U Of Pittsburgh 87; Wstng Hs 87; U Of Pittsburgh; Elect Engrng.

COLLINS, MIKE; North Pocono HS; Moscow, PA; (3); #49 In Class; Spanish Clb; Band; Chorus; Concert Band; Mrchg Band; Orch; Var L Bsbl; JV Bsktbl; Hon Roll; NHS; PA ST U; Bus.

COLLINS, PATRICK; West Scranton HS; Scranton, PA; (3); 30/250; Boys Clb Am; Letterman Clb; Varsity Clb; Im Ftbl; Var L Golf; Var L Tennis; Var L Trk; Var L Wrstlng; Hon Roll; NHS; Engrng.

COLLINS, SEAN; St Josephs Preparatory Schl; Philadelphia, PA; (4); 42/240; Cmnty Wkr; Var L Bsbl; Var Ftbl; High Hon Roll; NHS; Pres Schlr; Holy Crss, Loyola, Scranton, & Fordham Schlrshps 87-91; Coll Holy Cross; Accntng.

COLLINS, SHANITA; Peabody HS; Pittsburgh, PA; (4); 32/296; School Musical; Nwsp Stf; Rep Sr Cls; VP Stu Cncl; Pom Pon; Cit Awd; Hon Roll; NHS; Prfct Atten Awd; Rep Frsh Cls; Dance Comm Pres 84-85; Indstrl Mgmt.

COLLINS, STEPHANIE; Everett Area HS; Clearville, PA; (4); 10/107; Trs Spanish Clb; Band; Concert Band; Jazz Band; Mrchg Band; Pep Band; Trs Sr Cls; Var Capt Socr; Twrlr; NHS; Juniata Coll; Elem Educ.

COLLINS, SUSAN; Hopewell HS; Aliquippa, PA; (4); 44/245; French Clb; Hst Varsity Clb; Chorus; Drill Tm; Yrbk Bus Mgr; Stu Cncl; Powder Puff Ftbl; Var Trk; Hon Roll; NHS; Biochem.

COLLINS JR, THOMAS B; Emmaus HS; Macungie, PA; (3); Computer Clb; 1st Pl Rgnl, 5th Pl ST Olympcs Mind 85-86; Mech Engrng.

COLLINS, WILLIAM; Senior HS; Philadelphia, PA; (2); Art Clb; Church Yth Grp; Bsktbl; Ftbl; Wt Lftg; Spirit Of Cooperation 84; St Johns; Art.

COLLURA, JOSEPH; Palmyra HS; Palmyra, PA; (4); 40/180; Aud/Vis; French Clb; Wrstlng; Hon Roll; Peer Counseling 86-87; Gifted Prog 83-87; PA ST U; Psych.

COLMENARES, YVONNE M; Governor Mifflin HS; Reading, PA; (3); #23 In Class; Cheerleading; Vllybl; High Hon Roll; Princeton; Engrng.

COLOMBO, STACYLEE; Altoona Area HS; Altoona, PA; (3); French Clb; Nwsp Stf; Stu Cncl; Capt Var Cheerleading; Jr NHS; Girls League Pres 86-87; Princpls Advsry Comm 86-87; U MD.

COLON, CARMEN; Franklin Learning Center HS; Philadelphia, PA; (2); 2/23; Church Yth Grp; Red Cross Aide; Spanish Clb; Bsktbl; Gym; Sftbl; Swmmng; Trk; Vllybl; High Hon Roll; Amer Red Cross Youth Cncl 87; Med Trmnlgy Comptn 85-87; Emergency First Aid Comptn Tm 85-87; Harvard; Med.

COLONIAS, ATHANASIOS; Quigley HS; Aliquippa, PA; (3); 5/88; Church Yth Grp; Latin Clb; Math Tm; JV Var Bsktbl; High Hon Roll; Med.

COLONNA, ED; Center HS; Aliquippa, PA; (2); Spanish Clb; JV Im Bsbl; Im Bsktbl; Score Keeper; Im Wt Lftg; Hon Roll; Pres Schlr; Var Ftbl.

COLONNA, MATTHEW; Greensburg Centra Catholic HS; Greensburg, PA; (3); Boy Scts; Exploring; Hosp Aide; Red Cross Aide; Service Clb; Teachers Aide; Vllybl; High Hon Roll; NHS; JR Goodwill Ambsdr Awd 87; Stu Libr Awd 87; JR Fireman SW 87; US Air Force; Bus.

COLOSIMO III, FRANK; Moniteau JR-SR HS; West Sunbury, PA; (3); 4/139; Church Yth Grp; Cmnty Wkr; Exploring; Spanish Clb; SADD; Church Choir; Var Golf; High Hon Roll; NHS; Spanish NHS; Acad Games Tm Natl Finals GA 84-85; Natl Rural Elect Coop Yth Tour 87; U Pittsburgh; Phrmcy.

COLOSIMO, GENE; Carbondale Area JR SR HS; Carbondale, PA; (2); Boy Scts; Computer Clb; Ski Clb; Spanish Clb; High Hon Roll; 1st Pl Environmental Olympics 87.

COLPETZER, DEANNE; West York Area HS; York, PA; (2); Church Yth Grp; Chorus; Sftbl; High Hon Roll; Hon Roll.

COLPETZER, STACIE; Clarion-Limestone HS; Strattanville, PA; (2); 3/38; French Clb; SADD; Chorus; Lit Mag; Hon Roll; NHS; Prfct Atten Awd; PA Free Entrprs Wk 87.

COLPO, CHRIS; Franklin Regional HS; Murrysville, PA; (3); AFS; Drama Clb; Trs Exploring; Thesps; Chorus; School Play; Stage Crew; L Diving; Carnegie-Mellon; Biotech.

COLTON, KRISTEN; Notre Dame High Schl Of Green Pond; Easton, PA; (3); 1/90; Hosp Aide; Rep Frsh Cls; Sec Soph Cls; Var Bsktbl; Var Tennis; Var Trk; High Hon Roll; Hon Roll; NHS; Church Yth Grp; Cert Of Merit Hghst Hnr Sci & Math Soc Wmn Engrs 87; Outstndng Achvt Ltn I & II 85 & 86; Nrsng.

COLURSO, CARRIE; West Scranton HS; Scranton, PA; (2); Spanish Clb; Pom Pon; High Hon Roll; Hon Roll.

COLURSO, KIM; West Scranton SR HS; Scranton, PA; (4); Spanish Clb; Stu Cncl; Pom Pon; Marywood Coll; Elem Ed.

COLVIN, STEVE; Fort Le Boeuf HS; Erie, PA; (3); 2/180; Church Yth Grp; Var L Bsbl; Im Bowling; Im Vllybl; Var L Wrstlng; High Hon Roll; NHS; Math.

COLVIN, TRICIA; Punxsutawney Area HS; Punxsutawney, PA; (4); 83/245; Church Yth Grp; Math Tm; Band; Concert Band; Jazz Band; Mrchg Band; Pep Band; Variety Show; Hon Roll.

COLWELL, BEN; Central HS; Philadelphia, PA; (2); Boy Scts; Prfct Atten Awd; Bus.

COLWELL, BRANDY; Center Area HS; Monaca, PA; (2); Latin Clb; Yrbk Rptr; Rep Stu Cncl; Capt Bowling; Powder Puff Ftbl; Hon Roll; Gftd Pgm 85-87; Tulane U; Psych.

COLYER, DAVID; East Pennsboro Area HS; Camp Hill, PA; (2); Latin Clb; Var Wrstlng; High Hon Roll; Hon Roll; Engrng.

COLYVAS, ANGELA; Marple Newtown SR HS; Broomall, PA; (3); Nwsp Stf; Pres Stu Cncl; Mgr(s); Score Keeper; Stat Wrstlng; Cmnty Wkr; Intnl Clb; Service Clb; Yrbk Stf; JV Fld Hcky; Intl Rltns.

COMA, LISA; Central Catholic HS; Irwin, PA; (3); 111/234; Cmnty Wkr; Letterman Clb; Varsity Clb; Stat Bsktbl; Capt Var Bsktbl; Mgr(s); Var Trk; Var Im Vllybl; Hon Roll; Greensburg Tibn All Dist Bsktbll Tm & Pittsburgh Prs 87; Laurel Highlands Undrgrad Trnmnt MVP 87; Elem Ed.

COMBS, DEBRA; Rocky Grove HS; Franklin, PA; (3); Church Yth Grp; Girl Scts; Hosp Aide; Office Aide; Chorus; Hon Roll; Bradford Schl; Retail Mgmt.

COMELLA, KRISTEN; Academy HS; Erie, PA; (3); 31/226; Church Yth Grp; Color Guard; Jazz Band; Mrchg Band; Variety Show; JV Var Bsktbl; Var Trk; Hon Roll; NHS; Int Dsgn.

COMER, TONYA; Oliver HS; Pittsburgh, PA; (2); Church Yth Grp; Nwsp Ed-Chief; Pres Stu Cncl; Bsktbl; High Hon Roll; Prfct Atten Awd; SAR Awd; Acad All-Amrcn Schlr 87; Prjct Ld 87; Give Help 87; Law.

COMERFORD, JAMES; Dunmore HS; Dunmore, PA; (3); 19/146; Church Yth Grp; FBLA; Spanish Clb; Nwsp Phtg; Nwsp Rptr; Nwsp Stf; Ed Yrbk Ed-Chief; JV Golf; High Hon Roll; NHS; Lylty Day Awd 85; Engl.

COMERFORD, NICOLE J; Lackawanna Trail HS; Factoryville, PA; (3); 11/109; Cmnty Wkr; Drama Clb; Chorus; School Play; Var L Cheerleading; French Hon Soc; Hon Roll; NHS; Ntl Merit Ltr; Prfct Atten Awd; Deaf Educ.

COMFORT, STEPHANIE L; Saucon Valley SR HS; Bethlehem, PA; (3); 10/156; Am Leg Aux Girls St; Art Clb; Church Yth Grp; Drama Clb; 4-H; German Clb; Hosp Aide; Library Aide; Model UN; Band; Pres Acad Ftns Awd 85; Dickinson Coll; Math.

COMFORTI, MICHAEL; Connellsville Area SR HS; Connellsville, PA; (2); Church Yth Grp; Ftbl; Swmmng; Tchr.

COMLY, JIM; Upper Moreland HS; Hatboro, PA; (3); 48/275; Radio Clb; Var Capt Bowling; JV Trk; High Hon Roll; Drexel U; Mech Engrng.

COMMONS, DANIA; Carmichaels Area JR/Sr HS; Carmichaels, PA; (3); 3/112; French Clb; Pep Clb; Ski Clb; Var Bsktbl; DAR Awd; Hon Roll; NHS; Acad Fitness Awd 85; Algebra II Awd 85; Soph Engl Awd 86; U Of Pittsburgh; Phys Therapy.

COMPTON, GWENDOLYN L; Lewisburg Area HS; Lewisburg, PA; (3); 1/150; Am Leg Aux Girls St; Sec Band; Chorus; Orch; School Musical; Yrbk Stf; Rep Stu Cncl; Hon Roll; NHS; Latin Clb; Natl JR Clsscl Lge Latin Awd 85-86; Dist Band & Orch 86-87.

COMPTON, SUZANNE CARYL; Liberty JR SR HS; Liberty, PA; (2); Church Yth Grp; German Clb; Acpl Chr; Band; Chorus; Church Choir; Concert Band; Mrchg Band; Pep Band; Variety Show; Jrnlsm.

COMSTOCK, JOEL; Trinity HS; Washington, PA; (3).

CONAHAN, ANN; Notre Dame HS; Stroudsburg, PA; (3); 15/48; School Musical; Nwsp Stf; Yrbk Stf; Rep Frsh Cls; Pres Soph Cls; Fld Hcky; Sftbl; Gov Hon Prg Awd; NHS; Opt Clb Awd; Bstn Coll; Bus.

CONAHAN, JENNIFER; Haverford Twp SR HS; Havertown, PA; (4); 1/445; Am Leg Aux Girls St; Capt Flag Corp; Yrbk Stf; Swmmng; Gov Hon Prg Awd; Pres Schlr; Val; Hosp Aide; Spanish Clb; SADD; Harvard Book Awd 86; Phi Beta Kappa 87; Scty Womens Engrs 87; Princeton U; Pediatrics.

CONAWAY, CARRIE; State Coll Area Intermediate HS; State College, PA; (1); French Clb; Band; Mrchg Band; Symp Band; Nwsp Ed-Chief; Nwsp Rptr; Yrbk Ed-Chief; Yrbk Stf; Cit Awd; Hon Roll; Excllnc In Engl, Scl Stds, Bio 87; Cert Of Merit 87; Poem Pblshd In Schl Ltry Mgzn Hnbl Mntn 87; Jrnlsm.

CONAWAY, GEORGE; Bald Eagle-Nittany HS; Mill Hall, PA; (3); Drama Clb; Chorus; Concert Band; Madrigals; Mrchg Band; Orch; School Musical; Swing Chorus; NEDT Awd; Music.

CONBOY, DIANE; Elk Lake HS; Montrose, PA; (1); Spanish Clb; SADD; Band; Chorus; Jazz Band; Mrchg Band; School Musical; Swing Chorus; Off Frsh Cls; Stu Cncl; Frmr.

CONDE, DAWN; Penn-Trafford HS; Jeannette, PA; (3); 6/301; Cmnty Wkr; Hosp Aide; Math Clb; Chorus; Nwsp Bus Mgr; Ed Nwsp Stf; Im Sftbl; High Hon Roll; Sec NHS; Prfct Atten Awd; Acadc All Am Stu 87; Bus Adm.

CONDEELIS, JASON; Abington SR HS; Jenkintown, PA; (3); 124/507; Chorus; Madrigals; School Musical; Variety Show; Im Badmtn; JV Tennis; Im Vllybl.

CONDEL, MICHAEL; Western Wayne HS; Lake Ariel, PA; (2); 11/176; Boy Scts; Church Yth Grp; Chorus; Drm Mjr(t); Mrchg Band; Orch; Var Socr; Var Vllybl; High Hon Roll; NHS; Exch Stu Brazil 87-88; Black Belt Karate 85; Eagle Scout 87; PA ST; Crimnl Law.

CONDELLA, TAMMY; Mid Valley Secondary Ctr; Olyphant, PA; (2); Art Clb; Drama Clb; SADD; Stage Crew; Sec Jr Cls; Rep Stu Cncl; Vllybl; Hon Roll; U Scranton; Pre Med.

CONDEN, TARA; Wyoming Area HS; Wyoming, PA; (3); 5/250; Church Yth Grp; Key Clb; Math Clb; Spanish Clb; Rep Stu Cncl; Var L Sftbl; Var L Swmmng; High Hon Roll; NHS; Sraxton U; Pharmacy.

CONDO, MARK; Bald Eagle-Mittany HS; Mill Hall, PA; (3); 29/149; Church Yth Grp; Drama Clb; Ski Clb; Spanish Clb; Band; Concert Band; Jazz Band; Mrchg Band; School Musical; School Play; Woodsmn Wrld Outstndng Prfcncy Amer Hstry 87.

CONDON, HOPE; Old Forge HS; Old Forge, PA; (3); JV Var Bsktbl; Hon Roll; NHS; Photo Jrnlsm.

CONDRASKY, PAMELA; Cumberland Valley HS; Mechanicsburg, PA; (3); 17/582; Key Clb; Pep Clb; Ski Clb; JV Var Cheerleading; Sci.

CONDRON, ERIC; Shenango HS; New Castle, PA; (2); French Clb; JV Bsbl; Im Bsktbl; Hon Roll.

CONELIAS, MICHAEL; Freedom HS; Bethlehem, PA; (4); 112/456; Sec Church Yth Grp; Band; Rep Frsh Cls; Trs Sr Cls; Stu Cncl; JV Var Bsbl; JV L Bsktbl; Score Keeper; Cit Awd; Hon Roll; Bsbl All Star E PA Leag Ptchr, & Admnstrtv Apprctn Awd 87; U DE.

CONFER, ANGELA; Cranberry HS; Venus, PA; (3); 26/138; Trs Church Yth Grp; Pep Clb; Pres Science Clb; Spanish Clb; Band; Chorus; Church Choir; Pep Band; School Musical; Swing Chorus; Spnsh Prof.

CONFER, CHRIS; Huntingdon Area HS; Huntingdon, PA; (3); 57/217; VP Church Yth Grp; Ski Clb; Var L Golf; Hon Roll; Masonic Awd; Juniata Coll; Elctrcl Engr.

CONFER, JAMIE; Milton Senior HS; Milton, PA; (3); FHA; Trk; S W TX; Law Enfrcmnt.

CONFER, SEAN; Lock Haven SR HS; Howard, PA; (3); Church Yth Grp; Computer Clb; Spanish Clb; Var Bsbl; Var Bsktbl; High Hon Roll; Hon Roll; Lock Haven U; Bus Mgmt.

CONFINO, LORI; Owen J Roberts HS; Pottstown, PA; (2); 18/311; Boys Clb Am; Key Clb; Library Aide; Band; Chorus; Flag Corp; Mrchg Band; Stage Crew; Yrbk Rptr; Yrbk Stf; Bus.

CONFORTI, ALEXANDER N; B Reed Henderson HS; West Chester, PA; (3); Ski Clb; Ftbl; Wrstlng; Hon Roll; NHS; Arch.

CONFORTI, ROBERT; Riverside JR/Sr HS; Taylor, PA; (3); Ski Clb; Hon Roll; Meteorology.

CONGER, PAMELA; United HS; Armagh, PA; (4); 39/155; Camera Clb; Hosp Aide; Pep Clb; Ski Clb; Chorus; Lit Mag; Trk; Hon Roll; NHS; Smmr Hppng Photogrphy Hld IN U PA 85; Rochester Inst Of Tech; Biomed.

CONGER, WILLIAM; United HS; Armagh, PA; (3); 17/146; Boy Scts; Camera Clb; Church Yth Grp; Computer Clb; Sec Mu Alpha Theta; Band; Mrchg Band; School Musical; Yrbk Stf; NHS; RIT; Photo.

CONGERSKY, RICHARD; Windber Area HS; Windber, PA; (3); Church Yth Grp; Band; Concert Band; Mrchg Band; Stage Crew; Wt Lftg; MIT; Elec Engrng.

CONICELLO, FRANK; St John Neumann HS; Philadelphia, PA; (3); Yrbk Rptr; L Bsbl; L Ftbl; Penn ST; Mdcn.

CONIX, LUCINDA; West Catholic Girls HS; Philadelphia, PA; (4); Cmnty Wkr; Library Aide; Chorus; Hon Roll; Charles E Ellis Scholar 83-87; Rosemont Coll; Bus.

CONJELKO, BRIAN J; Richland HS; Johnstown, PA; (4); 1/158; Am Leg Boys St; Math Clb; Off Frsh Cls; Off Soph Cls; Bsktbl; Ftbl; Trk; NHS; SAR Awd; Val; St Francis Math Awd 87; Drftng, Schlr Athlt, Sci Awds 87; US Military Acad; Elec Engr.

CONJURA, ED; Our Lady Of Lourdes Regional HS; Shamokin, PA; (3); 25/89; Key Clb; Ski Clb; Spanish Clb; SADD; Varsity Clb; Nwsp Stf; Yrbk Stf; Stu Cncl; Ftbl; Tennis; Villanova; Bus Admin.

CONKLIN, ALISON; Bald Eagle Nittany HS; Lamar, PA; (3); 19/148; Church Yth Grp; Drama Clb; Sec Spanish Clb; SADD; Acpl Chr; Band; Chorus; Concert Band; Capt Drm Mjr(t); Madrigals; Intl.

CONKLIN, CICILY; Lock Haven HS; Castanea, PA; (4); FBLA; SADD; Drill Tm; Hon Roll; NEDT Awd; Excllnce Comm Dept 87; Williamsport Area CC; Med Sec.

CONKLIN, RICHARD; Lewistown Area HS; Lewistown, PA; (3); AFS; Boy Scts; Debate Tm; French Clb; Key Clb; Ski Clb; Off Jr Cls; L Golf; High Hon Roll; Hon Roll; Orthdntst.

CONKLIN, TIMOTHY ALLEN; Salisbury HS; Allentown, PA; (4); Debate Tm; Key Clb; Scholastic Bowl; School Musical; Nwsp Sprt Ed; Yrbk Rptr; Hon Roll; Ntl Merit Ltr; Hopwood Schlrshp & Grants To Lynchburg U 87; Lynchburg U; Jrnlsm.

CONKLING, AMY; State College Intermediate HS; State College, PA; (1); Band; Mrchg Band; Var Swmmng; Hon Roll; Cert Of Merit Frnch 86-87.

CONKO, GREGORY; Connellsville Area HS; Connellsville, PA; (3); 42/550; VP Art Clb; Sec Church Yth Grp; VP German Clb; Chorus; Var Swmmng; High Hon Roll; NHS; Grmn Natl Hnr Soc 86-87; Georgetown U; Intl Rltns.

CONLEN JR, JOHN J; Norristown Area HS; E Norriton, PA; (4); 69/450; Aud/Vis; Drama Clb; School Play; Stage Crew; Hon Roll; NHS; Prfct Atten Awd; Treas AIASA 86-87; Kutztown U; Telecomm.

CONLEY, JAMES; Hamburg Area HS; Hamburg, PA; (4); 13/144; VP Latin Clb; Spanish Clb; Var L Socr; Var L Tennis; Hon Roll; NHS; Rotary Awd; Plane Geometry Acad Awd 85; Physics Acad Awd 86; Econmcs Gvrmnt Acad Awd 87; Lehigh U; Electrical Engineerng.

CONLEY, ROSEMARIE; Mt St Joseph Acad; Richboro, PA; (4); Church Yth Grp; Cmnty Wkr; Girl Scts; Pres JCL; Sec Latin Clb; Model UN; Nwsp Stf; Rep Stu Cncl; Var Swmmng; Hon Roll; Metropltn Pres Cmmnty Svc Corps Archdiocese Phila 86-87; Natl Eagl Crss Wnnr 86; Ntl Ltn Hnr 85-87; Pre-Law.

CONLEY, SCOTT; Phil-Mont Christian Acad; Glenside, PA; (3); Aud/Vis; Chorus; Yrbk Bus Mgr; Stu Cncl; JV Capt Bsbl; JV Crs Cntry; Score Keeper; High Hon Roll; NHS; Drexel U; Chem Engrng.

CONLIN, MICHELLE; Warwick HS; Lititz, PA; (2); 78/320; Church Yth Grp; Girl Scts; JV Fld Hcky; Hon Roll; Girl Scouts Silver Awd 85.

CONN, CHRISTOPHER; Connellsville Area SR HS; Connellsville, PA; (3); Jazz Band; Mrchg Band; Symp Band; French Hon Soc; High Hon Roll; NHS; US Marine Corps.

CONN, GREG; Southmoreland HS; Scottdale, PA; (4); 14/223; German Clb; Letterman Clb; Math Clb; Ski Clb; Varsity Clb; Church Choir; JV Im Bsktbl; Socr; Im Vllybl; Hon Roll; German Natl Hnr Soc 85-87; Hgh Hnr Grad 87; Penn ST; Elec Engrng.

CONN, JASON M; Northgate HS; Bellevue, PA; (3); 14/168; Am Leg Boys St; JA; Var Trk; Hon Roll; Cum Laude Soc 86-87; Comp Sci.

CONN, LARRY; High Point Baptist Acad; Elverson, PA; (3); Bus.

CONN, LEANE; Cranberry Area HS; Seneca, PA; (2); 4-H; Teachers Aide; Band; Chorus; Im Bowling; Var Stat Trk; Hon Roll; Charles U; Archael.

CONN, REBECCA; Turkeyfoot Valley Area HS; Confluence, PA; (4); 2/57; Band; Chorus; Trs Frsh Cls; Trs Soph Cls; Trs Jr Cls; Var L Sftbl; Q&S; Ski Clb; Varsity Clb; Yrbk Stf; Al-Cnty Chorus 86; Al-Cnty Band 83-87; Al-Cnty Dist, Rgnl, Hnrs Band 86; OH U; Elec Engr.

CONNELL, SCOTT; Ft Cherry HS; Bulger, PA; (3); Science Clb; Spanish Clb; Varsity Clb; L Var Ftbl; High Hon Roll; Hon Roll.

CONNELLAN, SIOBHAN; Trinity HS; Mechanicsburg, PA; (4); Pep Clb; Chorus; School Musical; Nwsp Stf; Yrbk Stf; Stat Bsktbl; Kiwanis Awd; Benefcl Hodson Schlrshp 87; Rifle Sqd Band Frnt 85-87; Slvr Mdl Excllnc Comp Sci 87; Hood Coll; Mrktng.

CONNELLY, APRIL; Warwick SR HS; Lititz, PA; (2); 58/350; AFS; Spanish Clb; Acpl Chr; Band; Chorus; Concert Band; Mrchg Band; Orch; School Musical; School Play; Shw Choir 86-88; Cnty Chorus 86-87; Cnty Band 86-87; U DE; Comm.

CONNELLY, DEBORAH; Abraham Lincoln HS; Philadelphia, PA; (2); FBLA; JV Fld Hcky; Bus.

CONNELLY, GARRICK; Montoursville Area HS; Montoursville, PA; (3); Boy Scts; Church Yth Grp; FCA; French Clb; Letterman Clb; Varsity Clb; Var L Socr; Var L Tennis.

CONNELLY, GARY; Penn-Trafford HS; Trafford, PA; (2); JCL; Latin Clb; Tennis; God Cntry Awd; High Hon Roll; NHS; Schltc All Amer 87-88.

CONNELLY, KELLI; Greensburg Central Catholic HS; Hunker, PA; (3); 40/231; AFS; Hosp Aide; Capt Color Guard; Yrbk Stf; High Hon Roll; NHS; PA ST U; Psych.

CONNELLY, STEPHANIE; Bald Eagle Area HS; Howard, PA; (4); 5/191; SADD; Chorus; Yrbk Stf; Rep Stu Cncl; Im Powder Puff Ftbl; Capt Twrlr; DAR Awd; NHS; French Clb; Hosp Aide; Bruce E Knox Yth Svc Awd 86; Bus & Pro Wmns Clb Grl Of Yr 87; Jdg Shrp Mem Awd; Robert Morris Coll; Adm Spclst.

CONNER, DAWN; Bellwood-Antis HS; Tyrone, PA; (4); 55/113; Church Yth Grp; Key Clb; VICA; Band; Concert Band; Mrchg Band; Hon Roll; JA; Jazz Band; Pep Band; Vocatnl Indstrl Clbs Amer Preprd Spch 1st Rgnl Compttn, 2nd ST 87; Awds Vo-Tech 87; IN U Of PA; Mrktng.

CONNER, ELIZABETH; Danville HS; Danville, PA; (1); 4-H; Hosp Aide; JV Trk; High Hon Roll; Hon Roll; Pres Acdmc Fit Awd 86-87; Advrtsg Dsgn.

CONNER, ERIN; Bellwood Antis HS; Altoona, PA; (4); Library Aide; SADD; Chorus; Stage Crew; High Hon Roll; Hon Roll; Anthrplgy.

CONNER, KIRSTEN; Fairview HS; Fairview, PA; (4); French Clb; Varsity Clb; Nwsp Rptr; Crs Cntry; Swmmng; Trk; NHS; Natl Hnr Soc 86-87; Syracuse Univ; Advrtsng.

CONNER, KYLE; Henderson HS; West Chester, PA; (3); 12/377; Church Yth Grp; JCL; Band; Chorus; Church Choir; Jazz Band; School Musical; Variety Show; VP Jr Cls; French Hon Soc; Boys Spkng Cntst 2nd Pl 86; Music.

CONNER, PATRICK W; Quakertown HS; Quakertown, PA; (4); 54/290; Civic Clb; Teachers Aide; Var L Bsbl; Var Swmmng; Cit Awd; High Hon Roll; Hon Roll; Jr NHS; NHS; Opt Clb Awd; Amer Legion Awd 85; PHEAA Schlrshp Drexel U For 5 Yrs 87; Amer Legion Local Essay Wnnr 87; Drexel U; Elec Engr.

CONNERS, DANA; Council Rock HS; Richboro, PA; (2); High Hon Roll; Hon Roll.

CONNIFF, JOHN; Susquenanua Community HS; Lanesboro, PA; (2); Hon Roll.

CONNOLLY, CAROLYN; Wyoming Valley West HS; Kingston, PA; (3); Church Yth Grp; Key Clb; Nwsp Stf; Yrbk Stf; Rep Trs Stu Cncl; Var L Crs Cntry; Var L Swmmng; Cit Awd; High Hon Roll; NHS; Penn ST; Comms.

CONNOLLY, COLLEEN; Bethel Park SR HS; Bethel Pk, PA; (4); 146/519; FBLA; FHA; IN U.

CONNOLLY, CORINNE; Wyoming Area SR HS; Exeter, PA; (3); Key Clb; Spanish Clb; Capt Drill Tm; Swmmng; Hon Roll; NHS; Wilkes Coll; Pharmacy.

CONNOLLY, EILEEN P; Wyoming Valley West HS; Kingston, PA; (4); Trs Church Yth Grp; Cmnty Wkr; Key Clb; Pep Clb; SADD; Nwsp Stf; Yrbk Stf; Trs Stu Cncl; Capt L Sftbl; Co-Capt L Trk; Amer Bus Womns Asso Awd Schlrlshp 87; Amer Lgn Ctznshp Awd 87; Bell Of Penn Good Ctznshp Awd 87; Bloomsburg U; Comp Sci.

CONNOLLY, JOSEPH; Abington Heights HS; Clarks Summit, PA; (3); 66/292; Ski Clb; Concert Band; Mrchg Band; Hon Roll; NHS; PA JR Acad Sci 86.

CONNOLLY, KATHLEEN; Wyoming Valley West HS; Pringle, PA; (3); Trs Key Clb; Radio Clb; Chorus; Rep Stu Cncl; High Hon Roll; Hon Roll; NHS; Im Vllybl; Swmmng; Mgr(s); 1st Pl In Dist 5 Hist Day 86, 2nd Pl 87; Red Cross Voluntr 87.

CONNOLLY, MEGHAN; The Ellis Schl; Allison Park, PA; (3); Drama Clb; Hosp Aide; School Play; Stage Crew; Trs Jr Cls; Stu Cncl; JV Bsktbl; Var Tennis; Med.

CONNOLLY, SHAWN JAMES; Sacred Heart HS; Carbondale, PA; (3); 15/47; Debate Tm; Sec Frsh Cls; VP Bsbl; Hon Roll; Comms.

CONNOR, BLAINE; Hempfield HS; E Petersburg, PA; (4); 12/405; Pres Church Yth Grp; Quiz Bowl; Band; VP Chorus; Jazz Band; Mrchg Band; Pep Band; School Musical; Opt Clb Awd; Pres Schlr; 1stp L Bio Awd Fair 87; Lebaron Valley Coll; Vet.

CONNOR, CAROL ANN; Susquehanna Township HS; Harrisburg, PA; (4); VP AFS; Am Leg Aux Girls St; Key Clb; Model UN; Ski Clb; Flag Corp; Mrchg Band; VP Frsh Cls; Pres Soph Cls; Pres Jr Cls; Outstndng Acadc Achvr 86; P Powers Mem Schlrshp 87; AFS Exchng Peru 85; FL A&M U; Bus Admin.

CONNOR, CASEY; Scranton Prep Schl; Scranton, PA; (3); Dance Clb; Drama Clb; Pep Clb; School Musical; Yrbk Rptr; Cheerleading; Trk; U Scrntn; Pre-Law.

CONNOR, MICHAEL; Sacred Heart HS; Carbondale, PA; (4); FBLA; Ski Clb; Yrbk Rptr; Capt Var Bsbl; Var JV Bsktbl; Var Golf; High Hon Roll; NHS; Yng Cmmnty Ldrs Amer 87; PA ST U; Bus Admin.

CONNOR, TIMOTHY; John Bartram HS; Philadelphia, PA; (4); 6/625; Library Aide; High Hon Roll; NHS; Cert Achvt Excllnc Wrtg Rose K Zukin Foundtn 85; Acdmc Excllnc Awd 85; Spllg Bee Champ 84; Penn ST U; Bus.

CONNORS, BRENDA; Connellsville Area SR HS; Connellsville, PA; (3); VICA; High Hon Roll; Prfct Atten Awd; Dist 9 Comptn Comp Prgrmg 87; Secy.

CONNORS, CATHY; Penn Hills SR HS; Pittsburgh, PA; (3); Spanish Clb; Hon Roll.

CONNORS, KELLY; Baldwin HS; Pittsburgh, PA; (2); 18/481; Church Yth Grp; SADD; Rep Frsh Cls; Rep Stu Cncl; Mgr(s); High Hon Roll; PA ST U.

CONNORS, KERRI; Bethlehem Catholic HS; Bethlehem, PA; (3); Art Clb; Chorus; Drm Mjr(t); Fld Hcky; Twrlr; Med.

CONNORS, MATTHEW; Bethlehem Catholic HS; Bethlehem, PA; (3); 34/215; Ski Clb; Band; Concert Band; Drm & Bgl; Jazz Band; Mrchg Band; Pep Band; Tennis; Hon Roll; Diocesan Band; Rnsslr Polytech Inst; Aerosp.

CONOSHENTI, JOSEPH; Bishop Kenrick HS; Norristown, PA; (4); Dance Clb; Math Tm; Hon Roll; NHS; Opt Clb Awd; PA Coll Of Phrmcy Prtl Schlrshp 86; Dusqsuene U Prtl Schlrshp 87; Prncpls Awd 87; PA Coll Of Phrmcy; Ind Phrmcy.

CONRAD, AMBER; Liberty HS; Bethlehem, PA; (3); 29/429; Church Yth Grp; VP Spanish Clb; SADD; Chorus; Church Choir; Im JV Fld Hcky; Im JV Trk; High Hon Roll; Hon Roll; NHS.

CONRAD, CHARITY; Pine Grove Area HS; Pine Grove, PA; (3); Am Leg Aux Girls St; Varsity Clb; Chorus; Rep Jr Cls; Sec Rep Stu Cncl; JV Capt Cheerleading; JV Vllybl; Hon Roll; PA ST Univ; Acctng.

CONRAD, J JARED; Red Lion Area HS; Red Lion, PA; (2); 62/344; Boy Scts; VP Church Yth Grp; Stage Crew; JV Socr; Trk; Hon Roll; Prfct Atten Awd; Hstry Tchr.

CONRAD, JENNIFER; Cumberland Valley HS; New Kingstown, PA; (4); 212/519; Camera Clb; Pres Church Yth Grp; Sec German Clb; Girl Scts; Red Cross Aide; Ed Nwsp Phtg; Hon Roll; Natl Art Hnr Scty 85-87; HACC.

CONRAD, JOHN; Shikellamy HS; Sunbury, PA; (3); 50/312; Boy Scts; Key Clb; Spanish Clb; Hon Roll; Jr NHS; Sci.

CONRAD IV, JOHN B; West Perry HS; Shermans Dale, PA; (2); 20/222; Computer Clb; Band; Concert Band; Mrchg Band; JV Socr; Vllybl; Wrstlng; Hon Roll; 2 Awd For Comp Sci 85-87; Ltrs For Band-Marchng & Cncrt 84-87; Penn ST; Comp Sci.

CONRAD, LESLIE; Valley HS; New Kensington, PA; (2); French Clb; Chorus; High Hon Roll; Hon Roll; Prfct Atten Awd.

CONRAD, MELISSA L; Conrad Weiser HS; Wernersville, PA; (3); Cmnty Wkr; Rep Exploring; VP FNA; Hosp Aide; Science Clb; Rep Soph Cls; Rep Stu Cncl; JV Var Fld Hcky; Im Socr; JV Trk; Friendlst 84-85; Bus.

CONRAD, RENEE; Bishop Mc Devitt HS; Harrisburg, PA; (4); 24/187; Exploring; Scholastic Bowl; Band; Concert Band; Mrchg Band; Yrbk Stf; Hon Roll; NHS; Hnrbl Ment Essay Awd 86; Med Tech.

CONRAD, SUSAN; Bishop Carroll HS; Ashville, PA; (4); 26/107; Color Guard; Yrbk Ed-Chief; Yrbk Phtg; Yrbk Stf; Rep Soph Cls; Rep Jr Cls; Rep Sr Cls; Stat Bsktbl; Fshn Merch.

CONRAD, TERRI; Altoona Area HS; Altoona, PA; (4); 25/710; Computer Clb; Math Clb; Spanish Clb; Chorus; NHS; Penn ST U; Acctng.

CONRADY, CHRISTOPHER JON; Center HS; Aliquippa, PA; (2); German Clb; JV Bsktbl; Ftbl; Hon Roll; U Ptsbrg; Elec Engr.

CONRAN, SHAWN; West Catholic HS; Philadelphia, PA; (4); 93/287; Letterman Clb; Political Wkr; Red Cross Aide; Scholastic Bowl; School Play; Nwsp Stf; Yrbk Stf; Off Sr Cls; Stu Cncl; Bsbl; Jr Stu Cncl 86-87; Temple; Elec.

CONROY, KAREN; Bishop Guilfoyle HS; Altoona, PA; (3); Girl Scts; Library Aide; Color Guard; Mrchg Band; Yrbk Stf; Altoona Schl Commerce; Exec Sec.

CONROY, MELISSA; Greater Latrobe HS; Latrobe, PA; (3); 6/400; AFS; Letterman Clb; Concert Band; Symp Band; Var Swmmng; High Hon Roll; Hon Roll; NHS; Pres Schlr; Spanish NHS; Intl Stud.

CONROY, PAUL W P; Pocono Central Catholic HS; Canadensis, PA; (3); 8/32; Rep Am Leg Boys St; Church Yth Grp; Debate Tm; Chorus; School Play; Stage Crew; Voice Dem Awd; Art Clb; Camera Clb; Computer Clb; Stu Congrss 1st Pl Awds Cath Forn Lg 86-87; Stu Cngrss PA HS Spch Lg 5th Pl ST 86-87; Bus Adm.

CONROY, ROBERT; Devon Prep Schl; Malvern, PA; (4); 3/45; Computer Clb; Math Clb; Ski Clb; Varsity Clb; Yrbk Sprt Ed; Sec Sr Cls; Var Capt Crs Cntry; Var Capt Trk; High Hon Roll; NHS; Frnch & Math Awd; Spirit Awd Cross Cntry; Rensselaer Polytech; Elec Engr.

CONSIDER, DAVE; Ameadville Area SR HS; Meadville, PA; (3); Church Yth Grp; French Clb; JA; SADD; Bsktbl; Socr; Wt Lftg; Hon Roll.

CONSIGLIO, JACKIE; Bishop Guilfoyle HS; Altoona, PA; (4); French Clb; Science Clb; Ski Clb; Yrbk Stf; Rep Frsh Cls; Rep Soph Cls; Rep Sr Cls; Stu Cncl; Vllybl; High Hon Roll; Lttrd Vllybl 84-87; U Of Pittsburgh; Phys Thrpy.

CONSIGLIO, KELLIE L; Hollidaysburg Area HS; Hollidaysburg, PA; (4); 8/345; Spanish Clb; SADD; Varsity Clb; Lit Mag; Pres Frsh Cls; VP Soph Cls; VP Jr Cls; Capt Var Bsktbl; Sftbl; High Hon Roll.

CONSIGLIO, LISA; West Mifflin Area HS; Pittsburgh, PA; (4); 50/365; Key Clb; Flag Corp; Mrchg Band; Nwsp Stf; Yrbk Stf; Rep Stu Cncl; Wt Lftg; Hon Roll; NHS; Pres Acadmc Ftns Awd 87; U Of Pittsburgh; Phys Thrpy.

CONSIGLIO, TINA; West Mifflin Area HS; West Mifflin, PA; (2); Dance Clb; FBLA; Girl Scts; Pep Clb; Ski Clb; Spanish Clb; Chorus; Drill Tm; Mrchg Band; Yrbk Stf; Hig Hnr Roll 86-87; Ntl Hnr Soc 86-87; U Of Pittsburgh; Bus Admin.

CONSTANTINI, PAUL; Scranton Central HS; Scranton, PA; (4); 40/300; L Bsbl; NHS; Penn ST U; Envrnmntl Engrng.

CONSTANTINO, MICHAEL; Wyoming Area HS; W Pittston, PA; (4); 64/250; Art Clb; Nwsp Rptr; Nwsp Stf; Hon Roll; JETS Awd; Mc Cann Schl Of Bus; Accntng.

CONTAKES, CHRISTOPHER; Liberty HS; Bethlehem, PA; (3); 153/429; Pres Computer Clb; Ski Clb; Drill Tm; Ed Nwsp Phtg; Nwsp Rptr; Nwsp Stf; JV L Socr; Hon Roll; Schl Dist 1st Pl Comp Cmptn Awd 87; Comp Sci.

CONTANT, CLAUDINE; Daniel Boone HS; Douglassville, PA; (2); 43/172; German Clb; JA; Chorus; Harcum Coll; Equine.

CONTE, HEATHER; Central SR HS; York, PA; (3); Drama Clb; Ski Clb; Thesps; Band; Mrchg Band; School Play; Yrbk Stf; Hon Roll; Church Yth Grp; German Clb; Pres Clsrm Young Am 87; Twinning Exchng W Germany 87; Law.

CONTE, MARIA; Bishop Kenrick HS; Norristown, PA; (4); 39/285; Cmnty Wkr; Ski Clb; Spanish Clb; Hon Roll; NHS; Ntl Merit Ltr; Pres Schlrshp Widener Univ 87-88; Widener U; Nrsng.

CONTE, PERRY; South Philadelphia HS; Philadelphia, PA; (4); Debate Tm; Hosp Aide; Yrbk Ed-Chief; Yrbk Phtg; Sec Sr Cls; Var Tennis; Med.

CONTESTABILE, LISA; Greensburg Central Catholic HS; N Huntingdon, PA; (3); Art Clb; Church Yth Grp; Girl Scts; Rep Stu Cncl; Im Sftbl; Im Vllybl; High Hon Roll; Hon Roll; NHS; Hon Mntn Art Show 87; Comm.

CONTI, EMIDIO; Moniteau HS; Boyers, PA; (4); 1/132; Band; VP Soph Cls; Pres Jr Cls; Pres Stu Cncl; DAR Awd; High Hon Roll; JP Sousa Awd; NHS; Val; U Acad Schlrshp 87; Mst Versatile Sr 87; Mst Outstndng Section Ldr Band 86-87; Slippery Rock U; Communctns.

CONTI, ERIC; Mercer Area HS; Sharpsville, PA; (1); Cmnty Wkr; Hon Roll; Acad Games 86-87; Jr Acad Of Sci 86-87.

CONTI, JONATHAN; Mohawk Area HS; Wampum, PA; (3); 6/150; Church Yth Grp; Pres Spanish Clb; JV Bsbl; Hon Roll.

CONTI, LISA; Ambridge SR HS; Ambridge, PA; (3); Church Yth Grp; Pep Clb; SADD; Band; Concert Band; Mrchg Band; Pep Band; Symp Band; JV Golf; JV Vllybl; U Of Pittsburgh; Mgmt.

CONTI, TRICIA; Neshannock JR SR HS; Neshannock, PA; (3); Trs Sec Camera Clb; Cmnty Wkr; Exploring; Hosp Aide; Sec Trs Science Clb; SADD; Nwsp Phtg; Yrbk Ed-Chief; Yrbk Stf; NHS; Phrmcy.

CONTI, WILLIAM; Parkland HS; Orefield, PA; (2); School Musical; Pres Soph Cls; Pres Jr Cls; Var Crs Cntry; Var Diving; Hon Roll; Var Swmmng; Var Trk; Natl Yth Ftnss Tm-9th Natl, Dvng-Rnkd 13th ST 86-87; Bus.

CONTINO, BRIAN; Connellsville HS; Normalville, PA; (2); 14/580; Stage Crew; Cit Awd; High Hon Roll; Hon Roll; Jr NHS; Air Frc Acad; Pilot.

CONTORCHICK, CHERYL; Cambria Hts HS; Elmora, PA; (3); 4-H; Teachers Aide; Church Choir; Vllybl; 4-H Awd; Hon Roll; Gregg Shrthnd Awd Achvt 86-87; Pres Phys Fit Awd 84-85; PA ST; Bus Mgmt.

CONTRERAS, JACQUELINE; Little Flower HS; Philadelphia, PA; (3); Church Yth Grp; Library Aide; Spanish Clb; Chorus; Church Choir; Variety Show; Mgr(s); Trk; Vllybl; Prfct Atten Awd; Awd Hghst Grade Geomtry 85-86; Awd Cmmnty Svcs Corps 85-86; Physcl Thrpy.

CONVERSE, NOELLE; Williamsport Area HS; Williamsport, PA; (4); 8/512; Key Clb; Pep Clb; Ski Clb; Chorus; School Musical; Swing Chorus; Variety Show; Yrbk Rptr; Capt Cheerleading; High Hon Roll; Hermance & Wendell Schlrshps 87; Myrtle Stroup Music Awd 87; Key Club Awd 87; Franklin & Marshall Coll; Bio.

CONWAY, NOEL W; Dover Area HS; Dover, PA; (4); 17/240; Bsbl; Bsktbl; High Hon Roll; Hon Roll; NHS; Cls Of 87 Top Sales Rep 85; Boys Intermural Sports & Bsktbl Clb 84-87; Penn ST U; Math Educ.

CONWAY, STACY M; Hollidaysburg SR HS; Duncansville, PA; (1); 20/345; French Clb; Latin Clb; Science Clb; Band; Chorus; Yrbk Stf; Trs Jr Cls; Rep Stu Cncl; Twrlr; Hon Roll; IN U Of PA; Accntng.

CONWAY, SUSAN; Riverview HS; Verona, PA; (3); French Clb; Varsity Clb; Yrbk Stf; Jr Cls; Var Cheerleading; Powder Puff Ftbl; Im Sftbl; Var Trk; Hon Roll; NHS; Sprts Med.

CONWAY, TRACY; Lakeland JR SR HS; Jermyn, PA; (3); 15/178; FHA; Var JV Cheerleading; Score Keeper; Stat Trk; High Hon Roll; Hon Roll.

CONZ, CHRISTINE; Shikellamy HS; Sunbury, PA; (2); Girl Scts; NFL; Chorus; Church Choir; School Musical; Yrbk Stf; Lit Mag; Hon Roll; Lthrn Lvng Fth Awd 86; Grl Sct Slvr Awd 86.

CONZO, SUE; Altoona Area HS; Altoona, PA; (3); Aud/Vis; Spanish C Hon Roll; NEDT Awd; Pres Schlr; Acdmc Achvt Awd, Audio Visual Ai Awd 85; Awd Wrkng Preschl Chldrn Schl Yr 87; Paralgl.

COOCH, JANENE; Freedom HS; Bethlehem, PA; (4); 60/446; Intnl C Pep Clb; Science Clb; Spanish Clb; Chorus; School Musical; Bsktbl; (Cntry; Powder Puff Ftbl; Swmmng; Bethlehem Area Schl Dist Wmns C Awd 87; West Chester U.

COOK, ALISSA; Cocalico HS; Stevens, PA; (3); Camera Clb; Yrbk S Bio.

COOK, ALLANA; Sister Clara Muhammad HS; Philadelphia, PA; (Cmnty Wkr; Computer Clb; Dance Clb; Debate Tm; VP JA; Rptr Yr Rptr; Rep Soph Cls; Rep Jr Cls; Vllybl; Rcvd Hnr & Promo In Army Rsr 87; Rcvd Awd Dbtng Comp 87; Rcvd Awd Dts In JR Achiev 84; VA S Bus Mgmt.

COOK, AMANDA; Pequea Valley HS; Gap, PA; (3); AFS; Band; Chor Concert Band; Mrchg Band; Cheerleading; Dickinson U; Ed.

COOK, AMY S; Waynesboro Ares SR HS; Waynesboro, PA; (4); 46/3 Church Yth Grp; Church Choir; Rep Stu Cncl; Cit Awd; High Hon Ro Hon Roll.

COOK, ANDREA; Anville-Cleona HS; Annville, PA; (4); 2/112; Pr Church Yth Grp; Pres French Clb; Mrchg Band; Orch; Yrbk Bus Mgr; L Mag; Rep Stu Cncl; Dnfth Awd; VP NHS; Sal; Honor Roll 87; SICO Fnd Schlrshp 87; Amer Legion Ortcl Awd 87; Millersville U; Elem Ed.

COOK, ELIZABETH; Solanco HS; Nottingham, PA; (3); Church Y Grp; Ski Clb; Varsity Clb; Acpl Chr; Band; Chorus; School Musical; V Crs Cntry; Var Trk; High Hon Roll; Cnty Chorals 86; Chorale 86-8 Rotary Ldrshp Conf 87; Journalism.

COOK, ELLEN; Reynolds HS; Greenville, PA; (4); Church Yth G Spanish Clb; Hon Roll; General Guards 83; Brnz Palm 86; Med Asst.

COOK, GERGORY; Steel Valley SR HS; Homestead, PA; (3); Aud/Vi Church Yth Grp; Drama Clb; Latin Clb; Hon Roll; Var Bsbl; JV Bsktl Concert Band; School Play; Yrbk Stf; Acad Achvt 84-85; Athltc Ach 84-85; Pittsburgh; Med.

COOK, HEATHER; Northern Lehigh HS; Slatington, PA; (3); 5/16 Debate Tm; Ski Clb; School Musical; Variety Show; JV Var Fld Hcky; V Sftbl; Var Trk; High Hon Roll; Lion Awd; NHS; Hon Engl 86-88; Messi Coll; Chld Psychlgy.

COOK, JACKIE; Upper Darby HS; Clifton Hts, PA; (3); Dance Clb; Ho Aide; Library Aide; Office Aide; SADD; Teachers Aide; Chorus; Hon Ro Fvrt Stu Tchr Awd 85; Ms Teen All Am Pgnt 85-87; West Chester Co Fshn Dsgn.

COOK, JENNIFER; Parkland HS; Allentown, PA; (3); 146/481; Chur Yth Grp; SADD; Chorus; Variety Show; Yrbk Stf; VP Pres Stu Cn Tennis; Trk; Schlstc Gold Key Art Awd; Psych.

COOK, JOHN; Churchill HS; Pittsburgh, PA; (2); 18/220; Ski Clb; Ac Chr; Madrigals; School Musical; Yrbk Phtg; VP Soph Cls; Rep Stu Cn JV Socr; High Hon Roll; Hon Roll.

COOK, JOHN T; Warrior Run HS; Watsontown, PA; (3); 30/187; Am L Boys St; Varsity Clb; Pres Chorus; School Musical; Stage Crew; Off Jr C VP Pres Stu Cncl; Var L Bsbl; Var L Bsktbl; Hon Roll; Boston U Tanglw Inst Vocl Music Prog 87; Navl Sci.

COOK, KENNETH; Du Bois Area HS; Dubois, PA; (3); 91/262; Ban Chorus; Mrchg Band; School Musical; School Play; Diving; Ftbl; Swmmn Church Yth Grp; PAVAS; 3 Tm Ltr Wnnr-Swm Tm 84-87; 2 Yrs Dist Ch 86-87; 1 Yr Rgnl Chrs 86; Air Force; Phrmcy.

COOK, KIMBERLEY; Perry Traditional Acad; Pittsburgh, PA; (3 Church Yth Grp; Band; Mrchg Band; Variety Show; Nwsp Rptr; Yrbk St Stu Cncl; Tennis; Vllybl; Equestrian.

COOK, LORI; West Green Middle SR HS; Wind Ridge, PA; (4); 4/10 Church Yth Grp; Cmnty Wkr; Library Aide; Office Aide; Church Choi High Hon Roll; Hon Roll; NHS; Exec Scrtry.

COOK, MICHELLE; Highlands HS; Natrona Hts, PA; (3); Art Clb; Intr Clb; Office Aide; Yrbk Phtg; Rep Frsh Cls; Stu Cncl; Im L Trk; Btty Crck Awd; Hon Roll; Jr NHS; Med.

COOK JR, PHILLIP L; Waynesburg Central HS; Waynesburg, PA; (3 11/215; Lee Coll Cleveland TN.

COOK, STEPHANIE ANN; Bermudian Springs HS; East Berlin, PA (4); 37/121; Chorus; Madrigals; School Musical; Swing Chorus; Nwsp Pht Yrbk Phtg; Var L Fld Hcky; Bsktbl; Trk; Hon Roll; Class 1910 Schlrsh 87; 1st Pl PA ALASA Conf Prcss Seprtn 87; Grphc Arts Rcgntn Awd 8 Dean JC; Tech Theatre.

COOK, SUSAN; Hyndman Middle-SR HS; Hyndman, PA; (3); 3/5 Spanish Clb; SADD; Varsity Clb; Chorus; Flag Corp; Stu Cnc Cheerleading; Sftbl; Vllybl; NHS; Acctng.

COOK, THOMAS; Lampeter Strasburg HS; Lancaster, PA; (3); 6/14 Thesps; Varsity Clb; Band; Pres Chorus; Church Choir; Concert Band Jazz Band; Madrigals; Mrchg Band; School Musical; Cnty Dist Regnl & S Chrs 85-87; Rotary Stu Of Mnth 87; Sci Fair Awd Wnnr Chem 87; Engrng

COOK, TIM; Mt Pleasant Area JR/Sr HS; Mt Pleasant, PA; (3); Germa Clb; Rep Stu Cncl; Bsbl; Bsktbl; Ftbl; Wt Lftg; Hon Roll; Athltc Coach.

COOKE, DEREK; Blair Co Christian HS; Hollidaysburg, PA; (1); 19/2 Var Bsktbl; Var Socr; JV Trk; Pres Frsh Cls; Rep Stu Cncl; MVP All Sta Soccer 86-87.

COOKE, SHAUNA; Waynesburg Central HS; Prosperity, PA; (3); Ar Clb; Pep Clb; Ski Clb; Spanish Clb; VP Frsh Cls; VP Soph Cls; Stu Cnc Capt Cheerleading; JV Var Vllybl; Hon Roll; Scndry Art Educ.

COOLBAUGH, CHRISTINE; Wyoming Area SR HS; Harding, PA; (4 116/250; Art Clb; Key Clb; JV Var Sftbl; Misericordia Coll; Rad.

COOLBAUGH, EUGENE E; Schuylkill Haven HS; Schuylkill Haven PA; (4); Computer Clb; Hon Roll.

COOLE, SAMANTHA; Greensburg Central Catholic HS; Greensburg PA; (2); Sec Church Yth Grp; Girl Scts; Hosp Aide; Ski Clb; Elec Tech.

COOLEY, BRYAN; South Western HS; Hanover, PA; (2); 9/212; Ches Clb; Key Clb; Quiz Bowl; High Hon Roll; Adv Lf Savg; CPR; Comp Sci.

COON, LESLEY; Warren Area HS; Warren, PA; (3); 71/287; Church Yt Grp; Drama Clb; French Clb; Letterman Clb; Ski Clb; Varsity Clb; Acp Chr; Band; Chorus; School Musical; Slvr B Awd 85; Elem Ed.

COON, STACIE; Marion Center Area HS; Home, PA; (3); Office Aide Q&S; SADD; Intnl Clb; Stage Crew; Yrbk Rptr; Var Twrlr; High Hon Roll Hon Roll; Pre-Law.

COONEY, CHRISTINE; St Basil Acad; Philadelphia, PA; (3); Cmnty Wkr; Drama Clb; French Clb; Hosp Aide; SADD; Stage Crew; Nrsng.

COONEY, COLLEEN; West Scranton HS; Scranton, PA; (2); Spanish Clb; Var Cheerleading; JV Trk.

COONEY, JANET; Abraham Lincoln HS; Philadelphia, PA; (3); Spanish Clb; Sec Soph Cls; Var Capt Fld Hcky; Hon Roll; Prsdntl Phy Ftns Awd Hnr Roll Brnz Pin Awd; Pre-Schl Thrpy.

COONEY, KEVIN; Penn Hills SR HS; Pittsburgh, PA; (4); Pres AFS; Spanish Clb; Rep Stu Cncl; JV Bsbl; Im Vllybl; Hon Roll; U Of Pittsburgh; Med Tech.

COONEY, MICHELLE; Forest Hills SR HS; South Fork, PA; (3); 53/160; FBLA; Pep Clb; Pres Ski Clb; JV Cheerleading; Im Sftbl; L Trk; Im Vllybl; Hon Roll; PA ST; Accntnt.

COONEY, PAUL; Scranton Central HS; Scranton, PA; (3); 20/300; Church Yth Grp; Ski Clb; Var Bsbl; JV Var Bsktbl; Coach Actv; Var Socr; Im Vllybl; High Hon Roll; Med.

COOPER, ADAM MERTON; Saint Josephs Prep Schl; Philadelphia, PA; (4); 1/225; Math Tm; Sec Spanish Clb; Sec Concert Band; Ed Nwsp Stf; NHS; Ntl Merit SF; Prfct Atten Awd; Phila Area All-Cthlc Band 86-87; Natl Achvt Schlrshp 87; Natl Grk Exam Blue Rbbn 85 & 86; U WI Madison; Comp Sci.

COOPER, AMELIA; Villa Maria Acad; Erie, PA; (3); 53/182; Camera Clb; Cmnty Wkr; Trs Science Clb; Spanish Clb; Church Choir; Yrbk Phtg; Yrbk Stf; Hon Roll; NHS; Med Tech.

COOPER, ARTHUR; Faith Christian Schl; Blairstown, NJ; (4); 2/5; Chess Clb; Church Yth Grp; Computer Clb; Red Cross Aide; Stage Crew; Pres Sr Cls; Capt Socr; Wt Lftg; Hon Roll; Variety Show; Geom Awd 85-86; Bible Awd 85-86; Physcs Olympic Awd 85-86; Air Force; Electncs Engrng.

COOPER, BETH; Baldwin HS; Pittsburgh, PA; (3); 21/476; Math Clb; Capt Crs Cntry; Swmmng; Trk; High Hon Roll; NHS; Elem Ed.

COOPER, CARL; Notre Dame HS; Easton, PA; (3); Church Yth Grp; Ski Clb; Var L Trk; Hon Roll; Bus Admin.

COOPER, CHRISTY; Elkland HS; Elkland, PA; (3); Church Yth Grp; Drama Clb; SADD; Hon Roll; NHS; Lgl Sec.

COOPER, CONN; Halifax Area HS; Halifax, PA; (4); 25/100; Drama Clb; FHA; Varsity Clb; Concert Band; School Musical; School Play; Var Bsktbl; Var Ftbl; Hall Fdntn Schlrshp 87; Frostburg ST Coll; Bio.

COOPER, DAVE; Southmoreland SR HS; Scottdale, PA; (3); 3/230; Pres Church Yth Grp; Letterman Clb; Math Clb; Nwsp Rptr; Lit Mag; Trs Stu Cncl; L Socr; NHS; Ntl Merit Ltr; Grmn Natl Hnr Soc 85-86; Engnrng.

COOPER, DAWN; Lewistown Area SR HS; Lewistown, PA; (4); 14/246; AFS; Sec French Clb; Key Clb; Pep Clb; Ski Clb; Yrbk Bus Mgr; Yrbk Stf; High Hon Roll; Pres Schlr; Juniata Coll Alumni Schlrshp 87-88; Juniata Coll; Lbrl Arts.

COOPER, DI ANNA; Southmore Land SR HS; Scottdale, PA; (4); 47/222; Sec Church Yth Grp; Hosp Aide; Office Aide; Rep Pep Clb; Ski Clb; Spanish Clb; Teachers Aide; Chorus; School Musical; Im Powder Puff Ftbl; Eastern Mennonite Coll; RN.

COOPER, DOUG; Ringgold HS; Monongahela, PA; (2); Church Yth Grp; VP JA; Letterman Clb; Spanish Clb; SADD; Varsity Clb; School Musical; Bsbl; Socr; Hon Roll; Gftd Pgm 1st Grd 77-89; Medical.

COOPER, FELISHA; Penn Wood HS; Philadelphia, PA; (4); 141/335; Computer Clb; Dance Clb; GAA; Science Clb; Service Clb; Drill Tm; Orch; School Play; Var Trk; Hon Roll; Farleigh Dickerson; Phys Thrpy.

COOPER, JANE; Tunkhannock Area HS; Mehoopany, PA; (4); 2/290; Church Yth Grp; 4-H; Hosp Aide; Pres VP JA; Band; Concert Band; Mrchg Band; Cit Awd; DAR Awd; Kiwanis Awd; Outstndg Yng Bus Womn Of Yr 85; PA Govs Schl Ag 86; Carnegie Spkng & Hmn Rltns 85; Penn ST U; Engr.

COOPER, JEFFREY; Plymouth-Whitemarsh HS; Norristown, PA; (3); Band; Chorus; Church Choir; Concert Band; Jazz Band; Mrchg Band; School Musical; School Play; Swing Chorus; Harlequin Awd-Ldng Role Schl Musicl, Schl Musicl & Ply 86, 87; Cert-Rgnl & Dist Chorus 87; Music Prfrmnc.

COOPER, JOE; Upper Dauphin Area HS; Lykens, PA; (3); 19/115; Varsity Clb; Off Stu Cncl; Capt L Bsktbl; Capt L Ftbl; Hon Roll; Rotary Clb Stu Of Mnth 87; Ftbl Club 86-87; WHTM-TV Channel 27 News Plyr Of Yr Ftbl 86.

COOPER, JOHN; Wilmington Area HS; New Castle, PA; (3); 25/114; Church Yth Grp; L Bsktbl; L Ftbl; Im Sftbl; Hon Roll; Marine Bio.

COOPER, JULIE; Boiling Springs HS; Dillsburg, PA; (3); 30/123; Girl Scts; Chorus; Flag Corp; School Play; JV Var Mgr(s); Hon Roll; Prfct Atten Awd; CASAC 1st Pl Grnd Chmp 87; Frstry.

COOPER, KAREN; Franklin Regional SR HS; Murrysville, PA; (3); AFS; Church Yth Grp; Spanish Clb; Band; Chorus; Orch; Variety Show; U Of Pittsburgh; Pblc Rltns.

COOPER, KIM; Butler SR HS; Butler, PA; (3); French Clb; Office Aide; SADD; Thesps; Mrchg Band; School Musical; Symp Band; Rep Frsh Cls; Im Bsktbl; Acad Achvt Awd Butler SR HS 87; Ed.

COOPER, KIM; Chambersburg Area SR HS; Chambersburg, PA; (4); Trs Camera Clb; Key Clb; Pep Clb; Ski Clb; Spanish Clb; Rep Stu Cncl; Cheerleading; Crs Cntry; Trk; Hmcmng Ct 87; Penn ST Mont Alto; Bus Mgmt.

COOPER, KRISTEN E; Cheltenham HS; Glenside, PA; (4); 45/374; Hosp Aide; JCL; Chorus; Orch; School Musical; NHS; Pres Schlr; Dickinson Coll; Intl Stds.

COOPER, KRISTI; Millersburg Area HS; Millersburg, PA; (2); Church Yth Grp; VP Trs 4-H; Red Cross Aide; Spanish Clb; Band; Sec Chorus; Church Choir; Jazz Band; Mrchg Band; High Hon Roll; 4-H SR Div Clvr Awd Hm Econ 86; 3rd Pl Indvdl Clthng Textl ST Achvt Day 86; Acadmc Achvt Awd 85-86; Pharmacy.

COOPER, LINDA; Harbor Creek HS; Erie, PA; (4); Trs AFS; Office Aide; School Play; Ed Nwsp Stf; Yrbk Stf; Im Powder Puff Ftbl; Capt L Trk; Capt L Vllybl; Penn ST Behrend; Microbio.

COOPER, MARISSA; Churchill HS; Pittsburgh, PA; (4); 54/198; AFS; French Clb; Hosp Aide; Sec Temple Yth Grp; Tennis; Hon Roll; Vlntr Awd 84; Schl Advncd Jewish Stds 87; Presbyterian Hosp 400 Hrs Vlntr Wrk 86; Ithaca Coll; Bio.

COOPER, MARY; Tunkhannock HS; Mehoopany, PA; (2); 4/223; VP Church Yth Grp; Sec 4-H; Hosp Aide; VP JA; Key Clb; Spanish Clb; Band; Church Choir; Concert Band; Jazz Band; Super Slsprsn Of NE PA JR Achvt 86; Lock Haven U; Elem Educ.

COOPER, MEAGHEN E; Gwynedd Mercy Acad; Doylestown, PA; (4); 14/102; Church Yth Grp; Cmnty Wkr; Political Wkr; Service Clb; Yrbk Ed-Chief; Ed Yrbk Phtg; Var Capt Sftbl; Var Capt Tennis; Hon Roll; Pres Schlr; Outstndng Achvt In Bio 85; Hugh O Brian Ldrshp Awd 85; MVP Sftbl 86; Vndrblt U.

COOPER, MELISSA; Wyoming Valley West HS; Kingston, PA; (4); 50/398; FHA; Key Clb; Chorus; Stu Cncl; Capt Fld Hcky; Sftbl; Cit Awd; Hon Roll; NHS; Bloomsburg U; Mrktng.

COOPER, MISSI; Twin Valley HS; Honey Brook, PA; (4); 6/132; Pres 4-H; Spanish Clb; Teachers Aide; Varsity Clb; Rep Stu Cncl; Var Capt Fld Hcky; Var Capt Lcrss; Hon Roll; NHS; Pres Schlr; La Crosse MVP 85-87; US Army Rsrve Schlr/Athlete 87; Area II Trng Chmpn Hrsebck Rdng 84; U Of DE; Animal Sci.

COOPER, NEIL A; The Haverford Schl; Narberth, PA; (4); 2/83; Latin Clb; Model UN; Spanish Clb; Nwsp Rptr; Yrbk Sprt Ed; JV Bsbl; JV Tennis; DAR Awd; High Hon Roll; NHS; Brown U Awd Lit 86; Harvard U; Engl.

COOPER, NICOLE; Huntingdon HS; Huntingdon, PA; (4); 20/224; Pres Church Yth Grp; GAA; Concert Band; Yrbk Stf; Rep Soph Cls; Rep Jr Cls; Rep Sr Cls; Var Trk; L Var Vllybl; Hon Roll; Bucknell; Chem.

COOPER, SCOTT; Central York SR HS; York, PA; (4); Band; Chorus; Church Choir; Concert Band; Jazz Band; Mrchg Band; School Musical; Swing Chorus; Symp Band; Nwsp Stf; Shippensburg U; Ed.

COOPER, SHARON; Union City HS; Union City, PA; (2); Sec GAA; Pep Clb; SADD; Chorus; Var L Bsktbl; Var L Crs Cntry; Var L Trk; Var L Vllybl; High Hon Roll; Prfct Atten Awd; Prs Physcial Ftns Awd 86 & 87; Prs Acadmc Ftns Awd 86.

COOPER, STACY; Lincoln JR SR HS; Ellwood City, PA; (3); #112 In Class; Pres Church Yth Grp; FCA; Library Aide; SADD; High Hon Roll; Hon Roll; Bus.

COOPER, SUSAN; Marple Newtown SR HS; Broomall, PA; (3); 8/330; Ski Clb; Ed Spanish Clb; VP SADD; Nwsp Ed-Chief; Rep Stu Cncl; JV Lcrss; Stat Socr; JV Vllybl; Hon Roll; Prfct Atten Awd; Hstry Day Cmpttn 86; Dplma Of Merit, Excllnc-Spnsh 87; Lbrl Arts.

COOPERMAN, CINDY; Lancaster Country Day Schl; Reading, PA; (2); Chorus; Orch; School Play; Var Fld Hcky; Var Swmmng; High Hon Roll; Bio High Hnrs; Natl Latin Cntst Hnrs.

COOPERSMITH, ANDREW; Lower Moreland HS; Huntingdon Valley, PA; (3); Drama Clb; FBLA; School Musical; School Play; Yrbk Stf; Var Trk; High Hon Roll; Spnsh Merit Awds 85&86.

COOPIE, JENNIFER; Steel Valley HS; Munhall, PA; (4); 38/201; Cmnty Wkr; SADD; Nwsp Rptr; Capt Tennis; High Hon Roll; Hon Roll; NHS; MVP Vrsty Ten Tm 85-86; U Of Pittsburgh; Psych.

COOVER, JANE; Cumberland Valley HS; Mechanicsburg, PA; (3); 27/563; Trs Church Yth Grp; German Clb; Jazz Band; Mrchg Band; Orch; Symp Band; French Hon Soc; Hon Roll; NHS; Chem.

COOVER, MICHELLE L; Mechanicsburg Area SR HS; Mechanicsburg, PA; (2); Church Yth Grp; Pep Clb; Band; Concert Band; Nwsp Rptr; Nwsp Stf; Rep Stu Cncl; Vllybl; High Hon Roll.

COPE, KYLE; Bangor HS; Bangor, PA; (3); 3/213; Church Yth Grp; Computer Clb; Leo Clb; Band; Mrchg Band; Pep Band; Stu Cncl; JV Bsktbl; Var Tennis; High Hon Roll; Mst Outstndng Bio Awd 85-86; Mst Imprvd Tnns Plyr 86-87; Engrng.

COPE, SUSAN; Meadowbrook Christian HS; Danville, PA; (1); 2/12; Church Yth Grp; Drama Clb; Chorus; Church Choir; Hon Roll; Bus Math.

COPELAND, LATASHA; Little Flower H S For Girls; Philadelphia, PA; (3); 109/333; Church Yth Grp; Cmnty Wkr; Exploring; Girl Scts; NAACP; Chorus; Church Choir; School Play; Trk; Hon Roll; Black Std League 84-87; St Vincent Home For Children 84-87; Vocal Music Awd 84-86; Howard U; Psychlgy.

COPELAND, MARION; Yough SR HS; W Newton, PA; (4); Pres French Clb; Girl Scts; Office Aide; Spanish Clb; Band; Chorus; Concert Band; Drm Mjr(t); Jazz Band; Mrchg Band.

COPELAND, NANCY; Saint Maria Goretti HS; Philadelphia, PA; (3); 2/350; Math Clb; Pep Clb; PAVAS; Service Clb; Spanish Clb; Teachers Aide; Rep Jr Cls; JV Tennis; Hon Roll; NHS; Gld Mdl Rlgn 85-87; Gld Mdl Frnch 85-86; Gld Mdl Wrld Cltrs 87.

COPLAN, DAVID; Gateway SR HS; Monroeville, PA; (4); Chess Clb; Temple Yth Grp; Im Bsktbl; Jr NHS; Monroeville Police Benevoletn Assn 87; The Amer U.

COPPER, LEROY; University City HS; Philadelphia, PA; (4); Church Yth Grp; Cmnty Wkr; Exploring; Church Choir; Crs Cntry; Cit Awd; Prfct Atten Awd; Spanish NHS; Ctn Of Merit-Mtvtn 87; Spnsh Awd 87; Prfct Atten Awd 86-87; Karate Awd 86-87; Rose K & Zukin Fndtn Awd; Widener U; Law.

COPPULA, LISA; Mt Pleasant Area HS; Mt Pleasant, PA; (3); 21/250; GAA; Ski Clb; Pres Frsh Cls; Pres Soph Cls; Off Stu Cncl; Cheerleading; High Hon Roll; Pharmcy.

CORBA, MARYANN; St Maria Goretti HS; Philadelphia, PA; (4); Art Clb; GAA; Nwsp Stf; 2nd Hnrs 86-87.

CORBETT, DAVID; Jefferson-Morgan HS; Mather, PA; (3); 18/74; Varsity Clb; Var Ftbl; Navy.

CORBETT, JIM; Quigley HS; Baden, PA; (4); Var Bsbl; L Bsktbl; Var Ftbl; Var Golf; High Hon Roll; Hon Roll; NHS; PA ST.

CORBETT, SHIRLEY; Waynesburg Central HS; Spraggs, PA; (3); FCA; Mu Alpha Theta; Spanish Clb; Tennis; Trk; Vllybl; Hon Roll; Nrsng.

CORBIN, BRENDA; Franklin Area HS; Franklin, PA; (4); L Swmmng; Kiwanis Awd; Coaches Awd Swmmng 86-87; Clarion U; Accntng.

CORBIN, JEANNETTE; New Covenant Acad; Wellsboro, PA; (2); 2/5; Church Yth Grp; Drama Clb; Chorus; School Musical; School Play; Yrbk Stf; Socr; Houghton Coll.

CORBIN, STEPHANIE; Brockway Area HS; Reynoldsville, PA; (3); 1/110; Pres Sec 4-H; Speech Tm; Pres Concert Band; Pres Mrchg Band; Pres Pep Band; Yrbk Stf; Stu Cncl; 4-H Awd; Hon Roll; NHS; Jefferson Cnty Dairy Princess 87-88.

CORCORAN, JOHN; Council Rock HS; Churchville, PA; (2); High Hon Roll; Hon Roll; Pres Acad Ftns Awd 84-85; PA Math Leag Merit Cert 85; Bus.

CORCORAN, LAWRENCE; Girard College HS; Holland, PA; (3); 2/38; Exploring; Ski Clb; Nwsp Ed-Chief; Var L Bsbl; Var L Socr; Var L Swmmng; Cit Awd; High Hon Roll; NHS; Alumni Schlr Athl Awd 87; Naval Acad; Bus Admn.

CORDAN, JILL; Riverside HS; Beaver Fls, PA; (3); GAA; JV Bsktbl; Var L Trk; Im Vllybl; Hon Roll; NHS; Robert Morris; Acctng.

CORDAS, DAVID; Pennsbury HS; Yardley, PA; (4); 88/771; Rptr Stu Cncl; Im Bowling; Var L Diving; Var L Swmmng; Im Tennis; Hon Roll; Jr NHS; NHS; Outstndg Acad Achvmnt Awd 87; Lehigh U; Engrng.

CORDEK, CHRISTOPHER; Bishop Carroll HS; Ebensburg, PA; (3); Church Yth Grp; Bsbl; Bsktbl; Golf; Trk; Hon Roll.

CORDELL, COREY; Southmoreland SR HS; Scottdale, PA; (3); Church Yth Grp; French Clb; Tennis; Devry Inst Of Tech; Bus Comp.

CORDELL, GEOFFREY; Pequea Valley HS; Intercourse, PA; (3); 23/111; French Clb; FBLA; Varsity Clb; Trs Stu Cncl; Im Bsbl; Im Bsktbl; Var Tennis; Im Vllybl; High Hon Roll; U DE; Bus Adm.

CORDERO, BRENDA; Freedom HS; Bethlehem, PA; (4); 50/487; Art Clb; Chorus; High Hon Roll; Hon Roll; Jr NHS; NHS; Pres Schlr; Brd Of Govrns Schlrshp 87; Amer Assn Of Univ Women Schlrshp 87; Med Sci.

CORDIER, MELISSA; Freeport Area SR HS; Sarver, PA; (2); Hosp Aide; Mrchg Band; Symp Band; Nwsp Stf; Cheerleading; Sftbl; Trk; Twrlr; High Hon Roll; Hon Roll; PA ST; Med.

CORDISIO, GINO; Monongahelo Valley Catholic HS; Brownsville, PA; (3); 12/104; Boy Scts; Pres Exploring; Ski Clb; Spanish Clb; Bsbl; Bsktbl; Wt Lftg; NHS; Spanish NHS; Acadc All-Am 87; Ordr Arrw 85; Med.

CORDOVA, PERLITA; Lebanon Catholic HS; Lebanon, PA; (3); FHA; Spanish Clb; SADD; Chorus; Yrbk Stf; Swmmng; Wt Lftg.

CORDRAY, DIANE; The Agnes Irwin Schl; Berwyn, PA; (3); Church Yth Grp; Acpl Chr; Orch; Bsktbl; Lcrss; Socr; Tennis; High Hon Roll; Hon Roll; Ntl Merit SF.

CORDWELL, CURTIS; Blue Mt S D A Acad; Orwigsburg, PA; (3); Camera Clb; Church Yth Grp; Library Aide; Church Choir; Yrbk Phtg; Jr Cls; Capt Ftbl; Capt Sftbl; Capt Vllybl; High Hon Roll; Andrews U; Theolgy.

COREY, TASHA; Linesville HS; Linesville, PA; (3); 1/100; German Clb; SADD; Yrbk Stf; VP Jr Cls; Var Sftbl; Var Vllybl; High Hon Roll; NHS; Drama Clb; School Play; Prom Court 87; Hmcmng Court 84-86; Math.

CORKELL, THERESA; John S Fine SR HS; W Nanticoke, PA; (4); 21/256; Cmnty Wkr; 4-H; Yrbk Stf; Pres 4-H Awd; High Hon Roll; Hon Roll; Typing Awd 85-86; Consumer Ed Awd 86-87; Accntng/Bkkpng Awd 86-87; Luzerne Cnty CC; Telecomm.

CORKERY, DOROTHY; John Bartram HS; Philadelphia, PA; (4); 5/900; Cmnty Wkr; Dance Clb; French Clb; JA; Office Aide; Red Cross Aide; SADD; Teachers Aide; Fld Hcky; Gym; Ellis Schlrshp 84; Bartram Acad All Star Awd 86; Stu Wk Awd 86; French.

CORKERY, TRACY; West Catholic Girls HS; Philadelphia, PA; (3); Psychlgy.

CORKERY, WILLIAM; Monsignor Bonner HS; Folcroft, PA; (4); 10/317; Boys Clb Am; Cmnty Wkr; JV Bsbl; Im Bsktbl; Temple U Outstndg Achvt Scholar 87; AFGROTC Scholar 87; NROTC Scholar 87; Temple U; Engrng.

CORL, SUSAN; Windber Area HS; Windber, PA; (3); Hosp Aide; Quiz Bowl; Ski Clb; Yrbk Ed-Chief; Yrbk Phtg; JV Var Bsktbl; High Hon Roll; NHS; Ntl Merit Ltr; Pres Schlr; Pres Phy Ftns Awd 85-87; Bus.

CORLE, NICOLE; Claysburg-Kimmel HS; Imler, PA; (2); 19/98; Drama Clb; Ski Clb; Speech Tm; Concert Band; Mrchg Band; Frsh Cls; Twrlr; Hon Roll; Prfct Atten Awd; Ivy Leag Schl; Law.

CORLE, THERESA A; Northern Bedford County HS; New Enterprise, PA; (3); 19/105; Cmnty Wkr; Math Clb; Office Aide; Service Clb; Band; Chorus; Jazz Band; Mrchg Band; School Musical; Voice Dem Awd; Pre-Med.

CORMAS, JOHN; Penn Hills HS; Pittsburgh, PA; (4); 21/609; JV Bsbl; High Hon Roll; NHS; Penn ST U; Physcs.

CORMIER, BRENDA; Louis E Dieruff HS; Allentown, PA; (2); 86/340; Church Yth Grp; Cmnty Wkr; Sec JA; Political Wkr; Boy Scts; Drama Clb; Exploring; FBLA; Ski Clb; Mgr Swmmng; Champ Annual Splng Bee 85-86; Ldrshp Troika Awd 85-86; Lawyer.

CORNELIUSSEN, CARI; Panther Valley HS; Coaldale, PA; (3); 13/132; Pres Drama Clb; Chorus; Capt Flag Corp; Mrchg Band; School Musical; Nwsp Rptr; Hon Roll; NHS; Prfct Atten Awd; Acad All-Amer 87; Math Tchr.

CORNELL, CHAD; Stroudsburg HS; Stroudsburg, PA; (2); Art Clb; Im Ftbl; Hon Roll; Rotary Awd; Prncpls Awd, Art Awd 85; Best Prspctv In Art Show 85; Art Tchr.

CORNELL, KIM; Saltsburg JR-SR HS; Saltsburg, PA; (2); 8/97; Drama Clb; SADD; Varsity Clb; School Musical; School Play; Stage Crew; Yrbk Bus Mgr; Yrbk Rptr; Yrbk Stf; JV L Bsktbl; Penn ST; Psych.

CORNELL, LEE ANN; Moon SR HS; Coraopolis, PA; (3); FNA; Girl Scts; Hosp Aide; Spanish Clb; High Hon Roll; Hon Roll; Vet.

CORNELL, LEWIS; Forest Hills HS; Sidman, PA; (4); 8/160; Ski Clb; Var Capt Bsbl; Var Capt Ftbl; Wt Lftg; High Hon Roll; Jr NHS; Lion Awd; Pres Schlr; Rotary Awd; Spanish NHS; Acadmc Al-Amer 84-87; Penn ST U; Engrng.

CORNETT, CYNTHIA L; Delone Catholic HS; Gettysburg, PA; (4); 12/164; Am Leg Aux Girls St; Church Yth Grp; Ski Clb; Pres Soph Cls; Sec Stu Cncl; Var L Fld Hcky; Hon Roll; VP NHS; Pres Schlr; Teachers Aide; JR Miss Idams Cnty Schlrshp 86-87; Franklin Coll; Bus.

CORNIA, PAUL; North Hills HS; Pittsburgh, PA; (4); 10/467; Church Yth Grp; Scholastic Bowl; Var Tennis; High Hon Roll; Hon Roll; Prfct Atten Awd; Case Wstrn Rsrve U; Pre-Med.

CORNIBE, BRIAN P; Butler Area SR HS; Butler, PA; (3); Var L Ftbl; Hon Roll.

CORNISH, CARI; Coudersport JR SR HS; Coudersport, PA; (3); 11/90; Pep Clb; Ski Clb; Chorus; Concert Band; Jazz Band; Mrchg Band; Yrbk Stf; Powder Puff Ftbl; Trk; NHS; Med Tech.

CORNISH, MICHELE; Duquesne HS; Duquesne, PA; (3); 7/96; Drama Clb; FTA; Girl Scts; Y-Teens; Drill Tm; Yrbk Stf; Bsktbl; Trk; NHS; Prfct Atten Awd; Hampton U; Accntng.

CORNISTA, GLADYS; Governor Mifflin HS; Shillington, PA; (3); 22/387; Q&S; Stu Cncl; Fld Hcky; JA; Chorus; Madrigals; Nwsp Stf; Yrbk Stf; Trk; High Hon Roll; HS Hnr Soc 86-87; Drexel U; Elec Engr.

CORNMAN, ALAN; Dayton HS; Templeton, PA; (3); 4/52; Chess Clb; Church Yth Grp; Spanish Clb; Band; Chorus; Concert Band; Mrchg Band; Pep Band; School Musical; Pres Frsh Cls; IN U; Law.

CORNMAN, MICHELLE; Cumberland Valley HS; Boiling Springs, PA; (4); 90/518; 4-H; German Clb; Concert Band; 4-H Awd; Hon Roll; PA ST Dstngsh JR Mbr 84; Cumberland Cnty Otstndng 83; Dairy Sci.

CORNMAN, PAUL; Freeport SR HS; Freeport, PA; (3); 74/218; School Play; Stage Crew; Ftbl; Trk; Hon Roll.

CORNOG, ANGEL; Frankford HS; Philadelphia, PA; (3); 27/645; Office Aide; Rep Stu Cncl; Co-Capt Var Cheerleading; JV Fld Hcky; Mat Maids; Hon Roll; Manor JC; Ct Rprtng.

CORNOG, SHARON; Sun Valley SR HS; Media, PA; (3); 25/270; Girl Scts; SADD; Var Cheerleading; Stat Lcrss; Hon Roll; Nrsng.

CORONA, STACEY; Mount Carmel Area JR SR HS; Mt Carmel, PA; (3); AFS; FTA; Key Clb; Latin Clb; Library Aide; Pep Clb; Ski Clb; Spanish Clb; Rep Frsh Cls; Rep Soph Cls; X-Ray Tech.

CORPREW, WARREN; Blue Mountain Acad; Willow Grove, PA; (3); Computer Clb; Ski Clb; Varsity Clb; Band; Bsktbl; Swmmng; Vllybl; Cit Awd; Hon Roll; Prfct Atten Awd; Aerontcl Engrng.

CORR, WARREN; Wilson HS; Easton, PA; (4); 4/127; Boy Scts; Debate Tm; Model UN; Trs Band; VP Chorus; Church Choir; VP Stu Cncl; Var L Tennis; God Cntry Awd; Trs NHS; PA Schl Brd Assn Delg; Pres Clsrm Delg; Engrng.

CORRADENE, ALBERT; Valley HS; New Kensington, PA; (3); Key Clb; Pep Clb; Science Clb; Ski Clb; Spanish Clb; VP Frsh Cls; Stu Cncl; JV Bsbl; Var JV Ftbl; Hon Roll; Engrng.

CORRADINO, MICHAEL C; Penn Manor HS; Conestoga, PA; (4); 2/315; Model UN; Var Golf; Var Tennis; Bausch & Lomb Sci Awd; Cit Awd; Lion Awd; NHS; Ntl Merit Ltr; Pres Schlr; Sal; Brd Dirctrs 4 Yr Fll Tuit Schlrshp St Josephs 87; St Josephs U; Law.

CORRADINO, RANDY; Old Forge HS; Old Forge, PA; (4); 34/104; Var Bsktbl; Var Ftbl; High Hon Roll; Hon Roll; Villanova; Engr.

CORRADO, DIANA; Notre Dame HS; Easton, PA; (3); 38/90; Flag Corp; Hon Roll; PA ST; Psych.

CORRADO, JOI; Palmyra Area HS; Palmyra, PA; (4); Drama Clb; German Clb; Girl Scts; Ski Clb; Tennis; Hon Roll; Shippensburg U.

CORREIA, SEAN; Valley Forge Military Acad; Bristol, RI; (2); Drama Clb; Band; Mrchg Band; School Play; Im Bsbl; Im Diving; JV Socr; Im Swmmng; Var Trk; JV Wrstlng; USAFA Colorado Spgs; Pilot.

CORRELL, CATHY; Corry Area HS; Corry, PA; (3); 1/229; Church Yth Grp; German Clb; Rep Frsh Cls; Rep Soph Cls; Rep Jr Cls; Rep Stu Cncl; Swmmng; Trk; Vllybl; High Hon Roll; Znta Amela Earhrt Awd 87; JETS Compttn 87; Schl Treas 86-88; Med.

CORRELL, CRAIG; Hamburg Area HS; Hamburg, PA; (3); Exploring; Bsbl; Socr; Hon Roll; Rep Soph Cls; Carpenter.

CORRELL, SCOTT; Governor Mifflin HS; Reading, PA; (3); 41/375; Chess Clb; JV Swmmng; Var Tennis; Im Vllybl; Hon Roll; NHS; Pres Schlr; Phila Clsscl Soc Ltn Awds 85 & 86; Pres Acad Fit Awd 85; PIAA St Tennis Champ Qlfr, Mdl Awd 87; Bus Admin.

CORRIDONI, SUE; Wyoming Area HS; West Pittston, PA; (3); 3/250; Drama Clb; French Clb; Key Clb; Math Clb; Ski Clb; Var Bsktbl; Var Trk; High Hon Roll; JETS Awd; NHS; Rensslr Math/Sci Awd 87; PA Free Entrprse Schlrshp 87; JETS Tm 3rd Pl 87; Bus.

CORRIGAN, BRIAN; Downington SR HS; Downingtown, PA; (3); 6/680; Debate Tm; Ski Clb; Jazz Band; Mrchg Band; Rep Stu Cncl; Im Tennis; JV Trk; High Hon Roll; Ntl Merit SF; Pres Schlr; Air Frc Acad; Arspc Engrng.

CORRIGAN, HEATHER; State College Area HS; Port Matilda, PA; (2); FBLA; Bus Math Bus Awd 87; Acctg Bus Awd 87; Achvt Awd 87; South Hills Bus Schl; Bus.

CORRIGAN, KATHLEEN; Hanover Area HS; Wilkes Barre, PA; (3); 3/194; Key Clb; SADD; Yrbk Stf; Rep Jr Cls; Rep Stu Cncl; High Hon Roll; Jr NHS; NHS; WY Vly Yth Salute 87; Penn ST U; Finance.

CORRINNE, JANET; Purchase Line HS; Clymer, PA; (2); Pep Clb; Nwsp Phtg; Cheerleading; Pom Pon; Trk; High Hon Roll; Hnrd Spnsh Stu 86-87; Hnrd Frnch Stu 85-86; Legl Asst.

CORSELIUS, KRISTEN; Abington Heights HS; Clarks Summit, PA; (3); 36/292; Ski Clb; Chorus; School Musical; Off Stu Cncl; Var Fld Hcky; High Hon Roll; Hon Roll; NHS; Church Yth Grp; Band; 3rd Pl Rgnl Grmn Exam 86; 1st Pl Rgnl Ntl Hstry Day 86; Intl Bus.

CORSELLO, LISA; Council Rock HS; Holland, PA; (3); 21/908; Var Tennis; High Hon Roll; NHS; Pre-Vet Med.

CORSI, ANN K; Mcdowell HS; Erie, PA; (4); 1/611; Model UN; Mrchg Band; Orch; Sr Cls; Kiwanis Awd; NHS; Ntl Merit SF; Val; Biomed.

CORSI, DIANE; Cardinal O Hara HS; Broomall, PA; (3); 8/710; Off Church Yth Grp; Cmnty Wkr; Pres Spanish Clb; Off SADD; High Hon Roll; NHS; Spanish NHS; Office Aide; Hon Roll; Cert Merit Natl Spnsh Cont 86; Awd Acdmc Excllnc 85-87; Schltc Achvt Spnsh 86-87.

CORSI, KIMBERLY; Highlands SR HS; Natrona Heights, PA; (3); Hosp Aide; Intnl Clb; VP Rep JA; Office Aide; SADD; Teachers Aide; Color Guard; Nwsp Ed-Chief; Nwsp Rptr; Ed Nwsp Stf.

CORSON, PATRICK; Mount Union Area HS; Shirleysburg, PA; (3); Am Leg Boys St; Church Yth Grp; French Clb; FBLA; Band; Concert Band; Mrchg Band; School Play; Stage Crew; Bsktbl.

CORTES, CANDY; Meadville Area SR HS; Meadville, PA; (3); 28/348; Church Yth Grp; French Clb; SADD; Off Stu Cncl; JV Var Cheerleading; High Hon Roll; Hon Roll; Prfct Atten Awd; AAHPERD Yth Ftnss Achvt Awd 84-87; Med.

CORTESE, TERRI; Mid-Valley HS; Dickson City, PA; (3); Computer Clb; Drama Clb; French Clb; SADD; Chorus; School Musical; School Play; Nwsp Bus Mgr; Nwsp Rptr; Nwsp Stf; Hosp Admn.

CORTILESO, MELISSA; Leechburg Area HS; Leechburg, PA; (2); Drama Clb; School Play; Sec Frsh Cls; Cheerleading; Hon Roll; Prfct Atten Awd; Bradford Schl Bus; Legal Secry.

CORTOLILLO, SUSAN; Bethel Park SR HS; Bethel Park, PA; (4); Church Yth Grp; Drama Clb; Band; Concert Band; Drill Tm; Mrchg Band; Orch; School Musical; Symp Band; Variety Show; Penn ST; Spanish.

CORUJO, ROBERT; Thomas A Edison HS; Philadelphia, PA; (4); 2/300; Chess Clb; Nwsp Rptr; Lit Mag; Ftbl; Socr; Wt Lftg; High Hon Roll; NHS; Prfct Atten Awd; Sal; John C Fariera Scholar Awd 87; Dr Robert W Clarke Awd 87; Stewart C Raucsh/Amer Philosphcl Soc Awd 85; PA ST U; Sci.

CORY, SUSAN; Wilmington Area HS; New Wilmington, PA; (4); Key Clb; Concert Band; Mrchg Band; Pep Band; Nwsp Rptr; Band; Hon Roll; Otstndng Typst 86; Sctn Ldr Awd Bnd 87; Pep Bnd Hnr 4 Yr Pn 87; Slippery Rock U.

COSBEY, DAVID; Daniel Boone HS; Douglassville, PA; (3); Church Yth Grp; Dance Clb; JA; Political Wkr; VP Pres Stu Cncl; Var JV Bsktbl; Coach Actv; JV Mgr(s); JV Score Keeper; Var Socr; HOBY Ldrshp Seminar 86; Rotary Intl Camp Neidig Ldrshp 87; PA Free Enterprise Wk 87; Shippensburg; Educ Admin.

COSENZA, MARGARET; Saint Huberts HS For Girls; Philadelphia, PA; (3); 28/421; Church Yth Grp; Dance Clb; Color Guard; Orch; School Musical; Stage Crew; Hon Roll; Prfct Atten Awd; Music I Achvt Awd; Hmn Svcs.

COSGRIFF, WESLEY; Elizabethtown Area HS; Manheim, PA; (3); Church Yth Grp; Drama Clb; Bsktbl; Golf; Trk; Wrstlng; Bus Mrktng.

COSKIO, MELANIE; Carbondale Area JR SR HS; Carbondale, PA; (2); Church Yth Grp; Hosp Aide; Ski Clb; Spanish Clb; U Scranton; Law.

COSMO, NICHOLAS; Archbishop Wood HS; Huntingdon Valley, PA; (2); 37/254.

COSNEK, CARRIE; Avonworth JR SR HS; Pittsburgh, PA; (4); 1/100; Church Yth Grp; Latin Clb; Concert Band; Mrchg Band; Yrbk Ed-Chief; Lit Mag; Var L Bsktbl; Var L Sftbl; High Hon Roll; NHS; U Proyost Schlrshp 87-91; Engr Merit Schlrshp 87-91; U Pittsburgh; Elec Engr.

COSPER, SUSAN; Fairview HS; Fairview, PA; (3); 10/170; Sec 4-H; Hosp Aide; Ski Clb; Orch; Var Socr; JV Sftbl; Var Swmmng; Hon Roll; NHS; Dist, Regn & ST Orch 86-87.

COSSABOON, DAVID; Unionville HS; Chadds Ford, PA; (4); 54/317; Computer Clb; FBLA; Math Clb; Mu Alpha Theta; Crs Cntry; Capt Trk; High Hon Roll; Hon Roll; Mu Alpha Theta Awd; St Schlr; VA Tech; Engrng.

COSSABOON, STACY; Spring-Ford SR HS; Royersford, PA; (3); 128/258; Debate Tm; German Clb; Girl Scts; Hosp Aide; Math Clb; SADD; Band; Church Choir; Concert Band; Jazz Band; Girl Scout Slvr Awd 85; Ldrshp Awd For Girl Scouting 84; Bloomsburg Coll; Pltcl Sci.

COSSACK, TRACEY; West Hazleton HS; Nuremberg, PA; (3); 33/213; Pres Church Yth Grp; Science Clb; Thesps; Trs Band; Chorus; Trs Mrchg Band; School Play; High Hon Roll; JP Sousa Awd; Pres Schlr.

COSSICK, TERRI; Laurel Highlands HS; Uniontown, PA; (3); 4-H; Girl Scts; Office Aide; Var Capt Bsktbl; Var Sftbl; Hon Roll; Phy Therapy.

COSSITOR, RICHARD; Exeter Twp SR HS; Reading, PA; (4); Sec Trs Exploring; Trs Key Clb; Pres Trs Spanish Clb; Varsity Clb; VP Jr Cls; VP Sr Cls; Var Crs Cntry; Var Trk; Var Capt Wrstlng; Jr NHS; All Div Wrstlng Div Chmps 86-87; All Cnty Crss Cntry Chmps 83-86; Hmcmng Crt 87; US Navy; Nuclear Pgm.

COST, CATHY; Lakeland HS; Clarks Summit, PA; (4); 9/146; Spanish Clb; Yrbk Stf; Hon Roll; NHS; Boston Arch Ctr; Arch.

COSTA, CHERYL; Central Bucks HS East; Danboro, PA; (4); 54/470; Drama Clb; Chorus; Flag Corp; Madrigals; Mrchg Band; Hon Roll; Bucks Cnty Nrsng Assn Schlrshp 87; Cnty Chorus 84-87; East Stroudsburg ST U Of PA.

COSTA, PHILIP; Upper Dublin HS; Oreland, PA; (3); 5/300; Drama Clb; Intnl Clb; Ski Clb; Varsity Clb; Band; Chorus; School Musical; Variety Show; Bsktbl; Var Capt Socr; 1st Tm All Leag Sccr 86.

COSTA, TINA; Penn Hills SR HS; Verona, PA; (4); 58/609; AFS; Spanish Clb; Concert Band; Mrchg Band; Orch; Pep Band; School Musical; School Play; Mgr Swing Chorus; Yrbk Stf; Penn Hills Womens Clb Nrsng Schlrshp 87; IN U; Nrsng.

COSTABILE, RICHARD; Dover Area HS; Dover, PA; (4); JA; Spanish Clb; Varsity Clb; Var JV Socr; Var Trk; Hon Roll; York Technical Inst; Elec.

COSTANTINI, EILEEN; Pennsbury HS; Levittown, PA; (4); 182/771; Rep Frsh Cls; Rep Soph Cls; Bsktbl; Var L Fld Hcky; Var L Sftbl; Hon Roll; Stu Mnth 83-85; Bloomsburg.

COSTANTINO, MICHAEL; Wyoming Area HS; West Pittston, PA; (4); 64/240; Art Clb; Church Yth Grp; Nwsp Stf; Hon Roll; JETS Awd; Mc Cann; Mrktng.

COSTANZA, DEBBIE; Bishop Mc Devitt HS; Philadelphia, PA; (3); Art Clb; Dance Clb; Ski Clb; SADD; Fshn Merch.

COSTANZO, SARA; Dunmore HS; Dunmore, PA; (3); Drama Clb; French Clb; Latin Clb; School Musical; School Play; Variety Show; Stat Bsktbl; Mgr(s); Trk; Hon Roll; Accntnt.

COSTELLA, SEAN; Danville Area HS; Danville, PA; (2); Boy Scts; Computer Clb; Latin Clb; Ski Clb; High Hon Roll; Pres Acdmc Fit Awd 86; Latin Hon Soc 87; Penn ST; Chem Engrng.

COSTELLIC, ROBERT P; Penn-Trafford HS; Irwin, PA; (3); JCL; Latin Clb; Varsity Clb; Jazz Band; Im Ftbl; Var Golf; Im Sftbl; High Hon Roll; Hon Roll; Prfct Atten Awd; Pre-Med.

COSTELLO, CAROLE; Sun Valley HS; Aston, PA; (4); Pres Drama Clb; JA; SADD; Band; Concert Band; Mrchg Band; School Musical; Variety Show; Nwsp Stf; VP Capt Trk; Acad All-Amer 86; Mst Talented Of SR Class 87; Broadcast Comm.

COSTELLO, JUDY; Norristown Area HS; Norristown, PA; (2); 36/459; Church Yth Grp; Ski Clb; Concert Band; Mrchg Band; Im Bsktbl; JV Cheerleading; JV Sftbl; Photo.

COSTELLO, KEITH; Valley Forge Military Acad; Norristown, PA; (3); ROTC; School Play; Stage Crew; Im Bsbl; Im Bsktbl; JV Ftbl; Im Sftbl; Im Swmmng; JV Wrstlng; Mnl Of Arms Effcncy Bdg 85-87; Father Fontain Awd; Const Engr.

COSTELLO, KELLY; Northwestern Lehigh HS; Schnecksville, PA; (4); 7/158; Am Leg Aux Girls St; Nwsp Stf; Stu Cncl; Cheerleading; Trk; Dnfth Awd; NHS; 4-H; Chorus; Congressional Schlrs Prog 87; Coach-Knee Hi Chrldrs 84-86; U Of MI; Med.

COSTELLO, LINDA; Lancaster Catholic HS; Lancaster, PA; (3); 80/213; Church Yth Grp; Latin Clb; Model UN; Red Cross Aide; VP SADD; Stage Crew; JV Sftbl; Var Trk; Im Vllybl; Serteen Awd 87; Red Cross Awd 86; Poltcl Sci.

COSTELLO, TODD; Meadville Area SR HS; Meadville, PA; (2); Im Badmtn; High Hon Roll; Continentl Math Leag 3rd 86; Cert Achvt Natl Hstry Day-Hnrbl Mntn 87.

COSTENBADER, STEPHEN; Palmerton HS; Palmerton, PA; (3); 4/163; Boy Scts; Church Choir; Var L Crs Cntry; Var L Trk; Acdmc Awd In Spnsh & Algebra 85-86; Engrng.

COSTENTINE, COLETTE; Ambridge Area HS; Freedom, PA; (3); Church Yth Grp; Pep Clb; Band; Concert Band; Mrchg Band; Pep Band; Symp Band; Hon Roll; Pharm.

COSTIGAN III, JAMES J; Cardinal O Hara HS; Havertown, PA; (3); 7/710; Cmnty Wkr; Rep French Clb; Rep SADD; Ed Nwsp Stf; Lit Mag; Rep Frsh Cls; Rep Soph Cls; Rep Jr Cls; Rep Sr Cls; Rep Stu Cncl; Outstndng Achvt Sci, Art, & Frnch 84-85; Future Ldrs Tmrrw; 1st Pl DE Cnty Sci Fair 85-86; Duke U; Bus.

COTELLESSE, JERRY; West Catholic Boys HS; Morgantown, PA; (4); 40/265; JA; High Hon Roll; Hon Roll; NHS; Pres Schlr; Ntl Hnr Soc; Pres Acad Ftns Awd; Kutztown U; Mktg.

COTHREN, JEFF; Council Rock HS; Newtown, PA; (3); 134/968; Church Yth Grp; Drama Clb; School Play; Stage Crew; Var Crs Cntry; Var L Trk; Hon Roll; NHS.

COTT, TRAVIS; Riverside HS; Fombell, PA; (2); Computer Clb; Spanish Clb; Var Bowling; Var Golf; High Hon Roll; Mech Engrng.

COTTAGE, MICHELE; North Allegheny HS; Sewickley, PA; (3); 180/660; Art Clb; Office Aide; Im Vllybl; Hon Roll; Arch.

COTTENDEN, SUSAN; Phil-Mont Christian Acad; Hatboro, PA; (3); Church Yth Grp; Chorus; Church Choir; Var Bsktbl; Var Fld Hcky; Var Trk; High Hon Roll; Hon Roll; Ntl Merit Ltr.

COTTER, DANIELLE; Berks Christian Schl; Pottstown, PA; (3); 6/19; Church Yth Grp; Ski Clb; Trk; MV Track,Swimmer 85-86; Coaches Cup Track 87; Child Care.

COTTER, VANESSA; Haverford SR HS; Drexel Hill, PA; (2); Hon Roll.

COTTERALL, CHRISTINE C; Cardinal O Hara HS; Springfield, PA; (4); 24/772; Church Yth Grp; German Clb; Math Clb; Service Clb; SADD; Hon Roll; NHS; Ntl Merit SF; Stage Crew; German Natl Hon Soc 86; Cardinal O Hara Schlstc Awd Bio 85; Pres Awd Acdmc Excllnc 85-86; Engrng.

COTTOM, JACKI; Mc Keesport HS; Mc Keesport, PA; (4); 21/410; AFS; Church Yth Grp; Library Aide; Office Aide; Pep Clb; Acpl Chr; Church Choir; School Musical; High Hon Roll; NHS; Amercn Legn Awd 84; Penn ST U; Biomdcl Engrng.

COTTRELL, DAVID C; Selinsgrive Area HS; Winfield, PA; (2); Socr; Hon Roll; Math.

COTTRELL, GLENN; Parkland HS; Allentown, PA; (3); 20/481; Aud Vis; Church Yth Grp; Drama Clb; Exploring; Chorus; School Play; Stag Crew; High Hon Roll; NHS; Intl Thespian Scty 86; Arch.

COUDRIET, VICTORIA; St Marys Area HS; St Marys, PA; (3); Bsktbl; L Sftbl; JV Vllybl; Hon Roll; Forest Ranger.

COUGHENOUR, GAIL; Hershey HS; Hershey, PA; (4); 50/197; Hos Aide; School Play; Stage Crew; Lit Mag; Var Crs Cntry; Var L Tennis; Va L Trk; High Hon Roll; Hon Roll; Masonic Awd; Jobs Dghtrs Schlrshp, Se Breeze Awd 87; Shippensburg U; Crmnl Jstc.

COUGHLIN, JENNIFER; Smithfield-Ridgebury-Ulster HS; Wes Sunbury, PA; (4); Pres Trs Church Yth Grp; Spanish Clb; Band; Chorus Color Guard; Mrchg Band; Yrbk Stf; Var Trk; High Hon Roll; Hon Roll Slippery Rock U; Accntng.

COUGHLIN, LINDA; Notre Dame HS; Easton, PA; (2); Church Yt Grp; Bsktbl; Trk; Bus.

COULL, DONNA; Clarion Area HS; Clarion, PA; (3); Library Aide; Tr Pep Clb; SADD; Chorus; Yrbk Stf; JV L Cheerleading; Var L Ftbl; Var Wrstlng; Hon Roll; Pres Schlr; Dntl.

COUNTERMAN, CHRISTINA; Bangor Area SR HS; Bangor, PA; (3) 34/190; Church Yth Grp; Cmnty Wkr; Trs Exploring; Office Aide; Colo Guard; Mrchg Band; Stage Crew; Yrbk Stf; Hon Roll; Cert Merit Germa 86-87; Human Svcs.

COUNTRYMAN, MIKE; Berlin Brothersvalley HS; Berlin, PA; (4); 20 90; 4-H; FFA; Band; Nwsp Phtg; Yrbk Phtg; Socr; 4-H Awd; Hon Rol NHS; PA St 4-H Wnnr Phtgrphy Natl 4-H Clb Cngrss 86; Wstrn Rgnl Sta Farmer FFA 86; 3rd St Dairy Jdgng 86; Penn St; Dairy Nutritionist.

COUPER, LEANNE; Quaker Valley HS; Sewickley, PA; (4); 62/165 Church Yth Grp; English Clb; Chorus; School Musical; Stat Bsktbl; In Bowling; L Var Sftbl; Var L Vllybl; Office Aide; Varsity Clb; Teen Ins 85-86; Robert Morris Coll; Comms.

COURCHAIN, EDWARD; Archbishop Wood Boys HS; Warminster, PA (2); Cmnty Wkr; Red Cross Aide; SADD; Coach Actv; Mgr(s); Crdlgy.

COURIE, CARLA; Canon Mc Millan HS; Canonsburg, PA; (4); Ches Clb; French Clb; Science Clb; Varsity Clb; Nwsp Stf; Cheerleading; Ho Roll; Homecmng Ct 87; U Of Pittsburgh; Psych.

COURSER, KEN; Connellsville Area SR HS; Dunbar, PA; (3); 125/525 German Clb; Office Aide; Miltry.

COURTNEY, LORI; Sharpsville Area HS; Greenville, PA; (3); 4-H Band; Chorus; Concert Band; Mrchg Band; 4-H Awd; Hon Roll; NHS Nrsng.

COURTNEY, VANESSA; Cambridge Springs HS; Cambridge Spg, PA (3); 32/93; Am Leg Aux Girls St; Girl Scts; Hosp Aide; Teachers Aide Band; Chorus; Color Guard; Concert Band; Mrchg Band; Pep Band; Me Tech.

COURTOT, ROBERT; Penn Cambria HS; Lilly, PA; (3); Boy Scts; Trk Hon Roll.

COURTWRIGHT, JACOB; West Greene HS; Wind Ridge, PA; (4); 7 115; VP FFA; Trk; Hon Roll.

COURY, MARY; Homer-Center HS; Homer City, PA; (3); Church Yt Grp; French Clb; Library Aide; SADD; Concert Band; Mrchg Band; Schoo Musical; Nwsp Rptr; Nwsp Stf; Hon Roll; U Of Pittsburgh.

COUSINS, KAREN; Acad Of Notre Dame; Rosemont, PA; (3); Hos Aide; Service Clb; Off SADD; Variety Show; Var Cheerleading; Hon Rol Camera Clb; Church Yth Grp; Cmnty Wkr; Dance Clb; Natl Latin Exar Cum Laude 87; Phys Thrpy.

COUSLER, JULIE; Central HS; York, PA; (3); Drama Clb; Ski Clb Nwsp Rptr; Nwsp Stf; Sec Soph Cls; Stu Cncl; Cheerleading; Pom Por Powder Puff Ftbl; Trk; Temple U; Advrtsg.

COVAL, KARLENE; West Scranton HS; Scranton, PA; (2); Spanish Clb Speech Tm; Stage Crew; Var Cheerleading; High Hon Roll; Hon Rol VFW Awd; Marywood; Math Tchr.

COVERT, JASON; Southern Huntingdon Co Area HS; Orbisonia, PA (3); 25/150; Church Yth Grp; 4-H; Varsity Clb; Chorus; Church Choi School Play; Swing Chorus; Var Bsbl; JV Bsktbl; Ntl Merit Schol; Bu Mgnt.

COVIELLO, ALISA; Bishop O Hara HS; Jessup, PA; (2); 8/127; Churc Yth Grp; Latin Clb; Spanish Clb; Cheerleading; High Hon Roll; Prfc Atten Awd; Art Awd 85-86; Med.

COVONE, TRACY; Freeport Area SR HS; Freeport, PA; (3); 36/213 Church Yth Grp; Pres Stu Cncl; Var Bsktbl; Trk; Hon Roll; Prfct Atte Awd; Penn ST; Arch.

COWAN, CHRISTOPHER; Fort Le Boeuf HS; Waterford, PA; (3); 75 219; Church Yth Grp; Model UN; Rep Soph Cls; Rep Stu Cncl; In Bowling; Var L Ftbl; JV Trk; Im Vllybl; JV Wrstlng; Hon Roll; Slipper Rock U; Sports Med.

COWAN, KRISTINA CAROLINE; Mifflinburg Area HS; Mufflinburg PA; (2); French Clb; Hosp Aide; Library Aide; Chorus; High Hon Roll; Ho Roll; NHS; Vlntr Svc Pin 86; 2nd Pl Piano Recital Cert 85; French.

COWAN, LYNN; Ringold HS; Monogahela, PA; (4); Aud/Vis; Churc Yth Grp; PAVAS; Ski Clb; Acpl Chr; Chorus; School Musical; Stage Crew Variety Show; Waynesburg Coll; Communctns.

COWAN, WENDY; Shenango JR SR HS; New Castle, PA; (4); 11/111 Camera Clb; Hosp Aide; Intnl Clb; Red Cross Aide; Yrbk Stf; Jr NHS NHS; Ntl Merit Ltr; NEDT Awd; Pres Schlr; Masonic Svc Awds 85-87 Hnr Roll 83-87; Carow Coll Poetry Cntst 86-87; Grove City Coll; Psych.

COWARD, MICHELLE; Mars Area HS; Valencia, PA; (4); 10/141; GAA Varsity Clb; Yrbk Phtg; Rep Sr Cls; Rep Stu Cncl; Var Trk; Var Vllybl High Hon Roll; NHS; PA ST U; Engrng.

COWHER, DENNIS; Claysburg-Kimmel HS; Queen, PA; (4); 1/52 Varsity Clb; Nwsp Sprt Ed; Trs Soph Cls; Var Jr Cls; Stu Cncl; Capt Bsbl Capt Bsktbl; Capt Ftbl; NHS; U S Mltry Acad.

COWHER, STACEY; Claysburg-Kimmel HS; Imler, PA; (2); 30/97 Camera Clb; Concert Band; Drill Tm; Flag Corp; Sec Frsh Cls; Stenogrphr

COWLEY, AMY; Bethlehem Center HS; Brownsville, PA; (4); 19/143 GAA; Ski Clb; Spanish Clb; Chorus; High Hon Roll; Hon Roll; CA U O PA; Pre-Phrmcy.

COX, CHRISTENA; Beaver Falls SR HS; Beaver Falls, PA; (3); Churc Yth Grp; French Clb; Science Clb; Church Choir; Stage Crew; Yrbk Phtg Mgr(s); Hon Roll; Law.

COX, COURTNEY; Montrose Area JR SR HS; Brackney, PA; (3); Cmnty Wkr; Sec VP 4-H; Sec Spanish Clb; SADD; Varsity Clb; Drill Tm; Yrb Stf; JV Crs Cntry; Var Mgr(s); JV Socr; Aerospc Sci.

COX, HEATHER; Meadville Area SR HS; Meadville, PA; (2); Frencl Clb; Nwsp Stf; Yrbk Stf; Stu Cncl; Cheerleading; Score Keeper; JV Vllybl Hon Roll; Prfct Atten Awd.

COX, KATHRYN S; Wellsboro Area HS; Wellsboro, PA; (1); 2/200; Acpl Chr; Band; Chorus; Var Cheerleading; Var Crs Cntry; JV Trk; High Hon Roll; Drama Clb; Concert Band; Mrchg Band; Bucknell; Englsh.

COX, KEVIN; Pine Forge Acad; Richmond, VA; (4); 2/79; Acpl Chr; Yrbk Ed-Chief; Pres Soph Cls; Bsktbl; Score Keeper; High Hon Roll; Sal; Howard U; Mech Engnrng.

COX, MELISSA A; South Side Beaver HS; Clinton, PA; (3); 58/130; Am Leg Aux Girls St; Church Yth Grp; Girl Scts; VICA; Chorus; Stu Cncl; High Hon Roll; Hon Roll; Hnrs Clb.

COX, MICHAEL S; Lancaster Catholic HS; Lititz, PA; (4); 46/195; School Musical; School Play; Variety Show; Nwsp Stf; Hon Roll; Awd-Outstndng Serv Rtrded Ctzns 87; Villanova U; Finnc.

COX, MICHELLE; East Pennsboro Area HS; Marysville, PA; (2); Church Yth Grp; Spanish Clb; Band; Church Choir; Concert Band; Mrchg Band; Pep Band; Tennis; Hon Roll; Bible Quizzng Top Scorer Awd 87; Toccoa Fls Bibl Coll; Math.

COX, THOMAS; Scranton Central HS; Scranton, PA; (4); 99/307; French Clb; Pep Clb; Ski Clb; SADD; Im Bsktbl; Var Crs Cntry; High Hon Roll; Hon Roll; U Of Scranton; Bus Manag.

COX, TIMOTHY; Coatesville Area SR HS; Coatesville, PA; (3); 50/517; Ski Clb; Spanish Clb; Chorus; Rep Frsh Cls; Rep Soph Cls; Pres Jr Cls; Rep Stu Cncl; Hon Roll; Pre-Law.

COXE, BRENDA; Hazleton HS; Hazleton, PA; (3); Art Clb; Debate Tm; 4-H; FBLA; FHA; Speech Tm; SADD; VICA; Vllybl; NHS; Luzerne County CC; Food Svc.

COXON, AMY; Central Dauphin HS; Harrisburg, PA; (3); 38/369; Rep Church Yth Grp; Chorus; Madrigals; Hon Roll; NHS; Lab Asst & Yth For Christ Clb 86-87; Word Of Life Teens Involved Competition 84-87; Liberty U; Elem Educ.

COY, MARIE; Penns Manor HS; Clymer, PA; (3); 30/102; Church Yth Grp; SADD; Band; Concert Band; Flag Corp; Mrchg Band; School Musical; Yrbk Stf; Hon Roll; Prfct Atten Awd; IN U Of PA; Elem Ed.

COYLE, ARTHUR; Sayre Area HS; S Waverly, PA; (3); Var L Bsbl; Var L Ftbl; Hon Roll.

COYLE, CHERIE; Cardinal Dougherty HS; Philadelphia, PA; (3); 75/670; Church Yth Grp; Chorus; Rep Stu Cncl; Hon Roll; NHS; Cert Athl Accmplshmt 86; Cert Acdmc Prfcncy Typng 87; Cert Commndtn Bus Ed Cmte 87; Med.

COYLE, DAN; Freeport SR HS; Freeport, PA; (3); 55/210; Cmnty Wkr; Concert Band; L Bsbl; Hon Roll; Music.

COYLE, DONNA; Nazareth SR HS; Nazareth, PA; (4); 19/243; Drama Clb; Key Clb; Office Aide; Chorus; Drill Tm; School Musical; Capt Twrlr; JV Vllybl; Hon Roll; Pres Schlr; Outstndg Achvt-Actg Awd 87; Yth Schlrshp 87; PA ST U.

COYLE, KRISTEN; East Pennsboro HS; Camp Hill, PA; (3); 9/187; Drama Clb; Pres French Clb; Model UN; Ski Clb; Flag Corp; Yrbk Stf; Stu Cncl; Trk; High Hon Roll; NHS; Intl Bus.

COYNE, PATRICIA; Archbishop Kennedy HS; Conshohocken, PA; (4); 13/171; French Clb; JA; Var L Crs Cntry; Var L Trk; Hon Roll; Ursinus; Bus Admin.

CRABLE, JENNIFER; Uniontown Area HS; Uniontown, PA; (4); 20/287; French Clb; Office Aide; Trs Ski Clb; Band; Mrchg Band; Yrbk Stf; Twrlr; French Hon Soc; High Hon Roll; NHS; Mjrtt Capt & Band Treas 86-87; Pres Acad Ftns Awd 87; U Of Pittsburgh; Acctng.

CRABLE, SARA; Uniontown Area HS; Uniontown, PA; (3); 4/318; French Clb; Ski Clb; Band; Concert Band; Jazz Band; Mrchg Band; Nwsp Stf; Yrbk Stf; Trs Jr Cls; Sec Sr Cls; Delg Rtry Clb Wrld Affrs Inst 87; Fayette All-Cnty Band 85 & 86; PA ST U; Bus.

CRAFA, DANA; Pius X HS; Bangor, PA; (3); #5 In Class; Drama Clb; School Musical; School Play; Bsktbl; Sftbl; High Hon Roll; NCTE Awd; NHS; Physicians Assistant.

CRAFT, LYNNELL; Conestoga SR HS; Devon, PA; (2); Sec Church Yth Grp; Chorus; Church Choir; Bsktbl; Mgr(s); Trk; Accounting.

CRAFT, MELISSA; Punxsutawney HS; Punxsutawney, PA; (3); Church Yth Grp; SADD; Band; Color Guard; Drill Tm; Flag Corp; Mrchg Band; Twrlr; Twrlrs Clb 85-87; Wrstlng Assn 86-87; Bsbl Assn 86-87; Nrsng.

CRAFT, PAMELA; Emmaus HS; Emmaus, PA; (3); Key Clb; Hon Roll; NHS; Hnrbl Mntn-Lehigh Vly Cmmtte On Emplymnt 87; Presdntl Acad Fitness Awd 85; Phrmcy.

CRAFT, STEVE; Somerset Area SR HS; Somerset, PA; (4); English Clb; JA; Mu Alpha Theta; Ski Clb; Spanish Clb; High Hon Roll; Hon Roll; NHS; Prfct Atten Awd; Rotary Awd; Grove City Coll; Mech Engnrng.

CRAFTS, WENDY; Lakeland Jr Sr HS; Olyphant, PA; (3); FHA; JA; SADD; Color Guard; Flag Corp; Hon Roll; Pre-Law.

CRAGEN, MICHELE; Moon SR HS; Coraopolis, PA; (3); 32/308; Pres Church Yth Grp; Key Clb; Yrbk Stf; Trs Jr Cls; Trs Sr Cls; Trs Stu Cncl; Var L Socr; Var L Trk; High Hon Roll; Hon Roll; Comm.

CRAGLE, DANIELLE M; Bishop Hoban HS; Wilkes-Barre, PA; (2); Church Yth Grp; Hosp Aide; Mu Alpha Theta; Ski Clb; Chorus; Concert Band; Mrchg Band; High Hon Roll; Mu Alpha Theta Awd; NEDT Awd.

CRAGLE, KRISTIN; Lake-Lehman HS; Dallas, PA; (2); Church Yth Grp; Dance Clb; Ski Clb; Hon Roll; Jr NHS; Penn ST; Psychlgy.

CRAGO, BRANDON; Carmichaels Area HS; Carmichaels, PA; (4); 27/101; Boy Scts; French Clb; Letterman Clb; Pep Clb; Varsity Clb; JV Var Bsktbl; Golf; Im Vllybl; High Hon Roll; Lion Awd; CA U PA; Engrng.

CRAIG, CATHERINE; Central Catholic HS; Whitehall, PA; (3); Church Yth Grp; Key Clb; Math Clb; Im JV Bsktbl; Coach Actv; Im Ftbl; JV Score Keeper; Im Vllybl; Wt Lftg; Hon Roll; Bst Def Awd Keystone Bsktbl Camp 87; ST Champ PIAA-AAA Bsktbl Tm 86-87.

CRAIG, CINDY; Saint Cyril Acad; West Chester, PA; (3); Dance Clb; Debate Tm; Key Clb; Science Clb; School Play; Nwsp Stf; Yrbk Stf; Lit Mag; Hon Roll; Prfct Atten Awd; Long Isl U Schlrshp 87; Long Isl U-Southampton; Bio.

CRAIG, DONNA; West Allegheny HS; Imperial, PA; (4); 14/200; Pres VP Key Clb; Office Aide; Spanish Clb; SADD; VP Soph Cls; Stu Cncl; Capt Cheerleading; Powder Puff Ftbl; High Hon Roll; Rotary Awd; Edinboro; Elem Ed.

CRAIG, JAMIE; Union HS; Sligo, PA; (3); Church Yth Grp; Dance Clb; Drama Clb; English Clb; FCA; Hosp Aide; JA; Math Clb; Pep Clb; Yrbk Stf; Pre Law.

CRAIG, JENNIFER; Danville HS; Danville, PA; (3); Key Clb; Nwsp Stf; Yrbk Rptr; Mat Maids.

CRAIG, JENNIFER; Mohawk HS; New Castle, PA; (4); 8/137; Pres Church Yth Grp; Dance Clb; VP FHA; Spanish Clb; Band; Mrchg Band; Hon Roll; NHS; Lehigh Cnty CC; Physcl Thrpst.

CRAIG, LISA; Lawrence Co Vo Tech; New Castle, PA; (3); Art Clb; OEA; Mgr(s); DECA; Mrktng.

CRAIG, LORI; Snyder HS; Middleburg, PA; (2); 21/94; Church Yth Grp; 4-H; Science Clb; Varsity Clb; Chorus; School Musical; Var L Bsktbl; Var L Fld Hcky; JV L Sftbl; Military Coll; Vet.

CRAIG, LYNNE; Freedom HS; Bethlehem, PA; (4); 24/433; Art Clb; Science Clb; SADD; Nwsp Stf; Yrbk Stf; JV Bsktbl; JV Var Sftbl; NHS; Pres Schlr; Congrssnl Schlr 86; Lehigh U; Biochmcl Engrng.

CRAIG, MELISSA; Aliquippa JR SR HS; Aliquippa, PA; (3); French Clb; Jr Cls; Cheerleading; Hon Roll; Penn ST; Law.

CRAIG, MICHAEL; Carlynton JR/SR HS; Carnegie, PA; (2); Computer Clb; Exploring; FBLA; FNA; Hosp Aide; Math Clb; Math Tm; Science Clb; Teachers Aide; VICA; WVU; Meteorlgy.

CRAIG, SANDY; Avon Grove HS; Landenberg, PA; (3); 6/210; SADD; Concert Band; Jazz Band; Mrchg Band; School Musical; Cheerleading; Vllybl; High Hon Roll; NHS; Archtctr.

CRAIG, SHANNON; Greensburg Central Catholic HS; Murrysville, PA; (2); Psych.

CRAIG, SUZANNE; Connellsville SR HS; Normalville, PA; (2); 15/580; Dance Clb; Exploring; Hosp Aide; Mrchg Band; Orch; Nwsp Rptr; Rep Stu Cncl; French Hon Soc; High Hon Roll; Hon Roll; 1st Pl Regnl & ST Awd PA JR Acad Sci 86; 2nd Pl Regnl Awd PA JR Acad Sci 87; Med.

CRAIG, WILLIAM; Mc Guffey HS; Claysville, PA; (3); Church Yth Grp; Computer Clb; Spanish Clb; Rep Soph Cls; Rep Jr Cls; Rep Stu Cncl; Var L Bsbl; Var L Bsktbl; Var L Ftbl; High Hon Roll; Mbr Cntry Confrnce Champs 85; Natl Athletic Merit, Obsrvr Reprtr All-Dstrct Bsebl Tm 87; Law.

CRAIGHEAD, BENJAMIN; State Coll Area Intermediate HS; State College, PA; (1); 62/450; Hon Roll; Johns Hopkns Math & Vrbl Natl Tlnt Srch 85; Hgh Scrr Math SAT; Sci.

CRAIN, SHELLY; Loyalsock Township HS; Montoursville, PA; (3); 4-H; French Clb; Key Clb; Latin Clb; Letterman Clb; Ski Clb; Varsity Clb; Yrbk Stf; JV Var Bsktbl; Var Sftbl; Mrn Geolgy.

CRALEY, JAMES; Red Lion SR HS; Felton, PA; (4); 45/330; Church Yth Grp; Band; Chorus; Jazz Band; Mrchg Band; Orch; Pep Band; School Musical; Symp Band; Hon Roll; Music Ed.

CRALEY, TIM; Red Lion SR HS; Felton, PA; (4); 108/330; Church Yth Grp; Band; Concert Band; Jazz Band; Mrchg Band; Orch; Pep Band; School Musical; Swing Chorus; Symp Band; Elctrncs.

CRAM, MARGARET; St Hubert Catholic HS; Philadelphia, PA; (4); 53/364; Gym; Outstndg Achvmnt Home Ec; CSF Tutoring Cert; Immaculata Coll; Math.

CRAMER, BECKY; Mon Valley Catholic HS; Monongahela, PA; (2); Var L Bsktbl; Var L Sftbl; Var L Vllybl; Pre Med.

CRAMER, BRUCE; Purchase Line HS; Punxsutawney, PA; (3); Church Yth Grp; Nwsp Rptr; Yrbk Stf; Trk; Hon Roll; Law Enfrcmnt.

CRAMER, CHRISTOPHER; Hempfield HS; Columbia, PA; (3); 25/400; Dance Clb; Chorus; Jazz Band; Orch; School Musical; Var L Ftbl; Var L Wrstlng; Hon Roll; Penn ST; Mech Engr.

CRAMER, CHRISTOPHER; Purchase Line HS; Punxsutawney, PA; (2); Varsity Clb; Var L Trk; High Hon Roll; Hon Roll.

CRAMER, JEFF; Eastern York HS; York, PA; (2); Church Yth Grp; Drama Clb; Chorus; Nwsp Rptr; JV Bsbl; JV Bsktbl; Var Golf; JV Wrstlng; High Hon Roll; Hon Roll.

CRAMER, JENNIFER; Stroudsburg HS; Stroudsburg, PA; (3); 3/243; Drama Clb; French Clb; Chorus; Church Choir; Concert Band; Mrchg Band; School Musical; Swing Chorus; High Hon Roll; Pres NHS; Fred Warings US Chorus 86; Among 5 Best Splrs Semifnlst Status 85; PA Miss Teen Pagent 87; Forgn Lang.

CRAMER, JULIA; Blue Ridge HS; Great Bend, PA; (4); Drama Clb; Hosp Aide; Ski Clb; Chorus; Yrbk Ed-Chief; Yrbk Phtg; Trs Jr Cls; Var Capt Bsktbl; Var L Cheerleading; NHS; Distngshd Achvr Scholar IUP 87-91; Robert Wood Mem Scholar 87; IN U PA; Nrsng.

CRAMER, LORI; United HS; Blairsville, PA; (4); 13/155; Band; Chorus; Nwsp Ed-Chief; Lit Mag; Off Stu Cncl; Var L Trk; Var Capt Twrlr; Hon Roll; Mu Alpha Theta Awd; NHS; Penn ST; Lndscp Arch.

CRAMER, MARK; Peters Township HS; Mc Murray, PA; (2); Science Clb; Band; Concert Band; Mrchg Band; Orch; Pep Band; School Musical; Hon Roll; JETS 86-87.

CRAMER, MELISSA; Hempfield HS; Landisville, PA; (3); Drama Clb; Chorus; Drill Tm; Flag Corp; Hon Roll; Best Garmnt Awd 87; Hempfield Womns Clb Garmnt Cntst 3rd Pl 87; Bus.

CRAMER, MISSY; Belle Vernon Area HS; Fayette City, PA; (3); Art Clb; Church Yth Grp; Pep Clb; Sec Frsh Cls; Stu Cncl; Cheerleading; Hon Roll; Psych.

CRAMER, ROBERT; Blacklick Valley JR SR HS; Twin Rocks, PA; (2); 1/110; Camera Clb; Church Yth Grp; Pres 4-H; Library Aide; NFL; School Play; Off Stu Cncl; High Hon Roll; NHS; Acdmc All Amrcn Awd 86-87; Presdntl Acadmc Ftnss Awd 85-86; High Hnr Dept Awds Bio, Geo, Wrld Hstry; IN U Of PA; Sci.

CRAMER, STUART; Upper Merion HS; King Of Prussia, PA; (3); 18/300; Math Tm; Spanish Clb; JV Var Bsbl; Im Vllybl; High Hon Roll; Hon Roll; NHS; Prfct Atten Awd; DE U.

CRAMER, TERESA; New Brighton SR HS; New Brighton, PA; (4); 30/141; GAA; SADD; School Play; Nwsp Rptr; JV Trk; High Hon Roll; Hon Roll; Acdmc All Amer Awd 86; Natl Ldrshp & Svc Awd 86; Edward Dempster Merrick Awd 87; Pittsburgh Art Inst; Cmmrcl Art.

CRAMER, TRACY; Elizabethtown Area HS; Bainbridge, PA; (2); FFA; Bus.

CRAMER, VALERIE; Somerset Area SR HS; Friedens, PA; (3); Pres Church Yth Grp; Hosp Aide; SADD; Chorus; Yrbk Stf; Rep Stu Cncl; Hon Roll; Cmpstn Hire Hndcppd Awd 86-87.

CRAMER, VICKY; West Greene HS; New Free Port, PA; (3); 6/130; Sec Library Aide; Office Aide; Band; Church Choir; Mrchg Band; Nwsp Stf; Sec Frsh Cls; Sec Trs Stu Cncl; High Hon Roll; Hon Roll; PA JR Acat Sci Regnl 1st,3rd Pl 86; Sci Awd 86; U Pittsburgh; Physcl Thrpy.

CRAMER, WOLFGANG; Bishop Mc Devitt HS; Harrisburg, PA; (3); 20/220; FBLA; Speech Tm; Rep Soph Cls; Trs Jr Cls; Stu Cncl; Hon Roll; NHS.

CRAMSEY, CAROLYN; Emmaus HS; Allentown, PA; (3); 83/546; Church Yth Grp; Girl Scts; Hon Roll; Penn ST; Early Educ.

CRAMSEY, DENISE L; Central Catholic HS; Macungie, PA; (4); 4/208; Math Clb; Nwsp Sprt Ed; Stu Cncl; Bsktbl; Vllybl; NCTE Awd; NHS; Ntl Merit SF; Opt Clb Awd; Sheila Miller Memrl Awd Outstndng Wrtr Blair Smmr Schl Jrnlsm 86; Syracuse U; Jrnlsm.

CRANE, MARK; Greencastle Antrim HS; Greencastle, PA; (3); Letterman Clb; Varsity Clb; Sec Jr Cls; Var Bsbl; Var Bsktbl; Coach Actv; Var Ftbl; Hon Roll; Prfct Atten Awd; Voice Dem Awd; Acctng.

CRANN, DAN; St John Neumann HS; Philadelphia, PA; (3); 31/349; Dance Clb; Office Aide; Yrbk Stf; Stu Cncl; Var Bsktbl; High Hon Roll; Arch.

CRAPIS, MARY; Quigley HS; Sewickley, PA; (3); 32/83; Camera Clb; Math Tm; Service Clb; Yrbk Stf; Pres Frsh Cls; JV Var Bsktbl; Powder Puff Ftbl; Stat Trk; Hon Roll; Church Yth Grp; Cortez Peters Hnr Rll Paprs-Accrcy 87; Actvts Cmmtte 87; Math.

CRATTY, ADAM; Riverview HS; Oakmont, PA; (3); Camp Fr Inc; Varsity Clb; Bsbl; Bsktbl; Ftbl; Hon Roll.

CRATTY, COLLEEN; Belle Vernon Area HS; Belle Vernon, PA; (3); Band; Concert Band; Mrchg Band; Var L Bsktbl; Powder Puff Ftbl; Var L Sftbl; Capt Var Vllybl; High Hon Roll; Hon Roll; NHS; Outstndng Sci Stu Awd 85; US Air Force Acad; Arntcl Engr.

CRAUL, RAYMOND; Dover Area HS; Dover, PA; (3); Cmnty Wkr; Band; Concert Band; Mrchg Band; JV Bsbl; Im Bsktbl; Hon Roll; Crmnl Jstc.

CRAVEN, DOROTHY; Upper Dublin HS; Oreland, PA; (3); Church Yth Grp; Jazz Band; Mrchg Band; Var Bsktbl; Var Fld Hcky; NHS; Band; Chorus; Concert Band; Pep Band; Band-Dists & Regional French Horn 87; Orchestra-Dists & Regional French Horn 87; U Of MD; Phys Therapy.

CRAVEN, ROBIN; Big Beaver Falls SR HS; Beaver Falls, PA; (3); 61/170; Drama Clb; Chorus; School Musical; Pittsburgh Beauty Acad; Csmtlgy.

CRAVENER, PEGGYSUE; Highlands SR HS; Tarentum, PA; (3); Pres Church Yth Grp; FBLA; Pep Clb; Sec Trs Chorus; Off Jr Cls; Rep Stu Cncl; Jr NHS; Aud/Vis; Office Aide; Nwsp Stf; Gld Achvt Awd 87; 5th Pl Awd Imprmptu Spkng Comptn 87; Seton Hil Coll Ldrshp Smnr Rep 85; 5 Brwn Awds; Bus Admin.

CRAVENER, SHAWN; Neshaminy HS; Parkland, PA; (3); 66/770; Ice Hcky; Hon Roll; Prfct Atten Awd.

CRAVOTTA, SAMUEL; Tri Valley SR HS; Fairchance, PA; (2); Spanish Clb; Band; Concert Band; Mrchg Band; VP Frsh Cls; Sec Soph Cls; L Var Bsktbl; L Var Ftbl; High Hon Roll; NHS; All-Cnty Ftbl Tm 85; Trrfc 20 Bsktbll Tm Hnrbl Mntn 87.

CRAWFORD, ANDREW; Strath Haven HS; Wallingford, PA; (4); Aud/Vis; Cmnty Wkr; Office Aide; Red Cross Aide; High Hon Roll; NHS; Pres Schlr; Charles Marish Sci Awd 87; Sacred Heart Med Ctr Awd 87; S Meth U; Bio.

CRAWFORD, ANN; St Paul Cathedral HS; Pittsburgh, PA; (3); 1/53; Church Yth Grp; Hosp Aide; Latin Clb; VP Sec Red Cross Aide; Chorus; Ed Nwsp Rptr; Yrbk Stf; High Hon Roll; VP NHS; NEDT Awd; Cong Yth Ldrsshp Conf 86; PA Free Enterprise Wk 86.

CRAWFORD, CAROLYN; West Greene HS; New Freeport, PA; (2); Exploring; Band; Chorus; Color Guard; Var JV Bsktbl; JV Cheerleading; Var Sftbl; Var Trk; Hon Roll; WVU; Pdtrcn.

CRAWFORD, DAVID; Brockway Area HS; Brockway, PA; (3); Boy Scts; Exploring; Varsity Clb; Stage Crew; Stu Cncl; Var Bsbl; Var Bsktbl; Var Golf; Wt Lftg; DAR Awd.

CRAWFORD, JEFFREY; Connellsville Area HS; Connellsville, PA; (2).

CRAWFORD, JENNIFER; Hampton HS; Allison Park, PA; (4); 101/255; Cmnty Wkr; French Clb; Hosp Aide; Ski Clb; Hon Roll; Denison U; Psych.

CRAWFORD, KATHLEEN; Sacred Heart HS; Pittsburgh, PA; (4); 37/140; Church Yth Grp; French Clb; Service Clb; Yrbk Stf; Hon Roll; Robert Morris Coll; Accntng.

CRAWFORD, KATHLEEN; York County Vo-Tech Schl; York, PA; (4); 6/325; Am Leg Aux Girls St; Girl Scts; Varsity Clb; VICA; Band; Color Guard; Cheerleading; Mgr(s); High Hon Roll; NHS; Acad All Star 86-87.

CRAWFORD, KELLY; Tyrone Area HS; Tyrone, PA; (3); 11/209; Pres Church Yth Grp; Pres 4-H; Key Clb; NFL; Chorus; VP Jr Cls; VP Stu Cncl; High Hon Roll; Jr NHS; NHS; REA Yth Tour 85; Pres Clsrm 87; Juniata Coll; Pol Sci.

CRAWFORD, LESLIE; Strath-Haven HS; Swarthmore, PA; (3); Stu Cncl; Fld Hcky; Trk; Soc Of Women Engrs Awd Of Xclnc 87; Engrg.

CRAWFORD, LUKE; Brockway Area HS; Falls Crk, PA; (3); 33/110; Drama Clb; 4-H; Thesps; Sec Band; Chorus; Mrchg Band; School Musical; VP Sr Cls; DAR Awd; Boy Scts; Natl HS Choral Awd 87.

CRAWFORD, MICHELLE L; Christian School Of York; York, PA; (4); 14/58; Church Yth Grp; Hosp Aide; Band; Chorus; Church Choir; School Musical; Rep Stu Cncl; Fld Hcky; Hon Roll; Rapid Amer Schlrshp 87; Messiah Coll.

CRAWFORD, ROBERT; Blacklic Valley HS; Ebensburg, PA; (2); Ftbl; Trk; Hon Roll; NHS; Prfct Atten Awd.

CRAWFORD, ROBERT; Hazleton HS; Drums, PA; (3); 56/455; Ski Clb; Im Bsbl; Im Bsktbl; Var L Trk; Im Wt Lftg; Hon Roll; Intl Frgn Lang 87; Acdmc All Am 87; Engrng.

CRAWFORD, SCOTT; Richland HS; Gibsonia, PA; (3); Chess Clb; Var Capt Debate Tm; French Clb; Quiz Bowl; Speech Tm; Yrbk Bus Mgr; Trs Soph Cls; JV Var Ftbl; High Hon Roll; Pres NHS; North Hills Gifted Consortium Awds & Certs; Geneva Coll High Q Bowl Cert; U Of Pittsburg H S Bowl Cert; Ivy League; Law.

CRAWFORD, SHAWN JAMES; Richland HS; Gibsonia, PA; (4); Debate Tm; FBLA; VP JA; NFL; Nwsp Bus Mgr; Yrbk Bus Mgr; Var Ftbl; High Hon Roll; NHS; Ntl Merit Schol; U Of PA; Bus Econ.

CRAWFORD, TERRIE; Brownsville Area HS; W Brownsville, PA; (3); Trs Leo Clb; Library Aide; Variety Show; Lion Awd; CA U.

CRAWFORD, THERESA; Bradford Central Christian HS; Bradford, PA; (4); 4/26; VP Drama Clb; Nwsp Ed-Chief; Capt Cheerleading; High Hon Roll; NEDT Awd; Pres Schlr; Exploring; Letterman Clb; Pep Clb; Patrick Engel Drama Awd 87; Mst Vlbl Chrldr Awd 86; Miss Cngnlty PA Mdrn Miss Schlrshp Pgnt 86; IN U Of PA; Erly Chldhd.

CRAWFORD, TINA; Bradford Central Christian HS; Bradford, PA; (4); 4/26; Letterman Clb; School Musical; School Play; Nwsp Ed-Chief; JV L Cheerleading; High Hon Roll; NHS; NEDT Awd; Camera Clb; Drama Clb; PA Mdrn Ms 4th Rnnr Up 86; Chrldng MVP Awd At Otto-Eldred Christmas Tourn 85; Early Chldhld Ed.

CRAYS, MARK; Cambridge Springs HS; Venango, PA; (3); 4-H; JA; Key Clb; Band; Im Bsbl; VP L Ftbl; JV Vllybl; VP L Wrstlng; Dist 10 Wrstlng Chmpn 86; Homecmng Kng 87; Mike Hood Awd-Wrstlng 86; Cvl Engnrng.

CREA, JOSEPH; Cardinal Brennan HS; Shenandoah, PA; (3); 19/58; Boy Scts; Cmnty Wkr; Debate Tm; Library Aide; NFL; Chorus; Church Choir; Nwsp Stf; Var L Bsbl; Var L Ftbl; Creative Writing Awd-Catholic Daughters 87; PA ST U; Law.

CREARY, CHERYL; Little Flower Catholic HS; Philadelphia, PA; (3); 94/322; Cmnty Wkr; French Clb; Hosp Aide; JA; Red Cross Aide; Teachers Aide; Chorus; School Musical; Yrbk Stf; Rep Frsh Cls; Visiting Nrs Awd 84-85; Mntlly Hndcppd Tutor Awd 85-87; Frankford Schl Nrsg; RN.

CREE, KELLIE; Central Dauphin HS; Enhaut, PA; (4); 4/367; Church Yth Grp; Cmnty Wkr; Science Clb; Spanish Clb; Nwsp Ed-Chief; High Hon Roll; Lion Awd; NHS; Pres Schlr; Aud/Vis; SICO Schlrshp 87; Mdrn Music Mstrs 84-87; Sci Olympd Tm 86-87; Millersville U Of PA; Elem Ed.

CREEL, TAMMY; Brockway Area HS; Brockway, PA; (3); Debate Tm; Exploring; GAA; Pep Clb; Speech Tm; JV Bsktbl; Var Sftbl; Hon Roll; PA ST U; Pre Med.

CREELY, CURT; Hopewell SR HS; Aliquippa, PA; (3); 26/255; Pres German Clb; Pres JA; Band; Nwsp Rptr; God Cntry Awd; High Hon Roll; NHS; Westminster Hnrs Bnd & Mcdonalds Bnd 87; Psych.

CREIGHTON, CHRISTINE S; Methacton HS; Audubon, PA; (4); 49/375; Hosp Aide; Service Clb; Chorus; Var Crs Cntry; JV Fld Hcky; Var Trk; High Hon Roll; NHS; Pres Acdmc Fitness Awd 86-87; U Of Richmond; Intl Bus.

CREIGHTON, VICKIE; Manheim Central HS; Manheim, PA; (2); Church Yth Grp; Pres 4-H; Chorus; Church Choir; School Musical; JV Fld Hcky; JV Trk; 4-H Awd; High Hon Roll; NHS; Tstmstrs 87; Messiah Coll PA; Med.

CREMARD, MARYANN; Pittston Area HS; Duryea, PA; (3); 20/365; Key Clb; Ski Clb; SADD; Nwsp Rptr; Nwsp Stf; Yrbk Bus Mgr; High Hon Roll; Bloomsburg U; CPA.

CREMEANS, STACY; Cedarcrest HS; Lebanon, PA; (3); French Clb; German Clb; Hon Roll; Law.

CREMONESE, NICOLE; Greensburg Central Catholic HS; Greensburg, PA; (3); 97/246; Latin Clb; Pep Clb; Ski Clb; Yrbk Stf; Rep Soph Cls; Rep Jr Cls; Stu Cncl; Powder Puff Ftbl; High Hon Roll; Hon Roll; Stu Cncl Awd 87; Ntl Blood Drive Cert 87; Penn ST U; Sci.

CRENETI, THERESA; Archbishop Ryan HS For Girls; Philadelphia, PA; (3); 1/524; Sec Church Yth Grp; Trs Service Clb; Spanish Clb; JV Fld Hcky; Var Tennis; JV Trk; High Hon Roll; NHS; Prfct Atten Awd; Gnrl Avrg Vrsty Ltr Tns 84-86; Blgy Algbt Wrld Cltr I Awd Srvc Awd 84-85; Chem Algbr II Hlth Awd 86.

CREPS, KELLY; Bedford HS; Everett, PA; (4); 13/176; VP SADD; VP Band; Sec Chorus; Concert Band; Jazz Band; Capt Mrchg Band; Rep Stu Cncl; Hon Roll; Sec NHS; Pres Art Clb; Acad Med; Bio.

CRESCENZI, STACIA; Northern York HS; Dillsburg, PA; (4); #21 In Class; Quiz Bowl; SADD; Band; Nwsp Ed-Chief; Yrbk Stf; Var L Bsktbl; Hon Roll; Pres Schlr; Rotary Awd; Im Powder Puff Ftbl; Womens Club Schlrshp 87; Penn ST U; Psych.

CRESHO, MARYANN; Wyoming Valley West HS; Forty Fort, PA; (3); 44/419; Church Yth Grp; Key Clb; Library Aide; Pep Clb; Ski Clb; SADD; Chorus; Nwsp Stf; Yrbk Stf; Lit Mag; Times Ldr Sftbll All Star Tm 87; PA Coll Of Pharm; Bio Chem.

CRESKO, WILLIAM; Tunkhannock Area HS; Tunkhannock, PA; (3); 6/320; Boy Scts; Drama Clb; 4-H; Ski Clb; School Play; Yrbk Stf; L Crs Cntry; L Swmmng; L Trk; NHS.

CRESPO, DEBBY; Shenango HS; New Castle, PA; (4); 6/113; Church Yth Grp; Girl Scts; Yrbk Ed-Chief; Yrbk Stf; High Hon Roll; Lion Awd; NHS; NEDT Awd; Chorus; Hon Roll; Grl Sct Slvr Awd; Cndy Store Mgr; Bloomsburg U; Deaf Ed.

CRESSMAN, DAWN; St Basil Acad; Philadelphia, PA; (3); Drama Clb; German Clb; Hosp Aide; Thesps; Chorus; School Play; Tennis; Theatre.

CRESSMAN, LAURIE; Montoursville HS; Montoursville, PA; (3); 5/180; French Clb; Hon Roll; NHS; Acdmc All Amer Schlr Awd Pgm 87; Lock Haven U; Elem Ed.

CRESSWELL, KELLI; Lackawanna Trail HS; Dalton, PA; (3); Ski Clb; Yrbk Ed-Chief; Yrbk Stf; Trs Frsh Cls; Pres Soph Cls; Pres Jr Cls; L Cheerleading; Var Fld Hcky; Hon Roll; NHS; Svc Awd 86-87; Stud Mmth April 87; Psych.

CRESWELL, LAURA; Daniel Boone HS; Douglassville, PA; (3); 30/170; French Clb; Drill Tm; Yrbk Phtg; Lit Mag; Capt Cheerleading; Opt Clb Awd; Prtcpnt-Frdms Fndtn Yth Ldrhsp Conf 87; YFU Exchng Stu-Holland 87; Lbrl Arts.

CRESWELL, MARA; Warwick HS; Lititz, PA; (3); 71/300; Model UN; Speech Tm; Thesps; Concert Band; Orch; School Play; Yrbk Stf; Hon Roll; WI ST Spch Cmptn 85; Lancaster Cnty Wind Ensmbl 87; Commnctns.

CREWS, JASON B; Roman Catholic HS; Philadelphia, PA; (3); 24/124; Cmnty Wkr; Drama Clb; NAACP; Political Wkr; Nwsp Ed-Chief; Nwsp Stf; Pres Stu Cncl; High Hon Roll; Hon Roll; NHS; Engl Hnrs 84-85; Outstndng Perfrmnc Awd Soc Hlpng Deaf Chldrn 85-86; Romans Blck Cult Clb Awds 86-87; Morehouse Coll; Psych.

CREWS, ROSALIND; John W Hallahn HS; Philadelphia, PA; (3); 69/292; VP Exploring; Office Aide; Orch; Stu Cncl; Prfct Atten Awd; Math.

CRIBBS, HEATHER; Blairsville SR HS; Blairsville, PA; (1); 8/118; Band; Concert Band; Mrchg Band; School Musical; Stage Crew; Rep Stu Cncl; Var Twrlr; High Hon Roll; Speech Pathology.

CRICCO, STACEY; Connellsville Area HS; Dickerson, PA; (1); Church Yth Grp; Band; Chorus; Jazz Band; PA ST; Elem Tchr.

CRIDER, GARY; Fairchance Georges HS; Uniontown, PA; (3); Boy Scts; Pres Church Yth Grp; Spanish Clb; Church Choir; Ftbl; Sftbl; High Hon Roll; Hon Roll; Elec Engr.

CRIDER, JEFF; Seneca Valley HS; Evans Cty, PA; (2); Church Yth Grp; Letterman Clb; Varsity Clb; Capt Bsktbl; Capt Ftbl; Trk; Wt Lftg; High Hon Roll; Hon Roll; NHS; Ftbl Tms Acdmc Achvt Awd 85-86.

CRIDER, ROGER; Seneca Valley HS; Evans City, PA; (4); 40/340; Church Yth Grp; Letterman Clb; Varsity Clb; Ftbl; Trk; Wt Lftg; Hon Roll; 3rd Tm All ST & Hnbl Mntn All Amer Ftbl 86; Westminster Coll.

CRIGHTON, BARBARA; Yough SR HS; Smithton, PA; (3); Church Yth Grp; French Clb; Chorus; Color Guard; Mrchg Band; High Hon Roll; Hon Roll; NHS; Elem Ed.

CRILLEY, JOSEPH PETER; Northwestern SR HS; E Springfield, PA; (4); 20/143; Boys Clb Am; Computer Clb; Model UN; Quiz Bowl; VP Science Clb; Yrbk Stf; JV Trk; Hon Roll; Math & Comp Sci Awd 87; Acad Hnrs 87; Albion Area Chmbr Of Cmmrc Schlrshp 87; Penn ST U; Aero Engrng.

CRIM, MISSY; Ringgold HS; New Eagle, PA; (1); SADD; Drill Tm; Variety Show; Pom Pon; Math Teacher.

CRIMMEL, ANDREW; Newport HS; Newport, PA; (2); Church Yth Grp; Computer Clb; High Hon Roll; 2nd Pl Captl Area Sci Engrng Fair 86; Med.

CRIMMINS, TRACY; Notre Dame HS; Stroudsburg, PA; (3); Chorus; School Musical; School Play; Pres Stu Cncl; Var Bsktbl; Capt Var Fld Hcky; Hon Roll; NHS; Var Sftbl; Psych.

CRINTI, LISA; Lancaster Catholic HS; Lancaster, PA; (3); 53/192; Drama Clb; School Play; Stage Crew; Nwsp Stf; Gld Key Awd Schlstc Art Cmptn 87; 1st Pl Tm PA HS Spch Leag Drama Cmptn 85-86; Beth Bash Awd 85-87; Archtctr.

CRISCI, BRIAN; Shenango HS; New Castle, PA; (3); 28/125; Letterman Clb; Varsity Clb; Var Bsbl; Var Bsktbl; Var Capt Ftbl; Hon Roll; Engrng.

CRISCUOLO, TIMOTHY J; Mc Keesport Area SR HS; Mckeesport, PA; (3); 50/450; Aud/Vis; Office Aide; Band; Concert Band; School Musical; Stage Crew; Hon Roll; Allegheny Coll; Pre-Med.

CRISE, TRICIA; Belle Vernon Area HS; West Newton, PA; (3); Pres Church Yth Grp; VP JA; Hst NFL; Church Choir; Capt Color Guard; L Trk; Var Vllybl; High Hon Roll; NHS; Acdmc All-Amer Awd 84 & 85; Achvr Awd Jr Achvt 86; IN U Of PA; Criminology.

CRISMAN, TRACY; Allegheny-Clarion Valley HS; Emlenton, PA; (4); 1/90; Mrchg Band; Off Stu Cncl; Cheerleading; Vllybl; High Hon Roll; NHS; Val; Trk; Spanish Clb; VP Band; Presdntl Schlrshp Clarion U 87; Byrd Schlrshp 87; Emlenton Cvc Clb Schlrshp 87; Am Leg Essy 2nd 86; Clarion U; Elem Ed.

CRIST, BRIAN; Williams Valley HS; Mechanicsville, MD; (4); 12/103; Band; Concert Band; Jazz Band; Mrchg Band; Symp Band; Hon Roll; NEDT Awd; 4-H; Pep Clb; Chorus; Cnty Band 1st Chair, ST Twin Vly Band 84-87; Schuylkill Cnty Band Awd 87; Naval Acad; Elec Tech.

CRIST, JEREMY; Central Dauphin HS; Harrisburg, PA; (2); 1/400; Church Yth Grp; Band; Chorus; Drm & Bgl; School Musical; Cit Awd; High Hon Roll; Jr NHS; NHS; Pres Schlr; West Point; Offcr.

CRIST, MICHELLE; Halifax Area HS; Halifax, PA; (4); 22/98; Church Yth Grp; Pres Band; VP Chorus; Church Choir; Concert Band; Drm Mjr(t); Mrchg Band; Stage Crew; Vllybl; Hon Roll; Yth Schlrs Yth Pgm Lebanon Vly Coll 86; Severl Piano Awds 84-87; Chambersburg PA; Vet Med.

CRIST, MICHELLE DENISE; Eastern York HS; York, PA; (4); 6/167; Am Leg Aux Girls St; Varsity Clb; Bsktbl; Capt Vllybl; Hon Roll; JC Awd; NHS; Pres Church Yth Grp; Girl Scts; Hosp Aide; Acad All Stars 87; Prom Cr 87; Vllybl Cnty All Stars 87; Juniata Coll; Bio Ed.

CRIST, NICOLLE; Archbishop Prendergast HS; Collingdale, PA; (3); 66/342; Hosp Aide; Political Wkr; Spanish Clb; Nwsp Rptr; Cheerleading; Hon Roll; Intl Bus.

CRIST, WENDY; Claysburg-Kimmel HS; Queen, PA; (3); Varsity Clb; VICA; Chorus; Rep Stu Cncl; Var Capt Cheerleading; JV Sftbl; Hon Roll; Dntl Asst.

CRISTEA, CRISTOPHER; Warren Area HS; Warren, PA; (3); 53/300; Am Leg Boys St; Art Clb; Church Yth Grp; Spanish Clb; School Play; Bsbl; Mgr(s); High Hon Roll; Hon Roll; Goldn Key Awd-Art 87; Dsgnd Cls Flg 86; Art.

CROASMUN, VIRGINIA; Central Cambria HS; Vintondale, PA; (2); Key Clb; Awd Consistent B Avg Typing I 86-87; Law.

CROCCO, WENDY; Westmont Hilltop HS; Johnstown, PA; (3); Art Clb; Church Yth Grp; Dance Clb; Key Clb; Ski Clb; Chorus; School Musical; Tennis; Ed.

CROCETTI, LYDIA; Connellsville Area SR HS; Connellsville, PA; (3); Office Aide; Mrchg Band; Symp Band; Yrbk Stf; Rep Stu Cncl; High Hon Roll; NHS; Spanish NHS; Bus.

CROCHUNIS, DEBORAH; Nativity B V M; New Phila, PA; (3); 1/86; French Clb; Bsktbl; Trk; High Hon Roll; NHS; Hghst Avg In Chem 87; Hghst Avg In Alg I 85; Hghst Avg In Engl II 86; Math.

CROCKARD, JAMES; Carmichaels Area SR HS; Carmichaels, PA; (4); 2/101; Boy Scts; Spanish Clb; SADD; Mgr Band; Rep Sr Cls; Sec NHS; NEDT Awd; Cmnty Wkr; Drama Clb; Pep Clb; Gifted Enrchmnt Pgm 81-87; Stu Forum 86-87; Am Leg Awd 81; Corp Law.

CROCKER, KIMBERLY; West Scranton HS; Scranton, PA; (3); 12/260; Church Yth Grp; Capt Dance Clb; Ski Clb; Spanish Clb; High Hon Roll; Acad All Amer 87; Engrng.

CROCKETT, CHRIS; Susquenita HS; Duncannon, PA; (3); 7/157; Church Yth Grp; Spanish Clb; Church Choir; Nwsp Stf; Hon Roll; NHS; VP Natl Hnr Scty 88; Mech Engr.

CROFT, LANCE; Greensburg-Salem SR HS; Greensburg, PA; (4); 35/290; Ski Clb; Chorus; L Golf; L Ice Hcky; Engrng.

CROFTON, ANTHONY; Hopewell HS; Aliquippa, PA; (4); 10/245; Church Yth Grp; Pres Exploring; Spanish Clb; Rep Frsh Cls; Rep Soph Cls; Rep Jr Cls; Rep Sr Cls; Var Bsbl; Stat Bsktbl; Lion Awd; U Of Pittsburgh; Chem.

CROMIS, REBECCA; Danville SR HS; Washingtonville, PA; (3); 4-H; FHA; Hon Roll.

CROMLEY, JOAN; Danville SR HS; Danville, PA; (3); 24/195; Latin Clb; High Hon Roll; NHS; U Of WA; Marn Bio.

CROMLEY, LEANNE; Montoursville HS; Montoursville, PA; (3); FBLA; German Clb; Cheerleading; Pom Pon; Med Tech.

CROMPTON, MELISSA; Trinity HS; Washington, PA; (4); 103/322; VP French Clb; Math Clb; Drill Tm; Yrbk Bus Mgr; Trs Soph Cls; Rep Jr Cls; Sec Sr Cls; Rep Stu Cncl; L Var Vllybl; Hon Roll; Mst Vlble Stffr Yrbk Ads Co-Ed 87; U Of Pittsburgh.

CRONAUER, KIMBERLY; GAR Memorial HS; Wilkes-Barre, PA; (3); 15/152; Ski Clb; Chorus; Drill Tm; Stat Bsktbl; Var L Fld Hcky; Hon Roll; Jr NHS; NHS; Cmptrs.

CRONE, MARC; Dover HS; Dover, PA; (4); 4/240; VP Jr Cls; VP Sr Cls; Rep Stu Cncl; Var Bsbl; Var Ftbl; Var Trk; High Hon Roll; Hon Roll; NHS; Joan E Yinpling Awd Of Excllnc 86; US Army Res Schlr Athlt 87; Exchng Clb Of York Yth Of The Mnth 87; Columbia U; Engrng.

CRONIN, JULIE; Bishop Carroll HS; Cresson, PA; (3); 12/128; Drama Clb; NFL; Pep Clb; Spanish Clb; Speech Tm; Stage Crew; Cheerleading; Hon Roll; Pre Law.

CRONIN, MEGAN; Bishop Mc Devitt HS; Oreland, PA; (3); 56/350; Church Yth Grp; Cmnty Wkr; Spanish Clb; SADD; Yrbk Stf; Powder Puff Ftbl; Trk; Hon Roll; NHS; Prfct Atten Awd; Ed.

CROOK, JENIFER; Cambridge Springs HS; Cambridge Spg, PA; (3); 4/105; Sec Key Clb; SADD; Nwsp Ed-Chief; Yrbk Stf; Var Cheerleading; Var Sftbl; Var Vllybl; Hon Roll; NHS; U Pittsburgh; Med.

CROOM, ROCHELLE; Wilkinsburg JR SR HS; Pittsburgh, PA; (4); 7/142; French Clb; Y-Teens; Cheerleading; Coach Actv; Hon Roll; NHS; Cutest Smile 85; Bst Dncr 85-87; Mst Popular 85; Bradford Schl Bus; Sec Sci.

CROPP, RICHARD; Cathedral Prep; Erie, PA; (2); 19/193; Boy Scts; Church Yth Grp; French Clb; Ski Clb; Band; Concert Band; Mrchg Band; Stage Crew; High Hon Roll; Eagle Scout Awd Boys Scouts Of Amer 86; Engrng.

CROSBIE, MELISSA; Wyoming Area HS; Exeter, PA; (3); 8/250; Drama Clb; Key Clb; Ski Clb; Spanish Clb; Chorus; Yrbk Stf; Capt Var Cheerleading; Swmmng; Trk; High Hon Roll; PA Free Entrprs Wk Schlrshp 87; Grd Soc Studies Awd 87; Bus Mgmt.

CROSBY JR, EDWARD G; Cardinal Brown HS; Shenandoah, PA; (3); 4/58; Aud/Vis; Boy Scts; Chess Clb; Library Aide; NFL; Church Choir; School Musical; Nwsp Stf; High Hon Roll; NHS; 1st Relign & Soc Stud 84-86; Catholic U; Psych.

CROSBY, JAMES; Northeast Catholic HS; Philadelphia, PA; (2); 23/365; Church Yth Grp; School Musical; High Hon Roll; NHS; Prfct Atten Awd; Sci.

CROSBY, KRISTEN; North Allegheny SR HS; Pittsburgh, PA; (3); 95/649; Cmnty Wkr; Exploring; Nwsp Phtg; Rep Jr Cls; Rep Stu Cncl; Hon Roll; Jr NHS; NHS; Dstngshd Achvt Awd PASC ST Conf 85; Dstngshd Achvt 1st Fml Rwng Tm Allegheny Cnty.

CROSIER, KIMBERLY; Juniata HS; Mifflintown, PA; (3); Drama Clb; SADD; Varsity Clb; Concert Band; Mrchg Band; Variety Show; Yrbk Stf; JV Capt Cheerleading; Hon Roll; NHS; Aerosp Engr.

CROSKEY, YVETTE M; Mount Saint Joseph Acad; Sumter, SC; (4); Drama Clb; Math Clb; Math Tm; French Hon Soc; High Hon Roll; NHS; Ntl Merit Schol; Voice Dem Awd; French Clb; Chorus; U Schlrs Pgm U Of Richmond 87; Excel A P Physcs, Englsh, & Russn Hstry 87; Mst Prmsng Actrs 85; U Of Richmond; Psych.

CROSS, CHRISTY; Grove City HS; Volant, PA; (3); Church Yth Grp; Band; Concert Band; Mrchg Band; Pep Band; Var Powder Puff Ftbl; L Trk; Wt Lftg; Hon Roll; Secy.

CROSS, DAVID; Northeast Preparatory Schl; Philadelphia, PA; (4); Computer Clb; Latin Clb; Library Aide; Science Clb; School Play; Outstndng Contribution In Sci; La Salle U; Vet Med.

CROSS, MARY; Everett Area HS; Everett, PA; (2); 2/170; Church Yth Grp; Spanish Clb; Varsity Clb; Band; Yrbk Phtg; Rep Stu Cncl; Golf; Gym; Trk; High Hon Roll; Marine Bio.

CROSS, RAYMOND; Southmoreland HS; Scottdale, PA; (2); 6/254; French Clb; Letterman Clb; Concert Band; Stu Cncl; Var L Ftbl; Var Trk; Var L Wrstlng; French Hon Soc; High Hon Roll; Sports Med.

CROSS, SHARON; Lincoln HS; Philadelphia, PA; (2); Dance Clb; Spanish Clb; SADD; Penn ST; Nrsng.

CROSS, TAMMY; West Greene HS; Waynesburg, PA; (3); Church Yth Grp; French Clb; FHA; Chorus; Church Choir; Hon Roll.

CROSSLEY, LOUISE; Coudersport JR SR HS; Coudersport, PA; (3); Church Yth Grp; 4-H; Band; Chorus; Church Choir; Nwsp Ed-Chief; Yrbk Stf; Var Trk; High Hon Roll; NHS; Lancaster Bible Coll; Educ.

CROSSMAN, MICHELLE; Freeport SR HS; Sarver, PA; (2); Hosp Aide; Office Aide; Trs Soph Cls; Stu Cncl; Stat Bsktbl; VP Sftbl; Hon Roll; Med.

CROSSON, LORI; Lewistown HS; Lewistown, PA; (3); Church Yth Grp; Spanish Clb; Color Guard; Flag Corp; Mrchg Band; School Musical.

CROSTEN, JEFFREY; New Castle HS; New Castle, PA; (3); 15/297; Cmnty Wkr; Chorus; Tennis; Hon Roll; Penn ST U; Engrng.

CROTEAU, CRAIG; Wyoming Area SR HS; W Pittston, PA; (4); Chess Clb; French Clb; Nwsp Rptr; Nwswtch 16 Nwsgm Cert Merit; Natl Sci Olympd; Kings Coll; Chem.

CROUNSE, STEPHEN; Abington Heights HS; Clarks Summit, PA; (3); Letterman Clb; Acpl Chr; Trs Chorus; Madrigals; School Musical; School Play; Var L Bsbl; Var L Bsktbl; Var L Ftbl; Hon Roll; Rotary Ldrshp Camp Ldr Of Ldrs Awd 86; Dist Chorus 87; Lge All Star Bsebl Tm.

CROUSE, KIMBERLY; Central Dauphin HS; Harrisburg, PA; (3); Church Yth Grp; Key Clb; Ski Clb; Chorus; Off Soph Cls; Off Jr Cls; Off Stu Cncl; Var Capt Cheerleading; Sftbl; Hon Roll; PA ST; Advrtsng.

CROUSE, LORI; Middletown Area HS; Harrisburg, PA; (3); FCA; Band; Chorus; Concert Band; Mrchg Band; Nwsp Rptr; Nwsp Stf; Yrbk Phtg; Yrbk Stf; Hon Roll; Penn ST U; Sci.

CROUSE, SCHON; Connellsville SR HS; Acme, PA; (4); CAP; Wt Lftg; Hon Roll; Air Force; Comp Repair.

CROUSE, SHAWN; Southern Huntingdon HS; Shade Gap, PA; (2); VICA; L Trk; Wt Lftg; Hon Roll; Electrncs.

CROUSHORE, DEANNA ELAINE; Belle Vernon Area HS; Belle Vernon, PA; (4); 91/272; Art Clb; Pres Library Aide; Pep Clb; Ski Clb; Chorus; Stage Crew; Nwsp Rptr; Nwsp Stf; High Hon Roll; Hon Roll.

CROUSHORE JR, WILLIAM; Southmoreland HS; Ruffsdale, PA; (4); 18/230; JCL; Latin Clb; Letterman Clb; Ski Clb; Varsity Clb; Stu Cncl; Socr; Pres Schlr; Ltn Natl Hnr Soc, & Hnr Grad 87; Duquesne U Cmpttv Schlrshp; Duquesne U; Phrmcy.

CROW, BRYAN; Ringgold HS; Monongahela, PA; (3); 11/351; JV Ftbl; High Hon Roll; NHS; Sci-Math Hnr Soc 85-88; Army; Comp Pgmr.

CROWE, BOBBIE; Butler Area SR HS; Lyndora, PA; (3); Exploring; Spanish Clb; High Hon Roll; Hon Roll; Jr NHS; Ntl Merit Schol; Acad Achvt Awd 86-8m; Pharmacy.

CROWE, BRENDA; Waynesboro SR HS; Waynesboro, PA; (4); 18/357; Sec Trs Exploring; Chorus; School Musical; Variety Show; Var Capt Fld Hcky; Var Trk; High Hon Roll; NHS; Civcs Awd 84.

CROWELL, BRAD; Spring-Ford HS; Lamerick, PA; (3); 42/260; Hon Roll; Aerospc Engrng.

CROWL, JULIANNE; Penn Trafford HS; Jeannette, PA; (3); School Musical; Swing Chorus; Nwsp Stf; Comm.

CROWLEY, ANTOINETTE; Schenley HS; Pittsburgh, PA; (3); Exploring; JA; NAACP; Capt Cheerleading; High Hon Roll; Hon Roll; NHS; Prfct Atten Awd; Schlstc Pin & Bar 84-85; U Of Pittsburgh; Engr.

CROWNER, MATTHEW; Gettysburg SR HS; Gettysburg, PA; (2); Chess Clb; Quiz Bowl; Ski Clb; Varsity Clb; Band; Jazz Band; Orch; Lcrss; Socr; Tennis; Highest Avrg In Bio 86-87; Biochem.

CROWNOVER, HEATHER; Warwick HS; Lititz, PA; (2); 29/320; VP Church Yth Grp; Chorus; Church Choir; Mrchg Band; School Musical; Nwsp Stf; High Hon Roll; Hon Roll.

CROWNOVER, TIM; Huntington Area HS; Mill Creek, PA; (3); 52/236; Boy Scts; Pres Church Yth Grp; Band; Concert Band; Mrchg Band; JV Capt Bsktbl; Eagl Sct Awd 87; Coast Guard Awd; Aero Engrng.

CROYLE, LINDA; Penns Manor HS; Alverda, PA; (3); 5/100; Art Clb; Band; Flag Corp; VP Jr Cls; VP Pres Stu Cncl; Stat Bsktbl; Stat Trk; NHS; Prfct Atten Awd; IN U PA; Math Ed.

CROYLE, MARIA; Somerset Area SR HS; Somerset, PA; (4); 3/236; Hosp Aide; Sec Mu Alpha Theta; Q&S; Sec Band; Yrbk Stf; Trs Jr Cls; High Hon Roll; NHS; Pres Schlr; English Clb; Dale Carngie Hmn Rltns Crse Schlrshp 87; L W Miller Hnrary Math & Sci Awd 87; U Of Pittsburgh; Phrmcy.

CROYLE, TODDY; Moon SR HS; Coraopolis, PA; (3); Key Clb; Spanish Clb; Band; Stu Cncl; Capt L Bsktbl; L Sftbl; Bus Admin.

CROZIER, PATRICIA; Neshaminy SR HS; Langhorne, PA; (3); 13/824; Pep Clb; Trs Chorus; School Musical; School Play; Yrbk Stf; Co-Capt Cheerleading; Gym; Powder Puff Ftbl; High Hon Roll; Hon Roll; PA U; Secndry Ed.

CRUDUP, LARRY; Bishop Mc Devitt HS; Harrisburg, PA; (4); 4/196; Drama Clb; Pres FBLA; Office Aide; Band; Jazz Band; DAR Awd; Hon Roll; Pres Trs NHS; Computer Clb; Cmmnd Stu Among Blacks PSAT 86; Accntng.

CRULEY, STACY; Blacklick Valley HS; Nanty Glo, PA; (3); German Clb; High Hon Roll; Hon Roll; NHS; Acad All-Amer Schlrshp Awd 86; X-Ray Tech.

CRUM, DEANNA; Portage Area HS; Portage, PA; (3); Church Yth Grp; Varsity Clb; Hon Roll; Prfct Atten Awd; Gym Awds; Mt Aloysius JC; Secy.

CRUM, KATHRYN; Aliquippa HS; Aliquippa, PA; (3); #15 In Class; Art Clb; French Clb; Hosp Aide; Band; Concert Band; Drm Mjr(t); Mrchg Band; Pep Band; Twrlr; Hon Roll; Pittsburgh Art Inst; Cmmrcl Art.

CRUMLEY, PAUL; Donegal HS; Mount Joy, PA; (3); 21/180; Church Yth Grp; Rep Frsh Cls; JV Var Bsktbl; Var Capt Tennis; Im Vllybl; Hon Roll; Merit Ten Awd 85 & 86; Bsktbl Sprtsmnshp Awd 87.

CRUMLING, AMY; South Western HS; Hanover, PA; (2); Cmnty Wkr; Key Clb; Band; Church Choir; Concert Band; Mrchg Band; School Musical; School Play; Symp Band; Hon Roll; Outstndng Help & Svc Key Clb & 1st Chair Awd Symphonic Band 87; IN U Of PA; Psych.

CRUMMEY, CHRISTINA; Little Flower Catholic HS For Girls; Philadelphia, PA; (3); Art Clb; Cmnty Wkr; Girl Scts; Orch; School Musical; School Play; Hampton; Pre Med.

CRUMMY, TAMMI A; William Penn HS; Philadelphia, PA; (3); Church Yth Grp; Girl Scts; Spanish Clb; Rep Soph Cls; Rep Jr Cls; Capt Var Cheerleading; Swmmng; Hon Roll; Jr NHS; Prfct Atten Awd; Lgl Asst.

CRUMP, BRIAN; York Vo-Tech; York, PA; (3); 16/456; Boy Scts; Chess Clb; VICA; Hon Roll; OH Inst Diesel; Diesel Mech.

CRUMRINE, ALISON; Butler Area SR HS; Butler, PA; (3); Church Yth Grp; Office Aide; Pep Clb; Ski Clb; Spanish Clb; Chorus; Rep Frsh Cls; Rep Soph Cls; Rep Stu Cncl; Stat Bsbl; Elctd 85 Swthrt Crt; Bus.

CRUSE, JENNIFER; Allen HS; Allentown, PA; (2); Sec Church Yth Grp; Leo Clb; SADD; Varsity Clb; Band; Soph Cls; Var Gym; Var Trk; Hon Roll; Jr NHS; Physcl Thrpy.

CRUSE, LISEL; William Allen HS; Allentown, PA; (3); Leo Clb; SADD; Sec Band; Chorus; Concert Band; Mrchg Band; Pep Band; Swing Chorus; Hon Roll; NHS; Mary Alice Miller Mem Schlrshp 86.

CRUSE, TARA; Philadelphia HS For Girls; Philadelphia, PA; (2); Acpl Chr; Chorus; Orch; School Musical; Variety Show; CC Of Phila ACE Music Pgm Schlrshp 87; Jrnlsm.

CRUSE, WADE; William Allen HS; Allentown, PA; (3); Ski Clb; Band; Jazz Band; Stu Cncl; JV Wrstlng; Hon Roll; Masonic Awd; NHS.

CRUZ, RAMON; Mastbaum Voc Tech; Philadelphia, PA; (2); Prfct Atten Awd; Customer Svc Cert Excell 87; Comm Pilot.

CSANDL, ISAAC; William Allen HS; Allentown, PA; (3); Pres Computer Clb; Drama Clb; JCL; Latin Clb; SADD; Chorus; Hon Roll.

CSUHTA, CHRISTINE; Canon-Mc Millan HS; Canonsburg, PA; (1); Church Yth Grp; Dance Clb; Drama Clb; Band; Chorus; Concert Band; Drm Mjr(t); School Musical; School Play; Var Sftbl; St Marys Coll; Public Reltns.

CUADRA-VALENZUELA, SARA E; Quigley HS; Baden, PA; (3); 29/90; Church Yth Grp; Cmnty Wkr; Drama Clb; Lib Chorus; Drill Tm; School Musical; Lib Swing Chorus; Powder Puff Ftbl; Wrstlng; High Hon Roll; Dist Chorus-Western PA 87; MAPP Schlrshp To Penn St U 87; Svc Awd-Music Mnstry & Mnstry Tms 86; Psych.

CUCCARO, JACQUELYN; Shaler Area HS; Allison Pk, PA; (3); Radio Clb; SADD; Yrbk Phtg; Rep Stu Cncl; Var Tennis; French Hon Soc; Hon Roll; NHS; NEDT Awd; Rotary Awd; PA Jr Acad Of Sci 2nd Pl & Natl Sci Olympiad Awd For Excllnc 87.

CUFF, TOM; Cardinal Brennan HS; Frackville, PA; (4); Letterman Clb; Rep Soph Cls; Rep Sr Cls; Rep Stu Cncl; Var L Bsbl; Capt Var Ftbl; Wt Lftg; Elks Awd; Hon Roll; Acad All Amer 85-87; Millersville U; Bio.

CUKAUSKAS, GERARD A; Bishop Hafey HS; Freeland, PA; (2); Chess Clb; Church Yth Grp; High Hon Roll; Hon Roll; Pres Acad Fit Awd 86; Acad All Amer Awd 87.

CUKAUSKAS, MICHAEL; Bishop Hafey HS; Freeland, PA; (2); Sec Church Yth Grp; Im Tennis; High Hon Roll; Hon Roll; Hstry Awd 85-86; Spn Awd 85-86; Optmtry.

CULBERTSON, MATT; Mechanicsburg SR HS; Mechanicsburg, PA; (3); 56/358; Hon Roll; Shippensburg; Bus.

CULIN, JANICE; Ridley SR HS; Woodlyn, PA; (4); 75/407; Drama Clb; Thesps; Chorus; School Musical; School Play; Stage Crew; Nwsp Rptr; Lcrss; Hon Roll; NHS; Stu Mnth 86; Bloomsburg U; Med Tech.

CULLEN, DENNIS P; Asrchbishop Ryan HS; Philadelphia, PA; (2); Boy Scts; SADD; Band; Concert Band; Jazz Band; Mrchg Band; Temple U; Engr.

CULLEN, HEIDI; Pleasant Valley HS; Kunkletown, PA; (3); 8/223; Math Tm; Teachers Aide; Sec Band; Mrchg Band; Nwsp Stf; VP Frsh Cls; Rep Stu Cncl; JV Sftbl; High Hon Roll; Trs Jr NHS; Top 20 In Class 84-86.

CULLEN, LAURIE; Council Rock HS; Holland, PA; (2); Stat Im Bsktbl; Var Socr; Sbrbn I All Lg & Hnrbl Mntn Sccr 85-87; EPYSA ST Sccr Tm 87; Pre Law.

CULLEN, MARY; Wyalusing Valley JR SR HS; New Albany, PA; (4); German Clb; Ski Clb; SADD; Band; Concert Band; Mrchg Band; Orch; Trk; Hon Roll; NHS; Pres Schlrshp 87; Tyler Mem Schlrshp 87-88; Natl Hnr Scty 87-88; U Of Scranton; Nrsng.

CULLEN, THERESA; Wyalusing Valley JR/Sr HS; New Albany, PA; (4); 5/132; German Clb; Ski Clb; SADD; Band; Concert Band; Mrchg Band; Orch; Trk; Cit Awd; High Hon Roll; Prfct Attend Awd 84; Pres Schlrshp 87; U Of Scranton; Chem.

CULLER, BRENT; Mc Connellsburg HS; Mcconnellsburg, PA; (4); Varsity Clb; Rep Stu Cncl; JV Var Socr; Var L Trk; Cit Awd; God Cntry Awd; Amercnsm Awd 87; Dghtrs Of Amer Revltn 87; Senate Of PA Awd 87; U Of Pittsburgh; Pol Sci.

CULLISON, CHRISTINA; William Penn SR HS; York, PA; (4); 48/370; SADD; Stage Crew; JV Vllybl; Hon Roll; NHS; Prfct Atten Awd; Penn ST; Psych.

CULLISON, JAMES; Biglerville HS; Biglerville, PA; (2); 26/109; Band; Mrchg Band; JV Bsbl; U Of PA; Fin.

CULLY, LAURIE; Laurel Highlands SR HS; Hopwood, PA; (3); Stat Swmmng; High Hon Roll; Hon Roll; Gtfd Pgm 85-88; Acctng.

CULP, CATHY; Dallas SR HS; Dallas, PA; (3); Drama Clb; Hosp Aide; Key Clb; Stage Crew; JV Trk; Hon Roll; Phys Ther.

CULP, DAVID; United HS; New Florence, PA; (4); 11/157; Boy Scts; Pres Church Yth Grp; Church Choir; Concert Band; Pres Mrchg Band; JV Var Twrlr; High Hon Roll; Hon Roll; NHS; Prfct Atten Awd; IN U Of PA; Pltcl Sci.

CULP, JEFFREY; Rocky Grove JR-SR HS; Reno, PA; (3); 3/81; Aud/Vis; Var Golf; Var Wrstlng; VP NHS; Amer Lgn Schl Awd; Chem Engrng.

CULP, JILL; Ford City HS; Ford City, PA; (3); Scholastic Bowl; SADD; Chorus; School Musical; Sec Sr Cls; Capt Var Cheerleading; Var JV Vllybl; High Hon Roll; NHS; Church Yth Grp; Psychlgy.

CULP, KIMBERLY; Dallas SR HS; Dallas, PA; (4); 28/248; Hosp Aide; Sec Key Clb; Red Cross Aide; School Play; Yrbk Stf; Var Crs Cntry; Var Trk; Hon Roll; NHS; Pres Acdmc Ftnss Awds Pgm 86-87; Pres Phys Ftnss Awd 85-87; Kings Coll; Bio.

CULVER, LISA; Harry S Truman HS; Levittown, PA; (3); Hon Roll; Elem Ed.

CULVER, MELISSA; Dallas SR HS; Wyoming, PA; (3); Art Clb; Church Yth Grp; Hosp Aide; Key Clb; Band; Chorus; Yrbk Stf; Phrmcy.

CULVER, REBECCA; Corry Area HS; Corry, PA; (3); VP SADD; Chorus; School Musical; School Play; Yrbk Phtg; Yrbk Rptr; Yrbk Stf; Rep Jr Cls; Rep Stu Cncl; Stage Crew; Acad Awd 85-86; Comm.

CUMBERLAND, DAWN; Moniteau HS; Eau Claire, PA; (3); Hosp Aide; Spanish Clb; Hon Roll; NHS.

CUMBERLEDGE, BRIAN; Canon Mc Millon SR HS; Canonsburg, PA; (4); 76/355; Latin Clb; Var L Tennis; Hon Roll; Washington Coll; Acctg.

CUMBERLEDGE, KRISTIE; Waynesboro Central; Brave, PA; (4); Trs FHA; VICA; Hon Roll; Outstndng Stu Of 1st Sem 86.

CUMBERLEDGE, SHERRI; Elderton JR SR HS; Shelocta, PA; (3); 1/95; Church Yth Grp; Spanish Clb; Band; Yrbk Sprt Ed; Stat Bsktbl; Var L Cheerleading; Var L Vllybl; Bausch & Lomb Sci Awd; High Hon Roll; NHS; Sci Fld.

CUMBLIDGE, STEPHEN; Butler SR HS; Butler, PA; (3); JA; Spanish Clb; High Hon Roll; Ntl Merit SF; Carnegie Mellon U; Chem Engrng.

CUMMINGS, BOBBI; Hempfield Area HS; Youngwood, PA; (2); Art Clb; Church Yth Grp; Spanish Clb; High Hon Roll; Hon Roll; Trvl Agnt.

CUMMINGS, CASEY; Lake Lehman HS; Harveys Lk, PA; (2); JV Bsktbl; JV Fld Hcky; High Hon Roll; Hon Roll; Jr NHS; NHS; William & Mary; Law.

CUMMINGS, CRAIG; Sun Valley HS; Brookhaven, PA; (4); 4/310; Scholastic Bowl; Science Clb; Band; Variety Show; Yrbk Stf; Var Trk; High Hon Roll; Lion Awd; NHS; Ntl Merit Ltr; Lebanon Vly Yth Schlrs 86; Phldlpha Sci Cncl Test Fnlst 87; Bronze Mdl Sci Olympd 86; Behvrl Bio.

CUMMINGS, STEPHANIE; Moon SR HS; Corapolis, PA; (3); 69/306; Band; Concert Band; Mrchg Band; Symp Band; High Hon Roll; Hon Roll; Pittsburgh Beauty Acad; Csmtlgy.

CUMMINS, ERIN; Bradford Central Christian HS; Bradford, PA; (2); Trs Computer Clb; Drama Clb; French Clb; Pep Clb; Nwsp Rptr; High Hon Roll; Hon Roll; PA ST U; Fash Dsgn.

CUMMINS, JENNIFER; Mohawk HS; New Castle, PA; (3); Pres VP Church Yth Grp; French Clb; Nwsp Rptr; VP Stu Cncl; JV Bsbl; L Mgr(s); NHS; Score Keeper; Trk; Im Vllybl; Hugh Obrien Yth Fndtn Del 86; PA ST Grange Jr Prncss 85-86; Smr Sftbl Pgm ASA Of PA St Champs 86; Scndry Educ.

CUMMONS, JOY; Harry S Truman HS; Levittown, PA; (3); 36/599; Dance Clb; Stu Cncl; Var Cheerleading; High Hon Roll; Hon Roll; Stu Dance Tchrs Lcns 86; Elem Ed.

CUNNINGHAM, AMY BETH; Wyalusing Valley HS; Laceyville, PA; (3); VP Church Yth Grp; Pres Library Aide; Spanish Clb; Lib Band; Chorus; Orch; School Musical; Mgr(s); Hon Roll; NHS; 1st Pl In Tyler Mem Essay Cont 86.

CUNNINGHAM, ANDREA; Harrisburg HS; Harrisburg, PA; (3); 14/251; PAVAS; Chorus; School Musical; Sftbl; Hon Roll; Prfct Atten Awd; Rotary Awd; Music Therapy.

CUNNINGHAM, APRIL; Steel Valley SR HS; Homestead, PA; (3); 20/210; Trs Key Clb; Concert Band; Jazz Band; Mrchg Band; Hon Roll; NHS; Cmnty Wkr; Pep Band; Yrbk Stf; PA Dist Ky Clb Ltnt Gvrnr 87; GATE 86-87; Sgnt Srty 86-87; Scope Jb Prg 86-87; Cnslng.

CUNNINGHAM, BRIDGET; Chester HS; Chester, PA; (3); NAACP; Chorus; Church Choir; Mrchg Band; School Musical; School Play; Off Soph Cls; Off Jr Cls; Bsktbl; Trk; Track Awd 85; Orch Awd 85; Prfct Atten 85; Young Teens 85; Upward Bound Pgm 85-87; Yth Svc Awd 85; DE ST Coll; Music Ed.

CUNNINGHAM, CAROL; Bishop Carroll HS; Ebensburg, PA; (4); 3/107; Pep Clb; Red Cross Aide; SADD; Chorus; Stat Bsktbl; High Hon Roll; Hon Roll; NHS; Elem Ed.

CUNNINGHAM, CAROLYN; Carrick HS; Pittsburgh, PA; (3); Q&S; Ski Clb; Chorus; School Musical; Rep Jr Cls; Hon Roll; Ftbl Trainer 86-87; Grls Bsktbl Athl Trainer 85-87.

CUNNINGHAM, CHRIS; Jeannette SR HS; Jeannette, PA; (3); Church Yth Grp; French Clb; Spanish Clb; Var L Bsktbl; Var L Ftbl; Var L Trk; High Hon Roll; Hon Roll; U Of Pittsburgh; Engrng.

CUNNINGHAM, CHRIS; Mohawk HS; New Castle, PA; (3); Church Yth Grp; French Clb; FBLA; Girl Scts; Mrchg Band; School Musical; Nwsp Ed-Chief; Nwsp Phtg; Tennis; Stat Trk; MIP Tennis 85.

CUNNINGHAM, CHRISTOPHER; Greater Latrobe Sr HS; Latrobe, PA; (2); 19/381; Aud/Vis; Letterman Clb; Library Aide; JV Bsktbl; Var L Socr; High Hon Roll; Prfct Atten Awd.

CUNNINGHAM, CHRYSTEN; Bethlehem Catholic HS; Bethlehem, PA; (3); 5/200; Hosp Aide; Key Clb; Math Tm; Quiz Bowl; VP SADD; Chorus; Nwsp Rptr; Nwsp Sprt Ed; Nwsp Stf; Capt L Tennis; Bio Med.

CUNNINGHAM, CURT; Central Catholic HS; Pittsburgh, PA; (3); 88/300; Ski Clb; Band; Jazz Band; Hon Roll.

CUNNINGHAM, CYNTHIA; Bishop Carroll HS; Ebensburg, PA; (3); Spanish Clb; SADD; Chorus; JV Var Bsktbl; JV Trk; Hon Roll.

CUNNINGHAM, DANIEL; Langley HS; Pittsburgh, PA; (3); JA; Office Aide; Teachers Aide; Nwsp Bus Mgr; Nwsp Phtg; Nwsp Rptr; Nwsp Sprt Ed; Nwsp Stf; Yrbk Bus Mgr; Yrbk Ed-Chief; Pgm Dir Schls Radio Dept; Comm.

CUNNINGHAM, GAYLE; Jersey Shore Area SR HS; Avis, PA; (3); Trs Church Yth Grp; French Clb; FBLA; Band; Concert Band; Mrchg Band; Bloomsburg U; Accntng.

CUNNINGHAM, GREGORY GRAHAM; Mercer HS; Mercer, PA; (4); 47/143; Stage Crew; Variety Show; Nwsp Stf; Yrbk Phtg; Yrbk Stf; Pres Soph Cls; Pres Sr Cls; Bsktbl; Var L Swmmng; Var L Trk; 9th In St In 50 Free Swmmng Comp 86; Dist 10 Champ 50 Free & 100 Butterfly 2 Record; 2&4 In State; Marion U; Bus Adm.

CUNNINGHAM, JAMES; Upper Dauphin Area HS; Elizabethville, PA; (3); Computer Clb; Band; Concert Band; Jazz Band; Mrchg Band; Rep Stu Cncl; Trk; Marine Bio.

CUNNINGHAM, JEFFREY; Millersburg Area HS; Millersburg, PA; (3); 20/71; Ftbl; Trk; Wrstlng; Hon Roll.

CUNNINGHAM, JOHN; Moniteau HS; Harrisville, PA; (3); 4-H; FFA; VICA; Var JV Ftbl; Wt Lftg; Newcastle Schl Of Trades.

CUNNINGHAM, JOSEPH; Wyoming Area SR HS; Exeter, PA; (4); 22/247; Church Yth Grp; Cmnty Wkr; Computer Clb; German Clb; Key Clb; Var Wrstlng; High Hon Roll; Hon Roll; NHS; PA ST Fresh Schlrshp 87; John Evans Me M Awd 87; Ger Achvt Awd 85; PA ST; Elect Engrng.

CUNNINGHAM, JUDITH; Bethlehem Catholic HS; Bethlehem, PA; (3); 26/200; Sec Church Yth Grp; Hosp Aide; Key Clb; Science Clb; Rep Frsh Cls; Rep Soph Cls; Rep Jr Cls; Stu Cncl; High Hon Roll; Hon Roll; Nrsg.

CUNNINGHAM, KELLEY; Huntingdon Area HS; Huntingdon, PA; (4); Pres Church Yth Grp; Key Clb; Library Aide; Sec Chorus; Church Choir; Var L Sftbl; Var L Tennis; JV Vllybl; Hon Roll; NEDT Awd; Dist IV & Rgn III Chorus 85-87; Outstndng Choral Awd 86-87; DE Vly Coll; Bio-Chem.

CUNNINGHAM, LESLIE; Auella Area JR SR HS; Avella, PA; (3); Art Clb; French Clb; FBLA; FHA; Chorus; Color Guard; Nwsp Rptr; Nwsp Stf; Yrbk Stf; Hon Roll; Jrnlsm Nwspr Work 86-87; Outstndng Achvt Econ 86-87; Data Proc.

CUNNINGHAM, MARK; Highlands SR HS; Natrona Hgts, PA; (3); VP Key Clb; SADD; Concert Band; Jazz Band; Mrchg Band; Bsbl; Swmmng; Jr NHS; NHS; Alle Kiski Hnrs Band 86-87; Mid East Music Fest 87.

CUNNINGHAM, MICHAEL; Pocono Mountain HS; Pocono Pines, PA; (2); Boy Scts; Church Yth Grp; Pep Clb; Ski Clb; SADD; Im Wt Lftg; Hon Roll; CA ST; Psych.

CUNNINGHAM, PATRICK; Penn Cambria HS; Ebensburg, PA; (2); Speech Tm; Hon Roll; NHS; US Air Force Acad; Aerospace.

CUNNINGHAM, SHANNA; Huntingdon Area HS; Huntingdon, PA; (4); 1/224; Off Church Yth Grp; French Clb; Cit Awd; High Hon Roll; Sec NHS; Val; Huntington Cnty Dairy Prncss 86; Socl Stds Achvt Awd 86-87; Pres Acdmc Fit Awd 86-87.

CUNNINGHAM, SHANNON; West Mifflin Area HS; W Mifflin, PA; (3); Ski Clb; Concert Band; Drill Tm; Mrchg Band; Orch; Pep Band; Nwsp Stf; Im Trk; Hon Roll; NHS; Educ.

CUNNINGHAM, SHELBY; J P Mc Caskey HS; Lancaster, PA; (4); 84/400; AFS; Church Yth Grp; Chorus; Church Choir; Hon Roll; Brd Of Governors Schlrshp 87; Millersville U; Bio.

CUNNINGHAM, STACY; Benton Area JR SR HS; Benton, PA; (4); 26/51; Drama Clb; FTA; Keywanettes; Library Aide; Chorus; Drm Mjr(t); School Musical; School Play; Nwsp Rptr; Yrbk Phtg; Acct I Awd, Typng I Awd, CPR Cert; Clarion U; Tchng.

CUNNINGHAM, TANYA; Oxford Area HS; W Nottingham, PA; (2); Art Clb; 4-H; FFA; Biology Awd 86-87; Dist Dairy Shwmnshp FFA 86-87; Dist Rec Kpng FFA 86-87; Engrng.

CUNNINGHAM, THERESA; Valley View JR SR HS; Blakely, PA; (1); 4/204; Ski Clb; Chorus; Stu Cncl; Score Keeper; High Hon Roll.

CUNNINGHAM, TRUDY; Lincoln HS; Wampum, PA; (3); AFS; Spanish Clb; High Hon Roll; Sclgy.

CUPILLARI, KRISTIN A; Scranton Prep HS; Factoryville, PA; (4); 16/190; Dance Clb; Drama Clb; School Musical; School Play; Yrbk Stf; High Hon Roll; NHS; Part Scholar Williams MA Coll Smmr Dnce Prgm 84; Acad Hnrs 5 Gld 2 Slvr & 12 Hnrb Mntn Mdls 83-87; Coll Holy Cross.

CUPP, ERIC; Sto-Rox HS; Mc Kees Rocks, PA; (3); Boys Clb Am; Chess Clb; VICA; Chorus; Yrbk Stf; Pres Frsh Cls; JV Trk; Hon Roll; Music.

CUPP, MICHELLE; Center HS; Monaca, PA; (4); 25/186; Exploring; VP Latin Clb; Yrbk Stf; VP Frsh Cls; VP Soph Cls; Stu Cncl; Powder Puff Ftbl; Hon Roll; NHS; Pres Schlr; Gannon U; Mdcl Tech.

CUPPETT, KELLY; Northeastern HS; Dover, PA; (3); Church Yth Grp; Ski Clb; Varsity Clb; Church Choir; Color Guard; VP Jr Cls; VP Sr Cls; Var Cheerleading; Var Fld Hcky; L Trk; Mst Imprvd Chrldr 86-87; Trvl Agnt.

CURA, THOMAS J; Downington HS; Downingtown, PA; (3); Church Yth Grp; FTA; Model UN; Ski Clb; Chorus; Rep Stu Cncl; Var Crs Cntry; Var Trk; High Hon Roll; NHS; Hstry Ed.

CURCI, CINDY; Mt Pleasant HS; Acme, PA; (3); Church Yth Grp; GAA; Band; Rep Frsh Cls; Bsktbl; Hon Roll.

CURCIO, SHANNA; Freedom HS; Bethlehem, PA; (3); Drama Clb; PAVAS; Ski Clb; SADD; Thesps; School Play.

CURLEY, KAREN; Chartiers Valley HS; Pittsburgh, PA; (3); German Clb; Varsity Clb; Yrbk Stf; Rep Stu Cncl; Var Vllybl; Med.

CURRAN, AMY; Saltsburg HS; Saltsburg, PA; (3); 5/65; Teachers Aide; Varsity Clb; Yrbk Stf; Stat Bsktbl; Var Cheerleading; Powder Puff Ftbl; JV Sftbl; High Hon Roll; Hon Roll; NHS; Hugh O Brian Yth Fdn 86; Pres Acad Ftns Awd 84-85; Pre-Law.

CURRAN, DEANNA; Bishop Hafey HS; Hazleton, PA; (1); Ski Clb; Spanish Clb; Y-Teens; Capt Cheerleading; Tennis; Hon Roll; Prfct Atten Awd; Acad All Amer Schlr 87; Math Awd 87; Outstndng H S Stu 87.

CURRAN, JENNIFER; Nazareth Acad; Philadelphia, PA; (4); 20/120; Pres French Clb; Chorus; Off Church Choir; Orch; Off Stu Cncl; Sftbl; Tennis; Hon Roll; NHS; Drexel Music Awds Cert 1st Pl 86; Advncd Study Prog Schlrshp 86; Music Schlrshp Temple U, Trenton ST; Trenton ST Coll; Music Educ.

CURRAN, VINCENT; St Josephs Prep; Villanova, PA; (4); 16/240; Chess Clb; German Clb; Math Clb; Pep Clb; Service Clb; Nwsp Stf; Lit Mag; Off Frsh Cls; Off Soph Cls; Off Jr Cls; All Cathlc Bsktbl 87; Mc Donalds Regnl All Stars; Fergusson Schlr Athltc; Markward Bsktbl Clb Plyr Yr; U Of PA; Bus.

CURRIE III, JAMES E; St Josephs Prep; Drexel Hill, PA; (4); 42/245; Trs Church Yth Grp; Hosp Aide; Spanish Clb; Rep Frsh Cls; Rep Soph Cls; Rep Sr Cls; Var L Wrstlng; Pres Scholar Loyola Coll 87; U DE.

CURRIER, ALISON; Council Rock HS; Richboro, PA; (3); Civic Clb; Drama Clb; Intnl Clb.

CURRO, RICHARD; St John Neumann HS; Philadelphia, PA; (3); 67/380; Letterman Clb; Spanish Clb; Capt L Crs Cntry; L Trk; Prfct Atten Awd; Rep Frsh Cls; Temple U.

CURRY, ANGELA; Union HS; Rimersburg, PA; (2); Aud/Vis; Trs Church Yth Grp; SADD; Color Guard; JV Bsktbl; High Hon Roll; Hon Roll; NHS; Arch.

CURRY, JUAN; Uniontown Area HS; New Salem, PA; (3); 28/318; Church Yth Grp; Letterman Clb; L NFL; Ski Clb; Spanish Clb; L Bsbl; L Ftbl; High Hon Roll; NHS; Aerospace Engr.

CURRY, KATHY; Ambridge Area HS; S Heights, PA; (4); 48/265; Pres Church Yth Grp; Pep Clb; Red Cross Aide; Teachers Aide; Drill Tm; High Hon Roll; Hon Roll; Cert Merit Outstndng Secy Skls Prof Secy Intntl 87; Robert Morris Coll; Word Prcsng.

CURRY, REBECCA; Daniel Boone HS; Douglassville, PA; (2); 20/157; Spanish Clb; Color Guard; Mrchg Band; Hon Roll; Publ Rel.

CURRY, TODD; Phil-Mont Xian Acad; Oreland, PA; (3); Church Yth Grp; Chorus; Church Choir; Stage Crew; Variety Show; Var L Crs Cntry; Var L Trk; Stu Mnth Awd, 2nd Piano Solo Compttn, 1st 800 M Rce Trk Chmpnshps 87; Elec Engr.

CURTIS, COURTNEY; Academy Of Notre Dame; West Chester, PA; (3); Church Yth Grp; Dance Clb; SADD; Teachers Aide; School Play; Yrbk Stf; JV Bsktbl; Cheerleading; Lcrss; Var Capt Socr; Brdcstg.

CURTIS, DAN; Carmichaels Area SR HS; Carmichaels, PA; (3); Radio Clb; Ski Clb; Spanish Clb; Band; Chorus; Concert Band; Jazz Band; Mrchg Band; Pep Band; Stage Crew; Alderson-Broaddus; Music.

CURTIS, JASON; Solanco HS; Quarryville, PA; (2); Varsity Clb; Var Ftbl; JV Trk; Hon Roll; PA U; Comp Pgmng.

CUSAT, LINDA; Hazleton HS; Hazleton, PA; (4); 31/392; Church Yth Grp; Cmnty Wkr; FBLA; Chorus; Nwsp Stf; Var Capt Bsktbl; Tennis; Hon Roll; NHS; James J & Helen R Malatach Schlrshp 87; Dist II PIAA Acdmc Athletic Excllnc 87; Bloomsburg U; Accountant.

CUSH, MICHAEL; Steel Valley HS; Munhall, PA; (3); 87/216; JA; Var Bsbl; Var Wrstlng; Hon Roll; TX; Ecnmcs.

CUSHEY, ERICH; Ringgold SR HS; Finleyville, PA; (2); Church Yth Grp; Science Clb; Variety Show; Ftbl; High Hon Roll; Hon Roll; Sci & Mth Hnr Scty-High Hnrs 86-87; Music.

CUSHMAN, GREGORY; Owen J Roberts HS; Pottstown, PA; (3); 14/299; Church Yth Grp; Letterman Clb; Band; Drm & Bgl; Mrchg Band; Orch; Var Trk; Im Vllybl; Hon Roll; NHS; Elec Engr.

CUSIC, LORRAINE; South Park HS; Library, PA; (4); 30/215; Ski Clb; SADD; Color Guard; Nwsp Stf; Mgr(s); Var Tennis; High Hon Roll; Hon Roll; NHS; U Of Pittsburgh; Pharm.

CUSICK, JULIE; Salisbury HS; Allentown, PA; (3); 1/154; Am Leg Aux Girls St; Debate Tm; PAVAS; Political Wkr; School Musical; School Play; Rep Frsh Cls; Sec Soph Cls; Sec Jr Cls; Rep Stu Cncl; Bio Olympcs 87; Amer Lgn Axlry Grls 87; Attorney.

CUSICK, TIMOTHY P; Scranton Central HS; Scranton, PA; (4); Church Yth Grp; NFL; Pres Speech Tm; SADD; Thesps; Nwsp Stf; Yrbk Stf; NHS; Ntl Merit SF; Rotary Awd; 2nd Pl In ST Cmptn In Drama 85; Drama.

CUSSATT, DOMINIC; W Hazelton HS; Hazleton, PA; (4); 38/224; Drama Clb; Scholastic Bowl; Ski Clb; Spanish Clb; Thesps; School Play; Nwsp Rptr; Yrbk Phtg; Trk; High Hon Roll; Penn ST U; Chem.

CUSSINS, VICKI; Keystone HS; Knox, PA; (3); SADD; Chorus; Ofc Mgmt.

CUSTER, DAVID; Millersburg HS; Millersburg, PA; (3); 37/73; Boy Scts; Church Yth Grp; Spanish Clb; Band; Concert Band; Var Ftbl; Var Trk; Hon Roll; Bio.

CUSTER, JEFF; East Pennsboro HS; Enola, PA; (3); 12/184; Boy Scts; Latin Clb; School Musical; School Play; Nwsp Rptr; Pres Frsh Cls; Pres Soph Cls; Var L Ftbl; High Hon Roll; Pres NHS; Hugh Obrien Yth Ambassador; Stu Forum Rep; Hstry.

CUSTER, JERRY LYNN; Windber Area HS; Windber, PA; (4); 37/128; Chess Clb; Exploring; Pres Band; Concert Band; Jazz Band; Mrchg Band; Var JV Vllybl; High Hon Roll; Hon Roll; Cert Of Dstngshd Svc-Music 86-87; Stu Of The Mnth 86-87; Instrmntlst Awd 86-87; U Of Pittsburg; Sci.

CUSTER, RICHARD D; Palmyra Area SR HS; Palmyra, PA; (4); 2/200; Quiz Bowl; Ski Clb; Stage Crew; Socr; High Hon Roll; NHS; Ntl Merit Ltr; Pres Schlr; Cmnty Wkr; Penn ST U Schlrs Hnr Schlrshp 87-88; Acdmc All-Am 87; PA ST U; Comp Sci.

CUSTER, ROY; Bentworth HS; Finnleyville, PA; (4); 43/126; JV Bsbl; Hon Roll; De Vry Inst Of Tech; Engrng.

CUSTER, TESA; Shanksville Stony Creek HS; Stoystown, PA; (3); 5/34; Ski Clb; Yrbk Stf; Sec Soph Cls; Sec Jr Cls; Off Stu Cncl; Var L Bsktbl; Var L Vllybl; Hon Roll; NHS; Spanish NHS.

CUSTODIO, MARIBEL A; Bethlehem Catholic HS; Bethlehem, PA; (4); 10/195; Hosp Aide; Key Clb; Yrbk Sprt Ed; Im Fld Hcky; Hon Roll; NHS; Hghst Avg Spnsh I & II Awd 84-85; Ntl Lang Arts Olympd Gld Mdl 84; Boston Coll; Med.

CUTHBERTSON, ANDRE E; John Harris HS; Harrisburg, PA; (2); 26/468; Art Clb; Boys Clb Am; School Play; Bsbl; Hon Roll; Pittsburgh U; Theatre.

CUTHBERTSON, JILL; Bradford Area HS; Bradford, PA; (4); AFS; SADD; School Play; Variety Show; Var L Tennis; High Hon Roll; Jr NHS; NHS; NEDT Awd; Pres Schlr; Top Twenty Grad Out Of Class 87; IN ST Of PA; Optometrist.

CUTLER, BRAD; Fort Le Boeuf HS; Waterford, PA; (2); FCA; FFA; VICA; Var L Ftbl; Im Vllybl.

CUTLER, JONATHAN; Marple Newtown HS; Broomall, PA; (3); Temple Yth Grp; School Play; Nwsp Sprt Ed; Rep Stu Cncl; Hon Roll.

CUTLER, JULIA; Jenkintown HS; Jenkintown, PA; (4); 3/42; French Clb; Pres Speech Tm; Chorus; School Musical; Swing Chorus; Yrbk Bus Mgr; French Hon Soc; High Hon Roll; NHS; Ntl Merit Ltr; Outstndng Achvt In Vcl Music 87; Wmns Clb Schlrshp 87; Dist & Rgn Chrs 85-87; Harvard-Redcliffe U; Intl Bus.

CUTLER, MICHAEL; Curwensville HS; Curwensville, PA; (3); Church Yth Grp; Hon Roll; Military; Marine Corp.

CUTLIP, MICHELE KAY; Central SR HS; York, PA; (4); 24/201; Am Leg Aux Girls St; Church Yth Grp; NFL; Spanish Clb; Band; Concert Band; Mrchg Band; School Musical; Variety Show; Nwsp Ed-Chief; Bnk Mngmnt.

CUTONE, SUSAN K; Serra Catholic HS; Pgh, PA; (4); Exploring; Math Tm; PAVAS; Band; Chorus; Stage Crew; Yrbk Phtg; Im Ftbl; Var Vllybl; High Hon Roll; St Vincents Coll; Physics.

CUTRI, PETER; Cathedral Preparatory Schl; Erie, PA; (3); 20/200; Ski Clb; Nwsp Stf; Yrbk Stf; Im Bsktbl; Var Swmmng.

CUTRONE, JOSEPH; Canevin HS; Pittsburgh, PA; (3); 55/195; Chorus; JV Ftbl; JV Var Socr; Var Tennis; Hon Roll; Robert Morris Coll; Comm.

CUTRUFELLO, JOSELLE; West Hazleton SR HS; Berwick, PA; (4); Pep Clb; Ski Clb; Spanish Clb; Flag Corp; IN U PA; Intr Dsgn.

CUTSHALL, CATHERINE E; Grove City Area HS; Grove City, PA; (4); 36/200; Ski Clb; Rep Frsh Cls; Stu Cncl; Capt L Cheerleading; Capt Powder Puff Ftbl; Capt Trk; Var L Trk; High Hon Roll; Frank Jiggs Wolford Awd 87; Walt Prettco Mem Awd 87; Pres Acad Fit Awd 87; Westminster Coll.

CUTSHALL, JENNIFER; Hollidaysburg Area SR HS; Hollidaysburg, PA; (3); 17/371; Spanish Clb; Acpl Chr; Chorus; Mgr(s); Im Vllybl; High Hon Roll; Hon Roll; Hnbl Mntn Ntl Spnsh Exm 86; Hghst Grd Spnsh II Cls 85-86; Cnty Chrs 87; PA ST U.

CUTTS, BRIAN; Steel Valley HS; W Homestead, PA; (3); Church Yth Grp; Wt Lftg; High Hon Roll; Hon Roll; NHS; Law.

CUZZOLINA, ANGELA; Bishop Guilfoyle HS; Altoona, PA; (3); Hosp Aide; Latin Clb; Spanish Clb; Y-Teens; Rep Stu Cncl; JV Var Cheerleading; Im Gym; JV Tennis; Var Wt Lftg; High Hon Roll; Hgh Hnr Rl 85; Bus Adm.

CVETAN, ANGELA; Brownsville Area HS; Brownsville, PA; (4); 11/200; Math Clb; Math Tm; Office Aide; Ski Clb; Band; Yrbk Stf; High Hon Roll; NHS; Church Yth Grp; Hugh O Brian Otstndng Sphmr Awd 85; CA U; Spch Pthlgy.

CVRKEL, KAREN; Bishop Mc Cort HS; Johnstown, PA; (3); 19/178; Mu Alpha Theta; Ski Clb; Spanish Clb; Chorus; School Musical; Swmmng; Trk; Vllybl; High Hon Roll; NHS; Sci.

CWYNAR, ANTOINETTE; Shenango HS; New Castle, PA; (3); 5/125; Band; Camera Clb; School Play; VP Pres Stu Cncl; Pom Pon; JV Var Vllybl; Cit Awd; High Hon Roll; Hon Roll; NHS; Law.

CYMBOR, JAMES; Northern Cambria HS; Barnesboro, PA; (3); 38/152; Stat Bsbl; JV Var Score Keeper; Hon Roll.

CYPARSKI, LAURIE; Harbor Creek HS; Erie, PA; (4); 11/222; Computer Clb; Office Aide; Teachers Aide; School Play; High Hon Roll; Hon Roll; Schlrshp Erie Bus Center 87; Wrd Prcssr.

CYPHERS, ALICE; Pocono Mt SR HS; Henryville, PA; (4); 15/298; Library Aide; Pep Clb; Nwsp Rptr; Nwsp Stf; Yrbk Ed-Chief; Yrbk Stf; Lit Mag; JV Cheerleading; Hon Roll; NHS; Natl Law Bay 1st Pl Essy Monroe Co 86; PMEA Schlrshp 87; Washington & Lee U; Frnch.

CYPHERS, PAUL; Keystone Oaks HS; Pittsburgh, PA; (3); 9/265; Church Yth Grp; German Clb; Var L Socr; Im Vllybl; High Hon Roll; NHS; Psych.

CYPHERT, AMY; Wilmington Area HS; New Wilmington, PA; (4); 5/117; Drama Clb; Trs Key Clb; Trs Spanish Clb; High Hon Roll; Trs NHS; Penn ST; Engrng.

CYRON, RON; John S Fine HS; Nanticoke, PA; (4); 25/251; Golf; Tennis; Vllybl; High Hon Roll; Hon Roll; NHS; NEDT Awd; Moreau 87-88; Kings Coll; Med Tech.

CYTERSKI, MICHAEL; Cathedral Prep; Erie, PA; (3); 1/194; Church Yth Grp; Latin Clb; VP Soph Cls; Rep Stu Cncl; JV Bsbl; Im Bsktbl; Var L Ftbl; Wrstlng; High Hon Roll; Hon Roll; Marine Bio.

CYWINSKI, TARA; Bishop O Reilly HS; Swoyersville, PA; (2); Ski Clb; Spanish Clb; Chorus; Mrchg Band; School Musical; School Play; Variety Show; JV Cheerleading; Prfct Atten Awd; Spanish NHS; Villanova; Law.

CZAJKOWSKI, DAWN MARIE; St Hubert Catholic HS For Girls; Philadelphia, PA; (4); Am Leg Aux Girls St; Mgr Aud/Vis; VP Church Yth Grp; Pres Girl Scts; Office Aide; Service Clb; Chorus; Cit Awd; Grl Schl Gold Awd 86-87 & Town & Cntry Schlrshp 87; Philadelphia CC; Educ.

CZARNECKI, ANDREA; Nazareth Acad; Philadelphia, PA; (3); 1/125; Rep Cmnty Wkr; NFL; Spanish Clb; VP Speech Tm; Chorus; School Musical; Sec Stu Cncl; Vllybl; High Hon Roll; NHS; Advncd ST & Natl Compttn Cthlc Frnscs Leag 86-87; Librl Arts.

CZARNECKI, BARBARA; Nazareth Acad HS; Philadelphia, PA; (4); Church Yth Grp; Cmnty Wkr; English Clb; NFL; Service Clb; Speech Tm; School Play; Bowling; NHS; NEDT Awd; Adelphi; Socl Svc.

CZARNECKI, JOHN; Bishop Mc Devitt HS; Harrisburg, PA; (4); 8/190; Am Leg Boys St; Band; Jazz Band; Mrchg Band; Ed Nwsp Bus Mgr; Rep Stu Cncl; L Socr; High Hon Roll; NHS; Orch; Math.

CZECK, MARY LYNN; Crestwood HS; Mountaintop, PA; (3); Mu Alpha Theta; Ski Clb; NHS; Math Clb; Im Vllybl; Jr NHS; NEDT Awd; Crestwood Spnsh Awd.

CZOLNIK, LUCY; Aliquippa JR/SR HS; Aliquippa, PA; (4); VP Chess Clb; Yrbk Stf; Hon Roll; NHS; U Ptsbrg.

CZOP, KEELY; Henderson HS; West Chester, PA; (3); 36/377; Intnl Clb; Yrbk Phtg; Stu Cncl; Sec VP French Hon Soc; Hon Roll; NHS; Ntl Merit Ltr; 2nd Pl Lawd Day Essay Cntst 86; Pilot.

CZUBA, GERI LYNN; Mt Pleasant Area SR HS; Mt Pleasant, PA; (3); 26/250; French Clb; GAA; Hosp Aide; Concert Band; Mrchg Band; High Hon Roll; Scl Wrkr.

CZUCHAN, ANDREA; Cardinal O Hara HS; Media, PA; (3); 40/710; Aud/Vis; Cmnty Wkr; Concert Band; Mrchg Band; Off Stu Cncl; Var L Diving; NHS; 2nd Pl Eastern Invtnl Dvng Cont & 3rd Pl Natl Cath Dvng Cont, US Army Cert Super Achvt Div Wnnr 87; Nuclear Med.

CZULEWICZ, ROGER A; Cathedral Preparatory HS; Fairview, PA; (3); 60/221; Church Yth Grp; Var Debate Tm; German Clb; Latin Clb; NFL; Im Bsktbl; Im Vllybl; NHS; US Nvl Acad; Avtn.

CZUTNO, TARA; West Hazleton HS; Hazleton, PA; (3); 27/217; Dance Clb; Exploring; Pep Clb; Ski Clb; Thesps; Co-Capt Color Guard; Orch; Yrbk Stf; Mgr(s); Trk; Penn ST U; Engrng.

D ABRUZZO, STEPHANIE ANN; Peters Township HS; Pittsburgh, PA; (2); NFL; Thesps; Chorus; Church Choir; Mrchg Band; Orch; School Musical; School Play; High Hon Roll; 1st Lit PTA Reflections Cntst, 2nd Dist 85-86; Brdcstng.

D ALESSANDRO, SANDRA; St Maria Gorett HS; Philadelphia, PA; (4); 112/384; French Clb; Rep Soph Cls; Hon Roll; Hon Ment Ldrshp Awd Future Sec 86; Cert Of Cmmndtn Stenography I 86; Gregg Shrthnd Achvmnt Awd 86; La Salle U; Bus Mngmnt.

D ALESSANDRO, TONY; Council Rock HS; Newtown, PA; (3); 192/900; Cmnty Wkr; Pres Key Clb; SADD; Im Ftbl; Hon Roll; Mrn Bio.

D ALTERIO, TONI; Oxford Area HS; Cochranville, PA; (2); DECA; Var JV Tennis; Hon Roll; Typg Prof Awd 87; Japan Oceania Prof 87; Cmnst Cult Prof 87; Video Tech.

D AMATO, ELIZABETH; Mechanicsburg Area SR HS; Mechanicsburg, PA; (2); 16/309; Church Yth Grp; Cmnty Wkr; Office Aide; Service Clb; Speech Tm; Nwsp Stf; JV L Fld Hcky; High Hon Roll; NHS; Finance.

D AMATO, JOSEPH; St John Neumann HS; Philadelphia, PA; (3); 15/380; Computer Clb; Math Tm; Service Clb; High Hon Roll; NHS; Spanish NHS; Temple; Comp Pgmmng.

D AMBROSIO, JOHN; West Catholic Boys HS; Philadelphia, PA; (3); 42/247; Church Yth Grp; Office Aide; JV Var Bsbl; Im Bsktbl; JV Var Socr; Hon Roll; Prfct Atten Awd; Crew Tm Var Ltr 84-85; Prfct Conduct Awd 84-85 & 85-86; PAL Bsbl City Champs 86; Temple; Acctg.

D AMBROSIO, RALPH V; St John Neumann HS; Philadelphia, PA; (3); 42/349; High Hon Roll; Prfct Atten Awd.

D AMELIA, KATHLEEN; Bishop Kenrick HS; Audubon, PA; (3); 8/380; Dance Clb; Soph Cls; Jr Cls; Stu Cncl; Powder Puff Ftbl; Var Tennis; High Hon Roll; VP NHS; Frnch Excllnc Awd 85-86; Natl Math Exm 86-87; Advncd Plcmnt Engl 86-88; Erly Chldhd Ed.

D AMICO, ANTHONY; South Allegheny HS; Glassport, PA; (3); 16/182; Church Yth Grp; Spanish Clb; Rep Stu Cncl; JV Bsktbl; Var Trk; NHS; 2 Yr Hnr Rll Cert 84-86; Accntng.

D AMICO, JACK A; East Allegheny HS; North Versailles, PA; (3) Chorus; School Musical; Capt Ftbl; Prfct Atten Awd; Singing Cmptn 2nd 1st Pl 86 & 87; GATE Prog 85-87; PMEA Awd 87; Spprtng Role Smm Stck Coll Musicls.

D AMICO, MELANIE; Central HS; Scranton, PA; (4); German Clb; High Hon Roll; Hon Roll; Jr NHS; NHS; Prfct Atten Awd; Robert C Byrd Schlrshp 87; U Of Scranton; Accntng.

D AMORE, ANTHONY; St John Neumann HS; Philadelphia, PA; (2).

D AMORE, MELANIE; Elk County Christian HS; St Marys, PA; (4); 1 79; Hosp Aide; Pres VP SADD; Rep Frsh Cls; Rep Soph Cls; Rep Jr Cls Rep Sr Cls; High Hon Roll; NEDT Awd; JA; UNTD Atates Ntl Ldrshp Merit Awd 86-87; Ldrsp Dvlpmnt Schlrshp 84-85; Ed Deaf & Hearing.

D ANDREA, DANIELLE V; Bishop Conwell HS; Bensalem, PA; (4) 115/264; Art Clb; Dance Clb; GAA; Office Aide; School Musical; Tremaine Semi-Fnl Dnc Compttn Prfrmnce Awd 85-86; Tremaine Dnc Cnvntns Merit Awd 85-86; Bucks Cnty CC; Bus Mgmt.

D ANDREA, MICHELE LEE; Warren Area HS; Warren, PA; (4); 16/300; Am Leg Aux Girls St; Church Yth Grp; Hosp Aide; Pres SADD Varsity Clb; Sftbl; Vllybl; High Hon Roll; NHS; Gldn Drgn Awd; U PA Cup; IN U PA; Crmnlgy.

D ANGELO, JOHN M; St John Neumann HS; Philadelphia, PA; (2); 6/351; Chorus; Rep Soph Cls; Rep Stu Cncl; Bowling; High Hon Roll; Hon Roll; $200 From William Penn Fndtn 86; Pharm.

D ANGELO, TRACEY; Hazleton HS; Mcadoo, PA; (4); 69/396; Trs Drama Clb; French Clb; Pep Clb; Ski Clb; Stage Crew; Var Sftbl; Hon Roll Lion Awd; Pres Schlr; Penn ST.

D ANNUNZIO, DAWN; Upper Darby HS; Upper Darby, PA; (3); FBLA VICA; High Hon Roll; Hon Roll; Prfct Atten Awd; Secy.

D ANTONIO, ERIC; Montour HS; Mckees Rocks, PA; (3); Spanish Clb Bowling; Socr; High Hon Roll; Hon Roll; Jr NHS; NHS; Spanish NHS; U Of Pittsburgh; Engrng.

D ANTONIO, KRISTI; Henderson HS; W Chester, PA; (3); Debate Tm Drama Clb; Intnl Clb; Political Wkr; School Musical; Yrbk Stf; Lit Mag Rep Stu Cncl; JV Lcrss; NHS; Pol Sci.

D ARCANGELO, ANDREA; Trinity HS; Camp Hill, PA; (3); 5/140 Church Yth Grp; Cmnty Wkr; Hosp Aide; Model UN; Pep Clb; Spanish Clb; Yrbk Stf; Trk; High Hon Roll; Med Tech.

D ARCY JR, WILLIAM F; Archbishop Wood For Boys; Holland, PA; (4) 62/276; Computer Clb; Hon Roll; Spn Awd 87; Penn ST; Engrng.

D AURIA, RICHARD W; Connellsville Area HS; Connellsville, PA; (3) Boy Scts; Band; Concert Band; Jazz Band; Mrchg Band; Orch; Pep Band School Musical; Symp Band; Hon Roll; Music.

D AVANTI, ANTHONY; Our Lady Of Lourdes Regional HS; Kulpmont PA; (3); 18/89; Am Leg Boys St; Drama Clb; French Clb; Key Clb; Pres Band; Mrchg Band; Stage Crew; Var L Golf; Var L Wrstlng; Pep Band HOBY Fndtn Ldrshp Semnr 86; Elect Engr.

D IGNAZIO, GINA; Downingtown SR HS; Glenmore, PA; (3); Library Aide; PAVAS; Spanish Clb; Teachers Aide; Chorus; School Musical; Yrbk Stf; High Hon Roll; NHS; Fnlst Pgnts-Chester Cnty JR Miss & Miss TEEN, Dance Capt Schl Musical 86-87; Dance.

D URSO, JENNIFER R M; Williamsport Area HS; Williamsport, PA (4); 20/518; Nwsp Ed-Chief; Nwsp Rptr; Nwsp Stf; Yrbk Rptr; Hon Roll NCTE Awd; Kystn 1st Plc PSPA 86; Intrnl Rltns.

DABAGIAN, ELLEN MARIE; Archbishop Prendergast HS; Upper Darby, PA; (4); 32/325; Church Yth Grp; Cmnty Wkr; Hosp Aide; Office Aide; Quiz Bowl; Rep Stu Cncl; Var L Fld Hcky; Hon Roll; NHS; Upr Darby Rtry Clb Stu Mnth 86; Prsdntl Acdmc Ftnss Awd, Gold Mdl Ldrshp & Srvc 87; Loyola Coll MD; Math.

DACEY, TRESA; Panther Valley HS; Nesquehoning, PA; (2); 10/122 Library Aide; Capt ROTC; Flag Corp; Nwsp Rptr; Yrbk Stf; Stu Cncl; Bsktbl; Trk; High Hon Roll; VFW Awd; PA U; Oral Srgry.

DADDONA, KIMBERLY; William Allen HS; Allentown, PA; (2); Drama Clb; Hosp Aide; Pep Clb; Spanish Clb; Chorus; School Play; Crs Cntry Hon Roll; Psych.

DADHANIA, MANISH; Cumberland Valley HS; Mechanicsburg, PA; (3); 60/550; Camera Clb; Key Clb; Model UN; Nwsp Rptr; Socr; Tennis; NHS; PA Yth & Govt 88; 1st Pl PA St Wnnr In Bio In PA JR Acad Of Sci 88; Cumberland Vly Awd Of Excll 88.

DADIO, TERRI; Freedom HS; Easton, PA; (3); 62/503; VP French Clb; Science Clb; SADD; Nwsp Sprt Ed; Nwsp Stf; Lit Mag; Var L Bsktbl; Var L Vllybl; Hon Roll; NHS; 1st Tm All Stars E PA Leag-Vlybl 87, Bsktbl 87; Dist XI Girls Bsktbl Chmpns 87; Psych.

DAGEN, SPRING; Pequea Valley HS; Gordonville, PA; (3); AFS; Church Yth Grp; VP Pres FBLA; Chorus; Stage Crew; Fld Hcky; Hon Roll; 4th Pl Impromptu Spkg Sprng Ldrshp Conf 87; Grphc Art.

DAGER, ERIC; Central Bucks West HS; Chalfont, PA; (3); 138/481; Nwsp Stf; Crs Cntry; Var Trk; Hon Roll; Prfct Atten Awd; Winter Track MIP 84-85 & 85-86; Arch.

DAHLER, LAURIE; Ridgway Area HS; Ridgway, PA; (4); 11/107; Yrbk Phtg; Yrbk Stf; L Gym; Elks Awd; High Hon Roll; NHS; PIAA ST Champ Uneven Parallel Bars 87; U Pittsburg; Phrmcy.

DAIELLO, DEANA; Freedom HS; Easton, PA; (4); 81/446; Church Yth Grp; Exploring; Quiz Bowl; VICA; Var Cheerleading; Hon Roll; Pres Vo Tech Cmrcl Arts Cls 85-86; Illstrtn.

DAILEY, CAROLINE; Carrick HS; Pittsburgh, PA; (3); Camp Fr Inc; Dance Clb; Drama Clb; Hon Roll; Prfct Atten Awd; Stu Mnth 85; Chef.

DAILEY, CAROLINE; Gwynedd Mercy Acad; Warrington, PA; (2); Bsktbl; Vllybl; Hon Roll; Frnch, Latin & Math Awds 85-86; Law.

DAILEY, JENNIFER; Hempfield HS; York, PA; (4); 33/513; Cmnty Wkr; SADD; Varsity Clb; Stu Cncl; Var Tennis; Var L Vllybl; Bausch & Lomb Sci Awd; Hon Roll; Hugh O Brien Ldrshp Seminar Ambssdr 85 Outstndng Stu Of Yr 84-86; Stu Of Yr 84-85; Penn St; Liberal Arts.

DAILEY, MATT; Peters Township HS; Mcmurray, PA; (3); Ski Clb; Varsity Clb; Ftbl; Trk; Wt Lftg; Wrstlng; French Hon Soc; High Hon Roll; Hon Roll; U Of IL; Lbrl Arts.

DAINTY, DANIEL; Belle Vernon Area HS; Belle Vernon, PA; (4); 98/265; Boy Scts; Church Yth Grp; Computer Clb; Nwsp Sprt Ed; Var L Bsktbl; Var L Ftbl; Capt L Trk; USAF Acad Prep Schl In CO 87-88; Adam Mc Kelvey Mem Awd For Outstndng Yth; USAF Acad Prep Schl; Bus Admin.

DAISLEY, DAWN; Reynolds HS; Greenville, PA; (4); 22/147; DECA; Hosp Aide; Stu Cncl; Hon Roll; NHS; PA Distrbtv Educ Clbs Amer Schlrshp Awd 86-87; Hnr Grad 87; Outstndng Vo-Tech Awd 87; Duquesne U; Intl Bus.

DAIT, PIERRE; Perkiomen Schl; Lehighton, PA; (4); 7/64; Ski Clb; Varsity Clb; Nwsp Stf; Yrbk Stf; Rep Stu Cncl; Var L Bsbl; Capt Var Bsktbl; Capt Var Ftbl; Hon Roll; NHS; Frank S Riordan Awd 87; Lewie Kellar Mem Awd 87; Frank C Stefano Awd 85; Villanova; Accntng.

ALANSKY, STEPHEN P; Altoona Area HS; Altoona, PA; (4); 109/718; ierman Clb; Trk; Penn ST; Bus Mngmnt.

ALE, JON; West Branch Area HS; Morrisdale, PA; (3); VICA; JV Ftbl; ocr; God Cntry Awd; Hon Roll.

ALE, STEPHANIE; Hickory HS; Hermitage, PA; (3); Hosp Aide; ibrary Aide; Spanish Clb; Band; Flag Corp; Swmmng; VP Spanish NHS; r Svc Clb 86-87; U Of AZ; Flght Attndnt.

ALE, THOMAS A; Greensburg-Salem HS; Greensburg, PA; (4); 16/270; res German Clb; Math Tm; Ski Clb; Pres Soph Cls; Pres Jr Cls; Pres Sr ls; Var Capt Ftbl; Var Trk; High Hon Roll; NHS; Ftbl 1st Tm All Dist & ll Conf 86; Carnegie Mellon U; Indstrl Mgmt.

ALESANDRO, BRIAN; Bishop Hafey HS; Zion Grove, PA; (2); Church th Grp; Spanish Clb; Bsbl; Ftbl; Military.

ALESANDRO, HOLLY; Blairsville SR HS; Blairsville, PA; (3); SADD; arsity Clb; Concert Band; Mrchg Band; Sec Frsh Cls; Stu Cncl; Bsktbl; rk; Vllybl; Schlrshp PA ST Coca-Cola Bowling Tourn 86; CPA.

ALESSANDRI, JAMES; Aliquippa HS; Aliquippa, PA; (3); Chess Clb; hurch Yth Grp; Stat Ftbl; Hon Roll.

ALESSANDRI, SUSAN; Aliquippa HS; Aliquippa, PA; (4); 20/130; rench Clb; Office Aide; School Play; Yrbk Stf; Off Sr Cls; Hon Roll; NHS; eaver County CC; Med Lab Tech.

ALESSANDRO, LAURA; Council Rock HS; Newtown, PA; (2); Cmnty Vkr; Chrmn Key Clb; SADD; Var Bowling; JV Fld Hcky; Mgr(s); JV Sftbl; rk; High Hon Roll; Hon Roll; Vet Med.

ALEY, EDSEL; Blue Mountain Acad; Queens, NY; (3); Church Yth rp; CAP; JA; Chorus; Drill Tm; Drm & Bgl; Wt Lftg; Andrews U; Aerospc 'ech.

ALEY, KELLY ANN; W Philadelphia Cath HS For Girls; Philadelphia, A; (4); 99/246; Drama Clb; Spanish Clb; Acad Achvt Cert Alg II; Acad chvt Awd Child Dev; Stock Broker.

ALEY, SAM; Pittston Area HS; Pittston, PA; (4); Pres Aud/Vis; Pres rama Clb; School Play; Variety Show; Yrbk Sprt Ed; Var L Socr; Var L llybl; Hon Roll; Schl Brd Hnr Awd; U Of Miami FL; Flm Video.

ALIOUS, JENNA; Saucon Valley SR HS; Hellertown, PA; (1); Library ide; Model UN; Teachers Aide; Band; Concert Band; Jazz Band; JV Fld Icky; Var Trk; High Hon Roll; Jr NHS; Leon A Brown Awd Outstndng rshmn 87.

ALLAS, ANNE; Lower Merion HS; Merion, PA; (3); VP Church Yth rp; Trs Service Clb; Nwsp Stf; Lit Mag; Capt Tennis; JV Wrstlng; Hon oll; Sec NHS; Spanish NHS; JCL.

ALMAGRO, WILLIAM; Butler Area SR HS; Butler, PA; (3); xploring; German Clb; Jazz Band; Mrchg Band; Symp Band; Im Ftbl; ligh Hon Roll; Ntl Merit SF; Phrmcy.

ALPIAZ, HEATHER; Towanda Area HS; Monroeton, PA; (4); Girl cts; Hosp Aide; Ski Clb; SADD; Concert Band; Mrchg Band; Rep Stu ncl; Stat Bsktbl; Stat Crs Cntry; Stat Trk; Cnty Band 84-87; Hnrs Band 7; Outstndng Prgrss Music Awd 85; Misericordia Coll; Occptnl Thrp.

ALTON, BRIAN; Riman Catholic HS; Philadelphia, PA; (3); 8/121; ADD; Rep Frsh Cls; Im Bsktbl; Capt Ftbl; Hon Roll; Jr NHS; NHS; VFW wd; Bus.

ALTON, DENISE; Penns Manor Area HS; Clymer, PA; (3); Pres ADD; Yrbk Stf; Var Capt Cheerleading; Hon Roll; Hugh O Brien Yth drshp Sem 86; Arin IUP A Smmr Happening Dance & Drama 87; IN Cty 'nlst JR Miss 87; IN U Of PA; Med Res.

ALTON, MICHAEL; Meadville Area SR HS; Meadville, PA; (2); hurch Yth Grp; JCL; Key Clb; Latin Clb; Ski Clb; Spanish Clb; Var wmmng; High Hon Roll; Hon Roll; Prfct Atten Awd.

ALTON, MICHELE; St Benedict Acad; Erie, PA; (4); 17/60; Quiz Bowl; 'res Sr Cls; Rep Stu Cncl; Hon Roll; NHS; Natl Bus Hnr Soc; Tng Actn lb; Cmps Mnstry; Erie Bus Cntr; Accntnt.

ALTON, STEVEN; Conestogo HS; Wayne, PA; (3); 40/440; Intnl Clb; panish Clb; Hon Roll; NHS; Math.

ALUISIO, JEAN; Deer Lakes JR SR HS; Saxonburg, PA; (4); 30/166; horus; School Play; Yrbk Stf; L Stat Trk; Hon Roll; Grad With Hnrs 87; Of Pittsburgh; Pre-Law.

ALY, BRIAN; Monsignor Bonner HS; Lansdowne, PA; (3); 72/245; sbl; Bsktbl; 1st Tm All Cthlc-Phila Bsktbl 86-87; 1st Tm All Delco Bsktbl 6-87; Bus.

ALY, BRIAN; West Catholic For Bays HS; Philadelphia, PA; (3); 100/ 48; Millersvl; Mktng.

ALY, ERIN; Bishop Mc Cort HS; Johnstown, PA; (2); Band; Chorus; oncert Band; Mrchg Band; Orch; High Hon Roll; NHS.

ALY, ERIN; Lansdale Catholic HS; Chalfont, PA; (3); 30/233; Drama lb; SADD; Church Choir; School Musical; Nwsp Stf; Rep Stu Cncl; Var Cheerleading; Trk; Hon Roll; 10th Pl Natl Chrldng Cmptn 86; Gwynedd lercy; Nrsng.

ALY, MEGAN; Acad Of Notre Dame; Devon, PA; (3); Debate Tm; lodel UN; Political Wkr; Var L Crs Cntry; JV Capt Lcrss; Var Capt Trk; 'CA; Speech Tm; Chorus; School Musical; 3 JR Olympics Crss Cntry, -3rd Pl & 2-2nd Pl 84-86; Lawyer.

AM, CHAU; Red Lion Area SR HS; Red Lion, PA; (3); 26/342; Science lb; Varsity Clb; Chorus; School Musical; Rep Stu Cncl; JV Im Bsktbl; JV ar Fld Hcky; High Hon Roll; Hon Roll; Mdrn Music Mastrs Hnr Soc 87.

AMAN, TONYA; Rochester HS; New Brighton, PA; (3); Church Yth rp; French Clb; Ski Clb; Color Guard; Concert Band; Drill Tm; School lusical; School Play; Var Trk; Hon Roll; Med.

AMASKA, JENNIFER L; Eastern York HS; York, PA; (2); 21/155; JV lgr Bsbl; Gym; Bus Admn.

AMBACH, TRISTA; Seneca Valley HS; Evans Cty, PA; (2); High Hon oll; Hon Roll; Schltc Awd 1st Yr 87; Vet Med.

AMBECK, JOLENE; Bishop Guilpoyle HS; Altoona, PA; (3); Sec cience Clb; Ski Clb; Chorus; Rep Jr Cls; Rep Stu Cncl; L Cheerleading; Ion Roll; Penn ST.

AMBROSIA, CHRISTINE; Serra Catholic HS; Monroeville, PA; (4); FS; VP Exploring; NFL; Speech Tm; School Musical; Stage Crew; Stat rs Cntry; Powder Puff Ftbl; Hon Roll; NHS; U Pittsburgh; Biochem.

AMIANI, KIMBERLEE; Upper Darby HS; Upper Darby, PA; (3); Pep lb; Cheerleading; Wt Lftg; Hon Roll; Prfct Atten Awd; Photo.

AMORE, CHARLENE; St Marys Area HS; Saint Marys, PA; (4); 18/ 79; VP SADD; Yrbk Stf; Stat JV Bsktbl; Stat Trk; NHS; Pres Schlr; AUW Schlrshp 87; Stackpole Carbon Co Schlrshp 87; PA ST U; strophysicist.

AMORE, JOANNE; Dayton HS; Templeton, PA; (3); 10/55; Dance Clb; ibrary Aide; Chorus; Nwsp Ed-Chief; Nwsp Rptr; Nwsp Stf; Trs Frsh Cls; 'rs Soph Cls; Trs Jr Cls; Trs Sr Cls; Mdcl Prfssn.

DAMP, DAVID; Montour SR HS; Pittsburgh, PA; (3); Church Yth Grp; SADD; Band; Chorus; Concert Band; Mrchg Band; Pep Band; Symp Band; JV Var Vllybl; Hon Roll; Educ.

DAMPF, JULIE; Knoch JR-SR HS; Butler, PA; (4); 35/247; Girl Scts; Concert Band; Mrchg Band; Pep Band; School Musical; School Play; Yrbk Ed-Chief; God Cntry Awd; Hon Roll; NHS; Eliz Stewart Schlrshp, Thiel Grant 87-88; Thiel Coll; Nrsng.

DAMS, SCOTT; Emmaus HS; Emmaus, PA; (3); Boy Scts; Church Yth Grp; German Clb; Key Clb; Ski Clb; Socr; Hnr Roll Awd 85; Bus.

DANCISON, THOMAS J; North Catholic HS; Pittsburgh, PA; (4); Drama Clb; Exploring; Model UN; NFL; Pres Spanish Clb; Speech Tm; Chorus; School Musical; School Play; Variety Show; Ntl Yth Ldrshp Awd 86; St Frncs Coll Schlrshp 87-91; Prry Hghlnd Jnr Wmns Clb Schlrshp 87; St Francis-Loretto PA; Med.

DANEK, MICHAEL; Ringgold HS; Donora, PA; (2); 1/350; Exploring; Chorus; Church Choir; School Musical; Rep Stu Cncl; JV Ftbl; Hon Roll; NHS; Ringgold HS Hnr Soc Hgh Hnr 85-87; U Of Pittsburg; Bio Chem.

DANEK, TRICIA; Burgettstown Area HS; Atlasburg, PA; (4); 8/138; French Clb; Chorus; Concert Band; Ed Yrbk Stf; Var JV Cheerleading; High Hon Roll; High Hon Roll; NHS; Pres Schlr; IN U Of PA; Cmnctns Media.

DANELSKI, BARBARA; Western Wayne HS; Lake Ariel, PA; (3); SADD; School Play; Sec Frsh Cls; Sec Rep Stu Cncl; Bsktbl; Mgr(s); Score Keeper; Sftbl; Cit Awd; Hon Roll; Ntl Ldrshp & Serv Awd 87; US Ntl Stu Cncl Awd 86; Exec Secr.

DANESE, RICH; Central Bucks West HS; Warrington, PA; (3); Ski Clb; SADD; JV Var Socr; Bus.

DANG, TIEN; S Philadelphia HS; Philadelphia, PA; (4); 6/710; Nwsp Stf; Yrbk Stf; Tennis; Hon Roll; Army Rsrve Natl Essay Cont 1st Pl 84; Columbus Day Essay Cont 3rd Pl 85; Temple U.

DANGEL, TRACY; Hollidaysburg Area SR HS; Hollidaysburg, PA; (4); Church Yth Grp; French Clb; Band; Concert Band; Mrchg Band; Symp Band; Var Swmmng; Im Vllybl; Hollidaysburg Area Educ Assoc Schlrshp 87; Band Excllnc Awd 87; Trphy For 1st Choir At Rgnl Band 87; Clarion U; Early Chldhd.

DANGELO, MIKE; Du Bois Area HS; Dubois, PA; (2); Bsbl; Bsktbl; Socr; Bus.

DANGELO, NICOLE; Nazareth Acad; Philadelphia, PA; (3); 13/125; Church Yth Grp; Library Aide; Science Clb; Stage Crew; Hon Roll; Archdiocesan Schlrshp Fnlst 87; Villanova U; Phy Thrpy.

DANGLE, JAIMEE; S Williamsport Area JR SR HS; S Williamsport, PA; (3); Cmnty Wkr; Trs French Clb; Band; Concert Band; Mrchg Band; Symp Band; Yrbk Stf; Stu Cncl; Bsktbl; Hon Roll.

DANIAS, STACIE; Bradford Central Christian HS; Bradford, PA; (3); Pep Clb; JV Var Cheerleading; Hon Roll; Jr NHS.

DANIEL, LAURA; Downingtown SR HS; Downingtown, PA; (3); 22/648; Sec GAA; Ski Clb; Spanish Clb; Rep Jr Cls; JV Var Lcrss; JV Var Swmmng; High Hon Roll; NHS; Teachers Aide; Daisy Chain; Jr Ms Cnty Fnlst.

DANIEL, LORI; Upper Dauphin HS; Elizabethville, PA; (4); 24/108; Church Yth Grp; JA; Band; Chorus; Church Choir; Concert Band; Mrchg Band; School Musical; School Play; VP Sr Cls; PA All ST,Dist & Rgnl Bnd 86-87; Elizabethtown Coll; Physcl Thrp.

DANIEL, MARIA CRISTINA; Center Area HS; Monaca, PA; (2); Spanish Clb; Im Badmtn; Prfct Atten Awd; Sawyer Schl Of Bus; Airlns Wrk.

DANIELLO, DENNIS; Reynolds HS; Greenville, PA; (3); 6/168; Boy Scts; Cmnty Wkr; Latin Clb; Nwsp Phtg; Nwsp Rptr; Yrbk Ed-Chief; Hon Roll; NHS; Natl Acad All-Amer 85-87; Natl Ldrshp & Svc Awd 86-87; PA ST Cap Page 86; Med.

DANIELS, ANTOINETTE; Chester HS; Chester, PA; (3); 10/458; Spanish Clb; Mrchg Band; Var Sftbl; High Hon Roll; Hon Roll; Prfct Atten Awd; Outstndg Alg I Stu Awd 85; Outstndg Geom Stu Awd 86; Hghst Avg Span 3 Stu 87; Engnrng.

DANIELS, BOB; Hollidaysburg SR HS; Hollidaysburg, PA; (3); 49/359; Church Yth Grp; Band; Jazz Band; Mrchg Band; Hon Roll; NHS; Penn St.

DANIELS, CARLTON; Tunkhannock Area HS; Tunkhannock, PA; (4); 12/270; Church Yth Grp; Computer Clb; Exploring; Letterman Clb; Pep Clb; Bsktbl; Trk; Hon Roll; NHS; Ron Hbbs Mem Schlrshp 87; Ntl Schlr/Athlt Awd 87; Sr Athltc Awd 87; Bucknell U; Mech Engrng.

DANIELS, CARRIE; Carlisle SR HS; Gardners, PA; (3); 175/454; Church Yth Grp; Cmnty Wkr; Drama Clb; 4-H; School Play; Rep Stu Cncl; Var L Crs Cntry; 4-H Awd; Hon Roll; 1st Hstry Cmpttn 86; Am Horse Show Assn 85-87; Hood Coll.

DANIELS, DEANA; Springfield HS; Oreland, PA; (4); Cmnty Wkr; Varsity Clb; Rep Frsh Cls; Rep Soph Cls; Trs Jr Cls; Off Stu Cncl; Fld Hcky; Lcrss; Jane Vche Srv Awd-La Crsse; W Chester U; Bus.

DANIELS, DEBRA; Millersburg Area HS; Millersburg, PA; (4); 11/76; French Clb; Spanish Clb; Color Guard; Nwsp Stf; Yrbk Stf; Hon Roll; NHS; Ntl Merit Ltr; Spanish Awd 86-87; Hnrbl Mntn In Natl French Exam 87; Presdntl Acad Fitness Awd 87; Susquehanna U; Engl.

DANIELS, EDDIE; Mastbaum Avts HS; Philadelphia, PA; (3); VICA; Stage Crew; Off Frsh Cls; Off Soph Cls; JV Var Socr; Air Force.

DANIELS, ERICA; Fort Le Boeuf HS; Erie, PA; (2); Dance Clb; GAA; Drm & Bgl; Im Cheerleading; JV Diving; L Trk; High Hon Roll; Hon Roll; Miss Amer Co-Ed Pgnt ST Fnlst 86; Vllybl Stu Trnr, Mdlng & Prmtns By Rania Agncy 87; Scl Wrkr.

DANIELS, LISA D; Mc Connellsburg HS; Needmore, PA; (3); 2/65; Am Leg Aux Girls St; Band; Concert Band; Mrchg Band; Stage Crew; Yrbk Stf; High Hon Roll; Jr NHS; NHS; Awds Hlth, Eng, Chem 86-87; Phys Thrpy.

DANIELS, MELISSA; St Marys Area HS; St Marys, PA; (3); 4/300; Cmnty Wkr; Debate Tm; Hosp Aide; Bsktbl; Tennis; High Hon Roll; NHS; Seneca Highlands Smr Acad 86; Physcl Thrphy.

DANIELS, MICHAEL; Corry Area HS; Corry, PA; (2); Church Yth Grp; Chorus; L Var Ftbl; L Var Trk; High Hon Roll; Hon Roll; Phys Educ.

DANIELS, NICHOLE; Chester HS; Chester, PA; (3); 225/458; Spanish Clb; Hon Roll; Prfct Atten Awd; Data Proc.

DANIELS, PATRICE INEZ; Coatesville SR HS; Thorndale, PA; (3); Camera Clb; SADD; VICA; Off Jr Cls; Sec Stu Cncl; Bsktbl; Mgr(s); Var Trk; Hon Roll; Phys Ftns, Perf Attend 84-85; Cosmetology.

DANIELS, STEVEN P; Elk County Christian HS; Ridgway, PA; (4); Ski Clb; Nwsp Rptr; Rep Jr Cls; JV Var Bsktbl; Var Trk; Hon Roll; Kiwanis Awd; Natl Phy Ed Awd 85; U S Natl Bsktbl Awd 86; Duquesne U; Bus Mgmt.

DANIELSON, BRETT; Otto-Eldred HS; Duke Center, PA; (3); Church Yth Grp; Spanish Clb; SADD; Chorus; Church Choir; Nwsp Rptr; Var Trk; Mt Vernon Bible Coll; Yth Mnstr.

DANIK, MICHELLE; Freeport Area HS; Freeport, PA; (3); 11/200; Rep Stu Cncl; Mgr(s); Trk; High Hon Roll; Hon Roll.

DANISAVICH, ALEX; Mahanoy Area HS; Barnesville, PA; (4); 50/110; Trs Church Yth Grp; Variety Show; Nwsp Phtg; Yrbk Phtg; L Bsktbl; L Trk; Kutztown; Physics.

DANNA, JOHN; Avella JR/Sr HS; Avella, PA; (3); Art Clb; French Clb; Letterman Clb; Varsity Clb; Var L Bsktbl; Var L Ftbl; Wt Lftg; Hon Roll; Rep Frsh Cls; Off Soph Cls; Hnr Rll 84-85; Hnr Rll Lttr 85-86; Hnr Lttr Htmn Awd 86-87; Bus.

DANNA, MISSI; Auella JR SR HS; Avella, PA; (3); French Clb; Pep Clb; Ski Clb; Yrbk Stf; Cheerleading; Tennis; Vllybl; Hon Roll; Orthopedics.

DANNEKER, DOLORES; Loyalsock Township HS; Williamsport, PA; (3); 3/124; Chorus; Color Guard; Nwsp Ed-Chief; Nwsp Rptr; Var L Trk; Hon Roll; NHS; Ntl Merit Ltr; Church Yth Grp; French Clb; IN U PA Physics Tstng Comp 87; Stu Rcgntn Brkfst 85-87; Physics.

DANNER, NICOLE; East Pennsboro Area HS; Camp Hill, PA; (2); 52/ 189; Hon Roll; Poem Hnrbl Mntn 86-87; Acadc Achvt Awd Alg I 85-86; Savannah Coll Of GA; Int Dsgn.

DANNHARDT, MARGARET; Greensburg Central Catholic HS; Greensburg, PA; (3); Hosp Aide; Ski Clb; Im Sftbl; JV Var Vllybl; High Hon Roll; Hon Roll; NHS.

DANOWITZ, JOSHUA; Pocono Mountain HS; Stroudsburg, PA; (2); U Of ID; Wrtng.

DANOWITZ, MICHAEL; Central Dauphin HS; Harrisburg, PA; (4); Key Clb; Quiz Bowl; Temple Yth Grp; Yrbk Ed-Chief; Yrbk Phtg; Yrbk Sprt Ed; VP Soph Cls; VP Jr Cls; VP Sr Cls; Pres Stu Cncl; Woodmn Wrld Amer Hstry Awd 87; Princpls Meritious Svc Awd 87; Natl Cncl Soc Studs Scholar Awd 86; Duke U; Intl Law.

DANOWSKI, DENISE; Villa Maria Acad; Erie, PA; (4); Computer Clb; Exploring; SADD; Color Guard; Yrbk Stf; High Hon Roll; NHS; NEDT Awd; Prfct Atten Awd; Pres Schlr; Gannon U; Mech Engrng.

DANOWSKI, REBECCA; Hatboro-Horsham HS; Hatboro, PA; (4); 17/ 267; Girl Scts; Chorus; Concert Band; Powder Puff Ftbl; Tennis; Capt Var Trk; High Hon Roll; Hon Roll; Prfct Atten Awd; Rotary Awd; Acad Achvt Awd Wrld Lit 87; Girl Scout Gold Awd 87; Champ Learng Awd 84-87; Marywood Coll; Mngmnt.

DANYLO, NICOLE; Western Beaver HS; Industry, PA; (3); Sec Trs Church Yth Grp; Hosp Aide; Office Aide; Chorus; Drill Tm; Nwsp Stf; Yrbk Stf; Rep Stu Cncl; Bowling; Capt Pom Pon; Intl Bus.

DANZIS, LOREN; Central Bucks HS East; Doylestown, PA; (3); Boy Scts; Debate Tm; Pres Stu Cncl; Var L Socr; Var L Trk; DAR Awd; God Cntry Awd; Hon Roll; Church Yth Grp; Ski Clb; JR Cnslr CISV Intl Cmp Kids 87; MVP Indr Sccr Trvl Tm 85; Intl Rltns.

DAO, MINH; Allen HS; Allentown, PA; (3); Boys Clb Am; JA; Im Vllybl; Hon Roll; Elec Engrng.

DAQUELENTE, TONY; Richland HS; Wexford, PA; (3); Church Yth Grp; Drama Clb; NFL; School Play; High Hon Roll; Hon Roll; Amer Lgn Awd 84; Robert Morris; Bus Mgmt.

DARCANGELO, JIM; Schuylkill Haven HS; Sch Haven, PA; (2); 15/101; Spanish Clb; Im Bsbl; JV Var Bsktbl; Im Ftbl; Im Vllybl; Im Wt Lftg; Hon Roll.

DARESTA, ANNETTE; Unionville HS; West Chester, PA; (4); 30/316; NHS; Trk; Capt Cheerleading; FBLA; Capt Flag Corp; School Musical; Nwsp Stf; Yrbk Stf; Chorus; High Hon Roll; Schl On Map Awd; George Washington U; Pre-Law.

DARLING, CHRIS; Elk Lake HS; Meshoppen, PA; (4); 16/96; SADD; VP VICA; Stat Bsktbl; Capt Tennis; Cit Awd; Hon Roll; Kiwanis Awd; Williamsport Area CC Schlrshp 87-88; Outstndng Elec Awd 86-87; Ela Hnrs Awd 86-87; Williamsport Area CC; Elec.

DARLING, ELIZABETH; Elk Lake HS; Meshoppen, PA; (2); FHA; Ski Clb; Spanish Clb; SADD; JV Cheerleading; Mgr(s); Pom Pon; Chrldng Awd 86-87; Trk Mgr Awd 86-87; Pom-Pom Awd 85-86; Nrsng.

DARLING, ERIC; The Baptist HS; Nicholson, PA; (4); Chess Clb; French Clb; Acpl Chr; Chorus; Im Socr; PA ST; Psych.

DARNELL, BEVERLY; Connellsville SR HS; Dunbar, PA; (4); 27/521; Q&S; Nwsp Rptr; Yrbk Stf; French Hon Soc; High Hon Roll; NHS; Prfct Atten Awd; Acad Excllnce; German Honry Scty; Newspaper News Edtr; Marietta Coll; Journlsm.

DARNELL, BOB; Connellsville HS; Dunbar, PA; (3); Hon Roll; Highest Perfmnc Sci; Auto Body.

DARRAH, ELIZABETH L; Villa Joseph Marie HS; Langhorne, PA; (3); Am Leg Aux Girls St; Drama Clb; Service Clb; SADD; Chorus; School Play; Variety Show; Rep Stu Cncl; Cheerleading; Prfct Atten Awd; Stu Mnth 85; Erly Chldhd Ed.

DARRAUGH, SHAWN; Hazleton HS; Hazleton, PA; (2); Church Yth Grp; FBLA; Office Aide; Ski Clb; SADD; Rep Frsh Cls; JV Bsbl; Var Capt Bsktbl; Score Keeper; Im Trk.

DARRIGO, ROCHELLE; North Star HS; Gray, PA; (3); 28/108; Art Clb; Church Yth Grp; Cmnty Wkr; FCA; Yrbk Stf; Hon Roll.

DARROCH, MEGAN; Center HS; Aliquippa, PA; (2); Drama Clb; Spanish Clb; Nwsp Stf; Rep Stu Cncl; Co-Capt Cheerleading; Powder Puff Ftbl; Sftbl; Hon Roll; Comm.

DARRUP, CHERYL L; Mount Carmel Area JR/Sr HS; Mt Carmel, PA; (4); 6/173; Dance Clb; Pres FTA; Trs Key Clb; VP Q&S; Sec Sr Cls; Capt Bsktbl; Capt Crs Cntry; Trk; Kiwanis Awd; NHS; Irwin Herr Schlrshp 87; Deppen Schlrshp 87; Rotary Stu Mnth Sept 86; Bucknell U; Bus Admin.

DASCHER, HEIDI; Upper Dublin HS; Dresher, PA; (3); 29/318; Church Yth Grp; SADD; Yrbk Stf; Var JV Sftbl; Hon Roll; NHS; Schltc Wrting Hnrbl Mntn 87; Penn ST; Bus.

DASCOLI, TERRY C; Beaver HS; Midland, PA; (4); Yrbk Stf; Sec Jr Cls; Sec Stu Cncl; Capt Cheerleading; Powder Puff Ftbl; L Sftbl; Duffs Bus Inst; Prfssnl Scrtry.

DASH, ANITA; East Pennsboro Area HS; Camp Hill, PA; (3); Art Clb; Drama Clb; French Clb; Model UN; Band; Concert Band; Mrchg Band; Yrbk Stf; Stu Cncl; High Hon Roll; Med.

DASH, KEN; Pennsbury HS; Yardley, PA; (3); 2/850; Spanish Clb; JV Socr; Var Capt Tennis; CC Awd; High Hon Roll; Hon Roll; NHS; Prfct Atten Awd; Bucks Cnty Courier Tms Schltc Awd 87; Genl Elec Co Twn Mtg Tmrrw Ldrshp Pgm 86; PA Ldrshp Pgm 86.

DASH, MELISSA; Ringgold HS; Monongahela, PA; (3); #8 In Class; Ski Clb; Nwsp Stf; Yrbk Stf; Soph Cls; Var Diving; Var Golf; Var Swmmng; Var Trk; High Hon Roll; NHS; U Of Pittsburgh-Provst Day Wnr 87; Comp Engrng.

DASHEM, HOWARD; Penns Valley Area HS; Centre Hall, PA; (4); 4-H; Pres FFA; Band; Ftbl; Wt Lftg; Hon Roll; De Kalb Agri Acmplshmnt Awd 87; J Decker Agri Awd 87; Frm Crdt Outstndng Prjct Bk Awd 86-87.

DASHIELL, JULIANNE T; Ridley SR HS; Ridley Park, PA; (4); 106/407; Church Yth Grp; Dance Clb; Drama Clb; French Clb; Girl Scts; Library Aide; Ski Clb; Band; Chorus; Concert Band; Glassboro ST Coll; Psych.

DASKALAKIS, ARGYRO; Quaker Valley SR HS; Sewickley, PA; (2); Church Yth Grp; Drama Clb; Chorus; Church Choir; School Musical; VP Frsh Cls; High Hon Roll.

DASKALAKIS, KATINA; Quaker Valley SR HS; Sewickley, PA; (2); Church Yth Grp; Chorus; Church Choir; School Musical; Hon Roll; Most Outstndng Stu Chorus Awd 85-86.

DAUB, TINA; Tulpehocken HS; Bethel, PA; (2); Church Yth Grp; Spanish Clb; SADD; Band; Concert Band; Mrchg Band; School Musical; Bsktbl; Score Keeper; Trk; Advrtsng.

DAUBENSPECK, ERIC; Brockway Area HS; Brockway, PA; (3); 12/110; Varsity Clb; Var Bsbl; Var Bsktbl; Var Golf; High Hon Roll; Accntng.

DAUGHERTY, AMY; Annville-Cleona HS; Annville, PA; (3); 20/130; SADD; Varsity Clb; Nwsp Stf; Yrbk Stf; Var L Fld Hcky; Mat Maids; JV L Trk; NHS; Stat Sftbl; HOBY Fndtn Ldrshp Awd 86; Legal Asst.

DAUGHERTY, AMY; Cranberry HS; Franklin, PA; (3); French Clb; Science Clb; Sec Ski Clb; SADD; Teachers Aide; Nwsp Stf; Yrbk Stf; Trk; Hon Roll; Art Inst/Pittsburgh; Cmmrcl Art.

DAUGHERTY, CYNTHIA A; Derry Area SR HS; Derry, PA; (2); Church Yth Grp; Band; Chorus; Concert Band; Mrchg Band; Pep Band; School Musical; Symp Band; Yrbk Stf; High Hon Roll; PA Free Enterprise Week 87; 1st Pl In Derry Arts & Sci Fair 86; Penn ST; Commercial Art.

DAUGHERTY, DAVE; Center Area HS; Monaca, PA; (2); Exploring; Spanish Clb; Band; Concert Band; Jazz Band; Mrchg Band; Pep Band; Symp Band; High Hon Roll; Hon Roll; Spn Merit 85-86; Engrng.

DAUGHERTY, DIANE M; Serra Catholic HS; E Mckeesport, PA; (4); Cmnty Wkr; Exploring; Hosp Aide; Red Cross Aide; Service Clb; Spanish Clb; SADD; Nwsp Stf; Powder Puff Ftbl; Sftbl; Cmmnty Svc Awd 85; Amblnc Lt Cmmnty 86-87; Penn ST U; Hosp Adm.

DAUGHERTY, ERIC; West Perry SR HS; New Bloomfield, PA; (2); Church Yth Grp; Library Aide; Church Choir; Hon Roll; Word Of Life Coll; Bible.

DAUGHERTY, GINA; Philipsburg-Osceola Area HS; Philipsburg, PA; (4); 26/240; Church Yth Grp; Drama Clb; Band; Chorus; Capt Flag Corp; Mrchg Band; School Musical; School Play; Stage Crew; Yrbk Stf; Sci Awd 85; Duquesne U; Phrmcy.

DAUGHERTY, MICHELE; Apollo-Ridge HS; Apollo, PA; (4); FBLA; FHA; Pep Clb; Political Wkr; Ski Clb; Spanish Clb; SADD; Band; High Hon Roll; NHS; Schlrshp Pitts Beauty Acad 87-88; Pres Acad Ftns Awd 87; Pittsburgh Beauty Acad; Cosmtlg.

DAUKSHUS, KAREN; Marian Catholic HS; Tamaqua, PA; (3); 21/104; Church Yth Grp; Pep Clb; SADD; Rep Soph Cls; Var L Bsktbl; Var Trk; Hon Roll; Elem Educ.

DAUSON, TAMMIE; Fort Le Boeuf HS; Erie, PA; (3); 23/208; Drama Clb; Chorus; School Musical; School Play; Mgr Stage Crew; Nwsp Stf; Rep Stu Cncl; Var Bsktbl; JV Sftbl; High Hon Roll; Secy.

DAVANZO, PHILOMENA A; Bangor Area HS; Roseto, PA; (3); Pep Clb; Nwsp Stf; Lit Mag; Wrstlng; Hon Roll; NCACC; Legl Secy.

DAVELER, PHILLIP J; Ridley SR HS; Ridley Park, PA; (3); Mu Alpha Theta; Radio Clb; Band; Concert Band; Mrchg Band; Symp Band; Hon Roll; Comp Sci.

DAVELLI, LISA; South Allegheny HS; Port Vue, PA; (4); 9/187; Pres Sec Church Yth Grp; Trs French Clb; Hosp Aide; Office Aide; Sec Band; Jazz Band; Sec Mrchg Band; Rep Stu Cncl; Powder Puff Ftbl; Cit Awd; Century III Ldrshp Awd 86; District Orchestra 86-87; Organ Schlrshp 83-86; U Of Pgh; Pt.

DAVENPORT, DEBORAH; Dallas SR HS; Shaverstown, PA; (3); Band; Chorus; Church Choir; Concert Band; Madrigals; School Musical; School Play; Yrbk Stf; Fld Hcky; Hon Roll; Silver Awd 85; 1st Pl Duet Sing 87; Ed.

DAVENPORT, JULIE A; Jamestown HS; Greenville, PA; (2); French Clb; Bsktbl; Vllybl; Athl Awd 86-87; Air Force Acad; Bus.

DAVENPORT, SONYA; Susquehanna HS; Harrisburg, PA; (2); Dance Clb; NAACP; Chorus; Church Choir; Rep Soph Cls; Var JV Cheerleading; Coach Actv; Gym; Trk; Hampton U; Lawyr.

DAVEY, PATRICIA; Bishop Mc Devitt HS; Philadelphia, PA; (3); 128/349; Church Yth Grp; Spanish Clb; Powder Puff Ftbl; Hon Roll; Prfct Atten Awd; Educ.

DAVID, ALAN; Uniontown SR HS; Uniontown, PA; (3); Boy Scts; Pres Church Yth Grp; Debate Tm; JA; Spanish Clb; Jazz Band; Mrchg Band; Stat Trk; God Cntry Awd; Prfct Atten Awd; Penn ST U; Marine Bio.

DAVID, GLORIA; Altoona Area HS; Altoona, PA; (3); 11/796; Nwsp Stf; High Hon Roll; Pres Schlr.

DAVID, KIM; Laural Highlands SR HS; Uniontown, PA; (2); JA; Nwsp Stf; High Hon Roll; Hon Roll; Elem Ed.

DAVID, MOODY; Simon Gratz HS; Philadelphia, PA; (1); Bst Autobdy Wrkr Yr Awd 87; Welder.

DAVIDHEISER, SCOTT; Spring-Ford HS; Schwenksville, PA; (3); 56/256; Church Yth Grp; Ski Clb; Spanish Clb; Var Bsbl; Var Ftbl; Wrstlng; 1st Tm All Pac-8 Ftbl 86; 1st Tm All Pac-8 Bsbl 87.

DAVIDHIZAR, CARLA; Johnstown Christian HS; Hollsopple, PA; (2); 1/27; Chess Clb; Church Yth Grp; Drama Clb; 4-H; Science Clb; Chorus; Yrbk Stf; Trs Soph Cls; JV Bsktbl; Var Socr; Estn Monnonite Coll.

DAVIDICK, TIMOTHY; Hazleton SR HS; Hazleton, PA; (4); Church Yth Grp; Drama Clb; Leo Clb; Ski Clb; SADD; School Musical; Bsbl; Bowling; Penn ST U; Arch.

DAVIDOW, MICHELLE; Norwin HS; N Huntingdon, PA; (3); 216/571; Ski Clb; SADD; Band; Color Guard; Sec Sr Cls; Off Stu Cncl.

DAVIDSON, JULIE; Northwestern Lehigh HS; Orefield, PA; (3); 21/153; Debate Tm; SADD; Varsity Clb; Chorus; Sec Stu Cncl; Bsktbl; Fld Hcky; Sftbl; Hon Roll; Comp Awd 87; Psychtry.

DAVIDSON, KATHRYNE; Lincoln HS; Philadelphia, PA; (3); 5/500; Art Clb; Aud/Vis; Concert Band; Orch; Hon Roll; Ntl Merit SF; We The People 200, Yng Artsts 87, Wmns Spnsh Spkng Org Awd, 1st Pl Paramount Pctrs Essy Cont 87; Cmmrcl Art.

DAVIDSON, KEITH; Auquippa HS; Aliquippa, PA; (2); Church Yth Grp; Ski Clb; L Bsbl; Golf; Tennis; Wt Lftg; Hon Roll.

DAVIDSON, LYNN; Central Cambria HS; Ebensburg, PA; (3); Cmnty Wkr; Pres 4-H; French Clb; NFL; Y-Teens; Nwsp Rptr; Yrbk Stf; 4-H Awd; Hon Roll; Gftd Prgrm; Law.

DAVIDSON, MARI; Bishop O Hara HS; Dunmore, PA; (2); 6/127; Church Yth Grp; Dance Clb; French Clb; Latin Clb; Pep Clb; School Play; Cheerleading; High Hon Roll; Art Awd 85-86; Math.

DAVIDSON, RACHEL; Conestoga SR HS; Berwyn, PA; (2); Hosp Aide; SADD; Acpl Chr; Concert Band; Variety Show; Nwsp Rptr; Hon Roll; Opt Clb Awd; Exch Stu England 85-86; Peer Cnslr 87; Bus.

DAVIDSON, ROBERT; Blairsville HS; Blairsville, PA; (1); Art Clb; French Clb; Trk; Wrstlng; Phy Ftnss Awd; Penn ST U.

DAVIDSON, SCOTT; Seneca Valley SR HS; Zelienople, PA; (4); 27/340; Varsity Clb; Rep Jr Cls; VP Stu Cncl; Socr; Swmmng; Hon Roll; Pres NHS; Prfct Atten Awd; Rotary Awd; Acad Achvt Awd; Thomas J Prevish Mem Awd Swim; Swim Tm Capt; Allegheny Coll; Bio.

DAVIDYOCK, ANDREW; Liberty HS; Liberty, PA; (2); Computer Clb; German Clb; Capt Bsktbl; Socr; Trk; Hon Roll; Air Force Acad; Mltry Pilot.

DAVIE, DEBRA; Blacklick Valley HS; Vintondale, PA; (2); NFL; Ski Clb; Spanish Clb; Speech Tm; Varsity Clb; Stage Crew; Rep Frsh Cls; Rep Soph Cls; Rep Stu Cncl; Sftbl.

DAVIE, WILLIAM; Blacklick Valley HS; Vintondale, PA; (4); 1/91; Library Aide; Varsity Clb; Yrbk Ed-Chief; Var Bsktbl; Ftbl; Trk; High Hon Roll; Hon Roll; Pres NHS.

DAVIES, ERIN; Tunkhannock Area HS; Tunkhannock, PA; (3); French Clb; Key Clb; Yrbk Phtg; Yrbk Stf; Cheerleading; Mgr(s); Sftbl; Bus.

DAVIES, JENEFER M; Bishop Neumann HS; Montoursville, PA; (4); Model UN; Pep Clb; SADD; School Musical; Yrbk Bus Mgr; Ed Yrbk Stf; Bsktbl; Capt Cheerleading; High Hon Roll; NHS; Natl Advncmnt Arts 87; Mst Otstndng Chrldr 84-87; Awd Hgh Grds 87; Hollins Coll; Dnc.

DAVIES, JERRY; Lake Lehman HS; Dallas, PA; (2); Hon Roll; NEDT Awd 86; Hstry Tchr.

DAVIES, PENNY K; Upper Darby HS; Clifton Hts, PA; (3); 150/598; Hosp Aide; Chorus; Color Guard; Drill Tm; School Musical; Office Aide; Acpl Chr; Flag Corp; Mrchg Band; Psych.

DAVIN, MOLLY; Lansdale Catholic HS; Lansdale, PA; (3); 40/234; Drama Clb; Var L Math Tm; SADD; School Play; Nwsp Stf; Yrbk Stf; Co-Capt Swmmng; JV Trk; Hon Roll; Prfct Atten Awd; Phrmcy.

DAVIS, AMY; Meadowbrook Christian Schl; Lewisburg, PA; (1); 1/15; Chorus; Socr; Hon Roll; Opt Clb Awd.

DAVIS, ANTHONY; Harry S Truman HS; Levittown, PA; (3); Church Yth Grp; Chorus; Church Choir; Variety Show; VP Frsh Cls; VP Soph Cls; VP Jr Cls; Rep Stu Cncl; Hon Roll; Rotary Awd; Lincoln U; Psych.

DAVIS, B; Oxford Area HS; Oxford, PA; (3); 29/197; Varsity Clb; Yrbk Stf; Stu Cncl; Var Bsbl; Var Bsktbl; Var Capt Ftbl; Hon Roll; MVP Bsbl 87; Acctnt.

DAVIS, BARBARA; Central Cambria HS; Ebensburg, PA; (2); 1/200; 4-H; Hosp Aide; NFL; Ski Clb; Chorus; Stu Cncl; Cheerleading; Hon Roll; Medicine.

DAVIS, BARBARA; Souderton Area HS; Harleysville, PA; (3); Church Yth Grp; Church Choir; Hon Roll; Bus Educ Symp CC 87; Montgomery Cnty CC; Legal Sec.

DAVIS, BARBARA LYNN; Pennsbury HS; Morrisville, PA; (3); Church Yth Grp; SADD; Yrbk Stf; Rep Chrmn Stu Cncl; Im Bsktbl; Fld Hcky; JV Socr; Var JV Trk; Prfct Atten Awd; Nrsng.

DAVIS, BETH; Wyoming Valley West HS; Kingston, PA; (3); 29/419; Church Yth Grp; Key Clb; Radio Clb; SADD; L Swmmng; High Hon Roll; NHS; Yth Salute 87.

DAVIS, BOBBI J; Blacklick Valley JR SR HS; Belsano, PA; (2); Library Aide; Speech Tm; Concert Band; Nwsp Rptr; Hon Roll; NHS; Pres Schlr; Acadmc All Amer 85-86; Psych.

DAVIS, BRENDA; Blairsville SR HS; Blairsville, PA; (1); Art Clb; French Clb; Library Aide; Sftbl; High Hon Roll; Hon Roll.

DAVIS, BRENDA; Kiski Area HS; Vandergrift, PA; (4); 95/344; FHA; Band; Chorus; Concert Band; Mrchg Band; School Musical; Tennis; Twrlr; High Hon Roll; Cert Of Merit 87; Comp Sys Inst; Bus Adm.

DAVIS, BRENT; Pequea Valley HS; New Holland, PA; (3); AFS; Drama Clb; FBLA; German Clb; Band; Mrchg Band; School Musical; School Play; VP Frsh Cls; VP Jr Cls; Attorney.

DAVIS, BRIAN; Northeast Bradford HS; Le Raysville, PA; (4); 9/67; Varsity Clb; Var Capt Bsktbl; Hon Roll; Lycoming Coll; Bus Manag.

DAVIS, CARRIE; Girard HS; Girard, PA; (2); 1/200; Drama Clb; Drill Tm; Mrchg Band; School Musical; Ed Nwsp Stf; Yrbk Ed-Chief; Lit Mag; Rep Stu Cncl; High Hon Roll; Aud/Vis; James Merry Cmmndtn 86; 1st Pl Dist Lit Cont 85; Hgh Engl Score Teams Comp 87; Harvard U; Invstmnt Bkng.

DAVIS, CATHY; Columbia Montour Area Vo-Tech Schl; Berwick, PA; (3); 14/227; Girl Scts; Yrbk Stf; Hon Roll; 1st Pl Nrsg Asst 86; Geisinger Schl Of Nrsg; Nrsg.

DAVIS, CHANTALE; Waynesboro Area SR HS; Blue Ridge Summit, PA; (4); Dance Clb; Pep Clb; Ski Clb; School Musical; Yrbk Stf; Coach Actv; Capt Var Gym; Trk; NHS; Presdntl Acad Ftnss Awd 87; Fnlst PA Gvrnrs Schl Of Arts 85-86; 1st Pl Trphy Rdlnd Invtnls Chmpsh 83; Northeastern U.

DAVIS, CHRISTINA M; Ontario Street Baptist Schl; Philadelphia, PA; (4); 1/4; Church Yth Grp; Drama Clb; Hosp Aide; Math Clb; Teachers Aide; Church Choir; Yrbk Stf; High Hon Roll; Val; Hyles-Anderson Coll; Elem Educ.

DAVIS, CHRISTINE; Towanda Area HS; Monroeton, PA; (3); Trs Church Yth Grp; Pres FHA; Hosp Aide; Pres Sr Cls; Var Mgr(s); Capt Twrlr; Bucks County CC; Culinary Arts.

DAVIS, CRYSTAL; Moon SR HS; Coraopolis, PA; (3); Band; Mrchg Band; Rep Frsh Cls; Bsktbl; Trk; Hon Roll; U Of Pittsburgh; Law.

DAVIS, DARLA; Seneca Valley SR HS; Harmony, PA; (4); VP Church Yth Grp; Ski Clb; Varsity Clb; Chorus; Var L Crs Cntry; Beautyshp Quartet Baritone 85-87; Westminster Coll; Bus Admin.

DAVIS, DARREN; Northern York HS; Dillsburg, PA; (3); 99/232; Aud/Vis; Chess Clb; Church Yth Grp; Computer Clb; Pres DECA; FFA; Nwsp Stf; Crs Cntry; Trk; Messiah Coll; Secndry Ed.

DAVIS, DEANNA; Faith Christian Schl; Stroudsburg, PA; (4); 2/5; Church Yth Grp; Spanish Clb; Chorus; Trs Soph Cls; Trs Jr Cls; Trs Sr Cls; Off Stu Cncl; Stat Bsktbl; Sftbl; Hnr Rll 86; Chrstn Chrctr Awd 85-86; Christian Coll; OB.

DAVIS, DELORES; Susquehanna Community HS; Susquehanna, PA; (2); Church Yth Grp; VP SADD; Chorus; Nwsp Phtg; Nwsp Rptr; Ed Nwsp Stf; Lit Mag; Var Trk; Nwsp Phtg; Jrnlsm.

DAVIS, DENISE; Lake-Lehman HS; Sweet Valley, PA; (2); 2/199; Church Yth Grp; Pres Frsh Cls; Pres Soph Cls; Rep Stu Cncl; Im Sftbl; Var L Vllybl; High Hon Roll; Jr NHS; NEDT Awd; Hugh Obrian Yth Fndtn Ambssdr 86-87; 2nd Tm All Schlstc Vllybl WY Vlly Conf 86; Sprts Med.

DAVIS, DIANA; Sharpsville Area HS; Sharpsville, PA; (3); 22/102; V Chess Clb; Hosp Aide; Library Aide; Math Clb; SADD; School Musica Nwsp Rptr; Yrbk Ed-Chief; Yrbk Stf; Var Cheerleading; Art Cntst Wnn 1st Pl Lcl Cntst 85; Acadc Achvt Awd 84 & 85; Duquesne U.

DAVIS, DINA; Hazelton HS; Hazleton, PA; (3); Pep Clb; Yrbk Stf; Cheerleading; Fashion Inst Philadelphia; Fshn.

DAVIS, DONNA; Mount Pleasant Area HS; Mt Pleasant, PA; (3); IC Schl Of Bus; Trvl-Toursm.

DAVIS III, EDMUND C; Elizabethtown Area HS; Elizabethtown, PA (3); Boys Clb Am; Boy Scts; FFA; SADD; Air Force; Bldg Tech.

DAVIS, ERIN L; New Brighton Area HS; New Brighton, PA; (3); 6/18 Am Leg Aux Girls St; Varsity Clb; Nwsp Rptr; Yrbk Stf; Trs Soph Cls; Twrlr; High Hon Roll; Church Yth Grp; GAA; Girl Scts; Rtry Yth Ldrsh Conf 86-87; Outstndng JR-DRILL Tm-Mjrtte 86-87; Beaver Cnty JR Mis Fnlst 86-87; Penn ST U; Chld Psychlgy.

DAVIS, EVAN; Schuylkill Haven HS; Schuylkill Haven, PA; (3); 23/10 Boy Scts; Computer Clb; German Clb; School Musical; Stu Cncl; Ftbl; Tr School Play; Stage Crew; High Hon Roll; Penn ST; Electrnc Engrng.

DAVIS, GEORGE; Panther Valley HS; Coaldale, PA; (1); 21/127; Ftb Wt Lftg; JV Wrstlng; Hon Roll.

DAVIS, GERALD; Roxborough HS; Philadelphia, PA; (3); 21/35 Diving; Golf; Swmmng; Hon Roll; All Pub Diving City Champ Set Recor 87; Penn ST; Law.

DAVIS, GRETCHEN; Lackawanna Trail HS; Dalton, PA; (4); 5/8 Church Yth Grp; Cmnty Wkr; French Clb; Quiz Bowl; Scholastic Bow Science Clb; Ski Clb; Chorus; Madrigals; Score Keeper; Keystone JC Pharmacist.

DAVIS, IESHA; Martin Luther King HS; Philadelphia, PA; (3); Tr Church Yth Grp; Church Choir; Drill Tm; Yrbk Stf; Gym; Sftbl; Vllyb Hon Roll; Prfct Atten Awd; Pep Sqd 86; Comp Tech.

DAVIS, JAMES; Father Judge HS; Philadelphia, PA; (3); 55/402; Debat Tm; French Clb; Hon Roll; Penn ST; Aero Engrng.

DAVIS, JAMES C; Central Cambria HS; Colver, PA; (3); #1 In Class Church Yth Grp; Drama Clb; NFL; Speech Tm; Stu Cncl; High Hon Rol Mark S Singel Good Ctznshp Awds 83-84; Astrophysics.

DAVIS, JEFF; William Penn HS; York, PA; (4); 87/312; Bowling; Sftb Var Capt Wrstlng; Hon Roll.

DAVIS, JEFFREY; Waynesburg Central HS; Spraggs, PA; (3); Aud/Vi Camera Clb; Drama Clb; Ski Clb; Spanish Clb; JV Bsbl; JV Bsktbl; JV Cr Cntry; JV Socr; JV Trk; Brdcstng.

DAVIS, JEFFREY S; Canon Mc Millan HS; Canonsburg, PA; (3 Computer Clb; Trk; Hon Roll; Comp Engrng.

DAVIS, JENNIFER; Aliquippa HS; Aliquippa, PA; (3); 7/150; Churc Yth Grp; French Clb; Office Aide; Church Choir; Yrbk Stf; Off Jr Cls Sftbl; High Hon Roll; NAACP Hnrs Outstnding Achvt In Educ 83; Arch.

DAVIS, JENNIFER; Beaver Valley Christian Acad; New Brighton, PA (3); Church Yth Grp; Drama Clb; Speech Tm; School Musical; Yrbk St Pres Jr Cls; Bsktbl; Hon Roll; Debate Tm; VP Soph Cls.

DAVIS, JENNIFER; Bishop Hafey HS; Hazleton, PA; (4); 10/13 Drama Clb; VP Stu Cncl; Co-Capt Cheerleading; Cit Awd; Dnfth Aw Elks Awd; High Hon Roll; NHS; Church Yth Grp; Amer Lgn Aw 84fluzerne Cnty Jr Miss Fnlst 86; Top 8 Fnlsts In Miss Capital Dnc 87 Kings Coll; Mass Cmnctns.

DAVIS, JENNIFER; Emmaus HS; Macungie, PA; (3); 25/548; Exploring JA; Spanish Clb; Stage Crew; Hon Roll; NHS; Acctng.

DAVIS, JENNIFER; Freedom HS; Easton, PA; (3); 114/486; Pres FNA Hosp Aide; VICA; Concert Band; Mrchg Band; Hon Roll; Directors Forur Bethlehem Area Vo-Tech Schl 87; Northampton Cmnty Coll; Nrsng.

DAVIS, JENNIFER K; Biglerville HS; Biglerville, PA; (3); Girl Scts Hosp Aide; Library Aide; Nwsp Stf; Lit Mag; Sec Stu Cncl; Hon Rol Scholastic Writing Awd Merit Cert 87.

DAVIS, JENNIFER S; Knoch HS; Butler, PA; (3); Church Yth Gr SADD; Drill Tm; School Musical; Yrbk Stf; Trk; JV Vllybl; High Hon Rol NHS.

DAVIS JR, JOHN; Bald Eagle Area HS; Bellefonte, PA; (4); Bowling Elks Awd; High Hon Roll; NHS; William B Garver Schlrshp 87; PA ST U Bus.

DAVIS, JONATHAN; New Hope-Solebury JR SR HS; New Hope, PA (4); 7/79; Pres VP FBLA; Scholastic Bowl; Sec Soph Cls; Sec Jr Cls; Se Stu Cncl; Var L Bsbl; Var L Bsktbl; High Hon Roll; Hon Roll; NHS; Na Phy Ed Awd 86-87; Acadmc All Amer 85-86; Georgetown; Busnss Admin

DAVIS, KAREN; Mc Keesport Area HS; White Oak, PA; (3); 51/350 Church Yth Grp; German Clb; Girl Scts; School Musical; Wildlife Mgmt

DAVIS, KATHARINE; Lakeland JR SR HS; Clarks Summit, PA; (3); 4 143; FHA; JA; Library Aide; Color Guard; Flag Corp; Rep Stu Cnc Cheerleading; U Of Scranton; Jrnlsm.

DAVIS, KATHERINE; Greensburg Central Catholic HS; Ruffsdale, PA (3); 48/231; Church Yth Grp; Hosp Aide; Ski Clb; Yrbk Stf; Sec Sr Cls; Re Stu Cncl; Im Sftbl; Im Vllybl; High Hon Roll; Jr NHS; Nrsng.

DAVIS, KATHY; Plum Borough SR HS; Pittsburgh, PA; (4); Church Yt Grp; Spanish Clb; Socr; High Hon Roll; Hon Roll; Jr NHS; NHS; Natl Hn Soc 86; CCAC Boyce Campus.

DAVIS, KATHY JO; Pocono Central Catholic HS; Tobyhanna, PA; (3 1/30; Chorus; School Play; Nwsp Rptr; High Hon Roll; NHS; VFW Aw Voice Dem Awd; Physcl Thrpy.

DAVIS, KENDRA; Red Lion Area SR HS; Felton, PA; (3); 4/355; Scienc Clb; Varsity Clb; Jazz Band; Symp Band; Trs Fld Hcky; Swmmng; Frenc Hon Soc; High Hon Roll; NHS; Ntl Merit Ltr; Gov Schl Sci Alt 87; Cer Merit SE PA Sectn Amer Chem Soc 87; Early Admssns IUP 87-88; IN PA; Bio.

DAVIS, KIM; Plum SR HS; Pittsburgh, PA; (4); Library Aide; Drill Tn Yrbk Stf; Rep Frsh Cls; Rep Jr Cls; Rep Sr Cls; Stat Bsbl; JV Bsktbl; J Cheerleading; Swmmng; Plum Proud Awds 4.0 Avg; Grls Ldrs Asso Outstndng Svc Awd; Penn ST U; Chem.

DAVIS, KIMBERLY; Trinity HS; Washington, PA; (3); Art Clb; Pep Cl Acctnt.

DAVIS, KURTIS T; Marion Center Area HS; Plumville, PA; (3); 47/16 Church Yth Grp; Band; Chorus; Mrchg Band; Pep Band; Yrbk Stf; J Swmmng; JV Trk; Hon Roll; Dist Chrs 87; Cnty Chrs 85-87; Stingaires Sl Chr 86; IUP; Economics.

DAVIS, LAURA; Susquehannock HS; Glen Rock, PA; (2); 48/243; Gi Scts; Var Sftbl; Hon Roll; Penn ST U; Psychology.

DAVIS, LAURIE; Connellsville Area HS; Connellsville, PA; (2); Offic Aide; SADD; Teachers Aide; Chorus; School Musical; Rep Frsh Cls; Re Stu Cncl; Hon Roll.

DAVIS, LINDA; Creative & Performing Arts HS; Philadelphia, PA; (4); /128; Church Yth Grp; Computer Clb; Dance Clb; Teachers Aide; Rep Soph Cls; Rep Jr Cls; Rep Sr Cls; Rep Stu Cncl; High Hon Roll; NHS; Kutztaun U; Marine Bio.

DAVIS, MARY; Brokville Area JR SR HS; Brookville, PA; (4); 49/131; Boy Scts; Church Yth Grp; Cmnty Wkr; Pres FTA; German Clb; GAA; Key Clb; Letterman Clb; Pep Clb; Teachers Aide; Brookville Area Educ Assoc 87; Tchrs Schlrshp 87; Lucy A Valero Schlrshp 87; Clarion U Of Pa; Education.

DAVIS, MARY; Highlands SR HS; Natrona Heights, PA; (3); Church Yth Grp; Hosp Aide; Key Clb; Rep Soph Cls; Rep Jr Cls; Swmmng; WV U; Elem Educ.

DAVIS, MARYANN; Riverview HS; Verona, PA; (3); Varsity Clb; Band; Concert Band; Mrchg Band; Var Bsktbl; Var Trk; Var Vllybl; Sctn 15a Bsktbl All-Star, Eastern Suburbs Bsktbll All-Star, HS Vllybl Spr Srvr Awd 86-87; Real Est.

DAVIS, MEAGAN; Gateway SR HS; Monroeville, PA; (4); 106/475; DECA; JA; Pep Clb; Chorus; Sr Cls; Stu Cncl; Bsktbl; Trk; Hon Roll; WV U; Cmmnctns.

DAVIS, MELANIE; Wellsboro Area HS; Middlebury Center, PA; (2); 24/177; Church Yth Grp; CAP; Drama Clb; Sec Trs 4-H; German Clb; Chorus; Color Guard; Yrbk Stf; 4-H Awd; Hon Roll; Bus.

DAVIS, MELISSA; Chambersburg Area SR HS; Chambersburg, PA; (2); Church Yth Grp; Hosp Aide; Band; Chorus; Church Choir; Concert Band; Orch; Pep Band; High Hon Roll; Hon Roll; Phrmcy.

DAVIS, MICHAEL; Clarioni-Limestone HS; Strattanville, PA; (4); 7/66; Var Bsktbl; Var Trk; Hon Roll; NHS; Outstndng Sci Awd 86-87; Outsndng Awd In Vctnl & Indl Arts 86-87; U Ptsbrg; Engrng.

DAVIS, MICHELLE; Indiana JR HS; Indiana, PA; (1); Art Clb; SADD; JV Socr; Hosp Aide; Office Aide; Pep Clb; Teachers Aide; Band; Mrchg Band; Orch; Yth Fit Awd 85-86; Oper Babysttr 86; Shelocta Stu Of Mnth 86; Penn ST; Psych.

DAVIS, MINDY; Fairchance Georges HS; Uniontown, PA; (4); 11/150; Spanish Clb; Band; Concert Band; Mrchg Band; Capt Twrlr; Pres Frsh Cls; Sec Soph Cls; Pres Jr Cls; HS-COAL Queen Rep 86; Nrsng.

DAVIS, MONICA; Carlisle SR HS; Carlisle, PA; (3); 10/454; Art Clb; Color Guard; Stage Crew; Nwsp Rptr; Rep Stu Cncl; Swmmng; High Hon Roll; Hon Roll; VP NHS; Schlstc Art Awds Hnrbl Mntn 86.

DAVIS, MYRA E; Slippery Rock Area HS; Prospect, PA; (3); 9/189; Trs French Clb; Intnl Clb; Library Aide; Mrchg Band; Yrbk Rptr; Yrbk Stf; High Hon Roll; NHS; Church Yth Grp; Pep Clb; Boston U; Med.

DAVIS, NANCY; Mid-Valley Secondary Ctr; Throop, PA; (3); Drama Clb; Teachers Aide; Chorus; Color Guard; Drill Tm; School Play; Stage Crew; Nwsp Rptr; Nwsp Stf; High Hon Roll; Hd Layout Dsgn Nwsppr Staff 86-87; Lead Role Drama Clb 86-87; Tutr Shrthd & Hstry 86-87; Penn ST; Acctg.

DAVIS, NICOLE; Frankford HS; Philadelphia, PA; (3); 39/700; Church Yth Grp; Church Choir; Drill Tm; Sec Sr Cls; Bsktbl; JV Trk; Hon Roll; Pres Schlr; IN U; Med.

DAVIS, PHILIP; Greensburg Central Catholic HS; Irwin, PA; (3); Letterman Clb; Ski Clb; Varsity Clb; JV Bsktbl; Var Capt Crs Cntry; Im Sftbl; Var L Trk; Im Vllybl; Hon Roll; 7th In Cnty-Cross Cntry 86.

DAVIS, R DANIEL; Daniel Boone HS; Douglassville, PA; (2); Chess Clb; French Clb; Bowling; Ftbl; Wt Lftg; Wrstlng; Hon Roll; Pres Acdmc Ftnss Awd 86; Med.

DAVIS, REGINA; Cardinal Dougherty HS; Philadelphia, PA; (3); 52/670; Church Yth Grp; Cmnty Wkr; Teachers Aide; Hon Roll; NHS; Prfct Atten Awd; Prescl Tchr.

DAVIS, REGINA; Lansadle Catholic HS; Kulpsville, PA; (3); 56/224; Drama Clb; SADD; School Musical; Var Cheerleading; Score Keeper; JV Sftbl; Hon Roll; Excllnc Rlgn 86-87; Outstndng Ldr Stu Ldrshp Wk 86-87; Gwynedd-Mercy Coll; Bio.

DAVIS, RENEE; Penn-Trafford HS; Export, PA; (3); AFS; FBLA; Drm Mjr(t); Mrchg Band; Sftbl; Twrlr; High Hon Roll; Hon Roll; Bus.

DAVIS, ROBERT; Lakeland JR SR HS; Olyphant, PA; (3); Spanish Clb; Wt Lftg; PA ST U; Engrng.

DAVIS, ROBERT; Oxford Area HS; Cochranville, PA; (3); 11/205; Church Yth Grp; 4-H; Pres FFA; Yrbk Stf; JV Wrstlng; DAR Awd; High Hon Roll; Hon Roll; NHS; FFA ST Dairy Jdgng 2nd, Rcrd Kpng Slvr 86-87; Physics Achvt Awd 86-87; Ag & Indus Arts Prof Awd 84-7; Dairy Sci.

DAVIS, RONNIE; Greensburg Salem SR HS; Greensburg, PA; (2); 56/294; French Clb; Band; High Hon Roll; Hon Roll; Jr NHS.

DAVIS, ROSS; Churchill HS; Turtle Creek, PA; (2); 13/222; Church Yth Grp; Ski Clb; L Socr; L Tennis; High Hon Roll; Jrnlsm.

DAVIS, SALLY; Northern York HS; Dillsburg, PA; (4); Spanish Clb; Band; Concert Band; Mrchg Band; Rep Frsh Cls; Rep Soph Cls; Rep Jr Cls; Sec Stu Cncl; Mgr(s); Mat Maids; Prsdntl Acad Ftns Awd; E Stroudsburg U; Htl Mgmnt.

DAVIS, SHAWN; Riverside HS; Ellwood City, PA; (3); 14/167; Computer Clb; Elec Engrng.

DAVIS, STACEY; Jefferson-Morgan JR SR HS; Mather, PA; (2); 4/110; Spanish Clb; High Hon Roll; NEDT Awd; Foreign Lang Awd 86; Med.

DAVIS, STEPHEN T; Archbishop Ryan HS; Philadelphia, PA; (3); 3/414; JA; Spanish Clb; Capt Bowling; Coach Actv; High Hon Roll; Spanish NHS; Bio Alb Outstndng Perf 84-85.

DAVIS, SUSAN; Norwin SR HS; Irwin, PA; (4); 102/563; Office Aide; Spanish Clb; Trs Concert Band; Trs Mrchg Band; High Hon Roll; Hon Roll; Jr NHS; NHS; Band Dir Awd 84; PA ST U; Real Est.

DAVIS, TAMARA; Kennard-Dale HS; Stewartstown, PA; (3); French Clb; Chorus; Color Guard; Sec Soph Cls; Trs Jr Cls; Cheerleading; Hon Roll; York Coll Of PA; Tchr.

DAVIS, THERESA; Brandywine Heights HS; Macungie, PA; (2); FBLA; Band; Color Guard; Concert Band; Flag Corp; Mrchg Band; Hon Roll; Real Est.

DAVIS, THOMAS; Aliquippa JR/Sr HS; Aliquippa, PA; (2); Chess Clb; Band; Jazz Band; Mrchg Band; Pep Band; Rep Frsh Cls; Rep Soph Cls; Var Bsbl; Hon Roll.

DAVIS, THOMAS; Knoch HS; Butler, PA; (2); Church Yth Grp; Bsktbl; Ftbl; Trk; High Hon Roll; Hon Roll; Harvard; Med.

DAVIS, TIMOTHY; Council Rock HS; Holland, PA; (3); JV Var Socr; Hon Roll; NHS; Rep Stu Cncl; Math.

DAVIS, TIMOTHY; Shady Side Acad; Pittsburgh, PA; (3); Chess Clb; Church Yth Grp; Drama Clb; French Clb; Math Tm; Thesps; School Play; Nwsp Rptr; Nwsp Stf; JV Var Bsbl; Bus.

DAVIS, VICKI; Farrell Area SR HS; Farrell, PA; (3); Spanish Clb; Teachers Aide; Acpl Chr; Church Choir; Stage Crew; Yrbk Stf; Hon Roll; NHS; Intr Dsgn.

DAVIS, VICKIE; Central Dauphin HS; Harrisburg, PA; (2); 6/405; Chorus; School Musical; School Play; Yrbk Stf; Rep Stu Cncl; Stat Bsktbl; Stat Socr; High Hon Roll; Jr NHS; Pres Schlr; 3rd Pl Amer Math Exm 87.

DAVIS, W BRADLEY; Clearfield Area HS; Clearfield, PA; (4); 38/292; Pres Church Yth Grp; French Clb; Rptr FBLA; SADD; Im Bowling; Cheerleading; Im Ftbl; Var Trk; 2nd For Plcl Spkng At FBLA Rgnls 87; 1st For Sngng In Schl Tlnt Show 87; ICM Schl Of Bus; Accntng.

DAVIS, W STEVEN; Central Cambria HS; Ebensburg, PA; (4); 6/217; Boy Scts; Science Clb; Ski Clb; Var L Ftbl; High Hon Roll; NHS; Rotary Awd; PA ST U; Engrng.

DAVIS, WENDY; Brandywine Heights HS; Topton, PA; (2); Art Clb; Hosp Aide; Color Guard; Rep Soph Cls; JV Capt Bsktbl; Coach Actv; Var L Sftbl; Broadcasting.

DAVIS, WENDY; Daniel Boone HS; Birdsboro, PA; (3); 2/174; German Clb; Varsity Clb; Var Capt Bsktbl; Var Fld Hcky; Var Sftbl; High Hon Roll; NHS; Opt Clb Awd.

DAVISON, BRIAN D; Twin Valley HS; Honey Brook, PA; (4); 2/137; Am Leg Boys St; Aud/Vis; Church Yth Grp; Pres Computer Clb; Drama Clb; German Clb; VP JA; Quiz Bowl; Pres Radio Clb; Chorus; Outstndg Englsh Stu 86; Outstndg Bio Stu 85; Outstndg Math Stu 84; Comptr Engrng.

DAVISON, HEATHER; Hanover Area HS; Lower Askam, PA; (4); Drill Tm; Flag Corp; Gym; High Hon Roll; NHS; Atlantic Coast Champ Tsunami Blue Winter Guard 85-87; Highest Avg Bus Stu 87; Comp Sci Awd 87.

DAVISON, JACKIE; Saegertown HS; Saegertown, PA; (3); 8/125; Spanish Clb; SADD; Band; Concert Band; Yrbk Ed-Chief; Yrbk Stf; Hon Roll; Jr NHS; NHS; Edinboro U; Marine Bio.

DAVISON, LA TITIA; Wilkinsburg JRSR HS; Pittsburgh, PA; (4); 42/142; Drama Clb; Exploring; FBLA; Girl Scts; Spanish Clb; Chorus; School Play; Yrbk Stf; Hon Roll; Jr NHS; NHS; Pitt U; Med.

DAVISON, MICHELLE; Fairchance-Georges HS; Fairchance, PA; (3); Red Cross Aide; Spanish Clb; Concert Band; Mrchg Band; Yrbk Stf; Twrlr; Comms.

DAVISON, TAMMIE; Cambridge Springs HS; Cambridge Spgs, PA; (3); Spanish Clb; SADD; Yrbk Phtg; JV Sftbl; Hon Roll.

DAVISON, WILLIAM R; Northwestern HS; Albion, PA; (3); Pres Church Yth Grp; Computer Clb; Office Aide; Science Clb; Yrbk Stf; JV Crs Cntry; Hon Roll; Edinboro; Elec Engrng.

DAVY, TEREASA; Lock Haven SR HS; Blanchard, PA; (4); 37/242; VP Sec FHA; Trs Library Aide; Spanish Clb; SADD; Color Guard; FHA Mbr Of Yr; Encounter Degree; Comp Tech; Travel.

DAWES, CHRISTINE; Bishop Neuman HS; Williamsport, PA; (2); Model UN; Sec SADD; Yrbk Stf; Pres Frsh Cls; Rep Soph Cls; VP Jr Cls; Bsktbl; Cheerleading; High Hon Roll; NHS; Schltc Wrtg Awd 87; Hood Coll; Intl Relat.

DAWSON, AMY; Beaver Area JR SR HS; Beaver, PA; (3); 11/194; Am Leg Aux Girls St; Church Yth Grp; Hst JCL; Key Clb; Chorus; Church Choir; Powder Puff Ftbl; Var L Tennis; High Hon Roll; Trs NHS; Math.

DAWSON, CHRIS; Louis E Dieruff HS; Allentown, PA; (2); Ski Clb; JV Bsktbl; JV Socr; Jr NHS; USCGA; Mar Biol.

DAWSON, DAVID; Lower Merion HS; Bala Cynwyd, PA; (3); Boy Scts; JCL; Latin Clb; Var Crs Cntry; Hon Roll; Ntl Merit Ltr; 2nd Pl Awd WA DC City Wide Sci Fair 86; Mst Vlbl Oarsmn Awd-Crew Tm 86; 2nd Pl Shrt Story Cntst 86; Engrng.

DAWSON, DOUGLAS; Lampeter-Strasburg HS; Willow Street, PA; (3); Church Yth Grp; Varsity Clb; Rep Frsh Cls; Rep Soph Cls; Rep Jr Cls; JV Bsktbl; Var Ftbl; Arch Engr.

DAWSON, JASON; Mercer Area JR/Sr HS; Mercer, PA; (3); Church Yth Grp; Debate Tm; Drama Clb; Ski Clb; Speech Tm; Trk; Hon Roll.

DAWSON, JEFFREY; Bishop Mc Cort HS; Conemaugh, PA; (4); Cmnty Wkr; Mu Alpha Theta; Chorus; Hon Roll; Mu Alpha Theta Awd; IN U Of Pennsylvania; Comp Sci.

DAWSON III, JOHN T; Mifflinburg Area HS; Mifflinburg, PA; (2); Drama Clb; French Clb; Key Clb; Stage Crew; Bsktbl; Var Socr.

DAWSON, KIMBERLY J; North Hills HS; Pittsburgh, PA; (3); Keywanettes; Chorus; Rep Frsh Cls; Rep Soph Cls; Rep Jr Cls; Rep Stu Cncl; Var Capt Cheerleading; High Hon Roll; NHS; Music.

DAWSON, MARIE ELAINE; Carmichaels Area SR HS; Carmichaels, PA; (4); Trs Pres DECA; VICA; DECA-DIST Comptn 6th Pl 85-86; DECA-ST Comptn 7th Pl 85-86; Bradford Bus Schl; Rtl Mgmt.

DAWSON, PAM; Coudersport JR SR HS; Coudersport, PA; (4); 8/87; Trs Church Yth Grp; Drama Clb; French Clb; Ski Clb; SADD; Band; Chorus; Church Choir; School Play; Yrbk Stf; Geneva Schlrshp 87; Geneva Coll; Psych.

DAWSON, WILLIAM; Millville Area HS; Benton, PA; (3); Drama Clb; VP Exploring; FBLA; Band; School Play; South Hills Bus Schl; Bus Mgmt.

DAY, BETH; Jefferson Morgan HS; Jefferson, PA; (4); 8/90; Am Leg Aux Girls St; Art Clb; Sec Trs French Clb; Rep Frsh Cls; VP Soph Cls; VP Jr Cls; Hmcmg Ct 84 & 86; May Day Attendt 83; Bash Dsgn.

DAY, COLLEEN; York Catholic HS; York, PA; (3); 34/152; JA; Latin Clb; Spanish Clb; Chorus; School Musical; Yrbk Stf; Coach Actv; Capt Vllybl; Hon Roll; NHS; Solo Fnlst Japan US Schlrshp 86-87; Towson U; Spnsh.

DAY, MAUREEN; Gwynedd-Mercy Acad; Hatfield, PA; (2); 4-H; Service Clb; SADD; Stage Crew; Yrbk Stf; JV Tennis; Im Vllybl; Hghst Gnrl Avrg Awd For Wlrd Hstry 86; Hghst Gnrl Avrg Awd For Bio 87; Magna Cum Laude Awd 86; Bio.

DAY, MIRIAM; Montrose HS; Montrose, PA; (3); Trs Church Yth Grp; French Clb; Latin Clb; Letterman Clb; Varsity Clb; JV Crs Cntry; L Var Trk; Hon Roll; NHS; Prfct Atten Awd; Dist High Jmp Chmp 84-86; Mst Valubl Trk 85-86; Broome CC; Dentl Hygnst.

DAY, SANDI; Abington Heights HS; Clarks Summit, PA; (3); 71/292; Church Yth Grp; Drama Clb; Ski Clb; Stage Crew; Rep Stu Cncl; Hon Roll; Hon Mntn Natl French Exam AATF 86-87; Cmmnctns.

DAY, SHOREY; Mc Guffey HS; W Alexander, PA; (4); 10/203; Am Leg Aux Girls St; Pres Church Yth Grp; Pres French Clb; Sec Sr Cls; Trs Stu Cncl; Im Powder Puff Ftbl; Capt L Tennis; L Trk; NHS; Pep Clb; Hmcmng Qun 86; Penn ST; Htl-Restrnt Mgmt.

DAYANANDA, PRIYA; Lock Haven SR HS; Lock Haven, PA; (3); Church Yth Grp; Keywanettes; Model UN; Spanish Clb; SADD; Chorus; Variety Show; Cheerleading; Tennis; Intl Rel.

DAYETT, BRADLEY; Littlestown HS; Littlestown, PA; (3); Am Leg Boys St; Varsity Clb; Band; Concert Band; Mrchg Band; School Musical; School Play; Trk; Wrstlng; NHS.

DAYLIDA, DAWN; Bishop O Reilly HS; Shavertown, PA; (3); Latin Clb; Drill Tm; Rep Jr Cls; Rep Stu Cncl; JV Cheerleading; Var Fld Hcky; USAF Acad; Aerospc Tech.

DAYRIT, CHRISTINA; Cardinal Dougherty HS; Philadelphia, PA; (3); 26/670; Service Clb; Rep Stu Cncl; Var Tennis; Var Trk; High Hon Roll; NHS; Prfct Atten Awd; Latin II Prfcncy Awd 86; Pre Med.

DAYTNER, SANDI; New Castle SR HS; New Castle, PA; (3); 4-H; SADD; Rep Sr Cls; Stu Cncl; Trk; 4-H Awd; Hon Roll; PA Free Enterprise Wk; Acadmc Games; Slippery Rock U; Bus Adm.

DAYTON, CARRIE; Montrose Area JR/Sr HS; Montrose, PA; (3); 19/181; French Clb; Varsity Clb; Flag Corp; Var Bsktbl; Var Fld Hcky; JV Sftbl; Hon Roll.

DAZIO, STACEY; Coatesville Area SR HS; Coatesville, PA; (3); FBLA; Band; Concert Band; Mrchg Band; Rep Frsh Cls; Rep Soph Cls; Sec Jr Cls; Sec Sr Cls; Rep Stu Cncl; Hon Roll; Stu Cncl Awd 84-85; Penn ST; Acctng.

DE AGOSTINO, SHERRY; Altoona Area HS; Altoona, PA; (3); Spanish Clb; Var Bsktbl; Hon Roll; Prncpls Advsry Comm 85-87; Lady Lion Bsktbl Tm Natly Rnkd 1 Of Natns Top 25 Tms USA 85-87; Law.

DE ANGELIS, GINA; Lebanon Catholic HS; Hershey, PA; (3); 15/67; Chess Clb; German Clb; Color Guard; Drm Mjr(t); Mrchg Band; School Play; Nwsp Stf; High Hon Roll; Hon Roll; Excllnc Amer Hstry, Engl 3 86-87; Intl Rltns.

DE ANGELIS, MELISSA; Kennedy Christian HS; Hermitage, PA; (2); 5/96; Dance Clb; French Clb; Science Clb; Service Clb; Ski Clb; Var JV Cheerleading; High Hon Roll; PA JR Acad Sci 1st Awd 86.

DE ANGELIS, MICHAEL; Upper Moreland HS; Hatboro, PA; (4); 21/254; Key Clb; Concert Band; Jazz Band; Pres Mrchg Band; Rep Stu Cncl; Var Bsbl; Im Bsktbl; High Hon Roll; NHS; Rbrt C Byrd Hnrs Schlrshp 87-88; Penn ST; Fnnce.

DE ANGELO, CHRISTOPHER; Pittston Area HS; Duryea, PA; (3); 58/306; Art Clb; Boy Scts; Computer Clb; Science Clb; Ski Clb; Chorus; Mrchg Band; Hon Roll; Art Awd 86-87; Astrnmy.

DE ANGELO, DEBRA; Parkland HS; Allentown, PA; (4); 160/438; Church Yth Grp; Q&S; Yrbk Ed-Chief; Kutztown U; Bus Admin.

DE ANGELO, JANINE; West Scranton HS; Scranton, PA; (3); FNA; Trk; RN.

DE BALLI III, PETER; Central Cambria HS; Ebensburg, PA; (3); 2/220; Debate Tm; NFL; Ski Clb; Trs Speech Tm; School Play; Yrbk Rptr; High Hon Roll; NHS; HOBY Fndtn ST Ambssdr 86; Pre-Med.

DE BARR, MELISSA; Yough SR HS; Sutersville, PA; (3); 33/237; Church Yth Grp; Sec FBLA; Library Aide; Chorus; Church Choir; Hon Roll; NHS; Chrch Pianist & Orgnst 85; Secy.

DE BELLIS, KURT; Northampton Area HS; Northampton, PA; (3); 20/494; Drama Clb; Leo Clb; Chorus; School Musical; Rep Stu Cncl; JV Var Ftbl; High Hon Roll; Hon Roll; NHS; Bio-Engrng.

DE BENEDICTIS, LORI; Hatboro-Horsham SR HS; Hatboro, PA; (3); 12/258; Church Yth Grp; SADD; Powder Puff Ftbl; Var L Tennis; Cit Awd; High Hon Roll; Hon Roll; Bus.

DE BERARDINIS, RALPH; Salesianum HS; Aston, PA; (3); 1/300; Boy Scts; Church Yth Grp; JCL; SADD; Nwsp Rptr; Nwsp Stf; VP Soph Cls; Stu Cncl; Crs Cntry; JV Trk; Eagle Sct 85.

DE BERNARDO, CHRISTINA M; Mercyhurst Prep Schl; Harbor Creek, PA; (4); 11/155; Girl Scts; Spanish Clb; Yrbk Stf; High Hon Roll; NHS; PA ST Erie; Comp Sci.

DE BOARD, MATT; Boiling Springs HS; Carlisle, PA; (3); Church Yth Grp; Computer Clb; Spanish Clb; Band; Concert Band; Mrchg Band; Pep Band; Im Ftbl; Im Sftbl; Hon Roll; Messiah Coll; Med.

DE BOLT, RICHARD; Pennsbury HS; Fallsington, PA; (4); 93/771; Band; Chorus; Concert Band; Jazz Band; Mrchg Band; Orch; Pep Band; School Musical; Stage Crew; NHS; Drexel U; Elec Engr.

DE BONA, PAMELA ANN; Notre Dame Catholic HS; Easton, PA; (4); 3/92; Chorus; Church Choir; Color Guard; School Play; Bsbl; Sftbl; 1st Hnrs 84-87; Aeronaut Engr.

DE BORD, RISSIE LYNN; Brownsville Area HS; East Millsboro, PA; (3); Church Yth Grp; SADD; Church Choir; High Hon Roll; Hon Roll; US Natl Ldrshp Merit Awd 87; CPA.

DE BROFF, BRUCE; Taylor Allterdice HS; Pittsburgh, PA; (3); CAP; Exploring; FBLA; FFA; German Clb; NAACP; SADD; Band; Nwsp Ed-Chief; Yrbk Phtg; Harvard; Optmtlgy.

DE CAESTECKER, ANNIQUE; Villa Maria Acad; West Chester, PA; (3); 21/103; Cmnty Wkr; Lcrss; Hon Roll; Pasla 87; Captn La Crosse Tm 87-88; Med.

DE CAPUA, CAMILLE; Sharon HS; Sharon, PA; (2); 9/187; French Clb; Chorus; Yrbk Stf; Crs Cntry; Off Trk; Hon Roll; NHS; Med.

DE CARLO, KARI; Uniontown Area HS; Uniontown, PA; (4); 4/290; SADD; Concert Band; Mrchg Band; School Musical; Off Jr Cls; Sec Sr Cls; Cheerleading; DAR Awd; High Hon Roll; Sec NHS; Kiwanis SR Girl Awd, Prsdntl Acdmc Ftnss Awd, Natl Hnr Soc Srvc Awd 87; Washington & Jefferson; Chem Rs.

DE CARLO, MICHELLE; South Philadelphia HS; Philadelphia, PA; (4); Dance Clb; Library Aide; School Musical; Pres Frsh Cls; NHS; Ntl Merit SF; Temple U; Criminal Justice.

DE CARLUCCI, HENRY KEITH; Laurel Highlands SR HS; Uniontown, PA; (4); 14/350; Golf; Trk; Wt Lftg; High Hon Roll; Hon Roll; Jr NHS; NHS; Natl Ldrshp Merit Awd 86-87; Carnegie-Mellon U; Engrng.

DE CAROLIS, LEA; Central Bucks West HS; Chalfont, PA; (3); 19/477; Gym; High Hon Roll; Hon Roll; Jr NHS; NHS.

DE COOMAN, SHARIEE; Lincoln HS; Ellwood City, PA; (3); 2/162; French Clb; Y-Teens; Chorus; School Musical; L Tennis; Stat Trk; High Hon Roll; NHS; Prfct Atten Awd; Acmdc Achvmnt Awd; Educ.

DE COSMO, CASSIE; James M Coughlin HS; Wilkes-Barre, PA; (3); Church Yth Grp; Drama Clb; VP German Clb; Hosp Aide; Key Clb; Ski Clb; Chorus; School Play; Yrbk Stf; Hon Roll; Pres Acad Fit Awd 84-85; Dist Chorus 86-87; Early Chldhd Ed.

DE CRAY, JAMES; Haverford SR HS; Ardmore, PA; (3); 64/414; Band; Concert Band; Mrchg Band; Orch; Stage Crew; Symp Band; Hon Roll; PMEA Dist Band 86; Sound Of Amer Hon Band 87.

DE CROES JR, STEPHEN D; Dover Area HS; Dover, PA; (4); Band; Chorus; Concert Band; Drill Tm; Jazz Band; Mrchg Band; Orch; Pep Band; Tennis; Hon Roll; IN U Of PA; Comm-Media.

DE CROO, NICOLE; Leechburg Area HS; Leechburg, PA; (3); 17/87; Art Clb; Drama Clb; Math Tm; Chorus; School Play; Nwsp Rptr; Ed Nwsp Sprt Ed; Nwsp Stf; Yrbk Stf; Var Capt Cheerleading; Bus.

DE EULIO, DINA; New Caslte HS; New Castle, PA; (3); 15/293; Church Yth Grp; Girl Scts; Spanish Clb; Band; Chorus; Concert Band; Mrchg Band; Pep Band; Gym; Tennis; PA JR Acad Of Sci 85-86; Itln Clb Yth Agnst Cncr; Amer Hrt Assn Music Clb; Vet Med.

DE FAZIO, CHRISTA; Bellwood-Antis HS; Tipton, PA; (3); Key Clb; Ski Clb; Chorus; School Musical; Im Badmtn; Var Fld Hcky; Im Vllybl; Hon Roll; NHS; Physcl Thrpst.

DE FELICE, CAROLYN; Shenango JR-SR HS; New Castle, PA; (3); 15/125; Church Yth Grp; French Clb; Hosp Aide; Flag Corp; School Play; Hon Roll; NHS; IN U Of PA; Physcl Thrpy.

DE FEO, RICHARD; Upper Merion HS; King Of Prussia, PA; (3); 8/297; Math Tm; Var L Bsbl; Var L Ftbl; Wt Lftg; High Hon Roll; Pres NHS; Prfct Atten Awd; Bsbl 2nd Tm All-Lg Catcher 87; Ftbl 2nd Tm All-Lg Dfnsv Back 86; Wharton Coll; Bus.

DE FERRARI, PATRICIA; Aliquippa HS; Aliquippa, PA; (3); Pep Clb; Hst Frsh Cls; Hon Roll; NHS; U Of MA; Achlgy.

DE FLAVIS, MARIA; W B Saul HS; Philadelphia, PA; (3); Boys Clb Am; Computer Clb; Dance Clb; FFA; Radio Clb; SADD; Yrbk Stf; Bsktbl; Cheerleading; Sftbl; Hnr Soc Clb 86; Bus.

DE FORREST, JENNIFER; Harry S Truman HS; Croydon, PA; (4); 4/534; Stu Cncl; Var Mgr Fld Hcky; Sftbl; NHS; Pres Schlr; Stu Mnth 87; Waste Mgmt Scholar 87; PTA Scholar 87; Drexel U; Elec Engrng.

DE FRAIN, CHRIS; Wellsboro Area HS; Wellsboro, PA; (2); Drama Clb; Bowling; High Hon Roll; Hon Roll; PA Free Entrprs Wk Schlrshp 87; Bus Mgmt.

DE FRAIN, SHERRI; Emmaus HS; Emmaus, PA; (3); 82/525; SADD; Var L Cheerleading; Var JV Sftbl; Hon Roll; Dist XI 1st Tm All Star & Dist XI Champ Sftbl 87; Emmaus Sr Tm Cls B ASA ST Champ 87; Cosm.

DE FRANCESCO, ANDREA; Cedar Cliff HS; Camp Hill, PA; (3); 11/304; Am Leg Aux Girls St; Hosp Aide; Key Clb; SADD; Orch; Rep Stu Cncl; Var L Fld Hcky; NHS; Spanish NHS; GAA; Mi PA Cnfrnc All Str Tm/Fld Hcky 86; C S Ehresman Awd For Outstndng Fld Hcky Schlr Athlt 85-86; Engrng.

DE FRANCESCO, SALVATORE; Pittston Area HS; Avoca, PA; (4); 27/348; L Swmmng; Hon Roll; NHS; Accntg.

DE FRANCO, MARISA; Fairview HS; Fairview, PA; (3); 1/160; French Clb; Model UN; Ski Clb; Teachers Aide; Varsity Clb; Cheerleading; Swmmng; Trk; NHS; Val; Intensive Lang PSU 87; Rotary Clb Rep Ryla Cnvtn 87; U Of VA; Pol.

DE FRANK, LISA; Fairchance Georges HS; Uniontown, PA; (3); Spanish Clb; Yrbk Phtg; VP Soph Cls; High Hon Roll; Hon Roll; Jr NHS; NHS; Pres Schlr; U Of Pittsburgh.

DE FRANK, MATTHEW; Trinity HS; Camp Hill, PA; (4); Rep Stu Cncl; Bsktbl; Golf; Trk; Hon Roll; Capt Of Bsktbl Tm; Div Ii All Star-Bsktbl; Susquehanna U; Bus Mjr.

DE FRANK, STEPHEN; Uniontown Area HS; New Salem, PA; (4); 69/289; Latin Clb; Ski Clb; Spanish Clb; Helen Brice Mem Schlrshp 87; Foreign Lang Honor Society 85; Slippery Rock U; Pltcl Sci.

DE FREITAS, HEWLETTE A; Penn Wood HS; Yeadon, PA; (3); Aud/Vis; Church Yth Grp; Cmnty Wkr; Computer Clb; Church Choir; Nwsp Rptr; Nwsp Stf; JV Socr; JV Var Trk; Prfct Atten Awd; Adv Bio Sci 87; Track & Newspaper Awd; Bsktbl Hnr Awd; U Of PA; Sci.

DE GENNARO, SUSAN; Lake-Lehman HS; Shavertown, PA; (4); 9/154; Key Clb; Red Cross Aide; Ski Clb; SADD; School Play; Nwsp Rptr; Yrbk Phtg; Yrbk Stf; Rep Frsh Cls; VP Soph Cls; Hugh O Brien Yth Ldrshp Awd 84-85; WY Vlly Conf Fld Hcky All-Star Tm 86.

DE GEORGE, VINCENT J; Seton La Salle HS; Pittsburgh, PA; (4); 62/263; Drama Clb; Band; Chorus; Church Choir; Mrchg Band; School Musical; Pres Frsh Cls; Cvc Lght Opera Pttsbrgh Schlrshp 87; Bstncnsrvtry Prfrmng Arts Schlrshp 87; Ithca Coll Drm Schlrshp 87; Cinn Cnsrvtry; Musicl Theatr.

DE GRAAFF, R INGRID; Blue Mountain Acad; Wellsboro, PA; (2); Church Choir; Off Frsh Cls; VP Soph Cls; Var Im Sftbl; Var Im Vllybl; High Hon Roll; Anthrplgy.

DE GRAAFF, REBECCA; Blue Mountain Acad; Wellsboro, PA; (4); 6/55; Concert Band; Nwsp Stf; Yrbk Ed-Chief; Sec Soph Cls; Rep Stu Cncl; High Hon Roll; NHS; Church Yth Grp; Office Aide; School Play; James E Fegley Music Awd 87; Outdr Clb Pres 85-86; Ensmbl Tr Grp 84-87; Loma Linda U; Med.

DE GRASSE, MIKE; West Branch JR SR HS; Allport, PA; (3); German Clb; Ftbl; Socr; Wt Lftg; Wrstlng; Var Wrestling Ltr 84-85&86-87; Var Ftbl Ltr 86-87; Mech.

DE GREEN III, H PETER; Mc Caskey HS; Lancaster, PA; (1); Chess Clb; Church Yth Grp; Computer Clb; Church Choir; School Musical; Socr; Tennis; Hon Roll.

DE GREGORIO, JOSEPH; Montoursville HS; Montoursville, PA; (3); 1/185; German Clb; Key Clb; Math Tm; Rep Frsh Cls; Rep Soph Cls; Var Bsktbl; Var Socr; Hon Roll; Pres NHS; Acdmc All AM 87; Mongrm Clb 87-88; Engrng.

DE GRUTTOLA, AMY; Keystone Oaks HS; Pittsburgh, PA; (4); 30/268; Church Yth Grp; VP Exploring; German Clb; Office Aide; Pep Clb; Chorus; Nwsp Stf; High Hon Roll; Hon Roll; Hgh Hnr Rll 87; New Century Clb 87; Offc Aide 87; Slppry Rck U; Accntng.

DE GUZMAN, JOACHIM; Wellsboro SR HS; Middlebury Ctr, PA; (3); Rep Chess Clb; VP Church Yth Grp; Science Clb; Band; Church Choir; Concert Band; Jazz Band; Mrchg Band; Rep Stu Cncl; Trk; Culinary Inst Of Amer; Chef.

DE HAVEN, LEIGH; North Western SR HS; Albion, PA; (2); Art Clb; Drama Clb; Nwsp Stf; Hon Roll; Fashion.

DE HAVEN, MICHELE; Northwester Lehigh HS; New Tripoli, PA; (4); 45/162; Nwsp Stf; Var Capt Bsktbl; Var Capt Crs Cntry; Var Capt Trk; Hon Roll; Outstndng Cls Stu Awd Grls Crss Cntry, Grls Trk 86-87; Bnkng.

DE HECK, BETH ANNE; Central Bucks East HS; Jamison, PA; (4); Drama Clb; Girl Scts; Political Wkr; Pres Chorus; School Musical; Hon Roll; Penn ST U; Educ.

DE HOFF, JENNIFER; Central SR HS; York, PA; (4); Ski Clb; Varsity Clb; Nwsp Stf; Yrbk Stf; JV Var Cheerleading; Hon Roll; York Coll PA.

DE IULIIS, DINO; Central Catholic HS; Pittsburgh, PA; (3); Art Clb; JV Ice Hcky; Im Vllybl; Comm Art.

DE JESUS, JOSE; William Allen HS; Allentown, PA; (3); Church Yth Grp; Cmnty Wkr; Drama Clb; Intnl Clb; Leo Clb; Spanish Clb; SADD; School Play; Pres Frsh Cls; VP Jr Cls; Hispanics Acad Progress Prog Penn St 87; Lawyer.

DE JOHN, JERRY; West Catholic HS; Philadelphia, PA; (2); 11/248; JV Bsbl; Hon Roll; Cert Merit W 86-87; Cert Excllnce Chem 87; Grand Bryn Mawr Coll Wise Prgm 87; Bus Adm.

DE LANCEY, JIM; Valley SR HS; New Kensington, PA; (2); Church Yth Grp; Ski Clb; SADD; Band; Concert Band; Mrchg Band; Hon Roll; Prfct Atten Awd.

DE LANCEY, RICHARD; Dallastown Area HS; Dallastown, PA; (3); Aud/Vis; Pres Debate Tm; Drama Clb; Letterman Clb; NFL; Radio Clb; Pres Speech Tm; Chorus; School Play; High Hon Roll; Law.

DE LANEY, BOBBIE JO; Brookville Area HS; Brookville, PA; (3); Art Clb; Letterman Clb; Varsity Clb; Var L Sftbl; Hon Roll; Crmnl Jstice.

DE LATTRE, LARA; Kennard-Dale HS; Fawn Grove, PA; (3); 15/170; Art Clb; Pres Church Yth Grp; Drama Clb; Pres VP 4-H; French Clb; Ski Clb; Chorus; Church Choir; School Musical; VP Frsh Cls; ST 4-H Blue Rbbn Demo Spkr 85; Yrk Cnty JR 4-H Hrsmn & Judge 2nd Pl 86; Natl Awd Top 5% Stu NEDT 87; Math.

DE LAY, MICHELE; Fleetwood Area HS; Fleetwood, PA; (3); Camp Fr Inc; Office Aide; Ski Clb; Chorus; Color Guard; Drill Tm; Off Jr Cls; Off Sr Cls; Var Cheerleading; Capt Var Fld Hcky; Recgnzed At Schlrs Night; Occuptnl Thrpy.

DE LISIO, JEFF; Center HS; Aliquippa, PA; (3); Church Yth Grp; Spanish Clb; Varsity Clb; Var L Bsktbl; Hon Roll; AAA All Star Bsktbl 2nd Tm 86-87; Merit Diploma Spn II 85-86; Pre-Dntstry.

DE LONG, WENDY; Northampton SR HS; Bath, PA; (3); Drama Clb; VP VICA; Stage Crew; Yrbk Bus Mgr; Yrbk Phtg; Yrbk Stf; Hon Roll; Slvr Mdl Dstct Lvl Via Cmptn 87; UICA Achvmnt Prgrm Awd 87; Pittsburgh Boounty Acad; Csmtlg.

DE LOZIER, DANE; Hollidaysburg Area HS; Duncansville, PA; (3); Church Yth Grp; Chorus; Stu Cncl; Ftbl; Trk; Wrstlng; Cit Awd; Hon Roll.

DE LUCA, AARON; Charleroi Area HS; Charleroi, PA; (3); Boy Scts; Capt Scholastic Bowl; Science Clb; Nwsp Stf; Off Soph Cls; Off Jr Cls; Stu Cncl; Im Bsktbl; Var Golf; Var Trk; Rnslr Mdl Awd In Math & Sci 87; Eagle Scout 86; Engrng.

DE LUCA, ANDREW; Sun Valley HS; Aston, PA; (3); 32/270; Aud/Vis; Church Yth Grp; Computer Clb; JV Bsbl; JV Tennis; Hon Roll; Prfct Atten Awd; Frgn Languages.

DE LUCA, SUSAN; North Allegheny SR HS; Wexford, PA; (4); 310/660; Church Yth Grp; Cmnty Wkr; Exploring; School Musical; School Play; Sec Soph Cls; Stu Cncl; Var Tennis; Mst Imprvd Wrld Cultures II 84, World Cltrs I 83; Stu Cncl Activities 84; Bowling Green ST U; Intr Desgn.

DE LUCCA, D LEO; Hazleton SR HS; Hazleton, PA; (3); Drama Clb; Im Bsktbl; High Hon Roll; Hon Roll; Bloomsburg U; Educ.

DE LUCCA, DANIELLE; West Hazleton HS; West Hazleton, PA; (3); 7/217; Church Yth Grp; Girl Scts; Spanish Clb; Concert Band; Drm Mjr(t); Mrchg Band; Dnfth Awd; High Hon Roll; Pres Schlr; Spirit Of The Wildcat Marching Band Awd 87; Med.

DE MARCO, CHRISTOPHER; Tunkhannock Area HS; Tunkhannock, PA; (1); 3/275; Aud/Vis; Key Clb; Science Clb; Band; Concert Band; Mrchg Band; Stage Crew; JV L Socr; JV L Tennis; Hon Roll.

DE MARCO, JAMES; Saint John Neumann HS; Philadelphia, PA; (3); 69/349; Im Bsktbl; Hon Roll; Bus Mgmt.

DE MARCO, LAURIE; Tunkhannock Area HS; Tunkhannock, PA; (4); 2/290; Aud/Vis; Cmnty Wkr; French Clb; Pres Key Clb; Latin Clb; School Musical; Yrbk Rptr; Rep Stu Cncl; Stat Bsktbl; Var L Fld Hcky; PA Gvnrs Schl Intl Stds, 2nd Medal-Natl Latin Ii & 3rd Pl-NE PA-CONCOURS Natl De Francais Iii 86; Intl Stds.

DE MARZO, DAVE; Riverside JR SR HS; Taylor, PA; (2); JV Ftbl; JV L Trk; Hon Roll; Pdtrcn.

DE MASSE, BETH ANN; Carmichaels SR HS; Carmichaels, PA; (4); Am Leg Aux Girls St; Art Clb; Dance Clb; GAA; Spanish Clb; Varsity Clb; Band; Church Choir; Drm Mjr(t); Mrchg Band; Tchng.

DE MATT, TRICIA; Hazleton HS; Hazleton, PA; (3); Drama Clb; Latin Clb; Spanish Clb; Yrbk Stf; Hon Roll; Pres Acdmc Fit Awd 85.

DE MATTEIS, JOSEPH; Aliquippa JR SR HS; Aliquippa, PA; (2); Church Yth Grp; Band; Concert Band; Jazz Band; Mrchg Band; Pep Band; Hon Roll; Pa ST U; Mechncl Engr Tech.

DE MATTEO, STACY; Mohawk JR SR HS; Edinburg, PA; (3); French Clb; SADD; Drill Tm; Flag Corp; School Musical; Nwsp Rptr; Yrbk Stf; Stat Bsbl; Im Powder Puff Ftbl; Hon Roll; Pblc Rltns.

DE MEESTER, HEATHER; Bensalem HS; Bensalem, PA; (2); Sftbl; Trk; Hon Roll; Law.

DE MEESTER, TIFFANY; Bensalem HS; Bensalem, PA; (2); Key Clb; Teachers Aide; Color Guard; Off Soph Cls; JV Socr; JV Trk; High Hon Roll; NHS; Prfct Atten Awd; Cngrsnl Yth Ldrshp Cncl 87; Med.

DE MELFI JR, THOMAS M; Central Dauphin HS; Harrisburg, PA; (4); FCA; Capt Bsktbl; Vllybl; Sftbl; Bloomsburg U; Bio.

DE MILIO III, PHILIP; Pius X HS; Roseto, PA; (3); Pep Clb; Science Clb; Varsity Clb; Stage Crew; Off Stu Cncl; Var L Bsbl; Var L Bsktbl; Var L Ftbl; Wt Lftg; Hon Roll.

DE MORELAND, DONNA; Central Bucks East HS; Warrington, PA; (4); Church Yth Grp; Cmnty Wkr; Office Aide; Red Cross Aide; SADD; Band; Chorus; Church Choir; Color Guard; Drill Tm; X-Ray Tech.

DE MOSS, KATHLEEN; West Perry HS; Elliottsburg, PA; (2); Spanish Clb; School Play; Nwsp Rptr; Stu Cncl; Fld Hcky; Trk; Hon Roll; Cmnctns.

DE MOTT, JENNIFER; Connellsville Area HS; Dunbar, PA; (3); 35/500; Art Clb; Chorus; School Play; Hon Roll; Jr NHS; NHS; Spanish NHS; Acad Xclnc Awd 83-84; Sci Awd/Highst Prfrmnc 83-84; Penn ST; Law.

DE NERO, KRISTEN; Gateway SR HS; Monroeville, PA; (3); Church Yth Grp; Cmnty Wkr; Ski Clb; Chorus; Color Guard; Mrchg Band; School Musical; Sec Jr Cls; Sec Sr Cls; High Hon Roll; Pharmacy.

DE PAULIS, DAVID F; Mc Keesport HS; White Oak, PA; (3); 60/410; Church Yth Grp; NFL; Speech Tm; Yrbk Stf; Hon Roll; Notre Dame U; Law.

DE PHILLIPS, HOLLY; Rockwood Area HS; Somerset, PA; (2); Computer Clb; NFL; Speech Tm; Band; Mrchg Band; Off Stu Cncl; Cheerleading; Vllybl; Hon Roll.

DE PIETRO, FRANK; Dunmore HS; Dunmore, PA; (3); 40/146; Boy Scts; Computer Clb; French Clb; Ski Clb; Spanish Clb; Var Ftbl; High Hon Roll; Hon Roll; Temple Northeastern U; Phrmcy.

DE PIETRO, KATHLEEN; West Scranton HS; Scranton, PA; (2); 10/270; Spanish Clb; Stage Crew; Off Soph Cls; Cheerleading; Coach Actv; Jr NHS; U Of Scranton; Phrmcst.

DE PLANQUE, ALEXIS; Brandywine HS; Topton, PA; (2); Art Clb; Band; Concert Band; Drill Tm; Jazz Band; Mrchg Band; Pep Band; JV Bsktbl; Sftbl; Swmmng; Genetic Engrng.

DE PRIEST, HEATHER; Oil City SR HS; Oil City, PA; (3); Acpl Chr; L Diving; L Swmmng; Trk; Wt Lftg; Hon Roll.

DE PRIMIO, TRACY; Hempfield SR HS; Greensburg, PA; (2); Pep Clb; Ski Clb; Spanish Clb; Var Vllybl; High Hon Roll; Hon Roll; NHS; Spanish NHS; Pres Acad Fit Awd 85-86; Medicine.

DE RISO, DINA MARIE; Greater Works Acad; Pittsburgh, PA; (4); 4/31; Service Clb; Ski Clb; Yrbk Ed-Chief; Yrbk Stf; High Hon Roll; Hon Roll; Prfct Atten Awd; ICM Schl Of Bus Schlrshp 87; ICM Schl Of Bus; Accntng Mgmt.

DE ROBERTIS, MEREDITH; Union Area HS; New Castle, PA; (4); 12/66; Cmnty Wkr; Drama Clb; Office Aide; SADD; Pres Y-Teens; Chorus; Capt Color Guard; Madrigals; School Musical; Yrbk Stf; DAR Ctznshp Awd 87; Duffs Bus Inst; Fshn Merch.

DE ROSA, ANN; Central Bucks HS East; Danboro, PA; (4); 4-H; FBLA; Yrbk Stf; Mgr Sftbl; Sec 4-H Awd; Hon Roll; Millersville U; Spec Educ.

DE ROSE, DAVID; Beaver Falls SR HS; Beaver Falls, PA; (3); 40/171; Church Yth Grp; Science Clb; Spanish Clb; Yrbk Phtg; Rep Frsh Cls; Rep Soph Cls; JV Var Bsbl; JV Bsktbl; Hon Roll; Bus Admn.

DE ROSE, VERONICA L; Monongahela Valley Catholic HS; Elizabeth, PA; (2); 19/75; FBLA; Hosp Aide; Ski Clb; Spanish Clb; Band; Chorus; Bsktbl; Sftbl; Hon Roll; Spanish NHS; St Vincent Coll; Doctor.

DE ROSIA, SHARON; Beaver Valley Christian Acad; Freedom, PA; (2); Church Yth Grp; Library Aide; Chorus; School Musical; School Play; Pres Soph Cls; Rep Stu Cncl; JV Var Cheerleading; Sftbl; JV Vllybl; Pres Acdmc Ftns Awd 85-86.

DE ROSS, DANIEL; Saegertown HS; Saegertown, PA; (4); 12/114; Aud/Vis; Letterman Clb; Math Tm; Varsity Clb; Stage Crew; Var Vllybl; Var Wrstlng; Hon Roll; Jr NHS; NHS; Cajon Mem Awd 87; Edinboro U; Comp Sci.

DE RUBIS, LEIGH; Central Cambria HS; Ebensburg, PA; (3); Var Cheerleading; Nrsng.

DE SANTIS, CHRISTIAN L; Mt Penn HS; Reading, PA; (3); French Clb; Science Clb; Spanish Clb; Chorus; Govt.

DE SANTIS, DAMON; Butler Intermediate HS; Butler, PA; (2); French Clb; Rep Stu Cncl; Hon Roll; Jr NHS; Notre Dame; Engrng.

DE SANTIS, MAUREEN; Sacred Heart Acad; Berwyn, PA; (4); 2/39; VP Cmnty Wkr; Yrbk Stf; VP Sr Cls; Wt Lftg; High Hon Roll; NHS; Sal; Drexel U; Nutrtn Sci.

DE SARNO, MICHAEL FIORE; Penn Hills HS; Penn Hills, PA; (3); PITT; Accntng.

DE SHONG, ADAM E; Perkiomen Valley HS; Graterford, PA; (3); 15/200; Am Leg Boys St; Church Yth Grp; Ski Clb; Concert Band; Jazz Band; Var L Ftbl; L Golf; L Trk; Cit Awd; High Hon Roll; Keystone Boys ST 87; Accptnc Ursinus Coll 87; Acdmc Achvmnt Awd 85-87; Elec Engrng.

DE SIMONE, BETH; Plum SR HS; New Kensington, PA; (3); AFS; French Clb; FTA; SADD; Nwsp Ed-Chief; Yrbk Ed-Chief; Lit Mag; NHS; Teen Inst Ldrshp Trnng 86-87; Girls Ldrs Assn Outstndg Svc Awd 86-87; Boston U; Pre-Med.

DE SIPIO, SHARON; Cardinal O Hara HS; Springfield, PA; (3); 3/710; FNA; Spanish Clb; Yrbk Ed-Chief; Yrbk Stf; High Hon Roll; Hon Roll; NHS; Spanish NHS; Voice Dem Awd; Wrld Cltrs 84-85; Engl Awd 85-86 & 86-87; Amer Hstry Awd 86-87; Engl.

DE SIPIO, SUSAN; Lansdale Catholic HS; Souderton, PA; (4); 5/220; Cmnty Wkr; Math Tm; Pres Service Clb; Mgr(s); Powder Puff Ftbl; Swmmng; Dnfth Awd; High Hon Roll; Trs NHS; Pres Schlr; Hghst Grd Pt Avg In Geom, Eng-Gftd; Hghst GPA World Cult II, Eng, Bio; Hghst GPA Chem Stdy & Am Cul; Philadelphia Coll Pharm; Pharm.

DE SOTO, MICHAEL; Upper Dauphin Area HS; Elizabethville, PA; (3); 1/120; Church Yth Grp; Varsity Clb; Band; Pres Soph Cls; Pres Jr Cls; Bsktbl; Capt Trk; Rotary Awd; Mrchg Band; Crs Cntry; HOBY Fndtn Sem 86; Mktg.

DE SOUZA, MICHELE; Dallastown Area HS; Dallastown, PA; (4); 75/353; Hosp Aide; Temple Yth Grp; Varsity Clb; Var L Crs Cntry; Diving; Gym; Trk; God Cntry Awd; High Hon Roll; Rotary Awd; Rotry Intl Tdnt Exch 86-87; American U DC; Intl Rel.

DE STEFANO, ALBERT; Father Judge HS; Philadelphia, PA; (3); 5/405; Church Yth Grp; Cmnty Wkr; French Clb; Band; Chorus; Concert Band; Jazz Band; Madrigals; Mrchg Band; Orch; Bus.

DE STEFANO, JAMES; Nativity B V M HS; Pottsville, PA; (3); 6/97; Aud/Vis; Chess Clb; Band; Chorus; Concert Band; Mrchg Band; Variety Show; Nwsp Stf; Var Crs Cntry; Var Trk; All Amer Band Hall Fame 87; Nuclr Energy.

DE STEFANO, MARY ANN; Bishop Hannan HS; Scranton, PA; (4); Exploring; Hosp Aide; JA; Spanish Clb; Bowling; Hon Roll; NHS; Excllnc Sclgy,Wrld Cltrs Ii,Spnsh Ii & Spnsh I 84-86; Marywood Coll.

DE TULLIO, DAWN; Greenville SR HS; Greenville, PA; (4); 29/126; Sec French Clb; Yrbk Stf; Off Stu Cncl; Var L Cheerleading; Wt Lftg; Hon Roll; Office Aide; Pep Clb; Band; Chorus; U Of NC-CHARLOTTE; Acctg.

DE VAN JR, STANLEY M; Central HS; Philadelphia, PA; (3); 118/540; JV Trk; Hon Roll; Comp Engrng.

DE VICTORIA, JOELSON; South Philadelphia HS; Philadelphia, PA; (4); 5/550; Church Yth Grp; Acpl Chr; JV Bsbl; Tennis; Hon Roll; Prfct Atten Awd; PA ST U; Pre-Med.

DE VIRGILIS, ALEX THOMAS; Scranton Prep; Waverly, PA; (4); 100/180; Service Clb; Thesps; Chorus; School Musical; School Play; Hon Roll; Dickinson Coll; Law.

DE VIZIA, TANIA; James M Coughlin HS; Wilkes-Barre, PA; (3); Band; Concert Band; Mrchg Band; Orch; Pep Band; Symp Band; NHS; Church Yth Grp; High Hon Roll; PMEA Dist IX Band 87; PMEA Rgn IV ST Band 87; Music.

DE WALD, CHRISTINE E; Daniel Boone HS; Douglassville, PA; (4); 7/160; Capt Quiz Bowl; SADD; Concert Band; Jazz Band; Mrchg Band; Yrbk Sprt Ed; High Hon Roll; NHS; Ntl Merit SF; Opt Clb Awd; Villanova U; Chem Engrng.

DE WIRE, MARK; Clarion-Limestone HS; Strattanville, PA; (3); 11/86; Camera Clb; Ski Clb; Spanish Clb; Band; Concert Band; Mrchg Band; Pep Band; Yrbk Phtg; Yrbk Stf; Golf.

DEABENDERFER, CINDY; Penns Manor HS; Indiana, PA; (3); 27/105; Church Yth Grp; 4-H; Band; Flag Corp; Rep Soph Cls; Rep Jr Cls; Rep Stu Cncl; Hon Roll; IN Cnty Dairy Prncss 87-88; IUP; Elem Educ.

DEAL, ALLEN; Lawrence Co Vo Tech; New Castle, PA; (3); 70/296; Boy Scts; Church Yth Grp; VICA; Lab Rsrch.

DEAL, JESSE; Elizabethtown Area HS; Elizabethtown, PA; (3); 66/224; Art Clb; French Clb; FFA; Nwsp Ed-Chief; Yrbk Ed-Chief; Lit Mag; Masonic Awd; Close Up Prog 87; Temple U; Mrktng.

DEAMER, COLLEEN; Delone Catholic HS; Hanover, PA; (4); 10/163; Yrbk Stf; Cheerleading; High Hon Roll; Hon Roll; NHS; Excllnc Spns Awd 85-86; Tp Awd 83-86; Shippensburg U; Chem Pharm.

DEAN, JENNIFER; Jamestown Area HS; Jamestown, PA; (3); Spanish Clb; Varsity Clb; VICA; Band; Concert Band; Mrchg Band; School Musical; Variety Show; Var Cheerleading; Hon Roll; Cosmtlgst.

DEAN, LORI; Penn Trafford HS; Jeannette, PA; (2); Church Yth Grp; FBLA; Bsktbl; Sftbl; Htl Mgmt.

DEAN, SHUSHANE; Linden Hall HS; Montrose, PA; (3); Church Yth Grp; 4-H; French Clb; FBLA; Spanish Clb; Chorus; Church Choir; Pres Soph Cls; JV Fld Hcky; 4-H Awd; Rtry Exchng Stu Argentina 85-86; Bus Mgmt.

DEAN, VALLERIE R; Nativity B V M HS; Pine Grove, PA; (2); 10/78; Hosp Aide; Office Aide; Chorus; Hgh Hnrs 85-86; Hnrs 86-87; Med.

DEAN, VICTOR; Jamestown Area HS; Jamestown, PA; (4); 2/52; Spanish Clb; Varsity Clb; Stu Cncl; Var Bsktbl; High Hon Roll; NHS; Sal; Air Force; Elec.

DEANGELIS, MELISSA; Oil City HS; Oil City, PA; (4); 44/231; Art Clb; Cmnty Wkr; German Clb; Varsity Clb; Yrbk Rptr; Yrbk Stf; Pres Sr Cls; L Cheerleading; Vllybl; Hon Roll; Syracuse U; Bio.

DEANGELO, SCOTT; Hazleton HS; Hazleton, PA; (2); 23/380; Aud/Vis; Stage Crew; Wrstlng; Hon Roll; Pres Schlr.

DEARDORFF, ALISA; Big Spring HS; Carlisle, PA; (3); 54/258; Chorus; Sec Rep Stu Cncl; Mgr(s); Powder Puff Ftbl; Trk; Hon Roll; Pres Physcl Ftns Awd; Spcl Rcgntn Stu Cncl Awd.

DEARDORFF, BONNIE; Frazier HS; Perryopolis, PA; (3); Drama Clb; French Clb; Ski Clb; Yrbk Stf; Var Capt Cheerleading; Powder Puff Ftbl; Score Keeper; High Hon Roll; Hon Roll.

DEARDORFF, JIM; Dover Area HS; Dover, PA; (3); Boy Scts; Band; Chorus; Concert Band; Mrchg Band; School Musical; Var Crs Cntry.

DEARDORFF, RICHARD; Dover Area HS; Dover, PA; (3); Church Yth Grp; Band; Chorus; Concert Band; Mrchg Band; School Musical; Hon Roll; West Chester; Music.

DEASY, KEVIN; Devon Prep Schl; Wynnewood, PA; (3); Cmnty Wkr; Drama Clb; Ski Clb; Band; Stage Crew; Nwsp Phtg; Nwsp Sprt Ed; Nwsp Stf; Yrbk Phtg; Yrbk Sprt Ed; Law.

DEATER, LARISA; Meadville SR HS; Meadville, PA; (4); Key Clb; Science Clb; Varsity Clb; Rep Jr Cls; VP Sr Cls; Trs Stu Cncl; Capt Var Cheerleading; JV Trk; Hon Roll; Schlstc Hnr Soc; NY ST U Buffalo; Arch.

DEATS, KELLY; Williams JR SR HS; Lawrenceville, PA; (2); Sec Spanish Clb; Sec Soph Cls; JV Capt Bsktbl; JV Capt Vllybl; High Hon Roll; Jr NHS; NHS; Pres Schlr; Spanish Awd 86-87; Mansfield ST Coll; Med Rsrch.

DEAUNOVICH, BETH; Penn Hills SR HS; Pittsburgh, PA; (3); Spanish Clb; Band; Yrbk Stf; Off Jr Cls; High Hon Roll; NHS; Pres Acdmc Fit Awd 85; Psych Clb Sec 86-8 7; FL Atlntc U; Cmmnctns.

DEAVER, CLAUDINE; Henderson SR HS; West Chester, PA; (3); 6/371; SADD; Var Bsktbl; Var Tennis; High Hon Roll; Acdmc All-Amrcn, Radio Consttntl Moment & Sci Tm 86-87.

DEAVER, DAVID; Big Spring HS; Newville, PA; (3); 7/258; Var L Bsktbl; Coach Actv; Var Crs Cntry; JV Trk; High Hon Roll; NHS; U S Air Force; Career Offcr.

DEAVER, WENDY; Northern SR HS; Dillsburg, PA; (4); 46/200; Church Yth Grp; Hosp Aide; Chorus; Hon Roll; NHS; Prsdntl Acdmc Ftnss Awd 87; Messiah Coll; Family Cnslng.

DEAVOR III, WILLIAM H; Lewistown Area HS; Lewistown, PA; (3); Boy Scts; Church Yth Grp; French Clb; High Hon Roll; Hon Roll; Chem Engr.

DEBENEDICT, RAYMOND; Marian Catholic HS; Tamaqua, PA; (4); 15/110; Chess Clb; Concert Band; Jazz Band; Trs Mrchg Band; School Play; L Trk; Hon Roll; Band; Chorus; Pep Band; Schylkl Cnty Med Soc Awd 87; Zeswitz Music Awd 87; PA All ST Lions Band 86; Phila Coll Of Phrmcy & Sci; Phr.

DEBLASIO, DANIEL R; Norristown Area HS; Norristown, PA; (3); 1/500; VICA; Trk; High Hon Roll; Hon Roll; Outstndng Soc Stud Awd 86; Music Engrng.

DEC, THERESA A; Sacred Heart HS; Mc Kees Rocks, PA; (4); Exploring; Pres Library Aide; Mu Alpha Theta; NFL; Band; Hon Roll; Mu Alpha Theta Awd; NHS; Pres Schlr; Math Clb; 4-Yr Full Acad Scholar NM Inst Mine & Tech 87; Cert Merit PA Board Higher Ed 86; NM Inst M&T; Physcs.

DECAPUA, JAMI; Hickory HS; Hermitage, PA; (3); 23/167; Hosp Aide; Trs Latin Clb; School Play; Nwsp Stf; Yrbk Stf; Pres Frsh Cls; Capt L Cheerleading; Var L Tennis; NHS; Chrldng Acadc Awd 87; CLI 86; Swmrs Clb 85; Phrmcy.

DECARO, JOANNA; Mercy Vocational HS; Upper Darby, PA; (4); Church Yth Grp; Service Clb; Chorus; Church Choir; Variety Show; Bowling; Outstndng Svc To Schl 87; Clerical.

DECH, MATTHEW; Emmaus HS; Emmaus, PA; (3); 195/525; Cmnty Wkr; Key Clb; Var Bsktbl; Im Bowling; Var Trk; Im Vllybl; Hon Roll; Prfct Atten Awd; PA ST; Acctng.

DECH, NANCY; Red Lion Area SR HS; Red Lion, PA; (3); 24/342; Varsity Clb; Concert Band; Mrchg Band; Symp Band; Yrbk Stf; Var Swmmng; High Hon Roll; Hon Roll; NHS; Im Powder Puff Ftbl; Tri-M Mdrn Msc Mstrs Hnr Scty 87; Bio Chmstry.

DECHERT, LISA; Grace Christian Schl; Lebanon, PA; (4); 9/20; Church Yth Grp; Cmnty Wkr; Chorus; School Play; Yrbk Stf; Fld Hcky; Sftbl; High Hon Roll; Hon Roll; Score Keeper; Lebanon Vly Coll; Psych.

DECINTI, CAROLYN; G A R HS; Wilkes-Barre, PA; (4); French Clb; Chorus; Yrbk Stf; Stat Bsktbl; Var Cheerleading; Hon Roll; Jr NHS; NHS; Wilkes Clg Pa.

DECKER, ALFRED J; Neshaminy SR HS; Langhorne, PA; (3); 196/770; Aud/Vis; Chess Clb; Science Clb; Pres Stage Crew; Ntl Merit SF; Duquesne; Physcst.

DECKER, BEVERLY; Everett Area HS; Everett, PA; (2); 3/150; Sec Church Yth Grp; Sec Spanish Clb; Band; Drm Mjr(t); Pep Band; Sec Soph Cls; Stu Cncl; Golf; Score Keeper; High Hon Roll; Woodmen Of The Wrld For Hstry Proficiency 86.

DECKER, CHARLES; Neshaminy HS; Langhorne, PA; (3); 92/730; Key Clb; Stage Crew; Lit Mag; Hon Roll; Ntl Merit Ltr; Bus Admin.

DECKER, NATALIE TONWEN; Abington Hgts HS; Clarks Summit, PA; (4); JA; High Hon Roll; Ntl Merit Ltr; Abngtn Wmns Clb 87; Outstndng Achvt Prntng 87; Keystn JC Wrkshp Pottry Prntmkng 89-87.

DECKER, SHAY; Carmichaels Area JR HS; Carmichaels, PA; (1); French Clb; Color Guard; Nwsp Stf; High Hon Roll; Hon Roll; Homcmng Attendant 86-87.

DECKER, TOM; Archbishop Wood HS; Horsham, PA; (2); 78/254; Church Yth Grp; JV Wrstlng; Hon Roll; Sports Med.

DECKERT, DIANA; Mount St Joseph Acad; Warminster, PA; (2); Cmnty Wkr; French Clb; FBLA; JCL; Ed Science Clb; High Hon Roll; NEDT Awd; PA Gvrnrs Schl For Ag 87; 1st Pl PA Jr Acad Of Sci Rgnl & ST Cmptns 87; Silver Mdl Natl Ltn Exam 87; Vet.

DECKMAN, DENISE; Northwest Area HS; Shickshinny, PA; (4); 7/119; Sec Trs Church Yth Grp; Computer Clb; Drama Clb; Pres SADD; Chorus; Church Choir; School Musical; Swing Chorus; Off Frsh Cls; Off Soph Cls; Most Prmsng Underclsmn Chrl Awd 84; Voice Of Democracy Awd 2nd Pl 86; PMEA Rgnl Chorus 1st Pl 87; U Of Pittsburgh; Nrsng.

DECLAIR, GEORGEANN; West Mifflin Area HS; W Mifflin, PA; (3); Pep Clb; Ski Clb; Rep Frsh Cls; Rep Soph Cls; Rep Jr Cls; Powder Puff Ftbl; Vllybl; Nrsg.

DECOWSKI, NOELLE; Bishop Hafey HS; Freeland, PA; (1); Art Clb; Church Yth Grp; Library Aide; Spanish Clb; Chorus; Badmtn; Sftbl; Tennis; Michelle Branz Mem Awd 86.

DEDEL, KELLI; Unionville HS; West Chester, PA; (4); 54/315; Pep Clb; Nwsp Rptr; Off Sr Cls; Off Stu Cncl; Cheerleading; High Hon Roll; Hon Roll; Jr NHS; NHS; U Of Richmond; Crmnl Jstc.

DEE, MARY BETH; Nativity BVM HS; Pottsville, PA; (1); 31/95; Y-Teens; Chorus; JV Cheerleading; Stat Trk; Intr Dsgn.

DEEBEL, KATHY; Cardinal Brennan HS; Frackville, PA; (3); 7/58; Band; Rep Frsh Cls; Rep Soph Cls; Rep Jr Cls; Pres Sr Cls; Pres Stu Cncl; Hon Roll; Trs NHS; Scholastic Bowl; Chorus; Amer Cult, Engl II, German II & III, Govt Ec, Theo III & Med-Eng III Certs Of Outstndng Achvt; Law.

DEEGAN, GREGORY; Pottstown SR HS; Pottstown, PA; (4); 4/181; VP Key Clb; Band; Concert Band; Jazz Band; Mrchg Band; High Hon Roll; Trs NHS; Pres Schlr; PA ST U; Cvl Engnrng.

DEEGAN, SEAN; Southmoreland SR HS; Scottdale, PA; (3); French Clb; Letterman Clb; Varsity Clb; Socr; Hon Roll; Ecnmcs.

DEEMER, KIM; Fort Le Baeuf HS; Erie, PA; (3); 75/280; Dance Clb; Drama Clb; SADD; Drill Tm; School Play; Rep Jr Cls; Stat Bsktbl; Var Cheerleading; Messiah; Occ Therapist.

DEEMER, KIM; Seneca Valley HS; Evans City, PA; (4); Church Yth Grp; Cmnty Wkr; Pep Clb; Ski Clb; Lit Mag; Trk; Im 3rd Awd-Smmr Bst Two Wks Chrstn Cmp 85; VA Wesleyan Coll; Bus Manag.

DEEMER, PEGGY; Ligonier Valley HS; Ligonier, PA; (3); 4/156; NFL; Science Clb; SADD; Chorus; Flag Corp; School Play; Rep Stu Cncl; High Hon Roll; Jr NHS; NHS; PA Free Entrprs Wk Lockhaven U 86-87; Carnegie Mellon U; Heredty Rsrc.

DEEMER, ROBERT; Du Bois Area HS; Du Bois, PA; (3); 16/321; Chess Clb; Science Clb; Var L Golf; Hon Roll; NHS; Penn ST; Chem Engrng.

DEENIHAN, TIMOTHY; Serra Catholic HS; Wilmerding, PA; (3); 12/154; Drama Clb; Math Tm; NFL; Pres Speech Tm; Chorus; School Musical; Stu Cncl; High Hon Roll; NHS; NEDT Awd; Aerspc Engr.

DEERY, ANESSA; Upper Darby HS; Primos, PA; (4); 45/590; High Hon Roll; Hon Roll; Bus Educ Awd, Am Studies Awd 86; Exec Secry.

DEERY, PAMELA; Upper Darby HS; Primos, PA; (3); 48/598; Church Yth Grp; Acpl Chr; Church Choir; School Musical; Swing Chorus; High Hon Roll; Hon Roll; Prfct Atten Awd; Lgl Scrtry.

DEESING, ANGELA; Mahanoy Area HS; Delano, PA; (3); Spanish Clb; SADD; Chorus; School Play; Variety Show; Swmmng; Trk; Scl Wrk.

DEETER, JANE; Chestnut Ridge SR HS; Manns Choice, PA; (4); 9/137; SADD; Sec Trs Band; Nwsp Bus Mgr; Rep Stu Cncl; Var Mgr Trk; JP Sousa Awd; NHS; Hugh O Brian Ldrshp Awd 85; Intl Frgn Lang Awd 86; Pres Acdmc Fit Awd 87; Alleghany CC; Med Lab Tech.

DEETS, CHRISTINE; Oil City SR HS; Titusville, PA; (3); 28/218; Church Yth Grp; Office Aide; Sec Science Clb; Acpl Chr; Nwsp Stf; Co-Capt Cheerleading; Crs Cntry; Sftbl; Trk; Capt Vllybl; Photo Session Yth Opportn 86; Schlstc Exc 86; Ambassador Coll; Tchr.

DEFAZIO, GINA; Mid Valley HS; Dickson City, PA; (3); Yrbk Phtg; Yrbk Stf; Pharm.

DEFAZIO, THOMAS; Du Bois Central Christian HS; Dubois, PA; (2); Exploring; Math Tm; Ski Clb; Bsbl; Bsktbl; Crs Cntry; High Hon Roll; Prfct Atten Awd.

DEFFIBAUGH, ABIGAIL L; Claysburg-Kimmel HS; Imler, PA; (3); 13/78; VP FTA; Rep Stu Cncl; JV Var Mgr(s); Hon Roll; NHS; Prfct Atten Awd; Jrnlst.

DEFIBAUCH, DALLAS; Trinity Area HS; Washintgton, PA; (3); 113/425; Ski Clb; SADD; Band; Concert Band; Drm & Bgl; Jazz Band; Mrchg Band; Orch; Pep Band; Stage Crew.

DEFIBAUGH, DALLAS; Trinity HS; Washington, PA; (3); 131/428; Ski Clb; SADD; Band; Concert Band; Drm & Bgl; Jazz Band; Mrchg Band; Orch; Pep Band; Symp Band; Bus.

DEFIBAUGH, TRACY; Conemaugh Township Area HS; Hooversville, PA; (3); 9/117; Church Yth Grp; Chorus; Church Choir; Hon Roll; NHS; Spnsh Cert 85-87; Med.

DEFIGIO, DANIEL A; General Mc Lane HS; Edinboro, PA; (4); 8/187; Spanish Clb; Chorus; Jazz Band; Pep Band; School Musical; Chess Clb; Church Yth Grp; German Clb; Rep Stu Cncl; Bsktbl; Fredrick Chopin Piano Awd 87; Dist, Rgnl Chorus 86 & 87; Dist Jzz 86 & 87; Oberlin Cnsrvtry; Piano Prfrmnc.

DEFILIPPI, MATTHEW; Leechburg Area HS; Leechburg, PA; (4); 5/85; Drama Clb; Math Tm; Office Aide; Nwsp Stf; Yrbk Stf; Pres Sr Cls; VP Stu Cncl; High Hon Roll; NHS; Pres Schlr; Pres Acad Ftns Awd 87; Pre-Med.

DEFONTENY, LOUIS; Harry S Truman HS; Bristol, PA; (3); Teachers Aide; JV Capt Socr; JV Capt Wrstlng; High Hon Roll; Hon Roll; Fin.

DEFRANTZ, WALTRINA; G A R Memorial HS; Wilkes-Barre, PA; (4); 30/187; Church Yth Grp; Dance Clb; FBLA; Key Clb; Letterman Clb; Library Aide; NAACP; Pep Clb; Ski Clb; Spanish Clb; Natl Hnr Scty 84-87; Scty Distngshd Amer Hgh Schl Stdnts 87; Hnr Rll 84-87; Pre-Med.

DEGAUAGE, AMY; Hanover Area HS; Wilkes Barre, PA; (3); Hosp Aide; High Hon Roll; Hon Roll; NHS; Psychlgy.

DEGENHART, KRISTI; Peters Township HS; Venetia, PA; (3); Sec Church Yth Grp; FBLA; Thesps; Church Choir; School Play; Nwsp Stf; Rep Soph Cls; Co-Capt Cheerleading; Drama Clb; Secndry Eng Educ.

DEGILIO, MICHAEL; Marian Catholic HS; Lansford, PA; (4); 56/130; Church Yth Grp; Letterman Clb; Ski Clb; Varsity Clb; Bsktbl; Coach Actv; Ftbl; Trk; Wt Lftg; Allentown Coll; Crmnl Jstce.

DEGLER, DOUGLAS; Muhlenberg HS; Reading, PA; (4); 41/185; Boy Scts; Ski Clb; Jazz Band; Mrchg Band; Orch; School Musical; Bsktbl; Trk; NHS; Beaver Coll Schlrshp & Hnrs Prog 87; Beaver Coll; Phy Thrpy.

DEGLER, KRISTEN; Cedar Crest HS; Lebanon, PA; (3); Trs Church Yth Grp; Key Clb; Pep Clb; Spanish Clb; SADD; Band; Concert Band; Mrchg Band; Yrbk Stf; Im Vllybl; PA ST U; Soc Wrk.

DEGLER, SHARON; Conrad Weiser HS; Sinking Spring, PA; (3); 33/179; FBLA; Girl Scts; Trs Spanish Clb; Chorus; Mrchg Band; School Musical; Yrbk Stf; JV Var Cheerleading; Var Trk; Hon Roll.

DEGOL, ANTHONY; Bishop Guilfoyle HS; Altoona, PA; (3); Church Choir; Yrbk Stf; PA ST U; Bus.

DEGRUTTOLA, JASON; Blairsville SR HS; Blairsville, PA; (4); Church Yth Grp; Stu Cncl; Trk; High Hon Roll; Hon Roll; Blairsville Italian Soc Auxillary Schlrshp 87; Westminster Coll; Accntng.

DEGUS, LINDA E; Conestoga SR HS; Malvern, PA; (4); AFS; Cmnty Wkr; Band; Drill Tm; Nwsp Rptr; Nwsp Stf; Lit Mag; Rep Stu Cncl; Var JV Fld Hcky; Var JV Lcrss; Pioneer Mnth 87; Miss PA Coed Pgnt Fnlst 87; Immcltta Coll Poetry Awd 86; Penn ST U; Comm.

DEHAAS, DAWN; Tyrone Area HS; Tyrone, PA; (3); Key Clb; Spanish Clb; Chorus; Yrbk Stf; High Hon Roll; Hon Roll; X-Ray Tech.

DEHNER, CHERYL LORRAINE; Clarion-Limestone HS; Strattanville, PA; (3); 1/70; Church Yth Grp; French Clb; FHA; SADD; High Hon Roll; Hon Roll; NHS; Prfct Atten Awd; Math Tm; Hugh Obrn Yth Fntdtn ST Ldrshp Smnr 86; Acdmc Awds-Frnch, Home-Ec, Hstry, Englsh & Math 84-86; Intl Stds.

DEHNER, LISA; Cranberry Area HS; Seneca, PA; (2); 22/141; Church Yth Grp; Hosp Aide; Pep Clb; Science Clb; Spanish Clb; Orch; Stat Bsktbl; Stat Trk; JV Vllybl; Hon Roll.

DEHNER, STACY; Bishop Kenrick HS; Norristown, PA; (4); 12/287; Trs Science Clb; Chorus; Co-Capt Color Guard; School Musical; Variety Show; DAR Awd; NHS; JV Vllybl; Ralston Schlrshp 87; Christian Brthrs Schlrshp 87; Merit Schlrshp 87; La Salle U; Bio.

DEHNER, TERRY; Clarion-Limestone HS; Strattanville, PA; (1); Church Yth Grp; Var FCA; Var FFA; SADD; VICA; FFA Grnhnd Awd 86-87; FFA Star Grnhnd Awd 86-87; Auto Mech.

DEI GOA, ROY; Canevin Catholic HS; Carnegie, PA; (3); Socr; Air Force; Pilot.

DEIBERT, JULIE; Tri-Valley HS; Sacramento, PA; (4); 17/74; Quiz Bowl; Band; Yrbk Sprt Ed; Sec Jr Cls; Var Capt Bsktbl; Var L Sftbl; Var Capt Vllybl; Hon Roll; Rotary Awd; 1st Femal Athlt At Tri-Vly Bsktbl Tm 86-87; Rotary Stu Of Mnth For March 87; Tri-Vlys Femal Schlr 87; Lock Haven U; Sprts Med.

DEIBLER, JOAN; Tyrone Area HS; Warriors Mark, PA; (3); 4-H; Spanish Clb; Concert Band; Jazz Band; Mrchg Band; Hon Roll; Church Yth Grp; Pep Band; School Musical; Elem Ed.

DEIBLER, MICHAEL; Shikellamy HS; Sunbury, PA; (3); Boy Scts; Band; Concert Band; Mrchg Band; Hon Roll; Jr NHS; Army; Data Prcssng.

DEIBLER, MICHELE; Dover Area SR HS; Dover, PA; (2); 60/360; Church Yth Grp; Hosp Aide; Teachers Aide; Chorus; Hon Roll; Cmnty Wkr; School Musical; Crmnl Law.

DEIBLER, TARA M; Lewistown Area HS; Lewistown, PA; (4); 33/249; Church Yth Grp; French Clb; Pep Clb; Ski Clb; Acpl Chr; Band; Chorus; Church Choir; Concert Band; Mrchg Band; York Coll PA; Soclgy.

DEIGER, SHAWN; W Middlesex Area Schl; Pulaski, PA; (1); Boy Scts; Church Yth Grp; French Clb; High Hon Roll; Hon Roll; NY ST U; Forest Rngr.

DEILY, KRIS; Abington Heights HS; Scranton, PA; (1); Dance Clb; Ski Clb; Chorus; School Musical; School Play; Capt Cheerleading; JV Trk; Hon Roll; 2nd Pl Jr Acad Sci 87; 1st Pl Triathlon 87; NY ST Olympd Spoken Russian Awd 87; Ped.

DEILY, LISA; North Catholic HS; Pittsburgh, PA; (2); 57/232; Exploring; German Clb; Band; Concert Band; Jazz Band; Mrchg Band; Hon Roll; Mid East Band Fest 87; Carnegie Mellon U; Music.

DEIMLER, TONYA; Steelton-Highspire HS; Highspire, PA; (3); 13/102; Quiz Bowl; Spanish Clb; Band; School Musical; Yrbk Stf; Var Sftbl; High Hon Roll; Hon Roll; Jr NHS; NHS.

DEININGER, DONNA; Tamaqua Area HS; Tamaqua, PA; (4); 3/180; Trs Am Leg Aux Girls St; VP Church Yth Grp; Pres Drama Clb; Pres Girl Scts; Drm Mjr(t); School Musical; Rep Stu Cncl; NHS; Pep Clb; VP Science Clb; Hugh O Brien Yth Fndtn 85; All-Estrn Chrs, Fred Warings US Chrs 87; Ithaca Coll; Music Ed.

DEIPO, DONNA; Upper Moreland SR HS; Willow Grove, PA; (1); 27/251; Varsity Clb; JV L Socr; Var L Tennis; High Hon Roll; Princeton; Comm Lwyr.

DEISCHER, KRISTEN; Henderson SR HS; West Chester, PA; (2); 4/335; Church Choir; Jazz Band; Mrchg Band; School Musical; Nwsp Rptr; Lit Mag; Rep Stu Cncl; French Hon Soc; Hon Roll; Church Yth Grp; Saxophnst Amercn Music Abrd Smr Tour 87; Engr.

DEIST, DONNA; North Star HS; Boswell, PA; (3); 4/140; Sec 4-H; Mu Alpha Theta; Band; Chorus; Church Choir; 4-H Awd; Hon Roll; Frostburg ST Coll; Law.

DEIST, DONNA; Schuylkill Valley HS; Reading, PA; (4); 3/133; Sec Church Yth Grp; Pep Clb; SADD; Band; Chorus; Church Choir; Mrchg Band; School Musical; High Hon Roll; NHS; All Am Acad Awd 85-86; Outstndng Schlstc Achvt 86-87; Albright Coll; Surgeon.

DEITRICH, ANN; Williams Valley HS; Wiconisco, PA; (4); 1/97; Church Yth Grp; Girl Scts; Quiz Bowl; Chorus; Trs Sr Cls; Bausch & Lomb Sci Awd; God Cntry Awd; VP NHS; Val; Lebanon Vly Coll Prsdntl Schlrshp; Patriot Nws Schlrshp; Mary Margaret Nestor Fndtn Schlrshp; Lebanon Valley Coll; Math.

DEITRICH, JEFF; Elizabethtown Area HS; Elizabethtown, PA; (4); PA Schl Of Arts; Cmmrcl Art.

DEITZ, STACY; Union HS; Rimersburg, PA; (3); 17/94; Aud/Vis; Pep Clb; SADD; Color Guard; Flag Corp; Mrchg Band; School Musical; Bsktbl; Trk; High Hon Roll; IN U; Attrny.

DEL BORGO, ANN; Greater Johnstown HS; Johnstown, PA; (4); 41/277; Key Clb; Chorus; Yrbk Ed-Chief; Yrbk Phtg; Yrbk Rptr; Off Sr Cls; High Hon Roll; Hon Roll; Jr NHS; NHS; U Of Pittsburgh Johnstown; Bio.

DEL CAMPO, FRANK; St John Newmann HS; Philadelphia, PA; (3); 87/350; Var Ftbl; Phrmcy.

DEL CASTELLO, BRIAN; New Castle SR HS; New Castle, PA; (2); 34/263; Boy Scts; Church Yth Grp; Library Aide; Rep Stu Cncl; JV Crs Cntry; Im Vllybl; JV Wrstlng; Hon Roll; Anthrplgy.

DEL COTTO, GREGORY; Franklin Regional HS; Murrysville, PA; (3); Computer Clb; Spanish Clb; Band; Rep Frsh Cls; Stu Cncl; Bsktbl; Golf; High Hon Roll; Prfct Atten Awd.

DEL DUCA, MICHAEL; Seneca Valley HS; Mars, PA; (2); Crimin.

DEL GRECO, PAULA; Aliquippa HS; Aliquippa, PA; (4); 2/130; Exploring; French Clb; Office Aide; VP VICA; Concert Band; Mrchg Band; Yrbk Stf; VP Jr Cls; VP Sr Cls; Twrlr.

DEL ROMANO, NICHOLAS; Upper Darby HS; Upper Darby, PA; (3); Trk; Hon Roll.

DEL VALLE, ERICA; Central HS; Philadelphia, PA; (2); Teachers Aide; Chorus; JV Sftbl; JV Var Vllybl; Intl Rltns.

DEL VITTO, SHAUNA; Monongahela Valley Catholic HS; Monongahela, PA; (3); 11/98; Debate Tm; GAA; Rep Frsh Cls; Var L Bsktbl; Powder Puff Ftbl; Var L Sftbl; Var L Vllybl; French Hon Soc; High Hon Roll; Hon Roll; Pre Med.

DELACH, BETH; Bethel Park HS; Carmi, IL; (4); 110/519; Trs DECA; Band; School Play; Yrbk Bus Mgr; Capt Var Cheerleading; L Coach Actv; 2nd Pl Lcl, 3rd Pl ST, 3rd Pl Natl, Mrktng DECA Cmpttn 87; Robert Morris Coll; Mktg.

DELANEY, SEAN; Monsignor Bonner HS; Drexel Hill, PA; (4); 7/310; Church Yth Grp; Math Tm; Service Clb; L Stage Crew; Nwsp Rptr; JV Bowling; Im Sftbl; NHS; Ntl Merit SF; Commonwlth PA Cert Of Merit; Drexel U; Elec Engrng.

DELARA, GREG; Connellsville HS; Connellsville, PA; (3); 63/525; Office Aide; JV Ftbl; High Hon Roll; NHS.

DELAUTER, RONALD; Greencastle-Antrim HS; Greencastle, PA; (3); Boy Scts; Church Yth Grp; Chorus; Church Choir; Brthrhd, Ordr Of Arrow & Boy Scts Of Amer 84; PA ST U; Elec Engrng.

DELCAMP, MARC; Fleetwood Area HS; Fleetwood, PA; (4); 5/114; Aud/Vis; School Musical; JV Var Tennis; High Hon Roll; Hon Roll; NHS; Kutztown U; Acctng.

DELCONTE, LISA; Cardinal O Hara HS; Broomall, PA; (4); 82/771; French Clb; JA; Latin Clb; Church Choir; Flag Corp; Nwsp Stf; Yrbk Stf; Im Vllybl; Hon Roll; NHS; Rosemnt Coll Trustee Schlrshp 87; Acadmc Achvt Awd Widener U 87; Villanova U; Acctng.

DELEGRAM, JODY; Central Dauphin HS; Harrisburg, PA; (2); Drama Clb; Key Clb; Ski Clb; Chorus; School Musical; Nwsp Rptr; Nwsp Stf; Yrbk Stf; Vllybl; Hon Roll; Harrisburg Area CC; Nrsng.

DELETTO, BILL; Waynesburg Central HS; Waynesburg, PA; (3); Aud/Vis; French Clb; Ski Clb; JV Bsktbl; JV Var Ftbl; Hon Roll.

DELGADO, ABEL; St Josephs Prep; Philadelphia, PA; (4); 45/240; Church Yth Grp; Cmnty Wkr; Intnl Clb; Latin Clb; Library Aide; Model UN; Spanish Clb; Im Bsktbl; Hon Roll; NHS; Mayors Schlrshp Phil, Natl Hspnc Schlrshp, & Mnrty Schlrshp St Josephs U 87; U PA; Comm.

DELGAUDO, WALTER; Dallas SR HS; Dallas, PA; (3); 13/253; School Play; Yrbk Stf; Rep Soph Cls; Rep Jr Cls; L Ftbl; Var Trk; Im Wt Lftg; Hon Roll; NHS; NEDT Cert; U Pittsburgh; Pre-Med.

DELHAGEN, MARCY; Susquehanna Community HS; Thompson, PA; (2); Ski Clb; Var Cheerleading; Hon Roll.

DELIZZIO, JAMES; Cardinal O Hara HS; Broomall, PA; (3); 165/710; Chess Clb; Trs Church Yth Grp; JA; Office Aide; Nwsp Rptr; Nwsp Stf; Im Bsktbl; Im Bowling; Crmnlgy.

DELL, JASON; Somerset Area HS; Somerset, PA; (3); 5/230; French Clb; Math Clb; Math Tm; Mu Alpha Theta; Ski Clb; Varsity Clb; Var Socr; French Hon Soc; High Hon Roll; NHS; Engr.

DELL ORFANO, BETTINA; Dover Area HS; Dover, PA; (3); Am Leg Aux Girls St; Band; Mrchg Band; Yrbk Stf; Pres Soph Cls; Pres Jr Cls; Pres Sr Cls; L Var Swmmng; High Hon Roll; NHS; Outstndng Sci Stu 87; Pediatrician.

DELLAFIORA, JAMES M; Homer-Center HS; Homer City, PA; (3); Pres Church Yth Grp; Pres Library Aide; Varsity Clb; Band; Pres Sr Cls; VP Stu Cncl; L Trk; Hon Roll; Voice Dem Awd; French Clb; JR Acad Sci 1st Pl Awd 84-86; Mock Trl 87.

DELLAPINA, JENNIFER; Burgettstown Area JR-SR HS; Burgettstown, PA; (4); 17/137; Church Yth Grp; Yrbk Stf; Rep Stu Cncl; Mgr(s); Var Tennis; High Hon Roll; NHS; Pres Schlr; Purdue U Schl Conumer & Fmly Sci 87-88; Charles & Minnie Kelley Almni Schlrshp 87-88; Purdue U; Htl Adm.

DELLAROSE, LAURIE; Brownsville Area HS; La Belle, PA; (3); 1/200; Math Clb; Ski Clb; SADD; Band; Drm Mjr(t); Stu Cncl; High Hon Roll; NHS; Rotary Awd; Duquesne; Phrmcy.

DELLEMONACHE, CARLEEN; Sto-Rox HS; Mc Kees Rocks, PA; (4); 14/138; Church Yth Grp; FBLA; Office Aide; Drm Mjr(t); Yrbk Stf; VP Sr Cls; Twrlr; High Hon Roll; NHS; Boys Clb Am; Lone Str Cement Inc Hnbl Mntn Awd 87; IN U Of PA; Engl Ed.

DELLEVIONE, ELIZABETH; Bishop Shanahan HS; W Chester, PA; (4); 3/218; Art Clb; Hosp Aide; Math Tm; Quiz Bowl; Scholastic Bowl; Lit Mag; High Hon Roll; Jr NHS; NHS; Ntl Merit SF; Achvmnt Algebra II; Hghst Gnrl Avrg Awd ; Achvmnt Latin; Moore Coll; Art.

DELLICKER, TARA; Brandywine Heights HS; Topton, PA; (3); 3/120; Chorus; Drill Tm; Mrchg Band; Sec Jr Cls; Sec Sr Cls; Rep Stu Cncl; Var Capt Cheerleading; Var L Trk; High Hon Roll; NHS; Med.

DELLINGER, LAURA; Conrad Weiser HS; Sinking Spring, PA; (4); 69/195; Church Yth Grp; Hosp Aide; Spanish Clb; Chorus; School Musical; Rep Jr Cls; JV Trk; Hon Roll; Muscl Achvt Awd 87; IN U; Lawyer.

DELLINGER, MARK; New Oxford SR HS; New Oxford, PA; (4); 29/167; Boy Scts; Hst VP FFA; School Play; Hst Sr Cls; Rep Stu Cncl; JV Ftbl; FFA Schlrshp; John L Kratzort Memrl Schlrshp Top FFA Prsn; Parlmntry Proc Tm FFA; CO ST U; Vet Sci.

DELLIQUADRI, ERIC; Shenango JR SR HS; New Castle, PA; (2); Spanish Clb; Im Bsktbl; Var Ftbl; Hon Roll; Jr NHS; U Of Pittsburgh; Engrng.

DELLIQUADRI, MARIA; Shenango HS; New Castle, PA; (3); #3 In Class; Nwsp Rptr; Nwsp Stf; Stu Cncl; Cit Awd; High Hon Roll; Hon Roll; Jr NHS; NHS; Carnegie Mellon; Data Prcssng.

DELNERO, JEFFREY; Central Columbia HS; Bloomsburg, PA; (4); Church Yth Grp; DECA; German Clb; Radio Clb; Ski Clb; Nwsp Rptr; Bsbl; Bowling; Ftbl; Wt Lftg; USAF.

DELON, GERALD; Hopewell HS; Aliquippa, PA; (2); Church Yth Grp; Cmnty Wkr; Bsbl; Wt Lftg; High Hon Roll; Hon Roll; Robert Morris; Bus.

DELONG, ANDREA; Brandywine Heights HS; Mertztown, PA; (2); GAA; Chorus; Color Guard; Mrchg Band; Hon Roll; Kutztown; Occptnl Thrpst.

DELONG, DONNA; Northamption Area SR HS; Bath, PA; (3); 69/494; Trs DECA; Office Aide; Hon Roll; 1st Pl Wnnr DECA Dist Cmptn 87; St Cmptn DECA St Ldrshp 86-87; Pres Of Ntrthmptn DECA Chptr 87-88; Bus.

DELP, TRICIA; Archbishop Ryan HS; Philadelphia, PA; (4); 2/490; Church Yth Grp; Exploring; French Clb; Hosp Aide; Q&S; Science Clb; Nwsp Stf; Var L Tennis; French Hon Soc; NHS; Soc Of Wmn Engrs Awd Excel In Math,Sci 86; Excel In Adv Bio & Trignmtry 86; Physcl Thrpy.

DELSIGNORE, GEORGE; North Star HS; Boswell, PA; (2); 4/160; Mu Alpha Theta; Ski Clb; Trs Frsh Cls; Off Stu Cncl; Hon Roll; Pres Schlr; Hugh Obrian Yth Ambassador 87; Material Arts Black Belt 87; Mensa 86; UCLA; Corporate Finance.

DELUCA, DESIREE A; Norristown Area HS; Norristown, PA; (3); 63/491; Band; Chorus; Concert Band; Mrchg Band; Pep Band; Symp Band; Hnr Roll 2nd & 3rd 85-87.

DELUCCIA, HOLLY; Curwensville Area HS; Curwensville, PA; (3); French Clb; FBLA; Hosp Aide; Chorus; Acadmc All Am 87; Lock Haven.

DELUCREZIA, AIMEE; Bensalem SR HS; Bensalem, PA; (2); Wt Lftg; High Hon Roll; Hon Roll.

DELVECCHIO, LISA; Old Forge HS; Old Forge, PA; (4); 28/104; Drill Tm; Capt Pom Pon; Hon Roll; NHS; Marywood Coll; Psych.

DELVECCHIO, MELANIE; Dunmore HS; Dunmore, PA; (2); 30/140; Drama Clb; French Clb; Ski Clb; Spanish Clb; Band; Concert Band; Mrchg Band; School Musical; School Play; Stu Cncl; Cmmnctns.

DEMAGLIO, MICHELLE; Penn Hills SR HS; Verona, PA; (3); Girl Scts; Ski Clb; Band; Bowling.

DEMALON, STEPHANIE; Greensburg Central Catholic HS; Mckeesport, PA; (3); AFS; Church Yth Grp; Pep Clb; Mrchg Band; Hon Roll; Seton Hill; Early Ed.

DEMARCHI, KATHY; Penn-Trafford HS; Levelgreen, PA; (3); AFS; Drama Clb; Exploring; FBLA; Hosp Aide; Red Cross Aide; SADD; Hon Roll; Cmmnctns.

DEMARCO, KIMBERLY; Lancaster Catholic HS; Lancaster, PA; (3); Service Clb; Ski Clb; Varsity Clb; Rep Frsh Cls; Rep Soph Cls; Rep Jr Cls; Pres Sr Cls; Off Stu Cncl; Var Capt Fld Hcky; Var Co-Capt Trk; Bio.

DEMARK, NICHOLE; Pittston Area HS; Hughestown, PA; (3); Ski Clb; Psych.

DEMARTINO, DANA; Fort Le Boeuf HS; Erie, PA; (3); 11/207; Church Yth Grp; Cmnty Wkr; Ski Clb; Nwsp Rptr; Lit Mag; Score Keeper; High Hon Roll; Hon Roll; Cert Mert 86-87; Art Compttn 87.

DEMASE, MARIA; New Castle HS; New Castle, PA; (4); AFS; Office Aide; SADD; Drill Tm; Nwsp Rptr; Yrbk Stf; Rep Frsh Cls; Rep Soph Cls; Rep Jr Cls; Hon Roll; Hmcmng Qn; Treas Of Italian Clb; Medical Explorers; Westminster Coll.

DEMATTEO, JOHN; Pocono Central Catholic HS; Mt Pocono, PA; (3); Art Clb; Latin Clb; Pep Clb; Scholastic Bowl; Teachers Aide; Yrbk Stf; Var L Bsbl; Var L Bsktbl; High Hon Roll; Hon Roll; PA ST; Bus.

DEMELLIER, LEAH; E L Meyers HS; Wilkes Barre, PA; (4); Trs French Clb; Pres Key Clb; Ski Clb; Chorus; School Play; Nwsp Sprt Ed; Yrbk Stf; VP Jr Cls; VP Sr Cls; Var Crs Cntry; Outstndng Sr Girl 86-87; Photo.

DEMENIK, SHANNON; Northwestern HS; E Springfield, PA; (3); Exploring; Model UN; Sftbl; Vllybl; Chem.

DEMI, CHARISSA; Northern Cambria HS; Spangler, PA; (3); 9/152; Church Yth Grp; French Clb; Ski Clb; Color Guard; Concert Band; Yrbk Stf; High Hon Roll; NHS.

DEMIS, TARA; Mc Keesport Area HS; Mckeesport, PA; (3); 3/410; Pres AFS; Cmnty Wkr; Exploring; GAA; Library Aide; Pep Clb; Powder Puff Ftbl; High Hon Roll; VP NHS; Prfct Atten Awd.

DEMKO, STACEY; Plum SR HS; Pittsburgh, PA; (2); Dance Clb; GAA; SADD; Chorus; Sec Frsh Cls; Cheerleading; Sftbl; Trk; Hon Roll; Med.

DEMKOSKY, CHERYIL; Mid-Valley HS; Throop, PA; (3); Bsktbl; Mgr(s); High Hon Roll; JA; Hon Roll; Cert Of Merit-Frnch 84-85.

DEMMER, DEBORAH; Venanga Christian HS; Oil City, PA; (3); 1/35; Model UN; Yrbk Stf; VP Soph Cls; Pres Jr Cls; Rep Sr Cls; Rep Stu Cncl; Var Capt Cheerleading; High Hon Roll; NHS; NEDT Awd; Hugh Obrn Yth Ldrshp Semnr 86.

DEMMY, LISA RENEE; Butler Area SR HS; Butler, PA; (4); 99/756; Church Yth Grp; FBLA; Hosp Aide; Spanish Clb; SADD; Chorus; Rep Stu Cncl; Elks Awd; Jr NHS; Elks Schlrshp $500 87; Slippery Rock U.

DEMORA, SAM; Lakeland HS; Jermyn, PA; (4); 36/148; Hon Roll; Penn ST U; Law.

DEMOSKY, LEE; Greater Latrobe Schl Dist; Latrobe, PA; (3); 70/367; CAP; Computer Clb; Debate Tm; German Clb; NFL; Radio Clb; Lion Awd; Hnr Rll 84-87; Pitt U; Cvl Engr.

DEMPKOSKY, CHRISTINE; Wyoming Valley West HS; Larksville, PA; (4); Church Yth Grp; Hosp Aide; Key Clb; Library Aide; Ski Clb; High Hon Roll; NHS; Kings Coll; Phy Asst.

DEMPSEY, ANN MARIE; John S Fine HS; Nanticoke, PA; (3); Science Clb; High Hon Roll; Hon Roll; Sci Secy.

DEMPSEY, PATRICIA; Archbishop Kennedy HS; Philadelphia, PA; (4); Church Yth Grp; Sec Cmnty Wkr; Sec Intnl Clb; Lit Mag; Rep Stu Cncl; Var L Fld Hcky; Mgr(s); Var Tennis; NHS; Hon Roll; West Chester.

DEMPSEY, SUZANNE; Bishop Conwell HS; Levittown, PA; (3); 48/277; Office Aide; SADD; Band; Cheerleading; Mgr(s); Score Keeper; Hon Roll; Amer Lgn Auxlry 85; Cert Of Merit Spnsh 87; Cert Hgh Avg Alg 87; La Salle Coll; Law.

DEMYUN, MARC; Dallas SR HS; Shavertown, PA; (3); Chess Clb; Church Yth Grp; Hosp Aide; ROTC; Yrbk Bus Mgr; VP Frsh Cls; VP Soph Cls; Var L Tennis; Trk; Wt Lftg; 2 Gld Mdls, 1 Slvr, 1 Brnz-Trk 85; 3rd Pl E Cst Rgnls 86; VP Soph Cls 86.

DENEEN, PAM; Southern Fulton HS; Warfordsburg, PA; (3); FBLA; FHA; Spanish Clb; Band; Chorus; Stu Cncl; Mgr(s); High Hon Roll; Spanish NHS; Air Force.

DENGEL, TED; Monaca HS; Monaca, PA; (3); 1/90; Scholastic Bowl; SADD; Pres VP Band; School Musical; Pres VP Stage Crew; Stu Cncl; L Tennis; High Hon Roll; NHS; Ntl Merit SF; Carnegie-Mellon; Chem Engrng.

DENGLER, CHARLES; Steelton-Highspire HS; High Spire, PA; (3); Art Clb; Chess Clb; Church Yth Grp; Computer Clb; Model UN; Band; Mrchg Band; Hon Roll; Prfct Atten Awd; Doctor.

DENGLER, LORI; Exeter Township SR HS; Reading, PA; (3); 29/241; Varsity Clb; Band; Stu Cncl; Fld Hcky; Mgr(s); High Hon Roll; Jr NHS; NHS; Concert Band; Mrchg Band; Exec Cmt 85-87; Bus.

DENGLER, MICHAEL E; Lancaster Catholic HS; Lancaster, PA; (4); 43/192; Chess Clb; Church Yth Grp; Pep Clb; Chorus; Stage Crew; Yrbk Stf; Co-Capt Var Cheerleading; Natl Latin Exam Cum Laude 85-86; Kutztwn U Of PA; Crmnl Just.

DENITTI, LAURA; Yough HS; Smithton, PA; (3); French Clb; Office Aide; Chorus; Concert Band; Mrchg Band; Yrbk Stf; Twrlr; Med.

DENKER, AMY; Springside Schl; Philadelphia, PA; (3); Math Tm; SADD; Acpl Chr; Chorus; Madrigals; Lit Mag; Pres Stu Cncl; Var Socr; High Hon Roll; Ntl Merit SF; Jfrsn Bk Awd U Of VA 86-87.

DENLINGER, EMILY; High Point Baptist Acad; Morgantown, PA; (3); Church Yth Grp; Drama Clb; Speech Tm; School Play; Yrbk Stf; Sec Jr Cls; Stat Bsktbl; Var Sftbl; Var Vllybl; High Hon Roll; ST & Natl Chmpnshp-Duo Acting 86; ST Chmpnshp-Drama Intrprttn 84; Bob Jones U; Drama.

DENLINGER, ERIC; Hempfield HS; Mountville, PA; (3); Boy Scts; Radio Clb; JV Wrstlng; Penn St; Arch.

DENNE, CARLA; Duquesne SR HS; Duquesne, PA; (3); 3/96; French Clb; Y-Teens; Band; Ed Nwsp Stf; VP Jr Cls; Stu Cncl; Cheerleading; High Hon Roll; NHS; Hugh O Brien Ldrshp Awd 86.

DENNE, COLLEEN; South Allegheny HS; Mckeesport, PA; (4); 38/167; Church Yth Grp; JA; Y-Teens; Pres Chorus; High Hon Roll; Hon Roll; GATE; U Pittsburgh.

DENNEY, MINDI; Connellsville SR HS; Connellsville, PA; (4); Office Aide; Acpl Chr; Chorus; School Musical; Dance Clb; VP Sr Cls; VP Stu Cncl; JV Capt Cheerleading; Hon Roll; NHS; Stu Gvt Awd 86-87; WV U; Cmnctns.

DENNEY, MONICA; Brownsville Area HS; Isabella, PA; (4); Drama Clb; Math Tm; Pres SADD; Flag Corp; Mrchg Band; Nwsp Stf; Sec Jr Cls; VP Sr Cls; Hon Roll; Jr NHS; Embry Riddle U; Aerntcl Engr.

DENNIS, BRIAN M; Delaware Valley HS; Milford, PA; (4); 9/140; Re Sr Cls; Bsktbl; Socr; Tennis; Elks Awd; Hon Roll; NHS; VA Tech; Com Sci.

DENNIS, DIETRICH C; Blue Mountain Acad; Philadelphia, PA; (3); 1 75; Camera Clb; Chorus; School Play; Sec Frsh Cls; Sec Stu Cncl; J Bsktbl; Im Ftbl; Im Score Keeper; Im Sftbl; Im Vllybl; Andrews U; Geor

DENNIS, JIMI; Lincoln HS; Ellwood City, PA; (3); Chorus; Churc Choir; School Musical; Crtv Wrtng Awd Excell 85-86; Geneva Coll; Ele Ed.

DENNIS, LORENA; Valley View JR SR HS; Peckville, PA; (4); Danc Clb; Spanish Clb; Chorus; School Musical; School Play; Stu Cnc Cheerleading; Coach Actv; Trk; Vllybl; Award Of Excl Cheerldng 85 & 8 West Chester U.

DENNISON, ROBERT; Hyndman Middle SR HS; Hyadman, PA; (3 Aud/Vis; Church Yth Grp; Library Aide; Pres VICA; Tennis; Hon Ro Allehany CC; Elec Engr.

DENNLER, DENA M; North Catholic HS; Pittsburgh, PA; (4); 26/24 Church Yth Grp; Spanish Clb; SADD; Yrbk Ed-Chief; Stu Cncl; Bskth Hon Roll; NHS; Miss PA Amer Co-Ed 86; Acad All-Amer 86; Natl Ldrsh & Svc Awd 86; St Vincent Coll; Psych.

DENNY, AMY; Greater Johnstown HS; Johnstown, PA; (4); 35/277; T Key Clb; Capt Flag Corp; Nwsp Rptr; Yrbk Stf; Rep Sr Cls; High Ho Roll; NHS; Rotary Awd; Dirctrs Awd Color Grd 87; Band Qun 87; Scru Clb 87; Penn ST; Bus Adm.

DENNY, TIMOTHY; Butler SR HS; Butler, PA; (3); AFS; Var Tennis; NHS; JA; Library Aide; Var Swmmng; High Hon Roll; Hon Ro Dedication Awd Tennis 85-86; Lttred Vrsty Tennis 85-87; Lttrd JR Na Hon Soc 85-86; Politics.

DENO, KIMBERLY; Frankford HS; Philadelphia, PA; (3); Art Clb; Dr Mjr(t); Yrbk Stf; Rep Frsh Cls; Rep Soph Cls; Rep Jr Cls; Sec Stu Cnc High Hon Roll; Hon Roll; Photo.

DENOME, FRANK; Lincoln HS; Ellwood City, PA; (3); Bowling; Ho Roll; Chmcl Engr.

DENSMORE, VALERIE; Curwensville Area HS; Curwensville, PA; (3 Pres Church Yth Grp; Ski Clb; Chorus; Concert Band; Drm Mjr(t); Mrch Band; School Musical; Stu Cncl; High Hon Roll; NHS.

DENT, JEFF; El Meyers HS; Wiles Barre, PA; (4); 15/140; Choru Concert Band; Jazz Band; Mrchg Band; Orch; School Musical; Yrbk Pht Swmmng; NHS; Ntl Merit Ltr.

DENT, KIMBERLY; Hempfield HS; Greensburg, PA; (2); Church Y Grp; Cmnty Wkr; Computer Clb; French Clb; Hosp Aide; Ski Clb; Ban Concert Band; Yrbk Stf; Bsktbl; CU Boulder; Phys Therapy.

DENT, SUZANNE; Butler SR HS; Butler, PA; (4); Church Yth Gr Cmnty Wkr; Exploring; FBLA; JA; Office Aide; Spanish Clb; Teache Aide; School Musical; Variety Show; PA ST U; Fin.

DENT, TRACY; C B West HS; Warrington, PA; (3); 189/477; Camp F Inc; Church Yth Grp; JV Bsktbl; Var Socr; JV Vllybl; Bus Mgmt.

DENTLER, STACY; Mechanicsburg HS; Mechanicsburg, PA; (2); 6 304; Pep Clb; Nwsp Stf; VP Frsh Cls; JV Bsktbl; Stat Ftbl; Hon Rol Comms.

DENTON, DIRK C; Sewickley Acad; Pittsburgh, PA; (4); Computer Cl English Clb; German Clb; SADD; Concert Band; Jazz Band; Scho Musical; DAR Awd; High Hon Roll; JP Sousa Awd; Cum Laude Soc 86-8 Tufts U, Boston; Music.

DENTZEL, EDWARD; Leechburg Area HS; Leechburg, PA; (2); Dram Clb; Math Tm; Sec Chorus; Church Choir; School Musical; School Pla Trs Soph Cls; Off Stu Cncl; Bsbl; Bsktbl.

DENUNZIO, PHILIP; Greensburg Salem SR HS; Greensburg, PA; (3 Spanish Clb; Nwsp Stf; Bsktbl; Hon Roll; PA ST; Engr.

DEOM, FRANK; Bishop Hafey HS; Drums, PA; (4); Spanish Clb; Bsb JV Bsktbl; Hon Roll; NHS; Spanish NHS; Amer Legion Awd 84; Penn S

DEOM, STEPHANIE; Bishop Hafey HS; Drums, PA; (3); Girl Scts; Ke Clb; Math Clb; Science Clb; Chorus; Orch; School Play; High Hon Ro Hon Roll; Prfct Atten Awd; Grl Sct Slvr Awd 86; Marian Mdl 85; Law.

DEORIO, MARIA; St Basil Acad; Philadelphia, PA; (3); 16/81; Churc Yth Grp; Computer Clb; Drama Clb; Pres Spanish Clb; NHS; Ntl Mer Ltr; Spanish NHS; Ntl Sci Awd 84-85; Pre-Law.

DEPAOLIS, DIANE; Mon Valley Catholic HS; Donora, PA; (3); 49/9 Church Yth Grp; Cmnty Wkr; Ski Clb; Stage Crew; French Hon So Psych.

DEPASTINO, BLAKE A; Mount Lebanon HS; Pittsburgh, PA; (4); 4 550; Nwsp Rptr; Ed Lit Mag; Trk; High Hon Roll; Rep Stu Cncl; Columb U; Engl.

DEPEW, CHRISTINE; Susquehanna Community HS; Lanesboro, PA (3); Sec Library Aide; Cheerleading; Powder Puff Ftbl; Hon Roll; Penn S U; Secondary Educ.

DEPP, JULIE ANNE; North Catholic HS; Pittsburgh, PA; (4); 87/24 Church Yth Grp; Hosp Aide; Ski Clb; Spanish Clb; JV Var Bsktbl; Ho Roll; Most Vlbl Plyr-Bsktbll 85; Natl Achvmnt Awd-Phys Ed 85; Hon Awd 86; Edinboro Univ; Comp Sci.

DEPPEN, SUSAN R; Reading SR HS; Reading, PA; (2); 89/851; Se Exploring; Chorus; Color Guard; Mrchg Band; Stage Crew; Hon Ro NHS; 1st Pl ST Poster Contest 87; Art.

DEPTO, TINA MARIE; Glendale JR SR HS; Coalport, PA; (3); 18/7 Church Yth Grp; Science Clb; Band; Chorus; Flag Corp; Mrchg Ban Yrbk Phtg; JV Var Bsktbl; Hon Roll; Voice Dem Awd; PA Schl Of Nrsn Nrsng.

DERBY, JODY; Bradford Area HS; Bradford, PA; (3); Church Yth Gr French Clb; Band; Flag Corp; Tennis; Hon Roll; Jr NHS; Jamestown C Mortuary Sci.

DERESKA, MARK; Reading SR HS; Reading, PA; (2); 75/819; Var Swmmng; Wt Lftg; High Hon Roll; Hon Roll; Gld Mdl, All Amer 400 Y Freestyle Relay PIAA ST Swmmng Chmpnshps 87.

DERICKSON, KEVIN; Central Dauphin HS; Harrisburg, PA; (3); Bo Scts; Band; Concert Band; Stu Cncl; JV Socr; Im Vllybl; Im Wt Lftg; Ho Roll; Eagle Sct Awd; USAF; Airline Pilot.

DERIENZO, ANGELA; Monongahela Valley Catholic HS; Charleroi, PA (3); Church Yth Grp; Dance Clb; Hosp Aide; Spanish Clb; Teachers Aid Band; Chorus; Church Choir; School Musical; Variety Show.

DERK, KATHLEEN; Penncrest HS; Media, PA; (3); 133/344; Churc Yth Grp; Dance Clb; Office Aide; Ski Clb; Thesps; Band; Concert Ban School Musical; School Play; Stage Crew; Lock Haven U; Phy Thrpy.

DERMO, RUDY; Nativity B V M HS; Pottsville, PA; (3); 24/8 Exploring; Ftbl; Wt Lftg; Hon Roll; Bio,Med.

DERNOSHEK, ERIC; Canon Mc Millan SR HS; Mc Murray, PA; (4 Art Clb; Yrbk Ed-Chief; Yrbk Stf; High Hon Roll; Hon Roll; NHS; Pre Acdmc Ftnss Awd; Penn ST U; Engrng.

DERO, KAREN MICHELLE; Garden Spot HS; Honey Brook, PA; (3); 8/196; FFA; Library Aide; Nwsp Rptr; Rep Stu Cncl; High Hon Roll; Hon Roll; Jr NHS; NHS; Ntl Merit Ltr; Ambssdr Of Grdn Spot To The HOBY Fndtns Cntrl PA Ldrshp Smnr 86; Law.

DEROSKY JR, FRANK W; West Allegheny SR HS; Imperial, PA; (4); 11/201; Computer Clb; Exploring; Office Aide; Im Bsbl; High Hon Roll; Hon Roll; NHS; Passvnt Acdmc Awd 87; Elzbth Stewrt Hnrs Schlrshp 87; Thiel Coll; Comp Sci.

DERR, BONNIE; Northern Lebanon HS; Myerstown, PA; (3); 45/300; Library Aide; Pep Clb; JV Sftbl; Hon Roll; Med.

DERR, GENNEL; Governor Mifflin HS; Mohnton, PA; (3); 27/333; Model UN; Spanish Clb; Y-Teens; Mrchg Band; Pep Band; Nwsp Phtg; High Hon Roll; Typng Awd 86; Bio.

DERR, KESLEE; Milton SR HS; White Deer, PA; (2); 4-H; Girl Scts; Latin Clb; Band; Chorus; Mrchg Band; School Play; Sftbl; 4-H Awd; Hon Roll; Ltn Hnr Awd 90% & Abv 86-87; Bloomsburg Coll; Nrsng.

DERR, STACY; Milton HS; Milton, PA; (2); Intnl Clb; Y-Teens; Color Guard; Mrchg Band; JV Sftbl; Cls Brd 87; Cptn Of Rfls 87; Nrsng.

DERR, STEPHANIE L; Boyertown JR HS East; Gilbertsville, PA; (1); 3/226; Church Yth Grp; Chorus; Orch; Stage Crew; Sec Stu Cncl; Fld Hcky; Lcrss; Swmmng; High Hon Roll; Phys Thrpy.

DERR, VICKI; Donegal HS; Maytown, PA; (3); 73/175; Varsity Clb; Drm Mjr(t); VP Frsh Cls; VP Soph Cls; VP Jr Cls; VP Sr Cls; Trs Stu Cncl; Var Bsktbl; Var Fld Hcky; Var Sftbl; Elizabethtown Coll; Accntng.

DERRY, SONYA ANN; Neshaminy HS; Langhorne, PA; (4); Church Yth Grp; Office Aide; Teachers Aide; Chorus; Church Choir; Color Guard; Mrchg Band; Symp Band; Bsktbl; Fld Hcky; Bloomsburg Coll; Spec Educ Tchr.

DERSTINE, ANDRIA L; Souderton Area HS; Souderton, PA; (4); 2/320; AFS; Church Yth Grp; Intnl Clb; Yrbk Stf; Off Stu Cncl; High Hon Roll; Jr NHS; NHS; Ntl Merit SF; Drama Clb; AM Lgn Awd; Schlrs Bnqt; Stu Of Mo; Intrntl Rltns.

DERSTINE, LAURIE; Souderton HS; Harleysville, PA; (3); Band; Color Guard; Concert Band; Drill Tm; Drm & Bgl; Jazz Band; Mrchg Band; Pep Band; Sftbl; High Hon Roll; Nrsg.

DESALVO, CHRISTINA; Northern Cambria HS; Nicktown, PA; (3); 1/152; French Clb; Library Aide; Chorus; High Hon Roll; Hon Roll; NHS.

DESALVO, ROBERT; Greensburg Central Catholic HS; Greensburg, PA; (3); Cmnty Wkr; Yrbk Stf; High Hon Roll; NHS; U Of Pittsburgh; Dentistry.

DESANTIS, CAROL; Archbishop Kennedy HS; Conshohocken, PA; (4); 34/171; Office Aide; Yrbk Rptr; Yrbk Stf; Vllybl; Hon Roll; Temple U; Mrktng.

DESCAVISH, BARBARA; Moshannon Valley JR-SR HS; Houtzdale, PA; (3); Church Yth Grp; Spanish Clb; Varsity Clb; Chorus; Sec Frsh Cls; Off Soph Cls; Stu Cncl; JV Var Cheerleading; JV Var Sftbl; Hon Roll; Lock Haven U; Tchr.

DESCIAK, EDWARD; Bishop Hoban HS; Mountaintop, PA; (3); 19/203; Church Yth Grp; Computer Clb; Latin Clb; Var Bsktbl; Var Crs Cntry; Var Trk; High Hon Roll; NHS; NEDT Awd; Rotary Awd; Rtry Intl Ldrs Cmp Hmntrm Awd 86; Pre-Med.

DESHPANDE, PARAG; Cathedral Prep Schl; Erie, PA; (3); 7/193; Ski Clb; JV Wrstlng; High Hon Roll; Bio.

DESKEVICH, ANDREW; Blacklick HS; Nanty Glo, PA; (3); 2/100; Aud/Vis; Library Aide; Yrbk Ed-Chief; High Hon Roll; Pres Schlr; VISTOS; Philsphy.

DESKEVICH, DUANE; Somerset HS; Somerset, PA; (4); 20/240; Am Leg Boys St; German Clb; JA; Letterman Clb; Math Clb; Mu Alpha Theta; Q&S; Ski Clb; Varsity Clb; Nwsp Ed-Chief; American U; Pol Sci.

DESKIEWICZ, CARYN; Bensalem HS; Andalusia, PA; (2); Color Guard; Psych.

DESSOYE, DENISE; Coughlin HS; Plains, PA; (4); DECA; Hon Roll; DECA Clb Gen Merch 3rd Pl 86 & 4th 87; Luzerne Cnty; Human Svc.

DETAR, COREY; Greensburg Salem HS; Greensburg, PA; (2); FBLA; Ski Clb; Spanish Clb; Im Bsktbl; JV Crs Cntry; Im Ftbl; Var Wrstlng; High Hon Roll; Hon Roll; Rep Stu Cncl; Pltcl Sci.

DETERS, TROY; Williamsburg JR/Sr HS; Williamsburg, PA; (3); Church Yth Grp; Cmnty Wkr; VICA; Im Bsbl; Im JV Bsktbl; Coach Actv; Im Ftbl; Im Wt Lftg; Im Hon Roll; Elec Engr.

DETISCH, TIMOTHY; Cathedral Prep; Erie, PA; (4); 28/216; Pres Church Yth Grp; Office Aide; Im Bsktbl; Im Vllybl; Hon Roll; Gannon U; Acctg.

DETOURNAY, CHANTAL; Coatesville Area SR HS; Coatesville, PA; (3); 41/500; Drama Clb; Spanish Clb; Chorus; School Musical; School Play; Var Swmmng; Hon Roll; NHS; Temple; Lawyer.

DETRANE, SALVATOVE; St John Neumann HS; Philadelphia, PA; (2); 3/351; Band; High Hon Roll; Schlrshp 87; U Of MI; Bus.

DETTER, MICHAEL; West York SR HS; York, PA; (2); 13/170; Art Clb; Varsity Clb; Stage Crew; Var Bsbl; JV Bsktbl; Var Ftbl; High Hon Roll; Hon Roll; NHS; Prfct Atten Awd; Comm Art.

DETTINGER, RONDA M; Cumberland Valley HS; Mechanicsburg, PA; (3); Pres Church Yth Grp; FBLA; Church Choir; Bowling; Hon Roll; Schlstc Art Awds 86-87; Gold Key Awd 86; Fisher JC; Trvl.

DETTLING, DAWN MARIE; Montour HS; Pittsburgh, PA; (3); Church Yth Grp; Trs Girl Scts; SADD; Concert Band; Mrchg Band; Symp Band; Tennis; High Hon Roll; NHS; Band; Girl Scouts Slvr Ldrshp Awd 86; Civil Engrng.

DETTMER, TAMMY; Northampton SR HS; Northampton, PA; (4); AFS; Church Yth Grp; Library Aide; Church Choir; High Hon Roll; Hon Roll; Lion Awd; NHS; Libr Aide Of Yr 87; 3rd Hghst Avg Alg I 84; Moore Elem Schl PTA Schlrshp 87; Messiah Coll; Occup Ther.

DETTORE, ERIKA; Rochester JR SR HS; Rochester, PA; (3); 15/120; Service Clb; Ski Clb; Nwsp Rptr; Trs Soph Cls; Trs Jr Cls; Cheerleading; Powder Puff Ftbl; High Hon Roll; Trs NHS; Prfct Atten Awd; Carnegie-Mellon U; Pre Law.

DETURK, LISA; Oley Valley HS; Temple, PA; (3); 49/152; Cmnty Wkr; Hosp Aide; JA; Key Clb; Teachers Aide; Band; Concert Band; Mrchg Band; JV Var Vllybl; Hon Roll; Elem Ed.

DETWEILER, CINDI; Pen Argyl Area HS; Pen Argyl, PA; (3); 17/140; Church Yth Grp; Leo Clb; VICA; Band; Church Choir; Drm & Bgl; Flag Corp; Mrchg Band; Rep Frsh Cls; Rep Soph Cls; Proffsnl Dev Cert VICA 87; St Lukes Nrsng Schl; Pedtrcn.

DETWEILER, DANA; Bedford HS; Bedford, PA; (4); 56/160; Letterman Clb; Band; Concert Band; Jazz Band; Pep Band; JV Var Vllybl; Hon Roll; Bowling; JR Miss Cont 2nd Rnr Up 86-87; Cnty Band Dstrct Band 85, 86, 87; US Music Ambsdrs HI Tour 86; WV U; Dntl Hygne.

DETWEILER, DAVID; Palisades HS; Kintnersville, PA; (3); Art Clb; Camera Clb; Pep Band; Ski Clb; Nwsp Phtg; Yrbk Phtg; Crs Cntry; Trk; Wt Lftg; Hon Roll; Syracuse U; Cmmnctns.

DETWILER, AMEE; Northern Bedford County HS; Woodbury, PA; (4); Sec FBLA; FTA; SADD; Chorus; School Musical; Yrbk Stf; High Hon Roll; NHS; Pres Acdmc Fit Awd 87; Bus Ed Awd 87; Attoona Schl Of Commerce; Acctg.

DETWILER, JAMES; Beaver Area HS; Beaver, PA; (3); Band; Chorus; Orch; School Musical; VP Soph Cls; VP Jr Cls; VP Sr Cls; Dnfth Awd; NHS; Church Yth Grp; Hugh O Brien Yth Ldrshp Awd.

DETWILER, SHEILA; South Park HS; Library, PA; (3); Church Yth Grp; Office Aide; Pep Clb; Y-Teens; JV Capt Cheerleading; Var Hon Roll; Bus Acctng.

DEUTSCH, PAMELA; Seneca Valley SR HS; Mars, PA; (4); 131/347; JA; ROTC; Band; Mrchg Band; Nwsp Stf; Lit Mag; Var L Sftbl; Hon Roll; Schltc Awd 87; Crnbrry Twnshp Miss Congeniality 86; U Of Pittsburgh; Bus Mgnt.

DEVANZO, KAREN; Bishop Hafey HS; Hazleton, PA; (4); 23/129; Church Yth Grp; Spanish Clb; Y-Teens; Chorus; Church Choir; Orch; School Play; Hon Roll; Jr NHS; NHS; Outstndng Svc Cmmnty & Schl, Gen Excllnce Choral Music, 3rd Kiwanis 87; Geisinger Medcl Ctr; Nrsng.

DEVENNEY, PRESTON; Avella JR-SR HS; Washington, PA; (4); Boy Scts; Cmnty Wkr; Pres SADD; Pres Band; Nwsp Ed-Chief; Yrbk Bus Mgr; VP Jr Cls; Pres Sr Cls; Pres Stu Cncl; Pttsbrgh Prss WA Edtn Top 10 SR 87; West Liberty ST Coll; Acctng.

DEVER, DAVID; Cathedral Prep Schl; Erie, PA; (4); 30/214; JCL; Latin Clb; Church Choir; School Musical; Yrbk Ed-Chief; Yrbk Stf; Im Vllybl; Hon Roll; Ntl Merit Ltr; Penn ST U; Engrng.

DEVER, MARY ANN; Nazareth Acad; Philadelphia, PA; (4); Church Yth Grp; Cmnty Wkr; German Clb; Variety Show; Lit Mag; Prfct Atten Awd; Phila Coll Textls & Sci Schlrshp 87-88; Phila Coll Textls & Sci; Engrng.

DEVINE, AILEEN; Cardinal O Hara HS; Drexel Hill, PA; (4); 40/780; Art Clb; Church Yth Grp; Cmnty Wkr; Drama Clb; 4-H; French Clb; Latin Clb; School Play; Nwsp Stf; Bsktbl; Spiritual Ldr For CYO 83-85; Acad Schlrshp To Immaculata Coll 87; Immaculata Coll; Business.

DEVINE, KRISTAN; Upper Moreland HS; Hatboro, PA; (3); 30/280; Exploring; French Clb; Hosp Aide; SADD; Color Guard; Capt Mrchg Band; School Musical; Gov Hon Prg Awd; High Hon Roll; NHS; Nrsng.

DEVINE, MICHELLE; Lower Dauphin SR HS; Hershey, PA; (3); 79/276; Chorus; Mrchg Band; Hon Roll; Hershey Figure Skating Clb 84-87; Indoor Drumline 87; Indoor Guard 85 & 86.

DEVINE, THOMAS E; Nativity BVM HS; Port Carbon, PA; (2); 1/79; Chess Clb; Computer Clb; Science Clb; Var Bsbl; Var JV Bsktbl; High Hon Roll; Schl Sci Fair-1st Pl-Comp Sci 87; Jnr Acad Sci-2nd Pl-Comp Sci 87; Cptl Area Sci Fair-2nd-Comp Sci 87; Comp.

DEVINE, TOM; Nativity B V M HS; Port Carlon, PA; (2); 1/77; Chess Clb; Computer Clb; Math Clb; Math Tm; JV Bsbl; Stat Bsktbl; Stat Ftbl; Stat Vllybl; High Hon Roll; St Sci Fair 2nd Pl 86; PA JR Acad Sci 2nd Pl 86; Hghst Achvt Algbra & Geomtry 87; Comp Sci.

DEVINNEY, BRIAN; Seneca Valley HS; Mars, PA; (3); Trs Church Yth Grp; Ski Clb; Varsity Clb; Band; Im Ftbl; Var Golf; Var L Swmmng; Hon Roll; NHS; Engrng.

DEVLIN, DENNIS; Jules E Mastbaum HS; Philadelphia, PA; (4); JV Var Bsbl; Var Capt Ftbl; Engrng.

DEVLIN, HOLLY; Phoenixville Area HS; Phoenixville, PA; (2); 30/212; Spanish Clb; Nwsp Stf; Yrbk Stf; Rep Soph Cls; VP Cheerleading; VP Lcrss; Hon Roll; Jr NHS; Prfct Atten Awd; Pres Schlr; Law.

DEVLIN, JANE; Bishop Mc Devitt HS; Jenkintown, PA; (3); 196/349; Latin Clb; Powder Puff Ftbl; Sftbl; Hon Roll; Law.

DEVLIN, MICHAEL; Cardinal O Hara HS; Havertown, PA; (4); 251/771; Computer Clb; Bsbl; Bsktbl; Tennis; Hon Roll; PA ST U; Crimnl Justc.

DEVONSHIRE, VALERIE; Philadelphia HS For Girls; Philadelphia, PA; (1); Hosp Aide; Teachers Aide.

DEVORE, GARY; Rochester Area Schls; Rochester, PA; (3); French Clb; JA; Ski Clb; Spanish Clb; Nwsp Rptr; Nwsp Stf; High Hon Roll; NHS; Kent ST U Summer Acad Young Schlrs & Geneva Golden Tornado Invitational 4th Pl 87; Archeologist.

DEWALD, CINDY; Danville Area SR HS; Danville, PA; (3); French Clb; FFA; JV Mgr(s); Hon Roll; Grnhnd FFA 87; Schlrshp Awd Abv 90% FFA 87; Floricltr.

DEWALD, DAWN; Schuykill Haven Area HS; Auburn, PA; (3); 8/82; Trs Church Yth Grp; SADD; Concert Band; Drm Mjr(t); Mrchg Band; Capt Var Bsktbl; Capt Var Sftbl; Hon Roll; NHS; JR Hnr Guard 87; Med Sectry.

DEWALD, JOHN; Milton SR HS; Lewisburg, PA; (3); Computer Clb; Band; Concert Band; Drm Mjr(t); Mrchg Band; JV Trk; Hon Roll; NHS; Ntl Merit Ltr; Bucknell U; Engr.

DEWEESE, DANA; Kennedy Christian HS; Jamestown, PA; (2); 11/96; French Clb; Band; Concert Band; Jazz Band; Mrchg Band; High Hon Roll; Hon Roll; NEDT Awd; Penn ST U; Jrnlsm.

DEWEY, MARY LYNN; Chichester SR HS; Linwood, PA; (3); 33/293; Teachers Aide; JV Sftbl; Mgr Trk; Hon Roll; Jr NHS; Delo Grls Sftbl All-Str; Bus.

DEWIT, RICHARD; Moon SR HS; Coraopolis, PA; (3); Band; Rep Jr Cls; JV Bsbl; Hon Roll; Prfct Atten Awd; Mardi Gras King, Prom King 87; Arch.

DEWITT, ANDREW; Tunkhannock Area HS; Tunkhannock, PA; (3); JA; Spanish Clb; Accntng.

DEWITT, CHRISTINE; Upper Darby HS; Clifton Hts, PA; (3); Office Aide; Teachers Aide; Flag Corp; Lit Mag; Mgr Bsbl; Mgr Bsktbl; Temple U; Art.

DEWITT, KEVIN; Gov Mifflin HS; Shillington, PA; (3); 15/331; Boys Clb Am; CAP; Debate Tm; Key Clb; Model UN; Var Crs Cntry; Var Trk; NHS; Aerospace.

DEWITT, MIKE; Seneca Valley HS; Zelienople, PA; (2); ROTC; VP Ski Clb; Rep Frsh Cls; Rep Soph Cls; Rep Stu Cncl; Var L Ftbl; Var L Trk; Var Wt Lftg; Hon Roll; Prfct Atten Awd; Air Force Acad; Aviatn.

DEX, DANIEL D; Emmaus HS; Allentown, PA; (4); 4/475; Key Clb; Model UN; Chorus; School Musical; Stu Cncl; Var L Crs Cntry; Var Tennis; Pres NHS; Ntl Merit SF; Safe-Rides-VP; Intl Law.

DEY, LYNNE; Brandywine Heights HS; Fleetwood, PA; (4); 14/125; Chorus; Flag Corp; Mrchg Band; Ed Yrbk Stf; Golf; Hon Roll; NHS; Pres Acad Ftns Awd, Quill & Scroll Awd 86-87; Kutztown U; Cmmncrl Art.

DEYARMIN, HELEN M; United HS; Homer City, PA; (4); 8/155; Camera Clb; Mu Alpha Theta; Chorus; School Musical; Nwsp Bus Mgr; Lit Mag; Mgr(s); Powder Puff Ftbl; Stat Trk; NHS; Natl Eng Merit Awd 85; US Army Reverves; IUP.

DEZII, RANDOLPH; St John Neumann HS; Philadelphia, PA; (4); 90/384; Exploring; Rep Frsh Cls; Rep Sr Cls; Hon Roll; Outstndg Achvt Stud Cncl 87; Oustndg Achvt Drftg 87; Oustndg Achvt Acadcs 87; Temple U; Dnstry.

DEZZI JR, JOSEPH; Springfield HS; Springfield, PA; (4); 3/255; Art Clb; Pres Exploring; Cmnty Wkr; Nwsp Stf; Yrbk Stf; Lit Mag; Full Tution Schlrshp To Parsons Schl Of Design NY 87; William C Hollibaugh Art Awd 87; Parsons Schl Of Dsgn; Fine Art.

DHAYER, JANET L; Trinity HS; Washington, PA; (3); 72/402; Art Clb; Church Yth Grp; Cmnty Wkr; Drama Clb; 4-H; Ski Clb; Spanish Clb; Band; Church Choir; Concert Band; Physcian.

DHERIT, GREGORY; Northeastern HS; Manchester, PA; (4); Boy Scts; Computer Clb; Exploring; Band; Mrchg Band; Var Trk; Var L Wrstlng; God Cntry Awd; Hon Roll; Pres Clssrm 87; Egl Sct Brnz Plm 85; Yrk Coll PA; Scndry Ed.

DI BACCO, GARY; Avella HS; Avella, PA; (3); Chess Clb; French Clb; Letterman Clb; SADD; Pres Frsh Cls; Sec Soph Cls; Pres Jr Cls; L Bsktbl; L Ftbl; Var Wt Lftg; Phrmcy.

DI BARTOLA, DENISE; Bishop Mc Cort HS; Johnstown, PA; (3); Hosp Aide; JA; Latin Clb; Mu Alpha Theta; Pep Clb; Ski Clb; School Musical; Yrbk Rptr; Yrbk Stf; JV Cheerleading; Penn ST-UNIVERSITY Park; Bio.

DI BERNARDO, JEROME; Penn-Trafford HS; Irwin, PA; (3); Church Yth Grp; FCA; Ski Clb; Spanish Clb; Im Bsktbl; JV Var Ftbl; Mgr(s).

DI BLASI, CLAUDIA R; Academy Of Notre Dame De Namur; Upper Darby, PA; (3); 1/80; Church Yth Grp; Chorus; School Play; Yrbk Stf; Mgr(s); Score Keeper; Trk; High Hon Roll; Hon Roll; Ntl Merit Ltr; Diocesian Schlr 87; Dplm Frm Cowanova Studio 86; Engr.

DI BLASI, MARIA GRAZIA; Hazleton HS; Hazelton, PA; (4); 97/398; Civic Clb; Drama Clb; French Clb; FBLA; Swmmng; Tennis; Hon Roll; Lion Awd; Vrsty Ltrmn 83-86; Penn ST Univ; Phy Thrpy.

DI BONA, CATHERINE; Bensalem SR HS; Bensalem, PA; (3); Church Yth Grp; Drama Clb; ROTC; Spanish Clb; Orch; School Musical; Var JV Swmmng; Wt Lftg; Cit Awd; Hon Roll; Temple U; Psych.

DI BUONO, EMILY; Lawrence County Area Vo-Tech; Ellwood City, PA; (3); Drama Clb; FBLA; Hosp Aide; Spanish Clb; Y-Teens; Chorus; Nwsp Rptr; Rep Soph Cls; Im Bsbl; Im Powder Puff Ftbl; Wilma Boyd Bus Schl; Exec Secy.

DI CAMILLO, LINDA; S Allegheny JR-SR HS; Port Vue, PA; (4); 5/174; VP Spanish Clb; Yrbk Stf; VP Soph Cls; Sec Sr Cls; Capt Cheerleading; Twrlr; DAR Awd; High Hon Roll; NHS; US Bus Ed Awd 86; Penn ST U; Bus.

DI CAMILLO, LISA; S Allegheny JR SR HS; Port Vue, PA; (1); 6/170; Sec Spanish Clb; Drill Tm; Yrbk Stf; Pres Stu Cncl; JV Cheerleading; Capt Twrlr; High Hon Roll; US Busns Educ Awd 86; U Of Pittsburgh.

DI CARLANTONIO, MARIA; Gwynedd Mercy Acad; Sellersville, PA; (2); 2/86; Yrbk Stf; JV Sftbl; Im Vllybl; High Hon Roll; Amer Classcl Leag, Natl JR Classcl Leag Cert Hnrbl Merit Maxima Cum Laude, Natl Latin I Exam 85-86; Orthopdcs.

DI CELLO, MARK; Valley SR HS; New Kensington, PA; (3); 19/225; Chess Clb; Science Clb; Spanish Clb; Var JV Bsbl; Hon Roll; NHS.

DI CENSO, DARREN; Ringgold HS; Finleyville, PA; (3); 90/351; Church Yth Grp; Cmnty Wkr; Math Clb; Science Clb; Wt Lftg; Hon Roll; Prfct Atten Awd; Acctng.

DI CIANNA, ERIC; Brownsville HS; Republic, PA; (3); Drama Clb; VP Ski Clb; SADD; Nwsp Stf; Pres Jr Cls; Stu Cncl; Bowling; Hon Roll; Rotary Awd; Engr.

DI CICCO, AIMEE; Cornell HS; Coraopolis, PA; (3); 3/68; Church Yth Grp; Dance Clb; Key Clb; Science Clb; Spanish Clb; Pres Jr Cls; Capt Pom Pon; High Hon Roll; NHS; Publ Svc Anncmnt Scrpt Wrtg Contst Wnnr 87; Biochem.

DI CICCO, JENNIFER; Northern Chester County Tech HS; Berwyn, PA; (3); 8/124; Hon Roll; NHS; W Chester U; Math.

DI CICCO, MICHELLE; Our Lady Of HS; Aliquippa, PA; (3); Hosp Aide; Yrbk Stf; Sec Soph Cls; Rep Stu Cncl; L Sftbl; Vllybl; Hon Roll; NHS; Outstndng Achvt Amer Lit Jr Eng 87; Bus Admin.

DI CICCO, STEPHEN; North Catholic HS; Pittsburgh, PA; (3); 11/289; Church Yth Grp; FCA; VP German Clb; Ski Clb; Rep Stu Cncl; Var Capt Bsktbl; Crs Cntry; Stat Score Keeper; Hon Roll; NHS; Sprt & Trdtn Awd 86-87.

DI CLEMENTE, DIANE; Hershey HS; Hershey, PA; (3); 42/225; Pep Clb; Ski Clb; Nwsp Sprt Ed; Yrbk Sprt Ed; Var Swmmng; Var L Tennis; High Hon Roll; Hon Roll; Psych.

DI COLA, ANDREA; Neshannock HS; New Castle, PA; (3); Camera Clb; Church Yth Grp; FBLA; Library Aide; Ski Clb; Im Bsktbl; Twrlr; Svc Awd 84-85; Attrny.

DI DONATO, DAWN; Henderson HS; Downingtown, PA; (4); 32/348; Girl Scts; Hosp Aide; JA; Math Tm; Stage Crew; French Hon Soc; God Cntry Awd; Hon Roll; NHS; Opt Clb Awd; Cls 1982 Scholar 87; Lebanon Vly Coll; Actuarial Sci.

DI FEBO, DAVID; Cardinal O Hara HS; Glen Riddle, PA; (3); 40/710; Cmnty Wkr; Hon Roll; Recgntn PSAT Natl Merit Prgm 87; Engl.

DI FILIPPO, DEBORAH; Spring-Ford HS; Pottstown, PA; (3); 154/256; Cmnty Wkr; Pep Clb; Spanish Clb; Church Choir; Yrbk Stf; Stu Cncl; Bsktbl; Cheerleading; Lcrss; Philadelphia Coll; Phrmcst.

DI FLORIO, PETERINA; Jeannette SR HS; Jeannette, PA; (2); Church Yth Grp; French Clb; Hosp Aide; Ski Clb; Church Choir; JV Sftbl; Var Tennis; Hon Roll; MVP-TNNS Tm 87.

DI FRANCESCO, STEFAN; North Star HS; Boswell, PA; (3); Church Yth Grp; FCA; Chorus; Hon Roll; Sci Awd 85; RIT; Elec Engr.

DI IENNO, LISA MARIE; Sacred Heart Acad; Drexel Hill, PA; (4); School Play; Ed Nwsp Stf; Ed Yrbk Stf; Rep Stu Cncl; Var Bsktbl; Var Lcrss; High Hon Roll; NHS; Natl Merit Sci Awd Bio-Chem 85-86; Ursinus Coll; Cmmnctns.

DI LORENZO, JEFFREY R; Harry S Truman HS; Levittown, PA; (3); 3/599; Var Tennis; Hon Roll; NHS; Penn ST; Engrng.

DI LORETO JR, GREGORY T; Cathedral Prep HS; Edinboro, PA; (3); Art Clb; Ski Clb; JV Crs Cntry; Diving; JV Trk.

DI LUIGI, PATRICIA; Highlands HS; Natrona Hts, PA; (4); 64/276; DECA; Band; Concert Band; Mrchg Band; DECA Dist Comp-4th Pl 87; Schlstc Achvt Awd 87; Bradford Schl; Secty.

DI MAIO, MICHELLE; Notre Dame HS; Bethlehem, PA; (3); Pep Clb; Yrbk Stf; Rep Jr Cls; Rep Stu Cncl; Var Capt Cheerleading; Var Capt Sftbl; Hon Roll; Trs NHS; Prfct Atten Awd; Spanish NHS; MVP Sftbl 86; Bio.

DI MALANTA, MARK; Northeast Catholic HS; Philadelphia, PA; (3); Aud/Vis; Chess Clb; Office Aide; Band; Concert Band; Drill Tm; Mrchg Band; Orch; Hon Roll; Jr NHS; U Of PA; Bio Sci.

DI MASCIO, MICHAEL; Trinity HS; Camp Hill, PA; (2); Ski Clb; JV Im Bsktbl; Var JV Ftbl; Wt Lftg; Hon Roll; West Point; Accntnt.

DI MATTEO, DARIA; Philadelphia H S For Girls; Philadelphia, PA; (3); 192/402; JA; Variety Show; Hon Roll; PA ST; Bus Mgmt.

DI MINICO, MINDY; Neshaminy SR HS; Penndel, PA; (3); 6/770; Church Yth Grp; Dance Clb; Intnl Clb; Var Bsktbl; JV Var Cheerleading; Powder Puff Ftbl; Gov Hon Prg Awd; High Hon Roll; NHS; Accptnc PA Govr Schl For Ag 87; Distngshd Hnrs 85-87; Vet Med.

DI NARDO, DANIEL; Center Area HS; Monaca, PA; (3); 62/182; Latin Clb; Letterman Clb; Pres Varsity Clb; Im Bsktbl; Im Bowling; Coach Actv; Var L Ftbl; Im Wt Lftg; Hon Roll; Engrng.

DI NARDO, MICHAEL ANTHONY; Hopewell HS; Aliquippa, PA; (4); 32/245; Church Yth Grp; Band; Chorus; Concert Band; Mrchg Band; School Musical; Bsbl; Ftbl; Wt Lftg; High Hon Roll; Pizza Hut Schlr Athl Awd 86; Hnrb Mntn Ftbl 86; Schlr Ath 86-87; Grove City Coll; Biochem.

DI NICOLA, M TRAVIS; Mc Dowell HS; Erie, PA; (4); 120/600; Dance Clb; Pres Drama Clb; Acpl Chr; Chorus; School Musical; School Play; Stu Cncl; Var Cheerleading; Rotary Awd; PA Gov Schl Arts Theatre 86; James M Conner Mem Schlrshp 87; Penn ST; Theatre.

DI PAOLO, JOHN P; Holy Ghost Prepratory Schl; Philadelphia, PA; (4); 3/81; Pres Aud/Vis; JV Socr; Hon Roll; NHS; Schlrshp Wnnr 87; U Of PA; Math.

DI PERNA, JIM; Central Catholic HS; Pittsburgh, PA; (3); 4/265; Spanish Clb; Rep Stu Cncl; Var Capt Socr; Var Swmmng; Var Trk; High Hon Roll; Hon Roll; VP NHS; Spanish NHS; Top Spnsh Stu Cls 85 & 86; Engrng.

DI PIANO, JENNIFER; Perkiomen Valley HS; Collegeville, PA; (4); 14/168; Am Leg Aux Girls St; Varsity Clb; Yrbk Ed-Chief; Diving; Hon Roll; NHS; Pres Schlr; Schwenksvlle Wmns Cvc Clb Hgh Hnrs Art 87; Unisys Awd Gen Excllnc 87; Schwenksvlle Itm Jrnlsm Awd 87; Kutztown U; Comms Dsgn.

DI PRINZIO, MARC; Downingtown SR HS; Downingtown, PA; (3); 6/648; Chess Clb; Church Yth Grp; Computer Clb; German Clb; Model UN; Concert Band; Jazz Band; Var Tennis; High Hon Roll; NHS; Engnrng Sci.

DI RENZO, MICHAEL T; Cardinal O Hara HS; Springfield, PA; (4); 69/792; Church Yth Grp; FBLA; JA; Spanish Clb; Yrbk Stf; Jr Cls; Sr Cls; Stu Cncl; Bsktbl; Golf; Rose-Holmon Inst Of Tech Schlrshp 87; DE Cnty Sci Fair 2nd Pl 85; Drexel U; Engrng.

DI RUONO, JOHN; Lincoln HS; Ellwood City, PA; (3); 83/162; Var Capt Socr; Var L Trk; Spnsh.

DI SALVIO, CATHERINE; Neshaminy HS; Trevose, PA; (3); 160/788; Color Guard; Stat Trk; Hon Roll; Lwyr.

DI SANTE, MARGARET; Freedom SR HS; Bethlehem, PA; (4); 132/446; VICA; Mgr(s); Mat Maids; Score Keeper; Sftbl; Grdn Phllp Bty Schl Schlrshp 87; Otsdng SR Csmtlgy Awd 87; Grdn Phillips Bty Schl; Csmtlgy.

DI SANTO, MARIA; Hopewell SR HS; Aliquippa, PA; (3); 53/255; Trs Church Yth Grp; Cmnty Wkr; Latin Clb; Library Aide; Chorus; School Musical; Im Socr; High Hon Roll; Hon Roll; NHS; Cert Regntn Sccr 87; Cert PA ST Enviro-Olympcs 87; Elem Ed.

DI SIPIO, ANTHONY; Benton Area HS; Benton, PA; (4); 2/49; Trs Key Clb; Scholastic Bowl; Var Bsbl; Var Capt Bsktbl; High Hon Roll; VP NHS; Math Ad 85; Century 21 Typg & Acctg Awd 85 & 86; JETS Test Awd 87; Penn ST U; Micro-Biol.

DI SOMMA, CHRISTIANA; Immaculate Conception HS; Washington, PA; (3); Art Clb; Drama Clb; School Play; Stage Crew; Acad Excllnc Frnch Hnr 85-87; Lang.

DI STASI, LISA; Serra Catholic HS; Glassport, PA; (3); Church Yth Grp; Pep Clb; Trs Spanish Clb; SADD; Band; Powder Puff Ftbl; Hon Roll; NHS; Sec Spanish NHS; Indvdl Mdl Awd Outstndng Stu Chem,Spnsh 3 86-87; Indvdl Mdl Awd Outstndng Stu Hlth 85-86; Physcl Thrpst.

DI VECCHIO, LORI; Sto-Rox SR HS; Mc Kees Rocks, PA; (4); 52/138; Letterman Clb; Nwsp Ed-Chief; Nwsp Sprt Ed; Trs Jr Cls; Rep Sr Cls; Mgr VP Bsktbl; Coach Actv; L Sftbl; Hon Roll; Prfct Atten Awd; Athl Schlrshp Lock Hvn U 87; Lock Haven; Psych.

DIA, DIYE E; West Phila Catholic HS For Girls; Philadelphia, PA; (4); Aud/Vis; Cmnty Wkr; French Clb; Chorus; Orch; Gym; Concert Band; School Musical; Bowling; Swmmng; Albright Coll Cert Outstndng HS Achvt Awd 86; West Phil Catholic Grls HS Exem Stu Awd 86-87; Howard U; Microbio.

DIAMOND, ERIC; Beaver Area JR SR HS; Beaver, PA; (3); Art Clb; Church Yth Grp; German Clb; Ski Clb; Nwsp Rptr; Nwsp Stf; Hon Roll; U Of MA; Psych.

DIAMOND, MELANIE; Burgettstown Area JR-SR HS; Midway, PA; (3); Church Yth Grp; Ski Clb; Drm Mjr(t); Sec Stu Cncl; Twrlr; Vllybl; Hon Roll; PA Free Entrprs Wk Schlrshp 87; Bus.

DIAMOND, TRACY; Abington SR HS; Jenkintown, PA; (4); Pres Key Clb; Mrchg Band; Rep Frsh Cls; Rep Soph Cls; Rep Jr Cls; Rep Sr Cls; Rep Stu Cncl; Std Cncl Svc Awd 87; Principals Citizenshp Svc Awd 87; Hofstra U; Psychlgy.

DIANA, MICHELE; Plum SR HS; Pittsburgh, PA; (2); AFS; Church Yth Grp; French Clb; JA; Library Aide; Pep Clb; SADD; Yrbk Stf; Hon Roll; NEDT Awd; 6 Wk Classroom Awd In Literature I 86-87; Math.

DIANA, REGINA; Scranton Tech HS; Scranton, PA; (3); Red Cross Aide; VICA; Band; Concert Band; Jazz Band; Mrchg Band; Pep Band; Rep Stu Cncl; Stat Twrlr; Hon Roll; 2nd Pl UICA Hair Stylng Comp 85; CMC Of X-Ray; Techncn.

DIANGELO, MONA; Upper Darby HS; Upr Darby, PA; (3); Office Aide; Sftbl; Paralegal.

DIANNA, ALEXANDRA; Northern Lehigh HS; Walnutport, PA; (3); 21/166; Ski Clb; SADD; Nwsp Ed-Chief; Nwsp Phtg; Nwsp Rptr; Stat Trk; High Hon Roll; Ntl Merit Ltr; Jazz Band; Yrbk Phtg; EAST; Pre Med.

DIASCRO, MATTHEW; Perkiomen Schl; Red Hill, PA; (4); 2/64; Thesps; Yrbk Ed-Chief; Pres Soph Cls; VP Jr Cls; Var Lcrss; Capt Var Socr; Bausch & Lomb Sci Awd; Pres NHS; Rotary Awd; Sal; Alvin A Krauss Chem Awd 87; Norman Rockwell Bate Memrl Awd 87; Hillegass Jrnlsm Awd 87; Wesleyan U; Chem Engrng.

DIAZ, JEANETTE; Philadelphia High School For Girls; Philadelphia, PA; (3); 159/403; Spanish Clb; Teachers Aide; Mrchg Band; Spanish NHS; Accntnt.

DIAZ, JOHN; Sun Valley HS; Aston, PA; (3); 120/270; JV Tennis; Penn State; Liberal Arts.

DIAZ, NELSON; Father Judge HS; Philadelphia, PA; (3); 26/402; Pres Church Yth Grp; Varsity Clb; Var Crs Cntry; Im Ftbl; Var Trk; High Hon Roll; Hon Roll; NHS; Scrtry Of Cmnty Srv Crps 86-87; Drexel; Arch.

DIAZ, PAMELA G; Owen J Roberts HS; Pottstown, PA; (2); 3/311; Service Clb; Band; Mrchg Band; Stage Crew; Yrbk Stf; Hon Roll; Engrng.

DIAZ, VILMARIE; Engineering And Science HS; Philadelphia, PA; (3); 45/150; Church Yth Grp; Drill Tm; Metorious Reprt Crd 87; Bus Adm.

DIAZ-SANDI, EDUARDO LICURGO; Reading SR HS; Wyomissing Hills, PA; (4); 24/563; Gym; High Hon Roll; Hon Joseph E Coleman Acad Excllnce Achvt Awd 86; USGF Region 7 Gym Champ 86; Natl Gymn Champ 85; Chem Engrng.

DIBELER, SONYA; Saint Maria Goretti HS; Philadelphia, PA; (4); 12/398; Math Tm; Capt L Bowling; Capt L Tennis; NHS; Ntl Merit Ltr; Prfct Atten Awd; Pres Schlr; Half Tuition Schlrshp Phila Coll Pharm & Sci; Hnrbl Mntn Rlgn; Phila Coll; Psych.

DIBERT, AUDRA; Penn Cambria HS; Gallitzin, PA; (4); 27/197; Camera Clb; Drama Clb; Sec French Clb; NFL; Speech Tm; Chorus; School Play; Yrbk Phtg; High Hon Roll; Hon Roll; IN U Of PA; Jrnlsm.

DIBERT, CORY; Chestnut Ridge HS; Imler, PA; (3); Church Yth Grp; Cmnty Wkr; Ski Clb; SADD; Rep Jr Cls; Var Bsbl; Mgr(s); High Hon Roll; Hon Roll; Arch Drftg.

DIBERT, CREGG; Chestnut Ridge SR HS; Imler, PA; (4); 31/129; Chess Clb; School Play; Bsktbl; Ftbl; Bus.

DIBERT, TERESSA; Chestnut Ridge HS; New Paris, PA; (3); 2/147; Church Yth Grp; JV Socr; High Hon Roll; Hon Roll; Prfct Atten Awd; Chem I Awd; Secndry Math Tchr.

DIBILIO, MIKE; Pen Argyl Area HS; Pen Argyl, PA; (3); 7/163; Yrbk Rptr; Pres Stu Cncl; Var L Bsktbl; JV Ftbl; High Hon Roll; Hon Roll; Jr NHS; NHS; Pre-Law.

DIBONAVENTURA, WILLIAM; West Catholic Boys HS; Philadelphia, PA; (3); 90/247; Villanova U; Psych.

DICARO, JULIA; Highlands SR HS; Tarentum, PA; (3); Exploring; Hosp Aide; Intnl Clb; Trs Soph Cls; Pres Jr Cls; Rep Trs Stu Cncl; Swmmng; Hon Roll; Jr NHS; NHS; Marine Bio.

DICE, TINA; Waynesboro Area SR HS; Chambersburg, PA; (4); Pres Church Yth Grp; Computer Clb; Sec Math Clb; Chorus; Church Choir; Stage Crew; Var L Fld Hcky; Var JV Mgr(s); Var JV Score Keeper; High Hon Roll; Penn ST U; Sec Educ.

DICELLO, CHRISTINA; Pottsville Area HS; Pottsville, PA; (4); Q&S; Ski Clb; Concert Band; Mrchg Band; Yrbk Sprt Ed; Yrbk Stf; High Hon Roll; Hon Roll; Drama Clb; Exploring; Order Sons Of Italy Prsdntl Schlrshp & Prsdntl Academic Fitness Awd 87; Muhlenberg Coll; Veterinary.

DICICCO, MARCO; Hopewell SR HS; Aliquippa, PA; (4); 11/245; Church Yth Grp; Radio Clb; Thesps; School Musical; Rep Sr Cls; JV Bowling; JETS Awd; Lion Awd; NHS; Pres Schlr; Air Force ROTC Schlrshp 87; U Of Southern CA; Aero Engrng.

DICICCO, MARGARET; St Basil Acad; Philadelphia, PA; (3); 20/82; French Clb; Service Clb; Orch; Hon Roll; Cert Mrt Frnch Natl Cntst 87; Bus Admin.

DICK, ADRIENNE; Council Rock HS; Holland, PA; (3); 56/908; Spanish Clb; Yrbk Ed-Chief; Rep Stu Cncl; Im Mgr Powder Puff Ftbl; JV Tennis; High Hon Roll; Hon Roll; NHS.

DICK, BRIAN; Commadore Perry HS; Hadley, PA; (4); Pres Radio Clb; Band; Concert Band; Jazz Band; Mrchg Band; Pep Band; Yrbk Phtg; Yrbk Stf; JV Bsktbl; NHS; Mercer Co Star Jazz Band 86; SR Of Week 86; Chem Engrng.

DICK, CHRISTOPHER; Danville Area HS; Riverside, PA; (1); 41/231; Band; Concert Band; Mrchg Band; French Hon Soc; High Hon Roll; Pres Acadmc Ftns Awd 87.

DICK, KEVIN; Penns Manor HS; Penn Run, PA; (3); Chess Clb; Var Trk; High Hon Roll; Hon Roll; Cherryhill Tnshp Vlntr Fire Dept 84-87; Indiana U Of PA; Crmnlgy.

DICK, MICHELE; Danville Area HS; Riverside, PA; (3); Drama Clb; French Clb; Hosp Aide; Band; Concert Band; Mrchg Band; French Hon Soc; High Hon Roll; NHS; 1st Pl Ribbon Sci Fair 85; Elem Educ.

DICKEN, KIMBERLEY R; Claysburg-Kimmel HS; Imler, PA; (3); 2/79; Sec FTA; Chorus; Church Choir; High Hon Roll; Hon Roll; NHS; Natl Bus Hnr Soc-Secy 87; Med Secy.

DICKENSHEETS, SCOTT K; Southwestern HS; Hanover, PA; (3); 85/233; Camera Clb; Computer Clb; Varsity Clb; Im Bowling; Im Golf; Var L Swmmng; Im Wt Lftg; Med.

DICKENSHEETS, TRICIA; S Western HS; Hanover, PA; (3); Hosp Aide; Key Clb; JV Capt Cheerleading; Hon Roll; Psych.

DICKERSON, MICHAEL; Exeter Township SR HS; Reading, PA; (4); 3/222; Varsity Clb; VP Band; Jazz Band; Stu Cncl; Socr; Hon Roll; Jr NHS; NHS; Exploring; 4-H; Natl Latin Hnr Society 87; Eagle Awd-Outstndng In Math 87; Lorane Elem Schl Schlrshp $500 87; Penn ST U; Animal Biosci.

DICKERT, LYN H; Franklin Area SR HS; Franklin, PA; (3); 1/217; VP Spanish Clb; Capt Drill Tm; Yrbk Ed-Chief; Rep Stu Cncl; Capt Pom Pon; High Hon Roll; NHS; Church Yth Grp; Yrbk Bus Mgr; Brd Schl Dir Awd 84-87; Spnsh Comp Awd 84-87; Stu Mnth 87; Pre-Med.

DICKERT, NICCI; Geibel HS; S Connellsville, PA; (3); 1/100; Trs Pep Clb; SADD; High Hon Roll; Ntl Merit Ltr; Spanish NHS; St Vincent Coll; Accntng.

DICKEY, DINA; Beaver Valley Christian Acad; S Hts, PA; (3); 1/11; VP Church Yth Grp; Band; Chorus; School Musical; Nwsp Stf; Yrbk Stf; Var Bsktbl; Var Cheerleading; High Hon Roll; Ntl Merit SF.

DICKEY, JENNIFER; Butler Area SR HS; Butler, PA; (4); 240/755; Church Yth Grp; Girl Scts; Hosp Aide; Spanish Clb; Chorus; Church Choir; Clarion U PA; Elem Ed.

DICKEY, KEVIN; Ringold HS; New Eagle, PA; (1); Golf; Donora Dragons Soccer Team Won Western PA Yth Soccer Champshp 87; USAF Acad; Sci.

DICKHOFF, DAVID A; Kennedy Christian HS; New Castle, PA; (3); 14/19; Boy Scts; Trs Exploring; French Clb; High Hon Roll; Cheerleading.

DICKHOFF, ERIC; Kennedy Christian HS; New Castle, PA; (2); Boy Scts; Exploring; JA; JV Ftbl; Hon Roll; US Air Frc Acad; Pilot.

DICKINSON, MELISSA; Berks Christian Schl; Pottstown, PA; (3); Church Yth Grp; Drama Clb; Chorus; Church Choir; School Musical; School Play; Var JV Cheerleading; Var JV Trk; High Hon Roll; Hon Roll; Mst Spirtd Awd Chrldng 86-87; Lab Tech.

DICKINSON, ROBYN; Tunkhannock Area HS; Lake Winola, PA; (4); 15/280; Science Clb; Spanish Clb; Jazz Band; Rep Soph Cls; Rep Jr Cls; Rep Sr Cls; Mgr Var Fld Hcky; High Hon Roll; NHS; Ntl Merit Ltr; Natl Frat Stu Mscns Piano 84-87.

DICKINSON, TINA; Mohawk HS; New Galilee, PA; (3); Spanish Clb; Concert Band; Mrchg Band; Powder Puff Ftbl; Wt Lftg; High Hon Roll; Hon Roll; NHS; Pitt; Engrng.

DICKINSON, VIKI; Morrisville HS; Morrisville, PA; (3); 32/95; FNA; Hosp Aide; Red Cross Aide; Swmmng; Vllybl; High Hon Roll; Hon Roll; St Schlr; Val; Helene Field Nrsng Schl; Nrs.

DICKMAN, MEGAN; Seneca Valley HS; Mars, PA; (2); Art Clb; Yrbk Stf; Stat Ftbl; Hon Roll; Bio Med.

DICKS, DAWN; Trinity HS; Washington, PA; (3); Camera Clb; Nwsp Rptr; Vllybl; Penn ST; Chem.

DICKSON, MELISSA J; George Washington HS; Philadelphia, PA; (4) 22/750; Trs French Clb; Teachers Aide; Yrbk Stf; Var Capt Gym; French Hon Soc; High Hon Roll; L NHS; SADD; Hon Roll; Statler Fndtn Schlrshp 87-88; Pres Acdmc Fitness Awd & Frnch Clb Awd Excllnc Frnch 86-87; PA ST U; Hotel-Restaurant Mgt.

DICKSON, SHONA; Seneca Valley HS; Mars, PA; (4); Church Yth Grp; Ski Clb; Band; Trs Sr Cls; Sftbl; Med Careers Clb; Ecolgy Clb; Gannon U; Bio.

DICKSON, SUSAN; Conemaugh Township Area HS; Johnstown, PA; (4); 8/101; Drama Clb; French Clb; VP Spanish Clb; Ed Nwsp Ed-Chief; Ed Yrbk Phtg; Ed Lit Mag; L Bsktbl; L Vllybl; Lion Awd; Pres NHS; Exc In Frnch Awd 87; Pres Acad Ftns Awd 87; Cnmgh Twnshp Rtry Schlrshp & Srv & Schlstc Awds 87; IN U PA; Scndry Ed.

DICKSON, WILLIAM; Ambridge Ara HS; Freedom, PA; (2); Boy Scts; Spanish Clb; Band; Hon Roll; Law.

DICTON, DONNA; Wyoming Valley West HS; Forty Fort, PA; (2); Church Yth Grp; Cmnty Wkr; Key Clb; Sec Jr Cls; Rep Stu Cncl; Var Cheerleading; Var Sftbl; Cit Awd; High Hon Roll; Hon Roll; Princeton; Pre Med.

DIDA, JOHN; Chartiers Valley HS; Carnegie, PA; (3); VP Church Yth Grp; Culinary Inst Of NY; Chef.

DIEC, NGHI; Central HS; Philadelphia, PA; (2); Math Tm; Science Clb; Chorus; Orch; Var Capt Sftbl; JV Vllybl; Hon Roll; U Of PA; Acurl Sci.

DIECKS, DEBRA; Beaver Area JR-SR HS; Beaver, PA; (3); 64/214; Red Cross Aide; Sec Chorus; Powder Puff Ftbl; Hon Roll; Wrth Advsr-Assmbly 37-Intl Ordr Of Rnbw-Grls 87; Exec Sec.

DIEDERICH, MICHELLE; York Catholic HS; Jacobus, PA; (4); Drama Clb; Pres JA; Chorus; Nwsp Stf; Yrbk Stf; Crs Cntry; Trk; High Hon Roll; NHS; Pres Schlr; Law Day Essy Cntst 2nd Plc 85-86; Mck Trl Cntst 86-87; Bauder Fashion Coll; Fshn Dsgn.

DIEFENBACH, CHARITY; Villa Maria Acad; Erie, PA; (3); Science Clb; Ski Clb; Spanish Clb; SADD; Rep Frsh Cls; Rep Jr Cls; Rep Stu Cncl; Im Bsbl; Im Socr; Var Tennis; Sci.

DIEFENBACHER, ELIZABETH LOUISE; Great Valley HS; Malvern, PA; (4); Am Leg Aux Girls St; Church Yth Grp; Trs Service Clb; Sec Yrbk Stf; Pres Frsh Cls; Pres Jr Cls; Var Capt Fld Hcky; Var Capt Trk; Bausch & Lomb Sci Awd; SADD; U S Army Rsve Natl Schlr/Athltc Awd 87; U Of PA.

DIEFFENBACH, LISA; Tulpehocken HS; Bethel, PA; (2); 20/127; Drama Clb; Spanish Clb; Bsktbl; Hon Roll; Pre-Med.

DIEHL, CHERYL; Immaculate Conception HS; Washington, PA; (3); 1/38; Art Clb; Dance Clb; Math Tm; Yrbk Stf; Rep Frsh Cls; Rep Soph Cls; Rep Jr Cls; Rep Sr Cls; Vllybl; NHS; Phrmcy.

DIEHL, ERIC; Greater Latrobe SR HS; Latrobe, PA; (4); 86/405; Letterman Clb; Varsity Clb; Var L Bsbl; Var L Ftbl; Var L Wrstlng; High Hon Roll; Hon Roll; Rotary Awd; 1aaa 1st Team Catcher & PG-ALL East 1st Team Catcher 87; Shippensburg; Bus.

DIEHL, GREG; Dover Area HS; Dover, PA; (3); 127/320; Church Yth Grp; German Clb; Letterman Clb; Varsity Clb; L JV Bsbl; L JV Bsktbl; Var Ftbl; L Var Trk; Wt Lftg; Engrng.

DIEHL, JOANNE; Quakertown Communtiy HS; Quakertown, PA; (3); 103/310; Church Yth Grp; Dance Clb; SADD; Teachers Aide; Y-Teens; Chorus; Twrlr; Dncng Awds 85-86; Moravian; Behvrl Sci.

DIEHL, KATHY; Columbia Montour AVTS; Bloomsburg, PA; (3); Trs Soph Cls; High Hon Roll; Hon Roll.

DIEHL, LINETTE; Bedford HS; Bedford, PA; (3); 4-H; FBLA; Sec FFA; Hon Roll; Deg Greenhand FFA 84; Deg Chapter Farmer FFA 85; Outstndng Achvt Typing I,High Hnr Typing II 85-86.

DIEHL, LORI; Central Dauphin HS; Harrisburg, PA; (3); 28/397; Key Clb; Ski Clb; Band; Chorus; Concert Band; Mrchg Band; School Musical; Timer; Hon Roll; Jr NHS.

DIEHL, SHANNON; Bedford HS; Bedford, PA; (3); Chorus; School Musical; Hon Roll; Comp Pgmmr.

DIEHL, TRACI; Belle Vernon Area HS; Belle Vernon, PA; (3); Trs Church Yth Grp; Band; Concert Band; Mrchg Band; Pep Band; Nwsp Stf; Stat L Bsbl; JV Var Bsktbl; Stat L Vllybl; NHS; Bus Law.

DIEHM, BRANDON; Wissahicron HS; Norristown, PA; (4); 20/273; Math Clb; Variety Show; Pres Stu Cncl; Capt Socr; Capt Tennis; Var Wrstlng; Hon Roll; VP NHS; PA Free Entrpse Wk Schlrshp 85; Coll Of William & Mary.

DIEM, ANNETTE; Punxsutawney Area HS; Rochester Mills, PA; (3); Sec Trs Church Yth Grp; GAA; Band; Concert Band; Jazz Band; Mrchg Band; Pep Band; Hon Roll; IUP.

DIEM, DAWN; East Juniata HS; Mcalisterville, PA; (3); 7/119; Church Yth Grp; Sec FBLA; FHA; Chorus; Sec Frsh Cls; High Hon Roll; Hon Roll; NHS.

DIENER, JOHN; Elizabethtown Area HS; Elizabethtown, PA; (3); 9/250; Trs Church Yth Grp; Capt Math Tm; Ski Clb; L Var Golf; L Var Tennis; Bausch & Lomb Sci Awd; NHS; Ntl Merit Ltr; Exploring; Hugh O Brien Yth Fndtn Rep 86; Amer HS Math Exm Wnr 86 & 87; Amer Comp Sci Leag Al-Star 85-87; Engrng.

DIERINGER, NOELLE; Du Bois Area HS; Rockton, PA; (4); 59/273; Band; Church Choir; Orch; Hon Roll; 1st Pl Wnnr Of Du Bois Courier Exprss Chstms Essy 83-84; Clarion U Of PA Symp Orch 83-86; Canegie Mellon U; Music Perf.

DIERKES, LINDA; Upper Dublin HS; Ambler, PA; (3); 62/298; Intnl Clb; SADD; Chorus; Mrchg Band; Orch; School Musical; Im Vllybl; Yth Schlrs Pgm-Lebanon Vly Coll-Germn 87; Exch Stu To W Germany 87; St Chmpnshp Marchg Cardinals 86; Frgn Lang.

DIEROLF, BRIAN; Brandywine Heights HS; Bechtelsvle, PA; (4); 30/125; Var JV Bsbl; Var JV Bsktbl; PA ST U; Bus.

DIEROLF, TINA; Boyertown SR HS; Boyertown, PA; (3); FHA; Chorus; Color Guard; Sec Jr Cls; Cit Awd; Bandfrnt 84-87; Chld Dvlpmnt.

DIERS, ALICIA; Selins Grove HS; Selins Grove, PA; (3); Church Yth Grp; Cmnty Wkr; 4-H; SADD; Teachers Aide; Lit Mag; Library Aide; Tchrs Aide.

DIERTERLE, KEITH; Northeastern HS; Mt Wolf, PA; (3); Varsity Clb; Band; Jazz Band; School Musical; Chrmn Stu Cncl; Var L Crs Cntry; JV Golf; Var L Trk; Hon Roll; Biochem.

DIESEL, TRACY; Canon Mcmillan HS; Canonsburg, PA; (4); 14/35[illegible]; Cmnty Wkr; French Clb; SADD; Yrbk Sprt Ed; Yrbk Stf; High Hon Roll; Hon Roll; NHS; 2nd Pl Frnch Dcltn; U Of Pittsburgh; Psych.

DIETEL, SANDY; Bermudian Springs HS; East Berlin, PA; (3); Nwsp Phtg; Nwsp Rptr; Nwsp Stf; Cntrl PA Save The Anmls Wlkthn 85, 86 87; 2 Mile Rhbltn Hosp Walk 87; Csmtlgy.

DIETEMAN, DAVID; Cathedral Prep Schl; Erie, PA; (3); 8/193; Debate Tm; Model UN; NFL; Science Clb; Rep Frsh Cls; Rep Soph Cls; Sec Jr Cls; VP Sr Cls; Im Bsktbl; Im Vllybl; 1st Pl Reg & 2nd Pl St PA Jr Acad Of Sci 84-86; 20th Tm Catholic Natl Debate Trnmnt 86-87; Poli.

DIETER, BECKY; Hampton HS; Allison Park, PA; (3); 5/201; French Clb; GAA; Hosp Aide; Red Cross Aide; Rep Stu Cncl; Powder Puff Ftbl; Var L Sftbl; Var Capt Swmmng; Tennis; High Hon Roll; Swmmng MVP 85-87; Hmcmng Court 87; Prom Cmmttee 87.

DIETRICH, ANGELA; Lykens Christian Schl; Williamstown, PA; (3); Church Yth Grp; Quiz Bowl; Band; Chorus; Orch; Pep Band; School Musical; School Play; Yrbk Ed-Chief; Yrbk Stf; Pensacola Chrstn Coll; Accntng.

DIETRICH, CHRISTOPHER; Williams Valley HS; Wiconisco, PA; (4); Art Clb; Chess Clb; Chorus; Church Choir; Hon Roll; Prfct Atten Awd; Arch.

DIETRICH II, DAVID; Norwin HS; N Huntingdon, PA; (4); Church Yth Grp; Letterman Clb; Math Clb; Pep Clb; Ski Clb; SADD; Varsity Clb; L Swmmng; Hon Roll; PA ST U; Bus Admin.

DIETRICH, LAURIE; Tamaqua Area HS; Tamaqua, PA; (4); 3/186; Pep Clb; Spanish Clb; Mrchg Band; School Play; Nwsp Stf; Cheerleading; Pom Pon; High Hon Roll; Hon Roll; NHS; Boston U; Pre Med.

DIETRICH, LISA; Kutztown Area SR HS; Lenhartsville, PA; (4); Church Yth Grp; Band; Color Guard; Concert Band; Flag Corp; Mrchg Band; School Play; Variety Show; Trk; High Hon Roll; DE Vly Coll Hnrs Schlrshp 87; DE Vly Coll; Bio.

DIETRICH, MARCY; Hamburg Area JR- SR HS; Hamburg, PA; (3); German Clb; Pres Sec Latin Clb; Library Aide; Pres Soph Cls; VP Sec Stu Cncl; Capt Cheerleading; Stat Ftbl; Hon Roll; Travel.

DIETRICH, MIKE; Exeter Township HS; Reading, PA; (3); Exploring; Variety Show; Lit Mag; Hon Roll.

DIETRICH, PAMELA; Downingtown SR HS; Downingtown, PA; (3); 11/648; French Clb; VP Intnl Clb; Scholastic Bowl; Spanish Clb; SADD; Rep Stu Cncl; Score Keeper; High Hon Roll; NHS; NEDT Awd; Intl Stud.

DIETRICH, SHEILA; Bermudian Springs HS; York Springs, PA; (3); Church Yth Grp; FHA; Band; Concert Band; Mrchg Band; Nwsp Rptr; Capt Var Bsktbl; Var JV Sftbl; JV Vllybl; Cntrl PA Bus Schl; Acctng.

DIETRICH, TOM; Central Dauphin HS; Harrisburg, PA; (3); 25/370; Letterman Clb; Ski Clb; Varsity Clb; Rep Jr Cls; Var L Ftbl; Im Vllybl; Wt Lftg; High Hon Roll; Hon Roll; Jr NHS; Sci.

DIETTERICH, SUSAN; Pleasant Valley HS; Brodheadsville, PA; (2); 18/243; Drama Clb; Math Tm; Band; Chorus; Concert Band; Pep Band; School Play; Stage Crew; Lit Mag; Hon Roll; Lwyr.

DIETTERICK, JESSICA; Columbia-Montour AVTS HS; Berwick, PA; (3); 25/227; Church Yth Grp; Girl Scts; Chorus; Yrbk Stf; Var JV Cheerleading; Hon Roll; Jr NHS; Prfct Atten Awd; Hlth Occptns Stu Of Amer Prlmntrn 86-88; 1st Pl & 18th Pl Mdcl Splling In ST & Natl HOSA Cmpttn 87; Med.

DIETZ, EDWARD D; Conrad Weiser HS; Robesonia, PA; (2); Aud/Vis; Spanish Clb; Varsity Clb; Bowling; Crs Cntry; Ftbl; Trk; Hon Roll; Radlgst.

DIETZ, ERIN L; Northampton Area SR HS; Walnutport, PA; (2); 128/545; GAA; Art Clb; SADD; Teachers Aide; Rep Stu Cncl; Var L Bsktbl; Var L Sftbl; Hon Roll; Pres Acad Fit Awd 85-86; Phys Ed Tchr.

DIETZ, MARCY; South Western HS; Hanover, PA; (2); Church Yth Grp; Girl Scts; JV Capt Cheerleading; Var Mgr(s); JV Var Mat Maids; JV Var Score Keeper; Hon Roll; Sec Of Foreign Exchng Stu Clb 86-87; Air Force.

DIETZ, MELODY; Yough SR HS; Smithton, PA; (3); Church Yth Grp; Chorus; Church Choir; Color Guard; Flag Corp; Mrchg Band; School Musical; Prfct Atten Awd; Sawyer Bus Schl; Sec.

DIETZ, MICHELLE Y; York Vo-Tech; York, PA; (3); DECA; Lit Mag; Rep Stu Cncl; Var JV Cheerleading; French Hon Soc; Hon Roll; Bus Mgmt.

DIETZ I I, DAVID; Red Lion Area Sr HS; York, PA; (3); 64/342; Varsity Clb; Var Ftbl; Var Trk; Hon Roll.

DIFFENDERFER, CATHY; Jeannette HS; Jeannette, PA; (2); Dance Clb; French Clb; Ski Clb; Drm Mjr(t); Rep Frsh Cls; Rep Soph Cls; Tennis; Twrlr; Hon Roll.

DIFRANCESCO, CHRISTINA; Bishop Mccort HS; Johnstown, PA; (2); 10/180; Mu Alpha Theta; NFL; Pres Pep Clb; Trs VP Spanish Clb; Chorus; Trs Stu Cncl; Var Swmmng; High Hon Roll; NHS; Spanish NHS; Amer Leg Awd 87; Span Hnr Scty Awd Svc 87.

DIFRANCESCO, JUSTIN; North Star HS; Boswell, PA; (2); 10/150; FCA; Mu Alpha Theta; Hon Roll; Bus Mgmt.

DIFRANCESCO, STEFAN; North Star HS; Boswell, PA; (3); 5/150; Church Yth Grp; FCA; Chorus; Hon Roll; Sci Awd; US Air Force; Elec Engr.

DIGES, CAMILLE; West Greene HS; Waynesburg, PA; (2); 2/104; Church Yth Grp; FTA; Science Clb; Chorus; Yrbk Stf; High Hon Roll; Hon Roll; Rotary Awd; 1st Plc Rgnl Cmptn PA JR Acad Of Sci 87; 2nd Plc ST Cmptn PA JR Acad Of Sci 87; Boston U; Physcs.

DIGGAN, ERIC; Milton Area SR HS; Milton, PA; (3); 50/243; Varsity Clb; Var Bsktbl; Coach Actv; Var Ftbl; Powder Puff Ftbl; Wt Lftg; Pre-Law.

DIGGINS, JOSEPH P; Moon SR HS; Coraopolis, PA; (3); 80/306; Church Yth Grp; Exploring; JA; Key Clb; Rep Frsh Cls; Im Bsktbl; JV Socr; Hon Roll; Prfct Atten Awd; Yth Ldrshp Awd 86; Bus Admin.

DIGGINS, SHELLEY; Plum SR HS; New Kensington, PA; (4); AFS; FTA; Band; Mrchg Band; Orch; School Musical; DAR Awd; NHS; Pres Schlr; High Hon Roll; St Vincent Ldrshp Acdmc Schlrshps 87; St Vincent Coll; Bio.

DIGIACOMO, DAWN; Hempfield SR HS; Greensburg, PA; (2); Church Yth Grp; Girl Scts; Pep Clb; Ski Clb; Speech Tm; Band; Concert Band; Mrchg Band; Hon Roll; Med Sci.

DIGIACOMO, KIMBERLY; Danville SR HS; Danville, PA; (2); Church Yth Grp; 4-H; Band; Jazz Band; JV Bowling; High Hon Roll; Acad All Amercn 87; Dist Band 86.

DIGIORGIO, MARIA; Central HS; Philadelphia, PA; (2); Office Aide; Chorus; Church Choir; Rep Stu Cncl; High Hon Roll; Hon Roll; Med.

DIGIOVANNI, DEAN G; Norristown Area HS; Norristown, PA; (4); 46/568; DECA; English Clb; FBLA; Intnl Clb; Key Clb; Ski Clb; Nwsp Stf; Yrbk Stf; VP Jr Cls; VP Sr Cls; Finance.

DIGNEY, ROSEMARY; Perkiomen Preparatory School; Montclair, NJ; (4); 20/63; Church Yth Grp; Model UN; Ski Clb; Teachers Aide; School Play; JV Diving; JV Fld Hcky; Mgr(s); Im Socr; U Of NC; Psych.

DIGUILIO, EMIL; Montour HS; Mckees Rocks, PA; (3); Trs Frsh Cls; Rep Soph Cls; Rep Jr Cls; Rep Sr Cls; Rep Stu Cncl; Var Ftbl; Var L Trk; Slippery Rock U; Sports Med.

DIGWOOD, JEANETTE; Old Forge HS; Scranton, PA; (3); 3/105; Ski Clb; Var Sftbl; High Hon Roll; NHS; Dntl Hygn.

DILBERTO, MARY ANN; Hazleton HS; Hazleton, PA; (3); 120/450; Church Yth Grp; Drama Clb; FNA; Leo Clb; Ski Clb; Orch; Stat Crs Cntry; Stat Trk; French Hon Soc; Hon Roll; Schlstc All Amer 86-87; Pharm.

DILCHERD, ALICIA; William Allen HS; Allentown, PA; (2); Chorus; Color Guard; Swing Chorus; Powder Puff Ftbl; Hon Roll; Elec Engrng.

DILELLO, DEANN; Susquehanna Community HS; Lanesboro, PA; (4); SADD; Color Guard; Bsktbl; Cheerleading; Crs Cntry; Powder Puff Ftbl; Trk; Vllybl; PA ST; Early Childhood Educ.

DILG, CHERYL; Hatboro-Horsham HS; Horsham, PA; (3); Library Aide; Chorus; Color Guard; Mrchg Band; JV Mgr(s); JV Sftbl; Var Trk; Var Twrlr; Hon Roll; Prfct Atten Awd; Specl Achvt Awd-Clerical Work 86-7; Champ Of Learning Awd 85-6; FRA Natl Amercnsm Essay Cont 85-6; Bus.

DILISI, CHRISTINA; Lansdale Catholic HS; Lansdale, PA; (3); 48/223; SADD; Stage Crew; Crs Cntry; Trk; Hon Roll; Prfct Atten Awd; Phy Thrpy.

DILKS, JASON; Warren Area HS; Warren, PA; (3); Drama Clb; German Clb; Pep Clb; Spanish Clb; School Play; Stage Crew; Var Golf; Score Keeper; Tennis; Hon Roll; Cmmnctns.

DILKS, JENNIFER; Upper Merion Area HS; King Of Prussia, PA; (2); VP Frsh Cls; Pres Soph Cls; Pres Jr Cls; Var Cheerleading; Hon Roll; NHS; Church Yth Grp; SADD; HOBY, & King Prussia Rtry 4 Way Tst Wnnr Awd 87; Educ.

DILL, JULIE ANN; Peters Township HS; Erie, PA; (4); 35/245; Drill Tm; Nwsp Rptr; Yrbk Stf; Off Sr Cls; Off Stu Cncl; Cheerleading; Trk; High Hon Roll; Pres Schlr; Spanish NHS; PA ST U; Comm.

DILL, MICHELLE; United HS; Homer City, PA; (4); 36/155; Camera Clb; Church Yth Grp; Cmnty Wkr; Hosp Aide; Ski Clb; Rep Stu Cncl; L Trk; Hon Roll; Prfct Atten Awd; Congrssnl Yth Ldrshp Cncl 87; Penn ST; Pre Med.

DILL, TRACI; Fort Le Boeuf HS; Waterford, PA; (3); Chorus; School Musical; Sec Soph Cls; Rep Stu Cncl; Var Cheerleading; Var Score Keeper; Im Vllybl; High Hon Roll; Hon Roll; Church Yth Grp; Acad Achiev Awd 84-85; Med Lab Tech.

DILLALOGUE, JACKIE; Penn Cambria HS; Gallitzin, PA; (4); 29/200; Art Clb; Drama Clb; FBLA; Hon Roll; Jr NHS; NHS.

DILLARD, CAMELIA; St Paul Cathedral HS; Pittsburgh, PA; (3); Pres Church Yth Grp; Hosp Aide; Latin Clb; NAACP; Spanish Clb; Mrchg Band; Yrbk Stf; Sec Trs Stu Cncl; High Hon Roll; NHS; Natl Hstry Day Awd 3rd Pl 87; Latin I Awd Achvt 86; Engl Achvt Cert 86; U Of Pgh; Pdtrcs.

DILLARD, KELLY; Valley HS; New Kensington, PA; (2); Library Aide; Varsity Clb; JV Bsktbl; Mgr(s); Crmnlgst.

DILLIG, PAULA; Laurel Highlands SR HS; Hopwood, PA; (3); French Clb; Pep Clb; Ski Clb; Chorus; Yrbk Rptr; Sec Frsh Cls; Cit Awd; DAR Awd; Hon Roll.

DILLON, ERIKA; Linden Hall HS; Sacramento, CA; (3); Fld Hcky; Sftbl; Jr NHS; Engr.

DILLON, LAURA; Downingtown HS; Exton, PA; (2); 1/850; Church Yth Grp; Key Clb; Spanish Clb; Concert Band; Rep Stu Cncl; Var L Crs Cntry; Var L Swmmng; JV Trk; High Hon Roll; Rep Frsh Cls; PA Gov Schl Sci 87; Johns Hopkins U; Genetics.

DILLON, LAURA; Moshannon Valley HS; Houtzdale, PA; (3); Church Yth Grp; Ski Clb; Spanish Clb; SADD; Varsity Clb; Band; Drm Mjr(t); Orch; Stage Crew; Yrbk Stf; Pres Ftnss Awd 85-86; Psych.

DILLON, ROBIN; Plum SR HS; Verona, PA; (3); SADD; Varsity Clb; Yrbk Ed-Chief; Yrbk Phtg; Var L Swmmng; Var Tennis; Twrlr; High Hon Roll; NHS; NEDT Awd; Awd Rcgntn The Am Soc Of Engrs 87; Engineering.

DILLON, TINA MARIE; Philipsburg-Osceola Area HS; Philipsburg, PA; (4); 30/245; Church Yth Grp; Cmnty Wkr; Hosp Aide; Library Aide; Pep Clb; SADD; Band; Mrchg Band; Nwsp Stf; Yrbk Stf; Cntrl PA Schl/Nrsg; RN.

DILLOW, STEVE; Donegal HS; Mt Joy, PA; (3); 6/186; Church Yth Grp; Pres Band; Tennis; Wrstlng; Hon Roll; VP NHS; Rotary Awd; Acadmc All Amer Schlr 85; Lions Clb Ldrshp Conf 87; Lawyer.

DILMORE, JIM; Mc Keesport Area HS; Irwin, PA; (2); 6/440; Boy Scts; German Clb; Rep Stu Cncl; JV Ftbl; Cit Awd; DAR Awd; High Hon Roll; AFS; Church Yth Grp; NFL; Peer Grp Ldrshp Comm; Engnrng.

DILOSSI, JOE; St John Neumann HS; Philadelphia, PA; (3); 33/349; Church Yth Grp; Office Aide; High Hon Roll; Prfct Atten Awd; Elec Engr.

DILS, GLEN; Central Dauphin HS; Harrisburg, PA; (3); 3/369; Wrstlng; NHS; Legal.

DIMARINO, DAVID; Downingtown HS; Glenmoore, PA; (3); 24/648; German Clb; Band; Concert Band; Jazz Band; Mrchg Band; School Musical; Bowling; Trk; Musician Of Yr; Musician.

DIMATTIO, DAVID; Cathedral Prep; Erie, PA; (3); Church Yth Grp; Latin Clb; Hon Roll; Astrnmy.

DIMBOKOWITZ, STEVE; Perry Traditional Acad; Pittsburgh, PA; (3); 43/193; Ski Clb; Band; Hon Roll; Prfct Atten Awd; 1st Pl Dnc Cntst 85; US Navy; Bus.

DIMITRIOU, ELENI; Holy Name HS; Wyomissing, PA; (3); 17/119; Library Aide; Spanish Clb; Chorus; Church Choir; School Musical; Variety Show; Yrbk Stf; High Hon Roll; Hon Roll; NHS; Algrbr II Trg Awd 87; Immaculate Coll; Attrny.

DIMM, WILLIAM C; Springfield HS; Springfield, PA; (4); 1/247; Boy Scts; Church Yth Grp; Computer Clb; Pres Exploring; Capt Science Clb; Nwsp Rptr; Im Badmtn; Elks Awd; God Cntry Awd; NHS; Rensselaer Plytchnc Inst Math Sci Awd 86; 1st Pl St Josephs Cmptr Cmptn 87; Lehigh U; Mec Engrng.

DIMMICK, JACK; Mahanoy Area HS; Mahanoy City, PA; (4); 25/111; Camera Clb; Church Yth Grp; Civic Clb; Cmnty Wkr; Drama Clb; Letterman Clb; Scholastic Bowl; Ski Clb; SADD; Varsity Clb; All Cnty Tight End 86; Hnrb Mntn D-End 86; Kutztown U; Bus Adm.

DIMOFF, STEPHANIE; Mount Union Area HS; Mt Union, PA; (3); Art Clb; GAA; Spanish Clb; Sec Jr Cls; Sec Stu Cncl; Capt Bsktbl; Var Trk; Var Vllybl; NHS.

DIMUCCIO, JODI; New Castle SR HS; New Castle, PA; (4); 21/232; Exploring; Pres French Clb; Office Aide; SADD; Drill Tm; Nwsp Stf; Yrbk Stf; Stu Cncl; Hon Roll; Jr NHS; WV U; Phy Thrpy.

DINACCI, DINA; Downingtown SR HS; Glenmoore, PA; (3); 181/650; GAA; Ski Clb; SADD; Nwsp Stf; Yrbk Stf; JV Bsktbl; Mgr(s); Var Sftbl; High Hon Roll; Hon Roll; All Area Sftbl 87; All League 85-87.

DINAN, MELISSA JOAN; Gwynedd-Mercy Acad; Schwenksville, PA; (2); Office Aide; Chorus; School Musical; School Play; Variety Show.

DINARDO, JOHN; Bishop Guilfoyle HS; Altoona, PA; (3); 26/156; Church Yth Grp; Cmnty Wkr; Hosp Aide; Red Cross Aide; Science Clb; Off Jr Cls; Stu Cncl; Cit Awd; Hon Roll; Ntl Ldrshp Svc Awd US Achvt 87; Bio,Med.

DINDAK, SHARI; Mc Keesport HS; Mc Keesport, PA; (3); 2/410; Church Yth Grp; Hosp Aide; Office Aide; Drm & Bgl; Mrchg Band; Powder Puff Ftbl; Twrlr; High Hon Roll; NHS; Rotary Awd; Elem Ed.

DINGLE, KELLY; Fort Le Boeuf HS; Waterford, PA; (3); #11 In Class; Drama Clb; Pres 4-H; School Musical; VP Jr Cls; JV Sftbl; Var Trk; Stat Wrstlng; 4-H Awd; High Hon Roll; NHS; PA ST U; Ecnmcs.

DINGLE, SCOTT; Fort Le Boeuf HS; Mill Village, PA; (1); 7/209; Trs Church Yth Grp; Computer Clb; Band; Concert Band; Mrchg Band; School Play; Rep Stu Cncl; Bsbl; Bsktbl; Ftbl; Penn ST; Comp Sci.

DINH, MAI; Acad Of Notre Dame; Upper Darby, PA; (3); VP Debate Tm; VP Speech Tm; Chorus; Nwsp Rptr; Nwsp Stf; Lit Mag; Im Bsktbl; Computer Clb; U PA Schlr 87; George Washington U Smmr Schlr 87; PA Diocesan Schlar 87-88; Ntl Hist 2nd Pl 86; Bus Admn.

DINH, TUNG; Upper Darby HS; Upr Darby, PA; (3); High Hon Roll; Hon Roll; Prfct Atten Awd.

DININNO, DIANE; West Branch JR SR HS; Morrisdale, PA; (2); Spanish Clb; SADD; Stu Cncl; Gov Hon Prg Awd; High Hon Roll; Hon Roll; Prfct Atten Awd; Sal; Spanish NHS; Val; Bus.

DINNOCENTI, BRIAN; Spring-Ford HS; Royersford, PA; (4); 9/237; French Clb; JV Bsbl; Var L Ftbl; Var Tn; Im Vllybl; Var Wt Lftg; JV L Wrstlng; High Hon Roll; NHS; Pres Acdmc Ftns Awd 87; Hnr Awd 87; Wrtr Of Yr 86; PA ST; Engrng.

DINSMORE, DEBRA; Punxsutawney Area SR HS; Punxsutawney, PA; (4); 34/246; Church Yth Grp; French Clb; Speech Tm; Thesps; Acpl Chr; Chorus; Church Choir; School Musical; Variety Show; Hon Roll; Mry Ann Irvn Schlrshp 87; Jhn W Jnks Schlrshp 87; Wilson Coll; Vet Med.

DINSMORE, MATTHEW; Punxsutawney SR HS; Punxsutawney, PA; (3); Church Yth Grp; Cmnty Wkr; French Clb; Thesps; Stage Crew; Penn ST U.

DINUNZIO, ANDREA; Neshaminy HS; Langhorne, PA; (3); 1/790; Office Aide; Service Clb; Band; Chorus; Mrchg Band; School Musical; Variety Show; Var Crs Cntry; JV Var Gym; High Hon Roll; Math, Socl Stds, Engl Schlrshp Awds; Med.

DIODATO, GINA; York County Area Vo-Tech Schl; York, PA; (4); 91/358; Chess Clb; VICA; School Play; Hon Roll; Stu Mth 83-84; Co-Op Pgm 86-87.

DIOMEDO, ADAM; Notre Dame HS; Easton, PA; (4); VP NFL; Capt Scholastic Bowl; Teachers Aide; School Musical; Nwsp Stf; Yrbk Stf; Trs Stu Cncl; High Hon Roll; Pres Schlr; Art Awd 85-86; Exch Club Freedom Shrine Tst 2nd Pl 87; Kutztown U; Cmmnctn Desgn.

DIONNE, THERESA; Northampton SR HS; Walnutport, PA; (4); 3/450; Leo Clb; Chorus; Pres Frsh Cls; VP Soph Cls; VP Jr Cls; Trk; High Hon Roll; NHS; AFS; Ski Clb; Stu Mnth 86; Northampton Cnty 1st Rnnr Up JR Miss Scholar 86; Hghst Hlth Avg Awd; PA ST U; Child Psych.

DIORIO, RONALD; Shamokin Area HS; Shamokin, PA; (3); 3/223; Pres Science Clb; Pres Frsh Cls; Pres Soph Cls; Pres Jr Cls; Trs Stu Cncl; Var L Ftbl; Var L Trk; Var Wt Lftg; High Hon Roll; Ntl Merit Ltr; 3rd Pl PA ST Teenage Pwrlftng Meet 87; Harvard U; Pre Law.

DIPANGRAZIO, STEVE; Red Lion Area HS; Red Lion, PA; (3); 81/375; Am Leg Boys St; Nwsp Bus Mgr; Ftbl; Wrstlng.

DIPKO, BARBARA; Greater Johnstown HS; Johnstown, PA; (3); FNA; German Clb; Nwsp Rptr; Yrbk Stf; Sftbl; Vllybl; Hon Roll; NHS; Prfct Atten Awd; WV U; Psych.

DIPPERY, DEE; Penns Valley Area HS; Millheim, PA; (3); Church Yth Grp; Drama Clb; Pres Pep Clb; School Play; Nwsp Rptr; JV Bsktbl; Var Sftbl; Rotary Awd; Merit Awd Rotary Clb Cmmnty Svc; Platoon Ldr Awd Law Enfrcmnt Camp Cadet & Awd For Cmpltn 84-85; Air Force; Pre Law.

DIPPERY, DENISE; Centre County Christian Acad; Reedsville, PA; (3); Chorus; Church Choir; Var L Bsktbl; Im Mgr Coach Actv; Var L Socr; Var Trk; Church Yth Grp; Drama Clb; FHA; FTA; MVP Offns Sccr MVP Bsbl 3-1st Pl Ribbons Trck 85-87; 3 1st Pl Rbbns Trck 84-85; Phy Ed.

DIPPERY, JENNIFER; Middleburg HS; Middleburg, PA; (4); 4/114; Varsity Clb; Band; Concert Band; Jazz Band; Mrchg Band; Off Stu Cncl; Var L Bsktbl; Var L Fld Hcky; Var L Sftbl; Im Vllybl; Bsktbl MVP JV & Vrsty 85 & 87; 1st Tm All-Star Sftbl, Natl Schlr/Athlt Awd Army 87; 2nd Tm Hcky 86; Juniata Coll; Bio.

DIPPERY, JOY; Tyrone Area HS; Tyrone, PA; (3); 9/209; Sec Key Clb; Sec Science Clb; Mrchg Band; Yrbk Stf; Rep Soph Cls; Cheerleading; Swmmng; High Hon Roll; Jr NHS; NHS; Mini Triathln Trphy 87; Achvt Rprt Trphy Key Clb 87; Bio Asst Awd 87; PA ST U; Microbio.

DIPPOLD, SARA; Elk County Christian HS; St Marys, PA; (3); 30/72; Ski Clb; Yrbk Stf; Trs Frsh Cls; Bowling; Cheerleading; Trk; Vllybl; Hon Roll; Dietetics.

DIRENZO, STEPHEN; Kennedy Christian HS; Sharon, PA; (3); 9/97; Exploring; Latin Clb; Science Clb; Yrbk Stf; Var Trk; Im Vllybl; High Hon Roll; NHS; NEDT Awd; Cert Of Educ Devlpmnt Supr Prfrmnc Ntl Educ Devlpmnt Tsts 85; 2nd Pl PA JR Acad Of Sci 86; U Of PA; Med.

DIRICCO, JOHN; Central Catholic HS; Pittsburgh, PA; (3); 11/263; Church Yth Grp; Im Ftbl; High Hon Roll; Hon Roll; Spanish NHS.

DIRNBACH, ERIC; Central HS; Philadelphia, PA; (3); 28/540; Boy Scts; Yrbk Stf; Var Crs Cntry; Hon Roll; Ntl Merit SF; Engrng.

DISABATO, CHARLYN; Bishop Guilfoyle HS; Altoona, PA; (3); Bsktbl; Vllybl; Hon Roll.

DISCHER, CRISTI; St Huberts HS; Philadelphia, PA; (3); 221/460; Cmnty Wkr; Dance Clb; FBLA; Office Aide; Teachers Aide; Stage Crew; Nwsp Stf; Yrbk Stf; Cheerleading; Swmmng; Bus Mgmt.

DISHLER, STACEY; Lincoln HS; Ellwood City, PA; (3); 58/162; AFS; French Clb; Latin Clb; Y-Teens; Band; Mrchg Band; Powder Puff Ftbl; High Hon Roll; Hon Roll; Latin Awd 84-86; Frnch Awd 86-87; Band 84-86; Physcl Thrpst.

DISIDORE, MICHELLE MARIE; Pius X HS; Martins Crk, PA; (3); Church Yth Grp; Exploring; Pep Clb; Yrbk Stf; JV Sftbl; Biology.

DISNEY, SCOTT; East Pennsboro HS; Enola, PA; (3); French Clb; Varsity Clb; Band; Concert Band; Jazz Band; Mrchg Band; Pep Band; School Musical; JV Var Ftbl; Wt Lftg; Accntng.

DISSINGER, PAUL; Cedar Crest HS; Lebanon, PA; (2); 35/357; Church Yth Grp; Drama Clb; French Clb; Pep Clb; Sec Spanish Clb; Var Trk; Capt Vllybl; Hon Roll; NHS; Spanish NHS; Lebanon Vly Coll; Law.

DISSTON, COURTNEY; Springside Schl; Wyndmoor, PA; (3); Service Clb; Nwsp Rptr; Ed Yrbk Ed-Chief; Yrbk Stf; Im Lcrss; Var Tennis; JV Vllybl; Hon Roll; Math Hnrs; Stu Guides.

DISTEFANO, MARY; Bishop Shanahan HS; W Chester, PA; (4); 49/215; Cmnty Wkr; Dance Clb; Service Clb; Yrbk Stf; Lit Mag; Stat Bsktbl; Var Tennis; Var Trk; Hon Roll; Trstee Schlrshp-Acdmc Achvt 87-88; Pace U; Intl Manag.

DITCHEY, CARL; Bishop Mc Devitt HS; Harrisburg, PA; (3); 60/250; Art Clb; Church Yth Grp; Cmnty Wkr; Computer Clb; FBLA; Pep Clb; Red Cross Aide; Science Clb; Service Clb; Ski Clb; 1st, 2nd & 3rd Pl Sci Fair 85 & 86 & 84; Penn ST U; Arch Engrng.

DITRI, SALVADOR; Beaver Area HS; Midland, PA; (3); Yrbk Stf; Tennis.

DITRICH, DENISE; Mercyhurst Prep; Erie, PA; (3); 13/170; Church Yth Grp; French Clb; Variety Show; JV L Socr; Var L NHS; Frsh Acadc Schlrshp 84-85; Crew Tm Ltrs; Math.

DITRICH, LAURA; Villa Maria Academy HS; Erie, PA; (4); 5/130; Church Yth Grp; Cmnty Wkr; Latin Clb; School Musical; NHS; NEDT Awd; PA ST; Psych.

DITSIOUS, MARK A; Bradford Area HS; Bradford, PA; (3); Am Leg Boys St; French Clb; Key Clb; Ski Clb; Stu Cncl; Var Ftbl; Var Trk; Im Wt Lftg; High Hon Roll; Hon Roll; Aero Engrng.

DITTMAN, HEATHER; Pocono Mt HS; Bartonsville, PA; (3); Sftbl; Hon Roll; Bus.

DITTMAR, CLINT J; Norristown Area HS; Norristown, PA; (3); 10/524; Computer Clb; DECA; FBLA; Intnl Clb; JV L Socr; High Hon Roll; Hon Roll; Acad Excllnce 85; USA Today Statue Liberty Essay Cont Ellis Island Fndtn 85; Mktng.

DITTMER, MICHAEL A; Butler SR HS; Butler, PA; (3); Acad Achvt Awd 86-87; Pitt; Dental Med.

DITZ, CINDY; Hickory HS; Hermitage, PA; (3); 38/167; DECA; Library Aide; 3rd Pl Dist & ST Cmptn DECA 87; Library Aid Cert 86; Acctg.

DIVEGLIA III, EUGENE; Newport HS; Newport, PA; (2); VP Soph Cls; Rep Stu Cncl; High Hon Roll.

DIVELY, KEVIN; Berlin Brothersvalley HS; Berlin, PA; (2); Spanish Clb; Pres Frsh Cls; Pres Soph Cls; Rep Stu Cncl; Var L Bsbl; JV Var Bsktbl; Var L Ftbl; Wt Lftg; Wrstlng; Cit Awd.

DIVELY, MELISSA; Claysburg-Kimmel HS; Claysburg, PA; (3); 37/79; Hst Church Yth Grp; Drama Clb; Speech Tm; VP SADD; Teachers Aide; Chorus; School Musical; Stage Crew; Variety Show; Semi-Fnlst Gvrnrs Schl Arts 87; Elem Educ.

DIVELY, MONICA; Altoona Area HS; Altoona, PA; (3); 40/796; Computer Clb; Spanish Clb; High Hon Roll; Hon Roll; Jr NHS; NEDT Awd; Prfct Atten Awd; Pres Acad Fit Awd 84-85; Acad Achvt Awd 84-85.

DIVENS, VICTORIA; Kennedy Christian HS; Sharpsville, PA; (3); Church Yth Grp; Hosp Aide; Sec Spanish Clb; Nwsp Rptr; Nwsp Stf; Yrbk Rptr; Yrbk Stf; Stu Cncl; JV Bsktbl; Var L Cheerleading; U Pittsburgh; Phys Ther.

DIVENS, WILLIAM; Kennedy Christian HS; Sharpsville, PA; (2); 44/96; Art Clb; Spanish Clb; Var Bsbl; Var Ftbl; Var Wrstlng; Hon Roll.

DIVERS, WENDY; Milton SR HS; Milton, PA; (3); Girl Scts; Key Clb; Latin Clb; Library Aide; Band; Concert Band; Mrchg Band; Fld Hcky; Med Secy.

DIVIDO, TRICIA; Blacklick Valley HS; Nanty-Glo, PA; (3); 6/100; NFL; Ski Clb; Yrbk Stf; L Trk; High Hon Roll; NHS; Pres Acad Ftnss Awd 84; Acad All-Amer 86; Law.

DIVINS, DEE; Union HS; Sligo, PA; (4); 4/54; French Clb; SADD; Chorus; Flag Corp; Off Stu Cncl; High Hon Roll; Hon Roll; Pep Clb; Score Keeper; Hnr Stu, Outstndng SR Engl Dept 87; All A Awd 84-85 & 87; Clarion U Of PA; Math.

DIVIRGILIO, DANA; Penn Trafford HS; Claridge, PA; (2); AFS; Hosp Aide; JCL; Latin Clb; Teachers Aide; Chorus; High Hon Roll; Hon Roll; Corp Law.

DIXIT, PRIYA; Laurel Highlands SR HS; Uniontown, PA; (3); 1/363; Hosp Aide; Red Cross Aide; Temple Yth Grp; Madrigals; School Play; Rep Stu Cncl; CC Awd; NHS; JA; Math Tm; AP Hstry Clb; Indn Clsscl Dncng; Schl Tutr; Med.

DIXON, AMY; Central HS; Scranton, PA; (3); 134/325; Spanish Clb; SADD; Yrbk Stf; ESL Tutoring Clb Pres 86-87; ESL Tutoring Clb VP 85-86; Gregg Awd For Typing 87; Marywood Coll; Cmmnctn Disorder.

DIXON, ANGELA N; Harrisburgh HS; Harrisburg, PA; (2); 28/378; Church Yth Grp; ROTC; Church Choir; Variety Show; Nwsp Rptr; Bsktbl; Hon Roll; Prfct Atten Awd; USC; Jrnlsm.

DIXON, ANTHONY; Pittston Area HS; Pittston, PA; (4); Trs Aud/Vis; Pres Drama Clb; Ski Clb; Chorus; School Musical; School Play; Stage Crew; Variety Show; Yrbk Stf; Hon Roll; Marywood Coll; Comms.

DIXON, ANTON; Center HS; Aliquippa, PA; (2); Church Yth Grp; Spanish Clb; Church Choir; JV Bsbl; Bowling; Hon Roll; Stanford U; Crmnl Jstc.

DIXON, APRIL; Taylor Allderdice HS; Pittsburgh, PA; (3); Dance Clb; JA; Teachers Aide; Chorus; Psych.

DIXON, DEE DEE; United HS; Vintondale, PA; (4); 52/158; Ski Clb; Chorus; School Musical; Yrbk Stf; Sec Jr Cls; Sec Sr Cls; Sec Stu Cncl; JV Var Cheerleading; Hon Roll; Chorus Trea 86-87; Hmncng Ct 86-87; 1st Pl Cheer & Dance Local Comptn 86-87; Penn ST U; Lbrl Arts.

DIXON, DORENE; Langley HS; Pittsburgh, PA; (3); DAR Awd; Hon Roll; U Pittsburgh; Bus.

DIXON, JOHN M; Towanda Area HS; Wysox, PA; (4); Trk; Hon Roll; Penn ST U; Elem Ed.

DIXON JR, KENNETH C; Abington Heights HS; Clarks Summit, PA; (4); Boy Scts; Band; Mrchg Band; Var L Bsbl; Var L Golf; God Cntry Awd; Church Yth Grp; Egl Sct Awd 87; PA ST U; Htl Mng.

DIXON, LISA; West Scranton HS; Scranton, PA; (3); 8/400; Church Yth Grp; FNA; Church Choir; Twrlr; High Hon Roll; Jr NHS; Vet Med.

DIXON, ROCHELLE; Aliquippa SR HS; Aliquippa, PA; (2); Church Yth Grp; Cmnty Wkr; Computer Clb; French Clb; Girl Scts; Hosp Aide; Library Aide; NAACP; Band; Church Choir; NAACP Schlstc Achvt Awd 84-85; Gannon U; Child Psych.

DIXON, SHELLENE; Tunkhannock HS; Tunkhannock, PA; (3); 68/320; Art Clb; Computer Clb; Drama Clb; JA; Ski Clb; SADD; Fld Hcky; Hon Roll; Palmer Coll Chrprctc; Chrprctr.

DIXON, TAMMIE; Rochester JR SR Area HS; Rochester, PA; (4); 3/95; French Clb; Red Cross Aide; Service Clb; Ski Clb; Yrbk Ed-Chief; High Hon Roll; Rotary Awd; Pres Acad Ftns Awd 87; Outstndng Achvt Awd In Art 87; PA ST U; Acctng.

DIXON, TINA; Plymouth-Whitemarsh HS; Lafayette Hill, PA; (1); Art Clb; Church Yth Grp; Hosp Aide; VP JA; SADD; Band; Chorus; Pres Church Choir; School Musical; School Play; UCLA; Bio.

DIXSON, THOMAS; Homer Center JR SR HS; Lucernemines, PA; (3); 45/121; Church Yth Grp; French Clb; Ski Clb; Varsity Clb; Var Bsktbl; Var Capt Golf; Appalacian Conf Mdlst Golf 86; Optomtry.

DMYTRYSZYN, LANA; Central HS; Philadelphia, PA; (4); 71/340; Math Tm; Office Aide; Drill Tm; School Musical; VP Frsh Cls; Rep Stu Cncl; Im Sftbl; Hon Roll; US Student Council Awd 87; Drexel U; Intl Bus.

DO, MINH L; Engineering & Science HS; Philadelphia, PA; (4); 30/210; Hon Roll; NHS; Ruth W Hayre Scholar 87; Synod Trinity Mnrty Scholar 87; Drexel U; Elctrcl Engrng.

DOAN, DANA; Coatesville Area SR HS; Coatesville, PA; (3); Church Yth Grp; GAA; Girl Scts; Ski Clb; Spanish Clb; Varsity Clb; Band; Color Guard; Mrchg Band; Nwsp Rptr.

DOBB, MARC; Lower Dauphin HS; Hummelstown, PA; (3); 39/276; Cmnty Wkr; Var JV Bsbl; Var JV Bsktbl; Var JV Ftbl; Hon Roll; NHS; U Of Pittsburgh; Mrktng.

DOBBIE, KRISTA; Bellwood-Antis HS; Altoona, PA; (3); 4/115; VP Church Yth Grp; Ski Clb; Band; Chorus; School Musical; Yrbk Stf; Rep Stu Cncl; Fld Hcky; Hon Roll; NHS.

DOBBS, MARC; Ford City SR HS; Vandergrift, PA; (4); 24/140; Capt Quiz Bowl; Rep SADD; Trs Rep Chorus; School Musical; Variety Show; Var L Ftbl; Var L Trk; Dnfth Awd; Hon Roll; NHS; Outstndng 4-H Stu 86; Mayor For Day 87; PA ST U; Human Svc.

DOBBS, TERRI; Hampton HS; Gibsonia, PA; (3); 21/201; Church Yth Grp; Ski Clb; Spanish Clb; Im Powder Puff Ftbl; Var L Sftbl; High Hon Roll; NHS; Accntng.

DOBECK, DAWN; Southern Columbia HS; Elysburg, PA; (3); 41/107; Key Clb; Varsity Clb; Yrbk Sprt Ed; Yrbk Stf; VP L Sftbl; Hon Roll; Prfct Atten Awd; Voice Dem Awd; Letterman Southern Columbia Softball Tm 87; Teaching.

DOBERNECK, DIANE; State College Area SR HS; State College, PA; (4); Sec Intnl Clb; Mgr Mrchg Band; Im Socr; Im Vllybl; PA ST U; Art Hist.

DOBISHINSKY, MARIA; Lakeland HS; Jermyn, PA; (3); 30/147; FHA; SADD; Yrbk Stf; Off Stu Cncl; Cheerleading; Vllybl; Hon Roll; NHS; US Bus Educ Awd 87; Penn ST; Acctng.

DOBKIN, MAGGIE; Taylor Allderdice HS; Pittsburgh, PA; (3); SADD; Stage Crew; Nwsp Phtg; Yrbk Stf; Crs Cntry; High Hon Roll; Hon Roll; Studio Art.

DOBLES, MAX C; B Reed Henderson HS; Exton, PA; (4); 6/330; JCL; Scholastic Bowl; Var Capt Crs Cntry; JV Trk; Hon Roll; NHS; Ntl Merit SF; Natl Sci Olympd Awd 83; Engr.

DOBRANSKI, MICHELLE; Northwestern Lehigh HS; Germansville, PA; (4); Drama Clb; PAVAS; Lib Chorus; School Musical; School Play; Mgr Stage Crew; Swing Chorus; Nrthwstrn Lehigh Schlrshp Awd For Future Tchrs 87; N W Coraliers Music Awd 87; Phi Delta Kappa 87; Millersville U; Sec Ed.

DOBRINICK, TOM; Penn-Trafford HS; Trafford, PA; (3); 80/301; Spanish Clb; Im Bsktbl; Var L Ftbl; Im Wt Lftg; Sports Med.

DOBROWALSKI, LAUREN E; Coughlin HS; Laflin, PA; (3); 11/380; Hosp Aide; Key Clb; Nwsp Ed-Chief; Nwsp Rptr; Rep Stu Cncl; Var L Crs Cntry; Var L Trk; High Hon Roll; Hon Roll; NHS; Hstry.

DOBSON, CHRIS; Lower Dauphin HS; Middletown, PA; (3); Ski Clb; JV Ftbl; Stat Score Keeper; Wt Lftg; Hon Roll; Bus.

DOBSON, DANIELLE; Neshaminy HS; Levittown, PA; (3); 118/768; Lit Mag; Mgr(s); Powder Puff Ftbl; Stat Wrstlng; Hon Roll; Prfct Atten Awd; Penn ST.

DOBSON, JEFFERY; St John Neumann HS; Philadelphia, PA; (3); 8/349; Computer Clb; Science Clb; Var Socr; Hon Roll; NHS; VA Poly Insti; Engr.

DOBSON, SUSAN; Sun Valley HS; Aston, PA; (3); 90/270; Leo Clb; SADD; Chorus; Hon Roll; Law Enforc.

DOBZYNSKI, MARK; Cathedral Prep; Erie, PA; (3); 77/193; Church Yth Grp; Cmnty Wkr; Exploring; Library Aide; Im Bsktbl; Post Deputy Secty Of Transportation 87; Sports Med.

DOCALOVICH, EDWARD; Lakeland HS; Mayfield, PA; (3); Pres Frsh Cls; Pres Soph Cls; Pres Jr Cls; Pres Sr Cls; Off Stu Cncl; Bsbl; Bsktbl; Capt Ftbl; High Hon Roll; Hon Roll; Villanova; Elec Engrng.

DOCHERTY, KEVIN; Reading HS; Reading, PA; (3); 107/709; Aud/Vis; Computer Clb; Exploring; German Clb; Model UN; Co-Capt Quiz Bowl; Prfct Atten Awd; Aerospc Engr.

DOCK, CHRISTINE; Crestwood HS; Mountaintop, PA; (4); 40/197; FBLA; Ski Clb; Sec Jr Cls; Pres VP Stu Cncl; JV Var Cheerleading; L Var Crs Cntry; Sftbl; Capt L Trk; High Hon Roll; Hon Roll; Ntl Pres Ftns Awd 87; Prnt Tchrs Stu Assn Rcgntn Awd, Prlmntry Prcdrs 1st Pl Awd 86-87; Bloomsburg U; Accntng.

DOCKERY, LEONARD SHAWN; George Westinghouse HS; Pittsburgh, PA; (3); AFS; Church Yth Grp; Band; Church Choir; Im Bsktbl; JV Ftbl; JV Trk; Var L Vllybl; Hon Roll; NHS; Comp Engrng.

DOCKTOR, DAVID; York Suburban HS; York, PA; (3); 43/177; Ski Clb; Concert Band; Mrchg Band; Stage Crew; Var Vllybl; Engrng.

DODDS, DEBRA; Rockwood Area HS; Rockwood, PA; (3); 7/82; Rep Jr Cls; High Hon Roll; Hon Roll; Hgh Hnr Roll; Hrn Roll 85-86.

DODDS, JOHN; Williamson JR/Sr HS; Lawrenceville, PA; (3); CAP; Pres Computer Clb; Spanish Clb; Ed Yrbk Stf; Hon Roll; NHS; Embry-Riddle; Aerntcl Sci.

DODEK, RICHARD; Highlands SR HS; Brackenridge, PA; (4); 35/281; Key Clb; Teachers Aide; Trs Band; Jazz Band; Mrchg Band; Hon Roll; NHS; Church Yth Grp; Drama Clb; Concert Band; Prsdntl Acdmc Ftnss Awd, Semper Fidelis Awd, PMEA Dist I Band 87; U Of Pittsburgh; Phrmcy.

DODGE, AMY; Tunkhannock Area HS; Dalton, PA; (2); JV Bsktbl; Hon Roll.

DODGE, BRUCE; Sharpsville SR HS; Greenville, PA; (4); 4/119; Boy Scts; Hon Roll; NHS; Pres Schlr; Outstndg Physics Stu Yr; Comp Lit Awd; U Of Pittsburgh; Metlrgcl Engr.

DODGE, DANIELLE; Athens HS; Athens, PA; (3); Church Yth Grp; SADD; Band; Chorus; Sec Frsh Cls; Trs Sr Cls; Rep Stu Cncl; Var L Swmmng; Var Trk; German Clb; Eastern Coll; Mktg.

DODGE, JAMES; Tunkhannock Area HS; Dalton, PA; (3); Letterman Clb; Var Bsbl; Var Bsktbl; Cit Awd; Hon Roll; NHS; Ntl Merit Ltr.

DODGE, KEVIN; Warwick HS; Lititz, PA; (3); 29/260; Lib Band; Lib Chorus; Church Choir; Mrchg Band; Orch; School Musical; School Play; Symp Band; JV Tennis; High Hon Roll; Intl Bus.

DODSON JR, CARL; Central HS; Martinsburg, PA; (3); 34/187; FCA; Varsity Clb; Var L Bsbl; Var Bsktbl; Var L Ftbl; Hon Roll; NEDT Awd; Elec Engrng.

DODSON, GAYLE; Claysburg-Kimmel HS; Claysburg, PA; (4); 10/49 Am Leg Aux Girls St; Camera Clb; German Clb; Speech Tm; Band; Schoo Musical; Sec Soph Cls; Trs Jr Cls; Capt Twrlr; Hon Roll; Hmcmng Qn 86 1st Pl Dnc Mstrs Cmpttn Sigels Schl Dnc, & Claysburg Am Lgn Band Pos 522 Band Awd 87; PA ST U; Bus Admin.

DOEBLER, CHARLES; Lock Haven HS; Lock Haven, PA; (4); 3/250 Pres Model UN; Concert Band; Jazz Band; Mrchg Band; High Hon Roll NHS; Ntl Merit Ltr; Excllnce Physics & Chem 85-86; USAF Acad.

DOEL, PETER; Plum SR HS; Pittsburgh, PA; (4); AFS; Church Yth Grp French Clb; Acpl Chr; Chorus; Church Choir; School Musical; Hon Roll Grove City Coll; Math.

DOERFLER, J DOUGLAS; Lake-Lehman HS; Harveys Lake, PA; (3) 12/221; Church Yth Grp; Concert Band; Jazz Band; Mrchg Band; Var Socr; Var L Trk; High Hon Roll; Hon Roll; Jr NHS; NHS; PA & Atlanti Cst Band Chmpshps 84-86; Med.

DOERR, DOREEN; Phila HS For Girls; Philadelphia, PA; (2); GAA; Va Sftbl; Oceangrphy.

DOHANIC, JOHN; Northwestern HS; W Springfield, PA; (3); Art Clb Boy Scts; Chess Clb; Church Yth Grp; Hon Roll; Law.

DOHERTY, CLARE G; Lower Merion HS; Wynnewood, PA; (4); Intn Clb; School Play; Yrbk Stf; Stu Cncl; Hon Roll; NHS; Schlrshp PA Gvrnr Schl Arts 86; Schlstc Art Awds 86-87; U Chicago; Art.

DOHERTY, JEANMARIE; Nazareth Acad; Philadelphia, PA; (3) Church Yth Grp; Intnl Clb; Red Cross Aide; Spanish Clb; Color Guard Psych.

DOHERTY, KATHY; Tulpehocken HS; Bernville, PA; (2); Band; Mrchg Band; Hon Roll; UCLA.

DOHERTY, TRICIA; Abington Heights HS; Clarks Summit, PA; (1) Chorus; Rep Stu Cncl; Cheerleading; Hon Roll.

DOKAS, PATTY; Hanover Area JR/Sr HS; Wilkes Barre, PA; (4) Luzerne Cnty CC; Travel Mgmnt.

DOKMANOVICH, JENNIFER; Center HS; Aliquippa, PA; (3); German Clb; Powder Puff Ftbl; Hon Roll; Jr NHS; NHS; Ehrenur Kunde Grm Awd 87; Bus.

DOLACK, JOANNE; Archbishop Ryan HS For Girls; Philadelphia, PA (4); 5/491; Trs French Clb; Hosp Aide; Red Cross Aide; Science Clb; Var Capt Fld Hcky; L Var Sftbl; French Hon Soc; Hon Roll; NHS; PA Free Enterprise Wk Scholar 85; IPS Awd 84; Frnch Awd 85; Sci.

DOLAN, CAROL; Lock Haven :Sr HS; Blanchard, PA; (3); Trs FHA Spanish Clb; Bsktbl; Wheelock; Socl Wrk.

DOLAN, CHRISTINE; Athens HS; Athens, PA; (4); 6/142; Art Clb; Lit Mag; High Hon Roll; Hon Roll; NHS; Ntl Merit Ltr; Natl Schlrshp Art Cmptn 85; Tp 10 Schlstc Awd 87; Fll Schlrshp St Francis Coll 87; St Francis Coll; Vet.

DOLAN, HEATHER; Cameron County HS; Emporium, PA; (4); Pres Spanish Clb; Mrchg Band; VP Soph Cls; Rep Sr Cls; Capt Cheerleading Gym; Trk; Twrlr; Hon Roll; Prfct Atten Awd; Dstngshd Athl Awd 87; U Of Sonora Mexico; Intrprtng.

DOLAN, LORI; St Marys Area HS; St Marys, PA; (3); 3/300; Cmnty Wkr Off Frsh Cls; Off Soph Cls; Off Jr Cls; Pres Sr Cls; Stu Cncl; Capt Bsktbl Gym; High Hon Roll; NHS; Engrng.

DOLAN, THOMAS C; Sharpsville HS; Sharpsville, PA; (4); 2/130 Church Yth Grp; Ski Clb; Thesps; Band; Chorus; Drm Mjr(t); Jazz Band Mrchg Band; School Musical; Pres NHS; Alleheny Coll; Bio.

DOLCHIN, MELISSA; Bensalem HS; Bensalem, PA; (4); 7/500; Band High Hon Roll; Hon Roll; Kiwanis Awd; NHS; Acadmc All Am Schlr Pgm Temple U Pres Awd; Temple U; Pre-Med.

DOLECKI, LISA; Venango Christian HS; Oil City, PA; (3); 8/35; Art Clb Spanish Clb; SADD; Variety Show; Var Cheerleading; Stat Score Keeper Hon Roll; NHS.

DOLENCE, PHIL; Johnstown HS; Johnstown, PA; (4); Band; Chorus Orch; School Musical; Variety Show; Hnr Roll 87; U Of Pittsburg; Psych.

DOLES, BRAD; Butler SR HS; E Butler, PA; (3); Church Yth Grp Exploring; French Clb; Thesps; Chorus; Church Choir; School Musical Swing Chorus; Variety Show; Hon Roll.

DOLINSKI, KARA; Ambridge Area HS; Ambridge, PA; (3); Am Leg Aux Girls St; VP German Clb; Pep Clb; Red Cross Aide; Band; Off Jr Cls; Var L Bsktbl; Vllybl; High Hon Roll; NHS.

DOLIVEIRIA, JUDITH; Bishop Carroll HS; Nantyglo, PA; (4); 4/107 Drama Clb; Teachers Aide; Chorus; School Play; Hon Roll; NHS; Svc Awd 83; Catholic Dghtrs Of Amer Rlgn Awd 83; Princlpls Awd High Hnr 83; U Of PA Indiana; Acctng.

DOLL, KAREN; Northeastern HS; Mt Wolf, PA; (4); Chorus; Vet Med.

DOLL, KATHERINE; Jim Thorpe HS; Jim Thorpe, PA; (3); 3/96; Band; Chorus; Mrchg Band; Yrbk Stf; Capt Cheerleading; Capt Vllybl; High Hon Roll; NHS; Prfct Atten Awd.

DOLL, MARK; Cedar Crest HS; Lebanon, PA; (1); Church Yth Grp; German Clb; Pep Clb; Quiz Bowl; Band; Concert Band; Drm & Bgl; Jazz Band; Mrchg Band; Rep Frsh Cls.

DOLMAJER, JEFFREY; Highlands SR HS; Brackenridge, PA; (3); Exploring; Pres JA; SADD; Teachers Aide; Varsity Clb; JV Coach Actv; Var L Ftbl; JV Trk; Var L Wt Lftg; Var L Wrstlng; Wrestlng Capt Ldrshp Awd 85-86; Jr Achvmt Super Sls Awd 86; Mt Union Coll OH; Sports.

DOLNEY, JOSEPH; Southmoreland HS; Everson, PA; (3); French Clb; Letterman Clb; Var L Bsktbl; Bus.

DOLTON, JENNIFER; Hempfield Area SR HS; Greensburg, PA; (4), FBLA; Spanish Clb; Band; Concert Band; Mrchg Band; High Hon Roll; Hon Roll; Prfct Atten Awd; 2nd Pl Region II Conf FBLA Eng 87; 3rd Pl Eng PA ST Ldrshp Conf 87; Robert Morris Coll; Mgmt.

DOLTON, RENEE; Hempfield Area SR HS; Greensburg, PA; (2); French Clb; Concert Band; Mrchg Band; Pres Acad Ftns Awd 86; Med.

DOMACHOWSKI, STEVE; Butler Intermediate HS; Butler, PA; (2); French Clb; Teachers Aide; Rep Frsh Cls; Rep Soph Cls; Im Bsktbl; NHS.

DOMAN, ELMER; Trinity Area HS; Eighty Four, PA; (3); 26/400; Camera Clb; Computer Clb; Math Clb; Math Tm; Nwsp Phtg; Yrbk Phtg; High Hon Roll; Drftng.

DOMANSKI, BRENDA; Danville SR HS; Riverside, PA; (3); 1/187; Spanish Clb; Chorus; Color Guard; High Hon Roll; NHS; Chem.

DOMARECKI, LISA; Panther Valley HS; Summit Hill, PA; (2); #42 In Class; French Clb; Office Aide; Ski Clb; Band; Concert Band; Mrchg Band; Sftbl; Penn ST.

DOMBACH, CHRISTOPHER; Warwick HS; Lititz, PA; (2); 42/320; Church Yth Grp; Computer Clb; Church Choir; Var Trk; High Hon Roll; Hon Roll; Prfct Atten Awd; 1st Pl Lancstr Cnty Sci Fair 86; NASA Awd Lncstr Cnty Sci Fair 87; Bus Admin.

PENNSYLVANIA DORF 203

DOMBACH, DIANE; Lampeter Strasburg HS; Willow Street, PA; (3); 12/154; VP Church Yth Grp; VP FBLA; Chorus; Var Bsktbl; Hon Roll; NHS; Bus.

DOMBACH, J ERIC; Lancaster Mennonite HS; Quarryville, PA; (3); Chess Clb; Pres Church Yth Grp; Mgr Acpl Chr; Chorus; Church Choir; Orch; Ed Yrbk Stf; Hon Roll; Ntl Merit Ltr; Mdl Awd Outstndg Cntrbtns Music 87; Cert Awd Contrbtns Music 86; Comp Sci.

DOMBACH, KENNETH; Donegal HS; Mt Joy, PA; (4); 60/178; Church Yth Grp; FCA; Latin Clb; Rep Frsh Cls; Rep Jr Cls; Var Bsbl; Im Wt Lftg; Var Wrstlng; Lion Awd; Sctnl Chmp Wrstlng 87; Bus.

DOMBKOWSKI, TIMOTHY; N Pocono HS; Archbald, PA; (3); 10/300; High Hon Roll; NHS; Arspc Engrng.

DOMBROSKI, NANCY; Villa Maria Acad; Harborcreek, PA; (3); Church Yth Grp; Cmnty Wkr; Dance Clb; Exploring; Hosp Aide; Model UN; Science Clb; SADD; Off Stu Cncl; Im Bsktbl; Bio.

DOMBROWSKI, ANN; Plum SR HS; Pittsburgh, PA; (2); Church Yth Grp; Hosp Aide; Color Guard; Symp Band; Nwsp Stf; Yrbk Ed-Chief; Yrbk Stf; Var Swmmng; Hon Roll; Nrsng.

DOMER, CHRIS; South Fayette HS; Cuddy, PA; (3); Key Clb; JV Bsktbl; Hon Roll; NHS; Junior Mr Dance Of PA 84; Dance Masters Schlrshp 87; Civic Light Opera Ministar 87-88; Pitt U; Med.

DOMIN, AMY; North Pocono HS; Moscow, PA; (3); 32/250; Art Clb; Church Yth Grp; Ski Clb; Band; Chorus; Pres Lib Concert Band; Pres Lib Mrchg Band; VP Orch; Var Trk; Hon Roll; Arch.

DOMIN, JUSTINE; Emmaus HS; Wescosville, PA; (3); 23/560; Exploring; Var Im Cheerleading; Swmmng; High Hon Roll; Jr NHS; NHS; ME Yth Physcl Ftnss Tm-5th Natls 86-87; Med.

DOMIN, PATRICIA C; West Hazleton JR SR HS; West Hazleton, PA; (4); 14/224; Cmnty Wkr; FNA; Library Aide; Red Cross Aide; Ski Clb; SADD; Color Guard; Mrchg Band; Capt Twrlr; NHS; Intl Stu Ldrshp Awd; PA Free Enterprise Wk Schlrshp; 2nd Pl JR Acad Of Sci; Penn ST; Pharm.

DOMINGO, DEANNA; Moon Area HS; Coraopolis, PA; (3); Church Yth Grp; German Clb; Chorus; Ed Nwsp Ed-Chief; Rptr Nwsp Rptr; Cheerleading; Sftbl; High Hon Roll; Hon Roll; NHS; Aeronautical Engrng.

DOMINIC, JASON; Abington SR HS; Rockledge, PA; (3); Latin Clb; Spanish Clb; Bowling; Hon Roll; Med.

DOMINICK, JODI; Wyoming Area SR HS; Wyoming, PA; (3); Key Clb; Ski Clb; Spanish Clb; Capt Cheerleading; Vllybl; High Hon Roll; NHS.

DOMINICK, JOSEPH; Carlynton HS; Carnegie, PA; (3) 2/150; Trs German Clb; Nwsp Stf; Yrbk Stf; L Socr; High Hon Roll; Hon Roll; NHS; Chem Engrng.

DOMINICK, LISA MICHELE; Pittston Area HS; Pittston, PA; (4); Key Clb; Band; Concert Band; Mrchg Band; Luzerne Cty CC; Chld Devlpmt.

DOMINOWSKI, LESLEE; South Park HS; Library, PA; (3); 15/220; FBLA; Bsktbl; Tennis; High Hon Roll; NHS; Cmnty Wkr; Girl Scts; Library Aide; Political Wkr; VP NHS 87-88; Intl Free Throw Title/KC 85.

DOMITROVIC, RON; Central Catholic HS; Pittsburgh, PA; (3); 32/290; Boy Scts; Drama Clb; Pres School Musical; Pres School Play; Pres Stage Crew; JV Crs Cntry; Im Ftbl; JV Trk; High Hon Roll; Hon Roll; Cvl Engrng.

DOMITROVICH, LAURA; Our Lady Of The Sacred Heart HS; Aliquippa, PA; (4); 9/57; Co-Capt NFL; School Musical; School Play; Yrbk Ed-Chief; Hon Roll; NHS; Ntl Hstry & Gvt Awd; All Amer Acdmc Awd; U Of Pittsburgh; Phys Thrpy.

DOMONKOS, BILL; Mary Fuller Frazier Memorial HS; Perryopolis, PA; (3); Var Golf; High Hon Roll; Hon Roll; NHS; Engrng.

DOMRZALSKI, KATHY; Parkland HS; Coplay, PA; (3); 29/481; Cmnty Wkr; VP Pres SADD; Thesps; Chorus; School Musical; VP Soph Cls; VP Jr Cls; Stu Cncl; Hon Roll; Drama Clb; Delg Untd Ways Natl Yth Ldrshp Conf 87; Phys Thrpy.

DONACHY, COLETTE; St Marys Area HS; St Marys, PA; (3); 58/290; Yrbk Phtg; Yrbk Sprt Ed; Yrbk Stf; Var L Sftbl; Hon Roll; Outstndg JR Female-Phys Educ 87; SADD Slogan & Postr Contst Wnnr 86.

DONAHER, MAUREEN; Cardinal O Hara HS; Havertown, PA; (3); 45/710; Church Yth Grp; Office Aide; Service Clb; School Musical; Ed Yrbk Stf; Hon Roll; NHS; Hnrb Mntn DE Cnty Sci Fair 87; Acad Convoctn 85-87; Bus.

DONAHEY, JAMIE; Mt Pleasant Area HS; Norvelt, PA; (3); 3/253; GAA; Band; Nwsp Ed-Chief; Nwsp Stf; Var L Cheerleading; High Hon Roll; Psychology.

DONAHOE-GOLDBERG, SIDNEY A; Central HS; Philadelphia, PA; (4); 111/334; French Clb; Pres Trs Temple Yth Grp; Ed Yrbk Stf; Ntl Merit SF; Stanford; Business.

DONAHOO, JAMES; Sayre HS; Sayre, PA; (3); Letterman Clb; Var Bsbl; Var Bsktbl; Var Crs Cntry; Prfct Atten Awd; Acctnt.

DONAHUE, JENNIFER; Kennett HS; Chadds Ford, PA; (3); Model UN; Radio Clb; School Musical; Yrbk Sprt Ed; Stu Cncl; Crs Cntry; High Hon Roll; NHS; Church Yth Grp; French Clb; Frnch, Latn Awds 87; Comms.

DONAHUE, MARY E; Pittston Area SR HS; Pittston, PA; (4); 103/345; Church Yth Grp; Cmnty Wkr; Key Clb; Ski Clb; Yrbk Stf; Northampton CC; Travel.

DONAHUE, NANCY; Marion Ctr; Indiana, PA; (3); 21/156; Intnl Clb; Pep Clb; Varsity Clb; Band; Chorus; Concert Band; Flag Corp; Mrchg Band; VP Soph Cls; Rep Stu Cncl; IUP; Scndry Educ.

DONAHUE, STACEY A; Mountain View JR/Sr HS; Nicholson, PA; (2); Sec 4-H; Girl Scts; Chorus; Mrchg Band; Var Bsktbl; Var Trk; Engl Constitution Essay Hnr 87; Pres Phys Ftns Awd 87; Commrcl Art.

DONAHUE, TAMARA; South Park HS; Library, PA; (4); 20/200; FBLA; Office Aide; Spanish Clb; Drill Tm; Yrbk Stf; Rep Soph Cls; Rep Jr Cls; Rep Sr Cls; High Hon Roll; NHS.

DONALD, JAMES; Penn Hills SR HS; Pittsburgh, PA; (4); 147/577; Boy Scts; 4-H; Spanish Clb; Band; Bsbl; Bsktbl; Bowling; Hon Roll; Prfct Atten Awd; U Of Pittsburgh; Pharmacy.

DONALDSON, BOB; Cambridge Springs HS; Cambridge Springs, PA; (4); 22/107; French Clb; VP Key Clb; Bsbl; Ftbl; Wrstlng; Hon Roll; Pres Schlr; Edinboro U-PA; Crmnl Jstc.

DONALDSON, JERILYNN L; South Philadelphia HS Motivtn; Philadelphia, PA; (4); Color Guard; Pres Sr Cls; Rep Stu Cncl; Crs Cntry; Trk; High Hon Roll; Hon Roll; NHS; Prfct Atten Awd; Acad Achvt Pgm U PA 84-87; Adv Career Training 87; Math Ed Achvt 85-87; PA ST; Engrng.

DONALDSON, JONATHAN; Ambridge HS; Freedom, PA; (3); Aud/Vis; Exploring; German Clb; JA; Pep Clb; Var Crs Cntry; L Trk; Stat JV Vllybl; OH ST; Astro Engr.

DONALDSON, MATT; Hampton HS; Gibsonia, PA; (3); Church Yth Grp; Quiz Bowl; Spanish Clb; JV Bsbl; High Hon Roll; Hon Roll; Pre-Law.

DONAPEL, MICHAEL; Frankford HS; Philadelphia, PA; (3); Church Yth Grp; Teachers Aide; High Hon Roll; Hon Roll; Pres Schlr; Highest Math Avg In Cls; Accntng.

DONATELLI, CHRISTINE; Quaker Valley SR HS; Sewickley, PA; (2); Band; Drm Mjr(t); Twrlr; Hon Roll; Hosp Aide; Library Aide; Office Aide; Chorus; Concert Band; Mrchg Band; Mid-East Music Awd 86-87; Interior Decoratng.

DONATI, DAVID W; Fort Cherry HS; Hickory, PA; (4); Math Clb; Science Clb; Ski Clb; Varsity Clb; Jr Cls; Sr Cls; Stu Cncl; Bsbl; Wt Lftg; NHS; Aeron Engrng.

DONATI, DEBBIE; North Pocono HS; Moscow, PA; (4); Church Yth Grp; Co-Capt Tennis; Drama Clb; School Play; Yrbk Stf; Hon Roll; NHS; Vrsty Lttr & Bar; Spllng Schlrshp Amer Lgn Pst 579; East Stroudsburg U; Htl Mngmnt.

DONATI, JOANN; Marian HS; Jim Thorpe, PA; (4); Pres Church Yth Grp; SADD; School Play; Mgr L Ftbl; Var Capt Trk; French Hon Soc; Dlrs Sprtsmnshp Awd 87; A Kielbasa Mem Awd 87; E Strdsbrg U; Elem Ed.

DONATO, KRISTA; Upper Darby HS; Drexel Hill, PA; (3); Hosp Aide; Teachers Aide; Yrbk Stf; Stu Cncl; Fld Hcky; Lcrss; Mgr(s); Trk; High Hon Roll; Hon Roll; Bio.

DONATO, LISA; Little Flower Catholic HS; Philadelphia, PA; (3); 2/326; Hosp Aide; Office Aide; Orch; Nwsp Ed-Chief; Nwsp Rptr; Nwsp Stf; High Hon Roll; NHS; Ntl Merit Ltr; Prfct Atten Awd; HS Schlrshp 84-87; 2nd Pl Magna Carta Essy Cntst-Schlrshp 87; Voic-Vision Essy Cntst Postr-Fdrl Bldgs.

DONATO, MARK L; Penn Hills HS; Pittsburgh, PA; (4); 147/616; Ski Clb; Varsity Clb; Off Sr Cls; Stu Cncl; L Vllybl; High Hon Roll; Hon Roll; Robert Morris Coll; Bus Manag.

DONATO, MICHELE; Exeter SR HS; Reading, PA; (3); 25/260; Drama Clb; Concert Band; Mrchg Band; Orch; Rep Stu Cncl; JV Fld Hcky; High Hon Roll; Jr NHS; NHS; Coll Misericordia Schlrshp 87; Golden Eagle Awd-Acad Achvt 85; Early Admittnc To Coll Misericordia 87; Coll Misericordia; Nrsg.

DONCH, DANA; Northwestern HS; Albion, PA; (3); Church Yth Grp; Drama Clb; Red Cross Aide; Thesps; Chorus; Church Choir; Drill Tm; School Musical; School Play; Hon Roll; Dist, Regnl, ST Chorus; Music Ed.

DONCH, KRISTA; Cardinal O Hara HS; Brookhaven, PA; (3); 184/718; Art Clb; Church Yth Grp; Dance Clb; Intnl Clb; JA; School Play; Sec Frsh Cls; Bowling; Hon Roll; Bus Adm.

DONEL, TIM; Trinity HS; Washington, PA; (4); 71/322; Aud/Vis; Thesps; Mrchg Band; School Play; Stage Crew; Hon Roll; OH U; Audio Prdtcn.

DONELLI, JENNIFER L; North Allegheny SR HS; Allison Pk, PA; (3); Church Yth Grp; French Clb; Hosp Aide; Ski Clb; Chorus; Yrbk Ed-Chief; Yrbk Stf; High Hon Roll; Jr NHS; Dance Clb; Dstngshd Achvt PA Schl Press Assn 86; Med.

DONEY, DONNA; Punxsutawney Area SR HS; Punxsutawney, PA; (4); 92/264; Church Yth Grp; FCA; FBLA; Mary Ann Irvin Scholar; John W Jenks; IN U PA; Elem Ed.

DONEY, TARA; Parkland HS; Allentown, PA; (2); Hosp Aide; Office Aide; Y-Teens; Chrmn Frsh Cls; Rep Soph Cls; High Hon Roll; Hon Roll; Travel.

DONGAS, NOELLE A; E L Meyers HS; Wilkes Barre, PA; (3); 18/187; French Clb; Sec Key Clb; Library Aide; Pep Clb; SADD; Chorus; Yrbk Stf; Trk; Hon Roll; NHS; Outstndng Frnch Stu Awd 85-86; Key Clbr Mnth 87; Bloomsbrgu U; Medcl Tech.

DONGELL, LESLIE; Penn Cambria HS; Gallitzin, PA; (2); 5/235; Drama Clb; NFL; Spanish Clb; Speech Tm; SADD; Nwsp Rptr; Off Stu Cncl; Cheerleading; Socr; Hon Roll; Sci Fair Winner 86; Med.

DONGES, INGRID; Great Valley HS; Phoenixville, PA; (3); 3/267; Trs German Clb; Sec SADD; Acpl Chr; Chorus; JV Capt Cheerleading; NHS; Distinguished Hnr Roll 84-87; Dist 12 Rgnl Choruses 87; Athlete Of Wk,Mst Spritd Awd 86; MA Inst Of Tech; Engr.

DONGHIA, JAMES; Mohawk HS; New Castle, PA; (4); 12/140; Cmnty Wkr; Letterman Clb; Spanish Clb; Varsity Clb; Band; Concert Band; Ftbl; Trk; Wt Lftg; High Hon Roll; Outstndng Tm Plyr Ftbl 86; Duquesne U; Bus Admin.

DONHOFF, CONSTANCE; Seneca Valley HS; Harmony, PA; (4); 52/358; Var L Bsktbl; Var L Sftbl; Hon Roll; Gen Coll Schlrshp 87; Wstmnstr Athltc Grnt 87-91; Westminster Coll; Engrng.

DONINI, SAM; Charleroi Area HS; Charleroi, PA; (3); Church Yth Grp; VP French Clb; Ski Clb; SADD; Varsity Clb; Off Soph Cls; Stu Cncl; Var Bsbl; JV Bsktbl; Var Trk.

DONLAN, ROB; Shamokin Area HS; Shamokin, PA; (2); 16/260; Church Yth Grp; Cmnty Wkr; Key Clb; Pep Clb; Science Clb; Ski Clb; Varsity Clb; Orch; Ftbl; Trk; Dist Orch, Rgnl Orch 86-87; Teenage Powerlfting 1st Pl 86.

DONLEY, PAULA; Meyersdale Area HS; Meyersdale, PA; (3); French Clb; Band; Concert Band; Mrchg Band; School Musical; Yrbk Stf; Hon Roll; NHS; Elem Ed.

DONLIN JR, PAUL; Dallas SR HS; Dallas, PA; (3); Chess Clb; Computer Clb; Bsbl; Golf; Engrng.

DONMBROSKY, JENNIFER; Shenandoah Valley HS; Shenandoah, PA; (3); Computer Clb; Dance Clb; Pep Clb; Spanish Clb; SADD; Varsity Clb; Chorus; Rep Jr Cls; Off Stu Cncl; Cheerleading.

DONMOYER, NICOLE; Annville-Cleona HS; Lebanon, PA; (3); 18/127; FBLA; Varsity Clb; Chorus; Yrbk Stf; Stu Cncl; Cheerleading; Score Keeper; Sftbl; Vllybl; Jr NHS; Med Arts.

DONMOYER, RENEE; Pine Grove Area HS; Pine Grove, PA; (3); Church Yth Grp; SADD; School Musical; Yrbk Stf; Im Vllybl; High Hon Roll; Hon Roll; NHS; Frnch Engl Geom & Bio Awds 86; Spnsh Frnch Engl & Soc Stu Awds 87; PA Free Entrpse Wk Sem Schlrhsp 87; Bloomsburg U; Psych.

DONNACHIE, CRAIG; Cedar Crest HS; Lebanon, PA; (3); German Clb; Pep Clb; Ftbl; JV Socr; Hon Roll; U Of Pittsburgh; Envrnmt Engr.

DONNELLI, MARK; Fleetwood Area HS; Fleetwood, PA; (3); 9/115; Boy Scts; Band; Chorus; Color Guard; Concert Band; Drill Tm; Mrchg Band; School Musical; Trs Jr Cls; Pres Sr Cls; Sertoma Clb Recog Outstndng Stdnts 85-86; Intl Stds.

DONNELLY, BRIAN; Fairview HS; Fairview, PA; (4); 8/150; Cmnty Wkr; Debate Tm; Model UN; Teachers Aide; Varsity Clb; Nwsp Stf; Rep Stu Cncl; Var Crs Cntry; JV Socr; JV Trk; Wnnr Fr G Matthew Daly Schlrshp 87; Latn Natl Hnr Socty; Wnng Tm PA Free Entrprs Wk 86; Boston Coll.

DONNELLY, CAROL; Archbishop Ryan High Schl For Girls; Philadelphia, PA; (4); 6/490; French Clb; Library Aide; Science Clb; Nwsp Rptr; French Hon Soc; Hon Roll; NHS; JV Cheerleading; Phila Coll Phrmcy & Sci Pres Schlrshp 87; U Of Pitts Prvst Schlr 87; Phrmcy.

DONNELLY, COLEEN M; Padua Acad; Boothwyn, PA; (3); Art Clb; Church Yth Grp; Cmnty Wkr; JV Swmmng; Swathmore; Art.

DONNELLY, JOHN; Bethlehem Catholic HS; Hellertown, PA; (3); 63/200; Church Yth Grp; Scholastic Bowl; Science Clb; VP Sr Cls; Var L Bsktbl; Var L Ftbl; Im Vllybl; Var Wt Lftg; High Hon Roll; Sir Thomas J Lipton Awd 82; Natl League Arts Olumpiad 84; Finance.

DONNELLY, JUDY; Central Bucks East HS; Warrington, PA; (3); 2/488; Church Yth Grp; Hosp Aide; Band; Concert Band; Mrchg Band; Hon Roll; Fash Merch.

DONNELLY, KATHY; Notre Dame HS; Easton, PA; (3); 16/96; Hosp Aide; Office Aide; Pep Clb; Yrbk Stf; Rep Soph Cls; Stu Cncl; JV Cheerleading; Mgr(s); Score Keeper; Sftbl; Lafyette; Psych.

DONNELLY, KIMBERLY; Red Lion Area SR HS; Airville, PA; (3); 16/342; Am Leg Aux Girls St; Debate Tm; Mrchg Band; School Musical; Symp Band; Nwsp Rptr; Trs Frsh Cls; Pres Soph Cls; High Hon Roll; Hon Roll.

DONNELLY, MELODY A; Berwick Area SR HS; Berwick, PA; (2); Church Yth Grp; Keywanettes; Band; Color Guard; Concert Band; Mrchg Band; Hon Roll; Jr NHS; NHS; BYU; Secndry Ed.

DONNELLY, REGINA; Archbishop Kennedy HS; Philadelphia, PA; (2); Cmnty Wkr; Rep Frsh Cls; Trk; Vllybl; Prfct Atten Awd; Temple.

DONNELLY, SUSAN; Creative & Performing Arts HS; Philadelphia, PA; (4); 6/127; Chorus; Hon Roll; NHS; Red Cross Aide; Acpl Chr; School Musical; 1st Rnnr Up Talent Miss PA Teenager Pgnt 86; Ithaca Coll; Music Educ.

DONNER, MONICA; Greenville JR SR HS; Greenville, PA; (1); 19/160; Sec French Clb; Sec Trs Chorus; JV L Cheerleading; Hon Roll.

DONNIAN, PASQUALE; St John Neumann HS; Philadelphia, PA; (3); 48/349; Chess Clb; FBLA; SADD; Hon Roll; 2nd Hnrs 84-87; 1st Hnrs 86-87; Crmnl Jstc.

DONNINI, JOSEPH; E L Meyers HS; Wilkes Barre, PA; (3); 19/187; French Clb; Key Clb; Political Wkr; Ski Clb; SADD; Chorus; Yrbk Bus Mgr; VP Jr Cls; Trk; French Hon Soc.

DONOFRIO, JOHN; Coatesville Area SR HS; Coatesville, PA; (4); 7/470; Spanish Clb; Im Bsbl; Im Wrstlng; High Hon Roll; NHS; Pres Schlr; Temple U Pres Schlrshp 87; Cert Ed Devlpmt 85; Temple; Cmmncts.

DONOHUE, CHRISTINE M; Villa Maria Acad; Drexel Hill, PA; (4); Church Yth Grp; NFL; School Musical; Yrbk Ed-Chief; Im Fld Hcky; High Hon Roll; Mu Alpha Theta Awd; VP NHS; Ntl Merit SF; Spanish NHS; Villanova U; Sci.

DONOVAN, BRIAN; Forest City Regional HS; Forest City, PA; (3); Drama Clb; German Clb; Letterman Clb; Ski Clb; Varsity Clb; Band; Concert Band; Jazz Band; Mrchg Band; School Musical.

DONOVAN, COURTNEY; Haverford HS; Havertown, PA; (3); GAA; Service Clb; Spanish Clb; Stage Crew; Nwsp Rptr; Nwsp Stf; Rep Frsh Cls; Var Fld Hcky; JV Gym; Var Lcrss; Cmmnctns.

DONOVAN, GAYANNE; Daniel Boone HS; Douglasville, PA; (4); 61/165; French Clb; German Clb; JA; SADD; Varsity Clb; Flag Corp; Stu Cncl; JV Var Cheerleading; Mgr(s); Powder Puff Ftbl; Sportsmnshp Awd Bsktbl Chrldng 85-86; MVP Awd Ftbl Chrldng 86-87; U TN Knoxville; Phys Thrpy.

DONOVAN, HEATHER; Aliquippa HS; Aliquippa, PA; (3); Church Yth Grp; Drama Clb; Exploring; Sec French Clb; Office Aide; Band; Concert Band; Mrchg Band; School Play; JV Cheerleading; Gannon U; Dntstry.

DONOVAN, HEATHER; Wilson Area HS; Riegelsville, PA; (4); 6/135; Debate Tm; Ski Clb; Nwsp Ed-Chief; Yrbk Rptr; Ed Yrbk Stf; Rep Stu Cncl; Mgr(s); High Hon Roll; NHS; Pres Schlr; G Washington Schlr WA Coll 87; Flt Rsv Assoc Bond 87; Anna C Moyer Awd Eng 87; WA Coll; Eng.

DONOVAN, JEANNETTE; West Scranton HS; Scranton, PA; (2); Spanish Clb; Co-Capt Cheerleading; Hon Roll; Jr NHS.

DONOVAN, KIMBERLY; Riverside JR SR HS; Moosic, PA; (3); 16/146; Ski Clb; Flag Corp; Variety Show; Yrbk Stf; Pres Soph Cls; Pres Jr Cls; Off Stu Cncl; Var JV Cheerleading; High Hon Roll; NHS; Presdntl Acadmc Ftns Awd 85; Mrktng.

DONTEN, SUSAN M; Cedar Crest HS; Lebanon, PA; (4); 10/306; Art Clb; Cmnty Wkr; French Clb; Pep Clb; School Musical; Im Vllybl; High Hon Roll; NHS; Ntl Merit SF; Church Yth Grp; Honor Banquet 84-86.

DONTON, RUSSELL; Cedar Crest HS; Lebanon, PA; (2); Pep Clb; Golf; Hon Roll.

DOOLIN, CHRISTINE M; Kennedy Christian HS; W Middlesex, PA; (4); 2/93; Hosp Aide; Pres Science Clb; Band; Concert Band; Mrchg Band; NHS; NEDT Awd; Sal; Coll Womns Assn Schlrshp 87; Pres Acdmc Fit Awd 87; U Of Pittsburgh; Phy Thrpy.

DOOLING, MARK; Frankford HS; Philadelphia, PA; (3); 6/672; FBLA; Service Clb; Nwsp Stf; Bsbl; Ftbl; High Hon Roll; Hon Roll; NHS; Vrsty Bsbll MVP 87; Vrsty Bsbll All Public Catcher 87; Vrsty Bsbll All City 87; Bus.

DOPERA, KRISTINE; Parkland HS; Schnecksville, PA; (3); 90/481; Leo Clb; Library Aide; Bsktbl; Trk; Capt Twrlr; Hon Roll.

DOPERAK, VICKI; Gateway SR HS; Monroeville, PA; (3); Chorus; Off Frsh Cls; Off Soph Cls; Off Jr Cls; Off Sr Cls; Stu Cncl; Capt Var Cheerleading; Cit Awd; Hon Roll; Prfct Atten Awd; Cmmnctns.

DOPKO, MICHELLE; G A R JR SR Memorial HS; Wilkes-Barre, PA; (4); 9/172; Debate Tm; Key Clb; Chorus; Nwsp Stf; Off Stu Cncl; Tennis; Hon Roll; Jr NHS; NHS; Dbt Tm Awd 86; Advrtsng.

DOPP, JANE; Shaler Area SR HS; Glenshaw, PA; (3); 11/486; Church Yth Grp; SADD; Band; Mrchg Band; Symp Band; Ed Lit Mag; High Hon Roll; Hon Roll; NHS; NEDT Awd; Med.

DORAN, CHRISTOPHER; Monsignor Bonner HS; Yeadon, PA; (3); 17/250; SADD; Variety Show; Nwsp Stf; Rep Frsh Cls; Rep Soph Cls; Rep Jr Cls; Im Bsktbl; JV Swmmng; French Hon Soc; Hon Roll; Villanova; Comms.

DORAN, JANET WANDA; Upper Merion HS; King Of Prussia, PA; (2); Church Yth Grp; DECA; Trphy For 3rd Pl In Dist Cmptitns DECA, Mdl For 1st Pl Dist Cmptitn In DECA 87; Johnson & Wales; Real Estate.

DORAN, ROBERT; Archbishop Ryan HS For Boys; Philadelphia, PA; (2); 88/349; Political Wkr; Hon Roll; UCLA; Law.

DORAZIO, MICHELE; Fairchance-Georges HS; Smithfield, PA; (3); Library Aide; High Hon Roll; Hon Roll; Jr NHS; WV Career Inst; Secy.

DORENZO, NICOLE; Upper Darby HS; Clifton Heights, PA; (3); Hon Roll; Prfct Atten Awd; Perfct Atten 84-87; Psych.

DORF, JONATHAN; Marple Newtown HS; Broomall, PA; (2); 1/324; Chess Clb; Capt Debate Tm; Model UN; Trs Temple Yth Grp; Nwsp Ed-Chief; Var L Tennis; High Hon Roll; Amer Chem Scty Awd 86-87.

DORFI, ANNE; Kennedy Christian HS; Sharon, PA; (2); 14/96; Church Yth Grp; Office Aide; Service Clb; Spanish Clb; Band; Concert Band; Jazz Band; Mrchg Band; Hon Roll.

DORFIELD, JENNIFER; Butler SR HS; Butler, PA; (3); French Clb; Thesps; Color Guard; Drill Tm; School Play; Nwsp Ed-Chief; Trs Jr Cls; Rep Stu Cncl; Hon Roll; NHS; JR Natl Hnr Soc Acadmc Ltr Merit 86; Acadmc Achvt Awd 87; Butler Cnty JR Miss Fnlst 87; Lbrl Arts.

DORFMEISTER, JENNIFER; Altoona Area HS; Altoona, PA; (3); 12/796; Math Tm; Spanish Clb; Var L Bsktbl; High Hon Roll; VP Jr NHS; ST & Natl Bsktbl Champ 85-86; Grls Lg 86.

DORIS, CHRISTA; Marian Catholic HS; Hometown, PA; (3); 38/104; Church Yth Grp; Office Aide; Pep Clb; Yrbk Stf; Cheerleading; Amer Lgn Awd 84; Phys Thrpy.

DORISH, MOLLY; Wyoming Valley West HS; Kingston, PA; (4); 42/400; Key Clb; Library Aide; Pep Clb; Sec Jr Cls; Pres Stu Cncl; Im Bsktbl; Var Diving; Var Swmmng; Im Vllybl; Cit Awd; Acad Achvt Schlrshp To Kings Coll 87; Yth Ldr Of Yr 3rd Rnnr-Up 86; Kings Coll.

DORKO, MICHAEL; Steel Valley HS; Munhall, PA; (4); 10/201; Band; Concert Band; Mrchg Band; NHS; U Of Pittsburgh; Chem.

DORKO, MICHELLE; Steel Valley HS; Munhall, PA; (3); 9/209; Cmnty Wkr; Hosp Aide; Yrbk Stf; Stu Cncl; Capt Cheerleading; High Hon Roll; NHS; US Chrldr Achvt Awd, Natl Sci Merit Awd, Acdmc All Amer Schlr 86-87; U Of Pittsburgh; Phys Thrpy.

DORMAN, FRANCES; Faith Christian Schl; Pittsburgh, PA; (2); Drama Clb; Chorus; Church Choir; School Play; High Hon Roll; Hardest Wrkr Awd 86; Prncpls Hnr Awd 86; Med.

DORMAN, MICHAEL; Mifflinburg Area HS; Mifflinburg, PA; (4); 9/174; FBLA; Var Bsbl; Var L Ftbl; Var L Wrstlng; Cit Awd; High Hon Roll; Hon Roll; NHS; Bloomsburg U; Bus Admin.

DORMAN, MICHELE; Bellefonte Area HS; Pleasant Gap, PA; (4); 91/235; French Clb; SADD; Varsity Clb; Flag Corp; Yrbk Stf; Rep Sr Cls; Var L Cheerleading; L Capt Crs Cntry; Var Powder Puff Ftbl; Var L Trk; Outstndnt Sr Awd For Cross Cntry 87; Lock Haven U; Sociology.

DORMAN, TERESA; Bald Eagle Area HS; Fleming, PA; (4); 24/196; French Clb; Library Aide; Nwsp Stf; Hon Roll; Lock Haven U; Scndry Ed.

DORMER, TAMMY; Shamokin Area HS; Shamokin, PA; (4); 11/238; Drama Clb; German Clb; Key Clb; Pep Clb; Science Clb; Ski Clb; Varsity Clb; Color Guard; Yrbk Stf; Bsktbl; Ursinus Coll; Sprts Med.

DORN, CHERYL; Susquehannock HS; Shrewsbury, PA; (3); 16/194; AFS; Church Yth Grp; Orch; School Musical; School Play; Nwsp Rptr; Bsktbl; Hon Roll; NHS; Dist 7 Orchstra 87; York Yth Symphny 84-88; Acadc Ltr 86.

DORNBACH, JASON; North Hampton SR HS; Bath, PA; (3); 145/394; Church Yth Grp; DECA; Var Ftbl; JV Var Socr; Var Trk; Wt Lftg; JV Wrstlng; Hon Roll; 1st Pl Dist For DECA 86-87; Churchmans Bus Schl; Bus Admin.

DORNEY, GREG; Nazareth Area HS; Nazareth, PA; (3); 79/280; Computer Clb; German Clb; Letterman Clb; Varsity Clb; Var L Bsbl; Im Bsktbl; Im Ftbl; Im Sftbl; Im Tennis; Im Wt Lftg; 1st Tm Colonl Leag-Bsbl 86-87; Bus Manag.

DORNEY, MAUREEN; Steel Valley HS; Munhall, PA; (3); 25/216; Pres Key Clb; Band; Mrchg Band; Hon Roll; NHS; Penn ST U; Marine Bio.

DORNISCH, MAUREEN; Elk County Christian HS; St Marys, PA; (3); Color Guard; Vllybl; Hon Roll; Tchr.

DORRION, WILLIAM; Sheffield Area JR-SR HS; Tiona, PA; (3); 1/95; Computer Clb; Drama Clb; Band; Jazz Band; Pres Mrchg Band; Pep Band; School Musical; Symp Band; High Hon Roll; JETS Awd.

DORSCH, CURTIS; Conestoga HS; Paoli, PA; (3); 23/452; Ski Clb; JV Bsbl; JV Bsktbl; High Hon Roll; Hon Roll.

DORSHIMER, DAWNA; Lackawanna Trall HS; Factoryville, PA; (3); Drama Clb; Ski Clb; Chorus; Stu Cncl; Fld Hcky; Mgr(s); Score Keeper; French Hon Soc; Hon Roll; NHS; Pres Physcl Ftnss Awd 85-87; Messiah Coll.

DORSHIMER, RONDA; Pleasant Valley HS; Kunkletown, PA; (2); Drama Clb; Pep Clb; Off Soph Cls; Stu Cncl; Stat Bsktbl; JV Cheerleading; JV Sftbl; Hon Roll; Allentown Bus Schl; Bus Mgmt.

DORSI, SHEILA M; Pennridge HS; Sellersville, PA; (3); 112/409; SADD; Orch; Nwsp Stf; Stu Cncl; Var Fld Hcky; Trk; Hon Roll; Marine Bio.

DORWART, STEPHANIE; Valley HS; Arnold, PA; (3); 32/225; Art Clb; French Clb; Math Tm; Ski Clb; Chorus; Yrbk Ed-Chief; Yrbk Phtg; Hon Roll; Am Legn Awd 84; Acdmc All-Am 87; Wash & Jeff; Aeron Engrng.

DORWART, STEPHEN; Neshamiry HS; Trevose, PA; (4); 117/723; Var L Bsbl; Var L Ftbl; Im Wt Lftg; Hon Roll; Jr NHS; NHS; Ftbl Schlrshp Bucknell Defsmn Yr 85-86; All Lowr Bucks Alls Tr Ftbl Gm 87; Bucknell; Bio.

DOSCH, MARK T; North Allegheny SR HS; Pittsburgh, PA; (3); 9/649; Am Leg Boys St; Exploring; JA; Rep Jr Cls; Im Vllybl; Hon Roll; Jr NHS; NHS; Prfct Atten Awd; Bio Pre-Med.

DOSS, KEVIN; Pine Grove Area HS; Pine Grove, PA; (3); ROTC; Varsity Clb; Drill Tm; Rep Stu Cncl; Var Capt Ftbl; Im Sftbl; Var Wt Lftg; JV Wrstlng; Prfct Atten Awd; Church Yth Grp; Super Cadet Awd JROTC 87; Bus.

DOTSON, LESLIE A; Lower Merion HS; Boulder, CO; (3); Drama Clb; Hosp Aide; SADD; Thesps; Chorus; Color Guard; Intl Rltns.

DOTTER, CATHERINE; Pittston Area HS; Hughestown, PA; (3); 5/305; Drama Clb; Concert Band; Jazz Band; Mrchg Band; Orch; Symp Band; Computer Clb; Math Clb; Science Clb; Dist IX Band 85; Region IV Band 86; 2nd Marywood Coll Wind Ensmbl 86; Music Educ.

DOTTER, JENNIFER; Seneca Valley HS; Evans Cty, PA; (3); 13/370; Church Yth Grp; Natl Beta Clb; Sec SADD; Chorus; Jazz Band; Var Pom Pon; High Hon Roll; VP NHS; Sec Jr Cls; Pres Sr Cls; Jr Natl Hnr Soc 84-85; Honor Roll 84087; Secondary Educ.

DOTTER, TRACY; Seneca Valley HS; Evans Cty, PA; (3); 13/370; Church Yth Grp; Natl Beta Clb; SADD; Chorus; Jazz Band; VP Sr Cls; Off Stu Cncl; Pom Pon; Var L Swmmng; NHS; Jr Natl Hnr Soc 84-85; Hnr Roll 84-87; Engl Teacher.

DOTTERY, KEITH; William Allen HS; Allentown, PA; (3); 37/670; Exploring; JCL; Latin Clb; Ski Clb; Varsity Clb; Yrbk Stf; Hon Roll; Jr NHS; NHS; Engrng.

DOTTS, TAMMY; Owen J Roberts HS; Pottstown, PA; (4); 38/272; Pres Aud/Vis; Library Aide; Scholastic Bowl; School Musical; School Play; Lit Mag; Wright ST U; Theatre Arts.

DOUBLE, CHRISTINA; Karns City HS; Karns City, PA; (4); Yrbk Stf; Stat Bsktbl; Var L Vllybl; Hon Roll; NHS; Pres Acad Ftns Awd 87; Acad Lttr 86; Scrtry.

DOUBLE, GARY; Karns City HS; Karns City, PA; (3); Hon Roll; NHS.

DOUD, LISA; Williamson JR SR HS; Lawrenceville, PA; (3); 6/89; Computer Clb; Trs Spanish Clb; Yrbk Stf; Var L Trk; High Hon Roll; Hon Roll; NHS; Scl Stds Awd 87; Hnr Roll Awd 87; Med.

DOUDRICK, DORTHEY; West Perry HS; New Bloomfield, PA; (4); 13/192; Drama Clb; French Clb; Varsity Clb; Concert Band; Mrchg Band; Stage Crew; Yrbk Stf; Stat Sftbl; Hon Roll; NHS; Fine Arts Schlrshp Stdy Europe 86-87; Goucher Coll.

DOUDS, RENEE; Hempfield SR HS; Jeannette, PA; (3); GAA; Latin Clb; Pep Clb; Ski Clb; Spanish Clb; Yrbk Stf; Rep Stu Cncl; L Cheerleading; Powder Puff Ftbl; Trk; Pres Acad Awd 84-85; Chrldng Awd 84-87.

DOUGALAS, LAURA; Wyoming Valley West HS; Swoyersville, PA; (3); Key Clb; Ski Clb; L Var Fld Hcky; L Var Trk; Im Vllybl; Hon Roll; NHS; Boston U; Comms.

DOUGAN, BECKY; Meadville SR HS; Meadville, PA; (3); 21/350; French Clb; Girl Scts; Key Clb; Ski Clb; Band; Concert Band; Socr; Hon Roll; Dist Band 86; Rgnl Band 86; Ntl French Frgn Exch 86; Music.

DOUGERT, CARY; J M Coughlin HS; Wilkes Barre, PA; (3); Trs German Clb; Drill Tm; Trk; NHS.

DOUGHER, CHRISTINE; Pittston Area HS; Pittston, PA; (3); Church Yth Grp; Chorus; Hon Roll; Speech Thrpy.

DOUGHER, JAMES; Valley View JR SR HS; Archbald, PA; (3); 6/190; Church Yth Grp; Latin Clb; Spanish Clb; Church Choir; Coach Actv; Golf; Swmmng; High Hon Roll; Hon Roll; NHS; Lehigh Univ; Engnrng.

DOUGHER, LYNN; Valley View HS; Archbald, PA; (1); 28/204; Church Yth Grp; Ski Clb; Spanish Clb; Chorus; School Musical; Crs Cntry; Swmmng; Trk; Prfct Atten Awd.

DOUGHERTY, ANDREA; The Philadelphia HS For Girls; Philadelphia, PA; (3); Office Aide; Teachers Aide; Off Frsh Cls; Hon Roll; Prfct Atten Awd; Meretrious 85, 86 & 87; Bus.

DOUGHERTY, ANDREW; Cardinal O Hara HS; Broomall, PA; (3); 10/750; Debate Tm; Math Tm; NFL; Speech Tm; Nwsp Bus Mgr; Nwsp Ed-Chief; Var Golf; Chess Clb; Hon Roll; NHS; 1st Awds At DE Vly Sci Fairr 85-87; 1st Awds At P J A S ST Comp 83-87; Entre Con 87; Bus.

DOUGHERTY, ANN; Hazelton SR HS; Hazleton, PA; (3); Church Yth Grp; Leo Clb; Pep Clb; Ski Clb; Spanish Clb; Stu Cncl; Var Co-Capt Cheerleading; Hon Roll; Prfct Atten Awd; Govt.

DOUGHERTY, BOB; Emmaus HS; Wescosville, PA; (4); Math Clb; Math Tm; Band; Concert Band; Mrchg Band; JV Golf; Var Tennis; Hon Roll; Jr NHS; AHSME Semi-Fnlst 87; U Of DE; Chem Engnrng.

DOUGHERTY, BRANDON; Upper Darby HS; Upr Darby, PA; (3); Drama Clb; Office Aide; School Play; Rep Stu Cncl; Bsktbl; JV Var Mgr(s); High Hon Roll; Hon Roll; Outstndng Stu Awd 85-86; Phtgrphy.

DOUGHERTY, CLARK; Eastern York HS; York, PA; (2); Church Yth Grp; Drama Clb; Chorus; Church Choir; School Musical; High Hon Roll; Hon Roll; Marine Bio.

DOUGHERTY, COLLEEN; Bishop Hafey HS; Hazleton, PA; (4); Hosp Aide; Ski Clb; Spanish Clb; Sec Sr Cls; Off Stu Cncl; Cheerleading; CC Awd; Intnl Clb; Donald Mason Busnss Schlrshp 86; Century 21 Typing Awd 86; US Business Educ Awd 87; St Josephs U; Business Admin.

DOUGHERTY, DRAKE; York Catholic HS; York, PA; (3); 77/154; Church Yth Grp; Drama Clb; French Clb; Varsity Clb; School Play; Rep Frsh Cls; Rep Soph Cls; Rep Jr Cls; Rep Sr Cls; Rep Stu Cncl; Bus Mgmt.

DOUGHERTY, ERICA; Hamburg Area HS; Shoemakersville, PA; (3); 15/170; Library Aide; Speech Tm; Band; Chorus; School Musical; Hon Roll; NHS; Latin Clb; Spanish Clb; Acdmc Ltr Awds-Wrld Cltrs, Algbr II & Spnsh II; Intl Rltns.

DOUGHERTY, JENNIFER; Emmaus HS; Macungie, PA; (3); 123/520; French Clb; Varsity Clb; Band; Chorus; Concert Band; School Musical; School Play; Off Jr Cls; Var JV Bsktbl; Hon Roll.

DOUGHERTY, MARGARET; North Hills SR HS; Pittsburgh, PA; (3); Church Yth Grp; Key Clb; Chorus; Sec Trs Jr Cls; Rep Stu Cncl; Var JV Cheerleading; Trk; High Hon Roll; NHS; U Of Notre Dame; Advrtsng.

DOUGHERTY, MICHAEL; Quigley HS; Allison Park, PA; (3); Camera Clb; Church Yth Grp; German Clb; Hon Roll; Art & Hist Awds 85-86.

DOUGHERTY, MICHELE; Northwestern Lehigh HS; Germansville, PA; (4); 52/149; DECA; Rep Stu Cncl; Hon Roll; Lehigh Cnty CC; Trvl & Trsm.

DOUGHERTY, PATRICIA C; Boyertown HS; Gilbertsville, PA; (1); Dance Clb; French Clb; PAVAS; Teachers Aide; Yrbk Stf; Rep Frsh Cls; Stu Cncl; Cheerleading; Mgr(s); Hon Roll; Socl Sci.

DOUGHERTY, PATRICK; Lansdale Catholic HS; Lansdale, PA; (3); Boy Scts; Pres Frsh Cls; VP Soph Cls; JV Var Bsbl; JV Var Bsktbl; Ftbl; Hon Roll; Prfct Atten Awd; Rotary Awd.

DOUGHERTY, PAUL; West Scranton SR HS; Scranton, PA; (2); Church Yth Grp; JV Bsktbl; Var Crs Cntry; Hon Roll; Jr NHS.

DOUGHERTY, SHERMAN; Reading SR HS; Reading, PA; (4); 45/563; Debate Tm; Crs Cntry; Trk; Hon Roll; 4th Pl Rdng/Berks Sci Fair 86; JR Rtrn 86; Engnrng.

DOUGHMAN, CHERYL; Lancaster Christian Schl; Bird In Hand, PA; (3); Chorus; Var Bsktbl; Capt Fld Hcky; Hon Roll.

DOUGHTY, SHANNON; Montour HS; Coraopolis, PA; (2); Office Aide; SADD; Chorus; Yrbk Stf; Mgr(s); Timer; High Hon Roll; U Of Pgh; Psych.

DOUGLAS, AMY; Red Lion Area SR HS; Delta, PA; (3); 8/375; Debate Tm; Sec 4-H; School Musical; School Play; Nwsp Stf; Sec Soph Cls; 4-H Awd; Hon Roll; Prfct Atten Awd; Ed.

DOUGLAS, ANGELA; Elkland Area HS; Middlebury, PA; (3); 4/68; Drama Clb; French Clb; SADD; Band; Chorus; Concert Band; Mrchg Band; School Musical; School Play; Nwsp Stf; Pres Acad Ftns Awd 85; Gldn Poet Awd 86 & 87; Dstrct VIII Bnd 87; Elem Ed.

DOUGLAS, BRIANA MICHELLE; Villa Maria Acad; Phoenixville, PA; (3); Hosp Aide; Science Clb; Chorus; Church Choir; Madrigals; School Musical; Hon Roll; Tri-M Intl Music Hnr Scty 84-87,Histrn 87; Smmr Music Schlrshp 86; Natl Fat Stu Musicians ST 86-87; Med.

DOUGLAS, ELIZABETH; Villa Maria Acad; Wayne, PA; (3); Art Clb; Drama Clb; School Play; Yrbk Phtg; Yrbk Rptr; Lit Mag; High Hon Roll; NHS; Ntl Merit Schol; Cmmnctns.

DOUGLAS, MELISSA; Chambersburg Area SR HS; Chambersburg, PA; (2); French Clb; Ski Clb; Band; Chorus; Church Choir; Concert Band; Mrchg Band; High Hon Roll; Hon Roll; PA ST U.

DOUGLAS, MONICA; Elizabeth Forward HS; Elizabeth, PA; (3); Church Yth Grp; Cmnty Wkr; Nwsp Rptr; Yrbk Stf; Pres Soph Cls; Pres Jr Cls; Stat Trk; Stat Wrstlng; Hon Roll; Clarion U PA; Pre-Law.

DOUGLAS, MONICA; Valley HS; New Kensington, PA; (3); Ski Clb; Varsity Clb; Chorus; Concert Band; Mrchg Band; Pres Frsh Cls; Var Capt Cheerleading; JV Var Vllybl; High Hon Roll; Hon Roll; Medcl.

DOUGLAS, RENETTA; Hollidaysburg Area HS; Hollidaysburg, PA; (3); Drama Clb; FNA; German Clb; Latin Clb; Library Aide; SADD; Y-Teens; School Play; Stage Crew; Rep Frsh Cls; RN Nrsng.

DOUGLAS, STEPHANIE; Northeast HS; Philadelphia, PA; (4); 54/600; German Clb; Political Wkr; Band; Concert Band; Mrchg Band; Orch; School Musical; Hon Roll; NHS; Dr A Oswald Michener Instrmntl Awd 87; Sentate Svc Awd 87; U DE; Mrktng.

DOUGLAS, THOMAS; Trinity HS; Washington, PA; (3); Mgr(s); Hon Roll; Phrmcy.

DOUGLASS, KELLIE; Hempfield Area SR HS; Irwin, PA; (3); Trs Church Yth Grp; French Clb; Pep Clb; Ski Clb; Teachers Aide; Chorus; School Musical; Yrbk Stf; JV Cheerleading; Var Vllybl; Indvl Awd Chrldng Camp 84; Vlybl Vrsty Ltrmn 85; Sec Ed.

DOUTHAT, STEPHEN; Columbia-Montour Area Vo-Tech; Nescopeck, PA; (3); #21 In Class; FFA; JV Bsktbl.

DOUTRICH, MARK; Tulpehocken HS; Bethel, PA; (4); 3/100; Band; Chorus; School Musical; School Play; High Hon Roll; Hon Roll; NHS; PA ST U; Scndry Educ.

DOUTRICH, NOEL; Donegal HS; Maytown, PA; (3); 18/177; Varsity Clb; JV Var Bsktbl; L Var Fld Hcky; Var Powder Puff Ftbl; L Var Trk; High Hon Roll; Hon Roll; Most Outstndg Athl Trck Team 87; Good Sprtsmnshp Awd Bsktbl 86-87; Bus.

DOUTT, HEIDI; Cranberry HS; Seneca, PA; (3); 41/140; French Clb; Pep Clb; SADD; Varsity Clb; School Musical; Rep Stu Cncl; Cheerleading; Crs Cntry; Trk; Hon Roll; Med.

DOUTT, JENNIFER LYNN; Sharpsville HS; Clark, PA; (4); Hosp Aide; Library Aide; Spanish Clb; Thesps; Chorus; Yrbk Stf; Hon Roll; Acdmc Lttr 86-87; Yngstown ST U; Nutritn.

DOUTT, JOANNE; Cambridge Springs HS; Saegerton, PA; (2); 10/101; Church Yth Grp; VP Sec 4-H; Pep Clb; SADD; JV Bsktbl; JV Sftbl; JV Vllybl; 4-H Awd; Hon Roll; NHS; Elem Ed.

DOUTT, PAULA; Cambridge Springs HS; Saegertown, PA; (4); 5/100; Church Yth Grp; Pres 4-H; French Clb; Pep Clb; SADD; Yrbk Phtg; Yrbk Stf; VP Stu Cncl; Capt L Bsktbl; Capt L Sftbl; Houghton Coll-NY; Lbrl Arts.

DOUTY, KAMI; Juniata HS; Mifflintown, PA; (3); SADD; Varsity Clb; Mrchg Band; School Play; Yrbk Stf; Trs Soph Cls; Trs Jr Cls; Cheerleading; Hon Roll; NHS; Bus.

DOVERSPIKE, BRAD; Freeport Area HS; Sarver, PA; (3); JV Bsktbl; JV Var Ftbl; VFW Awd; U Of Pittsburgh; Phrmcy.

DOVIAK, TRACI; Northern Lennon HS; Jonestown, PA; (2); Art Clb; Band; Color Guard; Mrchg Band; School Musical; Stage Crew; Cheerleading; Mgr(s); Score Keeper; Sftbl.

DOVICHIN, ERIN; Villa Maria Acad; Erie, PA; (3); 6/168; Capt Model UN; NFL; PAVAS; Political Wkr; Capt Quiz Bowl; Science Clb; School Play; Stu Cncl; High Hon Roll; NHS; 1st Pl PA Ctzns Better Libraries Essay Cont 86; 2nd Pl Model UN 86; Amelia Erhart Ldrshp Awd 87; Lib Arts.

DOVIDAS, MARK; MMI Prep Schl; Mountaintop, PA; (3); Boy Scts; Science Clb; Var Bsbl; Var JV Golf; Hon Roll; PA JR Acad Of Sci 1st Awd ST Comp 85; German Lang Cntst 85; Johns Hopkins Pgm CSAT Tst 83; Drexel Univ; Bus.

DOVILLERS, CATHY; Jeannette SR HS; Jeannette, PA; (3); 9/134; Cmnty Wkr; Drama Clb; French Clb; Hosp Aide; Yrbk Stf; French Hon Soc; High Hon Roll; JC Awd; NHS; Rotary Awd; HOBY Ldrshp Awd 86; IN U; Med Technlgy.

DOWDY IV, THOMAS C; Archbishop Ryan For Boys; Philadelphia, PA; (4); 124/478; Yrbk Stf; JV Var Bowling; Hon Roll; Amer Inst Dsgn; Elec Mech Dsgn.

DOWEY, KAREN; Harmony Area HS; Cherry Tree, PA; (4); 9/50; Office Aide; Band; Chorus; Stage Crew; Nwsp Rptr; Trs Jr Cls; Mgr(s); High Hon Roll; NHS; Otstndng Vclst Awd 87; Pres Acad Ftnss Awd 87; PA ST U; Nrsng.

DOWLER, MIKE; Greenville HS; Greenville, PA; (4); 11/130; Letterman Clb; Ski Clb; Thesps; Varsity Clb; School Play; Golf; JV Var Socr; NHS; Ntl Merit Ltr; VFW Awd; Sem Top Engr Prspcts 86; Med Mssn Haiti 85; Lead Actor 86; Purdue U; Engrng.

DOWLER, RITA; Fort Cherry HS; Midway, PA; (4); Church Yth Grp; Computer Clb; Drama Clb; Math Clb; Ski Clb; Band; Chorus; Concert Band; Yrbk Ed-Chief; High Hon Roll; Westminster Coll; Sclgy.

DOWLING, MICHAEL; Bucktail Area HS; North Bend, PA; (2); Letterman Clb; Varsity Clb; Chorus; Concert Band; Mrchg Band; School Musical; School Play; Var L Bsbl; Prfct Atten Awd; Commrcl Artst.

DOWLING, REBECCA; West Mifflin Area HS; West Mifflin, PA; (2); 13/289; Church Yth Grp; German Clb; Orch; Var Crs Cntry; Var Trk; High Hon Roll; Jr NHS; NHS; PMEA HS Orchestra Fstvl Awd 87.

DOWNER, BETH; Waynesburg Central HS; Waynesburg, PA; (3); AFS; Camera Clb; French Clb; Band; Concert Band; Jazz Band; Mrchg Band; Orch; Pep Band; School Musical; Cnty, Dist, Hnrs Band, PA All ST Lions Band 85-87; Duquesne Schl Music Schlrshp 88; Duquesne Schl Music; Music Ed.

DOWNER, KRISTEN; Greenville HS; Greenville, PA; (3); French Clb; German Clb; JCL; Latin Clb; Sci.

DOWNES, CHRISTINE; Kiski Area HS; Export, PA; (3); Church Yth Grp; FBLA; Math Tm; SADD; Varsity Clb; Band; Church Choir; Swing Chorus; Symp Band; Stat Bsbl; PA ST U; Acctng.

DOWNEY, MICHELLE; Nazareth Acad; Philadelphia, PA; (3); JCL; Latin Clb; Yrbk Stf; Vllybl; Prfct Atten Awd; Hood Coll; Law.

DOWNEY, MICHELLE; Penn Hills SR HS; Pittsburgh, PA; (3); FTA; Sec VP JA; Trs Office Aide; Spanish Clb; School Play; Rep Soph Cls; Rep Jr Cls; Stu Cncl; Prfct Atten Awd; Elem Ed.

DOWNIE, RACHEL L; Beaver County Christian HS; Beaver Falls, PA; (4); Church Yth Grp; School Play; Nwsp Stf; Yrbk Ed-Chief; Yrbk Stf; Bsktbl; Vllybl; Hon Roll; Hnrs 87; Presdntl Acadc Ftns Awd 87; Geneva Coll; Cmnctns.

DOWNIN, AMY; Waynesboro SR HS; Quincy, PA; (4); 56/374; Church Yth Grp; Rep Soph Cls; Fld Hcky; Sftbl; Hagerstown Bus Coll Schlrshp 87; Fnlst Sr Girl Of The Yr Awd; Hagerstown Bus Coll; Lgl Secy.

DOWNING, LYNN; West Phila Catholic Girls HS; Philadelphia, PA; (3); 7/246; French Clb; Political Wkr; Spanish Clb; Speech Tm; School Play; Yrbk Stf; Hon Roll; NHS; Ellis Grnt Awd 84-87; White Williams Schlrshp 86; Drexel U; Comp Tech.

DOWNS, LISA; Sun Valley HS; Aston, PA; (3); 38/270; Art Clb; Camera Clb; Drama Clb; French Clb; SADD; School Musical; Yrbk Stf; Lit Mag; Hon Roll; Career Explrtn Med Profssns 86-87; West Chester U; Spch Pthlgy.

DOWNS, MICHELLE; Haverford SR HS; Havertown, PA; (2); Spanish Clb; Rep Soph Cls; Var L Crs Cntry; Var L Trk; Hon Roll; All Star-1st Tm Sprng Trck 3200 M 87; Georgetown; Math Bus.

DOXEY, JENNIFER; Upper Merion HS; W Conshohocken, PA; (3); 98/300; Church Yth Grp; Rep Jr Cls; Rep Sr Cls; Stu Cncl; Var JV Tennis; Hnr Roll 87; Bus Mngmnt.

DOYLE, ANN-MARIE V; Upper Moreland HS; Hatboro, PA; (4); 13/253; Church Yth Grp; Chrmn Key Clb; Teachers Aide; Nwsp Ed-Chief; Mgr Swmmng; High Hon Roll; NHS; Ntl Merit SF; Millersville U; Elem Tchr.

DOYLE, COLEEN; Nazareth Acad; Philadelphia, PA; (3); Cmnty Wkr; Debate Tm; Latin Clb; Model UN; NFL; Pep Clb; Service Clb; Stu Cncl; Rosemont Coll; Art Hstry.

DOYLE, JASON; Rocky Grove JR- SR HS; Cooperstown, PA; (3); Aud/Vis; Science Clb; Mgr(s); JV Stat Wrstlng; High Hon Roll; Hon Roll; JV Ltr-Wrstlng, Varsity Ltr-Acdmc & Plaque Acdmc; U Of Pittsburgh.

DOYLE, JOHN; West Catholic Boys HS; Darby, PA; (3); 7/248; Church Yth Grp; Cmnty Wkr; Math Tm; Nwsp Ed-Chief; High Hon Roll; NHS; Acadmc Ecllnc Chem & Relgn 86-87; Temple Law Mock Trl Awd 86-87; Ls Salle Coll; Law.

DOYLE, MARIA ELENA; Quigley HS; Baden, PA; (4); 1/98; Dance Clb; Model UN; Nwsp Ed-Chief; Trs Jr Cls; L Trk; Gov Hon Prg Awd; Ntl Merit Schol; Val; Voice Dem Awd; Church Yth Grp; Prfrmd In Pittsburgh Ballet Theatre In Nutcracker 83; Schlstc Ach Awd In Beaver Cnty JR Miss Pgm 86; Princeton U; Intl Affairs.

DOYLE, MARK; Nativity HS; New Philadelphia, PA; (3); 15/86; AFS; Aud/Vis; Computer Clb; Debate Tm; FBLA; JA; Math Clb; NFL; Science Clb; Spanish Clb; Spn III Awd 87; Spn I & II Awd 85-86; Alg 1 Awd 85; Engl I Awd 85; Phys Sci Awd 85; Penn ST.

DOYLE, MELANIE; Biglerville HS; Biglerville, PA; (2); 33/112; FFA; Varsity Clb; Yrbk Stf; Var Cheerleading; Gym; Mgr(s); Hon Roll; Penn ST.

DOYLE, PATTY; Gateway SR HS; Monroeville, PA; (4); 63/487; Church Yth Grp; Cmnty Wkr; Drama Clb; Exploring; NFL; Chorus; Church Choir; Nwsp Stf; Yrbk Stf; High Hon Roll; Pres Acdmc Ftnss Awd 87; Trphy Hghlnd Dncng & Mdls 85; U Pittsburgh; Psych.

DOYLE, SHANNON; Pottsgrove HS; Pottstown, PA; (3); 19/209; Debate Tm; Science Clb; Pres Spanish Clb; Varsity Clb; Chorus; School Musical; Nwsp Rptr; Rep Frsh Cls; Rep Soph Cls; Rep Jr Cls; Am Lgn Awd 84; Elem Ed.

DOYLE, STEPHANIE; Southwestern HS; Hanover, PA; (2); 4-H; Key Clb; Varsity Clb; JV Bsktbl; JV Trk; Var Vllybl; 4-H Awd; Hon Roll; U NC; Stock Broker.

DOYLE, THOMAS; Cathedral Prep; Erie, PA; (3); 9/221; Church Yth Grp; Civic Clb; CAP; Office Aide; Rep Jr Cls; Coach Actv; Swmmng; Timer; Im Vllybl; High Hon Roll; William E Daisley Sportsmnshp Awd 85-86; All City Water Polo Vrsty Tm 86-87; 1st Hnrs 84-87; Accntng.

DOYLE JR, WILLIAM F; Bishop Mc Devitt HS; Roslyn, PA; (4); 23/365; Church Yth Grp; Computer Clb; German Clb; Math Clb; Math Tm; Scholastic Bowl; Science Clb; Bsktbl; Mgr(s); Hon Roll; 2nd Pl PJAA 84-87; 1 Of 7 Coll Schlrshp Prog 86-87; Hnbl Mntn Phila Elec Co Spnsrd Comp Bwl 87; Drexel U; Elec Engrng.

DRABICK, SCOTT; Northwestern Lehigh HS; Orefield, PA; (3); 11/153; Church Yth Grp; Exploring; Nwsp Stf; Var Bsktbl; Var Crs Cntry; High Hon Roll; NHS; Grmn & Englsh Awds 86 & 87; Elec Engr.

DRABINSKY, JENNIFER; Boyertown Area SR HS; Boyertown, PA; (4); 10/427; Church Yth Grp; Math Tm; Nwsp Stf; Stat Bsktbl; Trk; Bausch & Lomb Sci Awd; Cit Awd; High Hon Roll; NHS; Pres Schlr; Freeland Scholar Ursinus Coll Merit Scholar 87; Leidy-Rhoads Scholar 87; Ursinus Coll; Pre-Med.

DRACH, CHRISTINE; Wyoming Area SR HS; Wyoming, PA; (3); Drama Clb; Key Clb; Spanish Clb; Chorus; Var Sftbl; Var Swmmng; High Hon Roll; NHS; Kings Coll; Cmnctns.

DRAGER, ALISON M; Donegal HS; Columbia, PA; (3); Am Leg Aux Girls St; Church Yth Grp; Color Guard; Nwsp Rptr; Nwsp Stf; Yrbk Stf; Hon Roll; NHS.

DRAGO, LISA; Garnet Valley HS; Glen Mills, PA; (2); French Clb; Intnl Clb; School Musical; Rep Frsh Cls; Rep Soph Cls; JV Fld Hcky; JV Socr; JV Trk; Hon Roll; Acad Excllnc 85-86; Med.

DRAGWA, RICHARD; Forest City Regional HS; Forest City, PA; (3); Boy Scts; Church Yth Grp; Ski Clb; Band; Concert Band; Jazz Band; Mrchg Band; Golf; Hon Roll; NHS; Black Belt In Karate 87.

DRAHUST, MARYANN; East Allegheny HS; North Versailles, PA; (3); Church Yth Grp; Dance Clb; Spanish Clb; Band; Color Guard; Sec L Concert Band; Mrchg Band; School Musical; Yrbk Stf; Soph Cls; 3rd Pl Mon Yough Sci Fair 83-84; Chld Care.

DRAKE, BOBBI; Wellsboro SR HS; Tioga, PA; (3); Sec Church Yth Grp; VP Drama Clb; VP FCA; Pep Clb; Chorus; Church Choir; Rep Stu Cncl; L Crs Cntry; Mgr(s); L Trk; Pres Phys Ftnss Awd 85; Toccoa Falls Coll; Socl Sci.

DRAKE, JEFFREY; Wellsboro HS; Tioga, PA; (2); Church Yth Grp; Drama Clb; French Clb; Church Choir; Rep Stu Cncl; JV Bsktbl; Var L Tennis; Var Trk; Hon Roll; Nyack Coll; Phy Thrpy.

DRAKE, NEIL; Maplewood HS; Townville, PA; (3); 16/154; Church Yth Grp; Exploring; JA; Pep Clb; Spanish Clb; Chorus; Church Choir; Hnr Cert 86-87; Law.

DRAKULIC, MILANA; Norwin HS; Ardara, PA; (4); VP Church Yth Grp; Dance Clb; Bowling; Sftbl; Intl Ordr Rnbw Grls-Grnd Lctr Dist 11 87, Grnd Rep OH 86 & Pst Wrthy Advsr, Irwn Assmbly 42 85; Penn ST; Elem Ed.

DRAN, SHARI; Bethlehem Center SR HS; Amity, PA; (4); 13/160; Church Yth Grp; Cmnty Wkr; 4-H; Girl Scts; Spanish Clb; Chorus; Color Guard; Mrchg Band; High Hon Roll; Hon Roll; Washington & Jefferson; Chem.

DRANCHAK, KATHY; Cambria Heights HS; Hastings, PA; (3); 88/190; Library Aide; Hon Roll; IN U Of PA; Tchng.

DRANSITE, JERILYNNE; Peters Township HS; Mcmurray, PA; (4); Jazz Band; School Musical; High Hon Roll; Hon Roll; Indiana U Of PA; Scl Sci.

DRAPCHO, A MATTHEW; Coudersport Area HS; Coudersport, PA; (3); Pres Drama Clb; French Clb; Varsity Clb; Jazz Band; Trs Jr Cls; Var L Bsktbl; Var L Ftbl; Var L Trk; Hon Roll; NHS; Falcon Spirit Awd 86; Drama Awd 87.

DRAPIEWSKI, JO ELLEN; Bishop O Reilly HS; Dallas, PA; (2); Ski Clb; Cheerleading; High Hon Roll; Hon Roll; NHS; Spanish NHS.

DRAPIEWSKI, JOELLEN; Bishop O Reilly HS; Dallas, PA; (2); Ski Clb; Cheerleading; High Hon Roll; Hon Roll; NHS; Spanish NHS.

DRASHER, JAMES M; Muhlenberg HS; Reading, PA; (4); Boy Scts; Ski Clb; Off Stu Cncl; JV Bsbl; Var Golf; Lion Awd; NHS; Off Soph Cls; Prsdntl Acdmc Ftnss Awd; Penn ST U-Main Campus.

DRASHER, ROBIN; Berwick Area SR HS; Berwick, PA; (4); Library Aide; Chorus; Color Guard; Flag Corp; Mrchg Band; Nwsp Stf; U Of S FL; Nrsng.

DRASKOVIC, JEANNE; Kennedy Christian HS; Pulaski, PA; (3); 8/97; Spanish Clb; Cheerleading; High Hon Roll; Hon Roll; NEDT Awd.

DRASS, RENEE MARIE; Altoona Area HS; Altoona, PA; (4); 41/718; PAVAS; Science Clb; Spanish Clb; Chorus; Orch; School-Musical; Hon Roll; Juniata Gap PTO Schlrshp 87; PA ST U; Bio.

DRAUS, SUSAN; James M Coughlin HS; Wilkes-Barre Twp, PA; (3); 1/374; Drama Clb; German Clb; Band; Chorus; Church Choir; Jazz Band; Yrbk Ed-Chief; Sec Jr Cls; Capt Pom Pon; Jr NHS; Hnr Soc 86-87; Engr.

DRAVK, STEPHANIE; Eastern York HS; Wrightsville, PA; (3); 5/172; Am Leg Aux Girls St; VP JA; Nwsp Stf; Im Bowling; High Hon Roll; Jr NHS; NHS; Hugh O Brien Yth Ldrshp Smnr 86; Assoc Edtr For Nwspr 86-87; Lbry Clb 85-86; IN U PA; Englsh.

DRAYER, SHERRI; Union HS; Sligo, PA; (3); 10/104; Rep SADD; Sec Soph Cls; VP Jr Cls; Rep Stu Cncl; JV Var Cheerleading; Vllybl; Hon Roll; NHS.

DRAYTON, TROY; Steelton Highspire HS; Steelton, PA; (3); 39/102; French Clb; School Musical; Yrbk Stf; Pres Stu Cncl; Bsktbl; Capt Ftbl; Trk; Wt Lftg; Div I Coll.

DRECHSLER, CYNTHIA S; South Allegheny JR SR HS; Port Vue, PA; (4); 15/187; Church Yth Grp; French Clb; FNA; Y-Teens; Stu Cncl; NHS; Carlow Coll; Nrsng.

DREES, BECKY; Jenkintown HS; Jenkintown, PA; (2); Chorus; School Musical; Ed Nwsp Rptr; Yrbk Stf; Pres Soph Cls; Rep Stu Cncl; Cheerleading; Tennis; French Hon Soc; NHS; Semi Fnlst Congress Bundestag Exchng 87.

DREGER, CHRISTINE M; Archbishop Prendergast HS; Drexel Hill, PA; (4); Latin Clb; Orch; Var JV Cheerleading; JV Coach Actv; Im Sftbl; Im Vllybl; Hon Roll; NHS; Acad Schlrshp Cabrini Coll 87; Presdntl Acad Ftns Awd 87; Cabrini Coll.

DREHER, CHRISTIAN; Beaver Falls SR HS; Beaver Falls, PA; (3); 57/170; French Clb; Var L Ftbl; Prfct Atten Awd; Bus Mgmt.

DREHER, MARIKA; Beaver Falls SR HS; Beaver Falls, PA; (3); 66/170; Aud/Vis; Library Aide; Office Aide; Speech Tm; Hon Roll; Bradford Bus Schl; Accntng.

DREHER, TARRA; Penn-Trafford HS; Irwin, PA; (2); Cmnty Wkr; Drama Clb; JCL; Latin Clb; Spanish Clb; Varsity Clb; Variety Show; Yrbk Stf; High Hon Roll; Var JV Bsktbl; Trphy Flag Ftbl 86-87; St John U; Opthmlgist.

DRESSLER, ANDREA; Selmsgrove Area HS; Selinsgrove, PA; (2); Church Yth Grp; 4-H; French Clb; 4-H Awd; Hon Roll; Child Pyschologist.

DRESSLER, ERIC; Du Bois Area HS; Dubois, PA; (3); Capt Swmmng.

DRESSLER, LISA; Shamokin Area HS; Danville, PA; (2); 84/250; Art Clb; SADD; Yrbk Stf; Hon Roll; Accntng.

DRESSLER, TRUDY; Selinsgrove Area HS; Selinsgrove, PA; (2); Church Yth Grp; 4-H; German Clb; SADD; Chorus; Church Choir; Stat Fld Hcky; Hon Roll; Elem Educ.

DRETAR, NICOLE; Abington Heights HS; Clarks Summit, PA; (1); 2/269; Ski Clb; Chorus; School Musical; Sec Frsh Cls; Rep Stu Cncl; Cheerleading; High Hon Roll; Elect Engrng.

DREWENCKI, BETH; Knoch JR SR HS; Cabot, PA; (4); Church Yth Grp; Cmnty Wkr; Dance Clb; Pep Clb; Ski Clb; SADD; Church Choir; Drill Tm; Pom Pon; Hon Roll; Gannon U; Sci.

DREWS, TARA; Lincoln HS; Philadelphia, PA; (3); Cmnty Wkr; Dance Clb; Exploring; FBLA; Girl Scts; Hon Roll; Rgnl Wnnr-4th Pl Bus Engl-FBLA 87; Pierce JC; Ct Rprtg.

DRISCOLL, JANE; Villa Maria Acad; Erie, PA; (4); 12/153; Science Clb; Ski Clb; Hon Roll; NHS.

DRISCOLL, TRACY; Hazleton HS; Hazleton, PA; (4); 90/400; FNA; Hosp Aide; Office Aide; Band; Chorus; Color Guard; Mrchg Band; Nwsp Rptr; Hon Roll; Stat Mgr(s); 1st Acdmc Hnrs 84-85; Schtz Schlrshp 86-87; Reading Hosp Schl Of Nrsng.

DRIVER, KERRY; Quakertown HS; Quakertown, PA; (3); Debate Tm; Drama Clb; Sec French Clb; Ski Clb; School Play; Trs Stu Cncl; Hon Roll; NHS; Church Yth Grp; Mgr Ftbl; Hugh Obrien Yth Fndn Ambsdr 86; Rep Bucks Cnty HOBY 86; Look Yr Smi Fnlst 87; Mdlng.

DROPIK, BARBARA; Mt Pleasant Area SR HS; Mt Pleasant, PA; (4); 7/250; GAA; Latin Clb; Band; Concert Band; Mrchg Band; Yrbk Stf; Trk; High Hon Roll; NHS; Pres Schlr; U Of Pittsburgh; Engrng.

DROSNER, JOHN; Central York SR HS; York, PA; (3); 12/289; JA; Varsity Clb; JV Bsktbl; JV Ftbl; JV Vllybl; High Hon Roll; Hon Roll; NHS; Opt Clb Awd; Engr.

DROSS, JENNIFER C; Pocono Central Catholic HS; Cresco, PA; (4); #1 In Class; VP Service Clb; Rep Frsh Cls; Pres Rep Soph Cls; VP Jr Cls; VP Stu Cncl; Church Yth Grp; Pep Clb; Quiz Bowl; Scholastic Bowl; Spanish Clb; Early Accptnc Penn ST U 86-87; PSU; Lbrl Arts.

DROST, SHERRY; Altoona Area HS; Altoona, PA; (4); 20/718; Church Yth Grp; Spanish Clb; Chorus; Mrchg Band; Var L Twrlr; Var L Vllybl; Hon Roll; Jr NHS; Penn ST; Accntng.

DROTTER, AMY; Schuylkill Haven Area HS; Sch Haven, PA; (2); 2/90; German Clb; Hosp Aide; Library Aide; Science Clb; SADD; Band; Chorus; Nwsp Rptr; Cheerleading; High Hon Roll; Pltcl Sci.

DROZDO, MICHAEL; Oil City Area SR HS; Seneca, PA; (4); 4-H; Acpl Chr; Band; Chorus; Concert Band; Jazz Band; Mrchg Band; Pep Band; School Musical; Symp Band; Clarion U PA; Music Ed.

DROZDOWSKI, JUNE; Seneca Valley HS; Mars, PA; (3); Church Yth Grp; Band; Jazz Band; Mrchg Band; Vet.

DROZDOWSKI, ROBERT; St John Neumann HS; Philadelphia, PA; (3); 37/349; Im Bsktbl.

DROZDOWSKI, STEPHEN; St John Neumann HS; Philadelphia, PA; (2); 13/354; Drexel U; Sec Educ.

DRUCK, KAREN; Abington Heights HS; Clarks Summit, PA; (4); 50/272; Cmnty Wkr; Letterman Clb; Yrbk Rptr; Ed Yrbk Stf; Rep Stu Cncl; Var Capt Cheerleading; Hon Roll; Booster Clb Awd Vrsty Ftbl Chrldng 86; Speaker For Graduatn 87; Coaches Awd Best Chrldr 87; PA ST U; Elem Ed.

DRUCK, SUSAN; Abington Heights HS; Clarks Summit, PA; (2); Letterman Clb; Ski Clb; Yrbk Stf; Rep Stu Cncl; Cheerleading.

DRUCKENMILLER, PAUL E; Catasauqua HS; Catasauqua, PA; (2); Boy Scts; Church Yth Grp; Cmnty Wkr; Drama Clb; Band; Chorus; Concert Band; Mrchg Band; School Musical; Symp Band; Moravian; Music.

DRUCKENMILLER, SCOTT; Northwestern Lehigh HS; Kempton, PA; (3); Band; JV Var Bsbl; JV Var Ftbl; JV Var Wrstlng; Hon Roll; Penn ST; Comp Engrng.

DRUCTOR, WENDY; Wyoming Area SR HS; Falls, PA; (3); 49/250; Church Yth Grp; French Clb; Key Clb; Ski Clb; Church Choir; Var Diving; Var Trk; High Hon Roll; Hon Roll; Penn ST; Bus Mgmt.

DRUGA, MARTY; Fort Cherry HS; Southview, PA; (3); Chorus; Mgr(s); Score Keeper; High Hon Roll; Bradford Schl; Bus.

DRUM, RAY; Columbia Montour AVTS; Berwick, PA; (4); Science Clb; Hon Roll; Pres Acad Fitness Awd Prgm 87; US Navy; Nuclear Prgm.

DRUMM, DENISE; Bradford Central Christian HS; Bradford, PA; (2); Pres Computer Clb; Pep Clb; Varsity Clb; Cheerleading; Hon Roll; Jr NHS; NHS; Presdntl Acdmc Ftnss Awds Pgm 87; Htl Mgmt.

DRUMMOND, BOB; Hazelton HS; Hazleton, PA; (2); Church Yth Grp; Var L Wrstlng; Bus Admin.

DRUMMOND, CINDY; North Star HS; Boswell, PA; (2); 8/125; Church Yth Grp; FCA; Capt Flag Corp; Nwsp Stf; Rep Stu Cncl; JV Var Bsktbl; Hon Roll; Actvty Boosters Stu Of Mnth 86; Lgl Secy.

DRUMMOND, FELICIA J; Westinghouse HS; Pittsburgh, PA; (4); 16/233; Pres Church Yth Grp; Sec Cmnty Wkr; Church Choir; Cit Awd; Hon Roll; NHS; Prfct Atten Awd; US Navy.

DRURY, DEBORAH J; Lampeter-Strasburg HS; Lancaster, PA; (4); Church Yth Grp; Red Cross Aide; SADD; Thesps; Chorus; Church Choir; School Musical; School Play; Stage Crew; Mgr Tennis; SCI Rsrch Soc Of N Amer Sigma XI 87; PA Inst Chemsts 87; Dept Of Energy 87; Moody Bible Inst; Chrstn Ed.

DRURY, JOHN; Wissahickon HS; Blue Bell, PA; (2); FBLA; Key Clb; Varsity Clb; Ftbl; Lcrss; Powder Puff Ftbl; Wt Lftg; Wrstlng; Bus Acctg.

DRYFOOS, ALISON; West Hazelton HS; Sugarloaf, PA; (2); Drama Clb; Thesps; Nwsp Rptr; Nwsp Stf; Var Cheerleading; Hi Jnks Clb; Sprt Clb.

DRYSIAK, BRENDALYN D; Cowanesque Valley HS; Westfield, PA; (4); 1/75; Girl Scts; Letterman Clb; Band; School Musical; Yrbk Ed-Chief; Tennis; JP Sousa Awd; NHS; Val; US Army Rsrv Natl Schlr Athlt Awd 87; Outstndg SR Instrmntlst 87; Edith H Clark Awd Englsh 87; Lebanon Vly Coll; Hotel Admin.

DRYZAL, JOHN; Central Cambria HS; Johnstown, PA; (4); 25/219; Var Wrstlng; Hon Roll; Commtr Hnr Schlrshp 87-88; Schlstc Prfrmnc Awd 87-88; St Francis Coll; Bio.

DRZAL, MARGARET; Windber Area HS; Windber, PA; (3); Speech Tm; Color Guard; Mrchg Band; Bsktbl; Capt Twrlr; High Hon Roll; Hon Roll; Jr NHS; NHS; Cmnty Wkr; Cambria/Somerset County Jr Miss Fnlst 88; U Of Pittsburgh; Cmnctns.

DSCHUHAN, HAROLD; Ambridge Area HS; Ambridge, PA; (3); Pep Clb; Spanish Clb; Teachers Aide; Off Jr Cls; Stu Cncl; Var JV Bsktbl; JV Ftbl; Wt Lftg; Hon Roll; Elec Engnrng.

DU BOIS, STACY; Bishop Guilfoyle HS; Altoona, PA; (3); Hosp Aide; Library Aide; Rep Stu Cncl; Capt L Cheerleading; Swmmng; Wt Lftg; High Hon Roll; Hon Roll; Jr NHS; VP NHS; Pilot.

DU PONT, MICHELLE; Conestoga HS; Wayne, PA; (2); Lit Mag; Sec Frsh Cls; Trs Soph Cls; Trs Jr Cls; Var Swmmng; Law.

DUARTE, DAIRA; Blue Mountain Acad; Narberth, PA; (3); Church Yth Grp; Library Aide; Office Aide; Teachers Aide; Acpl Chr; Chorus; Church Choir; School Play; Sec Soph Cls; Rep Jr Cls; Nuke U; Dentstry.

DUBBS, MICHAEL; Red Lion HS; Windsor, PA; (3); 41/342; Cmnty Wkr; JA; Hon Roll; Altin Cum Lauda Awd 86-87; Bio.

DUBBS, NICOLE; Lower Merion HS; Bala Cynwyd, PA; (3); French Clb; Service Clb; Nwsp Stf; Yrbk Stf; Stu Cncl; JV Var Fld Hcky; JV Var Lcrss; Var Swmmng; Hon Roll; NHS.

DUBBS, SCHERI DIANNA; Williams Valley JR SR HS; Reinerton, PA; (4); 36/106; Teachers Aide; Chorus; School Musical; Yrbk Bus Mgr; Yrbk Ed-Chief; Yrbk Phtg; Yrbk Stf; Powder Puff Ftbl; Mary Margaret Nestor Fndtn 87; David Hollenback Mem 87; Kutztown U; Bus Mgmt.

DUBE, MIKE; Penn Trafford HS; Irwin, PA; (4); Chess Clb; FBLA; JA; VICA; Hon Roll; Voctnl Indust Clbs Of Amer Apprnc Awd 86-87; Westmoreland Cnty CC; Bus.

DUBIEL, MARIE; Valley View JR-SR HS; Olyphant, PA; (2); 3/189; Rep Soph Cls; Rep Stu Cncl; Var Sftbl; Var Swmmng; Im Mgr Vllybl; High Hon Roll; NHS; Church Yth Grp; Latin Clb; SADD; Presdntl Ftnss Awd; Acad Excllnce Awd; WNEP Cert Of Merit; Ursinus Coll; Accntnt.

DUBIL, LORI; Lake Lehman HS; Shawarese, PA; (2); JV Bsktbl; JV Vllybl; Hon Roll; Marywood Coll; Retail Merch.

DUBNANSKY, RACHEL; Charleroi Area HS; Charleroi, PA; (3); 4/181; FNA; Spanish Clb; Band; Concert Band; Mrchg Band; School Musical; Nwsp Rptr; Vllybl; High Hon Roll; NHS; Vly Indepndnce Stu Forum Rep 87; Hlth.

DUBNER, KAREN L; Norristown Area HS; Norristown, PA; (2); 35/450; Cmnty Wkr; Hosp Aide; Intnl Clb; Math Clb; Sec Temple Yth Grp; Jazz Band; Pep Band; High Hon Roll; Hon Roll; Band; Underclsmn Awd For Band; U Of Miami; Music Ther.

DUBOTS, MICHELLE; Coudersport HS; Coudersport, PA; (3); Drama Clb; Letterman Clb; Band; School Play; VP Jr Cls; JV Var Cheerleading; High Hon Roll; NHS; Church Yth Grp; French Clb; Outstndng French Stu Awd 87; Hugh O Brien Yth Fndtn 86.

DUBROW, MICHAEL; Abington HS; Meadowbrook, PA; (3); 38/502; Boy Scts; French Clb; Nwsp Ed-Chief; Nwsp Phtg; Nwsp Stf; Hon Roll; Jr NHS; NHS.

DUBUC, JENNIFER; Conestoga HS; Devon, PA; (4); JA; Varsity Clb; Var L Bsktbl; Var Trk; Hon Roll; Dle Crngie Schlrshp & Grad 85-86; Susquehanna U; Accntng.

DUBYAK, MELISSA; Cambria Heights HS; Patton, PA; (4); Chorus; Church Choir; Capt Color Guard; Mrchg Band; School Play; Stage Crew; Var L Swmmng; IN U PA; Elem Educ.

DUCELLIER, MICHELLE; Quakertown SR HS; Quakertown, PA; (2); 1/334; Ski Clb; Acpl Chr; Madrigals; Orch; Trk; High Hon Roll; Jr NHS; Church Yth Grp; French Clb; Outstndng Frnch Stu 86; Outstndng Svc Awd 86; Natl Frnch Cont 86; Genetic Engrng.

DUCK, KIMBERLY; Southwestern HS; Hanover, PA; (2); Church Yth Grp; Key Clb; Band; Chorus; Church Choir; Concert Band; Mrchg Band; Hon Roll; NEDT Awd; Real Est.

DUCLOS, MOIRA; Bishop Hoban HS; Mountaintop, PA; (4); 14/230; Church Yth Grp; VP Computer Clb; French Clb; FBLA; Pres Trs Mu Alpha Theta; Chorus; Capt Var Crs Cntry; Im Socr; Stat Swmmng; Capt Var Trk; MVP Crss Cntry Tm 85 & 86; Fairfield U Schlrshp; Fairfield U; Math.

DUDA, CHERYL; Neshannock HS; New Castle, PA; (3); 1/114; Library Aide; Science Clb; Drm Mjr(t); Twrlr; Bausch & Lomb Sci Awd; High Hon Roll; NHS; Church Yth Grp; Math Tm; Quiz Bowl; PA JR Acad Of Sci 87; Amer Chmcl Soc Awd 87; WA Wrkshp Union Carbide Session 87; Bucknell U; Bio.

DUDA, DAWN; Villa Maria Acad; Erie, PA; (3); Science Clb; SADD; Im Bsktbl; JV Socr; JV Trk; Hon Roll; NHS; Nrsg.

DUDA, KARA; Taylor Allderdice HS; Homestead, PA; (3); Church Yth Grp; Med.

DUDA, SHERRIE; Shenango HS; New Castle, PA; (2); Church Yth Grp; 4-H; Girl Scts; Office Aide; Drill Tm; 4-H Awd; Hon Roll; Jr NHS; Bradford Schl; Hotel Mgmt.

DUDAK, MIKE; Pleasant Valley HS; Kunkletown, PA; (3); Math Clb; Rep Frsh Cls; Rep Soph Cls; Rep Jr Cls; Rep Pres Stu Cncl; Stat Coach Actv; Im Ice Hcky; Var Mgr(s); Im Var Socr; Stat Sftbl; Radio Brdcstng.

DUDAS, TRACI; Spring-Ford HS; Royersford, PA; (3); 87/262; Church Yth Grp; French Clb; Pep Clb; Yrbk Ed-Chief; Yrbk Phtg; Yrbk Stf; Hon Roll; Elem Ed.

DUDASH, JONNA; Ringgold HS; Eighty Four, PA; (3); Dance Clb; Off Frsh Cls; Off Soph Cls; Off Jr Cls; Cheerleading; Twrlr; Hon Roll; NHS; Mth & Sci Hnr Soc 85-87; Acctng.

DUDASKO, DIANE; Berwick Area HS; Berwick, PA; (4); Church Yth Grp; Exploring; Library Aide; Ski Clb; Hon Roll; Jr NHS; NHS; Brent Levan Mem Awd Biol 87; Penn ST U; Micro-Biol.

DUDDING, SUZETTE; Central Catholic HS; Allentown, PA; (3); Church Yth Grp; Girl Scts; Pres Key Clb; Library Aide; Math Clb; Math Tm; Pep Clb; Pres Spanish Clb; Var Capt Cheerleading; High Hon Roll; Ntl Ltn Cum Laude Awd 85 & 86; 2nd Pl Awd PA Jr Acad Of Sci 86; Bus Law.

DUDECK, DOREEN; Bishop Hafey HS; Harleigh, PA; (3); 17/121; VP Chess Clb; Church Yth Grp; Office Aide; Spanish Clb; Rep Stu Cncl; Bowling; Trk; High Hon Roll; Rep NHS; Opt Clb Awd; 2 Bowling Trophies 87; Various Acad Awds 86; Ofc Aid Awd 86; Penn ST; Bus.

DUDEK, MARK; Purchase Line HS; Arcadia, PA; (4); 1/100; Concert Band; Nwsp Rptr; Var Bsktbl; Im Ftbl; High Hon Roll; NHS; Ntl Merit Ltr; Am Lgn Awd; Marine Bio Qust 86; Penn ST; Engrng.

DUDEK, TARA; Purchase Line HS; Arcadia, PA; (2); 12/156; Church Yth Grp; 4-H; Concert Band; Mrchg Band; Sftbl; Twrlr; High Hon Roll; Hon Roll; NHS; Acadmc,Schlstc Al-Amer 86 & 87; Natl Ldrsh, Svc Awd 87; Phy Thrpy.

DUDINYAK, ELIZABETH; Bishop Hafey HS; Freeland, PA; (2); Ski Clb; Y-Teens; Rep Stu Cncl; JV Cheerleading; High Hon Roll; Hghst Engl Avg 86; Stu Cncl Ldrshp & Serv Awd 86; Top 10 Indvdl Awd US Chrldng Assc 86.

DUDO, DAVID; Center Area HS; Monaca, PA; (3); Latin Clb; Varsity Clb; Color Guard; Bsbl; Bsktbl; Bowling; Ftbl; Wt Lftg; Hon Roll; NHS.

DUFF, HEATHER; Kiski HS; Vandergrift, PA; (3); Church Yth Grp; Teachers Aide; Chorus; School Musical; Yrbk Stf; Bradford Bus Schl; Sec.

DUFFALO, DEIDRA LEE; Mechancisburg SR HS; Mechanicsburg, PA; (2); #11 In Class; Ski Clb; Chorus; Nwsp Ed-Chief; Rep Stu Cncl; Var Cheerleading; High Hon Roll; NHS.

DUFFIELD, BONNIE; Wyalusing Valley HS; Wyalusing, PA; (3); 10/145; Pres 4-H; FBLA; Hosp Aide; Spanish Clb; Orch; Sec Soph Cls; Trs Stu Cncl; 4-H Awd; High Hon Roll; Hon Roll; Pre Med.

DUFFNER, THERESA; Archbishop Ryan For Girls HS; Philadelphia, PA; (3); 4/508; Trs Church Yth Grp; French Clb; GAA; Science Clb; Yrbk Stf; Fld Hcky; High Hon Roll; NHS.

DUFFY, KRISTEN; Seton La Salle HS; Pittsburgh, PA; (4); Church Yth Grp; Ski Clb; Drill Tm; JV Co-Capt Cheerleading; Golf; JV Var Sftbl; Mrn Bio.

DUFFY, MICHELE; Danville HS; Danville, PA; (2); Church Yth Grp; Key Clb; Latin Clb; Letterman Clb; Pep Clb; Ski Clb; Spanish Clb; Varsity Clb; School Play; Rep Frsh Cls; Ath Awds 87; Schl Rcrd Breaker Triple Jump & Hgh Hurdles Hnr 87; AZ ST U; Lib Arts.

DUFFY, NANCY M; Archbishop Wood For Girls; Holland, PA; (1); 9/246; Church Yth Grp; Cmnty Wkr; Spanish Clb; Teachers Aide; Variety Show; Nwsp Rptr; Rep Frsh Cls; Rep Soph Cls; Rep Jr Cls; Trs Sr Cls; Mst Lkly Succd 87; Schlrshp Archbishp Wood Schl For Grls 83-84; ICGSL All-Star Sccr Tm 85; PA ST U; Bus Admin.

DUFFY, THERESA A; St Hubert Catholic HS For Girls; Philadelphia, PA; (3); Am Leg Aux Girls St; Cmnty Wkr; Dance Clb; Color Guard; Capt Gym; Prfct Atten Awd; Hnr Mntn Acctng I 87.

DUFNER, DAN; Archbishop Wood H S Boys; Southampton, PA; (3); 3/235; French Clb; Pres Stu Cncl; Var L Swmmng; High Hon Roll; NHS; French Awd; Notre Dame; Mktng.

DUGAN, KAREN; Claysburg-Kimmel HS; Imler, PA; (2); 7/97; Camera Clb; Varsity Clb; Band; Concert Band; Mrchg Band; Var JV Bsktbl; Var Sftbl; High Hon Roll; Prfct Atten Awd; MVP JV Bsktbl 86-87; Vrsty Foul Shtng Awd Bsktbl 86-87; Bus Prfssn.

DUGAN, LORIANN; North Star HS; Boswell, PA; (2); Art Clb; Church Yth Grp; Computer Clb; FCA; FHA; VICA; Color Guard; Mrchg Band; Yrbk Bus Mgr; Fashion Dsgnr.

DUGAN, MARY; Greensburg Central Catholic HS; Greensburg, PA; (3); Church Yth Grp; Computer Clb; French Clb; Girl Scts; Hosp Aide; Pep Clb; Service Clb; Ski Clb; SADD; Temple Yth Grp; Pre Med.

DUGAN, SEAN; Bald Eagle Area HS; Howard, PA; (4); FCA; Varsity Clb; Rep Soph Cls; Rep Jr Cls; Rep Stu Cncl; L Var Ftbl; Var Trk; Im Wt Lftg; Var L Wrstlng; High Hon Roll; Wdsmn Of Wrld Hstry Awd 84; Penn ST; Bio.

DUGDALE, TONY; Radnor HS; Bryn Mawr, PA; (4); 24/297; Aud/Vis; Boy Scts; Pres Exploring; NFL; Red Cross Aide; Speech Tm; Ed Yrbk Stf; Im Vllybl; High Hon Roll; NHS; Eagle Scout, Natl Cncl Uth Ldrshp Awd 86; Natl Chmpnshp Tm Stndrd 1st Aid Red Crss Comp 85; Haverford Coll; Med.

DUGGER, RUTH; Southmoreland SR HS; Everson, PA; (4); Church Yth Grp; Drama Clb; FFA; Library Aide; Pep Clb; Teachers Aide; Church Choir; School Play; Stu Cncl; Outstndng Hort Stu 87; Slvr Awd For Hort Stu.

DUGGINS, MICHELE; Pleasant Valley HS; Saylorsburg, PA; (4); 3/197; Math Tm; Scholastic Bowl; Band; Chorus; School Musical; Yrbk Stf; Rep Stu Cncl; High Hon Roll; Lion Awd; Pres NHS; Alfred & Ada Repp Schlrshp 87; Lioness Clb Schlrshp; Vee Ann Blakeslee Meml Schlrshp; PA ST U; Bio.

DUHARE, ELLEN; Upper Dublin HS; Ft Washington, PA; (3); 46/300; Church Yth Grp; Intnl Clb; Office Aide; Nwsp Stf; Stat Bsbl; Var Cheerleading; Hon Roll; NHS.

DUHARTE, ELLEN; Upper Dublin HS; Ft Washington, PA; (3); 46/300; Church Yth Grp; Intnl Clb; Office Aide; Nwsp Rptr; Nwsp Stf; Stat Bsbl; Var Cheerleading; NHS.

DUHOVIS, STEPHEN; Hershey SR HS; Hummelstown, PA; (3); 47/209; JV Var Bsbl; Spanish NHS; Sprts Med.

DUKE, GREGORY; Montgomery Area HS; Montgomery, PA; (1); Spanish Clb; Rep Stu Cncl; High Hon Roll; Schlrshp To Johns Hopkins U & 2 Courses Bucknell U 87-88.

DUKE, JOHN; Portage Area HS; Lilly, PA; (4); 4/123; Ski Clb; High Hon Roll; NHS; Pres Schlr; Chem II Awd 86; Jean H Kinley Math Awd 87; Pres Acad Awd 87; Duquesne U; Pharm.

DUKEMAN, LAURA; Pequea Valley HS; Narvon, PA; (3); 9/144; AFS; Drama Clb; Varsity Clb; Band; Concert Band; Mrchg Band; JV Capt Cheerleading; High Hon Roll; NHS; Prfct Atten Awd; Math.

DUKES, CARLA; Duquesne SR HS; Duquesne, PA; (3); 5/96; Rep Frsh Cls; Rep Soph Cls; Rep Jr Cls; High Hon Roll; Hon Roll; NHS; Prfct Atten Awd; US Ntnl Ldrshp Mrt Awd 86; Elec Engnr.

DUKES JR, JOSEPH; Duquesne HS; Duquesne, PA; (4); 23/89; French Clb; Var Capt Ftbl; Var Mgr(s); Hon Roll; Bus Adm.

DUKOVCIC, JOANNA; Hopewell HS; Aliquippa, PA; (4); #8 In Class; Church Yth Grp; VP Exploring; German Clb; Band; Chorus; Capt Drill Tm; Stu Cncl; High Hon Roll; NHS; Pres Schlr; Air Force ROTC Schlrshp 87; Pitt Engrng Alumni Schlrshp 87; Pitt Provosts Schlrshp 87; Pittsburgh U; Elec Engrng.

DULA, CHRISTINA; Rochester Area HS; Rochester, PA; (3); Church Yth Grp; Office Aide; SADD; Color Guard; Drill Tm; Flag Corp; Nwsp Rptr; Nwsp Stf; Pom Pon; Score Keeper; MODELING Schlrshp 85; Miss Jr Teen Pittsburgh 85-86; Kids Of Amer Natl Pagnt Fnlst 86; Travel Indstry.

DULA, PETER; Lancaster Mennonite HS; Millersville, PA; (3); Church Yth Grp; Chorus; Nwsp Ed-Chief; Nwsp Sprt Ed; Nwsp Stf; Rep Frsh Cls; Rep Soph Cls; JV Socr; Hon Roll; Goshen Coll; Jrnlsm.

DULANY, KELLY; Waynesburg Central HS; Spraggs, PA; (3); Letterman Clb; Ski Clb; Spanish Clb; JV L Cheerleading; L Trk; Var Vllybl; Wt Lftg; Hon Roll; MVP Grls Trck 85-86; Pschlgy.

DULEBA, CARLENE; Hickory SR HS; Hermitage, PA; (4); 17/170; Sec Rep Drama Clb; Latin Clb; Sec Stage Crew; Yrbk Stf; Cheerleading; NHS; Rep Soph Cls; Im Vllybl; Natl Latin Hon Soc 85-87; Acad All Amer 86; Nrsng.

DULEVITZ, MARK; Norristown Area HS; Norristown, PA; (4); 41/417; School Play; High Hon Roll; Hon Roll; PA Cert Of Merit-Outstndg Perf On SAT 86; U Of TX Austin; Physcs.

DULEY, ANGELA; Cecilian Acad; Philadelphia, PA; (3); 1/36; Pep Clb; Hon Roll; NEDT Awd; Natl Latin Exam Cert Hnrbl Mntn 87; Natl Sci Olympd Cert Dstnctn 87; Amer Chem Soc Cert Excllnc 87; Boston U; Pre Med.

DULICK, MICHELLE; Connellsville SR HS; Connellsville, PA; (2); Art Clb; Church Yth Grp; Dance Clb; Office Aide; SADD; Teachers Aide; Church Choir; Yrbk Stf; Rep Frsh Cls; High Hon Roll; Chld Dvlpmt.

DULLEN, KATHY; Central Dauphin HS; Harrisburg, PA; (2); 24/405; Ski Clb; Band; Concert Band; Mrchg Band; High Hon Roll; Hon Roll; Jr NHS; NHS; PTA Awd Excllnc Engl; Pres Acadmc Ftns Awd; Cnty & All Str Bnd; Comm.

DUM, BENJAMIN; West Perry HS; Elliottsburg, PA; (4); Sec Church Yth Grp; VP 4-H; Pres FFA; Quiz Bowl; Spanish Clb; Band; JV Bsktbl; Var Socr; JV Wrstlng; 4-H Awd; Dstngshd JR Stu PA Holstein Assn 84; S Cntrl ST Farmer FFA 87; Outstndg Vo-Ag Stu 84-87; Penn ST; Anim Biosci.

DUM, CHRISTOPHER; Louis E Dieruff HS; Allentown, PA; (3); ROTC; Yrbk Stf; Rep Stu Cncl; JV Var Ftbl; Im Wt Lftg; JV Var Wrstlng; Hon Roll; Jr NHS; NHS; Pres NHS; Prfct Atten Awd; PA ST U; Electrcl Engrng.

DUMBLOSKY, STEPHANIE; Steel Valley HS; Munhall, PA; (4); 3/201; Pres Church Yth Grp; Co-Capt Flag Corp; L Diving; High Hon Roll; Hon Roll; NHS; U Pittsburgh; Phys Thrpy.

DUMINSKE, CHRISTINE; Punxsutawney HS; Punxsutawney, PA; (2); Church Yth Grp; French Clb; SADD; Color Guard; Jazz Band; Mrchg Band; Pep Band; Twrlr; Hon Roll; PA ST U; Archtctrl Engrng.

DUMM, DENNIS H; Northern Cambria HS; Nicktown, PA; (3); 31/152; Art Clb; Boy Scts; VP 4-H; Trk; Wt Lftg; 4-H Awd; Hon Roll; Champ Sr Fitter Awd 4-H 86; Art.

DUMM, JOHN; Bishop Carroll HS; Barnesboro, PA; (3); 5/128; Aud/Vis; Computer Clb; Drama Clb; NFL; SADD; School Play; Pres Jr Cls; Stu Cncl; High Hon Roll.

DUMMYRE, SARA; Franklin Regional SR HS; Murrysville, PA; (4); 79/336; AFS; Church Yth Grp; French Clb; SADD; Chorus; Church Choir; Trk; Hon Roll; Allegheny Coll; French.

DUMNICH, CRAIG; Greensburg Salem HS; Greensburg, PA; (3); French Clb; Ftbl; Wt Lftg; Hon Roll; Bus.

DUMOND, CRAIG; Cranberry Area HS; Seneca, PA; (3); Aud/Vis; 4-H; Stu Cncl; Trk; Var JV Wrstlng; Heavy Mach Oper.

DUNA, LORI; Hazleton SR HS; Drums, PA; (2); Color Guard; Mrchg Band; High Hon Roll; JV Bowling; CPA.

DUNA, SCOTT; Hazleton SR HS; Drums, PA; (3); Acctg.

DUNBACK, JEAN; Dunmore HS; Dunmore, PA; (3); Church Yth Grp; Drama Clb; French Clb; Latin Clb; Ski Clb; School Musical; School Play; Nwsp Rptr; Rep Soph Cls; Cheerleading; Pharm.

DUNBAR, CHAVOCK; Harrisburg HS; Harrisburg, PA; (4); 5/101; Church Yth Grp; Rptr DECA; Trs Church Choir; Yrbk Stf; Hon Roll; Dstngshd Hnrs 87; Stu Of Mnth 85; Urban Lg Scholar Wnr 1st Pl 87; Millersville U; Mktg.

DUNBAR, COREY; Red Lion Area SR HS; Brogue, PA; (3); 40/364; Am Leg Boys St; Band; Drm Mjr(t); Mrchg Band; Orch; Symp Band; JV Bsktbl; Hon Roll; Mdrn Music Mstrs Hnr Soc Pres 87-88; Bus.

DUNCAN, ERIC; Springdale HS; Cheswick, PA; (4); 11/110; Trs German Clb; Nwsp Stf; Trs Jr Cls; Trs Sr Cls; Trs Stu Cncl; JV Bsbl; Var Ftbl; Var L Tennis; Pres Acdmc Fit Awd 87; Robert Morris Coll; Mgmt.

DUNCAN, FRANCENE; Wynesboro SR HS; Mont Alto, PA; (2); Computer Clb; Var Vllybl; Comp.

DUNCAN, JENNIFER L; Methacton SR HS; Audubon, PA; (4); 3/414; Church Yth Grp; Cmnty Wkr; Red Cross Aide; Band; Chorus; Lit Mag; Powder Puff Ftbl; High Hon Roll; NHS; Ntl Merit SF; PA Acad Decathlon Chmpns A Tm 85-86.

DUNCAN II, THOMAS; Mohawk JR SR HS; New Castle, PA; (4); Spanish Clb; School Musical; School Play; Penn ST; Engrng.

DUNCH, BRIAN; Yough SR HS; Sutersville, PA; (3); Computer Clb; Red Cross Aide; Spanish Clb; SADD; Var Bsktbl; Im Golf; Im Tennis; High Hon Roll; Hon Roll; NHS; Engrng.

DUNCHAK, LARA; Central Cambria HS; Ebensburg, PA; (3); Library Aide; NFL; Ski Clb; Speech Tm; Stu Cncl; High Hon Roll; Hon Roll; AZ ST U; Aerosp Engrng.

DUNHAM, ELLEN; Wellsboro Area HS; Wellsboro, PA; (3); 2/126; Band; Chorus; Trs Soph Cls; VP Jr Cls; Rep Stu Cncl; Var L Crs Cntry; Var Capt Swmmng; Var L Trk; High Hon Roll; NHS; PMEA Dstrct & Rgnl Bnd 85-87.

DUNHAM, PATRICIA; Cedar Crest HS; Lebanon, PA; (4); French Clb; Capt Drill Tm; Drm & Bgl; Capt Mrchg Band; Yrbk Stf; Capt Twrlr; Vllybl; Hon Roll; Mst Outstndng Stu In Bandfront 86-87.

DUNKEL, CAROL; Tyrone Area HS; Tyrone, PA; (3); Key Clb; Band; Chorus; Concert Band; Jazz Band; Mrchg Band; Pep Band; Lit Mag; Hon Roll; NHS; Awd Outstndg Achvt Plane Geom 87; Pre-Law.

DUNKEL, DEBRA; Tyrone Area HS; Tyrone, PA; (2); Band; Chorus; Color Guard; Drill Tm; Mrchg Band; Var Twrlr; Church Yth Grp; French Clb; Stage Crew; Pres Schlr; Wrtng Awd 87; Franklin & Marshall; Law.

DUNKELBERGER, KEVIN; Reading SR HS; Reading, PA; (3); 67/710; Political Wkr; Chorus; Orch; Stage Crew; Hon Roll; Penn ST; Crmnl Just.

DUNKERLEY, DAVID S; Central SR HS; York, PA; (2); Art Clb; JV Ftbl; Hon Roll; Ntl Art Hnr Soc 85-86; Envrnmtl Olympcs Tm 86-87.

DUNKERLEY, DOUG; Grove City HS; Grove City, PA; (4); 67/174; FFA; High Hon Roll; Hon Roll; Prfct Atten Awd; Natl FFA Fndtn Awd Ag Mech 85; OH Diesel Tech; Mech.

DUNKERLEY, KELLEE; Emmaus HS; Allentown, PA; (3); 135/518; Art Clb; German Clb; Chorus; JV Bsktbl; Im Sftbl; JV Trk; Hon Roll; German Hnrs Club 85-86; Med.

DUNKLE, JENNIFER; Northern HS; Dillsburg, PA; (4); 15/204; VP Church Yth Grp; Girl Scts; Spanish Clb; Chorus; Concert Band; Mrchg Band; School Musical; Yrbk Stf; Powder Puff Ftbl; Hon Roll; Pres Acad Fit Awd 87; U DE; Chem.

DUNKLE, KRISTI; Bedford HS; Everett, PA; (4); 40/176; Church Yth Grp; SADD; Chorus; School Musical; Yrbk Ed-Chief; Co-Capt Var Cheerleading; Crs Cntry; L Var Trk; Hon Roll; Track Outstndng Newcomer 84; Outstndng Runner 85; Coaches Awd 86; Shippensburg U; Jrnlsm.

DUNKLE, REBECCA; Sheffield JR-SR Area HS; Clarendon, PA; (4); Drama Clb; SADD; Varsity Clb; Jazz Band; School Musical; School Play; Nwsp Stf; Bsktbl; Trk; Hon Roll; Brbzn Mdlng Schl Grad 84; Bsktbl Ltr 86 & 87; IN U PA; Acting.

DUNKLE, REBECCA ANN; Mifflinburg Area HS; Mifflinburg, PA; (1); Church Yth Grp; Spanish Clb; Hon Roll; Prfct Atten Awd; Teaching.

DUNLAP, RICK; Blairsville HS; Blairsville, PA; (1); Church Yth Grp; Ftbl; Score Keeper; Trk; Hon Roll; Prfct Atten Awd.

DUNLEAVY, SIOBHAN; East Stroudsburg HS; E Stroudsburg, PA; (3); 49/237; Chorus; Var L Cheerleading; Var L Swmmng; Trk; High Hon Roll; Hon Roll; Prfct Atten Awd; Stu Trnr Vrsty Lttr 86-87.

DUNMIRE, LISA; Lewistown Area HS; Mc Veytown, PA; (3); Trs Church Yth Grp; 4-H; French Clb; Hosp Aide; High Hon Roll; Gertrude Kaup Memrl Awd Outstndng Bus Stu 86-87; Centre Bus Schl; Med Secr.

DUNMYER, NANCY J; Richland SR HS; Johnstown, PA; (4); 10/157; Letterman Clb; Mu Alpha Theta; Pep Clb; Stu Cncl; Bsktbl; Trk; Vllybl; High Hon Roll; Jr NHS; NHS; Schlrshps-Amer Lgn Aux, Martin Limestone, Elizbthtwn Acdmc 87; US Army Rsrv Schlr/Athl Awd 87; Elizabethtown Coll; Vet Med.

DUNN, COLLEEN MICHELE; Chestnut Ridge SR HS; New Paris, PA; (1); High Hon Roll; Hon Roll; Jr NHS; Law.

DUNN, EDITH; Engineering Of Science HS; Philadelphia, PA; (3); Church Yth Grp; Cmnty Wkr; Mu Alpha Theta; Office Aide; Teachers Aide; Drill Tm; Stage Crew; Yrbk Stf; Off Jr Cls; Off Sr Cls; Black Orch Awd 85-87; Comp Sci.

DUNN, GEORGIE; Cumberland Valley HS; Mechanicsburg, PA; (3); Rep Trs Art Clb; Computer Clb; Rep Key Clb; Rep Keywanettes; Office Aide; Rep PAVAS; Science Clb; Ski Clb; Rep Frsh Cls; Rep Soph Cls; PA Gov Schl Arts 87; Bio.

DUNN, KEARY; Lampeter-Strasburg HS; Strasburg, PA; (3); 27/153; Varsity Clb; Stu Cncl; Bsbl; Cheerleading; Wt Lftg; Wrstlng; Millersville U; Phrmcy.

DUNN, KEVIN M; Henderson HS; Downingtown, PA; (4); 23/348; Aud/Vis; Boy Scts; Cmnty Wkr; Computer Clb; Library Aide; Math Clb; Math Tm; Ski Clb; High Hon Roll; Hon Roll; Lehigh U Trustee, Mark C Croll Eductnl Schlrshps 87-88; Natl Hnr Rll 87; Lehigh U; Elec Engrng.

DUNN, MICHAEL P; East Stroudsburg HS; East Stroudsburg, PA; (3); 69/245; Church Yth Grp; Ski Clb; JV Bsbl; JV Bsktbl; Var Capt Socr; Var L Swmmng; Var L Tennis; Hon Roll; All Leag Sccr 86; U Of Scranton; Bus.

DUNN, MICHELE; Juniata HS; Mifflintown, PA; (3); FHA; Girl Scts; JV Sftbl; High Hon Roll; Hon Roll; NHS; Prfct Atten Awd; Sec.

DUNN, MIKE; West Allegheny HS; Oakdale, PA; (3); Capt L Ftbl; Var L Trk; Var Wt Lftg; Bus.

DUNN, ROBIN; Germantown HS; Philadelphia, PA; (3); 5/300; Cmnty Wkr; Girl Scts; Hosp Aide; Math Tm; Red Cross Aide; Chorus; Madrigals; Rep Jr Cls; Hon Roll; Psych.

DUNN, SHARON I; Strah Haven HS; Wallingford, PA; (4); Exploring; Intnl Clb; Yrbk Stf; Var Capt Swmmng; Hon Roll; Ntl Merit Ltr; Pres Schlr; JV Sftbl; Dsbld Vet Schlrshp; PA ST Smmr Hnrs Acad; Frnch Exchng; Wittenberg U.

DUNNACHIE, CAROLINE; Pius X HS; Bangor, PA; (3); 1/28; Pres Church Yth Grp; Pep Clb; Church Choir; Rep Stu Cncl; Var Bsktbl; High Hon Roll; NHS; Diocesan Schlrshp 84-85; Ambssdr Hugh Obrien Ldgrshp Sem 86; Northampton Co Rep HOBY Alumni Assn 86; Med.

DUNNE, RAYMOND; Penncrest HS; Media, PA; (3); 83/344; Boy Scts; Ski Clb; Varsity Clb; Variety Show; Rep Stu Cncl; Var Socr; JV Trk; MVP In Soccer 85.

DUNNING, JENNIFER; North Allegheny Intermediate HS; Pittsburgh, PA; (1); Pep Clb; Y-Teens; Cheerleading; Gym; Swmmng; Cit Awd; U Of TN; Nrsng.

DUNNING, SUZANNE; Highlands SR HS; Midwest City, OK; (3); Church Yth Grp; Library Aide; VP SADD; Church Choir; Concert Band; Mrchg Band; Pep Band; School Play; Bsktbl; Hon Roll.

DUNSEY, SHELLY; Carrick HS; Pittsburgh, PA; (3); Q&S; Ski Clb; School Musical; School Play; Nwsp Rptr; Nwsp Stf; Stu Cncl; Tennis; High Hon Roll; Hon Roll; IUP; Crmnl Lwyr.

DUNSKI, JONATHAN F; Whitehall HS; Whitehall, PA; (4); 2/233; Pres German Clb; Scholastic Bowl; Yrbk Phtg; VP Stu Cncl; High Hon Roll; Hon Roll; NHS; Sal; Pres-Magic Cir; Hghst Avg-Eng Cmmncmt Awd; PA ST U; Bio.

DUNSON, DAVID; State College Area HS; State College, PA; (1); Var Swmmng; JV Trk; Im Vllybl; Hon Roll; Arch Engrng.

DUPALY, DIANE; Baldwin HS; Pittsburgh, PA; (2); Church Yth Grp; Drama Clb; French Clb; Office Aide; Trk; Vllybl; High Hon Roll.

DUPIER, CHRISTINE; Bishop Boyle HS; Duquesne, PA; (2); 2/35; Hosp Aide; Yrbk Stf; JV Cheerleading; High Hon Roll; NHS; Merit Awd Engl II 87; Hnr Cert Alg, Soc Studs, French 86; Med.

DUPIER, DENISE; Duquesne HS; Duquesne, PA; (4); Exploring; Bsktbl; Hon Roll; ST Awd Cert DECA Career Dvlpmnt Conf Outstndng Ablty Mrktng Pgm Stdy 87; Mansfield U; Bus Admin.

DUPIN, KAREN; Central Cambria HS; Mineral Pt, PA; (2); French Clb; Stat Score Keeper; JV Vllybl; Hon Roll; Prfct Atten Awd; U Of Pittsburgh-Johnstown.

DUPPSTADT, ROBERT; Somerset Area HS; Somerset, PA; (3); 111/231; Church Yth Grp; Red Cross Aide; SADD; Hon Roll; English Clb; 4-H; German Clb; Chorus; Bsbl; Wt Lftg; Bus.

DUPREE, MARLO; Scotland School For Vet Children; Phila, PA; (3); FBLA; GAA; Girl Scts; ROTC; Band; Church Choir; Color Guard; Stu Cncl; Bsktbl; Trk; Outstndg Skills & Achvt Excell Bus Ed 87; Bus Admin.

DURA, LISA; West Hazelton HS; Ringtown, PA; (2); FBLA; Hon Roll; Mc Cann Schl Of Business.

DURAKOVICH, MICHAEL; Susquehannock HS; Shrewsbury, PA; (4); 60/220; Band; Concert Band; Mrchg Band; Pep Band; Hon Roll; NHS; US Navy; Nclr Engr.

DURAN, CARMEN M; Reading HS; Reading, PA; (2); 147/819; Law.

DURAN, KIRK; Ft Cherry HS; Bulger, PA; (2); Church Yth Grp; Computer Clb; Ski Clb; Varsity Clb; Var Ftbl; Var Wt Lftg; High Hon Roll; Hon Roll; Jr NHS.

DURANT, MELICA E; Philadelphia HS For Girls; Philadelphia, PA; (4); Debate Tm; Drama Clb; Hosp Aide; Library Aide; Teachers Aide; School Play; Variety Show; Stat Bsktbl; Score Keeper; Timer; Ruth B Hoffstein Lang Awd Latin 87; U Of Pittsburgh; Pre-Law.

DURANTE, STEVEN N; Norristown Area HS; Norristown, PA; (3); 1/500; Pres Church Yth Grp; FCA; VP Key Clb; Church Choir; Yrbk Stf; Off Frsh Cls; Off Soph Cls; Off Jr Cls; Off Stu Cncl; Var Capt Swmmng; Med.

DURASA, PAULA; Saegertown HS; Conneautville, PA; (4); 21/107; Church Yth Grp; Hosp Aide; Key Clb; Trs Spanish Clb; SADD; Band; Mrchg Band; Mgr Variety Show; Hon Roll; Jr NHS; U Of Pittsburgh.

DURBIN, LAURA; Bishop Guilfoyle HS; Altoona, PA; (3); Church Yth Grp; German Clb; NFL; Jr Cls; JV Sftbl; Vllybl; Elem Educ.

DURBIN, RICHARD; Mc Guffey HS; Washington, PA; (3); 3/240; Letterman Clb; Ski Clb; Spanish Clb; Yrbk Stf; Co-Capt Crs Cntry; Var L Trk; High Hon Roll; NHS; USAA Ldrshp-Svc Awd 86; Acadc Al-Amer 87.

DURBIN, THOMAS; Center HS; Aliquippa, PA; (2); Church Yth Grp; Computer Clb; Bowling; High Hon Roll; Hon Roll; Robotcl Engnr.

DURFEE, DONALD; SR HS; Pittsburgh, PA; (3); Drama Clb; PAVAS; Jazz Band; Orch; Lit Mag; Trk; Hon Roll; Carnegie Solo Awds 87; PA Music Tchrs Assn Perf Fest 85-86; Music Perf.

DURICH, JENNIFER; Louis E Dieruff HS; Allentown, PA; (2); French Clb; JA; Ski Clb; Var Crs Cntry; JV Fld Hcky; Var Trk; Art.

DURILLA, JUDITH; Panther Valley HS; Nesquehoning, PA; (1); 4/127; Drama Clb; Library Aide; Speech Tm; Band; Church Choir; Drm Mjr(t); School Musical; Nwsp Rptr; High Hon Roll; Pres Schlr; Outstndng Frshmn Band Mbr 87.

DURINSKY, MARK; Hopewell HS; Aliquippa, PA; (2); French Clb; Chorus; School Musical; Variety Show; Rep Frsh Cls; JV Ftbl; Hon Roll.

DURITSKY, ANDREA; Connellsville Area HS; Dunbar, PA; (1); Church Yth Grp; Yrbk Stf; Cit Awd; High Hon Roll; Jr NHS; U Of PittsburghLAW.

DURKIN, DAN; Du Bois Area HS; Du Bois, PA; (3); Ski Clb; Nwsp Sprt Ed; Ftbl; Ice Hcky; Jrnlsm.

DURKIN, NANCY; Abington Heights HS; Clarks Summit, PA; (4); 1/256; Hosp Aide; Scholastic Bowl; Lit Mag; Rep Jr Cls; Rep Sr Cls; Rep Stu Cncl; High Hon Roll; NHS; Ntl Merit SF; Val; PA Gvrnrs Schl-Intl Stds 85; Won Schls Engl & Scl Stds Awds 87; U Of PA; Bus.

DUROSS, JEANNETTE; West Phila Catholic Girls HS; Philadelphia, PA; (3); 69/246; Church Yth Grp; Science Clb; Spanish Clb; Hon Roll; Lab Tech.

DURRANT, JULIA; Nazareth Acad; Philadelphia, PA; (3); 29/125; French Clb; Math Clb; NFL; Speech Tm; Nwsp Rptr; Nwsp Stf; High Hon Roll; Hon Roll; Prfct Atten Awd; Frnscs Cert Of Excel 85-86; Med.

DURST, KENNETH JOHN; Northeast HS; Philadelphia, PA; (3); Dance Clb; FCA; JA; Math Tm; Varsity Clb; Drm & Bgl; Stage Crew; Pres Frsh Cls; VP Soph Cls; VP Jr Cls.

DURST, WENDY; Reynolds HS; Greenville, PA; (3); 14/160; Church Yth Grp; Latin Clb; SADD; Band; Chorus; Color Guard; Capt Drill Tm; Mrchg Band; Yrbk Stf; Capt Pom Pon; Psych.

DURYEA, SARA; Bishop Carroll HS; Loretto, PA; (3); Pep Clb; Ski Clb; SADD; Trk; Vllybl; Hon Roll; Crmnl Law.

DUSHAW, JOSEPH; Bradford Area HS; Derrick City, PA; (4); 19/268; Boy Scts; Trs FFA; Key Clb; Hon Roll; Jr NHS; NHS; Eagle Sct 87; Gvrnrs Schl Ag 86; Deklb Awd 87; U Of Pittsburgh-Bradford.

DUSHECK, CAROLINE; Hazleton HS; Hazleton, PA; (2); Dance Clb; Drama Clb; Pep Clb; Ed Nwsp Ed-Chief; Ed Yrbk Ed-Chief; Cheerleading; High Hon Roll; Amer Leg Awd 85-86; Qn Of Hearts 85-86; Acad Achvt Awd 85-86; Sci.

DUSTIN, CHRISTOPHER; Henderson SR HS; West Chester, PA; (2); 24/332; Boy Scts; Concert Band; Jazz Band; Mrchg Band; Spanish NHS.

DUTCH, JON; Kiski Area HS; Leechburg, PA; (3); German Clb; High Hon Roll; Hon Roll; Ntl Merit Ltr.

DUTCHKO, DONNA; Mon Valley Catholic HS; Elizabeth, PA; (4); 21/72; FBLA; Pep Clb; PAVAS; Nwsp Phtg; Yrbk Stf; Powder Puff Ftbl; High Hon Roll; Hon Roll; Ice Figure Skating Chmpn 81-87; Art Fstvl Banner Competition Wnr 87; Fashion Inst Of Pittsburgh.

DUTCHKO, STAN; Southmoreland HS; Ruffsdale, PA; (3); 153/212; Latin Clb; Letterman Clb; Ski Clb; Spanish Clb; Capt L Crs Cntry; Capt L Trk; Var L Wrstlng; Hon Roll; Crs Cntry-Record Holder 86; Sprts Med.

DUTKIEWICZ, BARBARA; Archbishop Ryan HS For Girls; Philadelphia, PA; (3); 7/508; Art Clb; French Clb; Math Tm; Ed Nwsp Stf; Im Bsktbl; High Hon Roll; NHS; Dance Clb; Q&S; Cert Of Profcncy-Art 84-85; Cert Of Profcncy-Rlgn 85-86; US-JPN Senate Schlrshp 86; Law.

DUTKIEWICZ, MARGIE; St Hubert HS; Philadelphia, PA; (4); 99/354; Chorus; School Musical; 2nd Hnrs 86-87; Phila Comm Coll; Acctng.

DUTKO, CHRISTINE; Marion Center HS; Chambersville, PA; (3); 9/153; Sec Art Clb; Latin Clb; Concert Band; Mrchg Band; Var Cheerleading; Var Trk; High Hon Roll; Jr NHS; NHS; Marion Ctr Wrkshp Art Wkend 86; IN U Of PA; Genetc Engnrng.

DUTROW, SUSAN; Tyrone Area HS; Tyrone, PA; (3); Church Yth Grp; Key Clb; Varsity Clb; Mrchg Band; Capt L Bsktbl; L Var Crs Cntry; L Var Trk; High Hon Roll; NHS; Latin Clb; Outstngn HS Athl Amer.

DUTTRY, JILL; Mechanicsburg Area SR HS; Mechanicsburg, PA; (4); 30/303; Church Yth Grp; Computer Clb; NFL; Speech Tm; Co-Capt Flag Corp; Yrbk Stf; Rep Stu Cncl; Im L Bsktbl; Hon Roll; Sec Trs NHS; Span Heritage Summer Homestay Schlrshp 86; Natl Hnr Scty Awd 87; Presdntl Acad Fit Awd 87; PA ST U; Elem Educ.

DUVALL, EDWARD; South Allegheny HS; Liberty Boro, PA; (3); 2/188; Church Yth Grp; Spanish Clb; Yrbk Stf; Off Jr Cls; Var Bsbl; JV Var Bsktbl; Coach Actv; High Hon Roll; Jr NHS; Prfct Atten Awd; MVP Bsebl 85; 2nd Pl Schl Sci Fair 86; Hon Ment Regnl Sci Fair 86; Pharm.

DUVALL, LISA; Bethlehem Center HS; Fredericktown, PA; (4); 13/153; Cmnty Wkr; Spanish Clb; Band; Capt Color Guard; Mrchg Band; Hon Roll; Lion Awd; Pres NHS; Mary Nass Schlrshp 87-88; CA U PA; Elem Ed.

DUZICKY, FRANK; Ambridge Area HS; Baden, PA; (3); German Clb; Pep Clb; Spanish Clb; SADD; Stu Cncl; Crs Cntry; Trk; Hon Roll.

DUZYK, JOHN; Mohawk HS; New Castle, PA; (3); 12/130; Church Yth Grp; Cmnty Wkr; French Clb; Letterman Clb; Varsity Clb; Band; Concert Band; Jazz Band; Mrchg Band; Pep Band; Spelling Bee Wnnr 85; Marine Bio.

DVORAK, JACINTA MARIE; Highlands SR HS; Natrona Hts, PA; (3); Church Yth Grp; Hosp Aide; SADD; Band; Nwsp Rptr; Trs Jr Cls; Rep Stu Cncl; L Swmmng; Hon Roll; Jr NHS; PA Free Entrprs Wk Schlrshp 86; Bus.

DVORCHIK, LAWRENCE; Upper Dublin HS; Ambler, PA; (3); FBLA; Intnl Clb; SADD; Temple Yth Grp; Off Stu Cncl; Bsbl; Im Bsktbl; Robert Lipson Memrl Schlrshp Awd-B Nai Brith Yth Orgnztn 87.

DWORSKY, CHAD; Du Bois Central Christian HS; Reynoldsville, PA; (2); Boy Scts; Math Clb; Var L Bsbl; Var L Socr; Hon Roll; NHS; PA ST U; Math.

DYCKMAN, ERIC; Sun Valley HS; Aston, PA; (3); 107/270; Capt Crs Cntry; Var Trk; Hon Roll; Mgmnt.

DYDYNSKI, LORI; Wyoming Valley West HS; Plymouth, PA; (4); Boy Scts; Pres Church Yth Grp; Hosp Aide; Pres Trs Intnl Clb; SADD; Concert Band; Mrchg Band; Hon Roll; NEDT Awd; Prfct Atten Awd; Intl Clb Svc Awd 86; Coll Misericordia; Occptnl Thrp.

DYE, PATRICK; Dover Area HS; Dover, PA; (3); Trs Church Yth Grp; Var L Socr; York Coll Of PA; Mgnt.

DYE, SHANNON; Northampton SR HS; Bath, PA; (3); AFS; Drama Clb; Chorus; Hon Roll; Computer Clb; SADD; Band; Stage Crew; Nwsp Stf; Swmmng; Spnsh IV 87-88; Kutztown U; Elem Educ.

DYER, CARLA; Hempfield SR HS; Greensburg, PA; (3); 38/693; Church Yth Grp; Office Aide; Spanish Clb; Church Choir; High Hon Roll; Jr NHS; NHS; Prfct Atten Awd; Pres Schlr; Spanish NHS; Elem Ed.

DYER, DARLENE RENE; Uniontown Area SR HS; Uniontown, PA; (4); Spanish Clb; High Hon Roll; Hon Roll; Prfct Atten Awd; Pres Schlr; Spanish NHS; Offc Wrkr.

DYER, LORRI; Octorara HS; Christiana, PA; (3); 72/157; DECA; Hosp Aide; Teachers Aide; Rep Stu Cncl; Var Capt Tennis; Hon Roll; Westchester U; Elem Ed.

DYER, STEPHANIE; West Allegheny SR HS; Imperial, PA; (3); 60/199; Spanish Clb; Stat Ftbl; JV Powder Puff Ftbl; Hon Roll.

DYER, SUSAN; Elizabeth Forward HS; Bunola, PA; (3); Spanish Clb; Band; Var Sftbl; Hon Roll; Prfct Atten Awd; Math.

DYGAN, BONNIE; Tidioute HS; Tidioute, PA; (3); 1/19; Church Yth Grp; Debate Tm; SADD; Band; Chorus; Church Choir; Yrbk Ed-Chief; Stu Cncl; Bsktbl; Pres NHS; Presbytrn Chrch, Tidioute PA, Elder 87; Stu Yr Exchng Clb Warren, PA 87; Philomel Music Awd 87; Allegheny Coll; Engrng.

DYKES, SETH; Susquehanna HS; Harrisburg, PA; (3); Cmnty Wkr; Red Cross Aide; Var L Ftbl; Var L Trk; Accntng.

DYLEWSKI, TED; Mercyhurst Prep Schl; Ripley, NY; (1); Chorus; Pep Band; High Hon Roll; Music.

DYMEK, MICHAEL; Riverside HS; Moosic, PA; (3); Boy Scts; Stu Cncl; Bsktbl; Hon Roll; Church Yth Grp; Dance Clb; Ski Clb; Color Guard; Bsbl; Engr.

DYRBOLA, CECELIA; Quakertown Community SR HS; Quakertown, PA; (3); Church Yth Grp; VICA; Band; Concert Band; School Musical; Stage Crew; Score Keeper; High Hon Roll; Hon Roll; NHS; 3rd Pl In Hair Show 85; 1st Pl Rifle Tm In League 87; Bus.

DYSARD, BONNIE; Clearfield Area HS; Clearfield, PA; (4); Church Yth Grp; Office Aide; Sec SADD; Chorus; High Hon Roll; Hon Roll; NHS.

DYSARD, SUZANNE; Mercersburg Acad; Lancaster, SC; (3); Church Yth Grp; Library Aide; Nwsp Stf; Yrbk Stf; Rep Frsh Cls; JV Sftbl; Var Vllybl; Hon Roll; Ntl Merit Ltr; French Clb; Mercersburg Acad Schlrshp.

DYSHUK, LARISSA; Central HS; Scranton, PA; (4); Dance Clb; Debate Tm; Drama Clb; NFL; Pep Clb; PAVAS; Ski Clb; Spanish Clb; Speech Tm; Orch; Temple U; Spnsh.

DYSZEL, STEVEN; Cardinal Brennon HS; Girardville, PA; (3); 25/58; Stage Crew; Yrbk Stf; Var Bsbl; JV Var Bsktbl; Hon Roll; Excllnc Math, Sci 86-87; Bus.

DZIAK, JASON; Bentworth HS; Bentleyville, PA; (4); 6/133; Ski Clb; School Play; Nwsp Rptr; Yrbk Stf; High Hon Roll; NHS; Mary Noss Schlrshp Awd 87; CA U Of PA; Psych.

DZIEDZICKI, JULIE; Connellsville HS; Dunbar, PA; (1); Church Yth Grp; 4-H; Band; Jazz Band; Vllybl; High Hon Roll; Trs Jr NHS.

DZUIBA, SEAN; Hazleton HS; Hazleton, PA; (4); 108/488; Computer Clb; Ski Clb; Golf; Hon Roll; Prfct Atten Awd; Microcomp Pgmmng 2nd Pl 85; Microcomp Engrng.

DZURICSKO, TAWNYA; Mercer HS; Mercer, PA; (4); 52/143; Church Yth Grp; Spanish Clb; Var Capt Bsktbl; Var Trk; JV Var Vllybl; Dist 10 Champs Bsktbl 86; 5th Pl ST Long Jump 86; Hmcmng Ct 86; Clarion U; Bus Adm.

DZURKO, LORI; Frazier HS; Perryopolis, PA; (3); Ski Clb; Color Guard; Co-Capt Drill Tm.

DZURKO, MICHAEL; Windber Area HS; Windber, PA; (3); Church Yth Grp; Math Clb; Spanish Clb; VP L Bsbl; JV VP Ftbl; JV Trk; JV VP Wt Lftg; Hon Roll; NHS; Stu Of Mnth Awd 85-87; Pres Phys Ftnss Awd 87.

DZURKOVICH, DONOVAN; Reading HS; Reading, PA; (3); 97/710; Im Ice Hcky; Var Socr; Elec.

DZWONCHYK, JOSEPH; Forest City Regional HS; Browndale, PA; (3); Letterman Clb; Band; Concert Band; Jazz Band; Var L Bsbl; Var L Bsktbl; Var L Crs Cntry; Hon Roll; NHS; Rotary Awd; Dist & Regnl Band 86-87; Hstry.

EACHUS, LORENA; Unionville Chadds Ford HS; Chadds Ford, PA; (3); 76/276; Church Yth Grp; Hosp Aide; Intnl Clb; Library Aide; SADD; Stat Bsktbl; Mgr(s); Hon Roll; Opt Clb Awd; Pre Med.

EADES, ANDREA; Minersville Area HS; Pottsville, PA; (3); Spanish Clb; Chorus; JV Bsktbl; High Hon Roll; Hon Roll; NHS.

EAGAL, SHANE; Butler Intermediate HS; Butler, PA; (2); ROTC; Band; Air Force.

EAGLE, STEVEN; Steel Valley HS; Munhall, PA; (4); 10/227; Chess Clb; Latin Clb; Ftbl; High Hon Roll; Hon Roll; Engrng.

EAGLER, KRISTA; East Juniata HS; Thompsontown, PA; (2); SADD; Band; Yrbk Sprt Ed; Yrbk Stf; Var Cheerleading; Var Fld Hcky; Var Trk; Twrlr; Hon Roll; NHS; Penn ST.

EAKIN, TERRI; Commodore Perry HS; Greenville, PA; (4); Art Clb; Library Aide; Office Aide; Chorus; Flag Corp; Mrchg Band; Yrbk Ed-Chief; Sec Soph Cls; Fd Mgmt.

EAKIN, TODD; Watsontown Christian Acad; Montgomery, PA; (4); 1/13; VP Trs Church Yth Grp; Pres VP 4-H; Yrbk Bus Mgr; Pres Sr Cls; VP Stu Cncl; Capt Bsktbl; 4-H Awd; High Hon Roll; Val; PA ST Chmpn 4-H Potato Grdng & Id Cntst Twice 86 & 87; 4-H Dlgt To Japan 86; 4-H Er Of Yr 86; Rochester Inst Of Tech; Engnrng.

EAKINS, SAM; Central Bucks West HS; Chalfont, PA; (3); Church Yth Grp; Chorus; JV Var Bsbl; JV Golf; Hon Roll; Ntl Merit SF; Ed.

EALER, JEFFERY; B Reed Henderson HS; West Chester, PA; (4); 2/349; Cmnty Wkr; Math Tm; Nwsp Stf; Lit Mag; Trs Soph Cls; VP Jr Cls; Socr; Hon Roll; VP NHS; Ntl Merit SF; Chem Engrng.

EARHART, NIGEL S; Hempfield HS; Lancaster, PA; (3); 50/420; Rep Am Leg Boys St; Exploring; School Play; Variety Show; Rep Jr Cls; Rep Sr Cls; Hon Roll; NHS; Lncstr Nwspr Dlvry Awd 84; Intl Rltns.

EARL, CHRISTA; Berwick Area SR HS; Berwick, PA; (3); Drama Clb; School Musical; School Play; Stage Crew; Var Cheerleading; JV Fld Hcky; High Hon Roll; Hon Roll; Jr NHS; NHS; American U; Cmmnctns.

EARL, SUSAN; Middletown Area HS; Middletown, PA; (3); 3/193; FCA; Key Clb; Library Aide; Chorus; Var Mgr(s); JV Socr; Stat Sftbl; High Hon Roll; Hon Roll; Prfct Atten Awd; Elem Ed.

EARLEY, AMY; Cedar Cliff HS; Camp Hill, PA; (2); 33/296; GAA; Key Clb; Model UN; Spanish Clb; Y-Teens; Trs Frsh Cls; L Var Sftbl; L Var Swmmng; Hon Roll; Spanish NHS; Connie S Ehresman Awd & Mid Penn Div I All-Star Hnrb Mntn For Field Hockey 86-87; Lehigh.

EARLEY, JENNIE; Peters Township HS; Venetia, PA; (4); VP Church Yth Grp; Dance Clb; Pep Clb; Varsity Clb; Church Choir; School Musical; Rep Frsh Cls; Rep Soph Cls; Rep Jr Cls; Cheerleading; Clarion U; Spch Path.

EARLS, MARGARET; Corry Area HS; Corry, PA; (4); Art Clb; Church Yth Grp; Trs French Clb; NHS; PA Top Qz Tm Chrch 85; Baptist Bible Coll; Tchr.

EARLY, ELIZABETH ANN; Upper Merion HS; King Of Prussia, PA; (4); 97/273; VP DECA; Var Sftbl; Hon Roll; Katharine Gibbs Schlrshp 87-88; 50 Svngs Bnd Stu Of Mnth 87; 2nd Pl DECA Compt 86-87; Katharine Gibbs Sch; Exec Secy.

EARNESTY, ANN; Connellsville SR HS; Connellsville, PA; (3); 59/533; Teachers Aide; Drm & Bgl; Mrchg Band; Symp Band; Nwsp Stf; Yrbk Stf; Stu Cncl; High Hon Roll; Jr NHS; Prfct Atten Awd; Prfct Atten 85-86; CA U PA; Bus Mgmt.

EARNSHAW, SCOTT; Owen J Roberts HS; Spring City, PA; (4); 30/270; Letterman Clb; Bsbl; Bsktbl; Golf; Vllybl; Shippensburg U Of PA; Acctg.

EARWOOD, JOHN SCOTT; Carlisle SR HS; Carlisle, PA; (4); 50/400; Boy Scts; Trs Church Yth Grp; Rep Stu Cncl; Var L Socr; Var Capt Swmmng; Var Trk; Hon Roll; AROTC Schlrshp; Villanova U; Bio.

EASLER, PAUL; Mc Keesport Area SR HS; Mckeesport, PA; (4); AFS; Boy Scts; Church Yth Grp; Drama Clb; JA; NFL; VP Acpl Chr; School Musical; School Play; Ntl Cngrssnl Yth Ldrshp Smnr DC 87; AFS Intl Exchng-New Zealand-Wntr Advntr 87; Penn ST; Intl Rltns.

EASLY, MIKE; Cathedral Prep; Erie, PA; (3); 30/199; Church Yth Grp; Var L Diving; Var L Swmmng; Hon Roll.

EASON, MATTHEW; Plymouth Whitemarsh HS; Norristown, PA; (3); Var Bsbl; Im Bsktbl; Var Ftbl; Wt Lftg; Hon Roll; CA ST U Long Beach; Ntrnst.

EAST, DENISE; Fort Le Boeuf HS; Waterford, PA; (2); Pep Clb; Rep Stu Cncl; JV Var Bsktbl; JV Cheerleading; JV Var Sftbl; Hon Roll; Prfct Atten Awd; Secy.

EASTMAN, JIM; Northeast Bradford HS; Rome, PA; (2); Chess Clb; Church Yth Grp; Trs 4-H; Radio Clb; Variety Show; JV Crs Cntry; Hon Roll.

EASTON, BARBARA; Salisbury Elk Lick HS; Springs, PA; (2); 2/33; Chorus; Concert Band; Mrchg Band; Yrbk Stf; Var Bsktbl; Var Sftbl; High Hon Roll; Hon Roll; Nrsng.

EASTWOOD, CRAIG B; Perkiomen Valley HS; Schwenksville, PA; (3); 11/186; Am Leg Boys St; Church Yth Grp; Math Tm; Ski Clb; Nwsp Stf; JV Wrstlng; Hon Roll; NHS; Outstndng Stdnt Awd 86; Outstndng Acad Achvt Awd 86-87; Penn ST U; Engrng.

EATON JR, JOHN; Red Lion Area SR HS; Windsor, PA; (4); 37/337; Boy Scts; Pres 4-H; Pres FFA; Band; Mrchg Band; Mgr 4-H Awd; Hon Roll; Pres Schlr; FFA Ag Accomplishmnt Awd 87; FFA 1st Pl Tm Livestock Judging 85; PA ST York; Animal Science.

EATON, NORM; Meadville Area SR HS; Meadville, PA; (2); French Clb; Var Golf; High Hon Roll; Hon Roll; U Of Boulder; Med.

EATON, SHERRY; New Brighton Area HS; New Brighton, PA; (4); 3/144; Am Leg Aux Girls St; GAA; Varsity Clb; Nwsp Stf; Capt Trk; High Hon Roll; Lion Awd; Gannon Acadc Schlrshp 87; Charles & Florence Wright Schlrshp 87; Anthony Krut Schlrshp 87; Gannon U; Pre-Law.

EBBERT, SHAWN; Carlynton HS; Carnegie, PA; (3); Art Clb; Boys Clb Am; Ski Clb; Nwsp Stf; JV Crs Cntry; Var Socr; JV Trk; High Hon Roll; Max Adolescent Potentls Prog 86; Presdnl Fit Awd 86-87.

EBERHARDT, ADAM; Mifflinburg Area HS; Lewisburg, PA; (3); Drama Clb; VP French Clb; Key Clb; PAVAS; School Musical; School Play; Stage Crew; Nwsp Ed-Chief; Var Socr; JV Trk; Commnctns.

EBERHARDT, EADIE; Jouderton Area HS; Philadelphia, PA; (3); Chorus; VP Frsh Cls; VP Soph Cls; Var Bsktbl; JV Cheerleading; Var Sftbl; High Hon Roll; Hon Roll; Stu Of Yr; Piano Awd; Frnch Clss Perfrmnc Awd; PA ST; Bus Adm.

EBERHART, CHRISTINE; Linesville HS; Linesville, PA; (2); 2/80; Church Yth Grp; Sec FHA; Pres Spanish Clb; Band; Chorus; Concert Band; Mrchg Band; Stu Cncl; Stat Bsktbl; Stat Ftbl; Awd FCVC Dist 10, 3rd ST Sftbl 87; Awd Screkpr FCVC 87; IN U Of PA; Tchng.

EBERHART II, LOYE; Mt Pleasant Area HS; Mt Pleasant, PA; (3); Chess Clb; Science Clb; High Hon Roll; Physics.

EBERLE, AMY; Penn Manor HS; Lancaster, PA; (4); Nwsp Rptr; Nwsp Stf; Hon Roll; Millersville U; Psych.

EBERLE, SANDRA A; Henderson HS; West Chester, PA; (4); 12/336; Hosp Aide; Intnl Clb; JCL; Latin Clb; Orch; Var Capt Sftbl; Hon Roll; NHS; Pres Schlr; Natl Latin Exm-Smma Cum Laud Slvr Mdl 84-85; Yth Undrstndng Smr Exchng Stu 85; Intl Rltns.

EBERLY, ERIC; Cocalico HS; Reinholds, PA; (3); 29/165; Boy Scts; Church Yth Grp; Church Choir; Im Socr; Var Wrstlng; Hon Roll; NHS; Ntl Merit Ltr; Arch.

EBERLY, LORIE; Dover Area HS; Dover, PA; (3); French Clb; Chorus; Church Choir; Concert Band; Mrchg Band; School Musical; Pres Frsh Cls; Pres Stu Cncl; Crs Cntry; Gym.

EBERLY, ROBERT; Middletown Area HS; Middletown, PA; (3); 51/193; FCA; Political Wkr; JV Bsktbl; Var JV Ftbl; Var Trk; Vllybl; Wt Lftg.

EBERLY, ROSE; Shalom Christian Acad; Fayetteville, PA; (3); Sec Church Yth Grp; FHA; Chorus; VP Frsh Cls; Pres Soph Cls; Pres Jr Cls; Var Fld Hcky; Capt Socr; Var Trk; Var Vllybl; Distngshd Chrstn Hs Stu 86-87.

EBERSOLE, AIMEE; Salisbury HS; Emmaus, PA; (3); Key Clb; Political Wkr; SADD; School Musical; Nwsp Rptr; Nwsp Stf; Swmmng; Hon Roll; Art Awd 84-85; Moravian Coll; Intl Rltns.

EBERSOLE, JOANNE; Donegal HS; Marietta, PA; (4); 15/160; Stage Crew; Hon Roll; Pres Acad Fit Awd 87; Central PA Bus Schl; Acctg.

EBERSOLE, JOE; Hempfield HS; Manheim, PA; (3); Key Clb; Nwsp Stf; Ftbl; Hon Roll; Acad All Am 87.

EBERT, BRIAN; Greater Works Acad; Pittsburgh, PA; (3); 1/42; Church Yth Grp; Pres Ski Clb; Stu Cncl; Im Vllybl; High Hon Roll; Prfct Atten Awd; Val; Presdntl Physcl Ftns Awd, Patch 85 & 87; Semi-Fnlst Grtr Wrks Acad Sci Fair 87; Capt Tm USA Hockey 85; Bio.

EBERT, MICHELLE; Allentown Central Catholic HS; Allentown, PA; (3); GAA; Pres JA; Color Guard; Drill Tm; Mrchg Band; Coach Actv; Im Sftbl; Hon Roll; Kutztown U; Acctng.

EBERT, TINA; Parkland HS; Fogelsville, PA; (3); 31/485; Key Clb; Office Aide; Band; Flag Corp; Stage Crew; Yrbk Stf; Trk; High Hon Roll; Hon Roll; Trs NHS; Psychlgy.

EBITZ, MELISSA; Riverview HS; Oakmont, PA; (3); French Clb; Varsity Clb; Jr Cls; Capt Bsktbl; Powder Puff Ftbl; Sftbl; VP Trk; Capt Twrlr; High Hon Roll; NHS.

EBLING, MATTHEW; Cocalico HS; Reinholds, PA; (3); 31/166; Art Clb; Boy Scts; Computer Clb; Drama Clb; Quiz Bowl; Science Clb; Chorus; Church Choir; School Musical; School Play; Gannon; Pre-Med.

EBLING, WILLIAM; Hamburg Area HS; Hamburg, PA; (3); Spanish Clb; Rep Stu Cncl; Im Bowling; Var L Ftbl; Hon Roll; JC Awd; All Acdmc Ftbl Tm 86; Math.

EBNER, GEORGE; Trinity HS; Bowmansdale, PA; (3); French Clb; Letterman Clb; Pep Clb; Red Cross Aide; Ski Clb; Spanish Clb; Im Bsktbl; Var Socr; Im Swmmng; Im Tennis; Psychlgst.

EBNER, JOHN; Northampton SR HS; Northampton, PA; (4); 60/430; Chorus; Church Choir; Co-Capt Swmmng; High Hon Roll; Hon Roll; NHS; Dist & Regl Chorus 84-87; Dist Swmg Medlst 86-87; Vrsty Ltr & Chorl Ltr 84-87; E Stroudsburg U; Phy Thrpy.

EBY, ANDREW; Lancaster Menn HS; Wash Boro, PA; (3); Chess Clb; VP Church Yth Grp; Drama Clb; FFA; Im Socr; Im Vllybl; Hon Roll.

EBY, DAVID; Ephrata HS; Ephrata, PA; (4); 67/253; Church Yth Grp; Trs FFA; Var L Ftbl; Hon Roll; Keystone FFA Degree 87; Hibshman Schlrshp 87; Messiah Coll; Bus Admin.

EBY, GALEN; Sullivan County HS; Canton, PA; (4); 6/84; Pres Church Yth Grp; Ski Clb; Lit Mag; Crs Cntry; Cit Awd; Hon Roll; Pres NHS; Nrthrn Cntrl Bnk Schlrshp 87; Messiah Coll; Accntng.

EBY, HEATHER WALKER; Carlisle SR HS; Carlisle, PA; (4); 13/387; Pres Church Yth Grp; Drama Clb; German Clb; JA; Science Clb; Color Guard; Mrchg Band; Yrbk Stf; NHS; Shwcs USA Solo Tap 3rd Pl 84; Acadc Excllnc Awd 86-87; Piano Achvt Awd 84; Drexel U; Bus Admin.

EBY, KRISTIN; Northampton Area SR HS; Northampton, PA; (4); AFS; Leo Clb; Color Guard; Trk; Hon Roll; Penn ST U.

ECCKER, KAREN; Athens Area HS; Sayre, PA; (4); 29/142; Band; Concert Band; Mrchg Band; Rep Frsh Cls; Rep Soph Cls; Rep Jr Cls; Rep Sr Cls; Rep Stu Cncl; Capt Bsktbl; L Sftbl; Class Advsrs Awd 87; IN U Of PA; Bio.

ECENRODE, RISHA; Governor Mifflin SR HS; Shillington, PA; (4); 94/257; FBLA; Key Clb; Chorus; Color Guard; Flag Corp; Mrchg Band; School Musical; School Play; Swing Chorus; Yrbk Phtg; Ursinus Coll; Law.

ECHALK, RAYMOND; Old Forge HS; Old Forge, PA; (3); 10/120; Church Yth Grp; Ski Clb; Var Golf; High Hon Roll; Hon Roll; NHS; Phrmcy.

ECHARD, JAMES; Laewistown Area HS; Mc Veytown, PA; (3); Church Yth Grp; Varsity Clb; Chorus; Var Bsbl; Var Bsktbl; Var Ftbl; High Hon Roll; NHS; Seven Mt Ftbll League All Star 86; Big 8 Ftbll League All Star 86; All Cnty Ftbll All Star; Comp Sci.

ECHEVARRIA, DEBORAH; Cedar Grove Christian Acad; Philadelphia, PA; (4); Church Yth Grp; Cmnty Wkr; Church Choir; Variety Show; Var Bsktbl; Var Crs Cntry; Var Sftbl; Var Tennis; Var Trk; Hon Roll; Sprtual Live Clb Awd 84-85; Cert Merit 84-87; Word/Life Bible Inst; Phys Ed.

ECK, CAROL; West Forest HS; Tionesta, PA; (4); 3/43; Sec Church Yth Grp; Model UN; Yrbk Ed-Chief; Yrbk Phtg; Rep Stu Cncl; Mgr Cheerleading; Mgr(s); JV Vllybl; NHS; Pres Schlr; Hnr Roll 84-85; Pres Acad Ftnss Awd 87; PA ST U.

ECK, JODIE; Lancaster Catholic HS; Columbia, PA; (4); 70/191; Church Yth Grp; Varsity Clb; Band; Chorus; Church Choir; Nwsp Rptr; Nwsp Stf; Yrbk Stf; Sftbl; Tennis; Westchester U; Lbrl Arts.

ECKARD, PHYLLIS; Perkiomen Valley HS; Collegeville, PA; (3); Church Yth Grp; Cmnty Wkr; Drama Clb; Band; Chorus; Church Choir; Concert Band; Jazz Band; Mrchg Band; Orch; Nursng.

ECKARD, STANLEY; Cumberland Valley HS; Carlisle, PA; (4); PAVAS; Band; Concert Band; Mrchg Band; Orch; Symp Band; Gov Hon Prg Awd; PA Gov Schl Arts Schlrshp, Harrisburg Symphony Yng Soloists Audition 86; John Mack Oboe Camp; Curtis Inst Music; Music.

ECKARDT, DIANE; West Scranton HS; Scranton, PA; (4); French Clb; JA; Ski Clb; Thesps; Nwsp Stf; Yrbk Stf; Pom Pon; Empire Beauty Schl; Csmtlgy.

ECKEL, THOMAS; Tunkhannock Area HS; Falls, PA; (2); Art Clb; Boy Scts; Chess Clb; Church Yth Grp; Var Ftbl; Var Vllybl; Blue Rbn Fnlst & Gld Key Wnr Schstcs Art Awds 86; Archtct.

ECKENDORF, ROBERT P; Academy HS; Erie, PA; (3); 13/226; Art Clb; Boy Scts; Church Yth Grp; Exploring; High Hon Roll; NHS; Prfct Atten Awd; Ad Altare Dei BSA Relgs Awd 85; Exprt NRA Trgt Shtr 87; Eagle Sct 87; Cmrcl Art.

ECKENROD, JERRY; SSVC HS; Cresson, PA; (3); Band; Concert Band; Drm Mjr(t); Jazz Band; Mrchg Band; Pep Band; Stage Crew; Symp Band; Bsbl; Cit Awd; Band Dir; Most Points Of Yr; Math Cert Awd; Air Force; Air Trffc Cntrll.

ECKENRODE, HOLLY; Cedar Crest HS; Lebanon, PA; (2); German Clb; Key Clb; Pep Clb; Cheerleading; Hon Roll; Nrs.

ECKENRODE, LISA; Bishop Guilfoyle HS; Altoona, PA; (3); Library Aide; Math Tm; Sftbl; Hon Roll; Bio.

ECKENRODE, LISA; Penn Cambria HS; Cresson, PA; (3); Drama Clb; NFL; Ski Clb; SADD; Mrchg Band; JV Bsktbl; JV Cheerleading; Hon Roll; NHS; Slippery Rock; Med.

ECKENRODE, ROBERT; Saltsburg JR SR HS; Saltsburg, PA; (2); JV Ftbl; Church Yth Grp; Computer Clb; French Clb; Spanish Clb; Var Trk; Hon Roll; IN U PA; Data Proc.

ECKER, JANICE; Northgate HS; Pittsburgh, PA; (4); JA; Library Aide; SADD; Band; Chorus; Church Choir; Color Guard; Concert Band; Mrchg Band; School Musical; Hnrs Dist Rgn & 1st In Sctn ST Choir 86-87; Natl Choral Awd 87; Prncpls Awd & Cert Of Merit 87; IN U Of PA; Music Ed.

ECKER, KRISTIN; Hazleton HS; Hazleton, PA; (3); 72/445; 4-H; Concert Band; Yrbk Stf; High Hon Roll.

ECKERD, KAREN; Cumberland Valley HS; Mechanicsburg, PA; (3); 88/591; Church Yth Grp; Sec 4-H; Church Choir; Color Guard; Mrchg Band; Ed Yrbk Stf; 4-H Awd; High Hon Roll; ST Fshn Revue 85; Elem Educ.

ECKEROD, MARY; Cambria Hgts HS; Ebensburg, PA; (3); 23/187; Church Yth Grp; Drama Clb; Chorus; School Musical; Nwsp Rptr; Nwsp Stf; Yrbk Stf; Hon Roll; NHS; Scndry Ed.

ECKERT, ANDY; Grace Christian HS; Myerstown, PA; (3); 4/21; Boy Scts; Trs 4-H; Ski Clb; Yrbk Phtg; Yrbk Stf; Pres Jr Cls; VP Bsbl; JV VP Socr; Hon Roll.

ECKERT, JULIE; Lebanon SR HS; Lebanon, PA; (4); VP Church Yth Grp; French Clb; Sec Girl Scts; Teachers Aide; Nwsp Stf; JV Var Fld Hcky; Hon Roll; NHS; Pres Schlr; Computer Clb; Grl Sct Gld Awd 87; Lebanon Ed Assn Schlrshp 87; Shippensburg U; Elem Ed.

ECKERT, MATTHEW D; Red Lion SR HS; Red Lion, PA; (3); #119 In Class; Am Leg Boys St; Boy Scts; Varsity Clb; Pres Band; Pres Chorus; Jazz Band; Mrchg Band; Orch; Symp Band; Capt Swmmng.

ECKERT, MICHELLE; Northeastern SR HS; York, PA; (3); 27/192; Church Yth Grp; JV Capt Fld Hcky; Trk; Hon Roll; NHS; Exhbtr Yrk Art Assoc 3rd Annl Stu Art Shw 87; Inter Dsgnr.

ECKHART, KATHLEEN; Crestwood HS; Mountaintop, PA; (4); 4-H; Pep Clb; Ski Clb; L Swmmng; Stat Socr; High Hon Roll; NHS; Syracuse U; Psych.

ECKHART, TRICIA; Northern Lehigh HS; Slatington, PA; (3); 18/160; Chorus; Mrchg Band; Trk; Wt Lftg; High Hon Roll; Hon Roll; Amer Music Abroad Tour Hnr 86.

ECKHOFF, NANCY; Mt View HS; Nicholson, PA; (3); 37/105; Office Aide; Teachers Aide; Chorus; Var Cheerleading; JV Fld Hcky; Var Gym; Wt Lftg; Median Schl Of Allied Hlth; Vet.

ECKLEY, DEVIN; Newport HS; Newport, PA; (4); 9/92; FFA; Hon Roll; Prfct Atten Awd.

ECKLEY, LINDA; Claysburg Kimmel HS; Claysburg, PA; (3); 11/77; Chrmn Cmnty Wkr; Speech Tm; Band; School Musical; Yrbk Phtg; Rep Stu Cncl; JV Var Bsktbl; Var Cheerleading; High Hon Roll; Trs NHS; Acad All Amrcn 86-87.

ECKLEY, NISSA; Newport HS; Newport, PA; (2); 43/117; Cmnty Wkr; 4-H; FBLA; 4-H Awd; Hon Roll; U Of FL; Math.

ECKMAN, DAVID; Solanco HS; Quarryville, PA; (2); Acpl Chr; Chorus; Rep Frsh Cls; Trs Jr Cls; Rep Stu Cncl; JV Bsbl; Var Ftbl; JV Wrstlng; Prfct Atten Awd; PA ST; Med.

ECKMAN, HEATHER; Pocono Mountain HS; Tannersville, PA; (3); 17/300; Chorus; School Musical; Yrbk Stf; JV Fld Hcky; High Hon Roll; Hon Roll; NHS.

ECKMAN, HOLLY; Performing Arts HS Of Phila; Pitman, NJ; (3); Drama Clb; Chorus; School Musical; School Play; Variety Show; Yrbk Stf; Trs Frsh Cls; Pres Soph Cls; Sec Jr Cls; Trs Stu Cncl; Theatre.

ECKRODE, LORI; Mahanoy Area HS; Barnesville, PA; (3); FHA; VICA; Chorus; Chef.

ECKROTE, KYM; West Hazleton HS; Conyngham, PA; (3); Church Yth Grp; Pep Clb; Ski Clb; Color Guard; Cheerleading; Gym; Drama Clb; French Clb; FBLA; FNA; Philadelphia Art Inst; Int Dsgn.

EDDOWES, ANNETTE; Upper Dublin HS; Ft Washington, PA; (4); Pres Sec Camera Clb; SADD; Color Guard; Mrchg Band; Nwsp Phtg; Capt Twrlr; Excng Pgm To Germany 87; IN U Of PA; Chem Toxicologst.

EDDY, DAVID; Mercyhurst Prep; Erie, PA; (4); Church Yth Grp; Debate Tm; French Clb; Church Choir; Wt Lftg; Hon Roll; NHS; U Of Pittsburgh; Engrng.

EDDY, KATHERINE; Marion Center HS; Creekside, PA; (4); 4/169; Intnl Clb; Latin Clb; Office Aide; SADD; Varsity Clb; Chorus; Drill Tm; School Play; Yrbk Stf; Rep Stu Cncl; U Of CO-BOULDER; Physics.

EDDY, ROBIN JO; Bradford Central Christian HS; Bradford, PA; (4); 5/26; Varsity Clb; Yrbk Ed-Chief; Pres Soph Cls; VP Jr Cls; VP Sr Cls; Var L Bsktbl; Capt VP Cheerleading; NHS; Pres Acadmc Ftns Awd 87; Wntr Crnvl Queen 87; PA ST U; Intl Bus.

EDELIN, MAUREEN; Hanover HS; Hanover, PA; (4); 42/108; Art Clb; Church Yth Grp; SADD; Teachers Aide; Fld Hcky; High Hon Roll; Hon Roll; York U; Accntnt.

EDELMAN, DEANNE; Northampton Area SR HS; Northampton, PA; (4); 27/430; AFS; Church Yth Grp; Girl Scts; Leo Clb; Chorus; Var Tennis; High Hon Roll; Hon Roll; NHS; Rotary Awd; Muhlenberg Coll; Acctng.

EDER, LORI; Jefferson-Morgan JR SR HS; Waynesburg, PA; (4); 11/86; Church Yth Grp; Intnl Clb; Varsity Clb; Var Bsktbl; Var Trk; Drama Clb; Letterman Clb; Spanish Clb; Band; Concert Band; Corp Psych.

EDER, PAUL; Bethlehem Catholic HS; Bethlehem, PA; (4); 89/195; Boy Scts; Trs Church Yth Grp; Hon Roll; Ad Altare Dei Rlgs Awd, & Boy Scts 84; Allentown Coll; Bus.

EDGAR, DAVID; Tunkhannock HS; Tunkhannock, PA; (2); 3/325; German Clb; Key Clb; High Hon Roll; Hon Roll; NHS; Pres Schlr; 2 Natl Chmpnshps Rifle 85; 6 Natl Rcds 85-86; US Olympc Trnng Ctr 84-86; Ecnmcs.

EDGAR, GINGER; North Hills SR HS; Pittsburgh, PA; (4); 9/457; Sec Drama Clb; NFL; Speech Tm; Thesps; Chorus; Ed Lit Mag; High Hon Roll; NHS; U Of Pittsburgh; Psych.

EDGAR, JASON; Chambersburg Area SR HS; Chambersburg, PA; (2); Rep Stu Cncl; L Golf.

EDGERTON, JOSEPH; New Castle SR HS; New Castle, PA; (3); 23/296; Church Yth Grp; Band; Church Choir; Jazz Band; Mrchg Band; Pep Band; Bowling; Tennis; High Hon Roll; Hon Roll; Tchr.

EDGREN, ANDREW; Fox Chapel HS; Pittsburgh, PA; (2); Church Yth Grp; Crs Cntry; Trk; Hon Roll; JETS Awd; 1st Pl Tm Intl Schlrshp-Alliance Coll 87; Bibl Qz Fnls Chrstn/Mssnry Alliance Coll 87.

EDINGER, ELAINE; Mifflinburg Area HS; Lewisburg, PA; (2); Church Yth Grp; Cmnty Wkr; FBLA; FHA; Hosp Aide; Church Choir; Hon Roll; Csmtlgy.

EDLEMAN, CHRISTINA; Owen J Roberts HS; Pottstown, PA; (4); Art Clb; Letterman Clb; Trk; Vllybl; Kutztown U; Art Educ.

EDMONDS, JAMES; Mercer JR SR HS; Mercer, PA; (2); Church Yth Grp; SADD; Bsbl; Ftbl; Sftbl; Swmmng; Trk; Wt Lftg; Wrstlng; Army.

EDMONDS, LINDA; Clarion-Limestone HS; Mayport, PA; (2); Church Yth Grp; French Clb; FNA; Girl Scts; SADD; Chorus; Church Choir; Color Guard; Mrchg Band; Hotel Mngmt.

EDMONDSON, JOHN; Chambersburg Area SR HS; Chambersburg, PA; (3); 210/657; Spanish Clb; Drm & Bgl; Stu Cncl; Var JV Ftbl; Hon Roll; Frdm & Ldrshp Awd From Frdms Fndtn At Vly Frg 86; Shpnsbrg ST U; Bus.

EDMONDSON, ROB T; Camp Hill HS; Camp Hill, PA; (3); 3/96; Church Yth Grp; Debate Tm; Nwsp Stf; Trs Jr Cls; Trs Sr Cls; Rep Stu Cncl; L Socr; L Trk; JETS Awd; NHS; Ctr Fr Acdmclly Tlntd Yth Thrgh Johns Hopkins U 84 & 85; :Govt.

EDMONDSON, SETH D; Camp Hill HS; Camp Hill, PA; (3); 6/97; Church Yth Grp; Debate Tm; Concert Band; Jazz Band; Nwsp Stf; Yrbk Stf; Var L Socr; Var L Trk; JETS Awd; NHS; Natl Latin Exm-Cum Laude Latin IV Prs 87; US Naval Acad; Engrng.

EDMONDSON, THOMAS H; Cedar Crest HS; Lebanon, PA; (3); Boy Scts; Church Yth Grp; Cmnty Wkr; Ski Clb; Spanish Clb; Varsity Clb; Band; Concert Band; Jazz Band; Mrchg Band; NC Music Educ Assn Instrmntl Solo Awd 86; Forestry.

EDMUND, ERIN B; Dover Area HS; Dover, PA; (3); 3/260; Sec Church Yth Grp; Hosp Aide; Capt Color Guard; Pres Yrbk Ed-Chief; Yrbk Phtg; Yrbk Sprt Ed; High Hon Roll; Sec NHS; Ski Clb; Chrmn Jr-Sr Prom 86-87; Engr.

EDMUNDS, AMY; Quaker Valley HS; Sewickley, PA; (2); Service Clb; Chorus; School Musical; Nwsp Phtg; Yrbk Ed-Chief; Yrbk Phtg; Yrbk Rptr; Lit Mag; Sftbl; Hon Roll; Bus.

EDMUNDS, SEAN; West Branch Area HS; Karthaus, PA; (3); Boy Scts; Church Yth Grp; Track Schl; Comp.

EDRIS, GREGORY; Blue Mountain Acad; Leesport, PA; (4); Ski Clb; Stu Cncl; JV Var Bsktbl; Im Ftbl; Var Gym; Im Sftbl; Im Vllybl; Im Wt Lftg; High Hon Roll; Andrews U; Acctnt.

EDWARD, KENNETH; Elizabeth Forward HS; Elizabeth, PA; (4); Church Yth Grp; Cmnty Wkr; FCA; Science Clb; Acpl Chr; Chorus; Church Choir; School Musical; Stage Crew; Frsh Cls.

EDWARDS, AIMEE; North Pocono SR HS; Lake Ariel, PA; (4); 8/250; Church Yth Grp; Drama Clb; Ski Clb; Rep Stu Cncl; Cheerleading; High Hon Roll; Hon Roll; Sec NHS; Minisink Lions Clb Schlrshp, Scott Donaghy Memrl Schlrshp 87; Mst Congnl Bsktbl Chrldr 86-87; Bloomsburg U; Bus Admin.

EDWARDS, ANTHONY JOHN; Punxsutawaney Area HS; Punxsutawney, PA; (3); Am Leg Boys St; Church Yth Grp; Letterman Clb; Science Clb; Spanish Clb; Varsity Clb; Off Sr Cls; Bsktbl; L Tennis; Hon Roll; Gov Schl Arts ST Smi Fnlst 87; Gftd Pgm 85-88; Penn ST U; Pre Law.

EDWARDS, BONNIE; Curwensville Area HS; Olanta, PA; (3); Drama Clb; French Clb; Sec Band; Chorus; Concert Band; Mrchg Band; Pep Band; Arion Awd 87; Grnd Assoc Mscn Rnbw Grls 86-87; 9th Grade Bnd Awd 85; Study Music.

EDWARDS, CARL A; Wyoming Valley West HS; Kingston, PA; (4); 31/397; Math Clb; Band; Capt Var Bsbl; Im JV Bsktbl; Im Bowling; L Var Ftbl; Im Vllybl; Im Wt Lftg; Hon Roll; NHS; Edwrd Jnjgn JR Gd Sprtsmnshp 87; Hnrb Mntn All Schlstc Ftbl 87; Blmsbrg U.

EDWARDS, CHERYL; West Perry SR HS; Landisburg, PA; (4); Cmnty Wkr; Office Aide; Service Clb; Spanish Clb; Teachers Aide; Varsity Clb; Yrbk Sprt Ed; Rep Stu Cncl; Var Capt Fld Hcky; Var Capt Sftbl; Schl & Cmnty Svc Awd, Mid-Penn All Star Defensive Plyr In Field Hockey & Dependable Stu Awd 87; Susquehanna U; Sociology.

EDWARDS, CHRISTOPHER; Seneca HS; Erie, PA; (3); 7/170; Var L Crs Cntry; Var L Trk; Hon Roll; NHS; Concert Band; Mrchg Band; Sec Soph Cls; VP Jr Cls; VP Sr Cls; Stu Cncl; All-Cnty X-Cntry & Trck 86-87; Math & Ldrshp Awd 85-86; Engnrng.

EDWARDS, DEANNA; Peters Township HS; Mcmurray, PA; (2); Trk; Hon Roll; Attendance Awd 86-87; Pa ST U; Vet.

EDWARDS, DOREEN; Villa Maria Academy; Erie, PA; (3); 2/151; Hosp Aide; Ski Clb; SADD; VP Frsh Cls; VP Soph Cls; VP Jr Cls; VP Sr Cls; High Hon Roll; NHS; Cert Merit Engrng & Sci Gannon U 86; Teen Action Club Board 87-88; Med.

EDWARDS, EDDIE; Octorara HS; Cochranville, PA; (3); 10/157; Chess Clb; Church Yth Grp; Drama Clb; Mgr Concert Band; Jazz Band; Mrchg Band; Var L Bsbl; JV Socr; High Hon Roll; Hon Roll; Gifted Pgm.

EDWARDS, EDWARD; West Perry SR HS; Landisburg, PA; (2); 33/223; Rep Stu Cncl; JV Bsbl; JV Ftbl; Im Wt Lftg; Hnr Roll 85; Mst Outstndng Phycl Ed Stu 86; AAHPERD Physcl Ftnss Achvt Awd 86-87.

EDWARDS, ERIN; Monaca HS; Monaca, PA; (4); 14/95; Church Yth Grp; Pep Clb; Drill Tm; Mrchg Band; Pom Pon; Hon Roll; NHS; Prfct Atten Awd; Futre Sec Clb 86-87; Leadrs Clb 84-87; Penn ST; Bus Mngmt.

EDWARDS, GLYNDA; Blairsville SR HS; Blairsville, PA; (4); 13/135; SADD; Band; Chorus; Concert Band; Mrchg Band; School Musical; High Hon Roll; NHS; Smmr Happng IUP 86; Seton Hl; Music.

EDWARDS, KIMBERLY; Minersville Area HS; Minersville, PA; (3); 1/150; Pep Clb; Spanish Clb; SADD; Mrchg Band; Nwsp Rptr; Pres Frsh Cls; Sec Soph Cls; Rep Stu Cncl; Cheerleading; High Hon Roll; Bloomsburg; Math.

EDWARDS, LISA; Strawberry Mansion HS; Phila, PA; (3); 7/108; Church Yth Grp; Cmnty Wkr; Dance Clb; Church Choir; Yrbk Stf; VP Jr Cls; Cit Awd; Prfct Atten Awd; Cncrn Blck Men Awd; Hampton U; Pedtrc Nrs.

EDWARDS, LYNN; North Pocono HS; Moscow, PA; (3); 9/240; Sec Church Yth Grp; Spanish Clb; Capt Drill Tm; Yrbk Stf; Lit Mag; VP Sr Cls; Rep Stu Cncl; Twrlr; High Hon Roll; NHS; Prncpls List 86; Law.

EDWARDS, MELISSA; Marion Center HS; Marion Center, PA; (3); Church Yth Grp; Intnl Clb; Band; Chorus; Church Choir; Concert Band; Flag Corp; IN U; Elem Educ.

EDWARDS, MICHAEL; William Penn HS; Philadelphia, PA; (4); 6/201; Boy Scts; Yrbk Phtg; Yrbk Sprt Ed; Var Bsbl; Var Ftbl; Hon Roll; Prfct Atten Awd; M L King Mem Essy Cont 87; Outstndng Achvt Eng 85; Hnrbl Mntn 4th Annl Essy Cont 85; Temple U; Radio.

EDWARDS, MOLLIE; Norwin HS; N Huntingdon, PA; (4); 135/568; Letterman Clb; Pep Clb; Ski Clb; Cheerleading; Powder Puff Ftbl; Vrsty Chrldng Let Awd 86-87; U Of Pittsburgh; Pharm.

EDWARDS, RONALD; Athens HS; Athens, PA; (3); German Clb; Math Clb; Nwsp Stf; Bsbl; Sftbl; Trk; Wt Lftg; High Hon Roll; Bio Awd 83-84; Accntnt.

EDWARDS, SHELLEY; Garden Spot HS; Terre Hill, PA; (4); Pres Church Yth Grp; Girl Scts; Library Aide; Political Wkr; Chorus; JV Var Bsktbl; Tennis; Hon Roll; Lion Awd; Lions Clb Trip Sicily Wrtg Essay Spirit Amer 87; Bst Offnse Plyr Awd Bsktbl 86; Tchr.

EDWARDS, STACEY; Mc Guffey HS; Claysville, PA; (2); VP JA; Pep Clb; Spanish Clb; Chorus; Yrbk Stf; High Hon Roll; Chld Psych.

EDWARDS, TAMARA; Oxford Area HS; Oxford, PA; (4); 25/174; FTA; Girl Scts; Red Cross Aide; Nwsp Rptr; Yrbk Stf; Hst Stu Cncl; JV Fld Hcky; Score Keeper; High Hon Roll; NHS.

EDWARDS, WENDY; Oxford Area SR HS; Cochranville, PA; (3); 32/197; Church Yth Grp; Civic Clb; VP FTA; Hosp Aide; Library Aide; SADD; Color Guard; School Play; Nwsp Rptr; Mgr(s); Profcncy-Latin 87; Profcncy-Adv Hist Of Hmn Dev 87; Outstndng-Vlntr Svc Cert 87; Northeastern U Boston; Hlth Sci.

EFFTING, VALERIE A; Freedom HS; Bethlehem, PA; (2); 144/431; CAP; Office Aide; Teachers Aide; Cit Awd; Hon Roll; Acctng.

EFIRD, HEATHER; Benton Area JR SR HS; Benton, PA; (2); Drama Clb; Band; Jazz Band; Mrchg Band; School Play; Radlgy.

EGAN, BARBARA; Harry S Truman HS; Levittown, PA; (3); Church Yth Grp; Drama Clb; Girl Scts; Chorus; School Play; Yrbk Phtg; Hst Sr Cls; Bus.

EGAN, MICHELE; Quakertown Community HS; Quakertown, PA; (3); 50/310; SADD; Stu Cncl; Cheerleading; Hon Roll; NHS; Ski Clb; Varsity Clb; Chorus; Nwsp Stf; Fld Hcky.

EGER, STACY; Penn Cambria HS; Cresson, PA; (3); Drama Clb; Hon Roll; Prfct Atten Awd; St Francis Coll; Accntng.

EGGERS, JENNIFER; Solanco HS; Quaryville, PA; (3); Art Clb; Chess Clb; Church Yth Grp; 4-H; Girl Scts; SADD; Y-Teens; Sftbl; Cit Awd; 4-H Awd; Dentstry.

EGGERS, TINA SUE; Rocky Grove HS; Franklin, PA; (3); DECA; Band; Chorus; Stu Cncl; JV Bsktbl; Mgr Sftbl; Mgr Vllybl; Hon Roll.

EGLI, SHELLY; Bellefonte Area HS; Bellefonte, PA; (3); 7/211; Pres SADD; Color Guard; Capt Mrchg Band; Trs Frsh Cls; Trs Soph Cls; Trs Jr Cls; Trs Sr Cls; High Hon Roll; Hon Roll; NHS; Miss Bellefonte 87-88; Elem Educ.

EGLISKIS, DAVID; Tunkhannock Area HS; Dallas, PA; (3); Church Yth Grp; French Clb; Key Clb; JV Crs Cntry; Var JV Socr; JV Trk; Hon Roll; Fin.

EHLERS, JENNIFER; Bishop Hafey HS; Hazleton, PA; (2); Drama Clb; French Clb; Key Clb; NFL; Science Clb; Chorus; Concert Band; Orch; School Play; Hon Roll; PA JR Acad 2nd Pl Awds 86-87.

EHLERS, JULIE; Bishop Hafey HS; Hazleton, PA; (2); Drama Clb; Key Clb; Math Clb; Science Clb; Chorus; Orch; School Play; Ntl Scl Std Olympd Wrld Cltrs Awd 85-86; PA Jnr Acad Of Sci Awds 86-87; Amercn Lgn Awd 86.

EHLINGER, MICHELE; Center HS; Monaca, PA; (3); 3/186; Spanish Clb; JV Vllybl; High Hon Roll; Hon Roll; Merit Dplma Spanish I, II, III 84-87; 2nd Pl Slippery Rock Comp Spanish IV; Acdmc All Stars 85-86; U Of Pittsburgh; Phy Therapy.

EHNI, EARLENE DAWN; Moon SR HS; Coraopolis, PA; (3); Camera Clb; Pres JA; Var JV Vllybl; Air Force; Law Enfrcmnt.

EHRENBERGER, JUDY; North Hills HS; Pittsburgh, PA; (4); 35/469; Church Yth Grp; Drama Clb; JA; Library Aide; Thesps; Bsktbl; High Hon Roll; JC Awd; Presdntl Acadc Ftns Awd 87; Slippery Rock U; Psych.

EHRENFELD, JOHN; Plum HS; Pittsburgh, PA; (4); Varsity Clb; School Play; Stat Bsktbl; Capt Crs Cntry; L Trk; Hon Roll; NHS; Grad Hnrs 87; U Of Pittsburgh; Engnrng.

EHRENSBERGER, KELLY; Elk County Christian HS; St Marys, PA; (2); 10/90; Dance Clb; Hosp Aide; SADD; Church Choir; Nwsp Rptr; Bowling; JV Var Cheerleading; High Hon Roll; NEDT Awd; Bus.

EHRENSBERGER, REBECKA; St Marys Area HS; St Marys, PA; (2); Boys Clb Am; Library Aide; Typng Cert Of Crdt; Vllybl Clb; Lbry Aide Svc Awd.

EHRENSBERGER, ROB; Elk County Christian HS; St Marys, PA; (3); 40/75; Cmnty Wkr; Varsity Clb; JV Var Bsktbl; JV Ftbl; Var Golf; Im Trk; Wt Lftg; 3 Yr Lttr Awd; Arch Engr.

EHRENZELLER, MICHELLE; Juniata HS; Pt Royal, PA; (3); Drama Clb; Varsity Clb; School Play; Stage Crew; Variety Show; Var L Bsktbl; Var L Sftbl; Im Tennis; Im Vllybl; Hon Roll; Jr Vrsty Ltr Bsktbl & Sftbl 84-86; Vrsty Ltr Bsktbl & Sftbl 86-87; Plc Offcr.

EHRET, LARRY; Fairview HS; Erie, PA; (4); 84/154; Band; Jazz Band; Mrchg Band; Pep Band; School Musical; Louis Armstrong Jazz Awd; Westminster Coll; Accntng.

EHRGOTT, DANIEL; Meadville Area SR HS; Meadville, PA; (4); 113/290; Pres VP Church Yth Grp; 4-H; Var L Trk; 4-H Awd; Hon Roll; Yth Group 5 Yrs; Jr Champ Medal For Track 87; Slippery Rock U; Evnr Sci.

EHRHARDT, BETH; N Pocono HS; Moscow, PA; (3); 40/230; Church Yth Grp; Dance Clb; Hst FBLA; Ski Clb; Band; Church Choir; Concert Band; Mrchg Band; Orch; Yrbk Stf; Gregg Shrthnd Awd 87; Keystone JC; Bus.

EHRHARDT, KATHY; Beaver Falls HS; Beaver Falls, PA; (3); Spanish Clb; Rep Stu Cncl; Var Score Keeper; High Hon Roll; Hon Roll; Gftd Prog 84-87; Engrng.

EHRHART, MATTHEW J; Pequea Valley HS; Narvon, PA; (4); 2/128; Trs VP FFA; Pres Sr Cls; Stu Cncl; JV Var Wt Lftg; DAR Awd; Pres NHS; Ntl Merit SF; Im Vllybl; 4-H; High Hon Roll; Hugh Obrian Yth Ldrshp Smnr 85; Star Grnhnd & Star Chptr Frmr Ffa 85-86; PA ST Cnsrvtn Ldrshp 87; PA ST U; Cvl Engrng.

EHRISMAN, DENA; Juniata HS; Mifflintown, PA; (3); Computer Clb; Drama Clb; 4-H; SADD; Varsity Clb; Sec Band; Chorus; VP Frsh Cls; Off Stu Cncl; Var JV Bsktbl; Tri M 84-88; Math.

EHRITZ, JACQUELINE; Northampton SR HS; Northampton, PA; (4); 34/430; Hosp Aide; SADD; Chorus; Capt Drill Tm; Swmmng; High Hon Roll; Hon Roll; NHS; Pom Squad Capt 86-87; Phy Olympcs 3rd Pl 86; U Of PA-PITTSBURGH; Phy Thrpy.

EHRLICH, DAVID; York Suburban SR HS; York, PA; (3); 34/180; Boy Scts; Ski Clb; Orch; Stage Crew; High Hon Roll; Hon Roll; Carnegie Mellon; Comp Sci.

EHRLICH, DEBORAH A; Blue Mt Acad; Hamburg, PA; (3); Chorus; Church Choir; Badmtn; Bsbl; Bowling; Golf; Swmmng; Tennis; Hon Roll; Acdmc Schlrshp Columbia Union Coll 88-89; Southern Adventist Coll; RN.

EHRMAN, JILL; Mount Alvernia HS; Pittsburgh, PA; (3); 3/54; VP JA; Red Cross Aide; Trs Frsh Cls; Bausch & Lomb Sci Awd; High Hon Roll; Hon Roll; NHS; Rtry Yth Ldrshp Ctr Awd 87; Hghst Avg Engl,Bio,Spnsh,Scl Stds Awds 84-85; Hghst Avg Spnsh,Eng 85-87; Duquesne U; Phrmcy.

EICHELBERGER, ERIN; Chartrers Valley HS; Pittsburgh, PA; (3); Church Yth Grp; Cmnty Wkr; Pep Clb; Spanish Clb; SADD; NHS; Bus.

EICHELBERGER, EUN HEE; Manheim Central HS; Manheim, PA; (4); Church Choir; 4 Way Tst Awd 87; MD Inst Coll Art; Comm Art.

EICHELBERGER, FRANK; Northern York HS; York Spgs, PA; (2); 100/250; Art Clb; French Clb; Science Clb; Stage Crew; Yrbk Stf; Rep Frsh Cls; Rep Soph Cls; Rep Jr Cls; Rep Sr Cls; Sec Stu Cncl; Arch.

EICHELBERGER, MICHAEL; Everett Area HS; Everett, PA; (3); Computer Clb; Exploring; Trs Frsh Cls; VP Stu Cncl; Var Bsbl; Im Bowling; Var Ftbl; Im Swmmng; AERONTCL Engrng.

EICHELBERGER, RON; Northern Bedford County HS; Hopewell, PA; (3); 5/104; FBLA; Ski Clb; Varsity Clb; Pres Band; Nwsp Stf; Trs Soph Cls; VP Jr Cls; Var L Wrstlng; High Hon Roll; NHS; FBLA 1st Pl Dist 5 Bus Math 86; PA ST U; Bus.

EICHER, BETH; Fairchance Georges JR SR HS; Fairchance, PA; (3); 4-H; Girl Scts; Band; Chorus; Concert Band; Drill Tm; Mrchg Band; JV Var Bsktbl; Mgr(s); Score Keeper; W VA U; Med Secr.

EICHER, CHARLES; Connellsville Area HS; Normalville, PA; (3); VICA; High Hon Roll; Dir List 85-87; U PA Fayette; Comp Prg.

EICHER, CLYDE; Seneca Valley HS; Ligonier, PA; (4); 17/350; Ski Clb; Hon Roll; U Of Pittsburgh; Engrng.

EICHER, GINA; Altoona Area HS; Altoona, PA; (3); Computer Clb; Trs German Clb; Band; Concert Band; Drm & Bgl; Mrchg Band; Orch; Pep Band; Symp Band; Var L Swmmng; Tri-Cnty Orchstr 85; PA Dist & Rgnl Band 87.

EICHER, KEITH; Northern Bedford HS; Roaring Spg, PA; (4); Pres Camera Clb; Speech Tm; Band; VP Chorus; Drm Mjr(t); School Musical; School Play; Swing Chorus; Ed Nwsp Phtg; Ed Yrbk Phtg; Natl Choral Awd 87; Dists & Rgnl Chorus 85-87; Juniata Coll; Pre Med.

EICHER JR, RICHARD W; Claysburg-Kimmel HS; East Freedom, PA; (4); 7/51; NFL; Speech Tm; Varsity Clb; Band; Yrbk Ed-Chief; Ftbl; NHS; High Hon Roll; Cmnty Wkr; Political Wkr; PA St Dlgt To YMCA Yt Conf On Ntnl Affrs 86; PA YMCA Yth & Gvmt Sntrl Bll Cttn 86:Snt Comm 85; US Air Force Acad; Aerospc.

EICHER, TRACY; Fairchance Georges JR/Sr HS; Fairchance, PA; (4); Church Yth Grp; Pres 4-H; Band; Concert Band; Drm Mjr(t); Mrchg Band; Bsktbl; Sftbl; Jr NHS; Sec NHS; X-Ray Tech.

EICHER, TRAVIS; Hollidaysburg SR HS; Hollidaysburg, PA; (3); Church Yth Grp; JV Crs Cntry; Var Trk; Altoono Schl/Commerce; Bus Mgmt.

EICHORN, KRISTEN; Upper Moreland HS; Hatboro, PA; (3); 161/275; Hosp Aide; JV Socr; Hon Roll; Air Force; Nrsng.

EIDSON, ANDREW; Central Bucks HS West; Chalfont, PA; (4); German Clb; Band; Concert Band; Mrchg Band; Var L Bsktbl; Var L Golf; Var L Socr; JV Tennis; Var L Vllybl; Im Wt Lftg; Marietta Coll; Bus.

EILENBERGER, DAVID; Stroudsburg HS; Saylorsburg, PA; (3); 5/231; Am Leg Boys St; French Clb; Scholastic Bowl; Science Clb; Nwsp Stf; Tennis; High Hon Roll; NHS; Poltcl Sci.

EILER, DAVID; Valley HS; New Kensington, PA; (3); Ski Clb; Spanish Clb; Chorus; High Hon Roll; NHS; Hnrs Awd 85; Engr.

EILER, TIMOTHY; Philipsburg Osceola Area HS; Philipsburg, PA; (4); 70/243; Letterman Clb; Yrbk Stf; Bsbl; Bsktbl; Crs Cntry; JV Ftbl; Central Penn League 1st Tm Bsbll Des Hitter 86 & 2nd Tm Bsbll Center Field 87; Mansfield U; Business Admstrtn.

EILL, LORI; Downingtown SR HS; Downingtown, PA; (3); French Clb; GAA; Ski Clb; SADD; Chorus; Mrchg Band; Var Diving; Stat Mgr(s); Var Sftbl; Hon Roll; Crmnl Just.

EIMERS, BRENDA; Mountain View HS; Forest City, PA; (2); 4/91; Band; Chorus; Nwsp Rptr; Yrbk Phtg; Var Bsktbl; Var Crs Cntry; Var Sftbl; Var Vllybl; High Hon Roll; Rotary Awd; Latin Hnr Scty 85-87; Stu Month 86; Dist Band & Chorus Alt Regnl 87; Med.

EINSEL, JASON; Cedar Crest HS; Lebanon, PA; (2); German Clb; Spanish Clb; JV Socr; Prfct Atten Awd.

EIRICH, MIKE; West Branch HS; Allport, PA; (2); Spanish Clb; SADD; Varsity Clb; Ftbl; Wt Lftg.

EISAMAN, JERRY; Norwin SR HS; N Huntingdon, PA; (3); Aud/Vis; German Clb; SADD; Stage Crew; JV Bsktbl; Var L Ice Hcky.

EISELE, SUSAN; Council Rock HS; Richboro, PA; (3); 113/840; Church Yth Grp; Intnl Clb; Key Clb; Church Choir; Rep Frsh Cls; Rep Jr Cls; JV Fld Hcky; Hon Roll; NHS; Physcl Thrpy.

EISENACHER, RONALD C; Sun Valley HS; Aston, PA; (4); Am Leg Boys St; Variety Show; VP Soph Cls; VP Jr Cls; Pres Stu Cncl; Socr; Var Wrstlng; Hon Roll; Styu Senate Achvt Awd 86-87; West Chester U; Comms.

EISENBERG, JUDITH; Carver HS For Science & Engr; Philladelphia, PA; (3); 6/200; Church Yth Grp; Hosp Aide; Temple Yth Grp; Church Choir; Orch; Nwsp Stf; Yrbk Stf; Rep Frsh Cls; Rep Soph Cls; Gov Hon Prg Awd; A Avg; Med Sci.

EISENBERG, STEVEN; Abington SR HS; Meadowbrook, PA; (3); 20/506; Chess Clb; French Clb; Quiz Bowl; Science Clb; Spanish Clb; Nwsp Stf; Yrbk Stf; Rep Frsh Cls; Rep Soph Cls; Rep Jr Cls; Bus.

EISENBERG, STEVEN; Upper Dublin HS; Ambler, PA; (3); 38/305; FBLA; Intnl Clb; SADD; Lit Mag; Rep Soph Cls; Rep Jr Cls; Im Bsktbl; JV Tennis; Im Vllybl; NHS; 5TH Pl FLBA Rgnl Cmptn/Grphc Arts 87; Sprts Med.

EISENHARD, LORI; Central Catholic HS; Allentown, PA; (3); Church Yth Grp; Key Clb; Ski Clb; Spanish Clb; Im Powder Puff Ftbl; Var L Sftbl; Var Vllybl; High Hon Roll; Hon Roll; Bus.

EISENHAUER, AMY; Cedar Crest HS; Lebanon, PA; (3); 92/342; Key Clb; Pep Clb; Drm Mjr(t); School Musical; Yrbk Sprt Ed; Var Bsktbl; Var L Fld Hcky; Var L Sftbl; Im Vllybl; Hon Roll; Socl Sci.

EISENHAUER, DOROTHY A; Cedar Crest HS; Lebanon, PA; (4); Pres Drama Clb; Pres French Clb; Key Clb; Pep Clb; Orch; School Musical; School Play; Stage Crew; NHS; Hnr Banquet; Franklin & Marshall; Mrktng.

EISENHOWER, FRANKLIN A; Curwensville Area HS; Curwensville, PA; (3); Ski Clb; Varsity Clb; Pres Jr Cls; Pres Stu Cncl; Var JV Bsbl; Var JV Bsktbl; Var JV Ftbl; High Hon Roll; Hon Roll; NHS; Acdmc All Am 86-87; JR Most Likely To Suceed 87; Penn ST; Engineering.

EISENMAN, BONNIE; North Clarion JR SR HS; Marble, PA; (3); French Clb; Hon Roll; Hlth.

EISERMAN, AMY; Cedar Crest HS; Cornwall, PA; (2); 118/345; Drama Clb; Trs FBLA; German Clb; Girl Scts; Library Aide; Pep Clb; School Musical; School Play; Stage Crew; L Var Bowling; Math.

EISMAN, JENNIFER; Du Bois SR HS; Luthersburg, PA; (2); SADD; Trk; Hon Roll; Social Svcs.

EITNIER, DIANE; Pequea Valley HS; New Holland, PA; (3); AFS; Varsity Clb; Band; Chorus; Mrchg Band; Pep Band; School Musical; School Play; Fld Hcky; NHS.

EKAS, MICHAEL; Freeport Area HS; Freeport, PA; (3); 5/220; Boy Scts; Math Tm; Scholastic Bowl; Stat Ftbl; High Hon Roll; Hon Roll; NHS; Ntl Merit SF; MIT; Aerontcl Engrng.

EKBERG, PAMELA; Danville HS; Danville, PA; (2); Church Yth Grp; French Clb; Key Clb; Latin Clb; Ski Clb; Cheerleading; Gym; CAP; Tennis; Trk.

EKDAHL, KRISTIN; Emmaus HS; Allentown, PA; (3); 104/548; Exploring; German Clb; Key Clb; Nwsp Stf; Soph Cls; Stu Cncl; Hon Roll; VFW Awd; Voice Dem Awd; Presdntl Acadmc Fts Awd 84-85; Marine Bio.

EKIS, CHRIS; Hickory HS; Hermitage, PA; (3); Church Yth Grp; German Clb; Fshn Dsgn.

EKLUND, KEITH L; Baldwin HS; Pittsburgh, PA; (4); 10/535; Boy Scts; Nwsp Phtg; Ed Nwsp Stf; Yrbk Ed-Chief; Ed Yrbk Stf; Var L Trk; NHS; Ntl Merit SF; Church Yth Grp; JA; Whitehall High Achvrs Cert 83-84; Seven Sprgs Yrbk Semnr 86; Capt Baldwin-Whitehll Athlc Assn 83-87; Mech Engr.

EL ATTRACHE, DEAN; Mt Pleasant Area SR HS; Mt Pleasant, PA; (4); 7/256; Ski Clb; Var Ftbl; NHS; Ntl Merit Ltr; Pres Schlr; Presdntl Clsrm 87; Stu Of Mnth 86; Keystone Conf AAA Div All-Conf Qrtrbk 86; Acad All Amer.

EL BASSUNI, NABILA; Stroudsburg HS; Stroudsburg, PA; (2); Dance Clb; French Clb; Quiz Bowl; School Musical; Bsktbl; Swmmng; Capt Tennis; Trk; Capt Vllybl; High Hon Roll; Med.

ELBIN, LANCE L; Southern Fulton HS; Warfordsburg, PA; (3); 3/76; Am Leg Aux Girls St; CAP; Band; Chorus; School Play; Bsbl; High Hon Roll; NHS; Ntl Merit SF; Embry-Riddle Aerontcl U.

ELBY, SHANNON; Connellsville SR HS; Connellsville, PA; (3); 24/550; Chorus; Drm Mjr(t); Mrchg Band; School Musical; Symp Band; Rep Stu Cncl; French Hon Soc; High Hon Roll; Masonic Awd; NHS; Law.

ELCHISAK, HOLLY; Shenandoah Valley JR/Sr HS; Shenandoah, PA; (3); 2/79; Mrchg Band; JV Bsktbl; JV Var Vllybl; High Hon Roll; NHS; Natl Ldrshp/Svc Awd 87; Acad Al Am Awd 86-87; Schlstc Achvt Awd 86; Span Tchr.

ELDER, DAVID; Tussey Mountain HS; Saxton, PA; (4); 7/116; Church Yth Grp; Nwsp Stf; Rep Frsh Cls; Rep Soph Cls; Rep Jr Cls; Bsbl; Bsktbl; Ftbl; Pres NHS; Tribune Dem Schlr Athlt Awd 87; Am Lgn Post 169 Gradtn Awd 87; Stoudnour Ctznshp Awd 87; Penn ST U; Acctg.

ELDER, DEANNA; Franklin Regional HS; Export, PA; (3); 112/329; Church Yth Grp; Cmnty Wkr; FNA; SADD; Thesps; Chorus; School Musical; School Play; Yrbk Stf; High Hon Roll; Pre Med.

ELDER, KAREN; Shenango HS; New Castle, PA; (3); Camera Clb; Church Yth Grp; French Clb; Office Aide; Flag Corp; School Play; Yrbk Stf; Prfct Atten Awd; Educ.

ELDER, ROMY; Freeport Area SR HS; Sarver, PA; (3); 5/213; FBLA; Office Aide; Nwsp Stf; Yrbk Stf; High Hon Roll; Hon Roll; Accntng.

ELDER, RYAN; Mt Pleasant Area HS; Mt Pleasant, PA; (2); JV Ftbl; Capt Wrstlng; Cit Awd; High Hon Roll; Engrng.

ELDER, SANDRA; Cardinal O Hara HS; Chester, PA; (4); 126/771; Church Yth Grp; Cmnty Wkr; Drama Clb; Spanish Clb; SADD; Hon Roll; W Chester U; Elem Ed.

ELDER, SCOTT; Danville SR HS; Danville, PA; (2); #5 In Class; Church Yth Grp; Socr; Trk; High Hon Roll; Arntcl Engrng.

ELDER, TERRY; Hanover SR HS; Hanover, PA; (4); 8/109; Aud/Vis; Math Tm; Red Cross Aide; Science Clb; Varsity Clb; Stage Crew; Var L Bsktbl; Coach Actv; Var L Trk; Hon Roll; Exchng Clb Schlrshp, Engrng Soc Yrk, & Pres Acdmc Ftnss Awd 87; PA ST U; Elec Engrng.

ELDER, TRUDY; Wilmington Area HS; New Wilmington, PA; (4); 17/125; Dance Clb; Drama Clb; Key Clb; Office Aide; Stage Crew; Capt Bsktbl; Powder Puff Ftbl; Hon Roll; NHS; Acdmc Achvt Awd 84; Prsdntl Ftnss/Schlr Awd 87; Kent ST U; Real Est.

ELDRIDGE, MICHAILE; West Philadelphia Catholic Gls HS; Philadelphia, PA; (4); 36/233; Hosp Aide; Band; Jazz Band; Orch; School Play; Rep Jr Cls; Rep Sr Cls; Rep Stu Cncl; Hon Roll; NHS; HOBY Fndtn Awd; Coll Of Holy Crs; Corp Law.

ELEK, KIRSTEN; Notre Dame HS; Easton, PA; (3); Chorus; Yrbk Stf; Trs Soph Cls; Capt Sftbl; Hon Roll; Church Yth Grp; Pep Clb; Ski Clb; Var Bsktbl; Church Choir; Educ.

ELEK, MARTIN; Carmichaels Area HS; Carmichaels, PA; (2); Stage Crew; High Hon Roll; Hon Roll.

ELENCHIK, PAMELA; Dallas SR HS; Pittston, PA; (3); Hosp Aide; Hon Roll; Yth Ftns Achvt Awd 87; Elem Educ.

ELFONT, RACHEL; Lower Moreland HS; Huntingdon Valley, PA; (3); Sec Drama Clb; SADD; Chorus; Madrigals; Pep Band; School Musical; School Play; Lit Mag; VP Frsh Cls; Rep Stu Cncl; Hntngdn Vly Wmns Clb Awd 85; Ntl Hbrn Hnr Soc 86; Ed.

ELIADES, KATHERINE; Penn Wood Schl; Lansdowne, PA; (3); Church Yth Grp; Dance Clb; FBLA; SADD; Yrbk Phtg; Yrbk Stf; Rep Frsh Cls; Rep Soph Cls; Rep Jr Cls; Rep Sr Cls; Bus.

ELIAS, DANIELLE; Center HS; Monaca, PA; (3); Spanish Clb; Var JV Sftbl; Hon Roll; CCBC; Aviation.

ELIAS, HOLLY; Northern Cambria HS; Barnesboro, PA; (3); 13/152; Hosp Aide; Spanish Clb; Band; Chorus; Concert Band; Drill Tm; Sec Jr Cls; High Hon Roll; NHS; Spanish NHS; PA ST U; Law.

ELIAS, JOHN JAY; Cambria Heights HS; Patton, PA; (3); Ski Clb; Chorus; Church Choir; Concert Band; Jazz Band; Mrchg Band; Pep Band; School Play; Stage Crew; Hon Roll; Optmtry.

ELIAS, MICHAEL D; Shenango HS; New Castle, PA; (3); Art Clb; French Clb; Speech Tm; Var JV Bsbl; Cert Of Achvt In Karate; Health.

ELIAS, PAMELA; Western Wayne HS; Lake Ariel, PA; (3); Church Yth Grp; Exploring; SADD; Band; Chorus; Church Choir; Concert Band; Mrchg Band; Trk; PIAA Dist 12 2nd Pl 3200 Rly & 3rd Pl 800 M, Alt PIAA ST Chmpnshp Trk 87; Intr Dcrtr.

ELIAS, SAM; E L Meyers HS; Wilkes Barre, PA; (3); German Clb; Chorus; Wrstlng; Hon Roll; Engr.

ELIASON, LYNN; Fort Le Boeuf HS; Erie, PA; (3); Trs Soph Cls; Var Bsktbl; Capt Var Sftbl; Capt Var Vllybl; High Hon Roll; VP NHS; Pharmacy.

ELICK, THOMAS; Coughlin HS; Wilkes Barre, PA; (3); Art Clb; Band; Concert Band; Mrchg Band; Jr Cls; Wt Lftg; Hon Roll; Jr NHS; Prfct Atten Awd; Drftng.

ELICKER, KAREN; South Western HS; Hanover, PA; (3); Sec Key Clb; School Play; Nwsp Stf; Yrbk Stf; VP Jr Cls; Sec Stu Cncl; Var L Cheerleading; Tennis; Hon Roll; NEDT Awd; Bus.

ELICKER, T SEAN; Northeastern HS; York, PA; (3); 1/175; Math Tm; Band; Concert Band; Orch; School Musical; Ed Lit Mag; Bsbl; Golf; Bausch & Lomb Sci Awd; High Hon Roll; USNA Summer Seminar 87; High Educ; Physics.

ELIE, JOHN; Waynesboro Area SR HS; Waynesboro, PA; (3); Boy Scts; Rep Frsh Cls; Rep Soph Cls; Var L Trk; Var L Wrstlng; Arch.

ELIJAH, TERRI; Sister Clara Muhammad HS; Philadelphia, PA; (1); 5/23; Hosp Aide; Chorus; Drill Tm; School Play; Stu Cncl; Vllybl; Prfct Atten Awd; UCLA; Arch.

ELINE, ROSEMARY; South Western HS; Hanover, PA; (3); 34/233; Church Yth Grp; Hosp Aide; Nwsp Stf; Yrbk Stf; Hon Roll; NHS; Bus Mngmnt.

ELKIN, CHRISTINA; Blairsville HS; Blairsville, PA; (1); Trk; Vllybl; Hon Roll; Fshn Merch.

ELKINS, ADAM; Lower Merion HS; Wynnewood, PA; (3); VP Temple Yth Grp; Concert Band; Jazz Band; Mrchg Band; Yrbk Phtg; Var L Ice Hcky; Var L Trk; French Hon Soc; Hon Roll; Trs NHS.

ELKINS, KAREN; Valley View JR-SR HS; Peckville, PA; (3); Church Yth Grp; French Clb; Hosp Aide; Spanish Clb; Chorus; Drill Tm; Im Coach Actv; Capt Pom Pon; Var Swmmng; Hon Roll.

ELLEBIE, MARK; Farrell SR HS; Farrell, PA; (3); 15/103.

ELLENBERGER, JULIE; Punxsutawney SR HS; Stump Creek, PA; (3); Art Clb; Drama Clb; Office Aide; Radio Clb; School Play; Nwsp Stf; Yrbk Stf; Rep Sr Cls; Cheerleading; Hon Roll; Slippery Rock; Comm.

ELLER, WENDY; Solanco HS; Peach Bottom, PA; (3); FHA; Flag Corp; Yrbk Stf; High Hon Roll; Bus.

ELLERS, KEVIN; Ridley HS; Ridley Pk, PA; (3); 30/484; Boys Clb Am; Spanish Clb; Lcrss; Vtd All-Amer 87; Bus.

ELLETSON, KYM; Academy HS; Erie, PA; (3); Exploring; Red Cross Aide; Var L Socr; Var L Sftbl; Pre Law.

ELLINGER, AMY; Lebanon Catholic HS; Quentin, PA; (4); Debate Tm; Pep Clb; Spanish Clb; Mgr(s); Hon Roll; Stu Month Svc & Spirit 87; Alvernia Coll; Counseling.

ELLIOTT, CYNTHIA; Souderton HS; Telford, PA; (4); 40/350; Var L Trk; Hon Roll; Eugene Klmvch Sci Awd 87; Widener U; Nrsng.

ELLIOTT, DANI; Windber Area HS; Windber, PA; (3); 49/128; Dance Clb; Drama Clb; French Clb; Chorus; Variety Show; Hon Roll; NY U; Dance Choreogrphr.

ELLIOTT, DAVID J; Allegheny Clarion Valley HS; Parker, PA; (3); 8/87; Am Leg Boys St; Boy Scts; Spanish Clb; Chorus; Pres Soph Cls; Pres Jr Cls; Rep Stu Cncl; Trk; High Hon Roll; NHS; Aero Engr.

ELLIOTT, HEIDI; Mechanicsburg Area SR HS; Mechanicsburg, PA; (2); Cmnty Wkr; Pep Clb; Band; Chorus; Flag Corp.

ELLIOTT, JANINE; Downingtown HS; West Chester, PA; (3); 57/648; GAA; Latin Clb; Pep Clb; Ski Clb; Spanish Clb; Chorus; Rep Frsh Cls; Cheerleading; Lcrss; Hon Roll; Social Work.

ELLIOTT, JEFFREY; Mc Guffey HS; Claysville, PA; (3); Boy Scts; JA; Spanish Clb; Band; Chorus; Mrchg Band; Bsktbl; FL Inst Tech; Bio.

ELLIOTT, SHEILA; Penns Manor HS; Alverda, PA; (3); 9/93; Office Aide; OEA; SADD; Teachers Aide; Varsity Clb; Church Choir; Vllybl; High Hon Roll; Hon Roll; NHS; Sec.

ELLIOTT, STEVEN J; Kiski Area HS; Apollo, PA; (3); Church Yth Grp; Debate Tm; Letterman Clb; Math Tm; Chorus; Yrbk Stf; Var L Crs Cntry; Var L Ftbl; Var L Swmmng; Var L Trk; Lamp Of Learning-Acad Lttr 86; Cornell; Physics.

ELLIOTT, SUE; Annville-Cleona HS; Lebanon, PA; (4); 16/119; Trs Church Yth Grp; Trs Rep FFA; Speech Tm; SADD; Acpl Chr; Chorus; Madrigals; School Musical; Var Co-Capt Fld Hcky; Hon Roll; Lancastr/Lebanon Fld Hcky Schlrshp 86-87; Farm Wmn Schlrshp 87; Millersville U; Elem Ed.

ELLIS, BRYAN; Garnet Valley HS; Glen Mills, PA; (4); 12/151; German Clb; Intnl Clb; Model UN; Scholastic Bowl; L Crs Cntry; L Trk; Ntl Merit Schol; Rice; Math.

ELLIS, CAROL; Cowanesque Valley HS; Knoxville, PA; (4); 5/100; Drama Clb; Letterman Clb; SADD; Band; Yrbk Stf; Trs Stu Cncl; Stat Bsktbl; Var Trk; JV Var Vllybl; High Hon Roll; Alfred ST Coll; RN.

ELLIS, JAMIE; Cumberland Valley HS; Mechanicsburg, PA; (3); Church Yth Grp; German Clb; GAA; Key Clb; Ski Clb; Im Socr; L Var Trk; Hon Roll; U Of FA; Accntnt.

ELLIS, JANENNE; West York Area HS; York, PA; (4); FCA; Teachers Aide; Pres Varsity Clb; Var Capt Bsktbl; Var L Fld Hcky; Var Capt Sftbl; Var L Trk; Var Capt Vllybl; NHS; Voice Dem Awd; Stu Athl Awd Sr Clss 87; Jo A Myeres Schlrshp 87; Yrk Dly Rcrd, Yrk Dsptch All Str Bsktbl 87; WV U; Sprts Physlgy.

ELLIS, JENNIFER; Quigley HS; Beaver Falls, PA; (3); Chorus; Bsktbl; Powder Puff Ftbl; Vllybl; Gov Hon Prg Awd; Church Yth Grp; Pep Clb; Church Choir; School Musical; Sm-Fnlst Govnrs Schl Arts 85-87; Accmpnst Cncrt Chr 86-87; Mrtn.

ELLIS, SHANNON; West Branch JR-SR HS; Morrisdale, PA; (2); Debate Tm; Drama Clb; Spanish Clb; SADD; Band; Concert Band; Mrchg Band; School Play; Hon Roll; Prfct Atten Awd; Eagle Scout Awd 87.

ELLIS, TAWNYA; West Branch Area HS; Morrisdale, PA; (3); 13/133; Science Clb; Spanish Clb; SADD; Band; Chorus; Concert Band; Mrchg Band; Nwsp Stf; Stu Cncl; Hon Roll; Bio.

ELLIS, TIFFANY ANNE; Schenley HS; Pittsburgh, PA; (3); Church Yth Grp; Dance Clb; Drama Clb; French Clb; Chorus; Church Choir; School Play; Rep Stu Cncl; High Hon Roll; Hon Roll; Stdnt Exch Canada 85; Sci Rsrch Apprntc Univ Pgh 86; Engrng.

ELLIS, VICKI MARIE; Sharpsville Area HS; Sharpsville, PA; (4); 5/121; Sec Trs Band; Chorus; Jazz Band; Mrchg Band; Pep Band; Nwsp Stf; Yrbk Stf; Capt Cheerleading; Vllybl; High Hon Roll; Acdmc Achvt Awds 85-87; Youngstown ST U; Chem Engrng.

ELLISON, ANGELA; Central HS; Philadelphia, PA; (2); Church Yth Grp; Cmnty Wkr; Girl Scts; Math Tm; High Hon Roll; Hrvrd; Law.

ELLISON, JAMES P; Hanover HS; Hanover, PA; (4); 3/104; Nwsp Rptr; Pres Frsh Cls; Pres Stu Cncl; JV Bsktbl; Var Tennis; Elks Awd; NHS; Ntl Merit SF; NEDT Awd; Rotary Awd; Outstndng Tennis Plyr 86.

ELLMAN, SUSAN; Lower Moreland HS; Huntingdon Valley, PA; (3); Drama Clb; FBLA; Hosp Aide; Temple Yth Grp; School Musical; Stage Crew; Pblc Rltns.

ELLSWORTH, KEVIN; Donegal HS; Marietta, PA; (4); 8/161; Pres Church Yth Grp; Pres Chorus; Capt Trk; Cit Awd; God Cntry Awd; Hon Roll; NHS; Ntl Merit SF; Opt Clb Awd; BYU.

ELLSWORTH, PAULETTE; GJA Vocational-Tech Schl; Radcliff, KY; (4); Church Yth Grp; ROTC; VICA; Hon Roll; Voctnl Technl Achvt Awd All Thru HS; Skin Care Spec.

ELLSWORTH, THOMAS; Burgettstown JR/Sr HS; Burgettstown, PA; (2); #4 In Class; French Clb; Band; Concert Band; Mrchg Band; Pep Band; Symp Band; High Hon Roll; Hon Roll; Sci.

ELLSWORTH, WENDY; Tunkhannock Area HS; Meshoppen, PA; (2); 19/330; 4-H; JV Bsktbl; JV Fld Hcky; JV Sftbl; 4-H Awd; Hon Roll.

ELMQUIST, RACHEL; Johnsonburg HS; Johnsonburg, PA; (3); Camera Clb; Church Yth Grp; Library Aide; Yrbk Stf; Trs Jr Cls; Var Cheerleading; Var Vllybl; Lwyr.

ELPHINSTONE, MICHAEL; Freeport Area HS; Sarver, PA; (4); 1/163; Church Yth Grp; Stage Crew; High Hon Roll; NHS; Opt Clb Awd; Pres Schlr; Prncpls Awd 87; Penn ST New Kensington; Engrng.

ELSER, NICOLA; Ephrata SR HS; Ephrata, PA; (3); 62/288; FBLA; Capt Flag Corp; Mrchg Band; Hon Roll; Bus.

ELTZ, WENDY; New Oxford HS; New Oxford, PA; (3); Teachers Aide; Rep Varsity Clb; Rep Stu Cncl; JV Bsktbl; Var L Trk; Var L Vllybl; Hon Roll; Vlybl Trphy 84-85; MVP Vlybl Trphy 86-87; Acctng.

ELY, DAVID; Seton La Salle Regional HS; Pittsburgh, PA; (3); 90/260; Rep Am Leg Boys St; Church Yth Grp; FBLA; JA; Pres Frsh Cls; Rep Soph Cls; Rep Jr Cls; Sec Stu Cncl; Var Capt Bsbl; Var Bsktbl; Med.

ELY, JENNIFER; Downingtown SR HS; Downingtown, PA; (3); 110/648; Church Yth Grp; French Clb; Ski Clb; SADD; Band; Chorus; Concert Band; Var L Mgr(s); Im Score Keeper; High Hon Roll; Phy Thrpy.

ELY, JILL; Sheffield Area JR-SR HS; Clarendon, PA; (4); 8/76; Church Yth Grp; SADD; Band; Concert Band; Jazz Band; Trs Mrchg Band; Symp Band; Nwsp Ed-Chief; NHS; Altar Guild Schlrshp 87; Joey Curtin Band Awd 87; Westminster Coll; Telecmmnctns.

ELY, KATHLEEN; Hikellamy HS; Sunbury, PA; (4); 3/301; Pres Library Aide; Teachers Aide; Yrbk Stf; Cheerleading; Hon Roll; NHS; Rotary Awd; Church Yth Grp; Spanish Clb; Fld Hcky; Lycoming Coll; Lbrl Arts.

ELY, MARNA; West Green JR SR HS; Sycamore, PA; (3); Dance Clb; Band; Concert Band; Mrchg Band; Trs Sr Cls; Sec Trs Stu Cncl; Var Trk; Stat Wrstlng; Hon Roll; French Clb; All Cnty Band 85-87; Rdlgc Tech.

EMADI, BAQIRALI A; Cumberland Valley HS; Mechanicsburg, PA; (4); Im Trk; Hon Roll; Drexel U; Mech Engr.

EMANUEL, DIANA; Saltsburg HS; New Alexandria, PA; (2); 10/91; SADD; Chorus; Mrchg Band; Nwsp Rptr; Mgr(s); Score Keeper; JV Vllybl; High Hon Roll; Hon Roll; Church Yth Grp; IN County SR Co Chorus 86-87; Duguesne U; Bus Mgt.

EMANUEL, PATRICK; Blairsville SR HS; Blairsville, PA; (3); 36/110; Letterman Clb; Varsity Clb; School Musical; Stage Crew; Bsktbl; Coach Actv; Var L Ftbl; Trk; Hon Roll; Tch.

EMBERG, JEFF; Kiski Area SR HS; Apollo, PA; (3); Aud/Vis; Church Yth Grp; Band; Jazz Band; Mrchg Band; Orch; Pep Band; Symp Band; Swmmng; Hon Roll; Comm.

EMBERSON, JACQUELENE; Phila HS For Girls; Philadelphia, PA; (3); 67/400; Chorus; Stage Crew; Variety Show; Yrbk Phtg; Yrbk Stf; Fld Hcky; Mgr(s); Sftbl; Trk; Hon Roll; Ellis Fund Schlrshp 87; U NH; Specl Ed.

EMERICH, LAURA; Central Cambria HS; Ebensburg, PA; (4); 1/214; Art Clb; Ski Clb; Band; Concert Band; Jazz Band; Mrchg Band; Pep Band; Stage Crew; Yrbk Stf; Var Trk; IN U; Chmstry.

EMERICH, SHELLY LYNN; Tulpehocken HS; Bethel, PA; (4); 38/100; Office Aide; Chorus; School Musical; Sec Jr Cls; Pres Stu Cncl; Var L Fld Hcky; Var Capt Sftbl; JR Miss 86; Duquesne U; Intl Rltns.

EMERICK, DAVID; Laurel Highlands HS; Glencoe, PA; (3); Chorus; Socr; ST Socr Champs 83-85; Diesel Mechnc.

EMERICK, JASON; Berlin Brothers Valley HS; Glencoe, PA; (2); Spanish Clb; Band; Sec Chorus; Church Choir; Concert Band; Mrchg Band; JV Var Bsktbl; Hon Roll; Cnty Chorus 4th Choir Tenor 87; Dist Chorus Tenor 87; Pckd For Rgnl Chorus 87; Brigham Young U; Music Tchr.

EMERICK, JENNIFER; Berlin Brothersvalley HS; Fairhope, PA; (3); 40/105; Church Yth Grp; French Clb; SADD; Chorus; Church Choir; Concert Band; Co-Capt Drm Mjr(t); School Play; Nwsp Rptr; Debate Tm; Ldrshp Dvlp Prog 86; Acadc All-Amer Schlr Prog 85; Jrnlst.

EMERICK, JODY; Somerset Area SR HS; Somerset, PA; (3); 51/230; English Clb; French Clb; JA; Office Aide; Teachers Aide; Chorus; JV Capt Cheerleading; Sftbl; French Hon Soc; High Hon Roll; Acadc Excllnc 85; Teaching.

EMERICK, WENDY; Hyndman Middle SR HS; Hyndman, PA; (3); Spanish Clb; Varsity Clb; Chorus; School Musical; JV Var Cheerleading; Sftbl; Tennis; Twrlr; Hon Roll; ACC; Bus.

EMERSON, JAA; Northern HS; Dillsburg, PA; (3); 8/239; Church Yth Grp; Church Choir; Nwsp Stf; Yrbk Ed-Chief; JV Bsktbl; Powder Puff Ftbl; Var L Sftbl; Hon Roll; NHS; Cmnty Wkr; US Naval Acad Talented & Gifted Pgm 85; US Naval Acad; Bus Adm.

EMERSON, JAMES; Plum SR HS; Verona, PA; (3); Hon Roll; Prfct Atten Awd; Penn ST U; Bus.

EMERY, ALISA; Seneca Valley SR HS; Mars, PA; (2); Art Clb; Church Yth Grp; Exploring; Girl Scts; Ski Clb; Chorus; Stage Crew; Crs Cntry; Gym; Trk; Schsltc Awd 86-87; Archtct.

EMERY, DENISE; Spring-Ford SR HS; Royersford, PA; (3); 74/256; Church Yth Grp; Pep Clb; Spanish Clb; Off Stu Cncl; Var Capt Cheerleading; JV Lcrss; Hon Roll; Med Tech.

EMERY, MELINDA; Northampton SR HS; Bath, PA; (3); 69/484; DECA; Drama Clb; Hosp Aide; Hon Roll; 3rd Pl Dist Lev Restrnt Mktng & Mgmt 86 & 87; ST Comptr PA DECA Conf 86 & 87; Johnson & Wales; Htl/Rest Mktng.

EMIG, LISA; Christian School Of York; Dover, PA; (2); Church Yth Grp; 4-H; Band; Chorus; Church Choir; Pep Band; Phtgrphr.

EMIG, TRAVIS; Red Lion SR HS; Red Lion, PA; (3); 13/342; L Var Golf; Science Clb; Varsity Clb; Yrbk Stf; High Hon Roll.

EMIGH, JAMES; West Branch Area HS; Morrisdale, PA; (3); 33/105; Ski Clb; Varsity Clb; Var L Ftbl; Var Wt Lftg; Mansfield U; Fish Cltr.

EMLING, CHRISTINA; Solanco HS; Nottingham, PA; (3); 18/268; JV Crs Cntry; Trk; High Hon Roll; Hon Roll; Trs NHS; Cert Of Achiev For Scl Stds 87.

EMMERICH JR, FRANK RICHARD; Archbishop Wood For Boys; Hatboro, PA; (3); 12/235; Pres Church Yth Grp; Speech Tm; Nwsp Rptr; Hon Roll; NHS; Amer Lgn Awd 84; Frdm Fndtn Yth Conf Rep 87; Brdcst Jrnlst.

EMMERT, LORI; St Marys Area HS; Kersey, PA; (2); Church Choir; JV L Cheerleading; Hon Roll; Bus.

EMMERT, PAUL; Hanover Area JR/Sr HS; Ashley, PA; (3); Drama Clb; Key Clb; Leo Clb; Ski Clb; Var Bsbl; JV Golf; Var Tennis; Hon Roll; JETS Awd; NHS; Temple U; Phrmcy.

EMMONDS, HEATHER; Ford City HS; Ford City, PA; (3); Church Yth Grp; Rep Spanish Clb; Chorus; Drill Tm; Off Jr Cls; Rep Stu Cncl; Co-Capt Cheerleading; Vllybl; Hon Roll; NHS; Stu Activities Awd 87.

EMREY, ERIC; Garden Spot HS; E Earl, PA; (2); Trs Boy Scts; Pres Church Yth Grp; JV Socr; Hon Roll; Pilot.

EMRICH, JEANNETTE; Northern Lebanon HS; Annville, PA; (4); 24/170; Sec Church Yth Grp; Office Aide; Chorus; Church Choir; Color Guard; Mrchg Band; School Musical; Stage Crew; High Hon Roll; Hon Roll.

EMS JR, FRANK W; East Stroudsburg Area HS; Marshalls Creek, PA; (3); 17/260; Am Leg Boys St; Church Yth Grp; School Play; Rep Stu Cncl; Var Bsbl; Var Ftbl; Var Swmmng; Var Wt Lftg; Hon Roll; NHS; Acad All Amer 87; All Area Hnrs In Ftbl 86; Engrng.

EMSWILER, BRIEN; North Star HS; Stoystown, PA; (2); Sec Soph Cls; JV Ftbl.

ENCISO, CHRIS; Penn Hills SR HS; Pittsburgh, PA; (3); High Hon Roll; Hon Roll; Cnstrctn.

ENCISO, MICHELLE; Valley HS; New Kensington, PA; (2); FBLA; Band; Concert Band; Mrchg Band; Pep Band; Sftbl; Vllybl; Hon Roll; Accnt.

ENCK, STEVE; Conestoga Valley HS; Lancaster, PA; (3); Rep Soph Cls; Rep Jr Cls; Im Ftbl; JV Wrstlng; Hon Roll; PA ST U; Engrng.

ENDERLE, ROBERTA; Pennsburg HS; Yardley, PA; (4); Church Yth Grp; German Clb; SADD; Band; Hon Roll; NHS; AZ ST U; Bus.

ENDERS, HOWIE; Council Rock HS; Richboro, PA; (2); Temple Yth Grp; Band; Concert Band; Mrchg Band; Pep Band; Hon Roll; Penn ST; Cvl Law.

ENDERS, RICHARD; Hamburg Area HS; Hamburg, PA; (2); Spanish Clb; Band; Concert Band; Jazz Band; Mrchg Band; Wrld Cltrs Acadc Awd 86; Wilkes Coll; Env Engr.

ENDLER, EDWARD F; E L Meyers HS; Wilkes-Barre, PA; (4); 2/160; Letterman Clb; Pep Clb; VP Ski Clb; SADD; Varsity Clb; Chorus; Yrbk Stf; Stu Cncl; Var L Bsbl; Var L Ftbl.

ENDLER, RENEE; Bishop Carroll HS; Nicktown, PA; (4); 8/107; Girl Scts; Pep Clb; Ski Clb; Concert Band; Mrchg Band; Crs Cntry; IUP; Natrl Sci.

ENDLISH, JASON; Leechburg Area HS; Leechburg, PA; (3); Ftbl; Vllybl; Hon Roll; NHS; Aeronmcs.

ENDY, MARK; Daniel Boone HS; Earlville, PA; (3); Aud/Vis; Boy Scts; Ski Clb; Chorus; Bsktbl; Bowling; Hon Roll; JR Fire Chief 86-87; Navy; Aviation.

ENG, MELANIE; Exeter HS; Reading, PA; (3); Drama Clb; Library Aide; Chorus; School Play; Mgr Bsktbl; Gym; Hon Roll.

ENGEL, GREGORY; Elk County Christian HS; St Marys, PA; (3); 9/72; Am Leg Boys St; Varsity Clb; Rep Soph Cls; Var JV Bsktbl; Var L Crs Cntry; Var L Trk; High Hon Roll; Hon Roll; Coaches Awd Cross Cntry 86-87; St Meet Track 7th Pl 1600m Relay 86-87; DK; Optometry.

ENGEL, JENNIFER; Elk County Christian HS; St Marys, PA; (3); Church Yth Grp; Band; Concert Band; Drm Mjr(t); Jazz Band; Mrchg Band; Var Trk; High Hon Roll; PA All ST Bands 86-87; PA Gov Schl Arts 87; Med Tech.

ENGEL, JOE; Canton Area HS; Ralston, PA; (3); FFA; Speech Tm; VP Frsh Cls; VP Soph Cls; JV Bsktbl; Var Crs Cntry; Var Trk; Hon Roll; Bradford Cnty Star Frmr Awd 87; Frstry.

ENGEL, KAREN; Montoursville HS; Montoursville, PA; (4); 14/157; Dance Clb; English Clb; Ski Clb; Pres Spanish Clb; School Musical; Im Swmmng; Var Tennis; Hon Roll; Pres Schlr; Acad Achvt Awd & Spnsh Clb Awd 87; Susquehanna U; Med.

ENGEL, KATHY; Carlynton HS; Pittsburgh, PA; (2); Cmnty Wkr; Ski Clb; Rep Frsh Cls; Var Bsktbl; Var Sftbl; High Hon Roll; Inst Of Sec/Tech; Detective.

ENGEL, KRISTIN; Elk County Christian HS; St Marys, PA; (1); 1/84; SADD; Band; Church Choir; Concert Band; Jazz Band; Mrchg Band; Pep Band; Rep Frsh Cls; Rep Stu Cncl; High Hon Roll; Music.

ENGEL, MICHELLE; Northern Lebanon HS; Lebanon, PA; (2); 11/210; French Clb; Hon Roll.

ENGEL, THOMAS; Canton Area HS; Ralston, PA; (3); 25/114; Jazz Band; Mrchg Band; JV Bsktbl; JV Ftbl; Temple Schl Of Music; Muscn.

ENGELHARDT, ALLISON A; Canon-Mc Millan SR HS; Canonsburg, PA; (3); 50/400; French Clb; Hosp Aide; Office Aide; Ski Clb; Drill Tm; Yrbk Stf; Pom Pon; Hon Roll; CA ST U Of PA Comptn Awd-Excllnc In Frnch 86; Cmmnty Svc Awd-585 Hrs Of Vlntr Hosp Wrk 86.

ENGELMAN, MARLA; Millville Area HS; Millville, PA; (4); French Clb; Q&S; School Play; Nwsp Rptr; Nwsp Stf; Yrbk Rptr; Yrbk Stf; Lit Mag; Cheerleading; Hon Roll; Bloomsburg U; Mass Cmnctns.

ENGELMAN, MARY; Bishop Guilfoyle HS; Altoona, PA; (3); Trs Sec Church Yth Grp; German Clb; SADD; Stu Cncl; JV Cheerleading; JV Var Sftbl; High Hon Roll; Hon Roll; NHS; Juniata Coll; Med.

ENGELSIEPEN, KELLY; Shaler Area SR HS; Pittsburgh, PA; (3); SADD; Flag Corp; Yrbk Stf; Hon Roll; Vet.

ENGLE, BETH; Bethlehem Center HS; Richeyville, PA; (3); 8/160; VP Sec Church Yth Grp; Spanish Clb; Pres Concert Band; Mrchg Band; High Hon Roll; NHS; MENC Ntl Musc Pgm-Celebrn Of Bicntennl Constitutn 87; Pre Law.

ENGLE, BETH; Montoursville Area HS; Montoursville, PA; (3); 18/185; Church Yth Grp; Spanish Clb; Chorus; Gym; High Hon Roll; Pittsburgh; Phys Thrpy.

ENGLE, DAVID; Cornwall-Lebanon HS; Lebanon, PA; (1); 52/350; Boy Scts; German Clb; Pep Clb; Band; Concert Band; Mrchg Band; Pep Band; JV Trk; Hon Roll.

ENGLE, JASON; Penn Wood HS; Lansdowne, PA; (3); 26/340; Aud/Vis; Boy Scts; Church Yth Grp; Intnl Clb; Rep Soph Cls; Trk; Cit Awd; God Cntry Awd; Hon Roll; Church Choir; Eagle Scout 86; Eagle Pjct Bst In Dist 87; Cmmctns.

ENGLE, JEFFREY; Palmerton Area HS; Bowmanstown, PA; (3); Art Clb; Boy Scts; Stat Bsbl; Var Mgr(s); Army; Arch.

ENGLE, KIM; Elizabethtown Area HS; Elizabethtown, PA; (3); Church Yth Grp; Office Aide; Band; Chorus; Church Choir; Concert Band; Mrchg Band; Orch; Hershey Medcl Ctr; Nrsng.

ENGLE, TERRY A; Upper Dauphin Area HS; Elizabethville, PA; (4); 19/101; Hst FFA; Trk; Hon Roll; NHS; Rotary Awd; Millersville U; Teacher.

ENGLE, TIMOTHY; Elizabethtown Area HS; Elizabethtown, PA; (3); 23/259; Trs Church Yth Grp; Pres 4-H; Teachers Aide; Pres Varsity Clb; VP Frsh Cls; Var Bsbl; Var Bsktbl; 4-H Awd; Rotary Awd; Messiah Coll; Bus Adm.

ENGLEKA, ELENA; Rockwood Area HS; Somerset, PA; (2); Band; Chorus; Drm Mjr(t); Mrchg Band; Trs Frsh Cls; Trs Soph Cls; Var L Bsktbl; Var L Vllybl; Hon Roll; Edu.

ENGLEMAN JR, CARL; Central Catholic HS; Oley, PA; (3); Boy Scts; Church Yth Grp; Cmnty Wkr; Exploring; German Clb; Scholastic Bowl; Ski Clb; Yrbk Stf; Vllybl; NHS; Lebanon Vly Coll Summr Sci Schlrshp 86; Pre-Med.

ENGLEMAN, KEVIN; Milton Area SR HS; Milton, PA; (2); Church Yth Grp; Spanish Clb; Band; Chorus; Church Choir; Concert Band; Mrchg Band; Pep Band; Music.

ENGLER, DOUGLAS W; Haverford HS; Havertown, PA; (4); 48/482; Church Yth Grp; Model UN; Ski Clb; Lcrss; High Hon Roll; Hon Roll; NHS; Ntl Merit SF; Boy Scts; Intl Exchng To Germany 86; U Of Penn; Bus.

ENGLERT JR, MICHAEL W; Hempfield HS; Columbia, PA; (3); 40/411; Dance Clb; Chorus; Trs Soph Cls; Trs Jr Cls; Trs Sr Cls; Rep Stu Cncl; Var L Gym; High Hon Roll; Hon Roll; NHS; Cls II ST Qulfr, 3rd Vault, 5th Parllel Bars, 6th High Bar 87; Engr.

ENGLERT, VICKI; Schuylkill Valley HS; Mohrsville, PA; (3); 9/138; Cmnty Wkr; SADD; Chorus; Mrchg Band; School Musical; Rep Stu Cncl; High Hon Roll; Hon Roll; VP NHS; Church Yth Grp; Reg Chorus 87; Nrsng.

ENGLISH, CAROL; Pittston Area HS; Pittston, PA; (4); Drama Clb; FBLA; Key Clb; Ski Clb; Bsbl; Hon Roll; NHS; Penn ST U.

ENGLISH, HEATHER; Williams Valley HS; Tower City, PA; (3); 27/102; Chorus; Capt Drm Mjr(t); Mrchg Band; Hst Soph Cls; Off Jr Cls; Sftbl; Capt Twrlr; Prfct Atten Awd.

ENGLISH, MARK; Montrose Area HS; Hallstead, PA; (3).

ENGLISH, RODNEY; West Branch JR SR HS; Morrisdale, PA; (4); 10/109; JA; Trs Spanish Clb; SADD; Band; Concert Band; Mrchg Band; Hon Roll; Lock Haven U; Physc Tchr.

ENGSTROM, DAVID W; Upper Dublin HS; Ambler, PA; (3); Boy Scts; Church Yth Grp; Intnl Clb; SADD; Varsity Clb; JV Capt Socr; Var L Trk; Im Wt Lftg; Hon Roll; NHS.

ENGSTROM, KRISTAN; Emmaus HS; Allentown, PA; (3).

ENLOW, ROBERT; Sayre HS; Sayre, PA; (3); Boy Scts; Pres Church Yth Grp; Cmnty Wkr; Chorus; Swing Chorus; Swmmng; Wrstlng; God Cntry Awd; High Hon Roll; Hon Roll; Penn Free Enterprise Wk-Lock Haven U 87; Music.

ENNIS, ANDREW; Sayre HS; S Waverly, PA; (3); Boy Scts; Chorus; JV Var Ftbl; Hon Roll; Prfct Atten Awd; Special Chorus Encore 84-85; Comp Analysis.

ENNIS, GENE; Archbishop Ryan For Boys HS; Philadelphia, PA; (3); 130/349; Band; Concert Band; Jazz Band; Mrchg Band; Temple; Music.

ENNIS, JANET; Seneca Valley SR HS; Harmony, PA; (4); 29/347; Sec Varsity Clb; Chorus; Symp Band; Rep Jr Cls; Var L Swmmng; Var L Trk; NHS; Math Tm; Band; Church Choir; Rotary Stu Month 87; Acad Achvt Awd 85-86; Phy Olympic Team 86-87; PA ST U; Law.

ENNIS, MARIBETH; Bristol JR/Sr HS; Bristol, PA; (3); Art Clb; Spanish Clb; SADD; Yrbk Stf; Stu Cncl; Var Cheerleading; JV Fld Hcky; Stu Of Mnth 87.

ENOCH, CHRISTOPHER L; Palisades SR HS; Ottsville, PA; (3); 43/182; Trs Am Leg Boys St; Church Yth Grp; Math Tm; Pep Clb; Ski Clb; SADD; Chorus; Madrigals; Stage Crew; Yrbk Stf; Arch.

ENOS, JEFFREY; Curwensville Area HS; Curwensville, PA; (4); 33/113; Boy Scts; Church Yth Grp; Ski Clb; Hon Roll; NHS; Pres Schlr; Rotary Awd; Ricks JC; Engr.

ENRIGHT, BARBARA; Freedom HS; Bethlehem, PA; (3); 60/486; Science Clb; Spanish Clb; Band; Concert Band; Mrchg Band; Pep Band; JV Var Fld Hcky; Psych.

ENSLIN, DONNA; Western Wayne HS; Lake Ariel, PA; (2); Church Yth Grp; Hosp Aide; SADD; Band; Concert Band; Tchr.

ENSMINGER, RYNELL; Grace Christian Schl; Lebanon, PA; (4); 2/20; Church Yth Grp; Pres 4-H; School Play; Yrbk Stf; Fld Hcky; 4-H Awd; High Hon Roll; Smmr Mssns Mexico 86; Smmnr Yth Schlrs Inst 86; Lebanon Vly Coll; Vet Med.

ENTENMAN, DOUGLAS; Valley Forge Military Acad; Norristown, PA; (3); Art Clb; Pres German Clb; Letterman Clb; ROTC; Science Clb; Varsity Clb; Drm & Bgl; JV Var Ftbl; Var L Trk; JV Var Wrstlng; Caplins Mdl 87; Chapel Vstry 86-87; Ath Schlrhsp 85-88; Med Sci.

ENTIS, PAUL; Bensalem SR HS; Bensalem, PA; (3); Capt Debate Tm; Hosp Aide; Pres Intnl Clb; Model UN; SADD; Nwsp Stf; High Hon Roll; NHS; Bro Yr, Sigma Alpha Rho Frat, Stu Mnth 87; Ray Kroc Yth Achvt Awd Bus 86; Intl Rltns.

EPERESI, CARRIE; Center HS; Monaca, PA; (4); 24/186; Latin Clb; Varsity Clb; VP Sr Cls; Rep Stu Cncl; Bowling; Var Capt Cheerleading; Score Keeper; Hon Roll; NHS; Pres Schlr; St Vincent Coll; Grphc Dsgn.

EPLER, ROBERT; Exeter Township SR HS; Reading, PA; (3); 3/241; Church Yth Grp; Key Clb; Quiz Bowl; Band; Mrchg Band; Socr; High Hon Roll; Hon Roll; NHS; Pres Schlr; Med.

EPPINGER, CHRISTY; Kennard Dale HS; Stewartstown, PA; (3); 25/175; Ski Clb; Varsity Clb; Yrbk Stf; Trs Soph Cls; Trs Jr Cls; Trs Sr Cls; Rep Stu Cncl; Var L Cheerleading; Hon Roll; NHS; Elem Educ.

EPPLEY, JOHN; North Star HS; Holsopple, PA; (3); Aud/Vis; Boy Scts; FCA; Band; Chorus; Stage Crew; Yrbk Phtg; Var Bsktbl; Var Golf; Hon Roll; Bio.

EPPOLITO, CHARLES; Methacton SR HS; Lansdale, PA; (3); 46/381; Church Yth Grp; Scholastic Bowl; High Hon Roll; Hon Roll; Bus.

EPPS, ERICA; Simon Gratz HS; Philadelphia, PA; (4); 8/375; Var Bsktbl; Trk; Hon Roll; NHS; Ntl Merit Ltr; Drexel U; Comp Engr.

EPPS, LISA; St Maria Goretti HS; Philadelphia, PA; (4); 75/347; Am Leg Aux Girls St; Camp Fr Inc; SADD; Pres Orch; Cert Acad Achvt 87; Spelman Coll; Psych.

EPPS, THERESA; Phila HS For Girls; Philadelphia, PA; (2); Dance Clb; Hosp Aide; Pep Clb; Variety Show; Off Frsh Cls; Off Soph Cls; Hon Roll; U Of S CA; Entrprnr.

EPSTEIN, JOANNE; Marple Newtown SR HS; Newtown Square, PA; (3); 29/332; Var Trk; High Hon Roll; Hon Roll; Prfct Atten Awd; MVP Indr Trck 85-86 & 86-87; MVP Outdoor Trck 87; DE County 300 M Indr Trck Champ 85-86 & 86-87; Law.

EPSTEIN, MARK; Wyoming Valley West HS; Kingston, PA; (4); 5/398; Chess Clb; Computer Clb; Exploring; Hosp Aide; Key Clb; VP Math Clb; Political Wkr; Nwsp Rptr; Nwsp Stf; Yrbk Rptr; PA Sci Olympiad 1st Pl, Outstndng Sci Stu Luzerne Cnty & Mock Trial Dist Cmpttn 1st Pl; U Of PA; Biophysics.

ERB, CHRISTINE; Solanco HS; Bart, PA; (3); 7/271; Pres VP Church Yth Grp; Varsity Clb; Capt Drill Tm; Rep Stu Cncl; JV Fld Hcky; Im Powder Puff Ftbl; Var L Sftbl; Im Vllybl; High Hon Roll; Sec NHS; Behavrl Sci.

ERB, HEIDI; Danville HS; Danville, PA; (1); Ski Clb; Sec Frsh Cls; Var Cheerleading; Im Gym; JV Tennis; JV Trk; High Hon Roll; Pres Acdmc Ftns Awd 87; PA ST; Arts.

ERB, JEFFREY D; Great Valley HS; Malvern, PA; (4); Art Clb; Yrbk Stf; Swmmng; Savings Bond Mural Desgn 87; Kutztown.

ERB, LESTER; Milton Area SR HS; Milton, PA; (4); Pres Varsity Clb; Var Capt Bsbl; Var Capt Bsktbl; Var Capt Ftbl; God Cntry Awd; Opt Clb Awd; Pres Schlr; Yng Amer Awd 86-87; Offnsv & Dfnsv Plyr Of Yr-All Conf, Ftbl 86 & 87; Outstndng Ftbl Plyr 87; Bucknell U; Lbrl Arts.

ERB, MICHELLE; Mifflinburg Area HS; Mifflinburg, PA; (4); Pres Off FHA; Office Aide; Capt Color Guard; Mrchg Band; Capt Bsktbl; Trk; Hon Roll; Young Amercn Awd 87; Bus & Profsnl Wmns Stu Of Month 87; Booster Club Schlrshp 87; Harrisburg Area CC; Corr Rehab.

ERB, PHILIP; Manheim Central HS; Manheim, PA; (4); Trs Pres Church Yth Grp; Capt L Crs Cntry; Capt L Trk; Hon Roll; Pres Schlr; 4 Way Test Awd 87; Abe Weidman Schlr Athl Awd 87; SR Athl Awd 87; Shppnsbrg U.

ERB, SHAWN; Donegal HS; Mount Joy, PA; (3); 1/180; Computer Clb; Math Clb; Spanish Clb; Band; Rep Frsh Cls; JV L Bsktbl; Var L Tennis; High Hon Roll; NHS; Prfct Atten Awd; Millerville Coll; Cmptr Sci.

ERB, STEVE; Cedar Crest HS; Lebanon, PA; (1); Boy Scts; German Clb; Hon Roll; Mech Engr.

ERB, SUZANNE; Northern Lebanon HS; Jonestown, PA; (4); 7/166; Quiz Bowl; School Play; Ed Lit Mag; L Bowling; Hon Roll; NHS; Pres Acad Fit Awd; Sr Outstanding In German; Olympics Of The Mind; Juniata Coll; Chemistry.

ERCOLINO, DENISE; Downingtown SR HS; Downingtown, PA; (3); Drama Clb; German Clb; Ski Clb; SADD; Chorus; School Musical; School Play; High Hon Roll; Hon Roll; NHS; Bus.

ERDELY, JUDY; Technical Memorial HS; Erie, PA; (3); 47/311; Yrbk Stf; Sec Frsh Cls; Trk; Vllybl; Bus.

ERDELY, MICHAEL; Charleroi Area JR Sr HS; Charleroi, PA; (4); 30/162; Varsity Clb; Mrchg Band; School Musical; Stage Crew; Im Bsktbl; Var L Trk; Hon Roll; W VA U; Aero Engr.

ERDLEY, SUSAN; Milton HS; Milton, PA; (3); 12/229; Computer Clb; Latin Clb; Band; Chorus; Color Guard; Concert Band; Mrchg Band; Rep Stu Cncl; Hon Roll; NHS; Dist Band 87; Bucknell U; Sec Math.

ERDMAN, KIRSTEN; Cedar Crest HS; Mt Gretna, PA; (4); 52/325; Art Clb; Drama Clb; French Clb; Pep Clb; Orch; School Musical; School Play; Nwsp Stf; Yrbk Stf; Var Crs Cntry; Duquesne U Acdmc Cmpttv Schlrshp 87-88; Duquesne U; Comm.

ERDMAN, KRISTIN L; Shikellamy HS; Sunbury, PA; (3); German Clb; NFL; Band; Concert Band; Flag Corp; Mrchg Band; School Musical; School Play; Stage Crew; Yrbk Phtg; FL Gold Coast Concrt Band Comptn 85; Susquehanna Vly Band 87; Susquehanna U; Persnnl Mgmt.

ERDMAN, LORI; Upper Dauphin Area HS; Gratz, PA; (3); 11/120; Church Yth Grp; Cmnty Wkr; Chorus; Church Choir; Hon Roll; Phys Thrpy.

ERGOTT, BLU; Jersey Shore SR HS; Avis, PA; (3); Cmnty Wkr; Service Clb; Ski Clb; JV Wrstlng; Williamsport Area CC Vo-Tech 86-87; PA ST U; Intl Rel.

ERHARD, GREGORY ROBBINS; Moon SR HS; Coraopolis, PA; (2); Church Yth Grp; Var Tennis; Hon Roll; Law.

ERICH, MARTIN; Elk County Christian HS; St Marys, PA; (1); 4/84; Hosp Aide; SADD; Rep Frsh Cls; Trk; JV Wrstlng; Hon Roll; U Of Pittsburgh; Phrmcst.

ERICKSON, DOUGLAS; Central Dauphin HS; Harrisburg, PA; (2); Boy Scts; Chorus; School Musical; School Play; Stage Crew; Variety Show; Hon Roll.

ERICKSON, KRISTEN; Downington SR HS; Chester Springs, PA; (4); 92/551; Dance Clb; Drama Clb; French Clb; Chorus; Madrigals; School Musical; Swing Chorus; Hon Roll; Pres Schlr; Church Yth Grp; Acdmc Schlrshp Wagner Coll 87; Pres Schlrshp Lebanon Vly Coll 87; Wagner Coll; Arts Admin.

ERICKSON, LORI; Franklin Regional SR HS; Murrysville, PA; (3); AFS; Church Yth Grp; Drama Clb; French Clb; Band; Church Choir; Concert Band; Mrchg Band; Nwsp Stf; Crs Cntry.

ERICKSON, MARCIE; Central HS; Roaring Spring, PA; (4); 30/187; FCA; GAA; Ski Clb; Varsity Clb; Rep Jr Cls; Var Capt Cheerleading; Var L Sftbl; Trk; Var L Vllybl; Hon Roll; Coaches Achvt Awd Vlybl 86; Hustle Awd & MVP Awd Sftbl 85 & 87; Acad All Am Schlr Dir 87; Shippensburg U; Secondary Educ.

ERICKSON, TAMMY; Bellwood-Antis HS; Bellwood, PA; (4); 17/118; Pres Church Yth Grp; Drama Clb; School Play; Yrbk Stf; Fld Hcky; Trk; High Hon Roll; NHS; Ntl Merit Schol; Prfct Atten Awd; Med Assist.

ERICSON, JENNIFER; Henderson HS; W Chester, PA; (3); Church Yth Grp; Yrbk Stf; Trs Soph Cls; Capt Cheerleading; Envrmntl Mgmnt.

ERICSSON, CAROL; Highlands SR HS; Natrona Hts, PA; (4); Girl Scts; Hosp Aide; Key Clb; Concert Band; Mrchg Band; School Musical; Symp Band; Sec Stu Cncl; High Hon Roll; NHS; Grl Sct Gld Awd 87; Outstndng Instrmntlst Awd 87; Penn ST U; Nrsng.

ERIN, VOCKE; Huntingdon Area HS; Huntingdon, PA; (2); 1/185; Pres Church Yth Grp; 4-H; Key Clb; Ski Clb; Concert Band; Var Vllybl; High Hon Roll; NHS; Ltrd In Vsty Vllybl 86-87; Chem.

ERITANO, REBECCA; Moon HS; Aliquippa, PA; (3); French Clb; JA; Off Soph Cls; Penn ST; Cmmnctns.

ERMILIO, JENNIFER; Conestoga SR HS; Paoli, PA; (2); Church Yth Grp; Dance Clb; Drama Clb; Hosp Aide; Model UN; School Musical; School Play; Variety Show; JV Tennis; Hon Roll.

ERMINE, KRISTIN; Southmoreland HS; Scottdale, PA; (2); 44/254; Church Yth Grp; French Clb; Letterman Clb; Varsity Clb; Score Keeper; Sftbl; Tennis; French Hon Soc; Occptnl Thrpy.

ERMISH, DAVID; G A R HS; Wilkes-Bare, PA; (3); 6/157; Computer Clb; French Clb; Concert Band; Orch; Stage Crew; Var L Bsbl; Var L Ftbl; Wt Lftg; Hon Roll; Jr NHS; Comp.

ERMISH, MARK; G A R HS; Wilkes-Bare, PA; (3); 9/157; Computer Clb; German Clb; Chorus; Concert Band; Orch; Stage Crew; Var L Bsbl; Var L Ftbl; Var Wt Lftg; Hon Roll; Engrng.

ERMLICH, TIMOTHY; Trinity HS; Camp Hill, PA; (2); 27/140; Ski Clb; Spanish Clb; Socr; Hon Roll; NEDT Awd; Rep Frsh Cls.

ERNEST, CHRISTOPHER; Danville SR HS; Danville, PA; (2); VP Church Yth Grp; Drama Clb; Key Clb; Ski Clb; Tennis; Poltcl Sci.

ERNST, BETH; Parkland HS; Schnecksville, PA; (3); 33/400; German Clb; Chorus; Flag Corp; School Musical; Stu Cncl; Mgr(s); High Hon Roll; Hon Roll; NHS; Penn ST.

ERNST, JENNIFER; William Allen HS; Allentown, PA; (2); 67/634; Varsity Clb; School Musical; Yrbk Stf; Sec Frsh Cls; Sec Soph Cls; Sec Jr Cls; Capt Var Cheerleading; Powder Puff Ftbl; Hon Roll.

ERNST, KRISTEN; Hamburg Area HS; Bernville, PA; (3); 25/180; Sec Latin Clb; Library Aide; Pres Spanish Clb; Yrbk Sprt Ed; Yrbk Stf; Rep Stu Cncl; Var Fld Hcky; Var Trk; Hon Roll; NHS; Acad Awd Wrld Cultrs 86; Acad Awd Engl 87; Pres Phys Ftnss Awd 82-87; Elem Educ.

ERNST, MICHAEL; Fleetwood Area HS; Fleetwood, PA; (3); Church Yth Grp; Ski Clb; Band; Concert Band; Mrchg Band; Bsktbl; Coach Actv; Socr; Trk; Soc Sci.

ERNWOOD, CATHERINE; Nazareth Acad; Phila, PA; (3); Cmnty Wkr; French Clb; Fld Hcky; Swmmng; Metro Chrprsn Of Childrens Actvs Cmnty Svc Corps 86-87; Metro Prgm Devlpr Cmnty Svc Corps 87-88; Microbio.

ERRETT, GWEN; Fort Cherry JR/Sr HS; Mc Donald, PA; (4); Church Yth Grp; Math Clb; Science Clb; Ski Clb; Spanish Clb; Band; Chorus; Mrchg Band; Yrbk Ed-Chief; Grad Hnrs 87; Waynesburg; Elem Ed.

ERRICO, MARY; Dunmore JR SR HS; Dunmore, PA; (3); Drama Clb; Band; Lib Chorus; Concert Band; Mrchg Band; School Musical; School Play; Yrbk Stf; High Hon Roll; Hon Roll; Marywood Coll; Mrktng.

ERTEL, STEPHEN; Blue Mountain Acad; Halifax, PA; (4); 10/57; Church Yth Grp; Computer Clb; Teachers Aide; School Musical; Stage Crew; Off Jr Cls; Vllybl; Hon Roll; Prncpls Awd For Outstndng Svc 87; Columbia U Coll; Math.

ERTELL, DEBORAH; Phoenixville Area HS; Phoenixville, PA; (2); Pep Clb; Spanish Clb; Band; Concert Band; Mrchg Band; School Musical; Hon Roll; Jr NHS; Pres Acdmc Ftnss Awd 86.

ERTH, STACEY; York Suburban SR HS; York, PA; (3); 20/189; Office Aide; Teachers Aide; Pres Trs Temple Yth Grp; Orch; School Musical; Nwsp Stf; Yrbk Stf; Stat Mgr Swmmng; Hon Roll; NHS; Intl Rel.

ERWIN, PAM; Frankford HS; Philadelphia, PA; (3); JV Sftbl; Var Trk; Hon Roll; Prfct Atten Awd; Handicapped Chldrn.

ESBENSHADE, KAREN; Donegal HS; Mount Joy, PA; (2); Church Yth Grp; 4-H; Band; Church Choir; Concert Band; Mrchg Band; Orch; Symp Band; 4-H Awd; Hon Roll.

ESCALANTE, CARLOS; Plum SR HS; Pittsburgh, PA; (3); 12/410; AFS; School Play; Nwsp Stf; Yrbk Stf; Rep Soph Cls; Rep Jr Cls; Pres Sr Cls; L Socr; Hon Roll; NHS; VA U; Bio.

ESCHBACH, TAMMY; Kutztown Area SR HS; Kutztown, PA; (3); FBLA; Var Sftbl; KYAA Sftbl Awd 86; Allentown Bus Schl; Scrtrl.

ESCHENMANN, JULIE; Annville-Cleona HS; Annville, PA; (4); German Clb; Varsity Clb; Sec Jr Cls; Sec Sr Cls; Stu Cncl; Mat Maids; Var Tennis; Var Trk; Stat Wrstlng; Jr NHS; Kiawanis Clb Awd-Art 87; Wilma Boyd Schl; Trvl.

ESH, RICKY; Pequea Valley HS; Gap, PA; (4); Church Yth Grp; FFA; Yrbk Phtg; Im Socr; Hon Roll; NHS; Hnr Rl Awd; Printing.

ESHBACH, DEBBIE; Freedom HS; Bethlehem, PA; (4); 17/446; French Clb; Mrchg Band; Pep Band; Rep Stu Cncl; Gym; Powder Puff Ftbl; Capt Twrlr; NHS; Pres Schlr; Nrthmptn Cnty JR Miss 2nd Rnnr Up; Am Assn U Wmn Schlrshp; W R & S Roberts Schlrshp; Gettysburg Coll; Mth.

ESHBACH, GREGORY; Bethlehem Catholic HS; Bethlehem, PA; (3); 118/200; Boy Scts; Math Tm; Band; Concert Band; Mrchg Band; Pep Band; School Musical; Stage Crew; Crs Cntry; Tennis; Acctng.

ESHBACH, MICHELLE; Emmaus HS; Old Zionsville, PA; (3); 66/518; Aud/Vis; Color Guard; Yrbk Phtg; Yrbk Stf; Sftbl; High Hon Roll; Hon Roll; NHS; Opt Clb Awd; JV Var Mgr(s); Polit Sci.

ESHBAUGH, PATRICIA; Keystone JR SR HS; Shippenville, PA; (3); 24/135; Sec Pres Church Yth Grp; Chorus; Church Choir; Concert Band; Var L Bsktbl; Var L Trk; Hon Roll; Ldrshp Conf At Seton Hill Coll 86; Clarion U Of PA; Elem Ed.

ESHBAUGH, SHARON; Brookville HS; Brookville, PA; (3); Trs Sec Church Yth Grp; French Clb; Stu Cncl; Mgr(s); Hon Roll; Jr NHS; Accntng.

ESHELMAN, NAOMI; Christian School Of York; Carlisle, PA; (4); 2/58; Church Yth Grp; Chorus; Church Choir; Yrbk Phtg; VP Jr Cls; VP Sr Cls; Capt Fld Hcky; Cit Awd; High Hon Roll; Sal; Grove City Coll; Bus Admin.

ESHELMAN, PAIGE LYNN; Ephrata SR HS; Ephrata, PA; (4); 4/257; Drama Clb; Teachers Aide; Chorus; Drill Tm; School Musical; School Play; Yrbk Ed-Chief; High Hon Roll; Sec NHS; Ntl Merit Ltr; Elizabeth W Shawb Wrtng Awd 87; Jostens Plbshng Excllnc In Jrnlsm Awd 87; NY U Schlrs Pgm & CAS Schr; NY U; Engl.

ESHELMAN, SCOTT; Elizabethtown Area HS; Elizabethtown, PA; (2); 13/309; VP Frsh Cls; Im Socr; Hon Roll; NHS; Law.

ESHENOWER, KRISTIN; Central Dauphin HS; Harrisburg, PA; (4); Var L Cheerleading; Im Vllybl; Millersville U; Elem Edu.

ESHLEMAN, D SCOTT; J P Mccaskey HS; Lancaster, PA; (4); 20/400; Chess Clb; FBLA; SADD; Variety Show; Im Vllybl; Im Wt Lftg; Hon Roll; NHS; Pres Schlr; Spanish NHS; Elizabethtown Coll; Accntng.

ESHLEMAN, DARYL; Lancaster Mennonite HS; Paradise, PA; (3); 18/155; Pres Church Yth Grp; Acpl Chr; Chorus; School Musical; Yrbk Bus Mgr; Yrbk Sprt Ed; Yrbk Stf; Hon Roll; NHS; Accounting.

ESHLEMAN, GAIL; Solanco HS; Peach Bottom, PA; (3); Dance Clb; Girl Scts; Spanish Clb; Band; Concert Band; Mrchg Band; Pep Band; Variety Show; Nwsp Stf; Mat Maids; Ctznshp Awd Amer Stds 87; Temple U; Law.

ESKETZIS, ELLEN; William Allen HS; Allentown, PA; (2); Church Yth Grp; German Clb; Hon Roll.

ESKIN, BETH; Abington HS; Rydal, PA; (4); 35/486; Sec Pres French Clb; Intnl Clb; Nwsp Stf; Ed Yrbk Ed-Chief; Rep Frsh Cls; Rep Soph Cls; Rep Jr Cls; Rep Sr Cls; Rep Stu Cncl; Hon Roll; Pres Acdmc Ftnss Awd 87; U PA.

ESPADA, ANASTACIA; Saint Benedict Acad; Erie, PA; (3); 14/53; Exploring; Model UN; Chorus; Rep Stu Cncl; Hon Roll; Trs NHS; Spnsh Schlrshp 85-86; Spnsh Awds 84-87; Gannon U; Nurse.

ESPADA, MARIA; Saint Benedict Acad; Erie, PA; (4); 10/63; Exploring; Model UN; Office Aide; School Play; Stage Crew; Variety Show; Rep Stu Cncl; High Hon Roll; Hon Roll; NHS; Spnsh Schlrshp 84-86; Spnsh Awd 84-87; Natl Hnr Scty Schlrshp 87; Gannon U; Nrsng.

ESPEJO, EMMA L; Philadelphia High School For Girls; Philadelphia, PA; (4); 46/365; Drama Clb; Hosp Aide; Library Aide; Teachers Aide; Acpl Chr; Chorus; Madrigals; School Musical; Lit Mag; Var L Fld Hcky; American U; Jstc.

ESPER, MARK C; Butler SR HS; Butler, PA; (3); JA; Math Tm; Spanish Clb; Cit Awd; High Hon Roll; Jr NHS; NHS; Acad Achvt Awd 87; Law.

ESPER, WILLIAM JOHN; Butler SR HS; Butler, PA; (4); SADD; Band; Concert Band; Mrchg Band; Symp Band; Im Ftbl; Hon Roll; Jr NHS; Duquesne U; Engl.

ESPOSITO, ANTHONY; St John Neumann HS; Philadelphia, PA; (2); 79/395; Drama Clb; Library Aide; School Play; Stage Crew; Rep Soph Cls; Bowling; Mgr(s); Trk; La Salle U; Pathlgy.

ESPOSITO, JOANNE; Hazleton HS; Hazleton, PA; (3); Church Yth Grp; Drama Clb; FNA; Pep Clb; Y-Teens; School Play; Var L Bsktbl; Var Crs Cntry; Var L Sftbl; Hon Roll; Allentown Wilkes; Nrsng.

ESPOSITO, JOHN; Old Forge HS; Old Forge, PA; (3); Ski Clb; Golf; High Hon Roll; Hon Roll; NHS; Cmmnctns.

ESPOSITO, JULEEN; Penn Hills SR HS; Verona, PA; (3); Ski Clb; Spanish Clb; Rep Soph Cls; Rep Jr Cls; Hon Roll; Accntng.

ESPOSITO, PATSY; Beaver Area HS; Midland, PA; (3); Church Yth Grp; Spanish Clb; SADD; Band; Rep Stu Cncl; Var L Bsbl; JV L Bsktbl; Var L Ftbl; Hon Roll; 1st Pl Tm-Wght Lftng Cmptn 87; 3rd Pl-5 Mile Run-Cancer 86; Penn ST; Engrng.

ESPOSITO, ROSA; Quigley HS; Midland, PA; (4); 11/100; Pres Church Yth Grp; Hosp Aide; Math Tm; Chorus; High Hon Roll; NHS; Typng Awd 85; Latin III Awd 86; Phrmcy.

ESPOTISO, JOHN; Old Forge HS; Old Forge, PA; (3); Ski Clb; Var Golf; High Hon Roll; Hon Roll; NHS; Comm.

ESSER, DENISE; Palisades HS; Upper Black Eddy, PA; (2); Library Aide; VICA; Drm Mjr(t); High Hon Roll; Hon Roll; Hair Dsgns Motion Vo-Tech 87; Cosmetlgy.

ESSEX, DAVID P C; Valley Forge Military Acad; Upper Marlboro, MD; (3); Boy Scts; French Clb; ROTC; SADD; Varsity Clb; Yrbk Stf; JV L Ftbl; Var Capt Swmmng; Var L Trk; Engl Awd 85; A Wayne Lgn Grd, Cptns Trp Hy Smmng 87; Citidel Coll; Nuclear Engr.

ESSIG, LYNN; Southern Columbia HS; Catawissa, PA; (3); Key Clb; Ski Clb; Varsity Clb; Yrbk Stf; JV Var Bsktbl; Var Capt Fld Hcky; Trk.

ESTEP, MELISSA; Williamsburg HS; Williamsburg, PA; (3); Pres Church Yth Grp; FBLA; FNA; Chorus; Mrchg Band; Yrbk Stf; JV Cheerleading; Capt Twrlr.

ESTHER JR, CHARLES R; Freedom HS; Bethlehem, PA; (1); 4/456; JA; Math Tm; Model UN; Chorus; Church Choir; Hon Roll; NHS; Ntl Merit SF; Distrct Chrs 86.

ESTKOWSKI, JACQUELINE; Lincoln HS; Ellwood City, PA; (3); 34/169; Sec Spanish Clb; Y-Teens; Chorus; Rep Stu Cncl; Co-Capt Cheerleading; Powder Puff Ftbl; High Hon Roll; Hon Roll; NHS.

ESTRADA, CROMWELL; Bethlehem Catholic HS; Bethlehem, PA; (3); 18/220; Hosp Aide; Key Clb; SADD; Var Crs Cntry; Ftbl; High Hon Roll; NHS; PA Math Lg Cert Merit 87; Natl Frnch Test Cert Merit 87; Medical Careers Club Sec & Treas 87-88; PA ST; Pre-Med.

ESTRIGHT, WILLIAM; Aliquippa JR-SR HS; Aliquippa, PA; (4); 2/95; Pres Church Yth Grp; Math Tm; Mrchg Band; Yrbk Phtg; Pres Jr Cls; Pres Sr Cls; Var L Wrstlng; High Hon Roll; Lion Awd; NHS; Yale U; Engr.

ESWAY, JENNIFER; Hempfield HS; Greensburg, PA; (3); GAA; Letterman Clb; Pep Clb; Ski Clb; Varsity Clb; Im Ftbl; Var L Swmmng; High Hon Roll; Hon Roll; Jr NHS; Cmmnctns.

ETCHBERGER, KELLY; Tulpehocken HS; Bethel, PA; (2); 36/115; Drama Clb; Band; Stage Crew; Sec Frsh Cls; Sec Soph Cls; JV Bsktbl; JV Sftbl; JV Trk; Hon Roll.

ETHERIDGE, JOEL ERIC; Rodnor SR HS; Wayne, PA; (4); Art Clb; Boy Scts; Church Yth Grp; Drama Clb; Latin Clb; NAACP; Chorus; Nwsp Stf; Yrbk Stf; Cheerleading; Ntl Hispanic Scholars Semi-Fnlst 86-87; Schl Nwsppr Ed 86-87; PMEA Dist 12 Chorus Tenor I 87; Pre-Law.

ETHERIDGE, WENDY; Methacton SR HS; Eagleville, PA; (3); 1/407; Church Yth Grp; Math Tm; Spanish Clb; School Musical; Variety Show; Rep Jr Cls; Var Cheerleading; Var Trk; DAR Awd; NHS; Ntl Sci,Soc Studies,Eng Awd 84-85; Princeton; Bio Resrch.

ETKIN, TERRI; HS Of Engr & Sci; Philadelphia, PA; (4); 90/210; Drama Clb; Temple Yth Grp; School Musical; School Play; Yrbk Stf; Rep Stu Cncl; Hon Roll; Bertha Pasternak Feldman Awd 87; Bnai Brith Wm Gerber Schlrshp 87; Bnai Brith Chain Weisman Lodge Schl; Temple U; Psych.

ETRISS, DIANE; Cardinal O Hara HS; Brookhaven, PA; (4); 129/771; Teachers Aide; Yrbk Stf; Hon Roll; Gregg Typng & Steno Awds 86-87; Crdnl O Hara Awd Steno 86-87; 4th Pl Archdcs 87; Bus Cmptn Shrthnd II; Katharine Gibbs Schl; Exec Sec.

ETTEER, CHRISTINE; Greencastle Antrim HS; Greencastle, PA; (3); VP Church Yth Grp; SADD; Chorus; Church Choir; Nwsp Stf; Rep Frsh Cls; Rep Soph Cls; Rep Jr Cls; Rep Sr Cls; Cosmtlgy.

ETTINGER, LISA; Lewistown Area SR HS; Lewistown, PA; (3); German Clb; Hosp Aide; VICA; Nwsp Stf; Hon Roll; Cndystrpr Pin For Wrkng More Than 100 Hrs 83; Erly Chldhd Edu.

ETTORE, CHRISTIE; Downingtown HS; Exton, PA; (3); Pres GAA; Ski Clb; Spanish Clb; Chorus; Var Fld Hcky; JV Lcrss; Mgr(s); Var Trk; Hon Roll; Phy Thrpy.

ETTWEJN, KEVIN; Cathedral Prep; Erie, PA; (3); CAP; German Clb; RPI; Arch Engrng.

ETZEL, LARA; Wellsboro HS; Wellsboro, PA; (4); Art Clb; Church Yth Grp; German Clb; Church Choir; Concert Band; Mrchg Band; Yrbk Stf; JV VP Bsktbl; Hon Roll; NHS; Mansfield U; Psych.

ETZWEILER, CINDY; Upper Dauphin Area HS; Halifax, PA; (3); 2/120; Trs Church Yth Grp; Chorus; Concert Band; Drill Tm; Mrchg Band; L Trk; NHS; Pnst For Gspl Sngng Grp 86 & 87; Spnsh.

EUBANKS, BARBIE; Warren Area HS; Warren, PA; (3); Church Yth Grp; German Clb; Office Aide; Band; Yrbk Stf; Sec L Bsktbl; High Hon Roll; Hon Roll; IN U; Elem Educ.

EULIANO, JOHN; Cathedral Prep; Erie, PA; (3); 14/193; Church Yth Grp; Cmnty Wkr; Im Bsktbl; High Hon Roll; Hon Roll; Ntl Merit Ltr; 1st Plc Frgn Lang Cmptn 87; Med.

EUSEBIO, CATALINO; Central HS; Philadelphia, PA; (2); Hon Roll; Barnwell Hnr Rl 86-87; Cert Merit-Amer Assoc Tchrs Span/Portugese Immaculate Coll 87; Comp Engrng.

EUSEBIO, MARILOU; Philadelphia HS For Girls; Philadelphia, PA; (3); 2/405; Office Aide; French Hon Soc; Gov Hon Prg Awd; Hon Roll; Engrng.

EUSTICE, AMY; Great Valley SR HS; Frazer, PA; (3); GAA; Spanish Clb; SADD; JV Co-Capt Cheerleading; Hon Roll; NHS; Intr Dsgn.

EUSTICE, CHRISTINE M; Bishop Hoban HS; Shickshinny Lake, PA; (3); 22/199; Sec Computer Clb; FBLA; Mu Alpha Theta; Teachers Aide; JV Bsktbl; Var L Sftbl; High Hon Roll; Hon Roll; NHS; NEDT Awd; Finance.

EUSTIS, STEVEN M; Abington Heights HS; Clarks Summit, PA; (3); 6/292; Boy Scts; Ski Clb; Band; Concert Band; Mrchg Band; Orch; Im Bowling; Var L Crs Cntry; Var Trk; Hon Roll; Govt Scouts Day-District Attorney 86; Engrng.

EUSTON, GREGORY; Moon Area SR HS; Coraopolis, PA; (4); Acpl Chr; Chorus; Drm Mjr(t); Mrchg Band; Pep Band; School Musical; Symp Band; Variety Show; Tiger Pride Awd 87; U Of Pittsburgh; Elec Engrng.

EUSTON, HEATHER; Moon SR HS; Coraopolis, PA; (2); Exploring; Band; Mrchg Band; Pep Band; Symp Band; Variety Show; Var Score Keeper; Var L Sftbl; Var Timer; Pub Rel.

EUTSEY, APRIL S; Connellsville Area HS; Mt Pleasant, PA; (4); 48/500; Church Yth Grp; GAA; Band; Rep Stu Cncl; Cheerleading; Var L Sftbl; Var L Trk; Var L Vllybl; Hon Roll; NHS; Hustler Awd In Vllbl 85-86; Best Hitter Awd Sftbl 85-86; Liberty U; Phy Ed.

EVACKO, PATRICIA; Forest Hills SR HS; Sidman, PA; (4); 1/157; Thesps; Capt Color Guard; School Musical; Yrbk Stf; Dnfth Awd; VP NHS; Pres Schlr; Spanish NHS; Val; Am Leg Aux Girls St; U Pittsburgh; Phrmcy.

EVAK, SHARON; Hempfield Area SR HS; Adamsburg, PA; (4); 89/693; Drama Clb; FBLA; Library Aide; Office Aide; Chorus; School Play; Cit Awd; High Hon Roll; Hon Roll; Westmoreland Cnty CC 87-88; FBLA Rrgnl Cmpttr 86; WCCC; Med Sec.

EVAN, MARK; E L Meyers HS; Wilkes Barre, PA; (3); Ski Clb; Concert Band; Jazz Band; Mrchg Band; NEDT Awd; Spanish NHS; Geology.

EVANCHICK, CHRISTINE; Northern Cambria HS; Barnesboro, PA; (3); 44/152; French Clb; Library Aide; Chorus; Yrbk Stf; High Hon Roll; Hon Roll.

EVANCHO, LISA; West Hazelton JR SR HS; West Hazelton, PA; (2); Spanish Clb; Nwsp Stf; JV Var Cheerleading; SADD; Nwsp Rptr; Yrbk Stf; Var Gym; Mgr(s); Hon Roll; Presdntl Acadmc Ftns Awd 86.

EVANCHOCK, DAWN; Windber Area HS; Windber, PA; (3); Church Yth Grp; Hosp Aide; Teachers Aide; Color Guard; Hon Roll; Bus Awd-Typng II 86-87; Bus.

EVANINA, TANYA; Valley View JR SR HS; Peckville, PA; (2); Off Soph Cls; Var Bsktbl; Var Sftbl; Crmnl Justice.

EVANKO, JANINE; Blairsville SR HS; Blairsville, PA; (3); Church Yth Grp; SADD; Varsity Clb; Color Guard; School Musical; Nwsp Stf; Yrbk Stf; Var Sftbl; Var L Vllybl; Hon Roll; St Vincent Coll; Bus.

EVANS, ALMEDA; Harrisburg HS; Harrisburg, PA; (3); 13/165; Cmnty Wkr; FBLA; Office Aide; Teachers Aide; Pres Stu Cncl; Trk; Cit Awd; High Hon Roll; Hon Roll; Prfct Atten Awd; Stu Of Month 86; Natl Hnr Scty Awd Ldrshhp Week 87; Ldrshp Awd ASETS 87; Vet Sci.

EVANS, ANDREA; Hempfield HS; Greensburg, PA; (4); Library Aide; Office Aide; Orch; High Hon Roll; Hon Roll; Jr NHS; Prfct Atten Awd; Spanish NHS; Westmoreland CC; Psych.

EVANS, ANNIE; Butler Area SR HS; Butler, PA; (3); Library Aide; Band; Chorus; Concert Band; Mrchg Band; School Musical; Hon Roll; Jr NHS.

EVANS, AUDRA; West Perry SR HS; Loysville, PA; (3); French Clb; Bsktbl; Sclgy.

EVANS, BARBARA; Crestwood HS; White Haven, PA; (4); 12/226; Church Yth Grp; Cmnty Wkr; Science Clb; Teachers Aide; Gov Hon Prg Awd; High Hon Roll; Pres Schlr; U Of Pittsburgh; Bio Chem.

EVANS, BRYAN; William Penn SR HS; York, PA; (3); JA; Variety Show; Rep Frsh Cls; Im Bsktbl; Im Ftbl; Hon Roll; Prfct Atten Awd; Pres Schlr; De Vry Inst; Comp Sci.

EVANS IV, CHARLES M; Cocalico HS; Adamstown, PA; (4); 36/163; Boy Scts; Camera Clb; Var Tennis; Im Wt Lftg; JV Var Wrstlng; PA ST U; Advrtsng.

EVANS, CHERYL; Waynesboro SR HS; Waynesboro, PA; (4); 6/382; Computer Clb; Chorus; Concert Band; Mrchg Band; Orch; Trs Sr Cls; High Hon Roll; NHS; Wynsbro Are Educ Assc Schlrshp 87; Instrmntlst Magzn Merit Awd 87; Penn ST; Bus.

EVANS, CHRISTINE; Penn Trafford HS; Harrison Cty, PA; (3); 60/296; AFS; Church Yth Grp; Drama Clb; Exploring; FBLA; Capt Hosp Aide; JCL; Latin Clb; Badmtn; High Hon Roll; Pediatrc Nrsng.

EVANS, CHRISTY LYNN; Greater Johnstown Area Vo-Tech Schl; Johnstown, PA; (3); 5/300; ROTC; Scholastic Bowl; VICA; Drill Tm; NHS; Church Yth Grp; JA; Church Choir; Natl Air Force Assn Awd Outstndng AFJROTC Cadet 87; Gr Johnstown Vo-Tech Awd Employability 86-87; Penn ST; Aerospace Engrng.

EVANS, CLAUDIA; Center HS; Monaca, PA; (3); Trs Church Yth Grp; Spanish Clb; Band; Church Choir; Concert Band; Drm Mjr(t); Mrchg Band; Hon Roll; Slippery Rock Frgn Lang Cmptn Hnrbl Mntn 86; Beaver Cnty Invtnl Hnrs Band 87; PA ST Schlrshp 87; Hampton U; Acctg.

EVANS, COREEN; Marion Catholic HS; Nesquenoning, PA; (3); 22/104; Church Yth Grp; French Clb; Pep Clb; Ski Clb; SADD; Nwsp Phtg; Cheerleading; Tennis; Trk.

EVANS, CRYSTAL; Waynesburg Central HS; Brave, PA; (4); 5/194; Office Aide; Teachers Aide; Chorus; Nwsp Stf; High Hon Roll; NHS; Typng I Awd; Girl Mnth Jan; Engl Awd; Outstndg Bus Stu.

EVANS JR, DAVID C; Stroudsburg HS; Stroudsburg, PA; (2); 67/364; Ski Clb; Varsity Clb; Capt Bowling; JV Ftbl; Trk; Vllybl; High Hon Roll; Hon Roll; Vrsty Lttr & Pin Awd Rifle Team 86-87; Med.

EVANS, DAWN; Neshaminy HS; Feasterville, PA; (3); VP Church Yth Grp; Girl Scts; Hosp Aide; Intnl Clb; Red Cross Aide; Church Choir; Var Trk; Stat Wrstlng; Nrsng.

EVANS, DENNIS; Altoona Area HS; Altoona, PA; (4); 4/718; Church Yth Grp; Computer Clb; Band; Concert Band; Mrchg Band; Orch; Jr NHS; NHS; Mid ST Bnk Schlstc Awd Band 84; Mnstry.

EVANS, DOUG; Indiana Area SR HS; Indiana, PA; (3); 46/322; Church Yth Grp; Red Cross Aide; SADD; Church Choir; School Musical; Crs Cntry; Swmmng; Trk; High Hon Roll; Hon Roll; Rep Graystone Chrch Yth 86; Engl.

EVANS, ELIZABETH ANN; Archbishop John Carroll HS; St Davids, PA; (4); 24/369; French Clb; Pres Soph Cls; Pres Jr Cls; Sr Cls; Pres Stu Cncl; Fld Hcky; French Hon Soc; Hon Roll; NHS; JR Sat Clb-Stu Of Yr 86-87; Bryn Mawr Rtry-Stu Of Mnth-Oct 86-87; Cmpbl Soup Schlrshp 86-87; Dickinson Coll; Hstry.

EVANS, HARRIETT; Susquehanna Twp HS; Harrisburg, PA; (2); SADD; Band; Chorus; Church Choir; Concert Band; Mrchg Band; Orch; School Musical; Capt Cheerleading; JV Sftbl; PA Sentrl Awd 85; Outstndng Feml Vclst, Prfrmr 86; Houghton Coll; Psych.

EVANS, JAMES; Sun Valley HS; Aston, PA; (3); 4/280; Church Yth Grp; FCA; German Clb; Science Clb; Var Socr; High Hon Roll; NHS.

EVANS, JENNIFER; The Ellis Schl; Pittsburgh, PA; (3); Church Yth Grp; GAA; Hosp Aide; Pep Clb; Ski Clb; SADD; Hon Roll; Sec Jr Cls; JV Var Bsktbl; JV Fld Hcky; Bus.

EVANS, JOANN; New Castle HS; New Castle, PA; (4); 40/272; Cmnty Wkr; Computer Clb; Hosp Aide; Red Cross Aide; Teachers Aide; Nwsp Stf; Rep Sr Cls; Im Vllybl; Hon Roll; Pres Schlr; Jean Schwartz Memrl Svc Awd 87; PA JR Acad Sci 84-87; Acad All Amer HS Stu 87; Grove City Coll; Bio.

EVANS, JOSEPH; Bishop Mc Cort HS; Johnstown, PA; (4); Latin Clb; Letterman Clb; Ski Clb; Rep Soph Cls; Var L Ice Hcky; God Cntry Awd; High Hon Roll; Hon Roll; Juniata Coll; Pre-Med.

EVANS, JUDITH K; North Penn SR HS; Lansdale, PA; (4); 7/651; Dance Clb; Exploring; Hosp Aide; Science Clb; Lit Mag; High Hon Roll; NHS; Ntl Merit SF; Psychlbio.

EVANS, KATHLEEN; Our Lady Of The Sacred Heart HS; Aliquippa, PA; (4); 6/60; Dance Clb; SADD; Trs Frsh Cls; Golf; Acad All-American; Duquesne U; Media Arts.

EVANS, KATHRYN; Sharon SR HS; Sharon, PA; (3); 26/210; Aud/Vis; Cmnty Wkr; Drama Clb; French Clb; Library Aide; Chorus; School Musical; Stage Crew; Nwsp Rptr; Nwsp Stf; Penn ST; Psych.

EVANS, KELLY; Carlisle SR HS; Carlisle, PA; (3); Church Yth Grp; Hosp Aide; Hon Roll; IN U PA; Elem Ed.

EVANS, KIMBERLY; Big Beaver Falls HS; Beaver Falls, PA; (3); 39/170; Bus.

EVANS, KRISTA; Abington Heights HS; Clarks Summit, PA; (3); Church Yth Grp; Drama Clb; Ski Clb; Vllybl; Elem Ed.

EVANS, LAKEY; Reading HS; Reading, PA; (3); 71/710; Dance Clb; Key Clb; SADD; School Play; VP Frsh Cls; VP Stu Cncl; Var Cheerleading; Var Fld Hcky; Var Swmmng; Prfct Atten Awd; PHILA Coll Perfrmng Art; Dance.

EVANS, LAURA; Henderson HS; W Chester, PA; (3); 116/367; Church Yth Grp; Chorus; Lit Mag; Rep Stu Cncl; Mgr(s); Score Keeper; Trk; Hon Roll; Associated Schls Inc; Bus.

EVANS, LAUREN; North Allegheny HS; Wexford, PA; (2); 145/630; Vllybl; Hon Roll.

EVANS, LINDA K; Weatherly Area HS; Weatherly, PA; (3); Church Yth Grp; Sec Computer Clb; FBLA; Sec Library Aide; Pep Clb; Nwsp Stf; VP Sr Cls; Rep Stu Cncl; Hon Roll; Spnsh Art Awd 85-86; Wilkes Coll; Scl Svcs.

EVANS, LISA; Plum HS; Verona, PA; (3); 6/410; Mrchg Band; Symp Band; High Hon Roll; NHS; Rifle Tm Lttr 87; 1st Pl In U Of Pittsburgs Sci Day 87; Rochester Inst Tech; Bio-Tech.

EVANS, LISA; Wyoming Valley West HS; Swoyersville, PA; (4); 62/410; Church Yth Grp; Hosp Aide; Latin Clb; Chorus; Church Choir; Color Guard; Hon Roll; Luzerne Cnty CC; Nrsng.

EVANS, MARK; Danville HS; Danville, PA; (3); Var L Bsbl; JV Bsktbl; Var L Ftbl; Hon Roll; NHS; Marketing.

EVANS, MINDY; Wyoming Valley West HS; Luzerne, PA; (2); 24/425; Pres Trs Church Yth Grp; Trs Key Clb; SADD; Var Trk; Var Vllybl; High Hon Roll; NHS.

EVANS, RAQUEL; G A R Memorial HS; Wilkes-Barre, PA; (4); 4/172; Band; Chorus; Yrbk Ed-Chief; Yrbk Stf; Trs Jr Cls; Cheerleading; High Hon Roll; Jr NHS; NHS; Penn ST U; Bus.

EVANS, REBECCA; Neshaminy HS; Langhorne, PA; (3); 90/770; Church Yth Grp; Chorus; Church Choir; Var Crs Cntry; Powder Puff Ftbl; JV JCL; Swmmng; Var Trk; High Hon Roll; Hon Roll; Jrnlsm.

EVANS, SCOTT; Owen J Roberts HS; Pottstown, PA; (4); 18/270; Boy Scts; Church Yth Grp; FFA; JA; Stu Cncl; Elks Awd; Hon Roll; NHS; Eagle Sct 85; Penn ST U; Envrmntl Eng.

EVANS, SHERRI; Bethlehem Center HS; Beallsville, PA; (3); 24/161; Art Clb; GAA; Pep Clb; Spanish Clb; Varsity Clb; JV Capt Cheerleading; Socr; Hon Roll; Air Force.

EVANS, SIMONE; West Catholic Girls HS; Philadelphia, PA; (4); 3/233; Math Tm; Spanish Clb; Orch; Nwsp Rptr; Nwsp Stf; NHS; Cornell U; Pre-Med.

EVANS, STACI; Steelton-Highspire HS; Steelton, PA; (3); 11/102; Library Aide; Spanish Clb; School Musical; Yrbk Ed-Chief; Rep Frsh Cls; Rep Jr Cls; Cheerleading; Stat Vllybl; Hon Roll; NHS; U HI Manoa; Interprtr.

EVANS, TAMMY; The Baptist HS; Clarks Summit, PA; (3); Church Yth Grp; Cmnty Wkr; FCA; Chorus; Church Choir; Sec Jr Cls; Capt L Bsktbl; Capt L Socr; Hon Roll; Prfct Atten Awd; Sccr Awd 86; Pres Awd Phys Ftns 85-87; Grand Rapids Bapt Coll; Soc.

EVANS, TRACEY; Big Spring HS; Newville, PA; (2); 2/297; Spanish Clb; Chorus; High Hon Roll; Hon Roll; NHS; Spanish NHS; Intl Frgn Lang Awd 87; Chorus Awd 87.

EVANS, TRICIA; Oley Valley HS; Oley, PA; (3); 18/142; Church Yth Grp; FFA; Girl Scts; Hon Roll; Vet.

EVANS, TROY; Blacklick Valley HS; Nanty-Glo, PA; (3); 15/100; Varsity Clb; Bsbl; Bsktbl; Gov Hon Prg Awd; High Hon Roll; Hon Roll; NHS.

EVANS JR, ULYSSES; Center HS; Burtonsville, MD; (4); Church Yth Grp; Computer Clb; Exploring; Band; Church Choir; Concert Band; Jazz Band; Mrchg Band; High Hon Roll; Hon Roll; ST Percssnst Church God 87; Regn I ST Band PA 87; Westminster Hnrs Band Westminster Coll 87; Howard U; Comp Sys Engrng.

EVANS, WENDY; West Allegheny HS; Oakdale, PA; (3); German Clb; JV Var Sftbl; Var Swmmng; Hon Roll; Penn ST; Aerontcl Engrng.

EVANS, WILLIAM; Boiling Springs HS; Carlisle, PA; (3); 13/130; Band; Concert Band; Jazz Band; Mrchg Band; Hon Roll; Shippensburg U; Comp.

EVANS, WILLIAM; Shaier Area HS; Pittsburgh, PA; (3); 144/486; Pep Clb; Ski Clb; Bsbl; Ftbl; Score Keeper; Sftbl; Wt Lftg; Duke U; Banking.

EVELAND, REBECCA; Shamokin Area HS; Shamokin, PA; (3); 8/232; Trs Key Clb; Pres Science Clb; Band; Chorus; Rep Frsh Cls; Rep Soph Cls; Rep Jr Cls; Trs Sr Cls; Var High Hon Roll; Art Clb; Outstndng Writer; Pres Phys Fit Awd; 3rd Pl ST Piano Comptn; Oberlin; Perf Music.

EVELSIZER, SUZANNE; Canon Mc Millan SR HS; Eighty Four, PA; (3); Rep Band; Concert Band; Mrchg Band; Hon Roll; Excllnt Rating PMEA Solo & Small Ens Fest 87; Acctng.

EVENS, JAMIE; Port Allegany HS; Port Allegany, PA; (4); 19/113; Debate Tm; ROTC; Sec Spanish Clb; Var Bsktbl; Var Ftbl; Trk; Hon Roll; PA Free Enterprise Week PFEW 86; PA Higher Educ Asst Agncy Cert Of Merit 86; IN U Of PA; Sports Mgmt.

EVENS, JULIE; Port Allegany HS; Port Allegany, PA; (3); 1/117; Library Aide; Office Aide; Yrbk Stf; Stat Mgr(s); Trk; High Hon Roll; Hon Roll; Jr NHS; NHS; Cert Excllnce All Yr Hnr Roll 85-87; O Lean Bus Inst; Bus Adm.

EVERARD, REBECCA; York Catholic HS; York, PA; (3); FBLA; Spanish Clb; Varsity Clb; Chorus; Im Bsktbl; Mgr(s); Sftbl; High Hon Roll; Accntng.

EVERETT, DANIELLE; Penn Hills HS; Verona, PA; (3); Key Clb; Library Aide; Spanish Clb; Yrbk Stf; Sec Soph Cls; Pres Jr Cls; Rep Sr Cls; Rep Stu Cncl; Trk; Hon Roll; Chatham Coll Upward Bound 85-88; Hampton; Pediatrics.

EVERETT, KELLY L; David B Oliver HS; Pittsburgh, PA; (4); 2/198; Hosp Aide; Math Clb; Band; Nwsp Rptr; Var L Tennis; High Hon Roll; NHS; Sal; Natl Achvt Schlrshp 87; Outstndng Amer Stus 87; MIT; Gntc Engrng.

EVERETT, MISSY; Mechanicsburg Area SR HS; Mechanicsburg, PA; (2); 93/313; Cmnty Wkr; Girl Scts; Key Clb; Ski Clb; SADD; Color Guard; Mrchg Band; Sec Jr Cls; Trk; Hon Roll; Teaching French To Elem Schl Chldrn 87.

EVERETT, SUSAN; West Hazleton HS; Conyngham, PA; (4); 7/224; Church Yth Grp; FTA; Letterman Clb; Pep Clb; Ski Clb; Spanish Clb; Varsity Clb; Var Cheerleading; God Cntry Awd; High Hon Roll; PA ST U; Elem Ed.

EVERITT, DENISE; Tunkhannock HS; Tunkhannock, PA; (3); Church Yth Grp; Cmnty Wkr; Band; Concert Band; Mrchg Band; Orch; School Play; Variety Show; High Hon Roll; NHS; Band Ltr 85-86; Med Tech.

EVERLY, CATHY; Uniontown HS; Farmington, PA; (3); Spanish Clb; Hon Roll; Accntng.

EVERLY, JODIE; Moniteau HS; Slippery Rock, PA; (2); Church Yth Grp; Drama Clb; 4-H; NFL; Science Clb; Spanish Clb; SADD; Mrchg Band; NHS; Voice Dem Awd; PA Jr Acad Of Sci Region Ix & State 87; HOBY Schlrshp Awd 87; Gov Schl Of Ag At Penn State 87; Penn ST; Vet Med.

EVES, LISA; Meadville Area SR HS; Meadville, PA; (3); 117/363; Church Yth Grp; French Clb; Key Clb; Varsity Clb; Nwsp Sprt Ed; Nwsp Stf; Yrbk Stf; VP Jr Cls; Rep Stu Cncl; JV Var Bsktbl; MVP Frnkln Bsktbll Trnmnt 85; Penn State; Physcl Thrpst.

EVEY, EILEEN; Bishop Guilfoyle HS; Hollidaysburg, PA; (3); Library Aide; Ski Clb; Speech Tm; Trs SADD; Chorus; Off Jr Cls; Stu Cncl; Var Tennis.

EVON, CHRISTINE; Southmoreland HS; Mt Pleasant, PA; (3); 93/222; Drama Clb; French Clb; GAA; Library Aide; Rep Pep Clb; Ski Clb; Nwsp Rptr; Nwsp Stf; Yrbk Stf; Lit Mag; Hon Mntn Humanities Day Proj 87; Geneva Coll; Bus Admin.

EVONICH, DEBORAH; Plum SR HS; Pittsburgh, PA; (3); Off Cmnty Wkr; Trs DECA; Library Aide; SADD; School Play; Ed Nwsp Stf; Stat Bsktbl; Hon Roll.

EWART, BEVIN; Plum SR HS; Pittsburgh, PA; (3); Church Yth Grp; Cmnty Wkr; French Clb; Library Aide; SADD; Bsktbl; Coach Actv; Socr; Trk; High Hon Roll; Honors Engl,Wrld Cltrs,Frnch,Fmly Rltns,Chld Dev Awds 86-87; Soccer Ltrs 85-87; Honor Roll 84-87; U Of Pittsburgh; Ped Nrsng.

EWEDOSH, MICHAEL; Monongahela Valley Catholic HS; Richeyville, PA; (3); 2/100; Drama Clb; Science Clb; School Play; Stage Crew; Nwsp Stf; French Hon Soc; Hon Roll; NHS; Ntl Sci Olympd Awd-Physcs 87; Biomed Engrng.

EWELL, SIDNEY; Harrisburg HS; Harrisburg, PA; (3); 66/265; ROTC; Var JV Bsktbl; Var Capt Ftbl; Wt Lftg; Hon Roll; NHS; Def Plyr Yr 86; Off Plyr Game 86.

EWELL, TODD; Carlisle SR HS; Carlisle, PA; (3); Computer Clb; Varsity Clb; Yrbk Stf; Var L Bsktbl; Hon Roll; NHS; Prfct Atten Awd; Comp.

EWING, JOSHUA; Montgomery HS; Montgomery, PA; (3); FBLA; SADD; Pres Soph Cls; Ftbl; Trk; Wt Lftg; Wrstlng; Hon Roll; NHS; IUP; Bus Mgr.

EWING, MICHAEL; Archbishop Wood HS For Boys; Langhorne, PA; (3); 16/234; Yrbk Stf; Crs Cntry; Trk; High Hon Roll; NHS; All Catholic Cross Cntry; 3rd Pl Med Hlth Delaware Vly Sci Fair; All Catholic Trkc.

EWING, PATRICIA; Archbishop Prendergast HS; Aldan, PA; (3); 15/327; GAA; Latin Clb; Service Clb; Stage Crew; Yrbk Stf; Im Sftbl; High Hon Roll; Hon Roll; Hon Mntn HS Schlrshp Cntst 84.

EWING, ROBIN; Hempfield Area SR HS; Greensburg, PA; (4); 264/700; FBLA; Pep Clb; Chorus; School Play; BCI; Accntng.

EWT, PAULA; Laurel Valley HS; New Florence, PA; (4); 1/87; Trs AFS; Capt Scholastic Bowl; Science Clb; Nwsp Ed-Chief; Yrbk Ed-Chief; Capt Twrlr; DAR Awd; NHS; Rotary Awd; Val; Marine Corp Schlrshp Fndtn Schlrshp 87; IUP Dstngshd Achvr Schlr 87; Abigail Noble Memrl Schlrshp 87; IN U Of PA; Chem.

EXLER, JENNIFER; Shaler Area HS; Pittsburgh, PA; (3); 28/500; VP SADD; Yrbk Stf; Rep Frsh Cls; Off Soph Cls; Off Jr Cls; Off Sr Cls; Sec Stu Cncl; JV L Bsktbl; Var L Sftbl; French Hon Soc; HOBY Ambssdr 85.

EYE, KURT S; Penn Manor HS; Lancaster, PA; (4); 12/315; Im Badmtn; Im Bowling; Im Vllybl; High Hon Roll; Hon Roll; NHS; Ntl Merit SF; U Of PA; German.

EYER, SHERRI; Hershey HS; Hershey, PA; (3); 65/230; Church Yth Grp; Variety Show; Lit Mag; Stu Cncl; Var L Bsktbl; Var L Crs Cntry; Im Powder Puff Ftbl; Var Capt Trk; Im Vllybl; Im Wt Lftg; Careers Hlth Clb 86-87; Med.

EYSTER, SHAWN; Bermudian Springs HS; E Berlin, PA; (3); Chess Clb; Church Yth Grp; Computer Clb; Library Aide; Sec Band; Church Choir; Concert Band; Jazz Band; Mrchg Band; Pep Band; 9th Natn Wide HS Chess Comptn 86; 1st Plc Cnty Comp Cont 86; Messiah Coll; Comp Prog.

EYTCHESON, ERIC; York County Area Vo Tech HS; York, PA; (4); Varsity Clb; VICA; Yrbk Stf; Var JV Ftbl; Score Keeper; Var L Trk; Var L Wrstlng; High Hon Roll; Hon Roll; Prfct Atten Awd; Mst Outstndng Awd Ftbl 86; Mst Verstl Athl Awd Trck 87; Stdt Mnth Awd May 87; Mech Dsgn.

EZDEBSKI, PAMELA; Danville Area HS; Danville, PA; (3); French Clb; Key Clb; Latin Clb; Yrbk Stf; Trk.

EZZELL, JOSEPH; State College Area Intermediat HS; State College, PA; (1); Office Aide; Teachers Aide; Im Bsktbl; Im Vllybl; Hon Roll.

FABBRI, LESLIE; Penn Cambria SR HS; Gallitzin, PA; (4); 20/200; Yrbk Stf; Var L Bsktbl; Var L Golf; Var Trk; Hon Roll; Schlr, Ath Awd 87; Pres Physcl Ftns Awd 84-87; PA ST U; Accntng.

FABER, EDWARD; Center Area HS; Monaca, PA; (3); 27/175; Am Leg Boys St; Latin Clb; Letterman Clb; Varsity Clb; Bsbl; Bsktbl; Golf; High Hon Roll; Hon Roll; NHS; Magna Cum Laude Latin Clb 87; Pre Med.

FABER, RAY; Bangor Area HS; Bangor, PA; (2); Church Yth Grp; German Clb; Office Aide; JV L Tennis; Hon Roll; Prfct Atten Awd; Pres Schlr; Pres Acad Ftns Awd 85-86; Natl Hist/Govt Awd USAA 86.

FABIAN, ANNE; Lebanon Catholic HS; Lebanon, PA; (3); 6/72; Hosp Aide; Spanish Clb; SADD; Chorus; Church Choir; School Play; Nwsp Rptr; Yrbk Ed-Chief; NHS; Govt.

FABIAN, JULIE; Seneca Valley HS; Evans City, PA; (3); JA; Hon Roll; Psych.

FABIAN, LISA R; Lancaster Christian Schl; Reinholds, PA; (4); 7/26; VP Church Yth Grp; Sec Chorus; Yrbk Bus Mgr; Var Bsktbl; Var Capt Cheerleading; Var Sftbl; Var Vllybl; Hon Roll; Teen Wk 86; Philadelphia Coll Bible; Socl.

FABICH, PAULA; Lincoln HS; Wampum, PA; (3); 12/165; SADD; Y-Teens; Hst Band; Mrchg Band; Orch; VP Frsh Cls; Var L Bsktbl; Sftbl; High Hon Roll; NHS; Elem Ed.

FABIE, CONNIE M; Christian School Of York; York, PA; (4); 5/59; Church Yth Grp; German Clb; Chorus; Church Choir; Color Guard; School Play; Rep Jr Cls; Trs Stu Cncl; High Hon Roll; Dist Chorus 86.

FABIO, JAMES; Faith Community Christian Schl; Bethel Park, PA; (2); Church Yth Grp; French Clb; Stage Crew; Nwsp Ed-Chief; Rep Stu Cncl; JV Bsktbl; Ftbl; Sftbl; High Hon Roll; US Air Frc Acad; Aerospc Engr.

FABYANIC, WILLIAM D; Plum SR HS; Pittsburgh, PA; (3); 180/431; Am Leg Boys St; Boy Scts; JA; Band; Symp Band; Hon Roll; Eagle Scout 87.

FACHIN, KATHARINA; Villa Maria Acad; West Chester, PA; (3); 2/98; Church Yth Grp; Debate Tm; NFL; Speech Tm; Lit Mag; JV Trk; NHS; High Hon Roll; Ntl Merit Ltr; Diocesan Schlr Yr 87-88; Vrsty Debate Dist PHSSL Leag 86-87; 2nd Pl JV Debate 85-86; Polt Sci.

FACKLER, ELIZABETH; Harrisbur Christian Schl; Harrisburg, PA; (2); 1/10; Church Yth Grp; Cmnty Wkr; School Play; Sec Stu Cncl; Var Capt Bsktbl; Var Capt Fld Hcky; Var L Sftbl; High Hon Roll; Hnr Soc 87; 1st Pl Piano At Fine Arts Cmptn 86.

FADALE, ERIC; Warren Area HS; Clarendon, PA; (3); 4/300; Boy Scts; Church Yth Grp; Letterman Clb; Math Tm; Scholastic Bowl; Ski Clb; Varsity Clb; Stage Crew; Trs Frsh Cls; VP Soph Cls; Hnrbl Mntn Hstry Fair 84; Williams Awd Otstndng Wrstlr 84.

FADDIS, SCOTT; Waynesburg Central HS; Waynesburg, PA; (4); 22/186; Pres AFS; Chess Clb; Church Yth Grp; French Clb; Political Wkr; Band; Concert Band; Drm Mjr(t); Mrchg Band; French Hon Soc; Anna G Meighen Hist Awd 86; Edward B Cordrag Hist Awd 87; Congrssnl Yth Ldrshp Cncl Awd 85; Shippensburg U; Hist.

FAETH, JENNIFER; Danville HS; Danville, PA; (3); Cmnty Wkr; Pep Clb; Red Cross Aide; Ski Clb; Spanish Clb; Band; Symp Band; Nwsp Rptr; Im Mat Maids; Hon Roll; WMSPT; Scl Svcs.

FAGAN, ERIN; North Allegheny HS; Sewickley, PA; (2); 111/630; Church Yth Grp; Chorus; Hon Roll; Jr NHS; Walk-A-Thon Cmmttee 86; Jr Tamburitzan Prfrmng Ensmbls; Duquesne U; Bus.

FAGLEY, KELLY; Clarion Area JR/Sr HS; Shippenville, PA; (3); Pres Church Yth Grp; Cmnty Wkr; FCA; Pep Clb; Chorus; Color Guard; Ed Yrbk Stf; Var L Bsktbl; Capt Var Vllybl; Hon Roll; Cmmncmnt Usher 87; Cvl Engr.

FAGLEY, MATTHEW J; Girard HS; Girard, PA; (3); 3/135; Am Leg Boys St; Drama Clb; Church Choir; Concert Band; Mrchg Band; Rep Stu Cncl; Var Tennis; NHS; All ST & US All Eastern Choirs 86-87; Schlrshp Erie Times News Pblshng Co 87; Aerontcl.

FAHEY, BRUCE; Old Forge HS; Old Forge, PA; (2); Camera Clb; Ski Clb; Sec Pres Band; Pres Concert Band; Pres Jazz Band; Sec Pres Mrchg Band; Sec Pres Orch; Sec Pres Pep Band; School Musical; School Play; Johnson Tech Inst; Electrician.

FAHEY, COLIN; Upper Darby Schl Of The Sciences; Clifton Hts, PA; (3); 1/757; Pres Debate Tm; Mu Alpha Theta; Pep Band; Capt Var Sftbl; Bausch & Lomb Sci Awd; French Hon Soc; High Hon Roll; JETS Awd; Ntl Merit Schol; Val; Govs Schl Of Sci 86; Phil Schl Textiles & Sci 87; Calculus Awd 87; MIT; Asto Physcst.

FAHNESTOCK, DOUGLAS; Manheim Central HS; Manheim, PA; (4); 71/235; Church Yth Grp; VICA; Var L Bsbl; Hon Roll; Outstndng Awd-Cbntmkng & Mllwrk 87; Crpntr.

FAHNESTOCK, LINN; Elizabethtown Area HS; Manheim, PA; (4); Church Yth Grp; VICA; Electrnc Inst; Electrncs.

FAHNESTOCK, MATTHEW C; Lower Dauphin HS; Hummelstown, PA; (3); 30/273; Art Clb; Church Yth Grp; Cmnty Wkr; Bsbl; Bsktbl; High Hon Roll; Hon Roll; JV Sccr MVP Awd, 1st Pl Art Awd, ST 85; Vrsty Mst Imprvd Plyr 86; Engrng.

FAHNESTOCK, WILLIAM; South Western HS; Hanover, PA; (2); Boy Scts; Chess Clb; School Play; Stage Crew; Variety Show; Natl Educ Devel Test 85-86; Interpretor.

FAHRENBACH, RANDY; Pequea Valley HS; Paradise, PA; (3); FFA; Hon Roll; NHS; Prfct Atten Awd; Star Greenhand FFA; FFA Treas & Pres; Mechnc.

FAHRENBACH, STACEY; Western Wayne HS; Lake Ariel, PA; (2); Sec Church Yth Grp; Chorus; Church Choir; School Musical; Stage Crew; Variety Show; Hon Roll.

FAHRINGER, BOYD; Danville Area SR HS; Catawissa, PA; (3); 6/183; Yrbk Rptr; Yrbk Sprt Ed; Yrbk Stf; High Hon Roll; Hon Roll; NHS.

FAHRNEY, JOE; Waynesboro SR HS; Waynesboro, PA; (3); Varsity Clb; Var Bsbl; JV Bsktbl.

FAIDLEY, MICHAEL; Rockwood Area HS; Markleton, PA; (2); VP Chess Clb; Computer Clb; Speech Tm; School Play; High Hon Roll; Hon Roll; Elec Engnrng.

FAIR, CRAIG D; Twin Valley HS; Elverson, PA; (3); Am Leg Boys St; Boy Scts; Spanish Clb; Band; Concert Band; Drm Mjr(t); Jazz Band; Mrchg Band; School Musical; JV Var Bsbl; Mrn Bio.

FAIR, JENNIFER; West Middlesex HS; West Middlesex, PA; (2); FBLA; Library Aide; Spanish Clb; Concert Band; Mrchg Band; JV Cheerleading; L Trk; JV Vllybl; Hon Roll; Med Tech.

FAIR, REBECCA; Liberty HS; Bethlehem, PA; (3); 4/445; Varsity Clb; Band; Church Choir; School Musical; Stat Bsbl; Tennis; High Hon Roll; NHS; Girl Scts; Concert Band; Gvrnrs Schl Intl Rltns 87.

FAIRBANKS, KIMBERLY; Performing Arts Schl; Wallingford, PA; (3); Dance Clb; Drama Clb; Chorus; School Musical; School Play; Stage Crew; High Hon Roll; VP Soph Cls; Pres Jr Cls; Rep Stu Cncl; Outstndng Acht In Acting & Choir; Crnge Mln; Cmnctns.

FAIRCHILD, LE ANN; Freeland HS; Freeland, PA; (3); 1/86; Church Yth Grp; Pep Clb; Scholastic Bowl; Chorus; Nwsp Stf; Yrbk Stf; Stu Cncl; Var Cheerleading; High Hon Roll; NHS; Law.

FAIRLEY, SHANNON; Panther Valley HS; Lansford, PA; (2); 14/120; Library Aide; Ski Clb; Yrbk Stf; Bsktbl; Sftbl; Vllybl.

FAIRMAN, KEVIN; Somerset Area HS; Somerset, PA; (1); FFA; School Play; Crpntry.

FAIRNAK, DAVID M; Valley Forge Military Acad; Piscataway, NJ; (3); 59/144; Aud/Vis; Drama Clb; Radio Clb; Spanish Clb; Chorus; Stage Crew; Nwsp Stf; Hon Roll; Model UN; ROTC; AWLG 84-87; Steven Foster Hon Soc Chrs & Music 84-85; Actvts Hon Unit Distnctn 84-87; Bus.

FAISON, STACEY; Dallas SR HS; Wyoming, PA; (3); Drama Clb; Band; Chorus; Flag Corp; School Musical; School Play; Nwsp Stf; Yrbk Phtg; Hon Roll; Semi Fnlst Gvrnrs Schl Dance 86; WV U; Math Educ.

FAJERSKI, KAREN; Carrick HS; Pittsburgh, PA; (3); Q&S; Nwsp Stf; Yrbk Stf; Stu Cncl; High Hon Roll; NHS; Co-Editor Newspaper; Slipper Rock U; Elem Ed.

FAKO, ROBIN; Hampton HS; Allison Park, PA; (3); Ski Clb; Spanish Clb; Varsity Clb; Nwsp Stf; Rep Frsh Cls; Rep Soph Cls; Rep Jr Cls; Rep Sr Cls; Stu Cncl; Tennis; Engl.

FALASCO, TARA; Sharon SR HS; Sharon, PA; (3); Art Clb; French Clb; Spanish Clb; Chorus; Flag Corp; Mrchg Band; Hon Roll; Penn ST U; Scl Wrkr.

FALCHECK, KELLY A; Bishop Hoban HS; Mountaintop, PA; (3); 6/196; Church Yth Grp; Pres French Clb; Hosp Aide; Mu Alpha Theta; Ski Clb; Chorus; Color Guard; Yrbk Stf; NHS; NEDT Awd; English Awd; Stu Discovery Prog; Med Profssn.

FALCO, SHARON; Cardinal O Hara HS; Springfield, PA; (3); 14/740; Cmnty Wkr; French Clb; Office Aide; SADD; Nwsp Stf; Yrbk Stf; French Hon Soc; High Hon Roll; Hon Roll; Jr NHS; Pres Cmnty Svc Corps 87; Med.

FALCONE, CINDY; Upper Darby HS; Upr Darby, PA; (3); Office Aide; Color Guard; Concert Band; Mrchg Band; Orch; Symp Band; Phys Thrpy.

FALCONE, JONI; Pius X HS; Roseto, PA; (3); Computer Clb; Pep Clb; Varsity Clb; Chorus; Yrbk Stf; Sec Stu Cncl; Var Bsktbl; Travel.

FALCONE, KEVIN; Lower Moreland HS; Huntingdon Valley, PA; (3); Church Yth Grp; Frsh Cls; Rep Soph Cls; Rep Jr Cls; Stu Cncl; JV Bsktbl; Var Socr; Var Trk; Hon Roll; Prfct Atten Awd; Philadelphia Athl Wk 86; Huntingdon Vly Athl Assoc Chmnshp Sccr 85-86; Lwr Moreland HS Plyr Awd 86.

FALCONE, LOUIS D; Salisbury SR HS; Bethlehem, PA; (3); Computer Clb; Key Clb; Teachers Aide; Prfct Atten Awd; Outstndng Nwscarrier Awd 87; Commnctns.

FALCONE, YVONNE; Pen Argyl HS; Pen Argyl, PA; (4); 6/119; Drama Clb; Scholastic Bowl; Ski Clb; Chorus; School Play; CC Awd; High Hon Roll; NHS; Computer Clb; Red Cross Aide; Prsdntl Acdmc & Ftnss Awd 87; Prsdntl Schlrshp 87; Pen Argy Alumni Assc Schlrshp 87; U Of Scranton; Psychlgy.

FALCONI, NICOLE; Ridley SR HS; Folsom, PA; (3); 6/423; French Clb; GAA; Office Aide; Varsity Clb; Var Capt Cheerleading; Var L Fld Hcky; High Hon Roll; NHS; Prfct Atten Awd; JV Lcrss; Best All Around Girl; MVP JV La Crosse As Goalie; Temple; Phys Thrpy.

FALES, DONNA; Conneaut Lake HS; Conneaut Lake, PA; (3); Pep Clb; Spanish Clb; Concert Band; Nwsp Rptr; Nwsp Stf; JV Var Cheerleading; High Hon Roll; Hon Roll; NHS; Comm.

FALEY, CHRISTINA; Chichester SR HS; Chester, PA; (3); 41/298; Drama Clb; Spanish Clb; SADD; Band; Chorus; Flag Corp; School Play; Hon Roll; Jr NHS; Spanish NHS; Crmnl Jstc,Law.

FALEY, JIM; Central Dauphin HS; Harrisburg, PA; (3); 42/370; Var L Bsktbl; Var L Ftbl; Im Vllybl; Im Wt Lftg; Jr NHS; NHS; Ftbl Capt 87-88; Vrsty Athlt Of Wk 86-87; Bus.

FALKLER, RACHEL; Kennard Dale HS; Stewartstown, PA; (2); Band; Chorus; Concert Band; Drm Mjr(t); Mrchg Band; Orch; Pep Band; Rep Stu Cncl; Stat Vllybl; High Hon Roll; Bio Sci.

FALKNER, JOSEPH; Highlands SR HS; Natrona Hgts, PA; (3); VICA; Wt Lftg; Hon Roll; Stu Of Mnth 86-87; Work Consuentious Awd 86-87; Brown Awd 85-86; Jrny Mech.

FALKNER, MERIDITH; Freeport SR HS; Sarver, PA; (3); FBLA; Hon Roll; Branford Schl Of Bus; Exec Sec.

FALKOWSKI, ED; Elmer L Meyers HS; Wilkes Barre, PA; (4); 1/171; VP German Clb; SADD; L Vllybl; VP NHS; Val; Wt Lftg; Hon Roll; Jr NHS; Pres Schlr; Full 4 Yr NROTC Schlrshp 87; USMA; Aerosp Engrng.

FALLECKER, LISA; Karns City HS; Chicora, PA; (3); 7/100; Art Clb; Off Stu Cncl; Trk; Hon Roll; NHS; Amer Lgn Awd 84; Academic Achvt Let.

FALLECKER, RAYLENE; Beaver JR SR HS; Beaver, PA; (2); Church Yth Grp; JCL; Latin Clb; Pep Clb; Ski Clb; Sec Soph Cls; Sec Jr Cls; Var Cheerleading; Var JV Socr; Trk; Med.

FALLOT, MELISSA; Knoch JR SR HS; Butler, PA; (2); Church Yth Grp; 4-H; Girl Scts; Orch; High Hon Roll; Prfct Atten Awd; Sci Rsrch.

FALSETTI, LISA; Fort Cherry HS; Westland, PA; (4); Drama Clb; FNA; Math Clb; Science Clb; Ski Clb; Spanish Clb; Thesps; Varsity Clb; Trs Chorus; Capt Cheerleading; Amer Lgn Awd 83; CA U; Elem Ed.

FALTON, PAULINE; Our Lady Of Lourdes Regional HS; Kulpmont, PA; (3); 20/89; Am Leg Aux Girls St; FBLA; PAVAS; SADD; JV Cheerleading; NHS; Prfct Atten Awd; Cmnty Wkr; Drama Clb; Leo Clb; Mss Shamokin Anthracite Hrtg Qn 86-87; Rspct For Lf Clb Asst Secty 86-87; Law.

FALVO, NICOLE; North Allegheny Intermediate HS; Powell, OH; (2); 49/630; Chorus; Var Tennis; High Hon Roll; Jr NHS; Acadc Awds-Spcfc Clses-Eurpn Hstry 85-86; Typng II 86-87; Ldrshp Dvlpmnt Cls 86-87; Psychlgy.

FALZONE, REGINA; Tunkhannock Area HS; Harveys Lake, PA; (4); Office Aide; Pep Clb; Spanish Clb; Yrbk Ed-Chief; Yrbk Stf; High Hon Roll; Hon Roll; NHS; Ntl Ldrshp Merit Awd; Ophthlmlgy.

FAMULARO, LISA; Pennsbury HS; Levittown, PA; (3); Rep Frsh Cls; Rep Soph Cls; Rep Jr Cls; Rep Stu Cncl; Var Cheerleading; JV Capt Socr; Hon Roll; NHS; Mst Respected JV Socr Plyr 86-87; Mst Val Off Socr Plyr JV 86-87; JV Chrldg Capt 85-86.

FANDRAY, SUSAN; Baldwin HS; Pittsburgh, PA; (4); Church Yth Grp; Ski Clb; JV Tennis; Hon Roll; Duquesne U; Bus.

FANG, ANDREW SUN; Freedom HS; Bethlehem, PA; (4); 33/433; Cmnty Wkr; Science Clb; Ski Clb; Capt Color Guard; Pres Orch; Rptr Nwsp Stf; Yrbk Stf; Var L Crs Cntry; Var L Tennis; Hon Roll; U MI; Pre-Med.

FANNIN, CATHY; St Marys Area HS; Weedville, PA; (4); 45/276; Yrbk Stf; Hon Roll; NHS; Ntl Bus Hnr Soc 86-87; Du Bois Bus Coll; Exec Sec.

FANNING, YVONNE; Kensington SR HS; Philadelphia, PA; (3); Drama Clb; Hosp Aide; Red Cross Aide; Teachers Aide; School Musical; School Play; Stage Crew; Variety Show; Nwsp Rptr; Nwsp Stf; Northeastern Hosp Schl; RN.

FAPORE, DESIREE D; Cameron County HS; Emporium, PA; (3); 1/92; German Clb; Mu Alpha Theta; Mrchg Band; Yrbk Ed-Chief; Trs Frsh Cls; Trs Soph Cls; Trs Jr Cls; Stu Cncl; High Hon Roll; NHS; Excllnce Chem 86; Htl/Rest Mgmt.

FAPORE, GRETCHEN; Cameron County HS; Emporium, PA; (2); Church Yth Grp; Varsity Clb; Mrchg Band; Yrbk Stf; Var L Bsktbl; Var L Cheerleading; Var L Golf; Var L Trk; High Hon Roll; Hon Roll; Delta Epsln Phi 86-87.

FARABAUGH, ANNE; Cambria Heights HS; Ebensburg, PA; (3); 7/190; Church Yth Grp; FHA; Library Aide; Speech Tm; Lib Band; Concert Band; Mrchg Band; School Play; Stage Crew; High Hon Roll; Ntl Engl Tchrs Wrtng Cntst 87; U Of Pittsburgh; Phy Thrpy.

FARABAUGH, MICHAEL; Bishop Mc Cort HS; Johnstown, PA; (3); Latin Clb; Math Tm; Mu Alpha Theta; Spanish Clb; JV Stat Bsktbl; Score Keeper; High Hon Roll; Hon Roll; Mu Alpha Theta Awd; Accntnt.

FARABAUGH, RICHARD; Northern Cambria HS; Spangler, PA; (3); 40/170; Chess Clb; Stage Crew; Ftbl; Trk; Hon Roll; PA ST; Engrng.

FARABAUGH, TAMMY; Blairsville SR HS; Blairsville, PA; (3); 16/109; Church Yth Grp; Var JV Bsktbl; High Hon Roll; NHS; IUP; Nrsg.

FARAK, ANITA MARIE; Seneca HS; Erie, PA; (4); 18/148; School Musical; School Play; VP Soph Cls; VP Jr Cls; VP Sr Cls; Rep Stu Cncl; Cheerleading; High Hon Roll; Hon Roll; NHS; Prnts, Tchr & Stu Union Schlrshp 87; Mercyhurst Coll; Elem Ed.

FARAONE, TONI; New Castle SR HS; New Castle, PA; (4); AFS; French Clb; Color Guard; Flag Corp; Rep Frsh Cls; Rep Soph Cls; Im Vllybl; Acdmc All Amer 87; CSX Schlrshp 87; U Of Pittsburgh; Journlsm.

FARDO, AMY; Ambridge Area HS; Ambridge, PA; (4); Chess Clb; German Clb; Teachers Aide; Concert Band; School Play; Off Stu Cncl; Capt Crs Cntry; Pom Pon; Capt Trk; NHS; Gvrnrs Schl Ag 86; U Pittsburgh Alumni Assn Schlrshp, Engrng Hnrs Schlr 87; U Of Pittsburgh; Elec Engrng.

FARGO, MICHAEL; Meadville Area SR HS; Meadville, PA; (4); 80/275; Church Yth Grp; Computer Clb; Math Clb; Science Clb; Pres Ski Clb; VP Spanish Clb; SADD; Yrbk Stf; Mgr Socr; Mgr Vllybl; U Of Pittsburgh; Comp Sci.

FARICH, JOHN; Yough HS; W Newton, PA; (3); 10/139; VP Computer Clb; French Clb; Math Clb; Spanish Clb; Elec Engr.

FARIS, MELINDA; Southmoreland HS; Scottdale, PA; (3); VP Church Yth Grp; Drama Clb; French Clb; Pres FNA; Office Aide; School Play; Stage Crew; Var Socr; Var L Swmmng; Cmnty Wkr; Wheeling Coll; Nrsng.

FARKAS, JAIMIE; Lancaster Catholic HS; Strasburg, PA; (3); 3/193; Church Yth Grp; Stage Crew; Nwsp Rptr; Ed Nwsp Stf; Rep Sr Cls; Var L Crs Cntry; Var L Trk; Hon Roll; NHS; Keystone Awd 86; Math Teacher.

FARKAS, NICHOL; Mc Keesport SR HS; White Oak, PA; (1).

FARLEY, BRAD; Spring Grove SR HS; Spring Grove, PA; (2); Q&S; Var JV Wrstlng; Hon Roll.

FARLEY, CRAIG; William Allen HS; Allentown, PA; (2); 47/600; German Clb; JCL; Latin Clb; Scholastic Bowl; Band; Chorus; Concert Band; Jazz Band; Mrchg Band; Pep Band; Music Perf.

FARLEY, DAVID; St Marys Area HS; Saint Marys, PA; (4); JA; Var L Trk; Hon Roll; NHS; Penn ST U; Mech Engrng.

FARLEY, JAMIE; Milton Area SR HS; New Columbia, PA; (2); 33/254; Rep Stu Cncl; JV Bsktbl; Var Sftbl; Hon Roll; Pres Acad Ftns Awd 85-86.

FARLEY, JENNIFER; Lake-Lehman HS; Shavertown, PA; (4); 39/158; Cmnty Wkr; Girl Scts; Ski Clb; Band; Concert Band; Mrchg Band; Symp Band; Hon Roll; Girl Sct Gold Awd 87; Penn ST U; Librl Arts.

FARLEY, JILL; Plum SR HS; Pittsburgh, PA; (2); Church Yth Grp; SADD; Yrbk Stf; Vllybl; High Hon Roll; Math.

FARLEY, ROBIN M; Academy Of Notre Dame; Gulph Mills, PA; (4); 1/74; Pres Debate Tm; Math Tm; Service Clb; Pres Speech Tm; School Musical; Nwsp Rptr; Lit Mag; Mgr(s); Ntl Merit SF; Val; Local Wnnr Natl Frnch Cntst 84-86; Pre Law.

FARLEY, TRACI; Montgomery Area JR-SR HS; Montgomery, PA; (3); French Clb; Var L Bsktbl; Var L Trk; High Hon Roll; NHS.

FARMAKIS, JASON; Sharpsville HS; Sharpsville, PA; (3); 2/100; Drama Clb; Math Clb; Science Clb; Thesps; Acpl Chr; Band; Chorus; Concert Band; Jazz Band; Mrchg Band; Dist Band & Chorus 86-87; Pittsburgh U; Pre-Law.

FARMER, ANDREA; Northern Lebanon HS; Fredericksburg, PA; (4); Art Clb; Church Yth Grp; Cmnty Wkr; 4-H; Model UN; Teachers Aide; Band; Chorus; Church Choir; Concert Band; Slvr Mdl Fencg Clb 85; Slvr Mdl Keystone ST Games Fncg 86; Penn ST; Lib Art.

FARMER, MARCELLA; Mc Keesport SR HS; Mc Keesport, PA; (2); 11/400; Church Yth Grp; Library Aide; Office Aide; Acpl Chr; Orch; School Musical; High Hon Roll; Hon Roll; Rgn/ST Orchstra Fstvls 87.

FARMER, TRACY; Baldwin HS; Pittsburgh, PA; (3); 116/477; Church Yth Grp; French Clb; Chorus; Church Choir; School Musical; Var Trk; Hon Roll; Accntng.

FARMER III, WILLIAM S; Elizabeth Forward SR HS; Elizabeth, PA; (2); 61/340; Church Yth Grp; Swmmng; Trk; Hon Roll; AP Amrcn Hstry Course/Coll Crdt 87.

FARMERIE, WENDY; Wilmington Area HS; New Wlmington, PA; (4); 16/112; Church Yth Grp; Key Clb; Math Tm; Spanish Clb; Speech Tm; Band; Variety Show; Hon Roll; NHS; Pres Schlr; Westminster Coll; Intercultrl.

FARNE, WILLIAM HEATH; Central Dauphin HS; Harrisburg, PA; (3); Civic Clb; Hon Roll; Penn ST; Bus.

FARNEY, LINDA; Linden Hall HS; E Petersburg, PA; (3); Girl Scts; Science Clb; Chorus; Nwsp Stf; JV Trk; High Hon Roll; Jobs Dghtrs; Algebra II Awd; Stage Dsgn.

FARNSWORTH, MICHELE; St Marys Area HS; St Marys, PA; (3); 38/288; Office Aide; Pep Clb; JV Var Cheerleading.

FAROLE, ANGELA; Allentown Central Catholic HS; Whitehall, PA; (3); 50/255; Church Yth Grp; Hosp Aide; Key Clb; Spanish Clb; Chorus; Church Choir; Flag Corp; Powder Puff Ftbl; High Hon Roll; Hon Roll; Psych.

FAROLE, DEANA; Quaker Valley HS; Sewickley, PA; (1); Drama Clb; Chorus; School Musical; School Play; Mgr(s); Score Keeper; High Hon Roll; Pres Schlr; Amer Red Cross, Yth Svc Of Pittsburgh Allegheny Cnty 87; Law.

FARQUER, KIMBERLY; Neshaminy HS; Langhorne, PA; (4); 90/640; Teachers Aide; Yrbk Stf; Im Vllybl; Cit Awd; Hon Roll; NHS; Elem Ed Schlrshp 87; Beaver Coll; Elem Ed.

FARR, JENNIFER; Montrose Area JR SR HS; Little Meadows, PA; (3); French Clb; SADD; Varsity Clb; Color Guard; Var Cheerleading; Var Mgr(s); Var Score Keeper; Hon Roll; Acctg.

FARR, ROBERT; Exeter Township SR HS; Reading, PA; (3); 1/241; Boy Scts; Key Clb; Varsity Clb; Var L Ftbl; High Hon Roll; Jr NHS; NHS; Pres Schlr; Egl Sct 86.

FARRAR, JEFFREY; Ambridge Area HS; Ambridge, PA; (4); 21/265; Aud/Vis; Math Clb; SADD; VICA; Co-Capt Vllybl; Hon Roll; Lion Awd; NHS; Prfct Atten Awd; Itailian Wmns Clb 87; PA ST U; Engrng.

FARRAR, TESSA; Montoursville HS; Montoursville, PA; (3); Cheerleading; Powder Puff Ftbl; Trk.

FARRELL, HEATHER; North Penn JR-SR HS; Blossburg, PA; (3); Camera Clb; Key Clb; Color Guard; Cheerleading; Hon Roll; Trvl.

FARRELL, KATHLEEN; Dallas SR HS; Dallas, PA; (4); 14/249; Yrbk Stf; Stu Cncl; Capt Cheerleading; Hon Roll; Lion Awd; NHS; Presdntl Schrlshp 87-88; U Of Scranton; Math.

FARRELL, KELLY ANNE; Nazareth Acad; Philadelphia, PA; (3); 20/120; Church Yth Grp; Cmnty Wkr; French Clb; Latin Clb; Yrbk Stf; Off Frsh Cls; Hon Roll; Prfct Atten Awd; Diocesian Schlrs Prog 87; Amsco Ntl Latin Exam Cert Of Excllnc 85; Jrnlsm.

FARRELL, MEGAN; Riverview HS; Oakmont, PA; (3); Ski Clb; Concert Band; Off Jr Cls; Stu Cncl; Var Bsktbl; Capt Pom Pon; Powder Puff Ftbl; High Hon Roll.

FARRELL, VICTORIA; Red Lion Area SR HS; Felton, PA; (3); 19/342; Am Leg Aux Girls St; Church Yth Grp; Flag Corp; Orch; School Musical; School Play; Yrbk Stf; French Hon Soc; High Hon Roll; NHS; Yth For Undrstndng Cert Of Merit 87; RR Electric Yth Tour WA DC Cert Of Prtcptn 87.

FARREN, SEAN; Central Catholic HS; Rankin, PA; (4); Exploring; Chorus; Bowling; High Hon Roll; Hon Roll; Latin Hnr Soc 84-85; Marquette U; Cmnctns.

FARRO, JEFF; Nativity BVM HS; Cressona, PA; (2); 8/78; VP Church Yth Grp; Latin Clb; JV Bsktbl; JV Ftbl; Wt Lftg; Hon Roll; Highst Achvt Latin I, Latin II, Physical Sci 86-87; Business.

FARRONE, TONI; New Castle SR HS; New Castle, PA; (4); AFS; French Clb; Color Guard; Flag Corp; Rep Frsh Cls; Rep Soph Cls; Rep Jr Cls; Rep Sr Cls; Vllybl; Hon Roll; Acadmc All Amercn 87; U Of Pittsburgh; Comm.

FARROW, RAY; Ambridge Area HS; Freedom, PA; (3); Church Yth Grp; FCA; French Clb; Pep Clb; SADD; VICA; Ftbl; Hon Roll.

FARRUGGIO, KIMBERLEE; Bishop Conwell HS; Yardley, PA; (3); 11/268; Hosp Aide; Spanish Clb; SADD; Nwsp Rptr; High Hon Roll; NHS; Hghst Avg Engl Villa Victoria Acad 84-85; PA ST; Pre-Med.

FARTINI, ANGELA; North Star HS; Stoystown, PA; (2); 15/139; Church Yth Grp; Cmnty Wkr; FCA; Ski Clb; SADD; Yrbk Stf; Var JV Cheerleading; Var Mat Maids; Hon Roll; Med.

FASANO, CAROL; Mifflinburg Area HS; Mifflinburg, PA; (4); 4/154; Pres VP French Clb; Key Clb; Trs Soph Cls; Sec Stu Cncl; Cheerleading; Var L Fld Hcky; JV Gym; JV L Sftbl; High Hon Roll; Hon Roll; Acadmc Fitness Awd 86-87; Outstndng Mbr Of Ntl Hnr Scty 86-87; Villanova U; Bus Adm.

FASHOUER, JACQUELINE; West Scranton HS; Scranton, PA; (2); Dance Clb; Drama Clb; NFL; Speech Tm; Thesps; School Play; Hon Roll; Aud/Vis; Spanish Clb; Cathlc Frnsc Leag Cert Superiorty 86; 2nd Pl Nvc Ortrcl Dclmtn Awd 86; Marywood Coll; Elem Ed.

FASNACHT, DARYLE; Annville-Cleona HS; Palmya, PA; (3); Church Yth Grp; Chorus; Church Choir; Madrigals; JV Bsbl; JV Ftbl; Prfct Atten Awd; CPA.

FASNACHT, LARRY; Cocalico HS; Denver, PA; (3); Boy Scts; Church Yth Grp; Ftbl; Wt Lftg; Hon Roll.

FASOLD, JENNIFER; Danville Area HS; Danville, PA; (4); Hosp Aide; Key Clb; Mrchg Band; Symp Band; Yrbk Ed-Chief; Yrbk Phtg; Yrbk Rptr; Yrbk Stf; High Hon Roll; NHS; PA ST U; Human Dev.

FASOLD, MELISSA; State College Intermediate HS; State College, PA; (1); Cmnty Wkr; Library Aide; Teachers Aide; High Hon Roll; Hon Roll; Cert Merit Outstndng Achvt Grmn 86-87; Power Paws 86-87; Engr.

FASOLT, REBECCA; Hempfield HS; Lancaster, PA; (3); 38/400; Trs Girl Scts; Concert Band; Mrchg Band; Orch; Symp Band; Rep Jr Cls; Stu Cncl; Var Sftbl; NHS; Service Clb; Bus.

FASSL, KRISTA; Bethlehem Catholic HS; Bethlehem, PA; (3); 8/205; Church Yth Grp; Hosp Aide; SADD; Church Choir; Nwsp Rptr; Hon Roll; NHS; Key Clb; Band; Mrchg Band; Folk Grp-Quitar 84-88; Outstndng Achvt German 85 & 86; Medical Careers Clb 85-88.

FATH JR, DAVID KELLY; Palmyra Area SR HS; Annville, PA; (4); 1/187; Am Leg Boys St; Church Yth Grp; Pres Band; Rep Stu Cncl; Var Bsbl; Var Bsktbl; DAR Awd; NHS; Pres Schlr; Rotary Awd; Cedarville Coll.

FATIGA, ANTHONY; Archbishop Wood HS; Willow Grove, PA; (2); 92/254; Im Coach Actv; JV Ftbl; Var Trk.

FATTA, SCOTT; Saltsburg JR SR HS; Clarksburg, PA; (3); Varsity Clb; Yrbk Stf; Trk; High Hon Roll; Hon Roll; NHS; Pres Ftns Awd; Math.

FATULA, KEITH; Greater Johnstown HS; Johnstown, PA; (4); 39/277; Drama Clb; Pres Trs Key Clb; Math Tm; NFL; Speech Tm; Concert Band; Jazz Band; Off Mrchg Band; School Musical; Trs Sr Cls; Dir Awd 87; IN U Of PA; Acctnt.

FATUR, ROY P; Greensburg Salem HS; Greensburg, PA; (4); 2/261; Exploring; Math Tm; Ski Clb; Band; Rep Stu Cncl; Var L Crs Cntry; Var L Trk; Jr NHS; Pres NHS; Sal; PA Higher Ed Assis Agncy Cert Of Merit 86; US Air Force; Aerospc Engnrng.

FATZINGER, TRACEY A; Saucon Valley SR HS; Bethlehem, PA; (4); 1/150; Scholastic Bowl; Chorus; Sec Sr Cls; Capt Crs Cntry; Swmmng; Trk; High Hon Roll; Yrbk Ed-Chief; NHS; Ntl Merit SF; Northamptn Cnty JR Miss Schlstc Achvmnt Awd 86; Leon Brown Outstndng Awd 84; Cross Cntry Leag All Str.

FAUL, KELLY; Warren Area HS; Warren, PA; (3); Trs Church Yth Grp; Band; Church Choir; Concert Band; Yrbk Stf; JV Cheerleading; Im Tennis; Cit Awd; Hon Roll; Office Aide; Bus Mgmt.

FAULKNER, GRETA; Mc Dowell HS; Erie, PA; (2); 179/629; Computer Clb; Girl Scts; Ski Clb; Spanish Clb; Yrbk Stf; Stu Cncl; JV Cheerleading; Tennis; Hon Roll; Tnns Rnkng 7th 86 16 Undr; Tnnr Rnkd 39th Mddl ST 16 Undr; Comm.

FAULSTICK, SCOTT E; William Tennent HS; Southampton, PA; (4); 13/590; Hosp Aide; Chorus; Church Choir; Madrigals; School Musical; NHS; Ntl Merit Ltr; Centennial Schlr 87; Hosp Vol 500 Hr Awd 86; Georgetown U; Lingstcs.

FAUNCE, SAMANTHA; Bensalem HS; Bensalem, PA; (2); Red Cross Aide; Spanish Clb; JV Fld Hcky; Capt Swmmng; Vllybl; High Hon Roll; Amer Ed Wk Essy Cntst Wnnr 86; Swmmng Mst Vlbl 85-86; Outstndng HS Ath Of Amer 85-86.

FAURL, RANDY; Emmaus HS; Macungie, PA; (3); 50/530; JA; Key Clb; Im JV Socr; Im JV Vllybl; High Hon Roll; Hon Roll; Jr NHS; NHS; Engrng.

FAUSER, PAUL D; Manheim Central HS; Manheim, PA; (4); 47/217; Boy Scts; Church Yth Grp; Cmnty Wkr; Off Jr Cls; Trs Sr Cls; Trk; God Cntry Awd; Hon Roll; Vlntr/Lrnbl Mntly Rtrded 86-87; Shippensburg U; Bus.

FAUSEY, JILL; Danville Area HS; Danville, PA; (3); 28/159; Hosp Aide; Color Guard; Mrchg Band.

FAUST, CAROLYN; West Allegheny HS; Oakdale, PA; (3); Teachers Aide; Yrbk Stf; Lit Mag; Hon Roll; Gifted Prog 76-88; Excercise Clb 87; Art Inst Of Pittsburgh; Artist.

FAUST, CYNTHIA; Pleasant Valley HS; Kresgeville, PA; (3); Art Clb; Dance Clb; Drama Clb; French Clb; Pep Clb; School Play; Stu Cncl; JV Var Cheerleading; JV Var Fld Hcky; Powder Puff Ftbl; Temple U; Frnch Educ.

FAUST, ERIN; Mc Keesport Area HS; Mckeesport, PA; (4); 15/335; French Clb; Powder Puff Ftbl; L Var Trk; High Hon Roll; Jr NHS; NHS; Prsdntl Acdmc Fitness Awd, Mc Keesport Coll Clb Schlrshp & Highest Hnrs Grad 87; U Of Pittsburgh; Med.

FAUST, JENNIFER; Lampeter Strasburg HS; Lancaster, PA; (4); AFS; Art Clb; Thesps; Chorus; Madrigals; School Musical; School Play; Nwsp Rptr; Lit Mag; Stat Bsktbl; Ithaca Coll; Cmnctns.

FAUST, LORI; Salisbury HS; Allentown, PA; (4); Cmnty Wkr; Hosp Aide; Pres Key Clb; Political Wkr; SADD; School Musical; Rep Frsh Cls; Church Yth Grp; Drama Clb; Red Cross Aide; Future Teachers Of Amer Awd & Frgn Lang Week Awd 87; Good Shepherd Home Rehab Hostp Vlntr Awd 85-86; Penn ST U; Spcl Educ.

FAUX, GREGORY; Tunkhannock Area HS; Falls, PA; (4); 27/270; Church Yth Grp; Latin Clb; Letterman Clb; Ski Clb; Yrbk Stf; Var L Crs Cntry; Var L Trk; Hon Roll; NHS.

FAVA, RACQUELLE; Mon Valley Catholic HS; Scenery Hill, PA; (3); Sec 4-H; French Clb; Ski Clb; Chorus; School Musical; Variety Show; Rep Jr Cls; Stu Cncl; Var JV Bsktbl; Powder Puff Ftbl; Htl,Rstrnt Mgmt.

FAVATA, FRANK; Liberty HS; Bethlehem, PA; (3); Band; Concert Band; Jazz Band; Pep Band; Hon Roll; Nwsppr Carrier Of Month 86; Penn ST U; Bus.

FAWCETT, JOSEPH B; Lakeland HS; Olyphant, PA; (3); 14/180; Nwsp Stf; Sec Jr Cls; Off Stu Cncl; L Var Ftbl; L Var Trk; Wt Lftg; High Hon Roll; Hon Roll; NHS; Lackawanna Cnty Trk/Fld Male Athl Yr 87; Pres Phys Ftnss Awd 83-87; All Schlstc Trk/Fld 86-87; Syracuse U; Pre Law.

FAWCETT, SYLVIA; Ambridge Area HS; Baden, PA; (3); Pres German Clb; SADD; VP Band; Jazz Band; Symp Band; L Sftbl; L Vllybl; Hon Roll; NHS; Acad All Amer 85; Sftbl All Star Catcher 87; Econ Powerhouse Sftbl Catcher 86; U Pittsburgh; Bus Adm.

FAYBIK, JASON P; Burrell SR HS; Arnold, PA; (3); Drama Clb; French Clb; Pres Trs Stu Cncl; PA ST; Anthslgst.

FAYO, CHARLENE; Duquesne SR HS; Duquesne, PA; (4); 3/82; Office Aide; Co-Capt Color Guard; Concert Band; Stu Cncl; High Hon Roll; Hon Roll; NHS; ICM Bus Schl; Mdcl Offc Astnt.

FAYOCAVITZ, DAVID; Abington Heights HS; Clarks Summit, PA; (4); 19/264; Co-Capt Wrstlng; Hon Roll; Lion Awd; NHS; Pres Schlr; All Star Wrstlng Tm 87; Dalton Lions Clb Wrstlng Trny Outstndg 87; John A Archangelo Schlrshp; Drexel U; Engrng.

FAZAKAS, CHRISTINE; Allentown Central Catholic HS; Whitehall, PA; (3); 24/265; Drama Clb; FBLA; Library Aide; Thesps; School Musical; Variety Show; Yrbk Stf; High Hon Roll; Lion Awd; NHS; 3rd Pl PJAS 84-85; Engl Educ.

FAZEKAS, LAURIE; Central Christian HS; Brockway, PA; (3); Exploring; Pres Pep Clb; Ski Clb; Nwsp Stf; Yrbk Stf; Var JV Vllybl; Hon Roll; Clarion Math Cmptn 87; Pitt; Phys Thrpy.

FAZIO, CHRISTOPHER; General Mc Lane HS; Edinboro, PA; (4); Band; Drm & Bgl; Jazz Band; Mrchg Band; Orch; School Play; Symp Band; Var L Trk; Hon Roll; Concert Band; Nans Music Schlrshp Awd 87; Kent St Mrchng Band Schlrshp 87; Kent St U; Music Educ.

FAZIO, FRANK; Hampton HS; Allison Park, PA; (4); 42/255; Ski Clb; Rep Frsh Cls; Rep Sr Cls; Im Coach Actv; Im Tennis; Trk; Hon Roll; U Of AZ; Pre Med.

FAZZI, HEATHER L; Dallas SR HS; Wyoming, PA; (4); 15/250; Drama Clb; School Musical; School Play; Stage Crew; Nwsp Phtg; Ed Nwsp Stf; Yrbk Ed-Chief; Yrbk Phtg; Yrbk Stf; Hon Roll; Partial Schlrshp & Art III Awd 87; N E PA Schlrshp Art Wrkshp 1st 86; Moore Coll Of Art; Art.

FEAGINS, WILLIAM; Westinghouse HS; Pittsburgh, PA; (2); Science Clb; Nwsp Stf; Cit Awd; Hon Roll; Cmrcl Artsts.

FEASER, MICHELLE; Cedar Crest HS; Lebanon, PA; (3); 23/343; FTA; Latin Clb; Pep Clb; Spanish Clb; Band; Concert Band; Mrchg Band; Pep Band; School Musical; Hon Roll; Arion Awd-Mst Outstndng JR In Band 87; Music.

FEASTER, CRAIG; Bedford HS; Bedford, PA; (3); 3/204; Chess Clb; Exploring; Math Tm; Chorus; Rep Stu Cncl; L Ftbl; Hon Roll; NHS; Ntl Merit Ltr; Voice Dem Awd; Outstndng 10th Gr Stu 85; 6th Pl FBLA Natls Bus,Math 85; 3rd Pl Allegany CC Math Schlrshp Comp 87; Penn ST; Med.

FEASTER, DEBBIE; Montgomery Area HS; Montgomery, PA; (4); 14/62; French Clb; Thesps; Capt Color Guard; Concert Band; Mrchg Band; School Play; Nwsp Stf; Yrbk Stf; High Hon Roll; Hon Roll; Susquehann U; Music Ed.

FEATENBY, JENNIFER; Danville HS; Danville, PA; (2); Exploring; Hosp Aide; Key Clb; Rep Frsh Cls; Rep Soph Cls; Var Cheerleading; Mat Maids; Powder Puff Ftbl; Var Sftbl; Pres Schlr; Psychlgy.

FEATENBY, SUSAN; Danville SR HS; Danville, PA; (3); 64/187; Church Yth Grp; French Clb; Hosp Aide; Band; Concert Band; Jazz Band; Bsktbl; Var Capt Sftbl; Tennis; Hon Roll; Bloomsburg U; Elem Ed.

FEATHER, ALLAN J; Hatboro-Horsham HS; Hatboro, PA; (3); Drama Clb; School Play; Variety Show; Yrbk Rptr; Bowling; Crs Cntry; Ice Hcky; Trk; High Hon Roll; Hon Roll; Gld Acadmc Awd 86-87; 2nd Pl Subrbn 1 Area Indvdl Bwlng Chmpnshps 87; 1st Pl Mxd Dbls Bwlng 86-87.

FEATHER, GREGORY M; Bedford HS; Bedford, PA; (4); 48/174; Ski Clb; Band; Chorus; Concert Band; Jazz Band; Mrchg Band; Pep Band; Trk; Hon Roll; Mst Imprvd Band Stu; U Of Pittsburgh; Acctng.

FEATHERMAN, WILLIAM D; Oxford Area HS; Oxford, PA; (4); 1/172; Boy Scts; Quiz Bowl; Ski Clb; SADD; Var Capt Bsbl; Var Crs Cntry; Im Golf; High Hon Roll; NHS; Ntl Merit SF; Archtctr.

FEATHERS, VICKI; Claysburg-Kimmel HS; Imler, PA; (2); 11/108; Drama Clb; Speech Tm; Y-Teens; Band; Chorus; Color Guard; Concert Band; School Play; Rep Stu Cncl; High Hon Roll; P S U; Jrnlsm.

FEBBO, LOUIS; Scranton Prep; Old Forge, PA; (1); Ftbl; Sci.

FEBUS, ROSA I; Reading SR HS; Reading, PA; (3); Acpl Chr; Chorus; Swing Chorus; Var Fld Hcky; Var Sftbl; Var Vllybl; Reading Area CC; Lab Tech.

FECZKO, JANINE; Greensburg Central Catholic HS; So Greensburg, PA; (3); Church Yth Grp; Variety Show; Lit Mag; High Hon Roll; Hon Roll; AFS; Pep Clb; Ski Clb; School Musical; School Play; Wrd Prcssng Cert 85; Cthlc Dghtrs Of Amer Cert Poetry Div II 84; Pre Med.

FEDAK, GARY; Chartiers Valley HS; Carnegie, PA; (4); 20/299; German Clb; Varsity Clb; Var Capt Bsktbl; Im Ftbl; NHS; Emplyee Mnth Roy Rgrs 86; U Dayton; Cvl Engrng.

FEDARTO, VICKI LYNN; Belle Vernon Area HS; Belle Vernon, PA; (2); Debate Tm; JA; Chorus; Nwsp Phtg.

FEDOR, CAREY; Riverside JR SR HS; Taylor, PA; (3); Art Clb; Color Guard; Variety Show; Cheerleading; Trk; MD; Beauty Schl.

FEDOR, LORY LEIGH; Northwestern HS; W Springfield, PA; (4); VP Thesps; Capt Color Guard; Mrchg Band; School Musical; VP Soph Cls; VP Jr Cls; VP Sr Cls; Pres Stu Cncl; Trs Ftbl; Trs Wrstlng; Albion Area Lions Clb Awd 87; Lock Haven U.

FEDORCHAK, SANDRA K; Mid-Valley Secondary Ctr; Olyphant, PA; (1); 3/112; Dance Clb; Drama Clb; Concert Band; Mrchg Band; School Musical; School Play; VP Frsh Cls; Rep Stu Cncl; Cheerleading; High Hon Roll; Bus.

FEE, J KEVIN; Plymouth-Whitemarsh HS; Lafayette Hill, PA; (3); Math Clb; Math Tm; Mu Alpha Theta; Var Bsktbl; High Hon Roll; Hon Roll; Law.

FEE, MATTHEW; St John Neumann HS; Philadelphia, PA; (2); 1/350; HS Full Scholar 86; Lngstcs.

FEEG, CHERYL; Conrad Weiser HS; Robesonia, PA; (3); 53/179; FBLA; JCL; Band; Chorus; Concert Band; Mrchg Band; School Musical; Yrbk Stf; Var Sftbl; Hon Roll; Typng II Awd 87; Bus Mgmt.

FEEGE, MICHAEL S; Boyertown JR HS; Perkiomenville, PA; (1); Cmnty Wkr; VICA; High Hon Roll; Hon Roll; Aerospc Engrng.

FEEHERY, TERRENCE; Cardinal O Hara HS; Springfield, PA; (4); 47/771; Rep Frsh Cls; Rep Soph Cls; Rep Jr Cls; Rep Sr Cls; Stu Cncl; Capt L Swmmng; High Hon Roll; Hon Roll; Lion Awd; NHS; La Salle U Swmng Schlrshp 87; Union League Gd Ctznshp Schlrshp 87; HS All Amer Swmr 83; La Salle U PA; Physcl Thrpy.

FEELEY, JENNIFER; Cheltenham HS; Cheltenham, PA; (2); Church Yth Grp; VP Sec 4-H; Chorus; Church Choir; Var Trk; 4-H Awd; Del Val Coll; Anml Sci.

FEENAN, SUSAN; Creative & Performing Arts HS; Philadelphia, PA; (3); Art Clb; Church Yth Grp; Drama Clb; PAVAS; Spanish Clb; Yrbk Stf; Hon Roll; Jr NHS; NHS; 1st Pl Frgn Lng Pst Cntst 87; Cmnctns.

FEESE, ERIC; Southern Columbia Area HS; Catawissa, PA; (3); Ftbl; Var L Wrstlng; High Hon Roll; NHS; Voice Dem Awd; Pinamonti Awd Most Dedicated Wrstlr 85-86; Pinamonti Awd Most Dedicated Wrstlr 86-87.

FEESER, ARTHUR; South Western SR HS; Brodbecks, PA; (3); JV Ftbl; Var JV Wrstlng; Pittsburg Inst Of Art; Art.

FEGELY, SHANE; Dallas SR HS; Trucksville, PA; (3); Boy Scts; Chess Clb; Drama Clb; School Musical; School Play; Socr; God Cntry Awd; High Hon Roll; Hon Roll; NEDT Top 10 Percent 84-86; Embry Riddle Aeronautical U.

FEGER, KYLE E; Schuylkill Haven Area HS; Schuylkill Haven, PA; (3); 4/103; Boy Scts; Trs FCA; Trs German Clb; VP Jr Cls; Rep Stu Cncl; L Bsbl; L Ftbl; Var Wrstlng; SADD; Hon Roll; HOBY Fndtn Ambssdr 86; Peer Eductn 86; US Naval Acad; Mech Engrng.

FEGLEY, DANIEL; G W Carver HS For Engrng & Sci; Phila, PA; (3); Chess Clb; Church Yth Grp; Exploring; Radio Clb; Variety Show; La Salle; Financl Mgmt.

FEGLEY, LAURA; Danville SR HS; Danville, PA; (3); Ski Clb; Spanish Clb; Trs Frsh Cls; Trs Soph Cls; Trs Jr Cls; Trs Sr Cls; Rep Stu Cncl; Var Cheerleading; Gym; JV Socr; Lock Haven U; Physcl Thrpy.

FEGLEY, SHERRY; Mahanoy Area HS; Barnesville, PA; (4); 3/110; Exploring; Ski Clb; Band; Chorus; Flag Corp; School Play; Nwsp Stf; Yrbk Stf; NHS; Pres Schlr; Schuyl Kill Cnsrvtn Awd, Mahanoy City Rtry Clb Schlrshp & Christ Untd Chrch Of Christ Schlrshp 87; Pennm ST; Sci.

FEHR, KRISTEN; Governor Mifflin SR HS; Reading, PA; (3); 38/300; Hosp Aide; Office Aide; Q&S; Teachers Aide; Flag Corp; Nwsp Stf; Yrbk Sprt Ed; JV Var Fld Hcky; High Hon Roll; Mrchg Band; Unified Achvmnt Awd 86-87; Nrsng.

FEHR, TRICIA; Pine Grove Area HS; Pine Grove, PA; (4); 5/116; Yrbk Ed-Chief; Yrbk Stf; High Hon Roll; Hon Roll; Patricia A Bush Mem Awd 87; Pres Acadmc Fitness Awd 87; Tremnt Wmns Club Awd 87; PA ST; Clerk Steno.

FEICHTEL, JOHN; Mechanicsburg Area HS; Mechanicsburg, PA; (4); 1/303; Am Leg Boys St; Varsity Clb; Nwsp Bus Mgr; Nwsp Rptr; VP Sr Cls; Var Bsbl; Capt Ftbl; Gov Hon Prg Awd; High Hon Roll; NHS; Am Leg Post 109 Awd 87; Fink/Steiner Ath Awd 87; US Marine Corps Dstngshd Ath Awd 87; US Naval Acad; Aerospc Engrng.

FEICK, MARIE; Elizabeth Forward HS; Monongahela, PA; (3); 42/345; Spanish Clb; Var L Bsktbl; Var L Crs Cntry; Var Trk; Hon Roll; Prfct Atten Awd; Nrsng.

FEIGHT, CORINNA; Everett Area HS; Breezewood, PA; (3); Computer Clb; FHA; GAA; Library Aide; SADD; VICA; Stat Bsktbl; Hon Roll; NHS; VICA Skll Olympcs 2nd Data Entry 87.

FEILKE, CHERYL; Upper Darby HS; Upr Darby, PA; (3); French Clb; Pep Clb; Stu Cncl; Bsktbl; Fld Hcky; JV Var Lcrss; Hon Roll; Jr NHS; Prfct Atten Awd; Wrkng With Chldrn.

FEINBERG, FERN; Hatboro-Horsham SR HS; Hatboro, PA; (3); Cmnty Wkr; Key Clb; SADD; Temple Yth Grp; Mrchg Band; Nwsp Stf; Yrbk Stf; Rep Soph Cls; Rep Jr Cls; Powder Puff Ftbl; Early Elem Ed.

FEINDT, FRANCES; Cardinal O Hara HS; Brookhaven, PA; (3); 2/710; Office Aide; Spanish Clb; Hon Roll; NHS; Exclinc Awd Engl 3, Shrthnd I, US Hstry, Relign 86-87; Exclinc Awd Spnsh 2 Natl Spnsh Exm Awd 85-86; Penn ST U; Bus Admin.

FEIOCK, JENNIFER; Canton JR-SR HS; Canton, PA; (2); French Clb; Letterman Clb; Spanish Clb; Chorus; School Musical; Rep Stu Cncl; Var Sftbl; JV Var Vllybl; High Hon Roll; Pres Phys Fit Awd 86-87; Phy Ed.

FEITERMAN, THEODORE; The Hill Schl; Boyertown, PA; (3); Varsity Clb; Chorus; Church Choir; Variety Show; Pres Frsh Cls; Pres Soph Cls; Var Bsbl; Var Bsktbl; Var Ftbl; Im Gym; Amer Lgn Ctznshp, Schlrshp & Ldrshp Awd 84; U Of PA; Engrng.

FELBERG, LINDA; Neshaminy HS; Levittown, PA; (4); 71/723; Political Wkr; Ski Clb; Nwsp Stf; Lit Mag; Hon Roll; NCTE Awd; NHS; Amer U; Intl Stdys.

FELDKAMP, JEFF; Souderton Area HS; Telford, PA; (4); 6/320; Church Yth Grp; Debate Tm; FCA; Hosp Aide; Service Clb; JV Socr; Var L Tennis; High Hon Roll; Hon Roll; VP NHS; Army ROTC Schlrshp 87; Herald Of Christ Awd 86; Pres Acad Ftns Awd 87; Le High U; Engr.

FELDKAMP, TOM; Soudeton Area HS; Telford, PA; (3); Chess Clb; Church Yth Grp; Computer Clb; Var Tennis; Hon Roll; Prfct Atten Awd; Penn ST; Engrng.

FELDMAN, MELISSA; Hillel Acad; Pittsburgh, PA; (1); Church Yth Grp; Cmnty Wkr; Hosp Aide; Stu Cncl; High Hon Roll; Econ.

FELDMAN, RONNEY SUE; Hill Top Prep; Havertown, PA; (3); Aud/Vis; Chess Clb; Hosp Aide; Library Aide; Pres Temple Yth Grp; Chorus; Yrbk Stf; Rep Stu Cncl; Sftbl; Trk; 43 Mile Out 50 Mile Swim Jr Lfsvng; U PA; Med.

FELDMAN, STACY; Abington SR HS; Huntingdon Valley, PA; (3); Cheerleading; Sftbl; Tennis; Subrbn I All Leag 85-87; Bus.

FELEGY, TANIA; William Allen HS; Allentown, PA; (4); 95/559; Hosp Aide; JCL; Latin Clb; Leo Clb; Y-Teens; Yrbk Stf; Rep Jr Cls; Hon Roll; Jr NHS; Contemporary Affairs; Latin Awds; Kings Coll; Physcns Asst.

FELICETTI, LAURA; Brookville Area HS; Brookville, PA; (3); 7/180; Drama Clb; German Clb; Varsity Clb; Orch; Var L Swmmng; Trk; High Hon Roll; Jr NHS; NHS.

FELICITA, JULIE; Sayre Area HS; Sayre, PA; (3); Dance Clb; Exploring; Chorus; Drm Mjr(t); Var Mgr(s); Var Score Keeper; Mgr Trk; Instrmntlst Magzn Merit Awd 87; Williamsport; Acctg.

FELIX, ANN; Elizabethtown Area HS; Elizabethtown, PA; (3); 34/259; Sec Church Yth Grp; Red Cross Aide; Nwsp Stf; Powder Puff Ftbl; Red Crss Vlntr Hnr Awd 86-87; Accntng.

FELIX, JOSEPH; Northstar HS; Hollsopple, PA; (2); 23/137; FCA; Bsbl; Im Bsktbl; JV Ftbl; Mgmnt.

FELIX, TRACY JO; Elizabethtown Area HS; Elizabethtown, PA; (4); 19/229; FHA; Chorus; Nwsp Rptr; Powder Puff Ftbl; Hon Roll; NHS; Lncstr Gen Hosp Nrsg Schl; RN.

FELLABAUM, CHRISTOPHER; New Castle HS; New Castle, PA; (3); AFS; VP French Clb; JV Crs Cntry; French Hon Soc; AFS Exchng Stu 87-88; Frnch Clb Vp 86-87; Air Force; Chinese Lang.

FELLENBAUM, GINA; Lancaster Catholic HS; Lancaster, PA; (3); Church Yth Grp; Hosp Aide; JA; Teachers Aide; Nwsp Rptr; Yrbk Rptr; Yrbk Stf; Hon Roll; Acad Awd In Engl II 86; Acad Awd In Clerical Typng 87; Typing Editor & Section Editor For Yrbk 87; PA ST U; Jrnlsm.

FELLER, ALEXA GRAM; Conrad Weiser HS; Reinholds, PA; (3); 40/163; Hosp Aide; JCL; Band; Chorus; Mrchg Band; School Musical; Bowling; Mgr Crs Cntry; Trk; Hon Roll.

FELLIN, BETH; West Hazleton HS; W Hazleton, PA; (2); Church Yth Grp; Scholastic Bowl; Boys Clb Am; SADD; Thesps; School Play; Nwsp Rptr; Yrbk Rptr; Bsktbl; Sftbl; ADVRTSNG.

FELLIN, DANIEL; Bishop Hatey HS; Weston, PA; (3); 1/117; Scholastic Bowl; School Musical; School Play; Ed Lit Mag; VP Jr Cls; JV Bsbl; Math Tm; Model UN; Speech Tm; Thesps; Natl Qualf Cathlc Fornsc Leag 87; 2nd Pl Kings Coll Frnch Cntst 84-85; Lib Arts.

FELLON, JASON D; Shikellamy HS; Northumberland, PA; (3); Am Leg Boys St; Boy Scts; German Clb; Red Cross Aide; Trs Stu Cncl; Hon Roll; PA ST; Ag Engrng.

FELTENBERGER, HOLLY; Franklin JR SR HS; Polk, PA; (2); Hosp Aide; Y-Teens; Chorus; Off Frsh Cls; Off Soph Cls; Var Cheerleading; High Hon Roll; Hon Roll; Schl Dir Awd 86-87; Obstrcl Nrs.

FELTENBERGER, JOSEPH; Central York HS; York, PA; (3); Var Trk; Hon Roll; PA ST York Campus; Elec Engr.

FELTENBERGER, MICHELLE; Franklin HS; Franklin, PA; (4); 6/220; Drill Tm; School Musical; Off Sr Cls; Stu Cncl; Trk; Elks Awd; High Hon Roll; Kiwanis Awd; NHS; Church Yth Grp; Wllms Schlrshp 87-88; Penn ST; Psychlgy.

FELTER, JOHN; Tunkhannock Area HS; Tunkhannock, PA; (4); 7/270; Letterman Clb; Pep Clb; Spanish Clb; Yrbk Sprt Ed; Var Capt Bsktbl; Hon Roll; NHS; Bsktbl Schlrshp To Wichita ST U 86; Wichita ST U; Areontcl Engr.

FELTON, DAVID; Greater Johnstown HS; Johnstown, PA; (4); 2/293; Art Clb; Boy Scts; JA; Math Tm; Scholastic Bowl; Spanish Clb; Nwsp Rptr; Yrbk Rptr; High Hon Roll; NHS; Cls Salutatrn 87; Jrnlsm Awd, PA JR Acad Sci Humnts Sympsm Awd 87; UPJ Coll Pres Schlrshp 87; U Of Pittsburgh Johnstwn; Engr.

FELTON, PAT; Williams Valley JR/Sr HS; Williamstown, PA; (4); 11/104; Chorus; Rep Frsh Cls; Var Ftbl; Var Wrstlng; Mary Margaret Nestor Fndtn Schlrshp 87; Neighbors In Need 87; Lock Haven U; Sprts Med.

FELTOVICH, GREGORY P; Peters Township HS; Mcmurray, PA; (2); Church Yth Grp; Computer Clb; Intnl Clb; Science Clb; Chorus; High Hon Roll; NHS; Cvl Engrng.

FELTY, CHRIS; Pine Grove Area HS; Pine Grove, PA; (3); Boys Clb Am; Band; Concert Band; Mrchg Band; Wrstlng.

FELTY, COLLEEN; Lake Lehman SR HS; Shavertown, PA; (4); 6/155; Sec Church Yth Grp; Cmnty Wkr; Hosp Aide; Teachers Aide; Church Choir; Yrbk Ed-Chief; Tennis; High Hon Roll; Jr NHS; NHS; Outstndng Grl Yr Awd 87; Virtuoso Pianist; PA ST U; Med.

FELTY, ERIC; Schuylkill Haven HS; Auburn, PA; (3); 14/83; Cmnty Wkr; Computer Clb; Yrbk Phtg; Im Wt Lftg; Hon Roll; Air Force Acad; Engrng.

FELTY, PAMELA; Tri-Valley HS; Hegins, PA; (3); FBLA; Girl Scts; Spanish Clb; Band; Concert Band; Yrbk Stf; Bsktbl; Cheerleading; Score Keeper; Columbia U; Psychtry.

FELTZ, LORIANNE; Villa Maria Acad; Erie, PA; (4); 6/126; PAVAS; Q&S; Nwsp Ed-Chief; Yrbk Stf; Off Stu Cncl; Var Sftbl; Var Tennis; High Hon Roll; NHS; SAR Awd; Class Grad Spkr 87; Outstndng Jrnlst Of 1987 1st Pl Ftrs Article 87; Bowling Green ST U; Jrnlsm.

FENDRICK, DANIELLE; Bishop Hafey HS; Drifton, PA; (2); 5/125; FNA; Key Clb; Latin Clb; Ski Clb; Capt JV Cheerleading; Gym; Swmmng; L Trk; High Hon Roll; Pres Schlr; Pres Acad Ftnss Awd 84-85; 3rd Pl Indvdl Chrldng Awd 86; Shlstc All-Amer Schlr Pgm 87; Dentist.

FENDROCK, DIANE; Carbondale Area JR SR HS; Carbondale, PA; (3); 13/120; German Clb; Chorus; Mrchg Band; School Musical; Rep Frsh Cls; Pres Soph Cls; Jr NHS; NHS.

FENG, WU-CHE; State College Area SR HS; State College, PA; (4); Im Bsktbl; JV Crs Cntry; Var Trk; High Hon Roll; Prfct Atten Awd; PA ST U; Engrng.

FENICAL, DAWN; Lower Dauphin HS; Hummelstown, PA; (3); Church Yth Grp; Ski Clb; Chorus; Church Choir; VP Frsh Cls; Rep Soph Cls; Hst Jr Cls; Sec Sr Cls; Stu Cncl.

FENIELLO, STACEY; Cornellsville Area HS; Connellsvl, PA; (3); Art Clb; Chess Clb; Library Aide; Office Aide; Stage Crew; High Hon Roll; Hon Roll; Psych.

FENNELL, SHERRY; Karns City JR SR HS; Chicora, PA; (4); 9/117; Church Yth Grp; FCA; SADD; Chorus; Yrbk Stf; Capt Var Bsktbl; Capt Var Vllybl; High Hon Roll; NHS; Ntl Merit Ltr; Beck Schlrshp 87; W Penn Schl Nrsng; Nrsng.

FENNESSEY, JULIA; Peters Township HS; Mcmurray, PA; (3); Ski Clb; SADD; Yrbk Stf; Ed Lit Mag; Jrnlsm.

FENNIE, CRAIG J; Archbishop Ryan For Boys; Philadelphia, PA; (2); 22/376; Ice Hcky; Cit Awd; High Hon Roll; Hon Roll; Prfct Atten Awd; Principals Awd 85-86 & 86-87; Princeton; Engineering.

FENNINGER, ANNETTE; Lancaster Christian Schl; Parkesburg, PA; (4); Drama Clb; Chorus; Yrbk Phtg; Yrbk Stf; Pres Jr Cls; Var Stat Bsktbl; Var Sftbl; Hon Roll; Lancaster Schl Of Cosmetolgy.

FENTON, CAROL; Said Eagle Nittany HS; Mill Hall, PA; (4); 3/120; French Clb; Hosp Aide; Band; Pres Sr Cls; Var Co-Capt Bsktbl; Hon Roll; NHS; Model UN; Nwsp Rptr; VP Soph Cls; Hosp Axlry Awd 87; Jf & Susan Smth Awd 87; U Scrntn; Physcl Thrpy.

FENTON, TRACI; Elizabeth Forward SR HS; Elizabeth, PA; (3); Library Aide; Ski Clb; Pep Band; Nwsp Stf; Capt Cheerleading; Var Swmmng; High Hon Roll; NHS; Schlstc Achvmnt Awd-Midpark HS 85.

FENWICK, JAMES; Tunkhannock Area HS; Mehoopany, PA; (3); 6/330; Boy Scts; Key Clb; JV Var Bsktbl; Hon Roll; NHS; Rotary Ldrshp Cmp 86; Acad All Amercn 86; Husky Bsktbl Camp 86; Aeronautical Engrng.

FEOLA, KRIS; Pocono Mountain HS; Tannersville, PA; (2); Church Yth Grp; Ski Clb; Band; Concert Band; Mrchg Band; Pep Band; JV Sftbl.

FEOLA, RITA; Jeannette SR HS; Jeannette, PA; (3); Office Aide; Ski Clb; Spanish Clb; Band; Jazz Band; Mrchg Band; L Var Sftbl; Capt L Tennis; Hon Roll; JC Awd; U Pittsburgh; Hlth Sci.

FERA, RENEE; John S Fine SR HS; Plymouth, PA; (2); 2/226; Church Yth Grp; Library Aide; Band; Concert Band; Mrchg Band; Yrbk Stf; Swmmng; High Hon Roll; NHS.

FERDARKO, KATHRYN; Valley HS; Arnold, PA; (3); 48/255; AFS; VP Church Yth Grp; Spanish Clb; Band; Concert Band; Mrchg Band; Stage Crew; High Hon Roll; Hon Roll.

FERENCE, BARB; Bishop Mc Cort HS; Johnstown, PA; (3); French Clb; Latin Clb; Pep Clb; Yrbk Stf; High Hon Roll; NHS; Pdtrcs.

FERENCE, JOHN; Kennedy Christian HS; Sharon, PA; (3); 2/97; Drama Clb; Library Aide; VP Spanish Clb; School Play; Nwsp Stf; Yrbk Stf; JV Golf; Im Mgr Vllybl; High Hon Roll; Rotary Awd.

FERENCE, MARY JEAN; Greensburg Central Catholic HS; Greensburg, PA; (3); 4/225; Sec AFS; Church Yth Grp; Cmnty Wkr; Exploring; Hosp Aide; Varsity Clb; Crs Cntry; Trk; High Hon Roll; NHS; St Vincent Chllng Prog Schlrshp 86; Amer Fld Svc Sec 87-88; Pre Med.

FERENCE, RON; Beaver Area SR HS; Beaver, PA; (2); Boy Scts; German Clb; JCL; Latin Clb; SADD; Chorus; Nwsp Rptr; Golf; High Hon Roll; Hon Roll; Schlstc Achvt Awd 87; Pediatrics.

FERENCUHA, LISA A; Connellsville Area SR HS; S Connellsville, PA; (3); 7/525; Church Yth Grp; GAA; Office Aide; Symp Band; Var L Bsktbl; JV Var Vllybl; French Hon Soc; High Hon Roll; NHS; FCCA All Cnty Bsktbl Tm 87; IN U; Rsprtry Thrpst.

FERGERSON, ANGELA; Hickory HS; Sharpsville, PA; (3); 36/167; Camera Clb; Library Aide; Service Clb; Band; Concert Band; Mrchg Band; Pep Band; Swmmng; Stat Trk; 4th Pl Still Life Photo PA Indus Arts Fair 85; Govt.

FERGUSON III, ALEXANDER J; Ringgold HS; Monongahela, PA; (3); Church Yth Grp; Computer Clb; Math Clb; Pep Clb; Political Wkr; Science Clb; Ski Clb; Trs Soph Cls; Trs Jr Cls; Stu Cncl; Engr.

FERGUSON, ANITA; Everett Christian Acad; New Paris, PA; (4); 2/8; Church Yth Grp; Band; Chorus; Church Choir; Concert Band; School Musical; Yrbk Stf; Stu Cncl; Bsktbl; Vllybl; Lee Coll; Bus.

FERGUSON, BETH; Brownsville Area HS; Brownsville, PA; (3); Drama Clb; FBLA; Office Aide; Ski Clb; SADD; Chorus; Nwsp Rptr; Nwsp Stf; Cheerleading; High Hon Roll; St Vincents; Acctg.

FERGUSON, CASSANDRA; Pocono Mountain HS; E Stroudsburg, PA; (4); AFS; JA; Pep Clb; SADD; Chorus; Madrigals; School Musical; Yrbk Stf; Rep Frsh Cls; Sec Soph Cls; E Stroudsburg U; Chem.

FERGUSON, HEIDI; E L Meyers HS; W B, PA; (3); Key Clb; Ski Clb; Chorus; Concert Band; Mrchg Band; Orch; JV Var Bsktbl; Var L Sftbl; Jr NHS; NHS; Elec Engr.

FERGUSON, JAN; Blairsville SR HS; Blairsville, PA; (1); Art Clb; Church Yth Grp; French Clb; School Musical; Pres Frsh Cls; Stu Cncl; High Hon Roll; Hon Roll.

FERGUSON, JARED; Tunkhannock Area HS; Tunkhannock, PA; (2); Church Yth Grp; French Clb; Chorus; JV Var Bsktbl; Var JV Ftbl; JV Trk; High Hon Roll; Hon Roll; Wt Lftg; FCA; Dist Chorus 87; JR Historians Club 85-86; Law.

FERGUSON, JILL; Richland HS; Gibsonia, PA; (3); 19/186; AFS; Off Church Yth Grp; French Clb; Chorus; School Play; Nwsp Stf; Yrbk Ed-Chief; Rep Soph Cls; Rep Jr Cls; Stat Bsktbl; Music.

FERGUSON, JOSEPH; Dunmore HS; Dunmore, PA; (3); Boys Clb Am; French Clb; Letterman Clb; Var Bsbl; Var Bsktbl; Var Golf; Hon Roll; Jr NHS; U Of Scranton; Accntng.

FERGUSON, KEN; Mc Guffey HS; Claysville, PA; (3); 7/240; Am Leg Boys St; Ski Clb; Spanish Clb; Variety Show; Crs Cntry; Golf; Tennis; Trk; High Hon Roll; NHS; Stu Rcgntn Awd 85-87.

FERGUSON, MICHELLE; Corry Area JR-SR HS; Columbus, PA; (4); 22/196; Church Yth Grp; French Clb; SADD; Band; Concert Band; Jazz Band; Mrchg Band; Betty White Schlrshp 87; U Of Pittsburgh; Crmnlgy.

FERGUSON, REBECCA; Abington SR HS; Abington, PA; (3); 103/527; Intnl Clb; Varsity Clb; Var Fld Hcky; Var Lcrss.

FERGUSON JR, ROBERT D; Upper Darby HS; Drexel Hill, PA; (3); 15/598; German Clb; Band; Concert Band; Jazz Band; Mrchg Band; School Musical; Im Bsktbl; Var Tennis; High Hon Roll.

FERGUSON, RON; Du Bois Area HS; Dubois, PA; (3); 48/280; Church Yth Grp; Cmnty Wkr; Computer Clb; Red Cross Aide; SADD; Chorus; Church Choir; Golf; Mgr(s); Hon Roll; Penn ST U; Accntng.

FERGUSON, SANDI; West Branch Area HS; Grassflat, PA; (3); DECA; Varsity Clb; VICA; Band; Color Guard; Concert Band; Mrchg Band; Bsktbl; Sftbl; Vllybl; PA ST U; Police Ofcr.

FERGUSON, TAMMIE; Bethel Park SR HS; Bethel Park, PA; (4); 100/519; Bsktbl; Socr; Hon Roll; Cheerleading; Powder Puff Ftbl; Sftbl; Trk; Armys Mst Vlbl Plyr Sccr 86-87; YMCA Pttsbrgh 13th Annl All Sprts Bnqt 87; Wstrn PA Coachs 85&86; Mercyhurst Coll; Elem Educ.

FERGUSON, TOM; Indiana Area SR HS; Indiana, PA; (3); 1/320; Boy Scts; Chess Clb; Exploring; JV Crs Cntry; JV Tennis; JV Trk; High Hon Roll; Prfct Atten Awd.

FERKO, BARB; North East HS; North East, PA; (3); AFS; Band; Concert Band; Mrchg Band; High Hon Roll; Prfct Atten Awd; Latin Exam Awd 86-87; Gammon U; Marine Bio.

FERKO, ED; Phoenixville Area HS; Phoenixville, PA; (3); Spanish Clb; Varsity Clb; Rep Stu Cncl; Var L Bsbl; Var L Bsktbl; Vllybl; NHS; All Leag Bsbl Ptchr-Pioneer Athl Conf 87; Pre Law.

FERKO, JON GARY; Hempfield HS; Holtwood, PA; (3); CAP; Exploring; Science Clb; Chorus; Orch; School Musical; Im Bsbl; Im Bsktbl; Coach Actv; JV Ftbl; Aerontcl Engrng.

FERKO, THOMAS; Shade-Central City HS; Central City, PA; (3); 1/75; Exploring; Ski Clb; Spanish Clb; Band; Pres Frsh Cls; Trk; NHS; Juniata Coll; Chmstry.

FERLITO, BECKY; Clearfield Area HS; Clearfield, PA; (4); 6/292; Trs Church Yth Grp; Pres French Clb; Ski Clb; Concert Band; Mrchg Band; Orch; Yrbk Ed-Chief; Stu Cncl; NHS; Penn St U; Bus Admin.

FERNANDES, DAVID; Archbishop Kennedy HS; Philadelphia, PA; (4); 4/170; Aud/Vis; Church Yth Grp; Library Aide; Service Clb; Nwsp Rptr; Rep Sr Cls; Trk; High Hon Roll; NHS; Prfct Atten Awd; St Joseph U; Bus Mngmnt.

FERNANDEZ, ANTHONY; St Joseph Prep; Philadelphia, PA; (4); 45/240; Spanish Clb; Im Bsktbl; Im Ftbl; JV Wrstlng; Hon Roll; NHS; Ntl Merit SF; Natl Hspnc Awds Prog SF 87; Bus.

FERNANDEZ, DANA; Shenango HS; New Castle, PA; (2); Church Yth Grp; French Clb; School Play; Pres Frsh Cls; Var JV Cheerleading; Hon Roll; Prfct Atten Awd.

FERNANDEZ, GINA; Mahanoy Area HS; Mahanoy City, PA; (3); Church Yth Grp; Drama Clb; FHA; Spanish Clb; Y-Teens; Flag Corp; Variety Show; Nwsp Stf; Yrbk Stf; Trk; Cert For Peer Cnslng Ed 85; Elem Ed.

FERNANDEZ, MELISSA; Pennsbury HS; Yardley, PA; (4); 93/771; Spanish Clb; Teachers Aide; Chorus; School Play; Var Swmmng; Hon Roll; NHS; Appalachian ST U.

FERNANDEZ, MICHAEL; Loyalstock Township HS; Montoursville, PA; (3); 22/130; Trs Church Yth Grp; French Clb; Key Clb; Ntl Merit SF; Librl Arts.

FERNANDEZ, SELENA; Nazareth Acad; Philadelphia, PA; (3); Church Yth Grp; Cmnty Wkr; Spanish Clb; VP Jr Cls; PA ST U; Int Dcrtng.

FERNANDEZ, TODD R; Methacton HS; Audubon, PA; (4); 1/361; Boy Scts; Debate Tm; Math Tm; Band; Chorus; Orch; Var Socr; Var Tennis; Bausch & Lomb Sci Awd; Ntl Merit SF; Physics.

FERNSLER, MATTHEW; Lancaster Country Day Schl; Quentin, PA; (2); Camera Clb; Chess Clb; Church Yth Grp; Math Clb; School Play; Hon Roll; Ford Fndtn Schlrshp 85; Acutary.

FERRA, CHUCK; Du Bois Area HS; Reynoldsvle, PA; (3); Varsity Clb; Var L Ftbl; Var L Trk; Var L Wrstlng; Hon Roll; Nice Kid Awd 85; Cmnctns.

FERRACO, MICHAEL; Hampton HS; Allison Park, PA; (3); JV Bsbl; JV Ice Hcky; Var JV Trk; High Hon Roll; NHS.

FERRARA, BRAD; Ringgold HS; Donora, PA; (3); 11/374; Math Clb; Science Clb; Varsity Clb; L Var Crs Cntry; Capt L Trk; High Hon Roll; NHS; Bio Olympics 86; Villanova; Med.

FERRARA, JENNIFER; Cumberland Valley HS; Mechanicsburg, PA; (3); 68/590; German Clb; Quiz Bowl; Speech Tm; Capt Flag Corp; School Play; Nwsp Stf; Opt Clb Awd; Schltc Wrtng Gold Keys Natl Hnrs 87; PA ST Spch Tournmnt 86; Exec Women Intl Schlrshp 87.

FERRARA, STEFANIE; Ne Castle HS; New Castle, PA; (2); Boy Scts; Church Yth Grp; Exploring; French Clb; Color Guard; Yrbk Stf; Stu Cncl; Trk; Hon Roll; Pitt; Phys Thrpst.

FERRARI, MAUREEN; Our Lady Of Lourdes Regional HS; Shamokin, PA; (4); 20/100; Church Yth Grp; Pep Clb; Spanish Clb; SADD; School Play; Nwsp Rptr; Yrbk Ed-Chief; Yrbk Stf; JV Cheerleading; Coach Actv; Hi Time Pblshng Corp Natl Prayer Comptn Hon Men Pblshd 87.

FERRARI, SONDRA; Danville HS; Riverside, PA; (3); Hst Key Clb; School Musical; School Play; Stage Crew; Nwsp Bus Mgr; Nwsp Phtg; Nwsp Rptr; Yrbk Bus Mgr; Yrbk Phtg; Mat Maids; Art Thrpy.

FERRARI, TONY; Connellsville Area JR HS; Champion, PA; (3); 53/530; Boy Scts; Chess Clb; Var Ftbl; Var Tennis; Wt Lftg; NHS; Comm.

FERRARINI, MELISSA; Hempfield SR HS; Greensburg, PA; (3); Church Yth Grp; Dance Clb; Pep Clb; Spanish Clb; Hon Roll; Jr NHS; NHS; Prfct Atten Awd; U Of PA Indiana; Nrsng.

FERRARO, KIM; Pittston Area SR HS; Hughestown, PA; (4); Pres Art Clb; Pres Aud/Vis; Drama Clb; French Clb; Office Aide; School Play; Yrbk Stf; Lit Mag; High Hon Roll; Semi-Fnlst Gov Schl Of Arts 85; Gold Key Awd-Schltc Art Awds 87; Hnrb Mntn-Schltc Art Awds 85-87; Parsons Schl Of Design; Fshn.

FERRARO, LOREDANA; Saint Huberts HS; Philadelphia, PA; (3); Computer Clb; Math Clb; Var Bsktbl; Var Sftbl; Prfct Atten Awd; Office Aide; Teachers Aide; Stage Crew; Temple U; Comp Tech.

FERRARO, MATTHEW; Nazareth Area SR HS; Nazareth, PA; (3); 23/265; Am Leg Boys St; Art Clb; Letterman Clb; Ski Clb; Yrbk Stf; L Ftbl; Im Wt Lftg; Hon Roll; Boys ST Cnslr 87; Pol Sci.

FERRARO, TRACY; Penn Hills SR HS; Pittsburgh, PA; (4); 102/690; JA; Teachers Aide; Stu Cncl; Gym; High Hon Roll; Secy Yr 87; Lamp Knwldg Awds,Awd Merit,Cert Profcncy 87; Pitt U; Bus.

FERREE, BRIAN L; Red Lion Area SR HS; Windsor, PA; (3); Church Yth Grp; Varsity Clb; Var Capt Socr; Hon Roll; US Air Force Acad; Pilot.

FERREE, CHRISTOPHER; Geibel HS; Uniontown, PA; (4); 21/85; Drama Clb; French Clb; School Musical; School Play; Yrbk Stf; Lit Mag; French Hon Soc; Hon Roll; Drama Awd 87; Lit Awd 87; 2nd Pl Frnch Oral Rctatn Hmnts Day Cmp 87; Otterbein Coll; Actr.

FERREE, JESSICA; Spring Grove SR HS; Spring Grove, PA; (4); 52/273; Church Yth Grp; French Clb; German Clb; Varsity Clb; Nwsp Rptr; Sec Soph Cls; Sec Jr Cls; Rep Stu Cncl; Var Capt Cheerleading; High Hon Roll; Antonelli Insti; Fshn.

FERREE, STEPHEN; South Western HS; Hanover, PA; (3); 7/225; Church Yth Grp; Computer Clb; Varsity Clb; L Var Bsktbl; L Var Ftbl; High Hon Roll; NHS; Engr.

FERRELL, CHRISTY; Lampeter Strasburg HS; Strasburg, PA; (4); 7/144; Pres Church Yth Grp; Pres VP JA; Band; Chorus; School Musical; School Play; Yrbk Bus Mgr; L Var Crs Cntry; L Var Trk; NHS; 3rd Natl JR Achvt VP Prsnnl 85-86; Sci Fair Awds 85-87; Grl Mnth May 87; US Air Force Acad; Bhvrl Sci.

FERRELL, FRANK; Devon Prep; Gladwyne, PA; (3); 2/40; Chess Clb; Church Yth Grp; Cmnty Wkr; Math Tm; JV Crs Cntry; High Hon Roll; NHS; Ntl Merit Ltr; Almni Awd Frm Benchmark 84; AP European Hstry Awd 86; AP Amer Hstry Awd 87.

FERRELL, JAMES; New Castle SR HS; New Castle, PA; (4); 23/232; Computer Clb; Var Ftbl; Wt Lftg; NHS; U Of Pittsburgh; Ind Engrng.

FERRENBERG, JAMES; Huntingdon Area HS; Huntington, PA; (3); 39/221; Hon Roll; US Air Force; Aviation.

FERRENCE, CHRIS; Blue Mountain HS; Summit Station, PA; (2); 15/230; School Play; Rep Stu Cncl; Var Wrstlng; Hon Roll; NEDT Awd; Hugh O Brian Yth 86; Bus.

FERRENCE, JENNIFER; Cambria Heights HS; St Benedict, PA; (3); 51/182; VP Church Yth Grp; Band; Chorus; Church Choir; Concert Band; Mrchg Band; Trk; Hon Roll.

FERRENCE, KRISTA; West York Area SR HS; York, PA; (3); 1/197; Sec Church Yth Grp; Rep Stu Cncl; Co-Capt Cheerleading; High Hon Roll; NHS; Ntl Merit Ltr; Asst Dir Of St Judes Superdance 87; Wnnr VFW We The People Spch Cntst 87; Dickinson; Law.

FERRETTI, MICHELLE; Leechburg Area HS; Leechburg, PA; (2); 20/87; Band; Chorus; Concert Band; Drm Mjr(t); Mrchg Band; Trs Soph Cls; Rep Stu Cncl; Var Capt Twrlr; Hon Roll; Penn St U; Cnslr Jvnl Dlnqnts.

FERRINGER, ELIZABETH; Keystone HS; Knox, PA; (3); FBLA; Pep Clb; Spanish Clb; SADD; Chorus; Nwsp Bus Mgr; Nwsp Rptr; Nwsp Stf; Rep Stu Cncl; JV Var Cheerleading; U Of Pittsburgh; Nrsng.

FERRINGER, TINA; Marion Center Area HS; Home, PA; (4); 8/169; Church Yth Grp; Pres FBLA; Office Aide; SADD; Varsity Clb; Cheerleading; High Hon Roll; Jr NHS; NHS; IN U Of PA; Ofc Adm.

FERRIS, LOUIS; Notre Dame HS; Easton, PA; (3); 18/90; Math Tm; Quiz Bowl; Varsity Clb; Bsbl; Wrstlng; High Hon Roll; Hon Roll; Most Improved Wrstlr 87; Acad Bowl Math 84; Pre-Med.

FERRO, DANIELLE; Berwick HS; Berwick, PA; (4); 12/202; Math Tm; Science Clb; Swmmng; High Hon Roll; Hon Roll; NHS; Ntl Merit SF; Pres Schlr; Bowman Ashe Scholar 87; U Miami; Finance.

FERROZZUTTI, AMY; Aliquippa HS; Aliquippa, PA; (3); 9/150; Pep Clb; Hon Roll.

FERRY, AMY; Bishop Conwell HS; Yardley, PA; (3); 131/277; Dance Clb; Chorus; Hon Roll; Prfct Atten Awd; Bucks County CC; Intl Rltns.

FERRY, CECELIA; Eisenhower HS; Russell, PA; (3); Church Yth Grp; German Clb; Key Clb; Pep Clb; Band; Church Choir; Drm & Bgl; Jazz Band; Mrchg Band; Orch; Hnr Bands & Orchestra 87; Edinboro U; Elem Educ.

FERRY, JOSEPH E; Norristown Area HS; Norristown, PA; (3); 50/522; FBLA; Key Clb; Yrbk Stf; Hon Roll; Tops An A In Bus Clss; Bus.

FERRY, MIKE; Warren Area HS; Warren, PA; (4); Scholastic Bowl; Varsity Clb; Var L Crs Cntry; JV Ftbl; Var Capt Trk; JV Wrstlng; Bausch & Lomb Sci Awd; High Hon Roll; Jr NHS; NHS; Allegheny Coll; Pre Med.

FERTAL, SCOTT; Hanover Area HS; Wilkes Barre, PA; (3); French Clb; Letterman Clb; Varsity Clb; Stu Cncl; L Var Bsbl; Im Var Bsktbl; Var VP Ftbl; Im Var Powder Puff Ftbl; Var Wt Lftg; Hon Roll; Dfnsv Plyr Gm 85-86; Coll Rcrtng Pmphlt 87; Shippensburg; Soc Svcs.

FESENMYER, SUSAN; Rocky Grove HS; Oil City, PA; (3); Dance Clb; Girl Scts; Chorus; Drm Mjr(t); Off Jr Cls; Bsktbl; Cheerleading; Crs Cntry; Hon Roll; Clarion; Bus Advrtsng.

FESSENDEN, WENDY; Athens HS; Sayre, PA; (3); Church Yth Grp; Teachers Aide; Band; Church Choir; Concert Band; Mrchg Band; Rep Frsh Cls; Bsktbl; Trk; Vllybl; USAF; Admin.

FESSLER JR, GARY LEE; Schuylkill Haven Area HS; Schuylkill Haven, PA; (3); 8/82; FCA; German Clb; Science Clb; SADD; Varsity Clb; VP Sr Cls; JV Var Ftbl; Wrstlng; Hon Roll; NHS; Honor Guard 87; Mech Engr.

FETCENKO, SUSAN MICHELLE; West Branch Area HS; Hawk Run, PA; (2); Church Yth Grp; SADD; Band; Chorus; Concert Band; Mrchg Band; Pep Band; School Musical; Rep Stu Cncl; Hon Roll; Bus.

FETCH, KRISTIN; Penn Trafford HS; Trafford, PA; (3); 42/296; AFS; Church Yth Grp; Exploring; JCL; Latin Clb; Chorus; Var Trk; High Hon Roll; Hon Roll; NHS.

FETCH, MICHELLE; Central SR HS; York, PA; (3); #20 In Class; Drama Clb; PAVAS; Stage Crew; High Hon Roll; Hon Roll; NHS; Opt Clb Awd; Music Compstn Awd 1st Pl Dist Lvl 86; Med Fld.

FETCH, TANYA; Wyoming Area SR HS; Harding, PA; (3); Aud/Vis; Drama Clb; Key Clb; Chorus; Stu Cncl; Var Civic Clb; Var Vllybl; Engl.

FETCHEN, KIMBERLY; Elizabeth Forward HS; Elizabeth, PA; (4); Church Yth Grp; Spanish Clb; Var Capt Socr; Hon Roll; NHS; Pres Schlr; WPIAL Coachs All Str Tm 86; Pres Ftnss Awd 84; Penn ST; Accntng.

FETCHKO, MATTHEW; Bishop Hafey HS; Hazleton, PA; (3); Art Clb; Church Yth Grp; Science Clb; Spanish Clb; Ed Yrbk Stf; Lit Mag; High Hon Roll; NHS; Ntl Merit Schol; PA JR Acad Of Sci-Excellence Awd 86; Art.

FETCKO, JODI; Caron-Mc Millan SR HS; Strabane, PA; (4); FBLA; VP JA; Office Aide; Band; Concert Band; Flag Corp; Nwsp Rptr; High Hon Roll; FBLA Rgnl 1st Pl Wnnr 4th Pl ST Stenogrphr II 87; Bradford Schl Of Bus; Exec Sec.

FETCKO, SHAWN; Canon Mc Millan SR HS; Strabane, PA; (3); 78/367; Varsity Clb; Nwsp Rptr; Var L Swmmng; Hon Roll; Prfct Atten Awd.

FETOCK, MARIA; Brownsville HS; Grindstone, PA; (4); 11/200; Drama Clb; Math Tm; Band; Mrchg Band; Nwsp Ed-Chief; Yrbk Stf; Vllybl; High Hon Roll; NHS.

FETSCO, RON; Carmichaels Area HS; Carmichaels, PA; (3); 16/113; Art Clb; Spanish Clb; Band; Mrchg Band; DAR Awd; High Hon Roll; Hon Roll; WVU; Radlgy.

FETSICK, LISA; Churchill HS; Pittsburgh, PA; (2); 12/222; French Clb; Leo Clb; Science Clb; Teachers Aide; Band; Concert Band; Jazz Band; Pep Band; Stage Crew; High Hon Roll; Rifle, Vrsty Ltr 85-87; Mrkmnshp; Maryland ST; Marine Bio.

FETSKO, CHRISTINE; Portage Area HS; Portage, PA; (4); Varsity Clb; Chorus; Variety Show; Stu Cncl; Capt Cheerleading; Hon Roll; Spcl Olympcs Hugger 84-87; IN U Of PA; Respiratry Thrpy.

FETTER, COLBY; Biglerville HS; Gettysburg, PA; (3); 20/110; Computer Clb; Nwsp Rptr; Comp Tech.

FETTER, VALERIE; Danville Area HS; Danville, PA; (3); 117/187; Exploring; French Clb; Latin Clb; Yrbk Phtg; Yrbk Stf; Psych.

FETTERHOFF, PAM; Upper Dauphin Area HS; Elizabethville, PA; (3); 7/115; Rep Church Yth Grp; Var Bsktbl; Stat Ftbl; Var L Sftbl; Hon Roll; NHS; Teachers Aide; Varsity Clb; Band; Stu Cncl Art Awd 86; 2nd Edtn Young Cmmnty Ldrs Amer 86-87; Bus Admin.

FETTERMAN, MISSEY; Punxsutawney HS; Punxsutawney, PA; (4); Cmnty Wkr; Debate Tm; French Clb; Hosp Aide; Radio Clb; Science Clb; Sec Speech Tm; Wt Lftg; Hon Roll; Frgn Exchng Stu Chle 86-87; IN U Of PA; Trnsltns.

FETTEROLF, JODI; Juniata HS; Mifflintown, PA; (4); Varsity Clb; Jazz Band; School Musical; School Play; Yrbk Ed-Chief; Trs Jr Cls; Var Capt Cheerleading; Var Fld Hcky; Var Tennis; NHS; PA ST U.

FETTEROLF, PAULA; Northwestern HS; Albion, PA; (2); 12/161; Flag Corp; Yrbk Stf; Rep Soph Cls; Stat Bsktbl; Var Trk; JV Vllybl; High Hon Roll; Hon Roll; Pres Physcl Ftns Awd 86; Edinboro U; Bus Mgmt.

FETTERS, JILL; Downingtown SR HS; Downingtown, PA; (4); 33/551; French Clb; GAA; Capt Color Guard; Sec Stu Cncl; JV Lcrss; Capt Twrlr; Cit Awd; DAR Awd; High Hon Roll; Sec NHS; Outstndg Amer Stu 86-87; Chester Cnty Jr Miss 2nd Rnnrr Up 86-87; Rotary Stu 86; Bus Admin.

FETTIS, RENEE; Baldwin HS; Pittsburgh, PA; (4); 52/535; Math Clb; Band; Concert Band; Jazz Band; Mrchg Band; Orch; School Musical; High Hon Roll; NHS.

FETZER, MICHELLE; Jersey Shore HS; Avis, PA; (3); Library Aide; Flag Corp; Hon Roll; Cosmetology.

FEUDALE, WM; Shamokin Area HS; Shamokin, PA; (3); 20/100; Aud/Vis; Rep Jr Cls; Bsktbl; Ftbl; Hon Roll; Corporate Lawyr.

FEY, ELIZABETH; Upper Darby HS; Drexel Hill, PA; (3); 19/681; Cmnty Wkr; VP Drama Clb; German Clb; Acpl Chr; Chorus; School Musical; School Play; Ed Nwsp Stf; Var Tennis; NHS; Wellesley Coll Bk Awd, CSC Ldrshp Awd 87.

FIALKOV, JONATHAN; Central Catholic HS; Monroeville, PA; (3); Computer Clb; Science Clb; High Hon Roll; Hon Roll; Pre-Law.

FIBBI, KENNETH; Monongahela Vly Catholic HS; Monongahela, PA; (2); 2/80; Band; Yrbk Phtg; Bsktbl; French Hon Soc; High Hon Roll.

FICAROTTA, TRACY; Morrisville HS; Morrisville, PA; (3); 7/92; GAA; Chorus; School Musical; VP Jr Cls; Capt JV Cheerleading; Capt JV Sftbl; Hon Roll; Jr NHS; NHS; Merit Awd Acdmc Engl, Spnsh I & Ii Outstndng Achvt; Fnlst Stu Rep Schl Brd.

FICCA, ROSE; Our Lady Of Lourdes HS; Atlas, PA; (3); 23/89; Library Aide; Spanish Clb; Yrbk Stf; Hon Roll; Sci.

FICHTNER, MICHELE; Solaneo HS; Quarryville, PA; (4); 21/243; Trs Acpl Chr; Trs Band; School Musical; Yrbk Ed-Chief; Stu Cncl; Sec NHS; Pres Schlr; Church Yth Grp; Computer Clb; Trs Girl Scts; SR Awd, Area Repblcns Schlrshp 87; Cnty Chorus 86 & 87; Elizabethtown Coll; Early Chld.

FICKE, ALANA; Lower Moreland HS; Huntingdon Valley, PA; (4); 29/201; Church Yth Grp; Drama Clb; German Clb; Office Aide; Acpl Chr; Band; Chorus; Concert Band; Jazz Band; Mrchg Band; Muhlenberg Coll; Pre Med.

FICKES, TEDENA; Chambersburg Area SR HS; Fayetteville, PA; (3); Office Aide; Spanish Clb; Chorus; Off Soph Cls; Off Jr Cls.

FICKINGER, KELLY; Canon Mc Millan HS; Eighty Four, PA; (4); 18/357; French Clb; Ski Clb; Sec Band; Cheerleading; Crs Cntry; Sftbl; Tennis; High Hon Roll; NHS; PA ST U; Bus Admin.

FICKINGER, MATTHEW; Williams Valley HS; Williamstown, PA; (2); Art Clb; Ski Clb; Spanish Clb; JV Bsbl; Im Bsktbl; High Hon Roll; Hon Roll; PA ST; Biol.

FIDLER, MATT; Milton SR HS; Milton, PA; (2); 20/250; Church Yth Grp; Dance Clb; French Clb; Key Clb; Ski Clb; Im Bsbl; Im Bsktbl; Im Vllybl; Hon Roll; Pres Schlr; Bloomsburg; Psychlgy.

FIDLER, STACY; Cumberland Valley HS; Camp Hill, PA; (4); 35/519; Red Cross Aide; Ski Clb; School Musical; JV Var Mgr(s); Im Vllybl; French Hon Soc; Hon Roll; NHS; James Madison U; Biol Sci.

FIDLER, STEVEN; Center Twp HS; Aliquippa, PA; (3); Spanish Clb; Chorus; Wt Lftg; Hon Roll; Natl Hnr Rl Soc 87; Actuary.

FIDYK JR, JOHN; Hanover Area JR SR HS; Wilkes-Barre, PA; (4); 30/157; Hon Roll; Jr NHS; Wilkes Coll; Comp Sci.

FIELD, COLLEEN; Western Wayne HS; Lake Ariel, PA; (2); FBLA; Spanish Clb; School Play; Fshn Dsgn.

FIELDING, TINA; Seneca HS; Wattsburg, PA; (3); 2/150; Pres Church Yth Grp; Chorus; Concert Band; Mrchg Band; Orch; High Hon Roll; NHS; Amelia Earhart Awd 86-87; Peer Jury 86-87; Pre-Law.

FIELDS, REX; Mc Connellsburg HS; Mcconnellsburg, PA; (4); 6/66; Church Yth Grp; Civic Clb; Science Clb; School Musical; School Play; Yrbk Rptr; Badmtn; Bsbl; Bsktbl; Socr; Millersville U Of PA; Med.

FIELDS, SHARON DENISE; Frankford HS; Philadelphia, PA; (3); 100/625; Church Yth Grp; Cmnty Wkr; Drama Clb; Library Aide; Teachers Aide; Church Choir; Nwsp Stf; NHS; Gamam Phi Delta Sorority Eastern Rgnl Schlrshp 87; Templ U; Comp Accntng.

FIENMAN, LISA; Marple-Newtown HS; Broomall, PA; (3); Dance Clb; Drama Clb; Pep Clb; Service Clb; SADD; Temple Yth Grp; School Play; Variety Show; Stu Cncl; Var JV Cheerleading.

FIENMAN, MARC; Marple Newtown HS; Broomall, PA; (3); 8/325; Model UN; Trs Service Clb; SADD; Temple Yth Grp; Off Stu Cncl; JV Tennis; Hon Roll; Ntl Hstry Day Grp Prjct Entry 1st Pl 85; 1st Pl Phldlphia Rgn Two Tls 2nd Pl State Ntls 97% No Place; Hstry.

FIERER, SARA A; Harrisburg Acad; Harrisburg, PA; (4); 3/30; Debate Tm; Orch; Yrbk Stf; Var Bsktbl; Var Crs Cntry; Var Fld Hcky; High Hon Roll; Ntl Merit Ltr; Pres Schlr; State Orchestra 85-86; Latin Awd 87; 2nd Pl Young Soloist-Harrisburg Symphony 86; Oberlin Coll; Cello.

FIERRO, MARIA; West Hazleton HS; Hazleton, PA; (2); #26 In Class; Pep Clb; Spanish Clb; Chorus; Sftbl; High Hon Roll; Penn ST U; Dntl Asst.

FIESTA, MELISSA; Moravian Acad; Macungie, PA; (4); 1/67; Hosp Aide; Yrbk Sprt Ed; Stu Cncl; Var Tennis; High Hon Roll; John Amos Comenius Awd Hgst Acadmc Avg 87; Frances H Storrs Awd Undrstndg Gntlnss For Others 87; Wellesley Coll.

FIGUEROA, NELSON; Northeast HS; Philadelphia, PA; (4); 152/600; Drexel Grant 87-88; Drexel U; Electrnc Engrng.

FIGURA, LISA; Jim Thorpe Area HS; Jim Thorpe, PA; (3); 11/93; FHA; Chorus; Nwsp Rptr; Yrbk Stf; Stu Cncl; Bsktbl; Sftbl; Vllybl; High Hon Roll; NHS; Lit.

FIKE, EUGENE; Somerset Area HS; Somerset, PA; (4); Church Yth Grp; English Clb; French Clb; JA; Varsity Clb; Stage Crew; Tennis; Hon Roll; Kiwanis Awd; James Madison U.

FIKE, MICHELLE; Du Bois Area HS; Sykesville, PA; (3); Off Stu Cncl; JV Tennis; Hon Roll; Penn ST.

FILBERN, MATTHEW; Yough SR HS; Ruffs Dale, PA; (3); 6/258; Computer Clb; Math Clb; Ski Clb; Spanish Clb; Jazz Band; Yrbk Rptr; Yrbk Stf; JV Bsbl; NHS; Band; Rotry Intl Affairs Cmte Debate 87; Aeronautical Engrng.

FILBEY, JOHN; Spring Grove SR HS; York, PA; (3); Varsity Clb; High Hon Roll; Hon Roll; NHS; Bsbl; Ftbl; Indstrl Engr.

FILBURN, RENAE; Connellsville Area HS; Connellsville, PA; (2); 11/580; VP Church Yth Grp; Office Aide; Chorus; Flag Corp; Symp Band; Rep Stu Cncl; Var L Vllybl; High Hon Roll; Spanish NHS; Acad Excllnce.

FILBY, DONNA JEAN; Chartiers-Houston HS; Houston, PA; (3); 16/136; Sec Trs Church Yth Grp; Trs Science Clb; Spanish Clb; Sec Concert Band; Sec Mrchg Band; Var L Sftbl; Var Vllybl; High Hon Roll; NHS; PA JR Acad Sci Rgnls 1st 87; PA JR Acadad Sci ST 2nd 87; PA Sci Tlnt Srch JR Awd 87; Chem.

FILBY, SANDRA; Hollidaysburg SR HS; Hollidaysburg, PA; (3); Latin Clb; Letterman Clb; Ski Clb; Varsity Clb; Variety Show; Capt Cheerleading; JV Var Sftbl; Var Swmmng; L Trk; Hon Roll.

FILER, ALAN; Pennsbury HS; Tullytown, PA; (3); Band; Concert Band; Jazz Band; Mrchg Band; Orch; Pep Band; School Musical; PA Gov Schl Perf Arts Schlrshp 86; Cnty Dist Rgnl Bands 86-87; All ST Jazz Band 87; N TX U; Music.

FILER, DARLA; Freeport SR HS; Freeport, PA; (4); FBLA; Band; Chorus; Concert Band; Mrchg Band; Pep Band; Stage Crew; Symp Band; Stat JV Ftbl; Hon Roll; Stu Mnth 85; Chrs Awd 87; Bradford Schl; Mdcl Scrtry.

FILER, KIRSTEN; Penn Trafford HS; Trafford, PA; (3); 12/301; Church Yth Grp; Drama Clb; Hosp Aide; JCL; Band; Chorus; Jazz Band; Orch; High Hon Roll; NHS; All ST Orch 87.

FILING, MICHELE; Oxford Area HS; Nottingham, PA; (3); Girl Scts; Ski Clb; Var Capt Cheerleading; Var Crs Cntry; Var Trk; Hon Roll; MVP Awd Cross Country 87; Bonne Belle Cir Elcllnce 87; Sccl All Star X Country Tm 87; Psych.

FILIPEK, MICHELLE; Abington Heights HS; Clarks Summit, PA; (3); Band; Concert Band; Jazz Band; Mrchg Band; Lit Mag; Ski Clb; Var Sftbl; Cum Laude Lat Awd 84-85; Marywood Hnrs Band 84-85; Band Awd 86-87; Dist Chorus Concert 86-87.

FILIPOWSKI, DAWN; North Catholic HS; Pittsburgh, PA; (3); Art Clb; Church Yth Grp; French Clb; Ski Clb; SADD; Hon Roll; Pep Clb; LIFE Grp 85-87; Prof Nrsng.

FILIPOWSKI, STEPHANIE; Villa Maria Acad; Erie, PA; (4); 22/127; Church Yth Grp; Service Clb; School Play; Variety Show; Trs Frsh Cls; Hon Roll; Trs NHS; Pres Schlr; Egn Schlrshp 87; Prsdntl Schlrshp 87; Tresa Bns Schlrshp 86; Mercyhurst Coll; Htl Manag.

FILIPPINI, SUSAN; James M Coughlin HS; Wilkes-Barre, PA; (3); Key Clb; Math Clb; Band; Concert Band; Jazz Band; Mrchg Band; Orch; Pep Band; Symp Band; Stfl; Luzerne Cnty CC; Srgcl Tech.

FILIPPO, FRANK; Father Judge HS; Philadelphia, PA; (3); 25/404; Im Bsktbl; Var Im Ftbl; Var L Golf; Jr NHS; NHS.

FILLER, TAMMEY; Juniata HS; Mifflintown, PA; (3); FHA; Girl Scts; Nwsp Rptr; Nwsp Stf; Yrbk Stf; Sftbl.

FILLER, WILLIAM; Central HS; Philadelphia, PA; (2); Im Wt Lftg; JV Wrstlng; Hon Roll; Clssfd Mntlly Gftd 86; Sci.

FILLING, JOEL; Quakertown S HS; Quakertown, PA; (3); Am Leg Boys St; German Clb; Bsbl; Ftbl; Hon Roll; Prsdntl Acdmc Fitness Awd; Old Dominion; Naval.

FILLIP, LISA; Ambridge Area HS; South Heights, PA; (3); Church Yth Grp; JA; Pep Clb; Var JV Cheerleading; Hon Roll; Accntnt.

FILLMORE, TRACY L; Dallastown Area HS; Dallastown, PA; (4); Camera Clb; JA; SADD; Var Diving; Mgr(s); Im Sftbl; Mgr Swmmng; Phtgrphy.

FILMAN, CHARISSA; Victory Christian Acad; Reading, PA; (1); Church Yth Grp; Acpl Chr; School Musical; Yrbk Stf; Cheerleading; Vllybl; High Hon Roll.

FILOR, FRANK; Milton Hershey Schl; Cooperstown, NY; (3); Am Leg Boys St; 4-H; Ski Clb; JV Socr; Wrstlng; 4-H Awd; High Hon Roll; Hon Roll; Stu Ldrshp Scty; Accntng.

FINAFROCK, JAYMES; Fairfield HS; Orrtanna, PA; (3); 15/73; Church Yth Grp; Pres FFA; Varsity Clb; Band; Mrchg Band; Swing Chorus; Pres Soph Cls; Pres Jr Cls; L Bsktbl; L Socr; Star Grnhnd FFA 84-85; Star Chptr Frmr FFA 86-87; Ag.

FINAMORE, JOAN; H S Creative & Performing Arts; Philadelphia, PA; (4); 3/130; Band; Orch; Nwsp Rptr; Nwsp Stf; Stu Cncl; High Hon Roll; Hon Roll; NHS; Otstndng Acad Achvt Awd-Temple U 87; Hnrbl Mntn In Edtrl Sec Of Temple U Press Trnmnt 87; Temple U; Jrnlsm.

FINAN, COLIN; Pittston Area HS; Pittston, PA; (3); 78/305; Band; Concert Band; Jazz Band; Mrchg Band; Pep Band; Symp Band; Tennis; Prfct Atten Awd; Sci.

FINARELLI III, AL; Bishop O Reilly HS; Dallas, PA; (2); Church Yth Grp; Bsktbl; Coach Actv; Hon Roll; Ltrd Bsktbl 86-87; Bus.

FINBERG, CRYSTAL; Plum SR HS; Pittsburgh, PA; (3); French Clb; Service Clb; SADD; Mrchg Band; Orch; Nwsp Stf; Yrbk Stf; Stat Bsktbl; Capt Twrlr; Hon Roll; Outstndg Svc Awd 87; St Marys Coll; Corp Law.

FINCH, BRIAN; Overbrook School For The Blind; Philadelphia, PA; (3); 1/7; Cmnty Wkr; Radio Clb; Acpl Chr; Chorus; Variety Show; Lit Mag; Rep Frsh Cls; Cit Awd; High Hon Roll; Radio Cmmnctns.

FINCH, CARLEEN; Peters Township HS; Mcmurray, PA; (4); Cmnty Wkr; FBLA; Girl Scts; Hosp Aide; Office Aide; PA ST U; Bus Admin.

FINCH, ERIC; Upper Darby HS; Upr Darby, PA; (3); 6/681; Church Yth Grp; Quiz Bowl; Scholastic Bowl; Swmmng; Tennis; High Hon Roll; Jr NHS; Ntl Merit Ltr; Law.

FINCH, JEFF; Fort Le Boeuf HS; Waterford, PA; (3); Ski Clb; Hon Roll; Edinboro U.

FINCH, LORI; Bellwood-Antis HS; Altoona, PA; (4); Church Yth Grp; Key Clb; Band; Chorus; Concert Band; Mrchg Band; Trk; Hon Roll; Penn ST; Human Dvlpmnt.

FINCH, LYLENN; Westinghouse HS; Pittsburgh, PA; (2); Exploring; Trk; Cit Awd; High Hon Roll; SAR Awd; Engr.

FINCH, MICHAEL; Quaker Valley HS; Sewickley, PA; (2); Church Yth Grp; German Clb; Key Clb; Math Tm; Nwsp Sprt Ed; JV Var Socr; High Hon Roll; Kiwanis Awd; Martin Luther King Essay Wnnr 86; Delta Epsilon Phi Natl German Hnr Soc 87; PA Cls Aa Socr Champs 86.

FINCK, STACEY; Montgomery Area HS; Montgomery, PA; (3); French Clb; Bsktbl; Cheerleading; Trk; Hon Roll; NHS.

FINCK, TRICIA; Milton Area SR HS; Milton, PA; (4); 33/193; SADD; Band; Concert Band; Mrchg Band; School Musical; Yrbk Stf; Hon Roll; NHS; Pres Schlr; Latin Clb; Pres Acadc Ftnss Awd 87; Bloomsburg U.

FINDISH, PATRICIA; Windber Area HS; Windber, PA; (3); Church Yth Grp; Pres French Clb; JA; Concert Band; Jazz Band; Mrchg Band; Yrbk Stf; Off Jr Cls; Hon Roll; Pres Schlr; Engl.

FINDLEY, LISA; Central Cambria HS; Vintondale, PA; (4); 11/214; Computer Clb; Sec Trs French Clb; FBLA; Library Aide; Swmmng; High Hon Roll.

FINDLEY, TRACY; Chambersburg Area HS; Chambersburg, PA; (3); Sec Exploring; French Clb; VICA; Band; Chorus; Mrchg Band; Pep Band; Vocational Achvt Awd 87; Med Asst.

FINE, CHRISTINE; Moniteau HS; West Sunbury, PA; (2); Spanish Clb; Band; Concert Band; Jazz Band; Mrchg Band; Orch; Variety Show; Stat Bsktbl; NHS; Louis Armstrong Jazz Awd 86.

FINE, JULIE; Winchester-Thurston HS; Pittsburgh, PA; (4); AFS; Cmnty Wkr; Political Wkr; Service Clb; Spanish Clb; Yrbk Bus Mgr; Lit Mag; Svc Awd Of Rcgntn 86; Macalester Coll.

FINE, MATTHEW; Lower Merion HS; Philadelphia, PA; (3); Rep Frsh Cls; Rep Soph Cls; Rep Jr Cls; Rep Stu Cncl; Capt Var Socr; Var Tennis; Capt Var Trk; Hon Roll; US Pan Am Maccabbi Tm 87; Bus.

FINEGAN, EILEEN R; St Hubert Catholic HS For Girls; Bensalem, PA; (3); 100/421; Drama Clb; Science Clb; Chorus; Orch; Hon Roll.

FINELLE, ANNETTE; Bishop Hannan HS; Scranton, PA; (4); 2/123; Church Yth Grp; Spanish Clb; Orch; High Hon Roll; NHS; Sal; IHM Schlrshp Marywood Coll 87; Outstndgn Achvt Mdrn & Clsscl Lang 87; Pres Acad Ftns Awd 87; Marywood Coll; Cmmrcl Art.

FINICLE, LORI; Williamsport Area HS; Williamsport, PA; (3); 23/600; Key Clb; Latin Clb; Office Aide; Chorus; Variety Show; Var L Cheerleading; Hon Roll; CHIP Awd 85-86; Psych.

FINK, ALLISON; Shenango JR-SR HS; New Castle, PA; (2); Church Yth Grp; Mrchg Band; Rep Stu Cncl; Co-Capt Twrlr.

FINK, ANN MARIE; Peters Township HS; Eighty Four, PA; (4); Dance Clb; Pres FBLA; Drill Tm; Yrbk Stf; Lit Mag; Cheerleading; Gym; Pom Pon; High Hon Roll; Hon Roll.

FINK, ANNE; Bethlehem Catholic HS; Bethlehem, PA; (3); Aud/Vis; Capt Color Guard; Yrbk Stf; Hon Roll; Pre-Med.

FINK, CHRIS; Beaver Area HS; Beaver, PA; (2); 67/240; Church Yth Grp; German Clb; Ski Clb; JV Ftbl; Var Trk; Im Wt Lftg; Hon Roll.

FINK, JAMES; The Christian Acad; Brookhaven, PA; (3); Church Yth Grp; Chorus; Var Crs Cntry; Var Trk; Mind Christ Awd 86; Crmnl Jstc.

FINK, JANINE; Everett Area HS; Everett, PA; (3); Pres Church Yth Grp; Spanish Clb; SADD; Chorus; Color Guard; Rep Stu Cncl; Stat Mgr(s); Hon Roll; NHS; Spanish NHS; Shippensburg U; Elem Educ.

FINK, JASON; Montgomery Area HS; Montgomery, PA; (3); Church Choir; VP Soph Cls; Capt L Ftbl; L Var Trk; Ldrshp Awd In Ftbl 86-87; Most Valbl Awd In Trk 86-87; Bill Hall Mem Awd For Trk 86-87; Sales.

FINK, JODI; Central Columbia HS; Berwick, PA; (4); Sec 4-H; Key Clb; Chorus; Var L Cheerleading; Im Sftbl; 4-H Awd; Nrsng.

FINK, MELANIE; Fleetwood Area HS; Fleetwood, PA; (3); Church Yth Grp; Hosp Aide; Band; Chorus; Color Guard; Concert Band; Drill Tm; Jazz Band; Mrchg Band; Rep Stu Cncl; Intr Dsgn.

FINK, MITCH; Fleetwood HS; Fleetwood, PA; (4); VP Church Yth Grp; Ski Clb; Band; Mrchg Band; Var Bsktbl; Var Tennis; Var Socr; Church Council Yth 86-87; Lycoming Coll; Bus Admin.

FINK, TRACY; Hamburg Area HS; Orwigsburg, PA; (4); 3/144; Pres Sec Church Yth Grp; Library Aide; Trs Spanish Clb; Chorus; Var Tennis; High Hon Roll; Hon Roll; Sec NHS; $500 Lthrn Brthrhd Schlrshp 87; Acad Ltr Awds In Spnsh IV 86 & Gmtry 85; Blmsbrg U; Accntng.

FINK, VANCE; Lampeter-Strasburg HS; Lancaster, PA; (3); 4/147; AFS; VP PAVAS; School Musical; School Play; Yrbk Ed-Chief; Yrbk Stf; Hon Roll; NHS; Ntl Merit Ltr; Pol Sci.

FINK, VICKIE; Belleforte Area HS; Bellefonte, PA; (4); 12/250; Trs Drama Clb; SADD; Band; Chorus; Color Guard; Mrchg Band; School Musical; Yrbk Stf; JR Miss Fnlst Centre Cnty 87; 3 Vrsty Ltrs Trk 85-87; Wrstlg Chrldr 84-86; Lock Haven U; Sec Ed.

FINKBEINER, JOHN A; Central Bucks HS West; New Britain, PA; (3); 19/483; Am Leg Boys St; Church Yth Grp; Cmnty Wkr; FCA; Chorus; VP Sr Cls; VP Stu Cncl; Bsbl; Capt Bsktbl; Ftbl; Keystone Boys St 86-87; Engrng.

FINKELSTEIN, KIM; St Maria Goretti HS; Philadelphia, PA; (4); 10/390; French Clb; Intnl Clb; Math Clb; Math Tm; French Hon Soc; High Hon Roll; NHS; Drill Tm; Rep Soph Cls; Hon Roll; Sci Hnr Scty; 200 Schlrshp; Ambssdr Sphmr Clss; Drexel U; Comp Sci.

FINKELSTEIN, MAGGIE; Cumberland Valley HS; Mechanicsburg, PA; (3); 39/578; Library Aide; Red Cross Aide; Teachers Aide; Swmmng; Hon Roll; NHS; All-Amrcn 2nd Tm Wtr Polo 85-86; Athltc Actvty-Wtr Polo 84-88; Bio.

FINKEN, APRIL; Pen Argyl Area HS; Pen Argyl, PA; (3); Church Yth Grp; Dance Clb; Drama Clb; Spanish Clb; Mrchg Band; School Play; Stage Crew; Cheerleading; Trk; Travl & Toursm.

FINKLESTINE, SCOTT; Penn Cambria SR HS; Gallitzin, PA; (3); Trs Trk; Hon Roll; NHS; Prfct Atten Awd; High Math Avg Awd 86; Juniata Coll; Chem.

FINLAN, MARTIN; Cardinal Brennan HS; Ashland, PA; (3); 14/58; Chorus; Concert Band; Mrchg Band; Bowling; Hon Roll; NHS; NFL; Allntwn Diocesan Chorus, Schuylkl Cnty Chorus 85-87; Amer Yth Cncrt Tour Euro 85-86.

FINLEY, STACEY D; Cedar Grove Christian Acad; Philadelphia, PA; (3); Church Yth Grp; Hosp Aide; Band; Nwsp Rptr; Yrbk Rptr; Yrbk Stf; Trs Jr Cls; Rep Stu Cncl; Bowling; Var Cheerleading; New Horizon Bapt Church Edctn Schlrshp 84-85; Bus.

FINLEY, STEPHEN; Bishop Mc Devitt HS; Glenside, PA; (3); 188/362; JV Bsbl; JV Wrstlng; PA ST; Comp.

FINN, ANNETTE; Bishop Carroll HS; Ebensburg, PA; (3); 17/128; Pep Clb; Ski Clb; Spanish Clb; Yrbk Stf; Trs Jr Cls; Hon Roll.

FINNAN, JOSEPH P; Bishop Hoban HS; Plains, PA; (2); Church Yth Grp; Latin Clb; Mu Alpha Theta; High Hon Roll; Lion Awd; NEDT Awd.

FINNEGAN, BEVERLY; W Greene HS; Aleppo, PA; (4); 14/106; FTA; Rep Frsh Cls; Trs Soph Cls; Off Stu Cncl; Mgr(s); Score Keeper; Vllybl; High Hon Roll; Hon Roll; NHS; Norfolk ST U.

FINNEGAN, BRIAN; Hazleton HS; Drums, PA; (2); French Clb; French Hon Soc; High Hon Roll.

FINNEGAN, JOHN; Msgr Bonner HS; Glenolden, PA; (4); Pres Schlrshp Widener U 87-91; Merit Schlrshps St Josephs U & Loyola/New Orleans 87; Widener U; Bus Admin.

FINNEGAN, KATHLEEN; Downingtown SR HS; Downingtown, PA; (3); 1/648; Sec Church Yth Grp; Sec Spanish Clb; Color Guard; Trs Stu Cncl; Var Swmmng; High Hon Roll; NHS; Pres Schlr; Ski Clb; Nwsp Stf; Stu Rep To Schl Board 87-88; Hugh Obrian Yth Fndtn Sem Schlrshp; Stu Forum.

FINNEGAN, LESLIE; Chambersburg SR HS; Chambersburg, PA; (4); 40/650; Chorus; Concert Band; Jazz Band; Madrigals; Mrchg Band; NHS; Chopin Piano & Chambersburg Wmns Clb Awds 87; Dist & Rgnl Chrs 86 & 87; West Chester U; Music Ed.

FINNERTY, ANNMARIE; New Castle SR HS; New Castle, PA; (3); 25/263; GAA; Office Aide; Spanish Clb; Varsity Clb; Band; Concert Band; Mrchg Band; JV Var Bsktbl; Var Tennis; Im Vllybl; :Communctns.

FINNEY, ALETA; Philadelphia HS For Girls; Philadelphia, PA; (3); 20/405; Church Yth Grp; Library Aide; Office Aide; Teachers Aide; Var JV Bowling; Var Cheerleading; JV Trk; French Hon Soc; High Hon Roll; Hon Roll; UCLA; Astrnmy.

FINNIN, JEN; Upper Merion Area HS; Bridgeport, PA; (4); 100/296; Cmnty Wkr; JA; Pep Clb; PAVAS; SADD; Varsity Clb; Variety Show; Rep Frsh Cls; Rep Soph Cls; Rep Jr Cls; W Chester U; Acctg.

FINO, TINA; West Scranton HS; Scranton, PA; (3); Dance Clb; Spanish Clb; Thesps; Off Frsh Cls; Off Soph Cls; Off Jr Cls; Off Sr Cls; Stu Cncl; Cheerleading; Hon Roll; Secy.

FINTON, CHRIS; Meadville SR HS; Meadville, PA; (4); #4 In Class; Boy Scts; Science Clb; Varsity Clb; Concert Band; Nwsp Phtg; Sec Jr Cls; Sec Stu Cncl; Var Capt Swmmng; God Cntry Awd; Hon Roll; David A Levinson Awd Swmmng 85-86; Meaqdville Trbn Edit Cntst Wnnr 86; Law.

FIORANI, PAULA; Bedford HS; Bedford, PA; (3); 24/204; Pres 4-H; JA; Ski Clb; JV Capt Cheerleading; Stat Trk; Hon Roll; Photogrphy.

FIORE, ANNETTE; Hazelton HS; Hazleton, PA; (3); Drama Clb; Hosp Aide; Pep Clb; Chorus; Yrbk Stf; Hon Roll; Dental Hygenist.

FIORE, CATHERINE; Bethlehem Catholic HS; Bethlehem, PA; (4); 81/205; Key Clb; Political Wkr; Sec Trs Science Clb; Nwsp Ed-Chief; Nwsp Phtg; Nwsp Stf; Rep Soph Cls; George Washington U; Intl Rltns.

FIORE, MARY JOAN; Hazleton SR HS; Hazleton, PA; (4); Drama Clb; FBLA; Chorus; Nwsp Stf; Yrbk Stf; E Stroudsburg U; Elem Ed.

FIORENTINI, HEIDI; Chartiers Valley SR HS; Bridgevi Le, PA; (3); Varsity Clb; Rep Stu Cncl; Var Cheerleading; L Capt Swmmng; Comp Grphcs.

FIORI, DAWN; Shikellamy HS; Northumberland, PA; (3); Debate Tm; FBLA; Library Aide; Red Cross Aide; Speech Tm; SADD; Band; Chorus; Concert Band; Mrchg Band; Hnr-1st Ch Frnch Horn Cncrt Band 85-86; Outstndg Undrclsmn Chr; Susquehanna U; Elem Educ.

FIORI, ROSE; Montour HS; Mckees Rocks, PA; (3); Church Yth Grp; Acpl Chr; Chorus; High Hon Roll; Span.

FIORILLO, BECKY; Spring-Ford HS; Collegeville, PA; (2); 31/289; Sec Drama Clb; French Clb; Thesps; Band; Chorus; Concert Band; Jazz Band; Mrchg Band; School Play; Variety Show; Wrtr Of Month.

FIORITO, DANIEL L; Bethel HS; Bethel Park, PA; (4); Chess Clb; French Clb; Science Clb; Ski Clb; JV Golf; Var Socr; Var Tennis; Var Vllybl; Hon Roll; Acdmc & Gnrl Schlrshp-Wstmnstr 87; Westminster; Bio Tech.

FIRCH, MICHAEL; Strong Vincent HS; Erie, PA; (4); 14/160; Office Aide; Red Cross Aide; Ski Clb; VP Spanish Clb; Yrbk Stf; Lit Mag; Ftbl; Swmmng; Trk; Wt Lftg; Scott Cmpbl Memrl Schlrshp 87; Slippry Rck U; Phys Thrpy.

FIRELY, AMY; Norristown Area HS; Norristown, PA; (3); 92/524; DECA; Office Aide; Rep Frsh Cls; Rep Soph Cls; Rep Jr Cls; Rep Stu Cncl; PA ST U; Med.

FIRESTINE, LYNN; Tunkhannock Area HS; Tunkhannock, PA; (2); 11/330; Church Yth Grp; Spanish Clb; Band; Church Choir; Concert Band; Mrchg Band; High Hon Roll; Schlrshp Bnqt 86.

FIRESTINE, SHAWN; Cocalico SR HS; Stevens, PA; (3); Camera Clb; Chess Clb; Computer Clb; Tennis; Prfct Atten Awd; Pol Sci.

FIRESTONE, DENISE; Laurel Highlands HS; Lemont Furnace, PA; (3); 154/331; Hon Roll; Accntng.

FIRKAL, PAMELA; Panther Valley SR HS; Summit Hill, PA; (2); 23/127; Drama Clb; FHA; Chorus; Mrchg Band; School Musical; School Play; Mgr(s); High Hon Roll; Hon Roll; Law.

FIRTH, TRACY; Ridley SR HS; Ridley Pk, PA; (3); 20/438; Church Yth Grp; GAA; Pep Clb; Spanish Clb; Varsity Clb; Band; Concert Band; Var Fld Hcky; Var Lcrss; Hon Roll; Physcl Ther.

FISCHER, BETH; Richland HS; Wexford, PA; (2); AFS; Debate Tm; Hosp Aide; NFL; SADD; Band; Chorus; Concert Band; Mrchg Band; School Musical; Allegheny Vly Hnrs Bnd 86; Frgn Lang.

FISCHER, CARA; Elizabethtown Area HS; Elizabethtown, PA; (2); 64/281; Teachers Aide; Nwsp Stf; JV Tennis; Stat Trk; Fshn Merch.

FISCHER, DANNY; Franklin JR SR HS; Franklin, PA; (4); Band; Concert Band; Mrchg Band; High Hon Roll; Hon Roll; Prfct Atten Awd; Schl Dist Awd 86; Slippery Rock U; Acctng.

FISCHER, DAVE; Knoch HS; Butler, PA; (4); Var Ftbl; VP NHS; Pres Acad Awd 87; RIT Coll Schlrshp 87; Rochester Inst Tech; Appld Mth.

FISCHER, JAMIE; Northern SR HS; Wellsville, PA; (3); 78/252; Art Clb; Chess Clb; Library Aide; Nwsp Ed-Chief; Nwsp Rptr; Nwsp Stf; Yrbk Stf; Im Tennis; Hon Roll; U Of DE; Art.

FISCHER, JENNIFER; Moon SR HS; Coraopolis, PA; (4); 71/304; Camera Clb; Office Aide; Chorus; CC Awd; Hon Roll; Chamber Of Commerce Schlrshp 87; Roberts Morris Coll; Bus Mgmt.

FISCHER, LISA M; Upper Moreland SR HS; Willow Grove, PA; (3); 121/275; Church Yth Grp; Ski Clb; Flag Corp; Mrchg Band; School Musical; Nwsp Stf; Yrbk Stf; Lit Mag; JV Var Bowling; Hon Roll; Cert Of Distngshd Svcs-Qtr Mstr 86-87; Comp Sci.

FISCHER, MARIA; Bishop Conwell HS; W Bristol, PA; (3); 42/269; Office Aide; Score Keeper; Dsgn Cls Phila Coll Txtls, Sci 87; Elem Ed.

FISCHER, MICHAEL R; Archbishop Ryan HS Boys; Philadelphia, PA; (4); 26/429; Church Yth Grp; German Clb; Concert Band; Jazz Band; Off Mrchg Band; Pep Band; Nwsp Rptr; Hon Roll; NHS; Otstndng Achvt In Music 85; Penn ST U Ogantz; Engr.

FISCHER, MICHELLE ANN; Lebanon HS; Lebanon, PA; (4); 8/279; German Clb; Key Clb; VP Latin Clb; Pep Clb; Science Clb; Teachers Aide; Trs Varsity Clb; Yrbk Sprt Ed; Rep Jr Cls; Var Capt Bsktbl; Hnrb Mntn Lancaster-Lebanon All-Star Fld Hcky Tm 85 & 86; Mount St Marys Coll; Bio.

FISCHER, MONNETTE; York Catholic HS; Shawsbury, PA; (2); Dance Clb; French Clb; FBLA; Pep Clb; Chorus; Variety Show; Sftbl; Trk; High Hon Roll; Hon Roll; 90/Abve Awd 85-86; Chld Psych.

FISCHER, RONALD; Cedar Grove Christian Acad; Philadelphia, PA; (4); 9/45; Nwsp Ed-Chief; Yrbk Ed-Chief; Pres Soph Cls; Pres Stu Cncl; Var Capt Socr; Var Capt Tennis; Kiwanis Awd; NHS; Church Yth Grp; Pep Clb; Bio.

FISCHER, SARA E; Trinity Christian HS; Pittsburgh, PA; (3); 4/13; Church Yth Grp; Drama Clb; Chorus; School Play; Yrbk Rptr; Frsh Cls; Soph Cls; Jr Cls; Stu Cncl; Bsktbl; Calvin Coll.

FISCHER, SCOTT W; Council Rock HS; Holland, PA; (3); 139/908; Boy Scts; Church Yth Grp; Debate Tm; Political Wkr; Stu Cncl; Hon Roll; Prfct Atten Awd; Pro Deo Et Patria Awd 85; Wrld Cnsrvtn Awd 86; Egl Sct 87.

FISCHER, SUSAN; St Basil Acad; Philadelphia, PA; (3); Cmnty Wkr; French Clb; Sec German Clb; Math Clb; Science Clb; Service Clb; SADD; Yrbk Stf; Temple U; Physcl Thrpy.

FISCHER, TOBE; Lancaster Catholic HS; Columbia, PA; (3); 15/200; Var L Bsbl; NHS; Algebra II Awd 87; Geomtry Awd 86; Spnsh I 85; Bus/Med.

FISCHL, BETH; Northampton SR HS; Bath, PA; (3); AFS; Computer Clb; DECA; Library Aide; SADD; Yrbk Stf; Powder Puff Ftbl; Hon Roll; Pres Schlr; PA DECA ST Wnnr 6th Pl & Dist Wnnr 1st Pl Advrtsng 87; Bus Admin.

FISCUS, THERESA; Our Lady Of Lourdes Regional HS; Shamokin, PA; (3); Camera Clb; Cmnty Wkr; Pep Clb; Spanish Clb; Concert Band; Pep Band; High Hon Roll; Hon Roll; Dists Cert Of Merit 87; Schltc Gld Key Awd 87.

FISH, AMY; Penn Cambria HS; Lilly, PA; (3); Drama Clb; French Clb; Spanish Clb; SADD; Chorus; Rep Stu Cncl; Gym; Trk; Vllybl; Hon Roll; Physcl Fitns Awd 87; Athltc Ltrs Track 86-87; French.

FISH, BRIAN; Cathedral Prep Schl; Erie, PA; (3); Church Yth Grp; Debate Tm; German Clb; NFL; Service Clb; Speech Tm; Im Bsktbl; Var Trk; Im Vllybl; Advncd Stndng Crs Gannon U 86-87; Schlrshp Gannons Tn U 86-87; Pol Sci.

FISH, JEREMY B; Coudersport JR/Sr HS; Coudersport, PA; (4); 4-H; Ski Clb; Band; Concert Band; Mrchg Band; Nwsp Phtg; Nwsp Rptr; Yrbk Phtg; Yrbk Stf; L Ftbl; Passavant Schlrshp Awd 87; Thiel Coll; Enviro Sci.

FISH, KATHY; Elkland Area HS; Elkland, PA; (3); 12/82; Church Yth Grp; Hosp Aide; Band; Chorus; Nwsp Stf; Yrbk Stf; VP Soph Cls; JV Var Cheerleading; High Hon Roll; NHS; Miss Teen Amer Pgnt 86; Prom Queen 87; Williamsport Area CC; Acctg.

FISH, TERRI ANNE R; Penn-Trafford HS; Level Green, PA; (3); AFS; Church Yth Grp; Cmnty Wkr; Drama Clb; FBLA; Pep Clb; Ski Clb; SADD; Trs Stu Cncl; Hon Roll; Pre Law.

FISHBACK, JED; Lower Moreland HS; Huntingdon Valley, PA; (2); Debate Tm; Key Clb; NFL; Temple Yth Grp; JV Socr; High Hon Roll; Hon Roll; Bus.

FISHEL, DAVID; Butler HS; Butler, PA; (2); French Clb; Im Bsktbl; Hon Roll; Jr NHS.

FISHER, ALLYSON; Bishop Hafey HS; Lattimer Mines, PA; (4); Pep Clb; Ski Clb; Spanish Clb; Drill Tm; Trs Stu Cncl; Var L Cheerleading; Pom Pon; Hon Roll; Prfct Atten Awd; Hghst Avg Accntg I 86; Extraordnry Stu Amer 87; DCA Ldrshp Awd 87; Elizabethtown Coll; Childhd Ed.

FISHER, AMY; Pine Grove Area HS; Pine Grove, PA; (3); Varsity Clb; Band; Chorus; Drill Tm; Yrbk Stf; Cheerleading; Hon Roll; Trs NHS.

FISHER, BRANT; Wilmington HS; New Wilmington, PA; (4); 7/121; Church Yth Grp; Concert Band; Mrchg Band; L Var Golf; God Cntry Awd; High Hon Roll; Pres NHS; Eagle Sct 86; Hnrs Band 87; Prsdntl Acdmc Ftnss Awd 87; Grove City Coll; Math.

FISHER, CINDY; Calvary Baptist Chirstian Sch; Lancaster, PA; (2); Church Yth Grp; Chorus; School Musical; Var Capt Bsktbl; Var Sftbl; Var Vllybl; High Hon Roll; Hon Roll.

FISHER, CLARK; Milton Hershey HS; Windber, PA; (4); Lit Mag; Stu Cncl; Crs Cntry; Swmmng; Capt Trk; High Hon Roll; Hon Roll; NHS; Stu Ldrshp Soc 85-87.

FISHER, CONRAD; Boyertown Area SR HS; Green Lane, PA; (3); 106/465; Art Clb; VP Sec 4-H; German Clb; Speech Tm; JV Var Crs Cntry; JV Trk; 4-H Awd; Hon Roll; Winter Track Jr Var 86; 4-H Capitol Days 86; Aerospace Engr.

FISHER, CORRINA; Crestwood HS; Mountaintop, PA; (3); Key Clb; Library Aide; Color Guard; Flag Corp; Mrchg Band; JV Var Fld Hcky; Var L Sftbl; Child Psych.

FISHER, DAN; Garden Spot HS; Narvan, PA; (3); Church Yth Grp; Concert Band; Trk.

FISHER, DANA; Exeter Twp SR HS; Reading, PA; (4); 23/220; Q&S; Y-Teens; Nwsp Rptr; Fld Hcky; Jr NHS; NHS; Lansdale Schl Of Bus; Acctng.

FISHER, DEBBIE; Cumberland Valley HS; Mechanicsburg, PA; (4); Church Yth Grp; Key Clb; Ski Clb; Color Guard; Nwsp Rptr; Lit Mag; JV Trk; U Of DE; Bio.

FISHER, DEBBIE; Meadville Area SR HS; Meadville, PA; (3); 8/363; Church Yth Grp; French Clb; Key Clb; Ski Clb; High Hon Roll; Hon Roll.

FISHER, DEBBIE; Wilmington Area HS; New Wilmington, PA; (4); Church Yth Grp; French Clb; Trs Stu Cncl; JV Bsktbl; Capt Powder Puff Ftbl; Score Keeper; Sftbl; Capt L Trk; Hon Roll; NHS; ST Trck Mt 86; 2nd Pl ST Trck Mt 87; U Of Pittsburgh.

FISHER, DENISE; Blairsville SR HS; Blairsville, PA; (3); Church Yth Grp; SADD; Band; Concert Band; Drm Mjr(t); Mrchg Band; Var Trk; Var Twrlr; Hon Roll; PA ST Hoop Champ 86, Intl Wrld Solo Champ 86, IN Cnty JR Miss Cntstnt 87 Cmpttv Baton; Law.

FISHER, DENISE M; Abraham Lincoln HS; Philadelphia, PA; (4); 18/430; Capt Drill Tm; Drm & Bgl; Flag Corp; Variety Show; Rep Stu Cncl; JV Sftbl; High Hon Roll; Hon Roll; NHS; Police Athl Leag Schlrshp 87; Bus Ed Assn Phil Awd 86; Outstndng Bus Mellon Bnk Awd 87; Temple U; Accntng.

FISHER, DIANE; Abraham Lincoln HS; Philadelphia, PA; (3); 27/450; Capt Drill Tm; Drm & Bgl; Flag Corp; Variety Show; Rep Stu Cncl; JV Sftbl; High Hon Roll; Hon Roll; NHS; Prfct Atten Awd; Fshn Dsgn.

FISHER, EDWARD T; Archbishop Ryan Boys HS; Philadelphia, PA; (3); 12/414; Church Yth Grp; SADD; High Hon Roll; Outstndng Stu Latin 86; Eng.

FISHER, GEORGINA C; Lampeter-Strasburg HS; Strasburg, PA; (4); 25/144; Band; Chorus; Concert Band; Mrchg Band; Pep Band; School Musical; Crs Cntry; Trk; High Hon Roll; Hon Roll; West Chester U; Spch Pthlgy.

FISHER, HEIDI; Pequia Valley HS; Paradise, PA; (4); Church Yth Grp; Varsity Clb; Acpl Chr; Sec Band; Chorus; Mrchg Band; School Musical; Fld Hcky; Sftbl; High Hon Roll; Co, Dist & Rgnl Chorus 86-87; Fld Hcky All Star 85-86; Fld Hcky & Sftbl All Star 86-87; U Of DE.

FISHER, HOLLY; Hamburg HS; Shoemakersville, PA; (3); Latin Clb; Library Aide; Spanish Clb; SADD; Varsity Clb; Nwsp Stf; Cheerleading; Mgr(s); Hon Roll.

FISHER, JAMIE; Uniontown Area SR HS; Markleysburg, PA; (2); French Clb; Sec JA; NFL; Speech Tm; VP Frsh Cls; High Hon Roll; Frmns Queen 86; WV U; Jrnlsm.

FISHER, JIM; Wilmington Area HS; New Wilmington, PA; (2); Chess Clb; Church Yth Grp; Spanish Clb; Band; Concert Band; Drm & Bgl; Mrchg Band; Crs Cntry; Socr; Hon Roll; Crmnl Just.

FISHER, JOHN; Cedar Crest HS; Lebanon, PA; (2); 40/345; Church Yth Grp; L Mgr(s); High Hon Roll; Basic & Advncd Stu Trainer Clinic 86-87; Phy Thrpy.

FISHER, JOHN; Liberty HS; Bethlehem, PA; (3); 30/429; Church Yth Grp; Stage Crew; Rep Sr Cls; Im Bsktbl; Var Swmmng; Im Wt Lftg; Law Crmnl Justice.

FISHER, JULIE; Hempfield SR HS; Hunker, PA; (2); Church Yth Grp; Hosp Aide; Ski Clb; Spanish Clb; Color Guard; High Hon Roll; Jr NHS; Spanish NHS; Englsh Awd 86.

FISHER, KEVIN; Carbondale Area JR SR HS; Simpson, PA; (4); Art Clb; English Clb; FBLA; Ski Clb; Comm Arts.

FISHER, KIMBERLY; Central Dauphin HS; Hummelstown, PA; (2); Girl Scts; Band; Chorus; Concert Band; Hon Roll; Bus.

FISHER, KRISTINA; Reading SR HS; Reading, PA; (3); 39/711; Key Clb; Chorus; Variety Show; Var Capt Bsktbl; Var Capt Cheerleading; Var Capt Fld Hcky; Sftbl; Mst Outstndng Bsktbl & Fld Hcky Plyr 87; Mst Outstndng Girl Athl 85; 2nd Pl Typng Cont 87; Reading Hosp Schl Nrsng; RN.

FISHER, LEVATO; Bermudian Springs HS; East Berlin, PA; (4); 20/128; Hosp Aide; Chorus; School Play; Nwsp Ed-Chief; Nwsp Rptr; Nwsp Stf; Yrbk Rptr; Yrbk Stf; Stu Cncl; Capt Cheerleading; Jrnlsm Awd 87; Chrldng Capt 86-87; Edtr Advrtsng/Literary Stf Yrbk 86-87; IN U Of PA; Cmnctns.

FISHER, LYNETTE; United HS; Armagh, PA; (4); 34/159; Library Aide; Ski Clb; Band; Drill Tm; Mrchg Band; Lit Mag; Trk; High Hon Roll; Hon Roll; Prfct Atten Awd; Gannon U; Radiolgcl Technlgy.

FISHER, MARGARET; Columbia Montour AVTS HS; Catawissa, PA; (3); 1/267; High Hon Roll; Hon Roll; NHS; Natl Sci Olympiad 87; Cosmetology Club 85-87; Acad Hair Designs.

FISHER, MARK; Hershey SR HS; Hummelstown, PA; (3); Chess Clb; Ski Clb; Acpl Chr; Band; Chorus; Concert Band; Drill Tm; Jazz Band; Mrchg Band; Pep Band; U Of CT; Physcs.

FISHER, MATT; Mc Dowell HS; Erie, PA; (4); 2/599; Drama Clb; German Clb; Math Tm; Mrchg Band; School Play; Lit Mag; Cit Awd; Gov Hon Prg Awd; Ntl Merit Schol; Sal; Westinghouse Sci Talent Srch Hnrs Group 86; PA Govrns Schl For Sci 86; Natl Fraternity Stu Muscns 86; Rensselaer Poly Inst; Mech Engr.

FISHER, MATTHEW; Sharon HS; Sharon, PA; (3); 57/200; French Clb; School Play; Stage Crew; Pres Jr Cls; Sec Sr Cls; Ftbl; Wrstlng; Hon Roll; Sci.

FISHER, MATTHEW R; Mc Dowell HS; Erie, PA; (4); 2/613; Boy Scts; Church Yth Grp; Drama Clb; German Clb; Science Clb; Mrchg Band; Rep Stu Cncl; Tennis; NHS; Sal; Natl Frat Of Stu Musicians 86-87; Natl Merit Semifnlst 86; PA Govs Schl For The Sci 86; Rensselaer Plytch Inst; Mech En.

FISHER, MICHAEL; Burrell SR HS; Lower Burrell, PA; (3); 5/178; Pres Church Yth Grp; Drama Clb; Spanish Clb; Band; Concert Band; Jazz Band; Mrchg Band; Pep Band; School Musical; Var JV Bsbl; Prfct Atten; Mid East All-Star Band; Dstngshd Hnr Roll; Med.

FISHER, MICHAEL; Center HS; Aliquippa, PA; (3); 8/186; Am Leg Boys St; Latin Clb; Varsity Clb; Rep Stu Cncl; Var L Bsbl; Im Bsktbl; High Hon Roll; Ntl Merit Ltr; Acadmc All Star 84-86; Acadmc All Star-Hrbl Mntn 86-87; Engrng.

FISHER, MICHAEL E; Solanco HS; Drumore, PA; (2); FFA; Var JV Wrstlng; High Hon Roll; Hon Roll; NHS; Penn ST.

FISHER, ROBERT; Conemaugh Valley JR/Sr HS; Conemaugh, PA; (4); 4/119; Computer Clb; Pep Clb; Varsity Clb; Bsktbl; Ftbl; Mgr(s); Cit Awd; High Hon Roll; Hon Roll; Jr NHS; Franklin Almni Assn 87; Prsdntl Acdmc Ftnss Awd 87; Outstndg Math Stu Awd 87; PA ST U; Elec Engnrng.

FISHER, SHANNON; Crestwood HS; Mtn Top, PA; (2); Boy Scts; Key Clb; Bsbl; Lincoln Tech; Comp Rpr.

FISHER, SHELIA; Lock Haven SR HS; Lock Haven, PA; (4); 19/247; Cmnty Wkr; German Clb; Keywanettes; SADD; JV Bsktbl; Hon Roll; Clarion U PA; Med Tech.

FISHER, STEPHANIE; Carlisle SR HS; Carlisle, PA; (3); Hnr Spnsh IV 86-87; Pre Med.

FISHER, THOMAS; Schuylkill Haven Area HS; Sch Haven, PA; (2); 27/108; German Clb; Yrbk Stf; Ftbl; USAF; Elec.

FISHER, TRACY; Central Dauphin HS; Harrisburg, PA; (2); Key Clb; Orch; Jr NHS.

FISHER, UNEVA; Mc Guffey HS; Washington, PA; (4); 7/210; VP Art Clb; French Clb; Concert Band; Drm Mjr(t); Jazz Band; Sec Mrchg Band; Pep Band; Stage Crew; Yrbk Ed-Chief; High Hon Roll; Mid Est Music Fstvl Symphnc Band 87; PA Govrnrs Schl-Intl Stds, PA Govrnrs Schl/Arts Smi-Fnlsts 86; Brdcst Jrnlsm.

FISHER, VALERIE; Washington HS; Washington, PA; (2); Spanish Clb; Band; Trs Soph Cls; Stu Cncl; Trk; Vllybl; High Hon Roll; Hon Roll; Letterman Clb; Concert Band; Hugh O Brian Yth Fndtn Ldrshp Awd 86-87; Chld Psych.

FISHINGER III, WILLIAM A; Shaler Area HS; Pittsburgh, PA; (3); 4/486; French Clb; Ski Clb; Chorus; School Play; Stage Crew; JV Var Ftbl; JV Trk; French Hon Soc; High Hon Roll; Hon Roll; US Air Frc Acad; Cmrcl Pilot.

FISICHELLA, BERNADETTE; St Maria Goretti HS; Philadelphia, PA; (4); 24/383; Church Yth Grp; Math Clb; Math Tm; Spanish Clb; Ed Yrbk Stf; Rep Frsh Cls; Rep Jr Cls; Var Tennis; NHS; Pres Schlr; Phila Coll Pharm & Sci; Med Tec.

FISK, JONATHAN; Danville Area HS; Danville, PA; (3); 15/197; Spanish Clb; Band; Trk; Lbrl Arts.

FISTER, COLLEEN; Hamburg Area Class HS; Hamburg, PA; (3); VP French Clb; Latin Clb; VP Band; Pres Chorus; Drm Mjr(t); High Hon Roll; NHS; Ntl Merit Schol; IN ST U; Music Ed.

FITCH, MICHAEL; Susquehanna Township HS; Harrisburg, PA; (3); 2/149; Pres Church Yth Grp; Quiz Bowl; Band; Chorus; Jazz Band; Bausch & Lomb Sci Awd; High Hon Roll; NHS; AFS; Drama Clb; Schlr Wk CTY Smmr Pgm 86; PA Gobnrs Schl Sci, Rgn V ST Chorus 87; Physics.

FITCH, PATRICK DOUGLAS; Waynesburg Central HS; Waynesburg, PA; (3); Cmnty Wkr; Spanish Clb; Band; Concert Band; Mrchg Band; Nwsp Stf; Var Bsktbl; Hon Roll; Drum Capt Mrchng & Cncert Band 85; Flr Hcky Tm Capt 85-87; All Cnty Band 84; Fulton-Montgomery; Air Sci.

FITE, ERIC; Millersburg Area HS; Millersburg, PA; (4); 33/76; Letterman Clb; Library Aide; Capt L Ftbl; Trk; Wt Lftg; High Hon Roll; Shippensburg U; Comp Sci.

FITSER, LORI; Calisbury HS; Allentown, PA; (3); Hosp Aide; Band; Mrchg Band; Rep Frsh Cls; Hon Roll; Bus Adm.

FITT, DAVID; Archbishop Wood HS For Boys; Hatboro, PA; (3); 5/264; Math Tm; SADD; Concert Band; Drm Mjr(t); Jazz Band; Mrchg Band; School Musical; High Hon Roll; NHS; Princeton; Math.

FITT, JASON; Danvile Area HS; Danville, PA; (3); Church Yth Grp; Key Clb; Rep Frsh Cls; Rep Stu Cncl; JV Ftbl; Var Trk; Wt Lftg; Gov Hon Prg Awd; High Hon Roll; Hon Roll; Engrng.

FITTERLING, TRAVIS; Dover Area HS; Dover, PA; (2); FFA; German Clb; Ftbl; 4-H Awd; PA ST U; Game Warden.

FITTON, JONATHAN W; Wyomissing Area HS; Wyomissing, PA; (4); 4/104; Spanish Clb; Concert Band; Jazz Band; Mrchg Band; VP Capt Crs Cntry; VP L Trk; High Hon Roll; NHS; Ntl Merit SF; Chess Clb; Wyomissng Area HS Math Awd 86; Lehigh U; Engrng.

FITZ, TANA; Northeastern HS; Manchester, PA; (3); Sec Church Yth Grp; GAA; Ski Clb; Band; Chorus; Church Choir; Concert Band; Mrchg Band; Sec Soph Cls; Sec Jr Cls; St Judes Cmte 84-86; Prom Cmte 86-87; Fndrsng Cls 84-87; Phys Ther.

FITZ GERALD, DEIRDRE; Sacred Heart HS; Jermyn, PA; (3); 1/43; Trs Latin Clb; Scholastic Bowl; Chorus; School Play; Nwsp Ed-Chief; Nwsp Rptr; Nwsp Stf; High Hon Roll; NHS; HS Schlrshp 84-85; UMBC; Archlgy.

FITZBIGGONS, JILL C; Mount Lebanon HS; Pittsburgh, PA; (3); Var Crs Cntry; Var Swmmng; Var Trk; Hon Roll; Ntl Merit Ltr; Pre-Med.

FITZGERALD, CYNTHIA; Ambridge Area HS; Sewickley, PA; (4); 8/265; Trs Church Yth Grp; Trs JA; Spanish Clb; SADD; Sr Cls; Golf; High Hon Roll; NHS; Pres Schlr; Penn ST CEO Schlrshp 87; Penn ST U; Bio.

FITZGERALD, GERALDINE; West Hazleton HS; Drums, PA; (4); 43/228; Church Yth Grp; FFA; FTA; PAVAS; Ski Clb; Spanish Clb; Varsity Clb; Stu Cncl; Var Co-Capt Cheerleading; NHS; Hmcmng Queen 86; PA ST U; Intl Bus.

FITZGERALD, JENNIFER; Somerset Area HS; Somerset, PA; (3); English Clb; Letterman Clb; Varsity Clb; Nwsp Stf; Yrbk Stf; Rep Stu Cncl; Var L Cheerleading; Trk; Hon Roll; Church Yth Grp; Actg.

FITZGERALD, JOSEPH; Ambridge HS; Baden, PA; (4); 85/206; Am Leg Boys St; Spanish Clb; Chorus; Ftbl; Vllybl; Wt Lftg; Wrstlng; J W Van Dike Schlrshp 87; Penn ST U.

FITZGERALD, KELLY; North Clarion JR SR HS; Tionesta, PA; (4); Spanish Clb; School Musical; Stage Crew; Stat Bsktbl; L Mgr(s); Stat Socr; JV Var Trk.

FITZGERALD, KEVIN; Central Catholic HS; Pittsburgh, PA; (3); 28/270; Var Bsktbl; Im Crs Cntry; Im Ftbl; Var Capt Golf; JV Ice Hcky; Im Score Keeper; Im Timer; Im Vllybl; High Hon Roll; Hon Roll; Ecnmcs.

FITZGERALD, PATRICIA; East Pennsboro HS; Hummelstown, PA; (3); Art Clb; French Clb; Yrbk Ed-Chief; Trs Jr Cls; Rep Stu Cncl; High Hon Roll; Natl Art Hnr Soc 85-87; Harrisburg Arts Magnet Schl Accptnce 87-88; Harrisburg Area CC Accolades Hnr; Comm Art.

FITZGERALD, ROBERT; The Haverford Schl; Haverford, PA; (2); Nwsp Rptr; Pres Jr Cls; Stu Cncl; Var Bsktbl; Var Ftbl; Memrl Awd Fr Potntl For Future Excllnc 86-87.

FITZHENRY, KATHLEEN; Nazareth Acad; Philadelphia, PA; (4); Church Yth Grp; German Clb; Hosp Aide; Pep Clb; Church Choir; Sec Frsh Cls; Trs Sr Cls; NHS; Prfct Atten Awd; Beaver Coll Schlrsp 87; 600 Hr Hosp Svc Awd; Beaver Coll; Bio.

FITZPATRICK, JAMES; Williams Valley JR SR HS; Williamstown, PA; (3); Schlr Ath Awd Fresh 85; Legsltv Art Exhbt 86; Law.

FITZPATRICK, KAREN; Central Christian HS; Du Bois, PA; (2); Church Yth Grp; Varsity Clb; VP Frsh Cls; Rep Stu Cncl; Var L Bsktbl; Var L Sftbl; Var L Vllybl; High Hon Roll.

FITZPATRICK, LISA; New Wilmington HS; Volant, PA; (2); Cmnty Wkr; 4-H; School Musical; VP Frsh Cls; L Mat Maids; Stat Trk; Stat Wrstlng; 4-H Awd; Hon Roll; Indstrl Arts Awd 85; St Fnlst In Miss American Co-Ed Pgnts 86; Bus.

FITZPATRICK, SHEILA; St Basil Acad; Philadelphia, PA; (3); Drama Clb; French Clb; Hosp Aide; SADD; Band; Prncpls Awd Chem 87; Nrsng.

FITZPATRICK, SHEILA M; Central Bucks West HS; Doylestown, PA; (4); 4/483; Am Leg Aux Girls St; Hosp Aide; Intnl Clb; Concert Band; School Musical; Lit Mag; Rep Stu Cncl; NHS; Ntl Merit SF; Prfct Atten Awd; PA SAT Cert Merit 87; Wrld Affairs Clb VP 85-87; Bucks Cnty Adv Sci Sem 85-86.

FITZSIMMONS, AMI; Clarion-Limestone HS; Corsica, PA; (3); #4 In Class; Pres Varsity Clb; Chorus; High Hon Roll; Hon Roll; NHS; Var L Bsktbl; Var L Cheerleading; Var L Trk; Amer Lgn Ctznshp Awd 85; Acctng.

FITZSIMMONS, BRIAN; Forest City Regional HS; Forest City, PA; (3); Church Yth Grp; Computer Clb; German Clb; Letterman Clb; Varsity Clb; Bsbl; Bsktbl; Golf; High Hon Roll; NHS; Bus Admin.

FITZSIMMONS, KAREN; Harriton HS; Gladwyne, PA; (4); Church Yth Grp; Cmnty Wkr; Intnl Clb; SADD; Concert Band; Mrchg Band; Var Capt Bsktbl; Var Capt Sftbl; Trk; Vllybl; Lee Scott Rubin Mem Bsktbl Schlrshp Awd 87; U Of Delaware; Sprts Med.

FITZSIMMONS, TONYA; Punxsutawney HS; Mayport, PA; (2); French Clb; Science Clb; Hon Roll; Marine Biology.

FITZWATER, LE ROY M; Upper Darby HS; Drexel Hill, PA; (3); Pres Church Yth Grp; German Clb; Acpl Chr; Chorus; Church Choir; Swing Chorus; Yrbk Phtg; Hon Roll; Indstrl Arts Soph Awd Arch; Prfct Attend Awd; Arch Engrng.

FIUMARA, THERESA; Catasauqua HS; Greensboro, NC; (4); 24/124; Church Yth Grp; Drama Clb; SADD; Teachers Aide; School Musical; School Play; Yrbk Stf; Stu Cncl; Hon Roll; John A Leidich Mem Schlrshp 87; U Of NC; Elem Educ.

FIX, CARLA; Penn Trafford HS; Trafford, PA; (2); 10/350; Drama Clb; Hosp Aide; JCL; Chorus; Church Choir; School Musical; School Play; Trs Frsh Cls; Rep Soph Cls; High Hon Roll; Frmns Esy Cntst 84; Amer Lgn Esy Cntst 84 & 85; All Amer Acadc Yrbk 87; Chem Engr.

FIX, JOSEPH; Salisbury HS; Allentown, PA; (3); SADD; Off Soph Cls; Off Jr Cls; Off Stu Cncl; L Socr; Lion Awd; Stu Forum 86-88; All-League 1st Tm Forward Soccer 86.

FLAHERTY, ERIN ANNE; G A R Memorial HS; Wilkes-Barre, PA; (4); 11/178; Key Clb; Band; Concert Band; Mrchg Band; Var L Vllybl; High Hon Roll; Hon Roll; Jr NHS; NHS; Kutztown U; Elem Ed.

FLAHERTY, JUDITH; G A R Memorial HS; Wilkes-Barre, PA; (3); 6/152; Church Yth Grp; Key Clb; Chorus; Church Choir; Jazz Band; Mrchg Band; Orch; Fld Hcky; Tennis; High Hon Roll.

FLAIG, KIM; Williamsburg JR SR HS; Williamsburg, PA; (3); FBLA; Chorus; Mrchg Band; School Musical; Nwsp Stf; Yrbk Stf; Stu Cncl; Cheerleading; Twrlr; Altoona Schl Of Cmrc; Med Sect.

FLAIL, DAWN; Harry S Truman HS; Levittown, PA; (3); Drama Clb; Pep Clb; SADD; Mrchg Band; School Musical; School Play; Rep Stu Cncl; Im Var Cheerleading; Im Diving; Im Gym; MI ST Coll; Counselor.

FLAIM, KATHY; West Hazelton HS; W Hazleton, PA; (3); 5/223; Cmnty Wkr; Leo Clb; Math Tm; Red Cross Aide; Scholastic Bowl; SADD; Thesps; Varsity Clb; Sec Band; Church Choir; Amer Legion Awd 86; Luzerne Cnty Jr Miss Fnlst 87; Easter Seals Lily Queen 87; Catholic U Of Amer; Biomed Engr.

FLAM, KAREN P; Central Bucks West HS; Doylestown, PA; (3); 74/481; Am Leg Aux Girls St; Cmnty Wkr; Office Aide; Red Cross Aide; Science Clb; Temple Yth Grp; Hon Roll; School Musical; Sci Olympd 86-87; Frnch Awd 84-85; Bio.

FLAMISH, JESSICA; Galeton Area HS; Galeton, PA; (3); 9/39; Sec French Clb; Band; Chorus; Yrbk Phtg; Yrbk Stf; Var JV Cheerleading; Var JV Trk; Hon Roll; NHS; VFW Awd; Presdntl Acadc Ftns Awd 84-85; Lang.

FLANAGAN, BRIGID; Villa Maria Acad; Erie, PA; (3); Ski Clb; Trs Jr Cls; Trs Sr Cls; Socr; Trk; Hon Roll; NHS.

FLANAGAN, PATRICK; Harry S Truman HS; Levittown, PA; (3); Var L Tennis; Hon Roll; NHS; PA ST U; Chem Engrng.

FLANDERS, JOHN; Newport HS; Liverpool, PA; (1); 20/123; Band; Chorus; Concert Band; School Musical; Im Ftbl; Hon Roll.

FLANDERS, SEAN; Montour HS; Mckees Rocks, PA; (3); Computer Clb; Spanish Clb; Rep Jr Cls; Im Bsktbl; JV Var Ftbl; JV Var Trk; JV Mgr Vllybl; High Hon Roll; Hon Roll; VA Tech; Engr.

FLANIGAN, MELISSA; Lock Haven SR HS; Lock Haven, PA; (3); Pres Church Yth Grp; German Clb; SADD; Hon Roll; Natl History & Govt Awd 87; Lock Haven U; Teaching.

FLANIGAN, SUSAN; West Mifflin Area HS; W Mifflin, PA; (2); Drama Clb; High Hon Roll; Jr NHS; NHS; OH ST U; Journlst.

FLANNERY, DAVID; West Scranton HS; Scranton, PA; (3); 6/270; Boys Clb Am; Church Yth Grp; Latin Clb; Letterman Clb; VP Sr Cls; Stu Cncl; Ftbl; High Hon Roll; NHS; Ntl Merit Ltr; Acad All-Am; Svc & Ldrshp Awd; Law.

FLANNERY, GERRI; Norwin SR HS; N Huntingdon, PA; (4); 138/557; Red Cross Aide; SADD; VICA; Chorus; Hon Roll; Median Schl Of Allied Hlth; Med.

FLANNERY, MICHELE; Scranton Prep Schl; Clarks Summit, PA; (4); 125/190; Church Yth Grp; Cmnty Wkr; Pep Clb; School Play; VP Rep Soph Cls; VP Rep Jr Cls; Capt Bsktbl; Capt Var Sftbl; Vrsty Sftbl Al-Star 85-87; Cavalier Awd 87; PA ST U; Rehbltatn Educ.

FLARTEY, KELLY; Hazleton HS; Hazleton, PA; (4); Church Yth Grp; Pep Clb; Chorus; Nwsp Stf; Yrbk Stf; Var Bsktbl; Var Trk; High Hon Roll; NHS; Michael M Minor Memrl Awd, Ladies Unioco Awd 87; Temple U; Phys Thrpy.

FLATI, RICHARD; Hershey HS; Hershey, PA; (3); Church Yth Grp; Quiz Bowl; School Musical; Yrbk Stf; Rep Frsh Cls; Rep Soph Cls; Var L Crs Cntry; High Hon Roll; Spanish NHS; Variety Show; 2nd Pl Bridge Bldg Event St Sci Olympd 86; Engr.

FLATNESS, LISA; Tunkhannock HS; Tunkhannock, PA; (2); 1/400; Drama Clb; Key Clb; School Musical; Sec Soph Cls; Stu Cncl; Var Cheerleading; JV Fld Hcky; Socr; Var Trk; High Hon Roll; Presdntl Physcl Ftns Awd; Presdntl Acadmc Ftns Awd 85-86; Oxford U; Philsphr.

FLAUGH, PATRICK; Bishop Mc Cort HS; Johnstown, PA; (3); Boy Scts; Church Yth Grp; Cmnty Wkr; Mu Alpha Theta; Spanish Clb; Nwsp Rptr; Nwsp Stf; Yrbk Bus Mgr; Yrbk Rptr; JV Var Crs Cntry; Penn ST; Bus.

FLAXENBURG, JESSE; Owen J Roberts HS; Elverson, PA; (3); 1/299; JV Bsbl; Var Socr; Im Vllybl; High Hon Roll; Hon Roll; NHS; Prfct Atten Awd.

FLECHER, MARK; Lincoln HS; Ellwood City, PA; (4); Church Yth Grp; Cmnty Wkr; Ski Clb; Socr; Indiana U Of PA; Sci.

FLECK, BRIAN; Montour HS; Mckees Rocks, PA; (2); SADD; Pres Soph Cls; Var JV Ftbl; Var Trk; High Hon Roll; Hon Roll; Sphmr Rep Of SAAD 86-87.

FLECK, JENNIFER; Oley Valley HS; Douglassville, PA; (3); 10/142; Cmnty Wkr; Chorus; School Musical; Nwsp Rptr; Cheerleading; High Hon Roll; Hon Roll; Sec NHS; Drama Clb; Yrbk Stf; Female Stu Mo 87; Aerobics Clb VP 87; Law.

FLECK, JON; Altoona Area HS; Altoona, PA; (4); 12/718; Computer Clb; Drama Clb; German Clb; Ski Clb; Variety Show; Nwsp Rptr; Nwsp Sprt Ed; Nwsp Stf; Score Keeper; High Hon Roll; 3 K Pins 81-83; 2nd Pl Keystone Awds 86; Elem Schl Schlrshp 87; PA ST; Journlsm.

FLECK, KEVIN; United HS; New Florence, PA; (3); 31/146; Trs Art Clb; Chess Clb; Ski Clb; Band; Chorus; Concert Band; Mrchg Band; Nwsp Stf; Var Bsbl; JV L Wrstlng.

FLECK, TODD; Montour HS; Mckees Rocks, PA; (3); Computer Clb; Exploring; Letterman Clb; SADD; Crs Cntry; Trk; Track & Cross Cntry Lttrs 85-87; Engr.

FLECKENSTEIN, DAWN; Coudersport Area HS; Coudersport, PA; (4); Computer Clb; French Clb; FTA; Pep Clb; Ski Clb; Spanish Clb; Band; Chorus; Concert Band; Mrchg Band; Lck Hvn U; Elem Ed.

FLECKER, TIM; Shaler Area SR HS; Glenshaw, PA; (3); 22/486; Chess Clb; Math Tm; Ski Clb; Rep Frsh Cls; Rep Soph Cls; Rep Jr Cls; Rep Stu Cncl; Var Socr; High Hon Roll; NHS; Engrng.

FLECKSTEINER, JOHN W; Bethlehem Catholic HS; Bethlehem, PA; (3); 115/183; Church Yth Grp; Hon Roll; Comp Sci.

FLEEGER, BRIAN; Moniteau HS; West Sunbury, PA; (1); Spanish Clb; Concert Band; Mrchg Band; Trk; Hon Roll; Jr NHS; Sci.

FLEEGLE, BARBARA; North Star HS; Jennerstown, PA; (4); FCA; Varsity Clb; Pres Frsh Cls; VP Jr Cls; Sec Stu Cncl; Var Bsktbl; Var Sftbl; Var Vllybl; Lion Awd; NHS; Lioness Clb Awd 87; Pblc Rltns.

FLEEGLE, LEE ANN; Ferndale Area HS; Johnstown, PA; (4); 1/69; Am Leg Aux Girls St; Pres SADD; Pres Band; Pres Chorus; Sec NHS; Pres Schlr; Val; Pres Church Yth Grp; VP Pres Leo Clb; Church Choir; Thiel Wmns Clb Schlrshp 87; Stewart Hnrs Schlrshp 87; Passavant Rcgntn Awd 87; Thiel Coll; Pre-Law.

FLEEGLE, RHONDA; North Star HS; Stoystown, PA; (4); #7 In Class; FCA; FBLA; Nwsp Stf; Hon Roll; Secty Nrth Str Bus Clb 87; Stu Of Mnth Apri 87.

FLEET, CHRISTINE; Duquesne SR HS; Duquesne, PA; (3); FBLA; Y-Teens; Nwsp Stf; Yrbk Stf; Sec Soph Cls; Rep Stu Cncl; Var Cheerleading; Hon Roll; Joseph M Gaydos Cls Secy Hnr 85-86; Cert Achvt Chrldng 84-85; Accntng.

FLEISCHER, STEPHEN; Strath Haven HS; Wallingford, PA; (3); Quiz Bowl; JV L Tennis; Bausch & Lomb Sci Awd; High Hon Roll; NHS; Cnfrnc On Ldrshp 86; Math Sci.

FLEISHER, ALYSIA; Lewistown Area HS; Granville, PA; (4); 5/248; AFS; French Clb; Key Clb; Pep Clb; Ski Clb; Mgr Fld Hcky; Mgr(s); Sftbl; High Hon Roll; NHS; Presdntl Acac Ftns Awd 87; Elizabethtown Coll; Pre-Law.

FLEISHER, ANTHONY; Newport HS; Newport, PA; (3); Var Bsbl; JV Wrstlng; Hon Roll.

FLEISHER, ERIC; Newport JR SR HS; Newport, PA; (1); 4-H; 4-H Awd.

FLEISSNER, JOELLE; Washington HS; Washington, PA; (2); Ski Clb; Spanish Clb; Rep Frsh Cls; Rep Soph Cls; Stu Cncl; JV Capt Cheerleading; High Hon Roll; Jrnlsm.

FLEMING, JENNIFER; Phil-Mont Christian Acad; Huntingdon Valley, PA; (3); Church Yth Grp; Dance Clb; Girl Scts; Hosp Aide; Chorus; Church Choir; School Play; Yrbk Rptr; Yrbk Sprt Ed; Yrbk Stf; Villanova; Comm.

FLEMING, JOHN; Brockway Area HS; Reynoldsville, PA; (4); 10/89; Boy Scts; Church Yth Grp; 4-H; FFA; Varsity Clb; Vllybl; Hon Roll; Lion Awd; Pres Schlr; Penn ST; Ag Engrng.

FLEMING, LISA; Knoch JR SR HS; Butler, PA; (4); 32/243; Concert Band; Mrchg Band; Sr Cls; Swmmng; Trk; High Hon Roll; Hon Roll; NHS; Pres Schlr; Eva M Knoch Schlrshp 87; Westminster Coll; Math.

FLEMING, MARCIA; Brookville Area HS; Sigel, PA; (4); 14/129; Pres French Clb; FBLA; Band; Yrbk Stf; Lit Mag; Off Stu Cncl; Trk; Vllybl; Jr NHS; NHS; Venango Cmps Schlrshp 87; Sigel Fire Queen 86; Prdntl Physcl Ftnss Awd 86 & 87; Vernango Campus Of Clarion.

FLEMING, MICHELE; Glendale JR SR HS; Coalport, PA; (4); 1/93; Mrchg Band; Yrbk Bus Mgr; Yrbk Stf; Hon Roll; Pres NHS; Val; Voice Dem Awd; Band; Concert Band; Coalprot-Irvona Rotary Club Engl Awd 87; Howard C New Comb Schlrshp 87; Pres Acad Fitnss Awd 87; IN U Of PA; Accntng.

FLEMING, PATRICIA; HS Of Engineering & Science; Philadelphia, PA; (3); 21/200; Drama Clb; Chorus; School Musical; School Play; Yrbk Bus Mgr; Yrbk Stf; Rep Frsh Cls; Hon Roll; Trs NHS; Church Yth Grp; Psych.

FLEMING, STEPHANIE; Moniteau HS; West Sunbury, PA; (4); 1/132; Sec 4-H; French Clb; Spanish Clb; Church Choir; Concert Band; Jazz Band; School Musical; Vllybl; High Hon Roll; NHS; Van Slyckct Reeside Ovrseas Schlrshp W Grmny 86; Cngrss Bundestag Ovrseas Schlrshp Altrnt 86; Duquesne U; Music Thrpy.

FLEMING, THERESA; Mc Guffey HS; Washington, PA; (4); Church Yth Grp; Chrmn Hosp Aide; JA; Pep Clb; Spanish Clb; Church Choir; 4-H Awd; Hon Roll; Outstndng Achvt Candy Strpr 85-86; WA Hosp; Radiolgy.

FLEMMENS, KIMBERLY K; Christian Schl Of York; Seven Valleys, PA; (4); Art Clb; Sec Church Yth Grp; Library Aide; Quiz Bowl; Trs Jr Cls; Trk; Hon Roll; Trck MVP Awd 85; Teacher.

FLENNER, KIM; Beaver Area JR SR HS; Beaver, PA; (2); French Clb; Key Clb; Latin Clb; SADD; High Hon Roll; Hon Roll; Penn ST U; Acctng.

FLENNER, MICHAEL; Carlynton JR-SR HS; Coraopolis, PA; (3); Im Bsbl; Var Wrstlng.

FLESHER, JONATHAN; Liberty HS; Bethlehem, PA; (3); 25/429; Chess Clb; Band; Chorus; Concert Band; Jazz Band; Mrchg Band; Orch; Var Tennis; Church Yth Grp; Cmnty Wkr; PA-NJ Indvdl Tourn 12th Pl 87; 1st Pl Moravian Gryhnd Tnns Cmp Tourn 86; Mst Imprvd Tnns Camp 86; Engrng.

FLESHMAN, KEVIN; Carlisle HS; Carlisle, PA; (4); 13/400; Sec Jr Cls; VP Sr Cls; JV Bsktbl; Var L Ftbl; Hon Roll; NHS; Rotary Awd; H R Ahl Schlrshp 87; Lafayette Coll.

FLETCHER, BENJAMIN; Shadyside Acad; Allison Park, PA; (3); Camera Clb; Church Yth Grp; French Clb; Ski Clb; SADD; JV Ftbl; JV Tennis; Engr.

FLETCHER, KIMBERLY; Scranton Central HS; Scranton, PA; (2); FBLA; Girl Scts; Spanish Clb; Pom Pon; Swmmng; Slvr Ldrshp Slvr Awd 86; Gld Ldrshp 87; U Of Scranton; Jvnle Prob Ofcr.

FLETCHER, MARLENE; Valley View JR/Sr HS; Blakely, PA; (2); Church Yth Grp; Child Care & Dev Classes 86-87; Sewing Classes 85-86; Piano Lessons 84; Pilot.

FLETCHER, MATTHEW; Montour SR HS; Pittsburgh, PA; (2); 20/250; High Hon Roll; Schl Amer H S Math Exam Ldr 87; ASHME Hnr Roll 87; Acad Achvmnt Awd 85-87; Math.

FLETCHER, SANDY; Bethel Christian Schl; Erie, PA; (3); 2/16; Church Yth Grp; Stage Crew; Variety Show; Nwsp Sprt Ed; Nwsp Stf; Yrbk Phtg; Yrbk Sprt Ed; Yrbk Stf; VP Frsh Cls; VP Jr Cls; MVP In Vlybl & Sftbl 85-86; Cdrvl; Phy Ed.

FLETCHER, TODD; Elizabeth Forward HS; Elizabeth, PA; (3); 34/345; Church Yth Grp; French Clb; Pres Trs Leo Clb; Jazz Band; Trs Mrchg Band; Hon Roll; Lion Awd; Leo Awd Hnr 86; Archit.

FLICK, DEBBIE; Ft Leboeuf HS; Waterford, PA; (3); Dance Clb; French Clb; Im Vllybl; Hon Roll; Air Force; Pilot.

FLICK, JOHN; Oil City HS; Oil City, PA; (3); 31/219; Church Yth Grp; German Clb; Varsity Clb; Var L Ftbl; JV Trk; Var L Wrstlng; NHS; Crmc Engrng.

FLICK, SAMUEL; Somerset Area HS; Somerset, PA; (4); 27/240; Mu Alpha Theta; Varsity Clb; Trk; Wt Lftg; Wrstlng; Hon Roll; NHS; Rotary Awd; English Clb; French Clb; Indiana U PA; Finance.

FLICK, TRACE; Butler HS; Butler, PA; (2); Church Yth Grp; FBLA; Hosp Aide; SADD; VICA; Chorus; Church Choir; Sftbl; Jr NHS; Pittsburgh Beauty Acad; Csmtlgy.

FLICKINGER, DANIEL; Owen J Roberts HS; Pottstown, PA; (2); 28/311; Band; Chorus; Church Choir; Concert Band; Mrchg Band; School Musical; Symp Band; Variety Show; JV Tennis; Im Vllybl.

FLICKINGER, DEBRA; Lehighton Area HS; Lehighton, PA; (1); 9/306; Pres Church Yth Grp; Debate Tm; Pres Girl Scts; SADD; Chorus; Church Choir; High Hon Roll; Hon Roll; Law.

FLICKINGER, ERIC; Warwick HS; Lititz, PA; (3); 4/280; Church Yth Grp; Cmnty Wkr; Pres Varsity Clb; Pres Frsh Cls; Capt Bsktbl; Capt Socr; Bausch & Lomb Sci Awd; High Hon Roll; NHS; Sci, Hstry, Math, Phys Ed Awds 87.

FLICKINGER, JENEEN; Newport HS; Newport, PA; (2); Varsity Clb; Chorus; School Musical; Trs Soph Cls; Off Stu Cncl; Co-Capt Bsktbl; Co-Capt Fld Hcky; Sftbl; Hon Roll; Acctng.

FLINCHBAUGH, ANNE; Penn Manor HS; Washington Boro, PA; (3); 15/315; Church Yth Grp; GAA; Varsity Clb; Pres Jr Cls; Pres Sr Cls; Var Bsktbl; Var Crs Cntry; Var Trk; High Hon Roll; NHS; Cmmnctn Art.

FLINN, NANCI; Gettysburg SR HS; Gettysburg, PA; (4); 89/233; Church Yth Grp; French Clb; Band; Color Guard; School Musical; Mgr Wrstlng; Hon Roll; Palmer Schl Chiroprctcs.

FLOHR, CHRISTOPHER; Carlisle SR HS; Mt Holly Spgs, PA; (3); Pres Key Clb; Im Bsktbl; Hon Roll; Math.

FLOREK, SCOTT; Ft Le Boeuf HS; Erie, PA; (2); 5/203; FCA; Var JV Bsktbl; Var L Ftbl; Var Trk; Wt Lftg; High Hon Roll; NHS; Southern Coll; Phys Thrpy.

FLORENCE, LISA; York Suburban HS; York, PA; (3); 26/176; VP Exploring; Trs Girl Scts; Concert Band; Drm Mjr(t); Mrchg Band; JV Var Bsktbl; Var Capt Sftbl; God Cntry Awd; Hon Roll; NHS; Elem Ed.

FLORENCE, RAYMOND; West Catholic HS; Philadelphia, PA; (3); Cmnty Wkr; Rep Frsh Cls; Rep Sr Cls; Rep Stu Cncl; Var L Ftbl; Hon Roll; Forestry.

FLORES, ELENA; Bishop Mc Devitt HS; Harrisburg, PA; (4); #10 In Class; Science Clb; Service Clb; Ski Clb; Chorus; Drill Tm; Capt Mrchg Band; VP Stu Cncl; Tennis; High Hon Roll; NHS; Bio.

FLORIG, JENNIFER; Pottsgrove HS; Pottstown, PA; (4); 63/227; French Clb; Trs FBLA; Key Clb; Library Aide; Science Clb; Varsity Clb; Color Guard; Stat Ftbl; Var Stat Sftbl; Widener U; Htl Manag.

FLOROS, NIKKI C; Hickory HS; Hermitage, PA; (2); Church Yth Grp; Drama Clb; Latin Clb; Varsity Clb; Chorus; School Musical; JV Bsktbl; Var L Vllybl; Rep Frsh Cls; Trk; Latin Hnr Scty 85-87; 3rd Pl Impromptu Essay YSU Eng Fest OH 86; Wrtng.

FLORY, DIANE; Chambersburg Area HS; Marion, PA; (2); Church Yth Grp; Rep French Clb; Girl Scts; Office Aide; SADD; Chorus; Drm & Bgl; Mrchg Band; Nwsp Ed-Chief; Rep Soph Cls; Sprt Wk-Hay Day 1st Pl 85-86; 1st Pl Feature Twrlr W/Drm & Bgle Corp 85-86; Spch Thrpst.

FLORY, DOUGLAS; Ringgold HS; Monongahela, PA; (3); Computer Clb; Office Aide; SADD; Varsity Clb; Stage Crew; Rep Frsh Cls; Rep Jr Cls; Rep Stu Cncl; L Ftbl; L Wrstlng; Prfct Atten; Warrant Offcr Flight Schl; Avtr.

FLOT, HEIDI WILSON; Trinity HS; New Cumberland, PA; (2); Church Yth Grp; Spanish Clb; VP Frsh Cls; Bsktbl; JV Cheerleading; JV Trk; NEDT Awd; Phy Thrpy.

FLOUT, KEVIN; Neshannock HS; New Castle, PA; (3); VP Drama Clb; School Play; Nwsp Sprt Ed; Var L Trk; PA St Police Acad Yth Wk 87; Youngstown ST U; Law Enfrcmnt.

FLOWERS, NAIMA; Frankford HS; Philadelphia, PA; (3); 7/600; Boys Clb Am; Var Trk; Hon Roll; NHS; Prfct Atten Awd; Pres Acdmc Ftnss Awd 85; Comp Pgmmng.

FLOYD, JOHN O; Taylor Allerdice HS; Pittsburgh, PA; (3); Boy Scts; Church Yth Grp; Cit Awd; High Hon Roll; Hon Roll; Ntl Merit Ltr; Hmnts Apprtcshp Prog Archlgy 86-87; Bd Ushrs 1st Bptst Chrch Ptsbrgh 84-87; ALCOA Ldrshp Dvlpmnt; Hstry.

FLUCK, RODNEY S; Quakertown SR HS; Quakertown, PA; (2); 4/350; Scholastic Bowl; Stage Crew; Nwsp Phtg; Nwsp Rptr; Nwsp Stf; Yrbk Stf; L Ftbl; Hon Roll; Jr NHS.

FLUHARTY, CINDY; Hopewell SR HS; Aliquippa, PA; (4); 50/245; Church Yth Grp; Drama Clb; German Clb; Hosp Aide; Office Aide; Chorus; Hon Roll; Westminster Coll; Ecnmcs.

FLYNN, ALISON; Scranton Central HS; Scranton, PA; (2); Ski Clb; SADD.

FLYNN, BILL; Father Judge HS; Philadelphia, PA; (4); 4/360; Var Golf; Var Swmmng; Hon Roll; NHS; Pres Schlr; Full Tutn Schlrshp-St Jsphs U 87; Hnrb Mntn-Comp Sci Awd & Phi Beta Kappa Awd 87; St Josephs U; Food Mrktng.

FLYNN, ELIZABETH; North Catholic HS; Pittsburgh, PA; (3); Rep Frsh Cls; Rep Soph Cls; Trs Jr Cls; Sec Sr Cls; Stu Cncl; Co-Capt Bsktbl; Sftbl; Tennis; Hon Roll; Nrth Cthlc Actvts Awd 86-87; Stu Cncl Awd & Hmcmng Rep 84-85; Stu Cncl Awd 85-86; Comms.

FLYNN, KEVIN; Towanda Area HS; Monroeton, PA; (3); Letterman Clb; Varsity Clb; Var L Bsbl; Var L Bsktbl; Var L Ftbl.

FLYNN, MAUREEN; Vincentian HS; Glenshaw, PA; (4); 3/61; Civic Clb; Service Clb; SADD; Trs Chorus; School Play; Yrbk Stf; Rep Soph Cls; High Hon Roll; NHS; Univ Schlr Duquesne Univ 87-88; Natl Engl Merit Awd 86-87; Duquesne Univ; Elem Ed.

FLYNN, MONICA; Lansdale Catholic HS; North Wales, PA; (3); Im Swmmng; JV Tennis; Hon Roll; Prfct Atten Awd; Psych.

FOCHT, ANNE; Williamsburg HS; Williamsburg, PA; (3); 1/68; Church Yth Grp; Band; Chorus; Concert Band; Jazz Band; Mrchg Band; Trs Jr Cls; JV Var Vllybl; Hon Roll; NHS; Rep HOBY Fndtn Ldrshp Smnr 85-86; Spnsh.

FOCHT JR, RICHARD L; Huntingdon Area HS; Huntingdon, PA; (3); 49/224; Boy Scts; Chess Clb; Church Yth Grp; Key Clb; Band; Concert Band; Mrchg Band; Pep Band; School Musical; God Cntry Awd; PA ST U; Law.

FOCHT, ROCHELLE; Central HS; Martinsburg, PA; (3); Church Yth Grp; FBLA; Hon Roll; Lgl Secy.

FOCHT, TAMARA; Tulpehocken HS; Bernville, PA; (4); 1/100; Band; Chorus; Jazz Band; Pep Band; School Musical; School Play; Var Capt Tennis; Bausch & Lomb Sci Awd; High Hon Roll; NHS; Muhlenberg Coll; Bio.

FOCHTMAN, CANDACE; Chambersburg Area HS; Chambersburg, PA; (2); Hosp Aide; Color Guard; Natl Ldrshp & Svc Awds 87; Peace Corps.

FODI, SCOT; North Catholic HS; Pgh, PA; (3); 133/285; Church Yth Grp; JA; JV Bsktbl; Im Sftbl; Am Leg Awd 84.

FODOR, PETER; Northampton SR HS; Northampton, PA; (3); Church Yth Grp; High Hon Roll; Hon Roll; Pres Acadmc Ftns Awd Prog 84-85; Vet.

FOFLYGEN, MONICA; Burgettstown Area JR SR HS; Atlasburg, PA; (3); Trs Church Yth Grp; Sec Drama Clb; Drm Mjr(t); Mrchg Band; School Musical; Symp Band; Stat Bsktbl; L Sftbl; High Hon Roll; NHS; Radiologic Tech.

FOGAL, ANN MARIE; Fannett,Metal HS; Doylesburg, PA; (3); Varsity Clb; Color Guard; Nwsp Stf; Yrbk Stf; Frsh Cls; Soph Cls; Bsktbl; Cheerleading; Sftbl; NHS; Acadmc All Amer 85-86; Hnr Roll; Journlsm.

FOGARTY, ELEANOR; Our Lady Of Lourdes Regional HS; Sunbury, PA; (4); Church Yth Grp; Girl Scts; Spanish Clb; Nwsp Bus Mgr; Yrbk Ed-Chief; Yrbk Stf; High Hon Roll; NHS; Spanish NHS; Immaculata Coll; Bus Admin.

FOGARTY, SHARON; Nativity BVM HS; Minersville, PA; (4); 32/93; Art Clb; Hosp Aide; Ski Clb; Variety Show; Nwsp Stf; Var Bowling; French Hon Soc; High Hon Roll; Hon Roll; Bus Awd; Phila Coll Text & Sci; Fshn Mrc.

FOGARTY, THERESA M; Central Catholic HS; Allentown, PA; (4); Key Clb; Math Clb; Q&S; Ski Clb; Chorus; Nwsp Stf; Lit Mag; Swmmng; High Hon Roll; NHS; 2nd Pl Lehigh Cnty For Stand Up For Life Essay 86; 1st Awd P A Schl Press Assoc 87; Colgate; Bio.

FOGLE, CAROLYN; Berlig Brothersvalley HS; Berlin, PA; (3); 4-H; Ski Clb; Spanish Clb; Speech Tm; SADD; Church Choir; Cheerleading; Hon Roll; Dentistry.

FOGLE, JON; Emmaus HS; Alburtis, PA; (3); Pres Church Yth Grp; Key Clb; Spanish Clb; Rep Jr Cls; Var L Vllybl; Physcl Thrpy.

FOGLE, KIM; East Juniata HS; Mcalisterville, PA; (4); 1/79; VP Chorus; Hst Sr Cls; Var Capt Cheerleading; Var Capt Fld Hcky; Var Trk; NHS; Ntl Merit Ltr; Speech Tm; School Musical; Nwsp Stf; Standard Steel Scholar 87; Roy Hart Drama Awd 87; Natl Army Res Schltc Ath Awd 87; IN U PA; Bio.

FOGLEMAN, MARY; East Juniata HS; Mifflintown, PA; (3); Aud/Vis; Church Yth Grp; Computer Clb; FBLA; Library Aide; OEA; Chorus; Church Choir; Hon Roll; Prfct Atten Awd.

FOGLIA, TRACEY; Ringgold HS; Monongahela, PA; (3); 5/372; Drama Clb; Varsity Clb; Nwsp Ed-Chief; Yrbk Sprt Ed; L Bsktbl; L Capt Socr; L Sftbl; High Hon Roll; NHS; Natl Math & Sci Hon Soc 85-87.

FOHR, SHERRY; Bradford Area HS; Bradford, PA; (3); AFS; Key Clb; Ski Clb; Chorus; Yrbk Phtg; Yrbk Rptr; Yrbk Stf; Tennis; High Hon Roll; Hon Roll; Psych.

FOKUO, GLORIA; Trinity Christian HS; Verona, PA; (3); 3/13; Church Yth Grp; Drama Clb; Chorus; Church Choir; School Play; Yrbk Stf; Vllybl; High Hon Roll; Hon Roll; Jr NHS; Med.

FOLEY, CINDY; Saint Pius X HS; Phoenixville, PA; (1); 56/146; Art Clb; Drama Clb; Chorus; School Play; Schl Prfrmng Arts.

FOLEY, DALE E; Otto Eldred HS; Eldred, PA; (3); 29/93; Chess Clb; Pres Library Aide; Spanish Clb; SADD; Chorus; Variety Show; Hon Roll; Var Mgr(s); Var Trk; Cert Outstndng Achvt 87; Optmlgy.

FOLEY, KAREN; Marple Newtown HS; Broomall, PA; (3); Cmnty Wkr; Office Aide; Teachers Aide; Nwsp Stf; Sec Jr Cls; Stu Cncl; Var Cheerleading; Mgr(s); Hon Roll; Prfct Atten Awd; Del Co Comm Coll; Hmn Rltns.

FOLEY, KEVIN P; Canon Mc Millan SR HS; Canonsburg, PA; (4); Chess Clb; Church Yth Grp; FBLA; Chorus; Nwsp Rptr; Hon Roll; Slippery Rock U; Spcl Ed.

FOLEY, NEIL; Lincoln HS; Ellwood City, PA; (3); 7/168; Boy Scts; Church Yth Grp; Ski Clb; Var Crs Cntry; High Hon Roll; Hon Roll; NHS; Sci Fld.

FOLEY, PAIGE L; Lancaster Catholic HS; Leola, PA; (4); 40/197; Pep Clb; Varsity Clb; Chorus; School Musical; Nwsp Phtg; Yrbk Phtg; Off Jr Cls; Sec Stu Cncl; Capt Cheerleading; Hon Roll; U Of DE.

FOLEY, SHARON; Pine Grove Area HS; Tremont, PA; (3); SADD; Chorus; Yrbk Stf; Rep Frsh Cls; Hon Roll; Pine Grove Area HS Spnsh Awd, Engl Awd, & Home Economics Awd 87; Social Work.

FOLINO, ANTHONY J; Natvitiy Bvm; Pottsville, PA; (3); 10/86; Boy Scts; Speech Tm; Var L Bsktbl; Trk; Hon Roll; NHS; Prfct Atten Awd; Intl Forgn Lang Awd 85-86; Acad All Amer 87; Psychstrst.

FOLK, HEATHER; Pen Argyl Area HS; Wind Gap, PA; (3); Church Yth Grp; Cmnty Wkr; Chorus; VP Frsh Cls; VP Soph Cls; VP Jr Cls; Var Bsktbl; Var Sftbl; Var Tennis; Prfct Atten Awd; Educ.

FOLK, MARY; Danville SR HS; Danville, PA; (3); Boy Scts; FFA; Latin Clb; JV L Sftbl; Green Hand Awd 85; Chptr Frmr 86; Schlrshp Awd 87; Bloomsgurg ST Coll; Nrsng.

FOLKES, AMY; Lansdale Catholic HS; Lansdale, PA; (3); 4-H; SADD; Nwsp Stf; Yrbk Stf; Hon Roll; Ultrasnd Tech.

FOLLETTE, GINA; Richland HS; Gibsonia, PA; (3); Library Aide; Color Guard; High Hon Roll; Hon Roll; Robert Morris; Acctng.

FOLMAR, BRIAN; Du Bois Area HS; Lutersburg, PA; (3); Aud/Vis; Boy Scts; Church Yth Grp; Varsity Clb; Stage Crew; Var L Swmmng; Swimmer Of Wk 87; Swimming Ltrs 86-87; Penn ST; Chem Tchr.

FOLMAR, KIRSTEN; West Branch Area HS; Morrisdale, PA; (3); Drama Clb; Hosp Aide; Office Aide; Science Clb; Spanish Clb; SADD; Teachers Aide; Flag Corp; Hon Roll; Penn ST; Nrsg.

FOLMAR, MARGARET; Moshannon Valley JR SR HS; Houtzdale, PA; (3); Sec Church Yth Grp; Spanish Clb; SADD; Church Choir; Nwsp Stf; Score Keeper; Hon Roll; Prfct Atten Awd; Erly Chldhd Educ.

FOLTZ, JERRY; Shade HS; Cairnbrook, PA; (4); 1/63; Boy Scts; Varsity Clb; Band; Yrbk Stf; Pres Jr Cls; Stu Cncl; L Bsbl; L Tennis; Cit Awd; High Hon Roll; 4 Yr AFROTC Schlrshp 87; USN Acad; Nvl Arch.

FOLTZ, TRACY; Warwick HS; Lititz, PA; (4); 56/236; Sec Church Yth Grp; Pres FBLA; Chorus; Concert Band; Mrchg Band; Orch; School Musical; Lit Mag; High Hon Roll; Lncstr-Lbnon CO Band; Jr All AM Hall Fame Band Hnrs; Millersville U; Elem Educ.

FONAROW, NICOLE; Hatboro Horsham HS; Horsham, PA; (4); 45/280; Key Clb; Color Guard; Drill Tm; Flag Corp; Mrchg Band; Stage Crew; Soph Cls; Jr Cls; Sr Cls; Swmmng; Ursinus; Scis.

FONDRK, DIANE; Kiski Area HS; Vandergrift, PA; (4); English Clb; Office Aide; Spanish Clb; Trk; DAR Awd; High Hon Roll; Penn ST; Bus Admin.

FONNER, ROBERT; Belle Vernon Area HS; West Newton, PA; (3); Church Yth Grp; Cmnty Wkr; Band; High Hon Roll; Hon Roll; U Of Pittsbugh; Law.

FONSECA, MARIA; Salisbury HS; Allentown, PA; (3); Cmnty Wkr; Drama Clb; Trs Pres Exploring; Stage Crew; JV Fld Hcky; Var L Sftbl; High Hon Roll; NHS; Yng Ldrs Conf-Untd Way 87; Nvl Acad Smmr Smnr 87; HOBY Fndtn Smnr 86; U Of MI; Nclr Engrng.

FONTAINE, IRIS; Chichester SR HS; Aston, PA; (3); 76/297; Church Yth Grp; 4-H; GAA; Girl Scts; Library Aide; Model UN; SADD; Band; Chorus; Mrchg Band; Outstndng Svc Awd 85; Penn ST; Pre-Med.

FONTANAZZA, MARIO; Mt Pleasant Area HS; Mt Pleasant, PA; (3); Band; Var JV Ftbl; JV Trk.

FONTANESI, CINDY; Moon SR HS; Coraopolis, PA; (4); Church Yth Grp; DECA; Stu Cncl; Sftbl; Hon Roll; Slippery Rock U; Pub Rel.

FONTICOBA, WILLIAM; Cardinal Dougherty HS; Philadelphia, PA; (3); 9/670; Var Capt Crs Cntry; Var Capt Trk; High Hon Roll; NHS; Acctng.

FOOR, DAMIEN; North Penn HS; Lansdale, PA; (3); 99/699; Hon Roll; NHS; Philadelphia Clsscl Soc Cum Laude 86 & 87; Am Clsscl Lg Lat Cum Laude 87; Intl Rel.

FOOR, JEFFREY; Everett Area HS; Everett, PA; (4); 10/115; Church Yth Grp; Varsity Clb; Yrbk Stf; Stu Cncl; Trk; Wrstlng; Hon Roll; Drexel Univ; Engrng.

FOOR, KIMBERLY; Everett Area HS; Everett, PA; (3); 23/128; Drama Clb; Library Aide; Spanish Clb; Color Guard; Flag Corp; Stage Crew; NHS; Nrsg.

FOOR, LINDA; Chestnut Ridge SR HS; Bedford, PA; (2); Camera Clb; FBLA; Color Guard; Yrbk Phtg; Trk; Hon Roll; Jr NHS; 2nd Pl Rgnl Typwrtng Awd 87; JV Trck Athl Awd 86-87; Secr.

FOOR, MICHELLE; Everett Area HS; Everett, PA; (3); 16/128; GAA; Band; Color Guard; Concert Band; Flag Corp; Var JV Bsktbl; Stat Mgr(s); Var Sftbl; Var JV Vllybl; Prfct Atten Awd; Spcl Educ.

FOOR, RONALD; Everett Area HS; Breezewood, PA; (3); Drama Clb; Varsity Clb; School Play; Stu Cncl; Var Golf; Var L Trk; Im Wt Lftg; Psych.

FOORE, WILLIAM; Sharon SR HS; Sharon, PA; (3); 25/203; Pres Church Yth Grp; Varsity Clb; Stage Crew; Crs Cntry; Ftbl; Sftbl; Trk; Wt Lftg; Wrstlng; High Hon Roll; Biol.

FOOTE, BRIAN; Quaker Valley HS; Sewickley Hls, PA; (1); Boy Scts; Band; Concert Band; Mrchg Band; Pep Band; Hon Roll; Pres Schlr; Pittsburgh Yth Symph Orch 86; Three Rivrs Yng Peoples Orch 86; Full Scholar Du Quesne U Early Adm 86; Music.

FORBES, DEBORAH; Mc Dowell HS; Erie, PA; (2); 368/629; Pep Clb; Bowling; Hon Roll.

FORBES, JOHN MYRON; Greenville SR HS; Greenville, PA; (4); 12/130; Off Church Yth Grp; German Clb; Thesps; Varsity Clb; School Play; Var L Crs Cntry; Var L Trk; Var L Wrstlng; Hon Roll; NHS; Rodney K Wentling Outstndg Wrstlr Awd 87; Thomas Mc Inturf Athl Awd 87; Grove City Coll; Math.

FORBES, MELISSA J; Greencastle Antrim HS; Greencastle, PA; (3); Church Yth Grp; Band; Chorus; Church Choir; Color Guard; Mrchg Band; L Trk.

FORBES, STACEY RENE; Tawanda Area HS; Towanda, PA; (4); Church Yth Grp; FBLA; SADD; Chorus; School Musical; Yrbk Stf; Cheerleading; Sftbl; Vllybl; NHS; Grad Distgshd Acdmc Hon 87; Liberty U; Journlsm.

FORCE, LISA; Hopewell HS; Aliquippa, PA; (3); 10/255; Art Clb; Church Yth Grp; French Clb; Band; Var L Bsktbl; Var L Sftbl; High Hon Roll; NHS.

FORCEY, ROBERT; West Branch HS; Morrisdale, PA; (4); 6/128; Trs VP Drama Clb; Band; Chorus; Concert Band; Mrchg Band; School Play; VP Jr Cls; Trs Sr Cls; Var L Bsktbl; VP NHS; Hugh O Brian Yth Fndtn Rep 85; Intl Rep.

FORCIER, KATHY; Hamburg Area HS; Hamburg, PA; (3); Computer Clb; Ski Clb; Spanish Clb; VP SADD; Rep Stu Cncl; Stat Ftbl; Var Trk; Cit Awd; High Hon Roll; Hon Roll; Psychlgy.

FORD, ALISA A; Bishop Mc Devitt HS; Philadelphia, PA; (4); Computer Clb; French Clb; FBLA; JA; SADD; Stu Cncl; Cheerleading; Powder Puff Ftbl; High Hon Roll; NHS; Bd Of Gvnrs Schlrshp 86-87; Ldrshp Awd 86&87; Clarion U Of PA; Acctg.

FORD, AMY; Central Bucks West HS; Warrington, PA; (3); Am Leg Aux Girls St; GAA; Band; Trs Frsh Cls; Rep Soph Cls; Capt Cheerleading; Capt Sftbl; L Tennis; Hon Roll; Opt Clb Awd; Dickinson; Engl.

FORD, BETHANY A; Downingtown HS; Downingtown, PA; (4); 5/561; Scholastic Bowl; Concert Band; Mrchg Band; Orch; School Musical; Symp Band; Nwsp Ed-Chief; NHS; Ntl Merit SF; Intnl Clb; Dist XII Bnd; Mathmtcs.

FORD, DAWN; Valley HS; New Kensington, PA; (1); Chorus; Cheerleading; Gym; Trk; High Hon Roll; Dentistry.

FORD, GLORIA; Bedford HS; Bedford, PA; (3); Church Yth Grp; FCA; SADD; Chorus; Church Choir; JV Var Bsktbl; Var Cheerleading; Bus.

FORD, JUDITH; Ambridge Area HS; Ambridge, PA; (4); 24/265; VP French Clb; Pres Pep Clb; VP Spanish Clb; Lib Band; Stu Cncl; Co-Capt Cheerleading; L Sftbl; High Hon Roll; NHS; Pres Acdmc Fit Awd 87; U S Chrldr Achvt Awd 87; Slippery Rock U; Elem Ed.

FORD, LAUREN; Meadville Area SR HS; Meadville, PA; (3); 16/328; Church Yth Grp; French Clb; Girl Scts; JCL; Key Clb; VP Latin Clb; High Hon Roll; Hon Roll; Engl.

FORD, ROBERT; Hampton HS; Allison Park, PA; (3); 19/206; Church Yth Grp; Ski Clb; Nwsp Stf; Im Bowling; Im Wt Lftg; High Hon Roll; Motocross Racing Awds 85-86; Engrng.

FORD, ROBERT; Hazelton HS; Hazleton, PA; (3); #11 In Class; Hosp Aide; VP Band; Jazz Band; Mrchg Band; School Play; Var L Tennis; French Hon Soc; PA ST U; Med.

FORD, SHAWNTEL; Creative & Performing Arts HS; Philadelphia, PA; (3); Church Yth Grp; Cmnty Wkr; Dance Clb; Debate Tm; JA; Drill Tm; School Musical; Stage Crew; Variety Show; Rep Frsh Cls; Human Reltns Awd 82; NY U; Pre Law.

FORD, STEPHEN; Central Cambria HS; Nantyglo, PA; (3); 13/210; Boy Scts; Sec Computer Clb; Band; Concert Band; Jazz Band; Mrchg Band; Pep Band; JV Bsbl; Hon Roll; Prfct Atten Awd; U Of Pittsburgh-Johnstwn; Acctg.

FORDYCE, KARRY; Trinity HS; Amity, PA; (2); Church Yth Grp; Cmnty Wkr; German Clb; Band; Concert Band; Mrchg Band; Pep Band; Hon Roll; Hstry Clb 87; PSYCH.

FOREMAN, CHRISTINE; Hughesville HS; Hughesville, PA; (3); 22/147; Trs Stu Cncl; Var L Bsktbl; Hon Roll; Ski Clb; Varsity Clb; Yrbk Stf; Var L Cheerleading; Var Trk; Athletic Awds Bsktbl & Chrldng; Lycoming Coll; Bus Adm.

FOREMAN JR, JOHN; Waynesboro Area SR HS; Waynesboro, PA; (3); Boy Scts; Nwsp Rptr; JV Crs Cntry; Hon Roll; Order Of Arrow Lodge Chief BS Natl Hnr Scty 86-87; Yth Rep Exec Brd Of Mason-Dixon Cncl BSA 86-87; PA ST.

FOREMNY, STEVE; Kennard-Dale HS; New Park, PA; (3); German Clb; Quiz Bowl; Ski Clb; School Play; Yrbk Stf; Socr; Trk; Hon Roll; NHS; Indiana U Of Pa Physcs Awd 87; Comp Sci.

FORESMAN, BRIAN C; Muncy HS; Muncy, PA; (4); 5/74; Boy Scts; Quiz Bowl; Varsity Clb; Var L Ftbl; Capt Wrstlng; High Hon Roll; NHS; Ntl Merit SF; Rotary Awd; All Cnfrnc Ftbll Lnbckr & Grd 86; Pre-Med.

FORGAS, KRISTA; Belle Vernon Area HS; Belle Vernon, PA; (3); Church Yth Grp; Pep Clb; Ski Clb; Nwsp Stf; Yrbk Stf; Hon Roll; Pre-Law.

FORINASH, RADA; Port Allegany HS; Port Allegany, PA; (3); French Clb; Mrchg Band; Score Keeper; Hon Roll; Wrstlng Score Keeper; Bryant; Exec Sec.

FORINASH, ROBERT A; Christian Schl Of York; York, PA; (3); 2/60; Church Yth Grp; Chorus; Sec Frsh Cls; Var Bsbl; High Hon Roll; 1st Plc Natl Soc Stds Olympd 86; John Hopkins U; Physcn.

FORINGER, BONNIE; Rocky Grove HS; Guys Mills, PA; (2); Hosp Aide; Chorus; Concert Band; Hon Roll; Drama Clb; Library Aide; Office Aide; Mst Vlntr Hrs At Franklin Hosp 87; Butler Cnty CC; Med Adm.

FORINGER, TRICIA; Ambridge Area HS; Ambridge, PA; (3); Church Yth Grp; Office Aide; Pep Clb; Red Cross Aide; Spanish Clb; SADD; Band; Concert Band; Mrchg Band; Pep Band.

FORKER, KRISTIN; Annville-Leona HS; Annville, PA; (3); 12/127; Church Yth Grp; Acpl Chr; Chorus; Rep Jr Cls; Hon Roll; Jr NHS; NHS; NEDT Awd; Prfct Atten Awd; Outstndng Stu Home Ec 86; Animal Sci.

FORMAN, EVAN; Central HS; Philadelphia, PA; (3); 26/500; Debate Tm; Yrbk Stf.

FORMICA, MICHAEL K; Quakertown SR HS; Quakertown, PA; (4); Scholastic Bowl; Yrbk Sprt Ed; Rep Stu Cncl; Capt Crs Cntry; Var Trk; High Hon Roll; Am Leg Boys St; Church Yth Grp; Computer Clb; Debate Tm; Schlr/Athl Awd 86-87; Natl Chmp Amer Comp Sci Leag 87; ST Chmpn 3000m Stplchse Trk 87; U Of Pitt Honors Coll; Engrng.

FORNELLI, JILL; Kennedy Christian HS; Hermitage, PA; (2); 21/98; Drama Clb; Latin Clb; Drill Tm; School Play; VP Frsh Cls; Pres Jr Cls; Var Cheerleading; Hon Roll; Attndnt Hmcmng Ct 86-87; Phys Ther.

FORNEY, GEOFF; Interboro HS; Prospect Park, PA; (3); Scholastic Bowl; Capt Bsbl; Im Bsktbl; Var Socr; Im Vllybl; High Hon Roll; Hon Roll; Jr NHS; NHS; Ntl Merit Ltr; Mechncl Engr.

FORNEY, MICHELE; Millersburg Area HS; Millersburg, PA; (3); 24/75; Church Yth Grp; Spanish Clb; Church Choir; Color Guard; Mrchg Band; Powder Puff Ftbl; Sftbl; Hon Roll; Elem Ed.

FORNWALT, DANIELLE; Middletown Area HS; Middletown, PA; (4); Cmnty Wkr; Debate Tm; GAA; Hosp Aide; Key Clb; Radio Clb; Teachers Aide; Bsktbl; Trk; Hon Roll; Miss Chrstms Seal 86; 1st Rnnr Up Essy Compttn PA Miss Natl Tnagr Pgnt 87; Fnlst Miss Tn Pgnt 86; Harrisburg Area CC; Nrsng.

FORREN, ANITA; The Christian Acad; Claymont, DE; (4); 11/60; FBLA; School Play; Pres Jr Cls; Rep Sr Cls; JV Cheerleading; Var Sftbl; Church Yth Grp; Nwsp Ed-Chief; Nwsp Rptr; Sftbl Plyr Of Yr; Jrnlsm & Accntng II Awd; Christian Growth Awd; Messiah Coll; Nrsng.

FORREST, ATHENA; Westinghouse HS; Pittsburgh, PA; (2); Cmnty Wkr; Teachers Aide; Chorus; Hon Roll; Gloria K Spencer Poetry Cont-1st Pl 87; Shakespeare Fest-Best Chorus 87; All-City Honors Choir 87; Poetry.

FORREST, WENDY; Panther Valley HS; Lansford, PA; (3); 11/132; Pres Library Aide; Ski Clb; Capt Drm Mjr(t); Jazz Band; Nwsp Bus Mgr; Yrbk Bus Mgr; Rep Stu Cncl; Pres NHS; Prfct Atten Awd.

FORRESTER, STEVE; Mercer HS; Mercer, PA; (3); 20/140; School Play; Nwsp Rptr; Yrbk Stf; Crs Cntry; Trk; Opt Clb Awd; ST Track Mt 3200m Rly 1st Pl 85; ST X Cntry Mt 12th Pl 85; ST X Cntry Mt 4th Pl 86.

FORREY, ALLISON; Hempfield HS; Lancaster, PA; (4); 17/425; Art Clb; Varsity Clb; JV Bsktbl; Var L Fld Hcky; Var L Sftbl; High Hon Roll; NHS; Presdntl Ftnss Awd 87; US Dept Of Army Schlr/Athlte Awd 87; Hempfld Educ Assn Schrlshp 87; Penn ST U; Law.

FORRY, TAMMIE; Eastern HS; Hallam, PA; (4); 46/167; English Clb; Exploring; SADD; Varsity Clb; School Musical; Nwsp Rptr; Yrbk Rptr; Rep Sr Cls; Rep Stu Cncl; Fld Hcky; Athltcs Schlrshp 87; SR All Star Fld Hockey Gm 86; IN U Of PA; Engl.

FORS, BRIAN; Academy Of The New Church; Huntingdon Vly, PA; (4); Key Clb; Math Clb; Science Clb; JV Bsbl; JV Crs Cntry; Hon Roll; Trs NHS; Outstndng Achvt Physcs Awd 85-86; Pres Acadmc Ftns Awd 86-87; Outstndng Achvt Math Awd 86-87; Lehigh U; Engr.

FORSBERG, DAWN; Northern Bedford County HS; Woodbury, PA; (3); Church Yth Grp; SADD; Varsity Clb; Color Guard; Yrbk Stf; Stu Cncl; Var L Cheerleading; L Mgr(s); Var Tennis; High Hon Roll; Ltr Color Guard & Capt Sr Yr; Pres Physcl Ftns Awd; Erly Chldhd Educ.

FORSEY, MICHELLE; Hanover Area JR SR HS; Wilkes Barre, PA; (4); 14/158; Band; Chorus; Concert Band; Drm Mjr(t); Mrchg Band; Nwsp Stf; Yrbk Ed-Chief; Yrbk Stf; High Hon Roll; NHS; PA Jr Acad Sci ST & Rgnl Wnnr; Tonys Food Svc Schlrshp Natl Food Svc Assn; Luzerne Cnty CC; Dietitician.

FORSYTHE, KELLY; Canevin HS; Bulger, PA; (3); Science Clb; Ski Clb; Band; Yrbk Bus Mgr; Yrbk Phtg; Yrbk Rptr; Yrbk Stf; Powder Puff Ftbl; Hon Roll; Sci Fair Awd 85-86; PA St U; Nuclear Physcs.

FORSYTHE, RAYNA; Southmoreland SR HS; Scottdale, PA; (4); 24/230; Church Yth Grp; Drama Clb; Chorus; Drm Mjr(t); Jazz Band; Mrchg Band; Nwsp Stf; Lit Mag; Swmmng; Cnty & Dist Band; Lock Haven U; Spec Ed.

FORT, DERON; West Chester Henderson HS; West Chester, PA; (3); 1/377; Spanish Clb; Im Bsktbl; JV Var Crs Cntry; JV Var Wrstlng; High Hon Roll; Hon Roll; Spanish NHS.

FORTE, AMY; Upper Darby HS; Upr Darby, PA; (3); 120/596; Hosp Aide; SADD; High Hon Roll; Hon Roll; Elem Schl Tchr.

FORTE, JANE A; Monongahela Vly Catholic HS; Ellsworth, PA; (4); 4/82; Spanish Clb; SADD; VP Band; Concert Band; Mrchg Band; Ed Yrbk Stf; Powder Puff Ftbl; Hon Roll; Pres NHS; Spanish NHS; ; Pre-Med.

FORTI, DAVID W; Trinity HS; Lemoyne, PA; (3); 7/145; Debate Tm; Model UN; Ski Clb; Spanish Clb; Speech Tm; VP Frsh Cls; L Bsbl; Im Bsktbl; Var Crs Cntry; JV Ftbl; Med.

FORTI, TRACY; Old Forge HS; Old Forge, PA; (3); Church Yth Grp; Drama Clb; Hosp Aide; Ski Clb; Thesps; Drm Mjr(t); School Musical; School Play; Variety Show; Twrlr; Ms Devilette 87; Majorette Capt 84-87; Wrld Twlrng Assn-Pon Pom, Mdlng, Twrlng 84-85.

FORTIER, KAREN; Baldwin HS; Pittsburgh, PA; (3); 35/477; VP French Clb; Math Clb; Color Guard; Mrchg Band; School Musical; Gym; Trk; High Hon Roll; NHS; Math.

FORTMAN, CARRIE; Susquehannock HS; Glen Rock, PA; (2); 15/243; Church Yth Grp; Hon Roll; Psych.

FORTNA, HEIDI; Ephrata SR HS; Ephrata, PA; (3); 17/287; Church Yth Grp; 4-H; Intnl Clb; Concert Band; School Musical; JV Var Tennis; 4-H Awd; Hon Roll; NHS; Schlstc Art Gld Key Awd 85; Math.

FORTNA, JONI; Northern Lebanon HS; Lebanon, PA; (3); 22/201; Ski Clb; Capt Color Guard; School Play; Pres Soph Cls; VP Sr Cls; Sec Stu Cncl; JV Var Cheerleading; JV Var Sftbl; Var Tennis; Hon Roll; WCTU Oratorical Awd 86-87; Trvl Profsn.

FORTNER, WILLIAM; Abington Heights HS; Clarks Summit, PA; (3); 4-H; SADD; Ed Nwsp Stf; Rep Sr Cls; Var Bsbl; Capt Ftbl; Capt Wrstlng; 4-H Awd; Hon Roll; NHS; Drexel; Psychtrst.

FORTSON, DON; Mount Union Area HS; Mt Union, PA; (3); 25/169; French Clb; Church Choir; Yrbk Stf; Var L Bsbl; JV Var Bsktbl; JV Var Ftbl; Im Wt Lftg; Hon Roll; PA ST U; Cmnctns.

FORTUNATO JR, JAMES; Shannock Valley HS; Rural Valley, PA; (3); 17/68; Boy Scts; Chess Clb; SADD; VICA; JV Bsktbl; Hon Roll; Comp Prog.

FORTUNATO, MARIE; Interboro SR HS; Norwood, PA; (3); Sec AFS; Key Clb; Trs Frsh Cls; Trs Soph Cls; Trs Jr Cls; Var Sftbl; High Hon Roll; Sec Jr NHS; Sec NHS; Natl Hnr Society-Secy; Debate Team; Philadelphia Coll; Pre-Med.

FORTWANGLER, CRYSTAL; Connellsville Area HS; Connellsville, PA; (2); Chorus; Nwsp Rptr; Rep Frsh Cls; Rep Soph Cls; Rep Stu Cncl; JV Swmmng; High Hon Roll; Hon Roll; Cert Of Acdmc Excllnc 85-86; Oceanographer.

FORWOOD, DAVID; Donegal HS; Marietta, PA; (2); Church Yth Grp; Latin Clb; Spanish Clb; JV Socr; Hon Roll; Plt.

FOSBENNER, CORY R; Upper Perkiomen HS; Zionsville, PA; (3); 88/244; Am Leg Boys St; Varsity Clb; Swmmng; Hon Roll; Pol Sci Awd; Communications.

FOSBRINK, CHRIS; Connellsville Area HS; Connellsville, PA; (3); VICA; High Hon Roll; Railroad Engr.

FOSBRINK, PAMELA; Southmoreland SR HS; Mt Pleasant, PA; (2); 3/254; French Clb; Pep Clb; Color Guard; Flag Corp; French Hon Soc; St Vincents Coll; Math.

FOSCO, DENISE; Mc Dowell HS; Erie, PA; (3); 74/577; Church Yth Grp; Dance Clb; Hosp Aide; Chorus; Pep Band; Yrbk Stf; Rep Stu Cncl; JV Sftbl; Var Swmmng; Hon Roll; Tressa Burns Arts Scholar; Mercyhurst Prep HS Ballet & Flute Scholar 85-86; Nwsp Wk 85; Piano Awds; PA ST; Phys Thrpy.

FOSKO, LEOCADIA; Wyoming Area HS; Wyoming, PA; (4); 73/249; Key Clb; Band; Church Choir; Concert Band; Mrchg Band; High Hon Roll; Kutztown U; Spcl Ed.

FOSKO, MARY THERESA; Wyoming Area SR HS; West Wyoming, PA; (3); 35/253; Drama Clb; Trs Key Clb; Ski Clb; Spanish Clb; Chorus; Var Sftbl; Var Vllybl; High Hon Roll; Hon Roll; NHS; Jrnlsm.

FOSNOT, BRIAN; Peters Township HS; Mc Murray, PA; (2); Spanish Clb; Yrbk Bus Mgr; Hon Roll; FBLA; Ski Clb; Band; Concert Band; Jazz Band; Yrbk Stf; Im Ftbl.

FOSSEE, CHRISTA; Quaker Valley SR HS; Sewickley, PA; (2); 1/180; Church Yth Grp; Drama Clb; French Clb; Chorus; School Play; Rep Frsh Cls; Trs Soph Cls; Var Socr; Var Swmmng; Hon Roll; Pres Acadmc Ftns Awd 85-86; Bus.

FOSTER, BRADLEY; South Park HS; Pittsburgh, PA; (3); 19/213; Drama Clb; Thesps; School Play; VP Jr Cls; VP Sr Cls; Rep Stu Cncl; High Hon Roll; NHS; Rotary Awd; JV Socr; Rotary Yth Ldrshp Awd 87; Mascot Ftbl Tm Trphy 86-87; Awd Cert Mascot Bsktbl 86-87; Engr.

FOSTER, BYRON; Mohawk Area JR/SR HS; Enon Valley, PA; (3); Off Boy Scts; VP Church Yth Grp; Dance Clb; French Clb; Latin Clb; Band; Church Choir; Concert Band; Drm & Bgl; Jazz Band; Novey; Aeronautical Engrng.

FOSTER, CARRIE; Mountain View HS; Union Dale, PA; (2); Girl Scts; High Hon Roll; Hon Roll; Prfct Atten Awd; Pres Schlr; Tchng.

FOSTER, CHRISTOPHER; Shady Side Acad; Pittsburgh, PA; (3); Church Yth Grp; Debate Tm; French Clb; Letterman Clb; Variety Show; Lit Mag; Var Capt Swmmng; VP Frsh Cls; Trk; Hon Roll; 100 Yrd Bckstrk Rcrd Hldr 87; 2nd Pl Leag Chmpnshps Bckstrk 87; MV Swmmr Capt 87-88; Intl Hstry.

FOSTER, DAWN; Corry Area HS; Corry, PA; (3); Girl Scts; Office Aide; Pep Clb; Teachers Aide; VICA; Y-Teens; Chorus; Mrchg Band; School Musical; School Play; J H Thompson; Cosmtlgst Tchr.

FOSTER, JANETTE; Philipsburg-Osceola Area HS; West Decatur, PA; (4); 5/250; Church Yth Grp; Band; Drill Tm; Yrbk Stf; Hon Roll; NHS; Ctzns Of Tomrrw 86-87; PA ST U; Bio.

FOSTER, JILL; Cardinal O Hara HS; Media, PA; (3); 128/710; Var Tennis; Var Trk; Hon Roll; 1st Tm All Cathlc Trk 85-86; 1st Tm All Cathlc Tnns 86-87; Hnrs Convctn Awd Top 10% Clss 85; Sprts Med.

FOSTER, KRISTEN; Penn-Trafford HS; Irwin, PA; (3); AFS; JCL; Band; Chorus; Hon Roll; Marine Bio.

FOSTER, LESLIE; Montrose Area JR/SR HS; Montrose, PA; (3); Sec 4-H; SADD; Varsity Clb; Mrchg Band; Off Stu Cncl; Var Capt Crs Cntry; Var Capt Trk; Hon Roll; Prfct Atten Awd; Mdls & Trphs Trck & Crs Cntry; Bucknell U; Elem Educ.

FOSTER, MICHAEL LAWRENCE; Otto-Eldred HS; Eldred, PA; (3); 18/93; Boy Scts; Church Yth Grp; Library Aide; SADD; Chorus; School Play; Nwsp Stf; Hon Roll; Prfct Atten Awd; Dist Chr 86-87; Rgnl Chr 86-87; Accntng.

FOSTER, PAMELA; Warren Area HS; Warren, PA; (3); 28/287; Art Clb; French Clb; Hosp Aide; PAVAS; Political Wkr; Cit Awd; Hon Roll; Poltcl Sci.

FOSTER, SEAN; Philipsburg-Osceola Area HS; West Decatur, PA; (4); 46/234; Chess Clb; Computer Clb; Ski Clb; SADD; Yrbk Stf; Trs Jr Cls; Trs Sr Cls; Stu Cncl; Ftbl; Wt Lftg; PA ST-ALTOONA; Bus.

FOSTER-BEY, JASON; Girard College HS; Philadelphia, PA; (3); Chess Clb; Radio Clb; Band; Concert Band; VP Soph Cls; Rep Stu Cncl; JV Tennis; Comp Sci.

FOTOPOULOS, AFRODITI; William Allen HS; Allentown, PA; (4); 80/559; Sec Chorus; Off Sr Cls; Twrlr; Hon Roll; Jr NHS; Lion Awd; NHS; Pres Spanish NHS; Mc Cormick Bk Awd 86; Moravian Coll; Elem Educ.

FOTOPOULOS, ANTONIA; Reading SR HS; Reading, PA; (4); 111/574; Aud/Vis; Pres Church Yth Grp; Service Clb; Spanish Clb; Chorus; Hon Roll; West Chester U; Tele Cmmnctns.

FOUNTAIN, THERESA; Central HS; Philadelphia, PA; (3); Mrchg Band; Var Mgr Diving; Var Mgr(s); Score Keeper; Var Mgr Swmmng; Hon Roll; Spanish NHS; Perfect Atten Awd & Barnwell Hnr Roll 84-87.

FOUST, CARI; Bloomsburg HS; Bloomsburg, PA; (2); 19/140; Church Yth Grp; Pep Clb; Chorus; Yrbk Stf; Pres Frsh Cls; Sec Soph Cls; JV Capt Cheerleading; Powder Puff Ftbl; Hon Roll; HOBY Ldrshp Awd 87; Phy Thrpy.

FOUST, DAVE; United HS; Homer City, PA; (4); Off Sr Cls; Var Ftbl; Var Wrstlng; High Hon Roll; Wrstlng & Ftbl All-Star 87; All-Conf Wrstlng Tm 87; Calif ST Coll PA; Indstrl Art.

FOUST, JILL; Center HS; Monaca, PA; (3); 21/180; Latin Clb; Chorus; Swing Chorus; High Hon Roll; Hon Roll; Ntl Merit Schol; Prfct Atten Awd; Magna Cum Laude Awd Latin 87; Phy Thrpst.

FOUST, KAREN; Danville SR HS; Riverside, PA; (4); French Clb; Ski Clb; Tennis; Chorus; School Musical; Rep Frsh Cls; Bowling; Mat Maids; High Hon Roll; Hon Roll; 13th Annl Bus Educ Sympsm-Wllmsprt PA 87; Geisngr Mdcl Ctr Schl; RN.

FOUST, ROB; Coudersport JR SR HS; Coudersport, PA; (3); Church Yth Grp; Drama Clb; FFA; Ski Clb; Band; Chorus; Church Choir; Concert Band; School Play; Nwsp Rptr; Bus Admn.

FOWLER, CHRISTOPHER; Mahanoy Area HS; Delano, PA; (3); Church Yth Grp; Drama Clb; Ski Clb; Spanish Clb; Band; Chorus; Concert Band; Mrchg Band; Pep Band; School Musical; Schuylkill Cnty Yth Cncl 85-87; Psych.

FOWLER, HOLLY; Bishop Conwell HS; Yardley, PA; (3); 97/277; Art Clb; Church Yth Grp; Cmnty Wkr; Hosp Aide; Spanish Clb; Chorus; Church Choir; Madrigals; Stage Crew; Crs Cntry; U OH Scrntn; Elem Ed.

FOWLER, IRENE; Sharpsville HS; Sharpsville, PA; (3); Library Aide; Math Clb; SADD; Yrbk Stf; VP Soph Cls; VP Jr Cls; Off Stu Cncl; Var Cheerleading; Hon Roll; NHS; Acctng.

FOWLER, JOHN; Oxford HS; Oxford, PA; (3); 40/200; Church Yth Grp; 4-H; Band; Chorus; Concert Band; Mrchg Band; Yrbk Stf; Bsktbl; Ftbl; Trk; U Of DE; Phscl Thrpy.

FOWLER, KIMBERLY; Jefferson-Morgan JR SR HS; Clarksville, PA; (2); 9/130; Spanish Clb; Varsity Clb; School Play; Pres Frsh Cls; Pres Soph Cls; Pres Jr Cls; Stu Cncl; Var L Bsktbl; JV Stat Sftbl; High Hon Roll; Carnegie Mellon.

FOWLER, KIMBERLY; Juniata HS; Mifflintown, PA; (3); Computer Clb; Drama Clb; SADD; Band; Variety Show; Nwsp Rptr; JV Var Fld Hcky; JV Sftbl; Hon Roll; Aerosp Engrng.

FOWLER, LAURA; Butler SR HS; Butler, PA; (3); Church Yth Grp; French Clb; Service Clb; Chorus; Orch; Hon Roll; Jr NHS; Ntl Merit Ltr; Taylor U; Elem Ed.

FOWLER, STEVE; Waynesburg Central HS; Waynesburg, PA; (3); 1/180; Church Yth Grp; Letterman Clb; Spanish Clb; Var Capt Bsktbl; Var L Crs Cntry; High Hon Roll; Pres NHS; NEDT Awd; Geolgy Awd-Waynesburg Coll Sci Fair 86; Engl III Awd, Chem III Awd 87.

FOWLES, MARK; State Coll Area Intermediate HS; Pine Grove Mills, PA; (1); Amer Assn Tchrs Ger Natl U S Test Prgm Cert Merit 87; ST Coll Area Schl Brd Cmmndtn 87; Mech Engr.

FOX, BRIAN W; Oley Valley HS; Fleetwood, PA; (4); 10/154; Pres Debate Tm; Scholastic Bowl; Teachers Aide; School Musical; School Play; Stage Crew; Nwsp Rptr; Nwsp Sprt Ed; Hon Roll; NHS; Outstndng Stu-Grmn & Engl 87; Wdrw Hrbn Merl Trst Fnd Awd-Vltry Schl Svc 87; Kutztown U; Scndry Educ.

FOX, CHRISTOPHER; Susquehanna Comm HS; Susquehanna, PA; (3); 7/84; Aud/Vis; Boy Scts; Church Yth Grp; Ski Clb; Bsbl; JV Var Bsktbl; High Hon Roll; Hon Roll; Ntl Merit Ltr; Penn ST U; Engrng.

FOX, DAVID; Cranberry HS; Kennerdell, PA; (3); Auto Transmssn Specist.

FOX, DENNIS; Waynesburg Central HS; Waynesburg, PA; (3); Letterman Clb; Library Aide; Ski Clb; SADD; Varsity Clb; School Play; Ftbl; Trk; Wt Lftg; Wrstlng; Slippery Rock; Englsh.

FOX, DUANE; William Allen HS; Allentown, PA; (2); 50/634; Church Yth Grp; Band; Chorus; Church Choir; Concert Band; Mrchg Band; Orch; Pep Band; School Musical; Hon Roll.

FOX, HEATHER; Oil City Area HS; Oil City, PA; (3); AFS; Church Yth Grp; Varsity Clb; Yrbk Stf; Stu Cncl; JV Capt Cheerleading; Hon Roll.

FOX, HELEN; State Coll Area Intermediate HS; State College, PA; (2); 5/497; Church Yth Grp; Cmnty Wkr; Cit Awd; Hon Roll; Prfct Atten Awd; Judge Richard M Sharp Awd Excllnc Acdmc & Cvc Achvt 86-87; Acdmc Achvt Awd Top 10 Pct Clss 86-87.

FOX, HOLLY; Gettysburg SR HS; Gettysburg, PA; (4); Ski Clb; SADD; Chorus; School Musical; School Play; Swing Chorus; Variety Show; Yrbk Ed-Chief; Yrbk Stf; Stu Cncl; Hildegard Hamme Schl Dance Trophy 86, Grad 87; Gettysburg Coll Summr Theatre Credts 86; Philadelphia Coll; Dance.

FOX, JASON; Central York HS; York, PA; (3); 21/248; Boy Scts; Church Yth Grp; Ski Clb; Socr; High Hon Roll; Hon Roll; NHS.

FOX, JENNIFER L; Western Wayne HS; Waymart, PA; (4); 24/142; Exploring; FBLA; Office Aide; Spanish Clb; Yrbk Stf; Mgr(s); Var Trk; Wrstlng; Hon Roll; NHS; Marymount U; Mktg.

FOX, JOSEPH M; Archbishop Ryan Boys HS; Philadelphia, PA; (2); 10/352; Off Soph Cls; JV Bsktbl; JV Ftbl; Hon Roll.

FOX, MELISSA ANN; Plymouth-Whitemarsh HS; Plymouth Meeting, PA; (4); Computer Clb; Hosp Aide; Intnl Clb; Mu Alpha Theta; Science Clb; Spanish Clb; VP Temple Yth Grp; Concert Band; Cheerleading; Mgr Golf; Med.

FOX, RONDA; Lock Haven SR HS; Flemington, PA; (3); Pres Hst FHA; Prfct Atten Awd; Srvc Awds Rainbow Grls 85; 1 Top Sllrs Daffodil Days Cancer Soc 84; Elem Educ.

FOX, SHANNON; Reading SR HS; Reading, PA; (3); 55/710; Library Aide; Model UN; Chorus; Elem Schl Tchr.

FOX, SUSAN; Purchase Line HS; Commodore, PA; (4); 2/106; Pres SADD; Trs Jr Cls; Stu Cncl; Capt Twrlr; High Hon Roll; Lion Awd; VP NHS; Hmcmng Crt 86; JR Prom Prncs 86; Elem Ed.

FOX, TINA; John Harris HS; Harrisburg, PA; (2); 51/356; Church Yth Grp; 4-H; ROTC; Chorus; Law.

FOX, TRISHA; Rocky Grove HS; Oil City, PA; (4); 20/96; French Clb; Yrbk Ed-Chief; Off Soph Cls; Off Jr Cls; Off Sr Cls; VP Stu Cncl; Var Vllybl; Hon Roll; Pres Schlr; Vrsty Vlybl MVP 85-87; Acadc Excel Awd 86-87; IN U PA; Psych.

FOX, VANCE; Council Rock HS; Washington, PA; (3); 112/905; Church Yth Grp; Rep Frsh Cls; L Bsbl; L Ftbl; Im Vllybl; Hon Roll; NHS; Bus.

FOXWORTH, REGGIE; Farrell SR HS; Farrell, PA; (3); Boy Scts; Computer Clb; Spanish Clb; Speech Tm; Varsity Clb; Pep Band; Yrbk Stf; Pres Soph Cls; Var L Trk; Hon Roll; NC A T & T; Comp Pgmr.

FOY, COLLEEN; John S Fine HS; Nanticoke, PA; (3); 24/228; Key Clb; Chorus; Concert Band; Mrchg Band; Swmmng; High Hon Roll; HOBY Fndtn Ambssdr 86; Yng Cmmnty Ldrs Of Amer 86; Spch Thrpst.

FOY, KARYN; St Basil Acad; Philadelphia, PA; (3); 8/82; Church Yth Grp; Drama Clb; French Clb; Science Clb; Varsity Clb; School Play; VP Soph Cls; VP Jr Cls; Off Stu Cncl; Var Bsktbl; High Honor Roll 86-87; Natl Merit Ltr Engl 86-87; Scty Dist Amer HS Studs 86-87; Crmnl Justice.

FOY, LISA; Venango Christian HS; Oil City, PA; (4); Cmnty Wkr; SADD; Variety Show; Nwsp Rptr; Yrbk Stf; L Var Bsktbl; L Var Cheerleading; High Hon Roll; Hon Roll; NHS; Gannon U; Humanities.

FOY, SEAN; Downington SR HS; Coatsville, PA; (3); 36/648; German Clb; Ski Clb; Band; Concert Band; Mrchg Band; Capt Bowling; High Hon Roll; Hon Roll; NHS; Ntl Merit SF; Comp Sci.

FOY, TAMMY; West Mifflin Area HS; W Mifflin, PA; (3); Drama Clb; Pep Clb; Orch; School Play; Off Stu Cncl; High Hon Roll; Hon Roll; Jr NHS; NHS; Ag Inst Mnrty Stu AIMS Pgm 86; Sndy Schl Atten Awd 84; Pitt; Math.

FOY, TINA; Venango Christian HS; Oil City, PA; (4); 18/36; Cmnty Wkr; SADD; Sftbl; High Hon Roll; Hon Roll; NHS; Bus Awd 87; Venango Campus; Bus.

FOZARD, DARLENE; Bishop Guilfoyle HS; Altoona, PA; (4); 13/123; Pres Speech Tm; Co-Capt Drill Tm; Nwsp Rptr; Rep Stu Cncl; High Hon Roll; Hon Roll; NHS; Voice Dem Awd; Sec Church Yth Grp; Cmnty Wkr; Hugh O Brian Fndtn Yth Ldrshp 84-85; Wrtg.

FRABLE, TAMIE; Mid-Valley HS; Olyphant, PA; (3); Drama Clb; French Clb; School Play; VP Soph Cls; Pres Jr Cls; Pres Sr Cls; Rep Stu Cncl; Crs Cntry.

FRADIN, CHRISTINA; Fox Chapel HS; Pittsburgh, PA; (3); Church Yth Grp; English Clb; French Clb; Key Clb; Ski Clb; SADD; Lit Mag; L Var Crs Cntry; High Hon Roll; NHS; Math.

FRAGIN, JODI; Abington Hgts HS; Clarks Green, PA; (3); 10/283; Ski Clb; Yrbk Stf; VP Lit Mag; Pres Frsh Cls; Off Stu Cncl; Trk; Co-Capt Twrlr; Cit Awd; Hon Roll; NHS; Schltc Art Awd, Cert Merit 86; Natl Hstry Day Dist Comptn 3rd Pl 86; 1st Awd 5 Man Triathln Team 86.

FRAIL, CHARLENE; E L Meyers HS; Wilkes-Barre, PA; (3); 31/188; Trs FBLA; German Clb; Hosp Aide; SADD; Chorus; Rep Stu Cncl; Var L Fld Hcky; High Hon Roll; Hon Roll; Jr NHS; Acdmc All Amer Frgn Lang 86; Accntng.

FRAILEY, TAMMY; Pocono Mountain HS; Swiftwater, PA; (3); 95/300; Church Yth Grp; Pep Clb; Q&S; SADD; Sec Band; Chorus; Church Choir; Concert Band; Mrchg Band; Pep Band; Music Bus.

FRALICK, JASON; Millersburg Area HS; Millersburg, PA; (2); Church Yth Grp; VP Soph Cls; Rep Stu Cncl; JV Bsktbl; Var Ftbl; Cit Awd; Hon Roll.

FRAMBES, CATHERINE M; Philadelphia HS For Girls; Philadelphia, PA; (3); 155/405; Teachers Aide; Var L Trk; Hon Roll; PA Coll; Physcl Thrpy.

FRAMPTON, MARSHA R; North Star HS; Boswell, PA; (4); FCA; Mu Alpha Theta; SADD; Chorus; Concert Band; Mrchg Band; School Play; Swing Chorus; Cit Awd; Venture Awd 87; Radlgy.

FRAMPTON, MATTHEW; West Perry SR HS; Shermansdale, PA; (2); 19/222; Spanish Clb; Chorus; Concert Band; Jazz Band; Mrchg Band; JV Socr; Trk; Military; Elec.

FRANCAVILLA, JILL; New Hope-Solebury HS; Lahaska, PA; (3); Ski Clb; Band; Drill Tm; Sec Frsh Cls; Sec Soph Cls; Stu Cncl; Var Fld Hcky; Score Keeper; Hon Roll; NHS; Hnrbl Mntn All Lgu Field Hcky 86.

FRANCESCHI, ELSA; Mon Valley Catholic HS; Belle Vernon, PA; (3); Am Leg Aux Girls St; Cmnty Wkr; French Clb; Ski Clb; Teachers Aide; Band; Mrchg Band; Nwsp Stf; Yrbk Stf; French Hon Soc.

FRANCESCHI, JAVIER; William Allen HS; Allentown, PA; (3); Key Clb; Rep Stu Cncl; JV Socr; JV Var Wrstlng; Hon Roll; Jr NHS; Penn ST U; Med.

FRANCESCHINA, GENE; North Hills HS; Pittsburgh, PA; (4); 14/467; Cmnty Wkr; JA; Concert Band; Mrchg Band; Pep Band; Symp Band; High Hon Roll; NHS; IUP Physics Awd 86; Carnegie Mellon U; Elec Engrng.

FRANCHAK, MICHAEL; Richland HS; Wexford, PA; (4); 1/183; Church Yth Grp; Scholastic Bowl; Nwsp Sprt Ed; Rep Stu Cncl; Var Capt Bsbl; Var Capt Ftbl; Var L Trk; High Hon Roll; NHS; Ntl Merit Ltr; Vet Med Apprentcshp; Pres Physcl Ftns Awd; Duke U; Elect Engr.

FRANCHEK, JENNIFER; West Allegheny HS; Imperial, PA; (3); Sec Art Clb; FBLA; Capt Color Guard; Drill Tm; Intl Bus Mgmt.

FRANCHI, DAYNA; Plum SR HS; Pittsburgh, PA; (3); SADD; Varsity Clb; Crs Cntry; Swmmng; Trk; Hon Roll; Vrsty Ltr Swmmng 85; Vrsty Ltr Crs Cntry 86; Vrsty Ltr Trk 86 & 87; U Pittsburgh; Chiro.

FRANCHOCK, NEAL; Moshannon Valley HS; Glen Hope, PA; (3); Church Yth Grp; FCA; Letterman Clb; Varsity Clb; L Var Bsbl; JV Wrstlng; Envrnmntl Sci.

FRANCIS, GREG; Conestoga HS; Strafford, PA; (2); Church Yth Grp; Drama Clb; School Play; Stage Crew; Lit Mag; Prfct Atten Awd; Psycht.

FRANCIS JR, JOSEPH M; Bishop Guilfoyle HS; Altoona, PA; (3); Church Yth Grp; Ski Clb; Ftbl; Golf; Hon Roll; Amer Lgn Awd 84; Bstn Coll; Chmstry.

FRANCIS, SANDRA; Upper Moreland HS; Willow Gr, PA; (3); 57/275; JV Cheerleading; High Hon Roll; Hon Roll; Penn ST; Math.

FRANCIS, STACEY; Western Beaver HS; Beaver, PA; (3); Cmnty Wkr; Chorus; School Musical; Bowling; Var JV Cheerleading; High Hon Roll; Hon Roll; Above-Avg Ctznshp 86-87; Sci.

FRANCISKO, JENNIFER; West Branch Area HS; Morrisdale, PA; (3); Office Aide; Spanish Clb; Trs SADD; Varsity Clb; Chorus; Mrchg Band; JV Cheerleading; Mgr(s); Socr; Sftbl; Mrktng.

FRANCK, LORIE; Warwick HS; Lititz, PA; (4); AFS; Church Yth Grp; Drama Clb; Color Guard; Drill Tm; Cheerleading; Twrlr; Artwrk Displyd Capitl Cngrssnl Art Awd 85-86; Numrs Wmns Club Art Awds 84-87; Savannah Coll Art & Dsgn; Grphc.

FRANEK, JENNIFER; Garnet Valley HS; Boothwyn, PA; (2); Church Yth Grp; French Clb; Intnl Clb; Ski Clb; JV Fld Hcky; JV Trk; Hon Roll; Prfct Atten Awd; Biochem.

FRANEK JR, JOHN J; Moshannon Valley HS; Ginter, PA; (3); 22/112; VICA; JV Ftbl; Masnry.

FRANEY, DAVID; Central Catholic District HS; E Pittsburgh, PA; (3); Im Fld Hcky; Im Ftbl; JV Wrstlng; High Hon Roll; Hon Roll; NHS; Duquesne U.

FRANGAKIS, JOHN ROBERT; West Middlesex JR-SR HS; West Middlesex, PA; (3); 1/110; Church Yth Grp; Key Clb; Spanish Clb; Band; Jazz Band; Pep Band; Nwsp Phtg; Yrbk Phtg; Off Stu Cncl; NHS; US Achvt Acad 85-86; High Hnr Rll 85-86; Hugh O Brien Yth Ldrshp Rep 86; Intl Rltns.

FRANGIONE, PEGGY; Eisenhower HS; Sugar Grove, PA; (4); Math Tm; Office Aide; Spanish Clb; Teachers Aide; Yrbk Phtg; Yrbk Stf; JV Vllybl; High Hon Roll; Hon Roll; NHS; Jets Tm Awd 86; Eagle Awd 86; FL Inst Of Tech; Marine Bio.

FRANK, ELLEN; Plymouth Whitemarsh HS; Norristown, PA; (4); 35/335; VP FTA; Teachers Aide; Flag Corp; Ed Nwsp Stf; Var Mat Maids; High Hon Roll; NHS; Pres Schlr; Future Educ Awd 87; Syracuse U; Elem Ed.

FRANK, GEORGE; Shenango HS; New Castle, PA; (2); Spanish Clb; High Hon Roll; Amer Chem Soc Awd 87; Phy.

FRANK, HEATHER; Downingtown SR HS; Exton, PA; (3); 1/648; Church Yth Grp; FTA; German Clb; Flag Corp; Swmmng; High Hon Roll; NHS; NEDT Awd; SADD; Band; NEDT Awd 86; German Awd 85; Dstngshd Hon Rroll 85-86; Math.

FRANK, JODI; Shenango HS; New Castle, PA; (3); 20/125; Church Yth Grp; 4-H; Speech Tm; Concert Band; Jazz Band; Mrchg Band; Pep Band; Vllybl; Hon Roll; Awds In Frnscs-Oral Intrprtn 85-86; Bus Admin.

FRANK, KEVIN; Sugar Valley HS; Loganton, PA; (4); Church Yth Grp; FFA; Leo Clb; Library Aide; Service Clb; Spanish Clb; Band; Chorus; Concert Band; Mrchg Band; Sm Gas Engines Awd 87; Police Acad; St Trpr.

FRANK, NICOLE; Bishop Carroll HS; Ebensburg, PA; (3); Drama Clb; SADD; Stage Crew; Var Trk; Hon Roll; Rehab Cnclng.

FRANK JR, ROBERT E; Norristown Area HS; Norristown, PA; (3); 31/467; Concert Band; Mgr Sftbl; Var Wrstlng.

FRANK, SHERRI; Central Cambria HS; Ebensburg, PA; (4); 3/214; Key Clb; Ski Clb; Yrbk Stf; Hst Frsh Cls; Sec Soph Cls; Sec Jr Cls; Sec Sr Cls; High Hon Roll; Hon Roll.

FRANK, STEPHANIE; Tamaqua Area HS; Tuscarora, PA; (3); 42/247; French Clb; Pep Clb; Q&S; Science Clb; Chorus; Church Choir; Ed Nwsp Ed-Chief; Cheerleading; Stat Ftbl; Mgr(s); PA ST Press Assn Kystn Awd 86; Ldrshp Cncl 86-87; Psych.

FRANK, TIM; Altoona Area HS; Altoona, PA; (2); Computer Clb; German Clb; Math Clb; Math Tm; Nwsp Rptr; JV Bsktbl; High Hon Roll; Jr NHS; NHS; Pres Schlr; Political Wkr; Hghst Avg Math Awd 86.

FRANK, TISHA; Chambersburg Area SR HS; Chambersburg, PA; (2); Spanish Clb; JV Capt Bsktbl; Var L Sftbl; Vllybl; Hon Roll; Child Psych.

FRANK II, VINCENT P; Altoona Area HS; Altoona, PA; (3); 31/762; Boy Scts; Chess Clb; German Clb; Math Clb; Math Tm; Political Wkr; Jazz Band; Var Swmmng; High Hon Roll; Pres Schlr; Soc Sci.

FRANK, WENDY; North Hills HS; Pittsburgh, PA; (3); Church Yth Grp; Cmnty Wkr; Hosp Aide; Chorus; Rep Stu Cncl; Cheerleading; Trk; High Hon Roll; Hon Roll; NHS; Bus.

FRANKE, PAUL; Frankford HS; Philadelphia, PA; (3); 15/679; Var Bsbl; Var Mgr(s); Im Sftbl; Hon Roll; Bus.

FRANKENBERRY, ROBERT N; North East HS; North East, PA; (4); 12/141; Sec Church Yth Grp; Speech Tm; Thesps; VP Chorus; Concert Band; Drm Mjr(t); Nwsp Stf; Var L Crs Cntry; Var L Trk; Ntl Merit Ltr; PA All ST Chorus 86-87; MENC Estrn Div Conf, All Estrn Chorus 87; Florne Wagner Schlrshp 86; D Angelo Schl Music; Piano.

FRANKHOUSER, MARK; Philipsburg-Osceola Area HS; Philipsburg, PA; (4); 16/234; Chess Clb; Computer Clb; Rep Stu Cncl; Hon Roll; Ctzns Of Tmrrw 86; PA ST U; Elec Engr.

FRANKLIN, ANDY; Northampton SR HS; Bath, PA; (3); 81/496; Leo Clb; Ski Clb; Yrbk Stf; Ftbl; Socr; Trk; Hon Roll; Pres Schlr; Aviation.

FRANKLIN, ANTHONY; Henderson HS; W Chester, PA; (3); Church Yth Grp; High Hon Roll; Hon Roll; Radlgst.

FRANKLIN JR, BARRETT M; Bishop Boyle HS; Homestead, PA; (4); Church Yth Grp; English Clb; NAACP; Bsktbl; Ftbl; High Hon Roll; Hon Roll; NHS; Merit Awd Amer Hist 83; Engl Awd 83; Soc Stds Awd 83; Penn ST U; Bus Adm.

FRANKLIN, BEN; Northern Cambria HS; Barnesboro, PA; (4); 28/128; Letterman Clb; Church Choir; Jr Cls; Rep Stu Cncl; Ftbl; Wt Lftg; High Hon Roll; Hon Roll; IUP; Bio.

FRANKLIN, CHRISTOPHER; Hatboro-Horsham HS; Horsham, PA; (3); 99/250; FCA; Red Cross Aide; Bsbl; Ftbl; Ice Hcky; Wrstlng; Rotary Awd; Letterman Clb; Varsity Clb; Coach Actv; Phys Ed Hghst Hnrs 86-87; 1st Tm All Area Wrstlng 86-87; 2nd Tm All Area Bsbl 86-87; Temple U; Comp Sci.

FRANKLIN, LISA; Ringgold HS; Finleyville, PA; (4); Teachers Aide; Chorus; Nwsp Stf; Hon Roll; Sawyer Bus Schl; Trvl Agnt.

FRANKO, GILLY; Meadville Area SR HS; Meadville, PA; (3); JCL; Latin Clb; Pres Frsh Cls; Rep Soph Cls; Pres Jr Cls; Rep Pres Stu Cncl; Var L Sftbl; Var L Vllybl; Hon Roll.

FRANKO, LISA; Tunkhannock HS; Tunkhannock, PA; (4); 3/286; Art Clb; Dance Clb; Math Tm; Scholastic Bowl; Science Clb; Yrbk Bus Mgr; Yrbk Ed-Chief; Yrbk Phtg; Trs Soph Cls; Crs Cntry; Acad Schlr Awd 84-86.

FRANKO, MARY; Plum SR HS; Pittsburgh, PA; (3); Dance Clb; French Clb; School Musical; Bsktbl; Tennis; Trk; Hon Roll; 1st Humnts Day Cont Frnch 87; Ed.

FRANKOVICH, LAURI; Shenango HS; New Castle, PA; (4); 19/111; Exploring; French Clb; Library Aide; Office Aide; Drill Tm; Stat Bsbl; NHS; Natl Merit Awd In Sci 86; Comptve Schlrshp 87; Duquesne U; Phar.

FRANKS, MELINDA; Kiski Area SR HS; New Kensington, PA; (3); Computer Clb; Spanish Clb; SADD; VICA; Symp Band; High Hon Roll; Hnrs & Cnty Band; Pres Phys Ftnss Awd; Certfd Nrs Asstnt 86-87; Med.

FRANKS, SHERRY; Penns Valley Area HS; Centre Hall, PA; (3); Art Clb; Church Yth Grp; Trs Girl Scts; Ski Clb; Sec Spanish Clb; Church Choir; JV Sftbl; Hon Roll; Natl Art Hnr Soc Treasr 86-87; Yrbk Artst 87-88; Bio.

FRANO, JOHN; Central Christian HS; Dubois, PA; (3); 10/48; Computer Clb; Exploring; JA; Var JV Bsbl; Var JV Bsktbl; Var Crs Cntry; Var Golf; High Hon Roll; Hon Roll; NHS; Penn ST; Bus Admin.

FRANSKO, MADELINE; Elizabeth-Forward HS; Elizabeth, PA; (2); Church Yth Grp; Dance Clb; French Clb; Pep Clb; Chorus; Yrbk Stf; Swmmng; French Hon Soc; Hon Roll; U Of Pittsburgh; Psych.

FRANTZ, BARBARA F; Williams Valley JR SR HS; Williamstown, PA; (2); Band; Chorus; Concert Band; Mrchg Band; School Musical; Symp Band; Rep Stu Cncl; Co-Capt Powder Puff Ftbl; Score Keeper; Mgr Sftbl; Penn ST; Chem Engr.

FRANTZ, CHRISTOPHER; South Western HS; Brodbecks, PA; (3); Y-Teens; Golf; NEDT Awd; Bus Admin.

FRANTZ, DEBRA D; East Stroudsburg HS; E Stroudsburg, PA; (4); 49/210; Art Clb; VP Exploring; Ski Clb; Stat Bsbl; Var Capt Cheerleading; Mgr(s); Var L Trk; Shippensburg U; Bus.

FRANTZ, MELISSA; Butler Area HS; Butler, PA; (3); Library Aide; Thesps; Concert Band; Mrchg Band; Stu Cncl; Hon Roll; Jr NHS; Rainbow Girls Worth Advisor 86; Psych.

FRANTZ, MICHELE; Donegal HS; Mount Joy, PA; (4); 6/158; Girl Scts; Teachers Aide; Band; Concert Band; Mrchg Band; School Play; Symp Band; Mgr(s); High Hon Roll; NHS; Am Clsscl Leag Cum Laude Awd; Lock Haven U; Scndry Math.

FRANTZ, PAMELA; Elizabethtown Area HS; Elizabethtown, PA; (4); 40/240; Camera Clb; Church Yth Grp; Teachers Aide; Church Choir; Nwsp Rptr; Yrbk Rptr; Yrbk Stf; Powder Puff Ftbl; Sftbl; Twrlr; Immaculata Coll.

FRANTZ, ROBERT; Bradford Central Christian HS; Bradford, PA; (3); 12/26; Computer Clb; Key Clb; Science Clb; Sec Soph Cls; Sec Jr Cls; Var L Bsbl; Var L Bsktbl; Triangle Tech; Comp Drftng.

FRANTZ, RUSSEL; Punxsutawney Area HS; Punxsutawney, PA; (3); Church Yth Grp; French Clb; Band; Mrchg Band; Orch; Pep Band; L Cheerleading; Var Crs Cntry; Var Trk; Hon Roll; US Chrldr Achvt Awd 86-87; Nrsng.

FRANTZ, SONIA; Parkland SR HS; Slatington, PA; (4); 43/438; Teachers Aide; Var Trk; High Hon Roll; Hon Roll; NHS; Prfct Atten Awd; Cert Of Apprctn For Leukemia 86; Kyston Awd For Outstndng Achvt In Bus Ed Crrclm 87; Olympa USA Awd; Southeastern Acad; Trvl.

FRANTZ, THOMAS; Selinsgrove HS; Winfield, PA; (1); Church Yth Grp; FFA; Hon Roll; CRPNTRY.

FRASER, BILL; Knoch JR-SR HS; Butler, PA; (4); Church Yth Grp; Science Clb; JV Bsktbl; Var Ftbl; Var Trk; Var Wt Lftg; High Hon Roll; Pres Schlr; Grove City Coll; Bus Admin.

FRASER, JACK; United HS; Seward, PA; (3); 55/147; Church Yth Grp; Cmnty Wkr; Ski Clb; VP Jr Cls; Off Stu Cncl; Var L Bsbl; Var L Bsktbl; Var L Ftbl; Wt Lftg; Hon Roll; Annual Blairsvl Disptch All Star Ftbll Team 86; All IN Gazette Ftbll Team 86.

FRASER, LAURIE; Upper Dublin HS; Maple Glen, PA; (3); 88/297; Church Yth Grp; Intnl Clb; Nwsp Stf; Lit Mag; Stat Fld Hcky; Powder Puff Ftbl; Psychlgy.

FRASK, SCOTT; Hazleton SR HS; Hazleton, PA; (3); VICA; Wrstlng; Hon Roll; Archt.

FRATANGELI, LISA; Aliquippa SR HS; Aliquippa, PA; (3); French Clb; Office Aide; Band; Mrchg Band; Twrlr; Engl Merit Awd 83-84; Music.

FRATI, SANDI; Old Forge HS; Old Forge, PA; (2); Dance Clb; Soph Cls; Cheerleading; Hon Roll; Nrsng.

FRATTO, RAYMOND; Montour HS; Mc Kees Rocks, PA; (4); 16/317; Church Yth Grp; Math Tm; SADD; Jazz Band; Pres Sr Cls; Var Bsktbl; Var Socr; Var Trk; Var High Hon Roll; NHS; Provost Smmr Schlrshp U Of Pitt 86; Carnegie Mellore U; Engr.

FRATTONE, MICHAEL; Saint John Neumann HS; Philadelphia, PA; (4); 3/336; Letterman Clb; Capt Math Clb; Math Tm; Pres Science Clb; Service Clb; Im Bsktbl; Var L Tennis; High Hon Roll; NHS; Ntl Merit Ltr; Archdiocese Of Phila Dstngshd Schlr Awd, City Schlrshp, St Josephs U Pres Schlrshp, KC Awd 87; St Josephs U; Bus.

FRAVEL, BRADLEY; Neshaminy HS; Levittown, PA; (3); Cmnty Wkr; Computer Clb; FCA; Nwsp Sprt Ed; Yrbk Sprt Ed; Stu Cncl; L Ftbl; L Trk; Var Wrstlng; Hon Roll; Penn ST U; Pltcl Sci.

FRAVEL, DEBORAH; Athens HS; Athens, PA; (4); 5/142; Art Clb; FBLA; Scholastic Bowl; SADD; Trs Soph Cls; Pres Stu Cncl; Capt L Bsktbl; Capt L Vllybl; Bausch & Lomb Sci Awd; VP NHS; Army Schlr/Athl Awd 87; Outstndng Cls Stu Athl Awd 87; HOBY Awd 85-86; Purdue U; Chem Engrng.

FRAVEL, KELLEY; Lock Haven HS; Flemington, PA; (3); Church Yth Grp; Spanish Clb; SADD; Color Guard; Drill Tm; Mat Maids; Prfct Atten Awd; PA Free Enterprise Wk 86-87; Girls Assn For Progress & Svc 86-87; Rainbow For Girls 85-87; Lock Haven U; Bus Mgmt.

FRAYNE, CATHRYN; Bensalem HS; Bensalem, PA; (3); Cmnty Wkr; Band; Color Guard; Co-Capt Drill Tm; Mrchg Band; High Hon Roll; Embry-Riddle; Aerontcl Engrng.

FRAZEE, JOHN; Rockwood Area HS; Somerset, PA; (3); 1/77; Aud/Vis; Computer Clb; Pres NFL; Speech Tm; Concert Band; Jazz Band; Mrchg Band; High Hon Roll; Pres Acadmc Ftns Awd 84-85; Natl Lang Arts Plympd Awd 85; Air Force; Elctrnc Engrng.

FRAZER, CHRISTIN; Homer Ctr; Homer City, PA; (4); Pres VP Library Aide; School Play; Hst Sr Cls; Stu Cncl; DAR Awd; Sec NHS; French Clb; FBLA; VP Soph Cls; VP Jr Cls; Health Careers Clb Schlrshp 87; Amer Lgn Post 493 Schlrshp 87; Sr Mnth Awd 87; Pres Acad Ftns Awd 87; Grove City Coll; Biology.

FRAZER, ROSS; Homer Center HS; Homer City, PA; (3); 6/111; Pres VP Church Yth Grp; French Clb; Library Aide; Pres SADD; Chorus; High Hon Roll; Hon Roll; Jr NHS; NHS; Bus.

FRAZEY, PAUL; West Chester Henderson HS; West Chester, PA; (3); 20/350; Church Yth Grp; Nwsp Rptr; Yrbk Rptr; Trs Frsh Cls; Var Ftbl; Var Tennis; Var Trk; Hon Roll; NHS; Spanish NHS; Drexel; Engr.

FRAZIER JR, ANDREW; Peabody HS; Pittsburgh, PA; (4); #11 In Class; JA; Math Tm; Co-Capt Tennis; High Hon Roll; NHS; Pres Classrm 86; Natl Achvt For Outstndng Negro Stu Semi-Fnlst 86; MITE Pgm At Howard U & U Of MD 85; Engrng.

FRAZIER, CINDY; Sto-Rox SR HS; Mckees Rocks, PA; (2); Church Yth Grp; FBLA; JA; Library Aide; Office Aide; Nwsp Stf; Yrbk Stf; Im Sftbl; Im Vllybl; Hon Roll; Robert Morris Coll; Bus Mgmt.

FRAZIER, DAVID; Eastern Lebanon County HS; Lebanon, PA; (4); 1/159; Chess Clb; Church Yth Grp; Quiz Bowl; Yrbk Phtg; Var L Bsktbl; Var L Socr; Bausch & Lomb Sci Awd; High Hon Roll; NHS; Bausch & Lomb Sci Awd 86; Natl Hnr Scty 85-87; Natl Merit Sci Awd 86; MIT; Engr.

FRAZIER, DAVID; Hollidaysburg Area SR HS; Duncansville, PA; (3); 84/385; Varsity Clb; Chorus; Variety Show; VP Rep Stu Cncl; Var L Golf; Var Trk; Var L Wrstlng.

FRAZIER, JODI; Connellsville Area SR HS; Connellsville, PA; (3); Exploring; VICA; Band; Hon Roll; Campus Life Stu Ldr 85-87; Dimensions Clb Sec 85-86; Nurses Aide 84-85; Uniontown Beauty Acad; Cosmtlgy.

FRAZIER, SCOTT; Gateway HS; Monroeville, PA; (2); JV Bsktbl; Var L Ftbl; Hon Roll.

FRAZIER, SCOTT; Lock Haven SR HS; Lock Haven, PA; (3); Boy Scts; Church Yth Grp; German Clb; Band; Chorus; Church Choir; Concert Band; Jazz Band; Mrchg Band; Orch; Kappa Kappa Psi Strive Hghst 87; Miriam Claster Scholar 87; Music Instr.

FRAZIER, SHANNON; South Fayette JR SR HS; Bridgeville, PA; (4); 7/71; FBLA; Key Clb; Science Clb; Co-Capt Cheerleading; Hon Roll; Sec NHS; Washington & Jefferson; Bus Adm.

FRAZIER, WOODROW; Duquesne HS; Duquesne, PA; (3); #17 In Class; Ftbl; Hon Roll; NHS; Air Frc Acad; Aviation.

FREAS, DAVID; Abington SR HS; Glenside, PA; (3); 73/502; Band; Concert Band; Jazz Band; Mrchg Band; Symp Band; Lcrss; NHS; Comp Sci.

FREAS, DAWN E; Abington SR HS; Glenside, PA; (4); 43/492; Church Yth Grp; VP Girl Scts; Sec Varsity Clb; Rep Stu Cncl; Var Fld Hcky; Var Lcrss; Hon Roll; Kiwanis Awd; NHS; Pres Schlr; Ind Arts Awd 86-87; W Eugene Stull Awd 86-87; Bst Female Ath 86-87; VA Tech; Arch.

FRECH, TIM; Marion Center Area HS; Home, PA; (4); 38/173; VICA; Hon Roll; OH ST U; Welding Engrng.

FRECHIONE, TINA; Trinity Christian Schl; Pittsburgh, PA; (1); 3/16; Chorus; Hon Roll; Jr NHS; NEDT Awd; U Pittsburgh; Zoology.

FREDELLA, BRADLEY; Mechanicsburg Area SR HS; Mechanicsburg, PA; (3); French Clb; Ski Clb; Hon Roll; U Of CA; Engrng.

FREDERICK, ALEX; Lake-Lehman HS; Harveys Lake, PA; (3); Ski Clb; SADD; Rep Stu Cncl; Var L Bsktbl; Var Ftbl; L Vllybl; Hon Roll; Jr NHS; NHS; Rotary Clb Ldrshp Camp 86; Nom For Hugh O Brien Yth Ldrshp Awd 86; Busi.

FREDERICK, AMY; Burrell HS; Lower Burrell, PA; (3); AFS; Am Leg Aux Girls St; French Clb; SADD; Band; Mrchg Band; Yrbk Stf; Pres Frsh Cls; VP Soph Cls; Pres Stu Cncl; Americn Lgn Awd 84; Rep At Studnt Forums 85; Duquesne U; Crmnlgy.

FREDERICK, AMY; North Star HS; Boswell, PA; (2); Dance Clb; FCA; Hosp Aide; Band; Chorus; Concert Band; Mgr Mrchg Band; JV Vllybl; Hon Roll; Cnty Band Awds 86-87; Cnty Chorus 87; Psych.

FREDERICK, JAMIE; Freeport HS; Sarver, PA; (3); 66/213; Hosp Aide; Drm Mjr(t); VP Soph Cls; Capt Twrlr; Hon Roll; Mrchg Band; Speech Pathology.

FREDERICK, KRISTOFER; Central Dauphing East HS; Enhaut Steelton, PA; (4); 11/237; Debate Tm; Political Wkr; Spanish Clb; Golf; NHS; Pres Schlr; Rotary Awd; Woodman Of Wrld Amer Hstry Awd 86-87; WA; Poltcl Sci.

FREDERICK, MARK; Mohawk HS; New Galilee, PA; (3); Spanish Clb; Bsbl; Ftbl; Wt Lftg; Hon Roll; Spanish NHS; Ltrmn Bsbl 84-87; Ltrmn Ftbl 85-86; Criminology.

FREDERICK, REBECCA; Brandywine Heights Area HS; Mertztown, PA; (3); 10/117; Church Yth Grp; Girl Scts; Chorus; School Play; Yrbk Stf; High Hon Roll; Hon Roll; NHS; Ntl Merit Ltr; Hosp Aide; Psychologist.

FREDERICK, ROBB; Moon SR HS; Corapolis, PA; (3); Boy Scts; Chess Clb; Computer Clb; German Clb; SADD; Rep Frsh Cls; Rep Soph Cls; Rep Jr Cls; Rep Stu Cncl; Var Diving; Bus Admin.

FREDERICKS, CHRISTOPHER J; East Allegheny HS; E Mc Keesport, PA; (4); 8/213; Ski Clb; School Musical; Bsktbl; High Hon Roll; Hon Roll; NHS; Ntl Merit SF; Opt Clb Awd; Amer Legn Awd 84; PA Cert Of Merit 86; U Of Southern CA; Wrtng.

FREDERICKS, JOHN R; Nativity BVM HS; Pottsville, PA; (4); 1/93; NFL; Variety Show; Nwsp Stf; Off Soph Cls; Off Jr Cls; Pres Stu Cncl; Stat Bsktbl; Score Keeper; Bausch & Lomb Sci Awd; High Hon Roll; Allentwn Diocesese Pro-Life Essay Wnr 86; PHSSL ST Radio Anncng Chmpn 86; Natl Jr Sci Sympsm 87; Kings Clg; Chem.

FREDERICKS, THAIS; Panther Valley HS; Lansford, PA; (2); 20/120; Church Yth Grp; Cheerleading; Hon Roll; Penn ST U; Psych.

FREEBERG, MICHELE; Moshannon Valley HS; Houtzdale, PA; (3); Church Yth Grp; Spanish Clb; Varsity Clb; Chorus; JV Var Cheerleading; JV Var Sftbl; Amer Cancer Soc Chrldr 84-86; Clarion; Bus Admn.

FREED, GLENN; Ambridge Area HS; Baden, PA; (3); Computer Clb; Math Tm; Pep Clb; Spanish Clb; SADD; High Hon Roll; Prfct Atten Awd; Secndry Math Ed.

FREED, JENNIFER AILEENE; East Pennsboro Area HS; Camp Hill, PA; (3); Sec Art Clb; Church Yth Grp; Drama Clb; GAA; Latin Clb; Model UN; Band; Chorus; Church Choir; Concert Band; Military; Arts.

FREED, JOSEPH; York Catholic HS; York, PA; (2); 4/146; Cmnty Wkr; Spanish Clb; Var L Golf; High Hon Roll; Hon Roll; York Cnty All-Star Glf 87; Bus.

FREED, LORI; Central Bucks HS East; New Hope, PA; (4); 63/452; Pres Trs Church Yth Grp; Pres Trs 4-H; Red Cross Aide; Ski Clb; Stage Crew; Yrbk Phtg; Yrbk Stf; 4-H Awd; High Hon Roll; Hon Roll; 1st Pl Math Cont 84; VA Polytechnc Inst; Pre Vet.

FREED, MICHELE LYNN; Hork Catholic HS; York, PA; (4); 2/166; FBLA; Chorus; School Musical; School Play; Nwsp Stf; Yrbk Ed-Chief; High Hon Roll; NHS; Opt Clb Awd; Sal; Sico Fndtn Scholar 87; Anna Dill Gamble Mem Scholar 87; Eta Chptr Delta Kappa Gamma Recrtmnt Grant 87; Millersville U PA; Elem Ed.

FREEDMAN, ABIGAIL; Hershey HS; Hershey, PA; (3); Pep Clb; Ski Clb; School Musical; School Play; Stage Crew; Nwsp Rptr; Lit Mag; Stu Cncl; Powder Puff Ftbl; Var Swmmng; ST Rep Internship 86; Intl Bus.

FREEDMAN, JEFFREY MARK; George Washington HS; Philadelphia, PA; (4); 23/800; Mu Alpha Theta; Chorus; Yrbk Ed-Chief; Var Gym; High Hon Roll; NHS; Spanish NHS; A M Vincent Trust Schlrshp 87; Sci Awd-Excel In Chem 87; Outstndng Svc Ldrshp & Spirit To Clss 87; PA ST U; Sci.

FREEDMAN, ROBIN; Plymouth Whitemarsh HS; Norristown, PA; (2); Temple Yth Grp; Nwsp Rptr; Nwsp Stf; Yrbk Stf; Lit Mag; Swmmng; Hon Roll; Jr NHS; People To People Stu Ambassador 87; Jrnlsm.

FREELAND, SEAN; Richland HS; Gibsonia, PA; (2); School Musical; Nwsp Stf; Yrbk Stf; Socr; PA ST Slct Sccr Tm-Play Trnmnts In Europe & Russia.

FREELAND, THERESA; Susquenita HS; Duncannon, PA; (4); 23/168; Leo Clb; Spanish Clb; Yrbk Sprt Ed; VP Soph Cls; VP Jr Cls; Pres Sr Cls; Stat Bsktbl; Var L Sftbl; Lion Awd; NHS; Patriot-News Outstndg Jrnlsm Achvt Awd 87; HACC.

FREEMAN, CAROL LEE; Jim Thorpe Area SR HS; Albrightsville, PA; (3); 15/92; FHA; Ski Clb; Speech Tm; Chorus; Color Guard; Flag Corp; Nwsp Rptr; Yrbk Stf; Hon Roll; Crbn Cnty Ortry-HS Lvl-2nd Pl 86-87; New Rochelle; Comm.

FREEMAN, DIANNE; Harbor Creek HS; Erie, PA; (4); 17/225; Church Yth Grp; Cmnty Wkr; French Clb; Office Aide; Church Choir; Nwsp Rptr; Powder Puff Ftbl; High Hon Roll; Hon Roll; NHS; SC Rep Stght A 83-84; Natl Beta Clb 83-84; Behrend Coll; Educ.

FREEMAN, ERICA K; Julia R Masterman HS; Philadelphia, PA; (4); Art Clb; Church Yth Grp; Church Choir; Orch; School Musical; Stage Crew; Nwsp Stf; Yrbk Stf; Lit Mag; Delaware Vly Tri-ST Schltc Art Awd Gold Key 85; Lit Magazine Cont Hnrb Mntn 86; Haverford Coll; Psych.

FREEMAN, HAROLD; Williamson JR SR HS; Lawrenceville, PA; (3); Pres Science Clb; Stat Bsktbl; Var Trk; High Hon Roll; Hon Roll; Prfct Atten Awd; Alg I 85; Alg II 86; Geom 87; AV Tech.

FREEMAN, KAREN G; Hempfield Area HS; Greensburg, PA; (4); Trs VP Intnl Clb; Spanish Clb; Trs Temple Yth Grp; Orch; Hon Roll; NHS; Spanish NHS; U Of Pittsburgh; Pharm.

FREEMAN, KELLY; Garnet Valley HS; Chester Heights, PA; (4); 8/148; Pres German Clb; Pres Intnl Clb; Model UN; Off Stu Cncl; NHS; Rotary Awd; Soroptimist Schlrshp, Walter J Udovich Humanitarian Awds 87; U Of Richmond; Psych.

FREEMAN, KELLY FRANCES; South Western HS; Hanover, PA; (4); 60/203; AFS; Teachers Aide; Nwsp Rptr; Nwsp Stf; Trs Sr Cls; Cheerleading; Lion Awd; Hmcmng Rep 85-86; Prom Committee 85-86; PA ST; Art.

FREEMAN, KENNETH; Freedom HS; Bethlehem, PA; (4); 24/445; Science Clb; Band; Chorus; Concert Band; Mrchg Band; Orch; Pep Band; Symp Band; High Hon Roll; NHS; Dist Band 85-86; Strghts A-S/1 Yr/Acdmc Swtr 85-86; Penn ST; Bio.

FREEMAN, LAMONT; Lincoln HS; Philadelphia, PA; (3); Hon Roll.

FREEMAN, NICOLE; Aliquippa HS; Aliquippa, PA; (3); Pres Library Aide; Band; Chorus; Church Choir; Concert Band; Mrchg Band; Pep Band; Rep Jr Cls; Hon Roll; Clarion U; Educ.

FREEMAN, ROBERT R; Garden Spot HS; Denver, PA; (3); FFA; Socr; Star Greenhnd 85; Star Chptr 86; Red Rose Degree 87; Alfred; Ag.

FREEMAN, RUDY; Perry Traditional Acad; Pittsburgh, PA; (3); Varsity Clb; Chorus; Off Stu Cncl; L Var Bsbl; JV Bsktbl; L Var Ftbl; Socr; Wt Lftg; Hon Roll; Ntl Merit Schol; Perfct Attend 84; Bsbl Stln Bases 87; Schl Tchr.

FREEMAN, SCOTT; Warren Area HS; Warren, PA; (3); Boy Scts; Church Yth Grp; VP Ski Clb; Varsity Clb; Band; Orch; Stu Cncl; Ftbl; Trk; High Hon Roll; Penn ST U; Bus.

FREEMAN, STEVE; Kennard-Dale HS; Stewartstown, PA; (2); Boy Scts; Ski Clb; Chorus; JV L Socr; Hon Roll; PA ST U; Pilt.

FREEMAN, TONYA; Chester HS; Brookhaven, PA; (3); French Clb; School Musical; Trs Frsh Cls; Trs Soph Cls; Trs Jr Cls; Var JV Cheerleading; French Hon Soc; Prfct Atten Awd; Fash Mdsg.

FREER, CHRISTINE; Franklin HS; Polk, PA; (2); 15/252; German Clb; Hosp Aide; Color Guard; Frsh Cls; Soph Cls; High Hon Roll; Prfct Atten Awd.

FREESE, GREGORY; Kennard-Dale HS; Stewartstown, PA; (2); Varsity Clb; Var Bsbl; Var Bsktbl; High Hon Roll; York Daily Record And York Dispatch County All-Star Baseball Team 87; Telecomm.

FREESE, KERRY; Solanco SR HS; Nottingham, PA; (2); Church Yth Grp; Sec 4-H; Trs FBLA; Red Cross Aide; Varsity Clb; JV Sftbl; Var JV Tennis; High Hon Roll; NHS; Natl Schltc Typng Cont 1st Pl Rgnl 87; Schl Schlr Drvrs Ed 87.

FREET, JOHN C; York Suburban SR HS; York, PA; (4); Boy Scts; Church Yth Grp; Ski Clb; School Musical; VP Jr Cls; Stu Cncl; Crs Cntry; Swmmng; High Hon Roll; Hon Roll; Presdntl Acadc Ftns Awd 87; Rtry Ldrshp Conf 86; NYU; Studio Art.

FREIDHOFF, JENNIFER; Conemaugh Valley HS; Johnstown, PA; (3); 11/105; Church Yth Grp; Concert Band; Co-Capt Flag Corp; Mrchg Band; Stu Cncl; Hon Roll; Jr NHS; NHS.

FREILICH, MARGARET; Upper Merion Area HS; Wayne, PA; (4); 8/276; Aud/Vis; Nwsp Stf; JV Fld Hcky; Var Capt Swmmng; DAR Awd; High Hon Roll; NHS; Ntl Merit Ltr; Math Tm; Lit Mag; Myls J Brennan Mem Shclrshp 87; Ntl Hnr Soc Book Schlrshp 87; Acad Fitness Awd 87; Tufts U; Sci.

FREILING, PATRICIA; Nazareth Acad; Philadelphia, PA; (4); 21/125; Capt Dance Clb; French Clb; Latin Clb; Chorus; School Musical; School Play; Variety Show; Var Cheerleading; Im Vllybl; High Hon Roll; Nalt Latin Exam Magna Cum Laude 87; Allentown Coll; Pre-Law.

FREIMAN JR, STEPHEN M; Western Wayne HS; Dickson City, PA; (3); Ski Clb; Spanish Clb; Im Wt Lftg; Cit Awd; High Hon Roll; Hon Roll; Rotary Awd; Penn ST U; Math.

FREITAG, JENNIFER; Central Bucks HS West; Doylestown, PA; (3); 12/481; Church Yth Grp; Ski Clb; Nwsp Ed-Chief; Mgr(s); Capt L Tennis; Cit Awd; High Hon Roll; Hon Roll; Jr NHS; NHS; Middle ST Rank Tnns Plyr 80-87; Tnns Tm MVP 85-86; Grls Tnns League Chmpn 86.

FREITICK, AMY; Villa Maria Acad; Newtown Square, PA; (3); 91/94; Art Clb; Varsity Clb; Variety Show; Var Bsktbl; Var Fld Hcky; Opt Clb Awd; Prfct Atten Awd; Bsktbls MVP & All Star 86-87; Athltc Of Wk Awd 87; Fld Hcky All Star & Athltc Of Wk Awd 86; Crmnl Justc.

FREIWALD, GRETCHEN; Bishop Mc Cort HS; Park Hill, PA; (3); German Clb; Chorus; School Musical; Hon Roll; U Of Pittsburg.

FRELICK, AMIBETH; Hempfield Area HS; Greensburg, PA; (3); VP 4-H; Wt Lftg; 4-H Awd; CA U Of PA; Educ Elem.

FRENCH, ANDY; Mercer JR SR HS; Mercer, PA; (3); Church Yth Grp; Drama Clb; NFL; Ski Clb; Speech Tm; Band; Chorus; Concert Band; Jazz Band; Mrchg Band; Outstndng Band Stu 86-87.

FRENCH, ARLENE; Shenango HS; New Castle, PA; (2); Dance Clb; Drill Tm; Mrchg Band; Var Cheerleading; Var Gym; High Hon Roll; Hon Roll.

FRENCH, JOHN; Brookville Area HS; Brookville, PA; (3); 39/177; Trs French Clb; Key Clb; SADD; Var JV Bsktbl; Var Golf; Var Trk; Hon Roll; VP Jr NHS; NHS; Grove City Coll; Accntng.

FRENCH, LLOYD; Northeast Bradford HS; Athens, PA; (2); Computer Clb; FFA; Ag Mech Awd Frm 86; Dairy Fds Awd & Dairy Prods Awd 86; Str Grnhd Awd 86; Frmg.

FRENCH, SUZANNE; Moon Area HS; Aliquippa, PA; (4); Church Yth Grp; Key Clb; Chorus; Trs Frsh Cls; Stu Cncl; Capt Var Swmmng; Hon Roll; NHS; Tiger Pride Awd 87; Moon Ed Assctn Tchrs Schlrshp 87; Grove City Coll; Elem Ed.

FRENCH, VERONICA; Center HS; Monaca, PA; (2); Church Yth Grp; Latin Clb; Varsity Clb; Church Choir; Var L Crs Cntry; Im Powder Puff Ftbl; Im Sftbl; Var L Trk; Hon Roll; Intl Banking.

FRENIA, DANIEL K; Hampton HS; Allison Park, PA; (3); 70/201; Cmnty Wkr; SADD; Rep Frsh Cls; Var L Swmmng; Hon Roll; JR Acad Sci-PA 87; WIPALS-WMMNG 87; Chem.

FRESCURA, CHRISTINA; Penn Trafford HS; Jeannette, PA; (2); Sec Pres Church Yth Grp; Varsity Clb; Lit Mag; JV Sftbl; L Swmmng; High Hon Roll; Hon Roll.

FRESH, LANE; Cumberland Valley HS; Mechanicsburg, PA; (3); 90/595; Boy Scts; Church Yth Grp; Debate Tm; Latin Clb; NFL; Speech Tm; School Musical; School Play; Stage Crew; Hon Roll; Eagle Sct Awd 86; 1st Bio St Mtng PA Jr Acad Sci 87; Med.

FRETZ, RENITA; Shalom Christian Acad; Marion, PA; (3); 1/30; Church Yth Grp; FHA; Hosp Aide; Acpl Chr; Yrbk Stf; Rep Sec Stu Cncl; High Hon Roll; Prfct Atten Awd; Bible Quiz Trphs 86-87; 1st Pl Teen Tlnt Cont Piano 86; Comp Sci.

FREW, LISA A; Minersville Area HS; Minersville, PA; (3); 1/100; German Clb; Band; Concert Band; Jazz Band; Mrchg Band; School Musical; High Hon Roll; NHS; NEDT Awd; Ltt Archy 86 & 87; Acad Achvt Awd 85-87; Engr.

FREW, MICHAEL; Minersville Area HS; Newtown, PA; (4); 28/131; French Clb; Hosp Aide; Pres SADD; Chorus; School Musical; Stage Crew; Nwsp Stf; Yrbk Stf; Cit Awd; NEDT Awd; Srptmst Awd 87; Paul Smiths Coll; Htl Manag.

FREY, AMY; Lewistown Area HS; Lewistown, PA; (3); French Clb; Ski Clb; Chorus; Pres Frsh Cls; JV L Cheerleading; Trk; High Hon Roll; NHS; Bus.

FREY, AMY; Nazareth Area SR HS; Nazareth, PA; (3); 11/255; Nwsp Sprt Ed; Yrbk Stf; Pres Frsh Cls; Trs Stu Cncl; Var L Gym; Var Mat Maids; Capt Var Sftbl; High Hon Roll; Hon Roll; NHS; 1st Tm All Lg Offender Fld Hcky 86; 2nd Tm All Lg 2nd Bsmn Sftbl 87; Phrmcy.

FREY, BRADLEY; Elk County Christian HS; Ridgway, PA; (4); 25/79; Boy Scts; Library Aide; Ski Clb; Yrbk Stf; Trk; Hon Roll; Lion Awd; Eagle Scout 84; St Vincent Coll; Bio.

FREY, CHRIS; North Allegheny SR HS; Pittsburgh, PA; (3); 179/650; Exploring; ROTC; Socr; Army Resrv Basic Trng Betwn JR & SR Yr Smmr 87; Army.

FREY, CHRISTY; Eastern York HS; Hellam, PA; (3); Church Yth Grp; SADD; School Musical; Swing Chorus; Rep Stu Cncl; Cheerleading; Sftbl; Trk; Vllybl; Varsity Clb; Pre-Law.

FREY, COBY; Dover Area HS; Dover, PA; (4); Sec Intnl Clb; Band; Chorus; Concert Band; Mrchg Band; Ed Nwsp Rptr; Nwsp Stf; Wilson Coll; Intl Banking.

FREY, CRYSTAL; Liberty JR SR HS; Liberty, PA; (3); 5/49; German Clb; Yrbk Stf; Stat Trk; Var JV Vllybl; Hon Roll; NHS; Indstrl Engrng.

FREY, DAVID; Carlisle HS; Carlisle, PA; (3); Cmnty Wkr; Debate Tm; Drama Clb; Church Choir; Orch; School Musical; School Play; Stage Crew; Nwsp Rptr; Hon Roll.

FREY, DAVID; Dieruff HS; Allentown, PA; (2); Church Yth Grp; JA; Rep Frsh Cls; Rep Soph Cls; Rep Stu Cncl; Prfct Atten Awd; CPA.

FREY, FRANCES; Dover Area HS; Dover, PA; (3); 31/260; Church Yth Grp; Cmnty Wkr; FFA; German Clb; Teachers Aide; Chorus; Fld Hcky; Hon Roll; FFA Chapter Schlrshp 85-86; Shippensburg U; Hstry.

FREY, HEATHER; Red Lion SR HS; Red Lion, PA; (3); 11/342; Debate Tm; SADD; Varsity Clb; Nwsp Rptr; Yrbk Sprt Ed; Yrbk Stf; Var Tennis; High Hon Roll; Hon Roll; NHS; Bus.

FREY, JENNIFER; MMI Prep Schl; Sugarloaf, PA; (4); Science Clb; Service Clb; SADD; Nwsp Rptr; Lit Mag; Var Crs Cntry; Sftbl; High Hon Roll; NHS; Nwsp Stf; PA Jr Acad Sci Cmptn-1st Pl Rgnl, St Lvls 85; Wellesley Coll; Chem.

FREY, KATHY; Shamokin Area HS; Sunbury, PA; (2); 2/254; Art Clb; Camera Clb; 4-H; Science Clb; SADD; Band; Concert Band; Mrchg Band; Swing Chorus; Yrbk Stf; Genetic Engrng.

FREY, KRISTEN; Red Lion Area SR HS; Red Lion, PA; (3); 33/342; Debate Tm; SADD; Capt Flag Corp; Mrchg Band; Yrbk Sprt Ed; Var Mgr(s); Var Timer; JV Trk; Im Wt Lftg; Hon Roll; Accntng.

FREY, KRISTIN; Central Dauphin HS; Harrisburg, PA; (2); Key Clb; Ski Clb; Yrbk Stf; VP Frsh Cls; VP Jr Cls; Var Bsktbl; Var Fld Hcky; Var Trk; Soc Sci.

FREY, MARY PAT; Elk County Christian HS; St Marys, PA; (2); 14/90; SADD; Church Choir; Nwsp Stf; JV Capt Cheerleading; High Hon Roll.

FREY, PASCHA; South Williamsport Area HS; S Williamsport, PA; (4); 8/140; Key Clb; Keywanettes; Ski Clb; Spanish Clb; Hst Sr Cls; Off Stu Cncl; Co-Capt Cheerleading; Trk; NHS; Drill Tm; Hmcmng Queen 86-87; Amer Lgn Awd Excllns Pblms Democrcy 87; Alumni Key Awd 87; PA ST U; Mass Comm.

FREY, PATRICIA; Newport HS; Newport, PA; (2); Flag Corp; Nwsp Rptr; High Hon Roll; Psych.

FREY, PATTI; Wallenpaupack Area HS; South Sterling, PA; (3); 7/154; Chorus; Mrchg Band; School Musical; Trs Frsh Cls; Trs Soph Cls; Trs Jr Cls; Trs Sr Cls; High Hon Roll; Jr NHS; NHS; Dist 9 Chorus 86-87; Frnch.

FREY, STACEY; Lampeter Strasburg HS; Lancaster, PA; (3); 14/146; Church Yth Grp; Band; Concert Band; Mrchg Band; Bsktbl; Hon Roll; NHS; Cmmnctns.

FREY, SUZANNE; Big Spring HS; Newville, PA; (2); 1/283; Quiz Bowl; School Musical; School Play; Nwsp Rptr; High Hon Roll; NHS; Undrclssmn Engl Awd, Jrnlsm Awd, Sci Awd 86-87; Engl.

FREY, VALERIE; Tyrone Area HS; Spruce Creek, PA; (3); Art Clb; Church Yth Grp; Library Aide; Chorus; Church Choir.

FREY II, WILLIAM R; Liberty JR-SR HS; Liberty, PA; (2); German Clb; Hon Roll.

FREYER, LESLIE; Freedom HS; Bethlehem, PA; (3); 140/500; French Clb; Varsity Clb; Nwsp Phtg; Nwsp Stf; Var Fld Hcky; Hon Roll; Econ.

FRICK, BECKY; Western Wayne HS; Sterling, PA; (3); Church Yth Grp; Flag Corp; Hon Roll; Prfct Atten Awd.

FRICK, RICHARD E; Plum HS; Pittsburgh, PA; (3); 3/410; AFS; SADD; VP Band; Mrchg Band; School Play; Symp Band; High Hon Roll; Trs NHS; NEDT Awd; Marine Phys Ftns Awd 84; Hnr Guard Cmncmnt 87; Vet Med.

FRICKERT, TAMI; Northampton Area SR HS; Bath, PA; (4); AFS; Sec DECA; Pres Drama Clb; FBLA; Pep Clb; Quiz Bowl; School Musical; School Play; Hon Roll; 2nd Pl Stdnt Of Yr 87; DECA 2nd Pl Gen Merchndsng 87; DECA 6th Pl Aprl & Accs 86; 3rd Pl Pub Spkng 86; Northampton Cnty CC; Bus Mgnt.

FRIDAY, BRET; Henderson HS; West Chester, PA; (2); 9/350; French Clb; Math Clb; Rep Frsh Cls; Var Ice Hcky; Var Socr; Var Trk; French Hon Soc; High Hon Roll; Hon Roll; MVP Sccr Tem 85; Biology.

FRIDAY, JOSEPH; Fort Cherry HS; Hickory, PA; (3); Drama Clb; Science Clb; Ski Clb; Spanish Clb; Stage Crew; JV Bsktbl; Ftbl; JV Wrstlng; High Hon Roll; Hon Roll; US Naval Acad; Accntnt.

FRIDRICK, KATHY; Western Beaver HS; Midland, PA; (4); 9/75; Church Yth Grp; Drama Clb; Chorus; Nwsp Stf; Yrbk Stf; Bowling; Hon Roll; NHS; Prsdntl Acdmc Ftnss Awd 87; Grad Hnr Stu 87; U Of Pittsburgh; Nrsng.

FRIEDE, SARAH; Bishop Kenrick HS; Norristown, PA; (4); 10/285; Math Tm; Science Clb; Service Clb; Capt Color Guard; School Musical; Nwsp Ed-Chief; Hon Roll; NHS; Ntl Merit Ltr; French Clb; Rotry Clb Stu Mth 87; U Of Dayton; Acctng.

FRIEDEL, JEFFREY; Central Dauphin East HS; Hummelstown, PA; (3); Church Yth Grp; Drama Clb; French Clb; Chorus; School Play; Nwsp Stf; Yrbk Stf; Stu Cncl; Tennis; Pres Schlr; Crmnl Justice.

FRIEDHOFER, CORINNE A; Hempfield HS; Lancaster, PA; (2); Church Yth Grp; Chorus; Hon Roll; Shippensburg U; Chld Care Dvlpm.

FRIEDLINE, MICHELE; North Star HS; Jennerstown, PA; (2); 21/150; FCA; Ski Clb; SADD; Stu Cncl; Mat Maids; Im Tennis; Im Vllybl; Hon Roll; Bus Admn.

FRIEDMAN, DARA; Council Rock HS; Churchville, PA; (2); Debate Tm; Drama Clb; Hst Key Clb; Math Tm; Political Wkr; SADD; Band; Soph Cls; Socr; High Hon Roll; Cnty Sci Smnr 86-87; Mrchng Band Lttr 86; Vrsty Debate Lttr 85-87; Biochem.

FRIEDMAN, JENNIFER; Cheltenham HS; Wyncote, PA; (2); Drama Clb; Quiz Bowl; Thesps; Acpl Chr; Chorus; School Musical; Swing Chorus; Variety Show; Stu Cncl; IN In IN N Wstrn; Vocal Music.

FRIEDMAN, JOANNE; Bensalem HS; Bensalem, PA; (2); Office Aide; Swmmng; Actvty Cmte 86-87; Stu Vlntr 86-87.

FRIEDMAN, LISA; Villa Maria HS; Campbell, OH; (3); 3/40; Art Clb; Rep Church Yth Grp; Drama Clb; Rep GAA; Key Clb; Office Aide; Spanish Clb; Thesps; School Musical; School Play.

FRIEDMAN, MATTHEW; Marple Newtown HS; Media, PA; (2); Temple Yth Grp; Stage Crew; JV Socr; JV Swmmng; Znst Yth Fed Hdrch Smnr-Israel 87.

FRIEDMAN, ROBERT C; Bethel Park HS; Bethel Pk, PA; (4); 50/520; Capt Ftbl; Hon Roll; Outstndng Acad Achvt 86-87; Cngrssnl & Pres Ftns Appntmnt Of US Nvl Acad 87; US Naval Acad; Elec Engrng.

FRIEDMAN, THERESA; Nazareth Acad; Phila, PA; (3); 7/128; Dance Clb; Debate Tm; French Clb; JV Speech Tm; School Musical; High Hon Roll; Schlrshp 84; Hnr Cert Merit Outstndng Schlstc Achvt 85-87; Ntl Frnscs Lgue Degree Excel 87; Sci.

FRIEDMAN, TODD; Lower Moreland HS; Huntingdon Valley, PA; (3); Science Clb; Pres Sec Temple Yth Grp; Nwsp Rptr; Yrbk Stf; JV Golf; High Hon Roll; Hon Roll; Bio.

FRIEDRICH, JOHN; Highlands SR HS; Natrona Hgts, PA; (3); Computer Clb; French Clb; Ntl Merit Ltr; Prfct Atten Awd; Pres Schlr; Gld Mdl & 6th Plc ST Sci Olympcs 87; Gld Awds 3.5 & QPA 85-87; PA U; Motion Pctr Indstry.

FRIEDRICH, JOHN; Plymouth Whitemarsh HS; Conshohocken, PA; (2); Ftbl; Wt Lftg; High Hon Roll; Hon Roll; Sci.

FRIEDRICH, MICHAEL A; Bensalem HS; Bensalem, PA; (2); Boy Scts; ROTC; Spanish Clb; Color Guard; Drill Tm; Rep Stu Cncl; Bsbl; Crs Cntry; Trk; Cit Awd; Naval Acad.

FRIEKO, ROBERTA; Bishop Mc Cort HS; Johnstown, PA; (2); Spanish Clb; High Hon Roll; Hon Roll; INDIANA U Of PA; Math.

FRIEL, COLEEN; Mt St Josephs Acad; Philadelphia, PA; (3); Art Clb; Church Yth Grp; Off Cmnty Wkr; Debate Tm; Intnl Clb; JCL; SADD; VP Socr; High Hon Roll; Sec Spanish NHS; Harvard Smmr Pgm 87; Schrlshp Gormanston Coll 86; 2nd Essy Wnnr 86; Intl Econ.

FRIEL, MATTHEW J; Butler SR HS; Butler, PA; (3); Church Yth Grp; FCA; Im Bsktbl; Var Ftbl; Hon Roll; AZ ST U; Poltcl Sci.

FRIEND, BRIAN; Warren Area HS; Warren, PA; (3); School Play; Var JV Bsbl; High Hon Roll; Hon Roll; Engrng.

FRIEND, ERIC; Chambersburg Area HS; Chambersburg, PA; (4); 42/553; Pres Church Yth Grp; Letterman Clb; Spanish Clb; Varsity Clb; Im Bsktbl; Var L Crs Cntry; Var L Trk; High Hon Roll; NHS; Luthern Brohd Membrshp Schlrshp 87-88; CA U Of PA; Bio.

FRIEND, GEORGE; Laurel Highlands HS; Hopwood, PA; (1); Church Yth Grp; Science Clb; Mrchg Band; Carnegie Mellon; Robotics.

FRIENDY, GINA; Hazleton HS; Hazleton, PA; (3); Church Yth Grp; FBLA; Leo Clb; Psych.

FRIES, ERIN; Chambersburg Area SR HS; Chambersburg, PA; (2); 5/730; JCL; Latin Clb; Chorus; Sec Symp Band; High Hon Roll; Amer Leg Aux Schl Awd 86.

FRIES, JEAN; Allentown Central Catholic HS; Allentown, PA; (3); Church Yth Grp; Exploring; JV Bsktbl; Var Vllybl; High Hon Roll; Hon Roll; Early Child Dev.

FRIESE, CAROL; Upper Merion SR HS; King Of Prussia, PA; (3); 31/298; Aud/Vis; Church Yth Grp; Math Tm; Concert Band; Mrchg Band; School Musical; Yrbk Ed-Chief; Hon Roll; NHS; Rotary Club Test Wnnr 86; Early Chldhd Ed.

FRIGM JR, PHILIP E; Central York HS; York, PA; (3); Church Yth Grp; Band; Chorus; Church Choir; Concert Band; Jazz Band; Mrchg Band; Orch; School Musical; Stage Crew; Aerospc Engrng.

FRINGUELLOTTI, CHRISSY; Valley View JR SR HS; Eynon, PA; (2); Rep Latin Clb; Rep Ski Clb; Rep Chorus; Rep Stu Cncl; Stat Bsktbl; Var Trk; Var Vllybl; Athltc Awd Trck & Fld, Prsdntl Awds Phys Ftnss 85-87.

FRIONI, CELENE; Center Area HS; Aliquippa, PA; (2); German Clb; Hon Roll; Phrmcy.

FRISCH, JOHANNA; Palmerton Area HS; Palmerton, PA; (3); Girl Scts; Hosp Aide; Chorus; Flag Corp; Yrbk Phtg; Yrbk Stf; Stat Bsktbl; Var JV Mgr(s); Trk; Hon Roll; Southeastern Acad; Trvl Agnt.

FRISCH, JOHN J; Northwestern Lehigh HS; Germansville, PA; (4); Letterman Clb; Ski Clb; Rep Stu Cncl; JV Bsbl; Var Ftbl; Var Trk; Hon Roll; NHS; Pres Acdmc Ftnss Awd 86-87; PA ST U; Hlth.

FRISHKORN, DAWN; Seneca Valley HS; Zelienople, PA; (3); Church Yth Grp; 4-H; Ski Clb; SADD; Color Guard; Yrbk Stf; Hon Roll; Marine Bio.

FRISINA, TONI; Meadville Area SR HS; Meadville, PA; (2); French Clb; Nwsp Rptr; Yrbk Stf; Stu Cncl; Stat Bsktbl; JV Var Mgr(s); Var Trk; High Hon Roll; Hon Roll; Phys Therapist.

FRITZ, ALAN; Monaca HS; Monaca, PA; (3); Am Leg Boys St; Ski Clb; Pres Soph Cls; Var Bsbl; Var Var Bowling; L Ftbl; Var Wt Lftg; Penn ST; Bio.

FRITZ, BARRY; North Star HS; Stoystown, PA; (2); Aud/Vis; Computer Clb; Band; Pres Stage Crew; Hon Roll; Music.

FRITZ, BRADLEY; Cocalico HS; Adamstown, PA; (3); 4/172; Aud/Vis; Camera Clb; Sec Soph Cls; Trs Jr Cls; JV Var Bsktbl; Var Vllybl; High Hon Roll; NHS; Soc Stud Ldrshp Awd; Sci.

FRITZ, GARY; Cathedral Prep; Erie, PA; (3); Boy Scts; Church Yth Grp; Cmnty Wkr; Bowling; Crs Cntry; Cit Awd; Hon Roll; Eagle Scout 87; Pope Pius XII & Ad Alteri Die Awds 86; Natl Page Pgm In Washington DC 86.

FRITZ, JOHN; Central York HS; York, PA; (3); Varsity Clb; Var Bsbl; Var Ftbl; Var Wt Lftg; Var Capt Wrstlng.

FRITZ, KELLY EVANS; North Hills HS; Pittsburgh, PA; (4); JA; Key Clb; Ski Clb; Chorus; Yrbk Stf; Stu Cncl; Bsktbl; Cheerleading; Trk; Vllybl; W VA U; Bus.

FRITZ, LANCE; Beaver Area HS; Beaver, PA; (3); Ski Clb; Spanish Clb; Ftbl; Trk; Hon Roll; Part-Time Job 86; Slippery Rock U; Athltc Trnng.

FRITZ, MARC; North Star HS; Stoystown, PA; (4); Hon Roll; U Of Pittsburgh; Pre-Law.

FRITZ, PAULA; Souderton Area HS; Mainland, PA; (3); Aud/Vis; Ski Clb; Rep Frsh Cls; Rep Soph Cls; Rep Jr Cls; Rep Stu Cncl; JV Fld Hcky; JV Lcrss; Var L Trk; Hon Roll; Elem Educ.

FRITZ, TAMMI; North Star HS; Boswell, PA; (2); Art Clb; Church Yth Grp; Letterman Clb; Ski Clb; Spanish Clb; SADD; Vllybl; Cit Awd; Hon Roll; FCA; Pres Acadmc Ftns Awd 85; Advrtsg.

FRITZ, TOBY; Greencastle-Antrim HS; Waynesboro, PA; (3); 11/180; Church Yth Grp; Latin Clb; School Play; Var L Ftbl; Var L Socr; L Trk; High Hon Roll; NHS; PIAA ST Champ AA Discus; Latin II & JR Geometry Hghst Grd Avg 86-87.

FRITZLEY, JIM; West Allegheny HS; Imperial, PA; (4); Drama Clb; Ski Clb; Spanish Clb; High Hon Roll; Hon Roll; Robert Morris Coll; Accntg.

FROATS, LISA; Avella HS; Avella, PA; (3); 12/85; Art Clb; French Clb; Band; Yrbk Stf; Bsktbl; High Hon Roll; Hon Roll; NHS; Outstndng Acad Wrk Wrld Cultures & Typing II 86-87; Anesthetist.

FROCK, PENNIE; South Western HS; Hanover, PA; (2); Band; Concert Band; Mrchg Band; Symp Band; Hon Roll; Phy Thrpy.

FROCK, ROBBYN; South Western HS; Hanover, PA; (3); Church Yth Grp; Exploring; Hosp Aide; L Band; Capt Color Guard; Capt Drill Tm; Stage Crew; Yrbk Stf; JV Cheerleading; NHS; Nrsng.

FROEHLICH, ANNETTE; Greater Johnstown SR HS; Johnstown, PA; (4); 11/293; German Clb; JA; Sec Key Clb; Math Clb; Chorus; Nwsp Rptr; Nwsp Stf; Yrbk Rptr; Yrbk Stf; High Hon Roll; Acdmc All Am 86-87; Washingon & Jefferson Coll.

FROEHLICH, JEANNE; Greater Johnstown HS; Johnstown, PA; (3); Drama Clb; Sec German Clb; NFL; Chorus; Variety Show; Nwsp Stf; Yrbk Stf; Hon Roll; NHS.

FROEHLICH, TANYA; Meadville HS; Meadville, PA; (3); 1/350; Pres 4-H; VP Key Clb; Orch; Rep Jr Cls; Socr; Elks Awd; High Hon Roll; Church Yth Grp; French Clb; 1st Pl In Reg Hstry Day Cmptn 86; Wnnr Of SR Merit Physcl Ftns Awd 85-86; Awd Schlrshp For PA 86.

FROGGATT, RORY; Monitteau HS; W Sunbury, PA; (4); 8/139; Ski Clb; Spanish Clb; Sec Soph Cls; Bsbl; Bsktbl; Ftbl; Hon Roll; Pres NHS; Prfct Atten Awd; Pres Schlr; Fndtn Schlrshp 87; Penn ST U; Bus Mgmt.

FROLA, KIMBERLY; Chestnut Ridge SR HS; Bedford, PA; (3); Cmnty Wkr; Scholastic Bowl; Nwsp Ed-Chief; High Hon Roll; NHS; VFW Awd; Voice Dem Awd; Camera Clb; Debate Tm; 4-H; PA ST U Lang Inst Schlrshp 87; Adv Bio & Physics Awds 87; Cngrs Bundestags Frgn Exch Schlrshp 87.

FROLLO, CATHY; Penn Hills HS; Verona, PA; (4); 63/609; Drama Clb; French Clb; School Play; Off Jr Cls; Stu Cncl; Hon Roll; NHS; SR Class Schlrshp 87; Robert Morris Coll; Paralegal.

FROMM, JASON; Kennard-Dale HS; Stewartstown, PA; (3); 2/167; Boy Scts; German Clb; Quiz Bowl; Varsity Clb; School Musical; Rep Stu Cncl; Crs Cntry; Trk; High Hon Roll; NHS; Eagle Sct.

FROMME, BILL; Williams Valley HS; Wiconisco, PA; (3); Aud/Vis; Stage Crew; Penn ST U; Engrng.

FROMMER, COREY; Northampton Area HS; Northampton, PA; (2); Exploring; Aviation.

FROMMER JR, JAMES F; Liberty HS; Bethlehem, PA; (3); 37/438; Church Yth Grp; Yrbk Stf; Var L Bsktbl; Trk; Var Vllybl; Hon Roll; Pre-Med.

FRONDUTI, AMY; Mt Lebanon HS; Pittsburgh, PA; (3); 2/550; Church Yth Grp; Hosp Aide; Science Clb; Color Guard; Sec Jr Cls; Var Swmmng; Renslr Awd For Outstndg Prfmnc-Math & Sci 87; Aerosp Engrng.

FRONHEISER, MEG; Bishop Carroll HS; Ebensburg, PA; (3); 16/128; Dance Clb; Drama Clb; NFL; Pep Clb; Speech Tm; SADD; Rep Stu Cncl; Powder Puff Ftbl; Hon Roll; 2nd Pl Dist Frnscs-Ortrcl Dclmtn, Prsuasv Spkng 85, 86; ST Frnscs Semifnlst 86; Lbrl Arts.

FRONHEISER, MONICA; Boyertown SR HS; Bally, PA; (3); 80/432; FBLA; Cit Awd; High Hon Roll; Hon Roll; Secy.

FRONTINO, AMY; Williamson JR SR HS; Lawrenceville, PA; (3); 16/79; Sec Spanish Clb; SADD; Yrbk Sprt Ed; Yrbk Stf; Sec Soph Cls; Var JV Cheerleading; Var Trk; Hon Roll; NHS; Prfct Atten Awd; Radiology Tech.

FRONTINO, ROBERT; Northern Cambria HS; Barnesboro, PA; (3); 31/152; French Clb; Pres Soph Cls; Pres Jr Cls; Rep Stu Cncl; Var L Bsbl; Var L Bsktbl; Var L Ftbl; Hon Roll.

FRONZAGLIA, PHYLLYS; Quigley HS; Aliquippa, PA; (3); 30/83; French Clb; Chorus; Stat Bsktbl; Mgr(s); Powder Puff Ftbl; High Hon Roll; Hon Roll; Math League 86-87; Homecoming Ct 86.

FRONZAGLIA, SANDY; Our Lady Of The Sacred Heart HS; Aliquippa, PA; (4); 13/70; Dance Clb; Pep Clb; Spanish Clb; Varsity Clb; Chorus; Pep Band; Yrbk Stf; VP Jr Cls; Co-Capt Bsktbl; Hon Roll; Dir Pep Clb, Beaver Cnty & Pittsburgh All-Star 1st Tm Bsktbl, MVP Bsktbl 85-87; Gannon U; Med Asst.

FROST, DOUGLAS; Laurel Highlands HS; Uniontown, PA; (3); Church Yth Grp; FCA; JA; Crs Cntry; L Trk; High Hon Roll; Hon Roll; WV U; Chem Engr.

FROST III, HARRY J; Yough HS; Smithton, PA; (4); 52/256; French Clb; Model UN; Ski Clb; Chorus; Church Choir; High Hon Roll; NHS; U Pittsburgh; Engrng.

FROST, MICHELE; Cavlisle SR HS; Carlisle, PA; (3); 197/409; JA; Spanish Clb; Rep Frsh Cls; L Trk; High Hon Roll; Hon Roll; Prfct Atten Awd; Cnty Bnd 87; Dist Band 87; Pharm.

FROST, SHAWN; Shikellamy HS; Sunbury, PA; (3); Boy Scts; Church Yth Grp; Cmnty Wkr; German Clb; Rep Stu Cncl; JV Var Trk; Hon Roll; Chem.

FRUCELLA, HEIDI; Linden Hall HS; Frederick, MD; (3); Art Clb; Debate Tm; Drama Clb; Political Wkr; Quiz Bowl; Ski Clb; School Musical; School Play; Variety Show; Nwsp Rptr; Prfct 87; Stu Of Mnth 87; Columbia; Jrnlsm.

FRUSCO, MELANIE; Nazareth Acad; Philadelphia, PA; (4); Cmnty Wkr; French Clb; Intnl Clb; Lit Mag; JV Capt Cheerleading; High Hon Roll; Merit Cert 86-87; Drexel U; Mrktng.

FRUTIGER, LISA; Bradford Area HS; Bradford, PA; (3); VP Girl Scts; Spanish Clb; Mrchg Band; Rep Stu Cncl; Coach Actv; Im Sftbl; Twrlr; Im Vllybl; Hon Roll; Gld Awd Grl Scts 85; Elem Ed.

FRY, BRIDGET; Butler Area HS; Butler, PA; (2); French Clb; Teachers Aide; Sftbl; Hon Roll; Jr NHS; Gftd Pgm 85-87; Ofc Held At Yth & Govt Model Legislature Harrisburg 86 & 87; Psych.

FRY, CHRIS; Fleetwood Area HS; Fleetwood, PA; (3); 20/180; Boy Scts; Church Yth Grp; Library Aide; Band; Chorus; Mrchg Band; School Play; Yrbk Rptr; Golf; Hon Roll; Phys Asst.

FRY, CHRISTOPHER; Mc Keesport Area HS; Mc Keesport, PA; (3); 39/410; Pres Church Yth Grp; Cmnty Wkr; Computer Clb; VP Exploring; German Clb; Chorus; Stage Crew; Nwsp Stf; Hon Roll; NHS; 1st Pl Sci Fair Awds 84-85; 6 Special Sci Fair Awds 84-85; Elec Engr.

FRY, JOYCE; Donegal HS; Mount Joy, PA; (2); GAA; Band; Chorus; Color Guard; Concert Band; Flag Corp; Mrchg Band; Pep Band; Fld Hcky; Mt Joy Cmmnty Sftbl League Champs 86; Central Penn; Lgl Sec.

FRY, JUDY; Boiling Springs JR SR HS; Carlisle, PA; (3); 2/140; Band; Concert Band; Mrchg Band; Yrbk Sprt Ed; Yrbk Stf; Sec Frsh Cls; Sec Soph Cls; JV Bsktbl; High Hon Roll; Sec NHS; Dickinson Coll Summer Schlrshp 87; Villanova Coll; Chld Psych.

FRY, KIMBERLY; Marion Center HS; Home, PA; (3); 5/153; VICA; School Play; Trs Jr Cls; High Hon Roll; Hon Roll; Parlmntry Procedure Team; Opening & Closing Team; Parlmntry Procedure All Star Team; Cosmtlgst.

FRY, LARRY; West Perry HS; New Bloomfield, PA; (3); 14/243; Var L Bsbl; Var L Ftbl; Var L Wrstlng; NHS; Spanish Clb; Varsity Clb; Spts Illus Faces In The Crowd 85; Top 10 Recvrs & Mid Penn All Star Def End Ftbl 86; Mid Penn All Star; Crim Just.

FRY, LISA; Moniteau JR SR HS; Chicora, PA; (3); Sec Church Yth Grp; FBLA; Chorus; Hon Roll; NHS; Butler Cnty CC; Rtl Mgmt.

FRY, MARC; Mechanisburg SR HS; Grantham, PA; (2); 69/319; Church Yth Grp; Capt Var Bsktbl; Hon Roll; MVP Bsktbl 86; Ldng Rbndr 86; Div III Chmpns Bsktbl 87; Hstry.

FRY, MARTHA; Moniteau HS; W Sunbury, PA; (4); 7/128; Church Yth Grp; Spanish Clb; Drill Tm; Hon Roll; NHS; Pres Acdmc Fitness Awd 87; Lillian Heck Schlrshp 87; Geneva Coll Schlrshp 87; Geneva Coll; Comm.

FRY, NATHAN; West Perry HS; Shermans Dale, PA; (3); 4/210; Church Yth Grp; Cmnty Wkr; Band; Chorus; Church Choir; Concert Band; High Hon Roll; Hon Roll; NHS; Prfct Atten Awd; Dist Chorus 86-87; Sndy Schl Assn Tlnt Awd 87; Drftng.

FRY, SHEILA M; Greensburg Salem SR HS; Greensburg, PA; (3); 115/302; Cmnty Wkr; Drama Clb; Library Aide; NFL; Spanish Clb; Color Guard; Mrchg Band; Nwsp Stf; Mat Maids; Scl Wrkr.

FRYDMAN, BARI; Bensalem HS; Bensalem, PA; (2); Key Clb; Office Aide; Spanish Clb; Off Frsh Cls; Sec Soph Cls; Off Stu Cncl; Capt Cheerleading; Mgr(s); Hon Roll; Soph Cls Secr 86-87; Chrldng Capt 87-88.

FRYE, BEATRICE; Susquehanna Community HS; Thompson, PA; (2); Church Yth Grp; Dance Clb; 4-H; SADD; Band; Chorus; Church Choir; Concert Band; Jazz Band; Mrchg Band; HOBY Fndtn 87; Comm.

FRYE, GARY; Center HS; Monaca, PA; (3); Art Clb; Letterman Clb; Spanish Clb; Varsity Clb; Yrbk Sprt Ed; L Var Bsbl; Capt Var Golf; Hon Roll; Prfct Atten Awd; Teachers Aide; U Of Miami-Wake Forest; Bus Adm.

FRYE JR, JAMES D; Jersey Shore SR HS; Jersey Shore, PA; (3); Computer Clb; JV Crs Cntry; Var Trk.

FRYE, JEFFREY; Fort Cherry HS; Washington, PA; (3); Church Yth Grp; Trs Drama Clb; Math Clb; Science Clb; Ski Clb; Spanish Clb; Thesps; Chorus; School Play; Trs Stu Cncl; Penn ST; Cinematography.

FRYE, MICHELLE; Altoona Area HS; Altoona, PA; (3); 1/796; Pres Church Yth Grp; Orch; Off Jr Cls; Tennis; High Hon Roll; NEDT Awd; Pres Schlr; Computer Clb; German Clb; Chorus; Cntrl PA Showcase Perf Arts Yth Piano 85; 1st Chair Viola Awd 85; Silvr Mdl Awd Natl Piano Audtns 84; Mth.

FRYER, BARBARA A; Norristown Area HS; Norristown, PA; (3); 6/491; Church Yth Grp; Band; Jazz Band; Orch; Symp Band; JV Bsktbl; JV Sftbl; Im Tennis; Hon Roll; Prfct Atten Awd.

FRYMOYER, HEIDI; East Pennsboro HS; Camp Hill, PA; (3); GAA; Spanish Clb; Chorus; School Musical; Pres Sr Cls; Var Capt Gym; Var Trk; Hon Roll; NHS; Church Yth Grp; 3rd Pl-Poem-Family & Children Svcs 85-86; Track-3rd Midpenn 400 Relay 86-87; COMMUNICATIONS.

FRYNKEWICZ, PAMELA; Ambridge HS; Freedom, PA; (3); French Clb; Hosp Aide; Office Aide; Pep Clb; Chorus; JV Trk; Hon Roll; Med.

FRYZLEWICZ, CHRISTINE; Portage Area HS; Portage, PA; (3); 31/124; Dance Clb; German Clb; Letterman Clb; Ski Clb; Varsity Clb; Sec Jr Cls; Stat Bsktbl; JV Cheerleading; Var Trk; Hon Roll; Presdntl Phy Ftns Awd 86 & 87; Schl Rcrd Hldr 200 Yd Dash-Trk 86-87; Bus.

FUERMAN, RICHARD; The Hill Schl; Pottstown, PA; (4); Cmnty Wkr; Library Aide; Model UN; Ski Clb; Band; Concert Band; Jazz Band; Mrchg Band; Yrbk Bus Mgr; Im Golf; Acdmc Achvt Pres Schlrshp Wilkes Coll 87-91; Wilkes Coll; Pre Med.

FUGE, JACQUELINE E; State College SR HS; State College, PA; (2); Cmnty Wkr; Dance Clb; Trk; Hon Roll; Typng Hnr Awd 86-87; Wrld Cultures Hnr Awd 86-87; Pres Physcl Ftns Awd 83-86; Penn ST; Psych.

FUHRER, MITCH; Fort Le Boeuf HS; Waterford, PA; (3); 94/217; FCA; Ski Clb; Pres Soph Cls; Trs Jr Cls; JV Bsbl; Var L Ftbl; Wt Lftg; Law.

FUHRMAN, BRIDY; South Western HS; Hanover, PA; (3); 51/233; Nwsp Stf; Var JV Bsktbl; JV Var Fld Hcky; Lang.

FUHRMAN, GLEN; South Western HS; Hanover, PA; (2); JV Ftbl; JV Var Wrstlng; Hon Roll; US Air Force.

FUHRMAN, JENNIFER; Hanover SR HS; Hanover, PA; (4); 9/110; Church Yth Grp; Pep Clb; Varsity Clb; Chorus; Co-Capt Vllybl; High Hon Roll; Hon Roll; Jr NHS; NHS; Rotary Awd; Outstndg Plyr Vlybl 87; Pres Acad Ftns Awd 87; Penn ST U; Lib Arts.

FUINI, MARK; Parkland HS; Schnecksville, PA; (3); Exploring; JV Ftbl; Var Trk; Hon Roll; Engrng.

FUISZ, JOS; Moravian Acad; Bethlehem, PA; (3); Model UN; Political Wkr; Scholastic Bowl; Lit Mag; Rep Frsh Cls; Pres Soph Cls; VP Jr Cls; High Hon Roll; Hon Roll; Ntl Merit Ltr; Outstndng Delg Mdl UN; Doseter Awd Engl; Cum Laud Soc; Law.

FULCO, DANIEL; Downingtown HS; Downingtown, PA; (3); 69/648; Letterman Clb; Ski Clb; Concert Band; JV Bsktbl; JV Socr; Var L Trk; Hon Roll; NHS; Spanish Clb; Pres Acad Fit Awd 84-85; Law.

FULENO, MELISSA; New Castle SR HS; New Castle, PA; (4); 18/240; Church Yth Grp; French Clb; Hosp Aide; Red Cross Aide; SADD; Rep Frsh Cls; Rep Soph Cls; Rep Sr Cls; Stu Cncl; Vllybl; Gannon U Acad Schlrshp 86; Gannon U; Pre-Med.

FULGINITI, AMY; Middletown Area HS; Middletown, PA; (3); Pres Key Clb; Advertising.

FULGINITI, ANGELA; Moshannon Valley JR-SR HS; Houtzdale, PA; (4); 4-H; Spanish Clb; Band; Chorus; Concert Band; Mrchg Band; Pep Band.

FULGINITI, JULIE; Living Word Acad; Lancaster, PA; (1); Rep Frsh Cls; Rep Stu Cncl; Var Bsktbl; Hon Roll.

FULKERSON, ALICIA; Shenango HS; New Castle, PA; (3); 5/121; AFS; Church Yth Grp; Spanish Clb; SADD; Flag Corp; Yrbk Stf; Stu Cncl; Var Mgr(s); Im Vllybl; Hon Roll; Pharm.

FULLER, CRAIG; Calvary Baptist Christian Acad; Conneautville, PA; (3); Chorus; Yrbk Ed-Chief; Yrbk Stf; Pres Jr Cls; Var Bsktbl; Hon Roll; Prfct Atten Awd; Church Yth Grp; Church Choir; School Play; JV Bsktbl MVP 85-86; Vrsty Bsktbl All Conf 1st Team 86-87; Vrsty Bsktbl 1st Leg In Rbnds 86-87; PA ST; Mech Engrng.

FULLER, DEBBIE; Aliquippa HS; Aliquippa, PA; (3); Exploring; French Clb; Hosp Aide; Band; Concert Band; Mrchg Band; Rep Jr Cls; Ntl Merit Ltr; Corp Law.

FULLER, JASON; Ford City HS; Ford City, PA; (3); 5/160; Trs Spanish Clb; Pres Soph Cls; Rep Jr Cls; Trs Sr Cls; Rep Stu Cncl; JV Bsbl; JV Bsktbl; High Hon Roll; Hon Roll; Ntl Merit Ltr; PA ST U; Engineering.

FULLER, KAREN; Riverside JR SR HS; Taylor, PA; (4); 44/172; Ski Clb; Variety Show; Pres Soph Cls; Pres Jr Cls; Pres Sr Cls; Rep Stu Cncl; Hon Roll; Art Clb; Spanish Clb; Ntl Yth Ldrshp Salute 86; E Stroudsburg U; Psych.

FULLER, MICHELLE; Geibel HS; Vanderbilt, PA; (3); Library Aide; Yrbk Stf; Var Bsktbl; Var Sftbl; Var Vllybl; High Hon Roll; Spanish NHS; Ltr Bsktbl, Vlybl, Sftbl 84-87.

FULLER II, ROY G; Geibel HS; Vanderbilt, PA; (3); 24/102; Drama Clb; Service Clb; Ski Clb; Var L Ftbl; High Hon Roll; Hon Roll; Prfct Atten Awd; PA JR Acad Sci 85-86; Hlth Prfssn.

FULLERTON, SUSAN; Elizabethtown Area HS; Elizabethtown, PA; (3); 14/259; Church Yth Grp; Library Aide; Chorus; Trs Frsh Cls; Hon Roll; NHS; Messiah Coll; Bus Mgmt.

FULMER, DIANA; Garden Spot HS; New Holland, PA; (2); 11/266; Sec Church Yth Grp; Rep PAVAS; Acpl Chr; Chorus; Orch; School Musical; Rep Stu Cncl; JV Bsktbl; Var Fld Hcky; High Hon Roll; Dist Chorus 87; All Actvts Awd 85; Natl Hnr Socty 86-87; Messiah; Elem Tchg.

FULMER, HOLLY; South Allegheny HS; Mckeesport, PA; (3); Spanish Clb; Y-Teens; Band; Concert Band; Mrchg Band; Pep Band; School Musical; Trk; Silver Poet Awd World Poetry 86.

FULMER, JANET; Yough SR HS; West Newton, PA; (3); French Clb; VICA; Color Guard; Pres Jr Cls; Hon Roll; West Cnty CC; Comp.

FULMER, JEFF; Purchase Line HS; Cherry Tree, PA; (3); 18/98; School Play; Hon Roll; French Clb; USAA Frgn Lang Achvt Awd 87; Lawyer.

FULMER, KATHERINE; J P Mc Caskey HS; Lancaster, PA; (4); AFS; FBLA; JA; Pep Clb; Ski Clb; Spanish Clb; Band; Chorus; Concert Band; Nwsp Rptr; MVP Awd-Fld Hcky 83-84; West Chester Coll; Elem Educ.

FULMER, LU ANNE; Yough SR HS; Yukon, PA; (3); Drama Clb; Ski Clb; Band; Chorus; Mrchg Band; School Play; Symp Band; Nwsp Rptr; Rep Stu Cncl; Var Sftbl; Theater.

FULMER, MISSY; Ft Cherry HS; Mc Donald, PA; (3); Drama Clb; Math Clb; Science Clb; Ski Clb; Spanish Clb; Varsity Clb; Chorus; Var Bsktbl; Mgr(s); Var L Sftbl; Pre-Med.

FULMER, TAMMY; Purchase Line HS; Clymer, PA; (2); VP FHA; Nwsp Stf; Hon Roll; Cosmtlgist.

FULMER, TIMOTHY; Saucon Valley HS; Bethlehem, PA; (3); 4/156; Church Yth Grp; Math Tm; VP Band; Concert Band; Jazz Band; Mrchg Band; Pep Band; Crs Cntry; Trk; High Hon Roll; Engrng.

FULMER, VICTORIA; Little Flower Catholic HS For Girls; Philadelphia, PA; (3); 6/365; Church Yth Grp; Cmnty Wkr; Office Aide; Teachers Aide; Acpl Chr; Chorus; School Musical; School Play; High Hon Roll; Hon Roll; Psych.

FULTON, DOREEN; Carmichaels Area SR HS; Carmichaels, PA; (4); 42/103; Church Yth Grp; French Clb; JA; Pep Clb; Sec Band; Concert Band; Mrchg Band; Hon Roll; NHS; Coll Schlrshp Music 87-88; Alderson Broaddus Coll; Music.

FULTON, GABRIELLE; Nazareth Acad; Philadelphia, PA; (3); Church Yth Grp; French Clb; Orch; Nwsp Rptr; Nwsp Sprt Ed; Psych.

FULTON, KRIS; Johnsonburg HS; Johnsonburg, PA; (3); 6/92; Trs Church Yth Grp; Pres French Clb; Varsity Clb; Band; Color Guard; Rep Stu Cncl; Var L Bsktbl; Score Keeper; Sftbl; L Var Tennis; Hugh O Brian Ambssdr 86; Mst Imprvd Tnns 86; Ntl Ldrshp Merit Awd 85-86; UCLA; Med.

FULTON, MIKE; Weatherly HS; Weatherly, PA; (3); Church Yth Grp; FBLA; Ski Clb; Nwsp Stf; Bryant Coll; Bnkng.

FULTON, NICOLE; Peters Township HS; Mc Murray, PA; (3); Dance Clb; Spanish Clb; Varsity Clb; Drm Mjr(t); Variety Show; Yrbk Stf; Rep Stu Cncl; Var L Cheerleading; Hon Roll; Spanish NHS.

FULTON, RHONDA; Central Cambria HS; Colver, PA; (3); Pres Church Yth Grp; FBLA; Yrbk Stf; Var Sftbl; Prfct Atten Awd; Shrthnd I Trnscrptn Awds 86-87; Hagerstown BC; Court Stenogrph.

FULTON, ROSE; Homer Center HS; Homer City, PA; (3); 16/110; French Clb; Sec SADD; Color Guard; Hon Roll; Jr NHS; NHS; Hme Eco Outstndng Stu Awd 85-86; Chld Psychlgy.

FULTON, RUSS; Scranton Central HS; Scranton, PA; (2); Ftbl; Trk; Ltr Ftbl; Sci.

FULTON, SUSAN; Saltsburg JR SR HS; Clarksburg, PA; (4); 10/88; Trs Sr Cls; Sec Stu Cncl; Capt Var Cheerleading; Powder Puff Ftbl; Var L Sftbl; High Hon Roll; NHS; Aud/Vis; Varsity Clb; Yrbk Stf; Bst All Arnd Chrldr Awd USCA Chrldng Cmp 84; All Gzt 1st Tm Sftbl 85-87; Hmcmng Queen 86; IN U PA; Cmnctns.

FULTON, WENDY; Taylor Allderdice HS; Pittsburgh, PA; (3); Church Yth Grp; Exploring; Model UN; Church Choir; Trk; Hon Roll; Spelman U; Med.

FULTZ, HAROLD; West Snyder HS; Beaver Spgs, PA; (2); 9/90; Camera Clb; Computer Clb; SADD; Chorus; Comp Sci.

FULTZ, SHARRI; Hopewell SR HS; Aliquippa, PA; (3); Exploring; JA; Church Choir; Rep Stu Cncl; Var Powder Puff Ftbl; Var Trk; Hon Roll; U Pittsburgh; OB/GYN.

FULTZ, SHAWN; West Snyder HS; Mc Clure, PA; (2); Camera Clb; VP Church Yth Grp; Computer Clb; Science Clb; SADD; Band; Chorus; School Musical; Nwsp Phtg; Yrbk Phtg; Comp Sci.

FUMANTI, KEVIN; Du Bois Area HS; Reynoldsville, PA; (3); Chess Clb; Hon Roll; Stu Of Wk Awd 85; Nice Kid Awd 87.

FUMANTI, MELISSA; Old Forge HS; Old Forge, PA; (4); Ski Clb; Yrbk Phtg; Cheerleading; Hon Roll; All Amer Chrldr Awd 1st Pl 86; Gregg Typg Awd 85; Chld Devlpmnt.

FUNARO, CAROL; Upper Darby HS; Upper Darby, PA; (3); Acpl Chr; Chorus; Tennis; Trk; Hon Roll; Adelphi Coll; Dance.

FUNG, MAYBO; Northeast HS; Philadelphia, PA; (4); Hosp Aide; Office Aide; Red Cross Aide; Service Clb; Teachers Aide; Prfct Atten Awd; Rep Frsh Cls; Off Soph Cls; Off Jr Cls; Off Sr Cls; Svc Awd; CDL Awd; Early Elem Educ.

FUNK, BARBARA; Danville SR HS; Danville, PA; (2); #15 In Class; Church Yth Grp; Hosp Aide; Band; Concert Band; Mrchg Band; Orch; Symp Band; JV Fld Hcky; High Hon Roll; Fshn Dsgn.

FUNK, BARRY; Donegal HS; Mount Joy, PA; (2); Ski Clb; Band; Mrchg Band; Bowling; Ftbl; Tennis; Wrstlng; Temple; Law.

FUNK, COLLEEN; Steelton-Highspine HS; Steelton, PA; (3); 22/102; Cmnty Wkr; Dance Clb; Drama Clb; Sec French Clb; Pep Clb; Stat Bsbl; Var JV Cheerleading; Var JV Sftbl; Prfct Atten Awd; Library Aide; All Amer Tlnt Awd 84; Danc Hrt Awd Merit 85; Millersville U; Frnch.

FUNK, DONNA; Homer Center HS; Homer City, PA; (2); French Clb; Hosp Aide; SADD; Band; Chorus; Jazz Band; Mrchg Band; School Musical; Hon Roll; NHS; Nursing.

FUNK, MICHAEL S; Spring Ford HS; Collegeville, PA; (3); 44/256; French Clb; Math Clb; Rep Soph Cls; JV Bsbl; JV Ftbl; Pharmcy.

FUNK, VIVIAN GAIL; Lincoln HS; Ellwood City, PA; (4); 89/169; 4-H; Girl Scts; Key Clb; Office Aide; Spanish Clb; SADD; Chorus; Church Choir; Flag Corp; Mgr(s).

FUNKHOUSER, MARK; Hopewell Area HS; Beaver Falls, PA; (4); 60/265; Rep Exploring; French Clb; Pep Clb; Thesps; Pres Band; Chorus; Concert Band; Jazz Band; Mrchg Band; Pep Band; PA ST U Music Actvty Schlrshp 87; Dist, Regl, All-St Chorus 86-87; May Court, Dist Band 86-87; PA ST U; Music Ed.

FUNYAK, JAMES; Steel Valley HS; Munhall, PA; (3); Varsity Clb; VICA; Stage Crew; JV Ftbl; Var Vllybl; High Hon Roll; NHS; 2nd Pl Dist VICA Cmptn Bldng Trds 86-87.

FUOSS, MARGIE; Montgomery JR SR HS; Montgomery, PA; (2); 8/103 Church Yth Grp; 4-H; FHA; Library Aide; Speech Tm; Varsity Clb Church Choir; Nwsp Rptr; Sec Soph Cls; Var L Tennis; Ten MVP 86-87, Lycoming Cnty Dairy Prncss 87; Lockhaven U; Scndry Educ.

FURCHT, KARISSA J; East HS; West Chester, PA; (3); French Clb; Ski Clb; SADD; Teachers Aide; JV Cheerleading; Var JV Mgr(s); JV Sftbl; U Of MI; Aerospc Tech.

FURCOLA, NICOLE; Philmont Christian Acad; Philadelphia, PA; (3); 12/48; Church Yth Grp; Chorus; Church Choir; School Play; Yrbk Ed-Chief; Var JV Fld Hcky; High Hon Roll; NHS; Temple U; Journlsm.

FURELLO, JILL; Dunmore HS; Dunmore, PA; (3); French Clb; Chorus, Yrbk Stf; Trk; High Hon Roll.

FUREY, APRIL; Old Forge HS; Old Forge, PA; (3); Hosp Aide; Church Choir; School Play; Yrbk Stf; Gov Hon Prg Awd; High Hon Roll; U Of Scranton; Educ.

FUREY, STEVE; Council Rock HS; Newtown, PA; (2); Spanish Clb; Ftbl; Hon Roll; Engrng.

FURFARI, ERIC; Bishop Carroll HS; Lilly, PA; (3); 9/189; Am Leg Boys St; Boy Scts; Stage Crew; Variety Show; Var L Ftbl; Hon Roll; NHS.

FURIA, FRED; The Haverford Schl; Haverford, PA; (2); 3/77; Church Yth Grp; Math Clb; Spanish Clb; Nwsp Stf; Swmmng; Tennis; High Hon Roll; Pendergrass Trphy Swmmng 86-87.

FURILLO, DOUG; Danville HS; Danville, PA; (3); French Clb; Ski Clb; Rep Soph Cls; Rep Jr Cls; Var L Bsbl; JV Bsktbl; Var L Ftbl; Hon Roll; U Of Pittsburg.

FURIMSKY, BENJAMIN; Rockwood Area HS; Rockwood, PA; (2); Church Yth Grp; Computer Clb; Ski Clb; School Play; Stage Crew; L Bsktbl; Crs Cntry; Var L Socr; Var L Trk; Hon Roll; Penn State.

FURLONG, BOB; Pleasant Valley HS; Saylorsburg, PA; (3); Debate Tm; Drama Clb; Concert Band; Mrchg Band; Pep Band; School Play; Stage Crew; Ed Yrbk Phtg; Yrbk Stf; Ed Lit Mag; Kodak Schlstc Photo Awds 86; PA Gvrnrs Schl Arts Smi-Fnlst Photo 87; 4 Day Schlrshp Smnr 85; NYU; Cnmtgrphy.

FURLONG, CHRISTOPHER; Cedar Cliff HS; Camp Hill, PA; (3); 130/304; Debate Tm; VP Drama Clb; German Clb; Latin Clb; Speech Tm; VP Thesps; Chorus; School Musical; School Play; Stage Crew; Drama.

FURLONG, DAVID; Brownsville Area HS; Brownsville, PA; (4); 8/227; Math Tm; Ski Clb; SADD; Yrbk Stf; Stu Cncl; L Var Bsbl; Var Capt Ftbl; Wt Lftg; High Hon Roll; Hon Roll; Jaycettes Outstndng Frshmn Awd 84; All Am Stu/Ath Awd 87; CA U; Chirprctc Med.

FURMAN, DAVE; Lower Moreland HS; Huntingdon Valley, PA; (2); FBLA; German Clb; Key Clb; Science Clb; JV Bsbl; High Hon Roll; Hon Roll.

FURMAN, STACEY; Fairview HS; Fairview, PA; (4); 53/154; Church Yth Grp; Drama Clb; Library Aide; Office Aide; Chorus; Capt Color Guard; Mrchg Band; School Musical; Lit Mag; Hon Roll; Gannon U; Acctng.

FURMAN, SUSAN; Coudersport JR SR HS; Coudersport, PA; (4); 4-H; French Clb; FBLA; FHA; 4-H Awd; Hon Roll; Olean Bus Inst; Acctg.

FURMANIAK, DIANNE; Cardinal O Hara HS; Media, PA; (4); 49/771; Ed Yrbk Stf; Off Jr Cls; Off Sr Cls; Stu Cncl; Hon Roll; Chrmn NHS; Hnrs Convocation 85, 86 & 87; Mt St Marys Schlrshp, Coll Holy Cross Schlrshp 87; U DE.

FURROW, ERIC J; Wilson HS; Reading, PA; (4); 15/330; Chess Clb; Math Clb; High Hon Roll; Hon Roll; NHS; Ntl Merit SF; Science Awd 85-86; Comp Sci.

FURST, SUSAN; Plymouth-Whitmarsh HS; Norristown, PA; (3); Pres Church Yth Grp; Chorus; Church Choir; Drm Mjr(t); Mrchg Band; School Musical; Sec Stu Cncl; Swmmng; Hon Roll; Harlequin Awd Lead King & I Musical 87; Rkie Yr Majorette Awd 85; Acadmc Awd 85-87.

FURST, TODD; Salisbury HS; Allentown, PA; (3); Church Yth Grp; Computer Clb; Key Clb; JV Bsktbl; High Hon Roll; Hon Roll; Lehigh U; Comp Sci.

FURTEK, RICHARD; Northeast Catholic HS; Philadelphia, PA; (4); Church Yth Grp; Political Wkr; Yrbk Ed-Chief; L Ftbl; NHS; Busi.

FUSARO, NANCY; Penn Hills SR HS; Verona, PA; (3); Yrbk Stf; High Hon Roll; Hon Roll; Exec Wmns Intl Outstndng Bus Stu 86-87; Cvl Srvc Stenogrphr.

FUSARO, WILLIAM; Moniteau HS; West Sunbury, PA; (4); 10/196; Spanish Clb; Chorus; Pres Soph Cls; VP Jr Cls; Rep Stu Cncl; Capt Bsbl; JV Bsktbl; Var L Ftbl; Var L Trk; Im Mgr Wt Lftg; Dstrct Chrs 86-87; Al Conf Ftbl Tm 86-87; Natl Hnr Socty 86-87; Slippery Rock U; Bus.

FUSS, MICHELE; Lampeter Strasburg HS; Lancaster, PA; (3); 40/148; AFS; Art Clb; Thesps; Varsity Clb; Concert Band; Flag Corp; School Play; Yrbk Phtg; L Trk; Opt Clb Awd; Secndry Ed.

FUSTING, HEATHER M; James Buchanan HS; St Thomas, PA; (3); 8/214; Am Leg Aux Girls St; School Play; Yrbk Ed-Chief; Trs Jr Cls; Trs Sr Cls; Trs Stu Cncl; Var Cheerleading; Var Trk; 4-H Awd; Hon Roll; Amer Legn Aux Awd 85; Pres Fit Awd 85-86; Franklin Cnty Lamb & Wool Qn 86-87; Pre-Law.

FYE, JAMES; St Marys Area HS; Weedville, PA; (3); 5/269; Am Leg Boys St; Band; Concert Band; Jazz Band; Capt Var Crs Cntry; Var L Trk; Hon Roll; NHS; MVP Crss Cntry 86-87; Pre-Med.

FYOCK, ELIZABETH; Purchase Line HS; Clymer, PA; (3); Sec 4-H; SADD; Varsity Clb; Chorus; Nwsp Sprt Ed; Var L Bsktbl; Var L Sftbl; Var L Vllybl; High Hon Roll; Hon Roll; Elem Educ.

GABEL, DIANNE; Plymouth Whitemarsh HS; Norristown, PA; (4); 15/324; 4-H; Spanish Clb; Sftbl; Vllybl; Hon Roll; Jr NHS; NHS; Pres Schlr; A H Ambler Awd For Peace & Scl Jstc 87; YMCA Schlrshp 87; Ursinus Coll; Med.

GABEL, MARTIN; Bishop O Reilly HS; Swoyersville, PA; (4); Am Leg Boys St; Spanish Clb; Chorus; Yrbk Rptr; JV Bsbl; JV Bsktbl; Var L Socr; Spanish NHS; Pres Acad Fitness Awd 85-86; Natl Sci Merit Awd 85-6; Kings Coll; Crmnl Jstc.

GABEL, MEREDITH; John S Fine HS; Nanticoke, PA; (4); 20/250; Key Clb; Sec Chorus; Yrbk Rptr; Yrbk Stf; Mgr(s); JV Vllybl; High Hon Roll; NHS; Acadmc All Amercn; Intl Bus.

GABEL, MICHELLE; John S Fine HS; Nanticoke, PA; (4); Key Clb; Chorus; Yrbk Stf; Mgr Bsbl; Mgr(s); Vllybl; High Hon Roll; NHS; Intl Bus.

GABLE, JIM; Elizabethtown Area HS; Bainbridge, PA; (2); 30/300; Church Yth Grp; Church Choir; Var Ftbl; Trk; Hon Roll; PIAA Dist 3 Rnnr Up Ftbl 86; Penn ST U; Bus Mngmt.

GABLE, JOHN; Elizabethtown Area HS; Bainbridge, PA; (3); Church Yth Grp; Church Choir; Yrbk Phtg; Yrbk Stf; Comrcl Art.

GABLE, SARAH JANE; Trinity HS; Camp Hill, PA; (3); Debate Tm; Model UN; Nwsp Stf; Var L Crs Cntry; Var L Trk; JETS Awd; NHS; Ntl Merit Schol; CAP; French Clb; US Army Rsrv Natl Schlrshp/Athl Awd 87; Maxima Zum Laude Natl JR Clsscl Leag 84-85; Wrtr 1 Act Cmptn.

GABLE, TARA L; Blue Mountain HS; Pottsville, PA; (4); 26/218; Hosp Aide; Mu Alpha Theta; Chorus; School Play; Nwsp Rptr; Yrbk Stf; Rep Sr Cls; Mgr(s); JV Trk; French Hon Soc; Bio Olympiad 85; Amer U; Intl Stds.

GABLE, WILLIAM; Pittston Area SR HS; Pittston, PA; (4); 12/328; Im Bsktbl; Hon Roll; NHS; Bus Admin.

GABODA, PETER BLAYZE; Central Cambria HS; Mineral Pt, PA; (2); Ski Clb; JV Bsbl; JV Ftbl; U Of Pittsburgh; Elec Engr.

GABONAY, LAUREN; Brownsville Area HS; New Salem, PA; (3); 8/210; Church Yth Grp; Civic Clb; Math Tm; High Hon Roll; Hon Roll; NHS; Ntl Merit Ltr; PA Govnrs Schl Ag 87.

GABRIEL, ALLISON; Harriton HS; Penn Valley, PA; (3); French Clb; SADD; Yrbk Stf; JV Bsktbl; Var Sftbl; High Hon Roll; Hon Roll; NHS; Bus.

GABRIEL, BRIAN; Carrick HS; Pittsburgh, PA; (4); 24/340; Nwsp Stf; Sec Jr Cls; VP Sr Cls; VP Stu Cncl; L Bsbl; Im Bsktbl; JV Crs Cntry; High Hon Roll; Hon Roll; Bsbll All Cty Shrtstp 86; Allegheny; Bus Admn.

GABRIEL, LORI; Brownsville Area HS; Merrittstown, PA; (3); Drama Clb; Latin Clb; Teachers Aide; Variety Show; Sec Frsh Cls; High Hon Roll; Hon Roll; Soph Homcmng Attendant 85; Nrsng.

GABRIEL, MICHAEL; Bishop Hafey HS; Hazleton, PA; (2); 18/106; Art Clb; Church Yth Grp; Yrbk Stf; Off Stu Cncl; Bsktbl; Tennis; Hon Roll; Amer Lgn Ldrshp Awd 85-86; Acadmc All-Amer 86.

GABRIELE, LISA; Bishop Conwell HS; Levittown, PA; (3); 104/277; Church Yth Grp; JV Cheerleading; Var Fld Hcky; JV Var Sftbl; Var Swmmng; Natl Phys Ed Awd 85-86; BUS.

GABURRI, MICHELE; Chartiers Valley HS; Carnegie, PA; (4); 50/303; Church Yth Grp; Spanish Clb; Ed Yrbk Stf; Hon Roll; NHS; Carlow Coll; Nrsng.

GACA, JEFFREY; Quaker Valley HS; Sewickley, PA; (2); VP Key Clb; Pres Soph Cls; L Bsktbl; L Trk; High Hon Roll; Hon Roll; All Sectn Bsktbl Vrsty.

GACH, DAN; Hempfield SR HS; Grapeville, PA; (3).

GACHA, TAMMY; Tunkhannock Area HS; Tunkhannock, PA; (3); Key Clb; Spanish Clb; Band; Concert Band; Mrchg Band; School Play; Cheerleading; Sftbl; Hon Roll; Spanish.

GACKENBACH, DIANE; William Allen HS; Allentown, PA; (3); 42/659; Hosp Aide; JA; JCL; Band; Orch; Hon Roll; NHS; Preschool Educ.

GADOLA JR, ANGELO M; Bishop Hafey HS; Hazleton, PA; (3); Cmnty Wkr; Computer Clb; Leo Clb; Ski Clb; Orch; Yrbk Stf; Bsbl; Bowling; Stat Trk; Yth Ldrshp Conf-Mltry Ordr Wrld Wars 87; Ntl Scl Stds Olympd 87; US Naval Acad; Avtn.

GADOLA, ANN MARIE; Hazleton HS; Hazleton, PA; (3); FBLA; Leo Clb; Spanish Clb; Mgr(s); Stat Swmmng; Intr Dsgn.

GADOLA, BART; Sharpsville HS; Sharpsville, PA; (3); Chess Clb; Church Yth Grp; Ski Clb; JV Cheerleading; School Play; Var Trk; Hon Roll; Envrnmntl Sci.

GADOLA III, GUY P; Sharpsville Area HS; Sharpsville, PA; (4); 1/120; Church Yth Grp; School Musical; Pres Stu Cncl; L Trk; Bausch & Lomb Sci Awd; DAR Awd; Val; Voice Dem Awd; HS Area Educ Assn Schlrshp 87; U Of Pittsburgh Eng Hnrs Schlrshp 87; Slippery Rock U Bk Awd 87; U Of Pittsburgh; Engr.

GADOLA, LISA; Kiski Area HS; Leechburg, PA; (3); Church Yth Grp; Band; Chorus; Trk; High Hon Roll; Nrsng.

GADOMSKI, LARA; Western Wayne HS; Waymart, PA; (4); 12/141; Ski Clb; SADD; Mrchg Band; Sec Soph Cls; Sec Jr Cls; Sec Sr Cls; Im Gym; Hon Roll; VP NHS; Presdntl Acad Fit Awd 8 7; Kings Coll; Elem Educ.

GADSDEN, JAMES L; Coatesville Area SR HS; Coatesville, PA; (4); 112/457; NAACP; Spanish Clb; Var Ftbl; Var Swmmng; Var Trk; Ntl Merit Ltr; Prfct Atten Awd; Minority Stu Schlrshp 87; Ftbl Mvp 86-87; Shippensburg U; Bio.

GADSDEN, THERESIA; Mechanicsburg Area HS; Mechanicsburg, PA; (2); 27/309; Church Yth Grp; Spanish Clb; Band; Church Choir; Mrchg Band; Orch; Symp Band; Hon Roll; Ntl Merit Ltr; Rgnl Bnd 86-87; Music.

GAFFNEY, KEVIN P; Upper Darby HS; Upper Darby, PA; (2); Bsktbl; Comp Prgmr.

GAFFNEY, MARY KATHRYN; Lansdale Catholic HS; Ambler, PA; (3); 15/223; Science Clb; SADD; Nwsp Stf; JV Bsktbl; Var L Fld Hcky; JV Socr; Var L Sftbl; Hon Roll; Sec NHS; Modern Bio Acad Excllnce Awd 86; Psych.

GAGE, KAREN; Strath Haven HS; Wallingford, PA; (4); FBLA; Intnl Clb; Color Guard; Yrbk Stf; Var Vllybl; High Hon Roll; NHS; Ntl Merit SF; Rotary Awd; PA Free Enterprise Wk Scholar 86; Duke U; Econ.

GAGLIANO, FRANCIS E; Mt Lebanon SR HS; Pittsburgh, PA; (4); Ski Clb; School Musical; School Play; Nwsp Rptr; Yrbk Phtg; Ed Lit Mag; High Hon Roll; Prfct 5 AP Engl Exam Lit 87; U Pittsburgh; Film Stds.

GAGLIARDI, BLAKE; MMI Prep Schl; Hazleton, PA; (3); Aud/Vis; Computer Clb; Math Clb; Pep Clb; Ski Clb; Im Bsktbl; Im Fld Hcky; Im Vllybl; High Hon Roll; Ntl Merit Ltr; Bio Olympcs Comptn 86; Temple U; Bio.

GAGNON, ANDREA; Bethlehem Center HS; Brownsville, PA; (3); 33/165; Spanish Clb; Flag Corp; Mrchg Band; Rptr Soph Cls; Rptr Jr Cls; Capt Cheerleading; Stat Trk; Prfct Atten Awd; Outstndng Achvmnt Accntng 87; Bradford Schl Of Bus; Accntnt.

GAGNON, PATRICK; Greensburg Central Catholic; Trafford, PA; (3); German Clb; Letterman Clb; Service Clb; Ski Clb; Varsity Clb; Stu Cncl; Bsbl; Ftbl; Socr; Swmmng.

GAGUZIS, TRACY; Quaker Valley HS; Fair Oaks, PA; (2); Church Yth Grp; JA; Latin Clb; Band; Concert Band; Mrchg Band; Pep Band; Symp Band; Hon Roll; Rd Crss Awd Wrtng Paper Lupus 85-86; Duquesne Mid-East Fstvl Music Awd 85-87; Elem Tchr.

GAHR, KATHY; St Marys HS; St Marys, PA; (2); 150/301; Hosp Aide; Band; Chorus; Concert Band; Mrchg Band; Governrs Schl For Arts 87; Psych.

GAHR, WENDY; Elk County Christian HS; Kersey, PA; (4); 44/81; Hosp Aide; Model UN; SADD; Concert Band; Mrchg Band; Symp Band; Yrbk Stf; Stat L Bsktbl; Hon Roll; Lion Awd; 3rd Pl SR Dvsn Mt Sci Fr 86; Fox Twp Lns Gd Ctzn & SR Music Awds 87; Gannon U; Chmstry.

GAINES, BARRI; Wm Allen HS; Allentown, PA; (4); SADD; Debate Tm; Drama Clb; VP Temple Yth Grp; Nwsp Rptr; Nwsp Stf; Yrbk Stf; Hon Roll; Jr NHS; ASD Ortrcl Cntst Fnlst; West Chester U; Elem Ed.

GAISBAUER, TOM; Exeter SR HS; Birdsboro, PA; (2); German Clb; Stage Crew; Crs Cntry; Trk; High Hon Roll; Jr NHS; NHS; Pres Schlr; Engrng.

GAISER, GWEN; Karns City HS; Petrolia, PA; (3); Exploring; FCA; Chorus; Drill Tm; Stage Crew; JV Pom Pon; Var Vllybl; High Hon Roll; Hon Roll; NHS; Physical Therapy.

GAISER, STACEY; St Huberts HS; Philadelphia, PA; (3); 172/421; Cmnty Wkr; FTA; Im Gym; Cit Awd; Hon Roll; Kutztown U; Cnslng.

GAITHER, THOMAS K; Slippery Rock Area HS; Slippery Rock, PA; (3); 18/192; Am Leg Boys St; Boy Scts; Church Yth Grp; Cmnty Wkr; German Clb; Var L Socr; High Hon Roll; Hon Roll; NHS; U Pittsburgh.

GAITO, JENNFIER; Valley HS; New Kensington, PA; (3); 101/224; JA; Ski Clb; Varsity Clb; Score Keeper; Sftbl; Tennis; Twrlr; Bus Mgmt.

GAJDOWSKI, ANASTASIA M; Saegertown HS; Saegertown, PA; (4); 4/107; Church Yth Grp; Library Aide; Varsity Clb; Concert Band; Mrchg Band; Mgr(s); Hon Roll; NHS; Pres Schlr; French Clb; Acadc Schlrshp-Gannon 87; Gannon U; Med.

GAJEWSKI, CAROL; Villa Maria Acad; Mckean, PA; (3); SADD; Phys Ther.

GALAMB, DASHIA; Greater Works Acad; Pittsburgh, PA; (4); 3/32; Service Clb; Ski Clb; Yrbk Bus Mgr; Yrbk Ed-Chief; Cheerleading; Sftbl; High Hon Roll; Prfct Atten Awd; Church Yth Grp; Snow Queen; Outstanding Achvt Short Stry Devolpmnt; Outstanding Achvt Lit; U Pittsburgh.

GALAND, TAMMY; Beaver Area JR SR HS; Beaver, PA; (3); Church Yth Grp; French Clb; Pep Clb; Ski Clb; SADD; Powder Puff Ftbl; Sftbl; Hon Roll; Nrsng.

GALANDA, LAUREL; Trinity HS; Washington, PA; (4); 50/322; Camera Clb; Chrmn Hosp Aide; Office Aide; Nwsp Phtg; Yrbk Phtg; Var Capt Swmmng; Stat Vllybl; Hon Roll; Hnrb Mntn Seton Hill Art Show 86; Pntng Slctd Legslatve Schl Art Exhibit 87; Duquesne U; Pharmacy.

GALANTE, ELAINE; Bensalem HS; Bensalem, PA; (4); 38/474; Aud/Vis; French Clb; Varsity Clb; Band; Mrchg Band; Off Stu Cncl; Mgr(s); Swmmng; High Hon Roll; Hon Roll; PTA Schlrshp 87; La Salle U; Cmnctns.

GALANTE, MARIE; Villa Maria Acad; Drexel Hill, PA; (3); 20/100; Church Yth Grp; Debate Tm; NFL; Science Clb; Speech Tm; Yrbk Ed-Chief; Im Fld Hcky; High Hon Roll; NHS; Wnnr Of Main Line Wmn Strike For Peace Essy 86; Peagus Poetry Scty Wnnr 87; 3rd Pl PA Debate 86; Pol Law.

GALAS, AMY; Center Area HS; Monaca, PA; (3); 11/191; Dance Clb; Hosp Aide; Latin Clb; Chorus; Drill Tm; Flag Corp; School Musical; Trs Soph Cls; Co-Capt Pom Pon; Hon Roll; Summa Cum Laude 87; ELEM Ed.

GALBRAITH, BARBIE JEAN; Keystone HS; Knox, PA; (4); 27/125; French Clb; FBLA; Nwsp Phtg; High Hon Roll; Hon Roll; Gen Bus Awd 83-84; 5th Pl Bus Engl Comptn 85-86; 5th Pl Accntng II Comptn 86-87; Bkkpng.

GALBRAITH, JACK; Carlisle SR HS; Carlisle, PA; (3); Letterman Clb; Im JV Socr; JV Var Trk; High Hon Roll; Hon Roll; Ntl Merit SF; Lib Art.

GALBRAITH, JODY; Northern Lebanon HS; Lebanon, PA; (4); 21/175; French Clb; German Clb; Spanish Clb; NHS; Amer Lgn Essy Cont 2nd Pl 86; Hmcmng Ct 86-87; Schlrshp-Gymnstcs-Tmpl U 87; Temple U; Med.

GALBRAITH, SARAH; Downingtown SR HS; Uwchland, PA; (4); 3/551; Church Yth Grp; German Clb; SADD; Acpl Chr; Jazz Band; Mrchg Band; School Musical; Symp Band; Nwsp Stf; NHS; Amer Eductn Week Stu Recogntn 86; Natl HS Awd-Acadmc Excllnc 87; Dist 12 Chorus 87.

GALBRAITH, WM; Carlisle HS; Carlisle, PA; (3); Church Yth Grp; Band; Concert Band; Mrchg Band; Trk; High Hon Roll; Hon Roll; Ntl Merit Ltr; PJAS Aci Awd 2nd Pl 87; Ntl Sci Olympd ST Fnls Slvr 87; Lbrl Arts.

GALBREATH, CHAD; Knoch HS; Butler, PA; (2); Hon Roll.

GALDABINI, KATIE; Hickory HS; Glendale, WI; (2); Church Yth Grp; Latin Clb; Letterman Clb; NFL; Varsity Clb; Chorus; Church Choir; Crs Cntry; Trk; Lat Hrnr Soc 85-86 & 86-87; Yngstwn St U Engl Fest 10th Pl Essy 86-87; Dist Trck Champs 2nd Pl 86-87; Nrsng.

GALENTINE, TAMMY; Du Bois Area SR HS; Luthersburg, PA; (4); 5/270; Science Clb; Chorus; Capt Mrchg Band; School Musical; Variety Show; Hon Roll; NHS; PA ST U; Chem Engr.

GALEZNIAK, SHERRY; William Allen HS; Allentown, PA; (2); 53/634; Church Yth Grp; JA; Leo Clb; SADD; Y-Teens; High Hon Roll; Hon Roll; Pennn ST.

GALFORD, DAPHNE; Cameron County HS; Emporium, PA; (2); Church Yth Grp; German Clb; Teachers Aide; Yrbk Stf; Var L Bsktbl; Var L Cheerleading; Var L Trk; Hon Roll; MIP V Bsktbl 86-87.

GALIATSATOS, NICHOLAS J; Marple Newtown SR HS; Springfield, PA; (3); 21/322; Boy Scts; Church Yth Grp; Church Choir; High Hon Roll; Hon Roll; Prfct Atten Awd; Med.

GALICIC, AMY; Canon Mc Millan JR HS; Cecil, PA; (1); Church Yth Grp; Library Aide; Chorus; JV Trk; High Hon Roll.

GALIK, MELISSA; Connellsville Area SR HS; Connellsville, PA; (2); 156/570; Hon Roll; Pre Law.

GALITSKY, LEON; Allentown Central Catholic HS; Whitehall, PA; (3); 8/239; Math Clb; Math Tm; Quiz Bowl; Teachers Aide; Lit Mag; High Hon Roll; NHS; Math Fld.

GALL, BERNADETTE; Windber Area HS; Windber, PA; (3); FTA; Math Clb; Yrbk Ed-Chief; Yrbk Stf; L Trk; High Hon Roll; NHS; Pres Schlr; Pres Phy Fit Awd 86; MVP Trck 87; Algbr II & Acdmc Engl Hnrs 87; Nrsg.

GALL, PATRICIA; Cambridge Springs HS; Edinboro, PA; (3); 37/93; Pres VP Church Yth Grp; SADD; Teachers Aide; Band; Chorus; Church Choir; Concert Band; Mrchg Band; Pep Band; Variety Show; 2nd Pl Vrty Shw 87; Edinboro U Of PA; Educ.

GALLA, SHANNON; Central Cambria HS; Ebensburg, PA; (2); French Clb; Hon Roll; Prfct Atten Awd; Law.

GALLA, TRACY; Chartiers Valley HS; Bridgeville, PA; (4); 101/299; Dance Clb; Library Aide; Pep Clb; Spanish Clb; Band; Hon Roll; Air Force.

GALLAGHER, ALLEN; Danville JR HS; Danville, PA; (1); JV L Crs Cntry; Var L Trk; High Hon Roll; Pres Acad Fit Awd 86-87.

GALLAGHER, ANDREW; Exeter HS; Reading, PA; (3); 31/241; Quiz Bowl; Varsity Clb; Lit Mag; Var L Socr; Var L Tennis; Hon Roll; Jr NHS; NHS; All Div Hnrbl Mntn Soccer 86; Jrnlsm.

GALLAGHER, BARBARA; Aliquippa HS; Alquippa, PA; (2); Band; Concert Band; Mrchg Band.

GALLAGHER, BARBARA; Dunmore HS; Dunmore, PA; (2); 7/140; Drama Clb; French Clb; Letterman Clb; Ski Clb; Spanish Clb; Var Cheerleading; Var Crs Cntry; Var Trk; High Hon Roll; NHS; Med.

GALLAGHER, CAROLYN; Interboro HS; Essington, PA; (4); Library Aide; VP Pres Spanish Clb; Nwsp Phtg; Nwsp Rptr; Nwsp Stf; Rep Soph Cls; Rep Chrmn Jr Cls; Rep Chrmn Sr Cls; High Hon Roll; Physcl Ed Mrt Awd 84; DE Cnty CC; Hrtclr.

GALLAGHER, COLLEEN; Allentown Central Catholic; Allentown, PA; (4); Sec Frsh Cls; Sec Soph Cls; Sec Jr Cls; Sec Sr Cls; Bsktbl; Crs Cntry; Sftbl; Carole Weil Schlrshp For Sftbl 87; All-E Penn League Sftbl Tm 87; Carole Weil Sftbl All-Star 87; Kings Coll-Wilkes Barre PA.

GALLAGHER, DANIEL; Father Judge HS; Philadelphia, PA; (3); 24/408; Pres Frsh Cls; Pres Soph Cls; Pres Jr Cls; Im Bsktbl; Var Ftbl; Hon Roll; All Cathlc Ftbl 86-87; Bus.

GALLAGHER, DANIELLE; Archbishop Prendergast HS; Collingdale, PA; (3); 67/327; French Clb; Latin Clb; VICA; Hon Roll; Secnd Hnrs 86; Outstndng Illstrtr Awd 85-87; Hussian Schl Of Art; Illstrtn.

GALLAGHER, DONNA; St Basil Acad; Philadelphia, PA; (3); German Clb; JV Fld Hcky; Var Socr; NCTE Awd; Acad All-Amer Schlr 87; Natl Sci Merit 87; U Of Notre Dame; Law.

GALLAGHER, ELIZABETH; Upper Merion Area HS; King Of Prussia, PA; (3); German Clb; Capt Drill Tm; Mrchg Band; Soph Cls; Jr Cls; JV Capt Bsktbl; Var Sftbl; Hon Roll; Prfct Atten Awd; Most Imprvd Plyr Awd JV Grls Bsktbl 85; Allied Hlth.

GALLAGHER, HETHER GLORIA LYNN; Ridley SR HS; Ridley Park, PA; (4); 91/407; Chorus; Ntl Merit Schol; Brandywine Coll; Trvl Trsm.

GALLAGHER, HUGH; North East Catholic HS; Philadelphia, PA; (2); Boy Scts; Ftbl; Trk; Wt Lftg; Wrstlng; Hon Roll; Phys Fitness Awd 85; Spanish Awd 86; U Of MIAMI; Law.

GALLAGHER, JEAN; Cardinal O Hara HS; Ridley Park, PA; (3); 24/710; Spanish Clb; Flag Corp; Hon Roll; NHS; Prfct Atten Awd; Spanish NHS; Diocesan Schlrs Pgm Of Phila 87; Prncpls Awd/Acad Excllnc 85-87; DE Vly Sci Fair Awd 86; Advtg.

GALLAGHER, JEANINE; St Hubert HS; Philadelphia, PA; (2); Girl Scts; Frankford Schl Of Nrsng.

GALLAGHER, JENNIFER; Riverside HS; Ellwood City, PA; (2); 75/203; Art Clb; Sec Camera Clb; Church Yth Grp; DECA; FHA; GAA; Sec Library Aide; SADD; Church Choir; Score Keeper; 2nd In St DECA Cmptn In Pepsi Learn & Earn 87; Fashn Int Dsgn.

GALLAGHER, JOCELYN; Shenandoah Valley HS; Shenandoah, PA; (4); 5/102; Nwsp Stf; Yrbk Stf; Sec Soph Cls; Stu Cncl; Var Co-Capt Cheerleading; High Hon Roll; NHS; Chorus; Wt Lftg; Acad All-Amer; PA ST U.

GALLAGHER, KAREN M; Souderton Area HS; Harleysville, PA; (4); 103/350; Aud/Vis; Ski Clb; School Musical; Nwsp Stf; Lit Mag; Rep Frsh Cls; Rep Soph Cls; Rep Jr Cls; Rep Sr Cls; Rep Stu Cncl; MVP-GYMNSTCS & Capt 86-87; E Stroudsburg U; Bio.

GALLAGHER, KELLI; Hazleton HS; Hazleton, PA; (2); FBLA; Pep Clb; Band; Chorus; Concert Band; Mrchg Band; Hon Roll; Bloomsburg U; Comp Info Sci.

GALLAGHER, KIMBERLY; St Huberts HS; Philadelphia, PA; (3); 28/430; Cmnty Wkr; Hon Roll; Psych.

GALLAGHER, KRISTEN; St Basil Acad; Philadelphia, PA; (3); French Clb; Hosp Aide; Science Clb; SADD; Im Cheerleading; Nrsg.

GALLAGHER, LAURIE ANN; Downingtown SR HS; Exton, PA; (4); 37/550; Church Yth Grp; Cmnty Wkr; Spanish Clb; SADD; Teachers Aide; Chorus; Var L Cheerleading; High Hon Roll; NHS; Bio.

GALLAGHER, MARIE; Allentown Central Catholic HS; Allentown, PA; (3); Key Clb; Pep Clb; Yrbk Stf; JV Cheerleading.

GALLAGHER, MATTHEW; Abington Heights HS; Clarks Summit, PA; (3); Ski Clb; Var L Socr; Trk; Var Vllybl; Hon Roll; Athlte Wk Awd Sccr 86-87; Outstndng Frwrd Bstr Clb Awd Sccr 86-87; Rookie Yr Bstr Clb Awd Vlybl 87; PA ST U.

GALLAGHER, MAUREEN; St Hubert HS For Girls; Philadelphia, PA; (3); 63/421; Church Yth Grp; Cmnty Wkr; French Clb; GAA; Hosp Aide; Service Clb; SADD; Nwsp Stf; Hon Roll; Yth Traffic Safety Cncl DUI Prevention 87; Cmnty Svc Corps & Perfect Atten Awd 85-86; Secondary Educ.

GALLAGHER, MICHAEL; Montour HS; Pittsburgh, PA; (3); Var L Bsbl; Var L Ftbl; Hon Roll; U Pittsburgh.

GALLAGHER, PATRICK; Lock Haven HS; Lock Haven, PA; (3); Key Clb; School Musical; Rep Stu Cncl; Var L Ftbl; Trk; High Hon Roll; Hon Roll; NHS; Prfct Atten Awd; Pre-Med.

GALLAGHER, SEAN; Central HS; Philadelphia, PA; (3); Var Bsbl; JV Wrstlng; Barnwell Honor Awd 85; Engr.

GALLAGHER, SEAN; Gateway SR HS; Monroeville, PA; (4); FBLA; Science Clb; Ski Clb; Spanish Clb; Band; Jazz Band; Madrigals; Orch; Off Sr Cls; Ftbl; U Of Pittsburgh; Intl Rltns.

GALLAHER, CAREENA; Homer-Center JR SR HS; Lucernemines, PA; (4); 8/86; Sec FBLA; School Play; High Hon Roll; Hon Roll; Jr NHS; NHS; Top Ten SR 87; Best All Around Bus Stu 86; Sec.

GALLATIN, MATTHEW; Hempfield SR HS; Greensburg, PA; (3); Church Yth Grp; French Clb; Latin Clb; Ski Clb; Im Bsktbl; Im Vllybl; High Hon Roll; Hon Roll; Jr NHS; NHS; Bus Admn.

GALLELLI, CLAUDIA; Nazareth Acad; Philadelphia, PA; (4); Hosp Aide; Spanish Clb; Church Choir; VP Orch; School Musical; SF Natl Hispanic Schlr Awd 87; Philadelphia Coll; Phrmcy.

GALLELLI, ROCCO; Central HS; Philadelphia, PA; (2); Art Clb; Science Clb; Teachers Aide; Nwsp Stf; Temple U; Bus Mgmt.

GALLENTINE, JAMES; Jefferson-Morgan JR- SR HS; Mather, PA; (3); Art Clb; French Clb; Rep Frsh Cls; Var Wt Lftg; Var Wrstlng; Hon Roll; Amer Lgn Awd 85; Graphic Arts.

GALLEY, RICHARD; Salisburg Elk Lick HS; Fort Hill, PA; (3); VP Church Yth Grp; VP 4-H; FFA; School Play; Nwsp Stf; Yrbk Stf; Pres Frsh Cls; Pres Soph Cls; Pres Jr Cls; Capt Bsktbl; PA ST U; Chem Engrng.

GALLI, STEPHANIE; Blacklick Valley HS; Nanty-Glo, PA; (3); 10/100; German Clb; Speech Tm; High Hon Roll; Acad All Amer 85.

GALLIMORE, TAMIKA L; Henderson SR HS; West Chester, PA; (3); Am Leg Aux Girls St; Pres FBLA; Opt Clb Awd; 1st Pl Pblc Spkng Awd 86; 2nd Pl Imprmptu Spkng Awd 85; Spkng Hnr Intro MLK III 87; Fin.

GALLIS, HEIDI; Geibel HS; Uniontown, PA; (3); Drama Clb; French Clb; School Musical; Trs Frsh Cls; Trs Soph Cls; Trs Jr Cls; Trs Sr Cls; Var L Cheerleading; French Hon Soc; High Hon Roll; 3rd Pl French Poetry Humanties Day Comp 87.

GALLO, CHRISTINE; North Catholic HS; Pgh, PA; (3); 61/325; Var Tennis; Hon Roll; Hnr Awd Outstndng Schlstc Achvt 85-86; U Of CA Santa Cruz; Marine Zoo.

GALLO, DANIEL J; Archbishop Ryan For Boys; Philadelphia, PA; (4); 22/438; Church Yth Grp; NHS; Awd 1st Hnrs; Mech Engrng.

GALLO, DEBORAH; Burgettstown JR-SR HS; Burgettstown, PA; (3); 2/161; Church Yth Grp; Band; Mrchg Band; Pep Band; Symp Band; Var L Bsktbl; High Hon Roll; NHS; Mbr Soc Dstngshd Amer HS Stu 86; Med.

GALLO, DONNA; Pittston Area HS; Pittston, PA; (4); 1/348; Key Clb; Math Clb; Pres Science Clb; Off Ski Clb; Yrbk Stf; Trs Sr Cls; Co-Capt Cheerleading; High Hon Roll; NHS; NEDT Awd; Outstndg Sci Stu Awd 84; Math.

GALLO, JEAN CHERYL; Connellsville HS; Connellsville, PA; (2); Drama Clb; Exploring; Chorus; School Musical; School Play; Stage Crew; Variety Show; High Hon Roll; Hon Roll; Home Ec Awd 85-86; Girls Ensbl 85-86; Spanish.

GALLO, JOSEPH; St John Neumann HS; Philadelphia, PA; (2); 4/357; Church Yth Grp; Latin Clb; Yrbk Stf; Im Bsktbl; High Hon Roll; Temple; Business.

GALLO, MARLA; Mohawk JR SR HS; Edinburg, PA; (3); Church Yth Grp; FBLA; Spanish Clb; SADD; Drill Tm; Nwsp Rptr; Yrbk Rptr; Hon Roll; Rotary Awd; Pres Jr Cls; Amer Legion Essay 85 & 87; Public Rltns.

GALLO, ROBERT; Central Catholic HS; Pittsburgh, PA; (3); Church Yth Grp; Math Clb; Quiz Bowl; Yrbk Stf; Im Bsktbl; Bowling; Mgr Ftbl; Hon Roll; Honors 84-85; MBA; Pre-Law.

GALLO, STEPHEN JOHN; Lancaster Catholic HS; Lancaster, PA; (3); Chess Clb; Drama Clb; VP Model UN; School Musical; Nwsp Rptr; Yrbk Rptr; Var Socr; Var Swmmng; Var Trk; Rotary Awd; Rtry Intl Frgn Exchng Stu 85-86.

GALLOWAY, DAVID; Fort Cherry HS; Mc Donald, PA; (4); 7/115; Drama Clb; Science Clb; Ski Clb; Spanish Clb; School Play; Wrstlng; High Hon Roll; Hon Roll; U Of Pgh; Math.

GALLOWAY, MICHELLE; West Allegheny HS; Imperial, PA; (2); 14/210; Church Yth Grp; Drama Clb; Band; Chorus; Church Choir; Concert Band; Mrchg Band; Pep Band; School Play; High Hon Roll.

GALLOWAY, WILLIAM; Fort Cherry HS; Mc Donald, PA; (3); Science Clb; Ski Clb; Spanish Clb; Varsity Clb; Ftbl; Wrstlng; Hon Roll.

GALLTON, DANIEL; Warwick HS; Lititz, PA; (3); 15/300; Boy Scts; Church Yth Grp; Chorus; School Musical; School Play; Im JV Bsktbl; Ftbl; Wt Lftg; High Hon Roll; NHS; Physics.

GALONSKI, JENNIE; Belle Vernon Area HS; Belle Vernon, PA; (3); Hosp Aide; VP SADD; Hon Roll; NHS; Nrsng.

GALT, DANIELLE; Harbor Creek HS; Erie, PA; (4); 14/221; Sec AFS; Dance Clb; Variety Show; Ed Nwsp Stf; Ed Yrbk Sprt Ed; Rep Stu Cncl; Pom Pon; High Hon Roll; NHS; Mrchg Band; Commencement Awd Frnch 87; PA ST U; Psych.

GALUPI, CRAIG; Ambridge HS; Baden, PA; (3); Chorus; School Musical; Bsbl; Ftbl; Hon Roll; Music.

GALVAN KOCH, JESSICA; Blue Mountain Acad; York, PA; (1); Church Yth Grp; Library Aide; Band; Chorus; Church Choir; High Hon Roll; Phrmcy.

GALVIN, LUANNE; New Castle SR HS; New Castle, PA; (3); Church Yth Grp; Office Aide; Spanish Clb; Chorus; Drill Tm; Vllybl; High Hon Roll; Hon Roll; Westminster Coll; Public Reltns.

GALZARANO, SHARON; Center Area HS; Monaca, PA; (3); Am Leg Aux Girls St; Pres Exploring; German Clb; Red Cross Aide; Concert Band; Jazz Band; Mrchg Band; School Musical; NHS; Latin Clb; 3rd Pl Grmn Cmptn 87; 200 Hr Vlntr Svc Awd 85; Band Awd 85; Duquesne U; Phrmcy.

GAMBACORTA, JOSEPH; Scranton Tech; Scranton, PA; (4); Johnsons Voc.

GAMBERONI, STEVEN; Hempfield Area HS; Youngwood, PA; (2); Camera Clb; Ski Clb; Jazz Band; Penn ST U; Marine Bio.

GAMBILL, SUSAN M; North Allegheny HS; Wexford, PA; (4); 65/680; Aud/Vis; Exploring; School Musical; School Play; Stage Crew; Lit Mag; Capt Fld Hcky; Hon Roll; Jr NHS; NHS; Talent Show Emcee 87; OH U; Tele-Comm.

GAMBIRASI, AMY; Ringgold HS; Finleyville, PA; (3); Pep Clb; Ski Clb; Drill Tm; Variety Show; Nwsp Stf; Yrbk Stf; Rep Frsh Cls; Rep Soph Cls; Rep Jr Cls; Cheerleading; Capt Chrldrs 84-85; Ltrd Sftbl 84-87; Ltrd Pom Poms 85-87; Fshn Inst Pgh; Fshn Merch.

GAMBLE, LESLIE; Mastbaum AVTS HS; Philadelphia, PA; (2); Church Yth Grp; Red Cross Aide; Chorus; Church Choir; Hon Roll; Prfct Atten Awd; Accntnt.

GAMBLER, EDW; Emmaus HS; Macungie, PA; (3); 49/545; Art Clb; Aud/Vis; Church Yth Grp; JV Vllybl; Hon Roll; Carnegie-Melon; Rbtcs Engrng.

GAMBONE, MICHELLE; Connellsville Area HS; Dunbar, PA; (2); Church Yth Grp; GAA; Office Aide; Pep Clb; Ski Clb; Rep SADD; Chorus; School Musical; Soph Cls; Pres Stu Cncl; Phys Fit Awd 85-86; Chem.

GAMMELL, CHANIN; Schuylkill Valley HS; Reading, PA; (2); FBLA; Red Cross Aide; Stu Cncl; Spanish Clb; SADD; School Play; Nwsp Rptr; Nwsp Stf; JV Capt Bsktbl; Fld Hcky; Pediatrician.

GAMMON, JEANEEN; Owen J Roberts HS; Glenmoore, PA; (4); 27/270; Letterman Clb; Band; Concert Band; Mrchg Band; Yrbk Stf; Var JV Fld Hcky; Var Lcrss; Hon Roll; NHS; Penn St U; Lbrl Arts.

GAMPO, BRETT; West Greene HS; New Freeport, PA; (3); Boy Scts; Church Yth Grp; Cmnty Wkr; Ski Clb; Chorus; Church Choir; Concert Band; Bsktbl; Bowling; Sftbl; Spec Olympc Games Awd 85-87.

GAMPO, TALBY; West Greene HS; New Freeport, PA; (2); Art Clb; Boy Scts; Math Tm; Band; Church Choir; Concert Band; Jazz Band; Mrchg Band; Orch; Wrstlng.

GANAS, CHRISTIE; Exeter Twp SR HS; Reading, PA; (4); 1/212; Trs Leo Clb; Capt Quiz Bowl; Varsity Clb; Trs Stu Cncl; Stat Bsktbl; Var Tennis; Jr NHS; Trs NHS; Val; High Hon Roll; Am Lgn Awd 84; Otto Fisher Math Awd 84; Provost Schlrshp U Of Pittsburgh 87; U Of Pittsburgh; Biology.

GANC, DENNIS; West Hazelton HS; Drums, PA; (2); Yrbk Stf; Var Bsbl; High Hon Roll; Hon Roll; Prfct Atten Awd.

GANDER, JENNIFER; Lakeview HS; Sandy Lake, PA; (4); 6/130; Science Clb; Varsity Clb; Band; Concert Band; Mrchg Band; Pep Band; School Play; Nwsp Stf; L Crs Cntry; Var L Trk; Penn ST.

GANDHI, SWATA; Danville SR HS; Danville, PA; (2); 9/233; Girl Scts; Engl, Span, French Awds 87.

GANDY, OHMAR; Strath Haven HS; Media, PA; (4); Boys Clb Am; Church Yth Grp; Var Bsktbl; Im Coach Actv; Var Ftbl; Hon Roll; Ntl Merit Schol; Comp Sci.

GANDZIARSKI, CATHERINE; Deer Lakes HS; Creighton, PA; (4); 11/161; Pres VP Church Yth Grp; Varsity Clb; Concert Band; Mrchg Band; School Musical; Yrbk Stf; Var L Cheerleading; Var L Trk; NHS; NEDT Awd; Duquesne U; Phrmcy.

GANGLOFF, BENJAMIN; York Catholic HS; York, PA; (2); 3/135; Varsity Clb; Yrbk Stf; Rep Soph Cls; Ftbl; Var L Socr; High Hon Roll; NHS.

GANNON, MARK; Towanda HS; Towanda, PA; (3); Art Clb; Camera Clb; Church Yth Grp; Letterman Clb; Ski Clb; Yrbk Phtg; Var L Bsktbl; Var L Ftbl; Var L Trk; Im Vllybl; Distnc Rnnr Yr Trk 86; Phtgrphy.

GANNON, SHAWN; Bishop Mc Devitt HS; Harrisburg, PA; (3); 8/209; Computer Clb; Red Cross Aide; Science Clb; Band; Concert Band; Jazz Band; Mrchg Band; High Hon Roll; NHS; Bio Sci.

GANO, JAYNE; Reading HS; Reading, PA; (4); 30/720; VP German Clb; Nwsp Stf; Yrbk Stf; Var Capt Bsktbl; JV Var Sftbl; Var L Tennis; Var L Vllybl; Hon Roll; NHS.

GANOE, CINDY; Keystone JR SR HS; Shippenville, PA; (3); Trs French Clb; SADD; Varsity Clb; Var Capt Bsktbl; Mgr(s); Var Trk; JV Vllybl; French Hon Soc; High Hon Roll; NHS; Exchange Stu Thru Youth For Understndng To Australia 88; Fashion Desgn.

GANS, STEPHANIE; Acad Of Notre Dame; Havertown, PA; (3); Cmnty Wkr; Hosp Aide; Service Clb; JV Tennis; Fash Merch.

GANSLEY-ORTIZ, DEIDRE; Harrisburg HS; Harrisburg, PA; (3); 55/258; Aud/Vis; Church Yth Grp; Speech Tm; Chorus; Church Choir; Nwsp Rptr; Nwsp Sprt Ed; Tennis; PA Gvrnrs Art Semi Fnlst 86-87; Jrnlsm.

GANTERT, BRIAN; Parkland SR HS; Allntwn, PA; (4); 44/438; Hon Roll; NHS; Penn ST; Bus Admin.

GANTT, CHRISTIAN; Trinity HS; Duncannon, PA; (3); Ski Clb; Acpl Chr; Band; Chorus; Concert Band; Jazz Band; Mrchg Band; Orch; Pep Band; School Musical; Snd Recrdg Tech.

GANTT, MATTHEW; Greenwood HS; Millerstown, PA; (1); Chorus; School Musical; Rep Stu Cncl; JV Bsktbl; JV Socr; High Hon Roll.

GANTT, SHAWNA; Elizabeth Forward HS; Buena Vista, PA; (3); Church Yth Grp; French Clb; Girl Scts; Capt Color Guard; Swim For Cancer 86-85; PA ST; Scndry Educ.

GANTZ, JOHN; Shenandoah Valley HS; Shenandoah, PA; (4); 3/102; JV Var Bsbl; JV Var Bsktbl; High Hon Roll; Prfct Atten Awd; Lincoln Tech Inst; Elec Tech.

GANZ, CHRISTINE; Altoona Area HS; Altoona, PA; (3); German Clb; Political Wkr; Nwsp Stf; Ed Yrbk Stf; Lit Mag; Stu Cncl; Hon Roll; Congress Bundestag Yth Exchng Prog 87; NEDT Achvt Awd 85; Class Edtr Yrbk 87-88; Penn ST; Comm.

GARAITONANDIA, MONICA; Upper Dublin HS; Maple Glen, PA; (3); 18/300; FBLA; Pres Intnl Clb; SADD; Lit Mag; Rep Frsh Cls; Rep Jr Cls; Stu Cncl; Capt Mat Maids; Powder Puff Ftbl; Hon Roll; 1st Pl Ntl Spanish Comp 87; Govr Schl Intl Studies Schlrshp Smmr 87; AFLT 1st Pl Oral Prof French 86; Schiller Intl U; Intl Rltns.

GARBACIK, GARY; Trinity HS; Camp Hill, PA; (4); Boy Scts; Drama Clb; French Clb; Trs Band; Chorus; Concert Band; Mrchg Band; School Musical; School Play; Eagle Scout 83-845; US Music Ambssdrs 85-86; Amer Wldrnss Ldrshp Schl 86-87; Penn ST U; Cvl Engrng.

GARBER, AARON; Bermudian Springs HS; Gardners, PA; (3); #5 In Class; Im Tennis; Hon Roll; Top 5 Prcnt Awd 87; Med.

GARBER, ANGELA D; Dauphin County Vo-Tech HS; Middletown, PA; (2); Cmnty Wkr; Rptr DECA; Library Aide; JV Bsktbl; JV Trk; Hon Roll; DECA Compttn 1st Pl Mrktng Bus Mngmt 87; Johnson & Wales Bus Coll; Trsm.

GARBER, CHARLES J; Waynesboro Central HS; Waynesburg, PA; (4); Boy Scts; Band; Concert Band; Mrchg Band; Drafting.

GARBER, DOUG; Elizabethtown Area HS; Elizabethtown, PA; (3); Church Yth Grp; FFA; Varsity Clb; Bsbl; Bsktbl.

GARBER, JOSEPH; Donegal HS; Marietta, PA; (3); 21/169; Church Yth Grp; 4-H; Concert Band; Mrchg Band; Hon Roll; Yrbk Phtg; Messiah Coll; Chem.

GARBER, KIMBERLY; Hanover Area HS; Wilkes Barre, PA; (3); Key Clb; Stage Crew; Stu Cncl; Vllybl; Hon Roll; Jr NHS; Physcl Thrpy.

GARBER, MELISSA; Lancaster Mennonite HS; Mt Joy, PA; (3); Off Church Yth Grp; Chorus; Church Choir; Nwsp Rptr; Fld Hcky; Sftbl; Vllybl.

GARBER, TODD; Parkland SR HS; Allentown, PA; (3); 3/500; Chess Clb; Scholastic Bowl; Trs Temple Yth Grp; Band; Concert Band; Jazz Band; Mrchg Band; School Play; Rep Stu Cncl; Im Mgr Socr.

GARBERA, KIMBERLY; Carbondale Area HS; Simpson, PA; (4); 20/146; English Clb; FHA; Ski Clb; Spanish Clb; Chorus; Drill Tm; School Musical; Hon Roll; Wilkes Coll; Phrmcy.

GARBES, PETER; Danville SR HS; Danville, PA; (2); 2/165; Ski Clb; Mrchg Band; High Hon Roll; NEDT Awd; Latin Hnr Soc 87; Natl Latin Exam Latin I Summa Cum Laude 87; ASHME Schl Wnnr 86; Sci.

GARCHER, MICHELE; Geibel HS; Masontown, PA; (4); 7/80; Spanish Clb; Nwsp Stf; Lit Mag; Crs Cntry; High Hon Roll; Spanish NHS; Art Awd; Scl Stds Awd; Pres Acdmc Ftnss Awd; Hgh Hnr Rll 4 Yrs; St Francis; Lbrl Arts.

GARCHINSKY, ELISSA; Cedar Crest HS; Lebanon, PA; (3); 79/342; Latin Clb; Sec Band; Concert Band; Jazz Band; Mrchg Band; Orch; Pep Band; School Musical; Symp Band; Hon Roll; Millersville U; Poly Sci.

GARCIA, ALEXIS C; Dieruff HS; Allentown, PA; (3); Cmnty Wkr; Drama Clb; Exploring; FBLA; Office Aide; School Play; Trk; Awd For Tutoring Yng Chldrn 84-87; Trk Ltrs 85-87; Law.

GARCIA, ALICIA; Albert Gallatine SR HS; Point Marion, PA; (3); Library Aide; VICA; High Hon Roll; Hon Roll.

GARCIA, DIANA; Carbondale Area HS; Carbondale, PA; (2); Pres Church Yth Grp; Dance Clb; Trs FBLA; Ski Clb; Spanish Clb; Band; Chorus; Church Choir; Variety Show; High Hon Roll; Pre Med.

GARCIA, MARIBEL; William Penn HS; Harrisburg, PA; (3); 9/150; FBLA; Yrbk Phtg; Yrbk Stf; Off Jr Cls; Hon Roll; Cert Achvt The Gregg Offc Jb Trng Pgm 86; PA ST; Bus.

GARCIA, MARY; Biglerville HS; Biglerville, PA; (3); 10/105; Church Yth Grp; Pres Drama Clb; FBLA; Trs Chorus; Church Choir; Color Guard; Concert Band; Capt Flag Corp; Mrchg Band; Pep Band; Central PA Bus Schl; Trvl.

GARCIA, MICHELLE; Mc Keesport Area HS; Mc Keesport, PA; (2); 30/410; Girl Scts; Library Aide; Spanish Clb; Band; Concert Band; Mrchg Band; Rep Stu Cncl; Hon Roll; Pres Schlr; Silver Awd Girl Scout 87.

GARCIA, RENEE; Albert Gallatin SR HS; Point Marion, PA; (3); #1 In Class; Hosp Aide; Spanish Clb; Band; Drm Mjr(t); Jazz Band; Mrchg Band; High Hon Roll; NHS; Jr NHS; Robert C Byrd Schlrshp 87; Deans Frosh List Schlrshp 87; Penn ST U; Ceramic Engrng.

GARCIA, VALINDA; Newport HS; Newport, PA; (1); Swing Chorus; Trs Frsh Cls; Off Stu Cncl; High Hon Roll; Art.

GARCIA-ZAYAS, RICARDO M; Blue Mountain Acad; Mayaguez, PR; (1); 1/50; Aud/Vis; Church Yth Grp; School Play; Trs Frsh Cls; JV Bsktbl; Var Ftbl; Var Vllybl; High Hon Roll; Ping Pong V 86; U Puerto Rico; Engr.

GARCSAR, SAMANTHA; Salisbury HS; Allentown, PA; (3); 37/150; Band; Mrchg Band; Yrbk Phtg; Yrbk Rptr; Yrbk Stf; Twrlr; Hon Roll; SECR.

GARDECKI, TODD; Reading HS; Reading, PA; (3); #10 In Class; VP Chess Clb; Debate Tm; Exploring; Model UN; Tennis; High Hon Roll; Ntl Merit Ltr; Prfct Atten Awd; Quiz Bowl; Stage Crew; Ntl Mntn Sci Fair 86-87; Sprntndnts Schltc Achvt Awd 85-87; No 1 Cnty Chss 86-87; No 1 Mth, Sci 85; Physcl Sci.

GARDINER, DIANE; Palmyra HS; Palmyra, PA; (4); 5/180; Drama Clb; German Clb; Ski Clb; Chorus; Church Choir; Sftbl; Stat Swmmng; Twrlr; High Hon Roll; NHS; Penn ST; Bus Admn.

GARDINER, GLENN; Chichester SR HS; Linwood, PA; (3); 63/297; Stage Crew; Var Bsbl; Var Ftbl; Var Wrstlng.

GARDINER, STEPHEN; Baldwin HS; Pittsburgh, PA; (2); Church Yth Grp; Exploring; French Clb; Rep Frsh Cls; Rep Soph Cls; Var JV Bsktbl; Var Golf; Hon Roll; Prfct Atten Awd; Systs Dsgn.

GARDNER, ANDREW; Roman Catholic HS; Philadelphia, PA; (3); Office Aide; Spanish Clb; Rep Jr Cls; Pres Sr Cls; Rep Stu Cncl; Var L Ftbl; Var L Golf; L Trk; Pres NHS; Ntl Merit Ltr; Schlrshp Roman Catholic HS 84; Law.

GARDNER, BARBARA; Saint Marys Area HS; St Marys, PA; (3); 13/288; Church Yth Grp; Sec Hosp Aide; Teachers Aide; Church Choir; Concert Band; Mrchg Band; Im Swmmng; Im Vllybl; High Hon Roll; Hon Roll; Astronautical Engineering.

GARDNER, BRITT; Susquenita HS; Duncannon, PA; (3); Church Yth Grp; Nwsp Ed-Chief; Nwsp Stf; Yrbk Sprt Ed; Yrbk Stf; VP Sr Cls; Capt Cheerleading; Hon Roll; Spanish Clb; Sci Fair 1st Pl Category Botany 86; GPA Hnrs Engl 87; Rcvd Superior Rbbns & Spirt Awd Chrldng Cmp 86; HACC; Scndry Engl Tchr.

GARDNER, CHRIS; North Allegheny HS; Pittsburgh, PA; (3); Art Clb; Church Yth Grp; Hosp Aide; Rep Stu Cncl; Var Lcrss; Var Tennis; U Of WI; Bio Chem.

GARDNER, CORINNE; Hopewell HS; Aliquippa, PA; (4); 1/245; Cmnty Wkr; Latin Clb; Library Aide; Concert Band; Mrchg Band; Trs Jr Cls; Trs Sr Cls; High Hon Roll; Lion Awd; NHS; PMEA Dist Band Fstvls 85-86; Century III Ldr 86-87; Westminster Coll; Psych.

GARDNER, GALE; Purchase Line HS; Glen Campbell, PA; (2); 43/156; FBLA; Pep Clb; Nwsp Rptr; Nwsp Stf; Off Soph Cls; Hon Roll; Otstndng Bus Awd 86-87; Pblc Spkng Awd 2nd Pl 87; Penn ST U; Scrtry.

GARDNER, HEIDI; Warwick HS; Lititz, PA; (3); 2/275; Model UN; School Musical; Stu Cncl; High Hon Roll; NHS; Sal; Church Yth Grp; Exploring; Political Wkr; PA Gvrnrs Schl Intl Stds; Hgh O Brn Yth Ldrshp; Georgetown U Jpns Schlrshp; Intl Corp Atty.

GARDNER, JOHN; Chestnut Ridge HS; Bedford, PA; (3); Im Bsktbl; Im Ftbl; Im Vllybl; Im Wt Lftg; Hon Roll.

GARDNER, JULIE; William Penn SR HS; York, PA; (3); Sec Church Yth Grp; Cmnty Wkr; Drama Clb; Sec Ski Clb; Mgr(s); JV L Sftbl; JV L Trk; Var L Wrstlng; Hon Roll; NHS; Mst Dedctd Stu-Wrstlng Tm 87; AZ ST U; Jrnlsm.

GARDNER, KIMBERLY; Portersville Christian HS; Ellwood, PA; (3); 1/10; Church Yth Grp; Hosp Aide; Chorus; Church Choir; Variety Show; Yrbk Stf; Off Stu Cncl; Cheerleading; JV Capt Vllybl; High Hon Roll; PA Jr Acad Sci 1st 86-87; PA Jr Acad Sci 2nd 83-86; Geneva Coll; Pre-Law.

GARDNER, KIMBERLY; Union Area HS; New Castle, PA; (4); 4/66; French Clb; Hosp Aide; Library Aide; Pep Clb; Nwsp Stf; Yrbk Stf; High Hon Roll; Hon Roll; NHS; Mildred Rodgers Schlrshp 87; Jameson Sch; Nrsng.

GARDNER, LESLEY; Elkland Area HS; Elkland, PA; (4); 2/80; Var Drama Clb; Band; Trs Yrbk Stf; Capt Bsktbl; Capt Trk; Capt Vllybl; Cit Awd; JP Sousa Awd; Trs NHS; Sal; Army Rsrv Schlr/Athlt Awd 87; Femal Athlt Yr-Elmira NY Star Gazette 86; Outstndng Drma Clb Stu 87; Keuka Coll; Jrnlsm.

GARDNER, MALORA; Avon Grove HS; New London, PA; (3); 42/210; Church Yth Grp; SADD; Church Choir; Capt Flag Corp; School Musical; High Hon Roll; Hon Roll; NHS; Engl Awd 86-87; West Chester Univ; Elem Educ.

GARDNER, MARGY; Portersville Christian Schl; Ellwood City, PA; (4); 1/15; Chorus; Yrbk Ed-Chief; Pres Stu Cncl; Var Bsktbl; Cheerleading; Capt Vllybl; Wt Lftg; NHS; Val; Debate Tm; Vllybl Schlrshp Geneva Coll 87; Geneva Coll; Pre Med.

GARDNER, MAYNARD; Newport HS; Newport, PA; (4); 42/95; Varsity Clb; Nwsp Stf; Var Capt Bsbl; Im Bowling; Im Ftbl; Im Golf; Im Socr; Im Sftbl; Im Vllybl; Var Wt Lftg; Bsbl-Tri-Vly League All Star 86-87; Hnrbl Mntn In The Big 9 87; Sprtsmns Clb-Trsr 86-87; Williamsport Area Comm; Lndscpe.

GARDNER, MICHELE; Milton SR HS; Milton, PA; (3); Church Yth Grp; Chorus; Church Choir; Nwsp Stf; Yrbk Stf; Jr Cls; Trk; Hon Roll; Certfct Of Achvmnt For Cntrl Regnl Trainng Svcs 86; Certfct For Latin I 87; Air Force; PT.

GARDNER, MOLLY; Pittston Area HS; Hughestown, PA; (4); 1/363; Computer Clb; Key Clb; Sec Math Clb; Science Clb; SADD; JV Bsktbl; Capt Sftbl; High Hon Roll; Trs NHS; NEDT Cert 84-85; Luzerne County Sci Tchrs Awd 83-84; Finance.

GARDNER, PAUL; St Josephs Prep; Philadelphia, PA; (4); 17/240; Spanish Clb; Yrbk Ed-Chief; Crs Cntry; Trk; Schlrshp 83-87; Elln Hrcrt Schlrshp 87-91; Case Wesenn Reserve.

GARDONE, BARBARA; Penn Hills SR HS; Pittsburgh, PA; (4); 87/609; Concert Band; High Hon Roll; St Vincent Coll; Accntng.

GARELL, CHERYL; Hickory HS; Hermitage, PA; (3); 16/180; Cmnty Wkr; French Clb; Math Clb; Band; Chorus; Concert Band; School Musical; Cheerleading; French Hon Soc; NHS; PA ST; Bus Adm.

GARELL, KAREN; Hickory HS; Hermitage, PA; (3); 11/180; French Clb; Hosp Aide; Math Clb; Chorus; Concert Band; Mrchg Band; Pep Band; School Musical; Cheerleading; NHS; Penn ST; Accntng.

GARFORTH, CHRISSY; Sacred Heart HS; Pittsburgh, PA; (3); 12/138; Civic Clb; French Clb; Hosp Aide; Off Ski Clb; SADD; Varsity Clb; Var L Swmmng; Var L Tennis; High Hon Roll; Hon Roll; Var Sweater & Ltr Ten 87; Var Ltr Swim 87; Duke U; Med.

GARG, MANEESH; Central Dauphin HS; Harrisburg, PA; (2); Chorus; Hon Roll; NHS; Med.

GARGASZ, JOE; Lakeview HS; Mercer, PA; (4); 5/127; Letterman Clb; Science Clb; Varsity Clb; Ftbl; Trk; Elks Awd; Elks Awd 86; Grove Cty Coll; Engrng.

GARGASZ, MARK; Wilmington Area HS; Volant, PA; (1); Church Yth Grp; FFA; Hon Roll; Star Greenhand 86-87; Fish & Wldlfe Mgmnt Awd 86-87; Penn ST.

GARGIULO, FRANK; Farrell Area HS; Farrell, PA; (4); 7/87; Aud/Vis; Cmnty Wkr; Pres Computer Clb; Science Clb; Rep Stu Cncl; JV Bsktbl; Elks Awd; Pres NHS; VFW Awd; Voice Dem Awd; $1100 Elks Ntl Merit Schlrshp 87; 3rd Pl Ntl Hlth & Comp Cntst 84; Youngstown ST U; Comm.

GARGIULO, MICHAEL; Farrell HS; Farrell, PA; (2); French Clb; L Swmmng; NHS.

GARGIULO, STEPHANIE; Bishop Mc Devitt Catholic HS; Harrisburg, PA; (2); 75/250; Church Yth Grp; Drama Clb; Service Clb; School Play; Cheerleading; Sci.

GARGON, FRANK; Trinity HS; Washington, PA; (3); Church Yth Grp; French Clb; Letterman Clb; Varsity Clb; Var Socr; OH ST U.

GARIBAY, JOHN; Chichester HS; Aston, PA; (3); 51/291; Model UN; SADD; Nwsp Rptr; Nwsp Stf; Lit Mag; Trk; Wrstlng; Hon Roll; Beaver Coll; Communications.

GARIBAY, SCOTT; Chichester HS; Aston, PA; (3); 50/293; Church Yth Grp; Rptr English Clb; SADD; Nwsp Rptr; Var Trk; JV Wrstlng; Hon Roll; Cmmnctns.

GARIEPY, JACK; West Scranton HS; Scranton, PA; (2); Letterman Clb; Ski Clb; Var Capt Bsbl; Var JV Ftbl; Wt Lftg; Var JV Wrstlng; Hon Roll; Jr NHS; Rotary Awd; Bus.

GARING, JOHN; Karns City HS; Chicora, PA; (3); Church Yth Grp; Spanish Clb; SADD; Concert Band; Sec Mrchg Band; Pep Band; VP Jr Cls; Var Crs Cntry; Var Trk; Hon Roll; Penn Free Enterprise Week 87; Pres Clsrm For Young Amer 87; Hugh O Brian Yth Ldrshp Smnr 86; Aerspc Engr.

GARLAND, STACY; South Western HS; Hanover, PA; (3); Aud/Vis; Hosp Aide; Teachers Aide; Varsity Clb; Nwsp Rptr; Yrbk Stf; Vllybl; Soc Wrk.

GARLICK, NONA; Northwestern HS; Albion, PA; (3); 8/147; Church Yth Grp; French Clb; Wt Lftg; Hon Roll; NHS; NACEL Frgn Exch Pgm France 87; Frgn Lang.

GARLING, CAMILLA; Big Spring HS; Newville, PA; (3); Chorus; Capt Soph Cls; Stat Bsktbl; Powder Puff Ftbl; Stat Trk; Hon Roll; Lion Awd; Messiah Coll; Chem.

GARLOFF, SAMUEL; Blue Mountain HS; Orwigsburg, PA; (4); 1/211; Am Leg Boys St; Mu Alpha Theta; Quiz Bowl; Concert Band; Jazz Band; Mrchg Band; Nwsp Stf; NHS; Ntl Merit Ltr; Bus Adm.

GARMAN, DAVE; Hershey SR HS; Hershey, PA; (4); Chorus; Concert Band; Jazz Band; Mrchg Band; School Musical; Swing Chorus; Variety Show; Trs Sr Cls; L Var Bsbl; L Var Golf; Outstndng Musician 87; Natl Choral Awd 87; Louis Armstrng Band Jazz Awd 87; Penn ST U; Musical Theatre.

GARMAN, MICHELLE; Danville SR HS; Danville, PA; (3); Church Yth Grp; Latin Clb; Ski Clb; Yrbk Stf; Var L Bsktbl; Im Socr; Var L Sftbl; Hon Roll; Pres Acad Ftns Awd 86; Ed.

GARNER, DEIRDRE RAE ANNA; St Marys Area HS; Saint Marys, PA; (4); Computer Clb; English Clb; French Clb; Hosp Aide; JA; Hon Roll; PA ST U; Bus Adm.

GARNER, HOLLY; Manheim Central HS; Manheim, PA; (2); 100/239; Hon Roll; Elizabethtown Coll; Comm.

GARNER, JENNIFER; Bishop Kenrick HS; Norristown, PA; (4); 10/295; Science Clb; Ski Clb; Rep Stu Cncl; Cheerleading; Powder Puff Ftbl; Swmmng; Trk; Hon Roll; NHS; Pres Schlr; Prsdntl Schlrshp 87; Drexel U; Intl Stds.

GARNER, JUDY; Warwick HS; Lititz, PA; (4); 34/232; VP Pres Church Yth Grp; Yrbk Ed-Chief; Yrbk Stf; High Hon Roll; Hon Roll; NHS; Outstndg Achvt-Stff Stu Of Schl Yrbk 87; Elizabethtown Coll; Acctg.

GARNER, KIMBERLY; Christian School Of York; Jacobus, PA; (2); Church Yth Grp; Hosp Aide; Band; Chorus; Var Cheerleading; Var Trk; Hon Roll; Psych.

GARNER, MARLENE MAE; Eastern York HS; E Prospect, PA; (4); Sec Trs Church Yth Grp; Dance Clb; FCA; GAA; Girl Scts; Hosp Aide; Pep Clb; SADD; Sec Varsity Clb; Pres Trs Chorus; Elizabethtown Hnr Chr 87; Pres Phys Ftnss Awd 87; Chrldg Awds 83-87; Millersville U PA; Elem Educ.

GARNER, SANDY; Huntingdon Area HS; James Creek, PA; (4); 1/224; Trs Church Yth Grp; Pres 4-H; Sec Key Clb; Yrbk Stf; Sec Sr Cls; Sec Stu Cncl; Var Capt Fld Hcky; Var Sftbl; High Hon Roll; NHS; Pres Acad Ftnss Awd 87; Schlr Athl Awd 87; Math Dept Awd 87; Allegheny Coll; Math Tchr.

GARNER, THERESSA; Milton SR HS; Milton, PA; (3); Chorus; Mgr(s); Hon Roll; Pres Acdmc Ftnss Awd 86; U Of Pittsburgh; Pre Med.

GARNSEY, KIMBERLY; Montrose Area HS; Montrose, PA; (3); Church Yth Grp; Cmnty Wkr; French Clb; Spanish Clb; Variety Show; Nwsp Rptr; Yrbk Rptr; French Hon Soc; Hon Roll; Spanish NHS; Social Work.

GARRETT, ANGELA; Mechanicsburg HS; Mechanicsburg, PA; (2); 55/309; Am Leg Aux Girls St; Library Aide; Pep Clb; Teachers Aide; Chorus; Flag Corp; Mrchg Band; DAR Awd; Hon Roll; Presdntl Ftns Awd 85; Educ.

GARRETT, JASON; Peters Township HS; Mc Murray, PA; (4); 22/249; Letterman Clb; Varsity Clb; Yrbk Stf; Stu Cncl; Capt L Bsbl; L Bsktbl; Capt JV Ftbl; High Hon Roll; Hon Roll; Spanish NHS; John Carroll Pres Scholar 87; Hnr Excllnce 84-85 & 87; John Carroll U; Bus Mgmt.

GARRETT, KATHLEEN; Bishop Carroll HS; Cresson, PA; (4); 5/107; Pep Clb; Spanish Clb; Chorus; SADD; Stu Cncl; Capt Cheerleading; High Hon Roll; Hon Roll; NHS; St Francis; Occuptnl Trpy.

GARRETT, LISA; W Middlesex Area HS; W Middlesex, PA; (4); 11/92; Band; Concert Band; Mrchg Band; Nwsp Rptr; Yrbk Stf; Hon Roll; Jr NHS; NHS; Spanish NHS; Bowling Green ST U; Jrnlsm.

GARRETT, LORI; Wilmington Area HS; New Wilmington, PA; (4); Church Yth Grp; 4-H; FBLA; Office Aide; Yrbk Stf; Stu Cncl; 4-H Awd; Hon Roll; Elem Ed.

GARRETT, OMORISHANLA; Wm W Bodine HS For Intl Affairs; Philadelphia, PA; (4); 28/96; Chess Clb; Cmnty Wkr; Computer Clb; Debate Tm; Intnl Clb; JA; Library Aide; Math Clb; Science Clb; Chorus; J V Phila Debtng Tm Chmpns 83; 4th PA Sci Olympd 84; Temple U Law Day Pgm 84; U Of Pittsburgh; Poltcl Sci.

GARRETT, PATTI; West Middlesex Area HS; West Middlesex, PA; (2); Spanish Clb; Band; Stat Trk; High Hon Roll; Jr NHS; NHS; Prfct Atten Awd; Pres Acad Ftns Awd 85-86; Physcl Thrpy.

GARRETT, TODD; South Western HS; Hanover, PA; (3); 25/236; Rep Frsh Cls; Rep Soph Cls; Rep Jr Cls; Rep Sr Cls; Wrstlng; Hon Roll; Arch.

GARRETY, AMY; Elizabethtown Area HS; Elizabethtown, PA; (4); 15/250; Rep Frsh Cls; Rep Soph Cls; Rep Stu Cncl; Var Cheerleading; NHS; Pres Schlr; Pittsburgh U; Law.

GARRICK, MELVIN; Ringgold HS; Monongahela, PA; (3); 69/351; Penn Tech; Elec Tech.

GARRICK, TERI; Belle Vernon Area HS; Belle Vernon, PA; (4); 36/270; Trs FBLA; Ski Clb; Color Guard; Powder Puff Ftbl; Trk; High Hon Roll; NHS; Medical Interest Club; PA ST U; Crmnl Justice.

GARRISON, GAIL; Mt Lebanon SR HS; Pittsburgh, PA; (4); Pres Church Yth Grp; Exploring; Pep Clb; Service Clb; Ski Clb; Spanish Clb; Off Sr Cls; Var Diving; Im Ftbl; WV U; Intl Bus.

GARRISON, JOHN; Tunkhannock Area HS; Falls, PA; (2); 47/330; Church Yth Grp; 4-H; JA; Acpl Chr; Chorus; Church Choir; Variety Show; Hon Roll; Marine Bio.

GARRISON, JOSEPH; Crestwood JR SR HS; Mountaintop, PA; (4); 4/217; FBLA; Math Clb; Ski Clb; School Play; Nwsp Sprt Ed; Capt L Socr; VP L Trk; High Hon Roll; Trs VP NHS; Pres Schlr; Prsdntl Schlrshp Lock Haven U; Shippensburg U Smr Hnrs Pgm; Natl Yng Ldrs Cnfrnc; Lock Haven U; Sprts Brdcstr.

GARRISON, LYNNE A; Westmont Hilltop HS; Johnstown, PA; (3); 4/150; Sec Church Yth Grp; Pep Clb; Ski Clb; Chorus; School Musical; JV Trk; High Hon Roll; NHS; Banking.

GARRISON, SCOTT; Conrad Weiser HS; Wernersville, PA; (2); 32/163; Boy Scts; Church Yth Grp; Exploring; Spanish Clb; Church Choir; Tennis; Hon Roll; Geolgy.

GARRITY, MAUREEN; Carlisle SR HS; Carlisle, PA; (3); 109/454; Art Clb; Church Yth Grp; Hon Roll; Mechanicsburg Art Scholar 87-88; Art Hnr Soc Pres 87-88; Art.

GARRITY, NANCY; Lebanon Catholic HS; Lebanon, PA; (3); Cmnty Wkr; Spanish Clb; Chorus; School Play; Nwsp Rptr; Yrbk Stf; Lit Mag; Hon Roll; 2nd Pl Awd Sci Fair 86-87.

GARRY, KRISTIN; Homer Center HS; Homer City, PA; (3); 19/102; Church Yth Grp; Computer Clb; French Clb; Girl Scts; Varsity Clb; Concert Band; Mrchg Band; Nwsp Stf; Var Bsktbl; Var Sftbl; ROTC; Finance.

GARRY, SEAN; Lancaster Catholic HS; Lancaster, PA; (3); Church Yth Grp; Service Clb; Spanish Clb; Nwsp Sprt Ed; Educ.

GARTH, DARNETTA D; David B Oliver HS; Pittsburgh, PA; (2); JA; Mu Alpha Theta; Y-Teens; Off Stu Cncl; JV Var Bsktbl; Var Trk; High Hon Roll; Math.

GARTHWAITE, SCOTT; Du Bois Area HS; Du Bois, PA; (3); 5/360; Church Yth Grp; Nwsp Rptr; Lit Mag; High Hon Roll; NCTE Awd; Wabash Coll; Engrng.

GARTLEY, BILL; Hopewell HS; Aliquippa, PA; (4); 22/240; Exploring; Office Aide; Var JV Bsbl; Stat Bsktbl; Fld Hcky; Var JV Ftbl; Ice Hcky; High Hon Roll; NHS; Pres Acad Fit Awd 87; Penn ST U; Elec Engrng.

GARTNER, PAUL; Archbishop Wood HS; Doylestown, PA; (3); Industrial Engrng.

GARUCCIO, JOSEPH; Moon HS; Coraopolis, PA; (4); 17/306; French Clb; Variety Show; Im Ftbl; High Hon Roll; Hon Roll; NHS; Wolves Clb Schlrshp 87; PA St U; Chmcl Engr.

GARVER, DARLA; North Allegheny HS; Pittsburgh, PA; (2); 119/630; Church Yth Grp; JV Capt Fld Hcky; Hon Roll; Hosp Aide; Red Cross Aide; SADD; Orch; School Musical; Off Soph Cls; PMEA Fest For Orchestra & PASC Stu Cncl Conf 86; Pre-Med.

GARVER, JOEL; Phil-Mont Christian Acad; Philadelphia, PA; (4); 1/35; Chorus; Rep Sr Cls; Trs Stu Cncl; High Hon Roll; NHS; Superior Art Awd 86; Soc Dstngshd Amer HS Stu Art Fstvl 85-87; 3rd Art Show 86; U Of PA.

GARVER, STEPHEN JOEL; Phil-Mont Christian Acad; Philadelphia, PA; (4); 1/34; Rep Trs Stu Cncl; High Hon Roll; NHS; Ntl Merit Ltr; Rotary Awd; Val; Bst Ctgry Acrylc Pntng 87; U Of PA; Englsh.

GARVER, TAMMY; New Castle HS; New Castle, PA; (4); Church Yth Grp; Computer Clb; Exploring; French Clb; Hosp Aide; Yrbk Stf; High Hon Roll; Hon Roll; Acadc All Am Awd 86-87; Presdntl Acadc Ftns Awd 87; U Pittsburgh; Phys Thrpst.

GARVER, TIMOTHY; Altoona Area HS; Altoona, PA; (4); 13/720; Sec English Clb; Math Tm; Spanish Clb; Rep Stu Cncl; Var JV Bsbl; Jr NHS; NHS; PA ST U; Engrng.

GARVEY, DELORIS; Nazareth Acad; Philadelphia, PA; (3); Cmnty Wkr; Pep Clb; Var Bowling; Capt Var Socr; Var Sftbl; Prfct Atten Awd; Prfct Atten 85-86; E PA Yth Sccr Assn Slct Tm 86-87; All Star Sccr 86-87; Phila Sccr Clb 84-87; Acctg.

GARVIN, GREGORY; Upper Darby HS; Drexel Hill, PA; (3); 4/600; Cmnty Wkr; German Clb; Office Aide; Color Guard; Orch; School Musical; Var JV Lcrss; High Hon Roll; NHS; Ntl Merit Ltr; Engl Awd; US Hstry Awd; SR Life Svng; Astrophysics.

GARVIN JR, VAUGHN M; Du Bois Area HS; Du Bois, PA; (2); Art Clb; Church Yth Grp; Cmnty Wkr; Library Aide; Chorus; Church Choir; School Musical; Swing Chorus; Hon Roll; MADD Pstr Cntst 1st Pl Awd 87; Arch.

GARY, BRIAN; Bishop Neumann HS; Williamsport, PA; (2); Church Yth Grp; Model UN; Pep Clb; SADD; School Musical; School Play; Stage Crew; Variety Show; Yrbk Rptr; Yrbk Stf; New Views Jrnlsm Wrkshp At Yale U 87; Stu Cncl Otstndng Svc Awd 87; Natl Sci Olympiad Bio 87; Med.

GARY, JODY; Rockwood HS; Rockwood, PA; (3); Computer Clb; Band; Mrchg Band; Pres Jr Cls; Var Bsbl; Var Bsktbl; Var Socr; Hon Roll; Elctd Snow Prince Clss 85-87; Phys Ed.

GARY, LATIFAH A; Norristown Area HS; Norristown, PA; (4); FBLA; Intnl Clb; JA; Rep Frsh Cls; Rep Soph Cls; Rep Jr Cls; Rep Stu Cncl; Var Lcrss; Hon Roll; Joseph E Coleman Acad Achvt Awd 86; Pltcl Sci.

GASBARRINI, JAMIE; Cmj HS; Canonsburg, PA; (1); Church Yth Grp; Nwsp Rptr; Nwsp Stf; Yrbk Rptr; Yrbk Stf; Hon Roll; Acctnt.

GASBARRO, DEBORAH; Kiski Area HS; Vandergrift, PA; (4); FBLA; Chorus; High Hon Roll; Hon Roll; Rotary Awd; Jazz Rock Ensemble 86-87; New Kensington Comm; Exec Secty.

GASHEL, PATRICIA JANE; Mc Guffey HS; Claysville, PA; (4); 13/195; Am Leg Aux Girls St; Pres German Clb; Varsity Clb; Yrbk Phtg; Sec Soph Cls; VP Sr Cls; Pres Stu Cncl; Trk; Var Co-Capt Vllybl; NHS; Al-Sctn Vllybl 87; Outstndng Stu Awd 84-87; WVU.

GASHGARIAN, BRENDA; Villa Maria Acad; Erie, PA; (3); 25/170; Dance Clb; Science Clb; High Hon Roll; NHS; Bio.

GASHI, SHIRLEY ANN; Wyalusing Valley HS; Laceyville, PA; (4); 18/132; Drama Clb; German Clb; Band; Chorus; Jazz Band; Orch; School Musical; Hon Roll; NHS; Church Yth Grp; York Coll Of PA Pres Schlrshp 87; Schlrs In Educ Awd 87; York Coll Of PA; Scndry Ed Bio.

GASIOR, BONNIE; Sto-Rox SR HS; Mc Kees Rocks, PA; (2); 12/150; Boys Clb Am; Chess Clb; Chorus; Nwsp Stf; Yrbk Stf; Pres Soph Cls; Trs Stu Cncl; Sftbl; Hon Roll; PA ST; Doctor.

GASKIN, CAROLYN; Westinghouse HS; Pittsburgh, PA; (3); Am Leg Aux Girls St; Computer Clb; DECA; FTA; GAA; JA; OEA; Scholastic Bowl; SADD; Teachers Aide; Elem Educ.

GASPER, ARVADA; Lincoln HS; Ellwood City, PA; (3); Camera Clb; Computer Clb; Drama Clb; Girl Scts; Key Clb; Library Aide; Office Aide; Spanish Clb; SADD; Y-Teens; FL U; English.

GASS, CHRIS; Danville SR HS; Danville, PA; (3); Computer Clb; Bsktbl; Trk; Bloomsburg U; Tchng.

GASSER, JOHNNA; Hazleton HS; Hazleton, PA; (2); Bsktbl; Trk; Med.

GASSER, KRISTIN; Carlisle HS; Carlisle, PA; (3); VP Exploring; Library Aide; Ski Clb; Mrchg Band; Orch; School Musical; Stage Crew; Hon Roll; Marine Bio.

GASSER, VALERIE; Upper Darby HS; Drexel Hill, PA; (3); 34/571; Cmnty Wkr; Office Aide; Yrbk Stf; Vllybl; High Hon Roll; Hon Roll; French Awd 85; Philadelphia Coll; Phrmcy.

GASSERT, CHERI; Wyoming Valley West HS; Plymouth, PA; (3); 6/419; Church Yth Grp; Church Choir; Mrchg Band; Var Capt Socr; JV Vllybl; High Hon Roll; NHS; NEDT Awd; IFLA Frgn Lang Awd Frnch 85-86; Bob Jones U; Educ.

GASSNER, DENISE; Hickory HS; West Middlesex, PA; (3); Drama Clb; French Clb; Acpl Chr; Concert Band; Capt Drill Tm; School Musical; Yrbk Stf; Trs Soph Cls; Trs Jr Cls; Trs Sr Cls.

GASTON, COLBY; Blue Mountain HS; Orwigsburg, PA; (4); 34/227; Church Yth Grp; Drama Clb; SADD; School Play; Nwsp Stf; Yrbk Ed-Chief; Yrbk Stf; Hon Roll; Natl Sci Olympd Bio.

GASTON, KELLI; Harmony HS; Westover, PA; (3); Sec Church Yth Grp; Cmnty Wkr; Office Aide; Ski Clb; Band; Chorus; Concert Band; Mrchg Band; Stat Bsktbl; Hon Roll; Medicine.

GASTON, NICK; Marion Center Area Schl District; Rochester Mills, PA; (4); Aud/Vis; Library Aide; Pep Clb; Chorus; Stage Crew; JV Bsbl; Hon Roll; NHS; IN Bnkrs Assn Schlrshp 87; Penn ST U-Altoona; Engrng.

GATES, ANN; Bedford HS; Bedford, PA; (3); Trs Church Yth Grp; FBLA; Band; Concert Band; Mrchg Band; Orch; Pep Band; Hon Roll; Htl Mngmnt.

GATES, CAROL; Moon Area SR HS; Glenwillard, PA; (4); 20/294; Pres Church Yth Grp; Chorus; Mrchg Band; Symp Band; Twrlr; High Hon Roll; NHS; Pres Acad Schlrshp Awd 87; U Of AZ; Pharmacy.

GATES, CRICKET; Donegal HS; Mount Joy, PA; (3); CAP; Trs Frsh Cls; Rep Soph Cls; Rep Jr Cls; Hon Roll; American U; Frgn Stds.

GATES, GRETCHEN; Seneca Valley HS; Evans City, PA; (3); Ski Clb; Varsity Clb; JV Var Bsktbl; Var L Crs Cntry; JV Var Sftbl; Hon Roll; NHS; Seneca Vly Schlrshp Awd 85-87; Vet.

GATES, JEFF; Milton Area HS; Watsontown, PA; (2); Key Clb; Latin Clb; Ski Clb; Vllybl; Wt Lftg; Btty Crckr Awd; Pres Schlr.

GATES, LOUISE; Bishop Guilfoyle HS; Altoona, PA; (3); Church Yth Grp; SADD; Stu Cncl; Var Bsktbl; Hon Roll.

GATES, ROBERT; Maplewood HS; Centerville, PA; (3); Model UN; Spanish Clb; Band; Chorus; Pep Band; Rep Frsh Cls; Var Bsbl; Var Ftbl; Hon Roll; NHS; Rsrch Bio.

GATES, ROGER; United HS; Seward, PA; (4); Office Aide; Red Cross Aide; Chrmn Jr Cls; Chrmn Sr Cls; Var L Bsktbl; Var L Ftbl; Natl Ldrshp Awd 87; Ftbll All-Stars 86-87; IUP; Bus Mgmt.

GATES, SHERRI; Forest Hills HS; Mineral Point, PA; (4); FBLA; Pep Clb; Y-Teens; Hon Roll; Jr NHS.

GATESMAN, SUSAN; Keystone HS; Shippenville, PA; (3); 11/144; Sec Pep Clb; Rep SADD; Chorus; School Musical; Sec Jr Cls; Var L Bsktbl; Var L Trk; Var L Vllybl; NHS; Smmr Acad Clarion U-Cmmnctns 87; Chld Psych.

GATHERS, BECKY; West Middlesex JR SR HS; New Wilmington, PA; (2); Band; Chorus; Concert Band; Mrchg Band; Pep Band; High Hon Roll; NHS; Jr NHS; Trs Church Yth Grp; Exploring; Prsdntl Acac Ftns Awd 85-86; Westminster Coll Hnrs Band 86-87; Med.

GATRELL JR, GARY; West Green SR Middle HS; Holbrook, PA; (4); FFA; Letterman Clb; Varsity Clb; School Musical; School Play; Bsbl; Ftbl; Wt Lftg; Hon Roll; All Conf Rnng Back 87; Defnsve Back Awd 87; Elec Engr.

GATTO, ANTONINE; Bishop Carroll HS; Ebensburg, PA; (4); 1/107; Pep Clb; SADD; Yrbk Stf; Rep Jr Cls; Hon Roll; NHS; Acad All Amer 85; US Stu Cncl Awd 85; Natl Ldrshp & Svc Awd 85; Engrng.

GATTO, JOSEPH C; Abington Heights HS; Clarks Summit, PA; (3); 2/292; Temple Yth Grp; JV Var Bsbl; Var L Golf; Hon Roll; NHS; Quiz Bowl; Ski Clb; Yrbk Rptr; Im Bsktbl; Rotary Awd; Golf MVP 86-87; 2nd Pl Amer Chem Scty Cont 85-86; Lackawanna Golf League All Star Tm 86-87; Engrng.

GATTUSO, TESS; Pittston Area SR High; Pittston, PA; (3); 6/305; FNA; Key Clb; Ski Clb; Var Cheerleading; Hon Roll; Med.

GATZKE, KELLY; Tunkhannock Area HS; Mehoopany, PA; (3); Pres Church Yth Grp; Dance Clb; FCA; 4-H; Ski Clb; Yrbk Stf; JV Crs Cntry; JV Fld Hcky; L Trk; Hon Roll; Bus.

GAUDET, LENORE; Littlestown SR HS; Littlestown, PA; (4); 14/115; Pres Church Yth Grp; Drama Clb; Office Aide; Varsity Clb; Band; Chorus; Nwsp Rptr; Yrbk Sprt Ed; Crs Cntry; Trk.

GAUDIELLO, BRENDA; Connellsville SR HS; Connellsville, PA; (1); Teachers Aide; Chorus; School Musical; School Play; Nwsp Ed-Chief; Nwsp Stf; Score Keeper; Var Tennis; Mgr Trk; Hon Roll; Engl Tchr.

GAUDIO, ALYSON C; Villa Maria HS; Youngstown, OH; (4); Cmnty Wkr; Pep Clb; Spanish Clb; Stage Crew; Nwsp Rptr; Yrbk Stf; Lit Mag; NEDT Awd; Spanish NHS; NEDT Awd 85; Youngstown ST U; Bus.

GAUDLIP, DENISE M; Donegal HS; Mt Joy, PA; (4); 10/168; Pres Church Yth Grp; Sec Trs Band; Yrbk Stf; Off Frsh Cls; Off Soph Cls; Stat Bsktbl; Var Fld Hcky; Powder Puff Ftbl; Cit Awd; DAR Awd; ESU Pres Scholar 87-88; E Stroudsburg U; Elem Ed.

GAUDLITZ, DEREK; Meadville Area SR HS; Houston, TX; (3); 19/382; French Clb; Key Clb; Mu Alpha Theta; Science Clb; Yrbk Phtg; Stat Bsktbl; JV Var Tennis; Hon Roll; Doyle Awd 87; TX A&M U; Aerospc Engrng.

GAUGHAN, KIM; West Scranton HS; Scranton, PA; (4); Latin Clb; Yrbk Stf; Hon Roll; PA ST U.

GAUGHAN, LAURA; Meadville Area SR HS; Meadville, PA; (4); Church Yth Grp; Letterman Clb; VP Science Clb; Varsity Clb; Off Jr Cls; Off Sr Cls; Stu Cncl; Capt Swmmng; Hon Roll; Pre-Law.

GAUGHAN, SARA; Exeter HS; Birdsbow, PA; (3); #35 In Class; Church Yth Grp; Drama Clb; Concert Band; Mrchg Band; Orch; School Musical; Stage Crew; Nwsp Ed-Chief; Bio Sci.

GAUGLER, DONNA; Bethlehem Catholic HS; Bethlehem, PA; (3); 25/210; Church Yth Grp; Var L Sftbl; Var L Vllybl; High Hon Roll; Hon Roll; NHS; Fnanc.

GAUL, NICOLE; Saint Basil Acad; Philadelphia, PA; (3); Computer Clb; Drama Clb; French Clb; German Clb; Science Clb; Spanish Clb; Stage Crew; Pre Med.

GAUMER, KRISTINE; Susquehanna Township HS; Harrisburg, PA; (3); Church Yth Grp; Band; Chorus; Concert Band; Mrchg Band; Orch; School Musical; Hon Roll; Lebanon Vly Coll Hnrs Band 87; Psych.

GAUS JR, FRANK; Tunkhannock Area HS; Tunkhannock, PA; (4); 37/270; VP Church Yth Grp; Drama Clb; Science Clb; Acpl Chr; Chorus; School Musical; School Play; Stage Crew; Var L Bsktbl; Im L Crs Cntry; Dist Chorus 86-87; Astrnmy.

GAUS, SHAUN; North Hills HS; Pittsburgh, PA; (3); 12/483; Key Clb; Ski Clb; Band; Concert Band; Mrchg Band; Symp Band; High Hon Roll; NHS; Prfct Atten Awd; Med.

GAUTNEY, HEATHER; Villa Maria Acad; West Chester, PA; (3); Lit Mag; Fld Hcky; Hon Roll.

GAVAZZI, ANN; Corry HS; Corry, PA; (3); 11/223; Chorus; Ed Yrbk Stf; Trs Stu Cncl; Var L Vllybl; High Hon Roll; Banking.

GAVAZZI, DIANE; Mon Valley Catholic HS; Ellsworth, PA; (2); Church Yth Grp; Girl Scts; Flag Corp; Mrchg Band; 1st Pl Amer Legion Poetry Cont 86; Marine Bio.

GAVAZZI, MARSHA; Burgettstown Area JR SR HS; Burgettstown, PA; (2); Church Yth Grp; Cmnty Wkr; Science Clb; SADD; Chorus; Church Choir; Yrbk Stf; Sftbl; High Hon Roll.

GAVIO, LISA; Bishop Hafey HS; Hazleton, PA; (4); 27/128; Church Yth Grp; Ski Clb; Spanish Clb; Pres Y-Teens; Drill Tm; Stu Cncl; Capt Cheerleading; Hon Roll; Spanish NHS; Hmcmng Queen 86; Bloomsburg U; Mrktng.

GAVITT, LAURIE; W Hazelton HS; Conyngham, PA; (4); 19/224; Cmnty Wkr; Ski Clb; Spanish Clb; Trs Thesps; School Play; Nwsp Stf; Yrbk Stf; Off Sr Cls; High Hon Roll; Trs NHS; Penn ST U; Jrnlsm.

GAVLICK, KIRK; Wyoming Area SR HS; Pittston, PA; (3); Church Yth Grp; Cmnty Wkr; Key Clb; Nwsp Stf; JV Vllybl; High Hon Roll; Spanish Clb; SADD; Nwsp Rptr; Im Bsktbl; U Of Scranton; Med.

GAVLINSKI, GEORGETTE; Bishop Hannan HS; Clarks Summit, PA; (4); 9/130; Debate Tm; Drama Clb; French Clb; Hosp Aide; Chorus; School Musical; School Play; Yrbk Ed-Chief; Hon Roll; Sec NHS; Marywood Coll; Art.

GAVULA, JENNIFER; Butler HS; Butler, PA; (3); Hosp Aide; Spanish Clb; SADD; Thesps; Chorus; School Musical; Swing Chorus; Variety Show; Hon Roll; Jr NHS.

GAWRYLIK, TRACI; Shenandoah Valley HS; Shenandoah, PA; (3); 7/102; Pep Clb; Spanish Clb; Band; Var Capt Cheerleading; Pom Pon; Sftbl; High Hon Roll; Hon Roll; NHS; All Am Acdmc Awd 87.

GAWRYS, BRENT; Abington Heights HS; Clarks Summit, PA; (3); 4/292; Ski Clb; Band; Concert Band; Jazz Band; Mrchg Band; Orch; Pep Band; School Musical; Stage Crew; High Hon Roll; 2nd Pl Am Hstry Day Prjct 85-86; Penn ST Hnrs Pgm; Mech Engrng.

GAY, DANIEL; Tunkhannock Area HS; Tunkhannock, PA; (4); Ski Clb; Var Bsbl; Im JV Bsktbl; French Hon Soc; U Of NE-LAS Vegas; Bus.

GAY, JAMES; Johnstown SR HS; Johnstown, PA; (3); Pres Band; School Musical; Swing Chorus; Church Yth Grp; NFL; Spanish Clb; Speech Tm; Chorus; Concert Band; Jazz Band; Poli Sci.

GAYDOS, DIANE; Center HS; Aliquippa, PA; (3); Spanish Clb; VP Band; Concert Band; Drm & Bgl; Jazz Band; Mrchg Band; Orch; Symp Band; Hon Roll; All ST Orch 86-87; Mc Donalds All Amer Band 87; Cnty Honors Band 86-87; WV U.

GAYDOS, JAMES; Abington SR HS; Elkins Pk, PA; (3); 16/502; Rep Jr Cls; Hon Roll; Jr NHS; NHS; Prfct Atten Awd.

GAYDOS, KATHLEEN; James M Coughlin HS; Wilkes Barre, PA; (4); 13/333; Church Yth Grp; Yrbk Stf; Var L Fld Hcky; Var L Sftbl; High Hon Roll; Jr NHS; NHS; Penn ST U.

GAYDOS, PHIL; Laurel Highlands HS; Hopwood, PA; (2); Church Yth Grp; Math Tm; Science Clb; Teachers Aide; JV Bsktbl; Var L Ftbl; Capt Vllybl; Var Wt Lftg; High Hon Roll; JETS Awd; Typing Awd 86; Engrng.

GAYLORD, LORIN; North Allegheny HS; Allison Pk, PA; (2); 64/630; Cmnty Wkr; GAA; Ski Clb; SADD; Rep Stu Cncl; Fld Hcky; Trk; High Hon Roll; NHS.

GAZDA, DAVID; Ambridge Area HS; Baden, PA; (3); Am Leg Boys St; Chess Clb; Spanish Clb; Vllybl; High Hon Roll; Hon Roll; Lion Awd; Penn ST U; Elec Engr.

GAZEWOOD, JASON; Fairview HS; Fairview, PA; (3); 6/156; Church Yth Grp; Spanish Clb; Speech Tm; Varsity Clb; L Bsktbl; L Ftbl; Im Wt Lftg; High Hon Roll; Hon Roll; Acdmc All Amer 87; Poltcl Sci.

GAZMEN, NINA; Abington Heights HS; Waverly, PA; (3); 44/252; Hosp Aide; Ski Clb; Chorus; Color Guard; Orch; Yrbk Stf; Mgr(s); Hon Roll; NHS; Mrchg Band; 2nd Pl Jr Acad Sci 85-86; Pre-Dntstry.

GAZZE, RONALD; Greensburg-Salem HS; Greensburg, PA; (2); Church Yth Grp; Debate Tm; French Clb; Model UN; NFL; Ski Clb; JV Bsktbl; Var Golf; Trs Jr NHS; Speech Tm; Anne Ziskind Schlrshp 86; Dstngshd Hnr Rl 85-87; NFL PA Dist Stndrd Debte Chmpn 87; Princeton U; Med.

GAZZO, KELLY; Kiski Area HS; Apollo, PA; (3); German Clb; Spanish Clb; Chorus; Hon Roll.

GBRUOSKI, RENEE; Monongahela Valley Catholic HS; Monongahela, PA; (3); 10/105; Hosp Aide; Spanish Clb; Church Choir; Wt Lftg; NHS; Spanish NHS; Med.

GEAGAN, SHAWN; Butler SR HS; Lyndora, PA; (2); French Clb; Office Aide; Ski Clb; Teachers Aide; Stat Bsbl; Coach Actv; Ftbl; Hon Roll; Jr NHS.

GEARHART, AMY; Huntingdon Area HS; Huntingdon, PA; (3); GAA; Hosp Aide; Rep Soph Cls; JV Bsktbl; Coach Actv; Var Crs Cntry; Var L Fld Hcky; Im Ftbl; Im Powder Puff Ftbl; Var L Sftbl; Air Force.

GEARHART, BARBARA; Hershey SR HS; Hershey, PA; (3); 8/206; Chorus; Color Guard; Nwsp Rptr; Var L Trk; High Hon Roll; NHS; Spanish NHS; Accntng.

GEARHART, BRAD; Hempfield HS; Mountville, PA; (3); Church Yth Grp; Key Clb; Rep Sr Cls; Var Ftbl; Var Wt Lftg; JV Wrstlng; Hon Roll; Bus Admin.

GEARHART, CHRISTOPHER; Watsontown Christian Acad; New Columbia, PA; (3); 3/11; JV Var Bsktbl; Var Socr; Penn ST; Frstry.

GEARHART, GARY; Altoona Area HS; Altoona, PA; (3); 60/800; Church Yth Grp; Computer Clb; Key Clb; Spanish Clb; Concert Band; Mrchg Band; Orch; High Hon Roll; Crng Mln U; Comp.

GEARHART, ROB; Homer-Center HS; Blairsville, PA; (3); Church Yth Grp; Cmnty Wkr; Ski Clb; Varsity Clb; Pres Band; Pres Concert Band; Jazz Band; Mrchg Band; Stu Cncl; Bsktbl; Dirctrs Awds Music, Graphic Arts Awd 87.

GEARHART, SCOTT; Purchase Line HS; Clymer, PA; (2); Yrbk Stf; Hon Roll; Libry Awd 86.

GEARING, CHRIS; Laurel Highlands HS; Uniontown, PA; (2); 11/348; Exploring; Science Clb; High Hon Roll; NEDT Awd; Engrng.

GEARY, CHRISTINE; Southmoreland SR HS; Scottdale, PA; (2); Church Yth Grp; Drama Clb; German Clb; Letterman Clb; Ski Clb; Acpl Chr; Color Guard; Rep Stu Cncl; Bsktbl; Sftbl; Cnty Chorus 85-86; Dist Chorus 85-86; WVU; Dentistry.

GEARY, COLEEN; Kiski Area HS; Apollo, PA; (3); Church Yth Grp; Office Aide; Pep Clb; Spanish Clb; Color Guard; Concert Band; Jazz Band; Mrchg Band; Symp Band; Hon Roll; Pol Sci.

GEARY, KIMBERLEY; Connellsville HS; Champion, PA; (4); Camera Clb; Trs FBLA; Office Aide; Teachers Aide; French Hon Soc; Hon Roll; U Of Pittsburgh; Pltcl Sci.

GEARY, LINDA; Frazier Memorial JR SR HS; Dawson, PA; (3); Drama Clb; FNA; Ski Clb; Yrbk Stf; Stat Bsktbl; JV Var Cheerleading; Powder Puff Ftbl; Sftbl; High Hon Roll; Hon Roll; VFW 86; Tchr.

GEARY, LOU; Connellsville SR HS; Normalville, PA; (3); 12/560; Church Yth Grp; GAA; Ski Clb; Spanish Clb; SADD; Jr Cls; Stu Cncl; Crs Cntry; Mgr(s); Sftbl; U Of Pittsburgh; Pre Med.

GEARY, MARLA; Harrisburg HS John Harris Campus; Harrisburg, PA; (3); 90/297; Girl Scts; Hon Roll; 2nd Hr 86-87; AF; Acctng.

GEARY, MICHELLE LEE; Belle Vernon Area HS; Belle Vernon, PA; (4); 116/267; Art Clb; Church Yth Grp; Drama Clb; Sec VICA; Nwsp Phtg; Hon Roll; Home Hlth Aid.

GEARY, SHANA; Pennsbury HS; Levittown, PA; (4); Spanish Clb; Concert Band; Mrchg Band; Im Bsktbl; NHS; Pres Acad Ftns Awd 87; Millersville U Of PA; Elem Ed.

GEARY, WENDY; Danville HS; Danville, PA; (3); Sec Church Yth Grp; Computer Clb; Latin Clb; JV Crs Cntry; JV Trk; High Hon Roll; NHS; Latin Hon Sco 87; Cum Laude Awd Natl Latin Exam 86; Rutgers U; Bio.

GEBERT, CHRIS; Western Wayne HS; Waymart, PA; (3); VICA; Ftbl; Hon Roll.

GEBHARDT, ALICIA; Mc Dowell HS; Erie, PA; (4); 197/610; VP Church Yth Grp; Pep Clb; Chorus; Drill Tm; Nwsp Rptr; Nwsp Sprt Ed; Stu Cncl; JV L Vllybl; Hon Roll; Opt Clb Awd; Erie Cntys Jr Miss 86-87; Penn ST-ERIE; Pltcl Sci.

GEBICKI, MICHAEL; Greensburg Central Catholic HS; Greensburg, PA; (3); 21/243; Letterman Clb; Yrbk Sprt Ed; Im Bsktbl; Var L Ftbl; Var Trk; Im Vllybl; Wt Lftg; High Hon Roll; NHS; Ntl Merit Ltr; Notre Dame; Bus Adm.

GEBROSKY, CHRISTINE; Lincoln HS; Ellwood City, PA; (3); Church Yth Grp; Girl Scts; Hosp Aide; Key Clb; Spanish Clb; Band; Concert Band; Mrchg Band; Physcn Asst.

GEBROSKY, LISA; Lincoln HS; Ellwood City, PA; (4); 16/165; Church Yth Grp; Library Aide; Service Clb; Spanish Clb; SADD; Y-Teens; Powder Puff Ftbl; Hon Roll; NHS; Pres Schlr; Ushr Clb, Crna D Italia Ldg 608, St Agatha Scl Clb, Amer Bus Wmn Assoc Schlrshps87; Penn St U; Elect Engrng.

GECI, CRYSTA; Elk County Christian HS; St Marys, PA; (1); 28/84; Hosp Aide; Intnl Clb; Nwsp Stf; Hon Roll; Nrsng.

GECKLE, DEAN; Hempfield Area HS; Greensburg, PA; (4); 47/692; Computer Clb; VICA; Stage Crew; Swing Chorus; High Hon Roll; Hon Roll; NHS; VICA Fall Ldrshp Wrkshp 86; De Vry; Comp Info Systms.

GEDMARK, ANN M; Red Land HS; New Cumberland, PA; (4); 5/268; Am Leg Aux Girls St; Trs Debate Tm; Quiz Bowl; SADD; Rep Stu Cncl; Capt Fld Hcky; Trk; High Hon Roll; VP NHS; Ntl Merit SF; Penn ST; Pre-Law.

GEDNEY, TONYA A; Norristown Area HS; Norristown, PA; (4); 43/478; DECA; Sec FBLA; Intnl Clb; Pep Clb; SADD; Chorus; Nwsp Rptr; Nwsp Stf; Yrbk Rptr; Yrbk Stf; Elig Le Natl Hnr Soc; Distngshd Chorus Hnr Awd 86; Pblc Rel.

GEDRAITIS, MICHAEL; St John Neumann HS; Philadelphia, PA; (3); JV Ftbl; Wt Lftg; NHS; Irish Club Essay Awd 86.

GEE, CHERYL; West Catholic Girls HS; Philadelphia, PA; (3); 35/249; Church Yth Grp; French Clb; Library Aide; Teachers Aide; Church Choir; Rep Soph Cls; Rep Stu Cncl; Var L Cheerleading; Prfct Atten Awd; Cheyney Math & Comp Sci Awd 84-85; West Philadelphia Catholic Girls HS Math Hnr Roll 86; Med.

GEE, SHALANE; State College Intermediate HS; State College, PA; (1); Church Yth Grp; Drama Clb; Thesps; School Musical; School Play; Stu Cncl; JV Cheerleading; Hon Roll; 2nd Pl Essay Cntst 86-87; Brghm Yng U; Law.

GEER, MICHELE; Burrell SR HS; Lower Burrell, PA; (3); 31/176; Pres Church Yth Grp; Spanish Clb; Chorus; Color Guard; Nwsp Rptr; Trk; High Hon Roll; Hon Roll; Jr NHS; FTA; Schl Trck Record 85; Indiana U Of PA; Chld Psychlgy.

GEER, RICHARD; Wyoming Valley West HS; Kingston, PA; (3); 20/423; Aud/Vis; French Clb; Key Clb; Math Clb; Science Clb; Nwsp Stf; Yrbk Stf; Lit Mag; Rep Frsh Cls; Im Stat Bsktbl; NEDT Cert Awd; Kings Coll Spnsh Test Hon Ment; Law.

GEERTS, LEANN; Tunkhannock Area HS; Tunkhannock, PA; (2); Aud/Vis; Key Clb; Spanish Clb; Band; Concert Band; Jazz Band; Mrchg Band; School Musical; Var Swmmng; Hon Roll.

GEFFERT, BETSY; Brookville Area HS; Brookville, PA; (3); French Clb; Yrbk Stf; Sftbl; High Hon Roll; Hon Roll; Legal Secy.

GEFRIDES, CHRIS; Montoursville Area HS; Montoursville, PA; (3); FCA; French Clb; Var L Ftbl; High Hon Roll; Hon Roll; SPARK 86-87; BIO-ENGRNG.

GEHMAN, ANDY; Warwick HS; Lititz, PA; (3); Varsity Clb; Nwsp Sprt Ed; Yrbk Sprt Ed; JV L Bsbl; Var L Golf; Jrnlsm.

GEHMAN, DEBORAH; Norristown Area HS; Norristown, PA; (4); 61/471; Key Clb; Ski Clb; Concert Band; Orch; Symp Band; Yrbk Stf; Sec Sr Cls; Capt Var Cheerleading; Hon Roll; Sec Rotary Awd; Typng II Merit Awd 86; Psych.

GEHMAN, JOY; Gateway Christian Schl; Bechtelsville, PA; (2); Church Yth Grp; Drama Clb; Chorus; Rep Stu Cncl; Vllybl; Hon Roll; Prfct Atten Awd.

GEHMAN, KATHY; Warwick HS; Lititz, PA; (3); #27 In Class; Church Yth Grp; Library Aide; Band; Concert Band; Mrchg Band; Var Bsktbl; Var Sftbl; High Hon Roll; Hon Roll; NHS; Messiah Col.

GEHMAN, MATT G; Cowanesque Valley HS; Knoxville, PA; (2); Church Yth Grp; CAP; Computer Clb; Letterman Clb; Ski Clb; JV Bsbl; Var Ftbl; Var Trk; Var Wt Lftg; Hon Roll; Engrng.

GEHMAN, TIMOTHY; Ephrata SR HS; Ephrata, PA; (3); 82/287; Boy Scts; Chess Clb; Var L Ftbl; Trk; Wt Lftg; Hon Roll; All Stars Ftbl Tm 86; Syracuse; Sports Med.

GEHO, GLENN; Charleroi Area SR HS; N Charleroi, PA; (4); 11/165; Art Clb; High Hon Roll; Hon Roll; NHS; N Charleroi Tst Strs Acdmc Awd,Outstndng Stu 87; CA U PA; Law.

GEHO, PATRICK; Ambridge Area HS; Baden, PA; (3); Pep Clb; Band; Pres Chorus; Concert Band; Mrchg Band; Pep Band; Hon Roll; Hnr Chrus 87; Head Drmmr Band 87-88; Mc Donald Emplyee Mnth 87.

GEHRIS, BRIAN; Reading HS; Reading, PA; (3); 69/709; Boys Clb Am; JA; Chorus; Nwsp Stf; Yrbk Rptr; Var L Bsktbl; Var L Bowling; Opt Clb Awd; Merit Roll 85 & 87; Acctng.

GEHRIS, ELIZABETH CATHERINE; William Allen HS; Allentown, PA; (4); 35/559; Church Yth Grp; ROTC; Chorus; Var L Bsktbl; Var L Trk; NHS; AF ROTC Schlrshp Bus Admn 87; Army Advncd Dsgn Schlrshp 87; Navy ROTC Schlrshp 87; Grove City Coll; Bus Admn.

GEHRIS, JANE; Nazareth SR HS; Nazareth, PA; (3); 41/278; Church Yth Grp; Computer Clb; Drama Clb; Key Clb; Ski Clb; Sftbl; Hon Roll.

GEHRIS, JUDITH; William Allen HS; Allentown, PA; (2); Var L Gym; Var Trk; Hon Roll.

GEHRKE, DENISE; Schuylkill Valley HS; Reading, PA; (4); 9/130; VP FTA; Band; Chorus; Drm Mjr(t); School Musical; Yrbk Ed-Chief; Sec Stu Cncl; Capt Cheerleading; NHS; Acad All Am; Berks Cty Stu Sec; HOBY Ldrshp Rep; Comm.

GEHRLEIN, ANDY; Corry Area HS; Corry, PA; (3); 21/214; Church Yth Grp; Pres Soph Cls; Pres Jr Cls; Crs Cntry; High Hon Roll; Hon Roll; Model UN; Rep Stu Cncl; Trk; Schlrshp PA Free Entrprse Wk 87; Hnr Awd Accntng II 87; Bus.

GEIB, AMY; Mahanoy Area HS; Mahanoy City, PA; (1); Spanish Clb; Cheerleading; Crs Cntry; Trk; Hon Roll; Jrnlsm.

GEIB, JERE; Donegal HS; Mount Joy, PA; (2); Var Bsbl; JV Ftbl; Wt Lftg; High Hon Roll; Hon Roll.

GEIB, KIM; Elizabethtown HS; Elizabethtown, PA; (3); Church Yth Grp; 4-H; Shrthnd I Awd 87; Sec.

GEICK, LYNN; Ringgold HS; Donora, PA; (4); 68/326; Drama Clb; Spanish Clb; Pres Chorus; Nwsp Rptr; Yrbk Stf; Hon Roll; IN U-PA; Crmnlgy.

GEIGAL, MANUEL; Henderson SR HS; W Chester, PA; (3); Hon Roll; Wiedner U; Bus Adm.

GEIGER, ALICEN; Bishop Hannan HS; Scranton, PA; (2); Church Yth Grp; Spanish Clb; Church Choir; Var JV Cheerleading; High Hon Roll; Hon Roll; NHS.

GEIGER, BRAD; Catasauqua HS; Catasauqua, PA; (3); 5/143; Scholastic Bowl; Ski Clb; Rep Stu Cncl; Var JV Bsbl; Hon Roll; NHS; Ntl Merit Ltr; JV Ftbl; Natl Sci Merit Awd 85-86; Natl Ldrshp Svc Awd 86-87; Marine Bio.

GEIGER, DEEDEE; Northwestern Lehigh HS; Orefield, PA; (4); 2/158; Pres Sec Church Yth Grp; VP Sec 4-H; Church Choir; Var JV Fld Hcky; Stat Ftbl; Var JV Sftbl; High Hon Roll; Pres NHS; Pres Scholar Cedar Crest Coll; Salutatrn 87; Dist XI Field Hockey Champs 86; Cedar Crest Coll; Nuclr Med.

GEIGER, JO ELLEN; Penn Trafford HS; Irwin, PA; (3); Trs Church Yth Grp; Drama Clb; French Clb; FBLA; Hon Roll; Bus.

GEIGER, TANYA; Philadelphia HS For Girls; Philadelphia, PA; (3); Church Yth Grp; Exploring; OEA; Teachers Aide; Drill Tm; Lit Mag; Rep Jr Cls; Pre Med.

GEILING, TINA; Newport JR-SR HS; Newport, PA; (2); Church Yth Grp; Band; Chorus; Church Choir; Concert Band; Mrchg Band; School Musical; Hon Roll; Head Hunters Acad Of Cosmntgy.

GEIMAN, JEFFREY; South Western HS; Hanover, PA; (3); Varsity Clb; Var Bsktbl; Var Ftbl; Var Trk; Hon Roll; Bus Admin.

GEINER, SUSAN; Altoona Area HS; Altoona, PA; (3); Pres Church Yth Grp; Computer Clb; English Clb; Science Clb; Ski Clb; Band; Lit Mag; High Hon Roll; Pres Schlr; Cmnty Wkr; Dept Chrmns Awd Straight 5 84-85; Acad Pins 84-85; PA ST U; Math Tchr.

GEIS, PAMELA; Bishop Guilfoyle HS; Altoona, PA; (3); Church Yth Grp; Office Aide; Bsktbl; High Hon Roll; Hon Roll; Grls Bsktbl Shmps Trphy 85-86; Penn ST; Medcl Fld.

GEIS, TADD; Seneca Valley HS; Zelienople, PA; (2); Aud/Vis; Church Yth Grp; Band; Concert Band; Jazz Band; Symp Band; Yrbk Stf.

GEIS, TERRY; Mon Valley Catholic HS; Monessen, PA; (3); 25/102; Church Yth Grp; Pres Stu Cncl; Var L Bsbl; Var L Bsktbl; Var L Golf; Powder Puff Ftbl; L Socr; Hon Roll; Engr.

GEISEL, DEBORAH; Johnstown HS; Johnstown, PA; (4); 36/277; Church Yth Grp; NFL; Band; Chorus; Color Guard; Nwsp Rptr; Yrbk Rptr; High Hon Roll; NHS; French Clb; U Of Pittsburgh-Johnstwn; Lawyr.

GEISEL, ELIZABETH; St Pius X HS; Douglasville, PA; (1); 20/146; JA; Pep Clb; JV Cheerleading; Var Trk.

GEISELMAN, CHRIS; Dover Area HS; Dover, PA; (4); Church Yth Grp; English Clb; Hosp Aide; Vllybl; Hon Roll.

GEISER, THOM; Wilmington Area JR/SR HS; West Middlesex, PA; (2); 1/122; Art Clb; Boy Scts; Chess Clb; Spanish Clb; School Musical; Nwsp Rptr; Bsbl; Socr; Cit Awd; High Hon Roll; Eagle Scout 85; Vigil Order Of Arrow 86; Aero Engrng.

GEISHAUSER, KURT; Bishop Guilfoyle HS; Altoona, PA; (3); Boy Scts; VP Church Yth Grp; Ski Clb; Speech Tm; Yrbk Stf; Rep Frsh Cls; Rep Soph Cls; VP Jr Cls; Stu Cncl; L Bsbl; Mech Engr.

GEISINGER, RACHELLE; Liberty JR SR HS; Liberty, PA; (2); Sec FHA; School Musical; Var Cheerleading; Hon Roll; NHS; Sec Church Yth Grp; Dance Clb; Debate Tm; Drama Clb; German Clb; PA Acad Theatrcl Arts 87; Miss Hemisphere ST Fnlst 87; ST Grange Creatv Wrtng Awd; PA ST U; Med.

GEISLER, DAVID; Washington HS; Washington, PA; (2); 13/194; Church Yth Grp; Drama Clb; Spanish Clb; Band; Church Choir; Concert Band; Jazz Band; Mrchg Band; High Hon Roll; Hon Roll; Sci.

GEISLER, RONALD J; Washington HS; Washington, PA; (4); 16/150; Chorus; Church Choir; NHS; Pres Schlr; Chess Clb; Church Yth Grp; Drama Clb; Spanish Clb; Madrigals; School Play; Robert Byrd Hnrs Schlrshp 87; WA County Chorus Festvl 86; Voice Of Demcrcy Semi-Finlst 86; Grove City; Religion.

GEISSINGER, MARGARET E; Emmaus HS; Zionsville, PA; (4); 121/467; Pres Church Yth Grp; Trs SADD; Acpl Chr; Chorus; Church Choir; School Musical; School Play; Variety Show; Hon Roll; Prfct Atten Awd; Vlybl Team Mgr,Vrsty Ltr & Sports Awd 87; Messiah Coll; Bus Admin.

GEIST, JERRY; Schuykill Haven HS; Schuykill Haven, PA; (4); 14/102; Aud/Vis; Church Yth Grp; Science Clb; SADD; School Play; Pres Sr Cls; Pres Stu Cncl; Stat Bsktbl; Capt Var Ftbl; Var Trk; Hugh O Brian 85 & 87; Hnr Grd 86; PTO & Studnt Cncl Schlrshp 87; Kings Coll; Med.

GEIST, KRISTINE; Jenkintown HS; Jenkintown, PA; (3); 8/37; Symp Band; Sec Soph Cls; Pres Jr Cls; VP Sr Cls; Trs Stu Cncl; Mgr Mgr(s); Score Keeper; Spcl Stu Cncl Awd 87; Spnsh Awd Hghst Avg 85-87; Phys Thrpy.

GEIST, SUSAN; Riverview HS; Oakmont, PA; (3); 1/100; Pres AFS; Band; Var Co-Capt Bsktbl; Var Co-Capt Trk; Var Co-Capt Sftbl; High Hon Roll; NHS; French Clb; GAA; Concert Band; Leg Art Exhbt-Harrisburg 85-87; Allegheny Vly Hnrs Band 85-87; PMEA Hnrs Band 85-87; PA Music Ed 86-7.

GEIST, TINA; Danville SR HS; Danville, PA; (3); Church Yth Grp; 4-H; FHA; Library Aide; Office Aide; Chorus; Church Choir; 4-H Awd; Gavel 4-H Pres 86; Military; Cook.

GEITNER, MICHELE; Elk County Christian HS; St Marys, PA; (3); Hosp Aide; Letterman Clb; Var L Trk; Var L Vllybl; High Hon Roll; Church Choir; Sec Soph Cls; Sec Jr Cls; Var Capt Bowling; JV Cheerleading; IUP; Acctng.

GELATKO, MICHELE; West Hazelton HS; Tresckow, PA; (4); 12/265; Church Yth Grp; Sec FBLA; FNA; L Sftbl; Hon Roll; NHS; Penn St U; Elec Engnrng.

GELETEI, KATHY; Charleroi HS; Charleroi, PA; (4); 46/162; Exploring; Office Aide; SADD; Chorus; Color Guard; Nwsp Ed-Chief; Yrbk Stf; Rep Sr Cls; Hon Roll; Kiwanis Awd; CA U Of PA; Elem Ed.

GELETKO, DON; Elizabeth Forward HS; Elizabeth, PA; (3); Church Yth Grp; Rep Frsh Cls; Rep Soph Cls; Rep Jr Cls; Var L Badmtn; JV Bsktbl; Var L Ftbl; Var L Trk; Im Wt Lftg; Hon Roll; Ftbll Letterman 85-86; Bus.

GELEZINSKY, VINCENT; Pocono Mountain HS; Tobyhanna, PA; (4); Ski Clb; Var L Ftbl; Hon Roll; Acdmc Hnrs 84; Athltc Awd 86; Gannon U; Pre Med.

GELFO, MARK; William Allen HS; Allentown, PA; (3); Exploring; Lit Mag; Var Trk; Wt Lftg; Hon Roll; Jr NHS; NHS; Boy Scts; JV Ftbl; Ntl Hnr Scty Ltr & Awd 87; Awds In Rqtbl 86-87; Slvr Tm Mdl In Vlybl 87; Archtctr.

GELLER, NICOLE; Nazareth Acad; Feasterville, PA; (3); GAA; NFL; Service Clb; Fld Hcky; Sftbl; Church Yth Grp; Bowling; Cheerleading; Attndnc Awd 84-87; Spkng Awds 84-85; Med.

GELLI, JENNIFER; James M Goughlin HS; Plains, PA; (4); Church Yth Grp; Drama Clb; Ski Clb; Orch; School Play; Var Cheerleading; Var Fld Hcky; Tennis; Hon Roll; Jr NHS; C Schlrshp 87; Scranton U; Engl.

GELMAN, DIANA; George Washington HS; Philadelphia, PA; (3); 69/800; Art Clb; Math Clb; Math Tm; Office Aide; Teachers Aide; High Hon Roll; Prfct Atten Awd; Art Awds; Grad Hghst Hnrs; Drexel U; Comp Sci.

GELNETT, LANCE; Millersburg Area HS; Millersburg, PA; (3); 20/80; Spanish Clb; Yrbk Stf; Trs Soph Cls; Trs Jr Cls; Var L Bsbl; Var L Bsktbl; JV Ftbl; Var L Golf; Hon Roll; NHS; Bus.

GELOVICH, STEVE; Saint John Neumann HS; Philadelphia, PA; (4); 2/331; Aud/Vis; Math Clb; Rptr Nwsp Rptr; Ed Lit Mag; Rep Stu Cncl; Vllybl; Pres NHS; Sal; Q&S; Rep Sr Cls; Recpnt St John Neumann Ldrshp Awd 87; Recpnt Gld Mdls Soc Studies & Frnch 87; Slv Mdls Rel & Engl 87; La Salle U; Bio.

GELSINGER, DARRIN; Bermudian Springs HS; Gardners, PA; (3); 30/128; Church Yth Grp; Hon Roll.

GEMAS, MARIA; Connellsville Area SR HS; Connellsville, PA; (3); 73/480; Sec Church Yth Grp; Chorus; Concert Band; Mrchg Band; Symp Band; Yrbk Stf; Var JV Sftbl; High Hon Roll; NHS; Spanish NHS; Bus.

GEMELLAS, JOHN; Riverview SR HS; Verona, PA; (2); Wrstlng; Hnr Rl 85-86; High Hnr Rl 85-86; Hnr Rl 85-86; Law.

GEMELLI, CASSANDRA; Middletown Area HS; Middletown, PA; (4); Pres FCA; Key Clb; Library Aide; Model UN; Chorus; Color Guard; Orch; Nwsp Stf; Yrbk Stf; Var JV Fld Hcky; Harrisburg Almni Panhllnc Awd 87; U DE; Psych.

GEMMILL, HEATHER S; Gettysburg SR HS; Gettysburg, PA; (3); Pep Clb; Spanish Clb; Nwsp Rptr; Var Capt Cheerleading; Hon Roll; Pres Acad Ftnss Awd 86; Art Hstry.

GENASEVICH, GARY; West Hazleton HS; West Hazleton, PA; (4); 50/224; Aud/Vis; Spanish Clb; L Bsbl; L Bsktbl; L Crs Cntry; High Hon Roll; NHS; Millersville U.

GENATO, RICHARD; Greensburg Central Catholic HS; Greensburg, PA; (3); 12/250; Church Yth Grp; JCL; Yrbk Stf; Im Bsktbl; Var Ftbl; Im Sftbl; L Trk; Im Vllybl; High Hon Roll; NHS; 6th Pl Westmoreland Cnty Coach Champ Tourn 87.

GENELL, JEFF; Old Forge HS; Old Forge, PA; (3); JV Var Bsbl; Hon Roll; NHS; U Sthrn FL; Pre-Med.

GENEROSE, HEATHER; Hazleton SR HS; Hazleton, PA; (3); Church Yth Grp; Cmnty Wkr; Pep Clb; Ski Clb; Y-Teens; Orch; Stage Crew; L Trk; High Hon Roll.

GENEROSE, ROSINA; Bishop Hafey HS; Hazleton, PA; (4); 7/127; Church Yth Grp; Drama Clb; FNA; Service Clb; Spanish Clb; Y-Teens; Chorus; School Play; High Hon Roll; Hghst Avg Rlgn 86-87; Ltn Awd 86-87; Hghst Avg Hstry 86; Sci Awd 86; Hghst Avg Spnsh 85-87; Wilkes Coll; Med.

GENETTI, JIM; Mining And Mechanical Inst; Weatherly, PA; (3); Aud/Vis; Computer Clb; School Play; High Hon Roll; Hon Roll; Grmn Natl Hnr Soc 87-88; PA ST; Hrtcltre.

GENICOLA, LANCE S; Whitehall HS; Whitehall, PA; (4); 50/256; Am Leg Boys St; VP German Clb; Letterman Clb; Science Clb; Drm Mjr(t); Trk; NHS; Computer Clb; Exploring; Leo Clb; Army ROTC Schlrshp 87; Exchng Clbs Stu Of Mnth 87; Grmn Ntl Hnr Soc 87; Syracuse U; Chem Engrgn.

GENOVESE, LYNNE; West Scranton HS; Scranton, PA; (2); 30/300; Latin Clb; Letterman Clb; Speech Tm; Var Bsktbl; Var Cheerleading; Var Trk; Jr NHS; Phy.

GENOVESE, MARIE; Northampton Area SR HS; Northampton, PA; (2); Church Yth Grp; Library Aide; Band; Drill Tm; Mrchg Band; Pom Pon; Hon Roll; Pres Schlr; VFW Awd; Voice Dem Awd.

GENSEL, BECKY; John S Fine SR HS; Plymouth, PA; (4); Church Yth Grp; Girl Scts; Library Aide; Ski Clb; Varsity Clb; Band; Chorus; Yrbk Phtg; Yrbk Stf; Rep Soph Cls; Photo.

GENSEL, CINDY; Lake-Lehman HS; Sweet Vly, PA; (2); Cmnty Wkr; SADD; Orch; JV Bsktbl; JV Vllybl; High Hon Roll; Jr NHS; NHS; Godl Music Awd-Distngshd Prfmnc Violin 86; Art.

GENSEMER, JEFF; Danville HS; Danville, PA; (1); Ski Clb; JV Bsktbl; JV Socr; JV Trk; Hon Roll; Prfct Atten Awd.

GENT, KRISTIN; Riverview HS; Oakmont, PA; (3); 5/112; Drama Clb; French Clb; Girl Scts; Nwsp Stf; High Hon Roll; NHS; NEDT Awd; Grl Sct Slvr Awd 85; Sprts Med.

GENTILE, DEANNA; Mt Alvernia HS; Pittsburgh, PA; (4); 13/71; Drama Clb; Yrbk Stf; Pres Frsh Cls; Pres Soph Cls; Pres Jr Cls; Sec Stu Cncl; Var Capt Bsktbl; Var Capt Socr; Var Capt Sftbl; Hon Roll; Mt Alvernia Athl Assn Stu Athl Awd 87; Army Rsrvs Schlr/Athl Awd 87; WA & Jefferson Coll; Bio.

GENTILE, KETHA; Boiling Springs JR SR HS; Carlisle, PA; (3); 12/128; Band; Church Choir; Mrchg Band; Nwsp Rptr; Nwsp Stf; Score Keeper; Sftbl; High Hon Roll; Hon Roll; NHS; Psych.

GENTILE, LAURA; Hopewell SR HS; Aliquippa, PA; (3); 18/260; Exploring; Latin Clb; Library Aide; Math Clb; High Hon Roll; NHS; Computer Clb; FNA; Carnegie Mellon U; Air Force.

GENTILE, LINDA; Highlands HS; Tarentum, PA; (3); 26/303; Church Yth Grp; Hst Band; Concert Band; Mrchg Band; Pep Band; School Musical; JV Bsktbl; JV Var Trk; Jr NHS; NHS; Elem Educ.

GENTILE, MICHELE; Gateway SR HS; Monroeville, PA; (3); 14/452; Pres JA; Rep Frsh Cls; Rep Soph Cls; Rep Jr Cls; Rep Sr Cls; Rep VP Stu Cncl; JV Var Cheerleading; Im Vllybl; High Hon Roll; NHS; Independence Day Queen 87; Communications.

GENTILE, ROBERT; Athens HS; Athens, PA; (3); Art Clb; German Clb; Bsbl; Bsktbl; Ftbl; Accntng.

GENTLES, PETER; Upper Darby HS; Upper Darby, PA; (2); High Hon Roll.

GENTRY, LORI; Bishop Mc Devitt HS; Huntingdon Vall, PA; (3); 44/349; Art Clb; Latin Clb; Im Bsktbl; High Hon Roll; Hon Roll; Philadelphia Clsscl Soc Awd Lat 86-87; 1st & 2nd Hnrs 85-87; Sci.

GENTZYEL, PAULA; Lock Haven HS; Lock Haven, PA; (4); 44/242; FBLA; Spanish Clb; SADD; Nwsp Stf; Yrbk Stf; Mgr(s); High Hon Roll; NHS; Excllnce Commercl Dept Awd 86-87; 1st Pl Clerk Typst Region 7 FBLA 87; Williamsport Schl; Bus Admin.

GENUNG, SEAN; Western Beaver HS; Midland, PA; (2); JA; MIT; Robotcs.

GENZLINGER, RACHEL; Acad Of The New Church Girls Schl; Huntingdon Valley, PA; (3); 3/38; Math Clb; Teachers Aide; Stage Crew; Yrbk Stf; JV Vllybl; High Hon Roll; NHS; Chorus; Natl Lat II Exam Magna Cum Laude 85-86; Accelrtd Geom Awd 85-86; Ceret Hist, Geom, Eng, Relgn & Latin; Acad Of The New Church Coll.

GEORG, JEFFREY; Dover Area HS; Dover, PA; (3); 57/260; Am Leg Boys St; Pres Boy Scts; Pres Exploring; Acpl Chr; Chorus; Mgr Stage Crew; Var L Ftbl; Hon Roll; Medcl Exploring Post 611 Excllncy Awd 86-87; Pre-Med.

GEORGAKIS, MARIA; Center Area HS; Monaca, PA; (2); Exploring; Letterman Clb; Spanish Clb; Varsity Clb; Off Stu Cncl; Var Cheerleading; High Hon Roll; Hon Roll; Slppry Rck U-Frgn Lang Comp, Hnrbl Mntn 87.

GEORGE, AIMEE; Home-Center JR-SR HS; Homer City, PA; (3); 26/120; French Clb; Drill Tm; Trs Soph Cls; Trs Jr Cls; Rep Stu Cncl; JV Bsktbl; Var Cheerleading; Var Sftbl; Hon Roll.

GEORGE, ALICE; Trinity HS; Washington, PA; (2); French Clb; SADD; Sec Frsh Cls; Sec Soph Cls; Sec Jr Cls; Rep Stu Cncl; Var Cheerleading; Var Trk; High Hon Roll; Ltr Trk & Chrldng 85-87; PA ST U; Phys Thrpy.

GEORGE, BERNADETTE; Hazleton HS; Hazleton, PA; (4); 25/367; FBLA; Y-Teens; Color Guard; Im Cheerleading; French Hon Soc; Hon Roll; NHS; FBLA Rgn 16 3rd Pl Ecnmcs Awd 87; PA ST U; Pre Law.

GEORGE, DAVID; Meadeville Area SR HS; Meadville, PA; (3); 96/356; Church Yth Grp; German Clb; Im Swmmng; Palmer Schl Chiropractics.

GEORGE, DOUGLAS; Cumberland Valley HS; Camp Hill, PA; (4); 47/550; Math Tm; Quiz Bowl; Orch; Stage Crew; Hon Roll; NHS; GA Inst Tech; Aero Engr.

GEORGE II, JAMES; Moon SR HS; Coraopolis, PA; (3); JA; Key Clb; Ski Clb; Drm Mjr(t); Jazz Band; Mrchg Band; Pep Band; Symp Band; Bowling; Diving; US Nvl Acad; Optometry.

GEORGE, JOSEPH; Central Catholic HS; Pittsburgh, PA; (2); 77/350; Pilot.

GEORGE, KELLI; Meadville Area SR HS; Meadville, PA; (2); JCL; Trs Latin Clb; Spanish Clb; Var Socr; DAR Awd; High Hon Roll; Hon Roll; 2nd Natl His Day Cntst 87; Diploma Merit Spanish I 87; Cert Hnrb Merit Cume Laude 86.

GEORGE, LARRY; Greensburg Salem HS; Greensburg, PA; (2); 59/288; Church Yth Grp; NFL; Ski Clb; Spanish Clb; Stu Cncl; JV Ftbl; Var Ice Hcky; Var Trk.

GEORGE, LARRY; Trinity HS; Washington, PA; (3); 42/406; French Clb; Pep Clb; Var L Bsbl; Var L Ftbl; Im Wt Lftg; High Hon Roll; Hon Roll; Accntng.

GEORGE, LISA; Conrad Weiser HS; Robesonia, PA; (4); 1/192; Computer Clb; Drama Clb; Chorus; School Musical; School Play; Yrbk Ed-Chief; High Hon Roll; NHS; Ntl Merit Ltr; Val; Jhn Mrshll Schlr-Indpndnt Rsrch 87; Grtr Rdng Brd Rltrs Schlrshp 87; Franklin & Marshall Coll; Bus.

GEORGE, PAMELA; Central Dauphin East HS; Harrisburg, PA; (3); 38/280; Art Clb; Drama Clb; French Clb; Stage Crew; Nwsp Stf; Yrbk Stf; Var JV Cheerleading; Trk; Jr NHS; NHS; People To People Stu Ambssdr 86; Phys Thrpy.

GEORGE, PATTI; Yough HS; West Newton, PA; (3); FBLA; Library Aide; Yrbk Stf; Hon Roll; Bradford Schl; Co-Op Sec.

GEORGE, RONALD; Shenango HS; New Castle, PA; (3); French Clb; Concert Band; Mrchg Band; Pep Band; Hon Roll; NHS; Clarion U.

GEORGE, SHERI; Windber Area HS; Windber, PA; (3); 39/134; Drama Clb; Chorus; Church Choir; Color Guard; Mrchg Band; School Play; Hon Roll; NHS; PA Free Entrprs Wk Schlrshp 87.

GEORGE, VIRGINIA; Beaver Area JR SR HS; Beaver, PA; (3); Church Yth Grp; Sec JCL; Key Clb; Chorus; Pres Sec Church Choir; Orch; School Musical; Stu Cncl; JV Socr; Sec NHS; Govrnrs Schl Prfrmng Arts 87; Schlstc Achvmnt Awd 87; Pttsbrgh Yth Smphny 85-87; Psychlgy.

GEORGEKUTTY, MINI; Penn Center Acad; Upper Darby, PA; (4); Rep Church Yth Grp; Debate Tm; Political Wkr; Teachers Aide; Nwsp Ed-Chief; Ed Nwsp Stf; Yrbk Rptr; Ed Yrbk Stf; Chrmn Stu Cncl; Pres NHS; INTRNL Stds.

GEORGELIS, ANTHONY M; Hempfield HS; Landisville, PA; (3); 15/425; Church Yth Grp; Chorus; School Musical; School Play; Nwsp Stf; Yrbk Stf; Stu Cncl; Var Tennis; High Hon Roll; NHS; Pre-Law.

GEORGELIS, WILLIAM; Cedar Crest HS; Lebanon, PA; (3); FCA; Pres Key Clb; VP Pep Clb; School Play; JV Var Bsbl; JV Var Bsktbl; JV Ftbl; Bus.

GEORGULIS, CHRISTOPHER; Belle Vernon Area HS; Belle Vernon, PA; (4); 3/290; Boy Scts; Chess Clb; Church Yth Grp; Ski Clb; Band; Concert Band; Orch; Golf; Powder Puff Ftbl; Wt Lftg; Math Dept Hnr Awd 87; Engl Dept Hnr Awd 87; PA ST Scholar 87; PA ST; Physicist.

GEORGVICH, JOHN; Kiski Area HS; Apollo, PA; (3); Pep Clb; Acpl Chr; Chorus; Rep Jr Cls; Rep Stu Cncl; Var Capt Bsktbl; Var Trk; Hon Roll; Cnty Chorus 86-87; Culinary Arts.

GEPHARDT, DEBRA; Highlands SR HS; Tarentum, PA; (3); Sec Church Yth Grp; Hosp Aide; Sec Key Clb; Library Aide; Chorus; Church Choir; Swing Chorus; Hon Roll; Jr NHS; NHS.

GERACE, MICHAEL; Nativity BVM HS; Auburn, PA; (3); Art Clb; Aud/Vis; Church Yth Grp; Exploring; Spanish Clb; Stage Crew; Nwsp Stf; Var Crs Cntry; JV Ftbl; Var Trk; PA Jr Acad Sci 2nd Pl 85-86; Schl Sci Fair 3rd Pl 85; Var Let Trck/Crss Cntry 86; USAF; Elec Engrng.

GERACI, DAVID; West Mifflin Area HS; W Mifflin, PA; (2).

GERAETS, DAVID F; Abington Heights HS; Clarks Summit, PA; (3); 69/292; Ski Clb; VP Band; VP Concert Band; VP Mrchg Band; Stage Crew; Hon Roll; Farspc Engrng.

GERAMITA JR, ANTHONY J; Neshannock HS; New Castle, PA; (3); Pep Clb; Ski Clb; Varsity Clb; Chorus; School Musical; School Play; Frsh Cls; Soph Cls; Jr Cls; Ftbl; Comp.

GERARD, JASON; Charlerdi Area HS; Charleroi, PA; (4); 13/165; Computer Clb; Science Clb; Bowling; Var L Golf; High Hon Roll; Hon Roll; NHS; Penn ST; Computer Science.

GERASIMEK, CAROL SUE; Sharpsville Area HS; Sharpsville, PA; (4); 30/129; Art Clb; Camera Clb; Church Yth Grp; Thesps; Pres Band; Chorus; Pres Concert Band; Mrchg Band; Pep Band; Stage Crew; Acadc Achvt Awds 84-87; US Ntl Band Awd 85-87; US Ntl Ldrshp Merit Awd 86-87; Grove City Coll; Elem Tchr.

GERBER JR, EDWIN L; New Brighton HS; New Brighton, PA; (3); Church Yth Grp; Spanish Clb; Ftbl; Wt Lftg; Hon Roll; Elctrncs.

GERBER, JULIE; Dover Area HS; Dover, PA; (3); 21/260; Trs Church Yth Grp; L Var Fld Hcky; Mat Maids; High Hon Roll; Hon Roll; NHS; Prfct Atten Awd; Psych.

GERBER, RONNA; Penns Manor HS; Clymer, PA; (4); 3/92; FBLA; Girl Scts; SADD; Band; Concert Band; Stat Trk; High Hon Roll; NHS; Flag Corp; School Musical; 1st Pl FBLA Rgn 3 Clrk Typst I 87; 5th Pl FBLA ST Comptn Clrk Typst I 86-87; Indiana U PA; Bio.

GERBER, WENDY; Penns Manor Area HS; Clymer, PA; (3); 14/97; FBLA; Pres FHA; Girl Scts; Capt Color Guard; Concert Band; Mrchg Band; Pep Band; Yrbk Stf; Hon Roll; NHS; Bus Admin.

GERCHUFSKY, KEVIN; Northern Lehigh HS; Slatington, PA; (3); 9/166; SADD; Nwsp Stf; Var Crs Cntry; Var L Trk; High Hon Roll; Prfct Atten Awd; Chem Engr.

GERCHUFSKY, MICHAEL B; Northern Lehigh HS; Slatington, PA; (4); 12/142; English Clb; French Clb; Spanish Clb; Nwsp Rptr; Trk; French Hon Soc; High Hon Roll; Hon Roll; Prfct Atten Awd; Pres Schlr; Allentown Coll.

GERDEMAN, JASON; Allentown Central Catholic HS; Allentown, PA; (3); 15/242; Drama Clb; Key Clb; Math Clb; JV Var Bsbl; JV Var Bsktbl; Var Crs Cntry; Ftbl; Hon Roll; NHS; PA JR Acad Sci 2nd 85-86; Pre Med.

GERDES III, JOE; Trinity HS; Wormleysburg, PA; (2); Church Yth Grp; French Clb; Ski Clb; Teachers Aide; Varsity Clb; Stage Crew; Rep Stu Cncl; JV Bsktbl; JV Var Socr; Im Sftbl.

GEREGACH, GEORGE; Montour HS; Coraopolis, PA; (4); 78/303; Rep Stu Cncl; Bsktbl; Golf; Hon Roll; Vrsty Clb Treas 86-87; Allegheny; Bus.

GEREK, SANDRA; Carbondlae Area JR SR HS; Simpson, PA; (4); 29/144; Computer Clb; FBLA; Spanish Clb; Band; Pep Band; High Hon Roll; Hon Roll; Penn ST; Bus.

GERENYI, PETER; Taylor Allderdice HS; Pittsburgh, PA; (2); Church Yth Grp; Drama Clb; Nwsp Rptr; Ftbl; Pltcl Sci.

GERGES, TAVIA; Wellsboro HS; Wellsboro, PA; (2); French Clb; Pep Clb; Band; Mrchg Band; Rep Frsh Cls; Rep Soph Cls; Var Cheerleading; L Trk; JV Vllybl; High Hon Roll; Phys Thrpy.

GERGITS, KASHA; Allentown Central Catholic HS; Allentown, PA; (3); Hosp Aide; Key Clb; Pep Clb; JV Var Cheerleading; Hon Roll; :Dance.

GERHARDT, CHRISTINE; Bishop Conwell HS; Levittown, PA; (3); 36/277; Church Yth Grp; Library Aide; Capt Cheerleading; Coach Actv; Capt Var Pom Pon; Trk; High Hon Roll; Hon Roll; Prfct Atten Awd; Missn Clb; Elctrcl Engrng.

GERHART, ARTIE; Quaktertown SR HS; Milford Sq, PA; (2); SADD; VICA; Nwsp Stf; Hon Roll; Outstndng Sales Little Lg 83; Elec Occptns.

GERHART, CHRIS; Boyertown Area SR HS; Gilbertsville, PA; (3); FBLA; Cit Awd; Hon Roll; Cert Strght A's Math 85; Bus Mgmt.

GERHART, JILL N; Ephrata SR HS; Ephrata, PA; (3); Rep Frsh Cls; Rep Soph Cls; Rep Jr Cls; Rep Stu Cncl; Mgr(s); JV Sftbl; JV Tennis; Hon Roll; Spec Ed.

GERHART, KRISTA; Red Lion Area SR HS; Windsor, PA; (3); 51/342; Church Yth Grp; GAA; Girl Scts; SADD; Chorus; Church Choir; School Musical; School Play; Stage Crew; Nwsp Stf; Merit Diploma 3 Yrs Spanish 87; Merit Cert Leukemia Type-A-Thon 85-86; Dsgning.

GERHART, MICHELE; Northern Lebanon HS; Fredericksburg, PA; (3); 12/213; Math Tm; Teachers Aide; Band; Concert Band; Mrchg Band; Sftbl; High Hon Roll; Hon Roll; JC Awd; Lebannon Valley Coll Hnrs Band 87; Comp Sci.

GERHEIM, BECKY; Leechburg Area HS; Leechburg, PA; (4); Computer Clb; Drama Clb; Pres 4-H; JA; Math Tm; Chorus; Concert Band; Drm Mjr(t); Mrchg Band; Pep Band; Alle-Kiski Hnrs Bnd & Rgn II Bnd; Engrng.

GERIAK, CHRISTINE; Ambridge Area HS; Ambridge, PA; (4); 32/265; German Clb; Math Tm; Pep Clb; Red Cross Aide; Band; Drill Tm; Soph Cls; Jr Cls; Sr Cls; Hon Roll; U Pittsburgh; Physical Therapy.

GERKE, CAROL R; Hershey HS; Hershey, PA; (4); 60/198; AFS; Hosp Aide; NFL; Q&S; Speech Tm; Band; Mrchg Band; Nwsp Rptr; Lit Mag; Stat Trk; Indiana U Of PA.

GERLACH, APRIL; Hazleton HS; Hazleton, PA; (2); Hon Roll; Presdntl Acadc Ftnss Awd 86; Bkkpr.

GERLACH, DOUG; Donegal HS; Mount Joy, PA; (3); Church Yth Grp; Hon Roll.

GERLACH, PAULA; Chambersburg Area SR HS; Fayetteville, PA; (2); Drama Clb; Hosp Aide; Chorus; Yrbk Stf; Hon Roll; Jrnlst.

GERLACH, ROBERT; William Allen HS; Allentown, PA; (3); Computer Clb; Bowling; Hon Roll; Comp Pgmng.

GERMAN, FRANK; Yough District HS; Herminie, PA; (3); 4/285; Civic Clb; French Clb; Political Wkr; Ski Clb; SADD; Var Yrbk Rptr; Bsbl; High Hon Roll; VP NHS; Med.

GERMAN, KURT; Dallas SR HS; Trucksville, PA; (3); Aud/Vis; Boys Clb Am; Drama Clb; French Clb; Ski Clb; School Play; Stage Crew; Yrbk Stf; Hon Roll; Dentstry.

GERMANI, MICHAEL; Shenango HS; New Castle, PA; (2); 1/110; Spanish Clb; Var Bsbl; High Hon Roll; Jr NHS; Prfct Atten Awd; Engr.

GERMICK, ELIZABETH; Red Lion Area SR HS; Red Lion, PA; (3); 48/342; Church Yth Grp; Hosp Aide; Teachers Aide; Band; Church Choir; Concert Band; Mrchg Band; School Musical; Im Powder Puff Ftbl; Hon Roll; Millersville U; Educ.

GERNER, TRACEY; Juniata HS; Pt Royal, PA; (3); Camera Clb; FHA; Girl Scts; Library Aide; SADD; School Play; Yrbk Stf; Hon Roll; Central PA Bus Schl; Legl Asst.

GERNERT, AMY; Waynesburg Central HS; Waynesburg, PA; (4); 4/186; Church Yth Grp; Spanish Clb; Sec Concert Band; Sec Mrchg Band; High Hon Roll; Lion Awd; VP NHS; NEDT Awd; Pres Schlr; Voice Dem Awd; Miss Merry Chrstms 86; All Cnty Band 87; Wynsbrg Volntr Fire Co Ladies Aux Schlrshp 87; IN U Of PA; Secndry Math.

GEROSKY, JEFF; Pittston Area HS; Pittston, PA; (4); French Clb; Band; Concert Band; Jazz Band; Mrchg Band; High Hon Roll; Hon Roll; NHS; Wilkes Coll; Music Educ.

GERRITY, LEANNE; W Scranton SR HS; Scranton, PA; (4); Exploring; French Clb; Thesps; School Play; Yrbk Stf; Rep Stu Cncl; Var Pom Pon; Var Trk; Hon Roll; NHS; Stu Tchrs Schlrshp 87; U Of Scranton; Mdcl Tech.

GERSHMAN, MICHAEL; George Washington HS; Philadelphia, PA; (4); 33/800; SADD; Y-Teens; Yrbk Stf; Hon Roll; NHS; Penn ST U; Bus.

GERST, BEN; Quaker Valley HS; Sewickley, PA; (1); Boy Scts; Church Yth Grp; Hosp Aide; Band; Hon Roll; Symp Band; Boston Coll; Accntng.

GERST, JAMES; Quigley HS; Baden, PA; (3); 33/88; Var L Ftbl; Var L Trk; Var JV Wrstlng; Hon Roll; Phys Sci Awd 86; Engr.

GERSTEIN, ERIC; Northeast HS; Philadelphia, PA; (3); Boy Scts; Computer Clb; FBLA; Band; Var Trk.

GERSTER, AMY; North Hills HS; Pittsburgh, PA; (4); Mrchg Band; Symp Band; Hon Roll; NHS; Exploring; Ski Clb; Band; US Navy; Airmen.

GERY, MONICA; Upper Moreland HS; Willow Gr, PA; (3); 129/275; Band; Rep Soph Cls; Rep Jr Cls; Im Bsktbl; Var Cheerleading; Var Lcrss; Cmmrcl.

GERZINA, CHRISTINE; Corry Area HS; Corry, PA; (4); 30/200; Drama Clb; German Clb; Cheerleading; Hon Roll; German Hon Soc 83-85; Tallahassee CC; Bus Mngmnt.

GESCHWINDT, PAMELA; Schuylkill Haven Area HS; Sch Haven, PA; (2); 1/101; Church Yth Grp; German Clb; Pep Clb; Science Clb; SADD; Chorus; Church Choir; Concert Band; Cheerleading; High Hon Roll.

GESFORD, DARRELL; Lower Dauphin SR HS; Hummelstown, PA; (3); 148/350; Church Yth Grp; Spanish Clb; Varsity Clb; Rep Soph Cls; VP Crs Cntry; L Capt Socr; L Var Trk; L Var Wrstlng; Hon Roll; Culinary Arts.

GESS, DEREK; Upper Moreland HS; Hatboro, PA; (3); 16/300; Pres Church Yth Grp; Church Choir; Rep Jr Cls; Var Crs Cntry; Var Trk; High Hon Roll; NHS; Electrical Engnr.

GESSNER, ANGELA; Shikellamy HS; Paxinos, PA; (3); 4/319; Trs Sec French Clb; Hosp Aide; Concert Band; Mrchg Band; Rptr Yrbk Stf; Var Trk; French Hon Soc; High Hon Roll; Jr NHS; Sec Trs NHS; Frnch IV Awd 87; Med.

GESUALDI, GREGORY; St John Neumann HS; Philadelphia, PA; (2); 9/352; Church Yth Grp; High Hon Roll; Valanova U; Med Fld.

GETMAN, LAURA; Central Dauphin HS; Harrisburg, PA; (4); 116/366; Church Yth Grp; ROTC; Science Clb; Chorus; School Musical; School Play; Yrbk Stf; Im Capt Vllybl; Modern Music Master Hnr Scty Tri-M 87; HACC; Marine Bio.

GETNER, MATT; Carrick HS; Pittsburgh, PA; (3); Q&S; Nwsp Stf; Hon Roll; Duquesne; Jrnlsm.

GETSON, BRIAN; Lower Merion HS; Merion, PA; (3); SADD; Concert Band; Mrchg Band; Yrbk Rptr; Rep Jr Cls; Bsktbl; JV Trk; French Hon Soc; Hon Roll; NHS.

GETTEMY, SHAWN; Greensburg Salem HS; Greensburg, PA; (2); 5/294; Boy Scts; Church Yth Grp; Spanish Clb; Band; Concert Band; Drm & Bgl; Mrchg Band; High Hon Roll; Jr NHS; Engrng.

GETTLE, LAURA J; Owen J Roberts HS; Pottstown, PA; (3); 7/300; JA; Sec Key Clb; Drill Tm; Mrchg Band; Yrbk Stf; Bsktbl; Mgr(s); Score Keeper; Stat Trk; High Hon Roll; Accntng.

GETTLER, SHELBY; Eastern Lebanon County HS; Myerstown, PA; (3); 27/169; Church Yth Grp; FHA; SADD; Color Guard; Mrchg Band; Off Jr Cls; NHS; Engr.

GETTS, DEBBIE; Riverside JR SR HS; Taylor, PA; (4); Church Yth Grp; Drama Clb; German Clb; Girl Scts; Hosp Aide; JA; Sec Stu Cncl; Var Trk; Empire Beauty Schl; Csmtlgy.

GETTY, COREY; Columbia Montour Vo-Tech; Catawissa, PA; (3); Boy Scts; Church Yth Grp; JV Ftbl; Cit Awd; God Cntry Awd; Hon Roll; Elect.

GETZ, DENNIS; Forest Hills HS; Salix, PA; (4); 26/156; Spanish Clb; Var L Bsbl; JV Ftbl; High Hon Roll; Hon Roll; Spanish NHS; Penn ST; Engr.

GETZ, JEAN; Bucktail Area HS; Renovo, PA; (3); Church Yth Grp; Letterman Clb; Varsity Clb; Band; Concert Band; Mrchg Band; Off Frsh Cls; JV Bsktbl; Var Sftbl; Prfct Atten Awd.

GETZ, JOYCE; Bucktail HS; Renovo, PA; (2); Letterman Clb; Varsity Clb; Band; Mrchg Band; Orch; Rep Stu Cncl; JV Bsktbl; Var Sftbl; Hon Roll; Prfct Atten Awd; Psych.

GETZ, KARLA; Mahanoy Area HS; Mahanoy City, PA; (1); Church Yth Grp; Spanish Clb; School Play; Stage Crew; JV Cheerleading; L Crs Cntry; Hon Roll; Acctng.

GEYER, ELLEN; Archbishop Prendergast HS; Upper Darby, PA; (3); VP Drama Clb; Hosp Aide; Intnl Clb; NFL; Ski Clb; Chorus; Madrigals; School Musical; Im Bowling; Tri-M 86; Temple U; Cmnctns.

GEYER, JODY; Bald Eagle-Nittary HS; Mill Hall, PA; (2); Church Yth Grp; French Clb; Key Clb; SADD; Sec Jr Cls; Sec Stu Cncl; Capt Var Cheerleading; Sftbl.

GHEEN, BECKY; Mc Guffey HS; W Alexander, PA; (4); 21/210; Am Leg Aux Girls St; JA; Office Aide; Spanish Clb; School Musical; Score Keeper; Trk; Vllybl; Hon Roll; NHS; Wheeling Coll; Accntng.

GHEORGHIU, CRISTINA; Kennedy Christian HS; Greenville, PA; (4); 12/93; French Clb; Intnl Clb; Political Wkr; Ski Clb; School Play; Stage Crew; French Hon Soc; High Hon Roll; Hon Roll; NHS; Yth Schlrs Psych Pgm 86; U Of Pittsburgh; Psych.

GHOSH, GREG; Danville HS; Danville, PA; (4); 16/199; Computer Clb; French Clb; Key Clb; Ski Clb; Stu Cncl; Bsbl; Golf; Socr; Tennis; High Hon Roll; Schlr/Athlt Awd 87; Worcester Polytech Inst; Biomed.

GIACOBBE, FRANK; Mahanoy Area HS; Mahanoy City, PA; (4); Church Yth Grp; Drama Clb; VP French Clb; Band; Chorus; Concert Band; Mrchg Band; School Play; Stage Crew; Variety Show; Airline Schl.

GIACOMETTI, JAMES; Old Forge HS; Old Forge, PA; (3); Ski Clb; JV Var Bsbl; JV Bsktbl; Hon Roll; Trs NHS; Pharm.

GIACOMIN, MELANIE ANN; Penn-Trafford HS; Irwin, PA; (4); 34/334; Am Leg Aux Girls St; Math Clb; Varsity Clb; Yrbk Stf; Rep Soph Cls; VP Jr Cls; Pres Sr Cls; Var Crs Cntry; Var Sftbl; NHS; Womens Club Girl Mnth Oct 86; Sftbl & Acad Schlrshp 87; Post Gazette Sftbl All Star 86-87; Gannon U; Pharm.

GIACOMO, ED; Sto-Rox HS; Mc Kees Rocks, PA; (3); 61/162; FBLA; Band; Concert Band; Jazz Band; Mrchg Band; Duquesne U Mid-East Fstvl 87; VP Schl Band 87-88; US Marine Corp; CPA.

GIALLONARDO, RENEE; Hempfield SR HS; Greensburg, PA; (2); GAA; Pep Clb; Science Clb; Ski Clb; Spanish Clb; Var L Cheerleading; Powder Puff Ftbl; JV Tennis; Hon Roll; Jr NHS.

GIALLORETO, JERRY PAUL; St John Neumann HS; Philadelphia, PA; (2); 13/351; Church Yth Grp; Hon Roll; Alter Boy Soc; Temple Law Schl; Law.

GIAMMARUTI, JAMES; Father Judge HS; Philadelphia, PA; (3); 62/402; Cmnty Wkr; French Clb; Band; Concert Band; Jazz Band; Mrchg Band; Orch; School Musical; School Play; Symp Band; PA ST U; Bus Admin.

GIAMPAOLO, ENRICO; Archbishop Ryan HS Boys; Philadelphia, PA; (4); 21/421; High Hon Roll; NHS; Pres Schlr; Employees Exchange Schlrshp-Budd Co & Phyics Achvt Awd 87; Bio Lab Achvt Awd 85; Drexel U; Mech Engrng.

GIAMPIETRO, MATTHEW; Phoenixville Area SR HS; Phoenixville, PA; (3); Band; Concert Band; Jazz Band; Mrchg Band; Hon Roll; Rep Soph Cls; Var Capt Trk; JV Wrstlng; Ntl Band Assoc Outstndng Jazz Stu Awd 85-86; Crmnl Justc.

GIANFERANTE, LISA; Danville HS; Riverside, PA; (4); 19/199; Sec Key Clb; Ski Clb; Spanish Clb; JV Cheerleading; Im Coach Actv; JV Var Fld Hcky; VP Pres Mat Maids; JV Im Swmmng; Hon Roll; NHS; Montour Cnty Med Auxlry Grant 87; 1 Yr Attndc Awd 87; Spnsh Merit Awd 87; Syracuse U; Clncl Dctn.

GIANGIULIO, JOANN; Lower Merion HS; Ardmore, PA; (3); Pres Service Clb; Spanish Clb; SADD; Band; Nwsp Rptr; Off Soph Cls; Off Jr Cls; Lcrss; Hon Roll; NHS; Rep LMHS In 750th Annvrsry Of Berlin 87; Bus.

GIANNINI, MIKE; Upper Darby HS; Clifton Hts, PA; (3); Computer Clb; DE Cnty Area Vo-Tech 1st Hnrs 86-87; Data Procsng.

GIANNOUTSOS, SPIROS; Taylor Allderdice HS; Pittsburgh, PA; (3); Church Yth Grp; Computer Clb; JA; Math Clb; Yrbk Stf; JV Var Coach Actv; JV Vllybl; Var Wrstlng; Cit Awd; High Hon Roll.

GIARDINE, JENNIE; Bishop Conwell HS; Levittown, PA; (3); 12/279; Library Aide; JV Var Cheerleading; JV Trk; High Hon Roll; Hon Roll; NHS; Prfct Atten Awd; Cert Of Mer Spanish 95.5 GPA 86-87; PA ST; Occptnl Thrpy.

GIBALA, JEFFREY ALLAN; Mckeesport SR HS; Mckeesport, PA; (3); 36/410; Office Aide; Penn ST; Elec Engrng.

GIBAS, MARIA A; Nativity B V M HS; New Philadelphia, PA; (2); 5/79; Chorus; Church Choir; Var Crs Cntry; Var Twrlr; High Hon Roll; Prfct Atten Awd; PJAS St Sci Fair 2nd Fl 87; Acad All-Amer Schlr Awd 87; Internatl Foreigh Lnge Awd 86-87.

GIBB, JOLYNN; Highlands SR HS; Natrona Hts, PA; (4); 7/275; AFS; Exploring; JA; Key Clb; School Play; Diving; NHS; Pres Schlr; Natl Merit Scie Awd 85; Prsdntl Schlrshp 87; U Of Pittsburgh; Bio.

GIBBEL, DEAN; Tulpehocken HS; Bethel, PA; (4); 18/100; Church Yth Grp; Spanish Clb; Band; Concert Band; Mrchg Band; Cit Awd; Hon Roll; NHS; Schlstc Awd 86 & 87; Phys Fitness Awd 84-87; Lincoln Tech Inst; Elec.

GIBBEL, JOHN; Living Word Acad; Lititz, PA; (3); Church Yth Grp; Stage Crew; Yrbk Stf; Stu Cncl; Bsktbl; Socr; Tennis; Hon Roll; Computer Clb.

GIBBONS, AMY; Connellsville Area SR HS; Dawson, PA; (3); FHA.

GIBBONS, HEATHER; William Allen HS; Allentown, PA; (3); Debate Tm; VP Key Clb; Ski Clb; SADD; Varsity Clb; Nwsp Ed-Chief; Nwsp Stf; Lit Mag; Sec Soph Cls; Sec Stu Cncl; Pltcl Jrnlst.

GIBBONS, MOLLY; Hopewell HS; Hookstown, PA; (4); 69/245; German Clb; SADD; Concert Band; Sec Flag Corp; Mrchg Band; Pep Band; School Musical; Yrbk Stf; High Hon Roll; Hon Roll; Prfssnl Sec Intl 87; Robert Morris Coll; Accntng.

GIBBONS, RICHARD; Trinity HS; Mechanicsburg, PA; (3); Model UN; Ski Clb; Spanish Clb; School Play; Nwsp Rptr; Rep Stu Cncl; JV Bsktbl; JV L Ftbl; Trk; Hon Roll; Chsn Hrdst Wrkr Ftbll Tm 85; U Of Pittsburgh; Bnkng.

GIBBONS, SHERRI; Yough SR HS; W Newton, PA; (3); 61/239; Cmnty Wkr; Drama Clb; French Clb; Concert Band; Jazz Band; Mrchg Band; Hon Roll; Speech Thrpy.

GIBBONS, THOMAS; Southern Huntingdon HS; Blairs Mills, PA; (2); Stu Cncl; Hon Roll.

GIBBS, JENNIFER; Wyoming Area HS; W Pittston, PA; (2); Drama Clb; French Clb; Ski Clb; Band; Concert Band; Mrchg Band; Rep Stu Cncl; JV Coach Actv; Swmmng; Var L Trk; Bloomsburg Coll; Elem Educ.

GIBBS, MICHAELA; Yough SR HS; Irwin, PA; (4); Band; Concert Band; Jazz Band; Mrchg Band; Pep Band; School Play; High Hon Roll; NHS; Girl Scts; Library Aide; Early Accptnc CA U PA 86-87; Natl Yth Ldrshp Cncl 86-87; Vrsty Lttrmn Sccr Leag Nrwn 83; CA U PA; Clncl Psych.

GIBEL, JEANNINE M; The Winchester-Thurston Schl; Pittsburgh, PA; (4); AFS; French Clb; Girl Scts; Hosp Aide; Political Wkr; Yrbk Ed-Chief; Fld Hcky; U Of Pittsburgh; Econ.

GIBERSON, SCOTT; Wyoming Area HS; W Wyoming, PA; (4); 5/250; Key Clb; Science Clb; Ski Clb; Spanish Clb; Off Stu Cncl; Var Bsbl; Var Bsktbl; Var Ftbl; High Hon Roll; NHS; Pres Schlrshp III U Scranton 87; U Of Scranton; Bio.

GIBSON, ALEX; Valley Forge Military Acad; Poolesville, MD; (2); Debate Tm; German Clb; ROTC; Church Choir; Var Ftbl; Var Trk; Hon Roll; NHS; French Clb; Science Clb; Major General Anthony Wayne Mdl For 1st In Cls 85-86; William I Harvey Mdl For Hghst Sci Grade 85-86.

GIBSON, ALISA; Karns City HS; Petrolia, PA; (3); Church Yth Grp; Library Aide; Teachers Aide; Band; Chorus; Church Choir; Variety Show; JV Var Cheerleading; Hon Roll; NHS; Secr.

GIBSON, CHRISTINA; Serra Catholic HS; Mc Keesport, PA; (3); Spanish Clb; SADD; Yrbk Stf; Hon Roll; NHS; Ntl Merit Ltr; Pres Spanish NHS; Pitt Prvst Day Schlrshp 87; Dickinson Coll; Intl Law.

GIBSON, DAWN; Little Flower H S For Girls; Philadelphia, PA; (3); 78/322; Orch; Hon Roll; Med Fld.

GIBSON, DEBORAH; Penn-Trafford HS; Trafford, PA; (2); Church Yth Grp; Cmnty Wkr; SADD; Band; Concert Band; Mrchg Band; Yrbk Stf; High Hon Roll; Hon Roll; Penn ST; Bus Mgmt.

GIBSON, JENNIFER; Cedar Crest HS; Lebanon, PA; (2); Pep Clb; Spanish Clb; JV Bsktbl; JV Capt Fld Hcky; Hon Roll; NHS; Hnr Banquet 85-86; OH ST; Vet Med.

GIBSON, JENNIFER; Shenango HS; New Castle, PA; (3); 13/125; Church Yth Grp; Exploring; Office Aide; Varsity Clb; Drill Tm; Gym; High Hon Roll; Hon Roll; NHS; WV U; Physcl Thrpy.

GIBSON, LORI L; Northern Lebanon HS; Jonestown, PA; (1); 35/217; Art Clb; Color Guard; Flag Corp; Cheerleading; Pom Pon; Hon Roll; All-Amer Chrldr Fnlst 87.

GIBSON, MARCIA; Gateway SR HS; Monroeville, PA; (3); Church Yth Grp; Girl Scts; NAACP; Chorus; Var JV Bsktbl; Score Keeper; Sftbl; Pittsburg Coll; Estate Brkr.

GIBSON, MELISSA; Nortahwestern SR HS; Albion, PA; (3); 2/147; Am Leg Aux Girls St; Pres 4-H; Chrmn Model UN; Nwsp Rptr; VP Soph Cls; Pres Jr Cls; Pres Sr Cls; VP Stu Cncl; JV Var Trk; NHS; Amelia Earheart Ldrshp Awd, PS Moose Club Stu Cngrs, Acad Tm Jr Engrng Tech Soc 87; Carnegie Mellon U; Cmmnctns.

GIBSON, NATALIE; Williams Valley HS; Orwin, PA; (4); Spanish Clb; Chorus; Concert Band; Mrchg Band; Symp Band; Co-Capt Powder Puff Ftbl; Hon Roll; Mary Margaret Nestor Fndtn Scholar 87; Amer Alliance Phys Fit Awd 87; Bloomsburg U; Med Lab Tech.

GIBSON, REGINA; Saint Maria Goretti HS; Philadelphia, PA; (4); 77/384; Church Yth Grp; Cmnty Wkr; GAA; Office Aide; Hon Roll; Pres Schlr; Widener U; Nrsng.

GIBSON, SHAWN; Northern Lebanon HS; Jonestown, PA; (4); 14/166; Quiz Bowl; Concert Band; Mrchg Band; Orch; School Musical; Nwsp Rptr; Bausch & Lomb Sci Awd; High Hon Roll; NHS; Prsdntl Schlrshp Widener U 87-88; Widener U; Chem Engrng.

GIBSON, TAMI; Hopewell HS; Aliquippa, PA; (3); 52/250; AFS; FHA; Spanish Clb; SADD; Band; Chorus; Sftbl; Hon Roll; Natl Machinery Awd 84-86; Vet Med.

GIBSON, TODD; Shenango HS; New Castle, PA; (2); Church Yth Grp; Jazz Band; Mrchg Band; Im Bsktbl; JV Trk; JV Wt Lftg; Cit Awd; High Hon Roll; Hon Roll; Prfct Atten Awd; Art.

GICK, BRYAN; Youngsville HS; Youngsville, PA; (3); 1/125; Math Tm; VP SADD; Yrbk Stf; Var Trk; High Hon Roll; NHS; Church Yth Grp; German Clb; Math Clb; Rep Spanish Clb; Free Enterprise Wk CEO 86; Dist Regnl Choir 86-87; Bus.

GIDDENS, BERNADETTE; Overbrook School For The Blind; Philadelphia, PA; (4); #1 In Class; Drama Clb; German Clb; GAA; Pep Clb; PAVAS; Political Wkr; Band; Symp Band; Lit Mag; Off Sr Cls; U Of PA; Info Procsng.

GIDDINGS, ANGELA; North Allegheny HS; Bradfordwoods, PA; (2); 65/630; JA; Orch; Hon Roll; Jr NHS.

GIDDINGS, SAMANTHA; Strawbery Mansion HS; Phila, PA; (3); Hosp Aide; Church Choir; Central ST; Psychlgy.

GIEBEL, JOY; Richland HS; Gibsonia, PA; (2); AFS; NFL; Chorus; Variety Show; Yrbk Stf; Rep Frsh Cls; High Hon Roll; Hon Roll; Outstndng Stu Cncl Activities 86; Med.

GIEDER, KEVIN; Vincentian HS; Mars, PA; (2); Boy Scts; SADD; Hon Roll.

GIENIEC, JENNIFER A; Lampeter-Strasburg HS; Lancaster, PA; (3); AFS; Thesps; Band; Concert Band; Mrchg Band; School Musical; School Play; Lit Mag; Chrmn Stu Cncl; Var Sftbl; Atten Myrs Yth Cncl 87; Law.

GIERCZYNSKI, LEE; Keystone Oaks HS; Pittsburgh, PA; (3); 16/293; Science Clb; Jazz Band; Mrchg Band; Symp Band; High Hon Roll; PA Dist I Hnrs & Rgn I ST Band 87; Music Educ.

GIERING, ELIZABETH; Exeter Township SR HS; Reading, PA; (3); 45/241; Church Yth Grp; French Clb; Leo Clb; Varsity Clb; Band; Concert Band; Mrchg Band; Rep Soph Cls; Var Fld Hcky; Hon Roll; Secndry Ed.

GIERL, KEN; North Catholic HS; Pittsburgh, PA; (3); 61/293; Church Yth Grp; French Clb; Office Aide; School Play; Var Tennis; High Hon Roll; Hon Roll; Pre-Med.

GIFFING, SHERYL; Solanco HS; New Providence, PA; (2); High Hon Roll; Hon Roll; Solanco Schlr Awd Area Of Bus 87.

GIFFORD, JASON; Allentown Central Catholic HS; Kutztown, PA; (3); Church Yth Grp; Key Clb; Letterman Clb; Math Clb; Service Clb; Varsity Clb; Var Wt Lftg; Var Wrstlng; High Hon Roll; JC Awd; Engr.

GIFFORD, KARIN; Beaver Area SR HS; Beaver, PA; (2); 25/278; Church Yth Grp; French Clb; JCL; Pep Clb; Ski Clb; Orch; L Swmmng; L Tennis; High Hon Roll; School Play; Schlstc Achvmnt Awd 87; Dentistry.

GIFFORD, KRISTIN; Beaver Area SR HS; Bridgewater, PA; (3); 43/225; Church Yth Grp; JCL; Sec Key Clb; Pep Clb; Ski Clb; Spanish Clb; Drill Tm; Rep Stu Cncl; Powder Puff Ftbl; Swmmng; Finance.

GIGANTINO, ADRIENNE; Dunmore HS; Canadensis, PA; (4); French Clb; FBLA; Ski Clb; Pres Trs Spanish Clb; Capt Flag Corp; Yrbk Rptr; Var Sftbl; U Of Pittsburgh; Spanish.

GIGER, JEFF; Columbia Montour Vo Tech; Bloomsburg, PA; (3); Boy Scts; Church Yth Grp; JV Bsktbl; JV Wrstlng; Cit Awd; God Cntry Awd; Hon Roll; Prfct Atten Awd; Eagle Sct 85; Engrng.

GIGLIOTTI, A JASON; Monessen JR SR HS; Monessen, PA; (3); 13/108; Var Lit Mag; Var Bsktbl; Var Ftbl; High Hon Roll; Hon Roll; NHS; Amer Lgn Awd 85; All Conf Team Ftbl 86; Allconf Bsktbl, All Conf Bsbl 87; Bus Adm.

GIGLIOTTI, SHARON; Baldwin HS; Pittsburgh, PA; (3); 39/477; Sec Pres FBLA; Teachers Aide; Rep Jr Cls; Stat Bsktbl; Var Tennis; High Hon Roll; Sec NHS; Dist Voc Evltn Advsry Comm 87-88.

GILBERT, JAMES; Marian Catholic HS; Summit Hill, PA; (4); 5/109; Chess Clb; Exploring; Ski Clb; Band; School Play; Stage Crew; Trk; Gov Hon Prg Awd; High Hon Roll; NHS; Ladies Lgn Axlry Schlrshp; Penn ST; Bus.

GILBERT, JASON R; Northern Lehigh HS; Slatington, PA; (3); 47/166; Am Leg Boys St; Ski Clb; JV Crs Cntry; Var Mgr(s); Var Trk; High Hon Roll; Hon Roll; Psych.

GILBERT, LISA; Du Bois Area SR HS; Dubois, PA; (3); Chorus; Color Guard; Mrchg Band; Bsktbl; Score Keeper; Sftbl; Twrlr; Med Sec.

GILBERT, MELISSA; Schuylkill Haven HS; Sch Haven, PA; (2); Church Yth Grp; Girl Scts; SADD; Nwsp Stf; Vllybl; Hon Roll; Acctng.

GILBERT, RAYMOND JOHN; North Penn HS; Lansdale, PA; (3); 51/700; Service Clb; Band; Concert Band; Mrchg Band; High Hon Roll; Hon Roll; Schlrshp To Smmr Inst In Sci & Engr Alfred U 87; Mechncl Engr.

GILBERT, TRACEY; Pottsgrove HS; Pottstown, PA; (4); 8/228; Debate Tm; Math Tm; Ski Clb; Spanish Clb; Varsity Clb; School Musical; Capt Tennis; Hon Roll; NHS; Church Yth Grp; Delg Ot Mdl OAS Debate 85-86; U Of Richmond; Bus.

GILCHRIST, CHRISTINE; Emmaus HS; Macungie, PA; (4); 12/468; Latin Clb; Model UN; Sec Spanish Clb; Var Swmmng; Var Trk; High Hon Roll; Hon Roll; Jr NHS; NHS; Ntl Merit Ltr; Outstndg Latin 87; Girl With Most Var Lets 87; Penn ST; Psychlgy.

GILDEA, JOHN; Marian HS; Lansford, PA; (3); 23/104; JA; Letterman Clb; Nwsp Sprt Ed; Var L Bsbl; Var L Ftbl; Wt Lftg; Bus.

GILDEA, THOMAS; G A R Memorial HS; Wilkes-Barre, PA; (3); 23/152; Church Yth Grp; Chorus; Church Choir; Jazz Band; Orch; Ftbl; Wt Lftg; Wrstlng; Hon Roll; Jr NHS; NEDT Tst Awd 84; 1st Pl Germn Awd 85; Dist Rgnl Chrs 86; Med.

GILDEIN, BARBARA JEAN; Abraham Lincoln HS; Philadelphia, PA; (4); 14/435; Sec Service Clb; SADD; Flag Corp; Yrbk Stf; Rep Stu Cncl; Var Sftbl; Hon Roll; NHS; Drama Clb; FBLA; Cabinet Awd Scholar & Schl Svc 87; Schl Vol Svc Awd 87; Penn ST U; Spts Med.

GILE, LAWRENCE; Kittanning SR HS; Adrian, PA; (2); Rep Stu Cncl; Var Bsbl; Var Ftbl; Wt Lftg; Var Wrstlng; Penn ST U; Police Sci.

GILES, ARTHUR; Monaca JR SR HS; Monaca, PA; (4); Am Leg Boys St; Band; Concert Band; Mrchg Band; Orch; Pep Band; School Play; Var Bsbl; Hon Roll; Prfct Atten Awd; Just Say No Alchl/Drgs Clb 87; Prm Cmte 86; Beaver Cnty CC; Prfssnl Pilot.

GILES, ERIC J; Blackhawk HS; Beaver Falls, PA; (4); 16/270; Trs Church Yth Grp; German Clb; Key Clb; Im Capt Bsktbl; Trk; High Hon Roll; Hon Roll; JETS Awd; NHS; SR Stu 6 Wks 87; Rcvd ROTC Schlrhp 87; Rcvd Recog Outstndng Stu Accmplshmnt Alg, Cal, Wlrd Cul Hstry; Grove City Coll; Elec Engrng.

GILES, MARK; Ambridge HS; Ambridge, PA; (3); Am Leg Boys St; Church Yth Grp; Pep Clb; SADD; Thesps; Band; School Musical; JV Bsktbl; JV Ftbl; Im Golf; Acdmc All Amrcn 87; Nutritn.

GILGHRIST, ROBIN; New Castle SR HS; New Castle, PA; (2); #7 In Class; Girl Scts; Math Tm; Band; Concert Band; Mrchg Band; Pep Band; Cheerleading; Hon Roll; Acdmc Games Awds 85-87; Allegheny Ballet Co Wrkshp Schlrshp 85.

GILHOUSEN, LINDA; Brookville Area HS; Brookville, PA; (3); FHA; Chorus.

GILIA, JAMES; Sacred Heart HS; Carbondale, PA; (3); 8/45; Church Yth Grp; Computer Clb; FBLA; Ski Clb; SADD; Nwsp Stf; Yrbk Stf; Stat Bsktbl; Hon Roll; Bus.

GILIBERTI, BRIAN; Warwick HS; Lititz, PA; (4); 96/232; Aud/Vis; Boy Scts; Church Yth Grp; Computer Clb; Bsktbl; Crs Cntry; Trk; Wt Lftg; US Army; Biomdcl Equip Tech.

GILIBERTI, DAVID; Warwick HS; Lititz, PA; (4); 102/232; Aud/Vis; Boy Scts; Church Yth Grp; Computer Clb; SADD; Bsktbl; Crs Cntry; Wt Lftg; Prfct Atten Awd; US Army; Technel Illstratr.

GILKEY, MICHELLE; Highlands HS; Natrona Hts, PA; (3); Church Yth Grp; DECA; FHA; Library Aide; Chorus; Swing Chorus; Mgr(s); Score Keeper; Timer.

GILKIN JR, ROBERT J; St John Neumahn HS; Philadelphia, PA; (3); 25/350; Q&S; Yrbk Sprt Ed; Rep Frsh Cls; VP Soph Cls; VP Jr Cls; VP Sr Cls; Var Capt Socr; Var Trk; Hon Roll; Philadelphia Coll; Phrmcy.

GILL, GREGORY KEITH; Aliquippa HS; Aliquippa, PA; (2); Civic Clb; Exploring; Varsity Clb; Ftbl; Hon Roll; Comp Sci.

GILL, JOHN; Owen J Roberts HS; Pottstown, PA; (2); Key Clb; Band; Concert Band; Mrchg Band; JV Var Crs Cntry; Var Trk; Hon Roll.

GILL, PRESTON; Gateway SR HS; Monroeville, PA; (3); Boy Scts; Church Yth Grp; Computer Clb; Exploring; JA; NAACP; SADD; Wrstlng; JR Achvt Offcr 85; Pre Law.

GILL, ROB; Harry S Truman HS; Levittown, PA; (3); Drama Clb; Letterman Clb; Yrbk Rptr; Yrbk Sprt Ed; Trs Soph Cls; VP Jr Cls; VP Stu Cncl; Bsbl; Wrstlng; Hon Roll; Chef.

GILL, TODD; Hampton HS; Allison Pk, PA; (4); Ski Clb; Rep Soph Cls; Var Bsktbl; Var L Crs Cntry; Var L Trk; High Hon Roll; NHS; Lehigh U; Engrng.

GILL, TOVE MARIE; Northern York Co HS; Dillsburg, PA; (3); 22/238; Band; Mrchg Band; Stat Bsktbl; Mgr(s); High Hon Roll; Hon Roll; Prfct Atten Awd; Vet Med.

GILL, WILLIAM; Liberty HS; Bethlehem, PA; (3); 100/420; Bsbl; Bsktbl; Ftbl; Wt Lftg; Hon Roll; U Ptsbrg; Bus.

GILLCK, MAURICE; Faith Mennonite HS; Dundee, NY; (4); Capt Quiz Bowl; Church Choir; School Play; Yrbk Ed-Chief; Yrbk Stf; Pres Jr Cls; Pres Stu Cncl; Var Capt Socr; High Hon Roll; Hon Roll; Houghton Coll; Hstry.

GILLESPIE, DIANNE; Northeastern SR HS; Manchester, PA; (3); Band; Chorus; Church Choir; Jazz Band; Mrchg Band; Yrbk Stf; Hon Roll; NY U; Wrtng.

GILLESPIE, KEVIN; Springdale HS; Cheswick, PA; (3); Am Leg Boys St; Church Yth Grp; JV Bsktbl; Hon Roll; Community Based Learning 87-88; Academic Games; MAPPS Ldrshp Prog; Law.

GILLESPY, TIMOTHY; Neshannock HS; New Castle, PA; (3); Aud/Vis; Church Yth Grp; Library Aide; Math Tm; Band; Pep Band; NHS; Presdntl Acad Fit Awd 85; PA Jr Acad Of Sci 1st At ST 85; U PA; Vet.

GILLETT, ALLEN; Connellsville SR HS; Connellsville, PA; (3); 39/550; Band; Jazz Band; Mrchg Band; Pep Band; School Musical; Symp Band; NHS; Engrng.

GILLETTE, MARGO; Dunmore HS; Dunmore, PA; (4); 8/150; French Clb; VP FNA; JA; Ski Clb; Spanish Clb; Color Guard; Mrchg Band; Yrbk Stf; High Hon Roll; Jr NHS; C Drazba Mem Schlrshp 87; PA ST U; Psych.

GILLETTE, MARIE; Dunmore HS; Dunmore, PA; (3); Computer Clb; Drama Clb; French Clb; Chorus; Concert Band; Yrbk Stf; Hon Roll; Jr NHS; JR All Amer Hall Of Fame 86-87; Amer Heart Assoc Awd 86-87.

GILLEYLEN, AIMEE; Gateway SR HS; Monroeville, PA; (3); 52/452; Concert Band; Sec Mrchg Band; Rep Frsh Cls; Rep Soph Cls; Rep Jr Cls; Rep Jr Cls; High Hon Roll; Hon Roll; Psych.

GILLILAND, BARBARA; Conneaut Valley HS; Conneautville, PA; (3); Church Yth Grp; Pres Drama Clb; Hosp Aide; Spanish Clb; SADD; School Play; Nwsp Ed-Chief; High Hon Roll; NHS; Sec Boy Scts; Grove City Coll; Sec Educ.

GILLILAND, GREER; Fox Chapel HS; Pittsburgh, PA; (3); Art Clb; French Clb; JA; Key Clb; Ski Clb; SADD; Powder Puff Ftbl; Var Capt Socr; Hon Roll; Keystone ST Gmes Schlstc Sccr Tm 87; Cup Chllng Tm 87; Sccr W Penn All Str Tm 86, Tm Chmps 85; Sports Nutrtn.

GILLILAND, JOAN; Troy Area HS; Troy, PA; (2); Church Yth Grp; 4-H; French Clb; Band; Chorus; Church Choir; Concert Band; Mrchg Band; Swing Chorus; Rep Frsh Cls; MD.

GILLILAND, KIMBERLY; Conneaut Valley HS; Albion, PA; (3); Drama Clb; German Clb; Pep Clb; SADD; Band; Chorus; Concert Band; Mrchg Band; Pep Band; School Musical; Accntng.

GILLILAND, PAMELA A; Tyrone Area HS; Warriors Mark, PA; (4); 5/177; Sec Trs French Clb; Key Clb; Ski Clb; Varsity Clb; Chorus; Chrmn Jr Cls; Chrmn Sr Cls; Var Capt Cheerleading; High Hon Roll; Sec NHS; Elks Girl Of Mo 86; Acad Spotlight 87; Tyrone Rotary Club Bus Awd 87; Penn ST U; Mktng.

GILLIOTTI, LISA; Carbondale Area HS; Carbondale, PA; (3); 18/119; Art Clb; FBLA; Ski Clb; Spanish Clb; Chorus; Capt Color Guard; JV Bsktbl; High Hon Roll; Psychlgy.

GILLIS, PAULETTE; Steelton-Highspire HS; Steelton, PA; (3); 6/102; Pres Spanish Clb; Band; Church Choir; School Musical; Ed Yrbk Stf; Trs Stu Cncl; High Hon Roll; Hon Roll; NHS; Rotary Awd; Attny.

GILLMAN, RENEE; Gettysburg SR HS; Gettysburg, PA; (2); Chorus; Swing Chorus; Yrbk Ed-Chief; Yrbk Stf; Hon Roll; Med.

GILLOTT, MARIANNE; Connellsville Area SR HS; Connellsville, PA; (3); 5/575; Office Aide; Acpl Chr; Church Choir; Madrigals; School Musical; Yrbk Stf; Swmmng; French Hon Soc; High Hon Roll; NHS; Acad Excel Awds 85-87.

GILMARTIN, STACEY; Parkland HS; Fogelsville, PA; (2); Church Yth Grp; Drama Clb; Library Aide; Chorus; Ed Yrbk Stf; Stu Cncl; Hon Roll.

GILMORE, KELLY; South Allegheny HS; Antioch, CA; (2); French Clb; Office Aide; Stu Cncl; Hon Roll; Penn ST U; Law.

GILMORE, KELLY; South Allegheny JR SR HS; Glassport, PA; (3); 5/188; French Clb; FBLA; JA; Y-Teens; Nwsp Stf; VP Soph Cls; VP Jr Cls; Var Bsktbl; High Hon Roll; FNA; Outstndng Sci Stu Awd 84-85 & Frnsh Stu 85-86; Bus Schl; Accntng.

GILMORE, KRISTINA; Bishop Mc Devitt HS; Dauphin, PA; (3); FBLA; Political Wkr; Service Clb; SADD; Chorus; Nwsp Stf; Yrbk Stf; Rep Stu Cncl; Var Capt Cheerleading; Office Aide; High Achvt In Religion 86; Peer Counselor 86-88; Political Science.

GILMORE, SHANE; Penn Wood HS; Yeadon, PA; (4); 50/350; Church Yth Grp; School Musical; Intnl Clb; Pres Jr Cls; Sec Sr Cls; Var Crs Cntry; Var Ftbl; Var Wrstlng; Hon Roll; Chorus; Eva Jay Jones Awd 87; Ntl Yng Ldrs Conf-Congressnl Schlr 87; Most Schl Spirit 87; Lincoln U; Crmnl Justc.

GILMORE, TRACIE; Meadville Area SR HS; Meadville, PA; (4); 11/306; Church Yth Grp; Dance Clb; Key Clb; Science Clb; Varsity Clb; Rep Jr Cls; Rep Stu Cncl; Var Capt Cheerleading; High Hon Roll; NHS; US Stu Council Achvnmnt Awd 86; Gannon U; Optometry.

GILPIN, LINDA; Ringgold HS; Monongahela, PA; (4); 44/309; Chorus; School Musical; School Play; Nwsp Phtg; Nwsp Stf; Yrbk Phtg; Yrbk Stf; Rep Jr Cls; Rep Sr Cls; Hon Roll; .piano & Organ Rctls 83, 85 & 87; Publications 86 & 87; CA U Of PA; Acctg.

GILROY, KRISTEN; Lakeland HS; Jermyn, PA; (4); French Clb; FHA; Cheerleading; Trk; Hon Roll; PA ST U; Spec Ed.

GILROY, ROBERT; Trinity HS; Mechanicsburg, PA; (4); Ski Clb; Spanish Clb; Stage Crew; JV Socr; Var Trk; Hon Roll; NHS; PA ST U; Pre-Med.

GILSON, ANGIE; Shippensburg Area SR HS; Shippensburg, PA; (2); 2/233; Church Yth Grp; French Clb; SADD; Mgr(s); Timer; Trk; Hon Roll; GPA Above 3.5 Recgntn 86-87; PCP&S; Phrmcst.

GILSON III, CHARLES A; Moshannon Valley HS; Smithmills, PA; (4); 25/127; Spanish Clb; Chorus; School Play; Mgr(s); Tennis; High Hon Roll; Phys Ftnss Awd 87; Lock Haven U; Engrng.

GILSON, JOHN; Moshannon Valley HS; Smith Mill, PA; (3); 19/140; Letterman Clb; Varsity Clb; Wrstlng; Hon Roll.

GIMBEL, RITA MARY; Saint Hubert HS; Philadelphia, PA; (4); 140/364; Office Aide; Nwsp Rptr; Nwsp Stf; Lit Mag; Coach Actv; Capt Var Crs Cntry; Capt Var Trk; Prfct Atten Awd; Cmnty Wkr; Hosp Aide; Pres Acdmc Ftns Awd 87; Prfct Atten Awds 84-87; 4 Yr Plaq Trk, Vrsty Ltrs Trk & Crss Cntry 87; Holy Family Coll; Nrsng.

GIMBLE, KIM; E L Meyers HS; Wilkes-Barre, PA; (3); 47/187; Church Yth Grp; SADD; Chorus; Bsktbl; Fld Hcky; Sftbl; Swmmng; Trk; Vllybl; Hon Roll; Tchr.

GINDER, DANA; Manheim Central HS; Lititz, PA; (2); 1/239; Church Yth Grp; Concert Band; JV Var Bsktbl; JV Fld Hcky; JV Sftbl; Var L Trk; Hon Roll; NHS; Engl Awd 86; Pres Fit Awd 87.

GINDER, DIANE; Red Lion Area SR HS; York, PA; (3); 31/342; Church Yth Grp; Chorus; School Musical; School Play; Stage Crew; Im Powder Puff Ftbl; Var Trk; Hon Roll; NHS; Ntl Merit SF; Physcl Ther.

GINDER, JOHN; Donegal HS; Mt Joy, PA; (3); 10/178; Boy Scts; Church Yth Grp; Socr; Tennis; Cit Awd; God Cntry Awd; Hon Roll; NHS; Spanish NHS; MVP Socr 85; Tchg.

GINDHART, DAWN; Saint Basil Acad; Philadelphia, PA; (3); Art Clb; Science Clb; Spanish Clb; SADD; Varsity Clb; JV Bsktbl; Var Socr; Hon Roll; Pre-Med.

GINDHART, JON; Upper Moreland HS; Hatboro, PA; (3); 95/275; Boy Scts; Key Clb; Mrchg Band; School Musical; School Play; Symp Band; Off Jr Cls; Crs Cntry; Trk; Hon Roll; Penn ST; Engrng.

GINDHART, KELI; Nazareth Acad; Philadelphia, PA; (3); JCL; Latin Clb; NFL; Band; Color Guard; Orch; School Musical; Lit Mag; High Hon Roll; NHS; Natl Latin Exam Cert Of Hnrbl Mntn Maxima Cul Laude 85-86; 4 Yr Schlrshp For Nazareth Acad 84; Scndry Ed.

GINDLESPERGER, KRISTINE; Forest Hills SR HS; Windber, PA; (4); 9/156; VP Soph Cls; VP Jr Cls; VP Sr Cls; VP Stu Cncl; Trk; Vllybl; DAR Awd; Jr NHS; NHS; Art Clb; All Amer Math Awd 83; All Amer Academic Awd 83; IN U Of PA; Nursing.

GINDLESPERGER, RONALD; Conemaugh Twp Area HS; Johnstown, PA; (4); 12/101; NFL; Scholastic Bowl; Spanish Clb; Nwsp Rptr; Lion Awd; Someset Cnty Ct Hse Essay Awd 87; Stu Rotarian Of Mnth 87; Lttr Cmmndtn Ntl Merit Schlrshp 86; U Of Pittsburgh; Elec Engrng.

GINGRICH, BRENDEN; Garden Spot HS; New Holland, PA; (2); 10/226; Church Yth Grp; VP Drama Clb; Chorus; Concert Band; School Musical; School Play; Rep Stu Cncl; Socr; High Hon Roll; NHS; Lions Club Intl Yth Exch 87; Best Prod Asst 87; Chem.

GINGRICH, DAVE; Annville-Cleona HS; Annville, PA; (4); 30/120; Civic Clb; Varsity Clb; Chorus; Stu Cncl; Var Capt Bsbl; Var Capt Ftbl; Var Capt Wrstlng; Cit Awd; Kiwanis Awd; NHS; Harry Zeiders Mem Athl Awd, Dick Fiebig Mem Athl Awd, & Kiwanis Schlr Athl Awd 86-87; Shippensburg U; Engrng.

GINGRICH, ERIC; Lancaster Christian HS; Lampeter, PA; (4); Pres Church Yth Grp; Yrbk Sprt Ed; Mgr(s); Var Socr; Houghton Coll.

GINGRICH, GLENDA; Lancaster Mennonite HS; New Holland, PA; (3); VP Church Yth Grp; Rptr 4-H; Acpl Chr; Chorus; Orch; School Musical; 4-H Awd; High Hon Roll; Hon Roll; NHS.

GINGRICH, JULIE; Lebanon Catholic HS; Palmyra, PA; (3); Church Yth Grp; Cmnty Wkr; English Clb; 4-H; FHA; Hosp Aide; Spanish Clb; SADD; Yrbk Stf; Bloomsburg U; Scndry Ed.

GINGRICH, KIM; Annville-Cleona HS; Annville, PA; (3); 30/139; Varsity Clb; Mrchg Band; Co-Capt Cheerleading; JV Var Fld Hcky; Mat Maids; Var Sftbl; Jr NHS; Crmnlgy.

GINN, MARK; Corry HS; Corry, PA; (3); Church Yth Grp; Bsktbl; Ftbl; Tennis; Wt Lftg; Engrng.

GINOCCHI, JAMES; New Castle HS; New Castle, PA; (3); 1/280; Church Yth Grp; Spanish Clb; Stu Cncl; High Hon Roll; Prfct Atten Awd; New Castle Nwsp Outstndng Carrier Yr 86; Notre Dame; Med.

GINSBERG, NEIL A; Scranton Central HS; Scranton, PA; (4); 35/300; NFL; Speech Tm; Trs Thesps; Chorus; Jazz Band; Mrchg Band; School Musical; Stage Crew; Hon Roll; NHS; PA Govrns Schl For Arts 85; All ST Cast 86; Hartt Coll Of Music.

GINTER, CHRISTINE; Saint Hubert HS; Philadelphia, PA; (3); 82/421; Pres Church Yth Grp; Cmnty Wkr; Office Aide; Pep Clb; Cheerleading; Gym; Swmmng; Trk; Prfct Atten Awd; Bus Admn.

GINTER, D BARRY; Homer-Center HS; Homer City, PA; (3); 7/109; Library Aide; High Hon Roll; Hon Roll; Jr NHS; NHS; Constr.

GINTHNER, JULI ANN; G A R HS; Wilkes-Barre, PA; (3); German Clb; Key Clb; Ski Clb; Teachers Aide; Chorus; Nwsp Stf; Bsktbl; Cheerleading; Hon Roll; NHS; Bloomsburg Coll; Med.

GIOFFRE, EDWARD; Northeast HS; Philadelphia, PA; (4); 55/600; Computer Clb; Math Clb; Acpl Chr; Nwsp Rptr; Lit Mag; PCAW 86-87; ACE 86-87; PA ST U; Advrtsng.

GIONTE, JOSEPH; Meadville SR HS; Meadville, PA; (4); 22/306; Key Clb; Nwsp Rptr; Nwsp Stf; VP Jr Cls; VP Stu Cncl; High Hon Roll; Hon Roll; NHS; Yng Ldrs Amer 86-87; West Point; Mech Engrng.

GIORDANO, DOMENIC; Holy Ghost Preparatory HS; Philadelphia, PA; (4); 9/81; Stage Crew; Yrbk Bus Mgr; Im Ftbl; NHS; VFW Awd; Voice Dem Awd; Holy Ghst Fthrs Awd Chrstn Lvng, SR Rlgn Awd 86-87; Excllnce Latn 84; Excllnce Spnsh 85-87; Math 85; La Salle Coll; Bus.

GIORDANO, MARC; Cardinal O Hara HS; Springfield, PA; (2); 122/647; Hon Roll; Engl Awd Grtst Imprvmnt 86-87; Hghst Avg Alg II 86-87; Bus.

GIORDANO, THOMAS; New Wilmington Area HS; New Wilmington, PA; (3); Spanish Clb; Yrbk Stf; Pres Soph Cls; Pres Jr Cls; Hon Roll; Engr.

GIORI, CLARISSA; Freeport SR HS; Sarver, PA; (3); Church Yth Grp; Drama Clb; School Play; Sftbl; Vllybl; Hon Roll; Sawyer Schl; Trvl.

GIOTTI, ALBERT; Msgr Bonner HS; Drexel Hill, PA; (3); 1/255; Math Tm; Varsity Clb; Frsh Cls; Soph Cls; Jr Cls; Ftbl; Var Ice Hcky; High Hon Roll; Hon Roll; NHS; Bob Clark Mst Imprvd Awd 86-87; 14 Acad Awds 85-87; Fnlst In Schlrshp Cmptn 85; Villanova U; Math.

GIOVANNELLI, BRENDA; Belle Vernon Area HS; Belle Vernon, PA; (3); Pres Art Clb; Church Yth Grp; NFL; Color Guard; Yrbk Stf; Stu Cncl; High Hon Roll; NHS; Exploring; Wnnr Cnty & Dist Drama Cmptn 87; Rnnr Up Miss Metro Pttsbrgh Pgnt 86; Physcl Thrpy.

GIPE, JARROD; Chambersburg Area SR HS; Chambersburg, PA; (2); 52/750; Chess Clb; Drama Clb; JCL; Latin Clb; School Play; Yrbk Stf; Rep Stu Cncl; JV Ftbl; Wt Lftg; High Hon Roll; Penn ST; Psychology.

GIPE, PHILIP; Eastern York HS; Hellam, PA; (3); Church Yth Grp; Band; Concert Band; Jazz Band; Mrchg Band; Pep Band; School Musical; School Play; Symp Band; Yrbk Phtg.

GIRARDI, NATALIE; Southern Columbia Area HS; Paxinos, PA; (3); 11/107; High Hon Roll; Hon Roll; NHS; Math Cert Of Exclnc 87; Bio.

GIRARDI, PAUL THOMAS; Du Bois Central Christian HS; Curwensville, PA; (4); Art Clb; Church Yth Grp; Drama Clb; Exploring; NFL; Ski Clb; SADD; Concert Band; School Play; Ed Yrbk Stf; St Vncnt Coll Ldrshp, Acdmc Schlrshps 87; St Vincent Coll; Librl Arts.

GIRDISH, DIANE; Bethlehem Center HS; Marianna, PA; (4); 8/154; Drama Clb; Mrchg Band; School Play; High Hon Roll; NHS; Lions Clb Awd/Acadmcs 87; Old Trls Bus/Pro Womens Clb Stu Of Mnth 87; WA & Jefferson.

GIRDWOOD, DEANA; Ambridge Area HS; Freedom, PA; (4); 100/265; Church Yth Grp; Pep Clb; Spanish Clb; Mrchg Band; Pep Band; Symp Band; Off Jr Cls; Off Sr Cls; Slippery Rock U; Elem Ed.

GIRER, TAMMY; Council Rock HS; Newtown, PA; (3); 164/908; Rep Frsh Cls; Rep Soph Cls; Cheerleading; Hon Roll; Psychlgst.

GIRONDA, ERIC; Wilson Christian Acad; White Oak, PA; (3); Church Yth Grp; Cmnty Wkr; Yrbk Stf; VP Sr Cls; Var L Bsktbl; Var L Ftbl; Var L Sftbl; Hon Roll; Acad All Amercn 86-87; Elec Eng.

GIRTON, ANDREA D; St Cyril Acad; Bloomsburg, PA; (3); Cmnty Wkr; Drama Clb; Exploring; Girl Scts; Key Clb; Spanish Clb; Chorus; Church Choir; School Musical; School Play; HOBY 85-86; Bloomsburg U; Accntng.

GIRVAN, LINDA; Neshannock HS; Neshannock, PA; (3); Library Aide; Band; Concert Band; Mrchg Band; Pep Band; School Musical; School Play; Nwsp Stf; Bsktbl.

GISH, MICHELE; Southern Columbia HS; Catawissa, PA; (4); 20/80; Drama Clb; Girl Scts; Teachers Aide; Varsity Clb; School Play; Yrbk Stf; Capt L Cheerleading; Hon Roll; NHS; Prfct Atten Awd; High Achvt Math 84-85; MVP Chlrldng 87; Blmsbrg U; Spcl Educ.

GITCHEL, JEFFREY; Hillell Acad Of Pittsbrg; Pittsburgh, PA; (4); Temple Yth Grp; Yrbk Bus Mgr; Yrbk Phtg; Capt Bsktbl; Capt Ftbl; L Sftbl; High Hon Roll; Hon Roll; Ntl Merit Ltr; Acad All Amer 84; Bsktbll Leag All Star 86-87; Oberlin Coll.

GITT, TINA; Cedar Cliff HS; Camp Hill, PA; (3); Spanish Clb; Color Guard; Bsktbl; Bowling; Sftbl; Spanish NHS; Bus.

GITTERE, MAGGIE; Villa Maria Acad; Girard, PA; (4); 4-H; Science Clb; 4-H Awd; Hon Roll; US Pony Clb 84-87; Cmbnd Trnng Cmpttn 85-87; Pres 4-H Clb 83; Radford U.

GITTINGS, DEAN; Cambria Heights HS; Carrolltown, PA; (3); 52/180; Letterman Clb; Ski Clb; Chorus; Rep Jr Cls; Var Bsbl; Var Ftbl; Wt Lftg; NEDT Cert Merit 85-86; Penn ST; Pre-Med.

GIUNTA, CAROLYN; Bishop Shanahan HS; West Chester, PA; (4); 63/217; Church Yth Grp; Office Aide; Pep Clb; Service Clb; Rep Frsh Cls; Rep Soph Cls; Rep Jr Cls; Pres Sr Cls; Capt Cheerleading; JV Fld Hcky; St Josephs U; Bus Mngmnt.

GIUNTA, MARNIE; Gateway SR HS; Monroeville, PA; (2); 12/452; Bsktbl; Crs Cntry; Swmmng; Trk; High Hon Roll; Prfct Atten Awd; Ltrd In 4 Vrsty Sprts; Notre Dame; Sci.

GIUNTA, REGINA; Cardinal O Hara HS; Springfield, PA; (3); 120/782; Church Yth Grp; Dance Clb; JA; Spanish Clb; SADD; Chorus; Lit Mag; Im Sftbl; Im Vllybl; Hon Roll; Awd Ntl Spnsh Cntst 85; PA ST U; Tchr.

GIVINSKI, BOBBI JO; Penn-Trafford HS; Jeannette, PA; (3); 112/296; VP AFS; SADD; Chorus; Yrbk Stf; Stat Trk; Prfct Atten Awd; Early Chldhd Educ.

GIVLER, CRYSTAL; Tyrone Area HS; Port Matilda, PA; (3); Am Leg Aux Girls St; Trs Key Clb; Speech Tm; Varsity Clb; Yrbk Ed-Chief; Stu Cncl; Trk; DAR Awd; High Hon Roll; NHS; PA ST U; Cmmnctns.

GIVLER, THOMAS; Emmaus HS; Alburtis, PA; (3); Lit Mag; Var L Trk; Mech Engr.

GIZDIC, JOHN; Wilmington Area HS; West Middlesex, PA; (3); 12/115; Church Yth Grp; Spanish Clb; Var L Bsbl; Var L Ftbl; Im Wt Lftg; God Cntry Awd; Hon Roll.

GIZELBACH, ANN MARIE; John S Fine SR HS; Nanticoke, PA; (3); 8/228; Chorus; Concert Band; Mrchg Band; Mgr(s); L Swmmng; High Hon Roll; NHS; NEDT Awd; Yng Cmmnty Ldrs Of Amer 86-87; Bio.

GJURICH, DANA; Penn Cambria HS; Cresson, PA; (4); 1/216; Drama Clb; Pres French Clb; Office Aide; VP SADD; Stu Cncl; French Hon Soc; High Hon Roll; Hon Roll; Pres NHS; Prfct Atten Awd; Hghst Score CA Achvt Tst; St Francis; Bio.

GLACKEN, JENNIFER L; Archbishop Prendergast HS; Upper Darby, PA; (4); 60/325; Church Yth Grp; French Clb; Latin Clb; Spanish Clb; Coach Actv; Mgr(s); Trk; Hon Roll; NHS; Spanish NHS; West Chester U; Elem Educ.

GLACKEN, STACY; Conemaugh Valley JR SR HS; Johnstown, PA; (3); Church Yth Grp; Exploring; Pep Clb; Flag Corp; Mrchg Band; Hon Roll; NHS; Cambria Rowe Bus Coll; Med.

GLACKENS, MARY; Bishop Conwell HS; Fairless Hills, PA; (3); 29/277; Computer Clb; French Clb; Office Aide; Stage Crew; High Hon Roll; Hon Roll.

GLACKIN, MARIE; Neshannock HS; New Castle, PA; (3); 18/120; Church Yth Grp; Drama Clb; Exploring; NFL; Var L Cheerleading; NHS; NEDT Awd; Prfct Atten Awd; Hnr Awd 84-85; Frnscs-Oral Intrprtn 84-87; Gd Ctzshp Awd 84; Med.

GLADFELTER, THERESA; Bermudian Springs HS; E Berlin, PA; (3); Church Yth Grp; Ski Clb; Chorus; Nwsp Rptr; Nwsp Stf; Var Bsktbl; Var Cheerleading; Var Crs Cntry; Hon Roll; Jrnlsm Svc Awd 87; Press Clb Secty 86-87; Assoc Schls Inc Miami; Airlines.

GLADIS, JENNIFER; Duquesne HS; Duquesne, PA; (3); 12/98; Church Yth Grp; French Clb; Capt Color Guard; Rep Jr Cls; High Hon Roll; Hon Roll; Y-Teens; Stage Crew; Rep Frsh Cls; Rep Soph Cls; Gannon U; Lwyr.

GLADISH, JON; Pittston Area HS; Pittston, PA; (3); #23 In Class; Ski Clb; Var Crs Cntry; Var Trk; Hon Roll; Elec Engrng.

GLADISH, SAMANTHA; Pittston Area HS; Pittston, PA; (4); 11/350; Church Yth Grp; Computer Clb; French Clb; Key Clb; VP Math Clb; Science Clb; Ski Clb; Pres Stu Cncl; Capt Cheerleading; High Hon Roll; Sci.

GLADU, JULIE; Gwynedd Mercy Acad; Horsham, PA; (2); Church Yth Grp; Service Clb; Stage Crew; Yrbk Stf; Rep Frsh Cls; Off Stu Cncl; JV Lcrss; JV Swmmng; JV Tennis; Hon Roll; Summa Cum Laude Phil Clscl Soc 85; Cum Laude Ltn Awd 86; Hstry.

GLADYS, TRACY; Karns City HS; Chicora, PA; (3); Church Yth Grp; Chorus; Church Choir; Im Bsktbl; Hon Roll; Dntl Hyg.

GLAGOLA, ANDY; Norwin HS; North Huntingdon, PA; (3); Trk; Hon Roll.

GLANCY, SHAWN; Liberty HS; Bethlehem, PA; (3); 53/429; Church Yth Grp; German Clb; Sec Service Clb; Band; Concert Band; Mrchg Band; Pep Band; School Musical; Hon Roll; GAPP Exhng Stu 87; A Ctznshp Grd 86-87; Psych.

GLANTZ, DAVE; Harry S Truman HS; Levittown, PA; (3); Library Aide; JV Bsbl; Hon Roll; Prfct Atten Awd; U Of Southern CA; Music.

GLANTZ, LEISA A; Ridgway Area HS; Ridgway, PA; (3); 2/95; Drama Clb; Ski Clb; Spanish Clb; Chorus; School Play; Stu Cncl; Tennis; Trk; High Hon Roll.

GLAS, WILLIAM; Salesianum HS; West Chester, PA; (3); 2/280; Dance Clb; French Clb; Nwsp Sprt Ed; Stu Cncl; Im Bsktbl; Im Bowling; JV Socr; JV Trk; High Hon Roll; NHS; 1st In Class 84-85; 2nd In Class 85-86; :Engr.

GLASBY JR, STUART F; Central Bucks HS East; Lahaska, PA; (4); Var Crs Cntry; Var Trk; Ntl Merit Ltr; Rotary Awd; Susquehanna U; Law.

GLASER, DAVID; Waynesburg Central HS; Waynesburg, PA; (4); Boy Scts; Church Yth Grp; Spanish Clb; Pres Band; Rep Frsh Cls; High Hon Roll; JP Sousa Awd; NHS; NEDT Awd; Pres Schlr; 1st Annual Anthony Ames Memrl Schlrshp Awd 87; Case Western Reserve; Elec Engr.

GLASER, MELISSA; Reading Central Catholic HS; Reading, PA; (3); 9/123; Church Yth Grp; Spanish Clb; Varsity Clb; School Musical; Stage Crew; Yrbk Bus Mgr; JV Var Bsktbl; JV Var Fld Hcky; High Hon Roll; NHS; Pre-Med.

GLASER, SALLY; Central Dauphin East HS; Oberlin, PA; (4); 7/234; French Clb; Spanish Clb; Color Guard; Flag Corp; Jr NHS; NHS; Pres Schlr; Elizabethtown Coll Acad Schlrshp 87-88; Jody Smith Mem Schlrshp 87-88; Princlpls Awd Excllnce Bio 86; Elizabethtown Coll; Occup Thrpy.

GLASER, TRACEY; Bensalem HS; Bensalem, PA; (2); SADD; Var Cheerleading; Trk; High Hon Roll; Hon Roll; NHS; Sports Med.

GLASGOW, KATHLEEN T; Little Flower HS; Philadelphia, PA; (2); Cmnty Wkr; Drama Clb; Office Aide; Chorus; School Musical; School Play; Hst Frsh Cls; Rep Soph Cls; Hon Roll; CSH H R Rep Awd 85-87; Theatre.

GLASL, CLIFF; Northwestern HS; Albion, PA; (3); Chess Clb; Nwsp Sprt Ed; Bsbl; JV Bsktbl; Ftbl; Mgr(s); Hon Roll; Hon Roll 84-86; Behrend Coll; Bus Adm.

GLASS, DONNA; Bishop Guilfoyle HS; Newry, PA; (3); Cmnty Wkr; Band; Mrchg Band; Pep Band; Hon Roll; Psych.

GLASS, MICHAEL; Plum HS; Pittsburgh, PA; (2); Symp Band; JV Bsbl; Hon Roll; Clssrm Awd 86-87; Bus Mgmt.

GLASS, NANCY E; Montour HS; Pittsburgh, PA; (4); 50/300; Church Yth Grp; SADD; Band; Concert Band; Mrchg Band; Pep Band; Yrbk Stf; High Hon Roll; Hon Roll; Pres Schlr; Geneva Schlr Awd 87; Acdmc Achvmnt Awd Chld Dev I 87; Geneva Coll; Elem Educ.

GLASS, PAUL; Bishop Shanahan HS; Westchester, PA; (4); Var Capt Bsktbl; Var Socr; Mst Outstndng Male Athlt Of Yr 87; 1st Team Bsktbl 87; Mst Vlbl Plyr Bsktbl 87; Montgomery Cty CC; Ftns Mngmnt.

GLASSBERG, MINDY; Hazleton SR HS; Beaver Meadows, PA; (3); Drama Clb; FBLA; Hosp Aide; Office Aide; Service Clb; Ski Clb; Nwsp Rptr; Mgr(s); Hon Roll; Ed.

GLASSE, JEFFREY; Monsignor Bonner HS; Upper Darby, PA; (3); 10/280; Chess Clb; Pres Computer Clb; Math Clb; Math Tm; Thesps; Concert Band; Mrchg Band; Orch; Nwsp Rptr; VP Jr Cls; Carnegie Mellon; Sci.

GLASSHARG, MINDY; Hazleton SR HS; Beaver Meadows, PA; (3); Drama Clb; FBLA; Office Aide; Ski Clb; Nwsp Stf; Mgr(s); Score Keeper; Hon Roll; Educ.

GLASSIC, MARY ANN; Shamokin Area HS; Shamokin, PA; (2); Cmnty Wkr; Key Clb; Chorus; Color Guard; Mrchg Band; Twrlr; Hon Roll; Art Clb; Ski Clb; SADD; Dstngshd Srvc Awd-Key Clb Intl 86; Stu Vlntr Awd-Northumberland Area Aging 86 & 87.

GLASSMAN, DANIEL M; Pennsbury HS; Yardley, PA; (3); Am Leg Boys St; Computer Clb; NFL; Political Wkr; Spanish Clb; School Musical; Bsbl; Var Trk; Hon Roll; NHS.

GLASSMAN, MATT; Emmaus HS; Allentown, PA; (3); Cmnty Wkr; Exploring; Key Clb; Sec Q&S; SADD; Teachers Aide; VP Temple Yth Grp; Nwsp Bus Mgr; Nwsp Stf; Hon Roll; Natl Jrnlsm Conf 87.

GLASSO, LOUIS; Hampton HS; Allison Park, PA; (3); Ski Clb; Var Ftbl; L Ice Hcky; Wt Lftg; Wstrn PA Acad All Star Tm 87.

GLATTHORN, ALISON; St Huberts HS; Philadelphia, PA; (3); 173/421; Church Yth Grp; Hosp Aide; JV Crs Cntry; Var Trk; Var Hon Roll; Var Prfct Atten Awd; Beaver; Nrsng.

GLATZ, LYDIA; West Side Area Vo-Tech Schl; Dallas, PA; (3); Pres Sr Cls; High Hon Roll; Hon Roll; NHS; Food Svc Indus.

GLAZENSKI, JOSEPH; Pittston Area HS; Pittston, PA; (2); High Hon Roll; Hon Roll; NHS; Sci.

GLEASON, SHAWN; Arch Bishop Wood For Boys; Warminster, PA; (2); 28/254; Boy Scts; Drama Clb; Im Bsbl; JV Socr; Hon Roll; Hnrs 85; Temple; Sci.

GLEBA, MICHAEL W; Central Catholic HS; Pittsburgh, PA; (4); 2/265; Boy Scts; Latin Clb; Science Clb; Lit Mag; Bowling; High Hon Roll; NHS; Ntl Merit SF; Sal; Eagl Awd 86; Hghst Genrl Avg 83-85; Westinghouse Sci Hnrs Inst 86; Carnegie Mellon U; Biomdcl Engr.

GLEE, TINA; Greencastle-Antrim HS; Greencastle, PA; (3); Church Yth Grp; Hosp Aide; Nwsp Rptr; Nwsp Stf; Hon Roll; Med.

GLEICH, LISA; Trinity HS; Camp Hill, PA; (4); Pep Clb; Spanish Clb; Yrbk Phtg; Ed Yrbk Stf; Rep Stu Cncl; Trk; Var Capt Vllybl; High Hon Roll; Hon Roll; Pres Spanish NHS; Cthlc War Vetrns Schlrshp 86-87; Slvr Mdl Excllnce 4 Yr Spnsh, Amrcn Bus Wmns Assn Schlrshp 87; Chestnut Hill Coll; Advrtsng.

GLEIXNER, ROBERT; Elk County Christian HS; St Marys, PA; (3); 1/72; Letterman Clb; Concert Band; Mrchg Band; Pres Frsh Cls; VP Soph Cls; VP Stu Cncl; Bsktbl; Crs Cntry; Trk; PA Gov Schl Sci 87; Materials Engrng.

GLEMBOCKI, CINDY; Reading SR HS; Reading, PA; (3); 40/710; Church Yth Grp; Hosp Aide; Key Clb; Church Choir; Yrbk Stf; Hon Roll; Temple U; Physcl Thrpy.

GLENN, CHENA; Juniata HS; Pt Royal, PA; (3); Pres Drama Clb; Pres 4-H; SADD; Yrbk Stf; VP Soph Cls; Pres Jr Cls; Sec Stu Cncl; Var L Cheerleading; Var L Trk; NHS; PA ST Champ JR Grooming & Showmnshp 4-H 84; Lawyer.

GLENN, JULIE; Peters Township HS; Mcmurray, PA; (3); 68/236; Art Clb; Cmnty Wkr; Am Leg Aux Girls St; Intnl Clb; SADD; Yrbk Rptr; Yrbk Stf; Rep Stu Cncl; Var Trk; JV Vllybl; Graphic Desgn.

GLENN, MARY ANN; Waynesboro Area SR HS; Waynesboro, PA; (4); Library Aide; Yrbk Stf; High Hon Roll; NHS; J E Fawley Mem Schlrshp 87; Wynsbr Hosp Axlry Schlrshp 87; Frmrs Bnk & Trst Co Bus Ed Schlrshp 87; Hgrstwn Bus Coll; Med Scrtry.

GLENN, MATTHEW; Steel Valley HS; Munhall, PA; (3); 4/230; Church Yth Grp; Ski Clb; Stu Cncl; Var L Bsbl; Var JV Bsktbl; Var L Crs Cntry; Var L Ftbl; JV Vllybl; Wt Lftg; High Hon Roll; Pre Med.

GLESNER, JOANN; Big Spring HS; Newville, PA; (2); 64/283; Church Yth Grp; Hosp Aide; Band; Color Guard; Concert Band; Jazz Band; Mrchg Band; Stage Crew; Hon Roll; NHS; RN.

GLESSNER, COLEEN; Trinity HS; Enola, PA; (3); 15/138; Model UN; NFL; Ski Clb; Teachers Aide; School Musical; Cheerleading; Crs Cntry; Diving; Hon Roll; Rep Stu Cncl; 1st Pl Sci Fair 85-86.

GLESSNER, JOHN; Berlin Brothers Valley HS; Berlin, PA; (3); French Clb; Nwsp Rptr; Var Ftbl; Outstndng Off Plyr Yr Ftbl 86; All Cnty Somerst Cnty Ftbl 1st Tm 86; Frnch Clbs Srgnt Arms 85-86.

GLESSNER, PATRICIA; Penn Cambria HS; Lilly, PA; (3); Drama Clb; Speech Tm; Accntng.

GLICK, CHRISTINE; Lewistown Area HS; Lewistown, PA; (2); Church Yth Grp; 4-H; German Clb; Chorus; Fld Hcky; Sftbl; Swmmng; Vllybl; 4-H Awd; High Hon Roll; 4-H Grand Champ Beef 86; 4-H PAFC Stu 87; Enrichment Pgm 85; Penn ST U; Vet.

GLICK, CYNTHIA; Lehighton Area HS; Whitehall, PA; (4); Debate Tm; FBLA; Q&S; Scholastic Bowl; School Play; Nwsp Rptr; Nwsp Stf; Yrbk Stf; Hon Roll; HOBY Schlrshp Awd 85; Pres Schlrshp 87; Cedar Crest Coll; Pre-Med.

GLICK, DENISE; Solanco HS; Quarryville, PA; (3); Sec Church Yth Grp; Cmnty Wkr; 4-H; Sec FFA; Church Choir; Hon Roll; Gold Medal Awd St FFA Pblc Spkng Comptn 86-87; FFA Red Rose Deg Awd 86-87; Chapter FFA Schlrshp Awd; Agri Bus.

GLICK, JACK; Chambersburg Area SR HS; Fayetteville, PA; (2); JCL; Latin Clb; Hon Roll; Duke U; Hstry.

GLICK, JAMES; Northeast Catholic HS For Boys; Philadelphia, PA; (4); 25/432; Red Cross Aide; Im Bsbl; Var L Golf; Im Socr; High Hon Roll; Hon Roll; NHS; Pre Med.

GLICK, JULIE HELENE; Lower Moreland HS; Huntingdon Valley, PA; (3); French Clb; FBLA; Trs Temple Yth Grp; School Musical; Off Stu Cncl; Stat Bsktbl; Pres-Shlm Bar Bnai Brth Grls 86-87; Scndry HS Grad-Hbrw 87; Orlck Mem Awd.

GLICKMAN, BRYAN; Neshaminy HS; Feasterville Tr, PA; (3); 32/784; Drama Clb; PAVAS; Chorus; School Musical; School Play; Nwsp Rptr; Lit Mag; Hon Roll; NHS; Ntl Merit SF; Engrng.

GLICKMAN, DAVID; Parkland HS; Allentown, PA; (4); 58/438; Hosp Aide; Q&S; Nwsp Rptr; Hon Roll; NHS; VFW Awd; Bnai Brith Yth Orgnztn 86-87; Nwspr Copy Edtr 86-87; Penn ST.

GLISAN, CARLA; Uniontown HS; Markleysburg, PA; (4); Sec Trs Church Yth Grp; French Clb; Sec Letterman Clb; Ski Clb; Varsity Clb; School Play; Yrbk Bus Mgr; Capt Cheerleading; Trk; French Hon Soc; Penn ST U.

GLODEK, ANDREW; Everett Area HS; Everett, PA; (4); Boy Scts; Church Yth Grp; Exploring; Letterman Clb; Math Tm; Spanish Clb; Varsity Clb; Stu Cncl; Var L Golf; Var Trk; Eagl Sct 87; NRA Cert Exprt Rifl Shot 86; Shippensburg U; Hstry Prof.

GLODEK, KATRINA; Everett Area HS; Everett, PA; (2); Church Yth Grp; Drama Clb; Varsity Clb; School Play; VP Stu Cncl; Capt Tennis; High Hon Roll; Hon Roll; Spanish NHS; Hugh Obrien Yth Fndtn Seminar 87; Penn ST; Engrng.

GLOMB, KRISTIE; Oxford Area HS; Oxford, PA; (3); Church Yth Grp; FTA; Varsity Clb; Chorus; Drill Tm; Var Capt Cheerleading; JV Sftbl; High Hon Roll; Hon Roll; Chrldg Vrsty Capt 86-87; Ed.

GLOSS, TINA; Harrisburg HS; Harrisburg, PA; (4); 41/276; Church Yth Grp; Drama Clb; Thesps; Chorus; School Musical; School Play; Stage Crew; Hon Roll; Pres Schlr; Vcl Music Awd, & Outstndng Achvt Theatre 87; 1st Pl Mxd Chorus Music Pks 85-87; Los Angeles Vly Coll; Mtn Pct.

GLOVA, MICHELLE; Cambria Hgts HS; St Benedict, PA; (3); Cmnty Wkr; FHA; NFL; SADD; Church Choir; Concert Band; Mrchg Band; Nwsp Rptr; Yrbk Rptr; Hon Roll; Dist Semi Finalist Forensics 86-87; Preliminary Semi Finalist Jr Miss Pgm 86-87; Secondary Educ.

GLOVER, JULIE; Johnsonburg HS; Johnsonburg, PA; (3); Church Yth Grp; French Clb; Varsity Clb; Rep Stu Cncl; Bsktbl; Score Keeper; Sftbl Timer; Trk; Vllybl.

GLOVER, JULIE; Spring-Ford SR HS; Royersford, PA; (3); 56/268 Hosp Aide; Pep Clb; Ski Clb; Spanish Clb; Mrchg Band; Lcrss; Twrlr; Hon Roll; Physcl Thrpy.

GLOWA, CAREN; Montour HS; Mc Kees Rocks, PA; (3); VP Church Yth Grp; Dance Clb; Exploring; Girl Scts; SADD; Band; Concert Band; Drill Tm; Mrchg Band; Pep Band; Math.

GLOWACKI, AMY; Villa Maria Acad; Erie, PA; (3); 30/152; French Clb Model UN; Science Clb; Ski Clb; SADD; Yrbk Stf; Sec Stu Cncl; Im Vllybl Hon Roll; Trs NHS; Bus.

GLOWASKI, JOSEPH; Danville Area HS; Danville, PA; (3); 40/198 Mrchg Band; Symp Band; Pres Sr Cls; Var L Socr; JV Tennis; NHS; PA ST U; Engr.

GLOYSTEIN, JOHN; Cathedral Prep; Erie, PA; (3); 7/22; French Clb Rep Soph Cls; Rep Jr Cls; Rep Sr Cls; Chrmn Stu Cncl; Var Diving; JV Socr; Var Swmmng; Hon Roll; Ntl Merit SF.

GLUCK, SCOTT; Quakertown Community Senior HS; Quakertown, PA (2); Capt JV Bsktbl; Capt Im Ftbl; Var Hon Roll; Jr NHS.

GLUCZKY, KIMBERLY; Du Bois Area SR HS; Du Bois, PA; (3); 36/335 Church Yth Grp; Girl Scts; Band; Concert Band; Mrchg Band; Hon Roll

GLUNT, RICHARD; Central HS; East Freedom, PA; (3); Varsity Clb Chorus; L Capt Ftbl; L Capt Wrstlng; Hon Roll; Tri-Cnty Wrstlng Champ 85-86; Comp Sci.

GNAGEY, CHRIS; Turkeyfoot HS; Confluence, PA; (4); Band; Chorus; Concert Band; Jazz Band; Mrchg Band; Orch; Symp Band; Var Bsktbl; High Hon Roll; Army.

GNALL, GARY; Mahonoy Area HS; Barnesville, PA; (2); Church Yth Grp; JV Var Ftbl; Penn ST U; Nuclear Engrng.

GNALL, KEVIN; Salisbury HS; Bethlehem, PA; (3); 61/150; Church Yth Grp; Im Bowling; Hon Roll; Penn ST; Aero Engr.

GNEGY, ELIZABETH A; Upper St Clair HS; Pittsburgh, PA; (4); 17/382; Dance Clb; French Clb; Ski Clb; SADD; Thesps; Chorus; High Hon Roll; NHS; Ntl Merit SF; Paul Harris Awd 85-86; Intl Fin.

GNIPP, JEFFREY; Canevin HS; Pittsburgh, PA; (3); Church Yth Grp; NFL; Ski Clb; Mrchg Band; School Musical; Rep Sr Cls; Hon Roll; Band; Concert Band; Jazz Band; Pilot.

GOBER, LOUIS; Wyoming Area HS; Exeter, PA; (2); Boy Scts; Church Yth Grp; Cmnty Wkr; SADD; Band; Concert Band; Jazz Band; Trk; PSYCHT.

GOBLE, JESSICA; Keystone HS; Knox, PA; (3); French Clb; VP Pep Clb; Yrbk Stf; Stu Cncl; Bsktbl; Cheerleading; Vllybl; Geomtry Achvts 85; US Cngrssnl Page 86-87; Lbrl Arts.

GOBRECHT, JENNIFER; Southwestern HS; Hanover, PA; (2); 6/252; Key Clb; Varsity Clb; Trs Frsh Cls; Trs Soph Cls; Trs Jr Cls; JV Swmmng; JV Var Vllybl; High Hon Roll.

GOBRECHT, NANCY; Parkland HS; Orefield, PA; (2); 65/476; Yrbk Stf; High Hon Roll; Hon Roll; Comm.

GOCH, JAMES; Hanover Area HS; Ashley, PA; (3); 13/194; Wt Lftg; High Hon Roll; Jr NHS; Sr Natl Hnr Soc 86-87; Penn ST; Athl Admin.

GOCHIN, ALAN; HS Of Engineering & Sci; Philadelphia, PA; (4); 65/197; Computer Clb; Drama Clb; Office Aide; Science Clb; Chorus; Yrbk Stf; Pres Soph Cls; Rep Jr Cls; Hon Roll; La Salle U; Premed.

GOCHNAUER, BRAD; Hempfield HS; Mountville, PA; (3); 85/393; Church Yth Grp; Science Clb; Im Bsktbl; Im Vllybl; Bio.

GOCHNOUR, ANDREA; Bedford HS; Everett, PA; (4); 24/176; SADD; Chorus; Church Choir; Trs Concert Band; Drm Mjr(t); School Musical; Stu Cncl; Gym; Trk; Hon Roll; Woodmen World Hist Awd 85; Schlstc Medal 85; Bedford Cty Jr Miss 86; WV U.

GOCHTOVTT, ANNABEL C; Bishop Shanahan HS; Exton, PA; (4); 4/215; Debate Tm; Drama Clb; School Musical; School Play; Lit Mag; High Hon Roll; NHS; Val; Chorus; Gen Excllnce Awd 86; Pres Acad Fit Awd 87; St Josephs U; Mktg.

GOCKLEY, LAMAR B; Garden Spot HS; Mohnton, PA; (4); 1/218; Pres Church Yth Grp; Pres FFA; Quiz Bowl; High Hon Roll; Hon Roll; NHS; Star Red Rose Frmr 86; Tri Cnty Ayrshire Calf Awd 85; Natl Dry Shwmshp Cont Gld Mtl 86; Agri.

GODANIS, JANET; Mahanoy Area HS; Barnesville, PA; (3); 4-H; Spanish Clb; SADD; Concert Band; Drill Tm; Nwsp Stf; Yrbk Stf; Trk; Capt Twrlr; Hon Roll; Paralegl.

GODDARD, DANIELLE; Central Bucks West HS; Doylestown, PA; (3); Chorus; Hon Roll.

GODDING, JOSEPH; Bradford Area HS; Bradford, PA; (4); 30/273; Boy Scts; Key Clb; Rep Stu Cncl; Ftbl; High Hon Roll; Hon Roll; Army; Mech Engr.

GODFREY, JOHN; Red Lion HS; Felton, PA; (2); 91/344; Church Yth Grp; Band; Jazz Band; Mrchg Band; Symp Band; Hon Roll.

GODFREY, KEITH; Bishop O Reilly HS; Kingston, PA; (2); Drama Clb; Ski Clb; Spanish Clb; Band; Concert Band; Mrchg Band; Pep Band; School Play; Stage Crew; Marywood Hnrs Band 85-86; Outstndng Achvt Sci 86-87; Kings Coll; Sci.

GODFREY, KRISTINE; Lampeter Strasburg HS; Willow Street, PA; (3); 13/147; Pres Church Yth Grp; FBLA; Band; Madrigals; Yrbk Stf; Sec Frsh Cls; Chorus; Church Choir; Color Guard; Sci Fair 3rd Pl 85, Hnrb Mntn 86 & 87; City Cnty Sci Fair-3rd Pl 87, Hnrb Mntn 86; Elem Educ.

GODFREY, RACHEL; Ringgold HS; Donora, PA; (3); Church Yth Grp; Spanish Clb; Concert Band; Jazz Band; Mrchg Band; JV Var Bsktbl; Var L Socr; High Hon Roll; NHS; Band; Math & Sci Hnr Soc Chrprsn 85-87; NC U; Med.

GODFREY, RICHARD; Central York SR HS; York, PA; (3); Church Yth Grp; Band; Chorus; Jazz Band; Mrchg Band; Orch; School Musical; Swing Chorus; Symp Band; Hon Roll.

GODISH, DONNA; Penn Cambria SR HS; Lilly, PA; (4); 33/205; Sec French Clb; Girl Scts; Band; Chorus; Concert Band; Mrchg Band; Hon Roll; Penn ST U; Accntng.

GODISH, VIRGINIA; Penn Cambria SR HS; Lilly, PA; (3); French Clb; FBLA; Girl Scts; Drm Mjr(t); Hon Roll; Air Force.

GODLEWSKI, ROQUEL; Punxsutawney Area HS; Punxsutawney, PA; (4); Art Clb; Drama Clb; GAA; Speech Tm; Variety Show; Nwsp Stf; JV Var Cheerleading; JV Golf; Mgr(s); Hon Roll; Penn ST U.

GODSHALL, STEPHEN; Lancaster Mennonite HS; Rheems, PA; (3); 1/150; Church Yth Grp; Varsity Clb; Acpl Chr; Chorus; Rep Frsh Cls; Pres Stu Cncl; JV Bsktbl; Var Socr; Hon Roll; NHS; Certificate Of Excllnc Piano 86; Estrn Mennonite Coll; Med.

GODULA, CHRISTINA; Pittston Area HS; Dupont, PA; (4); 22/348; Art Clb; Computer Clb; Hosp Aide; Key Clb; Band; Nwsp Rptr; Yrbk Stf; High Hon Roll; Hon Roll; NHS; U Scranton; Med Technlgy.

GODWIN, DOUGLAS P; South Fayette HS; Bridgeville, PA; (3); 5/100; Church Yth Grp; Letterman Clb; Ski Clb; Band; Concert Band; Jazz Band; Mrchg Band; Var L Bsbl; High Hon Roll; NHS.

GODZIN, JOE; South Allegheny HS; Pt Vue, PA; (3); 75/187; ROTC; Stage Crew; Off Jr Cls; Off Sr Cls; Bsktbl; Coach Actv; L Var Ftbl; Swmmng; Trk; Wt Lftg; Military Acad; Aerontc Cmmnctns.

GOEBEL, BRIAN; Lincoln HS; Wampum, PA; (4); 72/169; Pittsburgh Inst; Aeronautics.

GOEBL, PATRICK; Bradford Central Christian HS; Bradford, PA; (3); Computer Clb; VP Key Clb; SADD; Yrbk Stf; Im Bsbl; JV Bsktbl; Var Ftbl; Im Ice Hcky; Var Socr; Im Tennis; Excllnce Sci Merit 86; Pres Acad Fit Awd 87.

GOEDEKER, MELANIE; Center Area HS; Aliquippa, PA; (2); Camera Clb; Latin Clb; Nwsp Phtg; Nwsp Rptr; Yrbk Phtg; Yrbk Rptr; Yrbk Stf; Stu Cncl; JV Capt Cheerleading; Powder Puff Ftbl; Showcase USA Dance Cmpttn 85-86; ICF Outstndng Chrldr Awd 86; Investment Banker.

GOEHRING, MATTHEW; Rochester Area HS; Rochester, PA; (3); Am Leg Boys St; Mgr(s); Tennis; High Hon Roll; Hon Roll; Bus.

GOEHRING JR, ROBERT; New Brighton Area HS; New Brighton, PA; (3); VP Pres Church Yth Grp; Chorus; Swing Chorus; JV Bsbl; Hon Roll; Arch.

GOEL, AARTI; Central Dauphin HS; Harrisburg, PA; (3); Dance Clb; Key Clb; Science Clb; Chorus; Trs Sr Cls; Hon Roll; Jr NHS; NHS; Med.

GOEPFERT, JODIE; Butler SR HS; Butler, PA; (3); Exploring; Band; Hon Roll; Acadc Achvt Awd 86-87; Butler Cnty CC; Nrsng.

GOETTER, SCOTT; Bensalem HS; Bensalem, PA; (2); Boy Scts; JV Socr; JV Swmmng; JV Wrstlng; High Hon Roll; Hon Roll; Drexel U; Engrng.

GOETZ, KATIE; Canevin HS; Carnegie, PA; (3); FBLA; Ski Clb; Spanish Clb; School Musical; School Play; Variety Show; Cheerleading; Powder Puff Ftbl; Hon Roll; Pa ST; Entrprnr.

GOETZ, LAURA; Parkland HS; Allentown, PA; (4); 59/438; Church Yth Grp; Key Clb; Q&S; Ski Clb; Yrbk Stf; Stu Cncl; Hon Roll; NHS; Parkette Gymntcs Mst Imprvd Gymnst 85; PA ST U; Psych.

GOETZ, LYNN; St Marys Area HS; St Marys, PA; (3); 70/269; Chorus; Trk; Stat Wrstlng; Hon Roll; Temple U; Mrchndsng.

GOFF, JESSICA; Upper Moreland HS; Hatboro, PA; (2); Drama Clb; Lib Chorus; Church Choir; Mrchg Band; School Musical; School Play; Stage Crew; Yrbk Stf; Rep Frsh Cls; Hon Roll; Child Psych.

GOGA, CHRISTINE; Shade HS; Cairnbrook, PA; (3); FBLA; Hosp Aide; Sec Ski Clb; Varsity Clb; Trs Soph Cls; Cheerleading; Trk; Vllybl; Hon Roll; Shrthnd Trnscrptn-60 WPM 86-87; Jmp Rope For Hrt 85-87; Accntngs 86-87; X-Ray Tech.

GOGGANS, ANTONIO; Mercy Vocational HS; Philadelphia, PA; (4); Church Yth Grp; Math Clb; School Play; Bsktbl; Mgr(s); Vllybl; Hon Roll; Law.

GOGOLA, CHERYL; West Hazleton HS; Hazleton, PA; (4); 14/224; 4-H; French Clb; Ski Clb; Thesps; Rep Sr Cls; Mgr(s); Hon Roll; NHS; Penn ST U; Bus Admin.

GOHEEN, TRACEY; York Catholic HS; York, PA; (2); Art Clb; Boy Scts; Cmnty Wkr; Exploring; Girl Scts; Library Aide; SADD; Chorus; Stage Crew; Cit Awd.

GOIDA, CRAIG; Panther Valley HS; Lansford, PA; (2); 9/127; Bsbl; Bsktbl; Ftbl; High Hon Roll; Hon Roll.

GOIDA, PAUL E; Panther Valley HS; Lansford, PA; (4); 10/104; Am Leg Boys St; Drama Clb; Nwsp Stf; Bsktbl; Ftbl; Trk; High Hon Roll; Hon Roll; NHS; Rotary Awd; Johns Hopkins U; Engr.

GOINS, DANIELLE; Ringgold HS; Monongahela, PA; (3); Varsity Clb; Capt Cheerleading; Drama Clb; Ski Clb; Chorus; Vrsty Chrldng Cptn 87-88; Prm Qn 87; Miss Hon Vly Beauty Pgnt 87.

GOKHALE, ANIL; Cathedral Prep HS; Erie, PA; (3); 5/197; German Clb; Im Bsktbl; Im Vllybl; Hon Roll; Med.

GOLAB, RANDOLPH S; Mercyhurst Prep Schl; Erie, PA; (3); Scholastic Bowl; Ski Clb; Yrbk Stf; Off Jr Cls; Rep Stu Cncl; Crs Cntry; L Tennis; Hon Roll; NHS; Engrng.

GOLASZEWSKI, GARY; John S Fine HS; Nanticoke, PA; (3); Band; Concert Band; Mrchg Band; High Hon Roll; JETS Awd; NHS; Boy Scts; Im Bsktbl; Im Ftbl; Prsdntl Phys Fitness Awd 85; NEDT Cert 85 & 86; Penn ST U; Arch Engrng.

GOLD, MARY; Butler SR HS; Butler, PA; (3); Am Leg Aux Girls St; Office Aide; Spanish Clb; Concert Band; Hon Roll; Outstndng Acad Achvt Studnt Cncl 84; Butler CC; Med Lab Tech.

GOLDBERG, BART; Boiling Springs HS; Richmond, VA; (4); 10/109; Teachers Aide; Nwsp Ed-Chief; Var JV Bsktbl; Score Keeper; Var Capt Socr; High Hon Roll; Hon Roll; Lion Awd; NHS; Cvc Assoc Awd 87; Patriot-Nws Co Jrnlsm Achvt Awd 87; James Madison U.

GOLDBERG, BETH; Council Rock HS; Holland, PA; (3); 66/908; Rep Stu Cncl; Var Cheerleading; Hon Roll; Poli Sci.

GOLDBERG, DAWN; Pennsbury HS; Yardley, PA; (2); Church Yth Grp; Political Wkr; Concert Band; School Musical; Variety Show; Varsity Clb; Var Swmmng; Var Tennis; Rep Frsh Cls; Rep Soph Cls; Cornell U; Chld Psychlgy.

GOLDBERG, JULIA; Linden Hall HS; Penn Valley, PA; (4); 2/30; Q&S; Quiz Bowl; Nwsp Ed-Chief; Nwsp Rptr; Nwsp Stf; Yrbk Ed-Chief; Yrbk Stf; Lit Mag; Rep Jr Cls; High Hon Roll; Gld-Four Awd 87; Hghst Engl Avg 87; Stu Pblctns Awd 87; St Johns.

GOLDEN, JOYCE; Hazelton HS; Sugarloaf, PA; (3); FBLA; Pep Clb; Chorus; Color Guard; Mrchg Band; Yrbk Stf; Stu Cncl; Hon Roll; Bloomsburg U; Bus Adm.

GOLDEN, KERRY; Greencastle-Antrim HS; Greencastle, PA; (4); 9/176; Church Yth Grp; Drama Clb; Pres Sec 4-H; French Clb; Political Wkr; School Play; Dnfth Awd; 4-H Awd; Hon Roll; Trs NHS; PA Gvrnrs Schl/Ag 86; 4-H Kystn Awd 86 & 87; VFW Schlrshp 87; PA ST U; Ag.

GOLDEN, MARY; Williamson JR-SR HS; Tioga, PA; (3); 8/93; Ski Clb; Spanish Clb; Nwsp Phtg; Yrbk Phtg; Yrbk Rptr; Var L Trk; Var L Vllybl; Cit Awd; Hon Roll; NHS; 6th Pl-USGF ST Cmptn 85; Photo.

GOLDFARB, DINA; Abraham Lincoln HS; Philadelphia, PA; (3); English Clb; French Clb; Red Cross Aide; Teachers Aide; Varsity Clb; Trs Stu Cncl; Var Cheerleading; JV Pom Pon; Var Tennis; PA ST; Bus.

GOLDFEDER, PHILIP; Pennsbury HS; Yardley, PA; (2); Band; Jazz Band; Mrchg Band; Trk; Prfct Atten Awd; Biochem.

GOLDINGER, RICH; Butler SR HS; Butler, PA; (3); Church Yth Grp; French Clb; Math Clb; Band; Concert Band; Jazz Band; Mrchg Band; Im Bsktbl; Im Ftbl; Acctg.

GOLDMAN, AMY; Pennsbury HS; Yardley, PA; (4); 160/777; Drama Clb; German Clb; Acpl Chr; Chorus; Capt Flag Corp; Mrchg Band; Rep Soph Cls; Rep Sr Cls; Stu Cncl; Fld Hcky; Temple; Bus Mgmnt.

GOLDMAN, BRETT H; Norristown Area HS; Norristown, PA; (3); 5/500; Temple Yth Grp; Concert Band; Jazz Band; Orch; School Musical; Nwsp Sprt Ed; Lit Mag; Hon Roll; Jr NHS; 10th Grade Sci Awd 85-86; Plcd In Ptry Cntst 85-86; Jrnlsm.

GOLDMAN, DAVID; N Pocono HS; Moscow, PA; (3); 22/231; Band; Concert Band; Mrchg Band; Variety Show; Rep Frsh Cls; High Hon Roll; Hon Roll; NHS; Systms Anlyst.

GOLDMAN, GREG; Spring-Ford SR HS; Collegeville, PA; (3); 15/256; Spanish Clb; Ftbl; Wt Lftg; Wrstlng; High Hon Roll; NHS; Penn ST Univ; Aerontcl Engnrng.

GOLDMAN, SUZANNE; Harriton HS; Narberth, PA; (4); Model UN; Service Clb; Yrbk Rptr; Yrbk Stf; Tennis; High Hon Roll; Hon Roll; NHS.

GOLDSCHMIDT, ANDREW; Parkland HS; Allentown, PA; (3); 87/481; Church Yth Grp; Cmnty Wkr; SADD; Band; Chorus; Concert Band; Jazz Band; Mrchg Band; Pep Band; Hon Roll; European Tour W/Amer Music Abrd Jazz Band 86; 3rd Term On Teen Cncl 87-88; Bio.

GOLDSMITH, COLLEEN; Nazareth Acad; Phila, PA; (3); German Clb; NFL; Color Guard; Drill Tm; Mrchg Band; School Musical; Yrbk Rptr; Yrbk Stf; Im Vllybl; Speech Tm; Charles E Ellis Schlrshp 87-88; Peer Cnsalr; PA ST U; Law.

GOLDSMITH, JENNIFER; Springdale HS; Springdale, PA; (3); Sec Drama Clb; German Clb; Spanish Clb; Rep Acpl Chr; Chorus; School Play; Stage Crew; Im Vllybl; Hon Roll; Ldrshp Pgm Pitt U MAPS 84; GATE Pgm; Bnkng.

GOLDSTEIN, DANA; Upper Dublin HS; Ft Washington, PA; (3); SADD; Varsity Clb; Trs Frsh Cls; Stu Cncl; Var Bsktbl; Var Fld Hcky; Var Lcrss; Hon Roll; NHS.

GOLDSTEIN, MARTIN; Upper Dublin HS; Ambler, PA; (3); Camera Clb; FBLA; Hosp Aide; Temple Yth Grp; Nwsp Rptr; Rep Jr Cls; Rep Stu Cncl; Var Swmmng; Aerospc Engr.

GOLDSTEIN, RACHEL; Taylor Allderdice HS; Pittsburgh, PA; (1); Ski Clb; Temple Yth Grp; Cit Awd; High Hon Roll; Stu Of Mnth 83-84; Stu Of Yr 83; U Of PA.

GOLEMBESKY, ANTHONY; Taylor Allderdice HS; Pittsburgh, PA; (4); 180/420; Boy Scts; Letterman Clb; Ski Clb; Varsity Clb; Band; JV Bsktbl; Var Capt Golf; VP Capt Socr; Var L Trk; Hon Roll; Golf Schlrshps 87; Francis Marion Coll; Bus Admn.

GOLEMBIESKY, JENNIFER; Freeport Area HS; Freeport, PA; (4); 16/170; Church Yth Grp; Band; School Musical; Yrbk Stf; Mgr(s); Vllybl; High Hon Roll; Pres Acad Ftns Awd 87; Duquesne U Cmptv Schlr 87; Duquesne U; Pharm.

GOLINGAN, CAROL; Abington SR HS; Ardsley, PA; (4); 169/486; Color Guard; Drill Tm; Mrchg Band; Beaver Coll; Comp Grphcs.

GOLIS, GERALD; Montrose Area HS; Montrose, PA; (3); French Clb; Library Aide; Chorus; School Musical; Nwsp Rptr; Nwsp Stf; Hon Roll; Jrnlsm.

GOLLETZ, GEORGE; Ambridge Area HS; Baden, PA; (2); Church Yth Grp; German Clb; High Hon Roll; Avionics.

GOLOCK, CAMILLE; Norwin HS; N Huntingdon, PA; (3); Band; Chorus; Concert Band; Drill Tm; Mrchg Band; Chrs & Bnd Awd JR Hgh East 84-85; Bnd Cert Norwin SR Hgh 85-86; Nrsng.

GOLTON, ANITA DEBORAH; Springfield HS; Springfield, PA; (4); Drama Clb; Chorus; School Musical; School Play; Stage Crew; Swing Chorus; Lit Mag; Hon Roll; NHS; Brandeis U; Theatre Arts.

GOLUBIEWSKI, MICHAEL; John S Fine SR HS; Nanticoke, PA; (3); 24/230; Church Yth Grp; Library Aide; Spanish Clb; Chorus; Nwsp Stf; Yrbk Stf; High Hon Roll; NEDT Awd; Young Community Ldrs Amer 86; U Scranton; Engl.

GOMBAS, STEPHEN; Chartiers Valley HS; Pittsburgh, PA; (3); Cmnty Wkr; Letterman Clb; Ski Clb; Varsity Clb; Bsbl; Crs Cntry; Trk; U Of Tampa; Aerontcl Engrng.

GOMBERT, DEBRA E; Whitehall HS; Whitehall, PA; (3); 94/300; Am Leg Aux Girls St; German Clb; Band; Mrchg Band; JV Var Bsktbl; JV Var Sftbl; Hon Roll; Germn Natl Hnr Soc 87; Bloomsburg; Acctng.

GOMEZ, ANA; Little Flower HS For Girls; Philadelphia, PA; (3); 14/336; Church Yth Grp; Math Clb; Yrbk Stf; Lit Mag; High Hon Roll; NHS; Merit Awd Meritorious Achvt Schl Sci Fair 87; 2nd Awd PA JR Acad Sci 85; Temple U Bio-Med Sci Pgm; Drexel U; Nrsg.

GOMEZ, DANIELLE SIMONE; Philadelphia HS For Girls; Philadelphia, PA; (3); 51/405; Political Wkr; Varsity Clb; Chorus; Rep Soph Cls; Trs Jr Cls; Trs Sr Cls; Var Fld Hcky; JV Sftbl; Var Trk; Hon Roll; Patchs Sprtng Actvts 84-88; Sci.

GOMEZ, DAVID; Crestwood HS; Moutaintop, PA; (3); Exploring; Math Clb; Band; Concert Band; Drm Mjr(t); Jazz Band; Mrchg Band; Pep Band; Symp Band; Hon Roll; PA JR Acdmy Sci Rgnl 1st Awd 87; PA JR Acad 2nd Awd 87; Math Excllnc Awd Rgnl PJAS 87; Embry-Riddle; Aerontcl Engrng.

GOMEZ, WILFRED; Henderson HS; Downingtown, PA; (3); 23/277; JV Bsbl; Hon Roll; NHS; Spanish NHS; Cmmrcl Art.

GOMOLA, JOE; Sheffield Area HS; Sheffield, PA; (4); Drama Clb; Concert Band; Jazz Band; Mrchg Band; Orch; Pep Band; School Play; Wrstlng; High Hon Roll; Hon Roll; Outstndng-Ldrshp Instrmntl Music & Hstry Scl Stds Stu 86-87; Dist & Rgnl Band 86-87; Penn ST Erie; Chem.

GOMOLEKOFF, DANA; Cathedral Prep; Erie, PA; (3); 100/200; Cmnty Wkr; Y-Teens; Ftbl; Im Swmmng; Ice Hcky & Sccr 84-87; Bwlng Leag 84-87; Erie Business Schl; Bus.

GONASUN, GLENN; Bishop Mc Devitt HS; Jenkintown, PA; (3); Church Yth Grp; Im Bsktbl; JV Ftbl; JV Wt Lftg; Law Enforcment.

GONAZLEZ, MILDRED; Bethlehem Catholic HS; Bethlehem, PA; (3); #74 In Class; Church Yth Grp; Cmnty Wkr; Key Clb; Mrchg Band; Schlrshp For Frshmn Yr 84-85; Brdcst Jrnlsm.

GONDEK, BRIAN; Glendale JR-SR HS; Flinton, PA; (3); Science Clb; SADD; Band; Yrbk Stf; Rep Stu Cncl; Ftbl; Wrstlng; Sprts Med.

GONGAWARE, STEPHEN; Jeannette SR HS; Jeannette, PA; (3); 6/130; Boy Scts; Computer Clb; VP Exploring; French Clb; Ski Clb; Band; Mrchg Band; Bausch & Lomb Sci Awd; High Hon Roll; 3rd Pl IMU Comp Cont 84; U Of Pittsburgh; Engr.

GONTARSKI, ANN M; Central Bucks West HS; Doylestown, PA; (4); Dance Clb; Jazz Band; School Musical; Cheerleading; High Hon Roll; Hon Roll; Gvrnr Schl For Arts Schlrshp 85; Boston U; Music.

GONTARZ, JO ANNA; Methacton HS; Audubon, PA; (3); 3/381; Hosp Aide; Library Aide; Math Tm; JV Fld Hcky; Var Golf; Var Swmmng; JV Trk; NHS; Nrsng.

GONTIS, CHRISTINE; North Star HS; Gray, PA; (2); 2/150; Art Clb; Cmnty Wkr; Computer Clb; Debate Tm; FCA; GAA; Letterman Clb; SADD; Varsity Clb; Stu Cncl; Aerospc Engr.

GONTIS, JEANNINE; North Star HS; Gray, PA; (2); 23/139; Art Clb; FCA; Spanish Clb; SADD; Yrbk Stf; VP Jr Cls; JV Var Bsktbl; Mat Maids; Sftbl; Wt Lftg; Stu Mth 87; Art Awd Laurel Art Annl Somerset Cnty Art Exhbt 87; Pre-Law.

GONZAGA, GIAN; Haverford HS; Ardmore, PA; (3); Chess Clb; Church Yth Grp; Latin Clb; Mrchg Band; Nwsp Rptr; Var L Crs Cntry; Var L Trk; Boy Scts; JCL; Crss Cntry MVP 86; All Delaware Cnty 2nd Tm 87; Psych.

GONZALEZ, ANTONIO; Morrisville HS; Morrisville, PA; (3); 27/100; School Musical; Var Bsbl; Var Bowling; Var Socr; Cit Awd; High Hon Roll; Hon Roll; Prfct Atten Awd; Crmnl Jstc.

GONZALEZ, BELINDA; Little Flower HS; Philadelphia, PA; (2); Cmnty Wkr; Hosp Aide; Office Aide; Teachers Aide; Chorus; School Musical; Variety Show; Off Frsh Cls; Off Soph Cls; JC Awd; Penn ST U; Math.

GONZALEZ, DAWN; Villa Maria Acad; Erie, PA; (4); 28/128; Cmnty Wkr; JA; SADD; Sec Soph Cls; Sec Jr Cls; Rep Stu Cncl; Im Wt Lftg; High Hon Roll; NHS; Presdntl Acadc Ftns Awd 87fblck Blt Karate 85; Schlrshps Gannon U 87; Gannon U; Med.

GONZALEZ JR, JACK; Northampton Area Joint HS; Northampton, PA; (2); U Of Pittsburgh; Pharmacy.

GONZALEZ, JOHN; Reading SR HS; Reading, PA; (3); Church Yth Grp; Cmnty Wkr; German Clb; High Hon Roll; Hon Roll; Val; Art Achvt, Gftd, Tlntd & Math Achvt Awds 84-85; UCLA; Law.

GONZALEZ, LIZZETTE; Lancaster Catholic HS; Lancaster, PA; (4); 92/196; Church Yth Grp; Mnrty Recgntn Awd 87; Millersville U Of PA; Chld Psy.

GONZALEZ, TORI; Kennard Dale HS; Stewartstown, PA; (3); Hosp Aide; Latin Clb; Chorus; Color Guard; School Musical; School Play; Trk; Vllybl; Hon Roll; Nrsng.

GOOD, CATHLEEN MARIE; Faith Mennonite HS; Mohnton, PA; (4); Church Yth Grp; Library Aide; Teachers Aide; Chorus; Nwsp Rptr; Cit Awd; High Hon Roll; Hon Roll; Ntl Merit Ltr; Dept Hmmkng Cert 84.

GOOD, CHRISTINE; Garden Spot HS; Reinholds, PA; (4); Rep Church Yth Grp; Sec Spanish Clb; Hon Roll; Jr NHS; NHS; Shippensburg U; Comp Inf Systms.

GOOD, HEIDI; West Perry HS; New Bloomfield, PA; (4); Trs Spanish Clb; Varsity Clb; Capt Color Guard; Concert Band; Mrchg Band; Yrbk Bus Mgr; Yrbk Stf; Trs Frsh Cls; Rep Stu Cncl; JV Trk; Duquesne U; Pre-Law.

GOOD, JOSEPH; Lakeland HS; Jermyn, PA; (3); Art Clb; French Clb; Ski Clb; Ftbl; Trk; Wt Lftg; Hon Roll; PA ST U; Engrng.

GOOD, KAREN; Middletown Area HS; Harrisburg, PA; (3); 13/210; Drama Clb; FCA; Model UN; Sec Chorus; School Musical; School Play; Swing Chorus; Im Bsktbl; JV Tennis; Hon Roll; Dstrct 7 Chorus 87.

GOOD, KRISTEN; Aliquippa JR SR HS; Aliquippa, PA; (2); Church Yth Grp; Drama Clb; French Clb; School Musical; School Play; Cheerleading; Hon Roll; Cert Of Merit 85-86; Diplma Mdlng 85; Dance.

GOOD, LEE; Lancaster Mennonite HS; Lititz, PA; (3); FFA; Chorus; School Play; Hon Roll; E Mennonite Coll; Bio.

GOOD, LEONA; Penns Manor HS; Alverda, PA; (4); 18/81; SADD; Band; Concert Band; Co-Capt Flag Corp; Mrchg Band; Stat Trk; Hon Roll; NHS; Twrlr; Conemaugh Vly Schl; Nrsng.

GOOD, LORI; Pequea Valley HS; E Paradise, PA; (4); 30/120; GAA; Varsity Clb; Band; Chorus; Mrchg Band; Sec Frsh Cls; Sec Soph Cls; Rep Sr Cls; Stu Cncl; Var Capt Bsktbl; George P Summers Schlrshp Nrsng 87; St Joseph Schl Nrsng; Nrsng.

GOOD, ROBERT; Penn Trafford HS; Jeannette, PA; (2); AFS; Aud/Vis; Ski Clb; Im Bsbl; Im Ftbl; U Of Pittsburgh; Engrng.

GOOD, SCOTT; Donegal HS; Mt Joy, PA; (4); 43/161; Socr; Hon Roll; Penn ST U; Engrng.

GOOD, STACEY; Hempfield Area SR HS; Irwin, PA; (2); Dance Clb; Drm Mjr(t); Rep Frsh Cls; Rep Jr Cls; Rep Stu Cncl; Var Twrlr; Capt JV Vllybl; High Hon Roll; Hon Roll; Jr NHS; Spec Subj Awd-Sewing 85-86.

GOOD, SUZANNE; Bedford Area HS; Bedford, PA; (3); Church Yth Grp; Cmnty Wkr; FTA; Office Aide; Ski Clb; Chorus; Stu Cncl; Var L Cheerleading; Var Sftbl; Var Trk; Nrs.

GOODE, BETHANY; Abraham Lincoln HS; Philadelihia, PA; (3); Varsity Clb; Color Guard; Mrchg Band; Rep Soph Cls; JV Var Vllybl; Stat Wt Lftg; Comp Sci.

GOODELL, BETH; Knoch HS; Butler, PA; (2); Boy Scts; Ski Clb; Band; JV Var Vllybl; Law.

GOODELLE, JASON; Cathedral Prep; Erie, PA; (3); 40/200; Model UN; Ski Clb; Stu Cncl; Socr; Church Yth Grp; Exploring; Off Sr Cls; Pre Med.

GOODFORD, CAROLYN; Crestwood HS; Mountaintop, PA; (4); Hosp Aide; Var Twrlr; Pres Acdmc Ftnss Awd 87; Wilkes Coll; Accntng.

GOODLANDER, HEATHER I; East Pennsboro HS; Enola, PA; (4); English Clb; French Clb; Pep Clb; SADD; Hon Roll; John Hau Fndtn Schlrshp 87; St Chmpnshp Bwlng Tm 85; 4th Pl Drunk Drvng Slogan Cntst 84-85; Harcum JC; Anml Hlth Tech.

GOODLIN, DEREK; Altoona Area HS; Altoona, PA; (3); 31/720; Cmnty Wkr; Computer Clb; French Clb; Key Clb; Political Wkr; Varsity Clb; Bsbl; Crs Cntry; Ftbl; Trk; NEDT Exam 85; PA ST U; Mech Engrng.

GOODLIN, JANICE; Marion Center Area HS; Indiana, PA; (3); FBLA; FNA; Hosp Aide; SADD; VICA; Radiolgc Tech.

GOODLING, AMY; Mechanicsburg SR HS; Mechanicsburg, PA; (2); Band; Concert Band; Drill Tm; Mrchg Band; Orch; Symp Band; High Hon Roll; Hon Roll; Cumberland Cnty Band 87; Penn ST; Bus Admin.

GOODLING, CHRIS; Susquenita JR SR HS; Duncannon, PA; (3); 9/184; Quiz Bowl; Ski Clb; Spanish Clb; Rep Frsh Cls; Rep Soph Cls; Trs Stu Cncl; Var L Bsktbl; JV L Ftbl; Var L Trk; Hon Roll.

GOODLING, DENISE; Lock Haven HS; Howard, PA; (4); Art Clb; Church Yth Grp; French Clb; Vllybl; Frgn Lang.

GOODLING, KEITH; Middleburg HS; Middleburg, PA; (3); Varsity Clb; Band; JV Bsbl; Var JV Bsktbl; Var JV Socr; High Hon Roll; Hon Roll; NHS; JV Bsktbl MVP 86; Acdmc All Amer 87; Tri Vly, All Star Sccr 2nd Tm 85-86; Engrng.

GOODLING, TAMMY; Otto-Eldred HS; Rixford, PA; (3); 11/90; Church Yth Grp; Pres Library Aide; Spanish Clb; Chorus; Color Guard; Mrchg Band; School Musical; Trk; Hon Roll; Lock Haven U; Elementary Educ.

GOODMAN, ANN; Freeport SR HS; Sarver, PA; (3); 35/216; Chorus; Stu Cncl; Cheerleading; Gov Hon Prg Awd; Hon Roll; Smmr Hppnngs Arts August 87; Fshn Merch.

GOODMAN, BETH; Lower Moreland HS; Huntingdon Valley, PA; (3); FBLA; Key Clb; Office Aide; Red Cross Aide; Science Clb; SADD; Temple Yth Grp; Yrbk Phtg; Yrbk Stf; Rep Soph Cls; Law.

GOODMAN, CAROLYN; Oley Valley HS; Oley, PA; (3); 42/140; Camp Fr Inc; JA; Key Clb; Pep Clb; Yrbk Phtg; Hon Roll; Nursing.

GOODMAN, DONNA MARIE; W Philadelphia Cath HS For Girls; Philadelphia, PA; (3); 34/249; Church Yth Grp; Girl Scts; Library Aide; Spanish Clb; Chorus; Church Choir; School Play; Stu Cncl; Cheerleading; High Hon Roll; Merit Awd Spch 85; 3rd Pl Awd Miss Parasol 87; Acad Achvt Awd Geom & Alg 2 86-87; Bus Mgmt.

GOODMAN, JEANNETTE; Cardinal O Hara HS; Havertown, PA; (3); 100/700; Church Yth Grp; Dance Clb; JA; Office Aide; Trk; Hon Roll.

GOODMAN, LEON; Central HS; Philadelphia, PA; (3); 150/532; Church Yth Grp; Church Choir; JV Var Ftbl; JV Trk; Im Wt Lftg; Crmnl Jstc.

GOODMAN, LYNNE; Line Mountain HS; Trevorton, PA; (4); 15/121; Church Yth Grp; FBLA; Sec Key Clb; Drill Tm; Nwsp Stf; Stu Cncl; Score Keeper; Hon Roll; NHS; Eagles Nest Schlrshp Of $100 For Accntng 87; Bloomsburg U; Accntng.

GOODMAN, MARK; Cranberry HS; Oil City, PA; (2); Church Yth Grp; FHA; Science Clb; SADD; L Bsbl; Score Keeper; Hon Roll; Educ.

GOODMAN, SHIRA; Abington SR HS; Hungtindon Valley, PA; (3); 3/502; Trs French Clb; Q&S; VP Temple Yth Grp; Chorus; Ed Yrbk Stf; High Hon Roll; Pres Schlr; School Musical; Stage Crew; Nwsp Rptr; Outstndng Stu 86; Outstndng Wrld Civ II, Amer Study I 86 & 87; Outstndng Feml Wellesley Coll Awd 87; Hstry.

GOODMAN, TONY; Chaltonham HS; Laverock, PA; (2); FBLA; Bsktbl; Tennis; Law.

GOODMAN, WILLIAM D; Tunkhannock Area HS; Tunkhannock, PA; (3); Church Yth Grp; Computer Clb; Band; Chorus; Church Choir; Concert Band; Jazz Band; Mrchg Band; Hon Roll; NHS; Comp Sci.

GOODNOW, KIMBERLY; Philadelphia H S For Girls; Philadelphia, PA; (3); 8/502; Cmnty Wkr; Teachers Aide; Concert Band; Jazz Band; Mrchg Band; Mgr Orch; School Musical; Vllybl; High Hon Roll; Prfct Atten Awd; Lab Asst In U Of Penns Laser Lab 87; WISE Guide Woman In Sci Exhibit At Franlin Inst 86-87; Bio-Chem.

GOODREAU, JENNIFER; New Covenant Acad; Wellsboro, PA; (1); 2/7; Church Yth Grp; Ski Clb; Band; Chorus; JV Bsktbl; JV Socr.

GOODRICH, CHRIS A; Blacklick Valley HS; Nanty Glo, PA; (3); 13/97; Boy Scts; German Clb; Varsity Clb; L Bsbl; Bsktbl; L Ftbl; Wt Lftg; Hon Roll; NHS; Acad All Amer 85-86; PA ST U; Engr.

GOODRICH, DEBRA; Hampton HS; Glenshaw, PA; (4); 59/239; Chorus; Capt Color Guard; School Musical; VP Frsh Cls; Pres Soph Cls; Rep Jr Cls; VP Sr Cls; Off Stu Cncl; Powder Puff Ftbl; Hon Roll; Hgh Hnr Rll 83-87; Elfinwild Lions Clb Samuel Reno Schlrshp 87; Pres Allghny Intermdte Stu Forum 86-87; PA ST U; Biochem.

GOODSON, DIONNE; Simon Gratz HS; Philadelphia, PA; (3); #7 In Class; FBLA; Hosp Aide; Sftbl; Crt Rm Stenogrphr.

GOODWILL, LISA; Fort Leboeuf HS; Waterford, PA; (3); 4-H; Hosp Aide; Ski Clb; Rep Stu Cncl; Bsktbl; Cheerleading; DAR Awd; Hon Roll; Beautician.

GOODWIN, BRIAN T; Reading SR HS; Reading, PA; (4); 35/574; Stage Crew; Var Bsktbl; Im Vllybl; Cit Awd; Hon Roll; NHS; JR Rotarian 86; Shippensburg U; Physics.

GOODWIN, CATHERINE; Upper Darby HS; Upper Darby, PA; (3); Aud/Vis; Chorus; Hon Roll; Law.

GOODWIN, GEORGE; Milton SR HS; New Columbia, PA; (2); Letterman Clb; Varsity Clb; JV L Bsbl; JV Var Ftbl; JV Var Wrstlng.

GOODWIN, HOLLY; Oil City SR HS; Oil City, PA; (3); 52/250; Acpl Chr; Chorus; Yrbk Stf; Trk; Vllybl; Hon Roll.

GOODWIN, KIERAN W; Wilson HS; Wyomissing, PA; (4); 1/321; French Clb; Scholastic Bowl; Stu Cncl; Var L Bsktbl; Var L Crs Cntry; High Hon Roll; Pres NHS; Ntl Merit SF; Cmnty Wkr; Math Awd 86; 10th Pl Berks Cty Crss Cntry Conf Run 86; Ecnmcs.

GOODWIN, MICHAEL; Tunkhannock HS; Mehoopany, PA; (4); Letterman Clb; Pep Clb; ROTC; Pres Spanish Clb; Socr; Vllybl; Hon Roll; NHS; Ntl Merit Schol; E Stroudsburg; Physcs.

GOODYEAR, DONNA; Norristown HS Annex; Norristown, PA; (4); Church Yth Grp; FBLA; Hosp Aide; Office Aide; Teachers Aide; VICA; Chorus; Nwsp Stf; Stu Cncl; Hon Roll; Data Prcssng.

GOOKER, BETH; South Western HS; Hanover, PA; (2); Exploring; Band; Chorus; Concert Band; Mrchg Band; Pep Band; Stage Crew; Symp Band; Hon Roll; NEDT Awd; Med.

GOON, CHRISTOPHER; Altoona Area HS; Altoona, PA; (4); 139/710; Church Yth Grp; FCA; JA; VICA; Im Bsktbl; Im Vllybl; High Hon Roll; Hon Roll; Penn ST U; Cvl Engrng.

GOPEZ, NOREEN; Mechanicsburg HS; Chadds Ford, PA; (4); 8/307; Girl Scts; NFL; Chorus; Stage Crew; Var Fld Hcky; Var Trk; Hon Roll; Pres NHS; Pres Schlr; AFROTC Schlrshp 87; Stu Of Month-Rotary Club 86-87; Girl Of Month-Womens Club 86-87; PA ST U; Electrical Engrng.

GORAL, JOHN; Archbishop Ryan HS; Philadelphia, PA; (2); 93/349; Church Yth Grp; Drama Clb; Chorus; School Musical; School Play; Yrbk Stf; God Cntry Awd; Hon Roll; Wrld Afrs Cncl 86-87; Dstgshd Achvmnt Theology 86-87; CA Coll; Crminolgy.

GORDANIER, MIKE-JUDD; Carson Long Military HS; Linden, NJ; (4); ROTC; Ski Clb; Varsity Clb; Var Capt Bsbl; Var Bsktbl; JV Ftbl; JV Var Socr; Trk; Elks Awd; Gov Hon Prg Awd; Pres Phy Fit Awd 87; MP Sgt Arms 87; A Tm Ldr 87; Lit Socty 87; Syracuse U; Engrng.

GORDILLO, DONALD; Valley Forge Military Acad; New Orleans, LA; (3); 20/150; ROTC; Spanish Clb; Varsity Clb; Drill Tm; Im Socr; Im Tennis; Hon Roll; Deans List 85-87; Tulane U; Engrng.

GORDISH, ERIN; Kiski Area HS; Avonmore, PA; (3); Ski Clb; Jazz Band; Mrchg Band; Pep Band; Symp Band; Var Tennis; Stat Trk; High Hon Roll; NHS; Trs Church Yth Grp; Top 10 Cls 84-85; Duquesne U; Phrmcy.

GORDNER, DONNA LYNNE; Millville Area HS; Millville, PA; (4); 4-H; FBLA; Library Aide; Band; School Musical; Yrbk Stf; 4-H Awd; Hon Roll; NEDT Awd; Millville Mutual Ins Co Schlrshp 87; East Stroudsburg U; Leis Svcs.

GORDON, BRENDA; Uniontown Area HS; Smock, PA; (3); Church Yth Grp; French Clb; German Clb; Hosp Aide; JA; Spanish Clb; SADD; French Hon Soc; Hon Roll; Spanish NHS; Penn ST U; Intrprtr.

GORDON, CHARLOTTE; Girls HS; Philadelphia, PA; (4); 120/402; Church Yth Grp; Library Aide; Office Aide; Pep Clb; Sec SADD; Teachers Aide; Orch; School Play; Variety Show; JV Bowling; Pre-Law.

GORDON, CRYSTAL; Shenango JR-SR HS; New Castle, PA; (3); 19/125; Teachers Aide; Band; Concert Band; Mrchg Band; Pep Band; Trk; Hon Roll; Prfct Atten Awd; Bradford Schl Of Bus; Acctng.

GORDON, ELIZABETH; Central HS; Martinsburg, PA; (4); Drama Clb; Sec Trs Girl Scts; VP JA; Red Cross Aide; Sec SADD; Nwsp Rptr; Yrbk Stf; Hon Roll; IN U; Psychology.

GORDON, ERIN; Wallen Paupack Area HS; Hawley, PA; (3); 6/150; Ski Clb; Band; Concert Band; Jazz Band; Mrchg Band; Pep Band; School Musical; Fld Hcky; Sftbl; Trk.

GORDON, GAY LYNN; Christian Schl Of York; York, PA; (3); Church Yth Grp; Chorus; Church Choir; Stat Vllybl; Hon Roll; RN.

GORDON, JEFFREY; Pennsbury HS; Morrisville, PA; (4); Boy Scts; German Clb; Temple Yth Grp; JV Ftbl; Bentley Coll; Bus.

GORDON, JOHN; Fox Chapel HS; Pittsburgh, PA; (3); 50/360; Church Yth Grp; PAVAS; Acpl Chr; Chorus; Madrigals; School Musical; Swing Chorus; JV Var Ftbl; High Hon Roll; NHS; Engrng.

GORDON, JOYCE; Montour HS; Pittsburgh, PA; (4); 25/301; Drama Clb; Library Aide; Yrbk Stf; High Hon Roll; NHS; Acdmc Achvt Awd-Grmn II & IV 87 & 86; Prsdntl Acdmc Ftnss Awd 87; ICM Schl Of Business; Trvl.

GORDON, PAMELA C; Westinghouse HS; Pittsburgh, PA; (4); 3/250; Church Yth Grp; Cmnty Wkr; FHA; Office Aide; Church Choir; Rep Stu Cncl; High Hon Roll; Pres NHS; Voice Dem Awd; US Ntnl Ldrshp Mrt Awds 87; IN U Of PA; Tchr.

GORDON JR, R CRAIG; Abington SR HS; Hunt Valley, PA; (3); 21/502; Boy Scts; Church Yth Grp; VP JA; SADD; High Hon Roll; Jr NHS; JV Ftbl; JV Golf; JV Trk; Im Wt Lftg; Bus Law.

GORDON, RAM; Taylor Allderdice HS; Pittsburgh, PA; (2); Math Clb; Ski Clb; Nwsp Rptr; Nwsp Stf; Bowling; High Hon Roll; NHS; Jrnlsm.

GORDON, ROBIN; Exeter HS; Reading, PA; (4); 30/217; Varsity Clb Y-Teens; Concert Band; Soph Cls; Jr Cls; Sr Cls; Stu Cncl; Tennis; Twrlr NHS; Cmmnctns.

GORDON, SHAWN; Hazleton HS; Drums, PA; (2); Ski Clb; Ftbl; Trk Wt Lftg; Wrstlng; Hon Roll; U S Air Force Acad; Aeronautics.

GORDON, SHIRLENE; Towanda HS; Towanda, PA; (3); 8/145; French Clb; Trs Library Aide; SADD; Yrbk Stf; Hon Roll; NHS; Jrnlsm.

GORE, SACHIN; Council Rock HS; Holland, PA; (2); Boy Scts Computer Clb; Exploring; Im Badmtn; Im Socr; Im Tennis; Im Vllybl High Hon Roll; Hon Roll; Prfct Atten Awd; Comp Sci.

GORELL, LISEL; State Coll Area Intermediate HS; State College, PA (1); Drama Clb; Thesps; Band; School Musical; School Play; Rep Frsh Cls Hon Roll; VFW Awd.

GORGAS, STEPHANIE; Lincoln HS; Wampum, PA; (4); 92/165 Exploring; FBLA; Girl Scts; Key Clb; Y-Teens; Powder Puff Ftbl; Hon Roll; Prfct Atten Awd; Hm Ec Awd 87; Girl Sct Gld Awd 86; ITT Tech Inst; Bus Mgmt.

GORGONE, PETER; Pittston Area HS; Pittston, PA; (4); 1/350; French Clb; Math Clb; Math Tm; Quiz Bowl; Science Clb; Im Bsktbl; Var L Tennis; Hon Roll; NHS; Rotary Awd; Rotary Ldrshp Camp 85; Physics.

GORHAM, JOSH; Tunkhannock Area HS; Dalton, PA; (2); Church Yth Grp; JV Bsbl; JV Bsktbl; L Crs Cntry; God Cntry Awd; High Hon Roll.

GORKO, KELLI; Tunkhannock HS; Falls, PA; (4); 32/280; Ski Clb; Trs Spanish Clb; Band; Mrchg Band; Yrbk Stf; Rep Jr Cls; Rep Sr Cls; Stat Fld Hcky; High Hon Roll; NHS; Misericordia; Med Tech.

GORMAN, JAMES; St John Neumann HS; Philadelphia, PA; (4); 51/365; Band; Concert Band; Jazz Band; Pep Band; JV Ftbl; Hon Roll Outstndng Activity Band 86-87, Acad Hnr Rl 86-87; St Joseph U.

GORMAN JR, JAMES; Harriton HS; Narberth, PA; (3); Ski Clb; SADD; Ed Nwsp Phtg; Nwsp Rptr; Ed Nwsp Stf; Ed Yrbk Phtg; Var L Socr; High Hon Roll; NHS; Temple Press Tourn Edtrl Wrtng 3rd Pl 87; Rnnr-Up Phila Cntry Clb Champ Fnls 84; Bus.

GORMAN, KIMBERLY; Elk Lake Schl District; Owego, NY; (2); Camera Clb; SADD; VICA; Chorus; Yrbk Stf; Hon Roll; Stu Agnst Drvng Drnk 86-87; Vctnl Indstrl Clbs Amer 86-87; Hnr Rll 85-86; PA ST; Acctng.

GORMAN, MICHELLE; Sacred Heart HS; Pittsburgh, PA; (3); Q&S; Spanish Clb; Nwsp Rptr; Nwsp Stf; Yrbk Stf; Hon Roll; Engl.

GORMAN JR, PETER C; Montour HS; Pittsburgh, PA; (3); 29/279; Stat Coach Actv; JV Ftbl; High Hon Roll; NHS; Achvt Awd In Elec 86; Bus Mgnt.

GORMAN, TRACY; B Reed Henderson HS; W Chester, PA; (3); Office Aide; Pep Clb; Pep Band; Yrbk Phtg; Yrbk Stf; Var Gym; Hon Roll; 2 Vrsty Ltrs Gymnstcs 84-87; Math.

GORMELY, DAWN; Marple Newtown HS; Broomall, PA; (3); Thesps; School Play; Lit Mag; Off Stu Cncl; Fld Hcky; Mgr(s); Miss Petite USA ST PA Semifnlst 86-87; All Star Sftbl Tm 83-86; Advrtsng.

GORMLEY, SUZANNE; John W Hallahan HS; Philadelphia, PA; (3); 46/292; Cmnty Wkr; French Clb; Yrbk Stf; Rep Frsh Cls; Rep Soph Cls; Rep Jr Cls; Bsktbl; Score Keeper; Var Sftbl; Im Vllybl; PA ST U JR Acad Of Sci 2nd Pl 86-87; U Of PA; Physcl Therapy.

GORNIAK, TAMRA; Seneca HS; Erie, PA; (3); Pep Clb; Var L Bsktbl; Var L Sftbl; Var L Vllybl; Hon Roll; All County Hnrb Mntn Bsktbl 85-86; Flght Attndnt.

GORTON, JOHN; H S Truman HS; Bristol, PA; (3); 3/500; Boy Scts; Debate Tm; Drama Clb; NFL; Jazz Band; School Musical; High Hon Roll; NHS; Egl Sct 87; Jazz Band Awd 86-87; Elec Engr.

GORWALL, EMILY; Peters Township HS; Mcmurray, PA; (2); Church Yth Grp; Church Choir; Rep Stu Cncl; Trk; Hon Roll; Purdue; Engnrng.

GOSIEWSKI, LISA; Tunkhannock HS; Harveys Lake, PA; (4); 17/270; Spanish Clb; Sftbl; Capt Vllybl; Hon Roll; NHS; Vllybl Awds Coaches Awd & Mst Imprvd 85-85; U Of FL; Grphc Art.

GOSNELL, RICHARD; Cambridge Springs HS; Cambridge Springs, PA; (4); 4/104; Aud/Vis; Pres Ski Clb; Quiz Bowl; Pres Jr Cls; Pres Sr Cls; Trs Stu Cncl; Mgr Vllybl; Hon Roll; Kiwanis Awd; NHS; Homecoming King 85; Penn ST U; Physics.

GOSNELL, TIM; Cumberland Valley HS; Mechanicsburg, PA; (3); 19/540; Church Yth Grp; FCA; Key Clb; Band; Concert Band; Jazz Band; Mrchg Band; School Play; Symp Band; Trs Soph Cls; Smmr Sci Smnr US Air Force Acad 86; PA JR Acad Sci 1st Pl Rgn IV & ST, Natl Hnr Soc Schlrshp 87; Duke U; Elec Engrng.

GOSNEY, HEATHER; South Acad; Glassport, PA; (3); Office Aide; Y-Teens; Twrlr; NHS; U Of Pittsburgh; Bus.

GOSS, AMY; Chief Logan HS; Mcclure, PA; (3); 33/182; Computer Clb; Spanish Clb; Band; Church Choir; Concert Band; Mrchg Band; Pep Band; Yrbk Stf; Stu Cncl; Sftbl; Nrsng.

GOSS, RICHARD; York Catholic HS; York, PA; (3); Boy Scts; Library Aide; Spanish Clb; Stage Crew; Yrbk Stf; Hon Roll; NHS; Eagle Sct BSA 85; Comp Sci.

GOSSAR, KELLY; Moshannon Valley HS; Ginter, PA; (3); 35/120; Spanish Clb; Varsity Clb; Band; Chorus; Yrbk Stf; Sec Soph Cls; Sec Jr Cls; Var L Bsktbl; Score Keeper; Var L Sftbl.

GOSWEILER, SHANNON; Downingtown SR HS; Glenmore, PA; (2); GAA; Ski Clb; Spanish Clb; SADD; Fld Hcky; Lcrss; Hon Roll; MIP Fld Hcky & Lacrosse 85-86.

GOTJEN, DEIDRE; Somerset Area HS; Somerset, PA; (3); 39/230; Pres Church Yth Grp; Drama Clb; English Clb; Q&S; Chorus; Church Choir; School Play; Nwsp Stf; Yrbk Stf; Stu Cncl; Lib Art.

GOTSHALL, DONNA; Hillside Christian Acad; Lewisburg, PA; (2); 1/6; Church Yth Grp; Library Aide; Church Choir; Yrbk Stf; Var Socr; Var Sftbl; Var Vllybl; Cit Awd; Chrstn Chrctr 86-87; Hghst Sci Av 85-86; Tchng.

GOTTERBARN, LYNNE; Meadville SR HS; Meadville, PA; (3); GAA; JA; Sec Spanish Clb; Var L Socr; Hon Roll; U Of MA Amherst; Archlgy.

GOTTLIEB, JEFFREY A; Glen Mills Schls; Baltimore, MD; (4); 1/116; Aud/Vis; Chess Clb; CAP; Computer Clb; Teachers Aide; Nwsp Phtg; Yrbk Phtg; L Socr; Capt L Tennis; Hon Roll; U Of MI; Naval Arch.

GOTTLIEB, TERRI; George Washington HS; Philadelphia, PA; (4); 27/815; Spanish Clb; Temple Yth Grp; School Play; High Hon Roll; NHS; Spanish NHS; Mntly Gftd Prg; RKTSE Wrtng Cont Smi-Fnlst; Temple U; Bio.

GOTTRON, MARK; Vincentian HS; Gibsonia, PA; (2); Nwsp Stf; Var Bsktbl; Var Socr; Hon Roll; Allegeny Coll; Orthodonics.

GOTTSCHALK, AMY; Mc Guffey HS; Prosperity, PA; (4); 19/201; French Clb; Yrbk Sprt Ed; Yrbk Stf; Rep Jr Cls; Stat Ftbl; High Hon Roll; Hon Roll; NHS; Church Yth Grp; Stu Recgntn Awd 84-86.

GOTTSCHALK, JENNIFER; Riverview SR HS; Verona, PA; (3); Nwsp Rptr; Rep Jr Cls; Powder Puff Ftbl; Hon Roll.

GOTWALD, JUDI; Seneca Valley SR HS; Harmony, PA; (3); 4-H; Girl Scts; Pep Clb; ROTC; Madrigals; School Play; Nwsp Rptr; Nwsp Stf; Yrbk Stf; Hon Roll; TROA ROTC Mdl Excptnl Ptntl Ldrshp 87; Rotary Awd Attnd 5th Conf Of RYLA Westminster Coll 87; Bus Admin.

GOTWOLS, DANIELLE; Eastern York HS; Wrightsville, PA; (2); 16/155; SADD; School Musical; Yrbk Stf; Trs Frsh Cls; Trs Soph Cls; Trs Jr Cls; Stu Cncl; Var Capt Cheerleading; JV Vllybl; High Hon Roll; Crmnl Law.

GOUGH, CAROLYN; Somerset Area SR HS; Somerset, PA; (4); 44/240; Pres Church Yth Grp; English Clb; FCA; German Clb; Q&S; Sec Ski Clb; Varsity Clb; Jazz Band; School Play; Yrbk Stf; Lock Haven U; Elem Educ.

GOUGH, JASON; Hamburg Area HS; Shoemakersville, PA; (3); German Clb; Trk; Hon Roll; Pres Schlr; Grmn Hnr Soc; Rtry Ldrshp Camp; Engrng.

GOULD, AMY D; Greenville HS; Greenville, PA; (4); Thesps; Pres Chorus; Madrigals; School Musical; Mgr School Play; Variety Show; Rep Stu Cncl; JV Cheerleading; Var Trk; Hon Roll; Dist, Rgnl & ST Chorus 87; Merion Gebrich Schlrshp Music 87; West Chester U; Vocal Prfrmnce.

GOULD, ANDREW; Hershey SR HS; Hershey, PA; (3); 30/205; Church Yth Grp; Letterman Clb; Spanish Clb; Varsity Clb; Var L Bsbl; Var L Golf; Ice Hcky; High Hon Roll; Hon Roll; Spanish NHS; Demolay 86; U Of Pittsburgh; Dnstry.

GOULD, ELLEN; Upper Darby HS; Drexel Hill, PA; (3); 8/560; Cmnty Wkr; French Clb; Yrbk Rptr; Yrbk Stf; JV Cheerleading; Var JV Mgr(s); JV Swmmng; Var JV Tennis; High Hon Roll; Hon Roll; Arch Engrng.

GOULD, KARA D; N Allegheny SR HS; Pittsburgh, PA; (4); 46/652; Cmnty Wkr; French Clb; Acpl Chr; Chorus; School Musical; Lit Mag; Hon Roll; Jr NHS; NHS; Ntl Merit SF; Awd Bio; U Of WI Madison; Cmmnctns.

GOULD, TODD E; Lower Dauphin SR HS; Middletown, PA; (4); 2/237; Am Leg Boys St; Boy Scts; Mrchg Band; High Hon Roll; NHS; Sal; Concert Band; Orch; God Cntry Awd; Opt Clb Awd; AFROTC Schrlshp 87-91; Semper Fidelis & Prsdntl Acdmc Ftns Awds 87; 7 Boy Scts Of Amer Offcrs; Penn ST U; Aeronautical Engrng.

GOULDEN, STACI; Littlestown HS; Littlestown, PA; (3); Church Yth Grp; Teachers Aide; Band; Chorus; Color Guard; Mrchg Band; Yrbk Stf; Fld Hcky; Med Asst.

GOULDING, RICHARD; Mt Pleasant JR HS; Mt Pleasant, PA; (3); Pres 4-H; Ski Clb; VICA; Stage Crew; 1st Pl In PA Blue Forms In Vet Sci 85; 4-H Teen Ldr & EFNP Counslr 85; 2nd In Proj Bk Awd 85; HEATING & Air Cond.

GOUNDER, CHRIS; Jeannette SR HS; Jeannette, PA; (2); L Bsbl; L Ftbl; Wt Lftg; Engr.

GOURDIER, LISA; Cardinal O Hara HS; Aston, PA; (4); 82/771; VP Church Yth Grp; Office Aide; Teachers Aide; Sftbl; Hon Roll; NHS; Outstndng Bus Stu 87; West Chester U; Bus.

GOURLAY, SUSAN M; Neshaming HS; Langhorne, PA; (4); 1/690; Capt Dance Clb; Pres SADD; Chorus; School Musical; Nwsp Ed-Chief; NHS; Val; Drama Clb; Intnl Clb; Soc Wmn Engrs Awd 87; Coll Schlrshp 87; Exch Clb Stu-Of-Yr 87; Temple U; Vcl Prfrmnce.

GOURLEY, ANN MARIE; Villa Maria Acad; Norristown, PA; (3); Church Yth Grp; Cmnty Wkr; GAA; Girl Scts; Political Wkr; SADD; Teachers Aide; Chorus; Yrbk Rptr; JV Fld Hcky; Johnson & Wales; Trvl Mgmt.

GOURLEY, JILL; Curwensville Area HS; Curwensville, PA; (3); Drama Clb; Ski Clb; Varsity Clb; Nwsp Stf; Rep Stu Cncl; Var Cheerleading; Hon Roll; Erly Chldhd Ed.

GOURLEY, LARRY; Seneca HS; Wattsburg, PA; (4); 14/153; Ski Clb; School Musical; Bsbl; Ftbl; Hon Roll; NHS; Fclty Choice Grad Spkr 87; Dept Awd Soc Stud 87; Grove City Coll; Comp Syst.

GOUSIE, MALEITA; Governor Mifflin SR HS; Shillington, PA; (3); Key Clb; Model UN; Q&S; Y-Teens; Chorus; Concert Band; Orch; Nwsp Stf; Ed Yrbk Stf; Sec Stu Cncl; Am Leg Schl Awd 85; Maximus Hnr Unified Point System 85-87; Pres Acad Awd 85; Boston U; Ed.

GOVAN, CINDY; Lakeland HS; Olyphant, PA; (3); 46/136; Church Yth Grp; French Clb; FHA; Drill Tm; Yrbk Stf; Rep Stu Cncl; Hon Roll; Prfct Atten Awd; Archit.

GOVANUCCI, RENEE; Serra Catholic HS; Mc Keesport, PA; (4); AFS; Girl Scts; Library Aide; Concert Band; Drm & Bgl; Mrchg Band; School Play; Powder Puff Ftbl; Capt Twrlr; Hon Roll; Point Pk Coll; Psychlgy.

GOWARTY, MARK; West Scranton SR HS; Scranton, PA; (3); 89/269; Boy Scts; Church Yth Grp; Yrbk Stf; Stu Cncl; Hon Roll; Penn ST U; Pre-Med.

GOWATSKI, KELLY; Connellsville Area HS; Mt Pleasant, PA; (4); 17/520; Church Yth Grp; Band; Color Guard; Mrchg Band; Symp Band; Nwsp Sprt Ed; Stu Cncl; Score Keeper; French Hon Soc; High Hon Roll; U Of Pittsburgh; Phy Thrpy.

GOWATY, MARGARET; Mc Keesport Area HS; Mc Keesport, PA; (4); Cmnty Wkr; Girl Scts; VP JA; Acpl Chr; Band; School Musical; Nwsp Rptr; Mgr(s); Hon Roll; NEDT Awd; Ladies Axlry-VFW Ldrshp Citatn 87; Grl Sct Slvr Awd 87; JR Achvt-Bst Slsprsn Awd 87.

GOWNLEY, ERIN; Mahanoy Area HS; Mahanoy Plane, PA; (3); Church Yth Grp; Spanish Clb; School Play; Variety Show; Nwsp Stf; Yrbk Stf; VP Frsh Cls; JV Var Cheerleading; VP NHS; Elem Ed.

GOYAK, MARY JO; Western Beaver HS; Industry, PA; (3); Church Yth Grp; Girl Scts; Scholastic Bowl; SADD; Yrbk Stf; Acpl Chr; Chorus; Church Choir; Rep Stu Cncl; Bowling.

GOYNE, KIM; El Meyers HS; Wilkes-Barre, PA; (4); 28/152; FBLA; Key Clb; Ski Clb; Hon Roll; Spanish NHS; Hd Strt Schlrshp 87; Wilkes Coll; Chldhd Educ.

GOZA IV, GRANVILLE; Saegertown HS; Saegertown, PA; (4); 2/107; Boy Scts; Math Tm; Band; Var Pres Concert Band; Jazz Band; Var Pres Mrchg Band; Bowling; Hon Roll; NHS; Sal; Cainegie Mellon U; Math.

GOZIKOWSKI, SHARON; Wyoming Area SR HS; Falls, PA; (3); 114/250; 4-H; French Clb; FHA; JV Bsktbl; Var Sftbl; 4-H Awd; Med.

GRAB, JOSEPH A; Mtn View Bible Chrch Christian Schl; Middletown, PA; (4); 1/4; Chorus; Church Choir; School Play; Var L Bsktbl; Var L Socr; Var L Sftbl; High Hon Roll; Prfct Atten Awd; 1st Pl Math-KCEA, 2nd Pl Math-AACS 86; 1st Pl Math-KCEA, 3rd Pl Math-AACS 87; PA ST U; Engrng.

GRABAN, AMY; Villa Maria HS; Lowellville, OH; (4); 8/53; Cmnty Wkr; Drama Clb; French Clb; Key Clb; Thesps; Mrchg Band; Nwsp Stf; French Hon Soc; High Hon Roll; NHS; Pres Acdmc Fit Awd 86-87; Miami U; Mass Cmmnctns.

GRABARITS, RICHARD; Northampton Area HS; Northampton, PA; (4); 25/446; AFS; Exploring; Leo Clb; Ski Clb; Golf; High Hon Roll; NHS; Rotary Awd; Stu Mnth 87; Penn ST U; Aerospc Engrng.

GRABER, CRISTINA J; Ephrata SR HS; Akron, PA; (4); 1/256; Church Yth Grp; Intnl Clb; Library Aide; Quiz Bowl; Concert Band; Orch; Nwsp Stf; High Hon Roll; NHS; Ntl Merit SF; Ltn Amer Stds.

GRABIAK, BEVERLY L; Mt Pleasant A HS; Calumet, PA; (3); Art Clb; Sec 4-H; 4-H Awd; Hon Roll.

GRABIAK, LYNN; Greensburg Central Catholic HS; Greensburg, PA; (3); 52/233; Sec Church Yth Grp; Ski Clb; Yrbk Stf; Trs Soph Cls; Sec Jr Cls; Off Stu Cncl; Powder Puff Ftbl; Score Keeper; High Hon Roll; NHS; AFS & Medical Explorers 86-87; Pep Club 84-85.

GRABIAS, GAYLE; L E Dieruff HS; Allentown, PA; (3); Church Yth Grp; Rep Stu Cncl; JV Var Cheerleading; Powder Puff Ftbl; Spcl Hnr By City For Hstry Day Proj 85; Elem Ed Tchr.

GRABIEC, JENNIFER; Ford City HS; Ford City, PA; (3); 4/160; Spanish Clb; Chorus; VP Soph Cls; Rep Jr Cls; Rep Sr Cls; Rep Stu Cncl; Stat Ftbl; Var L Tennis; Bausch & Lomb Sci Awd; High Hon Roll; Acad Achvt Awd 85; USTA Ten Camp Scholar 87; Biomed Engrng.

GRABILL, STANLEY; Stoneboro Wesleyan Methodist HS; Ashville, NY; (2); Pep Clb; Band; Concert Band; Mrchg Band; Orch; Pep Band; School Musical; Ftbl; Trk; Hon Roll; Music.

GRABOFSKI, JANET; Elizabeth Forward HS; Elizabeth, PA; (3); 24/345; Church Yth Grp; Latin Clb; Band; Concert Band; Jazz Band; Mrchg Band; High Hon Roll; Hon Roll; NHS; Marine Bio.

GRABOSKE, ROBERT; John S Fine HS; Nanticoke, PA; (3); 40/222; Var Bsbl; Var Bsktbl; High Hon Roll.

GRABOWSKI, SHERRY; Mid-Valley HS; Throop, PA; (3); Drama Clb; Chorus; School Play; Variety Show; Rep Stu Cncl; High Hon Roll; Church Yth Grp; French Clb; GAA; Girl Scts; Merch Advrtsng.

GRABSKI, KRISTY; Beaver Area JR/Sr HS; Beaver, PA; (2); JCL; Latin Clb; Ski Clb; Cheerleading; Trk; High Hon Roll; Acadmc Achvmnt Awd 87; Med Fld.

GRABSKI, MARLO A; Burgettstown Area JR-SR HS; Burgettstown, PA; (4); 1/137; Am Leg Aux Girls St; Dance Clb; Spanish Clb; Chorus; Drm Mjr(t); Cit Awd; Lion Awd; Pres Schlr; Val; Voice Dem Awd; Heritage Schlrshp 87; Climax Schlrshp 87; Goulding Music Schlrshp 87; Denison U; Bio.

GRABY, CRAIG; Annville-Cleona HS; Lebanon, PA; (3); 7/127; Church Yth Grp; Math Tm; Model UN; Varsity Clb; Var L Socr; Var L Wrstlng; Hon Roll; NHS; NEDT Awd; Comp Sci.

GRACE, BEVERLY; West Allegheny HS; Oakdale, PA; (3); Exploring; FBLA; Teachers Aide; High Hon Roll; Hon Roll; Dirctrs List At Parkway W Area Voc Schl 86-87; Olympia Natl Schlstc Typing Cntst Awd 87; Comp Systems Inst; Comp Prog.

GRACE, CHRISTOPHER; Norristown Area HS; Norristown, PA; (3); 8/430; Computer Clb; Var Bowling; Top 10 Frsh Cls 84-85; Comp Awd 84-85; Comp Sci.

GRACE, LORIE; Northern York County HS; Dillsburg, PA; (3); 57/232; Library Aide; Rep Frsh Cls; Rep Soph Cls; Rep Jr Cls; High Hon Roll; Hon Roll; Messiah Coll; Nrsng.

GRACE, MICHELLE; Bishop Mc Devitt HS; Oreland, PA; (3); 34/349; Church Yth Grp; Cmnty Wkr; Dance Clb; Office Aide; Rep Jr Cls; Powder Puff Ftbl; Im Vllybl; Hon Roll; NHS; Math.

GRACZYK, HEATHER; William Tennent HS; Warminster, PA; (4); Cmnty Wkr; School Musical; Sec Stu Cncl; Var Golf; Mgr Socr; Hon Roll; All-State Music Awd Drums 83; St Finalst Miss Amer Co-Ed Pageant 86; Stud Cncl Schlrshp Temple U 87; Temple U; Liberal Arts.

GRADOS, ROBERT; Fox Chapel Area HS; Monessen, PA; (4); 30/322; French Clb; Key Clb; Ski Clb; Chorus; Nwsp Ed-Chief; Nwsp Stf; Var JV Ftbl; High Hon Roll; Hon Roll; U Of MI; Law.

GRADY, DANIEL M; Archbishop Ryan For Boys; Philadelphia, PA; (3); 18/414; Church Yth Grp; Computer Clb; Dance Clb; Spanish Clb; Band; Mrchg Band; School Play; JV Ftbl; Trk; High Hon Roll; Lectors Awd Partcptn Schl Masses 86-87; U PA; Bus Admin.

GRADY, LEIGH ANNE; Central Bucks West HS; Doylestown, PA; (3); 100/497; Church Yth Grp; Chorus; School Musical; School Play; Rep Soph Cls; Rep Jr Cls; Sec Sr Cls; Stu Cncl; Var L Cheerleading; High Hon Roll.

GRADY, MEGAN EILEEN; St Hubert HS; Philadelphia, PA; (3); 85/421; Spanish Clb; Yrbk Ed-Chief; Yrbk Stf; C E Ellis Schlrshps 85-87; Erly Chldhd Educ.

GRAEBER, DANELLE; Spring-Ford SR HS; Spring City, PA; (2); 84/289; French Clb; Intnl Clb; Pep Clb; Political Wkr; Ski Clb; Rep Soph Cls; Capt Cheerleading; Stat Wrstlng; Hon Roll; Pltcl Sci.

GRAEBER, JENNIFER; Warwick HS; Lititz, PA; (3); 57/295; Art Clb; Church Yth Grp; Drama Clb; Pep Clb; Radio Clb; Spanish Clb; Chorus; School Play; Stage Crew; Nwsp Rptr.

GRAEBNER, ROBERT; Arch Bishop Wood For Boys HS; Warminster, PA; (2); 118/254; Boy Scts; German Clb; Office Aide; SADD; Socr; Schl Scholar 85-89; Ldrshp Order Arrow BSA 87; WA Crossing Awd 85.

GRAF JR, KENNETH W; Northern HS; Dillsburg, PA; (3); 7/254; Ski Clb; Spanish Clb; Varsity Clb; Variety Show; Bsktbl; Coach Actv; Socr; Hon Roll; All-Star Soccer 1st Tm MVP 86; All-Star Basketball 1st Tm MVP 87; Teaching.

GRAF, ROBERT; Ridley SR HS; Holmes, PA; (4); 135/407; Varsity Clb; Var Ftbl; Var Capt Trk; Var Wrstlng; Hon Roll; Plyr Of Yr-Ftbl; All-Delco, Central, Schltc & Dist Channel 3 & All-Area Golden Eleven 86; Temple U; Physcl Educ.

GRAFENSTINE, THERESA; Bensalem HS; Bensalem, PA; (4); 23/477; Teachers Aide; Nwsp Rptr; High Hon Roll; Hon Roll; NHS; St Joseph U Schlrshp 87; Presdntl Acadc Ftns Awd 87; St Joseph U; Pre-Med.

GRAFF, DOUGLAS; Northwestern SR HS; Albion, PA; (2); 15/168; Exploring; High Hon Roll; Hon Roll; NHS; JR Firemn Yr 86; Pre-Med.

GRAFFIUS, ROBERT; Exeter Township HS; Reading, PA; (4); 16/220; Varsity Clb; Pres Soph Cls; Pres Jr Cls; Off Sr Cls; Capt Var Crs Cntry; Var Trk; Hon Roll; Jr NHS; NHS; Amer Lgn Awd 84; Berks All-Star Cross Cntry 83, 85 & 86 & Country Champ 86; Homecmng Ct 86.

GRAFT, RACHELLE MARIE; Connellsville SR HS; Connellsville, PA; (3); 116/500; GAA; Chorus; Bsktbl; Trk; NHS; Crmnlgy.

GRAFTON, RYAN; Freeport SR HS; Freeport, PA; (2); Church Yth Grp; Chorus; Church Choir; School Musical; JV Ftbl; High Hon Roll; Hon Roll; Bible Mnstry.

GRAFTON, SONJA; Kittanning SR HS; Worthington, PA; (3); Hosp Aide; Pep Clb; SADD; Sftbl; High Hon Roll; Hon Roll; NHS; RN.

GRAHAM, AARON; Butler Area SR HS; Renfrew, PA; (3); Aud/Vis; Church Yth Grp; Computer Clb; Rep Frsh Cls; Hon Roll; Pilot.

GRAHAM, AMANDA; Council Rock HS; New Hope, PA; (2); GAA; Rep Stu Cncl; JV Fld Hcky; JV Socr; Hon Roll; Lang.

GRAHAM, AMY; Juniata HS; Mifflintown, PA; (3); French Clb; FHA; SADD; Varsity Clb; Band; Drm Mjr(t); Mrchg Band; Stage Crew; Nwsp Rptr; Nwsp Sprt Ed; Acad Of Med Arts; Med Asst.

GRAHAM, ANITA; North Clarion HS; Tionesta, PA; (3); Girl Scts; Trk; Prfct Atten Awd; Clarion U.

GRAHAM, ANTONY; West Scranton HS; Dupont, PA; (4); Computer Clb; French Clb; Band; Concert Band; Jazz Band; Mrchg Band; Orch; Pep Band; Hon Roll; Nuclear Pwr Schl Orlando; Phycs.

GRAHAM, BRADLEY; Oil City HS; Oil City, PA; (3); 30/215; Camera Clb; Political Wkr; Sec Sr Cls; Rep Stu Cncl; Var Ftbl; Var Trk; Hon Roll; Prfct Atten Awd; Elec Engr.

GRAHAM, CHERI; Punxsutawney Area HS; Oliverburg, PA; (4); 10/249; VP Band; Yrbk Stf; Trs Sr Cls; Rep Stu Cncl; Trk; Elks Awd; NHS; Ntl Merit SF; Exploring; French Clb; James V Colonna Band Awd 87; Art Awd 87; Mary Ann Irving Memrl Schlrshp 87; Clarion U Of PA; Medcl Tech.

GRAHAM, JOANNA; Vincentian HS; Pittsburgh, PA; (4); 5/58; Drama Clb; JA; School Play; Stage Crew; Yrbk Stf; JV Bsktbl; Sec VP NHS; Prfct Atten Awd; Wrtrs Hnr Soc 84-85; Schlrshp-La Rche Coll; La Roche Coll; Intrior Dsgn.

GRAHAM, JODY; Elizabeth-Forward HS; Monongahela, PA; (4); Girl Scts; JA; Library Aide; Office Aide; SADD; Band; Concert Band; Mrchg Band; Bsktbl; Score Keeper; Rainbow 85-86; Alleghany CC; Bus Admin.

GRAHAM, KIM; Plum SR HS; Pittsburgh, PA; (3); DECA; Library Aide; Pep Clb; SADD; Color Guard; Allegney Cnty CC; Bus.

GRAHAM, KRISTEN; Crestwood HS; Wapwallopen, PA; (4); FBLA; Mu Alpha Theta; Ski Clb; Rep Stu Cncl; Var L Cheerleading; Var L Trk; NHS; PTSA 3rd VA & Stu Body Rep 86-87; HS Brd Of Educ Awd 87; Pres Acadc Ftns Awd 87; La Salle U; Acctng.

GRAHAM, SONYA L; Norristown Area HS; Norristown, PA; (4); 25/416; Church Yth Grp; Computer Clb; Dance Clb; FBLA; ROTC; Chorus; Drill Tm; Sftbl; Cit Awd; Hon Roll; Computer Maxwell Inst; Wrd Prsr.

GRAHAM, STACY; Chartiers Valley HS; Bridgeville, PA; (3); Church Yth Grp; Civic Clb; Pep Clb; SADD; School Play; Variety Show; Nwsp Rptr; Nwsp Stf; Shasda 87.

GRAHAM, SUZANNE ELIZABETH; Strath Haven HS; Wallingford, PA; (3); Church Yth Grp; FCA; Var Bsktbl; Var Fld Hcky; Var Lcrss; Hon Roll; Rotary Awd; Cmpr Of Wk-Schlrshp 86; Kystn Grls Hcky Tm; Mnstry.

GRAHAM, TIMOTHY; William Allen HS; Allentown, PA; (3); 270/625; Boy Scts; Computer Clb; Exploring; Letterman Clb; Chorus; Orch; Rep Stu Cncl; Var L Crs Cntry; JV Ftbl; Var L Trk; Comp Sci.

GRAHAM, VALERIE; Riverside HS; Fombell, PA; (3); #11 In Class; Church Yth Grp; Chorus; Church Choir; Nwsp Rptr; Nwsrprtng Awd 85-86; Hstry Awd 84-85; Hlth Awd 86-87; CA U Of PA; Brdcstng.

GRAHAM, WANDA; West Forest JR-SR HS; Tionesta, PA; (3); 1/45; Pres Stu Cncl; Capt L Bsktbl; Var L Sftbl; L Vllybl; Hon Roll; NHS; VP Frsh Cls; Rep Soph Cls; Rep Jr Cls; Pres Acad Fita Wd Cert 85-87; Cert Hgh Lvls Achvt Math Soc Sci & Sci 87; Envrmntl Ed Comp Cert 85-87; WVU; Mar Biol.

GRAHE, JULIE ANN; West York HS; York, PA; (4); 4/195; Sec Trs Church Yth Grp; Pres Sec German Clb; SADD; Teachers Aide; Cit Awd; High Hon Roll; NHS; Prfct Atten Awd; Pres Schlr; Stu Mon/Rtry Intl 87; Stu Mon/Exchng Club 87; Wilson Coll; Vet.

GRAHOR, JOSEPH; North Catholic HS; Pittsburgh, PA; (3); 1/289; Art Clb; Church Yth Grp; Ski Clb; Spanish Clb; Stage Crew; Hon Roll; NHS; Ntl Merit Ltr.

GRAJEWSKI, JOANNE; Northwest Area HS; Shickshinny, PA; (3); 4/111; Computer Clb; Var L Fld Hcky; Var L Trk; High Hon Roll; NHS; Law.

GRAJEWSKI, MARK; Shenandoah Valley HS; Shenandoah, PA; (3); 22/79; High Hon Roll; Hon Roll; Penn ST; Phys Ther.

GRAMLICH, KRISTINE; Bishop Mccort HS; Johnstown, PA; (3); 1/155; German Clb; Math Tm; Mu Alpha Theta; Speech Tm; Chorus; Yrbk Stf; High Hon Roll; NHS; Ntl Merit Ltr; Rookie Of Yr Chemistry 86; Economics.

GRAMMES, JILL; Saucon Valley SR HS; Hellertown, PA; (1); 20/142; Dance Clb; Chorus; School Musical; Rep Stu Cncl; Capt Cheerleading; High Hon Roll; Hon Roll; Jr NHS; Pres Acad Ftns Awd 87; J Hpkns Med Schl; Pdtrcs.

GRANADOS, CHRISTINE; Central Catholic HS; Reading, PA; (3); 6/117; Scholastic Bowl; School Play; Stage Crew; Pres Jr Cls; Sec Sr Cls; Var Bsktbl; Trs NHS; Prfct Atten Awd; Office Aide; Spanish Clb; Spnsh II Achvt Awd 86; Spnsh III Achvt Awd 87; Comm.

GRANAN, ANDREW W; Lansdale Catholic HS; Perkasie, PA; (4); 4/218; Computer Clb; Exploring; Math Tm; Science Clb; High Hon Roll; NHS; Ntl Merit SF; Maxima Cum Laude Natl Latin Exmntn 86; Physics.

GRANDE, CYNTHIA; Dunmore HS; Dunmore, PA; (3); French Clb; Letterman Clb; Spanish Clb; Yrbk Stf; Co-Capt Pom Pon; Var Sftbl; Fshn Rtlng.

GRANDE, DAVID; Kennedy Christian HS; Farrell, PA; (3); 7/97; Church Yth Grp; Spanish Clb; Concert Band; Jazz Band; Mrchg Band; Pres Sr Cls; Rep Stu Cncl; Bsktbl; High Hon Roll; Science Clb; Ottaway Nwspr Schlrshp 87; Mercyhurst; Bus Mgmt.

GRANDERSON, KENNETH; Central HS; Philadelphia, PA; (3); Church Yth Grp; Computer Clb; Library Aide; Church Choir; Ftbl; Var Trk; Hon Roll; Alcolyte; U Of Pittsburgh; Arch.

GRANEY, SUZANNE; Red Land HS; Etters, PA; (4); 23/257; SADD; Madrigals; School Musical; School Play; Nwsp Ed-Chief; Ed Yrbk Stf; Rep Stu Cncl; Church Yth Grp; Debate Tm; French Clb; HOBY 85; Newbrry PTO Schlrshp, & Patriot Nws Mst Vlbl Nwspaper Stff Awd 87; Shippensburg U; Jrnlsm.

GRANIGAN, MINDY; Baldwin HS; Pittsburgh, PA; (3); Boy Scts; Church Yth Grp; Drama Clb; French Clb; Band; Concert Band; Mrchg Band; Stu Cncl; Score Keeper; Hon Roll; Ed.

GRANKAUSKAS, KEITH; Montour HS; Mckees Rocks, PA; (2); Church Yth Grp; SADD; Teachers Aide; JV Bowling; Hon Roll; VFW Awd; Art Inst Of Pittsburgh; Art.

GRANNAS, CHRISTINE; Bellwood-Antis HS; Bellwood, PA; (4); 23/115; FBLA; JA; Key Clb; Chorus; Church Choir; Capt Color Guard; Nwsp Rptr; Stat Bsktbl; High Hon Roll; Hon Roll; Safety Rep Awd Altoona Vo-Tech 86-87.

GRANT, CAMERON; Chichester SR HS; Boothwyn, PA; (3); Art Clb; JV Var Ftbl; Wt Lftg; Ftbl.

GRANT, CARRIE ANN; Solanco HS; Oxford, PA; (3); Computer Clb; Dance Clb; French Clb; Hosp Aide; Library Aide; Office Aide; SADD; Band; Chorus; Concert Band; Phys Thrpy.

GRANT, CHRISTOPHER; Frankford HS; Philadelphia, PA; (3); Acpl Chr; Chorus; Variety Show; Crs Cntry; Timer; Trk; Engrng.

GRANT, DANA; East Allegheny HS; North Versailles, PA; (2); Trs French Clb; VP JA; Ski Clb; Band; Color Guard; Concert Band; Jazz Band; Yrbk Bus Mgr; Yrbk Stf; NHS; Psych.

GRANT, DANIEL; Pocono Mountain HS; Pocono Pines, PA; (4); 25/330; Var Capt Ftbl; Var Tennis; Var Capt Wrstlng; Hon Roll; Hnbl Mntn All Lg Ftbl 85-86; Hnbl Mntn Dfns Ftbl 86-87; Bio.

GRANT, JENNIFER; Ambridge Area HS; Sewickley, PA; (4); 20/265; Girl Scts; Pep Clb; Red Cross Aide; Band; Concert Band; Mrchg Band; Pep Band; Symp Band; Soph Cls; Jr Cls; Pres Ftnss Awd 87; Schlrshp Ambridge Area Wlvs Clb Den 3 87; Natl Hnr Soc 87; Robert Morris Coll; Bus Admin.

GRANT, JODY; Riverside HS; Ellwood City, PA; (3); Church Yth Grp; Library Aide; Office Aide; Spanish Clb; Acpl Chr; Chorus; Concert Band; Jazz Band; School Musical; School Play; Geneva; Music.

GRANT, KIA; Saul Ag Sci HS; Philadelphia, PA; (3); 10/168; Computer Clb; English Clb; FFA; FTA; Math Tm; NAACP; Spanish Clb; Orch; Rep Jr Cls; Cit Awd; GPB Ctznshp Awd 86; Cmnty Svc Awd 87; Ldrshp Awd AFNA 87; Georgetown U; Psych.

GRANT, KIRSTEN; Tunkhannock HS; Tunkhannock, PA; (2); 42/330; Var Fld Hcky; JV Sftbl; Var Swmmng; Hon Roll.

GRANT, MICHELLE; Olney HS; Philadelphia, PA; (4); 125/620; Pep Clb; Teachers Aide; Color Guard; Rep Sr Cls; Capt Var Bsktbl; Hon Roll; Prfct Atten Awd; Mc Donalds Double Dutch Leag Schlrshp 84-86; Temple; Mktng.

GRASS, SEAN; New Castle SR HS; New Castle, PA; (2); #1 In Class; Speech Tm; Im Vllybl; High Hon Roll; 1st Awd PA JR Acad Sci 87; Engl.

GRASSELL, JULIE; Greater Latrobe SR HS; Latrobe, PA; (4); 8/417; German Clb; Hosp Aide; Band; Concert Band; Mrchg Band; Symp Band; Trk; High Hon Roll; NHS; U Pittsburgh; Phys Thrpy.

GRASSI, ANTHONY; Tyrone Area HS; Tyrone, PA; (3); 43/209; Varsity Clb; Stage Crew; Rep Stu Cncl; JV Var Ftbl; JV Var Trk; JV Var Wt Lftg; Hon Roll; Penn ST; Elctrnc Engrng.

GRASSI, TONY; Tyrone Area HS; Tyrone, PA; (3); 42/209; Varsity Clb; Stage Crew; Rep Stu Cncl; Var Ftbl; Var Trk; Hon Roll; Elec Engrng.

GRASSO, MICHAEL; St John Neumann HS; Philadelphia, PA; (3); 27/349; Rep Soph Cls; Rep Jr Cls; Hon Roll; NHS.

GRASSO, PHILIP; St Josephs Preparatory Schl; Cherry Hill, NJ; (4); 10/225; Boy Scts; Camera Clb; Chess Clb; Church Yth Grp; Library Aide; Yrbk Ed-Chief; Bowling; High Hon Roll; NHS; Ntl Merit SF.

GRASSO, TAMMY; Downingtown SR HS; Downingtown, PA; (3); 56/648; Drama Clb; French Clb; SADD; Teachers Aide; Chorus; School Musical; Nwsp Ed-Chief; Nwsp Stf; Hon Roll; NHS; Jornlsm.

GRASTY, TAMMY; Chester HS; Chester, PA; (3); Hosp Aide; Teachers Aide; Chorus; Church Choir; School Play; Trk; Church Yth Grp; Widener U; Bus Admin.

GRATES, TRACY; Highlands SR HS; Tarentum, PA; (3); Exploring; JA; Letterman Clb; Office Aide; Rep Stu Cncl; Sftbl; High Hon Roll; Jr NHS; NHS; Pres Schlr; Math.

GRATKOWSKI, LEANE; Steelton-Highspire HS; Highspire, PA; (3); 13/102; Varsity Clb; Var Bsktbl; High Hon Roll; Hon Roll.

GRATTI, GEORGE; Shamokin Area HS; Shamokin, PA; (2); Aud/Vis; Camera Clb; Civic Clb; Cmnty Wkr; SADD; Band; Concert Band; Mrchg Band; Pep Band; Crs Cntry.

GRATTON, HOLLY; Plum SR HS; Pittsburgh, PA; (3); Sec Trs Church Yth Grp; DECA; Drama Clb; FTA; JA; Pep Clb; SADD; Drill Tm; Cit Awd; Hon Roll; Penn ST.

GRATZINGER, GREG; Southmoreland SR HS; Mtpleasant, PA; (4); JCL; Latin Clb; Letterman Clb; Pres Soph Cls; Bsbl; Bsktbl; Ftbl; Trk; Wt Lftg; Bus Mgmt.

GRAUERT, CHRISTOPHER; Exeter Twp SR HS; Reading, PA; (3); 13/241; Math Tm; Rep Jr Cls; Ftbl; Socr; Wrstlng; Hon Roll; Jr NHS; NHS; Engrng.

GRAUSAM, CHRISTINE; Bishop O Hara HS; Dunmore, PA; (2); Art Clb; Drama Clb; Latin Clb; Ski Clb; School Play; JV Bsktbl; Pro Life Clb; Pro Life Cnvntn 86; Pro Life March 86; Lay Ministry Church Lector; Harvard; Med.

GRAUSGRUBER, JASON; Susquehanna Comm HS; Susquehanna, PA; (3); Aud/Vis; Church Yth Grp; Computer Clb; Debate Tm; JA; Math Clb; Math Tm; Science Clb; Ski Clb; SADD; US Achvt Acad 84; Penn ST; Engr.

GRAUVOGEL, MICHELE; Engineering-Science HS; Philadelphia, PA; (3); Varsity Clb; Sftbl; Hon Roll; NHS; FL Inst Tech; Space Sci.

GRAVELY, SHAWNE; W Philadelphia HS; Phila, PA; (3); Cmnty Wkr; Teachers Aide; Nwsp Stf; Cit Awd; High Hon Roll; Hon Roll; White-Williams Fndtn Schlrshp 87; Exctv Secy.

GRAVER, PATRICK; Solanco HS; Oxford, PA; (3); 38/277; Varsity Clb; Var L Bsktbl; Var L Socr; Hon Roll; Acctnt.

GRAVES, BRIAN; Northwestern HS; Albion, PA; (3); Rep Jr Cls; Crs Cntry; Trk; Hon Roll; Prfct Atten Awd; 1st Tm All County Cross Country 86; U Of PA-EDINBORO; Bus Mgmt.

GRAVES, CEBRA; Quaker Valley HS; Sewickley, PA; (2); Debate Tm; Drama Clb; Key Clb; Chorus; School Musical; School Play; JV Socr; L Trk; High Hon Roll; Acting.

GRAVES, CLIFFORD S; Northern Potter HS; Ulysses, PA; (4); 14/74; Math Tm; Ski Clb; Score Keeper; High Hon Roll; NHS; Ntl Merit Ltr; Pres Schlr; Natl Bus Educ Awd 87; Clarkson U; Accntng.

GRAVES, ERIC; Conestoga SR HS; Devon, PA; (2); Camera Clb; French Clb; German Clb; Math Clb; Math Tm; Orch; Yrbk Bus Mgr; Yrbk Stf; High Hon Roll; Hon Roll; Prsdntl Acdmc Fitnes Awd 86.

GRAVES, KATHLEEN; Oho-Eldred JR-SR HS; Eldred, PA; (4); 1/74; Dance Clb; Varsity Clb; Chorus; Nwsp Stf; Var L Cheerleading; Var L Trk; High Hon Roll; NHS; Ntl Merit Ltr; Val; Harrington Acadmc Achvt Awd, Amrcn Lgn Awd 87; PA Schl Brds Assn Repr 86; IUP; Accntng.

GRAVES, KENTON; Williamson JR SR HS; Millerton, PA; (2); Boy Scts; Computer Clb; Spanish Clb; L Var Trk; L Var Wrstlng; High Hon Roll; Jr NHS; NHS; Prfct Atten Awd; Im Socr; Pres Acdmc Fit Awds Prg 84-85; Order Of Arrows Boy Scouts; Penn ST; Electrncs.

GRAVES, KIMBERLY MOORE; Northwestern HS; Lake City, PA; (3); Pep Clb; SADD; Band; Concert Band; Drill Tm; Mrchg Band; Stage Crew; Im Bsktbl; JV Cheerleading; JV Pom Pon; Elem Ed.

GRAVINESE, JILL; Plymouth-Whitemarsh HS; Conshohocken, PA; (3); Dance Clb; Off Jr Cls; Cheerleading; Pom Pon; Powder Puff Ftbl; Sftbl; Jr NHS; NHS; Villanova U; Accntng.

GRAY, BARBARA; Bellefonte HS; Bellefonte, PA; (3); Spanish Clb; Varsity Clb; Band; Concert Band; Jazz Band; Mrchg Band; Yrbk Phtg; JV Bsktbl; Var L Crs Cntry; Var L Trk; Hnrs Band Britain Tour, All Eastern Band 87; Army; Music.

GRAY, CINDY; Du Bois Area HS; Dubois, PA; (3); Trk; Du Bois Bus Coll; Prof Bus.

GRAY, CURTIS; Homer-Center HS; Indiana, PA; (3).

GRAY, DANIKA; Kennedy Christian HS; Mercer, PA; (3); 44/97; Varsity Clb; Band; Concert Band; Jazz Band; Mrchg Band; Pep Band; School Musical; Nwsp Rptr; Nwsp Stf; Yrbk Sprt Ed; Crss Cntry ST & Dist 10 86; Mercer Co Chmpnshp 86; Edinboro U; Intr Dsgn.

GRAY, DAVE; Charleroi Area JR SR HS; Charleroi, PA; (3); Sec Ski Clb; Spanish Clb; SADD; Im Bsktbl; High Hon Roll; Hon Roll; NHS; PA ST; Engrng.

GRAY, JEFF; Northern Lebanon JR SR HS; Jonestown, PA; (3); 3/213; Am Leg Boys St; Boy Scts; Church Yth Grp; Quiz Bowl; Ski Clb; School Play; Var L Ftbl; Wt Lftg; High Hon Roll; NHS; AFROTC; Aerospc Engnrng.

GRAY, JODY; Butler SR HS; Butler, PA; (2); Hon Roll; Phrmcy.

GRAY, JOSH; Danville SR HS; Danville, PA; (1); Bsbl; Wrstlng; 3rd Pl 9th Grade Winner Annual Sci Fair 87; Outstanding 9th Gr Wrestler 87; All Star Team Bsbll 87; Law.

GRAY, KELLY; Ligonier Valley SR HS; Ligonier, PA; (3); 5/154; Am Leg Aux Girls St; Art Clb; Rep Stu Cncl; JV L Bsktbl; Var L Trk; High Hon Roll; Jr NHS; NHS; Pres Natl Art Honor Soc 86-88; Pres Youth Group; Stu Council Ldrshp Awd 85.

GRAY, LARRY S; West Catholic HS For Boys; Philadelphia, PA; (3); 67/248; Chess Clb; Library Aide; Pep Clb; Red Cross Aide; Teachers Aide; High Hon Roll; Hon Roll; Drexel U; Elec Engr.

GRAY, LAURA; Governor Mifflin HS; Shillington, PA; (3); 68/326; Exploring; Hosp Aide; JA; Spanish Clb; Chorus; Color Guard; School Play; Hon Roll; Gov Mifflin Jr High Hnr Soc 83-84; Volunteer Easter Seal Soc 87; Emory U; Elem Educ.

GRAY, LAVAN; Chambersburg SR HS; Chambersburg, PA; (3); 50/650; AFS; Pep Clb; Ski Clb; Spanish Clb; Stu Cncl; Stu Cncl; Hon Roll; Pharmacist.

GRAY, LESLIE; Hopewell SR HS; Aliquippa, PA; (4); 15/250; Trs Church Yth Grp; German Clb; Hosp Aide; Chorus; Drill Tm; Rep Frsh Cls; Rep Soph Cls; Rep Jr Cls; Rep Sr Cls; High Hon Roll; Grove City Coll; Intl Bus.

GRAY, LUCINDA M; Moon SR HS; Coraopolis, PA; (3); German Clb; JA; Prfct Atten Awd; Robert Morris Coll; Bus Admin.

GRAY, MARLA L; Susquehanna HS; Harrisburg, PA; (4); 51/154; Sec AFS; Drama Clb; PAVAS; Chorus; Color Guard; School Musical; School Play; Capt Cheerleading; Twrlr; Hon Roll; YMCA Yth Of Yr 85-86; Outstndg Acad Achvr 85-86; IN U PA; Psych.

GRAY, MELISSA; Warren Area HS; Warren, PA; (3); Church Yth Grp; Cmnty Wkr; Hosp Aide; Spanish Clb; Chorus; Color Guard; Mrchg Band; School Play; High Hon Roll; Hon Roll; Silver B 85.

GRAY, MICHAEL; Devon Prep Schl; Newtown Sq, PA; (3); Chess Clb; Sec Stu Cncl; Var Bsbl; JV Bsktbl; Hon Roll; Spnsh Bk Awd 85; Sprng Dnc Co-Chrman 86; JR Cls Rng Cermny Spkr 87; Bus Admin.

GRAY, ROBERT F; Center Area HS; Monaca, PA; (2); Computer Clb; Latin Clb; Hon Roll; Latn Magna Cum Laude Awd 86-87; Aerontcl Engrng.

GRAY, SARA; Cumberland Valley HS; Mechanicsburg, PA; (3); 5/578; Church Yth Grp; German Clb; Model UN; Quiz Bowl; Speech Tm; Off Orch; Var L Bsktbl; Hon Roll; NHS; Ntl Merit Ltr; Keystone ST Games Regn III Soccr Tm 85 & 86; Exch Stu Switzerland Rotary Intl 87-88; William & Mary; Pol Sci.

GRAY, STACY; South Western HS; Hanover, PA; (2); Girl Scts; Fld Hcky; Honor Roll 86-87; Social Worker.

GRAY, TERRI; Coudersport JR SR HS; Coudersport, PA; (3); Hosp Aide; Pep Clb; Band; Chorus; Concert Band; Flag Corp; Mrchg Band; Yrbk Stf; Cheerleading; Vllybl; US Army; Mltry Police.

GRAY, THOMAS A; Williamsport Area HS; Williamsport, PA; (4); Var L Wrstlng; Hon Roll; Rotary Awd; Wrstlng Club Awd 86-87; E Dennis Slattery Schlrshp 86-87; U Of Pittsburgh; Bio Sci.

GRAY, TRACY; Connellsville SR HS; Vanderbilt, PA; (3); Pep Clb; SADD; Chorus; Mgr(s); Hon Roll; Penn ST Fayette; Chld Care.

GRAYBEAL, LISA; Solanco HS; Peach Bottom, PA; (2); Spanish Clb; Nwsp Rptr; Stat Bsktbl; Cheerleading; Score Keeper; Cit Awd; Prncpls Awd For Engl 87; Amer Soc For Micro Bio 1st Pl 85; Stu Of The Mrkng Period For Engl 87; Duke U; Bus.

GRAYBILL, BRENT; Dover Area HS; Dover, PA; (4); Socr; Wt Lftg; Wrstlng; Hon Roll; NHS; Prfct Atten Awd; P Billy Webb Wrstlng/Acadmc Excllnc Awd 86; Shippensburg U; Bio.

GRAYBILL, CHAD; Dover Area SR HS; Dover, PA; (3); Aud/Vis; Church Yth Grp; Computer Clb; German Clb; Stage Crew; Lit Mag; Jrnlsm.

GRAYBILL, MIKE; Lampeter Strausburg HS; Ronks, PA; (3); 38/160; Chess Clb; Church Yth Grp; Varsity Clb; School Musical; School Play; Pres Frsh Cls; Bsktbl; Ftbl; Wt Lftg; Scl Sci.

GRAYBILL, RACHEL; Exeter Township SR HS; Reading, PA; (4); Speech Tm; Varsity Clb; Off Stu Cncl; Var Capt Crs Cntry; Var Capt Trk; Hon Roll; Drama Clb; GAA; Y-Teens; Band; MVP Awd Berk Cnty Coaches 86-87; Awd Bers Cnty Bnk 87; Schlrshp U Hawaii 87-88; U Hawaii At Mandor; Psychology.

GRAZIANO, LEONARD; Devon Prep Schl; Buckingham, PA; (3); 10/43; Band; Chorus; Pres Frsh Cls; JV Bsktbl; Var L Tennis; High Hon Roll; Hon Roll; NHS; Engl Excel 84-85; Spnsh Excel 85-86; Tnns Coaches Awd 85-87; Cmnctns.

GRAZIANO, MARI JO; Old Forge HS; Old Forge, PA; (3); 32/130; Ski Clb; Spanish Clb; JV Var Bsktbl; Var Crs Cntry; JV Var Sftbl; Hon Roll; NHS; Bio Awd 84; Nrsng.

GRAZIANO, NICOLE; Cardinal Brenna HS; Frackville, PA; (3); 12/58; Office Aide; Nwsp Ed-Chief; Yrbk Rptr; Yrbk Stf; Jr Cls; Sec Sr Cls; JV Var Bsktbl; Hon Roll; NHS; Bloomsburg U; Erly Chldhd Ed.

GRAZNAK, JANIS; Mapletown JR SR HS; Greensboro, PA; (3); 4/75; GAA; Band; Concert Band; Mrchg Band; School Play; Stat Bsktbl; Im Vllybl; High Hon Roll; Hon Roll; Sec NHS; Cmmnctns.

GREAGER, KIM; Ridley SR HS; Ridley Pk, PA; (3); 131/423; FBLA; Teachers Aide; Band; Chorus; Concert Band; Jazz Band; Mrchg Band; Yrbk Stf; Hon Roll; 5th FBLA Regnls Comp 87; Bus.

GREALY, STEPHANIE M; Council Rock HS; Newtown, PA; (3); 177/960; Intnl Clb; Spanish Clb; Rep Soph Cls; Rep Jr Cls; Stu Cncl; Var Cheerleading; Im Vllybl; Hon Roll; IU Stu Forum Intermediate Unit Rep 86-87; Chrmn Prom Committee 86-87; Advrtsng.

GREASER, SHAWN; Hollidaysburg Area SR HS; Hollidaysburg, PA; (3); 11/385; Ski Clb; Chorus; Tennis; Trk; High Hon Roll; Hon Roll.

GREAVES, SONDRA; Tunkhannock Area HS; Tunkhannock, PA; (1); German Clb; VP Frsh Cls; VP Soph Cls; Stu Cncl; Var Cheerleading; Var Crs Cntry; Var Trk; Hon Roll; Law.

GREBINOSKI, ELIZABETH; North Catholic HS; Pittsburgh, PA; (4); 24/244; Yrbk Stf; Rep Stu Cncl; Var Bsktbl; Var Sftbl; NHS; Pep Clb; Chorus; School Musical; Var Cheerleading; High Hon Roll; Edinboro U Of PA; Scndry Ed.

GREBONISKI, MELISSA; Coughlin HS; Plains, PA; (4); Church Yth Grp; Hosp Aide; Ski Clb; SADD; Stat Bsbl; Var Capt Bsktbl; Cheerleading; High Hon Roll; Hon Roll; NHS; Penn ST U; Med.

GRECO, CATHERINE; Bishop Neumann HS; Williamsport, PA; (3); Church Yth Grp; Cmnty Wkr; Drama Clb; FBLA; SADD; Chorus; School Musical; School Play; Variety Show; Hon Roll; Cmmntns Advt.

GRECO, ELIZABETH; Ringgold HS; Donora, PA; (3); Pres Church Yth Grp; Intnl Clb; Office Aide; Spanish Clb; Nwsp Stf; Accntng.

GRECO JR, FRANK; Penn Hills HS; Verona, PA; (3); JV Var Bsktbl; Var Vllybl; High Hon Roll; Hon Roll; Arch.

GRECO, JOHN; M Ringgold HS; Donora, PA; (3); Church Yth Grp; Rep Frsh Cls; Rep Stu Cncl; Im Mgr Ftbl; High Hon Roll; Hon Roll; Post Gazette Outstndng Carrier 86; CA U; Acctg.

GRECO, JONATHAN; St John Neumann HS; Philadelphia, PA; (2); 62/351; Bsktbl; Hon Roll; Villanova.

GRECO, MARGARETTA; Upper Darby HS; Clifton Hts, PA; (3); Office Aide; Chorus; Hon Roll; Nuclear Med.

GRECO, TAMMIE; Ringgold HS; Donora, PA; (2); FNA; Spanish Clb; High Hon Roll; Pres Church Yth Grp; Teachers Aide; Acpl Chr; Church Choir; Cit Awd; Jr NHS; Math Sci Hnr Scty 85-87; Nrsng.

GREECH, JIMMY; West Hazleton HS; W Hazleton, PA; (3); 72/225; Am Leg Boys St; Exploring; JV Bsktbl; JV Ftbl; PA ST U; Military.

GREEN, ANNMARIE; Northern Le High HS; Slatington, PA; (3); 51/166; Var Fld Hcky; High Hon Roll; Hon Roll; Hlth Care.

GREEN, BRIAN; Sharon HS; Sharon, PA; (3); Computer Clb; Math Tm; Spanish Clb; Yrbk Stf; JV Bsbl; JV Var Bsktbl; JV Var Ftbl; JV Socr; Wt Lftg; High Hon Roll; Calculus Recognition Awd 87; 2 Yr Acdmc Letter Pin 87; Eng Festival Creative Writing Awd 86; Electrical Engrng.

GREEN, CAROLINE; Northampton SR HS; Northampton, PA; (3); 105/494; German Clb; Ski Clb; Chorus; Yrbk Stf; Trs Soph Cls; Stu Cncl; Stat Bsktbl; Var Tennis; Hon Roll; Journlsm.

GREEN, CATHY; Springdale HS; Springdale, PA; (3); Church Yth Grp; GAA; JA; Library Aide; Office Aide; SADD; Acpl Chr; Chorus; Church Choir; Yrbk Sprt Ed; Outstndng Ctznshp Act 85-86.

GREEN, DIANE M; Bishop Mc Devitt HS; Harrisburg, PA; (4); 17/195; Computer Clb; Spanish Clb; Chorus; Church Choir; Var Cheerleading; Var Sftbl; Var Tennis; Hon Roll; NHS; Rotary Awd; Peer Cnslr; PA Coll; Phrmcy.

GREEN, ELISABETH; Elk Lake HS; Montrose, PA; (2); 15/75; Church Yth Grp; 4-H; French Clb; SADD; Band; Church Choir; Mrchg Band; Yrbk Stf; Rep Stu Cncl; Var Bsktbl; Keystone ST Invtl Bsktbl Cmp 87; 2nd Tm All Str Bsktbl 87; Dist XII Bsktbl Champs 86-87; U Of Pittsburgh; Athl Trng.

GREEN, ELIZABETH; Carlisle SR HS; Carlisle, PA; (3); 1/250; Drama Clb; School Play; Pres Frsh Cls; Sec Jr Cls; JV Vllybl; NHS; Ntl Merit Ltr; Sec Rep Pep Clb; Rep Soph Cls; Rep Stu Cncl; Eagl Acadc Awd; Grmn Natl Hnr Soc; Intl Stu Ldrshp Inst-Brd Rgnts; Yale U; Pre-Law.

GREEN, HEIDI; Penn Wood HS; Lansdowne, PA; (4); 4/346; Dance Clb; Sec Drama Clb; Hosp Aide; Orch; School Play; Yrbk Stf; Off Stu Cncl; Mgr(s); NHS; Pres Schlr; Hnrs Yr 82-87; Rotry Intl Schlrshp, William Penn Assn Awd 87; Lycoming Coll; Intl Reltns.

GREEN, JENNA; Seneca Valley SR HS; Evans Cty, PA; (2); 4-H; ROTC; Drill Tm; Nwsp Rptr; Nwsp Stf; High Hon Roll; Hon Roll; Hse Of Rep Citation Awd; ROTC Superior Cadet Awd; Bus Mgmt.

GREEN, JENNIFER; Bishop Conwell HS; Yardley, PA; (3); 3/277; Hosp Aide; Office Aide; Service Clb; SADD; Church Choir; Crs Cntry; Mgr(s); Trk; High Hon Roll; NHS; Hugh O Brien Yth Ldrshp Smnr Ambssdr 86; Alternate Hoby Ambssdr Intl Smnr 86; Natl Roll 84-87; Physical Therapy.

GREEN, JENNIFER; North Pocono HS; Moscow, PA; (3); 3/260; Church Yth Grp; Cmnty Wkr; Political Wkr; Chorus; Color Guard; Variety Show; High Hon Roll; NHS; Var Awd 84-87; Penn ST; Med.

GREEN, JENNIFER; Philadelphis High Schl For Girls; Philadelphia, PA; (3); Political Wkr; Teachers Aide; Var Swmmng; Church Yth Grp; Girl Scts; Hosp Aide; Im Lcrss; Math.

GREEN, JOHANNA; Rocky Grove HS; Franklin, PA; (3); Yrbk Phtg; Stu Cncl; High Hon Roll; Hon Roll; Acdmc Achvt Hnr Awd 84-85; Photo Jrnlsm.

GREEN, JOHN; West Scranton HS; Scranton, PA; (3); Engr.

GREEN, JOSEPH; Shenandoah Valley HS; Shenandoah, PA; (3); 3/79; High Hon Roll; NHS; UCLA; Aerntcs.

GREEN, JOSHUA; Abington SR HS; Rydal, PA; (3); 1/502; Chess Clb; French Clb; Hosp Aide; Chorus; Yrbk Stf; Rep Soph Cls; High Hon Roll; NHS; Ntl Merit Ltr; Outstdng Cls Std 86; Alexander Hamilton Awd 87; St Anatomy Comptn Silver Medal 87; Med.

GREEN, JOSHUA B; Quaker Valley HS; Sewickley, PA; (3); 3/166; Am Leg Boys St; JA; Key Clb; Latin Clb; Math Tm; Spanish Clb; Nwsp Stf; Yrbk Bus Mgr; Yrbk Stf; Lit Mag.

GREEN, JUDY; Gateway SR HS; Monroeville, PA; (3); Acpl Chr; Chorus; High Hon Roll; Phys Ther.

GREEN, LORI; Lehighton Area HS; Lehighton, PA; (3); Church Yth Grp; FBLA; FNA; Hosp Aide; Office Aide; SADD; Teachers Aide; Stage Crew; Score Keeper; Cit Awd; Prjct SPARK 86-87; Sclgy.

GREEN, LORI; Weatherly Area HS; Weatherly, PA; (3); 7/60; Cmnty Wkr; Computer Clb; Library Aide; Spanish Clb; Color Guard; Flag Corp; Mrchg Band; Nwsp Ed-Chief; Nwsp Phtg; Nwsp Rptr; Natl Hnr Rll, Natl Ldrshp Awd 87; Law.

GREEN, MARY ELIZABETH; St Hubert HS; Phkladelphia, PA; (3); 81/421; Pres Camp Fr Inc; Church Yth Grp; Cmnty Wkr; Church Choir; Jazz Band; Orch; School Musical; Hon Roll; Catholic Natl Inst For Training Ldrshp & Svc Awd 86; Music Awd 85-87; Music.

GREEN, PEGGY SUE; Jim Thorpe Area SR HS; Jim Thorpe, PA; (3); VICA; Color Guard; Rep Jr Cls; Var Mgr(s); JV Mat Maids; High Hon Roll; Hon Roll; Fd Preprtn.

GREEN, RAUBIE; Strath Haven HS; Media, PA; (4); Aud/Vis; 4-H; Key Clb; Math Clb; Band; School Play; Stage Crew; Off Soph Cls; Bsktbl; Ftbl; Lincoln Peer Tutrng Awd 85; Millersville U; Acctnt.

GREEN, RHONDA; W Philadelphia Catholic Girls HS; Philadelphia, PA; (4); 19/233; French Clb; Service Clb; Yrbk Rptr; Hon Roll; NHS; Prfct Atten Awd; 2nd Pl Plq-Stngrphy I Cmptn 86; Presdntl Acadc Ftns Awd 87; ST Brd Of Gvrnrs Tutn Schlrshp 87; Clarion U Of PA; Accntng.

GREEN, RICHARD; Central HS; Philadelphia, PA; (3); Nwsp Phtg; Im Bsktbl; Hon Roll; Med.

GREEN, RICHARD; Hempfield HS; Lancaster, PA; (3); 10/450; Ski Clb; Variety Show; High Hon Roll; NHS; Red Crss Lfsvng 85-87; Microbio.

GREEN, RICHARD; Ringgold HS; Monongahela, PA; (2); Boy Scts; Church Yth Grp; French Clb; Var Bsbl; Var Bsktbl; Comm.

GREEN, THERESA; Butler Area HS; Butler, PA; (2); Church Yth Grp; French Clb; GAA; Office Aide; Sftbl; Capt L Vllybl; IUP; Law Enfrcmnt.

GREEN, VALERIE RENEE; Bensalem HS; Bensalem, PA; (2); Church Yth Grp; Rep NAACP; Spanish Clb; Chorus; Rep Soph Cls; JV Capt Cheerleading; Trk; Hon Roll; Prfct Atten Awd; Dance Clb; Spellman Coll; Med.

GREENAWALD, DALE; Montour HS; Coraopolis, PA; (3); L Trk.

GREENAWALT, DALE W; Sharon HS; Sharon, PA; (4); 5/159; Aud/Vis; Math Clb; Pep Clb; Science Clb; JV Ftbl; Gov Hon Prg Awd; High Hon Roll; Hon Roll; Kiwanis Awd; Opt Clb Awd; Acad Schlrshp Youngstown ST U 87; Youngstown ST U; Elec Engr.

GREENAWALT, PAM; Union HS; Sligo, PA; (3); FCA; SADD; Yrbk Stf; Stu Cncl; JV Var Bsktbl; JV Capt Bowling; JV Capt Cheerleading; Trk; Var Vllybl; Hon Roll; Allegheny Coll; Sec Ed.

GREENAWAY, LISA; Norwin SR HS; N Huntingdon, PA; (4); SADD; Stu Cncl; Co-Capt Cheerleading; Powder Puff Ftbl; JC Awd; Lion Awd; NHS; Rotary Awd; Miss Christmas Seal Pgnt 86; IN U; Comm.

GREENBERG, DANA; Allen HS; Allentown, PA; (2); Intnl Clb; Service Clb; Ski Clb; Yrbk Stf; Stu Cncl; Tennis; Hon Roll; Jr NHS; Law.

GREENBERG, JUDI; Lincoln HS; Ellwood, PA; (4); 75/168; Y-Teens; School Musical; Yrbk Ed-Chief; JV Cheerleading; Powder Puff Ftbl; Hon Roll; AFS; Ski Clb; Spanish Clb; Chorus; IN U PA; Fash Merch.

GREENBERG, SCOTT; Council Rock HS; Langhorne, PA; (3); 13/980; Cmnty Wkr; Math Tm; Mu Alpha Theta; Quiz Bowl; Hon Roll; NHS; Prsdntl Clsrm Rnnr Up 86-87; Olympics Mind 84-86; Bus.

GREENBLATT, BENJAMIN; Henderson HS; Paoli, PA; (2); 2/353; Computer Clb; Intnl Clb; Math Tm; Science Clb; Nwsp Stf; Ed Lit Mag; Trk; French Hon Soc; High Hon Roll; Comp Bowl/Energy Ed Advsry Cncl 87; MIT.

GREENDONER, DEBBI; Lock Haven SR HS; Blanchard, PA; (3); Church Yth Grp; Pres FHA; Library Aide; Service Clb; Spanish Clb; Nwsp Stf; L Bsktbl; Twrlr; Hon Roll; Natl Hstry & Govt Awd 87.

GREENDONER, DOREEN; Curwensville Area HS; Curwensville, PA; (3); FBLA; Nwsp Stf; Stu Cncl; Mat Maids; Hon Roll; 5th Regl FBLA Acctg Comp 87; Dubois Bus Coll; Acctg.

GREENE, BARTON; Neshaminy HS; Levittown, PA; (3); 169/768; JV Var Socr; Hon Roll; Prfct Atten Awd; Phys Thrpy.

GREENE, CORI; Bensalem HS; Bensalem, PA; (3); 121/500; Church Yth Grp; Chorus; Sr Cls; Var Bsktbl; Var Sftbl; Hon Roll; Temple; Law.

GREENE, DAYNE S; Westinghouse HS; Pittsburgh, PA; (3); Chess Clb; Cmnty Wkr; NAACP; Teachers Aide; Band; Concert Band; Jazz Band; Mrchg Band; Pep Band; Rep Sr Cls; All Cty Hnr Band Awd 87; Physcs Olympcs Awd 87; Pittsburgh Rep Engrng Pgm Awd 86; Engrng.

GREENE, KATHY; Cedar Crest HS; Lebanon, PA; (2); 49/345; French Clb; Pep Clb; Band; Concert Band; Jazz Band; Orch; Pep Band; Hon Roll; NHS; Mrchg Band; Dist Band 87; Cnty Chmbr Orchstra 87; Cnty Wind Emsmbl 86-87; Music Ed.

GREENE, KELLI; Marion Center HS; Indiana, PA; (3); 12/151; Church Yth Grp; FNA; Hosp Aide; Intnl Clb; Office Aide; Ski Clb; SADD; Band; Concert Band; Mrchg Band; Dist Band 86; Med.

GREENE, KIMBERLY; Jersey Shore HS; Jersey Shore, PA; (4); 118/240; Sec FFA; VICA; Yrbk Stf; Williamsport Area CC; Lndscpng.

GREENE, LEIGH; Central Dauphin HS; Harrisburg, PA; (3); Key Clb; School Musical; School Play; Yrbk Stf; Off Jr Cls; Off Sr Cls; Stat Ftbl; L Var Swmmng; Voice Dem Awd; Dauphin Cnty Seatblt Campgn TV PSA Wnnr 87; Stdnt Authr Accolades HACC Lit Magzn 87; Hood Coll; Cmnctns.

GREENE, MARKISHA; Philadelphia HS For Girls; Philadelphia, PA; (1); Office Aide; Band; Stage Crew; Stat Bsktbl; Hnr Cert Meritorious Schlstc Acvht 86-879; MIT; Computer Engineer.

GREENE, MICHAEL; Central HS; Philadelphia, PA; (4); Church Yth Grp; PA ST; Mech Engr.

GREENE, RICHARD; Quaker Valley SR HS; Fairfield, CT; (3); Key Clb; Science Clb; Spanish Clb; Chorus; VP Frsh Cls; Rep Stu Cncl; Socr; Trk; Wrstlng; Hon Roll; 1st Pl Rgnl Jr Sci Acdmy 87; 1st Pl ST Jr Sci Adcmy 87.

GREENE, TIMOTHY J; Jersey Shore SR HS; Jersey Shore, PA; (3); French Clb; Math Tm; Math Clb; Hon Roll; Math.

GREENEWALD, CHRISSI; Elizabeth Froward SR HS; Elizabeth, PA; (3); French Clb; Hosp Aide; JA; Library Aide; Pep Clb; Hst Jr Cls; Score Keeper; Swmmng; Stat Wrstlng; Hon Roll; Prom Qn 87; Cmmnctns.

GREENFIELD, ALLISON; Hillel Acad; Pittsburgh, PA; (1); Drama Clb; French Clb; Temple Yth Grp; School Play; Rep Stu Cncl; JV Gym; JV Swmmng; Wt Lftg; High Hon Roll; Hon Roll; NYC; Hist.

GREENJACK, ANDREW S; Unionville HS; W Chester, PA; (4); 92/317; Hst FBLA; Thesps; School Play; JV Bsbl; Var Crs Cntry; Var Trk; Hon Roll; Jr NHS; Outstndng Bus Prsn 87; Bus Schlrshp Awd 87; IUP Physics Awd 87; Penn ST U; Engrng.

GREENLEAF, ROBERT; Ringgold HS; Donora, PA; (3); Aud/Vis; Spanish Clb; Varsity Clb; Var Ftbl; Var L Trk; Hon Roll; CA U PA.

GREENLEAF, SARA; Springside Schl; Erdenheim, PA; (3); Church Yth Grp; Yrbk Stf; Lit Mag; JV Socr; JV Sftbl; High Hon Roll; Awd Dstnctn Math 85 & Spnsh 85-87; Educ.

GREENLEE, JOHN; Monongahela Valley Catholic HS; Fredericktown, PA; (3); French Clb; Ski Clb; School Musical; School Play; Pres Soph Cls; Pres Jr Cls; Pres Sr Cls; Golf; French Hon Soc; Hon Roll; Law.

GREENLEE, LAURA; Shalom Christian Academy; Waynesboro, PA; (3); Pres Church Yth Grp; Hosp Aide; Chorus; Nwsp Ed-Chief; Nwsp Stf; Yrbk Stf; High Hon Roll; Eng.

GREENOVER, BILL; Perkiomen Valley HS; Collegeville, PA; (3); Church Yth Grp; JV Tennis; Hon Roll; Sound Rcrdng Tech.

GREENTREE, JENNIFER; Avon Grove HS; Lincoln Univ, PA; (3); Trs FBLA; School Play; Yrbk Stf; Lit Mag; JV Fld Hcky; Hon Roll; Prfct Atten Awd; Villanova U; Crmnl Jstc.

GREER, KELLY; S Fayette HS; Cuddy, PA; (4); 1/71; Key Clb; Chorus; Yrbk Stf; Cheerleading; High Hon Roll; Hon Roll; NHS; Ntl Merit Ltr; Prfct Atten Awd; Val; Wstnghouse Sci Hnrs Inst 86-87; Med.

GREER, LORI; Deer Lakes JR/Sr HS; Valencia, PA; (4); 32/170; Church Yth Grp; Drama Clb; SADD; School Play; Stage Crew; Variety Show; High Hon Roll; Hon Roll; Acadc Achvt Awd 86fegans Hnr Schlrshp 87; Mercyhurst Coll; Psych.

GREGA, BRIAN; Dunmore HS; Dunmore, PA; (4); 30/150; Computer Clb; French Clb; Ski Clb; Y-Teens; Ftbl; U Of Scranton; Accntnt.

GREGG, STACEY; California Area HS; California, PA; (3); 26/123; Drama Clb; Band; Concert Band; Mrchg Band; School Musical; School Play; Stage Crew; Nwsp Rptr; Nwsp Stf; Yrbk Stf; Elizabeth Coll; Occptnl Thrpy.

GREGGS, LISA; Sharpsville Area HS; Sharpsville, PA; (3); Hosp Aide; Chorus; Concert Band; Drill Tm; Mrchg Band; Yrbk Bus Mgr; Hon Roll; NHS; Accntng.

GREGO, FRANK; Blairsville SR HS; Blairsville, PA; (1); Church Yth Grp; Varsity Clb; Band; Concert Band; Mrchg Band; Golf; High Hon Roll; U Pittsburgh; Med.

GREGOIRE, MICHELLE D; Hempfield HS; Landisville, PA; (4); 37/415; Office Aide; Q&S; School Play; Variety Show; Nwsp Ed-Chief; Nwsp Phtg; High Hon Roll; NCTE Awd; NHS; Opt Clb Awd; Millersville U; Englsh.

GREGORCHIK, EDDIE; Bishop Mc Cort HS; Johnstown, PA; (3); Trs Spanish Clb; Chorus; Stage Crew; Var Bsbl; Var Capt Ice Hcky; Var Trk; High Hon Roll; Hon Roll.

GREGOROWICZ, PAULA; John S Fine HS; Nanicoke, PA; (4); 4/251; Nwsp Rptr; Yrbk Stf; Bsktbl; Vllybl; High Hon Roll; NHS; NEDT Awd; Cert JETS Tm Tst 86.

GREGORY, ALLISON; North Star HS; Boswell, PA; (3); 12/144; FCA; Hosp Aide; Mu Alpha Theta; Ski Clb; Rep Stu Cncl; Mgr(s); Hon Roll; UNC.

GREGORY, CHRISTINE; Freeport SR HS; Sarver, PA; (4); 45/163; Church Yth Grp; Band; Mrchg Band; School Musical; Stage Crew; Symp Band; Yrbk Stf; Hon Roll; Drama Clb; Church Choir; Butler Cnty Schlrshp 87; Stage Crew Awd 87; Thiel Coll; Nrsng.

GREGORY, DALE; Jamestown HS; Jamestown, PA; (3); FCA; French Clb; Chorus; Concert Band; Capt Frsh Cls; Var Bsktbl; Var Crs Cntry; Var Trk; Hon Roll; NHS; Cngrssnl Yth Ldrshp Cncl 87; Natl Sci Olympd Qlfr 85; Slippery Rock ST Coll; Archlgy.

GREGORY, DAVID; Quaker Valley HS; Sewickley, PA; (4); Church Yth Grp; Science Clb; Ski Clb; Spanish Clb; Golf; Socr; Tennis; Hon Roll; 1st & 2nd Awds PA Jr Acad Of Sci 85 & 86; U Of Dayton; Bus.

GREGORY, DORTHEA; Laurel Valley HS; New Florence, PA; (3); VP Church Yth Grp; Pres VP Varsity Clb; Band; Chorus; Church Choir; Concert Band; Jazz Band; Mrchg Band; Pep Band; Yrbk Stf; Natnl Hnr Rl 87; Athltc Achvt Awd; Cls MVP Vllybll 85-86; Child Psychology.

GREGORY, JERRY; Oil City HS; Oil City, PA; (4); 17/256; Teachers Aide; High Hon Roll; Lion Awd; Venango Campus.

GREGORY, PATRICIA A; Aliquippa JR SR HS; Aliquippa, PA; (2); Trs Church Yth Grp; Computer Clb; Exploring; French Clb; Band; Concert Band; Jazz Band; Mrchg Band; Yrbk Stf; Sftbl; Psych.

GREIDER, JULIE; Hempfield HS; Columbia, PA; (3); Exploring; 4-H; Chorus; JV Var Bsktbl; JV Var Fld Hcky; Im Vllybl; 4-H Awd; High Hon Roll; NHS; Sci Awd 86; Ms Cngnlty Awd Dairy Prncs Pgnt 87; Alt Dairy Prncs 87; Law.

GREIF, ALYSSA; Hazelton HS; Hazleton, PA; (3); 16/476; FBLA; Service Clb; Ski Clb; Soroptimist; Spanish Clb; Temple Yth Grp; High Hon Roll; Hon Roll; Pres Acadmc Ftnss Awd 85; Bus.

GREIM, APRIL JEAN; Palisades HS; Kintnersville, PA; (4); #2 In Class; Debate Tm; Rep Stu Cncl; Cheerleading; Sftbl; High Hon Roll; Hon Roll; Jr NHS; NHS; Pres Schlr; Sal; Slctd As Yth For Undrstndng Frgn Exchng Stu To The Netherlands 85-86; U Of DE; Intl Rltns.

GREINER, JENNIFER; Catasauqua HS; Catasauqua, PA; (1); 1/160; SADD; Off Stu Cncl; JV Var Bsktbl; JV Fld Hcky; L Trk; Hon Roll.

GREINER, KAREN; Living Word Acad; Leola, PA; (2); Church Yth Grp; Chorus; Yrbk Stf; Var Bsktbl; Var Fld Hcky; Var Trk; Hon Roll; School Musical; Stage Crew; Var Vllybl; Pres Phy Fit Awd 85-86; ACSI Sci Fair Proj 1st 86; Char Hnr Rll 85-86; Bus.

GREINER, THERESA; Bishop Guilfoyle HS; Altoona, PA; (3); Cmnty Wkr; Hosp Aide; Band; Chorus; Mrchg Band; School Musical; Rep Stu Cncl; Hon Roll; Cnty Band 86 & 87; Dist Band 87; Nrsng.

GREISEMER, LORI; Upper Perkiomen HS; East Greenville, PA; (3); 40/266; Church Yth Grp; Drama Clb; Chorus; School Musical; School Play; Yrbk Stf; Var Trk; Hon Roll; Lbrl Arts.

GRELLA, RACHEL; Bishop Mc Devitt HS; Middletown, PA; (4); 3/176; Science Clb; Service Clb; Ski Clb; Band; Chorus; Church Choir; Madrigals; Mrchg Band; High Hon Roll; NHS; Blgy.

GRENCAVICH, RENEE; West Hazleton HS; Conyngham, PA; (3); Church Yth Grp; French Clb; Varsity Clb; Off Stu Cncl; Var L Bsktbl; Sftbl; Trk; Bsktbl-MVP 84-85; Penn ST U; Marine Sci.

GRESCO, BRIAN; Cambria Heights HS; Carrolltown, PA; (3); 29/185; Var Trk; Hon Roll; Engrng.

GRESHKO, CLIFFORD; Hazleton HS; Hazleton, PA; (2); FBLA; Letterman Clb; Spanish Clb; Varsity Clb; Bsbl; Bsktbl; Ftbl; Hon Roll; Pres Schlr; Orthodntst.

GRESHOCK, JENNIFER; Acad Of Notre Dame; Berwyn, PA; (3); Off Church Yth Grp; Math Tm; Pep Clb; SADD; School Musical; Variety Show; Nwsp Rptr; Yrbk Rptr; Lit Mag; VP Jr Cls.

GRESKO, JEANENE; Northern Cambria HS; Barnesboro, PA; (3); 13/152; French Clb; Chorus; Color Guard; Yrbk Stf; Trs Frsh Cls; Stu Cncl; Trk; Vllybl; High Hon Roll; NHS.

GRESKO JR, RONALD J; Saltsburg JR SR HS; Saltsburg, PA; (4); 19/94; FFA; VICA; Chorus; High Hon Roll; Hon Roll; Triangle Tech; Air Condtng.

GRESKO, VERONICA; Saltsburg JR SR HS; Saltsburg, PA; (1); Library Aide; Pep Clb; Spanish Clb; Teachers Aide; Yrbk Stf; High Hon Roll; Hon Roll; NHS; Spanish NHS; Soc Wrkr.

GRESKOVICH, MATTHEW; State College Intermediate HS; State College, PA; (1); Bsktbl; Ftbl; JV Tennis; Pwr Of Paws Awd 87; PA ST; Med.

GRESLICK, KAREN; Curwensville Area HS; Curwensville, PA; (3); Drama Clb; French Clb; Ski Clb; Varsity Clb; Nwsp Rptr; Yrbk Stf; Pres Soph Cls; Var Co-Capt Cheerleading; Hon Roll; NHS; Acad All Amercn 86-87; Psych.

GRESOCK, ROBERT; Du Bois Area SR HS; Sykesville, PA; (3); Church Yth Grp; Varsity Clb; Var L Tennis.

GRETZ, KENDRA; Norwin SR HS; N Huntingdon, PA; (4); 10/557; Sec Church Yth Grp; Pres FBLA; Sec Leo Clb; Office Aide; Pep Clb; High Hon Roll; Hon Roll; NHS; Rotary Awd; Ms Future Bus Ldr Of Amerca 87; Outstndngt Bus Stu Of Yr 85-87; Acad Exclince Shrthand 87; WCCC; Bus Admin.

GREVE, ALAN E; Norristown Area HS; Norristown, PA; (4); 17/427; Key Clb; Band; Jazz Band; Orch; School Musical; Var Bsbl; Var Capt Socr; Hon Roll; Off NHS; Rotary Awd.

GREVE, PHILLIP; Henderson SR HS; West Chester, PA; (3); 9/377; Church Yth Grp; Acpl Chr; Concert Band; Drm Mjr(t); Jazz Band; VP Mrchg Band; School Musical; High Hon Roll; Spanish NHS.

GREVERA, ROBERT; John S Fine HS; Nanticoke, PA; (2); 17/243; Chess Clb; Drama Clb; Spanish Clb; High Hon Roll; NHS; NEDT Awd; Carnegie-Mellon U; Chem Engrg.

GREW, TAMMIE; Shaler Area SR HS; Glenshaw, PA; (3); Dance Clb; Office Aide; Ski Clb; SADD; Varsity Clb; Nwsp Rptr; Rep Frsh Cls; Rep Soph Cls; Im Sftbl; Var L Swmmng; Grove City; Biol.

GREZLAK, JENNI; Pennsbury HS; Morrisville, PA; (3); French Clb; Office Aide; Chorus; Stage Crew; Im Bsktbl; JV Fld Hcky; JV Socr; Im Sftbl; Hon Roll; NHS; Intl Rltns.

GRIBBLE, TONJA; Rockwood Area HS; Somerset, PA; (2); Band; Chorus; Mrchg Band; Nwsp Stf; Pres Frsh Cls; Bsktbl; Sftbl; Vllybl; High Hon Roll; Hon Roll; 1st All Cty Sftbl Tm 85-86; Law.

GRIBSCHAW, WENDY; Elizabeth Forward HS; Mc Keesport, PA; (3); #38 In Class; Jazz Band; VP Sec Mrchg Band; Hon Roll; U Of Pittsburgh; Nurse Ansthtst.

GRICE, CLAYTON; Mount Union Area HS; Mt Union, PA; (3); Letterman Clb; Varsity Clb; Church Choir; Concert Band; Trs Frsh Cls; Trs Soph Cls; VP Jr Cls; Var L Ftbl; Var L Trk; Var Capt Wrstlng; Dist Champ Wrstlng, Trck 86-87; Keystone Game Wrstlng Champ 87; Crimnl Justc.

GRIEB, ELIZABETH; Williamsport Area HS; Cogan Station, PA; (3); Office Aide; Teachers Aide; Y-Teens; Chorus; VP Frsh Cls; JV Var Bsktbl; Im Bowling; Im Sftbl; JV Trk; JR Usher SR Cmmncmnt 87; Peer Helpr 87-88; Law.

GRIEB, VICKI; Lock Haven SR HS; Flemington, PA; (4); 34/243; Church Yth Grp; Computer Clb; Hosp Aide; Keywanettes; VP Sec Library Aide; Spanish Clb; SADD; Drm Mjr(t); Variety Show; Nwsp Stf; Cndystrpng Awd 86; Lock Haven U; Hlth Sci.

GRIEBEL, STEVE; Clarion-Limestone HS; Clarion, PA; (3); 3/85; Varsity Clb; Var Capt Bsktbl; Var L Ftbl; Var L Trk; Hon Roll; NHS; Engr.

GRIEFF, STACEY; Oil City SR HS; Oil City, PA; (3); AFS; Varsity Clb; Color Guard; Drill Tm; Mrchg Band; Trk; Photogrphrs.

GRIEGO, KIMBERLY; John S Fine HS; Glen Lyon, PA; (3); 10/228; Key Clb; Chorus; Church Choir; Color Guard; Flag Corp; High Hon Roll; NHS; Med.

GRIEMSMANN, SONJA; Mountain View HS; Nicholson, PA; (3); Band; Chorus; Concert Band; Mrchg Band; VP Stu Cncl; Hon Roll; Church Yth Grp; Ski Clb; Badmtn; Gym; Presdntl Phys Ftnss Awd 85 & 87; Bus Admin.

GRIER, KRISTIE; Bishop Hafey HS; Hazleton, PA; (3); Key Clb; Spanish Clb; Lit Mag; Stu Cncl; L Trk; High Hon Roll; NHS; Prfct Atten Awd; Spanish NHS; Eng Awd 85; Spnsh Awd 85; Amer Lgn Awd 85; Cmnctns.

GRIESACKER, PAULA; Villa Maria Acad; Erie, PA; (3); CAP; Sec Exploring; Latin Clb; Red Cross Aide; Color Guard; Drill Tm; Nwsp Ed-Chief; Mgr Var Crs Cntry; Var Swmmng; Var Trk; Billy Mitchell Awd Civil Air Patrol 86; Amelia Aerhart Awd 87; Hnr Recr Young Marines Boot Camp 85; Air Force Acad; Elec Engrng.

GRIESSER, MELISSA; Sun Valley HS; Aston, PA; (3); GAA; Spanish Clb; Band; Bsktbl; Coach Actv; Lcrss; Mgr(s); Sftbl; Wt Lftg; Hon Roll; Bus Mgmt.

GRIEST, BRYAN; Butler SR HS; Butler, PA; (3); CAP; Exploring; Library Aide; Teachers Aide; Acdmc Achvt Awd 87; Beaver CC; Pilot.

GRIFFIFTHS, TAMMI; West Scranton HS; Scranton, PA; (3); Girl Scts; Hosp Aide; Ski Clb; Spanish Clb; Chorus; Stat Bsktbl; Stat Sftbl; Stat Swmmng; Stat Tennis; Stat Vllybl; Social Fld.

GRIFFIN, AUDRA; Moniteau HS; Chicora, PA; (3); 6/136; Dance Clb; Band; Drill Tm; Sec Soph Cls; VP L Vllybl; High Hon Roll; NHS; Church Yth Grp; Drama Clb; 3rd Pl Natl Acad Games Propaganda 87; 1st Pl ST Acad Games Equations 87; Hearing Imprd Ed.

GRIFFIN, BRENDA; Carbondale Area JR SR HS; Carbondale, PA; (4); 9/144; Computer Clb; English Clb; French Clb; FBLA; Library Aide; Scholastic Bowl; Science Clb; Yrbk Stf; High Hon Roll; Mansfield U; Scndry Ed.

GRIFFIN, DEBORAH; Bethel Park SR HS; Bethel Park, PA; (4); 71/317; Art Clb; Church Yth Grp; Science Clb; Yrbk Ed-Chief; Hon Roll.

GRIFFIN III, JOSEPH; St Josephs Preparatory HS; Flourtown, PA; (4); Political Wkr; Service Clb; Im Bsktbl; High Hon Roll; NHS; Schlrshp To St Josephs U 87; Gold Medal In French, Silver In Biology 87; Prep Schlr 84-87; Drexel U; Business.

GRIFFIN, MARTIN T; Bishop Egan HS; Bensalem, PA; (3); Am Leg Boys St; Church Yth Grp; Exploring; Socr; Arch.

GRIFFIN, THOMAS; Dallas SR HS; Dallas, PA; (3); Art Clb; Church Yth Grp; Debate Tm; Hon Roll.

GRIFFIN, TODD; Trinity HS; Washington, PA; (4); 10/361; French Clb; L Bsktbl; L Ftbl; L Trk; NHS; All Dist Ftbl 86-87; All Conf Ftbl 85-86; U Of PA; Pre-Law.

GRIFFIS, DANA; Tunkhannock HS; Tunkhannock, PA; (3); Art Clb; French Clb; Letterman Clb; Spanish Clb; Var Swmmng; JV Tennis; Mgr Trk; Cit Awd; Hon Roll; NHS; Natl Frnch Cntst 3rd Pl Tunkhannock 86; Natl Frnch Cntst Cert Of Merit 87; Education.

GRIFFIS, DAYNA C; Tunkhannock HS; Tunkhannock, PA; (3); French Clb; Spanish Clb; Band; Mrchg Band; Var L Mgr(s); Var L Swmmng; Var L Tennis; Var L Trk; Cit Awd; Hon Roll; Le Cncrs Ntl De Frncs 85; Fshn Mrchndsng.

GRIFFIS, STEPHANIE; Tunkhannock Area HS; Tunkhannock, PA; (3); 60/323; Dance Clb; Girl Scts; Chorus; Drill Tm; Mrchg Band; Variety Show; Capt Twrlr; Spanish Clb; Flag Corp; Hon Roll; PA ST Champs-Jr Drill Tm & Pom Pons 87; World Twirling Assn-Sr Show Corps-Natl Champs 85; Teaching.

GRIFFITH, APRYLE L; Greater Latrobe HS; Latrobe, PA; (4); 18/422; Art Clb; Trs Computer Clb; Trs 4-H; German Clb; NHS; Ntl Merit SF; JA; JCL; High Hon Roll; PA Govnrs Schl For The Sci 85; Ntl Art Hnr Sco 86-87; Ntl Rcgntn PA Continental Math League Cont 84; Phrmcy.

GRIFFITH, BILLIE SUE; Charleroi Area JR SR HS; Charleroi, PA; (4); FBLA; Office Aide; Ski Clb; SADD; Nwsp Rptr; Nwsp Stf; Sec Sr Cls; Powder Puff Ftbl; Sftbl; Hon Roll; Hmcmng Ct 86; Prom Ct 87; IN U Of PA; Bus.

GRIFFITH, CAROLINE; Fairview HS; Erie, PA; (3); German Clb; Varsity Clb; Rep Soph Cls; Rep Jr Cls; Rep Sr Cls; Off Stu Cncl; Var Socr; Var Sftbl; High Hon Roll; NHS; Psych.

GRIFFITH, COLLEEN; Baldwin HS; Pittsburgh, PA; (3); 37/477; Pres Exploring; Trs French Clb; Key Clb; SADD; Rep Jr Cls; High Hon Roll; NHS; Pres Schlr; Yrbk Stf; Sci.

GRIFFITH, DAVID; Carlisle SR HS; Carlisle, PA; (3); 44/467; Boy Scts; Church Yth Grp; Spanish Clb; Nwsp Rptr; Nwsp Stf; JV Socr; Var L Swmmng; Cit Awd; High Hon Roll; Hon Roll; MVP & Hghst Point Awd Swmmng; Aerontcl Engrng.

GRIFFITH, ELLEN; Greater Johnstown HS; Johnstown, PA; (4); 52/277; Office Aide; Service Clb; Spanish Clb; Y-Teens; Rep Jr Cls; High Hon Roll; Hon Roll; IN U Of PA; Comp Prgrmr.

GRIFFITH, GEORGE; St John Neumann HS; Philadelphia, PA; (3); 20/349; Pres Church Yth Grp; Science Clb; Yrbk Sprt Ed; Rep Stu Cncl; Var L Tennis; High Hon Roll; Varsity Clb; Im Bsktbl; Im Coach Actv; Natl Hnr Soc Achvt Awd 87; St John Neumann Awd Dedctn Extra-Curric Activities 87; Pre-Med.

GRIFFITH, JOHN; United HS; Indiana, PA; (4); Camera Clb; JA; Ski Clb; Band; Nwsp Ed-Chief; High Hon Roll; Hon Roll; NHS; Prfct Atten Awd; Pres Schlr; Johnstown Tribune-Democrt Schlstc Jrnlst Awd 87; IN U Of PA; Jrnlsm.

GRIFFITH, KAREN; Garnet Valley HS; Boothwyn, PA; (3); 32/152; German Clb; Intnl Clb; Yrbk Stf; Off Stu Cncl; Mgr(s); Score Keeper; Vllybl; Hon Roll; Acadmc Excllnc Awd 85-87; Med Tech.

GRIFFITH, MICHELLE; United HS; Seward, PA; (4); 21/155; Pres Library Aide; Ski Clb; Chorus; Cheerleading; Trk; Hon Roll; Sec NHS; VP Church Yth Grp; FBLA; Hmcmng Queen 86-87; Ms SR Hall Of Fame 86-87; Grove City; Accntng.

GRIFFITH, TERRIE; Hazelton HS; Drums, PA; (3); Church Yth Grp; French Clb; Pep Clb; SADD; Band; Chorus; Church Choir; Mrchg Band; Pep Band; Bowling; Phy Thrpst.

GRIFFITH, TRACY; Cambria Heights HS; Hastings, PA; (3); Church Yth Grp; Drama Clb; FHA; Nwsp Rptr; Yrbk Stf; Hon Roll.

GRIFFITH, YAVETTE; Marion Center Area; Plumville, PA; (3); Drama Clb; FNA; Intnl Clb; Latin Clb; Q&S; SADD; Varsity Clb; School Play; Yrbk Stf; Cheerleading; Spcl Ed.

GRIFFITHS, DANA; Geigel HS; S Connellsville, PA; (1); Drama Clb; Pep Clb; Science Clb; Ski Clb; Pres Frsh Cls; Pres Soph Cls; Pres Stu Cncl; JV Bsktbl; Capt Cheerleading; JV Vllybl; Natl Chrldrs Assn Sprt Stck Awd 87; Chld Psych.

GRIFFITHS, ELIZABETH; Sharpsville Area HS; Sharpsville, PA; (3); #6 In Class; Camera Clb; Sec Chess Clb; Math Clb; Science Clb; Chorus; Color Guard; Flag Corp; Yrbk Stf; Hon Roll; NHS; Phys Therapy.

GRIFFITHS, LONNIE P; Montrose Area HS; Montrose, PA; (3); German Clb; Ski Clb; Varsity Clb; Band; Concert Band; Jazz Band; Mrchg Band; Socr; Trk; High Hon Roll; Top Grades Trk Awd 87; Penn ST U; Med.

GRIFFITHS, LYNN; Hazleton HS; Hazleton, PA; (4); 64/393; Church Yth Grp; Drama Clb; Sec Band; Concert Band; Mrchg Band; School Play; Hon Roll; JP Sousa Awd; Kiwanis Awd; NHS; PA Bandmstrs Awd 84; ST Band, & John P Schwartz Mem Awd 87; Millersville U; Music Ed.

GRIFFITHS, RUSSELL S; North Catholic HS; Pittsburgh, PA; (2); 89/213; Cmnty Wkr; Ski Clb; Swmmng; Nemerouse Swimming Awds; Aerontcs.

GRIGAS, ANTHONY; Greater Nanticoke Area HS; Nanticoke, PA; (2); Ski Clb; JV Bsbl; JV Bsktbl; JV Ftbl; High Hon Roll; Acctg.

GRIGAS, WAYNE; Shenandoah Valley HS; Shenandoah, PA; (3); VP Jr Cls; VP Sr Cls; JV Var Ftbl; Nwsp Stf; Rep Frsh Cls; Rep Stu Cncl; Im Wt Lftg; Hon Roll; Bloomsburg U; Law Enfrcmnt.

GRIGG, BRIAN; Gr-Johnstown AVTS; South Fork, PA; (4); 17/256; Letterman Clb; Pep Clb; ROTC; Science Clb; SADD; Flag Corp; Bsktbl; Sftbl; Trk; Hon Roll; Vet Of Forgn Wars US 87; U Pittsburgh; Engrng.

GRIGG, KAREN; Altoona Area HS; Altoona, PA; (4); 43/718; Church Yth Grp; PAVAS; Spanish Clb; SADD; Chorus; Church Choir; School Musical; Jr NHS; U Pittsburgh; Phys Thrpy.

GRIGGS, YVETTE; Quigley HS; Aliquippa, PA; (3); Dance Clb; Exploring; Chorus; School Musical; Powder Puff Ftbl; MAPP 87; Chld Psych.

GRIGLOCK, LORI; Pittston Area SR HS; Pittston, PA; (4); #24 In Class; FBLA; NHS; Paralgl.

GRIGUS, SHAWN; Nazareth Area SR HS; Nazareth, PA; (3); 79/275; Boys Clb Am; Church Yth Grp; Im Bsbl; JV Wrstlng; Hon Roll; Penn ST; Biochem.

GRILOUS, GEORGE; Conneaut Valley HS; Conneautville, PA; (3); Band; Chorus; Concert Band; Jazz Band; Mrchg Band; Pep Band; School Play; Nwsp Ed-Chief; Stu Cncl; NHS; CBS Jrnlsm Intrmnt 87; Brdcst Jrnlsm.

GRIM, BARBARA; Eastern York HS; Wrightsville, PA; (4); 18/169; Ski Clb; Trs Varsity Clb; Stat Bsktbl; Var Fld Hcky; Var Mgr(s); Im Powder Puff Ftbl; High Hon Roll; Hon Roll; Jr NHS; NHS; PA ST U; Engrng.

GRIM, BRADLEY K; Christian School Of York; Thomasville, PA; (3); Church Yth Grp; Drama Clb; Chorus; Church Choir; School Musical; Yrbk Stf; Pres Soph Cls; VP Jr Cls; Pres Stu Cncl; Hon Roll; Bus Mgmt.

GRIMAUD, BECKY; Tunkahnnock HS; Tunkhannock, PA; (2); 2/330; Church Yth Grp; French Clb; Key Clb; Chorus; VP Soph Cls; Var Bsktbl; JV Sftbl; JV Var Vllybl; Hon Roll; Pres Acadmc Ftnss Awd 85; JV Coachs Awd-Vllbl 85; JV MVP-BSKTBL 8586; MVP-SFTBL 86; Pediatrcn.

GRIME, SHERRY; Beaver Area HS; Beaver, PA; (2); Sec Church Yth Grp; JCL; Key Clb; Pep Clb; Band; Drm Mjr(t); School Musical; High Hon Roll; Church Choir; Concert Band; Wstmnstr Hnrs Band 87; Schlstc Achvt Awd 87; Mrn Bio.

GRIMES, DARREN; Chestnut Ridge SR HS; New Paris, PA; (3); Boy Scts; Chess Clb; Church Yth Grp; Computer Clb; JV Trk; Hon Roll; Chasis Engr.

GRIMES, FRANCIS; Mon Valley Catholic HS; Donora, PA; (3); Boy Scts; Ski Clb; Spanish Clb; Var L Ftbl; Wt Lftg; Robert Morris Coll; Banking.

GRIMES, LESLIE; Rockwood Area HS; Rockwood, PA; (4); 10/95; NFL; Band; Chorus; School Play; Yrbk Stf; Var Cheerleading; High Hon Roll; Hon Roll; VP NHS; HS Maple Prncs 87; Frmrs & Thrsrmns Jbl Queen 85-86; 1st Chr Soprano 86; PA ST U; Theatre Arts.

GRIMES, MICHELLE; Meadowbrook Christian HS; New Columbia, PA; (4); Sec Trs Church Yth Grp; Library Aide; Trs Yrbk Stf; Trs Frsh Cls; Trs Soph Cls; Trs Jr Cls; Trs Sr Cls; L Socr; Hon Roll; Hnr Roll; Amer Hstry, Bio, Trig, Geom & Phys Sci Awds; 5 Yrs Prfct Atten; Ovrll Acad Achvt; Pensacola Christian Coll; Nrsg.

GRIMES, PATRICK; Towanda HS; Wysox, PA; (4); Boy Scts; Letterman Clb; Science Clb; Concert Band; Var L Crs Cntry; Var L Trk; Var Wrstlng; Strctl Engrng.

GRIMES, RICHARD; Central Catholic HS; Pittsburgh, PA; (3); 9/275; Church Yth Grp; Exploring; Stage Crew; VP Frsh Cls; VP Soph Cls; Var L Tennis; Hon Roll; NHS; Ntl Merit Ltr; Spanish NHS.

GRIMES, TRAVIS; Northern Lebanon JR SR HS; Fredericksburg, PA; (3); Ski Clb; JV Var Bsbl; JV Var Bsktbl; Hon Roll; Aerontcl Engrng.

GRIMM, BRAD; Center Area HS; Aliquippa, PA; (2); Spanish Clb; Band; Concert Band; Jazz Band; Mrchg Band; School Musical; Hon Roll; Spanish NHS; Hnrs Band 87; Dist Band 87; Rgnl Band 87.

GRIMM, CHERI; Ligonier Valley SR HS; Ligonier, PA; (3); AFS; Sec Trs Chess Clb; Pres SADD; Capt Color Guard; Stage Crew; Yrbk Stf; Stu Cncl; High Hon Roll; Hon Roll; Jr NHS.

GRIMM, DANA; Lampeter-Strasburg HS; New Providence, PA; (4); 24/144; AFS; FHA; Teachers Aide; Lit Mag; Westchester U; Poly Sci.

GRIMM, JONATHAN; Eastern HS; York, PA; (3); 53/183; JV Bsbl; JV Bsktbl; Var Ftbl; Hon Roll; Lock Haven; Comp Sci.

GRIMM, LISA; Bethlehem Center SR HS; Washington, PA; (3); 73/165; Church Yth Grp; Spanish Clb; Computer Clb; Cruise Dir.

GRIMM, MARCUS; Solanco HS; Quarryville, PA; (2); 4/283; Church Yth Grp; Concert Band; Jazz Band; Mrchg Band; School Musical; Rep Stu Cncl; JV Crs Cntry; JV Trk; High Hon Roll; NHS; Pub Rel.

GRIMM, ROBERT; South Moreland HS; Scottdale, PA; (3); 22/224; JCL; Latin Clb; History.

GRIMM, SCOTT; Connellsville Area SR HS; Indian Head, PA; (3); 35/520; Aud/Vis; Boy Scts; Camera Clb; German Clb; Stat Ftbl; JV Trk; High Hon Roll; Hon Roll; NHS; Grmn Hnr Socty Delta Epsln Phi 86-87; FL Inst Of Tech; Marn Bio.

GRIMM, STACEY; Center HS; Aliquippa, PA; (3); #4 In Class; VP Exploring; Girl Scts; JA; Spanish Clb; Pres Band; Concert Band; Jazz Band; Mrchg Band; School Musical; High Hon Roll; Girl Scout Silver Awd 85.

GRIMM, TINA; South Moreland SR HS; Tarrs, PA; (3); VICA; Powder Puff Ftbl; Sftbl; Swmmng; Twrlr; Vllybl; Drama Clb; Pep Clb; Chorus; US Army; Photo.

GRIMM, TRACEY; Knoch HS; Butler, PA; (2); French Clb; Rep Frsh Cls; VP Soph Cls; Rep Stu Cncl; JV Stat Bsktbl; Stat Ftbl; JV Golf; Score Keeper; Tennis; Stat Trk; Outstndng Stu Cncl Rep 87; Law.

GRIMME, TIMOTHY; Conemough Twp Area HS; Holsapple, PA; (4); 14/107; Quiz Bowl; Scholastic Bowl; Varsity Clb; Yrbk Stf; Ftbl; Trk; Vllybl; NHS; Navy Nuclear Pwr Schl; Nclr Opr.

GRINARML, REBECCA; Rockwood Area HS; Markleton, PA; (2); 1/115; Computer Clb; NFL; Speech Tm; Band; Concert Band; Jazz Band; Mrchg Band; School Play; High Hon Roll; Natl Hnrs Socty Awd-Sci 85-86; Mdcl Sci.

GRINER, BRIAN SCOTT; Shikellamy HS; Northumberland, PA; (3); 2/323; Am Leg Boys St; Church Yth Grp; Quiz Bowl; Pres Rep Stu Cncl; Var L Ftbl; Var L Trk; God Cntry Awd; High Hon Roll; NHS; Spanish NHS; Drexel U; Med.

GRINNEN, AMY; Villa Maria Acad; Erie, PA; (3); 8/156; Science Clb; Hon Roll; NHS; Teeng Actn Clb 85-86 & 86-87; Msn Clb-VP 87-88; Bus Admin.

GRIPPI, JANET; Bishop Hannan HS; Scranton, PA; (2); Stu Cncl; Cheerleading; Sftbl; High Hon Roll; NHS; PA Jr Acdmy Sci 86-87; Rgnls & ST 1st Pl 86; Rgnl 2nd Pl 87.

GRIPPI, RICHARD F; Bishop Hannan HS; Scranton, PA; (4); 13/120; Debate Tm; Speech Tm; JV Bsbl; Capt Tennis; High Hon Roll; Trs NHS; Rotary Awd; U Of Scranton; Criminal Justice.

GRIPPO, CASSIE SUE; Southmoreland HS; Scottdale, PA; (3); Latin Clb; Pep Clb; Ski Clb; Teachers Aide; Capt Cheerleading; Im Gym; JV Var Powder Puff Ftbl; Sec Frsh Cls; Sec Soph Cls; VP Rep Stu Cncl; Pres Humanstcs Clb 86-87; Pres Ldrs Clb 86-87; Law.

GRISCAVAGE, JOHN; N Allegheny HS; Allison Pk, PA; (2); 1/630; Hosp Aide; Concert Band; Mrchg Band; School Musical; High Hon Roll; Church Yth Grp; Cmnty Wkr; Exploring; PA Music Edctrs Assn Dist I Hnrs Band 86; Allegheny Vly Hnrs Band 85-87; Chem Awd 86-87.

GRISE, MARCIA; Wilkinsburg JR SR HS; Wilkinsburg, PA; (3); French Clb; JA; Key Clb; Office Aide; High Hon Roll; Hon Roll; Jr NHS; NHS; Educ.

GRISER, NANCY BETH; Mc Keesport Area HS; Mc Keesport, PA; (4); AFS; Exploring; German Clb; JA; Orch; School Musical; Nwsp Stf; Hon Roll; Gannon Schlrshp Acdmc 87; Gannon U; Pre Med.

GRISILLO, CHRISTINA; Archbishop Prendergast HS; Yeadon, PA; (3); 120/365; Drill Tm; Orch; Rep Frsh Cls; Rep Soph Cls; Rep Jr Cls; William T Kerr Awd 85; Music Awd Hghst GPA 85; Engnrng.

GRISKEY, MARK; Hempfield Area HS; Greensburg, PA; (2); Camera Clb; Carnegie Mellon; Arch.

GROBINSKI, ANGELA; John S Fine HS; Nanticoke, PA; (3); 12/225; Spanish Clb; Var Cheerleading; High Hon Roll; NHS.

GROCE, MARK; Chambersburg Area SR HS; Shippensburg, PA; (2); 183/735; Boy Scts; Hon Roll; Physics.

GROCE, MICHELE; Chambersburg Area SR HS; Newburg, PA; (3); Church Yth Grp; Drama Clb; Spanish Clb; Band; Chorus; Church Choir; Concert Band; Variety Show; Crs Cntry; Fld Hcky.

GRODACK, CINDY; Western Wayne HS; Lake Ariel, PA; (3); 4-H; Mrchg Band; Nwsp Rptr; Yrbk Phtg; Yrbk Sprt Ed; Var Bsktbl; Var Socr; Var Sftbl; High Hon Roll; NHS; West Point; Sci.

GROFF, ANDY; Lampeter-Strasburg HS; Lancaster, PA; (2); VP FFA; Thesps; Band; VP Chorus; Concert Band; Jazz Band; Madrigals; Mrchg Band; School Musical; School Play; FFA Greenhand Degree 86, Chptr Farmer Degree 87, Fndtn Awds 86-87; Agri Engr.

GROFF, BARBRA; J P Mc Caskey HS; Bausman, PA; (4); 84/490; Chorus; Cheerleading; ST Joe Hosp Schl Nrsng; RN.

GROFF, DAVID K; North Penn HS; Hatfield, PA; (4); Yrbk Stf; Lit Mag; Off Sr Cls; Jr Cls; Hon Roll; Ntl Merit SF; US St Acad Decatualon 86.

GROFF, DONNA; Lancaster Mennonite HS; Lancaster, PA; (3); 25/180; Church Yth Grp; 4-H; Chorus; Orch; Stage Crew; JV Var Bsktbl; Var L Crs Cntry; NHS.

GROFF, JEFF; Garden Spot HS; Narvon, PA; (3); Church Yth Grp; Chorus; Stu Cncl; Socr; Wt Lftg; Wrstlng; High Hon Roll; Hon Roll; Jr NHS; Bloomsburg U; Phys Educ.

GROFF, KRISTIE; Mifflingburg Area HS; Millmont, PA; (1); Church Yth Grp; High Hon Roll; Dntstry.

GROFF, KRISTIN; Cumberland Vly HS; Mechanicsburg, PA; (3); Library Aide; Office Aide; Nwsp Ed-Chief; Nwsp Rptr; Nwsp Stf; Var Cheerleading; Var Pom Pon; Hon Roll; 20th Pl ST Natl Spnsh Exm, Hnrb Mntn Schl Sci Fair 85-86; Jrnlsm.

GROFF, MARCEY; Grace Christian Schl; Ephrata, PA; (4) Drama Clb; Teachers Aide; Chorus; Yrbk Stf; Var Capt Cheerleading; Var Fld Hcky; Var Sftbl; Var Tennis; Var Hon Roll; Prfct Atten Awd; V-Fld Hcky, Andrw Awd 86-87; V-Fld Hcky, Brnbs Awd 84-85; Alvernia Coll; Chld Psychlgy.

GROFF, RODNEY; Lancaster Mennonite HS; Kinzer, PA; (3); Chess Clb; VP Church Yth Grp; Cmnty Wkr; FFA; Chorus; Im Socr; Im Tennis; Hon Roll; NHS; Im Bsktbl; Chess Ltr 86 & 87; Cert Merit Frm HS Alumni Assn 87; Bus.

GROFF, TINA; J D Mccaskey HS; Lancaster, PA; (4); 145/455; AFS; Am Leg Aux Girls St; Teachers Aide; Chorus; Cheerleading; Trk; Hon Roll; Natl Chrldng Champ 83-87; Dist Trck Mt 85-86; Educ.

GROFF, WAYNE; Faith Mennonite HS; Gap, PA; (4); 2/27; Pres Church Yth Grp; Math Clb; Acpl Chr; Nwsp Stf; Pres Jr Cls; Pres Stu Cncl; High Hon Roll; Millersville U; Accntng.

GROGG, VICKY; South Western HS; Hanover, PA; (3); AFS; Key Clb; Concert Band; Mrchg Band; Exch Stu S Korea 86-87.

GROH, REBECCA; Northern Lebanon HS; Jonestown, PA; (3); 38/175; Varsity Clb; Var L Crs Cntry; JV Fld Hcky; Var L Trk; Hon Roll; Nuclear Engr.

GROHAL, MATT; Windber Area HS; Windber, PA; (3); Church Yth Grp; Cmnty Wkr; Letterman Clb; Pep Clb; Rep Frsh Cls; Rep Stu Cncl; Ftbl; Score Keeper; Trk; High Hon Roll; Sports Med.

GROHOWSKI, REBECCA; Quakertown Community SR HS; Quakertown, PA; (2); 25/359; Art Clb; Cmnty Wkr; Letterman Clb; High Hon Roll; Hon Roll; Jr NHS; Prfct Atten Awd; Bucks Cnty Cncl Arts JR HS Exhibit 86; Pres Acad Fit Awd 85-86; JR AAHPERD Awd 86; Fine Art.

GROLLER, MATTHEW S; Northampton Area SR HS; Bath, PA; (3); Church Yth Grp; VICA; Band; Concert Band; Jazz Band; Mrchg Band; Symp Band; Hon Roll; Engr.

GROMACKI, LESLEE; Villa Maria Acad; Erie, PA; (3); 2/151; Church Yth Grp; VP PAVAS; SADD; Chorus; Church Choir; School Musical; School Play; Variety Show; High Hon Roll; Hon Roll; Educ.

GROMAN, KRISTA; Spring Ford SR HS; Spring City, PA; (4); 26/240; Church Yth Grp; Varsity Clb; Capt Var Bsktbl; Var Fld Hcky; Capt Var Lcrss; Hon Roll; Lion Awd; French Clb; German Clb; GAA; MVP Bsktbll, Lacrss, Bstrs Fml Athlt 87; Gnrdi Awd Outstndg Fml Athlt 87; Outstndg Grmn Stu Awd 87; Lehigh U; Bus.

GRONAUER, ROBERT; G A R Memorial HS; Wilkes-Barre, PA; (4); 27/171; Letterman Clb; Chorus; Var Capt Bsbl; Coach Actv; Var Capt Ftbl; Var Wt Lftg; Hon Roll; Jr NHS; NHS; TV Clb Pres; All Schlstc Ftbl & Hnbl Mntn; Unico Ftbl Tm; Pre-Law.

GRONCZEWSKI, PETER; Cardinal Dougherty HS; Philadelphia, PA; (3); 98/676; Hon Roll; Prfct Atten Awd; Temple U; Lw Enfrcmnt.

GRONDWALSKI, ANDREA; Highlands SR HS; Natrona Hts, PA; (4); 69/281; Exploring; Hosp Aide; Key Clb; Var Sftbl; Hon Roll; Seton Hill Coll; Dietcs.

GRONINGER, TIMOTHY; Lewisburg Area HS; Lewisburg, PA; (3); 5/150; Science Clb; JV Var Bowling; Var Capt Socr; JV Var Tennis; Hon Roll; Jr NHS; NHS; Engrng.

GROOMS, REWA; Scotland Schl For Veterans Children; Philadelphia, PA; (3); Hosp Aide; ROTC; School Musical; School Play; Variety Show; JV Bsktbl; Fld Hcky; Var Trk; Temple U; B1siness Education.

GROOVER, TAMMY; Cowanesque Valley HS; Westfield, PA; (4); Church Yth Grp; Drill Tm; Flag Corp; Mrchg Band; Nwsp Ed-Chief; Nwsp Rptr; Nwsp Stf; Capt L Cheerleading; Capt L Pom Pon; Girl Scts; Phyllis Clark Awd-Hghst Typing Avg 87; Williamsport Schl; Exev Sec.

GROSCH, MICHAEL; Clarion Area HS; Shippenville, PA; (4); 2/97; Band; VP Chorus; Jazz Band; Pep Band; School Musical; High Hon Roll; JP Sousa Awd; NHS; Sal; U Of Houston; Chem Engr.

GROSCHOPP, KENNETH; Central Bucks West HS; Perkasie, PA; (3); FBLA; SADD; Band; Orch; Variety Show; Lit Mag; Off Stu Cncl; 4-H Awd; Hon Roll; Prfct Atten Awd; Grove City Coll; Pre-Law.

GROSCUP, BETSY; Daniel Boone JR SR HS; Birdsboro, PA; (2); 15/176; Church Yth Grp; French Clb; Color Guard; Mrchg Band; Stu Cncl; High Hon Roll; Hon Roll.

GROSS, ANGELA; Reading HS; Reading, PA; (4); 18/563; Hon Roll; NHS; Old Dominion; Bus Admin.

GROSS, BARBARA; Exeter Township HS; Douglassville, PA; (4); 31/218; Church Yth Grp; Exploring; Q&S; Quiz Bowl; Yrbk Stf; Lit Mag; JV Bowling; High Hon Roll; Hon Roll; Jr NHS; Yrbk Achvt Awd 86; Pres Acdmc Ftnss Schlrshp 87; Messiah Coll.

GROSS, DIANE; Bellefonte Area HS; Pleasant Gap, PA; (4); 57/237; French Clb; Pep Clb; Ski Clb; SADD; Varsity Clb; Band; Concert Band; Drill Tm; Drm Mjr(t); Mrchg Band; Outstndg Athl Awd-Gymnastics 87; Penn ST U; Human Dev.

GROSS, GRETTA A; Northeastern SR HS; Manchester, PA; (3); 5/188; Sec 4-H; Chorus; Orch; School Musical; Var L Bsktbl; L Var Sftbl; Var L Vllybl; High Hon Roll; Var NHS; Amer Yth Symphny European Tour 85; Sth Cntrl PA Cattlemns Assn Queen 87; SURGEON.

GROSS, JONATHAN; Archbishop Wood HS; Southampton, PA; (3); 25/256; Boy Scts; German Clb; Nwsp Ed-Chief; Nwsp Stf; Trk; High Hon Roll; Hon Roll; NHS; Engr.

GROSS, JULIE; Mifflinburg Area HS; Millmont, PA; (1); Girl Scts; Key Clb; High Hon Roll; Susquehanna U.

GROSS, KATH; Little Flower Catholic HS; Philadelphia, PA; (3); 19/322; Church Yth Grp; German Clb; GAA; Chorus; Nwsp Rptr; Nwsp Stf; Yrbk Stf; Socr; High Hon Roll; Hon Roll; Rnnr Up Columbus Day Esy Cont 87; Voices & Visions Esy Cont 87; Crmnl Jstc.

GROSS, KENNETH; Marple Newtown SR HS; Broomall, PA; (3); 85/362; Cmnty Wkr; Office Aide; Teachers Aide; Nwsp Bus Mgr; Hon Roll; GA Tech; Pre Med.

GROSS, LINDA; Bethlehem Catholic HS; Bethlehem, PA; (3); 1/200; Art Clb; Band; Drill Tm; Flag Corp; Mrchg Band; JV Bsktbl; Fld Hcky; High Hon Roll; NHS; Scholastic Bowl; Natl Frnch Cntst-Cert Of Merit 85-86; Cert Of Hnr-Outstndng Achvt/Hghst Avg Theolgy 86; Grphc Dsgn.

GROSS, LORI; Northeastern SR HS; Manchester, PA; (4); Chorus; Nwsp Rptr; Pres Frsh Cls; Rep Soph Cls; Rep Jr Cls; Rep Sr Cls; Stu Cncl; Hon Roll; Sec NHS; Voice Dem Awd; Shippensburg U; Ed.

GROSS, MARIA; Littlestown HS; Littlestown, PA; (4); 27/117; Band; Chorus; Concert Band; Jazz Band; Mrchg Band; School Musical; Rep Stu Cncl; Hon Roll; Arion Fndtn Awd Instrmntl 87; Cnty Band; Dist Band; Peg Horns Beauty; Cosmtlgy.

GROSS, TIMOTHY; Seneca Valley HS; Zelienople, PA; (3); Boy Scts; Church Yth Grp; Letterman Clb; Pep Clb; Ski Clb; Varsity Clb; Nwsp Rptr; JV Var Bsktbl; JV Var Golf; Hon Roll; Mst Outstndng Plyr Golf 86-87; Grove City Coll; Finance.

GROSS, WILLIAM ERNEST; Pocono Mountain HS; Mt Pocono, PA; (2); Boy Scts; Sec Church Yth Grp; Band; Chorus; Church Choir; Concert Band; Mrchg Band; School Musical; Swing Chorus; Music.

GROSSEK, PAMELA; Canon Mc Millian SR HS; Cecil, PA; (4); Drama Clb; Ski Clb; Band; Chorus; Concert Band; Flag Corp; Mrchg Band; School Play; High Hon Roll; Hon Roll; Kent ST U; Advrtsng.

GROSSER, CHERYL; Exetor Twp SR HS; Reading, PA; (3); 25/241; German Clb; Band; Concert Band; Mrchg Band; High Hon Roll; Hon Roll; Jr NHS; NHS; Pdtrcn.

GROSSER, RAE ANN; Connellsville Area SR HS; Connellsville, PA; (3); Library Aide; Q&S; Stage Crew; Nwsp Ed-Chief; Nwsp Rptr; Yrbk Stf; Hon Roll; NHS; Prfct Atten Awd; Natl Travel Schl.

GROSSER, STEVEN C; Owen J Roberts HS; Pottstown, PA; (3); Am Leg Boys St; Letterman Clb; Band; Concert Band; Drm & Bgl; Mrchg Band; School Musical; Symp Band; L Trk; Im Vllybl.

GROSSER, TORI; Pottstown SR HS; Pottstown, PA; (3); 2/179; VP FNA; Mrchg Band; Rep Sr Cls; Var Cheerleading; JV Capt Sftbl; High Hon Roll; NHS; Opt Clb Awd; Prfct Atten Awd; Sal; Nrsng.

GROSSI, PATRICIA A; Villa Maria Acad; King Of Prussia, PA; (3); 1/97; Math Tm; Mu Alpha Theta; Scholastic Bowl; Teachers Aide; School Musical; Lit Mag; Im Bsktbl; French Hon Soc; High Hon Roll; Sec NHS; PA Cncl Teachrs Engl 85; Awd Geo & Bio Essay Cont 85; French II & Alg II Awd 86; Civil Engrng.

GROSSMAN, ESTHER; Abington Hights HS; Clarks Summit, PA; (3); Dance Clb; Ski Clb; Temple Yth Grp; Chorus; Trs Frsh Cls; Pres Stu Cncl; Hon Roll; Ldrshp Awd 84-87; Ntl Piano Plyng Adtns 85; Chsn To Attnd PASC Confrnc 85 & 86; Intl Rltns.

GROSSMAN, KIRSTEN; Red Lion SR HS; Red Lion, PA; (3); 78/342; Aud/Vis; Teachers Aide; Varsity Clb; Rep Soph Cls; Rep Jr Cls; Off Sr Cls; Off Stu Cncl; Var Swmmng; Hon Roll; Jr NHS; Bus Adm.

GROSSMAN, MELISSA; Downingtown Sr HS; Downingtown, PA; (4); French Clb; Girl Scts; Intnl Clb; Teachers Aide; Chorus; Nwsp Rptr; Lit Mag; Trk; High Hon Roll; Hon Roll; Bus.

GROSSMAN, MELISSA; Moniteau HS; W Sunbury, PA; (4); 32/136; Church Yth Grp; Exploring; FBLA; Sec Library Aide; SADD; Nwsp Stf; Yrbk Stf; Lit Mag; High Hon Roll; Drama Clb; Bst Ovrll Bus 86-87; U S Army Reserve; Legl Spec.

GROSSMAN, PHILLIP; Cedar Cliff HS; Lemayne, PA; (3); 20/320; Boy Scts; Camera Clb; Key Clb; Latin Clb; Ski Clb; Nwsp Phtg; Pres Frsh Cls; Socr; High Hon Roll; Latin Hnr Scty 85-86; Cum Laude Natl Latin Exam 85-86; U Rochester; Optics Engr.

GROTE, SARA; Ellis HS; Pittsburgh, PA; (3); 7/35; Nwsp Rptr; Yrbk Stf; VP Frsh Cls; Pres Sr Cls; Fld Hcky; Hon Roll; Wllsly Clb Awd-Schlrshp, Chrctr & Ldrshp, Extra Curclr Actvts 87; Wrtng.

GROTH, DAVID; Daniel Boone HS; Douglassville, PA; (3); 42/172; Varsity Clb; Var Ftbl; Var Trk; Var Wrstlng; Hon Roll; Opt Clb Awd; Wrstlng 2nd Sectnls 3rd Rgnls ST Qualif O86-87; Ftbl All Berks Cnty Recvr 86.

GROTH, SUSIE; Jeannette HS; Jeannette, PA; (2); Ski Clb; Spanish Clb; Band; Color Guard; Mrchg Band; Sftbl; Hon Roll; Med.

GROTHE, BARRY; York Vo-Tech; New Freedom, PA; (3); VICA; Hon Roll; NHS; PA ST U; Cvl Engnrng.

GROTHE, CONNIE; Central SR HS; York, PA; (2); 1/264; Church Yth Grp; Varsity Clb; Pres Soph Cls; Var Capt Bsktbl; JV Vllybl; High Hon Roll; Med.

GROTHEN, CORY; Gettysburg SR HS; Gettysburg, PA; (4); Chess Clb; Spanish Clb; SADD; Pres Sr Cls; Rep Stu Cncl; Hon Roll; NHS; Opt Clb Awd; Yrk Tech Inst; Archt Drftr.

GROTTOLA, SHAWN; Northern SR HS; Dillsburg, PA; (3); Chess Clb; Computer Clb; Intnl Clb; Spanish Clb; Varsity Clb; Stage Crew; Nwsp Stf; Rep Soph Cls; Var Socr; Var Tennis.

GROVANNETTI, DOMINIC; The Swarthmore Acad; Drexel Hill, PA; (3); Office Aide; OEA; Ski Clb; Bsktbl; Socr; Sftbl.

GROVE, CAROL; Central Cambria HS; Ebensburg, PA; (2); Trs Church Yth Grp; Cmnty Wkr; Dance Clb; Hosp Aide; JA; Key Clb; Chorus; Rep Stu Cncl; Hon Roll; St Francis Coll; Bio.

GROVE, ERIC; Seneca Valley HS; Harmony, PA; (3); 77/395; Art Clb; Church Yth Grp; Radio Clb; Ski Clb; Band; Ftbl; Tennis; Wt Lftg; Hon Roll; Physcl Ed.

GROVE, JASON; Mifflinburg Area HS; Mifflinburg, PA; (1); Rptr 4-H; FFA; Concert Band; Hon Roll; SUN Area Envirolmpcs 1st 87; FFA Lvstck Judg 2nd 87; WOTC Essy Cntst 5th 87; Penn ST; Ag Engr.

GROVE, JEFFREY; Tunkhannock HS; Tunkhannock, PA; (3); 25/350; Church Yth Grp; Key Clb; JV Bsbl; JV Bsktbl; Cit Awd; Hon Roll; NHS; Acad All Am; West Chester U; Sports Med.

GROVE, KRISTIE; Middletown Area HS; Middletown, PA; (4); 10/176; Church Yth Grp; FCA; Band; Chorus; Concert Band; Jazz Band; Mrchg Band; Orch; Swing Chorus; Yrbk Stf; Ruth L Graham, Lions Clb Band Achvt & Semper Fidelis Awds 87; Bucknell U.

GROVE, LARISA; Mechanicsburg SR HS; Mechanicsburg, PA; (4); 23/313; Library Aide; Ski Clb; Band; Chorus; Mrchg Band; School Play; Symp Band; Stat Socr; Hon Roll; NHS; Pres Acdmc Ftnss Awd 87; Ltr Commndtn Natl Merit Schlrshp Pgm 87; PA Fish Commssn Cnsrvtn Awd 85; U Of DE; Biolgcl Sci.

GROVE, RAFE; Elizabethtown Area HS; Elizabethtown, PA; (4); 37/235; Chorus; Church Choir; VP Soph Cls; Stu Cncl; Cheerleading; Trk; Girl Mnth 87; Albright Coll; Polt Sci.

GROVE, TAMMY; Lincoln HS; Wampum, PA; (3); 70/162; Church Yth Grp; Chorus; Hon Roll; Geneva; Spec Educ.

GROVES, JENNIFER S; Karns City HS; Petrolia, PA; (4); 7/122; Am Leg Aux Girls St; Band; High Hon Roll; Hon Roll; NHS; Pres Schlr; VFW Awd; SADD; Chorus; Concert Band; PA Free Entrprs Wkm Schlrshp 86; Dist V Band 87; All Str Band/Band Hall Of Fame 85-87; Butler Co CC.

GROVES, KIM; Shikellamy HS; Northumberland, PA; (3); Church Yth Grp; Pres 4-H; Hosp Aide; Sec SADD; Chorus; Church Choir; Capt Color Guard; Concert Band; Drill Tm; Mrchg Band; Outstndng Band Frnt Awd 85-86; Occu Thrpst.

GROVES, TRACY; Bradford Central Christian HS; Bradford, PA; (4); 2/26; Drama Clb; Pep Clb; Ski Clb; SADD; Yrbk Stf; Rep Stu Cncl; High Hon Roll; Hon Roll; Jr NHS; NHS; IN U; Elem Ed.

GROVES, WILLIAM; Conneaut Valley HS; Springboro, PA; (3); Aud/Vis; Church Yth Grp; Drama Clb; Office Aide; Pep Clb; Spanish Clb; Teachers Aide; Varsity Clb; Band; Concert Band; PA Free Entrprs 86; Chrstn Ldrshp Inst 86; U AZ; Elec Engr.

GROW, LISA; Shamokin Area HS; Shamokin, PA; (4); 14/213; Sec Key Clb; Varsity Clb; Sec Frsh Cls; Sec Soph Cls; Sec Jr Cls; Sec Sr Cls; Sec Stu Cncl; Capt Cheerleading; Var Swmmng; Elks Awd; Shamokin Area HS Alumni Assn Schlrshp 87; Bloomburg U Schlr 87; Bloomsburg U; Elem Ed.

GROWDEN, MICHELLE; Ringgold HS; Finleyville, PA; (1); Chorus; Hon Roll.

GROZNIK, TERESA; Montour HS; Mc Kees Rocks, PA; (4); Church Yth Grp; GAA; Rep Stu Cncl; JV Var Cheerleading; Stat Sftbl; L Var Swmmng; Hon Roll; Daemn Coll Deans Schlrshp & Deptmntl Schlrshp 87; Daemen Coll; Phys Thrpy.

GRUBB, CHRIS; Spring-Ford HS; Royersford, PA; (4); French Clb; German Clb; Pep Clb; Ski Clb; Varsity Clb; Nwsp Stf; Yrbk Ed-Chief; Stu Cncl; Capt Cheerleading; Coach Actv; Kutztown; Elem Ed.

GRUBB, LINDA; Everett Area HS; Clearville, PA; (4); 13/104; Sec Trs FHA; GAA; Varsity Clb; Var Capt Sftbl; Var Capt Vllybl; Hon Roll; Lion Awd; Ntl Merit Ltr; Vrsty Clb 4 Yr Ltr 87; Johnson & Wales Coll; Pstry Chf.

GRUBB, LORIN V; Dover Area HS; Dover, PA; (4); 1/230; Pres Acpl Chr; Chorus; Concert Band; School Musical; Stu Cncl; DAR Awd; Pres NHS; Ntl Merit SF; Opt Clb Awd; 1st Co Bar Assoc Law Day Essay Cntst, Fnlst PA Gov Schl Arts, Hnrs Eng Achvt 86; Comp Sci.

GRUBB, SUSAN; Middletown Area HS; Middletown, PA; (4); Hon Roll.

GRUBBS, GRETCHEN; Albert Gallatin HS; Smithfield, PA; (4); Pres 4-H; VP Frsh Cls; Stu Cncl; Score Keeper; Cit Awd; 4-H Awd; High Hon Roll; Jr NHS; Ctzn Mth Awd; Acadc Top 10 Awd; Penn ST U; Educ.

GRUBBS, KATE; Avonworth JR/Sr HS; Pittsbg, PA; (4); 25/99; AFS; JCL; Latin Clb; Band; Ed Nwsp Stf; Pres Frsh Cls; Sec Jr Cls; Trs Sr Cls; Socr; Tennis; OH U; Intl Stds.

GRUBE, CHRISTINE; Reading SR HS; Reading, PA; (3); 254/710; Key Clb; Chorus; Yrbk Stf; Off Stu Cncl; Penn ST; Lab Tech.

GRUBE, ROBIN; Liberty HS; Bethlehem, PA; (4); 40/421; Pres Church Yth Grp; Church Choir; Var JV Fld Hcky; Hon Roll; NHS; Hnrs Grad 87; PA ST U; Elem Educ.

GRUBE, WILIAM; Nazareth HS; Nazareth, PA; (3); Art Clb; Computer Clb; Im JV Bsktbl; Hon Roll.

GRUBER, HEIDI; East Pennsboro Area HS; Enola, PA; (3); Art Clb; Sec Church Yth Grp; Sec German Clb; Trs GAA; Girl Scts; Mrchg Band; School Musical; Yrbk Stf; Sec Stu Cncl; Var Im Bsktbl; St Fnlst Miss PA Tnagr Pgnt 87; Semi-Fnlst Gvrnrs Schl Dance 86; Messiah Coll; Phys Thrpy.

GRUBER, KATHY; Northern York County HS; Dillsburg, PA; (3); 5/239; French Clb; Pres Girl Scts; Hosp Aide; Model UN; Band; Chorus; Church Choir; Concert Band; Jazz Band; Mrchg Band; Stu Council Acad Excllnc Awd 86.

GRUBER, MARK; East Pennsboro Area HS; Enola, PA; (4); VP German Clb; Trs Varsity Clb; School Musical; School Play; Pres Sr Cls; Var JV Bsbl; Var JV Socr; L Swmmng; High Hon Roll; NHS; Penn ST; Archtctrl Engr.

GRUBIC, MARK; Central York SR HS; York, PA; (3); Trs Exploring; High Hon Roll; Hon Roll; NHS; Enviro-Olympc Clb 85-87; Juniata; Mdcl Dr.

GRUBICH, MELISSA; Southmoreland HS; Mtpleasant, PA; (3); 11/224; Church Yth Grp; French Clb; Letterman Clb; Pep Clb; Nwsp Bus Mgr; Nwsp Ed-Chief; Nwsp Rptr; Nwsp Stf; Yrbk Stf; Lit Mag; Tnns Chmpnshp; Presdntl Ftns Awd; Bus.

GRUCA, EDWARD; Westmont Hilltop HS; Johnstown, PA; (2); 44/145; Boy Scts; VP Var Ftbl; Var L Trk; Comp Anlyst.

GRUCA, TRACY ANNE; Seneca Valey SR HS; Zelienople, PA; (4); Sec Church Yth Grp; Sec FTA; Thesps; Madrigals; School Musical; School Play; High Hon Roll; Hon Roll; NHS; SWBCEA Tchng Schlrshp 87; Clarion U; Elem Educ.

GRUDA, DEBBIE; Du Bois Area SR HS; Dubois, PA; (3); 55/430; Church Yth Grp; Hosp Aide; Chorus; Stu Cncl; Stat Bsktbl; JV Tennis; Hon Roll; Penn ST U; Business Admin.

GRUDKOWSKI, DAVID; John S Fine HS; Nanticoke, PA; (4); 9/251; Ski Clb; Golf; Trk; High Hon Roll; Trs NHS; Bucknell U; Chem Engr.

GRUDKOWSKI, EILEEN; John S Fine HS; Nanticoke, PA; (2); Key Clb; Ski Clb; Yrbk Stf; VP Frsh Cls; VP Soph Cls; JV Var Cheerleading; Diving; Civic Clb; Swmmng; Trk; Psychol.

GRUDZINSKI, CINDI; Allentown Central Catholic HS; Allentown, PA; (4); 17/204; Exploring; Pep Clb; Band; Concert Band; Drill Tm; Mrchg Band; Pep Band; High Hon Roll; NHS; Principals Awd 87; VA Tech; Arch.

GRUENLOH, JENNIE; John S Fine HS; Glen Lyon, PA; (4); 1/250; Church Yth Grp; Model UN; Speech Tm; Nwsp Stf; Lit Mag; High Hon Roll; Ntl Merit SF; NEDT Awd; Sons Italy Essay Cntst Wnr; Time Essy Cntst Natl Fnlst; Pre-Med.

GRUENLOH, MATTHEW; John S Fine SR HS; Glen Lyon, PA; (2); Cmnty Wkr; Nwsp Stf; NHS; NEDT Wnnr; Engr.

GRUESU, PAUL; Johnsonburg Area HS; Johnsonburg, PA; (3); Boy Scts; Camera Clb; Church Yth Grp; Red Cross Aide; Varsity Clb; Bsktbl; Tennis; High Hon Roll; Acad All Amer Scholar Awd 85.

GRUM, ALEXANDER; Pocono Central Catholic HS; E Stroudsburg, PA; (3); Latin Clb; Math Clb; Pep Clb; Ski Clb; Sec Frsh Cls; Sec Soph Cls; Var Bsbl; JV Bsktbl; Im Vllybl; Hon Roll; Cert Red Crs Lfgrd 85; Penn ST U; Engrng.

GRUM, GENA; Lakeland HS; Jermyn, PA; (3); FHA; SADD; Nwsp Stf; Sec Frsh Cls; Sec Soph Cls; Var Cheerleading; Var Hon Roll; Star Beauty Schl; Csmtlgy.

GRUMBINE, JENNIFER; Avon Grove HS; Landenberg, PA; (3); 2/215; Church Yth Grp; Mrchg Band; School Play; Yrbk Stf; Lit Mag; Trs Sr Cls; Var Tennis; NHS; Quiz Bowl; Band; Hugh O Brien Yth Ldrshp Fndtn 86; Outstndng Soph Of Avon Grove Yth Ed Assn 86; Engrng.

GRUMBINE, MICHAEL S; Susquehanna Township HS; Harrisburg, PA; (1); 20/170; Church Yth Grp; Trk; Hon Roll; Sci.

GRUMBLATT, ALAIS; Oley Valley HS; Oley, PA; (3); #20 In Class; Library Aide; Nwsp Stf; High Hon Roll; Hon Roll; Gilead; Mnstry.

GRUMBLING, WENDY; Cocalico HS; Denver, PA; (2); Computer Clb; Band; Color Guard; Concert Band; Stat Trk; Twrlr; Hon Roll; Vtrnrn.

GRUMELL, KRISTIN; Nazareth Acad; Philadelphia, PA; (3); Hosp Aide; JCL; Latin Clb; Yrbk Stf; JV Bowling; JV Cheerleading; Prfct Atten Awd; Cert Apprctn Frankford Hosp 85; Magna Cum Laude Jr Clsscl Leag Ltn 87; Educ.

GRUNDEN, JILL; Trinity Christian Schl; Pittsburgh, PA; (3); 4/13; Church Yth Grp; Chorus; Yrbk Rptr; Ed Yrbk Stf; Cheerleading; Hon Roll; Jr NHS; NHS.

GRUNDEN, KYLE; Waynesboro Area SR HS; Blue Ridge Summit, PA; (4); Boy Scts; JCL; Acpl Chr; Chorus; Concert Band; Jazz Band; Rep Stu Cncl; Var L Ftbl; Var L Wrstlng; NHS; Embry-Ripple U; Aero Engrng.

GRUNDER, ANDREW; Spring-Ford SR HS; Royersford, PA; (3); 119/250; Drama Clb; Radio Clb; Thesps; Chorus; School Musical; School Play; Stage Crew; Natl Trust For Hstrc Presrvtn 87; Westchester; Teacher.

GRUNEWALD, JEFFREY; Emmaus HS; Emmaus, PA; (3); Key Clb; Letterman Clb; Model UN; VP Q&S; Scholastic Bowl; Nwsp Rptr; Nwsp Sprt Ed; Hon Roll; Natl Hist Day 3rd Dist & Hnrb Mntn 87; Acad Hallmrks Natl Knowldg Master Open 87; Hist.

GRUNFELD, ERIC; Plymouth Whitemarsh HS; Plymouth Meeting, PA; (2); Math Clb; Bsktbl; High Hon Roll; Hon Roll; Hnr Chosen 87 HS Amb From PW HS 87; Nrthn Europe This Smmr Promoting USA.

GRUNWELL, ROSE; Chichester SR HS; Boothwyn, PA; (3); 36/296; Hosp Aide; SADD; Yrbk Phtg; Lit Mag; JV Mgr(s); Var JV Score Keeper; JV Sftbl; Vllybl; Hon Roll; Literary Awd; Engr.

GRUPPO, DEBBIE; Pleasant Valley HS; Saylorsburg, PA; (2); Ski Clb; SADD; Band; Concert Band; Mrchg Band; Pep Band; Hon Roll; Band Rbbn Achvt Awd 85; Photography.

GRURIC, MELISSA; Saltsburg JR SR HS; Saltsburg, PA; (1); Church Yth Grp; Dance Clb; GAA; Hosp Aide; SADD; Trs Frsh Cls; Stu Cncl; JV Cheerleading; Gym; Trk; Phy Fitns Awd 86-87; Intl Stu Ldrshp Awd; Color Coordntr.

GRUS, MISSY; Yough SR HS; Lowber, PA; (3); 68/237; FBLA; Office Aide; Pep Clb; Ski Clb; Rep Stu Cncl; High Hon Roll; Hon Roll; Robert Morris Coll; Sci.

GRUSHECKY, SHAWN; Warren Area HS; Warren, PA; (3); Church Yth Grp; Spanish Clb; Varsity Clb; Band; Concert Band; School Play; Stage Crew; JV Crs Cntry; JV Ftbl; Trk; Presdntl Physcl Ftnss Awd 85-86; Wldlf Bio.

GRUSZKA, LISA; Nazareth Acad; Philadelphia, PA; (3); Church Yth Grp; Hosp Aide; Chorus; JV Cheerleading; Hon Roll; Prfct Atten Awd; Med.

GRUVER, CHRISTINE; Blue Mountain HS; Cressona, PA; (3); Chorus; Drill Tm; Mrchg Band; Trk; Hon Roll; Cnty Chorus Sckuykill Cnty 86-87; Disablech Childrn Teacher.

GRUVER, JASON; Gov Mifflin HS; Reading, PA; (4); 32/257; Nwsp Stf; Rep Stu Cncl; Var Capt Socr; Var Trk; Im Vllybl; JV Wrstlng; Pres Acad Fit Awd 87; U Of FL; Bus.

GRUVER, KAREN; Redbank Valley HS; New Bethlehem, PA; (4); 7/137; Drama Clb; French Clb; Stage Crew; Score Keeper; High Hon Roll; NHS; Pres Schlr; IN U Of PA; Nrsng.

GRUVER, KATHY; Penn Hills HS; Pittsburgh, PA; (3); Church Yth Grp; Sec Drama Clb; French Clb; Spanish Clb; Chorus; School Musical; School Play; Variety Show; Nwsp Sprt Ed; Hon Roll; Prvst Day Schlrshp-Eng Cmptn 87; Gftd Pgm; Drama Clb-Sec; Hnr Rl; Prfct Atten Awd; Thtr.

GRUVER, LISA; B Reed Henderson SR HS; W Chester, PA; (3); Office Aide; Lit Mag; JV Trk; Hon Roll; Engl.

GRUVER, PATRICE; Quakertown HS; Quakertown, PA; (1); Church Yth Grp; GAA; Spanish Clb; Chorus; Rep Stu Cncl; Capt Bsktbl; Var Fld Hcky; Socr; Var Trk; JC Awd; Teacher.

GRUVER, PERRY; Montgomery Area HS; Montgomery, PA; (3); French Clb; Thesps; Chorus; Stage Crew; Var L Ftbl; Var L Trk; Var L Wrstlng; NHS; Ntl Merit Ltr; Mid-Penn Ftbl All Star Team 1st String Tackle 86-87; Mech Engr.

GRYCZKO, MARGARET; Scranton Prep Schl; Clarks Green, PA; (4); 147/192; Pres Church Yth Grp; Drm Clb; Debate Tm; Chorus; PA JR Acad Sci 83-87; Notre Dame U Intl Stu Ldrshp Insti 86; St Theresa Ctchsml Awd Scranton 86; Elizabeth Coll; Occptnl Thrpy.

GRZEGOREK, DENISE; Ambridge Area HS; Ambridge, PA; (2); Pep Clb; Spanish Clb; Teachers Aide; Band; Concert Band; Drill Tm; Mrchg Band; Pep Band; Gym; Pom Pon; Prfct Atten Catechism Cls 85-87; CA ST; Elem Ed.

GRZYWINSKI, PATRICIA; Southmoreland SR HS; Scottdale, PA; (4); Dance Clb; JCL; Latin Clb; Ski Clb; Sec Spanish Clb; Teachers Aide; Chorus; Powder Puff Ftbl; Trs Spanish NHS; Clarion U; Doc.

GUARAGNO, DANIEL; Morrisville HS; Morrisville, PA; (3); 19/89; Band; Jazz Band; Mrchg Band; Crs Cntry; Hon Roll; VFW Awd; Mech Engrng.

GUARINO, JOSEPH; Hempfield HS; Lancaster, PA; (3); 109/465; Nwsp Rptr; Church Yth Grp; Var Ftbl; Wt Lftg; Hon Roll; Comm.

GUARINO, LORI; Old Forge HS; Old Forge, PA; (2); Church Yth Grp; Dance Clb; Ski Clb; Spanish Clb; Color Guard; School Musical; School Play; Variety Show; Off Soph Cls; Cheerleading; Penn ST; Prof Dncr.

GUARLOTTI, MICHELE L; Greensburg Central Catholic HS; Jeannette, PA; (3); 20/47; NFL; Nwsp Phtg; Nwsp Sprt Ed; Rep Jr Cls; Pres Sr Cls; Var Golf; L Tennis; High Hon Roll; Trs NHS; Debate Tm; Ldrshp Schlrshp Awd 85; Pre Med.

GUBICZA, JENNIFER; Trinity HS; Camp Hill, PA; (3); Hosp Aide; Service Clb; Spanish Clb; Chorus; Color Guard; Rep Stu Cncl; High Hon Roll; Hon Roll; NHS; Hlth.

GUCKERT, DANA; North Penn HS; Lansdale, PA; (3); 134/647; Ski Clb; Rep Frsh Cls; Rep Soph Cls; Rep Jr Cls; Rep Sr Cls; Rep Stu Cncl; Var Cheerleading; JV Lcrss; Powder Puff Ftbl; Hon Roll; Drexel; Bio Sci.

GUCKERT, JEFFREY; Fairview HS; Fairview, PA; (3); 1/164; FBLA; Pres Math Clb; Natl Beta Clb; Speech Tm; Var Capt Bsbl; Var L Bsktbl; Var L Golf; High Hon Roll; Ntl Merit Ltr; Most Outstndng 9th Grade Boy 84-85.

GUDUKAS, TIMOTHY; West Mifflin Area HS; W Mifflin, PA; (2); Chess Clb; VP Exploring; JV Bsbl; JV Bsktbl; Var Golf; High Hon Roll; NHS; U S Naval Acad; Aviatr.

GUEDES, MATTHEW L; Palmerton HS; Palmerton, PA; (4); 7/142; Church Yth Grp; Pres Frsh Cls; Pres Soph Cls; Var Bsbl; Var Co-Capt Ftbl; Hon Roll; ROTC 3 Yr Schlrshp 88-91; Outstndng Ftbl Stu Awd 87; Dcknsn Coll.

GUERRA, CHERYL; Phil-Mont Christian Acad; Maple Glen, PA; (4); Church Yth Grp; Political Wkr; Chorus; Stat Bsktbl; High Hon Roll; Hon Roll; Montgomery Cty CC; Jrnlst.

GUERRIERI, AMY; Brownsville SR HS; Republic, PA; (4); 1/200; Drama Clb; Capt Math Tm; Drm Mjr(t); Rep Sr Cls; Stat Trk; VP NHS; Rotary Awd; Office Aide; Ski Clb; Penn ST Jnr Sci & Hmnts Sympsm 85; Med.

GUERRIERI, LESLIE; Penn Trafford HS; Export, PA; (2); Hosp Aide; Hst JCL; Math Clb; Nwsp Ed-Chief; Lit Mag; JV Var Sftbl; Var Swmmng; High Hon Roll; Acdmc All Amer 87; Pre-Med.

GUERRIERI, MICHELE; Parkland SR HS; Allentown, PA; (3); 74/481; JA; Leo Clb; Chorus; Hon Roll; Ntl Merit Schol; Bloomsburg U; Sociolgy.

GUERRISI, JOANN; Lebanon Catholic HS; Lebanon, PA; (3); German Clb; Ski Clb; School Play; Nwsp Bus Mgr; Golf; NHS; Golf Awds 83-87; Math.

GUERRY, SARAH; Lower Merion HS; Wynnewood, PA; (3); VP French Clb; Intnl Clb; Service Clb; Church Choir; Nwsp Ed-Chief; Nwsp Rptr; Yrbk Stf; Rep Stu Cncl; VP French Hon Soc; High Hon Roll; Med.

GUFFEY, TIMOTHY; Milton Area SR HS; New Columbia, PA; (4); Latin Clb; Varsity Clb; Chorus; Var Ftbl; Im Wt Lftg; JV Wrstlng; Amer Lgn Essy Cont Locl Wnnr 87; Latn Awd High Lvl Stdy & Prfcncy 85; Devry Inst Of Tech; Elec Engrng.

GUGER, KATHY; Gateway SR HS; Monroeville, PA; (3); 12/452; Concert Band; Mrchg Band; Orch; Lit Mag; Im Vllybl; High Hon Roll; Ntl Merit Ltr; Prfct Atten Awd; Mid-East Music Fstvl 87; Estrn Swm Assc Smmr Chmpsnshps-Brnz Mdl 86; Carnegie Mellon; Bio Chem.

GUGINO, LENNY; Lock Haven HS; Lock Haven, PA; (3); 12/250; Church Yth Grp; Pres Key Clb; Model UN; Spanish Clb; Chorus; Variety Show; Var L Bsktbl; Var L Trk; Hon Roll; NHS; Hotel-Restaurant Mgmt.

GUGLIUZZA, CHARLES R; Notre Dame HS; Easton, PA; (3); School Play; Rep Frsh Cls; Var Ftbl; Var Trk; Wt Lftg; Var Wrstlng; Hon Roll; Bus Admin.

GUIANEN, DAVE; Northwestern HS; Cranesville, PA; (4); 8/145; Capt Computer Clb; Capt Math Tm; Chrmn Model UN; Scholastic Bowl; Hon Roll; JETS Awd; NHS; Ntl Merit Ltr; PA Higher Educ Assistance Agncy Commendated Stu 86-87; Capt Compt Tm 1st Pl Gannon U Comp 86-87.

GUICHETEAU, MICHAEL; Bishop Mc Devitt HS; Fort Washington, PA; (3); Church Yth Grp; Computer Clb; Ski Clb; Im Bsktbl; JV Ftbl; Wt Lftg; Hon Roll.

GUIDA, ANTHONY; Wallenpaupack Area HS; Lakeville, PA; (3); 14/160; Cmnty Wkr; Ski Clb; VP Jr Cls; Var Ftbl; Var Tennis; Wt Lftg; High Hon Roll; NHS; Schlr Awds High Hnrs 84-86; Air Force Pilot.

GUILES, MARY ELLEN; Elizabethtown Area HS; Bainridge, PA; (3); 83/224; Band; Concert Band; Jazz Band; Mrchg Band; Pep Band; Yrbk Stf; Powder Puff Ftbl; Trk; Vllybl; Church Yth Grp; Shippensberg; Socl Wrk.

GUILEY, DEREK; Council Rock HS; Richboro, PA; (3); 192/908; Drama Clb; Yrbk Phtg; Lit Mag; Rep Jr Cls; Rep Sr Cls; Rep Stu Cncl; Im Vllybl; Rep Frsh Cls; Rep Soph Cls; Presdntl Clsrm For Yng Am 87; Yth Ldrshp Cnfrnc Lehigh U 86; Sv The Chldrn Wk 85; Flm.

GUILFOYLE, BRIDGET; Punxsutawney Area HS; Punxsutawney, PA; (4); 7/246; French Clb; Math Tm; Science Clb; Band; Capt Color Guard; Concert Band; Mrchg Band; Variety Show; Twrlr; High Hon Roll; Pnxstwny Coll Schlrshp 87; IN U Of PA; Engl.

GUILLE, SHERI; Spring Ford HS; Royersford, PA; (2); 3/289; French Clb; Pep Clb; Drill Tm; Yrbk Spt Ed; Rep Stu Cncl; Var Cheerleading; L Score Keeper; Hon Roll; NHS; Anchr Clb Treas 87; Phrmcy.

GUILLEUX, BEATRICE; Upper Dublin HS; Ambler, PA; (2); Church Yth Grp; Socr; Office Aide; SADD; Stu Cncl; Mgr(s); Var Swmmng; Var Tennis; Var Timer.

GUILLEUX, FRANCOIS; Upper Dublin HS; Ambler, PA; (4); 50/320; Boy Scts; Varsity Clb; Rep Frsh Cls; Rep Soph Cls; Rep Jr Cls; Rep Sr Cls; Chrmn Stu Cncl; L Ftbl; NHS; Pres Schlr; Carnegie-Mellon U.

GUINAN, COLLEEN; Saint Huberts HS; Philadelphia, PA; (3); 312/421; Clothing & Textiles Cert For Excllnc 86-87; Typg Cert 86-87; Bus Admin.

GUINEE, PATRICK; Bishop Carroll HS; Cresson, PA; (4); 2/107; Ski Clb; Yrbk Stf; Trs Stu Cncl; Bausch & Lomb Sci Awd; Hon Roll; NHS; Ntl Merit Ltr; NEDT Awd; Chem Awd 86; Natl Stu Cncl Awd 86; Yng Comm Ldrs Of Amer 86; St Francis; Bio.

GUINN-BAILEY, BERNICE; Milton Area SR HS; Milton, PA; (3); Intnl Clb; VP Varsity Clb; Y-Teens; Lit Mag; Pres Soph Cls; Pres Sec Stu Cncl; Var Bsktbl; Crs Cntry; Var Trk; Im Vllybl; Mst Outstndng Prfrmce Trk 85-87; Stu Cncl Awd 87; Paralgl.

GUISE, BRAD; Central York SR HS; York, PA; (4); 4-H; JV Ftbl; Im Vllybl; Hon Roll; PA ST U; Sci.

GUISE, LISA; Owen J Roberts HS; Pottstown, PA; (4); 5/291; Church Choir; Concert Band; Mrchg Band; School Musical; Off Stu Cncl; Stat Bsktbl; Im Vllybl; High Hon Roll; High Hon Roll; VP NHS; Chem.

GUISLER, LISA M; Beaver Area HS; Midland, PA; (4); JCL; Ski Clb; Drm Mjr(t); Trs Jr Cls; Bsktbl; Cheerleading; Twrlr; High Hon Roll; NHS; Pres Schlr; Army Schlr/Athl Awd 86; Rotary Club Stu Mnth May 87; Directors Awd Mrchng Band 86; Geneva Coll; Accntng.

GUISTO, ROCHELE L; Cameron County HS; Emporium, PA; (3); 3/87; Mu Alpha Theta; Yrbk Stf; Pres Soph Cls; Pres Jr Cls; Rep Stu Cncl; High Hon Roll; Hon Roll; Mu Alpha Theta Awd; NHS; Prfct Atten Awd; Law.

GUISTWHITE, DAVID; Mechanicsburg HS; Mechanicsburg, PA; (3); Band; Concert Band; Jazz Band; Mrchg Band; Orch; Symp Band; God Cntry Awd; High Hon Roll; Hon Roll; Church Yth Grp; Ntl Hnr Roll Yrbk 87.

GUJDA, MICHAEL J; Holy Ghost Preparatory Schl; Bristol, PA; (4); Art Clb; Math Tm; Scholastic Bowl; Var Crs Cntry; Var Trk; Hon Roll; NHS; Pres Schlr; Math Clb; Nwsp Stf; Excllnc In Advncd Lvl Frnch 86-87; Excllnc In Intrmdt Grmn, Hnbl Mntn 86; Lehigh U; Bus.

GULA III, JOSEPH F; Ringgold HS; Donora, PA; (3); 74/351; Office Aide; Var JV Bsktbl; Var JV Ftbl; Hon Roll; Pharm.

GULLA, TRACEY; Sharpsville SR HS; Sharpsville, PA; (3); Camera Clb; Yrbk Stf; NHS; Acdmc Achvt Awd 86-87; Penn ST U.

GUMAN, CYNTHIA; Brownsville Area HS; Grindstone, PA; (3); FBLA; Co-Capt Cheerleading; Gym; High Hon Roll; Hon Roll.

GUMAN, JOE; Valley View HS; Jessup, PA; (3); Art Clb; FFA; Latin Clb; Science Clb; Band; Chorus; Nwsp Stf; Public Spkng Awd 87; VP FFA 86-88.

GUMBERT, TAMMY; West Allegheny HS; Oakdale, PA; (3); Chorus; Lit Mag; Rep Stu Cncl; Cheerleading; Jr NHS; Law.

GUMBINER, HEATHER L; Owen J Roberts HS; Pottstown, PA; (2); 25/325; Church Yth Grp; French Clb; Intnl Clb; Key Clb; Service Clb; Band; Concert Band; Mrchg Band; School Musical; Symp Band; Distrct 12 Band Awd & Regnl 6 Band Awd 87; Med.

GUMBINER, LAURA M; Owen J Roberts HS; Pottstown, PA; (3); 4/299; German Clb; Key Clb; Band; Church Choir; Mrchg Band; Rep Stu Cncl; JV Sftbl; Vllybl; Hon Roll; NHS; Med Rsrch.

GUMINA, SCOTT J; Elizabeth Forward HS; Elizabeth, PA; (4); 69/293; Church Yth Grp; Pres Band; Concert Band; Drm & Bgl; Jazz Band; Mrchg Band; Pep Band; School Musical; Trk; Hon Roll; Music Prfrmnce Scholar WVU 87; Mc Keesport Music Clb Prfrmnce Scholar 87; Baldwin Whitehll Ed Scholar; WVU; Music.

GUMLOCK, DAVID A; Easton Area HS; Easton, PA; (4); 24/460; Debate Tm; Chorus; Orch; Hon Roll; Jr NHS; NHS; Ntl Merit SF; Earlham Coll; Pre-Arch.

GUMMO, RENEA; Bellwood Antis Jr Sr HS; Altoona, PA; (2); Nwsp Rptr; Nwsp Stf; L Bsktbl; Trk; High Hon Roll; Hon Roll; HOBY Ldrsh Awd 86-87; Natl Piano Plyng ST Member 86; Journlst.

GUMMO, TANYA; Tyrone Area HS; Tyrone, PA; (3); 28/198; Drama Clb; Pres Girl Scts; Spanish Clb; School Play; Yrbk Stf; High Hon Roll; Hon Roll; Art Clb; Twrlr; Outstndng Stu Drftng, Dsgn 87; Spnsh Tchr Elem Stu 86-87; Exchng Stu 87-88; US Air Frc; Arch.

GUNDY, DENISE; Philadelphia High School For Girls; Philadelphia, PA; (3); 15/405; Spanish Clb; Office Aide; Rep Service Clb; Stage Crew; Rep Stu Cncl; JV Bowling; Spanish NHS; Dstngshd Rprt Crds Hnr Keys 85-86; C E Ellis Schlrshp 85-87; Meritrs Awd 87; Med.

GUNST, SHAWN; Highlands HS; Natrona Heights, PA; (4); 88/277; School Play; Pres Stu Cncl; L Ftbl; L Trk; Var Vllybl; Hon Roll; Prfct Atten Awd; OH Wesleyan U; Hstry.

GUNTER, LAURA; West Branch Area HS; Morrisdale, PA; (2); Drama Clb; 4-H; Spanish Clb; Chorus; Stage Crew; 4-H Awd; Nrsng.

GUNTHER, TRICIA; Ambridge Area HS; Ambridge, PA; (3); Church Yth Grp; Pep Clb; Spanish Clb; Band; Mrchg Band; Symp Band; Hon Roll; Prfct Atten Awd; Phtgrphy.

GUNZBURGER, GREG; Coudersport JR SR HS; Coudersport, PA; (3); 18/77; FFA; Varsity Clb; Band; School Play; Pres Jr Cls; Var L Ftbl; Var L Trk; Var L Wrstlng; Hon Roll; Concert Band; Sports Boosters Spirit Awd 87; Penn ST; Bus Mgmt.

GUPTA, DHRUTI; Council Rock HS; Langhorne, PA; (3); Intnl Clb; Key Clb; SADD; Hon Roll.

GUPTA, RITA; Gateway SR HS; Monroeville, PA; (3); 8/475; Hosp Aide; JA; Math Tm; Science Clb; Orch; Trs Soph Cls; Stu Cncl; Socr; High Hon Roll; NHS; Engrng.

GURDAK, PAUL; Warren Area HS; Warren, PA; (3); Boy Scts; French Clb; Letterman Clb; Varsity Clb; Band; School Play; Im Bsbl; Var L Bsktbl; Im Wt Lftg; Hon Roll; Bus.

GURGANUS, SHELLY; Grace Christian HS; Lebanon, PA; (3); 6/22; Church Yth Grp; Drama Clb; Ski Clb; Speech Tm; Chorus; Church Choir; School Play; Yrbk Stf; Sec Frsh Cls; Sec Soph Cls; Fnlst PA Miss Natl Teenager Pgntn 86 & 87; Liberty U; Communications.

GURGIOLO, THOMAS; New Castle SR HS; New Castle, PA; (4); Church Yth Grp; Math Tm; Varsity Clb; Band; Jazz Band; Mrchg Band; Symp Band; Rep Frsh Cls; Tennis; Hon Roll; Womens Shelter Essay Cont Winner 87; OH Northern U; Math.

GURLEY, DENISE; Archbishop Ryan HS; Philadelphia, PA; (4); 276/490; Camp Fr Inc; Cmnty Wkr; JA; Q&S; Ed Nwsp Rptr; JV Bowling; 2nd Hnrs 86-87; ST Grnt 87-88; Bucks Co Comm Coll; Acctng.

GURNANI, SAILESH; Woodland Hills SR HS; Pittsburgh, PA; (2); 4/222; Math Clb; Acpl Chr; Band; Concert Band; Jazz Band; Mrchg Band; Orch; School Musical; Stu Cncl; Trk; 5th-Physcs Band Comp-PA Sci Olympd 87; Chmcl Engrng.

GURSKY, JOANN E; North Schuylkill HS; Frackville, PA; (4); 3/170; Church Yth Grp; Church Choir; Variety Show; Stat Bsktbl; Golf; Elks Awd; High Hon Roll; Hon Roll; NHS; N Schuylkill Trst Forgn Lang Awd 87; Enrlld Hnrs Prog Susquehanna U 87; Susquehanna Schlrshp 87; Susquehanna U; Comp Sci.

GUSKIEWICZ, LAURA; Greensburg Central Catholic HS; Greensburg, PA; (2); Lit Mag; Hon Roll; St Vincent Coll Prog Gifted & Talented 85-87; St Vincent Coll.

GUSTAFSON, KATHRYN; Greensburg Central Catholic HS; Jeannette, PA; (3); Church Yth Grp; Intnl Clb; NFL; Yrbk Stf; High Hon Roll; Hon Roll; NHS; Im Sftbl; Im Vllybl; Eng.

GUSTITIS, RANDAL D; Cardinal O Hara HS; Broomall, PA; (4); 3/772; Pres German Clb; Math Tm; Mrchg Band; Ed Yrbk Phtg; High Hon Roll; JETS Awd; Lion Awd; NHS; Ntl Merit SF; Computer Clb; Delta Epsilon Phi German Natl Hnr Soc 86; Amrcn Defns Assoc Awd 86; Navy Dstngshd Achvt Awd 86; Nuclear Engrng.

GUTH, DEANNA; Connellsville Area SR HS; Dawson, PA; (2); French Hon Soc; High Hon Roll; Hon Roll.

GUTHERIE, RUSSEL; Jefferson-Morgan HS; Jefferson, PA; (4); 11/90; Hon Roll.

GUTHRIDGE, SCOTT; Living Wood Acad; Manheim, PA; (3); Church Yth Grp; Stage Crew; Yrbk Phtg; Yrbk Stf; Pres Soph Cls; Stu Cncl; Socr; Trk; Hon Roll.

GUTHRIE, CHARLES; Du Bois Area HS; Falls Crk, PA; (2); Arts.

GUTHRIE, KRISTIE; Fairchance Georges SR HS; Fairchance, PA; (3); Church Yth Grp; FHA; NAACP; Spanish Clb; JV Bsktbl; High Hon Roll; Hon Roll; NHS.

GUTHRIE, LINDA; Bishop Boyle HS; Pittsburgh, PA; (2); Church Yth Grp; Chorus; Nwsp Rptr; VP Frsh Cls; JV Var Bsktbl; JV Var Vllybl; Hon Roll; PA Jr Acad Of Sci-2nd Awd 86.

GUTHRIE, LUCINDA; Youngsville HS; Irvine, PA; (4); #1 In Class; Math Tm; Spanish Clb; School Play; Stage Crew; Rep Stu Cncl; High Hon Roll; NHS; Prfct Atten Awd; Val; Mltry Plc Ofcr.

GUTHRIE, MELISSA; Pen Argyl Area HS; Pen Argyl, PA; (4); Church Yth Grp; Drama Clb; Math Clb; Ski Clb; Spanish Clb; Chorus; School Play; Var Capt Cheerleading; Sftbl; Pen Argyl Area Educ Assn Schlrshp 87; E Stroudsburg U; Elem Educ.

GUTHRIE, SANDRA; Curwensville Area HS; Grampian, PA; (3); Church Yth Grp; French Clb; Church Choir; Mat Maids; Accntng.

GUTIERREZ, MARCIA; Center HS; Monaca, PA; (2); Church Yth Grp; Cmnty Wkr; Hosp Aide; Spanish Clb; Yrbk Stf; Stu Cncl; L Gym; Powder Puff Ftbl; L Trk; High Hon Roll; Gifted Prog 85-86; Frgn Lang Awd Spanish I & II 86-87; Monaca Turners Gymnst Team 85-87.

GUTIERREZ, TERRI; Center Area HS; Monaca, PA; (3); Church Yth Grp; Spanish Clb; Chorus; Drill Tm; School Musical; Yrbk Stf; Stu Cncl; Pom Pon; High Hon Roll; NHS; Gifted Prog 84-87; Slipper Rock U Forgn Lang Comptn 2nd Pl Span III Voc 87; Band 2nd Cls 87; Law.

GUTKNECHT, KRISTIN; Danville SR HS; Danville, PA; (1); Church Yth Grp; Hosp Aide; Key Clb; Ski Clb; Var JV Cheerleading; High Hon Roll; Prsdntl Acadmc Ftns Awd 86-87; Hgh Frnch I Avg Awd-2nd Hghst Avg 86-87; Colgate U; Scl Wrk.

GUTOWSKI, JENNIFER; Du Bois Area HS; Dubois, PA; (3); Church Yth Grp; Hosp Aide; Band; Chorus; Concert Band; Mrchg Band; School Musical; Swing Chorus; Swmmng; Hon Roll; Med.

GUTOWSKI, PETER; Pittston Area HS; Pittston, PA; (2); 1/354; Church Yth Grp; French Clb; JV Wrstlng; High Hon Roll; NHS; Rotary Awd; PA ST; Econ.

GUTSHALL, BARBARA; Donegal HS; Marietta, PA; (2); Church Yth Grp; Band; Concert Band; Mrchg Band; JV Tennis; Hon Roll; Cnty Band Fest Symphnc Band 87.

GUTSHALL, BRENDA; Palmyra HS; Palmyra, PA; (4); Ski Clb; Chorus; Harrisburg Area CC; Phrmcy.

GUTSHALL, ERIC; Central Dauphin HS; Harrisburg, PA; (3); Church Yth Grp; Cmnty Wkr; FCA; Letterman Clb; Varsity Clb; School Play; Frsh Cls; Bsktbl; Golf; Cit Awd; Outstndg Carrier Contst 83-86; Young Colubus Trip Englnd & Sctlnd 85; Bus Admin.

GUTSHALL, JEFFREY; East Pennsboro Area HS; Enola, PA; (3); Ski Clb; Varsity Clb; Stat Socr; Var L Trk; High Hon Roll; Bucknell U; Engrng.

GUTTERMAN, FRANKLIN; MMI Prep; Hazleton, PA; (4); 1/29; Computer Clb; Ski Clb; Pres Sr Cls; Var Bsbl; JV Bowling; Var Crs Cntry; High Hon Roll; NHS; NEDT Awd; Spanish NHS; Excel In Cmptr Sci Awd 84; PA JR Acad Of Sci St Comp 83-85; Ntl Chem Scty Tst 86; Cmptr Sci.

GUTTERMAN, MERLE; MMI Prep Schl; Hazleton, PA; (3); Ski Clb; Nwsp Stf; Yrbk Stf; Rep Frsh Cls; Rep Soph Cls; Stu Cncl; JV Bowling; Hon Roll; NEDT Awd; Spanish NHS; Cmmnctns.

GUTTSHALL, BRET; Carlisle HS; Carlisle, PA; (3); Rep Jr Cls; Hon Roll; Prfct Atten Awd; Bus.

GUTZWILER, JIM; Portersville Christian Schl; Zelienople, PA; (3); Church Yth Grp; Ski Clb; Variety Show; Yrbk Bus Mgr; Yrbk Stf; Rep Jr Cls; Rep Stu Cncl; Bsktbl; Socr; High Hon Roll.

GUY, COLLEEN; Middletown Area HS; Middletown, PA; (4); 34/171; Key Clb; Chorus; Nwsp Stf; Var JV Cheerleading; Hon Roll; NHS; Allwine Schlrshp 87; Shppnsbrg U; Engl.

GUY, RACHEL; Lincoln HS; Wampum, PA; (3); 27/162; French Clb; Y-Teens; Chorus; High Hon Roll; Hon Roll.

GUY, TINA; Valley HS; Arnold, PA; (1); Chorus; Pittsburgh Beauty Acad; Csmtlgy.

GUYDISH, CHRISTA; Bishop O Reilly HS; Plains, PA; (3); Church Yth Grp; Hosp Aide; Spanish Clb; Stu Cncl; Crs Cntry; Tennis; Bus.

GUYER, KRISTA; Philipsburg-Osceola HS; Philipsburg, PA; (4); SADD; Band; Concert Band; Yrbk Stf; Rep Stu Cncl; Sftbl; Prom Cmmttee 86 & 87; IN U Of PA; Elem Educ.

GUYNN, PAULA; Southmoreland SR HS; Scottdale, PA; (2); Church Yth Grp; French Clb; Math Clb; Ski Clb; Vllybl; French Hon Soc; High Hon Roll; Splng Bee 84; Hgh Hnr Rl 83-84; Law.

GUYRE, GARRETT; Pocono Mountain HS; Blakeslee, PA; (4); Church Yth Grp; Cmnty Wkr; French Clb; Pep Clb; SADD; Teachers Aide; Var Bsbl; Hon Roll; Aeronautical Engrng.

GUZA, TRACY; Hazleton HS; Hazelton, PA; (4); 3/388; Drama Clb; Y-Teens; High Hon Roll; NHS; Pres Schlr; Art Leag Fine Arts Awd 87; Schlstc Art Awd 87; Fashion Inst Tech; Fshn Merch.

GUZIK, JEAN; Chartiers Valley HS; Pittsburgh, PA; (3); 75/360; Math Tm; Pres Pep Clb; Ski Clb; Variety Show; Var Vllybl; Rotary Awd; Schl Rep Teen Inst 86-87; U Pittsburgh; Elem Ed.

GUZOWSKI, NICOLE; Reading SR HS; Reading, PA; (4); 170/560; Pres Church Yth Grp; Nwsp Stf; Im Bsktbl; JV Diving; Var Sftbl; Im Vllybl; Prfct Atten Awd; Cedar Crest Coll; Med Tech.

GUZUR, RICH; Charleroi Area HS; Charleroi, PA; (3); 13/185; Trs Church Yth Grp; Varsity Clb; Mrchg Band; Orch; Symp Band; Var L Socr; Hon Roll; NHS; Prfct Atten Awd; Gannon U; Crmnl Jstc.

GUZZARDO, GARY; Fairview HS; Fairview, PA; (3); Model UN; Ski Clb; Trs Spanish Clb; Speech Tm; Varsity Clb; Sec Jr Cls; Pres Sr Cls; Var Socr; L Var Trk; Hon Roll; Arch.

GUZZY, JOHN; Greensburg Central Catholic HS; New Stanton, PA; (3); 14/250; Hosp Aide; Yrbk Stf; Rep Stu Cncl; Var L Bsktbl; Var L Ftbl; High Hon Roll; NHS; Pre-Med.

GWYNN, DAYNA; Carmichaels Area JR SR HS; Carmichaels, PA; (2); 6/115; Band; Concert Band; Mrchg Band; Nwsp Stf; High Hon Roll; Jr NHS; Prfct Atten Awd; Pres Acdmc Awds Pgm 85-86.

HA, DANIEL; Salanco SR HS; New Providence, PA; (3); Drama Clb; German Clb; High Hon Roll; Hon Roll; Ntl Merit SF; Schlrshp Awd Socl Stds 87; Bio.

HAAG, DANIEL; Central SR HS; York, PA; (4); 1/213; Pep Band; School Musical; Bausch & Lomb Sci Awd; High Hon Roll; Lion Awd; Hst NHS; Opt Clb Awd; Val; VFW Awd; Voice Dem Awd; Carnegie Mellon U; Chem Engr.

HAAG, MICHELLE; Oil City SR HS; Oil City, PA; (3); Church Yth Grp; Girl Scts; Trk; Wt Lftg; Stat Wrstlng; High Hon Roll; Hon Roll; Prfct Atten Awd; Gftd Acad Schlrshp-Clarion U, Free Entrprs Wk Schlrshp-Lockhaven U 87.

HAAS, ANDREW R; Loyalsock Township HS; Montoursville, PA; (3); 4/117; French Clb; Latin Clb; Ski Clb; SADD; Varsity Clb; Rep Stu Cncl; Bsktbl; Socr; Bausch & Lomb Sci Awd; NHS; Intl Sgnl Cntrl Grp Sci Test 3rd Pl 86; Knight-Pre-Calc Hnrs Chem 86-87; Franklin & Marshall; Med.

HAAS, CHRISTA; Mercyhurst Preparatory Schl; Erie, PA; (2); Church Yth Grp; Drama Clb; Chorus; Church Choir; School Musical; NCTE Awd; Mercyhurst Prep Schl Arts Schlrp 86-87.

HAAS, FARAH; Owen J Roberts HS; Pottstown, PA; (4); 26/270; Camera Clb; Dance Clb; Latin Clb; Varsity Clb; School Musical; Yrbk Stf; JV Var Fld Hcky; Var Capt Lcrss; Hon Roll; NHS; James Madison U; Cmmnctns.

HAAS, GEORGANNE; Pius X HS; Pen Argyl, PA; (4); 10/32; Pep Clb; Varsity Clb; Church Choir; Yrbk Stf; Sec Sr Cls; Sec Stu Cncl; Capt Var Bsktbl; Capt Var Sftbl; Hon Roll; Schlr Athlt Awd 87; Mst Outstndng Athlt Awd 87; W Yeisley Mem 87; Secy.

HAAS, GREGORY S; Kutztown Area HS; Kutztown, PA; (4); 2/147; Pres Church Yth Grp; Science Clb; Band; Church Choir; Concert Band; Jazz Band; Mrchg Band; School Musical; School Play; Variety Show; Pres Acad Fit Awd 87; Highest Ranking Math Stu Awd 87; U Of Pittsburgh; Engrng.

HAAS, HEATHER; Parkland HS; Schnecksville, PA; (4); Pres 4-H; JA; Math Tm; Off SADD; Rep Soph Cls; Rep Jr Cls; Rep Sr Cls; Stu Cncl; 4-H Awd; Hon Roll.

HAAS, JEFF; Brandywine Hts HS; Mertztown, PA; (2); Var Bsbl; JV Socr; Vllybl; Hon Roll; Defnse Atty.

HAAS, KAREN; Blue Mountain Acad; Emmaus, PA; (4); Chess Clb; Church Yth Grp; Library Aide; Chorus; Church Choir; Orch; Stage Crew; Yrbk Stf; Hon Roll; Prfct Atten Awd; Stu Dcnss 86-87; Prse Ensmble 85-87; Ushrtte 84-86; Hartland Coll; Chrstn Bus Admin.

HAAS, KEITH; Northeastern SR HS; Manchester, PA; (2); Yrbk Stf; Ed Lit Mag; Capt Golf; Var Wrstlng; High Hon Roll; Jr NHS; NHS; Ntl Merit Ltr; Physcis.

HAAS, MICHAEL; Central Dauphin HS; Harrisburg, PA; (3); 90/350; Ski Clb; Rep Soph Cls; Rep Jr Cls; Rep Sr Cls; Rep Stu Cncl; Var Socr; Hon Roll; Physics.

HAAS, PETER; Interboro HS; Prospect Park, PA; (3); Camp Fr Inc; French Clb; Band; Chorus; Church Choir; Jazz Band; Mrchg Band; School Play; Nwsp Ed-Chief; Nwsp Rptr; Astro Physcs.

HAAS, TRICIA; Warwick SR HS; Lititz, PA; (2); 14/240; Computer Clb; Girl Scts; Teachers Aide; Yrbk Stf; JV Capt Bsktbl; Var Sftbl; High Hon Roll; Lions Clb Yth Exch Stu Peru 87; Tchg.

HAASE, JENNIFER; Downingtown SR HS; Glenmoore, PA; (3); 148/650; Church Yth Grp; Drama Clb; French Clb; Intnl Clb; Ski Clb; School Play; Nwsp Stf; Rep Stu Cncl; Hon Roll; Pres Schlr; Psych.

HABA, DARLENE; Kennard-Dale HS; Oxford, PA; (4); 10/125; Exploring; Ski Clb; Band; Concert Band; Mrchg Band; Yrbk Rptr; Yrbk Stf; Hon Roll; NHS; Pres Schlr; York Cnty Acdmc All Str 87; Spch Thrpst.

HABAKUS, SCOTT; Governor Mifflin HS; Mohnton, PA; (4); 73/270; Chess Clb; Var Bsbl; Capt Bsktbl; Im Vllybl; PA ST U; Elec Engrng.

HABALAR, CAREY; Garden Spot HS; New Holland, PA; (2); Church Yth Grp; Bsktbl; Sftbl; Hon Roll; Jr NHS; Cmmnctns.

HABECKER, JENNY; Hempfield HS; Lancaster, PA; (3); Yrbk Bus Mgr; Fld Hcky; Mgr Swmmng; Hon Roll; Hotel-Rstrnt Mngt.

HABECKER, WENDY; William Allen HS; Allentown, PA; (3); Trs Leo Clb; Spanish Clb; SADD; Band; Concert Band; School Musical; Yrbk Stf; Powder Puff Ftbl; JV Sftbl; Pol Sci.

HABER, BRETT; Hamton HS; Gladwyne, PA; (3); Yrbk Bus Mgr; JV Tennis; Var Capt Trk; Hon Roll; NHS; All ST 300 Mtrs Hrdls Trck & Fld 86; 3 Time ST Champ Trck & Fld 87; Lib Arts.

HABER, JAMES; Northeast Catholic HS; Philadelphia, PA; (3); Aud/Vis; Church Yth Grp; SADD; Band; Concert Band; Mrchg Band; Orch; Pep Band; Stage Crew; Hon Roll; Natl Hnr Soc Awd Svc Tutorng 87; All Cathlc Band 86; Comm.

HABER, JENNIFER; Freedom HS; Easton, PA; (4); Pres Drama Clb; French Clb; Hosp Aide; Ski Clb; Trs SADD; School Play; Trs Jr Cls; Rep Stu Cncl; Var Capt Fld Hcky; Hon Roll; PA Plyhse Drama Awd 87; Wheaton Coll; Psych.

HABERBERGER, TAMMY; St Marys Area HS; Saint Marys, PA; (4); Stat Bsktbl; Stat Ftbl; Var Sftbl; Hon Roll; Gannon U; Law Assistnt.

HABERGERGER, MICHELLE; St Marys Area HS; Saint Marys, PA; (4); 8/278; VP Stu Cncl; JV Cheerleading; Var Capt Trk; JV Var Vllybl; Hon Roll; Lion Awd; NHS; Gannon Acad Schlrshp 87; Diane Johnson Mem Awd 87; Gannon U; Nrsng.

HABERLE, TROY; Boyertown SR HS; Boyertown, PA; (3); VICA; US Navy.

HABERLEN, JENNIFER; Ligonier Valley SR HS; Ligonier, PA; (4); 1/154; AFS; Yrbk Ed-Chief; Var L Bsktbl; Var L Trk; Bausch & Lomb Sci Awd; Elks Awd; Gov Hon Prg Awd; Val; Church Yth Grp; Model UN; Army & Air Force ROTC Schlrshps 87; Westinghouse Sci Hnrs Inst 87; Schlr/Athlete Awds 87; John Hopkins; Bio Med Engrng.

HABERSTROH, J TODD; Hempfield HS; Columbia, PA; (2); 140/447.

HABERSTUMPF, CRAIG; Emmaus HS; Emmaus, PA; (3); 52/530; Key Clb; Var L Swmmng; High Hon Roll; Hon Roll; Bloomsburg U; Accntng.

HABLE, KIM; Garden Spot HS; New Holland, PA; (4); Church Yth Grp; 4-H; Girl Scts; Sec Spanish Clb; SADD; Chorus; Pres Frsh Cls; Rep Soph Cls; Stu Cncl; Var JV Fld Hcky; Millersville U; Elem Educ.

HABOUSH, MICHAEL; Hopewell SR HS; Aliquippa, PA; (2); JV Bsktbl; Var Crs Cntry; L Var Vllybl; Hon Roll; 3rd Yr Spn ; Nwspr Carrier.

HACHENBERG, JODIE; Lock Haven HS; Lock Haven, PA; (3); Art Clb; Computer Clb; Drama Clb; 4-H; German Clb; Spanish Clb; SADD; Yrbk Bus Mgr; Yrbk Phtg; Yrbk Rptr; 4-H Dale Carnegie Course 86.

HACK, LYDIA; Juniata HS; Mifflintown, PA; (3); Trs Church Yth Grp; Girl Scts; Political Wkr; Pres Spanish Clb; Pres Band; Yrbk Stf; Bsktbl; 4-H Awd; NHS; Computer Clb; Band Outstndng JR 87; Schlstc Ltr 86-87; Atty.

HACK, VIRGINIA A; Burrell HS; Lower Burrell, PA; (4); 7/197; Spanish Clb; Chorus; Church Choir; Mrchg Band; Variety Show; High Hon Roll; NHS; Pres Schlr; Rotary Awd; Young People Alive Perfrmng Grp 83-87; Schlstc Achvmnt Awd 85-87; Regnl Dist Choir 87; Shenandoah Coll&consrvtry; Musi.

HACKENBERG, ERICK; Marian Catholic HS; Nesquehoning, PA; (3); 13/105; SADD; Rep Soph Cls; Rep Jr Cls; JV Var Bsktbl; JV Var Ftbl; High Hon Roll; NHS; Math Clb; Rep Frsh Cls; WQEQ Plyr Game-Chmpnshp Game Dist Ii 85; Schl Career/Single Seasn Passing Rcd 86; Pre-Med.

HACKENBERG, SHELLEY; Mechanicsburg HS; Mechanicsburg, PA; (2); Church Yth Grp; GAA; Pep Clb; JV Fld Hcky; Var Sftbl; Var Trk; Hon Roll; Csmtlgsy.

HACKENBURG, STEPHANIE; Middleburg HS; Middleburg, PA; (3); 9/120; VP Key Clb; Varsity Clb; Band; Yrbk Sprt Ed; Pres Jr Cls; Var Bsktbl; Var Fld Hcky; Var Sftbl; Var Hon Roll; NHS; Fld Hcky All Star Tm 85-87; PA Math Leag Cert Merit, & Dist Band 86-87; Educ.

HACKER, MONICA; Cheltenham HS; Wyncote, PA; (4); 70/365; Art Clb; Aud/Vis; Pep Clb; PAVAS; Ski Clb; Yrbk Phtg; VP Soph Cls; VP Jr Cls; VP Sr Cls; Stu Cncl; Clemson U SC; Textiles.

HACKETT, DENISE; Juniata HS; Mifflintown, PA; (3); SADD; Chorus; Nwsp Stf; Yrbk Stf; Hon Roll; Computer Clb; Spanish Clb; Concert Band; School Play; Stage Crew; Modern Music Masters Tri-M 82-88; Libry Asst 86-88; Vllybl Clb 86-87; OH Wesleyan Coll; Psych.

HACKETT, LISA; Shaler Area HS; Pittsburgh, PA; (4); 54/509; Yrbk Stf; JV Var Mgr(s); Hon Roll; Spanish NHS; Carlow Coll.

HACKETT JR, MICHAEL J; Archbishop Ryan HS For Boys; Philadelphia, PA; (2); 12/352; Im Coach Actv; Stat Powder Puff Ftbl; JV Socr; Hon Roll; PA ST U.

HACKMAN, JILL; Gateway SR HS; Monroeville, PA; (3); Chorus; Yrbk Stf; Off Frsh Cls; Off Soph Cls; Off Jr Cls; Off Sr Cls; Stu Cncl; JV Bsktbl.

HACKWORTH, JULIE; Solanco SR HS; Holtwood, PA; (3); 15/272; VP Church Yth Grp; Teachers Aide; Acpl Chr; Chorus; Flag Corp; Nwsp Ed-Chief; High Hon Roll; NHS; Salanco Schlr Art 85; TAG Prog 84-88; Jrnlst.

HADDAD, JOHN; Central Catholic HS; Allentown, PA; (3); JA; Chorus; Socr; Trk; Northampton Area Coll; Acctng.

HADDOCK, CRAIG; Belle Vernon Area HS; W Newton, PA; (4); 78/258; Capt Socr; Capt Vllybl; High Hon Roll; Hon Roll; Pl Tech Inst; Comp Aid Drftng.

HADLEY, TRACY; Central HS; Scranton, PA; (2); German Clb; SADD; Band; L Pom Pon; L Swmmng; L Trk.

HADVANCE, PAULA; GAR Memorial HS; Wilkes-Barre, PA; (4); 6/172; Key Clb; Library Aide; Ski Clb; Chorus; Yrbk Stf; Rep Stu Cncl; Capt Cheerleading; Jr NHS; NHS; Med.

HAEFNER, TONY; Lancaster Catholic HS; Lancaster, PA; (3); 50/193; Art Clb; Church Yth Grp; Cmnty Wkr; Service Clb; Hon Roll; Art.

HAEHN, LISA; Youngsville JR SR HS; Grand Valley, PA; (4); 27/96; Pres 4-H; Spanish Clb; Band; Color Guard; Concert Band; Mrchg Band; Yrbk Stf; Rep Stu Cncl; JV Bsktbl; Var Cheerleading; Hmmkrs Extnsn Schlrshp 87; Rotary Schlrshp 87; Warren Cnty Medcl Soc Auxlry 87; Franklin Rgnl Mdcl; X-Ray Tech.

HAERTSCH, HEIDI ANNE; Pocono Central Catholic HS; Swiftwater, PA; (4); Church Yth Grp; NFL; Service Clb; Teachers Aide; Chorus; School Musical; School Play; Cheerleading; High Hon Roll; Anne Jacoby Mem Awd 87; Musicians Protective Awd 87; MVP Chrldg Awd 87; W Chester U; Elem Ed.

HAERTTER, TIMOTHY; Catholic HS Of Lancastr; Lancaster, PA; (4); 48/188; Church Yth Grp; Pep Clb; Varsity Clb; Band; Chorus; Concert Band; Jazz Band; Mrchg Band; School Musical; Var Cheerleading; PA ST U; Engrng.

HAEUSER, DONNA; Bishop Conwell HS; Levittown, PA; (3); Band; Socr; Bucks Cnty CC; Comp.

HAFEMEISTER, CHRIS; Villa Maria HS; Mantua, OH; (4); 23/52; Pep Clb; Spanish Clb; Thesps; School Musical; Stage Crew; Var Vllybl; NHS; Spanish NHS; Kent ST U; Bus Adm.

HAFER, DAVID; Cumberland Valley HS; Camp Hill, PA; (3); 214/583; Var Swmmng; Bus.

HAFER, LANCE; Tamaqua Area HS; Tamaqua, PA; (3); German Clb; Sec Science Clb; Co-Capt Bsbl; Bsktbl; Ftbl; Hon Roll; NHS; Prfct Atten Awd; German Hnr Soc 86-87; Penn ST U; Arch.

HAFFLY, ELIZABETH; Middletown Area HS; Middletown, PA; (3); Art Clb; Church Yth Grp; Computer Clb; Library Aide; Political Wkr; Scholastic Bowl; SADD; School Musical; Hon Roll; Prfct Atten Awd; Art Awd 84; Comp.

HAFFNER, ANDREA; Bensalem HS; Bensalem, PA; (2); Hosp Aide; Teachers Aide; Mgr(s); JV Trk; High Hon Roll; NHS.

HAFNER, STEPHANIE; Altoona Area HS; Altoona, PA; (3); Church Yth Grp; FTA; German Clb; Band; Chorus; Church Choir; Concert Band; Orch; Hon Roll; Valley Forge Chrstn Coll; Music.

HAFTEL, BRETT L; Twin Valley HS; Reading, PA; (4); 15/132; FBLA; Scholastic Bowl; Pres Spanish Clb; School Musical; Nwsp Bus Mgr; Ed Yrbk Stf; JV Bowling; CC Awd; High Hon Roll; NHS; Schlrshp-PA Free Entrprs 86; Outstndng Bus Stu 84; Outstndng FBLA Stu 83-86; Dickinson Col6; Bus Adm.

HAGADUS, PAUL; Central Catholic HS; Allentown, PA; (3); Boy Scts; Church Yth Grp; Letterman Clb; Off Sr Cls; Bsbl; Im Bowling; Var L Ftbl; Wt Lftg; Var L Wrstlng; Hon Roll; Pittsburgh; Ed.

HAGAN, MELISSA; Canon Mc Millan HS; Canonsburg, PA; (4); VP NAACP; Sec Varsity Clb; Church Choir; Nwsp Stf; Yrbk Stf; Sec Sr Cls; Trs Stu Cncl; Var Capt Crs Cntry; Var Capt Trk; NHS; Mary Chptr 24 Eastern Star Schlrshp 87; Outstndg Avchvmnt Athlets Awd 87; Indiana U Of PA; Ecnmcs.

HAGEL, KATHRYN; Salem Christian Schl; Allentown, PA; (4); 1/17; Drama Clb; Chorus; School Musical; VP Sr Cls; Pres Stu Cncl; Var L Bsktbl; Capt Cheerleading; Var L Sftbl; High Hon Roll; Val; Elim Bible Inst; Yth Cnslng.

HAGEMANN, AMY; Liberty HS; Bethlehem, PA; (4); 19/421; Hosp Aide; Teachers Aide; Band; Chorus; Concert Band; Mrchg Band; Var Capt Fld Hcky; High Hon Roll; NHS; Clss 1920 Awd 87; Muhlenberg Coll; Chem.

HAGEN, STEPHEN; Beaver HS; Beaver, PA; (2); Chess Clb; Church Yth Grp; JCL; Latin Clb; Chorus; Church Choir; Trk; High Hon Roll; Hon Roll; Hnr Roll.

HAGER, TAWNIA; Conneaut Lake HS; Conneaut Lake, PA; (3); Drama Clb; Spanish Clb; Flag Corp; Nwsp Stf; Capt L Cheerleading; PA Free Entrprs Wk 86; Rtry Yth Ldrshp Awds 87.

HAGERMAN, KIMBERLY; Penns Manor HS; Clymer, PA; (3); 43/115; Art Clb; Varsity Clb; Var Capt Bsktbl; Im Vllybl; All Cnty & Appalachian-Bsktbl; U Of NC; Bsktbl.

HAGERMAN, TRACEY; Kutztown Area SR HS; Kutztown, PA; (4); 14/146; Chorus; School Musical; School Play; Variety Show; Nwsp Bus Mgr; Nwsp Rptr; Nwsp Sprt Ed; Yrbk Rptr; Sec Frsh Cls; Sec Soph Cls; Juniata Almni Schlrshp 87-88; Grimeey Trst Schlrshp 87-88; Juniata Coll; Prsnl Mgmt.

HAGERTY, MELISSA A; Upper Dublin SR HS; Fort Washington, PA; (3); 30/300; PAVAS; Science Clb; Chorus; School Play; Yrbk Stf; Lit Mag; Stu Cncl; Trk; High Hon Roll; NHS; Free Enterprise 87; Lifegrd 86-87; Advrtsng.

HAGERTY, STACIE; Laurel Highlands SR HS; Uniontown, PA; (3); Trs Church Yth Grp; Exploring; SADD; Mrchg Band; Co-Capt Twrlr; Im Vllybl; Hon Roll; Rotary Awd; HOBY Ambssdr 86.

HAGGE, CYNTHIA; Oley Valley HS; Boyertown, PA; (3); 59/150; Camp Fr Inc; Band; Concert Band; Mrchg Band; Pep Band; Nwsp Rptr; Yrbk Stf; Drama Clb; Key Clb; Library Aide; Elem Ed.

HAGGENMILLER, KRISTA; Cardinal O Hara HS; Media, PA; (4); 20/776; Math Tm; SADD; Capt Flag Corp; Hon Roll; NHS; Ntl Merit Ltr; German Clb; School Musical; Yrbk Stf; Rotary Awd; Mccabe Schlr 87; 1st Plc DE Vlly Sci Fr Physcs 87; German Natl Hon Soc 87; U VA; Elec Engr.

HAGGERTY, MICHAEL; St John Neumann HS; Philadelphia, PA; (3); Yrbk Stf; Crs Cntry; Trk; High Hon Roll; Hon Roll.

HAGGERTY, TIM; St John Neumann HS; Philadelphia, PA; (3); 73/349; Church Yth Grp; L Ftbl; JV Trk; High Hon Roll; Hon Roll; Elect Engrng.

HAGGERTY, WILLIAM; South Philadelphia HS; Philadelphia, PA; (3); Band; Orch; Symp Band; Rep Stu Cncl; Stat Sftbl; Cit Awd; Prfct Atten Awd; Navy.

HAGIS, PETER S; Northeast HS; Philadelphia, PA; (4); 19/690; Church Yth Grp; Pres Math Clb; Science Clb; Ski Clb; Hon Roll; NHS; Ntl Merit SF; Aerospace Engrng.

HAGUE, JUDY; Wyoming Area HS; Exeter, PA; (3); 49/250; Ski Clb; Spanish Clb; Sftbl; Hon Roll.

HAHM, KYUNG; Central HS; Philadelphia, PA; (2); Library Aide; Math Clb; Teachers Aide; Nwsp Phtg; Lit Mag; Tennis; Hon Roll; Clsscl Soc Of Philadelphia Latin 86-87; Barnwell Awd Bronze 85-86; Phila Pblc Leag Tnns Champs Awd 87; Orgnc Chem.

HAHN, COREY; Hanover HS; Hanover, PA; (3); Chess Clb; Varsity Clb; School Play; Var Bsbl; JV Bsktbl; Var Ftbl; Var Wrstlng; Hon Roll; Outstndng Offns Plyr, York Cnty Ldng Scrr Ftbl, 2nd Ldng Rshr York Cnty Ftbl 87.

HAHN, JOHN; Plymouth-Whitemarsh HS; Lafayette Hill, PA; (3); 4/382; Pres Boy Scts; Sec Church Yth Grp; Hosp Aide; Chorus; Nwsp Rptr; Var Tennis; NHS; Cmnty Wkr; Computer Clb; Exploring; Dstngshd Stu Awd 86-87; Twn Mtng Tmrrw Ldrshp Smnr Schl Rep 86-87; Phldlpha Bstkbl Natl Korean Amer 87; Dntstry.

HAHN, MELISSA; Northampton Area SR HS; Bath, PA; (3); Trs Church Yth Grp; Sec DECA; 4-H; Yrbk Stf; JV Fld Hcky; 4-H Awd; Hon Roll; Drama Clb; Flag Corp; Dist Level DECA 86-87; ST Level DECA 86 & 87; Northampton Area Drug Task Force 86-87; Mktg Tchr.

HAHN, STEPHEN; Brandywine Heights HS; Topton, PA; (2); Band; Chorus; Concert Band; Jazz Band; Mrchg Band; Var L Bsbl; Var L Bsktbl; Var L Socr; Hon Roll; NHS; U Of VA; Physcl Thrpy.

HAHNER, KELLY ANN; Steel Valley HS; Munhall, PA; (3); 23/209; Concert Band; Drill Tm; Jazz Band; Rep Mrchg Band; Sec Jr Cls; Sec Sr Cls; Rep Stu Cncl; Stat Wrstlng; Hon Roll; NHS; HOBYS 86.

HAHNLEN, CRAIG; Lower Dauphin HS; Hershey, PA; (2); Church Yth Grp; Bsktbl; JV Socr; Var Trk; Hon Roll.

HAID, LISA RENE; Altoona Area HS; Altoona, PA; (4); Church Yth Grp; German Clb; JA; Math Tm; Red Cross Aide; Rep Sr Cls; High Hon Roll; JV Bsktbl; Hon Roll; Church Yth Grp; Aaaha Outstndng Math Stu Schlstc Awd 87; Super Achvt PA Math Leag 87; Penn ST U; Psychlgy.

HAID, PAUL; Penn Cambria HS; Loretto, PA; (3); Church Yth Grp; NHS; Prfct Atten Awd; Drama Clb; SADD; Hon Roll.

HAIGH, CHRISTY; Leechburg Area HS; Leechburg, PA; (4); 6/83; Band; Chorus; Church Choir; Concert Band; Mrchg Band; Pep Band; High Hon Roll; Hon Roll; Sec NHS; Pres Schlr; Sec Of Mnth Awd-Prfsnl 86; Penn ST U; Bus Adm.

HAIGH, GABRIELLE; St Huberts HS; Philadelphia, PA; (3); 221/421; Drama Clb; Chorus; Church Choir; School Musical; School Play; Art.

HAIN, BRANDON; Exeter HS; Reading, PA; (3); Aud/Vis; Computer Clb; FBLA; Math Clb; Science Clb; Stage Crew; Bowling; Vllybl; Wrstlng; Ntl Merit Ltr; PA ST; Accntng.

HAIN, CRYSTAL; Northern Lebanon HS; Jonestown, PA; (2); 18/208; Varsity Clb; Rep Stu Cncl; Var Cheerleading; Hon Roll; Bus.

HAIN, MYRA; Spring Ford HS; Royersford, PA; (3); 21/256; Art Clb; French Clb; Math Clb; Rep Sr Cls; Var Trk; Hon Roll; NHS; Hofstra U; Biolgst.

HAIN, RICCI; Spring Ford HS; Royersford, PA; (4); Math Clb; Bsktbl; Ftbl; Trk; Vllybl; Stck Brck.

HAINES, ALLEN; Littlestown SR HS; Littlestown, PA; (3); Chess Clb; FFA; Var Tennis; Var Wt Lftg; JV Wrstlng; High Hon Roll; Prfct Atten Awd; Army.

HAINES, BARBARA; Lewisburg Area HS; Lewisburg, PA; (4); 32/163; Latin Clb; Band; Concert Band; Mrchg Band; Var Trk; Hon Roll; Masonic Awd; NHS; Latin Awd Excllnce 87; PA ST U; Pre Law.

HAINES, CHERYL; Waynesburg Central HS; Spraggs, PA; (1); Sec Church Yth Grp; 4-H; French Clb; FFA; 4-H Awd; Hon Roll; 1st Pl Creed Cont; 2nd Pl Parlmntry Procedure Cont 87; WV U; Agri.

HAINES, DAVID; Newport HS; Newport, PA; (4); 29/89; Church Yth Grp; Band; Concert Band; Jazz Band; Mrchg Band; School Musical; School Play; Hon Roll; Tri-M 84-87.

HAINES, JAMES; Lancaster Catholic HS; Lancaster, PA; (3); Lewistown; Fireman.

HAINES, LINDA; Mechanicsburg HS; Mechanicsburg, PA; (2); 13/309; Church Yth Grp; High Hon Roll; Hon Roll; NHS.

HAINES, MELINDA; Newport JR/SR HS; Newport, PA; (3); FBLA; FTA; Teachers Aide; Sec Frsh Cls; Rep Jr Cls; Rep Stu Cncl; Var Capt Cheerleading; Hon Roll; Prfct Atten Awd.

HAINES, STEPHANIE; Conemaugh Township Area HS; Holsopple, PA; (3); 6/121; Nwsp Ed-Chief; Pres Frsh Cls; VP Soph Cls; VP Jr Cls; Rep Stu Cncl; Var Capt Bsktbl; Var Sftbl; Var Vllybl; Hon Roll; NHS; 1st Tm All Cnty Girls Bsktbl 85-87; 1st Tm All Cnty Girls Vllybl 86; Rotary Yth Ldrshp 87; Cornell; Pre-Law.

HAINES, STEPHANIE; Moshannon Valley HS; Houtzdale, PA; (4); Dance Clb; Hosp Aide; Pep Clb; Spanish Clb; SADD; Band; Chorus; Flag Corp; Yrbk Bus Mgr; God Cntry Awd; Jacob George Mem Schlrshp 87; Miss TEEN PA Pgnt 86; Gannon U; Nrsng.

HAINESWORTH, MICHELLE; Hempfield SR HS; Greensburg, PA; (3); French Clb; Latin Clb; Pep Clb; Color Guard; Crs Cntry; Gym; Trk; Wt Lftg; Hon Roll; Ntl Merit SF; Track & Field Ltrs & Medals 84-87; IN U Of PA; Psych.

HAINLEY, KATHY; Altoona Area HS; Altoona, PA; (3); Church Yth Grp; Drama Clb; Hosp Aide; Chorus; Stage Crew; High Hon Roll.

HAIST, TERI; Downingtown SR HS; Downintown, PA; (3); 20/635; Church Yth Grp; German Clb; Ski Clb; Chorus; Church Choir; Capt Color Guard; Swing Chorus; Stat Bsktbl; High Hon Roll; Sec NHS; Child Psych.

HAJDUK, CHRISTINE; Frazier Memorial HS; Star Junction, PA; (4); 1/130; Church Yth Grp; Drama Clb; FNA; Red Cross Aide; Chorus; JV Bsktbl; Var Vllybl; High Hon Roll; Sec Trs NHS; Val; Natl Hnr Scty Schlrshp 87; Penn St Fayette Campus Schlrshp 87; Penn ST U; Bio.

HAJDUKIEWICZ, ANDREW J; Gateway HS; Monroeville, PA; (3); Church Yth Grp; Concert Band; Ftbl; Ice Hcky; Engr.

HAJEC, GLENDA; Corry Area HS; Spartansburg, PA; (4); 22/200; French Clb; Concert Band; Jazz Band; Mrchg Band; Rep Stu Cncl; Hon Roll; Acdmc Achvt Awd 87; U Of Dayton; Nuclear Med.

HAKALA, DENISE; Quakertown HS; Quakertown, PA; (3); Drama Clb; School Musical; School Play; Stage Crew; High Hon Roll; Hon Roll.

HAKE, CHRISTINE; Red Lion Area SR HS; Red Lion, PA; (3); 100/342; Varsity Clb; VP Jr Cls; Sec Stu Cncl; Var Cheerleading; JV Var Mgr(s); Powder Puff Ftbl; JV Var Vllybl; Hon Roll; Spanish NHS; 4-H; Penn ST; Bus Adm.

HAKIM, JOHN; E L Meyers HS; Wilkes Barre, PA; (4); German Clb; Pres Ski Clb; Chorus; School Musical; Yrbk Stf; VP Jr Cls; VP Sr Cls; Stu Cncl; Jr NHS; U Scranton.

HALAHAN, LORI; Greensburg Central Catholic HS; Trafford, PA; (4); 31/217; Ski Clb; Powder Puff Ftbl; Trk; High Hon Roll; NHS; Deptmntl Bus Awd 87; Bradford Bus Schl; Sec.

HALBEDL, NICOLE; Montour HS; Mckees Rocks, PA; (3); Church Yth Grp; Hosp Aide; SADD; Drill Tm; Rep Stu Cncl; Powder Puff Ftbl; Twrlr; Hon Roll; Psychlgy.

HALCOUSSIS, OURANIA SOPHIA; Hampton HS; Allison Pk, PA; (4); Trs Church Yth Grp; Concert Band; Jazz Band; Mrchg Band; Symp Band; Ntl Merit SF; IN U; Acctng.

HALDAMAN, ANN; Bethlehem Catholic HS; Bath, PA; (3); 87/202; Am Leg Aux Girls St; Church Yth Grp; Pres Sec Exploring; Church Choir; School Musical; High Hon Roll; Hon Roll; Intl Gymnstcs Tem Cls III 85-86; Educ.

HALDEMAN, HEATHER; Pine Grove Area HS; Schuylkill Hvn, PA; (4); 3/116; Varsity Clb; Chorus; Yrbk Stf; Rep Soph Cls; Rep Jr Cls; Rep Sr Cls; Rep Stu Cncl; Var Cheerleading; JV Sftbl; Im Vllybl; Schuylkill Cnsvtn Dist Awd 87; Presdntl Acadmc Ftns Awds; Penn ST U; Wildlife Scientist.

HALDEMAN, JENNIFER; Bellefonte Area HS; Bellefonte, PA; (3); Girl Scts; Ski Clb; SADD; Varsity Clb; Band; Concert Band; Mrchg Band; Bsktbl; Trk; Vllybl; Silver Awd 85; Gold Awd 88.

HALDEMAN, MICHELE; Cocalico HS; Denver, PA; (3); 6/169; Church Yth Grp; Girl Scts; Concert Band; Pep Band; High Hon Roll; Psych.

HALE, CHRISTOPHER; Montour HS; Mckees Rocks, PA; (4); 70/301; Boy Scts; Church Yth Grp; Math Tm; Political Wkr; Science Clb; Var Capt Vllybl; Hon Roll; Pttsbrgh Prss Pst Gztt Vllybl Plyr Wk 87; Eldrtn Vllybl Trnmnt MVP 86-87; WPIAL Vllybl Chmps 86-87; US Nvl Acad; Aerospc Engrng.

HALE, LORI; Bald Eagle-Nittany HS; Mill Hall, PA; (3); 40/148; Band; Mrchg Band; Bsktbl; High Hon Roll; Hon Roll; Centre County Area; Prctcl Nrs.

HALE, ROCKY; Garden Spot HS; New Holland, PA; (2); Chorus; Concert Band; Mrchg Band; Orch; Pep Band; Bsbl; Ftbl; Socr; Wrstlng; High Hon Roll; Insprtnl Wrstlng Awd 85-86; Ldrshp Wrstlng Awd 86-87.

HALES, MONIQUE; Cardinal O Hara HS; Chester, PA; (3); Church Yth Grp; Hosp Aide; JA; Office Aide; SADD; Chorus; School Musical; Rep Frsh Cls; Stu Cncl; Hon Roll; Poli Sci.

HALESKY, MICHELLE; Montrose Area HS; Montrose, PA; (3); Church Yth Grp; Cmnty Wkr; VP 4-H; German Clb; SADD; Band; Church Choir; Concert Band; Mrchg Band; Yrbk Stf; Salute Yth Natl Cncl Yth Ldrshp 87; PA Rep Modern Miss 87; Dist 12 Girls Golf Champ 86; Bus Adm.

HALESKY, SCOTT; Susquehanna Community HS; Thompson, PA; (2); Ftbl; Trk; Chem.

HALEWSKI, DEANNA; Dover Area HS; Dover, PA; (3); 23/300; Chorus; Nwsp Rptr; Yrbk Ed-Chief; High Hon Roll; NHS; Ntl Merit SF; Baylor U; Jrnlsm.

HALEY, JAMES; Center HS; Monaca, PA; (3); Am Leg Boys St; Computer Clb; Exploring; German Clb; Spanish Clb; Varsity Clb; School Musical; School Play; Stu Cncl; Bsbl; VP-ENGRNG Explrers Grp 87; Spksprsn & Rep-Rgnl Expo; Alt STEP Smnr-Prdue U 87; Engrng.

HALEY, MATTHEW; Carbondale Area JR SR HS; Carbondale, PA; (3); German Clb; Ski Clb; Var L Bsbl; High Hon Roll; Hon Roll; Amer Red Cross 1st Aid Awd 86-87; Amer Hrt Assoc CPR & Emer Crdc Care 86-87; Penn ST Univ; Neurology.

HALFAST, LARRY; Corry Area HS; Spartansburg, PA; (4); Trs FFA; Lucy A Morris Schlrshp 87; County Schl Inc; Trk Drvr.

HALFHILL, DOLLY; Connellsville SR HS; Vanderbilt, PA; (3); 94/550; FBLA; Hon Roll; Bus.

HALGAS, STACY; Leechburg Area HS; Leechburg, PA; (3); 4-H; Office Aide; Nwsp Stf; Yrbk Stf; Vllybl; 4-H Awd; Drama Clb; Spanish Clb; SADD; Nwsp Rptr.

HALL, BILL; Connellsville HS; Connellsville, PA; (1); Computer Clb; Office Aide; Radio Clb; Chorus; Nwsp Stf; Yrbk Stf; JV Ftbl; Sec Wrstlng; Hon Roll; Prfct Atten Awd; Penn ST; Comp Tech.

HALL, BRIAN; Bethel Park HS; Bethel Park, PA; (4); 50/509; Trs Church Yth Grp; Capt Quiz Bowl; Church Choir; NHS; Purdue U; Elec Engrng.

HALL, CHRISTINE; Fannett-Metal HS; Fannettsburg, PA; (4); 4/41; Drama Clb; Trs FBLA; Color Guard; Stage Crew; Pres Sec Stu Cncl; JV Bsktbl; VP Cheerleading; Stat Sftbl; Hon Roll; NHS; Acad All-Amer 85-87; Penn ST U; Bus Admin.

HALL, CONNIE; Moniteau HS; West Sunbury, PA; (2); Church Yth Grp; Girl Scts; Spanish Clb; Band; Church Choir; Concert Band; Jazz Band; Mrchg Band; NHS; God Cntry Awd; 2nd Pl SRU Frgn Lang Comp 86; Hnrb Mntn Frgn Lang Comp 87; Music.

HALL, CYNTHIA; Freedom HS; Bethlehem, PA; (4); 180/433; Church Yth Grp; Office Aide; Pep Clb; Acpl Chr; Band; Chorus; Church Choir; Color Guard; Concert Band; Drill Tm; Dist 10 PMEA Band 87; PA Yth Hnrs Cncrt Band 87; Miss Amer Coed St Fnlst 86; Lebanon Vly Coll; Elem Edu.

HALL, DARREN; Upper Moreland HS; Willow Gr, PA; (3); 74/275; Boy Scts; School Musical; Stage Crew; Lit Mag; Hon Roll; Taekwondo Karate Black Belt 85; Life Scout BSA 84; Arch.

HALL, DAVID JAMES; Lincoln HS; Ellwood City, PA; (4); 58/170; Spanish Clb; Im Bowling; Capt L Ftbl; L Var Trk; Im Wt Lftg; Hon Roll; Ushrs Clb Schrshp 87; Schlr Athlt Awd 86; Slippery Rock U; Phys Thrpy.

HALL, DEANNA; New Castle SR HS; New Castle, PA; (3); 36/263; Hon Roll; Italian Club 86-87; Yrbk Sales Rep 85; Accntng.

HALL, DEENA; Mary Fuller Frazier JR-SR HS; Dawson, PA; (3); Church Yth Grp; Pres Sec 4-H; High Hon Roll; Hon Roll; Jr NHS; Elem Educ.

HALL, ELIZABETH; Taylor Allderdice HS; Pittsburgh, PA; (3); Debate Tm; Intnl Clb; Cit Awd; Hon Roll; Brown; Law.

HALL, FLOYD; Bensalem SR HS; Bensalem, PA; (2); Bsktbl; Ftbl; Mgr(s); Score Keeper; Vllybl; Wt Lftg; Comp.

HALL, GARY; Center HS; Aliquippa, PA; (2); Exploring; Chorus; School Musical; Law.

HALL, HEATHER; Cedar Crest HS; Lebanon, PA; (2); 103/345; Church Yth Grp; Color Guard; Drill Tm; Lcrss; Sftbl; Twrlr; Vllybl; Pep Clb; Spanish Clb; SADD; Cert Hnrs Band 86-87; Bus.

HALL, HEATHER; Somerset Area SR HS; Friedens, PA; (3); 56/231; German Clb; Hosp Aide; Letterman Clb; Varsity Clb; Chorus; Socr; Hon Roll; Art Clb; Church Yth Grp; Orch.

HALL, HOWARD; Schuylkill Haven HS; Sch Haven, PA; (3); FCA; Chorus; Var L Bsbl; L Bsktbl; Var L Ftbl; Hon Roll; Aud/Vis; Church Yth Grp; Acdmc All Amer, 1st Pl Schuylkill Haven Sci Fair Adv Bio 87; Elect Engrng.

HALL, JAMES; Punxsutawney Area HS; Punxsutawney, PA; (3); Crs Cntry; Hon Roll; Indl Field.

HALL, JAMES; St John Newmann HS; Philadelphia, PA; (3); 6/349; Computer Clb; Math Clb; Math Tm; Science Clb; High Hon Roll; NHS; Archdcsn Schlr Prgm; Bio.

HALL, JEFF; North Penn JR/Sr HS; Blossburg, PA; (3); 12/58; Trs Key Clb; Pres Varsity Clb; VP Jr Cls; Var Bsbl; Capt Var Bsktbl; Trk; Hon Roll; Penn St; Engr.

HALL, JENNIFER LYNN; Methacton HS; Collegeville, PA; (3); 18/381; Pres Exploring; FHA; Office Aide; Rep Soph Cls; Rep Jr Cls; Rep Stu Cncl; Stat Swmmng; Timer; High Hon Roll; NHS; Acad Achvt Awd 85-87; Clemson U; Ceramic Engrng.

HALL, JENNY; Spring-Ford SR HS; Royersford, PA; (3); 50/294; French Clb; Ski Clb; Sec Frsh Cls; Sec Soph Cls; JV Lcrss; Var Tennis; Hon Roll; Church Yth Grp; Library Aide; SADD; U DE; Med Tech.

HALL III, JOHN T; Solanco HS; Christiana, PA; (3); Art Clb; Varsity Clb; Bowling; Var Socr; Var Trk; High Hon Roll; Hon Roll; Schlstc Art Show 2 Gold Keys & 6 Hon Ment 87; Art.

HALL, JULIA; Mt Lebanon HS; Pittsburgh, PA; (4); Church Yth Grp; SADD; Band; High Hon Roll; German Clb; Latin Clb; Off Frsh Cls; Off Soph Cls; Off Jr Cls; Slvr & Gld Mdlst Ice Dnc Compttns Tri-ST Area 83-87; Calvin Coll.

HALL, JULIE; Saltsburg JR SR HS; Saltsburg, PA; (3); Pep Clb; Ski Clb; Spanish Clb; Chorus; School Musical; Yrbk Stf; Powder Puff Ftbl; High Hon Roll; Hon Roll; Spanish NHS; UCLA; Math.

HALL, KEN; Lower Dauphin HS; Hummelstown, PA; (3); Science Clb; Chorus; Hon Roll; Sci.

HALL, KIM; Western Wayne HS; Newfoundland, PA; (3); 34/189; Church Yth Grp; FHA; Hon Roll.

HALL, KIMBERLEY; Dallas SR HS; Dallas, PA; (3); Art Clb; Church Yth Grp; Ski Clb; Off Jr Cls; Stu Cncl; Var L Cheerleading; Im Gym; Hon Roll; Chrldng Invitational St Champ 87; JR Prom Qn 87; Art Awd 86; Advrtsng.

HALL, KRISTEN; Newport HS; Newport, PA; (3); 11/117; GAA; Varsity Clb; Chorus; Concert Band; Pres Frsh Cls; Off Jr Cls; Var Cheerleading; JV Var Fld Hcky; Var L Sftbl; Wt Lftg; Manhattan Ville U; Fshn Dsgn.

HALL, LESLIE; Northern Bedford Co HS; New Enterprise, PA; (4); 19/94; Pres Church Yth Grp; FBLA; Varsity Clb; Sec Band; Chorus; Yrbk Ed-Chief; Stu Cncl; Capt Cheerleading; Socr; Hon Roll; Ldrshp Awd 87; Altoona Schl; Bus Admin.

HALL, LISA; St Hubert Catholic HS For Girls; Philadelphia, PA; (3); 76/421; Cmnty Wkr; Office Aide; Yrbk Bus Mgr; Hon Roll; Compu Sci.

HALL, LISA; Turkeyfoot Valley Area HS; Confluence, PA; (2); Library Aide; Chorus; Church Choir; Trs Frsh Cls; VP Soph Cls; Stat Ftbl; Sftbl; Cit Awd; DAR Awd; High Hon Roll; Comp Literacy Awd 85-86; Phys Ed Awd 85-87; Advanced Phys Sci 85-86; Bio.

HALL, MELISSA; Hazleton SR HS; Drums, PA; (3); Church Yth Grp; Pep Clb; Y-Teens; Band; Chorus; Concert Band; Mrchg Band; Var Swmmng; Hon Roll; PSU; Bus.

HALL, MELISSA; Middleburg HS; Middleburg, PA; (3); 21/130; Church Yth Grp; Ski Clb; Spanish Clb; Sec SADD; Nwsp Rptr; Yrbk Stf; JV Fld Hcky; Hon Roll; Psych.

HALL, MELISSA; Villa Maria Acad; West Chester, PA; (3); Cmnty Wkr; Hosp Aide; Capt Cheerleading; Tennis; Hon Roll; Pre Med.

HALL, REBECCA; Jefferson-Morgan HS; Waynesburg, PA; (4); 6/97; Church Yth Grp; Flag Corp; Nwsp Ed-Chief; Yrbk Stf; Stat DAR Awd; High Hon Roll; Lion Awd; NEDT Awd; Acad All Amer Awd; Bethany Coll Bethany WV; Comm.

HALL, REBEKAH; New Freedom Christian HS; Shrewsbury, PA; (3); 1/9; Church Yth Grp; Debate Tm; German Clb; Math Clb; Radio Clb; Science Clb; Speech Tm; Chorus; Var Bsktbl; Var Golf; 3rd Sci Fair 85-86; 1st Ju-Jitsu Trnmnt 86; Sci Fair Champ 87; Bob Jones U.

HALL, SHAWN; Bucktail Area HS; Renovo, PA; (2); Letterman Clb; Library Aide; Varsity Clb; Chorus; Church Choir; Concert Band; Mrchg Band; School Musical; School Play; Prfct Atten Awd; Band Awd 87; Comm Art.

HALL, STEVEN; Corry Area HS; Corry, PA; (2); Rep Church Yth Grp; PAVAS; Pres Thesps; Band; Chorus; Church Choir; Concert Band; Mrchg Band; Pep Band; School Musical; Duke U; Drama.

HALL, TAMELA; South Philadelphia HS; Philadelphia, PA; (3); Art Clb; Off Soph Cls; Off Jr Cls; JV Bsktbl; Prfct Atten Awd; Bus Mgmt.

HALL, TERENCE; West Philadelphia HS; Phila, PA; (3); JV Ftbl; Var Gym; Hon Roll; Drexel U; Comp Sci.

HALL, THOMAS; Everett Area HS; Everett, PA; (3); Boy Scts; Church Yth Grp; Chorus; JV Var Ftbl; L Wrstlng; Penn ST; Lndscp Arch.

HALL, VALERIE; Interboro HS; Glenolden, PA; (3); GAA; Teachers Aide; Mrchg Band; JV Bsktbl; Var Sftbl; High Hon Roll; Jr NHS; NHS; Pres Schlr; Northeastern U; Elec Engr.

HALLAHAN, SUSAN; George Schl; Lebanon, PA; (3); Cmnty Wkr; Drama Clb; French Clb; Hosp Aide; Pep Clb; Ski Clb; Swmmng; Hon Roll; Hnrs Awd 85-86; Librl Arts.

HALLAM, DANA; Fort Cherry HS; Midway, PA; (3); 7/147; Computer Clb; Math Clb; Science Clb; Ski Clb; VP Spanish Clb; Varsity Clb; Tennis; Twrlr; High Hon Roll; NHS; Duquesne U; Law.

HALLECK, LISA; Villa Maria Acad; Erie, PA; (3); 22/150; Church Yth Grp; Science Clb; Ski Clb; Stu Cncl; Cheerleading; Tennis; High Hon Roll; NHS; Intl Law.

HALLER, DAVID A; Monongohela Valley Catholic HS; Monongahela, PA; (3); 30/99; Pep Clb; Varsity Clb; Stage Crew; VP Stu Cncl; Var L Bsktbl; Im Coach Actv; Var L Socr; Im Wt Lftg; Hon Roll.

HALLER, JODI; Elk County Christian HS; Kersey, PA; (1); 1/84; Church Choir; Bsbl; JV Bsktbl; Hon Roll.

HALLER, NICHOLAS; Seton La Salle HS; Pittsburgh, PA; (3); Church Yth Grp; Cmnty Wkr; Library Aide; Red Cross Aide; Spanish Clb; High Hon Roll; Hon Roll; NHS; Exploring; Teachers Aide; Outstndng Vol Bapt Homes Awd 87; Stu Mnth 87; Med.

HALLER, NICOLE; Peters Township HS; Mc Murray, PA; (2); Dance Clb; GAA; Ski Clb; Spanish Clb; Speech Tm; Teachers Aide; Church Choir; Drill Tm; School Play; Off Soph Cls; Penn ST; Cmnctns.

HALLGREN, JOHN; Donegal HS; Mount Joy, PA; (2); JV Socr; Tennis; Hon Roll; Ntl Hstry & Govt Awd 86-87.

HALLINGER, MARK R; Council Rock HS; Newtown, PA; (4); 43/848; Church Yth Grp; JV Golf; JV Trk; Im Vllybl; Im Wt Lftg; Hon Roll; NHS; Ntl Merit SF; PA Hghr Ed Assist Aency Cert Merit 85; Schrlshp Carnegie Mellon U 86; Pre-Law.

HALLMAN, DANA; Stroudsburg HS; Stroudsburg, PA; (3); 4/250; Dance Clb; Drama Clb; French Clb; PAVAS; Service Clb; Thesps; Drm Mjr(t); Swing Chorus; DAR Awd; NHS; Dist Chorus 85-87; Regnl Chorus 85-86; Teach Music.

HALLMAN, ROB; Solanco SR HS; Oxford, PA; (3); Varsity Clb; JV Var Bsbl; JV Var Socr; Hon Roll; Peer Cnslng 85-87; Archt.

HALLOCK, MICHELE; Coughlin HS; Wilkes Barre, PA; (4); Church Yth Grp; Hosp Aide; Hon Roll; Luzerne Cnty CC; Accntng.

HALLOCK, SANDY; Tunkhannock HS; Tunkhannock, PA; (2); Drama Clb; Spanish Clb; School Play; Pres Frsh Cls; Rep Stu Cncl; Var Cheerleading; JV Sftbl; JV Vllybl; Hon Roll.

HALLORAN, BRIGITTE; Otto Eldred HS; Eldred, PA; (4); 15/83; Chorus; Nwsp Rptr; Nwsp Stf; Sec Jr Cls; Sec Sr Cls; JV Var Bsktbl; Hon Roll; NHS; Jr Homcmng Rep 85; Sr Homcmng Crt 86; Sr Prom Crt 87; Jamestown CC; Bus Mgmt.

HALLOWELL, KIMBERLY; Henderson HS; West Chester, PA; (3); 24/365; Church Yth Grp; Ski Clb; Church Choir; JV Cheerleading; Stat Lcrss; DAR Awd; Hon Roll; NHS; Acadc Achvt Awd 87.

HALLUM, SCOTT; West Allegheny HS; Oakdale, PA; (2); 29/216; Chorus; Rep Frsh Cls; JV Bsbl; Bsktbl; JV Ftbl; Wt Lftg; Hon Roll; Clss Rep 85-86; Ftbll & Bsbll Wghtlftg 85-87; Hnr Rll 85-87.

HALLUM, SUSAN; West Allegheny HS; Oakdale, PA; (4); 14/202; Cmnty Wkr; Hosp Aide; VP Chorus; Gov Hon Prg Awd; NHS; Lions Clb Nrsng Schlrshp 87; Outstndng Stu Parkway Tech-PM Cls 87; Sewickley Vly Hosp; Nrsng.

HALM, KERRY; Benton JR/Sr HS; Benton, PA; (2); Drama Clb; Keywanettes; Band; Church Choir; Concert Band; Mrchg Band; Pep Band; School Musical; Trs Soph Cls; Rep Stu Cncl; Mrn Bio.

HALMA, KIMBERLY; Emmaus HS; Allentown, PA; (3); JV Var Cheerleading; Var Diving; Hon Roll; Phys Ftnss Tm 5th Pl Ntls 87; SAFE Rds 87; Bus.

HALODA, CHRISTINE; Jefferson-Morgan JR SR HS; Jefferson, PA; (3); 2/69; Rep Church Yth Grp; Exploring; French Clb; Pep Clb; Yrbk Stf; High Hon Roll; Ntl Merit Ltr; Prfct Atten Awd; Wrld Cultrs Awd 86.

HALPER, JODI; Cedar Grove Christian Acad; Philadelphia, PA; (3); Pres Church Yth Grp; Hosp Aide; Church Choir; Nwsp Stf; Yrbk Ed-Chief; Yrbk Stf; Pres Frsh Cls; Capt Var Coach Actv; Var Fld Hcky; Var Sftbl; Tri-Cnty Grls Athltc Assn-Sftbl Hnrbl Mntn-Al-Star Leag Tm 86; Slvr Cert Intrprtv Readng 87; Mdcn.

HALPIN, CHAS; Immaculate Conception HS; Washington, PA; (2); Am Leg Boys St; Letterman Clb; Varsity Clb; Var L Bsbl; JV Bsktbl; Var L Ftbl; Crmnlgy.

HALPIN, JOANNA; Eastern York HS; Wrightsvlle, PA; (2); Drama Clb; Color Guard; School Musical; JV Cheerleading; Gym; High Hon Roll; Jr NHS; Pres Acad Fit Awd 85-86; Pres Phys Fit Awd 86-87; Comp Sci.

HALSEY, ANDREW; Emmaus HS; Emmaus, PA; (4); 5/473; Pres SADD; Coach Actv; Var Capt Socr; German Clb; Key Clb; Model UN; Cit Awd; High Hon Roll; Lion Awd; NHS; 1st Pl ST Lvl PJAS Sci Awd 87; VA Tech; Engrng.

HALTER, BRETT; Penns Valley Area HS; Spring Mills, PA; (3); Chrmn Varsity Clb; Var Capt Bsktbl; Var Crs Cntry; Ftbl; Var Golf; Var JV Trk; Pre-Law.

HALTERMAN, TIM; Danville SR HS; Danville, PA; (2); Letterman Clb; Varsity Clb; Rep Frsh Cls; Var Bsktbl; Var Socr; Var Trk; Hon Roll; Pres Schlr; Tchg.

HALUSCHAK, GREGORY; Frazier HS; Star Jct, PA; (3); Computer Clb; ROTC; Ftbl; Wt Lftg; US Army; Comp.

HALUSHAK, AMY; Northampton SR HS; Northampton, PA; (4); 94/444; Library Aide; Chorus; Hon Roll; Cedar Crest Coll; Bio.

HALVERSON, WILLIAM; Iaterboro HS; Essington, PA; (4); Computer Clb; SADD; Var Ftbl; Bus.

HALVORSEN, KRISTEN; Norristown Area HS; Norristown, PA; (4); 9/398; Girl Scts; Intnl Clb; SADD; Jazz Band; Mrchg Band; School Musical; Yrbk Stf; Lit Mag; NHS; Cngrss Bundestag Exchng Schlrshp 86-87; Natl Yng & Mrt 87; U Of Delaware; Intl Rltns.

HAMED, JOYA; Shenango JR SR HS; New Castle, PA; (2); Church Yth Grp; Girl Scts; Drill Tm; Yrbk Stf; VP Rep Stu Cncl; Hon Roll; Jr NHS; Cecchetti Methd Clsscl Ballet III 85; Modld Allegro Boutqs Sprng Fntsy 87; Intl Ordr Rnbw 85; Phys Thrpy.

HAMER, DENNIS; Peters Township HS; St Charles, MO; (4); Science Clb; Varsity Clb; Concert Band; VP Soph Cls; Var L Diving; Var L Ftbl; Var L Swmmng; Var L Trk; Hon Roll; Prfct Atten Awd; Dist Band Cntst & ST Band Centrl MO ST U 83-85; Dist I Band Fest 85-86; Mercyhurst Coll; Music.

HAMER, LORI; Mechanicsburg SR HS; Mechanicsburg, PA; (3); 197/338; Art Clb; Hon Roll; Interior Dsgn.

HAMER, WENDIE; Johnstown SR HS; Johnstown, PA; (4); 81/297; Exploring; French Clb; NFL; Chorus; Church Choir; Concert Band; Mrchg Band; Orch; School Musical; Nwsp Stf; Band Ltr 86-87; U Pittsburgh; Bus.

HAMIL, KATHY; Marion Center HS; Marion Center, PA; (3); 4-H; FNA; Hosp Aide; Latin Clb; Red Cross Aide; SADD; Teachers Aide; School Play; Hon Roll; Nursing.

HAMILTON, ADAM; Danville Area HS; Danville, PA; (2); Golf; Tennis; High Hon Roll; Bus Adm.

HAMILTON, ANITA; Yough SR HS; W Newton, PA; (4); 24/238; Computer Clb; French Clb; Girl Scts; Office Aide; Ski Clb; Spanish Clb; VP Band; Trs Chorus; VP Concert Band; VP Mrchg Band; Lions Club Schlrshp 87; PA ST U; Sci.

HAMILTON, BETTY JO; Mt Union Area HS; Mt Union, PA; (3); 13/152; Pres Church Yth Grp; VP FBLA; GAA; Band; Concert Band; Jazz Band; Mrchg Band; Var L Vllybl; Hon Roll; NHS; Dist, Rgnl Band 85-87; Juniata Coll; Acctng.

HAMILTON, CINDY; Lincoln HS; Ellwood City, PA; (3); Drama Clb; Spanish Clb; Y-Teens; Chorus; School Musical; School Play; Powder Puff Ftbl; High Hon Roll; Hon Roll; Pittsburg Bty Acad; Csmtlgy.

HAMILTON, CRYSTAL; Philadelphia HS For Girls; Philadelphia, PA; (3); Drexel U; Elec Engrng.

HAMILTON, DAMON; John S Fine HS; Nanticoke, PA; (2); 9/243; Rep Ski Clb; Im Bsktbl; JV Ftbl; Var L Trk; High Hon Roll; NHS; NEDT Awd; Variety Show; Rep Frsh Cls; Rep Soph Cls; Acdmc All Amer; Acdmc Ldrshp.

HAMILTON, DAWN; Union City Area HS; Union City, PA; (4); 8/79; Sec Camera Clb; Nwsp Rptr; Hst Soph Cls; Hst Jr Cls; Hst Sr Cls; Rep Stu Cncl; Bsktbl; Powder Puff Ftbl; Trk; Vllybl; Am Leg Scholar 87; Bears Clb Scholar 87; Pres Acad Awd 87; IN U PA; Biol.

HAMILTON, JAMIE; Jeannette SR HS; Jeannette, PA; (2); French Clb; Spanish Clb; Concert Band; VP Frsh Cls; Bsktbl; Twrlr; French Hon Soc; High Hon Roll; Optometry.

HAMILTON, JILL; Mechanicsburg Area HS; Grantham, PA; (3); 123/338; Sec Art Clb; Church Yth Grp; NFL; Speech Tm; Church Choir; School Play; Hon Roll; Ntl Art Hnr Soc; Messiah Coll; Art,Elem Ed.

HAMILTON, JIM; West Allegheny HS; Imperial, PA; (4); 10/202; Science Clb; Varsity Clb; Nwsp Sprt Ed; Capt L Crs Cntry; Capt L Trk; DAR Awd; High Hon Roll; Lion Awd; NHS; Prfct Atten Awd; Crs Cntry Trck Running Schlrshp 87; US Army Natl Acadmc Athl Awd 87; Prfct Atten Cert 87; U Of Pgh; Scndry Educ.

HAMILTON, KAREN; H S For Girls; Philadelphia, PA; (4); 103/345; Hosp Aide; Var Pom Pon; Hon Roll; Merit Awds 83-87; Cum Laude Awd 87; NC Central U; Acctg.

HAMILTON, KRISTEN; York Catholic HS; York, PA; (3); VP JA; Pres Pep Clb; Rep Spanish Clb; Chorus; School Musical; Var Capt Cheerleading; Hon Roll; Pres NHS; Church Yth Grp; Sec Yrk Catholc Music Assn 87-88; Fnlst Yrk Cnty JR Miss Pgm 87; Elem Ed.

HAMILTON JR, LARRY H; South Philadelphia HS; Philadelphia, PA; (3); JV Bsbl; Var Crs Cntry; Var Trk; Hon Roll; Vrsty Lttrs X-Cntry 85-87; Vrsty Lttr & Trphy Trck/Fld 85-86; JR Vrsty Lttr Bsbll 86-87; Comp Sci.

HAMILTON, LISA; Warren Area HS; Warren, PA; (3); Trs German Clb; Chorus; Church Choir; Concert Band; Mrchg Band; Orch; School Musical; Stat Bsbl; High Hon Roll; Jr NHS; Penn ST Prep Schl Hnrs 87; PA ST U; Lib Art.

HAMILTON, MATT; Beaver Area SR HS; Beaver, PA; (2); Church Yth Grp; JCL; Latin Clb; Ski Clb; School Play; Ftbl; High Hon Roll; Hon Roll; Pittsburgh U; Ped.

HAMILTON, MICHELLE; Butler SR HS; Butler, PA; (3); Library Aide; Science Clb; Jr NHS; Voice Dem Awd; Grove City; Math.

HAMILTON, MIKE; Curwensville Area HS; Curwensville, PA; (4); 30/120; Boy Scts; Chess Clb; VICA; Bsbl; NHS; Pres Schlr; Williamsport CC; Mech.

HAMILTON, SERENA; Milton SR HS; Milton, PA; (3); Art Clb; Boy Scts; Church Yth Grp; Spanish Clb; Var Socr; NHS; Exploring; Prom Committee 86-87; Early Childhd Dev.

HAMILTON, TAMMI; Lincoln HS; Ellwood City, PA; (3); Latin Clb; Y-Teens; Chorus; High Hon Roll; Hon Roll; NHS; Latin Achvt Awd 85.

HAMILTON, TRACY; Ambridge SR HS; Baden, PA; (4); Library Aide; Pep Clb; Spanish Clb; Teachers Aide; School Play; Nwsp Phtg; Nwsp Stf; Rep Frsh Cls; Rep Soph Cls; Rep Jr Cls; Sawyer Schl Of Bus; Travel.

HAMLEN, STEVEN; Northern Lebanon HS; Annville, PA; (3); 20/205; Church Yth Grp; Science Clb; School Play; Capt Socr; Var Trk; Var Wrstlng; High Hon Roll; 3rd In PA Math League In Region 83; Cert From Johns Hopkins Ctr For Talented Yth 84; MVP Sccr Assoc; Chem Engrng.

HAMLET, CAROL; Northern York HS; Dillsburg, PA; (4); 40/202; Band; Chorus; Concert Band; Jazz Band; Hon Roll; JP Sousa Awd; GPEA Schlrshp 87; Rotary Stu Dec 87; All ST Lions Club Band 86; Music Honors Scty 87; Millersville U; Music Ed.

HAMLET, DAVID; Norther York County HS; Dillsburg, PA; (3); 15/232; Am Leg Boys St; Boy Scts; Concert Band; Jazz Band; Mrchg Band; School Musical; Var Crs Cntry; Var Trk; NHS; Band; Trmpt Sectn Ldr 87; Cvl Engrng.

HAMLET, TANIA; Bristol JR-SR HS; Bristol, PA; (3); SADD; Yrbk Stf; Sec Frsh Cls; Sec Soph Cls; Sec Jr Cls; Sec Sr Cls; Rep Stu Cncl; Cheerleading; Hon Roll; Drama Clb; Stu Mnth 86; La Salle U; Bus Adm.

HAMM, BRETT; Donegal HS; Mt Joy, PA; (3); Air Force.

HAMM, DENISE; Fleetwood HS; Kutztown, PA; (3); 3/113; Chorus; Concert Band; Madrigals; Mrchg Band; School Musical; Variety Show; High Hon Roll; Hon Roll; NHS; Bynden Wood Yth Cnrt Fnlst Piano 87; Amer Legn Axlry Mdl Awd 84; Music.

HAMM, GREGORY; Meshannon Valley JR SR HS; Ramey, PA; (3); Computer Clb; Letterman Clb; Math Tm; Spanish Clb; Varsity Clb; Var Bsbl; JV Var Ftbl; Hon Roll; Penn ST; Ag Engrng.

HAMM, MARGARET; Bishop Neumann HS; Williamsport, PA; (2); 1/35; Cmnty Wkr; Model UN; Trs VP SADD; Sec Frsh Cls; Trs Soph Cls; Rep Stu Cncl; Var Sftbl; High Hon Roll; NHS; Prfct Atten Awd; PA ST U Smmr Instv Lang Inst 87; Lib Arts.

HAMM, MICHAEL; Seneca Valley HS; Mars, PA; (3); JA; Chorus; L Trk; Hon Roll; NHS; PA Soc Of Prfsnl Engrs Merit Cert 87; Engrng.

HAMM, MICHELE; Bishop Neumann HS; Williamsport, PA; (3); 1/39; Pep Clb; SADD; Yrbk Phtg; Tennis; High Hon Roll; Hon Roll; NHS; Ntl Merit Ltr; Prfct Atten Awd; Prncpls Acad Awd-1st Pl 85, 3rd Pl 86, 1st Pl 87; Most Impvd Ten 87; 2nd Pl Mxd Reg & Doubls 85; ROTC; Dntstry.

HAMM, MIKE; Manheim Central HS; Manheim, PA; (4); 18/240; Var Capt Ftbl; Var L Wrstlng; High Hon Roll; Hon Roll; NHS; Schlr Ath 87; Robert C Byrd Schlrshp 87; Stu Month Manheim Central Test Awd 87; Western MD.

HAMM, STACEY; Parkland HS; Schnecksville, PA; (3); 30/438; JA; Math Tm; SADD; Pres Trs Stu Cncl; Swmmng; DAR Awd; High Hon Roll; Hon Roll; NHS; Ntl Merit Ltr; Dist Chmp-Swmmng-200 Yr Freestyl 87; U Of Richmond.

HAMMAKER, KENNETH; Susquenita HS; Marysville, PA; (3); 3/159; Boy Scts; Church Yth Grp; French Clb; Office Aide; Quiz Bowl; Rep Stu Cncl; JV Wt Lftg; JV Wrstlng; Hon Roll; NHS; Winner Drug Driving Slogan Cntst 85.

HAMMAKER JR, KENNETH L; Cumberland Valley HS; Mechanicsburg, PA; (4); 32/512; Boy Scts; Ski Clb; Band; JV Wrstlng; God Cntry Awd; High Hon Roll; Eagle Scout 83; Villanova U; Bus Admin.

HAMMAKER, MICHELE; Susquenita HS; Marysville, PA; (4); 1/164; Ski Clb; Chorus; Church Choir; Mrchg Band; Off Stu Cncl; Mat Maids; Score Keeper; High Hon Roll; Val; Church Yth Grp; Dick Swank Engl Prize 87; Amer Auxiliary Essay Cntst Winner 83; Lycoming Coll.

HAMMAN, KAREN; W Perry HS; Landisburg, PA; (2); 66/222; Drama Clb; Spanish Clb; Band; Concert Band; Mrchg Band; School Play; Yrbk Stf; JV Fld Hcky; JV Sftbl; Penn ST; Elem Ed.

HAMME, DAVID; Henderson HS; West Chester, PA; (3); 10/377; Boy Scts; JA; Im JV Bsktbl; Hon Roll; Jr NHS; Prfct Atten Awd; U Of NC; Bus.

HAMME JR, JEFFREY E; Wm Penn SR HS; York, PA; (1); Church Yth Grp; JV Var Bsbl; JV L Bsktbl; JV Mgr(s); West York Optm Bowling Leag 76-87; Jr Travlng Leag High Aver Hnrs 85-87; Legion Bsbl Prog Bys Club; Phy Thrpst.

HAMME, MATTHEW; Dover Area HS; Dover, PA; (3); 34/320; Varsity Clb; Chorus; Var Bsbl; Var Socr; Hon Roll; Acctg.

HAMMER, JENNIFER; Hampton HS; Gibsonia, PA; (3); JA; Mrchg Band; Powder Puff Ftbl; High Hon Roll; Hon Roll; NHS; Sci.

HAMMER, MELISSA; Clairon-Limestone HS; Summerville, PA; (4); 2/65; Drama Clb; VP Spanish Clb; SADD; Varsity Clb; School Play; Trk; High Hon Roll; NHS; Sal; Presdntl Acadmc Fitness Awds 87; Robert Byrd Schlrshp 87-88; Clarion U.

HAMMERBACHER, NOELLE; E L Meyers HS; Wilkes-Barre, PA; (3); 22/186; Church Yth Grp; VP Key Clb; Ski Clb; SADD; Band; Chorus; Concert Band; Drm Mjr(t); Jazz Band; Orch; Kings Coll; Accntng.

HAMMERLY, AMY; Northeast Bradford JR SR HS; Leraysville, PA; (1); Church Yth Grp; Band; Mrchg Band; Off Frsh Cls; Stu Cncl; JV Cheerleading; Hon Roll; Med.

HAMMERS, KRISTIN; Kennedy Christian HS; Hubbard, OH; (2); 7/96; Church Yth Grp; French Clb; Girl Scts; Hosp Aide; Key Clb; Science Clb; Church Choir; Mat Maids; High Hon Roll.

HAMMERSMITH, AMY; Freedom HS; Bethlehem, PA; (4); 31/433; Debate Tm; Drama Clb; Model UN; Red Cross Aide; Capt Scholastic Bowl; VP Science Clb; Orch; Ed Nwsp Ed-Chief; Yrbk Stf; Var Crs Cntry; Pres Frshmn Schlrshp Drexel U 87; Outstndng Del Model UN Sec Council 87; Drexel U; Marketing.

HAMMOND, DANICA; New Castle SR HS; New Castle, PA; (2); #2 In Class; French Clb; Chorus; Drill Tm; High Hon Roll.

HAMMOND, DIANE; Bishop Conwell HS; Penndel, PA; (3); 4/277; Am Leg Aux Girls St; Church Yth Grp; Office Aide; Nwsp Stf; Im Bsktbl; Mgr(s); High Hon Roll; Trs NHS; Ntl Ldrshp & Svc Awd 86; Acadc All-Am 86; Cngrsnl Yth Ldrshp Cncl 87.

HAMMOND, KIMBERLY; Hampton HS; Allison Park, PA; (3); Art Clb; English Clb; Pep Clb; Spanish Clb; Varsity Clb; Yrbk Rptr; Yrbk Stf; Var Capt Cheerleading; Powder Puff Ftbl; Hon Roll; Allegheny Coll; Fshn Mrchndsng.

HAMMOND, MICHAEL W; Meadville Area SR HS; Meadville, PA; (4); 7/290; Boy Scts; Spanish Clb; Yrbk Phtg; Im Capt Bowling; Var L Trk; High Hon Roll; Pres Schlr; Church Yth Grp; Science Clb; Hon Roll; Meadville Area SR Schltc Hnr Scty 87; PA ST U; Engrng.

HAMMONDS, CLIFFORD; Clairton HS; Clairton, PA; (3); 23/95; Boys Clb Am; Computer Clb; JA; Spanish Clb; SADD; Nwsp Sprt Ed; Rep Jr Cls; Ftbl; Var Wt Lftg; High Hon Roll; Elec Engrng.

HAMMONDS, ROBERT; Mc Keesport SR HS; Mckeesport, PA; (3); AFS; Pep Clb; Nwsp Rptr; Swmmng; High Hon Roll; NHS; Val; Penn ST; Psych.

HAMMONS, LISA; Montour HS; Coraopolis, PA; (3); Art Clb; Dance Clb; Drama Clb; Exploring; SADD; School Play; Nwsp Phtg; Nwsp Rptr; Nwsp Stf; Vllybl; Mst Cmpltd Wrk Chrstn Schl 84; Psychlgy.

HAMPE, SHERRY; Hopewell SR HS; Aliquippa, PA; (3); 20/242; JA; Math Tm; Vllybl; High Hon Roll; NHS; Ltr Vllyvl 86; IN U PA; Acctng.

HAMPEL, BRIAN; Lake Lehman HS; Shavertown, PA; (1); Ski Clb; Hon Roll; NHS; Premed.

HAMPTON, CALEB; Exeter HS; Reading, PA; (3); 15/260; Boy Scts; Key Clb; Band; Jazz Band; School Musical; Jr NHS; NHS; Amer Leg Awd 85; Outstndng Yth Awd 85.

HAMPTON, CANDACE; Mt Carmel Area HS; Mt Carmel, PA; (2); 5/140; Art Clb; Cmnty Wkr; Key Clb; Latin Clb; Band; Concert Band; Jazz Band; Mrchg Band; Sftbl; High Hon Roll; Phy Thrpy.

HAMPTON, DARLENE M; Bedford HS; Bedford, PA; (4); VP Pres Church Yth Grp; Computer Clb; FBLA; Ski Clb; Chorus; Nwsp Rptr; Yrbk Stf; Bsktbl; Bowling; Hon Roll; Frostburg ST Coll; Cmmnctns.

HAMPTON, DAWN; Mt Carmel Area JR SR HS; Mt Carmel, PA; (3); 6/118; FNA; Hosp Aide; Key Clb; Band; Concert Band; Jazz Band; Mrchg Band; Sftbl; High Hon Roll; Hon Roll; Nrs.

HAMPTON, JOY D; Cameron County HS; Emporium, PA; (3); 2/92; Church Yth Grp; Mu Alpha Theta; Band; Mrchg Band; Yrbk Phtg; Rep Soph Cls; Rep Jr Cls; Cheerleading; Twrlr; High Hon Roll; Delta Epsilon Phi 86-87; Bnkng.

HAMPTON, MICHELLE D; Strath Haven HS; Swarthmore, PA; (4); Church Yth Grp; Girl Scts; Chorus; School Musical; School Play; Stage Crew; Rep Stu Cncl; Hon Roll; Ntl Merit Ltr; Pres Schlr; Grinnell Coll; Engl.

HAMPTON, REBECCA; Perry Traditional Acad; Pittsburgh, PA; (3); Drama Clb; Nwsp Rptr; Yrbk Rptr; Off Stu Cncl; Cheerleading; Sftbl; Chmcl Engrng.

HAMRIC, MARY; Washington HS; Washington, PA; (4); 9/147; Letterman Clb; Spanish Clb; Rep Soph Cls; Bsktbl; Tennis; Trk; High Hon Roll; NHS; Stdnt Mnth 86-87; U S Air Force Acad 87; PA ST U; Cvl Engrng.

HAMRICK, DANA; Cumberland Valley HS; Mechanicsburg, PA; (3); Sec Church Yth Grp; German Clb; Girl Scts; Key Clb; PAVAS; Church Choir; Lit Mag; DAR Awd; Hon Roll; Ntl Merit Ltr; Ntl Art Hnr Soc 85-86; Hlmrk Awd Sclstc Arts 87; 3 Gld Kys, 3 Blue Rbns Schlstc Arts 86-87; Art Hstrn.

HAMROCK, BRIDGET; United HS; Homer City, PA; (3); 45/147; Art Clb; Ski Clb; Chorus; Stu Cncl; Cheerleading; Hon Roll; Art.

HAMSCHER, JENNIFER; Emmaus HS; Emmaus, PA; (3); Latin Clb; Bsktbl; Sftbl; Penn ST; Elem Ed.

HAMSHER, ANGELA; Northern York SR HS; Dillsburg, PA; (4); 94/200; Church Yth Grp; Drama Clb; NFL; Band; Chorus; Church Choir; Rep Color Guard; Concert Band; Mrchg Band; West Chester U; Spch Thrpy.

HAMSON, CONNIE; Octorara HS; Cochranville, PA; (3); 6/157; Dance Clb; Girl Scts; Ski Clb; Band; Capt Color Guard; Concert Band; Flag Corp; Mrchg Band; School Musical; Variety Show; Dist Bnd 87; Cmptr Of The Week 87; Sci.

HAMULA, BROCK; Central Cambria HS; Johnstown, PA; (3); 19/220; Hosp Aide; Red Cross Aide; VP Stu Cncl; Bsktbl; Ftbl; Golf; Tennis; Trk; Cit Awd; High Hon Roll; PA Champshp Mock Trial Team 87; Pre-Med.

HAN, CHANG; Methacton HS; Audubon, PA; (3); Debate Tm; FBLA; Off Jr Cls; Stu Cncl; Socr; Tennis; Trk; Hon Roll; Engrng.

HAN, CLEMENCE; Cheltenham HS; Melrose Pk, PA; (4); Math Tm; Hon Roll; NHS; Penn ST U; Engrng.

HANAYIK, KEVIN; Purchase Line HS; Commodore, PA; (3); Chorus; Concert Band; Capt Drill Tm; Trs Mrchg Band; Pep Band; School Play; Bsktbl; Trk; Hon Roll.

HANCHAR, PATRICE; Cambria Heights HS; Carrolltown, PA; (3); Cmnty Wkr; Political Wkr; Band; Chorus; Church Choir; Color Guard; Concert Band; Mrchg Band; School Musical; Cit Awd; Penn ST U; Biochem.

HANCHARIK, MARK A; Hollidaysburg Area JR HS; Hollidaysburg, PA; (1); Chess Clb; Nwsp Rptr; Nwsp Stf; Lit Mag; Pres Frsh Cls; Stu Cncl; NEDT Awd.

HANCOCK, GUIDYNE; Mt Carmel Area JR SR HS; Atlas, PA; (3); 20/140; Cmnty Wkr; French Clb; FNA; FTA; Key Clb; Pep Clb; Red Cross Aide; Ski Clb; Pres Soph Cls; Pres Jr Cls; Crmnl Law.

HANCOCK, JENNIFER; Mercyhurst Prep; Erie, PA; (2); 3/202; Debate Tm; Chorus; Pep Band; School Musical; Var Cheerleading; JV Vllybl; Hon Roll; Acad Schlrshp 85-86; Msc Schlrsph 85-87; Cmmnctns.

HANCOCK, LISA L; St Hubert HS; Philadelphia, PA; (4); 17/383; French Clb; Girl Scts; Hosp Aide; Office Aide; Pres Pep Clb; Service Clb; Jazz Band; Orch; Stage Crew; Hon Roll; Corp Mgmt.

HANCOCK, SHANNON; Susquenita HS; Duncannon, PA; (3); French Clb; Rep Frsh Cls; Rep Soph Cls; Stat Coach Actv; Var L Crs Cntry; Mgr(s); L Trk; High Hon Roll; Hon Roll; Sec NHS; Cert Merit Achvt Phys Fit 86; Shippensburg U; Soc Sci.

HANCOVSKY, PAUL; Peters Township HS; Mcmurray, PA; (4); Varsity Clb; Capt Bsktbl; CC Awd; Rotary Awd; Penn ST Mc Keesport.

HANCZYC, MARTIN; Scranton Prep Schl; Duryea, PA; (3); 50/189; Latin Clb; Concert Band; Mgr Stage Crew; High Hon Roll; Hon Roll; PA ST U; Gentc Engrng.

HAND, JACQUELINE E; Saucon Valley SR HS; Bethlehem, PA; (4); 1/150; German Clb; Model UN; Chorus; School Musical; School Play; Nwsp Stf; Sec Stu Cncl; Capt Tennis; Pres NHS; Ntl Merit SF; Pre-Law.

HAND, JEFF; Lincoln HS; Ellwood City, PA; (3); 72/166; Church Yth Grp; Key Clb; Spanish Clb; Var Cheerleading; Var Ftbl; Var Trk; Hon Roll; CA ST U; Indus Arts Ed.

HAND, THOMAS; Honesdale HS; Lake Como, PA; (2); Naval Acad; Naval Career.

HANDEL, HEIDI; Conneaut Lake HS; Conneaut Lk, PA; (3); Drama Clb; Pep Clb; Spanish Clb; SADD; Nwsp Rptr; JV Bsktbl; Stat Sftbl; Var L Vllybl; High Hon Roll; NHS; U Of Pittsburgh.

HANDEL, KRISTEN; Portage Area HS; Portage, PA; (3); NFL; Yrbk Stf; Rep Stu Cncl; Trk; NHS; Hosp Aide; Chorus; Nwsp Stf; Rep Frsh Cls; Rep Jr Cls; Rtry Yth Ldrshp Adw 87; Pres Phys Ftns Awd 86 & 87; JR Acad Sci 86.

HANDERHAN, BRIAN; West Allegheny HS; Oakdale, PA; (3); 10/199; Spanish Clb; Rep Jr Cls; Var L Bsbl; Var L Ftbl; High Hon Roll; NHS.

HANDERHAN, COLEEN; Carlynton JR/Sr HS; Carnegie, PA; (4); Drama Clb; Ski Clb; Band; Chorus; Church Choir; Concert Band; Drm Mjr(t); Mrchg Band; Vllybl; Mid-East Music Conf 85-86; Dist & Rgn I Chorus Fest 85-87.

HANDKE, KATHLEEN; Gateway SR HS; Monroeville, PA; (3); 10/473; Girl Scts; Pres NFL; Trs Science Clb; Nwsp Stf; Ed Lit Mag; High Hon Roll; NHS; Membr 3rd Pl Team For Bio Olympics; Law.

HANDKE, PAUL; Greensburg Salem HS; Greensburg, PA; (2); 16/290; VP Sec 4-H; German Clb; Im Ftbl; 4-H Awd; High Hon Roll; Hon Roll; Jr NHS; Wldlf Mgmt.

HANDLER, MELISSA; Gwynedd Mercy Acad; Huntingdon Vly, PA; (2); Cmnty Wkr; SADD; Bsktbl; Sftbl; Hon Roll; Achvt Awd Spnsh 86-87; Achvt Awd Latn 86; PA Free Entrprse Schlrshp 87; Crmnlgy.

HANDWERK, JAMES; Bishop Neumann HS; Williamsport, PA; (2); Boy Scts; Model UN; Yrbk Stf; JV Socr; Comp Sci.

HANDWERK, JENNIFER; Emmaus HS; Macungie, PA; (3); Var Trk; Hon Roll; Bus.

HANDY, RALPH; Luthern HS; Philadelphia, PA; (2); Church Yth Grp; Debate Tm; NAACP; Church Choir; Stage Crew; Variety Show; Gym; Score Keeper; Svc Awd 87; AFNA Prtcpnt; Corp Law.

HANDYSIDE, HEATHER; Peters Township HS; Mcmurray, PA; (3); Key Clb; School Musical; School Play; Nwsp Ed-Chief; Nwsp Phtg; Nwsp Rptr; Nwsp Stf; Lit Mag; Rep Stu Cncl; Var Cmnty Wkr; Rotary Yth Ldrshp Awd 87; Jrnlsm.

HANDZUS, BERNADETTE; Archbishop Kennedy HS; Philadelphia, PA; (2); Girl Scts; Hosp Aide; Cit Awd; Hon Roll.

HANDZY, NESTOR Z; La Salle College HS; Philadelphia, PA; (3); Capt Chess Clb; Intnl Clb; Math Clb; Math Tm; Science Clb; Nwsp Rptr; Nwsp Stf; Pres Soph Cls; Rep Stu Cncl; NHS; Iron Hlls Math Leag Awd 85-86; Outstndng Wrk Schl Nwspaper & Math Tm 86-87; Math.

HANES JR, THOMAS; Elk County Christian HS; St Marys, PA; (3); Varsity Clb; Var L Ftbl; Var Trk; Hon Roll; Vrsty Lttr Ftbl 85-86 & 86-87; PA ST U; Forestry.

HANES, TIMOTHY; Elk County Christian HS; St Marys, PA; (3); 1/90; Var JV Ftbl; High Hon Roll; NEDT Awd.

HANEY, BARBRA; Hopewell HS; Monaca, PA; (4); 2/245; Cmnty Wkr; Sec Exploring; French Clb; Math Tm; Red Cross Aide; Rep Frsh Cls; Rep Soph Cls; Powder Puff Ftbl; High Hon Roll; Lion Awd; HOBY Ldrshp Awd 85; Mensa Awd 87; MI ST Acad Excllnce 87; MI ST U; Wildlife Vet.

HANEY, JEFFREY P; Lansdale Catholic HS; Lansdale, PA; (4); Math Tm; Crs Cntry; Trk; High Hon Roll; Hon Roll; Ntl Merit SF; Math.

HANEY, MICHELE A; Northern Lebanon HS; Jonestown, PA; (4); 10/166; Model UN; Varsity Clb; Concert Band; Mrchg Band; Pep Band; Sftbl; Tennis; NHS; Pres Acadmc Ftns Awd 87; PA ST U; Sci.

HANFORD, HOLLI; Highlands SR HS; Natrona Hgts, PA; (3); Am Leg Aux Girls St; Nwsp Stf; Yrbk Stf; VP Frsh Cls; VP Soph Cls; Sec Jr Cls; Sec Sr Cls; Var Capt Cheerleading; Hon Roll; Jr NHS; Ms All Amer Chrldr Pag 6th SF 87; Elem Ed.

HANGLEY, KATHERINE; Central HS Of Phila; Philadelphia, PA; (3); 53/538; Drama Clb; Political Wkr; Teachers Aide; Thesps; Acpl Chr; Chorus; Madrigals; School Play; Yrbk Stf; Lit Mag; Carnegie-Mellons Pre-Coll Smmr Pgm 87; Stu Peace, Phila Coaltn Cncrnd Yth; Theatre.

HANING, RON; Salisbury Elk Lick HS; Salisbury, PA; (4); Pres Church Yth Grp; Pres FFA; Yrbk Stf; Socr; Hon Roll; Diesel Mech.

HANKINSON, REED; Ambridge Area HS; Ambridge, PA; (3); Intnl Clb; JA; Variety Show; Var L Bsbl; Var L Bsktbl; Hon Roll; US Athl Awd/Schlrshp 85; Beaver Co Hoop Shoot Awd; WV U; Sprts Med.

HANKINSON, SEAN; Berlin Brothers Valley HS; New Balt, PA; (3); 10/100; Chess Clb; Scholastic Bowl; Spanish Clb; Pres Frsh Cls; VP Soph Cls; VP Jr Cls; VP Stu Cncl; Var Bsbl; VP Bsktbl; Ftbl; Yth Traffic Safety Council 87-88; Stu Forum 87-88; Elec Engrng.

HANKO, JIM; West Greene HS; Waynesburg, PA; (3); 8/103; FFA; School Musical; JV Var Ftbl; Hon Roll.

HANKO, PAMELA; Carmichaels Area HS; Crucible, PA; (1); Trs French Clb; Nwsp Stf; High Hon Roll; Jr NHS; NCTE Awd; Pres Schlr; Acad All-Amer 87.

HANKS, BRIAN; Huntingdon Area HS; Huntingdon, PA; (3); 50/230; Chorus; Concert Band; Mrchg Band; JV Var Bsbl; JV Var Bsktbl; Hon Roll; Opt Clb Awd; Bus Admn.

HANLEY, DEANNA D; Liberty Christian Acad; West Lawn, PA; (4); 1/3; Chorus; School Musical; Yrbk Ed-Chief; VP Frsh Cls; Pres Soph Cls; Pres Jr Cls; VP Sr Cls; Pres Stu Cncl; Im Bowling; Sftbl; Dean Scholar Messiah Coll 87; Messiah Coll.

HANLEY, DEANNE; Franklin Regional HS; Murrysville, PA; (3); French Clb; Ski Clb; SADD; Stu Cncl; L Swmmng; L Tennis; High Hon Roll; Hon Roll; Bus.

HANLEY, JEFFREY; Sharpsville HS; Sharpsville, PA; (4); Spanish Clb; SADD; Chorus; VP Stu Cncl; Var Bsktbl; Wt Lftg; Hon Roll; NHS; Pres Schlr.

HANLEY, KEVIN; Woodland Hills HS; Pittsburgh, PA; (2); 56/222; Church Yth Grp; French Clb; Hon Roll; Sci.

HANLEY, LORI; Spring Ford HS; Royersford, PA; (3); 58/262; SADD; Hon Roll; Engrng.

HANLEY, MARIA A; Mahanoy Area HS; Mahanoy City, PA; (3); Am Leg Aux Girls St; Church Yth Grp; Exploring; Ski Clb; SADD; Capt Color Guard; Concert Band; Swmmng; Amb To Hugh O Brian Yth Ldrshp Sem 86; Eagle Of Crss Awd Rgn Awd 87; Catholic Yth Cncl Of PA 86-87.

HANLEY, MARY; Carmichaels Area JR/Sr HS; Nemacolin, PA; (1); 15/120; Pres Stu Cncl; Sftbl; High Hon Roll; Hon Roll; Band; Concert Band; Mrchg Band; Nwsp Stf; Pres Frsh Cls; JV Bsktbl; WV U; Nursing.

HANLEY II, MICHAEL E; David B Oliver HS; Pittsburgh, PA; (2); Church Yth Grp; Cmnty Wkr; VP Exploring; Political Wkr; Red Cross Aide; SADD; Band; High Hon Roll; Prfct Atten Awd; Boys Clb Am; Prjct LEAD 87; 2nd Prz Sld 450 Rffl Tckts 86; The Chem People Inst Stu Rep 87; Law.

HANLIN, EDWARD; Big Spring HS; Newville, PA; (4); Trs Church Yth Grp; Chorus; Mrchg Band; School Musical; Rep Stu Cncl; Diving; Swmmng; Hon Roll; Outstndng Stdnt Cncl Membr 87; Stdnt Cncl Awd 87; Outstndng Musicn 87; Shippensburg U; Engl.

HANLON, CARRI; Penn Cambria HS; Loretto, PA; (4); 4/206; Drama Clb; Trs French Clb; SADD; Stage Crew; Sec Frsh Cls; Trs Jr Cls; High Hon Roll; Hon Roll; Trs NHS; Prfct Atten Awd; Jemima S Boyd Schlrshp 87; Lividus Chaptr Schlrshp 87; Hgh Achvt Awd 87; IN U Of PA; Elem Ed.

HANLON, CHERYL; Penn Cabria SR HS; Gallitzin, PA; (3); Art Clb; Church Yth Grp; Drama Clb; French Clb; Nwsp Rptr; Score Keeper; Sftbl; Prfct Atten Awd.

HANLON, LISA; Penn Cambria HS; Cresson, PA; (4); 16/206; VP Drama Clb; VP French Clb; Speech Tm; Chorus; Church Choir; Color Guard; School Musical; Sec Jr Cls; Sec Sr Cls; NHS; Marcn Lgn Ortucl Awd 85-87; Hnr Rll; Pharmcy.

HANLON, LYNN; North Allegheny HS; Sewickley, PA; (2); 44/630; Drm Mjr(t); Mrchg Band; Capt Twrlr; Hon Roll; Jr NHS; Acdmc.

HANLON JR, MATTHEW; John S Fine HS; Lower Askam, PA; (4); Drama Clb; Ski Clb; School Play; Stu Cncl; Hon Roll; HOBY 85; Upwrd Bnd Stu Govt 85-87; Rotry Yth Cmp 85; Wilkes Coll; Comms.

HANLON, SHERRI; Kiski Area SR HS; Apollo, PA; (4); Pep Clb; Spanish Clb; Chorus; Nwsp Rptr; Nwsp Stf; Sec Frsh Cls; Rep Jr Cls; Rep Sr Cls; Rep Stu Cncl; High Hon Roll; 3.5 & Abv Schl Yr 87; Sec Bldng Cmte 85-86; Grad Hnr Grd 85-86; Slippery Rock; Elem Ed.

HANN, LAWRENCE; Swarthmore Acad; Media, PA; (3); 1/22; Church Yth Grp; Ski Clb; Nwsp Rptr; Sec Frsh Cls; Var L Bsktbl; Var L Lcrss; Var Capt Socr; Var Tennis; High Hon Roll; Hon Roll; Outstndng Achvt Engl, Spnsh, Socl Stdy; Ovral Acadc Prfrmc 84-87; Coach Awd Sccr 84-85; MVP Sccr 85-87; Elec Engr.

HANN, LEAH; Mt Pleasant Area HS; Acme, PA; (4); 26/250; Exploring; Latin Clb; Sec Band; Mrchg Band; Rep Frsh Cls; Mat Maids; High Hon Roll; NHS; Martin Zabkar Jr Awd 86-87; Edinboro U Of PA; Pre-Law.

HANN, TRACY; Penn Trafford HS; Manor, PA; (2); Chess Clb; Math Clb; SADD; Band; Concert Band; Mrchg Band; Yrbk Stf; Lit Mag; High Hon Roll; All-Amer Acadmc 87; Acctng.

HANNA, BETH; Wilmington Area HS; New Wilmington, PA; (3); Spanish Clb; Nwsp Stf; JV Var Cheerleading; Powder Puff Ftbl; Im Vllybl; Hon Roll; Grove City Coll; Elem Ed.

HANNA, BRIAN; Washington HS; Washington, PA; (2); Church Yth Grp; Letterman Clb; JV Ftbl; Wt Lftg; Military; Pilot.

HANNA, BUSHRA; Allentown Central Catholic HS; Allentown, PA; (4); Stage Crew; Hon Roll; A Principles Awd & Strive Beyond Your Reach Awd 87; Child Psych.

HANNA, ROBERT; Devon Prep HS; Berwyn, PA; (3); 2/40; Chess Clb; Computer Clb; Math Clb; Math Tm; JV Bsbl; High Hon Roll; NHS; Ntl Merit Ltr; NEDT Awd; Math, Calacanctius, Physcs Awds; Sys Engrng.

HANNA, SHAWN; Tyrone Area HS; Warriors Mark, PA; (4); 6/177; Pres Church Yth Grp; Drama Clb; Math Tm; Ski Clb; Spanish Clb; Chorus; School Musical; Swing Chorus; Golf; NHS; US Air Force; Elect Engrng.

HANNAH, DAVID W; Pennsbury HS; Levittown, PA; (3); Band; Chorus; Church Choir; Concert Band; Mrchg Band; Orch; School Musical; School Play; Gym; Bucks Cnty Chorus 84, Orch 86 & 87; Elem Ed.

HANNAH, DAWN DICHELE; Merion Mercy Acad; Philadelphia, PA; (4); 16/81; Civic Clb; Cmnty Wkr; Science Clb; Service Clb; Spanish Clb; Acpl Chr; Stage Crew; Hon Roll; NHS; Ntl Merit Ltr; Art Hnr Socty 85-87; Georgetown U; Forgn Lang.

HANNAH, KATHY; Du Bois Area HS; Reynoldsville, PA; (4); 18/270; French Clb; Science Clb; Band; Concert Band; Mrchg Band; Orch; School Musical; Stu Cncl; High Hon Roll; Grove City Coll; Bio.

HANNAK, DIANNE; Marion Center Area HS; Creekside, PA; (3); 9/157; FNA; Hosp Aide; Latin Clb; Office Aide; Red Cross Aide; SADD; Chorus; Off Jr Cls; Mgr(s); High Hon Roll; IN U Of PA; Nrsng.

HANNAK, WILLIAM; Blacklick Valley HS; Twin Rocks, PA; (3); 3/100; Trs Church Yth Grp; Ski Clb; Speech Tm; School Play; Rep Stu Cncl; High Hon Roll; Mdcn.

HANNAN, KAREN L; North Allegheny HS; Pittsburgh, PA; (4); Chrmn FBLA; Yrbk Stf; Rep Frsh Cls; Rep Jr Cls; Sec Stu Cncl; Capt Var Cheerleading; Hon Roll; Jr NHS; NHS; Prfct Atten Awd; Bio Achvt Awd 86; Miami U Of OH; Acctng.

HANNER, TIMOTHY; Williamsport HS; Williamsport, PA; (3); Pres Church Yth Grp; Hosp Aide; Chorus; Church Choir; Mrchg Band; Orch; School Musical; Swing Chorus; Symp Band; Stu Cncl; J H Natl, Dist, Rgnl St & All Eastern Chorus 85-87; Dist & Rgnl Orch 85-87; Music.

HANNIBAL, MATTHEW; Cathedral Prep; Fairview, PA; (3); 7/193; Church Yth Grp; Model UN; Ski Clb; Var L Swmmng; High Hon Roll; Im Bsktbl; Im Bowling; JV Crs Cntry; JV Socr.

HANNIGAN, PATRICIA; Gateway SR HS; Monroeville, PA; (3); 90/454; Church Yth Grp; Color Guard; Mrchg Band; Off Frsh Cls; Off Frsh Cls; Trs Jr Cls; Trs Sr Cls; Hon Roll; Accntng.

HANNON, CATHIE; Chief Logan HS; Burnham, PA; (4); 4/198; Sec Computer Clb; Yrbk Ed-Chief; VP Frsh Cls; VP Soph Cls; VP Jr Cls; VP Sr Cls; Scrkpr Bsbl; Cheerleading; High Hon Roll; Pres NHS; Millers U Of PA; Math.

HANNON, CHRISTINE; Seton Catholic HS; Pittston, PA; (4); 3/89; Trs Church Yth Grp; Pres SADD; Madrigals; Nwsp Rptr; Yrbk Stf; Rep Stu Cncl; High Hon Roll; NHS; Ntl Merit Ltr; Natl Yth Salute 86-87; Natl Yth Ldrshp Conf 87; Duquesne U Schlr Awd 87; Duquesne U; Phrmcy.

HANNON, THOMAS; Athens Area HS; Sayre, PA; (3); Hon Roll; West Point; Engr.

HANRAHAN, KELLY; Punxsutawney Area HS; Punxsutawney, PA; (3); Varsity Clb; Nwsp Rptr; Nwsp Stf; Cheerleading; Hon Roll; IN U Of PA; Fshn Mdse.

HANSEL, BRIAN; Moshannon Valley HS; Houtzdale, PA; (3); 16/120; Boy Scts; JV Bsbl; Hon Roll; Jr NHS; Hist.

HANSEN, BECKY; Dunmore HS; Dunmore, PA; (4); 51/149; Trs French Clb; Ski Clb; Cheerleading; Swmmng; Trk; Twrlr; St Cloud ST U; Poltcl Sci.

HANSEN, BETH; Central Dauphin HS; Harrisburg, PA; (3); Ski Clb; Concert Band; Mrchg Band; Yrbk Stf; Stu Cncl; Tennis; Stat Trk; Intl Stdy.

HANSEN, CHRISTINA; Franklin Regional SR HS; Murrysville, PA; (3); FHA; Spanish Clb; SADD; VP Chorus; Sec Orch; School Musical; Sec Frsh Cls; Rep Stu Cncl; JV Bsktbl; High Hon Roll; Brigham Young U; Phrmcst.

HANSEN, MICHAEL W; Owen J Roberts HS; Glenmoore, PA; (4); School Play; Penn ST U; Elec Engrng.

HANSHE, RHONDA; Center HS; Monaca, PA; (2); German Clb; Hon Roll.

HANSHUE, JULIE; Juniata HS; E Waterford, PA; (3); Church Yth Grp; Drama Clb; 4-H; FHA; Pres Girl Scts; Library Aide; Chorus; School Play; Yrbk Stf; Hon Roll; Int Design.

HANSON, CHRISTOPHER; Jenkintown HS; Jenkintown, PA; (2); Intnl Clb; Model UN; Chorus; School Musical; Stage Crew; Rep Trs Stu Cncl; Var Crs Cntry; JV Tennis; Hon Roll; NHS; Chem.

HANSON, CRAIG; Eisenhower HS; Warren, PA; (3); Rep Frsh Cls; Rep Soph Cls; Var Wrstlng; Hon Roll; Comp Sci.

HANSON, LIDA; Mc Keesport HS; White Oak, PA; (2); Orch; School Musical; Var L Swmmng; High Hon Roll; Hon Roll; Prfct Atten Awd; Swmmng WPIAL Meet 85-87.

HANSOTTE, RON; Lawrence Cty Area Vo-Tech; New Castle, PA; (3); Aud/Vis; Church Yth Grp; VICA; Chorus; Stage Crew; Hon Roll.

HANSOTTE, SANDRA; Ford City HS; Ford City, PA; (3); Cmnty Wkr; VP Key Clb; Concert Band; Yrbk Stf; Stu Cncl; Capt Twrlr; High Hon Roll; Trs NHS; Dance Clb; German Clb; Marine Bio Quest Awd 86; PA Regional, District, & Cnty Band Fest 87; Intl Studies.

HANYCH, JEAN; Louis G Dieruff HS; Allentown, PA; (2); 17/340; Scholastic Bowl; Rep Frsh Cls; Rep Soph Cls; JV Var Bsktbl; Var Crs Cntry; Var Trk; JV Var Vllybl; Hon Roll; Jr NHS; Trck Awds-Leag, Dist & Invttnl Mdls 87; Med.

HANZELY, TOM; Dubois Area HS; Dubois, PA; (3); Boy Scts; Nwsp Stf; Mgr(s); Natl Rural Elec Yth Tour 87; Crmnl Just.

HARAYDA, MICHELE; Conneaut Valley HS; Springboro, PA; (3); Cmnty Wkr; Exploring; Library Aide; Spanish Clb; Nwsp Stf; Yrbk Stf; High Hon Roll; NHS.

HARBACH, TIM; Newport Pacific HS; Kenosha, WI; (4); School Musical; School Play; JV Bsbl; Engrng.

HARBAUGH, WENDY; Hempfield Area HS; Greensburg, PA; (4); French Clb; Pep Clb; Chorus; High Hon Roll; Hon Roll; U Of Pittsburgh; Mth.

HARBOLD, TANYA; Bermudian Springs HS; York Spgs, PA; (3); 3/120; Church Yth Grp; French Clb; Chorus; School Musical; Swing Chorus; Yrbk Rptr; Off Stu Cncl; Var Sftbl; Hon Roll; Psych.

HARCLERODE, JUSTIN; Everett Area HS; Everett, PA; (1); Church Yth Grp; Exploring; Pres Stu Cncl; Bsktbl; Medicine.

HARCLERODE, SONJA; Chestnut Ridge HS; New Paris, PA; (3); 1/137; 4-H; FBLA; SADD; Teachers Aide; Band; Concert Band; Mrchg Band; Pep Band; Sec Soph Cls; VP Stu Cncl; 2nd Pl PA FBLA Stenogrphr I Comptn 87; Homecmnt Crt Atten; Fall Foliage Queen Cont; Phys Thrpy.

HARCLERODE, TERRI; Windber Area HS; Windber, PA; (3); Church Yth Grp; French Clb; Band; Concert Band; Jazz Band; Yrbk Stf; Rep Jr Cls; Hon Roll; NHS; JA; Student Of Month 87; Pres Acad Fitness Awd 85.

HARDER, HOLLY; Blue Mountain Acad; Takoma Park, MD; (3); 5/76; FCA; Pep Clb; Ski Clb; Acpl Chr; Chorus; Rep Soph Cls; Stu Cncl; Stat Bsktbl; Score Keeper; High Hon Roll; Union Clg.

HARDIE, THOMAS; Senecca Valley SR HS; Zelienople, PA; (3); 3/400; Church Yth Grp; JA; Radio Clb; ROTC; Chorus; Stage Crew; Nwsp Rptr; Nwsp Stf; Lit Mag.

HARDING, HEATHER; Cocalico HS; Reamstown, PA; (3); 21/166; GAA; Rep Stu Cncl; Var L Cheerleading; Var L Fld Hcky; High Hon Roll; Bus.

HARDING, LAURA; Northern Lebanon SR HS; Lebanon, PA; (3); 30/201; Trs Church Yth Grp; Pres 4-H; FFA; Rep Stu Cncl; Var L Bsktbl; JV Fld Hcky; Var L Sftbl; Hon Roll; Dairy Sci.

HARDING, STEPHANIE; Freeport SR HS; Sarver, PA; (2); Var Stat Bsktbl; JV Trk; High Hon Roll; Hon Roll; Arch.

HARDING, TERRI; Waynesburg Central HS; Waynesburg, PA; (3); French Clb; Hosp Aide; Mu Alpha Theta; Natl Beta Clb; Ski Clb; Band; Capt Color Guard; Concert Band; Mrchg Band; Trk; Electrnc Engrng.

HARDING, TIM; Lampeter-Strasburg HS; Strasburg, PA; (4); 9/148; Band; Concert Band; Jazz Band; School Musical; School Play; VP Jr Cls; VP Sr Cls; Var Bsbl; JV Wrstlng; High Hon Roll; City/Cnty Sci Fair Awd 86-87; Pres Acdmc Fit Awd 87; USAF; Mech Engrng.

HARDWICK, CAROLE; Langley HS; Pittsburgh, PA; (3); Church Yth Grp; Band; Concert Band; Mrchg Band; Cit Awd; Hon Roll; Jr NHS; Prfct Atten Awd; Med.

HARDY JR, DAVID E; West Catholic HS Boys; Philadelphia, PA; (4); Debate Tm; Church Choir; Variety Show; Rep Stu Cncl; Bsktbl; Coach Actv; Score Keeper; Hon Roll; Prfct Atten Awd; Temple U; Law.

HARDY, JENNIFER; Gateway SR HS; Monroeville, PA; (3); 105/452; NAACP; Pep Clb; Chorus; Off Jr Cls; JV Bsktbl; Var L Trk; Hon Roll; Gold Mdl Trck 87; Med.

HARDY, JODI; East Pennsboro HS; Summerdale, PA; (2); VP Church Yth Grp; English Clb; Latin Clb; Church Choir; Yrbk Stf; High Hon Roll; Hon Roll; Asst Vet.

HARDY, KELLY; Mohawk Area JR-SR HS; Wampum, PA; (3); Church Yth Grp; Band; Jazz Band; Mrchg Band; Pep Band; School Musical; Nwsp Rptr; Var L Crs Cntry; Var Trk; Rep Western PA United Methodist Youth On A Mission Of Peace To The Soviet Union 87.

HARDY, MIA; Scott Intermediate HS; Coatesville, PA; (2); Drama Clb; Band; Color Guard; Concert Band; Mrchg Band; School Musical; Cheerleading; Sftbl; Trk; Hon Roll; Dr.

HARENSKI IV, JOSEPH E; Quaker Valley HS; Sewickley, PA; (2); German Clb; Math Tm; Band; Crs Cntry; Trk; High Hon Roll; Pres Schlr; Chem.

HARGER, PATRICIA; Monongabela Valley Catholic HS; Monessen, PA; (3); 15/94; Camp Fr Inc; Cmnty Wkr; Ski Clb; Chorus; Mgr(s); French Hon Soc; Hon Roll; 2nd Pl Humnts Dy Skt Cmptn Frnch; PA ST U; Psych.

HARGRAVES, JEROME; Chester HS; Chester, PA; (4); Church Yth Grp; Debate Tm; Bsktbl; Trk; Vllybl; High Hon Roll; NHS; Acadmc All Amer 86; Drexel U; Elec Engrng.

HARGRAVES, MICHAEL R; Central Columbia HS; Berwick, PA; (3); 69/169; Am Leg Boys St; Exploring; German Clb; JV Crs Cntry; Mgr(s); JV Trk; JV Wrstlng; Prfct Atten Awd; Mngr 5 People Wrk 87; Millersville U; Mngmt.

HARING, CORA; Fleetwood Area HS; Fleetwood, PA; (3); Ski Clb; Drill Tm; Sec Jr Cls; Var Cheerleading; Var Fld Hcky; Hon Roll; MVP Outstndng Chrldr 85-86; Air Force; Psych.

HARING, TIMOTHY J; Upper Perkiomen HS; Barto, PA; (3); 5/242; Am Leg Boys St; Cmnty Wkr; Var L Crs Cntry; Var L Trk; High Hon Roll; NHS; Im JV Socr; Magna Cum Laude Ntl Latin Exam 87; Outstndng Acad Achvt 11th Grd Engl 87; Oustndng Acad Achv Trig 87; Physcl Thrpy.

HARING, TRACY; Pottstown SR HS; Pottstown, PA; (3); 14/155; Trs Church Yth Grp; French Clb; Chorus; Flag Corp; Jr Cls; Var Tennis; High Hon Roll; NHS; Accntng.

HARKCOM, JONI LYNN; Somerset Area SR HS; Somerset, PA; (4); 26/232; English Clb; German Clb; JA; Band; Mrchg Band; Yrbk Bus Mgr; Trs Soph Cls; High Hon Roll; Hon Roll; NHS; Acad Achvt Awd 85-87; Soroptimist SR 86-87; Bus.

HARKELROAD, KRISTI; Bedford HS; Bedford, PA; (4); Sec VP Church Yth Grp; SADD; Teachers Aide; Chorus; Church Choir; Flag Corp; Mrchg Band; School Musical; Rep Stu Cncl; Mgr(s); Spcl Edu.

HARKER JR, ARNOLD; North Star HS; Hooversville, PA; (3); 16/141; Church Yth Grp; FCA; Mu Alpha Theta; Teachers Aide; Hon Roll; Mu Alpha Theta Indctn Cert 86; Cvl Engr.

HARKINS, DIANE; Purchase Line HS; Clymer, PA; (4); Band; Chorus; Concert Band; Mrchg Band; Pep Band; Stage Crew; Yrbk Stf; Hon Roll; Intl Frgn Lang Awd 86 & 87; ICM Schl Of Bus; Med Asst.

HARKINS, JOHN H; Mechanicsburg Area SR HS; Mechanicsburg, PA; (4); 33/305; Ski Clb; School Play; PSU; Elect Engr.

HARKINS, TAMMY; William Allen HS; Allentown, PA; (4); 2/626; Church Yth Grp; JCL; Latin Clb; SADD; Church Choir; Rep Soph Cls; High Hon Roll; Hon Roll; NHS; Opt Clb Awd; 2nd Pl Upper Yth Tm 86 & 87; Cedar Crest Coll; Math.

HARKNESS, SHANNON; Delaware Valley HS; Milford, PA; (3); 4/150; Mgr(s); Tennis; High Hon Roll; NHS; Intl Frgn Lang Awd & Acdmc All-Amer 86; US Natl Math Awd 87; Psych.

HARLAN, KELLI; Elizabeth Forward HS; Elizabeth, PA; (4); 11/294; AFS; Hosp Aide; VP Spanish Clb; Chorus; Flag Corp; Stat Bsktbl; Stat Trk; High Hon Roll; Trs NHS; Pres Schlr; Grove Cty Coll Acadc Schlrshp 87; Grove City Coll; Elem Educ.

HARLAN, MICHAEL; St Marys Area HS; Kersey, PA; (4); Boy Scts; Yrbk Stf; Swmmng; Vllybl; Wt Lftg; Army.

HARLESS, LESLIE; William Penn SR HS; York, PA; (4); 43/382; French Clb; High Hon Roll; Jrnlsm.

HARLEY, DONNA; Parkland HS; Allentown, PA; (3); 37/481; Band; Chorus; Concert Band; Jazz Band; Mrchg Band; Pep Band; School Musical; Hon Roll; NHS; Prfct Atten Awd; Bio.

HARLEY, GINNAE; The Ellis Schl; Export, PA; (3); Nwsp Stf; Pres Stu Cncl; Var L Bsktbl; Socr; Soph Awd 85-86; Bus.

HARLEY, MICHELE; Archbishop Ryan HS For Girls; Philadelphia, PA; (3); 32/508; Sec English Clb; Service Clb; SADD; Color Guard; Var JV Mrchg Band; Lit Mag; Im Bowling; High Hon Roll; Trs NHS; Prfct Atten Awd; Vet.

HARMAN, AMY; Fairview HS; Fairview, PA; (3); Church Yth Grp; French Clb; Nwsp Rptr; Bsktbl; Cheerleading; Hon Roll; NHS; $2000 Schlrshp Frm Times News Pblshng Co 87; Jrnlsm.

HARMAN, BRIAN; West Hazleton HS; Rock Glen, PA; (2); Spanish Clb; Golf; High Hon Roll; Hon Roll; Pre-Med.

HARMAN, JANE; Oliver HS; Pittsburgh, PA; (3); Sec JA; Red Cross Aide; Nwsp Rptr; Yrbk Stf; Capt Pom Pon; High Hon Roll; Hon Roll; Prfct Atten Awd; Prfct Attndnc Chrch 84; Awd Hstry, Govt 84-87; All Amer Awd 86; U Of Pittsburgh; Bio.

HARMAN, JILL; East Pennsboro Area HS; Enola, PA; (3); Church Yth Grp; Drama Clb; French Clb; Pres German Clb; Chorus; Church Choir; Concert Band; Jazz Band; Madrigals; Mrchg Band.

HARMAN, JODI; York County Area Voctnl Tech Schl; York, PA; (4); FHA; VICA; Sftbl; Vllybl; High Hon Roll; Hon Roll; Wmns AM ORT Awd, Mst Outstndng Fd Prep, FHA 2nd Pl Bkng Fd Svc 87; Gallaudet U; Bus Mngmt.

HARMAN, MICHELE; Upper Dauphin Area HS; Millersburg, PA; (3); 20/120; 4-H; Band; Chorus; Concert Band; Jazz Band; Mrchg Band; Cheerleading; Trk; Med Tech.

HARMAN, ORLAN; Mount Pleasant Area SR HS; Donegal, PA; (3); CAP; German Clb; Hon Roll; Acad All Amer Awd 85-86; Air Force Cand Schl; AF Offcr.

HARMAN JR, RONALD R; Freeland HS; Freeland, PA; (4); 1/87; Pres VP FBLA; Yrbk Ed-Chief; Yrbk Phtg; VP NHS; Ntl Merit SF; Pres Schlr; Val; VP Computer Clb; Scholastic Bowl; Spanish Clb; 4 Yr Navy ROTC Schlrshp 87; 4 Yr Schlrshp Wilkes Coll Mth Comptn 87; FBLA Ntl Ldrshp Conf Typng 87; Boston U; Aero Engrng.

HARMAN, SUE; Williamsport Area HS; Williamsport, PA; (3); 4/596; Capt Color Guard; Concert Band; Orch; Yrbk Stf; Sec Soph Cls; Pres Jr Cls; Rep Sr Cls; Rep Stu Cncl; High Hon Roll; NHS; Typg Prof Awd 85; Psych.

HARMON, EDDIE; West Greene HS; New Freeport, PA; (3); 28/102; Boys Clb Am; Computer Clb; FFA; Teachers Aide; Stage Crew; JV VP Bsktbl; FFA Dbtng Tm 85-86; Lttrs Bsktbl 3 Yrs; OK U; Comp Sci.

HARMON, KATRINA; Honesdale HS; Honesdale, PA; (2); Letterman Clb; Ski Clb; Temple Yth Grp; Varsity Clb; Y-Teens; Off Stu Cncl; Stat Bsktbl; Var L Tennis; JV Trk; Hon Roll; Publc Reltns.

HARMON, MICHAEL; Shanksville Stonycreek HS; Berlin, PA; (4); Chess Clb; Ski Clb; Pres Jr Cls; Wt Lftg; Tap SR Awds 86-87; Somerset Bldg Assoc Awds 86-87; Heating & Plmbng Awd 86-87; Williams Area Coll; Rfrg & Air.

HARMON, MIKE; Mc Guffey HS; Washington, PA; (3); 1/250; Exploring; Ski Clb; Speech Tm; Var Capt Crs Cntry; JV Socr; Var Trk; High Hon Roll; NHS; HS Awds Ger Sci Math Hlth SS 84-86; Grmny Speech Fest 86; Track Cross Cntry 85 & 86; Bio Engr.

HARMON, NICHOLE C; Philadelphia HS For Girls; Philadelphia, PA; (4); 26/365; Pres Church Yth Grp; Hosp Aide; Nwsp Phtg; Nwsp Stf; Lit Mag; Stu Cncl; NHS; Spanish NHS; Service Clb; High Hon Roll; Ntl Achvt Schlr; Stu Soc Awareness; 3rd Pl Essay Cntst; Wesleyan U; Chem.

HARMON, SHANNON; Burrell HS; New Kensington, PA; (3); FBLA; Chorus; Color Guard; New Kensington Comm Schl; Bus.

HARNER, CAROL L; Wayside Christian Schl; Boyertown, PA; (4); 1/5; Church Yth Grp; Chorus; Church Choir; School Musical; Yrbk Stf; Rep Frsh Cls; Rep Soph Cls; Rep Jr Cls; Rep Sr Cls; Trs Stu Cncl.

HARNER, LAURA; Blue Mountain Acad; Hanover, PA; (3); Drama Clb; Teachers Aide; Church Choir; Nwsp Ed-Chief; Nwsp Rptr; Nwsp Stf; Sec Frsh Cls; Var Im Bsktbl; Capt Im Vllybl; Hon Roll; Comms.

HARNER, ROBERT; Pottstown SR HS; Pottstown, PA; (3); 35/155; French Clb; Key Clb; Var L Bsktbl; Hon Roll; Accntng.

HARNER, STEVE; Schuylkill Haven Area HS; Sch Haven, PA; (2); Spanish Clb; Pres Frsh Cls; Pres Soph Cls; Pres Jr Cls; Rep Stu Cncl; Bsbl; Ftbl; Hon Roll; Air Force Acad; Airline Pilot.

HARNISH, BRETT; Hempfield HS; Lancaster, PA; (3); 54/400; Science Clb; JV Bsktbl; High Hon Roll; Hon Roll; NHS; Marines.

HARNISH, BRIAN; Solanco HS; Christiana, PA; (4); Trs Church Yth Grp; Pres 4-H; Pres FFA; High Hon Roll; Hon Roll; Star Cptr Frmr FFA 85; Star Greenhand 84; Farmer.

HARNISH, ERIC; Dover Area HS; Dover, PA; (4); 2/230; Quiz Bowl; Band; School Musical; Var L Socr; Var L Tennis; Ntl Merit Ltr; Sal; Am Chem Soc Awd 85; Renssnc Elite Choir 84-87; AAL All Coll Schlrshp Fnlst 87; Duke U; Chem.

HARNISH, JENNIFER; Solanco HS; Christiana, PA; (2); 13/282; Church Yth Grp; Pres 4-H; FFA; Band; Concert Band; Mrchg Band; JV Bsktbl; High Hon Roll; NHS; Girl Scts; Star Chapter Farmer 87.

HARNISH, SARAH; Hempfield HS; Lancaster, PA; (4); Drama Clb; JA; Chorus; Mrchg Band; School Musical; Variety Show; Hon Roll; Modrn Music Mstrs Hnr Soc 85-87; Dist Chorus 85-87; Cnty Chorus 84-87; Kutztown U; Elem Educ.

HARP, CHADWICK A; Norristown Area HS; Norristown, PA; (4); 10/413; Aud/Vis; Orch; School Play; Ed Nwsp Phtg; Yrbk Ed-Chief; Lit Mag; Off Sr Cls; Tennis; NHS; Cornell U; Gov.

HARPER, ADRIENNE; Chester HS; Chester, PA; (4); 9/390; Church Yth Grp; Capt FCA; French Clb; Church Choir; Var Bsktbl; Hon Roll; NHS; Temple; Psych.

HARPER, AMY; Venango Christian HS; Rouseville, PA; (3); SADD; Variety Show; Cheerleading; Hon Roll; Psych.

HARPER, CAROL; Bishop Mc Devitt HS; Philadelphia, PA; (4); 195/357; Cmnty Wkr; VP JA; Service Clb; Spanish Clb; VICA; Variety Show; Yrbk Stf; Stu Cncl; Powder Puff Ftbl; NHS; JR Achvt, Outstndng Achvr Awd 85; Comp Inf Systems.

HARPER, CYNDI; Mc Guffey HS; Amity, PA; (4); Church Yth Grp; French Clb; Trs JA; Pep Clb; Ski Clb; Spanish Clb; Rep Frsh Cls; Rep Soph Cls; Rep Jr Cls; Rep Sr Cls; Bus Admin.

HARPER, JAY; Archbishop Wood HS For Boys; Feasterville, PA; (3); 5/241; Mgr Crs Cntry; Trk; High Hon Roll; NHS; Ntl Merit SF; Best Sci Fair Awd 85-87; HS Scholar; Marine Bio.

HARPER, LISA; The Christian Acad; Brookhaven, PA; (3); Library Aide; Chorus; Church Choir; Stage Crew; Nwsp Ed-Chief; Nwsp Rptr; Nwsp Sprt Ed; Nwsp Stf; Stu Cncl; JV Stat Bsktbl; Messiah Coll; Cmnctns.

HARPER JR, RICHARD BIDDLE; Conrad Weiser JR SR HS; Robesonia, PA; (4); 1/189; Computer Clb; Latin Clb; Scholastic Bowl; Chorus; Jazz Band; School Musical; JV Var Socr; High Hon Roll; NHS; Val; Outsndng Mth Stu Clss 87; Outsndng Scl Stds Stu Clss 87; Scer Ldrshp Awd 87; Emory U; Bus Admin.

HARPER, SHELLEY; Conrad Weiser HS; Robesonia, PA; (2); 27/169; Drama Clb; JCL; Chorus; School Play; Stu Cncl; JV Cheerleading; JV Fld Hcky; Trk; Mgr Wrstlng; Hon Roll.

HARPER, THOMAS; Archbishop Wood For Boys HS; Feasterville, PA; (2); 6/260; Church Yth Grp; Math Clb; Math Tm; Nwsp Rptr; Nwsp Stf; Im Bsktbl; Im Vllybl; High Hon Roll; Silv Mdl Bst Fair Bucks Cnty Sci Fair 86-87; Hghst Avg Religion 85-86; Hghst Avg Spn 86-87.

HARPER, TRACI; Meyersdale Area HS; Meyersdale, PA; (4); Pres Church Yth Grp; FBLA; Pep Clb; VP Spanish Clb; Yrbk Stf; Hon Roll; NHS; Intl Frgn Lang Awds 86-87.

HARPST, CHRISTOPHER; Commodore Perry HS; Hadley, PA; (4); Math Tm; Stage Crew; Bsbl; Crs Cntry; L Wrstlng; Hon Roll; NHS.

HARPST, RENITA; Reynolds HS; Fredonia, PA; (3); 6/142; Latin Clb; Letterman Clb; Spanish Clb; Stu Cncl; Var L Bsktbl; Var Cheerleading; Var Trk; Var L Vllybl; Hon Roll; NHS; Mdcl.

HARPST, TODD; Coudersport Area JR SR HS; Coudersport, PA; (3); Art Clb; French Clb; Varsity Clb; Band; Concert Band; Mrchg Band; School Play; VP Frsh Cls; Sec Soph Cls; Pres Stu Cncl; Bus Adm.

HARPSTER, CHARLES; Bellwood-Antis HS; Altoona, PA; (3); Boy Scts; Off Frsh Cls; Hon Roll; Prfct Atten Awd; Prfct Attndnc 86; Bucknell Univ.

HARPSTER, HEATHER; State Clg Area Intermediate HS; Port Matilda, PA; (2); Cit Awd; Hon Roll; Bus Educ Awd 87; Penn ST U.

HARPSTER, PAMELA; Juniata HS; E Waterford, PA; (4); Church Yth Grp; FHA; Library Aide; VICA; School Play; Yrbk Stf; High Hon Roll; NHS; Jr NHS; Sr Csmtlgy Awd 86-87; Schlrshp-Pttsbrgh Beauty Acad 86-87; Pittsburgh Beauty Acad; Csmtlgy.

HARR, KIMBERLY; Hollidaysburg Area SR HS; Hollidaysburg, PA; (4); 84/330; German Clb; Y-Teens; Mgr(s); Score Keeper; Sftbl; Vllybl; Prfct Atten Awd; Associated Schls; Flight Atten.

HARR, SHAUN; Claysburg-Kimmel HS; Imler, PA; (1); 2/83; Church Yth Grp; Drama Clb; Ski Clb; SADD; Pres Chorus; Wrstlng; High Hon Roll; Hon Roll; Amer Legn Awd 86; Corp Law.

HARRAR, JAMES CRAIG; Central Bucks East HS; Pipersville, PA; (3); Ski Clb; JV Swmmng; Var L Tennis; Cit Awd; Hon Roll; Penn ST; Psych.

HARRELL, CHRIS; Gateway SR HS; Monroeville, PA; (3); Boys Clb Am; Im Bsktbl; Comp Sci.

HARRELL, STEPHEN; G Westinghse/Taylor Allderdice HS; Pittsburgh, PA; (3); SADD; Band; Cert Artistic Recognition; Otis/Parsons Art Inst; Art.

HARRIGAN, OKIFA; Phila HS For Girls; Philadelphia, PA; (3); Church Yth Grp; Cmnty Wkr; Computer Clb; Debate Tm; English Clb; FNA; Hosp Aide; Math Clb; Office Aide; Sec Teachers Aide; U Of PA; Med.

HARRIGER, PAUL; Du Bois Area HS; Reynoldsville, PA; (3); Church Yth Grp; Pres 4-H; Letterman Clb; Quiz Bowl; Scholastic Bowl; Science Clb; Stage Crew; Wrstlng; 4-H Awd; Hon Roll; Outstndng Offcrs Awd 4-H 86; Aerontcs.

HARRIGLE JR, DALE; Catasauqua HS; Catasauqua, PA; (3); 8/128; Exploring; Ed Lit Mag; Var Crs Cntry; Var Trk; Hon Roll; Ntl Merit Ltr; Prfct Atten Awd; Mech Engrng.

HARRINGTON, EILEEN; Cardinal Dougherty HS; Philadelphia, PA; (3); 24/670; Church Yth Grp; Varsity Clb; Var JV Sftbl; High Hon Roll; Hon Roll; NHS; Nrsng.

HARRINGTON, LISA; Pittston Area SR HS; Avoca, PA; (3); Pres Church Yth Grp; Hosp Aide; Math Clb; Hon Roll; JV Trk; 4-H Awd; 4-H; Band; Mrchg Band; USN.

HARRINGTON, NIKOLE; West York HS; York, PA; (3); Church Yth Grp; Dance Clb; Drama Clb; FFA; JA; Library Aide; NFL; Spanish Clb; Speech Tm; SADD; Seafood Qun 86; Penn ST; Arts-Fshn.

HARRINGTON, SUE ELLEN; Gwynedd-Mercy Acad; Blue Bell, PA; (2); Church Yth Grp; Cmnty Wkr; JV Sftbl; JV Tennis; Cert Hnrb Merit Cum Laude 85-86; Diploma De Merit Spn 85-86; Notre Dame; Legl.

HARRIS, CRYSTAL; Little Flower HS; Philadelphia, PA; (3); Church Yth Grp; German Clb; Church Choir; Stage Crew; Hon Roll; Acctnt.

HARRIS, DAIVD; Slippery Rock Area HS; Slippery Rock, PA; (4); Office Aide; Band; Concert Band; Jazz Band; Mrchg Band; School Musical; Var Socr; Allegheny Coll.

HARRIS, DAVID; Council Rock HS; Richbow, PA; (3); 76/908; Debate Tm; Key Clb; Political Wkr; Rep Frsh Cls; Rep Soph Cls; Rep Jr Cls; Im Mgr Badmtn; Im Mgr Bsktbl; Im Mgr Vllybl; Im Mgr Socr; Wnnr Prsdntl Clssrm Schlrshp 87; Poly Sci.

HARRIS, DENISE; International Affairs HS; Philadelphia, PA; (3); Church Yth Grp; Cmnty Wkr; Girl Scts; Band; Church Choir; Concert Band; Orch; Sftbl; Trk; Prfct Atten Awd; Amer Chemical Soc Awd 87; West Pt US Military Acad.

HARRIS, DESIREE; Chester HS; Chester, PA; (3); 16/485; VP Sec Church Yth Grp; GAA; Spanish Clb; VP Church Choir; JV L Bsktbl; Var JV Mgr(s); High Hon Roll; Hon Roll; Prfct Atten Awd; Math Awd 85-86; Lang Awd-Spnsh 85-86 & 86-87; Georgetown U; Med.

HARRIS, GEORGE; Mifflinburg Area HS; Mifflinburg, PA; (4); 21/164; Cmnty Wkr; French Clb; Key Clb; Service Clb; SADD; School Musical; Stage Crew; JV Bsktbl; L Socr; Cit Awd; Hobart & William; Psych.

HARRIS, JAUNA; Union HS; Rimersburg, PA; (4); 7/56; FCA; Trs French Clb; Pep Clb; Chorus; School Musical; Nwsp Ed-Chief; Yrbk Ed-Chief; Rep Stu Cncl; Capt Var Bsktbl; Capt Var Vllybl; Hon Roll 83-87; IN U Of PA; Engr.

HARRIS, JEFFREY; Pennsbury HS; Morrisville, PA; (4); 180/777; Church Yth Grp; FCA; German Clb; Var Ftbl; Var Trk; Pennsbury Schlrshp; VA Tech.

HARRIS, JENNIFER; Central HS; Philadelphia, PA; (3); Latin Clb; JV Swmmng; Open Door Stu Exchng To France 87.

HARRIS, JILL; Millersburg Area HS; Millersburg, PA; (3); 25/70; Art Clb; Sec Church Yth Grp; French Clb; Spanish Clb; Color Guard; Hon Roll; Elem Educ.

HARRIS, JOHN; Monsignor Bonner HS; Glenolden, PA; (3); 21/259; Chess Clb; Math Tm; Im Ftbl; High Hon Roll; Hon Roll; Comp Literacy Cert Of Achvt 85; Frnch Cert Of Achvt 87; Drexel U; Elec Engr.

HARRIS, LISA; Portage Area HS; Portage, PA; (4); 40/128; Ski Clb; Speech Tm; Varsity Clb; Chorus; Stat Bsktbl; JV Cheerleading; Hon Roll; U Pittsburgh; Pre-Law.

HARRIS, MARIJANE; Mifflinburg Area HS; Mifflinburg, PA; (1); Sec Drama Clb; French Clb; Key Clb; Chorus; School Musical; School Play; Stu Cncl; Hon Roll; Lbrl Arts.

HARRIS, MEAGAN; Taylor Allderdice HS; Pittsburgh, PA; (2); Ski Clb; High Hon Roll; NHS; Acad Letter For 4 Of 4 Terms High Hnr Roll 86 & 87; Medicine.

HARRIS, ROBYN; Waynesboro Area SR HS; Waynesboro, PA; (3); 52/355; AFS; Church Yth Grp; Dance Clb; Band; Color Guard; Flag Corp; Mrchg Band; L Diving; L Swmmng; Hon Roll; Early Chldhd Ed.

HARRIS, RUTHANN; New Castle SR HS; New Castle, PA; (3); 49/263; Church Yth Grp; Spanish Clb; Church Choir; Trk; Air Force.

HARRIS, SANDRA; Williamson HS; Lawrenceville, PA; (3); Trs Church Yth Grp; SADD; Band; Chorus; Church Choir; Yrbk Stf; High Hon Roll; NHS; Prfct Atten Awd; Elmira Bus Inst; Scrtry.

HARRIS, SCOTT; South Williamsport Area HS; Williamsport, PA; (3); 15/100; Hst Frsh Cls; Hst Soph Cls; Hst Jr Cls; Hst Sr Cls; Rep Stu Cncl; L Bsktbl; High Hon Roll; Hon Roll; Vet-Med.

HARRIS, TASHA; West Catholic Girls HS; Philadelphia, PA; (3); 29/248; Church Yth Grp; Girl Scts; NFL; Service Clb; Spanish Clb; Orch; Yrbk Stf; Rep Stu Cncl; Hon Roll; Prfct Atten Awd; Ellis Grant Schlrshp 84-88; White-Wllms Schlrshp 87-88; Villanova U; Ecs.

HARRIS, TERRANCE; Walter Biddle Saul HS; Philadelphia, PA; (3); FFA; Church Choir; Yrbk Stf; Bsktbl; Ftbl; Sftbl; Temple U; Cmmnctns.

HARRIS, TODD; Mercer JR & SR HS; Mercer, PA; (3); Varsity Clb; Yrbk Stf; Var Capt Bsktbl; JV Ftbl; L Capt Trk; High Hon Roll; OH Northern; Phrmcy.

HARRIS, TONYA L; Penn Manor HS; Millersville, PA; (3); Pres Church Yth Grp; FBLA; Girl Scts; Library Aide; SADD; School Musical; School Play; Powder Puff Ftbl; High Hon Roll; Bus Mgmt.

HARRISON, CATHERINE; Red Lion Area SR HS; Red Lion, PA; (3); 25/342; JCL; School Musical; School Play; Symp Band; Yrbk Ed-Chief; Stu Cncl; High Hon Roll; NHS; U Of PA.

HARRISON, DAVID TODD; Conneaut Lake HS; Conneaut Lake, PA; (3); Ski Clb; Trs Spanish Clb; Im Bsbl; JV Ftbl; Hon Roll; NHS; PA Chem Olympcs 87; JETS Tst Chem, Bio 87; U Of Pittsburg; Phrmcy.

HARRISON, JULIE; Burrell SR HS; Lower Burrell, PA; (2); 23/214; Cmnty Wkr; Intnl Clb; Ski Clb; Concert Band; Mrchg Band; VP Frsh Cls; Swmmng; Tennis; High Hon Roll; Hon Roll; 1st Pl Sci Fair 86.

HARRISON, KAREN; Columbia Montour Area Vo-Tech Schl; Stillwater, PA; (4); 9/206; DECA; SADD; VICA; High Hon Roll; Hon Roll; NHS; Rotary Awd; Church Yth Grp; Chorus; Church Choir; Bloomsburg Rotary Clb Stu Of Mnth 87; DECA ST Finlst 85; DECA Dist-3rd Pl 85; DECA Dist 4th Pl 84; Bus Admn.

HARRISON, KIETA; Philadelphia HS For Girls; Philadelphia, PA; (3); 78/400; Hon Roll; Jr NHS; Mntlly Gftd Pgm; Prime Pgm 85-86; Howard U; Phy Therapy.

HARRISON, MARGARET; Saegertown HS; Saegertown, PA; (4); 7/124; VP Key Clb; Ski Clb; Pres Spanish Clb; Mrchg Band; VP Jr Cls; Pres Sr Cls; Rep Stu Cncl; JV Var Cheerleading; JV Var Sftbl; NHS; Pres Acad Ftns Awd 87; Wmns Imprvmnt Clb Awd For Scl Stds 87; Hamilton Coll; Pre-Med.

HARRISON, MATTHEW; Eastern York HS; York, PA; (2); 6/144; Church Yth Grp; School Musical; JV L Bsktbl; Var L Socr; Var Trk; High Hon Roll; Jr NHS; JV Golf; Natl Piano Plyng Auditns Intl Lvl 87; Sci Dept Cls Awd 87; Pre Med.

HARRISON, MELISSA; North Allegheny HS; Wexford, PA; (2); Church Choir; Mrchg Band; Nwsp Stf; Hon Roll; Comm.

HARRISON, SCOTT; Mercyhurst Prep; Erie, PA; (1); Chorus; Catholic Daugh Am Essay 1st Pl 86.

HARRISON, SHAWN; Big Spring HS; Newville, PA; (2); French Clb; Hon Roll; U Of S CA; Med.

HARRISON, TRACY JANE T; Nativity BVM HS; Pottsville, PA; (3); Exploring; 4-H; Hosp Aide; Band; Chorus; Drill Tm; Flag Corp; Mrchg Band; Hghst Achvt Alg I 84-85; Hghst Achvt Engl III, Miss Amer Co-Ed Pgnt 86-87; Bloomsburg U; Spcl Ed.

HARRISON, VICTOR; Pine Forge Acad; River Rouge, MI; (3); Church Yth Grp; JA; Math Clb; School Play; Sec Jr Cls; Im Bsbl; Var Bsktbl; L Vllybl; Hon Roll; JA Awd 84-85; Pine Forge Acad; Elect Engrng.

HARRISON, VIRGINIA KATHLEEN; Unionville HS; Wilmington, DE; (4); 70/316; Am Leg Boys St; Boy Scts; Debate Tm; Band; Drm Mjr(t); Jazz Band; Mrchg Band; School Musical; Vllybl; Lion Awd; U Of DE; Phys Ed.

HARRITY, DANIEL; Bishop Hannan HS; Scranton, PA; (4); 20/144; Church Yth Grp; French Clb; Nwsp Ed-Chief; Yrbk Ed-Chief; NHS; Excllnc AP Engl, Frnch IV & Theolgy IV 87; U Of Scranton; Intl Bus.

HARROLD, DONNA; Hempfield Area SR HS; Greensburg, PA; (4); 135/693; FBLA; Pep Clb; Wt Lftg; High Hon Roll; Hon Roll; Kiwanis Awd; Camera Clb; Bus Law Awd-2nd Pl; Westmoreland CC; Prlgl.

HARRY, JEFF; Scott Intermediate Schl; Coatesville, PA; (2); Nwsp Rptr; Crs Cntry; Hon Roll; NHS; NEDT Awd; Acdmc Dstnctn 87; Pres Acdmc Ftnss Awd 87; Natl Ed Dev Awd 87; Military.

HARRY, LANCE; Council Rock HS; Holland, PA; (3); 35/980; Model UN; JV Bsbl; Var Ice Hcky; High Hon Roll; Hon Roll; NHS; Engrng.

HARRY, TRACY; Franklin Area HS; Franklin, PA; (4); 8/237; Drama Clb; French Clb; Hosp Aide; PAVAS; Radio Clb; SADD; Band; Chorus; Co-Capt Color Guard; Drill Tm; Schl Dir Awd 84-87; Penn ST U; Cmmnctns.

HARRY, VICTORIA; Bishop Hafey HS; Hazleton, PA; (2); Church Yth Grp; Dance Clb; Key Clb; Math Tm; Pep Clb; Ski Clb; Rep Stu Cncl; High Hon Roll; Ntl Merit Ltr; USNMA 87; Educ.

HARSCH, MATTHEW E; Council Rock HS; Richboro, PA; (3); Band; Concert Band; Jazz Band; Mrchg Band; Orch; School Musical; Symp Band; Hon Roll; Music.

HARSH, CHERYL; Garden Spot SR HS; New Holland, PA; (2); 4/226; Church Yth Grp; Yrbk Stf; Rep Jr Cls; JV Var Ftbl; Mgr(s); JV Sftbl; High Hon Roll; Hon Roll; NHS; Schlstc Art Awds, Cert Merit, Hnr Pass Stu GPA 3.5 Or Abv 86-87.

HARSHAW, APRIL; Marple-Newtown HS; Newtown, PA; (4); 23/330; Drama Clb; Service Clb; Swmmng; Capt Tennis; High Hon Roll; NHS; Stu Mnth 87; Frgn Lang Awd 87; Young Life Campgnr 87; Eckerd Coll; Intl Bus.

HARSHBARGER, BETSY; Lewistown Area HS; Mc Veytown, PA; (2); Church Yth Grp; French Clb; Chorus; Church Choir; High Hon Roll; Hon Roll; Tchng.

HARSHBERGER, DANA; Johnstown Christian Schl; Boswell, PA; (2); 3/26; Chess Clb; Drama Clb; Science Clb; Chorus; Stage Crew; Yrbk Stf; Sec Frsh Cls; Sec Soph Cls; Var Cheerleading; Socr; E Mennonite Coll.

HARSHMAN, CHRISTY; Laurel Highlands SR HS; Uniontown, PA; (4); Church Yth Grp; Hosp Aide; Chorus; Church Choir; School Play; Yrbk Rptr; High Hon Roll; NHS; Socl Stds Awd 87; Messiah Coll; Psych.

HARSHMAN, REBECCA; Bellwood-Antis JR SR HS; Tyrone, PA; (1); Chorus; Church Choir; School Musical; Nwsp Rptr; High Hon Roll; Prfct Atten Awd; Acad All-Amer; Stud Of The Week.

HART, DAVID; Juniata HS; E Waterford, PA; (3); SADD; Varsity Clb; Sec Soph Cls; Wrstlng; High Hon Roll; Lion Awd; NHS; PIAA ST Champ 155 Lbs Wrstlng 87.

HART, JAMIE; South Western HS; Hanover, PA; (3); 46/225; Key Clb; Letterman Clb; Varsity Clb; School Musical; Nwsp Stf; Yrbk Stf; Hst Frsh Cls; Hst Soph Cls; Hst Jr Cls; Hst Sr Cls.

HART, JOANNE; West Allegheny SR HS; Oakdale, PA; (4); 17/202; Color Guard; Mrchg Band; Nwsp Stf; Stu Cncl; Powder Puff Ftbl; Hon Roll; U Of Pittsburgh; Pre Law.

HART, KASHA; Northeast Prep HS; Philadelphia, PA; (4); Smmr Yth Prog 85; Soc Sci Awd 86-87; Pierce JC; Bus.

HART, KIMBERLY; Moon SR HS; Coraopolis, PA; (3); 23/305; JA; Band; Drill Tm; Jazz Band; Mrchg Band; Pep Band; Symp Band; JV L Sftbl; High Hon Roll; NHS; IN U; Pre Law.

HART, KRISTENA; Trinity SR HS; Amity, PA; (4); Debate Tm; French Clb; Key Clb; Math Tm; NFL; Spanish Clb; Church Choir; Orch; Powder Puff Ftbl; Var Tennis; U Of Pittsburg; Intl Bus.

HART, KRISTI; Boyertown Area HS; Boyertown, PA; (3); Rep Stu Cncl; Var Capt Bsktbl; Var Fld Hcky; Var Lcrss; Var Sftbl; Cit Awd; Hon Roll; Prfct Atten Awd; Rehabilitaton Therapist.

HART, LORI; Central SR HS; York, PA; (3); Band; Mrchg Band; Var L Bsktbl; JV Vllybl; Hon Roll; Sci.

HART, ROBERT ALLEN; Acad HS; Erie, PA; (4); 31/232; Chess Clb; Computer Clb; Band; Concert Band; Drm & Bgl; Mrchg Band; School Musical; Variety Show; Masonic Awd; Slippery Rock U; Med Tech.

HART, TONY; Interboro HS; Prospect Park, PA; (4); Computer Clb; Ski Clb; Hon Roll; DE Cnty CC; Mech Engrng.

HART, TRACEY; Burgettstown Area JR SR HS; Bulger, PA; (4); VP Drama Clb; Pres Exploring; French Clb; Speech Tm; Band; Concert Band; Mrchg Band; Pep Band; School Musical; School Play; William & Mary; Psych.

HARTENSTINE, DAVID; Emmaus HS; Allentown, PA; (3); 12/548; Boy Scts; Key Clb; SADD; Var L Crs Cntry; Var L Trk; Im Wt Lftg; High Hon Roll; NCTE Awd; NHS; Ntl Merit Ltr; Foreign Svc.

HARTENSTINE, DON; Williams Valley HS; Williamstown, PA; (3); Chorus; Yrbk Stf; VP Soph Cls; Var L Bsbl; Var L Bsktbl; Var L Ftbl; Var L Wrstlng; Hon Roll; Schvykill Cnty 2nd Tm W R Ftbl 86; Bus Admin.

HARTER, CHRISTOPHER; Cedar Crest HS; Lebanon, PA; (2); 32/350; Band; Concert Band; Mrchg Band; JV Ftbl; JV Trk; Im Wt Lftg; Var L Wrstlng; High Hon Roll; Hon Roll; NHS; MVP JV Wrstlr 86-87; Schlstc Hnr Banquet 86-87.

HARTER, COURTNEY; Bald Eagle Nittany HS; Mill Hall, PA; (2); 18/136; Drama Clb; Chorus; School Musical; Swing Chorus; Twrlr; Elem Educatn.

HARTER, MICHAEL; Middletown Area HS; Middletown, PA; (3); Hon Roll; PA ST; Vet.

HARTER, REBEKAH; Benton Area JR/SR HS; Stillwater, PA; (4); 10/47; Church Yth Grp; Teachers Aide; High Hon Roll; NHS; Cert Of Prfcncy Awd Typng I & II, Accntng I & II 85-87; Loyality Awd 87; Bus Clb, Karate Clb; Exec Sec.

HARTER, SUZANNA E; Bethel Park SR HS; Bethel Park, PA; (4); #28 In Class; Church Yth Grp; Drill Tm; Mrchg Band; School Musical; Symp Band; Variety Show; High Hon Roll; NHS; Ntl Merit SF; Intnl Relations.

HARTKOPF, TAMARA; Upper Merion Area HS; King Of Prussia, PA; (3); DECA; Cheerleading; Sftbl; Hon Roll; Rotary Awd; Elem Ed.

HARTLAUB, KELLIE; Littlestown HS; Gettysburg, PA; (3); Art Clb; DECA; FHA; Girl Scts; Hon Roll; Harrisburg CC; Culinary.

HARTLAUB, MICHELLE; Spring Grove SR HS; Spring Grove, PA; (3); Church Yth Grp; FHA; Varsity Clb; Mrchg Band; Sec Jr Cls; Fld Hcky; Powder Puff Ftbl; Twrlr; Sec.

HARTLE, AMY; Beaver Area JR SR HS; Beaver, PA; (3); Church Yth Grp; Key Clb; Pep Clb; Spanish Clb; Powder Puff Ftbl.

HARTLE, JENISE; Union HS; Rimersburg, PA; (3); 5/107; FCA; SADD; Nwsp Stf; Yrbk Stf; Var Bsktbl; Var Trk; Var Vllybl; Hon Roll; NHS; Awd Ntl Schlstc Typng Cntst 86-87; 1st Rnnr Up Rmrsbrg Frmns Queen 87; Bus.

HARTLE, LAURA; Karns City HS; Chicora, PA; (3); 1/97; Church Yth Grp; Band; Concert Band; Drm Mjr(t); Mrchg Band; Pep Band; Stu Cncl; High Hon Roll; Hon Roll; NHS; Bus Mgmt.

HARTLE, MICHAEL; Lock Haven SR HS; Flemington, PA; (3); 30/256; Pres Church Yth Grp; Spanish Clb; Band; Chorus; Concert Band; Jazz Band; Variety Show; Ftbl; Trk; Hon Roll; JR Cls Chmstry Awd 87; Bus Admin.

HARTLE, SUSAN M; North Clarion HS; Lucinda, PA; (4); 3/83; Church Yth Grp; Cmnty Wkr; Drama Clb; 4-H; Letterman Clb; Library Aide; Spanish Clb; SADD; Varsity Clb; Chorus; Pres Acad Ftns Awd 87; Arion Awd 87; Pittsburgh Tech Inst; Comp Dsgn.

HARTLEY, HEIDI; Elkland Area HS; Knoxville, PA; (3); 1/68; Drama Clb; French Clb; SADD; Yrbk Ed-Chief; Var Stu Cncl; Var Mgr(s); Var L Tennis; Pres NHS; Ntl Merit Ltr; Pres Schlr; Vet.

HARTLEY, JODI; Solanco SR HS; New Providence, PA; (3); 18/300; Sec Church Yth Grp; ROTC; Chorus; Concert Band; Drm Mjr(t); Mrchg Band; Orch; School Musical; High Hon Roll; NHS; Dist Band 86; Art Schlr 86; Schltc Art Awd 85-87; Art.

HARTLEY, MELISSA L; South Williamsport Area HS; S Williamsport, PA; (4); Key Clb; Sec Spanish Clb; Capt Mrchg Band; Nwsp Ed-Chief; Cit Awd; NHS; Pres Schlr; Pres FBLA; Flag Corp; Nwsp Rptr; PTA Schlrshp Grad 87; Alumni Awd Grad Gold Cord & Key 87; Millersville Univ; Mass Cmmnctn.

HARTLEY, SUSAN; Steel Valley HS; Munhall, PA; (4); Church Yth Grp; Band; Symp Band; Yrbk Stf; Score Keeper; High Hon Roll; Hon Roll; NHS.

HARTMAN, ANTHONY; Central Catholic HS; Verona, PA; (2); 73/300; Im Bsktbl; Im Bowling; Im Ftbl; Im Vllybl; Hon Roll; U Of Pittsburgh; Med.

HARTMAN, CATHERINE A; Plum HS; New Kensington, PA; (3); 2/410; Trs AFS; Church Yth Grp; Sec Exploring; French Clb; Pres Mrchg Band; Capt L Tennis; NHS; Ntl Merit SF; Sal; FTA; US Nvl Acad Smmr Sci Sem 87; GATE 85-87; Sci.

HARTMAN, CHRISTINE; Oley Valley HS; Fleetwood, PA; (3); 2/150; Camp Fr Inc; Drama Clb; Pep Clb; Chorus; School Musical; School Play; Nwsp Rptr; Nwsp Sprt Ed; High Hon Roll; NHS; U Of PA; Math.

HARTMAN, CHRISTINE; West Mifflin Area HS; W Mifflin, PA; (4); 23/339; VP Band; Chorus; Concert Band; Jazz Band; VP Mrchg Band; Trs Orch; Off Jr Cls; Hon Roll; NHS; Pres Schlr; PA ST U; Psych.

HARTMAN, CHRISTOPHER; Central Catholic HS; Verona, PA; (3); 53/332; Im Bsktbl; Hon Roll; Pitt; Elec Engrng.

HARTMAN, DUSTY; Biglerville HS; Bendersville, PA; (3); 15/100; Spanish Clb; JV Bsktbl; Hon Roll; Treas Spnsh Clb 86-87.

HARTMAN, HARRY; Perry Traditional Acad; Pittsburgh, PA; (3); 11/190; Am Leg Boys St; Nwsp Phtg; Nwsp Rptr; Yrbk Stf; Lit Mag; Rep Stu Cncl; Var Bsbl; Var Crs Cntry; Hon Roll; NHS; Toastmstrs Intl Publ Spkng Awd 85.

HARTMAN, HEATHER; Central Catholic HS; Center Valley, PA; (3); Girl Scts; Band; Mrchg Band; Pep Band; School Musical; Orch; School Play; Yrbk Stf; PA ST U; Pre Law.

HARTMAN, JEFF; Central Dauphin SR HS; Harrisbrg, PA; (2); 14/406; Chess Clb; Ski Clb; Crs Cntry; Socr; Tennis; Jr NHS; Engrng.

HARTMAN, JENNIFER; Palmyra Area SR HS; Annville, PA; (3); Sec Church Yth Grp; Chorus; Concert Band; Sec Soph Cls; Sec Jr Cls; Sec Sr Cls; Stu Cncl; Stat Bsktbl; Twrlr; VFW Awd; Psych.

HARTMAN, KARIN; Fairview HS; Fairview, PA; (4); 30/154; Hosp Aide; Ski Clb; Teachers Aide; Nwsp Phtg; Rep Frsh Cls; Rep Soph Cls; Rep Jr Cls; Rep Sr Cls; Cheerleading; Hon Roll; PA JR Sci Awd 14st Pl Dist 86-87; E Carolina U; Physcl Thrpy.

HARTMAN, KATHY; Parkland HS; Allentown, PA; (4); 93/438; Var L Bsktbl; Var L Sftbl; Hon Roll; Outstndng Plyr, Div II E Penn Conf All Stars & All Conf All Stars Sftbl 87; Shippensburg U; Bio.

HARTMAN, KIMBERLY; Susquehanna Township HS; Harrisburg, PA; (3); 23/150; Art Clb; Model UN; Stage Crew; Yrbk Stf; Rep Frsh Cls; Var Capt Cheerleading; Stat Ftbl; Var JV Sftbl; Hon Roll; NHS; Schlstc Art Awd-Cert Merit 85; Dfnsv Plyr Yr-Sftbl 86; Bus Mgmt.

HARTMAN, PAMELA; Benton Area JR/Sr HS; Benton, PA; (2); Band; Concert Band; Mrchg Band; School Musical; Stage Crew; Symp Band; Nwsp Stf; Mgr(s); Hon Roll.

HARTMAN, RAYMOND; Pennsbury HS; Morrisville, PA; (4); 107/800; Band; Chorus; Concert Band; Jazz Band; Mrchg Band; Orch; Pep Band; School Musical; School Play; Crs Cntry; Pres Acdmc Ftnss Awd 87; Best Musicn 87; Med.

HARTMAN, SIMONE; Saint Basil Acad; Philadelphia, PA; (3); Pres Computer Clb; Drama Clb; Rep GAA; Scholastic Bowl; Spanish Clb; Variety Show; Sec Soph Cls; Im Bsktbl; Coach Actv; Var Fld Hcky; Fin Sec JR Div AOH 87-88; Peer Cnslr 87-88; PA ST.

HARTMANN, KARL; Archbishop Wood For Boys; Warminster, PA; (3); 4/235; German Clb; Quiz Bowl; Scholastic Bowl; Rep Frsh Cls; JV Ftbl; JV Var Wrstlng; High Hon Roll; VP NHS; 3rd Pl DE Vly Sci Fair Chemstry Div 85; Rcpnt Dcsn Schlrshp Awd 87; Notre Dame; Law.

HARTMANN, MELISSA; Carbondale Area HS; Carbondale, PA; (2); Sec Church Yth Grp; Spanish Clb; Band; Church Choir; Concert Band; Mrchg Band; Off Stu Cncl; Hon Roll.

HARTNER, SHERRY; Saint Basil Acad; Philadelphia, PA; (3); 10/88; Drama Clb; French Clb; Pep Clb; Science Clb; Trs Jr Cls; Trs Stu Cncl; Im Bsktbl; Var Fld Hcky; French Hon Soc; Hon Roll; Religion Awd 84; Natl Engl Merit Awd 87; Phys Thrpy.

HARTRANFT, CATHY; Kutztown Area HS; Kutztown, PA; (4); 1/147; Sec Church Yth Grp; School Play; Variety Show; Var Capt Bsktbl; Var Capt Fld Hcky; DAR Awd; High Hon Roll; NHS; Pres Schlr; Val; Schlr Athl Awd Brks Cnty 87; U Of DE.

HARTRANFT, JEREMY; Garden Spot HS; Narvon, PA; (1); Church Yth Grp; FFA; Concert Band; Mrchg Band; Socr; JV Trk; Hon Roll; Star Grnhnd Awd In FFA 87; Grnhnd Awd In FFA 87; Frst Mgnt Awd In FFA 87; PA ST; Wildlife Mgr.

HARTSOCK, JARED; Uniontown SR HS; Chalk Hill, PA; (3); 58/318; JA; Letterman Clb; Im Vllybl; Capt L Wrstlng; High Hon Roll; Hon Roll; Gftd Pgm; Nvl Pilot.

HARTUNG, ALICIA; Vincentian HS; Glenshaw, PA; (2); Service Clb; Chorus; Church Choir; Hon Roll; Educ.

HARTY, KRISTIN; Sacred Heart HS; Pittsburgh, PA; (3); 12/139; Church Yth Grp; Dance Clb; French Clb; Girl Scts; Hosp Aide; Library Aide; Band; Trs Jr Cls; Rep Sr Cls; Stu Cncl; Joan Marc Mdlln Vlntr Svc & 2nd Pl PA JR Acad Sci 87; PA ST; Ed.

HARTZ, CARL; Freeland HS; Freeland, PA; (3); 13/74; JV Var Bsktbl; JV Var Ftbl; Hnr Roll 84-87.

HARTZ, DESSA; Downingtown SR HS; Downington, PA; (3); 101/648; Art Clb; French Clb; Pep Clb; Ski Clb; SADD; Concert Band; Flag Corp; Yrbk Stf; Rep Stu Cncl; Mgr Bsktbl; Fshn Merch.

HARTZEL, DOUGLAS J; Biglerville HS; Biglerville, PA; (3); Drama Clb; Chorus; School Musical; Nwsp Rptr; Nwsp Stf; Yrbk Stf; Rep Stu Cncl; Hon Roll; Jr NHS.

HARTZELL, ANGIE; Carlisle SR HS; Carlisle, PA; (3); Exploring; Chorus; Coach Actv; Fld Hcky; Sftbl; Hon Roll; Wesley; Phy Therapist.

HARTZELL, MICHELLE; Mc Guffey HS; Washington, PA; (3); 19/250; French Clb; Ski Clb; Yrbk Bus Mgr; Yrbk Rptr; Yrbk Stf; Off Jr Cls; High Hon Roll; NHS; Stu Rcgntn Awd 86; Robotics.

HARTZELL, TONIA; Northeastern HS; Manchester, PA; (3); Ski Clb; Chorus; Var Capt Cheerleading; Hon Roll; NHS; York Coll; Acctnt.

HARTZELL, WENDY; Seneca Valley HS; Renfrew, PA; (3); 27/360; Art Clb; Church Yth Grp; Rep Frsh Cls; Rep Soph Cls; Rep Jr Cls; Var Cheerleading; Var Trk; High Hon Roll; Hon Roll; NHS; Arch.

HARTZLER, KIMBERLY; Lancaster Country Day Schl; Mt Joy, PA; (2); Church Yth Grp; Debate Tm; 4-H; French Clb; GAA; School Play; Nwsp Stf; Var Bsktbl; High Hon Roll; Hon Roll; Psych.

HARVATH, MARGARET ANNE; Purchase Line HS; Punxsutawney, PA; (2); Church Yth Grp; Sec FHA; Band; Concert Band; Flag Corp; Mrchg Band; Hon Roll; Dntl Asst.

HARVATINE, LAURA; Forest City Regional HS; Thompson, PA; (3); 4-H; German Clb; Ski Clb; Band; High Hon Roll; NHS; Gftd Pgm 84-87; Natl Merit Sci Awd 86; Natl Merit Chem Awd 87; Phrmcy.

HARVEY, BETSY; Tunkhannock HS; Tunkhannock, PA; (3); 1/300; French Clb; Latin Clb; Science Clb; Chorus; Church Choir; Fld Hcky; High Hon Roll; NHS; Val; Dstrct & Rgn Chorus 86-87; Doctor.

HARVEY, CALLIE; Freeport HS; Sarver, PA; (2); Library Aide; Rep Stu Cncl; Stat Bsbl; JV Var Cheerleading; Hon Roll; Pittsburgh Beauty; Csmtlgy.

HARVEY, CHENNITA; Cecilian Acad; Willingboro, NJ; (3); 7/36; Boys Clb Am; Church Yth Grp; Cmnty Wkr; Model UN; Science Clb; Variety Show; Nwsp Stf; Var Capt Bsktbl; Var Capt Sftbl; US Army Rsrv Ntl Schlr/Athle Awd 86; Ntl Hnr Roll 87.

HARVEY, CHRISTINE ANN; Seneca Valley HS; Zelienople, PA; (3); FNA; Ski Clb.

HARVEY, DEBORAH; Pennsbury HS; Yardley, PA; (3); French Clb; Intnl Clb; Rep Frsh Cls; Rep Soph Cls; Rep Jr Cls; Im Cheerleading; JV Socr; French Hon Soc; Hon Roll; NHS; Crmnl Law.

HARVEY, ELISABETH; Country Day Schl Of The Sacred Heart; Merion, PA; (4); Church Yth Grp; Church Choir; Mgr Bsbl; Var Fld Hcky; Lcrss; Mgr(s); High Hon Roll; Hon Roll; 1st Hnrs, 2nd Hnrs; Dickinson Coll; Bio.

HARVEY, JAMIE; Connellsville Area SR HS; Connellsville, PA; (3); GAA; Office Aide; Pep Clb; Chorus; Stage Crew; Bsktbl; Hon Roll.

HARVEY, JOHN; Harborcreek HS; Harborcreek, PA; (3); ROTC; Var L Bsbl; Var L Ftbl; L Wrstlng; TROA ROTC Medl 87; Mltry Perfrmnce Awd 87; Cmmndng Offcr Harbr Crk NE NJ ROTC 87-88.

HARVEY, JULIET; Elizabeth Forward HS; Elizabeth, PA; (4); 1/293; Trs Church Yth Grp; Cmnty Wkr; Library Aide; Spanish Clb; Sec Church Choir; Nwsp Stf; Cit Awd; DAR Awd; High Hon Roll; NHS; OH Nrthrn Pres Schlr Awd 87; Best Physics Stu Natl Assoc Physics Tchrs 87; Chaplains Awd 87; OH Northern U; Engr.

HARVEY, KIMBERLY; Mary Fuller Frazier Mem HS; Layton, PA; (4); Am Leg Aux Girls St; Band; Color Guard; Capt Mrchg Band; School Play; Nwsp Stf; Capt Bsktbl; Powder Puff Ftbl; Capt Sftbl; MVP Female Athl 87; CA U; Elem Educ.

HARVEY, SUE ANN; Central Cambria HS; Ebensburg, PA; (3); Art Clb; Church Yth Grp; Trs 4-H; FBLA; JV Vllybl; Hon Roll; 2nd Regl Comptn Acctg I FBLA 87; 4th ST Comptn Acctg I FBLA 87; IN U PA; Finc.

HARVEY, TAMMY; Trinity HS; Washington, PA; (3); 88/402; Art Clb; Camera Clb; Pep Clb; Ski Clb; Drm Mjr(t); Mrchg Band; Yrbk Bus Mgr; Yrbk Stf; Co-Capt Twrlr; High Hon Roll; Natl Art Hnr Soc; Acctg.

HARVEY, WENDY; Downington HS; Downingtown, PA; (4); 46/553; Sec Trs French Clb; Intnl Clb; Acpl Chr; Chorus; Co-Capt Flag Corp; School Musical; Swing Chorus; High Hon Roll; NHS; NEDT Awd; Elizabethtown Coll Acad Schrlshp 86-87; Outstndng Amercn Stu 86-87; Elizabethtown Coll; Intl Bus.

HARVILLA, JESSLENE; Nativity BVM HS; Minersville, PA; (1); 17/96; Girl Scts; Spanish Clb; Color Guard; Crs Cntry; High Hon Roll.

HARWOOD, CAROLYN M; Bishop Conwell HS; Levittown, PA; (3); 33/277; Art Clb; French Clb; Socr; Smmr Schlrhsp-Moore Coll Art 87; Clmbia Schlstc Prss Assc Smmr Jrnlsm Wrkshp 87; Fine Arts.

HARWOOD, LORI; Bensalem HS; Bensalem, PA; (3); SADD; Trs Temple Yth Grp; Rep Jr Cls; Var JV Fld Hcky; Var Socr; Stat Wrstlng; Hon Roll; Acctng.

HARZINSKI, DEBBIE; Curwensville Area HS; Curwensville, PA; (4); 29/115; Drama Clb; Pres French Clb; Sec Letterman Clb; Pep Clb; Varsity Clb; School Musical; Capt Co-Capt Cheerleading; Pom Pon; Hon Roll; Pres Schlr; Mst Sprtd Chrldr Awd 83-84; Mst Outstndng Chrldr Awd 82-83; Captain Awds 84-87.

HASCHETS, BRIAN; Belle Vernon Area HS; West Newton, PA; (3); Church Yth Grp; Band; Drm & Bgl; Pep Band; NHS; Natl Art Awd 84-85; Dentstry.

HASELHORST, HEIDI; Lancaster Mennonite HS; Narvon, PA; (3); 2/155; Church Yth Grp; Teachers Aide; Chorus; Nwsp Rptr; Nwsp Stf; Rep Stu Cncl; High Hon Roll; Pres NHS; Ntl Merit SF; Rotary Awd; Rotary Clb Loyalty To Schl Awd 86-87; Lancaster Mennonite Schlrshps 84-87; Piano Silver Cert 86; Sci.

HASELOW, STACEY; West Greene HS; West Finley, PA; (3); French Clb; FHA; Var JV Bsktbl; Var Trk; Hon Roll; Phy Educ.

HASELTINE, TODD; The Christian Acad; Brookhaven, PA; (3); Church Yth Grp; Rep Soph Cls; JV Var Bsbl; JV Bsktbl; JV Socr; Hon Roll; Christian Chrctr Awd Mnd Chrst 85-87; Yth Actn Mnstrs Chrstn Chrctr Awd 87; Cedarville Coll; Tree Srgn.

HASENPLUG, KAREN; Sharpsville Area HS; Transfer, PA; (4); 24/120; Church Yth Grp; FBLA; Sec Trs FHA; Library Aide; Office Aide; High Hon Roll; NHS; $50 Bond From Mercer Cnty Lgl Sec 87; $50 Bond For Home Ec GPA 87; Highest Grade Pnt Avg Bus Clss 87; Du Bois Bus Coll; Exec Sec.

HASH, SUZANNE; Kennard-Dale HS; New Park, PA; (3); 7/165; Church Yth Grp; Pres Sec 4-H; Band; Chorus; Orch; Yrbk Stf; Hon Roll; NHS; Sec FFA; Church Choir; Yrk Cnty Dairy Prncss, & Pres Yrk Cnty FFA 87; Ag.

HASINECZ, JEANNIE; Pittston Area SR HS; Avoca, PA; (3); 11/300; FBLA; FNA; Science Clb; Ski Clb; High Hon Roll; Hon Roll; NHS; Bus Admin.

HASKINS, DENISE; Newport HS; Newport, PA; (3); 2/117; Pres Trs Girl Scts; Quiz Bowl; Chorus; School Musical; School Play; Swing Chorus; Stat Bsbl; Stat Bsktbl; Mgr Ftbl; NHS; Physlgy.

HASKINS, JEFF; Coudersport Area HS; Coudersport, PA; (4); 11/87; VP FFA; Trs Varsity Clb; Trs Jr Cls; VP Stu Cncl; Var L Ftbl; Var L Trk; Hon Roll; NHS; Gagnon Awd 87; Du Bois Campus; Bus Admin.

HASKINS, LISA; New Wilmington HS; Volant, PA; (3); Bsktbl; Powder Puff Ftbl; Vllybl; Polc Offcr.

HASKINS, SHANNON; Coudersport Area JR SR HS; Coudersport, PA; (3); Chorus; High Hon Roll; Hon Roll; NHS; Amer Chem Soc Chem Awd 87.

HASLAM, ROBERT K; Central HS; Philadelphia, PA; (4); Ed Lit Mag; Trk; NEDT Awd; Spcl Tlnt Schlrshp-Crtv Wrtng-Eckrd Coll 87; J L Haney Ptry Prz 87; Gld Svc Awd-HS 87; Eckerd Coll-FL; Rsssn Area Std.

HASSINGER, LAEL; Millersburg Area HS; Millersburg, PA; (4); 6/85; Art Clb; Spanish Clb; Concert Band; Jazz Band; Mrchg Band; Stage Crew; Ed Nwsp Rptr; Yrbk Stf; High Hon Roll; Hon Roll; Bnd Lttr & Pns 84-87; Fnlst In Voice Of Dmcrcy 86; Natl Ldrshp Awd 86; Harrisburg Area; Crmnl Law.

HASSLER, MARYBETH; Twin Valley HS; Morgantown, PA; (1); 15/184; Bsktbl; High Hon Roll; Hnr Stu 86-87; Star Grnhnd FFA 86-87; U Of DE; Vet Med.

HASSLER, STEPHANIE; Cocalico HS; Denver, PA; (2); Church Yth Grp; Chorus; Church Choir; Sec Frsh Cls; Sec Soph Cls; Rep Stu Cncl; JV Cheerleading; Var Tennis; Var Trk; High Hon Roll; Millersville U; Tchg.

HASSON, CATHY; Northern Cambria HS; Nicktown, PA; (4); Church Yth Grp; 4-H; NFL; Spanish Clb; Speech Tm; Band; Concert Band; Mrchg Band; Nwsp Stf; Trk; 1st & 2nd Pl St Hstry Day Comptn 85-86; IN U Of PA; Jrnlsm.

HASSON, TRACI; Bristol JR SR HS; Bristol, PA; (4); 10/80; VP SADD; Mrchg Band; Yrbk Bus Mgr; Sec Jr Cls; Sec Sr Cls; Stu Cncl; Var Fld Hcky; Stat Sftbl; Hon Roll; NHS; Mrlyn Myr Schlrshp 87; Millersville U; Elem Ed.

HASTINGS, ELIZABETH; St Benedict Acad; Erie, PA; (3); 6/53; School Musical; High Hon Roll; Hon Roll; NHS; Bus Mngmt.

HATCH, DEBRA; Corry Area HS; Corry, PA; (2); Drama Clb; Spanish Clb; SADD.

HATCH, JEFFREY; Lampeter-Strasburg HS; Willow Street, PA; (3); 16/148; AFS; Church Yth Grp; Exploring; Thesps; Band; Chorus; Concert Band; Madrigals; School Musical; School Play; Gov Schl Arts Semifnlst 87; Pol Sci.

HATCH, MARLENE; Corry Area HS; Corry, PA; (4); 14/192; Trs Drama Clb; German Clb; SADD; Band; Concert Band; Mrchg Band; Pep Band; School Play; High Hon Roll; Hon Roll; Acad Achvt Awd 87; IN U PA; Comp Sci.

HATCH, NICOL; Altoona Area HS; Altoona, PA; (3); Ski Clb; Speech Tm; Capt Flag Corp; Nwsp Stf; Rep Stu Cncl; Sec Jr NHS; NEDT Awd; Pres Schlr; Rotary Awd.

HATCHER, BRIGELLA; Pine Forge Acad; Rapidan, VA; (3); Church Choir; Nwsp Stf; Off Frsh Cls; Pres Soph Cls; Pres Jr Cls; Off Stu Cncl; Miss PFA 84-85; Oakwood Coll; Hstry.

HATFIELD, LESLIE; Waynesburg Central HS; Mt Morris, PA; (4); Camera Clb; French Clb; GAA; Letterman Clb; Band; Yrbk Stf; Var L Bsktbl; Var L Sftbl; MVP Sftbl 85-87; MVP Lady Raider Tourn 86; Bsktbl 86; All Conf Bsktbl Awd 86-87; Sprts Med.

HATHAWAY, KENNETH; Mc Guffey HS; Washington, PA; (3); Computer Clb; Var Bsktbl; High Hon Roll; Hon Roll; Natl Ldrshp Awd 84.

HATHAWAY, KRISTEN; Villa Maria Acad; Erie, PA; (3); Hosp Aide; Office Aide; Science Clb; SADD; Stu Cncl; Hon Roll; NHS; Cert Apprec Outstndg Vol Svc 87; Thiel Coll; Nrsg.

HATHAWAY, PATRICIA; Trinity HS; Washington, PA; (4); 77/361; Key Clb; Pep Clb; Drill Tm; Otstnsng Bus Stu 87; Point Park Coll; Bus.

HATLEY, MELITA; Schenly Center; Pittsburgh, PA; (3); Church Yth Grp; French Clb; Chorus; Church Choir; School Play; VP Jr Cls; Sec Stu Cncl; Capt Pom Pon; High Hon Roll; Hon Roll; Ms Blck Teenag 1st Rnr-Up 86; Lmabda Kappa Mu Sorority Kopelles Pres 86-87; Frnch Awd 4th Lvl 87; Hampton U; Bus Adm.

HATTEN, SHANNON; Curwensville Area HS; Grampian, PA; (3); Sec Church Yth Grp; Drama Clb; French Clb; Chorus; JV Bsktbl; JV Vllybl; French Hon Soc; Hon Roll; 5th Dist Mrktng Supr Lvl 87; Gen Mrktng.

HATTER, DONALD; Henderson HS; W Chester, PA; (3); 18/367; Ski Clb; Hon Roll; NHS; Var Bsktbl; Var Ftbl; Var Trk; Im Wt Lftg; Harvard; Accntng.

HATTER, RENEE; Southmoreland HS; Mt Pleasant, PA; (2); Church Yth Grp; French Clb; Math Clb; French Hon Soc.

HATTERSLEY JR, WILLIAM; Forest City Regional HS; Pleasant Mt, PA; (3); 25/62; Letterman Clb; Band; Concert Band; Mrchg Band; Var L Bsbl; L Bsktbl; Var L Socr; Hon Roll; NHS; Elec Engrng.

HATTON, JENNIFER; Mechanicsburg Area SR HS; Mechanicsburg, PA; (3); 119/309; Hosp Aide; Pres SADD; Band; Chorus; Color Guard; Concert Band; Drill Tm; Mrchg Band; Symp Band; Twrlr; Penn ST U; Music Thrpst.

HATTOUM, VANESSA; Greensburg Central Catholic HS; Jeannette, PA; (3); Art Clb; Ski Clb; Spanish Clb; Rep Soph Cls; Trk; Wrstlng; Hon Roll; Debate Tm; Library Aide; Sftbl; Gvrnrs Schl Arts Schlrshp 87; Am Coll Paris; Art.

HATZISTAVRAKIS, IRENE; Mt Penn HS; Mt Penn, PA; (4); 25/70; VP Sec Church Yth Grp; FTA; Chorus; Flag Corp; Nwsp Rptr; Nwsp Stf; Hon Roll; Elem Educ.

HAU, MILLIE; Lancaster Catholic HS; Lancaster, PA; (3); 28/192; Service Clb; Chorus; School Musical; Nwsp Ed-Chief; Nwsp Rptr; JV Trk; High Hon Roll; Hon Roll; PA Schl Press Assn 1st Pl Awd Nws Stry; Elem Ed.

HAUCK, CHARLES; Abington Heights HS; Clarks Summit, PA; (2); Boy Scts; Band; Concert Band; Jazz Band; Mrchg Band; JV Bsbl; JV Bsktbl; Hon Roll; Rotary Awd; Eagle Sct 86; Rotry Ldrshp Cmp 87; Engrng.

HAUCK, JESSICA L; Ephrata SR HS; Ephrata, PA; (4); 65/260; Rep Soph Cls; Rep Jr Cls; Var L Crs Cntry; JV Fld Hcky; Im Gym; Powder Puff Ftbl; JV Sftbl; JV Trk; Im Vllybl; Hon Roll; Shippensburg U; Crimnl Justc.

HAUCK, LINDA D; Sharon SR HS; Sharon, PA; (4); Hosp Aide; Y-Teens; Band; Concert Band; Mrchg Band; Mat Maids; PA ST U; Nrsng.

HAUCK, NICHOLE; Everett Area JR-SR HS; Everett, PA; (2); 30/120; Art Clb; French Clb; GAA; SADD; Varsity Clb; Sec Chorus; School Musical; Rep Soph Cls; Stu Cncl; Var L Cheerleading; Air Force; Nrsng.

HAUDENSHIELD, NANCY; Peters Twp HS; Mc Murray, PA; (3); Art Clb; Church Yth Grp; Hosp Aide; Yrbk Stf; JV Socr; Var JV Vllybl; Hon Roll; Ski Clb; Prom Cmte 87; Lifegrd Cert 85; Lbrl Arts.

HAUEISEN, LAINIE; Conrad Weiser HS; Robesonia, PA; (3); 19/179; Church Yth Grp; Band; Chorus; Color Guard; School Musical; Rep Stu Cncl; JV Bsktbl; JV Fld Hcky; Var Tennis; Hon Roll; Superior Performance In Natl Educ Dvlpmnt Tsts 85; Advrtsng.

HAUGER, GARTH P; Somerset Area SR HS; Somerset, PA; (3); 7/235; Am Leg Boys St; Church Yth Grp; Drama Clb; English Clb; German Clb; FA; NFL; Quiz Bowl; Scholastic Bowl; Speech Tm; Pres Ntl Hnrs Soc 87-88; Keystone Bys St 87; Engl.

HAUGER, KEITH; Mt Pleasant Area HS; Stahlstown, PA; (3); Chess Clb; German Clb; VICA; Hon Roll; Bus.

HAUGHEY, KERRIE; Mastbaum AVTS; Philadelphia, PA; (3); Trs Jr Cls; Hon Roll; Temple U.

HAUGHNEY, CEANE; Mahanoy Area HS; Mahanoy City, PA; (2); Hosp Aide; Band; Variety Show; Nwsp Stf; Off Frsh Cls; JV Var Bsktbl; JV Var Cheerleading; Trk.

HAUGHT, PAT; Waynesburg Central HS; Waynesburg, PA; (3); Letterman Clb; Spanish Clb; Var L Bsbl; Var L Ftbl; Var Wt Lftg; Hon Roll.

HAUPT, MARY BETH; Villa Maria Acad; Waterford, PA; (3); PAVAS; Science Clb; Spanish Clb; SADD; Band; Church Choir; Concert Band; Mrchg Band; Hon Roll; NHS; Music Schlrshp Organ 83-84; Pre Law.

HAUPT, MELISSA; Nazareth Area SR HS; Nazareth, PA; (4); 5/227; Church Yth Grp; 4-H; Girl Scts; Key Clb; Yrbk Stf; Rep Stu Cncl; Var L Mat Maids; High Hon Roll; Hon Roll; NHS; Honor Grad 87; NAHS Alumni Schlrshp 87; Fashion Inst Tech; Fshn Merch.

HAUPT, PAMELA; Conemaugh Valley HS; Mineral Point, PA; (3); 7/104; Church Yth Grp; Band; Var L Bsktbl; Im Coach Actv; Var L Sftbl; Var L Vllybl; Hon Roll; Jr NHS; NHS; Outstndng-Girls Phys Ed 85; U Of Pittsburg; Pharm.

HAUS, SHANNON; Milton HS; West Milton, PA; (3); 41/202; Spanish Clb; Varsity Clb; Rep Stu Cncl; Var Crs Cntry; Var Trk; Hon Roll; Rotary Awd; Ray Ulrich Memorial Awd Outstndng Perfrmnc/Cross Country 85; 2 Time State Qulfr Cross Country 84 & 85.

HAUSER, BRIAN; Denn Hills HS; Pittsburgh, PA; (4); 1/609; Church Yth Grp; German Clb; Ski Clb; Band; Concert Band; Mrchg Band; High Hon Roll; Kiwanis Awd; NHS; Val; U Of Richmnd Acdmc Grnt 87; U Of Richmond; Pre Med.

HAUSER, DANIEL; Clarion Area HS; Clarion, PA; (3); 3/95; Chess Clb; Church Yth Grp; Band; Concert Band; Jazz Band; Mrchg Band; Wrstlng; High Hon Roll; Hon Roll; NHS; IV No 6 Hnrs Band 1st Chair Alto Sax 86; Biology.

HAUSER, ELISABETH A; Neshaminy HS; Penn Del, PA; (3); Intnl Clb; Math Tm; Sec SADD; Chorus; Orch; School Musical; NHS; Natl Sci Olympiad Cert 85; Spanish.

HAUSER, JACKIE; Villa Maria Acad; Erie, PA; (4); Church Yth Grp; Cmnty Wkr; GAA; Hosp Aide; Library Aide; Science Clb; Chorus; Im Bsktbl; Im Socr; Sftbl; PA ST Behrend; Engr.

HAUSER, KIRSTEN; State College Area Intrmdt Schl; State College, PA; (2); 72/554; Dance Clb; Rep Frsh Cls; Rep Stu Cncl; Powder Puff Ftbl; High Hon Roll; Bllt Schlrshp 86-87; Ntl Wnnr Intrmdt Clss Ntl Piano Aud 86; Cert Of Mrt In Recog Ostndng Aciev Bio 86; Sci.

HAUSERMAN, DAVID; Pennsbury HS; Yardley, PA; (3); L Crs Cntry; L Trk; Hon Roll; NHS; U Of PA; Bus.

HAUSHALTER, KURT; State College Area HS; State College, PA; (4); 7/541; Pres Church Yth Grp; Im Capt Bsktbl; JV Var Ftbl; Powder Puff Ftbl; Im Capt Vllybl; Cit Awd; Hon Roll; Church Choir; Coaches Awd Ftbl 86-87; Clss Of 76 Schlrshp 87; Faculty Schlr Awd 87; PA ST; Phy Educ.

HAUSSMANN, ROBERT; William Allen HS; Allentown, PA; (4); 5/550; Trs German Clb; Ski Clb; Nwsp Phtg; Yrbk Phtg; Lit Mag; Off Sr Cls; Chrmn Stu Cncl; Trs NHS; Ntl Merit Ltr; Math Tm; Sons Of Amer Revoltn Good Ctznshp Medl 87; Muhlenberg Phi Beta Kappa Awd 87; Drew U; Comp Sci.

HAUX, CAROL; Archbishop Kennedy HS; Plymouth Mtg, PA; (4); 1/176; Pres French Clb; Pres Service Clb; Nwsp Sprt Ed; Rep Stu Cncl; Var L Crs Cntry; Var L Trk; Hon Roll; NHS; St Schlr; Track Schlrshp 87; PA Yth Of Yr 87; Quaker Chem Fndtn Schlrshp 87; Villanova U; Bus Admin.

HAVEN, CHRISTINE; Hempfield HS; Landisville, PA; (3); 40/400; Drama Clb; Chorus; School Play; Yrbk Stf; Lit Mag; High Hon Roll; Hon Roll; NHS; Sci Fair Awd 86; Purdue U; Engrng.

HAVENS, CHRISTIAN; Valley Forge Military Acad; Lawrencevl, NJ; (3); ROTC; Var Bsbl; Im Ftbl; Im Socr; Hon Roll; Acad Red Stars 86-87; Bus.

HAVER, DENISE; Gateway SR HS; Monroeville, PA; (4); 10/484; Church Yth Grp; Girl Scts; Capt Color Guard; Trs Orch; School Musical; Yrbk Ed-Chief; Yrbk Phtg; High Hon Roll; NHS; Pres Schlr; John Carroll Schlrshp, Prsdntl Awd & Amer Values Schlrshp 87; John Carroll U; Engl.

HAVERT, PAMELA; Conestoga HS; Berwyn, PA; (2); Art Clb; Aud/Vis; Girl Scts; Pep Clb; Chorus; School Musical; Stage Crew; Arch.

HAVEY, HEATHER; Hopewell SR HS; Aliquippa, PA; (3); 45/255; French Clb; JA; Latin Clb; Chorus; Stu Cncl; Crs Cntry; Trk; High Hon Roll; NHS; Schlr Athlt Awd; Gannon U; Bio.

HAVILAND, DOLORES; St Basil Acad; Philadelphia, PA; (4); Science Clb; Service Clb; Yrbk Stf; Tennis; High Hon Roll; Ntl Merit Ltr; Schlrshp St Basil Acad 83-87; Bio.

HAVILAND, TRACEY; St Basil Acad; Philadelphia, PA; (3); Dance Clb; French Clb; GAA; Spanish Clb; SADD; School Musical; Im Cheerleading; Im Coach Actv; Var Tennis; Im Trk; MVP Ten Tm 86-87.

HAVRILLA, ANGELA; Portage Area HS; Portage, PA; (3); 15/110; Var Trk; High Hon Roll; Hon Roll; U Of Pittsburgh; Compu.

HAVRILLA, TODD; Portage Area HS; Portage, PA; (3); 45/109; Var JV Ftbl; Im Wt Lftg; Hon Roll.

HAWES, GRETA; Coatesville Area SR HS; Coatesville, PA; (3); 57/516; Dance Clb; French Clb; Ski Clb; SADD; Band; Church Choir; Yrbk Stf; Im Bsktbl; Im Bowling; Hon Roll; Presdntl Phys Ftns Awd 84-86; Goldie Beacon; Accnt.

HAWK, DEBRA; Central Dauphin HS; Harrisburg, PA; (3); Key Clb; Ski Clb; Chorus; Sec Stu Cncl; JV Fld Hcky; Im Vllybl; High Hon Roll; Hon Roll; NHS; Intl Stds.

HAWK, GEORGE; Connellsville Area HS; Normalville, PA; (3); 167/500; Church Yth Grp; Crpntr.

HAWK, JOE; Southmoreland SR HS; Scottdale, PA; (3); 22/224; Pres Church Yth Grp; Cmnty Wkr; Trs German Clb; Letterman Clb; Church Choir; Var L Bsbl; Var L Socr; Var L Trk; JV Bsktbl; Germn Ntl Hnr Soc Treas; Yth Assn Wrld Affrs.

HAWK, JOSEPH W; Pittston Area SR HS; Hughestown, PA; (4); Trs Art Clb; Cmnty Wkr; French Clb; FBLA; Key Clb; Math Clb; Stage Crew; Hon Roll; Schltc Art Achvt Awd 86; Luzerne Cnty CC; Dntl.

HAWK, SCOTT; Waynesburg Central HS; Waynesburg, PA; (3); Chess Clb; Letterman Clb; Sec Spanish Clb; Socr; Wrstlng; Hon Roll; Wrstlng/2 Yr Ltrmn 85-87; WV U; Comm.

HAWK, TIM; Plum SR HS; Pittsburgh, PA; (3); Nwsp Rptr; Yrbk Stf; Swmmng; Hon Roll; Prfct Atten Awd; Varsity Clb; Chorus; School Play; Variety Show; PA ST U; Advrtsng.

HAWK, WILL; Burrell SR HS; Lower Burrell, PA; (3); Cmnty Wkr; French Clb; Teachers Aide; High Hon Roll; Jr NHS; Am Leg Natrlztn Ceremony Cnty Court House 85-86; PA ST U; Acctng.

HAWKINS, COLLEEN; Oil City SR HS; Oil City, PA; (3); 1/218; Varsity Clb; School Musical; Variety Show; Sec Stu Cncl; Var L Bsktbl; Var L Vllybl; High Hon Roll; Hon Roll; Trs NHS; Engr.

HAWKINS, JOE; Red Lion Area SR HS; Windsor, PA; (3); 22/342; Am Leg Boys St; Varsity Clb; Var L Swmmng; Var L Tennis; High Hon Roll; Hon Roll; Engr.

HAWKINS, JOSEPH D; Red Lion SR HS; Windsor, PA; (3); 22/324; Am Leg Boys St; Varsity Clb; Var Capt Swmmng; Var L Tennis; High Hon Roll; Engr.

HAWKINS, LESLIE; Donegal HS; Mount Joy, PA; (2); Girl Scts; Chorus; Church Choir; JV Bsktbl; Var Fld Hcky; JV Sftbl; JV Trk; High Hon Roll; Hon Roll; VFW Awd; Grl Scout Slvr Awd 86; Teacher.

HAWKINS, ROBERT; Hanover Area JR/Sr HS; Ashley, PA; (3); 51/194; Church Yth Grp; Intnl Clb; Yrbk Stf; Var Crs Cntry; Im Ftbl; Var Trk; Capt Wrstlng; Hon Roll; Im Tennis; Im Vllybl; Dist II Wrstlng Champ 87 & 3rd Pl Wnnr 86; Dist II Crss Cntry Plwnnr 86; Forestry.

HAWKINS, TERESA; Everett Area HS; Breezewood, PA; (3); Concert Band; Mrchg Band; Pep Band; Yrbk Ed-Chief; Sr Cls; Stu Cncl; JV Bsktbl; JV Var Vllybl; French Hon Soc; Hon Roll; Schlrshp-Gttysbrg Yrbk Exprnc-Smmr Wrkshp 87; Arch.

HAWKS, DACEY; Butler Intermediate HS; Butler, PA; (2); SADD; Orch; Sftbl; Musician Note 86; U Pittsburgh PA; Phys Thrpst.

HAWKSLEY, TOM; West Scranton HS; Scranton, PA; (2); Comp Prgrmng.

HAWLEY, BILLIE; Sayre Area HS; Sayre, PA; (3); Art Clb; Church Yth Grp; Computer Clb; Drama Clb; Girl Scts; Band; Acpl Chr; School Play; Gym; Vllybl; Bus.

HAWLEY, PATRICIA; Nazareth Acad; Philadelphia, PA; (3); French Clb; Jazz Band; Orch; School Musical; School Play; Yrbk Stf; Rep Soph Cls; Rep Jr Cls; Trs Sr Cls; Im Bsktbl; Judg Lois Forer Awd 84-85; Bus Admin.

HAWLEY, VIRGINIA; Montrose Area HS; Montrose, PA; (3); 4-H; French Clb; Concert Band; Sec Mrchg Band; Socr; Hon Roll; Sprts Med.

HAWN, PAMELA E; Biglerville HS; Gettysburg, PA; (4); 12/78; Computer Clb; 4-H; Spanish Clb; SADD; Frsh Cls; Soph Cls; Jr Cls; Sr Cls; Bsktbl; Dthfh Awd; Cls Secy, Pres; Penn ST U; Bus.

HAWRANKO, ALYSSA; Mary Fuller Frazier HS; Perryopolis, PA; (4); 1/130; Drama Clb; VP Chorus; Capt Flag Corp; Bausch & Lomb Sci Awd; NHS; Val; FNA; Library Aide; Science Clb; HOBY Ldrshp 85; Gannon 1 Acad Schlrshp 87; Dmnd ST/Bell Of PA Schlrshp Acad 87; Gannon U; Fam Med.

HAWRYLAK, MICHELE; Riverside HS; Beaver Falls, PA; (2); AFS; Letterman Clb; Band; Trs Soph Cls; Trs Jr Cls; Stu Cncl; JV Var Cheerleading; Coach Actv; Var L Gym; High Hon Roll.

HAWRYLAK, VALERIE; Shaler Area HS; Glenshaw, PA; (3); Dance Clb; Hosp Aide; SADD; Teachers Aide; Concert Band; Capt Flag Corp; Yrbk Stf; Hon Roll; Spanish NHS; 1st Pl Dance Cmptn 86; Physcl Thrpy.

HAWTHORNE, SUSAN; Little Flower Catholic HS; Philadelphia, PA; (3); 7/322; Nwsp Stf; Yrbk Stf; Rep Stu Cncl; Co-Capt Var Cheerleading; Hon Roll; NHS; Prfct Atten Awd; Bus Admin.

HAY, KEITH; Berlin Brothers Valley HS; Berlin, PA; (1); Church Yth Grp; 4-H; FFA; Band; Concert Band; Mrchg Band; Im Bsktbl; High Hon Roll; Hon Roll; FFA Star Greenhand Awd 86-87; PA ST U; Ag.

HAY, KELLY; Northampton SR HS; Bath, PA; (4); 92/430; Drama Clb; Leo Clb; Chorus; School Musical; School Play; Stage Crew; Hon Roll; Bloomsburg U; Bus Mgmt.

HAY, KIMBERLY; Berlin Brothers Valley HS; Berlin, PA; (4); 24/81; Church Yth Grp; French Clb; FBLA; Chorus; Church Choir; Drill Tm; School Play; FBLA 2nd Pl Bus Law 87; Bus Ldrs Amer Sprng Ldrshp; Cambria Rowe; Acctng.

HAY, THOMAS; Peters Township HS; Venetia, PA; (2); Varsity Clb; Var L Bsbl; Var L Swmmng; High Hon Roll; St Chmpn 100 Yd Bttrfly-Swmmng 87; Al-Dist Hnrbl Mntn-Bsbl-Pitchr 87.

HAYCISAK, JENNIFER; Cambria Heights HS; St Benedict, PA; (3); FHA; Yrbk Stf; Hon Roll; Mt Aloysius JC; Cardvslr Tech.

HAYDEN, AMY; Riverview HS; Verona, PA; (3); 29/107; Office Aide; Rep Jr Cls; Rep Sr Cls; Rep Stu Cncl; Pom Pon; Powder Puff Ftbl; Hon Roll; French Clb; Yrbk Ed-Chief; Yrbk Stf; Art Inst Of Pittsburgh; Int Dsn.

HAYDEN, DEBORAH; Juniata HS; Mifflintown, PA; (4); Art Clb; Computer Clb; Spanish Clb; Speech Tm; Varsity Clb; Nwsp Rptr; Fld Hcky; Hon Roll; NHS; Pres Schlr; Cntrl PA Bus Schl; Rtl Mgt.

HAYDEN, JENNIFER; Aliquippa SR HS; Aliquippa, PA; (2); Band; Concert Band; Mrchg Band; Twrlr; Hon Roll; Jr NHS; PA ST U; Accntg Mgmt.

HAYDEN, LEE; Butler Area SR HS; Butler, PA; (3); 1/723; Church Yth Grp; Exploring; NFL; Pres Service Clb; Speech Tm; Band; Concert Band; Jazz Band; Mrchg Band; Orch; Fin Pitts Provost Day 87; PCBL ST Essay Cont 1st Pl 87; James V Colonna Band Awd 85.

HAYDEN, MICHELLE; Beaver Falls SR HS; Beaver Falls, PA; (3); 97/170; GAA; Drm Mjr(t); Yrbk Stf; Sec Soph Cls; Sec Jr Cls; Stat Gym; Capt Trk; L Twrlr; Hon Roll; Bus Admin.

HAYDT, TRICIA; Pleasant Valley HS; Kunkletown, PA; (2); Math Tm; SADD; Fld Hcky; High Hon Roll; Hon Roll; Social Svcs.

HAYES, BERNADETTE; Archbishop Kennedy HS; Conshohocken, PA; (4); 67/169; Yrbk Stf; Var L Cheerleading; Var L Trk; Var L Vllybl; La Salle U; Acctg.

HAYES, CHRISTOPHER N; Archbishop Ryan HS; Philadelphia, PA; (4); 10/424; Church Yth Grp; Science Clb; Varsity Clb; Nwsp Stf; Rptr Yrbk Stf; Lit Mag; Var Bsbl; High Hon Roll; NHS; Outstnd Acad Achvmnt Awd General Studies 85; Acad Achvmnt Biology, Theology I & Ii 84 & 86; Notre Dame; Bus.

HAYES, CINDY; Calvary Baptist Acad; Clymer, PA; (4); 1/5; Band; Trs Sr Cls; Var Bsktbl; Var Vllybl; High Hon Roll; Val; VP Church Yth Grp; Acpl Chr; Chorus; Church Choir; Acdmic All-Amrcn Awd 87; Bible Quiz Tm 86 & 87; KECA Rgnl Essy Cmpttn Exclnt Awd 86 & 87; Bob Jones U.

HAYES, CRISTIN; Strong Vincent HS; Erie, PA; (3); 50/191; Church Yth Grp; Exploring; Science Clb; Jrnlsm.

HAYES, DONNA; Central Bucks HS West; Chalfont, PA; (4); 8/485; Intnl Clb; Band; Nwsp Ed-Chief; Ed Lit Mag; Lion Awd; NHS; Ntl Merit Schol; Hosp Aide; Mrchg Band; School Musical; CBEA Schlrshp 87; Prsdntl Acad Fitness Awd 87; Natl Sci Olympiad Awd 87; U Of DE; Intl Relatns.

HAYES, DOUG; Greater Johnstown Cntrl SR HS; Johnstown, PA; (3); 2/292; VP German Clb; Capt Quiz Bowl; Speech Tm; Band; Chorus; High Hon Roll; NHS; Church Yth Grp; Math Clb; Concert Band; Grmn Clb Awds 85-87.

HAYES, MELISSA; Jim Thorpe Area HS; Jim Thorpe, PA; (2); Speech Tm; Drm Mjr(t); Flag Corp; Nwsp Stf; Stu Cncl; JV Cheerleading; Stat Coach Actv; Stat Mgr(s); JV Sftbl; Trs Var Twrlr; Most Outstndng Peer Cnslr 86-87; Air Force.

HAYES, MICHAEL; Crestwood HS; Mountaintop, PA; (4); 2/193; Math Clb; Ski Clb; VP Ftbl; VP Trk; VP Wt Lftg; High Hon Roll; Kiwanis Awd; Lion Awd; NHS; NEDT Awd; Pres & Carpenter Schlrshps 87; Wilkes Coll; Elec Engrng.

HAYES, MICHAEL; Mahanoy Area HS; Barnesville, PA; (3); Ski Clb; Y-Teens; Var L Ftbl; Var L Trk; Var Wt Lftg; Im Wrstlng; NHS; Law.

HAYES, SCOTT; Methacton SR HS; Norristown, PA; (3); 50/381; VICA; High Hon Roll.

HAYES, TERR LEE; Corry Area HS; Corry, PA; (4); 30/205; Radio Clb; Ftbl; Wt Lftg; Wrstlng; Hon Roll; Lion Awd; Carmen Piccirillo Awd Ftbl 86-87; Bst Dfnsv Plyr Awd Ftbl 86-87; Thiel Coll.

HAYGOOD, DEON; Harrisburg HS; Harrisburg, PA; (3); 24/263; Cmnty Wkr; Math Clb; Science Clb; Orch; Sec Stu Cncl; Var Trk; Hon Roll; Prfct Atten Awd; Upward Bound 85-88; Yth Against Cancer Soc 86-87; Stu Mnth 85; Med Tech.

HAYLETT, KEVIN; Conneaut Lake HS; Conn Lake, PA; (3); SADD; Nwsp Phtg; Nwsp Rptr; Pres Jr Cls; Pres Stu Cncl; Var L Ftbl; Im Vllybl; Var Wt Lftg; Phrmcst.

HAYLETT, WENDY; Meadville Area SR HS; Meadville, PA; (3); 77/363; Church Yth Grp; French Clb; Science Clb; SADD; Cheerleading; Hon Roll; Med.

HAYNEY, FRANCIS V; St Josephs Prep Schl; Camden, NJ; (4); 20/225; Chess Clb; Math Tm; Hon Roll; NHS; Prfct Atten Awd; Pres Schlr; Slvr Medl Greek, Latin 87; U Of PA; Clsscs.

HAYNIE, GAIL; Penn Wood HS; Aldan, PA; (3); 17/341; Church Yth Grp; Sec FBLA; Nwsp Stf; Yrbk Stf; Var Bsktbl; JV Capt Lcrss; Sftbl; Var Tennis; High Hon Roll; Hon Roll; JR Ldrshp Awd Ftr Secys 87; PA Free Entrprs Wk Schlrshp 87; Outstndng Stu In Bus 87; Bus.

HAYS, DONALD; Uniontown Area HS; Uniontown, PA; (3); Art Clb; Latin Clb; Ski Clb; Spanish Clb; Hon Roll.

HAYS, MARK; Riverview HS; Oakmont, PA; (2); 6/70; Socr; High Hon Roll; U Of Pittsburgh; Med.

HAYS, STEVEN; Central HS; Philadelphia, PA; (3); 144/538; Library Aide; Hon Roll; Barnwell Hnr Rll 86 & 87; Mntlly Gftd Pgm 84; Phrmcy.

HAYWALD, KENNETH; Tunkhannock Area HS; Falls, PA; (4); 55/280; FCA; Var Ftbl; Var Wt Lftg; Cntry 21 Accntng III Awd 87; All Schlstc Ftbl-Cntr 87; Keystone JC; Accntng.

HAZEL, MARY; Boyertown Area HS; Boyertown, PA; (3); 112/470; Band; Chorus; Concert Band; Mrchg Band; Orch; Pep Band; School Musical; Cit Awd; Hon Roll.

HAZELTINE, BEV; Lake-Lehman SR HS; Harveys Lake, PA; (3); Church Yth Grp; Drill Tm; Flag Corp; Mrchg Band; Var L Cheerleading; Art Clb; Band; Church Choir; Color Guard; L Var Twrlr; Ltr Chrldng Wrstlng 86-87; Ltr Band Twrlr 85-86; Air Force.

HAZEN, LENORA; Lakeview HS; Mercer, PA; (4); 9/128; Church Yth Grp; Intnl Clb; Library Aide; Chorus; Mgr School Play; Exploring; 4-H; Latin Clb; Church Choir; Stage Crew; Latin Cert 85-84; Stu Lbrrn Cert 85-86; Grove City Coll; Mech Engrng.

HAZLETT, BONITA; Freeport SR HS; Sarver, PA; (4); Hosp Aide; Mrchg Band; Pep Band; Stage Crew; Nwsp Rptr; Rep Frsh Cls; Var Stat Bsktbl; Coach Actv; Var L Sftbl; Im Swmmng; Acdmc All Amer 85-86; Gannon U; Nrsng.

HAZLETT, DARIN; Lakeview HS; Stoneboro, PA; (4); VP 4-H; Science Clb; Band; Chorus; Concert Band; Jazz Band; Mrchg Band; Pep Band; School Play; 4-H Awd; Seat W/Greenville Symphny & Yth Symphny 86; Dstrct 5 Band Fstvl 87; Mercer Co Res 4-H Captl Days 86; Indiana U Of PA; Music.

HAZLETT, GENE; Highlands HS; Natrona Hgts, PA; (3); 65/359; Band; Var JV Bsbl; JV Bsktbl; Var Golf; Hon Roll; Jr NHS; Prfct Atten Awd; Ntl Sci Mrt Awd 85 & 86.

HAZUKA, MELISSA; Plum SR HS; Pittsburgh, PA; (3); DECA; French Clb; FTA; Yrbk Stf; Rep Soph Cls; Rep Jr Cls; Rep Sr Cls; JV Im Cheerleading; High Hon Roll; Hon Roll; U Pittsburgh; Med.

HEACOCK, KIMBERLY; Lake-Lehmon HS; Sweet Valley, PA; (2); 7/199; SADD; Sec Frsh Cls; Sec Soph Cls; Var Cheerleading; High Hon Roll; Hon Roll; NHS; NEDT Awd; Princeton; Bus Adm.

HEADER, CLINT; Pottsville Area HS; Pottsville, PA; (1); Aud/Vis; Camera Clb; Church Yth Grp; Chorus; Church Choir; JV Bsbl; PA ST U; Sci.

HEADLEY, KERRY; J P Mc Caskey HS; Landisville, PA; (4); 54/400; Drama Clb; Pep Clb; Q&S; Nwsp Rptr; Nwsp Stf; Cheerleading; Hnrbl Mntn Temples Jrnlsm Cnvntn 86; Schl Of Visual Arts Prtl Schlrshp 87; Jrnlsm.

HEADLEY JR, ROBERT F; Carmichaels Area HS; Carmichaels, PA; (4); 10/110; Boy Scts; Church Yth Grp; Cmnty Wkr; Library Aide; Ski Clb; Spanish Clb; Band; Concert Band; Mrchg Band; Pres Frsh Cls; Waynesburg Coll Schlrshp 87; Govs Schl Math-Sch, Hstry-Scl Study 86; Waynesburg Coll; Chem.

HEAGY, JENNIFER; Christian School Of York; York, PA; (3); Church Yth Grp; Library Aide; Band; Chorus; Concert Band; Mrchg Band; Hon Roll; Acdmc All Amer 86-87; Farquhar-Lyles Yth Awd Vlntr Svc 86-87; Libry Sci.

HEAL, CHARLES; Wyoming Area HS; W Pittston, PA; (3); Key Clb; Ski Clb; Hon Roll; Prfct Atten Awd; U Of Scranton; Biochem.

HEALEY, ANGIE; Ambridge Area HS; Ambridge, PA; (3); Pep Clb; Spanish Clb; Band; Concert Band; Mrchg Band; Symp Band; Score Keeper; Wrstlng; Hon Roll; Cmnty Wkr; Sawyer Schl Bus; Legal Secy.

HEALEY JR, BOB; Cardinal O Hara HS; Glenolden, PA; (3); Church Yth Grp; Civic Clb; JA; Varsity Clb; Lit Mag; Im Bsktbl; Hon Roll; Engrng.

HEALEY, LISA; West Scranton SR HS; Scranton, PA; (2); Dance Clb; French Clb; Hosp Aide; Hon Roll.

HEALEY, MARILYN; Coughlin HS; Laflin, PA; (3); 50/400; 4-H; Girl Scts; Hosp Aide; Ski Clb; Var L Trk; High Hon Roll; Hon Roll; Jr NHS; NHS; Nwsp Rptr; Pres Acad Fit Awd 87; Med.

HEALEY, SEAN; Mercyhurst Prep; Erie, PA; (3); 17/170; NHS; JV Bsktbl; Var L Socr; Var L Tennis.

HEANEY, DONALD F; North Hills HS; Pittsburgh, PA; (4); 51/467; Boy Scts; Cmnty Wkr; Exploring; Ski Clb; High Hon Roll; Hon Roll; Eagl Sct 87; Penn ST; Engrng.

HEANEY, SUSAN; Cardinal O Hara HS; Havertown, PA; (3); 59/719; Church Yth Grp; Cmnty Wkr; Service Clb; SADD; Yrbk Sprt Ed; JV Coach Actv; Swmmng; Hon Roll; NHS; Prfct Atten Awd; Med.

HEARD, PAMELA; Wyoming Area HS; Wyoming, PA; (4); Hosp Aide; Spanish Clb; Color Guard; Mrchg Band; Orch; Yrbk Stf; Trk; Music Schlrshp-Wilkes Coll-PA 86-87; Wilkes Coll-PA; Music.

HEARD, SUZANNE; Bangor Area SR HS; Bangor, PA; (3); 9/213; Church Yth Grp; Cmnty Wkr; Hosp Aide; VP Science Clb; Sec Soph Cls; Stat Bsktbl; High Hon Roll; Jr NHS; VP NHS; Nrsng.

HEARN, KRISTINA; Warwick HS; Lititz, PA; (4); 10/252; Ski Clb; Rep Frsh Cls; Rep Jr Cls; Var Crs Cntry; High Hon Roll; Jr NHS; NHS; NEDT Awd; ABWA Schlrshp; Gftd Pgm; Philadelphia Coll Phrmcy; Phrmc.

HEARN, MICHELLE; Rockwood Area HS; Somerset, PA; (4); 5/95; Chorus; School Play; Yrbk Stf; Trs Stu Cncl; Stat Bsktbl; Var Cheerleading; Stat Vllybl; High Hon Roll; NHS; Sci Awd 84; Poli Sci.

HEARON, STEVE; Downingtown SR HS; Exton, PA; (3); 37/648; Pres German Clb; Letterman Clb; Band; Rep Frsh Cls; Rep Soph Cls; Rep Jr Cls; Rep Stu Cncl; Var L Ftbl; Stat Lcrss; Wt Lftg; Stu Ldrshp Conf Lehigh Coll 86.

HEARSON, PATRICIA; Cedar Crest HS; Lebanon, PA; (2); Church Yth Grp; Spanish Clb; Band; Concert Band; Drm Mjr(t); Jazz Band; Mrchg Band; Orch; Pep Band; Symp Band; Dist Band PA 87; All-St Band 86; Rgnl Band 87.

HEASLEY, CHRISTINA; Belle Vernon Area HS; Belle Vernon, PA; (4); 135/275; Dance Clb; Pep Clb; Variety Show; JV Var Cheerleading; Var Powder Puff Ftbl; Var Trk; Gov Hon Prg Awd; Hon Roll; 2nd Pl Fred Astire Dance Comptn 87; Westmoreland Cnty CC; Accntng.

HEASLEY, JENNIFER; East Juniata HS; Thompsontown, PA; (3); Chess Clb; Band; Concert Band; Mrchg Band; Pep Band; School Musical; School Play; Yrbk Stf; Var L Bsktbl; Var L Fld Hcky; Dist Band 87; Dist Truck 87.

HEATER, KATHY; Elkland Area HS; Osceola, PA; (3); 12/65; Church Yth Grp; Office Aide; Teachers Aide; Yrbk Stf; Stat Bsktbl; Mgr(s); Hon Roll; NHS; Pres Awd 85-86.

HEATH, DENNIS; Elizabeth Forward HS; Greenock, PA; (3); Trs Church Yth Grp; Exploring; JA; Trs Leo Clb; Church Choir; JV Bsktbl; JV Trk; Lion Awd; Prfct Atten Awd; Hnr PA Lions Laser Ctr 85; Amer Red Cross Cert Life Guard 87; Pre-Med.

HEATH, JENNIFER; Middletown Area HS; Middletown, PA; (3); 21/193; FBLA; Band; Chorus; Color Guard; Mrchg Band; Advrtsng.

HEATH, LIZ; Boyertown Area HS; Douglassville, PA; (4); Hosp Aide; Library Aide; Sec VICA; Church Choir; Mrchg Band; Nwsp Rptr; Cit Awd; Hon Roll; Lion Awd; Mst Outstndng Stu Food Preprtn 87; Mst Outstndng Vo-Tech Stu 87; New England Culinary Inst; Chef.

HEATHERINGTON, KATHERINE S; Mc Keesport Area SR HS; Mc Keesport, PA; (3); Church Yth Grp; NFL; Trs Acpl Chr; School Musical; Nwsp Ed-Chief; Var Cheerleading; NHS; French Clb; Sec Girl Scts; Hosp Aide; PMEA Dist I Hnrs Choir 84 86; U Of Pittsburgh.

HEATLEY, WENDY; Liberty JR SR HS; Roaring Brnch, PA; (3); Camera Clb; Var Capt Crs Cntry; Var Capt Trk; High Hon Roll; NHS; FHA; Yrbk Phtg; Var JV Bsktbl; Var JV Vllybl; Outstndng Female Ath 86-87; MVP Crs Cntry 86 & 87, Track 87; ST Qlfr Crs Cntry 86, Track 87; Jrnlsm.

HEATWOLE JR, WILLIAM E; Towanda Area HS; Towanda, PA; (4); Boy Scts; Church Yth Grp; Letterman Clb; Science Clb; Ftbl; Trk; Outstndng Sprinter 86-87; Clutch Awd 86; James Madison U; Finance.

HEAVEY, KAREN; Nazareth Acad; Phila, PA; (3); Dance Clb; French Clb; Hosp Aide; School Musical; Yrbk Stf; Sec Soph Cls; Sec Jr Cls; Cheerleading; Hon Roll; Prfct Atten Awd; Yellow Belt Tae Kwon Do 87; Intl Bus.

HEBDEN, ROBERTA; Mid Valley HS; Throop, PA; (3); Drama Clb; Nwsp Stf; High Hon Roll; Hon Roll; Csmtlgst.

HEBERLE, DOUGLAS M; Bethel Park HS; Bethel Park, PA; (3); Am Leg Boys St; Drama Clb; VP Key Clb; Pres NFL; Pres Trs Stu Cncl; Diving; High Hon Roll; NHS; Ntl Merit Ltr; SADD; Phyclgst.

HEBERT, BRIAN; Chief Logan HS; Mc Clure, PA; (4); 7/200; Pres Church Yth Grp; Pres Computer Clb; Science Clb; Varsity Clb; Var L Bsbl; Var L Ftbl; High Hon Roll; Prfct Atten Awd; French Clb; Math Clb; HS Schltc Perfrmnce Awd 87; Schlrhsp Chief Logan Lions Club 87; 1st Pl Sci Olympiad Laser Shoot 87; St Francis Coll; Math.

HEBERT, RICHARD; Danville HS; Danville, PA; (2); Cmnty Wkr; Red Cross Aide; Ski Clb; Socr; Trk; High Hon Roll; PA ST U; Chem.

HEBRANK, JAMES; Hempfield Area SR HS; Greensburg, PA; (4); 128/693; AFS; Church Yth Grp; Drama Clb; JA; NFL; Spanish Clb; School Play; Yrbk Stf; High Hon Roll; Hon Roll; IN U Of PA; Finance.

HECK, BRIDGET; Wilson HS; W Lawn, PA; (3); 60/304; Dance Clb; Leo Clb; Spanish Clb; School Musical; Stu Cncl; Im Bsktbl; JV Cheerleading; Var Crs Cntry; Var L Trk; Im Wt Lftg; Dist III AAA High Jmp Champ 85; Berks Cntry Trk & Fld All-Star 85; Bloomsburg U; Phys Thrpy.

HECK, MELISSA G; Spring-Ford HS; Royersford, PA; (4); 54/235; Pep Clb; Cheerleading; Lcrss; Data Entry.

HECK, RENEE; E L Meyers HS; Wilkes Bare, PA; (4); Church Yth Grp; German Clb; Key Clb; Pep Clb; Sec Ski Clb; SADD; Chorus; Flag Corp; Trk; Jr NHS; Misericordia; Nrsng.

HECKARD, ANN-MARIE; State Coll Area Intermediate HS; State College, PA; (1); Band; Concert Band; Jazz Band; JV Tennis; Cit Awd; Hon Roll; Frnch Awd 87.

HECKARD, BARRY; Mechanicsburg SR HS; Mechanicsburg, PA; (2); 24/309; French Clb; SADD; Nwsp Stf; Trk; High Hon Roll; NHS; Peer Advct SLAM 87; Spch Tm 87-88; Jrnlsm.

HECKER, TOM; Archbishop Wood For Boys; Oakford, PA; (2); 6/260; Yrbk Rptr; JV Bsbl; Im Vllybl; High Hon Roll; NHS; Intl Frgn Lang Awd 86-87; Acdmc All Am Awd 86-87.

HECKETHORN, LINDA; Montour HS; Mckees Rocks, PA; (3); SADD; Mrchg Band; Powder Puff Ftbl; Swmmng; Twrlr; High Hon Roll; NHS; Sci Olympic Team 87; Geometry Awd 86; Engrng.

HECKLER, KIMIE; Kieruff HS; Allentown, PA; (3); 42/390; Art Clb; Hon Roll; Prfct Atten Awd.

HECKMAN, CHRISTOPHER; Milton SR HS; Milton, PA; (2); Boy Scts; Bucknell U; Engr.

HECKMAN, JODY; East Pennsboro Area HS; Enola, PA; (3); Art Clb; Church Yth Grp; Ski Clb; Spanish Clb; VP SADD; Chorus; Madrigals; Pres Stu Cncl; Var Fld Hcky; Hon Roll; Schltc Art Awd 84; Bus Mgmt.

HECKMAN, JULIE A; Norristown Area HS; Norristown, PA; (3); 25/524; GAA; Key Clb; VP Pep Clb; Rep Jr Cls; Pres Stu Cncl; Var Bsktbl; Im Vllybl; High Hon Roll; NHS; Rotary Awd; Town Mtng Tomrrow 86; Accountng.

HECKMAN, KIM; Crestwood HS; Mountain Top, PA; (3); 25/198; Science Clb; Ski Clb; Yrbk Stf; Rep Stu Cncl; JV Var Cheerleading; Mgr(s); Trk; High Hon Roll; Med Dctr.

HECKMAN, MICHELLE R; Brookville Area HS; Brookville, PA; (3); Pres Church Yth Grp; FTA; Library Aide; Chorus; School Musical; Hon Roll; Jr NHS; NHS; US Achvt Acad 86; Elem Ed.

HECKMAN, SHELBI; Middleburg HS; Mt Pleasant Mills, PA; (3); 26/140; Key Clb; Ski Clb; Varsity Clb; Nwsp Stf; Yrbk Stf; Stu Cncl; Fld Hcky; VP Soph Cls.

HECKMAN, TAMMY; Northeastern HS; York Haven, PA; (3); 3/266; Art Clb; Church Yth Grp; Red Cross Aide; Spanish Clb; Church Choir; High Hon Roll; NHS; Ntl Merit Ltr; Dance Clb; JA; Natl Hon Roll 86-87; Zembo Shrine Circus Poster Wnnr 85; Psychology.

HEDDAEUS, MARK; Richland HS; Wexford, PA; (3); Boy Scts; German Clb; Chorus; Socr; High Hon Roll; NHS; Comp Sci.

HEDDINGS, JEFFREY; Milton SR HS; Potts Grove, PA; (2); 69/254; VICA; Socr; PA ST U; Machnst.

HEDDINGS, MATTHEW; Danville SR HS; Danville, PA; (2); Church Yth Grp; Key Clb; Ski Clb; Gym; JV Socr; Var L Trk; God Cntry Awd; High Hon Roll; Hon Roll; Pres Acad Ftnss Awd 85-86; Arch.

HEDGLIN, BRETT; Montieau HS; Boyers, PA; (3); 25/140; Church Yth Grp; Spanish Clb; Bsktbl; Golf; High Hon Roll; Hon Roll; NHS; Crmnlgy.

HEDIN, ANDY; Upper Darby HS; Drexel Hill, PA; (3); Acpl Chr; Chorus; Yrbk Phtg; Yrbk Stf; High Hon Roll; Hon Roll; Prfct Atten Awd; Rochester Inst Of Tech; Photo.

HEDLAND, DAWN; Neshannock HS; New Castle, PA; (3); 30/112; Boy Scts; English Clb; Exploring; Latin Clb; Library Aide; NFL; Pep Clb; Ski Clb; Speech Tm; SADD; 2nd Pl Rbn Forensic Comptn 85-86; Psychlgy.

HEDMAN, MEGAN; Indiana Area SR HS; Indiana, PA; (3); Var Key Clb; Acpl Chr; Madrigals; Nwsp Stf; Rep Stu Cncl; Tennis; Hon Roll; Jr NHS; NEDT Awd; Prfct Atten Awd; YTSC Sec; Brdcst Jrnlsm.

HEDQUIST, CELESTE; Peters Township HS; Mcmurray, PA; (2); Church Yth Grp; High Hon Roll; Hon Roll; Brigham Youth U; Bus Mgmt.

HEDRICH, KATHLEEN M; Interboro HS; Prospect Park, PA; (3); Drama Clb; VP French Clb; Flag Corp; Mrchg Band; School Play; Rep Frsh Cls; Rep Soph Cls; Rep Jr Cls; High Hon Roll; NHS; Cmnctns.

HEDRICK, V MATTHEW; Owen J Roberts HS; Pottstown, PA; (2); 21/311; JV Socr; Hon Roll; Actry.

HEDZIK, STEVEN; Ambridge Area HS; Baden, PA; (3); Church Yth Grp; Pep Clb; VICA; JV Bsbl; Var Wt Lftg; JV Wrstlng; Hon Roll; PA Tech; Elec.

HEENAN, MELANIE J; Tidioute HS; Tidioute, PA; (3); Trs Church Yth Grp; Debate Tm; Letterman Clb; Office Aide; SADD; Varsity Clb; Church Choir; Yrbk Stf; Trs Frsh Cls; Trs Soph Cls; Mercyhurst; Soc Wk.

HEER, JON; Ringgold SR HS; Monongahela, PA; (1); 10/380; Office Aide; Chorus; School Musical; Swing Chorus; Variety Show; Rep Stu Cncl; Hon Roll; Jr NHS; Carnegie Mellon U; Med.

HEETER, TAMRA; Union JR SR HS; Sligo, PA; (2); Pres Church Yth Grp; FCA; L Trk; L Var Vllybl; French Clb; SADD; School Musical; Yrbk Stf; Trs Soph Cls; Rep Stu Cncl; Westminster Coll; Law.

HEFFELFINGER, LORI A; Marian Catholic HS; Lansford, PA; (4); 30/109; Hosp Aide; Office Aide; Pep Clb; Chorus; School Play; Var Capt Cheerleading; JV Sftbl; Hon Roll; Panther Vly Chamber Commerce Awd 87; Immaculata Coll; Chem.

HEFFELFINGER, RONALD; Neshaminy HS; Penndel, PA; (4); 18/687; Band; Chorus; Jazz Band; School Musical; Bsktbl; Socr; High Hon Roll; Hon Roll; NHS; Villanova U; Commerce.

HEFFENTRAGER, JANE; Louis E Dieruff HS; Allentown, PA; (2); 4/340; Mrchg Band; Pep Band; Nwsp Rptr; Nwsp Stf; Rep Frsh Cls; Rep Soph Cls; Mgr(s); Stat Swmmng; Hon Roll; Prfct Atten Awd; Engrng.

HEFFNER, LORA; Elizabethtown HS; Elizabethtown, PA; (3); Varsity Clb; Bsktbl; Fld Hcky; Powder Puff Ftbl; Sftbl; Wt Lftg; French Clb; Spanish Clb; SADD; Off Sr Cls.

HEFFNER, RICHELLE; Schuylkill Haven HS; Schuylkill Haven, PA; (4); German Clb; Science Clb; SADD; Teachers Aide; Band; Color Guard; Drill Tm; Mrchg Band; Yrbk Stf; Sec Sr Cls; Jr Hnr Guard 86; Mst Likely To Succeed-Bus 87.

HEFLIN, DAVID E; Northgate JR SR HS; Bellevue, PA; (3); 19/154; Sec Am Leg Boys St; Red Cross Aide; Var L Ftbl; Var L Swmmng; Var L Trk; Cit Awd; High Hon Roll; Hon Roll; Prncpls Awd Outstndng Schlrshp 87.

HEFLIN, MATTHEW; Saint Pius X HS; Pottstown, PA; (1); 22/145; Boy Scts; Latin Clb; Stage Crew; Socr; Hon Roll; Hnr Roll 87; Penn ST; Med.

HEFTY, JANICE; Du Bois Area HS; Falls Creek, PA; (3); 19/321; Girl Scts; Varsity Clb; Chorus; School Musical; JV Capt Bsktbl; Var Trk; Var Vllybl; Hon Roll; NHS; Nice Kid Awd; Elem Educ.

HEGADUS, ANGIE; North Star HS; Stoystown, PA; (4); 23/130; Varsity Clb; School Play; Sec Sr Cls; Rep Stu Cncl; Var L Cheerleading; Capt Mat Maids; Var L Vllybl; FCA; Yrbk Stf; Stat Wrstlng; Lioness Of Mnth 87; Nrth Str Actvts Bstr Stu Of Mnt 84 & 87; Cmnctns.

HEGARTY, MAUREEN E; Central Catholic HS; Whitehall, PA; (4); Church Yth Grp; Cmnty Wkr; Hosp Aide; Key Clb; Mrchg Band; Nwsp Stf; Kings Coll; Phrmcy.

HEGEDIS, CHRISSANDA DAWN; Mapletown JR SR HS; Bobtown, PA; (4); 7/76; GAA; Ski Clb; Ed Nwsp Phtg; Ed Yrbk Phtg; Trs Sr Cls; Vllybl; Hon Roll; Trs NHS; Stud Mnth Dec 87; Youth Educ Assoc 85-87; Radiology.

HEGEDUS, SHERRY; Connellsville SR HS; Mt Pleasant, PA; (3); Concert Band; Flag Corp; Mrchg Band; Pres Frsh Cls; Pres Soph Cls; Rep Jr Cls; Rep Stu Cncl; Hon Roll; NHS; Prfct Atten Awd; Bus Adm.

HEH, KELLY; Cumberland Valley HS; Camp Hill, PA; (4); German Clb; Hosp Aide; Red Cross Aide; Ski Clb; School Play; Hon Roll; Ntl Merit Ltr; Johns Hopkins U; Pre-Med.

HEIBERGER, BRIAN; St Marys Area HS; St Marys, PA; (2); 86/301; Var L Bsbl; Knoth3le Bsbl 86-87.

HEID, CHRISTY; Highlands HS; Natrona Hts, PA; (4); 5/280; Intnl Clb; Key Clb; Band; Church Choir; Concert Band; Mrchg Band; Orch; Pep Band; School Musical; Symp Band; HEA Schlrshp 87; Westminster Alumni Schlrshp 87; Westminster Coll; Engrng.

HEIDE, BILLIE; Mt Pleasant Area HS; Mammoth, PA; (2); 44/240; GAA; Letterman Clb; Band; Concert Band; Mrchg Band; Pep Band; Sftbl; High Hon Roll; Hon Roll; Arch.

HEIDE, LINDA; Mt Pleasant Area HS; Mt Pleasant, PA; (3); Latin Clb; Ski Clb; Band; Nwsp Sprt Ed; Stu Cncl; Tennis; Hon Roll; Rl Est.

HEIDECKER, JOHN; Hazleton HS; Ebervale, PA; (2); Aud/Vis; CAP Cmnty Wkr; Exploring; Radio Clb; ROTC; SADD; VICA; Penn ST; Bus Mngmt.

HEIDECKER, ROBYN; Harbor Creek HS; Erie, PA; (4); 21/224; AFS Sec Church Yth Grp; Flag Corp; Yrbk Stf; Powder Puff Ftbl; High Hon Roll; Hon Roll; NHS; Bus Awd 86-87; IUP; Bus Ed.

HEIDENREICH, MARK; North Catholic HS; Pittsburgh, PA; (3); 26/267; Math Tm; NFL; Speech Tm; Hon Roll; NEDT Awd; Aerospc Engrng.

HEIDENREICH, MARY ANNE; St Francis Acad; Pittsburgh, PA; (4) 1/34; Drama Clb; Pres JA; Math Clb; Pres NFL; Pep Clb; Service Clb; Chorus; School Musical; School Play; Nwsp Rptr; Ntl Pro-Life Ortrcl Wnnr 86; Bus.

HEIDENRICH, DIANNE; Peters Twp HS; Mc Murray, PA; (3); VP Varsity Clb; VP Frsh Cls; VP Jr Cls; Stu Cncl; Var Cheerleading; Var Diving; Var Gym; Score Keeper; Var Trk; Var Vllybl.

HEIDORN, DONNA; Windbar Area HS; Windber, PA; (4); Am Leg Aux Girls St; Hosp Aide; Band; Chorus; Color Guard; Flag Corp; Mrchg Band; Hon Roll; Clr Grd Awds 84; Stu Of Mon 87; Prfct Atten 87; PA Acad Of Cosmetology.

HEIDT, DEAN; Cathedral Prep; Erie, PA; (3); 2/194; VP Frsh Cls; Trs Soph Cls; Rep Jr Cls; Stu Cncl; Var JV Bsktbl; Var JV Ftbl; JV Wt Lftg; High Hon Roll; Engrng.

HEIGES, JEFFREY; Hickory HS; Hermitage, PA; (4); 3/175; Pres Computer Clb; Math Clb; Varsity Clb; Acpl Chr; School Musical; Nwsp Sprt Ed; Rep Sr Cls; Var Bsbl; Capt Crs Cntry; NHS; PA Soc Of Prof Engrs Awd 86; Congrssnl Page US House Of Rep 86; Private Pilots License 87; US Nvl Acad; Aeros Engrng.

HEIKES, SUSAN; Juniata HS; Mifflintown, PA; (3); Sec Church Yth Grp; SADD; Varsity Clb; Chorus; Concert Band; Yrbk Stf; Stat Mgr(s); High Hon Roll; NHS; Schlstc J 85-87; Music Hnr Awd 84-85; Central PA Bus Schl; Acctng.

HEILER, CHRISTINA; Cardinal O Hara HS; Holmes, PA; (3); 53/710 Pres Church Yth Grp; Cmnty Wkr; Service Clb; Chorus; Yrbk Stf; Lit Mag; Im Bsktbl; Im Sftbl; Hon Roll; NHS; Acadc Convctn 85-87; Educ.

HEILMAN, DARIN T; Lebanon Catholic HS; Lebanon, PA; (3); 4/67 Chess Clb; Math Tm; Science Clb; Yrbk Rptr; JV Var Bsktbl; Capt Ftbl Wt Lftg; Bausch & Lomb Sci Awd; High Hon Roll; NHS; Math Awd 85-87 Chem Awd 87; Elec Engr.

HEILMAN, NATHAN; Freeport Area SR HS; Sarver, PA; (2); 4-H; Trk 4-H Awd; High Hon Roll; Vet.

HEILMAN, NICOLE; Northeastern HS; Mt Wolf, PA; (3); Pep Clb Varsity Clb; Band; Chorus; Concert Band; Mrchg Band; School Musical Variety Show; Capt L Cheerleading; Hon Roll; Bus Mgmt.

HEILMAN, SUSAN L; Norristown Area HS; Norristown, PA; (3); 25/491 Intnl Clb; Chorus; Concert Band; Mrchg Band; Pep Band; Symp Band Hon Roll; Pre Med.

HEILMAN, TRACY; Central York HS; York, PA; (3); Varsity Clb School Musical; Variety Show; Nwsp Stf; Yrbk Stf; Co-Capt Cheerleading Hon Roll; Early Childhood Care.

HEIM, ANGIE; South Western HS; Hanover, PA; (3); Cmnty Wkr; Pres Key Clb; Varsity Clb; School Play; Yrbk Stf; L Var Bsktbl; Capt Var Fld Hcky; Hon Roll; NEDT Awd; Key Clbbr Mnth Awd 86; Outstndng Cmmnty Svc Awd 87; Cmmnctns.

HEIM, HEATHER; Line Mountain HS; Dalmatia, PA; (4); 6/117; Am Leg Aux Girls St; FBLA; Pres Varsity Clb; Yrbk Stf; Sec Sr Cls; Capt Fld Hcky; Pres NHS; Key Clb; Elks Awd; Hon Roll; Yng Amer Awd 87 Kiwanis Clb Scholar 87; Robert H Myers Mem Awd 87; Shippensburg U Biol.

HEIM, JILL; Nazareth Acad; Phila, PA; (3); Library Aide; Stage Crew Sec Frsh Cls; Trs Jr Cls; Im Gym; Peer Cnslng; Wrld Affrs; Cntstnt Teens Encouraging Excllnc Nationally; Psych.

HEIM, KAREN; Tri-Valley HS; Pitman, PA; (3); 14/76; Computer Clb FBLA; Nwsp Rptr; Nwsp Stf; Yrbk Stf; Rep Stu Cncl; Sftbl; Hon Roll Med Secr.

HEIM, LISA; Scranton Central HS; Scranton, PA; (4); Aud/Vis; Church Yth Grp; Pep Clb; SADD; Trs Chorus; Capt Color Guard; School Musical Northeast Inst Of Educ; Acctng.

HEIM, MARLIN; Tri-Valley HS; Pitman, PA; (3); 13/76; Am Leg Boys St; Ski Clb; Spanish Clb; Varsity Clb; Var L Bsbl; Var L Ftbl; Im Wt Lftg Var L Wrstlng; Hon Roll; Dist AA Wrestling Champ In PA 87; Tri-Valley Ftbl Team Eastern Conf Champs 85; 8 Ltts; Engr Field.

HEIM, SCOTT; Danville SR HS; Danville, PA; (3); 31/198; Trs Church Yth Grp; French Clb; Church Choir; Var Capt Crs Cntry; Var Trk; High Hon Roll; NHS; Geo Hghst GPA 85; Amer Chmcl Soc 2nd Pl Score 87 Math.

HEIM, SCOTT; Shikellamy HS; Northumberland, PA; (3); Stage Crew Ftbl; Sftbl; Wt Lftg; Hon Roll; Aerontcl Sci.

HEIMBACH, GRETA; East Pennsboro Area HS; Enola, PA; (3); 2/191 Church Yth Grp; Model UN; VP Spanish Clb; Nwsp Ed-Chief; Yrbk Ed-Chief; Rep Stu Cncl; L Var Trk; High Hon Roll; NHS; Art Clb; Ntl Soc Studies Olympd 2nd Pl 87; SE Penn Amer Chem Soc Cert Merit 86; Pre Law.

HEIMBACH, JENNIFER; Boyertown Area SR HS; Boyertown, PA; (3) 103/451; Computer Clb; FBLA; Library Aide; Hon Roll; Diplomas Merit Spnsh II & III 85-87; Intrprtng.

HEIMBACH, KAREN; Boyertown SR HS; Boyertown, PA; (3); 54/451 FBLA; Library Aide; Teachers Aide; Cit Awd; High Hon Roll; Hon Roll Opt Clb Awd; Prfct Atten Awd; Pres Schlr; Reading Area CC; Bus.

HEIMBACH, MARY ANN; Boyertown Area SR HS; Boyertown, PA; (4) 108/435; Church Yth Grp; Hosp Aide; Church Choir; Mrchg Band; Nwsp Stf; Twrlr; Hon Roll; Library Aide; SADD; Nwsp Rptr; Wrd Life Clbs Schlrshp Awd 85; Bandfront 3 Yr Plaq Awd 85-87; Hosp Aid Cert Apprctn 86; Reading Area CC; Med Sec.

HEIMEL, DENISE; Coudersport JR/Sr HS; Coudersport, PA; (3) Drama Clb; French Clb; Chorus; School Play; Hon Roll; Mltry.

HEIN, DAVID; West Scranton HS; Scranton, PA; (4); 16/250; Boy Scts Pres Church Yth Grp; VP JA; Ski Clb; VP Orch; Yrbk Stf; Off Stu Cncl God Cntry Awd; Jr NHS; NHS; Bloomsburg ST U; Accntng.

HEIN, DOUGLAS A; West Scranton HS; Scranton, PA; (4); 21/260 Church Yth Grp; JA; Ski Clb; Yrbk Stf; Stu Cncl; Jr NHS; Amer Lgn Axlr Mdl Awd; Bloomsburg U; Accntng.

HEINDEL, ALYSSA; Spring Grove SR HS; York, PA; (4); 32/289 Church Yth Grp; JA; SADD; Chorus; Church Choir; Hon Roll; NHS; W Chester U; Business.

HEINDEL, CRAIG; Spring Grove HS; Hanover, PA; (2); 51/290; Church Yth Grp; JA; Church Choir; High Hon Roll; Hon Roll; Pres Acad Fitn Awd 86; Spring Grove Schlrshp Awd 86.

HEINDEL, SHERRY; Eastern York HS; Hellam, PA; (3); 15/170; Pres Church Yth Grp; Varsity Clb; Drm Mjr(t); Stat Var Bsbl; Mgr(s); Powder Puff Ftbl; Twrlr; High Hon Roll; Hon Roll; Jr NHS; PA ST.

HEINE, DANA; Big Spring HS; Newville, PA; (3); 4-H; Teachers Aide; Chorus; School Musical; 4-H Awd; Hon Roll; NHS; Prfct Atten Awd; Eastern Ntnl 4-H Horse Rndup 85; 4-H ST Fashn Revw 86; Equestrian Sci.

HEINEY, JEFFREY; Lampeter Strasburg HS; Lancaster, PA; (4); AFS; Drama Clb; FBLA; Chorus; School Musical; School Play; Nwsp Ed-Chief; Nwsp Stf; Lit Mag; Natl FBLA Cmptn St Awd Wnr 87; Millersville U; Cmnctns.

HEININGER, ROCHELL; Springdale HS; Springdale, PA; (4); 17/104; FHA; GAA; SADD; Yrbk Phtg; Yrbk Stf; L Bsktbl; High Hon Roll; Hon Roll; NCTE Awd; Girls Bsktbl Tm Sectn Wnnr; NCSU; Bus Mgmt.

HEINLEIN IV, JOHN; Taylor Allderdice HS; Pittsburgh, PA; (3); Pres Computer Clb; Math Clb; Math Tm; High Hon Roll; Jr NHS; NHS; Ntl Merit Ltr; Chess Clb; French Clb; Cit Awd; Am HS Math Exam 87; Hnrd Am Chem Soc Chem Stu Yr 86; Smmr Schlrshp Carnegie-Mellon U 85-86; Carnegie-Mellon U; Comp Engrng.

HEINLY, SAMANTHA; Reading SR HS; Kissimmee, FL; (4); 58/568.

HEINRICH, ANGIE; York Suburban SR HS; York, PA; (3); 15/180; Church Yth Grp; Varsity Clb; Band; Concert Band; Mrchg Band; JV Var Bsktbl; Var Trk; Hon Roll; NHS; NC ST U; Bio Sci.

HEINRICH, JEAN M; Bishop Carroll HS; Portage, PA; (3); Drama Clb; NFL; Ski Clb; School Play; Rep Frsh Cls; Rep Soph Cls; Rep Jr Cls; Trs Stu Cncl; Stat Bsbl; Hon Roll; Yng Ldrs Amer 85; Stu Cncl Ldrshp Awd 87; Law.

HEINRICH, JEFF; Windber Area HS; Windber, PA; (3); Var Bsbl; Var L Ftbl; Hon Roll; NHS.

HEINTZEL, LINDA; Villa Maria Acad; Erie, PA; (4); 7/133; PAVAS; SADD; School Musical; Stage Crew; Yrbk Stf; Trk; High Hon Roll; Hon Roll; NHS; NEDT Awd; Awd Outstndng Achvt French Lang 86; IN U Pennsylvania; Chld Ed.

HEINTZELMAN, ANDREA; Mifflinburg Area HS; Mifflinburg, PA; (1); 57/191; German Clb; JV Sftbl; High Hon Roll; Hon Roll.

HEINTZELMAN, KEVIN; Parkland HS; Whitehall, PA; (2); Church Yth Grp; Cit Awd; High Hon Roll; Hon Roll; Med.

HEINTZELMAN, LISA; Mechanicsburg Area HS; Mechanicsburg, PA; (3); 141/338; Church Yth Grp; NFL; Speech Tm; SADD; Chorus; School Play; Hon Roll; Schlstc Wrtng Awds Cert Merit 87; Psych.

HEINY, MATTHEW; Northampton SR HS; Danielsville, PA; (3); 18/496; Cmnty Wkr; Pres Frsh Cls; Pres Soph Cls; VP Stu Cncl; Var L Ftbl; JV Trk; Im Wt Lftg; Var Wrstlng; High Hon Roll; PA ST U.

HEINZ, KEVIN; Mechanicsburg SR HS; Mechanicsburg, PA; (3); 142/338; Key Clb; JV Ftbl; Hon Roll; Bio.

HEINZER, JOSEPH; Venango Christian HS; Oil City, PA; (1); Boy Scts; JV Golf; High Hon Roll; Hon Roll.

HEIRENDT, MICHELLE; Fort Cherry HS; Mcdonald, PA; (2); Computer Clb; Drama Clb; Math Clb; Science Clb; Ski Clb; Spanish Clb; Pres Chorus; Church Choir; School Musical; Hon Roll; Comp Pgmmng.

HEISER, JULIE; Upper Dublin HS; Oreland, PA; (3); 103/250; Church Yth Grp; Drama Clb; SADD; Teachers Aide; Stage Crew; Yrbk Stf; Rep Soph Cls; JV Fld Hcky; JV Lcrss; Lion Awd; Chem.

HEISER, KELLY; Eastern Lebanon Co Schls; Schaefferstown, PA; (2); 1/175; Trs Church Yth Grp; Chorus; Church Choir; Sec Frsh Cls; Off Soph Cls; Stu Cncl; JV Bsktbl; Var L Fld Hcky; Gym; Var L Trk; Mem Of Acad All-Amer 86-87; Natl Sci Acad Mem 86-87; TV New Brdcstr.

HEISER, LORI; Central Bucks East HS; Doylestown, PA; (3); Ski Clb; Yrbk Stf; Var Capt Swmmng; JV Tennis; High Hon Roll; Hon Roll; NHS; Pres Acdmc Ftnss Awd 84-85; Schltc Lttr 85-86; Coachs Awd Swmmng 86-87; Bus.

HEISEY, ANGIE; Manheim Central HS; Manheim, PA; (4); 4-H; Yrbk Stf; Stu Cncl; Fld Hcky; Dnfth Awd; Hon Roll; Grl Of Mon 87; Hmcmng Qn Hnr Attndnt 86; Gettysburg Coll.

HEISEY, DEB; Donegal HS; Mount Joy, PA; (3); 20/177; Church Yth Grp; Hon Roll.

HEISEY, JULIE; Elizabethtown Area HS; Elizabethtown, PA; (4); 15/229; Trs AFS; VP Rep Band; Mrchg Band; Rep Frsh Cls; Trs Soph Cls; Rep Sr Cls; Trs Stu Cncl; Tennis; NHS; Pres Schlr; Acad Schlrshp 87; Messiah Coll; Phrmcy.

HEISEY, LEON; Manheim Central HS; Manheim, PA; (4); 12/217; Church Yth Grp; Pres FFA; High Hon Roll; NHS; Prfct Atten Awd; Rotary Awd; Keystne Frmr Degree, Deklab Ag Awd 87; 4 Way Tst Awd 86; PA ST U; Mech Engrng.

HEISEY, MARK; EA HS; Elizabethtown, PA; (3); Band; Concert Band; Mrchg Band; School Play; Stage Crew; Nwsp Rptr; Lit Mag; Var Socr; Var Tennis.

HEISEY, SHELDON; Elizabethtown Area HS; Elizabethtown, PA; (3); 26/289; Church Yth Grp; 4-H; FFA; Var Ftbl; Future Frmrs Of Amer Star Grnhnd 85.

HEISEY, TERI; Daniel Boone HS; Douglassville, PA; (3); Cmnty Wkr; French Clb; Intnl Clb; Letterman Clb; Service Clb; Ski Clb; Varsity Clb; VP Jr Cls; Off Stu Cncl; Var Cheerleading; PENN ST U; Cmptr Prgrmmr.

HEISHMAN, AMY; Waynesboro Area SR HS; Mont Alto, PA; (4); 11/353; Trs Church Yth Grp; JCL; Yrbk Bus Mgr; Yrbk Stf; Stat Trk; High Hon Roll; Voice Dem Awd; Amer Bus Wmns Assn Scholar 87; Blubaugh Math Awd 87; Pinebrook JC; Sec Sci.

HEISHMAN, TODD; Waynesboro Area HS; Mont Alto, PA; (4); 45/382; Am Leg Boys St; Church Yth Grp; Library Aide; Stat Bsktbl; JV Var Trk; Cit Awd; High Hon Roll; Hon Roll; NHS; Tnns Keystn ST Gms 86; Washington Bible Coll; Tchng.

HEISLER, KIMBERLY; Pennsbury HS; Yardley, PA; (3); French Clb; Chorus; Yrbk Stf; JV Fld Hcky; Liberal Arts.

HEISLER, SUSAN; Canon Mc Millan SR HS; Bridgeville, PA; (4); 96/364; Art Clb; Exploring; French Clb; Hosp Aide; Office Aide; Church Choir; Tennis; High Hon Roll; Hon Roll; Prfct Atten Awd; 2nd Pl Awd Frnch Compttn Intl Day; CA U PA; Modrn Lang.

HEISNER, KELLY; Nativity BVM HS; Middleport, PA; (2); 22/72; Spanish Clb; Drill Tm.

HEISS, JOHN; Archbishop Carroll HS; Wayne, PA; (4); 98/365; Band; Concert Band; Jazz Band; Mrchg Band; Var L Bsbl; Im Bsktbl; Capt Im Ftbl; Var L Trk; Im Vllybl; Hon Roll; Ntl Hnr Soc Awd 86; Rev John J Hickey Awd-Relgious Actvts 87; Villanova U; Pre Law.

HEISS, MARNIE; M S Hershey HS; Hummelstown, PA; (2); 10/213; Boy Scts; Dance Clb; English Clb; Pep Clb; Ski Clb; Color Guard; Stage Crew; Nwsp Stf; Var Swmmng; High Hon Roll.

HEIST, LAUREN; Council Rock HS; Newtown, PA; (3); 66/908; Church Yth Grp; Drama Clb; JV Bsktbl; Var JV Fld Hcky; Var JV Sftbl; Hon Roll; NHS; All Star Tm Intercllgt Fld Hcky Cmp Norton MA 86; Metrorlgy.

HEIST, ROERT; Dallas SR HS; Wyoming, PA; (3); 17/232; Church Yth Grp; Ski Clb; School Play; Yrbk Stf; Pres Jr Cls; Pres Sr Cls; Golf; Trk; Hon Roll; NHS; Natl Ldrshp Yth Salte 87.

HEISTER, KRISTIN A; Hershey HS; Hershey, PA; (4); 15/200; Church Yth Grp; Spanish Clb; Teachers Aide; Cheerleading; Gym; Powder Puff Ftbl; High Hon Roll; Hon Roll; NHS; Spanish NHS; Intl Frgn Lang Awd 85-86; Fedrtd Wmns Clb Schlrshp 86-87; Shippensburg U; Elem Ed.

HEISTER, KURT A; Conestoga HS; Wayne, PA; (3); Church Yth Grp; Key Clb; Model UN; Political Wkr; JV Bsbl; Im Bsktbl; Im Ftbl; Im Wt Lftg; Hon Roll; Engrng.

HEITZENRATER, MIKE; Punxsutawney Area HS; Punxsutawney, PA; (4); 57/245; Varsity Clb; Golf; Trk; Hon Roll; Gftd Pgm 83-87; Penn ST U; Geolgy.

HEIZMANN, NOELLE BETH; Central Bucks HS East; Doylestown, PA; (4); Am Leg Aux Girls St; Debate Tm; Pres Band; Mrchg Band; Ed Yrbk Stf; Cit Awd; High Hon Roll; NHS; Bnd Svc & Dedctn Awd, Cntrl Bucks Ed Schlrshp, Srptmst Ctznshp Awd 86-87; Trenton ST Coll; Bio.

HELD, DAVE; Jeannette SR HS; Jeannette, PA; (2); 12/135; Church Yth Grp; Civic Clb; Drama Clb; French Clb; Service Clb; Ski Clb; Spanish Clb; SADD; Rep Stu Cncl; High Hon Roll; Jrnlsm.

HELD, KEVIN; Pleasant Valley HS; Kunkeltown, PA; (3); Yrbk Ed-Chief; Yrbk Phtg; Yrbk Rptr; Yrbk Sprt Ed; Yrbk Stf; Capt Golf.

HELFENSTEIN, MARY; Monongahela Valley Catholic HS; Donora, PA; (3); 4/100; Dance Clb; Teachers Aide; Church Choir; French Hon Soc; Hon Roll; NHS; 1st Frnch Cmpstn 87; Concours Natl De Francais Cert De Merit 87; Engl.

HELFRICH, MICHAEL; West York Area HS; York, PA; (3); 4/186; Var Boy Scts; Var German Clb; Var Spanish Clb; Hst Soph Cls; Var Stat Bsktbl; JV Golf; Im Socr; Im Wt Lftg; High Hon Roll; Hon Roll; HOBY Fndtn 86; Freedom Fndtn Geo Wshngtn Hnr Mdl 85; 3 Schlrshps-AFL-CIO Essy Cntsts 84-86; Archeolgy.

HELIG, SCOTT; Central HS; Philadelphia, PA; (2); Jrnlsm.

HELIGER, MATTHEW; Oley Valley HS; Oley, PA; (3); 62/142; Chess Clb; Church Yth Grp; Varsity Clb; Var JV Bsbl; Var Bsktbl; JV Socr; Hon Roll.

HELLER, ALISA; Danville SR HS; Riverside, PA; (3); 27/187; Spanish Clb; Band; Concert Band; Mrchg Band; School Play; JV Fld Hcky; High Hon Roll; NHS.

HELLER, CHRISTOPHER; Eastern York HS; York, PA; (2); Trk; High Hon Roll; Hon Roll; Jr NHS; Pres Schlr; Bio.

HELLER, HEIDI; Delaware Valley HS; Milford, PA; (3); 33/145; SADD; Trs Frsh Cls; Trs Soph Cls; Stu Cncl; Stat Bsktbl; JV Fld Hcky; Var Gym; Var Mgr(s); Var Sftbl; Scrtrl.

HELLER, JUDY; Slippery Rock Area HS; Portersville, PA; (4); 64/172; Pep Clb; Concert Band; Mrchg Band; Stat Bsktbl; Im Powder Puff Ftbl; Hon Roll; Natl Travel Schl; Travel.

HELLER, KIM; Tulpehocken HS; Bernville, PA; (2); Drama Clb; Spanish Clb; Tennis; High Hon Roll; Hon Roll; Pres Phys Fit Awd 86; 3rd Pl Frgn Lang Comptn 87; Girls Tnns Cert Awd 85-86; Bus Mgmt.

HELLER, LESLEY; Bald Eagle Nittany HS; Mill Hall, PA; (3); 31/148; Computer Clb; Spanish Clb; SADD; Bald Eagle Nittany Peace Prz 85; Fash Dsgn.

HELLER, LUKE; Nativity BVM HS; Pottsville, PA; (3); 17/86; Chess Clb; Cmnty Wkr; Computer Clb; Nwsp Rptr; Trk; Wt Lftg; Hon Roll; Dickinson Coll; Law.

HELLER, VICKY; Freeland HS; Freeland, PA; (4); 12/86; Church Yth Grp; VP FBLA; Yrbk Stf; Var Capt Bsktbl; Var L Sftbl; Elks Awd; High Hon Roll; NHS; Mansfield U; Comp Sci.

HELM, JODI; Elizabethtown Area HS; Elizabethtown, PA; (3); 48/260; Hosp Aide; Teachers Aide; Band; Chorus; Color Guard; Mrchg Band; Fld Hcky; Vllybl; Med.

HELM, LORI; Waynesboro Area SR HS; Waynesboro, PA; (3); Church Yth Grp; French Clb; Ski Clb; Chorus; Church Choir; School Play; Stage Crew; Hon Roll; PA ST U; Flm Cmnctns.

HELMAN, DAVID; Mount Calvary Christian Schl; Palmyra, PA; (4); 2/17; Camera Clb; School Play; Yrbk Phtg; Rep Frsh Cls; Rep Stu Cncl; Var Bsbl; Var Bsktbl; Var Socr; Cit Awd; Hon Roll; Bob Jones U; Finance.

HELMAN, VALERIE; Seneca Valley SR HS; Zelienople, PA; (3); Church Yth Grp; Cmnty Wkr; Girl Scts; Stage Crew; God Cntry Awd; High Hon Roll; Hon Roll; Prfct Atten Awd; Pep Clb; Ntl Acad Games Champs Trphs 85-87; ST Acad Games Champs Trphs 85-87; Frnsc Pathlgy.

HELMICK, KATHLEEN; Beaver Area JR-SR HS; Beaver, PA; (3); Pep Clb; High Hon Roll; Hon Roll; Int Dcrtng.

HELMICK, LORI; Laurel Highlands HS; Brownfield, PA; (3); 13/500; Trs FBLA; High Hon Roll; NHS; Acctng.

HELMON, AMY; Windber Area HS; Windber, PA; (3); Church Yth Grp; Math Clb; Pep Clb; SADD; Chorus; Capt Cheerleading; L Trk; Hon Roll; Stu Of Mnth 86 & 87; Psych.

HELMUTH, HEATHER; Calvary Baptist Christian Schl; Lancaster, PA; (4); Church Yth Grp; Pep Clb; Band; Chorus; Concert Band; School Play; Yrbk Stf; Capt Bsktbl; Var Sftbl; Capt Vllybl; Wheaton Coll; Phy Thrpy.

HELOCK, ANDREA R; West Halzeton JR-SR HS; Sheppton, PA; (2); French Clb; Chorus; Color Guard; High Hon Roll; Hon Roll; Tri-High Chrs 86-87; Vet.

HELON, DAVID; North Hills HS; Pittsburgh, PA; (3); 11/490; Var Bsbl; Var L Ftbl; High Hon Roll; NHS; Sci.

HELSEL, BRIAN; Claysburg-Kimmel HS; E Freedom, PA; (2); 7/110; JV Var Bsbl; JV Var Ftbl; Tennis; Vllybl; Wt Lftg; Wrstlng; High Hon Roll; U Of Pittsburgh; Nuclr Phy.

HELSEL, MIKE; West Branch HS; Philipsburg, PA; (3); 40/125; Letterman Clb; Scholastic Bowl; Varsity Clb; Var L Bsbl; Var L Ftbl; Var L Wt Lftg; Var L Wrstlng; Penn ST U; Cvl Engrng.

HELSEL, RONALD; Hollidaysburg SR HS; Duncansville, PA; (3); Letterman Clb; Varsity Clb; Var Capt Bsbl; Ftbl; Swmmng; Wt Lftg; Hon Roll; Tiger Trphy Lttrmns Coat Cptn Bsbl MVP Trphy 87; Sprtsmnshp Awd Ltr Swmng 85-86; Coaches Awd 85-86; WV Coll; Bus Mgmt.

HELTERBRAN, TRACEY; Ambridge Area HS; Baden, PA; (4); 35/265; Red Cross Aide; Spanish Clb; Band; Concert Band; Mrchg Band; Off Soph Cls; Off Jr Cls; Off Sr Cls; Hon Roll; NHS; Wolvs Clb Achvt Awd Outstndng Secr Stu 87; Bradford Schl; Secr.

HELTZEL, TONYA; Hanover HS; Hanover, PA; (3); 4/206; Church Yth Grp; Chorus; Church Choir; School Musical; Swing Chorus; Nwsp Rptr; Var L Vllybl; High Hon Roll; NHS; Ntl Merit Ltr; Acadc Hnrs-Schltc Achvt 84-87; Engrng.

HELVESTON, DANA; Upper Moreland HS; Willow Grove, PA; (2); 6/254; SADD; Chorus; Orch; School Musical; JV Cheerleading; JV Socr; Swmmng; High Hon Roll; NHS; Penn ST; Bio.

HELZLSOUER, TIM; West Mifflin Area HS; West Mifflin, PA; (3); 46/312; Concert Band; Jazz Band; Mrchg Band; Ftbl; High Hon Roll; Hon Roll; Jr NHS; NHS; Penn ST; Chem.

HEMBURY, LYNN; Sullivan County HS; Dushore, PA; (4); 6/85; Church Yth Grp; Pres VP 4-H; FBLA; Scholastic Bowl; Band; Concert Band; Jazz Band; Mrchg Band; Yrbk Stf; VP Frsh Cls; Pres Acad Ftnss Awd 87; Bridgewater Coll; Bus Admin.

HEMING, KELLI; United HS; Robinson, PA; (4); Var L Bsktbl; Powder Puff Ftbl; Var L Sftbl; Var L Vllybl; Hon Roll; U Of Pittsburgh-Johnstwn; Educ.

HEMINGWAY JR, DAVID C; Coatesville Area Schl District; Downingtown, PA; (4); 3/470; Yrbk Ed-Chief; Yrbk Sprt Ed; Var Capt Crs Cntry; Var Capt Wrstlng; Cit Awd; NHS; NEDT Awd; JA; Chorus; Frsh Cls; Pres Scholar U DE 87-90; Robert C Byrd Hnr Scholar 87; Cls 1936 Mem Scholar 87; Schlr Ath Awd 87; U DE; Elect Engrng.

HEMLOCK, MELISSA; Bishop O Hara HS; Peckville, PA; (2); 13/127; Latin Clb; Spanish Clb; Cheerleading; Med.

HEMMA, CHRISTI; Shaler Area SR HS; Glenshaw, PA; (3); 104/486; Camp Fr Inc; Dance Clb; Pep Clb; SADD; Chorus; Flag Corp; School Musical; Yrbk Stf; Vllybl; Hon Roll; Secy.

HEMMINGER, CRAIG; West Middlesex HS; Pulaski, PA; (2); Spanish Clb; High Hon Roll; Hon Roll; Jr NHS; NHS; Prfct Atten Awd; Pres Acdmc Ftns Awd 85-86; Accntnt.

HEMMINGS, NICOLE; Mon Vly Catholic HS; Monongahela, PA; (2); Spanish Clb; Color Guard; Drill Tm; Flag Corp; Mrchg Band; VP Frsh Cls; Rep Soph Cls; Spanish NHS; Natl Sci Olympiad 86-87; Penn ST U; Accntng.

HEMSTREET, REBECCA; Northwestern HS; Albion, PA; (2); #20 In Class; Hon Roll; Vet Med.

HENCK, WENDY; Altoona Area HS; Altoona, PA; (3); Computer Clb; Drama Clb; Key Clb; Ski Clb; Spanish Clb; Speech Tm; Chorus; School Play; Stage Crew; Mgr(s); IUP; Med Tech.

HENDERSHOT, SHARON; Southern Fulton HS; Warfordsburg, PA; (3); Church Yth Grp; FBLA; FHA; Chorus; Church Choir; Hon Roll; LDS Coll; Fshn Mrchndsng.

HENDERSHOTT, MIKE; Greencastle HS; Greencastle, PA; (3); 33/180; Letterman Clb; Varsity Clb; Var L Bsktbl; Coach Actv; Wt Lftg; Hon Roll; Comp Sci.

HENDERSON, CARRIE; Hershey HS; Hershey, PA; (4); 70/187; Church Yth Grp; Cmnty Wkr; Exploring; Model UN; Service Clb; Ski Clb; Spanish Clb; Teachers Aide; Band; Chorus; Amer Assn U Womn Schlrshp 87; Intl Ordr Jobs Dghtrs Schlrshp 87; Penn ST; Psychtrc Nrsg.

HENDERSON, CELENE; Simon Coratz HS; Philadelphia, PA; (4); 13/385; Church Yth Grp; Hosp Aide; Office Aide; Nwsp Rptr; Yrbk Ed-Chief; Trs Jr Cls; Rep Sr Cls; Trs Stu Cncl; Cit Awd; Prfct Atten Awd; Pedtrcn.

HENDERSON, DAN; St John Neumann HS; Philadelphia, PA; (3); 10/349; Church Yth Grp; Cmnty Wkr; Im Ftbl; High Hon Roll; Jr NHS; NHS; Med.

HENDERSON, DAWN; Ridley SR HS; Woodlyn, PA; (4); 68/407; Church Yth Grp; JV Var Lcrss; Hon Roll; Pres Schlr; Gym Mjr Pgm At Ridley; Eastern Coll; Hlth Sci.

HENDERSON, ERIN; Meadville Area HS; Meadville, PA; (4); Church Yth Grp; Drama Clb; SADD; Varsity Clb; Nwsp Phtg; Nwsp Rptr; JV Var Socr; JV Var Wrstlng; Hon Roll; Gannon U; Optmtry.

HENDERSON, HEATHER; Churchill HS; Braddock, PA; (2); 68/222; Pres Scholastic Bowl; Chorus; Lit Mag; Stu Cncl; Mgr(s); U Of PA Pittsburgh; Med.

HENDERSON, KRISTI; Trinity HS; Washington, PA; (4); 11/322; Church Yth Grp; Key Clb; Pep Clb; High Hon Roll; Kiwanis Awd; NHS; Stu Cncl Awd 87; Case Western Reserve; CPA.

HENDERSON, KRISTY; Beaver Area SR HS; Beaver, PA; (3); German Clb; Key Clb; Pep Clb; Powder Puff Ftbl; Hon Roll; Elem Teaching.

HENDERSON, MARK P; Middletown Area HS; Middletown, PA; (3); Am Leg Boys St; FCA; Model UN; Political Wkr; Chorus; Mrchg Band; School Musical; Swing Chorus; Yrbk Stf; Boy Scts; Egl Sct; Duquesne U; Pol Sci.

HENDERSON, MEGAN; Bishop Newmann HS; Montoursville, PA; (3); Cmnty Wkr; 4-H; FBLA; Hosp Aide; SADD; Chorus; Variety Show; Var L Bsktbl; 4-H Awd; Hon Roll; CPR Adv Life Sppt 85-86; Health Svcs.

HENDERSON, MICHAEL; Bangor Area SR HS; Bangor, PA; (3); Chess Clb; French Clb; Off Sr Cls; Im Bsbl; Im Bsktbl; JV Var Ftbl; Swmmng; Lincoln Tech; Engr.

HENDERSON, RHONDA; Academy HS; Erie, PA; (3); 31/226; Church Yth Grp; Drama Clb; JA; Pep Clb; Acpl Chr; Chorus; Church Choir; Swing Chorus; Variety Show; Off Jr Cls; Dist & Rgnl Ii Chrs 85-87; PA ST U.

HENDERSON, RICHARD; Valley Forge Military Acad; Roswell, GA; (3); Boy Scts; Debate Tm; French Clb; FBLA; Soroptimist; ROTC; Nwsp Stf; L Swmmng; God Cntry Awd; Stu Anthony Wayne Lgn Grd Mltry Hnr Effncy Awd 86; Law.

HENDERSON, ROSALYN; Oxford Area HS; Oxford, PA; (3); 26/174; FBLA; Pep Clb; SADD; Chorus; Yrbk Stf; Pres Stu Cncl; JV Var Bsktbl; Hon Roll; NHS; Brnz Mlt Fo Ldrshp 87; Fhsn Dsgn.

HENDERSON, SCOTT; Indiana Wesleyen Schl; Aultman, PA; (4); Aud/Vis; French Clb; Chorus; School Play; Yrbk Ed-Chief; Yrbk Phtg; Yrbk Stf; High Hon Roll; Hon Roll; Pres Acadmc Ftns Awd 86-87; Radlgic Tech.

HENDERSON, TINA; Western Beaver HS; Industry, PA; (3); Chorus; Yrbk Ed-Chief; Yrbk Stf; Trs Jr Cls; JV Capt Bowling; JV Var Cheerleading; Trk; Hon Roll; NHS; Mth.

HENDRICKS, SHAWN D; Pine Grove HS; Pine Grove, PA; (3); Am Leg Boys St; Boy Scts; ROTC; Var Ftbl; Var Wrstlng; God Cntry Awd; God & Family 80; Jet Eng Tech.

HENDRICKSON, BARRY; Danville SR HS; Danville, PA; (2); Band; Concert Band; Jazz Band; Mrchg Band; Pep Band; Pres Acad Ftnss Awd 86; Musician.

HENDRICKSON, CHRISTOPHER; Danville HS; Danville, PA; (3); Cmnty Wkr; Spanish Clb; Nwsp Sprt Ed; Nwsp Stf; Yrbk Stf; VP Jr Cls; Bsbl; Bsktbl; Ftbl; Chsn To Attnd PA St Police Acad 87; Crmnlgy.

HENDRICKSON, MICHAEL; Oxford Area HS; Oxford, PA; (3); VICA; Var Wrstlng; Hon Roll; Elect Engrng.

HENDRICKSON, TRACEY; Avon Grove HS; Nottingham, PA; (3); Red Cross Aide; SADD; Temple Yth Grp; Band; Concert Band; School Musical; Hst Frsh Cls; Rep Stu Cncl; Var Capt Cheerleading; Mgr(s); Amer Music Abroad 87; Slippery Rock; Phy Therapy.

HENERY, KAYE D; Towanda HS; Towanda, PA; (4); Art Clb; Drama Clb; English Clb; French Clb; Model UN; Thesps; School Play; French Hon Soc; Gov Hon Prg Awd; NHS; PA Govs Schl For Arts, Crtv Wrtng 85; Pinhas & Davidson Lit Awd 87; Arts Stu 87; Reed Coll.

HENES, BRIAN; Father Judge HS; Philadelphia, PA; (4); 15/353; Church Yth Grp; Debate Tm; Hosp Aide; NFL; School Play; Ed Nwsp Stf; JV Bowling; Lion Awd; NHS; Pres Schlr; APA Trnsprt Schlrshp, U Scrantn Pres Schlrshp, De Sales Schlrshp Allentown Coll 87; U Of Scranton; Poltcl Sci.

HENGELSBERG, MICHAEL; Hampton HS; Allison Pk, PA; (3); Drama Clb; Exploring; Acpl Chr; Band; Chorus; Church Choir; Jazz Band; Madrigals; School Musical; Variety Show; Allegeheny Coll; Optmtry.

HENGEN, ROBERT SCOTT; York Suburban SR HS; York, PA; (4); Church Yth Grp; Drama Clb; SADD; Thesps; School Musical; School Play; Mgr Stage Crew; Nwsp Phtg; Mgr Ftbl; Socr; Fulton Opera House Lancaster PA Outstndng Cher Creation 86-87; U Of Sthrn CA; B A Drama.

HENGST, KELLY; Chestnut Ridge SR HS; New Paris, PA; (4); 23/139; Church Yth Grp; GAA; Band; Concert Band; Drm Mjr(t); Mrchg Band; Variety Show; Var Capt Bsktbl; Var Capt Vllybl; Hon Roll; Miss Offense-Vllybll 87; Mvp Ldng Scorer-Bsktbl 87; Center Specialist-Vllybll 86; Best Offense-Sftbll; Conemaugh Vly Mem Hosp; Nurse.

HENGST, TINA; Greenwood HS; Millerstown, PA; (4); VP Church Yth Grp; Sec Chorus; School Play; Yrbk Bus Mgr; Var Capt Cheerleading; Cit Awd; Hon Roll; VFW Awd; Art.

HENISE, MARK; Eastern York HS; York, PA; (3); 7/150; Church Yth Grp; Nwsp Bus Mgr; Var L Socr; Var Trk; High Hon Roll; Jr NHS; NHS; Hnr Roll 84-87; Natl Hnr Soc & Vrsty Soccer Let 86-87; Math.

HENKE, KRISTIN; Bradford Area HS; Bradford, PA; (4); 26/276; AFS; Pep Clb; School Play; Ed Nwsp Stf; Var Capt Cheerleading; Hon Roll; VP Jr NHS; Erly Chld Ed.

HENKEL, CHRISTINE; Butler SR HS; Butler, PA; (3); Church Yth Grp; Cmnty Wkr; French Clb; Library Aide; Mrchg Band; Orch; Symp Band; Var L Swmmng; Hon Roll; Jr NHS; Acadc Achvt Awd 87; Mssnry.

HENKEL, DAVID W; Mt Pleasant Area HS; Mt Pleasant, PA; (4); Chess Clb; Band; Concert Band; Mrchg Band; Im Bsktbl; Stat Timer; Im Vllybl; Hon Roll; Prfct Atten Awd; 3rd Pl-Engl Wrtng, Humnts Day & Pttsbrgh Prss Ntl Stck Mrkt Game; Shippensburg U; Psychlgy.

HENKEL, SCOTT; Mount Pleasant Area SR HS; Mt Pleasant, PA; (2); 27/275; Debate Tm; Pres German Clb; Latin Clb; Science Clb; SADD; Band; Wt Lftg; High Hon Roll; Hon Roll; Pres Schlr; U Of Pitts-Grnsbrg-1st Pl Awd-Debate Tm 85; 1st Pl Grmn Poetry Rctl-Hmanties Day-HS 85; U Of Pittsburgh; Engrng.

HENNE, TERRANCE; Shaler Area HS; Pittsburgh, PA; (3); 20/490; French Clb; Var L Bsbl; JV Bsktbl; Var L Ftbl; French Hon Soc; High Hon Roll; Hon Roll; NHS; Pre-Law.

HENNEGAN, BERNADETTE A; Cheltenham HS; Cheltenham, PA; (3); Church Yth Grp; JV Bsktbl; JV Var Fld Hcky; JV Sftbl; Bus Educ Stdnt Of Mnth For Typng I 86; Acntng.

HENNESSEY, GERELLA; Bishop Guilfoyle HS; Hollidaysburg, PA; (3); Church Yth Grp; Spanish Clb; Hon Roll; Secy Chch Yth Grp 85-86; Pres Chch Yth Grp 86-87; Hm Art Schlrshp Art Inst Schls 85-86; Penn ST U; Jrnlsm.

HENNESSEY, MEGAN; Conestoga SR HS; Malvern, PA; (3); VP AFS; Cmnty Wkr; Hosp Aide; Spanish Clb; SADD; Tennis; Public Svc Paoli Memrl Hosp 87; Tnns Recognition Awd 85-86; St Marys Coll; Nrsng.

HENNESSY, LISA; North Catholic HS; Pgh, PA; (3); Church Yth Grp; Cmnty Wkr; Library Aide; Ski Clb; Spanish Clb; Nwsp Rptr; Nwsp Stf; Rep Stu Cncl; JV Cheerleading; Hosp Aide; Natl Sci Testing; Sociology.

HENNIGAN, PATRICIA; Wyoming Area HS; Exeter, PA; (3); Art Clb; Aud/Vis; Drama Clb; French Clb; Key Clb; Chorus; School Musical; School Play; Trs Jr Cls; Trs Sr Cls; Pre-Elem Ed.

HENNIGER, JASON; Tyrone Area HS; Tyrone, PA; (3); 4/194; Boy Scts; Key Clb; Latin Clb; Science Clb; Speech Tm; Band; Concert Band; Mrchg Band; Yrbk Stf; Rep Stu Cncl.

HENNING, JAMES; Tunkhannock Area HS; Mehoopany, PA; (2); #4 In Class; Church Yth Grp; German Clb; Latin Clb; Band; Concert Band; Mrchg Band; Pep Band; School Musical; Cit Awd; Hon Roll; Psych.

HENNING, KATIE; Turkhannock Area HS; Laceyville, PA; (3); 48/350; Key Clb; Band; Concert Band; Mrchg Band; School Musical; JV Bsktbl; Hon Roll; Medcl Technlgy.

HENNING, LISA; General Mc Lane HS; Edinboro, PA; (4); Drama Clb; Model UN; Teachers Aide; Band; Concert Band; Jazz Band; Mrchg Band; Lit Mag; Edinboro U Of PA; Elem Ed.

HENNINGER, DION; William Allen HS; Allentown, PA; (3); Computer Clb; Exploring; Chorus; Penn ST; Chem.

HENNINGER, SHERI; Upper Dauphin Area HS; Elizabethville, PA; (4); 4/102; Sec Church Yth Grp; Varsity Clb; Chorus; Yrbk Stf; Sec Sr Cls; Var JV Bsktbl; Var Capt Sftbl; Hon Roll; Sec NHS; Prfct Atten Awd; John Hall Schlrshp 87; Presdntl Acad Fit Awd 87; Glen Chaptr Order Of Eastern Star Awd 87; Juniata Coll; Elem Educ.

HENNINGER, THAD E; Huntingdon Area HS; Petersburg, PA; (4); 11/234; Am Leg Boys St; Key Clb; Band; Concert Band; Yrbk Sprt Ed; L Var Ftbl; L Trk; High Hon Roll; NHS; Pres Schlr; Life Sct 85; Ordr Arrw Brthrhd 83; Penn ST U; Engrng.

HENNINGS, LISA; Pocono Mountain SR HS; Reeders, PA; (3); 24/330; Office Aide; Band; Concert Band; Drm Mjr(t); Mrchg Band; Stage Crew; Powder Puff Ftbl; Trk; Hon Roll; Ntl Olympia Typg Awd 86-87; US Navy; Med Sec.

HENNON, LEANNE; Lincoln HS; Ellwood City, PA; (3); 76/162; Sec Church Yth Grp; Spanish Clb; Y-Teens; Band; Concert Band; Mrchg Band; Powder Puff Ftbl; Hon Roll; Med.

HENNON, MELINDA; West Allegheny HS; Oakdale, PA; (3); 19/195; Church Yth Grp; Chorus; VP Frsh Cls; Pres Jr Cls; Capt Cheerleading; Diving; Co-Capt Sftbl; High Hon Roll; Jr NHS; WPIAL Diving Champ 6th Pl 87; MAC Diving Comptn 2nd Pl 87; Busch Gardens Choral Fest 1st Pl 87.

HENOFER, MATTHEW J; Central HS; Philadelphia, PA; (3); Hon Roll; Masonic Awd; Med.

HENRICHSEN, PAUL; Methacton HS; Norristown, PA; (3); 40/389; Boy Scts; Pres Sec Church Yth Grp; Exploring; Math Tm; Office Aide; Church Choir; Nwsp Ed-Chief; High Hon Roll; Hon Roll; NHS; Fnlst PA Govrnrs Schl Arts 87; Montgomery Cnty Mathmtclly Precocious Yth Pgm 84-86; Brighm Young U; Aerospc Indstry.

HENRIQUES, AMY; Central Bucks West HS; Warrington, PA; (3); 180/420; SADD; Pres Temple Yth Grp; Chorus; Yrbk Stf; Capt L Cheerleading; Mgr(s); Swmmng; Hon Roll; Prfct Atten Awd; Stu Govt Orgnztn 86; Amer Allnce Hlth, Phys Ed & Dnce 85; IN U Of PA; Fshn Merch.

HENRY, AMY; Boiling Springs HS; Boiling Spgs, PA; (2); Church Yth Grp; Band; Trs Soph Cls; Var Bsktbl; Var Fld Hcky; Wrestling Ct 86-87.

HENRY, BRENTON; Redbank Valley HS; New Bethlehem, PA; (4); 15/140; Church Yth Grp; 4-H; VP FFA; JV Bsktbl; 4-H Awd; Gov Hon Prg Awd; Hon Roll; FFA Keystone Frmrs Degree 87; Hnr Scty 86-87; Alfred ST Coll; Anml Husbandry.

HENRY, DAVID; Indiana Area HS; Indiana, PA; (3); JA; Math Tm; Scholastic Bowl; Spanish Clb; Speech Tm; Acpl Chr; Chorus; Rep Stu Cncl; High Hon Roll; NHS; Acdmc Lttr 85-86; Accntng.

HENRY, DEBBIE; Tyrone Area HS; Tyrone, PA; (4); Church Yth Grp; Latin Clb; VP SADD; Band; Chorus; Concert Band; Mrchg Band; School Musical; Var Twrlr; Hon Roll; Atlntc Coast Conf Chmpns-Mjrtte 82-86; Miss Laurel Hghlnds 87; PA ST Chmpns-Mjrtte 84-85.

HENRY, DON; Philipsburg-Osceola Area HS; Osceola Mills, PA; (3); 12/243; VP Pres Church Yth Grp; Thesps; Acpl Chr; Chorus; Church Choir; Mrchg Band; Hon Roll; NHS; Art Clb; Dist Vand 87; Clarion U; Music Education.

HENRY, DOUGLAS; North Star HS; Jennerstown, PA; (4); 16/136; FCA; Sec Trs Mu Alpha Theta; Varsity Clb; Concert Band; School Play; Yrbk Stf; Var L Bsbl; Var L Bsktbl; Var L Ftbl; BSA Crtfct Mrt 79; Cvl Engr.

HENRY, EDWARD; Shenango HS; New Castle, PA; (3); Church Yth Grp; Band; Concert Band; Mrchg Band; Pep Band; Hon Roll; Art.

HENRY, ERIC; Fleetwood Area HS; Fleetwood, PA; (3); 6/112; Bsbl; Bsktbl; Golf; Socr; Tennis; Vllybl; High Hon Roll; Hon Roll; NHS; Sls Mgr.

HENRY, GLORY; Garden Spot HS; New Holland, PA; (2); 83/226; German Clb; Chorus; Mrchg Band; Orch; School Play; Rep Stu Cncl; Var Crs Cntry; JV Sftbl; L Var Trk; Hon Roll; Dntl.

HENRY, GRACE; Waynesboro Area SR HS; Waynesboro, PA; (4); Art Clb; Intnl Clb; Chorus; Concert Band; Mrchg Band; School Musical; Swing Chorus; Var Crs Cntry; Var Trk; Hon Roll; Prsdntl Acad Ftns Awd 87; Instrmntl Mgzn Mscnshp Awd 87; Cnty Bnd & Cnty Chorus 87; Syracuse U; Sci.

HENRY, JANET LYNN; Lampeter-Strasburg HS; Willow Street, PA; (3); 36/145; Church Yth Grp; SADD; Church Choir; Stage Crew; Rep Jr Cls; JV Fld Hcky; JV Sftbl; Hon Roll; Yth Southrn Bapt ST Bibl Drll Wnnr 85; New Prov Bapt Chrch Acteens Qn 85; Nrsg.

HENRY, JEAN; Chartiers Valley HS; Pittsburgh, PA; (4); 26/297; Civic Clb; Ski Clb; Drill Tm; School Musical; Stu Cncl; Sftbl; NHS; Robert C Byrd Schlrshp 87-88; Pres Acad Ftnss Awd 87; Washington/Jefferson Coll; Dntl.

HENRY, JEREMY; Roman Catholic HS; Philadelphia, PA; (3); Art Clb; Teachers Aide; Y-Teens; Temple U; Bus.

HENRY, JOHN S; Mt Penn HS; Mt Penn, PA; (4); 6/64; Trs Model UN; Scholastic Bowl; Varsity Clb; Variety Show; Bsktbl; Co-Capt Socr; Trs Spanish Clb; Yrbk Phtg; VP Sr Cls; Pres Stu Cncl; Air Force ROTC Schlrshp Up To $7000 87-91; Male SR Athlt Of Yr 84; US Army Rsrv Natl Schlr Awd 87; Penn ST U; Engr.

HENRY, JOYCE; Comellsville Area SR HS; White, PA; (3); 75/550; Art Clb; VP Church Yth Grp; Exploring; Hosp Aide; Teachers Aide; Hon Roll; PA ST Sndy Schl Assoc Poster Cont; 1st Pl Cnty Wnnr 84,1st Pl ST Wnnr 84,2(d Pl 85,1st Pl ST 86; Med Lab Tech.

HENRY, KEVIN; Solanco HS; Nottingham, PA; (3); Pres Church Yth Grp; CAP; JA; SADD; Band; Church Choir; Im VP Socr; High Hon Roll; Hon Roll; Wt Lftg; Phrmclgy.

HENRY, KIERA; Bensalem HS; Andalusia, PA; (2); Spanish Clb; SADD; Church Choir; Orch; JV Jr Cls; JV L Bsktbl; JV L Fld Hcky; Var L Trk; Hon Roll; PA Sub Hnrb Mntn Trk Tm 87; 1st Pl Frgn Lang Forn Tourn Spn Intermed 87; Harvard Med Schl; Plstc Srgry.

HENRY, KIMBERLY; Connellsville SR HS; Connellsville, PA; (2); Red Cross Aide; Hon Roll; Psychlgy.

HENRY, LISA; Newport HS; Newport, PA; (4); 23/89; FBLA; Sec FTA; Sec Office Aide; Teachers Aide; Temple Yth Grp; Color Guard; Yrbk Stf; Hon Roll; Bnk Tllr.

HENRY, MELINDA; Harmony HS; Cherry Tree, PA; (4); 7/50; Pres Church Yth Grp; Office Aide; VP Ski Clb; Band; Chorus; Concert Band; Sec Stu Cncl; Co-Capt Cheerleading; Var Sftbl; High Hon Roll; Outstndng Chrldr 87; Mst Imprvd Plyr 87; IN U Of PA.

HENRY, MICHAEL; Rockwood Area HS; Rockwood, PA; (4); Church Yth Grp; Band; Chorus; Concert Band; Mrchg Band; School Play; JV Var Bsktbl; Capt Var Golf; Var Trk; Dnfth Awd; WVU; Engnrng.

HENRY, PAM; Abington Hts HS; Clarks Summit, PA; (3); Band; Trs Soph Cls; JV Bsktbl; Var L Crs Cntry; Var L Trk; Hon Roll; Crss Cntry Coaches Awd & Dedicated Rnnr Trophy 86; Cum Laude Awd 84.

HENRY, PATTI; Shenango HS; New Castle, PA; (4); 10/112; Office Aide; Co-Capt Cheerleading; Stat Gym; Hon Roll; VP NHS; Bus Adm.

HENRY, REBECCA; Cumberland Valley HS; Carlisle, PA; (3); Pres Church Yth Grp; Chorus; Church Choir; Variety Show; High Hon Roll; Hon Roll; Swimmers Aide; Interprative Dance For Schl Concrt; Studied With Royal Danish Ballett; Ballet.

HENRY, RHONDA; Union HS; Rimersburg, PA; (3); 4/104; Art Clb; Library Aide; Pep Clb; SADD; Band; Color Guard; Mrchg Band; High Hon Roll; Hon Roll; Secrtry.

HENRY, SHARON; Juniata HS; Honey Grove, PA; (4); 1/142; VP Church Yth Grp; Varsity Clb; Cit Awd; DAR Awd; High Hon Roll; NCTE Awd; Pres NHS; Pres Schlr; Val; Band; Fld Hockey,Bsktbl & Sftbl Tri-Vly Leag All STAR 85-87; Outstndg Athl Awd 86-87; Otstndg Sci Stu 86-87; US Naval Acad; Ocngrphy.

HENRY, SHAWN; Fort Le Boeuf HS; Erie, PA; (3); Boy Scts; Band; Concert Band; Jazz Band; Mrchg Band; Pep Band; High Hon Roll; Prfct Atten Awd.

HENRY, STACY ANN; Central Cambria HS; Ebensburg, PA; (2); Ski Clb; Chorus; VP Jr Cls; Off Stu Cncl; Cheerleading; High Hon Roll; Pharmacy.

HENRY, STEPHEN; Charleroi JR SR HS; Charleroi, PA; (4); 10/165; Church Yth Grp; Science Clb; Ski Clb; Varsity Clb; Rep Stu Cncl; Var Ftbl; Var Trk; Hon Roll; Lion Awd; NHS; PA ST; Arch.

HENRY, TAMMY R; Calvary Christian Acad; Mill Creek, PA; (3); 1/11; Church Yth Grp; Political Wkr; Chorus; Yrbk Bus Mgr; Var Bsktbl; Var Cheerleading; Cit Awd; High Hon Roll; Voice Dem Awd; Sprtsmnshp Awd-Bsktbl 85-86.

HENRY, TIFFANY; Purchase Line HS; Clymer, PA; (3); #2 In Class; Church Yth Grp; SADD; Chorus; Nwsp Ed-Chief; High Hon Roll; NHS; Law.

HENRY, TRACI; Schuylkill Haven; Sch Haven, PA; (3); Church Yth Grp; Pep Clb; Science Clb; SADD; Teachers Aide; Mrchg Band; Im Bsktbl; Var Capt Cheerleading; JV Mgr(s); JV Sftbl; York Coll; Law Enfrcmt.

HENSCHEN, SHANE; Rennard-Dale HS; Stewartstown, PA; (3); 31/167; German Clb; Ski Clb; Varsity Clb; JV Bsbl; Var Bsktbl; Var Socr; Hon Roll; Intllgnc Anlyztn.

HENSEL, SUZANNE; Mars Area HS; Mars, PA; (4); French Clb; Varsity Clb; Stu Cncl; Bsktbl; Var Trk; Var Vllybl; High Hon Roll; Pres NHS; Mst Outstndng Trck Awd 87; Cincinnati U; Arch.

HENSEL, TAMMY; Connellsville Area SR HS; Mill Run, PA; (4); 63/520; Art Clb; Dance Clb; Model UN; Band; School Play; Stage Crew; Nwsp Stf; Hon Roll; Prfct Atten Awd; Penn ST; Nrsng.

HEOVIK, DARCEY E; Radnor HS; Wayne, PA; (4); 27/300; Church Yth Grp; Pres Drama Clb; Chorus; Church Choir; School Musical; School Play; Stage Crew; High Hon Roll; NHS; 1st Pl Voice-Tri Cnty Concert Assoc Comp 86; All State Chorus 87; Wnnr Combs Coll H S Vocal Comp 85; IN U; Voice Perf.

HEPBURN, KIMBERLY; Montoursville HS; Cogan Station, PA; (3); 47/185; Hosp Aide; Spanish Clb; Var Pom Pon; Var Powder Puff Ftbl; Bloomsburg U; Medcl Tech.

HEPLER, JENNIFER; Wilmington Area HS; Volant, PA; (2); Hosp Aide; Yrbk Stf; High Hon Roll; Hon Roll; NHS; Law.

HEPLER, RENA; Keystone JR SR HS; Knox, PA; (3); 7/135; Pres French Clb; Model UN; Sec Pep Clb; Yrbk Sprt Ed; Rep Stu Cncl; Bsktbl; French Hon Soc; High Hon Roll; NHS; Med Tech.

HERB, NICOLE S; Shady Side Acad; Pittsburgh, PA; (4); 18/124; English Clb; Pres German Clb; Letterman Clb; Q&S; Ski Clb; SADD; Varsity Clb; Orch; Symp Band; Variety Show; Natl Wnnr Travel-Study Trip W Germny 86; Radcliffe Coll Natl Schlr 87; Cncrt Mistrss Pttsbgh Yth Symph; Harvard Coll; German.

HERBEIN, TARA; Souderton Area HS; Telford, PA; (4); AFS; Aud/Vis; Drama Clb; Intnl Clb; SADD; Nwsp Stf; Stu Cncl; Var Cheerleading; Var L Tennis; Var L Trk; Mark Knaefler Awd 87; Penn ST U; Math.

HERBER, BRIAN; Hamburg Area HS; Shoemakersville, PA; (4); 20/145; 4-H; Var JV Bsbl; High Hon Roll; Hon Roll; NHS; Lions Clb Of Hamburg Schlrshp & Zions UCC Schlrshp 87; Penn ST; Chem Engrng.

HERBERT, RANDY; Connellsville Area HS; Vanderbilt, PA; (2); PA ST; Crmnlgy.

HERBERT, ROBERTA; Shenango HS; New Castle, PA; (4); 24/111; Letterman Clb; Varsity Clb; Trs Frsh Cls; Trs Soph Cls; Trs Jr Cls; Trs Sr Cls; Stat Ftbl; Var Capt Gym; Var Sftbl; L Trk; Qualified For Dist For Gymnastics 83-87; Trinity Lutheran Schlrshp 87; Clarion U; Accntng.

HERBINKO, MIKE; Hazleton SR HS; Hazleton, PA; (2); 121/380; Boy Scts; Letterman Clb; Ftbl; Wt Lftg; Wrstlng; Hon Roll; USAF ROTC.

HERBRUCK, MATTHEW; Beaver Area HS; Beaver, PA; (3); Church Yth Grp; JCL; Latin Clb; Letterman Clb; Q&S; Nwsp Ed-Chief; Var L Crs Cntry; Var L Trk; Ntl Merit SF; Pltcl Sci.

HERBST, CHRIS; Central Bucks HS East; Doylestown, PA; (3); Chorus; Yrbk Stf; Bus.

HERBSTER, BILL; Linesville HS; Espyville, PA; (4); 13/91; Church Yth Grp; VP German Clb; Pep Clb; VP Ski Clb; Var L Bsbl; Bsktbl; JV Var Ftbl; Wt Lftg; High Hon Roll; Hon Roll; Hmcmg Kng 86-87; Ftbll MVP 86-87; Grove City Coll; Bus Mgmt.

HERBSTER, MATT; Kiski Area SR HS; Apollo, PA; (4); Church Yth Grp; Math Tm; Model UN; Pep Clb; SADD; Nwsp Ed-Chief; Nwsp Stf; Pres Soph Cls; Pres Jr Cls; JV Bsbl; Rotary Yth Ldrshp Awd 86; PA ST U; Comm.

HERBSTRITT, MATTHEW; Elk County Christian HS; St Marys, PA; (4); 5/77; Boy Scts; Intnl Clb; Varsity Clb; Jazz Band; Pres Soph Cls; Pres Jr Cls; Pres Sr Cls; Rep Stu Cncl; Ftbl; Cit Awd; CD Of A Ctznshp Awd; Capt Of Trck Tm; BSA Egl Awd; PA ST U; Indstrl Engrng.

HERCEG, KEN; Nazareth Area SR HS; Nazareth, PA; (3); 50/275; German Clb; Letterman Clb; JV Bsbl; Im Wt Lftg; Var Capt Wrstlng; Hon Roll; Orthpdcs.

HERCHKO, CLAUDIA; Connellsville HS; Dunbar, PA; (3); FBLA; Library Aide; Band; Chorus; Concert Band; Drm Mjr(t); Flag Corp; Mrchg Band; Pep Band; Symp Band; Bus.

HERLEMAN, MICHAEL B; Carlynton HS; Carnegie, PA; (4); 9/161; Rep Sr Cls; Var L Ftbl; Var L Trk; High Hon Roll; Hon Roll; Acadmc All Amer 85-86; Pres Acadmc Ftnss Awd 86-87; Aerospc Engr.

HERLEY, COLLEEN; East HS; West Cheseter, PA; (3); 19/429; Exploring; Hosp Aide; SADD; Jr Cls; Var Cheerleading; Hon Roll; Spanish NHS; Physcl Thrpy.

HERMAN, AMY; Dover Area HS; Dover, PA; (4); 5/234; Church Yth Grp; Dance Clb; Band; Chorus; Church Choir; Concert Band; Mrchg Band; School Musical; Yrbk Ed-Chief; Yrbk Stf; HOBY Ldrshp Awd 85; York Dispatch Acdmc All-Star, Acdmc Schlrshp Elizabethtown Coll 87; Elizabethtown Coll; Chem.

HERMAN, BRAD; Northeastern HS; Manchester, PA; (4); 5/167; Boy Scts; Exploring; Varsity Clb; Band; Chorus; Var Crs Cntry; Var Trk; God Cntry Awd; High Hon Roll; VP NHS; Nrtheastrn Educ Assn Schlrshp 87; Walter A Brunhouse Schlrshp 87; Penn ST U; Arch.

HERMAN, CAROL; Fort Le Boeuf HS; Erie, PA; (3); French Clb; Concert Band; Mrchg Band; Orch; Pep Band; School Musical; High Hon Roll; Hon Roll; Prfct Atten Awd; PA All-ST Lions Band 86; Erie Plyhs Orchstra 85-87; Erie Phlhrmnc Yth Orchstra 86; Vet.

HERMAN, CHRIS; Biglerville HS; Arendtsville, PA; (2); 29/117; Hon Roll; HACC; Firefghtng.

HERMAN, COREY; Shikellamy HS; Northumberland, PA; (4); 16/297; Drama Clb; English Clb; Key Clb; Aud/Vis; Speech Tm; School Musical; School Play; JV Bowling; NHS; Pres Schlr; Ntl Frnsc League Degree Dstnctn 87; PA Hghr Educ Assist Agncy Cert Of Merit 86; Penn St; Tlcmnctns.

HERMAN, DAVID; Southwestern HS; Hanover, PA; (2); Key Clb; Ski Clb; Nwsp Rptr; Nwsp Stf; Hst Frsh Cls; VP Jr Cls; VP Ftbl; JV Var Wrstlng; Hon Roll; Pres Schlr; Phy Thrpy.

HERMAN, DINA; Central Catholic HS; Whitehall, PA; (3); Hosp Aide; Spanish Clb; Cheerleading; Swmmng; Hon Roll; Volunteerng Awds 84 & 87; Nrs.

HERMAN, JEFF; Eastern York HS; York, PA; (3); 21/170; Church Yth Grp; Church Choir; Nwsp Bus Mgr; Nwsp Rptr; Var L Golf; Im Vllybl; High Hon Roll; Hon Roll; Voice Dem Awd.

HERMAN, JODIE; Middleburg Joint HS; Middleburg, PA; (3); Computer Clb; Ski Clb; Varsity Clb; Color Guard; Mrchg Band; Var JV Fld Hcky; Gym; Var Mgr(s); JV Var Sftbl; Yth Ftnss Achvt Awds 83-86; Williamsport Area CC; Mgmt.

HERMAN, JOE; Abington Hts North Campus HS; Clarks Summit, PA; (3); 30/300; Church Yth Grp; Var L Bsktbl; Var Trk; High Hon Roll; Hon Roll; NHS; Russian Awd Excell 87; Sci.

HERMAN, PAMELA L; North Hills SR HS; Glenshaw, PA; (4); AFS; Key Clb; Sec VP Temple Yth Grp; Yrbk Stf; Penn ST; Bus.

HERMAN, SUSAN; Milton HS; New Columbia, PA; (2); Church Yth Grp; German Clb; Sec Library Aide; Y-Teens; Band; Chorus; Concert Band; Mrchg Band; Nwsp Rptr; Stu Cncl; Educ.

HERMAN, TERESA; Canton Area HS; Roaring Branch, PA; (4); 15/120; Church Yth Grp; 4-H; Letterman Clb; Chorus; Concert Band; Mrchg Band; School Play; Pres Sr Cls; Stu Cncl; Cheerleading; Tioga Cnty Dairy Prin ST Fnlst 86; Tioga Cnty 4-H Schlrshp; Keystone Wnr 4-H; Wilkes Coll; Comm.

HERMAN, TONY; Northern HS; Dillsburg, PA; (3); 67/232; Art Clb; Rep Frsh Cls; Rep Soph Cls; JV Bsktbl; Im Vllybl; L Hon Roll; Drexel-MD; Mrktng.

HERMANN, CHAD; Wyomissing Area; Wyomissing, PA; (4); 2/102; Church Yth Grp; Model UN; Scholastic Bowl; Yrbk Sprt Ed; Lit Mag; Im Var Bsktbl; Ntl Merit Ltr; St Schlr; Cmnty Wkr; Dartmouth Bk Awd 86; Duquesne U; Jrnlsm.

HERMANN, JOHN; Fort Le Boeuf HS; Waterford, PA; (4); 1/162; Church Yth Grp; Rep Stu Cncl; Var Ftbl; Var Trk; Im Vllybl; Var Wrstlng; Cit Awd; DAR Awd; High Hon Roll; Pres NHS; Stu Cncl Achvmnt Awd 84-87; Acdmc Athltc Awd 87; Outstndg SR Engl 87; PA ST U; Engnrng.

HERMANN, JOHN; Holy Ghost Prep; Yardley, PA; (4); 3/82; Cmnty Wkr; Library Aide; Math Clb; Pres Science Clb; High Hon Roll; NHS; Pres Schlr; French Clb; Texaco Philan Trophic Schlrshp; Katherine Ryan Schlrshp; Acad Stipend; MI ST; Vet Med.

HERMANN, MARGARET; Lampeter-Strasburg HS; Lancaster, PA; (4); 3/142; VP Sec AFS; Trs Band; Trs Mrchg Band; Nwsp Ed-Chief; Var L Trk; Hon Roll; Trs NHS; Pres Schlr; Church Yth Grp; Ursinus Coll Dirs Schlrshp 87; Natl Merit Cmmnd Stu 87; Ursinus Coll; Math.

HERMANOFSKI, ROBERT; John S Fine HS; Nanticoke, PA; (3); Ski Clb; Im Ftbl; JV Wrstlng; High Hon Roll; NHS; Ntl Merit SF; NEDT Awd; Ntl Ldrshp & Svc Awd 85; Yng Comm Ldrs Of Amer 86; Med.

HERMANSDERFER, JON; Steel Valley HS; Munhall, PA; (2); Var Golf; Var L Swmmng; Var L Tennis; High Hon Roll; 2nd Pl Wstrn Penn Swim Chmpnshp 87; Elec Engrng.

HERMICK, ERIC; Rochester Area HS; Rochester, PA; (3); Cmnty Wkr; SADD; Trs Frsh Cls; Capt Bsbl; Fld Hcky; Ftbl; Ice Hcky; Powder Puff Ftbl; Wt Lftg; High Hon Roll; Amer Leg Awd Walter S Roth 84; All Section 1st Team Catcher Bsbl 87; Hnr Roll Awd 87; Sports Med.

HERMSDORF, PAMELA; Fort Le Boeuf HS; Erie, PA; (2); FHA; Stage Crew; Hon Roll; PI.

HERNANDEZ, ANACESILIA; Allen HS; Allentown, PA; (3); 4-H; Girl Scts; Chorus; School Musical; School Play; Variety Show; Swmmng; Hon Roll; Lehigh Cnty CC; Comp.

HERNANDEZ, MARK; Waynesburg Central HS; Waynesburg, PA; (3); Chess Clb; Church Yth Grp; Cmnty Wkr; Letterman Clb; Spanish Clb; L Var Bsbl; L Var Ftbl; Swmmng; Tennis; L Var Trk; Lee Coll; Phrmcy.

HEROLD, DANIELLE; Butler Area SR HS; Butler, PA; (3); Exploring; 4-H; Office Aide; Sec Jr Cls; Sec Sr Cls; Rep Stu Cncl; Var L Socr; Var L Trk; L Jr NHS; Rookie Yr Grls Trk 85; Intl Stds.

HEROLD, SHERRY ANN; Butler SR HS; Butler, PA; (4); 8/699; Church Yth Grp; Pres VP 4-H; German Clb; Library Aide; SADD; High Hon Roll; Jr NHS; NHS; Natl Prsbytrn Schlrshp 87-88; Grove City Coll; Biochem.

HERR, CAROLYN J; Lancaster Mennonite HS; Lancaster, PA; (4); 28/151; VP Pres Church Yth Grp; Cmnty Wkr; Hosp Aide; Sec Acpl Chr; Madrigals; Stage Crew; Ed Lit Mag; Sec Stu Cncl; Cit Awd; Hon Roll; Hnrs Schlrshp For EMC 87; Poetry Div Of Schlstc Wrtng Awds 87; Peace Essay Cntst 87; Eastern Menonite Coll.

HERR JR, DALE; Solanco SR HS; Kirkwood, PA; (3); VP FFA; Varsity Clb; VP Sr Cls; Rep Stu Cncl; Var Wrstlng; High Hon Roll; Hon Roll; Princpls Awd Ag 86-87; FFA Stanred Rose Degree Cnty 86-87.

HERR, DARIN; Lancaster Mennonite HS; Ephrata, PA; (3); 15/155; Chess Clb; Church Yth Grp; Computer Clb; Math Clb; Nwsp Stf; Im Tennis; Im Vllybl; Im Wt Lftg; Hon Roll; Comp Pgm & Article Publshd In Rainbow Magazine 86; Comp Sci.

HERR, DEBORAH L; Conestoga Valley HS; Leola, PA; (3); 55/209; Teachers Aide; Yrbk Stf; Bsktbl; Crs Cntry; Ftbl; Sftbl; Capt Trk; Hon Roll; Spec Ed.

HERR, LINDA; Mt Alvernia HS; Pittsburgh, PA; (3); Ski Clb; Chorus; Variety Show; Yrbk Stf; Sec Jr Cls; Trs Stu Cncl; Hon Roll; Bus Hnr Soc 87-88; Bus.

HERR, SANDY; Northern Lebanon HS; Jonestown, PA; (4); 1/170; Pres Varsity Clb; Var Capt Bsktbl; Var Capt Fld Hcky; Var Capt Sftbl; High Hon Roll; Lion Awd; NHS; Magna Cum Laude 87; US Army Rsrv Schlr Athl 86-87; Leag All Star Fld Hcky,Bsktbl & Sftbl 86-87; Bloomsburg U; Pre-Med.

HERREMA, KEVIN; Abington Heights HS; Clarks Summit, PA; (2); 45/300; Church Yth Grp; German Clb; Ski Clb; Chorus; Church Choir; Concert Band; Mrchg Band; Var Trk; Hon Roll; Computer Clb; PA JR Acad Of Sci 2 Rgnl 1st Awds 1 ST 9th Awd 1 ST 2nd Awd 86 & 87; Sci.

HERRERA, ANDRES; Northeast Catholic HS; Philadelphia, PA; (4); 27/369; Nwsp Phtg; Nwsp Rptr; Hon Roll; NHS; Ntl Merit SF; Sprng/Fall Crew Vrsty 84-87; Bus.

HERRERA, MONIQUE; St Cyril Acad; Sun Valley, CA; (4); Drama Clb; Chorus; Church Choir; School Play; Nwsp Stf; Yrbk Stf; Var Vllybl; Cit Awd; High Hon Roll; Hon Roll; Arts Recg & Tlnt Search Hon Mntn 87; Music.

HERRICK, KATIE; Red Lion SR HS; Red Lion, PA; (3); 70/342; Church Yth Grp; Hosp Aide; SADD; School Musical; Nwsp Rptr; Yrbk Stf; Lit Mag; Im Bowling; Timer; Hon Roll; 1st Pl Wnnr-MADD Postr Cont 87; PA Schl Of Arts; Cmmnctns Art.

HERRICK, TODD; Mercer Area HS; Mercer, PA; (4); 19/143; Nwsp Sprt Ed; Nwsp Stf; Yrbk Stf; Stu Cncl; Bsktbl; Crs Cntry; Golf; Trk; Hon Roll; Prfct Atten Awd; Grove City Coll; Elem Ed.

HERRING, APRIL LYNN; Southern Lehigh HS; Center Valley, PA; (4); 6/225; Church Yth Grp; Key Clb; Rep Varsity Clb; Pres Band; Nwsp Stf; Yrbk Sprt Ed; Rep Stu Cncl; Capt Sftbl; Capt Tennis; High Hon Roll; 1st Tm All Leag Ctchr 87; Links Bev Positv Attd Awd 87; Jimmie Schaeffer Sftbl Awd 87; Messiah Coll; Cmmnctns.

HERRING, DARA M; Central HS Of Phila; Philadelphia, PA; (2); Acpl Chr; Chorus; Trk; Hon Roll; Prfct Atten Awd; Pres Schlr; Pres Acdmc Ftnss Awd 86.

HERRING, JULI; Bangor Area SR HS; Bangor, PA; (3); Computer Clb; Sec Leo Clb; SADD; Sec Varsity Clb; Ed Nwsp Rptr; Ed Lit Mag; Rep Jr Cls; Sr Cls; Stat Badmtn; JV Bsktbl; Commnctns.

HERRING, LOREN; Tri-Valley HS; Valley View, PA; (2); 8/85; Church Yth Grp; Quiz Bowl; Bsktbl; High Hon Roll; Hon Roll; Envir-Olympcs 3rd Pl 86-87; Schuylkill Snsrvtn Dist Essy Cntst 1st Pl 86; All Amer Ftns Awd 87; Engl.

HERRING, MARCY; St Francis Acad; Pittsburgh, PA; (3); #7 In Class; Church Yth Grp; Drama Clb; Hosp Aide; Math Clb; Trs SADD; School Play; Stage Crew; Yrbk Phtg; Yrbk Stf; High Hon Roll; Carnegie Mellon U; Bus Mgmnt.

HERRING, NADEEN; Harrisburg HS; Harrisburg, PA; (4); 16/225; Pep Clb; Speech Tm; Nwsp Ed-Chief; Nwsp Rptr; Nwsp Stf; Stu Cncl; Hon Roll; Debate Tm; Outstndng Jrnlsm Awd 86; Schlrshp Summer Sessions Dickinson Coll 86; Spelman Coll; Eng.

HERRING, SHEILA; Pine Grove Area HS; Pine Grove, PA; (3); SADD; Varsity Clb; Chorus; Yrbk Stf; Pres Stu Cncl; Stat Bsktbl; Var Cheerleading; Hon Roll; NHS; JA Awd Math 83-84; Elem Ed.

HERRINGTON, MATTHEW; Garden Spot HS; New Holland, PA; (2); Church Yth Grp; SADD; Rep Frsh Cls; Rep Stu Cncl; JV Var Bsktbl; Coach Actv; JV Var Socr; JV Trk; Law Enfrcmnt.

HERRIOTT, BILL; Canon Mc Millian HS; Canonsburg, PA; (3); 55/367; Varsity Clb; Socr; Timer; Bus Admin.

HERRMANN, ALISA; Riverview HS; Verona, PA; (2); 11/100; Chorus; Concert Band; Mrchg Band; Nwsp Stf; Yrbk Stf; Stu Cncl; Pom Pon; JV Trk; JV Vllybl; Psychlgy.

HERROLD, APRIL ANNE; Parkand SR HS; Orefield, PA; (2); Church Yth Grp; Church Choir; Hon Roll.

HERROLD, ROBERT; Mt Carmel Area HS; Mt Carmel, PA; (3); Ski Clb; Band; Concert Band; Jazz Band; Mrchg Band; Pep Band; Hon Roll; Lion Awd; PMEA Dist & Rgnl Bands 86 & 87; PMEA ST Band, Lions Clb PA ST Band 87; Susquehanna U; Music.

HERRON, JENNIFER; Carrick HS; Pittsburgh, PA; (4); DECA; JA; Q&S; SADD; Nwsp Stf; Powder Puff Ftbl; Hon Roll; Pre-Law.

HERSCH JR, DARYL; Cathedral Prep HS; Erie, PA; (3); 103/193; Church Yth Grp; Nwsp Phtg; Nwsp Rptr; Nwsp Stf.

HERSCHMAN, CATHY; Northampton SR HS; Northampton, PA; (3); 136/494; German Clb; Hosp Aide; Ski Clb; Ed Yrbk Stf; Stat Bsktbl; Var Tennis; Hon Roll; Pharmacy.

HERSHBERGER, MARCIA; Perkiomen Valley HS; Perkiomenville, PA; (3); Church Yth Grp; Yrbk Stf; Rep Jr Cls; Rep Stu Cncl; Var Cheerleading; High Hon Roll; Hon Roll; NHS; Pre-Med.

HERSHBINE, TODD; State College Area SR HS; State College, PA; (4); 167/567; Pres Church Yth Grp; Acpl Chr; Pres Stu Cncl; Var L Crs Cntry; JV L Ftbl; Var L Trk; Cit Awd; Hon Roll; PIAA Crss Cntry ST Champns All ST Tm 86; Citatn Hous Rep Commwlth PA 86; Power Paws 86; PA ST U; Public Rltns.

HERSHEY, CHRISTINE; Pequea Valley HS; Gap, PA; (3); Church Yth Grp; Drama Clb; Hosp Aide; Library Aide; Chorus; Church Choir; School Play; Nwsp Stf; Hon Roll.

HERSHEY, JILL; Elizabethtown Area HS; Elizabethtown, PA; (4); 1/260; Rep Soph Cls; Rep Jr Cls; JV Bsktbl; Var Cheerleading; Var Capt Fld Hcky; Var Capt Trk; High Hon Roll; NHS; Val; Hugh O Brian Ldrshp Awd 85; Role Model Awd 87; U DE; Phys Ther.

HERSHEY, JULIE; Octorara HS; Cochranville, PA; (3); Church Yth Grp; Color Guard; School Musical; School Play; Nwsp Phtg; Rep Stu Cncl; Var Fld Hcky; Hon Roll; NHS; Drama Clb; Pblc Rltns.

HERSHEY, KEVIN F D B; Pequea Valley HS; Gap, PA; (3); VP AFS; VP Drama Clb; School Play; Pres Frsh Cls; Pres Soph Cls; Pres Jr Cls; Pres Sr Cls; Hon Roll; NHS; Rotary Awd; Hugh O Brn Ldrshp Smnr 86; Pres Prom Cmmtee 87.

HERSHEY, LARRY; Coudersport JR SR HS; Coudersport, PA; (3); Off Church Yth Grp; Ski Clb; Band; Chorus; Church Choir; Mrchg Band; Pep Band; Ftbl; Trk; Hon Roll; Music.

HERSHEY, LYLE; Pequea Valley HS; Kinzers, PA; (4); Pres Trs Church Yth Grp; Concert Band; Mrchg Band; Bsbl; Capt Socr; Hon Roll; Grove City Coll; Bus.

HERSHEY, MICHELE; Pequea Vly HS; Gordonville, PA; (3); 48/152; AFS; Church Yth Grp; Pep Clb; Varsity Clb; VP Capt Cheerleading; Fld Hcky; Gym; Hon Roll; JC Awd; Penn ST U; Phy Ed.

HERSHEY, RHONDA; Octorara HS; Atglen, PA; (3); 13/151; Art Clb; Church Yth Grp; Drama Clb; Band; Concert Band; Mrchg Band; School Musical; School Play; Nwsp Stf; Cheerleading; Hnrbl Mntn Schlstc Art Cntst 87; Textl Dsgn.

HERSHMAN, ALISON; Garden Spot HS; New Holland, PA; (2); Political Wkr; Hon Roll; PA Bndmstrs Assn Outstndng Musician Awd 83; Military; Intlgnce.

HERSPERGER, STEPHANIE; Tyrone Area HS; Tyrone, PA; (3); Church Yth Grp; Key Clb; Ski Clb; VP Soph Cls; JV Cheerleading; High Hon Roll; Law.

HERTZOG, CYNTHIA; William Allen HS; Allentown, PA; (2); Sec Church Yth Grp; SADD; Drama Clb; Exploring; FBLA; Girl Scts; JA; Red Cross Aide; Church Choir; Eckerd Coll; Med.

HERTZOG, DONNA; Grace Christian HS; Newmanstown, PA; (4); 5/20; Chorus; Yrbk Stf; Rep Sr Cls; High Hon Roll; Hon Roll; Presdntl Acadc Ftns Awd 87; Emprie Beauty Schl; Csmtlgy.

HERTZOG, K S; Garden Spot HS; Ephrata, PA; (1); Church Yth Grp; Pres 4-H; VP FFA; Quiz Bowl; Orch; 4-H Awd; Hon Roll; Ag.

HERTZOG, KERRY; Northern Cambria HS; Barnesboro, PA; (3); 48/152; High Hon Roll; Hon Roll; Sign Lang Course 87; Poetry Cont Awds 87.

HERTZOG, STEPHANIE; Ephrata SR HS; Ephrata, PA; (3); Camera Clb; English Clb; 4-H; Science Clb; Spanish Clb; JV Fld Hcky; JV Var Mgr(s); Im Tennis; Im Vllybl; Hon Roll; Fld Hcky 85; JV Fld Hcky Mgr 86; Hnr Rl Cmpltn 85-87; PA Schl Of Arts; Intr Dsgn.

HERVEY, BETHANN D; Hampton HS; Allison Pk, PA; (4); Church Yth Grp; Service Clb; Band; Church Choir; Mrchg Band; Yrbk Sprt Ed; Capt Var Cheerleading; High Hon Roll; Hon Roll; Stu Store 87; Westminster Coll; Elem Ed.

HERZING, NANCY; Du Bois Area SR HS; Penfield, PA; (4); 6/288; Cmnty Wkr; Science Clb; Teachers Aide; Chorus; School Musical; High Hon Roll; Pres NHS; Prfct Atten Awd; Rotary Awd; Voice Dem Awd; Engl Awd 87; Huston Twnshp Alumni Schlrshp 87; Du Bois Bus/Prof Wmns Schlrshp 87; Gannon U; Sci.

HESIDENCE, ROBIN; Butler SR HS; Butler, PA; (3); Office Aide; Teachers Aide; Chorus; Hon Roll; Gldn Acdmc Achvt Awd 87; Dntl Tech.

HESKY, MICHELLE; Butler SR HS; Butler, PA; (3); Church Yth Grp; Cmnty Wkr; Exploring; JA; Chorus; Hon Roll; Johnson & Wales Cllg-2 Yr Schlrshp 86; ST Finlist Miss Natl Teen Pageant 86; Outstndng Acad Achvt Awd; Business Mgmt.

HESLIN, HEATHER; Liberty HS; Bethlehem, PA; (4); 100/421; Dance Clb; Hosp Aide; Chorus; Sftbl; Hon Roll; Choraliers Awd 87; E Stroudsburg U; Spcl Ed.

HESS, ANGELIQUE; Elizabethtown Area HS; Elizabethtown, PA; (3); 38/259; Band; Chorus; Concert Band; Flag Corp; Jazz Band; Mrchg Band; Orch; Swing Chorus; Sftbl; Vllybl; PA Fed Of Music Clbs Music Camp Schlrshp Outstndng Voclst 86; All Amer Yth Hnr Choir HI Tour 86; Music Pfmnc.

HESS, CHRISSY; Hempfield HS; Lancaster, PA; (3); Chorus; Nwsp Stf; Powder Puff Ftbl; Mgr Sftbl; High Hon Roll; Chef.

HESS, CORRIE; Northern HS; Dillsburg, PA; (3); 2/232; Rep Church Yth Grp; Off Band; Pres Chorus; Jazz Band; Trs Jr Cls; Capt Var Cheerleading; Var L Trk; NHS; Cmnty Wkr; Model UN; Music Hnr Soc 87; Acadc Exclnc Awd 86-87; Messiah Coll; Law.

HESS, DAWN; Lancaster Mennonite HS; Smoketown, PA; (3); Chess Clb; Church Yth Grp; Acpl Chr; Chorus; Orch; School Play; Fld Hcky; Mgr(s); Hon Roll; Music Awd 85-87; Messiah Coll.

HESS, DAWN; Oxford HS; Oxford, PA; (3); 44/197; Art Clb; Church Yth Grp; Hosp Aide; Chorus; Church Choir; Var JV Bsktbl; Var JV Sftbl; Swmmng; Var JV Vllybl; Kuztown U; Comrcl Art.

HESS, ERIC; Altoona Area HS; Altoona, PA; (4); 55/718; German Clb; Key Clb; Band; Concert Band; Jazz Band; Mrchg Band; Symp Band; Pres Schlr; St Schlr; Hghst Rnkng Jazz Bnd In US 87; IN U Of PA; Accntng.

HESS, EUGENE; Lancaster Mennonite HS; Marietta, PA; (3); Church Yth Grp; 4-H; FNA; Hon Roll; NHS; 4-H Dairy Proj Awd 86; Dairy Frmr.

HESS, JENNIFER; William Penn SR HS; York, PA; (3); 110/374; Am Leg Aux Girls St; Church Yth Grp; Hosp Aide; JA; Chorus; Church Choir; Mrchg Band; Mgr Crs Cntry; Var Mgr(s); Mgr Trk; Lancaster General Schl; Nrsg.

HESS, JULIE; Eastern York SR HS; York, PA; (2); 23/155; Cmnty Wkr; Varsity Clb; Rep Stu Cncl; Var L Trk; Var L Vllybl; High Hon Roll; Hon Roll; Var L Bsktbl; Im Gym; YCIAA Yrk Cnty Vllybl Al-Star 86; Marine Corp Physcl Ftns Awd 86 & 87; Presdntl Phy Ftns Awd 83-86; Comp Fld.

HESS, KELLY; Donegal HS; Mount Joy, PA; (4); 25/168; Chorus; Church Choir; School Play; Stage Crew; Rep Frsh Cls; Stat Crs Cntry; Powder Puff Ftbl; Stat Trk; Hon Roll.

HESS, KEVIN; Fairview HS; Erie, PA; (4); 5/154; Teachers Aide; Varsity Clb; VP Stu Cncl; Var JV Bsbl; Var Capt Bsktbl; Var Golf; High Hon Roll; Hon Roll; JC Awd; NHS; Mike George Awd Ldrshp, Athltcs, Comm & Schlstc 87; 1st Tm All Conf Bsktbl 86-87; Grove City Coll; Bus.

HESS, LEAH; Millville HS; Bloomsburg, PA; (4); FBLA; FFA; FHA; Band; Hon Roll; Lion Awd; Acdmc Achvt Awd 87; Hort.

HESS, LISA D; Solanco HS; Quarryville, PA; (4); Thesps; Varsity Clb; Band; Flag Corp; Mrchg Band; Orch; School Musical; Trk; Wt Lftg; High Hon Roll; Penn ST U; Bus Admin.

HESS, MARCY; Faith Mennonile HS; Drumore, PA; (4); 1/27; Church Yth Grp; Library Aide; Acpl Chr; Chorus; Church Choir; Yrbk Ed-Chief; High Hon Roll; St Joseph Schl Of Nrsg; Nrsg.

HESS, MARCY A; Bishop Mc Cort HS; Johnstown, PA; (3); 32/155; Art Clb; Drama Clb; Hosp Aide; Acpl Chr; Chorus; School Musical; High Hon Roll; Hon Roll; NHS; 4.0 Clb 86; Cncrt Solost Vocal 2 Prfrmncs 86; Dickinson U; Psych.

HESS, MATTHEW; Upper Dauphin Area HS; Gratz, PA; (3); Band; Chorus; Concert Band; Jazz Band; Mrchg Band; Rep Stu Cncl; Hon Roll; PA ST U; Aerospace Engrng.

HESS, RENEE; Gateway Christian HS; Alburtis, PA; (4); School Play; Yrbk Stf; Rep Jr Cls; Vllybl; Bus.

HESS, ROBERT; Bangor Area SR HS; Bangor, PA; (3); Boy Scts; Church Yth Grp; Computer Clb; Pep Clb; Hon Roll; Engnrng.

HESS, ROY; Connellsville Area HS; Dawson, PA; (3); 82/540; Pres Church Yth Grp; Chorus; Mrchg Band; School Musical; School Play; Hon Roll; NHS; Conf Yth Cncl Mnstry; PA JR Acad Sci; Dist Untd Meth Yth VP 87-88; U Pittsburgh; Bus Adm.

HESS, RUSTON; Williamson JR SR HS; Millerton, PA; (3); Computer Clb; Ski Clb; High Hon Roll; NHS; German Clb; Motocross Rcng 86; 1st & 4th Amtr Mdfd & Stck 87; Opmtry.

HESS, SHERRY L; Monaca Jr-Sr HS; Monaca, PA; (3); 3/88; Am Leg Aux Girls St; Church Yth Grp; French Clb; Hosp Aide; Pres Library Aide; Office Aide; Pep Clb; VP Red Cross Aide; High Hon Roll; NHS; Gannon; Obstetrics.

HESS, STACEY; Dieruff HS; Allentown, PA; (3); JV Var Cheerleading; Var Gym.

HESSENAUER, MEGHAN; Avon Grove HS; Avondale, PA; (3); 17/215; Church Yth Grp; Cmnty Wkr; Intnl Clb; Radio Clb; Nwsp Sprt Ed; Capt Var Bsktbl; Capt Var Fld Hcky; Var Sftbl; High Hon Roll; NHS; Foods Here & Abroad Awd 86-87; Marine Bio.

HESSER, ANGELA; Lewiston Area HS; Lewistown, PA; (3); Pres Church Yth Grp; German Clb; Church Choir; Yrbk Phtg; Yrbk Stf; Cit Awd; High Hon Roll; NHS; Girl Scts; Acdmc Ltr 85-87; Chrch Band 87; Temple U; Photo.

HESSER JR, RICHARD; Lewistown Area HS; Lewistown, PA; (3); Church Yth Grp; Varsity Clb; SADD; Church Choir; JV Var Ftbl; Im Wt Lftg; Hon Roll; 14th Yr Perfect Church Attndnce Awd Pin 87.

HESSLER, HEIDI; Chambersburg Area SR HS; Chambersburg, PA; (2); JCL; Latin Clb; NFL; Chorus; Nwsp Stf; Rep Stu Cncl; High Hon Roll.

HESSON, KAREN; Southmoreland SR HS; Scottdale, PA; (4); Sec Pres Church Yth Grp; DECA; Library Aide; Pep Clb; DECA 2nd Pl Dist Comptn & 3rd Pl ST Comptn Gen Merch Evnt 86-87; Kiwanis Clb Jan Stdnt Mnth 86-87; Mktg.

HESTER, JENNIFER; Central York SR HS; York, PA; (3); Ski Clb; Varsity Clb; Chorus; Capt Mrchg Band; School Musical; School Play; Rep Stu Cncl; Capt Cheerleading; Trk; High Hon Roll; Mrktng.

HETH, DAWN; Hollidaysburg Area HS; Hollidaysburg, PA; (3); 15/300; Church Yth Grp; Ski Clb; Band; Chorus; Concert Band; Mrchg Band; Stage Crew; Hon Roll; Messiah Coll; Nrs.

HETRICK, BARBARA; Newport HS; Newport, PA; (3); 9/117; Church Yth Grp; 4-H; Varsity Clb; Band; Church Choir; Concert Band; Mrchg Band; Rep Frsh Cls; Pres Soph Cls; Pres Jr Cls; Tri M 87.

HETRICK, DAWNNE D; Fairview HS; Fairview, PA; (4); 59/159; Pres Church Yth Grp; Drama Clb; Pres Girl Scts; Teachers Aide; Thesps; Acpl Chr; Chorus; Church Choir; Capt Color Guard; Drill Tm; Fairview Ed Assn Schlrshp 87; Clarion U Of PA; Spcl Ed.

HETRICK, GARY; Redbank Valley HS; New Bethlehem, PA; (4); 23/139; 4-H; FFA; Varsity Clb; Ftbl; Trk; 4-H Awd; Hon Roll; NHS; Prfct Atten Awd; Keystone Farmer Degree 87.

HETRICK, GEORGIA; Claysburg Kimmel HS; Claysburg, PA; (1); VP Church Yth Grp; Chorus; Church Choir; Sec Frsh Cls; Rep Stu Cncl; Cheerleading; Sftbl; High Hon Roll; Hon Roll; Tri Hi Y Prlmntrn; Penn ST; Ed.

HETRICK, KATHY ANN; Penncrest HS; Media, PA; (3); 97/344; Pep Clb; SADD; Chorus; Variety Show; Nwsp Phtg; JV Var Bsktbl; JV Var Sftbl; Hon Roll; Rotary Awd; Drama Clb; Law.

HETRICK, KATRINA; Boiling Springs HS; Mt Holly Springs, PA; (3); Chess Clb; Chorus; Yrbk Stf; Hon Roll; Psych, Law & US Hist Coll Level Courses Boston Coll 87; Corporate Lawyer.

HETRICK, KRISTINE; Salisbury Elk Lick HS; Fort Hill, PA; (4); Trs FFA; Band; Nwsp Phtg; Nwsp Stf; Yrbk Phtg; Yrbk Stf; Trs Sr Cls; Sftbl; DAR Awd; Hon Roll; Cambria Rowe; Acctng.

HETRICK, LAVONE; Jefferson-Morgan HS; Clarksville, PA; (4); 12/97; Intnl Clb; Red Cross Aide; Church Choir; Yrbk Stf; High Hon Roll; Hon Roll; Schlrshp Awd Filer-Sodlek Post 954 87; Waynesburg Coll; Nrsng.

HETRICK, SUSAN; Mohawk Area HS; Edinburg, PA; (3); VP FBLA; Chorus; Capt Drill Tm; Capt Flag Corp; School Musical; Stage Crew; Nwsp Rptr; Nwsp Stf; 1st Pl Inbus Grphcs Awd 87; Art Awds 86-87; Cmmrcl Art.

HETRICK II, WILBUR; Jefferson Morgan JR SR HS; Clarksville, PA; (3); 7/76; Computer Clb; Spanish Clb; Band; Concert Band; Mrchg Band; Bsbl; High Hon Roll; Hon Roll; Spanish NHS; Medcl.

HETTES, CHRISTEL; Wallenpaupack Area HS; Greentown, PA; (3); 9/151; Church Yth Grp; Var L Bsktbl; Var L Fld Hcky; Var L Sftbl; High Hon Roll; Hon Roll; NHS; Sec Natl Hnr Soc 87; Thrptc Rec.

HETTLER, PAUL; Elizabeth-Forward SR HS; Mckeesport, PA; (2); Church Yth Grp; Computer Clb; French Clb; Math Clb; High Hon Roll; Arch.

HETZEL, MARCIA; Northern Lebanon HS; Grantville, PA; (3); 25/215; Art Clb; 4-H; Chorus; School Musical; Var Tennis; Var Trk; Flght Attndnt.

HETZLEIN, ALAINA; Faith Community HS; Pittsburgh, PA; (4); 1/29; Computer Clb; Office Aide; Pep Clb; Spanish Clb; Nwsp Rptr; Nwsp Stf; Yrbk Rptr; Yrbk Stf; Stu Cncl; Sftbl; U Of Pittsburgh.

HEUSTON, KRISTINA; Harry S Truman HS; Levittown, PA; (3); 38/599; Computer Clb; German Clb; NFL; ROTC; Chorus; Drill Tm; Bowling; High Hon Roll; NHS; Salem Coll; Med.

HEVALOW, KATHY; The Christian Acad; Trainer, PA; (3); Acpl Chr; Chorus; School Play; Sec Sr Cls; High Hon Roll; Prfct Atten Awd; Acadc Excel Awd French I Awd 84-85; Acadc Excel Awds Acadc 85-87; Jrnlst.

HEVENER, CATHY; Warwick HS; Lititz, PA; (3); 10/267; Church Yth Grp; Varsity Clb; Var Capt Bsktbl; Var Sftbl; Var Tennis; High Hon Roll; Sec NHS; Hnrbl Mntn Schltc Wrtng Awd 87; Palmyra Cougar Clb Rndbl Clsc All Star Tm 86; Pres Anti Drg Grp 87-88; Secndry Educ.

HEVERLY, AMY; Lock Haven HS; Howard, PA; (3); Church Yth Grp; French Clb; SADD; Chorus; VP Jr Cls; Stu Cncl; Socr; Hon Roll; NHS; NEDT Awd; Penn ST.

HEVERLY, BARBIE; Lock Haven HS; Howard, PA; (3); Spanish Clb; SADD; Band; Chorus; Church Choir; School Musical; Bsktbl; Socl Wrk.

HEVERLY, BETH; Jersey Shore SR HS; Jersey Shore, PA; (4); Church Yth Grp; Cmnty Wkr; 4-H; French Clb; FBLA; Girl Scts; Red Cross Aide; Ski Clb; Teachers Aide; Stage Crew; Girl Scout Gold Awd 87; Fash Revue 4-H 3 Yrs Fnlst 85-87; High Achvmnt Awd In Phys Ed 87; Bus Field.

HEWETT, STEFANIE; Pen Argyl Area HS; Pen Argyl, PA; (3); 4/160; Church Yth Grp; Spanish Clb; Chorus; Cheerleading; Tennis; Trk; Twrlr; High Hon Roll; NHS; Hstry Day Wnnr.

HEWITT, ERIC; Highlands SR HS; Tarentum, PA; (3); Boy Scts; Intnl Clb; Key Clb; SADD; Band; Concert Band; Mrchg Band; Symp Band; Jr NHS; Prfct Atten Awd; St Vincent Coll; Pre-Med.

HEWITT, THOMAS F; Chapel Christian Schl; Belle Vernon, PA; (4); 2/5; Boy Scts; Church Yth Grp; School Play; Yrbk Stf; Capt Bsktbl; Im Bowling; Capt Ftbl; Sftbl; Vllybl; Hon Roll; Sci.

HEYD, ED; Bethel Christian Schl; North East, PA; (2); 1/20; Church Yth Grp; Band; Variety Show; Rep Frsh Cls; Sec Soph Cls; Stu Cncl; Var L Bsktbl; Var L Sftbl; High Hon Roll; Crtfct Excllnc Acad Exclnc 86; Bible Schlr Awd 86; Bst Dfnsve Plyr Sftbl 86; PA ST U; Aero.

HEYD, RUTH; Bethel Christian Schl; North East, PA; (1); 2/10; 4-H; Office Aide; Band; Chorus; Church Choir; Variety Show; VP Frsh Cls; Stu Cncl; Sftbl; 4-H Awd; Schl Chr Accmpnst 86; Chrch Argnst 86; Music.

HEYDT, ALLISON; Coatesville Area HS; Coatesville, PA; (3); 32/540; Church Yth Grp; French Clb; Ski Clb; Chorus; Off Soph Cls; Off Jr Cls; Off Sr Cls; Stu Cncl; Cheerleading; High Hon Roll; Psych.

HEYER, TARA; Plum SR HS; New Kensington, PA; (3); Q&S; School Play; Nwsp Stf; Hon Roll; Prfct Atten Awd; Clss Awds Amrcn Hstry, Bio, Engl, Health I 85-86; Clss Awds Wrld Cultres, Shrthnd I Amrcn Lit 86-87; Bus.

HEYL, CHRIS; Loyalsock HS; Williamsport, PA; (4); 52/104; Ski Clb; Spanish Clb; Band; Chorus; Jazz Band; Madrigals; Mrchg Band; Pep Band; School Musical; Trk; Ltrmn & Conf Champ Trk 85-87; Pres Ski Clb 87; VP Ski Clb 86; PA ST U; Admin.

HEYN, CHRISTOPHER; Lampeter-Strasburg HS; Strasburg, PA; (2); 13/165; Chess Clb; Cmnty Wkr; Quiz Bowl; Varsity Clb; Yrbk Stf; Var L Crs Cntry; Var Trk; Hon Roll; Sci Fair 1st Pl Comp, Air Force Awd & Hon Ment Physics Cnty & Local 85-87; Sci.

HEYS, GAYLE LYNN; Thomas Jefferson HS; Pittsburgh, PA; (4); 7/257; Church Yth Grp; Drama Clb; French Clb; Church Choir; Stage Crew; Yrbk Stf; Score Keeper; High Hon Roll; Trs NHS; Grove City Coll; Accntng.

HEYSHAM, AMY; Elkland Area HS; Elkland, PA; (3); 9/88; Drama Clb; 4-H; French Clb; SADD; Chorus; School Musical; Yrbk Stf; VP Stu Cncl; Hon Roll; NHS; Physcn Asstnt.

HIBBERT, SHARON; Trinity HS; Washington, PA; (3); 4/404; Art Clb; Aud/Vis; Dance Clb; French Clb; PAVAS; Q&S; Chorus; Nwsp Ed-Chief; Nwsp Rptr; Nwsp Stf; Cmnctns.

HIBBS, ANDREW; Middleburg Joint HS; Middleburg, PA; (3); 23/133; Church Yth Grp; NHS; Stu Of Mnth 85; PA ST U; Cvl Engr.

HIBSHMAN, HEIDI A; Eastern Lebanon County HS; Myerstown, PA; (3); 26/146; Church Yth Grp; SADD; Chorus; Variety Show; Off Sr Cls; Sec Stu Cncl; Var Capt Cheerleading; High Hon Roll; Hon Roll; NHS; Shippensburg U; Jrnlsm.

HICE, MARY JANE; Jefferson Morgan HS; Jefferson, PA; (4); 15/97; Art Clb; Spanish Clb; Acpl Chr; Chorus; Madrigals; Swing Chorus; Stat Sftbl; Hon Roll; WV U; Intr Dsgn.

HICKERNELL, DONNA; Eastern Lebanon County HS; Robesonia, PA; (3); 3/169; Sec FHA; Hosp Aide; SADD; Hon Roll; NHS; Nrsng.

HICKERSON, MURPHY J; Rochester Area HS; Rochester, PA; (4); 12/94; NAACP; Chorus; Pres Church Choir; Pres Soph Cls; Pres Jr Cls; Pres Sr Cls; High Hon Roll; NHS; Pres Schlr; Chllng Schlrshp U Pittsburgh 87; Outstndng Cls Stu Awd Vocal Music 87; NAACP Schlrshp; U Of Pittsburgh; Pre Med.

HICKEY, ALLISAN; Daniel Boone JRSR HS; Douglassville, PA; (2); 36/166; Church Yth Grp; Drama Clb; Sec French Clb; Girl Scts; Library Aide; Chorus; Flag Corp; School Musical; Nwsp Stf; Hon Roll; U Of NE-LINCOLN; Law.

HICKEY, DAVID; Seneca Valley SR HS; Dillsbury, PA; (4); Boy Scts; Pres Church Yth Grp; Exploring; ROTC; Chorus; NHS; Eagle Sct Rnk 85; Penn ST; Lawyr.

HICKLE, EDWARD; Hempfield SR HS; Luxor, PA; (3); Boy Scts; Library Aide; VICA; Band; Stage Crew; Nwsp Stf; Bowling; Mgr(s); Trk; Wt Lftg.

HICKMAN, AMY; Mc Guffey HS; Prosperity, PA; (3); 5/250; German Clb; Sec Band; Concert Band; Jazz Band; Mrchg Band; School Musical; High Hon Roll; NHS; Church Yth Grp; Pep Band; PA Govr Schl Of The Arts Music 86; Congrssnl Yth Ldrshp Cncl Wash D C 86; Acad All Amer 85; Music Ed.

HICKMAN, BRETT; Juniata HS; Port Royal, PA; (4); Varsity Clb; School Play; Var L Ftbl; Var L Trk; Hon Roll; Lincoln Tech Inst; Comp Drftg.

HICKMAN, JASON; Wilmington Area HS; New Wilmington, PA; (3); 13/115; Church Yth Grp; Drama Clb; Latin Clb; School Play; Stage Crew; Crs Cntry; Trk; High Hon Roll; Hon Roll.

HICKMAN, LISA; Hopewell SR HS; Aliquippa, PA; (2); Drama Clb; JA; Latin Clb; Thesps; Concert Band; Drm Mjr(t); Mrchg Band; School Play; JV Tennis; Hon Roll; Psych.

HICKMAN, LISA; Waynesburg Central HS; Waynesburg, PA; (4); Art Clb; Ski Clb; Spanish Clb; Hon Roll; WV Career Coll; Accntng.

HICKS III, ARTHUR T; Pine Forge Acad; Castle Hayne, NC; (3); Church Yth Grp; Quiz Bowl; Chorus; Church Choir; School Musical; School Play; Nwsp Sprt Ed; Pres Frsh Cls; Bsktbl; Hon Roll; Cngrsnl Schlr Cngrsnl Yth Ldrshp Cncl 87; Oakwood Coll AL; Med.

HICKS, JAMES; Cambria Hts HS; St Benedict, PA; (3); Cmnty Wkr; Ski Clb; JV Bsbl; JV Ftbl; L Swmmng; Hon Roll; NEDT Awd; Comp Prgmr.

HICKS, JAY; Windber Area HS; Windber, PA; (3); Chess Clb; FTA; Library Aide; Math Clb; Office Aide; Ski Clb; Spanish Clb; SADD; Sec Soph Cls; Var Bsbl; Smrst Cnty All Star 1st Tm Dfns Ftbl 86; Dist Ldr Qrtrbck Sacks 86; 2nd Pl Swmmng Dists 84-86; Engrng.

HICKS, JOSEPH G; Central Catholic HS; Verona, PA; (2); Art Clb; Church Yth Grp; Cmnty Wkr; Dance Clb; Drama Clb; Exploring; French Clb; JA; Pep Clb; Thesps; Top Sales-Dist JA; Trvl.

HICKS, LISA; Donegal HS; Maytown, PA; (3); 100/177; Art Clb; Camera Clb; FBLA; Color Guard; Drill Tm; Flag Corp; Yrbk Phtg; Mgr(s); Church Yth Grp; Nwsp Phtg; Gold Ky Schlstc Art Shw 87; Semi Fnlst Gvrnrs Schl Photo 87; PA Schl Of Photo; Photo.

HICKS, MICHAEL; Greencastle-Antrim HS; Greencastle, PA; (3); 10/180; School Play; Stage Crew; Stat Bsbl; JV Bsktbl; Var L Ftbl; Hon Roll; NHS; Boy Scts; Exploring; Latin Clb; Elec Engrng.

HICKS, RANEE; Homer Center HS; Indiana, PA; (4); FBLA; Office Aide; SADD; Band; Chorus; Concert Band; Jazz Band; Mrchg Band; Hon Roll; NHS; Homer City Wmns Clb Schlrshp 87 & Band Bstr Schlrshp 87; 1st Pl Rgn III FBLA Typng I Awd 86; Indiana U Of PA; Accntng.

HICKS, STACY; Southern Huntingdon Cnty HS; Todd, PA; (4); 7/108; French Clb; GAA; SADD; Band; Chorus; Pep Band; Var Fld Hcky; French Hon Soc; Hon Roll; NHS; NEC Thompson Inst; Elec Tech.

HICKS, SUSAN; Burgettstown JR SR HS; Bulger, PA; (3); Ski Clb; Spanish Clb; Concert Band; Drill Tm; Stu Cncl; Twrlr; High Hon Roll; Hon Roll; Jr NHS; NHS; Pre-Med.

HICKS, TAMMY; Jim Thorpe HS; Lake Harmony, PA; (3); 17/92; Color Guard; Hon Roll; Trvl.

HICKS, TERESSA R; Saltsburg HS; Saltsburg, PA; (3); 11/91; FTA; Teachers Aide; Band; Lit Mag; JV Bsktbl; High Hon Roll; Concert Band; Mrchg Band; Stage Crew; Hon Roll; Pres Acad Fit Awd 86; Clarion U Arts Fest Publctn 86; Above & Beyond Ldr Awd 86; Engl.

HICKS, TRACY; Cedar Crest HS; Lebanon, PA; (2); 39/345; Church Yth Grp; Pep Clb; Spanish Clb; SADD; Band; Church Choir; Concert Band; JV Stat Bsbl; Hon Roll; Jrnlsm.

HIESTAND, CHRISTOPHER; Emmaus HS; Zionsville, PA; (2); Church Yth Grp; Var JV Bsbl; Hon Roll; Acctng.

HIESTER, EMILY; Hershey HS; Hershey, PA; (4); 4/200; Chorus; Mrchg Band; School Musical; Ed Yrbk Stf; Fld Hcky; High Hon Roll; Kiwanis Awd; NHS; Spanish NHS; JR Wmns Clb Schlrshp 87; Kenyon Coll.

HIESTER, JENNIFER; Fleetwood Area HS; Kutztown, PA; (3); 8/108; French Clb; Rep Stu Cncl; Hon Roll; Prsdntl Acdmc Ftnss Awd 84-85.

HIGBEE, BETH; Central Catholic HS; Allentown, PA; (3); Church Yth Grp; Ski Clb; School Musical; Nwsp Rptr; Nwsp Stf; Tennis; High Hon Roll; Hon Roll; Stu Newspr Advsry Prgrm Mbr 86-87; Advncd Plcmnt Englsh 87-88; Cmmnctns.

HIGGINS, BETHANN; Norristown Area HS; Norristown, PA; (3); 3/491; Church Yth Grp; DECA; FBLA; Pep Clb; Yrbk Stf; Rep Soph Cls; Rep Jr Cls; Im JV Bsktbl; Var Diving; Im Fld Hcky; Top Ten Awd Cls 84-85; X Ray Tech.

HIGGINS, JENNIFER; Lock Haven HS; Lock Haven, PA; (3); Art Clb; Cmnty Wkr; Spanish Clb; Yrbk Stf.

HIGGINS, JOSEPH A; Marian HS; Nesquehoning, PA; (4); Am Leg Boys St; VP Church Yth Grp; L Ftbl; High Hon Roll; Lion Awd; VP NHS; Rotary Awd; Aud/Vis; Chess Clb; Cmnty Wkr; Swarthmore Acdmc Grnt 87; Robert C Byrd Hnrs Schlrshp Awd 87; Peter Lobosky Schlrshp Awd 87; Swarthmore; Elctrcl Engrng.

HIGGINS, MARIA; Crestwood HS; White Haven, PA; (2); 23/173; Ski Clb; Var L Cheerleading; Var L Trk; High Hon Roll; NEDT Awd; Elsie Baker Awd 86 & 87.

HIGGINS, PAM; Marian HS; Nesquehoning, PA; (3); 1/104; Am Leg Aux Girls St; Sec Church Yth Grp; Cheerleading; Cit Awd; French Hon Soc; High Hon Roll; Lion Awd; NHS; Math Clb; Pep Clb; Avmets Dstngshd Ser Awd 83-84; Schlrshp To Marian HS 84-85; Hugh Obrn Yth Foundtn Ambssdr 85-86; Bio Sci.

HIGGINS, POLLY; North Hills HS; Pittsburgh, PA; (4); 37/495; AFS; Ski Clb; Sec Thesps; Chorus; Flag Corp; Stage Crew; Lit Mag; Var Trk; NHS; Jrnlsm.

HIGGS, JENNIFER; Norristown Area HS; Norristown, PA; (4); DECA; FCA; Key Clb; Rep Stu Cncl; Var Capt Diving; JV Sftbl; JV Swmmng; Hon Roll; NHS.

HIGH, ERIC DONOVAN; Central HS; Philadelphia, PA; (3); 52/304; Church Yth Grp; Band; Church Choir; Concert Band; Jazz Band; Mrchg Band; Orch; JV Wrstlng; Jr NHS; Honor Roll 83-85; Charles Bowser Schlrshp 87; Central ST U; Chem.

HIGHLAND, GIGI DENISE; Grove City HS; Grove City, PA; (4); 12/172; Cmnty Wkr; French Clb; Key Clb; Science Clb; Band; Concert Band; Mrchg Band; Orch; Pep Band; School Musical; Coopers Energy Cmmnty Svc Schlrshp 87; Acad All Amer 85; Honors Band 86; Penn ST U.

HIGHLANDS, RICHARD; Jeannette SR HS; Jeannette, PA; (3); 1/126; Am Leg Boys St; Spanish Clb; Stu Cncl; Bsktbl; Trk; High Hon Roll; Hon Roll; NHS; Sprts Med.

HIGINBOTHAM, DAVE; Brownsville Area HS; Merrittstown, PA; (3); Church Yth Grp; Cmnty Wkr; Ski Clb; SADD; Band; Church Choir; Concert Band; Mrchg Band; Variety Show; Nwsp Stf; Govnrs Schl Arts-Dance Bucknel U 87; Dancng Schl Ownr.

HILBERT, STEVE; Fleetwood HS; Fleetwood, PA; (3); Bsbl; Socr; Tennis; Wrstlng; Music.

HILBERT, TAMMY; Tunkhannock Area HS; Dallas, PA; (3); Art Clb; Ski Clb; Spanish Clb; Flag Corp; Art.

HILBURN, PERRY; Cambridge Springs HS; Cambridge Spg, PA; (3); 22/98; Band; Drm & Bgl; Mrchg Band; Im Bsbl; Var L Ftbl; Var L Mgr(s); Im Wt Lftg; Var L Wrstlng; Hon Roll; Fav Ftbl Plyr Of Yr 86; Fastest Pin Awd-Wrstlng 86.

HILDEBRAND, CRAIG; Central York SR HS; York, PA; (3); 17/250; Art Clb; Varsity Clb; Var L Bsktbl; Var L Ftbl; Trk; Im Wt Lftg; High Hon Roll; Prfct Atten Awd; Art Hnr Soc 84-88; Engrng.

HILDEBRAND, HEATHER; Altoona HS; Altoona, PA; (3); Pres Church Yth Grp; Chorus; Church Choir; Drm & Bgl; Drm Mjr(t); Mrchg Band; Swing Chorus; JV Sftbl; Var Trk; JV Var Vllybl; Williamsport Area CC; Arch.

HILDEBRAND, SCOTT; Karns City HS; Petrolia, PA; (3); Church Yth Grp; Cmnty Wkr; Chorus; Ftbl; Hon Roll; Hahnemann U; Physcn Asst.

HILDENBRAND, JENNIFER; Jenkintown HS; Jenkintown, PA; (4); Drama Clb; Acpl Chr; Church Choir; Concert Band; Jazz Band; School Musical; Swing Chorus; JV Lcrss; Pres Yth Fllwshp United Meth Chrch 85-87; PMEA Dist Chrs 87; Westchester U; Music.

HILDENBRAND, SUZANNE; Yough SR HS; Arona, PA; (3); Office Aide; Ski Clb; Pres Spanish Clb; Var L Bsktbl; Capt Powder Puff Ftbl; Var L Trk; Var L Vllybl; Hon Roll; NHS; Prfct Atten Awd; Med.

HILDESHEIM, DEBORAH; Mount Calvary HS; Elizabethtown, PA; (3); 3/23; Chorus; Yrbk Bus Mgr; Sec Bsbl; Var Bsktbl; Var Cheerleading; Var Sftbl; Var Trk; Hon Roll; NHS; Poli Sci.

HILE, JENNIFER; Penns Valley Area HS; Centre Hall, PA; (3); 41/150; Sec Church Yth Grp; French Clb; Band; Chorus; Concert Band; Mrchg Band; Nwsp Stf; Yrbk Stf; Var Crs Cntry; Var Trk; Penn ST U.

HILE, MICHELLE; Reading HS; Reading, PA; (3); 44/710; Acpl Chr; Band; Chorus; Color Guard; Capt Flag Corp; Mrchg Band; School Musical; School Play; Swing Chorus.

HILEMAN, CAROL; Saltsburg JR SR HS; Clarksburg, PA; (1); SADD; Concert Band; Mrchg Band; Stat Vllybl; High Hon Roll.

HILEMAN, KEITH; Hollidaysburg SR HS; Hollidaysburg, PA; (4); 19/356; VP Church Yth Grp; Science Clb; Varsity Clb; Chorus; Concert Band; Jazz Band; Mrchg Band; Variety Show; Off Stu Cncl; Wrstlng; Neil Dlzr Schlrshp Fund-Wrstlng 87; Penn ST U.

HILEMAN, KEVIN; Hollidaysburg HS; Hollidaysburg, PA; (4); Church Yth Grp; Letterman Clb; Science Clb; SADD; Varsity Clb; JV Bsbl; Im Swmmng; JV Tennis; Im Vllybl; Var Capt Wrstlng; Penn ST; Acctg.

HILEMAN, LORI; Rockwood Area HS; Somerset, PA; (2); Computer Clb; FHA; Pres Stu Cncl; Var JV Vllybl; Hon Roll; Bus.

HILES, CANDI; Connellsville Area SR HS; Dawson, PA; (3); Art Clb; FBLA; Stage Crew; Hon Roll; Bus.

HILES, LISA; Wilmington Area HS; New Bedford, PA; (3); VP Pres FBLA; Spanish Clb; Color Guard; Capt Powder Puff Ftbl; Chorus; Trk; Vllybl; Hon Roll; Masonic Awd; Shclrshp PA Free Enterprise Wk 86; Awd Bus & Math 3rd Pl 86; Awd Accntng I 3rd Pl 87; US Air Force; Nrsng.

HILF, JEFFREY; Moon Area HS; Corapolis, PA; (3); Church Yth Grp; German Clb; Key Clb; JV Bsbl; Im Bsktbl; JV Ftbl; Var Golf; Engrng.

HILFERTY, JOSEPH R; Saint Josephs Prep; West Chester, PA; (4); Yrbk Rptr; Ftbl; Capt Wrstlng; U Of Pittsburgh; Law.

HILKERT, MELANY; Danville SR HS; Danville, PA; (3); French Clb.

HILL, AMANDA; Conestoga HS; Malvern, PA; (2); Intnl Clb; Variety Show; Yrbk Phtg; Off Frsh Cls; Rep Soph Cls; Var Fld Hcky; Var JV Lcrss; Hon Roll; Marine Phys Ftns Awd-1st Pl 86.

HILL, BRADY; Wm Penn SR HS; York, PA; (4); Letterman Clb; Varsity Clb; Capt L Wt Lftg; Swmmng; Aud/Vis; Computer Clb; PAVAS; Band; Concert Band; Jazz Band; IUP Of PA; Bus Mgnt.

HILL, CARRIE; Great Valley SR HS; Frazer, PA; (3); Cmnty Wkr; Pres French Clb; Intnl Clb; Ski Clb; SADD; Var JV Cheerleading; Mgr(s); Hon Roll; Psychlgy.

HILL, CHRISTINA; Elkland Area HS; Nelson, PA; (4); 3/84; Pres 4-H; FTA; Ed Nwsp Stf; Trk; DAR Awd; High Hon Roll; Pres Schlr; Drama Clb; Library Aide; Teachers Aide; PA Maple Swthrt 86-87; Outstndng Amer Stu 87; HOBY Ldrshp Fndtn Smnr 85; PA ST U; Elem Ed.

HILL, DAVID S; Cedar Cliff HS; Camp Hill, PA; (3); 45/305; Boy Scts; Cmnty Wkr; Drama Clb; Sec JCL; Mrchg Band; Orch; School Musical; Symp Band; Hon Roll; NHS; Harrisburg Yth Sym Orch; Elec Engr.

HILL, HARDY-AMES; William Penn SR HS; York, PA; (3); Church Yth Grp; Ski Clb; Varsity Clb; Band; Concert Band; School Musical; School Play; Symp Band; Var L Socr; Var L Swmmng; Marketing.

HILL, JAMES; Hempfield HS; Ladisville, PA; (2); Im Bsbl; Im Bowling; Var Ftbl; Im Ice Hcky; Hon Roll; Engrng.

HILL, JASON; Ne Ca HS; New Castle, PA; (2); 40/276; Sci.

HILL, JENNIFER; Meadville SR HS; Meadville, PA; (4); Church Yth Grp; Latin Clb; Nwsp Stf; Yrbk Stf; Stu Cncl; Stat Bsktbl; Co-Capt Socr; Hon Roll; U S Army MVP Soccer Awd 87; Seton Hill Coll; Pre-Med.

HILL, JENNIFER; West Hazelton HS; Nuremberg, PA; (4); Drama Clb; French Clb; FTA; Girl Scts; Thesps; Band; Chorus; Concert Band; Hon Roll; William Habel Memrl Awd 87; Dist Chrs 85 & 87; JR Acad Sci 85 & 87; Luzenne Comm Coll; Art.

HILL, JUDITH A; Souderton Area HS; Souderton, PA; (4); Aud/Vis; Church Yth Grp; Color Guard; Mrchg Band; School Musical; School Play; Trk; Hon Roll; Track & Field Ltr 86; Marching Band Ltr 86 & 87; PA ST U; Spanish.

HILL, KAREN; Brownsville Area HS; Labelle, PA; (3); Ski Clb; Past Wrthy Advsr Brwnsvlle Rnbow Assmbly 86; Elem Educ.

HILL, KAREN; Chamberburg Area SR HS; Chambersburg, PA; (3); AFS; JCL; Latin Clb; Letterman Clb; Pep Clb; Cheerleading; Tennis; Trk; Vllybl; US Chrldr Achvt Awd 86.

HILL, KARI; Tunkhannock Area HS; Tunkhannock, PA; (2); Spanish Clb; Tennis; Hon Roll.

HILL, MARCUS R; Aliquippa SR HS; Aliquippa, PA; (3); Bsbl; Bsktbl; Ftbl; IN ST; Arch.

HILL, MICHAEL; Southern Columbia Area HS; Elysburg, PA; (3); 3/110; Nwsp Rptr; Nwsp Stf; Yrbk Phtg; Trk; High Hon Roll; NHS; Voice Dem Awd; HS Math Awds 86 & 87; Amercn Assn Of U Wmn Essy Cntst Hrbl Mntn 84; Engrng.

HILL, MICHELLE; Lock Haven SR HS; Flemington, PA; (3); Sec FHA; German Clb; SADD; Band; Chorus; Concert Band; Jazz Band; Mrchg Band; Orch; Pep Band.

HILL, MILON E; West Philadelphia Catholic HS; Philadelphia, PA; (3); 14/200; Chess Clb; Church Yth Grp; CAP; CC Awd; Hon Roll; Union Leag Of Phila 87.

HILL, PAMELA; Montgomery JR SR HS; Allenwood, PA; (3); French Clb; Thesps; Chorus; School Musical; Bsktbl; Var Trk; Hon Roll.

HILL, PETER; Athens Area HS; Sayre, PA; (3); Acpl Chr; Chorus; Concert Band; Mrchg Band; JV Crs Cntry; JV Trk; Hon Roll; Red Cross Aide; Musicl Soc Schlrshp-Piano 87; Annl Litrry Cntst-Poetry Catgry 2nd, 6rd Pl 86; Red Crs Yth Ldrshp Conf; Bucknell; Med.

HILL, SUSAN; New Brighton Area HS; New Brighton, PA; (4); 35/141; Church Yth Grp; GAA; Letterman Clb; Varsity Clb; Chorus; Church Choir; Yrbk Sprt Ed; JV Var Cheerleading; L Trk; Hon Roll; Mt Union Coll; Sprts Med.

HILL, TERA L; Southern Fulton HS; Needmore, PA; (3); 1/90; Am Leg Aux Girls St; Science Clb; Trs Jr Cls; VP Stu Cncl; Var Bsktbl; Var Sftbl; Var Vllybl; Bausch & Lomb Sci Awd; High Hon Roll; Trs NHS; Ntl Sci Merit Awds 86; Intl Frgn Lang Awd 86; Shippensburg U; Accntng.

HILL, THOMAS; Cedar Grove Christian Acad; Philadelphia, PA; (3); Church Yth Grp; Yrbk Stf; Var Bsbl; Var Socr; Hon Roll; Temple; Finance.

HILL, WILBERT; Penns Manor HS; Clymer, PA; (3); 1/97; Boy Scts; VP Chess Clb; Church Yth Grp; Chorus; School Musical; Pres Jr Cls; High Hon Roll; NHS; COMP Sci.

HILLAND, MERLINDA; Connellsville HS; Mt Pleasant, PA; (3); Art Clb; FBLA; Office Aide; Spanish Clb; Rep Stu Cncl; Var JV Sftbl; Var Vllybl; Hon Roll; Vlybl Ltr 84-85; Connellsville.

HILLEBRAND, JULIE; Elk County Christian HS; St Marys, PA; (4); 15/79; Letterman Clb; Pep Clb; Ski Clb; Band; Concert Band; Var L Crs Cntry; Var L Trk; High Hon Roll; Hon Roll; Rotary Awd; 4 Yr Vrsty Ltr Wnr In Cross Cntry & Track & Field 83-87; IN U Of PA; Bus.

HILLEGAS, HEIDI; Shanksville-Stonycreek HS; Friedens, PA; (3) 8/34; Church Yth Grp; Mrchg Band; Yrbk Stf; Stu Cncl; Var Cheerleading; Twrlr; Hon Roll; Spanish NHS; Trvl Bus.

HILLENBRAND, DEBRA; Council Rock HS; Holland, PA; (3); 66/908; Cmnty Wkr; Library Aide; L Bsktbl; Im Coach Actv; L Sftbl; High Hon Roll; NHS; Dvlpmntl Psych.

HILLER, DAWN; Quaker Valley HS; Leetsdale, PA; (4); 25/157; Church Yth Grp; Exploring; Chorus; Flag Corp; Var JV Bsktbl; Crs Cntry; Var Trk; Var Capt Vllybl; High Hon Roll; Hon Roll; FBLA Awd Typng 85; U Of Pittsburgh; Orthdntst.

HILLER, MELISSA; Donegal HS; Mount Joy, PA; (2); Drama Clb; Hon Roll; Outstndng Prtcptn-Creativity 87; Engl.

HILLER, PAUL; Northeast Catholic HS; Philadelphia, PA; (4); 14/358; Im Bowling; High Hon Roll; Hon Roll; NHS; Awd For 1st Pl Hnrs Smstr Brk 84-86; Abv Avrg Mrk Grmn For Smstr 84-87; Holy Fmly Coll; Scndry Ed.

HILLIARD, CATHERINE; Big Spring HS; Newville, PA; (4); 18/188; Pres 4-H; Chorus; Var Capt Crs Cntry; Var L Trk; Hon Roll; NHS; VFW Awd; US Army Reserve Natl Schlr Athl Awd 87; Carlisle Barracks PA Acad Achvt Awd 87; Female Ath Yr 87; Western MD Coll; Phy Therapy.

HILLIARD, CHAD; Shaler SR HS; Pittsburgh, PA; (3); 119/496; JA; French Hon Soc; High Hon Roll; Hon Roll; Art Inst Of Pittsburg; Advrtsng.

HILLIARD, KEITH; Homer-Center HS; Homer City, PA; (3); 33/120; Camera Clb; Letterman Clb; Ski Clb; Varsity Clb; Band; Jazz Band; Yrbk Phtg; Rep Stu Cncl; Var L Ftbl; Var Capt Trk; U Of Pittsburgh; Bio.

HILLIARD, MARK; Alizuippa JR SR HS; Aliquippa, PA; (2); Church Yth Grp; Math Tm; Band; Ftbl; Wt Lftg; High Hon Roll; Hon Roll.

HILLIARD, PATTI; Butler SR HS; Renfrew, PA; (4); Pres Church Yth Grp; Cmnty Wkr; French Clb; Office Aide; Chorus; Church Choir; School Musical; Rep Stu Cncl; Vllybl; Hon Roll; Fnlst Butler Cnty JR Miss Pgnt 87; Slippery Rck U; Elem Spcl Ed.

HILLIARD, ROY; Cumberland Valley HS; Camp Hill, PA; (3); Am Leg Boys St; Trs Pres SADD; Jazz Band; Mrchg Band; Symp Band; Trs Pres Stu Cncl; JV Var Bsbl; JV Socr; Hon Roll; Key Clb; Hugh O Brian Ldrshp Awd 86; Stu Advsry Bd Harrisburg Yth Forum 87; Stu Cncl Adv Ldrshp Pgm 86; Bus.

HILLIBUSH, ROXANNE; Mahanoy Area HS; Mahanoy City, PA; (3); SADD; Drill Tm; Mrchg Band; Nwsp Stf; Yrbk Stf; Twrlr; Hon Roll; Cmnty Wkr; FHA; Spanish Clb; Hnr Soc 85-86; Bus Adm.

HILLIS, SHELLY; Du Bois Area SR HS; Reynoldsvl, PA; (2); VP Pres 4-H; Chorus; Stu Cncl; 4-H Awd; Mst Imprvd Hrs & Rdr 4-H 85; Outstndng 4-H Stu 85; Rsrv Grnd Chmpn 86; Marine Bio.

HILLMAN, DENISE; Pottstown HS; Pottstown, PA; (4); Sec French Clb; Key Clb; Band; Concert Band; Jazz Band; Mrchg Band; Nwsp Rptr; Yrbk Stf; NHS; Kutztown U; Poltcl Sci.

HILSEN, KERRI; South Allegheny HS; Port Vue, PA; (3); 5/187; French Clb; Girl Scts; VP JA; Y-Teens; Band; Chorus; School Musical; Yrbk Stf; Powder Puff Ftbl; NHS; Engrng.

HILSON, NICOLE; West Scranton HS; Scranton, PA; (2); 2/317; Church Yth Grp; FNA; JA; Latin Clb; Ski Clb; Orch; Var Trk; High Hon Roll; Jr NHS; Vet.

HILSTOLSKY, KIM; Wyoming Area HS; Pittston, PA; (3); Art Clb; Spanish Clb; Gym.

HILTEBEITEL, JESSICA; Springford SR HS; Royersford, PA; (2); 15/289; Band; Concert Band; Jazz Band; Mrchg Band; Orch; Yrbk Phtg; High Hon Roll; Hon Roll; NHS; Music.

HILTON JR, JAMES; Elizabethtown Area Schl Dist HS; Elizabethtown, PA; (3); 28/259; Var L Bsktbl; Var L Socr; Hon Roll.

HILTZ, HEATHER; Solanco HS; New Providence, PA; (2); 60/289; Band; Jazz Band; Mrchg Band; Sec Soph Cls; Sec Jr Cls; Var Bsktbl; Var Fld Hcky; Var Sftbl; Jr NHS; MVP Hcky Tm Goalie 86; Stck Brkr.

HILWIG, STUART J; Emmaus HS; Macungie, PA; (4); 45/453; AFS; Cmnty Wkr; Exploring; German Clb; Hosp Aide; Key Clb; Model UN; Ski Clb; SADD; Orch; Schlrshp From German Gvrmnt Smmr Exch Prog 84; Pre-Med.

HILYARD, SHARON; Henderson HS; W Chester, PA; (3); 147/367; Church Yth Grp; Key Clb; Band; Mrchg Band; All-St Band; Dist Band; Psych.

HIMELRIGHT, ERIC; Cedar Crest HS; Lebanon, PA; (1); Boy Scts; Church Yth Grp; German Clb; Pep Clb; Y-Teens; L Swmmng; God Cntry Awd; Hon Roll; Supr Prfrmnce Awd 83; Penn ST U.

HIMES, CATHY; West Perry SR HS; New Bloomfield, PA; (3); 21/257; Office Aide; Spanish Clb; Varsity Clb; Band; Concert Band; Jazz Band; Mrchg Band; Pep Band; Certfd Prfsnl Modl 87; Bus.

HIMES, CHRISTINE; Lewistown Area HS; Lewistown, PA; (3); AFS; French Clb; VP Key Clb; Varsity Clb; Var Fld Hcky; Var Trk; High Hon Roll; NHS.

HIMES, DEBORAH; Blairsville SR HS; Blairsville, PA; (4); 7/123; Drama Clb; Band; Co-Capt Color Guard; Concert Band; Mrchg Band; Nwsp Rptr; NHS; Pres Schlr; Duquesne U Schlr 87; Stu Cncl Schlrshp 87; Jobs Daughter Schlrshp 87; Duquesne U; Bus Mgmt.

HIMES, GINA; Biglerville HS; Aspers, PA; (3); 36/109; Library Aide; Spanish Clb; Varsity Clb; Var Cheerleading; Var Fld Hcky; Var Sftbl; Hon Roll; Dental Hygentist.

HIMES, JULIE; Dubois Area HS; Reynoldsvl, PA; (3); Med Prof.

HIMES, LAURA; Hollidaysburg Area SR HS; Hollidaysburg, PA; (4); 37/365; Hosp Aide; JA; Latin Clb; SADD; Varsity Clb; Sftbl; Vllybl; Hon Roll; NHS; Wmns Clb Schlrshp 87; Acad H Awd 87; Mst Pnts Awd-Vllybll 87; U Pittsburgh Johnstown; Phys Th.

HIMES, MICHELLE; St Marys Area HS; Kersey, PA; (3); 13/269; Hosp Aide; Sec VP SADD; Chorus; Concert Band; Mrchg Band; Stat Trk; Hon Roll; NHS; Ntl Merit Ltr; Govrs Schl For Intl Stud 87; Humannities Dept U Of Pittsburg Bradfor 87; Comm.

HIMES, MISSI; St Marys Area HS; St Marys, PA; (2); FBLA; Jmstwn Bus Coll; Accntnt.

HIMMEL, ALAN; Taylor Allderdice HS; Pittsburgh, PA; (3); Sec Trs Church Yth Grp; Ski Clb; Yrbk Stf; Bus.

HINCHEE, KELLY; Mount Union Area HS; Huntingdon, PA; (3); 22/152; Church Yth Grp; FBLA; Hosp Aide; SADD; Band; Concert Band; Drm Mjr(t); Jazz Band; Yrbk Stf; Twrlr; Shippensburg U; Elem Ed.

HINCHER, TIMOTHY; West Perry HS; New Germantown, PA; (3); Varsity Clb; JV Crs Cntry; JV Diving; Var Socr; Im Swmmng; Var Trk; Im Vllybl; Var Wrstlng; Hon Roll; Electrncs.

HINCHLIFFE, MICHAEL T; Council Park HS; Holland, PA; (3); German Clb; Ftbl; Prfct Atten Awd.

HINCY, VALERIE; Ringgold HS; Eighty Four, PA; (4); 20/379; Church Yth Grp; Girl Scts; Pep Clb; Chorus; Drill Tm; Variety Show; Off Soph Cls; Pom Pon; Hon Roll; Grl Sct Slvr Awd 84.

HINDMAN, JENNIFER A; Central HS; Philadelphia, PA; (4); 30/340; Dance Clb; French Clb; Office Aide; Teachers Aide; Drill Tm; Orch; Stu Cncl; God Cntry Awd; Hon Roll; Ntl Merit SF; NYU; Dance.

HINDMAN, PAM; Moniteau HS; Boyers, PA; (3); FBLA; Chorus; Cheerleading; Vllybl; Exec Sec.

HINDS, CHERI; Seneca HS; N East, PA; (3); 7/160; Spanish Clb; Drill Tm; Pom Pon; High Hon Roll; Hon Roll; NHS; Intr Design.

HINDSLEY, COLLEEN; Archbishop Carroll HS; Villanova, PA; (3); Intnl Clb; School Musical; Var Capt Cheerleading; French Hon Soc; High Hon Roll; Hon Roll; Diocesan Schlrs Awd 86-87; Frgn Lang.

HINDSMAN, KYLE; Abington SR HS; Willow Grove, PA; (3); 114/502; Chess Clb; Chorus; Madrigals; Rep Stu Cncl; Camera Clb; Stage Crew; Bus Admin.

HINDSON, KAMRON; Fairview HS; Fairview, PA; (3); French Clb; Varsity Clb; Nwsp Stf; Rep Frsh Cls; Rep Soph Cls; Rep Jr Cls; Tennis; Trk; Hon Roll; NHS; Comms.

HINE, LORI; Coughlin HS; Wilkes Barre, PA; (4); Concert Band; Drm Mjr(t); Mrchg Band; Stat L Bsktbl; Var L Fld Hcky; L Mgr(s); L Score Keeper; L Stat Vllybl; Hon Roll.

HINELINE, MICHELE; Western Wayne HS; Lake Ariel, PA; (3); 32/189; SADD; Hon Roll; Prfct Atten Awd.

HINER, KRISTI; Corry Area HS; Corry, PA; (3); Teachers Aide; Drm Mjr(t); Stat Bsktbl; Score Keeper; Twrlr; Hon Roll; Pres Schlr; Delta Epsilon Phi Germn Hnr Soc 85; Clarion U; Bus Admin.

HINERMAN, DANA; Elizabeth Forward HS; Mckeesport, PA; (3); 53/350; French Clb; Library Aide; Chorus; Co-Capt Color Guard; Mrchg Band; Twrlr; Hon Roll; Psych.

HINES, JAMIE; Elizabeth Forward HS; Elizabeth, PA; (3); Chorus; School Musical; School Play; Diving; Socr; Dstngshd AM HS Stu 86; Med Secr.

HINES, SHEILA; Bishop Carroll HS; Cresson, PA; (4); 12/107; Pep Clb; Spanish Clb; SADD; Yrbk Stf; Var Capt Bsktbl; Hon Roll; NHS; Bio.

HINES, WILLIAM; Hazelton SR HS; Beaver Mdws, PA; (2); Boy Scts; Cmnty Wkr; French Clb; Band; Stage Crew; Yrbk Stf; Var Bowling; Hon Roll; Am Leg Axlry Dept PA Schl Awd 83; Sct Of Yr 84; Kng-Qn Hrts Ct 86; Penn ST; Elec Engrng.

HINISH, KAREN; Bedford Area HS; Bedford, PA; (4); 39/176; Trs Church Yth Grp; Ski Clb; SADD; Band; Concert Band; Mrchg Band; Pep Band; Hon Roll; Williamsport Area CC; Srgcl Te.

HINISH, MARY; Everett Area HS; Everett, PA; (4); 5/106; Computer Clb; French Clb; Math Clb; Varsity Clb; Band; Pres Soph Cls; Off Stu Cncl; Sftbl; High Hon Roll; NHS; U Of DE; Poltcl Sci.

HINK, STEPHANIE; Union Area HS; New Castle, PA; (3); Drama Clb; French Clb; Teachers Aide; Band; Concert Band; Jazz Band; Mrchg Band; Pep Band; Rptr Chess Clb; Lit Mag; Cert Merit Am Chem Soc 87; Cmnctns.

HINKEL, CHRISTOPHER; Danville SR HS; Danville, PA; (2); Ski Clb; Rep Frsh Cls; JV Bsbl; Var Golf; DAR Awd; High Hon Roll.

HINKLE, CRAIG; Bermudian Springs HS; York Spgs, PA; (3); 4/120; Boy Scts; Letterman Clb; Varsity Clb; JV Bsktbl; Var L Ftbl; Var L Trk; High Hon Roll; Hon Roll; Church Yth Grp; Band; Acctg.

HINKLE, DAVID; Blacklick Valley HS; Nanty Glo, PA; (2); Trs Church Yth Grp; Computer Clb; Concert Band; Mrchg Band; Nwsp Rptr; High Hon Roll; Hon Roll; Prfct Atten Awd; VISTOS Tutor 86-87; Frnscs 86; Physcn.

HINKLE, JULIE; Northern Lebanon HS; Lebanon, PA; (4); 15/167; Church Yth Grp; Office Aide; Band; Chorus; Church Choir; Mrchg Band; School Musical; School Play; Stage Crew; Nwsp Ed-Chief; Cedar Crest Coll; Psych.

HINKLE, MARCI B; Springfield HS; Wyndmoor, PA; (3); Cmnty Wkr; JV Bsktbl; Socr; JV Sftbl; Im Vllybl; EPYSA U-14 U-16 Sccr 83-86; Rgnl Camp Sccr 84-85.

HINKLE, MICHELLE; Fleetwood Area HS; Fleetwood, PA; (3); 33/116; Spanish Clb; Flag Corp; JV Fld Hcky; Phrmcy.

HINKLE, RANDY; Fleetwood Area HS; Fleetwood, PA; (4); 5/116; Aud/Vis; Church Yth Grp; Library Aide; Chorus; School Musical; Yrbk Bus Mgr; Yrbk Stf; Lit Mag; Rep VP Stu Cncl; Tennis; Millersville; Chem.

HINKLE, SHARON; Hazleton HS; Drums, PA; (3); Church Yth Grp; Drama Clb; Girl Scts; Chorus; Color Guard; Mgr(s); Slvr Awd 87; Natl Awd Wnnr Frnch 84-85; Slvr Ldrshp Awd 87.

HINKLE, STACEY; Eastern York SR JR HS; Wrightsville, PA; (3); Church Yth Grp; SADD; Band; Concert Band; Jazz Band; Mrchg Band; Pep Band; Jr NHS; Voice Dem Awd; High Hon Roll.

HINKLE, THERESA; Weatherly Area HS; Weatherly, PA; (3); 3/55; Trs Computer Clb; FBLA; Sec Frsh Cls; Sec Soph Cls; Sec Jr Cls; Stu Cncl; JV Bsktbl; Var Sftbl; Hon Roll; Germ Achvt Awd 2nd Highest Ave; Engl Achvt Awd Highest Ave; Kutztown U.

HINKLE, TOBY; Greensburg Salem HS; Greensburg, PA; (2); 22/296; Church Yth Grp; German Clb; Hosp Aide; Ski Clb; Var Bsktbl; Sftbl; Var Vllybl; High Hon Roll; Jr NHS; Pre-Law.

HINKLER, DAVID ROSS; Fort Le Boeuf HS; Erie, PA; (4); 13/167; Church Yth Grp; Ftbl; Gym; Swmmng; Vllybl; Wrstlng; High Hon Roll; NHS; Ntl Merit Schol; Blck Blt Karate 87; Penn ST Erie; Elctrcl Engrng.

HINKO, VALERIE; Wyoming Seminary Prep Schl; Hudson, PA; (4); 7/86; Sec Cmnty Wkr; Drama Clb; Madrigals; Nwsp Ed-Chief; Ntl Merit SF; Hosp Aide; SADD; Chorus; School Musical; School Play; Tllrd Assoc Smmr Prgrm Schlrshp 86; A L Green Dvnprt Schlshp SR Yr 86; Cumlaude & March Ptry Prz 86; English.

HINMAN, ALICE; Cowanesque Valley HS; Westfield, PA; (2); Chess Clb; Church Yth Grp; Drama Clb; School Musical; Yrbk Stf; Stu Cncl; Trk; Stu Of Mo Awd 86-87; Bus.

HINMAN, REGINA; Cowanesque Valley HS; Westfield, PA; (3); Church Yth Grp; Drama Clb; SADD; School Musical; Yrbk Ed-Chief; Stu Cncl; Var Cheerleading; High Hon Roll; NHS; Stu Mnth Feb/Oct 86; Math.

HINSON, KEVIN; Homer Center HS; Lucernemines, PA; (3); Varsity Clb; Band; Chorus; Concert Band; Mrchg Band; Orch; School Musical; Var Ftbl; Var L Trk; Hon Roll; Carnegie Mellon; Music.

HINTON, BRIAN; Ridgway Area HS; Ridgway, PA; (3); Church Yth Grp; Cmnty Wkr; Spanish Clb; Ftbl; Trk; Wt Lftg; Wrstlng; Hon Roll; IN U; Law Enfrcmnt.

HINTON, KIMBERLY; Kennard Dale HS; Stewartstown, PA; (2); Art Clb; Dance Clb; French Clb; Chorus; Concert Band; Orch; Var Trk; DAR Awd; High Hon Roll; Dance Clb; Sci/Engrng Aprntcshp At Abrdn Prvng Grnd MD 87; U DE; Nclr Engr.

HINZ, ELLEN; North Pocono HS; Moscow, PA; (4); 12/235; Church Yth Grp; Dance Clb; Concert Band; Mrchg Band; Orch; Yrbk Stf; Var Capt Trk; High Hon Roll; NHS; H Lrn Clmnts Schlrshp 87; MVP Trck 87; Trck Dist II 200 M & 1600 M Rly Tm 87; Outstndng Perfmnc PE; U Of Scranton; Math Educ.

HIPP, CAROLINE; Spring-Ford SR HS; Royersford, PA; (2); Math Clb; Spanish Clb; Concert Band; Mrchg Band; JV Lcrss; Hon Roll; NHS; Sci.

HIPPERT, KIM; Fleetwood HS; Kutztown, PA; (3); 15/120; Model UN; Ski Clb; School Musical; VP Jr Cls; VP Sr Cls; Var Fld Hcky; Im Vllybl; Hon Roll; Bus Mgmt.

HIPPLE, ANDREW; Montoursville HS; Trout Run, PA; (3); 20/185; VP Rptr FFA; Key Clb; Gov Hon Prg Awd; Hon Roll; NHS; PA Gov Schl For Ag 87; PA ST U; Ag Educ.

HIPPLE, BECKY; Montoursville HS; Trout Run, PA; (4); 25/174; FBLA; FFA; German Clb; Office Aide; Teachers Aide; Chorus; Church Choir; Hon Roll; Lycoming Cnty Dairy Princess 86; Central PA Bus Schl; Paralegal.

HIPPLE, DORI; Meadville Area SR HS; Meadville, PA; (2); French Clb; Chorus; Nwsp Stf; JV L Cheerleading; L Trk; High Hon Roll; Hon Roll.

HIPWELL, TIM L; North Allegheny HS; Bradfordwoods, PA; (4); 46/659; JA; Thesps; Chorus; School Musical; School Play; Variety Show; Stu Cncl; Trk; Hon Roll; Jr NHS; JR Rotarian 86-87; Outstndng Merit Phys Ed Awd 86; Bucknell U; Polit Sci.

HIRIAK, MARY LYNNE; Saint Pius X HS; Pottstown, PA; (1); 4/148; PAVAS; High Hon Roll; Physcl Sci Awd 87.

HIRIAK, NICHOLAS F; St Pius X HS; Pottstown, PA; (4); Aud/Vis; Science Clb; School Play; Stage Crew; Trk; Hon Roll; NHS; I Dare You Ldrshp & Father Bally Knights Columbus Awds 87; York Coll; Accntng.

HIRSCH, JEFF; Hempfield HS; Lancaster, PA; (3); 40/400; Church Yth Grp; Im Bsktbl; Var Golf; Var Ice Hcky; JV Socr; Hon Roll; NHS; Bus.

HIRSCH, KAREN; Abington SR HS; Abington, PA; (3); 51/502; Orch; School Musical; Nwsp Rptr; Nwsp Stf; Yrbk Stf; Lit Mag; Hon Roll; Ntl Merit Ltr; Hosp Aide; Sec Frsh Cls; Schlstc Wrtng Awd Hnrbl Mntn Poetry 87; Govs Schl For Arts Poetry 87; Engl.

HIRSH, JEREMY L; Akiba Hebrew Acad; Philadelphia, PA; (4); DECA; FBLA; Nwsp Ed-Chief; Nwsp Rptr; Yrbk Ed-Chief; Yrbk Phtg; Lit Mag; JV Crs Cntry; Swmmng; Bausch & Lomb Sci Awd; Hugh O Brien Yth Fndtn; Temple U Math Cmptn 3rd Pl; Temple U Nwswrtng Cntst 2nd Pl.

HIRSHEY, ANDY; Lower Merwin HS; Philadelphia, PA; (3); Var JV Ice Hcky; Communciations.

HISCHEMELLOR, STEVE; North Catholic HS; Pittsburgh, PA; (3); Debate Tm; German Clb; Ski Clb; Hon Roll; PA ST U; Aerospace Engnrng.

HISIRO, CARRIE; Charleroi Area HS; Charleroi, PA; (3); Ski Clb; Varsity Clb; Off Frsh Cls; Rep Soph Cls; Off Jr Cls; Bsktbl; Powder Puff Ftbl; Socr; Sftbl; Hon Roll; PA Free Enterprize Week 86; U Of Pittsburgh; Dental Hygn.

HISSONG, BRIAN; James Buchanan HS; Lemasters, PA; (2); Church Yth Grp; Varsity Clb; VP Jr Cls; Var Socr; Band; Concert Band; Mrchg Band; Off Frsh Cls; Off Soph Cls; Swmmng; PA ST Mont Alto; Architecture.

HISSONG, CRAIG; James Buchanan HS; Lemasters, PA; (3); Church Yth Grp; Cmnty Wkr; Debate Tm; Letterman Clb; Mrchg Band; Pres Stu Cncl; Var Socr; Capt Swmmng; Wt Lftg; Hon Roll; Law.

HITCHCOCK, LESLEY; Elk Lake HS; Montrose, PA; (2); Church Yth Grp; 4-H; Band; Chorus; JV Var Bsktbl; Var JV Fld Hcky; Var JV Sftbl; Hon Roll.

HITCHCOCK, MONICA; Elk Lake HS; Montrose, PA; (2); Church Yth Grp; 4-H; Band; JV Var Bsktbl; Var Fld Hcky; Var Trk; Hon Roll.

HITCHINS, ALISSA; Plum SR HS; Pittsburgh, PA; (3); Rptr FBLA; Office Aide; Hon Roll; Pittsburgh Art Inst; Comm Art.

HITE, KIMBERLY; Bishop Carroll HS; Loretto, PA; (4); 33/106; Drama Clb; 4-H; Pep Clb; Ski Clb; Spanish Clb; SADD; Mrchg Band; Yrbk Stf; Cheerleading; Hon Roll; Bucknell Ldrshp Conf Bucknell U 86; U Of Pitt Johnstown; Psych.

HITNER, LISA; Upper Dublin HS; Ft Washington, PA; (4); JA; Teachers Aide; Fld Hcky; Socr; Hon Roll.

HITTINGER, JAIME; Freedom HS; Bethlehem, PA; (3); 39/509; Church Yth Grp; Exploring; Hosp Aide; Pep Clb; SADD; Chorus; Yrbk Bus Mgr; Hon Roll; NHS; Dntstry.

HITZ, KYLE; Central Dauphin HS; Harrisubrg, PA; (2); French Clb; Ftbl; Tennis; Trk; Hon Roll; Jr NHS; Penn ST; Comp Pgmr.

HIXENBAUGH, SHARON; Canan-Mc Millan SR HS; Mcdonald, PA; (4); 125/367; French Clb; FBLA; Ski Clb; JV Cheerleading; Hon Roll; Sawyer Bus Schl; Trvl Ind.

HIXON, KEVIN; Plum Borough SR HS; Pittsburgh, PA; (2); 154/410; Boy Scts; Chess Clb; Church Yth Grp; Drama Clb; JV Ftbl; Socr; Hon Roll; Sgn Lng Boyce Comm Coll 86; Boliva Drm Grp 87; Military Svc; Frstry.

HIXSON, EMILY; Southmoreland SR HS; Scottdale, PA; (4); 8/230; Drama Clb; German Clb; Math Clb; Chorus; Church Choir; School Musical; School Play; Variety Show; Nwsp Stf; Yrbk Stf; Grmn Natl Hnr Soc Awd 86-87; Pres Acdmc Ftnss Awd 86-87; Houghton Coll; Music Ther.

HIZA, KIMBERLY; Hazleton HS; Hazleton, PA; (3); 110/425; FBLA; Pep Clb; Chorus; JV Im Bsktbl; Hon Roll; Cdts Clb 86-87; ROTC; Acctng.

HLADCZUK, THOMAS; HS Of Engr & Sci; Pliladelphia, PA; (3); High Hon Roll; NHS; 4th Pl Ordrs Sons Italy Law Day Esy Cntst 86; Alpha Delta Kappa Wrtng Prtflo Cmptn Hnr Mntn 87; Temple U Schl Cmnctns; Jrnlsm.

HLAVAC, JULIE ANNE; Bishop O Reilly HS; Swoyersville, PA; (4); Church Yth Grp; Cmnty Wkr; Dance Clb; Drama Clb; English Clb; JA; Math Clb; Pep Clb; Political Wkr; Science Clb; Spn Awd 83-86; Chem Awd 84; Natl Hstry Day Cont Awd 84; U Scranton; Pre-Med.

HLAVAC, KERRY ANN; Bishop O Reilly HS; Swoyersville, PA; (3); Spanish Clb; SADD; Stu Cncl; Cheerleading; Sftbl; Hon Roll; NHS; Spanish NHS; Bloomsburg; Chldhd Devlpmnt.

HLAVATY, JOHN; Pine Grove Area HS; Pine Grove, PA; (3); Boy Scts; ROTC; JV Var Ftbl; Prfct Atten Awd; PA Fish Cmssn Cnsrvtn Awd & JROTC Officer 86; Wrld Cnsrvtn Awd 85; Penn ST.

HLUSHAK, MIKE; Bishop Mc Devitt HS; Harrisburg, PA; (3); 3/225; FBLA; Service Clb; Rep Frsh Cls; Rep Soph Cls; Rep Jr Cls; Rep Stu Cncl; JV Bsbl; Bsktbl; High Hon Roll; NHS; Bus.

HLUSHAK, TRACEY; Bishop Mc Devitt HS; Harrisburg, PA; (4); 11/200; Service Clb; Rep Stu Cncl; Capt Cheerleading; NHS; Elem Educ.

HNARAS, ANNA STACIE; Fairchance-Georges HS; Uniontown, PA; (3); Church Yth Grp; French Clb; Yrbk Stf; Var JV Bsktbl; Hon Roll; Jr NHS; Pres Schlr.

HNASKO, SCOTT; Hazleton HS; Hazleton, PA; (2); Capt Scholastic Bowl; Mgr Nwsp Bus Mgr; Rptr Nwsp Stf; Rep Stu Cncl; Hon Roll; Penn ST U; Writing.

HNAT, BRIAN; West Hazleton HS; W Hazleton, PA; (2); 21/255; Var Ftbl; Im Wt Lftg; Var Wrstlng; Hon Roll; Pres Acadmc Ftns Awd 86.

HNAT, JAMES; Methaeton HS; Collegeville, PA; (3); 24/381; Debate Tm; French Clb; Intnl Clb; Model UN; Office Aide; Red Cross Aide; Concert Band; Orch; School Musical; Socr; Schykill Vly Orchstra 84; Rotary Ldrshp Cmp 87.

HO, DANG L T; John Harris HS; Harrisburg, PA; (1); #12 In Class; Socr; Tennis.

HO, HUONG; John Harris HS; Harrisburg, PA; (3); 9/274; French Clb; Library Aide; Varsity Clb; Yrbk Stf; Off Jr Cls; Tennis; Hon Roll; Prfct Atten Awd; 2nd Hnrs 85-87; Penn ST; Pharmcst.

HO, QUI; Olney HS; Philadelphia, PA; (4); #11 In Class; Art Clb; Math Tm; Hon Roll; NHS; Scholar Wente & Williams 86-87; Spring Garden Coll; Mech Engr.

HO, VU CHAU; John Harris Campus HS; Harrisburg, PA; (1); 21/468; Tennis.

HO, WARREN; Unionville HS; West Chester, PA; (4); 1/316; FBLA; Mu Alpha Theta; Nwsp Sprt Ed; Trs Sr Cls; Rep Stu Cncl; Co-Capt Tennis; Ntl Merit Schol; Val; Natl Soc Profssnl Engrs Schlrshp; Community Schlrshp; Princeton U; Engrng.

HOAG, MARK; Ft Cherry HS; Mcdonald, PA; (4); Computer Clb; Drama Clb; Thesps; Band; Concert Band; Mrchg Band; Orch; Pep Band; School Play; Stage Crew; Bst Thspn 87; U Pittsburgh Bradford; Icthylgy.

HOAGLAND, KIMBERLY; Shenandoah Valley JR SR HS; Shenandoah, PA; (4); Nwsp Stf; Yrbk Stf; Co-Capt Crs Cntry; Capt Sftbl; Hon Roll; NHS.

HOATS, BRENDA; West Hazelton HS; Tresckow, PA; (3); 9/221; Church Yth Grp; Office Aide; Pep Clb; Ski Clb; Varsity Clb; Off Stu Cncl; Var JV Cheerleading; Coach Actv; High Hon Roll; NHS; Bloomsburg U; Offc Admin.

HOBBS, DAVE; Methacton SR HS; Norristown, PA; (3); JV Bsbl; JV Bsktbl; Im Crs Cntry; Im Ftbl; Im Lcrss; Im Swmmng; Im Wt Lftg; Cit Awd; High Hon Roll; Bus.

HOBBS, DUANE; Fairfield HS; Fairfield, PA; (3); 37/73; Band; Concert Band; Mrchg Band; School Musical; School Play; Swing Chorus; Var Crs Cntry; Var Trk; PA ST.

HOBBS, TRACY; Trinity HS; Washington, PA; (3); 50/400; French Clb; Pep Clb; High Hon Roll; Hon Roll.

HOBEREK, JODY LYNN; Burgettstown Area JR SR HS; Burgettstown, PA; (4); Drama Clb; French Clb; Mrchg Band; Symp Band; Tennis; Hon Roll; Jr NHS; NHS; Schlrshp Free Entrprs Wk, Mdrn Miss Pgnt, Pitt-Mc Donald Band Drm Corps East Semi-Fnls 86; WV U; Intl Stds.

HOCH, ERIC; Nazareth Area HS; Nazareth, PA; (3); 38/265; Boy Scts; Church Yth Grp; Drama Clb; School Musical; Stage Crew; Rep Stu Cncl; Crs Cntry; Trk; High Hon Roll; Hon Roll; PA ST; Biochem.

HOCH, JEREMY; Penn-Trafford HS; Irwin, PA; (2); JCL; Latin Clb; Math Clb; Varsity Clb; Crs Cntry; Trk; High Hon Roll; Natl Ltn Exam Slvr Mdl 87; Physics.

HOCH, KIMBERLY; Mechanicsburg SR HS; Mechanicsburg, PA; (3); 117/343; Am Leg Aux Girls St; Art Clb; Band; Concert Band; Mrchg Band; School Play; Chld Psych.

HOCHBERG, KATHERINE; Huntingdon Area HS; Huntingdon, PA; (4); 7/224; Pres SADD; Yrbk Ed-Chief; Cit Awd; DAR Awd; High Hon Roll; VP NHS; Pres Schlr; Pres Clsrm For Yng Amer 86; Sandy Ninninger Awd Key Clb-Hghst Awd 87; Svc To Schl 87; American U; Sclgy.

HOCK, KAREN; William Allen HS; Allentown, PA; (3); 25/610; Trs Pres Leo Clb; SADD; Yrbk Stf; Im Bowling; Hon Roll; Jr NHS; Lion Awd; NHS; 4th Pl History Day-Sr Project Div 86; Gifted Student 84-88.

HOCK, KRISTIE; Bloomsburg HS; Bloomsburg, PA; (4); 18/140; Drama Clb; FCA; Thesps; Varsity Clb; Chorus; Rep Stu Cncl; Capt Var Cheerleading; Socr; Hon Roll; NHS; Bloomsburg U; Bus Admin.

HOCKENBERRY, BARBARA; Shippensburg Area SR HS; Shippensburg, PA; (4); 15/217; Church Yth Grp; Capt Quiz Bowl; Band; Chorus; Jazz Band; School Musical; NHS; Qz Tm Tp Avrg & Mst Vlb Plyr 87-86; Shippensburg U; Math.

HOCKENBERRY, CARMIE; Fannett-Metal HS; Fannettsburg, PA; (4); Drama Clb; Varsity Clb; VICA; Color Guard; VP Frsh Cls; VP Soph Cls; VP Jr Cls; VP Sr Cls; Capt Cheerleading; Sftbl; Acad All Amer 85-86; Army.

HOCKENBERRY, DAWN; Penn-Trafford HS; Trafford, PA; (3); 15/301; Church Yth Grp; Hosp Aide; JCL; High Hon Roll; NHS; AFS; Drama Clb; Latin Clb; Acpl Chr; Band; HOBY Rep 86; Japan-US Sen Scholar SF 87; Congress-Bundestag Scholar Exch 87; Intl Rltns.

HOCKENBERRY, DOUGLAS; Lakeview HS; Mercer, PA; (4); 7/128; Pres Science Clb; Band; Concert Band; Mrchg Band; PA St U; Chmcl Engnrng.

HOCKENBERRY, JASON; Newport JR SR HS; Newport, PA; (3); 4/117; Stage Crew; Var Bsbl; Vllybl; Wt Lftg; High Hon Roll; NHS; Ntl Merit Ltr.

HOCKENBERRY, JOSEPH; Nazareth Area SR HS; Nazareth, PA; (3); 3/280; Church Yth Grp; Cmnty Wkr; JCL; Rep Frsh Cls; Var L Bsktbl; Var L Trk; High Hon Roll; Hon Roll; NHS; Prfct Atten Awd.

HOCKENBERRY, KELLY; Glendale JR SR HS; Flinton, PA; (4); 7/93; Pres Science Clb; Chorus; Yrbk Stf; Stat Sftbl; Hon Roll; NHS; Library Aide; Band; Flag Corp; Stat Bsktbl; Pres Acad Ftnss Awd 87; PA ST U; Bus Admin.

HOCKENBERRY, LORI; Newport JR SR HS; Newport, PA; (2); Band; Concert Band; Jazz Band; Mrchg Band; Pep Band; Hon Roll; Bnd Ltr 86; Hrsbrg Acad Med Arts; Dntl Astn.

HOCKENBERRY, MICHELLE; Newport HS; Newport, PA; (3); 6/117; School Play; Stu Cncl; Var Bsktbl; Var Fld Hcky; JV Sftbl; Trk; High Hon Roll; Hon Roll; NHS; Psych.

HOCKENBERRY, SHENDELLE; Juniata HS; Honey Grove, PA; (3); Chorus; Color Guard; Concert Band; Mrchg Band; Capt Yrbk Stf; Pres Frsh Cls; Cert Merit Outstndng Achvt Schlrshp 82-83; Cert Merit Outstndng Achvt Schlrshp 83-84; Crmnl Jstc.

HOCKER, AMY; Ridley SR HS; Milmont Park, PA; (3); 95/423; Church Yth Grp; Pep Clb; Trs Soph Cls; Trs Jr Cls; Trs Sr Cls; Rep Stu Cncl; Var JV Fld Hcky; JV Lcrss; JV Trk; Ski Clb; Hugh O Brian Yth Fndtn Ldrshp Sem 86; Nrsg.

HOCKINS, SHANE; Windber Area HS; Windber, PA; (3); 19/128; Debate Tm; Drama Clb; French Clb; Capt Quiz Bowl; Band; Jazz Band; Mrchg Band; Nwsp Ed-Chief; NHS; Pres Schlr; Attended 1987 PA Governor's Schl For Internatl Studies; Intl Stdy.

HODGE, MELISSA; Yough SR HS; W Newton, PA; (3); Sec Church Yth Grp; Mgr Drama Clb; French Clb; FBLA; Library Aide; Pep Clb; Band; Chorus; Church Choir; Concert Band.

HODGE, SABRINA; Exeter SR HS; Reading, PA; (3); 33/241; Church Yth Grp; JA; Varsity Clb; Chorus; Mrchg Band; Yrbk Ed-Chief; Var Bsktbl; Var Fld Hcky; Var Trk; Hon Roll; Exec Yth Rep For St James Chapel Corp 86; Penn; Accntnt.

HODGE, SELENA; Little Flower Catholic HS For Girls; Philadelphia, PA; (3); #90 In Class; Church Yth Grp; Spanish Clb; Teachers Aide; Chorus; Church Choir; School Musical; School Play; Stage Crew; Rep Frsh Cls; Capt Trk; Treas Blck Stu Lg 85-86; VP Blck Stu Lg 86-87; Flowerette 87-88; Pierce JC; Real Est.

HODGSON, CHRISTINE; Chichester SR HS; Aston, PA; (3); 51/297; GAA; Spanish Clb; Varsity Clb; Stu Cncl; Var Cheerleading; JV Sftbl; Twrlr; Hon Roll; Spanish NHS; Penn ST; Nrsg.

HODIL, BRYAN M; Shaler Area SR HS; Pittsburgh, PA; (4); 84/509; Church Yth Grp; Ski Clb; L Var Crs Cntry; Var Capt Trk; High Hon Roll; Hon Roll; MVP Trck 87; Grove City Coll; Engrng.

HODOS, BRYAN; Bishop Mc Cort HS; Johnstown, PA; (3); Math Tm; Mu Alpha Theta; Spanish Clb; Chorus; School Musical; Pres Jr Cls; Ice Hcky; High Hon Roll; NHS; Spanish NHS.

HODOWANEC, STEFANIE; Reading SR HS; Reading, PA; (3); 16/720; Church Yth Grp; Math Tm; Band; Chorus; Concert Band; Drm Mjr(t); Jazz Band; Mrchg Band; Orch; Pep Band; Zeswitz Music Awd 85; Long Fmly Stu Athlt Awd 85; Schlstc Pin 86; Med.

HODOWANEC, TANYA MARIE; Exeter Township HS; Birdsboro, PA; (4); 4/216; Drama Clb; Quiz Bowl; Co-Capt Flag Corp; School Play; Variety Show; VP Sr Cls; Bsktbl; Tennis; High Hon Roll; Jr NHS; HOBY Rep 85; Outstndng Grmn Stu 87; Exeter Twp Educ Assn Awd 87; Millersvl U; Scndry Educ.

HOEGEL, ERICH; Hempfield SR HS; Greensburg, PA; (3); Am Leg Boys St; Exploring; VICA; Hon Roll; Am Lgn Bsbl 87; Hempfield Rcrtn Bsbl 76-86; Army; Mason.

HOEHN, BRIAN; Central Bucks East HS; Pipersville, PA; (3); 80/505; Aud/Vis; Boy Scts; Church Yth Grp; Cmnty Wkr; Red Cross Aide; Stage Crew; JV Var Bsbl; Var Bsktbl; JV Var Ftbl; Lion Awd; Eagle Sct Awd 86.

HOENIG JR, RONALD M; Rochester Area HS; Rochester, PA; (3); 12/174; Church Yth Grp; VP JA; Ski Clb; Yrbk Stf; High Hon Roll; Prfct Atten Awd; Areonautical Engr.

HOEPFL, SUZANNE; Upper Darby HS; Upr Darby, PA; (3); GAA; Chorus; Stage Crew; Sftbl; Hon Roll; Boca Ratton/Villinova; Psych.

HOERGER, HOLLY; Bethel Park SR HS; Pgh, PA; (4); VP FBLA; CC Awd; Hon Roll; IN U Of PA; Finance.

HOETZLEIN, SUSAN; Baldwin HS; Pittsburgh, PA; (3); 98/473; Church Yth Grp; French Clb; Ski Clb; Nwsp Rptr; Rep Jr Cls; Rep Sr Cls; Var L Crs Cntry; Var L Trk; Hon Roll; Arts Apprntceshp Pgm Dimension Arch 87-88; Arch.

HOEY, ERIN; Norwin SR HS; N Huntingdon, PA; (3); GAA; SADD; Teachers Aide; VICA; Hon Roll; 3rd Pl Local Cake Decrtng Comptn 87; Sec VICA Club 87; Johnson & Wales; Pastry Chef.

HOFF, BRAQUEL; Spring Grove Area SR HS; Codorus, PA; (3); 7/304; Sec Church Yth Grp; JA; Varsity Clb; Church Choir; Rep Stu Cncl; Var L Fld Hcky; Var L Trk; High Hon Roll; Pres NHS; VFW Awd; Jr Achvt Outstndng Emply Rnnr-Up 86-87; 3rd Pl St Trck 86 & 87; Outstndng Grl Athltc 86 & 87.

HOFF, JOSH; Upper Moreland HS; Horsham, PA; (4); 6/254; Computer Clb; Math Clb; Jazz Band; Mrchg Band; High Hon Roll; NHS; Ntl Merit Ltr; Chess Clb; French Clb; Key Clb; Stu Of Month 86; Chem Excllnc Awd 86 & 87; Philadelphia Sci Cncl Tlnt Srch Fnlst 87; U Of PA; Comp Sci Engr.

HOFFA, STEFANIE; Conrad Weiser HS; Wernersville, PA; (3); Church Yth Grp; Exploring; JCL; VICA; Mrchg Band; Hon Roll; Stu Of Quartr 86-87; Csmtlgst.

HOFFACKER, WHITNEY; Hickory HS; Hermitage, PA; (3); 23/180; Boy Scts; Varsity Clb; Band; Chorus; School Musical; Stage Crew; Crs Cntry; Wrstlng; NHS; Spanish NHS; PA ST; Civil Engrng.

HOFFEDITZ, STEVE; James Buchanan HS; Mercersburg, PA; (4); Pres VP FFA; Varsity Clb; Rep Stu Cncl; JV Bsktbl; JV Var Socr; Cit Awd; Hon Roll; NHS; Prfct Atten Awd; Wlbr Grssnckl Awd 87; Agricltr.

HOFFER, BETH; Northern Lebanon HS; Jonestown, PA; (2); 35/208; Church Yth Grp; Pres 4-H; Quiz Bowl; Science Clb; Stage Crew; L Crs Cntry; Mgr(s); Trk; Hon Roll.

HOFFER, BRADLEY; Cedar Crest HS; Lebanon, PA; (3); French Clb; German Clb; Hon Roll; Music.

HOFFER, CAROL; Hempfield HS; E Petersburg, PA; (4); 5/415; Chess Clb; VP Pres Church Yth Grp; Math Tm; Quiz Bowl; Rep Stu Cncl; Coach Actv; Fld Hcky; High Hon Roll; NHS; Stu Mnth 87; Lanco Credit Union Gerald Fortney Mem Scholar 87; Yorktowne Bus Inst Bus Olymps 1st 87; Elizabethtown Coll; Acctng.

HOFFER, DENISE; Abraham Lincoln HS; Philadelphia, PA; (3); 39/519; Church Yth Grp; Band; Sec Chorus; Church Choir; Concert Band; Drm Mjr(t); Jazz Band; Madrigals; Mrchg Band; Orch; Biochem.

HOFFER, KIMBERLY; Mt Pleasant Area HS; Latrobe, PA; (2); Church Yth Grp; German Clb; Ski Clb; Concert Band; Mrchg Band; Rep Frsh Cls; Hnrb Mntn Humanities Day Ethnic Foods 85-86; Audiolgy.

HOFFER, LEANN; Allentown Central Catholic HS; Whitehall, PA; (3); Dance Clb; Key Clb; Spanish Clb; Dance Awds 82 & 87; ST & Natl Dance Comptns Bst Perf 82, Tlnt Comptn Overall Achvr 83; Philadelphia Coll; Dance.

HOFFERT, KURT; Exeter SR HS; Reading, PA; (3); 8/250; Key Clb; Band; Concert Band; Jazz Band; Mrchg Band; Orch; Pep Band; School Musical; Stu Cncl; High Hon Roll; Dist Orch 84-86; Co Band & Orch 84-87; Bio.

HOFFMAN, AMANDA; Freedom HS; Bethlehem, PA; (4); 200/433; Hosp Aide; Spanish Clb; Bsktbl; Crs Cntry; Sftbl; Hon Roll; G F Goodwin Schlrshp 87; IN U; Bio.

HOFFMAN, AMY; Belle Vernon Area HS; Belle Vernon, PA; (3); Debate Tm; NFL; Pep Clb; Nwsp Stf; Ed Yrbk Stf; Powder Puff Ftbl; L Sftbl; High Hon Roll; Jr NHS; NHS; Amer Lgn Awd 84; PA ST U.

HOFFMAN, ANDRE; St John Nueman HS; Philadelphia, PA; (2); 63/361; Boy Scts; Band; JV Bsktbl; JV Ftbl; Var JV Score Keeper; Cit Awd; High Hon Roll; Prfct Atten Awd; Schlrshp Awd Trphy 82-83; Outstndng Music Trphy 83-84; Cert Of Outstndng Reading 83-84; Penn ST U; Law.

HOFFMAN, ANGEL; SR HS; Schuylkill Havn, PA; (2); 1/100; Pres Church Yth Grp; German Clb; Hosp Aide; Library Aide; Science Clb; Spanish Clb; SADD; Chorus; Church Choir; School Musical; Delphian Soc Awd 85; Principals Awd 87; County Music Competition 85.

HOFFMAN, ANGELA; Millersburg Area HS; Millersburg, PA; (3); Letterman Clb; Pres Spanish Clb; Yrbk Stf; Trs Soph Cls; Bsktbl; Powder Puff Ftbl; Trk; Hon Roll.

HOFFMAN, BARBARA; Southern Huntingdon County HS; Orbisonia, PA; (3); French Clb; GAA; SADD; Varsity Clb; School Play; L Fld Hcky; NHS; Ntl Merit Ltr; Math Ed.

HOFFMAN, BETHANY; West Branch Area JR SR HS; Karthaus, PA; (3); 18/120; Sec Church Yth Grp; Spanish Clb; Varsity Clb; Yrbk Ed-Chief; Sec Jr Cls; Bsktbl; DAR Awd.

HOFFMAN, BEVERLY; Brookville Area JR/Sr HS; Brookville, PA; (4); 34/131; French Clb; FFA; Hosp Aide; Library Aide; Stat Coach Actv; Clarion U PA; Med.

HOFFMAN, BRIAN; Quigley HS; Rochester, PA; (3); 19/86; Trk; Hon Roll; Var Bsbl; Var Ftbl; Carpentry.

HOFFMAN, BRIDGET; Cardinal O Hara HS; Boothwyn, PA; (3); 314/710; Church Yth Grp; Dance Clb; SADD; Hon Roll; Prfct Atten Awd; Penn ST; Cmmnctns.

HOFFMAN, BRIDGETT; York Catholic HS; York, PA; (3); Church Yth Grp; Drama Clb; French Clb; Ski Clb; Nwsp Bus Mgr; Nwsp Stf; Yrbk Stf; Crs Cntry; Mgr(s); Trk; Chestnut Hill Coll In Search Of Ldrs Smmr Schlrshp 87; Advrtsng.

HOFFMAN, CHARLOTTE; Weatherly HS; Weatherly, PA; (3); VP Church Yth Grp; Hosp Aide; VP Library Aide; Office Aide; Teachers Aide; Pres Jr Cls; Stu Cncl; Var Sftbl; Hon Roll; Highst Hnrs Entire Class 85-86; Bio.

HOFFMAN, CINDY; Salem Christian Schl; Whitehall, PA; (4); 3/17; Church Yth Grp; Office Aide; Chorus; School Musical; Sec Sr Cls; Trs Stu Cncl; Var L Vllybl; Hon Roll; Philadelphia Coll Of Bible; Sec.

HOFFMAN, CRAIG; Blacklick Valley HS; Ebensburg, PA; (3); Church Yth Grp; Library Aide; NFL; Ski Clb; Spanish Clb; Varsity Clb; Trk; Hon Roll; St Frncs Coll PA; Nrsng.

HOFFMAN, CRAIG; Sch Haven Area HS; Schuylkill Haven, PA; (3); 1/103; Boy Scts; Off FCA; VP German Clb; Science Clb; Varsity Clb; Var L Bsbl; Var L Ftbl; High Hon Roll; Hon Roll; Biomed Engrng.

HOFFMAN, DEANA; Sto Rox SR HS; Mckees Rocks, PA; (2); Church Yth Grp; Office Aide; Nwsp Stf; Hon Roll; Atty.

HOFFMAN, DENISE; Lower Dauphin SR HS; Hummelstown, PA; (3); Sec Art Clb; Cheerleading; Sftbl; Hon Roll; Ski Clb; Chorus; Ntl Art Hnr Soc 85-87.

HOFFMAN, DIANE; Springdale HS; Springdale, PA; (3); Art Clb; Church Yth Grp; GAA; Hosp Aide; Band; Color Guard; Concert Band; Mrchg Band; Yrbk Rptr; Yrbk Stf; Advrtsng.

HOFFMAN, DOUGLAS P; Boyertown HS; Barto, PA; (1); High Hon Roll; Drftsmn.

HOFFMAN, EDWARD; Rockwood HS; Rockwood, PA; (3); 4-H; VICA; 4-H Awd; Hon Roll; Carpntr.

HOFFMAN, ERIC; Pleasant Valley HS; Brodheadsville, PA; (4); 30/171; VICA; Cit Awd; High Hon Roll; Dir Awd Mnr Cnty Area Vo-Tech Schl 87; Mach Shp Awd 87; Advnc Plcmnt Schlrshp 87; MVEA Schlrshp 87; Williamsport CC; Mach & Tl Tec.

HOFFMAN, GREG; Milton HS; Milton, PA; (3); Boy Scts; Varsity Clb; Rep Stu Cncl; Var Bsbl; Im Vllybl; Im Wt Lftg; Hon Roll.

HOFFMAN, GRETA; Williams Valley JR SR HS; Williamstown, PA; (1); Church Yth Grp; Chorus; Mrchg Band; Twrlr; Accntnt.

HOFFMAN, JENNIFER; Central SR HS; York, PA; (3); 26/248; Cmnty Wkr; Trs JA; NFL; Band; Concert Band; Mrchg Band; Stage Crew; Nwsp Stf; Yrbk Stf; JV Bsktbl; Attended Washington DC Jrnlsm Inst Amer U 87; Comms.

HOFFMAN, JENNIFER; Hickory HS; Hermitage, PA; (3); Church Yth Grp; Drama Clb; German Clb; Y-Teens; Acpl Chr; Chorus; Prfct Atten Awd; Music.

HOFFMAN, JOANNE; Boyertown Area SR HS; Barto, PA; (3); 143/470; Art Clb; Chorus; Rep Frsh Cls; JV Bsktbl; Var Capt Sftbl; Cit Awd; Sftbl Bttlng Chmpn Awd MVP 85-87; Physcl Ed.

HOFFMAN, JOHN; East Juniata HS; Mcalisterville, PA; (3); Chess Clb; Computer Clb; Science Clb; Band; Concert Band; Mrchg Band; Pep Band; Im Bsktbl; Indiana Inst; Cmptr Pgmng.

HOFFMAN, JOHN A; Williams Valley HS; Tower City, PA; (4); 4/100; VP Band; Chorus; Jazz Band; Mrchg Band; Orch; VP Sr Cls; Capt L Ftbl; Hon Roll; NHS; Dickinson Coll.

HOFFMAN, JONATHAN; Hazleton HS; Mcadoo, PA; (3); VICA.

HOFFMAN, JULEE; Halifax Area HS; Halifax, PA; (4); 17/101; Drama Clb; Varsity Clb; Chorus; School Musical; School Play; Nwsp Rptr; Var Capt Cheerleading; High Hon Roll; FTA; STAT 86-87; Harrisburg Area CC.

HOFFMAN, JULIE; Somerset Area SR HS; Somerset, PA; (3); 13/231; English Clb; Q&S; Varsity Clb; Nwsp Stf; Stat Bsktbl; Capt Socr; Var L Trk; High Hon Roll; NHS; Pres Schlr; Accntng.

HOFFMAN, KAREN; Owen J Roberts HS; Chester Springs, PA; (2); 22/311; Church Yth Grp; 4-H; Band; Concert Band; Mrchg Band; Im Vllybl; High Hon Roll; Natl Piano Audition ST Winner 86; Physical Therapy.

HOFFMAN, KELLY; Pottstown SR HS; Pottstown, PA; (3); 38/155; Art Clb; Drama Clb; French Clb; Key Clb; Thesps; Chorus; School Musical; School Play; Hon Roll; Prfct Atten Awd; Best Actress 87; 3rd Yr Awd-Key Clb & Chorus 87; 3rd Pl-Schl Art Show 87.

HOFFMAN, KIM; Boiling Springs HS; Mt Holly Spgs, PA; (2); Band; Concert Band; Mrchg Band; JV Bsktbl; Hon Roll.

HOFFMAN, KIM; Mt Calvary Christian Schl; Palmyra, PA; (4); 1/17; Church Yth Grp; Quiz Bowl; Teachers Aide; Concert Band; Mrchg Band; Yrbk Stf; Var JV Trk; High Hon Roll; NHS; Val; Dist Band 84-86; Hnrs Band 86; Hghst Math Awd 84; Messiah Coll.

HOFFMAN, LUANN; Donegal HS; Mount Joy, PA; (2); Church Yth Grp; Color Guard; Powder Puff Ftbl; Hon Roll; Hnr Rll 85-87; Elizabethtown Coll.

HOFFMAN, MARKHAM D; Hanover HS; Hanover, PA; (3); Art Clb; Ski Clb; Varsity Clb; School Play; Var L Ftbl; Bus.

HOFFMAN, MARY; Susquenita JR SR HS; Duncannon, PA; (3); 22/157; VP Church Yth Grp; Drama Clb; Library Aide; Quiz Bowl; Acpl Chr; Chorus; Church Choir; School Musical; School Play; Nwsp Stf; Spcl Ed.

HOFFMAN, MICHELE; Northampton SR HS; Bath, PA; (4); 116/430; AFS; Cmnty Wkr; Drama Clb; FBLA; Library Aide; School Musical; School Play; Stage Crew; Hon Roll; JC Awd; George Wolf PTA Schlrshp 87; Churchman Bus Schl; Acctg.

HOFFMAN, MICHELLE; Chambersburg Area SR HS; Fayetteville, PA; (4); 7/641; French Clb; VP Pep Clb; Stage Crew; Yrbk Stf; Var Capt Cheerleading; French Hon Soc; High Hon Roll; Hon Roll; NHS; Shippensburg U; Acctng.

HOFFMAN, NEAL; Hanover HS; Hanover, PA; (3); 40/126; Art Clb; Ski Clb; VP Jr Cls; JV Ftbl; JV Wrstlng; Bus.

HOFFMAN, RICHARD; Cathedral Preparatory Schl; Erie, PA; (3); 50/190; Boy Scts; Service Clb; Spanish Clb; Yrbk Stf; Im Bsktbl; Im Vllybl; Ntl Merit SF; Vet Med.

HOFFMAN, ROCK; Abington SR HS; Abington, PA; (3); 185/502; Nwsp Stf; Asst Coach Abington Raiders Pop Warner Ftbl Clb 85-87; Cmmnctns.

HOFFMAN, ROXANNE CATHERINE; Shippensburg Area SR HS; Newburg, PA; (4); 12/215; Am Leg Aux Girls St; Ski Clb; Varsity Clb; Band; School Musical; Rep Pres Stu Cncl; Capt Swmmng; High Hon Roll; NHS; Dickinson Coll Smmr Schlrshp 86; Shippensburg U Schlrshp 86-87; PA ST U.

HOFFMAN, SCOTT; Berlin-Brothersvalley HS; Berlin, PA; (2); Chess Clb; Spanish Clb; JV Bsbl; JV Var Ftbl; Wt Lftg; Im Wrstlng; Hon Roll; Presdntl Acad Ftnss Awd 85-86; WV U; Cmmnctns.

HOFFMAN, SHARON; Montour HS; Coraopolis, PA; (4); 94/301; Church Yth Grp; Hosp Aide; Office Aide; Teachers Aide; Church Choir; Concert Band; Mrchg Band; Pep Band; School Musical; Hon Roll; Acad Achvt Awd Advncd Typng 87; Robert Morris Coll; Exec Sec.

HOFFMAN, TERRI M; Northern SR HS; Dillsburg, PA; (4); 33/200; Sec DECA; Yrbk Stf; JV Trk; Hon Roll; Gld Key Schlstc Arts 87; Deca 2nd & Cmptncy Awd Dist Lvl 87; Deca 3rd Pl Manl Cvc Cnscns St Lvl 87; Harrisburg CC; Bus Adm.

HOFFMAN, THOMAS R; Waynesboro Area SR HS; Waynesboro, PA; (3); 83/400; FCA; Church Yth Grp; Var L Bsktbl; Var L Ftbl; Var L Trk; Cit Awd; Hon Roll; All Leag Ftbl Def Bck; Offnsv MVP Ftbl.

HOFFMAN, TRACEY; Mahanoy Area HS; Shenandoah, PA; (2); Comp Pgmmr.

HOFFMAN, TRACY R; Mercer Area JR SR HS; Mercer, PA; (3); Varsity Clb; Chorus; Bsktbl; Mgr(s); Trk; Vllybl; Vrsty Ltr Bsktbl, Vlybl, & Trk 85-87; Nice Kid Awd 86; Mrchndsng.

HOFFMAN-DILLION, LISA; Franklin HS; Franklin, PA; (4); French Clb; Girl Scts; Hosp Aide; SADD; Off Soph Cls; Off Jr Cls; Sftbl; Hon Roll.

HOFFMANN, CARYN; Shaler Area HS; Pittsburgh, PA; (3); 29/486; Math Tm; Pep Clb; Var L Bsktbl; Var L Socr; Im L Sftbl; High Hon Roll; NHS; Rotary Awd; Spanish NHS; Bsktbl-Nwsp All Star Team, Chrstms TournMVP 87; Schlr/Ath Awd 85; Bio Awd 85; PSYCH.

HOFFMANN, PAUL; Montrose Area JR- SR HS; Montrose, PA; (3); Concert Band; Jazz Band; Mrchg Band; NHS; Dist Band & Orchestra, Rgnl Orchestra 87; Elect Engrng.

HOFFMASTER, ALICE; Susquehannock HS; Shrewsbury, PA; (4); 66/220; AFS; Drama Clb; Teachers Aide; School Play; Rep Frsh Cls; Prm Cmt 85-86; Twsn ST U; Scl Wrkr.

HOFFMEYER, DEAN; North Star HS; Boswell, PA; (3); FCA; French Clb; Letterman Clb; Ski Clb; Varsity Clb; Sec Sr Cls; Var L Ftbl; Wt Lftg.

HOFFMEYER, JON; North Star HS; Boswell, PA; (3); 28/139; FCA; French Clb; Ski Clb; Varsity Clb; Yrbk Stf; Var L Ftbl; Wt Lftg; Hon Roll; Dist V All Star Ftbl 85-86; Elec Engrng.

HOFFNER, BROOKE; Pleasant Valley HS; Brodheadsville, PA; (3); Church Yth Grp; Ski Clb; Socl Wrk.

HOFFNER, KELLY; West Branch Area JR/Sr HS; Morrisdale, PA; (2); 4-H; SADD; Band; Concert Band; Mrchg Band; Rep Stu Cncl; Stat Wrstlng; 4-H Awd; Hon Roll; Elem Ed.

HOFFNER, TARA; Louis E Dieruff HS; Allentown, PA; (2); 3/340; Drama Clb; Madrigals; School Play; Nwsp Rptr; Trs Soph Cls; Rep Stu Cncl; Stat Bsktbl; Tennis; Trk; Hon Roll.

HOFIUS, BECKY; Sharpsville Area HS; Sharpsville, PA; (4); Pres Camera Clb; Church Yth Grp; Civic Clb; SADD; Nwsp Stf; Yrbk Phtg; Cheerleading; Vllybl; Hon Roll; NHS; 3rd Acdmc Achvt Awd 86-87; Hnrs Bio; Youngstown U.

HOFMANN, JOHANNA; Linden Hall HS; Richland, PA; (4); Church Yth Grp; Hosp Aide; Model UN; Trs Frsh Cls; Trs Soph Cls; Cit Awd; DAR Awd; High Hon Roll; Jr NHS; NHS; Tour Guide Awd 83-87; Stu Of The Mnth 84; Outstndng Lang Awd 87; Bkstr Wrkr 83-87; Rep To Jpns Girls 84; Mt Vernon Coll; Spnsh Intrp.

HOFMANN, LORI; Upper Dublin HS; Dresher, PA; (3); 46/300; Church Yth Grp; Math Tm; Science Clb; SADD; Teachers Aide; Yrbk Stf; Var L Bowling; Im Powder Puff Ftbl; Var L Socr; Im Vllybl; 1st Pl Delaware Vly Sci Fair 86; US Naval Awd 86; US Air Force Awd 87; Bio.

HOFMANN, MELISSA; Quigley HS; Sewickley, PA; (3); NFL; Yrbk Stf; High Hon Roll; Rotary Awd; Drama Clb; Drm Mjr(t); School Play; Twrlr; Hon Roll; Duquesne U Smmr Wrld Affrs Prog; Rotary Yth Ldrshp Awd; Wnnr Yrbk Artist; Miami U Of OH; Bus Admin.

HOFMANN, STEVEN T; Governor Mifflin SR HS; Shillington, PA; (3); 28/337; Sec Model UN; Scholastic Bowl; Chorus; School Musical; Var Capt Crs Cntry; Var Trk; Hon Roll; Aud/Vis; Boy Scts; Chess Clb; Schlrshp To PA Free Enterprise Wk 87; Unified Achvt Awd 86-87; Intl Reltns.

HOFMANN, TAMMY; William Allen HS; Allentown, PA; (3); Exploring; Intnl Clb; Hon Roll; NHS; Allentown Bus Schl; Data Prcsng.

HOFMANNER, RON; Daniel Boone JR SR HS; Douglassville, PA; (2); Trs German Clb; JV Crs Cntry; Var Trk; Var Wrstlng; High Hon Roll; Hon Roll; Comp Sci.

HOFSASS, KENNETH; Mechanicsburg Area HS; Mechanicsburg, PA; (2); 5/355; Mrchg Band; Symp Band; High Hon Roll; NHS; Elec Engrng.

HOGAN, COLLEEN; Bishop O Hara HS; Olyphant, PA; (4); 15/115; Drama Clb; Latin Clb; Letterman Clb; Spanish Clb; Varsity Clb; Chorus; School Play; Capt Cheerleading; Hon Roll; NHS; Presdntl Schlrshp Marywood Coll 87; HS Schlrshp Scranton Prep 83; HS Schlrshp Bishop O Hara 83; Marywood Coll; Acctng.

HOGAN JR, EDWARD JAMES; Father Judge HS; Philadelphia, PA; (4); 34/353; Boy Scts; Latin Clb; Ftbl; Trk; Hon Roll; NHS; Acdmc Achvt Awd 85-87; Drexel U; Bus.

HOGAN, KATHLEEN; Rochester Area HS; Rochester, PA; (3); 30/105; Church Yth Grp; French Clb; Service Clb; Concert Band; Mrchg Band; Orch; Yrbk Stf; Powder Puff Ftbl; Tennis; Hon Roll; Cnty Band 87; Miss TEEN PA 86; U Pittsburgh; Dntl Hygnst.

HOGAN, KENDALL; Haverford SR HS; Havertown, PA; (3); 22/403; Jazz Band; Orch; School Musical; Symp Band; Var Tennis; JV Trk; Hon Roll; NHS.

HOGAN, KRIS; Seneca Valley SR HS; Renfrew, PA; (2); Church Yth Grp; 4-H; Latin Clb; Math Tm; ROTC; Hon Roll; Bus Adm.

HOGAN, SARAH; East Stroudsburg HS; East Stroudsburg, PA; (1); 1/264; Church Yth Grp; French Clb; Math Tm; Model UN; Chorus; School Musical; High Hon Roll.

HOGAN, SEAN; G A R Memorial HS; Wilkes-Barre, PA; (3); 21/158; French Clb; Ski Clb; Stage Crew; Wt Lftg; Hon Roll; Jr NHS; NHS; Acctg.

HOGAN, TIFFANY; St Marys Area HS; St Marys, PA; (3); Hosp Aide; Var L Bsktbl; Bowling; Coach Actv; Var L Sftbl; Var L Vllybl; Hon Roll; NHS.

HOGE, AMY; Mcguffey HS; Washington, PA; (4); 15/201; VP Church Yth Grp; Spanish Clb; Trs Band; Concert Band; Drm Mjr(t); Mrchg Band; Yrbk Stf; High Hon Roll; Hon Roll; NHS; Stdnt Recog 83-86; Nrsg.

HOGG JR, RONALD L; Lampeter-Strasburg HS; Lancaster, PA; (3); 1/147; JV Bsbl; VP Ftbl; Im Mgr DAR Awd; JV Wrstlng; Hon Roll; NHS; Willow St Sertoma Schlr-Athlete Wrstlnd Awd, 1st Pl Forest Fire Awd & Burrowes Math Schlr 86-87; Meteorologist.

HOGG, SCOTT; Lampeter-Strasburg HS; Lancaster, PA; (3); 5/147; JV Bsbl; VP Ftbl; Im Mgr DAR Awd; Hon Roll.

HOGGA, MICHAEL; Northern Chester County Tech; Phoenixville, PA; (4); 1/120; Church Yth Grp; Stage Crew; High Hon Roll; Hon Roll; NHS; Pres Schlr; Val; Penn ST U.

HOGUE, CARALEE; Lincoln HS; New Castle, PA; (3); Sec German Clb; Ski Clb; Y-Teens; Band; Chrmn Jr Cls; VP Stu Cncl; Powder Puff Ftbl; Var Sftbl; Stat Trk; High Hon Roll; Elem Ed.

HOGUE, JOSEPH; Kiski Area HS; Vandergrift, PA; (4); German Clb; Teachers Aide; Band; Concert Band; Mrchg Band; Bsktbl; Ftbl; Mgr(s); Hon Roll; Val Tech; Auto Tech.

HOGUE, LORI; Hughesville HS; Hughesville, PA; (3); 3/140; Varsity Clb; Band; Chorus; JV Var Bsktbl; Var Trk; NHS; Church Yth Grp; Trs French Clb; Hon Roll; Nrsg.

HOH, LEO; Elk County Christian HS; Johnsonburg, PA; (4); Aud/Vis; Chess Clb; Bowling; Hon Roll; Gannon U.

HOHL, MIKE; Garden Spot HS; Morgantown, PA; (3); Varsity Clb; Capt Ftbl; Var Wt Lftg; JV Wrstlng; Hon Roll; PA ST; Srvyng.

HOHL, PETER; Notre Dame HS; Easton, PA; (2); French Clb; Ski Clb; Varsity Clb; JV Bsktbl; Var Crs Cntry; Var Trk; Im Vllybl; Hon Roll.

HOHL, VICKI L; Emmaus HS; Wescosville, PA; (4); 26/468; Key Clb; Spanish Clb; High Hon Roll; Jr NHS; NHS; Wmns Clb Outstndng Bio, Prsdntl Acdmc Ftnss Awd 87; Bloomsburg U; Bio.

HOHMAN, TAMI; South Park HS; Library, PA; (3); 43/235; Church Yth Grp; Ski Clb; Church Choir; Color Guard; Yrbk Stf; Var Swmmng; Hon Roll; Elem Ed.

HOHMANN, DALE; Deer Lakes HS; Gibsonia, PA; (4); Aud/Vis; Pres VICA; Church Choir; Hon Roll; Hnr Grad-Prfct Atten Awd; Auto Mchnc.

HOJNOWSKI, HEIDI; John S Fine HS; Sheatown, PA; (2); 1/243; Debate Tm; Model UN; Spanish Clb; Speech Tm; Nwsp Stf; Yrbk Rptr; Rep Soph Cls; High Hon Roll; NHS; Ntl Merit Ltr; Natl Hist Day Histrcl Paper 84-86; Natl PTA Rflctns Cntst 85-86; Qlfd Natl Spch Debt Comptn 86.

HOKE, DAVID; Millersburg Area HS; Millersburg, PA; (4); 1/76; Concert Band; Jazz Band; Mrchg Band; VP Sr Cls; Bowling; Golf; Vllybl; NHS.

HOKE, KAREN; Spring Grove Area SR HS; Spring Grove, PA; (3); 5/301; VP 4-H; Hosp Aide; Library Aide; Band; Mrchg Band; Stat Bsktbl; 4-H Awd; High Hon Roll; NHS; Mst Outstndng Frnch Stu, Sprng Grv 85; Yth Schlrs Inst, Lebanon Vly Coll 87; Biochem.

HOKE, MARK; Dover Area HS; E Berlin, PA; (3); 38/265; Quiz Bowl; Varsity Clb; Var Ftbl; JV Trk; Im Vllybl; Var Wrstlng; JA; Off Stu Cncl; Im Bsktbl; Hon Roll; Hofstra U; Brdcstng.

HOKE, ROD; Newport JR/Sr HS; Newport, PA; (3); Ftbl; Wt Lftg; USMC; Elctrncs.

HOKE, SALLY; Hanover SR HS; Hanover, PA; (3); Red Cross Aide; Band; Concert Band; Jazz Band; Mrchg Band; Orch; School Musical; School Play; Im Bsktbl; Hon Roll; Padi Intl Diving Coll; Scuba In.

HOLABAUGH, PAULA M; Maplewood HS; Guys Mills, PA; (3); Church Yth Grp; Cmnty Wkr; Pres Exploring; Hosp Aide; Spanish Clb; Color Guard; Concert Band; Pep Band; Yrbk Sprt Ed; Acad All Am Awd 86; Med.

HOLBEN, GREGORY; Brookville Area HS; Brookville, PA; (3); Chess Clb; Yrbk Stf; Accntng.

HOLCOMB, CHRIS; Liberty JR SR HS; Liberty, PA; (4); 7/44; Chorus; School Musical; Stage Crew; Var Capt Bsktbl; Var L Crs Cntry; Var L Socr; Var L Tennis; Hon Roll; NHS; Harry Smith Awd Acadmcs Athlcs; PTO Schlrshp Ctznshp; Geo Washngtn U; Civl Engrng.

HOLCOMBE, STEPHANIE; Susquehanna Township HS; Harrisburg, PA; (3); GAA; SADD; Band; Chorus; Mrchg Band; School Musical; Lit Mag; Mgr(s); Rotary Awd; Concert Band; Hnr Rll; Spch Pthlgy.

HOLDEN, SCOTT; Philipsburg-Osceola Area HS; Philipsburg, PA; (4); 23/237; Boy Scts; Church Yth Grp; Ski Clb; SADD; Band; JV Bsktbl; Var L Crs Cntry; NHS; Penn ST; Cvl Engr.

HOLDERMAN, AMY; Bellefonte Area HS; Bellefonte, PA; (3); Drama Clb; French Clb; Hosp Aide; Library Aide; SADD; Band; Chorus; Church Choir; Mrchg Band; School Play; Psych.

HOLDREDGE, DANIEL; Dallas SR HS; Dallas, PA; (3); 52/211; Boy Scts; Church Yth Grp; School Play; Yrbk Stf; Rep Stu Cncl; JV Socr; Var Trk; God Cntry Awd; High Hon Roll; Hon Roll; Eagl Sct 85; VP Untd Meth Yth Fllwshp 86-87; Med Tech.

HOLDREN, KELLY; Danville HS; Danville, PA; (2); #25 In Class; Church Yth Grp; Hosp Aide; Key Clb; Ski Clb; Spanish Clb; Teachers Aide; Score Keeper; Hon Roll; Pres Acadc Ftns Awd 86; Psych.

HOLDREN, MARK; Danville SR HS; Danville, PA; (3); High Hon Roll; Hon Roll; Presdntl Acadc Ftns Awd 84-85.

HOLECEK, MARK; Hughesville HS; Muncy, PA; (3); Varsity Clb; Var L Bsktbl; Var Capt Socr; Im Vllybl; High Hon Roll; Boy Scts; Hon Roll; U Of Southern CA; Engr.

HOLES, TODD; Bellwood-Antis HS; Bellwood, PA; (3); 15/115; Var Bsbl; Var Trk; High Hon Roll; Stu Of Wk 87; PA ST U; Wildlife Tech.

HOLLAND, DANA; Ambridge Area HS; Baden, PA; (3); German Clb; Pep Clb; SADD; Band; Concert Band; Mrchg Band; Pep Band; Yrbk Stf; Stu Cncl; Hon Roll; PA ST U; Advrtsg.

HOLLAND, DAVID S; York Suburban HS; York, PA; (4); 44/188; Aud/Vis; Boy Scts; Computer Clb; Dance Clb; Pres Drama Clb; Exploring; Letterman Clb; PAVAS; Thesps; Acpl Chr; Hgh Obrn Yth Fndtn Ambsdr 85-87; Montgmry Coll; Info Sys Proc.

HOLLAND, JULIA; Glendale JR SR HS; Glasgow, PA; (3); 10/70; Sec Church Yth Grp; Drama Clb; Science Clb; SADD; Capt Co-Capt Color Guard; Nwsp Rptr; Nwsp Stf; Yrbk Stf; Hon Roll; NHS.

HOLLAND, MICHAEL; Henderson HS; Westchester, PA; (3); 16/377; FCA; Math Tm; Ski Clb; Spanish Clb; Bsbl; Bsktbl; Ftbl; Lcrss; Hon Roll; Ntl Merit Ltr; Auburn U; Engrg.

HOLLAND, PAM; Towanda Area HS; Towanda, PA; (4); 34/138; Sec Church Yth Grp; Drama Clb; Band; Chorus; Concert Band; Madrigals; Mrchg Band; School Play; Swing Chorus; Yrbk Stf; Actng.

HOLLAS, CHRISTINE; St Paul Cathedral HS; Pittsburgh, PA; (2); SADD; Chorus; Church Choir; Stu Cncl; NHS; NEDT Awd; High Hon Roll; 1st Pl Ntl Hstry Day Cmptn 86-87; Outstndng Achvt Awd In Spnsh 84-87; Duquesne U; Music.

HOLLEN, GARETH ERIC; Greater Johnstown SR HS; Johnstown, PA; (4); 58/277; Pres Church Yth Grp; JA; Chorus; Concert Band; Trs Mrchg Band; Orch; Rep Jr Cls; Rep Stu Cncl; VP Tennis; Hon Roll; IN U PAACCNTNG.

HOLLEN, SHELLY; Tyrone Area HS; Tyrone, PA; (3); Key Clb; Latin Clb; Spanish Clb; SADD; Chorus; JV Trk; Bus Admin.

HOLLENBACH, DEAN; Shikellamy HS; Sunbury, PA; (4); Boy Scts; CAP; JV Wrstlng; Hon Roll; Lincoln Tech Inst; Comp Elec.

HOLLENBACH, ROBERT H; Montour HS; Mckees Rocks, PA; (3); 19/206; Boy Scts; Chess Clb; Leo Clb; Spanish Clb; SADD; Band; Hon Roll; Mortuary Sci.

HOLLENBACH, SUSAN T; Hamburg Area JR SR HS; Bernville, PA; (2); Sec 4-H; Sec FFA; German Clb; Ski Clb; JV Bowling; Im Fld Hcky; 4-H Awd; Hon Roll; NHS; Pres Schlr; Penn ST U; Ag.

HOLLENBACK, MICHELE; Troy Area HS; Towanda, PA; (3); 46/184; 4-H; Hosp Aide; Band; Chorus; Concert Band; Jazz Band; Mrchg Band; Cheerleading; Twrlr; 4-H Awd; Radiolgcl Tech.

HOLLENBAUGH, DAVID; New Hope-Solebury HS; Solebury, PA; (4); 3/78; VP FBLA; Math Tm; Quiz Bowl; Ski Clb; Yrbk Ed-Chief; Stu Cncl; Bsbl; L Socr; VP NHS; Math & Bus Law Awd 86; Bus.

HOLLENBAUGH, KENNETH; Boiling Springs JR SR HS; Boiling Spgs, PA; (4); 31/107; Aud/Vis; Boy Scts; Ski Clb; Im Bsbl; Im Crs Cntry; JV Var Ftbl; Im Trk; Hon Roll; NPEA 84; NLSA 85; Bloomsburg U; Acctng.

HOLLENSHEAD II, KAREN; Gwynedd Mercy Acad; Harleysville, PA; (2); Aud/Vis; PAVAS; Varsity Clb; Chorus; School Play; Lit Mag; High Hon Roll; Ntl Merit Ltr; Pres Schlr; Harvard U; Pediatrcn.

HOLLER, CATHERINE; Riverview HS; Oakmont, PA; (3); 6/107; Chorus; Yrbk Ed-Chief; Yrbk Rptr; Off Jr Cls; Stat Bsbl; Capt Cheerleading; High Hon Roll; NHS; Secndry Ed.

HOLLER, DAVID; Hyndman Middle SR HS; Hyndman, PA; (3); 7/48; Church Yth Grp; Red Cross Aide; Science Clb; Ski Clb; Spanish Clb; SADD; Band; Chorus; Concert Band; Mrchg Band; Frostburg ST Coll; Phrmcy.

HOLLER, LORI; Salisbury Elk Lick HS; Salisbury, PA; (3); FHA; Yrbk Stf; JV Var Bsktbl; Sftbl; Penn ST U; Nrsng.

HOLLER, WILLIAM; William Allen HS; Allentown, PA; (3); 68/695; Pres Church Yth Grp; German Clb; JV Bsbl; Im Bowling; Var Vllybl; Hon Roll; Ntl Merit Ltr; Elect Engr.

HOLLEY, ROXANNE; North Penn HS; Morris Run, PA; (3); 30/58; Camera Clb; Church Yth Grp; Drama Clb; Exploring; GAA; Library Aide; Band; Chorus; Concert Band; Mrchg Band; Ltr Trck 85-87; WACC; Bus.

HOLLIDAY, JENNIFER; Highlands SR HS; Natrona Hgts, PA; (3); 10/303; Key Clb; SADD; Color Guard; Off Soph Cls; Off Jr Cls; Stu Cncl; Trk; NHS; Pres Schlr; Gold Awds 85, 86 & 87; Aerontcl Engrng.

HOLLIDAY, MICHELLE; Central Bucks HS West; Doyleston, PA; (3); 170/477; Church Yth Grp; Drama Clb; Hosp Aide; Sec SADD; Chorus; Nwsp Ed-Chief; Nwsp Rptr; Fld Hcky; Hon Roll; SADD Fndnr Awd 86; Schl Exchng Prog 85; Bus Mngmnt.

HOLLIHAN, ALLISON; Seneca Valley HS; Harmony, PA; (2); Ski Clb; Yrbk Stf; Rep Frsh Cls; High Hon Roll; Hon Roll; 1st Yr Awd Acad Achvt 86-87; Sci.

HOLLINGER JR, EDWARD; Northeastern HS; Mt Wolf, PA; (3); 17/236; Band; Chorus; Concert Band; Jazz Band; Mrchg Band; Orch; School Musical; Off Sr Cls; Pa ST U; Nuclear Sci.

HOLLINGER, JANICE; Riverview HS; Verona, PA; (4); 5/120; Church Yth Grp; French Clb; Key Clb; Pres Speech Tm; Nwsp Ed-Chief; Yrbk Stf; High Hon Roll; NHS; NEDT Awd; U Of Pittsburgh.

HOLLINGER, KATHLEEN E; Lebanon SR HS; Lebanon, PA; (4); #35 In Class; VP FBLA; Girl Scts; Band; Church Choir; Concert Band; Mrchg Band; Orch; School Musical; Rep Frsh Cls; Hon Roll; Outstndng Bus Stu Awd Quota Clb 86-87; Hnrs Grad 87; Cedar Awd 87; Cntrl PA Bus Schl; Med Secr.

HOLLINGER, KURT; York Suburban HS; York, PA; (3); 10/180; Ski Clb; Band; Concert Band; Jazz Band; Mrchg Band; Orch; Pep Band; School Musical; High Hon Roll; NHS; Top Math Stu 87; Top 5 Prcnt Of Cls 85-86; Top 10 Prcnt Of Cls 87; Arspc Engrng.

HOLLINGER, MELISA; Garden Spot HS; New Holland, PA; (2); Church Yth Grp; Stage Crew; JV Fld Hcky; Hon Roll; Intr Dctrtng.

HOLLINGER, PAM; Penn Cambria HS; Lilly, PA; (4); Art Clb; Drama Clb; Yrbk Stf; Presdntl Phys Fitness Awds 83-87; Med Asst.

HOLLINGER, SHAWN; Garden Spot HS; New Holland, PA; (2); Off Church Yth Grp; Chorus; Church Choir; Bsktbl; Socr; Trk; Vllybl; Photo.

HOLLINGSHEAD, ROHNA; Bishop Guilfoyle HS; Altoona, PA; (3); Church Yth Grp; Cmnty Wkr; Hosp Aide; Spanish Clb; SADD; Drm Mjr(t); Capt Twrlr; Hon Roll.

HOLLINGSWORTH, G SCOTT; Blacklick Valley HS; Ebensburg, PA; (4); Boy Scts; Computer Clb; Yrbk Phtg; Trk; Hon Roll; Pres Schlr; VISTOS 88; Penn ST; Mech Engrng.

HOLLINGSWORTH, SCOTT; Blacklick Valley HS; Ebensburg, PA; (4); 15/89; Camera Clb; Computer Clb; Ski Clb; Yrbk Phtg; Yrbk Stf; Var Trk; Hon Roll; Penn ST; Mech Engr.

HOLLINSHEAD, SUSAN; Bethel Park HS; Bethel Park, PA; (4); 15/502; Civic Clb; Pres JA; Key Clb; Spanish Clb; SADD; Acpl Chr; Chorus; Church Choir; Swing Chorus; Variety Show; Bucknell.

HOLLIS, CHRISTINA; Leechburg Area HS; Leechburg, PA; (4); 3/84; Drama Clb; JA; Chorus; School Play; Nwsp Stf; Yrbk Stf; Hon Roll; Pres NHS; Sec Soph Cls; Sec Sr Cls; Franklin & Marshall Coll.

HOLLIS, MARK; Bentworth HS; Bentleyville, PA; (4); Boy Scts; Church Yth Grp; School Play; God Cntry Awd; Hon Roll; Ski Clb; Order Arrow 83; Egl Sct Awd 87; Natl Yng Ldrs Conf 87; CA U PA; Comp Engr.

HOLLIS, ROBERT; Yrichland HS; Johnstown, PA; (3); Math Clb; NAACP; Mrchg Band; Orch; Var L Vllybl; Gov Hon Prg Awd; Prfct Atten Awd; Cmnty Wkr; Exploring; Pep Clb; Louis E King Natl Schltc Awd Gettysburh Coll 86; PA All ST Band Phildlphia Acd Msc 87; ABC Lead 87; Engrng.

HOLLIS, RONALD; Jeannette SR HS; Jeannette, PA; (3); 48/131; Spanish Clb; Stu Mnth 85.

HOLLISH, BARBARA; Morrisville HS; Oakford, PA; (4); 3/96; Band; Yrbk Stf; Trs Stu Cncl; Var Capt Cheerleading; Var Sftbl; High Hon Roll; NHS; Sec Soph Cls; Exc Stu Mnth 87; Bucks Cty Intermedia Sci Sem 86; Phrmcy.

HOLLISTER, CRISTINE; Lancaster Catholic HS; Lancaster, PA; (3); 13/210; Pep Clb; Varsity Clb; Stage Crew; Bsktbl; Sftbl; Hon Roll; NHS; Phy Thrpy.

HOLLMAN, DEIRDRE; Harrisburg HS; Harrisburg, PA; (4); 3/235; Drama Clb; Model UN; Pres Science Clb; Chorus; Var Tennis; Kiwanis Awd; Pres NHS; VFW Awd; Smith Coll Book Awd 87; Alpha Phi Alpha Schlrshp Awd 87; Princeton U; Comm.

HOLLOCK, LORI; Crestwood HS; Mountaintop, PA; (4); Ski Clb; Stat Bsktbl; Capt Var Fld Hcky; Capt Var Sftbl; Brd Of Educ Awd 87; Presdntl Phys Fitness Awd 87; E Stroudsburg U; Bio.

HOLLOMAN, CARLA; Geibel HS; Uniontown, PA; (3); Var L Bsktbl; L Sftbl; Var L Vllybl; Yrbk Sprt Ed; High Hon Roll; Hon Roll; Spanish NHS; MVP Sftbl 86; MVP Vllybl-All WPIAL Vllybl & Bstkbl 86; All Cnty Sftbl & Bsktbl 85, 86 & 87; Psychlgy.

HOLLOWAY, AMY E; Mcguffey HS; Washington, PA; (3); 20/244; Church Yth Grp; Exploring; French Clb; Ski Clb; Powder Puff Ftbl; Tennis; High Hon Roll; Hon Roll; NHS; Stu Recog Awd 85-87; Poli Sci.

HOLLOWAY JR, ARTHUR D; Valley Forge Military Acad; Baltimore, MD; (2); 18/160; ROTC; Varsity Clb; Drill Tm; JV Bsktbl; Var Ftbl; Var Trk; U Of FL; Engr.

HOLLOWAY, SHAORN; Abraham Lincoln HS; Philadelphia, PA; (3); Teachers Aide; Acpl Chr; Band; Chorus; Church Choir; Concert Band; Jazz Band; Madrigals; Orch; Yrbk Stf; Tchng.

HOLLOWBUSH, KELLY; Brandywine Heights HS; Topton, PA; (4); 10/120; Band; Jazz Band; School Play; Swing Chorus; Yrbk Phtg; VP Sr Cls; Sec Stu Cncl; Tennis; Pres NHS; Drama Clb; Rtry Clb Schlrshp; AM Lgn Prz-Drmtcs; Prsdntl Acdmc Ftnss Awd; U Of DE; Nrsng.

HOLLY, CHRISTINA; Hazleton HS; Lattimer, PA; (3); 44/400; French Clb; Hosp Aide; Pep Clb; Chorus; Flag Corp; Bowling; Hon Roll; Kings Coll; Physns Asst.

HOLLY, MICHELE; Perry Traditional Acad; Pittsburgh, PA; (3); 21/190; Church Yth Grp; Band; Nwsp Rptr; Lit Mag; Rep Stu Cncl; Var L Sftbl; Var L Vllybl; Hon Roll; Jr NHS; Rotary Awd; Upwrd Bnd Prjct; Educ Admin.

HOLMAN, RANDY; Susquenita HS; Duncannon, PA; (3); 2/164; Church Yth Grp; Quiz Bowl; Rep Soph Cls; Sec Stu Cncl; Crs Cntry; JV Var Wrstlng; High Hon Roll; Lion Awd; NHS; NEDT Awd; Natl Educ Development Cert Of Merit 84-85; Amer HS Math Exam 2nd Pl 86; Annual Math Cont 1st Pl 87; US Naval Acad; Pilot.

HOLMES, ANDRE; Lower Merion HS; Merion, PA; (3); Intnl Clb; Ski Clb; SADD; Band; Concert Band; Mrchg Band; Orch; Rep Frsh Cls; Rep Jr Cls; Rep Stu Cncl; Sci.

HOLMES, DIANE; Kiski Area HS; Vandergrift, PA; (3); FBLA; Band; Color Guard; Concert Band; Mrchg Band; Stu Cncl; High Hon Roll; Hon Roll; Bus Steno.

HOLMES, ELIZABETH; Neshaminy SR HS; Langhorne, PA; (3); Church Yth Grp; Mrchg Band; Var L Swmmng; JV Trk; Hon Roll; Prfct Atten Awd; Lang Tchr.

HOLMES, KEITH; Northampton Area SR HS; Northampton, PA; (2); Church Yth Grp; FBLA; Im Bsktbl; Im Ftbl; Var Golf; Hon Roll; Villanova; Law.

HOLMES, LEE; Saucon Valley HS; Bethlehem, PA; (4); 3/138; Am Leg Aux Girls St; German Clb; Chorus; Swing Chorus; Variety Show; Capt Cheerleading; Mgr(s); Lion Awd; NHS; Pres Schlr; Most Outstndng SR Ath Chrldng 87; PA ST; Bus Admin.

HOLMES, LEE C; Hopewell HS; Aliquippa, PA; (4); Pres 4-H; Letterman Clb; Varsity Clb; JV Var Ftbl; Var Score Keeper; Var Wt Lftg; Var L Wrstlng; High Hon Roll; Hon Roll.

HOLMES, NICOLE; Little Flower Catholic HS; Philadelphia, PA; (3); Church Yth Grp; Cmnty Wkr; Hosp Aide; Intnl Clb; Political Wkr; Church Choir; School Play; Im Crs Cntry; Im Trk; Hon Roll; Prfct Atndnc 87; NC Cntrl U; Hlth.

HOLMES, STACEY; Southwark Motivation HS; Philadelphia, PA; (4); 40/520; Art Clb; Hosp Aide; JV Sftbl; Var Tennis; Cit Awd; Hon Roll; NHS; Prfct Atten Awd; Tnns 86; Drwng & Paintng 86; Bst Athlt-U Of PA Ntl Yth Sprts Pgm 84; Lincoln U; Nrsng.

HOLMES, TERILYN; Blue Mountain Acad; Atkinson, NH; (3); Church Yth Grp; Teachers Aide; Chorus; Sftbl; Vllybl; Hon Roll; Prfct Atten Awd; Atlantic Union Coll.

HOLOVACK, LORI; Washington HS; Washington, PA; (2); Dance Clb; Letterman Clb; Temple Yth Grp; Varsity Clb; Trk; Hon Roll; WA & Jefferson.

HOLOWACH, DEBBIE; Upper Dublin HS; Ambler, PA; (4); 110/313; Pep Clb; Yrbk Stf; Cheerleading; Tennis; IUP.

HOLSAPFEL, BROOK; West Middlesex HS; Sharon, PA; (3); #11 In Class; Church Yth Grp; Dance Clb; Exploring; Spanish Clb; Band; Chorus; Concert Band; Jazz Band; Mrchg Band; Stu Cncl; IN U; Secdnry Educ.

HOLSOPPLE, COLLEEN; Central Cambria HS; Johnstown, PA; (3); 13/210; Church Yth Grp; Chorus; Sec Sr Cls; Crs Cntry; Trk; Cit Awd; Hon Roll; Prfct Atten Awd; Art Clb; Educ.

HOLT, KIMBERLY; West Branch HS; Philipsburg, PA; (3); 17/110; Ski Clb; Spanish Clb; SADD; Varsity Clb; VICA; Band; Chorus; Concert Band; Mrchg Band; Yrbk Stf; PA ST; Comp Sci.

HOLT, LYNN; Du Bois Area HS; Du Bois, PA; (4); 48/270; Trs Girl Scts; Trs Intnl Clb; Teachers Aide; Color Guard; Flag Corp; Mrchg Band; School Musical; Alumni Assoc Schlrshp 87; Sci Team 87; Rainbow Girls Past Wrthy Adv & Grnd Page 85 & 87; PA ST U; Rad Tech.

HOLT, MELISSA; York Catholic HS; York, PA; (4); 10/166; Girl Scts; JA; Nwsp Rptr; High Hon Roll; Hon Roll; NHS; York Cnty Merit Schlrshp, Religion Excllnc Awd & Bus Ed Hnrb Mntn In Excllnc 87; York Coll Of PA; Accntng.

HOLT, NICOLE; Kennard Dale HS; Stewartstown, PA; (3); 36/165; Varsity Clb; Band; Concert Band; Mrchg Band; School Musical; School Play; Mgr(s); JV Trk; Var Vllybl; Hon Roll; Bus Mgmt.

HOLT, PEGGY; Centre County Christian Acad; Julian, PA; (3); 2/15; Church Yth Grp; Teachers Aide; School Play; Trk; Hon Roll; Prfct Atten Awd; PA Math Leag Awd 85-87.

HOLT, TINA; Butler SR HS; Butler, PA; (3); Church Yth Grp; Mrchg Band; Orch; School Musical; Swing Chorus; Rep Stu Cncl; Var Capt Twrlr; Hon Roll; Jr NHS; Penn ST U; Med.

HOLT, TINA; Kennedy Christian HS; Sharon, PA; (2); 28/96; Hosp Aide; Office Aide; Spanish Clb; Cheerleading; Hon Roll; Headmasters Incentive Schlrshp 85; Natl Edctnl Devlpmnt Awd 85 & 86; Marine Bio.

HOLTZ, AMY; Villa Maria Acad; Erie, PA; (3); Church Yth Grp; Science Clb; Off Stu Cncl; Socr; Hon Roll; VP NHS; Bus.

HOLTZHAUSER, HEIDI; Conneaut Lake HS; Conneaut Lake, PA; (3); Key Clb; Ski Clb; SADD; Capt Mrchg Band; Pep Band; Rptr Nwsp Stf; Rep Stu Cncl; JV Cheerleading; Hon Roll; 2nd & 3rd Pl Mdls Wstmnstr Fig Sktng Comptn 87; Gannon Coll; Bus.

HOLTZLEICER, DEBRA; Catasauqua HS; Catasauqua, PA; (4); Computer Clb; Lit Mag; Cheerleading; Fld Hcky; Powder Puff Ftbl; Trk; Hon Roll; Rotary Awd; U PA; Chem.

HOLTZMAN, CHERYL; Mc Keesport SR HS; Mc Keesport, PA; (4); Powder Puff Ftbl; U Of Pittsburg; Psych.

HOLTZMAN, JUDITH; Bishop Mc Cort HS; Johnstown, PA; (3); 3/155; JA; Math Tm; Mu Alpha Theta; Chorus; Im Socr; L Im Trk; High Hon Roll; NHS; Acdmc All Amer HS Stu 86-87.

HOLUBOWSKY, VICTOR; Archbishop Ryan HS For Boys; Philadelphia, PA; (2); Im Trk.

HOLUPKA, HEIDI; Kiski Area HS; Leechburg, PA; (4); JA; Spanish Clb; SADD; Chorus; Color Guard; Yrbk Stf; Mgr(s); Trk; High Hon Roll; NHS; DAR Awd; Top 15; Top 10; PA ST U; Pre-Law.

HOLZAPFEL, FAITH A; Hickory HS; Hermitage, PA; (3); 16/167; Art Clb; Church Yth Grp; DECA; Exploring; 4-H; VP JA; Latin Clb; Service Clb; Yrbk Stf; NHS; Natl Latin Hnr Soc 84-87; Bradford Schl; Retail Mgmt.

HOM, LINDA; Penn Wood HS; Lansdowne, PA; (4); 2/332; Intnl Clb; Chorus; Lit Mag; Var Trk; Bausch & Lomb Sci Awd; High Hon Roll; Masonic Awd; NHS; Prfct Atten Awd; Sal; Na Cncl Supvsrs Math 87; Nalt Sci Olympiad 87; Pres Acad Ftns Awd 87; Phila Coll Of Pharm; Pharm.

HOMAN, DAVID; Salisbury-Elk Lick HS; Salisbury, PA; (3); 1/28; VP Church Yth Grp; School Play; Nwsp Bus Mgr; Nwsp Rptr; JV Bsktbl; High Hon Roll; Hon Roll; Trs 4-H; Nwsp Stf; Yrbk Stf; Schlrshp Frstburg ST Coll 86; Altrnt Cndt PA Gvrns Schl Sci 86; Elec Engr.

HOMER, JANELL; Grove City HS; Grove City, PA; (4); 73/167; FBLA; Powder Puff Ftbl; Vllybl; Edinboro U; Crmnl Jstc.

HOMER, JULIE; Greenwood HS; Millerstown, PA; (1); 4/67; Church Yth Grp; GAA; Chorus; School Musical; Off Frsh Cls; Off Stu Cncl; Bsktbl; Fld Hcky; Sftbl; High Hon Roll; Pres Acad Fit Awd 85.

HOMICK JR, PAUL S; Highlands SR HS; Brackenridge, PA; (4); 27/275; Intnl Clb; SADD; School Play; Pres Stu Cncl; High Hon Roll; NHS; Pres Schlr; Rotary Awd; Computer Clb; Drama Clb; Stu Rep To Schl Brd 86-87; Cong Yth Ldrshp Cncl 86; St Vincent Coll; Pre-Med.

HOMISON, RENE; Hempfield Area HS; Greensburg, PA; (4); 99/693; Chess Clb; Library Aide; Pep Clb; Spanish Clb; Nwsp Stf; Yrbk Stf; High Hon Roll; Hon Roll; NHS; Spanish NHS; PA ST U; Frgn Rltns.

HOMITZ, DANIEL; Quigley HS; Monaca, PA; (3); 4/80; Camera Clb; Math Tm; Chorus; Yrbk Stf; Swmmng; High Hon Roll; Span Awd 85; Engrg.

HOMME, JACKIE; Bentworth HS; Ellsworth, PA; (4); Exploring; Band; Concert Band; Flag Corp; JV Bsktbl; High Hon Roll; Hon Roll; NHS; Prfct Atten Awd; Pres Schlr; WA & Jefferson; Doctor.

HOMMEL, KEVIN; Line Mountain HS; Herndon, PA; (2); Boy Scts; Ed VP Jazz Band; JV Wrstlng; Hon Roll.

HOMNACK, KERRYANN; John S Fine HS; Nanticoke, PA; (2); Girl Scts; VICA; Chorus; Swmmng; Hon Roll; Food Prep.

HOMNACK, PAUL; J S Fine & W B A Vo Tech; Nanticoke, PA; (4); Boy Scts; Computer Clb; Red Cross Aide; VICA; L Swmmng; Hon Roll; Prfct Atten Awd; Sons Of Italy Comm Awd 86-87; Scientific Data Procsng Awd 86-87; VICA Comptn 1st Pl 85-86; US Army; Comp.

HOMROCK, CHRIS; Connellsville Area HS; Connellsville, PA; (1); SADD; Nwsp Sprt Ed; Hon Roll; Law.

HONARD III, HARRY W; Academy HS; Erie, PA; (3); 31/226; Church Yth Grp; German Clb; Concert Band; Jazz Band; Mrchg Band; Variety Show; MIP Mrchng Band 86; SES W Germany 86; Eric Civic Orch 84-86; Music.

HONDROS, KRISTIN M; Agnes Irwin Schl; St Davids, PA; (4); Art Clb; Nwsp Sprt Ed; Lit Mag; Capt Bsktbl; Var Fld Hcky; Var Lcrss; Hon Roll; Ntl Merit SF; Natl Latin Hnr Scty; Sec/Tres Of Athltc Assn.

HONEY, CHRISTINE; Strong Vincent HS; Erie, PA; (4); 46/160; FBLA; Hon Roll; Bradford Schl; Exec Sec.

HONEYMAN, THOMAS; Frankford HS; Philadelphia, PA; (3); 30/679; Chess Clb; French Clb; Service Clb; Yrbk Stf; Stu Cncl; Var Bsbl; Var Ftbl; Var Capt Socr; Hon Roll; Duke U; Mrn Bio.

HONS, TIFFANY; Fort Cherry HS; Mc Donald, PA; (3); 11/147; Drama Clb; FNA; Trs Library Aide; Math Clb; Ski Clb; Spanish Clb; Sec Band; School Play; High Hon Roll; NHS; Miss Teen Pageant 87; Psych.

HONSEL, JASON; Notre Dame HS; Nazareth, PA; (3); 13/96; Scholastic Bowl; Nwsp Stf; Trs Stu Cncl; Bsbl; Bsktbl; Crs Cntry; Hon Roll; Quiz Bowl; High Hon Roll; Lehigh U; Econ.

HOOBER, ALISSA; Garden Spot HS; New Holland, PA; (2); Church Yth Grp; VP 4-H; German Clb; Chorus; Orch; School Musical; Stage Crew; Rep Stu Cncl; Bsktbl; Fld Hcky; All Am Pgnt Semi Fnlst 87; 1st Pl 4-H St Wnnr Swng 87; Home Econ.

HOOD, AMY; Ephrata SR HS; Ephrata, PA; (3); Camera Clb; Church Yth Grp; Chorus; Church Choir; Rep Stu Cncl; JV Bsktbl; Powder Puff Ftbl; JV Sftbl; Wt Lftg; Hon Roll; Fshn Merch.

HOOD, CAROL; Lourdesmont HS; Chester, PA; (3); Church Yth Grp; Dance Clb; 4-H; Library Aide; Math Tm; Church Choir; Bsktbl; Sftbl; Cit Awd; Dnfth Awd; Bio.

HOOD, JENNIFER; Northern Cambria HS; Barnesboro, PA; (3); 11/152; Church Yth Grp; French Clb; High Hon Roll; Penn ST U.

HOOD, KATRINA; Avon Grove HS; West Grove, PA; (3); 12/210; Pres FNA; OEA; Service Clb; Capt Drm Mjr(t); Mrchg Band; Variety Show; Lit Mag; JV Fld Hcky; Capt Twrlr; High Hon Roll; Awd Cls Rank 6th Out Of 218 84-85; Typg Awd 85-86; Vrsty Ltr 86-87.

HOOK, MICHELLE; Hempfield Area SR HS; Greensburg, PA; (4); AFS; Cmnty Wkr; Exploring; Spanish Clb; High Hon Roll; Jr NHS; NHS; Ntl Merit Ltr; Pres Schlr; Spanish NHS; 7th Pl Gnnon Spnsh Tst 86; 4 Yr $1000 Schlrshp 87; 3rd Pl Spnsh Drmtc Prsntatn 87; IN U Of PA; Spnsh.

HOOKER, KAREN; Loyalsock Township HS; Williamsport, PA; (3); 26/120; French Clb; Trs Key Clb; Chorus; Color Guard; Drill Tm; Mrchg Band; School Musical; Yrbk Stf; Sftbl; Twrlr; PA ST; Bus Adm.

HOOKS, CHRISTINA; Ford City JR SR HS; Ford City, PA; (3); Trs 4-H; 4-H Awd; Intrmdt Fttr 85; Bradford Schl; Secr.

HOOPER, JENNIFER; Hickory HS; Hermitage, PA; (1); Latin Clb; Chorus; Capt Cheerleading; Diving; Trk.

HOOPER, PATRICK; Elk Co Christian HS; St Marys, PA; (3); 9/88; Church Yth Grp; Letterman Clb; SADD; Varsity Clb; Pres Jr Cls; Stu Cncl; Var Bsktbl; Var L Golf; Trk; High Hon Roll; Boy Scts 81; Amer Legn Schl Awd 84; Yth Ftnss Achvt Awd 84; Optmtry.

HOOPES, ANDREW; Ridley SR HS; Ridley Pk, PA; (3); 131/417; Bsbl; Socr; Soccer.

HOOS, JESSICA; Liberty HS; Bethlehem, PA; (3); 121/429; Office Aide; SADD; Pres Band; Pres Concert Band; Pres Mrchg Band; Pres Orch; Nwsp Stf; Yrbk Stf; Sftbl; Hon Roll; Med.

HOOVER, BRYAN; Central Dauphin HS; Harrisburg, PA; (3); 9/387; Church Yth Grp; Concert Band; Jazz Band; Mrchg Band; JV Trk; JV Wrstlng; High Hon Roll; Hon Roll; Jr NHS; NHS; PA ST U; Civil Engr.

HOOVER, CHRISTINE; Corry Area HS; Corry, PA; (2); Church Yth Grp; German Clb; SADD; Chorus; Church Choir; High Hon Roll; Amer Hstry, Plane Geom, Acad Bio Acad Achvt Awds; PA ST U; Math Tchr.

HOOVER, DAN; Shenango JR SR HS; New Castle, PA; (3); 12/125; Exploring; Varsity Clb; Pres Jr Cls; Var Bsktbl; Var Ftbl; High Hon Roll; Hon Roll; Jr NHS; NHS; 1st Tm All Cnty Defnse Ftbl 85-86; Med.

HOOVER, DARYL; Eastern York HS; York, PA; (4); Church Yth Grp; High Hon Roll; Deans List 86-87; Hnrs Pgm Penn ST 86-87; Acad All Star 86-87; Penn ST; Hosp Admin.

HOOVER, DARYL; Lancaster Mennonito HS; Ephrata, PA; (3); 69/155; Pres Church Yth Grp; FFA; Bsbl.

HOOVER, DONNA; Waynesboro Area SR HS; Waynesboro, PA; (3); 12/400; Chorus; Yrbk Phtg; Yrbk Stf; Rep Frsh Cls; Var Capt Cheerleading; High Hon Roll; Hon Roll; NHS; Presdntl Acadc Ftns Awd; Chrldng Achvt Awd; Intl Frgn Lang Awd; IN U PA; Psych.

HOOVER, GINA; Grace Christian Schl; Myerstown, PA; (3); Church Yth Grp; 4-H; Var Fld Hcky; Var Sftbl; Var Trk; 4-H Awd; Hon Roll; CAP; Var Cheerleading; All Str Fld Hcky Awds 85-86; Outstndng HS Athlts In Amer 86; Amateur Athltc Union Of US 84-87; Phys Educ.

HOOVER, J MARK; Moon SR HS; Coraopolis, PA; (4); Pres German Clb; Key Clb; Band; Symp Band; Off Frsh Cls; Off Soph Cls; Off Jr Cls; Off Sr Cls; Trs Stu Cncl; Im Bsktbl; Soc Distngshd Amer HS Stu; Acad All Star Allegheny Times.

HOOVER, JAMES; Cocalico HS; Denver, PA; (3); Boy Scts; Camera Clb; Church Yth Grp; Ftbl; Var Tennis; Var Trk; Hon Roll; Lion Awd; Penn ST U; Bus Admin.

HOOVER, JOELLE; Big Spring HS; Newville, PA; (3); 22/258; Nwsp Ed-Chief; Rep Jr Cls; Sec Sr Cls; Sec Stu Cncl; Capt Cheerleading; Powder Puff Ftbl; High Hon Roll; NHS; Church Yth Grp; Math Tm; JR Mnth Awd 87; Shippensburg U; Cmnctns.

HOOVER, JON; Marion Center Area HS; Home, PA; (3); Aud/Vis; Band; Concert Band; Mrchg Band; Stage Crew; Stu Cncl; Swmmng; Hon Roll; Ntl Coll Chiropractic; Chrprctr.

HOOVER, KATHY; Keystone JR SR HS; Marble, PA; (3); 15/140; FBLA; Band; Concert Band; Jazz Band; Mrchg Band; Pep Band; School Musical; Hon Roll; Accntng.

HOOVER, KATY; Southwestern HS; Hanover, PA; (3); 19/210; Church Yth Grp; Key Clb; Ski Clb; Varsity Clb; Yrbk Stf; JV Fld Hcky; Var Swmmng; Hon Roll; NHS; NEDT Awd; Bus Adm.

HOOVER, MARCY; Fannett Metal HS; Ft Loudon, PA; (4); 9/41; Am Leg Aux Girls St; Art Clb; Church Yth Grp; Drama Clb; Chorus; Color Guard; Swing Chorus; Nwsp Stf; High Hon Roll; NHS; 2nd Pl-Amer Lgn Essy Cntst 86; Acadmc All Amer 84; Hghst Avg-Frnch Clss 84-86; Shippensburg U; Wrtnt/Art.

HOOVER, REBECCA; Spring Ford HS; Royersford, PA; (2); 30/289; Art Clb; Church Yth Grp; French Clb; SADD; Nwsp Stf; Var JV Lcrss; Mgr(s); Hon Roll; NHS; Lit Mag; Writer Of Mnth Awd 85-87; Art.

HOOVER, RICH; Northwestern HS; Albion, PA; (4); 7/150; SADD; School Play; Cheerleading; Var Capt Crs Cntry; Var Capt Trk; Pres NHS; Church Yth Grp; Model UN; Scholastic Bowl; Babe Ruth Sprtsmnshp Awd, Hasthan Character Awd, Wesley Freeburg Jr Mem Awd 87; Penn ST U Univ Park; Envrmntl.

HOOVER, ROBERT; Ligonier Valley HS; Stablstown, PA; (3); AFS; Church Yth Grp; Computer Clb; Spanish Clb; Band; Concert Band; Jazz Band; Mrchg Band; Hon Roll; Prfct Atten Awd; Acctg.

HOOVER, STEPHEN; Dover Area HS; Dover, PA; (3); 5/260; Computer Clb; Varsity Clb; L Var Tennis; High Hon Roll; Hon Roll; Prncpls Awd Outstndng Sci 87; Chem Engrng.

HOOVER, TAMMY; Northern Bedford County HS; Hopewell, PA; (3); 1/95; SADD; Band; Chorus; Nwsp Stf; VP Soph Cls; Capt Cheerleading; Var Socr; Var Trk; High Hon Roll; NHS; Pres Phys Fit Awd 83-87; Juniata Coll; Pre-Med.

HOOVER, VERNA; Bald Eagle Area HS; Karthaus, PA; (4); 35/190; Pres Church Yth Grp; VP SADD; Chorus; Concert Band; Mrchg Band; School Musical; Im Powder Puff Ftbl; Var JV Sftbl; High Hon Roll; Prfct Atten Awd; Lock Haven U; Med.

HOOVER, WENDY; Western Wayne HS; Hamlin, PA; (3); Church Yth Grp; Girl Scts; Spanish Clb; Church Choir; Hon Roll; MUSIC-PIANO.

HOOVLER, MARK; General Mc Lane HS; Mckean, PA; (4); 19/196; Boy Scts; Spanish Clb; Teachers Aide; Rep Yrbk Stf; Rep Stu Cncl; High Hon Roll; Hon Roll; Pres Schlr; Stu For Acad Excellence 86-87; Robert L Fleek Awd 87; Penn ST Behrend; Ed.

HOPE, CHARLES; Northeast HS; Philadelphia, PA; (3); Church Yth Grp; DECA; FBLA; Ntl Hnr Roll 86-87; Cmptr Prgrmr.

HOPE, JOHN; Harrisburg HS; Harrisburg, PA; (3); Model UN; Nwsp Rptr; Nwsp Stf; Hon Roll; NHS; Lewis Clark Coll; Frgn Lang.

HOPF, CHRISTINA; Peters Twp HS; Mcmurray, PA; (3); 3/235; Chess Clb; Exploring; Key Clb; Teachers Aide; Varsity Clb; Lit Mag; Capt VP Crs Cntry; VP L Trk; High Hon Roll; NHS; PA Govrns Schl Schl For Sci 87; Chem Olympd Fnls 87; TAC Natl Jr Olympcs Fnlst Track/Fld 86; Engrng.

HOPF, JENNIFER; Council Rock HS; Churchville, PA; (2); Hosp Aide; Key Clb; Band; Drill Tm; Mrchg Band; Hon Roll; Psych.

HOPF, NATHAN; Northern York County HS; Dillsburg, PA; (3); 8/232; Chess Clb; Church Yth Grp; SADD; Band; Concert Band; Drill Tm; Mrchg Band; High Hon Roll; 3 Schltc Cert 85-87; Tech Engrng.

HOPKINS, BRADLEY; Tunkhannock Area HS; Dalton, PA; (3); 4/235; Church Yth Grp; VP Pres 4-H; Key Clb; 4-H Awd; High Hon Roll; JETS Awd; NHS; Prfct Atten Awd; Mech Engr.

HOPKINS, GAIL; Penn Cambria HS; Cresson, PA; (3); 18/210; Spanish Clb; SADD; Band; Color Guard; Rep Frsh Cls; L Var Bsktbl; L Var Vllybl; NHS; IN U; Law.

HOPKINS, GARY; West Greene HS; Nineveh, PA; (4); 5/102; Trs Church Yth Grp; Drama Clb; Ski Clb; Yrbk Bus Mgr; VP Jr Cls; Stu Cncl; Trk; High Hon Roll; NHS; PITT Fresh Erly Admssn Prg 86-87; U Of Pittsburgh; Bus Admin.

HOPKINS, JENNIFER; Downingtown SR HS; Exton, PA; (3); French Clb; Hosp Aide; Ski Clb; Band; Color Guard; Concert Band; Flag Corp; Mrchg Band; School Musical; Stage Crew.

HOPKINS, KRISTA; Brookville Area HS; Brookville, PA; (3); 6/178; German Clb; Key Clb; Varsity Clb; Capt L Cheerleading; High Hon Roll; Hon Roll; NHS; FTA; Chorus; Rep Stu Cncl; PA Free Entrprs 86; Accntng I Hnrs 87.

HOPKINS, MAUREEN; Upper Darby HS; Drexel Hill, PA; (3); Pep Clb; Nwsp Rptr; Rep Frsh Cls; Rep Soph Cls; Crs Cntry; Gym; Trk; Pediatrics.

HOPKINS, SEAN; Sto Rox HS; Mckees Rocks, PA; (2); Boys Clb Am; Letterman Clb; Varsity Clb; Pres Soph Cls; VP Bsbl; JV Bsktbl; VP Ftbl; High Hon Roll; Duquesne U; Corp Lawyer.

HOPKINS, SHARON; Saint Basil Acad; Rydal, PA; (3); Drama Clb; German Clb; Hosp Aide; Spanish Clb; School Play; Yrbk Stf; Hon Roll; Elem Ed Tchr.

HOPKINS, SHERRY; State College Area SR HS; State College, PA; (4); 147/541; Church Yth Grp; Pres 4-H; 4-H Awd; High Hon Roll; NEDT Awd; FHA; Orch; PA ST U.

HOPKINSON, JAMES; Belle Vernon Area HS; West Newton, PA; (3); Pom Pon; Hon Roll.

HOPPEL, ANGELLA; Philadelphia HS For Girls; Philadelphia, PA; (3); Hosp Aide; Latin Clb; Library Aide; Office Aide; Science Clb; Spanish Clb; Teachers Aide; Varsity Clb; Im Bsktbl; Im Var Cheerleading; Made All-Public Swmtm 86; Marine Bio.

HOPPLE, ALLYSON; Annville-Cleona HS; Cleona, PA; (4); 47/125; Cmnty Wkr; French Clb; SADD; Band; Mrchg Band; Orch; School Musical; Nwsp Sprt Ed; Yrbk Stf; NHS; Lock Haven U; Erly Chldhd Educ.

HOPPLE, KIM; Cumberland Valley HS; Mechanicsburg, PA; (4); 48/585; Church Yth Grp; Pres 4-H; FBLA; Pres FFA; Quiz Bowl; Band; JV Bsktbl; Var L Fld Hcky; NHS; FFA Outstndg Girl 86; Keystone Frmr Degree 87; FFA Star Greenhand 85; Penn ST; Ag.

HOPPY, JASON; Hazleton HS; Hazleton, PA; (2); Church Yth Grp; FBLA; Stu Cncl; Bsbl; Capt Bsktbl; Wt Lftg; Hon Roll; Cmptd For Typng Awd In FBLA 86-87; Accntnt.

HOPSHIRE, JOHN; Warren Area HS; Warren, PA; (4); 5/285; Boy Scts; Varsity Clb; Concert Band; Ftbl; Capt Trk; Wt Lftg; High Hon Roll; Jr NHS; NHS; Pres Schlr; Qlfd For Rgnls ACS Chem Olympd 86; Penn ST U; Chem Engrng.

HORAN, DIANNE; Abington Heights HS; Clarks Green, PA; (3); 109/292; Boy Scts; Church Yth Grp; JA; Ski Clb; Hon Roll; Crimnl Justc.

HORAN, KERIE; Belle Vernon Area HS; Belle Vernon, PA; (3); FBLA; Library Aide; Pep Clb; Ski Clb; Teachers Aide; Band; Concert Band; Mrchg Band; Yrbk Stf; Score Keeper; Intl Order Of The Rainbow For Girls Worthy Advisor 86; CA U Of PA; Pre-Elem Tchr.

HORCHOLIC, DANA; Swissvale HS; Pittsburg, PA; (4); 5/196; Church Yth Grp; VP French Clb; Hosp Aide; Y-Teens; Acpl Chr; Band; Concert Band; Mrchg Band; Pep Band; School Musical; IBEW Local Union No 5 & Wstrn PA Chptr NECA 87; PTSA Scholar 87; Womens Clb Swissvale 87; PA ST U; Elec Engrng.

HORENSKY, SUSAN; Hazleton HS; Drums, PA; (4); FBLA; CC Awd; High Hon Roll; NHS; AFL CIO Labr Cncl Awd 87; Shawn Zanolini Memrl Awd 87; Albert Arnoff Awd 87; Penn ST; Bus Adm.

HORENZY, TAMMI; Freeport SR HS; Sarver, PA; (3); Church Yth Grp; Hosp Aide; School Musical; School Play; Nwsp Rptr; Nwsp Stf; Yrbk Stf; Trk; Vllybl; Hon Roll; Bwlng Grn ST U; Spch Pathlgn.

HORICK, NICOLE; Carlisle SR HS; Gardners, PA; (3); 21/467; JA; Key Clb; Yrbk Stf; High Hon Roll; Hon Roll; NHS; Crmnl Just.

HORLACHER, MAUREEN; Lancstermennonite HS; Mt Gretna, PA; (3); Art Clb; Pres Sec Church Yth Grp; FTA; Latin Clb; Nwsp Rptr; High Hon Roll; Hon Roll; NHS.

HORN, BRAD; Plum HS; New Kensington, PA; (2); JV Aud/Vis; Boy Scts; Band; Concert Band; Symp Band; Var Ftbl; Wt Lftg; Hon Roll; NEDT Awd; Ftbl Lttr Wnnr; Tutor 85-86; Penn ST; Engrng.

HORN, HOLLY; Carlisle SR HS; Carlisle, PA; (3); 34/454; JA; Office Aide; Color Guard; Stage Crew; Mgr(s); Trk; High Hon Roll; Hon Roll; NHS; Cert Of Awd Of Acad Excllnce 86-87; IN U; Psych.

HORN, LISA; Liberty HS; Bethlehem, PA; (3); 168/429; Elem Ed.

HORN, MIKE; Du Bois Area HS; Rockton, PA; (3); Band; Concert Band; Mrchg Band; Pep Band; PA ST; Pre Law.

HORN, PENNY; Chambersburg Area SR HS; Upper Strasberg, PA; (2); Church Yth Grp; German Clb; Hon Roll; Outstndng Atten In Chrch 83-87; Newspaper Staff Camp Joy-El 84; Cert From Faithful Bible Invstgtrs 82.

HORN, STEPHEN; Penns Manor SR HS; Penn Run, PA; (3); 19/105; Boy Scts; Band; Concert Band; Jazz Band; Mrchg Band; Stu Cncl; Ftbl; L Trk; Hon Roll; IN U PA HS Hnrs Band 84-85; UCLA; Cnmtgrphy.

HORN, TROY; Chambersburg Area SR HS; Chambersburg, PA; (2); Boy Scts; German Clb; Ski Clb; Spanish Clb; Off Soph Cls; Off Stu Cncl; Bsbl; Ftbl; Golf; Tennis.

HORNAK, GENA NICOLE; Boyertown HS; Perkiomenville, PA; (4); 40/440; Hosp Aide; JA; Spanish Clb; SADD; Teachers Aide; Drill Tm; Mrchg Band; Cit Awd; Hon Roll; Ursinus Coll; Bio.

HORNBERGER, DALE; Millersburg Area HS; Millersburg, PA; (4); 16/76; Boy Scts; Trs Church Yth Grp; Var Ftbl; Var Wrstlng; Hon Roll; NHS; National Ed Ctr; Elec Engrng.

HORNBERGER, WENDY; Bensalem HS; Bensalem, PA; (2); Church Yth Grp; Drama Clb; Chorus; Church Choir; School Play; Off Soph Cls; Crs Cntry; Trk; High Hon Roll; Law.

HORNCHEK, ERIC; Harry S Truman HS; Fairless Hills, PA; (4); 7/575; Aud/Vis; Computer Clb; Library Aide; NFL; Pres Y-Teens; High Hon Roll; NHS; Prfct Atten Awd; Pres Schlr; Comp Mth Awd 86; Outstndng Stu Chem Awd 87; Bristol Twp PT Schlrshp 87; Carnegie Mellon U; Engrng.

HORNE, GREGORY; Columbia-Mobtour AVTS HS; Berwick, PA; (4); 1/177; Yrbk Stf; Pres Soph Cls; Pres Jr Cls; Pres Sr Cls; Var Ftbl; Var Wrstlng; Pres NHS; Val; Letterman Clb; Math Tm; Army Rsrv Schlr-Athlete Awd; Most Valuable Linesman Awd; Drftng-Dsgn Outstndng Sr Awd; Rtry Schlrshp; Penn ST U; Mech Engrng.

HORNE, HEATHER; Yough HS; W Newton, PA; (4); Church Yth Grp; French Clb; Library Aide; Ski Clb; Mgr(s); Powder Puff Ftbl; Sftbl; Vllybl; Hon Roll; NHS; St Francis-Pittsburgh; Thrpy.

HORNE, JAMES; North Catholic HS; Glenshaw, PA; (3); 53/285; Church Yth Grp; FCA; Ski Clb; SADD; Rep Jr Cls; Var L Bsbl; Var L Bsktbl; Var L Golf; Hon Roll; NHS; Bio.

HORNE, JAMI; Quakertown Community HS; Richlandtown, PA; (2); Church Yth Grp; Dance Clb; Drama Clb; French Clb; Office Aide; SADD; Band; Chorus; Church Choir; Concert Band; Pres Physcl Ftns Awd 85-87; Physcl Thrpy.

HORNER, DEANA; E Pennsboro Area HS; Summerdale, PA; (3); Church Yth Grp; Dance Clb; Drama Clb; French Clb; SADD; Church Choir; Stu Cncl; High Hon Roll; Hon Roll; NHS; Carlisle Prof/Central PA Youth Ballet 85-87; PA Ballet Co 84-85; Chautauqun Dance Fstvl Co 87; Dance.

HORNER, JANE; Beaver County Christian Schl; New Brighton, PA; (1); 1/11; Church Yth Grp; Library Aide; Trs Band; Chorus; Church Choir; JV Var Vllybl; Ntl Merit SF; Carnegie Mellon; Elec Engrng.

HORNER, JULIE; Bellefonte Area SR HS; Bellefonte, PA; (3); 5/211; SADD; Band; Chorus; Jazz Band; School Musical; Nwsp Ed-Chief; Yrbk Bus Mgr; Rep Stu Cncl; NHS; Drama Clb; PMEA All-St, Regnl & Dist Band 86-87; PA ST U.

HORNER, KEVIN; St Marys HS; Ephrata, PA; (2); 1/9; Cmnty Wkr; Chorus; School Play; Pres Soph Cls; Var Bsbl; Var Bsktbl; Var Crs Cntry; Var Socr; Hon Roll; NHS; St Joes Prep Semnry; Clrgy.

HORNER, MELISSA; Berlin Brothers Valley HS; Berlin, PA; (3); 12/97; Church Yth Grp; French Clb; SADD; Band; VP Chorus; Church Choir; Concert Band; Drm Mjr(t); Mrchg Band; Hon Roll; Cnty Chorus 2nd Alto 86-87; Chorus VP 86-87; Vocal Perf.

HORNER, TODD; Punsutawney Area HS; Punxsutawney, PA; (3); Math Tm; Science Clb; Teachers Aide; Variety Show; Var L Bsbl; Hon Roll; NHS; Ntl Merit Ltr; Gifted Prog 85-88; Pharmacy.

HORNICK, SCOTT; Corry Area HS; Corry, PA; (4); 2/200; Model UN; Spanish Clb; Yrbk Ed-Chief; Rep Soph Cls; Rep Jr Cls; Pres Sr Cls; Rep Stu Cncl; Ftbl; Trk; Sal; PA Byrd Schlrshp 87; Hgh Hnr Roll 85-87; Outstndng Schlr Athlt 86-87; U Of Dayto(; Elec Engr.

HORNIG, TIMOTHY; Ridley SR HS; Ridley Park, PA; (3); 67/453; Boy Scts; Ski Clb; Spanish Clb; Varsity Clb; Var JV Bsbl; Capt Var Bsktbl; Var JV Ftbl; West Chester; Secndry Educ.

HORNINGER, BETH; Liberty HS; Bethlehem, PA; (4); 15/421; Cmnty Wkr; Hosp Aide; Var Capt Cheerleading; Powder Puff Ftbl; Cit Awd; High Hon Roll; NHS; SAR Awd; Key Clb; Y-Teens; AM Assc U Wmn Schlrshp 87; Lmp Of Knwldg 87; Strght A-S 4 Yrs; PA Mtr Trck Assc Schlrshp 87; PA ST U; Med.

HORNSTEIN, KEN; Conneaut Lake HS; Conneaut Lake, PA; (3); 1/80; JA; Key Clb; Spanish Clb; Mgr Mrchg Band; Stage Crew; High Hon Roll; Ntl Merit SF; Drama Clb; Math Tm; Quiz Bowl; 1st Chem Div JETS, 3rd Tm Chem Olympic,Qlfr Chem Olympiad 87; Elec Engrng.

HORODOWICH, ELIZABETH; Pennsbury HS; Yardley, PA; (3); Am Leg Aux Girls St; Art Clb; French Clb; Nwsp Stf; Yrbk Phtg; Yrbk Stf; Lit Mag; Stu Cncl; Hon Roll; Sec NHS; Schlrshp To Moore Coll Of Art 84-85; Gov ST Art Awd 85-86; Bcks Cnty Cncl For Arts Awd 86-87; Art.

HOROSCHAK, SIGRID; Northern Lehigh HS; Slatington, PA; (3); 4/166; Debate Tm; Ski Clb; Jazz Band; Mrchg Band; School Musical; Nwsp Stf; Yrbk Stf; Pres Soph Cls; Twrlr; High Hon Roll; ST Wide Mck Trl Tm 86-87; Physics.

HORR, DIANNA; West Greene HS; Waynesburg, PA; (4); 27/105; Dance Clb; Varsity Clb; Nwsp Stf; Yrbk Stf; Sec Sr Cls; Rep Sec Stu Cncl; Var Capt Cheerleading; Var L Vllybl; Hon Roll; Letterman Clb; Outstndng Chrldr Coog Fnlst 85; All Cmp Elite Sqd Chrldng Cmp WV U 85; 14th Pl Ntl Chrldr Cmptn 86; U Pittsburgh; Public Rltns.

HORSLEY, CHRISTIN; Eisenhower HS; Russell, PA; (3); 1/122; Hosp Aide; Chorus; Church Choir; Madrigals; Yrbk Stf; Rep Stu Cncl; JV Var Bsktbl; JV Cheerleading; Var Trk; NHS; Law.

HORST, JOHN; Central York HS; York, PA; (2); Church Yth Grp; High Hon Roll; Hon Roll; Acad Ltr 86-87.

HORST, LYNNAE; Faith Mennonite HS; Ronks, PA; (3); Church Yth Grp; Acpl Chr; Chorus; Nwsp Rptr; Ed Nwsp Stf; Sec Frsh Cls; Rep Sec Stu Cncl; High Hon Roll; Hon Roll; Prfct Atten Awd; Ruth Awd Charactr Qlty Awd 84 86; Bus.

HORST, SUSAN; Lancaster Mennonite HS; Palo Alto, PA; (3); Pres Church Yth Grp; Drama Clb; Chorus; Church Choir; Orch; Hon Roll; Elem Ed.

HORST, WENDY S; Chambersburg Area SR HS; Chambersburg, PA; (3); 31/697; Pres Church Yth Grp; Sec FTA; Pres German Clb; Chorus; Church Choir; Concert Band; Mrchg Band; Orch; Yrbk Stf; Hon Roll; 1st Pl Dist Grmn Comptn Catgry Compstn 86; Millersville U; Grmn.

HORSTMAN, RONALD DALE; Lakeview HS; Mercer, PA; (4); 4/128; Varsity Clb; School Play; Nwsp Rptr; Nwsp Stf; Var L Ftbl; Capt Var Trk; Elks Awd; NHS; Air Force ROTC Schlrshp 87; Penn St; Aerospc Engnrng.

HORT, JASON; Danville JR HS; Danville, PA; (1); Rep Frsh Cls; Im Bsktbl; Im Ftbl; Var Trk; High Hon Roll; Pres Schlr.

HORT, KURT; Shikellamy HS; Northumberland, PA; (4); 11/311; Am Leg Boys St; Capt L Bsktbl; Capt L Ftbl; Hon Roll; NHS; Dickinson; Pre-Med.

HORTING, ELISABETH; Newport JR SR HS; Newport, PA; (2); 3/117; Church Yth Grp; Band; Chorus; Church Choir; Concert Band; Jazz Band; Mrchg Band; Pep Band; School Musical; Swing Chorus; 1st Pl At Millersville U Piano Fstvl 86.

HORTING, SHANNON; Newport HS; Newport, PA; (4); 16/89; Am Leg Aux Girls St; Varsity Clb; Chorus; School Musical; Yrbk Sprt Ed; Var JV Bsktbl; Var Capt Fld Hcky; Hon Roll; NHS; Shippensburg U PA; Elem Ed.

HORTMAN, TIM; Mountain View HS; Hop Bottom, PA; (3); 10/105; Boy Scts; Chess Clb; 4-H; Teachers Aide; Band; Chorus; Socr; Hon Roll; Prfct Atten 84-87.

HORTON, CARRIE; North Penn HS; Covington, PA; (3); 1/60; Church Yth Grp; Drama Clb; Band; Chorus; Concert Band; School Play; Nwsp Stf; High Hon Roll; Hon Roll; NHS; District Band 85-86; Soc Of Dist Am H S Stu 85-86; Mansfield U; Bus.

HORTON, MELINDA; Frazier HS; Perryopolis, PA; (3); Pres Church Yth Grp; Drama Clb; VP Band; Church Choir; Color Guard; Drill Tm; Flag Corp; Mrchg Band; School Play; JV Bsktbl; Psych.

HORTON, MELISSA; Nativity BVM; Pine Grove, PA; (2); 20/77; Latin Clb; Church Choir; Hon Roll; Pres Schlr; Intl Frgn Lang Awd 85-86.

HORTON, RANCE; Lower Dauphin HS; Hummelstown, PA; (2); Ski Clb; Bsbl; Bsktbl; Golf; Tennis; Hon Roll.

HORVATH, JENNIFER; Scranton Central HS; Scranton, PA; (2); Dance Clb; 4-H; French Clb; Hosp Aide; Office Aide; SADD; PA ST; Nursng.

HORVATH, THERESA; Lakeland JR SR HS; Carbondale, PA; (4); Computer Clb; SADD; Yrbk Stf; Cheerleading; Hon Roll; Flag Corp; Pep Band; Marywood Coll; Elem Ed.

HORWATH, JOSEPH F; Freedom HS; Bethlehem, PA; (3); 114/509; Boys Clb Am; Spanish Clb; Hon Roll; Allentown Coll; Pre Med.

HORWATH, KIRSTEN; Bethlehem Catholic HS; Bethlehem, PA; (4); 96/205; Var L Cheerleading; Slovak Catholic Sokal Schlrshp 87; PA St U.

HOSBACH, THOMAS; New Hope Solebury HS; New Hope, PA; (4); 35/77; Civic Clb; Cmnty Wkr; JA; Ski Clb; Varsity Clb; Band; Concert Band; Jazz Band; Mrchg Band; Orch; Army & Marine Corps Soccer Awd 87; MVP Soccer & Bsebl 87; Cmmnty Assoc Schlrshp 87; West Chester; Music.

HOSCHAR, AARON; Greensburg Salem SR HS; Greensburg, PA; (2); French Clb; Model UN; NFL; Rep Soph Cls; High Hon Roll; Hon Roll.

HOSFELD, MATTHEW; Liberty HS; Bethlehem, PA; (4); 170/434; Boys Clb Am; Letterman Clb; Ski Clb; Varsity Clb; Band; Concert Band; Jazz Band; Mrchg Band; JV Var Socr; Hon Roll; Michael J Glenn Mem Awd 87; Moravian Coll; Bio.

HOSKINSON, MIKE; Waynesburg Central HS; Mount Morris, PA; (3); 10/200; Chess Clb; Church Yth Grp; Ski Clb; Spanish Clb; Varsity Clb; Church Choir; Bsktbl; High Hon Roll; NHS.

HOSLER, DAWN; Juniata HS; Pt Royal, PA; (3); Varsity Clb; Concert Band; Mrchg Band; Stage Crew; Stat Bsktbl; JV Var Socr; Var L Sftbl; JV Var Trk; Hon Roll; NHS.

HOSLER, MATTHEW; Freeport HS; Sarver, PA; (3); 9/200; Pres Church Yth Grp; Church Choir; Concert Band; Mrchg Band; Symp Band; Rep Stu Cncl; Trk; High Hon Roll; Pep Band; Hon Roll; ARIN Intermdt Unit Marine Bio Quest 86; Studnt Schl Board Rep 86; Biophysics.

HOSLER, MICHAEL; Juniata HS; Thompsontown, PA; (3); Chess Clb; Drama Clb; SADD; Band; Concert Band; Jazz Band; Mrchg Band; School Play; Variety Show; Yrbk Ed-Chief; Theatre Arts.

HOSPELHORN, SHARON; Waynesboro Area SR HS; Wa Nesboro, PA; (2); Church Yth Grp; Library Aide; Chorus; Church Choir; Yrbk Stf; Capt Cheerleading; Crs Cntry; Trk; Hon Roll.

HOSTAL, PAMELA; South Park HS; Library, PA; (3); 13/227; Ski Clb; Teachers Aide; Capt Var Cheerleading; High Hon Roll; NHS; Prfct Atten Awd; PITT Penn ST; Pre Med.

HOSTERMAN, TROY; Bellefonte Area HS; Bellefonte, PA; (3); 16/250; Var Bsbl; Im Coach Actv; Var Ftbl; Im Wt Lftg; Hon Roll; PA ST; Bus Mgnt.

HOSTETLER, PATRICIA; Mt Pleasant Area HS; Jones Mills, PA; (3); Church Yth Grp; French Clb; GAA; Library Aide; Nwsp Stf; Yrbk Stf; High Hon Roll; Exec Secy.

HOSTETTER, KIRK; North Hills HS; Pittsburgh, PA; (3); Ski Clb; Band; Concert Band; Jazz Band; Mrchg Band; Orch; Pep Band; JV Trk; High Hon Roll; Pres N Hills Band 88.

HOSTETTER, MICHELLE; Elizabethtown Area HS; Elizabethtown, PA; (2); 58/281; Art Clb; Church Yth Grp; French Clb; JV Tennis; JV Trk; Interior Dsgn.

HOSTETTER, NATHAN; Lancaster Christian Schl; Lancaster, PA; (3); Chorus; Yrbk Phtg; VP Soph Cls; Pres Jr Cls; Var L Bsktbl; Var L Socr; Hon Roll; Pres Schlr; HOBY Fndtn Sem 86; HOBY CLEW Treas 87; Drexel; Bus Adm.

HOSTLER, CHRIS; Bellwood-Antis HS; Tyrone, PA; (1); Wrstlng; Hon Roll; Penn State; Jrnlst.

HOSTLER, ROBERT; Dover Area HS; Dover, PA; (4); Varsity Clb; Bsbl; Ftbl; Trk; Hon Roll; MVP JV Ftbl 84-85; Yrk City Sprtsmn Awd Ftbl 86; Mst Schl Sprt 86; WV U; Bus.

HOSTRANDER, BRIDGETTE; Wellsboro Area HS; Wellsboro, PA; (2); Pep Clb; Band; Chorus; Concert Band; Mrchg Band; Pep Band; Bsktbl; Sftbl; DAR Awd; Hon Roll.

HOSU, KARLA; Harborcreek HS; Erie, PA; (3); JV Bsktbl; Var Powder Puff Ftbl; Var Capt Sftbl; Var Capt Vllybl; Hnrb Mntn All County Sftbll 1st Base 87; Law.

HOTCHKISS, JENNIFER; Dover Area HS; Dover, PA; (3); 56/260; Sec Church Yth Grp; Cmnty Wkr; Trs 4-H; Library Aide; Varsity Clb; Chorus; Color Guard; Yrbk Stf; JV Fld Hcky; Cit Awd; Hugh O Brian Yth Fndtn Ldrshp Smnr 86; Educ.

HOTCHKISS, LORI; Conneaut Valley HS; Springboro, PA; (2); Pres Church Yth Grp; Science Clb; Spanish Clb; Chorus; Church Choir; Rep Stu Cncl; High Hon Roll; NHS; TEAMS Comptn JETS Testing 87; Math.

HOTT, CHRISTINE; Everett Area HS; Everett, PA; (3); Church Yth Grp; Computer Clb; FBLA; GAA; SADD; Band; Concert Band; Mrchg Band; Pep Band; Hon Roll; Wrd Proc.

HOTTENSTEIN, JOHN; Hempfield HS; Lancaster, PA; (4); Church Yth Grp; Exploring; Chorus; Stage Crew; Hon Roll; Frnst De Vry Schlrshp 87; Dr Vry; Elec Engrng.

HOUCK, DEANA; Greencastle-Antrim HS; Greencastle, PA; (3); Rptr FNA; Pep Clb; Varsity Clb; Nwsp Rptr; Stat Bsktbl; Var Cheerleading; Hon Roll; 3rd Pl In Sci Bio Fair 85-86; Rad Tech.

HOUCK, JEFF; Greensburg Central Catholic HS; Greensburg, PA; (3); Var JV Ftbl; Im Mgr Wt Lftg; Marn Bio.

HOUCK, JEFFREY; Huntington Area HS; Huntington, PA; (2); 78/224; Red Cross Aide; SADD; Teachers Aide; Yrbk Stf; Rep Soph Cls; Stu Cncl; VP Bsbl; VP Bsktbl; VP Ftbl; Hon Roll; MD U; Biochem.

HOUCK, JEREMIAH; Hampton HS; Gibsonia, PA; (3); Church Yth Grp; Red Cross Aide; Var Capt Swmmng; Hon Roll; Most Valuable Swimmer 85-87; Civil Engnr.

HOUCK, KEVIN; Hickory HS; Hermitage, PA; (3); German Clb; Letterman Clb; Varsity Clb; Nwsp Rptr; Var L Ftbl; Var L Trk; Wt Lftg; NHS; Acadmc All Am 87; Bus Admin.

HOUCK JR, WILLIAM P; Chambersburg Area HS; Chambersburg, PA; (2); Chess Clb; Church Yth Grp; Teachers Aide; Penn ST U; Math.

HOUGGY, KATHERINE; Hampton HS; Allison Park, PA; (3); Church Yth Grp; French Clb; Ski Clb; Symp Band; VP Frsh Cls; VP Soph Cls; Pres Jr Cls; Pres Sr Cls; High Hon Roll; NHS; Cornell U; Med.

HOUGH, MIKE; Girard HS; Girard, PA; (4); 2/145; Am Leg Boys St; Drama Clb; French Clb; Letterman Clb; Math Tm; Band; Concert Band; Jazz Band; Mrchg Band; Pep Band; Exchnge Clb Yth Mnth 87; Grove City Coll; Mech Engrng.

HOUGH II, THOMAS H M; North Allegheny SR HS; Pittsburgh, PA; (3); 344/649; Nwsp Rptr; Nwsp Stf; Lit Mag; Prfct Atten Awd; TV Prdctn.

HOUGHTALING, LAURA; Cowanesque Vly HS; Westfield, PA; (2); Church Yth Grp; Computer Clb; FFA; Girl Scts; Quiz Bowl; Chorus; Church Choir; Color Guard; Drill Tm; Mrchg Band; Penn ST; Art.

HOUGHTON, CAROL; Gtr Johnstown Area Vo Tech; Johnstown, PA; (3); Trs Church Yth Grp; DECA; Hosp Aide; VICA; Church Choir; Cert Aprctn Cndy Strpr 85; Vo-Tech Achvt Awd Schl Shp 86; Bus Ed.

HOUGHTON, CHERYL; Cardinal O Hara HS; Glenolden, PA; (3); 111/723; Dance Clb; Hosp Aide; SADD; Yrbk Stf; JV Fld Hcky; French Hon Soc; Hon Roll; Prfct Atten Awd; Math Stu Of Month 87; Med.

HOUIDES, DEBORAH; Allen HS; Allentown, PA; (3); Art Clb; Camera Clb; Ski Clb; Ed Nwsp Phtg; Off Frsh Cls; Off Soph Cls; Hon Roll; Intnl Clb; JCL; Hst Latin Clb.

HOUP, GLENDA; Calvary Christian Acad; James Creek, PA; (3); Church Yth Grp; Cmnty Wkr; 4-H; Band; Yrbk Sprt Ed; Cheerleading; Socr; Cit Awd; 4-H Awd; Sec Pep Clb; 2nd Rnnr Up In All Amer Tn Grl Pgnt; Miss Marklesburg Fire Qn 87; JR Grange Ldr 85; Liberty U; Bus Admin.

HOUPTLEY, LORI; Brandywine Hts HS; Fleetwood, PA; (2); 43/140; Church Yth Grp; Socr; Tennis; Hon Roll; Phys Ther.

HOURI, MARIE; Lebanon Catholic HS; Palmyra, PA; (3); 7/72; Church Yth Grp; Ski Clb; Spanish Clb; School Play; Yrbk Ed-Chief; Hon Roll; Pres NHS; 3rd Pl Sci Fair 87; Intntl Bus.

HOUSE, KARI; Fairview HS; Fairview, PA; (4); 21/154; Am Leg Aux Girls St; Ski Clb; Varsity Clb; Lit Mag; Rep Stu Cncl; JV Var Cheerleading; L Crs Cntry; L Capt Trk; Hon Roll; Trs NHS; Coaches Awd Track 87; Babe Ruth Awd 87; Purdue U; Hlth Sci.

HOUSEHOLDER, ALLEN; Elizabeth-Forward SR HS; Elizabeth, PA; (2); 8/325; Church Yth Grp; Exploring; French Clb; Leo Clb; Band; Church Choir; Concert Band; Mrchg Band; High Hon Roll; Hon Roll; Fast Paced Math Pgm Coll Crdt 86; Physics.

HOUSEHOLDER, TRISHA; Lincoln HS; Ellwood City, PA; (3); 14/167; Hosp Aide; Sec Trs Spanish Clb; SADD; Y-Teens; Chorus; Rep Frsh Cls; Pres Soph Cls; Trs Sr Cls; Stu Cncl; Im JV Cheerleading; Trk MVP Tri Cnty 85; Beaver Cnty 87; Cntr Inv 87; Ath Of Wk 86; Hgh Pnt Awd Of Trk Team 85-87; Math.

HOUSEKNECHT, JEFFREY; Montgomery Area JR SR HS; Montgomery, PA; (3); 17/84; Thesps; Band; Chorus; Concert Band; Jazz Band; Mrchg Band; School Musical; School Play; Stage Crew; Var L Ftbl; USMC; Mltry Plc.

HOUSEKNECHT, TRACY; Hughesville HS; Hughesville, PA; (3); 46/147; Church Yth Grp; 4-H; FTA; Girl Scts; Hosp Aide; Key Clb; Spanish Clb; Teachers Aide; Band; Chorus; SR Hgh Cnty Band Awd 86; Ed.

HOUSEL, SUSAN; Meyersdale HS; Meyersdale, PA; (4); 4/116; French Clb; Chorus; Yrbk Stf; Rep Stu Cncl; Var Capt Cheerleading; High Hon Roll; NHS; Hnr Ltr Hgh GPA; ACC Math Cmptn Schlrshp 86; French Hnr Awd Hgh GPA 85; U Pgh Johnstwn; Educatn.

HOUSER, BETH; South Park HS; Library, PA; (3); 36/260; Rep Jr Cls; Var L Bsktbl; Capt Cheerleading; Coach Actv; Var L Crs Cntry; Var L Trk; Secndry Ed.

HOUSER, GRETCHEN; Eastern York JR/Sr HS; E Prospect, PA; (4); Sec Church Yth Grp; Sec VP 4-H; Chorus; Concert Band; Mrchg Band; Yrbk Stf; Aud/Vis; Band; School Musical; Nwsp Rptr; Pres Phy Ftns Awd; PA 4-H ST Captl Days Rep; Mary Salome Billmeyer Baker Schlrshp; Wilson Coll; Vet Sci.

HOUSER, MARK; New Castle HS; New Castle, PA; (4); 11/253; AFS; Jazz Band; School Play; Var L Cheerleading; High Hon Roll; NHS; Ntl Merit Ltr; Church Yth Grp; Drama Clb; Quiz Bowl; Ntl Ldrshp Merit Awd 85-86; Acotr Musician 85-86; OH U; Telecomm.

HOUSER, MATT; New Castle SR HS; New Castle, PA; (3); 19/263; Church Yth Grp; French Clb; Varsity Clb; Band; Concert Band; Mrchg Band; Pep Band; Rep Stu Cncl; Cheerleading; Crs Cntry; Academic All Am 84; Duquesne; Presthd.

HOUSER, MELANIE; Upper Moreland HS; Hatboro, PA; (3); 30/275; Spanish Clb; Band; Church Choir; Concert Band; Mrchg Band; School Musical; Symp Band; Mgr(s); Score Keeper; Timer.

HOUSER, MITCHELL; New Castle SR HS; New Castle, PA; (2); AFS; CAP; French Clb; Pep Clb; Concert Band; Jazz Band; Mrchg Band; Pep Band; Rep Frsh Cls; Rep Soph Cls; Miami U Coral Gab; Crimnlgy.

HOUSHOLDER, DARRYL J; Seneca Valley SR HS; Zelienople, PA; (3); JA; Bsbl.

HOUSLEY JR, WILLIAM H; Philipsburg-Osceola Area SR HS; Philipsburg, PA; (3); Letterman Clb; Var Capt Bsktbl; Var Capt Ftbl; Wt Lftg; Hon Roll; NHS.

HOUSTON, AMY; Danville SR HS; Danville, PA; (3); Debate Tm; Key Clb; Latin Clb; Nwsp Ed-Chief; Rep Frsh Cls; Rep Soph Cls; Rep Jr Cls; Rep Stu Cncl; Capt Cheerleading; Var L Crs Cntry; Natl Latin Honor Scty; Alg Awd.

HOUSTON, CLAIRE; Abraham Lincoln HS; Philadelphia, PA; (3); Sec Church Yth Grp; Trs Girl Scts; Capt ROTC; Capt Flag Corp; School Musical; Rep Frsh Cls; Rep Soph Cls; Rep Jr Cls; Hon Roll; Drill Tm; Girl Scout Silver Awd 87; Acctng.

HOUSTON, NICOLE; Carrick HS; Pittsburgh, PA; (4); 47/341; High Hon Roll; Hon Roll; Robert Morris Coll; Acctng.

HOUTMAN, KATIE; Mt Pleasant Area SR HS; Acme, PA; (2); 4/250; Church Yth Grp; GAA; Pres Concert Band; Mrchg Band; VP Frsh Cls; Stu Cncl; Var L Bsktbl; Var L Sftbl; High Hon Roll; Pres Schlr; County Band.

HOUTZ, JAMES; Montgomery Area HS; Allenwood, PA; (4); Hon Roll; Bus Amd.

HOUTZ, KELLY; Bellefonte Area HS; Bellefonte, PA; (3); French Clb; Library Aide; Yrbk Stf; High Hon Roll; NHS.

HOUTZ, SHANNON; Big Spring HS; Newville, PA; (2); 14/283; Pep Clb; Yrbk Stf; Stu Cncl; JV Var Vllybl; Hon Roll; Prfct Atten Awd; Acctg.

HOUZE, JONATHAN; Highlands HS; Natrona Hgts, PA; (3); SADD; Concert Band; Jazz Band; Rep Stu Cncl; Prfct Atten Awd; 1st Pl Comp Pgmmng ST Sci Olympd 87; Chem.

HOVANEC, TERRI; Center HS; Monaca, PA; (3); 1/186; JA; Pres Latin Clb; Library Aide; VP Frsh Cls; Rep Stu Cncl; NHS; Ntl Merit Ltr; Val; Summa Cum Laude Latin Awd 87; Consistent Highest Hnr Roll Rnkng 85-87; PA ST U; Elec Engrng.

HOVIS, HOLLY; Mercer HS; New Wilmington, PA; (3); Ski Clb; Concert Band; Jazz Band; Mrchg Band; Stage Crew; JV Bsktbl; Var Trk; Hon Roll; Intl Stud.

HOVIS, JOSEPH; Cranberry HS; Oil City, PA; (2); CAP; French Clb; Science Clb; Teachers Aide; Crs Cntry; Trk; JV Wrstlng; Hon Roll; Vrsty Eclgy Tm 2nd Pl Fnls 87; Envrnmtl Sci.

HOWALD, MARYANN; Abington SR HS; Elkins Park, PA; (4); 23/505; Concert Band; Jazz Band; Mrchg Band; Rep Stu Cncl; Lcrss; Trk; Twrlr; Cit Awd; Hon Roll; Masonic Awd; Abingtn Alumni Schlrshp 87; Abngtn Chapt Natl JR Hnr Soc Schlrshp 87; 4 Yr Tuit Temple U 87; Temple U; Phys Thrpy.

HOWALD, MATTHEW; Abington SR HS; Elkins Park, PA; (3); Church Yth Grp; FCA; Intnl Clb; Var JV Bsbl; Im Bsktbl; Ftbl; Bus Admin.

HOWANITZ, JOHN; Lakeland HS; Olyphant, PA; (3); French Clb; Hon Roll.

HOWAR, DENNIS; Meyerside HS; Meyersdale, PA; (4); Boy Scts; Church Yth Grp; VP French Clb; Band; Concert Band; Jazz Band; Mrchg Band; Pep Band; Bsktbl; Lion Awd; WV U; Bus.

HOWARD, ALICIA PETRICE; Harrisburg HS; Harrisburg, PA; (2); Science Clb; Band; Chorus; Church Choir; Concert Band; Jazz Band; Mrchg Band; Orch; Hon Roll; Palmer Schl Cert Of Merit Deans List 87; Med Tech.

HOWARD, AMY; Red Lion Area HS; Brogue, PA; (3); 62/342; Varsity Clb; Tennis; Hon Roll; Bus.

HOWARD, DEAN; Ridgway HS; Ridgway, PA; (4); 8/105; Stu Cncl; Bsktbl; Trk; Hon Roll; NHS; Finance.

HOWARD III, EDWARD H; Union HS; Rimersburg, PA; (3); 24/105; Pres Church Yth Grp; FCA; SADD; School Musical; Yrbk Stf; Var L Bsktbl; Var Golf.

HOWARD, JANINE; Chichester SR HS; Boothwyn, PA; (3); 14/296; SADD; JV Fld Hcky; Mgr(s); High Hon Roll; Hon Roll; Jr NHS; Pres Schlr; Spanish NHS; Church Yth Grp; Stage Crew; Dstngshd Hnr Roll 84; Athltc Dir Sprtsmnshp Awd 86; Pol Sci.

HOWARD, MELISSA; Jim Thorpe SR HS; Lake Harmony, PA; (4); Ski Clb; School Play; Nwsp Ed-Chief; Yrbk Phtg; Vllybl; High Hon Roll; NHS; Pres Schlr; Rotary Awd; Villanova; Econ.

HOWARD, RHONDA; Juniata HS; Mifflintown, PA; (4); Trs Spanish Clb; Chorus; Church Choir; School Musical; Variety Show; Yrbk Bus Mgr; Hon Roll; NHS; FHA; Band; Schlstc J Awd; Prsdntl Acdmc Ftnss Awd; Susquehana U; Math.

HOWARD, ROBERT; Kutztown Area HS; Kutztown, PA; (4); VP Church Yth Grp; Chorus; School Musical; School Play; Variety Show; Rep Stu Cncl; Capt Bsbl; Capt Socr; High Hon Roll; Trs NHS; Penn ST; Pre-Med.

HOWARD, ROBERT; Salisbury HS; Allentown, PA; (3); 16/150; Church Yth Grp; L Crs Cntry; Var Trk; High Hon Roll; Hon Roll; NHS; Bio.

HOWARD II, RONALD F; Grove City SR HS; Grove City, PA; (4); 18/205; Boy Scts; Science Clb; Ski Clb; Stu Cncl; Bsktbl; Ftbl; Powder Puff Ftbl; Trk; Vllybl; CC Awd; Grad Culver Swim Naval Prog 87; Mercer Co Athletic Hall Of Fame Best Athlete 87; U Of Pittsburgh; Phrmcy.

HOWARD, THERESA; Creative & Performing Arts HS; Philadelphia, PA; (3); Church Yth Grp; Dance Clb; Drama Clb; Library Aide; School Musical; School Play; Hon Roll; Schlrshp For Dance Theatre Of Harlem 83-84; Prfmng Arts Schl Awds 82-85; NY U.

HOWARD, TRACEY; Hershey HS; Hummelstown, PA; (3); 54/209; Exploring; Ski Clb; Spanish Clb; Concert Band; Jazz Band; Mrchg Band; School Musical; Hon Roll; Lion Awd; Spanish NHS; Penn ST U; Bus Admin.

HOWE, JENNIFER; Warren Area HS; Warren, PA; (3); Art Clb; French Clb; Ski Clb; Orch; Rep Frsh Cls; Rep Soph Cls; Stu Cncl; Stat Trk; High Hon Roll; Hon Roll; Acctng.

HOWE, LAURA; Camp Hill HS; Camp Hill, PA; (3); 24/98; Debate Tm; Chorus; Flag Corp; School Musical; School Play; Stage Crew; Yrbk Stf; Var Trk; High Hon Roll; NHS; Outstndng Acadc Achvt Presdntl Acadc Ftns Awds Prg 85; Engr.

HOWE, MONIKA; Salisbury HS; Bethlehem, PA; (4); Cmnty Wkr; German Clb; Key Clb; SADD; Hon Roll; Outstndg Achvt Awd German 86-87; Good Speherd Vol Awd 84-85; SE Acad; Trvl.

HOWE, ROBERT; Upper Moreland HS; Hatboro, PA; (3); 71/275; Key Clb; Ski Clb; Rep Frsh Cls; Rep Soph Cls; Rep Jr Cls; Rep Sr Cls; Rep Stu Cncl; Var Capt Crs Cntry; Socr; Tennis; Phys Thrpy.

HOWE, SHAWN; Lewistown HS; Mc Veytown, PA; (2); 4-H; JV Bsktbl; Var L Golf; Im Vllybl; Pilot.

HOWE, TIM; West Branch Area HS; Hawk Run, PA; (2); Spanish Clb; Varsity Clb; JV Bsktbl.

HOWE, TRACY; Warren Area HS; Warren, PA; (3); Church Yth Grp; Trs French Clb; Sec Varsity Clb; Sec Jr Cls; Sec Sr Cls; Rep Stu Cncl; Var Sftbl; Var Vllybl; Hon Roll; PA ST; Elem Ed.

HOWELL, EUNICE; Pine Forge Acad; Richmond, VA; (2); Church Choir; Yrbk Stf; Cit Awd; Hon Roll; Prfct Atten Awd; Oakwood Coll; Lawyer.

HOWELL, JAMES; Solanco HS; Oxford, PA; (2); Varsity Clb; Rep Stu Cncl; Var Bsbl; JV Socr; Hon Roll; Vrsty Bsbl MVP Awd 87.

HOWELL, JENNIFER; Curwensville Area HS; Curwensville, PA; (3); Church Yth Grp; Drama Clb; Ski Clb; Spanish Clb; Flag Corp; Nwsp Rptr; Ed Yrbk Stf.

HOWELL, TAMMY; Cowanesque Valley HS; Westfield, PA; (4); 9/77; Sec Letterman Clb; SADD; Chorus; Yrbk Stf; Sec Soph Cls; Stat Bsktbl; Var Trk; JV Var Vllybl; High Hon Roll; Sec NHS; Schlr Athlt Trophy 85 & 86; E Stroudsburg U; Hsptlty Mgmt.

HOWELLS, DEBBIE; Marion Center Area HS; Marion Center, PA; (4); 16/159; FBLA; Teachers Aide; VP Varsity Clb; Var JV Cheerleading; High Hon Roll; Jr NHS; NHS; Acctnt II Awd 87; Office Prcdrs 3rd Pl FBLA 87; Typing Awd 86.

HOWELLS, RICHARD; Northern Bedford County HS; Roaring Spring, PA; (3); FBLA; Ski Clb; Pres SADD; Varsity Clb; Trs Chorus; School Musical; Yrbk Stf; Var Ftbl; High Hon Roll; NHS; 1st Tm All-Bedford Cnty Ftbll 86; Med.

HOWER, JONATHAN; Moon Area HS; Coraopolis, PA; (4); 63/304; Rep Soph Cls; Rep Jr Cls; Rep Stu Cncl; L Bsbl; Hon Roll; U Of Pittsburgh; Engrng.

HOWER, KIMBERLY; Northampton SR HS; Northampton, PA; (3); 15/494; AFS; Sec Drama Clb; Pres 4-H; Leo Clb; Chorus; School Musical; School Play; 4-H Awd; High Hon Roll; Sec NHS; Psych.

HOWES, AMANDA; Bethlehem Center HS; Brownsville, PA; (4); 3/153; Church Yth Grp; Spanish Clb; Band; Yrbk Stf; Trs Jr Cls; Stu Cncl; Vllybl; DAR Awd; High Hon Roll; NHS; Schl Board Rep 86-87; WV U; Chld Psych.

HOWIE, JOHN; Downingtown SR HS; Downington, PA; (3); Ski Clb; Band; Concert Band; Mrchg Band; Stage Crew; Bowling; Hon Roll; ED.

HOWLAND, KEITH; Lower Moreland SR HS; Huntingdon Valley, PA; (3); Chess Clb; Church Yth Grp; Drama Clb; Acpl Chr; Church Choir; School Musical; School Play; Stage Crew; Hon Roll; NHS.

HOWLAND, MICHELE; Lower Moreland HS; Huntingdon Valley, PA; (3); Church Yth Grp; FBLA; German Clb; Varsity Clb; Hon Roll; JV Crs Cntry; Capt Trk; Bio.

HOWLES, VALERIE; Cambridge Springs HS; Saegertown, PA; (4); Church Yth Grp; Spanish Clb; Teachers Aide; Band; Concert Band; Mrchg Band; Pep Band; School Musical; Hon Roll; Villa Maria Coll; Nrsng.

HOWSARE, ANGELA; Bedford HS; Bedford, PA; (3); Church Yth Grp; FCA; Hosp Aide; SADD; Band; Chorus; Color Guard; Mrchg Band; School Musical; Art Clb; Bedford Cnty Fall Foliage Queen Cont 86; Scndry Tchng.

HOWSARE, CHRISTINE L; Upper Moreland SR HS; Hatboro, PA; (4); 1/259; Key Clb; Flag Corp; Yrbk Ed-Chief; Rep Frsh Cls; Rep Soph Cls; Rep Jr Cls; Rep Sr Cls; High Hon Roll; NHS; Ntl Merit SF; Acdmc All Amer 86; PA Hghr Ed Asstnc Agncy Cert Of Merit 86; U PA; Chem Engrng.

HOWSARE, JACQUELINE; Hatboro Horsham HS; Hatboro, PA; (4); Drama Clb; Intnl Clb; Key Clb; Concert Band; Mrchg Band; School Play; High Hon Roll; NHS; Ntl Merit Ltr; Band; AATG Hnrb Mntn-German 85-87; Lock Haven U Of PA; Theatre.

HOY, LISA; Parkland HS; Coplay, PA; (4); 97/438; Church Yth Grp; Exploring; Hosp Aide; Band; Hon Roll; York Coll Of PA; Nrsng.

HOY, MELISSA; Waynesburg Central HS; Spraggs, PA; (3); AFS; Church Yth Grp; Cmnty Wkr; 4-H; Natl Beta Clb; Spanish Clb; Church Choir; Concert Band; Mrchg Band; School Musical; Agribus.

HOY, ROBERT TODD; Waynesburg Central HS; Waynesburg, PA; (4); Boy Scts; Church Yth Grp; Letterman Clb; Ski Clb; Spanish Clb; Variety Show; Fld Hcky; Socr; Wrstlng; Hon Roll; Cement Lab Tech.

HOYES, BROCK; Danville SR HS; Danville, PA; (1); Im Capt Bsktbl; Im Capt Ftbl; Var Trk; High Hon Roll; Hon Roll; Pres Acad Ftns Awd 86-87; Phy Ed Tchrs Awd 86-87.

HOYMAN, JACQUELINE M; Connelsville Area SR HS; Connellsville, PA; (2); 156/566; GAA; Sec Girl Scts; Teachers Aide; Band; Color Guard; Mgr Concert Band; Mrchg Band; Hon Roll.

HOYMAN, LINDA; Berlin Brothersvalley HS; Berlin, PA; (3); 8/94; Art Clb; Church Yth Grp; Rptr FBLA; Chorus; Stat Wrstlng; High Hon Roll; NHS; Engl Awd 85; Bus.

HOYT, DAVID; Ridgway Area HS; Ridgway, PA; (4); 14/105; Ftbl; Trk; Wrstlng; High Hon Roll; Hon Roll; Crmnl Justc.

HOYT, MARGARET; Cumberland Valley HS; Mechanicsburg, PA; (3); 24/584; Church Yth Grp; Key Clb; Latin Clb; Ski Clb; Church Choir; Orch; School Musical; Im Vllybl; High Hon Roll; NHS; Lebanon Vly Hnrs Orchestra 86; Cumberland Cnty Orchestra & Latin Achvt Awd 2nd Pl 87; Psychobiology.

HOYT, TAMARA; G A R Memorial HS; Wilkes-Barre, PA; (4); 22/174; Chorus; Nwsp Ed-Chief; Yrbk Stf; High Hon Roll; Hon Roll; Jr NHS; NHS; Key Clb; Church Choir; Hugh O Brien Yth Ldrshp Fndtn 84; Kings Coll; Cmnctns.

HOYT, WADE; Lake-Lehman HS; Shavertown, PA; (2); Key Clb; ROTC; Ski Clb; SADD; Hon Roll; NHS; PA ST U; Law.

HRACH, JENNIFER S; Mt Alvernia HS; Pittsburgh, PA; (4); Church Yth Grp; Computer Clb; French Clb; Math Clb; Chorus; JV Capt Bsktbl; Var Crs Cntry; Var Trk; Hon Roll; Stu/Ath Awd 87; WA & Jefferson Coll; Bio.

HREZIK, KIM; Schuylkill Valley HS; Leesport, PA; (4); 26/132; Pep Clb; SADD; Chorus; School Play; Nwsp Stf; Yrbk Stf; VP Sr Cls; Var Capt Cheerleading; L Trk; NHS; Mrt Rl Sts Yr 86-87; West Chester U; Sprts Med.

HRIN, ERIC; Jefferson-Morgan JR SR HS; Jefferson, PA; (4); 12/93; Civic Clb; Cmnty Wkr; Nwsp Rptr; Nwsp Stf; Yrbk Rptr; Yrbk Stf; VP Frsh Cls; Rep Jr Cls; Cit Awd; High Hon Roll; Amer Legn Essy Awd 1st Pl 86; Tri Cnty Cncl Amer Legn Essy Awd 1st Pl 86; Knghts Colmbs Essy Awd 86; Law.

HRIVNAK, MICHAEL; Seneca Valley HS; Zelienople, PA; (3); Pres Church Yth Grp; Varsity Clb; Acpl Chr; Jazz Band; Madrigals; Swing Chorus; Rep Jr Cls; Var L Ftbl; Var Capt Socr; Var L Swmmng; Bio.

HRIVNAK, PATTI; Gateway SR HS; Monroeville, PA; (3); 17/452; Color Guard; Concert Band; Mrchg Band; Orch; Yrbk Ed-Chief; Yrbk Sprt Ed; Yrbk Stf; NHS; PA All St Band 87; Sound Of Amer Natl Hnrs Band 87; U Of PA.

HRIZO, JOHN; Gateway HS; Monroeville, PA; (4); Boy Scts; Exploring; Band; Jazz Band; Orch; Amer Chem Socty Pittsburgh Outstndng Chem Stdnt 85-86; Penn ST; Elctrcl Engrng Tech.

HROMYAK, MICHAEL; Tamaqua Area HS; Tamaqua, PA; (3); 47/208; Church Yth Grp; Var L Bsbl; Var L Bsktbl; Var L Crs Cntry; Ftbl.

HRUTKAY, HEATHER; Mon Valley Catholic HS; Bentlyville, PA; (3); Hosp Aide; Ski Clb; Spanish Clb; Chorus; Nwsp Stf; Yrbk Stf; Powder Puff Ftbl; Spanish NHS; 1st Pl Spnch Level III Art Cntst 87; Awd In Spnsh I For A Avrge 85; Awd In Spnsh II For A Avrge 86; Indiana U; Accntng.

HRZIC, JENNIFER; Montoursville HS; Montoursville, PA; (3); 23/183; Dance Clb; German Clb; Var JV Bsktbl; Stat Socr; Var Trk; Hon Roll; NHS; Acad All Amer 86-87; Arch.

HSIEH, MICHAEL; Conestoga SR HS; Wayne, PA; (3); SADD; Corp Law.

HSIEH, STEPHEN; Central HS Of Phila; Philadelphia, PA; (2); Orch; Hon Roll; Comp Engr.

HSU, STAN; Henderson HS; West Chester, PA; (2); 8/353; Latin Clb; High Hon Roll; Ltn Hnr Society 85.

HU, CHRISTINE; Cardinal Brennan HS; Shenandoah, PA; (3); 1/58; Hosp Aide; Trs Pres Library Aide; Science Clb; Pres Chorus; Ed Nwsp Ed-Chief; Yrbk Ed-Chief; Gov Hon Prg Awd; Hon Roll; NHS; Nthwstrn U Smmr Music Pgm 84-85; Ambssdr Hugh O Brien Yth Fndtn Smnr 85-86; 3rd Rnnr Up Miss PA 86-87; Pre Med.

HU, JAMES Y; State College Area SR HS; Kensington, CA; (4); 2/541; Cmnty Wkr; Debate Tm; Trs Model UN; Scholastic Bowl; Yrbk Stf; Cit Awd; High Hon Roll; JETS Awd; NEDT Awd; U Of CA-BERKELEY; Mech Engrng.

HUA, LINH; Philadelphia HS For Girls; Philadelphia, PA; (2); Exploring; Badmtn; Hon Roll; Prfct Atten Awd; U PA.

HUBAL, DEBRA; Valley-View HS; Eynon, PA; (3); 20/193; Sec Church Yth Grp; Spanish Clb; Acpl Chr; Cheerleading; Hon Roll; Elem Educ.

HUBBARD, AMY; Freedom HS; Bethlehem, PA; (4); Science Clb; Spanish Clb; Church Choir; Lit Mag; Var Mgr(s); Var Swmmng; Var Trk; Hon Roll; NHS; Pres Schlr; U Of ND; Phys Thrpy.

HUBBARD, TRACEY M; Forest City Regional HS; Pleasant Mt, PA; (3); 13/65; Letterman Clb; Spanish Clb; Band; Nwsp Stf; Rep Frsh Cls; Var Sftbl; Hon Roll; NHS; Gregg Typng Awd, Ltr Sftbl 87; Pre Law.

HUBBERT, KOREN; Greenwood HS; Millerstown, PA; (2); Teachers Aide; Chorus; School Musical; VP Frsh Cls; JV Fld Hcky; JV Sftbl; Var JV Trk; High Hon Roll; Hon Roll; Ntl Englsh Mrt Awd 86-87; Med.

HUBENTHAL, PAT; Neshannock HS; New Castle, PA; (3); 3/102; Boy Scts; Drama Clb; Speech Tm; Jazz Band; School Musical; School Play; Rep Jr Cls; High Hon Roll; NHS; Ntl Merit SF.

HUBER, BRIAN; Harry S Truman HS; Levittown, PA; (3); 209/599; Boy Scts; Band; Chorus; Concert Band; Mrchg Band; Pep Band; Hon Roll; Vlntr Water-Front Cnslr Spec Ed Camping Trip 87; PA ST U; Aerontcl Engr.

HUBER, CHRISTOPHER; Tech Memorial HS; Erie, PA; (3); 3/311; CAP; French Clb; VICA; Rep Jr Cls; Rep Stu Cncl; Stat Bsbl; Stat Bsktbl; JV Socr; NHS; Comp.

HUBER, CURTIS; Bethlehem Catholic HS; Bethlehem, PA; (3); 68/215; Church Yth Grp; Bsbl; Bsktbl; Bowling; Ftbl; Wt Lftg; Hon Roll; Prfct Atten Awd; Bus.

HUBER, DELVIN J; Garden Spot HS; East Earl, PA; (4); 32/206; Church Yth Grp; 4-H; FFA; 4-H Awd; High Hon Roll; Hon Roll; Prfct Atten Awd; Keystone Awd 87; Red Rose Awd 86.

HUBER, GREGORY B; Garden Spot HS; East Earl, PA; (2); Church Yth Grp; 4-H; FFA; High Hon Roll; Hon Roll; Jr NHS; Star Greenhand Awd.

HUBER, JEFFREY; Huntingdon Valley HS; Huntingdon Valley, PA; (3); Boy Scts; Church Yth Grp; German Clb; JV Bsbl; JV Crs Cntry; JV Trk; Hon Roll; Eagle Sct Boy Scts; Aviation.

HUBER, JENNI; Indiana Area HS; Indiana, PA; (1); Key Clb; SADD; Band; Concert Band; Jazz Band; Mrchg Band; Orch; L Var Swmmng; JV Trk; Hon Roll; Phy Thrpy.

HUBER, LENNY; Penn Manor HS; Millersville, PA; (3); #39 In Class; Im Socr; VP Trk; Im Vllybl; Hon Roll; NHS.

HUBER, MITCHELL; Richland HS; Gibsonia, PA; (3); Trs Church Yth Grp; NFL; Speech Tm; Chorus; Var L Socr; High Hon Roll; VP NHS; Rotry Yth Ldrs Awd 87; Bus.

HUBER, PAM; Pequea Valley HS; Paradise, PA; (3); Trs 4-H; FBLA; Varsity Clb; Drill Tm; Var JV Cheerleading; Hon Roll; AFS; Teachers Aide.

HUBER, PATRICIA; Sacred Heart HS; Pittsburgh, PA; (3); 17/135; French Clb; Latin Clb; Service Clb; Chorus; Yrbk Stf; Var Sftbl; Im Vllybl; High Hon Roll; Hon Roll; Ed.

HUBER, RANDY; Danville Area SR HS; Danville, PA; (2); Church Yth Grp; Spanish Clb; Varsity Clb; Yrbk Stf; Var L Bsbl; JV L Bsktbl; Im L Ftbl; High Hon Roll; Hon Roll; Pres Schlr; Hstrcl Awd Avrg 86; Nclr Physisist.

HUBER, STEVE; Wilmington Area HS; Pulaski, PA; (3); 3/115; Pres Church Yth Grp; Drama Clb; Latin Clb; Concert Band; Jazz Band; Mrchg Band; School Play; Rep Stu Cncl; God Cntry Awd; High Hon Roll; Drama Clb-Outstndng Debut Prfrmnc Awd 85-6; Dist Band 86-7; Amer Legion Schl Awd 85.

HUBER, TAMMIE; Solanco SR HS; New Providence, PA; (4); 76/235; Cmnty Wkr; Sec VP Drama Clb; Office Aide; Thesps; Chorus; School Play; Nwsp Rptr; Mgr Fld Hcky; Cit Awd; Hon Roll; Elem Educ.

HUBLER, DENISE; Spring Grove HS; Spring Grove, PA; (3); 89/308; Church Yth Grp; FNA; Hosp Aide; Varsity Clb; Acpl Chr; Chorus; Church Choir; School Musical; Stat Bsktbl; JV Fld Hcky; Vlntr Svc Awd Pin 85; 100 Point Acadmc Pin 86.

HUBLER, FRED; Schuylkill Haven Area HS; Pt Clinton, PA; (3); 16/89; Chess Clb; German Clb; Ftbl; Trk; Wt Lftg; High Hon Roll; Hon Roll; NHS; Natl Acdmy Math Awd 87; Comp Tech.

HUCKABONE, MARY JO; Warren Area HS; Warren, PA; (3); 46/390; Dance Clb; Band; Concert Band; Mrchg Band; Orch; Variety Show; Cit Awd; Hon Roll; Prfct Atten Awd; Elem Ed.

HUCKEL, JEFFREY; Bishop Shanahan HS; Coastesville, PA; (4); 43/215; Political Wkr; Nwsp Rptr; Nwsp Sprt Ed; Im Bsktbl; Im Ice Hcky; Elks Awd; Outstndng Achvmnt In Social Studies 87; 2nd Hnrs On Report Card 83-87; Lock Haven U; Jrnlsm.

HUCKESTEIN, ANGIE; Seneca Valley HS; Evans City, PA; (4); 42/340; VP FTA; Mrchg Band; Symp Band; JV Var Mgr(s); L Stat Wrstlng; Hon Roll; Mrchng Band Ltr 86; Schlstc Achvt Awd 85-87; Symphny Band Cert Of Merit 87.

HUDACHEK, BARBARA; West Scranton HS; Scranton, PA; (3); FBLA; Church Yth Grp; Bsktbl; Trk; Hon Roll; Acctg.

HUDACSEK, CHRISTINE; Ambridge Area HS; Ambridge, PA; (3); French Clb; Pep Clb; Band; Concert Band; Mrchg Band; Orch; High Hon Roll; Hon Roll; Prfct Atten Awd; Music.

HUDAK, JODI; Ambridge Area HS; Baden, PA; (3); Pep Clb; Chorus; Off Frsh Cls; Off Soph Cls; Off Jr Cls; Off Sr Cls; Tennis; Hon Roll; Cosmetlgy.

HUDAK, KRISTEN A; Liberty HS; Bethlehem, PA; (3); 100/447; Nwsp Phtg; Nwsp Rptr; Nwsp Stf; Awds For Ftr Artcles In Schl Nwspr 85-86; Writer.

HUDAK, MONICA; Notre Dame HS; Easton, PA; (3); Yrbk Stf; Var L Bsktbl; JV Cheerleading; Var L Sftbl; Im Vllybl; Hon Roll; MVP Sftbl 86-87; Outstndg Effrt Alg 86-87; Mst Imprvd Plyr Sftbl 85-86; Phy Thrpy.

HUDGEONS, ALESHA; Lansdale Catholic HS; Lansdale, PA; (3); 42/223; VP Cmnty Wkr; Hosp Aide; Chorus; School Musical; Hon Roll; Natl Spnsh Cont, Religous Acdmc Awd 85; Natl Spnsh Cont 86; Educ.

HUDOCK, AMY ELIZABETH; Butler Area SR HS; Butler, PA; (2); 47/740; Church Yth Grp; French Clb; Hosp Aide; Band; Capt Cheerleading; Gym; Pom Pon; High Hon Roll; NHS; Med.

HUDOCK, RICHARD N; Hazleton HS; Hazleton, PA; (2); Aud/Vis; Church Yth Grp; FCA; Ski Clb; Teachers Aide; Rep Stu Cncl; Co-Capt L Bsktbl; Coach Actv; Golf; Tennis; 1st Hnr Rl 86-87; Pres Ftnss Awd 86; Bsktbl Dist Chmpn Tm 86-87; Librl Arts.

HUDOCK, ROBERT; Geibel HS; Uniontown, PA; (4); 11/81; Computer Clb; Drama Clb; Science Clb; Trs Frsh Cls; Stat Bsktbl; Var Capt Ftbl; Wt Lftg; High Hon Roll; Hon Roll; NEDT Awd; Bell PA & Cnty Mrkt Schlrshp 87; Cngrsnl Schlr 87; Carnegie Mellon U; Bio.

HUDOCK, SHERRY A; Shikellamy HS; Northumberland, PA; (3); 56/312; Church Yth Grp; Spanish Clb; Lit Mag; JV Bowling; Var JV Fld Hcky; Hon Roll; SCNDRY Educ.

HUDSICK, AMY; Du Bois Area HS; Penfield, PA; (2); 79/327; Pres Girl Scts; Chorus; School Musical; Hon Roll; Exec Secr.

HUDSON, BETH; Shaler Area SR HS; Allison Pk, PA; (3); 63/490; Flag Corp; Mrchg Band; Symp Band; Nwsp Stf; Var Swmmng; French Hon Soc; Hon Roll; NEDT Awd.

HUDSON, HILLARY; Central York SR HS; York, PA; (3); 32/266; Art Clb; 4-H; Ski Clb; Y-Teens; Stage Crew; Crs Cntry; Trk; High Hon Roll; Hon Roll; NHS; Outstndng Frshmn Artist 85.

HUDSON, MONICA; Penn Hills SR HS; Pittsburgh, PA; (3); Pep Clb; Band; Concert Band; Mrchg Band; Rep Jr Cls; Rep Badmtn; Mgr(s); Hon Roll; Lmp Of Knwldg Awd 86 & 87; Pre Med.

HUDSON, WILLIAM; West York Area SR HS; York, PA; (2); 26/209; VP French Clb; Var JV Vllybl; Hon Roll; Med.

HUDY, KELLY; Fort Le Boeuf HS; Waterford, PA; (4); Dance Clb; French Clb; Spanish Clb; Capt Cheerleading; Gym; Trk; Vllybl; High Hon Roll; Hon Roll; NHS; Frgn Lang Awd 86-87; PA Free Entrprs Wk 85-86; Hgh Hnr Grad; Behrend; Bus Manag.

HUEBNER, JENNIFER; Mechanicsburg Area HS; Mechanicsburg, PA; (2); 46/309; Church Yth Grp; Girl Scts; Band; Chorus; Color Guard; Concert Band; Mrchg Band; Nwsp Stf; Mgr Bsktbl; Mgr(s); Intr Dsgn.

HUEMME, JANICE; Plum SR HS; Pittsburgh, PA; (3); AFS; SADD; Band; Drill Tm; Symp Band; L Bsktbl; Trk; JV Vllybl; Hon Roll.

HUETTER, SUSAN; Baldwin HS; Pittsburgh, PA; (2); 99/481; Church Yth Grp; French Clb; Key Clb; Yrbk Stf; Rep Stu Cncl; High Hon Roll; Pres Schlr; Pres Acadmc Ftns Awd 85; Paralegal.

HUEY, BRENT; Academy HS; Erie, PA; (3); 6/232; Pres Church Yth Grp; Ed Yrbk Phtg; Rep Stu Cncl; Var Capt Bsbl; NHS; Aerospace Engrng.

HUEY, SUSAN; Oil City SR HS; Oil City, PA; (3); Varsity Clb; Stu Cncl; Var Capt Cheerleading; Gym; L Trk; Elem Ed.

HUEY, VICKIE; Hamburg Area HS; Hamburg, PA; (4); Exploring; FBLA; SADD; Band; Chorus; School Musical; Fld Hcky; Twrlr; Hon Roll; Masonic Awd; Acdmc Ltr Awd 86; Stu Librarn Cert 86; Vrsty Ltr Band Chorus 87; Allentown Bus; Accntng.

HUFF, DAVID; Bellwood-Antis HS; Altoona, PA; (4); 10/112; Key Clb; VICA; VP Band; Drm Mjr(t); Mrchg Band; Pres Sr Cls; High Hon Roll; NHS; Prfct Atten Awd; Pres Schlr; Outstndng Voc Stu Of The Yr Awd 87; Acad All-Amer Awd 87; Vo-Tech SR Awd 87; Altoona Campus; Electrical Engr.

HUFF, DIANE; Lancaster Catholic HS; Denver, PA; (3); Cmnty Wkr; Chorus; Concert Band; Mrchg Band; Pep Band; Stage Crew; Cabrini; Elem Educ.

HUFF, DONNAMARIE; Lancaster Catholic HS; Denver, PA; (4); 21/191; JCL; Model UN; Service Clb; Stage Crew; Ed Nwsp Rptr; NHS; Yth Day Gvrnmnt Trffc Cntrlr; Meadowbrook Ests Cvc Assn Awd; Pres Acad Fit Awd; Syracuse U; Bio.

HUFF, MACHELLE; Karns City HS; Chicora, PA; (4); 20/110; SADD; Concert Band; Sec Jr Cls; Rep Stu Cncl; Im Bsktbl; Capt Pom Pon; High Hon Roll; Hon Roll; NHS; Shng Star Awd-Super Star Drill Tm Cmp 86; Trophies-All Stars No 1 Tm-Grls Sftbl 83-84; Butler CC; Bus Mgmt.

HUFF, MICK; Shenango JR-SR HS; New Castle, PA; (2); Art Clb; Chorus; Jazz Band; Hon Roll; Youngstown ST U; Music.

HUFF, REBECCA; Knoch HS; Butler, PA; (4); 6/243; Hosp Aide; Band; Concert Band; Mrchg Band; Pep Band; School Musical; School Play; High Hon Roll; NHS; Pres Schlr; Penn Twp Womens Guide Schlrshp 87-88; Daemen Dpet & Deans Schlrshps 87-88; Daemen Coll; Physical Therapy.

HUFF, SHARON; Bedford HS; Bedford, PA; (3); Church Yth Grp; Chorus; Church Choir; School Musical; School Play; Hon Roll; Outstndng Achvt-Rcrd Kpng 87; Frostburg U; Music.

HUFF, SHERRY; Karns City HS; Chicora, PA; (3); Pom Pon; High Hon Roll; Hon Roll; NHS; 4-H; Band; Concert Band; Bsktbl; Sftbl; Accntng.

HUFF, STEPHANIE; Mercyhurst Prep; Erie, PA; (4); 40/155; VP Church Yth Grp; Sec JCL; Thesps; Chorus; School Musical; Stage Crew; Nwsp Rptr; Lit Mag; Rep Stu Cncl; Cmnty Wkr; CTE 83; Penn ST Erie; Elem Ed.

HUFF, SUSAN; West Hazleton HS; Conyngham, PA; (4); 30/220; Trs French Clb; FTA; Ski Clb; SADD; Sec Varsity Clb; Stu Cncl; Var Capt Cheerleading; Elks Awd; High Hon Roll; NHS; Channel 16 Sports Awd Fridays Hero Chrldng 86; PA ST; Elem Ed.

HUFFCUT, STACY; Northeast Bradford JR SR HS; Rome, PA; (3); 12/104; Chess Clb; 4-H; Office Aide; Teachers Aide; Band; Chorus; VP Soph Cls; Rep Stu Cncl; JV Cheerleading; Gym; Sslvr Schlr Plaq-Hnr Roll 82-83; 1st Pl Bradford Cnty 4-H Rndup 85; Hmcmng Ct 86-87.

HUFFMAN, BRENT A; Blairsville SR HS; Blacklick, PA; (3); 8/110; SADD; Chorus; Concert Band; Drm Mjr(t); School Musical; High Hon Roll; VP NHS; Church Yth Grp; Library Aide; Office Aide; All ST Chorus 87; Gov Schl Arts 87; PA All ST Lions Band Taiwan 87; Music Theatre.

HUFFMAN, CYNTHIA; Lewistown Area HS; Lewistown, PA; (2); Sec Church Yth Grp; 4-H; Spanish Clb; Church Choir; Concert Band; Mrchg Band; High Hon Roll; Hon Roll; NHS; Acadc Ltr 86; Acadc Star 87; Nrs.

HUFFMAN, JENNY; Corry Area JR SR HS; Corry, PA; (2); Boys Clb Am; Boy Scts; Church Yth Grp; Exploring; German Clb; GAA; Girl Scts; VICA; SADD; Chorus; Nrsng.

HUFFMAN, JOYCE; Meyersdale Area HS; Hyndman, PA; (4); Sec French Clb; FBLA; Library Aide; Chorus; Yrbk Stf; Cheerleading; Sftbl; Vllybl; Hon Roll; NHS; Alleghany CC; Nrsng.

HUFFMAN, MARYANN; Brownsville Area HS; Smock, PA; (4); Yrbk Stf.

HUFFMAN, PAMELA; Mowhawk Area JR SR HS; Edinburg, PA; (4); 20/125; French Clb; Band; Mrchg Band; Powder Puff Ftbl; U Of Pittsburgh; Biochem.

HUFFMAN, SOUNDRA L; South Allegheny HS; Port Vue, PA; (3); 18/187; Church Yth Grp; JA; Y-Teens; Band; Concert Band; Pep Band; Stu Cncl; Powder Puff Ftbl; Hon Roll; NHS; Elem Educ.

HUFFNAGLE, HEATHER; Lancaster Country Day Schl; Lancaster, PA; (3); Chorus; Yrbk Stf; Lit Mag; Var JV Fld Hcky; Var Tennis; Hon Roll; Helen M Powilson Awd Svc To Schl 87; Vrsty Ltr In Tennis 87; Am Cancer Soc Awd For Swm For Cancer 84.

HUFFORD, CHRISTINE; Central HS; Martinsburg, PA; (4); 33/189; Hon Roll; Acdmc All Amer 87; Penn ST; Psych.

HUFFORD, KIMBERLY; Portage Area HS; Portage, PA; (4); 25/120; Band; Chorus; Concert Band; Jazz Band; Mrchg Band; Pep Band; Stage Crew; Variety Show; Im Vllybl; Hon Roll; IN U Of PA; Med Tech.

HUFNAGEL, CHRISTINE; Plum SR HS; Pittsburgh, PA; (3); SADD; Band; Mrchg Band; Symp Band; Yrbk Stf; Stat Bsktbl; Stat Trk; Hon Roll; Prfct Atten Awd; U Pittsburgh; Pre Med.

HUGE, LISA; Stroudsburg HS; Sciota, PA; (2); Spanish Clb; Chorus; High Hon Roll; Spanish NHS; E Stroudsburg U.

HUGHES, BRIAN P; Hanover Area JR SR HS; Wilkes-Barre, PA; (3); 15/196; Church Yth Grp; Red Cross Aide; Rep Stu Cncl; Var Bsktbl; Var L Ftbl; Var L Trk; High Hon Roll; Hon Roll; Jr NHS; NHS; Dist II Track Champ 85-86; Lifeguard Cert 87; Pre-Dental.

HUGHES, CATHY; West Allegheny SR HS; Imperial, PA; (3); Exploring; Trs FBLA; High Hon Roll; Hon Roll; Outstndng Bus Stu 87; 2nd Pl Job IntrvwFBLA 87; 4th Pl Typng FBLA 86-87; Secr.

HUGHES II, CHARLES E; Pen Argyl HS; Pen Argyl, PA; (4); 5/119; Computer Clb; Yrbk Stf; Trs Sr Cls; Var L Bsbl; Var L Bsktbl; Var L Ftbl; NHS; SAR Awd; Natl Ftbl Fed Schlr Athl 87; Pres Ftns Awd 87; IN U Bloomington; Bus Admin.

HUGHES, CHRISTOPHER; Roman Catholic HS; Philadelphia, PA; (3); 9/121; Church Yth Grp; Teachers Aide; Var VP Socr; High Hon Roll; NHS; Physcl Sci Awd Outstndng Schltc Achvt 85; U Of FL; Phrmcst.

HUGHES, CINDY; North Clarion JR SR HS; Tionesta, PA; (3); Spanish Clb; Drill Tm; Mrchg Band; School Musical; Yrbk Stf; Pom Pon; Crimenology.

HUGHES, DANIEL; Chief Logan HS; Lewistown, PA; (4); 28/200; Ski Clb; Spanish Clb; Band; Chorus; Concert Band; Var Capt Crs Cntry; Var Capt Trk; Hon Roll; Susquehanna U; Engr.

HUGHES, DAVID; Danville SR HS; Danville, PA; (2); Church Yth Grp; Ski Clb; JV Socr; Var Trk; High Hon Roll.

HUGHES, DENISE; Pittston Area SR HS; Avoca, PA; (3); Art Clb; Church Yth Grp; FBLA; FNA.

HUGHES, DOUGLAS; Cedar Crest HS; Cornwall, PA; (4); 13/312; Pres Drama Clb; FBLA; VP Spanish Clb; School Musical; School Play; Capt Swmmng; High Hon Roll; NHS; Ntl Merit Ltr; Hnrs Banquet 83-87; Penn ST; Engrng.

HUGHES, HEATHER; Steelton-Highspire HS; Highspire, PA; (3); 18/102; Hosp Aide; School Musical; Yrbk Ed-Chief; Var Twrlr; Hon Roll; NHS; Church Yth Grp; Cmnty Wkr; Dance Clb; Drama Clb; HOBY Ldrshp Awd 85; 1st Rnnr Up To Miss Amer Coed PA 87; Gftd Pgm 79-87; Psych.

HUGHES, JENNIFER; Academy Of Notre Dame De Namur; West Chester, PA; (3); Art Clb; SADD; School Musical; School Play; Lit Mag; JV Bsktbl; JV Lcrss; JV Socr; Im Swmmng; High Hon Roll; Moore Coll Of Art Achlrshp 86-87; Congrsmn Shultz Congrsnl Art Awd 84-85; 1st Pl Drwng Art Exhbit 87.

HUGHES, KAREN; Avon Grove HS; Landenberg, PA; (3); 13/180; GAA; SADD; Teachers Aide; School Play; Stage Crew; Nwsp Stf; Yrbk Stf; Stu Cncl; Fld Hcky; Gym.

HUGHES, KATHRYN; Meadville Area SR HS; Meadville, PA; (3); Rptr Hst VICA; Band; High Hon Roll; 3rd Pl-Preprd Spch ST VICA Cmptn 87; Cmnctns.

HUGHES, KELLY; Hempfield Area SR HS; Greensburg, PA; (2); French Clb; Ski Clb; Yrbk Stf; Rep Stu Cncl; High Hon Roll; Hon Roll; Jr NHS; Straight A Exclnt Hnr 86-87.

HUGHES, KRISTIE; Connellsville Area HS; Vanderbilt, PA; (3); 87/530; Church Yth Grp; Chorus; Church Choir; Concert Band; Mrchg Band; Pep Band; High Hon Roll; Hon Roll; Jr NHS; CA ST U; Elem Ed.

HUGHES, LAURIE JO; Archbishop Ryan HS For Girls; Philadelphia, PA; (3); 23/507; French Clb; French Hon Soc; High Hon Roll; Schlrshp Archbshp Ryan Girls 84-85; Intl Stds.

HUGHES, LISA; Central York HS; York, PA; (2); Church Yth Grp; Varsity Clb; Band; Concert Band; Mrchg Band; Symp Band; Var Capt Cheerleading; High Hon Roll; Hon Roll; Sci.

HUGHES, LORI; Highlands SR HS; Natrona Hgts, PA; (3); Art Clb; FHA; Crs Cntry; Mgr(s); Trk; Vllybl; Puppet Shows; Psych.

HUGHES, MARK; Avello Area HS; Avella, PA; (3); 5/72; Computer Clb; French Clb; Letterman Clb; School Play; Lit Mag; JV Ftbl; Var JV Mgr(s); High Hon Roll; Hon Roll; NHS; Tutoring 86-87; Engrng.

HUGHES, MICHAEL; Central York SR HS; York, PA; (3); Varsity Clb; Bsktbl; Ftbl; Trk; Vllybl; Hon Roll.

HUGHES, MICHELLE; Central Dauphin HS; Penbrook, PA; (4); Dance Clb; Science Clb; Chorus; Yrbk Sprt Ed; Yrbk Stf; Golf; Gym; Hon Roll; Louis Eugene King Schlr Gettysbrg Coll 87; Gettysbrg Coll; Genetcst.

HUGHES, MIKE; Meyersdale Area HS; Meyersdale, PA; (4); 12/116; Spanish Clb; Chorus; School Musical; School Play; Yrbk Stf; Bsktbl; Score Keeper; High Hon Roll; Hon Roll; NHS; Pre-Law.

HUGHES, PAMELA; Southside HS; Georgetown, PA; (3); Pres FBLA; Teachers Aide; Varsity Clb; Yrbk Stf; Coach Actv; Score Keeper; Vllybl; Hon Roll; 2nd Pl Entrprnsrshp II Regnl Comp 87; Travel.

HUGHES, PATTI; North Penn HS; Lansdale, PA; (4); Ski Clb; Bowling; High Hon Roll; Hon Roll; Temple U; Bus.

HUGHES, PEGGY; Wellsboro Area HS; Trout Run, PA; (2); Pep Clb; SADD; Band; Chorus; Hon Roll; PA ST U; Bus Mgmt.

HUGHES, SHAWN; Leechburg HS; Leechburg, PA; (4); JA; Pep Clb; Band; Concert Band; Jazz Band; Mrchg Band; Pep Band; Var L Bsbl; Pres Fit Awd 87; Alle-Kiski Hnrs Band 86; Clarion U PA; Bus.

HUGHES, SUSAN; J W Hallahan Catholic Girls HS; Philadelphia, PA; (4); 12/299; Church Yth Grp; VP JA; Math Clb; Math Tm; Chorus; Sec Nwsp Stf; High Hon Roll; NHS; Pres Schlr; Drama Clb; Sci Schlrshp Judson Coll 87-88; Judson Coll; Pre Med.

HUGHES, SUSAN G; Du Bois Central Christian HS; Rockton, PA; (4); Civic Clb; Cmnty Wkr; Computer Clb; Drama Clb; FBLA; German Clb; Hosp Aide; NFL; Radio Clb; Service Clb; Numrs Eqstrn Awds 83-87; ST Fnlst Miss Natl Teen Agr Pagnt 83; Intl Bus.

HUGHES, THOMAS; Central Catholic HS; Pittsburgh, PA; (3); 21/260; Ntl Merit Ltr; Med.

HUGHES, THOMAS; Serra Catholic HS; W Mifflin, PA; (3); 7/160; Spanish Clb; Nwsp Stf; Pres Jr Cls; Rep Stu Cncl; Tennis; High Hon Roll; Hon Roll; NHS; Ntl Merit Ltr; Spanish NHS; Med.

HUGHES, THOMAS; West Catholic H S For Boys; Philadelphia, PA; (3); Cmnty Wkr; Var JV Bsktbl; Im Wt Lftg; Bus Mgmt.

HUGHES, TIFFANY; Abington Heights HS; Clarks Summit, PA; (3); Dance Clb; Ski Clb; School Play; Hon Roll; Russian Lang Awd; Psych.

HUGUES, KEVIN; Henderson HS; W Chester, PA; (3); Var L Bsbl; Var L Wrstlng; Hon Roll; Engr.

HUGULEY, HEATHER L; Wilkinsburg JR SR HS; Pittsburgh, PA; (4); 1/150; Church Yth Grp; Hosp Aide; Pres Sec Key Clb; Spanish Clb; Yrbk Ed-Chief; VP Stu Cncl; Co-Capt Cheerleading; NHS; Val; Renssalaer Awd Math & Sci 86; Hugh O Brien Outstndg Stu 85; Athl Awd Vrsty Ltr Chrldng 86; Penn ST U; Med.

HUHA, EILEEN; Beaver Area JRSR HS; Beaver, PA; (2); Church Yth Grp; French Clb; Hosp Aide; Key Clb; Pep Clb; School Musical; Nwsp Stf; Yrbk Ed-Chief; High Hon Roll; Schlstc Achvt Awd 87; PA ST U; Pre Med.

HULICK, PATRICIA; Souderton Area HS; Schwenksville, PA; (4); 1/340; Intnl Clb; Spanish Clb; Yrbk Stf; Rep Frsh Cls; Rep Stu Cncl; DAR Awd; High Hon Roll; NHS; NEDT Awd; Val; Outstndng Stu Physics 87; Excllnce Sci & Math 87; Pres Acad Fit Awd 87; Franklin & Marshall; Sci.

HULICK, STEVAN; Burgettstown Area JR SR HS; Burgettstown, PA; (4); 14/137; Spanish Clb; Var L Bsktbl; Var JV Ftbl; High Hon Roll; Hon Roll; Jr NHS; NHS; Ntl Merit Ltr; Presdntl Acad Fit Awd 87; OH U; Athl Training.

HULING, DEBORAH; Richard SR HS; Gibsonia, PA; (3); Debate Tm; Hosp Aide; Speech Tm; Band; Mrchg Band; School Musical; Nwsp Stf; Yrbk Stf; High Hon Roll; NHS; Pres Yth Grp Chrch 83-85; Duquesne U; Pre-Law.

HULL, EDWARD; Bishop Kenrick HS; Norristown, PA; (4); 2/291; Varsity Clb; VP Stu Cncl; High Hon Roll; JC Awd; NHS; Rotary Awd; 3rd Tm-Rgnl All Amer-Sccr 86-87; Acdmc All Amer 86-87; All Cthlc-Bsbl & Bsktbl 86-87; U Of PA.

HULL, MARGO; Central SR HS; York, PA; (2); Church Yth Grp; JV Timer; Hon Roll; Lab Tech.

HULL, TAMI L; Pennridge HS; Sellersville, PA; (4); 6/398; Capt Mrchg Band; Yrbk Stf; Lit Mag; Mgr(s); DAR Awd; High Hon Roll; NHS; Pres Schlr; Pratt Ntl Tlnt Srch Schlrshp 87; Gannett Fndtn Schlrshp 87; Zmmrmn Schlrshp 87; Pratt Inst; Fshn Dsgn.

HULLAK, ANDREA; Canon Mc Millan SR HS; Canonsburg, PA; (4); Church Yth Grp; FBLA; Library Aide; Pep Clb; Chorus; Nwsp Stf; Pom Pon; Trk; Hon Roll; PA Commercial; Acctg.

HULS, CHRISTA; Greensburg Salem SR HS; Greensburg, PA; (2); Sec Church Yth Grp; German Clb; Hosp Aide; Church Choir; Nwsp Rptr; Nwsp Stf; JV Vllybl; High Hon Roll; Jr NHS; Full Schlrshp PA Free Enterprise Wk Smmr 87.

HULSHART, ERIC; Daniel Boone HS; Douglassville, PA; (2); Quiz Bowl; Spanish Clb; Stage Crew; Hon Roll; Cmmnctns.

HUMAY, JENNIFER A; Norristown Area HS; Norristown, PA; (3); 31/428; Cmnty Wkr; Ski Clb; SADD; Rep Soph Cls; Sec Jr Cls; Stu Cncl; Stat Bsktbl; Stat Fld Hcky; Mgr(s); Btty Crckr Awd; Villanova Univ; Bilgcl Sci.

HUMBEGER, ANTHONY; Jeanette SR HS; Jeannette, PA; (3); FBLA; Spanish Clb; Var Bsbl; Var Wrstlng; Hon Roll; Accntng.

HUMBERGER, DORIS LEE; Hempfield Area SR HS; Grapeville, PA; (4); 123/693; Sec FBLA; Library Aide; Pep Clb; Color Guard; Powder Puff Ftbl; Vllybl; Cit Awd; Hon Roll; Computer Systems Inst; Sys Anly.

HUMBERT, JONATHAN; Mt Calvary Christian Schl; Columbia, PA; (3); Chess Clb; Chorus; School Play; Yrbk Stf; Hon Roll; NHS; Crmnlgy.

HUMBERT, SHERRI; Shade HS; Boswell, PA; (4); Sec Computer Clb; Hosp Aide; Yrbk Stf; Hon Roll.

HUMBERT, STEVEN; Somerset Area HS; Friedens, PA; (4); Boy Scts; JA; VICA; Sftbl; Hon Roll; Marine Corp; Comp.

HUMBERT, TARA; Warren Area HS; Warren, PA; (3); Drama Clb; French Clb; Concert Band; Drm Mjr(t); Jazz Band; Mrchg Band; School Musical; School Play; Sftbl; High Hon Roll; Slvr B Awd 85; I U P.

HUMBLE, JENNIFER; Coughlin HS; Laflin, PA; (3); 12/374; Math Clb; Yrbk Ed-Chief; Yrbk Stf; Var Cheerleading; JV Sftbl; Var Trk; High Hon Roll; Hon Roll; Jr NHS; NHS; Pres Acdmc Ftnss Awd 85; Acdmc Cert Merit 85; Pre Vet.

HUMES, KATE; Mechanicsburg HS; Mechanicsburg, PA; (3); Pep Clb; Ski Clb; Var Fld Hcky; Trk; Hon Roll; Fshn Merch.

HUMMEL, CAMILLE I; Mifflinburg HS; New Berlin, PA; (4); 20/154; Sec French Clb; Concert Band; Mrchg Band; Pep Band; Ed Yrbk Stf; Mgr Stu Cncl; Var L Fld Hcky; Var Capt Sftbl; Hon Roll; Cntrl Susqhn Intr Unit Schlrshp 87; Most Athl 87; May Day Ct 86; Penn ST U; Bus Admin.

HUMMEL, CANDY; West Middlesex HS; West Middlesex, PA; (3); 13/104; Art Clb; Church Yth Grp; Chorus; Concert Band; Mrchg Band; Variety Show; Score Keeper; Sftbl; Jr NHS; NHS; Prfct Attndnt Awd 84; Pres Phy Ftns Awd 85; Gustavus Adolphus Coll; Music.

HUMMEL, DOUG; Shamokin Area HS; Shamokin, PA; (4); 16/235; Pres Ski Clb; Varsity Clb; Ftbl; Swmmng; Hon Roll; NHS; Penn ST U; Energy.

HUMMEL, HARVEY; Bensalem HS; Bensalem, PA; (4); 22/529; Boy Scts; Church Yth Grp; High Hon Roll; Hon Roll; Ursinus Coll; Vet Med.

HUMMEL, JENNIFER; Daniel Boone HS; Birdsboro, PA; (2); 20/250; Church Yth Grp; Cmnty Wkr; DECA; Drama Clb; German Clb; SADD; Chorus; Church Choir; Yrbk Stf; Rep Frsh Cls; Sci.

HUMMEL, KARLA; Hempfield HS; Lancaster, PA; (3); Cmnty Wkr; Exploring; Hosp Aide; Yrbk Stf; Mgr(s); NHS.

HUMMEL, NATALIE; Shikellamy HS; Northumberland, PA; (3); 41/312; VP Trs Church Yth Grp; German Clb; Color Guard; Rep Stu Cncl; Elem Ed.

HUMMEL, SHANNON; Blairsville SR HS; Pittsburgh, PA; (3); Bsktbl; High Hon Roll; Hon Roll.

HUMMEL, THOMAS; Bensalem HS; Bensalem, PA; (2); Boy Scts; French Clb; Model UN; Science Clb; JV Trk; Im Wrstlng; MA Inst Of Tech; Comp Sci.

HUMMELL, AMY; Washington HS; Washington, PA; (4); 9/153; Pres Church Yth Grp; Chrmn Hosp Aide; Key Clb; Letterman Clb; Chorus; Church Choir; Mrchg Band; Symp Band; JP Sousa Awd; Sec NHS; Pres Acad Fit Awd 87; Am Yth Symphnc Bnc-European Grande Concrt Tour 85; WV U Honors Bnd 85; Bucknell U; Chemical Engrng.

HUMMER, JODY; Hershey HS; Hershey, PA; (3); 31/208; Spanish Clb; Teachers Aide; Concert Band; Mrchg Band; Sftbl; Hon Roll; Spanish NHS; Intl Frgn Lang Awd-Spnsh 86-87.

HUMMER, TRACY; Danville Area HS; Danville, PA; (2); 50/170; Exploring; Key Clb; Ski Clb; Var Cheerleading; Var JV Fld Hcky; Mat Maids; Swmmng; High Hon Roll; Pres Schlr; Med.

HUMPHREY, KRISTEN; Plum SR HS; Pittsburgh, PA; (3); 69/410; French Clb; Band; Nwsp Rptr; Lit Mag; Hon Roll; Grls Ldrshp Assn Outstndng Svc Awd 86-87; Jrnslm.

HUMPHREY, MONICA; Coatesville HS; Wagontown, PA; (3); Cmnty Wkr; ROTC; Spanish Clb; SADD; Drill Tm; Rep Stu Cncl; Stat Crs Cntry; Hon Roll; Military Order Of Wrld Wars Mdl 85; Retired Offcrs Assn Mdl; PA Modern Miss Pageant Cngnlty Wnnr 87; Pblc Rltns.

HUMPHREY, SALLY; Reynolds HS; Greenville, PA; (3); Library Aide; Q&S; Spanish Clb; Chorus; Nwsp Rptr; Nwsp Stf; Yrbk Sprt Ed; Yrbk Stf; Mgr(s); Voice Dem Awd; Mercer Cnty Sunday Schl Assn Pstr Cntst-1st Pl 85 & 87; Rgnl Sunday Schl Assn Pstr Cntst-1st Pl 85; Southwest Indian Schl; Msnry.

HUMPHREY, SUSAN; Highlands HS; Natrona Hts, PA; (4); Girl Scts; Mrchg Band; School Play; Rep Stu Cncl; Var Crs Cntry; Var Swmmng; Var Tennis; Jr NHS; NHS; U S Army Rsrv Natl Schlr/Athlete Awd 87; Natl Sci Merit & Ldrshp Awds 86-87; Juniata Coll; Chem.

HUMPHREY, TREVOR; Pine Grove Area HS; Pine Grove, PA; (3); ROTC; Varsity Clb; VP Stu Cncl; Capt Var Wrstlng; Hon Roll; VP NHS; Assn US Army Ldrshp Awd 86-87; Achvt Awd Algebra II 86-87; Co Cmndr Pine Grove JROTC Corps 87-88; AF ROTC; Math.

HUMPHREYS, CYNTHIA; Centre County Christian Acad; Howard, PA; (4); Drama Clb; Teachers Aide; Sec Frsh Cls; Sec Jr Cls; Sec Sr Cls; Sec Stu Cncl; Capt L Bsktbl; Var L Cheerleading; Var Capt Socr; L Capt Sftbl; Lock Haven U; Phys Educ.

HUMPHRIES, KAREN; John S Fine SR HS; Mocanaqua, PA; (3); 3/228; Ski Clb; High Hon Roll; NHS; Intl Drctry Of Dstngshd Ldrshp 86; Acadmc All Amercn 84; Ntl Ldrshp & Svc Awds 85; U Of Scranton; Premed.

HUNDERTMARK, JAY; Bethlehem Center HS; Fredericktown, PA; (4); 3/157; Spanish Clb; Varsity Clb; Band; Concert Band; Mrchg Band; Var Bsktbl; High Hon Roll; Lion Awd; NHS; Mst Musicl 87; Emiren Battaglini Awd 87; Amrcn Lgn Awd 84; CA U Of PA.

HUNGER, JILL; Pennsbury HS; Yardley, PA; (2); Band; Church Choir; Concert Band; Mrchg Band; Var L Trk; Hon Roll; Penn Relay 87.

HUNGSAVAISYA, RACHANEEPORN; Abington SR HS; Rydale, PA; (3); 22/534; Hosp Aide; VP Pres Intnl Clb; Key Clb; Sec Latin Clb; Library Aide; Spanish Clb; Yrbk Stf; High Hon Roll; Hon Roll; NHS; Magna Cum Laude/Ntl Ltn Exam 85; Pres Acad Ftns Awd 84-85; Summa Cum Laude/Ntl Ltn Exam 86; U PA; Med.

HUNNELL, SHERRY LYNN; Waynesburg Central HS; Waynesburg, PA; (2); 1/227; Church Yth Grp; Cmnty Wkr; French Clb; Natl Beta Clb; Band; Stu Cncl; Cheerleading; High Hon Roll; NEDT Awd; Law Day Essay Cntst Wnnr 86; Awd Exc Frnch,Englsh,Sp Sci,Geo,Civics 86; 1st Rnnr Up Sewng Cntst 86; Pre-Law.

HUNSBERGER, ERIC; Spring-Ford HS; Collegeville, PA; (3); 35/256; Pres Church Yth Grp; German Clb; Chorus; Church Choir; JV Bsktbl; JV Socr; Hon Roll; Purdue; Comp Engrng.

HUNSBERGER, KI; Souderton Area HS; Harleysville, PA; (3); Aud/Vis; Boys Clb Am; Yrbk Stf; Natl Socl Stdy Olympd 85; 2-Yr Awd Socl Stdy Olympd 85; Hstry Tchr.

HUNSECKER, DARYL; Shalom Christian Acad; Chambersburg, PA; (3); Church Yth Grp; Computer Clb; Acpl Chr; Church Choir; Hon Roll; Prfct Atten Awd; Comp Sci.

HUNSICKER, CHRIS M; North Allegheny SR HS; Pittsburgh, PA; (3); DECA; Hon Roll.

HUNSICKER, LISA; Cedar Crest HS; Lebanon, PA; (3); Key Clb; Latin Clb; Pep Clb; SADD; Chorus; Capt Crs Cntry; Trk; Trck 3200 Rly, 2nd Pl & 1600 M Run 6th Pl 87; Trck M Run 5th Pl 86; Gls C Cntry 28th 85; Nrsng.

HUNSINGER, KIMBERLY; Elk Lake HS; Springville, PA; (1); 3/104; Art Clb; French Clb; SADD; Rep Stu Cncl; Mgr(s); Pom Pon; Hon Roll.

HUNSINGER, NATHAN; Hazelton HS; St Johns, PA; (3); 192/445; Church Yth Grp; French Clb; FBLA; Hosp Aide; ROTC; Bowling; Ftbl; Vllybl; Wrstlng; Hon Roll; 1st Pl Chmpnshp Trphy Mdfd Kart Rcng 85 & 86; 3d Pl Awd Imprmptv Spkng FBLA 87; Bloomsburg U; Corp Lawyer.

HUNSINGER, TAMI; Elk Lake HS; Montrose, PA; (2); Spanish Clb; SADD; Rep Stu Cncl; JV Var Bsktbl; Var Sftbl; JV Vllybl; Bsktbl, Sftbl Chmpns 86-87; 2nd Tm Al-Star Sftbl 86-87.

HUNT, ANNEMARIE; Avon Grove HS; Cochranville, PA; (3); 54/210; Church Yth Grp; Girl Scts; Hosp Aide; Band; Concert Band; Mrchg Band; School Musical; Variety Show; Yrbk Bus Mgr; Rep Stu Cncl; Harcum JR Coll; Physcl Thrpy.

HUNT, CHAD; West Hazleton HS; Weston, PA; (4); 38/224; FTA; Rep Letterman Clb; Rep Spanish Clb; SADD; Thesps; Band; Var L Crs Cntry; Var Trk; NHS; Drama Clb; Intl Thespian Society 85-87; Penn ST; Comm.

HUNT, CHRIS; Nazareth Area SR HS; Nazareth, PA; (3); Church Yth Grp; Bsktbl.

HUNT, DANIEL; Monsignor Bonner HS; Drexel Hill, PA; (3); 38/255; Church Yth Grp; SADD; Nwsp Stf; JV Crs Cntry; Hon Roll; Jr NHS; NHS; Monsignor Bonner Crew Tm 85; Phil Ingr Schlrshp Pgm 85-87; Monsignor Bonner St Edmonds Gld 85-87; Acctng.

HUNT, DAVID; Neshannock JR/SR HS; Neshannock, PA; (3); 16/120; Drama Clb; Speech Tm; Sec VP Band; Concert Band; Jazz Band; Mrchg Band; School Musical; School Play; NHS; Church Yth Grp; Westminister Hnrs Band.

HUNT, DENISE; Connellsville HS; Connellsville, PA; (2); 42/566; Chorus; Var Crs Cntry; Var JV Trk; High Hon Roll; Hon Roll; Spanish NHS; Acdmc Excllnc 85-86.

HUNT, ELISA; Corry Area HS; Corry, PA; (4); Art Clb; Church Yth Grp; Cmnty Wkr; Library Aide; School Play; Chorus; Mercyhurst Coll; Elem Educ.

HUNT, NANCY; Williamson JR SR HS; Millerton, PA; (3); Sec German Clb; Yrbk Stf; VP Soph Cls; Rep Stu Cncl; Var L Trk; Var L Vllybl; High Hon Roll; Hon Roll; Sec Jr NHS; NHS; Grmn Awd 85-87; Dntl Hygnst.

HUNT, REGINA; Brownsville HS; Republic, PA; (3); 19/200; Pres Church Yth Grp; Math Tm; Office Aide; SADD; Chorus; Nwsp Rptr; Var Bsktbl; High Hon Roll; NHS; Ntl Schlrshp Ldrshp Merit Awd 87; Pdtrcn.

HUNT, REGINA; Brownsville SR HS; Adah, PA; (3); 19/200; Pres Church Yth Grp; Math Tm; SADD; Chorus; Variety Show; Nwsp Rptr; JV Var Bsktbl; High Hon Roll; NHS; Pre-Med.

HUNT, ROBERTA; Seneca HS; Wattsburg, PA; (4); 4/149; Chorus; Sec Trs Concert Band; Capt Drm Mjr(t); Mrchg Band; Orch; Yrbk Stf; Var Twrlr; High Hon Roll; JP Sousa Awd; NHS; Pres Acad Fnts Awd 87; Villa Maria Coll; Prof Nrsng.

HUNTER, DOREEN; Leechburg Area HS; Leechburg, PA; (2); 5/95; Church Yth Grp; Chorus; Color Guard; Yrbk Stf; Hon Roll; 4-H; Girl Scts; Hstry Tchng.

HUNTER, HOLLY; N Hills HS; Glenshaw, PA; (4); 16/467; Exploring; Keywanettes; Ski Clb; Yrbk Stf; VP Jr Cls; Rep Stu Cncl; High Hon Roll; NHS.

HUNTER, JENNIFER; Kiski Area HS; Leechburg, PA; (3); Pres Church Yth Grp; Varsity Clb; Chorus; Church Choir; Nwsp Stf; Rep Stu Cncl; Var L Crs Cntry; Var Trk; High Hon Roll; Hon Roll; Ftns Awd 87; Health.

HUNTER, MELISSA; Carbondale Area JR-SR HS; Carbondale, PA; (2); Cmnty Wkr; Computer Clb; Ski Clb; Spanish Clb; Drill Tm; Sftbl; Swmmng; Vllybl; Hon Roll; Med Fld.

HUNTER, SHAWN; Danville HS; Washingtonvl, PA; (2); 19/159; Key Clb; Ski Clb; School Musical; Var JV Cheerleading; JV Fld Hcky; Mat Maids; JV Tennis; High Hon Roll; Exploring; Im Bsktbl; Natl Latin Hnr Soc 86-7.

HUNTER, SHERRI; Elk Lake HS; Montrose, PA; (3); Spanish Clb; Sftbl.

HUNTER, TODD R; Unionville HS; Chadds Ford, PA; (4); 13/300; Scholastic Bowl; Science Clb; Mgr Nwsp Stf; Bausch & Lomb Sci Awd; High Hon Roll; Jr NHS; NHS; Ntl Merit SF; NEDT Awd; Amer Assn Phys Tchrs Awd 86; Wnnr IN U Of PA Phys Tstng Cmptn 86; Awd Excel Engl 85-86; PA ST U; Astrophys.

HUNTLEY, STEVE; Bensalem HS; Bensalem, PA; (3); Pres Church Yth Grp; CAP; ROTC; Ftbl; Wt Lftg; Wrstlng; Cit Awd; High Hon Roll; NHS; Bronze Medal Schlstc Excllnc 87; Bus Admin.

HUNTSBERGER, MICHAEL L; Montrose Area HS; New Milford, PA; (4); 11/164; Art Clb; Pres VP 4-H; Ski Clb; Spanish Clb; SADD; Varsity Clb; Yrbk Stf; Rep Stu Cncl; JV Var Socr; Var Trk; Ntl Hallmark Hnr Awd 87; PA ST U.

HUNTZINGER, DAPHNE; Tri-Valley HS; Spring Glen, PA; (4); 6/87; Church Yth Grp; Drama Clb; VP Sec 4-H; Concert Band; Jazz Band; Mrchg Band; School Play; Yrbk Stf; Hon Roll; NHS; Elizabethtown Coll; Bus Admn.

HUNTZINGER, JENNIFER; Minersville Area HS; Minersville, PA; (3); 8/111; Pep Clb; Spanish Clb; SADD; Yrbk Ed-Chief; Sec Soph Cls; Sec Jr Cls; Stat Bsktbl; Var Score Keeper; Var L Sftbl; Var L Vllybl.

HUNTZINGER, KIM; Pine Grove Area HS; Pine Grove, PA; (1); ROTC; SADD; Pres Frsh Cls; Rep Stu Cncl; JV Var Cheerleading; Hon Roll; Varsity Clb; Chorus; Drill Tm; Mc Cann Schl Of Bus; Exec.

HUNTZINGER, MICHELE; Pine Grove Area HS; Pine Grove, PA; (3); ROTC; SADD; Varsity Clb; Band; Chorus; Drill Tm; VP Soph Cls; VP Jr Cls; Capt Cheerleading; Hon Roll; JROTC Supr Cadet Decor 86-87; Am Leg Mltry Excllnce Awd 87; Bloomsburg U; Nrsg.

HUNZER, KATHLEEN; Neshaminy HS; Feasterville, PA; (4); 21/690; Girl Scts; SADD; Concert Band; Mrchg Band; School Play; Yrbk Ed-Chief; Sec Soph Cls; Lion Awd; NHS; Rotary Awd; Penn ST U; Comm.

HURCHICK, PEGGY; W Scranton HS; Scranton, PA; (3); 22/263; Pep Clb; Spanish Clb; Yrbk Stf; Off Stu Cncl; Var Trk; High Hon Roll; Jr NHS; NHS; Acadmc All Amer 87; Mktng.

HURD, WILLIAM; Clearfield Area HS; Clearfield, PA; (4); Band; Concert Band; Jazz Band; Mrchg Band; Pep Band; MAT Scholar W Chester U 87; West Chester U; Bus Mgmt.

HURLBUTT, JANET; Blairsville SR HS; Black Lick, PA; (4); 3/123; Sec Church Yth Grp; Office Aide; SADD; Stage Crew; VP Frsh Cls; Sec Soph Cls; Score Keeper; High Hon Roll; Jr NHS; NHS; Pres Acad Ftness Awd, Acad All Amer, PA ST U Essay 87; PA ST U; Bus Mgmnt.

HURLEY, DENISE; Churchill/Woodland Hills HS; Pittsburgh, PA; (2); Chorus; Rep Stu Cncl; JV Vllybl; High Hon Roll; Hon Roll; Vet.

HURLEY, KATHRYN M; Fox Chapel Area HS; Pittsburgh, PA; (3); 37/361; Church Yth Grp; Science Clb; Yrbk Stf; Var L Fld Hcky; Var Trk; High Hon Roll; Hon Roll; NHS; Nutritionist.

HURLEY, PAMELA; Central Cambria HS; Ebensburg, PA; (3); 6/210; Drama Clb; NFL; Ski Clb; Speech Tm; School Musical; School Play; Nwsp Rptr; High Hon Roll; Library Aide.

HURLEY, SHANNON M; Elizabeth Forward HS; Elizabeth, PA; (4); 12/293; Church Yth Grp; Exploring; GAA; Ski Clb; Spanish Clb; JV L Bsktbl; Var L Sftbl; Var L Vllybl; High Hon Roll; NHS; U Pittsburgh Merit Schlrshp, Pres Acdmc Ftnss Awd 87; Cert Merit PHEAA; U Of Pittsburgh; Phys Thrpy.

HURLOCK, PATRICIA; Pennsbury HS; Fairless Hls, PA; (3); Church Yth Grp; Girl Scts; Intnl Clb; SADD; Church Choir; Orch; School Musical; Nwsp Stf; Stud Mnth Oct 84,May 86; Bio.

HURRELL, DANELLE; Norristown Area HS; Norristown, PA; (3); 104/531; Art Clb; VICA; Sec Jr Cls; Stu Cncl; Var Capt Bowling; JV Fld Hcky; JV Lcrss; JV Sftbl; Im Vllybl; IN U Of PA; Hstry.

HURRIANKO, MEGAN; Greensburg Central Catholic HS; Greensburg, PA; (3); 18/231; AFS; Hosp Aide; Chorus; Color Guard; School Play; Yrbk Stf; High Hon Roll; NHS.

HURSEN, ERIN; Carlisle HS; Carlisle, PA; (3); 18/455; Hosp Aide; Office Aide; Service Clb; Color Guard; Nwsp Rptr; Off Sr Cls; High Hon Roll; NHS; Bus.

HURSH, MELISSA; Conestoga Valley HS; Leola, PA; (4); 132/253; Church Yth Grp; Var Capt Gym; Hon Roll; SR Athltc Awd Gymnstcs, Hlf Schlrshp Palmer Schl 87; Palmer Schl; Lgl Secr.

HURST, AIMEE; Garden Spot HS; New Holland, PA; (2); 20/226; Church Yth Grp; German Clb; Chorus; Church Choir; Stage Crew; Fld Hcky; Mgr(s); Hon Roll; Jr NHS; NHS; Med.

HURST, AUDREY; Lancaster Mennonile HS; Ephrata, PA; (3); Church Yth Grp; Chorus; Church Choir; High Hon Roll; Lancaster Gen Schl Nrsng; Nrsng.

HURST, DORLEE; Lancaster Mennonite HS; New Holland, PA; (3); Church Yth Grp; Cmnty Wkr; Chorus; Hnrb Mntn Sclptr 85; Flrst.

HURST, DOUG; Garden Spot HS; Bowmansville, PA; (3); VP FFA; JV Bsktbl; Var Socr; L Trk.

HURST, KENDRA; Harrisburg HS; Harrisburg, PA; (2); 72/358; Variety Show; Var JV Cheerleading; JV Pom Pon; Delta Sigma Theta Jabberwock Awd 86; Howard U; Cvl Engr.

HURST, LEIGH A; Middletown Area HS; Middletown, PA; (3); 19/193; Key Clb; Model UN; Chorus; School Musical; Swing Chorus; VP Frsh Cls; Pres Soph Cls; Pres Jr Cls; Stu Cncl; Var L Sftbl; Penn ST U; Advtamnt.

HURST, MAURA; Lampeter Strasburg HS; Ronks, PA; (3); 34/145; AFS; Art Clb; Drama Clb; Pres FBLA; Thesps; School Musical; School Play; Yrbk Stf; Score Keeper; Stat Trk; Educ.

HURST, STACEY; Danville HS; Danville, PA; (3); French Clb; Key Clb; Rep Frsh Cls; Rep Jr Cls; Gym; Socr; Tennis; Trk; High Hon Roll; NHS; French & Geometry Awd; Frgn Reltns.

HURWITCH, MELISSA; Du Bois Area SR HS; Dubois, PA; (3); Hosp Aide; Varsity Clb; Nwsp Rptr; VP Soph Cls; Stu Cncl; Tennis; U Of PA; Elem Ed.

HURWITZ, DANIEL; The Christian Acad; Folcroft, PA; (3); Computer Clb; Radio Clb; Ski Clb; Bsbl; Ftbl; Lcrss; Wt Lftg; Hon Roll; Med.

HURWITZ, JAMIE; Lower Merion HS; Philadelphia, PA; (3); Debate Tm; Var Fld Hcky; Capt Var Trk; French Hon Soc; High Hon Roll; NHS; Wellesley Bk Awd 87; Mary I Turner Awd 86.

HURWITZ, WENDY; Central Bucks H S East; Doylestown, PA; (4); Debate Tm; FBLA; Soroptimist; Chorus; Nwsp Bus Mgr; Nwsp Rptr; Nwsp Stf; Yrbk Bus Mgr; Rep Frsh Cls; Rep Jr Cls; John G Stripe Soc Schlrs Emory U 87; Emory U; Mktng.

HUSAK, HEIDE; Ambridge Area HS; Ambridge, PA; (3); VP Church Yth Grp; German Clb; Pep Clb; Red Cross Aide; Chorus; School Musical; Soph Cls; Jr Cls; JV Var Cheerleading; Hon Roll; Sewickley Vly Hosp Schl/Nrsg.

HUSBAND, JOAN; Connellsville SR HS; Connellsvl, PA; (3); 13/550; Church Yth Grp; Office Aide; School Musical; French Hon Soc; High Hon Roll; NHS; Acad Exclnce 85.

HUSBAND, MARY LOU; Connellsville Area SR HS; Connellsville, PA; (4); 1/500; Church Yth Grp; FTA; Q&S; School Musical; Yrbk Sprt Ed; Bausch & Lomb Sci Awd; French Hon Soc; High Hon Roll; NHS; Val; Dstngshd Achvr Schlrshp IN U Of PA 87; IN U Of PA; Chemistry.

HUSE, KAREN A; Morrisville HS; Morrisville, PA; (3); 18/92; FFA; Spanish Clb; Band; Color Guard; Sec Jr Cls; Cit Awd; High Hon Roll; Hon Roll; Engl Imprvmnt Attitude 86; Sci, Engl Achvt 86; Art Inst Phila; Interior Decrtr.

HUSICK, MICHAEL; Chambersburg Area SR HS; Chambersburg, PA; (3); Church Yth Grp; French Clb; Key Clb; Office Aide; Pep Clb; Yrbk Stf; Hon Roll; Prfct Atten Awd; Robotic Tech.

HUSKEY, JEFF; Fairview HS; Erie, PA; (3); Church Yth Grp; Computer Clb; German Clb; Ski Clb; Nwsp Phtg; Nwsp Rptr; JV Var Bsbl; JV Ftbl; Var Mgr(s); Pblc Rltns.

HUSS, BECCI D; Chambersburg Area HS; Fayetteville, PA; (2); 278/735; Church Yth Grp; French Clb; JCL; Red Cross Aide; SADD; Chorus; Nwsp Rptr; Messiah Coll; Secndry Ed.

HUSTEAD III, DELLAS C; Jeannette SR HS; Jeannette, PA; (4); 10/128; Am Leg Boys St; French Clb; Ski Clb; Varsity Clb; Variety Show; Var Bsbl; Var L Wrstlng; High Hon Roll; Hon Roll; NHS; Juvnl Justc Essy Cntst Wnnr Westmoreland Cnty 86; Westnghse Sci Hnrs Inst 86-87; U Of Pittsburgh; Engrng.

HUSTED, THOMAS; Hempfield HS; Mountville, PA; (3); Boy Scts; Church Yth Grp; Wrstlng; Lancaster Schl Drftng; Arch.

HUSTON, SCOTT; Mercy Vocational HS; Philadelphia, PA; (4); 6/130; Drama Clb; Varsity Clb; Bsktbl; Ftbl; Trk; Wrstlng; Hon Roll; Prfct Atten Awd; Amer Inst Of Dsgn.

HUSTOSKY, KEITH; Southmoreland HS; Mt Pleasant, PA; (3); German Clb; Concert Band; Jazz Band; Nwsp Stf; JV Golf; NHS; Grmn Natl Hnr Soc; Engrng.

HUTCHIN, DARCIE; Faith Community Christian HS; Eighty Four, PA; (3); 1/28; VP Church Yth Grp; Drama Clb; French Clb; Church Choir; Yrbk Stf; VP Jr Cls; Cheerleading; High Hon Roll; NHS; NEDT Awd; Grove City Coll; Jrnlsm.

HUTCHINS, ANDREA; Slippery Rock Area HS; Slippery Rock, PA; (4); Aud/Vis; Chorus; Flag Corp; Nwsp Rptr; Rep Frsh Cls; Var Crs Cntry; Trk; High Hon Roll; NHS; Pres Bibl Clb 86-87; Presdntl Acadc Ftns Awd 86-87; Grl Sct Slvr Awd 83-84; Slippery Rock U; Chem.

HUTCHINS, HOLLY; Millersburg Area HS; Millersburg, PA; (3); 24/73; French Clb; Color Guard; Mrchg Band; Nwsp Stf; High Hon Roll; Hon Roll; Careers Hlth Clb 86-87; Consrvtn Clb 86-88; Duquesne U; Engl Tchr.

HUTCHINSON, BARBARA; Juniata HS; Mifflin, PA; (4); Art Clb; 4-H; FHA; SADD; 4-H Awd; High Hon Roll; Hon Roll; Jr NHS; NHS; Home Ec Hnr 87; Pres Acad Ftns Awd 87; Schltc J Awd 84-87; Ntl Ed Ctr Thompson Inst; Accnt.

HUTCHINSON, JACKIE; Daniel Broone HS; Douglassville, PA; (3); Spanish Clb; Band; Capt Color Guard; Capt Drill Tm; Capt Flag Corp; Mrchg Band; Yrbk Stf; Stat Bsktbl; Mgr(s); Score Keeper; Tchng Spcl Educ.

HUTCHINSON, KRISTAL D; South Moreland SR HS; Mt Pleasant, PA; (2); Church Yth Grp; Girl Scts; JCL; Latin Clb; Service Clb; Teachers Aide; Chorus; Pres Frsh Cls; Rep Stu Cncl; Cheerleading; Intl Ordr Rnbw Girls Chpln 85; Penn ST U.

HUTCHINSON, WENDI ADELE; Warwick HS; Lititz, PA; (2); 69/325; VP Church Yth Grp; Exploring; Mrchg Band; Nwsp Rptr; Yrbk Rptr; Stat Trk; Hon Roll; Cmmnctns.

HUTCHISON, BARRY A; Cumberland Valley HS; Mechanicsburg, PA; (3); Aud/Vis; Letterman Clb; Science Clb; Varsity Clb; Orch; Nwsp Stf; Rep Var Stu Cncl; Var Swmmng; High Hon Roll; Prfct Atten Awd; ROTC; Aerospce Engrng.

HUTCHISON, JAMES D; South Allegheny HS; Mc Keesport, PA; (3); 34/187; Concert Band; Mrchg Band; Hon Roll; NHS; Schlstc Achvt Awd 86-87; Penn ST U; Engr.

HUTCHISON, JANNETTE; Mon Valley Catholic HS; Monessen, PA; (2); 12/75; Spanish Clb; Chorus; Yrbk Stf; High Hon Roll; Spanish NHS; Sci.

HUTH, PATRICK; Freeport Area HS; Freeport, PA; (3); 26/200; Church Yth Grp; L Bsbl; Hon Roll.

HUTSELL, SCOTT; Bethel Perk HS; Library, PA; (4); Drama Clb; Math Clb; Science Clb; Chorus; School Musical; School Play; Swing Chorus; Hon Roll; Penn ST; Engr.

HUTT, KEVIN D; Northeast Catholic HS For Boys; Philadelphia, PA; (3); 61/328; Church Yth Grp; Office Aide; Cit Awd; Hon Roll; NHS; Spnsh Merit Awd 85-86; Temple U; Law.

HUTTON, HEIDI; Clearfield Area HS; Clearfield, PA; (4); 80/318; Band; Concert Band; Mrchg Band; Var Swmmng; Var Trk; Capt Var Vllybl; Cit Awd; Church Yth Grp; Key Clb; Red Cross Aide; Elks Nrsng Schlrshp 87; Lions Schlrshp 87; Clrfld Hosp Nrs Alum Assoc 87; Geisinger Med Schl; Nrs.

HUTTON, JENNIFER L; Harmony Area Schls; Mahaffey, PA; (4); 4/50; Church Yth Grp; VP Band; Chorus; School Play; Nwsp Stf; Trs Sr Cls; NHS; Pres Schlr; Office Aide; Concert Band; Jhnstwn Trbn-Dmcrt Schlstc Jrnlsm Awd 87; Hghtn Coll Trustees Schlrshp 87; Houghton Coll; Engl.

HUTTON, JOSEPH; Monsignor Bonner HS; East Lansdowne, PA; (4); 96/302; Letterman Clb; Library Aide; Office Aide; SADD; Varsity Clb; Var Ftbl; Mgr(s); Dedctd Tm Mgr Awd 87; Clss Awd SADD Slvr Mdl & Lbrry Aide Slvr Mdl 87; RETS Elec Schls; Elec Tech.

HUTZ, DIANE; James M Coughlin HS; Wilkes Barre, PA; (4); Hon Roll; Jr NHS; NHS; Luzerne County CC; Trvl.

HUTZEL, GREG J; Exeter HS; Reading, PA; (3); Am Leg Boys St; Church Yth Grp; French Clb; Crs Cntry; JV Ftbl; JV Tennis; Var L Trk; Hon Roll; NHS; Arch.

HUWE, GIGI; St Francis Acad; Pittsburgh, PA; (3); Math Clb; Bsktbl; Vllybl; High Hon Roll; Bus.

HUWEART, ERIC; Quaker Valley HS; Sewickley, PA; (4); 11/156; German Clb; Key Clb; Concert Band; Mrchg Band; Pep Band; Var L Socr; High Hon Roll; Kiwanis Awd; NHS; Pres Schlr; Case Wstrn Rsrv U; Biomed Engr.

HUYA, TIM; Northwestern SR HS; Cranesville, PA; (3); 10/168; Cmnty Wkr; Library Aide; Model UN; Red Cross Aide; Yrbk Sprt Ed; Off Stu Cncl; L Var Trk; High Hon Roll; NHS; Ntl Merit Ltr; Cert Apprctn Untd Way 86; JR Frmn Yr, Mbr Cranesville Volntr Fire Dept 84; Forestry.

HUYNH, HUONG; Churchill HS; Braddock, PA; (2); 31/222; French Clb; Band; Pitt U.

HUYNH, KHENG; Philadelphia HS For Girls; Philadelphia, PA; (3); Intnl Clb; Trs Science Clb; Teachers Aide; Meritorious Awd 8 7; U PA; Engrng.

HUYNH, KHOA DANG; John Harris HS; Harrisburg, PA; (4); 1/273; Chess Clb; Math Clb; Office Aide; Stu Cncl; Socr; Tennis; High Hon Roll; Val; Hghst Hnr Stu SR Cls 87; Hghst Stndng In Math 3 Yrs 85-87; Delta Sigma Theta Annl Coll Schlrshp 87; Penn ST U; Mech Engrng Dsgnr.

HUYNH, NGOC; Hempfield HS; E Petersburg, PA; (3); 70/393; Chorus; Variety Show; Rep Soph Cls; Rep Stu Cncl; High Hon Roll; Hon Roll; Doctor.

HUYNH, VAN; Pottstown SR HS; Pottstown, PA; (3); 1/155; French Clb; Key Clb; Spanish Clb; Rep Jr Cls; Sr Cls; JV Fld Hcky; JV Lcrss; High Hon Roll; NHS; Val; Acctng.

HVIZDA, SHERRY; Jefferson-Morgan HS; Waynesburg, PA; (3); 20/92; Am Leg Aux Girls St; 4-H; Office Aide; Yrbk Ed-Chief; Yrbk Stf; Rep Soph Cls; Rep Stu Cncl; Cit Awd; DAR Awd; High Hon Roll; Yth Traffic Sfty Cncl 86-87.

HVOZDA, ERIC; Homer Center HS; Homer City, PA; (4); Aud/Vis; Computer Clb; Stage Crew; Bst Drftsmn Awd; Penn ST Altoona; Comp Sci.

HWANG, THOMAS; Marple Newtown SR HS; Broomall, PA; (3); 1/322; Art Clb; JV Capt Math Tm; Pres Service Clb; Chorus; Orch; Var L Crs Cntry; Bausch & Lomb Sci Awd; High Hon Roll; NHS; PA Gov Schl Sci 87; Elec Engrng.

HWOSTOW, CHRIS; Hampton HS; Allison Park, PA; (3); French Clb; Spanish Clb; Band; Drill Tm; Symp Band; L Pom Pon; Im Powder Puff Ftbl; High Hon Roll; Hon Roll; Intl Bus.

HYATT, RICHARD; Berlin Brothers Valley HS; Berlin, PA; (2); Boy Scts; Chess Clb; Computer Clb; 4-H; FFA; Library Aide; Office Aide; Ski Clb; Spanish Clb; Cit Awd; W VA U; Comp Sci.

HYDOCK, MICHAEL T; Nativity B V M HS; Pottsville, PA; (4); 8/93; Chess Clb; VP Band; Chorus; Concert Band; Mrchg Band; Stage Crew; Variety Show; Hon Roll; NHS; Prfct Atten Awd; PA ST U; Engrng.

HYDRO, PATRICE; Marian Catholic HS; Jim Thorpe, PA; (3); 46/104; Yrbk Stf; JV Sftbl; Peer Fcltr; Physcl Thrpy.

HYDRUSKO, LAURA; Pleasant Valley HS; Saylorsburg, PA; (3); Drama Clb; Ski Clb; SADD; L Drill Tm; Stage Crew; Stu Cncl; JV Cheerleading; Trk; L Twrlr; Hon Roll; Law.

HYDUK, STEPHANIE; Norwin SR HS; N Huntingdon, PA; (4); 70/563; Sec FBLA; Office Aide; Hon Roll; FBLA Job Interview Awd 2nd Pl 86-87; Secy.

HYKES, MARCIA; Greencastle-Antrim HS; Greencastle, PA; (3); 1/166; VP Church Yth Grp; Chorus; Nwsp Stf; VP Stu Cncl; Var L Fld Hcky; L Trk; High Hon Roll; NHS; Ntl Merit Ltr; Part In PA All-St Chorus 87; Psych.

HYLER, HOLLY; Peters Township HS; Mcmurray, PA; (2); Trs Soph Cls; Rep Stu Cncl; JV Cheerleading; WA & Jefferson Coll; Elem Ed.

HYMAN, WAYNE; Emmavs HS; Wescosville, PA; (4); 17/473; Church Yth Grp; Var Bsktbl; High Hon Roll; NHS; 2nd Pl Awd PA JR Acad Of Sci 87; Presdnl Acad Fit Awd 87; PA ST U; Engrng.

HYND, LISA; West Branch Area HS; Lanse, PA; (3); 1/118; Drama Clb; Ski Clb; Chorus; Concert Band; Mrchg Band; Yrbk Stf; Rep Stu Cncl; Hon Roll; NHS; Penn ST; Jrnlsm.

HYNICK, RICHARD; Lake Lehman HS; Hunlock Crk, PA; (2); Church Yth Grp; JV Var Bsbl; JV Bsktbl; Hon Roll; Jr NHS; Soc Sci.

HYNOK, CHRISTINA; West Mifflin Area HS; W Mifflin, PA; (2); Art Clb; Ski Clb; Yrbk Stf; Rep Stu Cncl; Im Cheerleading; Im Trk; High Hon Roll; Hon Roll; Jr NHS; Med.

HYSELL, BRIDGETT; Lincoln HS; Ellwood City, PA; (3); 59/160; Hosp Aide; Latin Clb; SADD; Y-Teens; Chorus; Variety Show.

I GOE, TINA; St Huberts HS; Philadelphia, PA; (3); Drama Clb; Chorus; School Play; Office Aide; Teachers Aide; Church Choir; School Musical; Gym; Typng Awd 87; Wilfred Acad; Csmtlgy.

IACAVAZZI, PETER; West Scranton SR HS; Scranton, PA; (2); Latin Clb; Letterman Clb; L Bsbl; L Ftbl; Trk; Wt Lftg; Hon Roll; Jr NHS; NHS; VFW Awd; Princeton Univ; Med.

IACCIO, CHRISTOPHER; Bangor Area HS; Bangor, PA; (2); 49/213; Church Yth Grp; Ski Clb; Coach Actv; JV Var Ftbl; Var Trk; Im Vllybl; Hon Roll; Part Churchs Session 87; Pre-Med.

IACONO, CARLO; Chichester SR HS; Twin Oaks, PA; (3); 25/293; Model UN; Nwsp Ed-Chief; Nwsp Sprt Ed; Stu Cncl; Hon Roll; Jr NHS; NHS; Spanish NHS; Spanish Clb; School Play; 3 Rd Pl DE Cnty Prss Clb-Sprts Wrtng 86; 3rd Pl DE Cnty Prss Clb-Sprts Wrtng 87; Lbrl Arts.

IACONO, MICHELLE; Dover HS; Dover, PA; (3); GAA; Varsity Clb; Var Bsktbl; Stat Fld Hcky; Im Sftbl; Var Vllybl; All Star Tm Sftbl 87; Bloomsburg Coll.

IACOVANGELO, LORI; Ringgold HS; Monongahela, PA; (4); 29/350; Ski Clb; Variety Show; Sec Stu Cncl; Capt Pom Pon; Math Science Hon Soc 86-87; U Of Pittsburgh; Physical Ther.

IACOVELLA, FOSCA L; Archbishop Prendergast HS; Havertown, PA; (4); 6/325; Church Yth Grp; Cmnty Wkr; Latin Clb; Service Clb; Spanish Clb; Im Vllybl; High Hon Roll; VP Spanish NHS; Jesuit Schlrshp, Patroness Awd & Prsdntl Acdmc Fitness Awd 87; St Josephs U; Bus.

IACULLO, BARBARA; St Huberts HS; Philadelphia, PA; (3); Dance Clb; Office Aide; Red Cross Aide; SADD; Gordon Phillips; Csmtlgy.

IADONATO, SHAWN; Punxsutawney Area HS; Punxsutawney, PA; (4); 6/250; French Clb; Math Tm; Science Clb; Band; Concert Band; Jazz Band; Mrchg Band; Pep Band; Variety Show; Yrbk Phtg; U PA; Doctor.

IAMS, MELISSA J; Jefferson-Morgan JR SR HS; Jefferson, PA; (4); 13/97; French Clb; Teachers Aide; Varsity Clb; Rep Jr Cls; Sftbl; Hon Roll; Rotary Awd; Boy Scts; Quiz Bowl; Cmmnwlth PA Wldlf Cnsrvtn Awd 85; Outstdndng Athlt Sftbl 87; Waynesbrg Coll; Bio.

IANETTI, MICHELE; Haverford HS; Havertown, PA; (3); 60/423; GAA; Orch; Stage Crew; Symp Band; Stu Cncl; Sftbl; Hon Roll; IN U Of PA; Cmmnctns Tech.

IANNACONE, PAUL; S Philadelphia HS; Philadelphia, PA; (4); 2/30; School Play; Lit Mag; High Hon Roll; Hon Roll; Prfct Atten Awd; Schlrshp-Community Coll 87; Community Coll.

IANNIELLI, FRANK; Bishop O Hara HS; Dunmore, PA; (2); Boy Scts; Ski Clb; Spanish Clb; Penn ST; Engr.

IANNOTTA, DENNIS; Emmaus HS; Wescosville, PA; (3); Computer Clb; Band; Concert Band; Mrchg Band; Lcrss; Hon Roll; Acad Awd 84-85; Bus Mgmt.

IANNUCCI, MIKE; Penncrest HS; Media, PA; (3); Church Yth Grp; Exploring; German Clb; Scholastic Bowl; Ski Clb; Stage Crew; JV Var Bowling; JV Var Gym; Im Socr; PA ST; Heating Air Cond.

IANSON, BERT; Cowanesque Valley HS; Middlebury Ctr, PA; (4); Pres Church Yth Grp; Drama Clb; FFA; Letterman Clb; School Play; Stage Crew; Yrbk Stf; Ftbl; NHS; Mansfield U; Math.

IANSON, BRYONNA; Cowanesque Valley HS; Middlebury Ctr, PA; (2); Camera Clb; Trs Church Yth Grp; Trs FFA; Rptr Girl Scts; Letterman Clb; Trs Soph Cls; Var Trk; Stat Wrstlng; Hon Roll; Slvr Awd Grl Scts 87; Star Chptr Frmr Awd FFA 87; Farm Credit Svc Awd FFA 87; Mansfield U.

IAWNACONE, PAUL; South Philadelphia HS; Philadelphia, PA; (4); 2/30; Lit Mag; High Hon Roll; Hon Roll; CC 2 Yr Schlrshp 87; Community Coll.

IBINSON, LINDA; North Catholic HS; Pittsburgh, PA; (3); Art Clb; Camera Clb; Church Yth Grp; German Clb; NFL; Speech Tm; Band; Stage Crew; Nwsp Stf; Hon Roll; Baldwin-Wallace Coll; Art.

ICKES, CAROL; Altoona Area HS; Altoona, PA; (4); 2/718; Church Yth Grp; Math Clb; Office Aide; Trs Spanish Clb; Var Capt Vllybl; DAR Awd; Jr NHS; Trs NHS; NEDT Awd; Coaches Awd Vllybl, Weightlifting Imprvmnt Awds 85; High Scorer Awd Vllybl 86; Phys Ther.

ICKES, CHRIS; North Star HS; Boswell, PA; (4); Boy Scts; Church Yth Grp; FCA; School Play; Yrbk Ed-Chief; Stu Cncl; JV Trk; Cit Awd; Lion Awd; Prfct Atten Awd; St Vincent Coll; Accnting.

ICKES, CHRISTY M; Clearfield Area HS; Clearfield, PA; (3); 8/350; Key Clb; Ski Clb; Spanish Clb; Concert Band; Yrbk Stf; VP Soph Cls; VP Jr Cls; Var Cheerleading; Trk; High Hon Roll; Bus Admin.

ICKES, JENNIFER; Benton JR SR HS; Orangeville, PA; (2); Sec Art Clb; Drama Clb; Girl Scts; Keywanettes; Chorus; Church Choir; Concert Band; School Musical; Stu Cncl; Var Bsktbl; Hugh Obrian Yth Fndtn Ldrshp Ambsdr 86-87; Frank C Laubach Ltrcy Awd 85; Kutztown; Cmrcl Art.

ICKES, MARK; Blairsville SR HS; Blairsville, PA; (3); Computer Clb; Library Aide; Yrbk Stf; High Hon Roll; NHS; 2nd Pl-Intrmrl Wrstlng 87; Penn ST U; Arch.

ICKES, MICHELLE; Claysburg-Kimmel HS; Claysburg, PA; (2); Trs Church Yth Grp; Y-Teens; Drama Clb; Hon Roll; Prfct Atten Awd; Cashr.

IDE, GWENDOLYN; Tunkhannock Area HS; Mehoopany, PA; (3); Drama Clb; 4-H; French Clb; Chorus; Flag Corp; Mrchg Band; School Play; Var Crs Cntry; Cit Awd; Hon Roll; Trophy Most Ded X-Cntry Rnnr 86; Phys Ther.

IDEN, MATT J; Rochester Area JR SR HS; Rochester, PA; (3); 18/110; Am Leg Boys St; JA; Concert Band; Mrchg Band; Orch; School Musical; Variety Show; Nwsp Rptr; Nwsp Stf; Var Trk; Crvt Wrtng Awd 86; Pblshd In Natl Mgzn 87; Crtv Wrtng.

IENI, LISA; Franklin Regional HS; Export, PA; (3); 96/329; Stu Cncl; Cheerleading; Art Clb; Yrbk Stf; High Hon Roll; Chrldng Squad At Natl Level 86-87; PA Miss All Amercn Chlrdlr 87; U DE; Mgmt.

IGNAT, DIANE; West Mifflin Area HS; W Mifflin, PA; (3); 50/320; Art Clb; Teachers Aide; Chorus; Nwsp Stf; Yrbk Stf; Off Frsh Cls; Off Soph Cls; Off Jr Cls; Sec Stu Cncl; JV Cheerleading; Amer Lgn Awd 86; Penn ST; Nrsng.

IGNOTZ, BRIAN; Brownsville HS; Allison, PA; (3); 2/200; Boy Scts; Math Tm; Ski Clb; Band; Jazz Band; Nwsp Stf; Im Bsktbl; Var Trk; Pres Jr NHS; NHS; Drexel U; Chmcl Engrng.

IGNOZZI, JEFFERY S; Burrell SR HS; Lower Burrell, PA; (3); VP JA; Varsity Clb; Var L Ftbl; Trk; Var L Wrstlng; Rotary Awd; Undefeated Aa Champs 86; MVP In Ftbl 86.

IGOU, MICHAEL; Tyrone Area HS; Tyrone, PA; (3); French Clb; JV Bsbl; Im Wt Lftg; High Hon Roll; Hon Roll; NHS; Law.

IHNAT, MARY ELAINE; Avella HS; Avella, PA; (3); Church Yth Grp; Drama Clb; Pres 4-H; French Clb; Trs SADD; Varsity Clb; Band; Chorus; Concert Band; Drm Mjr(t); Cnty Chorus 85-87; Cnty Band 86; Dist Chorus 84; Grove City CC; Music.

IHRIG, SALLY; Boyertown Area SR HS; Boyertown, PA; (4); 19/426; Church Yth Grp; FBLA; Teachers Aide; Teachers Aide; School Play; Var Capt Bsktbl; Var Capt Fld Hcky; Var Capt Lcrss; Cit Awd; High Hon Roll; Ath Schlrshp Coll Of William & Mary 87; William & Mary Coll.

IIAMS, LINDA; Avella HS; Avella, PA; (4); 4/50; Art Clb; Church Yth Grp; Trs French Clb; Teachers Aide; Church Choir; School Musical; Variety Show; Yrbk Stf; High Hon Roll; NHS; Duffs Bus Inst; Secrtrl.

ILES, JOSEPH; Abington HS; Abington, PA; (3); 98/502; Boy Scts; Church Yth Grp; Intnl Clb; Band; Mrchg Band; Jr NHS; Rotary Awd; Eagle Sct Awd 86; Union Leag Citiz Awd 87.

ILGEN, AMY; Central York SR HS; York, PA; (2); Ski Clb; Chorus; Color Guard; Mrchg Band; Mgr(s); Trk; High Hon Roll; Pres Schlr; Hosp Vlntr; Med.

ILGENFRITZ, CRAIG; Boiling Springs HS; Carlisle, PA; (3); 34/142; Computer Clb; Dance Clb; Spanish Clb; Band; Chorus; Mrchg Band; Pep Band; Swing Chorus; Bsbl; Bsktbl; Carlisle Area Sci Fair 2nd Pl 86; Wrtg Cont 1st Pl 84; Sci Fair Hnrbl Mntn 85; Comp Prgmg.

ILGENFRITZ, JENNIFER; Susquehannock HS; Glen Rock, PA; (3); 98/194; Office Aide; Teachers Aide; Chorus; Church Choir; Central Penn Bus Schl; Bus Mngt.

ILIK, BOB; Boyertown Area SR HS; Gilbertsville, PA; (4); 75/437; Band; Concert Band; Jazz Band; Mrchg Band; Pep Band; Var Crs Cntry; Var Swmmng; Var Capt Trk; Hon Roll; Athltc Grant Track 87-91; La Salle U; Acctg.

ILLAR, TINAMARIE; Leechburg Area HS; West Leechburg, PA; (3); 15/95; Pres Art Clb; Drama Clb; Nwsp Stf; Yrbk Stf.

ILOV, ALYSSA C; Quigley HS; Aliquippa, PA; (3); 18/83; French Clb; Math Tm; Chorus; Sec Soph Cls; Sec Jr Cls; Sec Sr Cls; Stat Bsktbl; Var Trk; Hon Roll; NHS; Natl Hnr Roll 87.

IMBARLINA, SERGIO; Plum SR HS; New Kensington, PA; (3); Exploring; Office Aide; Teachers Aide; Nwsp Rptr; Nwsp Stf; Hon Roll; NHS; Oscar Ritchie Mem Schrlshp 87; Clrsm Awds-Spnsh, Art, Amer Hstry 85-86; Knowledgemaster Tm 85 & 87; Physics.

IMBROGNO, LISA; Cardinal O Hara HS; Brookhaven, PA; (3); 51/710; Church Yth Grp; Civic Clb; Hon Roll; Ntl Merit Ltr; Chem.

IMBURGIA, DEBORAH; Cardinal O Hara HS; Boothwyn, PA; (3); 75/710; Aud/Vis; Pres Cmnty Wkr; Dance Clb; Chorus; School Musical; School Play; Var JV Cheerleading; French Hon Soc; Hon Roll; Prncpls Awd Vcl Music 85.

IMLER, GARY; Chestnut Ridge HS; New Paris, PA; (3); SADD; Var Ftbl; Var Wrstlng; Air Force; Elec.

IMLER, JAMES; Claysburg-Kimmel HS; Claysburg, PA; (3); 7/90; Varsity Clb; Chorus; School Musical; Var L Bsbl; Var L Bsktbl; Var L Ftbl; Var Tennis; Var Wt Lftg; Hon Roll; NHS; PA ST; Cmmnctns.

IMLER, JAMES L; Claysburg Kimmel HS; Imler, PA; (1); Pres Frsh Cls; Rep Stu Cncl; Hon Roll; Prfct Atten Awd; Bus Mgmnt.

IMLER, KELLY; Bedford HS; Bedford, PA; (3); Chorus; Co-Capt L Cheerleading; L Trk; Hon Roll; High Hnr Record Kpng 86-87; Track Awd Outstndng Newcomer 86-87; Central Penn Bus Schl.

IMLER, LORI; Bellwood-Antis HS; Tyrone, PA; (3); 7/115; Varsity Clb; Var Fld Hcky; Var Trk; High Hon Roll; Comp In Natl JR Olympcs 86.

IMPECIATI, DANIELLE C; Pittston SR HS; Pittston, PA; (3); FNA; Pep Clb; Nwsp Stf; Yrbk Stf; Accntng.

IMPERIALE, CHRISTOPHER; Sacred Heart HS; Carbondale, PA; (3); 18/45; Sec Off Church Yth Grp; Computer Clb; Ski Clb; SADD; Nwsp Stf; Yrbk Stf; Var Capt Bsbl; JV Var Bsktbl; Var Golf; Score Keeper.

INCH, ANNA MARIE; East Juniata HS; Richfield, PA; (3); Art Clb; Camera Clb; FBLA; Library Aide; School Musical; Yrbk Stf; Stat Bsktbl; Hon Roll; Central PA Bus Schl; Hlt Mngmn.

INCH, CHRISTINE; Central Dauphin HS; Harrisburg, PA; (3); Key Clb; Band; Chorus; Jazz Band; Madrigals; Orch; School Musical; School Play; Lion Awd; NHS; Wldlf Sci.

INDELICATO, RICH; Bethlehem Catholic HS; Bethlehem, PA; (4); 54/210; Jazz Band; School Musical; Stage Crew; Rep Frsh Cls; L Crs Cntry; Hon Roll; Berklee Coll Of Music; Music.

INDOF, MARIANNE; Belle Vernon Area HS; Belle Vernon, PA; (3); FNA; Ski Clb; VICA; Color Guard; Powder Puff Ftbl; Hon Roll; Westmoreland CC; Nrsng.

INGRAM, CHRISTOPHER; Washington HS; Washington, PA; (4); 9/173; Band; Jazz Band; Mrchg Band; Symp Band; High Hon Roll; JP Sousa Awd; NHS; Pres Schlr; Math Tm; Spanish Clb; State Jazz Band 2nd In Trombone In State 87; Richard A Byrd Schlrshp Acad Hnrs 87; PMEA Ensmble 85-87; U Of Cincinnati; Jazz.

INGRAM, JIMMIE; Harrisburg HS John Harris Campus; Harrisburg, PA; (3); 66/274; Boys Clb Am; Cmnty Wkr; FBLA; JA; Library Aide; Varsity Clb; Var Ftbl; Var Wt Lftg; Cit Awd; High Hon Roll; Ftbl MVP Offnsv Plyr 86; Boston Coll; Comp Sci.

INGRAM, MICHAEL; St Marys Area HS; Weedville, PA; (4); Am Leg Boys St; Boy Scts; Var L Ftbl; Var L Trk; Var L Wrstlng; Hon Roll; NHS; Bennetts Vly Alumni Schlrshp 87; Alfred U; Ceramic Engrng.

INGRAM, PAM; Seneca Valley HS; Mars, PA; (4); 80/360; Art Clb; Hosp Aide; Ski Clb; Stage Crew; Sec Stu Cncl; Var L Cheerleading; Hon Roll; U Of Pgh; Phys Thrpy.

INGRAM, YVETTE; Bellefonte SR HS; Bellefonte, PA; (3); Rep Frsh Cls; Rep Soph Cls; Var Pres Stu Cncl; Hon Roll; Stu Athl Trainer; Schl Bd Rep; Sports Med.

INGRASSIA, RALPH; Delaware Valley HS; Shohola, PA; (3); 12/158; Boy Scts; Drama Clb; Ski Clb; Band; Concert Band; Jazz Band; School Musical; School Play; Stage Crew; JV Crs Cntry; Aerospc Engr.

INMAN, DOUGLAS; Parkland HS; Allentown, PA; (2); Church Yth Grp; Stage Crew; Var Ftbl; Wt Lftg; Kutztown.

INMAN, DRUE; West Side Tech; Hunlock Creek, PA; (2); Chess Clb; Band; High Hon Roll; Hon Roll.

INMAN, SHARON; Academy HS; Erie, PA; (3); 13/226; Church Yth Grp; German Clb; Concert Band; Mrchg Band; Orch; Hon Roll; NHS; Mc Donalds All Erie Cnty Mrchng Band 85-87; Flute Sec Ldr Acad Mrchng Band 86-87; Dent Hygn.

INNAMORATI, ANNMARIE; Wyoming Valley West HS; Forty Ft, PA; (3); Church Yth Grp; Letterman Clb; Library Aide; Ski Clb; Rep Frsh Cls; Rep Soph Cls; Rep Jr Cls; Score Keeper; Var Tennis; Hon Roll; Coachs Awd Ten 86; Fordham; Atty.

INSALACA, SARINA; Notre Dame HS; Easton, PA; (2); Pep Clb; Chorus; Yrbk Phtg; Yrbk Stf; VP Jr Cls; Var Cheerleading; Var Trk; Counslng.

INSKIPT, JAMES; West Allegheny HS; Oakdale, PA; (3); Boy Scts; Drama Clb; Band; Chorus; Concert Band; Drm Mjr(t); Jazz Band; Mrchg Band; School Play; Stage Crew; Psych.

IOLI, MARK; Central Catholic HS; Pittsburgh, PA; (3); 78/225; Hon Roll; Comp Sci.

IONADI, DEOBRAH; Peabody HS; Pittsburgh, PA; (4); 3/292; DECA; Library Aide; Office Aide; Sec Soph Cls; Sec Sr Cls; High Hon Roll; NHS; All Amer Schlr Awd 86.

IONNI, JULIE; Central Dauphin HS; Harrisburg, PA; (2); Key Clb; Model UN; Ski Clb; Chorus; Nwsp Rptr; Nwsp Stf; Yrbk Sprt Ed; Yrbk Stf; Cheerleading; Tennis; Bst Prsnlty Awd 85; Vrsty Ltr Tennis, Trck, Chrldng 85 & 86; Hmrm Rep Stu Cncl 85 & 86; Commnctns.

IOZZI, NICK; Penn Hills SR HS; Verona, PA; (3); Im Ftbl; Im Wrstlng; Hon Roll; Finance.

IRANI, JENNIFER; Central Bucks East HS; Warrington, PA; (4); Church Yth Grp; Ski Clb; Chorus; Church Choir; Lit Mag; JV Fld Hcky; Mgr(s); Hon Roll; Jr NHS; Excell Musicianship Awd 84; U Of DE; Lib Arts.

IRELAND, KRISTA; Fairview HS; Erie, PA; (3); Q&S; Ski Clb; Varsity Clb; Nwsp Sprt Ed; Rep Soph Cls; Var L Sftbl; L Tennis; Hon Roll; Hnrbl Mntn 2nd Tm All Cnty Sftbll 85; Bus Admin.

IRETON, ALLISON; Villa Maria Acad; Devon, PA; (3); 16/100; Debate Tm; GAA; NFL; Speech Tm; SADD; Lcrss; Mgr(s); Hon Roll; NHS; 2nd Plc Dbt PCFL Trnmnt 85-86; Jffrsn Frm C-D Dbts 1st Plc 87; Finance.

IRIZARRY, CHRISTINA; Middletown Area HS; Middletown, PA; (3); 26/193; Key Clb; Var Cheerleading; Hon Roll; Physcl Ther.

IRONS, KAREN; Linesville HS; Linesville, PA; (2); 21/55; Cmnty Wkr; Computer Clb; FBLA; FNA; FTA; Math Clb; Office Aide; OEA; Political Wkr; SADD; Soc Wrkr.

IRONS, TRACY; Hopewell SR HS; Aliquippa, PA; (4); 58/245; Boys Clb Am; Church Yth Grp; Spanish Clb; SADD; Chorus; Church Choir; School Musical; Stage Crew; Sftbl; Hon Roll; Shadyside Hosp Schl Nrsng; Nrsn.

IRVIN, DOUGLAS; Bishop Guilfoyle HS; Hollidaysburg, PA; (3); 4-H; Bsktbl; Ftbl; Bus.

IRVIN, HEATHER; Glendale JR SR HS; Irvona, PA; (2); Art Clb; Drama Clb; Science Clb; SADD; Concert Band; Mrchg Band; Nwsp Rptr; Powder Puff Ftbl; Sftbl; Hon Roll; Pittsburgh Art Inst; Intr Dsgnr.

IRVIN, SCOTT; Arch Bishop Wood HS; Doylestown, PA; (2); Swmmng; Wt Lftg; Penn State; Naval Avaitor.

IRVIN, TY; Lower Dauphin HS; Palmyra, PA; (3); Boy Scts; Church Yth Grp; Computer Clb; Off Stu Cncl; Hon Roll; Prfct Atten Awd; Eagle Sct 87; Drexel; Elec Engrng.

IRVINE, PAM; North Clarion HS; Lucinda, PA; (3); Art Clb; French Clb; Varsity Clb; Flag Corp; School Musical; Var L Cheerleading; Trk; Hon Roll; Soc Work.

IRWIN, CARMELLA; Blairsville SR HS; Torrance, PA; (3); Chess Clb; Cmnty Wkr; Debate Tm; Hosp Aide; VICA; Chorus; School Play; Bowling; Swmmng; Prfct Atten Awd; Phys Ftns Awd; Pittsburg Beauty Acad; Nrsng.

IRWIN III, JAMES; Lincoln HS; New Castle, PA; (3); 8/162; German Clb; Radio Clb; Ski Clb; Band; School Musical; High Hon Roll; NHS; Ntl Merit SF; VFW Awd; AFS; Bus.

IRWIN JR, JEFFERY; Warren Area HS; Warren, PA; (4); 58/300; Church Yth Grp; French Clb; Bsbl; Bowling; High Hon Roll; Hon Roll; Jamestown CC; Bus Mgmt.

IRWIN, JENNIFER LINNEA; Somerset Area SR HS; Somerset, PA; (3); 62/231; CAP; English Clb; JA; NFL; Sec Spanish Clb; Chorus; Church Choir; Orch; Hon Roll; NHS; Acad Spanish Awd Outstndng Underclssmn 85-86; 1st Prose Catagorie Forensics 86-87; Spanish.

IRWIN, JILL; Palmyra Area SR HS; Annville, PA; (4); 79/187; Church Yth Grp; French Clb; Spanish Clb; SADD; Teachers Aide; Chorus; Stat Wrstlng; Hon Roll; Messiah Coll.

IRWIN, TODD; Northern SR HS; Dillsburg, PA; (3); 40/255; Ski Clb; Socr; Tennis; Hon Roll; Aerospc Engrng.

ISAAC, KRISTIN; Wilson Area HS; Easton, PA; (4); 12/127; Pres Sr Cls; Sec Stu Cncl; Var Capt Bsktbl; Var Capt Fld Hcky; Var Capt Sftbl; High Hon Roll; Hon Roll; Jr NHS; Estn Exchng Clb Stu Of Mnth 86; Sftbl MVP 86; Muhlenberg Coll; Premed.

ISAAC, ROBERT; Shenango JR-SR HS; New Castle, PA; (2); 3/140; Church Yth Grp; Sec Trs Spanish Clb; Concert Band; Mrchg Band; Pep Band; Golf; God Cntry Awd; High Hon Roll; Jr NHS; PA Keystone Bwl Undef Equatns & Onsets Acdmc Gms 85; Med.

ISAACS, SARAH; Towanda HS; Towanda, PA; (3); Church Yth Grp; FBLA; FHA; Variety Show; Yng Wmns Medln 87; Semnry Cert 87; 13th Annl Bus Educ Sympsm Wmspt Coll 87; Htl Mgmt.

ISAMAN, ANNETTE; Port Allegany HS; Perry, NY; (4); Camera Clb; Church Yth Grp; Computer Clb; Drama Clb; FHA; FTA; Math Tm; Red Cross Aide; Chorus; School Play; Alfred ST Coll; RN.

ISENBERG, ALEXIS; Shikellamy HS; Sunbury, PA; (1); 1/325; Trs Frsh Cls; Rep Stu Cncl; JV Cheerleading; High Hon Roll; Hon Roll; Jr NHS; Outstndng Girl Amer Lgn 85-86; Bucknell; Chem Engr.

ISENBERG, JULIE; Huntingdon Area HS; Huntingdon, PA; (3); Pres Church Yth Grp; Key Clb; Pres Soroptimist; Yrbk Stf; High Hon Roll; Hon Roll; NHS; Ntl Merit Ltr; NEDT Awd; Prfct Atten Awd; Psychtry.

ISENBERG, THOMAS L; Shikellamy HS; Sunbury, PA; (3); 8/312; Am Leg Boys St; VP Frsh Cls; VP Soph Cls; VP Jr Cls; VP Sr Cls; Rep Stu Cncl; JV Var Bsktbl; JV Ftbl; JV Golf; JV Var Tennis; Schl Board Rep; Villanova; Engrng.

ISHLER, BETH; State College Intermed; Julian, PA; (1); Hosp Aide; Ski Clb; Concert Band; Drm Mjr(t); Var Mgr(s); Twrlr; Hon Roll; PA ST U; Med Lab Tech.

ISHMAN, CHRISTINE; Du Bois Area SR HS; Reynoldsville, PA; (4); Band; Chorus; Church Choir; Concert Band; Drm Mjr(t); Mrchg Band; School Musical; Swing Chorus; Hon Roll; Natl Chrl Awd; ICM Schl Bus; Trvl.

ISKRA, LAURA; Pittston Area HS; Pt Blanchard, PA; (2); 35/240; Aud/Vis; French Clb; Key Clb; High Hon Roll; Hon Roll; NHS; Legl Prfssn.

ISOM, JANAI E; Harrisburg HS; Harrisburg, PA; (3); #38 In Class; Pep Clb; Band; Church Choir; Mrchg Band; Rep Stu Cncl; Var Bsbl; Var Bsktbl; Var Twrlr; Hon Roll; Prfct Atten Awd; Ms Jabberwock 86; Acadmc All Amer 87; 3rd Pl Black Hist Cntst 87; Hampton U; Tele Comm.

ISOM, JEMIR; Harrisburg HS; Harrisburg, PA; (3); 7/305; Church Choir; Mrchg Band; Var Bsktbl; Var Fld Hcky; Capt Twrlr; Hon Roll; NHS; Comp Tech.

ISOVITSCH, LEANN; Knoch HS; Butler, PA; (2); Church Yth Grp; FBLA; Chorus; Church Choir; Yrbk Stf; Co-Capt Twrlr; Hon Roll; Prfct Atten Awd; Bus Mgmt.

ISRAEL, JAMES; Butler HS; Lyndora, PA; (3); Boy Scts; Chess Clb; French Clb; JA; Band; Concert Band; Mrchg Band; Nwsp Stf; Im Ftbl; Hon Roll; Eng Tchr.

ISWALT, KATHLEEN; Pottstown SR HS; Pottstown, PA; (3); Concert Band; Mrchg Band; Ed Nwsp Rptr; Trs Jr Cls; Stu Cncl; High Hon Roll; NHS; Band; Jazz Band; School Musical; Anchr Clb VP & Pres 86-88; Dist Band 86-87; Acctg.

ITALIA, JOHN; Center Area HS; Monaca, PA; (2); Computer Clb; Pres Latin Clb; Letterman Clb; Varsity Clb; Rep Stu Cncl; Im Bowling; Var L Golf; High Hon Roll; Schlr Ath Beaver Cnty Times 85-86; Allegheny Singer Rsrch Comp 86; Dntstry.

ITALIANO, STEPHEN; Lincoln HS; Ellwood City, PA; (3); Spanish Clb; Pres Frsh Cls; Pres Rep Stu Cncl; Var L Bsbl; Bsktbl; Trk; Hon Roll; Syracuse U; Engineering.

ITLE, MARGARET; Trinity HS; Lewisberry, PA; (3); Church Yth Grp; Rptr VP 4-H; Political Wkr; Red Cross Aide; Spanish Clb; Drill Tm; JV Bsktbl; Var Trk; 4-H Awd; Equine Mgmt.

ITSKOWITZ, AMY; Hillel Acad; Pittsburgh, PA; (4); Hosp Aide; Temple Yth Grp; Chorus; Yrbk Ed-Chief; Rep Badmtn; Bsktbl; Vllybl; High Hon Roll; NHS; Yeshiva U; Lawyer.

ITSKOWITZ, MARC; Hillel Acad Of Pttsbrgh; Pittsburgh, PA; (1); Rep Stu Cncl; Var Bsktbl; Var Ftbl; Var Sftbl; High Hon Roll; PA JR Acad Sci 87; Med.

IVAN, MICHELLE; West Mifflin Area HS; Pittsburgh, PA; (4); Church Yth Grp; Ski Clb; Orch; Rep Soph Cls; Rep Stu Cncl; Im Sftbl; High Hon Roll; Hon Roll; NHS; Awd From US Acvhmnt Acad 86; Acad Schlrshp From Mercyhurst Coll 87; Mercyhurst Coll.

IVASKA, JENNIFER; West Mifflin Area HS; W Mifflin, PA; (3); Exploring; FBLA; Off Jr Cls; High Hon Roll; Hon Roll; Jr NHS; NHS; FTA; Office Aide; Off Soph Cls; Hlth.

IVCIC, JULIE; West Allegheny HS; Oakdale, PA; (4); 1/200; Math Tm; Drill Tm; Sec Frsh Cls; Pres Jr Cls; Pres Sr Cls; Trs Stu Cncl; Var Trk; High Hon Roll; NHS; Voice Dem Awd; Eng Awd 87; Soc Studies Awd 87; Century II Ldrshp Awd 87; Penn ST; Acctng.

IVES, JEFF; Mechanicsburg Area SR HS; Mechanicsburg, PA; (4); 3/303; Church Yth Grp; Yrbk Stf; Pres Frsh Cls; Pres Soph Cls; Pres Jr Cls; Pres Stu Cncl; Var Capt Socr; DAR Awd; NHS; Rotary Awd; Haverford Coll; Econ.

IVEY, JENNIFER; Central Bucks East HS; Doylestown, PA; (3); Cmnty Wkr; Concert Band; Mrchg Band; Mgr(s); Var Sftbl.

IVEY, PATRICIA; Northern York County HS; Dillsburg, PA; (3); 13/232; Band; Concert Band; Mrchg Band; School Musical; Stage Crew; Stat Bsktbl; High Hon Roll; Tri-M Music Hnr Soc Trea 87-88; Prom Cmmtte 86-87; Actrl Sci.

IVINS, LISA; Bensalem HS; Bensalem, PA; (3); Church Yth Grp; Dance Clb; Key Clb; Office Aide; Church Choir; Var Cheerleading; Hon Roll; Prfct Atten Awd; Animal Tech.

IVORY, HEATHER; Cambria Heights HS; Ashville, PA; (3); 22/183; Ski Clb; Chorus; L Var Bsktbl; VP L Trk; Hon Roll; NHS.

IWANCIW, NATALIE; Phoenixville Area HS; Phoenixville, PA; (2); Spanish Clb; Hon Roll; Prfct Atten Awd; Lawyer.

IZZO, CELESTE; Connellsville HS; Dunbar, PA; (3); 40/550; Sec Aud/Vis; Band; Chorus; Concert Band; Mrchg Band; School Musical; Rep Frsh Cls; Pres Soph Cls; Pres Jr Cls; Rep Stu Cncl; Miss Natl Teenger Essy Wnnr 85; Miss Westrn PA ST Fnlst 85; Miss Amer Coed ST Fnlst 86; CA U Of PA; Ed.

IZZO, TRICIA; Ellwood City Lincoln HS; Ellwood City, PA; (4); 95/165; French Clb; L Key Clb; Ski Clb; Spanish Clb; L Y-Teens; Chorus; Im JV Cheerleading; Powder Puff Ftbl; Sftbl; Hon Roll; SR Srvc Awd 87; Acdmc Achvt Awds 83 & 84; Slippery Rock U; Corrctv Thrpy.

JABARA, ROBBI; Greensburg-Salem HS; Greensburg, PA; (4); 57/261; Drama Clb; Pep Clb; Ski Clb; VP Spanish Clb; School Play; Variety Show; Bsktbl; Mat Maids; Sftbl; Trk; Kent ST; Zoology.

JABCO, LISA; Bellefonte Area HS; Pleasant Gap, PA; (3); Church Yth Grp; Band; Chorus; Church Choir; Concert Band; Mrchg Band; Off Stu Cncl; Hon Roll; South Hills Bus Schl.

JABLONSKI, CHRISTINA; Du Bois Area HS; Dubois, PA; (3); 15/324; Varsity Clb; Trk; Hon Roll; Pres NHS; Lawyer.

JABLONSKI, DANA; South Side HS; Hookstown, PA; (3); Church Yth Grp; Band; JV Ftbl; JV Trk; JV Wrstlng; High Hon Roll; Hon Roll.

JABLONSKI, LINDA L; Technical HS; Scranton, PA; (4); 1/195; FBLA; Letterman Clb; Scholastic Bowl; Nwsp Ed-Chief; Yrbk Ed-Chief; VP Stu Cncl; Pres NHS; Val; Q&S; L Sftbl; Pres Schlrshp 87; Marywood Coll; Bio.

JABLONSKI, LYNN; John S Fine HS; Nanticoke, PA; (3); 7/250; NHS.

JACAVAGE, MICHELLE; Shenandoah Valley JR SR HS; Shenandoah, PA; (3); 20/80; Nwsp Stf; Yrbk Stf; Hst Sr Cls; Var Capt Bsktbl; Var L Trk; Var Capt Vllybl; Hon Roll; Acad All-Amer 85-87.

JACHIMOWICZ, DIANE; Lake-Lehman HS; Shavertown, PA; (4); 20/152; School Play; Lit Mag; Capt L Bsktbl; JV Fld Hcky; Stat Sftbl; Stat Vllybl; Hon Roll; Millersville U Of PA; Psych.

JACINTO, LUIS; Bethlehem Catholic HS; Bethlehem, PA; (3); Hon Roll; Northampton CC.

JACK, SCOTT; Butler Area HS; Butler, PA; (2); Trs Church Yth Grp; ROTC; Spanish Clb; Hon Roll; Masonic Awd.

JACK, TODD; Allegheny-Clarion Valley HS; Lamartine, PA; (4); Aud/Vis; Boy Scts; Church Yth Grp; 4-H; Ftbl; Eagle Scout Awd 87; Triangle-Tech; Comp Ad Drftng.

JACK, TROY; Highlands SR HS; Natrona Hts, PA; (4); 19/275; Art Clb; Intnl Clb; NHS; Pres Schlr; PA ST U; Bio.

JACK III, WILLIAM H; Solanco HS; Kirkwood, PA; (3); Boy Scts; Computer Clb; Ski Clb; Teachers Aide; Varsity Clb; Co-Capt Var Socr; JV Trk; Vllybl; Capt Var Wrstlng; Hon Roll; Bus Law.

JACKAL, YVONNE; Sharpsville HS; Sharpsville, PA; (3); Sec Camera Clb; Chess Clb; Library Aide; Chorus; Nwsp Stf; Pres Soph Cls; Pres Stu Cncl; Var JV Cheerleading; Dnfth Awd; Hon Roll; TODD Sqd TODDS Chldrns Hosp; Elem Ed.

JACKMAN, MIKE; St John Neumann HS; Philadelphia, PA; (3); 22/349; Boy Scts; Church Yth Grp; Letterman Clb; Varsity Clb; Yrbk Stf; Sec Sr Cls; Bsbl; Ftbl; Socr; High Hon Roll; US Naval Acad; Mech Engrng.

JACKOWIAK, FRANK; Mahanoy Area HS; Gilberton, PA; (2); Church Yth Grp; Library Aide; Rep Soph Cls; Rep Stu Cncl; Ftbl; Stu Cncl Awd 87; Lbrry Awd 86-87; Electrncs.

JACKOWITZ, STEPHANIE; Mid-Valley HS; Olyphant, PA; (3); Rep Frsh Cls; Trs Soph Cls; VP Jr Cls; Rep Stu Cncl; Var Cheerleading; Var Crs Cntry; Var Sftbl; Vllybl; Hon Roll; Cert Of Merit Math & Sci 86; Fnlst All Amer Chrldr 86; Excptnl Knwldg Current Events In NE 86; Pltcl Sci.

JACKOWSKI, KAREN; Elizabeth Forward HS; Mc Keesport, PA; (3); French Clb; Office Aide; Chorus; Im Badmtn; Stat Bsktbl; Score Keeper; U Pittsburgh; Psych.

JACKSON, ALICE; Waynesboro SR HS; Waynesboro, PA; (3); Hosp Aide; Pep Clb; Yrbk Stf; Rep Stu Cncl; Stat Bsktbl; Im Cheerleading; Mgr(s); Cit Awd; Admin Sec.

JACKSON, AUDREY; Upper Merion Area HS; King Of Prussia, PA; (4); 95/290; Pres DECA; Var Powder Puff Ftbl; Var Sftbl; King Prussia Prof Bus Womens Clb Grl Of The Mnth 86; Katherine Gibbs; Sec.

JACKSON, BRENT; Port Allegany HS; Port Allegany, PA; (3); 3/115; Spanish Clb; SADD; JV Var Bsktbl; L Trk; High Hon Roll; Hon Roll; L Trk; High Hon Roll; Hon Roll; VP NHS; Elec Engr.

JACKSON, CANDI; Oil City Area Senior HS; Oil City, PA; (3); Church Yth Grp; Debate Tm; German Clb; Library Aide; Y-Teens; Band; Chorus; Church Choir; Yrbk Stf; Hon Roll; Psych.

JACKSON, CHRISTINE; Mast Baum AVTS HS; Philadelphia, PA; (2); Church Yth Grp; Var JV Bowling; UCLA; Accntnt.

JACKSON, CLINT; Freeport Area SR HS; Sarver, PA; (3); 1/200; Mrchg Band; Pep Band; School Musical; Symp Band; High Hon Roll; PA Gvrnrs Schl Sci 85; Marien Bio Quest 85; Carnegie-Mellon U; Psych.

JACKSON, ERICA; Hempfield Area SR HS; Greensburg, PA; (3); Letterman Clb; Yrbk Stf; Var L Crs Cntry; Var L Trk; High Hon Roll; Jr NHS; NHS; Sprts Med.

JACKSON, EVERETT D; Rochester JR-SR HS; Rochester, PA; (3); Am Leg Boys St; Office Aide; Teachers Aide; Var L Ftbl; L Mgr(s); JV Tennis; Var L Trk; Hon Roll; VFW Awd; Voice Dem Awd; Boys Nation 87; Elem Ed.

JACKSON, JANELL E; Penncrest HS; Media, PA; (4); Church Yth Grp; Library Aide; NAACP; Variety Show; Stat Bsktbl; Trk; 2nd Wnnr NAACP ST Essay Cntst 86; Hampton U; Spch Path.

JACKSON, JANET; Saltsburg JR SR HS; Saltsburg, PA; (4); 5/90; Church Yth Grp; Cmnty Wkr; Library Aide; ROTC; SADD; School Play; Variety Show; Ed Lit Mag; Bsktbl; Powder Puff Ftbl; GA Inst Tech; Psych.

JACKSON, JENNIFER; Ridgway Area HS; Ridgway, PA; (4); 6/105; Ski Clb; Nwsp Stf; Rep Stu Cncl; Cheerleading; High Hon Roll; Hon Roll; IN U Of PA; Med Tech.

JACKSON, JENNIFER CLAIRE; North Allegheny SR HS; Pittsburgh, PA; (3); AFS; Girl Scts; Political Wkr; Band; Pep Band; Swing Chorus; Yrbk Phtg; JV Vllybl; Jr NHS; NHS; Intl Rel.

JACKSON, JILL; Moon SR HS; Coraopolis, PA; (3); 27/309; Church Yth Grp; Hst French Clb; Chorus; School Musical; JV Cheerleading; Hon Roll; NHS; Dance Clb; Am Lgn Awd 84; Ctznshp Awd 84; Chatham Coll; Dance.

JACKSON, JOHN; Bethlehem Center HS; Brownsville, PA; (3); Boy Scts; Drama Clb; Exploring; Political Wkr; Band; Concert Band; Mrchg Band; School Play; Wshngtn Cnty Band 86-87; Yth Trffc Sfty Cncl 86-87.

JACKSON, JUANITA; Bodine HS For Intl Affairs; Philadelphia, PA; (3); 2/100; Library Aide; Varsity Clb; Var Bsktbl; Var Sftbl; Hon Roll; Jr NHS; Prfct Atten Awd; Erth Sci Awd 85; Awd Excllnc PA Sci Olympd 85; Anthrplgst.

JACKSON, JULIE; Mechanicsburg SR HS; Shiremanstown, PA; (3); 9/338; Debate Tm; Concert Band; Mrchg Band; Yrbk Stf; High Hon Roll; NHS; Washngtn Wrkshps 86; Law.

JACKSON, KAREN; Meadville HS; Meadville, PA; (3); 38/363; Letterman Clb; Varsity Clb; Rep Frsh Cls; Rep Soph Cls; Rep Jr Cls; Var L Swmmng; Var L Tennis; Stu Cncl; Hon Roll.

JACKSON, KEITH; HS Of Engineering & Sci; Philadelphia, PA; (4); 14/212; Church Yth Grp; JA; Ftbl; High Hon Roll; Hon Roll; NHS; Pres Schlr; U Of Pittsburgh Engr Impact Awd 87; Wayland Temple Bapt Chrch Schlrshp 86-87; U Of Pittsburgh; Mat Sci Engr.

JACKSON, KELLY; York Catholic HS; Dover, PA; (3); Pres Church Yth Grp; Latin Clb; Spanish Clb; Varsity Clb; Nwsp Stf; Rep Soph Cls; Rep Jr Cls; Rep Sr Cls; Var Bsktbl; Hon Roll; Clgt Miss Schlrshp Pgnt 88; U Ptsbrg; Physcl Thrpy.

JACKSON, KIMBERLY; Quaker Valley SR HS; Sewickley, PA; (3); Church Yth Grp; Dance Clb; Drama Clb; Latin Clb; Chorus; School Musical; High Hon Roll; Northwestern; Pre-Med.

JACKSON, KIMBERLY G; Hampton HS; Allison Park, PA; (4); 11/255; High Hon Roll; NHS; Ntl Merit SF; Wnnr Carnegiw Awd Solo Comptn 84-85; Wnnr Pittsbrgh Cncrt Soc Yng Artst Comptn 85; III USA Intl Bllt; Eastman Schl Music; Cellist.

JACKSON, LISA; Fort Cherry JR SR HS; Mcdonald, PA; (2); Church Yth Grp; French Clb; Math Clb; Chorus; Church Choir; Hon Roll; Secr.

JACKSON, LISA D; Creative & Performing Arts HS; Philadelphia, PA; (4); 43/136; Office Aide; Nwsp Ed-Chief; Voice Dem Awd; Private Industry Cncl Incentive Awd 86; West Chester U; Poltcl Sci.

JACKSON, LORI A; Moravian Acad; Reading, PA; (4); 7/67; Key Clb; Chorus; School Musical; Nwsp Stf; Yrbk Ed-Chief; Rep Stu Cncl; JV Crs Cntry; Var Fld Hcky; JV Lcrss; High Hon Roll; In Top 6th Percentile Yng Black Achievers 86-87; Cum Laude Soc 85-87; Brown Univ; Psych.

JACKSON, MARY; HS Of Engineering And Science; Philadelphia, PA; (3); 22/241; VP Church Yth Grp; Cmnty Wkr; SADD; Church Choir; Yrbk Stf; Hon Roll; NHS; Hnrs Prgrm & 1 Yr Schlrshp; Spelman Coll; Med.

JACKSON, MEREDITH L; HS Of Engineering & Science; Philadelphia, PA; (4); 32/220; Church Yth Grp; Church Choir; Cmnty Wkr; Quiz Bowl; Rep Frsh Cls; Rep Soph Cls; Rep Jr Cls; Var Bsktbl; Drexel U; Arch Engrng.

JACKSON, MIA P; Westinghouse HS; Pittsburgh, PA; (4); 9/221; Band; Concert Band; Jazz Band; Mrchg Band; Off Sr Cls; Swmmng; Hon Roll; All Cty Sr Hons Band 86-87; Bus & Fin Acad 84-87; Cntrs Musclly Tintd 83-85; Delaware ST Coll; Tchng Ed.

JACKSON, MICHAEL; St Marys HS Seminary; Jackson, GA; (2); 5/9; Ski Clb; School Play; Nwsp Stf; Sec Soph Cls; Var Socr; Var Sftbl.

JACKSON, MICHELLE; Edward Bok AVT HS; Philadelphia, PA; (3); FNA; Red Cross Aide; Yrbk Stf; Pep Clb; Nrsng.

JACKSON, SHARITA; West Phila Catholic Girls HS; Philadelphia, PA; (3); 37/248; VP Church Yth Grp; Hosp Aide; Intnl Clb; Office Aide; Chorus; Church Choir; Capt Vllybl; High Hon Roll; Hon Roll; Prfct Atten Awd; Intl Training Comm Spch Contst 87; Hi-Avg Geom Awd 86; Hi-Avg Latin Awd 87; Spelman Coll; Resrch Law.

JACKSON, SHELBY; Central HS; Philadelphia, PA; (2); Computer Clb; Var Trk; JV Vllybl; Hon Roll; Columbia U.

JACKSON, SUSAN; S Allegheny JR SR HS; Liberty Boro, PA; (3); 4/187; VP German Clb; Scholastic Bowl; Y-Teens; Concert Band; Mrchg Band; Pep Band; School Musical; Yrbk Sprt Ed; Off Jr Cls; Hon Roll; Elem Educ.

JACKSON, SUSANNA; Richland HS; Gibsonia, PA; (3); Church Yth Grp; Drama Clb; NFL; Chorus; School Musical; Swing Chorus; Nwsp Rptr; Trk; Hon Roll; Publctn Amer Poetry Annology 85; Super Rtng Pgh Piano Tchrs Recital Awds 85-86; U Of CA Brkley; Music.

JACKSON, TIA; William Penn SR HS; York, PA; (3); Church Yth Grp; JA; Mrchg Band; JV Bsktbl; Twrlr; Hon Roll; Penn ST; Acctg.

JACKSON, TRACY; Pennsbury HS; Levittown, PA; (4); 57/777; Rep Frsh Cls; Rep Soph Cls; Rep Jr Cls; Rep Stu Cncl; Hon Roll; Presdntl Acadc Awd 87; Boston U; Communications.

JACKSON, TRICIA; Kiski Area HS; Apollo, PA; (2); FBLA; Pep Clb; Teachers Aide; Rep Frsh Cls; Trs Soph Cls; Capt JV Cheerleading; Fashn Merchdsng.

JACKSON, VERNISE; Bok AVT; Philadelphia, PA; (3); FNA; Red Cross Aide; Stage Crew; Yrbk Stf; Vllybl; Nrsng.

JACOB, ELIZABETH ANN; Somerset Area SR HS; Somerset, PA; (4); 36/232; English Clb; JA; Pep Clb; Varsity Clb; Chorus; Orch; School Play; L Cheerleading; Im Swmmng; L Tennis; St Vincent Coll.

JACOB, LARRY; Emmaus HS; Macungie, PA; (4); 147/473; Ski Clb; Band; Concert Band; Jazz Band; Mrchg Band; Pep Band; Bsbl; PA ST Behrend Campus; Engrng.

JACOB, MATTHEW; Butler HS; Butler, PA; (3); Church Yth Grp; Cmnty Wkr; BHS Rfl Tm-Ltr 87; Edinboro U; Crmnl Jstc.

JACOB, RANDALL; Hempfield HS; Irwin, PA; (4); Band; Concert Band; Jazz Band; Mrchg Band; Pep Band; Symp Band; High Hon Roll; Hon Roll; Music Excllnc Awd 84; Penn ST U; Bus Mgmt.

JACOB, WILLIAM; Central Catholic HS; Pittsburgh, PA; (3); 14/256; FBLA; German Clb; Letterman Clb; Math Tm; Varsity Clb; Wrstlng; High Hon Roll; Hon Roll; NHS; Carnegie Mellon; Mech Engr.

JACOBETZ, DIANNE; Wilson Christian Acad; Mckeesport, PA; (3); Art Clb; Var Bsktbl; Swmmng; Vllybl; High Hon Roll; Hon Roll; NHS; Prfct Atten Awd; Athletic Awd Bsktbll Mst Dedctd 85-86.

JACOBS, ANDREW MARC; Abington SR HS; Rydal, PA; (3); Red Cross Aide; Chorus; Madrigals; School Musical; School Play; High Hon Roll; NHS; Ntl Merit Ltr; P T Gantt Awd-Bst Male Actor 86 & 87; European Hstry Awd 87; Thtr.

JACOBS, CHERYL; Harry S Truman HS; Levittown, PA; (3); Hon Roll; Prfct Atten Awd; Voltr Certfct Wrk Bucks Cnty Spcl Olymcs 83-87; Psychlgy.

JACOBS, DONNA; Yough HS; Irwin, PA; (3); FBLA; Ski Clb; Band; Chorus; Church Choir; Concert Band; Jazz Band; Mrchg Band; High Hon Roll; Ntl Merit Schol; Acad All Amer 87; Bradford Schl Of Bus; Exec Sec.

JACOBS, DOUG; Daniel Boone HS; Douglassville, PA; (3); 21/179; German Clb; Letterman Clb; Yrbk Stf; Crs Cntry; Trk; Wrstlng; Rotary Awd; Attnd Hugh O Brian Smnr 86-87; UCLA; Biochem.

JACOBS, HOLLY LYNN; South Allegheny HS; Port Vue, PA; (3); 68/178; Church Yth Grp; French Clb; VP FNA; Library Aide; Teachers Aide; Y-Teens; Chorus; Color Guard; Yrbk Stf; Capt Powder Puff Ftbl; Psych.

JACOBS, IAN G; High Schl For Engineering And Science; Philadelphia, PA; (4); Model UN; Nwsp Rptr; Rep Frsh Cls; Pres Soph Cls; Pres Jr Cls; Rep Sr Cls; Hon Roll; Ntl Merit SF; Drama Clb; Intnl Clb; Pres, Crrspndng Secy Wrld Affrs Cncl Philadlphia Steerng Cmmtte 86; Stu Prgrssv Action 83-86; Jrnlsm.

JACOBS, JEFFREY; Wyoming Area HS; West Pittston, PA; (3); 95/250; Boy Scts; Church Yth Grp; JV Var Bsktbl; Penn ST; Bus.

JACOBS, JOHN; Downingtown HS; Downington, PA; (3); Im Bowling; Hon Roll; Accntng.

JACOBS, JOHN; Shady Side Acad; Glenshaw, PA; (4); Ftbl; Trk; Wt Lftg; Hon Roll; Vanderbilt U; Engr.

JACOBS, KATHLEEN; Shaler Area HS; Glenshaw, PA; (4); SADD; Drill Tm; Co-Capt Swmmng; Hon Roll; Mst Outstndng Female Ath; Loylaty Awd Swim; U Pittsburgh; Early Chldhd Dev.

JACOBS, LEISEL; Elizabethtown Area HS; Mt Joy, PA; (3); Key Clb; Concert Band; Mrchg Band; Orch; Pep Band; Yrbk Phtg; Im Powder Puff Ftbl; Var Im Vllybl; Natl Sci Olymp Awd; Close-Up Pgm; Thomas Jefferson U; Phys Therpy.

JACOBS, M ELAINE; Indiana Area SR HS; Indiana, PA; (3); Drama Clb; French Clb; Orch; Nwsp Rptr; Socr; L Tennis; High Hon Roll; Hon Roll; Jr NHS; Sci.

JACOBS, ROBERT; West Scranton HS; Scranton, PA; (2); Hon Roll; Acctng.

JACOBS, STEPHEN; West Mifflin Area HS; W Mifflin, PA; (4); #23 In Class; Band; Concert Band; Mrchg Band; Orch; Hon Roll; Jr NHS; Pres Schlr; U Of Pittsbugh; Elect Engrng.

JACOBSON, LISA; Crestwood HS; Mountaintop, PA; (3); Mrchg Band; High Hon Roll; Hon Roll; Jr NHS; NHS; Nrs.

JACOBY, BONNIE; Hanover SR HS; Hanover, PA; (4); Varsity Clb; Var Capt Fld Hcky; High Hon Roll; Military; Nrs.

JACOBY, CHANIN; Northampton SR HS; Northampton, PA; (3); 96/494; Dance Clb; Pep Clb; Ski Clb; SADD; Chorus; Rep Stu Cncl; Var Crs Cntry; Var Powder Puff Ftbl; Var Swmmng; Var Trk.

JACOBY, HEIDI; Hamburg Area HS; Hamburg, PA; (3); Library Aide; Ski Clb; Spanish Clb; Yrbk Ed-Chief; Yrbk Stf; Stat Ftbl; High Hon Roll; NHS; Pres Acad Fit Awd 85; Fash Mrchndsng.

JACOBY, MISSY; Donegal HS; Mount Joy, PA; (2); Spanish Clb; Hon Roll; Hnr Roll 85-86; Travel.

JACOBY, MONICA; Northampton SR HS; Northampton, PA; (4); Office Aide; Chorus; Rep Soph Cls; Rep Jr Cls; Var Swmmng; High Hon Roll; Hon Roll; Schl Ltr Chorus 87; Bloomsburg; Nrsng.

JACOBY, PAMELA; Butler SR HS; Butler, PA; (3); Cmnty Wkr; French Clb; SADD; Thesps; Mrchg Band; Symp Band; Var L Tennis; Jr NHS; NHS; Allegheny Coll; Psych.

JACOBY, PAUL; Lower Merion HS; Merion, PA; (3); 2/320; Math Tm; Scholastic Bowl; Spanish Clb; Nwsp Rptr; Nwsp Sprt Ed; Yrbk Stf; Pres Frsh Cls; Pres Soph Cls; Off Jr Cls; Stu Cncl.

JACOBY, RICHARD; Hamburg Area HS; Hamburg, PA; (3); 61/181; French Clb; German Clb; Latin Clb; Ftbl; Wrstlng; God Cntry Awd; Hon Roll; HS Acadc Hnr 85-87; Med.

JACSON, KELLY; York Catholic HS; Dover, PA; (3); Pres Church Yth Grp; Latin Clb; Spanish Clb; Rep Stu Cncl; VP Bsktbl; Hon Roll; NHS; IVP; Crmnlgy.

JADIK, TAMARA; Abington Heights HS; Clarks Summit, PA; (2); 1/296; Trs 4-H; Ski Clb; Concert Band; Jazz Band; Mrchg Band; Yrbk Stf; Rep Stu Cncl; Hon Roll; Band; Chorus; 2nd Pl Amer HS Math Exm & Achvd Merit Rl, 2nd Area 4 A Exm Amer Chemcl Soc 87; Russian Olympiad 86.

JAFARI, MARYAM; Allentown Central Catholic HS; Allentown, PA; (4); 6/203; Exploring; Key Clb; Math Clb; Math Tm; Ski Clb; Yrbk Phtg; Tennis; High Hon Roll; Trs NHS; Pres Schlr; 2nd Pl-PA JR Acdmy Sci 85-86; Hghst Screr Math Exam 86-87; NYU; Sci.

JAFFE, FREDRIC; Cheltenham HS; Elkins Pk, PA; (3); 67/355; Y-Teens; Rep Frsh Cls; Rep Soph Cls; Var Ice Hcky; Var Tennis; Span Achvt Awd 85-86 & 86-87; Lawyer.

JAGERSKI, BETH A; Center HS; Aliquippa, PA; (4); 50/181; Church Yth Grp; German Clb; Band; Concert Band; Mrchg Band; School Musical; Rep Stu Cncl; Socr; Hon Roll; Prfct Atten Awd; German Clb Awd 86; IN U PA; Med Technlgy.

JAGGER, ANTHONY; Tunkhannock Area HS; Tunkhannock, PA; (2); 4/350; Spanish Clb; Hon Roll; Pres Schlr.

JAGGER, BRADLEY; Tunkannock Area HS; Tunkhannock, PA; (3); Ski Clb; Hon Roll; Culnry Arts.

JAHODA, HOLLY; Purchase Line HS; Clymer, PA; (2); 17/156; Church Yth Grp; Band; Concert Band; Trs Soph Cls; Stu Cncl; Bsktbl; Hon Roll; NEDT Awd; IUP; Hlth Fld.

JAKSCH, MARLA; Hempfield SR HS; Greensburg, PA; (3); Art Clb; Camera Clb; Church Yth Grp; French Clb; German Clb; GAA; Pep Clb; Ski Clb; Chorus; School Musical; PA Gvrnrs Schl Of The Arts; Art.

JAKUBETZ, JO ANNE; Canon Mc Millan HS; Canonsburg, PA; (4); 72/360; Capt Drill Tm; Nwsp Stf; Duquesne U; Phrmcy.

JAMAN, ANDREW; Solebury HS; Monroe, NY; (3); Chess Clb; Drama Clb; School Musical; School Play; Lit Mag; JV Bsktbl; Swmmng; High Hon Roll; Hon Roll; Prfct Atten Awd.

JAMANN, FREDERICK; Liberty HS; Bethlehem, PA; (4); 40/475; Cmnty Wkr; VP Computer Clb; Lit Mag; Hon Roll; Prfct Atten Awd; PA ST U; Engrng.

JAMES, AMY; Montour HS; Mckees Rocks, PA; (2); Mrchg Band; Symp Band; Yrbk Stf; Jr Cls; Vllybl; High Hon Roll; Hon Roll; OH ST; Aviation.

JAMES, CAROLYN; Lake-Lehman HS; Dallas, PA; (2); Church Yth Grp; Stu Cncl; Var L Bsktbl; Var L Fld Hcky; Trk; Hon Roll.

JAMES, CHRISTOPHER P; Hazletown HS; Drums, PA; (3).

JAMES, CLARK; Savcon Valley SR HS; Hellertown, PA; (4); 21/147; Ski Clb; Spanish Clb; Band; Concert Band; Jazz Band; Mrchg Band; Orch; Pep Band; School Play; Crs Cntry; Lehigh U; Pltcl Sci.

JAMES, JEFF; Carbondale Area JR SR HS; Carbondale, PA; (3); 13/119; German Clb; Ski Clb; Bsbl; Golf; High Hon Roll; Hon Roll; NHS.

JAMES, JONI; Bald Eagle-Nittany HS; Mill Hall, PA; (3); 36/148; French Clb; Varsity Clb; Var Capt Bsktbl; Score Keeper; PA Sprts Hall Fame 87; All Star Trnmnt Tm 85-86; W Brnch 3rd & 1st All Star Tm 85-86; Educ.

JAMES, LISA; Mid Valley HS; Olyphant, PA; (4); 1/130; DAR Awd; High Hon Roll; NHS; Sal; Rep Frsh Cls; Rep Soph Cls; Rep Jr Cls; Sec Rep Sr Cls; Stu Yr Awd 87; Engl Awd 87; Accntng Awd 87; Bloomsburg U; Bus Educ.

JAMES, LISA; Villa Maria Acad; Erie, PA; (3); SADD; Pres Frsh Cls; Pres Soph Cls; Pres Jr Cls; Pres Sr Cls; Var Crs Cntry; Capt Var Trk; Hon Roll; NHS; Psych.

JAMES, LORINE; Abington SR HS; Willow Grove, PA; (3); Gov Hon Prg Awd; High Hon Roll; Pres Schlr; Psych.

JAMES, WILLIAM; Maplewood HS; Guys Mills, PA; (3); Office Aide; Varsity Clb; Rep Frsh Cls; Rep Soph Cls; Rep Jr Cls; Rep Sr Cls; Rep Stu Cncl; Var L Ftbl; Var L Vllybl; Wt Lftg; Elem Ed.

JAMESON, WILLIAM; Jersey Shore HS; Avis, PA; (3); Cmnty Wkr; 4-H; Ftbl; Trk; Wt Lftg; Wrstlng; 4-H Awd; Hon Roll; Art.

JAMIESON, NANCY; Warren Area HS; Warren, PA; (4); 6/281; Church Yth Grp; Church Choir; Bowling; Jr NHS; High Hon Roll; Jr NHS; NHS; Pres Schlr; Hosp Aide; Office Aide; Gldn Dragon Ctznshp 87; Zonta Clb 87; IN U Of PA; Hstry.

JAMIESON, ROB; Pennsbury HS; Yardley, PA; (4); 49/778; Church Yth Grp; Cmnty Wkr; Debate Tm; Intnl Clb; Model UN; NFL; Political Wkr; Quiz Bowl; Red Cross Aide; Scholastic Bowl; Camp Neidig Ldrshp Schlrshp; Lck Hvn U Schlrshp; U PA Schlrshp; Stnfrd U; Ecnmcs.

JAMIL, ALIYA; Bradford Central Christian HS; Bradford, PA; (3); Computer Clb; Drama Clb; French Clb; Pep Clb; Ski Clb; JV Bsktbl; JV Sftbl; Hon Roll; NHS.

JAMISON, AMY; Union HS; Rimersburg, PA; (3); 1/104; Pres Sec FCA; SADD; Nwsp Ed-Chief; Rep Stu Cncl; JV Var Bsktbl; Var Trk; JV Var Vllybl; High Hon Roll; Hon Roll; Pres NHS; U Of Pittsburgh; Phrmcy.

JAMISON, SCOTT; Steel Valley HS; W Homestead, PA; (4); Hon Roll; Allegheny CC; Gnrl Studies.

JAMISON, STEPHEN; Elizabeth Forward HS; Mckeesport, PA; (2); Boy Scts; JA; Jazz Band; Crs Cntry; L Trk; God Cntry Awd; High Hon Roll; Hon Roll; Eagle Scout 86; Bus.

JAMISON, WILLIAM; Hyndman HS; Hyndman, PA; (3); 1/53; Drama Clb; Varsity Clb; Band; Mrchg Band; School Play; Bsktbl; Tennis; Hon Roll; Jr NHS; NHS; Brdcstng.

JAMULA, MARK; Hanover Area JR SR HS; Wilkes Barre, PA; (3); Var L Bsbl; Var Golf; Psychlgy.

JANARDHANA, SHIVA; Cedar Cliff HS; Camp Hill, PA; (3); 4/305; VP Computer Clb; Debate Tm; JCL; Key Clb; Latin Clb; Tennis; High Hon Roll; NHS; Natl Ltn Exm-Cum Laud 85 & 87; Ltn Hnr Scty; Woodmn Wrld Amer Hstry Awd 87; Elec Engr.

JANECK, AMY; Beaver Area JR SR HS; Beaver, PA; (2); Church Yth Grp; French Clb; Mrchg Band; School Musical; School Play; Var Twrlr; U Of Pittsburgh; Chld Psych.

JANI, KRISTIE; Salisbury HS; Allentown, PA; (4); 38/128; FBLA; Key Clb; Chorus; Rep Frsh Cls; Var Cheerleading; Hon Roll; FBLA Clerk Typist I 7th Pl & Outstndng Accntng II Stu 87; Bloomsburg ST U; Acctng.

JANIDLO, KAREN; Franklin HS; Franklin, PA; (4); VP Church Yth Grp; German Clb; Varsity Clb; Color Guard; Variety Show; Coach Actv; Trk; Vllybl; Hon Roll; Prfct Atten Awd; Brd Schl Drctrs & Prncpls Art Awds 87; ICM Schl Of Bus; Med Asstnt.

JANIK, CAROLINE; Trinity HS; Camp Hill, PA; (3); Drama Clb; Speech Tm; School Musical; School Play; Stage Crew; Nwsp Rptr; Yrbk Phtg; Hon Roll; Schlstc Wrtg Awd Wnnr 86-87; Dist 1 Act Ly Comptn Wnnr 86-87; George Washington U; Drama.

JANIK, DIANE; Cumberland Valley HS; Camp Hill, PA; (4); 3/512; Church Yth Grp; Teachers Aide; Color Guard; French Hon Soc; High Hon Roll; Kiwanis Awd; NHS; Amer Leg Aux Distngshd Achvt Awd 87; Harrisburg Kiwanis Schlrshp 87; Amer Bus Wmns Assoc Schlrshp 87; Villnova U; Acctng.

JANIKOWSKI, JAN; Cathedral Prep Schl; Erie, PA; (4); 24/212; Latin Clb; Chorus; Im Bsktbl; Bowling; High Hon Roll; Hon Roll; Ntl Merit Schol; Pres Schlr; Latin Honor Scty 84-86; John Carroll U; Bus.

JANIS, CRYSTAL; Wilmington Area HS; Volant, PA; (1); Chess Clb; Church Yth Grp; JV Powder Puff Ftbl; JV Tennis; Art Inst Of Pittsburgh; Int Dsg.

JANKOVICH, JEFF; Mercer Area JR SR HS; Mercer, PA; (3); Computer Clb; Science Clb; Pres Jr Cls; Capt Bsbl; JV Bsktbl; Capt L Ftbl; High Hon Roll; Hon Roll; NHS; Var L Trk; Dist Free Throw Champ K Of C 84; Hnrb Mntn All Tri-Cnty Ftbl 86; Pre-Med.

JANNOT, JASON; Meadville Area SR HS; Meadville, PA; (3); 49/365; Aud/Vis; Church Yth Grp; Var Golf; Var Ice Hcky; JV Socr; Hon Roll; Chiro.

JANORA, LISA; John S Fine HS; Nanticoke, PA; (4); 23/251; Trs VP Key Clb; Chorus; Yrbk Stf; Var Capt Fld Hcky; High Hon Roll; NHS; Physcl Thrpy.

JANOTKA, JEFFREY; Northampton SR HS; Bath, PA; (3); 12/494; Church Yth Grp; Science Clb; VP Soph Cls; Sec Jr Cls; Rep Stu Cncl; Var L Ftbl; Var Trk; Var Wt Lftg; High Hon Roll; Med.

JANOVICH, MARIE; Shamokin Area HS; Ranshaw, PA; (3); 80/223; German Clb; Science Clb; Ski Clb; Rep Frsh Cls; Rep Soph Cls; Rep Jr Cls; Rep Sr Cls; Rep Stu Cncl; Var Capt Cheerleading; Var Capt Mat Maids; Med.

JANOWIAK, JOSEPH; Central Catholic Allentown HS; Allentown, PA; (3); Boy Scts; Church Yth Grp; Lcrss; Wt Lftg; Prfct Atten Awd; Mt Aloysius JC; Bus Admin.

JANSEN, STEVE; Freeport Area HS; Freeport, PA; (2); Var Bsktbl; Var Trk; Hon Roll.

JANSHEGO, DAWN; Conemaugh Township HS; Johnstown, PA; (3); Aud/Vis; Drama Clb; Key Clb; Color Guard; Flag Corp; Mrchg Band; School Musical; School Play; Nwsp Bus Mgr; Nwsp Stf; Spnsh Awd 85; Bradford Bus Schl; Exec Secy.

JANUARY, SHARI; Highlands HS; Natrona Heights, PA; (4); DECA; JA; Sec Soph Cls; Sec Jr Cls; Sec Sr Cls; Stu Cncl; Bsktbl; Tennis; Hon Roll; Jr NHS; 1st Pl Awds DECA Sts 86-87; 1st Pl Awds DECA Dist 86-87; Hmcmng Ct 86-87; Bradford Schl; Exec Secr.

JANUSZKO, ROBERT C; James M Coughlin HS; Wilkes Barre, PA; (3); Aud/Vis; Key Clb; Math Clb; Acpl Chr; Band; Chorus; Concert Band; Mrchg Band; Im Crs Cntry; Hon Roll; PA ST U; Atmsphrc Sci.

JAQUITH, DOUGLAS; Conestoga Valley SR HS; Lancaster, PA; (4); 97/258; Chorus; Im Bsktbl; Var L Ftbl; Var Socr; Var L Trk; Im Wt Lftg; Prfct Atten Awd; U DE; Anthrplgy.

JAQUITH, NICOLE; Correy Area HS; Corry, PA; (2); 4-H; French Clb; FTA; Office Aide; Chorus; Penn ST; Scndry Teacher.

JARONIESKI, PAULA; Bishop Guilfoyle HS; Altoona, PA; (3); GAA; Library Aide; Red Cross Aide; Science Clb; SADD; Var Vllybl; Hon Roll; Asst Treas Chem Clb 86; Capt Vllybl Tm Juniata Clg Vllybl Cmp 86; Cmmrcl Airlns.

JAROSINSKI, AMY; Highlands SR HS; Natrona Hgts, PA; (3); Dance Clb; Office Aide; Pep Clb; Chorus; Rep Stu Cncl; Var JV Cheerleading; High Hon Roll; Jr NHS; VP NHS; Rtry Ldrshp Schlrshp 87; Soph & JR Cls VP 86-87; PA Ms All Am Chrldr Pgnt St Fnlst 87; Elem Ed.

JAROSZ, DAVE; St College Area Intermediate HS; St College, PA; (2); Church Yth Grp; Hosp Aide; L Bsktbl; Capt Im Ftbl; Powder Puff Ftbl; Power Of Paws 86-87; PSU; Bus.

JARRETT, JAMES; Bradford Area HS; Bradford, PA; (4); 5/275; Aud/Vis; Trs Key Clb; Rep Stu Cncl; Vllybl; High Hon Roll; Jr NHS; NHS; Ntl Merit Schol; NEDT Awd; RIT Hnr Schlrshp Cmptn 87; Rochester Inst Of Tech; Comp.

JARRETT, KRISTINA; Juniata HS; E Waterford, PA; (3); SADD; School Play; Sftbl; Vet Tech.

JARRETT, MATTHEW; Faith Christian Schl; Wind Gap, PA; (3); 4/15; Camera Clb; Stage Crew; Variety Show; Yrbk Phtg; Yrbk Stf; Trs Soph Cls; Trs Jr Cls; Bsktbl; Var Sftbl; Hon Roll; Elec Engr.

JARVIS, BRIAN; Lower Moreland HS; Huntingdon Valley, PA; (2); Church Yth Grp; French Clb; FBLA; Office Aide; Science Clb; JV Crs Cntry; JV Trk; Legal Admin.

JARVIS, MATTHEW; Carlisle HS; Carlisle, PA; (2); Drama Clb; Quiz Bowl; Chorus; School Musical; School Play; Variety Show; Pres Soph Cls; JV Socr; High Hon Roll; Pres Schlr; MVP Var Ten Tm 86-87; Intl Law.

JARVIS, TINA; Laurel Valley JR/Sr HS; Bolivar, PA; (3); 5/87; FBLA; Chorus; Wt Lftg; High Hon Roll; Hon Roll.

JASIEWICZ, TERI; Serra Catholic HS; Mc Keesport, PA; (4); Church Yth Grp; Drama Clb; Q&S; Red Cross Aide; Chorus; Color Guard; School Musical; Nwsp Ed-Chief; Nwsp Stf; Score Keeper; U Of Pittsburgh; Nrsng.

JASKO, MARK D; Ringgold HS; Finleyville, PA; (3); 15/351; Computer Clb; Spanish Clb; Varsity Clb; Var Bsktbl; JV Golf; Var Socr; Var Tennis; JV Trk; High Hon Roll; Hon Roll; Accntng.

JASKOWIAK, MEREDITH; St Huberts HS; Philadelphia, PA; (3); 177/409; Art Clb; Camera Clb; Cmnty Wkr; Library Aide; SADD; Yrbk Phtg; Lit Mag; Schlrshp-Smmr Course-Coll 87; Photo.

JASKULSKI, JODI; West Mifflin Area HS; West Mifflin, PA; (4); 50/338; Art Clb; Key Clb; Teachers Aide; Chorus; Drill Tm; Rep Jr Cls; Rep Sr Cls; Var Vllybl; Hon Roll; NHS; Lebanon Wmns Clb Schlrshp 87; Duquesne Smns Clb Schlrshp 87; Sr Actvty Awd 87; U Of Pittsburgh; Phrmcy.

JASLAR, MICHAEL; Hanover JR SR HS; Wilkes Barre, PA; (3); 57/194; Var L Bsbl; Ftbl; Var L Wrstlng; Hon Roll; Arch.

JASLOW, REBECCA; Abington HS; Abington, PA; (3); 2/502; French Clb; Hosp Aide; Pres Key Clb; Red Cross Aide; SADD; Chorus; Orch; School Musical; Nwsp Bus Mgr; Nwsp Rptr; 1st Pl Winnr Impromptu Essay Cont Key Clb Convntn 87; Med.

JASNIEWICZ, ANN; Benton JR SR HS; Benton, PA; (3); Art Clb; Library Aide; Chorus; Stage Crew; Hon Roll; NHS; Auto Mech.

JASPER, TOBI I; Moravian Acad; Allentown, PA; (3); Cmnty Wkr; Temple Yth Grp; Chorus; Variety Show; Yrbk Bus Mgr; Ed Lit Mag; Off Jr Cls; JV Fld Hcky; High Hon Roll; Hon Roll.

JASPER, TODD E; Neshaminy HS; Penndel, PA; (3); 16/780; Ski Clb; Concert Band; Mrchg Band; Yrbk Bus Mgr; High Hon Roll; Hon Roll; NHS; Prsdntl Clsrm Yng Amrncs 87; Tomorrows Ldrs Conf 87; Arntcl.

JASTROMB, TRACY; Meadville Area SR HS; Meadville, PA; (4); Church Yth Grp; Girl Scts; Hosp Aide; SADD; CPA.

JASTRZAB, JEFFREY; Greater Johnstown HS; Johnstown, PA; (4); 26/293; Math Clb; Ski Clb; Spanish Clb; Stage Crew; Trk; Wt Lftg; High Hon Roll; NHS; Rotary Awd; PA ST; Engrng.

JASTRZEMBSKI, KIMBERLY; Governor Mifflin SR HS; Reading, PA; (3); 11/300; Art Clb; Church Yth Grp; Dance Clb; Debate Tm; JA; Chorus; Church Choir; High Hon Roll; Hon Roll; Pres Schlr; Schl Hnr Soc 84-85 & 87; Bio Rsrch.

JAUSS, ELISABETH; Central Bucks HS West; Chalfont, PA; (3); Church Yth Grp; German Clb; Band; Hon Roll; Jr NHS; Pres Schlr; Germn Lang Excllnc Awd 87; Intl Bus.

JAVORKA, MICHAEL JOHN; Liberty HS; Bethlehem, PA; (3); 73/421; Computer Clb; Variety Show; Rep Frsh Cls; Hon Roll; Davidson Schlrshp 87; U Of TX Austin; Robotcs.

JAWORSKI, JOHN; Mt Pleasant Area HS; Mt Pleasant, PA; (3); 55/244; German Clb; JV Bsbl; Var L Ftbl; Hon Roll.

JAWORSKI, TRACY L; Daniel Boone HS; Douglassville, PA; (3); 14/170; Drama Clb; German Clb; JA; Var Cheerleading; Im Gym; Var Pom Pon; Hon Roll; Brandywine Of Widner U; Toursm.

JAYAKUMAR, SUNITA; Immaculate Conception HS; Washington, PA; (2); 1/37; Art Clb; Church Yth Grp; Math Tm; Pep Clb; Ski Clb; Yrbk Stf; Trs Frsh Cls; Rep Stu Cncl; Var Sftbl; High Hon Roll; Acdmc Excllnc Alg II Awd 86; Acadmc Excllnc Awds-Engl, Frnch 86 & 87; Med.

JAYMES, SHARON; Chambersburg Area SR HS; Orrstown, PA; (2); Church Yth Grp; Drama Clb; Hosp Aide; Ski Clb; SADD; Band; Chorus; Church Choir; Mrchg Band; Hon Roll.

JAYNE, KEVIN; Sullivan County HS; Mont Alto, PA; (4); 10/85; Trs Church Yth Grp; VP Key Clb; Band; VP Chorus; Jazz Band; Nwsp Rptr; Yrbk Stf; VP Sr Cls; High Hon Roll; Mgr NHS; Hgh Schl Band Dirs Awd 85-86; Pres Acdmc Fit Awd 86-87; Hghland Harold Rprtr 86-87; Penn ST U; Aerosp Engrng.

JAYNE, TAMRA; Wyalusing Valley HS; Laceyville, PA; (4); 25/132; Sec German Clb; Sec Jr Cls; Sec Sr Cls; Bowling; Cheerleading; Capt Sftbl; Capt Vllybl; High Hon Roll; Hon Roll; NHS; Le Hermans Clb Awd-Outstndg Sftbl Plyr 87; Kutztown U; Germn Educ.

JAYNES, BETH; Connellsville Area SR HS; Connellsville, PA; (3); 70/550; Band; Chorus; Color Guard; Flag Corp; Mrchg Band; School Musical; Pres Frsh Cls; Pres Soph Cls; Pres Stu Cncl; Stat Bsktbl; Physcly Hndcppd.

JAYNES, RANDY; Northeast Bradford HS; Stevensville, PA; (4); Trs Varsity Clb; Chorus; Concert Band; Capt Drm Mjr(t); Mrchg Band; Yrbk Phtg; Rep Stu Cncl; Var JV Bsktbl; High Hon Roll; Hon Roll; Rochestr Inst Tech; Comp Engrng.

JEDROSKO, MATTHEW; Bradford Area HS; Bradford, PA; (4); Aud/Vis; Band; Concert Band; Jazz Band; Mrchg Band; Hon Roll; Defiance Coll; Crmnl Jstc.

JEFFERIS, AMANDA; Henderson HS; W Chester, PA; (3); 56/360; Intnl Clb; Chorus; Orch; Mgr Crs Cntry; Acctng.

JEFFERSON, TOM; Laurel Highlands SR HS; Uniontown, PA; (2); Boy Scts; Science Clb; Ski Clb; Band; Concert Band; Jazz Band; Mrchg Band; Hon Roll; JETS Awd; Amrcn Lgn Hstry Awd 85; Sci.

JEFFREY, CHRISTOPHER; Burgettstown Area JR SR HS; Burgettstown, PA; (3); 24/164; Sec Drama Clb; Band; Chorus; Drm Mjr(t); School Musical; Off Stu Cncl; Hon Roll; NHS; Spanish Clb; Church Choir; Snd Amer Hnr Chorus, Barbershp Qrtet 87; Postive Teen Action 86 & 87; Poli Sci.

JEFFREY, KIMBERLY D; Dover Area HS; York, PA; (4); Varsity Clb; Var Cheerleading; Hon Roll; IN U Of PA; Fshn Merch.

JEFFRIES, ANGIE; West Perry SR HS; Blain, PA; (2); Psych.

JEFFRIES, JESSICA; Carlisle SR HS; Carlisle, PA; (3); Art Clb; Pep Clb; Service Clb; Stage Crew; Lit Mag; Stat Bsktbl; Var Stat Fld Hcky; Mgr(s); Var Stat Swmmng; Hon Roll; 2 Vrsty Mgr Lttrs Swmmng & Hcky 86; 1 Vrsty Mgr Lttr & Star Hcky 87; Ed.

JEGLINSKI, MELISSA; S Fayette JR SR HS; Bridgeville, PA; (4); 11/72; Drama Clb; Key Clb; VP Library Aide; Chorus; School Play; Nwsp Stf; Yrbk Ed-Chief; High Hon Roll; Hon Roll; NHS; Clarion U At PA; Englsh.

JEKARL, EDWARD KAP; Plymouth-Whitemarsh HS; Lafayette Hill, PA; (4); 22/365; Computer Clb; Mu Alpha Theta; Teachers Aide; Rep Frsh Cls; Trs Soph Cls; Rep Jr Cls; Rep Stu Cncl; Var Socr; JV Swmmng; High Hon Roll; Bio-Chem.

JELENSITS, ANDREA; William Allen HS; Allentown, PA; (3); 23/689; JA; Rep Jr Cls; Stu Cncl; Hon Roll; Jr NHS; NHS; Jennifer Pethick Mem Awd Sportsmnshp 87.

JELSTROM, KRISTINE; Mechanicsburg Area SR HS; Mechanicsburg, PA; (3); 84/338; Speech Tm; Nwsp Ed-Chief; Nwsp Rptr; Genetics.

JEMO, MIKE; Hazleton HS; Hazleton, PA; (3); 76/445; Chess Clb; Church Yth Grp; Trs FBLA; Yrbk Stf; Rep Frsh Cls; JV Bsktbl; Capt Var Crs Cntry; L Trk; Im Vllybl; Hon Roll; Pres Frgn Lang Organ; 5th Pl Data Proc Regnl FBLA Comp; Bloomsburg; Accntng.

JEMO, NICK; Weatherly Area HS; Weatherly, PA; (4); 3/66; Capt Bsbl; JV Capt Bsktbl; Capt Golf; Cit Awd; High Hon Roll; NHS; Penn ST U; Engnrng.

JENA, MATTHEW; Beaver Falls HS; Beaver Falls, PA; (3); French Clb; JA; High Hon Roll.

JENCKA, LISA; Greensburg Central Catholic HS; Irwin, PA; (4); French Clb; High Hon Roll; NHS; Prfct Atten Awd; WV Wesleyan.

JENCO, JENNIFER; West Mifflin Area HS; W Mifflin, PA; (3); Church Yth Grp; FBLA; Teachers Aide; Jr NHS; NHS; Jr Tamburitzans; Duquesne U; Comp Bus Mgt.

JENDREK, ROBIN; Mountain View HS; Nicholson, PA; (3); Chess Clb; Cmnty Wkr; Teachers Aide; Band; Chorus; Stu Cncl; Bsktbl; Fld Hcky; Sftbl; Trvl Agnt.

JENKINS, AISHA L; Fairview HS; Fairview, PA; (4); 3/154; Am Leg Aux Girls St; Model UN; Drm Mjr(t); Jazz Band; Pep Band; Lit Mag; High Hon Roll; JP Sousa Awd; NHS; Teachers Aide; Chem Olympd 1st & 2nd Lvl Tsts, Fairview Sci Dept Awd 87; Penn ST U; Engrng.

JENKINS III, EDWARD G; Cambria Heights HS; Mc Keesport, PA; (3); Sec Church Yth Grp; ROTC; Speech Tm; SADD; Church Choir; School Play; Yrbk Stf; Bsktbl; L Swmmng; Hon Roll; Engr.

JENKINS, ELIZABETH; Plum SR HS; Pittsburgh, PA; (3); DECA; SADD; Band; Chorus; Var L Swmmng; Timer; Hon Roll; 1st Pl DECA Rgnls 87; Mrktng.

JENKINS, ERICA; North Penn HS; Hatfield, PA; (4); Rep Frsh Cls; JV Powder Puff Ftbl; Hon Roll; Ntl Merit Ltr; PA ST U; Bus Admn.

JENKINS, JASON; Allen HS; Allentown, PA; (2); 90/726; Key Clb; SADD; Varsity Clb; Yrbk Stf; Var Stu Cncl; Ftbl; Var L Wrstlng; Hon Roll; Jr NHS; Schlstc Achvt Awd 85; Berkley; Law.

JENKINS, JAY W; Owen J Roberts HS; Glenmoore, PA; (4); 14/270; Band; Concert Band; Mrchg Band; School Play; Stage Crew; Symp Band; Var Tennis; Im Capt Vllybl; Hon Roll; NHS; Intl Dirctry Dstngshd Yng Ldrshp 86-87; Writng.

JENKINS, KAREN; Central HS; Scranton, PA; (3); 55/300; Trs Exploring; Pep Clb; Ski Clb; Spanish Clb; SADD; JV Capt Cheerleading; L Sftbl; Hon Roll; Jr NHS; Prfct Atten Awd; Pediatrc Nrs.

JENKINS, KATHLEEN; Deer Lakes JR SR HS; Gibsonia, PA; (4); 10/170; Office Aide; Teachers Aide; High Hon Roll; NHS; Pres Schlr; Grl Yr Awd Allghny Cnty Bus & Prfssnl Wmns Clb 87; Allegheny Cnty CC; Bus.

JENKINS, KATHRYN; Neshaminy HS; Langhorne, PA; (4); 10/680; Scholastic Bowl; Nwsp Stf; Lit Mag; Rep Stu Cncl; Stat Bsktbl; Var Crs Cntry; JV Fld Hcky; Var Capt Trk; NHS; Phila Coll Txtls & Sci Bus Merit Schlrshp 87; Schltc Schlrshp 87; Svc Awd 87; Phila Coll Txtls/Sci; Fash Mdsg.

JENKINS, KEVIN; Kennard-Dale HS; Fawn Grove, PA; (3); 10/170; Band; Concert Band; Mrchg Band; Orch; Variety Show; Yrbk Stf; Pres Sr Cls; Rep Stu Cncl; Var Mgr(s); Hon Roll; Rotary Ldrs Conf 87; Band Pres 87-88; Orch VP 86-87; Jrnlsm.

JENKINS, KIM; Frazier HS; Perryopolis, PA; (3); Church Yth Grp; Drama Clb; Trs 4-H; High Hon Roll; Hon Roll; NHS; 4-H Cert Cmpltn 84 & 86; Horse Brdr.

JENKINS, MARY KATHERINE; Cambria Heights HS; Mc Keesport, PA; (4); 21/189; Drama Clb; FHA; Library Aide; Chorus; Church Choir; Yrbk Rptr; Mat Maids; Hon Roll; NHS; Pres Schlr; Lock Haven U; Erly Chldhd Educ.

JENKINS, NEIL; Wyoming Valley West HS; Kingston, PA; (3); 2/412; High Hon Roll; Jr NHS; NHS; Ntl Merit Ltr; Rgnl Awd, Amer Chemcl Soc 86; Paderewski Gld Mdl 87; Natl Hnr Soc 87; Physcs.

JENKINS, RONDA; Greensburg Central Catholic HS; Trafford, PA; (2); L Tennis; High Hon Roll; Pitt Greensburg Humanities Day 3rd Pl Fren Poster 87; Sftbl AWGSL West Sect Runner Up 85; Advertising.

JENKINS, SHANNON M; Fairview HS; Fairview, PA; (3); Am Leg Aux Girls St; Drama Clb; Q&S; Speech Tm; Thesps; Chorus; Flag Corp; Lit Mag; Var L Swmmng; Church Yth Grp; Smmr Schl Of Excllnc Sci 87; Hstry.

JENKINS, WENDY; Rocky Grove HS; Franklin, PA; (3); Pres Church Yth Grp; Library Aide; SADD; Chorus; Yrbk Ed-Chief; Yrbk Sprt Ed; Var Cheerleading; Hon Roll; Rotary Yth Ldrshp Awds 87; Dist 3 Choir 86; Phrmcy.

JENKINS, YALANDA; Overbrook School For The Blind; Philadelphia, PA; (2); 1/4; Chorus; Color Guard; School Musical; Pres Frsh Cls; VP Soph Cls; Cheerleading; Swmmng; Capt Trk; Cit Awd; Hon Roll; Most Outstndg & Most Vlbl Athl 85 & 86; Gold, Slvr, & Brnz Medls USABA Ntls-Trck & Swmmg 85 & 86; Comp Sci.

JENKINSON, WILLIAM; Upper Moreland HS; Willow Grove, PA; (2); 28/245; Key Clb; Rep Stu Cncl; Var Bsbl; JV Bsktbl; JV Ftbl; High Hon Roll; NHS.

JENKO, CHRISTOPHER; Elizabeth-Forward HS; Elizabeth, PA; (3); 24/345; French Clb; Latin Clb; Yrbk Stf; Rep Frsh Cls; Tennis; High Hon Roll; Hon Roll; NHS; Acdmc All Amer 87; Ecnmcs.

JENNES, RENEE; Bishop O Hara HS; Throop, PA; (3); 13/96; Camera Clb; Ski Clb; Spanish Clb; School Play; Nwsp Stf; Hon Roll; Bishop O Hara Schlrshp 84; Marywood; Photo.

JENNINGS, BETH; Laurel Highlands HS; Hopwood, PA; (3); 19/310; Hosp Aide; Varsity Clb; Madrigals; School Musical; Swing Chorus; Rep Stu Cncl; Var Capt Swmmng; High Hon Roll; Jr NHS; NHS; William Kusinar Schlrshp Awd 87; Army Rsrv Schlstc/Athltc Excel Awd 87; PA ST U.

JENNINGS, BOBBI; Northeastern SR HS; Manchester, PA; (3); Dance Clb; Pep Clb; Ski Clb; Chorus; Color Guard; Sftbl; Twrlr; High Hon Roll; Hon Roll; Thesps; Jrnlsm.

JENNINGS, CURT; C A S HS; Coatesville, PA; (3); 32/445; Church Yth Grp; NAACP; Spanish Clb; High Hon Roll; CASH Hnr Soc 87; Howard U; Med.

JENNINGS, DEBRA; Downingtown SR HS; Downingtown, PA; (2); Intnl Clb; Ski Clb; Spanish Clb; Chorus; Stat Fld Hcky; Mgr(s); High Hon Roll; Hon Roll; Police Offcr.

JENNINGS, JEFF; Sharon HS; Sharon, PA; (4); 69/175; Cmnty Wkr; Office Aide; Red Cross Aide; Teachers Aide; Nwsp Phtg; Yrbk Phtg; Bsbl; Hon Roll; Food Mgmt.

JENNINGS, JENNI; Blue Mountain Acad; Hamburg, PA; (1); 2/50; Church Yth Grp; Concert Band; School Play; Variety Show; Pres Frsh Cls; Gym; High Hon Roll; Prfct Atten Awd; Typing Awd 87; Blue Mountain Acad.

JENNINGS, KATHLEEN; Blue Mountain Acad; Hamburg, PA; (4); 2/59; Band; Nwsp Stf; Yrbk Stf; Pres Frsh Cls; Pres Soph Cls; VP Sr Cls; Rep Stu Cncl; Im Gym; High Hon Roll; NHS; Souther Coll; Cmmnctns.

JENNINGS, MELISSA; Pine Grove HS; Pine Grove, PA; (4); Drama Clb; School Musical; Nwsp Rptr; Yrbk Stf; Mgr Wrstlng; Hon Roll; Stu Mnth 87; Hgh Hnrs Frnch 87; Wilkes Coll; Occptnl Thrpy.

JENNINGS, MICHAEL; Central HS; Philadelphia, PA; (3); Office Aide; Bus Mgmt.

JENNINGS, NIKOLE D; Delaware Valley HS; Milford, PA; (3); 20/150; Drama Clb; 4-H; SADD; School Musical; School Play; Stage Crew; Nwsp Rptr; Yrbk Stf; Lit Mag; 4-H Awd; PA Gvrnrs Schl Arts Creatv Wrtng Semi-Fnlst 86; Seeing Eye Inc 85; Natl Hnr Roll 87; Jrnlsm.

JENNINGS, RHODA; Chartiers Valley HS; Bridgeville, PA; (3); Cmnty Wkr; Dance Clb; School Musical; School Play; Variety Show; Rep Frsh Cls; Twrlr; Miss Pittsburgh Teen 86-87; Miss Marjorette Of PA 86-87; Wrld Grnd Natl Champ Twrlng Prdctn 84-85; Miami U Of OH; Prfrmng Arts.

JENSEN, GEORGE; Newport HS; Newport, PA; (4); 11/88; Church Yth Grp; Cmnty Wkr; Band; Wrstlng; High Hon Roll; Hon Roll; Tri-M; Millersville U; Math.

JENSEN, KERI; Leechburg Area HS; Leechburg, PA; (2); Mrchg Band; Yrbk Stf; Var Sftbl; Var Twrlr; Prfct Atten Awd.

JENTGENS, BRIAN D; Highlands HS; Natrona Heights, PA; (3); DECA; PA ST U; Ecs.

JERAULD, LORI; Montrose Area JR-SR HS; Montrose, PA; (3); Art Clb; Ski Clb; Band; Concert Band; Mrchg Band; Nwsp Stf; Yrbk Stf; Stu Cncl; Penn ST; Comms.

JERITZA, JERRY; Eisenhower HS; Russell, PA; (3); Pres Church Yth Grp; Pres Drama Clb; Trs 4-H; Acpl Chr; Band; Chorus; Concert Band; Drm Mjr(t); Jazz Band; Mrchg Band.

JERVIS, ANDREA; Tunkhannock HS; Factoryville, PA; (1); Spanish Clb; Pres Frsh Cls; Stu Cncl; Cheerleading; JV Stat Ftbl; Hon Roll.

JERVIS, MELISSA; Tunkhannock HS; Factoryville, PA; (4); 27/270; Ski Clb; Band; Concert Band; Mrchg Band; Stu Cncl; Cheerleading; Gym; Tennis; Hon Roll; NHS; Hmcmg Ct 86; Manor Coll; Opt Tech.

JESBERGER, MICHAEL; Archbishop Ryan HS; Philadelphia, PA; (2); 116/349; Ice Hcky; Hon Roll; Catholic Ed Essay Awd 86; Hockey Awd 86-87; Ray Staszak Mem Awd 86-87; Bus.

JESCHONEK, TONYA; Greater Johnstown HS; Johnstown, PA; (4); 5/293; Concert Band; Drm Mjr(t); Mrchg Band; Orch; School Musical; High Hon Roll; NHS; Bnd Ldrshp Awd 87; Arion Awd 87; Dist VI Bnd & Rgn III Bnd 84-87; IN U Of PA; Comp Sci.

JESENSKY, ERIN; South Side HS; Clinton, PA; (3); Library Aide; Teachers Aide; Chorus; Nwsp Rptr; Pres Jr Cls; Cheerleading; Var Powder Puff Ftbl; Trk; High Hon Roll; Hon Roll; UCLA.

JESENSKY, JAMES; Keystone Oaks HS; Pittsburgh, PA; (3); Church Yth Grp; Computer Clb; JV Golf; Capt Wrstlng; Hon Roll; Capt Of Fresh Wrstlng Team 84-85; Hon Rl 84-87; Comp Clb 84-87; Rose Hulman Inst; Comp Engrng.

JESIOLOWSKI, JILL; Nazareth Acad; Phila, PA; (3); 40/125; Hosp Aide; Band; Church Choir; Jazz Band; Mrchg Band; Orch; School Musical; Yrbk Rptr; Yrbk Stf; Hon Roll; Nrsg.

JESKO, JENNIFER; Gwynedd Mercy Acad; Huntingdon Vally, PA; (2); Cmnty Wkr; Drama Clb; JV Lcrss; JV Tennis; Geom Awd 87; Ltn Achvt Awd 86; Hnrs 1st, Spnsh Awd, Alg Awd 86; Comm.

JESKY, MICHAEL; Hazleton SR HS; Hazleton, PA; (2); Nwsp Bus Mgr; Nwsp Rptr; Nwsp Stf; Hon Roll.

JESSE, JENNIFER; John S Fine HS; Plymouth, PA; (2); 20/243; Key Clb; Ski Clb; Color Guard; Flag Corp; Mrchg Band; Yrbk Stf; Var Swmmng; High Hon Roll; NHS; NEDT Awd; Chem.

JESSUP, JEREMY; Peters Township HS; Mc Murray, PA; (2); Church Yth Grp; Computer Clb; Spanish Clb; JV Var Bsbl; High Hon Roll; Hon Roll; Spanish NHS; Wheeling WV Bsbl Compttn Wnnr & Lttrs Of Appreciation From ST Senator 85-86; Case Western Reserve; Engr.

JESSUP JR, OLIVER; Northeast Prep HS; Philadelphia, PA; (3).

JESTEADT, TIMMI; Butler SR HS; Butler, PA; (2); Church Yth Grp; 4-H; French Clb; Library Aide; SADD; Chorus; Trk; Jr NHS; Washington & Jefferson; Vet.

JESTER, WAYDE; Henderson HS; West Chester, PA; (2); 30/353; JA; Ski Clb; Yrbk Stf.

JETER, SHAYNNA; Aliquippa JR SR HS; Aliquippa, PA; (2); Library Aide; Office Aide; Chorus; JV Cheerleading; Trk; Hon Roll; Law.

JEWART, MICHELLE; Curwensville Area HS; Curwensville, PA; (3); Church Yth Grp; Drama Clb; Ski Clb; Flag Corp; Mrchg Band; Art Inst; Fshn.

JEWELL, AARON; Monessen SR HS; Monessen, PA; (3); Stage Crew; Ftbl; Ice Hcky; IN U.

JEWELL, JENNIFER; Delaware Valley HS; Milford, PA; (3); Library Aide; Ski Clb; SADD; Teachers Aide; Yrbk Stf; Lit Mag; Hon Roll; Pol Sci.

JEWELL, JUSTIN; Monessen HS; Monessen, PA; (3); 31/122; French Clb; Stage Crew; Trs Sr Cls; Var Ftbl; High Hon Roll; Hon Roll; Gftd Pgm 83-88; U Of Pittsburgh; Phys Thrpy.

JEWELL, STEVE; Mercer Area JR SR HS; Mercer, PA; (2); FFA; Band; Concert Band; Jazz Band; Mrchg Band; Pep Band; Stage Crew; Slippery Rock U.

JEWELL, WILLIAM MARK; Commodore Perry HS; Fredonia, PA; (4); 5/65; Yrbk Phtg; Yrbk Stf; Hon Roll; Elec Engr.

JEWETT, PATRICIA; Northeast Bradford JR SR HS; Rome, PA; (3); Computer Clb; French Clb; FHA; SADD; Chorus; High Hon Roll; Hon Roll; NHS; Accntng.

JEZEWSKI, VICKI; Carmichaels Area HS; Carmichaels, PA; (4); Library Aide; Spanish Clb; Hon Roll; Laurel Bus Inst; Accntng.

JINDAL, SHIVANI; Central Dahphin East HS; Harrisburg, PA; (4); 29/324; Var Debate Tm; Drama Clb; Pres French Clb; Chorus; Hon Roll; NHS; Rotary Awd; Ind Cltrl Dncng Hnrs Cert 85-87; Yng Lwyrs Assn 86-87; Mock Cert Trls 2nd St PA 85-86; Dickinson Coll; Law.

JIWA, SHEMINA; Ephrata SR HS; Ephrata, PA; (4); 16/252; Ed Ed Nwsp Ed-Chief; Nwsp Rptr; Pres Jr Cls; Trs Rep Stu Cncl; High Hon Roll; Hon Roll; VP NHS; Rotary Stu Of The Mnth Of October 86; J Harry Hibshman Schlrshp 87; Wolf Fndtn For Ed Awd 87; Philadelphia Coll; Pharmacy.

JOBES, KIRK; Mc Guffey HS; Claysville, PA; (3); Am Leg Boys St; Spanish Clb; Band; Mrchg Band; Nwsp Stf; High Hon Roll; Hon Roll; Jr NHS; NHS; Stu Rcgntn Awd; Rifle Tm; Med.

JODUN, WADE; Bald Eagle Nittany HS; Mill Hall, PA; (3); 14/148; Computer Clb; Model UN; Spanish Clb; Hon Roll.

JOHANSEN, AURORA; Upper Dauphin Area HS; Halifax, PA; (3); 2/105; Pres Church Yth Grp; Band; Chorus; Concert Band; Mrchg Band; Rep Frsh Cls; JV Var Trk; Outstndng Bnd Stu 85; HACC PA ST; Speech Pathlgy.

JOHN, ERIC; Archbishop Wood HS; Hatboro, PA; (2); 11/254; Aud/Vis; Church Yth Grp; German Clb; Nwsp Ed-Chief; High Hon Roll; Amer Lgn Awd For Courage Hnr Ldrshp Patriotsm & Svc 86; 1st Pl Envmntl Sci Bucks Cnty Sci Fair 87; Penn ST Univ.

JOHN, JEFFREY; Henderson SR HS; W Chester, PA; (3); Boy Scts; Intnl Clb; Ski Clb; Rep Stu Cncl; JV Bsbl; JV Lcrss; Var Wrstlng; VP Spanish NHS; Sect Champ In Wrstlng 87; Comp Sci.

JOHN, LIBY; High School Of Engineering & Science; Philadelphia, PA; (4); 6/210; Church Yth Grp; Yrbk Stf; Rep Frsh Cls; Rep Soph Cls; Hon Roll; Sec NHS; 2nd Prz George Washington Carrer Sci Fair 84-85; Drexel U; Elect Engr.

JOHNS, BINDHU; Hollidaysburg Area SR HS; Duncansville, PA; (3); 4/385; Drama Clb; French Clb; SADD; Band; Concert Band; Mrchg Band; Stage Crew; French Hon Soc; High Hon Roll; NHS; Jr Sci & Humanities Sympsm 86.

JOHNS, DONSHAE; Frankford HS; Philadelphia, PA; (3); 4/500; Church Yth Grp; Church Choir; Nwsp Stf; Hon Roll; NHS; Prfct Atten Awd; Pthlgst.

JOHNS, GWYN; Lock Haven SR HS; Lock Haven, PA; (3); Spanish Clb; SADD; Nwsp Rptr; JV Bsktbl; Mgr(s); JV Tennis; High Hon Roll; Hon Roll; NHS; Prfct Atten Awd; Girls Assn Progress & Svc; Psych.

JOHNS, JEFF; Oil City SR HS; Oil City, PA; (3); 25/233; Church Yth Grp; 4-H; 4-H Awd; High Hon Roll; Hon Roll; Prfct Atten Awd; Venango Cnty Indstrl Arts Awd 87; Sportsmnlike Driving Cert Achvt 86; Elec.

JOHNS, JEFF; Phoenixville HS; Phoenixville, PA; (3); Boy Scts; Spanish Clb; Yrbk Stf; Crs Cntry; Timer; Trk; God Cntry Awd; Prfct Atten Awd; Vrsty Ltr Crss Cntry Sprng Trk & Wntr Trk 85-87; Scndry Educ.

JOHNS, KAREN; Chambersburg Area SR HS; Orrstown, PA; (3); Church Yth Grp; 4-H; Girl Scts; Chorus; Church Choir; 4-H Awd; Hon Roll; Huntington Coll; Bus.

JOHNS, KELLY; South Western HS; Hanover, PA; (2); Computer Clb; Key Clb; Band; Chorus; Concert Band; Mrchg Band; Pep Band; School Musical; Symp Band; Hon Roll; Mth.

JOHNS, KERRY; Lakeview HS; Fredonia, PA; (4); 10/130; Varsity Clb; Chorus; Concert Band; Mrchg Band; Pep Band; School Play; Nwsp Ed-Chief; Var L Crs Cntry; Var Trk; NHS; Slippery Rock U; Physcl Ed.

JOHNS, KIMBERLY; Bishop Mc Devitt HS; Harrisburg, PA; (4); 6/176; Church Yth Grp; Service Clb; Ski Clb; Chorus; Madrigals; School Musical; School Play; Var Capt Cheerleading; NHS; PA ST U; Psychlgy.

JOHNS, MICHELLE; Tri-Valley HS; Hegins, PA; (3); 21/76; Art Clb; Computer Clb; Am Leg Aux Girls St; Varsity Clb; Yrbk Stf; Trs Jr Cls; JV Capt Cheerleading; Var L Mgr(s); Hon Roll; NHS; 1st Pl Locl Comp Cont 86; Awds Cmnty Arts Show 84-86; Penn ST; Bus Admin.

JOHNS, ROBERT C; Bishop Kenrick HS; Norristown, PA; (4); 3/290; Church Yth Grp; Math Tm; Science Clb; Spanish Clb; Rep Soph Cls; Var Bsbl; JV Bsktbl; High Hon Roll; VP NHS; Econ Medal 87; Cngrssnl Medal Merit 87; AFL-CIO PA ST Schlrshp 86; Notre Dame U; Bus.

JOHNS, TRACEY; Kiski Area HS; Sahsburg, PA; (3); Church Yth Grp; Pep Clb; Teachers Aide; Chorus; Stage Crew; Hon Roll; Secrtrl.

JOHNSON, ALICIA; Butler Area SR HS; Butler, PA; (3); Church Yth Grp; Exploring; FNA; Office Aide; Teachers Aide; Chorus; Church Choir; Orch; Yth Pin Vlntrng VA Hosp 86; Dntl Asst.

JOHNSON, ANGEL; Philadelphia High School For Girls; Philadelphia, PA; (3); 22/406; Trs Church Yth Grp; Rep GAA; Teachers Aide; Ed Nwsp Stf; Var L Trk; NHS; Prfct Atten Awd; Spnsh Honor Scty 87; Meritorious Achvts 85 & 87; Bailey-Williams Natl Honor Key Awd 86; Actrl Sci.

JOHNSON, ANGELICA; Mc Keesport Area HS; Mc Keesport, PA; (4); Trs Church Yth Grp; Sec Church Choir; Bk Rprt Awd Wnr Rdng 86-87; Mst Otstndng Stu Rdng 86-87; Art Inst Of Pittsburgh; Art.

JOHNSON, ANN; Philadelphia H S For Girls; Philadelphia, PA; (3); Church Yth Grp; Office Aide; Church Choir; Trk; Hon Roll; Med.

JOHNSON, ANTHONY; Roman Catholic HS; Philadelphia, PA; (3); 1/126; Cmnty Wkr; NAACP; Church Choir; Nwsp Rptr; Var L Trk; High Hon Roll; VP NHS; Varsity Clb; Acpl Chr; JV L Crs Cntry; V P Of Black Culture Club 87-88; Schlstc Achvt Awd From Concerned Black Men 87; Diocesan Schlrs 87; Bus Admin.

JOHNSON, ASTRID; Altoona Area HS; Altoona, PA; (3); Cmnty Wkr; German Clb; Marn Bio.

JOHNSON, BETSY; Millville Area HS; Millville, PA; (4); 11/78; VP Pres 4-H; VP FBLA; Pep Clb; Trs Band; School Play; Yrbk Stf; Sec Jr Cls; 4-H Awd; NHS; JV Sftbl; Hmcmng Qn 86; Outstndg Girl In 4-H 87; County & Dist Bands 85-86; Brandywine Coll; Fshn Merch.

JOHNSON, BRIAN; Elizabeth-Forward HS; Elizabeth, PA; (3); Boy Scts; Church Yth Grp; Dance Clb; Girl Scts; Concert Band; Im Bsbl; Im Bowling; Var Cheerleading; JV Ftbl; Var Ice Hcky; Girl Scts Good Ctzn Awd 87; UC Berkeley; Music.

JOHNSON, BRYANT; Pine Forge Acad; Philadelphia, PA; (4); 1/80; Church Yth Grp; Pres Chorus; Nwsp Rptr; Pres Frsh Cls; Pres Stu Cncl; High Hon Roll; NHS; Val; Acad Schlrs Of Amer 84-85; Oakwood Coll; Biol.

JOHNSON, CARLA; Greenville HS; Greenville, PA; (4); 12/130; Art Clb; Hst Church Yth Grp; Hosp Aide; Letterman Clb; Band; Concert Band; Orch; Pep Band; Vllybl; NHS; PPG Schlrshp Finlst 87; Meritorious Awd 82; Cedarville Coll; Chemistry.

JOHNSON, CARLA; Jefferson-Morgan HS; Jefferson, PA; (3); 3/77; Library Aide; Chorus; Nwsp Rptr; Yrbk Stf; High Hon Roll; NEDT Awd; Church Yth Grp; Acdmc All AM; Interct Club-Brd Of Dirctrs; Enrichmnt Pgm.

JOHNSON, CHAD; Eisenhower HS; Russell, PA; (3); 29/116; Hst Boy Scts; Pres Church Yth Grp; Exploring; Pres VP Leo Clb; Var L Wrstlng; High Hon Roll; Hon Roll.

JOHNSON, CHRIS; Cedar Crest HS; Lebanon, PA; (2); Boy Scts; Church Yth Grp; German Clb; Pep Clb; Hon Roll; Booster Clb Acdmc Merit Awd 87; Musical Cert Of Achvt 86; Psych.

JOHNSON, CHRISTINA; Archbishop Prendergast HS; Norwood, PA; (3); Latin Clb; Office Aide; Nrsng.

JOHNSON, CHRISTOPHER; Roman Catholic HS; Philadelphia, PA; (4); 2/137; Church Yth Grp; Computer Clb; Dance Clb; JA; Letterman Clb; Office Aide; Pep Clb; SADD; Nwsp Sprt Ed; Yrbk Stf; Amer Assn Physcs Tchrs Awd; Phi Beta Kppa Assn DE Vly Excllncy Stdy; Natl Yng Ldrs Cnfrnc Yth Ldr Awd; Temple U.

JOHNSON, CHRISTY L; Owen J Roberts HS; St Peters, PA; (4); 23/243; Pres Exploring; Sec Service Clb; SADD; NHS; Im Vllybl; Spring Garden Clg; Intr Dsgn.

JOHNSON, CLARENCE ROSCO; Chichester HS; Twin Oaks, PA; (3); Church Yth Grp; Office Aide; Pres Sr Cls; Var L Bsktbl; Var L Ftbl; Var Trk; Wt Lftg; Off Bck Of Yr Chichester Hgh, Pres Physcl Fttnss Awd, Prtcptd PA ST Dstrct Lng Jmp 86; Sprts Med.

JOHNSON, DANIEL; Southmoreland HS; Scottdale, PA; (3); Church Yth Grp; Intnl Clb; Political Wkr; Spanish Clb; JV Golf; Penn ST, Fayette Cmps Constitutnl Cnvntn 87; Accntng.

JOHNSON, DARLENE ANDREA; Wallenpaupack Area HS; Hawley, PA; (4); 4/144; Am Leg Aux Girls St; Chorus; Color Guard; School Play; Rep Stu Cncl; High Hon Roll; Jr NHS; NHS; Ski Clb; School Musical; Schlr Awd; Edctn Assn Schlrshp & Amer Assn Of Univ Womn Schlrshp; Bloomsburg U; Erly Chldhd Ed.

JOHNSON, DAVID; Avon Grove HS; Landenberg, PA; (3); 29/216; Aud/Vis; Camera Clb; JA; Yrbk Phtg; High Hon Roll; Hon Roll; Otstndng Achvt Accntg Awd 86-87; Physcs.

JOHNSON, DAVID; Jeannette SR HS; Jeannette, PA; (3); 4/140; Spanish Clb; Stu Cncl; High Hon Roll; Hon Roll; NHS; Ntl Merit SF; Penn ST U; Nuclear Engrng.

JOHNSON, DAVID S; Twin Valley HS; Elverson, PA; (3); 51/182; Am Leg Boys St; Trs Drama Clb; VP French Clb; Chorus; Concert Band; Jazz Band; Mrchg Band; School Musical; Nwsp Rptr; Ed Yrbk Stf; Outstndng Vcl Soloist Wlmsbrg Trnmnt Of Msc 87; Cnty Chrs 87; Msc Ed.

JOHNSON, DENISE; Curwensville Area HS; Curwensville, PA; (3); Church Yth Grp; Drama Clb; Mrchg Band; Yrbk Stf; Trs Stu Cncl; Mat Maids; Twrlr; Du Bois Penn ST; Accounting.

JOHNSON, DENISE; Fort Le Boeuf HS; Erie, PA; (3); 18/230; Drama Clb; Pep Clb; Teachers Aide; Chorus; School Musical; Stat Bsktbl; High Hon Roll; Hon Roll; Elem Edu.

JOHNSON, DENISE L; Philadelphia High Schl For Girls; Philadelphia, PA; (4); 55/365; Pres Church Yth Grp; Var Debate Tm; Lib Concert Band; Jazz Band; Orch; Nwsp Rptr; JV Badmtn; Capt Cheerleading; JV Fld Hcky; High Hon Roll; Blck Achvt Awd 86-87; Acad Achvt Awd 84-87; Summa Cum Laude Grad 87; PA ST U; Engl.

JOHNSON, DIRK; Butler SR HS; Butler, PA; (3); Church Yth Grp; Cmnty Wkr; Spanish Clb; Rep Stu Cncl; JV Var Bsbl; Im JV Bsktbl; JV Var Ftbl; JV L Trk; Bus.

JOHNSON, EMILIE; Coatesville Area SR HS; Coatesville, PA; (3); Drama Clb; Spanish Clb; SADD; Chorus; Yrbk Stf; High Hon Roll; Cmnty Wkr; Leo Clb; PAVAS; Ski Clb; Temple U; Law.

JOHNSON, ERIC; Palmyra HS; Annville, PA; (4); Church Yth Grp; Var L Crs Cntry; Capt L Wrstlng; Dnfth Awd; Hon Roll; NHS; FCA; French Clb; Concert Band; Jazz Band; Lycoming Coll.

JOHNSON, FAITH M; Philadelphia Montgomery Chrstn Acad; Philadelphia, PA; (3); Church Yth Grp; Cmnty Wkr; Library Aide; Chorus; Church Choir; VP Stu Cncl; Var Bsktbl; JV Fld Hcky; Hon Roll; Real Estate.

JOHNSON, GENINE; Warren Area HS; Warren, PA; (3); Sec Church Yth Grp; Drama Clb; French Clb; Band; Drm & Bgl; Orch; School Musical; Gym; High Hon Roll; Jr NHS; Intr Dsgnng.

JOHNSON, GERALD R; Warren Area HS; Warren, PA; (3); Church Yth Grp; Concert Band; Jazz Band; Mrchg Band; Pep Band; School Musical; Variety Show; Wt Lftg; High Hon Roll; Hon Roll.

JOHNSON, GREGG; Bishop Mc Cort HS; Johnstown, PA; (4); 5/130; Letterman Clb; Mu Alpha Theta; Ski Clb; Yrbk Stf; JV Bsktbl; Var L Crs Cntry; Var L Golf; Var L Trk; High Hon Roll; Rotary Awd; Air Force ROTC Schlrshp & Univ Schlrs 87; PA ST U; Arch Engrng.

JOHNSON, HEATHER; West Mifflin Area HS; W Mifflin, PA; (3); 6/310; Church Yth Grp; Capt Quiz Bowl; Mrchg Band; Orch; Nwsp Ed-Chief; Jr Cls; High Hon Roll; Jr NHS; NHS; 1st Pl Bible Qzzng Trphy 87; Piano Fdrtn Of Music Clbs PFMC Cmptitn Trphy 85; Scndry Educ.

JOHNSON, JEANNE; Meyersdale Area HS; Garrett, PA; (4); 1/116; Trs Spanish Clb; Band; Rep Stu Cncl; Var Bsktbl; Dnfth Awd; Hon Roll; Pres NHS; Intl Frgn Lang Awd; Pres Physcl Ftns Awd; Venture Clb Stu Of Mnth; Pittsburgh U.

JOHNSON, JEFF; Hopewell HS; Aliquippa, PA; (3); 118/255; Church Yth Grp; VP Soph Cls; Var L Ftbl; Var L Trk; Wt Lftg; Boy Scts; Exploring; Thomas Kolenda Awd Outstndng Athl & Schlr 84; MAC Coachs Assn Ftbl All Str 1st Tm All Sctn Rnng Bck.

JOHNSON, JEFFREY; Carlisle HS; Carlisle, PA; (3); Art Clb; German Clb; Ski Clb; Church Choir; Rep Jr Cls; Golf; Tennis.

JOHNSON, JENNIFER; Bald Eagle-Nittany HS; Beech Crk, PA; (3); 20/150; Cmnty Wkr; French Clb; Hosp Aide; Key Clb; Pep Clb; Ski Clb; Varsity Clb; Stu Cncl; Var Cheerleading; Var Gym; Lock Haven U; Elem Ed.

JOHNSON, JENNIFER; Linesville HS; Linesville, PA; (2); Spanish Clb; Band; Concert Band; Jazz Band; Mrchg Band; Pep Band; Stage Crew; Nwsp Rptr; Nwsp Stf; JV Crs Cntry; Amer Fed Musicns 87; Music.

JOHNSON, JENNIFER; Milton Area SR HS; New Columbia, PA; (2); Band; Concert Band; Mrchg Band; Nrsng.

JOHNSON, JERRY; Nazareth Area HS; Nazareth, PA; (3); VICA; JV Wrstlng; Auto Body Repair.

JOHNSON, JILL; Hazleton SR HS; Hazleton, PA; (3); Cmnty Wkr; Drama Clb; Office Aide; SADD; Teachers Aide; School Play; Stage Crew; High Hon Roll; Hon Roll; Actrl Sci.

JOHNSON, JILL; North Schuylkill HS; La Velle, PA; (2); 4/199; JV Capt Cheerleading; High Hon Roll; Hon Roll; Woodsmen Of Wrld Hstry Awd 87; Math Tutor 86; Gregg Shrthnd Awd 86; Optmtrst.

JOHNSON, JOHN; Central HS; Philadelphia, PA; (3); Chess Clb; Intnl Clb; JCL; Band; Hon Roll; Bus Mngmt.

JOHNSON, JOSEPH L; Germantown Acad; Ft Washington, PA; (4); Bausch & Lomb Sci Awd; Hon Roll; Ntl Merit SF; Vrsty Water Polo-Capt 87; Cum Laude Soc 86; Geomtry Awd 84; Biochem.

JOHNSON, KAREN; Hickory HS; Hermitage, PA; (3); Office Aide; Chorus; Yrbk Stf; L Bsktbl; Var Crs Cntry; L Trk; Elem Educ.

JOHNSON, LA SHAWN; Middletown Area HS; Middletown, PA; (3); Pres Church Yth Grp; FCA; FBLA; Model UN; Office Aide; Church Choir; Color Guard; Flag Corp; Yrbk Stf; JV Var Bsktbl; Howard U; Bus Admin.

JOHNSON, LAURA; Southside Beaver HS; Georgetown, PA; (3); 11/131; Church Yth Grp; 4-H; Library Aide; Teachers Aide; Band; Concert Band; Drm Mjr(t); Mrchg Band; Stat Bsbl; Capt Twrlr; Sthsd Hnrs Clb 84-87; Gftd & Tlntd Prgm 84-88; Marietta Coll; Elem Ed.

JOHNSON, LAWRENCE A; Chester HS; Chester, PA; (3); Church Yth Grp; Band; Mrchg Band; School Musical; Off Sr Cls; Socr; Capt Tennis; Cmnty Wkr; Church Choir; Concert Band; Swarthmore Coll Upwrd Bnd 85-87; Nghts Of Pythgras Masnc Grp 87; Arch.

JOHNSON, LISA; Chartiers Valley HS; Pittsburgh, PA; (4); 16/300; Letterman Clb; Varsity Clb; Band; Mrchg Band; Stu Cncl; Var Cheerleading; Powder Puff Ftbl; Hon Roll; NHS; Rotry Ldrshp Conf 86; Acad Schlrshp 87; Westminster Coll; Bus Admin.

JOHNSON, LISA; Emmaus HS; Macungie, PA; (4); 56/488; Girl Scts; Lib Mrchg Band; Symp Band; High Hon Roll; Hon Roll; Jr NHS; NHS; Prfct Atten Awd; Pres Acadmc Ftns Awd 87; Robert C Byrd Hnrs Schlrshp 87; Band Dir Svc Awd 87; Carnegie Melln U; Arch.

JOHNSON, LISA; Overbrook HS; Philadelphia, PA; (4); 3/421; Cmnty Wkr; Office Aide; Drm Mjr(t); Nwsp Stf; Mgr(s); Hon Roll; NHS; Soc Of Wmns Engrns Awd For Hgh Hnr Math & Sci 86-87; U Of DE; Cmnctns.

JOHNSON, MARC; Roman Catholic HS; Philadelphia, PA; (3); 29/126; NAACP; Church Choir; Var Capt Crs Cntry; Var Stat Trk; NHS; Prfct Atten Awd; Cmnty Wkr; Varsity Clb; Acpl Chr; Timer; Mst Imprvd Crss Cntry 86; Acdmc Achvt Awd Bkck Cultr Clb, Schlstc Achvt Awd Frm Cncrnd Blck Mn Inc 87.

JOHNSON, MARCIA; Sheffield Area HS; Clarendon, PA; (3); 3/89; Math Tm; Band; Concert Band; Mrchg Band; Pep Band; Symp Band; Var Sftbl; High Hon Roll; Hon Roll; NHS; Acadc Ltr 87.

JOHNSON, MARGARET; Archbishop Ryan HS For Girls; Philadelphia, PA; (3); 5/508; Math Tm; Q&S; Pres Spanish Clb; Nwsp Rptr; Nwsp Stf; High Hon Roll; NHS; Spanish NHS; Engl Awd 85; Essay Schlrshp From Assoc Of Catholic Tchrs 85; Drexel U; Acctng.

JOHNSON, MARK; Cardinal O Hara HS; Springfield, PA; (3); 87/710; Hon Roll; Schltc Achvt Awd 84-85; Grphc Dsgn.

JOHNSON, MARNA; Pennsbury HS; Yardley, PA; (3); SADD; Yrbk Phtg; Yrbk Stf; JV Bsktbl; Im Vllybl; Hon Roll; Mktg.

JOHNSON, MARY; Venango Christian HS; Cooperstown, PA; (3); 18/36; Sec Trs Spanish Clb; SADD; VP Jr Cls; Pres Sr Cls; Rep Stu Cncl; Var Capt Cheerleading; Var Sftbl; Var JV Vllybl; Hon Roll; Rotary Awd; Natl Hosp Ldrshp & Svc Awd 86; Psych.

JOHNSON, MEGAN; Abington HS; Glenside, PA; (3); Hosp Aide; Key Clb; Spanish Clb; SADD; Varsity Clb; Yrbk Stf; Sec Jr Cls; Stu Cncl; Fld Hcky; Lcrss; W Chester; Nrsng.

JOHNSON, MICHAEL; North Pocono HS; Moscow, PA; (4); 13/265; Trs Church Yth Grp; Drama Clb; Ski Clb; Band; Concert Band; Mrchg Band; Orch; School Play; Nwsp Stf; Trs Sr Cls; Psychlgy.

JOHNSON, MICHELLE; Upper Moreland HS; Hatboro, PA; (3); Church Yth Grp; Key Clb; SADD; Rep Frsh Cls; Rep Soph Cls; Rep Jr Cls; Rep Sr Cls; Stu Cncl; Var Cheerleading; Hon Roll; Permission To Skip SR Yr & Go Directly To Brandywine Coll & The Return To Grad With Class 88; Brandywine Coll; Fash Merch.

JOHNSON, MIKE; Kennard-Dale HS; Delta, PA; (3); 1/180; Boy Scts; Church Yth Grp; German Clb; Quiz Bowl; School Musical; Var L Trk; Bausch & Lomb Sci Awd; Pres NHS; Ntl Merit SF; NEDT Awd; LIU Stu Forum 86-87; JR Sci & Humanities Sympsm 86; Cert IN U Physics Tstng Comptn 87; Engrng.

JOHNSON, NATHANIEL; Avon Grove HS; Avondale, PA; (3); FBLA; JV Var Bsbl; JV Var Bsktbl; Var Trk; JV Var Wt Lftg; Hon Roll; Engl Awd 85; Algbr Awd 86.

JOHNSON, RHONDA; Connellsville JR H S West; Dunbar, PA; (1); Church Yth Grp; Pep Clb; Chorus; School Musical; Mgr(s); Score Keeper; Vllybl; Hon Roll; Jr NHS; Nrse.

JOHNSON, RICHARD; Geibel HS; Scottdale, PA; (3); VP Church Yth Grp; Drama Clb; French Clb; School Musical; Stage Crew; Yrbk Stf; JV Crs Cntry; French Hon Soc; High Hon Roll; NHS; Penn ST; Admn Jstc.

JOHNSON, SCOTT; Hempfield HS; E Petersburg, PA; (3); Chess Clb; Church Yth Grp; Im Wt Lftg; JV Wrstlng; Hon Roll; Bowling Capt 84-87; Ice & Street Hockey; CIT Of The Yr; Marine Bio.

JOHNSON, SCOTT; Manesen HS; Monessen, PA; (4); 2/93; Pres Stage Crew; Yrbk Phtg; Yrbk Sprt Ed; Stat Bsktbl; Capt Golf; Capt Tennis; Bausch & Lomb Sci Awd; High Hon Roll; NHS; Sal; Mnssn Hall Hnr Plque Awd & Schlrshp 86-87; Mlln Bnk Spcl Schlrshp 86-87; Amer Lgn Rnnr Up 83-84; U Of PA; Chem Engrng.

JOHNSON, SEAN; Brownsville HS; Brier-Hill, PA; (3); SADD; Band; Concert Band; Mrchg Band; Pep Band; Stage Crew; Fayette Cnty Band 87; Law.

JOHNSON, SEAN; Geibel HS; Connelsville, PA; (3); Boy Scts; Drama Clb; Pep Clb; Science Clb; Ski Clb; School Musical; School Play; Stage Crew; Crs Cntry; Ftbl; Pre-Dntstry.

JOHNSON, SHANNON M; J R Masterson HS; Philadelphia, PA; (4); 14/28; Church Yth Grp; Dance Clb; Stage Crew; Yrbk Stf; Var Tennis; Var Capt Vllybl; Hon Roll; Prfct Atten Awd; 1st Tm All Public Vllybl 86; 2nd Tm All Public Vllybl 85; Temple U; Pre-Med.

JOHNSON, SHELLEY; East Pennsboro HS; Enola, PA; (3); VP Spanish Clb; Var L Sftbl; Stat Trk; High Hon Roll; Hon Roll.

JOHNSON, SHERRI; Penn-Trafford HS; Jeannette, PA; (3); Drama Clb; FBLA; Hosp Aide; Latin Clb; Ski Clb; SADD; Rep Frsh Cls; Rep Soph Cls; High Hon Roll; Hon Roll; Nrse.

JOHNSON, SHERRY; Lehighton SR HS; Weissport, PA; (3); FHA; VICA; Flag Corp; High Hon Roll; Hon Roll; Csmtlgy.

JOHNSON, SHERRY; Western Beaver HS; Midland, PA; (3); Church Yth Grp; Cmnty Wkr; Drama Clb; FHA; Teachers Aide; Chorus; Concert Band; Mrchg Band; Symp Band; High Hon Roll; Pstv People Pwr Awd 87; IN U Of PA; Spec Educ.

JOHNSON, SIMON; West Catholic HS; Philadelphia, PA; (3); Girl Scts; Latin Clb; Library Aide; Scholastic Bowl; Science Clb; Chorus; Church Choir; Rep Jr Cls; Hon Roll; Sci Olympd Awd 85-86; Typwrtng Cert 87; Exmplry Stu Awd 87; Temple U; Nrsng.

JOHNSON, STEPHEN; Northwestern HS; Edinboro, PA; (3); Art Clb; Church Yth Grp; Cmnty Wkr; Trk; Hon Roll; Slippery Rock U; Phy Thrpy.

JOHNSON, TARIA; Chester HS; Chester, PA; (3); Chorus; Church Choir; Hon Roll; Prfct Atten Awd; 2 Excel Lttrs C Acadmc Achvmtn 85-87; UCLA; Bus.

JOHNSON, TERRY; Somerset Area SR HS; Somerset, PA; (3); Church Yth Grp; 4-H; FFA; SADD; Vllybl; CC Awd; High Hon Roll; Hon Roll; NHS; FFA Forestry Cntst Cnty, St, Natl 86; Allegany CC; Forestry.

JOHNSON, TIFFANY; Chester HS; Chester, PA; (3); 14/458; Art Clb; Spanish Clb; Teachers Aide; Stage Crew; Off Soph Cls; VP Stu Cncl; JV Mgr(s); Sftbl; Jr NHS; Prfct Atten Awd; Hghst Avg Trophy Span 86; Cert Merit Soc Studies 85-86 & 86-87; Excl Ltr Acadmc Achvt 87; U Of MD; Fshn Merch.

JOHNSON, TINA; Purchase Line HS; Mahaffey, PA; (2); VP Church Yth Grp; Pep Clb; Spanish Clb; Var Cheerleading; Stat Trk; Hon Roll; Math.

JOHNSON, TINNA; Towanda Area HS; Towanda, PA; (4); Capt Cheerleading; Sftbl; Hon Roll; Outstndng Edctn Stu Of Yr Awd 86-87; Spr Sprt Awd 86-87; Outstndng Schlstc Achvt Typng Awd 85-86; Bus Admin.

JOHNSON, TODD; Donegal HS; Mount Joy, PA; (4); Drama Clb; Chorus; Rep Frsh Cls; Musicn.

JOHNSON, TODD; Lincoln HS; Philadelphia, PA; (3); Computer Clb; Varsity Clb; Acpl Chr; Chorus; Madrigals; Variety Show; Var Capt Trk; Hon Roll; Prfct Atten Awd; Finc.

JOHNSON, TOMIKA; Creative & Performing Arts HS; Philadelphia, PA; (3); Dance Clb; Variety Show; Hon Roll; Chstnt Hill Coll; Bus Mngmnt.

JOHNSON, TORRI; The Ellis Schl; Clairton, PA; (3); Church Yth Grp; Speech Tm; SADD; Trs Church Choir; School Play; Pres Jr Cls; Im Badmtn; M L Tilley Schlrshp 84; Math.

JOHNSON, TREVOR; West Forest HS; Tionesta, PA; (3); Ski Clb; Var L Bsbl; Var L Bsktbl; Var L Socr; Hon Roll; Engrng.

JOHNSON, WADE; Pen Argyl Area HS; Wind Gap, PA; (3); 6/160; Boy Scts; Sec Church Yth Grp; Band; Chorus; Church Choir; Concert Band; Jazz Band; Mrchg Band; Pep Band; Variety Show; Bloomsburg U; Pre-Law.

JOHNSON, WESLEY D; York Suburban HS; York, PA; (3); Boy Scts; Church Yth Grp; Drama Clb; Ski Clb; Chorus; School Musical; School Play; Swing Chorus; JETS Awd; NHS; SE PA Section Of Am Chem Soc Schlrshp Awd In Chem 87; IUP Physics Testnt Comp Winner Of Recog 87; Medical Engrng.

JOHNSTON, ALYCE C; Central Dauphin East HS; Harrisburg, PA; (4); 12/247; Am Leg Aux Girls St; Art Clb; Pres Church Yth Grp; Ski Clb; Varsity Clb; Band; Chorus; Drill Tm; Drm Mjr(t); Jazz Band; Delta Sigma Theta Srty Schlrshp 87-88; Top 10 Pct JR Engrng Tst 87; Prncpls Awd Music, PE 87; Penn ST.

JOHNSTON, BARBARA; Washington HS; Washington, PA; (4); 7/149; Am Leg Aux Girls St; Pres French Clb; Girl Scts; Hosp Aide; Ski Clb; Band; Concert Band; Drm Mjr(t); Jazz Band; Mrchg Band; L Armstrng Jazz Awd 87; Alpha Delta Kappa Educ Schlrshp 87; Stu Of Mnth 87; IN U Of PA; Elem Educ.

JOHNSTON, BETH; East Pennsboro Area HS; Enola, PA; (3); 11/184; GAA; Model UN; Chorus; Concert Band; Madrigals; Mrchg Band; School Musical; Var Diving; Var L Tennis; Var L Trk; Travel.

JOHNSTON, CLARK; Penn Trafford HS; Irwin, PA; (4); Computer Clb; FBLA; Var Bsbl; Im Bsktbl; Im Ftbl; Im Capt Sftbl; Im Vllybl; Im Wrstlng; Hon Roll; Prfct Atten Awd; ICM Schl Of Business; Comps.

JOHNSTON, DAMIAN; Governor Mifflin HS; Shillington, PA; (3); 60/387; Chorus; Flag Corp; School Musical; Hon Roll; Madrigals; Mrchg Band; Orch; Variety Show; Yrbk Stf; Temple U; Bus Mgmt.

JOHNSTON, DAREN; Marion Center Area HS; Creekside, PA; (4); 15/169; VP FFA; Teachers Aide; Chorus; Church Choir; School Play; Mgr Stage Crew; High Hon Roll; Hon Roll; Star Chptr Frmr Deg 85; Str Grnhnd Deg 84; Kystn Frmr Deg 87; Educ.

JOHNSTON, DENNIS L; Beaver Area HS; Beaver, PA; (3); Band; Chorus; Jazz Band; School Musical; Var L Swmmng; High Hon Roll; NHS; Ntl Merit Ltr; Dist 5 Honors Band 87; Top Score Natl Math Exam 87.

JOHNSTON, DIANE; Saegertown HS; Ft Pierce, FL; (4); 13/105; Varsity Clb; Concert Band; Mrchg Band; Trs Jr Cls; Trs Sr Cls; L Sftbl; Co-Capt Vllybl; DAR Awd; Hon Roll; NHS; US Army Res Natl Schlr Ath Awd 87; Indian River CC Vllybl Scholar 87; DAR 86-87; Indian River CC; Bus Mgmt.

JOHNSTON, JULIE; St Marys Area HS; Kersey, PA; (2); Nrsng.

JOHNSTON, KRISTI; Mc Keesport Area SR HS; White Oak, PA; (3); NFL; Pep Clb; Speech Tm; Pres Acpl Chr; School Musical; School Play; Nwsp Rptr; Ed Nwsp Stf; Powder Puff Ftbl; Var Vllybl; Natl Forensic League Degree Merit & Hnr 86-87; Comm.

JOHNSTON, LAUREL; Freeport Area HS; Sarver, PA; (2); Drm Mjr(t); Nwsp Stf; Mgr(s); Twrlr; High Hon Roll; Hon Roll; Math.

JOHNSTON, MELANIE; North East HS; North East, PA; (4); 34/141; 4-H; Latin Clb; Bowling; Score Keeper; Sftbl; Vllybl; 4-H Awd; Hon Roll; Pres Schlr; Alg II High Hnrs Bst Grds 85-86; Engl High Hnrs 84-85; Wilson Coll; Vet Med Tech.

JOHNSTON, MICHELE; Lewistown Area HS; Lewistown, PA; (3); AFS; Key Clb; Acpl Chr; Chorus; School Musical; Rep Soph Cls; JV Capt Cheerleading; Im JV Fld Hcky; JV Trk; Hon Roll; Journlsm.

JOHNSTON, RHONDA; Ft Cherry JR SR HS; Mc Donald, PA; (3); 41/147; Drama Clb; Science Clb; Ski Clb; Chorus; High Hon Roll; Pittsburgh U; Nrs.

JOHNSTON, TRACEY; Punxsutawney Area HS; Big Run, PA; (2); Church Yth Grp; Cmnty Wkr; French Clb; Office Aide; Band; Concert Band; Drm Mjr(t); Mrchg Band; Trk; Hon Roll.

JOHNSTON, TRACY; Canon-Mc Millan SR HS; Canonsburg, PA; (4); Camera Clb; Drama Clb; FBLA; Ski Clb; Chorus; Church Choir; School Play; Nwsp Stf; High Hon Roll; NHS; Pres Phys Ftns Awd 87; Rgnl Secy Of Ftr Bus Ldrs 86-87; Drftng.

JOHNSTON, VICKI; Harmony Area HS; Westover, PA; (4); 1/50; Sec Trs Church Yth Grp; Teachers Aide; Band; Chorus; Church Choir; Mrchg Band; School Play; Nwsp Ed-Chief; VP Jr Cls; Stat Bsktbl; U Acad & Bonnie Winder Music Schlrshps 87; Slippery Rock U; Music.

JOHNSTONBAUGH, CASSIE; Bellefonte Area SR HS; Bellefonte, PA; (3); Trs Church Yth Grp; Chorus; Rep Frsh Cls; Pres Stu Cncl; Capt Twrlr; 3rd Pl Solo Comptn 87.

JOHOVIC, BARB; Shaler SR HS; Pittsburgh, PA; (3); 30/486; Church Yth Grp; Cheerleading; Mgr(s); Trk; Wt Lftg; Hnr Roll; Gvnrs Schl Applctn; Bnkng.

JOHREND, URSULA; Governor Mifflin HS; Reading, PA; (3); 51/326; Rep Jr Cls; Var L Cheerleading; Hon Roll; Jr NHS; Kutztown U; Elem Ed.

JOLL, SCOTT; Elizabeth Forward SR HS; Monongahela, PA; (3); Church Yth Grp; JV Bsbl; Var Golf; Hon Roll; Accntng.

JOLLEY, HEATHER; Scranton Central HS; Dunmore, PA; (3); Hst Art Clb; French Clb; JA.

JOLLY, ROBERT; Archbishop Wood For Boys; Warminster, PA; (3); Camera Clb; Stage Crew; Scholastic Bowl; Indvdl Hnr Engl; Bus Mgmt.

JONES, ADAM; Laurel Highlands HS; Uniontown, PA; (3); Ski Clb; Varsity Clb; Pres Soph Cls; Bsktbl; Ftbl; Wt Lftg; Penn ST; Psych.

JONES, ALBERT; Carlisle HS; Carlisle, PA; (4); 49/400; Boy Scts; Church Yth Grp; 4-H; Var L Bsbl; God Cntry Awd; Hon Roll; Elizabeth Adams Schlrshp, Allison United Methodist Chrch Schlrshp & George L Bowne Jr Accntng Awd 87; Shippensburg U; Bus Mgmt.

JONES, ALEXIS; Johnstown HS; Johnstown, PA; (3); Pep Clb; Rep Soph Cls; Rep Jr Cls; Var Bsktbl; Cit Awd; Hon Roll; Temple U; Bus Admin.

JONES, AMY; Juniata HS; Thompsontown, PA; (3); Church Yth Grp; Drama Clb; SADD; Concert Band; Mrchg Band; High Hon Roll; Hon Roll; NHS; Elem Tchng.

JONES, BETH; Mechanicsburg SR HS; Mechanicsburg, PA; (2); 39/309; Exploring; Girl Scts; Hosp Aide; SADD; School Play; Hon Roll; Girl Scout Slvr Awd 86; Fnlst Miss PA Natl Teenager 87; Order Of Red Flame Girl Scout 87; Dplmt.

JONES, BETH ANN; Charleroi Area HS; Charleroi, PA; (3); Church Yth Grp; Sec Pres 4-H; Hosp Aide; Spanish Clb; Rep SADD; Nwsp Rptr; Yrbk Phtg; Yrbk Stf; Stu Cncl; Hon Roll; Nrsng.

JONES, BRIAN; West Scranton HS; Scranton, PA; (3); Advrtsng.

JONES, CARRIE; Purchase Line HS; Mahaffey, PA; (2); FBLA; Pep Clb; Band; Concert Band; Flag Corp; Mrchg Band; Bus.

JONES, CHERRITTA CRAIG; Chester HS; Chester, PA; (3); 61/458; French Clb; FNA; Drill Tm; Sftbl; Howard U; Nurs.

JONES, CHRISTINE; Central HS; Philadelphia, PA; (3); Church Yth Grp; Civic Clb; Library Aide; Teachers Aide; Church Choir; School Musical; School Play; Variety Show; Yrbk Stf; High Hon Roll; Pre-Med.

JONES, CHRISTOPHER; North Clarion HS; Leeper, PA; (4); Boys Clb Am; Spanish Clb; Orch; Var Bsktbl; Var Tennis; Var Trk; Hon Roll; Jr NHS; 2nd Pl Dist IX Hgh Jmp 87; Clarion U; Finance.

JONES, CHRISTOPHER; Scott Intermediate HS; Coatesville, PA; (2); Pres Church Yth Grp; Chorus; Church Choir; Concert Band; Jazz Band; Mrchg Band; Orch; School Musical; Symp Band; High Hon Roll; Pres Acdmc Ftnss Awd 86-87; Music Ed.

JONES, CLARISSA; Pine Forge Acad; St Louis, MO; (3); Church Yth Grp; Hosp Aide; Pep Clb; Band; Chorus; Church Choir; School Play; Nwsp Stf; Off Frsh Cls; Cheerleading.

JONES, DAMON; Girard College; Philadelphia, PA; (3); VP Sr Cls; Var Wrstlng; High Hon Roll; Hon Roll; Boy Scts; Chess Clb; Exploring; Ski Clb; JV Bsbl; Daniel Fink Essy Awd-Cntst 81-82; Mst Imprvd Wrstlr 85-86; Bus Admin.

JONES II, DAVID; Newport JR SR HS; Newport, PA; (2); Pres Frsh Cls; JV Bsbl; JV Ftbl; Im Wt Lftg; Var Wrstlng; Hon Roll; Hugh Obrn Yth Awd 87; Bus Mangmnt.

JONES, DEBBIE; Meadville SR HS; Meadville, PA; (2); Church Yth Grp; French Clb; Off Stu Cncl; Hon Roll; Penn ST U; Acctng.

JONES, DEBORAH; Philadelphia-Montgomery Chrstn Acad; Ambler, PA; (3); 1/48; Art Clb; Church Yth Grp; Hosp Aide; Varsity Clb; VP Stu Cncl; JV Var Bsktbl; Var Capt Fld Hcky; JV Var Sftbl; High Hon Roll; NHS; Art.

JONES, DEBORAH; Wyoming Valley West HS; Larksville, PA; (2); Cmnty Wkr; French Clb; Hosp Aide; JV Fld Hcky; High Hon Roll; NHS; Prfct Atten Awd; Natl Hstry Day Dist Cont 2nd Pl 86-87; Vet.

JONES, DRAE MONIQUE; Villa Maria Acad; West Chester, PA; (3); 21/98; Library Aide; Chorus; Madrigals; Rep Soph Cls; Stu Cncl; U Of PA; Pol Sci.

JONES, ERIC; Perry Traditional Acad; Pittsburgh, PA; (3); 40/200; Drama Clb; Letterman Clb; Band; Concert Band; Jazz Band; Mrchg Band; Symp Band; Nwsp Phtg; Yrbk Phtg; Trk; U Of Pittsburgh; Pol Sci.

JONES, EVAN; Blue Mountain HS; Orwigsburg, PA; (4); 70/215; Quiz Bowl; School Play; Stage Crew; Nwsp Rptr; Nwsp Stf; Lit Mag; Stat Bsbl; JV Bsktbl; Hon Roll; Ntl German Hnr Soc; Jrnlst.

JONES, FELICIA; Aliquippa HS; Aliquippa, PA; (2); Church Yth Grp; Cmnty Wkr; French Clb; Hosp Aide; Library Aide; NAACP; Red Cross Aide; Trk; Hon Roll; Pres Schlr; Accntng.

JONES, GEORGE; Peters Township HS; Venetia, PA; (3); Varsity Clb; Var L Ftbl; Var L Trk; Wt Lftg; Mst Vlbl Jr 87 Track Team 87; Boston U; Physcl Thrpy.

JONES, HAZEL LYNNETTE; Villa Maria HS; Wheatland, PA; (4); 10/52; Church Yth Grp; Cmnty Wkr; French Clb; Hosp Aide; NAACP; Pep Clb; Yrbk Rptr; Lit Mag; French Hon Soc; NHS; Ldrshp Ed Devlpmt Cert Achvt Wharton Bus Schl U Of Penn 86; U Of PA; Nrsg.

JONES, HEATHER; Mahanoy Area HS; Mahanoy City, PA; (4); 5/110; French Clb; Band; Chorus; Concert Band; Mrchg Band; School Musical; Yrbk Stf; NHS; Drama Clb; FHA; Pres Acad Ftnss Awd 87; Schuykill Cnty Med Scty Awd 87; Muhlenberg Coll; Pre-Med.

JONES, HELEN; Blacklick Valley HS; Vintondale, PA; (3); 4/100; Church Yth Grp; JA; Spanish Clb; High Hon Roll; Jr NHS; Prfct Atten Awd; Rutgers U.

JONES, HELENA; Bucktail Area HS; Renovo, PA; (2); Church Yth Grp; Library Aide; Varsity Clb; Band; Concert Band; Mrchg Band; Pep Band; Bsktbl; Sftbl; Hon Roll; Outstndng JR Hgh Band Cmp Musician 85-86; PA ST U; Engrng.

JONES, JASON H; Saltsburg JR SR HS; Slickville, PA; (1); Cmnty Wkr; Variety Show; Rep Stu Cncl; Ftbl; Wrstlng; High Hon Roll; Penn ST U; Engrng.

JONES, JEFFREY; Burgettstown Area HS; Joffre, PA; (3); Church Yth Grp; French Clb; Ski Clb; Var L Ftbl; Wt Lftg; Hon Roll; Jr NHS; NHS; Embry-Riddle Aero U; Aero Sci.

JONES, JILL; Tussey Mountain HS; Robertsdale, PA; (4); 5/116; AFS; Band; Yrbk Stf; High Hon Roll; NHS; Pres Schlr; VFW Awd; Hlth Career Schlrshp 87; Slippery Rock U; Phys Thrpy.

JONES, JOE; Philipsburg SR HS; Philipsburg, PA; (4); Letterman Clb; Hon Roll; Var L Bsbl; Im Wt Lftg; JV Wrstlng; Alf Jones Awd Mst Imprvd Bsbl Plyr 87; Altoona U; Sprts Med.

JONES, JOHN; Middleburg HS; Middleburg, PA; (3); Chess Clb; Pres Varsity Clb; JV Bsbl; JV Var Bsktbl; JV Var Socr; Hon Roll; Prfct Atten Awd; Computer Science.

JONES, JONATHAN; Father Judge HS; Philadelphia, PA; (4); 33/358; Var Crs Cntry; Var JV Trk; La Salle U; Accntng.

JONES, KADIJAH; Philadelphia HS For Girls; Philadelphia, PA; (4); 27/365; Teachers Aide; Var L Trk; French Hon Soc; Hon Roll; NHS; Ntl Merit Ltr; Natl Achvt Fin 86; PSPE Chptr Fin 87; Board Ed Awd Achvt 87; Johns Hopkins U; Biomed Engr.

JONES, KAREN; Downingtown SR HS; Downingtown, PA; (4); 56/551; Church Yth Grp; Red Cross Aide; VP Spanish Clb; Capt Mrchg Band; Stu Cncl; Var Capt Bsktbl; High Hon Roll; Hon Roll; NHS; GAA; Hnrb John E Colman Acad Achvt Awd 86; Outstndg Amer Stu Awd 86-87; Gregg Typing Awd 85; Temple U; Pre-Med.

JONES, KATHERINE; Warren Area HS; Warren, PA; (3); Church Yth Grp; Cmnty Wkr; French Clb; Hosp Aide; High Hon Roll; Hon Roll; Jr NHS.

JONES, KATHLEEN; Saint Huberts HS; Philadelphia, PA; (3); 11/421; Hon Roll; Excel Engl Awd; Survey Am Cltr; Hnrb Mntn Acctng Awd; Bus Adm.

JONES, KATHY; Bishop Mc Devitt HS; Harrisburg, PA; (4); 28/176; FBLA; Church Choir; Yrbk Stf; Hon Roll; NHS; Church Yth Grp; Computer Clb; 4-H; Library Aide; Service Clb; Cert Merit Frnch II 85; 2nd Steno Rgnl Ldrshp Conf 86; Acctg.

JONES, KATRINA; Johnsonburg Area JR-SR HS; Johnsonburg, PA; (3); Camera Clb; Pres Church Yth Grp; Varsity Clb; VP Jr Cls; Sec VP Stu Cncl; Var Capt Cheerleading; Hon Roll; Prfct Atten Awd; Acad All-Amer 85 & 86; Hotel Mgmnt.

JONES, KEVIN; Danville Area HS; Danville, PA; (2); 9/165; Church Yth Grp; Letterman Clb; Trk; God Cntry Awd; Hon Roll; The Pres Acad Fit Awd 86; Astronomy.

JONES, KIMBERLY; Windber Area HS; Windber, PA; (3); Sec Band; Concert Band; Mrchg Band; Yrbk Bus Mgr; High Hon Roll; VP NHS; Pres Schlr; French Clb; Pep Band; Nwsp Stf; IN U Of PA Hnrs Band; Dist & Rgnl ST Band; Hlth.

JONES, KRISTIN; West Mifflin Area HS; W Mifflin, PA; (3); 78/310; JA; Key Clb; Pep Clb; Ski Clb; Color Guard; VP Jr Cls; Sr Cls; Sec Bsbl; Hon Roll; NHS; Indiana U Of PA; Pre-Law.

JONES, LARA; Pittston Area HS; Pittston, PA; (4); Church Yth Grp; Computer Clb; Key Clb; Math Clb; VP Science Clb; SADD; Var Capt Swmmng; Hon Roll; Drexel U; Fnc.

JONES, LAURA J; Kutztown Area HS; Kutztown, PA; (4); 6/149; Band; Chorus; School Musical; School Play; Variety Show; Stat Bsktbl; Var Tennis; High Hon Roll; NHS; Ntl Merit SF; Ursinus Coll.

JONES, LEAH; Central Bucks East HS; Gardenville, PA; (4); FBLA; Color Guard; High Hon Roll; Hon Roll; La Salle U; Chem.

JONES, LEIGH; Juniata HS; Thompsontown, PA; (3); 1/200; Drama Clb; SADD; Band; Mrchg Band; School Musical; School Play; Yrbk Stf; JV Sftbl; High Hon Roll; NHS.

JONES, LISA; Pittston Area SR HS; Avoca, PA; (3); 82/305; Dance Clb; Drama Clb; Key Clb; Ski Clb; Color Guard; Diving; Bio.

JONES, LORI A; Sacred Heart HS; Pittsburgh, PA; (4); Church Yth Grp; Latin Clb; Chorus; School Musical; Variety Show; High Hon Roll; Hon Roll; Natl Achvt Scholar Fin 87; Inroads 84-85; Howard U; Bio.

JONES, MAURICE K; Murrell Dobbins AVTS; Philadelphia, PA; (4); 8/450; VICA; JV Ftbl; Var Trk; Hon Roll; NHS; Delta Sigma Theta Scholar 87-88; Omega Psi Phi Scholar 87-88; Instrmnt Soc Amer Awd 86-87; NC A&T ST U; Elctcl Engrng.

JONES, MEGAN M; Palisades HS; Springtown, PA; (3); 1/240; Am Leg Aux Girls St; Art Clb; Church Yth Grp; Chorus; Madrigals; School Musical; Rep Stu Cncl; Var Fld Hcky; High Hon Roll; Pres NHS; ST Future Problm Tm-ST Champns 85; Yth Schlrs Inst At Lebanon Vly 87; Applied Sci.

JONES, MEREDITH; Peters Township HS; Mcmurray, PA; (3); 45/280; SADD; Yrbk Bus Mgr; Powder Puff Ftbl; Var Vllybl; Spanish NHS; Vllybll Ltrmn 87; Law.

JONES, MICHELLE; Oswayo Valley JR SR HS; Shinglehouse, PA; (3); French Clb; Letterman Clb; Ski Clb; Varsity Clb; Color Guard; Madrigals; Off Soph Cls; Mgr(s); Vllybl; NHS; Sec Sci.

JONES, MICHELLE; Purchase Line HS; Commodore, PA; (2); Pep Clb; Scholastic Bowl; Spanish Clb; Band; Mrchg Band; Cheerleading; High Hon Roll; Prfct Atten Awd; 2nd Pl Nwsp Ed Awd 86; American U; Lawyr.

JONES, MICHELLE J; Philadelphia HS For Girls; Philadelphia, PA; (3); 185/405; Office Aide; Nwsp Rptr; Bus Mngmnt.

JONES, MIKE; Bradford Area HS; Bradford, PA; (3); Art Clb; Pres Chess Clb; VP Computer Clb; Hon Roll; Prfct Atten Awd; NY HS Stu Chss Chmpn 85-87; USA Jr Chss Olympics Chss Chmpn 84-87; East Syracuse Schlstc Co-Chmp 84.

JONES, MIKE; Penn Hills SR HS; Pittsburgh, PA; (3); Spanish Clb; Hon Roll; Physical Therapy.

JONES, NANCIANNE; West Scranton HS; Scranton, PA; (2); Church Yth Grp; Dance Clb; Drama Clb; FBLA; Hosp Aide; Spanish Clb; Thesps; Hon Roll; US Nvl Acad; US Navy.

JONES, NICOLE; Portage Area HS; Portage, PA; (3); 1/110; Church Yth Grp; Chorus; Capt Twrlr; High Hon Roll; Chem 1 Awd 85-86; Biochem.

JONES, NICOLE MARIA; Carlisle SR HS; Carlisle, PA; (4); 241/397; Church Yth Grp; Office Aide; Political Wkr; Y-Teens; Variety Show; Im Bsktbl; Cheerleading; JV Score Keeper; Im Sftbl; Var Capt Trk; FL A&M Outstndng Stdnt Awd 86; Attnd PA 8th Annl Blck Hstry Semnr 85; PA Free Entrprs Wk 86; Francis Marion Coll; Army Ofcr.

JONES, PAIGE; North Allegheny SR HS; Pittsburgh, PA; (3); GAA; Hosp Aide; Radio Clb; Service Clb; VP Jr Cls; Rep Stu Cncl; Im Powder Puff Ftbl; L JV Sftbl; JV Vllybl; Im Wt Lftg; 1st Pl Schl Sci Fair 84-85; Awd Cert Cmpltng Prjct Bus 86; Instrctr Ldrshp Wrkshps Stu Cncl Conf 85-87; Pre-Law.

JONES, PAMELA; Bishop O Reilly HS; Larksville, PA; (3); Cmnty Wkr; Stage Crew; JV Var Fld Hcky; Score Keeper; Hon Roll; PA JR Acad Sci ST Meet 2nd Awd 85-87, Rgnl 2nd Awd 86, & Rgnl 1st Awd 85-87; Pre Med.

JONES, PATRICIA; Northeast Bradford HS; Rome, PA; (4); 5/78; VP Pres 4-H; Sec Varsity Clb; Band; Chorus; JV Cheerleading; Gym; High Hon Roll; NHS; Cntstnt-Brffrd/Sllvn Cnty JR Miss Pgnt 86; Kystn ST Gms-Gymnstcs 86; Schlrshp-Mdcl Fld 87; Mansfield U; Nrsng.

JONES, PAUL; Wyoming Valley West HS; Kingston, PA; (4); 27/380.

JONES, PAULA M; Villa Maria Acad; Malvern, PA; (3); 47/97; Math Tm; Rep Frsh Cls; Rep Jr Cls; Sec Stu Cncl; Fld Hcky; Hon Roll; Supr Plus Rtng Natl Guild Audtions 87; 1st Pl PMTA Fstvl 86 & 87; Msc Prfrmr.

JONES, RANDY; Waynesburg Central HS; Spraggs, PA; (4); Computer Clb; Chorus; Concert Band; Mrchg Band; Mgr(s); Trk; Wrstlng; High Hon Roll; Hon Roll; NHS; Computer Sys Inst; Comp Prgmr.

JONES, RAY; North Catholic HS; Allison Park, PA; (3); German Clb; Red Cross Aide; Spanish Clb; School Play; Yrbk Stf; Stat Bsktbl; Outstndg Partcptn In JR Clss N Catholic 87; Hist.

JONES, REBECCA; Penn-Trafford HS; Harrison City, PA; (2); FBLA; Girl Scts; JCL; Latin Clb; Quiz Bowl; Teachers Aide; Nwsp Stf; Lit Mag; High Hon Roll; Hon Roll; 1st Pl Natl ST Knwldg Mstrs Bowl Open 85; ST Latin Certamen 2nd Pl 87; Region Latin Oratory 2nd Pl; Med.

JONES, REBECCA; Philadelphia Christian Acad; Ambler, PA; (1); Church Yth Grp; Chorus; Church Choir; Bsktbl; Fld Hcky; Sftbl; High Hon Roll.

JONES, RICHARD; Carver HS Of Engineering & Science; Philadelphia, PA; (3); 91/241; Chess Clb; Debate Tm; Model UN; Stage Crew; Yrbk Stf; Mock Trail Team 86-87; Law.

JONES JR, RICHARD D; Penn Hills HS; Pittsburgh, PA; (4); 75/610; French Clb; Ski Clb; Bsbl; Ftbl; Golf; Wt Lftg; Hon Roll; NHS; Penn ST U; Bus Admin.

JONES, SHARON; John W Hallahan HS; Philadelphia, PA; (3); 77/328; Church Yth Grp; Hosp Aide; Library Aide; Office Aide; Cit Awd; Ellis Grnt 84-88; Excllnc Acctng I 87; Career Explrtn Prjct 84-88; Drexel U; Bus Admin.

JONES, STEPHANIE; Parkland SR HS; Neffs, PA; (2); Office Aide; JV Fld Hcky; JV Sftbl.

JONES, STEPHEN; Hershey SR HS; Hershey, PA; (3); 5/209; School Musical; Stage Crew; Yrbk Stf; JV Socr; High Hon Roll; NHS; Finance.

JONES, STEVE; James Buchanan HS; St Thomas, PA; (3); Trs 4-H; Boy Scts; Pres FFA; Hon Roll; 4-H Baby Beef & Pig & Rabt Clbs; Ag.

JONES, STEVEN; Connellsville SR HS; Mt Pleasant, PA; (2); VP Soph Cls; Hon Roll; Gftd Pgm; Med.

JONES, SUE; Solanco HS; Nottingham, PA; (4); Church Yth Grp; Cmnty Wkr; Hosp Aide; Office Aide; Band; Concert Band; Mrchg Band; School Musical; Yrbk Stf; Crs Cntry; Shippensburg U; Acctng.

JONES, TAMMY; Panther Valley HS; Nesquehoning, PA; (3); 38/139; Am Leg Aux Girls St; Church Yth Grp; ROTC; Cheerleading; Hon Roll; Allentown Coll; Accntng.

JONES, TASHA; Magnet Program Of Grmntwn; Philadelphia, PA; (4); Church Yth Grp; Civic Clb; Cmnty Wkr; Debate Tm; Drama Clb; Office Aide; Political Wkr; Teachers Aide; Pep Band; Vllybl; Schl Dist Awd 3rd Pl Ortrcl Cont 86; Cncl City Phila 86; Pol Sci.

JONES, TERRENCE; John Bartram HS; Philadelphia, PA; (3); Computer Clb; Exploring; 4-H; Library Aide; Band; Church Choir; Mrchg Band; Orch; Rep Jr Cls; Hon Roll; Comp Sci.

JONES, TERRY; York Catholic HS; York, PA; (3); FBLA; Varsity Clb; Chorus; Var Bsktbl; Var Ftbl; Var Trk; Acctng.

JONES, THEODORE; Owen J Roberts SR HS; Pottstown, PA; (2); 4/311; Boy Scts; Church Yth Grp; JV Socr; JV Trk; High Hon Roll; Hon Roll; Math.

JONES, THOMAS; West Perry HS; Shermansdale, PA; (3); Boy Scts; Computer Clb; Var Ftbl; Var Trk; Var Wrstlng; Hon Roll; Coaches Awd-Wrstlng 86-87; Elect.

JONES JR, THOMAS; Penn-Trafford HS; Manor, PA; (3); Var L Golf; Im Sftbl; JV Trk.

JONES, THOS; Carlisle SR HS; Carlisle, PA; (3); 107/547; JA; Political Wkr; Hon Roll; Carlisle Area Sci Advsry Cmmtte 4th Pl Bio 85.

JONES, TODD; West Allegheny HS; Imperial, PA; (4); 28/202; Chorus; Nwsp Rptr; Nwsp Stf; Lit Mag; Cheerleading; Coach Actv; Swmmng; High Hon Roll; Hon Roll; Lion Awd; Top 6 In ST Swmmng; Schlrshp For Swmmng; Dist Chorus; IN U Of PA; Comm.

JONES, TODD M; Burgettstown Area HS; Paris, PA; (2); French Clb; Ski Clb; Band; Jazz Band; Mrchg Band; Pep Band; VP Stu Cncl; Tennis; Hon Roll; Jr NHS; Rutgers; Med.

JONES, TRACEY; West Allegheny HS; Oakdale, PA; (2); 25/230; Art Clb; Drama Clb; Spanish Clb; Band; Chorus; Color Guard; Flag Corp; Mrchg Band; Swmmng; Hon Roll; 3rd Pl-Art Shw 87; Art.

JONES, TRACY; Germantown HS; Philadelphia, PA; (4); 3/362; Cmnty Wkr; Teachers Aide; Yrbk Ed-Chief; High Hon Roll; Jr NHS; NHS; Spanish NHS; Voice Dem Awd; Merit Afro-Amrcn Stds; G-Pin Awd Svc & Hgh Stndrds; Philadelphia Coll; Med Tech.

JONES, VALERIE; Wyoming Area Senior HS; West Pittston, PA; (3); Church Yth Grp; Civic Clb; German Clb; Chorus; Color Guard; Flag Corp; Mrchg Band; Band; Gold Music Awd, Lake Lehman March Of Champions 1st 86; Penn ST; Marine Bio.

JONES, VICTORIA; Blue Mountain HS; Orwigsburg, PA; (1); 30/217; Hosp Aide; Stage Crew; Hon Roll; Radiology.

JONES, WENDY; William Allen HS; Allentown, PA; (2); Exploring; Hon Roll; Jr NHS.

JONES, WILLIAM; Roman Catholic HS; Philadelphia, PA; (3); Art Clb; Civic Clb; Hon Roll; Bus Adm.

JONES, YOLANDA; John Harris HBG HS; Harrisburg, PA; (1); 35/500; Church Choir; Hon Roll; Prfct Atten Awd; Pittsburg U; Sec Sci.

JONESII, DAVID W; Allen HS; Allentown, PA; (3); 150/700; Ski Clb; Varsity Clb; Var Capt Bsbl; Var JV Bsktbl; Var Capt Ftbl; Hon Roll; NHS; Chem.

JORDAN, CHRIS; Keystone JR-SR HS; Parker, PA; (3); Chess Clb; Church Yth Grp; VP FFA; Spanish Clb; Rep Stu Cncl; Hon Roll; Star Greenhand FFA 85; Star Chptr Farmer FFA 86; Comp Engr.

JORDAN, DANA MARIE; Philadelphia HS For Girls; Philadelphia, PA; (4); 89/365; Pres Church Yth Grp; Civic Clb; Hosp Aide; Office Aide; Acpl Chr; Pres Church Choir; Yrbk Stf; Hon Roll; Hnrbl Joseph E Coleman Acdmc Achvmnt Awd 86; Lauretta W Carter JR Svc Awd 87; Dozoretz Natl Inst 87; Norfolk ST U; Comp Sci.

JORDAN, JEANNETTE; Montour HS; Pittsburgh, PA; (3); Church Yth Grp; Girl Scts; SADD; Concert Band; Mrchg Band; Yrbk Stf; Bowling; Var Swmmng; High Hon Roll; Hon Roll; NHS; Math.

JORDAN, JEFFREY; Geibel HS; Uniontown, PA; (3); 23/109; Boy Scts; Drama Clb; Stage Crew; Nwsp Rptr; Yrbk Phtg; Yrbk Stf; High Hon Roll; PJAS 1st Pl Region & 2nd St 86; U Pittsburgh; Phy Thrpst.

JORDAN, JOE; Mc Keesport Area HS; Mckeesport, PA; (4); 47/350; U Of Pittsburgh; Mech Engr.

JORDAN, JONATHAN; Delaware County Christian Schl; Kennett Sq, PA; (4); Church Yth Grp; Nwsp Rptr; Rep Soph Cls; Rep Sr Cls; Var JV Bsbl; Tennis; High Hon Roll; Pres Schlr; ACSI; Dstnghd Chrstn HS Stu Awd 86; Bates Coll; Law.

JORDAN, KAREN; St Marys Area HS; Kersey, PA; (4); Trs Sec Church Yth Grp; Cmnty Wkr; Capt Color Guard; Hon Roll; Prfct Atten Awd; Outstndng Band Stu, Capt Rifl Sqd 86-87; Waynesburg Coll; Chem.

JORDAN, KATHLEEN; Nazareth Acad; Phila, PA; (4); Hosp Aide; JCL; Latin Clb; Math Clb; Service Clb; Spanish Clb; Chorus; Orch; School Musical; Nwsp Rptr; Summa Cum Laude-Latin I 87; Pltcl Sci.

JORDAN, KELI; Otto-Eldred JR- SR HS; Eldred, PA; (3); Spanish Clb; SADD; Varsity Clb; Lit Mag; Stu Cncl; JV Capt Bsktbl; Trk; Twrlr; Hon Roll; NHS; Phy Ed & Engl IIA Awd 87; Gannon U; Optometry.

JORDAN, KELLY LYNN; North Schuykill HS; Frackville, PA; (4); 1/170; Trs Science Clb; Ski Clb; Stat Bsbl; Var Capt Cheerleading; Trk; High Hon Roll; Trs NHS; Val; Hugh O Brien Yth Awd 85; Goulds Pump Co Awd For Math & Sci 87; UNICO Cnty Chapter Schlrshp 87; Villanova U; Elec Engrng.

JORDAN, KRISTIE; North Schuylkill HS; Trackville, PA; (3); 14/200; Aud/Vis; Math Tm; Rep Jr Cls; Sec Stu Cncl; Cheerleading; Gym; Trk; High Hon Roll; Hon Roll; Art.

JORDAN, MARCI; Punxsutawney Area SR HS; Punxsutawney, PA; (4); 91/245; Color Guard; Mrchg Band; Variety Show; Masonic Awd; Mary Ann Irvin Schlrshp 87; Gftd Prog 83-87; IN U Of PA; Acctg.

JORDAN, MARK; Brownsville Area HS; Grindstone, PA; (3); Var Wrstlng; High Hon Roll; Jr NHS; Army.

JORDAN, MICHAEL; Devon Prep; Broomall, PA; (1); Pres Frsh Cls; Rep Stu Cncl; Var Bsbl; Bsktbl; High Hon Roll; Harvard; Engrng.

JORDAN, SHARLENE; Neshaminy HS; Langhorne, PA; (3); 89/780; Pep Clb; Ski Clb; Band; Chorus; Concert Band; Jazz Band; Mrchg Band; Orch; Symp Band; Cheerleading; Psych.

JORDAN, SUZANNE; Schuylkill Valley HS; Mohrsville, PA; (4); Ski Clb; Temple Yth Grp; Chorus; Church Choir; School Musical; Nwsp Rptr; Nwsp Stf; Yrbk Ed-Chief; Yrbk Stf; Pres Soph Cls; Antonelli Inst/Art/Photo; Photo.

JORDAN, TIMOTHY; Tunkhannock Area HS; Tunkhannock, PA; (3); Computer Clb; Drama Clb; Latin Clb; Chorus; School Musical; School Play; Swmmng; Natl Latin Exam Cert Of Merit Cum Laude 85-86; Natl Schlstc Art Cont Cert Of Merit 86-87; Psych.

JORDAN, TONY; Quaker Valley HS; Fair Oaks, PA; (2); Church Yth Grp; JV Bsktbl; Hon Roll; Ntl Merit Ltr; Acad All-Amer 86; Acctng.

JORDEN, AMY; Bishop Guilfoyle HS; Altoona, PA; (3); 8/156; Science Clb; Ski Clb; Spanish Clb; SADD; Teachers Aide; High Hon Roll; Hon Roll; Bio Tchr.

JORGENSEN, KARIN L; Pennsbury HS; Yardley, PA; (3); Church Yth Grp; Concert Band; Mrchg Band; Orch; School Musical; School Play; Stage Crew; Rep Stu Cncl; Hon Roll; Bucks County Band 85-87; Dist II Band & Orchestra 86-87.

JORGENSON, DAN; Saltsburg JR SR HS; Clarksburg, PA; (1); 25/74; Church Yth Grp; Rep Stu Cncl; Bsktbl; Hon Roll; Crmnlgy.

JORIS, LORI; Belle Vernon Area HS; Belle Vernon, PA; (4); 17/267; Ski Clb; VP Band; VP Concert Band; VP Mrchg Band; Powder Puff Ftbl; High Hon Roll; NHS; St Vincent Coll Acdmc Schlrshp; Grad 10 Pct Clss; St Vincent Coll; Chem.

JORSTAD, GUY; Knoch JR/Sr HS; Cabot, PA; (4); Church Yth Grp; Chorus; School Musical; School Play; Stage Crew; High Hon Roll; Hon Roll; NHS; Voice Dem Awd; Grove City Coll; Engrng.

JOSE, SONIA; Du Bois Area SR HS; Dubois, PA; (2); 74/311; Chorus; Church Choir; Flag Corp; Mrchg Band; Hon Roll; 10th Pl Xmas Essy Cont 86; Biology Education.

JOSEPH, ALLAN; Hanover Area HS; Wilkes Barre, PA; (4); 9/160; Golf; High Hon Roll; Pres NHS; NPAAA Achvmnt Schlrshp 87; Penn ST U Park; Lib Arts.

JOSEPH, BETH; Kiski Area HS; Export, PA; (4); Church Yth Grp; Cmnty Wkr; Drama Clb; French Clb; NFL; Chorus; School Play; Ed Nwsp Rptr; Rep Frsh Cls; Hon Roll; Co Chrs-Westmoreland 86-87; IN U Of PA; Scndry Educ.

JOSEPH, DIANA; New Castle SR HS; New Castle, PA; (3); Cmnty Wkr; French Clb; NFL; Concert Band; Mrchg Band; Nwsp Rptr; Stu Cncl; Hon Roll; Acdmc Gms Locl & ST & Natl Levls 84-87; Yth Pg 86-87; U Of Pittsburgh.

JOSEPH, JOHN; Connellsville Area HS; Connellsville, PA; (1); Church Yth Grp; Teachers Aide; Capt L Bsktbl; Var L Trk; JC Awd; Sec Jr NHS; Presdntl Physcl Ftnss Awd 87; Mst Wtty 86; Prfct Atten 87; Bus Mgmt.

JOSEPH, JOHNYEL; Coatesville Area SR HS; Coatesville, PA; (3); 210/510; FBLA; Off Sr Cls; Stu Cncl; JV Bsktbl; Hon Roll; Girl Scts; SADD; Awd For Most Teachable 84-85; Bsktbl Awd 85-86; Accntng.

JOSEPH, LAURIE; Connellsville Area HS; Connellsville, PA; (4); 7/560; GAA; Spanish Clb; Varsity Clb; Chorus; Pres Soph Cls; Pres Sr Cls; Rep Stu Cncl; Var Capt Bsktbl; Stat Mgr(s); Var L Trk; Gettysburg; Pre-Vet.

JOSEPH, PETER T; East Stroudsburg HS; E Stroudsburg, PA; (4); Cmnty Wkr; Model UN; Political Wkr; Var L Ftbl; Var Capt Tennis; High Hon Roll; Best All Around Male Ath Of Yr 87; Muhlenberg; Law.

JOSHI, APARNA; Slippery Rock Area HS; Slippery Rock, PA; (4); 1/172; Am Leg Aux Girls St; Hosp Aide; Sec JCL; Math Tm; Mrchg Band; Pres Sr Cls; Bausch & Lomb Sci Awd; DAR Awd; Pres NHS; Val; Northwestern U; Med Ed.

JOSHI, KALPESH; Cedar Crest HS; Lebanon, PA; (4); 16/306; FBLA; German Clb; Var L Socr; Var L Tennis; High Hon Roll; NHS; Sect Champs Tnns 87; U PA; Intl Finance.

JOSHI, MANISH; Liberty HS; Bethlehem, PA; (3); 16/429; Bsktbl; High Hon Roll; Hon Roll; NHS; Cert Of Achvt In Math Contest At Lehigh U 86-87; Cert Of Achvt In Nat Hist Day 87; Math.

JOSHI, PARUL; Methacton HS; Audubon, PA; (3); 24/381; JA; Red Cross Aide; Nwsp Rptr; Rep Jr Cls; Mgr(s); JV Tennis; JV Trk; High Hon Roll; Hon Roll; Jr NHS; Shmr Achvt Awd 86; Med.

JOSLIN, CINDY; Northwestern HS; W Springfield, PA; (3); French Clb; Nwsp Stf; Powder Puff Ftbl; JV Var Sftbl; Hon Roll; Erie Bus Ctr; Exec Secy.

JOVER, DOREEN; Valleyview HS; Peckville, PA; (4); 7/195; French Clb; Latin Clb; Vllybl; High Hon Roll; Hon Roll; NHS; Hnrb Mntn Natl Fren Cont; Amer Bus Womns Assoc Schlrshp; U Scranton; Psych.

JOY, JASON; Laurel Highlands HS; Uniontown, PA; (3); 1/375; Church Yth Grp; Hosp Aide; Science Clb; Band; Concert Band; Jazz Band; Mrchg Band; Pep Band; Nwsp Rptr; CC Awd; Provost Day Math Comp U Pittsburgh 1st Pl 87; Chem.

JOY, MARY; West Hazelton HS; Drums, PA; (3); 48/221; Dance Clb; Varsity Clb; Pres Band; Concert Band; Pres Mrchg Band; Var Cheerleading; Hon Roll; NHS; Pres Schlr; Marywood Coll; Intr Dsgn.

JOY, WILLIAM T; West Hazleton HS; Drums, PA; (2); French Clb; Stage Crew; Yrbk Phtg; Yrbk Stf; Im Bsktbl; Var Golf; Im Vllybl.

JOYCE, ALANA; West Scranton HS; Scranton, PA; (2); Cheerleading; Sftbl; Hosp Aide; Letterman Clb; Spanish Clb; Dentst.

JOYCE, PATRICK A; Shady Side Acad; Pittsburgh, PA; (4); Letterman Clb; Jazz Band; Yrbk Rptr; Lcrss; Socr; High Hon Roll; Hon Roll; Ntl Merit SF; German Clb; Variety Show; 1st Yr German Prz 83; John L Gray Lang Awd 84; Ltr Wnr Sccr & Lacrosse 84-86; Comm.

JOYCE, TRACY; Penn-Trafford HS; Manor, PA; (2); FBLA; SADD; Yrbk Stf; Advertisement.

JOYNES, ALAN; Bock AVT Schl; Philadelphia, PA; (3); 3/260; Church Yth Grp; Varsity Clb; Rep Sr Cls; Var Bsbl; Var JV Ftbl; Var Trk; Hon Roll; NHS; Stu Of Mnth 87; Class Advsry Pres 86; Elect Tech.

JOZEFIK, DREW; West Branch Area JR/SR HS; Kylertown, PA; (4); 1/129; Boy Scts; Drama Clb; Science Clb; SADD; Band; Chorus; Concert Band; Mrchg Band; Nwsp Ed-Chief; Var Bsktbl; Eagle Scout 83; Eastern Nazarene Coll; Law.

JUANG, OLIVER; Mc Dowell HS; Erie, PA; (3); 2/600; Debate Tm; German Clb; Model UN; Ski Clb; Trk; High Hon Roll; Kiwanis Awd; NHS; Ntl Merit Ltr; Med.

JUCHNO, ROBERT T; Fort Le Boeuf HS; Erie, PA; (3); Church Yth Grp; Nwsp Stf; Var Bsbl; Var Capt Bsktbl; Im Ftbl; Im Socr; Im Sftbl; Im Vllybl; High Hon Roll; Hon Roll.

JUCKNIK, STACY; Louis E Dieruff HS; Allentown, PA; (2); 18/403; Church Yth Grp; Quiz Bowl; Var Capt Cheerleading; Stat Gym; Var Powder Puff Ftbl; Stat Score Keeper; Hon Roll; Opt Clb Awd; Prfct Atten Awd; Hstry Day 85; Psych.

JUDD, BRYAN; Abraham Lincoln HS; Philadelphia, PA; (3); 25/600; Hon Roll; Drexel Coll; Elctrcl Engrng.

JUDGE, JOHN; West Scranton HS; Scranton, PA; (3); Boys Clb Am; Church Yth Grp; Letterman Clb; Political Wkr; Spanish Clb; Rep Frsh Cls; Rep Soph Cls; JV Ftbl; Var Golf; JV Trk; Crmnl Just.

JUDGE, LESLIE; G. A. R. Memorial HS; Wilkes-Barre, PA; (4); 4/171; Church Choir; Flag Corp; Orch; Pres Sr Cls; Stu Cncl; Bsktbl; High Hon Roll; Jr NHS; NHS; Outstndng Sci Stu 84; Comp Sci.

JUGAN, DONALD J; Owen J Roberts HS; Phoenixville, PA; (3); 11/299; German Clb; Library Aide; Quiz Bowl; School Musical; School Play; Yrbk Stf; Socr; Hon Roll; NHS; PA ST; Elec Engrng.

JULIAN, SHANE; Tyrone Area HS; Altoona, PA; (3); Computer Clb; Math Tm; Ski Clb; Spanish Clb; Bsbl; Ftbl; Wrstlng; High Hon Roll; Math Leag 3rd Pl 87; Outstndng Comp Stu 87; Altoona Campus Penn ST; Math.

JULIAN, SHARON; Clairton HS; Clairton, PA; (3); Drill Tm; Sec Jr Cls; High Hon Roll; NHS.

JULIAN, VALERIE; Elizabeth Forward HS; Monongahela, PA; (3); 69/330; Latin Clb; Yrbk Phtg; Yrbk Stf; Vllybl; High Hon Roll; Hon Roll; U Of Pittsburgh; Occu Thrpy.

JULIAS, CHRIS; Carlisle SR HS; Carlisle, PA; (3); 128/474; Yrbk Phtg; JV Crs Cntry; JV Wrstlng; Chem.

JUNAS, KRISTIN; Hazelton HS; Hazleton, PA; (2); FBLA; Office Aide; Co-Capt JV Cheerleading; Gym; US Chrldng Assn All Amer Natl Chmpn 86.

JUNAS, PAUL; Hazleton HS; Hazleton, PA; (4); 40/387; Civic Clb; Drama Clb; Pres Ski Clb; Stage Crew; High Hon Roll; Trs NHS; Gifted Pgm; Penn ST Coll; Bus Mgmt.

JUNGE, MATT; Cornell Education Ctr; Coraopolis, PA; (3); Boy Scts; JA; Band; Mrchg Band; Var L Bsbl; Var Golf; Hon Roll; U Of Pittsburgh; Marine Bio.

JUNKER, HEATHER; Mc Keesport HS; White Oak, PA; (3); 82/420; Church Yth Grp; Hosp Aide; Band; Concert Band; Jazz Band; Mrchg Band; Orch; School Musical; Symp Band; Prfct Atten Awd; Band Treas 87-88; Duquesne; Music.

JUPENA, NICHOLAS; Jeannette HS; Jeannette, PA; (3); 5/130; Letterman Clb; Pres Frsh Cls; Pres Soph Cls; Pres Jr Cls; Rep Stu Cncl; Var Bsbl; Var Bsktbl; High Hon Roll; W VA; Physcl Ther.

JURACKA, STEPHANIE; Panther Valley HS; Summit Hill, PA; (3); 14/132; Library Aide; Flag Corp; Nwsp Rptr; Bsktbl; Trk; Hon Roll; NHS; Pediatrics.

JURASITS, MONICA; Northampton SR HS; Northampton, PA; (3); 19/492; Drama Clb; Band; Chorus; Concert Band; Drm Mjr(t); Mrchg Band; School Musical; Stage Crew; High Hon Roll; Hon Roll; Med.

JURASKO, DIANE; Hopewell HS; Aliquippa, PA; (4); 30/245; German Clb; Trs Chorus; Mrchg Band; School Musical; Rep Sr Cls; Sec Stu Cncl; Pom Pon; Powder Puff Ftbl; High Hon Roll; Sec NHS; IN U Of PA.

JURATA, JOHN; Spring-Ford HS; Mt Clare, PA; (3); 12/265; Math Clb; Radio Clb; Trs Concert Band; Jazz Band; Capt Mrchg Band; Rep Jr Cls; NHS; Church Yth Grp; Spanish Clb; Band; PA All ST Dist & Rgn Bands; Rtry Intl Dist 743 Ldrshp Cmp; Mgr Of Schl Store; Govt.

JURCHAK, TIM; Elk Lake Schl; Meshoppen, PA; (1); Boy Scts; Church Yth Grp; 4-H; French Clb; Ski Clb; Prfct Atten Awd; Frstry.

JURISTA, BRENT; Tunkhannock Area HS; Tunkhannock, PA; (4); 40/270; Church Yth Grp; Pep Clb; Science Clb; Crs Cntry; Socr; Var L Trk; Gov Hon Prg Awd; Hon Roll; NHS; Penn ST U; Mech Engrng.

JURKOVIC, RYAN; Mt Pleasant Area HS; Mt Pleasant, PA; (2); Latin Clb; Yrbk Sprt Ed; Yrbk Stf; JV Bsbl; Ftbl; Wrstlng; High Hon Roll.

JURY, DAVID; Yough HS; Rillton, PA; (3); 5/280; Debate Tm; Concert Band; Mrchg Band; Nwsp Stf; Pres Jr Cls; High Hon Roll; NHS; Church Yth Grp; Computer Clb; Gftd Pgm 85-87; Ambssdr-HOBY Fndtn Ldrshp Smnr 86; Stu Rep-Schl Brd 87; Duquesne U; Pltcl Sci.

JUSCZAK, CAROL; St Hubert HS; Philadelphia, PA; (3); 16/421; Yrbk Stf; NHS; Hon Roll; SR Edtr Yrbk 87-88.

JUSKO, BECKY; Penns Manor HS; Clymer, PA; (3); 25/105; Church Yth Grp; Cmnty Wkr; FBLA; Band; Concert Band; Drm Mjr(t); Mrchg Band; Pep Band; School Musical; Yrbk Stf; Prncss Pinecone 85; Cnty Band 86-87; IUP; Nrsng.

JUSTI, DIANE; Quigley HS; New Brighton, PA; (3); Dance Clb; Drama Clb; School Musical; School Play; Ed Yrbk Stf; Pep Clb; Chorus; Church Choir; Mgr Powder Puff Ftbl; Stat Trk; Otstndng JR Yrbk Stff 87; Comp Sci.

JUSTICE, WILLIAM; Tunkhannock Area HS; Tunkhannock, PA; (4); #8 In Class; Boy Scts; Church Yth Grp; Golf; Hon Roll; NHS; Ntl Merit Ltr; Ntl Merit Ltr Of Comndtn; ST Golf Trnmnt; All Star Golf Awd; Pre-Med.

JUSTIN, KARI; Meadville SR HS; Meadville, PA; (4); Library Aide; Nwsp Ed-Chief; Nwsp Stf; Vllybl; Hon Roll; Fshn Inst Of Pittsburgh; Fshn.

KACHLINE, ANGIE; Quakertown Community SR HS; Quakertown, PA; (3); Nwsp Stf; Yrbk Stf; High Hon Roll; Hon Roll; Liberal Arts.

KACINKO, DAVID M; Churchill HS; Pittsburgh, PA; (4); 73/190; Church Yth Grp; Stage Crew; Var L Crs Cntry; Ftbl; Var L Trk; Hon Roll; Rifle Ltr 86-87; Pittsburgh Tech Inst; Mech Draf.

KACINKO, JOHN; Churchill HS; Pittsburgh, PA; (2); 41/222; Chorus; School Musical; School Play; Stage Crew; High Hon Roll; Hon Roll; Rifle JV Statistcn 86-87.

KACSMAR, BRUCE; Pittston Area HS; Hughestown, PA; (3); Im Bsbl; Im Bsktbl; High Hon Roll; Hon Roll; NHS; Rotary Awd; Sci.

KACZMAREK, KRISTINE; South Williamsport HS; S Williamsport, PA; (3); Leo Clb; Letterman Clb; VP Jr Cls; Hon Roll; Cheerleading; Trk; Hon Roll; Bio.

KACZMAREK, MARIA; Mt Carmel Area JR SR HS; Mt Carmel, PA; (4); 18/159; Key Clb; Q&S; Spanish Clb; Chorus; School Musical; Nwsp Stf; JV Var Cheerleading; Var Trk; High Hon Roll; NHS; Albright Coll; Psych.

KACZMARSKI, DEBBIE; Bishop Shanahan HS; W Chester, PA; (4); 16/215; Drama Clb; VP Chorus; VP Madrigals; School Play; JV Sftbl; Hon Roll; Prfct Atten Awd; Pres Schlr; Penn ST U; Elem Ed.

KACZYNSKI, KRIS; North Hills HS; Pittsburgh, PA; (4); Exploring; Pres FBLA; VP JA; Key Clb; Library Aide; Office Aide; Yrbk Stf; Stu Cncl; High Hon Roll; Robert Morris Coll; Accntng.

KADAR, KATHY; South Allegheny HS; Elizabeth, PA; (3); 12/186; Girl Scts; Y-Teens; Band; Concert Band; Jazz Band; Mrchg Band; Powder Puff Ftbl; Hon Roll; NHS; Slvr Awd 84; Marian Awd 85; U Of Pittsburgh; Phys Thrpy.

KADAR, TONI L; Ringgold HS; Monongahela, PA; (3); Ski Clb; Chorus; Drill Tm; L Cheerleading; Mgr(s); L Pom Pon; Trk; PA ST; Anesthtst.

KADER, CHARLES J; Strong Vincent HS; Erie, PA; (4); 31/160; Church Yth Grp; Cmnty Wkr; Political Wkr; VP Stu Cncl; JV Var Ftbl; Wt Lftg; NHS; Aud/Vis; French Clb; Office Aide; Stu Cncl Schlrshp, Clarion U Fndtn Hnrs Schlrshp, & Erie Cnty Yth Govt Awd 87; Clarion U; Pol Sci.

KAFEL, JEFF; Archbishop Wood For Boys HS; Willow Grove, PA; (3); 17/235; Ftbl; High Hon Roll; Hon Roll; NHS; CYO Bsktbl Awd 86; Mrktng.

KAFFENES, HARRY; Aliquippa JR SR HS; Aliquippa, PA; (3); 1/140; Pres Church Yth Grp; Drama Clb; Exploring; French Clb; Math Clb; Math Tm; Band; Concert Band; Jazz Band; Mrchg Band; Engrng.

KAGARISE, BRIAN; Northern Bedford County HS; Loysburg, PA; (4); 1/92; Pres Varsity Clb; Nwsp Sprt Ed; Pres Stu Cncl; Capt Var Bsbl; Capt Var Ftbl; Var L Wrstlng; Cit Awd; NHS; Pres Schlr; Val; Robert C Byrd Schlrshp 87; PA ST U; Engrng.

KAGARISE, WENDY; Everett Area HS; Clearville, PA; (2); Computer Clb; Math Tm; Spanish Clb; Band; Concert Band; Mrchg Band; Trk; Hon Roll; Prfct Atten Awd; Spanish NHS; Math.

KAHKONEN, SONJA; Trinity HS; Washington, PA; (4); Church Yth Grp; French Clb; Math Tm; Speech Tm; Thesps; Concert Band; Mrchg Band; High Hon Roll; Hon Roll; Tae Kwon Do Red Belt; Apprnc Faces Intntl; Coll Wooster; Psych.

KAHL, KAREN; Bethlehem Catholic HS; Bethlehem, PA; (4); 5/195; Key Clb; Color Guard; Capt Flag Corp; High Hon Roll; NHS; Outstndng Achvt Pre Calculus, Alg Ii, Trig; Soc Wmn Engrs Hnr; Am Assoc U Wmns Schlrshp; Rensselaer; Nuclear Engrng.

KAHLE, PATRICK; Clarion Area HS; Sligo, PA; (3); FCA; VP Frsh Cls; VP Soph Cls; VP Jr Cls; Var Bsktbl; Var Ftbl; Var Wt Lftg; High Hon Roll; Hon Roll; NHS; Clarion U Of PA.

KAHLER, MICHELE; Mifflinburg Area HS; Laurelton, PA; (1); Church Yth Grp; French Clb; Girl Scts; Psych.

KAHN, MIKE; Upper Dublin HS; Ft Washington, PA; (2); FBLA; Rep Frsh Cls; Rep Soph Cls; Rep Stu Cncl; Im Bsktbl; JV Im Socr; Im Wt Lftg.

KAIL, BILL; Peters Township HS; Mcmurray, PA; (2); Var L Bsbl; Var L Wrstlng; Bus.

KAIN, RICHARD; Taylor-Allderdice HS; Pittsburgh, PA; (2); Chess Clb; Church Yth Grp; Debate Tm; Hosp Aide; Political Wkr; Speech Tm; JV Crs Cntry; Var L Trk; Im Tennis; High Hon Roll; Slctd For US-SOVIET Exchng, Intitive For Undrstndng Prgrm 87; Humnts Apprntnshp Prgrm 87.

KAIN, RICHARD D; Neshaminy HS; Trevose, PA; (3); 130/780; Church Yth Grp; Computer Clb; Band; Im Tennis; Hon Roll; Socl Svcs.

KAIN, SHANNON; Elizabethtown Area HS; Bainbridge, PA; (3); 4-H; Pres Frsh Cls; Pres Soph Cls; Rep Jr Cls; Rep Stu Cncl; JV Trk; Educ.

KAIN, STACY; Newport HS; Newport, PA; (2); Var Cheerleading; Hon Roll; SOCIAL Svc.

KAISER, CHRISTOPHER; Henderson HS; W Chester, PA; (3); Ski Clb; Var L Bsbl; Var L Ftbl; Librl Arts.

KAISER, JENNIFER; Quakertown HS; Quakertown, PA; (3); Church Yth Grp; Dance Clb; Ski Clb; SADD; Varsity Clb; Church Choir; Variety Show; Nwsp Ed-Chief; Nwsp Rptr; Nwsp Stf; Presdntl Acadc & Ftns 85; Allentown Coll; Engl.

KAISER, MARTHA-JANE; Uniontown Area HS; Farmington, PA; (3); Church Yth Grp; Cmnty Wkr; German Clb; SADD; Church Choir; Concert Band; Orch; High Hon Roll; NHS; Secondary Educ.

KAISER, MARY BETH; St Hubert HS; Philadelphia, PA; (3); 1/421; Math Clb; Chorus; Orch; Nwsp Rptr; Ed Lit Mag; High Hon Roll; VP NHS; Prfct Atten Awd; Soc Womens Engnrs Cert Mrt 87; Jr 1st Pl Awd 87; Urban Studies Awd 87; Bus.

KAISER, SUZANNE; Hickory HS; Hermitage, PA; (3); Church Yth Grp; Drama Clb; Library Aide; Spanish Clb; Teachers Aide; Varsity Clb; Acpl Chr; Chorus; Church Choir; School Musical; Acadmc All Amer 86; All Amer Chrldng 86; Chem Tchr.

KAISER, TERESA; Plum SR HS; Pittsburgh, PA; (3); Scholastic Bowl; Acpl Chr; Chorus; JV Bsktbl; Var Trk; NHS; Phys Thrpy.

KAISER, VICKI; Conneaut Valley HS; Springboro, PA; (3); FFA; German Clb; Pep Clb; Ski Clb; Varsity Clb; Yrbk Stf; Rep Sr Cls; Rep Stu Cncl; Stat Ftbl; Var Vllybl; FFA Creed Cont 1st 84; Pblc Spkng 2nd Pl 84; Pharm.

KALAMASZ, ANN; Center HS; Aliquippa, PA; (4); 68/225; FHA; FNA; Band; Hon Roll; Bus.

KALAN, CHANTEL; Cecil JR HS; Cecil, PA; (1); Church Yth Grp; Band; Capt Color Guard; Nwsp Stf; High Hon Roll.

KALASINSKI, RENEA; Carbondale Area HS; Carbondale, PA; (2); Art Clb; Computer Clb; Spanish Clb; Hon Roll; Stngrphr.

KALBAUGH, JENNIFER; Biglerville HS; Arendtsville, PA; (2); 5/104; Chorus; Concert Band; Mrchg Band; School Musical; Yrbk Ed-Chief; Trk; Jr NHS; NHS; Church Yth Grp; High Hon Roll; Yth Advsry Dlgt Presbytrn Chrch 87; Cngrssnl Aide 87.

KALEMBA, DOUGLAS; Mt Pleasant Area SR HS; Mt Pleasant, PA; (3); 6/250; Golf; High Hon Roll; Engnrng.

KALEY, GRANT; Coatesville Area SR HS; Coatesville, PA; (3); 23/500; Church Yth Grp; French Clb; Leo Clb; Ski Clb; Acpl Chr; Chorus; School Musical; Yrbk Ed-Chief; Rep Frsh Cls; Rep Soph Cls.

KALGREN, KAREN; Du Bois Central Christian HS; Falls Creek, PA; (2); 7/40; CAP; Drama Clb; 4-H; Trs Pep Clb; Ski Clb; SADD; Band; School Play; Var Bsktbl; 4-H Awd; Buckeye Awd-Ldrshp Trngn 87; Sci.

KALGREN, MICHELLE; Dubois Area SR HS; Rockton, PA; (2); 52/300; Church Yth Grp; Flag Corp; Hon Roll; PA ST U; Elem Ed.

KALICH, KELLY M; Winchester Thurston HS; Mc Keesport, PA; (4); Dance Clb; Drama Clb; SADD; Orch; Nwsp Stf; Yrbk Bus Mgr; Yrbk Stf; Cheerleading; High Hon Roll; Matthews Intl Corp Schlrshp 87; Mst Outstndng Physcs Stdnt Amer Socty Physcs Tchrs; Northwestern U; Bus.

KALICH, MICHAEL S; Laurel Highlands HS; Oliver, PA; (2); Computer Clb; Science Clb; Sec Soph Cls; Golf; Socr; High Hon Roll; FL Inst Tech; Space Sci.

KALIK, RICH; Plum SR HS; Pittsburgh, PA; (3); 27/461; DECA; Trk; Wt Lftg; High Hon Roll; Hon Roll; NHS; Exclnc Awd Natl Hist Day 86; Plum Pride Patch QPA 86-87; Various Bowling Awds 85-87; Penn ST.

KALIMON, REBECCA; Heritage Christian Acad; Erie, PA; (3); 1/4; Church Yth Grp; Drama Clb; Library Aide; Pep Clb; School Play; Yrbk Stf; Capt Cheerleading; Var Sftbl; Hon Roll; NHS; Phys Thrpy.

KALINA, DONNA; Frankford HS; Philadelphia, PA; (3); Church Yth Grp; Acpl Chr; Church Choir; Scholastic Bowl; Band; School Musical; Mgr(s); Prg Anlyst.

KALINER, DANIEL J; Haverford SR HS; Philadelphia, PA; (3); 28/450; Debate Tm; French Clb; Speech Tm; Band; Mrchg Band; Nwsp Rptr; Tennis; Hon Roll; Jr NHS; NHS; Frnch & Engl Achvt Awds 85.

KALINIK, CHRISTINE; Belle Vernon Area HS; Belle Vernon, PA; (3); Pres Church Yth Grp; Drama Clb; Pep Clb; Ski Clb; Spanish Clb; Church Choir; School Play; Stage Crew; U Pittsburgh; Law.

KALINOSKI, GREGORY; Seneca Valley SR HS; Evans Cty, PA; (2); JA; Math Tm; Tennis; High Hon Roll; Hon Roll; CMU; Engr.

KALINOVICH, MARY; Bishop Hafey HS; Drums, PA; (4); 14/128; Drama Clb; French Clb; Ski Clb; Y-Teens; Chorus; Yrbk Stf; Bowling; French Hon Soc; NHS; Ntl Merit Ltr; Hist, Art Awds 83-84; Penn ST; Frgn Lang.

KALINOWSKI, CHRISTINE; St Huberts HS; Philadelphia, PA; (3); Intnl Clb; Office Aide; Pep Clb; Spanish Clb; Stage Crew; Hon Roll; Cmptr Sci.

KALISH, ILENE; Bensalem HS; Bensalem, PA; (3); Drama Clb; Key Clb; SADD; Color Guard; Nwsp Stf; Trs Sr Cls; Rep Stu Cncl; Tennis; Twrlr; Hon Roll; Engl.

KALISKY, LORI; York Catholic HS; York, PA; (4); 23/169; French Clb; FBLA; Rep Frsh Cls; Rep Soph Cls; Rep Sr Cls; Rep Stu Cncl; L Trk; Hon Roll; Trs NHS; Pres Schlr; Rev William Fitzpatrick Memrl Schlrshp; U Of Pittsburgh; Engrng.

KALKSTEIN, LESLIE; Penn Hills SR HS; Pittsburgh, PA; (3); Hon Roll; AAU Natl Gymnstcs 87; Advncd Optnl ST & Sctnls Gynmstcs 87; Acctng.

KALLAY, MICHAEL; Montour HS; Mckees Rocks, PA; (3); Letterman Clb; SADD; Varsity Clb; Variety Show; Rep Frsh Cls; JV Bsbl; JV Bsktbl; Ftbl; Golf; Wt Lftg; Cedarburg 500 Clb; Top Lftr Clb; Miami U Of OH; Bus Adm.

KALLIMANIS, JOHN; Lower Dauphin HS; Hershey, PA; (2); Socr; Hon Roll; Prfct Atten Awd.

KALOCHIE, JENNIFER; Minersville Area HS; Minersville, PA; (4); 1/114; Trs Spanish Clb; Capt Drill Tm; Yrbk Stf; Sec Sr Cls; Var Bsktbl; Var Capt Sftbl; Var Capt Vllybl; NHS; NEDT Awd; Val; Female Schlr Athlete 86-87; Rotary Clb Good Ctznshp Awd 87; Bio Awd 87; Bucknell; Pre Med.

KALP, LISA; Mt Pleasant Area HS; Acme, PA; (3); 14/240; Pres Church Yth Grp; French Clb; Trs Band; Concert Band; Mrchg Band; Yrbk Stf; Hon Roll; NHS; Prfct Atten Awd; Elem Ed.

KALP, TAMMY; Mt Pleasant SR HS; Acme, PA; (3); Church Yth Grp; Exploring; FBLA; Band; Church Choir; Mrchg Band; Nwsp Stf; Yrbk Stf; Im JV Vllybl; Bus.

KALUGDAN, IRENE; Bensalem HS; Bensalem, PA; (3); Intnl Clb; Key Clb; Teachers Aide; Orch; Nwsp Sprt Ed; Yrbk Rptr; Stat Bsbl; Hon Roll; Drama Clb; French Clb; YWCA Teen Recognition Awd Cmnty Svc 87; Stu Of Month 86; Wharton; Accntng.

KALUPANOV, KYRA; Steel Valley HS; Munhall, PA; (4); Art Clb; Church Yth Grp; Pep Clb; Ski Clb; SADD; Varsity Clb; Variety Show; Var Capt Cheerleading; Score Keeper; Hon Roll; Mst Vlbl Prsn Chrldng 87; U Of Pgh; Occptnl Thrpy.

KAMDAR, FALGU; Moon SR HS; Coraopolis, PA; (3); 2/306; Camera Clb; Cmnty Wkr; Hosp Aide; JA; Spanish Clb; High Hon Roll; NHS; Prfct Atten Awd; Pres Schlr.

KAMDAR, MELISSA; Saint Basil Acad; Rydal, PA; (4); 3/97; French Clb; Hosp Aide; Science Clb; Yrbk Rptr; Stu Cncl; Swmmng; French Hon Soc; High Hon Roll; NHS; HOBY Found 85; Ldrshp Awd 85; Pre-Med.

KAMINSKI, BRIAN; G A R Memorial HS; Wilkes-Barre, PA; (3); Computer Clb; FBLA; SADD; Chorus; Stage Crew; Rep Frsh Cls; Pres Soph Cls; Rep Jr Cls; Pres Stu Cncl; Hon Roll; Penn ST; Med.

KAMINSKI III, PETER P; Reading Central Catholic HS; Reading, PA; (4); Boy Scts; Chess Clb; German Clb; Chorus; Church Choir; VP Mrchg Band; Pep Band; School Play; Stage Crew; Variety Show; Albright Coll Grnt, Eagle Sct Awd 87; Albright Coll; Chem.

KAMINSKI, STEVE; Neshaminy HS; Feasterville, PA; (3); 35/722; Band; Concert Band; Jazz Band; Mrchg Band; Orch; High Hon Roll; Hon Roll; NHS; Spcl Citatn-Oustndng Muscnshp Frm NAJE; Prtcpnt Rgn VI Band & Dist XI Band-PMEA 86 & 87.

KAMINSKI-FENK, CHRISTINE; South Park HS; Library, PA; (3); Chorus; School Musical; Variety Show; Hon Roll; Psych.

KAMINSKY, JASON; Shade HS; Stoystown, PA; (3); Aud/Vis; Math Tm; Scholastic Bowl; Spanish Clb; Varsity Clb; Nwsp Sprt Ed; Capt Bsbl; Var Bsktbl; High Hon Roll; Hon Roll; PA Math Leag 83 & 84; Amer Lgn Awd 84.

KAMMERER, ERIC; Big Spring HS; Carlisle, PA; (3); 28/286; Aud/Vis; Spanish Clb; Y-Teens; JV Ftbl; Mgr(s); Wt Lftg; Hon Roll; NHS; Drexel U; Cvl Engr.

KAMON, MATTAN; State College Area SR HS; State College, PA; (4); 5/540; Computer Clb; Math Clb; Math Tm; Mu Alpha Theta; Science Clb; Concert Band; Mrchg Band; Symp Band; Rep Sr Cls; Im Bsktbl; HRB Smmr Sci Pgm 86; PA ST U; Engrng.

KAN, AMY; Philadelphia HS For Girls; Philadelphia, PA; (3); Art.

KANAPESKY, CHRISTINE; Beaver Area HS; Beaver, PA; (2); 39/240; Dance Clb; Chrmn French Clb; SADD; Teachers Aide; Color Guard; Stage Crew; High Hon Roll; Hon Roll; PA ST Univ-PA Cncl Of Tchrs Of Engl Essay Cntst Commdtn 85-86; Clncl Nutritn.

KANCZ, FAITHE; West Allegheny SR HS; Imperial, PA; (3); Cmnty Wkr; Rep German Clb; Ski Clb; Rep Stu Cncl; Im Powder Puff Ftbl; Var Sftbl; Var Tennis; Hon Roll; Teen Inst 86-87; IL Miss Teen Pgnt 86.

KANDEL, LISA; Burrell HS; Lower Burrell, PA; (3); Spanish Clb; SADD; Hon Roll; Jr NHS.

KANE, CAROL; Trinity HS; Amity, PA; (3); Art Clb; Spanish Clb; SADD; Pres Soph Cls; High Hon Roll; Hon Roll; Cert Achvmnt Bio Eng Art; Art Inst Pittsburgh; Cmrcl Art.

KANE, DEBORAH L; Linden Hall Schl; Bernardsville, NJ; (1); 3/18; School Play; Variety Show; Sftbl; High Hon Roll; Hon Roll; Linden Hall Golf Four Awd 87; Stu Of Month 87.

KANE, JAMES; Nativity BVM HS; Pottsville, PA; (2); 23/77; Aud/Vis; Chess Clb; Stat Bsktbl; Stat Ftbl; Var Golf; JV Score Keeper; Stat Trk; Stat Vllybl; Hon Roll; 2nd Pl Microbio Div Nativity Sci Fair 87; Highest Achvt Compt Literacy 87; Vrsty Cert Boys Bsktbl 87.

KANE, JENNIFER; Nazareth Acad; Philadelphia, PA; (3); Boy Scts; Church Yth Grp; French Clb; Service Clb; Lit Mag; Capt JV Bsktbl; Hon Roll; Villanova U; Englsh.

KANE JR, JOSEPH; Valley View JR SR HS; Jessup, PA; (3); Art Clb; Latin Clb; PA ST U; Dentstry.

KANE, KATHLEEN; Steel Valley HS; Munhall, PA; (3); 1/217; Church Yth Grp; Exploring; Varsity Clb; Var L Swmmng; Var L Tennis; Hon Roll; NHS; JR Mrshll 87 Grad Ceremny 87.

KANE, KATHY; Bishop O Reilly HS; Trucksville, PA; (2); Ski Clb; Bsktbl; Fld Hcky; Hon Roll; Prfct Atten Awd.

KANE, KELLY; Bedford HS; Bedford, PA; (3); Trs Church Yth Grp; FTA; Red Cross Aide; Ski Clb; SADD; Chorus; Trs Soph Cls; Rep Stu Cncl; JV VP Cheerleading; High Hon Roll; Med.

KANE, KEVIN; Northeast Catholic HS; Philadelphia, PA; (3); Ftbl; Hon Roll; NHS; Temple; Acct.

KANE, MEGAN; Wilmington Area HS; New Wilmington, PA; (3); 6/117; Spanish Clb; Pres Soph Cls; Pres Jr Cls; Var L Cheerleading; Powder Puff Ftbl; Swmmng; Var L Trk; High Hon Roll; Hon Roll; Acadmc Awd 84-86.

KANE, MICHELLE; Cardinal O Hara HS; Swarthmore, PA; (3); 90/710; Cmnty Wkr; Dance Clb; School Musical; Score Keeper; Hon Roll; Opt Clb Awd; A Mem Awd Exclinc In Acadc Achvt 84; Most Imprvd Awd Dance 86; Sci.

KANE, RICHARD; Lancaster Catholic HS; Lancaster, PA; (3); Cmnty Wkr; Var Crs Cntry; Landscape Dsgnr.

KANE, ROBIN LYNNE; Canevin Catholic HS; Carnegie, PA; (3); 28/198; Dance Clb; Pep Clb; Ski Clb; Stage Crew; Stu Cncl; Cheerleading; Powder Puff Ftbl; Hon Roll; Art Achvt Awd 87; PA ST; Advrtsng.

KANE, SCOTT A; Huntingdon Area HS; Huntingdon, PA; (3); 6/224; Boy Scts; Science Clb; Yrbk Ed-Chief; Cit Awd; High Hon Roll; Jr NHS; NHS; PA Govr Schl For Agri 86; PA Govr Schl For Intl Studies 87; Engr.

KANE, SEAN; St Josephs Prep Schl; Collingswood, NJ; (4); 100/250; Church Yth Grp; Cmnty Wkr; Pep Clb; SADD; Varsity Clb; Var Sftbl; L Bsbl; L Ftbl; Wt Lftg; Hon Roll; Philadelphia Nwsprs Inc Schlrshp Wnnr 85-87; St Joseph Prep Schl Spirit Awd, Pride Awd 87; MVP Bsbl; Miami U Oxford OH; Bus Mgmt.

KANE, TABATHA; Academy Of Notre Dame; Wayne, PA; (3); Cmnty Wkr; GAA; Sec Trs Jr Cls; Pres Sr Cls; JV Capt Lcrss; Var Socr; High Hon Roll; Church Yth Grp; Service Clb; Varsity Clb; Distnshd Hnrs Acad 86-87; Psych.

KANE, THERESA; Abington Heights HS; Clarks Summit, PA; (2); 8/296; Ski Clb; Band; Concert Band; Mrchg Band; Nwsp Stf; Rep Stu Cncl; Hon Roll; Cum Hnr Maximo Egregio Awd Natl Latin Exam & Magna Cum Laude 86 & 87.

KANE, TIM; West Catholic HS; Colwyn, PA; (3); 15/279; Off Church Yth Grp; Band; Nwsp Phtg; Wrstlng; Hon Roll; Prfct Atten Awd; Chrstn Schlr Applcnt 87; Temple Mock Trial 87; Brooks Inst Photo; Cinmtgrphy.

KANECK, SHELLY; Quigley HS; New Brighton, PA; (2); Pres Church Yth Grp; JA; Math Tm; Mrchg Band; Yrbk Stf; Band; Concert Band; Hstrn.

KANFOUSH, CAROL; Hopewell HS; Aliquippa, PA; (3); 44/255; Church Yth Grp; Spanish Clb; Chorus; Rep Stu Cncl; Powder Puff Ftbl; Trk; High Hon Roll; NHS; Psych.

KANG, RYOUNG; Bensalem HS; Bensalem, PA; (2); FBLA; Key Clb; Math Tm; Model UN; Science Clb; SADD; Orch; Stu Cncl; High Hon Roll; NHS; 4th Chr-All Cnty Orchestra Violin 86-7; 2nd Chr-All Cnty Orchestra Violin 85-6; Bryn Mawr; Polit Sci.

KANG, SHULAMITH DEBORAH; Upper Merion Area HS; Gulph Mills, PA; (3); 11/297; Church Yth Grp; Pres French Clb; Math Tm; Pres Model UN; Chorus; Mrchg Band; VP Orch; Nwsp Rptr; Hon Roll; Sec NHS; Brown U Bk Awd 87; Natl Sci Olympiad Bio & Physics Awd 85&87; Exchng Clb Stu Rcgntn Awd 87.

KANG, SUNGMIN; Allderdice HS; Pittsburgh, PA; (2); Boys Clb Am; Chess Clb; Computer Clb; Math Tm; High Hon Roll; Hon Roll; Jr NHS; Opt Clb Awd; Prfct Atten Awd; Cert Rcgntn Superbwl Prblm Slvn 87; Cert Achvmnt Rngr Pgm 85; Cert Prtcptn Marine Sci Pgm 86; MIT; Engnrng Physcs.

KANG, YOON; Emmaus HS; Macungie, PA; (4); 1/473; Chorus; School Musical; VP Frsh Cls; VP Soph Cls; Trs Sr Cls; JV VP Stu Cncl; Var Crs Cntry; Var Trk; NHS; Ntl Merit SF; Lee Iacocca Ldrshp Awd 87; DAR Good Ctzn Awd 87; Western Exchange Club Awd 87; U Of PA; Med.

KANIA, BRIAN; Cambridge Springs HS; Union City, PA; (3); Church Yth Grp; 4-H; Band; Church Choir; Concert Band; Mrchg Band; Pep Band; Off Jr Cls; Wrstlng; 4-H Awd.

KANIA, MICHAEL; North Allegheny Intermediate HS; Pittsburgh, PA; (2); 28/630; JA; Ski Clb; JV Ftbl; JV Ice Hcky; High Hon Roll; Orthopdc Srgn.

KANIA, MICHELE; Geibel HS; Uniontown, PA; (3); Dance Clb; Drama Clb; Hosp Aide; Pep Clb; Stage Crew; Yrbk Stf; High Hon Roll; NHS; NEDT Awd; Spanish NHS; Svc Awd 86; 400 Vlntr Hrs-Cndy Strpr 87; Comp.

KANICH, WILLIAM; Blacklick Valley HS; Nanty-Glo, PA; (2); 11/105; Varsity Clb; Church Choir; Concert Band; Nwsp Rptr; Rep Stu Cncl; Bsbl; Bsktbl; Ftbl; High Hon Roll; Pres Schlr.

KANIPER, NIKKI; Nazareth HS; Nazareth, PA; (3); Key Clb; Swing Chorus; Stu Cncl; Var Cheerleading; High Hon Roll; Rep Frsh Cls; Rep Soph Cls; Rep Jr Cls; Miss PA US Teen Pag Schlr & Cmmnty Actv Awds 87; Northampton Cnty Stu Forum 86-87; Sherman Bio Awd; Med.

KANISH, KELI; Schuylkill Haven HS; Schuylkill Haven, PA; (4); 7/85; Science Clb; SADD; Chorus; School Musical; Nwsp Stf; Var Cheerleading; Trk; Hon Roll; NHS; Ntl Merit Ltr; HS Wmns Clb Awd 87; Ashley Alonge Mem Schlrshp Fnd Bllt 85; Phila Coll Phrmcy & Sci; Phrmcy.

KANJORSKI, MARK; J S Fine SR HS; Nanticoke, PA; (2); Aud/Vis; Camera Clb; Political Wkr; Ski Clb; Stage Crew; Variety Show; Pres Soph Cls; High Hon Roll; NHS.

KANJORSKI, RUSSELL; J S Fine SR HS; Nanticoke, PA; (4); #2 In Class; Model UN; Political Wkr; Variety Show; Nwsp Rptr; Var L Ftbl; Var Trk; Pres NHS; Ntl Merit SF; U PA; Cmmnctns.

KANN, MIKE; Dover Area HS; Spring Grove, PA; (4); 57/235; Church Yth Grp; 4-H; FFA; Band; Chorus; Var Bsbl; 4-H Awd; Hon Roll; FFA Star Agri Bsnsmn Awd 87; FFA Keystone Frmr Awd 87; York Cnty Amer Leg Bsbl Schlrshp 87; York Coll; Bus Admin.

KANOUFF, BARBARA; Ambridge Area HS; Baden, PA; (3); Church Yth Grp; German Clb; Hosp Aide; Pep Clb; Hon Roll; Nrsing.

KANOUFF, DOUGLAS; Plum SR HS; Pittsburgh, PA; (3); Church Yth Grp; French Clb; Varsity Clb; Stage Crew; Symp Band; JV L Bsktbl; Var L Golf; JV L Trk; Var L Vllybl; Hon Roll.

KANTZ, JOSEPH; Selinsgrove HS; Selinsgrove, PA; (2); Boy Scts; Pres Church Yth Grp; Drama Clb; SADD; Chorus; School Musical; JV Ftbl; Im Trk; Im Wrstlng; Hon Roll; Susquehanna U; Engl.

KANUCH, TAMMY; Montour HS; Coraopolis, PA; (2); JA; SADD; Mrchg Band; Symp Band; Yrbk Stf; Stat Trk; High Hon Roll; Band; Concert Band; Pep Band; Trvlng Teenage Sftbl 1st Pl 86-87; Bio.

KANYAN, DENISE; Homer Center HS; Indiana, PA; (3); 17/129; Cmnty Wkr; Trs Computer Clb; Red Cross Aide; Chorus; Swing Chorus; High Hon Roll; Hon Roll; NHS; Hlth Careers Clb VP; Acadmc Chlng Engl Cls 85-87; IN U Of PA; Med Tech.

KAO, AN-CHIAN; MMI Prep Schl; Mountaintop, PA; (3); Science Clb; Ski Clb; School Play; Var Tennis; High Hon Roll; Hon Roll; NHS; NEDT Awd; Art Clb; Stage Crew; PA Jnr Acad Of Sci-1st Awd Rgnls 84-87; Intrvw PA Gvrnr Schl For Arts 87; Grmn Ntl Hnr Soc 85-87.

KAO, ELIZABETH; North Allegheny Intermediate HS; Pittsburg, PA; (2); 104/630; Boy Scts; VP Church Yth Grp; Exploring; Hosp Aide; Hon Roll; Hgh Hnr Awd Sci Fair 85-86; Ntl Math Leg ,Geo 86-87; Amer Music Schlrshp Assoc 87; Cert Of Merit Engl; Med.

KAPALA, SHERRI; Northwestern HS; Albion, PA; (3); 33/144; Computer Clb; Library Aide; Church Choir; Hon Roll.

KAPANYKO, WENDI; Hopewell SR HS; Aliquippa, PA; (3); 83/255; Church Yth Grp; Computer Clb; Exploring; French Clb; Girl Scts; SADD; Chorus; Yrbk Ed-Chief; Var Powder Puff Ftbl; Var JV Socr; Pre Med.

KAPELAN, JULIEANN; Coughlin HS; Wilkes Barre, PA; (3); Church Yth Grp; Band; Chorus; Church Choir; Concert Band; Jazz Band; Mrchg Band; Orch; Symp Band; Jr Mozart Club Of Wilkes-Barre PA 86-88; U Of Bridgeport CT; Music.

KAPLAN, DAVID; Reading SR HS; Reading, PA; (4); 4/563; Key Clb; SADD; Teachers Aide; School Play; Yrbk Stf; Im Socr; Hon Roll; NHS; Ntl Merit Ltr; Superintndnts Schlstc Recgntn 85-87; Econ.

KAPLAN, STEPHANIE; Hempfield HS; Landisville, PA; (3); 35/393; Dance Clb; Drama Clb; Capt Flag Corp; School Musical; School Play; JV L Cheerleading; Powder Puff Ftbl; High Hon Roll; Hon Roll; NHS; Constoga Vly Assn Sci Fair Awd 85-86; Bus.

KAPOOR, ALOK; Hempfield HS; Mt Joy, PA; (3); Computer Clb; Debate Tm; Nwsp Stf; JV Crs Cntry; Hon Roll; JR Div Fnlst Patrio News Nwsppr Crrs Yr84; Cert Prtcptn Comp Prblm Slvng Cont 85 & 86; Comp Sci.

KAPOURELOS, MARIA; Bishop Shanahan HS; W Chester, PA; (4); 23/217; Drama Clb; Math Tm; Service Clb; Nwsp Ed-Chief; Nwsp Stf; Mgr(s); Hon Roll; NHS; Pres Schlr; Stat Socr; Acdmc All Amer Schlr 84; Latin & Spnsh Awd For Excel 86; American U; Intl Bus.

KAPP, BRIAN; North Clarion JR SR HS; Venus, PA; (3); 7/105; Pres Church Yth Grp; French Clb; Mgr(s); Var Socr; NHS; NEDT Awd; Yrbk Stf; Engrng.

KAPP, MICHELLE; West Perry HS; Shermons Dale, PA; (4); Spanish Clb; Varsity Clb; Color Guard; Yrbk Ed-Chief; Sec Soph Cls; Sec Jr Cls; Sec Sr Cls; Rep Stu Cncl; Var JV Fld Hcky; JV Capt Sftbl; Antonellis; Fash Merch.

KAPP, PATRICK; Cranberry HS; Venus, PA; (2); CAP; Science Clb; Trk; Hon Roll; USAF; Aviation.

KAPPEL, JEFFREY; Canon-Mc Millan HS; Mcdonald, PA; (4); Spanish Clb; Trk; High Hon Roll; Hon Roll; NHS; Pres Schlr; Spanish NHS; PA Hghr Educ Awd 87; Penn ST U; Engrng.

KAPPEL, MARIA; Center HS; Monaca, PA; (3); Dance Clb; Spanish Clb; Variety Show; Var Co-Capt Cheerleading; Gov Hon Prg Awd; Hon Roll; Math Clb; Chorus; Score Keeper; Dnc-Won Nmrous ST & Ntl Cmptns 84-87; Chrldr Co-Capt-Vrsty Squad Won 2 1st Pl Trphs 87; U Of FL; Tchr.

KAPPEL III, WALTER; Phoenixville Area HS; Phoenixville, PA; (3); VP Church Yth Grp; Ski Clb; Jazz Band; SADD; Band; Concert Band; Mrchg Band; Yrbk Stf; Vllybl; Hon Roll; Hotel Mgmt.

KAPPLER, MICHELLE; Bradford Area HS; Bradford, PA; (3); 54/302; Church Yth Grp; Ski Clb; Pres Frsh Cls; Rep Soph Cls; VP Jr Cls; Chrmn Sr Cls; Var Cheerleading; Crs Cntry; Trk; Hon Roll; Pre-Med.

KAPSICK, DAVID; Wyoming Valley West HS; Edwardsville, PA; (3); Yrbk Stf; JV Var Bsbl; Im Bsktbl; Var Capt Ftbl; Im Vllybl; Im Wt Lftg; JV Wrstlng; Hon Roll; NHS; Bus.

KAPUSTA, AMY; Richland HS; Gibsonia, PA; (2); AFS; Cmnty Wkr; Hosp Aide; SADD; Teachers Aide; Chorus; Drill Tm; Pom Pon; Tennis; Hon Roll; Penn ST.

KAPUSTIN, WENDY; Lower Moreland HS; Huntingdon Valley, PA; (4); 38/202; Drama Clb; French Clb; FBLA; Intnl Clb; Key Clb; Science Clb; School Play; Rep Stu Cncl; Swmmng; High Hon Roll; Rtry Intl Stdy In Spain 87-88; American U; Intl Law.

KAPUSTYNSKI, KEVIN; Canon Mc Millan SR HS; Canonsburg, PA; (4); 72/355; Boy Scts; Church Yth Grp; Pres Exploring; Science Clb; Spanish Clb; Stage Crew; Ftbl; Trk; High Hon Roll; Spanish NHS; Comrcl Dvng.

KARABA, MONICA; Monongahela Valley Catholic HS; Scenery Hl, PA; (3); 1/99; Political Wkr; Soph Cls; Off Stu Cncl; Sftbl; JV Capt Vllybl; Bausch & Lomb Sci Awd; High Hon Roll; NHS; Spanish NHS; Cmnty Wkr; Penn Govnrs Schl Sci 87; Aerosp Engrng.

KARABELNIK, LISA; Governor Mifflin SR HS; Mohnton, PA; (3); 8/365; Sec Model UN; VP Spanish Clb; Trs Temple Yth Grp; Chorus; Nwsp Stf; Yrbk Stf; JV Var Fld Hcky; NHS; Ntl Merit Ltr; High Hon Roll; Wellesly Awd Excel 87; Pitt; Chld Psych.

KARAFFA, LARYSSA; Central Bucks HS East; Wrightstown, PA; (4); VP Sec 4-H; Var Cheerleading; Trk; Hon Roll; NHS; Phys Thrpy.

KARAHUTA, LORI LEE; Shenandoah Valley HS; Shenandoah, PA; (2); 1/104; Pep Clb; Chorus; Nwsp Rptr; Cheerleading; Gym; Sftbl; Vllybl; High Hon Roll; Val; Acadc All Am Hnr 87; Ltr Vlybl 87; Cert Sftbl 87; PA ST Bloomsburg; Atty.

KARALIS, SPIRO; Upper Darby HS; Upr Darby, PA; (4); 165/600; Church Yth Grp; Var Bsktbl; Im Ice Hcky; Im Socr; Var Trk; Im Wt Lftg; Var Wrstlng; Hon Roll; Temple U; Phrmcy.

KARAS, KRISTIN; Fort Cherry HS; Mcdonald, PA; (3); 14/149; Sec Church Yth Grp; Math Clb; Science Clb; Ski Clb; Varsity Clb; Band; Drm Mjr(t); Var L Tennis; Capt Twrlr; NHS; JR High Yth Grp 86-87; Chrprsn Of WA Dist Yth Cncl 85-88; Psychlgy.

KARASEK, MARK; Purchase Line HS; Clymer, PA; (2); FFA; Library Aide; Hon Roll; Star Grnhnd 86; Chptr Frmr 87; FFA Demonstratn Tm 87; Penn ST; Ag.

KARASTURY, SHANNON; Meadville Area SR HS; Meadville, PA; (4); Church Yth Grp; Drama Clb; SADD; Band; Stage Crew; Nwsp Phtg; Nwsp Rptr; Nwsp Stf; Yrbk Phtg; Yrbk Rptr; Clarion U; Cmmnctns.

KARCESKY, CARLA; Center HS; Aliquippa, PA; (2); Spanish Clb; Hon Roll.

KARCHNER, BONNIE; Berwick SR HS; Nescopeck, PA; (4); Church Yth Grp; Key Clb; Chorus; Church Choir; Yrbk Stf; Sftbl; High Hon Roll; Hon Roll; NHS; Bus Std Of Mnth 87; Prom Cmmttee 86; Bank Tllr.

KARDASZ, ERIC; Ambridge Area HS; Conway, PA; (3); Boy Scts; German Clb; Pep Clb; Band; Concert Band; Jazz Band; Mrchg Band; Robert Morriss Coll; Bus Mgmt.

KARDIAN, JOHN; North Allegheny SR HS; Pittsburgh, PA; (4); 144/648; Latin Clb; Mu Alpha Theta; Jazz Band; Orch; Nwsp Stf; Yrbk Stf; Lit Mag; Stu Cncl; Socr; NHS; Grad With Honor 87; U Of MD.

KARES, APRIL; Nazareth Area SR HS; Nazareth, PA; (3); Chorus; Church Choir; Rep Frsh Cls; Rep Soph Cls; Rep Stu Cncl; Var JV Fld Hcky; Stat Mat Maids; JV Trk; Hon Roll; Phys Ther.

KARG, PAT; Venango Christian HS; Kennerdal, PA; (3); 4/38; Aud/Vis; Boy Scts; Computer Clb; Model UN; Nwsp Rptr; Yrbk Phtg; L Ftbl; Var Wrstlng; Hon Roll; Prfct Atten Awd; Engrng.

KARGLE, MICHELE; Yough SR HS; West Newton, PA; (4); 12/250; Office Aide; Ski Clb; Spanish Clb; Mrchg Band; Yrbk Stf; Powder Puff Ftbl; L Trk; Co-Capt Twrlr; Im Vllybl; High Hon Roll; Westmoreland Cnty Hgh Jmp Champ 86; PA St U; Engnrng.

KARGO, RAY; Portage Area HS; Portage, PA; (4); 10/122; Church Yth Grp; Varsity Clb; Bsbl; Bsktbl; Ftbl; Wt Lftg; Hon Roll; NHS; Acad All Amer Awd 85-86; Sports Med.

KARHAN, HEATHER; Coudersport HS; Coudersport, PA; (4); French Clb; Pep Clb; Band; Concert Band; Mrchg Band; Pep Band; Yrbk Stf; Seton Hl Coll; Photo.

KARKALLA, AMY; Bethel Park HS; Bethel Park, PA; (4); 70/525; German Clb; Office Aide; Chorus; Drill Tm; School Musical; Variety Show; Pom Pon; Powder Puff Ftbl; High Hon Roll; NHS; Robert Morris Coll; CPA.

KARL, LORI; Bishop Mc Devitt HS; Harrisburg, PA; (4); #2 In Class; Red Cross Aide; Scholastic Bowl; Service Clb; Spanish Clb; Color Guard; High Hon Roll; Trs NHS; Natl Ldrshp & Svc Awds In Math 84-85; Lehigh U; Econ.

KARLOTSKY, JAMIE; Wyoming Valley West HS; Luzerne, PA; (3); Chorus; Bus.

KARMAZON, AMY; Fort Le Boeuf HS; Waterford, PA; (3); 47/215; Ski Clb; Stu Cncl; Cheerleading; Sftbl; Trk; Vllybl; Hon Roll.

KARNS, DAVID; Meadville Area HS; Meadville, PA; (2); Exploring; JV Crs Cntry; Var Trk; Boy Scts; Church Yth Grp; Var Hon Roll; Edinboro U; Lwyr.

KARNS, GARRICK; Everett HS; Everett, PA; (1); Church Yth Grp; Chorus; Capt Wrstlng.

KARNS, SCOTT; New Castle HS; New Castle, PA; (3); 20/293; Church Yth Grp; Letterman Clb; Bsbl; Hon Roll.

KAROL, BORIS; Engineering & Science HS; Philladelphia, PA; (3); 9/241; JA; NHS; Amercn U; Fin.

KAROLESKI, MICHAEL; Trinity HS; Washington, PA; (3); 13/402; Computer Clb; Math Clb; Math Tm; High Hon Roll; MD.

KARP, ALYSSA; Bensalem HS; Bensalem, PA; (4); 18/499; Teachers Aide; Nwsp Rptr; Rep Frsh Cls; Rep Soph Cls; Rep Jr Cls; Rep Sr Cls; Rep Stu Cncl; Hon Roll; NHS; Pres Schlr; Drexel U; Psych.

KARP, MARY ANN; Mt Saint Joseph Acad; Lafayette Hill, PA; (3); Art Clb; Hosp Aide; Pres SADD; Yrbk Stf; Hon Roll; NHS; NEDT Awd; Cmnty Wkr; JCL; Latin Clb; Exclince Religion Awd; Exclince 3-D Clay Awd; Pre-Med.

KARPIAK, TIM; Uniontown HS; Vanderbilt, PA; (4); 48/329; Letterman Clb; Spanish Clb; Varsity Clb; Off Frsh Cls; Off Soph Cls; Ftbl; Trk; DAR Awd; Hon Roll; Al-St B-Nai Brith Awd 87; Al Conf, An Cnty B-Nai Brith Awd 86-87; WVU; Sports Mdcn.

KARPIEN, JOHN; E L Meyers HS; Wilkes Barre, PA; (3); Ski Clb; Chorus; Var Bsbl; Var Ftbl; Var Wt Lftg; Jr NHS; NHS; NEDT Awd; Pres Schlr; Spanish NHS; Pres Schlrshp St Vincents Coll 85 & 86; Acad Tlntd Prog; Hnrs Math & Engl.

KARPINSKI, MARK; Karns City HS; Chicora, PA; (3); Boy Scts; Church Yth Grp; FCA; Var Capt Bsktbl; Var Capt Ftbl; Var L Trk; Hon Roll; Jr NHS; NHS; All Conf Ftbl Tm 87; All Star Bsktbl Tm 86; Naval Acad; Chem.

KARPOUZIS, KATERINA P; J P Mc Caskey HS; Lancaster, PA; (3); #49 In Class; AFS; Pres Church Yth Grp; Acpl Chr; Nwsp Rptr; Nwsp Sprt Ed; Trs Soph Cls; Trs Jr Cls; Trs Sr Cls; Hon Roll; Jr NHS; PMEA Dist Choral Fstvl 87.

KARR, TONY; Oswayo Valley HS; Shinglehouse, PA; (3); 11/80; Ski Clb; Varsity Clb; Var Bsbl; Var L Bsktbl; Var Crs Cntry; Im Socr; Var L Trk; NHS.

KARSTETTER, RENEE; Bishop Mc Devitt HS; Harrisburg, PA; (4); 40/190; FBLA; Service Clb; Bsktbl; Ftbl; Mgr(s); Hon Roll; NHS; PA ST U; Sprts.

KARTESZ, KRISTA; Rockwood Area HS; Rockwood, PA; (4); 6/98; JA; School Play; Rep Sr Cls; Rep Stu Cncl; Gov Hon Prg Awd; High Hon Roll; NHS; Spanish Clb; SADD; I U D; Dietician.

KARUZIE, LISA; Old Forge HS; Old Forge, PA; (4); Hosp Aide; Ski Clb; Yrbk Stf; Jr Cls; Sr Cls; Cheerleading; Hon Roll; PA ST U.

KARWASKI, MAUREEN; Bishop Hannan HS; Moosic, PA; (4); 15/122; Hon Roll; NHS; Hnrb Mntn Certs-Engl IV, Amrcn Govt, Music Theory I 87; Marywood Coll; Music-Piano.

KARWOWSKI, DIANE; Neshaminy HS; Langhorne, PA; (3); Art Clb; Drama Clb; Intnl Clb; Chorus; Stage Crew; Lit Mag; Pre Law.

KASBEE, VICKI; Reynolds HS; Fredonia, PA; (3); #35 In Class; Church Yth Grp; 4-H; FBLA; Sec FFA; Latin Clb; Capt Pep Clb; Chorus; Trs Frsh Cls; Var Capt Cheerleading; 4-H Awd; Robert Morris Coll; Bus Admin.

KASBEKAR, NISHAMINY; Archbishop Ryan HS For Girls; Philadelphia, PA; (3); 50/510; Am Leg Aux Girls St; Cmnty Wkr; French Clb; Intnl Clb; Rep Frsh Cls; Stu Cncl; French Hon Soc; High Hon Roll; Religion Awd Cert Of Achvt Fren 85; Cert Achvt Fren, Bio & Geom 86; NCCJ Yth Conf 86; Keystone Grls; Pharmacy.

KASCSAK, DAVID J; Northampton SR HS; Walnutport, PA; (3); VICA; Wt Lftg; Wrstlng; Vo-Tech Auto Body 85-88; OH Diesel Tech; Auto Tech.

KASDIN, TOVAH; Abington HS; Jenkintown, PA; (3); 30/502; Pres Temple Yth Grp; Nwsp Ed-Chief; Nwsp Rptr; Lit Mag; Rep Jr Cls; Rep Sr Cls; Rep Stu Cncl; Capt JV Bsktbl; High Hon Roll; NHS; Am Lgn Awd 85; Pblc Rltns Awd 87; Outstndng Acdmc & Ctznshp Awds Hbrw HS 85-86; Vet Med.

KASE, JULIE; Shamokin Area HS; Danville, PA; (3); 17/235; Trs Drama Clb; German Clb; NFL; Science Clb; Speech Tm; SADD; Chorus; Color Guard; School Play; Var Trk; Mst Outstndng In Spch 86-87; Outstndng Stu Dir 87.

KASE JR, THOMAS F; William Allen HS; Allentown, PA; (3); Church Yth Grp; Nwsp Stf; Hon Roll; Mansfield U; Sprtscaster.

KASECKY, TONYA; Blacklick Valley JR SR HS; Ebensburg, PA; (3); 4/100; Church Yth Grp; Library Aide; Ski Clb; Varsity Clb; Yrbk Stf; Stu Cncl; Capt JV Cheerleading; High Hon Roll; Pres Schlr; Acdmc All Amer Schlr 85; Hnbl Mntn Johnstown PA Chptr Natl Orgnztn 86; IN U PA; Math.

KASH, BRIAN; Henderson HS; W Chester, PA; (3); Speech Tm; School Play; Var Ice Hcky; Capt Lcrss; Drama Clb; Thesps; School Musical; Variety Show; Nwsp Phtg; Rep Stu Cncl; 1st Tm All Lg Lacrsse Goalie 86-87, 1st Tm All Area 87, 2nd Tm All ST 87; Pre-Law.

KASHLAK, KATHY; West Mifflin Area HS; W Mifflin, PA; (2); Pep Clb; Ski Clb; Mrchg Band; Hon Roll; Outstndng Svc Home Econ Awd 86; Bus.

KASHNER, WENDY; Danville SR HS; Danville, PA; (2); 62/159; Church Yth Grp; Key Clb; Ski Clb; Rep Frsh Cls; Cheerleading; Swmmng; JV Tennis; High Hon Roll; Hon Roll; Pres Acad Ftnss Awd 85-86; Ec.

KASHNICKI, LOU; John S Fine HS; Nanticoke, PA; (4); 45/256; Swmmng; High Hon Roll; Rcvd Accntng II, Typng II, Bus Engl 87; Cnsmr Ed 87.

KASHUBARA, PETE; New Castle HS; New Castle, PA; (3); 23/273; Church Yth Grp; Cmnty Wkr; French Clb; Letterman Clb; Varsity Clb; Band; Concert Band; Bsktbl; Coach Actv; Ftbl; Schlr Athlt Awd 84; US Mltry Acad; Arch.

KASIAN, BRIAN; Coatesville SR HS; Coatesville, PA; (2); French Clb; Capt Bsbl; Var Ftbl; Capt Ice Hcky; Wt Lftg; Hon Roll.

KASICK, KIMBERLY; Riverside JR SR HS; Taylor, PA; (3); Hon Roll; NEDT Awd; PSYCH.

KASICK, KRISTI; Williamson JR SR HS; Millerton, PA; (3); Drama Clb; FNA; Pep Clb; Spanish Clb; SADD; Stu Cncl; Cheerleading; Mgr(s); Trk; Vllybl; Robert Packard; Radiolgcl Tech.

KASKEY, RICHARD; Wyoming Valley West HS; Larksville, PA; (3); 29/420; Am Leg Boys St; Pres Church Yth Grp; JV Var Bsbl; Var Capt Bsktbl; Cit Awd; High Hon Roll; Hon Roll; NHS; NEDT Awd; Rotary Awd; U S Naval Acad; Elctrcl Engrng.

KASKO, MARY ANN; Lake-Lehman HS; Shavertown, PA; (2); Hosp Aide; Concert Band; Mrchg Band; Kiwanis Awd; Jr NHS; NHS; Pres Schlr; Band; Orch; Symp Band; Dist Band, Orch, Rgnl Orch 87.

KASNER, ERICA; Northeast HS; Philadelphia, PA; (4); 102/690; Hosp Aide; Temple Yth Grp; Orch; School Musical; Yrbk Stf; Rep Stu Cncl; Hon Roll; Prfct Atten Awd; Penn ST U; Elem Educ.

KASPER, JASON; Plum SR HS; Plum, PA; (3); Drama Clb; Teachers Aide; Drm Mjr(t); Jazz Band; Mrchg Band; School Musical; School Play; Symp Band; High Hon Roll; NHS; U Of Pittsburgh; Math.

KASPER, MARK; Chartiers Valley HS; Bridgeville, PA; (3); Church Yth Grp; German Clb; Letterman Clb; Ski Clb; Varsity Clb; Capt Socr; Rotary Awd; PA ST U; Finance.

KASPER, WILLIAM; Nativity BVM HS; Pottsville, PA; (2); Church Yth Grp; Computer Clb; Band; Concert Band; Mrchg Band; Stage Crew; Nwsp Rptr; Stat Bsktbl; Bowling; Hon Roll; Harvard Medical Schl; Med.

KASPICK, WAYNE; Tyrone Area HS; Tyrone, PA; (3); 20/206; VP Spanish Clb; Im Bsktbl; JV Var Crs Cntry; JV Ftbl; Im Vllybl; Var Wt Lftg; JV Wrstlng; High Hon Roll; Pres Schlr; Clarion U Of PA; Math.

KASPRENSKI, KRISTA; Allentown Central Catholic HS; Allentown, PA; (3); Key Clb; Math Tm; Scholastic Bowl; Off Stu Cncl; Tennis; High Hon Roll; VP NHS; Pres Schlr; Lehigh Law Leag Schlrshp Pres Clssrm 87; PA JR Acad Sci 1st 85-86; Prncpls Awd Scintfc Rsrch 86.

KASPUTIS, MARY LYNN; Seneca Valley SR HS; Evans City, PA; (4); 69/374; JA; Ski Clb; Teachers Aide; Drm Mjr(t); Mrchg Band; Pep Band; Nwsp Stf; Yrbk Phtg; Ed Lit Mag; Rep Sr Cls; Anna Jean Shoop Awd 85-87; Stu Mnth 87; Lttrd Mjrtte 87; IN U; Physcs.

KASSIS, NANCY; Notre Dame HS; Easton, PA; (2); 35/90; Pep Clb; Yrbk Stf; Cheerleading; Trk; Hon Roll; Spanish NHS.

KASTAWA, RON; Valley View JR SR HS; Archbald, PA; (3); JV Bsbl; Trk.

KASTER, SALLY; Williams Valley JR SR HS; Wiconisco, PA; (3); 21/91; Chorus; Stu Cncl; Var L Bsktbl; Im Ftbl; Harrisburg Area CC.

KASTRIBA, LINDA; Ambridge Area HS; Ambridge, PA; (2); Pres Church Yth Grp; German Clb; Pep Clb; Off Frsh Cls; Pres Soph Cls; Sec Stu Cncl; Im Capt Cheerleading; Hon Roll; Soph Class Rep On Hmcmng Crt 86; Penn ST; Oprtng Rm Nrs.

KASULIS, WILLIAM; West Side HS; Scranton, PA; (2); Boys Clb Am; Boy Scts; Letterman Clb; Ftbl; Hon Roll.

KASUN, PAIGE; J P Mccaskey HS; Lancaster, PA; (4); 100/400; AFS; Hosp Aide; Band; Orch; Nwsp Bus Mgr; Cheerleading; Hon Roll; OH ST U; Jrnlsm.

KASZOWSKI, TAMMY; Wilmington Area HS; New Wilmington, PA; (3); 1/115; Drama Clb; French Clb; Band; Concert Band; Mrchg Band; Pep Band; School Play; High Hon Roll; Hon Roll.

KASZUBA, DAVID C; Bishop Hoban HS; Mountain Top, PA; (4); Computer Clb; Latin Clb; Mu Alpha Theta; Yrbk Rptr; Lit Mag; High Hon Roll; Kiwanis Awd; NHS; Pres Schlr; Wilkes Coll Presidential Schlrshp 87-91; Wilkes Coll; Communications.

KASZUPSKI, JIM; Neshaminy HS; Feasterville, PA; (3); 59/800; Var Gym; Var Socr; Var Trk; Hon Roll; NHS; MVP JV Soccr 84-85; PA ST.

KASZYNSKI, KYRA; Emmaus HS; Londonderry, NH; (4); French Clb; Key Clb; JV Bsktbl; Var JV Fld Hcky; NHS; Opt Clb Awd; Cert Astan Ski Instrctr 85-87; Scrtry Sfrds 86-87; U Of VT.

KATCHMORE, DANIELLE; Carbondale Area JR/Sr HS; Carbondale, PA; (3); FBLA; Ski Clb; Spanish Clb; JV Bsktbl; Var Tennis; Hon Roll.

KATEKOVICH, KATHLEEN; Beaver Area JR-SR HS; Beaver, PA; (4); French Clb; JA; Ski Clb; Spanish Clb; Nwsp Phtg; Nwsp Rptr; Nwsp Stf; Lit Mag; Rep Stu Cncl; Var Powder Puff Ftbl; IN U Of PA; Prsnnl Mgmt.

KATES, HEATHER; Mt St Joseph Acad; Philadelphia, PA; (3); Computer Clb; Debate Tm; Math Clb; Math Tm; NFL; Science Clb; Spanish Clb; SADD; Ed Yrbk Stf; VP Frsh Cls; Irish Culture Clb VP 86-87; 1st Pl PA Acad Sci 86; Fnlst HOBY 85-86; Bio.

KATES, KELLY; Chichester SR HS; Marcus Hook, PA; (3); 46/297; French Clb; JA; Office Aide; SADD; Lit Mag; Bsktbl; Fld Hcky; Mgr(s); Hon Roll; Prfct Atten Awd; West Chester U; Math.

KATRISHEN, LEANNE; Hazleton HS; Hazleton, PA; (3); Pep Clb; Y-Teens; Off Frsh Cls; Rep Stu Cncl; Bsktbl; Crs Cntry; Sftbl; Hon Roll; Bsktbl Lttr 87; Sftbl Lttr 86-87; PA ST; Educ.

KATSOFF, ROBYN; Lower Merion HS; Pennwynne, PA; (3); Service Clb; SADD; Schltc Art Aws 86-87.

KATTOUF, JONATHAN; Central Dauphin HS; Harrisburg, PA; (3); 27/369; Rep Key Clb; Pres Soph Cls; Pres Jr Cls; Var Ftbl; Im Wt Lftg; NHS; Ntl Merit Ltr; Voice Dem Awd; Hon Roll; VFW Awd; HOBY Fndtn Ldrshp Sem 86; Pres Clssrm 87; Am Leg Oratorcl Awd 87.

KATTOUT, JONATHAN; Central Dauphin HS; Harrisburg, PA; (3); 27/369; Rep Key Clb; Pres Soph Cls; Pres Jr Cls; Var Ftbl; Im Wt Lftg; NHS; Ntl Merit Ltr; Voice Dem Awd; Exploring; JV Bsbl; Hgh Obrn Yth Fndtn Ldrshp Smnr 86; Pres Clssrm 87; Am Lgn Oratrcl Awd 87.

KATULIS, SEAN; Central Dauphin HS; Harrisburg, PA; (3); Pres Church Yth Grp; Jr NHS; Psych.

KATYAL, SHALINI; Shaler Area SR HS; Allison Park, PA; (3); 15/486; Hosp Aide; SADD; Temple Yth Grp; Yrbk Stf; French Hon Soc; High Hon Roll; NHS; Prfct Atten Awd; U Of MI; Med.

KATYNSKI, LARA; Freedom HS; Bethlehem, PA; (3); 144/487; Pep Clb; SADD; Lit Mag; Mgr(s); Score Keeper; Socr; Timer; Hon Roll.

KATZ, ERIC; Neshominy HS; Langhorne, PA; (4); 31/687; Boy Scts; Computer Clb; Math Tm; Teachers Aide; Rep Soph Cls; Trk; Hon Roll; NHS; P Mc Keaney Memrl Schlrshp 87-88; B M Fine Schlrshp 87-88; Drexel U; Comp Sci.

KATZ, JASON; Mount Lebanon HS; Pittsburgh, PA; (4); Chess Clb; Church Yth Grp; Latin Clb; Varsity Clb; Orch; School Musical; Im Bsktbl; Var L Ice Hcky; Var JV Trk; Hon Roll; Dist Orchstra 86; Gradtd With Hnrs 87; Kent ST U; Bus.

KATZ, LISA MICHELE; Lower Moreland HS; Huntingdon Valley, PA; (3); Sec VP FBLA; Hosp Aide; Science Clb; SADD; Teachers Aide; School Musical; Var Cheerleading; Stat Trk; Hon Roll; NHS; Rgnl VP FBLA 86-87; Entrecon Wharton Schl Of Bus 86; Lib Arts.

KATZENBACH, GEORGE; Plymouth Whitemarsh HS; Lafayette Hill, PA; (3); 29/382; Math Clb; Mu Alpha Theta; Nwsp Rptr; Nwsp Stf; Bsbl; Bsktbl; Socr; High Hon Roll; NHS; U Of PA; Sports Med.

KATZMAN, RONALD; Cumberland Valley HS; Mechanicsburg, PA; (3); Church Yth Grp; French Clb; FBLA; Key Clb; Ski Clb; Varsity Clb; Var L Socr; JV Tennis; French Hon Soc; Hon Roll; ST Slct Soccer Tm 87.

KATZMAR, DENISE; Harry S Truman HS; Levittown, PA; (3); Drama Clb; School Musical; Rep Stu Cncl; Var Capt Cheerleading; Coach Actv; Var JV Socr; Hon Roll; All Star Ftbl Chrldr 86; Engl Tchr.

KAUFFAMN, DAVID; North Allegheny HS; Pittsburgh, PA; (2); Art Clb; Cmnty Wkr; Math Clb; Math Tm; SADD; Teachers Aide; Stage Crew; Lit Mag; Jr NHS; NHS; Amer Lgn Awd 87; Ftbll JV 86; Engr.

KAUFFMAN, BRAD; New Wilmington Area HS; New Wilmington, PA; (3); Spanish Clb; Yrbk Stf; Stu Cncl; Var JV Bsbl; JV Bsktbl; Var JV Ftbl; Hon Roll; Bus.

KAUFFMAN, DANA; St Basil Acad; Philadelphia, PA; (3); Pres GAA; Spanish Clb; SADD; Nwsp Sprt Ed; Var Bsktbl; Socr; Sftbl; NHS; Athlt Wk Phila Inquirer-Bsktbl 87; Brdcstr.

KAUFFMAN, JACQUELINE; Lampeter-Strasburg HS; Strasburg, PA; (3); 29/147; Hosp Aide; Varsity Clb; Chorus; Color Guard; Concert Band; Mrchg Band; School Musical; Stu Cncl; Var Capt Cheerleading; Hon Roll; Med Tech.

KAUFFMAN, JACQUELYN; Bishop Mc Devitt HS; Harrisburg, PA; (3); 30/230; FBLA; Library Aide; Service Clb; Color Guard; Mrchg Band; NHS.

KAUFFMAN, JASON M; Halifax Area HS; Halifax, PA; (3); 4-H; Orch; 4-H Awd; Arch.

KAUFFMAN, LISA; Greencastle-Antrim SR HS; Greencastle, PA; (1); 1/194; Pres Church Yth Grp; Drama Clb; Chorus; Church Choir; School Play; Yrbk Rptr; High Hon Roll; Engl Awd 87; Chem.

KAUFFMAN, MELANIE; Wilmington Area HS; Volant, PA; (4); 29/110; Office Aide; Spanish Clb; Nwsp Ed-Chief; Stat Bsktbl; Stat Trk; Stat Vllybl; Westminster Coll; Engl.

KAUFFMAN, PAMELA; Red Lion Area SR HS; Red Lion, PA; (4); 1/330; Am Leg Aux Girls St; Drm Mjr(t); School Musical; Symp Band; Nwsp Stf; Trs Jr Cls; VP Sr Cls; Rep Stu Cncl; NHS; Ntl Merit Ltr; Ecnmcs.

KAUFFMAN, STEPHANIE; Ephrata SR HS; Ephrata, PA; (4); 34/243; Pres Pep Clb; Rep Sr Cls; Var Capt Cheerleading; Powder Puff Ftbl; Stat Trk; Hon Roll; Lancaster Schl Csmtlgy; Csmtlgy.

KAUFFMAN, SUE; Brandywine Heights HS; Mertztown, PA; (4); Art Clb; Pep Clb; Ski Clb; Band; Color Guard; Drill Tm; Mrchg Band; Stage Crew; Stu Cncl; Hon Roll; Antonelli Inst; Commrcl Artist.

KAUFMAN, AMY; Greensburg Salem SR HS; New Alexandria, PA; (3); 5/288; Church Yth Grp; Sec Trs 4-H; French Clb; Yrbk Stf; Sftbl; 4-H Awd; High Hon Roll; Jr NHS; Sec NHS; Equine Sci.

KAUFMAN, DAVID ALAN; Altoona Area HS; Altoona, PA; (3); Trs Science Clb; Speech Tm; VP Temple Yth Grp; Nwsp Ed-Chief; Stat Bsktbl; Stat Ftbl; Jr NHS; Pres Schlr; Chess Clb; Computer Clb; Acad Sci 1st Pl Region 87; Am Leg Good Citznshp Awd 85; Stu Cncl Conv Finance Chrmn 86.

KAUFMAN, KEVIN; Wissahickon HS; Ambler, PA; (3); 83/296; Key Clb; SADD; Varsity Clb; Nwsp Rptr; Nwsp Stf; JV Socr; JV Tennis; Var Wrstlng; Hon Roll; PA ST U; Jrnlsm.

KAUFMAN, MELISSA; Pleasant Valley HS; Sciota, PA; (3); 104/228; 4-H; Letterman Clb; Math Clb; Ski Clb; Varsity Clb; Rep Stu Cncl; Var JV Fld Hcky; Var JV Sftbl; JV Trk; Phys Thrpy.

KAUFMAN, RONA; North Hills HS; Pittsburgh, PA; (3); Trs Temple Yth Grp; Band; Concert Band; Mrchg Band; Orch; School Play; Symp Band; Yrbk Stf; High Hon Roll; NHS; Law.

KAUFMANN, RONALD; Northeast HS; Philadelphia, PA; (4); 22/600; Computer Clb; 4-H; VP Radio Clb; Mgr Science Clb; Nwsp Bus Mgr; NHS; GA Tech; Physcs.

KAUFOLD, HEATHER; Cumberland Valley HS; Mechanicsburg, PA; (3); 73/578; Art Clb; Latin Clb; Ski Clb; Speech Tm; Socr; Var L Swmmng; Hon Roll; Natl Art Hnr Soc 86-87; Bus.

KAUNE, DOUGLAS; Devon Prep Schl; Wayne, PA; (3); Church Yth Grp; Spanish Clb; Stage Crew; Nwsp Rptr; Yrbk Stf; Rep Soph Cls; Rep Jr Cls; Capt Bsktbl; Capt Tennis; Hon Roll; Pre Law.

KAUR, HARPREET; Pittston Area SR HS; Pittston, PA; (3); 15/305; Computer Clb; French Clb; FNA; Math Clb; Science Clb; Ski Clb; NEDT Awd; Bus.

KAUS, JUDENE; Riverview HS; Oakmont, PA; (3); Trs French Clb; Varsity Clb; Band; Concert Band; Drill Tm; Off Jr Cls; Var L Bsktbl; Powder Puff Ftbl; Var L Trk; Twrlr.

KAVANAGH, KATHLEEN; Trinity HS; Mechanicsburg, PA; (4); Drama Clb; Pep Clb; Ski Clb; Spanish Clb; Band; Mrchg Band; Yrbk Stf; Spanish NHS; Pres Acdmc Ftnss Awd 86-87; U Of DE; Bus Adm.

KAVELAK, ANDY; Curwensville Area HS; Curwensville, PA; (3); Chess Clb; French Clb; JV Ftbl; JV Wrstlng; High Hon Roll; Hon Roll; Penn ST; Engrng.

KAVULA, KEITH; Pleasant Valley HS; Kunkletown, PA; (4); Church Yth Grp; Civic Clb; Computer Clb; Debate Tm; Drama Clb; English Clb; Letterman Clb; Math Clb; Q&S; Ski Clb; Stroudsburg Music Clb Schlrshp 87; Friends Of Music Schlrshp Awd NM 87; Caf Jacksn Comp Fnlst 86; U Of NM; Piano Prmnc.

KAVULA, SCOTT; Pleasant Valley HS; Kunkletown, PA; (2); Aud/Vis; Church Yth Grp; Ski Clb; Band; Concert Band; Jazz Band; Mrchg Band; Pep Band; School Musical; School Play.

KAWALEC III, ADOLPH P; Notre Dame HS; E Stroudsburg, PA; (3); 11/48; Ski Clb; Stage Crew; Yrbk Stf; JV Bsktbl; Var Socr; Comm Art.

KAWCHAK, TAMMY LYNNE; Greater Johnstown HS; Johnstown, PA; (3); Key Clb; NFL; Spanish Clb; Chorus; Mrchg Band; School Musical; Yrbk Rptr; Rep Stu Cncl; High Hon Roll; NHS; Elem Ed.

KAY, MYRA; Pine Forge Acad; Lincoln, NE; (3); Office Aide; Teachers Aide; Chorus; Concert Band; Im Bsbl; Cit Awd; High Hon Roll; Prfct Atten Awd; Temprnc Essay Awd 85; Band Schlrshp 86-87; Oakwood Coll; Tchr.

KAY, SANDRA; Laurel Valley HS; New Florence, PA; (4); 10/90; AFS; Ski Clb; Chorus; Concert Band; Drm Mjr(t); Mrchg Band; Ed Yrbk Ed-Chief; Powder Puff Ftbl; NHS; SR Hgh Cnty Bnd 86; Comp Sci.

KAYLA, JACQUELINE; Rochester Area HS; Rochester, PA; (3); 1/105; Pres Church Yth Grp; VP JA; Q&S; Spanish Clb; Off Band; Concert Band; Mrchg Band; Orch; School Musical; Nwsp Ed-Chief; 2nd Rnnr-Up Bvr Cnty JR Miss Pgm 87; Rep To HOBY Smnr 86; Duquesne U; Cmnctns.

KAYLOR, PAMELA; Connellsville Area HS; Dunbar, PA; (3); Church Yth Grp; GAA; Pep Clb; Teachers Aide; Chorus; Church Choir; JV Var Bsktbl; Bowling; Mgr(s); High Hon Roll.

KAYLOR, STACY; Elizabethtown Area HS; Elizabethtown, PA; (3); Spanish Clb; Nwsp Ed-Chief; Trk; Hon Roll; Elizabethtown Coll; Radiolgy.

KAZA, LAURA; Punxsutowney Area HS; Punxsutawney, PA; (3); Art Clb; FBLA; Hosp Aide; SADD; Nwsp Phtg; Nwsp Rptr; Nwsp Stf; IN U; Hstry Tchr.

KAZIMERSKI, CHERYL; Frankford HS; Philadelphia, PA; (3); DECA; Drama Clb; Hosp Aide; Teachers Aide; School Play; Variety Show; Rep Frsh Cls; JV Fld Hcky; Cmmndtn 86-87; Paralgl.

KAZIO, CLAUDINE; Cardinal O Hara HS; Brookhaven, PA; (3); 30/715; Church Yth Grp; Cmnty Wkr; Office Aide; Spanish Clb; Teachers Aide; Cheerleading; Hon Roll; NHS; Opt Clb Awd; Spanish NHS; 2nd Pl Essy Cntst 87; Phrmcy.

KAZNICKI, LOIS; Arch Bishop Ryan High Schl For Girls; Philadelphia, PA; (3); 6/520; High Hon Roll; Hon Roll; Prfct Atten Awd; Schlrshp Archbishop Ryau HS Girls 84-85; Full Schlrshp Temple U Gftd Stu 86; Wrld Affrs Cncl Drmmr; Music.

KEACH III, ELMER R; Red Land HS; Etters, PA; (3); 50/311; Am Leg Boys St; Boy Scts; Cmnty Wkr; Quiz Bowl; SADD; Chorus; Mrchg Band; Yrbk Stf; God Cntry Awd; High Hon Roll.

KEAGY, ELIZABETH; Central York SR HS; York, PA; (3); Church Yth Grp; NFL; SADD; Band; Chorus; Church Choir; Concert Band; Drm Mjr(t); Jazz Band; Mrchg Band; Dist Band 87; PA Ambssdrs Music Europe Tour 87.

KEAN, MARY BETH; Cardinal O Hara HS; Drexel Hill, PA; (4); 4/772; Church Yth Grp; JCL; Math Tm; Service Clb; Concert Band; Mrchg Band; Nwsp Rptr; High Hon Roll; NHS; Presdntl Schlrshp Fort Immaculata Coll 87; Immaculata Coll; Math.

KEANE, ROSEMARY BETH; Downingtown SR HS; Exton, PA; (3); 95/648; Off Church Yth Grp; Drama Clb; Intnl Clb; Pep Clb; Political Wkr; Spanish Clb; SADD; Chorus; School Musical; Stage Crew; W Chstr U Schlrshp 86; Outstndng Merit Awd Spanish 86; Penn ST; Pol Sci.

KEAR, KRISTEN LAURA; Liberty HS; Bethlehem, PA; (4); 90/390; Church Yth Grp; Cmnty Wkr; Chorus; School Play; Nwsp Stf; Lit Mag; Trk; Hon Roll; La Salle U; Engl.

KEAR, PATRICIA; St Marys Area HS; Saint Marys, PA; (4); 14/287; Vllybl; High Hon Roll; NHS; Best Overall Spkr In Yth Ldrshp 86; U Of Pittsburgh; Pharmacy.

KEARNEY, ANTHONY; Old Forge HS; Old Forge, PA; (3); Exploring; Ski Clb; Nwsp Stf; Capt Crs Cntry; High Hon Roll; Hon Roll; NHS; Ntl Merit Schol; Aero Engrng.

KEARNEY, BARBARA; Annville-Cleona HS; Annville, PA; (3); 15/127; French Clb; Acpl Chr; Band; Chorus; Concert Band; Mrchg Band; Lit Mag; JV Fld Hcky; NHS; NEDT Awd; Intl Studies.

KEARNEY, ERIN; John S Fine SR HS; Nanticoke, PA; (2); 6/243; Spanish Clb; Chorus; Yrbk Stf; Cheerleading; Trk; High Hon Roll; NHS; Pomeroys Teen Brd 86-87; Temple; Pharm.

KEARNEY, HOPE; University City HS; Philadelphia, PA; (3); Church Yth Grp; 4-H; Church Choir; Nwsp Stf; Yrbk Stf; U Of PA Upwrd Bnd Pgm 85-88; Boy Scts Explr Pgm 86-87; Engr.

KEARNEY, KEVIN; Shamokin Area HS; Shamokin, PA; (2); #37 In Class; AFS; German Clb; Key Clb; Letterman Clb; Science Clb; Ski Clb; Spanish Clb; Varsity Clb; Ftbl; Hon Roll; Exchng Stu Mexico 84-85.

KEARNEY, SHAWN; Du Bois Area HS; Du Bois, PA; (2); Church Yth Grp; Nwsp Rptr; Nwsp Sprt Ed; Nwsp Stf; JV Golf; Hon Roll; Scty Dist Amer Stus 87; Jrnlsm.

KEARNEY, SHELLY; Hollidaysburg Area SR HS; Hollidaysburg, PA; (3); 3/385; Model UN; Hosp Aide; Latin Clb; Chorus; School Musical; Yrbk Ed-Chief; Ed Yrbk Stf; Lit Mag; Rep Stu Cncl; Hon Roll; Med Fld.

KEARNEY, TRACEY; Shamokin Area HS; Paxinos, PA; (2); 29/215; Art Clb; 4-H; Band; Concert Band; Mrchg Band; Orch; Yrbk Stf; 4-H Awd; Hon Roll; Bloomsburg U; Med.

KEARNEY, WILLIAM; Penn Cambria HS; Lilly, PA; (3); Library Aide; Mrchg Band; Stage Crew; JV Bsktbl; Im Vllybl; Hon Roll; High Avrg Frnch.

KEARNS, KIMBERLY; Methacton HS; Trooper, PA; (3); 17/381; JV Capt Fld Hcky; Stat Lcrss; High Hon Roll; NHS; HOBY Fntdn Smnr 86; Phila Coll Phrmcy Sci; Phrmcy.

KEARNS, KIMBERLY; Ringgold SR HS; Finleyville, PA; (4); Church Yth Grp; French Clb; Office Aide; Pep Clb; Ski Clb; Band; Chorus; Mrchg Band; Variety Show; Cheerleading; Sales.

KEAT, KEVIN; Pen Argyl Area HS; Pen Argyl, PA; (3); Math Clb; Science Clb; Ski Clb; Im Bsbl; Var Crs Cntry; JV Ftbl; Im Socr; Var JV Trk; Var Wt Lftg; Math.

KEATING, JAMES ALAN; Penn Trafford HS; Level Green, PA; (4); 24/344; Chess Clb; JCL; Latin Clb; High Hon Roll; Hon Roll; Lion Awd; NHS; Pres Schlr; St Vincent Coll Merit Schrlshp 87; Jr Clscl League St Meeting 86-87; St Vincent Coll; Bio.

KEATING, LORI; Dunmore HS; Dunmore, PA; (3); 38/146; Drama Clb; French Clb; FBLA; JA; Ski Clb; Spanish Clb; Chorus; Capt Pom Pon; Hon Roll; Jr NHS; Bus.

KEATING, REBECCA JO; Penn Trafford HS; Level Green, PA; (2); Chess Clb; JCL; Latin Clb; High Hon Roll; Hon Roll; St Vincent Coll; Psychtrst.

KEAY, SANDY; North Catholic HS; Pittsburgh, PA; (3); Church Yth Grp; Drama Clb; Ski Clb; Spanish Clb; Variety Show; Bsktbl; Score Keeper; Hon Roll; Allegheny Comm Coll; Mngmnt.

KEBERT, ROB; Meadville Area SR HS; Meadville, PA; (3); 103/328; Church Yth Grp; SADD; JV Socr; Hon Roll; Penn ST; Law.

KEBUZ, LANA; Lower Moreland HS; Huntingdon Valley, PA; (4); 39/201; Church Yth Grp; Drama Clb; FBLA; Key Clb; Science Clb; Crs Cntry; Trk; Vllybl; Hon Roll; NHS; U Of TX; Bus.

KECK, ARIES CLAIRE; Upper Dauphin Area HS; Pillow, PA; (3); 12/115; Drama Clb; Varsity Clb; Band; Concert Band; Mrchg Band; Socr; Trk; Hon Roll; Cmmnctns.

KECK, GINA; Little Flower Catholic HS; Philadelphia, PA; (3); 73/322; Service Clb; Hon Roll; Prfct Atten Awd; Ped Nrsng.

KECK, GORDON J; Knoch HS; Sarver, PA; (3); 17/230; Church Yth Grp; German Clb; Political Wkr; High Hon Roll; Hon Roll; Law School.

KECK JR, ROBERT; Mahanoy Area HS; Barnesville, PA; (3); Band; Concert Band; School Play; Ftbl; JV Trk; Var L Wrstlng; Hon Roll; NHS; Drexel U; Elec Engrng.

KEEBLER JR, JOSEPH; Oil City HS; Oil City, PA; (3); 16/192; Boy Scts; Trs Church Yth Grp; German Clb; Band; Ftbl; Swmmng; Hon Roll; NHS; Chem Engr.

KEECH, SUSAN; Hollidaysburg SR HS; Hollidaysburg, PA; (3); Library Aide; Band; Flag Corp; School Play; Variety Show; Yrbk Stf; Rep Stu Cncl; Vllybl; Hon Roll; PA ST.

KEEFER, ERIC; Central HS; York, PA; (3); Off Art Clb; Off Church Yth Grp; Cmnty Wkr; Dance Clb; Drama Clb; Pres JA; Latin Clb; PAVAS; Off Service Clb; Chorus; Natl Art Hnr Scty 85-87; NC ST U; Archt.

KEEFER, ERIN; Lake-Lehman HS; Shavertown, PA; (2); Sec Frsh Cls; JV Fld Hcky; Hon Roll; Jr NHS; NEDT Awd; NEDT Awd 86; Acting.

KEEFER, JANELLE; Shikellamy HS; Sunbury, PA; (3); 25/319; French Clb; NFL; Chorus; Drill Tm; School Musical; Variety Show; Nwsp Rptr; Hon Roll; Jr NHS; Cmnctns.

KEEFER, JENNIFER; Seneca Valley HS; Harmony, PA; (2); JA; Hon Roll; JA Sales Awd 87; Schlstc Awd 87.

KEEFER, JOANNE; Upper Dublin HS; Dresher, PA; (4); 63/320; Church Yth Grp; Teachers Aide; Church Choir; JV Cheerleading; Montgomery County CC; Nrsng.

KEEFER, KAREN S; Connellsville SR HS; Indian Head, PA; (4); 70/550; GAA; Teachers Aide; VP Soph Cls; VP Jr Cls; Var Vllybl; High Hon Roll; Hon Roll.

KEEFER, KELLY; Big Spring HS; Shippensburg, PA; (3); 2/260; Pres Jr Cls; Pres Sr Cls; Rep Stu Cncl; Capt Var Cheerleading; Var Powder Puff Ftbl; Var High Hon Roll; Pres NHS; Art Clb; School Musical; Outstndng Prfcncy Amer Hstry Awd 85; Dstngshd Hnrs Awd 85; Ed.

KEEFER, LEONA; Dover Area HS; Dover, PA; (4); Church Yth Grp; Cmnty Wkr; Chorus; Church Choir; Concert Band; Mgr Vllybl; CC Awd; High Hon Roll; Hon Roll; NHS; PA DE Dist Fine Arts Fstvl 86 & 87; Top 10th Cls Hnr Mdl 87; Messiah Coll.

KEEFER, MICHELLE; Meadville Area SR HS; Meadville, PA; (4); 30/306; Science Clb; Spanish Clb; Varsity Clb; Band; Trs Jr Cls; Trs Stu Cncl; Swmmng; Trk; High Hon Roll; Hon Roll; US Stu Cncl Achvt Awd 86.

KEEFER, SANDRA; Palmyra Area SR HS; Palmyra, PA; (4); 3/186; Church Yth Grp; Hosp Aide; Pep Clb; Teachers Aide; High Hon Roll; NHS; Stu Mnth 83-84; Lancaster Gen Hosp Schl Nrsng.

KEEFER, SCOTT; Mt Pleasant Area HS; Mt Pleasant, PA; (3); 50/250; Ski Clb; Im Bsktbl; JV Var Ftbl; JV Trk; Im Vllybl; High Hon Roll; Hon Roll; Law.

KEEFER, STACEY; Connellsville Area SR HS; Connellsville, PA; (3); 47/500; FTA; Band; Mrchg Band; Stage Crew; Nwsp Stf; Yrbk Stf; Rep Stu Cncl; High Hon Roll; Prfct Atten Awd; Church Yth Grp; 1st Pl 1st Yr Alg Cont Fayette Cnty; Math.

KEEFER, WILLIAM; Connellsville HS; S Connellsville, PA; (4); 144/520; Var L Bsktbl; Var L Wrstlng; High Hon Roll; NHS; Natl Hnr Soc 87; Ltr-Wrstlng & Bsbl 86-87; Penn ST U.

KEEFRIDER, ROBERT; Archbishop Wood For Boys HS; Warminster, PA; (2); 100/258; Church Yth Grp.

KEELER, BRYAN; Dover Area HS; Dover, PA; (3); 17/260; JV Bsktbl; Var L Socr; Hon Roll; Engrng.

KEELER, KRISTYN; Lebanon Catholic HS; Lebanon, PA; (3); 13/75; German Clb; Key Clb; Science Clb; Capt Color Guard; Capt Drill Tm; Jazz Band; School Play; Yrbk Rptr; Hon Roll; Ntl Merit Ltr; Best Actress For 1 Act Plys 87; Drexel; Commerce.

KEELER, LISA; Mt Pleasant Area HS; Mt Pleasant, PA; (2); German Clb; Girl Scts; Latin Clb; Science Clb; Ski Clb; Band; Concert Band; Mrchg Band; Bsktbl; Diving; Viking Rcgntn Awd Humanities & Phys Ed.

KEELER, SARAH; Ford City HS; Ford City, PA; (3); Church Yth Grp; German Clb; Girl Scts; SADD; Band; Chorus; Church Choir; Concert Band; Var Tennis; High Hon Roll; Acad Achvt 85; Acctng.

KEELEY, DENISE M; Cardinal Dougherty HS; Philadelphia, PA; (4); 13/696; Sec Church Yth Grp; Cmnty Wkr; Latin Clb; Math Clb; Church Choir; Hon Roll; NHS; Allied Hlth Schlrshp 87-88; Manor JC; Med Asst.

KEELEY, SEAN; Hopewell SR HS; Aliquippa, PA; (3); 22/230; Var Bsbl; L Var Bsktbl; Im Coach Actv; High Hon Roll; Schlr/Athl Awd 86-87; Bus Mgmt.

KEEN, CYNTHIA; W B Saul HS; Philadelphia, PA; (4); FFA; Girl Scts; Spanish Clb; Teachers Aide; Hst Jr Cls; Sec Sr Cls; Capt Vllybl; Outstndg Dairy Awd 85-86; Sales & Svcs 85; Flwr Show Exhibit Mgmt 85; James Martin Schl Nrsng.

KEEN, VANESSA; Lock Haven HS; Lock Haven, PA; (4); FBLA; Twrlr; Awd 4th Pl Bus Law Rgn 7 Sprng Ldrshp Conf 87; SECY.

KEENA, JOSEPH; Monsignor Bonner HS; Glenolden, PA; (4); 10/308; Boys Clb Am; Stage Crew; Nwsp Ed-Chief; Nwsp Stf; Yrbk Stf; Im Ftbl; High Hon Roll; Hon Roll; NHS; Opt Clb Awd; Pre Med.

KEENAN, AIMEE; Moon Area SR HS; Coraopolis, PA; (3); #79 In Class; DECA; Q&S; Yrbk Ed-Chief; Yrbk Phtg; Stat Var Bsktbl; Var JV Mgr(s); JV Score Keeper; JV Var Socr; Hon Roll; Key Clb; Fshn Mrchndsng.

KEENAN, WENDY; Chartiers-Houston HS; Washington, PA; (3); Cmnty Wkr; Drama Clb; Library Aide; Science Clb; Spanish Clb; Variety Show; Rep Stu Cncl; JV Vllybl; High Hon Roll; NHS; PA Govs Schl Crtv Wrtg Semi-Fnlst 87; Fndtn Free Enterprs Ed Schlrshp 87; Engl.

KEENE, CHRIS; Fort Le Boeut HS; Erie, PA; (4); 7/163; Model UN; Off Stu Cncl; Capt Wrstlng; High Hon Roll; Pres Schlr; Duke U Athlt Schlrshp 87; Duke U; Psych.

KEENE, DEBORAH A; Indiana Area SR HS; Indiana, PA; (4); 2/325; English Clb; Acpl Chr; Chorus; Church Choir; School Play; NCTE Awd; NHS; Ntl Merit SF; NEDT Awd; Lang Awds Engl, Spnsh, Latn; Math Awd; Hstry Day Merit Awd Regnl; IN U Of PA; Engl.

KEENE, MATTHEW E; Faith Christian HS; Ft Washington, PA; (3); Church Yth Grp; Pres Stu Cncl; JV Bsbl; JV Socr; High Hon Roll; Hon Roll; Prfct Atten Awd; PSAT/NMSQT Semi-Finalist 87.

KEENE, TRACY; Spring Grove Area HS; Spring Grove, PA; (3); Pres Church Yth Grp; Cmnty Wkr; JA; Ski Clb; Band; Concert Band; Mrchg Band; JV Bsktbl; Var Powder Puff Ftbl; Sftbl; Bus Admin.

KEENER, KELLY; Elizabethtown HS; Elizabethtown, PA; (4); Teachers Aide; VP Jr Cls; Fld Hcky; Powder Puff Ftbl; Trk; Hon Roll; Hcky Awd Ldng Screr & Mst Imprvd Trk 86-87; James Madison U; Psych.

KEENER, MARCIE; Reading SR HS; Reading, PA; (2); 192/819; JA; Acpl Chr; Ed Chorus; Fld Hcky; Hon Roll; Phy Thrpy.

KEENER, REBECCA; Steel Valley HS; W Homestead, PA; (3); Varsity Clb; Band; Concert Band; Mrchg Band; Yrbk Ed-Chief; Yrbk Sprt Ed; Yrbk Stf; Off Stu Cncl; Var JV Bsktbl; Wt Lftg; Communctns.

KEENEY, COLLEEN; Allentown Central Catholic HS; Northampton, PA; (3); 21/220; Hosp Aide; Key Clb; Pep Clb; Spanish Clb; Yrbk Stf; Im Powder Puff Ftbl; NHS; Nrsng.

KEENEY, MAURITA; Coughlin HS; Wlks Barr Twp, PA; (3); 34/347; Chess Clb; Math Clb; Stu Cncl; Cheerleading; Trk; Hon Roll; Jr NHS; NHS; Pres Schlr; Wilkes Coll; Corp Law.

KEENEY, SHANNON; Chestnut Ridge HS; Alum Bank, PA; (3); 17/131; GAA; Ski Clb; Trs Jr Cls; Stu Cncl; Bsktbl; Trk; Vllybl; Hon Roll; Var Ltrs-Vllybl, Basktbl & Trk 85-87; Bio.

KEENEY, YVONNE; Central SR HS; York, PA; (4); 2/211; VP Church Yth Grp; Intnl Clb; Drill Tm; Stat Bsktbl; High Hon Roll; Trs NHS; Pres Schlr; Sal; Hosp Aide; Sci Olympd 86; Acad Ltr & 3 Bars 85-87; Towson ST U; Chld Psych.

KEENY, LINDA; Red Lion Area SR HS; Stewartstown, PA; (3); 54/342; Library Aide; High Hon Roll; Hon Roll; RN.

KEEPORT, KENDRA; Penn Manor HS; Millersville, PA; (3); 80/300; Church Yth Grp; Peer Cnslr 85-87; Millersville U; Architecture.

KEER, COLLEEN; Marian Catholic HS; Coaldale, PA; (3); 4/104; Var Bsktbl; Var Trk; High Hon Roll; NHS; Spanish NHS; Engrng.

KEER, KAREN; Lehighton Area HS; Lehighton, PA; (4); 1/230; Art Clb; SADD; Chorus; Yrbk Stf; Rep Stu Cncl; Var L Cheerleading; Var L Fld Hcky; Var L Trk; High Hon Roll; NHS; C L Barry Mem Schlrshp 87; Thos J Mc Call Mem Schlrshp 87; Track MVP, Cls Schlr Ath 87; Allentown Coll; Bio.

KEETER, PAIGE; Pottsville Area HS; Pottsville, PA; (3); Drama Clb; Girl Scts; Hosp Aide; Q&S; Acpl Chr; Flag Corp; Yrbk Stf; High Hon Roll; NEDT Awd; Spanish Clb; Natl Ldrshp & Srvc Awd Wnnr 85; Psych.

KEETON, KIMBERLY; Seneca Valley SR HS; Harmony, PA; (4); 2/340; Sec Varsity Clb; Capt Mrchg Band; Mgr School Play; Symp Band; Yrbk Ed-Chief; Rep Stu Cncl; JP Sousa Awd; NHS; Sal; Math Tm; Outstndng Physcs Stu Of Yr 86-87; PMEA Hnrs, Dist & Regnl Band Fstvls 85-87; Carnegie Mellon U; Engrng.

KEFALOGIANNIS, CHRISTINE; Churchill HS; Pittsburgh, PA; (4); 47/190; Church Yth Grp; French Clb; Ski Clb; Yrbk Stf; JV Bsktbl; JV Trk; Var Capt Vllybl; High Hon Roll; Hon Roll; Hmcmng Ct 4th Rnnr Up 87; U Of Pittsburgh.

KEFER, MELANIE; Downington HS; Coatesvl, PA; (3); 33/672; Church Yth Grp; German Clb; GAA; Latin Clb; Ski Clb; Mrchg Band; Mgr(s); JV Var Tennis; High Hon Roll; NHS; Prsdntl Acdmc Ftnss Awd; Physcl Thrpy.

KEFFER, JOHN; York Catholic HS; York, PA; (2); 27/170; Dance Clb; JA; Spanish Clb; Varsity Clb; Rep Soph Cls; Rep Stu Cncl; JV Bsbl; JV Var Bsktbl; JV Var Ftbl; JV Golf; ST Champ Bsktbl Team 87; Mag Drive Rep 85; Irish Swpstks Rep 86; Psych.

KEGARISE, KEVIN; Manheim Central HS; Manheim, PA; (4); Church Yth Grp; Var Capt Bsktbl; Var L Ftbl; Var Capt Trk; Hon Roll; US Marine Corps Distngshd Ath Awd 86; VFW Def Back Awd 86; Athletic Awd 87; Grove City Coll; Mech Engrng.

KEGEL, SCOTT; Hempfield HS; Lancaster, PA; (3); 25/407; Ski Clb; JV Bsktbl; Var Crs Cntry; JV Socr; Var Trk; Im Wt Lftg; High Hon Roll; Hon Roll; Crs Cntry Ltr 85.

KEGERISE, TINA; Oley Valley HS; Oley, PA; (3); JA; Chorus; Color Guard; School Musical; Rep Stu Cncl; Var Capt Cheerleading; JV Sftbl; Cedar Crest Coll.

KEGLEY, WENDY; Hyndman Middle SR HS; Ellerslie, MD; (3); Art Clb; Camp Fr Inc; Computer Clb; Girl Scts; Letterman Clb; Ski Clb; Spanish Clb; SADD; Varsity Clb; Color Guard; Acctg.

KEHL, DAWN; Brandywine Heights HS; Mertztown, PA; (4); Camp Fr Inc; Church Yth Grp; FBLA; Hosp Aide; Library Aide; Pep Clb; Chorus; Yrbk Bus Mgr; High Hon Roll; Prfct Atten Awd; Lgn Essy Cont; Kutztown U; Bus Admin.

KEHL, STEVE; Tech Memorial HS; Erie, PA; (3); 20/311; JV Bsbl; Athltc Hnrs Soc 86-87; Elec.

KEHLER, GEORGIA; Shamokin Area HS; Shamokin, PA; (2); 65/250; Pep Clb; JV Sftbl; Law.

KEHLER, KIM; Shikellamy HS; Sunbury, PA; (3); 25/324; French Clb; Yrbk Stf; JV Cheerleading; French Hon Soc; Hon Roll; Jr NHS; Hst Frsh Cls; Hst Soph Cls; Hst Jr Cls; Hst Sr Cls; Elem Ed.

KEHLER, MELISSA; Boyertown SR HS; Bechtelsville, PA; (1); High Hon Roll; Hon Roll; Cmmrcl Artst.

KEHN, KIM; Fort Cherry HS; Mcdonald, PA; (3); Drama Clb; French Clb; FBLA; Library Aide; Math Clb; Science Clb; Ski Clb; NHS; Bradford Schl Of Bus; Accntng.

KEHRLI, KATHY; Lackawanna Trail HS; Factoryville, PA; (3); Drama Clb; Chorus; School Musical; School Play; Rep Stu Cncl; French Hon Soc; High Hon Roll; NHS; 1st Pl HS Math Exam 87; Hon Mntn Natl Frnch Cont 85-86.

KEIDERLING, HEATHER; Pittston Area HS; Wilkes Barre, PA; (4); FBLA; Key Clb; Science Clb; L Mgr(s); Stat Score Keeper; Var L Vllybl; Hon Roll; Gftd Cls; Cert Of Recgntn Devlpmnt PA Hnrs Tst 87; 2nd Rnnr-Up Prm Qn 87; Psych.

KEIFER II, CHARLES E; Lewisburg Area HS; West Milton, PA; (3); Var JV Ftbl; Im Tennis; JV Trk; Im Vllybl; Im Wt Lftg; High Hon Roll; Hon Roll; NHS; Retail Mgt.

KEIFER, ERIK; Peabody HS; Pittsburgh, PA; (4); 16/300; Band; Concert Band; Jazz Band; Mrchg Band; Pres Jr Cls; Pres Sr Cls; Crs Cntry; Swmmng; Trk; Hon Roll; Acad All Amer; Embry-Riddle Arntcl U; Pilot.

KEIFFER, JEFFREY M; Northwestern Le HS; New Tripoli, PA; (4); 13/165; Boy Scts; Nwsp Rptr; Yrbk Rptr; Var L Bsktbl; Var Capt Ftbl; High Hon Roll; Hon Roll; NHS; Susquehanna U; Bus Admin.

KEILEN, SEAN; Bishop Carroll HS; Loretto, PA; (3); 1/128; Drama Clb; Ski Clb; Speech Tm; Teachers Aide; Yrbk Stf; Rep Jr Cls; High Hon Roll; NHS; Voice Dem Awd; Computer Clb; Frncs Dist Champ Humrus Drmtc Interptn 85; Ldng Role Schl Play & Local Theatre 86; English Prof.

KEIM, DAVID; North Hills HS; Pittsburgh, PA; (4); 18/465; Church Yth Grp; Key Clb; Band; Concert Band; Mrchg Band; Symp Band; Pres Sr Cls; Var Crs Cntry; L Capt Swmmng; High Hon Roll; Comp Sci.

KEIM, KATHY; Phoenixville Area HS; Phoenixville, PA; (4); Key Clb; Yrbk Stf; High Hon Roll; Hon Roll; Cngrssnl Schlr Natl Yng Ldrs Conf 87.

KEINER, JENNIFER; John S Fine SR HS; Nanticoke, PA; (4); 20/265; Key Clb; Ski Clb; Chorus; Stat Bsktbl; L Crs Cntry; High Hon Roll; NHS; Nanticoke Cltrl & Hstrcl Socty Awd 887; Bloomsburg U; Elem Ed.

KEIPER, KRISTEN; Wyoming Area HS; West Wyoming, PA; (3); Trs Church Yth Grp; Key Clb; Spanish Clb; Band; Concert Band; Mrchg Band; Kings Coll; Accntng.

KEIPER, MICHAEL; Elk Lake HS; Springville, PA; (2); Spanish Clb; SADD; Band; Mrchg Band; Off Soph Cls; Bsktbl; Prfct Atten Awd; Comp Engrng.

KEISER, AMY; Milton SR HS; Milton, PA; (2); Intnl Clb; Y-Teens; Band; Concert Band; Mrchg Band; Rep Frsh Cls; Sec Soph Cls; Rep Stu Cncl.

KEISER, CHRISTOPHER; Ft Le Bouf HS; Waterford, PA; (2); 52/227; Debate Tm; Political Wkr; Red Cross Aide; Nwsp Sprt Ed; VP Church Yth Grp; Var Bowling; Var Golf; Var Vllybl; High Hon Roll; Hon Roll; Ganon U; Nuclr Engr.

KEISER, JENNIFER; Parkland SR HS; Allentown, PA; (2); 30/463; Key Clb; Library Aide; Lit Mag; Im Swmmng; L Trk; High Hon Roll.

KEISER, JONATHAN; Hazelton HS; Hazleton, PA; (2); Drama Clb; Exploring; VP Leo Clb; Ski Clb; Spanish Clb; Stage Crew; Nwsp Stf; Yrbk Rptr; Stu Cncl; Crs Cntry; Diggers Clb & Advntrs Clb 86-87; Psych.

KEISER, MARYBETH; Bishop Conwell HS; Levittown, PA; (3); 6/277; Church Yth Grp; Latin Clb; Teachers Aide; Var Bsktbl; JV Var Socr; High Hon Roll; NHS; Engrng.

KEISTER, ANDREW; Mifflinburg Area HS; Laurelton, PA; (3); 18/169; Pres Church Yth Grp; German Clb; Key Clb; Yrbk Stf; Im Bsktbl; Var L Tennis; High Hon Roll; Trs NHS; Penn ST U; Engr.

KEISTER, LORETTA; East Pennsboro HS; Harrisburg, PA; (3); French Clb; German Clb; Spanish Clb; Varsity Clb; Crs Cntry; Tennis; Trk; High Hon Roll; Hon Roll; NHS; Georgetown U; Lang.

KEISTER, SHAUN B; Middleburg Joint HS; Middleburg, PA; (3); SADD; Nwsp Stf; Yrbk Phtg; Yrbk Stf; Stu Cncl; Hon Roll; Jrnlsm.

KEITER, SANDRA M; Halifax HS; Halifax, PA; (4); 2/99; Church Yth Grp; Pres Spanish Clb; Band; Var Capt Bsktbl; Dnfth Awd; VP NHS; Sal; Varsity Clb; Concert Band; Amer Lgn Mdl; GIZ Awd; Army Resrv Natl Schlr Athl Awd; Messiah Coll; Engrng.

KEITH, LA MAR R; Northern Bedford County HS; Roaring Sprgs, PA; (3); 36/104; Church Yth Grp; VP Sec 4-H; FFA; Band; Chorus; Church Choir; Concert Band; Mrchg Band; 4-H Awd; Hon Roll; Auto Mech.

KEITH, LISA; Northern Cambria HS; Barnesboro, PA; (4); 9/125; Church Yth Grp; French Clb; Band; Concert Band; Mrchg Band; Stu Cncl; High Hon Roll; Hon Roll; NHS; IN U; Elem Ed.

KEITH, ROBERT; Sunvalley HS; Aston, PA; (3); 59/275; Chorus; Ice Hcky; Wrstlng; High Hon Roll; Hon Roll; Phrmclgy.

KEITH, SHANNON; Franklin HS; Franklin, PA; (2); Ski Clb; Varsity Clb; Rep Soph Cls; Bsktbl; Swmmng; Trk; Hon Roll; Board Of Schl Dir Awd 86-87.

KELBERG, SHARON; Pennsbury HS; Fairless Hls, PA; (4); 106/771; Drama Clb; French Clb; German Clb; Library Aide; Band; Stage Crew; Lit Mag; Tennis; French Hon Soc; Hon Roll; Stu Of Mnth 85; Pennsbury Scholar 87; Frgn Lang Achvt 84-87; Millersville U; Bus.

KELCHNER, KRISTIN; Elizabethtown Area HS; Elizabethtown, PA; (2); 53/281; Church Yth Grp; Church Choir; JV Fld Hcky; Trk; Hon Roll.

KELCHNER III, RALPH H; Berwick SR HS; Berwick, PA; (3); FFA; JC Awd; Engrng.

KELDSEN, DAN; Valley HS; New Kensington, PA; (3); Science Clb; Chorus; High Hon Roll; NHS; Berklee Schl Of Music; Compstn.

KELIIKIPI, JOSEPH; Washington HS; Washington, PA; (3); French Clb; Ski Clb; Varsity Clb; Yrbk Sprt Ed; Pres Stu Cncl; L Bsbl; JV Bsktbl; Var Crs Cntry; L Ftbl; L Tennis; Jrnlsm.

KELL, DAVID; West Perry HS; New Bloomfield, PA; (4); 12/188; French Clb; Spanish Clb; Pres Sr Cls; Var L Bsbl; Var L Ftbl; High Hon Roll; Hon Roll; NHS; NROTC Schlrshp 87; PA ST; Aero Engrng.

KELLAR, MATTHEW; Punxsutawney HS; Big Run, PA; (2); 1/295; French Clb; Math Tm; Spanish Clb; Varsity Clb; Rep Jr Cls; JV Bsktbl; L Tennis; High Hon Roll.

KELLEHER, KATHLEEN; Greensburg Central Catholic HS; Latrobe, PA; (3); Church Yth Grp; Drama Clb; Ski Clb; Chorus; Yrbk Bus Mgr; Yrbk Stf; Cheerleading; Powder Puff Ftbl; Hon Roll; Mrktng.

KELLER, DAVID; Chambersburg Area SR HS; Chambersburg, PA; (4); 76/604; Am Leg Boys St; Boy Scts; Letterman Clb; Hst Band; Pres Chorus; Pres Sr Cls; DAR Awd; God Cntry Awd; Rotary Awd; Pres Jazz Band; Paul Lucas Choral Awd 87; Frnkln & Mrshll Coll; Govt.

KELLER, JULIA; Yough SR HS; W Newton, PA; (3); #2 In Class; Church Yth Grp; French Clb; Library Aide; Chorus; Color Guard; High Hon Roll; NHS; Ntl Merit Ltr.

KELLER, KIMBERLY; Susquehanna Community HS; Susquehanna, PA; (2); Band; Chorus; Concert Band; Mrchg Band; Var JV Cheerleading; JV Sftbl; Hon Roll; Photo.

KELLER, KIRK; York Catholic HS; York, PA; (4); 26/169; Varsity Clb; Band; Concert Band; Jazz Band; Mrchg Band; L Capt Socr; Var L Trk; Hon Roll; NHS; Pres Schlr; York Dsptch Athlte Wk 86; Hon Mntn All Yrk Cnty Sccr Tm, Yrk Cnty Wstrn Div All Str Sccr Tm 87; OH Wesleyan U; Comp Sci.

KELLER, KRISTY; Oley Valley HS; Reading, PA; (3); Art Clb; Teachers Aide; Var Crs Cntry; Var Trk; Hon Roll; Reading Area CC; Chld Devlpmnt.

KELLER, MICHELLE; Hatboro Horsham SR HS; Hatboro, PA; (3); Art Clb; JV Bsktbl; JV Fld Hcky; JV Lcrss; Hon Roll; Spec Awd Sci Achvts 86-87; Binghamton U; Psychobiol.

KELLER, MICHELLE; William Penn SR HS; York, PA; (3); 71/365; Church Yth Grp; Cmnty Wkr; Hosp Aide; Chorus; JV Trk; Hon Roll; Prfct Atten Awd; Bio.

KELLER, NICOLE; Farrell HS; Farrell, PA; (2); JA; NAACP; SADD; Stu Cncl; High Hon Roll; Val; French Clb; Hosp Aide; SADD; Cheerleading; Pediatrcn.

KELLER, PAMELA; Catasauqua HS; Catasauqua, PA; (4); 9/124; SADD; Color Guard; Yrbk Stf; Lit Mag; Off Stu Cncl; Var Fld Hcky; Powder Puff Ftbl; High Hon Roll; NHS; NEDT Awd; Andrew Hudsco Memrl Awd 87; PA ST U; Criminal Justice.

KELLER, SCOTT; Wissahickon HS; Norristown, PA; (4); 17/287; Church Yth Grp; Intnl Clb; Ski Clb; Band; Concert Band; Jazz Band; Mrchg Band; Var Lcrss; Hon Roll; NHS; Dstrct Bnd 87; Rgnl Bnd IV 87; Natl Assoc Grmn Awd 85-86; Drexel U; Intrntl Areas Stds.

KELLER, SEAN; Beaver Area HS; Beaver, PA; (3); 1/220; VP JCL; Pres Latin Clb; Q&S; Nwsp Ed-Chief; Var L Socr; Var L Swmmng; Var L Trk; Bausch & Lomb Sci Awd; Ntl Merit SF; German Clb; PA Gvrnrs Schl Bus 87.

KELLER, STEPHANIE; Bovertown HS; Bechtelsville, PA; (4); French Clb; Mrchg Band; Pep Band; Symp Band; Nwsp Stf; Hon Roll; Ctznshp Awd 86; Cub Art Awd 87; Flight Svc.

KELLER, TRACEY; Warwick HS; Lititz, PA; (3); #46 In Class; SADD; Varsity Clb; Bsktbl; Mgr(s); Tennis; Hon Roll; NHS.

KELLERMAN, DARREN; Bald Eagle Area JR & SR HS; Julian, PA; (4); 3/191; Spanish Clb; Rep Stu Cncl; High Hon Roll; NHS; Ntl Merit Ltr; U Schlr PA ST; PA ST U; Pol Sci.

KELLERMAN, WILLIAM; Bald Eagle-Nittany HS; Beech Creek, PA; (3); VP Drama Clb; Key Clb; Band; Chorus; Jazz Band; Mrchg Band; Orch; School Musical; Swing Chorus; Symp Band; PMEA Dstct 4 Rgn III Bnd Chrs Orchstra All ST Chrs 86; Miriam Clstr Music Schlrshp Prvt Stdy 86; Music Educ.

KELLEY, COLLEEN; Bensalem HS; Oakford, PA; (3); Key Clb; Pep Clb; SADD; Varsity Clb; Yrbk Stf; Capt Cheerleading; Wt Lftg; High Hon Roll; Hon Roll; Jr NHS; Mst Spirited Var Chrldng Sqd 86-87; Mst Spirited Over-All 86; Marietta; Phys Ther.

KELLEY, JACKIE; Archbishop Kennedy HS; Philadelphia, PA; (3); Library Aide; Concert Band; Lit Mag; Hon Roll; U Of PA; Law.

KELLEY, JOE; Saltsburgh JR SR HS; New Alexandria, PA; (3); 2/65; Letterman Clb; Nwsp Stf; Ftbl; Wt Lftg; Wrstlng; High Hon Roll; NHS.

KELLEY, KATIE; Meadville Area SR HS; Meadville, PA; (3); 91/362; Var L Diving.

KELLEY, LAURA; Delone Catholic HS; Hanover, PA; (4); Varsity Clb; Yrbk Stf; Var Cheerleading; Hon Roll; NHS; Penn ST.

KELLEY, LISA; Nazareth Acad; Philadelphia, PA; (3); Red Cross Aide; Moore Coll; Fine Arts.

KELLEY, MICHELLE; Uniontown Area SR HS; Farmington, PA; (3); Exploring; JA; Stu Cncl; Hon Roll; U Of Pttsbrgh; Psych.

KELLEY, RAQUEL; Methacton HS; Norristown, PA; (3); 15/381; Church Yth Grp; Chorus; Church Choir; Color Guard; Flag Corp; School Musical; Ed Yrbk Stf; High Hon Roll; NHS; Drama Clb; Gold Mdl Drama Rgnl Fest Life At Eastern Nazarene Coll 86 & Silver Mdl Pencil Drwng Regn Fest 87; Englsh.

KELLEY, SCOTT; Central Dauphin HS; Harrisburg, PA; (3); Church Yth Grp; Ski Clb; JV Tennis; Im Vllybl; Hon Roll; Chem.

KELLEY, SHARON E; Connellsville Area HS; Connellsville, PA; (4); 3/521; School Musical; School Play; French Hon Soc; High Hon Roll; Kiwanis Awd; NHS; Prfct Atten Awd; Church Yth Grp; FTA; Science Clb; Robt P Mc Luckey Mem Schlrshp 87; Gftd Pgm 80-87; Acad Excllnc; Hnrs Art 82-87; U Schlr Hnrs Pgm; U Of Pittsburgh.

KELLEY, SHAWNIE; Cheswick Christian Acad; Cheswick, PA; (3); Chorus; Nwsp Rptr; Yrbk Bus Mgr; Yrbk Ed-Chief; Yrbk Phtg; Rep Soph Cls; Sec Stu Cncl; Cheerleading; Sftbl; NHS; Law.

KELLINGTON, ALISA; Montour HS; Pittsburgh, PA; (2); JA; SADD; Mrchg Band; Yrbk Phtg; Yrbk Sprt Ed; Yrbk Stf; Pom Pon; Sftbl; Hon Roll; JR Achvmnt Awd 86; U Of Pittsburgh; Med.

KELLMAN, ANDREW; Wyoming Seminary; Shavertown, PA; (4); Computer Clb; Drama Clb; Math Clb; PAVAS; Scholastic Bowl; School Musical; School Play; French Hon Soc; High Hon Roll; Hon Roll; 1st Degree Black Belt Tae Kwon Do & Hapkido 86; Brandeis U; Med.

KELLNER, CORINNE; Panther Valley HS; Coaldale, PA; (3); 51/136; Drama Clb; French Clb; SADD; Band; Chorus; Church Choir; Concert Band; Jazz Band; Mrchg Band; School Musical; Frnch.

KELLOGG, MEGHAN; Turtle Creek HS; Pittsburgh, PA; (3); 7/200; Church Yth Grp; Cmnty Wkr; Pep Clb; Spanish Clb; Acpl Chr; Band; Church Choir; Concert Band; Mrchg Band; Cheerleading; Grove City Coll; Elem Ed.

KELLON, AMY; Perkiomen Valley HS; Collegeville, PA; (3); Rep Soph Cls; Rep Jr Cls; Rep Stu Cncl; Var Cheerleading; High Hon Roll; Hon Roll; NHS; Stu Mnth 86; Bio.

KELLY, ALEX; Sacred Heart HS; Carbondale, PA; (3); 2/44; Computer Clb; Latin Clb; Scholastic Bowl; Band; JV Var Bsktbl; Ntl Merit Ltr; VFW Awd; Voice Dem Awd; Church Yth Grp; 4 Yr Acad Schlrshp 84; Aerosp Engrng.

KELLY, ANN MARIE; Dunmore HS; Dunmore, PA; (3); 10/150; Drama Clb; French Clb; Letterman Clb; Science Clb; Spanish Clb; Chorus; Church Choir; School Musical; School Play; Nwsp Rptr; Sci.

KELLY, CHARLA; Bishop Mc De Vitt HS; Philadelphia, PA; (4); 131/357; Church Yth Grp; Hosp Aide; Spanish Clb; Powder Puff Ftbl; Cit Awd; Hon Roll; Millersville U; Political Sci.

KELLY, CHRIS; Penn Trafford HS; Jeannette, PA; (2); JCL; Latin Clb; Letterman Clb; Ski Clb; Varsity Clb; Im Bsktbl; JV Ftbl; Var L Trk; Wt Lftg; High Hon Roll; Acadmc All Amer.

KELLY, DAVID; Spring Grove Area SR HS; York, PA; (3); 9/301; Boy Scts; Drama Clb; Varsity Clb; School Play; JV Crs Cntry; Var L Trk; Hon Roll; NHS; Ntl Merit Ltr; Pres Schlr; Vet Med.

KELLY, DEBORAH ANN; Conrad Weiser HS; Sinking Spring, PA; (3); 74/179; Church Yth Grp; Off Spanish Clb; Chorus; Church Choir; Color Guard; Mrchg Band; School Musical; School Play; Yrbk Stf; Rep Stu Cncl; Prncpls List; Bloomsburg U; Nrsng.

KELLY, GEORGE; Ridley SR HS; Crumlynne, PA; (3); 37/488; Science Clb; SADD; Hon Roll; Syracuse; Elec Engr.

KELLY, JAMES; Cardinal O Hara HS; Springfield, PA; (4); 5/771; Church Yth Grp; French Clb; Pres Latin Clb; Science Clb; Ed Nwsp Stf; Rep Stu Cncl; Var Crs Cntry; Var Swmmng; Cit Awd; DAR Awd; Crnll U Fllwshp 87; Amrcn Chem Soc Achvmnt Awd 87; Outstndg Achvmnt Calculus & Physcs 87; Cornell U; Chem.

KELLY JR, JAMES R; Canon Mc Millan HS; Eighty Four, PA; (4); Cmnty Wkr; French Clb; Ski Clb; OH HS Rodeo Assoc 87; Ntl HS Rodeo Fnls Pueblo CO 87; Northwest OK ST U; Engr.

KELLY, JEFFREY; Beaver Area HS; Beaver, PA; (3); German Clb; Bsbl; Bsktbl; Ftbl; Powder Puff Ftbl; High Hon Roll; Hon Roll; NHS.

KELLY, JOAN M; Norristown Area HS; Norristown, PA; (3); 41/491; Church Yth Grp; Rep Soph Cls; Rep Jr Cls; Trs Stu Cncl; Im JV Bsktbl; L Sftbl; Hon Roll; Schl Rep PASC St Conf 86; Bus Admin.

KELLY, JOANNE; Lake Lehman HS; Harveys Lake, PA; (3); Sec Church Yth Grp; Pres Trs Key Clb; Office Aide; Chorus; Yrbk Stf; Fld Hcky; Yth Salute 87; Outstndng Treas Awd-Key Clb 86.

KELLY, JOSEPH; Plum HS; Pittsburgh, PA; (2); Art Clb; Church Yth Grp; Var Crs Cntry; JV Socr; Var Trk; Hon Roll; Pilot.

KELLY, JUDY; Vincentarian HS; Pittsburgh, PA; (3); Cmnty Wkr; Q&S; Service Clb; Chorus; Rep Soph Cls; Pres Jr Cls; Hon Roll; NHS; Med.

KELLY, KAREN; Archbishop Prendergast HS; Clifton Hghts, PA; (3); Church Yth Grp; Library Aide; Office Aide; Pres Rep Jr Cls; Hon Roll; Prfct Atten Awd; Natl Bus Hnr Scty 87; Bus.

KELLY, KATHLEEN; Dunmore HS; Dunmore, PA; (4); 6/141; Drama Clb; French Clb; Letterman Clb; Church Choir; School Musical; Yrbk Stf; Crs Cntry; Trk; Jr NHS; NHS; Helen C Spellman Awd 87; Bloomsburg U.

KELLY, KERRY; Peters Township HS; Mc Murray, PA; (2); Ski Clb; Sec Soph Cls; JV Bsktbl; Capt JV Cheerleading; Trk; Hon Roll.

KELLY, KEVIN; Butler SR HS; Butler, PA; (2); German Clb; Latin Clb; Var JV Ftbl; Jr NHS; NHS.

KELLY, KEVIN; Pennsbury HS; Yardley, PA; (3); Camera Clb; Church Yth Grp; Cmnty Wkr; Letterman Clb; Nwsp Phtg; Im Bsktbl; Im Coach Actv; Var L Ftbl; Var Wt Lftg; Hon Roll; Christian Ldrshp Awd 86; Rdg Awd 84.

KELLY, KIM; Union City Area HS; Centerville, PA; (2); Sec Trs Church Yth Grp; Spanish Clb; Varsity Clb; Im Trk; Var Vllybl; DAR Awd; High Hon Roll; Hon Roll; Amer Leg Auxlry Awd 86; Pres Acad Ftns Awd 85.

KELLY, KIMBERLY; Bishop Shanehan HS; Coatesville, PA; (3); 28/202; Chorus; Hon Roll; Jr NHS; Prfct Atten Awd; Spanish NHS; Cmmnctns.

KELLY, LISA; Archbishop Carroll HS; Devon, PA; (3); 44/376; Cmnty Wkr; Hon Roll; Jr NHS; NHS; Accntng Awd 87; Bus Mngmt.

KELLY, MICHELLE; Archbishop Wood For Girls; Holland, PA; (4); 3/246; Model UN; Service Clb; School Play; Var Cheerleading; High Hon Roll; NHS; Anna M Vincent Schlrshp, Soc Of Women Engrs Highest Hnr Math & Sci, & Pres Acdmc Fitness Awd 87; Rchstr Inst/Tech; Polymer Tech.

KELLY, MONICA; Butler Intermediate HS; Evans City, PA; (2); Girl Scts; ROTC; SADD; Teachers Aide; Chorus; Church Choir; Flag Corp; School Musical; Hon Roll; Jr NHS; 4 Yrs Prfct Parde Atten Robntts 85; Extra Effrt Awd 86; Bus.

KELLY, MORGEN; Ellis Schl; Pittsburgh, PA; (3); Pres Drama Clb; VP Chorus; School Play; Stage Crew; Pres Soph Cls; Var JV Lcrss; Pres Political Wkr; SADD; Acpl Chr; Swing Chorus; 2nd Pl Soph Spch Cont.

KELLY, PAUL A; Holy Name HS; Wyomissing, PA; (3); 4/134; Math Tm; Pep Clb; JV Bsbl; Var L Bsktbl; Var L Ftbl; Trk; Wt Lftg; High Hon Roll; NHS; Ntl Merit Ltr; Natl Math League 8th Pl.

KELLY, RENEE; Susquehanna Community HS; Susquehanna, PA; (3); Church Yth Grp; Library Aide; Teachers Aide; Color Guard; Flag Corp; Var Cheerleading; Var Crs Cntry; Var Trk; Var Twrlr; Hon Roll; Penn ST; Elem Educ.

KELLY, SEAN; Devon Preparatory Schl; Exton, PA; (3); Trs Church Yth Grp; Math Tm; Nwsp Rptr; Var Crs Cntry; Im Ftbl; Var Trk; High Hon Roll; Ntl Merit Ltr; Math Awd 86-87; Elec Engr.

KELLY, SHARON; Freeport Area HS; Freeport, PA; (3); 1/200; Cmnty Wkr; Girl Scts; VP Mrchg Band; Pep Band; School Musical; Stage Crew; Symp Band; High Hon Roll; Jr All Amer Hall Fame Band Hnrs 85-86; Psych.

KELLY, SUSAN; Villa Maria Acad; West Chester, PA; (3); 20/100; Cmnty Wkr; Hosp Aide; Science Clb; Spanish Clb; SADD; Yrbk Stf; Lit Mag; Swmmng; High Hon Roll; Spanish NHS; Hosp Vlntr Svc Awd 86-87; Acadc Hnrs 85-87; Villanova; Med.

KELLY, SUZANNE; Nazareth Area HS; Mt Laurel, NJ; (3); 15/265; Library Aide; Yrbk Stf; High Hon Roll; Hon Roll; NHS; Pre Med.

KELLY, TAMMY; Altoona Area HS; Altoona, PA; (4); 62/718; Church Yth Grp; German Clb; Key Clb; Science Clb; Drill Tm; Flag Corp; Twrlr; Penn ST U.

KELMEREIT, LAURA C; Moon SR HS; Coraopolis, PA; (2); 43/350; French Clb; JA; Chorus; Im Fld Hcky; Hon Roll; TX A&M; Marine Bio.

KELSCH, JEFF; Carbondale Area HS; Carbondale, PA; (3); FBLA; Ski Clb; Spanish Clb; Band; Mrchg Band; Bsbl; Ftbl; Trk; Hon Roll; Penn ST U; Aerontcl Sci.

KELSEA, CHRISTAL; Karns City JRSR HS; Chicora, PA; (4); 47/116; Band; School Play; Stage Crew; JV Cheerleading; Stat Trk; High Hon Roll; Hon Roll; ICM Schl Of Bus; Stewardess.

KELSEY, KERRY; Corry Area HS; Corry, PA; (2); Church Yth Grp; German Clb; SADD; Drill Tm; Yrbk Stf; Twrlr; Htl/Rstrnt Mngmnt.

KELSEY, MICHAEL; Living Word Acad; Ephrata, PA; (2); Church Yth Grp; Chorus; School Play; Stage Crew; Stu Cncl; Bsbl; Bsktbl; Socr; Trk; Hon Roll; ASCI Stud Ldrshp Conf 86; Busi Admn.

KELSHAW, RACHEL; Quaker Valley HS; Sewickely, PA; (3); Art Clb; Church Yth Grp; Sec Civic Clb; Drama Clb; Spanish Clb; Chorus; Church Choir; School Musical; School Play; Lit Mag; Teen Insti, Schlstcs & Church Cmp Cnslr Awds 85-87; Elem Ed.

KELSO, CARRIE; Taylor Allderdice HS; Pittsburgh, PA; (3); French Clb; Model UN; Ski Clb; Band; Orch; Off Stu Cncl; High Hon Roll; Yth For Undrstnding Summer Stu To Netherlands 86; Generations Together 86-87.

KELTZ, CANDY; Oil City SR HS; Oil City, PA; (3); 30/232; AFS; Sec Pres FBLA; Varsity Clb; Color Guard; School Musical; Twrlr; Hon Roll; Prfct Atten Awd; 5th Pl Awd FBLA Bus Grphcs 87; Erie Schl Of Bus; Bus.

KEMERER, JOHN; Jeannette SR HS; Jeannette, PA; (2); 9/100; Ski Clb; Spanish Clb; Y-Teens.

KEMMERER, KATHY; Brockway Area HS; Brockway, PA; (3); 19/110; Church Yth Grp; Debate Tm; Exploring; Girl Scts; Chorus; Flag Corp; Mrchg Band; Stage Crew; Hon Roll; Med.

KEMMERLING, GLENDA; Shaler Area HS; Millvale, PA; (3); 12/502; Pep Clb; Variety Show; High Hon Roll; NHS; Spanish NHS; Cert Excllnc Spnsh 85; Succs Awd Currnt Evnts 87; Chld Care.

KEMMERLING, KEITH; Pine Grove Area HS; Pine Grove, PA; (3); Am Leg Boys St; ROTC; Chorus; Drill Tm; Im Sftbl; Im Vllybl; Wt Lftg; JV Var Wrstlng; Military; Elect.

KEMP, AMY; Hopewell Area HS; Aliquippa, PA; (3); 3/265; Latin Clb; Math Tm; Concert Band; Mrchg Band; School Play; Yrbk Stf; Var L Sftbl; NHS; Acdmc All-Amer 87; Beaver Cnty Hnrs Band & Schlr/Athlete 86-87.

KEMP, BRIAN; Columbia Montour Area Vo Tech Schl; Lake Worth, FL; (4); Boys Clb Am; Chess Clb; Church Yth Grp; Cmnty Wkr; Letterman Clb; JV Var Bsbl; JV Var Bsktbl; Stat Ftbl; High Hon Roll; Stnly Goldn Hmmr Awd 87; Cert Achvt 1st Hm Bldng Prjct 87; Coachs Awd Bsktbl 87; Crpntry.

KEMP, MARK; Connellsville Area SR HS; Normalville, PA; (3); 25/511; Office Aide; Band; Chorus; Jazz Band; Mrchg Band; Orch; School Musical; Symp Band; High Hon Roll; NHS; Bio Engr.

KEMP, RHONDA; Quigley HS; Industry, PA; (4); 4/98; Math Tm; Chorus; Drill Tm; Var Capt Bsktbl; Powder Puff Ftbl; Var L Sftbl; High Hon Roll; NHS; Rotary Awd; Acadmc All Amer & All Str; Wittenberg.

KEMP, RICHARD; Connellsville Area HS; Normalville, PA; (2); Church Yth Grp; Var Ftbl.

KEMPF, CARRA; Northwestern SR HS; Cranesville, PA; (2); Concert Band; Flag Corp; Pep Band; Yrbk Stf; Trk; PA ST; Psych.

KEMPF III, EDWARD J; Northwestern HS; Cranesville, PA; (4); 16/147; Boy Scts; Band; Chorus; Concert Band; Madrigals; Mrchg Band; School Musical; School Play; Stage Crew; JV Var Bsktbl; Ntl Choral Awd 87; Natl Band Awd 87; IN U Of PA; Bus Mgmt.

KEMPF, GWENDOLYN; Towanda Area HS; Towanda, PA; (4); 11/147; English Clb; Letterman Clb; Science Clb; Ski Clb; Spanish Clb; Varsity Clb; Var Capt Crs Cntry; Var Capt Swmmng; Tennis; Capt L Trk; VA Tech; Pre Vet Med.

KEMPFF, CYNTHIA; Harry S Truman HS; Bensalem, PA; (4); 47/534; ROTC; Chorus; Var L Trk; VFW Awd; James Funari Mem Schlrshp 87; The TROA Mdl, Plq & Schlrshp 87; Mercer Medical Ctr; Nrsng.

KEMPINSKI, DAWN; Wallenpaupauck Area HS; Hawley, PA; (3); 36/161; Church Yth Grp; Red Cross Aide; Ski Clb; Varsity Clb; JV Sftbl; Var Tennis; JV Trk; Im Wt Lftg; Ftns Ad 87; Sci Fair Awd 87; Engl.

KEMPTER, JOY; Archbishop Wood HS For Girls; Holland, PA; (4); 6/246; Church Yth Grp; Dance Clb; Math Tm; Scholastic Bowl; Service Clb; High Hon Roll; NHS; French Clb; Teachers Aide; Prfct Atten Awd; Hnrm Schlrshp U Scrntn 87; Chem Awd 86; Hnrbl Mntn Sci Fair 84,86; U Scranton; Math.

KENDALL, JOE; Laurel Highlands HS; Uniontown, PA; (3); Drama Clb; French Clb; JA; Hon Roll; Boston Coll; Stock Brkr.

KENDALL, MIKE; Hopewell Area HS; Monaca, PA; (3); 13/261; Boy Scts; Church Yth Grp; French Clb; Math Clb; Bsktbl; Ftbl; High Hon Roll; PA ST U; Engrng.

KENDER, TRACI; Bishop Hafey HS; Hazleton, PA; (3); Trs FNA; Key Clb; Library Aide; Office Aide; Ski Clb; Spanish Clb; Co-Capt Trs Y-Teens; Bus.

KENDERDINE, CHARLENE; Pocono Mountain HS; Henryville, PA; (3); Sec Church Yth Grp; Hosp Aide; Color Guard; Mrchg Band; Prmry Ed Tchr.

KENDI, THOMAS; Central Catholic HS; Monroeville, PA; (3); 5/260; Church Yth Grp; Math Clb; Teachers Aide; Band; Concert Band; Mrchg Band; Yrbk Stf; High Hon Roll; NHS; Spanish NHS; Social Studies Dept Awd Ldrshp Training MAPS U Of Pittsburgh; Engrng.

KENDIG, LISA; Donegal HS; Marietta, PA; (2); Sec Church Yth Grp; Band; Color Guard; Concert Band; Mrchg Band; Rep Frsh Cls; Sec Jr Cls; Rep Stu Cncl; JV Bsktbl; JV Var Mgr(s); Harvard; Med Sci.

KENDIG, VICKI; Northeastern HS; Mt Wolf, PA; (4); 11/159; Sec Band; Chorus; Sec Concert Band; Orch; School Play; Ed Nwsp Stf; Hon Roll; JP Sousa Awd; Rptr NHS; Voice Dem Awd; Prsdntl Acdmc Ftnss Awd 86-87; York Coll; Offc Admin.

KENDRA, CHRISTOPHER; Central Dauphin HS; Harrisburg, PA; (3); Exploring; Thesps; Band; Chorus; Concert Band; Jazz Band; Madrigals; School Musical; School Play; JV Ftbl; Theatre Arts.

KENDRA, JOHN; Trinity HS; Mechanicsburg, PA; (3); 35/140; Boy Scts; Model UN; Spanish Clb; Jazz Band; JV Var Ftbl; CAP; Ski Clb; Band; Concert Band; Hon Roll; PA ST; Mech Engr.

KENDZOR, BONNIE; Pittston Area HS; Pittston, PA; (4); Art Clb; Church Yth Grp; Exploring; FBLA; Key Clb; Math Clb; Science Clb; SADD; Yrbk Stf; L Var Socr; U Of Scranton; Lbrl Arts.

KENGER, AMBER; James M Coughlin HS; Wilkes Barre, PA; (4); 35/340; Yrbk Rptr; Yrbk Stf; Score Keeper; Mgr Vllybl; Hon Roll; Jr NHS; NHS; Acad Achvt Awd-Kings Coll 87; Kings Coll; Law.

KENISH, CHRISTINE; Kutztown Area HS; Kutztown, PA; (3); 17/178; School Play; Yrbk Phtg; Yrbk Stf; JV Cheerleading; High Hon Roll; Hon Roll; NHS.

KENJAROKI, ANN; Cumberland Valley HS; Camp Hill, PA; (3); Key Clb; Model UN; Pres Frsh Cls; Pres Soph Cls; Pres Jr Cls; Stu Cncl; Bsktbl; Fld Hcky; Sftbl; Hon Roll; Bus.

KENNADAY, PETER; New Castle SR HS; New Castle, PA; (3); 7/293; Church Yth Grp; Speech Tm; Band; Concert Band; Jazz Band; Mrchg Band; Pep Band; JV Tennis; Im Vllybl; Penn ST; Aerosp Engrng.

KENNEDY, BARB; Knoch HS; Butler, PA; (4); 46/245; Church Yth Grp; Trs FBLA; Band; Concert Band; Mrchg Band; Pep Band; Stage Crew; High Hon Roll; Pres Schlr; Butler Cnty CC; Accntnt.

KENNEDY, CHRISTIE A; Wallenpaupack Area HS; Hawley, PA; (3); 4/155; Band; Mrchg Band; Stu Cncl; Var Bsktbl; Var Sftbl; Var Tennis; Wt Lftg; High Hon Roll; Jr NHS; NHS; JR Olympcs-Natl Champs Bsktbl 85 & 87; Keystone ST Games Bsktbl 86; Tennis ST Champs Sngls 85; Phy Thrpy.

KENNEDY, COLLEEN; Interboro HS; Prospect Park, PA; (3); AFS; German Clb; Concert Band; JV Bsktbl; Var Sftbl; Vrsty Ltr Sftbl 85-86; Penn ST; Nrsng.

KENNEDY, CONNIE; Monaca JR SR HS; Monaca, PA; (3); 13/80; Am Leg Aux Girls St; Church Yth Grp; Cmnty Wkr; Girl Scts; Red Cross Aide; Science Clb; Band; Chorus; Concert Band; Mrchg Band; Chld Psychlgy.

KENNEDY, DAVE; Lock Haven SR HS; Lock Haven, PA; (3); Germa Clb; SADD; Mrchg Band; Musician.

KENNEDY, DEANNA; Ringgold HS; Monongahela, PA; (3); Civic Clb Ski Clb; Cheerleading; Trk; Hon Roll; Phys Thrpy.

KENNEDY, DOUGLAS; Waynesboro Area SR HS; Zullinger, PA; (3) Trs Church Yth Grp; Math Clb; Science Clb; High Hon Roll; Hon Roll NHS; Voice Dem Awd; PA ST; Elec.

KENNEDY, GREG; Uniontown HS; Uniontown, PA; (4); Boy Scts Computer Clb; Exploring; Science Clb; Ski Clb; Teachers Aide; Pgh Tech Inst; Comp Drftng.

KENNEDY, JAMES; Seneca Valley HS; Evans Cty, PA; (2); Church Yth Grp; ROTC; Church Choir; Yrbk Stf; JV Trk; High Hon Roll; Prfct Atten Awd; Schltc Awd 86-87; Super Cadet Awd ROTC 85-86; Merit Awd Chrch Yth Grp 83-84; Comp Sci.

KENNEDY, JEFFREY; York Catholic HS; York, PA; (3); Church Yth Grp; Latin Clb; Rep Band; Rep Concert Band; Jazz Band; Mrchg Band School Musical; Var Crs Cntry; Var Trk; Hon Roll; Crss Cntry ST Chmpns 85; Dist III Trk Chmpns 87; Bus Admin.

KENNEDY, JOHN; Northeastern HS; York, PA; (4); 8/181; Chess Clb Ski Clb; Chorus; Var JV Golf; JV Vllybl; Bausch & Lomb Sci Awd; High Hon Roll; NHS; Brunhouse Schlrshp, Acdmc All Star 87; Penn ST Engrng.

KENNEDY, JOHN O; Wyoming Valley West HS; Plymouth, PA; (3) Church Yth Grp; Chorus; School Musical; Variety Show; Hon Roll; NEDT Awd; Solost-Rgn 4 Rgnl Chrs Fstvl & Dist 9 Dist Chrs Fstvl 87; Theatr.

KENNEDY, KELLY; Waynesboro Area SR HS; Waynesboro, PA; (3); 20/369; Hosp Aide; Math Clb; Yrbk Stf; High Hon Roll; Hon Roll; NHS; Bus Clb Treas; AFS Friends Intl; Bus.

KENNEDY, KEVIN; Hempfield HS; Lancaster, PA; (3); 26/393; Am Leg Boys St; Boy Scts; Church Yth Grp; Exploring; Ski Clb; Orch; Ed Nwsp Phtg; Trs Stu Cncl; Var L Socr; Var L Trk; Outstndng Nwsppr Crrier Yr 85; Inter ST Circultn Mgrs Assoc Ctznshp Awd 85; Engrng.

KENNEDY, KIM; Penn Trafford HS; Jeannette, PA; (2); Cmnty Wkr FBLA; Hosp Aide; SADD; High Hon Roll; Hon Roll; Bus.

KENNEDY, KIMBERLY; Northeastern HS; Manchester, PA; (3); 27/172; SADD; Varsity Clb; Chorus; Church Choir; Concert Band; Jazz Band Orch; Var L Fld Hcky; Hon Roll; NHS; Hnrb Mntn York Cnty Svc Essy Cntst 86; Elizabethtown Coll; Bus.

KENNEDY, MARK; Northeastern HS; Manchester, PA; (4); 19/173 Aud/Vis; Stage Crew; Hon Roll; NHS; Camera Clb; Yrbk Phtg; Trk.

KENNEDY, MAUREEN; Tunkhannock HS; Tunkhannock, PA; (3); 39/320; French Clb; Concert Band; Mrchg Band; Var Fld Hcky; Var Swmmng Var Trk; Hon Roll.

KENNEDY, MEGAN; Hazleton HS; Hazleton, PA; (3); 60/445; French Clb; Latin Clb; Ski Clb; Crs Cntry; Trk; French Hon Soc; Hon Roll; Frgn Rltns.

KENNEDY, MICHAEL; Lincoln HS; Ellwood City, PA; (4); 73/165 Church Yth Grp; Latin Clb; Slippery Rock U; Educ.

KENNEDY, PAMELA; Big Spring HS; Newville, PA; (3); 2/269; Art Clb JV L Bsktbl; High Hon Roll; NHS; Prfct Atten Awd; Most Outstndng Span Stu Yr 87; Dist Hnr Roll 85-87; Bus.

KENNEDY, RACHEL; St Cyril Acad; Stillwater, PA; (3); Drama Clb Chorus; School Play; Nwsp Stf; Sec Frsh Cls; Rep Jr Cls; Vllybl; High Hon Roll; Stage Crew; Badmtn; NAHNS Essy Cntst Abt St John Vercelli 86-87 Bio.

KENNEDY, SEAN; Archbishop Wood HS For Boys; Ambler, PA; (2); 97/254; Band; Concert Band; Jazz Band; Mrchg Band; Orch; Mllbrk Lyceum Yth Shwcs Piano Solo 87; Bus.

KENNEDY, SEAN; Bermudian Springs HS; E Berlin, PA; (3); Band Nwsp Stf; Cmrcl Advrtsng.

KENNEDY, SEAN; Loyalsock Township HS; Williamsport, PA; (3); JA Key Clb; Latin Clb; Letterman Clb; Ski Clb; Spanish Clb; Im Bsktbl; Im Ftbl; Im Socr; Var L Tennis.

KENNEDY, SHANNON; Fairview HS; Erie, PA; (4); 11/154; Debate Tm; German Clb; Latin Clb; Model UN; Q&S; Ed Nwsp Stf; Yrbk Stf High Hon Roll; Hon Roll; Sec NHS; Oddfellows United Nations Plgrmge Yth; PA Free Enterprise Wk 87; Tri ST Jrnlsm Cont Hnrb Mntn; Boston U; Jrnlsm.

KENNEDY, SHANNON; Yough SR HS; Herminie, PA; (4); Ski Clb Spanish Clb; Chorus; Vllybl; High Hon Roll; NHS; Rotary Awd; U Of Pittsburgh; Pre Dentstry.

KENNEDY, SHAWN; East Pennsboro HS; Enola, PA; (3); Ski Clb Spanish Clb; Varsity Clb; Nwsp Rptr; Nwsp Sprt Ed; Nwsp Stf; Var Bsbl Var Socr; Hon Roll; Slippery Rock; Oceangrphy.

KENNEDY, SUSAN; Bensalem HS; Bensalem, PA; (4); 5/477; Service Clb; SADD; Pres Varsity Clb; Stu Cncl; Capt Cheerleading; High Hon Roll; NHS; Rotary Awd; Mst Valuable Chrldr 85; Stu Of Mnth 86; Med.

KENNEDY, TERRY; Trinity HS; Camp Hill, PA; (3); Church Yth Grp Pep Clb; Yrbk Stf; Rep Frsh Cls; Rep Soph Cls; VP Powder Puff Ftbl; Im Sftbl; Im Vllybl; DAR Awd; Hon Roll; Schltc Wrtg Cont Gold Key Wnnr Penn ST; Bus.

KENNEDY, TIMOTHY; Marion Center Area HS; Home, PA; (3); 1/153 Church Yth Grp; Band; Chorus; Church Choir; Concert Band; Mrchg Band; Pep Band; High Hon Roll; NHS; Natl Socl Studs Olympd 86-87.

KENNELLY, JOHN; Hopewell HS; Aliquippa, PA; (3); Var L Bsktbl Hon Roll; Arch Engrng.

KENNELLY, MARIE M; Phoenixville HS; Phoenixville, PA; (4); 62/200 Girl Scts; Key Clb; Pep Clb; Mrchg Band; School Musical; School Play; Im Vllybl; DAR Awd; Hon Roll; Prfct Atten Awd; Excllnc Acad 86; Wmns Clb Awd 87; West Chester U; Bus Admin.

KENNELLY, ROBERT; Hopewell HS; Aliquippa, PA; (2); Church Yth Grp; Nwsp Bus Mgr; Nwsp Rptr; Nwsp Stf; JV Bsktbl; JV Vllybl; Hon Roll; PA ST U; Intl Bus.

KENNEMUTH, JENNIFER; Brookville Area HS; Brookville, PA; (3) 41/175; French Clb; Sec Band; Church Choir; Sec Concert Band; Flag Corp; Sec Mrchg Band; Pep Band; School Musical; Rep Soph Cls; Rep Jr Cls; IN U Of PA; Tchr.

KENNESON, DAVID; William Allen HS; Allentown, PA; (2); Aud/Vis Boy Scts; Chess Clb; Church Yth Grp; Computer Clb; Exploring; Latin Clb; Ski Clb; Trs SADD; Nwsp Stf; Hnr Rl 87; Muhlenberg; Pre-Med.

KENNESON, JENNIFER; William Allen HS; Allentown, PA; (3); 57/657; Intnl Clb; Ski Clb; Spanish Clb; SADD; Color Guard; Yrbk Rptr; Yrbk Stf; Stu Cncl; Twrlr; Cdr Crst Coll; Tchr.

KENNEWEG, DAWN; Fort Cherry JR/Sr HS; Mcdonald, PA; (4); 23/115; Drama Clb; FNA; Math Clb; Science Clb; Ski Clb; Spanish Clb Varsity Clb; Chorus; Drill Tm; Mrchg Band; Schltc Achvt Awd 85-87; Phys Ftns Awd 83-87; CA U Of PA; Accntng.

KENNEY, DANIEL; William Tennent SR HS; Warminster, PA; (4); 118/576; Cmnty Wkr; German Clb; Red Cross Aide; Varsity Clb; Var Socr; Im Tennis; Var Vllybl; Hon Roll; U Of CT; Bus Law.

KENNEY, DONNA; Sayre Area HS; Sayre, PA; (3); Church Yth Grp; Dance Clb; Hosp Aide; School Play; Lit Mag; Trs Rep Stu Cncl; Var L Sftbl; Trk; JV Vllybl; High Hon Roll; Spnsh & Frnch.

KENNEY, JAMIE; Donegal HS; Mount Joy, PA; (3); Hon Roll.

KENNEY, KATHY; Moshannon Valley HS; Houtzdale, PA; (4); 10/120; Trs Ski Clb; Mrchg Band; Pep Band; School Play; High Hon Roll; NHS; Pres Acdmc Ftns Awd 87; Clarion U; Elem Ed.

KENNEY, MICHELLE; Duquesne HS; Duquesne, PA; (4); 11/81; Boys Clb Am; Exploring; Letterman Clb; Office Aide; Pep Clb; Varsity Clb; VICA; Y-Teens; VP Sr Cls; Cheerleading; Typng & Amer Hist Strght A; Kent ST; Sociology.

KENNEY, TARA; Geibel HS; Scottdale, PA; (3); Boy Scts; Church Yth Grp; Drama Clb; Girl Scts; Pep Clb; School Play; JV Var Bsktbl; High Hon Roll; Hon Roll; Nrsng.

KENNY, ALAN; Quigley HS; Sewickley, PA; (3); German Clb; JA; Math Clb; Math Tm; Rep Stu Cncl; Ftbl; Powder Puff Ftbl; Tennis; Wrstlng; Bio Chem.

KENNY, CATHY; Bensalem HS; Bensalem, PA; (4); 82/474; Drama Clb; SADD; Rep Frsh Cls; Sec Soph Cls; Rep Jr Cls; Rep Sr Cls; JV Var Cheerleading; JV Fld Hcky; High Hon Roll; Hon Roll; Secondary Eductn.

KENNY, GRETCHEN; Bishop Guilfoyle HS; Altoona, PA; (4); 19/123; Trs Science Clb; Pres SADD; Chorus; Yrbk Stf; Off Sr Cls; Var L Vllybl; High Hon Roll; Ntl Merit Ltr; IN U; Nrsng.

KENNY, THOMAS; Northeast Catholic HS; Philadelphia, PA; (3); 5/328; Chess Clb; Math Clb; Math Tm; Science Clb; High Hon Roll; Jr NHS; NHS; Computer Clb; Scholastic Bowl; Hon Roll; NE Catholic Schl Chess Champ 84-86; Cert Merit Top 5 Class 84-87; Schlrshp La Salle U 87-88; Liberal Arts,Bus Admn.

KENNY, WILLIAM; Bensalem HS; Bensalem, PA; (3); Cmnty Wkr; Letterman Clb; Model UN; Varsity Clb; Yrbk Phtg; Yrbk Rptr; Var Crs Cntry; Var Trk; Im Vllybl; Hon Roll; Jrnlsm.

KENSINGER, ANISSA; Juniata Valley HS; Petersburg, PA; (4); Art Clb; Church Yth Grp; VP 4-H; FFA; Teachers Aide; Yrbk Stf; Var L Trk; 4-H Awd; Hon Roll; Grnhnd Awd FFA 85-86; Chptr Frmr Awd 86-87; Hntngdn Cnty Alt Dry Prncss 87-88; Thompson Inst Of Tech; Exec Dta.

KENT, CHRISTOPHER; Punxsutawney Area HS; Punxsutawney, PA; (4); 19/249; Church Yth Grp; Varsity Clb; Variety Show; VP Jr Cls; Var Capt Bsktbl; Var Capt Ftbl; Var L Trk; High Hon Roll; Hon Roll; NHS; PA Free Entrprs Schlrshp; John W Jenks Schlrshp; U Of Pittsburgh; Fnncl Sci.

KENT, EDWARD; Trinity HS; Mechanicsburg, PA; (2); 1/149; Drama Clb; School Musical; School Play; Yrbk Stf; Hon Roll; NHS; NEDT Awd; HOBY Fndtn Ambssdr 86-87.

KENT, GLENN; Trinity HS; Mechanicsburg, PA; (3); Var Crs Cntry; Var Trk; Hon Roll; Math.

KENT, GREG; West Branch HS; Morrisdale, PA; (2); Boy Scts; Varsity Clb; JV Ftbl; JV Socr; Sftbl; Wt Lftg; Wrstlng; God Cntry Awd; Prfct Atten Awd; Arrow Of Lght 83; Comp Prgm.

KENT, JENNIFER; Bishop Mc Devitt HS; Harrisburg, PA; (3); Girl Scts; Hosp Aide; Pep Clb; Service Clb; Spanish Clb; SADD; Georgetown U; Pre Med.

KENT, JENNIFER; Villa Maria Acad; Newtown Sq, PA; (3); 28/98; Dance Clb; Service Clb; SADD; Lit Mag; Trk; High Hon Roll; Math.

KENT, KAREN; Williamson HS; Fillmore, NY; (3); Pres Church Yth Grp; Sec Computer Clb; Spanish Clb; Church Choir; High Hon Roll; NHS; Chorus; Jazz Band; Cit Awd; Spn Awd 85-87; Comp Awd 85-87; Amer Hstry Awd 87; Houghton Coll; Spn.

KENT, LEROY; Blue Mountain Acad; Brockway, PA; (3); Church Choir; Nwsp Phtg; Var Ftbl; Var Sftbl; Capt Vllybl; Var Wt Lftg; Hon Roll; PA ST; Law Enfrcmnt.

KENT, MICHAEL; Columbia Montour Vo-Tech; Nescopeck, PA; (3); Boy Scts; Exploring; Letterman Clb; Varsity Clb; Var Bsbl; Hon Roll; US Air Force; Comp.

KENT, SUSAN C; South Western HS; Hanover, PA; (3); 7/233; Church Yth Grp; Key Clb; Chorus; Church Choir; Mrchg Band; Symp Band; High Hon Roll; Hon Roll; NHS; Rotary Awd; Rotary Ldrs Conf 87; JR Rep Mrchng Band 86-87; Treas Chrch Yth Grp 87; UNC; Phrmcy.

KENT, TINA; Williamson JR SR HS; Millerton, PA; (3); Pres Spanish Clb; Yrbk Stf; Pres Sec Stu Cncl; Trk; Vllybl; High Hon Roll; Pres VP Jr NHS; Pres NHS; Mansfield U.

KENVIN, ROBERT; Freeland HS; Freeland, PA; (3); Aud/Vis; Bsktbl; Vllybl; Hon Roll; Chmpnshp Bsbl Tm 85 & 86; Bloomsburg U; Archeolgy.

KENWORTHY, DONNA; Bishop Conwell HS; Levittown, PA; (3); 11/279; Latin Clb; Quiz Bowl; Spanish Clb; Chorus; Madrigals; School Play; Nwsp Stf; High Hon Roll; NHS; Acadc All Am Awd 84-85 & 85-86.

KENYHERZ, DANA; Sacred Heart HS; Pittsburgh, PA; (3); Sec Church Yth Grp; Dance Clb; French Clb; PAVAS; Chorus; Orch; Hon Roll; NHS; Science Clb; Smrset Music Fest Schlrshp 86; PA Jr Acad Sci 2nd Pl Awd 86; Buhl Sci Fair Awd 86; Music.

KENYON, MARGARET; Souderton Area HS; Harleysville, PA; (4); 32/355; Exploring; Intnl Clb; Nwsp Rptr; Ed Lit Mag; Cit Awd; Hon Roll; Jr NHS; Spanish Clb; Chorus; School Musical; Samuel Blnk Schlrshp, & Yth Educ Assn Hstrn 87; Spnsh Cert Merit 84-87; Temple U; Jrnlsm.

KEONIG, ERIC; Carrick HS; Pittsburgh, PA; (3); 5/434; Church Yth Grp; German Clb; Math Tm; SADD; School Play; Nwsp Phtg; Yrbk Phtg; VP Jr Cls; Var Crs Cntry; High Hon Roll; Penn ST; Chem Engr.

KEPHART, AMY; Moshannon Valley HS; Houtzdale, PA; (4); 13/114; Church Yth Grp; VP Ski Clb; Band; Chorus; Concert Band; Flag Corp; Mrchg Band; Pep Band; School Play; Yrbk Ed-Chief; U Of Pittsburgh; Athl Trng.

KEPHART, JODY; Mc Shannon Valley HS; Brisbin, PA; (3); Church Yth Grp; Red Cross Aide; SADD; Varsity Clb; Band; Chorus; Yrbk Stf; Sftbl; High Hon Roll; Hon Roll; ICM Schl Of Bus; Sec Sci.

KEPHART, KATHRYN G; Penns Manor HS; Strongstown, PA; (3); 26/97; Sec Church Yth Grp; Band; Chorus; Church Choir; Concert Band; Jazz Band; Mrchg Band; Pep Band; School Musical; School Play; County Band 84-87; Vocal Ensemble 85-87; Food Mgmt.

KEPNER, STEVE; Hughesville HS; Hughesville, PA; (3); FFA; Var Bsbl; Var L Ftbl; Var Sftbl; Var Trk; Var Vllybl; Hon Roll; WACC; Forstry.

KEPPLE, CRAIG; Freeport Area SR HS; Sarver, PA; (3); 86/216; Band; Concert Band; Jazz Band; Mrchg Band; Pep Band; Symp Band; Nwsp Stf; God Cntry Awd; Hon Roll; Pharmacist.

KEPPLE, KEN; Franklin Regional HS; Delmont, PA; (4); Sec Trs Church Yth Grp; Drama Clb; SADD; Thesps; Sec Trs Chorus; Church Choir; School Musical; School Play; Swing Chorus; Rep Stu Cncl; IN U Of PA; Fine Arts.

KEPPLE, LANCE; Freeport Area HS; Sarver, PA; (3); 13/225; Church Yth Grp; 4-H; Letterman Clb; Var L Ftbl; Var Trk; Wt Lftg; High Hon Roll; PA Math Lg Awd 86.

KERCH, DANIEL; Portage Area HS; Portage, PA; (4); 19/121; Church Yth Grp; JA; Letterman Clb; Varsity Clb; Rep Stu Cncl; Var L Ftbl; Im Wt Lftg; 4-H Awd; High Hon Roll; Hon Roll; Penn ST; Comm.

KERCHNER, JEFFREY A; Boyertown Area JR High East; Bechtelsville, PA; (1); Aud/Vis; Church Yth Grp; German Clb; Stage Crew; Im Bsktbl; JV Socr; Var Trk; High Hon Roll; Pres Schlr.

KERCSMAR, MICHAEL; Central Bucks HS West; Chalfont, PA; (4); 31/487; Church Yth Grp; Computer Clb; Science Clb; High Hon Roll; Hon Roll; NHS; Math Tm; Ski Clb; Off Frsh Cls; Pres Schlr; Comp Achvt Awd 86; Naval Air Dev Ctr Sci Awd 87; Amer Chem Soc Chem Awd 86; PA ST; Engrng.

KEREKGYARTO, JULIA; Sacred Heart HS; Pittsburgh, PA; (3); Art Clb; Cmnty Wkr; Pep Clb; Ski Clb; Spanish Clb; SADD; Yrbk Stf; Crs Cntry; Girl Scts; Aerontcl.

KERIAZES, ELLENA P; Hanover SR HS; Hanover, PA; (3); Church Yth Grp; Chorus; School Musical; School Play; Swing Chorus; Var Tennis; NHS; Rotary Awd; Band; Nwsp Rptr; Bst Ply Drama Night 84-85; Best Actress Drama Night 86-87; Elctd Schl Bd Stu Repres 86-88; Bus Admin.

KERILLA, MICHAEL; Blue Ridge HS; Great Bend, PA; (3); VP Jr Cls; Var L Bsbl; Var L Bsktbl; High Hon Roll; Hon Roll.

KERKOWSKI, SCOTT; Lake Lehman HS; Dallas, PA; (4); 18/154; SADD; Varsity Clb; School Play; Nwsp Rptr; Sec Soph Cls; Sec Jr Cls; Sec Sr Cls; Capt Ftbl; Var Trk; High Hon Roll; Natl Coun Yth Ldrshp 86; Hnrb Mntn Citzns Voice All Star Ftbl 87; Chem Sec Educ.

KERN, CHARLENE; Mc Guffey HS; Claysville, PA; (4); 12/203; French Clb; Band; Drill Tm; Mrchg Band; Trs Jr Cls; Trs Sr Cls; Stat Trk; High Hon Roll; Lion Awd; NHS; Hmcmng Court 84-86; Prom Queen 86; Mary Knox Scholar 87; CA U PA; Elem Ed.

KERN, DEBBIE; Fort Le Boeuf HS; Waterford, PA; (3); Camera Clb; Church Yth Grp; Yrbk Stf; Stat Bsktbl; Var Trk; Hon Roll; Acadc Achvt Awd 84-85; Bus.

KERN, KEVIN; Southwestern HS; Hanover, PA; (3); 23/233; High Hon Roll; Hon Roll.

KERN, KIM; Shikellamy HS; Sunbury, PA; (3); Trs 4-H; French Clb; Chorus; Variety Show; 4-H Awd; Hon Roll; Pre Vet.

KERN, KRISTI; Trinity HS; Washington, PA; (3); 26/402; Key Clb; Pep Clb; Ski Clb; Spanish Clb; SADD; Sec Jr Cls; Sec Sr Cls; Rep Stu Cncl; Var Capt Cheerleading; Var L Trk; PA ST U; Phys Ther.

KERN, KRISTINA; Fort Le Boeuf HS; Waterford, PA; (2); 68/310; Cmnty Wkr; SADD; Nwsp Rptr; Hon Roll; SCI.

KERN, MARK; Grace Christian Schl; Richland, PA; (3); Church Yth Grp; Teachers Aide; Stage Crew; Pres Frsh Cls; Pres Soph Cls; Hon Roll; Wheaton Coll; TV Comm.

KERN, MELODY; David B Oliver HS; Pittsburgh, PA; (4); 7/238; Pres Exploring; Pres Math Clb; Math Tm; Pres Mu Alpha Theta; Ski Clb; Nwsp Stf; Rep Stu Cncl; Capt Swmmng; High Hon Roll; NHS; Sportsmnshp Awd 87; Silv E Exploring 87; Outstndng Acad Achvt Soc Studs 87; PA ST U; Engrng.

KERN, RENEE; Mahanoy Area HS; Mahanoy City, PA; (3); Church Yth Grp; Spanish Clb; School Musical; School Play; Variety Show; Yrbk Stf; Capt Bsktbl; Var L Sftbl; Hon Roll; NHS; All Are Tm-Girls Bsktbl 86; 1st Tm All Anthrcite-Girls Bsktbl 86; Nrsg.

KERN, SEAN; Dover Area HS; York, PA; (3); 7/260; Quiz Bowl; Varsity Clb; Nwsp Stf; Stu Cncl; Var L Crs Cntry; Var L Swmmng; Var L Trk; Im Vllybl; High Hon Roll; Trs NHS; U Of DE; Chem.

KERN, TAMMY; Connellsville Area SR HS; Connellsville, PA; (3); Church Yth Grp; Dance Clb; Church Choir; Flag Corp; School Musical; Off Stu Cncl; Var Vllybl; Hon Roll; Debate Tm; Library Aide; Bst Drssd Girl 84-85; Uniontwn Schl Nrsng; Nrsng.

KERNAN, DEBORAH; Nazareth Acad; Philadelphia, PA; (3); #8 In Class; Cmnty Wkr; Spanish Clb; Pres Chorus; Drill Tm; School Musical; Nwsp Rptr; Nwsp Stf; Yrbk Stf; High Hon Roll; NHS; Pre-Med.

KERNER, ANN MARIE; St Benedict Acad; Erie, PA; (4); 8/60; Am Leg Aux Girls St; Church Yth Grp; Girl Scts; Model UN; Teachers Aide; Cheerleading; Tennis; Hon Roll; NHS; Villa Maria Coll Schlrshp 87; PA JR Acad Sci-1st, 2nd Awd 84; Villa Maria Coll; Elem Ed.

KERNICK, CHRISTOPHER; Allentown Central Catholic HS; Coopersburg, PA; (3); Church Yth Grp; Computer Clb; German Clb; JV Var Bsbl; Im Bsktbl; Im Ice Hcky; Im Wt Lftg; Im Wrstlng; Hon Roll; Connie Mack ST Champ Bsbl 85-86.

KERNOSCHAK, JOHN M; Carbondale Area HS; Carbondale, PA; (4); 18/144; Computer Clb; English Clb; Ski Clb; Spanish Clb; Pres Soph Cls; VP Stu Cncl; Bsbl; Bsktbl; Ftbl; High Hon Roll; Coaches Awd 86-87; PA ST U; Elctrcl Engrng.

KERNOZEK, KYLE; Methacton HS; Phoenixville, PA; (3); 76/381; VICA; Arch.

KERNS, CHARLES; South Side Area HS; Georgetown, PA; (3); 12/150; Varsity Clb; Chorus; School Play; Var L Bsbl; JV Var Bsktbl; Var Golf; High Hon Roll; Hon Roll; NHS.

KERNS, KRISTI; West York HS; York, PA; (3); Sec Church Yth Grp; German Clb; JA; Varsity Clb; Yrbk Stf; Im Sftbl; Var Capt Tennis; Im Vllybl; Hon Roll; Dbls Awds Prtnr Kerri Kohr 86-87; Art Awd 86; Phys Thrpy.

KERPER, PATRICIA; Garden Spot HS; Narvon, PA; (2); Church Yth Grp; Library Aide; School Play; JV Cheerleading; Csmtlgst.

KERR, ANDREW; Marple Newtown SR HS; Newtown Sq, PA; (3); 9/322; Intnl Clb; Stat Golf; JV Trk.

KERR, DANIEL J; Panther Valley HS; Landsford, PA; (3); 30/132; Am Leg Boys St; Aud/Vis; Boys Clb Am; Chess Clb; ROTC; Var Trk; Prfct Atten Awd; PA ST U; Engrng.

KERR, GWEN; Waynesburg Central HS; Waynesburg, PA; (3); GAA; Natl Beta Clb; Pep Clb; Chorus; Church Choir; Stat Mgr Bsktbl; High Hon Roll; Hon Roll; Interior Dsgn.

KERR, JAMES; Avon Grove HS; West Grove, PA; (3); Boy Scts; Library Aide; Crs Cntry; Trk; Hon Roll; Prfct Atten Awd.

KERR, JENNIFER; Cambridge Springs HS; Cambridge Spg, PA; (3); French Clb; SADD; Concert Band; Mrchg Band; Pep Band; Jr Cls; Stu Cncl; Stat Bsktbl; VP Cheerleading; Hon Roll; Audio Tech.

KERR, JUDITH; Carmichaels Area HS; Carmichaels, PA; (3); 5/112; 4-H; Pep Clb; Spanish Clb; Band; Concert Band; Mrchg Band; VP Jr Cls; Im Sftbl; High Hon Roll; NHS; Accntng.

KERR, LAURA BETH; Pennsbury HS; Yardley, PA; (4); Church Yth Grp; Civic Clb; Debate Tm; Drama Clb; French Clb; PAVAS; Service Clb; SADD; Thesps; Acpl Chr; Best Actress Critics Awd 86; NY U; Drama.

KERR, THOMAS; Pottstown SR HS; Pottstown, PA; (3); 52/152; Key Clb; School Play; Yrbk Stf; Rep Soph Cls; Rep Jr Cls; Rep Sr Cls; Rep Stu Cncl; Var L Bsbl; Var L Ftbl; Hon Roll; Cmmnctns.

KERR, TRISHA; Shaler Area HS; Allison Park, PA; (3); 31/490; Church Yth Grp; Girl Scts; Ski Clb; Mgr(s); Score Keeper; Socr; French Hon Soc; High Hon Roll; Hon Roll; NHS; Slvr Awd In Girl Scouts 85; Ldrshp Awd In Girl Scouts 84; Coaches Soccer Hnr Awd 86; Educ.

KERRIDGE, JANE; Council Rock HS; Richboro, PA; (3); 155/908; Key Clb; Concert Band; Mrchg Band; Pep Band; Stage Crew; Rep Soph Cls; Rep Jr Cls; Powder Puff Ftbl; Hon Roll; Prfct Atten Awd; Elem Educ.

KERRIGAN, SEAN P; Bensalem HS; Bensalem, PA; (3); Art Clb; Boy Scts; Church Yth Grp; Math Tm; Science Clb; High Hon Roll; Prfct Atten Awd; Cngrssnl Schlr 87; Art.

KERRIS, DIANE; Lourdes Regional HS; Mt Carmel, PA; (4); 1/90; Stu Cncl; Capt Cheerleading; Golf; High Hon Roll; NHS; Spanish NHS; Presdntl Acadc Ftnss Awd 87; Am Assn U Of Wmn Awd 87; Hghst Avg Sci 87; Gannon U; Med.

KERSAINT, MARTINE; Archbishop John Carroll HS; Philadelphia, PA; (2); Art Clb; Dance Clb; Drama Clb; English Clb; FBLA; JA; NFL; Science Clb; Yrbk Stf; Stu Cncl; Ellis Grant 85-86; Home Ec & Libry Aide Awd 85-86; Minority Affairs Awd 85-86; Princeton; Med.

KERSHNER, JENNIFER; William Allen HS; Allentown, PA; (2); Exploring; Girl Scts; Band; Concert Band; Mrchg Band; Trk; Hon Roll; Vet Med.

KERSHNER, MELISSA; Hamburg Area JR/Sr HS; Hamburg, PA; (3); Sec Church Yth Grp; FBLA; German Clb; Girl Scts; SADD; Band; Concert Band; Jazz Band; JV Var Bsktbl; Hon Roll.

KERSHNER, TIFFANY; West Haqzleton HS; Hazleton, PA; (2); Spanish Clb; SADD; Thesps; Chorus; Church Choir; School Musical; Capt Twrlr; High Hon Roll; Pres Schlr; Hstry Awd Hghst Avg 86; U FL; Radio.

KERSTETTER, BRIAN; Warwick HS; Lititz, PA; (2); 26/327; Church Yth Grp; Var Socr; JV Trk; Im Vllybl; High Hon Roll; Hon Roll; Jr Natl Hnr Scty 85; Wheaton U; Bus Admin.

KERSTETTER, TODD; Shamekin Area HS; Shamokin, PA; (2); 7/250; Trs Church Yth Grp; Cmnty Wkr; Band; Concert Band; Jazz Band; Mrchg Band; Symp Band; High Hon Roll; Hon Roll; Law.

KERTES, CHRISTINA; Penn Cambria HS; Lilly, PA; (3); 7/186; Am Leg Aux Girls St; Library Aide; Chorus; Nwsp Stf; Off Frsh Cls; Sec Stu Cncl; JV Cheerleading; Trk; High Hon Roll; Hon Roll; Pres Phy Ftns Awd 85-86; Pres Acad Achvt 86; Good Ctznshp Awd 86; Lockhaven; Ped.

KERTULIS, KIMBERLY; East Pennsboro Area HS; Enola, PA; (2); 28/190; French Clb; Yrbk Stf; Hon Roll.

KERWIN, ANGELA; Millersburg Area HS; Millersburg, PA; (3); 2/72; Spanish Clb; Band; Concert Band; Drm Mjr(t); Jazz Band; Mrchg Band; Yrbk Rptr; Yrbk Stf; Var Sftbl; High Hon Roll; Med.

KERYAN, AMY; Hickory HS; Hermitage, PA; (4); 10/170; Drama Clb; Exploring; Latin Clb; Math Clb; Varsity Clb; Band; Chorus; Concert Band; Drill Tm; VP Mrchg Band; Statue Of Liberty Drill Team 86; Nrs.

KESHISHIAN, AROUSIAG; St Basil Acad; Phila, PA; (4); Sec Drama Clb; French Clb; Service Clb; SADD; School Play; Stage Crew; Variety Show; Trs Soph Cls; Trs Sr Cls; Trs Stu Cncl; NY U Schlrshp 87; Temple U Grant 87; Temple U; Pre-Law.

KESLAR, CONNIE; Meyersdale Area HS; Meyersdale, PA; (4); 6/116; VP Church Yth Grp; VP 4-H; Trs French Clb; Church Choir; Color Guard; Yrbk Stf; Var L Vllybl; Hon Roll; NHS; Frnch Hnr Awd 85; Scndry Ed.

KESSEL, JULIE; Hanover SR HS; Hanover, PA; (3); Dance Clb; Band; Chorus; Concert Band; Jazz Band; Mrchg Band; Orch; School Play; Swing Chorus; Rep Stu Cncl; Archaeology.

KESSEL, STEVEN; Bishop Mc Cort HS; Johnstown, PA; (3); German Clb; Vllybl; High Hon Roll; Hon Roll; Acctng.

KESSLER, AMY; Du Bois Area HS; Dubois, PA; (3); 75/400; Teachers Aide; Capt Var Bsktbl; Var Sftbl; Var Trk; Var Vllybl; Wt Lftg; MVP Bsktbl 86-87.

KESSLER, BOB; York Vo-Tech; Hanover, PA; (4); 7/413; JA; VICA; High Hon Roll; Hon Roll; NHS; Amercn All Stars Top 10 Pct Cls 87; 2nd Pl Amercn HS Math Exam 87; Most Likely To Succeed Comp Technl; Comp Oper.

KESSLER, DAVID; HS For Creative & Performing Arts; Philadelphia, PA; (3); 4/140; School Musical; Lit Mag; Jr Cls; High Hon Roll; Mst Promising Artist 84-85; Black Explorers In Medicine Art Cntst 2nd Pl 87; Soviet Jewry Art 1st 86; Parsons; Graphic Artist.

KESSLER, G BRIAN; Monessen JR SR HS; Monessen, PA; (3); 20/108; French Clb; Pres Sr Cls; Var JV Bsktbl; Ftbl; High Hon Roll; Hon Roll; The Vly Indpndnt Carrier Of Yr 86.

KESSLER, JOHNATHAN; Marion Center Area HS; Marion Center, PA; (3); Latin Clb; PA ST; Bio.

KESSLER, JOSEPH; Du Bois Area SR HS; Du Bois, PA; (3); 4/291; Science Clb; Yrbk Phtg; Var L Tennis; High Hon Roll; NHS; Aud/Vis; Camera Clb; Chess Clb; Varsity Clb; Church Choir; Nice Kid Awd 85; Courier Exprss Chrstms Essy Cont 84; JR Leg Bwlng Champ 85; Engrng.

KESSLER, LISA; Central York SR HS; York, PA; (3); Varsity Clb; Mrchg Band; Nwsp Stf; Rep Frsh Cls; Rep Soph Cls; VP Jr Cls; Pres Sr Cls; Var Bsktbl; Var Sftbl; Hon Roll; Elem Ed.

KESSLER, NADINE; Danville HS; Danville, PA; (3); Drama Clb; Key Clb; Latin Clb; NFL; Spanish Clb; Speech Tm; Nwsp Rptr; Rep Jr Cls; High Hon Roll; NHS; TV Brdcstng.

KESSLER, PAULA; Haverford HS; Havertown, PA; (3); 78/420; Office Aide; Yrbk Stf; Mgr Lcrss; Mgr Wrstlng; Hon Roll; Pres Schlr; Phrmcy.

KESSLER, SASHA; Bensalem HS; Bensalem, PA; (3); Church Yth Grp; Math Tm; Model UN; Scholastic Bowl; Speech Tm; Nwsp Stf; Socr; High Hon Roll; NHS; Ntl Merit Ltr; FPS Tm PA ST Chmpns SR Div, Smmr Smnr Physics US Naval Acad 87; U Of PA; Physics.

KESSLER, STACY; Central Columbia HS; Bloomsburg, PA; (3); Pres German Clb; Hosp Aide; Ski Clb; Teachers Aide; Color Guard; Var Cheerleading; JV Diving; Var Fld Hcky; Hon Roll; Cmnty Wkr; Bloomsburg U; Specl Ed.

KESSLER, SYBIL B; Performing Arts School Of Phila; Woodbury Hghts, NJ; (4); 3/25; Thesps; Acpl Chr; Chorus; Madrigals; School Musical; School Play; Stage Crew; Yrbk Stf; Trs Jr Cls; Swmmng; Smmr Arts Inst 85; ST Teens Arts Fstvl, & All South Jersey Chorus 84; Rutgers Coll; Theatre.

KESSLER, WALLY; Du Bois Area SR HS; Du Bois, PA; (2); 9/320; Cmnty Wkr; Science Clb; Band; Mrchg Band; Crs Cntry; High Hon Roll; NHS; Dist Coke Tourn-Bowlng 86; Altr Boy-St Mchls 79-87; 10th Pl-Cour Chrstmn Essy Cntst 86; Bio.

KESTENBAUM, DAVID S; Springfield Township HS; Glenside, PA; (4); 3/143; AFS; Capt Computer Clb; Capt Math Tm; Trs Thesps; School Musical; School Play; Lit Mag; Rep Stu Cncl; Tennis; Ntl Merit SF; Rennselaer Poly Tec Inst Math & Sci Awd 86; Yale U; Physics.

KESTER, CHARLES; Curwensville Area SR HS; Curwensville, PA; (3); Chess Clb; VICA; Chorus; Hon Roll; Drftsmn.

KESTER, KATHI; Curwensville Area HS; Mahaffey, PA; (3); Band; Concert Band; Mrchg Band; High Hon Roll; Hon Roll; NHS.

KESTER, KYRA K; Corry Area HS; Spring Creek, PA; (4); German Clb; Chorus; Concert Band; Mrchg Band; Orch; High Hon Roll; Hon Roll; Pres Schlr; Music Tchrs Natl Assn H S Cmpt 1st Rnr Up Natl Lvl 85-87; Erie Music Tchrs Assn Cmpt Jr Div 1st Pl 84; Cleveland Inst Of Music; Music.

KESTER, MICHAEL; Dallas SR HS; Shavertown, PA; (3); Art Clb; Chess Clb; Pres Church Yth Grp; Cmnty Wkr; Letterman Clb; Pep Clb; Ski Clb; Yrbk Stf; JV Golf; Var L Vllybl; U Of PA; Bus.

KESTER, SUSAN M; Sun Valley SR HS; Aston, PA; (3); 13/270; Am Leg Aux Girls St; Intnl Clb; Scholastic Bowl; Science Clb; SADD; Band; Yrbk Stf; JV Var Tennis; High Hon Roll; NHS; West Chester U; Math Tchr.

KESTNER, JENNIFER; Franklin Regional HS; Delmont, PA; (3); Cmnty Wkr; FNA; Hosp Aide; Chorus; Stage Crew; Nwsp Rptr; NHS; Clarion U PA; Educ.

KESZELI, GEORGE; Haverford HS; Haverford, PA; (3); Art Clb; Church Yth Grp; Cmnty Wkr; Drama Clb; Pres French Clb; Pep Clb; Acpl Chr; Chorus; School Musical; School Play; Concours Natl De Francais/Cert Merit 84-87; Art Awd-Tempera 85; Frnch.

KETCH, MARK; Sch Hoven HS; Sch Haven, PA; (3); Pres Church Yth Grp; Computer Clb; Science Clb; JV Bsktbl; JV Trk; Wt Lftg; Hon Roll.

KETCHA, KAREN; Valley View JR SR HS; Archbald, PA; (1); 3/180; French Clb; Ski Clb; Drill Tm; High Hon Roll.

KETH, KIMBERLY; Punxsutawney Area SR HS; Punxsutawney, PA; (3); FBLA; Trk; Csmtlgy.

KETH, PHILIP; Clarion Limestone HS; Clarion, PA; (4); Math Tm; Varsity Clb; Chorus; Madrigals; Swing Chorus; Var L Ftbl; Var L Trk; French Clb; Variety Show; Tm MVP Trck 86-87; Athlt Yr 86-87; Otstndng Chrl Stu 86-87; Clarion U PA; Comp Sci.

KETLER, ROBERT; Archbishop Ryan Hs For Boys; Philadelphia, PA; (4); 18/423; Church Yth Grp; Im Socr; JV Tennis; Hon Roll; Widener U; Engineering.

KETNER, CHRISTINE; Blue Mountain HS; Schuylkill Havn, PA; (4); 13/218; Latin Clb; Trs Mu Alpha Theta; Chorus; Nwsp Stf; Trk; High Hon Roll; Hon Roll; NHS; NEDT Awd; H S Wanger Mem Nrsng Awd 87; Bloomsburg U; Nrsng.

KETTELL, KIM; St Huberts HS; Philadelphia, PA; (4); Church Yth Grp; Stage Crew; Hon Roll.

KETTER, JILL; Trinity HS; Washington, PA; (3); Cmnty Wkr; French Clb; Girl Scts; Hosp Aide; Ski Clb; Band; Concert Band; Mrchg Band; Yrbk Stf; DAR Awd; Pre-Med.

KETTERER, DAVID CHRISTOPHER; Lincoln HS; Ellwood City, PA; (3); 62/162; Ski Clb; Spanish Clb; Var L Bsbl; Bsktbl; Var L Ftbl; Hon Roll; Schlr/Athl Awd 87.

KETTERER, KEITH; Daniel Boone HS; Douglassville, PA; (3); #25 In Class; Varsity Clb; Ftbl; Wrstlng; Hon Roll; Bus.

KETTERER, LINDA; Penn Hills HS; Pittsburgh, PA; (3); French Clb; Ski Clb; JV Var Bsktbl; Hon Roll; Penn ST U; Psych.

KETTERING III, CHARLES H; Sharpsville HS; Sharpsville, PA; (3); Church Yth Grp; JA; Library Aide; Ski Clb; VICA; Chorus; Church Choir; Mgr Bsktbl; Mgr Ftbl; Mgr(s); Acad Ltr; Ftbl Mgr Ltr; Data Proc Grad.

KETTERING, JANINE; Connellsvile Area SR HS; Connellsville, PA; (4); 36/550; Office Aide; Chorus; Jazz Band; School Musical; Symp Band; Nwsp Rptr; Trs Sr Cls; Var Cheerleading; High Hon Roll; NHS; Alt Govrns Schl Music 86; Homecoming Atten 86-87; IN U PA; Music Ed.

KEVERLINE, MARGARET; Bradford Central Christian HS; Bradford, PA; (4); 1/26; Camera Clb; Drama Clb; Pep Clb; SADD; Varsity Clb; Stage Crew; Yrbk Stf; Rep Stu Cncl; Capt Cheerleading; Bausch & Lomb Sci Awd; Amer Chem Soc Penn York Awd 86; Dietetics.

KEY, ELLIOTT; Ambridge HS; Ambridge, PA; (3); FCA; Var Bsktbl; Var Ftbl; Bus Mgmt.

KEY, MARK; Claysburg Kimmel HS; Claysburgh, PA; (2); 1/97; Art Clb; Church Yth Grp; Drama Clb; German Clb; PAVAS; Spanish Clb; SADD; Stage Crew; JV Bsbl; JV Bsktbl; Cert Of Achvt-Hgh Acadmc Hnr 86; Penn ST; Comp Pgmng.

KEYES, MARK; Wyoming Area HS; Falls, PA; (3); Cmnty Wkr; Golf; Wilkes; ROTC.

KEYES IV, WILLIAM R; Norristown Area HS; Norristown, PA; (4); 47/478; Service Clb; JV Bsbl; Hon Roll; PA; Advrtsng.

KEYS, RICHARD D; Beth-Center HS; Brownsville, PA; (4); 16/156; Capt Wrstlng; Letterman Clb; Ski Clb; Varsity Clb; Sftbl; Trk; High Hon Roll; Hon Roll; Lion Awd; PA Honors Test Awd; CA U Of PA; Scndry Physics.

KEYSER, CRAIG; Hatboro-Horsham HS; Hatboro, PA; (3); Church Yth Grp; English Clb; Ski Clb; Spanish Clb; SADD; Varsity Clb; Yrbk Ed-Chief; Yrbk Sprt Ed; Yrbk Stf; Lit Mag; PA ST.

KEYSO, RUTH ANN; Bishop Conwell HS; Levittown, PA; (4); 1/271; Math Tm; Capt Crs Cntry; Capt Trk; Elks Awd; High Hon Roll; VP NHS; Prfct Atten Awd; Sal; Quiz Bowl; Scholastic Bowl; U Notre Dame Dailey Memrl Schlrshp 87; Coaches Awd Crss Cntry 87; Hghst Gen Avg Math Calculss 87; U Of Notre Dame; Engrng.

KEZMAN, JAMES; Greensburg Central Catholic HS; Ligonier, PA; (3); VP Jr Cls; Off Sr Cls; Powder Puff Ftbl; Im Capt Sftbl; Im Capt Vllybl; High Hon Roll; Hon Roll; COMM.

KHA, KO; Pequea Valley HS; Gordonville, PA; (3); Church Yth Grp; Church Choir; Stage Crew; Yrbk Phtg; Yrbk Stf; Rep Stu Cncl; Vllybl; Cit Awd; High Hon Roll; NHS; Vlybl JV Ltr 85; Vlybl Pin 86; Photo.

KHANDHAR, ALPA; Neshaminy HS; Feasterville, PA; (3); 4/824; Cmnty Wkr; Intnl Clb; Sec Trs Service Clb; Variety Show; Nwsp Rptr; Nwsp Stf; Rep Stu Cncl; Im Tennis; High Hon Roll; Pres NHS; Outstndng Achvt Humanties 85; 2(d Pl Essay Cont 86; Intl Rltns.

KHANUJA, ASHOO; Villa Maria HS; Warren, OH; (4); 5/52; Art Clb; Hosp Aide; Key Clb; Pep Clb; Spanish Clb; Temple Yth Grp; Yrbk Phtg; Lit Mag; NHS; Pres Schlr; Awd 100 Hrs Vlntr Wrk 87; Mc Dougal Littell & Co Prfct Sprt Awd 87; Case Western Reserve U; Biomed.

KHOV, HING; Mastbaum AVT HS; Philadelphia, PA; (4); 3/320; Exploring; Hosp Aide; Science Clb; SADD; Lit Mag; Bsktbl; Swmmng; Bausch & Lomb Sci Awd; Val; Merit Awd 84-87; Phldlpha Fedrtn Tchr, Celia Pincr Awd, Pres Acadmc Ftns Awd 87; Phldlpha Coll Textiles & Sci.

KIBLER, ROBERT; Seneca Valley HS; Mars, PA; (3); 36/330; Teachers Aide; Hon Roll; Acad Achvt Awd 86-87; Bus Admin.

KICHLINE, EDWIN; Parkland HS; Allentown, PA; (2); Pres Church Yth Grp; JA; Chorus; School Play; Nwsp Stf; High Hon Roll; Hon Roll; Prfct Atten Awd; Pres Schlr; HOBY 87; Law.

KICHULA, JOHN R; La Salle College HS; Warminster, PA; (4); 9/243; Nwsp Stf; Im Bsktbl; Im Ftbl; Im Vllybl; Hon Roll; NHS; Ntl Merit SF; Crew Cptn Vrsty Lttr JR Ntl Tm 84-87; Acad Lttrs 84-87; Hghst Hnrs Chem Math Grmn Rlgn 84-86; U Of PA; Elec Engr.

KICK, CLARE; Portage Area HS; Portage, PA; (4); 7/128; Band; Chorus; Concert Band; Mrchg Band; Pep Band; High Hon Roll; Hon Roll; NHS; Prsdntl Acdmc Awd 86-87; U Of Pittsburg; Med.

KICSKA, JEFFREY; Notre Dame HS; Easton, PA; (3); Art Clb; Boy Scts; Church Yth Grp; Ski Clb; Band; Var Crs Cntry; Var Trk; JV Wrstlng; Hon Roll; Bio.

KIDD, BILLIE; Mt Union Area HS; Mt Union, PA; (3); Church Yth Grp; GAA; Spanish Clb; Var Sftbl; Hon Roll; NHS; Accntng.

KIDD, BONNIE; Mt Union Area HS; Mt Union, PA; (4); 11/171; French Clb; GAA; SADD; Band; Concert Band; Jazz Band; Mrchg Band; Var JV Cheerleading; Hon Roll; NHS; Pres Acdmc Ftns Awd 87; Elem Ed.

KIDD, CAROLYN; Parklandd HS; Orefield, PA; (3); 60/523; Drama Clb; Leo Clb; School Musical; School Play; High Hon Roll; Hon Roll; NHS; Candystriper Awd; Publc Rltns.

KIDD, SHAWN; Meadville Area HS; Meadville, PA; (3); 65/365; Aud/Vis; Church Yth Grp; Debate Tm; Pres Exploring; NFL; Speech Tm; Im Badmtn; JV Var Socr; Ntl Merit Ltr; Psych.

KIDDER, MICHELLE; West Allegheny HS; Imperial, PA; (3); Church Yth Grp; Cmnty Wkr; Library Aide; Office Aide; Teachers Aide; Hon Roll; Accntng.

KIDWELL, JOHN; Archbishop Ryan HS For Boys; Philadelphia, PA; (2); 119/356; Church Yth Grp; Civic Clb; U Of PA; Comms.

KIEFER, APRIL; Biglerville HS; Arendtsville, PA; (3); 4/105; Computer Clb; Library Aide; Spanish Clb; Nwsp Rptr; High Hon Roll; Jr NHS; NHS; Acctg.

KIEFER, JOSEPH; Abington Heights HS; Clarks Summit, PA; (1); Ski Clb; Var L Socr; JV Trk; Hon Roll; ACL NJCL Natl Latin Exam Summa Cum Laude 87; Engrng.

KIEHL, WENDY S; Warwick HS; Lititz, PA; (3); 7/267; Am Leg Aux Girls St; Church Yth Grp; Varsity Clb; Orch; JV Var Bsktbl; JV Var Sftbl; High Hon Roll; NHS; 3rd Pl Lancaster Cnty Sci & Engrng Fair 85; VP Natl Hon Soc 87-88; Scndry Sci.

KIEHN, MARK; Northern High School HS; Dillsburg, PA; (3); 66/232; Spanish Clb; Band; Concert Band; Mrchg Band; Golf; High Hon Roll; Glf Cert 87; Ltr Dstngsh Hnr 88; Psych.

KIELB, MAUREEN E; Lancaster Catholic HS; Landisville, PA; (3); 29/194; Church Yth Grp; Service Clb; Nwsp Rptr; Var Cheerleading; Im Fld Hcky; Var Pom Pon; Hon Roll; Bus.

KIELY, JENNIFER; Arch Bishop Prendergast HS; Glenolden, PA; (3); 20/327; Latin Clb; Pres Math Tm; Crs Cntry; Trk; Hon Roll; Sec NHS; Med.

KIELY, KITTY; Archbishop Carroll HS; Havertown, PA; (4); 28/367; Church Yth Grp; Intnl Clb; Spanish Clb; Nwsp Rptr; Rep Jr Cls; Cheerleading; Crs Cntry; High Hon Roll; Pres Schlr; Engrng Schlrshp Wilkes Coll 87; Drexel U; Commrc.

KIENINGER, THAD; Latrobe HS; Greensburg, PA; (3); 9/374; Boy Scts; German Clb; Letterman Clb; Ski Clb; Concert Band; L Mrchg Band; Var L Trk; High Hon Roll; Lion Awd; Art Clb; Air Force Acad; Astrntcs.

KIERSNOWSKI, JENNIFER; Shamokin Area HS; Shamokin, PA; (2); 90/250; Camera Clb; Church Yth Grp; Drama Clb; Girl Scts; Key Clb; Pep Clb; Ski Clb; SADD; Med.

KIERZEK, SUSAN; Nazareth Acad; Phila, PA; (3); Spanish Clb; Concert Band; Orch; School Musical; Variety Show; Yrbk Phtg; Yrbk Rptr; Yrbk Stf; Rep Soph Cls; Off Stu Cncl; Temple U; Communctns.

KIESAU, MARIN; Exeter SR HS; Reading, PA; (4); 19/250; Band; Capt Flag Corp; Orch; Stu Cncl; Mgr(s); Sftbl; Tennis; High Hon Roll; Jr NHS; NHS; Med.

KIESEWETTER, KENT; Bishop Guilfoyle HS; Altoona, PA; (3); 5/156; NFL; Science Clb; Ski Clb; SADD; Chorus; Im Bsktbl; Var Mgr(s); Var Vllybl; High Hon Roll; Hon Roll; UCLA.

KIESINGER, JENNIFER; Mifflinburg Area HS; Mifflinburg, PA; (2); JV Bsktbl; High Hon Roll; Pedtrcn.

KIGHTLINGER, MARCAIL; Meadville Avea SR HS; Meadville, PA; (2); Trs Exploring; French Clb; JA; JCL; Latin Clb; Mrchg Band; Pep Band; Sftbl; Hon Roll; Prfct Atten Awd; 1st Pl Dist Cont Natl Hstry Day 87; Cert Hnrb Mntn Cum Laude Natl Lat Exam 86; Cnty Yth Cnsrvation Cmp.

KIGHTLINGER, PAMELA; Seneca HS; Erie, PA; (3); 12/155; FBLA; Capt Color Guard; Mrchg Band; School Musical; Stage Crew; Yrbk Stf; Sec Stu Cncl; Trk; Hon Roll; NHS; Track Ltr & Mdl 86-87; Hnr Roll Ltr & Pin 86-87; FBLA Trophy Shorthand 86-87.

KIKUCHI, ALICIA; Strath Haven HS; Swarthmore, PA; (4); Girl Scts; Chorus; Church Choir; School Musical; School Play; Stage Crew; Hon Roll; NHS; Ntl Merit Ltr; Pres Schlr; Girl Scout Silver,Gold Awd 82-86; Acad Ltrs 85-87; Swarthmore Coll; Spcl Ed.

KILBURN, AMBER; Kennard Dale HS; Stewartstown, PA; (3); Church Yth Grp; Trs French Clb; Letterman Clb; Pep Clb; Varsity Clb; Stage Crew; Var Capt Cheerleading; Hon Roll; Most Dedicated Chrldr 86-87; Bus Mgmt.

KILDOO, JIM; Moniteau JR SR HS; Butler, PA; (1); Church Yth Grp; Dance Clb; Spanish Clb; Band; Concert Band; Mrchg Band; Swing Chorus; Trk; Hon Roll; Jr NHS.

KILE, JOHN; Hempfield HS; Landisville, PA; (3); 22/400; Band; Var Golf; NHS; Ntl Merit Ltr; William & Mary; Comp Sci.

KILGORE, HEIDI TRIS ANN; Butler SR HS; Butler, PA; (3); Church Yth Grp; JA; Library Aide; Spanish Clb; SADD; Hon Roll; NHS; ST Fnlst Miss Amer Cood Pageant 86; Butler Area SR HS Acad Achvt Awd 86-87; Social Work.

KILGORE, MAXINE; Red Lion Area SR HS; Brogue, PA; (3); 1/375; Exploring; JA; School Play; School Musical; Pres Frsh Cls; Rep Stu Cncl; Stat Bsbl; Cheerleading; High Hon Roll; HOBY Ldrshp Awd 86; Engrng.

KILGORE, PATRICIA; Northern HS; Dillsburg, PA; (3); Camp Fr Inc; Rep Soph Cls; Rep Jr Cls; Var Cheerleading; Var Crs Cntry; Var Powder Puff Ftbl; Var Trk; Physcl Thrpst.

KILHEFNER, SCOTT; Ephrata HS; Ephrata, PA; (3); VP Church Yth Grp; Intnl Clb; L Var Ftbl; Var Trk; Hon Roll.

KILIANY, LISA; Geibel HS; Scottdale, PA; (4); 18/80; Drama Clb; Pep Clb; Stage Crew; Lit Mag; Mgr(s); Hon Roll; NHS; Spanish NHS; Spanish Clb; School Musical; Duquesne U; Acctng.

KILIANY, ROSS; Southmoreland HS; Ruffsdale, PA; (3); Boy Scts; Drama Clb; Trs Exploring; German Clb; Letterman Clb; School Play; Nwsp Rptr; Nwsp Stf; Yrbk Stf; Lit Mag; Penn ST; Mdcl Prfssn.

KILKER, TARA; Bishop O Hara HS; Blakely, PA; (4); Drama Clb; Latin Clb; Spanish Clb; Chorus; Church Choir; School Play; Nwsp Ed-Chief; Nwsp Rptr; Hon Roll; NHS; George Washington U; Pol Sci.

KILLAM, SANDRA; Council Rock HS; Holland, PA; (2); SADD; Var Diving; JV Fld Hcky; JV Sftbl; Var Swmmng; Hon Roll; Penn ST.

KILLAR, CLAUDINE; Elizabeth Forward HS; Springboro, OH; (3); Rep Church Yth Grp; Exploring; JA; Sec Leo Clb; Q&S; Chorus; Mrchg Band; Nwsp Rptr; High Hon Roll; NHS.

KILLCRECE, LISA; Freeport SR HS; Freeport, PA; (3); Cmnty Wkr; Capt Drill Tm; Mrchg Band; Mgr(s); Asst Vet.

KILLEEN, MICHAEL S; Bellefonte SR HS; Bellefonte, PA; (3); 41/211; JV Crs Cntry; Gym; JV Trk; Hon Roll; Cert Of Educ Devlpmnt Ntl-NEDT 86; Offc Of Nvl Rsrch-HS Stu Intrn Pgm 87; Penn ST U; Dntstry.

KILLEN, DAWN; Nazareth Acad; Philadelphia, PA; (4); Cmnty Wkr; Debate Tm; French Clb; Math Clb; NFL; NHS; Acad All Amer 86-87; Philadelphia Coll; Phrmcy.

KILLIAN, AMY; Archbishop Prendergast HS; Drexel Hill, PA; (3); 30/356; Church Yth Grp; French Clb; Latin Clb; Stu Cncl; Coach Actv; JV Capt Fld Hcky; Hon Roll; NHS; Nrsng.

KILLIAN, KATHIE; Conemaugh Valley HS; Conemaugh, PA; (4); 3/118; FBLA; NFL; Office Aide; Pep Clb; Speech Tm; Band; Concert Band; Co-Capt Flag Corp; Mrchg Band; Nwsp Rptr; Bus Awd-Stngrphc & Clrcl 87; Rcgnzd-Jhnstwn Rtry Clb 87; Alx Rbgh & Rbrt C Bryd Schlrshps 87; Indiana U Of PA; Accntng.

KILLIAN, KATHRYN M; Central Catholic HS; Birdsboro, PA; (3); 10/130; Church Yth Grp; Quiz Bowl; Spanish Clb; Varsity Clb; School Musical; Yrbk Sprt Ed; Bsktbl; Sftbl; High Hon Roll; NHS; 1st Team Div I All-Star Bsktbl 86-87; Intnsv Lang Inst Penn ST 87; Intl Rltns.

KILLIAN, KELLY; Warwick HS; Lititz, PA; (2); 32/325; Camera Clb; Church Yth Grp; Cmnty Wkr; Computer Clb; French Clb; Red Cross Aide; Jr Cls; Fld Hcky.

KILLIAN, SUSAN; Little Flower HS For Girls; Philadelphia, PA; (3); 103/322; Church Yth Grp; GAA; Office Aide; Rep Frsh Cls; Rep Soph Cls; Im Bsktbl; JV Cheerleading; Capt Var Tennis; Hon Roll; PA ST; Advrtsng.

KILLIANY, KRISTINA; Western Wayne HS; Lake Ariel, PA; (3); Spanish Clb; Nwsp Rptr; Pres Jr Cls; Pres Sr Cls; Var Tennis; High Hon Roll; Hon Roll; Grls Tnns MVP 85 & 87; Dist 12 Grls Tnns Chmpn Sngls 86; Dist 12 Grls Tnns Chmpn Dbls 85; Bus Fnncng.

KILLINGER, TAMMY; Jersey Shore Area SR HS; Jersey Shore, PA; (4); 100/218; Church Yth Grp; Cmnty Wkr; Drama Clb; VP Trs 4-H; FBLA; Hosp Aide; Ski Clb; Band; Lit Mag; Rep Stu Cncl; Hghst Avrg Dvlpmnt Rdng 85-86; Lycoming Coll; Bus Admin.

KILLINGSWORTH, KRISTIN; Emmaus HS; Emmaus, PA; (3); Church Yth Grp; Key Clb; Spanish Clb; Chorus; Yrbk Sprt Ed; Hon Roll; Jr NHS; NHS.

KILLINO, MICHELLE; Old Forge HS; Old Forge, PA; (4); Church Yth Grp; Ski Clb; Yrbk Phtg; Cheerleading; Twrlr; Gregg Typing Awd 85; Chld Dvlvpmnt.

KILLION, JEFFREY; Archbishop Ryan HS For Boys; Philadelphia, PA; (2); 6/353; Chess Clb; Im Bsktbl; High Hon Roll; Outstndng Acad Achvt Span 85-86; Frgn Lang.

KILMER, VICTORIA; Blue Mt Acad; Hop Bottom, PA; (4); 3/58; Red Cross Aide; Band; Nwsp Rptr; Sec Jr Cls; Sec Stu Cncl; Gym; Im Sftbl; High Hon Roll; Prfct Atten Awd; Penn ST U.

KILYANEK, ANNE; Pittston Area HS; Duryea, PA; (4); 1/360; Pres Computer Clb; Hosp Aide; Key Clb; Math Clb; Ski Clb; SADD; High Hon Roll; NHS; NEDT Awd; Wlks Coll Trstees Schlrshp 87; NEDT Cert; Wilkes Coll; Comp Sci.

KIM, CHAE; Olney HS; Philadelphia, PA; (4); 17/700; Cmnty Wkr; Math Clb; Math Tm; Hon Roll; NHS; Trphy-Hnr Rll 84; Awd & Mdl-Outstndng Achvt-Hstry & Comp Sci 84; Temple U; Mdcl Lab Technlgy.

KIM, DEBORAH; Taylor Allderdice HS; Pittsburgh, PA; (3); French Clb; Math Clb; Ski Clb; Vllybl; High Hon Roll; NHS; Phrmcy.

KIM, HAE EUN; Pocono Mountain HS; Effort, PA; (3); Church Yth Grp; High Hon Roll; Hon Roll; Gregg Typng Awd 85-87; Rutgers Schl Phrmcy; Phrmcy.

KIM, HEERAK; Phil-Mont Christian Acad; Philadelphia, PA; (4); Pres Church Yth Grp; Church Choir; Sec Jr Cls; Rep Sr Cls; Sec Stu Cncl; JV Trk; High Hon Roll; NHS; Gold Cert In Oil Pntng & Mxd Media At Mddl Atlantic Chrstn Schls Assn 86; Tch Sndy Schl & Trtng 86-87; Mnstr.

KIM, HELEN; Blue Mountain Acad; Millville, NJ; (2); Church Yth Grp; Drama Clb; Sec Frsh Cls; Sec Stu Cncl; JV Bsktbl; JV Tennis; Var Vllybl; High Hon Roll; Andrews U; Physcl Thrpst.

KIM, HUI JUNG; Susquehanna Township HS; Harrisburg, PA; (3); 3/170; Am Leg Aux Girls St; Church Yth Grp; Sec GAA; Pres Key Clb; Model UN; Nwsp Stf; Var L Fld Hcky; Var Sftbl; High Hon Roll; Sec Trs NHS; Latn Awd 85; Med.

KIM, HYON; Downington SR HS; Downingtown, PA; (4); 1/523; French Clb; Capt Quiz Bowl; Acpl Chr; Nwsp Stf; Var JV Tennis; Bausch & Lomb Sci Awd; Gov Hon Prg Awd; VP NHS; Ntl Merit Schol; Val; Rensselaer Polytech Inst Math & Sci Awd, & Brwn U Bk Awd 86; Intl Frgn Lang Awd 87; Yale U; Corp Law.

KIM, HYUN CHIN; Abington SR HS; Roslyn, PA; (3); French Clb; Latin Clb; Yrbk Stf; Lcrss; High Hon Roll; Hon Roll; NHS; Lat Awd 85-86; Art Awd 84-85.

KIM, JIYOUNG; Schenley HS; Pittsburgh, PA; (3); Art Clb; Math Tm; Science Clb; Church Yth Grp; Intnl Clb; Math Clb; Speech Tm; School Musical; Pres Frsh Cls; Timer; Natl Math Lg 2nd 84-85; Chem Concept Tst 1st 84-85; Med.

KIM, JOHN; Cheltenham HS; Elkins Park, PA; (4); 3/365; Church Yth Grp; VP Intnl Clb; Math Tm; Capt Swmmng; NHS; Prsdntl Acdmc Fitness Awd & Paul J Whiteley Math Awd 87; DE Vly Sci Fair 1st Pl 85; MIT; Elec Engr.

KIM, JULIE; Laurel Highlands HS; Uniontown, PA; (2); 15/375; Art Clb; Church Yth Grp; English Clb; VP JA; Ski Clb; Church Choir; School Play; Sec Stu Cncl; Stat Bsktbl; High Hon Roll.

KIM, SUNG; Downingtown SR HS; Downingtown, PA; (3); 154/648; VP Model UN; Spanish Clb; Band; Jazz Band; Mrchg Band; Symp Band; Nwsp Sprt Ed; Yrbk Sprt Ed; Ed Lit Mag; Rep Jr Cls; Boston U; Med.

KIM, SUNG; Upper Darby HS; Upper Darby, PA; (3); 25/650; Church Yth Grp; Intnl Clb; JV Var Socr; Le High U; Comp Sci.

KIM, TAEYEON; Olney HS; Philadelphia, PA; (4); 6/701; Church Yth Grp; Math Clb; Math Tm; Orch; Badmtn; High Hon Roll; Hon Roll; NHS; Drexel U; Nutrion.

KIM, THOMAS; Wilson HS; Wyomissing, PA; (4); Debate Tm; German Clb; Math Clb; Chorus; Orch; L Var Tennis; Im Vllybl; High Hon Roll; Ntl Merit SF; Church Choir; PIAA Dist Orch-1st Chair 86; U Of PA; Med.

KIM, WON; Haverford SR HS; Havertown, PA; (3); Cmnty Wkr; Computer Clb; English Clb; Gym; High Hon Roll; Hon Roll; Electrncs.

KIM, YONG; Harry S Truman HS; Fairless Hills, PA; (3); #8 In Class; Church Yth Grp; Debate Tm; Var Tennis; Capt Wrstlng; Hon Roll; Prfct Atten Awd; Amer Lgn Cert Of Schl Awd & Stu Of Month 84-85; Pres Physical Ftnss Awd 85-86; RI Schl Of Dsgn; Cmmrcl Art.

KIMBERLAND, KELLY ANN; Canon-Mc Millan SR HS; Eighty Four, PA; (4); 31/357; Cmnty Wkr; French Clb; Science Clb; Teachers Aide; Band; Chorus; Drm Mjr(t); Jazz Band; Mrchg Band; Rep Frsh Cls; Outstndng Pianist Awd 84; Washington & Jefferson; Bio.

KIMBERLY, SHAUNA; Bellwood-Antis HS; Tyrone, PA; (1); Key Clb; Political Wkr; Chorus; School Play; Variety Show; Bsktbl; Mgr(s); Score Keeper; Timer; Penn ST; Law.

KIMBLE, LORRIE; Jersey Shore Area HS; Avis, PA; (3); Hon Roll; Williamsport Area CC; Food Prp.

KIMBLE, SUSAN; Meyersdale Area HS; Meyersdale, PA; (4); 1/116; Pres Church Yth Grp; Soroptimist; Sec Spanish Clb; Band; Concert Band; Mrchg Band; Hon Roll; NHS; Acdmc Awd 85 & 86; Acdmc All Amer 86.

KIMBLE, TODD; Williamsport Area HS; Williamsport, PA; (3); Wrstlng.

KIME, AMY; Harmony HS; Cherry Tree, PA; (4); 10/50; Concert Band; Drm Mjr(t); School Play; Yrbk Bus Mgr; Trs Stu Cncl; Capt Cheerleading; Dnfth Awd; NHS; IN U Of PA; Sci Ed.

KIMICATA, LESLIE; Sacred Heart HS; Pittsburgh, PA; (3); 26/120; Cmnty Wkr; Exploring; French Clb; Intnl Clb; VP Ski Clb; Color Guard; Stage Crew; Bsktbl; Score Keeper; Hon Roll; OH U; Chld Psych.

KIMMEL, AUDREY; Tri-Valley HS; Hegins, PA; (3); 1/76; Trs Church Yth Grp; Computer Clb; 4-H; Math Tm; Quiz Bowl; Church Choir; Yrbk Sprt Ed; Off Stu Cncl; Var Bsktbl; NHS; Woodsmn Of Wrld Awd 85 & 86; Bucknell Math Awd 86 & 87; Envir-O-Lympcs Champs 85; Chem Engrng.

KIMMEL, DIANE; Somerset SR HS; Somerset, PA; (4); Pres Church Yth Grp; English Clb; French Clb; FTA; GAA; JA; Letterman Clb; Pres Frsh Cls; Pres Soph Cls; VP Jr Cls; Prsdntl Phys Ftnss Awd 81-87; U Of Pittsburgh; Elem Educ.

KIMMEL, GLEN; The Christian Acad; Sharon Hill, PA; (3); Church Yth Grp; FNA; Sec FBLA; Hosp Aide; Chorus; Church Choir; Yrbk Phtg; Yrbk Sprt Ed; Im Vllybl; Hon Roll; 3rd Pl FBLA Acctng Cmptns Rgnl 87; Acctng Hnrs 87; Drexel U; Acctng.

KIMMEL, HEIDI; Wyoming Area HS; Falls, PA; (3); Church Yth Grp; French Clb; Ski Clb; Band; Chorus; Concert Band; Mrchg Band; School Musical; Rep Stu Cncl; Trk; Engrng.

KIMMEL, JEFFREY; Berlin-Brothervalley HS; Berlin, PA; (4); 20/85; Pres Church Yth Grp; VP 4-H; VP FFA; School Play; Mgr(s); Hon Roll; Bsktbl; Sftbl; Vllybl; Keystone Farmer Degree 87; Chapter Degree 85; Greenhand Degree 84; Penn ST U; Ag Educ.

KIMMEL, MICHELE; Connellsville Area SR HS; Normalville, PA; (2); VP Church Yth Grp; GAA; Office Aide; Pep Clb; Teachers Aide; Rep Stu Cncl; Cheerleading; Var Sftbl; Var Capt Vllybl; High Hon Roll; Presdntl Phy Fit Awd 86; U Pittsburgh; Anesthslgy.

KIMMEL, MISSY; Nativity BVM; St Clair, PA; (3); Nwsp Rptr; Rep Frsh Cls; Rep Soph Cls; JV Bsktbl; Var L Vllybl; Stu Cncl Awd 85-87; Tchr.

KIMMICK, AMY; Greater Johnstown Vo Tech Schl; Johnstown, PA; (3); 1/300; Pep Clb; VICA; Rep Stu Cncl; High Hon Roll; NHS; Ntl Merit Ltr; Exchng Stu Schlrshp 87.

KIMPEL, SAMANTHA; Kennedy Christian HS; Farmdale, OH; (4); 23/98; Pres Church Yth Grp; Mrchg Band; School Play; High Hon Roll; NEDT Awd; Pres Schlr; Drama Clb; French Clb; Latin Clb; J A Garfield Schlrshp To Hiram Coll 87; PA Jr Acad Of Sci Awd 85; Hiram Coll; Art Hstry.

KINARD, BRIAN; Central York SR HS; York, PA; (4); 10/218; Trs Church Yth Grp; German Clb; Varsity Clb; Yrbk Sprt Ed; Var L Ftbl; Im Wt Lftg; High Hon Roll; Lion Awd; NHS; AFROTC Schlrshp 87; VA Tech; Engrng.

KINARD, MELISSA; Spring Grove SR HS; Spring Grove, PA; (3); 19/306; JA; Varsity Clb; Nwsp Ed-Chief; Nwsp Stf; JV Bsktbl; JV Crs Cntry; Var Trk; High Hon Roll; Hon Roll; NHS; Med.

KINBACK, RITA; Abington Heights HS; Clarks Green, PA; (3); 1/292; Cmnty Wkr; Nwsp Stf; Ed Yrbk Stf; Lit Mag; Rep Stu Cncl; NHS; Val; Scholastic Bowl; Hon Roll; PA JR Acad Sci 1st Awd Rgnls & STS 86; ACL & NJCL Ntl Latin Exam Summa Cum Laude 85-87; Bk Awd; Pre-Med.

KINCAIDBEST, EDWARD; Valley View HS; Blakely, PA; (2); #19 In Class; Boy Scts; Church Yth Grp; Science Clb; School Play; Stu Cncl; Bsktbl; Vllybl; Hon Roll; Bus.

KINDEL, VALERIE; Brookville Area HS; Brookville, PA; (3); 4/150; Church Yth Grp; German Clb; Chorus; School Musical; Stat Bsktbl; Hon Roll; Jr NHS.

KINDER, JENNIFER M; Northeastern SR HS; Mt Wolf, PA; (3); Trs Church Yth Grp; Chorus; Concert Band; Jazz Band; Mrchg Band; School Musical; Yrbk Stf; Rep Jr Cls; Hon Roll; NHS; Hlth.

KINDIG, SCOTT; Central York HS; York, PA; (3); 18/245; Church Yth Grp; Ski Clb; Varsity Clb; Rep Frsh Cls; Rep Soph Cls; Var Co-Capt Wrstlng; Hon Roll; NHS; York Rot Clb Stu Month 87; IN Arts Awd Outstndng Jr 87; PIAA Dist III Sec Wrstlng Cham 87; Engr.

KINDLE, KATHLEEN; Lincoln HS; Ellwood City, PA; (3); #31 In Class; Drama Clb; Key Clb; Spanish Clb; SADD; Y-Teens; Chorus; Church Choir; School Musical; Hon Roll; NHS; OH Nrthrn U; Pre Law.

KINDON, MATTHEW; South Western HS; Hanover, PA; (2); 29/252; Cmnty Wkr; VP 4-H; Key Clb; Mgr Ftbl; Mgr(s); Trk; 4-H Awd; Hon Roll; Prfct Atten Awd; Elem Ed.

KINDRED, TRICIA; Yough HS; Lowber, PA; (3); FBLA; Pep Clb; Band; Chorus; Concert Band; Mrchg Band; Mgr(s); Mat Maids; Score Keeper; Hon Roll; Acctng.

KINDYA, ANDREW; United HS; Johnstown, PA; (4); 6/158; Computer Clb; Ski Clb; Stat Bsktbl; Ftbl; High Hon Roll; Hon Roll; Prfct Atten Awd; Penn ST; Engrng.

KING, AMY; Waynesburg Central HS; Waynesburg, PA; (4); 16/144; Pres Camera Clb; Trs French Clb; Office Aide; Chorus; Stu Cncl; Stat Trk; NHS; Church Yth Grp; Mu Alpha Theta; Natl Beta Clb; February Girl Of Month & Sr Attendant At Cinderella Ball 87; Stage Hand Vocalist 86-87; Alderson-Broaddus Coll.

KING, APRIL; Blackhawk HS; Beaver Falls, PA; (4); 15/270; Am Leg Aux Girls St; French Clb; Symp Band; Nwsp Ed-Chief; Yrbk Stf; Var L Crs Cntry; Var L Trk; High Hon Roll; Hon Roll; Kiwanis Awd; Duqesne Comptv Schlrshp 87; Seton Athl Awd Crs Cntry 86; Duquesne U; Phrmcy.

KING, BETSY; Mercyhurst Preparatory Schl; Erie, PA; (4); 39/160; Church Yth Grp; JCL; Yrbk Phtg; Yrbk Stf; Pres Frsh Cls; Pres Jr Cls; Stu Cncl; Im Ftbl; Im Vllybl.

KING, BRENDA; Dallas SR HS; Dallas, PA; (3); Art Clb; Cmnty Wkr; Stage Crew; Yrbk Stf; Hon Roll; Gold Key Wnnr Schltc Art Awds & Top Stu Awd Outstndng Schltc Achvt Art I 86-87; Dallas SH Art Shw 87.

KING, BRIAN; Mc Dowell HS; Erie, PA; (4); 31/599; German Clb; High Hon Roll; Hon Roll; $4000 Acadc Schlrsph-Gannon U 87; 1st Pl-Physcs-Lcl JETS Tm Comptn 87; Gannon U; Comp Sci.

KING, CURT; Plymouth Whitemarsh HS; Conshohocken, PA; (3); Bsbl; Ftbl; Trk; Wt Lftg; Prfct Atten Awd; Mrn Bio.

KING, DAVID; Apollo-Ridge HS; North Apollo, PA; (4); Math Clb; Varsity Clb; Concert Band; Rep Stu Cncl; Ftbl; Trk; Wt Lftg; Wrstlng; High Hon Roll; Rotary Awd.

KING, DEBORAH; Dover Area HS; Dover, PA; (4); 10/270; VP JA; Acpl Chr; Chorus; School Musical; Var Capt Cheerleading; High Hon Roll; NHS; Ntl Merit Ltr; PA ST U.

KING, DONALD; Monessen HS; Monessen, PA; (4); 4/93; Drama Clb; School Play; Variety Show; Nwsp Ed-Chief; Yrbk Ed-Chief; VP NHS; French Clb; Band; High Hon Roll; Carl Ann Naccarato Schlrshp, Waynesburg Hnr Schlrshp 87; Waynesburg Coll; Comm.

KING, ED; Mechanicsburg Area HS; Mechanicsburg, PA; (3); 58/338; Bsbl; Bowling; Hon Roll; Bus Admn.

KING, FRANKLIN; Montgomery Area HS; Montgomery, PA; (3); JV Var Ftbl; Wt Lftg; JV Var Wrstlng; Hon Roll; Bio.

KING, GREGORY; Devon Preparatory Schl; Bryn Mawr, PA; (3); 13/46; Church Yth Grp; Computer Clb; Ski Clb; Var Bsktbl; Var Trk; Hon Roll; NEDT Awd; Law.

KING, GWEN; Du Bois Area HS; Luthersburg, PA; (2); 8/327; Church Yth Grp; Varsity Clb; Variety Show; Pres Soph Cls; Rep Stu Cncl; Var L Crs Cntry; Var L Trk; High Hon Roll; Hon Roll; NHS; Nice Kid Awd 85-86.

KING, JAMES; Saucon Valley HS; Bethlehem, PA; (2); Band; Chorus; Concert Band; Jazz Band; Mrchg Band; Orch; School Musical; School Play; Swing Chorus; JP Sousa Awd; Hugh O'brien Youth Foundation 84; WHEATON Conservatory Of Music.

KING, JANE; Riverview HS; Oakmont, PA; (2); 2/104; French Clb; Key Clb; Band; Concert Band; Jazz Band; Mrchg Band; Nwsp Stf; High Hon Roll; NEDT Awd; Bio.

KING, JASON; Belle Vernon Area HS; Fayette City, PA; (3); Church Yth Grp; JV Ftbl; Hon Roll; Prfct Atten Awd; Asst Coach Fayette City Midget Ftbl 86.

KING, JENNIFER; Wissahickon HS; Gwynedd Valley, PA; (3); Church Yth Grp; Keywanettes; Chorus; Bus.

KING, JESSICA; Southmoreland SR HS; Everson, PA; (4); 20/230; Church Yth Grp; Exploring; French Clb; VICA; Church Choir; Trk; French Hon Soc; Hon Roll; Prfct Atten Awd; Westmoreland Cnty CC Schlrshp 87-88; Pres Acdmc Fit Awd 87; WCCC; Acctnt.

KING, JOHN; Living Word Acad; Leola, PA; (1); Church Yth Grp; Chorus; School Musical; Yrbk Stf; JV Bsbl; NHS; Character Awd 86.

KING, JOHN E; East HS; West Chester, PA; (4); 18/397; Political Wkr; Concert Band; Lit Mag; JV Crs Cntry; JV Socr; JV Trk; Hon Roll; NHS; Ntl Merit SF; Stu Of The Mnth 86; Eastern Coll.

KING, KATHLEEN; Fort City JR SR HS; Vandergrift, PA; (3); 14/150; Key Clb; SADD; High Hon Roll; Hon Roll; Eclgy.

KING, KEITH; Freeport Area SR HS; Freeport, PA; (2); 50/202; JV Ftbl; Hon Roll; Pittsburgh U; Elec Engr.

KING, KRISTEN H; Dover Area HS; Dover, PA; (4); 19/239; Church Yth Grp; Girl Scts; Red Cross Aide; Band; Chorus; Church Choir; Concert Band; High Hon Roll; Hon Roll; NHS; Christa Mc Auliffe Schlrshp Fund York Co 87; Semi Fnlst For PA Christa Mc Aulffie Schlrshp 87; Shippensburg U Of PA; Chem Edu.

KING, LEIGH A; Beaver Falls SR HS; Beaver Falls, PA; (3); 31/170; AFS; VP Church Yth Grp; Radio Clb; Prfct Atten Awd; Pblc Reltns.

KING, LISA; Center HS; Aliquippa, PA; (3); Latin Clb; Spanish Clb; Nwsp Rptr; Nwsp Stf; Yrbk Rptr; Yrbk Stf; Off Stu Cncl; Hon Roll; NHS; Church Yth Grp; Ntl Hnr Roll 87; Hampton U; TV Media.

KING, LORI; Lakeland JR-SR HS; Olyphant, PA; (3); 25/136; French Clb; Nwsp Stf; VP Frsh Cls; VP Soph Cls; Stat Bsktbl; Var Sftbl; Var L Trk; Hon Roll; Air Frc ROTC; Aeronaut Engr.

KING, LORI; Steel Valley HS; Munhall, PA; (3); 3/216; Art Clb; VP FBLA; VP JA; Tennis; Wt Lftg; High Hon Roll; NHS; Drwng Hung-Cptl Bldng-Hrrsbrg 87; The Cooper Union; Arch.

KING, LYNN; St Benedict Acad; Erie, PA; (3); 18/53; Church Yth Grp; Drama Clb; Exploring; Model UN; Q&S; Chorus; Color Guard; School Musical; Variety Show; Yrbk Stf; Edinboro U; Comms.

KING, MICHAEL L; Dover Area HS; Dover, PA; (4); 47/236; Varsity Clb; JV Bsbl; Var L Bsktbl; Var L Crs Cntry; JV Ftbl; Var L Tennis; High Hon Roll; Hon Roll; Penn ST; Bus.

KING, MICHELE KAY; Northeastern HS; Manchester, PA; (3); Church Yth Grp; Cmnty Wkr; FCA; Math Clb; Red Cross Aide; Ski Clb; Hon Roll; Central Penn Bus Schl; Accntng.

KING, MICHELLE; Brookville Area HS; Brookville, PA; (2); 4-H; French Clb; FTA; Acpl Chr; Chorus; School Musical; Bsktbl; High Hon Roll; Hon Roll; Jr NHS; Grove City Coll.

KING, MICHELLE; State College SR HS; Pennsylvna Frnc, PA; (2); Church Yth Grp; Hosp Aide; Acpl Chr; Chorus; Church Choir; Im Gym; Hon Roll; Awd Trngn All Assgnmnts For Eng; Pwr Of Paws Awd; PA ST; Eng.

KING, NIKKI; Neshaminy HS; Langhorne, PA; (3); 62/780; Chorus; Rep Frsh Cls; Trs Soph Cls; Trs Jr Cls; Trs Sr Cls; Stat Bsktbl; JV Fld Hcky; Var Powder Puff Ftbl; JV Sftbl; Stat Wrstlng.

KING, PAMELA; Pocono Mountain HS; Long Pond, PA; (4); 31/296; Pep Clb; SADD; Variety Show; Off Sr Cls; L Var Cheerleading; Var JV Trk; Hon Roll; Pres Jr NHS; JA; Service Clb; Wnnr Creatve Prrmng Arts Awd JR Miss Pgnt 86; Knghts Columbs Schlrshp Wnnr 87; Boston U; Intl Rltns.

KING, PETER; Hempfield Area SR HS; Greensburg, PA; (4); 65/692; JV Bsktbl; Stat Ftbl; Stat Trk; High Hon Roll; Hon Roll; VP Jr NHS; Rotary Awd; Spanish NHS; Hnr Rll-Math Assn Of Amer Tst 87; Penn ST U; Elec Engrng.

KING, RENEE N; Liberty HS; Bethlehem, PA; (4); 38/390; Girl Scts; Scholastic Bowl; Band; Chorus; School Musical; Yrbk Stf; Hon Roll; NHS; Concert Band; Mrchg Band; WA Coll 1782 Scty Schlrshp 87-88; WA Coll George Washington Schlr Schlrshp 87-88; WA Coll; Bio.

KING, RICHARD A; Ringgold HS; Eighty Four, PA; (4); Boy Scts; Cmnty Wkr; Hon Roll; Prfct Atten Awd; Eagle Scout 87; Penn ST U; Elec Engrng.

KING, ROB; Connellsville Area SR HS; Connellsville, PA; (2); Boy Scts; Jazz Band; Mrchg Band; Symp Band; VP L Swmmng; God Cntry Awd; Hon Roll.

KING III, RUDOLPH E; West Catholic HS; Philadelphia, PA; (3); Boy Scts; CAP; Computer Clb; Band; Drill Tm; Stage Crew; Im Bsktbl; Var Ftbl; Score Keeper; Acctng.

KING, SAMUEL T; Big Spring HS; Shippensburg, PA; (3); 12/268; Hon Roll; Outstndg Indus Arts Awd 87; Hnr Cert Scholar 85-87; Hnr Stu Pin 85-86; Crmlgy.

KING, SHELLI; Butler Area SR HS; Butler, PA; (3); Church Yth Grp; Office Aide; Spanish Clb; Varsity Clb; Drill Tm; Mrchg Band; Rep Stu Cncl; Score Keeper; Tennis; Hon Roll; Wnr UOL Ed Cmsn Essay Cntst 85; Hlth.

KING, STANLEY; Butler Area SR HS; Renfrew, PA; (3); Spanish Clb; Rep Stu Cncl; Hon Roll; Acad Achiev Awd 87; Jrnlsm.

KING, STEPHEN; Sun Valley HS; Media, PA; (4); 27/310; Scholastic Bowl; Pres Band; Pres Capt Mrchg Band; School Musical; Nwsp Stf; Pres Jr NHS; Lion Awd; Pres Concert Band; Jazz Band; Pep Band; All-ST Band 86; All-Eastern Band 87; Dist & Rgnl Band 85-87; Drexel U; Mech Engnrng.

KING, STEPHEN; Tunkhannock Area HS; Tunkhannock, PA; (3); Boy Scts; Church Yth Grp; Letterman Clb; Ski Clb; Band; Concert Band; Var Ftbl; Trk; Var Wt Lftg; 1st Degree Black Belt Hapkido & Tae Kwon Do 85; Elec Engrng.

KING, STEVE; Franklin HS; Polk, PA; (4); 43/217; French Clb; L Band; L Concert Band; L Jazz Band; L Mrchg Band; L Pep Band; L High Hon Roll; US Steelwrkrs Schlrshp, Hnrs Schlrshp 87; Edinboro U Of PA; Comp Sci.

KING, TERESA ANN; Ford City HS; Ford City, PA; (3); Church Yth Grp; Dance Clb; Drama Clb; FBLA; Chorus; Rep Frsh Cls; Rep Soph Cls; Cheerleading; Vllybl; Chrldng Awd 85; Fshn.

KING, TERRY; Schenley HS; Pittsburgh, PA; (2); Drm & Bgl; JV Bsktbl; L Swmmng; JV Var Vllybl; Sociolgy.

KING, TIM; Union HS; Rimersburg, PA; (2); 2/80; Aud/Vis; Chess Clb; Computer Clb; Golf; High Hon Roll; Hon Roll; Prfct Atten Awd; Church Yth Grp; French Clb; Bsbl; Chamber Commerce Design Awd 1st Pl 85; Memorial Day Svc Prog 85; Prog For Acad Talentd Kindgrtn-87; Computer Sci.

KING, TRACI; Dover Area HS; Dover, PA; (3); 21/270; Church Yth Grp; Teachers Aide; Varsity Clb; Chorus; School Musical; Yrbk Stf; Cheerleading; Hon Roll; NHS; Frnch Awd; Shippensburg U; Accntng.

KING, TRACIE; Otto-Elared JR-SR HS; Cuba, NY; (4); 13/92; Pep Clb; Varsity Clb; Chorus; Yrbk Stf; Pom Pon; Trk; Hon Roll; NHS; Deans Schlrshp 87-88; Amer Govt & Ecnmcs Awd 86; Daemen Coll; Physcl Thrpy.

KING, TUSHA; Northwestern HS; Astabula, OH; (4); Yrbk Stf; Bsktbl; Trk; Vllybl; Hon Roll; Math Awd 83; Pres Ftns Awd 83; Schl Ltr Awds 82-87; Manor JC; Psych.

KING, VENUS; Northeastern SR HS; Manchester, PA; (3); JA; Ski Clb; Chorus; Stage Crew; Lit Mag; Var Capt Cheerleading; Hon Roll; Air Force; Teaching.

KING, WENDEL L; Lancaster Mennonite HS; Cochranville, PA; (3); Pres Church Yth Grp; Drama Clb; FFA; Capt Varsity Clb; Var Capt Bsbl; Var Capt Crs Cntry; Var Capt Socr; Hon Roll; Messiah; Bus Mngmt.

KINGAN, GARY A; Jefferson-Morgan HS; Clarksville, PA; (4); 27/97; Ski Clb; Yrbk Stf; Hon Roll; Air Force.

KINGHAM, JENNIFER; Strath Haven HS; Swarthmore, PA; (4); Cmnty Wkr; Ski Clb; Fld Hcky; Lcrss; Socr; Hnr Rll 86-87; Widdner; Mrn Blgy.

KINGIG, SCOTT; Central York HS; York, PA; (3); 18/245; Church Yth Grp; Ski Clb; Varsity Clb; Rep Frsh Cls; Rep Soph Cls; Wrstlng; Hon Roll; NHS; Hnr Mntn Top 100 PA Wrstlrs 86; Sectnl Wrstlng Chmpn 87; Ind Arts Awd Centrl Yrk 87.

KINGSLEY, CYNTHIA; Villa Maria Academy; Jeffersonville, PA; (3); 24/98; Art Clb; Cmnty Wkr; Hosp Aide; JA; Off Service Clb; SADD; Stage Crew; Lit Mag; French Hon Soc; Hon Roll; Selected For Town Mtng On Tomorrow 86; Psych.

KINKAID, SUSAN; Governor Mifflin HS; Reading, PA; (3); VP Pres Key Clb; Stage Crew; Jr NHS; Northland Coll; Cnsrvtn Law.

KINLEY, TAMMY; Bishop Mc Cort HS; Johnstown, PA; (3); 40/155; French Clb; Girl Scts; Hosp Aide; Pep Clb; School Musical; High Hon Roll; Hon Roll; NHS; Chorus; Slvr Awd Girl Sctng 85; 200 Hr Awd Cndy Strpng.

KINNAN, MARCI; Saltsburg JR SR HS; Clarksburg, PA; (2); 11/100; Teachers Aide; VP Frsh Cls; VP Soph Cls; Capt L Cheerleading; JV Sftbl; High Hon Roll; Hon Roll.

KINNEER, EARL; Connellsville SR HS; Connellsville, PA; (2); VP Church Yth Grp; Pres 4-H; Math Tm; 4-H Awd; Hon Roll.

KINNEY, KATHLEEN; Trinity HS; Mechanicsburg, PA; (2); French Clb; Pep Clb; Variety Show; Trk; High Hon Roll; Hon Roll; Schlstc Wrtng Awds Cert Merit 86-87; Cert Ntl Ed Dvlpmnt 86-87.

KINNEY, NANCY; Fort Cherry HS; Mcdonald, PA; (3); 16/167; Drama Clb; French Clb; Math Clb; Science Clb; Ski Clb; Varsity Clb; Chorus; L Capt Vllybl; High Hon Roll; NHS; Math Awd 85; Sawyer Schl; Trvl.

KINSEY, PAMELA LEE; Solanco HS; Paradise, PA; (4); 22/241; Sec Church Yth Grp; Band; Rep Soph Cls; Rep Jr Cls; Rep Sr Cls; JV Bsktbl; Var Capt Fld Hcky; High Hon Roll; Hon Roll; NHS; Artisans Coll, Chala Fmly Schlrshps, PA Hnrs Test 87; Millersville U; Pol Sci.

KINSINGER, JOSH; Turkeyfoot Valley Area HS; Addison, PA; (2); Church Yth Grp; Drama Clb; Library Aide; Ski Clb; Varsity Clb; Chorus; School Play; Sec Frsh Cls; Var Bsbl; Var Ftbl; Comp Engr.

KINSMAN, MICHELLE; Crestwood HS; Mountaintop, PA; (3); Cmnty Wkr; Library Aide; School Musical; School Play; Nwsp Rptr; Nwsp Stf; JV Fld Hcky; High Hon Roll; Jr NHS; NHS; Jrnlsm.

KINTER II, HERMAN; Newport HS; Newport, PA; (2); Quiz Bowl; JV Var Ftbl; Var Wt Lftg; Hon Roll; Prfct Atten Awd.

KINTNER, JENNIFER; Tunkhannock HS; Tunkhannock, PA; (2); 47/305; Pep Clb; Ski Clb; Off Stu Cncl; Cheerleading; Hon Roll.

KINTZER, BRAD; Millersburg Area HS; Millersburg, PA; (3); 22/63; Co-Capt Art Clb; Computer Clb; French Clb; Spanish Clb; SADD; Bsbl; Bsktbl; Ftbl; Golf; Hon Roll; Health.

KINZLER, FREDERICK; Frankford HS; Philadelphia, PA; (4); 2/395; Computer Clb; Mrchg Band; Nwsp Stf; Rep Stu Cncl; Var Bsbl; Capt Var Bowling; High Hon Roll; NHS; Prfct Atten Awd; Sal; Dr David F Maxwell Memrl Grnt 87; Geraldine & John Simons Awd 87; Assoc 13 Clb 87; Boston U; Comp Ci.

KINZLER, MICHELLE; Quigley HS; Baden, PA; (4); VP 4-H; French Clb; NFL; Pep Clb; Chorus; Powder Puff Ftbl; 4-H Awd; Comp Tech Of Pittsburgh; Trvl.

KIOUMOURTZIS, SANDRA; Warren Area HS; Warren, PA; (3); French Clb; Hosp Aide; Chorus; Orch; School Musical; Cit Awd; Hon Roll; Prfct Atten Awd; Clarion U PA; Elem Ed.

KIPA, PETER; Freedom HS; Bethlehem, PA; (3); 36/509; Spanish Clb; Im Bsbl; NHS; Penn ST; Engr.

KIPFERL, KELLY; Williamson JR-SR HS; Lawrenceville, PA; (3); Computer Clb; Var JV Bsktbl; L Trk; North Penn X-Mas Trnmnt MVP 86; Comp II Awd 87; Elec Engr.

KIPP, AMY L; Newport HS; Newport, PA; (2); 34/120; Church Yth Grp; Mrchg Band; Gym; Wt Lftg; Hon Roll; Shippensburg; Phys Ed.

KIPP, DIANE; Newport HS; Newport, PA; (3); 34/125; Church Yth Grp; FTA; Varsity Clb; Band; Concert Band; Drm Mjr(t); Mrchg Band; School Musical; JV Var Bsktbl; JV Var Fld Hcky; Home Ec Awd 84-85 & 86-87; Elem Ed.

KIPP, JAY; Juniata HS; Mifflintown, PA; (3); Church Yth Grp; SADD; Stage Crew; Var L Bsbl; Var L Bsktbl; Var L Ftbl; High Hon Roll; Hon Roll; NHS; Prfct Atten Awd; 1st Team & Hnrb Mntn All Star Ftbl 85-86; 2nd Team Bsktbl All Stars 86-87; 1st Team All Star Bsbl 87; Educ.

KIPP, RODNEY; Quakertown Community HS; Quakertown, PA; (3); 16/303; VP Church Yth Grp; Band; Concert Band; Jazz Band; Mrchg Band; School Play; Var JV Vllybl; High Hon Roll; Hon Roll; Jr NHS.

KIR, LAURIE; Uniontown Area HS; Uniontown, PA; (2); French Clb; Library Aide; Teachers Aide; High Hon Roll; Hon Roll.

KIRBY, BERNICE; Charleroi Area JR/Sr HS; Charleroi, PA; (4); 17/162; Pres Frsh Cls; VP Soph Cls; VP Jr Cls; VP Sr Cls; Rep Stu Cncl; Capt Var Swmmng; NHS; Pres Schlr; VP French Clb; Office Aide; Prm Queen, Chrch May Queen & Hmcmng Crt 86-87; Acadc All Am 87; Charthene Clb Grl Mth 86; Edinboro U PA; Bus Adm.

KIRBY, DENNIS P; Archbishop Ryan H S For Boys; Philadelphia, PA; (2); 2/354; JV Ftbl; High Hon Roll; Hon Roll; Pres Schlr; Bio, Spnsh, Theology Awd 86.

KIRBY, JOSEPH J; Archbishop Ryan H S For Boys; Philadelphia, PA; (4); 40/422; VP Trs Church Yth Grp; Exploring; French Clb; Ed Nwsp Rptr; Yrbk Stf; Im Bsktbl; Im Socr; Hon Roll; Crystal Test Tube Awd Chem; Allentown Coll; Acctg.

KIRBY, TONI; Brownsville Area HS; Fairbank, PA; (4); 10/200; VP Church Yth Grp; Intnl Clb; SADD; Band; Chorus; Church Choir; Rep Sr Cls; NHS; Drama Clb; Stu Of Mnth Jan 87; Chrstn Educ Awd 85-86; Yth Educ Assoc Clb 86-87; Penn ST U; Engrng.

KIRCH, JEFFREY D; Bethel Park HS; Bethel Park, PA; (4); Church Yth Grp; JA; High Hon Roll; NHS; U Of Pittsburgh; Engrng.

KIRCHHOFER, SEAN; Nazareth Area SR HS; Nazareth, PA; (3); Rptr Jr Cls; Stu Cncl; JV Bsbl; Hon Roll; Law.

KIRCHNER, BRYAN; Meyersdale Area HS; Meyersdale, PA; (4); 22/126; Letterman Clb; Spanish Clb; Varsity Clb; School Musical; Yrbk Stf; Bsbl; Ftbl; Wt Lftg; Wrstlng; Hon Roll; IN U PA; Elec Eng.

KIRCHNER, ERIC; Hempfield HS; Lancaster, PA; (3); 69/450; Key Clb; Socr; Var Wrstlng; High Hon Roll; Outstndng Wrstlng Awd 85-87; Bus Admin.

KIRCHNER, JEFFREY; Keystone Oaks HS; Pittsburgh, PA; (3); 1/288; Art Clb; Church Yth Grp; Cmnty Wkr; JV Bsktbl; Tennis; High Hon Roll; Hon Roll; NHS.

KIRCHNER, JILL; Bedford Area HS; Bedford, PA; (3); 49/204; FTA; Ski Clb; Chorus; VP Frsh Cls; VP Soph Cls; VP Jr Cls; Stu Cncl; Cheerleading; Sftbl; Hon Roll; Shpnsbrg U; Eleme D.

KIRCHNER, KEVIN; Hempfield HS; Greensburg, PA; (4); 250/693; Aud/Vis; Computer Clb; Service Clb; Im Wt Lftg; Hon Roll; USAF.

KIRIK, RICH; North East HS; North East, PA; (4); 4/142; Church Yth Grp; Letterman Clb; Q&S; Nwsp Sprt Ed; Var Wrstlng; NHS; Ntl Merit Ltr; Yrbk Phtg; Var Ftbl; Im Wt Lftg; Exchng Clb Yth Of Mnth 87; Gannon U Acadc Schlrshp 87; Wrstlng Awd/Hrdst Wrkr 87; Gannon U; Elec Engr.

KIRISH, ANASTASIA; Ambridge Area HS; Ambridge, PA; (3); Hst German Clb; Pep Clb; Band; Concert Band; Mrchg Band; Off Soph Cls; Off Jr Cls; Off Sr Cls; Sftbl; Trk; IN U; Phrmcy.

KIRK, JULIANN; Mc Keesport Area SR HS; White Oak, PA; (2); Hosp Aide; Band; Color Guard; Concert Band; Drm & Bgl; Mrchg Band; Symp Band; High Hon Roll; Hon Roll; Im Powder Puff Ftbl; Amer Lgn Awd Medal Hnr 85; Sci Fair 3rd Pl Engrng 86; Outstndng Stu All Sbjcts 87; Phrmcy.

KIRK, KENDRA; Haverford HS; Drexel Hill, PA; (3); 45/423; Rep Frsh Cls; Sec Soph Cls; Sec Jr Cls; Sec Sr Cls; JV Fld Hcky; Var Capt Lcrss; Swmmng; Hon Roll; NHS; Bus.

KIRK, LISA; Carmichaels Area HS; Carmichaels, PA; (2); Art Clb; Church Yth Grp; Pep Clb; Ski Clb; Spanish Clb; School Play; Rep Stu Cncl; Cheerleading; Pom Pon; JV Var Score Keeper; Hmcmng Attndnt 86.

KIRK, SAMUEL; Central Christian HS; Dubois, PA; (3); Boy Scts; Debate Tm; Exploring; Varsity Clb; Nwsp Sprt Ed; Nwsp Stf; Yrbk Stf; Pres Sr Cls; Rep Stu Cncl; L Var Bsbl; Accntng.

KIRK, TERRY; Frankford HS; Philadelphia, PA; (3); Drama Clb; Red Cross Aide; School Play; Cheerleading; Hon Roll; Med.

KIRK, THOMAS; Msgr Bonner HS; Drexel Hill, PA; (3); 43/255; Computer Clb; Model UN; Ski Clb; SADD; Varsity Clb; Rep Jr Cls; Var L Socr; JV Ftbl; Prfct Atten Awd; Rowing-3 V Let,Cath League Champs 85-87; Wald Affairs Clb 86-87; Natl French Cntst 87; Engrng.

KIRKLAND, MARK; Central HS; Philadelphia, PA; (3); 20/500; Math Clb; Math Tm; Hon Roll; Jr NHS; Barnwell Hon Pin 85; Indstrl Dsgn.

KIRKMAN, MICHELE; Brookville Area HS; Brookville, PA; (3); Pres Church Yth Grp; French Clb; Trs Band; Concert Band; Pep Band; Vllybl; Hon Roll; IN U Of PA.

KIRKPARICK, LYNN; Upper Moreland HS; Willow Grove, PA; (2); 76/242; Aud/Vis; Rep Stu Cncl; Trk; Hon Roll; Intr Dsgn.

KIRKPATRICK, AMY BETH; Bell Vernon Area HS; Belle Vernon, PA; (4); 128/270; Church Yth Grp; FBLA; FNA; Hosp Aide; Pep Clb; SADD; Chorus; Color Guard; Variety Show; Hon Roll; Cap 50 Hr Awd, Pin 100 Hr Svc Awd Hosp Vlntr 84-86; 2 Awds Med Intrst Clb JR Cordtr 85-86, Sec 86-87; Bradford Schl Of Bus; Legl Sec.

KIRKPATRICK, JOHN C; Delone Catholic HS; Westminster, MD; (4); 11/167; Boy Scts; Computer Clb; Model UN; Variety Show; Yrbk Bus Mgr; High Hon Roll; NHS; Pres Schlr; St Schlr; Cert Mock Trial Cmptn 86-87; Villanova; Elec Engrng.

KIRKPATRICK, PATRICIA; Bishop Guilfoyle HS; Altoona, PA; (4); 47/117; Church Yth Grp; Science Clb; SADD; Chorus; Variety Show; Rep Sr Cls; Rep Stu Cncl; Var L Sftbl; Var Capt Vllybl; Hon Roll; Blair Med Socty Aux Awd 87; Sftbl MVP SR Yr; U Of Pittsburgh; Phy Thrpy.

KIRKPATRICK, PAULA; Homer Center JR-SR HS; Lucernemines, PA; (4); 4/90; Church Yth Grp; Cmnty Wkr; Drama Clb; Sec Pres FBLA; Hosp Aide; Office Aide; Sec VP SADD; Teachers Aide; Acpl Chr; Band; Michael J Supinka Jr Mem Schlrshp, Band Boosters Schlrshp, Top 10 SR 87; Indiana U Of PA; Bus Educ.

KIRLIN, CRAIG; Pottsgrove HS; Stowe, PA; (4); 58/226; Chess Clb; Latin Clb; Pres Leo Clb; Varsity Clb; Ftbl; Wrstlng; Pres Acdmc Ftnss Awd 87; Nvl Elec Tech.

KIRLIN, KERRY; St Maria Goretti HS; Philadelphia, PA; (4); 182/384; Church Yth Grp; Dance Clb; Office Aide; Variety Show; Score Keeper; Hon Roll; Brandywine Coll; Travel/Trsm.

KIRSCH, DONNA; Northern Cambria HS; Spangler, PA; (3); 10/152; Drama Clb; Hosp Aide; Library Aide; NFL; Teachers Aide; Chorus; School Play; High Hon Roll; Hon Roll; NHS; Girls Ensmbl 85-87; Cnty Chorus Fest 85-87; Dist Chorus 1st Alt 86-87; Jrnlsm.

KIRSCH, GRETCHEN; Northern Cambria HS; Spangler, PA; (3); 34/159; Church Yth Grp; Computer Clb; French Clb; Chorus; High Hon Roll; Hon Roll; NHS; PA ST U; Psych.

KIRSCH, HEIDI; Northwestern HS; E Springfield, PA; (3); Drama Clb; Thesps; Chorus; Church Choir; School Musical; School Play; Stage Crew; Variety Show; Hon Roll; NHS.

KIRSCH, LINDA; Cambria Heights HS; St Benedict, PA; (4); Concert Band; Mrchg Band; Hon Roll; NEDT Awd; X-Ray Tech.

KIRSCH, PAULA; Northern Cambria HS; Nicktown, PA; (3); 1/152; Computer Clb; Library Aide; Chorus; Pres Frsh Cls; Rep Jr Cls; Bsktbl; Var L Trk; Var L Vllybl; High Hon Roll; NHS; IN U Of PA.

KIRSCHNER, JULIE; Harriton HS; Penn Valley, PA; (3); Church Yth Grp; Cmnty Wkr; Hosp Aide; Service Clb; Pres Temple Yth Grp; Mgr(s); Score Keeper; Vllybl.

KIRSHNER, JAMES; Connellsville Area SR HS; Connellsville, PA; (2); VP Chess Clb; CA U; Bus.

KIRWIN, COLLEEN; St Huberts HS; Philadelphia, PA; (3); 20/421; Stage Crew; Ed Yrbk Stf; Cheerleading; Hon Roll; NHS; Prfct Atten Awd; Med Tech.

KIS HALAS, KRISZTINA; Upper Merion Area SR HS; King Of Prussia, PA; (4); 32/285; French Clb; Math Tm; Chorus; Concert Band; Mrchg Band; School Musical; Powder Puff Ftbl; JV Tennis; JV Var Trk; Im Vllybl; Cert Merit PA Highr Ed Asst Agcy 87; Nalt Sci Olympiad 85-86; Pres Acadc Ftns Awds Pgm 87; U Of CA Berkeley; Astrnmy.

KISAK, MICHAEL; Shaler Area HS; Glenshaw, PA; (3); 48/486; Boy Scts; Ski Clb; Stage Crew; Var Bowling; Var Trk; Hon Roll; Lion Awd; U Pittsburgh; Engrng.

KISAMORE, MICHAEL; Susquehannock HS; New Freedom, PA; (2); 34/243; Boy Scts; Computer Clb; Stage Crew; Elec Engr.

KISCADDEN, JENNIFER JO; Cedar Crest HS; Lebanon, PA; (4); Pep Clb; VP Concert Band; Drill Tm; Drm Mjr(t); Flag Corp; Mrchg Band; Pep Band; Hon Roll; Dist Band 86; Hnr Bnqt 87; Millersville U; Soc Wrk.

KISER, KELLIE; Warren Area HS; Warren, PA; (3); Art Clb; Pres Church Yth Grp; Cmnty Wkr; Hosp Aide; Spanish Clb; Y-Teens; Acpl Chr; Chorus; Church Choir; School Musical; Slvr B Awd Schl 85; Art Inst Pittsburgh; Intr Dsgng.

KISH, BETH; Palmyra Area SR HS; Palmyra, PA; (4); 9/186; Hosp Aide; Var JV Tennis; NHS; Tnns Trphy-Tm Ldr 86-87; Outstndng Typst-Shrthnd Awd, Bus Clb Awd 86-87; Liberty U; Elem Ed.

KISH, GREG; Penn Trafford HS; Harrison Cty, PA; (3); 65/360; Chess Clb; FBLA; Ski Clb; Im Ftbl; Im Ice Hcky; High Hon Roll; Hon Roll; PA ST.

KISH, JOSEPH; Bishop Hafey HS; Freeland, PA; (3); Chess Clb; Ski Clb; Var L Bsbl; Var Ftbl; Hon Roll; Prfct Atten Awd; Bst Phys Ed Awd 86-87.

KISH, MONIQUE; Crestwood HS; Mountaintop, PA; (4); 80/231; Art Clb; FBLA; Science Clb; Ski Clb; SADD; Rep Sr Cls; Var Trk; High Hon Roll; Hon Roll; Cmmrcl Dsgn.

KISHBAUGH, SUSAN; Lakeview HS; Jackson Center, PA; (4); 11/125; Church Yth Grp; Exploring; Hosp Aide; Intnl Clb; Science Clb; Band; Concert Band; Mrchg Band; Pep Band; School Play; Gannon U Acad Schlrshp 87; Gannon U; Pdtrcn.

KISHBAUGH, WAYNE; Wyalusing Valley HS; Laceyville, PA; (4); Boy Scts; Pres Church Yth Grp; 4-H; FBLA; Pres Band; Church Choir; Mrchg Band; School Musical; Yrbk Stf; Sr Cls; Egl Sct 85; Gradtd Top Bus Stu In Cls 87; 4-H Awd Top Scorer-Archry 86; Air Force; CPA.

KISHEL, CAROLYN; Mid Valley HS; Dickson, PA; (3); Computer Clb; Drama Clb; French Clb; Chorus; Drill Tm; School Musical; School Play; Nwsp Rptr; Nwsp Stf; Hon Roll; Geisinger; Nrsng.

KISHEL, KIMBERLY; Brownsville Area HS; Allison, PA; (3); Am Leg Aux Girls St; Sec Church Yth Grp; Girl Scts; Ski Clb; SADD; Church Choir; Brownsville Area Cmnty Queen 86-87; Pst Wrthy Advsr 87; PA ST; Cmnctns.

KISHEL, SUSAN; Brownsville Area HS; Allison, PA; (3); Church Yth Grp; Girl Scts; Ski Clb; SADD; Church Choir; High Hon Roll; Hon Roll; Drftng.

KISIDAY, PAULETTE; Ambridge HS; Freedom, PA; (3); Church Yth Grp; Hosp Aide; Pep Clb; Red Cross Aide; Concert Band; Mrchg Band; Symp Band; Rep Jr Cls; Im Capt Cheerleading; Stat Score Keeper; Ldrshp Seminar 84-85.

KISKO, TERRY; Minersville Area HS; Tremont, PA; (3); #5 In Class; Spanish Clb; Nwsp Stf; Yrbk Stf; High Hon Roll; Hon Roll; NHS; Elem Ed.

KISLAN, THOMAS; Bishop Hafey HS; Harleigh, PA; (3); 13/113; Math Clb; Spanish Clb; Var L Bsbl; Var Bowling; Var Ftbl; Golf; High Hon Roll; Hon Roll; Spanish NHS; PA JR Acad Of Sci; Scranton Univ; Pre Med.

KISLOFF, MICHELLE; Woodland Hills HS; Pittsburgh, PA; (2); 1/222; Church Yth Grp; Dance Clb; Hosp Aide; Ski Clb; Acpl Chr; School Musical; Yrbk Stf; Rep Stu Cncl; JV Capt Cheerleading; High Hon Roll; 3rd Pl Slippery Rock Lang Comp French Grammar 86.

KISNER, CINDY; Freedom HS; Bethlehem, PA; (3); 94/486; Church Yth Grp; French Clb; Science Clb; Ski Clb; SADD; Var Fld Hcky; Hon Roll; Sci.

KISOW, CARL; West Allegheny HS; Mcdonald, PA; (3); Hon Roll; Elctrcn.

KISS, SUZANNE; W Allegheny HS; Oakdale, PA; (2); 12/230; Church Yth Grp; Spanish Clb; Off Stu Cncl; Capt Cheerleading; JV Sftbl; High Hon Roll; Hon Roll; Jr NHS; Penn ST; Phys Thrpy.

KIST, ANTHONY; Great Johnstown Area Vo Tech; Johnstown, PA; (3); Art Clb; Church Yth Grp; German Clb; Library Aide; VICA; Var JV Ftbl; Wt Lftg; High Hon Roll; Hon Roll; NHS; Ltr Cert Employablty 86; Mdcl Technlgy.

KIST, PATRICIA; Conemaugh Valley HS; Johnstown, PA; (3); 1/105; Am Leg Aux Girls St; Church Yth Grp; Drama Clb; French Clb; NFL; School Play; Stage Crew; Yrbk Stf; Jr NHS; NHS; Penn ST U; Dr.

KISTLER, CYNTHIA; Emmaus HS; Emmaus, PA; (4); 34/468; Hst Key Clb; Trs Soph Cls; Trs Jr Cls; Hst Sr Cls; Stu Cncl; JV Fld Hcky; Capt Vllybl; Jr NHS; NHS; Mgr(s); Outstndng Volntr Svc Awd 87; Svc Abv Slf Awd 87; Extra Currclr Actvts Awds 87; Dickinson Coll; Econ.

KISTLER, GRETA; Northwestern Lehigh HS; Kempton, PA; (3); 10/150; 4-H; Fld Hcky; Trk; High Hon Roll; NHS; Natl Schl Trffc Safety Pstr Pgm 86; Art Electv I Awd 85.

KISTLER, JENNIFER; Chambersburg Area SR HS; Chambersburg, PA; (2); Church Yth Grp; JCL; Latin Clb; Spanish Clb; Chorus; Orch; Symp Band; Off Soph Cls; Crs Cntry; Hon Roll.

KISTLER, JOYCE; Bishop Hafey HS; White Haven, PA; (3); Church Yth Grp; French Clb; Girl Scts; Hosp Aide; Key Clb; Ski Clb; Chorus; Crmnl Law.

KITA, SUSAN; Washington HS; Washington, PA; (3); Nwsp Stf; Yrbk Stf; JV Bsktbl.

KITCHEN, IVY; Uniontown Area HS; Uniontown, PA; (3); Pres Trs French Clb; SADD; Band; Flag Corp; Mrchg Band; Stu Cncl; French Hon Soc; High Hon Roll; Hon Roll; Slippery Rock; Accntng.

KITCHEN, MICHELE; Council Rock HS; Wash Cross, PA; (3); Church Yth Grp; Flag Corp; Yrbk Stf; Stu Cncl; Hon Roll; Bus.

KITHCART, RICHELLE; West Branch JR-SR HS; Grassflat, PA; (2); Pres Church Yth Grp; Girl Scts; Red Cross Aide; SADD; Band; Chorus; Church Choir; Mrchg Band; Pep Band; Drama Clb; Nrs.

KITNER, ANDY; West Perry HS; Shermansdale, PA; (4); 24/184; VP Church Yth Grp; French Clb; Varsity Clb; JCL; Capt Trk; Embry-Riddle Aero U; Aero Engr.

KITNER, TINA; Central SR HS; Emigsville, PA; (3); Sec Church Yth Grp; Hosp Aide; Library Aide; High Hon Roll; Hon Roll; NHS; York Coll; Nrsng.

KITTLE, AMY; Lake-Lehman HS; Shavertown, PA; (2); Ski Clb; Vllybl; Hon Roll; Jr NHS; Engrng.

KITTLE, KERRY; Bangor SR HS; Bangor, PA; (3); Computer Clb; Varsity Clb; Band; Nwsp Ed-Chief; Nwsp Sprt Ed; Lit Mag; Off Soph Cls; Off Jr Cls; VP Sr Cls; Var JV Fld Hcky; Jr Natl Hnr Soc; 3 Yrs Exec Cncl Stu Gvnmt; Comm.

KITZMILLER, CHARLES; Riverview HS; Oakmont, PA; (2); Church Yth Grp; Stat Bsktbl; Elec Engr.

KIZIS, JENNIFER; Wyoming Area HS; Exeter, PA; (3); 1/240; Art Clb; German Clb; Key Clb; Math Clb; Var Swmmng; Var Trk; Var Vllybl; High Hon Roll; NHS; HOBY Schlrshp Wnnr 86; Kings Coll Dscvry Pgm Schlrshp 87; Keystone Gms Vllybl Team 87; Arch.

KLAAS, AIMEE; Faith Community Christian Schl; Clairton, PA; (4); 5/29; Church Yth Grp; French Clb; Pep Clb; Chorus; Church Choir; Nwsp Rptr; Yrbk Rptr; Yrbk Stf; VP Stu Cncl; High Hon Roll; Meritorious Conduct Awd 86-87; Music.

KLACZAK, CAROLYN; Archbishop Wood-Girls HS; Warminster, PA; (3); 20/239; Exploring; Girl Scts; Hosp Aide; Math Tm; Spanish Clb; Stage Crew; Yrbk Stf; Hon Roll; Prfct Atten Awd; Church Yth Grp; Hnrb Mntn Schl Sci Fair 86; Silver Awd GS 85.

KLADIAS, PAULA; Center Area HS; Aliquippa, PA; (2); German Clb; Hon Roll; Prfct Atten Awd; Debate Team Awd 85; Bus Mgmt.

KLADNY, KIMBERLY; Freeport SR HS; Sarver, PA; (4); 17/167; Girl Scts; Hosp Aide; Chorus; Drill Tm; School Musical; Stage Crew; High Hon Roll; NHS; Evening Club Schlrshp 87; PTO Schlrshp 87; SLD Awd 86; Gannon U; Nrsng.

KLADNY, STEPHEN; Freeport HS; Sarver, PA; (3); 7/213; Band; Concert Band; Jazz Band; Mrchg Band; Pep Band; School Musical; Stage Crew; Symp Band; Yrbk Phtg; High Hon Roll; Engrng.

KLANCHAR, BILL; Mary Fuller Frazier HS; Perryopolis, PA; (3); VICA; VP Jr Cls; Wt Lftg; Hon Roll; Dirctrs List Auto Mech N Fayette Area Vo-Tech Schl 87; Dist 9 VICA Comptn Auto Svc Specl 87; ST Ldrs; Rosedale Tech Inst; Diesel Mech.

KLANICA, CHRIS; Kiski Area HS; Freeport, PA; (4); Pep Clb; SADD; Mrchg Band; Symp Band; High Hon Roll; Aud/Vis; Band; Chorus; Orch; Pep Band; Semper Fidelis Awd 87; IUP; Sfty Eng.

KLAPATCH, MARK; Valley View HS; Peckville, PA; (4); 12/200; Church Yth Grp; Spanish Clb; Coach Actv; Capt Crs Cntry; Trk; Vllybl; High Hon Roll; NHS; Rotary Awd; SOAR Schlrshp 87; PA ST U; Athltc Trning.

KLAPCHAR, SCOTT; Archbishop Ryan-Boys HS; Philadelphia, PA; (3); 149/413; Church Yth Grp; Im Bsktbl; Cert Of Awd For Engl 87; Cert Of Hnr For US Hist 87; Dstngshd Hrns & 2nd Hnrs 87; Shippensburg U; Law Enforcemnt.

KLAPKOWSKI, KRISTIN; Mc Guffy HS; Claysville, PA; (4); 3/200; Am Leg Aux Girls St; French Clb; Pep Clb; Varsity Clb; VP Soph Cls; Stu Cncl; Capt Cheerleading; NHS; Rotary Awd; Rep Jr Cls; Penn ST U; Lbrl Arts.

KLAPTHAR, BRYAN; Fort Le Boeuf HS; Waterford, PA; (3); 4/200; Chess Clb; Church Yth Grp; FCA; Var Wrstlng; High Hon Roll; JETS Awd; NHS; Rotary Yth Ldrshp Awd Wnnr 87; Engrng.

KLAPUT, MELANIE; Ford City HS; Ford City, PA; (3); 16/160; Key Clb; Concert Band; Mrchg Band; High Hon Roll; Hon Roll; NHS; Ecology.

KLATKA, SHERRI; Mahanoy Area HS; Mahanoy City, PA; (2); Drama Clb; French Clb; FHA; SADD; Chorus; Variety Show; Nwsp Stf; Trk; Hon Roll; NHS.

KLAUS, BRIAN; Council Rock HS; Richboro, PA; (3); 170/908; Boy Scts; Drama Clb; Pres Exploring; Mrchg Band; School Musical; School Play; Hon Roll; Concert Band; Pep Band; Symp Band; Eagle Scout 87; Penn ST U; Bus.

KLAUSMAN, ELIZABETH; General Mc Lane HS; Edinboro, PA; (3); 5/225; Church Yth Grp; German Clb; Model UN; Church Choir; Mrchg Band; Orch; Symp Band; High Hon Roll; NHS; Ntl Merit Ltr; PA Governs Schl For Arts Schlrsp 87; All Earsn Hnrs Band 87; PA All ST Band 86; Eng.

KLEBE, TIFFANY; Mohawk JR SR HS; New Castle, PA; (3); 1/170; Church Yth Grp; JCL; VP Trs Latin Clb; SADD; Band; Chorus; Concert Band; School Musical; Yrbk Sprt Ed; Stat Bsbl; Acdmc All Amer 84-87; Amer Chmcl Scty 86; Top Stu In Sci & Math 86; Chmcl Engrng.

KLEBES, HEIDI; Villa Maria Acad; Erie, PA; (4); Trs Sec Church Yth Grp; Ski Clb; Spanish Clb; VP Soph Cls; Rep Stu Cncl; Im Socr; Capt Tennis; Im Vllybl; Hon Roll; NHS; Dist X Dbls Chmpn-Tnns 85; Penn ST U; Htl, Rstrnt Mgmt.

KLEBSCH, CRAIG; Lancaster Catholic HS; Drumore, PA; (3); 1/195; Nwsp Ed-Chief; Rep Stu Cncl; Bausch & Lomb Sci Awd; High Hon Roll; NHS; Ntl Merit Ltr; Rotary Awd; Church Yth Grp; Intnl Clb; Model UN; USAF Awd Superior Proj Envrmntl Sci 87; Superior Certfctn Hist Proj Natl Level 87; Excllcne Phy IN U; Engrng.

KLECKNER, JACQUE; Lock Haven SR HS; Lock Haven, PA; (4); 2/242; Chess Clb; Pres Service Clb; Trs SADD; Trs Chorus; Capt Cheerleading; Cit Awd; High Hon Roll; Trs NHS; Prfct Atten Awd; St Schlr; Miss PA Natl Tnagr 87; Natl Josten Schlrshp Fnlst 87; Phi Delta Kappa Natl Schlrshp Awd 87; Penn ST U; Anthrplgy.

KLECKNER, JACQUELINE; B Reed Henderson HS; W Chester, PA; (3); Cmnty Wkr; Ski Clb; SADD; Var Cheerleading; Stat Lcrss; JV Socr; Var Tennis; Var Trk; Hon Roll; Jr NHS; Ed.

KLECKNER, JACQUELINE; Lockhaven SR HS; Lock Haven, PA; (4); 2/247; Pres Service Clb; Trs SADD; Trs Chorus; Trs Jr Cls; Trs Sr Cls; Rep Stu Cncl; Capt Cheerleading; Trs NHS; Sal; VFW Awd; Cntry III Ldrs Schlrshp 86; Jstns Fndtn & Phi Delta Kappa Schlrshp 87; Penn ST U; Anthrplgy.

KLECKNER, MICHELLE; Hazleton HS; Hazleton, PA; (2); Pep Clb; Service Clb; Band; Church Choir; Concert Band; Mrchg Band; Pep Band; Hon Roll.

KLECKNER, ZOE; Delaware County Christian Schl; Haverton, PA; (4); 2/73; Pres Soph Cls; Pres Jr Cls; Pres Sr Cls; Var Cheerleading; Capt Var Fld Hcky; Var Sftbl; NHS; Sal; Math Clb; Office Aide; US Army Rsrv Ntl Schlr/Athlt Awd 87; William & Mary.

KLEE, TERRI; Pleasant Valley JRSR HS; Brodheadsville, PA; (3); Pep Clb; Yrbk Rptr; Yrbk Stf; Jr Cls; Cheerleading; Vrsty Chrldg Coach Awd 85-86; Chrldg Spirit Awd 84-85; Elem Ed.

KLEIGLENG, MARIE; Amridge Area SR HS; Baden, PA; (3); Am Leg Aux Girls St; Church Yth Grp; Spanish Clb; Mrchg Band; School Musical; Symp Band; Off Jr Cls; Trs Stu Cncl; High Hon Roll; NHS; Math.

KLEIMAN, DAVID; Cheltenham HS; Elkins Pk, PA; (4).

KLEIN, CHRIS; Saltsbury JR SR HS; Saltsburg, PA; (1); FFA; Capt Ftbl; Var Trk; Var L Wrstlng; Hon Roll; Greenhnd Frmr Awd FFA 86-87; Grnd Chmpn Carcass Lamb 2N Cnty Fair 84; Penn ST; Ag Bus.

KLEIN, DENISE; Carmichaels Area HS; Nemacolin, PA; (3); 6/120; Spanish Clb; Band; Concert Band; Rep Jr Cls; Rep Stu Cncl; Gov Hon Prg Awd; High Hon Roll; Hon Roll; NHS; Pep Clb; Elem Ed.

KLEIN, ERICA; Springside Schl; Philadelphia, PA; (3); School Play; Yrbk Phtg; Yrbk Stf; Lit Mag; Im Lcrss; Hon Roll; NHS; Hghst Score In HS Amer HS Math Exam 86; Cum Laude Soc 87; Wellesley Bk Awd 87; Bus.

KLEIN, KAREN; Peters Twp HS; Mc Murray, PA; (4); 27/243; Dance Clb; Intnl Clb; VP Science Clb; Drill Tm; Gym; CC Awd; Pres Schlr; Rotary Awd; Church Yth Grp; Key Clb; Natl Schl Orch Awd 87; ST Regnl & Dist Orch PA 87; Valparaiso U; Mech Engr.

KLEIN, MICHAEL; Lower Moreland HS; Huntingdon Valley, PA; (3); FBLA; JV Bsbl; JV Bowling; JV Trk; Hon Roll; 5th Pl FBLA Meet 86; Law.

KLEINMEYER, ROBERT; Conemaugh Twp HS; Davidsville, PA; (3); 42/121; Church Yth Grp; Stu Cncl; Crs Cntry; Golf; Trk; Hon Roll; Recipient Of PA Free Entrprs Week Schlrshp 87; Bus Admin.

KLEINSAK, MICHELLE; Bishop Mc Devitt HS; Harrisburg, PA; (3); Dance Clb; Drama Clb; Service Clb; Ski Clb; Color Guard; School Play; Nwsp Stf; Engl.

KLEINSTUBER, ELLEN L; Lampeter-Strasburg HS; Lancaster, PA; (3); 11/148; Girl Scts; SADD; Varsity Clb; Concert Band; Drm Mjr(t); Mrchg Band; L Var Cheerleading; Hon Roll; NHS; Church Yth Grp; Rotary Clb Stu Of The Month 86.

KLEINTOP, JEFF; Pleasant Valley HS; Saylorsburg, PA; (2); 36/243; Band; Concert Band; Jazz Band; Mrchg Band; Pep Band; Cnsrvtn.

KLEIST, MELANIE; Mc Keesport Area HS; White Oak, PA; (2); Hst AFS; Library Aide; Office Aide; Speech Tm; Stu Cncl; Powder Puff Ftbl; JV Vllybl; High Hon Roll; Outstndng Stu Spanish II 86-87.

KLEIST, STACEY; Meadville Area HS; Meadville, PA; (4); Sec Frsh Cls; Capt Cheerleading; Hon Roll; U Of Pittsburgh.

KLEJKA, BERNADINE; Greensburg Central Catholic HS; Mt Pleasant, PA; (3); 32/240; Pres 4-H; JCL; Pep Clb; Ski Clb; Chorus; Powder Puff Ftbl; 4-H Awd; High Hon Roll; Hon Roll; NHS; Pre Med.

KLEMANS, JENIFER; Duquesne SR HS; Duquesne, PA; (3); 15/96; French Clb; Rep Stu Cncl; Cheerleading; Hon Roll; NHS; Trs Frsh Cls; 4-H Awd; Rotary Awd; Mdcl Technlgy.

KLEMER, JENNIFER; Elizabethtown Area HS; Elizabethtown, PA; (2); 29/281; Hosp Aide; Model UN; VP Thesps; Capt Flag Corp; Mrchg Band; School Play; Stage Crew; Rep Stu Cncl; Hon Roll; Ski Clb; Physcl Thrpy.

KLEMER, JOHN; Shenandoah Valley JR SR HS; Shenandoah, PA; (3); 1/79; VP Frsh Cls; Rep Soph Cls; Rep Stu Cncl; JV Bsktbl; Capt L Crs Cntry; Var L Trk; High Hon Roll; NHS; Acad All Amer Awd 85-87; Top Acad Mdl Awd JR Cls 86-87; Rochester Inst Tech; Biomed Cmp.

KLEMM, KIMBERLY; Academy HS; Erie, PA; (3); 24/226; Drama Clb; German Clb; Vllybl; Penn ST; Engl Lit.

KLEMM, LARRY; Northwestern HS; Albion, PA; (2); #18 In Class; Rep Frsh Cls; JV Bsktbl; Slippery Rock U; Electronics.

KLEMOW, DANIELLE; Hazleton HS; Hazleton, PA; (2); Drama Clb; Pres Pep Clb; Ski Clb; SADD; Temple Yth Grp; JV Cheerleading; High Hon Roll; 2nd Pl JR Acad Sci Awd, & USCA Natl Champ Top 10 Cheerldng 86-87; Pres Acdmc Ftnss Awd 85-87; Princeton; Law.

KLENOVICH, JANICE; Bethlehem Catholic HS; Bethlehem, PA; (4); 72/200; Red Cross Aide; Coach Actv; Fld Hcky; Mgr(s); Powder Puff Ftbl; Score Keeper; Hon Roll; Northampton Cnty CC; Reg Nrse.

KLEPFER, ZANDRA; Brookville Area HS; Sigel, PA; (3); 30/175; Trs Church Yth Grp; FTA; German Clb; Key Clb; Office Aide; Pep Clb; Varsity Clb; Chorus; JV Capt Cheerleading; Hon Roll; Educ.

KLEPPER, PAULA; Hatboro-Horsham SR HS; Hatboro, PA; (4); 65/266; Church Yth Grp; FCA; Natl Beta Clb; Pep Clb; Science Clb; Spanish Clb; SADD; Church Choir; Mrchg Band; Var Crs Cntry; J J Vanfleck Mem Awd 87; Presdntl Acadc Ftns Awd 87; Mrchng Band Awd 87; Manor JC; Bio.

KLEPPINGER, ALISON; Quakertown HS; Pennsburg, PA; (2); Band; Concert Band; Jazz Band; Orch; Mgr(s); Score Keeper; JV Sftbl; JV Vllybl; Hon Roll; NHS; PA ST; Phy Thrpst.

KLEPPINGER, FAITH; Parkland HS; Schnecksville, PA; (2); Aud/Vis; Band; Nwsp Stf; Yrbk Stf; Rep Stu Cncl; JV Sftbl; Hon Roll; Pres Acad Ftnss Awd 85-86; Stu Tutr 85-86; Capt-JR Schltc Scrmmg 83-86; Edtr Nswpr 87-88; Engl.

KLEPSER, CHERYL A; Port Allegany HS; Snyder, NY; (4); 1/110; Trs French Clb; Varsity Clb; Chorus; Concert Band; Drm Mjr(t); Mrchg Band; L Bsktbl; Bausch & Lomb Sci Awd; NHS; Ntl Merit SF; Amer Chmcl Soc 86; Engrng.

KLETZLI, NANCY M; South Side HS; Clinton, PA; (3); 7/140; Science Clb; Spanish Clb; Church Choir; Var Trk; Hon Roll; NHS; PA JR Acad Sci 2nd Pl Regnl Comp 87; Acad All Amer 86; Natl Sci Merit Awd 86-87; U Detroit; Biochem Rsrch.

KLEVANSKY, JON; Lock Haven SR HS; Lock Haven, PA; (3); Spanish Clb; Band; JV Bsktbl; JV Tennis; High Hon Roll; Hon Roll; NHS.

KLEVENE, VALERIE; Hazleton SR HS; Hazleton, PA; (2); Office Aide; Band; Concert Band; Mrchg Band; Hon Roll.

KLEYNOWSKI, RICHARD; Pittston Area HS; Pittston, PA; (3); 21/305; Computer Clb; Math Clb; Band; Concert Band; Jazz Band; Mrchg Band; High Hon Roll; NHS; Prfct Atten Awd; Acad All Amer 86; Pharmacy.

KLIAMOVICH, JIM; Lake-Lehman HS; Hunlock Creek, PA; (4); 32/165; Pres Ski Clb; Band; Jazz Band; Rep Stu Cncl; L Golf; Hon Roll; Kings Coll; Pre Med.

KLIBER, ALLISON; Cambridge Springs HS; Springboro, PA; (2); 1/106; Sec Pres 4-H; Trs Model UN; Pres Spanish Clb; Chorus; Church Choir; JV Bsktbl; High Hon Roll; NHS; Math Tm; HOBY Ldrshp Smnr Schlrshp 87; Dale Carnegie Crs Effctv Spkng & Hmn Rel Grad 87.

KLICK, KEITH; Fort Le Boeuf HS; Erie, PA; (2); Church Yth Grp; FCA; Ftbl; Trk; Wt Lftg; High Hon Roll; NHS; Pres Schlr; Physical Therpist.

KLIEN, JANICE; Abington Heights HS; Clarks Summit, PA; (3); 12/285; Color Guard; Mrchg Band; Trk; Capt Twrlr; Hon Roll; NHS; Dist Wnnr US Army Rsrv Natl Essy Cntst 86; Cert Achvt Natl Hstry Day 86; Bus Adm.

KLIMCHAK, SUSAN; Center HS; Aliquippa, PA; (3); Am Leg Aux Girls St; Church Yth Grp; Latin Clb; Varsity Clb; Yrbk Stf; Off Stu Cncl; Var JV Bsktbl; JV Sftbl; Var Trk; High Hon Roll.

KLIMEK, BRIAN; Neshaminy HS; Feasterville, PA; (4); 4/680; Math Clb; Math Tm; Ski Clb; Nwsp Stf; Im Bsktbl; Im Ftbl; Var Trk; High Hon Roll; NHS; Rotary Awd; Sectys Schlrshp 87; 1st Plc Amrcn HS Math Tst 86-87; Sci Awd 84-87; Lafayette Coll; Bus.

KLIMEK, JOHN; Crestwood HS; Mountaintop, PA; (4); 4-H; Key Clb; Math Clb; Science Clb; 4-H Awd; High Hon Roll; Hon Roll; JETS Awd; NEDT Awd; Pres Schlr; Natl Eductnl Dvlpmnt Tst Awd 83-85; Prsdntl Acdmc Ftnss Awd 87; Times Ldr Nwspaper Carriers Awd 87; PA ST U; Engnrng.

KLIMPKE, HEIDI; Butler Area HS; Butler, PA; (3); French Clb; Hosp Aide; Concert Band; Mrchg Band; Orch; Symp Band; Im Bsktbl; Hon Roll; Butler County JR Miss Fnlst 87.

KLINE, AMY; The Agnes Irwin Scshl; Berwyn, PA; (3); Church Yth Grp; VP Dance Clb; Drama Clb; Chorus; Nwsp Stf; Ed Lit Mag; Rep Stu Cncl; Fld Hcky; Var Lcrss; Hon Roll; Implse Prz Best Poetry 87; Pres Clsrm Yng Amer 87.

KLINE, ANGELA; Waynesboro Area HS; Waynesboro, PA; (4); 14/336; Yrbk Stf; Var L Bsktbl; Var L Trk; High Hon Roll; NHS; Waynesboro Coll Clb Schlrshp 87; WAEA Schlrshp 87; Spnsh Awd 87; Penn ST U; Spcl Ed.

KLINE, BARB; St Marys Area HS; Kersey, PA; (4); 56/279; Concert Band; Jazz Band; Mrchg Band; NHS; SR IN U 9 Bnd 86; IN U; Crmnlgy.

KLINE, BARBARA; Hempfield SR HS; Greensburg, PA; (3); Debate Tm; Hosp Aide; VP Latin Clb; NFL; Political Wkr; Speech Tm; Orch; Hon Roll; Concert Orch Mistress 86-87; Shenendoah Coll; Music.

KLINE, BARBARA; William Allen HS; Allentown, PA; (3); Leo Clb; Church Choir; Fld Hcky; Intnl Clb; Mgr.

KLINE, BETH; Eastern HS; Wrightsville, PA; (4); Concert Band; Jazz Band; Mrchg Band; Orch; Pep Band; Yrbk Stf; Hon Roll; JP Sousa Awd; Bus Bkkpng Awd 87; PA Ambssdr Of Music 87; Shippensburg U; Accntng.

KLINE, BETH; General Mc Lane HS; Edinboro, PA; (3); German Clb; Band; Mrchg Band; Trk; Vllybl; Hon Roll; Ltrd Vllybl Jr Yr 86-87; PA ST; Bus.

KLINE JR, CRAIG; Holy Name HS; Shillington, PA; (3); Church Yth Grp; Rep Soph Cls; Pres Jr Cls; Pres Sr Cls; Pres Stu Cncl; Var L Bsktbl; U DE; Bus Adm.

KLINE, DALE; Spring Grove HS; Thomasville, PA; (3); Aud/Vis; Varsity Clb; JV Crs Cntry; Var L Trk; US Navy; Data Systems Tech.

KLINE, DAVID CORY; Pocono Mountain HS; Canadensis, PA; (3); VP Church Yth Grp; ROTC; JV Crs Cntry; Var Wrstlng; Prfct Atten Awd; KS ST Chmpn, Sctnl Chmpn Rifle Tm 87; Natl 4 Pos Tm Chmpn 86; Penn ST.

KLINE, DEBRA; Glendale JR SR HS; Irvona, PA; (3); 12/70; Art Clb; Library Aide; Red Cross Aide; Science Clb; SADD; Nwsp Rptr; Nwsp Sprt Ed; Hon Roll; Voice Dem Awd; Clarion U Of PA; Acctng.

KLINE, DIANE; Mahanoy Area HS; Mahanoy City, PA; (4); 10/110; VP Art Clb; Drama Clb; Spanish Clb; Band; Chorus; Capt Drill Tm; Nwsp Stf; Ed Yrbk Rptr; Trk; NHS; Central PA Bus Schl; Off Comm.

KLINE, EMILY; Solebury Schl; Lambertville, NJ; (3); Office Aide; Variety Show; Lit Mag; Rep Frsh Cls; High Hon Roll; PA Ballet Smr Pgm 85; Latn, Engl, Hstry Awds 86; Acadmc Cmmtte 86.

KLINE, FRANCESCA; Lock Haven SR HS; Lock Haven, PA; (4); 24/247; Spanish Clb; Trs Band; Chorus; Trs Concert Band; Jazz Band; Trs Mrchg Band; Orch; Hon Roll; JP Sousa Awd; Church Yth Grp; Bertha Mastellar Schlrshp 87; Kappa Kappa Psi-Band 86; Miss 4th July-Clntn Cnty 85; Lock Haven U; Mdcl Tech.

KLINE, HEIDI; Eisenhower HS; Russell, PA; (3); Hosp Aide; Key Clb; Office Aide; Teachers Aide; Band; Chorus; Concert Band; Jazz Band; Mrchg Band; Hon Roll; Dist Band 84-86; Regnl Band 85-86; Sound Amer Hnr Band 87; Spec Ed.

KLINE, JEFF; Danville Area HS; Danville, PA; (3); Math Teacher.

KLINE, JENNIFER; Saucon Valley SR HS; Hellertown, PA; (4); 13/138; Church Yth Grp; 4-H; Math Clb; Math Tm; Science Clb; Spanish Clb; Teachers Aide; School Musical; High Hon Roll; NHS; PA ST U; Gentc Engr.

KLINE, JULIE MARIE; Northern Cambria HS; Nicktown, PA; (4); 18/135; VP Drama Clb; Chorus; Nwsp Ed-Chief; Nwsp Rptr; Yrbk Stf; Var Capt Bsktbl; Twrlr; High Hon Roll; Hon Roll; NHS; Tribune-Democrat Schlstc Jrnlst Awd, IN Dist Hstry Day 1st Pl Indvdl Prjct Awd 87; Lock Haven U; Jrnlsm.

KLINE, KELLIE; Greencastle-Antrim HS; Greencastle, PA; (3); High Hon Roll; Hon Roll.

KLINE, KELLY; Berwick HS; Nescopeck, PA; (4); Pres Aud/Vis; FBLA; Chorus; Stage Crew; Nwsp Phtg; Nwsp Stf; Fld Hcky; Hon Roll; Bus Stu Mnth 87; Murray D Watts Acctng, Bus Law, Mgmt Awd 87; Zippy Food Bag Annl Schlrshp 87; Keystone JC; Fshn Merch.

KLINE, KELLY; Oley Valley HS; Reading, PA; (3); 40/144; School Musical; Nwsp Phtg; JV Var Sftbl; Hon Roll; Photo.

KLINE, KIMBERLY; Knoch HS; Butler, PA; (4); Pres Computer Clb; FBLA; FHA; JA; Stage Crew; Yrbk Stf; High Hon Roll; NHS; Pres Schlr; Comp Pgmr.

KLINE, KIMBERLY; Upper Darby HS; Drexel Hill, PA; (3); Church Yth Grp; Office Aide; Spanish Clb; Yrbk Stf; Rep Frsh Cls; Rep Soph Cls; Rep Jr Cls; Cheerleading; DAR Awd; Freedom Fndtn Ldrshp Conf & Ldrshp & Svc Awd 87; Intl Law.

KLINE, MICHELLE; St Marys Area HS; Kersey, PA; (4); 30/276; Hosp Aide; SADD; Yrbk Stf; Stu Cncl; Coach Actv; Var L Gym; Var L Trk; Hon Roll; Outstndng Jr In Art 86; MVP-GYMNAST & Columbia Art Schlrshp 87; Gannon U; Mech Engrng.

KLINE, MIKE; Newport HS; Newport, PA; (4); Varsity Clb; Var Capt Ftbl; Var Capt Wrstlng; 1st Team Dfnsv Bck, Hnrb Mntn QB & Tri Vly League MVP 86; 2nd Team Tri-Vly League Wrstlng 83-87; DE Vly Coll; Bus Adm.

KLINE, NOEL; Waynesboro Area SR HS; Waynesboro, PA; (3); Church Yth Grp; JCL; Latin Clb; Pres Science Clb; Chorus; School Musical; Stage Crew; Variety Show; Prfct Atten Awd; Yng Ctznshp Awd 85; Armed Frcs Comm & Elec Assoc 1st & 2nd 85-86; PA Music Ed Assoc 86; Temple U; Telecomm.

KLINE, PAMELA; Annville-Cleona HS; Annville, PA; (4); 20/120; Church Yth Grp; German Clb; Pres SADD; Chorus; Co-Capt Flag Corp; School Musical; Yrbk Ed-Chief; DAR Awd; NHS; Voice Dem Awd; Wmn Of Today Awd, Cls Of 1930 Awd 87; Lancaster Gnrl Hsptl Schl; Nrs.

KLINE, PATRICK; Greater Johnstown Area Vo-Tech Schl; Summerhill, PA; (3); 30/298; Ski Clb; VICA; Hon Roll; Vo Tech Awd Emplyablty 86 & 87; Accntng.

KLINE, SCOTT; Schuylkill Haven Area HS; Sch Haven, PA; (2); Aud/Vis; Spanish Clb; Im Ftbl; Hon Roll; Penn ST; Bus Mgmt.

KLINE, SHAUN; Milton Area SR HS; Milton, PA; (3); French Clb; Girl Scts; Intnl Clb; SADD; Chorus; School Musical; Nwsp Stf; Yrbk Stf; Peer Jury 86-88; Liberty U; Pol Sci.

KLINE, STACIE; North Clarion JR-SR HS; Leeper, PA; (3); 31/105; Church Yth Grp; Varsity Clb; Rep Stu Cncl; Var L Bsktbl; Trk; Hon Roll; Vrsty Ltr 86-87; Photo.

KLINE, STEPHANIE; Brandywine Heights HS; Mertztown, PA; (3); 36/124; Art Clb; Church Yth Grp; Library Aide; School Play; Stage Crew; Yrbk Stf; Sec Soph Cls; Hon Roll; Mrktng.

KLINE, STEPHANIE; Pen Argyl HS; Pen Argyl, PA; (3); 21/164; Ski Clb; Chorus; Sec Soph Cls; Sec Jr Cls; Var L Fld Hcky; JV Var Sftbl; Hon Roll; Psych.

KLINE, SUSAN; Canevin Catholic HS; Pittsburgh, PA; (3); 25/192; Church Yth Grp; JV Bsktbl; JV Var Sftbl; L Capt Vllybl; Hon Roll; Intl Bus.

KLINE, SUSAN; Fleetwood Area HS; Fleetwood, PA; (3); 17/112; Camp Fr Inc; Church Yth Grp; Fld Hcky; Mgr(s); Hon Roll; Accntng.

KLINE, TINA; Easton Area HS; Easton, PA; (4); Church Yth Grp; Dance Clb; Office Aide; Speech Tm; SADD; Chorus; JV Cheerleading; Var L Sftbl; Var L Trk; Hon Roll; IN U Pennsylvania; Bio.

KLINE, TOM; Cedar Crest HS; Lebanon, PA; (3); Pep Clb; Socr; Mst Outstndng Offensive Plyr Of Yr-Sccr 85-86; EPYSC 87; Lincoln Tech; Comp.

KLINE, TONYA L; Eastern Lebanon County HS; Myerstown, PA; (4); 19/159; Pres Church Yth Grp; Band; Chorus; Concert Band; Mrchg Band; Bowling; Vllybl; Hon Roll; NHS; SICO Fndtn Schlrshp 87; Helen Noonan Memrl Schlrshp 87; Kutztown U; Psych.

KLINE, TUESDAY L; Boyerton Area Jr High East; Gilbertsville, PA; (1); Hon Roll; Intr Dcrtng.

KLINEDINST, JULIE; York County Vo Tech; Red Lion, PA; (2); Church Yth Grp; Cmnty Wkr; DECA; Letterman Clb; Varsity Clb; Y-Teens; Var Bsktbl; Var Capt Vllybl; Hon Roll; Bus.

KLINEDINST, KATHY; Dover Area HS; Dover, PA; (3); Church Yth Grp; Varsity Clb; Color Guard; School Play; Yrbk Stf; Trk; Twrlr; Hon Roll; Opt Clb Awd.

KLINEFELTER, MICHELLE; Seneca Valley SR HS; Zelienople, PA; (3); 62/333; Art Clb; Office Aide; ROTC; Science Clb; Teachers Aide; Chorus; Stage Crew; High Hon Roll; Hon Roll; NHS; Psych.

KLINEHANS, STACY; Blacklick Valley JR SR HS; Nanty-Glo, PA; (2); Church Yth Grp; Varsity Clb; Yrbk Stf; Sftbl; Hon Roll; Pres Schlr; Pres Acadmc All Amer Fitness Awds 85-86; SEC.

KLINESMITH, MOWANA; Lawrence County Vo-Tech; New Castle, PA; (2); 16/268; Church Yth Grp; Cmnty Wkr; Hosp Aide; Red Cross Aide; SADD; VICA; Hon Roll; Art.

KLINETOB, MICHAEL; Berwick Area SR HS; Berwick, PA; (4); Boy Scts; Church Yth Grp; Exploring; Nwsp Phtg; Nwsp Stf; Yrbk Phtg; Yrbk Stf; Ftbl; Trk; Hon Roll; Eagle Sct Awd 83; Brnz, Gld, & Slvr Palms 84-86; Army.

KLING, ALICIA; Southern Huntingdon HS; Burnt Cabins, PA; (4); 1/102; Pres GAA; SADD; Varsity Clb; Yrbk Stf; Capt Cheerleading; Im Gym; High Hon Roll; NHS; Ntl Merit Ltr; Val; Reading Hosp; Radiology.

KLING, ERIC; Northeastern HS; Mt Wolf, PA; (3); 31/185; Aud/Vis; Varsity Clb; Band; Chorus; Stage Crew; Crs Cntry; Trk; Hon Roll; NHS; Egl Sct Awd 86.

KLING, TRACEY; Northeastern HS; Mt Wolf, PA; (3); Am Leg Aux Girls St; Church Yth Grp; Dance Clb; Drama Clb; FBLA; Girl Scts; Chorus; School Musical; School Play; Bsktbl; Chrldng Awd Of Trophy Vrsty Awd & Pres Ftnss Awd 85; Msc Awd Chorus 84; Med.

KLINGAMAN, RANDY; Parkland HS; Trexlertown, PA; (4); 10/438; Socr; Trk; High Hon Roll; NHS; Physcl Ftns Team Cptn 86-87; Wst Point.

KLINGEL, ROREE; Tunkhannock Area HS; Tunkhannock, PA; (3); 29/330; Key Clb; Ski Clb; Spanish Clb; Varsity Clb; Off Frsh Cls; Off Soph Cls; Off Jr Cls; Stat L Bsktbl; L Trk; Hon Roll; Law.

KLINGENSMITH, AMY; Ambridge Area SR HS; Ambridge, PA; (2); French Clb; Band; Mrchg Band; High Hon Roll; Hon Roll; Lwyr.

KLINGENSMITH, BONNIE; Seneca Valley HS; Evans City, PA; (4); 4-H; Hosp Aide; JA; Mrchg Band; Symp Band; Nwsp Stf; Yrbk Stf; Mgr Swmmng; High Hon Roll; NHS; Acad Schlrshp-Gannon U 87-88; Gannon U; Business.

KLINGER, BETH A; Owen J Roberts HS; Pottstown, PA; (2); 17/311; Mrchg Band; Rep Soph Cls; Rep Stu Cncl; JV Bsktbl; Var Sftbl; Twrlr; Hon Roll; Physcl Thrpst.

KLINGER, RITA; Tri-Valley HS; Valley View, PA; (4); 2/78; Sec Church Yth Grp; Quiz Bowl; Science Clb; Ski Clb; SADD; Sec Chorus; School Musical; Sec Stu Cncl; NHS; Sal; Presdntl Acadmc Ftns Awd 87; Achvt Schlrshp Wilkes Coll 87; Shwartz Maurer Awd Vcl Music, Spn-Sci 87; Wilkes Coll; Chemistry.

KLINGER, ROBERT A; Lykens Christian HS; Wiconsco, PA; (4); Church Yth Grp; FCA; Church Choir; School Musical; School Play; Stage Crew; Yrbk Phtg; Yrbk Stf; Pres Sr Cls; Bsktbl; Auto Mech.

KLINGER, STACEY; State College Area HS; Boalsburg, PA; (2); FFA; Library Aide; Office Aide; Hon Roll; R E Smith Awd 87; Brz Awd Meat Jdgng ST FFA 87; 1st Pl JMC PAFC 87; PA ST U; Ag.

KLINGERMAN, JAMIE; Bloomsburg HS; Bloomsburg, PA; (3); Drama Clb; Pep Clb; Thesps; Varsity Clb; Flag Corp; Mrchg Band; School Play; Rep Stu Cncl; Var Cheerleading; Powder Puff Ftbl; U PA Shippensburg; Elem Ed.

KLINGERMAN, KIM; Gateway HS; Pitcairn, PA; (3); Drama Clb; Girl Scts; Office Aide; Pep Clb; Ski Clb; Spanish Clb; Teachers Aide; Varsity Clb; Chorus; School Musical; U Of Pittsburgh; Nrsng.

KLINGLER, JAMES; Marian HS; Summit Hill, PA; (3); 5/107; Math Clb; Scholastic Bowl; Nwsp Stf; Hon Roll.

KLINK III, HARRY WILLIAM; Connellsville Area HS; Dunbar, PA; (3); Scholastic Bowl; Chorus; Var Crs Cntry; L Trk; High Hon Roll; Hon Roll; Jr NHS; Accntng.

KLINKSIEK, REBECCA; Chartiers Valley HS; Carnegie, PA; (3); 21/238; Spanish Clb; Drill Tm; Nwsp Ed-Chief; Frsh Cls; Pom Pon; Hon Roll; NHS; Dance Clb; Pep Clb; Mrchg Band; Rep Congressional Conf Young Ldrs Of Amer 87; Jrnlsm.

KLINZING, ANDREA M; Mon Valley Catholic HS; Monongahela, PA; (4); 13/80; Pep Clb; Spanish Clb; SADD; Concert Band; Nwsp Rptr; JV Var Cheerleading; Var Powder Puff Ftbl; Hon Roll; NHS; Spanish NHS; Span Recitatn Awd Recog 86; Kent St U; Audiolgy.

KLIPPI, MARCI; Connellsville Area SR HS; S Connellsville, PA; (3); German Clb; Library Aide; Teachers Aide; Band; Concert Band; Mrchg Band; Sec Soph Cls; High Hon Roll; Hon Roll; Ger Hnr Soc 87; Exec Secy.

KLIR, AMY; Shaler Area HS; Pittsburgh, PA; (3); 87/486; Office Aide; Ski Clb; Nwsp Stf; Yrbk Stf; Stu Cncl; Cheerleading; Hon Roll.

KLIVANSKY, STEVEN; George Carver HS Of Engrng & Science; Philadelphia, PA; (3); CAP; Computer Clb; Model UN; Stage Crew; High Hon Roll; Ntl Merit SF; Prfct Atten Awd; Omin Schlrshp Elec Engrng 87; Drexel U; Elec Engrng.

KLOBCAR, KAREN; Peters Township HS; Venetia, PA; (3); Hosp Aide; Science Clb; Ski Clb; Concert Band; Jazz Band; Mrchg Band; Pep Band; High Hon Roll; Hon Roll; Prfct Atten Awd; Cnty Band Washngtn Co Music Ed Assoc 85-87; Duquesne U Mid E Music Fest 85-87.

KLOCEK, CHRISTINE M; Bishop Hafey HS; Hazleton, PA; (4); #5 In Class; French Clb; Chorus; Color Guard; Nwsp Rptr; Yrbk Stf; French Hon Soc; Hon Roll; NCTE Awd; Pres NHS; Crtv Wrtg.

KLOCK, JODI; Shikellamy HS; Sunbury, PA; (4); Trs 4-H; FBLA; Girl Scts; Key Clb; Spanish Clb; Stat Bsktbl; Mgr(s); Score Keeper; 4-H Awd; Hon Roll; Mc Cann Bus Schl; Accntng.

KLOECKER, MELANIE; Villa Maria Acad; Erie, PA; (3); Science Clb; Spanish Clb; Varsity Clb; Im Bsktbl; Var Gym; Im Socr; Im Sftbl; Im Vllybl; Hon Roll; NHS; 2nd Pl Dist Sectnls Gymnstcs 86-87; Engr.

KLOECKER, RITA; Villa Maria Acad; Erie, PA; (3); Latin Clb; Model UN; SADD; School Play; Var Sftbl; Hon Roll; Jr NHS; NHS; PIAA Dist 10 Sftbl Champs & 4th Pl ST Sftbl Champs 87; Tresa Burns Ltn Schlrshp 87-88.

KLOMP, SARAH A; Great Valley SR HS; Malvern, PA; (3); 10/260; Am Leg Aux Girls St; Church Yth Grp; Office Aide; Rep Jr Cls; Stu Cncl; Dnfth Awd; High Hon Roll; NHS; French Clb; Nwsp Rptr; Tchng Awd Sun Schl; Schlrshp PA Free Entrprs Week; Political Sci.

KLONITSKO, CHRISTINE; Marian HS; Mcadoo, PA; (3); 49/104; Church Yth Grp; Library Aide; Mrchg Band; Var Sftbl; USAF; Radial Tech.

KLOSINSKI, JEAN; Venango Christian HS; Oil City, PA; (3); 5/35; Sec Model UN; Sec Spanish Clb; VP Sr Cls; Sec Stu Cncl; JV Var Bsktbl; Var Capt Cheerleading; Var Sftbl; High Hon Roll; Hon Roll; VP NHS; Athltc Awd-Mst Imprvd Plyr Sftbl 87; Pre-Med.

KLOSS, BRIAN; Notre Dame HS; Stroudsburg, PA; (3); 3/48; Math Tm; Scholastic Bowl; School Musical; VP Soph Cls; Trs Stu Cncl; Var Bsbl; Var Bsktbl; Var Socr; High Hon Roll; NHS; Spartan Athlt Awd 86; U Of Scrantan; Corp Law.

KLOTONOWITCH, PETE; Minersville Area HS; Minersville, PA; (3); Boy Scts; German Clb; Stat Crs Cntry; JV Wrstlng; Arrow Of Light 83; Bus Mngmnt.

KLOTZ, DARRELL; Somerset Area SR HS; Somerset, PA; (4); 8/236; VP JA; VP Mu Alpha Theta; Q&S; Varsity Clb; Stage Crew; Yrbk Stf; Frsh Cls; Var Capt Tennis; High Hon Roll; VP NHS; Bucknell U; Pre-Med.

KLOTZ, KEVIN; Alllentown Central Catholic HS; Allentown, PA; (4); 68/208; Church Yth Grp; Exploring; VP FBLA; Stage Crew; Hon Roll; Prfct Atten Awd; Allentown Coll Schlrshp 87; Allentown Coll; Comp Sci.

KLOTZ, MARIGRACE B; Archbishop Prendergast HS; Yeadon, PA; (4); 40/325; Aud/Vis; Church Yth Grp; Exploring; French Clb; Nwsp Rptr; Hon Roll; NHS; Prfct Atten Awd; Cert Rcgntn Scl Stds 85; Rnnr Up Miss Flg Day 86; Lankenau Hosp; Rdlgy.

KLOTZ, MAUREEN ANN; Shaler Area SR HS; Pittsburgh, PA; (3); Exploring; FBLA; Sec JA; SADD; Sec Stu Cncl; Capt JV Sftbl; High Hon Roll; Hon Roll; Rotary Awd; Pep Clb; JR Achvt Sales Awd 85-86; Niagara U; Bus Admin.

KLUCHUROSKY, MICHELLE; Purchase Line HS; Marion Ctr, PA; (2); 4-H; Spanish Clb; High Hon Roll; Vet Med.

KLUCK, CAROLYN; Carbondale Area JR SR HS; Simpson, PA; (4); Art Clb; Church Yth Grp; Computer Clb; FBLA; Spanish Clb; Fld Hcky; Trk; Hon Roll; Shippensburg U; Bus.

KLUCK, JOHN; Venango Christian HS; Rouseville, PA; (4); 11/36; Nwsp Stf; Yrbk Phtg; Rep Stu Cncl; Cit Awd; DAR Awd; Hon Roll; NHS; Prfct Atten Awd; Church Yth Grp; Computer Clb; St Joseph Mdl For Excllnc In Comp Sci 87; Amer Leg Awd For Courage, Hnr, Ldrshp, Ptrtsm 87; Gannon U; Comp Sci.

KLUGH, KELLY; Danville SR HS; Danville, PA; (4); Church Yth Grp; Exploring; Key Clb; Spanish Clb; SADD; Stu Cncl; Var Crs Cntry; Var Trk; High Hon Roll; Hon Roll; Shippensburg U.

KLUGH, TERRY; Moon HS; Coraopolis, PA; (3); 30/306; Church Yth Grp; Rep Soph Cls; Rep Jr Cls; Rep Stu Cncl; JV Bsktbl; High Hon Roll; Hon Roll; NHS; Med.

KLUN, KRISTIN; Yough SR HS; W Newton, PA; (3); 14/239; Concert Band; Jazz Band; Mrchg Band; Nwsp Ed-Chief; Rep Stu Cncl; High Hon Roll; NHS; Ski Clb; Spanish Clb; Rep Soph Cls; Natl Engl Merit Wad 86-87; PA ST Stu Cncl 86; Intrmed Unit Forum 85-87; Human Svcs.

KLUNK, BRADLEY; Dover Area HS; Dover, PA; (3); Church Yth Grp; Computer Clb; Im Bsktbl; JV Socr; Im Swmmng; Acctng.

KLUNK, TROY; Gettysburg SR HS; Gettysburg, PA; (2); Hon Roll; Prfct Atten Awd; Arch.

KLUSMAN, TOMYLA; Montgomery JR-SR HS; Montgomery, PA; (4); Bowling; Cheerleading; High Hon Roll; Hon Roll; NHS; Bloomsburg U.

KLYNOWSKY, DENISE; Weatherly HS; Weatherly, PA; (4); FBLA; Library Aide; Nwsp Ed-Chief; Trs Sr Cls; Pres Stu Cncl; Mgr Bsktbl; Bausch & Lomb Sci Awd; High Hon Roll; NHS; Ntl Merit Ltr; Hugh Obrien Yth Ldrshp Smnr 85; Acad All Amer 86; Univ Of Rochester; Pre-Med.

KMAN, BRIDGETTE; Tunkhannock Area HS; Tunkhannock, PA; (3); French Clb; Letterman Clb; Ski Clb; Stat Bsktbl; Var Tennis; Var Trk; Hon Roll; Cmmnctns.

KMETZ, KELLY; Jim Thorpe SR HS; Jim Thorpe, PA; (4); 10/87; Library Aide; School Play; Nwsp Stf; Sec Jr Cls; Stu Cncl; Capt Var Cheerleading; Var Mgr(s); High Hon Roll; Principals List 87; Girls Amer Legion Awd 84; E Stroudsburg U; Elem Ed.

KMETZ, LORI; St Marys Area HS; St Marys, PA; (3); Pep Clb; Yrbk Stf; Stat Ftbl; Stat Mgr(s); High Hon Roll; Hon Roll; UCLA; Law.

KMETZ, MELISSA; John S Fine HS; Nanticoke, PA; (4); Varsity Clb; Chorus; Color Guard; Rep Frsh Cls; Rep Soph Cls; Rep Jr Cls; Capt Twrlr; High Hon Roll; Hon Roll; NHS; Kings Coll.

KNABB, LISA; Kutztown SR HS; Kutztown, PA; (4); 8/151; Church Yth Grp; Chorus; School Play; Yrbk Stf; Var Capt Bsktbl; High Hon Roll; NHS; Pres Schlr; Library Aide; Office Aide; Scty Wmn Engrs 86; Kutztowns Wmns Prfsnl Clb Awd 87; Wilkes Coll; Optometry.

KNABE, MIRRELL M; Langley HS; Pittsburgh, PA; (3); Boys Clb Am; Boy Scts; Church Yth Grp; Cmnty Wkr; VP Soph Cls; Cit Awd; Hon Roll; Jr NHS; Color Guard; Life Sct 87; Karate-Yellow Belt 87; Comp Sci.

KNAPEK, KURT; Beaver HS; Beaver, PA; (3); JCL; Ski Clb; Nwsp Phtg; Nwsp Rptr; Nwsp Sprt Ed; Nwsp Stf; Var L Socr; Var L Tennis; Latin Clb; Quill & Scroll Awd For Jrnlsts 87; Jrnlsm.

KNAPICH, MARY G; Bishop Hoban HS; Shickshinny, PA; (4); Mu Alpha Theta; School Musical; Swing Chorus; Stu Cncl; Pom Pon; High Hon Roll; Hon Roll; NHS; Luzerne Cnty JR Ms Fnlst 86; Dist Chorus 86 & 87; Rlgn Awd 86; GFWC PA Fdrtn Wmns Clb ST Dance Awd; Penn ST; Math Educ.

KNAPP, JEANENE; Curwensville Area HS; Curwensville, PA; (4); 4/117; Pres AFS; Trs Church Yth Grp; VP Concert Band; Mrchg Band; Nwsp Rptr; Yrbk Ed-Chief; Yrbk Phtg; Gov Hon Prg Awd; Pres NHS; Pres Schlr; PA ST U; Hlth Plng Admin.

KNAPP, KRISTEN; Plum SR HS; Verona, PA; (3); Church Yth Grp; Dance Clb; French Clb; FHA; Color Guard; Drill Tm; School Play; Symp Band; Yrbk Stf; High Hon Roll; Grove City Coll.

KNAPP, LISA; Shade HS; Central City, PA; (3); Church Yth Grp; Ski Clb; Spanish Clb; Varsity Clb; Chorus; Church Choir; Concert Band; Mrchg Band; Var Bsktbl; Var Cheerleading; Nrsng.

KNAPP, MARY; William Allen HS; Allentown, PA; (3); Church Yth Grp; German Clb; Service Clb; SADD; Chorus; Church Choir; Stat Bsktbl; Var Trk; Hon Roll; Jr NHS; Sec Ed.

KNAPP, SHANNON; Plum SR HS; Verona, PA; (2); Church Yth Grp; French Clb; Hosp Aide; SADD; Teachers Aide; Band; Yrbk Stf; Sec Stu Cncl; Cheerleading; High Hon Roll.

KNAPP, TIM; East Pennsboro HS; Enola, PA; (3); 11/184; Chess Clb; Latin Clb; Library Aide; High Hon Roll; Natl Scl Stds Olympiad 4th 87; Acad Achvt Awd Alg II 87; Engr.

KNAPP, TIMOTHY; Plum SR HS; Verona, PA; (3); French Clb; SADD; Varsity Clb; Acpl Chr; Chorus; School Musical; Yrbk Bus Mgr; Yrbk Phtg; Rep Frsh Cls; JV Ftbl; Hlth.

KNARR, LEANNE; Dubois Area SR HS; Dubois, PA; (3); Teachers Aide; Drill Tm; Stage Crew; Im Bsktbl; Im Sftbl; Im Swmmng; Penn ST; Physcl Thrpst.

KNAUB, AMY; Eastern HS; York, PA; (2); Chorus; Color Guard; Nwsp Rptr; JV Bsktbl; JV Trk; Stat Vllybl; Hon Roll; Trvl/Trsm.

KNAUB, ANGIE; Eastern York JR SR HS; Windsor, PA; (2); Art Clb; Dance Clb; Drama Clb; Ski Clb; SADD; Concert Band; Mrchg Band; School Play; JV Cheerleading; JV Gym; York Little Theater Hnr 86; York Coll; Psych.

KNAUB, BRIAN; Harrisburg Christian School; Linglestown, PA; (3); Church Yth Grp; Yrbk Sprt Ed; Yrbk Stf; VP Jr Cls; Rep Stu Cncl; Var L Bsbl; Var L Bsktbl; Var L Socr; Hon Roll; MVP Bsktbl & Socr 86-87; All Conf Socr 86; MVP Socr Bsktbl & Bsbl 85-86; Bst Chrstn Testmny Bsktbl.

KNAUER, MICHELE; Souderton Area HS; Lederach, PA; (3); Ski Clb; Chorus; Mgr Trk; Hon Roll; Hmcmng Qn At Indian Vly JR HS 84-85; Hmcmng Princess 85-86; Real Estate.

KNAUFF, KYLE; Seneca Valley SR HS; Evans City, PA; (4); 52/347; Church Yth Grp; Nwsp Sprt Ed; Hon Roll; U Pittsburgh; Media Cmmnctns.

KNEAS, DAWN; Jim Thorpe SR HS; Jim Thorpe, PA; (3); Chess Clb; Hosp Aide; Office Aide; High Hon Roll; Hon Roll; Mc Cann; Wrd Prcssng.

KNECHT, ANDREW T; Somerset Area SR HS; Somerset, PA; (4); 61/237; VP JA; NFL; Q&S; Chorus; Concert Band; Jazz Band; Mrchg Band; VP Yr Mrktng JR Achvt 86; U Of Pittsburgh; Pre-Med.

KNECHT, KEVIN S; Council Rock HS; Churchville, PA; (3); 62/908; Concert Band; Mrchg Band; Pep Band; Symp Band; Capt Bowling; Sbrbn 1 Bwlng Tourn 4th Pl 86; Top 10 Aver Sbrbn 1 Lg 87; PA ST U; Bus Admin.

KNECHT, MATTHEW; Emmaus HS; Emmaus, PA; (3); 2/548; Chorus; Concert Band; Jazz Band; Mrchg Band; Pep Band; School Play; High Hon Roll; Jr NHS; Exploring; German Clb; Schlstc Scrmmage Team; Pres Acadc Ftns Awd; US Naval Acad; Engr.

KNEE, RON; Moshannon Vly JR & Sr HS; Smith Mill, PA; (3); Church Yth Grp; Band; Concert Band; Jazz Band; Mrchg Band; Pep Band; Bus.

KNEISEL, CHAD; Tunkhannock HS; Tunkhannock, PA; (2); Art Clb; Dance Clb; Ski Clb; Spanish Clb; SADD; Trk; High Hon Roll; Hon Roll; Ntl Merit Ltr; Psychlgy.

KNEPP, BRENDA J; Chief Logan HS; Mc Clure, PA; (3); 42/186; Pres Library Aide; Hon Roll; Pet Shop Ownr.

KNEPP, CATHY; Middleburg HS; Middleburg, PA; (3); VP German Clb; Girl Scts; Key Clb; Teachers Aide; Chorus; Mgr(s); Timer; Spcl Educ.

KNEPP, DENISE; Chief Logan HS; Burnham, PA; (4); 2/190; Girl Scts; Library Aide; Spanish Clb; Speech Tm; Varsity Clb; Fld Hcky; Cit Awd; High Hon Roll; NHS; Sal; Josten Ctznshp Awd 87; Dist Honor Roll Acadf Prof 84-87; Juniata Coll.

KNEPPER, GREG; Lower Merion HS; Bala Cynwyd, PA; (3); Rep Stu Cncl; Var Bsbl; Var Golf; Var Socr; Var Wrstlng; Hon Roll; NHS; All Main Line Soccer 86-87; All Main Line Wrstlng 86-87; 2nd JR Four Oared Shells Natl Crew 86-87; Air Force; Law.

KNEPPER, LEANN; Southern Huntingdon Cnty HS; Blairs Mills, PA; (2); French Clb; GAA; SADD; Varsity Clb; Chorus; Frsh Cls; Var L Bsktbl; Var JV Fld Hcky; Var L Sftbl; Hon Roll; Physcl Ftnss SR Mrt Awd 86-87; Yth Ftnss Achvt Awd 85-86.

KNEPSHIELD, BETHANN; Leechburg Area HS; Leechburg, PA; (2); Art Clb; Church Yth Grp; Pep Clb; Spanish Clb; Band; Chorus; Concert Band; Mrchg Band; Orch; Pep Band; Prfct Atten Sunday Schl 12 Yrs; Med.

KNERAM, HEATHER; New Castle HS; New Castle, PA; (2); AFS; Trk.

KNERLER, LORI; Faith Community Christian Schl; Upper St Clair, PA; (3); 2/28; Church Yth Grp; Drama Clb; French Clb; Sec Jr Cls; Capt Cheerleading; Sftbl; Vllybl; High Hon Roll; NHS; Marine Bio.

KNERR, JIM; William Allen HS; Allentown, PA; (3); Exploring; Var Bowling; JV Ftbl; Var Wt Lftg; Hon Roll; Crmnl Jstc.

KNESTRICK, RACHEL; Trinity HS; Amity, PA; (2); Dance Clb; French Clb; Hon Roll; Bus Mgmt.

KNEZEVICH, COLLEEN; Gateway HS; Monroeville, PA; (3); Ski Clb; Yrbk Stf; Rep Soph Cls; Rep Jr Cls; Rep Sr Cls; Cheerleading; Hon Roll; Hotel Mngmnt.

KNICKERBOCKER, STEVE H; Downingtown SR HS; Downingtown, PA; (4); 10/551; French Clb; JA; Ski Clb; Teachers Aide; Band; Mrchg Band; Im Bowling; High Hon Roll; NHS; Ntl Merit SF; Aero Engr.

KNIES, KRISTIN; Acad Of Notre Dame; Malvern, PA; (3); Church Yth Grp; Cmnty Wkr; French Clb; Hosp Aide; Intnl Clb; SADD; Nwsp Stf; Yrbk Stf; Lit Mag; Lcrss; Acad Sch3lar Notre Dame Acad 84-89; Scholar Frnch Intl Stud Assn 87.

KNIESS, AARON; Rochester Area HS; Rochester, PA; (3); 4/108; Drama Clb; Spanish Clb; Chorus; School Musical; Ed Nwsp Stf; High Hon Roll; NHS; Prfct Atten Awd; PA Dist 5 Chrl Fstvl & PA Reg 1 Chrl Fstvl 87; Bio Sci.

KNIFFIN, PAMELA D; North Allegheny SR HS; Pittsburgh, PA; (4); 456/660; Art Clb; DECA; JA; Math Tm; Band; DECA Fin & Crdt Wrttn Event 86; Distngshd Achvt Awd 86.

KNIGHT, AMY; Bald Eagle Nittany HS; Mill Hall, PA; (2); 17/136; 4-H; French Clb; Nwsp Stf; 4-H Awd; Hon Roll; PA ST U; Vet.

KNIGHT, CHRISTINE; United HS; Indiana, PA; (3); 14/147; Church Yth Grp; Ski Clb; Chorus; Church Choir; Nwsp Stf; Rep Stu Cncl; Var L Trk; Hon Roll; Jr NHS; Pres Ftnss Awd 85-86.

KNIGHT, ELIZABETH; Frazier HS; Perryopolis, PA; (4); Library Aide; Ski Clb; Band; Chorus; Color Guard; Mrchg Band; Nwsp Stf; Yrbk Stf; Var Cheerleading; Var Powder Puff Ftbl; CA U; Elem Educ.

KNIGHT, GLORIA; Cranberry JR SR HS; Venus, PA; (2); Sec 4-H; French Clb; Pep Clb; Science Clb; SADD; Band; Chorus; Church Choir; JV Cheerleading; Var Trk; Pittsburgh U.

KNIGHT, KATHLEEN; Seneca Valley SR HS; Mars, PA; (3); 33/333; Church Yth Grp; Dance Clb; VP JA; Ski Clb; Ed Nwsp Stf; Stat L Trk; Hon Roll; Debate Tm; ACCNTNG.

KNIGHT, KIM; Fort Cherry HS; Mc Donald, PA; (4); 36/111; Church Yth Grp; Math Clb; Science Clb; Chorus; Nwsp Rptr; Estrn Nazarene Coll; Pre-Med.

KNIGHT, MICHELE; St Marys Area HS; St Marys, PA; (3); Cmnty Wkr; German Clb; Letterman Clb; Office Aide; Teachers Aide; Varsity Clb; Bsktbl; Cheerleading; Score Keeper; Gov Hon Prg Awd; U Of Pittsburgh; Occptnl Thrpy.

KNIGHT, RHONDA; Elizabeth Forward HS; Elizabeth, PA; (4); Pres Spanish Clb; Capt Bsktbl; Capt Crs Cntry; Capt Trk; Hon Roll; 4 Yr Bsktbl Schlrshp Lafayete Coll 87-91; Lafayette Coll; Pre Med.

KNIGHT, RICHARD; Danville Area SR HS; Danville, PA; (3); Debate Tm; Drama Clb; Speech Tm; School Play; Nwsp Stf; Yrbk Rptr; Var Ftbl; Var Tennis; Hon Roll; Pres Schlr; Bloomsbrg U Intl Day Spnsh Awd 85; Natl Frnscs Leag Interp Awd 87; PA ST U; Comm.

KNIGHT, RICHARD; Jefferson-Morgan HS; Jefferson, PA; (3); Boy Scts; Varsity Clb; L Ftbl; L Wrstlng.

KNIGHT, SHANNON; West Scranton SR HS; Scranton, PA; (2); Aud/Vis; Letterman Clb; Spanish Clb; Band; Concert Band; Mrchg Band; Orch; Var Tennis; JP Sousa Awd; Solo Flutist SR Play, & 1st Chair Flute Trphy 86-87; Westchester U; Music Ed.

KNIGHT, SHERRY; Cranberry HS; Oil City, PA; (3); Church Yth Grp; Cmnty Wkr; 4-H; FBLA; High Hon Roll; Hon Roll; Highest Acad Aver-Engl 85-86; Human Sci.

KNIGHT, SUSAN; Yidioute HS; Tidioute, PA; (2); Church Yth Grp; SADD; Varsity Clb; Yrbk Stf; Pres Frsh Cls; Trs Stu Cncl; Var Bsktbl; Var Sftbl; Var Vllybl; NHS.

KNIGHTS II, WARREN CHARLES; G W C HS; Philadelphia, PA; (4); 130/230; Chess Clb; Spanish Clb; Teachers Aide; Varsity Clb; Rep Stu Cncl; Var Bsktbl; Im Ftbl; Penn ST; Bus.

KNIHA, LISA; Belle Vernon Area HS; Belle Vernon, PA; (3); Pep Clb; Band; Concert Band; Mrchg Band; Pep Band; High Hon Roll.

KNIPPLE, BRIAN K; East HS; Harrisburg, PA; (2); Church Yth Grp; Var Spanish Clb; JV Ftbl; Var Trk; Im Vllybl; Im Wt Lftg; JV Wrstlng; HACC; Rn.

KNIPPLE, DOUGLAS; Geibel HS; Scottdale, PA; (4); 4/82; Church Yth Grp; Drama Clb; Science Clb; Spanish Clb; Stage Crew; NHS; NEDT Awd; Prfct Atten Awd; Pres Schlr; Anchor Glass Schlrhsp $1000 86-87; St Vincent Acad Schlrshp 86-87; St Vincent Coll; Engr.

KNIPPLE, INDY; Southmoreland HS; Scottdale, PA; (3); 31/276; French Clb; Office Aide; French Hon Soc.

KNIPPLE, WINDY; Southmoreland HS; Scottdale, PA; (3); 23/230; French Clb; French Hon Soc.

KNISEL, LYNNE; Forest Hills HS; Summerhill, PA; (4); 51/160; Church Yth Grp; Girl Scts; Pep Clb; Y-Teens; Band; Chorus; Concert Band; Jazz Band; Mrchg Band; Off Stu Cncl; Band Pres 83-84; Mrchng Band Pres 86-87; Cnty Band, Chorus 83-84; U Of Pgh Jhnstwn.

KNISELY, LISA; Claysburg Kimmel HS; Claysburg, PA; (2); 12/97; Band; Chorus; Concert Band; Jazz Band; Mrchg Band; School Musical; High Hon Roll; Hon Roll; Prfct Atten Awd; Altoona Schl Of Commerce; Bus.

KNISELY, LORI; Punxsutawney Area HS; Punxsutawney, PA; (4); 18/245; Pres Art Clb; French Clb; VP Varsity Clb; Variety Show; Trs Jr Cls; VP Sr Cls; Capt Cheerleading; NHS; Rotary Awd; Capt Of Ntl ACA Chrldg Team 87; Ftbl Queens Ct 87; Rtry Exchng Stu To Chile 87-88; Lang.

KNISLEY, PAM; Waynesburg Central HS; Waynesburg, PA; (3); Church Yth Grp; Spanish Clb; Yrbk Rptr; Yrbk Stf; High Hon Roll; NHS; Span II & III Awd 85-87; Acctng.

KNITTLE, CHRISTA; Hazleton HS; Drums, PA; (3); Pres VICA; Chorus; Hairdresser.

KNIZE, SHARON; Highlands SR HS; Tarentum, PA; (3); DECA; FBLA; JA; Office Aide; Teachers Aide; Bsktbl; Hon Roll; Brown Awd 85-86; Bradford; Accntng.

KNIZNER, KEITH; Immaculate Conception HS; Washington, PA; (4); 15/52; Boy Scts; Computer Clb; Pep Clb; Var Capt Ftbl; U Of Pittsburgh; Comm.

KNOEBEL, DIANE L; Norristown Area HS; Norristown, PA; (3); 290/491; VICA; Hon Roll; Psych.

KNOEBEL, JENNIFER; Methacton SR HS; Audubon, PA; (3); Band; Chorus; Concert Band; Mrchg Band; Nwsp Stf; High Hon Roll; Hon Roll.

KNOEBEL, KRIS; Perkiomen Valley HS; Trappe, PA; (3); Varsity Clb; Var Capt Bsktbl; Var Fld Hcky; Var Capt Trk; Hon Roll; Trk-Most Vlbl Fld Persn 87; Bsktbl-Most Vlbl Offnsv Plyr 86-87; Fld Hcky St Chmpnshp Tm 86-87; Bus.

KNOEBEL, RICK; Southern Columbia Area HS; Elysburg, PA; (3); 13/105; Boy Scts; Church Yth Grp; Computer Clb; Debate Tm; Band; Mrchg Band; Stage Crew; Nwsp Stf; Trk; NHS; Engrng.

KNOLL, BARBIE; Central Dauphin HS; Harrisburg, PA; (3); 22/369; Church Yth Grp; Acpl Chr; Chorus; Church Choir; Sec Trs Orch; School Musical; School Play; Swing Chorus; Hon Roll; Sec NHS; Modern Music Masters Secy 85-88; Piano Accmpnst 84-88; Exec Secy.

KNOLLES, BETTE A; Wyalusing Valley JR SR HS; Wyalusing, PA; (3); Am Leg Aux Girls St; Letterman Clb; Spanish Clb; Var Bsktbl; Var Sftbl; Var Vllybl; Hon Roll; N T L East All-Star For Bsktbll 86-87.

KNOLLES, ERIC A; Athens Area HS; Athens, PA; (3); Church Yth Grp; Hosp Aide; Letterman Clb; SADD; Pres Frsh Cls; Pres Soph Cls; Rep Jr Cls; Rep Sr Cls; Pres Stu Cncl; Var L Crs Cntry; Legal.

KNOPF, TERI; Northampton HS; Walnutport, PA; (4); 8/452; AFS; Sec Leo Clb; Ski Clb; Rep Stu Cncl; Var Capt Fld Hcky; High Hon Roll; Jr NHS; NHS; Rotary Awd; Breifogal Scholar 87; Top Ten Awd 87; Kutztown U; Psych.

KNOPFEL, DREW; Plum SR HS; Pittsburgh, PA; (2); Computer Clb; Teachers Aide; Band; Concert Band; Mrchg Band; Symp Band; Crs Cntry; Socr; Wt Lftg; Wrstlng; 1st Pl Sci Fair Awd 86; Marine Fitnss Acadc Awd 86; Carneige Mellon; Comp Engrng.

KNOPP, BRENDA; Watsontown Christian Acad; Muncy, PA; (1); Church Yth Grp; Chorus; Church Choir; School Play; Stage Crew; Pres Frsh Cls; Capt Var Bsktbl; Var Socr; Hon Roll; Prfct Atten Awd; Al-Star Plyr Bsktbl Tnrmt 87; Nyack Coll.

KNOPP, PAMELA; Center HS; Monaca, PA; (3); 57/186; Camera Clb; Church Yth Grp; Latin Clb; Yrbk Stf; Cheerleading; Hon Roll; Pittsburgh Tech Inst; Comp Drft.

KNORR, BONNIE; Tri-Valley HS; Hegins, PA; (4); 29/74; Sftbl; Vllybl; Acad All-Amer 87; Alld Artst Awd 87.

KNORR, DANA; Altoona Area HS; Altoona, PA; (3); Church Yth Grp; Drama Clb; Spanish Clb; Chorus; School Play; Stage Crew; Yrbk Stf; Lit Mag; Im Vllybl; High Hon Roll; K-Pin Acad Achvt Awd 84-85.

KNORR, ERIC; James M Coughlin HS; Wilkes Barre, PA; (4); 9/342; Drama Clb; SADD; Band; Stage Crew; High Hon Roll; Jr NHS; Pres NHS; Ntl Merit Ltr; NEDT Awd; Pres Schlr; Wilkes Coll Prsdntl Schlrshp 87; Grace Kimball Mem Schlrshp 87; PA Hghr Ed Asst Agcy Cert Merit 86; Wilkes Coll; Bio.

KNORR, SCOTT; Schuylkill Haven HS; Schuylkill Haven, PA; (3); 3/103; Church Yth Grp; FCA; German Clb; Science Clb; Rep Stu Cncl; Bsbl; Ftbl; Wt Lftg; High Hon Roll; Hon Roll; Grmn Awd-Blmsbrg U 84; Engrng.

KNOTTS, MICHELLE; Altoona Area HS; Altoona, PA; (4); 33/718; Capt Dance Clb; Red Cross Aide; Chorus; Stu Cncl; Cheerleading; Capt Pom Pon; NEDT Awd; Pres Schlr; Key Clb; Ski Clb; Early To College Pgm 86-87; ST Stu Councl Chairpersn For 86 ST Conference; Penn ST U; Commnctns.

KNOTTS, TINA; Meyersdale Area HS; Meyersdale, PA; (3); Pres Church Yth Grp; French Clb; Hosp Aide; Band; Chorus; Concert Band; Mrchg Band; School Musical; School Play; Yrbk Stf; Elem Tchr.

KNOUSE, BRIAN; Ambridge Area SR HS; Freedom, PA; (2); German Clb; Chorus; Var Socr; Hon Roll; Beavr Cnty Consrvtn Schl Awd 85; US Air Force; Cvl Engrng.

KNOUSE, LISA; Milton SR HS; New Columbia, PA; (2); Color Guard; Flag Corp; Mrchg Band; Prfct Atten Awd.

KNOUSE, MATTHEW; Council Rock HS; Newtown, PA; (3); Pres Church Yth Grp; Ski Clb; Rep Stu Cncl; Im Bsktbl; JV Socr; JV Tennis; Im Vllybl; Cit Awd; Hon Roll; AFS; CIA.

KNOWLES, DONNA ALINDA; Chichester SR HS; Twin Oaks, PA; (3); 32/293; Model UN; Pres SADD; Band; Chorus; Concert Band; Mrchg Band; School Musical; School Play; NHS; Sec Spanish NHS; Spch Hrng Thrpst.

KNOWLTON, DAVID; Caudersport JR SR HS; Coudersport, PA; (3); Church Yth Grp; Drama Clb; Pep Clb; Ski Clb; Varsity Clb; School Play; Yrbk Stf; Im Bsktbl; L Mgr(s); Im Sftbl; Artst.

KNOWLTON, KELLY L; State College Area HS; State College, PA; (4); 30/600; Art Clb; Pres Service Clb; Mgr Mrchg Band; Ed Lit Mag; Rep Frsh Cls; Rep Soph Cls; Rep Jr Cls; Rep Sr Cls; JV Vllybl; Schltc Achvt Schlrshp Centre Cnty JR Miss 86; PA ST U; Arts.

KNOX, CHRISTINE; Conemaugh Valley HS; Johnstown, PA; (3); 13/104; Church Yth Grp; Color Guard; Mrchg Band; Rep Frsh Cls; Rep Soph Cls; Pres Jr Cls; Stu Cncl; Stat Bsktbl; Hon Roll; NHS; Sec.

KNOX, GARY; Franklin HS; Franklin, PA; (2); Exploring; Stat Bsbl; High Hon Roll; Hon Roll.

KNOX, HILLARY; Delaware Valley HS; Milford, PA; (3); Church Yth Grp; Library Aide; SADD; Chorus; Gym; Wilkes Coll; Pilot.

KNOX, MARIE; Mastbaum Area Vo-Tech Schl; Philadelphia, PA; (3); Gym; Temple U; Bus.

KNOX, MARK; Punxsutawney HS; Rochester Mills, PA; (4); 77/245; Pres VP Church Yth Grp; 4-H; Band; Concert Band; Mrchg Band; Pep Band; 4-H Awd; Hon Roll; Slippery Rock U; Bio.

KNOX, RAYMOND; Brockway Area HS; Brockway, PA; (1); FFA; Agronomy.

KNOX, WILLIAM; Central HS; Philadelphia, PA; (2); Science Clb; Hon Roll; 2nd Pl Amercn Assoc Of Teachers Span & Porg Cont 87; Med.

KNUPP, JASON; North Star HS; Jennerstown, PA; (2); 6/133; Boy Scts; FCA; Mu Alpha Theta; JV Bsktbl; Var L Ftbl; Im Socr; Im Wt Lftg; Hon Roll; Pol Sci.

KNUPP, ROBERT; Johnstown HS; Johnstown, PA; (3); Band; Chorus; Concert Band; Mrchg Band; School Musical; Hon Roll; NHS; Al-Amer Music Fstvl Apopka FL-OUTSTNDNG Choral Accmpnst 87; Natl Frdm JR Fstvl-Supr Rtng-Organ 86; Susquehanna U; Chrch Music-Orgn.

KNUPP, SUSANNE; Plymouth-Whitemarsh HS; Conshohocken, PA; (4); Drama Clb; French Clb; Chorus; School Musical; School Play; Ed Nwsp Sprt Ed; Stat Socr; Stat Wrstlng; High Hon Roll; Chem Engr.

KNUPPEL, MATTHEW; Central HS; Philadelphia, PA; (3); 72/550; Art Clb; Nwsp Stf; Lit Mag; JV Crs Cntry; Hon Roll; Jr NHS; Art.

KNURR, SHARON; Susquehanna Twp HS; Harrisburg, PA; (3); GAA; Key Clb; Trs Temple Yth Grp; Yrbk Stf; JV Mgr Diving; Stat Fld Hcky; L Mgr(s); JV Sftbl; Var Trk; Hon Roll; Physics.

KNYCH, STACEY; Hanover Area JR SR HS; Marion Terr, PA; (3); 27/191; Hosp Aide; Ski Clb; Concert Band; Jazz Band; Mrchg Band; Orch; School Musical; School Play; Variety Show; NHS; Mst Imprvd Musician 85; Pre-Med.

KO, JAY; Bensalem HS; Bensalem, PA; (3); Chess Clb; Math Tm; Spanish Clb; Nwsp Ed-Chief; Yrbk Stf; High Hon Roll; NHS; Prfct Atten Awd.

KOBALLA, ROBERT; Connellsville Area SR HS; Connellsville, PA; (3); Cmnty Wkr; JV Golf; NHS; High Hon Roll; Penn ST; Tchng.

KOBER, CHRISTOPHER; William Allen HS; Allentown, PA; (3); 109/600; Pres Key Clb; Leo Clb; Ski Clb; Nwsp Rptr; Nwsp Stf; Yrbk Rptr; Trs Frsh Cls; Trs Soph Cls; Trs Stu Cncl; Ftbl; PA Schl Prss Assoc 1st Pl Artcl In Schl Paper 85-86; Crmnl Jstc.

KOBERLEIN, CHRIS; Trinity HS; Camp Hill, PA; (3); Ski Clb; Spanish Clb; School Play; Im Bsktbl; Var Ftbl; JV Score Keeper; Im Wt Lftg; Bus Mgmt.

KOBERLEIN, FREDERICK; Danville Area HS; Danville, PA; (2); Var Socr; L Trk; Var Wrstlng; Marine Aviation.

KOBERT III, ALBERT O; Shaler Area HS; Allison Pk, PA; (2); 123/549; Chorus; Yrbk Stf; Hon Roll; Mech Engrng.

KOBLER, KATHRYN; Creative & Performing Arts HS; Philadelphia, PA; (4); #2 In Class; Drama Clb; Chorus; School Play; Var Fld Hcky; Var Trk; High Hon Roll; Jr NHS; NHS; Best Actress Theatre Group 86; Classical Theater.

KOBUCK, LORI; Tyrone Area HS; Warriors Mk, PA; (3); Art Clb; Church Yth Grp; Key Clb; Office Aide; Spanish Clb; Varsity Clb; Chorus; Stu Cncl; Cheerleading; Hon Roll; Penn ST U; Elem Educ.

KOBYLARZ, DAWN; John S Fine HS; Nanticoke, PA; (3); Spanish Clb; Var L Vllybl; High Hon Roll; NHS; NEDT Awd; UNSUNG Hero-Vllybl 87; Physcl Thrpst.

KOBZIEWICZ, MICHELE; Wyoming Area HS; Pittston, PA; (3); Art Clb; Church Yth Grp; Ski Clb; Spanish Clb; Yrbk Stf; Trk; Elem Ed.

KOCH, BECKY; Coughlin HS; Wlks Barr Twp, PA; (3); Art Clb; Math Clb; Math Tm; SADD; Nwsp Stf; Stu Cncl; Var L Cheerleading; Var Swmmng; High Hon Roll; Jr NHS; Med.

KOCH, CAROL; Notre Dame Acad; Ridley Park, PA; (3); PAVAS; SADD; School Musical; School Play; Cheerleading; Fld Hcky; Bus.

KOCH, CHRISTOPHER; William Allen HS; Allentown, PA; (3); VP JA; Dale Carnagie Schlrshp, Awds 86-87; PA ST U; Archt.

KOCH, EDWARD M; Neshaminy HS; Feasterville Tr, PA; (3); 55/800; Jazz Band; Mrchg Band; Orch; Pep Band; Nwsp Ed-Chief; Trs Frsh Cls; Trs Stu Cncl; God Cntry Awd; NHS; Prfct Atten Awd; Pol Sci.

KOCH, JODY; Jersey Shore SR HS; Jersey Shore, PA; (3); Sec Church Yth Grp; FBLA; Library Aide; Chorus; Church Choir; School Musical; Most Impvd Math Awd 86; Most Impvd Sci Awd 85; Elem Tchr.

KOCH, JULIE; Nativity BVM HS; New Ringgold, PA; (3); 32/87; Drama Clb; French Clb; Ski Clb; Band; Chorus; Concert Band; Mrchg Band; Rep Frsh Cls; Crs Cntry; Hon Roll.

KOCH, LEE; Methacton HS; Audubon, PA; (3); Debate Tm; Varsity Clb; Nwsp Sprt Ed; Rep Jr Cls; Off Sr Cls; Ftbl; Wt Lftg; Wrstlng; High Hon Roll; Hon Roll; Natl Scl Stds Olympd 84; U S Acdmc Decathln 86; Intgrty Cncl Ryl Arcanum 85; Law.

KOCH, LORI; Minersville Area HS; Llewellyn, PA; (3); 7/123; German Clb; High Hon Roll; NHS; Garland Group 87; Physical Therapy.

KOCH, RODDNEY; Conrad Weiser HS; Robesonia, PA; (3); 82/179; Church Yth Grp; Red Cross Aide; VICA; Chorus; Yrbk Phtg; Yrbk Stf; Bsbl; Golf; Wrstlng; Navy; Photogrphy.

KOCH, SHANNON; Oil City Area HS; Oil City, PA; (4); 17/233; AFS; Church Yth Grp; French Clb; SADD; Sec Teachers Aide; Concert Band; Mrchg Band; Pep Band; Clarion U PA; Ed.

KOCH, STEPHANIE; Altoona Area HS; Altoona, PA; (2); Keywanettes; Variety Show; Yrbk Rptr; Cheerleading; Tennis; Trk; Hon Roll; Drama Clb; French Clb; Political Wkr; U Of PA; Business Admn.

KOCHAN, JON; Schuylkill Valley HS; Leesport, PA; (4); SADD; Concert Band; Mrchg Band; Orch; School Musical; Nwsp Rptr; Stu Cncl; Bsbl; Swmmng; Tennis; Kutztown U; Cmnctn Dsgn.

KOCHANOWSKI, ROBERT; Pittston Area SR HS; Duryea, PA; (4); 51/363; Art Clb; Computer Clb; Pres JA; Im Bsktbl; Im Sftbl; JV Trk; Var JV Vllybl; Hon Roll; Air Force; Crmnl Jstc.

KOCHENASH, FRANK; Bethlehem Catholic HS; Bethlehem, PA; (3); 1/202; Scholastic Bowl; Concert Band; Sec Mrchg Band; Rep Jr Cls; VP Stu Cncl; Var Bsktbl; High Hon Roll; Hon Roll; Pres NHS; Ntl Merit Ltr; Indstrl Engrng.

KOCHENDERFER, SUE; Pennridge HS; Perkasie, PA; (4); Rep Frsh Cls; Rep Soph Cls; Rep Jr Cls; Rep Stu Cncl; Var Capt Cheerleading; Var Powder Puff Ftbl; Var Capt Sftbl; Hon Roll; Allentown Bus Schl; Trvl Agnt.

KOCHER, CYNTHIA; Pen Argyl HS; Pen Argyl, PA; (3); FBLA; Leo Clb; Chorus; Color Guard; Yrbk Stf; Hon Roll; Prfct Atten Awd; Bus.

KOCHER, JAMI; Susquenita HS; Duncannon, PA; (4); Church Yth Grp; Library Aide; Trs Spanish Clb; Ed Yrbk Stf; Stu Cncl; Var L Cheerleading; Var L Trk; Hon Roll; NHS; NEDT Awd; IN U Of PA; Intl Rltns.

KOCHER, KRISTEN; Hanover Area JR SR HS; Wilkes Barre, PA; (3); 16/194; Key Clb; Mrchg Band; Off Stu Cncl; Vllybl; Wrstlng; High Hon Roll; Jr NHS; NHS; Yth Salte 87; Kngs Coll Dscvry Pgm 87; Kings Coll; Guidnce Cnslr.

KOCHER, LAURA; Benton Area HS; Benton, PA; (4); 13/48; Trs Keywanettes; Band; Chorus; Concert Band; Mrchg Band; School Musical; School Play; Nwsp Rptr; Yrbk Stf; Sec Frsh Cls; Bntn Lns Clb Schlrshp 87; PA ST U Wlks Br Cmps Schlrshp 87; BEST Schlrshp 87; PA ST; Bus Adm.

KOCHER, LISA; Upper Dauphin Area HS; Elizaebthville, PA; (4); 12/111; VP Trs Church Yth Grp; Trs Drama Clb; Chorus; Church Choir; Drill Tm; Flag Corp; School Musical; School Play; Rep Stu Cncl; Var JV Cheerleading; Most Musical Girl Chorus 87; Nestor Fndtn Schlrshp 87; Pres Acadmc Ftnss Awd 87; Millersvl U; Elem Educ.

KOCHER, ROBERT; State College Intermediate HS; Pa Furnace, PA; (1); 10/476; Church Yth Grp; Ski Clb; Concert Band; Mrchg Band; Hon Roll.

KOCHINSKI, CHRISTINE; St Francis Acad; Library, PA; (3); 2/50; Exploring; SADD; School Play; Nwsp Rptr; Yrbk Phtg; Pres Soph Cls; VP Jr Cls; L Gym; NHS; Ntl Merit SF; Princeton; Arch.

KOCHIS, KATHRYN L; Laurel Highlands SR HS; Uniontown, PA; (3); 2/230; Cmnty Wkr; Math Tm; Spanish Clb; Teachers Aide; CC Awd; High Hon Roll; NHS; Cert Ed Dvlp Ntl 85; PA ST U Cert Cmmndtn Dlgt Mock Cnstnl Cnvntn 87; PA ST U; Ed.

KOCIELA, JENNIFER; Penn Trafford Hugh HS; Irwin, PA; (2); Church Yth Grp; Math Clb; Spanish Clb; Chorus; Socr; Hon Roll; Nrsry Ed.

KOCIOLEK, DAVID; Bishop Mc Devitt HS; Harrisburg, PA; (4); 4/160; Cmnty Wkr; Computer Clb; Debate Tm; Drama Clb; Science Clb; Speech Tm; Teachers Aide; School Play; Hon Roll; NHS; CCD Sunday Schl Trchr 86-87; Acadmc All Amer 84; Comp Sci.

KOCIS, CHRISTINE; Connellsville Area SR HS; Cnlvle, PA; (4); 60/520; Office Aide; Chorus; Flag Corp; Mrchg Band; School Musical; School Play; Yrbk Stf; Rep Frsh Cls; Rep Soph Cls; Rep Jr Cls; Tri Hi Y Clb; CA U Of PA; Comm.

KOCUDAK, JASON; Burrell HS; Lower Burrell, PA; (3); Spanish Clb; Var Tennis; High Hon Roll; Jr NHS; NHS; Ntl Merit Ltr; Prfct Atten Awd; Natl Sci Olympd Awd 84-85; Penn ST; Accntng.

KOCZAJA, KAREN; South Fayette JR SR HS; Mc Donald, PA; (3); 1/90; Ski Clb; Band; Chorus; Concert Band; Jazz Band; Mrchg Band; Variety Show; Rep Sr Cls; High Hon Roll; Hon Roll; Psych.

KODER, NICOLE; Quakertown SR HS; Milford Sq, PA; (3); 81/310; PAVAS; Ski Clb; Chorus; Stu Cncl; Capt Cheerleading; Hon Roll; Prfct Atten Awd; Cls Exec Committee 87; Dance.

KOEGLER, ED; Seneca Valley HS; Zelienople, PA; (4); Boy Scts; ROTC; Ski Clb; Drill Tm; Coach Actv; CC Beaver County; Pilot.

KOEHLER, ANNE; Emmaus HS; Emmaus, PA; (3); Girl Scts; JA; Band; Chorus; Church Choir; Concert Band; Mrchg Band; Orch; Ntl Merit SF; Physcl Thrpy.

KOEHLER, BRENDA; Oley Valley HS; Oley, PA; (3); 27/142; Cmnty Wkr; Drama Clb; Pep Clb; Teachers Aide; Flag Corp; Nwsp Ed-Chief; Nwsp Rptr; Cheerleading; Mgr(s); Twrlr; Educ.

KOEHLER, DUANE; Bangor HS; Bangor, PA; (3); 9/213; 4-H; Tennis; Trk; High Hon Roll; Thesps; Pres Acadmc Ftnss Awd 85; 3rd Plc Annual Mathmtcs Test 87; Aerospace Engr.

KOEHLER, KAREN; Wilson HS; Sinking Spring, PA; (4); 58/310; FBLA; Spanish Clb; Yrbk Stf; Stu Cncl; Capt Swmmng; Trk; High Hon Roll; Hon Roll; All Lg 500 Frstyl 85; All ST 400 Frstyl Rly; Reading Area CC; Accounting.

KOEHLER, KURT; Emmaus HS; Emmaus, PA; (3); JA; Key Clb; Pres Ski Clb; Spanish Clb; SADD; Trs Stu Cncl; Var L Diving; Var L Golf; Var L Trk; Hon Roll; IN U; Mrktng.

KOEHLER, MELISSA; Northampton HS; Bath, PA; (4); 150/430; Sec Church Yth Grp; FBLA; Pep Clb; Chorus; Church Choir; Hon Roll; 4th Pl Cerk Typst Cert 85; 2nd Pl Steno I Cert & Plaque 86; NCACC; Secy.

KOEHLER, SHEILA; Villa Maria Acad HS; W Chester, PA; (3); 10/98; SADD; Chorus; Yrbk Rptr; Yrbk Stf; French Hon Soc; High Hon Roll; NHS; Villa Maria Acad Schlrshps 84-88.

KOEHN, DEBORAH; Bishop Hafey HS; Drums, PA; (1); 6/101; NFL; Ski Clb; School Play; Lit Mag; Trk; Hon Roll; PA Music Tchrs Assoc 86; Natl Guild Auditions 86; Notre Dame; Med.

KOENIG, ELISSA I; Bensalem HS; Bensalem, PA; (4); 2/474; Mrchg Band; Off Sr Cls; Bausch & Lomb Sci Awd; High Hon Roll; Pres NHS; Ntl Merit SF; Sal; Math Clb; Scholastic Bowl; Band; Full Acadm Schlrshp CMU Smmr Stu 86; Full Tuition Schlrshp GWU Smmr Stu 86; Acad Sci 1st Awd 86; Physics.

KOEPFER, MICHELLE; Moon SR HS; Coraopolis, PA; (3); 32/306; Q&S; Yrbk Ed-Chief; Hst Soph Cls; Hst Jr Cls; Var Sr Cls; Sec Stu Cncl; Var L Cheerleading; Hon Roll; NHS; Yrbk Stf; Yth Ldrshp Awd HOBY 86.

KOESTER, JAS; Penn Wood HS; Lansdowne, PA; (3); 90/350; Chorus; Rep Soph Cls; JV Var Bsbl; Hon Roll; Var Capt Socr; Prfct Atten Awd; Most Athletic; Bus Educ.

KOFALT, NANCY ANN; Quigley HS; Beaver, PA; (4); Cmnty Wkr; Hosp Aide; Math Clb; Chorus; School Play; Swing Chorus; Yrbk Stf; Cheerleading; Mgr(s); Score Keeper; Seaton Hill Coll Ldrshp Awd 83-84; Eucharistic Mnstr; Tap Ballet Pointe & Jazz Dance; Barry U; Lib Art.

KOGER, FRANK; Our Lady Of The Sacred Heart HS; Mckees Rocks, PA; (4); 3/59; Church Yth Grp; Chorus; School Musical; School Play; Stage Crew; VP Soph Cls; Im Vllybl; High Hon Roll; NHS; Prfct Atten Awd; Carnegie Sci Awd 87; PHEAA ST Grant 87; Robert Morris Coll; Sys Analys.

KOGER, KEVIN; Seneca Valley HS; Harmony, PA; (3); VP JA; Ski Clb; Varsity Clb; Band; L Socr; L Swmmng; Hon Roll; Bus.

KOGOY, CHRISTINE A; Bishop Hoban HS; Ashley, PA; (4); 4/225; French Clb; Math Clb; Mu Alpha Theta; Pep Clb; Mrchg Band; Variety Show; Capt Twrlr; High Hon Roll; NHS; NEDT Awd; Acad All Amer Awd 87; Natl Band Awd 86-87; U Of Pittsburgh; Phrmcy.

KOHAN, CHRISTOPHER; Cambria Heights HS; St Benedict, PA; (3); 44/182; ROTC; Chorus; Var Bsbl; Hon Roll; Acadmc Ribbon-ROTC 84-88; US Navy; Cvl Engrng.

KOHARSKI, SANDY; Shamokin Area HS; Shamokin, PA; (2); Pep Clb; Color Guard; Yrbk Stf; Stat Trk; Hon Roll; Mc Canns Schl Of Bus; Leg Sec.

KOHL, THOMAS; Reading HS; Reading, PA; (3); 9/720; Capt Swmmng; Hon Roll; NHS; Var Sftbl; Pres Acad Fitns Awd 85; Sports Med.

KOHLBUS, THERESA; Red Lion Area SR HS; Red Lion, PA; (3); Orch; School Musical; Symp Band; Nwsp Ed-Chief; French Hon Soc; High Hon Roll; French Clb; JA; Band; Concert Band; PA Ambass Music 87; York Yth Symph 1st Chr Clar 86-87; Mod Music Mstrs Soc 87; PA Lwr 7th Dist Band; Advrtsg.

KOHLER, DEBORAH; Upper Moreland HS; Hatboro, PA; (3); Hosp Aide; Key Clb; Bowling; Mgr(s); Score Keeper; Trk; Hon Roll; Prfct Atten Awd; Phys Thrpy.

KOHLER, DEE; Northeastern HS; Manchester, PA; (3); SADD; Color Guard; Yrbk Stf; High Hon Roll; Hon Roll; NHS; Bus.

KOHLER, LANCE; Muncy HS; Muncy, PA; (4); 9/75; Varsity Clb; Rep Stu Cncl; Capt Ftbl; Socr; Im Vllybl; Capt Wrstlng; Cit Awd; High Hon Roll; NHS.

KOHLHAAS, HEIDI; Cumberland Valley HS; Mechanicsburg, PA; (3); Rep Key Clb; Rep Stu Cncl; Swmmng; Hon Roll; Var Ltr 85-87.

KOHLI, ERIC; Pennsbury HS; Levittown, PA; (4); 29/777; Capt Math Clb; Capt Math Tm; Stu Cncl; Im Bsktbl; Var Bowling; Im Vllybl; High Hon Roll; NHS; Prfct Atten Awd; Rotary Awd; Pennsbury Schlrshp Fndtn Grnt 87-88; Cert Excllnc Comp Sci 87; Cert Excllnc Soclgy 87; Penn ST U; Math Tchr.

KOHLMEIER, EDWARD; Upper Merion Area HS; King Of Prussia, PA; (3); Off Sr Cls; Schl Spnsrd Athltc Actvtys Crew JR, Var & Capt 84-87; Rutgers; Bus Adm.

KOHN, JOHN; Allentown Central Catholic HS; Allentown, PA; (4); 25/205; Church Yth Grp; Cmnty Wkr; Math Tm; Y-Teens; Im Bsktbl; High Hon Roll; Hon Roll; Temple U Pres Awd 87; Muhlenberg Coll; Med.

KOHR, KERRI; Central HS; York, PA; (3); Sec 4-H; Ski Clb; Varsity Clb; Yrbk Stf; Bsktbl; Var Capt Tennis; 4-H Awd; Hon Roll; Tnns 3rd Cnty Sngls, & 4th Dbls 86; Bus.

KOHUT, MARK; Central HS; Philadelphia, PA; (3); Boy Scts; Debate Tm; Library Aide; JV Golf; Var Lcrss; Var Socr; Micro-Bio Aide Einstein Med Ctr; Externshp Prog Central High 87-88; Mentally Gifted Prog 84-88; Micro Bio.

KOKINDA, JOHAN; Bishop Hafey HS; Beaver Meadows, PA; (2); Church Yth Grp; Debate Tm; French Clb; Math Clb; NFL; Science Clb; Speech Tm; Rep Stu Cncl; JV Bsktbl; Hon Roll; 1st Pl JR Acad Sci 87; Penn ST U; Nuclr Hlth Physct.

KOKORDIK, ROBERT; Monsignor Bonner HS; Lansdowne, PA; (3); 50/272; Chess Clb; Computer Clb; Debate Tm; NFL; Speech Tm; Im Bsbl; High Hon Roll; Hon Roll; Penn ST U; Accntng.

KOKOSKA, DENISE; Monagahela Catholic HS; Monessen, PA; (2); JA; Ski Clb; Spanish Clb; Nwsp Stf; Yrbk Phtg; Yrbk Stf; Trs Soph Cls; Spanish NHS; Stu Tutr 8-87; Med.

KOKOSKI, CARRIE; Ambridge Area HS; Ambridge, PA; (3); Trs Church Yth Grp; Office Aide; Pep Clb; Red Cross Aide; Spanish Clb; Jr Cls; Stu Cncl; Tennis; High Hon Roll; NHS.

KOKOSKI, LISA; Trinity HS; Mechanicsburg, PA; (2); 7/136; Church Yth Grp; French Clb; Ski Clb; Yrbk Bus Mgr; Yrbk Stf; Rep Stu Cncl; High Hon Roll; Hon Roll; NEDT Awd; VFW Awd; Patriot News Cert Of Merit For Creative Wrtng 86; Cert Of Apprectn For Volunteer Svcs CCD Pgm 87; Boston Coll; Chem Engrng.

KOLANDER, JEFF; Riverside JR/Sr HS; Moosic, PA; (3); Boy Scts; Church Yth Grp; Ski Clb; Variety Show; God Cntry Awd; Hon Roll; NHS; NEDT Cert, Black Belt-Tang So Doo Karate,Pres Acad Ftns Awd, Comp Natl Piano Plyng Aud; Lehigh U; Elec Engrng.

KOLB, E ANDERS; Central Bucks East HS; Doylestown, PA; (3); Am Leg Boys St; Science Clb; Ski Clb; Coach Actv; Coach Actv; Socr; Trk; High Hon Roll; Mock Constitutional Cnvntn Delg 87; Sci Olympiad 87; Indpndnt Experimentation-Sci 87-88; Pre-Med.

KOLB, JEFF; Plum SR HS; Pittsburgh, PA; (3); Church Yth Grp; Jazz Band; Symp Band; Var Trk; Hon Roll; NHS; Arch.

KOLB, SHAWN; Pocono Central Catholic HS; Tobyhanna, PA; (3); 11/31; Art Clb; JA; Library Aide; Ski Clb; Teachers Aide; Bsktbl; Cheerleading; Var Capt Fld Hcky; Socr; Sftbl; 1 Of 5 Top Spllrs Cls 86 & 87; Comp Sci.

KOLBUSH, MARIA; Hazelton HS; Mc Adoo, PA; (2); Drama Clb; FBLA; Hosp Aide; JV Cheerleading; Gym; High Hon Roll; Prsdntl Acadmc Ftnss Awd 86; Gifted Cls 86-87; Optometry.

KOLDE, KRISTIN; Southern Lehigh HS; Coopersburg, PA; (4); 5/230; Hosp Aide; Key Clb; Acpl Chr; Band; Chorus; Church Choir; Orch; Rep Stu Cncl; High Hon Roll; NHS; U Of Scranton; Physcl Thrpy.

KOLEK, MELISSA A; Mon Valley Catholic HS; Merrittstown, PA; (2); Church Yth Grp; Dance Clb; Band; Concert Band; Mrchg Band; Stat Bsktbl; Score Keeper.

KOLESSAR, MELISSA; Pottsgrove HS; Pottstown, PA; (4); 24/226; Spanish Clb; Concert Band; Mrchg Band; Pep Band; School Musical; Nwsp Rptr; Hon Roll; Opt Clb Awd; Pres Schlr; Am Bus Clbs Schltc Achvt Awd 87; Kutztown ST U; Elem Ed.

KOLINOSKI, TRACY; Johnsonburg Area HS; Wilcox, PA; (4); Church Yth Grp; Exploring; French Clb; Chorus; School Play; Nwsp Stf; Yrbk Stf; Cheerleading; French Hon Soc; Hon Roll; Intl Language Awd French & Engl 86; Clarion U; Accntng.

KOLIVOSKY, JOHN; W Branch Area HS; Morrisdale, PA; (3); 1/135; Camera Clb; Varsity Clb; Yrbk Phtg; Yrbk Stf; JV Bsktbl; Elks Awd; High Hon Roll; NHS; Engrng.

KOLLER, AMY; Canon Mc Millan HS; Eighty Four, PA; (4); 57/357; Church Yth Grp; French Clb; Hosp Aide; Chorus; Yrbk Stf; Vllybl; High Hon Roll; Hon Roll; Girl Sct Slvr Awd 85; SAD 87; OH Northern U; Phrmcy.

KOLLER, KIM; Hempfield SR HS; Greensburg, PA; (4); 94/694; Art Clb; GAA; Color Guard; Vllybl; Wt Lftg; High Hon Roll; Hon Roll; Prfct Atten Awd; Spanish NHS; Hensler Irvin Art Schlrshp 87; Physcl Ftnss Sr Merit 86; Certft Achvmnt Hempfield Artin Spartan 87; Seton Hill Coll; Art.

KOLLING, CARRIE; Jeannette SR HS; Jeannette, PA; (3); French Clb; Ski Clb; Spanish Clb; Band; Chorus; Drm Mjr(t); Mrchg Band; Var L Bsktbl; Hon Roll; JC Awd; Colorgrd Mjrtte; Cncrt Band; Sftbl Vrsyt Ltr; Elem Ed.

KOLOC, CINDY; Norr Pocono HS; Lake Ariel, PA; (3); 75/245; FBLA; Hosp Aide; Hon Roll; NHS; Comm Med Ctr; Nrsng.

KOLODZIEJ, CAROL A; Bishop Hoban HS; Wilkes Barre, PA; (2); Church Yth Grp; Cmnty Wkr; Dance Clb; Math Clb; Mu Alpha Theta; Office Aide; Spanish Clb; VP Jr Cls; Stu Cncl; Trk; PA ST; Acctnt.

KOLODZIEJCZAK, PILAR; Tunkhannock HS; Tunkhannock, PA; (2); Art Clb; Cit Awd; High Hon Roll; Hon Roll; NHS; Prfct Atten Awd; Cmmrcl Art.

KOLODZIEJSKI, LISA; Highlands SR HS; Natrona Hgts, PA; (3); VP Pres Church Yth Grp; JA; Chorus; Rep Soph Cls; Rep Jr Cls; Var L Trk; Hon Roll; Jr NHS; NEDT Awd; Brwn & Gold Awds 85-87; Marine Bio.

KOLOGE, KIM; Pittston Area HS; Avoca, PA; (4); FBLA; Key Clb; Math Clb; Science Clb; Ski Clb; Yrbk Stf; Var L Swmmng; High Hon Roll; Hon Roll; NHS; Bloomsburg U.

KOLOJEJCHICK, ANDREW; Wyoming Valley West HS; Swoyersville, PA; (4); 28/394; Am Leg Boys St; Chorus; Church Choir; Jazz Band; Mrchg Band; Orch; School Musical; High Hon Roll; Kiwanis Awd; NHS; Meyers Stage Band Fstvl Otstndng Sax Soloist 86; Wilkes Coll; Music Ed.

KOLP, REBECCA; Council Rock HS; Furlong, PA; (4); 2/854; Sec Intnl Clb; Orch; School Musical; Lit Mag; Powder Puff Ftbl; High Hon Roll; NHS; Ntl Merit SF; Pres Clsrm Schlrshp 86; Ursinus Coll; Bio.

KOLUMBAN, DEANNA; Big Beaver Falls HS; Darlington, PA; (3); 23/170; Art Clb; Girl Scts; JA; Spanish Clb; Stage Crew; Yrbk Stf; L Gym; Var Trk; High Hon Roll; Hon Roll; Sales Club; Med.

KOMANCHECK, JAMES; Garden Spot HS; New Holland, PA; (2); Boy Scts; Spanish Clb; Bsktbl; Golf; Tennis; Hon Roll; Jr NHS; NHS.

KOMANCHECK JR, JOHN J; Garden Spot HS; New Holland, PA; (4); 36/209; Boy Scts; Chess Clb; FBLA; Spanish Clb; Rep Sr Cls; Golf; Socr; Tennis; Hon Roll; Jr NHS; Grove City Coll; Math.

KOMATT, THOMAS; Central HS; Philadelphia, PA; (2); Mrchg Band; Drexel U; Engr.

KOMNATH, DAVID; Emmaus HS; Macungie, PA; (3); Hon Roll; Boys Clb Am; Hgh Advntr FL Sea Base; Wrk Shep Hlls Cntry Clb; Mrktng.

KOMOROSKI, DONALD; Central Catholic HS; Pittsburgh, PA; (3); Church Yth Grp; JA; Im Bsktbl; Var Trk; Hon Roll; Kiwanis Awd; Bus Admin.

KOMOSA, KATHLEEN; Sto-Rox HS; Mckees Rocks, PA; (3); FBLA; High Hon Roll; Hon Roll; Mrktng.

KOMULA, MATT; Jefferson-Morgan HS; Mather, PA; (4); 20/100; Am Leg Boys St; Church Yth Grp; French Clb; Pep Clb; Spanish Clb; Acpl Chr; Pres Band; Chorus; Church Choir; Concert Band; Mercyhrst U Tlnt Schlrshp 87; Dugheshe U Tlnt Schlrhp 87; Dugueshe U; Music Ed.

KONCHAK, TINA MARIE; Sacred Heart HS; N Versailles, PA; (3); Church Yth Grp; Cmnty Wkr; Computer Clb; Ski Clb; Teachers Aide; PA ST U; Law.

KONCHAR, MARK; Beaver Area SR HS; Beaver, PA; (2); Ice Hcky; Church Yth Grp; FCA; Latin Clb; Ski Clb; Bsbl; Bsktbl; Trk; Hon Roll.

KONCLE, KATHRYN; Warwick HS; Lititz, PA; (3); 11/286; PAVAS; Concert Band; Orch; Tennis; High Hon Roll; NHS; PFA Yth Conf 87; Schlrshp Elizabethtown Music Camp 85; 3rd Pl Wnnr Lititz Wmns Clb 87; Cmmnctns.

KONCSICS, MICHAEL; Louis E Dieruff HS; Allentown, PA; (2); Band; Chorus; Church Choir; Concert Band; Jazz Band; Mrchg Band; Orch; Pep Band; JV Tennis; Hon Roll; Cty Fnl Splng Bee 86; Music.

KONDASH, BILL; Bishop Hafey HS; Freeland, PA; (3); Orch; L Bsbl.

KONDISKO, LISA; Exeter Township SR HS; Reading, PA; (3); 16/241; Drama Clb; Leo Clb; Ski Clb; School Musical; School Play; Nwsp Ed-Chief; Nwsp Rptr; JV Bsktbl; High Hon Roll; Jr NHS; Pres Acdmc Ftns Awd.

KONDRAD, MICHELE; Hempfield HS; Irwin, PA; (3); Church Yth Grp; French Clb; Pep Clb; Pres Stu Cncl; Var Capt Cheerleading; Cit Awd; High Hon Roll; Jr NHS; NHS; Pres Schlr; Hugh O Brien Yth Fndtn 2nd Pl 85; Pre Law.

KONDRAVY, JAMES; Parkland SR HS; Coplay, PA; (3); 113/481; Church Yth Grp; VP Debate Tm; Math Tm; Rep Soph Cls; Rep Jr Cls; Rep Stu Cncl; JV Bsktbl; Var L Trk; Hon Roll; Poltcl Sci.

KONEN, ELIZABETH; Northwestern HS; Erie, PA; (4); Computer Clb; Drama Clb; 4-H; Pep Clb; Yrbk Phtg; Yrbk Rptr; Yrbk Sprt Ed; Yrbk Stf; Var Cheerleading; Var Powder Puff Ftbl; Travel.

KONICKY, COLETTE; Bishop Mc Cort HS; Johnstown, PA; (4); Cmnty Wkr; German Clb; Pep Clb; Ski Clb; Chorus; School Musical; Vllybl; High Hon Roll; NHS.

KONIECZNY, KRISTIN; Geibel HS; Mt Pleasant, PA; (4); Sec Frsh Cls; VP Soph Cls; Sec Sr Cls; Sec Stu Cncl; Var L Golf; French Hon Soc; High Hon Roll; NHS; Prfct Atten Awd; Army Schlr Athlte Awd; Pope John Paul II Svc Awd; St Vincent Coll Latrobe; Ecnmcs.

KONIECZNY, NOELLE; Geibel HS; Mount Pleasant, PA; (3); Church Yth Grp; Sec Frsh Cls; Rep Soph Cls; Var L Golf; Trs French Hon Soc; High Hon Roll; Hon Roll; Trs NHS; Prfct Atten Awd; Svc Awd 85-86; St Vincents, Latrobe; Educ.

KONIECZNY, VICKIE; Louis E Dieruff HS; Allentown, PA; (3); 98/420; Ski Clb; Chorus; Church Choir; Concert Band; Jazz Band; Orch; Var Cheerleading; Var Capt Gym; Var Mgr(s); Trk; Aquatics Clb 84-87 Vp 86-87; Lock Haven Univ; Pre Dntl.

KONIOR, ROBERTA; Cambria Heights HS; Hastings, PA; (4); 15/190; Q&S; Ski Clb; School Play; Yrbk Stf; NHS; Hnr Grad 87; IN Univ Of PA; CPA.

KONJURA, TRICIA; Shamokin Area HS; Shamokin, PA; (3); Pep Clb; Ski Clb; SADD; Varsity Clb; Band; Var Cheerleading; Var Swmmng; Hon Roll; JV Trk; Rep Frsh Cls; Schl Nwspr Edtr 86-87; 3rd Pl Dist Cltrl Arts Esy 86; Wrtr Mrkng Period 86; Pre-Med.

KONKLE, ELAINE; Perry Traditional Acad; Pittsbg, PA; (3); Church Yth Grp; Nwsp Phtg; Nwsp Rptr; Rep Soph Cls; Var L Bsktbl; Capt Stat Mgr(s); Var L Sftbl; Var Vllybl; High Hon Roll; Prfct Atten Awd; Penn ST; Marine Bio.

KONL, DEBORAH; Beaver Area HS; Buffalo Grove, IL; (2); Art Clb; Boy Scts; French Clb; Band; Concert Band; Mrchg Band; Pep Band; Symp Band; Yrbk Stf; Rep Frsh Cls; Acad Achvt Awd 87; Med.

KONLEY, JASON; Canevin HS; Pittsburgh, PA; (3); Aud/Vis; Church Yth Grp; FBLA; Ski Clb; Socr; 1st Pl Rgnl FBLA Bus Mth 86; 1st Pl Rgnl FBLA Acctng I 87; Bus.

KONOPATSKI, THOMAS; Elk Lake HS; Springville, PA; (1); Church Yth Grp; Spanish Clb.

KONSTANCE II, RICHARD P; Archbishop Ryan For Boys HS; Philadelphia, PA; (2); 7/355; JV Ftbl; Var Swmmng; Im Wt Lftg; High Hon Roll; Hon Roll; Pres Schlr; Bio Awd 86; Lehigh U; Mchncl Engrng.

KONSTANTINOU, JESSICA; Canon Mc Millan SR HS; Canonsburg, PA; (4); Sec Church Yth Grp; Office Aide; Nwsp Stf; Yrbk Stf; Twrlr; Hon Roll; IN U Of PA; Fshn Merch.

KONSUGAR, LISA; Charleroi Area JR SR HS; Charleroi, PA; (3); Spanish Clb; Varsity Clb; Color Guard; Var L Swmmng; Hon Roll; NHS; Pharm.

KONYHA, KLINT; Cambridge Springs HS; Cambridge Spg, PA; (3); 6/100; Hon Roll; Edinboro U; Math.

KOOIBAN, KRISTEN ANN; Lansdale Catholic HS; Hatfield, PA; (3); Cmnty Wkr; Debate Tm; Drama Clb; SADD; Varsity Clb; School Musical; Nwsp Stf; Rep Frsh Cls; Rep Soph Cls; Var Cheerleading; Cum Laude Natl Latin Exam 86-87; Highest Avg Religion 85-86; U Of NC; Pharmacy.

KOOL, LISA; Harriton HS; Pen Vly, PA; (4); SADD; Nwsp Rptr; Swmmng; Vllybl; Hon Roll; Trenton ST Coll; Spch Path.

KOON, TRACEY; Brownsville Area HS; Grindstone, PA; (3); Drama Clb; FBLA; Office Aide; SADD; Teachers Aide; Color Guard; Nwsp Rptr; Stu Cncl; High Hon Roll; U Of Pittsburgh; Law.

KOONS, JENNIFER; Oley Valley HS; Fleetwood, PA; (3); 34/142; Art Clb; Drama Clb; School Musical; School Play; Trk; Hon Roll; Pltcl Sci.

KOONS, JOHN; Pine Grove Area HS; Pine Grove, PA; (4); Cmnty Wkr; ROTC; VICA; Bsbl; Bowling; Lion Awd; Carpenter.

KOONS, MARY; Shenandoah Valley HS; Shenandoah, PA; (3); Chorus; Color Guard; Nwsp Stf; Mgr(s); Vllybl; Hon Roll; Liberal Arts.

KOONS, MELISSA; Eastern York HS; York, PA; (2); 5/145; Flag Corp; Nwsp Stf; Rep Stu Cncl; Mgr(s); Trk; High Hon Roll; Jr NHS.

KOONS, MICHAEL; Notre Dame HS; Bethlehem, PA; (3); 1/90; Trs Jr Cls; Trs Sr Cls; JV Bsbl; Var L Bsktbl; Var L Crs Cntry; Var L Trk; Pres NHS; Bio Awd 85-86; High General Avg & X-Cntry MV Runner 86-87; Aernautical Engr.

KOONS, SHELLY; Lehighton Area SR HS; Lehighton, PA; (3); Sec Church Yth Grp; Debate Tm; Girl Scts; Mrchg Band; Capt Twrlr; Cit Awd; Olympcs Mind ST Champ, & 8th Pl Wrld 85; Grl Sct Slvr & Siler Ldrshp Awds 86; Delg Natl GS Cnvntn 87; Dntl Hygn.

KOONS, SUSAN; Danville HS; Danville, PA; (2); Drama Clb; Hosp Aide; Key Clb; NFL; Red Cross Aide; Ski Clb; High Hon Roll; Spnsh Awd 86; Perfct Atten Rcgntn 85-86; Pres Acadmc Ftnss Awd 85-86.

KOONTZ, BRAD; Bedford HS; Bedford, PA; (3); 4/204; Church Yth Grp; Chorus; Church Choir; Variety Show; JV Crs Cntry; JV Trk; JV Wrstlng; High Hon Roll; JC Awd; Jr NHS; Otstndng Stu 84-85.

KOONTZ, JULIE; Northern Bedford County HS; Everett, PA; (3); Math Tm; SADD; Varsity Clb; Chorus; Yrbk Rptr; Var L Bsktbl; Var L Sftbl; Var L Vllybl; Hon Roll; NHS; %utstndng Vllybl Undrclsmn 84; MV Bsktbl Undrclsmn 85-86; Outstndng Rbnder-Bsktbl 86-87; Athltc Trnr.

KOONTZ, TINA ANN; Everett Area HS; Everett, PA; (4); Church Yth Grp; Chorus; Church Choir; School Musical; Sftbl; Pep Clb; SADD; Varsity Clb; Nwsp Rptr; Nwsp Stf; Altoona Beaty Acad; Csmtlgy.

KOOSER, JEFF; Connellsville SR HS; Dickerson Run, PA; (1); Yrbk Stf; Capt Ftbl; Hon Roll; Prfct Atten Awd; U Of Pittsburgh; Phrmcy.

KOPANIC, JULIE; Belle Vernon Area HS; Belle Vernon, PA; (3); 1/270; NFL; Sec Band; Nwsp Ed-Chief; Yrbk Ed-Chief; Yrbk Stf; Stu Cncl; Bausch & Lomb Sci Awd; High Hon Roll; NHS; Prfct Atten Awd; Wstmrlnd Cnty Band 86; CA U Of PA Frnch Cmptn 85&86; Mst Lkly Succeed 85; Chem Engnr.

KOPAS, JAMES; Fairchance Georges SR HS; Fairchance, PA; (3); Math Tm; Spanish Clb; High Hon Roll; Hon Roll; Jr NHS; Ski Clb; Band; Concert Band; Mrchg Band; Im Bsktbl; Prof Stds.

KOPASKO, KELLI; Pennsbury HS; Morrisville, PA; (4); Spanish Clb; Rep Frsh Cls; JV Var Tennis; Hon Roll; Jr NHS; PA ST U; Adv.

KOPEC, GEORGE; Fort Le Boeuf HS; Erie, PA; (3); 28/230; Computer Clb; French Clb; Spanish Clb; Stage Crew; High Hon Roll; Psych.

KOPECZKY, OTTO; Bensalem SR HS; Bensalem, PA; (2); Boy Scts; Chess Clb; Var Swmmng; Temple.

KOPENSKY, SUSAN; Gwynedd Mercy Acad; Blue Bell, PA; (2); Dance Clb; Drama Clb; French Clb; Office Aide; Chorus; School Musical; School Play; High Hon Roll; Achvt Latn 85-86; Achvt Geom 86-87; Achvt Music 86-87; Prfrmng Arts.

KOPER, DONALD; Belle Vernon Area HS; Belle Vernon, PA; (4); 40/267; Art Clb; Spanish Clb; JV Var Ftbl; Hon Roll; Jr NHS; NHS; Penn ST U; Scndry Ed-Physcs.

KOPERNA, GEORGE; Line Mountain HS; Herndon, PA; (4); 8/121; Sec 4-H; FBLA; Key Clb; Varsity Clb; Capt Bsktbl; Crs Cntry; High Hon Roll; Hon Roll; Trs NHS; Pres Schlr; Hghst Avg Amer Hstry Spn III & Geom 85-86; 3rd Pl Econ FBLA Regnl Comp 85-86; Hghst Avg Spn 86-87; UWV; Petro Engrng.

KOPERVOS, AILEEN P; Northeast HS; Philadelphia, PA; (3); Teachers Aide; Chorus; Church Choir; School Musical; Yrbk Stf; Rep Jr Cls; JV Var Fld Hcky; Jr NHS; Church Yth Grp; Drama Clb; Philadelphia Assn Schl Adminstrts Cert Of Achvt 85; Fndrs Awd-Gd Ctznshp 85; Delaware Vly Coll/Ag/Sci; Med.

KOPIAK, STEPHEN; Wyoming Area HS; Exeter, PA; (4); 78/249; Boy Scts; Debate Tm; 4-H; FBLA; SADD; Bsbl; Bsktbl; Bowling; Ftbl; Gym; Acdmc Excllnc Achvmnt Awd 83-84; Acdmc Excllnc Achvmnt Awd 84-85; Sprts Cmptn Gms Achvmnt Awd 87; PA ST U; Elec Engnrng.

KOPICZ, CHARLES; Fleetwood Area HS; Fleetwood, PA; (3); 11/112; Aud/Vis; Boy Scts; Quiz Bowl; Stage Crew; Nwsp Ed-Chief; Yrbk Ed-Chief; Cit Awd; Hon Roll; NHS; Natl Yth Ldrshp Conf 85; Aerospc Engrng.

KOPIE, KELLY; W Mifflin Area HS; W Mifflin, PA; (3); Church Yth Grp; Pep Clb; Hon Roll; Jr NHS; NHS; Public Hlth.

KOPKO, JOE; Pen Argyl Area HS; Wind Gap, PA; (3); 7/160; Ski Clb; Yrbk Stf; L Var Bsbl; L Var Ftbl; Wt Lftg; High Hon Roll; Hon Roll; Jr NHS; NHS; 1st Tm All Colonial Lg Ftbl Tm Sfty 86-87.

KOPKO, LARRY; Warren Area HS; Warren, PA; (3); Boy Scts; Church Yth Grp; Letterman Clb; SADD; Varsity Clb; Orch; Swmmng; Spanish Clb; Band; Nwsp Phtg; Eagle Sct 85; Ordr Arrow Vice Chf 87; Guest Page PA Hse Reps 86; Lbrl Arts.

KOPNICKY, AIMEE; Highlands SR HS; Natrona Hgts, PA; (3); Church Yth Grp; Cmnty Wkr; Exploring; Intnl Clb; JA; SADD; Sftbl; Swmmng; High Hon Roll; Jr NHS; Pres Kennedys Acdmc Ftnss Awd; Pres Kennedys Phys Ftnss Awd; Med.

KOPOLOVICH, ANNA; Burgettstown JR SR HS; Burgettstown, PA; (2); French Clb; Band; Chorus; Concert Band; Mrchg Band; Symp Band; Yrbk Stf; Pres Stu Cncl; Hon Roll; Jr NHS; Pitt U; Psych.

KOPOSKO, ANTHONY; Windber Area HS; Windber, PA; (3); 24/132; Band; Concert Band; Jazz Band; Mrchg Band; Hon Roll; U S Naval Acad; Mech Engr.

KOPP, COLLEEN; Central Christian HS; Dubois, PA; (3); NFL; Nwsp Rptr; Yrbk Rptr.

KOPP, MICHAEL J; Fox Chapel Area HS; Sharpsburg, PA; (4); Aud/Vis; Computer Clb; Political Wkr; Band; Concert Band; Jazz Band; Mrchg Band; School Musical; Symp Band; Hon Roll; Wilner Schlrshp 87; Audio-Visual Awd 87; U Of Pittsburgh; Comp Sci.

KOPPENHAVER, BRIAN; Cedar Crest HS; Lebanon, PA; (2); 13/345; Church Yth Grp; German Clb; Pep Clb; High Hon Roll; Hon Roll; NHS; Prfct Atten Awd; Millersville U; Teacher.

KOPPENHAVER, KATHY; Millersburg Area HS; Millersburg, PA; (3); Church Yth Grp; GAA; Spanish Clb; Band; Concert Band; Jazz Band; Mrchg Band; Yrbk Stf; Var Stu Cncl; Im Bowling; Music Therapy.

KOPPENHAVER, KELLY; Halifax Area HS; Halifax, PA; (4); Drama Clb; Band; Chorus; School Musical; Nwsp Rptr; Ed Yrbk Sprt Ed; Stu Cncl; Hon Roll; 4-H; FHA; John Hall Schlrshp 87; HACC; Mass Comm.

KOPPENHEFFER, ANGELA; Millersburg Area HS; Millersburg, PA; (3); 13/72; Church Yth Grp; Concert Band; Mrchg Band; Nwsp Phtg; Yrbk Stf; Sftbl; Hon Roll; Harrisburg Area CC; Math.

KOPYCIENSKI, DANIEL; Father Judge HS; Philadelphia, PA; (3); 17/403; Art Clb; Aud/Vis; Chess Clb; Cmnty Wkr; Hosp Aide; Yrbk Stf; Lit Mag; Var Hon Roll; NHS; Artwork 87; Cmmsn Soc Jstic Columbus Day Essy Cntst 86; Arch.

KOPYSCIANSKI, DENISE; Mt Carmel JR-SR HS; Mt Carmel, PA; (4); Key Clb; Pep Clb; Spanish Clb; Varsity Clb; Chorus; Cheerleading; Score Keeper; Wt Lftg; Natl Athl Hnr Socty; Cedar Crest Coll; Med Tech.

KORAIDO, MARY LYNN; Fort Cherry HS; Mc Donald, PA; (3); 1/147; Church Yth Grp; Cmnty Wkr; Hosp Aide; Library Aide; Ski Clb; Chorus; Mrchg Band; Var Tennis; Var Twrlr; NHS; U Of Pittsburgh; Physical Thrpy.

KORATICH, CHAD; Jefferson-Morgan JR SR HS; Rices Landing, PA; (2); 1/110; VP Chorus; Concert Band; Jazz Band; Mrchg Band; School Play; Yrbk Stf; Rep Soph Cls; Trk; High Hon Roll; PMEA Dist I Band Fstvl 87; Rgn I Band 87; All Cnty Band 86-87; Shippensburg U; TV Jrnlsm.

KORB, MATTHEW; Hazleton HS; Hazleton, PA; (3); 33/445; Drama Clb; FBLA; Leo Clb; Scholastic Bowl; Ski Clb; Nwsp Stf; Yrbk Stf; Hon Roll; Pres Acad Fit Awd 85; Hnrb Mntn PA Spn Cont 85; Mktng.

KORBER, KRISTIN; Yough SR HS; Yukon, PA; (3); Office Aide; Ski Clb; Spanish Clb; SADD; Nwsp Stf; JV Bsktbl; Powder Puff Ftbl; Var L Sftbl; Early Educ.

KORCZYNSKI, SHERRY; Highlands SR HS; Natrona Hts, PA; (4); 14/281; Drama Clb; Hosp Aide; Intnl Clb; Trs Key Clb; Office Aide; Sec SADD; Teachers Aide; Varsity Clb; Band; Concert Band; PA Free Entrprse Wk Schlrshp 86; Highlnds Educ Assn Schlrshp & Marine Distngshd Athlete Awd 87; PA ST U; Mrktng.

KORDEK, MICHAEL; York County Vo Tech; New Freedom, PA; (4); AFS; Aud/Vis; Boy Scts; Church Yth Grp; Drama Clb; VICA; School Play; Stage Crew; Hon Roll; NHS; De Vry Inst Of Tech; Elec.

KORDES, JEFF; Meadville Area SR HS; Meadville, PA; (4); Trs German Clb; Science Clb; Varsity Clb; Var L Diving; Var L Swmmng; Hon Roll; Dist 10 Diving Chmpn 87; Edinboro U Athl & Engrng Schlrshps 87; Edinboro U Of PA; Engrng.

KORDISH, MARK T; Bishop Carroll HS; Hastings, PA; (3); Bowling; Hon Roll; Prfct Atten Awd; Marines; Mechnc.

KORDISH, RANDY; Valley View HS; Jessup, PA; (3); 60/193; Nwsp Rptr; Nwsp Sprt Ed; Nwsp Stf; Var L Ftbl; Var L Wrstlng; All Schlstc Running Back Big II, All Schlstc Wrestler Lg 86; Mst Outstndng Wrester Elk Lake Tourn 87.

KORELKO, CAROLYN; Laurel Highlands HS; Lemont Furnace, PA; (2); 44/358; Office Aide; JV Cheerleading; High Hon Roll; Hon Roll; St Vincents.

KOREN, CHRISTOPHER; Mc Keesport HS; White Oak, PA; (3); 15/400; Art Clb; Debate Tm; German Clb; NFL; Q&S; Speech Tm; Stage Crew; Nwsp Stf; High Hon Roll; NHS; Duguesne U; Crtv Arts.

KOREN, DAVID; Pottstown HS; Pottstown, PA; (3); 3/155; Boy Scts; Drama Clb; School Play; Nwsp Ed-Chief; Yrbk Stf; Lit Mag; Bausch & Lomb Sci Awd; NHS; Key Clb; Spanish Clb; 1st Plc ST Natl Hstry Day 87; Brwn U Bk Awd 87; Cmmnctns.

KOREN, MARTINA; Hopewell Area HS; Aliquippa, PA; (3); 18/300; Church Yth Grp; Exploring; Hosp Aide; Latin Clb; Math Tm; Spanish Clb; Powder Puff Ftbl; L Vllybl; High Hon Roll; NHS; Psych.

KORENKIEWICZ, PAULA; Garnet Valley HS; Boothwyn, PA; (3); Trs FBLA; Varsity Clb; Rep Soph Cls; Rep Jr Cls; Rep Sr Cls; Var L Bsktbl; Var L Fld Hcky; Var L Sftbl; Prfct Atten Awd; Hon Roll; Rgnl Scrtry FBLA 87; Tpyng I & II Awds 86-87; Elzbthtwn-Blmsbrg; Med Scrtry.

KORENYI-BOTH, GEORGE; Devan Prep Schl; Havertown, PA; (3); Boy Scts; Computer Clb; Ski Clb; School Play; Hon Roll; Band; Dance Clb; Math Clb; Math Tm; Prom Cmte Chairman 87-88; RP Classes & 1st Track 85-88; U Of PA.

KORKIE, JEFF; Boyertown Area SR HS; Boyertown, PA; (3); #134 In Class; Church Yth Grp; Drama Clb; Teachers Aide; Band; Concert Band; Mrchg Band; Orch; School Musical; Variety Show; JV Bsktbl; Scl Stds.

KORKIE, JUNIPER; Daniel Boone HS; Douglassville, PA; (2); 39/160; Church Yth Grp; Drama Clb; German Clb; Intnl Clb; Flag Corp; Sftbl; Hon Roll; Temple; Comms.

KORMAN, KARLA; Penns Valley Area HS; Centre Hall, PA; (3); Church Yth Grp; Ski Clb; SADD; Chorus; Co-Capt Flag Corp; School Musical; Trk; High Hon Roll; NHS; Pep Clb; Pres Acad Ftnss Awd 85-86; Air Force; Mrktng.

KORMAS, LISA; Villa Maria Acad; Erie, PA; (3); Church Yth Grp; Model UN; PAVAS; Science Clb; Ski Clb; SADD; School Musical; Rep Stu Cncl; Hon Roll; School Play; Fnlst Miss Teen USA Pgnt 86; John Carroll U; Bio.

KORMOS, KARLA; Brownsville Area HS; Brownsville, PA; (3); 9/200; Pres Church Yth Grp; Drama Clb; Pres FBLA; Ski Clb; SADD; Nwsp Stf; Sec Jr Cls; Stu Cncl; High Hon Roll; Sec NHS; 3rd Pl FBLA Cnfrnc In Shrthnd I 86; IN U; Bus Ed.

KORNACKI, JULIE; Elk County Christian HS; St Marys, PA; (4); 6/72; Hosp Aide; Ski Clb; Varsity Clb; Band; Concert Band; Jazz Band; Mrchg Band; Bsktbl; Crs Cntry; Trk; Crss Cntry Ltr 85 & 86; Trck Ltr 87; Band Ltr 86; Phys Thrpy.

KORNBOU, LEANNE; Central SR HS; York, PA; (2); Church Yth Grp; Exploring; High Hon Roll; Achvmnt Math Awd 85; Pres Acad Ftnss Awd 84-85; Acad Lttr 87; Duquesne; Phrmcst.

KORNICK, SCOTT; Unionville HS; Kennett Sq, PA; (3); Var Bsbl; Var Bsktbl; Var Ftbl; All Pioneer Vly Bsktbl 86; All Southern Chester Cty Bsktbl 87.

KORO, TANYA; Ambridge Area SR HS; Ambridge, PA; (3); Pep Clb; Red Cross Aide; Chorus; Stage Crew; Variety Show; Rep Soph Cls; Rep Jr Cls; Hon Roll; Usherette 86-87; GATE-COLL Lvl Gftd Engl Cls 84-87; Music.

KOROWICKI, LISA; Immaculate Conception HS; Washington, PA; (4); 2/52; Art Clb; Trs Church Yth Grp; JA; Political Wkr; Ski Clb; Spanish Clb; Yrbk Phtg; Yrbk Stf; Capt Bowling; Var Sftbl; Carlow Schlrshp 87; PA ST Bwlng Champ 86; Blue Rbbns Artwrk Art Cmpttns 84-87; Carlow Coll; Art Ther.

KOROWICKI, RACHEL; Mc Guffey HS; Washington, PA; (3); VP Church Yth Grp; French Clb; Pep Clb; Ski Clb; L Var Bsktbl; L Var Trk; High Hon Roll; Hon Roll; JA; Im Var Powder Puff Ftbl; 1st Pl High Jmp Centry Conf AAA Westrn PA 87; Western PA Trk Rgnls 87; Phys Thrpy.

KORPELA, SARAH; Oil City SR HS; Oil City, PA; (3); 11/192; Pres AFS; Varsity Clb; Acpl Chr; School Musical; Yrbk Stf; Var L Bsktbl; L Trk; Var Vllybl; Hon Roll; NHS; Schlrshp Free Enterprise Wk Lock Haven U 87; Phrmcy.

KORTY, JANET K; Richland HS; Johnstown, PA; (4); 44/158; Church Yth Grp; Band; Chorus; Concert Band; Mrchg Band; Orch; Pep Band; School Musical; JP Sousa Awd; Madrigals; Otstndng Vclst Awd 87; Dist Chorus 87; Rgnl Chorus 87; IN U Of PA; Bus Mngmnt.

KORZI, MICHAEL; Windber HS; Windber, PA; (4); Cmnty Wkr; FTA; Math Clb; Concert Band; School Musical; Variety Show; Yrbk Phtg; Yrbk Sprt Ed; Yrbk Stf; Bsktbl; U Of Pittsburgh; Law.

KOSAK, PHILL; Trinity HS; Washington, PA; (3); VICA; Hon Roll; Electrnc Tech.

KOSANOVICH, KAREN; Our Lady Of The Sacred Heart HS; Aliquippa, PA; (2); 1/77; Church Yth Grp; NFL; Pres Soph Cls; Rep Stu Cncl; High Hon Roll; JETS Awd; NHS; Hugh O Brian Yth Fndtn Ldrshp Smnr 87; Penn ST U; Biomed Engr.

KOSANOVICH III, MILAN; Awestern Beaver HS; Industry, PA; (3); 6/110; Am Leg Boys St; Red Cross Aide; Pres Frsh Cls; Pres Sr Cls; Rep Stu Cncl; Var L Bsktbl; Var L Ftbl; Cit Awd; Hon Roll; NHS; Law.

KOSCIOLEK, ELLEN; Northampton SR HS; Northampton, PA; (3); AFS; Church Yth Grp; Yrbk Bus Mgr; Yrbk Stf; Coach Actv; Hon Roll.

KOSCO, PAM; Belle Vernon Area HS; Belle Vernon, PA; (4); Art Clb; Church Yth Grp; Exploring; FNA; Hosp Aide; JA; Math Clb; Ski Clb; SADD; Band; U Pittsburgh; Nrsng.

KOSEMPEL, PAUL; Council Rock HS; Holland, PA; (3); 109/908; Cmnty Wkr; VP Key Clb; Rep Soph Cls; Rep Jr Cls; Im Vllybl; High Hon Roll; Hon Roll; Kiwanis Awd; NHS; Prfct Atten Awd; U Of VT; Prelaw.

KOSER, TINA; Lewistown Area HS; Mc Veytown, PA; (4); 58/246; Art Clb; Church Yth Grp; German Clb; Varsity Clb; School Musical; Bsktbl; Fld Hcky; Sftbl; High Hon Roll; Hon Roll; Rgnl Art Awds; Kutztown U; Scndry Art Educ.

KOSHAR, ERICA; Greensburg Central Catholic HS; Greensburg, PA; (3); Cmnty Wkr; Computer Clb; Dance Clb; NFL; Band; Concert Band; Mrchg Band; Stage Crew; Hon Roll; Advrtsng.

KOSHT, MALORIE; Seneca Valley HS; Zelienople, PA; (3); 3/331; Math Tm; Drm Mjr(t); Mrchg Band; Symp Band; Yrbk Bus Mgr; Yrbk Ed-Chief; Lit Mag; High Hon Roll; Lion Awd; NHS; Psych.

KOSHY, ELIZABETH; Penn Wood HS; Lansdowne, PA; (4); 13/342; Drama Clb; Nwsp Rptr; Yrbk Rptr; Lit Mag; NHS; Prfct Atten Awd; Church Yth Grp; Intnl Clb; Office Aide; Church Choir; Dstngshd Hnr Mdl 84; St Peter Claver Scholar St Josephs U 87; Pres Acad Fit Awd 87; Home & Schl Awds 87; St Josephs U; Bus Adm.

KOSIEROWSKI, STEVE; Wyoming Area HS; Exeter, PA; (3); Ski Clb; Hon Roll; PA ST U; Engr.

KOSIOR, JON; Lincoln HS; Wampum, PA; (3); 24/162; Church Yth Grp; Library Aide; Spanish Clb; JV Bsbl; Var Bsktbl; Im Coach Actv; Im Powder Puff Ftbl; High Hon Roll; Hon Roll.

KOSKO, LISA; Steel Valley HS; Munhall, PA; (4); 25/206; SADD; Nwsp Stf; Yrbk Stf; Mgr(s); High Hon Roll; Hon Roll; Jr NHS; NHS; Prfct Atten Awd; U Of Pittsburgh; Psychology.

KOSLOSKY, JOHN; St John Neumann HS; Philadelphia, PA; (3); 117/349; Drexel U; Bus Adm.

KOSMOWSKI, KELLY; Kennedy Christian HS; Greenville, PA; (4); 15/98; Drama Clb; Ski Clb; Spanish Clb; Band; Chorus; Church Choir; Yrbk Stf; Sec Sr Cls; Crs Cntry; NHS; Cristo Severie Awd 87; U Of Pittsburgh; Pharm.

KOSOR, SCOTT; Yough HS; Ruffsdale, PA; (3); 66/239; Spanish Clb; Bsbl; Bsktbl; Hon Roll.

KOSS, DIANA; Central Cambria HS; Revloc, PA; (4); 40/212; 4-H; FBLA; Hosp Aide; Office Aide; Ski Clb; Chorus; Pres Stu Cncl; Capt Cheerleading; High Hon Roll; Hon Roll; Hmcmng Queen 86-87; U PA Ptsbrg; Elem Ed.

KOSSAR, TODD; Belle Vernon Area HS; Belle Vernon, PA; (4); Aud/Vis; Church Yth Grp; Ski Clb; JV Powder Puff Ftbl; Vllybl; California U PA; Marine Bio.

KOSSMANN, BILL; Hazleton HS; Hazleton, PA; (2); Cmnty Wkr; French Clb; Chorus; School Play; Ftbl; Hon Roll; Comp Pgrmr.

KOSSMANN, BOBBI; Hazleton HS; Hazleton, PA; (4); 66/400; Civic Clb; Drama Clb; French Clb; FBLA; Hosp Aide; Pep Clb; SADD; Hon Roll; NHS; Pres Ftnss Awd 87; Penn ST; Comms.

KOST, BRIAN; Quigley HS; Freedom, PA; (4); 24/98; Stage Crew; Bsktbl; Co-Capt L Crs Cntry; Var L Trk; High Hon Roll; Lion Awd; NHS; Gvrnrs Schl For Ag 86; Math League 86-87; Otstndng SR 87; Navy; Nuclear Tech.

KOST, KAREN; West Branch JR SR HS; Allport, PA; (2); Church Yth Grp; Spanish Clb; Chorus; Var JV Mgr(s).

KOSTANESKY, ROBIN; Hazleton HS; Drums, PA; (2); French Clb; Yrbk Stf; Rep Stu Cncl; Hon Roll; Pres Schlr; Sci.

KOSTEK, LYNN MARIE; St Benedict Acad; Erie, PA; (3); 13/52; Model UN; Q&S; Yrbk Ed-Chief; Yrbk Rptr; Yrbk Stf; Lit Mag; Var L Vllybl; High Hon Roll; Hon Roll; NHS; PSPA 2nd Pl Wrtng Awd 85; PSPA 1st Pl Srtng Awd Yrbk 86; Internship WSEE TV As Rptr 87; PA ST U; Comm.

KOSTELAC, JENNIFER; Montour HS; Pittsburgh, PA; (4); 22/300; Mgr Bsktbl; Mgr Swmmng; NHS; Merit Schlrshp Duquesne U 87; Duquesne U; Phrmcy.

KOSTER, MATTHEW; Harbor Creek HS; Erie, PA; (3); Computer Clb; Hon Roll; Elec Engrng.

KOSTIAL, CRAIG; Hempfield SR HS; Greensburg, PA; (2); Var L Trk; High Hon Roll; Jr NHS.

KOSTICK, HEATHER; Exeter Twp SR HS; Reading, PA; (3); 49/200; Church Yth Grp; Sec Leo Clb; Varsity Clb; Band; Concert Band; Mrchg Band; Pep Band; Var Cheerleading; Hon Roll; Jr NHS.

KOSTIVAL, DARREN; Governor Mifflin HS; Kenhorst, PA; (3); Chorus; School Musical; School Play; Swing Chorus; Tennis; West Chester U; Comp Sci.

KOSTLICH, DAWN-MARIE; Hopewell HS; Aliquippa, PA; (4); 49/250; Church Yth Grp; VP German Clb; Chorus; Yrbk Ed-Chief; Pres Sr Cls; Rep Stu Cncl; Co-Capt Cheerleading; Powder Puff Ftbl; Hon Roll; NHS; Beaver Cnty JR Miss 1st Runnr Up 86; W PA Prfct Teen 85; Hmcng Qn 86; PA ST U; Tlcmntctns.

KOSTOVICK, JOSEPH; North Penn JR SR HS; Covington, PA; (3); Boy Scts; Church Yth Grp; Exploring; ROTC; Stu Cncl; Wt Lftg; Wrstlng; Hon Roll; Eagle Sct 87; West Point; Army.

KOSTOWSKIE, JOHN; Shenandoah Valley HS; Shenandoah, PA; (3); Rep Frsh Cls; Rep Soph Cls; Hon Roll.

KOSTRYK, ANGELA; Purchase Line HS; Dixonville, PA; (2); Church Yth Grp; Pep Clb; SADD; Varsity Clb; VP Soph Cls; JV Var Bsktbl; Coach Actv; Var Sftbl; JV Var Vllybl; Hon Roll.

KOSTURA III, JAMES; Notre Dame HS; Easton, PA; (3); 16/89; Church Yth Grp; Variety Show; Rep Frsh Cls; Pres Jr Cls; VP Stu Cncl; JV Bsbl; JV Ftbl; Var Wrstlng; Hon Roll; Ntl Catholic Yth Cnvtn 85; Math.

KOSTURA, STACEY; Nativity BVM; Minersville, PA; (2); 15/80; Latin Clb; Chorus; Flag Corp; Nwsp Stf; Var Crs Cntry; Prfct Atten Awd; Bndfrnt Vrsty Ltr 87; Sci Fair, PJAS Sci Fair 2nd Pl 87; Latin Awds 85 & 86.

KOSUT, KATHLEEN; Altoona Area HS; Altoona, PA; (3); 36/796; Spanish Clb; Band; Jazz Band; Mrchg Band; Orch; Var L Swmmng; High Hon Roll; Pres Acadmc Ftnss Awd; Bus.

KOSZOWSKI, VICTORIA; Bensalem HS; Bensalem, PA; (3); Teachers Aide; Capt Var Swmmng; Capt Var Tennis; Dstcts Wmng 86-87; Dstcts Tnns 87; Gut Awd & Mst Cnstnt Smmr 87.

KOT, DENISE; West York Area SR HS; York, PA; (3); Teachers Aide; Varsity Clb; Rep Soph Cls; Rep Jr Cls; Stu Cncl; Var Capt Cheerleading; Coach Actv; Gym; Trk; Hon Roll; IN U Of PA; Elem Ed.

KOTARSKI, ANTHONY; James M Coughlin HS; Laflin, PA; (4); 1/340; Boy Scts; Chess Clb; Pres Church Yth Grp; Math Clb; Math Tm; Ski Clb; Yrbk Stf; Var L Golf; Var L Vllybl; High Hon Roll; Pres Acdmc Fitness Awd 87; US Naval Acad; Elect Engrng.

KOTCH, CHRISTOPHER; Wissahickon HS; Blue Bell, PA; (2); Boy Scts; Church Yth Grp; CAP; Exploring; Orch; Swmmng; Hon Roll; Amercn Legn Awd 85; Hi Awd Of Merit-Sfty Ptrl 85; Athltc Union Awd 85; Military; Arntcl Engrng.

KOTCHKA, SUZANN; Center Area HS; Aliquippa, PA; (2); Cmnty Wkr; Computer Clb; Spanish Clb; School Play; Yrbk Stf; Bsktbl; JV Cheerleading; Powder Puff Ftbl; Hon Roll; Spanish NHS; Outstndng Cheerldr Awd 86-87; Spnsh Awd 85-86; Bio.

KOTCHMAR, JULIE; Mohawk JR SR HS; New Castle, PA; (3); #1 In Class; Pres Church Yth Grp; JCL; Latin Clb; SADD; Band; Concert Band; Mrchg Band; Var Capt Cheerleading; High Hon Roll; NHS; U Of Notre Dame; Engrng.

KOTECKI, NATHAN D; York Catholic HS; York, PA; (2); Varsity Clb; Chorus; School Musical; Variety Show; High Hon Roll; NHS; Arch.

KOTELNICKI, LORI; Blacklick Valley HS; Nanty-Glo, PA; (2); Varsity Clb; Var Cheerleading; Hon Roll; Acdmc All Amer 86.

KOTERBA, JASON; Brownsville HS; Penncraft, PA; (3); Church Yth Grp; Ski Clb; Pres Stu Cncl; High Hon Roll; Hon Roll; Phys Thrpy.

KOTERSKI, AMY; Unionville HS; Chadds Ford, PA; (4); 50/316; French Clb; Pep Clb; Yrbk Stf; JV Fld Hcky; JV Trk; French Hon Soc; NHS; Villanova; Nrsng.

KOTHARI, LISA; Trinity HS; Westlake, OH; (3); Church Yth Grp; Cmnty Wkr; Drama Clb; French Clb; Pep Clb; School Play; Variety Show; Nwsp Rptr; Yrbk Stf; Bus Law.

KOTHMANN, HOLLY; Churchill HS; Pittsburgh, PA; (4); 1/190; AFS; Spanish Clb; Sec Acpl Chr; Chorus; School Musical; High Hon Roll; SF Pittsburgh Press All Stars 87; PA ST.

KOTLINSKI, CORINNE; Sto-Rox SR HS; Mckees Rocks, PA; (3); Boys Clb Am; French Clb; FBLA; Spanish Clb; SADD; Y-Teens; Band; Yrbk Stf; Sec Stu Cncl; High Hon Roll; U Of Pittsburgh; Bus Admin.

KOTOFSKY, ARON; Council Rock HS; Holland, PA; (3); 164/906; Cmnty Wkr; Key Clb; Temple Yth Grp; Im Badmtn; Im Bsktbl; Im Lcrss; Im Vllybl; Hon Roll; NHS; Prfct Atten Awd; Coll Of William & Mary; Adv.

KOTSAGRELOS, MICHELLE MARIE; Bethel Park SENIOR HS; Bethel Park, PA; (4); 64/519; Sec Church Yth Grp; Dance Clb; Political Wkr; JV Var Cheerleading; High Hon Roll; Hon Roll; Pres Schlr; Dance Clb; Sec Girl Scts; Chorus; Ahepa Dist Schlrshp Awd 87; Outstndg Chrldr Awd 86; U Of Pittsburgh; Pharm.

KOTSKO, JOHN; John S Fine HS; Nanticoke, PA; (4); 18/260; FBLA; Model UN; Ftbl; Trk; High Hon Roll; NHS; Syracus U; Bus.

KOTSKO, JUDE; Hazleton HS; Hazleton, PA; (3); Latin Clb; School Play; Nwsp Ed-Chief; Yrbk Ed-Chief; Pres Frsh Cls; Var Socr; Wrstlng; Hon Roll; NHS; ST Champ Bowling 85-86; Reg Judo Champ 86; U Of Miami; Med.

KOTT, DAVID; Yough SR HS; Herminie, PA; (3); French Clb; Band; Concert Band; Jazz Band; Mrchg Band; Pep Band; High Hon Roll; NHS; Mc Donalds All-Am HS Band 87; Penn ST; Engrng.

KOTT, DENISE; West Hazleton HS; Hazleton, PA; (4); 35/221; FBLA; SADD; Rep Sr Cls; Rep Stu Cncl; JV Cheerleading; Hon Roll; NHS; Cmnty Wkr; Office Aide; Y-Teens; Stu Cncl Awd Natl 84-85; Sec Natl Hnr Soc 86-87; Typg I Hghst Awd 85-86; Penn ST U; Paralegl.

KOTTACMP, BILLIE; Northeastern HS; Manchester, PA; (4); Church Yth Grp; Drama Clb; Red Cross Aide; Chorus; Church Choir; School Musical; Yrbk Stf; Hon Roll; Girl Scts; Thesps; Outstndng SR Awd Yrbk, Music Boosters Schlrshps, Coll Choir Schlrshp & Untd Brethen Schlrshp 86-87; Huntington Coll; Vocal Prfrmnc.

KOTTMEYER, KIM; Downingtown SR HS; Downingtown, PA; (4); 17/531; Intnl Clb; Spanish Clb; Trs SADD; Band; Chorus; Mrchg Band; School Musical; High Hon Roll; NHS; Prfct Atten Awd; Penn ST U; Spnsh.

KOTVAS, GEORGE D; Leechburg Area HS; Leechburg, PA; (3); JV Bsbl; Bus.

KOTZ, JOHN; John S Fine HS; Nanticoke, PA; (2); 39/226; Bsbl; Hon Roll.

KOTZEN JR, RICH; Daniel Boone HS; Birdsboro, PA; (3); Band; Concert Band; Jazz Band; Mrchg Band; Guitar Summerwork Shop Scholar 85; Outstndng Rhythm Awd 85; Berklee Schl Music; Music.

KOUKOSKI, CHRISTOPHER; Archbishop HS For Boys; Philadelphia, PA; (3); 56/416.

KOURSAROS, JOHN; Reading SR HS; Reading, PA; (3); 9/720; Aud/Vis; Stage Crew; Hon Roll; NHS; Prfct Atten Awd; Rotary Awd; Engl & Scl Stds 1st Prz Awd 85 & 84-85; Supts Schltc Recognition Awd 85-87; Engrng.

KOUTCH, PAUL; Lourdes Regional HS; Ashland, PA; (3); 26/92; Rep Frsh Cls; Rep Sr Cls; Im Bsktbl; Var Ftbl; JV Wrstlng; Bus.

KOUTOULAKIS, DIANE; Quigley HS; Conway, PA; (3); 33/83; Church Yth Grp; Chorus; Yrbk Stf; JV Bsktbl; Var Tennis; Var Trk; Hon Roll; Grove City Coll; Ed.

KOUTOULAKIS, KRISTINE; Hopewell HS; Aliquippa, PA; (3); 15/255; Church Yth Grp; Girl Scts; JA; Math Clb; Band; JV Var Bsktbl; Var L Tennis; Var Trk; High Hon Roll; NHS; Beavear Co Times Athl/Schlr Hnbl Mntn 85-87; Slipp)ry Rock U Span Comp Hnbl Mntn 87; Grove City Coll; Math Tchr.

KOUTROULIS, DEBBIE; St Hubert Catholic High For Girls; Philadelphia, PA; (3); Chorus; Manor JR Coll; Comp Pgm.

KOUVARAS, GEORGIA MARIE; Seneca Valley SR HS; Zelienople, PA; (4); Art Clb; Band; Hon Roll; Bradford Bus Schl; Retail Mgmt.

KOUVOLO, LISA; Ambridge Area HS; Freedom, PA; (3); VP Church Yth Grp; Pep Clb; Sec Chorus; Church Choir; Drill Tm; School Musical; Pom Pon; Hon Roll; Red Cross Aide; Spanish Clb; Comms.

KOVAC, CRAIG; Freeport HS; Sarver, PA; (4); Band; Concert Band; Mrchg Band; Symp Band; Stu Cncl; High Hon Roll; NHS; Pres Acad Fit Awd 87; Sumona Cum Laude 87; Miami U Oxford; Aeronautics.

KOVAC, MATT; Canon-Mc Millian HS; Canonsburg, PA; (4); Boy Scts; Ski Clb; Hon Roll; US Navy; Avtn.

KOVACH, DONNELLA; West Branch Area HS; Morrisdale, PA; (3); Drama Clb; Ski Clb; Spanish Clb; SADD; Band; Chorus; Church Choir; Concert Band; Drm Mjr(t); Mrchg Band; Music.

KOVACH, KIMBERLY; Geibel HS; Uniontown, PA; (3); Art Clb; Church Yth Grp; Dance Clb; Pep Clb; SADD; School Play; Yrbk Stf; Lit Mag; High Hon Roll; Voice Dem Awd; Pre-Med.

KOVACH, KRISTIN; Oswayo Valley JR SR HS; Shinglehouse, PA; (2); German Clb; Ski Clb; Varsity Clb; VP Frsh Cls; Var Capt Bsktbl; Var L Trk; Var Capt Vllybl; Elklnd Chrstms Trnmnt All Trny Team 86.

KOVACH, MELISSA; Homer-Center HS; Aultman, PA; (3); 9/111; French Clb; Library Aide; Band; Church Choir; Concert Band; Jazz Band; Mrchg Band; School Play; Stat Bsktbl; High Hon Roll.

KOVACH, RICHARD P; Butler Area SR HS; Butler, PA; (3); Exploring; Library Aide; Math Tm; Spanish Clb; Off Frsh Cls; Rep Soph Cls; Rep Stu Cncl; Hon Roll; L Jr NHS; NHS; Acad Achvt Awd 86-87; U Of Pittsburgh; Bus.

KOVACH, THOMAS; Ambridge Area HS; Baden, PA; (3); Church Yth Grp; CAP; Var Socr; High Hon Roll; Hon Roll; Crpntry.

KOVACIC, SHELLEY; Greater Johnstown SR HS; Johnstown, PA; (3); FBLA; Hosp Aide; Key Clb; Band; Chorus; Concert Band; Mrchg Band; Orch; School Musical; Hon Roll; Cambria Rowe Bus Coll; Med Sec.

KOVAL, DAWNA; Center HS; Monaca, PA; (3); German Clb; Chorus; Color Guard; Capt Drm Mjr(t); School Musical; Stu Cncl; Capt Twrlr; Htl Mgmnt.

KOVALCHICK, CHARLES J; Lackawanna Trail HS; Tukhannock, PA; (3); Stu Cncl; JV Bsbl; Var L Crs Cntry; JV Ftbl; Var Trk; Hon Roll; NHS; NAC Crs Cntry All Star 85-86; St Crs Cntry Trnmnt 85-86; Frgn Lang Awd 86-87; Med.

KOVALCHICK, MICHELLE; Tunkhannock HS; Tunkhannock, PA; (4); 4/254; Trs Key Clb; Yrbk Stf; Rep Sr Cls; Fld Hcky; Score Keeper; Cit Awd; High Hon Roll; Trs NHS; Sci.

KOVALCHIK, KATHLEEN; Napletown HS; Greensboro, PA; (4); 20/75; VP Church Yth Grp; Library Aide; Varsity Clb; Stu Cncl; Var Bsktbl; Var Sftbl; Im Vllybl; Wt Lftg; High Hon Roll; Hon Roll; Civic Clb Girl Mnth 87; Soc Distngshd Am HS Stu 86-87; Luarel Bus Inst; Banking.

KOVALCIK, PAMELA; Mount Alvernia HS; Pittsburgh, PA; (3); 9/54; Drama Clb; Lit Mag; Hon Roll; Sawyer Bus Schl; Med Secy.

KOVALESKI, KIRSTEN ANNE; Sacred Heart HS; Carbondale, PA; (3); 11/56; Pres Church Yth Grp; Computer Clb; Dance Clb; Drama Clb; English Clb; FBLA; Pres Girl Scts; NFL; Speech Tm; Slvr Awd Grl Scts 86; ISLI Mst Ldrshp Awd 86; U Of Scranton; Psychlgy.

KOVALOSKI, JAMES; Glendale JR SR HS; Irvona, PA; (4); 2/95; Yrbk Ed-Chief; JV Bsbl; Var Bsktbl; Bausch & Lomb Sci Awd; DAR Awd; Hon Roll; NHS; Sal; U Of Pgh; Mec Engrng.

KOVALOVICH, KAROL; Our Lady Of Lourdes Regional HS; Strong, PA; (3); 4/89; Drama Clb; French Clb; VP Library Aide; Nwsp Rptr; JV Bsktbl; JV Var Sftbl; French Hon Soc; Hon Roll; Lion Awd; Sec NHS; Hstry.

KOVALY, BETH; South Allegheny HS; Port Vue, PA; (3); 8/180; Church Yth Grp; Dance Clb; Chorus; School Musical; Rep Stu Cncl; Stat Bsktbl; JV Trk; FNA; Library Aide; Spanish Clb; PMEA Dist & Rgnl Choir 86-87; PMEA Dist Chorus 85-86; PMEA JR Chorus Fest 84; Pitt U.

KOVATCH, CHARLES; Crestwood HS; Mountain Top, PA; (3); Mrchg Band; School Musical; JV Bsktbl; Var L Trk; Hon Roll; SAR Awd; VFW Awd; Boy Scts; Church Yth Grp; French Clb; Eagle Scout BSA Highest Hnr 86; Order Of Arrow BSA Honored Campers & Ldrs 85; Pre-Dent.

KOVATCH, KATHY; Panther Valley HS; Nesquehoning, PA; (2); 46/120; Aud/Vis; Church Yth Grp; Drama Clb; French Clb; Ski Clb; Speech Tm; Flag Corp; Mrchg Band; School Musical; Mgr(s); Law.

KOVITCH, JOHN D; Central Columbia HS; Bloomsburg, PA; (3); 8/168; Ski Clb; Im Wt Lftg; Var Wrstlng; High Hon Roll; NHS; Ntl Merit SF; Ntl Sci Merit Awd 83-85; Pre-Med.

KOVSCEK, MARK; Belle Vernon Area HS; Belle Vernon, PA; (3); Debate Tm; VP NFL; Ski Clb; Band; Mrchg Band; Rep Jr Cls; High Hon Roll; NHS; Voice Dem Awd.

KOWALCHICK, CHRISTINE; Southern Columbia Area HS; Elysburg, PA; (3); Varsity Clb; Nwsp Stf; Sec Soph Cls; Pres Jr Cls; Trs Rep Stu Cncl; Var Bsktbl; Var L Fld Hcky; Var L Sftbl; Hon Roll; Voice Dem Awd; Bloomsburg U; Scndry Math Tchr.

KOWALCHICK, DAVID; Cocalico HS; Denver, PA; (3); Boy Scts; Church Yth Grp; Drm Mjr(t); Var Bsbl; Im Bsktbl; Var Ftbl; Im Sftbl; Im Wt Lftg; Hon Roll; Bus Admin.

KOWALCZYK, STEPHEN; Ft Le Boeuf HS; Waterford, PA; (2); 28/210; Church Yth Grp; 4-H; Ftbl; Wrstlng; Hon Roll; Dntstry.

KOWALEWSKI, CAROLINE; Carmichaels Area HS; Crucible, PA; (4); 32/99; Pep Clb; Spanish Clb; Hon Roll; Sci Tchr.

KOWALO JR, DAN; Canon Mc Millian HS; Mc Donald, PA; (4); 45/435; Chess Clb; Church Yth Grp; Letterman Clb; Acpl Chr; Chorus; Ftbl; Vllybl; Wt Lftg; Wrstlng; Hon Roll; CA U Of PA; Ag Cnsrvtn.

KOWALO, FREDERICK E; Canon Mc Millan HS; Mcdonald, PA; (4); Art Clb; Drama Clb; French Clb; Thesps; School Musical; School Play; Nwsp Stf; Ftbl; Trk; JV Wrstlng; Ca U; Film.

KOWALSKI, CATHERINE; Bishop Guilfoyle HS; Altoona, PA; (3); Church Yth Grp; SADD; Chorus; Color Guard; Yrbk Stf; Lock Haven U; Erly Chldhd Educ.

KOWALSKI, JENNIFER; Altoona Area HS; Altoona, PA; (2); German Clb; Church Choir; Capt Flag Corp; Mrchg Band; Orch; Hon Roll; Jr NHS; NEDT Awd; Mid ST Bnk Schlrshp Awd Music 86; Presdntl Acadc Ftnss Awd 86; Altoona Dnc Co 1st Pl SR Div 87; Med.

KOWALSKI, KATHLEEN; Villa Marie Acad; Erie, PA; (3); 12/168; Church Yth Grp; Red Cross Aide; SADD; Rep Stu Cncl; Cheerleading; Hon Roll; NHS; PTO Schlrshp 84-85; Tresa Burns Schlrshp In Frgn Lng 86-87.

KOWALSKI, RITA; Bensalem SR HS; Bensalem, PA; (4); #15 In Class; SADD; High Hon Roll; Val; Valedctrn Bus Typewrtr 87; Offc Wrk.

KOWALSKI, SANDRA; Ambridge Area HS; Baden, PA; (2); Church Yth Grp; Cmnty Wkr; French Clb; Pep Clb; SADD; Band; Concert Band; Mrchg Band; Pep Band; Stat Trk; Public Relations.

KOWALSKI, TRACEY; Mid-Valley HS; Olyphant, PA; (3); Drama Clb; SADD; Stage Crew; Nwsp Stf; Yrbk Stf; Rep Stu Cncl; Vllybl; Hon Roll; VP Frsh Cls; Trs Jr Cls.

KOWCHECK, ALYSSA; Avella Area JR SR HS; Avella, PA; (3); French Clb; Hosp Aide; Ski Clb; Var Cheerleading; Var Vllybl; High Hon Roll; NHS; Pres Schlr; Med.

KOWELL, PAULA; Mon Valley Catholic HS; Monessen, PA; (2); 5/74; Am Leg Aux Girls St; Church Yth Grp; Dance Clb; JA; Science Clb; Ski Clb; Teachers Aide; Chorus; Drill Tm; Mrchg Band; Amer Legion Aux Awd 85; Med.

KOWKER, JACKIE; Mahanoy Area HS; Gilberton, PA; (3); Spanish Clb; Variety Show; Nwsp Stf; Yrbk Stf; Pres Frsh Cls; Pres Soph Cls; Cheerleading; Diving; Swmmng; Trk; Occupational Thrpy.

KOWKER, KIMBERLY; Trinity HS; Camp Hill, PA; (2); 4/136; French Clb; Girl Scts; Math Tm; Pep Clb; Var Cheerleading; Var Trk; High Hon Roll; NHS; NEDT Awd; Quiz Bowl; Natl Latin Exam Awd 86; Med.

KOWKER, TRISH; Mahanoy Area HS; Gilberton, PA; (2); Ski Clb; Spanish Clb; Chorus; Drill Tm; School Play; Variety Show; Nwsp Stf; Diving; Swmmng; Var L Trk; Nrsng.

KOWNACKI, PAUL; Boiling Springs HS; Boiling Spgs, PA; (2); 2/123; Chess Clb; Trk; Wt Lftg; High Hon Roll; NHS; Carlisle Area Sci Fair 1st Pl 86; Capital Area Sci & Engrng Fair 3rd Comp & Physics 86-87; Math.

KOYACK, JIM; Shamokin Area HS; Ranshaw, PA; (4); Capt Chess Clb; Orch; Hon Roll; NBICL Tourn Chmpn-Chess 84-87; Blck Diamnd Tourn Chmpn-Chess 86; Top 10-States Tourn-Chess 86-87; Bloomsburg U; Comp Sci.

KOZA, STEPHANIE; Portage Area HS; Portage, PA; (4); 16/120; Chorus; Church Choir; Bsktbl; Trk; NHS; Chorus Treas 86-87; Ntl Hnr Soc Sec 86-87; Bus Adm.

KOZAK, BARBARA; Altoona Area HS; Altoona, PA; (3); Political Wkr; Nwsp Ed-Chief; Stat Bsktbl; Socr; Im Sftbl; Im Vllybl; Wt Lftg; Jr NHS; NEDT 84-85; Clncl Psych.

KOZAK, KORY; Emmaus HS; Macungie, PA; (3); 130/548; Sec Soph Cls; JV Bsbl; Capt Var Ftbl; Im Wt Lftg; Chem Engnrng.

KOZAK, MICHAEL; Thomas Jefferson HS; Bradford, PA; (4); 126/260; Church Yth Grp; Ski Clb; Varsity Clb; VP Concert Band; Sec Stu Cncl; JV Bsbl; Var L Ftbl; Im Wt Lftg; Hon Roll; U Of Pittsburgh-Bradford; Dntl.

KOZAR, JOHN; Connellsville SR HS; Dickerson Run, PA; (2); Science Clb; Rep Frsh Cls; JV Bsbl; Hon Roll; Law Enfrcmt.

KOZAR, SCOTT; Cornell HS; Coraopolis, PA; (3); 4/75; Church Yth Grp; Key Clb; Spanish Clb; Yrbk Ed-Chief; Yrbk Stf; Pres Frsh Cls; Var L Bsbl; Var L Bsktbl; Var L Ftbl; High Hon Roll; KDKA-TV Extra Effort Awd 87; Finance.

KOZDEN, MICHAEL; Southern Lehigh HS; Center Valley, PA; (4); 20/230; Varsity Clb; JV Bsbl; JV Var Ftbl; Var Trk; High Hon Roll; Hon Roll; NHS; Ntl Merit Ltr; Schlr Ath 87; Princpls List 84-85; Air Force Acad; Aerospc Engrng.

KOZEL, CYNTHIA; Langley HS; Pittsburgh, PA; (3); Ski Clb; Nwsp Ed-Chief; Nwsp Rptr; JV Vllybl; High Hon Roll; Hon Roll; NHS; U Of Pittsburgh; Bus Mgmnt.

KOZEN, LISA; Langley HS; Pittsburgh, PA; (3); Drama Clb; JA; Drill Tm; School Musical; Stage Crew; Var Pom Pon; Hon Roll; Jr NHS; St Schlr; Church Yth Grp; Vlntr Hndcppd 84; Purdue U; Engrng.

KOZERSKI, BRENDA; James M Coughlin HS; Wilkes Barre, PA; (3); 28/374; Cmnty Wkr; Chorus; Church Choir; Color Guard; Drill Tm; Pom Pon; High Hon Roll; Jr NHS; NHS; NEDT Awd; Elem Educ.

KOZICKY, LILIA; Moravian Acad; Bethlehem, PA; (3); Chess Clb; Key Clb; Model UN; NFL; Scholastic Bowl; School Play; Nwsp Ed-Chief; Yrbk Stf; Bsktbl; Tennis; Intl Law.

KOZIELEC, LAURA; Conemaugh Township HS; Hollsopple, PA; (3); 17/119; Drama Clb; L Varsity Clb; Sec Chorus; School Musical; Nwsp Bus Mgr; Nwsp Rptr; Nwsp Stf; Rep Stu Cncl; Cheerleading; Rotary Awd; Ryla, Rotary Yth Ldrshp Assn 86-87; Polish Heritg Cncl 86 & 87; Spcl Olympcs Vlntr 83-87; Bradford; Fshn.

KOZIKOWSKI, DENISE; Pequea Valley HS; Paradise, PA; (4); 37/114; Church Yth Grp; Sec Varsity Clb; Acpl Chr; Trs Band; Chorus; Jazz Band; Trs Stu Cncl; Var Fld Hcky; Capt Var Sftbl; Hon Roll; Jaycees Awd; Immaculata Coll; Lib Arts.

KOZLOFF, SAMUEL; Wyomissing Area HS; Wyomissing, PA; (4); 13/99; Pres French Clb; JCL; Model UN; Band; Yrbk Sprt Ed; NHS; Pres Schlr; Ski Clb; Concert Band; Jazz Band; Natl Latin Hnr Soc 86-87; Frgn Lang Achvt Awd 87; All Amer Yth Hnr Musician 85-87; U Of PA; Poltcl Sci.

KOZLOWSKI III, EDMUND J; Northampton Area SR HS; Bath, PA; (4); 24/430; AFS; Library Aide; Pres VICA; High Hon Roll; Hon Roll; NHS; Yth Of Month 86; Outstndg Sr Sci Compu Applctn 86-87; USAF.

KOZMA, CORINNE; Liberty HS; Bethlehem, PA; (3); 20/445; Capt Dance Clb; Mrchg Band; Im Score Keeper; Var Twrlr; Hon Roll; NHS; Prfct Atten Awd; Bio.

KOZMINSKI, FRANCIS; St Marys Area HS; Force, PA; (3); 13/298; Hon Roll; NHS.

KOZMINSKI, MIKE; Seneca Valley SR HS; Zelienople, PA; (4); 52/340; Boy Scts; Church Yth Grp; Ski Clb; Ftbl; Wt Lftg; Hon Roll; 1st Yr Awd Acadmc Achvt 86-87; Pittsburgh U; Bio Chem.

KOZUSKO, ANNA M; Indiana Area SR HS; Indiana, PA; (3); 18/320; Church Yth Grp; Key Clb; School Musical; Yrbk Ed-Chief; Yrbk Stf; Cheerleading; Socr; High Hon Roll; Jr NHS; NHS; Englsh Awd 85; Grphics Awd-Gettysburg Yrbk Exprnc 86; Penn ST U; Jrnlsm.

KRACH, MICHAEL; Du-Bois Area HS; Luthersburg, PA; (2); Church Yth Grp; Band; Concert Band; Jazz Band; Mrchg Band; School Musical; Variety Show; Nice Kid Awd 85-86; I U 6 Honors Band 86-87; Music.

KRACK, DAVID; Warren County Christian Schl; Irvine, PA; (1); Church Yth Grp; Rep Stu Cncl; JV Bsktbl; Sftbl; High Hon Roll.

KRACZ, DIANNE; Northern Chester County Tech Schl; Phoenixville, PA; (3); 12/128; Pep Clb; Nwsp Ed-Chief; Nwsp Rptr; Yrbk Stf; Brdcst Jrnlsm.

KRAEMER, ERIC; Carrick HS; Pittsburgh, PA; (4); 11/381; Math Tm; Q&S; Ski Clb; School Musical; Sec Sr Cls; Stu Cncl; Im Var Bsktbl; Var L Vllybl; High Hon Roll; NHS.

KRAFFT, MARQUERITE; Archbishop Kennedy HS; Philadelphia, PA; (3); Church Yth Grp; Cmnty Wkr; Trs French Clb; Office Aide; Church Choir; Knghts Clmbs Rlgn Awd 84; Educ.

KRAFT, AMIE; Phoenixville Area HS; Phoenixville, PA; (3); Key Clb; Pep Clb; Varsity Clb; Church Choir; Var Fld Hcky; Var Lcrss; High Hon Roll.

KRAFT, MARGARET; Bishop Mc Cort HS; Johnstown, PA; (3); Girl Scts; Math Tm; Mu Alpha Theta; Spanish Clb; Speech Tm; Tennis; High Hon Roll; NHS; Spanish NHS.

KRAFT, MELISSA; Freedom SR HS; Bethlehem, PA; (4); 58/446; Church Yth Grp; Cmnty Wkr; Hosp Aide; Pep Clb; Chorus; Capt Cheerleading; High Hon Roll; Hon Roll; Hnr Rl; Lehigh U; Gov.

KRAHE, MELANIE; Girard HS; Girard, PA; (3); 3/133; Concert Band; Drm Mjr(t); Jazz Band; Mrchg Band; Trs Pres Stu Cncl; Trk; High Hon Roll; NHS; Ntl Merit Ltr; Band; Schlrshp PA Governrs Schl Sci 87.

KRAHULEC, JIM; Cumberland Valley HS; Boiling Springs, PA; (3); 7/600; Spanish Clb; Band; Jazz Band; Mrchg Band; Orch; Stage Crew; Symp Band; Hon Roll; NHS; Math.

KRAISINGER, REGE; Mt Pleasant Area SR; Mt Pleasant, PA; (4); 17/240; Boy Scts; Church Yth Grp; Cmnty Wkr; German Clb; Letterman Clb; Var L Ftbl; High Hon Roll; NHS; NEDT Awd; Comp Engrng.

KRAISNITSKY, MARIA; Nativity BVM HS; Pottsville, PA; (2); 15/78; French Clb; Girl Scts; Hosp Aide; Math Clb; Ski Clb; Color Guard; Drill Tm; Capt Cheerleading; Var Crs Cntry; Hon Roll; Villanova; Accntng.

KRAJACIC, JEFFRY; Mc Keesport Area HS; Mc Keesport, PA; (2); Bsbl; Bsktbl; Ftbl.

KRAJACIC, TINA; Avella Area HS; Washington, PA; (3); Art Clb; 4-H; French Clb; Letterman Clb; Pep Clb; Ski Clb; Varsity Clb; Cheerleading; Score Keeper; 4-H Awd; Pres Acad Awd 85; Sci Fair Awd 87; CA U; Med.

KRAJCI, TRACEY; Central Bucks HS West; New Britain, PA; (4); 73/489; Church Yth Grp; SADD; Teachers Aide; Capt Var Cheerleading; High Hon Roll; Hon Roll; NHS; Beaver Coll; Elem Educ.

KRAJEWSKI, SANDRA; St Hubert HS; Philadelphia, PA; (3); 45/421; Art Clb; Church Yth Grp; Office Aide; Var JV Bowling; L Var Sftbl; Hon Roll; Prfct Atten 86-87.

KRAJNAK, MARK; Bishop O Reilley HS; Swoyersville, PA; (3); Spanish Clb; VP Frsh Cls; Stu Cncl; Var L Bsktbl; Var Capt Crs Cntry; Hon Roll; Prfct Atten Awd; Spanish NHS; Comm.

KRAJNIKOVICH, KIMBERLY; Butler SR HS; Bulter, PA; (4); Cmnty Wkr; French Clb; Drm & Bgl; Drm Mjr(t); Mrchg Band; School Musical; Twrlr; Hon Roll; Thesps; Stage Crew; Miss Butler Cnty & Miss Amer Pgnt 87; Butler Cnty JR Miss Pgnt 87; Clarion U; Intl Bus.

KRALL JR, LEONARD D; Center HS; Monaca, PA; (3); 18/187; Am Leg Boys St; German Clb; Quiz Bowl; Varsity Clb; Color Guard; JV Im Bsktbl; Var Mgr(s); Var Capt Trk; High Hon Roll; NHS; Yth For Understndng Intl Exchng Merit Cert & Frgn Lang Comp Hnrb Mntn 87; Military Sci.

KRALL, MELISSA; Eastern Lebanon County HS; Schaefferstown, PA; (3); 29/146; Church Yth Grp; Hosp Aide; Ski Clb; Rep Jr Cls; Var Bsktbl; Var L Sftbl.

KRALLY, DARRIN; Chartiers Valley HS; Carnegie, PA; (3); Church Yth Grp; Band; Jazz Band; Pep Band; School Musical; JV Bsbl; NHS; Crmnlgy.

KRAMARSKI, ROSANNE; Southmoreland SR HS; Scottdale, PA; (4); 39/230; Letterman Clb; Spanish Clb; Yrbk Stf; Trs Soph Cls; Trs Jr Cls; Trs Sr Cls; Rep Stu Cncl; Bsktbl; Sftbl; Tennis; Army Schlr/Athl Awd 87; Most Athltc 87; Clarion U Of PA.

KRAMER, CRYSTAL; Shamokin Area HS; Shamokin, PA; (2); 11/250; Church Yth Grp; Pep Clb; High Hon Roll; Hon Roll; Psychology.

KRAMER, KRISTA; Conemaugh Township Area HS; Hollsopple, PA; (3); 5/121; Church Yth Grp; Trs Key Clb; Concert Band; Mrchg Band; School Musical; Trs Jr Cls; Rep Stu Cncl; Hon Roll; Trs NHS; Hosp Aide; Rotary Yth Ldrshp Awd 87; Pharm.

KRAMER, LISA; Central Dauphin HS; Harrisburg, PA; (2); 20/400; Art Clb; Chorus; Var JV Cheerleading; JV Sftbl; Im Vllybl; High Hon Roll; Hon Roll; Prfct Atten Awd; Pres Schlr; Notre Dame; Psych.

KRAMER, MICHELE; Monaca HS; Monaca, PA; (3); 4/88; Pep Clb; Ski Clb; Drill Tm; Yrbk Ed-Chief; Yrbk Stf; Rep Stu Cncl; JV Cheerleading; High Hon Roll; Hon Roll; NHS; Gftd Art Pgm 84-87; Kent ST; Grphc Dsgn.

KRAMER, MITCHELL; Solebury Schl; Jenkintown, PA; (4); 3/22; Drama Clb; Quiz Bowl; Teachers Aide; School Musical; School Play; Variety Show; Yrbk Phtg; Yrbk Stf; Lit Mag; Pres Frsh Cls; Art Histry.

KRAMER, NADINE; St Clair Area HS; St Clair, PA; (4); 7/77; Drama Clb; Mu Alpha Theta; Co-Capt Drill Tm; Nwsp Stf; Yrbk Stf; Off Frsh Cls; Off Soph Cls; Off Jr Cls; Dnfth Awd; Kiwanis Awd; Susquehanna U; Occuptnl Thrpy.

KRAMER, SCOTT; Trinity Christian Schl; Pittsburgh, PA; (2); 4/20; Church Yth Grp; Stage Crew; Yrbk Phtg; JV Bsktbl; JV Socr; Jr NHS.

KRAMER, SUSAN; East Pennsboro Area HS; Camp Hill, PA; (2); 6/190; Spanish Clb; Flag Corp; Mrchg Band; Score Keeper; High Hon Roll; NHS.

KRAMER, WILLIAM; Hamburg Area SR JR HS; Hamburg, PA; (4); 42/144; Pres Church Yth Grp; Var Stat Socr; Hon Roll; Rotary Awd; Physcs Acadmc Awd 86; Mark Musser Mem Awd 87; Best Arch Stu Awd 87; Spring Garden Coll; Arch.

KRAMMES, MARY; Tri-Valley HS; Hegins, PA; (3); 9/76; Ski Clb; Band; Concert Band; Drm Mjr(t); Mrchg Band; Yrbk Sprt Ed; Stat Bsktbl; Var L Sftbl; JV Var Vllybl; NHS; Phys Ther.

KRAMRICH, AMI; Bethlehem Center HS; Denbo, PA; (2); 16/156; Drama Clb; FBLA; Ski Clb; Color Guard; Yrbk Stf; Hon Roll; Accntng.

KRANACK, KATRINA; Bishop Boyle HS; Pittsburgh, PA; (3); Cmnty Wkr; French Clb; Hosp Aide; Chorus; Nwsp Stf; Yrbk Stf; Hon Roll; Chrs Awd 86; Bus Awd For Typng 87; Jaon Of Arc Mdlln 87; Pharm.

KRANAK, JOAN; Plum SR HS; Pittsburgh, PA; (3); AFS; French Clb; Chorus; Church Choir; School Musical; School Play; Tennis; NHS; Prfct Atten Awd; Rotary Awd; WPIAL Sctn IV Champs Tennis 85; Hnr Grd Plum Cmmncmnt Ceremonies 87; Ltr In Tennis 86-87; Law.

KRANCE, AMY CHRISTINE; Moon SR HS; Corapolis, PA; (4); Church Yth Grp; Hosp Aide; Key Clb; Acpl Chr; Chorus; School Musical; School Play; Yrbk Rptr; Off Stu Cncl; Var Stat Crs Cntry; Prom Crt 86; Hmcmng Qn 86-87; Bethany Coll; Comm.

KRANKOWSKI, KIMBERLY; Lebanon Catholic HS; Fredericksburg, PA; (3); German Clb; Hosp Aide; Chorus; Hon Roll; NHS.

KRAPF, DANIELLE; Louis E Dieruff HS; Allentown, PA; (2); Art Clb; Dance Clb; Key Clb; Math Tm; Pep Clb; Science Clb; Ski Clb; Band; Chorus; Concert Band; Mrtn Lthr Kng Essy Cntst 86; Psyctry.

KRAPF, JACQUELINE; Carbondale Area HS; Simpson, PA; (3); Art Clb; FBLA; Sec German Clb; Ski Clb; Spanish Clb; Chorus; Flag Corp; High Hon Roll; Hon Roll; Htl Mngmnt.

KRAPF, LORI ANN; Hazleton HS; Hazleton, PA; (2); Church Yth Grp; Office Aide; Pep Clb; Yrbk Stf; Im Bsktbl; Var Diving; Var Swmmng; High Hon Roll; Hon Roll; Spanish NHS; Kngs Coll Spnsh Cont 4th Pl Awd 86; Penn ST U.

KRAPP JR, DONALD; Northeast Catholic HS; Philadelphia, PA; (4); 5/362; Boy Scts; Science Clb; Concert Band; Jazz Band; Mrchg Band; NHS; Ntl Merit SF; Grmn Awd; Math.

KRAPPWEIS, RICH; Baldwin HS; Pittsburgh, PA; (2); 80/481; Cmnty Wkr; Hon Roll; U Of Pittsburg.

KRASAS, JENNIFER L; Academy Of Notre Dame De Namur; Newtown Square, PA; (4); 1/74; Hosp Aide; Math Tm; Chorus; Yrbk Stf; Var Lcrss Mgr(s); High Hon Roll; Ntl Merit SF; Natl Hstry Day 1st Dist 86; Alumn Rep 87; Intl Rltns.

KRASHNAK, LAURA; Coughlin HS; Wilkes Barre, PA; (3); Pre German Clb; Key Clb; Library Aide; Stu Cncl; Vllybl; Hon Roll; NHS; Lt Wnnr Vlybl 87; Psych.

KRASINSKI, PAUL; Mc Dowell HS; Erie, PA; (4); 41/599; Ski Clb; High Hon Roll; Hon Roll; NHS; Penn ST Cmmnwlth Campus Schlrshp 87; Penn ST U; Elec Engr.

KRASKI, AMY; Carrick HS; Pittsburgh, PA; (3); Pres Church Yth Grp; Q&S; Nwsp Stf; Stu Cncl; Cheerleading; Powder Puff Ftbl; Hon Roll.

KRASKO, KRISTEN; Lindeh Hall HS; Lititz, PA; (3); 5/40; School Play; Nwsp Phtg; Lit Mag; Stu Cncl; Mgr(s); Capt Tennis; High Hon Roll; Hon Roll; NHS.

KRASKO, KRISTEN; Linden Hall HS; Rumson, NJ; (3); 6/35; Office Aide; Q&S; Varsity Clb; School Play; Nwsp Phtg; Lit Mag; Stu Cncl; Fld Hcky; Capt Co-Capt Tennis; High Hon Roll; HOBY Awd 86; Ed.

KRASUCKI, COLLEEN; Muncy HS; Muncy, PA; (4); 4/75; Church Yth Grp; Sec French Clb; Pep Clb; Varsity Clb; Yrbk Ed-Chief; Yrbk Phtg; Yrbk Stf; Rep Stu Cncl; JV Var Socr; Var L Sftbl; PA ST U; Psych.

KRASZEWSKI, KELLY; Pennsbury HS; Yardley, PA; (4); 39/770; Spanish Clb; Var Trk; Im Vllybl; Hon Roll; NHS; Pres Acad Ftnss Awd 86-87; Pennsbury Schlrshp 87; Penn ST; Bus.

KRATER, BRADLEY; Blair County Christian HS; Altoona, PA; (4); 3/4; Church Yth Grp; Chorus; Nwsp Stf; Pres Jr Cls; Pres Sr Cls; Pres Stu Cncl; Capt L Bsktbl; Im Ftbl; Capt L Socr; Var Trk; All Lg Socr MVP 86-87; All Lg Bsktbl MVP 86-87; Cedarville; Pre-Law.

KRATZ, AMY; Emmaus HS; Macungie, PA; (3); 20/450; Church Yth Grp; Key Clb; Model UN; Spanish Clb; Band; High Hon Roll; JP Sousa Awd; NHS; Opt Clb Awd; Pres Schlr; Profsnl Actor Dinner Theatre; 1st Dist Bnd; Perfect Attndnc; Pre Law.

KRATZ, GIRARD; G A R Memorial HS; Wilkes-Barre, PA; (3); German Clb; Key Clb; Band; Chorus; Concert Band; Jazz Band; Mrchg Band; Orch; Stage Crew; Stu Cncl.

KRATZ, HEATHER; Quakertown Community HS; Quakertown, PA; (1); German Clb; Yrbk Stf; Rep Frsh Cls; Stu Cncl; Capt Cheerleading; Jr NHS; Penn ST U; Arch.

KRATZ, KEITH; Souderton Area HS; Telford, PA; (4); 8/350; Church Yth Grp; Bsktbl; Socr; Tennis; High Hon Roll; Pres Schlr; Eugene Klimovich Sci Awd 87; Cornell U; Nutrtnl Sci.

KRATZ, RUTH; Methacton HS; Norristown, PA; (3); 78/381; FBLA; Teachers Aide; Church Choir; Hon Roll; Nrstwn Bus & Prfsnl Wmns Clb Awd 87; K Gibbs Schl Vly Frg Ldrshp Awd 87; Scrtrl.

KRATZER, DANELLE; Middleburg HS; Middleburg, PA; (3); 19/138; Pres Church Yth Grp; Ski Clb; Pres SADD; Band; Chorus; School Musical; Nwsp Stf; Yrbk Stf; Stu Cncl; Hon Roll; Prfct Attnd Awd 86-87; Elem Ed.

KRATZER, KATRINA; West Snyder HS; Beavertown, PA; (3); Chorus; Nwsp Ed-Chief; Nwsp Rptr; Nwsp Stf; Yrbk Rptr; Yrbk Stf; Hon Roll; Accntng I Awd 87; S Hills Bus Schl; Accntng.

KRATZER, KIMBERLY LYN; Emmaus HS; Emmaus, PA; (4); 57/469; Color Guard; High Hon Roll; Hon Roll; NHS; Ntl Merit Schol; Clercl Engl Awd 87; Offc Prctc Awd 87; Pres Acdmc Ftnss Awd 87; Trvl.

KRATZER, RUSTY; Central Dauphin HS; Harrisburg, PA; (3); 73/269; Key Clb; VP Soph Cls; VP Jr Cls; VP Sr Cls; Stu Cncl; Vllybl; High Hon Roll; Hon Roll; Jr NHS; NCTE Awd; Jrnlsm.

KRATZER, TROY; Middleburg HS; Middleburg, PA; (3); 13/135; Chess Clb; Church Yth Grp; Bsbl; Bsktbl; Comp Sci.

KRAUSE, BILL; Moshannon Valley HS; Houtzdale, PA; (3); Church Yth Grp; Varsity Clb; Bsbl; Ftbl; U Of Pittsburgh; Frstry.

KRAUSE, CHRISTINE; Mahanoy Area HS; Morea, PA; (2); French Clb; Chorus; Color Guard; Mrchg Band; Variety Show; Trk; Twrlr; Air Force; Nrsng.

KRAUSE, CHRISTOPHER J; Conestoga SR HS; Paoli, PA; (3); AFS; Am Leg Boys St; Church Yth Grp; Cmnty Wkr; Latin Clb; Service Clb; Stage Crew; Rep Frsh Cls; Rep Soph Cls; Rep Jr Cls; Arch.

KRAUSE, DEBRA; Northern Lehigh HS; Slatington, PA; (3); 1/166; Trs 4-H; Ski Clb; VP Soph Cls; Stu Cncl; Capt Var Crs Cntry; Var Trk; 4-H Awd; High Hon Roll; Lion Awd; NHS; Acctng.

KRAUSE, KIMBERLY ANN; Pine Grove Area HS; Pine Grove, PA; (4); 11/116; Am Leg Aux Girls St; Office Aide; SADD; Chorus; Mrchg Band; Ed Yrbk Stf; Sec NHS; Hon Roll; May Stu Of Month 87; Freeman Agcy Awd 87; Homeroom Rep 87; PA ST U; Teaching.

KRAUSE, MAURA FRANCES; Franklin Regional HS; Murrysville, PA; (4); Pres Spanish Clb; Nwsp Ed-Chief; Yrbk Stf; High Hon Roll; NHS; Wstnghs Sci Hnrs Inst 86-87; Sprntndnts Advsry Cncl 86-87; Pgh Pres Fnlst Hgh Achvr Awd 87; U Of Notre Dame; Engrng.

KRAVER, MELISSA; Canevin HS; Pgh, PA; (4); 15/198; Drama Clb; French Clb; FBLA; School Play; Yrbk Stf; VP Frsh Cls; VP Soph Cls; Rep Jr Cls; Rep Sr Cls; JV Cheerleading; Secy FBLA 87-88; No Absncs 86-87; Natl Hnr Socty; Robert Morris; Mgr Schl Gym.

KRAVETSKY, LAURIE; Kiski Area HS; Avonmore, PA; (4); Church Yth Grp; Pres Computer Clb; Pres Library Aide; Sec Office Aide; Science Clb; Ed Spanish Clb; Chorus; Nwsp Phtg; Var Trk; Hon Roll; IN U PA; Accntng.

KRAWIEC, FRANK; Belle Vernon Area HS; Webster, PA; (4); 31/270; FBLA; High Hon Roll; NHS; Robert Morris Coll; Acctng.

KRAYBILL, SHEILA; Elizabethtown Area HS; Elizabethtown, PA; (3); 15/250; Church Yth Grp; Pres VP 4-H; Band; Chorus; Church Choir; Concert Band; Mrchg Band; 4-H Awd; NHS; Schltc Wrtng Awd 1st Pl Essay Cnty Natl Hnrn Mntn 85; 3rd Pl Jr Rider Middle Dist ECTRA Trail Rides; Humanities.

KRAYCER, JO ANN; Bishop O Hara HS; Olyphant, PA; (3); 27/102; French Clb; Chorus; Pres Frsh Cls; Rep Stu Cncl; Stat Bsktbl; Vet Med.

KRAYCIK, TREVOR; Brandywine Heights HS; Mertztown, PA; (3); School Play; Yrbk Rptr; Yrbk Stf; Var Tennis; Broadcasting.

KRAYNACK, NATHAN; Tunkhannock Area HS; Tunkhannock, PA; (2); #2 In Class; Intnl Clb; Letterman Clb; Crs Cntry; Trk; High Hon Roll; Hon Roll; NHS; Exploring; German Clb; Key Clb.

KRAYNAK, JAMES S; Connellsville Area HS; Connellsville, PA; (4); 90/550; Band; Concert Band; Var L Ftbl; Capt L Wrstlng; Hon Roll; Jr NHS; NHS; WPIAL Wrstlng Champ 85-86; WPIAL Wrstlng Rnrup 87; Mst V Wrstlng Tm Pts Undrclsmn 86; CA U PA; Bus.

KRAYNAK, STEVEN; Lansdale Catholic HS; Hatfield, PA; (3); 24/224; Office Aide; Varsity Clb; Lit Mag; Var JV Bsktbl; Var JV Crs Cntry; JV Trk; Prfct Atten Awd; Schl Svc Awd 86-87; Outstndng Religion Stu 86-87; Hnrs Awd 84-88; Bio Sci.

KRCHNAR, CHRISTINA; Manheim Central HS; Manheim, PA; (4); 6/217; Chorus; School Musical; Yrbk Stf; Capt L Cheerleading; Var Trk; NHS; Pres Schlr; Church Yth Grp; Library Aide; Pep Clb; Amer Chmcl Soc Awd 87; Yrbk Awd 87; Lbry Aide Awd 87; Penn ST U; Chmstry.

KREBS, KIMBERLY; Milton Area SR HS; Milton, PA; (2); Trs Church Yth Grp; Intnl Clb; Band; Chorus; Color Guard; Concert Band; Mrchg Band; Capt Twrlr; Hon Roll; Prfct Atten Awd; Stu Mnth 87; Susquehnna Vly Band 87; Albright Coll; Pre Med.

KREBS, MICHELLE L; Christian School Of York; York, PA; (3); 6/60; Church Yth Grp; Chorus; Church Choir; Var Co-Capt Cheerleading; Trk; High Hon Roll; Hon Roll; Bible Quizzing Team Capt 86; E Nazarene Coll; Nrsng.

KREBS, ROBERT; Clearfield Area HS; Clearfield, PA; (4); Pres Church Yth Grp; Bsktbl; Ftbl; Wt Lftg; Hon Roll; Congressional Yth Ldrshp Cncl 87; IN U Of PA; Criminology.

KREBS, RYAN; Christian School Of York; York, PA; (2); Church Yth Grp; Drama Clb; Band; Church Choir; Var Bsbl; JV Bsktbl; Hon Roll; Eastern Nazarene Coll.

KRECH, MICHELE; Punxsutawney HS; Punxsutawney, PA; (4); 15/245; Church Yth Grp; French Clb; Hosp Aide; Church Choir; Mrchg Band; Pep Band; Spanish NHS; Vally Forge Christian; Elem Ed.

KREDEL, LYNN; Butler SR HS; Butler, PA; (3); Debate Tm; Pres 4-H; French Clb; Hosp Aide; Library Aide; Variety Show; Im Bsktbl; 4-H Awd; Hon Roll; Jr NHS.

KREEGER, TONYA; York Catholic HS; York, PA; (3); Church Yth Grp; French Clb; FBLA; Thesps; Nwsp Rptr; Im JV Bsktbl; VP L Mgr(s); VP Score Keeper; Hon Roll; Accntng.

KREGER, LISA; Villo Maria Acad; Lake City, PA; (4); 1/127; Science Clb; High Hon Roll; NHS; NEDT Awd; Val; PA Govs Schl For Sci 86; Schlrshp Duquesne U Acdmc Achvmnt 87; PA JR Sci & Gmnts 86; Duquesne U; Pharmacy.

KREGER, MELISSA; Rockwood Area HS; Rockwood, PA; (2); 15/107; Computer Clb; 4-H; Chorus; School Play; High Hon Roll; Hon Roll; Schlastic Awd 85-86; Principals Awd 85; Natl Sci Olympiad 81-82; Temple U; Pharmacy.

KREGLOW, KELLY; Easton Area HS; Orange Park, FL; (4); 67/487; Debate Tm; Drama Clb; Political Wkr; Ski Clb; Thesps; Acpl Chr; School Musical; School Play; Yrbk Ed-Chief; Yrbk Rptr; Bclrt Spkr 87; Svc & Ctznshp For Ldrshp Awd 87; H L Minder Awd 87; FL ST U; Drama.

KREIDER, ALISON; Exeter Twp SR HS; Reading, PA; (3); 14/241; Varsity Clb; School Play; Yrbk Stf; Cheerleading; Powder Puff Ftbl; Hon Roll; Jr NHS; NHS; Med.

KREIDER, CINDY; Lancaster Mennonite HS; Oxford, PA; (3); 23/155; Sec Trs Church Yth Grp; Sec 4-H; Acpl Chr; Chorus; Trs Orch; Sec Jr Cls; Off Stu Cncl; JV Fld Hcky; High Hon Roll; NHS; Med.

KREIDER, CRAIG; Solanco HS; Quarryville, PA; (3); 14/286; Church Yth Grp; Trs VP 4-H; FFA; Chorus; Church Choir; School Musical; JV Socr; Trk; High Hon Roll; Hon Roll; FFA Star Greenhand Awd 84-85; Solaneo Schlr Ag 84-85; Ag.

KREIDER, DEBORAH; Elizabethtown Area HS; Elizabethtown, PA; (3); Sec Rep Church Yth Grp; Chorus; Vllybl; NHS.

KREIDER, HOLLY J; Solanco HS; Quarryville, PA; (3); 1/273; Drama Clb; Exploring; VP Rptr 4-H; Trs Girl Scts; Hosp Aide; Spanish Clb; School Play; High Hon Roll; NHS; Ntl Merit Ltr.

KREIDER, LORI D; Garden Spot HS; E Earl, PA; (4); Church Yth Grp; Drama Clb; 4-H; Spanish Clb; Band; Concert Band; Stage Crew; Nwsp Ed-Chief; Nwsp Rptr; Rotary Awd; Lang.

KREIG, ERICA; Central Scranton HS; Scranton, PA; (2); Hosp Aide; Spanish Clb; SADD; Chorus; Color Guard; Ftbl; Trk; Villanova; Sociology.

KREIGER, DEANNA; West Branch HS; Kylertown, PA; (3); 4/120; Drama Clb; VP Spanish Clb; SADD; Band; Chorus; Church Choir; Concert Band; Mrchg Band; Rep Stu Cncl; NHS; Music Prfmnce.

KREINBROOK, STACY; Connellsville Area SR HS; Mount Pleasant, PA; (3); 2/550; Office Aide; Sec Service Clb; Chorus; Mrchg Band; Yrbk Stf; Stu Cncl; Stat Bsktbl; High Hon Roll; NHS; Spanish NHS; Spec Ed.

KREINDLER, LIZ; Delaware HS; Milford, PA; (3); SADD; Flag Corp; Nwsp Rptr; Nwsp Stf; Rep Soph Cls; Rep Jr Cls; Stu Cncl; Cheerleading; Mgr(s); Sftbl; Syracuse U; Physlgy.

KREISER, JOE; Northern Lebanon HS; Annville, PA; (2); 18/180; JV Bsbl; L Bsktbl; Hon Roll; Jr NHS.

KREISER, KARLA E; Lower Dauphin HS; Hershey, PA; (4); Am Leg Aux Girls St; VP Exploring; Hosp Aide; Chorus; School Musical; Nwsp Rptr; Nwsp Stf; Yrbk Stf; Rep Sr Cls; Rep Stu Cncl; Grls Ensmbl; Stage Crew; AZ ST U; Arch.

KREISER, LARRY; Cedar Crest HS; Lebanon, PA; (2); Church Yth Grp; Var Bowling.

KREISER, TODD M; Eastern Lebanon County HS; Newmanstown, PA; (4); 30/177; VICA; Hon Roll; NHS; Drftng Stdnt Yr 87; Lincoln Tech Inst; Drftng Tech.

KREISLER, AMY; Elkland Area HS; Elkland, PA; (4); 7/75; French Clb; SADD; Nwsp Stf; Stat Bsktbl; Trk; Hon Roll; NHS; Williamsport Area CC; Nrsng.

KREITZ, DUSTIN; Montoursville Area HS; Trout Run, PA; (3); 35/170; Boy Scts; Civic Clb; German Clb; Ski Clb; JV Ftbl; JV Wrstlng; Crmnl Just.

KREITZER, DANNY; Hanover Area JR SR HS; Wilkes Barre, PA; (4); 3/156; VP Key Clb; Ski Clb; Off Stu Cncl; High Hon Roll; NHS; PA JR Acad Sci 3rd Awd; Pres Acdmc Ftns Awd; U Of Scranton; Phys Thrpy.

KREITZER JR, EUGENE; Northern Lebanon HS; Fredericksburg, PA; (4); 1/150; Pres Church Yth Grp; Pres FFA; Model UN; Teachers Aide; Church Choir; Ftbl; Powder Puff Ftbl; Trk; Dnfth Awd; High Hon Roll; Achvt Amer Hstry 84 & 86; Outstndng Ag Stu 86; Star Grnhnd, Star Chptr Frmr 84-87; Ag.

KREJNUS, SUSAN; Cambria Heights HS; Elmora, PA; (4); 25/189; Drama Clb; FHA; Library Aide; NFL; Concert Band; Mrchg Band; Yrbk Stf; High Hon Roll; NHS; Modren Miss Schlrshp Pgnt 83-84.

KREM, CHRIS; Bethlehem Catholic HS; Bethlehem, PA; (3); Engrng.

KREMER, BETH; Uniontown Area SR HS; Uniontown, PA; (4); French Clb; JA; SADD; Color Guard; Flag Corp; Mrchg Band; School Play; French Hon Soc; High Hon Roll; Pittsburgh U; Legl.

KREMER, CHERI; Eisenhower HS; Russell, PA; (3); Teachers Aide; Stage Crew; Vllybl; High Hon Roll; NHS; Zoolgy.

KREMPA, LISA; Coatesville Area SR HS; Coatesville, PA; (3); 141/509; FBLA; Girl Scts; Service Clb; Ski Clb; SADD; Color Guard; Mrchg Band; Nwsp Ed-Chief; Nwsp Rptr; Nwsp Stf; Jrnlsm Awd Keystone Awd 86; Color Guard Capt Awd 87; Goldey Beacon; Sec.

KREMPASKY, JOHN; Danville Area HS; Danville, PA; (3); 15/194; Debate Tm; Key Clb; NFL; Speech Tm; High Hon Roll; NHS; Ntl Merit Schol.

KREMPOSKY, JANICE; Brownsville Area HS; Allison, PA; (3); Drama Clb; FBLA; SADD; Teachers Aide; School Musical; High Hon Roll; Hon Roll; Hmcmng Crt 86-87; ICM Schl Of Business; Trvl.

KREMUS, PAMELA; Northampton SR HS; Northampton, PA; (4); Rep Stu Cncl; Powder Puff Ftbl; Var Capt Swmmng; Var Trk; High Hon Roll; Hon Roll; E PA Interschltc Ath Conf All Star Tm 85-86 & 86-87; Kutztown U; Elem Ed.

KRENTZ, TAMMY; Warwick HS; Lititz, PA; (3); 6/267; Varsity Clb; Yrbk Phtg; Yrbk Stf; Stat Bsktbl; Stat Fld Hcky; Var Mgr(s); Stat Trk; High Hon Roll; NHS.

KREPAK, CRAIG; Northwestern Lehigh HS; New Tripoli, PA; (3); 31/153; 4-H; JV L Wrstlng; Hon Roll; Arch.

KRESGE, ROXANE; Pleasant Valley HS; Nazareth, PA; (4); Math Tm; Scholastic Bowl; Ski Clb; Teachers Aide; Varsity Clb; Rep Sr Cls; Rep Stu Cncl; Var L Bsktbl; Var L Cheerleading; Var L Sftbl; Acad All Amer Awd 85-86; Bloomsburg U; Bus.

KRESHON, JIMMY; Lincoln HS; Ellwood City, PA; (3); 24/162; Spanish Clb; Chorus; VP Jr Cls; Bsktbl; Capt Golf; High Hon Roll; Hon Roll; NHS; U Wake Forest; Pre-Med.

KRESPAN, STACEY; Eisenhower HS; Sugargrove, PA; (3); Chorus; Church Choir; Madrigals; Pres Orch; Stu Cncl; JV Var Bsktbl; JV Var Vllybl; Hon Roll; Rep Frsh Cls; Rep Jr Cls; Dist Chorus 86-87; Regional Chorus 86-87; All ST Chours 86-87; Music.

KRESS, BRIAN; Coughlin HS; Hudson, PA; (3); Aud/Vis; Math Clb; Ski Clb; Yrbk Stf; High Hon Roll; Hon Roll; Lion Awd; NHS; NEDT Awd; Sta Membr WRKC-FM; NY U; Film.

KRESSLER, JILL; Saucon Valley SR HS; Hellertown, PA; (4); 8/156; Church Yth Grp; Hosp Aide; Model UN; Spanish Clb; Yrbk Stf; Stat L Wrstlng; High Hon Roll; Lion Awd; NHS; Pres Schlr; Dolrs Luna/Spnsh Clb Awd 87; Bloomsburg U Of PA; Nrsng.

KRESSLEY, CARSON; Northwestern Lehigh HS; Orefield, PA; (4); 14/168; 4-H; Nwsp Rptr; Yrbk Phtg; High Hon Roll; NHS; Pres Schlr; Grmn Awd 85-87; Pres Acdmc Ftns Awd 87; Kutztown U; Bus Admin.

KRESTAR, DIANE; Greater Johnstown Vo-Tech; S Fork, PA; (2).

KRETCHMAN, SUSAN; Meyersdale Area HS; Meyersdale, PA; (3); Sec Church Yth Grp; Sec VP French Clb; Chorus; Church Choir; Concert Band; Mrchg Band; School Musical; School Play; Yrbk Stf; Sec Bsktbl; Crtv Wrtng Awd 85; Cmnctns.

KRETCHMAR, JENNIFER; State College Area SR HS; State College, PA; (2); 1/536; Church Yth Grp; Var Bsktbl; Powder Puff Ftbl; JV Sftbl; Im Tennis; Cit Awd; High Hon Roll; Biology Awd; German Awd; 1st Tm All-Star Mid-Allegheny Conf-Bsktbll; Lib Arts.

KRETT, KIM M; Scranton Preparatory Schl; Olyphant, PA; (2); 55/190; Dance Clb; VP Hosp Aide; Chorus; School Play; Yrbk Phtg; Var Mgr(s); JV Score Keeper; Var L Trk; High Hon Roll; Hon Roll; Med Dctr.

KREUTER, CHRISTINE; Belle Vernon Area HS; Belle Vernon, PA; (3); Chess Clb; Cmnty Wkr; Pep Clb; Concert Band; Mrchg Band; Pep Band; Powder Puff Ftbl; Sftbl; Vllybl; Hon Roll; Spnsh Awd; Vlybl Letter; Nrsng.

KREZANOSKY, TOM; Pottstown SR HS; Pottstown, PA; (3); 37/155; Computer Clb; JA; Var Bsbl; Accntng.

KRIDER, GLENDA; Tyrone Area HS; Tyrone, PA; (2); Library Aide Awd 86 & 87; Social Wrkr.

KRIDLER, BRIAN; Mercyhurst Prep HS; Erie, PA; (4); 8/155; Thesps; Sec Stu Cncl; Bsktbl; Socr; Trk; Hon Roll; Kiwanis Awd; NHS; SR Maura Smith Athltc Awd, George B Stimmell Memrl Schlrshp, US Army Rsrv Schlr/Athlt Awd 87; Kutztown U Of PA; Comm Dsgn.

KRIEG, HEIDI; St Marys Area HS; St Marys, PA; (3); Hosp Aide; Stat Ftbl; Trk; Hon Roll; Phys Ther.

KRIEGER, BILL; Fort Cherry HS; Mc Donald, PA; (3); 9/147; Computer Clb; Drama Clb; French Clb; Math Clb; Science Clb; Ski Clb; Thesps; School Play; High Hon Roll; NHS; Pre Med.

KRIEGER, ERIC; Connellsville Area HS; Connellsville, PA; (4); 25/521; Church Yth Grp; Drama Clb; High Hon Roll; NHS; Acdmc All-Amrcn 85-86; VFW Teen Bsbll ST Chmp Tm 84; WV U; Engnrng.

KRIEGER, KAREN; Shamokin Area HS; Shamokin, PA; (2); 59/250; Drama Clb; Pep Clb; Science Clb; SADD; Var Trk; Hon Roll; Law.

KRIEGER, WILLIAM; Fort Cherry HS; Mc Donald, PA; (3); Boy Scts; Church Yth Grp; Drama Clb; French Clb; Math Clb; Science Clb; School Play; High Hon Roll; Pre Med.

KRIFCHER, RONALD; Shady Side Acad; Uniontown, PA; (4); Chess Clb; Science Clb; Ski Clb; Spanish Clb; Temple Yth Grp; JV Tennis; JV Trk; High Hon Roll; JV Wt Lftg; Hon Roll; Smifnlst Ntl Hspnc Schlr Awds Pgm 87; PA Cert Of Merit-Outstndng Prfrmnc SAT 87; Eco.

KRILEY, BRIAN; Butler Area HS; Butler, PA; (3); Church Yth Grp; French Clb; Band; Concert Band; Jazz Band; Mrchg Band; Symp Band; Variety Show; PA ST U; Elec Engrng.

KRILEY, ERIC; Butler SR HS; Butler, PA; (3); Thesps; Acpl Chr; Chorus; Church Choir; School Musical; Swing Chorus; Hon Roll; Eastern Chorus 87, ST Chorus 87-88; Music Ed.

KRIMERSHMOYS, GARY; Central HS; Philadelphia, PA; (2); JV Gym; Hon Roll; PRIME Smmr Pgm 85-86; Princeton; Engrng.

KRINER, KEVIN; Athens Area HS; Ulster, PA; (3); Crmnl Just.

KRINER, MICHAEL; Lower Dauphin HS; Grantville, PA; (3); 16/277; Boy Scts; Pres Exploring; Var L Bsbl; Var L Socr; Var L Wrstlng; High Hon Roll; NHS; Prfct Atten Awd; Rotary Awd; Church Yth Grp; Dist Ldrshp Camp 87; Engrng.

KRINGER, ANN MARIE; Hazleton HS; Hazleton, PA; (4); 30/376; Cmnty Wkr; Office Aide; Variety Show; Nwsp Stf; Yrbk Stf; Var L Bsktbl; Var L Sftbl; High Hon Roll; NHS; U Scranton; Pre-Med.

KRIPPEL, NICOLE; Nazareth Acad; Phila, PA; (3); Debate Tm; NFL; Spanish Clb; Speech Tm; Chorus; Ed Lit Mag; Im Bowling; JV Var Mgr(s); JV Var Score Keeper; Im Vllybl; Psych.

KRISCIUNAS, HELENE M; St Hubert HS; Philadelphia, PA; (3); 109/421; Church Yth Grp; Office Aide; Pep Clb; Rep Stu Cncl; JV Capt Bsktbl; Var Socr; Var Sftbl; Var Trk; Hon Roll.

KRISCIUNAS, JOHN; Council Rock HS; Holland, PA; (3); 96/976; Cmnty Wkr; Spanish Clb; Im Bsktbl; Im Gym; Im Vllybl; Im Vllybl; JV Wrstlng; High Hon Roll; Hon Roll; NHS; Mr Bucks Cnty-Body Building 3rd Pl 86; Physcl Thrpy.

KRISE, BENJAMIN; Seneca Valley HS; Mars, PA; (2); Letterman Clb; Rep Frsh Cls; Var L Bsbl; Var L Bsktbl; JV Var Ftbl; High Hon Roll; Hon Roll; Schltc Achvt Awd 86-87; Rotary Intl Exch Stu Mexico 87-88; Aviation.

KRISE, JEFFREY; St Marys Area HS; Kersey, PA; (3); 35/250; JV Tennis; JV Wrstlng; Hon Roll; PITT; Phrmcy.

KRISER, ROBYN; Punxsutawney Area HS; Delancey, PA; (4); 62/245; French Clb; Letterman Clb; Variety Show; Rep Frsh Cls; Rep Stu Cncl; Stat Bsktbl; Cheerleading; Vllybl; Hon Roll.

KRISKO, KAREN; Bishop Carroll HS; Portage, PA; (3); 25/128; Red Cross Aide; Ski Clb; Band; Church Choir; Concert Band; Mrchg Band; Rep Frsh Cls; Trk; Vllybl; IN U Of PA; Bus.

KRISOVITCH, MICHAEL; Western Wayne HS; Lake Ariel, PA; (3); 7/194; Chess Clb; Computer Clb; Spanish Clb; High Hon Roll; Hon Roll; NHS.

KRISPIN, JONATHAN; Phil-Mont Acad; Philadelphia, PA; (4); Chorus; School Play; Rep Jr Cls; Pres Stu Cncl; Var Bsbl; Var Bsktbl; JV Bowling; Var Capt Crs Cntry; High Hon Roll; Hon Roll; Geneva Coll; Pre-Med.

KRISPIN, TIMOTHY; Phil-Mont Christian HS; Philadelphia, PA; (2); Church Yth Grp; Chorus; Concert Band; Bsktbl; Crs Cntry; Trk; High Hon Roll; Plyr Of Yr-Crss Cntry 85-86; Plyr Of Wk-Phila Inqr X-Cntry 86.

KRISS, STEPHEN; Johnstown Christian HS; Davidsville, PA; (1); VP Church Yth Grp; Pres Frsh Cls; Hon Roll; Pres Schlr; Chrch Rcrdng Secy 86.

KRISTEN, SCOT; Elizabeth Forward HS; Mckeesport, PA; (4); Boy Scts; Chess Clb; Spanish Clb; Band; Concert Band; Jazz Band; Mrchg Band; Hon Roll; Prfct Atten Awd; Var JV Bsbl; Robert Morris Coll; Acctg.

KRISTIAN, DANA; Aliquippa HS; Aliquippa, PA; (2); French Clb; Yrbk Stf; Hon Roll; Cnty Alg Tst-Hgh Rnk 86.

KRISTICK, JEFFREY; Central SR HS; York, PA; (2); 25/250; Varsity Clb; Stu Cncl; Golf; Vllybl; High Hon Roll; Hon Roll; U Of CA-LOS Angeles; Engrng.

KRISTOFF, JAN; Burgettstown Area JR SR HS; Burgettstown, PA; (2); 1/170; French Clb; Ski Clb; Concert Band; Mrchg Band; Pep Band; Symp Band; Yrbk Stf; High Hon Roll; Jr NHS; NHS; Med.

KRISTOFF, MARCY; Meadville Area SR HS; Meadville, PA; (3); Church Yth Grp; SADD; Chorus; Church Choir; Orch; School Play; Hon Roll; NHS; Meadville Sktg Clb-6 Yrs Sktg, 3 Yrs Cmptv; Nrsg.

KRITIKOS, KAREN A; Waynesboro Area SR HS; Martinsburg, WV; (4); Art Clb; Yrbk Stf; Var Fld Hcky; Var Mat Maids; Hon Roll; Shepherd Coll; Bus.

KRIVACEK, PAUL D; Hempfield Area SR HS; Greensburg, PA; (4); 4/693; French Clb; Math Tm; Ski Clb; French Hon Soc; High Hon Roll; NHS; Ntl Merit SF; Jr NHS; Cert Of Merit-IN U PA Physcs Tstg 86; Math Fnlstpitts Provost Day 86; Carnegie Mellon U; Elec Engrng.

KRIVANEK, MICHELE; Vincentian HS; Allison Park, PA; (4); GAA; Service Clb; Trs Sr Cls; Im Badmtn; Var Capt Bsktbl; Var Fld Hcky; Im Ftbl; JV Var Sftbl; Var Tennis; Im Vllybl; $1000 Duquesne U 87; Duquesne U; Finance.

KRIVENKO, LINDSEY; Dallas SR HS; Dallas, PA; (3); Ski Clb; Yrbk Phtg; Rep Stu Cncl; Stat Bsktbl; Var L Fld Hcky; Im Gym; Var Sftbl; L Tennis; Yth Ftnss Achvt Awd 87; Rookie & Plyr Of Yr Awd Field Hockey 85 & 86; Bio.

KRIVONICK, AMY; Marion Center HS; Marion Center, PA; (3); #1 In Class; Varsity Clb; Band; Drm Mjr(t); Pres Stu Cncl; Var Bsktbl; Var Crs Cntry; Var Trk; High Hon Roll; NHS; Hugh O Brian Yth Ldrshp Outstndng Soph 86; Comm.

KRIZANSKY, ROBERT; Hazelton HS; Hazleton, PA; (3); 42/800.

KROEHLER, TIM; Manheim Township HS; Lancaster, PA; (3); 15/321; Church Yth Grp; Computer Clb; Chorus; Church Choir; Mrchg Band; School Musical; JV Socr; Var JV Swmmng; Hon Roll; NHS; Tchr.

KROENER, KELLY; Cumberland Valley HS; Camp Hill, PA; (3); 15/650; Computer Clb; Key Clb; Model UN; Ski Clb; Spanish Clb; Teachers Aide; Rep Stu Cncl; Hon Roll; NHS; Rotary Awd; Rotary Ldrs Conf 87; Outstndng Frgn Lang Awd 85-87; Bus.

KROESEN, RICK; Wilmington Area HS; Pulaski, PA; (3); 15/130; FCA; Bsktbl; Hon Roll; Penn ST; Sprtscstr.

KROFT, JAMES; Oil City SR HS; Oil City, PA; (3); Church Yth Grp; SADD; Y-Teens; Badmtn; Bsktbl; Wt Lftg; Wrstlng; Hon Roll; Prfct Atten Awd; Vale Tech; Auto Tech.

KROH, KRISTA; Bradford Area HS; Bradford, PA; (4); AFS; Ski Clb; Band; Jazz Band; Mrchg Band; Hon Roll; Kiwanis Awd; Computer Clb; Service Clb; Pep Band; Carole Moore Mem Awd 87; Key Clb Ldrshp Awd 87; U Of PA Edinboro; Elem Educ.

KROH, MARK; The Hill Schl; Aaronsburg, PA; (4); Service Clb; Chorus; L Diving; Hon Roll; Ntl Merit SF; Georgetown; Russian Major.

KROH, TINA; Avon Grove HS; Avondale, PA; (3); Library Aide; SADD; Band; Concert Band; High Hon Roll; Hon Roll; Hnr Rl; Acctng.

KROHN, LISA; MMI Preparatory Schl; Hazleton, PA; (3); Art Clb; Science Clb; Bausch & Lomb Sci Awd; High Hon Roll; NHS; Ntl Merit Ltr; NEDT Awd; Chess Clb; Church Yth Grp; Computer Clb; PA Gvnrs Schls Sci & Ag 87; PJAS Sci Comptn 1st Pl Rgnl & 1st Pl ST 84-85; German Ntl Hnr Sci 87; Chem.

KROKOS, JOHN; G A R Memorial HS; Wilkes Barre, PA; (4); 27/169; Letterman Clb; SADD; Band; Chorus; Concert Band; Drm Mjr(t); Jazz Band; Mrchg Band; Orch; Vllybl; St Regnl & All ST Alt Chrs 85-87; Natl Schl Chrl Awd 87; Semper Fidelis Awd 87; Westchester U; Music Ed.

KROLICK, AMY JO; Garnet Valley JR SR HS; Boothwyn, PA; (2); 17/171; Spanish Clb; JV Lcrss; JV Vllybl; Hon Roll; Chem.

KROLICK, CARLA; Purchase Line HS; Dixonville, PA; (4); 15/102; FBLA; SADD; Varsity Clb; Yrbk Stf; Var L Bsktbl; Var L Sftbl; Var L Vllybl; Hon Roll; NHS.

KROLL, JULIANNE; Riverside HS; Fombell, PA; (4); Cmnty Wkr; 4-H; Hosp Aide; Concert Band; Mrchg Band; 4-H Awd; Hon Roll; Health Careers Club Secy; Jameson Mem Schl Nrsng; RN.

KROMER, DAVID; Northampton Area SR HS; Danielsville, PA; (3); VICA; High Hon Roll; Hon Roll; NHS; Prfct Atten Awd; Intl Assn Electrcl Inspctrs 87; Electrcl.

KRONE, AMY; Dover Area HS; Dover, PA; (4); 21/237; Church Yth Grp; Swmmng; Vllybl; High Hon Roll; Hon Roll; NHS; Schlrshp U Of IA 87; ST Champ 87; York Outstndng Swmmr Awd 87; U Of IA.

KRONE, SU ANN; Northeastern HS; York, PA; (4); 9/163; Ski Clb; School Play; Nwsp Rptr; Bsktbl; Tennis; High Hon Roll; Hon Roll; Pres NHS; Schlrshps Ins Women York & Soroptimist 87; Shippensburg U; Intntl Bus.

KRONER, KRISTEN; Quaker Valley SR HS; Sewickley, PA; (2); Band; Mrchg Band; Cheerleading; Trk; Cmmnctns.

KROPIEWNICKI, JOSEPH; John S Fine HS; Nanticoke, PA; (4); 7/257; Church Yth Grp; Red Cross Aide; Ski Clb; JV Im Bsktbl; Capt Var Golf; Capt Var Vllybl; High Hon Roll; NHS; Bicentennical Cmmtt Schlrshp 86-87; MVP Golf Capt 84-87; Unsung Hero Vlybl 86-87; Villanova; Pre-Med.

KROPP, CAROLINE; Lake-Lehman HS; Shavertown, PA; (4); 28/155; Key Clb; SADD; JV Bsktbl; Stat Fld Hcky; Var L Sftbl; Hon Roll; Jr NHS; NHS; Hmcmng Crt 86; Ice Princess Crt 86; Prm Crt 87; Shpnsbrg Coll; Phrmcst.

KROPP, KRISTIN; Lansdale Catholic HS; Lansdale, PA; (3); Drama Clb; French Clb; Chorus; Church Choir; School Musical; School Play; Variety Show; Lit Mag; Hon Roll; Law.

KROUS, KRISTA; Hempfield HS; Lancaster, PA; (3); 37/393; Church Yth Grp; Dance Clb; Pres 4-H; Girl Scts; Variety Show; Hst Soph Cls; Capt Cheerleading; High Hon Roll; NHS; Cmnty Wkr; Schlstc Art Shw-Gold Key Awd 85-86; Comms.

KROUSE, JEFFREY D; Freedom HS; Bethlehem, PA; (4); 1/465; Church Yth Grp; Pres JA; Math Tm; Model UN; Ed Yrbk Ed-Chief; Var Swmmng; High Hon Roll; NHS; Ntl Merit SF; Drtmth Bk Awd 85-86; PA ST U.

KROUSE, KELLY; Bradford Area HS; Bradford, PA; (3); Cmnty Wkr; Trs Key Clb; Library Aide; Spanish Clb; Pres Varsity Clb; Chorus; Color Guard; Yrbk Stf; Rep Sr Cls; Var L Bsktbl; Acadmc Excllnc Awd 85; Amer Exchng Stu Fnlst 87; MVP Crs Cntry 86; Air Frc; Pre Med.

KROUT, DEREK; West York HS; York, PA; (2); German Clb; School Musical; School Play; Rep Soph Cls; Rep Stu Cncl; Capt Bowling; JV Capt Ftbl; JV Var Vllybl; High Hon Roll; Hon Roll; Outstndng Art Awd 86.

KROUT, TRACY; Blue Mountain Acad; York, PA; (1); Computer Clb; Ftbl; Powder Puff Ftbl; Vllybl; High Hon Roll; Columbia Union Coll; Med.

KROUT, WENDY; Cumberland Valley HS; Boiling Springs, PA; (4); Art Clb; German Clb; Drill Tm; Orch; School Musical; Var Pom Pon; Im Swmmng; JV Tennis; Hon Roll; Ntl Merit Ltr; Cert Of Rcgntn Schlstc Wrtng 87; Natl Art Hnr Soc 84-87; Lehigh U; Bio.

KROW, BRADLEY; Steelton-Highspire HS; Steelton, PA; (3); 7/102; Church Yth Grp; English Clb; Latin Clb; Spanish Clb; Chorus; Variety Show; Ed Yrbk Stf; Var Trk; Var Wrstlng; Hon Roll; Rensselaer Medal 87; U Of Miami; Arch Engr.

KRUEGER, ANDREA; Hempfield HS; Lancaster, PA; (3); 58/300; Chorus; Stage Crew; Mgr(s); Powder Puff Ftbl; High Hon Roll; NHS; Schlstc Art Assoc Cert Mrt 87; 1st Pl Rbn Grphc Dsgn Hempfields Art Fstvl 86; Bus.

KRUEGER, JULIE; Upper Moreland HS; Hatboro, PA; (2); 25/242; Ski Clb; Teachers Aide; Nwsp Rptr; Coach Actv; Fld Hcky; High Hon Roll; Hon Roll.

KRUFKA, MARCI; Coughlin HS; Wilkes Barre, PA; (3); 25/362; Church Yth Grp; Key Clb; Orch; Yrbk Stf; High Hon Roll; Hon Roll; NHS; Presdntl Acadc Ftns 85; NEDT Cert-Score Over 90% 85; Lwyr.

KRUG, ERIC J; North East HS; North East, PA; (4); 2/143; Boy Scts; Quiz Bowl; Science Clb; Nwsp Rptr; DAR Awd; High Hon Roll; Hon Roll; Ntl Merit SF; VFW Awd; Latin Clb; Life Scout 86; Sci.

KRUG, ERIC R; Bishop Carroll HS; Nicktown, PA; (3); Church Yth Grp; Var L Ftbl; Var L Trk; Hon Roll; Aeronautical Engrng.

KRUG, JODI; Chartiers Valley HS; Pittsburgh, PA; (4); 33/299; Dance Clb; Capt Drill Tm; School Musical; School Play; Pres Frsh Cls; Pres Soph Cls; Pres Jr Cls; Pres Sr Cls; NHS; Cheerleading; Hmcmng Queen 86; Pitt; Chiropractor.

KRUG, STEPHEN; South Western HS; Hanover, PA; (3); 1/233; Quiz Bowl; Band; Jazz Band; Mrchg Band; Pep Band; School Musical; Symp Band; High Hon Roll; Hon Roll; Prfct Atten Awd; Mst Imprvd Muscn 86; Lwr Brss Sctn Head; 1st Chair Tuba; OH Wesleyan U; Math.

KRUG, THOMAS; Greater Johnstown Area Votech Schl; South Fork, PA; (2); High Hon Roll; Hon Roll; Jr NHS; Pres Acadmc Ftns Awd 85-86; Electrncs.

KRUHM, BRIAN; Penn-Trafford HS; Irwin, PA; (2); Church Yth Grp; JV Stat Socr; High Hon Roll.

KRUIS, KIM; Tyrone Area HS; Altoona, PA; (3); Art Clb; Cmnty Wkr; French Clb; SADD; Hon Roll; Grntlgy.

KRUKOWSKI, BRIAN; Saucon Valley SR HS; Hellertown, PA; (3); 3/156; High Hon Roll; Hon Roll; Jr NHS; NHS; Pres Schlr; Cert Achvt Brd Schl Drctrs 85-87; Allentown Coll; Math.

KRUKOWSKI, MELISSA; Abington Heights HS; Clarks Summit, PA; (3); 40/292; Lit Mag; Hon Roll; US Natl Ldrshp Mrt Awd 85; U Of Scranton; Med.

KRULL, JAMES; Devon Prep; Strafford, PA; (1); 1/55; Math Tm; Swmmng; High Hon Roll; Schlrshp-Devon Prep 86-90; Scntst.

KRULL, ROBERT E; Wyoming Valley West HS; Swoyersville, PA; (3); Stat Am Leg Boys St; Boy Scts; Latin Clb; Science Clb; JV Ftbl; Var L Vllybl; Im Wt Lftg; High Hon Roll; Chemst.

KRUM, LESLIE; Coatesville Area SR HS; Coatesville, PA; (3); 105/509; Aud/Vis; Church Yth Grp; Spanish Clb; Chorus; Church Choir; School Musical; Var Swmmng; Hon Roll; Cmmnctns.

KRUMENACKER, STEVE; Archbishop Wood Boys; Doylestown, PA; (2); 21/260; SADD; JV Socr; Hon Roll; Arch.

KRUMENAKER, COREY; Penn Cambria HS; Lilly, PA; (3); Am Leg Boys St; Boy Scts; Drama Clb; French Clb; NFL; Scholastic Bowl; Ski Clb; Concert Band; Mrchg Band; Yrbk Phtg; U Of Pittsburgh; Bio.

KRUMPHOLZ, KRISTEN; St Huberts HS; Philadelphia, PA; (3); Boy Scts; Cmnty Wkr; SADD; Lit Mag; SADD Hnr Awd 87; Cmmnctns.

KRUPA, TODD; Lake-Lehman HS; Shavertown, PA; (4); 9/155; Aud/Vis; SADD; Var Capt Bsbl; L Bsktbl; Var Capt Golf; High Hon Roll; Jr NHS; NHS; Rotary Awd; Spts Staff Writer The Times Ldr 86-87; Syracuse U; Nwspr.

KRUPILIS, PAULA; West Hazleton JR SR HS; Ringtown, PA; (2); 35/220; FNA; Office Aide; Color Guard; Capt Flag Corp; Capt Twrlr; Hon Roll; RN.

KRUPKA, TIMOTHY SCOTT; Louis E Dieruff HS; Allentown, PA; (2); ROTC; Band; Chorus; Concert Band; Jazz Band; Mrchg Band; Orch; Pep Band; Soph Cls; Var L Trk; Elec.

KRUPP, MICHELE; Wyoming Area SR HS; Exeter, PA; (3); Capt Color Guard; Mrchg Band; Capt Twrlr; High Hon Roll; Hon Roll; NHS; Mrktng.

KRUSE, KARLA; Penn Manor HS; Millersville, PA; (3); Camera Clb; Church Yth Grp; Drama Clb; PAVAS; Radio Clb; Ski Clb; Thesps; School Musical; School Play; Stage Crew; Smmr Arts Pgm Gftd 84 & 85; Phtgrphy.

KRUSHINSKY, KARA; Bishop O Hara HS; Moscow, PA; (4); 27/113; Church Yth Grp; Letterman Clb; Spanish Clb; Pres Frsh Cls; Pres Jr Cls; VP Stu Cncl; Bsktbl; Sftbl; High Hon Roll; NHS; Business.

KRUSINSKY, EDW; Shenandoah Valley HS; Shenandoah, PA; (3); 18/79; Var Ftbl; Hon Roll; Accntng.

KRUSZEWSKI, JOSEPH; Serra Catholic HS; W Mifflin, PA; (4); 50/157; Church Yth Grp; Spanish Clb; Teachers Aide; Var Ftbl; Mgr(s); Var Trk; Wt Lftg; Hon Roll; Jednota Schlrshp 87; IN U Of PA; Bus.

KRUTCH, MICHELE; Conemaugh Valley JR/Sr HS; Park Hill, PA; (4); 31/125; Drama Clb; French Clb; Hosp Aide; Scholastic Bowl; Concert Band; Mrchg Band; School Play; Nwsp Ed-Chief; Nwsp Rptr; Yrbk Stf; Johnstown Tribune-Democrt Schlstc-Jrnlst Awd 87; IN U Of PA.

KRUTH, PAUL; Shaler Area HS; Pittsburgh, PA; (4); 85/510; Computer Clb; Ski Clb; Spanish Clb; Band; Jazz Band; Var L Crs Cntry; Var L Trk; Spanish NHS; Stu Cncl; Hon Roll; Acdmc Schlrshp Grove City Coll 87-88; Grove City Coll; Pre-Dntstry.

KRYSIAK, BRENDALYN; Cowanesque Valley HS; Westfield, PA; (4); 1/84; Church Yth Grp; Girl Scts; Letterman Clb; Band; School Musical; Yrbk Ed-Chief; Jr Cls; Tennis; NHS; Cnsrvtn Essy Awd 83; Lecrd Mdrn Prse Awd 84; HOBY Ldrshp Ambssdr 84; Htl-Rest Mngt.

KRYWOKULSKI, BETH; Newport HS; Newport, PA; (4); 18/60; Art Clb; Spanish Clb; Stat Bsktbl; JV Sftbl; High Hon Roll; Hon Roll; Schlstc Art Awd 85-86; Artist Mnth 85-86; Art.

KRZECZOWSKI, KEVIN; Burgettstown JR/Sr HS; Langeloth, PA; (3); 7/161; Church Yth Grp; Cmnty Wkr; GAA; Science Clb; Pres Spanish Clb; Rep Jr Cls; Capt Var Bsktbl; High Hon Roll; Hon Roll; NHS; W & J Coll; Pre Dntstry.

KRZYWIEC, JOELLEN K; Valley View HS; Archibald, PA; (3); 29/193; Church Yth Grp; French Clb; Girl Scts; Math Clb; School Musical; Nwsp Stf; Yrbk Stf; Var Crs Cntry; Var Trk; Var Vllybl; U Of Scranton; Psych.

KUBA, JENNIFER; Valley HS; Arnold, PA; (3); Drama Clb; French Clb; Mgr(s); Score Keeper; Stat Wrstlng; Yrbk Phtg; Hon Roll; Vrst Lttr Wrstlng 87; Penn ST U; Cmmnctns.

KUBACKI, JANE; Lake-Lehman HS; Shaverstown, PA; (3); Key Clb; SADD; Yrbk Stf; Cheerleading; Fld Hcky; High Hon Roll; Hon Roll; Jr NHS; NHS.

KUBACKI, MICHELE; Nazareth Acad; Phila, PA; (3); Camp Fr Inc; Pres Hosp Aide; Math Clb; Pep Clb; Spanish Clb; Pres Frsh Cls; Pres Soph Cls; Pres Jr Cls; Hon Roll; Psych.

KUBANCSEK, WENDY; West Mifflin Area HS; W Mifflin, PA; (3); 10/300; Hosp Aide; Flag Corp; Orch; Rep Frsh Cls; Rep Soph Cls; Rep Jr Cls; Rep Stu Cncl; High Hon Roll; Hon Roll; NHS; Ofc Of Vctnl Rhbltn Schlrshp; U Of Pittsburgh; Bio.

KUBEL, JOHN; Notre Dame HS; Easton, PA; (4); 27/185; Letterman Clb; Yrbk Stf; Coach Actv; Tennis; Var Trk; Hon Roll; Ntl Merit Ltr; Penn ST U; Bio.

KUBIAK, SUSAN M; Parkway Gamma HS; Philadelphia, PA; (4); Church Yth Grp; Cmnty Wkr; Hosp Aide; Math Clb; Office Aide; Science Clb; Teachers Aide; Chorus; School Musical; Hon Roll; Lankenau Hosp Schl Nrsg; Nrsng.

KUBICK, PATTI; Abington Heights HS; Falls, PA; (3); 22/283; Var L Crs Cntry; Var Trk; Hon Roll; Cum Laud Cert Natl Ltn Cntst 84 & 85; Jr Acad Sci 2nd Pl Awd 85 & 86; Sci.

KUBICKI, JODY; G A R HS; Wilkes-Barre, PA; (3); Ski Clb; Yrbk Ed-Chief; Yrbk Sprt Ed; Yrbk Stf; Bsbl; Ftbl; Wt Lftg; Wrstlng; High Hon Roll; Hon Roll; Per Med.

KUBICKI, MICHELE A; Greater Latrube SR HS; Latrobe, PA; (4); Letterman Clb; JV Var Bsktbl; Var Capt Sftbl; Var Capt Vllybl; Hon Roll; Prfct Atten Awd; Hon Mntn Sctn Tm Vllybl, & Vllybl Schlrshp Waynesburg 87; Waynesburg Coll; Bus.

KUBIK, TAMI; Aliquippa HS; Aliquippa, PA; (3); Church Yth Grp; Cmnty Wkr; French Clb; Hosp Aide; SADD; Teachers Aide; Mrchg Band; Var Pom Pon; Hon Roll; Prfct Atten Awd; Scrtry For The Pom Pon Squad 87-88.

KUBINCANEK, MICHAEL; Trinity HS; Washington, PA; (3); 31/402; German Clb; JV Var Bsbl; JV Var Bsktbl; Hon Roll; Engrng.

KUBRAK, STEPHEN; Mastbaum Area Vo Tech; Philadelphia, PA; (3); Hon Roll.

KUBRICKI, SANDRA; Greater Nanticoke Area HS; Wapwallopen, PA; (2); 17/226; Pres Church Yth Grp; Key Clb; Spanish Clb; Chorus; Color Guard; Yrbk Stf; High Hon Roll; Hon Roll.

KUCERA, DEBORAH; Southmoreland SR HS; Mt Pleasant, PA; (3); 56/208; Aud/Vis; Girl Scts; Hosp Aide; Latin Clb; Office Aide; Pep Clb; Teachers Aide; Chorus; Stage Crew; Rep Soph Cls; Pres Phys Fit Awd 84-85; Phys Thrpy.

KUCH, KAREN; Coatesville Area SR HS; Coatesville, PA; (3); 30/509; FBLA; Leo Clb; Ski Clb; Spanish Clb; Varsity Clb; Band; Color Guard; Off Jr Cls; JV Sftbl; JV Swmmng; ACCTNT,Bus.

KUCINSKI, GINA; Hazleton HS; Hazleton, PA; (3); Cheerleading; Hon Roll.

KUCSKAR, KATHRYN; Bishop Conwell HS; Bensalem, PA; (3); 21/277; Church Choir; Concert Band; Nwsp Stf; JV Crs Cntry; Mgr(s); JV Trk; High Hon Roll; Hon Roll; NHS; Prfct Atten Awd; Settlement Music Schl Piano & Flute Certs & PJAS 85.

KUCZINSKI, BRIAN; Chartiers Valley HS; Pittsburgh, PA; (3); 19/328; Ski Clb; Spanish Clb; Varsity Clb; Nwsp Ed-Chief; Trs Jr Cls; Stu Cncl; Mgr(s); Swmmng; NHS; Accntng.

KUCZYNSKI, KELLY; Mahanoy Area HS; Mahanoy City, PA; (2); French Clb; Hosp Aide; Ski Clb; SADD; Teachers Aide; Chorus; Variety Show; Cheerleading; Pom Pon; Trk; Bio.

KUCZYNSKI, KURT; Mon Valley Catholic HS; Belle Vernon, PA; (3); Church Yth Grp; Ski Clb; Auto Engnrng.

KUDLAC, ANN; Beth-Center HS; Richeyville, PA; (3); Church Yth Grp; High Hon Roll; Hon Roll.

KUDLIK, CHERYL; Monessen JR-SR HS; Monessen, PA; (4); 42/92; Camp Fr Inc; Hosp Aide; Pep Clb; PAVAS; Band; Yrbk Stf; Cheerleading; Bradford Schl; Accntng.

KUDRNA, JOHN D; Ambridge Area HS; Freedom, PA; (3); Church Yth Grp; Band; Mrchg Band; Pep Band; U Of Pittsburgh.

KUEHNE, THOMAS; Behtlehem Catholic HS; Bethlehem, PA; (3); 96/211; Band; Concert Band; Jazz Band; Mrchg Band; Orch; Pep Band; School Musical; Symp Band; Boy Scts; Amer Yth In Concrt 86; Sound Of Amer 87; Med.

KUENY, FRAN; Mastbaum AVTS; Philadelphia, PA; (3); Var Bowling; JV Ftbl; Hon Roll; Ntl Merit Ltr; Drexel U; Mech Engrng.

KUERT, LISA; Freeport Area HS; Sarver, PA; (3); 16/213; Church Yth Grp; Church Choir; School Play; Trs Soph Cls; VP Jr Cls; Trk; High Hon Roll; English Clb; Nwsp Stf; Yrbk Stf; Teen Tlnt Awds-Snging & Piano 86; Ltrd-Trck 86; Comm.

KUFFA, BRIAN; Boiling Springs HS; Carlisle, PA; (4); 4/107; Ski Clb; Im Bsktbl; Im Ftbl; Var Socr; High Hon Roll; Hon Roll; NHS; Prfct Atten Awd; Shoppensburg U; Comp Sci.

KUFROVICH, JAMES; Mahanoy Area HS; Mahanoy City, PA; (4); 12/110; Band; Chorus; Concert Band; Jazz Band; Mrchg Band; School Play; Variety Show; Im Bsktbl; Var Trk; NHS; Mansfield U; Music Educ.

KUGLER, MICHELE; Saint Huberts H S For Girls; Philadelphia, PA; (4); 126/364; Office Aide; Mrchg Band; Hon Roll; Prfct Atten Awd; Plaque For Ldrshp, Svc, Dedication, And Ctznshp 87; Comp.

KUHARCIK, FRANK; Wyoming Valley West HS; Larksville, PA; (4); 9/397; School Musical; Stage Crew; JV Crs Cntry; JV Trk; Im Wt Lftg; High Hon Roll; Hon Roll; JETS Awd; NHS; NEDT Awd; Electronics Awd Fclty WVW 87; Ltr Rcgntn Helping Set Stndrds PA Hnrs Test 87; PA ST; Elec Engr.

KUHLMAN, KAREN; Marple Newtown HS; Media, PA; (4); 4/330; Var Bsktbl; Capt Sftbl; High Hon Roll; NHS; Ntl Merit Ltr; U VA.

KUHLS, AMY; Oil City SR HS; Oil City, PA; (4); Church Yth Grp; Band; Concert Band; Mrchg Band; Cnty Band; Dist Band; Hnrs Band; Rdlgst.

KUHN, BRENDA; Southmoreland SR HS; Alverton, PA; (3); Pres FFA; Pep Clb; VICA; Horticltr.

KUHN, CRAIG; Fort Le Boeuf HS; Waterford, PA; (3); 52/215; FCA; Var L Ftbl; Im Vllybl; Im Wt Lftg; Hon Roll; Prfct Atten Awd; 1st Tm All Cnty Ftbl 86-87; Attrny At Law.

KUHN, DAVID; Mt Pleasat Area HS; Mt Pleasant, PA; (2); German Clb; Var Bsbl; JV Bsktbl.

KUHN, JEFFREY; Coatesville Area SR HS; Coatesville, PA; (4); 34/470; Church Yth Grp; Computer Clb; Ski Clb; Spanish Clb; Church Choir; Bsbl; Swmmng; Hon Roll; NHS; Prfct Atten Awd; Millersville U; Ed.

KUHN, JONATHAN; Meadville Area SR HS; Meadville, PA; (3); 72/365; SADD; JV Var Vllybl; Hon Roll; Carnegie-Mellon U; Arch.

KUHN, KATHERINE; Highlands SR HS; Brackenridge, PA; (3); Exploring; Key Clb; SADD; Band; Mrchg Band; Jr Cls; Stu Cncl; Tennis; Jr NHS; NHS; Presdntl Acadmc Ftns Awd 85; Schltc Achvt Awd 87; Med.

KUHN, MICHAEL; Downington SR HS; Exton, PA; (3); Church Yth Grp; Model UN; Ski Clb; Spanish Clb; Band; Jazz Band; Mrchg Band; Hon Roll; NHS; Comp Sci.

KUHN, STEVEN M; Middletown Area HS; Middletown, PA; (3); 41/161; Am Leg Boys St; Boy Scts; Im Wt Lftg; Wrstlng; God Cntry Awd; High Hon Roll; Hon Roll; Boy Scout Eagle Awd 87; Bus.

KUHNS, TRICIA; United HS; Armagh, PA; (4); 9/160; Sec Church Yth Grp; Rep Sec FBLA; Ski Clb; Band; Capt Drill Tm; Yrbk Stf; High Hon Roll; Prfct Atten Awd; Pres Natl Bus Hnr Soc 86-87; Bradford Schl; Sec.

KUHS, SARA; Downingtown SR HS; Chester Springs, PA; (3); 89/648; Drama Clb; French Clb; Ski Clb; Band; Concert Band; Mrchg Band; Symp Band; Im Bowling; Im Vllybl; Hon Roll; Air Force; Zoolgy.

KUKLA, CHRISTOPHER; Oil City Area SR HS; Oil City, PA; (3); 45/245; JV Var Bsktbl; Var L Tennis; Im Vllybl; Hon Roll; NHS; Rep Stu Cncl; Im Socr.

KUKLES, MICHAEL; Pen Argyl Area HS; Pen Argyl, PA; (3); 15/160; Boy Scts; Church Yth Grp; Exploring; Band; Concert Band; Jazz Band; Mrchg Band; High Hon Roll; Hon Roll; Arch.

KUKLEWICZ, DAWN; Hanover JR-SR HS; Sugar Notch, PA; (3); Cmnty Wkr; Band; Chorus; Concert Band; Mrchg Band; School Musical; Rep Stu Cncl; Swmmng; Hon Roll; Jr NHS; Amer Red Cross Cert Lfgrd 87; Luzerne Cnty CC; Nrsng.

KUKLO, THERESA; North Pocono HS; Moscow, PA; (4); 6/240; FBLA; Concert Band; Var Capt Cheerleading; Var L Trk; High Hon Roll; NHS; Ntl Hnr Soc Schlrshp 87; Boosters Clb Schlr Athlte Schlrshp 87; Penn ST U; Accntng.

KUKOL, JASON; Reynolds HS; Transfer, PA; (3); Latin Clb; Spanish Clb; Trk; U Of Pittsburgh.

KUKOWSKI, RENEE; Pittston Area SR HS; Pittston, PA; (3); Church Yth Grp; Computer Clb; French Clb; FNA; Math Clb; Ski Clb; Chorus; L Trk; High Hon Roll; NHS; Ntl Hnr Soc Awd 85-86; Vrsty Trk Lttr; Kings Coll; Physcn Asstnt.

KUKUDA, RITA; Cambridge Springs HS; Cambridge Springs, PA; (2); 14/101; Sec Chorus; Hon Roll; U Of PA; Vet Med.

KUKULA, JENNY; Central Christian HS; Reynoldsvl, PA; (2); Camera Clb; Drama Clb; SADD; Chorus; School Play; Variety Show; Var Cheerleading; Psych.

KULAKOWSKI, J BIANKA; State College Area HS; Lemont, PA; (2); Am Leg Aux Girls St; Church Yth Grp; Hosp Aide; Duke U.

KULBACK, KRYSTEEN; Greater Johnstown Area Vo-Tech Schl; Windber, PA; (4); 27/258; Key Clb; VP Trs VICA; Chorus; Yrbk Stf; Stu Cncl; Hon Roll; Rotary 87; Awd Of Employablty 85-87.

KULCHAR, ANDREW C; Devon Prep Schl; Rosemont, PA; (3); 3/43; Chess Clb; Cmnty Wkr; Hosp Aide; Library Aide; Math Tm; Radio Clb; High Hon Roll; Amer Classical Lg Natl Latin Exam Hnrb Merit Maxima Cum Laude 86; Elec Engrng.

KULCZAK, CHERYL; Mt Pleasant Area HS; Mt Pleasant, PA; (4); 12/250; Church Yth Grp; Nwsp Stf; Yrbk Stf; High Hon Roll; NHS; Prfct Atten Awd; Bus Club Pres 86-87; Toys For Tots 85-87; Bus Stu Month 84-87; US Army; Admin Speclst.

KULICH, PAM; St Benedict Acad; Erie, PA; (4); 2/62; Office Aide; Ed Q&S; Yrbk Ed-Chief; Yrbk Rptr; Yrbk Stf; Stu Cncl; Wt Lftg; High Hon Roll; NHS; Sal; E Side Fdrtn Schlrshp 87; Gld Crd-Excllnc 4 Yrs Cmmnctns 87; 1st Hnrs-4 Yrs HS; Penn ST U; Physcl Thrpy.

KULICK, DAWN MARIE; Bishop Mc Devitt HS; Harrisburg, PA; (3); 23/217; Drama Clb; Service Clb; SADD; Chorus; Color Guard; School Musical; School Play; L Twrlr; Hon Roll; NHS; Sci Fair-Hnrbl Mntn 84-86; Bst Spprtng Actrss 85-86; 1st Pl Ply Awd Consts-Bst Dir 86-87; Chathum Coll; Psych.

KULICK, LISA; Bishop Mc Devitt HS; Harrisburg, PA; (3); 19/270; Drama Clb; Service Clb; SADD; Chorus; Color Guard; School Musical; School Play; L Twrlr; Hon Roll; NHS; Best Actress Awd Play Cont 86; Chatham Coll; Engl.

KULIG, GERALD; Freeland JR SR HS; Freeland, PA; (3); 3/84; Scholastic Bowl; Pres SADD; Pres Band; Pres Soph Cls; Pres Jr Cls; Bsbl; JV Var Bsktbl; Jr NHS; NHS; HOBY Awd; Boston U.

KULIKOWICH, NATALIE; Wyoming Valley West HS; Edwardsville, PA; (3); Church Yth Grp; Key Clb; Library Aide; Ski Clb; SADD; Crs Cntry; Fld Hcky; Drama Clb; Sftbl; Trk; Ed.

KULIKOWSKI, DIANE; Forest City Regional HS; Pleasant Mt, PA; (3); 12/65; Cmnty Wkr; German Clb; Sec Jr Cls; Stat Bsktbl; Stat Sftbl; High Hon Roll; Hon Roll; NHS; Nrsg.

KULIN, ANNA MARI; Butler SR HS; Butler, PA; (3); Sec Trs Church Yth Grp; Chorus; Church Choir; School Musical; Trs Jr NHS; Library Aide; Teachers Aide; Gld Acad Achiev Awd 86-87.

KULINSKI, MARIA; Forest City Regional HS; Forest City, PA; (3); Am Leg Aux Girls St; Trs 4-H; German Clb; Nwsp Ed-Chief; Trs Jr Cls; Dnfth Awd; High Hon Roll; Hon Roll; NHS; Bus Adm.

KULISH, JANICE; Canon Mc Millan HS; Canonsburg, PA; (4); 113/351; Latin Clb; Chorus; Chatham Coll; Optmtry.

KULKA, KATHI; Shaler Area HS; Glenshaw, PA; (3); 139/486; Church Yth Grp; Exploring; Office Aide; Pep Clb; Ski Clb; SADD; Church Choir; Yrbk Stf; Hon Roll; Pre-Schl Tchng.

KULL, CARRIE L; Montrose Area JR SR HS; Friendsville, PA; (4); 1/165; Pres German Clb; Latin Clb; Scholastic Bowl; Ski Clb; Varsity Clb; Yrbk Stf; Sec Frsh Cls; Sec Stu Cncl; Var L Fld Hcky; Var L Trk; Biolgcl Sci.

KULLY, KEVIN; Quakertown Community HS; Quakertown, PA; (2); Computer Clb; Var JV Bsbl; Prfct Atten Awd; Acclrtd Algebra II A 87; Fine Arts I 87; Lehigh U; Engr.

KULP, DENISE R; Reading SR HS; Reading, PA; (3); 15/720; Concert Band; Jazz Band; Mrchg Band; Orch; Pep Band; School Musical; Sftbl; Hon Roll; NHS; GAA; Spnsh I Awd Excllnc 85.

KULP JR, PAUL T; Wayside Christian Schl; Oley, PA; (3); 1/4; Church Yth Grp; Computer Clb; Political Wkr; Teachers Aide; Chorus; Rep Jr Cls; High Hon Roll; Band; Rep Stu Cncl; Computer.

KULP, RUTHANNA; Trinity HS; Mechanicsburg, PA; (4); 3/141; Drama Clb; Hosp Aide; Model UN; School Musical; School Play; Stage Crew; Rep Stu Cncl; Stat Socr; VP NHS; Ntl Merit Ltr; BMW Nrth Am Schlrshp Exchng W Grmny 86; Schlrshp Harnsburg Acad Smmr Enrchmnt Pgm 85; Carnegie Mellon; Drama.

KULP, SUSAN; Council Rock HS; Holland, PA; (2); Church Yth Grp; Hosp Aide; Trs Spanish Clb; Church Choir; Pensacola Christin Coll; Nrsng.

KULP, SUSAN; Exeter Twp HS; Reading, PA; (3); Drama Clb; Varsity Clb; Band; Variety Show; Rep Jr Cls; Rep Stu Cncl; Var Cheerleading; Hon Roll; Jr NHS; Mansfield U; Music Ed.

KUNA, DEBBIE; Pittston Area SR HS; Dupont, PA; (4); Drama Clb; French Clb; FNA; Hosp Aide; Key Clb; Chorus; Drill Tm; Swing Chorus; Variety Show; Yrbk Stf; Ladies Aid Schlrshp 87; St Lukes Nrsng Schl; Nrs.

KUNASZ, MARTA; Metacton SR HS; Audubon, PA; (3); Intnl Clb; Key Clb; Orch; Var Trk; French Clb; School Musical; Symp Band; JV Socr; Hon Roll; 1st In Discus At Leagues 1st Tm Suburban I 87; Dist & Rgnl Band & Orchestra 87; Top Point Scr Trck 87; Millersville U; Languages.

KUND, SEAN; Archbishop Wood HS For Boys; Willow Grove, PA; (2); 16/268; Church Yth Grp; Drama Clb; SADD; School Play; Rep Frsh Cls; Rep Soph Cls; Golf; High Hon Roll; Finances.

KUNDER, AARON; Monessen HS; Monessen, PA; (3); Rep Stu Cncl; Var L Bsbl; JV Var Bsktbl; Var Mgr(s); Var L Socr; Im Vllybl; Hon Roll.

KUNDRAT III, GEORGE; Yough SR HS; West Newton, PA; (3); 7/239; Computer Clb; Spanish Clb; Ftbl; High Hon Roll; NHS; Engrng.

KUNEC, MICHELLE; Bishop Hoban HS; Plains, PA; (4); FBLA; Math Clb; Mu Alpha Theta; Ski Clb; Rep Stu Cncl; Var Cheerleading; Mgr(s); Score Keeper; Var Trk; Stat Wrstlng; U Of Scranton; Pre Med.

KUNEMAN, RENEE; Fairview HS; Fairview, PA; (4); 55/155; French Clb; Varsity Clb; Bsktbl; Crs Cntry; Trk; Penn ST U.

KUNES, SNU; St Marys Area HS; Weedville, PA; (2).

KUNIG, ANETTE; Saltsburg HS; Saltsburg, PA; (3); 1/65; Camera Clb; Drama Clb; Varsity Clb; Yrbk Stf; Powder Puff Ftbl; Var L Swmmng; Var Trk; High Hon Roll; NHS; Pres Schlr; Cert Space Shttl Stu Invlvmnt Prgrm 86; Mst Outstndg Swmmr Awd Vly Leag Winter Chmpnshps 86; U Of Pittsburgh; Med.

KUNIG, SABINE; Saltsburg JR SR HS; Saltsburg, PA; (2); 1/95; Varsity Clb; JV Bsktbl; Var L Swmmng; Var L Trk; Gov Hon Prg Awd; High Hon Roll; Pres Schlr.

KUNKEL, AMY; Tamaqua Area SR HS; Tamaqua, PA; (3); 30/207; Church Yth Grp; Acpl Chr; Concert Band; Mrchg Band; Ed Yrbk Stf; Var L Crs Cntry; Var L Swmmng; Var L Trk; French Hon Soc; Hon Roll; Smmr Exchng Stu 87; PA U; Pre Vet.

KUNKEL, ANN; Parkland SR HS; Allentown, PA; (3); 11/505; Acpl Chr; Chorus; Church Choir; Color Guard; Jazz Band; Madrigals; Swing Chorus; High Hon Roll; NHS; Ntl Merit Ltr; Cnty & Dist Chorus 86-87; Aerosp Engr.

KUNKELY, TRACEY; Upper Morehand HS; Willow Grove, PA; (3); Band; Chorus; Concert Band; Mrchg Band; Orch; School Musical; School Play; Lit Mag; Church Yth Grp; German Clb; Drm Mjr Mrchng Band 87-88; Westchester U; Music Educ.

KUNKLE, DEAN A; Garden Spot HS; E Earl, PA; (4); 14/216; Church Yth Grp; Drama Clb; German Clb; Band; Chorus; Orch; DAR Awd; Hon Roll; NHS; Rotary Awd; Eastrn Lancastr Cnty Schl Dist Schlrshp 87; SR Natl Hnr Socty Schlrshp 87; Pres Acdmc Fit Awd 87; Villanova U; Modrn Lang.

KUNKLE, ERIC; Waynesboro SR HS; Mont Alto, PA; (4); 54/370; Am Leg Boys St; Bsbl; Bsktbl; Socr; Cit Awd; High Hon Roll; Hon Roll; Penn ST U; Bus.

KUNKLE, JENNIFER; Lehighton Area HS; Lehighton, PA; (2); Pres VP FHA; SADD; Chorus; Nwsp Rptr; Bsktbl; Crs Cntry; Trk; Hon Roll; Bloomsburg U; Spch Ther.

KUNKLE, MICHELLE; Blue Mountain HS; New Ringgold, PA; (3); 36/215; Band; Concert Band; Jazz Band; Mrchg Band; Hon Roll.

KUNKLE, PAIGE; Emmaus HS; Allentown, PA; (4); 29/473; Nwsp Rptr; Ed Nwsp Stf; High Hon Roll; Hon Roll; Jr NHS; Lion Awd; NHS; Prfct Atten Awd; Natl Lagn Arts Olympd 84; Pres Acad Fit Awd 87; Bloomsburg U; Acctng.

KUNKO, VIVIAN; Portage Area HS; Portage, PA; (3); 16/109; Mrchg Band; Off Stu Cncl; Trk; Twrlr; Im Vllybl; High Hon Roll; IN U Of PA; Ed.

KUNS, BETH; Nazareth Acad; Philadelphia, PA; (4); 11/117; Church Yth Grp; Service Clb; Capt Bowling; High Hon Roll; Prfct Atten Awd; Schlrhsp Phildlpha Coll Of Textiles & Sci 87; CSFN Schlrshp Holy Family Coll 87; Philadelphia Coll; Retail Mgmt.

KUNSELMAN, CHERYL; Dubois Area HS; Reynoldsville, PA; (3); 35/321; Church Yth Grp; Varsity Clb; Chorus; Stu Cncl; Var Capt Cheerleading; Hon Roll; Stu In Sptlght 86-87; Carrier Of Mnth 84-85; DAR Awd 83-84; NRGNG.

KUNSELMAN, LORI; Punxsutawney Area HS; Punxsutawney, PA; (2); French Clb; Rep Soph Cls; Stu Cncl; Stat Bsktbl; Stat Trk; Hon Roll; Law.

KUNTZ, DEBRA; Du Bois Area HS; Dubois, PA; (3); Church Yth Grp; Exploring; Intnl Clb; Chorus; School Musical; Nwsp Stf; Hon Roll; Trs NHS; Penn ST; Bus.

KUNTZ, DONNA M; Penn Hills HS; Pittsburgh, PA; (2); 1/700; Am Leg Aux Girls St; Church Yth Grp; French Clb; Girl Scts; Ski Clb; Sec Band; Yrbk Stf; Var L Crs Cntry; Var L Trk; High Hon Roll; Arspc Engr.

KUNZ, LISA; Southern Huntingdon HS; Blairs Mills, PA; (2); French Clb; GAA; SADD; Varsity Clb; Concert Band; JV Var Cheerleading; JV Var Pom Pon; L Trk; French Hon Soc; Hon Roll; Gldn Pt Awd Wrld Ptry 87.

KUO, ROO MEI; John W Hallahan HS; Philadelphia, PA; (4); 4/300; Art Clb; Exploring; JA; Math Clb; Orch; Nwsp Rptr; High Hon Roll; NHS; Prfct Atten Awd; Pres Schlr; 1st ST PA JR Acad Sci,Recpnt Phila Cty Schlrshp & Myrs Schlrshp, Soc Wmns Engr Hnr Sci & Math 87; U Of PA; Med.

KUPCHELLA, KAREN; Blacklick Valley HS; Nanty Glo, PA; (3); Camera Clb; Drama Clb; Library Aide; Trs NFL; Ski Clb; Varsity Clb; Mrchg Band; School Play; Yrbk Stf; Var L Trk; Pitt; Physio Thrpy.

KUPCHINSKY, LAUREN; Central SR HS; York, PA; (3); Am Leg Aux Girls St; Varsity Clb; Band; Mrchg Band; Symp Band; Yrbk Stf; Rep Stu Cncl; Cheerleading; High Hon Roll; NHS; Ctznshp Awd 85-86.

KUPEC, AMY; Kiski Area HS; Lower Burrell, PA; (4); Pep Clb; Varsity Clb; Symp Band; Nwsp Bus Mgr; Trs Jr Cls; Stu Cncl; Var L Cheerleading; Var Trk; High Hon Roll; Hon Roll; Hnrs Band 84-87; USAA Band 87; WV Univ; Bus.

KUPFER, DEBORAH A; Taylor Allderdice HS; Pittsburgh, PA; (4); #4 In Class; Q&S; Ski Clb; Nwsp Sprt Ed; Trs Soph Cls; Trs Jr Cls; Pres Stu Cncl; Capt L Tennis; High Hon Roll; NHS; Tennis Gold Mdl Mixed Doub Cty Champ 86; Silver Doub Cty Champ 85; Bronze Doub Cty Champ 84; U Of PA.

KUPFER, JENNIFER E; Meadville Area SR HS; Meadville, PA; (4); 31/309; French Clb; Ski Clb; SADD; Varsity Clb; Rep Sr Cls; Off Stu Cncl; Socr; Trk; High Hon Roll; Key Clb; Pres Acdmc Ftnss Awd; Schlstc Hnr Soc; INN U PA; Sci.

KUPFER, NANCY; Taylor Allderdice HS; Pittsburgh, PA; (3); JA; Nwsp Stf; Sec Frsh Cls; Rep Stu Cncl; Var Bsktbl; Var Crs Cntry; Var Trk; Hon Roll; MVP Bsktbl; Intl Stds.

KUPPELWEISER, TONI; Cameron County HS; Driftwood, PA; (2); German Clb; Color Guard; Yrbk Stf; Hon Roll; Prfct Atten Awd; Delta Epsilon Phi 86-87; Penn ST; Communications.

KUPSTAS, KATHERINE; Tunkhannock Area HS; Tunkhannock, PA; (3); 46/330; Art Clb; Fld Hcky; Hon Roll; 2 Certs Mrt Schlstc Art Comp 85-86; Dsgnd Pub Bllbd Lcl Mrchnt 85; 1st Grd Lvl Cntst SPCA 84; Cmmrcl Art.

KURAK, KIM; Jim Thorpe Area HS; Jim Thorpe, PA; (2); FHA; Ski Clb; Chorus; Yrbk Bus Mgr; Rep Stu Cncl; Stat Bsktbl; JV Capt Cheerleading; St Lukes Nrsng Schl; Pedtrc Nrs.

KURCLKO, TRICIA; Kennedy Christian HS; Sharon, PA; (2); 31/96; Church Yth Grp; Latin Clb; Concert Band; Mrchg Band; Rep Stu Cncl; JV Bsktbl; JV Vllybl; Hon Roll.

KURCZEWSKI, MICHELE; Governor Mifflin HS; Shillington, PA; (3); 80/300; Chorus; Jazz Band; Capt Mrchg Band; Orch; School Musical; Stage Crew; JV Cheerleading; Hon Roll; Girl Scts; Concert Band; Outstndng Bassist NYU Adjdctn 87; Unfd Achvt Awd 86 & 87; Psych.

KURILLA, JAMES; Susquehannock HS; Glen Rock, PA; (2); 10/243; Crs Cntry; Trk; High Hon Roll; Hon Roll; NHS; Lttrd Trck 87; PA ST U; Engr.

KURINKO, SHERRI LYNN; Saegertown HS; Saegertown, PA; (4); 25/107; 4-H; Ski Clb; SADD; Band; Church Choir; VP Stu Cncl; Cheerleading; Hon Roll; Jr NHS; Masonic Awd; CA U Of PA; Pre-Chiropractic.

KURMAN, JEFF; Hempfield Area SR HS; Greensburg, PA; (3); Cmnty Wkr; Spanish Clb; VP Temple Yth Grp; Concert Band; Mrchg Band; High Hon Roll; Jr NHS; NHS; Pres Schlr; Spanish NHS; Pre-Law.

KURNIAWAN, HANDANI; South Fayette JR SR HS; Mc Donald, PA; (4); 9/72; Key Clb; Math Tm; Spanish Clb; Yrbk Stf; High Hon Roll; Hon Roll; Kiwanis Awd; NHS; Prfct Atten Awd; South Fayette Schlrshp 87; Penn ST Behrend Coll; Engrng.

KURNIAWAN, MARIANI; South Fayette HS; Mc Donald, PA; (3); 9/90; Drama Clb; Key Clb; Library Aide; Church Choir; Stage Crew; Nwsp Rptr; Nwsp Stf; High Hon Roll; Hon Roll; NHS; Photo.

KURNIK, AMY; Charleroi Area HS; N Charleroi, PA; (4); Office Aide; SADD; Chorus; Swmmng; Hon Roll; IN U Of PA; Psych.

KURTINECZ, MICHELE; Steelton-Highspire HS; Steelton, PA; (3); 2/102; English Clb; French Clb; Girl Scts; Yrbk Stf; Bausch & Lomb Sci Awd; High Hon Roll; NHS; Dist Schlstc Art Cert Merit 87; Sci.

KURTZ, BRYAN; Cambria Higts HS; Hastings, PA; (3); 33/187; SADD; VICA; Chorus; VP Jr Cls; Stu Cncl; Hon Roll.

KURTZ, DANIEL; Central HS; Philadelphia, PA; (4); 60/362; Pres Intnl Clb; Office Aide; Nwsp Stf; Yrbk Ed-Chief; Lit Mag; Rep Sr Cls; Var Capt Ftbl; Hon Roll; Operation Undrstndng 86; Pres Clsrm For Yng Amercns 87.

KURTZ, DEE; Dieruff HS; Allentown, PA; (3); 71/390; Var Capt Cheerleading; Hon Roll; Jr NHS; Dntl Hygn.

KURTZ, HEATHER; Mifflinburg Area SR HS; Swengel, PA; (1); French Clb; Key Clb; Pep Clb; Chorus; Cheerleading; Pom Pon; High Hon Roll; Hon Roll; Chld Psych.

KURTZ, JAMES; Reading SR HS; Reading, PA; (3); 173/710; Exploring; Chorus; Rep Stu Cncl; Cmrcl Advrtsng Artst.

KURTZ, JEFFREY; Phoenixville Area HS; Phoenixville, PA; (3); Key Clb; Pep Clb; Red Cross Aide; Ski Clb; SADD; Variety Show; Pres Jr Cls; Rep Stu Cncl; Ftbl; Capt Swmmng; Auburn U; Accntng.

KURTZ, KAREN; Eastern Lebanon County HS; Myerstown, PA; (4); FBLA; NHS; Southeastern Acad; Trvl.

KURTZ, KENNETH; Seneca Valley HS; Mars, PA; (2); Pres Church Yth Grp; Library Aide; JV Bsktbl; Var L Crs Cntry; Var Trk; Cit Awd; Hon Roll; Comp Drftng.

KURTZ, MELISSA; St Pius X HS; East Greenville, PA; (4); 13/150; Art Clb; Girl Scts; Pep Clb; Science Clb; Spanish Clb; Drill Tm; Hon Roll; NHS; Millersville U; Bio.

KURTZ, MICHELLE; Carbondale Area JR SR HS; Forest City, PA; (4); 10/144; Art Clb; FBLA; Ski Clb; Chorus; Church Choir; Bsktbl; Trk.

KURTZ, RACHEL; Schuylkill Haven HS; Schuylkill Haven, PA; (4); 9/97; Am Leg Aux Girls St; SADD; Band; Chorus; Concert Band; Mrchg Band; Nwsp Phtg; Nwsp Rptr; Nwsp Stf; Yrbk Ed-Chief; 1st Pl Phtgrphy Cntst 86; Region V Band Fstvl 87 & Dist 10 Band Fstvl 87; Elizabethtown Coll; Pblc Rltns.

KURTZ, RICHARD; Chief Logan HS; Mcclure, PA; (3); Chess Clb; Computer Clb; FFA; FFA Pltry Awd 87; PA ST U; Ag Bus.

KURTZROCK, SHEILA; Shaler Area HS; Glenshaw, PA; (3); 65/486; Church Yth Grp; French Clb; Hosp Aide; SADD; Camera Clb; Yrbk Stf; French Hon Soc; High Hon Roll; Hon Roll; Daughters Of Amer Revolution 84; Frnch Hnr Awd 85; Sci Hnr Awd 84; Bio.

KURUCZ, ROB; Archbishop Wood HS; Pipersville, PA; (2); Aud/Vis; SADD; Band; Concert Band; Mrchg Band; Elec.

KURYWCHAK, JOHN; North Allegheny HS; Wexford, PA; (3); VP JA; JR Achvt Sales Awd 85-86; Arch.

KURZ, VALERIE MULLER; Quaker Valley HS; Sewickley, PA; (2); Debate Tm; Math Tm; Spanish Clb; School Play; Swmmng; Vllybl; Sci.

KURZWEIL, DENA; West Scranton HS; Scranton, PA; (4); 4/263; VP Aud/Vis; Speech Tm; Orch; School Play; Stage Crew; Yrbk Stf; NHS; Ntl Merit Ltr; Ursinus Coll; Genetic Engr.

KURZWEIL, ROBYN; West Scranton HS; Scranton, PA; (2); Hon Roll; Jr NHS; Hlth Careers Clb.

KUSH, BETHANEY; Kiski Area HS; Hyde Pk, PA; (3); Chorus; Color Guard; School Musical; Nwsp Stf; Yrbk Stf; Stat Bsktbl; Mgr(s); L Trk.

KUSH, MARLA A; Bishop Hoban HS; Nanticoke, PA; (3); 14/199; FBLA; Math Clb; Mu Alpha Theta; Mrchg Band; Rep Frsh Cls; High Hon Roll; Hon Roll; Mu Alpha Theta Awd; NHS; U Pittsburgh; Pre-Dent.

KUSHMA, ANDREW; Mohawk Area JR-SR HS; Edinburg, PA; (2); Boy Scts; Church Yth Grp; Dance Clb; 4-H; FFA; L Var Mgr(s); Trk; God Cntry Awd; Penn ST; Ag Engr.

KUSHMEDER, MICHELE ANN; Hazleton HS; Hazleton, PA; (4); 77/376; Church Yth Grp; Library Aide; Pep Clb; Band; Concert Band; Jazz Band; Trs Mrchg Band; Nwsp Stf; Hon Roll; Pres Schlr; Prsdntl Acdmc Ftnss Awd 87; Lock Haven U; Elem Ed.

KUSHNIR, LAWRENCE; East Allegheny HS; North Versailles, PA; (3); Am Leg Boys St; Var Bsktbl; Var Ftbl; Hon Roll; NHS; Engrng.

KUSTABORDER, LAURA; Altoona Area HS; Altoona, PA; (3); 3/796; Computer Clb; German Clb; Key Clb; Chorus; High Hon Roll; NEDT Awd; Pres Schlr; Pres Church Yth Grp; Penn ST; Archit.

KUSTRON, KIM; Monogahela Valley Catholic HS; Monongahela, PA; (2); 23/86; Girl Scts; Color Guard; Flag Corp; Rep Frsh Cls; Hon Roll; Spanish NHS; Bus.

KUTCH, DAWN; Western Wayne HS; South Canaan, PA; (2); Church Yth Grp; Band; Concert Band; Mrchg Band; School Musical; Cheerleading; High Hon Roll; Hon Roll; NHS; Cnty Band 87.

KUTCH, LARA; Lakeland JR/Sr HS; Jermyn, PA; (4); Church Yth Grp; Dance Clb; FHA; Hon Roll; Presdntl Acadc Ftnss Awd 87; Penn ST; Engrng.

KUTCH, MICHAEL J; Nativity Blessed Virgin Mary HS; Pottsville, PA; (1); 7/94; Chess Clb; Church Yth Grp; Debate Tm; Hosp Aide; Speech Tm; JV Ftbl; JV Trk; High Hon Roll; Kiwanis Awd; Med Prof.

KUTCH, PAULA; Forest City Regional HS; Forest City, PA; (3); Church Yth Grp; FFA; VICA; High Hon Roll; Hon Roll; Public Spkng Cont 86-87; Marywood Coll; Fash Desgn.

KUTCHER, JENNIFER; West York Area HS; York, PA; (3); 25/185; French Clb; Varsity Clb; Sec Civic Clb; Sec Soph Cls; Sec Jr Cls; Sec Sr Cls; VP Stu Cncl; Capt Bsktbl; Var Cheerleading; JV Tennis; 4th Pl VFW We The People Spch Cntst 87; Pol Sci.

KUTCHER, MARY; Danville SR HS; Riverside, PA; (3); Church Yth Grp; Ski Clb; Band; Concert Band; Drill Tm; Mrchg Band; Hon Roll.

KUTRUFF, TAMMY; Cambria Heights HS; Patton, PA; (3); 37/182; Drama Clb; Pres 4-H; Pres FHA; Band; Concert Band; Mrchg Band; School Play; Stage Crew; Yrbk Stf; Hon Roll; FHA Chptr Of Yr 87; Natl Educ Dvlpmnt Test Awd 86; Cnmgh Vly Mem Hsp; Rdlgc Tech.

KUTSICK, GREGORY; Northern Cambria HS; Barnesboro, PA; (4); 2/125; French Clb; Hosp Aide; Nwsp Rptr; Nwsp Stf; Stu Cncl; Ftbl; Wt Lftg; NHS; Sal; Natl Hnr Soc Pres 87; Ltrmn Ftbl 85-87; U Of Pgh Jnstwn; Phys Thrpy.

KUTZ, JASON; Bermudian Springs HS; York Spgs, PA; (3); Pres Band; Chorus; Concert Band; Jazz Band; Madrigals; Mrchg Band; School Musical; JV Bsktbl; Comp Tech.

KUTZ, RENEE LYNN; Spring-Ford HS; Collegeville, PA; (4); 39/250; Letterman Clb; Ski Clb; Spanish Clb; Lit Mag; Tennis; Trk; Hon Roll; Wrtr Of Mnth 86-87; Spn Awd 84-85; West Chester U; Bus Mgmt.

KUTZLER, DAVID; Liberty HS; Bethlehem, PA; (3); 64/430; Church Yth Grp; SADD; Band; Concert Band; Mrchg Band; Orch; Bsbl; Bsktbl; Bowling; Hon Roll; Sci.

KUYKENDALL, CHRISTY L; Athens HS; Sayre, PA; (3); Church Yth Grp; Dance Clb; FHA; Ski Clb; Band; Chorus; Off Stu Cncl; Var L Cheerleading; Var L Swmmng; Hnry Hgr Good Ctznshp Awd 84.

KUZDZAL, TODD W; Mc Dowell HS; Erie, PA; (4); 104/600; Var Wrstlng; Hon Roll; Spanish NHS; Wrstlng Boosters Schlrshp 87; Span Speaking Awd 85; Edinboro U; Grphc Arts.

KUZIO, NICOLE; South Allegheny HS; Port Vue, PA; (3); Dance Clb; French Clb; Girl Scts; JA; Y-Teens; Im Powder Puff Ftbl; French Hon Soc; Hon Roll; The Natl Soc Daughters Of Amer Rvltn 84; Keep PA Beautiful Day 83; Serv Awd Being Bus Ptrl Offc 84; Penn ST; Dent.

KUZMA, KERI; Tunkhannock Area HS; Tunkhannock, PA; (3); Church Yth Grp; French Clb; Sec SADD; Band; Concert Band; Mrchg Band; Var Sftbl; Zeswitz Awd-Most Valuable Jr 87; Dfnsv Plyr Yr-Varsity Sftbl 87; Keystone JC; Med Sec.

KUZMIAK, TINA MARIE; Bishop Mc Cort HS; Johnstown, PA; (3); Drm Mjr(t); High Hon Roll; NHS; French Clb; Latin Clb; Pep Clb; Ski Clb; Chorus; Socr; Trk.

KUZMICH, LORI; Riverside JR-SR HS; Taylor, PA; (4); Drama Clb; German Clb; Pep Clb; Ski Clb; Off Frsh Cls; Pom Pon; Antnl; Intr Dsgn.

KUZMINSKI, KATHY; Elmer L Meyers HS; Wilkes Barre, PA; (3); Hosp Aide; Key Clb; Pep Clb; SADD; Yrbk Stf; Trs Stu Cncl; Cheerleading; High Hon Roll; Hon Roll; Jr NHS; Hnr Socty 84-86; Med.

KUZMITSKY, TAMI; West Hazleton HS; Brandonville, PA; (3); 17/224; Scholastic Bowl; Thesps; Varsity Clb; Y-Teens; Chorus; Stu Cncl; Cheerleading; Hon Roll; Pres Schlr; Millersville U; Bio.

KUZNAR, SUSAN; Mon Valley Catholic HS; Cardale, PA; (1); GAA; JV Vllybl; Sci.

KUZNICKI, NOEL M; Lake-Lahman HS; Shavertown, PA; (4); 57/155; Key Clb; Var Cheerleading; Var Fld Hcky; Var Capt Sftbl; Hm Ec Awd 87; Dietcs.

KUZUPAS, LISA; Shade Central City HS; Cairnbrook, PA; (4); 3/61; Pres Band; Chorus; Color Guard; Concert Band; Drm Mjr(t); Mrchg Band; School Play; Yrbk Ed-Chief; VP Pres NHS; Edinboro ST U; Cmnctns.

KUZY, LISA; Immaculate Conception HS; Washington, PA; (2); 1/44; Sec Stu Cncl; Vllybl; High Hon Roll; Art Clb; Math Tm; Ski Clb; School Play; Yrbk Stf; Sftbl.

KWAIT, RICHARD A; Plymouth Whitemarsh HS; Plymouth Meeting, PA; (3); 7/389; Chess Clb; Math Tm; Mu Alpha Theta; Temple Yth Grp; Jr Cls; Stu Cncl; Bsbl; Golf; High Hon Roll; Hon Roll; HOBY Rep For Soph Clss 86.

KWAIT, ROBERT; Plmouth Whitemarsh HS; Plymouth Meeting, PA; (3); 8/389; VP Frsh Cls; Rep Jr Cls; VP Stu Cncl; JV Var Bsbl; JV Var Golf; High Hon Roll; Hon Roll; Jr NHS; NHS; Chess Clb; Rnnr Up HOBY 86.

KWELLER, JON; William Allen HS; Allentown, PA; (4); 110/559; Key Clb; Ski Clb; Temple Yth Grp; Varsity Clb; Jazz Band; Rep Jr Cls; Rep Sr Cls; Trk; Wt Lftg; Wrstlng; Robert M Friedman Awd Track 86; Athl Chrmn AZA 86; Liberal Arts.

KWIATEK, BRANDON; William Allen HS; Allentown, PA; (3); 35/609; Debate Tm; German Clb; Band; Concert Band; Mrchg Band; Nwsp Stf; Lit Mag; High Hon Roll; Hon Roll; NHS; Engl.

KWIATKOWSKI, ANN; West Scranton HS; Scranton, PA; (4); 6/242; Church Yth Grp; Spanish Clb; Varsity Clb; Yrbk Stf; VP Stu Cncl; Cheerleading; High Hon Roll; NHS; Pres Schlr; Spanish NHS; Presdntl Schlrshp 87; U Of Scranton; Medical Tech.

KWON, DANNY; Marple Newtown HS; Newtown Square, PA; (3); Church Yth Grp; German Clb; Intnl Clb; Math Clb; Variety Show; Nwsp Stf; Yrbk Stf; Lit Mag; Rep Frsh Cls; Rep Soph Cls; Dntstry.

KYLE, BILL; Blackhawk HS; Darlington, PA; (3); 70/234; Church Yth Grp; 4-H; FFA; VICA; 4-H Awd; High Hon Roll; Hon Roll; Natl FFA Fndtn Awd 87; Treator Driving 87; Notch Awd For Machine Shop 87; Pttsburg Inst Arntcs; Airpl Tch.

KYLE, KEITH; Mount Union Area HS; Mt Union, PA; (3); Church Yth Grp; Bsbl; Bsktbl; Ftbl.

KYLE, MAGGIE; Saucon Valley HS; Bethlehem, PA; (1); Church Yth Grp; Hosp Aide; Library Aide; Model UN; JV Tennis; High Hon Roll; Hon Roll; NHS; Ntl Sci Olympd 87; Pres Acad Ftns Awd 87.

KYLER, DARLA; West Branch Area HS; Kylertown, PA; (3); #3 In Class; Drama Clb; Science Clb; Spanish Clb; Chorus; Concert Band; Mrchg Band; High Hon Roll; NHS; Church Yth Grp.

KYLER, KELLY; Chester HS; Chester, PA; (3); DECA; Drama Clb; Yrbk Stf; DE CC; Hotel Mgmt.

KYLER, RACHAEL; Rocky Grove HS; Cooperstown, PA; (3); 1/81; Band; Chorus; Concert Band; Pep Band; Var JV Bsktbl; Var JV Vllybl; High Hon Roll; Hon Roll.

KYPER, ALEISA E; Mechanicsburg Area SR HS; Grantham, PA; (4); 6/305; Chorus; Church Choir; Concert Band; Mrchg Band; Yrbk Bus Mgr; Hon Roll; NHS; Ntl Merit SF; Pres Schlr; Church Yth Grp; Upper Allen Wmns Club AHFA 87; Ist Pl Ladies Aux Unit 109 Essay Cntst 87; Schlrshp Messiah Coll 87; Messiah Coll; Nrnsg.

KYPTA, JEFF; Hopewell Area HS; Clinton, PA; (2); 4-H; French Clb; Band; JV Ftbl; Var Trk; Robotics.

KYTE, JANINE; West Hazleton HS; Weston, PA; (2); 29/255; Scholastic Bowl; Spanish Clb; Yrbk Stf; Var Bsktbl; Hon Roll; Prose Writing 1st Pl 85-86; Phys.

KYTIC, EVELYN; Montour HS; Mc Kees Rocks, PA; (3); Red Cross Aide; Chorus; Concert Band; Mrchg Band; Var L Trk; High Hon Roll; NHS; Cmnty Wkr; Band; Pep Band; Acadc Achvt Awd Frnch III 86; Acadc Achvt Awd Occptnl Explrtn 87; Rookie Yr-Mrchng Band 86; Math Tchr.

KYTTLE, TONYA; Danville SR HS; Riverside, PA; (3); 65/189; Art Clb; Hosp Aide; Band; Chorus; Color Guard; Mrchg Band; School Musical; Symp Band; Var Crs Cntry; Hon Roll; Art Ed.

LA BARRE, LAURIE; Northeast Bradford HS; Rome, PA; (4); 12/73; Scholastic Bowl; Varsity Clb; VP Stu Cncl; Mgr Bsbl; Var Cheerleading; High Hon Roll; Hon Roll; Pres Schlr; Rotary Awd; Church Yth Grp; Rtry Exchng Stu Venezuela 87-88; Pre-Law.

LA BELLA, LARRY; St John Neumann HS; Philadelphia, PA; (4); Bsktbl; Hon Roll; Awd 1st Hnrs 87; St Josephs U; Accntng.

LA COE, JODI; Abington Heights HS; Clarks Summit, PA; (2); 41/296; Ski Clb; Chorus; School Musical; Rep Stu Cncl; Hon Roll; Rep To The NEIU Stu Forum 86-89; Arch.

LA CROSS, CATHLEEN; Bellefonte Area HS; Bellefonte, PA; (3); 1/211; Sec Drama Clb; Trs Model UN; Flag Corp; Stage Crew; Yrbk Stf; High Hon Roll; NHS; Outstndg Delg Awd Model UN 87; Intnsv Lang Inst 87.

LA CROSS, FRANCIS; Archbishop Ryan HS For Boys; Philadelphia, PA; (4); 26/450; Cmnty Wkr; Political Wkr; JV Crs Cntry; High Hon Roll; Hon Roll; Pres Schlr; John Mc Kee Schlrshp 87; Physics, Geom, A & Chem, Engl, Germ, & Wrld Culture Awd; Drexel U; Physics.

LA FASHIA, SUSAN; Cardinal O Hara HS; Springfield, PA; (3); 50/710; Cmnty Wkr; Office Aide; School Musical; Nwsp Stf; Yrbk Stf; High Hon Roll; Hon Roll; NHS; Spanish NHS; Church Yth Grp; Acdmc Convocation Hnr 85-87; Bus Admin.

LA FAVE, ANGELA; Pocono Central Catholic HS; Newfoundland, PA; (4); 5/30; Art Clb; Church Yth Grp; Pep Clb; School Play; Yrbk Stf; Rep Jr Cls; Bsktbl; Fld Hcky; Sftbl; High Hon Roll; Soc Distngshd Amer HS Stu 85-86; Voice Of Dem 85-86; Srvc Awd 84-85; Elem Ed.

LA FORGIA, PALMA; Jim Thorpe HS; Albrightsville, PA; (3); FHA; Spanish Clb; Nwsp Phtg; Nwsp Rptr; Nwsp Stf; Hon Roll; E Stroudsburg U; Elem Teacher.

LA LUNA, CHRISTINA; Abington Heights N Campus; Clarks Summit, PA; (3); 41/283; Church Yth Grp; Exploring; Ski Clb; SADD; Lit Mag; Rep Stu Cncl; Hon Roll; PA JR Acad Of Sci Rgnls & ST 1st 86; Marine Bio.

LA NUNZIATA, MARISA; Dunmore HS; Dunmore, PA; (4); 20/149; Computer Clb; Dance Clb; Drama Clb; French Clb; FBLA; Pep Clb; Spanish Clb; School Play; Variety Show; Ed Nwsp Sprt Ed; Meta Alta Chptr-Ntl Hnr Soc 86-87; Penn ST-WRTHNGTN Cmps; Bus Adm.

LA PIERRE, DAN; Harry S Truman HS; Levittown, PA; (3); Var Socr; Hon Roll; Prfct Atten Awd; All ST Soccer Tm 86; Temple U; Bus Adm.

LA PORTA, JEFF; Shade Central City HS; Cairnbrook, PA; (3); Art Clb; Boy Scts; Chess Clb; Church Yth Grp; Computer Clb; Q&S; Red Cross Aide; SADD; Varsity Clb; Yrbk Stf; Prfct Atten 82; Sci Awd 84; Lttr Trk 87; Pitt; Art.

LA PORTE, MATTHEW; North Hills HS; Pittsburgh, PA; (4); 10/490; Key Clb; Ski Clb; Mrchg Band; Orch; Im Bsbl; JV Bsktbl; JV Ftbl; High Hon Roll; NHS; Bucknell U; Chemistry.

LA POSTA, ANGELA; Washington HS; Washington, PA; (2); Key Clb; Ski Clb; Spanish Clb; SADD; Var Tennis; Hon Roll.

LA RUE, DENNIS; Tunkhannock Area HS; Tunkhannock, PA; (2); Nwsp Rptr; Nwsp Sprt Ed; Nwsp Stf; JV Bsktbl; Im Var Crs Cntry; Im Ftbl; Var Trk; Hon Roll; Baylor U; TV Brdcstng.

LA RUE SCHLICK, DENIELLE; Pottstown HS; Pottstown, PA; (4); French Clb; DE Coll Of Sci & Agr; Pre Vet.

LA SCOLA, AMY; Meadville SR HS; Meadville, PA; (3); 90/363; Yrbk Stf; Sec Jr Cls; Stu Cncl; JV Var Cheerleading; Hon Roll; Prfct Atten Awd; Reunir Sorority 85-88; Homecomg Queen 86.

LA VELLA, TONI; Hempfield Area SR HS; Irwin, PA; (3); Letterman Clb; Chorus; Nwsp Rptr; Stu Cncl; Capt Var Cheerleading; Hon Roll; Art Clb; French Clb; Office Aide; Pep Clb; Carnegie Mellon U; Adv.

LABATE, NICOLA; Central Catholic HS; Glenshaw, PA; (3); Yrbk Stf; Trk; High Hon Roll; Hon Roll; NHS; Spanish NHS; Duquesne U; Acctg.

LABEKA, BRETT; Sto-Rox HS; Mckees Rocks, PA; (2).

LABELLA, LOU; Methalton HS; Eagleville, PA; (3); 23/318; Chorus; Concert Band; Jazz Band; Orch; VP Frsh Cls; Var Ftbl; JV Trk; Var Wrstlng; Dnfth Awd; High Hon Roll; Havard Bk Awd 86-87; Rotary Intl Camp Neidig Tomorrows Ldrs 86-87; Natn Hnr Soc Pres 87-88; Bio.

LABELLA, RENIEA; Sto-Rox SR HS; Mckees Rocks, PA; (2); Chorus; Yrbk Stf; Pblc Rltns.

LABELLARTE, JOSEPH; Baldwin HS; Pittsburgh, PA; (3); Var Letterman Clb; SADD; Rep Jr Cls; JV Var Bsbl; JV Var Ice Hcky; Wrstlng; Hon Roll; Ntl Merit Ltr; Penn ST U; Real Estate.

LABENBERG, LYNN; W Hazleton HS; Zion Grove, PA; (4); 69/22 Cmnty Wkr; Drama Clb; French Clb; SADD; Teachers Aide; Thesp Chorus; Stage Crew; High Hon Roll; NHS; Penna JR Acdmy Sci 85-8 Luzerne CO CC; Chef.

LABENNE, BOB; Iroquois HS; Erie, PA; (4); 32/142; Letterman Cl Concert Band; Pep Band; Pres Frsh Cls; Pres Soph Cls; Pres Jr Cls; Pr Sr Cls; Var L Ftbl; Var Trk; Im Wt Lftg; Mercyhurst Coll; Crmnl Justic

LABERT, JOE; West Hazleton HS; Tresckow, PA; (2); Boy Scts; SAD Rep Frsh Cls; Rep Soph Cls; Rep Stu Cncl; JV L Ftbl; JV Var Wrstln Hon Roll; PA ST; Engrng.

LABORDE, KRISTEN; Du Bois Area HS; Dubois, PA; (3); 29/29 Church Yth Grp; Band; Concert Band; Mrchg Band; Hon Roll; Chur Yth Group; Sundy Schl Sec; VBS Tchr; Sec Mission Rdng Books JR, Te & Adult; SR High Cls Sec; Mt Vernon Nazarene Coll; Bus.

LABROSKY, JOHN; Riverside HS; Taylor, PA; (3); German Clb; J Science Clb; Ski Clb; JV Ftbl; High Hon Roll; Hon Roll; NHS; U Scranto Dentstry.

LABUDA, KIM; Geibel HS; Connellsville, PA; (4); Drama Clb; Pep Cl Spanish Clb; SADD; Lit Mag; High Hon Roll; Hon Roll; Spanish NH Bishop Hugh Lamb Awd 86-87; Spnsh Awd 85-87; CA ST U; Spani Teacher.

LABUDA, PAT; Mt Pleasant Area HS; Acme, PA; (3); Pres Church Y Grp; Ski Clb; Var L Ftbl; Im Vllybl; Hon Roll; Lwyr.

LACABA, RICHARD; Upper Darby HS; Milbourne, PA; (3); Science Cl Socr; Wrstlng; Hon Roll; Amer Indus Arts Stu Assn Awds 86 & 87; Drex U; Elec Engrng.

LACEY, NANCY JO; Bishop Boyle HS; North Braddock, PA; (4); 9/6 Aud/Vis; Dance Clb; Intnl Clb; Pep Clb; Spanish Clb; Im Bsktbl; I Powder Puff Ftbl; Im Sftbl; Im Tennis; Hon Roll; Mathmtcl Exclnc 8 Acctng.

LACHAT, LISA; Lock Haven SR HS; Castanea, PA; (4); 29/242; Chur Yth Grp; FHA; Spanish Clb; Teachers Aide; NEDT Awd; Prfct Atten Aw Lock Haven U; Elem Ed.

LACKEY, SHEILA; Franklin HS; Franklin, PA; (4); 32/240; Radio C Yrbk Stf; Off Frsh Cls; Off Soph Cls; Off Jr Cls; Off Sr Cls; Sec Stu Cn Trs NHS; Pres Schlr; Edinboro U PA Honors Pgm Schlrshp 87; Edinbo U Of PA; Comm.

LACKEY, THOMAS; Norwin SR HS; N Huntingdon, PA; (3); VIC Hon Roll; Jr NHS; Automtv Tech.

LACKI, ISABELLA; Wyoming Valley West HS; Kingston, PA; (2); Ho Aide; Key Clb; Chorus; L Diving; Hon Roll; NHS; Prfct Atten Awd; M Cert NEDT Tsts 87; Amer Red Cross Volunteer Svcs 87.

LACKO, JENNIFER; Northampton Area SR HS; Walnutport, PA; (45/445; Leo Clb; SADD; Chorus; Stu Cncl; High Hon Roll; Hon Roll; Li Awd; NHS; Spec Olympcs Vol 84-87; Stu Of Mnth Bus & Prof Wmns C 87; Alverna Coll; Bus.

LACOCK, CYNDI; Pequea Valley HS; Paradise, PA; (3); Church Y Grp; Varsity Clb; Band; Chorus; Church Choir; Concert Band; Jazz Ban Mrchg Band; Pep Band; Nwsp Rptr; Poetry Awd Natl 87; Nwsp Edtrl 8 Inst Of Amer Lit 87; Journlsm.

LACOMB, KRISTA; Keystone HS; Knox, PA; (3); 1/140; Trs Pep C Band; Chorus; Var L Bsktbl; Im Sftbl; Var L Trk; High Hon Roll; NH Clarion Cnty All Star Bsktbl 86-87; Jr Vrsty Bsktbl Capt 85-86; Math.

LACOUNT, ROB; Waynesburg Central HS; Waynesburg, PA; (4); 6/18 Boy Scts; Mrchg Band; DAR Awd; High Hon Roll; JP Sousa Awd; Li Awd; NHS; Church Yth Grp; French Clb; Concert Band; Order Arrow B Scouts 83; Robert C Byrd Scholar 87; Boy Yr 87; Wittenberg U; Bus Ad

LACROSS, FRANCIS R; Archbishop Ryan H S For Boys; Philadelph PA; (4); 26/450; Cmnty Wkr; Crs Cntry; High Hon Roll; Hon Roll; Hons 2nd Hons; Wrld Cltr; Grmn; Geo; Eng; Prncpls Awd; Drexel Physics.

LACY, SARAH; Central Bucks West HS; Doyleston, PA; (3); 69/4 Chorus; Rep Soph Cls; JV Lcrss; High Hon Roll; Hon Roll; Jr NHS; Prf Atten Awd; Pres Schlr; Tchr.

LADIG, PETER; Garnet Valley HS; Glen Mills, PA; (2); 3/169; Intnl C Model UN; Ski Clb; Spanish Clb; Varsity Clb; School Play; Trs Jr Cls; S Cncl; Var L Bsbl; Var L Socr; Bsbl Plyr.

LADLEE, KENNETH; E Stroudsburg HS; E Strdbg, PA; (4); Chur Yth Grp; Cmnty Wkr; JA; Var Tennis; Im Wt Lftg; Hon Ro Williamsport CC; Aviatn.

LADNER, TRACY; Montrose Area HS; Hallstead, PA; (3); Church Y Grp; Cmnty Wkr; German Clb; Girl Scts; Hosp Aide; Office Aide; SAD Varsity Clb; Capt Concert Band; Capt Flag Corp; Internshp Montro Independent 85-86; Jrnlsm.

LAFFERTY, ERIC; Gar Memorial HS; Nanticoke, PA; (4); 2/1 German Clb; Letterman Clb; Varsity Clb; Nwsp Sprt Ed; Off Stu Cncl; V L Vllybl; Var L Wrstlng; DAR Awd; NHS; Ntl Merit SF; U S Naval Ac Engrng.

LAFLEY, BRENDA; Central Dauphin HS; Harrisburg, PA; (3); Key C Red Cross Aide; Ski Clb; Teachers Aide; Var JV Cheerleading; Var L Gy Var L Trk; Im Vllybl; Hon Roll; 1st Pl Amer HS Math Exm 86-87; Ma

LAGIOVANE, SHARON; Shaler Area SR HS; Allison Park, PA; (4); 509; School Musical; School Play; Variety Show; Nwsp Stf; Mgr(s); Fren Hon Soc; High Hon Roll; Pres Schlr; Yrbk Rsrch Edtr 86-87; OH Cmnctns.

LAGODA, HEATHER; West Hazleton JR/Sr HS; Sugarloaf, PA; (French Clb; Girl Scts; Yrbk Stf; JV Bsktbl; Trk; God Cntry Awd; P Schlr; 2nd Pl Kings Coll Ntl Frnch Contst 86; Luzerne Cnty PFA Yth C 87; Girl Sct Gold Ldrshp Awd 86.

LAGOLA, RENEE; Minersville Area HS; Llewellyn, PA; (3); #9 In Cla German Clb; Yrbk Stf; JV Cheerleading; High Hon Roll; Jr Garland Gro 86-87; Acdmc Achvt Awd 84-85; Ftnss Achvt Awds 85-87; Comp Pgmn

LAGYAK, JEFFREY; Steelton-Highspire HS; Steelton, PA; (3); Che Clb; Spanish Clb; Swmmng; Trk; Wrstlng; Gov Hon Prg Awd; Harrisbu Area CC; Nrsng.

LAHART, CHRISTINA; Nazareth Acad; Philadelphia, PA; (4); Dra Clb; Red Cross Aide; Chorus; School Musical; Yrbk Rptr; Yrbk Stf; Hi Hon Roll; Hon Roll; Jr NHS; Penn ST U; Med.

LAHART, STEFANIE; Nazareth Acad HS; Phila, PA; (3); Church Y Grp; Cmnty Wkr; Pep Clb; Political Wkr; Chorus; Stage Crew; Yrbk S Lit Mag; Hon Roll; Prtcpnt Smmr Schlrshp Prog Wrkshps 87; Phila C Txtls & Sci; Fshn.

LAHIRI, INDRA; Solebury Schl; Chalfont, PA; (4); Church Yth G Chorus; Church Choir; School Musical; School Play; Lit Mag; Vllybl; Hi Hon Roll; Hon Roll; Catholic U Of America; Psychlgy.

LAHR, MELISSA; Shamokin Area HS; Shamokin, PA; (3); 48/246; P Church Yth Grp; Hosp Aide; Varsity Clb; Sec Concert Band; Sec Mrc Band; Yrbk Rptr; Bsbl; Var L Sftbl; Hon Roll; Physcl Thrpy.

LAHR, WILLIAM D; Upper Dauphin Area HS; Lykens, PA; (4); 21/101; Church Yth Grp; Trs FFA; Varsity Clb; Sec Band; Chorus; Mrchg Band; Symp Band; L Var Bsbl; Hon Roll; NHS; Plant Sci.

LAI, HANG; Lebanon Catholic HS; Annville, PA; (3); FHA; Library Aide; Spanish Clb; Yrbk Stf; Wt Lftg; Hon Roll; NHS; Stage Crew; Excel Spnsh 1 86; Excel Spnsh 2 87; U Of MD; Lang.

LAI, JENNIFER; Easton Area HS; Easton, PA; (4); 6/461; Hosp Aide; Chorus; Orch; Lit Mag; JV Crs Cntry; NCTE Awd; Ntl Merit Ltr; Modern Music Mstrs; PA Govr Schl For The Arts; Prncpl Viola Of ST Orch; Viola Prfmnc.

LAI, TRUC; Parkland HS; Allentown, PA; (2); JA; High Hon Roll; Med.

LAIB, SHAWN; Wallenpaupack HS; Hawley, PA; (3); Boy Scts; Church Yth Grp; Ski Clb; Var L Ftbl; Im Wt Lftg; Var L Wrstlng; Penn ST; Engrng.

LAIBE, GREG; Exeter SR HS; Reading, PA; (3); 12/241; Church Yth Grp; Drama Clb; German Clb; Quiz Bowl; Band; Church Choir; Concert Band; Mrchg Band; NHS; MIT; Elec Engrng.

LAIDLAW, PATRICK; Butler HS; Butler, PA; (2); Church Yth Grp; Spanish Clb; Var L Socr; Hon Roll; Jr NHS; Acad MVP Vrsty Sccr 86-87; Lttrd JR Ntl Hnr Soc 86-87; Hnr Stu Schlrshp Awd 85-87; Stanford; Law.

LAILONE, LAURA; Cardinal O Hara HS; Broomall, PA; (3); 23/720; Church Yth Grp; Office Aide; Service Clb; School Musical; Ed Yrbk Stf; Stu Cncl; Hon Roll; NHS; Ntl Merit Ltr; 1st Delaware Cnty Sci Fair 87; Hnrs Convctn Top 10 Pct Clss 85-87; Hnrb Mntn DE Vlly Sci Fair 87; Jrnlsm.

LAIRD, AARON; Dover Area SR HS; East Berlin, PA; (3); VP Pres Church Yth Grp; 4-H; Chorus; Outstdng Conservation Camp Std 86.

LAIRD, KAREN; Bensalem HS; Bensalem, PA; (3); Teachers Aide; Acpl Chr; Band; Chorus; Concert Band; Jazz Band; Mrchg Band; Orch; Socr; Dist & Rgnl Band 86-87; Marine Bio.

LAIRD, KATHY; West Allegheny HS; Imperial, PA; (3); 28/198; VP Sec JA; Spanish Clb; Band; Mrchg Band; Drama Clb; Ski Clb; Concert Band; Pep Band; Bsktbl; Powder Puff Ftbl; JR Achvmnt VP Prsnnl & Exec Secty Of Moon Ctr 86; Mrchng Bands Of Amrca Achvmnt Awd 86; Mgr.

LAKATA, YVONNE; Panther Valley HS; Nesquehoning, PA; (1); 8/127; Ski Clb; Rep Stu Cncl; JV Var Cheerleading; Var Trk; High Hon Roll; Medical.

LAKATOS JR, ANDREW S; Allentown Central Catholic HS; Allentown, PA; (3); 42/241; Church Yth Grp; Cmnty Wkr; JA; Math Clb; Ski Clb; Im Fld Hcky; Im Wt Lftg; Hon Roll; Elec Engrng.

LAKE JR, GERALD A; Blairsville SR HS; Blairsville, PA; (1); Boy Scts; JV Wrstlng; God Cntry Awd; Hon Roll; Penn ST U; Bio.

LAKEY, JENNIFER; Northampton SR HS; Bath, PA; (2); Church Yth Grp; DECA; Drama Clb; Fld Hcky; Churchmans Bus Schl; Bus.

LAKHANI, DEVAL; Villa Maria HS; Boardman, OH; (4); Pres Art Clb; Red Cross Aide; Spanish Clb; Ed Yrbk Stf; Tennis; NHS; Spanish NHS; Bio.

LAKIN, BETH; Mt Pleasant Area JR SR HS; Mt Pleasant, PA; (4); VP GAA; Ski Clb; Rep Jr Cls; Rep Stu Cncl; Capt Swmmng; Hon Roll.

LAKITSKY, MICHELLE; Tamaqua Area HS; Andreas, PA; (4); Exploring; 4-H; Pep Clb; Flag Corp; Mrchg Band; Yrbk Stf; Rep Jr Cls; Rep Sr Cls; Var Crs Cntry; Var Trk; Penn ST; Math.

LAKKIS, PASCALE; G A R Memorial HS; Wilkes-Barre, PA; (3); 10/152; Church Yth Grp; Ski Clb; Chorus; Off Stu Cncl; Tennis; Vllybl; Hon Roll; Jr NHS; NHS; Law.

LAKSO, KATIE; Huntingdale Area HS; Huntingdon, PA; (3); Church Yth Grp; GAA; Key Clb; SADD; Concert Band; Nwsp Stf; Yrbk Stf; Stu Cncl; Bsktbl; Fld Hcky; Pres Phys Ftns Awd 86-87; John Carroll U; Educ.

LALLEY, COLLEEN; Bishop Hannan HS; Scranton, PA; (3); Hosp Aide; Trs Jr Cls; Var Capt Cheerleading; U Of Scranton.

LAM, FAI JASON; Roman Catholic HS; Philadelphia, PA; (3); 5/121; Camera Clb; Math Clb; Math Tm; SADD; Rep Frsh Cls; Rep Stu Cncl; High Hon Roll; Hon Roll; Jr NHS; NHS; Thlgy I, Hstry I, & Algbr I Hnr Awds 84-85; Bus Mngmnt.

LAM, HUNG; Upper Moreland HS; Willow Grove, PA; (3); 90/256; Church Yth Grp; Debate Tm; Key Clb; Red Cross Aide; Science Clb; Speech Tm; SADD; Varsity Clb; Yrbk Phtg; Off Jr Cls; Physcl Educ Awd 85-86; MVP Awd Outstndng Trk 87; PA ST U; Tech Engrng.

LAM, PHAT; William Penn HS; York, PA; (3); Science Clb; Nwsp Phtg; Yrbk Ed-Chief; Yrbk Phtg; Yrbk Stf; Socr.

LAM, TY; Girard HS; Girard, PA; (3); Am Leg Boys St; Church Yth Grp; Varsity Clb; Bsktbl; Socr; Wt Lftg; Hon Roll; Elec Engr.

LAMANTIA, RUTH; Indiana Area HS; Indiana, PA; (3); Church Yth Grp; Drama Clb; Acpl Chr; School Musical; School Play; Diving; High Hon Roll; Jr NHS; NEDT Awd; Intl Frgn Lng Awd 86; Am Lgn Awd 85; Dickinson Coll; Pltcl Sci.

LAMB JR, JIM; Devon Prep; Wayne, PA; (3); Cmnty Wkr; Computer Clb; Trs FBLA; Math Tm; Ski Clb; Im Mgr Bsktbl; Capt Crs Cntry; Im Mgr Ftbl; Im Mgr Golf; Var Trk; Elctrcl Engrng; Elctrcl Eng.

LAMB, JOHN; Mohawk Area HS; New Castle, PA; (2); 4-H; FFA; Latin Clb; Political Wkr; JV Bsktbl; Hon Roll; PA Free Enterprise Wk 87; Bus.

LAMB, PEGGY; Saint Huberts Catholic HS; Philadelphia, PA; (3); 21/421; Church Yth Grp; Cmnty Wkr; Orch; School Musical; Hon Roll; NHS; Schlstc Al-Amer 86-87; Psych.

LAMBERT, AIMEE; Ringgold SR HS; Monongahela, PA; (4); Pep Clb; Ski Clb; Drm Mjr(t); Mrchg Band; Variety Show; Nwsp Stf; Yrbk Stf; Off Soph Cls; Stu Cncl; Cheerleading; IN U; Nursing.

LAMBERT, BRIAN; West Allegheny HS; Imperial, PA; (2); Varsity Clb; Chorus; Stu Cncl; Var Bsbl; JV Bsktbl; JV Var Ftbl; Hon Roll; Vrsty Ftbl Lttrmn 86; Vrsty Bsbl Lttrmn 87.

LAMBERT, CONNIE; Punxsutawney Area HS; Punxsutawney, PA; (3); Art Clb; FBLA; Vllybl; Hon Roll; 5th ST Ldrshp Conf Bus Graphcs FBLA 87.

LAMBERT, KELLY; Pen Argyl Area Joint HS; Pen Argyl, PA; (3); 36/140; Ski Clb; Sec Chorus; Fld Hcky; Sftbl; Hon Roll; Psych.

LAMBERT, VICKY; H S Of Performing Arts; Philadelphia, PA; (3); VP Church Yth Grp; Dance Clb; Library Aide; Teachers Aide; Acpl Chr; Chorus; Church Choir; School Play; Rep Stu Cncl; High Hon Roll; Full Scholar PA Ballet Co 87; Trphy Excptnlly Hgh Athltc Excllnce 85; Part Scholar Prfrmg Art 86-87; Phys Ther.

LAMBERT, VIRGINIA; Seneca Valley HS; Mars, PA; (2); Aud/Vis; Church Yth Grp; Dance Clb; Library Aide; Stage Crew; High Hon Roll; Hon Roll; Senca Vly 1st Yr Schlstc Awd 86-87; TV Prdctn Clb Awd 86-87; Comms.

LAMBIASE, MARIO; Liberty HS; Bethlehem, PA; (3); 97/454; Church Yth Grp; Cmnty Wkr; Latin Clb; Y-Teens; Bsktbl; Ftbl; Wt Lftg; Hon Roll; Prfct Atten Awd; Kutztown U; Rl Est.

LAMBORN, KIM; Spring-Ford HS; Phoenixville, PA; (3); 32/256; German Clb; Lcrss; Mgr(s); Hon Roll.

LAMIE, DANIELLE; Saucen Valley SR HS; Bethlehem, PA; (4); 9/138; French Clb; Yrbk Ed-Chief; Trs Sr Cls; Capt L Bsktbl; Capt L Bsktbl; Capt Lcrss; Capt L Sftbl; High Hon Roll; Hon Roll; Jr NHS; Fld Hcky All Str Tm 85-87; Pres Acdmc Ftns Awd 87; Outstndng Athlte Awd 86-87; Dickinson Coll; Bio.

LAMKEN, BRIAN SANER; Harriton HS; Penn Valley, PA; (3); VP Chorus; Madrigals; School Musical; School Play; Ed Lit Mag; VP NHS; Creative Arts.

LAMM, LORI A; Mercyhurst Prep; Erie, PA; (3); Am Leg Aux Girls St; Church Yth Grp; Cmnty Wkr; Nwsp Rptr; Rep Sec Stu Cncl; Var L Crs Cntry; Stat Sftbl; Hon Roll; Cmnctns.

LAMNATOS, THEODORA; Willia Penn SR HS; York, PA; (3); 2/452; Pres Church Yth Grp; SADD; Soph Cls; Rep Jr Cls; Hon Roll; NHS; Poltcl Sci.

LAMONT, LINDA; Northern Cambria HS; Barnesboro, PA; (4); 27/152; French Clb; GAA; Band; Concert Band; Jazz Band; Mrchg Band; Trk; High Hon Roll; Hon Roll; NHS; Hlth Fld.

LAMONTE, PAMELA; Williams Valley HS; Williamstown, PA; (1); Art Clb; Office Aide; Spanish Clb; SADD; Teachers Aide; Chorus; Acdmc All Amer 86; US Achvt Awd 87; Nrs.

LAMOREAUX, PAULA MAE; Lake Lehman SR HS; Hunlock Creek, PA; (4); 67/155; Sec Church Yth Grp; Key Clb; SADD; Chorus; Church Choir; Nwsp Rptr; Nwsp Stf; Yrbk Stf; Chiro.

LAMPE, SHANNON; Fairview HS; Erie, PA; (3); 9/165; French Clb; Model UN; Ski Clb; Varsity Clb; Rep Stu Cncl; JV Crs Cntry; Var Swmmng; Im Wt Lftg; Hon Roll; NHS.

LAMPE, SHERRI; Southside HS; Shippingport, PA; (3); 26/135; Church Yth Grp; FBLA; Hosp Aide; Library Aide; Yrbk Stf; Mgr(s); High Hon Roll; NHS; St Fnlst Miss Ntl Teenager 87; Social Wrk.

LAMPKIN, LAURA; Mercyhurst Prep; N East, PA; (3); Church Yth Grp; Debate Tm; French Clb; Service Clb; Ski Clb; School Musical; School Play; Var Crs Cntry; Hon Roll; Bus Mrktng.

LAMPKINS-FIELDER, RAINA; Quaker Valley SR HS; Sewickley, PA; (3); Key Clb; NFL; Q&S; Speech Tm; Band; Ed Nwsp Rptr; Ed Lit Mag; NHS; Debate Tm; French Clb; PALGOV Schl Arts Schlrshp, PA Poetry Soc 2nd Pl Awd 87; Natl Frnsc ST Cmpttn/Orgnl Oratory 3rd 85; Engl.

LAMPLE, CINDY; Lincoln HS; Ellwood City, PA; (3); Drama Clb; German Clb; Hosp Aide; SADD; Y-Teens; Chorus; Color Guard; Bradford; Bus.

LAMPMAN, CHRISTINE; Harry S Truman HS; Fairless Hills, PA; (3); 43/602; Debate Tm; Girl Scts; NFL; Fld Hcky; High Hon Roll; Hon Roll; Prfct Atten Awd; Poly Sci.

LAMPRINOS, MICHAEL; Milton SR HS; Milton, PA; (3); Computer Clb; FTA; Library Aide; Spanish Clb; Chorus; School Musical; High Hon Roll; Hon Roll; NHS; Schl Spnsrd Totl Fit Awd 86-87; Bloomsburg U; Ed.

LANAGER, DONNA; Clearfield Area HS; Hyde, PA; (4); 60/280; Drama Clb; French Clb; Chorus; School Musical; Nwsp Rptr; Nwsp Stf; Sftbl; Var Vllybl; Anna Aeillio Trst Schlrshp 87; Gannon U; Humanities.

LANAGER, JAMIE; Curwensville A HS; Curwensville, PA; (3); Drama Clb; French Clb; Ski Clb; Varsity Clb; L Cheerleading; Gym; Hon Roll.

LANCASTER, JAMES; Fairchance-Georges JR/Sr HS; Smithfield, PA; (3); Hon Roll; Ntl Merit SF; Pres Schlr; Gftd & Tlntd Stu 83-88; Tv/Radio Brdcstng.

LANCASTER, JONATHAN; Mercer HS; Mercer, PA; (2); Church Yth Grp; Exploring; Q&S; Variety Show; Nwsp Rptr; Nwsp Stf; Yrbk Rptr; Yrbk Stf; Golf; Clemson U; Frnch.

LANCASTER, PAUL; Brownsville Area HS; Hiller, PA; (3); Rep Soph Cls; Rep Jr Cls; Rep Stu Cncl; Var L Bsktbl; Var L Trk; Pre Dntstry.

LANCASTER, TAMMY; Mount Union Area HS; Mt Union, PA; (3); VICA; Hon Roll; Flrst.

LANCE, BARBARA; Roxborough HS; Philadelphia, PA; (4); 7/265; GAA; Hosp Aide; Chorus; School Musical; Nwsp Rptr; Rep Sr Cls; Var Gym; Var Sftbl; Capt Twrlr; Var NHS; High Hnr Roll 83-87; Book Allow Nalt Hnr Scty 87; Chestnut Hill Coll; Occ Thrpy.

LANCE, HOPE; Tunkhannock Area HS; Dalton, PA; (3); Art Clb; 4-H; Girl Scts; Key Clb; Concert Band; Mrchg Band; 4-H Awd; High Hon Roll; Hon Roll; Bus Mngmnt.

LANDAU, KATE; Allentown Central Catholic HS; Emmaus, PA; (3); Trs Church Yth Grp; Drama Clb; French Clb; JA; Key Clb; Pep Clb; Yrbk Stf; Crs Cntry; Hon Roll.

LANDEFELD, NATHAN; Beaver Area JR SR HS; Beaver, PA; (2); 1/200; Concert Band; Jazz Band; Mrchg Band; L Socr; Church Yth Grp; German Clb; Band; Pep Band; High Hon Roll; Hon Roll; Westminster Hnrs Band 87; Schltc Achvt Awd 87; Archit.

LANDER, GEORGE; Yough SR HS; Rillton, PA; (3); 47/237; French Clb; Math Clb; Chorus; Concert Band; Drm & Bgl; Jazz Band; Mrchg Band; Stage Crew; Symp Band; NHS; Sci.

LANDER, JENNIFER; Fort Leboeuf HS; Erie, PA; (2); Pep Clb; Band; Color Guard; Concert Band; Mrchg Band; High Hon Roll; Hon Roll.

LANDER, MARTIN; Fort Cherry HS; Midway, PA; (3); Boy Scts; Church Yth Grp; Drama Clb; Math Clb; Science Clb; Ski Clb; Spanish Clb; SADD; Chorus; High Hon Roll; Comp Sci.

LANDER, MICHELLE; Burgettstown HS; Joffre, PA; (3); French Clb; Science Clb; Chorus; Yrbk Phtg; Yrbk Stf; JV Var Bsktbl; Var Mgr(s); Var Sftbl; Hon Roll; ICM Bus Schl; Accntng.

LANDER, MIKE; North Clarion JR SR HS; Lucinda, PA; (3); Constrctn.

LANDERKIN, KELLY; Central HS; Makakilo, HI; (4); 42/397; Camera Clb; Service Clb; Acpl Chr; Chorus; Madrigals; Orch; Mgr Crs Cntry; Timer; Trk; Cit Awd; Scii Awd 87; Spnsh Comp At Immaculate Coll 86; U Of Delaware; Physics.

LANDES, KIMBERLY; Elk Lake HS; Montrose, PA; (1); Band; Chorus; Jazz Band; Mrchg Band; Swing Chorus; Bsktbl; Fld Hcky; Trk; Law.

LANDFRIED, ANGEL; Ambridge Area HS; Ambridge, PA; (3); Church Yth Grp; French Clb; Office Aide; Pep Clb; Red Cross Aide; Teachers Aide; Off Soph Cls; Off Jr Cls; Trk; Wt Lftg; U Of Gainesville; Paralgl.

LANDIS, AMY; Red Lion Area SR HS; Red Lion, PA; (3); Color Guard; Mrchg Band; Secy.

LANDIS, CINDY; Lampeter Strasburg HS; Ronks, PA; (2); Church Yth Grp.

LANDIS, DAWN; Kiski Area HS; E Vandergrift, PA; (4); Church Yth Grp; Computer Clb; French Clb; Chorus; High Hon Roll; Hon Roll; Acadmt Ltr 84-85; Pres Acadmc Ftns Awd 87; Trivial Pursuit Clb 86-87.

LANDIS, KELLY S; Hanover SR HS; Hanover, PA; (3); Church Yth Grp; Hosp Aide; Chorus; Swing Chorus; Nwsp Stf; High Hon Roll; Hon Roll; Erly Chldhd Educ.

LANDIS, KIM; Canton Area JR-SR HS; Troy, PA; (4); 4/118; Sec Trs Church Yth Grp; Trs Rep Letterman Clb; Pres Band; Drm Mjr(t); Pres Frsh Cls; Pres Soph Cls; Pres Jr Cls; Var Capt Cheerleading; JV Vllybl; Hon Roll; JR Prom Queen 86; JR Miss Fnlst 86; Laurel Fest Rep 87; Messiah Coll; Math Tchr.

LANDIS, MARLA; Bellefonte Area HS; Howard, PA; (4); 67/237; Church Yth Grp; Teachers Aide; Rep Stu Cncl; Var Cheerleading; JV Sftbl; Hon Roll; Courtesy Awd 87; SR Hmkng Awd 87; Driver Trainee Awd 87; Undine Awd 87; Vly Forge Chrstn Coll; Elem Ed.

LANDIS, MICHAEL; Lebanon Catholic HS; Lebanon, PA; (3); Cmnty Wkr; Exploring; Hosp Aide; Spanish Clb; School Play; Stage Crew; Golf; Hon Roll; NHS; Bowling; Stu Mnth 87; Phys Thrpy.

LANDIS, PAUL; Cedar Cliff HS; Mechanicsburg, PA; (3); 33/309; Church Yth Grp; German Clb; SADD; Var Trk; High Hon Roll; JETS Awd; NHS; Korean Martial Art Black Belt 85; Chldrns Self-Defense Cls 85-87; Ocean Engrng.

LANDIS, RAYMOND; Souderton Area HS; Hatfield, PA; (4); 35/340; Church Choir; Concert Band; Jazz Band; Mrchg Band; School Musical; Hon Roll; JP Sousa Awd; Dist Band 87; Rgnl Band 87; Abe Pool Mem Awd 87; Messiah Coll; Music.

LANDIS, SANDY; Christian School Of York; York, PA; (2); Concert Band; JV Bsktbl; Var Cheerleading; Var Trk; Hon Roll; MVP Trck 86; Trck Dist 86-87; Sci Fair Hnbl Mntn 87; Vet.

LANDIS, SCOTT; Berlin Brothersvalley HS; Berlin, PA; (4); 12/85; Church Yth Grp; Pres FFA; Speech Tm; Church Choir; School Play; Stage Crew; Yrbk Bus Mgr; Yrbk Stf; High Hon Roll; JC Awd; Keystone Frmr Degree 86; Slippery Rock U; Soil Cnsrvtn.

LANDIS, VICKI; Penn Manor HS; Lancaster, PA; (4); 91/315; Church Yth Grp; Thesps; L Chorus; Church Choir; Capt Color Guard; Mrchg Band; School Musical; Variety Show; Im Vllybl; Lancaster Bible Coll.

LANDIS, VICTOR; Elizabethtown Area HS; Bainbridge, PA; (3); FFA; Var L Ftbl; Var L Trk; Im Wt Lftg; Law Enfrcmnt.

LANDMESSER, CHRIS; Lake-Lehman HS; Shavertown, PA; (4); Cmnty Wkr; Ski Clb; Var L Bsktbl; Var Capt Bsktbl; Var L Ftbl; Var L Golf; High Hon Roll; Hon Roll; All Schlstc-Ftbl Awds 86; PIAA Acdmc Athlt Awd 87; Sprts VIP Awd 86; Lycoming; Chem.

LANDMESSER, PATRICIA; Bishop O Reilly HS; Larksville, PA; (4); 46/110; Chorus; Sftbl; Latin Hnr Soc 84; Acadc Achvt Awd-Genrl Chem 85-86; Prtl Schlrshp-Empire Bty Schl 87; Empire Beauty Schl; Csmtlgy.

LANDOLINA, MARIA; Shaler Area SR HS; Glenshaw, PA; (4); 20/510; Yrbk Stf; Stu Cncl; Swmmng; High Hon Roll; NHS; NEDT Awd; Spanish NHS; U Of Miami; Math.

LANDON, CHRISTA; Montoursville Area HS; Montoursville, PA; (1); Trs Spanish Clb; Stu Cncl; Cheerleading; Powder Puff Ftbl; Sftbl; Spn Tchr.

LANDREY, CHRISTOPHER; N Allegheny SR HS; Pittsburgh, PA; (3); 250/649; Church Yth Grp; Cmnty Wkr; Chorus; Church Choir; Rep Frsh Cls; Im Socr; Hon Roll; Orng Blt-Krate 87; Arch.

LANDSMANN, MELISSA; St Basil Acad; Philadelphia, PA; (3); Pres Church Yth Grp; VP Drama Clb; Science Clb; Spanish Clb; SADD; Nwsp Ed-Chief; Nwsp Rptr; Lit Mag; Ntl Merit SF; Spnsh Achvt Awd 86; Lbrl Arts.

LANDVATER, TRICIA; Donegal HS; Maytown, PA; (2); Church Yth Grp; Hosp Aide; Rep Jr Cls; Rep Stu Cncl; Var Cheerleading; High Hon Roll; Spanish NHS; Outstndng Cheerldr Yr 86-87.

LANDY, JOSEPH; Bethel Park HS; Bethel Pk, PA; (4); #27 In Class; Church Yth Grp; German Clb; Science Clb; Var Bsktbl; NHS; Ntl Merit Ltr; Pres Schlr; Certfd Scuba Diver; VA Tech-Blacksburg; Engr.

LANE, ALYSSA KIM; Coudersport JR/SR HS; Coudersport, PA; (4); 19/87; Trs Drama Clb; Hosp Aide; Varsity Clb; Band; Chorus; School Play; Nwsp Stf; Var JV Cheerleading; Var L Trk; Var JV Vllybl; IU 9 Band 84 & 86; Dist Chorus 87; 30 Pt Ltr 87; Indiana U Of PA; Psychology.

LANE, CRAIG; Danville HS; Danville, PA; (2); Ski Clb; Rep Frsh Cls; JV Socr; Hon Roll; Marine Bio.

LANE, DENISE; Lewistown Area HS; Lewistown, PA; (4); 10/249; Trs Spanish Clb; Varsity Clb; Pres Frsh Cls; VP Soph Cls; Off Jr Cls; Var Capt Bsktbl; Var Capt Fld Hcky; Var Capt Sftbl; High Hon Roll; NHS; Penn ST U; Spec Ed.

LANE, DONNA; Moshannon Valley HS; Smoke Run, PA; (3); VP 4-H; Ski Clb; SADD; Varsity Clb; Band; Chorus; School Play; Nwsp Stf; Cheerleading; Sftbl; PA ST U; Jrnlsm.

LANE JR, JAMES A; Bethlehem Center; Millsboro, PA; (3); Art Clb; Chess Clb; Church Yth Grp; FCA; Spanish Clb; Varsity Clb; JV Var Bsktbl; Coach Actv; Ftbl; Var Trk.

LANE, PATTI; Trinity HS; Camp Hill, PA; (3); Church Yth Grp; Exploring; Hosp Aide; Pep Clb; Spanish Clb; Variety Show; Yrbk Bus Mgr; Yrbk Stf; Rep Stu Cncl; Var Trk; Lgl Asstnt.

LANE, SARA M; Central Cambria HS; Ebensburg, PA; (4); 23/214; Art Clb; Band; Color Guard; Mrchg Band; Var Trk; High Hon Roll; Hon Roll; Prfct Atten Awd; Penn ST U; Landscape Arch.

LANE, SUSAN; Seneca Valley SR HS; Evans City, PA; (3); Church Yth Grp; JA; Band; Symp Band; Yrbk Sprt Ed; Rep Stu Cncl; Swmmng; Hon Roll; NHS; Rotary Awd; Med.

LANEY, KETURAH; Mercer Area JR SR HS; Mercer, PA; (4); 12/139; Concert Band; Jazz Band; Mrchg Band; Pep Band; Trk; Hon Roll; NHS; Prfct Atten Awd; Elks Awd; US Army Resrv Ntl Schlr/Athlet Awd 87; La Salle U; Socl Wrk.

LANG, AMY; High Point Baptist Acad; Elverson, PA; (3); 2/35; Church Choir; Yrbk Bus Mgr; Yrbk Ed-Chief; Sec Soph Cls; VP Jr Cls; Bsktbl; Score Keeper; Sftbl; High Hon Roll; Cedarville Coll; Med.

LANG, CHRISTINE; Methacton HS; Audubon, PA; (3); 43/384; Church Yth Grp; NFL; Speech Tm; Crs Cntry; Trk; Cit Awd; High Hon Roll; NHS; Pres Clssrm Schlrshp 87; Bonnie Bell Awd 86-87; U Of Richmond; Bus.

LANG, COLLEEN; Burrell HS; New Kensington, PA; (4); 6/203; Library Aide; Spanish Clb; SADD; High Hon Roll; Hon Roll; Jr NHS; NHS; Cngrssnl Schlr 87; Schltc Achvt Awd 87; Dstngshd Hnrs 86-87; Ctzns Gen Schl Nrsng; RN.

LANG, DAVID; Mercyhurst Prep Schl; Erie, PA; (3); 14/179; Trs Thesps; Chorus; Madrigals; School Musical; School Play; Nwsp Rptr; Trs Stu Cncl; Trk; Hon Roll.

LANG, DEBORAH ANN; Cochranton JR SR HS; Cochranton, PA; (4); 24/64; SADD; Band; Concert Band; High Hon Roll; Hon Roll; Meadville Vo-Tech; Nrsng.

LANG, MATTHEW; Methacton SR HS; Audubon, PA; (3); Church Yth Grp; Debate Tm; Math Tm; NFL; Church Choir; Concert Band; Var Crs Cntry; Im Swmmng; JV Trk; Chem.

LANG, MAUREEN; Our Lady Of The Sacred Heart HS; Pittsburgh, PA; (3); Cmnty Wkr; Pep Clb; Church Choir; Variety Show; Nwsp Stf; VP Sr Cls; Off Stu Cncl; Capt L English Clb; Capt L Sftbl; Capt L Vllybl; Mst Imprvd Sftbl 85; Mst Valuble Vlybl, All Star Tm Sftbl 86-87; Awd No Absnce 87; Pitt.

LANG, SEAN; Meadville Area SR HS; Meadville, PA; (3); 5/363; Aud/Vis; Ski Clb; Variety Show; Rep Stu Cncl; High Hon Roll; Hon Roll; Canned Food Dr Chrmn 88; Bus.

LANG, SHELLY; Seneca Valley HS; Renfrew, PA; (3); 54/336; Art Clb; Cmnty Wkr; Drama Clb; Teachers Aide; Varsity Clb; School Play; Lit Mag; Capt Cheerleading; Hon Roll; Sec Frsh Cls; Chld Psychlgy.

LANGAN, BILL; Trinity HS; Camp Hill, PA; (2); Ski Clb; Spanish Clb; JV L Socr; Hon Roll; NEDT Awd; Cert Of Ed Dev Ntl 86; U Of Notre Dame; Bus.

LANGAN, KAREN; Villa Maria Acad; Exton, PA; (3); 3/98; NFL; Speech Tm; Yrbk Ed-Chief; Lit Mag; Tennis; French Hon Soc; High Hon Roll; NCTE Awd; NHS; Church Yth Grp; Engl & Hstry Awds 85-86; Engl Awd 86-87.

LANGAN, NINA; Scranton Central HS; Scranton, PA; (2); Church Yth Grp; Hosp Aide; JA; SADD; Band; Concert Band; Mrchg Band; Nrs.

LANGE, JAMES; Upper Darby HS; Drexel Hl, PA; (4); Varsity Clb; Rep Sr Cls; Rep Stu Cncl; JV Var Bsktbl; JV Var Lcrss; JV Var Socr; High Hon Roll; Hon Roll; Prfct Atten Awd; Pres Schlr; Fred A Leinberger Mem Schlrshp 87; Pres Acad Ftnss Awd 87; 2 Home & Schl Assn Schlrshp 87; Penn ST U; Engrng.

LANGE, THOMAS; Tunkhannock HS; Tunkhannock, PA; (4); Drama Clb; Sec Key Clb; Latin Clb; School Play; Hon Roll; Sec NHS; Mech Engnrng.

LANGHURST, WENDY; Canon Mc Millar JR HS; Mc Donald, PA; (1); Church Yth Grp; Girl Scts; Office Aide; Chorus; Stage Crew; Sec Stu Cncl; L Bsktbl; High Hon Roll; French Clb; Pres Acad Fit Awd 85-86; Stwrdss.

LANGLEY, CHERYL; Carlisle SR HS; Carlisle, PA; (3); 100/467; Church Yth Grp; Cmnty Wkr; Band; Chorus; Church Choir; Concert Band; Mrchg Band; School Musical; Hon Roll; Prfct Atten Awd; Cnty Chrs & Bndy 85-87; Dstrct Chorus 86-87; Msc Ed.

LANGSDALE, CHRISTINE; Quaker Valley HS; Sewickley, PA; (3); Cmnty Wkr; Lit Mag; Psych.

LANGSTAFF, DAVID; West Greene HS; Chagrin Falls, OH; (4); 25/104; French Clb; School Musical; Hon Roll; GA Cmps Kent ST; Elec.

LANGSTON, JEFFREY; Keystone Oaks HS; Pittsburgh, PA; (3); 16/285; Boy Scts; Exploring; Symp Band; Ftbl; Wrstlng; Hon Roll; Penn ST U; Sci.

LANGTON, ANNETTE; Hopewell SR HS; Aliquippa, PA; (4); 35/247; VP Spanish Clb; Band; Chorus; Concert Band; Mrchg Band; High Hon Roll; NHS; Kent ST U; Pre Med.

LANIER, DANIELLE; Butler Intermediate HS; Butler, PA; (2); Church Yth Grp; Drama Clb; SADD; School Play; Sftbl; Hon Roll; Jr NHS; French Clb; School Musical; Stage Crew; Duquesne U; Law.

LANNAN, CURT; Jersey Shore HS; Jersey Shore, PA; (3); Church Yth Grp; Teachers Aide; JV Ftbl; Hon Roll; Prfct Atten Awd; Pres Schlr; Williamsport Area CC; Carpntry.

LANNO, CHRISTINA; Upper Darby HS; Drexel Hill, PA; (3); Church Yth Grp; VICA; Coach Actv; Fld Hcky; Lcrss; Mgr(s); Score Keeper; Timer; High Hon Roll; Hon Roll; Bus Admin.

LANRAIN, EDWARD; Lincoln HS; Ellwood City, PA; (3); 120/245; Art Clb; Boy Scts; Church Yth Grp; Computer Clb; Latin Clb; Ski Clb; SADD; Pres Frsh Cls; Bowling; Ftbl; JR Ltrmn Ellwood Cty Ftbl 87; VP Photo Clb 87; Pres Ski Clb 84-87; Slipper Rock U; Bus Mngmt.

LANTZ, BRIAN; William Penn HS; York, PA; (3); 23/374; Rep Jr Cls; JV Bsktbl; Hon Roll; Elctrcl Engrng.

LANTZ, CHANDRA D; Carlisle HS; Carlisle, PA; (4); JA; Ski Clb; Jr Cls; Sr Cls; Var L Fld Hcky; Var Capt Sftbl; Hon Roll; Ntl Merit Ltr; 1st Pl Cptl Area Sci & Engr Fair 87; 1st Pl Carlisle Area Sci Fair 87; CT Coll.

LANTZ, DENNIS; Athens HS; Ulster, PA; (3); Pres Church Yth Grp; Rep Stu Cncl; Ftbl; Hon Roll; NHS; Intl Relations.

LANTZ, TODD; Towanda HS; Towanda, PA; (3); Williamsport; Acctg.

LANZEL, BONNIE; Elk County Christian HS; St Marys, PA; (4); 28/80; Ski Clb; Var L Cheerleading; Hon Roll; Susquehannall U; Cmmnctns.

LANZENDORFER, CLEMENT; Cambria Heights HS; Carrolltown, PA; (3); Church Yth Grp; Cmnty Wkr; ROTC; VICA; Hon Roll; ROTC Acad Awd 85-86; ROTC Phy Fit Awd 85-86; Williamsport Area CC; Mech.

LANZONI, SANDRA MARY; Brockway HS; Brockway, PA; (3); Art Clb; Church Yth Grp; Cmnty Wkr; Debate Tm; Exploring; Varsity Clb; Variety Show; Off Stu Cncl; Var Co-Capt Cheerleading; Gym; Achvt Acdm 86; Acdmc All Amer 87; All Amer Chrldr Fnlst 86; Phrmcy.

LAO, ALICE; York Suburban SR HS; York, PA; (3); 3/175; Drama Clb; Capt Color Guard; Pres Frsh Cls; Pres Soph Cls; Sec Jr Cls; VP Stu Cncl; High Hon Roll; NHS; Intl Rltns Smmr Prog 87; Rtry Ldrs Conf 87; Georgetown U; Intl Rltns.

LAOV, PERT; H S For Creative & Performing Arts; Philadelphia, PA; (3); 1st Pz Halocaust Mem Art Phila 86-87; 3rd Pl Art Dinasaur Cont 85-86; Hnrb Mntn Energy Cont 85-87.

LAPCEVICH, MICHELE; Hickory HS; Hermitage, PA; (3); Drama Clb; French Clb; Band; Chorus; Drill Tm; Mrchg Band; School Musical; School Play; Stage Crew; NHS; Lawyer.

LAPCHAK, BRIAN; Freeland HS; Freeland, PA; (3); 10/100; Var Bsbl; Var L Bsktbl; Var L Bowling; Var Golf; Im Score Keeper; Im Tennis; Im Vllybl; Hon Roll; Jr NHS; Dist Xi Chmpnshp Bsktbl Tm 87; Sports Med.

LAPE, DIANA; Rockwood Area HS; Somerset, PA; (2); Church Yth Grp; Rep Frsh Cls; Rep Soph Cls; High Hon Roll; Hon Roll; Bus.

LAPE, JENNIFER; Conrad Weiser HS; Robesonia, PA; (3); 55/179; Spanish Clb; Chorus; Hon Roll; Penn ST; Cmrcl Art.

LAPE, REBECCA; Freeport SR HS; Sarver, PA; (3); 66/216; Church Yth Grp; Library Aide; Yrbk Stf; Rep Jr Cls; Rep Stu Cncl; Stat Bsktbl; Mgr(s); Hon Roll; Church Choir; Im Swmmng; Carnegie Mellon U Pre-Coll Art Schlrshp 87; Art.

LAPE, TODD; Mohawk JR SR HS; New Castle, PA; (3); Church Yth Grp; French Clb; Band; Nwsp Stf; L Bsktbl; Var Coach Actv; L Crs Cntry; Var Mgr(s); L Trk; Cit Awd; Comm.

LAPHAM, KIMBERLY; Gettysburg SR HS; Gettysburg, PA; (2); VP Church Yth Grp; Band; Church Choir; Concert Band; Mrchg Band; Symp Band; Var L Fld Hcky; Var L Vllybl; Hon Roll; SCI.

LAPHEN, MARYBETH; Lansdale Catholic HS; Lansdale, PA; (3); Cmnty Wkr; Drama Clb; Exploring; Hosp Aide; Office Aide; Service Clb; Ski Clb; SADD; VP Chorus; Yrbk Ed-Chief; Customer Srvc Rcgntn 87; Phys Thrpy.

LAPIKAS, LAURI; Sharon HS; Sharon, PA; (3); #10 In Class; French Clb; Latin Clb; Yrbk Stf; Var Cheerleading; High Hon Roll; Hon Roll; NHS.

LAPINA, JENNIFER; Jeannette SR HS; Jeannette, PA; (2); 1/130; Church Yth Grp; Drama Clb; Ski Clb; Spanish Clb; Chorus; Rep Stu Cncl; Tennis; Twrlr; High Hon Roll.

LAPINA, JOHN J; Jannette SR HS; Jeannette, PA; (4); 1/123; Service Clb; Ski Clb; Spanish Clb; Rep Stu Cncl; L Golf; L Trk; High Hon Roll; NHS; Rotary Awd; Val; Jr Rotrn 86; Kiwanian Of Mnth 87; US Naval Acad; Engr.

LAPINSKI, PAMELA; Mc Keesort Area HS; Mckeesport, PA; (4); 18/365; FBLA; Office Aide; Pep Clb; Yrbk Bus Mgr; Yrbk Stf; Bowling; Powder Puff Ftbl; High Hon Roll; Hon Roll; NHS; Robert Morris Coll; Mgmt.

LAPINSKY, CHRIS; Danville HS; Danville, PA; (2); Key Clb; Ski Clb; Fld Hcky; Mat Maids; Trk; High Hon Roll; Hon Roll; Fld Hockey Ltr; Piano Audition Awds; U Of PA; Mrktng.

LAPP, CANDICE; York Catholic HS; York, PA; (1); Letterman Clb; Pep Clb; Chorus; Rep Stu Cncl; Cheerleading; Cert Vlntr Achvt Martin Lib 85-87; Cert Fnlst Mdrn Miss Pageant 87; Cert Alpha Peer Cnslng Grp 87-88; Dance.

LAPP, MISSY; Pequea Valley HS; Paradise, PA; (3); 17/141; AFS; GAA; Varsity Clb; Chorus; School Play; Rep Stu Cncl; Var Bsktbl; Var Fld Hcky; JV Sftbl; Hon Roll; Prevet Med.

LAPP, RENEE; Halifax Area HS; Halifax, PA; (4); 5/96; Rep Church Yth Grp; Pres 4-H; FHA; Sec SADD; Varsity Clb; Chorus; Rep Sec Stu Cncl; Capt Cheerleading; Dnfth Awd; Pres NHS; Miriam S Gotlieb, William & Arthur Stambaugh & Halifax Educ Assocn Schlrshps 87; West Chester U; Music.

LAPPANO, DIANE; Steelton-Highspire HS; Steelton, PA; (3); 26/102; Pep Clb; Spanish Clb; Varsity Clb; School Musical; Yrbk Ed-Chief; Cheerleading; Sftbl; Hon Roll; NHS; Accntng.

LAPPE, TERRENCE; Archbishop Ryan HS For Boys; Philadelphia, PA; (2); Cmnty Wkr; Political Wkr; Stage Crew; Ftbl; Air Force Acad; Air Force Pilot.

LAPRAIRIE, DANIELE; Christian School Of York HS; Dover, PA; (4); Hosp Aide; Library Aide; Teachers Aide; School Play; Stage Crew; Mgr(s); Hon Roll; Lancaster Bible Coll; Elem Educ.

LARABEE, ERIN; Warren Area HS; Warren, PA; (3); French Clb; SADD; Varsity Clb; Concert Band; Var Bsktbl; Var Crs Cntry; Var Trk; JV Vllybl; High Hon Roll; Hon Roll; U Of Pittsburgh; Physcl Thrpst.

LARCK, KELLY; Riverview HS; Oakmont, PA; (4); 60/120; French Clb; SADD; Color Guard; Flag Corp; Yrbk Stf; Stu Cncl; Hon Roll; Duquesner U; Psych.

LARDO, SHERIE; Perry Traditional Acad; Pittsburgh, PA; (2); Computer Clb; Girl Scts; Swmmng; Cit Awd; Hon Roll; Vet.

LARIMER, MARK; Freedom HS; Bethlehem, PA; (3); Science Clb; JV Socr; Marine Bio.

LARK, ALETHIA; Franklin Learning Ctr; Philadelphia, PA; (3); Pres Church Yth Grp; Hosp Aide; Red Cross Aide; Rep Jr Cls; Hon Roll; Teachers Aide; Splng Bee Awd 83; Recgntn Awd Vltr 86; HOSA Awd 86; Podtry.

LARKIN, JON; Conestoga HS; Berwyn, PA; (2); Church Yth Grp; Cmnty Wkr; Service Clb; Stage Crew; Lit Mag; JV Bsbl; Coach Actv; JV Socr; Hon Roll; Yrbk Stf; Cmpr Of Yr Awd 86; 1st Pl Lttl Leag Tm-Bsbl-3rd Bsmn 86.

LARKIN, TERESA; Dunmore HS; Scranton, PA; (3); 6/155; Computer Clb; Hosp Aide; Chorus; Orch; School Musical; Ed Yrbk Stf; JV Cheerleading; Tennis; High Hon Roll; NHS; Dist Orchestra 86-87; Regnl Orchstra 87; Math.

LARKO, SUSAN; Mt Pleasant Area HS; Mount Pleasant, PA; (4); Art Clb; 4-H; German Clb; Band; Concert Band; Mrchg Band; 4-H Awd; Hon Roll; Kiwanis Awd; IN U Of PA; Art Educ.

LARLICK, MATTHEW; Central Bucks East HS; Doylestown, PA; (4); 91/468; Boy Scts; Chorus; JV Var Socr; Ntl Merit SF; Miltry.

LARME, MELISSA; Warren Area HS; Warren, PA; (4); 32/200; Art Clb; Church Yth Grp; Office Aide; Varsity Clb; Pres Jr Cls; Pres Sr Cls; Pres Stu Cncl; Capt Bsktbl; Capt Trk; Capt Vllybl; Yth Grp Schlrshp For Invlmnt 87; Fclty Apprctn Awd 87; IN U.

LAROUERE, KELLY; Norwin SR HS; N Huntingdon, PA; (3); 138/571; GAA; Letterman Clb; Pep Clb; SADD; Varsity Clb; Bsktbl; Diving; Jr NHS; Most Valuable Driver Awd 86-87; Sftbl Jr Olympic Tm Pittsburgh Metro Sftbl Chmpn 85.

LARRAZABAL, EMILIE; Academy Of Notre Dame De Namur; Glen Mills, PA; (3); Computer Clb; Hosp Aide; Nwsp Stf; Yrbk Stf; Sec Stu Cncl; Im Tennis; Hon Roll.

LARRIMORE, GREGORY; Bishop Guilfoyle HS; Altoona, PA; (3); 2/150; Science Clb; Chorus; High Hon Roll.

LARRY, VENETTA; Central HS; Philadelphia, PA; (2); Drama Clb; Library Aide; NAACP; Capt Pep Clb; Capt Drill Tm; Rep Frsh Cls; Sec Soph Cls; Stu Cncl; Var Bsktbl; Var Capt Cheerleading; Psych.

LARSEN, ANDREA; Dallastown Area HS; York, PA; (2); FCA; Ski Clb; Acpl Chr; Var Cheerleading; JV Tennis; JV Vllybl; High Hon Roll; Pep Clb; Church Choir; Drill Tm; Amer Schlr Awd 85; Natl Jr Hrn Scty 85.

LARSEN, HEATHER; Northwestern HS; Albion, PA; (2); 6/167; Library Aide; Pep Clb; SADD; Teachers Aide; Rep Stu Cncl; JV Sftbl; High Hon Roll; Hon Roll; Pres Physcl Ftns Awd 86; Pre-Med.

LARSEN, MARY K; Loudersport JR-SR HS; Coudersport, PA; (3); 10/90; French Clb; Varsity Clb; Chorus; School Play; Rep Frsh Cls; Rep Soph Cls; Rep Jr Cls; Capt Var Cheerleading; Var Trk; Var Vllybl; Frnch Spkng Mst Vlntly 87; Am Leg Axlry Awd 84.

LARSEN, MICHELLE; Steelton-Highspire HS; Highspire, PA; (3); 16/102; FBLA; Im Socr; Im Vllybl; High Hon Roll; NHS; Official Steamroller Cert In Chem 87; Penn ST; Comp.

LARSON, APRIL; Methacton SR HS; Worcester, PA; (3); Rep Church Yth Grp; Church Choir; Nwsp Rptr; Nwsp Stf; Vllybl; Philadelphia Harp Ensmble 87; Eastern Nazarene Coll; Optmtry.

LARSON, BRENDA; Warren Area HS; Warren, PA; (3); French Clb; Spanish Clb; Band; Concert Band; Jazz Band; Mrchg Band; Orch; Yrbk Stf; Slvr B 85; Psychlgy.

LARSON, KIM; Wilmington Area HS; New Castle, PA; (3); Church Yth Grp; Spanish Clb; Yrbk Stf; Var L Cheerleading; Powder Puff Ftbl; Score Keeper; Var L Trk; Hon Roll; Rotary Awd.

LARSON, KIRSTEN; Mc Keesport Area HS; Mc Keesport, PA; (3); 88/410; German Clb; ROTC; Scholastic Bowl; Speech Tm; School Play; Swmmng; Hon Roll; 4th Pl Rbbn Rolling Rock Est Horse Shw 85; 5th Pl Rbbn Oglebay Fest Horse Shw 86; Yrly Hnr Rll 84-85.

LARSON, KRISTIN J; Greater Latrobe HS; Latrobe, PA; (4); Ski Clb; Teachers Aide; Trs Chorus; Mrchg Band; School Musical; School Play; Variety Show; High Hon Roll; Hon Roll; NHS; Pres Acad Ftns Awd 87; PA ST U; Elem Educ.

LARSON, MICHELE; Villa Maria Acad; Erie, PA; (3); 51/150; Hosp Aide; Model UN; Political Wkr; Science Clb; Stu Cncl; Hon Roll; NHS; Campus Mnstry; Teenage Actn Clb; Amnsty Intl; Merryhurst Coll; Fash Merch.

LARSON, PAULA; Clarion-Limestone HS; Strattanville, PA; (4); 5/65; Am Leg Aux Girls St; English Clb; French Clb; Math Tm; SADD; Band; Trk; Hon Roll; NHS; Hosp Aide; Pres Acdmc Fit Awd 87; Outstndng Acdmc Achvt Adlt Roles & Fnctns March 86; Clarion U; Bio.

LARY, KIMBERLY; Reynolds HS; Greenville, PA; (3); 16/159; German Clb; Math Clb; Concert Band; Drill Tm; Mrchg Band; Yrbk Stf; Trs Jr Cls; Trs Sr Cls; Sec Stu Cncl; Pom Pon; Acad All Amer; Westminster Coll; Math.

LASANTA, LISA; West Catholic Girls HS; Philadelphia, PA; (3); 18/248; Church Yth Grp; Computer Clb; Trs NFL; School Musical; School Play; Nwsp Rptr; Lit Mag; High Hon Roll; Hon Roll; NHS; PHSSL Pin & Cert 1st In Infrmtve Spkng At Dist 87; 2 Cert Of Supr For Orgnl Story Tllng 86-87; Comm.

LASCUOLA, GINA; Butler Area SR HS; Butler, PA; (4); 29/699; AFS; Exploring; Office Aide; Pep Clb; Spanish Clb; SADD; School Musical; High Hon Roll; Jr NHS; NHS; Pres Acad Fit Awd 86-87; U Pittsburgh; Phys Thrpy.

LASH, ADAM; Center HS; Monaca, PA; (2); Letterman Clb; Varsity Clb; Socr; Tennis; Hon Roll.

LASH, DAVID; Curwensville Area HS; Curwensville, PA; (3); Cmnty Wkr; Letterman Clb; Science Clb; L Ftbl; Wt Lftg; L Wrstlng; DAR Awd; High Hon Roll; NHS; Acad All Amer 85-87; Natl Sci Merit Awds 85-87; Penn ST U; Civil Engr.

LASH, IRVIN M; Upper Perkiomen HS; Red Hill, PA; (2); 30/260; Church Yth Grp; JV Socr; Wt Lftg; Hon Roll; Sci.

LASHER, CANDY; Mercer Area JR SR HS; Mercer, PA; (4); 4/143; Var L Bsktbl; Var L Trk; Var L Vllybl; High Hon Roll; NHS; County Vllybl Honrbl Mentn; Elks Clb Stu Of Mnth; Sports Med.

LASHER, TAMMY; Annville-Cleona HS; Lebanon, PA; (4); Church Yth Grp; 4-H; Hst FFA; Chorus; Elenor Whitmeyer Awd 86-87; Prog Book Awds 83-86; Profcncy Awd Horse Jdng Awd 86-87.

LASHINSKY, LESLIE; Moshannon Valley HS; Houtzdale, PA; (3); 4/114; Spanish Clb; SADD; Chorus; Concert Band; School Play; Nwsp Ed-Chief; Yrbk Ed-Chief; Twrlr; High Hon Roll; NHS; Dstrct Band 87; PA ST U; Accntngn.

LASHLEY, TRACIE; Bedford HS; Bedford, PA; (4); 29/176; SADD; Band; Chorus; Flag Corp; School Musical; Sec Stu Cncl; Mgr(s); Trk; Hon Roll; NHS; Nrsng.

LASIK, ADAM; Central York SR HS; York, PA; (1); JV Var Socr; Hon Roll; 4th Pl Inter Schl Karate Champ 87; GA Tech; Arntcl Engr.

LASITIS, BONNIE; Penn Trafford HS; Irwin, PA; (4); Cmnty Wkr; French Clb; FBLA; Library Aide; High Hon Roll; Hon Roll; Prfct Atten Awd; A Cert Accntng I 85; 2nd Pl Entrpnrshp II FBLA Rgn II Conf 87; Fnlst Bus Mngmt Prjct 87; Armed Svcs; Mngmt.

LASKEY, JAYNI; Butler SR HS; Butler, PA; (4); 121/757; Church Yth Grp; Trs Exploring; French Clb; Hosp Aide; Office Aide; SADD; Thesps; Hon Roll; L Jr NHS; Presdntl Acadc & Ftns Awd 87; White Cert-HS 87; $500 Grnt-Mrqutte U 87; Marquette U; Phys Thrpy.

LASKEY, TODD; Hollidaysburg SR HS; Duncansville, PA; (3); Ftbl; Wt Lftg; Wrstlng.

LASKOS, CARRIE; West Hazelton HS; Sugarloaf, PA; (2); 3/224; Drama Clb; Pep Clb; Spanish Clb; SADD; Thesps; Concert Band; Mrchg Band; JV Tennis; High Hon Roll; Pres Schlr; Med.

LASKOSKY, MICHAEL; Hazleton HS; Drums, PA; (3); Science Clb; Teachers Aide; High Hon Roll; Hon Roll; Sci.

LASKY, WILLIAM; Annville Cleona HS; Annville, PA; (3); 7/127.

LASLO, MICHELLE; Moon Area HS; Coraopolis, PA; (2); DECA; Key Clb; Rep Soph Cls; Var L Socr; Hon Roll; Bus.

LASLOW, RICHARD; Plum SR HS; Pittsburgh, PA; (3); 18/410; Exploring; JA; Quiz Bowl; School Play; Stage Crew; JV Vllybl; High Hon Roll; NHS; Ntl Merit Ltr; Prfct Atten Awd; Acad Achvt Ltr 84-85; PSU; Engrng.

LASSAK, RANDY; Central Dauphin HS; Harrisburg, PA; (2); Church Yth Grp; Computer Clb; JV Bsktbl; JV Socr; JV Vllybl; Penn ST U; Comp Sci.

LASSITER, CASSANDRA; HS Of Engineering & Science; Philadelphia, PA; (3); 31/241; Drama Clb; Drill Tm; Yrbk Stf; High Hon Roll; NHS; U Of PA SAT Schrshp 86-88; Wnnr Trp Afrca Blck Hstry Contst 87; Duquesne U; Bus Mgmt.

LASSITER, DEBBIE; Owen J Roberts HS; Pottstown, PA; (4); 87/271; Exploring; Trs FBLA; Yrbk Stf; Hon Roll; Bus Svc Awd 87; Drexel U; Accntng.

LASUT, MIKE; Shade Central City HS; Cairnbrook, PA; (3); Church Yth Grp; Ski Clb; Spanish Clb; Bsbl; Hon Roll.

LASWELL, HEATHER; G A R Memorial HS; Wilkes-Barre, PA; (4); 10/172; Debate Tm; SADD; Nwsp Stf; Tennis; Hon Roll; Jr NHS; NHS; WY Valley Yth Salute; Debate Tm Awd; Acacm All Amer; Kutztown U; Geology.

LASZKIEWICZ, JULIE; Moon SR HS; Coraopolis, PA; (2); 31/331; Lib Computer Clb; Band; Hon Roll; Bus Mgmt.

LATCHEM, BRIAN; Mon Valley HS; Monessen, PA; (3); Art Awrd 1st Pl 86.

LATEEF, VILLIA A; Sister Clara Muhammad HS; Philadelphia, PA; (4); Cmnty Wkr; Debate Tm; English Clb; Girl Scts; Science Clb; Teachers Aide; Drill Tm; School Musical; School Play; Stage Crew; 1st Pl Sci Fair 85 & 87, 3rd Pl 86; Philadelphia Coll; Bus Mgmt.

LATERZA, SAM; Downington SR HS; Downington, PA; (3); Art Clb; Chess Clb; Capt Church Yth Grp; VP JA; Model UN; Chorus; Mrchg Band; Variety Show; Sec Stu Cncl; Ntl Merit Ltr; All Amer Stu Awd 84-85; Natl Ldrshp Merit Awd 85-86; Natl Engl Merit Awd 84-85; Biogrphcl Illstrtn.

LATIMER, PATRICK; Warren Area HS; Sheffield, PA; (3); 2/287; Spanish Clb; Chorus; Stage Crew; Bsktbl; Var Ftbl; Cit Awd; High Hon Roll; Jr NHS; NHS; Acdmc Letter 86; U Of PA; Pre-Law.

LATIMORE, KAREN; Moniteau JR SR HS; W Sunbury, PA; (4); French Clb; Library Aide; Color Guard; Mrchg Band; Nwsp Stf; Yrbk Rptr; Lit Mag; Hon Roll; NHS; Pres Acad Ftns Aws 86-87.

LATINA, RAENA; Henderson HS; West Chester, PA; (2); 10/330; Dance Clb; Girl Scts; SADD; Orch; Nwsp Rptr; Lit Mag; Rep Stu Cncl; JV Capt Cheerleading; Lcrss; Hon Roll; Girl Scout Gold Leadrshp Awd 86; 2nd Pl Pen & Ink-Womens Fed Of Chester Cnty Art Exhibit 86; Photojournlsm.

LATOUF, VIOLET; New Castle HS; New Castle, PA; (3); 47/263; GAA; Varsity Clb; Jr Cls; Stu Cncl; Ftbl; Trk; Athltc Trainer-Ftbl 87; Mdcl.

LATOUR, MARIE-FRANCE; Springside Schl; Penn Valley, PA; (3); Acpl Chr; Chorus; Rep Soph Cls; Sec Jr Cls; Rep Sr Cls; JV Fld Hcky; JV Lcrss; High Hon Roll; Cum Laude Soc 86-87; Harvard Bk Wd 86-87; Natl Frnch & Lat Cont 85-87; Med.

LATSHA, JODI; Shikellamy HS; Sunbury, PA; (1); French Clb; Hosp Aide; Rep Frsh Cls; Rep Stu Cncl; JV Var Cheerleading; Psych.

LATSHA, LUCINDA; Upper Dauphin Area HS; Pillow, PA; (3); Church Yth Grp; Cmnty Wkr; Band; Chorus; Church Choir; Concert Band; Mrchg Band; School Musical; Yrbk Ed-Chief; Hon Roll; Rtry Clb Stu Mnth 86-87; Mst Musicl JR Awd 86-87; Dauphin Co Chrs Fstvl 84-87; Elem Ed.

LATSHA, TIM; Line Mountain HS; Herndon, PA; (4); 7/121; Church Yth Grp; Chorus; Mrchg Band; School Musical; VP Stu Cncl; Mgr(s); JP Sousa Awd; NHS; Computer Clb; FBLA; PA Gvrns Schl Arts Schrlshp 86; Mansfield U; Music Ed.

LATTANZA, JESSICA; Mifflinburg Area HS; Mifflinburg, PA; (2); French Clb; Trs Key Clb; Chorus; School Musical; Yrbk Stf; Sec Stu Cncl; JV Capt Cheerleading; JV Fld Hcky; High Hon Roll; NHS; Dist Chorus.

LAU, ELAINE; Northeastern SR HS; York, PA; (3); Chorus; School Musical; Yrbk Stf; Var Capt Bsktbl; Im JV Vllybl; High Hon Roll; Hon Roll; Ski Clb; Art.

LAU, MICHAEL; Northeastern HS; York, PA; (3); 45/195; Aud/Vis; Varsity Clb; Chorus; Rep Jr Cls; JV Bsktbl; Var Trk; Var Vllybl; Aviation.

LAUBACH, CHRIS; Mifflinburg HS; Mifflinburg, PA; (2); Drama Clb; Sec 4-H; French Clb; Stage Crew; Sftbl; High Hon Roll; Hon Roll; Willmsprt Area CC; Comp Pgmmg.

LAUBACH, CRAIG; Lock Haven HS; Lock Haven, PA; (3); Red Cross Aide; Crtnst.

LAUBACH, JOELLA; Bald Eagle-Nittany HS; Mill Hall, PA; (3); Hon Roll.

LAUBACH, MICHAEL V; Saucon Valley SR HS; Hellertown, PA; (2); Boy Scts; Computer Clb; 4-H; Math Clb; SADD; Chorus; Church Choir; School Musical; Stage Crew; Hon Roll; Ltr Jckt Rflry 87; Arch Engrng.

LAUBACH, RACHELLE; Danville SR HS; Riverside, PA; (4); Church Yth Grp; Ski Clb; Var L Bsktbl; JV Var Fld Hcky; Gym; Socr; JV Var Sftbl; Swmmng; Edinboro U; Spch Pathlgy.

LAUBACH, W JEFFREY; Lancaster Country Day HS; Wyomissing, PA; (3); Rep Church Yth Grp; Mu Alpha Theta; VP Chorus; Church Choir; Stage Crew; Pres Jr Cls; Rep Stu Cncl; JV Var Bsktbl; Var L Socr.

LAUBENSTEIN, KATHY; Schuylkill Haven Area HS; Schuylkill Haven, PA; (3); 6/103; German Clb; Science Clb; SADD; VP Soph Cls; Stu Cncl; JV Bsktbl; Var Sftbl; Var Vllybl; High Hon Roll; Law.

LAUBER, ELLEN; Villa Maria Acad; West Chester, PA; (3); 51/108; Church Yth Grp; Cmnty Wkr; GAA; Hosp Aide; Yrbk Phtg; Yrbk Stf; Var JV Bsktbl; Var Sftbl; Hon Roll; Mrktng.

LAUBER, KELLYANNE; St Basil Acad; Philadelphia, PA; (4); 5/97; Church Yth Grp; French Clb; Pres FBLA; German Clb; High Hon Roll; Hon Roll; Jr NHS; NHS; Admin Sec.

LAUBSCHER, KRISTEN; Lock Haven SR HS; Lock Haven, PA; (3); SADD; Chorus; Color Guard; Flag Corp; 4-H; French Clb; FHA; School Musical; Hon Roll; Nrsg.

LAUBSCHER, LESLEY; Lock Haven HS; Howard, PA; (3); Art Clb; French Clb; SADD; Nwsp Rptr; JV Bsktbl; Hon Roll; NHS; GAPS Treasure.

LAUCHLAN, CHRISTINA; Cumberland Valley HS; Mechanicsburg, PA; (4); Church Yth Grp; French Clb; Pres Girl Scts; Nwsp Rptr; Yrbk Stf; Socr; High Hon Roll; NHS; Ntl Merit Ltr; Ntl Merit Fnlst 87; Grl Sct Slvr Awd 87; Cert Of Merit-Ptriot-Nws Schltc Wrtng Cont 87; U Of PA.

LAUCHNOR, DEBBI; Emmaus HS; Allentown, PA; (2); SADD; Rep Frsh Cls; Rep Soph Cls; Rep Stu Cncl; Capt Bsktbl; Hon Roll; Jr NHS; Pres Schlr; Penn ST; Pediatrician.

LAUDENBERGER, CURTIS; Lancaster Catholic HS; Lancaster, PA; (3); 61/250; Service Clb; Concert Band; JV Bsbl; Hon Roll; Bus Admin.

LAUDO, LEIGH; West Middlesex HS; West Middlesex, PA; (4); 1/96; FBLA; Library Aide; Office Aide; Pep Clb; Spanish Clb; Chorus; Trs Stu Cncl; Trk; High Hon Roll; NHS; Natl Sci Merit Awd 84-86; Pres Acad Fit Awd 84-86; Acctng.

LAUER, APRIL; Dover Area HS; Dover, PA; (3); Church Yth Grp; FCA; Band; Church Choir; Mrchg Band; Millersville U; Psych.

LAUER, CONNIE; North Clarion HS; Shippenville, PA; (4); Dance Clb; FBLA; FHA; SADD; Lit Mag; Hon Roll; Library Aide; Nwsp Stf; Prm Cmtn 86.

LAUER, KARLA; E Stroudsburg HS; E Stroudsburg, PA; (4); 3/210; AFS; Camera Clb; German Clb; Hosp Aide; Intnl Clb; Key Clb; Math Clb; Math Tm; Model UN; Science Clb; U Of Pittsburgh; Med.

LAUER, KIMBERLY; Northern Lebanon JR SR HS; Harrisburg, PA; (4); Church Yth Grp; FBLA; Math Clb; Office Aide; Chorus; School Musical; Trk; Hon Roll; Central Penn Business Schl.

LAUER, LINDA; Central Cambria HS; Ebensburg, PA; (3); 18/210; Church Yth Grp; Key Clb; Color Guard; Yrbk Stf; Trs Jr Cls; Trs Sr Cls; Stu Cncl; Var Cheerleading; Hon Roll; IN U Of PA; Nrsng.

LAUER, LISA; Shanksville Stonycreek HS; Friedens, PA; (3); 1/34; Pres Sec Church Yth Grp; Pres FHA; Pres Girl Scts; Band; Chorus; NHS; Spanish NHS; Spanish Clb; Concert Band; Mrchg Band; Grl Scout Silv Ldrshp Awd 85; Girl Scout Silv Awd 86; Grl Scout Gold Ldrshp Awd 87; Nrsng.

LAUER, MARK; North Clarion HS; Lucinda, PA; (3); 9/107; Spanish Clb; Var L Socr; Penn ST U; Engrng.

LAUFFENBERGER, CAROL; Warren Area HS; Russell, PA; (3); Color Guard; Concert Band; Mrchg Band; Orch; Hon Roll; Presdntl Phys Ftns Awd 82; Lawyrs Asst.

LAUGHERY, DAN; Highlands HS; Tarentum, PA; (3); DECA; JA; Ftbl; Hon Roll; Brown Cert 86 & 87; Acctng.

LAUGHERY, JUNIA; Union City Area HS; Union City, PA; (4); 10/79; Pres 4-H; Pres FFA; Pep Clb; Pres SADD; Yrbk Stf; Powder Puff Ftbl; Stat Trk; Cit Awd; High Hon Roll; Gannon U; Legal Asst.

LAUGHLIN, AMY; Union HS; Sligo, PA; (3); 16/105; FCA; SADD; Yrbk Stf; Stu Cncl; Bsktbl; Cheerleading; Trk; Vllybl; Hon Roll; Bus.

LAUGHLIN, JONATHON; Trinity Christian Schl; Pittsburgh, PA; (2); Boy Scts; Church Yth Grp; Drama Clb; German Clb; Band; Chorus; School Play; Yrbk Stf; Hon Roll; Jr NHS; Archlgy.

LAUGHLIN, MARY; Union HS; Rimersburg, PA; (2); Pres Church Yth Grp; FCA; French Clb; Girl Scts; Pep Clb; SADD; Flag Corp; School Musical; Variety Show; Pres Frsh Cls; Med.

LAUGHLIN, MERRY; Cameron County HS; Emporium, PA; (2); Church Yth Grp; German Clb; Yrbk Stf; Crs Cntry; Trk; Hon Roll; Delta Epsln Phi 86-87; Mst Trk Points Rnng 86-87.

LAUGHLIN, RICK; South Side HS; Hookstown, PA; (3); 9/142; Church Yth Grp; Varsity Clb; Band; Variety Show; Nwsp Stf; Ftbl; L Wrstlng; High Hon Roll; NHS; Ntl Merit Ltr; Beaver Cnty JR Grange King 84; All Star Tm Contntl Bible Quiz 86; 2nd Pl Infcms Mrthn Minds-Buhl 87; Penn ST; Rbtcs.

LAUGHNER, JIM; Ambridge Area HS; Baden, PA; (3); Band; Mrchg Band; Pep Band; Radiolgy Tech.

LAUGHNER, LAURIE; Blackhawk HS; Darlington, PA; (4); 17/271; AFS; Band; Concert Band; Jazz Band; Mrchg Band; Pep Band; Symp Band; Var L Sftbl; High Hon Roll; Hon Roll; Acad Scholar 87; Gannon U; Nrsng.

LAUMEISTER, RENEE; Upper Moreland HS; Willow Grove, PA; (3); 52/276; Pres Church Yth Grp; Hosp Aide; Chorus; Color Guard; Concert Band; Drm Mjr(t); Mrchg Band; School Musical; Symp Band; Music.

LAURENCE, GABRIEL; South Western HS; Hanover, PA; (2); Camera Clb; Church Yth Grp; Ftbl; Wrstlng; Hon Roll.

LAURENTI, MIKE; Kiski Area HS; Apollo, PA; (3); Chorus; Bsbl; Golf; Socr; Hon Roll; PA ST U; Elec Engr.

LAURENTO, DAVID; Coatesville Area SR HS; Coatesville, PA; (3); 13/517; Spanish Clb; JV Var Bsbl; Bowling; JV Var Socr; Hon Roll; NHS.

LAURIA, JUDI; St Maria Goretti HS; Philadelphia, PA; (4); Hon Roll; Prfct Attndc 83-87.

LAURICK, ED; Fort Cherry JR SR HS; Hickory, PA; (3); Drama Clb; Science Clb; Ski Clb; VICA; Band; Jazz Band; Mrchg Band; L Bsbl; High Hon Roll; NHS; Self-Emplyd.

LAURIE, CHRISTINA; Schuylkill Haven HS; Sch Haven, PA; (3); Library Aide; Pep Clb; Science Clb; SADD; Teachers Aide; Chorus; Rep Stu Cncl; Cheerleading; Hon Roll; Elem Ed.

LAURINATIS, JEANNE; Leechburg Area HS; Leechburg, PA; (3); Drama Clb; Office Aide; School Play; Nwsp Rptr; Yrbk Stf; JV Var Cheerleading; Im Vllybl; Hon Roll; NHS; Prfct Atten Awd; Hgh Acadc Achvt Awd 87.

LAURNOFF, AMY; Mercyhurst Prep Schl; Erie, PA; (3); 58/170; Cmnty Wkr; Dance Clb; French Clb; Hosp Aide; School Musical; Rep Frsh Cls; Var Cheerleading; Var Vllybl; Hon Roll; Slppry Rck U; Phys Educ.

LAUSCHUS, KIM; Riverview HS; Oakmont, PA; (4); 20/116; French Clb; Key Clb; Library Aide; Yrbk Stf; JV Cheerleading; Var Trk; Stat Wrstlng; Hon Roll; NHS; U Of Pittsburgh; Psych.

LAVALLEE, GUY; Bishop Neumann HS; Williamsport, PA; (2); Boy Scts; Model UN; Pep Clb; L Bsbl; L Bsktbl; L Socr; L Tennis; Order Arrow 86; Mech Engrng.

LAVAN, MARIANNE; Keystone HS; Shippenville, PA; (3); 1/130; Trs SADD; Chorus; Church Choir; Concert Band; Mrchg Band; School Play; Yrbk Ed-Chief; Trk; High Hon Roll; NHS; US Achvt Acdmy 85-86 & 86-87.

LAVENDER, KIA; Central HS; Philadelphia, PA; (3); Church Yth Grp; Chorus; Church Choir; Madrigals; Cheerleading; Vllybl; Prfct Atten Awd; Cmmnctns.

LAVERY, DENA; Pennsbury HS; Yardley, PA; (4); 61/777; Church Yth Grp; Chorus; Yrbk Stf; Hon Roll; NHS; U DE; Engl Ed.

LAVIN, MARY BETH; Donegal HS; Marietta, PA; (2); 15/200; Hst Band; Chorus; Color Guard; VP Frsh Cls; VP Soph Cls; Pres Jr Cls; Rep Stu Cncl; Var Cheerleading; Hon Roll; Spanish NHS; HOBY Yth Fndtn Rep 87; Penn ST U; Comms.

LAVIN, MICHELLE; Donegal HS; Marietta, PA; (3); Cmnty Wkr; FNA; Varsity Clb; Sec Band; Sec Concert Band; Sec Mrchg Band; Yrbk Stf; Trs Jr Cls; Stat Bsbl; Var Capt Cheerleading; Ntl Hstry & Govt Awd 85-86; PA ST; Nrsg.

LAVIN, PATRICK; Bishop Shanahan HS; Westchester, PA; (4); Red Cross Aide; Service Clb; Rep Frsh Cls; Rep Soph Cls; Rep Jr Cls; Trs Sr Cls; Stu Cncl; JV Bsbl; Im Bsktbl; JV Im Ftbl; Amer Red Cross Bld Svcs Awd 87; St Francis Coll; Bus Admin.

LAVIN, SEAN; Hershey HS; Hershey, PA; (3); 23/209; Debate Tm; School Musical; School Play; Stage Crew; Lit Mag; Mgr(s); Wt Lftg; High Hon Roll; NHS.

LAVINE, ROGER; Reading HS; Reading, PA; (2); Camera Clb; Pres Stu Cncl; Var L Bsbl; Hon Roll; Var L Wrstlng; Merit Roll 85-86/86-87; NC U; Bus.

LAW, ANNE-MARIE; Blackhawk HS; Beaver Falls, PA; (3); Church Yth Grp; Debate Tm; Pres Sec 4-H; Model UN; NFL; Speech Tm; Band; Chorus; School Play; Rep Stu Cncl.

LAW, CHARLES; Blacklick Valley HS; Nanty Glo, PA; (4); 4/91; Pres Boy Scts; Pres Church Yth Grp; Drama Clb; Pres NFL; Yrbk Sprt Ed; L Bsktbl; Capt Crs Cntry; Capt Trk; God Cntry Awd; High Hon Roll; Eagle Scout 85; Dist Champ St Qlfr Cross Cntry 86; Track & Field All Star Team Distance Rnnr 85.

LAW III, LA MAR DAVID; Cumberland Valley HS; Mechanicsburg, PA; (4); Key Clb; Ski Clb; Var L Ftbl; Wt Lftg; Susquehanna U.

LAW, MIKE; Somerset Area HS; Somerset, PA; (3); 37/230; Church Yth Grp; French Clb; Letterman Clb; Im Badmtn; Im Bsktbl; Im Bowling; Var Socr; Hon Roll; Prfct Atten Awd; Engrng.

LAW, WILLIAM; Red Land HS; Etters, PA; (4); 14/255; Boy Scts; German Clb; Quiz Bowl; Ftbl; Swmmng; Trk; Wt Lftg; High Hon Roll; NHS; Walter A Brunhouse Scholar 87; Eagle Sct Awd 87; Pres Acad Fit Awd; Penn ST; Engrng.

LAWHEAD, JAMIE; Central Dauphin HS; Harrisburg, PA; (3); Service Clb; Ski Clb; Yrbk Stf; Cit Awd; Cmnty Wkr; Church Choir; Nwsp Stf; Im Vllybl; Yth Art Awd 87; Art Awd 87; C Smith Mem Awd 85; Graphic Dsgn.

LAWLER, GLORIA; Canevin HS; Pittsburgh, PA; (3); FBLA; Stage Crew; Nwsp Stf; 1st Pl FBLA Rgnl Bus Grphcs 86-87; U Of Pittsburgh; Engl.

LAWLER, JANE; Bishop Mc Devitt HS; Harrisburg, PA; (4); 19/176; Art Clb; French Clb; Ski Clb; Concert Band; Jazz Band; Mrchg Band; School Musical; Ed Yrbk Stf; Stu Cncl; Hon Roll; Hghst Avg Awd 86; Mrktng.

LAWLER, MICHAEL; Archbishop Wood Boys HS; Feasterville, PA; (3); 14/230; Chess Clb; Hosp Aide; Library Aide; Math Clb; Math Tm; Political Wkr; Science Clb; High Hon Roll; NHS; 2nd Pl Bucks Cnty Sci Fair 86; Hnrb Mntn-DE Vly Sci Fair, Bucks Cnty Sci Fair 86, 87; U Of Notre Dame.

LAWLEY, HEATHER; Dallas SR HS; Shaverstown, PA; (3); 20/211; NFL; Ski Clb; Variety Show; Pres Soph Cls; VP Stu Cncl; Var Cheerleading; JV Fld Hcky; Var Trk; High Hon Roll; NHS; Chrldng Qlfrs & ST Chmpns 86 & 87; NEDT Awd 85; Advrtsng.

LAWLOR, MARJORIE; Archbishop Prendergast HS; Glenolden, PA; (3); 26/327; Church Yth Grp; Cmnty Wkr; GAA; Rep Stu Cncl; Mgr(s); Var Sftbl; Var Tennis; High Hon Roll; Hon Roll; NHS; Spn Awd 87; Scholar PA Free Entrprse Wk 86; Intl Rel.

LAWNICZAK, LORI; Moniteau HS; West Sunbury, PA; (3); Spanish Clb; Chorus; Pres Jr Cls; Trs Rep Stu Cncl; Var Capt Bsktbl; Stat Ftbl; Wt Lftg; Cit Awd; Hon Roll; NHS; Amer Lgn Awd Ldrshp, Courge 83-84; MVP Awd Vrsty Bsktbl 84-87; Athltc Awd & Sprtsmnshp Awd; Occuptnl Thrpst.

LAWRENCE, CHRISTINA; Panther Valley HS; Summit Hill, PA; (3); 6/132; Mrchg Band; Stage Crew; Yrbk Stf; Var Cheerleading; Gym; Trk; High Hon Roll; Hon Roll; NHS; Pre-Dntl.

LAWRENCE, DAVID; Hempfield HS; Lancaster, PA; (4); 4/425; Church Yth Grp; Computer Clb; Science Clb; Ski Clb; Nwsp Stf; VP Stu Cncl; Im JV Socr; NHS; Pres Schlr; Rotary Awd; James Hale Steinman Fndtn Scholar 87; Lancaster Cnty Sci & Engrng Fair Awds 85 & 87; U PA; Chem.

LAWRENCE, DWAYNE N; Northern York HS; Dillsburg, PA; (4); 119/204; Art Clb; Church Yth Grp; Pres DECA; Library Aide; Variety Show; 3rd Pl Gen Mrktng Dist DECA 86,5th Pl ST 86,2nd Pl Dist 87; Mrktng.

LAWRENCE, HANS; Shikellamy SR HS; Sunbury, PA; (3); 102/315; Debate Tm; German Clb; NFL; Speech Tm; Acpl Chr; Nwsp Phtg; Lit Mag; Bowling; Trk; Degree Hnr Natl Frnscs Leag 86; Penn ST; Psycht.

LAWRENCE, KRISTIN; Owen J Roberts HS; Coventryville, PA; (3); 19/299; Church Yth Grp; Stage Crew; Rep Soph Cls; Bsktbl; Fld Hcky; Score Keeper; Swmmng; Vllybl; High Hon Roll; Hon Roll; Ocngrphy.

LAWRENCE, MELISSA; Southwestern HS; Hanover, PA; (2); Church Yth Grp; Color Guard; Mrchg Band; Vet.

LAWRENCE, MICHAEL; Elk Lake HS; Meshoppen, PA; (2); 4-H; Spanish Clb; SADD; JV Bsbl; Bowling; Hon Roll; Law.

LAWRENCE, SALLY; Wilmington Area HS; Pulaski, PA; (4); 12/112; VP French Clb; Trs Jr Cls; Trs Sr Cls; Stu Cncl; VP Cheerleading; Hon Roll; Sec NHS; Pres Ftnss Acadmc Achvt Awd 87; U Of Pgh; Comp Sci.

LAWRENCE, TERRY; Elk Lake HS; Montrose, PA; (3); Drama Clb; 4-H; Ski Clb; Chorus; School Musical; School Play; Symp Band; Wrstlng.

LAWSON, EDW; Shenandoah Valley HS; Shenandoah, PA; (3); 9/89; Var L Bsktbl; High Hon Roll; Comp Sci.

LAWSON, JANICE; Central HS; Philadelphia, PA; (3); Church Yth Grp; Teachers Aide; Church Choir; Im Tennis; Hon Roll; Psych.

LAWSON, JERRY; St John Neumann HS; Philadelphia, PA; (3); 52/349; Band; Concert Band; Jazz Band; Pep Band; School Musical; Var L Bsbl; Hon Roll; Cert Hnr Outstndng Achvt Band 87.

LAWSON, KAREN; Warren Area HS; Warren, PA; (3); Pres Church Yth Grp; French Clb; Varsity Clb; JV Sftbl; Hon Roll; Jr NHS; Silver B Awd 84-85; Houghton; Sclgy.

LAWSON, LAURA; Frankford HS; Philadelphia, PA; (3); 102/654; Church Yth Grp; FBLA; Natl Beta Clb; Pep Clb; Service Clb; School Play; Yrbk Stf; Rep Soph Cls; Sec Jr Cls; VP Sr Cls; Pres Donaides 87-88; VP Cls 87-88; Co-Capt Var Chrldng 87-88; Holy Family; Early Ed.

LAWSON, MARK; Crestwood HS; Mountaintop, PA; (3); Boy Scts; Bsbl; Bsktbl; Vllybl; Hon Roll; NEDT Awd; Cnstrctn Fld.

LAWSON, MAUREEN; Villa Joseph Marie HS; Bensalem, PA; (4); 1/65; Sec Library Aide; Math Clb; Science Clb; SADD; Teachers Aide; Gov Hon Prg Awd; High Hon Roll; NHS; NEDT Awd; Prfct Atten Awd; Schlrshp To Temple U 87; Temple U; Bus Admin.

LAWSON, MICHELLE; Central HS; Philadelphia, PA; (3); 90/538; Debate Tm; Mrchg Band; Nwsp Stf; Var Badmtn; Tennis; Hon Roll; Jr Oratorical Cntst 87; VP Of Stu Assn 87; Law.

LAWSON, TIM; Center HS; Aliquppa, PA; (3); Am Leg Boys St; Camera Clb; Pres Latin Clb; Scholastic Bowl; Mgr(s); High Hon Roll; NHS; Latin Summa Cum Laude Awd 87; Gifted Pgm 85-87; Commnctns.

LAWTON, DENNIS; Southmoreland HS; Scottdale, PA; (4); 23/230; JCL; Latin Clb; Letterman Clb; Math Clb; Nwsp Stf; Var L Socr; Var L Trk; Clarion U PA; Math.

LAWTON, HOLLY; Columbia Montove Vo Tech; Bloomsburg, PA; (3); 67/227; Church Yth Grp; Exploring; Hosp Aide; Chorus; Hon Roll; Williamsport CC; Surgeon.

LAY, LISA; Carlynton HS; Carnegie, PA; (4); 40/172; French Clb; Girl Scts; Drill Tm; Passivant Awd 87; Thiel Coll; Psych.

LAYTON, CYNTHIA; Henderson HS; West Chester, PA; (2); 3/330; VP Church Yth Grp; Math Tm; Ski Clb; Concert Band; Mrchg Band; Orch; Lit Mag; Hon Roll; Trs Spanish NHS; Band; Arch.

LAYTON, HEATHER; Governor Mifflin HS; Reading, PA; (3); 4/350; Key Clb; Band; Chorus; Concert Band; Mrchg Band; Orch; School Musical; Gov Mifflin Hnr Scty 87-88; Unified Pt Awd 87-88; PA ST Ufastrnmy.

LAYTON, JOY; Garden Spot HS; New Holland, PA; (4); 56/200; Church Yth Grp; Pres Trs 4-H; Chorus; 4-H Awd; Hon Roll; Jr NHS; Grange 83-87; Mt Vernon Nazarene Coll; Hm Ec.

LAYTON, MICHELLE; Bishop Hafey HS; Conyngham, PA; (4); 16/127; German Clb; Hosp Aide; Service Clb; Ski Clb; Color Guard; Orch; Yrbk Rptr; Lit Mag; Twrlr; Hon Roll; W Chester U; Crmnl Jstc.

LAZAR, GREGORY; Bishop Hafey HS; Beaver Mdws, PA; (3); 20/120; Aud/Vis; Trs Church Yth Grp; Ski Clb; Pres Jr Cls; Rep Stu Cncl; Trk; Wt Lftg; Hon Roll; Prfct Atten Awd; Spnsh Cont 84-85; Math Cont 86-87; PA ST U; Arch.

LAZAR, TOM; Penn Trafford HS; Jeannette, PA; (3); High Hon Roll; Hon Roll; Penn ST; Ag.

LAZARCHICK, PAULA; Schuylkill Haven HS; Sch Haven, PA; (3); 28/82; Pep Clb; SADD; Teachers Aide; Yrbk Rptr; Yrbk Stf; Trs Frsh Cls; Trs Soph Cls; Trs Sr Cls; Var Vllybl; Hon Roll; Dntl Hygn.

LAZARUS, LAURA; Harriton HS; Rosemont, PA; (4); Cmnty Wkr; Pres Pep Clb; Yrbk Bus Mgr; Off Frsh Cls; Off Soph Cls; Off Jr Cls; Off Sr Cls; Var Tennis; Natl Chmpnshps-Crew-Brnz 87; U Of PA.

LAZARUS, MARK; Milton Area SR HS; Milton, PA; (3); 9/229; Pres Church Yth Grp; FBLA; Latin Clb; Trs Library Aide; Chorus; Church Choir; Nwsp Stf; Yrbk Stf; Hon Roll; NHS; Acctg.

LAZEVNICK, CAREY; Pittston Area HS; Pittston, PA; (3); FNA; Key Clb; Variety Show; Var Cheerleading; Sftbl; High Hon Roll; NHS.

LAZOR, JENNIFER; Greensburg Central Catholic HS; Greensburg, PA; (3); Latin Clb; Service Clb; Chorus; High Hon Roll; Hon Roll; Ivanhoe Inst; Dntl Asst.

LAZORCHICK, SUSAN; Emmaus HS; Allentown, PA; (3); 52/525; Church Yth Grp; French Clb; Key Clb; Model UN; SADD; Chorus; Church Choir; School Musical; JV Fld Hcky; NHS; Pltcl Law.

LAZORICK, CHARLENE; Marian Catholic HS; Jim Thorpe, PA; (3); 7/104; Pep Clb; Science Clb; Stu Cncl; Cheerleading; Spanish NHS; Sci.

LAZORISAK, DARRYL; Ambridge Area HS; Ambridge, PA; (2); Var Bsbl; JV Bsktbl; Hon Roll; Otstndng Prfrnc & Achvt Awd 87; Acad All Strs; U Of Pittsburgh.

LAZUR, JANINE M; Bishop Mc Devitt HS; Harrisburg, PA; (3); 10/250; Art Clb; Cmnty Wkr; Computer Clb; Science Clb; Band; Yrbk Ed-Chief; JV Socr; Var Sftbl; NHS; Ntl Merit Ltr; Schlstc Wrtng Awd 87; Div Battng Ldng & Mid Penn Div III Stfbl All Star 86; Bio.

LAZUR, RANEE; Tamaqua Area HS; Tamaqua, PA; (3); 15/208; Band; Concert Band; Mrchg Band; Trs Stu Cncl; L Var Crs Cntry; L Var Swmmng; L Var Trk; Trs French Hon Soc; Hon Roll; NHS.

LAZZARETTI, JUDY; Our Lady Of The Sacred Heart HS; Ambridge, PA; (4); 8/57; Capt NFL; School Play; Yrbk Ed-Chief; VP Sr Cls; Hon Roll; Sec NHS; Philosphy Awd 87; Engl Awd 86; Allegheny Coll; Bio.

LE, DAVE; Cumberland Valley HS; Camp Hill, PA; (3); Varsity Clb; JV Bsktbl; Var Socr; Var Trk; Cornell U; Intl Bus.

LE, HOAI; Philadelphia HS For Girls; Philadelphia, PA; (3); Latin Clb; Library Aide; Teachers Aide; Golf; Latin Hnr 85-86; Meritorious 86-87; Med.

LE, NGA; Harry S Truman HS; Levittown, PA; (3); Hon Roll; NHS; Temple U; Arch.

LE, NGA KIM; William Penn HS; York, PA; (4); 16/373; Hosp Aide; Pep Clb; Science Clb; Rep Jr Cls; Tennis; Trk; L High Hon Roll; Hon Roll; NHS; Prfct Atten Awd; 3rd Pl Awd York Cnty Sci & Engrng Fair 86; Temple U; Dentstry.

LE, NGUYET; York Catholic HS; York, PA; (3); French Clb; JA; Service Clb; Hon Roll; Acctng.

LE, THANH; Central HS; Philadelphia, PA; (3); Intnl Clb; Var Socr; Stat Vllybl; Hon Roll; A & B 84-85; Drexel U; Engr.

LE, TUNG T; Harrisburg HS; Harrisburg, PA; (3); 5/295; Computer Clb; Math Clb; Model UN; Science Clb; Socr; Tennis; Hon Roll; Natl Ldrshp Awd 87; Harvard U; Physcst.

LE BAR, MARY FRANCES; Stroudsburg HS; Stroudsburg, PA; (3); 17/259; Dance Clb; French Clb; Hosp Aide; Scholastic Bowl; Varsity Clb; Chorus; Yrbk Stf; Var JV Tennis; High Hon Roll; NHS; Childhood Educ.

LE BEAU, CHRISTINA; Clearfield HS; Hyde, PA; (1); Hosp Aide; JV Cheerleading; Policewoman.

LE BLANC, IRENE; Saint Hubert HS; Philadelphia, PA; (3); Color Guard; Stage Crew; Anml Stds.

LE COMTE, ALISA; Penn Cambria SR HS; Cresson, PA; (3); Drama Clb; Rptr FBLA; SADD; Sftbl; Trophies & Cert For Outstndng Accmplshmnt In Dance, Ballet-Tap-Jazz 85-87; Bus Adm.

LE COMTE, MICHELE; Meadville Area SR HS; Meadville, PA; (3); 8/363; Church Yth Grp; Cmnty Wkr; Off Stu Cncl; Crs Cntry; High Hon Roll; Yth Ftns Achvt Awd 86; Frnch High Hnrs Awd 84fhstry Awd For Hstry Day Actvts 85; Psycl Thrpst.

LE DONNE, GINA; Hampton HS; Allison Pk, PA; (4); Yrbk Sprt Ed; Var Capt Cheerleading; Capt Powder Puff Ftbl; Var Trk; High Hon Roll; Hon Roll; NHS; Pres Schlr; Schlrshp To WV Wslyn 87; Schlrshp To U Of Pttsbrgh; PA ST U; Bus.

LE FEBVRE, JEROME; Western Beaver HS; Industry, PA; (4); 18/84; Chess Clb; Exploring; Math Clb; Mrchg Band; Stage Crew; Bowling; Mgr(s); Wt Lftg; NHS; Prfct Atten Awd; Childrens Hosp Cmte, 2ng Pl Ovrll Power Indx Wghtlftng Cmpttn 87; De Vry Inst Of Tech; Lazer Engr.

LE FEVER, MICHELLE; Bishop Neuman HS; Williamsport, PA; (3); Pep Clb; SADD; Sec Frsh Cls; Var L Bsktbl; Var L Sftbl; Hon Roll; Church Yth Grp; FBLA; Im Vllybl; Cls Svc Awd Sec 85; Svc Awd Tutor 87; Natl Hnr Rl 87; York Coll PA; Bus Mgmt.

LE FUR, JESSICA I; Northwestern Lehigh HS; New Tripoli, PA; (4); 6/140; AFS; 4-H; French Clb; Sec German Clb; Science Clb; Color Guard; School Musical; Trk; High Hon Roll; Pres Schlr; Penn ST U; Pre-Med.

LE PAR, FELICE; Abington SR HS; Rydal, PA; (3); 2/507; French Clb; Hosp Aide; VP Key Clb; Temple Yth Grp; Band; Nwsp Ed-Chief; Off Frsh Cls; Off Soph Cls; Off Jr Cls; High Hon Roll; Outstndng Engl Stu Awds 85-87; Rensselaer Math/Sci Awd, Harvard Bk Awd 86-87; 4th Pl Natl Frnch 84-85; Med.

LE PERA, KEELY MARIE; Mt Saint Joseph Acad; Upper Southampton, PA; (3); Computer Clb; VP Latin Clb; Math Tm; NFL; Science Clb; Service Clb; Yrbk Stf; Swmmng; NHS; NEDT Awd; Fnlst-Outstndng HOBY Orgnztn 85; PA Jnr Acad Of Sci-1st Pl ST & Regnl 86; Latin Hnr Soc 86; Sci.

LE PERA, KRISTA; Mt Saint Joseph Acad; Upper Southampton, PA; (2); Cmnty Wkr; JCL; Latin Clb; Math Tm; NFL; Science Clb; Service Clb; Pres Spanish Clb; SADD; Var Cheerleading; Fnlst Outstndng Soph HOBY Ldrshp Awd 86; Ust Annl Ldrshp Confrnc HS 86; Spnsh Achvt Awd 85; Lbrl Arts.

LE POSA, VICKI; Quakertown Community HS; Quakertown, PA; (3); 47/303; Drama Clb; FBLA; Chorus; School Play; Stage Crew; Var Trk; Hon Roll; Accntng.

LEACH, DANIEL; Mon Valley Catholic HS; Monongahela, PA; (2); 26/76; Pep Clb; Ski Clb; Var L Ftbl; Wt Lftg; Phrmcy.

LEACH, KATHY; Quakertown Community HS; Trumbauersville, PA; (4); Chorus; Church Choir; School Musical; Stage Crew; Htl Mngmnt.

LEACH, LISA; Peters Township HS; Venetia, PA; (2); FBLA; NFL; Church Choir; Hon Roll; Spanish NHS.

LEACH, MARK; Cedar Crest HS; Lebanon, PA; (3); 3/342; Boy Scts; Church Yth Grp; Exploring; Trs German Clb; Latin Clb; Pep Clb; Quiz Bowl; Trs Band; Jazz Band; Mrchg Band; Altar Srvr; Dist Band 86; Cnty Band 85-87.

LEACH, PATRICK; Mon Valley Catholic HS; Monongahela, PA; (1); Pep Clb; Pres Frsh Cls; Var Bsbl; JV Bsktbl; Var L Ftbl; Wt Lftg; Natl Sci Olympd Awd 87; Med.

LEAH, MAIOLATESI; Scranton Prep; Peckville, PA; (3); 59/190; Cmnty Wkr; School Musical; School Play; Var Cheerleading; Var Trk; High Hon Roll; Hon Roll.

LEAKEY, LESTIE; Garden Spot HS; Blue Ball, PA; (4); 87/218; Church Yth Grp; Cmnty Wkr; Drama Clb; FBLA; Hosp Aide; Spanish Clb; Chorus; Church Choir; School Musical; School Play; Vlntr Cert 85-86; Kutztown U; Spcl Educ.

LEAMAN, ANITA; Garden Spot HS; E Earl, PA; (2); 7/226; Church Yth Grp; Chorus; Church Choir; High Hon Roll; Hon Roll; Jr NHS; NHS.

LEAMAN, MONICA; Chambersburg Area SR HS; Chambersburg, PA; (2); 5/735; Sec Church Yth Grp; Chorus; Church Choir; High Hon Roll; Tabor Coll; Bus Adm.

LEAMER, MICHAEL; Purchase Line HS; Commodore, PA; (2); Church Yth Grp; Trk; Hon Roll; Navy.

LEANDRI, HOLLY; Bishop O Reilly HS; Dallas, PA; (1); 14/87; Cmnty Wkr; GAA; Spanish Clb; Pres Soph Cls; Pres Soph Cls; JV Var Cheerleading; Hon Roll; Math Tm; Coach Actv; Natl Wnnr Natl Piano Audtns 87; Legl Profssn.

LEANDRO, PAULO; Cambridge Springs HS; Cambridge Spgs, PA; (4); 3/102; French Clb; Pep Clb; Var Capt Bsktbl; Var L Vllybl; Hon Roll; NHS; Prfct Atten Awd; JETS Acadmc Games 85-87; Acadmc Schlrshp Gannon U 87-91; Gannon U; Math.

LEAP, BARBARA; Pem Cambria SR HS; Lilly, PA; (2); French Clb; Ski Clb; SADD; Gov Hon Prg Awd; High Hon Roll; NHS; Intl Frgn Lang Awd Frnch 87; Cornell; Pedtrcn.

LEAP, KAREN; Greater Johnstown HS; Johnstown, PA; (3); Church Yth Grp; German Clb; Chorus; Concert Band; Mrchg Band; Pep Band; Hon Roll; Bradford Schl Bus; Sec.

LEAPHART, SUSAN; The Cecilian Acad; Philadelphia, PA; (3); 9/36; Drama Clb; Girl Scts; Hosp Aide; School Play; Schlrshp Finishg HS At Cecilian Acad 84-88; Corp Law.

LEAR, CHRISTIAN; Upper Moreland HS; Willow Grove, PA; (3); 79/275; Rep Stu Cncl; JV Bsbl; Capt Swmmng; Cit Awd; Hon Roll; Mech Engr.

LEAR, HEATHER; Crestwood JR/Sr HS; Mountaintop, PA; (4); 6/217; Trs Church Yth Grp; Girl Scts; Pres Key Clb; Library Aide; Band; Chorus; Church Choir; Concert Band; Mrchg Band; School Musical; Ed Assn Scholar 86-87; Marilyn Hay Awd 86-87; PA ST Campus Schlr Hnrs Prgm 87; Penn ST U; Meteorlgy.

LEAR, MATTHEW; Altoona Area HS; Altoona, PA; (3); Letterman Clb; Varsity Clb; Crs Cntry; Trk; High Hon Roll; Aerosp Engr.

LEARDI, MARY; Cardinal Ohara HS; Springfield, PA; (3); 26/710; Aud/Vis; Cmnty Wkr; Girl Scts; Band; Jazz Band; School Musical; School Play; Rep Frsh Cls; Rep Soph Cls; Rep Sr Cls; All Cthlc Bnd 84; DE Vly Sci Fair Nrs Awd 86; St Jsphs U; Pltcl Sci.

LEARN, DAVID; Penn Trafford HS; Trafford, PA; (3); 24/301; AFS; Cmnty Wkr; Acpl Chr; Chorus; Concert Band; Mrchg Band; Symp Band; High Hon Roll; NHS; Ltr Cmndtn Natl Merit Schlrshp Brd 87; Genetcs.

LEARN, JERRY; Purchase Line HS; Commodore, PA; (3); 7/104; Spanish Clb; Band; Mrchg Band; Nwsp Rptr; Var Trk; High Hon Roll; NHS; PA ST U; Mech Engnrng.

LEARN, MICHELE; Elkland Area HS; Elkland, PA; (3); 1/70; French Clb; School Musical; School Play; VP Soph Cls; VP Jr Cls; Var Bsktbl; Var Trk; Var Vllybl; High Hon Roll; Sec NHS; Hghst Gr Pt Avg 86-87; Pcpnt Penn ST Essy Cont 85-86; Med.

LEARN, PENNY; Punxsutawhey Area HS; Punxsutawney, PA; (4); 11/249; French Clb; Math Tm; Science Clb; Band; Concert Band; Mrchg Band; Variety Show; Hon Roll; JP Sousa Awd; NHS; IN U Of PA Hnrs Band 84-86; Natl Hnr Soc Quiz Team 86-87.

LEARN, TRISHA; Elkland Area HS; Elkland, PA; (3); 4/65; French Clb; GAA; SADD; Varsity Clb; Band; Mrchg Band; Bsktbl; Trk; Vllybl; High Hon Roll; Bus.

LEARY, JULIE; Jamestown Area HS; Jamestown, PA; (3); Band; School Musical; Variety Show; Sec Jr Cls; VP Stu Cncl; Var Cheerleading; High Hon Roll; NHS; Speech Pathology.

LEARY, MAUREEN; Lampeter-Strasburg HS; Lancaster, PA; (4); 4/142; Yrbk Rptr; Lit Mag; Stat Tennis; Hon Roll; NHS; Ntl Merit Ltr; Opt Clb Awd; Hnr Mntn Shrt/Shrt Stry Locl Schlstc Wrtng Awd; 1st Pl Shrt Stry Locl Schl Schlstc Wrtng Awd; Franklin Coll; Govt.

LEASGANG, LISA; St Marys Area HS; Kersey, PA; (4); 64/274; Sec Trs Church Yth Grp; FBLA; L Cheerleading; Hon Roll; Natl Bus Hnr Scty 86-87; Outdoor Clb 86-87; Stu Secr 86-87; J H Thompson Acad; Med Secr.

LEASURE, TOM; Hempfield SR HS; Hunker, PA; (3); Boy Scts; VICA; Hon Roll; Elec Wiring.

LEATHERMAN, JUDITH; Lancaster Mennonite HS; Coatesville, PA; (3); Pres Church Yth Grp; Chorus; Orch; Stage Crew; High Hon Roll; NHS; Acad Schlrshp 86; Stu Mnth Rotary Club 87; E Mennonite Coll; Bio.

LEATHERMAN, MICHELLE; Wellsboro SR HS; Wellsboro, PA; (2); Church Yth Grp; Drama Clb; Rptr 4-H; German Clb; Hosp Aide; Pep Clb; Chorus; Flag Corp; School Musical; High Hon Roll; Cosmotologist.

LEATHERMAN, NEAL B; Hope Christian Acad; Tamaqua, PA; (4); School Musical; Yrbk Stf; Hon Roll; Messiah Coll.

LEATHERMAN, TIM; Gettysburg SR HS; Gettysburg, PA; (2); CAP; Exploring; Ski Clb; SADD; Bsbl; Bsktbl; Crs Cntry; Ftbl; Ice Hcky; Wt Lftg; Crpntr.

LEATHERS, JOY; High Point Baptist Acad; Birdsboro, PA; (4); 2/34; Church Yth Grp; Church Choir; Stage Crew; Sec Jr Cls; Sec Sr Cls; Cheerleading; High Hon Roll; Pres Schlr; Sal.

LEAVY, JANINE; St Basil Acad; Philadelphia, PA; (3); Church Yth Grp; Drama Clb; French Clb; GAA; SADD; Rep Jr Cls; VP Sr Cls; Var Bsktbl; Im Coach Actv; Var Fld Hcky; Ntl Hnr Roll 86-87; Ntl Frnch Cntst 87.

LEAVY, THOMAS J; Arch Bishop Ryan HS; Philadelphia, PA; (2); 27/352; Church Yth Grp; Latin Clb; School Play; Diving; Ftbl; Swmmng; High Hon Roll; Hon Roll; Cert Of Awd Latin I 86.

LEBANNO, RENEE; Moniteau JR/SR HS; Slippery Rock, PA; (2); Pres Church Yth Grp; French Clb; Library Aide; Band; Chorus; Concert Band; Jazz Band; Mrchg Band; Butler Cnty All-Star Band 87; PA Jr Acad Sci 2nd Pl Awd 87; Capt Bible Quiz Tm; Psych.

LEBDA, DOUGLAS R; Lewisburg HS; Lewisburg, PA; (3); 6/149; Am Leg Boys St; Pres Chorus; School Musical; Nwsp Phtg; Pres Soph Cls; Pres Jr Cls; Capt Crs Cntry; Var Trk; NHS; Church Yth Grp; Bus.

LEBER, CHRISTOPHER E; Eastern York County HS; Hellom, PA; (2); Bowling; High Hon Roll; Hon Roll; Jr NHS; Millersville U; Comp Prog.

LEBER, CHRISTOPHER W V; Bermudian Springs HS; New Oxford, PA; (3); Off FFA; Nwsp Rptr; Hon Roll; Schlrshp Awd Cmmtte Chrmn 86; Soil & Water Mgnt Fndtn Awd FFA 87; 1st Pl FFA Cnty Frstry Cntst 85; Mt Alto Campus; Wldlf & Frst.

LEBERKNIGHT, JILL; Mechanicsburg Area HS; Mechanicsburg, PA; (2); 95/317; Dance Clb; Drama Clb; Speech Tm; Variety Show; Capt Cheerleading; Hon Roll; Church Yth Grp; Pep Clb; Chorus; School Musical; Profssnl Perfrmr.

LEBIEDZINSKI, KAREN M; Mount Saint Joseph Acad; Warminster, PA; (4); Rep Cmnty Wkr; Pres Girl Scts; Rep Service Clb; Ed Lit Mag; French Hon Soc; Pres NHS; Ntl Merit SF; Church Yth Grp; Drama Clb; French Clb; Japan USSSP Pa Smi-Fnlst 86; Awd Merit U Of Pa 86; Girl Scout Gold Awd 87; Aero Engr.

LEBKICHER, MICHAEL; Juniata HS; Mifflintown, PA; (3); SADD; JV Trk; GA Tech; Military.

LEBO, JEFFERY; East Pennsboro Area HS; Enola, PA; (4); 20/200; Boy Scts; Pres Chess Clb; Model UN; Spanish Clb; Hst Jr Cls; Hst Sr Cls; Trk; Hon Roll; NHS; Schlstc Art Comp Merits 84 & 86; Elec.

LEBO, MARCI; Mechanicsburg Area SR HS; Mechanicsburg, PA; (3); 2 338; SADD; Acpl Chr; Chorus; Nwsp Rptr; Nwsp Stf; Rep Stu Cncl; H Roll; Penn ST U; Psychlgy.

LEBO, SHARON; Millersburg Area HS; Millersburg, PA; (4); 5/90; S Church Yth Grp; Trs Spanish Clb; Band; Concert Band; Jazz Band; S Cncl; Var Trk; Cit Awd; High Hon Roll; NHS; Temple; Sports Medicin

LECCIA, BRAD; West Mifflin Area HS; W Mifflin, PA; (2); Boy Sc Chess Clb; Exploring; Science Clb; Spanish Clb; School Play; Off Soph C Bowling; Mgr(s); Socr; Astronomer.

LECH, COLLEEN; Belle Vernon Area HS; Belle Vernon, PA; (3); Ban High Hon Roll; Hon Roll; NHS; Nrsng.

LECHAK, BRIAN; Bishop O Reilly HS; Courtdale, PA; (3); Comput Clb; JV Capt Bsbl; Var Socr; Hon Roll; NEDT Awd; Penn ST; Bus.

LECHER, MARK CHRISTOPHER; Blue Ridge HS; Great Bend, P (3); Boy Scts; SADD; Varsity Clb; Var Bsktbl; L Crs Cntry; L Trk; Prf Atten Awd; Trste Grt Bnd Vlntr Fr Dept 86-87.

LECHMAN, ERIC R; Center HS; Aliquippa, PA; (4); 29/185; Am L Boys St; German Clb; School Musical; Nwsp Rptr; Bsktbl; Bowling; H Roll; NHS; Pres Schlr; Allegheny Coll.

LECHNER, BRENT; Carmichaels Area SR HS; Nemacolin, PA; (2); 100; Letterman Clb; Quiz Bowl; Spanish Clb; Varsity Clb; Nwsp Stf; V L Bsbl; Var L Bsktbl; Var L Ftbl; Cit Awd; DAR Awd; W Pt Military Aca Pilot.

LECHNER, BRIAN; Bradford SR HS; Bradford, PA; (4); 40/265; K Clb; Rep Stu Cncl; Im Vllybl; Lttrr Rfl Team MVP 84-85; Ntl Champ Ri Team 84; Brian Lechner Mem Voctnl Schlrshp Estblshd.

LECHNER, LAURI; Shenango HS; Wampum, PA; (3); 36/125; Dra Clb; French Clb; Flag Corp; School Play; Stage Crew; Nwsp Rptr; Nw Stf; Yrbk Rptr; Yrbk Stf; Hon Roll; Comm.

LECHNER, LYNN; Saucon Valley HS; Nazareth, PA; (4); 11/147; Ho Aide; Pres Spanish Clb; Nwsp Stf; Yrbk Stf; Stat Wrstlng; High Hon Ro Hon Roll; Jr NHS; NHS; Prsdntl Acdmc Ftnss, SVHS Fclty Mae Cwh & A J Oplngr Awds 87; Brd Schl Dir Awd 87; Millersville U-PA; Ele Educ.

LECKER, BRADY J; Elk County Christian HS; St Marys, PA; (1); 23/8 Hon Roll; Engrng.

LECKEY, IVY; Jersey Shore Area HS; Jersey Shore, PA; (3); French C Chorus; School Musical; Var Bsktbl; Var Capt Trk; Outstndng-Trck Dist 4 AAA Champ-Shot Put 87; West Branch Champ 86-87; Med Tec

LECKRONE, TOM; Christian School Of York; York, PA; (2); Church Y Grp; Chorus; Concert Band; Orch; Pres Soph Cls; Cit Awd; High Hon R PMEA Dstrct Bng & Chrs 86-87; Awd York Cntry Sci & Engr Fair 86

LECKRONE, WESLEY; Bishop Mc Devitt HS; Harrisburg, PA; (4); 3 186; Church Yth Grp; Computer Clb; Debate Tm; Ski Clb; Capt Spee Tm; VP SADD; Chorus; Madrigals; Off Sr Cls; Trs Stu Cncl; Law.

LECKY, KEITH; Harriton HS; Gladwyne, PA; (3); Wrstlng; Socr; Lcr Hon Roll; Varsity Clb; Letterman Clb; FCA; Yrbk Stf; Hnr Mntn N Merit 86; Duke U; Adv.

LECRONE, K MARK; Spring Grove Area HS; Spring Grove, PA; (3); 365; Boy Scts; Trs Church Yth Grp; Band; Chorus; Church Choir; Ja Band; School Musical; JETS Awd; NHS; Rotary Awd; Yth Schlrs In Lebanon Vly Coll 87; U ME Pulp Paper Fndtn Smmr Pgm Gftd Stu 8 Mech Engrng.

LECRONE, KELLY; Portage Area HS; Portage, PA; (4); 16/123; Chor High Hon Roll; NHS; Exec Secy.

LEDBETTER, JACQUELINE; Southmoreland SR HS; Mtpleasant, P (3); 9/222; Church Yth Grp; Pep Clb; Spanish Clb; Color Guard; NH Spanish NHS; SOCLGY.

LEDBETTER, WILLIAM; Cambridge Springs HS; Saegertown, PA; (Key Clb; Pep Clb; Spanish Clb; School Play; JV Ftbl; JV Vllybl; J Wrstlng; Edinboro U Of PA; Bus Admin.

LEDERER, CHRISTINE; Little Flower HS; Philadelphia, PA; (3); 5 396; Art Clb; Camera Clb; Church Yth Grp; Cmnty Wkr; Computer C English Clb; FBLA; German Clb; GAA; Hosp Aide; Bus.

LEDERER, HOWARD; Allderdice HS; Pittsburgh, PA; (3); Ski Clb; Ja Band; Ice Hcky; High Hon Roll; Hon Roll; NHS; U Of Pittsburgh; Med

LEDSTER, DANIELLE; Hempfield HS; Lancaster, PA; (3); Drama C Chorus; Drill Tm; School Musical; School Play; Nwsp Stf; Yrbk Stf; R Sr Cls; Hon Roll.

LEE, ADRIENNE R; Pine Forge Acad; El Paso, TX; (2); Church Y Grp; Office Aide; Church Choir; Pres Frsh Cls; Pres Soph Cls; Cit Aw Hon Roll; NHS; Oakwood Coll; Elem Educ.

LEE, AMY; Philadelphia HS For Girls; Philadelphia, PA; (1); Science C Gym; Ice Hcky; High Hon Roll; Hon Roll; St Schlr.

LEE, AMY; Spring-Ford SR HS; Royersford, PA; (2); 54/289; French C Nwsp Rptr; Yrbk Stf; Rep Soph Cls; Var JV Bsktbl; Var Fld Hcky; Va Trk; Intnl Clb; SADD; Chorus; Outstndng Frnch Stu Awd 86-87; Wrtr Mnth Awd 86-87; Fld Hcky Outstndng Offnsv Plyr 86; Engl.

LEE, ANDREW; West Forest JR-SR HS; Tionesta, PA; (3); 5/55; B Scts; Trs Church Yth Grp; Ski Clb; Chorus; Sec Frsh Cls; VP Stu Cncl; V L Bsbl; Var L Socr; NHS; Bio Chem.

LEE, BERNICE; Penn Cambria HS; Portage, PA; (3); Spanish Clb; H Roll; Med.

LEE, BILL; Palmyra HS; Palmyra, PA; (4); 39/190; VP German C Science Clb; Varsity Clb; Chorus; Nwsp Rptr; Nwsp Stf; L Bsktbl; L Ft Capt L Trk; Hon Roll; Trck Athltc Schlrshp; Shippensburg U; Ec.

LEE, BRADLEY C; Greensburg Salem SR HS; Greensburg, PA; (3); 288; Trs Pres Drama Clb; Exploring; French Clb; Math Tm; Thesp French Hon Soc; High Hon Roll; Jr NHS; Trs NHS; Ntl Merit S Outstndng Schltc Achvt 85; Chem.

LEE, CAROLENE; Farrell HS; Farrell, PA; (2); Church Yth Grp; Ho Aide; JA; Key Clb; Spanish Clb; Church Choir; Swmmng; Trk; Hon Ro Spanish NHS; Gerontlgy.

LEE, CHI; Central HS; Philadelphia, PA; (4); Chess Clb; Latin C Library Aide; Math Tm; Science Clb; Nwsp Stf; Var Badmtn; Hon Ro Mayor Schlrhp 86-90; Phldlpha Cty Schlrshp 86-90; White Wlm Schlrs 83-85; U PA; Physcs.

LEE, DAVID; Cedar Crest HS; Lebanon, PA; (3); German Clb; Pep C Science Clb; Rep Stu Cncl; Var Swmmng; Var Tennis; High Hon Ro NHS; Cornell U; Pre-Med.

LEE, DAVID; Conneaut Valley HS; Enola, PA; (4); 15/75; Drama C Political Wkr; Sec Trs Ski Clb; Spanish Clb; Nwsp Rptr; VP Jr Cls; Pr Stu Cncl; DAR Awd; Hon Roll; Atten Cngrsnl Smnr 86; Dickinson Coll.

LEE, DIANE; Portage Area HS; Portage, PA; (4); French Clb; Choru Hon Roll.

LEE, EDWARD; Lower Merion HS; Philadelphia, PA; (3); Trs Church Yth Grp; Hosp Aide; High Hon Roll; 4-H; JCL; Church Choir; JV Socr; Trk; French Hon Soc.

LEE, ERIC; Central SR HS; York, PA; (3); JV Socr; JV Tennis; High Hon Roll; NHS; Natl Sci Olympiad 87; PTSA Reflections Scheme Awd 85; Aerospace Engrng.

LEE, EUGENE; Cheltenham HS; Cheltenham, PA; (2).

LEE, GINA; Mathaeton SR HS; Eagleville, PA; (4); Aud/Vis; Church Yth Grp; Cmnty Wkr; Office Aide; Radio Clb; Band; Color Guard; Concert Band; Drm Mjr(t); Jazz Band; M Awd 84; County Jr Miss Physcl Fitnss Awd 86; Communctns.

LEE, HAN; Montour HS; Pittsburgh, PA; (2); Var JV Ftbl; JV Vllybl; High Hon Roll; Hon Roll; Amercn Lgn Awd 84-85; Acad Achvt Awds 86-87; Johns Hopkins U; Med.

LEE, HEATHER L; Bloomsburg Area SR HS; Bloomsburg, PA; (3); Am Leg Aux Girls St; Pep Clb; Varsity Clb; VP Jr Cls; JV Cheerleading; Var Powder Puff Ftbl; JV Sftbl; Robotics.

LEE, HEE SUN; Meadville Area SR HS; Meadville, PA; (4); 7/306; Church Yth Grp; Sec Trs Varsity Clb; Band; Tennis; Var Vllybl; High Hon Roll; Hon Roll; Pharmacy.

LEE, IRENE; Philadelphia High Schl For Girls; Philadelphia, PA; (3); 23/405; Office Aide; Hon Roll; NHS; Latin Hnr Soc 87; U Of PA.

LEE, JANE; Salisbury SR HS; Allentown, PA; (4); 4/122; Key Clb; Off Jr Cls; Stu Cncl; Stat Bsbl; Stat Bsktbl; Socr; Capt Swmmng; High Hon Roll; Hon Roll; Trs NHS; Pres Acad Fit Awd 87; Soc Wmn Engrs Hnr 87; Lafayette Coll; Chem Engrng.

LEE, JERRY; Athens Area HS; Athens, PA; (4); 4-H; FFA; Library Aide; Red Cross Aide; SADD; Hon Roll; Bradford Area Farmer Degree 86-87; Athens HS Wild Life Trphy 85; Bradford Cnty FFA Wldlf Trphy 85-86; Masonary.

LEE, KEE; Hatboro Horsham SR HS; Horsham, PA; (4); Socr; Var Trk; High Hon Roll; Hon Roll; NHS; Prfct Atten Awd; Pres Schlr; Gen Excllnc Awd 87; U Of PA; Chem.

LEE, KELLY; Quaker Valley HS; Sewickley, PA; (4); Band; Mrchg Band; Pep Band; Symp Band; Yrbk Sprt Ed; Capt Bsktbl; Capt Sftbl; Var L Vllybl; Hon Roll; Penn ST; Food Sci.

LEE, LISA; Governor Mifflin HS; Reading, PA; (4); 49/300; Cmnty Wkr; Dance Clb; FBLA; Key Clb; Math Clb; Orch; High Hon Roll; Hon Roll; Temples Pres Awd 87; Pres Fit Awd 87; Temple U; Intl Bus.

LEE, MARK; Bethel Park HS; Bethel Park, PA; (4); 5/519; Church Yth Grp; Capt Math Tm; Ski Clb; Var L Socr; Var L Tennis; NHS; Marshal Hahn Engnrng Schlrshp VA Tech 87; Natl Schlr/Athlt Awd 87; VA Tech; Engnrng.

LEE, MARSHA; Coatesville Area SR HS; Coatesville, PA; (4); Leo Clb; Ski Clb; Spanish Clb; Rep Stu Cncl; Mgr(s); JV Swmmng; JV Tennis; Speech Pthlgy.

LEE, MICHELLE; Emmaus HS; Macungie, PA; (4); 64/474; Rep Key Clb; Q&S; Acpl Chr; Yrbk Ed-Chief; Sec Soph Cls; Rep Sr Cls; Rep Stu Cncl; Var Capt Cheerleading; Sec NHS; Kiwanis Clb Schlrshp Wnr 87; LA ST U; Broadcast Jrnlsm.

LEE, MICHELLE; South Western HS; Hanover, PA; (3); Key Clb; Nwsp Stf; Yrbk Stf; JV Var Fld Hcky; JV Trk.

LEE, MISSY; York Suburban HS; York, PA; (3); Hosp Aide; Hon Roll; Econ.

LEE, PETER; Cardinal O Hara HS; Broomall, PA; (3); 49/721; Boy Scts; Chess Clb; Church Yth Grp; Cmnty Wkr; Math Tm; Service Clb; Concert Band; Mrchg Band; Ntl Merit Ltr; Pres Of Mensa Club Asst Instrctr Of Karate Club 86-87; Engrng.

LEE, RAY; New Castle SR HS; New Castle, PA; (2); Art Clb; CAP; Computer Clb; Dance Clb; FHA; Boys Clb Am; SADD; Church Choir; Nwsp Bus Mgr; Nwsp Phtg.

LEE, RENEE; Lawrence County Vo-Tech; New Castle, PA; (2); Cmnty Wkr; Chorus; Church Choir; School Musical; Variety Show; JV Var Cheerleading; Hon Roll; Modern Miss Acad Pgnt 1st Rnnr Up 87,1st Rnnr Up Talent 87; Music.

LEE, ROGER; Conestoga SR HS; Berwyn, PA; (2); Camera Clb; Concert Band; Mrchg Band; Orch; School Musical; Symp Band; Lit Mag; Princeton U; Photo.

LEE, RONALD; Central Catholic HS; Pittsburgh, PA; (4); 28/268; Drama Clb; School Musical; School Play; Nwsp Ed-Chief; JV Var Bowling; JV Trk; High Hon Roll; Hon Roll; Jr NHS; Nwsp Phtg; N C Miller Awd Svc In Nwsp 87; Carnegie-Mellon U; Bus.

LEE, S ERNIE; Oxford Area HS; Lincoln Univ, PA; (4); 35/172; Church Yth Grp; Bsbl; Ftbl; Trk; High Hon Roll; Hon Roll; Commended Stu Natl Achvt Schlrshp Prog Outstndng Negro Stu 86; 4 Yr Athltc Schlrshp 87; Lafayette Coll; Bus.

LEE, SEUNAH; Lower Moreland HS; Huntingdon Valley, PA; (4); 40/201; Church Yth Grp; Drama Clb; Library Aide; Science Clb; Church Choir; Stage Crew; Lit Mag; Stat Swmmng; Hon Roll; NHS; Haverford Coll; Biochem.

LEE, SHELLY; Bloomsburg HS; Bloomsburg, PA; (1); Pep Clb; Chorus; Mrchg Band; Yrbk Stf; JV Capt Cheerleading; Hon Roll.

LEE, STACY; Langley HS; Pittsburgh, PA; (3); Church Yth Grp; Hosp Aide; Pep Clb; Band; Concert Band; Mrchg Band; School Musical; Sftbl; Hon Roll.

LEE, SUNG; Cedar Crest HS; Bethlehem, PA; (4); 1/303; FBLA; Math Tm; Quiz Bowl; Orch; JV Tennis; High Hon Roll; NHS; Ntl Merit Schol; Val; Voice Dem Awd; Booster Clb Schlrshp 87; Brown U; Pre-Med.

LEE, TERESA; Coatesville HS; Coatesville, PA; (2); 29/434; 4-H; Teachers Aide; Chorus; Off Stu Cncl; Bsktbl; High Hon Roll; NEDT Awd; Prfct Atten Awd.

LEE, TOMEKA; Philadelphia HS For Girls; Philadelphia, PA; (3); 132/402; Church Yth Grp; Cmnty Wkr; Girl Scts; NAACP; SADD; Church Choir; Hon Roll; Hampton U; Bus Admin.

LEE, TRACEY; Girard Coll; Wilmington, DE; (3); 9/40; Chess Clb; Dance Clb; Letterman Clb; Math Clb; Quiz Bowl; Radio Clb; Ski Clb; Speech Tm; Varsity Clb; Stage Crew; All Penn NJ Crs Cntry 85; Friend Slct Trnmnt All Star 86; Morehouse Coll; Cmmnctns.

LEE, TRACI; Connellsville Area SR HS; Mount Pleasant, PA; (2); Church Yth Grp; French Clb; Girl Scts; Office Aide; Teachers Aide; Concert Band; Mrchg Band; Symp Band; High Hon Roll; Hon Roll; Socl Wrk.

LEE, VICTORIA; Upper Dublin HS; Ft Washington, PA; (3); 4/300; Capt Math Tm; Science Clb; Concert Band; Pres Mrchg Band; Orch; Lit Mag; Rep Stu Cncl; Gov Hon Prg Awd; Hon Roll; NHS; 1st Plcs ST Lvl Sci Fair PJAS 85-87; 1st Chr Flutist Cnty Band 87; Awds Air Force & Navy NASA 86; Biochem.

LEE JR, WILLIAM G; Freedom HS; Bethlehem, PA; (3); 9/513; Church Yth Grp; German Clb; Math Clb; Math Tm; Model UN; Gov Hon Prg Awd; Hon Roll; NHS; PA Math Leag Cert Merit 85; Cert Acdmc Attainmnt 86; Astrophysics.

LEE, YISHANE; Radnor HS; Villanova, PA; (4); 6/297; Hosp Aide; JA; Model UN; Service Clb; Stage Crew; Nwsp Sprt Ed; NHS; Ntl Merit Schol; Aud/Vis; School Play; Natl Cncl On Yth Ldrshp Schlrshp Fnlst 86; Peace Committee Exec Mem 86-87; Brown U.

LEE, YONG J; Mechanicsburg SR HS; Mechanicsburg, PA; (3); 10/364; Am Leg Boys St; Band; Orch; School Play; Yrbk Stf; Rep Jr Cls; Trs Stu Cncl; Var Capt Socr; High Hon Roll; NHS; Smfnlst & Attrnt Grmn Stu 87-88; Mltry Wrld Wrs Rep 87-88; WA Wrkshp Pgm 88; Bus.

LEECH, BETH; Albert Gallatin HS; Smithfield, PA; (4); 10/135; Ski Clb; Cheerleading; High Hon Roll; Hon Roll; Jr NHS; NHS; Stud Mnth 87; Pres Acad Ftns Awd 87; David Mallick Schlrshp Awd 87; Uniontown Schl Nrsng; Nrsng.

LEECH, JILL; Swissvale HS; Pittsburgh, PA; (4); 13/196; German Clb; Acpl Chr; Chorus; Nwsp Stf; Capt Bowling; High Hon Roll; Parent, Teacher & Stu Assn Schlrshp Awd 87; Schl Play Productions 85-87; Allegheny CC; Comp Sci.

LEECH, SANDRA; Gettysburg HS; Gettysburg, PA; (2); Church Yth Grp; Library Aide; Ski Clb; Teachers Aide; Yrbk Rptr; Yrbk Stf; Rep Frsh Cls; Sec Jr Cls; Bsktbl; Coach Actv; Physcl Ftns Awd 87; Athlt Ltrs In Bsktbl, Trck & Crs Cntry 86-87; Mlrsvl U; Rn.

LEEDS, FAITH M; Steel Valley HS; Munhall, PA; (3); Church Yth Grp; Dance Clb; French Clb; Girl Scts; Speech Tm; SADD; Cheerleading; High Hon Roll; Hon Roll; U Pittsburgh; Psych.

LEEDS, FRED; Big Spring HS; Newville, PA; (3); 80/280; Church Yth Grp; Drama Clb; Political Wkr; Band; Concert Band; Drm Mjr(t); Jazz Band; Mrchg Band; Trk; Hon Roll; Stu Mnth 86-87; Bio-Chem.

LEEDS, STEPHANIE; West Snyder HS; Middleburg, PA; (2); 3/90; Chorus; School Musical; Rep Frsh Cls; Rep Soph Cls; JV Mgr(s); JV Stat Sftbl; Hon Roll; Full Schlrshp PA Free Entrprs Wk; Cmnctns.

LEEDY, KRISTINA; Lower Dauphin HS; Palmyra, PA; (4); Camera Clb; Church Yth Grp; Hosp Aide; Ski Clb; Spanish Clb; Hon Roll; Miss Christmas Seal Am Lung Assoc 86-87; :Physcl Thrpy.

LEEDY, TAMMY; Northern Lebanon HS; Fredericksburg, PA; (3); Church Yth Grp; Pep Clb; JV Var Sftbl; Hon Roll; NHS; Ntl Merit Ltr; Psyc.

LEEPER JR, FRANK; Northern Lebanon HS; Jonestown, PA; (3); 13/218; Boy Scts; Trs 4-H; Band; Concert Band; Mrchg Band; Pep Band; Var L Bowling; 4-H Awd; Hon Roll; Boy Sct Postr Cntst Lancaster Lebanon Cncl 1st & 2nd 87; Culnry Arts.

LEEPER, GILLIAN; The Academy Of The New Church; Atlanta, GA; (2); Church Yth Grp; Sec Trs Soph Cls; Var Vllybl; Acad Of New Church Outstanding Achvt In Sci Awd 86-87; Member Deka; Architectural Engr.

LEES, GREGORY; Danville HS; Danville, PA; (2); Boy Scts; Trs 4-H; School Play; Gym; Var Socr; Wrstlng; Cit Awd; Hon Roll; Psychlgy.

LEESE, BRYAN; Boiling Springs HS; Dillsburg, PA; (3); Chess Clb; Church Yth Grp; Rep Stu Cncl; JV Bsbl; JV Ftbl; Var L Socr; JV Trk; Var Capt Wrstlng; Hon Roll; Mst Vlbl Wrstlr 85-86; Mst Imprvd Sccr 86; Mid Penn Div III Wrstlng All Star Tm 85; Sports Med.

LEESER, JODI; Milton SR HS; Milton, PA; (2); Trs Church Yth Grp; Sec German Clb; Varsity Clb; Chorus; Nwsp Bus Mgr; Rep Stu Cncl; Var Cheerleading; Var Crs Cntry; Pres Schlr; Exploring; Advsry Brd Schl Admn 86-87; Outdr Clb 85-87; Ed.

LEFEBURE, CINDY JO; Cambria Heights HS; Hastings, PA; (3); 33/182; Aud/Vis; Concert Band; Mrchg Band; Pep Band; Nwsp Phtg; Nwsp Rptr; Yrbk Rptr; Sftbl; Hon Roll; NHS; Phrmcst.

LEFEBURE, VALERIE; Purchase Line HS; Cherry Tree, PA; (2); 10/158; Church Yth Grp; French Clb; Hosp Aide; Band; Concert Band; High Hon Roll; Top Hnr Frnch Sectn Lang Clb 86-87; Radlgy.

LEFEBVRE, PAUL; Pennsbury HS; Morrisville, PA; (3); JV L Ice Hcky; Bus.

LEFEVER, DEBORAH; Milton Area HS; Milton, PA; (3); Pres Church Yth Grp; Service Clb; Spanish Clb; Varsity Clb; Yrbk Stf; Trs Sr Cls; Rep Stu Cncl; Var Trk; Hon Roll; NHS; Phys Ther.

LEFEVER, KIMBERLY; Elizabethtown Area HS; Mt Joy, PA; (3); 24/256; Am Leg Aux Girls St; Church Yth Grp; Cmnty Wkr; Library Aide; Band; Chorus; Rep Stu Cncl; Im Vllybl; Im Wt Lftg; REACH Amer Pgm 87; Psych.

LEFEVER, PAMELA; Elizabethtown Area HS; Mt Joy, PA; (4); 22/237; Church Yth Grp; Drama Clb; Library Aide; Spanish Clb; Teachers Aide; Chorus; Church Choir; School Musical; Powder Puff Ftbl; High Hon Roll; Girl Mnth 87; Pres Fit Awd 87; Elizabeth Hughes Soc Awd Outstndng Achvt 87; Lancaster Gen Hosp; Nrsng.

LEFEVRE, DOUGLAS; Brookville Area HS; Brookville, PA; (3); 22/175; Pres Key Clb; Pres Varsity Clb; VP Jr Cls; Var Ftbl; Var Swmmng; Var Trk; Trs Jr NHS; Trs NHS; Trs Frsh Cls; Trs Soph Cls; Underclass Athl Of Yr 86-87; PA Free Enterprise Wk 87; Pres Physcl Ftnss Awd 85-86; Psych.

LEFFAKIS, ZACHARY; Schenley HS; Pittsburgh, PA; (3); Boys Clb Am; Rep Stu Cncl; Var Ftbl; Wt Lftg; High Hon Roll; Hon Roll; NHS; Prfct Atten Awd; Connellex Ctr; Elec Engr.

LEFFLER, ANGELICA; Columbia Montour AVTS; Berwick, PA; (3); Church Yth Grp; Exploring; Letterman Clb; Chorus; Church Choir; Yrbk Ed-Chief; Stat Bsbl; Capt Cheerleading; VP & Pres HOSA Chptr 84-88; Pres MV Chrldr Stu Amer 86-87; Geisinger Med Ctr; Optmtrst.

LEFFLER, TAMMY; Bishop Mc Cort HS; Johnstown, PA; (3); Church Choir; High Hon Roll; Hon Roll; NHS; Pre-Law.

LEFLER, PATRICIA; Gettysburg SR HS; Gettysburg, PA; (3); Girl Scts; Fld Hcky; Sftbl; Hon Roll; Dance.

LEGENSTEIN, ANTHONY; Lancaster Catholic HS; Lancaster, PA; (4); Church Yth Grp; Cmnty Wkr; Exploring; Ski Clb; Var Ftbl; Var Trk; Wt Lftg; Wrstlng; Pks Mgmnts.

LEGG, REBECCA; Greensburg Salem SR HS; Greensburg, PA; (4); Church Yth Grp; Drama Clb; NFL; PAVAS; Ski Clb; Pres Spanish Clb; Chorus; VP Sr Cls; Rep Stu Cncl; Capt Cheerleading; County,Dist Chorus 84-86; Ensemble 86; U Pittsburgh; Psychlgy.

LEGGE, JENNIFER A; Greater Latrobe SR HS; Latrobe, PA; (3); AFS; Am Leg Aux Girls St; Church Yth Grp; Exploring; Sec French Clb; Stu Cncl; Mat Maids; Twrlr; Hon Roll; Rep Soph Cls; City Cnclmn & Cnty Treas At Kystn Grls ST 87; U Of Pittsburgh; Dntl Hygnst.

LEGGORE, LISA A; Dauphin County Technical Schl; Middletown, PA; (2); 12/253; DECA; Chorus; High Hon Roll; Hon Roll; 2nd Pl Gnrl Mrktng At Dist Cmptn DECA 87; Johnson; Mngmnt.

LEGLER, JEFFREY; Washington HS; Washington, PA; (2); Church Yth Grp; Trs Exploring; Acpl Chr; Chorus; Madrigals; School Musical; Hon Roll; Regnl Chorus 86-87; Music.

LEGOWSKI, GREG; Peters Township HS; Venetia, PA; (3); 13/556; Computer Clb; JCL; Latin Clb; Science Clb; High Hon Roll; NHS; Amer Comp Sci League Team 1st Pl 86-87.

LEGOWSKI, KRISTEN; Peters Township HS; Venetia, PA; (2); 6/514; JCL; Latin Clb; Yrbk Stf; High Hon Roll; Hon Roll; Law.

LEGRAND, RON; Cambria Heights SR HS; Hastings, PA; (3); Red Cross Aide; ROTC; Capt Var Swmmng; Hon Roll; VFW Awd; CC Of The Air Force.

LEGUTKO, ROBERT; Mahanoy Area HS; Mahanoy City, PA; (4); 10/110; Pres Band; Sec Chorus; Nwsp Ed-Chief; Var L Bsbl; Var L Crs Cntry; JP Sousa Awd; NHS; Im Bsktbl; Hon Roll; Pres Schlr; Elks Teenager Of Month 87; Schuylkill Cnty Div II Bsbl All Star 87; PA Dist 10 Band 87; Bloomburg U; Liberal Arts.

LEHENY, JULIE; St Francis Acad; Pittsburgh, PA; (3); Church Yth Grp; Drama Clb; VP SADD; Chorus; School Play; Nwsp Stf; Yrbk Phtg; Rep Jr Cls; NHS; Voice Dem Awd.

LEHET, MICHAEL; Benton Area JR SR HS; Benton, PA; (4); 16/49; Pres Drama Clb; Key Clb; Band; Pres Chorus; School Musical; School Play; DAR Awd; Hon Roll; NHS; Pres Art Clb; Dist Chorus; Reg Chorus; Natl Schl Choral Awd; Penn ST U; Elec Engr Tech.

LEHETT, AMY; West Middlesex HS; West Middlesex, PA; (4); 13/96; French Clb; Library Aide; Pep Clb; Drm Mjr(t); Nwsp Rptr; Yrbk Ed-Chief; Hon Roll; Jr NHS; Prfct Atten Awd; Natl Sci Merit Awd 86; Elem Ed.

LEHIGH, MITCH; Hanover SR HS; Hanover, PA; (3); 11/126; Varsity Clb; School Play; Yrbk Stf; Var L Bsbl; Var L Bsktbl; Coach Actv; Var L Ftbl; High Hon Roll; NHS; Mech Engr.

LEHMAN, CHRISTINE; Central York SR HS; Emigsville, PA; (4); Art Clb; Hon Roll; Ntl Art Hnr Soc 87; Secrtrl.

LEHMAN, CINDY; Shikellamy HS; Sunbury, PA; (4); German Clb; Var Fld Hcky; Var Capt Sftbl; Hon Roll; Jr NHS; NHS; Prfct Atten Awd; Pres Schlr; German Hnr Soc 87; Stu Athlt Awd 87; MD U; Phrmcy.

LEHMAN, CRISTI; East Pennsboro Area HS; Enola, PA; (3); Art Clb; Drama Clb; Latin Clb; School Play; Stage Crew; Nwsp Stf; Yrbk Stf; Hon Roll; Ntl Merit SF; Cert Merit Art 86; Cazenovia; Art.

LEHMAN, DAVID; Cheltenham HS; Cheltenham, PA; (4); Boy Scts; Church Yth Grp; Cmnty Wkr; Nwsp Rptr; Yrbk Phtg; Stu Cncl; Crs Cntry; Trk; Temple U; Cmmnctns.

LEHMAN, DAWN; Indiana Area HS; Indiana, PA; (3); 14/330; Church Yth Grp; Red Cross Aide; Acpl Chr; Church Choir; Concert Band; Mrchg Band; Orch; Jr NHS; NEDT Awd.

LEHMAN, DIANN; Greencastle Antrim HS; Greencastle, PA; (3); Church Yth Grp; Library Aide; Chorus; Yrbk Stf; Hon Roll; Hagerstown Bus Schl; Legal Sec.

LEHMAN, JOHN; Southmoreland HS; Scottdale, PA; (3); Drama Clb; Exploring; German Clb; Letterman Clb; School Play; Nwsp Phtg; Nwsp Stf; Yrbk Phtg; Golf; Grmn Natl Hnr Socty 86; Jrnlsm.

LEHMAN, JULIE; Elizabethtown Area HS; Elizabethtown, PA; (3); 5/230; Church Yth Grp; Band; Chorus; Concert Band; Drm Mjr(t); Mrchg Band; Orch; School Musical; High Hon Roll; NHS; Adolescent Psych.

LEHMAN, LORETTA; Mt Pleasant Area HS; Mt Pleasant, PA; (4); 13/250; Office Aide; Concert Band; Mrchg Band; Trk; CC Awd; High Hon Roll; NHS; Prfct Atten Awd; Yrbk Layout Editor 87; Bradford Schl.

LEHMAN, MELANIE M; Nativity B U M HS; Ravine, PA; (4); 5/93; French Clb; Hosp Aide; Science Clb; Flag Corp; Rep Stu Cncl; Bsktbl; High Hon Roll; Hon Roll; NHS; Pres Schlr; Hnrbl Mtn Cptl Area SCI Engr 84-85; US Natl Math Awd 86-87; Acad All Armcn Awd 86-87; Beaver Coll; Physcl Thrpst.

LEHMAN, ROBERT; Hempfield Area HS; Greensburg, PA; (3); Computer Clb; Spanish Clb; Var Bsktbl; Var L Ftbl; Var L Trk; Im Wt Lftg; High Hon Roll; Hon Roll; Jr NHS; NHS; Med.

LEHMAN, SAMANTHA; Mechanicsburg Area SR HS; Mechanicsburg, PA; (3); 19/338; SADD; Band; Chorus; Concert Band; Mrchg Band; School Play; Symp Band; Yrbk Stf; Stu Cncl; Hon Roll; Hstry.

LEHMAN, SANDY; Shikellamy HS; Sunbury, PA; (4); German Clb; Var Capt Fld Hcky; Sftbl; High Hon Roll; Hon Roll; Jr NHS; Prfct Atten Awd; Ams B Myr Schlrshp 87; U Of PA Bloomsburg; Psychlgy.

LEHMAN, SHIRLEY; Central SR HS; York, PA; (2); Church Yth Grp; Hosp Aide; Spanish Clb; SADD; Church Choir; High Hon Roll; Hon Roll; Acadmc Ltr Awd 86-87.

LEHMAN, STEPHANIE; Chambersburg SR HS; Chambersburg, PA; (3); Art Clb; Church Yth Grp; Spanish Clb; JV Cheerleading; Hon Roll; Shippensburg U; Elem Ed.

LEHMAN, STEVEN; Garden Spot HS; New Holland, PA; (3); 50/200; Church Yth Grp; School Play; Var Bsbl; JV Bsktbl; Im Ice Hcky; Var Socr; JV Wrstlng.

LEHMAN, TODD; Red Lion Area SR HS; Red Lion, PA; (3); 131/342; Boy Scts; Church Yth Grp; Varsity Clb; Church Choir; Sftbl; Trk; Hon Roll; Prfct Atten Awd; PA ST Ufelec Engrng.

LEHMANN, CHRISTOPHER; Pennsbury HS; Yardley, PA; (2); Political Wkr; SADD; Chorus; School Musical; School Play; Nwsp Ed-Chief; Nwsp Rptr; Yrbk Phtg; Yrbk Stf; Rep Frsh Cls; Awd Cert Of Mert Stu Cncl 87; Awd Cert Of Merit Newspaper 87; Columbia; Englsh.

LEHMANN, MICHAEL; Emmaus HS; Wescosville, PA; (2); Key Clb; Var Capt Bsbl; JV Bsktbl; Hon Roll; Jr NHS; NHS; Bus.

LEHMANN, RICHARD; Northeast Catholic HS; Philadelphia, PA; (3); 74/332; FCA; JV Crs Cntry; JV Trk; Hon Roll; Ntl Merit Ltr; Vrsty Crew Tm 85-87.

LEHN, KRISTEN E; Cedar Crest HS; Lebanon, PA; (4); JA; Key Clb; Pep Clb; Nwsp Sprt Ed; Sftbl; Tennis; Vllybl; Hon Roll; NHS; Hnr Rl 87; U Of DE; Intl Rltns.

LEHNER, AMY; Elizabeth Forward HS; Mckeesport, PA; (3); 1/345; French Clb; GAA; Latin Clb; Temple Yth Grp; Rep Jr Cls; Capt Var Bsktbl; High Hon Roll; NHS; All ST Hnrbl Mntn, All Sctn Bsktbl 86-87; Pre Med.

LEHNERT, JENNIFER L; Bishop Hoban HS; Mt Top, PA; (1); 5/219; Cmnty Wkr; FBLA; Math Clb; Mu Alpha Theta; Var L Diving; High Hon Roll; Mu Alpha Theta Awd; NEDT Awd; Phrmcy.

LEHNERT, RICHARD; M M I Preparatory Schl; Mountaintop, PA; (3); 3/39; Trs Aud/Vis; Debate Tm; Math Tm; NHS; Ntl Merit SF; NEDT Awd; Pres Schlr; Vllybl; German Natl Hnr Soc, PA Jr Acad Of Sci 1st Pl, Math Competition 5th Pl Luzerne Cnty 87; Bio Sci.

LEHR, DEBRA; Northampton Area SR HS; Treichlers, PA; (4); 30/436; Sec Soph Cls; Sec Jr Cls; Sec Sr Cls; Stu Cncl; Var Capt Cheerleading; Var Trk; DAR Awd; High Hon Roll; Hon Roll; NHS; Girl Of Mnth 86.

LEHR, LISA; Central SR HS; York, PA; (2); Art Clb; Varsity Clb; School Musical; Var Capt Cheerleading; High Hon Roll; Hon Roll; Performing Arts.

LEHR, MATTHEW; Solanco HS; Kirkwood, PA; (3); Aud/Vis; Chess Clb; Computer Clb; Science Clb; Spanish Clb; Lit Mag; Hon Roll; Prfct Atten Awd; Lbrl Arts.

LEHRER, DANA C; Moravian Acad; Allentown, PA; (3); 3/61; Chess Clb; Cmnty Wkr; Ski Clb; Trs Temple Yth Grp; Yrbk Stf; JV Tennis; High Hon Roll; Hon Roll; Arch.

LEHTO, ANN; W Middlesex HS; New Wilmington, PA; (3); 3/108; 4-H; Band; Chorus; Concert Band; Mrchg Band; Stu Cncl; Cheerleading; 4-H Awd; Jr NHS; NHS; Pres Acad Ftnss Awd 85; Engnr.

LEIB, JESSICA; West Hazleton HS; Sugarloaf, PA; (2); Church Yth Grp; Hosp Aide; Ski Clb; Spanish Clb; Cheerleading; Gym; Tennis; Radiolgy.

LEIB, MIKE; Boiling Springs HS; Mt Holly Spgs, PA; (3); Band; Concert Band; Jazz Band; Mrchg Band; Orch; Pep Band; School Play; Symp Band; Nwsp Stf; Score Keeper; Music Ed.

LEIBACH, KIM; Vincentian HS; Pittsburgh, PA; (3); JA; Red Cross Aide; Science Clb; Teachers Aide; Band; Chorus; Nwsp Rptr; Nwsp Stf; Hon Roll; Prfct Atten Awd; PA JR Acad Sci 1st Awds 85-8l.

LEIBMAN, KAREN; James M Coughlin HS; Wilkes Barre, PA; (4); 1/324; Church Yth Grp; Nwsp Ed-Chief; Nwsp Rptr; Bsktbl; Capt Vllybl; Cit Awd; High Hon Roll; Jr NHS; NHS; Val; Dist Ii PIAA Excllnc Awd 87; Pres Acdmc Fit Awd 87; Lycoming Coll; Ed.

LEIBY, KRAIG; Kutztown Area HS; Kutztown, PA; (4); 30/150; Boy Scts; Chorus; Drm Mjr(t); Jazz Band; Swing Chorus; Variety Show; God Cntry Awd; High Hon Roll; NHS; Church Yth Grp; Eagle Sct 85; Phys Thrpy.

LEICHNER, KAREN; Lansdale Catholic HS; North Wales, PA; (3); Yrbk Stf; 2nd Hnrs 84-87.

LEICHT, DOUGLAS; Northwestern HS; Albion, PA; (4); 12/163; Varsity Clb; Capt Bsktbl; Capt Ftbl; CC Awd; Hon Roll; Albion Clnc Fndtn Schlrshp 87; Penna ST U; Engrng.

LEID, WM TROY; Cocalico HS; Reinholds, PA; (3); 33/160; Capt Ftbl; L Trk; High Hon Roll.

LEIDICH, DAWN; Wilson Area HS; Easton, PA; (3); 22/160; Debate Tm; Drama Clb; NFL; Speech Tm; SADD; School Musical; School Play; Stage Crew; NHS; Opt Clb Awd; Miss TEEN Pagnt Miss Congnlty 86; Secdry Engl Ed.

LEIDIG, JEFFREY; Chambersburg Area SR HS; Chambersburg, PA; (2); 38/734; Church Yth Grp; German Clb; Band; Chorus; Jazz Band; Mrchg Band; Bsktbl; Jr Indp Merch Mnth 86; Bus Admin.

LEIDING, JENNIFER; Johnsonburg Area HS; Johnsonburg, PA; (4); Hon Roll; Ntl Merit Ltr; Nrsng.

LEIDY, JILL; Conemaugh Valley HS; Conemaugh, PA; (3); 14/105; NFL; Pep Clb; Ski Clb; Band; Nwsp Rptr; Yrbk Stf; Stat Bsktbl; Hon Roll; NHS; Prfct Atten Awd; Hmmkr Of Yr 85; Penn ST; CPA.

LEIDY, MARK; Everett Area HS; Breezewood, PA; (3); Varsity Clb; Pres Frsh Cls; Pres Jr Cls; Stu Cncl; Var L Bsbl; Var Ftbl; Hon Roll; Spanish NHS; Computer Clb; Acdmc All AM 86.

LEIDY, PAMELA; Mount Union Area HS; Shirleysburg, PA; (4); 42/172; Church Yth Grp; FBLA; GAA; Band; Concert Band; Mrchg Band; Sftbl; Hon Roll; Typng I Awd 84-85; Typng II Awd 85-86; Cnty Band 86-87; Empire Beauty Schl; Csmtlgy.

LEIGH, ALESIA C; Forest Hills HS; Summerhill, PA; (3); 1/158; Am Leg Aux Girls St; NFL; Ski Clb; Chorus; Swing Chorus; Nwsp Ed-Chief; Vllybl; NHS; Spanish NHS; Val; Penn ST U; Obstrcn.

LEIGH, ANGELA; Shikellamy HS; Northumberland, PA; (3); 4/315; Church Yth Grp; Key Clb; Library Aide; NFL; Chorus; School Musical; French Hon Soc; Hon Roll; NHS; Qtr Fnlst Cthlc Frncsc Lg Ntl Trnmnt 87; Med.

LEIGH, SPENCER; Shikellamy HS; Northumberland, PA; (4); Boy Scts; Church Yth Grp; Library Aide; Red Cross Aide; Acpl Chr; Chorus; Church Choir; High Hon Roll; Pres Acad Ftnss Awd 86-87; Eagle Scout 87; Brigham Young U; Micro Bio.

LEIGHT, DEBORAH; Eastern York HS; Windsor, PA; (3); 12/177; Church Yth Grp; SADD; Chorus; Church Choir; Color Guard; School Musical; Swing Chorus; High Hon Roll; Rotary Awd; Jr NHS; Rotary Ldrs Conf 87; Music.

LEIGHTHARDT, JOSEPH; Archbishop Ryan HS For Boys; Philadelphia, PA; (4); 100/485; Pres Cmnty Wkr; Pres Exploring; Hosp Aide; JA; Political Wkr; Pres Service Clb; Nwsp Stf; Cit Awd; Secret Svc Law Enfrcmnt Asstnc Awd 87; St Francis Peace Awd 87; Chapel Of 4 Chaplains Awd 86; La Salle; Law Enfrcmnt.

LEIGHTON, MELISSA; Owen J Roberts HS; Pottstown, PA; (3); 26/299; Letterman Clb; Service Clb; Rep Frsh Cls; JV Lcrss; Var Capt Tennis; Hon Roll.

LEIGHTY, SUSAN; Jefferson-Morgan HS; Jefferson, PA; (1); 4/109; Sec Trs Church Yth Grp; Library Aide; Office Aide; High Hon Roll; Rotary Awd; Intl Frgn Lang Awd 86 & 87; Penn St; Math.

LEIK, DOUGLAS; Central York SR HS; York, PA; (3); 15/248; High Hon Roll; Hon Roll; 1 Wk Schlrshp PA Free Enterprise Wk Lock Haven 87.

LEINBACH, JEFFREY; Biglerville HS; Biglerville, PA; (3); 10/97; Boy Scts; Drama Clb; Varsity Clb; School Play; Hon Roll; Jr NHS; Aud/Vis; Chorus; Tennis; Wrstlng; Clss Pres 86-87; Clss VP 87-88; Athltc Trnr, Eagl Sct Awd 84-88; Thtrcl Arts.

LEININGER, BETH; Warwick HS; Lititz, PA; (3); 10/270; Church Yth Grp; 4-H; Acpl Chr; Chorus; VP Mrchg Band; Orch; School Musical; Symp Band; NHS; Schlr Awd Music Band 87; Math.

LEIPHART, FRANCINE S; Red Lion Area HS; Red Lion, PA; (4); 6/330; Church Yth Grp; SADD; School Musical; School Play; Nwsp Rptr; Ed Nwsp Stf; High Hon Roll; NHS; Ntl Merit SF; Prfct Atten Awd; American U; Eng.

LEIS, ERIC; Canon Mc Millan HS; Canonsburg, PA; (3); 44/349; Chess Clb; Var Cheerleading; Var L Ftbl; Var Wt Lftg; Hon Roll; Sci.

LEISENRING, THERESA; William Penn SR HS; York, PA; (3); Aud/Vis; Girl Scts; JA; Office Aide; PAVAS; Chorus; Church Choir; School Play; PTSA Lit Awd 86-87; Drma.

LEISTER, BRENDA; Hanover SR HS; Hanover, PA; (3); 17/126; Church Yth Grp; Band; Chorus; Concert Band; Mrchg Band; Stage Crew; Swing Chorus; Lit Mag; Hon Roll; NEDT Awd.

LEISTER, DAWN; Eastern York JR-SR HS; York, PA; (3); VP Church Yth Grp; Pres 4-H; Girl Scts; SADD; Chorus; Church Choir; School Musical; Var Mgr(s); Stat Vllybl; 4-H Awd; Slvr & Gld Ldrshp Awds Grl Sctng 85-87; Med.

LEISTER, JENNIFER; St Pius X HS; Gilbertsville, PA; (1); 8/148; Cmnty Wkr; Yrbk Stf; JV Cheerleading; High Hon Roll; Hon Roll; Astronomy.

LEISTER, MONICA; Avonworth JR/Sr HS; Sewickley, PA; (3); Am Leg Aux Girls St; Church Yth Grp; JA; Spanish Clb; Hon Roll; Law.

LEISTER, PAMELA L; Boyertown JR High East Center; Gilbertsville, PA; (1); Art Clb; Aud/Vis; Church Yth Grp; French Clb; Church Choir; Color Guard; Stage Crew; High Hon Roll; Hon Roll; Bus Admin.

LEISTER, WENDY; Eastern York HS; E Prospect, PA; (2); Sec Church Yth Grp; Sec 4-H; Chorus; Nwsp Rptr; Nwsp Sprt Ed; Rep Stu Cncl; JV Cheerleading; L Gym; L Var Sftbl; Chrldng 85-87; Stu Cncl 86; Sftbl 87; Int Dsgnr.

LEISTNER, BILLIE JO; Connellsville Area HS; Connellsville, PA; (3); 223/500; Yrbk Phtg; Yrbk Stf; Prfct Atten Awd; Child Care & Devel.

LEISURE, LONDON; Pottstown SR HS; Pottstown, PA; (3); 75/155; Church Yth Grp; Latin Clb; Var Bsktbl; Elks Awd; Banking.

LEITZEL, DOUG; Mifflinburg HS; Mifflinburg, PA; (2); VP Church Yth Grp; French Clb; JV Bsktbl; Var JV Ftbl; Hon Roll.

LEITZEL, HEATHER; Upper Dauphin Area HS; Elizabethville, PA; (3); Church Yth Grp; Hosp Aide; Varsity Clb; Band; Chorus; Drm Mjr(t); Mrchg Band; School Musical; Stage Crew; Yrbk Phtg; Psych.

LEITZEL, TONIA; Millersburg Area HS; Millersburg, PA; (4); Ski Clb; Spanish Clb; Church Choir; Yrbk Stf; Bowling; Co-Capt Cheerleading; Mgr(s); Trk; Hon Roll; Pres Schlr; Enrchmnt Pgm 84-86; Shippensburg U; Mktg.

LELII, KIM; Upper Darby HS; Drexel Hill, PA; (3); Cmnty Wkr; Hosp Aide; Office Aide; Teachers Aide; Varsity Clb; Rep Frsh Cls; Rep Soph Cls; Rep Jr Cls; Rep Stu Cncl; Var Capt Trk; Temple U; Scl Wrk.

LEMANSKY, RAY; Tri Valley HS; Uniontown, PA; (3); Bausch & Lomb Sci Awd; Hon Roll; NHS; Engrng.

LEMKE, ERIKA L; Norwin SR HS; North Huntingdon, PA; (3); 164/571; Am Leg Aux Girls St; French Clb; Office Aide; Pep Clb; Sec Rep SADD; Concert Band; Mrchg Band; Nwsp Stf; Jr NHS; SADD Ofcrs Awd 86-87; Cert Of Achvt Keystone Girls ST 87; Music.

LEMLEY, SANDRA; Waynesburg Central HS; Waynesburg, PA; (3); Drama Clb; French Clb; Hosp Aide; Natl Beta Clb; Ski Clb; Chorus; Yrbk Stf.

LEMMERT, MICHILLE; Southern Fulton HS; Wardfordsburg, PA; (4); 17/70; Church Yth Grp; VP FBLA; FHA; Spanish Clb; VP Band; Chorus; Concert Band; Jazz Band; Mrchg Band; School Play; Hgrstwn Bus Admin Schlrshp 87-88; Hagerstown Bus Coll; Accntng.

LEMOCK, KELLI; Fort Le Boeuf HS; Waterford, PA; (3); Art Clb; Drama Clb; Ski Clb; Thesps; Chorus; School Musical; Stage Crew; Score Keeper; Stat Vllybl; Hon Roll; Awd For Set Dsgn Schl Musical 87; Interior Dsgn.

LEMON, CINDY LYNN; Rochester Area HS; Rochester, PA; (4); Q&S; Service Clb; Stage Crew; Nwsp Rptr; Nwsp Stf; Yrbk Stf; Co-Capt Cheerleading; Powder Puff Ftbl; Trk; NHS; Pres Acdmc Fit All Str 87; Flgt Attndt.

LEMON, SUSAN; Quakertown SR HS; Pennsburg, PA; (2); French Clb; Stage Crew; JV Tennis; Timer; Vllybl; High Hon Roll; Hon Roll; Jr NHS; NHS; Pres Acad Fit Awd 86; PA ST U; Sci.

LENCHAK, EMIL; William Allen HS; Allentown, PA; (2); 10/634; JA; JCL; Latin Clb; Im Bowling; High Hon Roll; Hon Roll; JETS Awd; Natl Lat Hnr Soc 87; Lat ST Cnvtn 87; Gld Mdl Natl Lat Exm 87; Engrng.

LENGEL, EDWARD; Lackawanna Trail HS; Nicholson, PA; (3); 2/109; CAP; Yrbk Ed-Chief; VP Jr Cls; Ftbl; Wt Lftg; High Hon Roll; NHS; Air Force; Appld Physcs.

LENGEL, EDWARD; Tulpehocken HS; Bernville, PA; (2); Boy Scts; JA; Quiz Bowl; Nwsp Rptr; Hon Roll; Air Force; Aerospace Engr.

LENGEL, THOMAS; Lackawanna Trail HS; Nicholson, PA; (4); Ski Clb; VP Jr Cls; L Ftbl; Wt Lftg; Wrstlng; Hon Roll; Stu Mnth 87; SR Pullup Rcd 87; East Stroundsburg U; Tchr.

LENGYEL, JEFF; Bethel Park HS; Bethel Park, PA; (4); Acadc Awd 86-87; Spd Rlng Sktng 83-86; WV U; Engr.

LENGYEL, VALERIE; Hopewell HS; Aliquippa, PA; (4); Exploring; Latin Clb; Sec Pres Science Clb; Chorus; Yrbk Stf; High Hon Roll; L F Blaney Cnsrvtn Awd 87; Cnty Enrivo-Lympics Tm 85 & 87; U Of Pittsburgh; Pre-Med.

LENHARD, BRIAN; Episcopal Acad; Villanova, PA; (4); Science Clb; Spanish Clb; Yrbk Phtg; JV Crs Cntry; JV Wrstlng; Hon Roll; Ntl Merit SF; Cum Laude 86; Aerontcl Law.

LENHARDT, RICHARD; Conneaut Valley HS; Conneautville, PA; (3); Boy Scts; Church Yth Grp; FFA; German Clb; Pep Clb; Spanish Clb; SADD; Varsity Clb; VICA; Bsbl; Crmnl Jstc.

LENHART, JENNIFER; Bishop Guilfoyle HS; Altoona, PA; (3); Church Yth Grp; Hosp Aide; Red Cross Aide; SADD; Var Twrlr; Penn ST U; Bus.

LENHART, NATALIE; Brandywine Heights Area HS; Mertztown, PA; (2); 6/164; Lib Band; Lib Chorus; Lib Jazz Band; School Play; High Hon Roll; NHS; Dist & Rgnl Band 86 & 87; Pre Med.

LENKER, JESSICA; Williams Valley JR SR HS; Wiconisco, PA; (1); Girl Scts; Office Aide; Pep Clb; Spanish Clb; Teachers Aide; Chorus; Mrchg Band; Twrlr; High Hon Roll; Hon Roll; Penn ST U; Sci.

LENN, MARIE; Union Area HS; New Castle, PA; (2); 17/268; FBLA; Latin Clb; SADD; Band; Concert Band; Mrchg Band; Pep Band; Nwsp Rptr; Trk; Hon Roll.

LENNON, AMY; Villa Maria Acad; Exton, PA; (3); 32/98; SADD; School Musical; Yrbk Stf; Lit Mag; Rep Frsh Cls; Sec Soph Cls; Rep Jr Cls; Pres Sr Cls; Rep Stu Cncl; Im Fld Hcky; Vet Med.

LENNON, JOHN; Hazleton SR HS; Beaver Meadows, PA; (3); 14/445; Pres English Clb; Capt Quiz Bowl; Capt Scholastic Bowl; Pres Science Clb; Band; Mrchg Band; Sec Sr Cls; Var Powder Puff Ftbl; Btty Crckr Awd; French Hon Soc; Carbon Cnty Strwbry Flds Awd 80; PA ST U; Lib Arts.

LENOX, MICHAEL; Pennsbury HS; Morrisville, PA; (2); Church Yth Grp; Band; Concert Band; Jazz Band; Mrchg Band; Bsktbl; Trk; High Hon Roll; Hon Roll; Engnrng.

LENTINI, ROBERT M; Holy Ghost Preparatory Schl; Philadelphia, PA; (4); Exploring; Math Clb; Math Tm; Var Trk; Hon Roll; NHS; Ntl Merit SF; Math.

LENTINI, RUSSELL; Our Lady Of Lourdes Regional HS; Kulpmont, PA; (2); 19/92; Boy Scts; Key Clb; Leo Clb; Rep Frsh Cls; Stat Im Bsktbl; Im Vllybl; Stat Wrstlng; Millersville U; Comp Sci.

LENTZ, BARRY; Shamokin Area HS; Gowen City, PA; (4); German Clb; Science Clb; Stage Crew; Golf; Wrstlng; Lycoming Coll; Mass Commcntns.

LENTZ, BRIAN; Moon SR HS; Coraopolis, PA; (3); 6/319; Church Yth Grp; Church Choir; Concert Band; Mrchg Band; Symp Band; Im Bsktbl; Capt Socr; High Hon Roll; Hon Roll; NHS.

LENTZ, KRISTINA; Pocono Mountain HS; Reeders, PA; (3); Hosp Aide; Band; Concert Band; Mrchg Band; Hon Roll; Drama Clb; 4-H; German Clb; Stage Crew; Occptnl Thrpy.

LENTZ, NATHAN; Northern York County HS; Rossville, PA; (3); 30/250; Art Clb; Debate Tm; Yrbk Stf; Score Keeper; Socr; French Hon Soc; Hon Roll; Ntl Merit SF; Schlstc Art Awds 87; Pratt Inst; Art.

LENTZ, VICKI; Millersburg Area HS; Millersburg, PA; (3); 5/72; Spanish Clb; Yrbk Bus Mgr; Yrbk Stf; Rep Stu Cncl; Var Bsktbl; Var Cheerleading; Var Trk; High Hon Roll; NHS; Engr.

LENTZ, WILLIAM K; Penn-Trafford HS; Irwin, PA; (3); Drama Clb; FBLA; Band; Chorus; Concert Band; Mrchg Band; Hon Roll; Prfct Atten Awd; Phrmcst.

LENZ, MARY; Indiana SR HS; Indiana, PA; (3); Church Yth Grp; Dance Clb; Drm Mjr(t); School Musical; School Play; Im Socr; Gov Hon Prg Awd; High Hon Roll; Jr NHS; NCTE Awd; Drama Awd 85; Twrlg Achvt Awds 85-86.

LENZ, PATRICK K; Penn Cambria SR HS; Gallitzin, PA; (3); Drama Clb; Band; Chorus; Concert Band; Mrchg Band; Hon Roll; Physcn.

LENZE, GRETCHEN; Elk County Christian HS; St Marys, PA; (3); 5/75; Ski Clb; Varsity Clb; Band; Church Choir; Concert Band; Jazz Band; Mrchg Band; Rep Stu Cncl; Var L Tennis; Hon Roll; Ed.

LENZI, STEVEN; Monongalela Valley Catholic HS; Monongahela, PA; (3); 13/100; Spanish Clb; Var Bsbl; JV Ftbl; High Hon Roll; Spanish NHS.

LEO, DARCY; Hickory HS; Hermitage, PA; (2); Latin Clb; Band; Chorus; Mrchg Band; Orch; Pep Band; Score Keeper; Stat Trk; Twrlr; Ltn Hnr Soc 84-87; Hmrm Pres 86-87; IN U Park; Bus.

LEO, MONICA; William Allen HS; Allentown, PA; (2); Church Yth Grp; JA; Leo Clb; SADD; Hon Roll; SADD 86-87; JA 85-87; Leo Club 86-87; Psych.

LEON, JEANETTE; Notre Dame HS; Nazareth, PA; (3); Hosp Aide; Nwsp Rptr; Nwsp Stf; JV Tennis; High Hon Roll; Hon Roll; Prfct Atten Awd; Drama Clb; Chorus; Yrbk Stf; Hugh Obrien St Ldrshp Smnr 86; PA JR Acad Of Sci 2nd Pl Rgnl 86; Temple U Press Trnmnt 3rd Pl 87; Med.

LEON, SANDRA; Northern HS; Dillsburg, PA; (3); 59/232; Drama Clb; 4-H; Temple Yth Grp; Drill Tm; Stage Crew; Twrlr; Hon Roll; Bus.

LEONARD, BRENDA; Hazleton HS; Hazleton, PA; (2); Leo Clb; Spanish Clb; Chorus; Nwsp Rptr; JV Cheerleading; Stat Trk.

LEONARD, CHRIS; Blairsville HS; Blairsville, PA; (4); 17/131; Varsity Clb; Bsktbl; Bowling; Crs Cntry; Sftbl; Trk; High Hon Roll; Hon Roll; NHS; Rotary Awd-Track, ST Track Meet & Acdmc All Amer 87; U Of Pittsburgh; Physcl Thrpy.

LEONARD, CHRISTIAN; Southmoreland SR HS; Scottdale, PA; (3); French Clb; Math Clb; Nwsp Stf; Lit Mag; French Hon Soc; NHS; Ntl Merit Ltr.

LEONARD, DEBORAH; Du Bois Area HS; Grampian, PA; (4); 36/274; Pres Church Yth Grp; Office Aide; Chorus; Var Sftbl; High Hon Roll; Hon Roll; NHS; Ntl Merit Ltr; Pres Schlr; Oral Roberts U; Pre-Med.

LEONARD, ELAINE; Hazleton HS; Hazleton, PA; (3); Leo Clb; Chorus; Nwsp Rptr; Var Capt Cheerleading; L Crs Cntry; L Trk; Hon Roll; Nrs.

LEONARD, HEATHER; Donegal HS; Marietta, PA; (3); Church Yth Grp; Band; Concert Band; Mrchg Band; Orch; Symp Band; Capt Cheerleading; Mgr(s); Powder Puff Ftbl; Bus.

LEONARD, HEATHER; North Star HS; Boswell, PA; (2); #37 In Class; FCA; SADD; Yrbk Stf; Sec Jr Cls; Var L Bsktbl; Var L Sftbl; Wt Lftg; Cit Awd; Hon Roll; Prfct Atten Awd.

LEONARD, JAMIE; Brownsville Area HS; Brownsville, PA; (4); 7/225; Trs Church Yth Grp; Drama Clb; Math Clb; SADD; Band; Church Choir; Mrchg Band; Variety Show; Nwsp Stf; Yrbk Stf; Bus.

LEONARD, JENNIFER; Penn-Trafford HS; Jeannette, PA; (3); AFS; Hosp Aide; JCL; Latin Clb; SADD; Chorus; Chld Psych.

LEONARD, JODY; Upper Merion Area HS; King Of Prussia, PA; (4); Church Yth Grp; Cmnty Wkr; German Clb; Im Ftbl; Lcrss; Swmmng; Trk; Gov Hon Prg Awd; High Hon Roll; Hon Roll; Pres Acad Ftns Awd 87; Lehigh U; Bus.

LEONARD, LORI; Bishop Mc Devitt HS; Harrisburg, PA; (3); 93/216; Cmnty Wkr; Drama Clb; Exploring; VP FBLA; Ski Clb; School Play; Rep Soph Cls; Tennis; Dance Clb; Service Clb; Qn Dphn Cnty Frmns Conv 85-86; Hsptlty Cmte-St Cthrn Lbr Prsh 85-87; Cmte Serv-Wrkng Fstvls 85-87; Psychlgy.

LEONARD, LUCINDA; Tidioute HS; Warren, PA; (4); 2/23; Debate Tm; Pres SADD; Varsity Clb; Stat Var Bsktbl; JV Stat Vllybl; Cit Awd; Trs NHS; Sal; Cmnty Wkr; Yrbk Stf; Engl Awd 87; Penn-New York Sect Amer Chem Soc Awd 87; Warren Cnty Hstrcl Soc Awd 87; Clarion U Of PA; Spec Educ.

LEONARD, MARIA; Blacklick Valley HS; Nanty Glo, PA; (4); Church Yth Grp; Ski Clb; Varsity Clb; Pres Jr Cls; Pres Sr Cls; Sec Stu Cncl; Capt Cheerleading; Swmmng; Hon Roll; NHS; Busi.

LEONARD, MARSHA; Penncrest HS; Media, PA; (3); 76/344; Church Yth Grp; Chorus; Drill Tm; Flag Corp; Mrchg Band; Variety Show; Yrbk Phtg; Stat Bsktbl; Lcrss; Hon Roll; Mrn Bio.

LEONARD, PHILIP; Abington HS; Rockledge, PA; (4); 40/442; Church Yth Grp; Cmnty Wkr; Computer Clb; Varsity Clb; Rep Sr Cls; Rep Stu Cncl; Var Trk; Im Vllybl; Var Wt Lftg; Var Capt Wrstlng; Lehigh U; Mech Engrng.

LEONARD, SUSAN; Chichester SR HS; Boothwyn, PA; (3); 11/297; Am Leg Aux Girls St; Nwsp Phtg; Ed Nwsp Stf; Yrbk Phtg; Yrbk Stf; Var L Fld Hcky; Var L Sftbl; High Hon Roll; Hon Roll; NHS.

LEONARD, TINA; Southmoreland SR HS; Ruffsdale, PA; (2); Band; Chorus; Concert Band; Jazz Band; Mrchg Band; Monsour Medical Ctr; Radlgy.

LEONE, CHRISTOPHER; Western Wayne HS; Moscow, PA; (3); Var Bsbl; Hon Roll; Arch.

LEONE, KRISTEN; Nativity BVM HS; New Philadelphia, PA; (2); 28/77; Art Clb; Spanish Clb; Sftbl; Hon Roll; Mst Dedctd Sftbl Plyr 87; Vrsty Ltr Sftbl 87.

LEONE, NICOLE; Bensalem HS; Bensalem, PA; (2); JV Socr; JV Var Tennis; High Hon Roll; NHS; Arch.

LEONE, TINA; Tunkhannock HS; Mehoopany, PA; (2); German Clb; Key Clb; Chorus; Concert Band; Drm Mjr(t); Jazz Band; Mrchg Band; JV Trk; Cit Awd; JA; Maywood Coll JR Hnr Band 85.

LEONG, GEORGE; Baldwin HS; Pittsburgh, PA; (3); Rep Soph Cls; Rep Jr Cls; Im Ftbl; Mchnc.

LEONHARDT, CHERYL; St Pius X HS; Pottstown, PA; (4); Art Clb; Cmnty Wkr; Hosp Aide; Service Clb; SADD; Varsity Clb; Stu Cncl; Fld Hcky; Score Keeper; Hon Roll; Amer Yth Fndtn I Dare You Awd/Ldrshp Awd 87; Admin Awd 87; Fr Leo Ltrhs K Of C Awd 87; U Of Scranton; Psych.

LEONOVICH, KAREN; Southern Columbia Area HS; Elysburg, PA; (4); 12/78; VP Jazz Band; VP Mrchg Band; VP Pep Band; Stu Cncl; Elks Awd; High Hon Roll; Hon Roll; NHS; Pres Schlr; Voice Dem Awd; Bloomsburg U; Psych.

LEONOWICZ, BEVERLY; Bishop Conwell HS; Bensalem, PA; (3); 56/279; Drama Clb; Office Aide; Chorus; Madrigals; Nwsp Stf; Var Socr; JV Swmmng; St Joseph U Dioceson Choral Fstvl Awd 85; Cert In French 86; Cert In Chorus 87; Psych.

LEOPOLD, BETH; Altoona Area HS; Altoona, PA; (3); Drama Clb; FTA; Key Clb; Math Tm; Spanish Clb; Speech Tm; SADD; VP Temple Yth Grp; Chorus; Nwsp Rptr; Tchng.

LEPERA, SHANNON; Norristown Area HS; Norristown, PA; (3); 60/491; Church Yth Grp; DECA; FCA; Rep Frsh Cls; Hon Roll; Hnr Soc 86-87; Messiah Coll; Elem Educ.

LEPLEY, MICHAEL A; West Snyder HS; Beaver Spgs, PA; (4); 7/92; Church Yth Grp; Computer Clb; Varsity Clb; Var Bsbl; Im Vllybl; Hon Roll; NHS; Var Capt Socr; Var Capt Wrstlng; PA JR Acad Sci 2nd Pl Regnl Comptn 85, 2nd Pl ST 86; 2nd Tm Tri Vly Lg Soccr All Star 85, 1st 86; PA ST U; Astrophyscst.

LEPO, TAIT; Bethlehem Center SR HS; Clarksville, PA; (3); 11/160; Art Clb; Church Yth Grp; Drama Clb; Ski Clb; Spanish Clb; Church Choir; Nwsp Rptr; Nwsp Stf; High Hon Roll; Hon Roll; Prfct Atten 85-87; CA U; Biol.

LEPPERT, KEITH; Chestnut Ridge SR HS; New Paris, PA; (3); 4/150; Concert Band; Mrchg Band; Var L Trk; High Hon Roll; Hon Roll; NHS; Chem I Awd 85-86; Aerospc Engrng.

LEPPERT, MICHELLE; Shade HS; Central City, PA; (3); 3/76; Library Aide; Color Guard; Drill Tm; Mrchg Band; Nwsp Rptr; Yrbk Stf; Hon Roll; NHS; Prfct Atten Awd; Hugh O Brian Yth Fndtn Western PA Ldrshp Semnr Ambssdr 86; Chem.

LEPPERT, TAMMY; Trinity HS; Washington, PA; (4); 21/322; Debate Tm; German Clb; Hosp Aide; Math Clb; Math Tm; Ski Clb; Chorus; Swmmng; High Hon Roll; Mary Noss Schlrshp CA U 87; Trinity H S Alumuni Schlrshp 87; Teachers Educ Schlrshp 87; CA U; Educ.

LEPRE, JENNIFER; Carbondale Area HS; Carbondale, PA; (3); FBLA; Spanish Clb; Crs Cntry; Trk; Hon Roll; Nrsng.

LEPRE, LYNNETTE; Carbondale Area HS; Carbondale, PA; (4); 12/144; FBLA; Ski Clb; Chorus; Yrbk Stf; Var Score Keeper; Sftbl; Twrlr; High Hon Roll; NHS; 1st Pl Talent Search 86.

LEPRE, RENE; Carbondale Area HS; Carbondale, PA; (2); Computer Clb; Ski Clb; Spanish Clb.

LERCH, CHRIS; Gov Mifflin SR HS; Reading, PA; (4); 43/260; Vllybl; Hon Roll; Joe Jackson Memrl Awd & Amateur Athl Union Of US Outstndng Achvt 87; Hnr Roll 85-87; Bus.

LERCH, CHRISTINA ELIZABETH; Interboro HS; Glenolden, PA; (3); Art Clb; Church Yth Grp; Drama Clb; Girl Scts; Latin Clb; Chorus; Mrchg Band; School Play; Stage Crew; Nwsp Stf.

LERCH, JENNIFER; Pen Argyl HS; Nazareth, PA; (4); Ski Clb; Band; Pres Chorus; Concert Band; Jazz Band; Mrchg Band; Lib Orch; Pep Band; Yrbk Stf; Rep Stu Cncl; Concert Band 1st Chair Flute & Sectional Ldr Marching Band 86-87; Elite Singing Grp 85-87; Lock Haven U; Comp Sci.

LERCH, SUZANNE; Middletown Area HS; Middletown, PA; (4); 1/171; FCA; Varsity Clb; Band; Sec Chorus; Concert Band; Mrchg Band; School Musical; Nwsp Rptr; Yrbk Stf; Trs Frsh Cls; Natl Hnr Scty; Elks Natl Fndtn Schlrshp 87; Patriot Nws Co; Jamesway Vldctrn 87; Middletown Alumni Assoc; PA ST U; Pre Vet.

LERNER, HENRY; Susquehanna Township HS; Harrisburg, PA; (4); 32/156; Quiz Bowl; Teachers Aide; Temple Yth Grp; Band; Chorus; Jazz Band; Mrchg Band; School Musical; Hon Roll; Ntl Merit Ltr; Am Lgn Esy Cont 85-86; U Pittsburgh.

LERSCH, DAWN; California Area HS; Coal Center, PA; (4); 13/95; Camera Clb; Church Yth Grp; Drama Clb; Pres 4-H; FNA; Chorus; Church Choir; Nwsp Stf; 4-H Awd; Hon Roll; CA U P A; Bus Mgmt.

LERTZMAN, BROOKE; Bensalem HS; Bensalem, PA; (2); Art Clb; Office Aide; Pres Temple Yth Grp; Stu Cncl; Var Swmmng; High Hon Roll; Hon Roll; HOBY Schlrshp Awd 87; Stu Govnmnt Class Rep 86-87.

LESAKO, MARK; Bethlehem Center HS; Brownsville, PA; (2); #49 In Class; Stu Cncl; JV Bsktbl; Hon Roll.

LESE, ANN MARIE; St Pius X HS; Phoenixville, PA; (1); 18/146; FTA; JV Tennis; High Hon Roll; Phrmcy.

LESE, VICKIE; Bentworth HS; Bentleyville, PA; (4); 45/133; GAA; Letterman Clb; Varsity Clb; Capt Drill Tm; Stu Cncl; Var Bsktbl; Var Sftbl; Var Vllybl; Hon Roll; US Army Resv Ntl Schlr & Athlte Awd 87; Bus & Profsnl Womens Stu Of Mnth In Sports 87; All Arnd Athlt; Pittsburgh U; Dntl Hugnst.

LESEK, JEFF; West Scranton HS; Scranton, PA; (3); Ski Clb; Golf; Swmmng; Engrng.

LESGOLD, JACOB; Taylor Allderdice HS; Pittsburgh, PA; (2); Exploring; Math Clb; Math Tm; High Hon Roll; Prfct Atten Awd; Amrcn HS Math Exmntn Hnr Rll; Acad Ltr; Mlclr Blgy.

LESH, JULIE; Bedford HS; Bedford, PA; (4); 22/187; VP Sec Church Yth Grp; Chorus; Stu Cncl; Var L Bsktbl; Var L Vllybl; Hon Roll; Schlstc Mdl Wnr 84-86; Pitt; Med.

LESHEN, SHANNON; West Mifflin Area HS; West Mifflin, PA; (4); 95/330; Varsity Clb; Capt Color Guard; Stu Cncl; Var L Bsktbl; Powder Puff Ftbl; Var L Sftbl; Var L Vllybl; NHS; Sftbl Schlrshp To Pt Park Coll 87; MVP Vlybl Tm; Point Park Coll; Pblc Admn.

LESHER, BETH; Reading SR HS; Reading, PA; (3); 58/710; Church Yth Grp; Band; Church Choir; Concert Band; Jazz Band; Mrchg Band; Orch; School Musical; Symp Band; Vllybl; Music.

LESHER, CYNTHIA; Cocalico HS; Denver, PA; (3); 34/172; Pres VP Church Yth Grp; VP Band; Chorus; Church Choir; VP Concert Band; Jazz Band; VP Mrchg Band; Pep Band; Var JV Sftbl; High Hon Roll; Lebanon Vly Hnrs Band 87; Cnty Band 86; Accntng.

LESHER, DONALD; Cocalico HS; Reinholds, PA; (3); Drama Clb; Teachers Aide; Stage Crew; Nwsp Sprt Ed; Nwsp Stf; L Var Bsbl; L Var Bsktbl; Var Ftbl; L Var Socr; High Hon Roll; Stu Mnth 86; Bus Mgmt.

LESHER JR, JAMES M; Upper Dauphin Area HS; Gratz, PA; (4); 4-H; FFA; Var L Bsbl; L Wrstlng; 4-H Awd; Alferd ST; Ag Sci.

LESHER, JENNIFER; East Juniata HS; Thompstontown, PA; (3); 8/100; Chess Clb; Church Yth Grp; SADD; Mrchg Band; Yrbk Stf; Pres Frsh Cls; Pres Jr Cls; Var JV Bsktbl; Var JV Fld Hcky; Var Trk; Nrsng.

LESHER, JULIANA; Gateway Christian Schl; Kutztown, PA; (3); 1/5; VP Church Yth Grp; Cmnty Wkr; Chorus; Variety Show; Nwsp Rptr; Pres Stu Cncl; High Hon Roll; Chrstn Witnss 86; Bible Memry Awd 86; Optimst Oratrcl Awd 86; Messiah Coll; Cmnctns.

LESHER, JULIE; Kutztown Area SR HS; Lenhartsville, PA; (4); 6/150; Pres Church Yth Grp; Band; Chorus; Co-Capt Drill Tm; Yrbk Stf; Rep Stu Cncl; L Var Trk; High Hon Roll; NHS; Pres Schlr; HOBY Fndtn Awd 85; Physics & German Awds 87; York Coll Of PA; Speech Cmmntn.

LESHKO, DANIEL; Hazleton HS; Mcadoo, PA; (3); 95/405; Church Yth Grp; Cmnty Wkr; FBLA; Red Cross Aide; Trk; Hon Roll; MD U; Fire Sci.

LESHKO, MARY ELIZABETH; Hazleton HS; Hazleton, PA; (3); FBLA; Chorus; Variety Show; Diving; Mgr(s); Score Keeper; L Swmmng; Hon Roll; NE Inst; Trvl.

LESHNER, SHARON; Bensalem SR HS; Bensalem, PA; (3); Key Clb; Office Aide; SADD; Varsity Clb; Nwsp Stf; Yrbk Stf; Cheerleading; Var Trk; High Hon Roll; NHS.

LESHOCK, CARL; Palmerton Area HS; Palmerton, PA; (3); 8/173; Boy Scts; Capt Debate Tm; Nwsp Stf; Yrbk Stf; JV Golf; Var Tennis; Hon Roll; NHS; Acadc Physcs Awd 87; Sci.

LESHOCK, DEBBIE; Southern Columbia Area HS; Shamokin, PA; (3); Ski Clb; Band; Chorus; Concert Band; Mrchg Band; Pep Band; Mgr Nwsp Stf; Hon Roll; Tchng.

LESISKO, JODI; Newport HS; Liverpool, PA; (3); 47/100; Chorus; School Musical; Mgr(s); Hon Roll; Cntre Hills Bus Schl; Comp.

LESKEY, MATTHEW; Rockwood Area HS; Rockwood, PA; (3); Computer Clb; NFL; Speech Tm; School Play; Yrbk Stf; Socr; High Hon Roll; Elctrcl Engrng.

LESKO, MAUREEN; Cardinal Brennan HS; Shenandoah, PA; (3); 23/58; Capt Color Guard; Drill Tm; Yrbk Stf; Vllybl; Hon Roll; Cert Honor Alg II 87; Penn ST U; Sci.

LESKO, RACHEL; Serra Central HS; Duquesne, PA; (2); Cmnty Wkr; Drama Clb; Hosp Aide; Science Clb; Teachers Aide; Chorus; Yrbk Phtg; Yrbk Stf; Trs Soph Cls; High Hon Roll; PA JA Sci 1st Pl 87; Cert Compltn Coll Cours Vet I-II 87; Bio Awds 86-87; U Of PA; Vet Sci.

LESKO, TINA M; Steel Valley HS; W Homestead, PA; (3); 65/207; Stage Crew; Nwsp Stf; Hon Roll; Engrng.

LESKOWYAK, BETH; Western Beaver HS; Beaver, PA; (4); Pres 4-H; FHA; Chorus; Mrchg Band; Bowling; Twrlr; Hon Roll; Median Schl; Med Sec.

LESKY, THERESA; Nativity BVM HS; Pottsville, PA; (2); Hosp Aide; Spanish Clb; Color Guard; Nwsp Stf; Stage Crew; Us Air Force Sci & Engr Fair Outstdng Proj Awd 87; Pres Phy Ftns 85-87; Most Progressv Band Awd 87; Cornell U; Hotel & Rest Mgmt.

LESLIE, HEATHER; Wilson Area HS; W Easton, PA; (4); 7/126; Debate Tm; Drama Clb; Mrchg Band; Mgr(s); Twrlr; High Hon Roll; Hon Roll; Pres Jr NHS; Sec NHS; Pres Acdmc Ftnss Awd 86-87; Soc Wmn Engrs Cert Merit Hnr Sci, Math 86-87; Bloomsburg U; Elem Ed.

LESLIE, JONATHAN; Gateway HS; Monroeville, PA; (2); 115/452; Boy Scts; Church Yth Grp; Ski Clb; JV Socr; God Cntry Awd; High Hon Roll; Hon Roll; Eagle Sct 86; Naval Aviation.

LESLIE, KAREN; Mohawk JR SR HS; Enon Valley, PA; (4); Pres Church Yth Grp; Sec FFA; FHA; School Play; Nwsp Rptr; Nwsp Stf; Pres Sr Cls; Var L Trk; DAR Awd; NHS; Westminster Coll; Elem Educ.

LESLIE, KATHLEEN E; Seneca Valley HS; Mars, PA; (3); 131/331; SADD; Band; Color Guard; Mrchg Band; Pep Band; Yrbk Stf; Hon Roll; Colorguard Ltr; Intr Desgn.

LESLIE, KELLY; Rockwood Area HS; Rockwood, PA; (3); 8/82; Yrbk Stf; Rep Stu Cncl; Sftbl; Vllybl; High Hon Roll; Hon Roll; Psych.

LESLIE, LEANNE; Dunmore HS; Dunmore, PA; (3); Drama Clb; Ski Clb; Spanish Clb; Flag Corp; Stage Crew; Nwsp Phtg; Yrbk Stf; Hon Roll; Penn ST U; Poli Sci.

LESLIE, MARY ANN; Fox Chapel HS; Pittsburgh, PA; (3); Church Yth Grp; GAA; Hosp Aide; Key Clb; Sec Mrchg Band; Symp Band; Var L Sftbl; Var Swmmng; Var L Vllybl; NHS.

LESLIE, THOMAS; Mohawk JR SR HS; New Galilee, PA; (3); VP Church Yth Grp; Sec French Clb; School Musical; Yrbk Stf; Var L Ftbl; Powder Puff Ftbl; Var L Trk; Wt Lftg; Hon Roll; Physcl Thrpy.

LESNAK, DANIELLE; Young SR HS; West Newton, PA; (3); Trs FBLA; Concert Band; Mrchg Band; Symp Band; Off Frsh Cls; Stu Cncl; Stat Bsktbl; Powder Puff Ftbl; Hon Roll; Bus.

LESNAK, LYNETTE; Marion Ctr Area HS; Indiana, PA; (4); 4/170; Q&S; Band; School Play; Yrbk Bus Mgr; Yrbk Rptr; High Hon Roll; NHS; Ntl Merit Ltr; Church Yth Grp; Commnded Stdnt Ntl Merit, Cert Merit Outstndng Perf SAT 86; Quill Scrll Histrn 86-87; Psych.

LESNETT, VICKY; West Greene HS; Waynesburg, PA; (2); French Clb; FHA; Pres Girl Scts; Library Aide; Math Clb; SADD; Var Sftbl; Var Vllybl; High Hon Roll; Pres Schlr; WV U; Pedtrcn.

LESNEY, MELISSA; Butler Area HS; Butler, PA; (3); German Clb; Pres Hosp Aide; JA; Science Clb; Thesps; Mrchg Band; School Musical; School Play; Nwsp Stf; Rep Stu Cncl; Duquesne U; Pharmacy.

LESNIAKOWSKI, BRIAN; Peters Twp HS; Mcmurray, PA; (4); Computer Clb; Var Ftbl; JV Wrstlng; High Hon Roll; PA ST; Comp Sci.

LESSIG, KURT; Exeter SR HS; Reading, PA; (3); Varsity Clb; Band; Concert Band; Mrchg Band; Orch; Crs Cntry; Trk; Bus.

LESSMAN, KARIN; Charleroi Area JR-SR HS; Charleroi, PA; (3); Pres Church Yth Grp; Rep FBLA; VP JA; Office Aide; Spanish Clb; Yrbk Ed-Chief; Stu Cncl; Powder Puff Ftbl; High Hon Roll; NHS; Offcr Of Yr JR Achvmnt VP Admin 87; PA ST U; Aerospc Engnrng.

LESSMAN, SHAWN; Connellsville SR HS; Mt Pleasant, PA; (2); Camera Clb; Ftbl; Trk; High Hon Roll; Hon Roll; PENN ST U; Elctrncs.

LESTER, JAMIE; Aliquippa HS; Aliquippa, PA; (2); Computer Clb; French Clb; VP Trs Girl Scts; Library Aide; School Play; Stage Crew; Hon Roll; Pre Law.

LESTER, KAREN L; Boyertown JR High East; Perkiomenville, PA; (1); Art Clb; Aud/Vis; French Clb; Chorus; Flag Corp; Stage Crew; High Hon Roll; Hon Roll; Prfct Atten Awd; Architecture.

LESTER, MELISSA; Punxsutawney Area HS; Punxsutawney, PA; (3); French Clb; Varsity Clb; Variety Show; Var L Cheerleading; Stat Wrstlng; Hon Roll; Boyd Schl; Airline Stewrds.

LESTER, MICHELLE; Pocono Central Catholic HS; E Stroudsburg, PA; (3); VP Frsh Cls; Sec Soph Cls; Trs Stu Cncl; L Sftbl; Co-Capt Cheerleading; Cit Awd; DAR Awd; High Hon Roll; NHS; VFW Awd; Excllence In Spllng Awd 85-86; Penn ST; Jrnlsm.

LESTER, THOMAS; Notre Dame HS; Stroudsburg, PA; (3); Stage Crew; Sec Stu Cncl; Capt Var Bsktbl; Coach Actv; Stat Score Keeper; Capt Im Vllybl; Prfct Atten Awd.

LESTRANGE, KAMI; Towanda Area HS; Monroeton, PA; (3); 15/170; Letterman Clb; Ski Clb; Var L Cheerleading; Var L Trk; Hon Roll; Phrmcst.

LESZCZYNSKI, RENEE; Hampton HS; Allison Park, PA; (3); 19/212; Concert Band; Mrchg Band; School Musical; Symp Band; Hon Roll; Allegheny Vlly Hnrs Band 85-86; Tri-M Music Hnr Soc 86-87.

LESZCZYNSKI, THERESA; Hampton HS; Allison Pk, PA; (4); 23/248; Jazz Band; Mrchg Band; School Musical; Symp Band; Powder Puff Ftbl; High Hon Roll; NHS; Pres Schlr; Arion Awd For Outstndng Mscnshp 87; Invlvmnt In Nmrs Hnrs Bands 82-87; Indaian U Of PA; Music.

LETIZIA, KRISTA; Central Cambria HS; Mineral Pt, PA; (3); Ski Clb; Rep Frsh Cls; Sec Soph Cls; Sec Jr Cls; Pres Stu Cncl; Cheerleading; Hon Roll; U Ptsbrgh; Phrmcy.

LETIZIO, ANDREA; Villa Maria Acad; Erie, PA; (3); Science Clb; Ski Clb; SADD; Yrbk Stf; Trk; Hon Roll; Penn ST; Psychlgy.

LETRENT, MARY; Bedford HS; Bedford, PA; (4); 4/176; Band; Chorus; Sec Frsh Cls; Sec Soph Cls; Sec Jr Cls; Sec Sr Cls; Rep Stu Cncl; Hon Roll; NHS; Concert Band; Outstndg 11th Grd Grl 85-86; Bio.

LETSCHE, NICOLE; Hamburg Area HS; Hamburg, PA; (3); Church Yth Grp; German Clb; Library Aide; SADD; Yrbk Stf; Rep Stu Cncl; Var L Cheerleading; Var L Ftbl; Hon Roll; Acad Ltr Awd Grmn II, III 86 & 87; Grmn Natl Hnr Soc Delta Epsilon Pin 86-87; Grmn.

LETSO, THOMAS; Cambria Heights HS; Patton, PA; (3); Church Yth Grp; Debate Tm; Ski Clb; SADD; Chorus; School Play; Stu Cncl; Swmmng; Amer Lgn Awd; Penn ST.

LETTIERI, MICHAEL; Old Forge HS; Old Forge, PA; (4); Ski Clb; Var Bsbl; JV Var Bsktbl; JV Var Ftbl; Hon Roll; Old Forge AA Outstndng Off Awd Ftbl 86-87; Old Forge Booster Club Hnrs Off Plyr Awd Ftbl 86-87; U Scranton; Acctng.

LETTIERI, STEVEN; Mercer JR SR HS; Mercer, PA; (2); Bsbl; Ftbl; Trk; Law Enfrcmt.

LEUSCHNER, GREER; Williams Valley HS; Williamstown, PA; (1); 1/119; Art Clb; Pep Clb; VP Spanish Clb; Lib Chorus; Church Choir; Flag Corp; High Hon Roll; Mst Vlbl Chorus Awd 87; Lebanon Valley Coll; Pre Law.

LEUSCHNER, GUY; Annville-Cleona HS; Annville, PA; (3); FBLA; Nwsp Stf; Yrbk Stf; Var Ftbl; Var Trk; Jr NHS; Phys Thrpy.

LEVAN, KAREN; Montgomery Area HS; Montgomery, PA; (3); Trs Pres Girl Scts; Yrbk Stf; Trs Soph Cls; Trs Jr Cls; Pres Stu Cncl; Tennis; Bob Jones U; Intr Design.

LEVAN, MICHELLE; Sch Haven HS; Sch Haven, PA; (2); 5/101; Church Yth Grp; Science Clb; Varsity Clb; Band; Chorus; School Musical; JV Cheerleading; Var L Trk; High Hon Roll; Pres Schlr; Dawn Klinger Awd Ldrshp & Schltc 84; Bio.

LEVAN, PAMELA; Pine Grove Area HS; Pine Grove, PA; (4); 38/116; Teachers Aide; Varsity Clb; Off Jr Cls; Off Sr Cls; Var Bsktbl; Var Sftbl; Pres Schlr; Odd Fllws Untd Natns Rep 86; Elizabthtwn Coll PA; Scndry Ed.

LEVANDOSKI, MELISSA; Wyoming Area HS; W Pittston, PA; (3); Cmnty Wkr; Girl Scts; Chorus; JV Var Cheerleading; JV Var Trk; Nrsng.

LEVENDUSKI, ANN; Saint Marys Area HS; Weedville, PA; (3); Church Yth Grp; Cmnty Wkr; Girl Scts; Pep Clb; Teachers Aide; Yrbk Phtg; Yrbk Rptr; Yrbk Sprt Ed; Yrbk Stf; Stat Bsktbl; Tch 4th Grd Rlgs Inst At Church 85-87; Chld Psych.

LEVENGOOD, AMY; Daniel Boone HS; Douglassville, PA; (3); 8/170; French Clb; Model UN; Quiz Bowl; Chorus; High Hon Roll; Hon Roll; NHS; Chorus Awd 85; Frgn Ang Cmpttn Awd 87; Psycht.

LEVENS, DOUGLAS; Cedar Crest HS; Lebanon, PA; (3); 17/342; Boy Scts; Pres German Clb; Pep Clb; L Ftbl; Var Trk; Im Vllybl; L Wrstlng; Hon Roll; NHS.

LEVENTHAL, MARK; Upper Dublin HS; Dresher, PA; (4); 16/316; Am Leg Boys St; FBLA; Yrbk Stf; Sec Jr Cls; Sec Sr Cls; Im Bsktbl; CC Awd; Hon Roll; NHS; Entre Con Wharton Schl U Of PA 86; Le High U; Acctg.

LEVENTRY, CHERI; Johnstown Area Vo-Tech; Windber, PA; (3); 14/320; Church Yth Grp; VICA; Cheerleading; Trk; Hon Roll; NHS; Recog Awd Peer Tutor 87; Phys Thrpst.

LEVICOFF, ROBERT; Central HS; Philadelphia, PA; (3); 24/536; Drama Clb; Science Clb; School Play; Yrbk Ed-Chief; Var L Crs Cntry; Hon Roll; Ntl Merit Ltr; Val; U Of PA; Pre Med.

LEVIN, ALISON; Pocono Mountain HS; E Stroudsburg, PA; (2); Cmnty Wkr; Color Guard; Mrchg Band; Twrlr; Hon Roll; NHS; Presented Mem Plaque To Concord HS Hnrng Christa Mc Auliffe 86; Gregg Typing Awd 87; U Of PA; Pub Rel.

LEVIN, JENNIFER; Hempfield HS; Lancaster, PA; (3); Dance Clb; Chorus; Variety Show; Sec Frsh Cls; Rep Soph Cls; Rep Jr Cls; Rep Sr Cls; Var L Cheerleading; Hon Roll; 1st Pl Local Dance Solo Cmptn 85-86; 1st Co Dance Solo Cmptn 85-86; 2nd Pl Dist Dance Solo Cmptn 85-86; Pediatrics.

LEVIN, JODI; Council Rock HS; Newtown, PA; (3); 202/908; VP Soph Cls; Var Cheerleading; JV Socr; Hon Roll; Dance Clb; Rep Stu Cncl; Var Mgr(s).

LEVIN, WENDY; Clearfield Area HS; Clearfield, PA; (4); 7/294; Cmnty Wkr; French Clb; SADD; Chorus; Church Choir; Im Bowling; High Hon Roll; NHS; U Of Pittsburgh Johnstown; Med.

LEVINE, AMY; West Greene HS; Holbrook, PA; (3); 2/103; Pres Ski Clb; School Musical; Pres Jr Cls; Var Bsktbl; Capt Trk; Var Vllybl; High Hon Roll; Drama Clb; French Clb; Letterman Clb; Western PA Ldrshp Conf 86; Yth Undrstng Intl Exchange 87; Pres Clssrm Yng Amer 87; U Of Pittsburgh; Cmmnctns.

LEVINGER, TIMOTHY; Hopewell HS; Aliquippa, PA; (2); Camera Clb; Church Yth Grp; French Clb; Stage Crew; Nwsp Phtg; Yrbk Phtg; Yrbk Rptr; Yrbk Stf; Var Socr; Var Swmmng; U Of NC; Elec Engr.

LEVITAS, ALLYSON S; Lower Merion HS; Ardmore, PA; (4); 78/370; Church Yth Grp; Chess Clb; Off JCL; Political Wkr; Thesps; Flag Corp; School Play; Lit Mag; Ntl Merit SF; French Hon Soc; Cum Laude Cert In Latin 86; Offc In Stu Coalition For Peace 84-87; Mdrn Lang.

LEVITT, LORA; Parkland SR HS; Allentown, PA; (3); 224/481; Hosp Aide; Library Aide; Teachers Aide; Temple Yth Grp; Chorus; School Musical; Yrbk Phtg; Var Twrlr; Bnai Brith Arnold Tenenbaum Mem Scholar 86.

LEVRANT, ROBERT; Council Rock HS; Holland, PA; (2); Boy Scts; Drama Clb; Sec Key Clb; SADD; Temple Yth Grp; Orch; School Musical; Hon Roll; Ner Tamid 85; Memrl Awd, Hewrew Hnr Soc 86; Harry Auspitz Memrl Prz 87; Intl Rltns.

LEVY, ARLENA R; George Westinghouse HS; Pittsburgh, PA; (4); 8/191; Church Yth Grp; Pep Clb; Lit Mag; Sftbl; Vllybl; Trs NHS; Hnr Soc 86-87; U CO; Arts.

LEVY, MARK; Freedom HS; Bethlehem, PA; (4); 48/433; Yrbk Rptr; Var Ftbl; Im Wt Lftg; Var Wrstlng; George Washington U; Engrng.

LEWANDOWSKI, DIANE; Geibel HS; Mount Pleasant, PA; (3); French Clb; Pep Clb; Sec Soph Cls; Sec Pres Stu Cncl; Var Capt Bsktbl; Var Sftbl; Var Capt Vllybl; French Hon Soc; High Hon Roll; NHS; WPIAL Cls A Plyr Yr Bsktbl 86-87; MVP Bsktbl 85-87; Math Ed.

LEWANDOWSKI, ERIC; Cathedral Prep; Erie, PA; (3); 23/217; Bsktbl; Ftbl; Wt Lftg; Hon Roll; Psych.

LEWANDOWSKI, HELEN; Academy HS; Erie, PA; (4); 18/197; Drama Clb; French Clb; Chrmn Model UN; Chorus; Variety Show; Yrbk Stf; VP L Vllybl; Prsdntl Acdmc Ftnss Awd 86-87; PA ST Coll-Behrend.

LEWANDOWSKI, LINDA; Bishop Conwell HS; Morrisville, PA; (3); 26/277; Library Aide; Teachers Aide; JV Capt Cheerleading; Hon Roll; La Salle U; Psych.

LEWANDOWSKI, PATRICIA; Academy HS; Erie, PA; (1); Chess Clb; Church Yth Grp; Drama Clb; French Clb; Model UN; Orch; Yrbk Ed-Chief; NHS; Pres Schlr; Egan Schlr Schlrshp Mercyhurst Coll 87; Bishop Watson Schlrshp 87; Merchurst Coll; Spcl Educ.

LEWARS, MARIE; Liberty HS; Bethlehem, PA; (3); 47/429; VP SADD; Thesps; Chorus; School Musical; Trs Frsh Cls; Trs Jr Cls; Rep Stu Cncl; Var Cheerleading; Hon Roll; Tripshp Schlrshp To Japan 87; Nrsng.

LEWELLEN IV, JOHN W; Holy Ghost Prep; Southampton, PA; (4); Aud/Vis; Library Aide; Math Clb; Math Tm; Scholastic Bowl; Science Clb; Church Choir; School Play; Nwsp Sprt Ed; Nwsp Stf; PA Govr Schl For Sci 85; U S Naval Acad Smmr Sci Smnr 86; Case Inst Of Tech; Physics.

LEWERT, SHARON; Pittston Area SR HS; Pittston, PA; (4); Church Yth Grp; Drama Clb; French Clb; Hosp Aide; Key Clb; Science Clb; Ski Clb; Nwsp Stf; Hon Roll; Penn ST U.

LEWGOOD, LESLIE; Monessen JR-SR HS; Monessen, PA; (3); Camp Fr Inc; Church Yth Grp; JA; PAVAS; Nwsp Stf; Rep Frsh Cls; VP Soph Cls; VP Jr Cls; High Hon Roll; NHS; PA ST U; Elctrcl Engrng.

LEWINGER, ALEX; Academy HS; Erie, PA; (3); 19/226; Church Yth Grp; Hosp Aide; Yrbk Stf; Rep Stu Cncl; Var Socr; Var Swmmng; Hon Roll.

LEWIS, AARON; Susquehanna Township HS; Harrisburg, PA; (3); SADD; Varsity Clb; Bsktbl; Ftbl; Trk; Opt Clb Awd; U DE; Elec Engr.

LEWIS, AMY; Nativity BVM HS; Pottsville, PA; (2); Girl Scts; Capt Var Drill Tm; Flag Corp; School Musical; Variety Show; Crs Cntry; Var Sftbl; Albright; Cmmnctns.

LEWIS, ANDREA; Lincoln HS; Ellwood City, PA; (4); 47/180; Speech Tm; Thesps; Concert Band; Drm Mjr(t); Mrchg Band; School Musical; Hon Roll; NEDT Awd; Church Yth Grp; French Clb; Louise Plasemeyer Awd & Semper Fedelis Awd 87; Geneva Coll; Med.

LEWIS, ARLEY; Punxsutawney Area SAR HS; Punxsutawney, PA; (3); French Clb; Math Tm; Science Clb; Yrbk Phtg; Off Stu Cncl; NHS; Rotary Awd; HOBY Awd.

LEWIS, BETHANY; West Perry HS; New Bloomfield, PA; (2); 47/220; Trs Church Yth Grp; Trs French Clb; Math Tm; JV Cheerleading; Stat Trk; Hon Roll; Penn ST U; Med.

LEWIS, BRET; Beaver Area HS; Beaver, PA; (3); 30/200; FCA; Ski Clb; Spanish Clb; Yrbk Ed-Chief; Yrbk Stf; Bsbl; Ftbl; Trk; Hon Roll; Engrng.

LEWIS, CHARLES W; Gettysburg HS; Gettysburg, PA; (2); 1/300; Model UN; Quiz Bowl; Band; Jazz Band; Orch; L Crs Cntry; Sec Soph Cls; L Tennis; High Hon Roll; Chess Clb; High Boy; Hgh Avg Alg II & Bio; 1st Plc ST Chesapeake Bay Essay Contest; West Point; Military Sci.

LEWIS, CHERYL; Pine Forge Acad; Pottstown, PA; (3); Church Choir; Swmmng; Hon Roll; Prfct Atten Awd; Good & Responsible Worker Awd 84; Mickey Awd For Pantomine In Engl 86; Child Psych.

LEWIS, CHRISTINA; German SR HS; Mc Clellandtown, PA; (3); Pres Art Clb; VP Jr Cls; Stu Cncl; Var Bsktbl; Var Cheerleading; High Hon Roll; Hon Roll; Pres Jr NHS; NHS; Red Cross Aide; COBBE Awd 87; Pres Culture Clb 86-87; Upward Bound 85-87; Boston U; Phy Thrpy.

LEWIS JR, DANA; Harbor Creek JRSR HS; Erie, PA; (3); 17/200; Boy Scts; Band; Concert Band; Mrchg Band; Pep Band; Variety Show; Hon Roll; Pop Piux XUU Religs Awd Boy Scts 85; Music.

LEWIS, DANA C; Nativity BVM HS; Pottsville, PA; (1); 8/94; Math Clb; Drill Tm; Variety Show; JV Bsktbl; JV Vllybl; Hon Roll; Intl Frgn Lang Awds Spn; Allentown Cath Diocese Scholar Awd; Putting On The Hits Perf Arts Show; Chem Engr.

LEWIS, DAVE; Marion Catholic HS; Tamaqua, PA; (3); 34/104; Var L Bsbl; Var L Bsktbl; Var L Ftbl; Bloomsburg; Sci.

LEWIS, DAVE; Mon Valley Catholic HS; Monongahela, PA; (2); Church Yth Grp; JA; Bsbl; Natl Sci Olympd; U Of PA; Cvl Engr.

LEWIS, DAVID; Emmaus HS; Emmaus, PA; (4); 65/470; Sec Trs Church Yth Grp; Exploring; German Clb; Key Clb; Scholastic Bowl; High Hon Roll; Hon Roll; Jr NHS; Ntl Merit Ltr; PA ST U; Comp Engrng.

LEWIS, DAWN; Penn Trofford HS; Irwin, PA; (2); 117/311; Carlow; Nrs.

LEWIS, DEBRA; Harry S Truman HS; Levittown, PA; (3); 75/602; Mrchg Band; Trs Stu Cncl; JV Bowling; Var Fld Hcky; Hon Roll; Bucks Cnty CC; Elem Educ.

LEWIS, DESIREE; William Allen HS; Allentown, PA; (3); 50/700; GAA; JA; Teachers Aide; Varsity Clb; VP Frsh Cls; Pres Soph Cls; Pres Jr Cls; Pres Sr Cls; Rep Stu Cncl; Var Bsktbl; Clss Pres 86-88; Stu Govt Sen; Psychlgy.

LEWIS, DIONEE; Northumberland Christian Schl; Northumberland, PA; (3); 1/6; Girl Scts; Hosp Aide; Chorus; School Play; Yrbk Stf; Var Bsktbl; Var Cheerleading; Var Socr; Var Vllybl; Opt Clb Awd; Girl Scout Silver Awd 87; Med Tech.

LEWIS, EDWARD; Cornell HS; Coraopolis, PA; (3); French Clb; VP JA; Band; Var Bsbl; JV Var Ftbl; Var Golf; Jr NHS; NHS; Air Force Acad; Pilot.

LEWIS, GARY; Fort Le Boeuf HS; Waterford, PA; (4); Church Yth Grp; Band; Concert Band; Jazz Band; Mrchg Band; Pep Band; JV Var Bsbl; Im Ftbl; Hon Roll; U Ptsbrg/Titsvl; Nght Clb Mgr.

LEWIS, GEORJ; Connellsville HS; Connellsville, PA; (2); NAACP; Bsktbl; Ftbl; Trk; Hon Roll; Jr NHS; Accntnt.

LEWIS, GRETCHEN; West Forest JR SR HS; Tionesta, PA; (3); Pres Church Yth Grp; Model UN; Chorus; Swing Chorus; Yrbk Ed-Chief; Stu Cncl; Capt JV Cheerleading; High Hon Roll; NHS; Pres Schlr; American U; Intl Stds.

LEWIS III, JAMES T; Owen J Roberts HS; Pottstown, PA; (3); 19/299; Boy Scts; Scholastic Bowl; Im Bsktbl; Im Vllybl; Hon Roll; NHS; Engr.

LEWIS, JENNIFER; Hempfield HS; Landisville, PA; (3); 84/400; Dance Clb; Band; Chorus; Concert Band; Jazz Band; Mrchg Band; Orch; School Musical; Symp Band; Rep Sr Cls; Glgy.

LEWIS, JENNIFER; Notre Dame HS; Easton, PA; (3); 14/100; Dance Clb; Pep Clb; Teachers Aide; Yrbk Phtg; Yrbk Stf; Mgr(s); Score Keeper; Trk; Hon Roll; Prfct Atten Awd.

LEWIS, JOHN A; Owen J Roberts HS; Pottstown, PA; (2); 5/311; Boy Scts; JV Socr; L Wrstlng; High Hon Roll; Hon Roll; Surgeon.

LEWIS, KRISTA; Mercyhurst Prep HS; Erie, PA; (3); 14/170; Church Yth Grp; Ski Clb; JV L Sftbl; Var L Trk; Hon Roll; NHS; Mercyhurst Coll; Psych.

LEWIS, LESLIE; Valley HS; New Kensington, PA; (1); Band; Chorus; Color Guard; Concert Band; Mrchg Band; Westmoreland Cnty Music Fstvl 87; Georgetown; Med.

LEWIS, LYNN; Warren Area HS; Warren, PA; (3); French Clb; Library Aide; Spanish Clb; Y-Teens; Chorus; Color Guard; Yrbk Stf; Sftbl; High Hon Roll; Hon Roll; Accntng.

LEWIS, MATTHEW R; Port Allegany HS; Port Allegany, PA; (1); 11/111; Rep Stu Cncl; NHS; Church Yth Grp; French Clb; Quiz Bowl; Acpl Chr; Chorus; School Musical; School Play; Hon Roll; U Of PA; Engrng.

LEWIS, MELISSA A; St Marys Area HS; Weedville, PA; (3); Church Yth Grp; Trk; Sociology.

LEWIS, MELVA; Center HS; Monaca, PA; (2); Church Yth Grp; Dance Clb; Church Choir; Prfct Atten Awd.

LEWIS, MICHELE; Clarion Area HS; Clarion, PA; (3); FHA; Pep Clb; Acpl Chr; Variety Show; Yrbk Stf; Trs Stu Cncl; Stat Bsktbl; Stat Ftbl; Var L Trk; JV Capt Vllybl; Presdntl Phys Fitness Awd 86-87; Clarion U Of PA; Phys Thrpy.

LEWIS, MICHELLE; Garden Spot HS; New Holland, PA; (4); 25/201; Spanish Clb; Band; Chorus; Concert Band; Mrchg Band; Orch; Rep Stu Cncl; Var JV Cheerleading; Jr NHS; Sec NHS; Sparticus Chldr Awd & Stu Of Month 87; Penn ST U; Liberal Arts.

LEWIS, MISHA; Abington HS; Glenside, PA; (3); 100/507; Spanish Clb; Temple Yth Grp; Lcrss; Hon Roll; Pol Sci.

LEWIS, NICOLE; Seneca Valley HS; Mars, PA; (3); Computer Clb; Hosp Aide; Math Tm; Pep Clb; Ski Clb; Trk; Hon Roll; Am Hrt Assoc 86; March Dimes 85; Med.

LEWIS, ROBERT E; Ringgold HS; Finleyville, PA; (3); Ski Clb; JA; Variety Show; Rep Frsh Cls; Hon Roll; Fnlst Provosts Day 87; Stu High-Q Tm Cmpttn Geneva Coll 87; Capt High-Q Tm 88; Med.

LEWIS, SCOTT; Oil City SR HS; Oil City, PA; (4); Rep Soph Cls; Var Ftbl; Var Trk; Wt Lftg; Wrstlng; Hon Roll; Prfct Atten Awd; PA ST-BEHREND; Arch Engrng.

LEWIS, TODD; Penntrafford HS; Export, PA; (3); Drama Clb; Sec FBLA; School Musical; VP Crs Cntry; Ftbl; Ice Hcky; Sftbl; VP Trk; JV Wrstlng; Hon Roll; FBLA Rgn Conf 5th Pl Acctng II 87; Marrietta; Math.

LEWIS, VENITA; Boiling Springs HS; Boiling Spgs, PA; (3); Church Yth Grp; Girl Scts; Hosp Aide; Chorus; Church Choir; School Play; Var L Bsktbl; Var L Fld Hcky; Var Timer; Var L Trk; Nwsp Hnr Carrier 85; PA ST Sunday Schl Dist Essay Wnnr, Rgnl Poetry Wnnr 85; Cmnctn Art.

LEWULLIS, KAREN; Central Catholic HS; Allentown, PA; (4); 13/210; Church Yth Grp; Exploring; Math Clb; Service Clb; Ski Clb; Tennis; High Hon Roll; Hon Roll; NHS; Schlrshp Elzbthtwn Coll 87-91; Emplyee Mnth Awd 87; NCACC; Dentl Hyg.

LEX, KENNETH; Langley HS; Pittsburgh, PA; (3); Band; Mgr Ftbl; NHS.

LEX, MICHELE; Cardinal O Hara HS; Aston, PA; (3); 64/719; Church Yth Grp; Cmnty Wkr; Dance Clb; JA; School Play; Rep Frsh Cls; NHS; Model UN; Scnd Hnrs 84-87; Top 10 Prcnt 84-87; Photo Awd For Medias Miss Hampshere Pgnt 86; Advrtsng.

LEZYNSKI, MICHAEL D; Archbishop Wood Boys HS; Holland, PA; (4); Yrbk Ed-Chief; Yrbk Stf; Rep Stu Cncl; JV Ftbl; Var Wrstlng; NHS; Anna M Vincnt Schlrshp 87; A Marlyn Moyer Jr Schlrshp 87; U Of Notre Dame; Bus.

LI, JOYCE; Parkland HS; Allentown, PA; (2); Chess Clb; JA; Library Aide; Church Choir; High Hon Roll.

LIANG, MICHAEL; Gateway SR HS; Monroeville, PA; (2); Off Debate Tm; NFL; Speech Tm; Orch; Yrbk Phtg; Tennis; High Hon Roll; Science Clb; Mrchg Band; Nwsp Phtg; Med.

LIANG, MING; Central Dauphin HS; Harrisburg, PA; (4); 35/386; Art Clb; Camera Clb; Computer Clb; Intnl Clb; Math Clb; Science Clb; Speech Tm; Vllybl; Hon Roll; Kiwanis Awd; PA ST U; Elec Engr.

LIAW, DANNY; Plymouth-Whitemarsh HS; Lafayette Hill, PA; (3); 2/382; Computer Clb; Hosp Aide; Pres Math Clb; Pres Mu Alpha Theta; Rep Jr Cls; High Hon Roll; NHS; Prfct Atten Awd; PA Jr Acad Of Sci-1st Pl Microbio Awd 85; Med.

LIBBY, LISA; Mechanicsburg HS; Mechanicsburg, PA; (3); 46/338; Rep Stu Cncl; Var L Bsktbl; Var L Fld Hcky; Var L Sftbl; Hon Roll; Mid PA Div I Sftbl All Star Tm 86-87; Keystone St Gms-Fld Hcky 87; Atty.

LIBBY, PAULA; Shikellamy HS; Sunbury, PA; (3); Cmnty Wkr; FCA; SADD; Var Capt Bowling; Fld Hcky; Var Sftbl; Jr NHS; All Star Tm Field Hocky 85-86; Pittsburg U; Phrmcy.

LIBBY, TIFFANY; Mifflinburg Area HS; Mifflinburg, PA; (1); Sec Church Yth Grp; French Clb; Key Clb; Fld Hcky; Sftbl; Hon Roll; Wnnr Of Essay Cntst Womens Christian Temperance Union87.

LIBBY, TRICIA; Pennsbury HS; Fairless Hls, PA; (3); VP Church Yth Grp; Cmnty Wkr; French Clb; School Musical; School Play; Stage Crew; Var Trk; Cit Awd; French Hon Soc; Hon Roll; Kutztown U; Soc.

LIBERASKI, CHRISTINE; G A R Memoreial HS; Wilkes-Barre, PA; (3); 3/152; Key Clb; Library Aide; Yrbk Bus Mgr; Yrbk Stf; Pres Jr Cls; Fld Hcky; High Hon Roll; Hon Roll; Jr NHS; NHS.

LIBERATO, LYNNE; Blue Mountain HS; Auburn, PA; (4); 19/218; Trs SADD; Co-Capt Cheerleading; Trk; French Hon Soc; School Musical; Ybk Stf; Swmmng; Hon Roll; 1st Acctng Stu 87; PA ST U; Bus.

LIBERMAN, DANIEL; Stroudsburg HS; Stroudsburg, PA; (3); 3/313; Math Tm; Scholastic Bowl; Trs Temple Yth Grp; Rep Stu Cncl; JV Bsktbl; Var Capt Golf; NHS; PA JR Acad Of Sci 1st Rgnl & 2nd ST 87; Acad All Amer 86 & 87; PA Gov Schl Bus Alt To Smmr Pgm 87; Bus.

LIBERTA, NICOLE; Notre Dame HS; Easton, PA; (3); 10/90; Yrbk Stf; Bsktbl; Sftbl; High Hon Roll; Hon Roll; Med.

LIBERTO, MURIEL M; Central Catholic HS; Allentown, PA; (4); 6/208; Exploring; Ski Clb; Yrbk Ed-Chief; Yrbk Phtg; Ed Lit Mag; High Hon Roll; NCTE Awd; NHS; Ntl Merit Ltr; PA Gvrnrs Schl Scncs 86; Equstrn Sprts 83-86; Vet Med.

LIBERTY, LISA; Beaver Falls HS; Beaver Falls, PA; (3); 8/177; AFS; Aud/Vis; Pres Trs Spanish Clb; VP Fresh Cls; Sec Stu Cncl; Var JV Cheerleading; Var Sftbl; Twrlr; High Hon Roll; NHS; Fnlst Beaver Cnty Jr Miss 87; U Of PA; Orthopedic Surgeon.

LIBHART, ERICA; Mechanicsburg Area SR HS; Mechanicsburg, PA; (2); 38/309; Pep Clb; Band; Concert Band; Mrchg Band; Stat Fld Hcky; Cit Awd; Hon Roll; Pres Acad Ftnss Awd 85.

LIBONATI, GENENE; Hazleton HS; Hazleton, PA; (4); 5/400; French Clb; Scholastic Bowl; Teachers Aide; Co-Capt Color Guard; Nwsp Ed-Chief; Sec Trs Stu Cncl; Co-Capt Cheerleading; Gym; Elks Awd; French Hon Soc; Amer Lgn Axlry Awd Wnnr 84; Wellesley Bk Wnnr 86; Englsh Achvt Awd 87; Kings Coll; Pre-Law.

LIBRANDI, DONNA; Bishop Mc Devitt HS; Steelton, PA; (3); 53/250; JV Var Bsktbl; High Hon Roll; Hon Roll.

LIBUS, CHRISTOPHER; John S Fine SR HS; Nanticoke, PA; (2); 11/243; Rep Soph Cls; High Hon Roll; NHS; Elec Engrng.

LICHTENBERGER, PAUL; Oil City SR HS; Oil City, PA; (3); Varsity Clb; Var L Ftbl; Wt Lftg; Var L Wrstlng; Hon Roll; Prfct Atten Awd.

LICHTENWALNER, CHARLES; Freedom HS; Bethlehem, PA; (4); 99/446; French Clb; Band; Chorus; Concert Band; Drm Mjr(t); Jazz Band; Mrchg Band; Orch; School Musical; School Play; Thursbey Music Schlrshp 87; Moravich; Music.

LICKER, LORANE; Lebanon HS; Lebanon, PA; (4); VP Camera Clb; Drama Clb; French Clb; Key Clb; Chorus; Nwsp Phtg; Yrbk Phtg; Hon Roll; Church Yth Grp; Pep Clb; Bnai Brith U Mem Amer Awd 87; Miss Christmas Seal For Lung Assoc 86-87; PA Ambssdrs Of Music 85; Messiah Coll; Psych.

LIDONNICE, JOHN; Penn Cambria HS; Lilly, PA; (3); Nwsp Sprt Ed; Nwsp Stf; JV Var Bsktbl; High Hon Roll; Hon Roll; NHS; MPV Bkstbl Tourn 85; Hghst Frnch Avg 85; Penn ST U; Engr.

LIEB, DAVID ANDREW; Hanover HS; Hanover, PA; (4); 12/110; Chess Clb; Science Clb; Varsity Clb; JV Bsbl; JV Var Bsktbl; JV Var Ftbl; JV Trk; Elks Awd; Hon Roll; Rotary Awd; PA ST U; Bio.

LIEB, DOUGLAS; Hanover SR HS; Hanover, PA; (3); 1/120; Math Tm; Science Clb; Band; Nwsp Stf; JV Bsbl; High Hon Roll; NHS; Chess Clb; Concert Band; Jazz Band; PA Govrs Schl For Intl Stud; Math Awd; Math Leag Chmpn.

LIEB, KIRSTIE; Cambria Heights HS; Carrolltown, PA; (3); 4-H; SADD; Band; Concert Band; Mrchg Band; Pep Band; Yrbk Stf; Cheerleading; Sftbl; Bus.

LIEBAL, RICHARD; Williamsburg HS; Williamsburg, PA; (3); 16/76; JA; Red Cross Aide; SADD; Varsity Clb; VICA; Rep Frsh Cls; Rep Soph Cls; Rep Jr Cls; JV Var Bsbl; JV Var Ftbl; Williamsport; Carpentry.

LIEBERMAN, JASON; Quakertown Community HS; Quakertown, PA; (3); Math Clb; Var L Socr; High Hon Roll; Hon Roll; Pres Schlr; Comp Sci.

LIEBERMAN, JILL; Dallas SR HS; Dallas, PA; (3); Political Wkr; Temple Yth Grp; School Musical; Sec Jr Cls; Pres Stu Cncl; Cit Awd; Hon Roll; Aud/Vis; Cmnty Wkr; Red Cross Aide; Pennsylvanians Aware; PA St Ldrshp Trng Pgm; Stu Cncl Rgnl Conf; Pre-Law.

LIEBERMAN, KELLY JO; Pen Argyl Area SR HS; Pen Argyl, PA; (3); 54/160; Church Yth Grp; Drama Clb; Sec Chorus; Capt Flag Corp; Mrchg Band; School Play; Variety Show; Var Powder Puff Ftbl; Capt Twrlr; Cmnctns.

LIEBERUM, MICHAEL; West Mifflin Area HS; W Mifflin, PA; (3); Varsity Clb; Var L Socr; Hon Roll; Jr NHS; NHS; Varsity Lttr Soccer 86-87; PA ST U; Engr.

LIEBLER, CHRISTINE; Karns City HS; Chicora, PA; (4); Drill Tm; School Play; Variety Show; Var Pom Pon; Pres Schlr; Physics Awd 87; Grove City Coll; Theatre.

LIEBLER, LAUREN; Trinity HS; Camp Hill, PA; (2); Drama Clb; French Clb; Pep Clb; Ski Clb; School Play; Variety Show; Yrbk Stf; Crs Cntry; Hon Roll; Jrnlsm.

LIEBMAN, LIONEL; North Hills HS; Pittsburgh, PA; (4); 23/475; Church Yth Grp; VP JA; Pres Key Clb; Science Clb; Ski Clb; JV Var Ftbl; JV Var Trk; Wt Lftg; High Hon Roll; Trs NHS; Westinghouse Hon Inst Of Sci 86-87; Engrng.

LIED, JODI; Cocalico HS; Reinholds, PA; (3); Sec Frsh Cls; JV VP Cheerleading; JV VP Fld Hcky; Stck Brkr.

LIED, KATIE; Peters Township HS; Mc Murray, PA; (3); Letterman Clb; Spanish Clb; Varsity Clb; Yrbk Stf; Stu Cncl; Cheerleading; Vllybl; Dnfth Awd; Hlth Svcs.

LIED, TRACY; Ephrata SR HS; Ephrata, PA; (4); 16/257; Church Yth Grp; Cmnty Wkr; Teachers Aide; Church Choir; Stage Crew; Rep Stu Cncl; JV Fld Hcky; JV Var Trk; Hon Roll; NHS; Hibshman Scholar 87-91; Messiah Coll Cert Acad Scholar 87-88; Messiah Coll; Psych.

LIEN, MARCUS C; Gateway SR HS; Monroeville, PA; (4); 1/501; Math Tm; Pres NFL; Ed Nwsp Stf; Ed Yrbk Stf; Ed Lit Mag; Tennis; Gov Hon Prg Awd; High Hon Roll; NHS; Ntl Merit SF; Med.

LIENARD, SHERILYN; Canon Mc Millan HS; Mc Donald, PA; (1); Church Yth Grp; Band; Chorus; Concert Band; Nwsp Rptr; High Hon Roll; Hon Roll; Frshmn Rep Band Prnts Assn 86-87.

LIETO, SUZANNE; Wallenpaupack Area HS; Hawley, PA; (4); 17/147; Pres 4-H; Ski Clb; Pres Band; Pres Concert Band; Pres Mrchg Band; Pres Stu Cncl; Var Bsktbl; Var Trk; DAR Awd; High Hon Roll; Hmcmng Qn 86; Needs Assessmnt Cmte 86-87; PA ST.

LIEUX, DOUGLAS M; Penncrest HS; Media, PA; (3); 223/344; Intnl Clb; Band; Chorus; Concert Band; Jazz Band; Mrchg Band; Pep Band; School Musical; Variety Show; Stat Bsbl; Music.

LIGGITT, TAMY; Watsontown Christian Acad; Muncy, PA; (2); 1/16; Church Yth Grp; Capt Quiz Bowl; Pres Soph Cls; Var L Bsktbl; High Hon Roll; NEDT Awd; Pres Acad Fit Awd 86; Top Acdmc Schl 86; Natl Hon Soc Christian Schls 87; Math.

LIGHT, ANGELA SUE; Eastern Lebanon County HS; Myerstown, PA; (3); #13 In Class; Church Yth Grp; Hosp Aide; Band; Concert Band; Mrchg Band; High Hon Roll; Hon Roll; NHS; Schlrshp Awd Hghst Yr Avg Chem 86; Merit Awd Chem II 87; Cert Apprctn Candy Striping 85; Scl Wrk.

LIGHT, JASON; Christian Schl Of York; Dover, PA; (2); Church Yth Grp; JA; Var Bsbl; High Hon Roll; Hon Roll; Natl Engl Merit Awd 87; Acad All Amer 87.

LIGHT, LORA; Tyrone Area HS; Tyrone, PA; (2); NHS.

LIGHTNER, BETHANY; Reading HS; Reading, PA; (3); 19/720; Pres Church Yth Grp; Debate Tm; Drama Clb; VP JA; Model UN; Church Choir; Yrbk Stf; Var Fld Hcky; Hon Roll; NHS; Hampshire Coll; Geolgcl Engr.

LIGHTNER, DEBBIE; Southern Huntingdon County HS; Shade Gap, PA; (3); 14/178; GAA; SADD; Varsity Clb; Concert Band; Mrchg Band; Nwsp Phtg; VP Soph Cls; Bsktbl; Fld Hcky; Sftbl; Resp Thrpy.

LIGHTNER, MICHAEL; Lewistown Area HS; Lewistown, PA; (3); Pep Clb; SADD; Varsity Clb; Pres Soph Cls; Pres Jr Cls; Var Capt Bsbl; Var Capt Crs Cntry; Im Wt Lftg; Var Capt Wrstlng; Hon Roll; Rode Tate Mem Awd-Wrstlng 86-87; Panther Athlt Awd-Crss Cntry, Wrstlng; Stu Mnth; Accntng.

IGHTNER, MIKE; Hollidaysburg Area SR HS; Duncansville, PA; (3); 0/385; Band; Concert Band; Mrchg Band; Orch; Vllybl; Wt Lftg; Hon oll; JETS Awd; NEDT Awd; Congrssnl Awd 87; U S Mltry Acad; Nclr ngnrng.

IGHTNER, SHARI; Central Dauphin HS; Harrisburgh, PA; (3); 24/370; hurch Yth Grp; Ski Clb; Flag Corp; Nwsp Ed-Chief; Gym; Trk; Hon Roll; r NHS; NHS; Presdntl Acadc Ftnss Awd 85; Nrsng.

IGUS, PAULA; Montour HS; Coraopolis, PA; (4); Pep Clb; High Hon oll; Hon Roll; NHS; PA JR Acad Sci 86; Sci Olympcs Tm & Presdntl cad Ftns Awd 87; U Of Pittsburgh; Dietician.

IHOTA, MIKE; Marple Newtown HS; Media, PA; (3); 15/320; Intnl Clb; ADD; Stu Cncl; Var Capt Bsktbl; NHS; Ntl Merit Ltr; Church Yth Grp; ki Clb; Variety Show; Nwsp Rptr; Bsktbl MVP; Engrng.

ILIENTHAL, TAMMY; Henderson HS; West Chester, PA; (3); Hosp ide; Service Clb; SADD; Nwsp Rptr; Lit Mag; Rep Frsh Cls; Rep Soph ls; Rep Jr Cls; JV Var Lcrss; High Hon Roll; Bnkng.

ILLEY, CHANDRA; Manheim Township HS; Lancaster, PA; (4); chool Musical; Nwsp Rptr; Var Cheerleading; Trk; Hon Roll; Danc Awds 5-87; PA ST U; Lbrl Arts.

ILLEY, CHRISTA; Connellsville SR HS; Mount Pleasant, PA; (3); 39/ 00; SADD; Y-Teens; Flag Corp; School Musical; Nwsp Stf; Yrbk Stf; Rep tu Cncl; High Hon Roll; NHS; Band; Grmn Natl Hnr Soc 86-87; Fshn sgn.

ILLIOCK, KIMBERLY; Connellsville Area HS; Dunbar, PA; (1); hurch Yth Grp; Office Aide; Ski Clb; Nwsp Stf; Yrbk Stf; Trk; Wrstlng; on Roll; NHS; CA U Of PA; Tchr.

ILLY JR, GARY JAMES; Highlands SR HS; Natrona Hgts, PA; (3); mnty Wkr; Intnl Clb; SADD; Off Jr Cls; NHS; Ortho Surgeon.

ILLY III, HOWARD; Emmaus HS; Zionsville, PA; (3); JV Mgr(s); Hon oll; Physcs.

ILLY, JENNIFER; Ringgold HS; Finleyville, PA; (3); Sec VP Church th Grp; Band; Chorus; Concert Band; Mrchg Band; School Musical; wsp Stf; Yrbk Stf; High Hon Roll; NHS; Coll In HS Comp II & Calculus 6-88; Sci Math Hnr Soc 85-88.

ILYQUIST, MICHELLE; Bald Eagle Area HS; Milesburg, PA; (4); 11/ 87; Pres Church Yth Grp; Church Choir; Stu Cncl; JV Cheerleading; High on Roll; NHS; Pep Clb; SADD; Teachers Aide; Acadc Excllnc Awd 86; op Fnlst JR Miss 86; Hi Hnrs Awd 87; Penn ST U; Advrtsng.

IM, AI-LI; Lower Merion HS; Narberth, PA; (3); Rep Drama Clb; Pres hesps; Band; Drm Mjr(t); Stage Crew; Yrbk Stf; Var Swmmng; Gov Hon rg Awd; Hon Roll; NHS.

IMBACHER, JOHN E; Knoch JR SR HS; Saxonburg, PA; (4); Am Leg oys St; VP FBLA; Concert Band; Mrchg Band; Pep Band; School usical; School Play; Stage Crew; High Hon Roll; NHS; Indiana U PA; cndry Ed.

IMONGELLI, ANTHONY; Wyoming Area HS; Pittston, PA; (3); Key lb; Ski Clb; Spanish Clb; Trk; PA ST; Gen Studies.

IMRICK, CHRISTOPHER; Punxsutawawney Area SR HS; unxsutawney, PA; (3); Stage Crew.

IMRICK, SHAWN; Seneca HS; Waterford, PA; (3); Boy Scts; Pres hurch Yth Grp; Concert Band; Mrchg Band; Orch; School Musical; God ntry Awd; Bsktbl; JV Var Ftbl.

IN, ANGELA H; Ephrata SR HS; Ephrata, PA; (4); 26/253; Trs Church th Grp; Jazz Band; Sec Orch; Nwsp Rptr; Gov Hon Prg Awd; Hon Roll; HS; Germn Awds 85; Music Awds 87; U Of PA; Music.

IN, CYNTHIA; Hickory HS; Hermitage, PA; (2); 5/200; Boy Scts; NFL; cholastic Bowl; Spanish Clb; Varsity Clb; Chorus; Orch; Var L Crs Cntry; ar Trk; Spanish NHS; Med.

IN, DAVE; Emmaus HS; Allentown, PA; (3); German Clb; Nwsp d-Chief; Yrbk Ed-Chief; Pres Jr Cls; Var L Crs Cntry; Var L Tennis; HS; Ntl Merit Ltr; Pres Schlr; Pres JA; Jr Achvt Pres Of Yr 86 & VP rdctn Of Yr 87; Dale Carnegie Course Schlrshp 87.

IN, EMILY; Gateway SR HS; Monroeville, PA; (2); Computer Clb; cience Clb; Orch; Hon Roll; Jr NHS; Prfct Atten Awd; Vars Awds PMEA ist/Rgnl/ST Orchestra 86-87; Grnhse Clb, Tres Chic, Teen Inst, Lab ech 85-87; U Of PA; Music.

IN, JEN; Plymouth-Whitemarsh HS; Plymouth Mtg, PA; (3); School usical; Nwsp Stf; Stu Cncl; JV Tennis; High Hon Roll; NHS; Ntl Merit tr; Art Clb; Math Clb; Chorus.

INBERGER, DONNA; Quakertown Community HS; Quakertown, PA;); Church Yth Grp; FBLA; Chorus; Church Choir; School Musical; JV ar Sftbl; Var Vllybl; High Hon Roll; Hon Roll; Varsity Clb; Bible Quiz bbns & Trphy 84-87; Sprts Cert & Ltr 85-87; Chorus Plq 87; CO hristian U.

INCK, KRISTI; West Allegheny HS; Oakdale, PA; (2); Church Yth Grp; rama Clb; Color Guard; Mrchg Band; School Play; Stage Crew; Hon Roll; rt Awds 86-87; Tchg/Advrtsng.

INCOLN, DIANE; Portage Area HS; Portage, PA; (3); Sec Church Yth rp; Church Choir; Co-Capt Color Guard; Mrchg Band; Nwsp Stf; Yrbk tf; Nrsng.

INCOLN JR, WAYNE; Freeport SR HS; Sarver, PA; (3); Ftbl; High on Roll; Hon Roll.

IND, EMILY J; Norristown Area HS; Norristown, PA; (4); Drama Clb; ADD; Orch; School Musical; School Play; Yrbk Rptr; DAR Awd; NHS; horus; Nwsp Rptr; Newspaper SR Spotlight/Faculty Focus Editor; Schl able News Chnl; Intrnl Affairs.

INDAUER, DAVID; Yough SR HS; W Newton, PA; (3); 8/241; omputer Clb; Ski Clb; Spanish Clb; Chorus; Tennis; High Hon Roll; Hon oll; NHS; Powder Puff Ftbl; Dstngshd Hnr Roll; NEMA 84-85; Pre-Law.

INDAUER JR, FRANK; Yough SR HS; W Newton, PA; (3); 35/239; JV ar Bsktbl; Golf; High Hon Roll; Hon Roll; Arch.

INDBERG, ERIK J; Central HS; Martinsburg, PA; (3); 39/190; Im llybl; Bus Admin.

INDBERG, JOELANE ELIZABETH; Ephrata SR HS; Ephrata, PA;); 30/253; Civic Clb; CAP; Exploring; Library Aide; Red Cross Aide; JV ld Hcky; Var L Swmmng; Var L Trk; Hon Roll; NHS; Hibshman 87; rove City Coll; Comp Sys.

INDBLAD, ERIC; Gateway SR HS; Monroeville, PA; (3); Math Clb; ath Tm; Var L Swmmng; NHS; Prfct Atten Awd; PA Gov Schl Sci Top tu ST 87; US Math Olympd Trnng Pgm Top Stu US 87; Rsrch Sci Inst op Stu 87.

INDEMAN, KENT; Elizabethtown Area HS; Elizabethtown, PA; (3); 2 In Class; Church Yth Grp; Chorus; Orch; Variety Show; Var Ftbl; Var ennis; High Hon Roll; Hon Roll; NHS; JV Bsbl; Close Up Program 87; olt Sci.

LINDEMUTH, STAN; Brockway Area HS; Reynoldsville, PA; (3); 30/ 120; Art Clb; Boy Scts; Church Yth Grp; Debate Tm; Exploring; Library Aide; Speech Tm; Band; Chorus; Mrchg Band; Good Ctznshp Awd For PA ST Senate 85-86; Penn ST; Psych.

LINDENBERG, MICHAEL; Susquehanna Township HS; Harrisburg, PA; (3); Temple Yth Grp; Varsity Clb; Im Bsktbl; Capt Var Ftbl; Var Socr; Var Trk; Wt Lftg; Hon Roll; NHS; Spkrs Awd Penn ST Model UN 86; Franklin; Psych.

LINDENBERG, SARA; Northern Lebanon HS; Jonestown, PA; (4); 3/ 177; Chorus; Church Choir; Concert Band; Mrchg Band; School Musical; School Play; Var L Tennis; NHS; Acpl Chr; Arion Awd; Lions Club Stu Mnth, Lebanon JR Womens Clb Stu Mnth; Intl Rel.

LINDENBERGER, BRYON; Fairview HS; Erie, PA; (4); Nwsp Rptr; Lit Mag; Hon Roll; Pblshd Fctn New Blood Magzn 87; Egan Schlrshp 87; Mercyhurst Coll; Engl Crtv Wrtn.

LINDENMUTH, JEFFERY; Emmaus HS; Emmaus, PA; (3); Art Clb; Boy Scts; Camera Clb; Church Yth Grp; Trs JA; Wt Lftg; Wrstlng; Hon Roll; Prfct Atten Awd; Eagle Scout 85; Art.

LINDER, ANDREW; Northwestern HS; Albion, PA; (3); Church Yth Grp; Model UN; L Bsbl; L Crs Cntry; L Capt Wrstlng; Hon Roll; Free Enterprise Wk 87; Comms.

LINDER, ILONA A; Shaler SR HS; Glenshaw, PA; (3); Cmnty Wkr; Hosp Aide; Concert Band; Mrchg Band; Symp Band; High Hon Roll; Hon Roll; NHS; Spanish NHS; Duquesne U Schl Music Mideast Instrmntl Music Fstvl 85.

LINDER, MARK; Williamson JR SR HS; Tioga, PA; (2); Boy Scts; 4-H; Chorus; Church Choir; Im Bsbl; Im Bsktbl; Im Wrstlng; Cit Awd; 4-H Awd; Hon Roll; Cnty 4-H Safty Blue-Form Wnr 87.

LINDNER, ALYSE M; North Penn HS; North Wales, PA; (4); 54/653; Church Yth Grp; Chorus; JV Powder Puff Ftbl; Hon Roll; NHS; Pres Schlrshp 5 Yrs 87-92; N Penn Area Schlrshp Merch-Sharp & Dohme 87-88; Pres Acdmc Ftnss Awd 87; Philadelphia Coll Pharm; Pharm.

LINDNER, JEFFREY; Lincoln HS; Ellwood City, PA; (3); 68/185; German Clb; Latin Clb; SADD; Rep Jr Cls; Var L Bsktbl; Var L Ftbl; Mst Imprvd Plyr Bsktbl Tm ST Semi-Fnls 86-87; Educ.

LINDNER, JENNIFER N; The Baldwin Schl; Hayerford, PA; (4); Drama Clb; French Clb; German Clb; Service Clb; Acpl Chr; Chorus; Orch; Stage Crew; Yrbk Stf; Rep Stu Cncl; Colby Coll Bk Prz 86; Outstndg Contrib Life Of Schl Awd 86; Awds Acadmc Exchng 84-87; U Of PA; Art History.

LINDQUIST II, DAVID; Octorara HS; Christiana, PA; (3); 24/157; VP Church Yth Grp; VP Band; Concert Band; Mrchg Band; School Musical; School Play; Nwsp Ed-Chief; Cmnty Wkr; Sec Trs Drama Clb; PAVAS; Arch.

LINDSAY, ALICE; Cecilian Acad; Philadelphia, PA; (2); Church Yth Grp; Girl Scts; Science Clb; Church Choir; Variety Show; Prfct Atten Awd; PA ST; Psyc.

LINDSAY, BOBBIJO; Greencastle-Antrim HS; Greencastle, PA; (3); Camera Clb; Band; Concert Band; Mrchg Band; Hon Roll.

LINDSAY, CHRISTOPHER; Mohawk JR SR HS; New Galilee, PA; (3); 3/137; Boy Scts; Chess Clb; Church Yth Grp; Latin Clb; SADD; Church Choir; Trk; High Hon Roll; Hon Roll; NHS.

LINDSAY, LE VONNE; Abington SR HS; Roslyn, PA; (3); 14/507; Band; Mrchg Band; Rep Jr Cls; JV Cheerleading; JV Lcrss; High Hon Roll; Jr NHS; Presdntl Acadmc Ftns Awd 84-85; Ctzns Prgrss Acadmc Achvt Awd 84-85; Outstndng Achvt Art 84-85; Phila Coll-Textiles; Fshn Dsgn.

LINDSEY, KELLIE; Corry Area JR SR HS; Corry, PA; (3); VP Pres Church Yth Grp; Cmnty Wkr; German Clb; Ski Clb; Church Choir; School Musical; Yrbk Stf; Rep Stu Cncl; Var Vllybl; Stat Wrstlng; Zonta Intl Svc Awd 87; Hlth Fld.

LINDSEY, LORI; Mohawk JR/SR HS; New Castle, PA; (3); Church Yth Grp; FNA; Hosp Aide; Office Aide; Red Cross Aide; Teachers Aide; Band; Chorus; Church Choir; Concert Band; St Francis Schl Rdlgy; Radiolgy.

LINDSEY, PEGGY; Laurel Highlands SR HS; Hopwood, PA; (2); Cit Awd; High Hon Roll; Hon Roll.

LINDSEY, SHERRY; Northampton Area SR HS; Northampton, PA; (4); 47/430; Pres DECA; Leo Clb; Model UN; SADD; Mrchg Band; Twrlr; Hon Roll; NHS; 6th Pl Fin & Credit DECA Dist Comp 86; 5th Pl Fin & Credit DECA Dist Comp 87; Bloomsburg U; Bus Adm.

LINDSEY, TAMMY; Boiling Springs HS; Winchester, VA; (3); Camp Fr Inc; 4-H; FHA; Nwsp Rptr; Socr; Hon Roll; James Wood Ridge Campus.

LINDSTROM, LYNN M; Clearfield HS; Clearfield, PA; (4); 1/315; French Clb; SADD; Chorus; High Hon Roll; NHS; Ntl Merit SF; Bio.

LINEHAN, JEANINE; Cardinal O Hara HS; Clifton Hts, PA; (4); 94/ 778; Church Yth Grp; Cmnty Wkr; Var Capt Cheerleading; Presdntl Schlrshp U Of Scranton 87; U Of Scranton; Law.

LINEN, BRENTON; John Harris HS; Harrisburg, PA; (2); 135/434; Church Yth Grp; Church Choir; Jazz Band; Mrchg Band; Wt Lftg; Electrnc Engrng.

LINER, RON; Norwin HS; N Huntingdon, PA; (4); 26/547; Ski Clb; SADD; VICA; Var L Trk; High Hon Roll; Hon Roll; Kiwanis Awd; Prfct Atten Awd; 3 Yr Hon Grad 84-87; Machnst.

LINGENFELTER, DWIGHT; West Branch JR-SR HS; Morrisdale, PA; (3); VP Church Yth Grp; Cmnty Wkr; Varsity Clb; JV Var Bsbl; Var L Bsktbl; Prfct Atten Awd; Penn St; Agrnmst.

LINGER, VICKI; Cornell HS; Coraopolis, PA; (3); 1/75; Computer Clb; JA; Trs Key Clb; Math Clb; Spanish Clb; Color Guard; Flag Corp; Nwsp Rptr; Nwsp Stf; Yrbk Stf; HOBY Ambsdr 86; Educ.

LINGLE, CHERIE; Susquehanna Twp HS; Harrisburg, PA; (3); Church Yth Grp; Band; Chorus; Church Choir; Concert Band; Jazz Band; Mrchg Band; Orch; School Musical; Symp Band; Cnty Bands & Orch 83 & 85; Lebanon Vly Hnrs Band 85-87; Church Bell Choir 83-87; Music Educ.

LINGLE, DON; Grove City HS; Grove City, PA; (3); 11/210; Church Yth Grp; Science Clb; Trs Jr Cls; JV Bsktbl; Var L Crs Cntry; Var L Trk; Im Vllybl; High Hon Roll; Hon Roll; NHS; Comp Sci.

LINGLER, CONAN; Karns City Area HS; Chicora, PA; (3); Exploring; Band; Concert Band; Mrchg Band; Pep Band; Variety Show; Hon Roll; NHS; Arch.

LINGREL, TONYA; Waynesboro Area HS; Waynesboro, PA; (2); Drama Clb; Girl Scts; Hosp Aide; Color Guard; Yrbk Stf; Rep Soph Cls; Var Cheerleading; JV Fld Hcky; JV Trk; Hon Roll; Grl Scts Slvr Awd 86.

LINHART, CATHY; Freeport HS; Freeport, PA; (3); Church Yth Grp; Chorus; Church Choir; Yrbk Stf; Trk; Hon Roll; Butler CC; Acctg.

LININGER, CHRISTINE; Fairchance-Georges SR HS; Fairchance, PA; (3); Library Aide; Spanish Clb; High Hon Roll; Hon Roll; Jr NHS; NHS; Uniontown Schl Of Nrsng; Nrsng.

LINK, CAREY; Susquenita HS; New Buffalo, PA; (3); Art Clb; Ski Clb; Variety Show; Nwsp Rptr; Nwsp Stf; Trs Soph Cls; Rep Jr Cls; Rep Stu Cncl; Stat Bsbl; Var Capt Fld Hcky; 1st Pl Perry Co Cncl Arts 86; 3rd Pl Susquenita HS Ltry Arts Fest 87; Ed.

LINK, JILL; Cambria Heights HS; Patton, PA; (3); 9/187; SADD; Chorus; Yrbk Stf; Pres Jr Cls; VP Stu Cncl; Var L Bsktbl; Var L Sftbl; Hon Roll; NHS; NEDT Awd; HOBY Ldrshp Smnr PA 86; Ntl Merit Sci Awd 87; Phrmcy.

LINK, JOHN; West York SR HS; York, PA; (3); 71/186; Varsity Clb; Nwsp Stf; Rep Stu Cncl; Var L Bsbl; Var L Bsktbl; Var L Golf; Hon Roll.

LINK, KRISTIN; Gwynedd Mercy Acad; Bluebell, PA; (2); SADD; School Musical; School Play; Nwsp Rptr; Yrbk Rptr; JV Bsktbl; Var Cheerleading; High Hon Roll; Mt St Josephs Acad Schlrshp 85; Sci.

LINK, MATTHEW; Cambria Heights SR HS; Dysart, PA; (3); 60/182; Church Yth Grp; ROTC; SADD; Chorus; Ftbl; Vllybl; Hon Roll; Air Force ROTC Superior Performance Ribbon; Penn ST; Pre-Med.

LINKENHEIMER, TAMMY; Seneca Valley SR HS; Harmony, PA; (3); Art Clb; JA; ROTC; Ski Clb; Bsktbl; Crs Cntry; Trk; High Hon Roll; Hon Roll; NHS; Schltc Excllnce Awd Natl Hnr Scty 87; Army.

LINKEVICH, PAM; Tamaqua Area School District; Tamaqua, PA; (3); 20/220; Church Yth Grp; Drama Clb; French Clb; Girl Scts; Library Aide; Chorus; Yrbk Stf; Var L Crs Cntry; Var L Swmmng; Var L Trk.

LINKO JR, DAVID; Connellsville Area N Fayette Vo-Tech; Dunbar, PA; (3); Boy Scts; VICA; JV Ftbl; Eagle Awd Boy Scts 86; Pres Auto Mech Cls 86-87; Investment Clb 85-86; Vale Tech; Auto Mech.

LINKO, JEFF; Connellville Area SR HS; Dunbar, PA; (1); Boy Scts; L Ftbl; High Hon Roll; Jr NHS; Eagle Awd Boy Scts 87; Gold Pin Acad Excllnce 87; Hghst Achvt Geog.

LINN, ANDY; Central Dauphin HS; Harrisburg, PA; (2); Church Yth Grp; Chorus; Jazz Band; School Musical; Var Socr; Swmmng; Hon Roll; Jr NHS; Naval Acad; Mechcl Engrng.

LINN, DANIEL; Chambersburg Area SR HS; Chambersburg, PA; (2); Quiz Bowl; Orch; Sci.

LINN, JENNIFER; Bald Eagle-Nittany HS; Mill Hall, PA; (3); 4/148; Spanish Clb; High Hon Roll; Hon Roll; Rtry Clb-Stu Of Mnth-Apr 87; Wmsprt Schl/Cmmrc; Mdcl Rcrds T.

LINN, KEN; Greenwood HS; Liverpool, PA; (2); 1/69; Church Yth Grp; Chorus; Concert Band; Mrchg Band; Trs Soph Cls; JV Bsbl; JV Bsktbl; Var Socr; High Hon Roll; Amer Legn Schl Awd 85; Penn ST; Acctng.

LINN, LISA M; Danville SR HS; Danville, PA; (3); Dance Clb; Drama Clb; Pres VP 4-H; NFL; Spanish Clb; Band; Concert Band; Nwsp Phtg; Yrbk Stf; NHS; Natl Forensics Lge 86-87; Intl Studies.

LINN, STEPHANIE; Middletown Area HS; Middletown, PA; (3); 25/193; FBLA; Key Clb; JV Sftbl; Hon Roll; Scndry Ed.

LINT, DIANE; Quakertown Community HS; Quakertown, PA; (4); 7/291; Girl Scts; SADD; Chorus; Concert Band; Mrchg Band; School Musical; Fld Hcky; High Hon Roll; Jr NHS; NHS; Westchester U; Elementary Educ.

LINT, TRACEY; Southmoreland HS; Ruffsdale, PA; (3); French Clb; Latin Clb; Spanish Clb; Sec Frsh Cls; Off Stu Cncl; JV Cheerleading; Powder Puff Ftbl; French Hon Soc; High Hon Roll; Hon Roll; Edinboro U; French.

LINTON, BRYAN; Washington HS; Washington, PA; (3); Letterman Clb; Spanish Clb; Varsity Clb; Yrbk Sprt Ed; Yrbk Stf; Var Bsbl; Var L Bsktbl; Var L Ftbl; Hon Roll; Phy Thrpy.

LINTZ, WILLIAM; Beaver Area SR HS; Beaver, PA; (3); Art Clb; Church Yth Grp; German Clb; Letterman Clb; Yrbk Stf; Bsktbl; Tennis; High Hon Roll; NHS; U Notre Dame; Elect Engrng.

LINUS, JOSEPH; Bishop Egau HS; Yardley, PA; (4); 2/214; Pres Cmnty Wkr; Concert Band; Jazz Band; Pep Band; Nwsp Rptr; Yrbk Stf; High Hon Roll; NHS; Rotary Awd; Sal; Music & Math Dept Awd; U Notre Dame; Bus Adm.

LIOTT, JAMES; Hazleton HS; Hazleton, PA; (2); FBLA; Var Bsktbl; Hon Roll; Chiropractry.

LIOTT, NATALIE; Hazleton HS; Hazleton, PA; (4); 132/388; Church Yth Grp; FBLA; Yrbk Stf; Bloomsburg Univ.

LIPEZ, ZOE; Lock Haven HS; Lock Haven, PA; (3); 28/250; Art Clb; Cmnty Wkr; Computer Clb; Spanish Clb; SADD; Nwsp Stf; Var Capt Bsktbl; Mgr(s); Score Keeper; Socr; PA Sports Hall Fm Meritorious Achvt Awd 87; Lock Haven U; Sports Med.

LIPINSKI, DOREEN; Bishop O Reilly HS; Swoyersville, PA; (4); 2/111; Ski Clb; Chorus; School Musical; Yrbk Stf; VP Stu Cncl; Cheerleading; High Hon Roll; NHS; Spanish NHS; Ntl Acad Sci Awd 85-86; Kings Coll; Cmmnctn Brdcstng.

LIPINSKI, JOSPEH; Scranton Central HS; Scranton, PA; (4); 63/305; JA; Pep Clb; Spanish Clb; SADD; Chorus; Bsbl; Ftbl; Trk; Hon Roll; NHS; Dick Holmes Awd Sprtmnshp Ftbl 86-87; Relay Rcrd Brkng Tm 87; U Of Scranton; Pre Med.

LIPINSKI, LEANE; Bishop O Reilly HS; Swoyersville, PA; (2); Ski Clb; Chorus; School Play; VP Soph Cls; Trs Stu Cncl; Capt Cheerleading; NHS; NEDT Awd; Trs Spanish NHS; Prfct Atten 86-87; Intl Frgn Lang Awds 87; Hnr Rll 86-87.

LIPINSKI, MICHELLE; Saint Huberts HS; Philadelphia, PA; (4); 31/ 384; French Clb; Rep Soph Cls; Rep Jr Cls; Trs Sr Cls; Trs Stu Cncl; Cheerleading; High Hon Roll; NHS; Prfct Atten Awd; U Tampa Ldrshp Schlr 87; Spcl Tlnt Ldrshp Schlrshp 87; All Acad Amer Stu 87; Eckerd Coll; Chmstry.

LIPKA, LEON; Wyoming Area HS; West Wyoming, PA; (3); 7/250; Key Clb; Spanish Clb; Pres Soph Cls; VP Jr Cls; VP Sr Cls; Rep Stu Cncl; Var Bsbl; Var Bsktbl; Var Ftbl; NHS; Bucknell; Engr.

LIPKO, DAVID; Nativity BVM HS; Llewellyn, PA; (2); 15/80; Church Yth Grp; Computer Clb; French Clb; Letterman Clb; SADD; Rep Frsh Cls; Var L Bsbl; Var L Bsktbl; Hon Roll.

LIPP, THERESA; St Hubert Catholic HS For Girls; Philadelphia, PA; (4); 29/364; Cmnty Wkr; Office Aide; Jazz Band; Orch; Nwsp Stf; Hon Roll; NHS; Presdntl Acad Fit Awd 8m.

LIPPARD, D BROOKS; Upper Darby HS; Drexel Hill, PA; (3); 75/650; Aud/Vis; Office Aide; Bsbl; Wt Lftg; High Hon Roll; Hon Roll; Rick Conetti Awd 86; Duke U; Math.

LIPPARD, LOUISA A; Kane Area HS; Kane, PA; (1); Key Clb; SADD; JV Bsktbl; JV Sftbl; Ithaca U NY; Sci.

LIPPE, GORDON; Church Farm Schl; Silver Spring, MD; (3); 9/17; Cmnty Wkr; Varsity Clb; Stu Cncl; Var L Tennis; Var L Wrstlng; Art Clb; Letterman Clb; Office Aide; Ski Clb; Nwsp Stf; Oustndg Wrk SR Ctzns, Chldrn, & Am Red Cross 87; 1 MD; Bio.

LIPPENCOTT, ERIN; Peters Township HS; Mc Murray, PA; (3); Dance Clb; FBLA; Varsity Clb; Yrbk Stf; Rep Frsh Cls; Pres Rep Soph Cls; Rep Jr Cls; Rep Stu Cncl; JV Var Cheerleading; Trk; Hmcmng Rep 86.

LIPPERT, BRIAN; Quigley HS; Baden, PA; (4); 8/96; Cmnty Wkr; Math Tm; Var Capt Bsbl; Var Capt Bsktbl; Var Capt Ftbl; Wt Lftg; High Hon Roll; Jr NHS; Lion Awd; NHS.

LIPPERT, DENNIS; Shaler Area SR HS; Pittsburgh, PA; (3); Exploring; Hon Roll; Mech Engrng.

LIPPERT, KELLY; Lincoln HS; Ellwood City, PA; (3); 13/160; French Clb; GAA; Key Clb; Ski Clb; Y-Teens; Chorus; Powder Puff Ftbl; Sftbl; High Hon Roll; NHS; Psych.

LIPPERT, MARELL; Blue Mountain HS; Schuylkill Haven, PA; (2); 10/216; SADD; Chorus; Concert Band; Mrchg Band; Stage Crew; Rep Frsh Cls; Trk; High Hon Roll; Schltc Art Awd 86; PA Legisltv Schl Art Awd 86.

LIPPINCOTT, LISA; Hickory HS; Hermitage, PA; (2); Church Yth Grp; VP FCA; French Clb; Church Choir; Yrbk Stf; Hon Roll; Stat Gym; Var L Trk; Var L Vllybl; Phys Ed.

LIPPOLD, CHRISTINE; Butler HS; Butler, PA; (2); Church Yth Grp; Library Aide; Office Aide; Spanish Clb; SADD; Hon Roll; Jr NHS; Ntl Merit Ltr.

LIPPY, DANIELLE RENEE; Chambersburg Area HS; Chambersburg, PA; (2); Art Clb; Trs Church Yth Grp; French Clb; Service Clb; Band; Mrchg Band; Hon Roll; Art Inst-Philadelphia; Comm Art.

LIPPY, JEFFREY; Middletown Area HS; Middletown, PA; (3); 22/193; Drama Clb; Exploring; Chorus; Church Choir; Tennis.

LIPPY, KELIE; Northeastern HS; Gettysburg, PA; (4); Office Aide; School Play; Hon Roll; Grdn Phlps Bty Schl; Csmtlgy.

LIPSCOMB, NICOLE; John Harris Campus HS; Harrisburg, PA; (3); 27/305; Chess Clb; Drama Clb; ROTC; Chorus; Mgr Stage Crew; Hon Roll; Art Inst Of Philadelphia; Photo.

LIPSETT, ANDREW; Minersville Area HS; Minersville, PA; (4); 9/114; Boy Scts; Exploring; Ski Clb; Spanish Clb; Yrbk Stf; Ftbl; Var L Wrstlng; High Hon Roll; Hon Roll; NHS; Penn ST U; Engrng.

LIPSKY, ROBERT; Minersville Area HS; Minersville, PA; (4); 2/114; French Clb; Ski Clb; JV Var Bsbl; Var L Wrstlng; Dnfth Awd; High Hon Roll; Pres NHS; NEDT Awd; Sal; Penn ST U; Engineering.

LIPYANIC, SHEILA; Nazareth Area SR HS; Wind Gap, PA; (3); Computer Clb; Library Aide; Chorus; Hon Roll; Data Prcssng.

LISAC, MICHELE; Kennedy Christian HS; Sharpsville, PA; (4); 18/94; JA; Science Clb; Spanish Clb; Yrbk Stf; JV Bsktbl; L Capt Crs Cntry; Sftbl; L Trk; High Hon Roll; NHS; Excllnc In Spnsh Awd 87; CA U Of PA; Pre-Vet Med.

LISBON, HOLLIE; North Star HS; Jenners, PA; (2); 14/250; Art Clb; FCA; SADD; Yrbk Stf; Var Mat Maids; Var Sftbl; Cit Awd; Hon Roll; Lion Awd; Tribune Democtra Awd 87; Penn ST U; Clinical Psych.

LISCHNER, JAMES; West Mifflin Area HS; W Mifflin, PA; (3); Band; Orch; Trk; PMEA Dist Orchestra Rep; Three Rivers Yth Orchestra & Meadowmount & Interlochen Music Camp; Music.

LISCINSKI, RICK; Johnsonburg Area HS; Johnsonburg, PA; (4); Cmnty Wkr; Band; Concert Band; Mrchg Band; Trs Frsh Cls; Tennis; Hon Roll; NHS; Prfct Atten Awd; Natl Hstry & Govt Awd 86; Natl Eng Merit Awd 86; Indiana U Of PA; Acctng.

LISCO, DANA; St Joseph HS; Natrona Hgts, PA; (3); Exploring; Hosp Aide; Office Aide; Off Frsh Cls; Sec Soph Cls; Off Jr Cls; Off Stu Cncl; Swmmng; Trk; Jr NHS; Full Schlrshp Free Entrprs Wk Lock Hvn U 87; Bus.

LISHER, SANDRA; Abraham Lincoln HS; Philadelphia, PA; (4); Church Yth Grp; Hosp Aide; Lit Mag; Pres Soph Cls; JV Vllybl; Hon Roll; Cmnty Wkr; Girl Scts; Rep Frsh Cls; Rep Jr Cls; Temple U; Lbrl Arts.

LISHINSKY, DAVID; Punxsutawney Area HS; Punxsutawney, PA; (4); 4/245; Church Yth Grp; Math Tm; Trs Science Clb; Spanish Clb; Varsity Clb; Var L Bsbl; Var L Golf; High Hon Roll; NHS; Variety Show; U Pittsburgh Merit Scholar 87-91; Rotary Boy Mnth 87; U Pittsburgh; Phys Thrpy.

LISHMAN, AMY; Brandywine Heights HS; Topton, PA; (2); Sec Church Yth Grp; Band; Chorus; Church Choir; Concert Band; Mrchg Band; Swing Chorus; Trs Frsh Cls; Hon Roll.

LISHMAN, JENNIFER; Brandywine Heights Area HS; Topton, PA; (4); 27/132; Pres Church Yth Grp; Cmnty Wkr; Q&S; Band; Church Choir; Concert Band; Mrchg Band; Pep Band; School Play; Ed Yrbk Stf; Kutztown U; Elem Educ.

LISICKI, LORRAINE; Nazareth Acad; Phila, PA; (3); Cmnty Wkr; French Clb; Hosp Aide; Library Aide; Color Guard; Drill Tm; Flag Corp; Im Vllybl; High Hon Roll; Hon Roll; Knights Of Columbus Awd 84; Band Awd 86; Frankford Hosp; Nrsng.

LISIEWSKI, LISA; Carbondale Area HS; Simpson, PA; (3); 1/125; Cmnty Wkr; German Clb; Spanish Clb; High Hon Roll; NHS; Prfct Atten Awd; Schlstc Art Awd 86; Literary Awd 86; Hghst Avg 2nd Yr German Clss 86; Psychlgy.

LISS, ALLISON; Gateway SR HS; Monroeville, PA; (3); Girl Scts; Trs Temple Yth Grp; Flag Corp; Mrchg Band; Orch; Trs Frsh Cls; Rep Soph Cls; Rep Sr Cls; Rep Stu Cncl; Var L Socr; Grl Sct Slvr Awd; Ithaca Coll; Physcl Thrpy.

LISS, JENNIFER; Neshaminy HS; Langhorne, PA; (4); Drama Clb; Chorus; School Musical; School Play; Prfct Atten Awd; Penn ST; Comm.

LIST, KEVIN; Oxford Area HS; Oxford, PA; (3); 10/197; Chorus; Yrbk Stf; VP Frsh Cls; VP Soph Cls; VP Jr Cls; Rep Stu Cncl; Var Bsbl; Var Ftbl; Var Capt Wrstlng; High Hon Roll; Bio Awd 86; 4th Pl Rgnl Wrstlng Compttn 87; Leag Wrstlng Chmpn 85-87; Ophthalmolgy.

LIST, MICHELE; Newport HS; Newport, PA; (3); 23/125; German Clb; Band; Chorus; Church Choir; Concert Band; Drm Mjr(t); Jazz Band; Mrchg Band; Pep Band; School Musical; Physical Thrpy.

LISTER, SANDIA; Pine Forge Acad; New York, NY; (2); Church Choir; Hon Roll; Stu Mnth 85; Scl Attndc Awd 85; Splng Bee Rbbn 84; Oakwood Coll; Obstetrcn.

LISTON, JOHN M; Hopewell HS; Aliquippa, PA; (3); Latin Clb; Im Bsktbl; PA ST U; Aero Engr.

LISZCZ, LYDIA I; Garden Spot HS; Terre Hill, PA; (2); 8/226; Chorus; Orch; School Musical; School Play; Rep Jr Cls; High Hon Roll; NHS; Prfrmnc/Music Theory Schlrshps Cshey Smmr Schl Music 85-86; Cnty, Dist & Rgnl Orch, Cncrt Mstrs 85-87; Music Ed.

LITAK, MARY; Bethlehem Catholic HS; Bethlehem, PA; (3); Church Yth Grp; Rep Jr Cls; Var JV Bsktbl; High Hon Roll.

LITCHKOWSKI, SHARON; John S Fine HS; Nanticoke, PA; (2); 28/243; Church Yth Grp; Key Clb; JV Var Cheerleading; NHS.

LITTELL, AMANDA; Abington Heights HS; Waverly, PA; (3); 8/292; VP Trs Drama Clb; Ski Clb; School Play; Stage Crew; Trs Jr Cls; Rep Stu Cncl; Var Tennis; Hon Roll; Pres NHS; Hugh O Brian Yth Fndtn Ldrshp Smnr HS Rep 86; Bus.

LITTELL, KIRK ANDREW; Richland HS; Gibsonia, PA; (4); 48/185; Exploring; French Clb; Ski Clb; Nwsp Sprt Ed; Var Bsbl; Stat Ice Hcky; Capt Socr; Var Trk; 3 Rivers Arts Fest-Pittsburgh Hnrb Mntn 86 & 87; N Hius Arts Fest-Hnrb Mntn 87; Kent ST U; Graphic Dsgn.

LITTLE, BETH; Cedar Cliff HS; New Cumberland, PA; (3); 42/304; Camera Clb; German Clb; Grmn Natl Hnr Scty 85-87; Psych.

LITTLE, BRIDGET; Gettysburg Area SR HS; Gettysburg, PA; (2); French Clb; Varsity Clb; Mgr(s); Var Tennis; High Hon Roll; Pres Acad Ftns Awd 86; 2nd Hghst Acad GPA 86; U Of VA; Bus-Hotel Mgmt.

LITTLE, CHRISTY; Laurel Highlands HS; Hopwood, PA; (3); 58/365; Red Cross Aide; SADD; Rep Frsh Cls; Rep Soph Cls; Rep Jr Cls; Capt Cheerleading; Vllybl; Hon Roll; JETS Awd.

LITTLE, CRYSTAL LYNNE; Mc Keesport SR HS; Mckeesport, PA; (4); 94/344; Office Aide; Sec Band; Sec Concert Band; Sec Mrchg Band; Sec Symp Band; Bsktbl; Cheerleading; Powder Puff Ftbl; Trk; Bsktbl Scholar St Francis Coll 87; Hnr Grad Top Half Cls 87; Best Smile 87; St Francis; Acctng.

LITTLE, DANIEL; Cambria Heights SR HS; Patton, PA; (3); 1/183; Nwsp Stf; Bsbl; Trk; Wrstlng; NHS; NEDT Awd; SAR Awd; VFW Awd; Voice Dem Awd; Daedalion Awd For Achvmnt 87; Sci Awd From Amer Chmcl Society 87; Naval Acad; Chemist.

LITTLE, DARREN; West Branch HS; Winburne, PA; (2); Spanish Clb.

LITTLE, DERRICK; Gettysburg SR HS; Littlestown, PA; (2); JV Wrstlng; Hon Roll; Presdntl Acadmc Ftnss Awd 86; Mathmtcs.

LITTLE, HEATHER; Richland HS; Gibsonia, PA; (4); 8/177; French Clb; Band; Jazz Band; Pep Band; School Musical; Powder Puff Ftbl; High Hon Roll; NHS; Pres Schlr; Campus Exctv Offcr Schlrshp Beaver Penn ST 87-88; Penn ST U; Psych.

LITTLE, JOSEPH E; Trinity HS; Camp Hill, PA; (3); Ski Clb; Ftbl; Wt Lftg; CO ST U; Photography.

LITTLE, KARI; Central Dauphin HS; Harrisburg, PA; (4); 20/366; Ski Clb; Band; Orch; School Musical; Crs Cntry; Socr; Trk; High Hon Roll; NHS; Ntl Merit Ltr; Drew U Scholar 87; Mst Valuable Runner Awd 86; Dist Band Rep 87; Drew U; Lib Arts.

LITTLE, LANCE; Hughesville HS; Hughesville, PA; (4); Computer Clb; Library Aide; Comp Prgrmr.

LITTLE, LYNELLE; South Western HS; Hanover, PA; (3); Church Yth Grp; Hosp Aide; Swmmng; Hon Roll; Paralegal.

LITTLE, MELISSA; Kennard Dale HS; Stewartstown, PA; (4); 6/114; Ski Clb; Varsity Clb; Trs Chorus; School Musical; Yrbk Stf; Stu Cncl; Capt Cheerleading; Vllybl; Hon Roll; NHS; Fnlst Adms Elctrc Yth Tour-Wshngtn 86-87; Yrk Dspth, Yrk Dly Rcrd Acdmc All Str 87; Elizabethtown Coll; Pltcl Sci.

LITTLE, MICHAEL; Cardinal Brennan HS; Frackville, PA; (3); 32/58; German Clb; Bsbl; Vllybl; Bus.

LITTLE, RICHIE; Berlin Brothersvalley HS; Berlin, PA; (3); 45/94; FFA; SADD; Wrstlng; Rosedale Tech; Mech.

LITTLE, SANDY; Mary Fuller Frazier HS; Perryopolis, PA; (4); Church Yth Grp; Drama Clb; Girl Scts; Library Aide; Pep Clb; Band; Concert Band; Mrchg Band; Pep Band; School Play; Washington & Jefferson; Psych.

LITTS, ERIC; Central Bucks East HS; Doylestown, PA; (3); Art Clb; Camera Clb; Ski Clb; Varsity Clb; Chorus; Orch; Yrbk Stf; Socr; Trk; Vllybl.

LITVIN, YAAKOV; Yeshiva Achei Tmimim HS; Milwaukee, WI; (2); FBLA; Rabbincal Schl.

LITZ, DENNY; Curwensville Area HS; Curwensville, PA; (3); Letterman Clb; Bsbl; Bsktbl; Ftbl; High Hon Roll; NHS.

LITZ, REBECCA; Danville HS; Riverside, PA; (3); 13/185; Church Yth Grp; Spanish Clb; SADD; Chorus; Church Choir; Yrbk Stf; High Hon Roll; NHS; NEDT Awd; Pres Schlr; Antonelli; Cmmrcl Art.

LITZELMAN, BRIAN; Liberty JR SR HS; Liberty, PA; (3); German Clb; VP Stu Cncl; Var L Bsktbl; Var Socr; Var Tennis; Hon Roll.

LITZENBERGER, DINA; Boyertown Area SR HS; Boyertown, PA; (4); 3/437; Pres Church Yth Grp; Girl Scts; Chorus; High Hon Roll; NHS; Pres Schlr; Computer Clb; Library Aide; Math Tm; Girl Sct Gold Awd 86; Natl Schl Orchestra Awd 87; Blanche R Boyer Schlrshp 87; Lebanon Valley Coll; Health.

LITZENBERGER, SARA; Bethleham Catholic HS; Riegelsville, PA; (4); 25/200; Key Clb; Ski Clb; Var Bsktbl; Mgr Ftbl; Var Powder Puff Ftbl; Var Capt Sftbl; High Hon Roll; NHS; Natl Lat Awd 86; Boston Coll.

LIU, EDWIN; Greensburg Salem SR HS; Greensburg, PA; (3); Pres German Clb; Band; Concert Band; Jazz Band; Mrchg Band; Orch; Var Tennis; Cit Awd; High Hon Roll; VP Jr NHS; Sci.

LIVELY, MICHELE; Bethlehem Catholic HS; Bethlehem, PA; (3); 40/210; Hosp Aide; Red Cross Aide; SADD; Color Guard; High Hon Roll; First Honors 84-87; Psych.

LIVENGOOD, BRYAN; Freeport Area HS; Sarver, PA; (3); 1/200; Science Clb; Var Bsbl; JV Bsktbl; High Hon Roll; NHS.

LIVENGOOD, JENNIFER; Peters Township HS; Mc Murray, PA; (4); Computer Clb; Dance Clb; FBLA; Letterman Clb; Pep Clb; Ski Clb; SADD; Varsity Clb; Drill Tm; Drm Mjr(t); World Grand Natl Twrlng & Show Corps Champ 78-86; Bus.

LIVERMORE, PATRICE; Nazareth Acad; Phila, PA; (3); Boys Clb Am; Cmnty Wkr; Var Socr; Hon Roll; NHS; Prfct Atten Awd; Sec Frsh Cls; Sec Soph Cls; Sec Jr Cls; Stu Cncl; Sir Thomas J Lipton Bys Clb Sprtsmanshp Awd; Scl Wrk.

LIVI, MICHAEL; Meadville Area SR HS; Meadville, PA; (3); 56/316; Church Yth Grp; School Play; Rep Stu Cncl; Var L Socr; JV Trk; High Hon Roll; Hon Roll.

LIVINGSTON, ANDREW; Quakertown Community HS; Quakertown, PA; (3); Church Yth Grp; Y-Teens; JV Bsktbl; Var Capt Socr; Var Trk; JV Vllybl; High Hon Roll; Hon Roll; Jr NHS; NHS; Am Leg 85; Pres Acad Fit 85; IN U PA; Comp Engrng.

LIVINGSTON, CAMILLE; HS Of Engineering And Science; Philadelphia, PA; (3); 19/250; Cmnty Wkr; Drama Clb; Political Wkr; School Play; Variety Show; Yrbk Stf; High Hon Roll; Hon Roll; NHS; Men Of BACA Art Awd Chrls E Ellis Schlrshp 86; WCAU Radio Play Wrtng Cntst 87; Stu U Penna Cad 86-88; Arch Dsgn.

LIVINGSTON, EDWARD; G Washington Carver HS Engrng & Sci; Philadelphia, PA; (3); 147/256; Art Clb; Camera Clb; Computer Clb; Engrng.

LIVINGSTON, HOLLY; Quakertown Community HS; Quakertown, PA; (3); Cmnty Wkr; Sec Computer Clb; French Clb; Rptr Nwsp Stf; Rptr Yrbk Stf; Tennis; Hon Roll; Jr NHS; NHS; Ntl Merit Ltr; Nwspr Ed Comp Club 85-86; Pres Phys Ftns Awd 85-86 & 86-87.

LIVINGSTON, IVY J; The Episcopal Acad; Philadelphia, PA; (4); Drama Clb; Nwsp Rptr; Var L Fld Hcky; Ntl Merit SF; Science Clb; Spanish Clb; School Musical; School Play; Stage Crew; JV Capt Bsktbl; Cum Laude Society 86; Natl Achvt Schlrshp For Negro Stu Semifnlst 86; John Plant Classics Schlrshp 86; Brown U; Classics.

LIVINGSTON, KELLEY; Fairchance-Georges HS; Smithfield, PA; (4); Church Yth Grp; Dance Clb; FHA; Library Aide; Office Aide; Red Cross Aide; VICA; Chorus; Church Choir; School Play; Choir Stu Of Yr Awd 85; Homcmng Qn 86-87; Creative Wrtng-Singing Cmpttn Awd 86; Singer.

LIVINGSTON, LIZ; Downingtown HS; Exton, PA; (3); 105/648; French Clb; GAA; Ski Clb; SADD; Chorus; Stu Cncl; JV Cheerleading; JV Trk; Hon Roll; Elem Ed.

LIVINGSTON, TIMOTHY; Elizabethtown Area HS; Elizabethtown, PA; (4); 35/224; Teachers Aide; Trs Varsity Clb; Capt Bsbl; Capt Ftbl; Wrstlng; Lion Awd; Athltc Schlrshp For Millersville U 87; Otstndng Athlts In Amer 87; John Campbell Mem Awd Ldrshp 87; Millersville U.

LIVOLSI, JEFFREY; Canon-Mc Millan JR HS; Cecil, PA; (1); Chorus; Hon Roll.

LIVSEY, KRISTENE; Columbia Montour AVTS; Danville, PA; (3); 18/208; Church Yth Grp; SADD; Band; Concert Band; Mrchg Band; Stage Crew; Hon Roll; NHS; Cosmtlgy Clb 85-87; Lock Haven U Of PA; Psych.

LLOYD, BETHANN; Greater Latrobe HS; Latrobe, PA; (4); 67/410; Letterman Clb; Pep Clb; Band; Concert Band; Mrchg Band; Pep Band; Symp Band; Var L Sftbl; High Hon Roll; Prfct Atten Awd; 1st Chr & Solo Cnty Bnd 85; Engsh Stu Mnth 87; IN U; Crmnlgy.

LLOYD, DIANE; Exeter SR HS; Reading, PA; (4); 18/217; Leo Clb; High Hon Roll; Hon Roll; Alvernia Coll; Accntng.

LLOYD, KEVIN; Springdale HS; Springdale, PA; (3); Office Aide; Rep Frsh Cls; Rep Soph Cls; Rep Jr Cls; Rep Stu Cncl; Var Bsktbl; Var Ftbl; Stat Score Keeper; Var Swmmng; Hon Roll; Outstndng Clsrm Achvt Awd 86-87; PA ST Police Amer Leg Yth Wk Dplma 87; Cmmtny Bsd Lrning Law Firm; U Of MI; Bus.

LLOYD, MARK W; Susquehanna Township HS; Harrisburg, PA; (4); 4/155; Am Leg Boys St; Model UN; Teachers Aide; Yrbk Stf; Stu Cncl; Var Bsktbl; High Hon Roll; Hon Roll; NHS; Pres Schlr; Dstngshd Schlr Dplm 87; Annl Schl Sprtsmnshp Awd 86-87; Top 10 Div Scrng Bsktbl 86-87; PA ST U; Engrng.

LLOYD, STEFFANIE; Reading SR HS; Reading, PA; (3); 108/710; Cmnty Wkr; Dance Clb; Drama Clb; FBLA; Pep Clb; PAVAS; Spanish Clb; Teachers Aide; School Musical; School Play.

LLOYD, TAMMANY; Purchase Line HS; Cherry Tree, PA; (2); Spanish Clb; Band; Chorus; Concert Band; Flag Corp; Mrchg Band; Var Twrlr; Hon Roll; Intl Frgn Lang Awd 86-87; Acadc All Am Spnsh 86-87.

LO BELLO, SHANNON; Central HS; Martinsburg, PA; (3); 5/188; Church Yth Grp; FCA; Chorus; Church Choir; High Hon Roll; NHS; Penn ST; Secdry Ed.

LO FASO, RANDALL; Lincoln HS; Ellwood City, PA; (3); French Clb; Acpl Chr; Chorus; Bsktbl; Ftbl; Engrng.

LOBAUGH, TAMARA; Biglerville HS; Aspers, PA; (4); 23/78; Pres Church Yth Grp; Pres FFA; Chorus; Church Choir; Lib Concert Band; School Musical; Hon Roll; Jr NHS; Yrbk Stf; FFA De Kalb Awd 87; Stu Mnth Awd 87; Pres Acdmc Ftnss Awd 87; Wilson Coll; Vet Med Tech.

LOBRON, NEIL; Saint Josephs Prep Schl; Philadelphia, PA; (4); Cmnty Wkr; Drama Clb; German Clb; Science Clb; Service Clb; Yrbk Phtg; Yrbk Stf; JV Socr; Prfct Atten Awd; Grmn Soc PA Schlrshp 87-88; Drexel U Grnt 87-88; PA ST Grnt 87-88; Drexel U.

LOCH, AMY; Elk Lake HS; Springville, PA; (1); 1/108; Art Clb; Trs Church Yth Grp; Spanish Clb; SADD; Band; Jazz Band; Mrchg Band; Var Tennis; High Hon Roll; Vet Med.

LOCH, JAMES; Mountain View JR/Sr HS; Nicholson, PA; (3); 10/105; Camera Clb; Chess Clb; Computer Clb; 4-H; Science Clb; Ski Clb; Band; Concert Band; Mrchg Band; Nwsp Rptr; Mech Engr.

LOCH, JENNIFER; Tunkhannock Area HS; Lake Winola, PA; (2); 6/320; Drama Clb; French Clb; Key Clb; Latin Clb; Letterman Clb; Pep Clb; Political Wkr; Ski Clb; Var Cheerleading; High Hon Roll.

LOCHER, DEAN; North Hills HS; Pittsburgh, PA; (4); 9/490; Science Clb; Pres Band; Drm Mjr(t); Mrchg Band; Orch; Pep Band; Rep Sr Cls; VP Stu Cncl; Hon Roll; NHS; U Of Pittsburgh; Cvl Engrng.

LOCK, RICHARD R; Devon Prep Schl; Paoli, PA; (4); 3/45; Hosp Aide; Nwsp Sprt Ed; Pres Jr Cls; Pres Stu Cncl; Var Socr; Capt Trk; High Hon Roll; NHS; Ntl Merit SF; NEDT Awd; Harvard Bk Awd 86; Devon Prep Gen Exc Awd 86; Devon Prep AP Biol Awd 85; Physcn.

LOCKARD, JENNIFER; Immaculate Conception HS; Washington, PA; (4); 8/52; Yrbk Stf; L Sftbl; High Hon Roll; Hon Roll; Pres NHS; Pres Schlr; Acadmc All Amer 85-86; John Carroll U; Acctng.

LOCKARD, KATHY; Homer-Center HS; Blairsville, PA; (3); #8 In Class; Trs Church Yth Grp; French Clb; Library Aide; Trs SADD; Band; Concert Band; Mrchg Band; Nwsp Stf; NHS.

LOCKE, CAMILLE; General Mc Lane HS; Mc Kean, PA; (3); 32/217; Spanish Clb; Band; Concert Band; Mrchg Band; Pep Band; Yrbk Stf; Rep Stu Cncl; Hon Roll; Rainbow Girl-Wrthy Advsr 87; Schltc Achvt Awds; Stu For Acad Excllnc Advsr; IN U PA; Scndry Educ.

LOCKE, DIANNE; A Lincoln HS; Philadelphia, PA; (3); 40/480; Boy Scts; Hosp Aide; Varsity Clb; Var Vllybl; Hon Roll; X-Ray Tech.

LOCKE, MARIANNE; York Catholic HS; New Freedom, PA; (3); 1/180; Church Yth Grp; Exploring; French Clb; Ski Clb; Varsity Clb; Chorus; L Mgr(s); Var Socr; High Hon Roll; Val.

LOCKE, MICHELLE; Brownsville Area HS; Chestnut Ridge, PA; (4); #14 In Class; Math Clb; Band; Concert Band; Mrchg Band; Hon Roll; Sclgy.

LOCKE, MISSY; Wellsboro Area HS; Wellsboro, PA; (3); 8/175; Drama Clb; Pep Clb; Band; Chorus; Concert Band; Jazz Band; Mrchg Band; Nwsp Rptr; Nwsp Stf; Yrbk Stf; Sprt Am Hnr Band & Chrs Erpn Tr-Dcknsn Coll 87.

LOCKE, PAM; Lincoln HS; Ellwood City, PA; (3); French Clb; Key Clb; SADD; Y-Teens; Chorus; Drill Tm; Mrchg Band; High Hon Roll; Hon Roll; Med.

LOCKE, SUSAN; Sacred Heart Acad; Villanova, PA; (4); Art Clb; Stage Crew; Yrbk Stf; Rep Frsh Cls; Rep Soph Cls; Rep Jr Cls; Sec Sr Cls; Bsktbl; Ftbl; Lcrss.

LOCKE, THERESA; Chesnut Ridge SR HS; New Paris, PA; (2); GAA; Ski Clb; Stat Bsktbl; Var Socr; JV Trk; Hon Roll; Chef.

LOCKERMAN, LAURIE; Vincentian HS; Pittsburgh, PA; (4); 13/61; VP Church Yth Grp; Nwsp Rptr; Yrbk Stf; Pres Frsh Cls; VP Stu Cncl; Var Capt Bsktbl; Sftbl; Hon Roll; NHS; Phy Thrpy.

LOCKEY, KRISTIN; Seneca Valley HS; Harmony, PA; (3); Ski Clb; Capt Pom Pon; High Hon Roll; Hon Roll; NHS; Schltc Achvt Awd 86 & 87.

LOCKHART, AUTUMN; Mc Keesport HS; White Oak, PA; (2); Hosp Aide; Spanish Clb; Orch; School Musical; Hon Roll; Psych.

LOCKLIN, ANN; Rockwood HS; Champion, PA; (3); 13/88; Drama Clb; NFL; Ski Clb; Band; Chorus; School Play; Nwsp Stf; VP Stu Cncl; Cheerleading; Stat Sftbl; Comm.

LOCKLIN, JAY; Western Wayne HS; Moscow, PA; (2); Hon Roll; Prfct Atten Awd; Natl Gld Piano Plyrs 86.

LOCKWOOD, CAROLYN; New Covenant Acad; Wellsboro, PA; (3); 1/10; Church Yth Grp; Debate Tm; Drama Clb; Ski Clb; School Musical; School Play; Yrbk Ed-Chief; Capt Bsktbl; Capt Socr; 1st Pl Hgh Schl Sci Fair 85; 2nd Pl Instrmntl Teen Tlnt Cntst 86; VP Grls Guild 85-87; Lwyr.

LOCKWOOD, PHILIP; South Western HS; Hanover, PA; (2); Pres Church Yth Grp; JA; Key Clb; School Musical; Nwsp Stf; Yrbk Stf; JV Capt Ftbl; Im Wrstlng; Hon Roll; Rotry Intl Exch Stu 87-88.

LOCY, DENNIS; Trinity HS; Washington, PA; (3); 4-H; FFA; German Clb; Publc Spkng 85; Penn ST; Electrcl Engr.

LODATO, ROBERT; Council Rock HS; Churchville, PA; (3); 356/908; Mrchg Band; BFA.

LODKEY, DIANE; Perry Traditional Acad; Pittsburgh, PA; (3); 4/190; Church Yth Grp; Drama Clb; Band; Church Choir; Ed Nwsp Ed-Chief; Rep Frsh Cls; Cheerleading; High Hon Roll; Jr NHS; NHS; Bus.

LODY, JOHN; Shade Central City HS; Central City, PA; (3); 5/80; CAP; Letterman Clb; Varsity Clb; Sec Soph Cls; VP Jr Cls; Var L Bsktbl; Var L Tennis; Var L Trk; Hon Roll; NHS; U Of Pittsburgh.

LOEB, RICHARD; Ridley HS; Woodlyn, PA; (3); 9/436; Thesps; School Musical; School Play; Stage Crew; JV Lcrss; JV Trk; High Hon Roll; Hon Roll; Pres Schlr; Most Academic Boy 84-85; VA Tech; Chem Engr.

LOEDDING, MARK; Ambridge Area HS; Sewickley, PA; (3); Am Leg Boys St; Church Yth Grp; Pep Clb; Var Bsbl; Hon Roll; Frstry.

LOEFFLER, JULIA; St Marys Area HS; St Marys, PA; (2); 3/301; Cmnty Wkr; Hosp Aide; Stu Cncl; JV L Cheerleading; Var L Swmmng; Hon Roll; HOBY Ldrshp Sem Ambssdr 87; Seneca Highlands Summr Acad Gifted/Tlntd Stu 87; Spn Cert Merit 87.

LOEFFLER, SHARON; Bishop Conwell HS; Langhorne, PA; (3); 4/278; Library Aide; Scholastic Bowl; SADD; Teachers Aide; JV Trk; High Hon Roll; Sec NHS; Prfct Atten Awd; Vet.

LOFGREN, KENNETH; South Allegheny HS; Elizabeth, PA; (3); Band; Concert Band; Jazz Band; Mrchg Band; Elec Engr.

LOFTS, ROY; Yough HS; W Newton, PA; (3); Boy Scts; Computer Clb; Math Tm; Tennis; Trk; Wt Lftg; Wrstlng; Navy.

LOFTUS, ANNETTE; Cumberland Valley HS; Camp Hill, PA; (3); 4/595; Key Clb; Latin Clb; Rep Stu Cncl; JV Capt Cheerleading; High Hon Roll; Amer Lgn Schl Awd 84; Ntl Hnr Scty 85; Ntl Art Hnr Scty 86; Fine Arts Mgmt.

LOFTUS, KENNY; Mahanoy Area HS; Mahanoy City, PA; (3); Spanish Clb; SADD; Band; Concert Band; Mrchg Band; Var Swmmng; Hon Roll; Cmnty Wkr; Nwsp Rptr; Nwsp Stf; Lttmn Swtr For Bnd, News Edtr For Nwspapr 86-87; Penn ST; Elem Ed.

LOGAN, KAY M; Youngsville HS; Youngsville, PA; (4); FBLA; Spanish Clb; NHS; Outstndng Stu-Chem Srvy-Phtgrphy Crce 87; Hghst Avg Spnsh IV 87; Scl Sci 87; Army; Trrn Anlys.

LOGAN, KRISTIANNE; Daniel Boone HS; Douglassville, PA; (2); 2/172; Church Yth Grp; French Clb; Trs JA; Yrbk Stf; Var Cheerleading; Trk; High Hon Roll; Opt Clb Awd; PA Gov Schl Arts Modern Dance 87; Child Psych.

LOGAN, LARA; Connellsville Area HS; Connellsville, PA; (3); 34/530; Church Yth Grp; Dance Clb; French Clb; Girl Scts; Pep Clb; Acpl Chr; Chorus; Drm Mjr(t); Mrchg Band; School Musical; Denison U; Dance.

LOGAR, DAVID; Girard HS; Girard, PA; (2); Var L Bsbl; JV Bsktbl; Hon Roll; Prfct Atten Awd; Hon Men Cnty Leag Bsebl 87.

LOGERO, CHRIS; Leechburg Area HS; Leechburg, PA; (2); 24/96; Art Clb; Math Tm; Spanish Clb; Varsity Clb; Sec Frsh Cls; Stu Cncl; Var L Bsbl; Var L Bsktbl; Var Capt Ftbl; Wt Lftg; Pittsburgh U; Arch.

LOGHING, DAVID L; Lower Moreland HS; Huntingdon Vly, PA; (4); 13/200; Intnl Clb; Nwsp Rptr; Lit Mag; High Hon Roll; Ntl Merit SF; St Schlr; 11th Grade Hstry Awd; Materials Sci.

LOGIC, JOSEPH; Octorara HS; Christiana, PA; (3); Computer Clb; Var Crs Cntry; JV Trk; Hon Roll; Bus.

LOGUE, ADRIAN; Chestnut Ridge HS; Manns Choice, PA; (3); 18/137; Band; Mrchg Band; Var Bsbl; Var Bsktbl; NHS; Accntng.

LOH, LAWRENCE; Carlisle SR HS; Carlisle, PA; (3); 57/454; Church Yth Grp; Concert Band; Drm Mjr(t); Mrchg Band; School Musical; Tennis; Trk; Hon Roll; Schlstc Achvt Awd; Co Dist & Reg Band; Med.

LOHMAN, DEBRA; Cumberland Valley HS; Mechanicsburg, PA; (3); 51/571; Key Clb; Latin Clb; Chorus; Hon Roll; NHS; Latn Hnrs 85-87; Centrl PA Schlstc Awd Wrtng Shrt Stry, 1st Pl Cptl Area Clsscs Fstvl Comp Pgm 87; Smith Coll; Poltcl Sci.

LOHR, AMY; Open Door Christian Acad; Greensburg, PA; (4); Church Yth Grp; Quiz Bowl; Teachers Aide; Chorus; Yrbk Ed-Chief; Vllybl; Hon Roll; 1st Pl Vllybl Cmptn 85-86; Pensacola Christian Coll; Ed.

LOHR, SUSAN E; Mifflinburg Area HS; Mifflinburg, PA; (3); Am Leg Aux Girls St; Key Clb; Spanish Clb; Band; Concert Band; Mrchg Band; Pep Band; Trk; High Hon Roll; NHS; Marine Bio.

LOIELO, DANIEL; Central HS; Philadelphia, PA; (2); Boy Scts; Computer Clb; Hon Roll.

LOIZES, STELLA K; Penn Hills SR HS; Verona, PA; (4); 73/616; Sec Church Yth Grp; Drama Clb; Hosp Aide; Science Clb; Spanish Clb; Nwsp Bus Mgr; Stu Cncl; Im Vllybl; Hon Roll; NHS; Med.

LOKAY, JOSETTE; Allentown Central Catholic HS; Northampton, PA; (3); Key Clb; Pep Clb; Ski Clb; Co-Capt Color Guard; Co-Capt Drill Tm; Stat Bsktbl; Mgr(s); Powder Puff Ftbl; Score Keeper; Hon Roll; Drexel; Bus.

LOMAGO, DEAN; Ringgold HS; Monongahela, PA; (4); 1/343; Aud/Vis; Trs Church Yth Grp; Var L Golf; Var L Socr; Bausch & Lomb Sci Awd; High Hon Roll; Pres NHS; Ntl Merit Ltr; Val; Amer Leg Schl Awd Dist Achvt 84; High Q Comptn Geneva Coll Rnrs Up Team Capt 86; WA & Jeff Coll; Medicine.

LOMAISTRO, STEVEN; Central HS; Philadelphia, PA; (2); Im Bsktbl; Var Crs Cntry; Var Trk; Hon Roll; Invstmnt Bnkr.

LOMAS, RHONDA; Mahanoy Area HS; Mahanoy Plane, PA; (3); FHA; Spanish Clb; Capt Color Guard; Nwsp Stf; Trk; Hon Roll; Sec Trs NHS; Bus Adm.

LOMAX, ANDREW; York Suburban HS; York, PA; (3); 16/176; Church Yth Grp; Nwsp Sprt Ed; Var L Socr; Var L Vllybl; High Hon Roll; Hon Roll; NHS; Ntl Merit Ltr; IN U Of PA Physics Tstng Comptn Wnnr.

LOMBARD, BARBARA; Gwynedd-Mercy Acad; Centre Sq, PA; (2); Service Clb; Im Fld Hcky; JV Lcrss; Intr Dsgn.

LOMBARDI, BECKY; Mon Valley Catholic HS; Charleroi, PA; (3); 2/98; Church Yth Grp; Pres Service Clb; Nwsp Rptr; Ed Yrbk Stf; Var JV Cheerleading; Hon Roll; NHS; Spanish NHS; Cmnty Wkr; Library Aide; HOBY Ldrshp Awd 85-86; Pittsburgh Diocesean Yth Cncl 86-88; 2nd Pl Awd Spanish Hum Day 86-87; Notre Dame; Bus Adm.

LOMBARDI, CHRISTOPHER; Ringgold HS; Finleyville, PA; (3); Drama Clb; School Musical; School Play; Variety Show; Pres Jr Cls; Ftbl; Gov Hon Prg Awd; High Hon Roll; Boy Scts; Ski Clb; Sci/Math Hnr Soc 86; ST Fnlst-PA Govrs Schl For Prfmg Era 85; MVP Vrsty Ftbl 84; Cmmnctns.

LOMBARDI, CHRISTOPHER J; Seneca Valley HS; Mars, PA; (3); 48/350; Am Leg Boys St; ROTC; JV Bsktbl; High Hon Roll; Hon Roll; Prfct Atten Awd; Superior Cadet Awd JROTC & Acad Achvt Awd 86-87; Bus Admin.

LOMBARDI, JAMIE; Meadville Area SR HS; Meadville, PA; (2); German Clb; Socr; Trk; High Hon Roll; 2nd Pl Dist 10 87; 3rd Pl ST PA Hstry Day 87; 3rd Pl Grmn Vocab Tst Slippery Rock U Frgn Lang Day 87.

LOMBARDO, ALICIA; Bishop Guilfoyle HS; Altoona, PA; (3); Dance Clb; Library Aide; SADD; Chorus; Var JV Cheerleading; High Hon Roll; Hon Roll; Fnlst All-Amer Chrldr 86; Dance Schlrshp-Alleghy Dance Co84; Chrldng Squad 1st Pl Tri-Cnty Comptn 86; Temple; Physcl Thrpst.

LOMBARDO, DIANA; Mohawk JR SR HS; New Castle, PA; (4); 20/135; Pres Latin Clb; Chorus; Color Guard; Flag Corp; School Musical; School Play; Stage Crew; Yrbk Phtg; Yrbk Stf; Stat Bsktbl; Penn ST U; Elec Engr.

LOMBARDO, DONNA; Exeter Township SR HS; Birdsboro, PA; (3); Drama Clb; Leo Clb; Library Aide; Red Cross Aide; Y-Teens; Score Keeper; Hon Roll; Pre-Law.

LOMBARDO, FRANCIS; Pittson Area SR HS; Pittston, PA; (3); 6/305; Math Clb; Crs Cntry; Trk; L Wrstlng; High Hon Roll; NHS; Scranton U; Pre-Med.

LOMBARDO, LOUIS; Center HS; Monaca, PA; (3); Drama Clb; Library Aide; Spanish Clb; Chorus; School Musical; Nwsp Rptr; Hon Roll; Ucla; Drama.

LOMBOY, CRAIG; William Allen HS; Allentown, PA; (2); Var L Tennis; Hon Roll; Jr NHS.

LONAS, JENNIFER; United HS; New Florence, PA; (1); Band; Concert Band; Mrchg Band; Trk; Vllybl; Stat Wrstlng; High Hon Roll; Hon Roll; Prfct Atten Awd.

LONCZYNSKI, JEANINE; West Hazleton HS; W Hazleton, PA; (2); Church Yth Grp; Dance Clb; Girl Scts; Pep Clb; PAVAS; Spanish Clb; SADD; Thesps; Chorus; Color Guard; Psych.

LONDON, JASON; Parkland HS; Allentown, PA; (3); 49/481; Aud/Vis; Library Aide; Ski Clb; Var Socr.

LONDON, KAREN; Curwensville HS; Curwensville, PA; (3); Drama Clb; Ski Clb; Varsity Clb; Yrbk Stf; Sec Soph Cls; VP Jr Cls; Capt Cheerleading; Gym; High Hon Roll; NHS.

LONDON, SUSAN; Upper Merion Area HS; King Of Prussa, PA; (4); 8/276; Pres Intnl Clb; Pres Model UN; Pres Service Clb; Chorus; NHS; Ntl Merit Ltr; Pres Schlr; Rotary Awd; Hosp Aide; Math Tm; Outstndng Achvt Schlrshp Temple U 87; Soc Studies Deptmnt Awd 87; Peace & Freedom Awd 87; Temple U; Psychlgy.

LONERGAN, LAUREN; Cardinal O Hara HS; Broomall, PA; (3); 5/737; Latin Clb; Spanish Clb; Nwsp Rptr; Ed Nwsp Stf; Lit Mag; Rep Frsh Cls; Rep Soph Cls; Rep Sr Cls; Rep Stu Cncl; Bsktbl; Prncpl Awd For Acadc Excllnc; Hghst Gen Avg Awd Sbjct Geom & Hstry; Pol Sci.

LONG, ANDREA; Quakertown SR HS; Quakertown, PA; (2); 49/359; Chorus; Stage Crew; Rep Stu Cncl; Stat Fld Hcky; Hon Roll; Jr NHS; NHS; Mgr(s); Pres Acad Ftns & Physcl Ftns Mrt Achct Awds 86-87; Fshn Dsgn.

LONG, ANTHONY; Hazleton SR HS; Hazleton, PA; (2); Church Yth Grp; Nwsp Ed-Chief; Yrbk Stf; JV Bsktbl; Var Golf; Hon Roll; Hugh O Brian Outstndng Soph 86-87; Pres Acdmc Fit Awd 85-86; Am Legn Awd 85-86.

LONG, BRIAN; Upper Darby HS; Upr Darby, PA; (2); Church Yth Grp; School Musical; Swmmng; Tennis.

LONG, CARLEEN M; Cambria Heights SR HS; Carrolltown, PA; (3); SADD; Teachers Aide; Band; Concert Band; Jazz Band; Mrchg Band; Mgr(s); Hon Roll; Ski Clb; Cambria County Band Fest 84-85 & 87; PA Music Educ Assn Dist 6 Band Fest 86; ICM Schl Bus.

LONG, CAROLYN; Baldwin HS; Pittsburgh, PA; (3); 69/477; Band; Sec Sr Cls; Var Bsktbl; Var Trk; Var Vllybl; Hon Roll; Pres Acdmc Achvt Awd 85; Elem Educ.

LONG, CAROLYN; Meyersdale Area HS; Hyndman, PA; (3); Church Yth Grp; French Clb; Chorus; Church Choir; Yrbk Stf; Hon Roll; Frostburg ST U; Dntstry.

LONG, CATHY; Vincetian HS; Gibsonia, PA; (3); Service Clb; Chorus; Off Jr Cls; JV Fld Hcky; High Hon Roll; Bstn Coll Hrvrd; Psychlgy.

LONG, DANIEL; Bishop Carroll HS; Ebensburg, PA; (3); 6/128; Church Yth Grp; Ski Clb; Spanish Clb; Stage Crew; L Ftbl; NHS; Engrng.

LONG, DAWN; Perkiomen Valley HS; Trappe, PA; (3); Church Yth Grp; Cmnty Wkr; Office Aide; Teachers Aide; Chorus; Church Choir; Color Guard; JV Cheerleading; Hon Roll; NHS; Acadmc Achvt Awd 87; Speech Pthlgy.

LONG, DEANNA; Wyoming Valley West; Kingston, PA; (2); Radio Clb; Ski Clb; Hon Roll.

LONG, GORDON; Shamokin Area HS; Shamokin, PA; (2); 46/240; Camera Clb; Rep Soph Cls; JV Bsbl; Hon Roll; Med.

LONG, GREGG; Corry Area HS; Corry, PA; (3); Boy Scts; Church Yth Grp; 4-H; Spanish Clb; VICA; Bsktbl; Trk; Cit Awd; Hon Roll; Carpntr.

LONG, HEATHER; Pleasant Valley HS; Effort, PA; (3); Drama Clb; VP German Clb; Math Tm; Ski Clb; Lit Mag; Rep Soph Cls; JV Bsktbl; Var Fld Hcky; JV Trk; Hon Roll; Top 20 85-86; Bio.

LONG, JAMES; Bensalem HS; Trevose, PA; (2); Church Yth Grp; Band; Chorus; Church Choir; Concert Band; Madrigals; Mrchg Band; Ftbl; Trk; Hon Roll; MIP Trk 87.

LONG, JENNIFER; State College Area Schl District; State College, PA; (1); Church Yth Grp; Drama Clb; Thesps; Band; Concert Band; School Musical; Yrbk Phtg; Yrbk Stf; Vllybl; JV Vllybl Ltrd 86; Golden Poet Awd 87; Great Amercn Poetry Anthology Publctn 87.

LONG, JENNIFER; State College Intermediate HS; Pine Grove Mills, PA; (3); Art Clb; 4-H; Chorus; Church Choir; Hon Roll.

LONG, JEROME; Harrisburg HS; Harrisburg, PA; (3); 29/275; Am Leg Boys St; Yrbk Stf; Rep Soph Cls; Rep Jr Cls; Elks Awd; Hon Roll; NHS; Prfct Atten Awd; Var Bsbl; Var JV Bsktbl; Elks Oratrcl Cont Wnnr 85; Accntng.

LONG, JULIE; Northwestern HS; W Springfield, PA; (3); 20/160; Drama Clb; Thesps; Mrchg Band; Stage Crew; Var Trk; Hon Roll; Band; Concert Band; Athltc Trnr Bsktbl 86-87; Cls Histrn 86-88; Pre-Medicine.

LONG, KELLI; Lehighton Area HS; Lehighton, PA; (3); 9/246; Pres Church Yth Grp; Girl Scts; Hosp Aide; SADD; Sec Soph Cls; VP Jr Cls; VP Sr Cls; Pres Stu Cncl; Var JV Cheerleading; Coach Actv; Am Leg Essay Cont Fin 86-87; Elem Ed.

LONG JR, KEVIN; Warren Area HS; Warren, PA; (3); Church Yth Grp; Cmnty Wkr; Letterman Clb; Varsity Clb; School Play; JV Var Bsktbl; Var Golf; High Hon Roll; Hon Roll; Slvr B 84; PA ST U; Engrng.

LONG, KIM; Harrisburg Christian HS; Harrisburg, PA; (2); Church Yth Grp; School Play; Var L Cheerleading; Hon Roll; Schl Hnr Soc 86-87.

LONG, KIM; Shamokin Area HS; Shamokin, PA; (2); Drama Clb; German Clb; Key Clb; Pep Clb; Science Clb; SADD; Hon Roll; Bloomsburg U; Engl Tchr.

LONG, KIMBERLY; Elizabeth Forward HS; Bunola, PA; (3); 12/345; Church Yth Grp; Concert Band; Mrchg Band; High Hon Roll; NHS; Bio.

LONG, KRISTINE; Valley HS; New Kensington, PA; (3); 8/260; Pep Clb; Sec Science Clb; Spanish Clb; Varsity Clb; Yrbk Stf; Var L Tennis; Capt Twrlr; JV Vllybl; High Hon Roll; NHS; Acad All-Amer 86; Pharm.

LONG, LORI B; Bishop Guilfoyle HS; Altoona, PA; (3); 12/156; Yrbk Stf; Jr Cls; Cheerleading; High Hon Roll; Hon Roll; Law.

LONG, LORRAINE; Harrisburg HS; Harrisburg, PA; (4); 11/227; Church Yth Grp; Cmnty Wkr; Band; Chorus; Church Choir; Concert Band; Jazz Band; Mrchg Band; Orch; Rep Stu Cncl; Most Outstndng Stu Music 84; 1st Rnnr Up Most Talntd 86-87; Millersville U; Music Ed.

LONG, MELISSA; Seneca Valley HS; Zelienople, PA; (4); 3/357; Ski Clb; Thesps; Chorus; L Mrchg Band; Symp Band; Var L Trk; NHS; 1st & 2nd Yr Schltc Achvt Awds 85-87; Sthwst Btlr Cnty Educ Assn Schlrshp 87; Geneva Coll; Bio.

LONG, MICHAEL; Brandywine Heights HS; Alburtis, PA; (2); Cmnty Wkr; Political Wkr.

LONG, MICHAEL; Mt Pleasant Area SR HS; Mt Pleasant, PA; (2); Church Yth Grp; German Clb; Church Choir; Concert Band; Jazz Band; Mrchg Band; Pep Band; Hon Roll; Pres Schlr; County Band 86; Musician.

LONG, MICHELE; Penns Valley Area HS; Centre Hall, PA; (3); 42/146; Church Yth Grp; Pep Clb; Varsity Clb; Band; Concert Band; Mrchg Band; Capt Bsktbl; Var Sftbl; Clarion ST U; Elem Educ.

LONG, MICHELLE; Mt Pleasant SR HS; Latrobe, PA; (4); 87/250; Art Clb; FBLA; FHA; GAA; Spanish Clb; Color Guard; Mat Maids; Hon Roll; Spanish NHS; Mt Pleasant Bus Club Schlrshp 87; Mary Zabkar Home Ec Awd Schlrshp 87; Gregg Filing Awd 87; Bus Careers Inst; Accounting.

LONG, PAMELA; Ringgold HS; Donora, PA; (4); 19/300; Church Yth Grp; FHA; Band; Concert Band; Mrchg Band; High Hon Roll; Hon Roll; NHS; Camp Fr Inc; SADD; Donora Forecast Awd 86-87; Monongaheld Womens Club Hmkng Awd 86-87; Erly Chldhd Educ.

LONG, PENNY; Pine Grove Area HS; Tremont, PA; (4); 1/116; Quiz Bowl; Yrbk Ed-Chief; Rep Stu Cncl; JV Vllybl; Dnfth Awd; NHS; Val; Chorus; School Musical; Yrbk Stf; Stu Month 86; HOBY Awd 85; Stu Forum Sec 86-87; Albright Coll; Bus Adm.

LONG, SANDY; Downingtown HS; Downingtown, PA; (4); Exploring; Hosp Aide; Ski Clb; SADD; Flag Corp; Yrbk Stf; Sftbl; Mgr Wrstlng; Cit Awd; Hon Roll; Living Arts Awd 86 & 87; Immaculata; Med.

LONG, SHEREE; Washington HS; Washington, PA; (3); French Clb; Letterman Clb; SADD; Band; Concert Band; Mrchg Band; Pres Orch; Yrbk Stf; Trk; Hon Roll; PMEA SR High Dist Orchstra 84-87; Hnr Strings & Bnd 86; Crimnl Law.

LONG, SHIRLEY; Bishop Carroll HS; Ebensburg, PA; (3); Spanish Clb; Trk; Hon Roll.

LONG, STACEY; Monongahela Valley Cath HS; Beallsville, PA; (3); 27/107; Church Yth Grp; Drama Clb; Ski Clb; School Musical; School Play; Nwsp Phtg; Yrbk Phtg; Yrbk Stf; Sec Frsh Cls; Natl Sci Olympd Chem 87; Johnson & Wales; Culinary Arts.

LONG, TRACY; Leechburg Area HS; Leechburg, PA; (3); Art Clb; Nwsp Stf; Stat Bsktbl; Hon Roll; NHS.

LONG, TRACY; Waynesburg Central HS; Waynesburg, PA; (3); Art Clb; Cmnty Wkr; Computer Clb; 4-H; JA; Model UN; Pep Clb; Ski Clb; Yrbk Phtg; Yrbk Stf; Associated Schools Inc; Trvl.

LONG, TRICIA; Chambersburg Area SR HS; Chambersburg, PA; (3); 14/635; Am Leg Aux Girls St; Church Yth Grp; Office Aide; Varsity Clb; Orch; JCL; Latin Clb; Pep Clb; Stu Cncl; JV Bsktbl; Natl Hyist Day Awd 86; Miss Amercn Co-Ed ST Finlst 87; All East Tourney Team Sftbbl 86; West Point; Physics.

LONG JR, WILLIAM A; Lock Haven HS; Blanchard, PA; (4); 1/242; Pres Church Yth Grp; French Clb; Sec Key Clb; Jazz Band; Variety Show; Bsktbl; High Hon Roll; Prfct Atten Awd; Rotary Awd; Val; Delg Hugh O Brian Yth Ldrshp Smnr 85; Excell Physics 86; Assoc Cnty Educ Schlrshp 87; PA ST U; Engr.

LONGACRE, MELISSA; Perkiomen Valley HS; Collegeville, PA; (3); Church Yth Grp; Debate Tm; Office Aide; VP Acpl Chr; Chorus; Church Choir; School Musical; School Play; Lit Mag; Stu Cncl; Allentown Coll; Actng Thtr.

LONGACRE, TAMMY; East Juniata HS; Richfield, PA; (4); Chess Clb; Stat Bsktbl; Var Fld Hcky; Stat Ftbl; Stat Trk; Blmsbrg U.

LONGAKER, MARK S; The Hill Schl; Pottstown, PA; (4); Cmnty Wkr; Hosp Aide; Latin Clb; Im Gym; Im Socr; Im Tennis; High Hon Roll; Ntl Merit SF; Rotary Awd; Latin, Greek & Eng Hnrs, Natl Greek Exam Hi Hnrs, Latin Prze, Alg Hnrs, Alumnus Prze, Rotary Awd.

LONGENBACH, DAVID; Parkland SR HS; Coplay, PA; (3); 201/481; German Clb.

LONGENBACH, LYNN; Allentown Central Catholic HS; Allentown, PA; (4); Church Yth Grp; School Musical; Nwsp Stf; Rep Soph Cls; Rep Stu Cncl; Mgr(s); Score Keeper; Hon Roll; Prfct Atten Awd; U Of Pittsburgh; Pre-Law.

LONGENBERGER, LORI; Bloomsburg HS; Bloomsburg, PA; (3); Pep Clb; Varsity Clb; Band; Symp Band; Hst Soph Cls; Hst Stu Cncl; Cheerleading; Powder Puff Ftbl; Capt Sftbl; Capt Twrlr; Bloomsburg U; Bus Adm.

LONGENECKER, AMY; Lebanon SR HS; Lebanon, PA; (4); 27/266; JCL; Key Clb; Keywanettes; SADD; Teachers Aide; School Musical; NHS; Church Yth Grp; Latin Clb; Chorus; Muscial Theatre Awd 87; Cedar Awd 87; Cert Tutrng Non-Engl Spkng Stu 85; Millersville U; Bio.

LONGENECKER, CHUCK; Hollidaysburg SR HS; Duncansville, PA; (3); 197/371; German Clb; ROTC; SADD; Sec Trs Soph Cls; JV Ftbl; Engr.

LONGENECKER, JENNIFER; Juniata HS; Pt Royal, PA; (3); Cmnty Wkr; Computer Clb; 4-H; Spanish Clb; SADD; Band; Concert Band; Jazz Band; Mrchg Band; JV Trk; ST Spllng Bee 83-84; Vet Asst.

LONGENECKER, KATHY; Donegal HS; Mount Joy, PA; (3); 17/176; Pres Church Yth Grp; Band; Yrbk Stf; Var Crs Cntry; Powder Puff Ftbl; Hon Roll; Soc Sci.

LONGLEY, JENNIFER JO; Nazareth Area SR HS; Easton, PA; (3); Key Clb; Chorus; Color Guard; Flag Corp; Mrchg Band; School Musical; Yrbk Stf; Lgl Secty.

LONGLEY, KIM; Northampton HS; Bath, PA; (4); 120/430; FBLA; Fld Hcky; Wilma Boyd Schl; Bus.

LONTZ, LORI; Williams Valley HS; Wiconisco, PA; (1); Church Yth Grp; Dance Clb; Band; Chorus; Concert Band; Mrchg Band; Pep Band; Symp Band; Twrlr; Hon Roll.

LONZETTA, LORI; Bishop Hafey HS; Hazleton, PA; (2); French Clb; Hosp Aide; Key Clb; Ski Clb; High Hon Roll.

LOOKGBILL, SCOTT; Hershey SR HS; Hummelstown, PA; (3); 81/203; Pep Clb; Ski Clb; Concert Band; Lit Mag; Var L Crs Cntry; Var Trk; High Hon Roll; Ntl Merit SF; Spanish NHS; Silver & Bronze Medal Natl Sci Olympiad 85; Gold Mdls PA ST Sci Olympiad 85; PA ST; Geology.

LOPARDO, LISA; New Hope-Solebury HS; New Hope, PA; (3); 1/70; Ski Clb; Band; Sec Frsh Cls; Trs Jr Cls; Rep Stu Cncl; L Fld Hcky; Socr; Cit Awd; High Hon Roll; NHS; Acad All Amer 86; Pre-Law.

LOPATA, ANDREA; Aliquippa JR SR HS; Aliquippa, PA; (4); 7/141; French Clb; Hosp Aide; Concert Band; Mrchg Band; Yrbk Stf; Off Jr Cls; Off Sr Cls; High Hon Roll; Hon Roll; PA ST U; Pre-Law.

LOPER, JILL DIANE; North Allegheny HS; Pittsburgh, PA; (4); JA; Yrbk Stf; JV Fld Hcky; Penn ST.

LOPER, LISA; Chester HS; Chester, PA; (3); Drama Clb; Exploring; Pep Clb; Spanish Clb; School Play; Off Jr Cls; Cheerleading; Sftbl; Cit Awd; Spnsh Awd 86-87; Penn ST U; Med.

LOPER, PHIL; North Allegheny Intermediate HS; Pittsburgh, PA; (2); 148/630; JV Ice Hcky; Hon Roll; Bus Mgmt.

LOPES, ALICIA; Big Beaver Falls SR HS; Beaver Falls, PA; (3); 26/170; Hst FHA; Band; Chorus; Mrchg Band; Trs Soph Cls; L Stat Trk; Hon Roll; IUP; X-Ray Tech.

LOPEZ, DONATO; Pennsbury HS; Fairless Hills, PA; (4); 284/777; French Clb; SADD; Stu Cncl; Ftbl; Trk; Wrstlng; Hon Roll; Drexel U; Mech Engrng.

LOPEZ, FLOR; Mastbaum Voc Tech; Philadelphia, PA; (4); Temple U; Comp Sci.

LOPINSKI, JULIE; Northern HS; Dillsburg, PA; (4); 38/201; Church Yth Grp; Quiz Bowl; Band; Chorus; School Musical; Stage Crew; Nwsp Stf; French Hon Soc; NHS; Peer Cnslr 85-87; IN U Of PA; Spch Path.

LOPUS, ALLEN; Peters Township HS; Venetia, PA; (3); Varsity Clb; Var JV Bsktbl; Coach Actv; L Var Socr; High Hon Roll; Hon Roll; NHS; Ntl Merit Ltr; Garner Acadmc Awd 84-86.

LOPUS, CINDY; Warren Area HS; Buffalo, NY; (3); High Hon Roll; Hon Roll; Merit Roll 84-85; Art Dsgn.

LORAH, MELISSA; Mahanoy Area HS; Delano, PA; (4); 8/112; Church Yth Grp; Drama Clb; Trs French Clb; Chorus; Pep Band; Nwsp Stf; Trk; Hon Roll; NHS; NEDT Awd; Early Admissn To Penn ST U 86-87; Kunkle Schlrshp 86-87; Rotary Schlrshp 86-87; Cathlc Dghts Awd 86-87; Penn ST U; Telecommnctns Tech.

LORAH, MICHAEL; Mahonoy Area HS; Mahanoy City, PA; (3); JV Bsktbl; JV Var Ftbl; JV Var Wt Lftg; God Cntry Awd; Acad All Amercn 86; PA ST; Engrng.

LORAH, PAM; Tamaqua Area HS; Tamaqua, PA; (3); Church Yth Grp; Drama Clb; Girl Scts; Q&S; Flag Corp; School Musical; Nwsp Rptr; Nwsp Stf; Swmmng; High Hon Roll; Keystone Awd Jrnlsm 87; Penn ST U; Bus Admin.

LORAH, TAMMY; Lehighton Area HS; Lehighton, PA; (1); Church Yth Grp; VP Girl Scts; Hosp Aide; Library Aide; SADD; Hon Roll; PA ST U; Archeolgy.

LORD, CYNTHIA; Altoona Area HS; Altoona, PA; (3); 465/796; FTA; Key Clb; Band; Concert Band; Mrchg Band; Lit Mag; Sec Church Yth Grp; Penn ST U; Tchr.

LORD, LAURA; Yough HS; Irwin, PA; (3); 21/250; Sec Trs 4-H; Office Aide; Spanish Clb; Yrbk Ed-Chief; Powder Puff Ftbl; 4-H Awd; High Hon Roll; NHS.

LORD, LAUREL; Wyalusing Valley HS; New Albany, PA; (3); German Clb; Girl Scts; Science Clb; Spanish Clb; SADD; Cit Awd; Hon Roll; Ntl Merit Ltr; Penn ST; Scdnry Ed.

LORD, LISA; Purchase Line HS; Cherry Tree, PA; (2); Spanish Clb; Concert Band; Mrchg Band; Stat Bsktbl; Stat Ftbl; Hon Roll; Acadc Al-Amer 85-87; Comp Pgmng.

LORD, LOUISE; Purchase Line HS; Cherry Tree, PA; (4); 30/109; Hst Trs FBLA; Stat Trk; Hon Roll; Acdmc All Amer, Prsdntl Acdmc Ftnss Awd 87; Outstndng Bus Stu Awd 85 & 86; Du Bois Business Coll; Accntng.

LORD, LYNDA; Minersville Area HS; Minersville, PA; (3); 17/120; Cmnty Wkr; Ski Clb; Chorus; School Musical; Pres Soph Cls; VP Jr Cls; Off Stu Cncl; Cheerleading; Sftbl; JR Garland Group; Bus.

LORD, MELISSA KAY; Lake-Lehman HS; Wilkes-Barre, PA; (4); 4/156; Pep Clb; SADD; School Play; Rep Stu Cncl; Var Cheerleading; High Hon Roll; Jr NHS; NHS; Prsdntl Schlrshp Susquhnna U 87; Susquehanna U; Med Tech.

LORD, MICHELL; Lake Lehman HS; Hunlock Crk, PA; (4); 54/162; SADD; PA ST; Phys Thrpy.

LORD, RICHARD; Conrad Weiser HS; Robesonia, PA; (2); 9/163; Drama Clb; JCL; Key Clb; Quiz Bowl; Spanish Clb; Chorus; School Musical; Bsktbl; Trk; Hon Roll; Prsdntl Ftnss Awd 87; Aerontcl Engrng.

LOREK, MICHELLE; Henderson HS; West Chester, PA; (3); 48/390; Church Yth Grp; Cmnty Wkr; Red Cross Aide; Nwsp Stf; Rep Jr Cls; Stu Cncl; JV Lcrss; Im Vllybl; Hon Roll; NHS; Comm.

LORELLI, DAWN; Punxsutawney Area HS; Anita, PA; (4); 44/380; Art Clb; Church Yth Grp; Drama Clb; French Clb; GAA; Variety Show; Capt Cheerleading; Var L Vllybl; High Hon Roll; IN U PA Accptnce 87; Mary Jacobs Scholar 87; IUP; Elem Ed.

LORELLI, LISA; Punxsutawney Area HS; Punxsutawney, PA; (3); Art Clb; French Clb; FNA; Hosp Aide; Church Choir; Cheerleading; Amer Lgn Awd 84; Nrsng.

LORENCE, COLLEEN; Peters Township HS; Mc Murray, PA; (3); Dance Clb; FBLA; Varsity Clb; School Play; Yrbk Stf; Rep Stu Cncl; Var Capt Cheerleading; Trk; Fash Merch.

LORENCE, KRISTEN; Plymouth-Whitemarsh HS; Plymouth Meeting, PA; (2); 32/250; Drama Clb; Intnl Clb; Lcrss; Score Keeper; Vllybl; High Hon Roll; Hon Roll; Jr NHS; NHS; Prfct Atten Awd; Off Frsh Cls; MIP Jr Vrsty Lacrosse Plyr 87; Frgn Rltns.

LORENZI, MICHELLE; Moon Area SR HS; Coraopolis, PA; (3); 34/306; Sec French Clb; Hosp Aide; VP JA; Band; Concert Band; Mrchg Band; Pep Band; Symp Band; Hon Roll; Prfct Atten Awd; Engrng.

LORENZO, JULIE; Belle Vernon Area HS; Belle Vernon, PA; (3); Band; Concert Band; Mrchg Band; Pep Band; JV Bsktbl; Powder Puff Ftbl; Var L Sftbl; Hon Roll; Marietta Coll.

LORENZO, RICH; Ringgold HS; Monongahela, PA; (3); Am Leg Boys St; Boys Clb Am; Boy Scts; Church Yth Grp; Computer Clb; Dance Clb; Letterman Clb; Science Clb; Varsity Clb; Rep Frsh Cls; Amer Legn Awd 84; MVP Ftbl Team 84; Vrsty Let-Ftbl, Track & Bsktbl 84-86; Med.

LORENZO, ROSE; Belle Vernon Area HS; Belle Vernon, PA; (3); Pep Clb; Band; Concert Band; Mrchg Band; Pep Band; High Hon Roll; Hon Roll; NHS; Prfct Atten Awd.

LORIA, JOSEPHINE; Central Bucks HS East; Warrington, PA; (4); Cmnty Wkr; FBLA; Chorus; Yrbk Stf; Hon Roll; NHS; Pres Schlr; Boston U; Psych.

LORIGAN, BRIAN; Bishop O Reilly HS; Edwardsville, PA; (2); Spanish Clb; VP L Bsbl; JV L Bsktbl; High Hon Roll; Hon Roll; NEDT Awd; Spanish NHS.

LORISO, ANTHONY; Burgettstown JR-SR HS; Coraopolis, PA; (3); 27/165; Spanish Clb; Ftbl; Wt Lftg; Hon Roll; NHS; Med.

LORISO, ROBERT; South Park HS; Library, PA; (4); Art Clb; Church Yth Grp; Swmmng; Hon Roll; Rvrs Art Fstvl Hnbl Mntn 86; Allegheny Cnty CC; Pilot.

LORKOVICH, PAUL; Aliquippa HS; Aliquippa, PA; (2); 1/150; Boy Scts; VP Church Yth Grp; VP French Clb; Math Tm; Concert Band; Mrchg Band; Yrbk Stf; High Hon Roll; Computer Clb; Exploring; High Q Team 86-87; Stu Rep For Stu Forum 87-88; PA ST U; Aerospace Engrng.

LORY, THOMAS; Hempfield Area SR HS; Greensburg, PA; (2); Church Yth Grp; Exploring; Im Wrstlng; Hon Roll; Prsdntl Acdmc Ftnss Awd 85-86; Med.

LOSCA, TINA; Ambridge HS; Sewickley, PA; (2); French Clb; Pep Clb; Off Soph Cls; Trk; Jrnlsm.

LOSCALZO, NIKKI; Council Rock HS; Newtown, PA; (2); Drama Clb; Key Clb; Spanish Clb; School Musical; School Play; Stage Crew; Rep Frsh Cls; Rep Soph Cls; High Hon Roll; Hon Roll.

LOSCO, THERESA; St Hubert HS; Philadelphia, PA; (3); 128/421; JV Var Bowling; Prfct Atten Awd; Holy Family; Ped.

LOSER, AMY; Elizabethtown Area HS; Elizabethtown, PA; (3); Church Yth Grp; Cmnty Wkr; Band; Chorus; Church Choir; Mrchg Band; Lit Mag; JV Var Bsktbl; Capt Cheerleading; Close Up Pgm 87; Soc Sci.

LOSITO, LISA; Avon Grove HS; West Grove, PA; (2); 12/250; Var Cheerleading; Im Wt Lftg; Hon Roll; Avon Grove Yth Educ Assn 85-87; Bio Awd 85-86; Lbrl Arts.

LOSS, AMY; Middleburg HS; Middleburg, PA; (3); 17/138; Church Yth Grp; Key Clb; Ski Clb; SADD; Varsity Clb; Chorus; JV Var Bsktbl; Var Stat Fld Hcky; JV Var Sftbl; Hon Roll; Early Chldhd Ed.

LOSTEN, DIANE E; Jeannette SR HS; Jeannette, PA; (2); 26/137; Church Yth Grp; Cmnty Wkr; Computer Clb; Spanish Clb; Chorus; High Hon Roll; Hon Roll.

LOTH, JULEE; Neshannock HS; Neshannock, PA; (3); 29/102; Drama Clb; Chorus; School Musical; School Play; Tennis; Hon Roll; Svc Awd 87; St Vincent; Fash Merch.

LOTMAN, MAURICE; Friends Central Schl; Bala-Cynwyd, PA; (4); Chorus; School Play; JV Bsbl; Bsktbl; Im Vllybl; Wt Lftg; Ntl Merit Schol; Hnr Mntn Grnd Cncrs Statewde Frnch Cont 83; Cert Merit, Pa Hghr Ed Asstnce Agncy 86; Cum Laude Soc 87; Trinity Coll Hartford.

LOTT, APRIL; Phila HS For Girls; Philadelphia, PA; (3); 181/405; Library Aide; Lit Mag; Alice N Boenesh Awd Excllnc Art 85; H A & S G Warshaw Mem Awd Excllnc Geom 85; Gftd Pgm 78-87; Comp Sci.

LOTT, DEBBIE; Penn Hills SR HS; Pittsburgh, PA; (3); Spanish Clb; Yrbk Stf; Stu Cncl; Hon Roll; Stu Sec Orgnztn VP 87-88; Bradford Bus Schl; Exec Sec.

LOTTICK, KAREN; Wyoming Seminary; Kingston, PA; (4); 34/76; Pres Church Yth Grp; Cmnty Wkr; Service Clb; Ski Clb; Varsity Clb; Stage Crew; Yrbk Stf; Var Fld Hcky; JV Sftbl; Union Coll.

LOTZ, MARY; Mechanicsburg HS; Mechanicsburg, PA; (4); 58/306; Church Yth Grp; Chorus; Church Choir; Orch; Sftbl; Swmmng; Trk; High Hon Roll; Hon Roll; NHS; Vrsty Lttr Swmmng 87; Vrsty Lttr Trk 85-87; Towson ST; Occptnl Ther.

LOUCKS, AMY; Eastern York HS; York, PA; (3); 5/177; Varsity Clb; VP Band; Jazz Band; Trs Sr Cls; Var Capt Bsktbl; Var L Trk; Pres Jr NHS; NHS; Ntl Merit Ltr; High Hon Roll; Dist Band 85-87; Rgnl St Band 86-87; Math.

LOUCKS, DANIEL; Elkland Area HS; Osceola, PA; (3); Chess Clb; Bsbl; L Bsktbl; L Socr; Trk; Hon Roll; AF; Ar Trf Cntrl.

LOUCKS, JEFF; Elkland Area HS; Osceola, PA; (4); 5/75; Am Leg Boys St; Library Aide; Varsity Clb; Yrbk Sprt Ed; Yrbk Stf; VP Sr Cls; Rep Stu Cncl; Var Bsbl; Var Bsktbl; Var Capt Socr; JD Rumsey Awd Outstndg Schlr Ath 87; Army Natl Soccer Coaches MVP 87; PA ST U; Chem Engr.

LOUCKS, THADD; Altoona Area HS; Altoona, PA; (4); 36/719; Art Clb; French Clb; Crs Cntry; Trk; French Hon Soc; NHS; Juniata Coll; Bio.

LOUDENSLAGER, SUSAN R; Elkland Area HS; Elkland, PA; (3); 5/85; Trs Church Yth Grp; SADD; Teachers Aide; Ed Yrbk Stf; Mgr(s); High Hon Roll; NHS; Ntl Merit Ltr; Prfct Atten Awd; Off Stu Cncl; Pres Acad Fitness Awd 85; Weekly Column Local Newspaper 86-87; Pre-Law.

LOUDER, DANA; Clarion Area HS; Clarion, PA; (4); Acpl Chr; Band; Chorus; Church Choir; Jazz Band; Sec Madrigals; Mrchg Band; School Musical; Swing Chorus; Bsktbl; Pres Phy Ftns Awd; Accptd Live Adtns Govrnrs Schl For The Hits; Accptd 2 Yrs Fred Warings U S Chorus; IN U Of PA; Vocal Performance.

LOUGHER, KIMBERLY; Jeannette SR HS; Jeannette, PA; (3); 67/124; Real Estate.

LOUGHMAN, KATHLEEN; Governor Mifflin HS; Shillington, PA; (3); 35/360; Key Clb; Model UN; Band; Concert Band; Mrchg Band; Orch; Nwsp Stf; Var L Sftbl; Hon Roll; Jr NHS; Unfd Achvt Awd 86-87; Cnty Band 86; US Navy Fleet Rsrv Essy Cont; 2ndry Ed.

LOUGHMAN, MARCI; West Greene HS; Sycamore, PA; (3); Pres Church Yth Grp; Dance Clb; Drama Clb; Varsity Clb; School Musical; Variety Show; Nwsp Rptr; Stu Cncl; Cheerleading; Hon Roll; Frnk P Ross Achvt Awd 84; 1st Pl Splng Bee & 1st Pl Kds Quiz 84; Point Park Coll; Prfssnl Dncr.

LOUGHNER, BARB; Jeannette SR HS; Jeannette, PA; (2); Exploring; French Clb; FBLA; Hosp Aide; Spanish Clb; Phys.

LOUGHNER, KIMBERLY; Jeannette SR HS; Jeannette, PA; (3); 67/124; Church Yth Grp.

LOUGHNER, SHARI; Penn Trafford HS; Jeannette, PA; (3); Drama Clb; Hosp Aide; Hst Band; Chorus; Jazz Band; School Musical; Im Ftbl; High Hon Roll; NHS; Schlstc All Am Awd 87; Elem Ed.

LOUGHNEY, CAROL; Pittston Area HS; Pittston, PA; (4); 8/348; Key Clb; Math Clb; Ski Clb; SADD; Yrbk Stf; Capt Vllybl; NHS; St Schlr; Pol Sci.

LOUGHRAN, MIKE; Greensburg Salem HS; Greensburg, PA; (4); Pres French Clb; Ski Clb; Chorus; Rep Jr Cls; Rep Sr Cls; Rep Stu Cncl; Capt Golf; Capt Ice Hcky; Var Twrlr; Hon Roll; Duquesne U; Pharm.

LOUIS, JENNIFER; Mercyhurst Preparatory Schl; Erie, PA; (4); 40/155; Church Yth Grp; Drama Clb; Thesps; School Musical; School Play; Sec Jr Cls; Pres Sr Cls; L Swmmng; DAR Awd; PA Jr Acad Of Sci 1st Pl City & St 84; VP Intl, Thespian Soc 86; Hon Thespian Lttrmn 85; U Of Pittsburgh; Psychlgy.

LOUNSBURY, RACHEL; Owen J Roberts HS; Chester Springs, PA; (3); 13/299; Church Yth Grp; FBLA; Trs Key Clb; Mrchg Band; School Play; Hon Roll; NHS; Debate Tm; Drama Clb; Sec 4-H; Dist 12 Orch 86; Comm Orch 85-86; Bus.

LOVE, DANIEL; Juniata HS; E Waterford, PA; (3); Pres Church Yth Grp; Pres 4-H; Pres FFA; SADD; Varsity Clb; Chorus; Church Choir; Yrbk Sprt Ed; Ftbl; 4-H Awd; Star Agri-Bus FFA Chptr 85-86; ST 4-H Pblc Spkng 85-86.

LOVE, KATHRYN ANN; Freeport SR HS; Freeport, PA; (3); Church Yth Grp; Office Aide; Band; Drm Mjr(t); Mrchg Band; Pep Band; School Musical; Stage Crew; Symp Band; High Hon Roll; Acad All-Amer Awd 86-87; US Achvt Acad 86-87; Penn ST; Engrng.

LOVE, KIMBERLY; Cornell HS; Coraopolis, PA; (4); 1/76; Key Clb; Sec Band; Nwsp Rptr; Var JV Cheerleading; JP Sousa Awd; Sec NHS; Val; Church Yth Grp; Hosp Aide; Science Clb; Corrn Mnk Whr Schlrhsp-IUP 87; PMEA Dist Band Fstvl, Schl Rep 87; Wstnghs Sci Hnrs Inst 86-87; Indiana U Of PA.

LOVE, KRISTIN; Plymouth-Whitemarsh SR HS; Conshohocken, PA; (3); Art Clb; Church Yth Grp; Teachers Aide; Sftbl; Exec Secr.

LOVE, MERITA; Bok AVT HS; Philadelphia, PA; (3); Computer Clb; Dance Clb; Drama Clb; GAA; Capt Color Guard; School Play; Yrbk Stf; Var Bsbl; Tennis; Trk; Bus.

LOVELESS, KIM; Sayre Area HS; Stone Mtn, GA; (4); 11/109; Drama Clb; French Clb; Ed Yrbk Stf; Lit Mag; Rep Jr Cls; Mat Maids; High Hon Roll; Yrbk Prdct Staff Awd 87; U GA; Jrnlsm.

LOVELESS, MICHAEL; Strath Haven HS; Media, PA; (3); Aud/Vis; Cmnty Wkr; Red Cross Aide; Chorus; School Musical; JV Bsbl; Var JV Socr; JV Swmmng; Hon Roll; PA Free Enterprise Week Schlrshp & Swartmore Coll Selected Writing Asst 87; Comms.

LOVELY, ERIC; Spring Ford HS; Spring City, PA; (3); 56/256; Exploring; German Clb; Var Library Aide; Off Stu Cncl; Hon Roll; Bloomsburg U; Bio.

LOVERA, PAM; Chichester SR HS; Aston, PA; (3); 9/293; Church Yth Grp; Model UN; Scholastic Bowl; SADD; Ed Lit Mag; Hon Roll; Jr NHS; NHS; Ntl Merit Ltr; Pres Schlr; Biochem.

LOVERIDGE, BEN J; West Middlesex JR SR HS; West Middlesex, PA; (3); Cmnty Wkr; FBLA; Nwsp Stf; Yrbk Stf; Var L Ftbl; Hon Roll; Ntl Merit Schol; Rgnl Pres FBLA 87-88; Bus.

LOVETT, JACK; General Mc Lane HS; Edinboro, PA; (3); 18/200; Church Yth Grp; Teachers Aide; Band; Mrchg Band; Var L Bsbl; JV Var Bsktbl; Var L Crs Cntry; JV Ftbl; NHS.

LOVETT, LANE; Charleroi HS; Charleroi, PA; (3); Church Yth Grp; Cmnty Wkr; French Clb; Science Clb; Ski Clb; Hon Roll.

LOVETT, MICHELE; Archbishop Ryan For Girls; Phila, PA; (3); 359/508; Cmnty Wkr; Dance Clb; Intnl Clb; Stage Crew; Vllybl; 2 Achvt Awds Rdng & Math 84-85; Accntnt.

LOVING, DEBBIE; Bethlehem Catholic HS; Hellertown, PA; (4); Color Guard; Mrchg Band; Mst Outstndng Bandfrnt Stu 86-87; Northampton Area CC; Bus Mgmt.

LOVING, GEORGE; Upper Darby HS; Drexel Hill, PA; (3); Band; Concert Band; Jazz Band; Mrchg Band; Orch; School Musical; Symp Band; Variety Show; Var Swmmng; Boy Scts; Bass Inst/Tech; Music.

LOVING, LELA; East Allegheny HS; East Mc Keesport, PA; (2); French Clb; Ski Clb; Band; Yrbk Stf; Stu Cncl; JV Im Cheerleading; Mgr(s); L Trk; Hon Roll; NHS; Engrng.

LOVIS, MICHELE; Frazier Mem JR SR HS; Vanderbilt, PA; (3); Church Yth Grp; Dance Clb; Spanish Clb; Church Choir; Cheerleading; Gym; Swmmng; Hon Roll.

LOVRINIC, CHRISTINE; Tunkhanhock Area HS; Tunkahannock, PA; (4); Art Clb; 4-H; French Clb; JA; Color Guard; Mrchg Band; Hon Roll; NHS; Airforce.

LOVRINIC, MATTHEW; Bishop Hafey HS; Hazleton, PA; (3); 30/113; Art Clb; Pres Ski Clb; Var Crs Cntry; Var Socr; Var Trk; Hon Roll; Bus.

LOW, ROBERT; Bishop Mc Cort HS; Windber, PA; (2); Chorus; Bsktbl; High Hon Roll.

LOWE, BARRY; West Perry HS; Shermansdale, PA; (4); Church Yth Grp; Pres French Clb; Rep Stu Cncl; JV Bsbl; Var Bsktbl; Var Ftbl; Var Trk; Hon Roll; Prfct Atten Awd; Shippensburg U.

LOWE, CATHY; York Suburban HS; York, PA; (3); GAA; Girl Scts; Pep Clb; Spanish Clb; Varsity Clb; Rep Jr Cls; Var Capt Bsktbl; JV Capt Cheerleading; Var Trk; DAR Awd; Var Bsktbl Capt 86-87; Rep For JR Cls 86-87; Daughtrs Of Amer Revltn 84.

LOWE, DIANE; Millersburg Area HS; Millersburg, PA; (4); 7/74; Church Yth Grp; French Clb; Key Clb; Spanish Clb; Church Choir; Yrbk Ed-Chief; Powder Puff Ftbl; French Hon Soc; Hon Roll; Penn ST U; Frnch.

LOWE, ERIC; Manheim Central HS; Manheim, PA; (4); Church Yth Grp; 4-H; Rep FFA; Hon Roll; Rotary Club Agri Awd 87; Kunkle Schlrshp PA ST 87; Pa ST U; Agri Engrng.

LOWE, KAREN; Franklin Regional HS; Murrysville, PA; (4); Varsity Clb; Var Bsktbl; Var Sftbl; High Hon Roll; Lttrd Sftbl 86; Outstndg Acad Achvt Pres Acad Ftns Awds Prgrm 87; Clarion U Of PA; Speech Pthlgy.

LOWE, ROD; Great Valley SR HS; Malvern, PA; (4); 19/258; Trs Am Leg Boys St; FBLA; Ski Clb; Varsity Clb; Var Bsktbl; Var Ftbl; Var Trk; Wt Lftg; NHS; Pres Schlr; Acad Fit Awd 87; Adv ST Comptn Bsktbl 86-87; PA ST U; Acctng.

LOWE, ROY; Liberty JR SR HS; Roaring Branch, PA; (3); Church Yth Grp; Computer Clb; German Clb; Wrstlng; Comp Sci.

LOWE, SCOTT; Connellsville Area HS; Mill Run, PA; (3); 21/550; Church Yth Grp; Church Choir; Nwsp Ed-Chief; Nwsp Rptr; Nwsp Stf; Capt Swmmng; JV Trk; French Hon Soc; High Hon Roll; NHS; Law.

LOWE, STACEY; Lampeter Strasburg HS; Lancaster, PA; (3); 38/145; Church Yth Grp; Chorus; JV Bsktbl; JV Capt Cheerleading; Im Mgr(s); Stat Socr; Accntng.

LOWENBERG, MARC; Methaeton HS; Trooper, PA; (3); 52/381; Var Socr; Var Capt Trk; Hon Roll; NHS; Ntl Hstyr Olympd; Ursinus Coll; Pre Law.

LOWENSCHUSS, ALAN; Harriton HS; Gladwyne, PA; (4); Cmnty Wkr; Concert Band; Jazz Band; Mrchg Band; Orch; Bsbl; Crs Cntry; Trk; Hon Roll; NHS; Bucknell U.

LOWERS, SEAN; Franklin Regional HS; Delmont, PA; (3); AFS; Math Tm; SADD; Nwsp Stf; High Hon Roll; Early Admissions St Vincent Coll Merit Schlrshp 87; ST Rep To Dist 20 PA ST Demolay Assn 86-87; St Vincent Coll; Intl Bus.

LOWERY, LISA; Meyersdale Area HS; Meyersdale, PA; (3); 25/108; Cmnty Wkr; Dance Clb; Spanish Clb; Band; Concert Band; Mrchg Band; School Musical; Stu Cncl; Capt Var Cheerleading; Hon Roll; Bus Admn.

LOWRANCE, ANDREA; Upattinas Schl; Phoenixville, PA; (4); School Play; Key Clb; Scholastic Bowl; JV Lcrss; High Hon Roll; Brd Natl Coaltns Altrntv Cmnty Schls 86-87; Stu Rep Upattinas Schl Brd 86-87; Marlboro Coll.

LOWRY, ADAM; Connellsville Area SR HS; Dunbar, PA; (3); 25/530; Var L Swmmng; High Hon Roll; Jr NHS; NHS; Coast Guard Acad; Engrng.

LOWRY, SHARON; Riverside HS; Beaver Falls, PA; (2); DECA; FHA; Hosp Aide; Red Cross Aide; Swmmng; Hon Roll; Mrn Bio.

LOWRY, TIM; Fort Cherry HS; Washington, PA; (4); Computer Clb; 4-H; FFA; Science Clb; Varsity Clb; Stat Bsktbl; Hon Roll; NHS; Dekalb Ag Acmplsmnt Awd 87; Star Chptr Frmr Awd; ST Rcrd Kppng Gold Awd; PA ST U; Ag Sci.

LOWSON, ALAN; Waynesboro Area SR HS; Mont Alto, PA; (4); 15/365; Boy Scts; Trs Church Yth Grp; Concert Band; Jazz Band; Capt Ftbl; Var L Trk; Wt Lftg; High Hon Roll; Pres NHS; Appntmt US Mil Acad 87; USMA West Pt; Biochem.

LOWSON, HETHER; Waynesboro SR HS; Mont Alto, PA; (3); JCL; Band; Chorus; Concert Band; Mrchg Band; Yrbk Stf; Hon Roll; Bus Mgmt.

LOWTHER, AMY; Connellsville Area SR HS; Vanderbilt, PA; (1); Hosp Aide; Pres Pep Clb; Chorus; Nwsp Stf; Sec Stu Cncl; Var Vllybl; Hon Roll; Vlntn Qn 87; Bst Prsnlty 87; MVP Pep Clb 87; Bus.

LOY, RICHARD J; Quakertown SR HS; Pennsburg, PA; (3); 17/310; VP Soph Cls; VP Jr Cls; VP Sr Cls; Var Ftbl; High Hon Roll; Jr NHS; NHS; Prfct Atten Awd; Am Leg Boys St; Church Yth Grp; Aero Engr.

LOYER, JAKE; Mercyhurst Prep Schl; W Springfield, PA; (2); Aud/Vis; Drama Clb; Thesps; Acpl Chr; Chorus; Madrigals; School Musical; School Play; Stage Crew; Wt Lftg; Schlrshp Art, Musc 85-87.

LOYER, MATTHEW; Mechanicsburg Area HS; Mechanicsburg, PA; (2); 14/309; Church Yth Grp; Quiz Bowl; Var L Crs Cntry; Var Trk; High Hon Roll; NHS; Christian Svc.

LOZINAK, LISA; Forest City Regional HS; Forest City, PA; (4); 8/57; Library Aide; Office Aide; Spanish Clb; SADD; Hon Roll; NHS; Natl Sci Awd 87; Accntng.

LU, ANDREW; Upper Dublin HS; Dresher, PA; (3); 12/295; Am Leg Boys St; Nwsp Stf; Yrbk Stf; Intnl Clb; Sec Frsh Cls; Sec Soph Cls; Stu Cncl; JV Bsbl; NHS; TMOT Ldrshp Prog 86; Engrng.

LU, KAI-WEI; North Penn SR HS; Lansdale, PA; (4); Orch; Rep Sr Cls; Var Trk; Gov Hon Prg Awd; High Hon Roll; Hon Roll; NHS; Prfct Atten Awd; Pres Schlr; 1st Intl Grn Drgn Tourn Karate 86; 3rd Annl Ovrsea Chinese Tlnt Comptn 85; Parsns Schl Dsgn; Fshn Dsgnr.

LU, THAT; Unionville HS; Embreeville, PA; (4); FBLA; L JV Lcrss; Var JV Socr; Var L Trk; Vllybl; Var Wrstlng; Hon Roll; NHS; Outstndng Wrstlng 87; Cngrssmn Merit Mdl 87; Stu Of Month 87; Crmnl Justce.

LUBA, ROMAN; Central HS; Philadelphia, PA; (3); 50/535; Art Clb; Boy Scts; Debate Tm; Library Aide; Concert Band; Yrbk Phtg; Yrbk Stf; Socr; Hon Roll; Arch.

LUBAK, MARY; Everett Area HS; Everett, PA; (3); Art Clb; Camera Clb; Church Yth Grp; Drama Clb; FHA; Girl Scts; Library Aide; Band; Stage Crew; Yrbk Stf; Med.

LUBAS, JOHN; Exeter SR HS; Reading, PA; (3); 72/246; Pep Clb; Band; Concert Band; Drill Tm; Jazz Band; Mrchg Band; Orch; Pep Band; School Musical; Variety Show; Natl Ldrshp Awd 86; Natl Music Awd 85; Penn ST U; Bus Admin.

LUBASZEWSKI, JILL; Forest City Regional HS; Uniondale, PA; (3); FHA; German Clb; Ski Clb; Yrbk Phtg; Yrbk Stf; Sftbl; Comm.

LUBBEKE, LYNNE; Berks Christian Schl; W Reading, PA; (3); Church Yth Grp; Hosp Aide; Ski Clb; Nwsp Rptr; Yrbk Bus Mgr; Yrbk Stf; Stat Bsktbl; Timer; Var Trk; Harcum JC; Fshn Merch.

LUBERT, CYNTHIA; Cambria Heights HS; Patton, PA; (3); Library Aide; Q&S; Ski Clb; Speech Tm; Chorus; Church Choir; Yrbk Stf; NHS; Educ.

LUBERT, MICHELLE; Monaca JR SR HS; Monaca, PA; (4); 17/90; Library Aide; Pep Clb; Spanish Clb; Hon Roll; NHS; U Of Pittsburgh; Pre-Med.

LUBIC, SHAWN; Geibel HS; Connellsville, PA; (3); French Clb; Pep Clb; SADD; Stage Crew; French Hon Soc; High Hon Roll; Arch.

LUBICKY, DANIEL; Father Judge HS; Philadelphia, PA; (3); 68/402; Boys Clb Am; Math.

LUBIN, JAMES D; Carbondale Area JR & SR HS; Carbondale, PA; (2); Computer Clb; Ski Clb; Spanish Clb; Rep Frsh Cls; Hon Roll; PA ST; Avtn.

LUBINSKY, DENNIS S; Butler Area SR HS; Butler, PA; (3); German Clb; Capt Socr; Trk; Wt Lftg; Wrstlng; High Hon Roll; Jr NHS; Latin Clb; Hon Roll; Pittsburgh Press All Star Soccer Slctn 85-86; European Soviet Cup Tour 87; PA ST Soccer Tm 84-87; Bus.

LUBINSKY, KEVIN; Nativity BVM HS; Cumbola, PA; (3); Aud/Vis; Church Yth Grp; Computer Clb; Exploring; Stage Crew; Nwsp Ed-Chief; Nwsp Rptr; Nwsp Stf; Im Stat Bsktbl; Hon Roll; Corp Law.

LUBINSKY, MICHELLE; Nativity BUM HS; Cumbola, PA; (2); Hosp Aide; Spanish Clb; Drm Mjr(t); Nwsp Rptr; Nwsp Stf; Rep Soph Cls; Bus Admin.

LUBISKI, KRISTINE; Little Flower HS For Girls; Philadelphia, PA; (3); 7/322; Cmnty Wkr; Exploring; Science Clb; Orch; School Musical; School Play; Nwsp Rptr; NHS; Prfct Atten Awd; Spnsh Awd 86; Law.

LUBOLD, WILLIAM; Central Oduphin HS; Harrisburg, PA; (3); Boy Scts; Band; Chorus; Concert Band; Mrchg Band; Penn ST U.

LUBRAGGE, WILLIAM; Upper Darby HS; Upr Darby, PA; (3); Church Yth Grp; High Hon Roll; Hon Roll; Prfct Atten Awd; Penn ST; Arch.

LUBRANI, RUSSELL; Belle Vernon Area HS; Belle Vernon, PA; (3); Var Bsbl; Var Bsktbl; High Hon Roll.

LUBY, JAMES; Scranton Central HS; Moscow, PA; (2); Cmnty Wkr; German Clb; Science Clb; Ski Clb; JTI.

LUCA, SHERRY; Lincoln HS; Ellwood City, PA; (4); 48/165; French Clb; Key Clb; Band; Concert Band; Mrchg Band; Bowling; Powder Puff Ftbl; Hon Roll; Prfct Atten Awd; Penn ST U; Engrng.

LUCARELLI, ANGELA; Hempfield HS; Irwin, PA; (4); Library Aide; Office Aide; Pep Clb; Ski Clb; Spanish Clb; Color Guard; High Hon Roll; Hon Roll; Jr NHS; Spanish NHS; Edinboro; Psych.

LUCARELLI, ARTHUR; Old Forge HS; Old Forge, PA; (3); Trs Sr Cls; Var Bsbl; Var JV Bsktbl; JV Ftbl; Var Golf; Hon Roll; NHS.

LUCARELLI, MICHELLE; Mohawk HS; Edinburg, PA; (4); 16/137; Church Yth Grp; Spanish Clb; Band; Mrchg Band; Nwsp Stf; Yrbk Stf; VP Soph Cls; Rep Stu Cncl; Var L Bsktbl; Mgr(s); Elem Ed.

LUCARELLI, NICOLE; Mohawk HS; Edinburg, PA; (4); 4/135; Church Yth Grp; French Clb; SADD; Band; Mrchg Band; Yrbk Ed-Chief; Var L Tennis; Stat Trk; High Hon Roll; Hon Roll; Mst Imprvd Tnns Plyr; 1st Chair Clrnt; Duquesne U; Acctg.

LUCAS, CHRISTINE; Shaler Area HS; Pittsburgh, PA; (4); 7/509; SADD; Nwsp Stf; Yrbk Bus Mgr; Off Frsh Cls; Off Sr Cls; Vllybl; High Hon Roll; NHS; PA ST U; Acctng.

LUCAS, DIETTRA; Monessen SR HS; Monessen, PA; (3); JA; VICA; Chorus; Nwsp Rptr; Hon Roll; Csmtlgs.

LUCAS, JENNIFER; Emmaus HS; Emmaus, PA; (3); 112/545; Trs French Clb; Latin Clb; SADD; Chorus; School Musical; Var Capt Bsktbl; Hon Roll; NHS; Church Yth Grp; School Play; PA Jr Acad Of Sci 2nd Pl 86; Moravian Coll Frgn Lang Cmpttn 4th Pl 85; Lang.

LUCAS, JOSEPH; Shaler Area SR HS; Pittsburgh, PA; (3); 141/486; Church Yth Grp; Cmnty Wkr; High Hon Roll; Ntl Sci Olympd 85-86; Elec Engr.

LUCAS, KATHLEEN; Steel Valley HS; Munhall, PA; (4); JCL; Key Clb; Latin Clb; Varsity Clb; Rep Frsh Cls; Capt Swmmng; Vllybl; Wt Lftg; Hon Roll; NHS; PTO Schlrshp Awd 87; Gannon U; Phrmcy.

LUCAS, KEITH; Council Rock HS; Newtown, PA; (2); Trs Computer Clb; Drexel Coll; Electrncl Engr.

LUCAS, KELLIE; Kazleton HS; Hazleton, PA; (3); Church Yth Grp; Cmnty Wkr; French Clb; FNA; Hosp Aide; Leo Clb; Pep Clb; Flag Corp; School Musical; Yrbk Stf; 100 Hr Awd For Vlntrng As Candy Striper 85; 200 Hr Awd For 86; Nrs.

LUCAS, KELLY; North Allegheny SR HS; Pittsburgh, PA; (4); 82/660; Exploring; German Clb; Ski Clb; High Hon Roll; Hon Roll; Jr NHS; NHS; Bio Lab Asst 86-87; IN U PA; Elem Ed.

LUCAS, KELLY; Waynesburg Central HS; Waynesburg, PA; (3); Trs Drama Clb; Hosp Aide; Chorus; Yrbk Stf; Sec Stu Cncl; JV Cheerleading; Cit Awd; High Hon Roll; NHS; NEDT Awd; Franklin & Marshall; Comm.

LUCAS, KIMBERLY; Ridley HS; Morton, PA; (4); 39/407; Office Aide; Spanish Clb; Chorus; Nwsp Stf; Score Keeper; Timer; Trk; Hon Roll; NHS; Ridley Permanent Scholar Fund 87; Pres Acad Fit Awd 87; Millersville U; Psych.

LUCAS, KRIS; Dover Area HS; Dover, PA; (4); 10/239; Church Yth Grp; Girl Scts; Library Aide; Nwsp Stf; Var Stat Bsbl; High Hon Roll; NHS; Woodmen Of The World Amer Hist Awd 86; Std Month Rotar Clb & Lions Clb 87; Acadmc All Stars 87; Shippensburg U; Hist.

LUCAS, LISA; Cashs HS; Chambersburg, PA; (4); 122/552; Art Clb; Drama Clb; English Clb; Chorus; School Musical; School Play; Lit Mag; Church Yth Grp; Service Clb; Drexel U; Art.

LUCAS, LORI; Warren Area HS; Warren, PA; (3); French Clb; Library Aide; Office Aide; Spanish Clb; Teachers Aide; Y-Teens; Chorus; Yrbk Stf; Stu Cncl; Trk; Psych.

LUCAS, LORIE; West Branch Area HS; Munson, PA; (2); Drama Clb; Science Clb; Spanish Clb; SADD; Varsity Clb; Stage Crew; Rep Stu Cncl; Var Cheerleading; Hon Roll; NHS; Acad.

LUCAS, LYNN; Mt Pleasant Area SR HS; Mt Pleasant, PA; (2); Ski Clb; Rep Stu Cncl; Hon Roll; Math.

LUCAS, SHANE; Shikellamy HS; Sunbury, PA; (3); 4/300; VP German Clb; VP Key Clb; NFL; Chorus; School Musical; Rep Soph Cls; JV Var Cheerleading; Trk; High Hon Roll; Jr NHS; Grgtwn U; Intl Bus.

LUCAS, STEPHENSON; W Catholic HS For Boys; Philadelphia, PA; (4); 67/265; Boy Scts; Computer Clb; French Clb; Chorus; Church Choir; Var Crs Cntry; Var Trk; Hon Roll; White Williams Fndtn Schlrshp 86-87; Temple U; Brdcstng.

LUCAS, TIM; Mt Pleasant Area SR HS; Mt Pleasant, PA; (3); #51 In Class; Latin Clb; Ski Clb; Var Golf; Var Tennis; High Hon Roll; Viking Recgntn Awd Maturity, Svc 85; 2nd Pl Art Awd Latin Humanties Day 85; Penn ST U; Math.

LUCCI, STEPHANIE; Pennsbury HS; Yardley, PA; (2); Church Yth Grp; Hosp Aide; VP Chorus; Yrbk Stf; Stu Cncl; Fld Hcky; Trk; Hon Roll; Prfct Atten Awd.

LUCE, JOSEPH; Elk Lake HS; Springville, PA; (2); Church Yth Grp; Spanish Clb; Comp Prgmr.

LUCERA, RICHARD; Methacton HS; Audubon, PA; (3); 5/383; Bsbl; Socr; DAR Awd; High Hon Roll; U Of DE; Civil Engr.

LUCERNE, DAVID; Downington SR HS; Downingtown, PA; (4); 19/561; Art Clb; Dance Clb; French Clb; Letterman Clb; Teachers Aide; Rep Stu Cncl; Var Crs Cntry; Capt Wrstlng; High Hon Roll; NHS; Living Arts Weekend Awds 85-87; NEDT Cert Accomplshmnt 84; PHEAA Cert Merit Outstndng Perf SAT 86; Finance.

LUCHAN, JAMES; Ambridge HS; Ambridge, PA; (2); Hon Roll; CNSRVTN.

LUCHETA, SUSAN; Franklin Regional SR HS; Murrysville, PA; (4); 1/310; Math Tm; Spanish Clb; SADD; High Hon Roll; NHS; Ntl Merit Ltr; Wstnghs Fmly Schlrshp 87; Frnkln Rgnl HS Spnsh Awd 87; PA JR Acdmy Sci-1st & 2nd Awds 84; Grove City Coll; Spnsh.

LUCIANI, DIANE; Monessen HS; Monessen, PA; (3); 17/108; JA; Teachers Aide; Band; Concert Band; Mrchg Band; Tennis; Med Scrtry.

LUCID, HENRY; North Hills HS; Pittsburgh, PA; (4); 40/460; Camera Clb; NFL; Q&S; Ski Clb; Yrbk Phtg; Trk; High Hon Roll; NHS; U Of TX Austin; Med.

LUCKANGELO, FRANK; Archbishop Ryan HS; Philadelphia, PA; (2); 84/349; Var Tennis; Outstndng Engl Awd 86-87.

LUCKENBAUGH, CHARLES; Hanover HS; Hanover, PA; (3); Chess Clb; Varsity Clb; Band; Concert Band; Jazz Band; Mrchg Band; School Musical; School Play; Pres Frsh Cls; Var Tennis; Engrng.

LUCKENBAUGH, KIMBERLY S; Newoxford SR HS; Hanover, PA; (4); 11/187; Drama Clb; Chorus; School Musical; School Play; High Hon Roll; Hon Roll; Lion Awd; Pres Schlr; Bst Actrss 85 & 86; Most Impvd 86; Natl Schl Chrl Awd 87; Shippensburg U; Scndry Educ.

LUCKETT, ROY Q; Bishop Mc Devitt Schl; Harrisburg, PA; (3); 62/245; Am Leg Boys St; Drama Clb; FBLA; Service Clb; School Play; VP Soph Cls; Pres Jr Cls; VP Sr Cls; Pres Stu Cncl; Im Bsktbl; Law.

LUCKEY, JUDITH; Elizabeth Forward HS; Elizabeth, PA; (4); 45/273; Acpl Chr; Concert Band; Drm Mjr(t); Mrchg Band; School Musical; Hon Roll; NHS; Mid-East Music Fstvl 86 & 87; Amer Lgn Ldrshp/Patriotism Awd 87; Mercyhurst Coll; Htl/Rest Mgmt.

LUCKOWSKI, ERIC; Henderson HS; Downingtown, PA; (3); 4/350; Debate Tm; Intnl Clb; Science Clb; School Musical; French Hon Soc; Hon Roll; 4th Pl Rgnl Sci Olympd 87; Hnrbl Mntn Immaculata U Wrtng Cont 87; Carnegie-Mellon U; Engrng.

LUCKSHIRE, DANIEL; Upper Darby SR HS; Drexel Hill, PA; (3); JV L Bsbl; Im Bsktbl; Var L Ftbl; Wt Lftg; Var L Wrstlng; High Hon Roll; Hon Roll; Prfct Atten Awd; Accntng II Awd 87; U Of PA; Bus.

LUDGATE, LAURIE; Reading HS; Reading, PA; (3); 1/710; Dance Clb; Key Clb; Service Clb; Teachers Aide; School Musical; Cheerleading; Im Gym; Mgr(s); Hon Roll; NHS; Am Lgn Awd 85; Med.

LUDICA, TAMMY; Mc Guffey HS; Claysville, PA; (3); VP Jr Cls; Off Stu Cncl; Var L Cheerleading; Hon Roll; NHS; Spanish Clb; VP Soph Cls; Mgr(s); Powder Puff Ftbl; Trk; Stu Recog Awd 86-87.

LUDT, SHARI L; Big Spring HS; Carlisle, PA; (4); 2/181; Pres Church Yth Grp; Nwsp Rptr; Yrbk Ed-Chief; VP Sr Cls; Capt Var Cheerleading; Capt Powder Puff Ftbl; L Var Trk; DAR Awd; High Hon Roll; NHS; UTS Schlrshp 87; Natl Elks Schlrshp 87; Locl Elks Schlrshp 87; Penn ST U; Frgn Lang.

LUDWICZAK, BRENDA; Valley HS; New Kensington, PA; (3); AFS; Exploring; Library Aide; Hon Roll; Accntnt.

LUDWIG, JEFFREY; Tri-Valley HS; Ashland, PA; (3); 5/76; Church Yth Grp; Drama Clb; Band; Chorus; Jazz Band; School Musical; Hon Roll; NHS; Penn ST; Chem.

LUDWIG, TAMMY; Cocalico HS; Denver, PA; (2); 33/193; Chorus; Concert Band; Jazz Band; Mrchg Band; Pep Band; Stat Bsktbl; Stat Trk; Hon Roll; Prfct Atten Awd; Lebanon Valley Coll Hnrs Bnd 86-87.

LUEPKE, LARRY; West Allegheny SR HS; Oakdale, PA; (2); 37/200; Ski Clb; Chorus; Golf; Hon Roll; Accntnt.

LUFF III, JOSEPH B; Council Rock HS; Washington Crsng, PA; (2); Socr; Tennis.

LUFT, DONNA; Exeter SR HS; Reading, PA; (4); 10/215; Pres Church Yth Grp; VP Leo Clb; Varsity Clb; Pres Y-Teens; Drm Mjr(t); Var Capt Bsktbl; Var Capt Fld Hcky; Var Capt Sftbl; Hon Roll; NHS; All Berks Field Hockey,Bsktbl Tm 86-87; Math Ed.

LUGG, ROBERT; Elkland Area HS; Nelson, PA; (3); Aud/Vis; Computer Clb; Drama Clb; French Clb; Ski Clb; Nwsp Stf; Stu Cncl; Var L Socr; Var L Tennis; Hon Roll; Elec Engr.

LUGIN, LEANDRA; Moon SR HS; Coraopolis, PA; (4); 83/304; Chorus; Robert Morris Coll; Bus Admin.

LUGO, BEILA; J P Mc Caskey HS; Lancaster, PA; (3); 112/517; Church Yth Grp; Library Aide; Chorus; Lit Mag; Wt Lftg; High Hon Roll; Hon Roll; U Of Pittsburgh; Pharm.

LUGO, GINA-MARIE; Seneca Valley HS; Mars, PA; (3); 35/331; Church Yth Grp; SADD; Chorus; Flag Corp; Yrbk Ed-Chief; Hon Roll; NHS; Dely PA Moose Stu Cngrss Against Drugs 87; Hofstra U; Lwyr.

LUISI, KIMBERLY P; Kiski Area HS; Apollo, PA; (4); Math Clb; Spanish Clb; Band; Capt Color Guard; Ed Yrbk Ed-Chief; Sftbl; High Hon Roll; Lion Awd; Top 10 84; IUP; Math.

LUISO, MARIKA; Chalutzim HS; Philadelphia, PA; (4); Church Yth Grp; Church Choir; School Play; Yrbk Stf; High Hon Roll; Ntl Merit Ltr; Val; ST Josephs U; Intl Rltns.

LUK, JASON C; Archbishop Ryan H S For Boys; Philadelphia, PA; (3); #45 In Class; Chess Clb; Arch.

LUKAS, AMY; Laurel HS; New Castle, PA; (3); 11/114; 4-H; SADD; Capt Drm Mjr(t); Yrbk Stf; Stu Cncl; Trk; 4-H Awd; High Hon Roll; Hon Roll; NHS; Most Dedicated Majorette 84; Citznshp Awdin ST 85; Wilma Boyd; Travel.

LUKAS, EMMA; Seton-La Salle HS; Pittsburgh, PA; (3); 18/245; Ski Clb; Band; Concert Band; Mrchg Band; Stage Crew; Yrbk Ed-Chief; Yrbk Stf; Powder Puff Ftbl; High Hon Roll; NHS; Achvt Awd-Acad Chem I 86; Acnvt Awds Spnsh I II 85-86; Phrmcy.

LUKAS, PAUL; Trinity HS; Washington, PA; (2); German Clb; Ski Clb; Socr.

LUKASAVAGE, ALLYSON; Lake Lehman HS; Dallas, PA; (2); 24/199; Cmnty Wkr; Var L Cheerleading; Var Trk; Hon Roll; Jr NHS.

LUKASIK, DAWN; Hempfeild SR HS; Greensburg, PA; (2); Office Aide; Chorus; High Hon Roll; Hon Roll; Jr NHS; Pres Schlr; Accntnt.

LUKASIK, STEPHEN; Bishop Ohara HS; Olyphant, PA; (2); 6/127; Latin Clb; JV Bsktbl; High Hon Roll; Boston Coll; Marene Geology.

LUKE, CHRISTINE; Penn Cambria HS; Ashville, PA; (3); Camera Clb; Church Yth Grp; Drama Clb; SADD; Chorus; Variety Show; Im Bsktbl; Im Vllybl; Hon Roll; Oceangrphy.

LUKE, EDDIE; Chartiers Valley HS; Pittsburgh, PA; (3); 56/323; Service Clb; Ski Clb; Nwsp Sprt Ed; Nwsp Stf; Off Soph Cls; Im Ftbl; NHS; Aerospc Engrng.

LUKE, LISA MARIE; Penn Cambria HS; Gallitzin, PA; (4); Drama Clb; French Clb; Girl Scts; Stage Crew; Yrbk Stf; Hon Roll; Prfct Atten Awd; PA ST U; Hlth.

LUKITSCH, KRISTEN L; Franklin Regional HS; Murrysville, PA; (4); 1/338; VP Pres Key Clb; Math Tm; Chorus; School Musical; Stu Cncl; Capt Cheerleading; Pom Pon; NHS; Ntl Merit SF; Val; Amer Assn Tchrs French Awd 85-86; Natl HS Chrldng Champnshps 85 & 86; Westinghse Hnrs Sci Inst 86-87; Biochem.

LUKOWSKY, ANN; Ford City JR SR HS; Ford City, PA; (4); Church Yth Grp; Spanish Clb; Nwsp Rptr; Var Capt Bsktbl; Im Cheerleading; Hon Roll; NHS; St Vincents Coll; Sclgy.

LULEWICZ, BETH ANN; Hanover Area JR/Sr HS; Wilkes-Barre, PA; (3); 41/194; Mrchg Band; Stage Crew; Hon Roll; PA ST U; Arch.

LUMLEY, SARAH; Meadville SR HS; Meadville, PA; (2); Church Yth Grp; Hosp Aide; Key Clb; Letterman Clb; Spanish Clb; Varsity Clb; Chorus; Church Choir; Socr; Swmmng; Penn St; Sprts Med.

LUMPKIN, STRAUGHN; Danville SR HS; Danville, PA; (2); Var L Bsbl; JV Tennis; Var L Ftbl.

LUND JR, JOHN M; Upper Moreland HS; Hatboro, PA; (4); 66/250; FCA; Key Clb; SADD; Bsbl; Bsktbl; Ftbl; Hon Roll; Grant Awd Muhlenberg Coll, Babe Ruth Awd 87; Muhlenberg Coll; Bus.

LUNDAY, BRIAN; Carlisle HS; Carlisle, PA; (3); Boy Scts; Quiz Bowl; Ski Clb; JV Crs Cntry; JV Trk; High Hon Roll; NHS; Ntl Merit SF; 1st Pl Sci & Engrng Fair 87; Anl Rtry Ldrs Cnfrnc/Crlsl Rtry Clb 87; Engrng.

LUNDBERG, MARCIE; Brockway Area HS; Brockway, PA; (3); Varsity Clb; Variety Show; Stu Cncl; JV Capt Cheerleading; Var Vllybl; Lwyr.

LUNDVALL, CHRISTINE; Lewistown Area HS; Lewistown, PA; (2); 4-H; French Clb; Ski Clb; 4-H Awd; High Hon Roll; NHS; 4-H ST Champ Jr Hunt Seat Eqltn Over Fences 85; 4-H 7th Pl At ST Horse Show Sr Hunt Seat Eq 86; PA ST U.

LUNDY, KAREN; Jersey Shore SR HS; Jersey Shore, PA; (3); FBLA; Grl Scts; Library Aide; Hon Roll; Grl Scts Gld Awd 86; Acad Achvt In Rdng 85-86.

LUNG, MATTHEW; Norht Allegheny SR HS; Pittsburgh, PA; (2); Band; Concert Band; Jazz Band; Mrchg Band; Pep Band; School Musical; Stage Crew; Symp Band; ST Mth Cont 87; Sci Fr 3rd Pl 87; Aud Engrng.

LUNGER, KEVIN; Northeastern SR HS; Manchester, PA; (3); Band; Chorus; Concert Band; Mrchg Band; Orch; Lit Mag; Hon Roll; Voice Dem Awd; Arch.

LUNGHOFER, RHONDA; Altoona Area SR HS; Altoona, PA; (3); GAA; Girl Scts; Y-Teens; Rep Stu Cncl; Mgr(s); Var L Swmmng; Penn ST U; Drftg.

LUNIFELD, AMY; Penn Hills HS; Pittsburgh, PA; (4); 24/616; Drama Clb; Hosp Aide; Ski Clb; Mrchg Band; Orch; School Play; High Hon Roll; JP Sousa Awd; Kiwanis Awd; NHS; Rd Crs Yth Ldrshp Dvlpmnt Ctr; Miami U; Systms Anlysis.

LUNNEY, CHRIS; Scranton Central HS; Scranton, PA; (2); Cmnty Wkr; FBLA; Spanish Clb; Var JV Bsbl; JV Var Bsktbl; JV Var Ftbl; Hon Roll; U Of Scranton; Lwyr.

LUNOVA, KAREN; Archbishop Wood HS For Girls; Churchville, PA; (4); 5/248; Pres 4-H; Trs German Clb; Ed Yrbk Stf; Cit Awd; Dnfth Awd; 4-H Awd; NHS; Library Aide; Math Tm; Scholastic Bowl; Ursns Coll Freelnd Mrt Schlrshp 87; Ursinus Coll; Poltcl Sci.

LUNT, JENNIFER; Montoursville HS; Montoursville, PA; (3); 30/187; 4-H; Key Clb; Chorus; Mrchg Band; School Musical; Rep Jr Cls; JV Socr; 4-H Awd; Hon Roll; German Clb; Acad All-Amer 87.

LUONG, QUANG; Central Dauphin HS; Harrisburg, PA; (2); 50/405; Computer Clb; Ski Clb; Hon Roll; Jr NHS.

LUONGO, CAROL; Dunmore HS; Dunmore, PA; (3); 23/150; Drama Clb; Yrbk Stf; JV Var Cheerleading; Capt Crs Cntry; Swmmng; Trk; High Hon Roll; Hon Roll; Jr NHS; NHS; Crss Cntry Alumnae Awd 86; Nrsng.

LUONGO, PAT; Dunmore HS; Dunmore, PA; (4); 40/150; Church Yth Grp; Computer Clb; Drama Clb; French Clb; Letterman Clb; Ski Clb; Im Bsktbl; JV Ftbl; Var L Trk; Var Wt Lftg; U Of Scranton; Comp Sci.

LUPINACCI, MARY; Saint Paul Cathedral HS; Pittsburgh, PA; (4); Dance Clb; Hosp Aide; Red Cross Aide; Chorus; High Hon Roll; NHS; Rotary Awd; 2nd Pl Sci Fair 85; 2nd Pl Carnegie Mellon U Hstry Day 86; Rcgntn Physcs 87; U Of Pittsburgh.

LUPINETTI, ANDREA; Penn Cambria SR HS; Gallitzin, PA; (4); 3/298; Drama Clb; French Clb; Girl Scts; SADD; Stage Crew; Rep Frsh Cls; Rep Soph Cls; Rep Jr Cls; Rep Sr Cls; Off Stu Cncl; Juniata COLL; Pre Med.

LUPINSKI, DAVID; Tunkhannock Area HS; Tunkhannock, PA; (3); 2/337; Key Clb; Var L Bsbl; Var L Socr; Var L Swmmng; Cit Awd; Hon Roll; Kiwanis Awd; NHS; Hnrs Banquet 84-87; Bio.

LUPOLE, RICHARD; Coughlin HS; Wilkes Barre, PA; (3); Church Yth Grp; ROTC; Band; Mrchg Band; JV Bsbl; JV Ftbl; Hon Roll; Soroptimist; Mrchg Band; Var Bsktbl; $40000 ROTC Schlrshp 4 Yr 90; Bsbl Teener All Star 86; Phys Fitness Awd 85; Penn ST U; Phys Therapy.

LUPOLI, CHRISTOPHER; Pennsburg HS; Yardley, PA; (3); 4/95; Natl Beta Clb; Chorus; Rep Frsh Cls; Rep Soph Cls; JV Var Socr; Var L Tennis; Var High Hon Roll; Var Hon Roll; NHS; FCA; PA ST U; Mrktng.

LUPTAK, LISA MARIE; Union Area HS; New Castle, PA; (4); 6/66; Art Clb; French Clb; FHA; High Hon Roll; Hon Roll; NHS; PA ST Coll Beaver Campus.

LUPYAK, MARION; Sacred Heart HS; Carbondale, PA; (3); 12/40; Church Yth Grp; Dance Clb; French Clb; Ski Clb; VP SADD; School Play; Variety Show; Trs Jr Cls; NHS.

LURE, REBECCA; State College Area SR HS; State College, PA; (3); German Clb; Ski Clb; SADD; Chorus; Church Choir; Flag Corp; Yrbk Stf; JV L Trk; Hon Roll; Prfct Atten Awd; Penn ST; Paramedc.

LURIE, LEANNE; Lower Merion HS; Philadelphia, PA; (3); Pep Clb; SADD; Rep Jr Cls; JV Cheerleading; JV Swmmng; Hon Roll; PA ST U; Ed.

LUROWIST, KRISTIN; Central Columbia HS; Bloomsburg, PA; (4); 12/170; JV Var Fld Hcky; High Hon Roll; NHS; Varsity Clb; Band; Concert Band; School Musical; Stat Wrstlng; French Hon Soc; Pres Schlr; Susquehanna Schlrshp 87-88; Marion T Adams Meml Schlrshp 87; Susquehanna U; Psych.

LUSCKAY, DORI; West Mifflin Area HS; W Mifflin, PA; (4); 30/365; FBLA; GAA; Office Aide; Powder Puff Ftbl; Sftbl; High Hon Roll; Jr NHS; NHS; Pres Schlr; Exploring; Secr Stu Yr, Typst Yr, & Mendelson Mem Awd Shrthnd 87; Lgl Secr.

LUSCOMBE, JAMES; Council Rock HS; Washington, PA; (2); Church Yth Grp; Ski Clb; JV Bsktbl; JV Ftbl; Im Vllybl.

LUSH, JENNIFER; Mechanicsburg Area SR HS; Shiremanstown, PA; (4); Pep Clb; Mgr(s); Score Keeper; Mgr Swmmng; Mgr Vllybl; Hon Roll; Enrchmnt Spec Intrst Gftd 81; St Athltc Trnr 87-88; CPA.

LUSK, STEVE; Chapel Christian Schl; Bentleyville, PA; (3); Church Yth Grp; 4-H; Church Choir; School Play; Yrbk Rptr; Var Bsktbl; Var Ftbl; Var Sftbl; High Hon Roll; Schlrshp Awd 86.

LUSKIN, LAURA; Upper Moreland HS; Willow Grove, PA; (2); 64/242; Chorus; School Musical; Stage Crew; Hon Roll; Prfssnl Musician.

LUSSIER, ELLEN; York Suburban HS; York, PA; (3); 39/176; SADD; JV Var Cheerleading; High Hon Roll; Hon Roll; Home Economics Hnrs Awd 86; Bus Admin.

LUSTIG, JON; Lancaster Mennonite HS; Mount Joy, PA; (2); 29/149; Church Yth Grp; Var Mgr(s); PA Math Leag-Supr Achvt 87; Math Assn Of Amer-Outstndg Prfcncy 87; Math.

LUTCAVAGE, CATHERINE; Spring-Ford SR HS; Royersford, PA; (3); 47/256; Church Yth Grp; German Clb; Girl Scts; Hosp Aide; SADD; Yrbk Sprt Ed; Yrbk Stf; Rep Frsh Cls; Rep Soph Cls; Rep Jr Cls; Medical Prfssnl & Career Acad.

LUTCAVAGE, CHRISTOPHER; Danville HS; Danville, PA; (2); Band; Concert Band; Mrchg Band; JV Crs Cntry; JV Trk; High Hon Roll; Latin Hon Soc 86-87; Pres Acdmc Fit Awd 85-86; Pre Med.

LUTES, ANDREA; Washington HS; Washington, PA; (3); 53/170; French Clb; Letterman Clb; Sec Frsh Cls; Sec Soph Cls; Sec Jr Cls; Stu Cncl; Vllybl; Hon Roll; Seton Hill Coll; Hstry.

LUTES, DIANE; Bishop Mc Devitt HS; Hummelstown, PA; (1); Spanish Clb; Capt Cheerleading; Hon Roll; Dcknsn; Htl Ownr.

LUTES, JUDY; Carrick HS; Pittsburgh, PA; (3); 69/325; Q&S; Ski Clb; SADD; Chorus; Nwsp Stf; Bsktbl; Powder Puff Ftbl; Hon Roll; Med.

LUTHER, CAROL; Bishop Guilfoyle HS; Altoona, PA; (3); 24/156; Science Clb; Chorus; Church Choir; High Hon Roll; Hon Roll; St Francis Coll; Med Fld.

LUTHER, MATTHEW; Cambria Heights HS; Carrolltown, PA; (4); 8/189; Pres Jr Cls; Pres Sr Cls; Pres Stu Cncl; Cit Awd; NHS; L Var Bsbl; L Var Ftbl; L Var Wrstlng; Faculty Awd 87; Bsbl 2 Records For Most Runs Scored & Stolen Bases 86-87; IN U; Acctng.

LUTHY, MATT; Central Catholic HS; Pittsburgh, PA; (2); 50/333; Band; Concert Band; Mrchg Band; Pep Band; Im Bsktbl; Im Crs Cntry; Im Ftbl; JV Socr; Im Vllybl; Hon Roll; PJAS Awds 85-87; Georgetown Notre Dame; Psych.

LUTJE, MARGARETHA; Allentown Central Catholic HS; Allentown, PA; (3); Church Yth Grp; German Clb; Key Clb; Math Tm; Service Clb; Chorus; Ed Lit Mag; High Hon Roll; NHS.

LUTSKA, BRANT; Monessen HS; Monessen, PA; (3); 39/126; VP Trs Church Yth Grp; Drama Clb; French Clb; VP FBLA; JA; Sec OEA; Radio Clb; Teachers Aide; Band; Yrbk Ed-Chief; Pittsburgh U; Bus Admin.

LUTSKO, JEFF; W Mifflin Area HS; W Mifflin, PA; (2); Boy Scts; Letterman Clb; Var Crs Cntry; Var JV Trk; High Hon Roll; Hon Roll; Jr NHS; Comm Pilot.

LUTTERSCHMIDT, TIMOTHY; William Allen HS; Allentown, PA; (4); 16/518; Pres Exploring; German Clb; ROTC; VP Ski Clb; Chorus; L Ftbl; Capt L Vllybl; Hon Roll; Jr NHS; VP NHS; ESU Deans Schlrshp 87; ESU; Law.

LUTTY, DARLENE; Deer Lakes HS; Cheswick, PA; (4); 26/180; Varsity Clb; Chorus; Capt Flag Corp; School Musical; School Play; Stage Crew; Nwsp Rptr; Yrbk Phtg; Capt Trk; Hon Roll; Band Awd & Drama Awd 87; Spch Acvhmnt Awd 85; ICM Schl Of Bus; Med Asst.

LUTZ, AMY; Lancaster Country Day HS; Columbia, PA; (3); Hst Drama Clb; GAA; Teachers Aide; Capt Var Bsktbl; Capt Var Tennis; Church Yth Grp; Model UN; PAVAS; School Play; Awd MVP Tennis Tm 85 86; Coaches Awd Tennis 87; Fshn Dsgn.

LUTZ, CARLA; Kutztown Area SR HS; Lenhartsville, PA; (4); 4/147; Pres Church Yth Grp; Hosp Aide; Band; Color Guard; Concert Band; Bausch & Lomb Sci Awd; High Hon Roll; NHS; Prfct Atten Awd; Pres Schlr; Wllm S Myr Awd-Muscl Excllnc 87; Ktztwn Myrs Awd-Outstndng Instrmntl-Mscn 87; Oscr & Mrn Stn Schlrshp; Bloomsburg U; Nrsng.

LUTZ, CARLA; Lincoln HS; Ellwood City, PA; (3); #36 In Class; Pres Church Yth Grp; Library Aide; High Hon Roll; Hon Roll; Socl Welfare.

LUTZ, CHRISTINE; Portage Area HS; Portage, PA; (4); 22/120; Ski Clb; Band; VP Chorus; Concert Band; Jazz Band; Pep Band; Sec Bowling; Im Vllybl; High Hon Roll; NHS; Pre-Dnt.

LUTZ, DIANE; Bishop Hafey HS; W Hazleton, PA; (3); Key Clb; Spanish Clb; Sec Y-Teens; High Hon Roll; Hon Roll; Hghst Av Spnsh II 85-86; PA ST U; Educ.

LUTZ, GEORGE; Columbia Montour Vo Tech; Danville, PA; (4); Teachers Aide; VICA; Chorus; Rep Jr Cls; Rep Sr Cls; Rep Stu Cncl; JV Wt Lftg; Hon Roll; NHS.

LUTZ, HEIDI; Wissahickon HS; Ambler, PA; (4); 11/287; VP Art Clb; Sec Pres Church Yth Grp; Ed Lit Mag; High Hon Roll; Hon Roll; NHS; Opt Clb Awd; Dr Franklin C Kelton Schlrshp Awd 87; Juniata Coll; Bio.

LUTZ, KEVIN; Portage Area HS; Portage, PA; (4); 7/120; Computer Clb; 4-H; French Clb; Letterman Clb; Varsity Clb; JV Var Ftbl; Wrstlng; High Hon Roll; VP NHS; Socr; PA State U; Elec Engnrng.

LUTZ, LESLIE; Montour HS; Mckees Rks, PA; (3); Office Aide; SADD; Teachers Aide; Band; Mrchg Band; Yrbk Stf; Stu Cncl; Pom Pon; Powder Puff Ftbl; Trk; U Pittsburgh; Tchg.

LUTZ, LISA; Lincoln HS; Ellwood City, PA; (3); 43/163; French Clb; Y-Teens; Powder Puff Ftbl; High Hon Roll; Hon Roll.

LUTZ, LISA; Moshannon Valley HS; Houtzdale, PA; (3); GAA; Ski Clb; Varsity Clb; Band; Concert Band; Mrchg Band; Pep Band; Yrbk Stf; Bsktbl; Twrlr.

LUTZ, MATTHEW; Immaculate Conception HS; Washington, PA; (2); 11/35; Math Tm; Ski Clb; Pres Soph Cls; Rep Stu Cncl; Var L Bsbl; Var Bsktbl; Var L Ftbl; Biol.

LUTZ, MICHAEL; Danville Area HS; Danville, PA; (4); JV Bsbl; JV Ftbl; Var Golf; High Hon Roll; NHS; Natl Acdmc All Amer Awd, Natl Ldrshp & Svcs Awd, Nattl Math & Sci Awds 84; Temple U; Actuarial Sci.

LUTZ, PATRICIA; Pennsburg HS; Yardley, PA; (3); Church Yth Grp; Cmnty Wkr; French Clb; SADD; Crs Cntry; Trk; Hon Roll; Psych.

LUTZ, PAULA; Nazareth SR HS; Nazareth, PA; (3); Church Yth Grp; Girl Scts; Hosp Aide; Color Guard; Drill Tm; Mrchg Band; Rep Stu Cncl; Twrlr; Hon Roll; Flght Atndnt.

LUTZ, REBECCA; Oley Valley HS; Temple, PA; (3); 46/142; Drama Clb; Model UN; Red Cross Aide; Chorus; Church Choir; Hon Roll; Marine Bio.

LUTZ, RENEE; Jefferson-Morgan HS; Rice Landing, PA; (4); 10/98; Intnl Clb; Spanish Clb; Yrbk Stf; High Hon Roll; Hon Roll.

LUTZ, ROBERT; South Hill Christian HS; Monongahela, PA; (3); 2/16; Church Yth Grp; School Play; Stage Crew; Yrbk Phtg; Yrbk Stf; Pres Jr Cls; Var Bsktbl; Var Socr; High Hon Roll; Hon Roll; Bio, Engl Top Achvt Awd 86; Physcl Sci Awd 85; Geneva Coll; Mdcl Rsrch.

LUTZ, STACEY; Lakeland HS; Jermyn, PA; (3); Church Yth Grp; French Clb; Stu Cncl; Stat Bsbl; JV Bsktbl; Var Cheerleading; Score Keeper; High Hon Roll; Hon Roll; NHS; U PA; Frnch.

LUTZ, SUSAN; Wilmington Area HS; Volant, PA; (3); Office Aide; Spanish Clb; Yrbk Stf; Sec Soph Cls; Sec Jr Cls; JV Cheerleading; Powder Puff Ftbl; Cit Awd; High Hon Roll; Hon Roll; Good Ctznshp Awd 85; Prom Prncss 87; Prncpls Lst 87; Grove City Coll; Educ.

LUTZ, TIM; Wyalusing Valley HS; Wyalusing, PA; (3).

LUTZ, TRACY; Portage Area HS; Portage, PA; (3); 33/112; Drama Clb; Letterman Clb; NFL; Varsity Clb; School Play; Nwsp Stf; Yrbk Stf; Trs Jr Cls; Var Trk; Stat Vllybl; Pres Phy Ftns Awd 85-87; Accntng.

LUX, KIRK; Harbor Creek HS; Erie, PA; (3); Computer Clb; Im Bsktbl; Var L Ftbl; Im Golf; Im Vllybl; Im Wt Lftg; High Hon Roll; Hon Roll; Engrng.

LUXON, LUELLA; Imperial Christian Acad; Clinton, PA; (3); Church Yth Grp; Debate Tm; French Clb; Quiz Bowl; Chorus; Variety Show; Nwsp Stf; Cheerleading; Var Sftbl; Var Tennis; Robert Morris Coll; Bus Manag.

LUYK, DEREK A; Burrell SR HS; Lower Burrell, PA; (3); 8/176; Church Yth Grp; Cmnty Wkr; Spanish Clb; Concert Band; Jazz Band; Var JV Bsktbl; L Trk; High Hon Roll; Jr NHS; NHS; 1ST Pl Savlation Army E Trrtry Star Srch Intermed Piano Solo Comp 85; Engrng.

LY, KIET; Lampeter-Strasburg HS; Strasburg, PA; (3); Band; Concert Band; Mrchg Band; Pep Band; Var Ftbl; Var Trk; Wt Lftg; Hon Roll; Penn ST; Mech Engrng.

LYANSKY, YAN; Bensalem HS; Bensalem, PA; (2); Chess Clb; Hon Roll; U PA; Stock Broker.

LYDIC, LISA; North Hills HS; Pittsburgh, PA; (3); Church Yth Grp; Exploring; Sec Band; Mrchg Band; High Hon Roll; Hon Roll; Sec NHS; Ntl Merit Ltr; Cmnty Wkr; Hosp Aide; Athl Awd 85; Optmtrst.

LYDON, CHRISTA; Nazareth Acad HS; Bensalem, PA; (3); French Clb; NFL; Pep Clb; Chorus; Chorus; School Musical; Stage Crew; Ed Lit Mag; Im Vllybl; Temple U; Jrnlsm.

LYKENS, JOHN; Conrad Weiser JR/Sr HS; Wernersville, PA; (3); 2/179; Exploring; Rep Stu Cncl; JV Bsbl; Im Bsktbl; Socr; JV Trk; High Hon Roll; Hon Roll; Rotary Intl Ldrshp Camp 87; Air Force ROTC Coll; Med.

LYKENS, KRISTEN; Clearfield Area HS; Clearfield, PA; (3); 15/300; Church Yth Grp; Key Clb; Ski Clb; Spanish Clb; Var L Cheerleading; Im Mgr Gym; Im Mgr Socr; L Var Trk; Stat Wrstlng; Cit Awd; Schl Rcrd In Trpl Jump In Trck 86.

LYLES, TAMMY G; John Harris HS; Harrisburg, PA; (1); Church Yth Grp; ROTC; Teachers Aide; Band; Church Choir; Mrchg Band; Pep Band; Off Frsh Cls; Sftbl; Hon Roll.

LYMAN, VERONICA; West Hazleton HS; Conyngham, PA; (4); 41/224; Church Yth Grp; Pres Spanish Clb; SADD; Varsity Clb; Nwsp Stf; Yrbk Stf; Var Capt Bsktbl; JV Cheerleading; Var Sftbl; Hon Roll; PA ST U; Hotel-Restrnt Mgmt.

LYNAM, BEN; West Middlesex HS; Pulaski, PA; (3); #1 In Class; French Clb; Science Clb; Pres Frsh Cls; Pres Soph Cls; Pres Jr Cls; Var Bsktbl; L Var Ftbl; High Hon Roll; Jr NHS; NHS.

LYNAM, JIM; West Middlesex Area HS; Pulaski, PA; (2); Cmnty Wkr; Var L Ftbl; Var L Trk; Hon Roll; Jr NHS.

LYNCH, ANDREA; Lackawanna Trail HS; Nicholson, PA; (3); 9/110; Hosp Aide; Ski Clb; Church Choir; Madrigals; French Hon Soc; Hon Roll; Trs NHS.

LYNCH, BETH A; Blue Mountain HS; Orwigsburg, PA; (4); 9/215; Mu Alpha Theta; Chorus; Nwsp Stf; Swmmng; JV Var Vllybl; Hon Roll; Sec NHS; NEDT Awd; Latin Hnr Soc; Pres Acad Ftnss Awd; Kutztown U; Math.

LYNCH, BRIAN; Meadville Area SR HS; Meadville, PA; (3); 10/363; Im Badmtn; Im Bowling; Ntl Merit Ltr; Biotechnlgy.

LYNCH, CHRISTINE; Bangor Area HS; Mount Bethel, PA; (2); Ski Clb; Varsity Clb; Var Fld Hcky; Art Clb; Band; Chorus; Im Bsktbl; JV Sftbl; JV Trk; Hon Roll; 2nd Hnrs 85-87; Marine Bio.

LYNCH, CHRISTOPHER; Coughlin HS; Wilkes-Barre, PA; (3); Ski Clb; Spanish Clb; Var Capt Golf; Hon Roll; Jr NHS; Acad All Amer 85-86; Pre-Law.

LYNCH, DAVE; Moon SR HS; Coraopolis, PA; (4); 10/304; German Clb; Key Clb; Rep Frsh Cls; L Crs Cntry; JV Socr; L Trk; High Hon Roll; NHS; Ntl Merit Schol; Acadc Excel Schlrshp 87; Chubb Fnftn Schlrshp 87; John Hopkins Schlrshp 87; PA ST U; Engr.

LYNCH, DAVID; West Catholic Boys HS; Philadelphia, PA; (2); 15/250; Temple; Sci.

LYNCH, KATHLEEN V; Cardinal Dougherty HS; Cheltenham, PA; (4); 34/696; Am Leg Aux Girls St; German Clb; Capt Band; Concert Band; Jazz Band; Mrchg Band; Orch; School Musical; School Play; Nwsp Rptr; Frtrnl Ordr Of Police 87; Raymond Russell Mem Schlrshp 87; PA & Natl Marine Corps Leag Schlrshp 87; Temple U; Music.

LYNCH, KRIS; Archbishop Wood For Boys; Warminster, PA; (4); Computer Clb; Scholastic Bowl; Pres SADD; Jazz Band; Mrchg Band; Nwsp Rptr; Yrbk Rptr; Lit Mag; Kiwanis Awd; Mscl Achvt Awd 87; Bloomsburg U; AM Hstry.

LYNCH, LISA; West Mifflin Area HS; W Mifflin, PA; (3); #1 In Class; Band; Chorus; Concert Band; Mrchg Band; Orch; Nwsp Rptr; Nwsp Stf; High Hon Roll; Jr NHS; NHS; PA Music Ed Assn Awd 85; Elec Engr.

LYNCH, LORI; West Mifflin Area HS; West Mifflin, PA; (3); #1 In Class; Band; Concert Band; Mrchg Band; Orch; Nwsp Rptr; Nwsp Stf; High Hon Roll; Hon Roll; Jr NHS; NHS; PA Music Educators Assn Awd 85; Engrng.

LYNCH, MARCY; Mt Pleasant Area HS; Mt Pleasant, PA; (3); 4/245; Chrmn SADD; Concert Band; Mrchg Band; Yrbk Bus Mgr; Rep Frsh Cls; Sec Jr Cls; JV Var Sftbl; Im Vllybl; High Hon Roll; William & Mary; Bus Admin.

LYNCH, SEAN; Upper Moreland SR HS; Willow Grove, PA; (3); 124/276; Rep Soph Cls; Var Ftbl; Var Trk; JV Wrstlng; Hon Roll.

LYNCH, THEODORE D; Honesdale HS; Honesdale, PA; (4); 6/238; Off Stu Cncl; Capt Bsbl; Capt Bsktbl; Capt Ftbl; Trs NHS; Cmnty Wkr; Drama Clb; School Musical; Yrbk Stf; High Hon Roll; 4 Yr NROTC & AFROTC Schlrshps, Hnsdle Area Jayces Outstndng Mle Stu Athl, Hnsdle Rtry Svc Slf Awd; PA ST U; Aerospce Engrng.

LYNN, DANA; Canevin HS; Coraopolis, PA; (3); French Clb; Spanish Clb; Stage Crew; Hon Roll; Lang.

LYNN, DONALD; Downingtown HS; Downingtown, PA; (3); 9/650; Letterman Clb; Spanish Clb; Rep Stu Cncl; Var Bsbl; Var Bsktbl; Var Ftbl; Var Socr; High Hon Roll; NHS; NEDT Awd.

LYNN, ELIZABETH K; Ligonier Valley SR HS; Ligonier, PA; (3); 9/154; Am Leg Aux Girls St; Hosp Aide; NFL; Ski Clb; SADD; Stu Cncl; Var Cheerleading; High Hon Roll; Hon Roll; Jr NHS; Hugh O Brian Yth Smnr Rep 86; Psych.

LYNN, STEPHEN W; Central HS; Phila, PA; (4); 2/341; Var Tennis; High Hon Roll; Ntl Merit SF; Brwn U Book Awd 86; John Seely Hart Engl Awd 86; Albert H Smyth Ltrature Prize 86; Engrng.

LYON, MELISSA; Caron Mc Millan HS; Eighty Four, PA; (3); Hosp Aide; Office Aide; Spanish Clb; Varsity Clb; Capt L Swmmng; Hon Roll; Penn ST U; Accntng.

LYONS, DENISE; St Marys Area HS; Saint Marys, PA; (4); JV Var Bsktbl; High Hon Roll; Hon Roll; NHS; Allegany CC; Dntl Hygiene.

LYONS, EILEEN T; Upper Dublin SR HS; Ambler, PA; (4); 57/318; SADD; Capt Color Guard; Capt Mrchg Band; Yrbk Stf; Hon Roll; NHS; Harold S Maynard Memorial Schlrshp 87; Ruthie Lemmel Memorial Awd 87; Presdntl Acad Fitness Awd 87; Fairfield U; Psychlgy.

LYONS, MICHAEL; Hughesville HS; Hughesville, PA; (3); Varsity Clb; Var L Ftbl; Capt Var Trk; Var L Wrstlng; High Hon Roll; NHS; Mst Prmsng-Wrstlng; Top Fld-Trk.

LYSIC, CATHY; Penn Cambria HS; Lilly, PA; (3); Drama Clb; Pres FBLA; Rep Frsh Cls; Trs Jr Cls; JV Var Bsktbl; Courtroom Stenographer.

LYTER, AMY; Greenwood HS; Millerstown, PA; (2); 5/69; Church Yth Grp; 4-H; GAA; Chorus; Swing Chorus; JV Bsktbl; VP Fld Hcky; VP Sftbl; 4-H Awd; Hon Roll; Penn ST; Spnsh.

LYTER, KRISTA; Middletown Area HS; Middletown, PA; (3); 28/197; Church Yth Grp; Band; Chorus; Church Choir; Concert Band; Mrchg Band; Orch; School Musical; School Play; Swing Chorus; Dawphin Cnty Chorus 85-86; Messiah Coll; Music Educ.

LYTER, MARTHA J; Bradford Area HS; Bradford, PA; (3); AFS; Hosp Aide; Pep Clb; Concert Band; Jazz Band; Mrchg Band; Pep Band; Yrbk Stf; Hon Roll; Music Therapy & Music Perf.

LYTLE, CHRISTIAN ROSS; Franklin Area HS; Franklin, PA; (4); 37/214; Band; Concert Band; Jazz Band; Pep Band; School Musical; School Play; Variety Show; Yrbk Phtg; Yrbk Sprt Ed; Hon Roll; Fnlst PA Gvrnrs Schl For Art-Photo 86; Tylr Yrbk Co Smmr Wrkshp Schlrshp 85; F D Williams Schlrshp 87; IN U Of PA; Media Pblctns.

LYTLE, ELIZABETH I; Hollidaysburg Area HS; Duncansville, PA; (4); #25 In Class; Drama Clb; Pres French Clb; SADD; Band; Chorus; Church Choir; Concert Band; Flag Corp; Orch; School Play; Wachter Fndtn Schlrshp 87; PA ST U; Bus.

LYTTLE, WILLIAM; Monessen JR-SR HS; Monessen, PA; (3); 52/110; High Hon Roll; Hon Roll; Comp Prgrmmr.

MA, OANH; Milton Hershey HS; Lancaster, PA; (4); Hst Drama Clb; Thesps; School Play; Stage Crew; Nwsp Rptr; Nwsp Stf; Lit Mag; Rep Frsh Cls; Capt Cheerleading; Capt Gym.

MA COY, DENISE J; Big Spring HS; Shippensburg, PA; (3); Church Yth Grp; JA; Pep Clb; Band; Chorus; Swing Chorus; Rep Stu Cncl; Stat Crs Cntry; Hon Roll; Prfct Atten Awd; Law.

MA LONE, CHRISTOPHER; Moon SR HS; Coraopolis, PA; (2); Chess Clb; French Clb; Band; Jazz Band; Symp Band; Variety Show; Nwsp Rptr; Nwsp Stf; Hon Roll; Trnsltr.

MAADDI, SHADI; St John Neumann HS; Philadelphia, PA; (4); #1 In Class; Computer Clb; Capt Math Tm; Science Clb; Yrbk Stf; NHS; Val; Math High Scorer 85-86.

MAAS, JENNIFER; Dowingintown SR HS; Downingtown, PA; (3); 21/648; Ski Clb; SADD; Chorus; Var L Tennis; High Hon Roll; Soph Art Stu Of Month 86; Arch.

MAAS, MICHELE; Fairview HS; Fairview, PA; (3); 4/160; Boy Scts; French Clb; Yrbk Stf; Rep Frsh Cls; Im Sftbl; Im Tennis; Hon Roll; NHS.

MABRY, TARA; Pine Grove Area HS; Pine Grove, PA; (3); ROTC; Drill Tm; Nwsp Ed-Chief; Nwsp Rptr; Sec Sr Cls; JV Var Sftbl; Lgl Secy.

MAC ARTHUR, DOUGLAS; Strong Vincent HS; Erie, PA; (3); 14/191; Var L Bsbl; JV Ftbl; Hnrb Mntn All Metro Bsbl Tm 87; Hotel Mgmt.

MAC ARTHUR, JOSH; Abington Heights HS; Dalton, PA; (3); 96/296; Socr; Vllybl; Hon Roll; Vrsty Lttr Sccr 85-87; Vrsty Lttr Vllybl 86-87; Marine Arch.

MAC BLANE, SHELLY; Marion Center Area HS; Home, PA; (3); FNA; Latin Clb; Chorus; Color Guard; Flag Corp; Mrchg Band; Yrbk Stf; Var Mgr(s); JV Var Trk; Aud/Vis; Vet Med.

MAC BRIDE, STEVE; York Suburban HS; York, PA; (3); SADD; Band; Concert Band; Mrchg Band; Orch; Pep Band; Variety Show; Hon Roll; Ntl Merit SF; U Of PA; Bus.

MAC CRACKEN, TIMOTHY; Father Judge HS; Philadelphia, PA; (3); 64/384; French Clb; Im Powder Puff Ftbl; Bus Admin.

MAC CRUM, KRISTY; North Allegheny SR HS; Wexford, PA; (2); 61/630; AFS; JA; Hon Roll; Hgh Achvt Newfne Math Cont 87; 1st Pl ST PA Natl Music Wk Essay Cont 85; Outstndng Achvt Chem 86-87; Engrng.

MAC DONALD, BRIAN J; Scranton Prep; Scranton, PA; (4); 41/190; Boys Clb Am; Boy Scts; Stage Crew; Capt Crs Cntry; Capt Trk; High Hon Roll; Lion Awd; NHS; VFW Awd; Eagle Sct 87; Lehigh U; Elec Engrng.

MAC DONALD, CHAD; Moniteau JR SR HS; West Sunbury, PA; (3); 15/140; Drama Clb; Spanish Clb; Concert Band; Jazz Band; Mrchg Band; School Play; Var Socr; Hon Roll; NHS; Ntl Merit Ltr; HOBY Awd 86; Mascot Awd 87; Natl Acdmc Gms Tm 82-87; U Of Miami; Ocean Engr.

MAC DONALD, HELEN; West Phila Catholic H S For Girls; Philadelphia, PA; (3); 46/246; French Clb; Girl Scts; Hon Roll; Prfct Atten Awd; Hotel Mgt.

MAC DONALD, KRISTIN; Greensburg Central Catholic HS; Murrysville, PA; (4); 18/222; Hosp Aide; Mgr Service Clb; Pres Chorus; School Musical; Stage Crew; Yrbk Stf; NHS; Hghst Hnr 84-87; Wstnghse Fmly Schlrshp 87; John C, Kathryn S Rdmnd Schlrshp 87; Chstnut Hll Coll; Math.

MAC DONALD, MARIA; School Street JR HS; Bradford, PA; (1); Office Aide; Ski Clb; VP Frsh Cls; Stu Cncl; Bsktbl; Cheerleading; High Hon Roll; Hon Roll; Jr NHS.

MAC DONALD, MARILYN; Riverside HS; Avoca, PA; (4); 35/170; Art Clb; FBLA; Spanish Clb; High Hon Roll; Hon Roll; NHS; Prfct Atten Awd; PTA Merit Awd Creative Wrtng 84; Chrch Yth Grp 83-86; U Of CT; Psychlgy.

MAC DONALD, MARK; State Coll Area Intermediate HS; State College, PA; (2); 3/600; Math Clb; Nwsp Stf; Im Bsktbl; Var L Tennis; Im Vllybl; Cit Awd; French Hon Soc; High Hon Roll; IHS Acdmc Excllnc Awd 87; Advncd Chem Awd 87; Advncd Alg II Awd 87; Math.

MAC DONALD, MICHAEL; Greensburg Central Catholic HS; Murrysville, PA; (2); Art Clb; Debate Tm; French Clb; Ski Clb; Speech Tm; Rep Frsh Cls; Var Crs Cntry; High Hon Roll; Coll Preview Acad Schlrshp 87; Cert Merit Cnty Art Exhbt 87; Cert Merit Amer Assn Frnch Tchrs 87.

MAC DOUGALL, JOHN W; Upper Merion Area HS; King Of Prussia, PA; (3); 11/295; Church Yth Grp; Math Tm; Yrbk Stf; JV Bsbl; Im Bsktbl; Var Swmmng; Im Vllybl; High Hon Roll; NHS; Rotary Awd; Lbrty Div All Leag Slctn 3 Swmng Evnts 87; Engr.

MAC DOWELL, JULIE; Gettysburg SR HS; Gettysburg, PA; (2); #11 In Class; Pres Church Yth Grp; French Clb; Model UN; Varsity Clb; Church Choir; Orch; VP Soph Cls; JV Capt Fld Hcky; Trk; High Hon Roll; Psych.

MAC FADDEN, MARY; Chambersburg Area HS; Chambersburg, PA; (2); Church Yth Grp; Drama Clb; JCL; Concert Band; Mrchg Band; High Hon Roll.

MAC FARLAND, MIKE; Carlynton HS; Carnegie, PA; (4); #33 In Class; Letterman Clb; Varsity Clb; Bsbl; Golf; Hon Roll; Allegheny Coll; Cmmnctns.

MAC GRADY, SUSAN; Lower Moreland HS; Huntingdon Valley, PA; (3); Science Clb; Rep Stu Cncl; JV Bsktbl; Var Capt Cheerleading; JV Var Sftbl.

MAC INTYRE, JULIE; Chestnut Ridge HS; Alum Bank, PA; (3); SADD; Band; Church Choir; Mrchg Band; Yrbk Stf; Stat Trk; JV Var Vllybl; Hon Roll; Jr NHS; NHS; U Of Pgh.

MAC KINNEY, KATHERINE; Downingtown SR HS; Exton, PA; (3); 47/648; French Clb; Ski Clb; Band; Concert Band; Mrchg Band; Hon Roll; NHS; NEDT Awd; Excllnt Rtng PMTA ST Adtns 86; Mem 85 ST Champ Mrchng Bnd 85; Rcgnzd Engl Dept Natl Ed Week 86; OH U; Scndry Ed.

MAC LURE, ANNE MARIE; Archbishop Prendergast HS; Havertown, PA; (3); 24/346; Church Yth Grp; Hosp Aide; Intnl Clb; Latin Clb; Service Clb; Spanish Clb; Hon Roll; NHS; Ntl Merit SF; Phila Coll Of Pharmacy.

MAC MAIN, NANCY; Morrisville JR SR HS; Morrisville, PA; (3); 14/85; VP Church Yth Grp; Hosp Aide; Church Choir; Concert Band; Mrchg Band; JV Bsktbl; JV Sftbl; Hon Roll; Elem Ed.

MAC MURRAY, PATRICIA; Cedar Cliff HS; Camp Hill, PA; (3); 65/304; Camera Clb; Yrbk Stf; High Hon Roll; Hon Roll; Spanish NHS; Photo.

MAC NAB, LORNA; Performing Arts Schl Of Phila; Mt Holly, NJ; (3); School Musical; School Play; Stage Crew; Yrbk Stf; Lit Mag; Hon Roll; All Around Theatre Awd 85 & 86; Hist Awd 85 & 86; Ed Fndtn For Foreign Study 86; Yr Abroad In Gr Britn; Artistic Director.

MACASEK, DAWN; Moon HS; Coraopolis, PA; (3); 63/306; Dance Clb; Art Clb; French Clb; Nwsp Stf; Rep Soph Cls; Rep Stu Cncl; JV L Socr; Var L Swmmng; Timer; Hon Roll; Painting Dsplyd At 3 Rivers Arts Fstvl 87; Tap Ballet Jazz 85-87; Indiana U; Optmtrst.

MACAULAY, CATHERINE; Lower Moreland HS; Huntingdon Valley, PA; (4); Church Yth Grp; FBLA; Key Clb; Science Clb; School Musical; Pres Jr Cls; Pres Sr Cls; VP Stu Cncl; Sftbl; Hon Roll; Asian Culters Smnr; Bus.

MACCALLUM, BILL; Mid Valley HS; Dickson City, PA; (4); Cmnty Wkr; Political Wkr; JV Var Bsbl; JV Var Bsktbl; Mansfield U; Radiology.

MACCARELLI, LISA MARIE; Gateway SR HS; Monroeville, PA; (4); Am Leg Aux Girls St; Pres VP Chorus; Sec Frsh Cls; Sec Soph Cls; Sec Jr Cls; Rep Sr Cls; Rep Stu Cncl; Var JV Cheerleading; Var Sftbl; Hon Roll; Monroeville Arts Cncl Schlrshp & Pres Acdmc Ftnss Awd 87; U Of Pittsburgh; Comms.

MACE, ELAINE; Pottstown SR HS; Pottstown, PA; (4); 17/181; Sec Trs Art Clb; Pep Clb; Stage Crew; Nwsp Stf; Yrbk Stf; Rep Frsh Cls; Var Lcrss; High Hon Roll; Hon Roll; NHS; Art Svc Awd 87; Art Show Awd 86; Lansdale Schl Bus; Paralgl.

MACE, MELISSA; Seton La Salle HS; Library, PA; (3); Church Yth Grp; Ski Clb; Varsity Clb; Y-Teens; Bsktbl; Powder Puff Ftbl; Trk; Vllybl; Vlybl Captn MVP 86-87; Vlybl Mst Dedctd Plyr 85-86; Bus.

MACE, PATRICIA; Hazleton HS; Hazleton, PA; (4); French Clb; FBLA; Intnl Clb; Stat Var Bsbl; Hon Roll; Bloomsburg Univ; Spch Pathology.

MACENCZAK, CHRISTINE; North Star HS; Jenners, PA; (3); 3/141; FCA; Hosp Aide; Math Clb; Mu Alpha Theta; Band; Church Choir; Concert Band; Var Cheerleading; Hon Roll.

MACENCZAK, SHARON; North Star HS; Jenners, PA; (2); 16/139; FCA; Hosp Aide; Mu Alpha Theta; Band; Church Choir; Color Guard; Hon Roll; Lwyr.

MACEVOY, ERICA; Penn Trafford HS; Trafford, PA; (4); 29/344; FBLA; JCL; High Hon Roll; Lion Awd; NHS; Prfct Atten Awd; Womens Club Awd 87; PA ST U; Finance.

MACEY, MATT; Greater Latrobe SR HS; Latrobe, PA; (2); 35/395; Boy Scts; VP Band; JV Ftbl; L Trk; High Hon Roll; Hon Roll; Astronomy.

MACHALIK, PAM; Panther Valley HS; Summit Hill, PA; (1); 35/129; Ski Clb; Trk; Vllybl; High Hon Roll; Hon Roll; Chld Psych.

MACHAMER, JODI; Cardinal O Hara HS; Parkside, PA; (3); 5/720; Hosp Aide; Spanish Clb; School Musical; Var JV Cheerleading; High Hon Roll; Hon Roll; NHS; Spanish NHS; Acad Convocation 86-7; Acad Excllnc Awds-Engl, Chem & Spanish 87; U Of PA; Pre-Med.

MACHINAK, DARLA; Jefferson-Morgan HS; Clarksville, PA; (2); 9/109; Exploring; Intnl Clb; Library Aide; Band; Yrbk Stf; Rep Stu Cncl; JV Var Bsktbl; Var Sftbl; Hon Roll; Bio.

MACHULSKY, MICHAEL; Coughlin HS; Plains, PA; (3); Church Yth Grp; Band; Concert Band; Mrchg Band; School Musical; JV Bsbl; Var Bsktbl; JV Ftbl; Var Vllybl; High Hon Roll; Luzerne Cnty Schltc Art Awd 84; Pres Acad Fit Awd 85; Alter Boy Awd 84.

MACIEJEWSKI, MARK; Punxsutawney HS; Big Run, PA; (3); Church Yth Grp; Cmnty Wkr; Letterman Clb; Varsity Clb; Variety Show; Var Bsbl; Var Ftbl.

MACIJOWSKY, CARRIE; Tunkhannock Area HS; Dalton, PA; (2); 6/322; German Clb; Letterman Clb; Band; Chorus; Concert Band; Jazz Band; Mrchg Band; Orch; Var Trk; Hon Roll; Hnrs Band 85; Penn ST U; Music.

MACIOCE, LISA; Sacred Heart HS; Pittsburgh, PA; (3); 4/135; Hosp Aide; Library Aide; Spanish Clb; High Hon Roll; Hon Roll; NHS; Serv Awd Yth In Serv-Eldrly 87; Stu Of Wk Hnr 87; Accntng.

MACK, CHRISTINE; Central Dauphin HS; Harrisburg, PA; (4); 4-H; Ski Clb; Chorus; Flag Corp; Im Vllybl; 4-H Awd; NHS; Hgh Pt Awd H & H Tack Shop Equitahon & Chldrens Hunter 86; Hollins Coll; Biochem.

MACK, JANEEN; Mt View HS; Kingsley, PA; (3); 3/105; Teachers Aide; Yrbk Stf; Var Sftbl; French Hon Soc; High Hon Roll; NHS; Pres Physical Fitness Awd 86-87; Susquehanna Cnty Bus Comptn 2nk Pl Acctng 86; Math Educ.

MACK, JANELLE; Chambersburg SR HS; Shippensburg, PA; (2); Church Yth Grp; JCL; Latin Clb; Band; Chorus; Church Choir; Mrchg Band; Var JV Fld Hcky; JV Swmmng; JV Trk; Corp Attrny.

MACK, JEFF; Pine Grove Area HS; Tremont, PA; (3); Boy Scts; ROTC; Band; Chorus; Concert Band; Mrchg Band; Bsktbl; Ftbl; Hon Roll; PA ST; Drftng.

MACK, KA RENE; Trinity Christian HS; Pittsburgh, PA; (3); Sec Church Yth Grp; Chorus; Co-Capt Cheerleading; Hon Roll; Jr NHS; NHS; Messiah Coll; Early Chld Dev.

MACK, KAREN; Butler Area SR HS; Butler, PA; (3); Exploring; French Clb; SADD; Jazz Band; Mrchg Band; Sec Stu Cncl; JV Im Bsktbl; L Tennis; L Trk; Sec Jr NHS; Hugh O Brian Ldrshp Awd 85-86; MVP Girls Tennis 86-87; Cnty JR Miss Fnlst 86-87; Notre Dame; Math.

MACK, LISA; Pen Argyl Area HS; Pen Argyl, PA; (4); 2/113; Church Yth Grp; Scholastic Bowl; Ski Clb; Band; Orch; School Play; Nwsp Stf; Yrbk Stf; High Hon Roll; Hon Roll; Sal; Philadelphia Coll; Phys Thrpy.

MACK, PETER; Conemough Township Area HS; Hollsopple, PA; (3); 23/120; Var L Trk; Bio.

MACK, STEPH; Northern Lehigh HS; Slatington, PA; (3); 18/166; Yrbk Stf; Trs Stu Cncl; Var Capt Bsktbl; Stat Crs Cntry; Var L Sftbl; NHS; Alth Yr 85-87; All Leag Team Bsktbl 1st Team 85-87; All Leag Sftbl 2nd Team 86,1st Team 87; Accntng.

MACKARA, DINA; Ridley SR HS; Morton, PA; (3); 92/473; Ski Clb; Teachers Aide; Drill Tm; JV Var Cheerleading; Var Trk; Hon Roll; Prfct Atten Awd; Keystone Schl Of Bus; Bus.

MACKCOVIAK, APRIL; St Marys Area HS; Weedville, PA; (4); Pres FBLA; Yrbk Phtg; Sec Yrbk Stf; Var L Cheerleading; Vllybl; Penn ST U; Bus Admin.

MACKENZIE, KRISTI; Bangor Area SR HS; Bangor, PA; (2); Boy Scts; Church Yth Grp; Drama Clb; Library Aide; Office Aide; JV Mgr(s); JV Tennis; Hon Roll; Pntng Tecnqs.

MACKEY, AMY; Bellwood Antis JR SR HS; Bellwood, PA; (1); Chorus; School Musical; JV Fld Hcky; JV Trk; High Hon Roll; Hon Roll.

MACKEY, BRIAN T; Towanda Area HS; Towanda, PA; (4); 1/150; Church Yth Grp; Trs Science Clb; SADD; Off Sr Cls; Stu Cncl; Bsktbl; Golf; Hon Roll; Ntl Merit SF; Acad All Amer 86; US Military Acad; Mech Engrng.

MACKEY, DAVE; Greater Latrobe SR HS; Greensburg, PA; (4); 14/420; Pres Church Yth Grp; German Clb; Letterman Clb; Math Tm; Ski Clb; Im Bsktbl; Var Tennis; High Hon Roll; NHS; Ntl Merit SF; PA ST U; Gntc Rsrchr.

MACKEY IV, FELIX; Canevin HS; Oakdale, PA; (3); 56/192; FBLA; Ftbl; 1st Tm Dfns Hnrb Mntn Offns Ftbl 86; Gtwy Wst Pblctns-1st Tm Ftbl; Bus.

MACKEY, LISA; Monessen JR SR HS; Monessen, PA; (3); Key Clb; High Hon Roll; Hon Roll; Trvl Mngmt.

MACKIE, CECELIA; Bishop Hannan HS; Scranton, PA; (4); Art Clb; Camera Clb; Drama Clb; FHA; Pep Clb; School Play; Stage Crew; Cheerleading; Excel Hnrs In Sclgy 85-86; Art II Awd 85-86; Theology III Awd 85-86.

MACKIE, MAURY; Scranton Central HS; Scranton, PA; (3); 31/300; French Clb; Pep Clb; SADD; Teachers Aide; Chorus; Yrbk Phtg; Rep Stu Cncl; Capt Cheerleading; Trk; NHS; Educ.

MACKIN, ADRIENNE; St Hubert Catholic High Schl/ Girls; Philadelphia, PA; (3); 180/421; Church Yth Grp; Cmnty Wkr; Computer Clb; Exploring; Office Aide; Spanish Clb; Speech Tm; Nwsp Stf; Lit Mag; Prfct Atten Awd; PA ST U; Crmnl Jstc.

MACKINTOSH, HEATHER; Ambridge Area HS; Baden, PA; (3); Thesps; Band; Chorus; Concert Band; Mrchg Band; Orch; School Musical; School Play; Symp Band; Hon Roll; Vcl Prfrmncs Bridger Brss Jzz Band 87; Sing Natl Anthm Band Sportng Evnts 86-87; Comps.

MACKLEY, BRANT; Red Lion Area SR HS; Delta, PA; (3); School Musical; Yrbk Phtg; JV Tennis; Law.

MACKLIN, ELLA; Schenley HS Teacher Center; Pittsburgh, PA; (3); Pres Church Yth Grp; Cmnty Wkr; French Clb; Var Trk; Cit Awd; High Hon Roll; Hon Roll; Pres NHS; Cert Recog Sprtl Grwth & Outstndng Ldrshp Qual Monumntl Bapt Chrch Schlrshp Comm 86; Engl Tchr.

MACKO, NICOLE; Penn-Trafford HS; Jeannette, PA; (3); Trs AFS; Hosp Aide; SADD; Chorus; Nwsp Rptr; Nwsp Stf; Yrbk Ed-Chief; Stat Trk; Hon Roll; Norfolk ST U; Socl Wrk.

MACKO, RENEE; Monongahela Valley Catholic HS; Charleroi, PA; (2); Art Clb; Church Yth Grp; Ski Clb; Spanish Clb; Chorus; Drm Mjr(t); Mrchg Band; Twrlr; Jr NHS; Spanish NHS; 2nd Art Comp Span 87; Slvr Mdl Ice Skating 85; Span.

MACKOR, KIM; Bethlehem Center HS; Beallsville, PA; (4); Rep Varsity Clb; Nwsp Rptr; Nwsp Stf; Yrbk Stf; Trs Soph Cls; Rep Jr Cls; Rep Sr Cls; Pres Stu Cncl; Stat Bsbl; Capt Bsktbl; Pres Stu Cncl 86-87; Hnrb Mntn Bsktbl 86-87; MIP Bsktbl 85-86; Waynesburg Coll; Comm.

MACKY, CAMERON; Wilmington Area HS; New Wilmington, PA; (4); 1/117; Drama Clb; Band; Mrchg Band; School Play; Stage Crew; Nwsp Sprt Ed; Off Stu Cncl; JV Capt Bsktbl; Capt L Crs Cntry; L Trk; Stanford U.

MACLEAN, MARC; Plymouth-Whitmarsh HS; Lafayette Hill, PA; (3); Pres French Clb; Hosp Aide; Red Cross Aide; ROTC; School Musical; Swing Chorus; Nwsp Rptr; Var Socr; Var Trk; Hon Roll; U Of NC-CHAPEL Hill; Bio Tech.

MACLEAN, SCOTT; The Christian Acad; West Chester, PA; (3); Church Yth Grp; Math Tm; High Hon Roll; Hon Roll; NHS; Teen Prchng Awd 86-87; Word Life Clb Schrlshp 85-87; Word Of Life Bible Inst; Msn Wk.

MACLER, MARK L; Hickory HS; Hermitage, PA; (2); Church Yth Grp; DECA; SADD; Capt Tennis; Hon Roll; MVP Vsty Tnns 85-87; Bus Mgmt.

MACMINN, CAROL; Phoenixville Area HS; Phoenixville, PA; (3); Church Yth Grp; SADD; Chorus; Church Choir; School Musical; School Play; Swing Chorus; Yrbk Stf; Tennis; Trk; Nrsng.

MACOM, AARON; Avella HS; Avella, PA; (3); Art Clb; Nwsp Rptr; Nwsp Stf; Pres Ftns Awd 84-85; Accntng.

MACONAGHY, JEFFREY D; Abraham Lincoln HS; Philadelphia, PA; (3); 20/450; Computer Clb; Letterman Clb; Service Clb; SADD; Varsity Clb; Nwsp Rptr; Nwsp Stf; Yrbk Stf; Pres Stu Cncl; Var JV Bsbl; All Public, All City, All Schlstc Soccer 86; All Public Swmmng 87; Pol Sci.

MACOSKO, KRISTEN; Sharpsville Area HS; Sharpsville, PA; (3); Church Yth Grp; Hosp Aide; Acpl Chr; Chorus; Church Choir; Capt Flag Corp; Jazz Band; Pep Band; NHS; Acad Achvmnt Awd 85-87; Grove Cty Coll; Music Elem Educ.

MACOSTA, SCOTT; Charleroi Area JR & SR HS; N Charleroi, PA; (3); Trk; Hon Roll; WV U; Engrng.

MACRI, DEAN; Wilmington Area HS; Pulaski, PA; (4); 3/118; Pres Chess Clb; Latin Clb; Band; Co-Capt L Crs Cntry; Trk; High Hon Roll; Hon Roll; Prfct Atten Awd; Pres Schlr; Sal; St Vincent Acad Schlrshp 87; St Vincent Coll; Math.

MACRI, LISA; Bishop Mc Cort HS; Johnstown, PA; (3); Pep Clb; Spanish Clb; Chorus; L Cheerleading; Sftbl; High Hon Roll; Hon Roll; Spanish NHS; Natl Sci Olypiad-Chem Cntst 9th Pl 87; Pharmacy.

MACURAK, BEVERLY; Karns City JR SR HS; Chicora, PA; (3); Church Yth Grp; Pep Clb; Chorus; JV Bsktbl; JV Cheerleading; Butler CC; Bus.

MACUS, JENNIFER; Serra Catholic HS; Mifflin, PA; (3); Spanish Clb; Chorus; Yrbk Stf; Trs Frsh Cls; Trs Soph Cls; Trs Jr Cls; Pres Sr Cls; Rep Stu Cncl; Capt Powder Puff Ftbl; Var Sftbl; Intl Bus.

MACUS, MATTHEW; Bishop Hafey HS; Sheppton, PA; (3); Chess Clb; L Ftbl; Philadelphia Coll; Phrmcy.

MACWITHEY, PAMELA; Warren Area HS; Warren, PA; (3); Church Yth Grp; French Clb; Varsity Clb; Band; Chorus; School Play; JV Var Cheerleading; High Hon Roll; Hon Roll; Pre-Med.

MACY, KRISTEN; South Park HS; Library, PA; (3); 13/240; Exploring; Trs FBLA; JA; Nwsp Phtg; Yrbk Phtg; Yrbk Stf; High Hon Roll; Hon Roll; Trs NHS; Prfct Atten Awd; Acctg.

MADAR, DARLA; Yough SR HS; Smithton, PA; (3); 28/252; Trs Cmnty Wkr; Ski Clb; SADD; Rep Frsh Cls; High Hon Roll; Hon Roll; Jr NHS; NHS; CA U Of PA; Bus Admin.

MADDAS, JOSEPH; Connellsville HS; Vanderbilt, PA; (2); 329/550; Computer Clb; Mgr(s); Hon Roll; High Achvmnt Awd Computers 85-86; U Of Pittsburgh; Phys Thrpst.

MADDEN, COLLEEN; Allderdice HS; Pittsburgh, PA; (3); Drama Clb; School Play; Acting.

MADDEN, DANIEL; Archbishop Wood H S For Boys; Churchville, PA; (2); 32/256; Var L Swmmng; Hon Roll.

MADDEN, JASON; Upper Moreland HS; Willow Grove, PA; (2); 44/242; Boy Scts; Key Clb; SADD; Varsity Clb; Var Gym; Var Bsktbl; Var Ftbl; Var Wt Lftg; Hon Roll; FL ST; Real Est.

MADDEN, LISA-ANN; Bishop O Reilly HS; Forty Fort, PA; (2); Hosp Aide; Red Cross Aide; Sec Spanish Clb; Chorus; Nwsp Rptr; VP Jr Cls; Hon Roll; NHS; Spanish NHS; Hnrb Mntn Natl Spn Exam 85-86; Duquesne; Phrmcy.

MADDEN, PAULA; North Hills HS; Pittsburgh, PA; (4); 23/467; Chorus; Yrbk Stf; Lit Mag; Sr Cls; Rep Stu Cncl; High Hon Roll; Hon Roll; NHS; Interior Dsgn.

MADDY, MISSY; Shade HS; Central City, PA; (4); 6/61; Pres Spanish Clb; Chorus; Nwsp Stf; Yrbk Stf; Sec Frsh Cls; Hon Roll; Sec NHS; Am Legion Awd 87; Army; Dental Spec.

MADEA, ERIKA; Northampton Area SR HS; Walnutport, PA; (3); 78/494; AFS; German Clb; GAA; Library Aide; Pep Clb; SADD; Chorus; Stu Cncl; Coach Actv; JV Fld Hcky; Acad All Amercn 85; U KY; Acctng.

MADEIRA, CHRISTEN; Rockwood Area HS; Rockwood, PA; (4); 1/95; Chorus; School Play; Nwsp Rptr; Yrbk Ed-Chief; Var Cheerleading; High Hon Roll; NHS; Val; New Cntrvl Jubilee 2nd Rnr-Up 85-86; PA ST U; Fin.

MADEJ, JEANNE; St Francis Acad; Bethlehem, PA; (4); 1/20; Q&S; Service Clb; Chorus; Scholastic Bowl; Nwsp Rptr; Pres Frsh Cls; Capt Cheerleading; Bausch & Lomb Sci Awd; High Hon Roll; NHS; Soc Wmn Engrs Hnr Math Sci; U DE; Bus Admin.

MADER, KATHLEEN; Susquenita HS; Marysville, PA; (3); Library Aide; Hon Roll; 1st Pl At Art Exhbt 86-87; 6th Pl In Cngrssnl Art Exhbt 86-87.

MADER, LORI; Burgettstown Area JR SR HS; Langeloth, PA; (4); 16/138; Ski Clb; Sec Spanish Clb; Var Capt Cheerleading; High Hon Roll; Hon Roll; Sec NHS; Tony Pappas Mem Awd Schlrshp 87; Indiana U Of PA; Bus.

MADEY, MARK; Baldwin SR HS; Pittsburgh, PA; (2); 134/481; Penn ST; Engrng.

MADEY, SHAWN; Berlin Brothers Valley HS; Berlin, PA; (3); 7/105; Band; Concert Band; Jazz Band; Variety Show; Co-Capt Bsktbl; Ftbl; Socr; Trk; Hon Roll; NHS; Music.

MADHATHERI, SWARNA; Philadelphia HS For Girls; Philadelphia, PA; (3); 4/405; Teachers Aide; French Hon Soc; High Hon Roll; Hon Roll; U PA Book Awd 87; Temple U; Bio.

MADONNA, NAN; Ambridge HS; Alquippa, PA; (4); Church Yth Grp; French Clb; Pep Clb; Band; Color Guard; Off Soph Cls; Off Jr Cls; Cheerleading; Mat Maids; Hon Roll; Chrldr Achvt Awd 86; Aliquippa Hosp Schl; X-Ray.

MADORE, ERIC; Connellsville Area SR HS; Cnlvle, PA; (4); 58/550; Concert Band; Symp Band; Capt Var Diving; Capt Var Swmmng; Var Trk; High Hon Roll; Hon Roll; NHS; Prfct Atten Awd; Rotary Awd; WPIAL Dvng Qlfr 86-87; JR Wst 83-84; Duquesne U; Bus Admin.

MADYUN, RASHIDA; Westinghouse HS; Pittsburgh, PA; (3); 4-H; Office Aide; Girl Scts; Teachers Aide; Y-Teens; Drill Tm; Bowling; Swmmng; Trk; Cit Awd.

MAFFEO, JOE; Norwin SR HS; N Huntingdon, PA; (3); Ski Clb; Spanish Clb; SADD; Im Bsbl; Im Bsktbl; Im Ftbl; Elctrcl Engrng.

MAGARGEE, JACKIE; Mercer HS; Mercer, PA; (3); Sec FFA; Chptr Frmrs Degree 85; Area Frmrs Degree 86; Keystone Frmrs Degree 87; Crmnlgy.

MAGARO, STEPHANIE; Northern HS; Wellsville, PA; (4); 5/195; Drama Clb; Pres Sec Speech Tm; Chorus; Nwsp Rptr; NHS; Pres Schlr; Rotary Awd; Debate Tm; French Clb; Quiz Bowl; IN U PA Distngshd Achvt Schlrshp 87; Womns Clb Dillsbg Schlrshp 87; Smll Grp Sngr Bers Sngrs 84-87; IN U Of PA; Secdry Ed.

MAGAS, NICOLE; Marion Center Area HS; Indiana, PA; (2); Pres 4-H; Intnl Clb; Varsity Clb; Band; Concert Band; Mrchg Band; Crs Cntry; Trk; 4-H Awd; Mentorship Sci Prg 87; Marine Bio Quest 87; Dist Chap Hist Day 87.

MAGAZZU, JAMIE; Bishop Hafey HS; Hazleton, PA; (1); 1/98; French Clb; Hosp Aide; Science Clb; Ski Clb; JV Cheerleading; High Hon Roll; Jr NHS; Amer Legn Awd Womn Aux 86; JR Acad Of Sci 1st Pl Behvrl Psych 87; Cathlc Schls Essay Cntst 1st Pl 86; Ed.

MAGAZZU, JODI; Hazleton HS; Hazleton, PA; (3); Church Yth Grp; Drama Clb; Leo Clb; Red Cross Aide; Ski Clb; Spanish Clb; Y-Teens; Chorus; Rep Stu Cncl; Var L Cheerleading; Am Lgn Aux Awd 84; JR Acad Sci Awd 85.

MAGDA, JULIE; Marian HS; Hazleton, PA; (3); 6/104; Hosp Aide; Concert Band; Mrchg Band; French Hon Soc; High Hon Roll; NHS; Med.

MAGDA, KURT; Arch Bishop Wood HS; Warrington, PA; (2); Art Clb; Advrtsng.

MAGDA, MICHELLE; G A R Memorial HS; Wilkes-Barre, PA; (4); 8/177; FBLA; Key Clb; Stage Crew; Hon Roll; NHS; Typing Ii 70 WPM 86; Shrthnd I 60 Wmp 86; Med.

MAGDICH, MARY ANNE; Canon Mc Millan SR HS; Canonsburg, PA; (4); Church Yth Grp; Latin Clb; Band; Concert Band; Mrchg Band; School Play; Yrbk Stf; Hon Roll; PA ST U; Math.

MAGEE, REGINA; Upper Darby HS; Drexel Hill, PA; (3); Office Aide; Concert Band; Jazz Band; Mrchg Band; Orch; High Hon Roll; Hon Roll; Hnr Music Awd 86-87.

MAGEE, ROBERT; Moon SR HS; Coraopolis, PA; (2); Mrchg Band; Pep Band; Symp Band; Rep Soph Cls; Tennis; Hon Roll.

MAGER, LINDA; Little Flower HS; Philadelphia, PA; (3); 113/326; Hon Roll; PSI Inst; Comp Tech.

MAGERA, GEORGE; Bentworth SR HS; Cokeburg, PA; (4); 2/131; Varsity Clb; Off Stu Cncl; Var Bsktbl; Im Bowling; Var Ftbl; Im Wt Lftg; High Hon Roll; NHS; Sal; Thomas Vaira Awd Outstndng Ftbl Plyr Schlr 87; Washington & Jeff Coll; Ecnmcs.

MAGILL, JONI L; Hollidaysburg Area HS; Duncansville, PA; (4); 2/345; German Clb; Science Clb; Band; Orch; Yrbk Stf; Ed Lit Mag; Hon Roll; NHS; Ntl Merit SF; German Awd 85 & 86; All-Amer Hall Of Fame HS Musicians & Womens Clb JR Acdmc Awd 86; Engrng.

MAGILTON, MONICA; Nazareth Acad; Langhorne, PA; (3); Cmnty Wkr; Math Clb; NFL; Child Psych.

MAGISKE, KELLY; Belle Vernon Area HS; Belle Vernon, PA; (3); Girl Scts; Pres Pep Clb; Ski Clb; Yrbk Bus Mgr; Sec Frsh Cls; Sec Soph Cls; Var L Cheerleading; High Hon Roll; NHS; HOBY Ldrshp Awd 86; Exemplary Stu 85; Med.

MAGLIOCCHETTI, DIANA; Pottstown SR HS; Pottstown, PA; (3); 18/155; Girl Scts; Key Clb; Pep Clb; Ski Clb; Spanish Clb; SADD; Yrbk Ed-Chief; Yrbk Stf; Pres Frsh Cls; Pres Soph Cls; Millersville U; Educ.

MAGNETTA, REBECCA; Freeport Area HS; Freeport, PA; (3); 12/213; School Musical; Pres Jr Cls; JV Cheerleading; Var Mgr(s); Var Trk; Hon Roll; Engrng.

MAGNI, KIM; Lebanon Catholic HS; Lebanon, PA; (4); FCA; French Clb; FHA; German Clb; Key Clb; Rep Stu Cncl; Var Cheerleading; Lebanon Cnty Medcl Soc Aux Schlrshp, Caplan Nrsngn Schlrshp, ABWA Hemlck Chptr Schlrshp 87; Lancstr Genl Schl Nrsng; Nrsng.

MAGNIER, MAURA; Conestoga SR HS; Berwyn, PA; (2); Hosp Aide; Intnl Clb; Latin Clb; Drill Tm; Variety Show; Rep Soph Cls; Var Gym; JV Lcrss; Hon Roll; Opt Clb Awd; Math Awd Alg I 86; U Of VA; Med.

MAGNOTTA, ALYSIA; North Pocono HS; Moscow, PA; (1); Church Yth Grp; Band; Concert Band; Mrchg Band; Var Cheerleading; Hon Roll; Prfct Atten Awd; Corp Law.

MAGNOTTA, JOE H; Center HS; Monaca, PA; (4); 1/185; Am Leg Boys St; Pres Computer Clb; German Clb; Letterman Clb; Varsity Clb; VP Capt Bsbl; Bsktbl; High Hon Roll; Lion Awd; Pres NHS; Most Likely To Succeed 87; Schlr Athlt 87; Center High Q Tm 86-87; Gftd & Tlntd Pgm 87; Grove City Coll; Elect Engrng.

MAGNOTTA, MARC C; North Pocono HS; Moscow, PA; (4); 63/264; Var Bsktbl; Var Capt Golf; Hon Roll; NHS; Golf MVP 85-87; Golf Outstndng Sr Athl & Bsktbl-Best Foul Shooter 87; Villanova; Engrng.

MAGNUSON, PETE; Phoenixville Area HS; Phoenixville, PA; (2); Church Yth Grp; Rep Stu Cncl; JV Bsktbl; JV Golf; Im Vllybl; Cit Awd; High Hon Roll; Hon Roll; Ntl Merit Schol; Pres Acdmc Excllnc 85-86; Comm.

MAGOR, ERIKA; Old Forge HS; Old Forge, PA; (4); 8/104; Church Yth Grp; Drama Clb; Color Guard; Drill Tm; School Musical; School Play; High Hon Roll; NHS; Acdmc Schlrshp & Band Booster Awd Bon 87; Misericordia; Erly Chldhd Educ.

MAGOUN, CHRIS; New Castle SR HS; New Castle, PA; (3); 3/250; Band; Concert Band; Mrchg Band; Pep Band; Trk; NHS; Secndry Ed.

MAGRAW, DEBRA; Villa Maria Acad; Erie, PA; (3); GAA; Pep Clb; Science Clb; Spanish Clb; SADD; Varsity Clb; Y-Teens; Socr; Hon Roll; Phys Thrpy.

MAGRINEY, CHRIS; Hershey SR HS; Hershey, PA; (2); 15/220; Ski Clb; Rep Soph Cls; High Hon Roll; Hon Roll; Physics.

MAGUIRE, HEATHER; Emmaus HS; Wescosville, PA; (3); 100/530; Exploring; Hosp Aide; Key Clb; Spanish Clb; SADD; Chorus; Nwsp Rptr.

MAGUIRE, MICHELE; Upper Merion Area HS; Swedesburg, PA; (3); Cmnty Wkr; Pres Jr Cls; Pres Sr Cls; Sftbl; Hon Roll; Outstndng Stu Class Cmmtmnt ; Cmmtte Chrprsn Class Actvts; Elem Ed.

MAGUIRE, SEAN ABRAHAM; Central HS; Philadelphia, PA; (4); 59/296; Church Yth Grp; Yrbk Stf; JV Crs Cntry; Var L Golf; Im Capt Vllybl; Hon Roll; Ntl Merit Ltr; Philadelphia Coll Pharm; Toxlgy.

MAGYOR, TAMMY; Mt Pleasant Area SR HS; Mt Pleasant, PA; (4); FBLA; Color Guard; Nwsp Stf; Yrbk Stf; Hon Roll; Bus Stu Of Mnth.

MAHAFKEY, CINDY; Seneca Valley HS; Mars, PA; (3); 90/400; Varsity Clb; Color Guard; Sftbl; Twrlr; Hon Roll; Embry-Riddle Aerontcl; Aeronics.

MAHAJAN, SUNIT; Fox Chapel Area HS; Pittsburgh, PA; (3); 30/340; Chess Clb; Math Clb; Math Tm; Mu Alpha Theta; Nwsp Stf; Yrbk Stf; Wrstlng; High Hon Roll; NHS; 1st Pl Sci Olympd 84-86; Med.

MAHALIDGE, JODI; Valley View JR SR HS; Jessup, PA; (2); 2/189; French Clb; Chorus; School Musical; Rep Stu Cncl; Var Cheerleading; High Hon Roll; NHS; Prfct Atten Awd; Acdmc Awd Excllnc 85-87; Cert Hnr Natl Frnch Cntst 87; Bus.

MAHAN, AMY; Trinity HS; Washington, PA; (4); FHA; German Clb; Hon Roll; Co-Capt Trnty Rifle Tm 87; Mediean Health Schl; Med Asst.

MAHAN, ERIC; Central Dauphin HS; Harrisburg, PA; (3); 1/370; VP Church Yth Grp; Trs Key Clb; Quiz Bowl; Stu Cncl; Bsktbl; Vllybl; Hon Roll; Jr NHS; NHS; Ntl Merit Ltr.

MAHAN, KIMBERLY; Acad Of Notre Dame De Namur; Rosemont, PA; (3); 16/80; Hon Roll; SADD; JV Fld Hcky; Lcrss; JV Var Mgr(s); Sftbl; Trk; High Hon Roll; Hon Roll; Villanova U; Acctng.

MAHAR, ANDREW; Cumberland Valley HS; Mechanicsburg, PA; (3); 142/578; Var Socr; Var Trk; Biol.

MAHAR, TRICIA; Upper Merion HS; King Of Prussa, PA; (4); Capt Math Tm; Lit Mag; Var Capt Bsktbl; Var Capt Socr; Pres NHS; U Of PA; Pre Med.

MAHARTY, DAVID; G A R Memorial HS; Wilkes-Barre, PA; (4); 20/172; Aud/Vis; French Clb; Ski Clb; Acpl Chr; Chorus; Var Capt Ftbl; Wt Lftg; Hon Roll; Jr NHS; NHS; Al-Schlstc Ftbl 86-87; Bio.

MAHEADY, MAUREEN; Bishop O Reilly HS; Kingston, PA; (4); 4/103; Trs Church Yth Grp; Sec FBLA; Chorus; VP Frsh Cls; Sec Soph Cls; Sec Jr Cls; Rep Stu Cncl; Capt Pom Pon; NHS; NEDT Awd; Cmptr Sci.

MAHER, CONNIE; Abington SR HS; Elkins Pk, PA; (4); 124/491; French Clb; Key Clb; Letterman Clb; SADD; Band; Color Guard; Flag Corp; Mrchg Band; Var L Swmmng; Hon Roll; Early Decision Schlrshp Awd 87; Stockton ST Coll; Marine Sci.

MAHER JR, ROBERT; Cambria Heights HS; Patton, PA; (3); 10/180; Chorus; School Play; Bsktbl; Ftbl; Hon Roll; NHS; Natl Sci Merit Awd 86; U Of Pittsburgh PA; Pharm.

MAHERS, CHRISTINE; Henderson SR HS; W Chester, PA; (3); Sec DECA; JCL; Drill Tm; Twrlr; DECA Dist Comp Apprl & Access 2nd Pl Troph; 1 Dist Medlln & 1 ST Comp Medlln Commn Core; Boston U.

MAHIDHARA, RAJA S; Shady Side Acad; Pittsburgh, PA; (4); Chess Clb; Spanish Clb; SADD; Teachers Aide; Temple Yth Grp; Nwsp Stf; Var Sftbl; Tennis; High Hon Roll; Hon Roll; Squash-Vrsty Tm Lttrd; Brown U; Phys.

MAHLON, COBY; Clearfield Area HS; Clearfield, PA; (4); 13/292; Church Yth Grp; Concert Band; Mrchg Band; Orch; School Musical; Var Capt Bsktbl; JV Vllybl; High Hon Roll; Natl Sci Merit Awd 87; Clarion U; Elem Ed.

MAHON, DAPHNE; Coudersport Area JR-SR HS; Coudersport, PA; (3); Chorus; Mrchg Band; Cheerleading; Twrlr; Hon Roll; Jamestown CC; Lgl Secr.

MAHON, ERIN; Bishop O Reilly HS; Shavertown, PA; (3); 11/110; Church Yth Grp; Latin Clb; Capt Pep Clb; Capt Cheerleading; Sftbl; Hon Roll; Wikes Coll; Engrng.

MAHONEY, BUD; Woodland Hills HS; Pittsburgh, PA; (2); 17/220; Ski Clb; Chemsts.

MAHONEY, CHRISTINE; Danville SR HS; Danville, PA; (3); Exploring; Hosp Aide; Latin Clb; Ski Clb; Yrbk Stf; Mat Maids; Trk; Nrs.

MAHONEY, DEBORAH; Philadelphia HS For Girls; Philadelphia, PA; (4); Church Yth Grp; Cmnty Wkr; Girl Scts; Hosp Aide; NFL; Teachers Aide; Church Choir; Drill Tm; Stage Crew; Off Soph Cls; PA ST U; Elec Engr.

MAHONEY, GREGORY; Carlisle SR HS; Carlisle, PA; (3); 63/467; Church Yth Grp; Chorus; School Musical; Rep Stu Cncl; Var L Crs Cntry; Var Trk; Hon Roll; Prfct Atten Awd; Boy Scts; Camera Clb; Eagle Scout 84; 2nd Pl St Gymnstc Champ 87; Aero Space Tech.

MAHONEY, JENNIFER; Cardinal Dougherty HS; Huntingdon Valley, PA; (3); 227/767; Hosp Aide; JA; Drill Tm; School Play; Archdcs Of Phila Awd For Typng Comptn 87; Cert Of Acad Prfcncy In Rlgn 85; Nrsng.

MAHONEY, MATTHEW; Freedom HS; Bethlehem, PA; (4); 87/445; Stage Crew; Yrbk Phtg; Hon Roll; Gettysburg Coll; Hist.

MAHONEY, NATHANIEL; Scotland Schl Vets Chld; Philadelphia, PA; (3); Art Clb; Church Yth Grp; Cmnty Wkr; Drama Clb; ROTC; Var Ftbl; Swmmng; Im Trk; Var Wt Lftg; Hon Roll; Cazanovia; Intr Decor.

MAHONEY, SHANE; Ambridge Area HS; Ambridge, PA; (4); Boy Scts; German Clb; Band; Hon Roll; Pres Japanese Clb 87; Triangle Tech Inst; Comp Drftng.

MAHONEY, YVONNE; Mckeesport SR HS; Mckeesport, PA; (4); 76/330; AFS; French Clb; Hosp Aide; Band; Powder Puff Ftbl; Hon Roll; Vlntr Wrk Mckeesport Hospitl Awd 85; Dy Cr Svcs.

MAHOOD, JULIE; Moniteau HS; Hilliards, PA; (4); 11/132; Art Clb; VP Chorus; Drill Tm; Jazz Band; Pres Sr Cls; Sec Stu Cncl; Var Bsktbl; Var Trk; Var Vllybl; Trs NHS; Dist Choir 87; Edinboro U; Fine Arts.

MAHR, CANDICE; Moon SR HS; Coraopolis, PA; (3); 93/306; Political Wkr; Concert Band; Mrchg Band; Var L Sftbl; Hon Roll.

MAI, HOANG; South Philaddelphia HS; Philadelphia, PA; (4); Jr NHS.

MAIALE, STEPHEN; Archbishop Ryan HS; Philadelphia, PA; (2); 53/374; JV Crs Cntry; High Hon Roll; Theology I Awd 86; Theology II, Mod Wrld Awd 87; Princ Hnrs Awd, Bio Awd 87.

MAIDEN, HOPE ELIZABETH; Millersburg Area HS; Millersburg, PA; (4); 18/78; Yrbk Stf; Pres Frsh Cls; Pres Soph Cls; Pres Jr Cls; Sec Cheerleading; Powder Puff Ftbl; High Hon Roll; Hon Roll; NHS; Harcum JC; Intrior Dsgn.

MAIELLA, PATRICK; New Castle SR HS; New Castle, PA; (3); 5/293; Boys Clb Am; Cmnty Wkr; Exploring; Intnl Clb; Library Aide; Office Aide; Chorus; High Hon Roll; Hon Roll; Brown U; Surgeon.

MAIER, AMY; Laurel Highlands HS; Uniontown, PA; (2); 15/375; VP JA; Library Aide; High Hon Roll; Hon Roll; NEDT Awd; Pres Frsh Cls; VP Soph Cls; Rep Stu Cncl; Stat Bsktbl; L Swmmng; Intl Bus.

MAIER, MARK; Butler HS; Butler, PA; (3); Church Yth Grp; Variety Show; Nwsp Sprt Ed; Var L Bsktbl; Im Ftbl; Hon Roll; MVP Bsktbl Tm 86-87; 1st Tm All Sect Bsktbl 86-87; Engrng.

MAIER, SANDRA; Quaker Valley HS; Sewickley, PA; (2); Church Yth Grp; Hosp Aide; Service Clb; Chorus; Lit Mag; Sec Soph Cls; Stu Cncl; Coach Actv; Var L Sftbl; Hon Roll; PA ST U; Physcl Thrpy.

MAIER, TRACI; Rocky Grove JR/Sr HS; Cooperstown, PA; (3); 18/81; Camera Clb; Hosp Aide; Library Aide; Science Clb; SADD; Chorus; Hon Roll; Vrsty Ltr Chorus 86.

MAILE, KRISTIN; Forest City Regional HS; Forest City, PA; (3); Camera Clb; German Clb; Letterman Clb; Band; Mrchg Band; VP Jr Cls; Off Stu Cncl; L Var Bsktbl; High Hon Roll; NHS; Med Tech.

MAILKI, MARK; Downingtown HS; Downingtown, PA; (3); 50/650; Church Yth Grp; Band; Concert Band; Jazz Band; Mrchg Band; Orch; School Musical; Symp Band; Yrbk Phtg; DAR Awd; Pres Acdmc Fit Awd 85; Dstngshd Hon Roll 3 Yrs 85; Chem Engr.

MAIMON, GILLIAN B; Springfield HS; Philadelphia, PA; (4); 9/140; Nwsp Rptr; Yrbk Ed-Chief; VP Soph Cls; Rep Stu Cncl; Var Lcrss; Var Swmmng; Ntl Merit SF; Political Wkr; Thesps; School Musical; PA Acdmc Decathlon, Co Intensive Frgn Lang Pgm 86; 1st Talent Show 83; Theater.

MAIN, BECCA; Pennsbury HS; Yardley, PA; (2); Church Yth Grp; Rep Stu Cncl; Bsktbl; JV Fld Hcky; Var Trk; Phys Fit Awd 86-87; Best Athlete 86; PA U HS 4x100 Relay Tm 87; Art.

MAIN, KEITH; West Greene SR HS; Waynesburg, PA; (4); 7/105; Church Yth Grp; Math Tm; VICA; High Hon Roll; NHS; VICA Dstrct Cmptn Arch Drftng 86; VICA ST Cmptn 86; Greene Cnty Vo-Tech Drftng 86; Archt.

MAIN, KEVIN; West Green Middle SR HS; Waynesburg, PA; (4); 2/105; Drama Clb; Pres Science Clb; Chorus; School Musical; Nwsp Stf; High Hon Roll; Lion Awd; VP NHS; NEDT Awd; PA JR Acad Of Sci 2nd Pl Awd 86; Wallps Isld Mrne Sci 85; W Greene HS Schltc Awd 86; Bio Sci.

MAIN, KIMBERLY; Blairsville SR HS; Blairsville, PA; (3); SADD; Color Guard; Mrchg Band; Stage Crew; Twrlr; High Hon Roll; Hon Roll; Med Scrtry.

MAINELLO, JULIE; Daniel Boone JR SR HS; Douglassville, PA; (3); 36/168; Hosp Aide; JA; Varsity Clb; Cheerleading; JV Sftbl; Hon Roll; Swmmng; Tennis; Candy Strpr 50 Hr Pin 86; Ed.

MAINES, LYNN; Altoona Area HS; Altoona, PA; (3); 50/700; French Clb; High Hon Roll; Prfct Atten Awd; PA ST U; Pre-Med.

MAINS, CHRISTINE; S Allegheny HS; Port Vue, PA; (4); 12/177; Hosp Aide; Y-Teens; Concert Band; Mrchg Band; Off Soph Cls; Off Sr Cls; Powder Puff Ftbl; Hon Roll; Sec NHS; Sci Fair Hon Mntn 84-85; PA ST U.

MAINS, CHRISTOPHER; Gettysburg SR HS; Gettysburg, PA; (2); Church Yth Grp; Quiz Bowl; Crs Cntry; Lcrss; High Hon Roll; Hon Roll; Prfct Atten Awd; Bio.

MAINS, KAREN; Susquenita JR-SR HS; Duncannon, PA; (4); 6/144; Church Yth Grp; 4-H; Quiz Bowl; Band; Chorus; Concert Band; Mrchg Band; School Play; Stat Bsktbl; Capt L Crs Cntry; Schlrshp-Duncannon Fr Co 87; PA ST U; Nrsng.

MAINS, TODD M; East Pennsboro HS; Enola, PA; (3); Boy Scts; Church Yth Grp; German Clb; Band; Concert Band; Mrchg Band; Pep Band; Stu Of Mnth Awd Commrcl Art 87.

MAIO, WENDI; Freedom HS; Bethlehem, PA; (4); 59/433; Dance Clb; Intnl Clb; Pep Clb; Band; Mrchg Band; Twrlr; Hon Roll; Pres Acdmc Ftnss Awd 87; NBTA Twrlng Awds 83-84; Bloomsburg U; Pre Law.

MAIORANO, ROSANNE; St Maria Goretti HS; Philadelphia, PA; (4); 68/384; Sec Exploring; GAA; Hosp Aide; Yrbk Sprt Ed; Var Capt Bowling; Var Tennis; Prfct Atten Awd; Paul Smith Scholar 87-88; Yth & Polit Sys Sem La Salle U 85-86; Paul Smith Coll; Hsptlty Mgmt.

MAISENHALTER, HEATHER; Bethlehem Catholic HS; Kinternersvle, PA; (3); 59/202; Key Clb; SADD; Chorus; Yrbk Stf; Hon Roll; Hghst Avg Jr Class Algb II 87.

MAISTO, GINA M; Bishop Boyle HS; Braddock, PA; (4); Drama Clb; Pep Clb; Spanish Clb; School Play; Nwsp Stf; Im Bsktbl; JV Capt Cheerleading; Im Ftbl; Im Sftbl; Hon Roll; U Pittsburgh; Comm.

MAITLAND, ANDREA; Andrea Maitland HS; Cranberry, PA; (3); 25/134; French Clb; Pres Pep Clb; SADD; Chorus; School Musical; Pres Jr Cls; Capt Var Cheerleading; French Hon Soc; Hon Roll; Miss Teen Autumn Leaf Fstvl Queen 86-87; Art Educ.

MAIZER, ROBERT; Elizabeth Forward HS; Elizabeth, PA; (3); FBLA; Socr; Hon Roll; Pres Acctg Clss 86-87; Robert Morris; Actg.

MAJCHROWICZ, KRISTIN; Hazleton HS; Hazleton, PA; (3); Church Yth Grp; Cmnty Wkr; Office Aide; Pep Clb; Y-Teens; Coach Actv; Mgr(s); High Hon Roll; Accntng.

MAJESKY, BETH; Immaculate Conception HS; Marianna, PA; (3); 11/18; Boy Scts; Math Clb; Math Tm; Variety Show; Sec Soph Cls; Rep Stu Cncl; Var JV Cheerleading; Im Socr; High Hon Roll; Hon Roll.

MAJOR, HELEN; Shamokin Area HS; Paxinos, PA; (3); 57/223; Church Yth Grp; Pres 4-H; Intnl Clb; Varsity Clb; Band; Concert Band; Drm Mjr(t); Jazz Band; Mrchg Band; Var L Swmmng; Lebanon Vly Coll; Pre Med.

MAJOR, J MATTHEW; Trinity HS; Mechansburg, PA; (3); Boy Scts; Ski Clb; Spanish Clb; Band; Concert Band; Jazz Band; School Play; Ftbl; Trk; Wt Lftg; Pre Law.

MAJOR, MITCHELL C; Council Rock HS; Newtown, PA; (4); 128/848; Church Choir; 4-H Awd; Pres Schlrshp 87-91; KY Wesleyan Coll; Poltcl Sci.

MAJOR, ROB; Richland HS; Gibsonia, PA; (3); French Clb; Ski Clb; Varsity Clb; Band; Concert Band; Jazz Band; Mrchg Band; Pep Band; Crs Cntry; Ftbl; Vrsty Lttr Awds Trck X-Cntry 85-87; Bus.

MAJORIS, TIFFANY; Westmont Hilltop HS; Johnstown, PA; (3); Rep Stu Cncl; Var Capt Bsktbl; Var L Tennis; Var L Trk; Ski Clb; Rep Frsh Cls; Sec Jr Cls; Rep Sr Cls; Var Sftbl; Ntl Hnr Soc 85-86; Pltcl Sci.

MAKARA, DAVID; Hazleton HS; Hazleton, PA; (2).

MAKARAVAGE, DONNA; G A R Memorial HS; Wilkes-Barre, PA; (4); 26/172; FBLA; Hosp Aide; Key Clb; Ski Clb; Chorus; Stage Crew; Nwsp Stf; Yrbk Stf; Var Trk; Var JV Vllybl; Ntl Hnr Soc Cert; Hnr Rl Cert; Med.

MAKARY, MARTIN; Danville SR HS; Danville, PA; (2); 20/165; Church Yth Grp; Debate Tm; Key Clb; NFL; Political Wkr; Red Cross Aide; Speech Tm; Golf; Tennis; High Hon Roll; 2nd Pl Sci Fair 86; 1st Pl PA AIASA Regnl Ldrshp Conf 86; Ltnm Hnrs Soctm APSL 87.

MAKHDOMI, SABINA; Moravian Acad; Easton, PA; (3); Hosp Aide; Model UN; Ski Clb; Chorus; Variety Show; Yrbk Stf; Trs Frsh Cls; Crs Cntry; Lcrss; High Hon Roll; Sci.

MAKIN, CASSIE; New Covemant Acad; Wellsboro, PA; (4); 1/2; Church Yth Grp; Debate Tm; Hosp Aide; Chorus; School Musical; School Play; Nwsp Rptr; Yrbk Stf; Sec Trs Sr Cls; Mansfield U; Bus Adm.

MAKITKA, DAN; Pocono Mt HS; Stroudsburg, PA; (3); 55/325; Pres VP Bowling; Var Tennis; Var Trk; High Hon Roll; Hon Roll; Capt Physic Olympc Tm 86; Bus Mgmt.

MAKOS, CYNTHIA; Allentown Central Catholic HS; Allentown, PA; (3); Key Clb; Pep Clb; Ski Clb; Spanish Clb; Chorus; Drill Tm; Nwsp Stf; Im Powder Puff Ftbl; Hon Roll; PA JR Acad Sci 1st Pl & Savngs Bond Top 5 85; Bus Adm.

MAKOSEY, BETH; Hempfield Area HS; Irwin, PA; (4); 155/699; Camera Clb; Debate Tm; French Clb; Ski Clb; Nwsp Ed-Chief; Nwsp Phtg; Nwsp Rptr; Yrbk Ed-Chief; High Hon Roll; Hon Roll; IN U Of PA; Cmmnctns.

MALACKANICH, KIMBERLY; Aliquippa JR- SR HS; Aliquippa, PA; (2); Exploring; 4-H; Library Aide; Band; Hon Roll; PA ST Coll; Med.

MALAS, LYNDA; Pocono Mountain HS; Stroudsburg, PA; (2); JV Bsktbl; JV Cheerleading; Im Gym; Var L Trk; Hon Roll; Scranton U; Phy Thrpy.

MALASAVAGE, ADELE; Marian HS; Mahanoy City, PA; (4); 20/119; Trs Church Yth Grp; Chorus; Mrchg Band; School Play; JV Capt Cheerleading; Trk; High Hon Roll; Hon Roll; NHS; Spanish NHS; Theology Awd Hghst Acadmc Avg 85; Rose Buddy Awd Reta Sigma Phi Sor 87; St Marys Wmns Gld Schlrshp 87; Cabrini Coll; Spec Educ.

MALASKA, TARA; Panther Valley HS; Nesquehoning, PA; (3); 10/132; Trs Church Yth Grp; FHA; Hosp Aide; Library Aide; Flag Corp; Nwsp Stf; Yrbk Stf; Cheerleading; High Hon Roll; Hon Roll; Acdmc All Amer; Genetic Engr.

MALATESTA, LAURIE; Sharpsville Area HS; Sharpsville, PA; (4); 9/120; Camera Clb; Hosp Aide; Office Aide; Ski Clb; SADD; Chorus; School Musical; Nwsp Rptr; Var Cheerleading; Hon Roll; Prsdntl Acdmc Ftnss Awd 87; Acdmc Achvt Awds 85-87; U Of Pittsburgh; Pre-Med.

MALCOLM, IVY; Western Wayne HS; Moscow, PA; (3); 29/200; Church Yth Grp; Mrchg Band; Sec Jr Cls; Sec Sr Cls; Var Mgr(s); Capt Twrlr; High Hon Roll; Hon Roll; Sci Awd 84-85.

MALDONADO, ARNALDO; Mastbaum Vo-Tech; Philadelphia, PA; (2); Church Yth Grp; Spanish Clb; SADD; Yrbk Phtg; JV Bsbl; JV Ftbl; Elctrcl Engr.

MALE, THERON; Henderson HS; W Chester, PA; (3); 83/378; DECA; Var Ice Hcky; Spanish NHS; Villanova; Bus.

MALEC, RON; Elizabeth Forward HS; Elizabeth, PA; (2); Soph Cls; Var Trk; Var Hon Roll.

MALENCHEK, GREGORY; Boyertown HS; Barto, PA; (4); 56/426; Boy Scts; CAP; SADD; Band; Bsbl; Ftbl; Wrstlng; Cit Awd; Hon Roll; Tech Future Awd 87; De Vry Inst Tech; Elec Engrng.

MALENICH, DANIEL; Fort Cherry HS; Mcdonald, PA; (2); Church Yth Grp; Computer Clb; Spanish Clb; Chorus; L Mgr(s); High Hon Roll; Hon Roll.

MALESKY, PAULA; Mt Pleasant Area HS; United, PA; (3); 40/240; Pres FTA; GAA; Teachers Aide; Yrbk Stf; Rep Frsh Cls; Rep Sr Cls; VP Stu Cncl; Var L Sftbl; Im Capt Vllybl; High Hon Roll.

MALESON, STEPHEN E; Cheltenham HS; Elkins Park, PA; (4); 4/360; Off Lit Mag; Rep Stu Cncl; Im Bowling; Var L Golf; Var L Tennis; NHS; Ntl Merit SF; Pres Schlr; Cilumbia U Alexander Hamilton Awd Schlrshp & Ldrshp 86; Clnl Phil Hstrcl Scty Hnrbl Mntn Essy 85; Engl.

MALETSKY, MICHAEL J; Upper Perkiomen HS; Pennsburg, PA; (3); 50/250; Trs Computer Clb; FBLA; JV Bsbl; Im Socr; Hon Roll; Accntng.

MALEY, DEBBIE; Bentworth HS; Cokeburg, PA; (3); FBLA; Girl Scts; Ski Clb; SADD; Teachers Aide; Drill Tm; Mrchg Band; Yrbk Stf; Soph Cls; Jr Cls; Prom Queen Candidate 87; Bradford Schl; Med Sec.

MALFARA, KRISTIN; West Catholic Girls HS; Philadelphia, PA; (3); School Play; Stage Crew; Rep Stu Cncl; Hon Roll; Itln Clb 84-86; Forn Chem.

MALFARA, TIMOTHY; St Josephs Prep; Philadelphia, PA; (4); 27/240; Trs Church Yth Grp; Math Tm; Im Bsktbl; Im Ftbl; Var Trk; High Hon Roll; NHS; Ntl Merit SF; Boy Scts; Pres Scholar St Josephs U 87; Mayors Scholar 87; U PA Grant; U PA; Pre-Med.

MALGAPO, JOSEPHINE; Philadelphia HS For Girls; Philadelphia, PA; (3); 1/405; Church Yth Grp; Office Aide; JV Vllybl; French Hon Soc; Hon Roll; NHS; Schlrshp PA Gvrnrs Schl Sci 87; Harvard Prz Bk 87; Bailey-Williams Hnr Key Awd 86-87; Law.

MALICK JR, EARL J; Shikellamy HS; Sunbury, PA; (4); Church Yth Grp; German Clb; VICA; Im Coach Actv; Var L Ftbl; Wt Lftg; Var L Wrstlng; Hon Roll; Kiwanis Awd; Rotary Awd; Chris Kohl Mem Awd 87; Young Amer Awd 86-87; Penn ST; Elec Engr.

MALICK, THERESA; Cardinal O Hara HS; Upland, PA; (4); 197/771; Church Yth Grp; Cmnty Wkr; Dance Clb; Spanish Clb; SADD; Hon Roll; Nuemann Coll; Med Tech.

MALIK, TASNEEM; Mechanicsburg HS; Mechanicsburg, PA; (3); 18/346; Hosp Aide; Orch; Yrbk Stf; High Hon Roll; Natl Fren Exam Merit Awd 87; Ldrshp Council Peer Counsling Prog 86-87; Med.

MALIKOWSKI, LISA; Crestwood HS; Mounatintop, PA; (4); 11/193; FBLA; Girl Scts; Trs Key Clb; Red Cross Aide; Chorus; School Musical; School Play; Nwsp Stf; Yrbk Stf; NHS; Full Pres Schlrshp To Marywood Coll, Scranton PA 87; Acad Fitness Awd 87; Crestwood Schl Bd Awd 87; Marywood Coll; Art.

MALIN, CATHY; St Huberts HS; Philadelphia, PA; (3); 56/421; Church Yth Grp; Dance Clb; French Clb; Intnl Clb; Office Aide; Nwsp Stf; Lit Mag; HS Acadc Dcthln-1st Prz-Schlrshp 83; Art Inst Of Philadelphia; Art.

MALIN, MATT; Central Bucks HS West; Chalfont, PA; (4); 83/489; Boy Scts; Ski Clb; Concert Band; Mrchg Band; JV Socr; Var Swmmng; Var JV Vllybl; NHS; Bucknell U; Geology.

MALIN, TAMI; West Chester East HS; West Chester, PA; (2); GAA; JV Fld Hcky; JV Lcrss; MVP Awd 86; Emplymnt Custmr Care Awd 87; Crmnl Justc.

MALINA, JEFF; Cathedral Prep; Erie, PA; (3); 69/200; Service Clb; Socr; Trk; Hon Roll; Prfct Atten Awd; Engr.

MALINAUSKAS, CRAIG; Abington Heights HS; Clarks Summit, PA; (3); 76/305; Ski Clb; SADD; Bsbl; Ftbl; Hon Roll; Var Ltr-Bsbl 87-88; Mrthn Dnc For Drbrl Plsy 87.

MALINCHAK, CHRISTINA SUE; Mc Keesport HS; Mckeesport, PA; (4); Band; Concert Band; Symp Band; JV Vllybl; High Hon Roll; Pres Schlr; Erly Admssn Penn ST Coll Engrng; Littl Sistr Alpha Kappa Lamba Frat; Penn ST; Chem Engr.

MALINCHAK, JAMES; Monessen HS; Monessen, PA; (3); Nwsp Rptr; Rep Stu Cncl; Bsbl; Bsktbl; Coach Actv; Golf; Acad All-Am 87; Athletic Admn.

MALINGOWSKI, CARRIE; York Catholic HS; York, PA; (3); Church Yth Grp; Exploring; FBLA; Pep Clb; Ski Clb; Chorus; Stage Crew; Vllybl; Hon Roll; Penn ST.

MALINGOWSKI, CHRIS; Bethel Park HS; Bethel Pk, PA; (4); 120/519; Am Leg Aux Girls St; FHA; Science Clb; SADD; Off Stu Cncl; Crs Cntry; Powder Puff Ftbl; 2 1st Pl Awds PA JR Acad Sci 84; 1st Pl Frnsc Awds 85; Kent ST U; Telecomms.

MALINOFF, JOSH; George Washington HS; Philadelphia, PA; (4); 62/800; VP Computer Clb; French Clb; JA; Math Tm; Mu Alpha Theta; Spanish Clb; SADD; High Hon Roll; NHS; Pres Schlr; 1st Pl-Drxl U Ctywide Comp Cont 84; Bst Of Wshngtn-Awd-Word Prcssng 87; U Of DE; Accntng.

MALINOSKI, DAN; Central Dauphin HS; Harrisburg, PA; (3); 5/369; Key Clb; Yrbk Stf; Hon Roll; NHS; Psych.

MALINOSKY, CAROL; German Township HS; Mc Clellandtown, PA; (3); Band; Concert Band; Mrchg Band; High Hon Roll; Jr NHS; NHS; Amer Leg Aux Dprt PA Schl Awd 85; Stu Of Mnth 85-86; Cert Educ Dvlpmnt 85; Yth Of Yr 85; Washington & Jffrsn Coll; Educ.

MALINOWSKI, JENNIFER; G A R Memorial HS; Wilkes-Barre, PA; (3); Key Clb; Library Aide; Ski Clb; Chorus; Nwsp Stf; Stu Cncl; Var Fld Hcky; JV Vllybl; Hon Roll; Jr NHS; Phrmcy.

MALINS, WENDY; Ambridge Area HS; Baden, PA; (3); Pep Clb; Spanish Clb; Var L Bsktbl; Sftbl; Var Capt Vllybl; High Hon Roll; Hon Roll; Jr NHS; NHS; Prfct Atten Awd; All-Section Bsktbl-1st Tm & 1st Tm WPIAL Vllybl Tm 86-87.

MALINSKI, MARY ANN; Bishop Hannan HS; Scranton, PA; (4); 4/126; Computer Clb; Scholastic Bowl; Stu Cncl; High Hon Roll; NHS; Pres Schlr; Girl Of Yr BPW Clb 87; Prsdntl Acadmc Ftns Awd 87; St John Neumann Awd Tching CCD 86; Marywood Coll; CPA.

MALISZEWSKI, SHANE; Freeport HS; Sarver, PA; (2); Var Trk; U Of Pittsburgh; Dntstry.

MALITSCH, DONNA L; Whitehall HS; Whitehall, PA; (4); 129/267; Church Yth Grp; VP DECA; Band; Chorus; Church Choir; Mrchg Band; School Musical; Hon Roll; Outstndng Attend Awd 87; Excllnc Vocal Music Awd 87; Natl Educ Ctr A B S; Acctg.

MALITSKY, KRISTIN; Tunkhannack Area HS; Tunkhannock, PA; (4); 1/273; Spanish Clb; Yrbk Stf; Var Capt Tennis; Cit Awd; Hon Roll; NHS; Ntl Merit Ltr; Acdmc All Amer; Natl Cncl Yth Ldrshp; SR Histrns Pres; Engrng.

MALIZIA, CHERYL; Bishop Mc Devitt HS; Harrisburg, PA; (4); 15/200; Art Clb; Church Yth Grp; Computer Clb; Exploring; French Clb; FBLA; Science Clb; Service Clb; Ski Clb; SADD; PA ST U; Pre Me.

MALLERY, SHERRY; Hyndman HS; Hyndman, PA; (3); Church Yth Grp; Spanish Clb; SADD; Band; Chorus; Concert Band; Mrchg Band; Hon Roll; Mt Vernon Nazarene; Elem Ed.

MALLICK, RICHARD; Owen J Roberts HS; Pottstown, PA; (2); Church Yth Grp; Chorus; School Play; Elec Engr.

MALLIN, MATT; Fairview HS; Erie, PA; (4); 74/164; Boy Scts; Drama Clb; Thesps; Band; Concert Band; Drm Mjr(t); Jazz Band; Mrchg Band; Orch; Pep Band; Eagle Scout Awd 87; IN U Of PA; Rcrtn Indstry Mgr.

MALLIN, STACY; West Branch HS; Lanse, PA; (2); Church Yth Grp; SADD; Band; Chorus; Church Choir; Concert Band; Mrchg Band; Twrlr; Hon Roll; NHS; Asbury Coll KY; Elem Educ.

MALLOY, BERNADETTE M; Christian School Of York; York, PA; (4); School Musical; Yrbk Stf; Rep Frsh Cls; Off Jr Cls; Pres Stu Cncl; Var Capt Cheerleading; Var Sftbl; Dnfth Awd; Hon Roll; State Fnlst MPNTP 86-87; ACSILC 84-86; Sep Stu Mnth 86; Pshch.

MALLOY, CAROLYN; Abington SR HS; Glenside, PA; (3); 125/502; Yrbk Stf; Rep Frsh Cls; Rep Jr Cls; Rep Stu Cncl; JV Capt Fld Hcky; Var JV Lcrss; Pres Schlr; Lbrl Arts.

MALLOY, DAN; Northgate JR SR HS; Pittsburgh, PA; (3); 2/167; Boy Scts; Church Yth Grp; Exploring; Math Tm; Pres Soph Cls; Var L Crs Cntry; Var L Trk; High Hon Roll; Prfct Atten Awd; Penn ST U.

MALLUZZO, MARIA; Du Bois Area HS; Dubois, PA; (2); 20/310; High Hon Roll; Hon Roll; NHS; DAH Nice Kid Awd 86-87; Du Bois Bus Coll; Bus.

MALONE, JAN; Conrad Weiser JR SR HS; Womelsdorf, PA; (2); 9/163; Latin Clb; Chorus; School Musical; Var Sftbl; Hon Roll; Hnr Rl Awd 85-86 & 86-87; Archlgy.

MALONE, JOHN; Penncrest HS; Media, PA; (1); Concert Band; Jazz Band; Mrchg Band; Magna Cum Laude Natl Latn Exm 86; Johnson & Wales Coll; Clnry Art.

MALONEY, DENNIS; Northeast Bradford HS; Rome, PA; (3); Boy Scts; Sec FFA; Rep Stu Cncl; High Hon Roll; Hon Roll; Grnhnd Awd-FFA 84-85; Chptr Frmr Awd-FFA 85-86; Flrcltr Awd-FFA 84-85; Air Force; Pilot.

MALONEY, PATRICK; Greater Latrobe SR HS; Latrobe, PA; (2); 9/381; Boy Scts; Church Yth Grp; NFL; Trk; High Hon Roll; Pres Schlr; Cntnntl Math League-Math Cntst Wnnr 86.

MALONEY, TIMOTHY J; Springdale HS; Springdale, PA; (3); Art Clb; Boy Scts; Exploring; VP Spanish Clb; SADD; Rep Stu Cncl; Var L Ftbl; High Hon Roll; Hon Roll; NHS; Hlth Ed Awd Outstndg Clssrm Prfrmnce 86-87; FL A&M; Archit.

MALONEY, TRACEY; Upper Darby HS; Drexel Hill, PA; (3); Civic Clb; Political Wkr; Ski Clb; Rep Soph Cls; Newumann Coll; Bus.

MALONOSKI, LESLIE; Phoenixville Area HS; Phoenixville, PA; (3); Key Clb; Pep Clb; Spanish Clb; SADD; Pres Chorus; Jr Cls; Stu Cncl; Stat Socr; Hon Roll; Prfct Atten Awd; Phys Thrpy.

MALSOM, JENNIFER; West Middlesex HS; West Middlesex, PA; (3); 21/104; Spanish Clb; Band; Chorus; Church Choir; Concert Band; Mrchg Band; High Hon Roll; Hon Roll; NHS; Prfct Atten Awd; Pres Acdmc Fit Awd Prg 85-86; Merit Awd Accntng I 86-87; Ecnmcs.

MALUSH, TAMMIE JO; Belle Vernon Area HS; Belle Vernon, PA; (3); Church Yth Grp; Drama Clb; Chorus; Powder Puff Ftbl; High Hon Roll; Hon Roll; Prfct Atten Awd; CA U Of PA; Spch Pthlgy.

MALUTIC, SALENA; Villa Maria HS; Campbell, OH; (4); 9/52; Hosp Aide; Ski Clb; Spanish Clb; Yrbk Ed-Chief; Sec Trs Bowling; JV Tennis; High Hon Roll; NHS; Spanish NHS; John Carroll Grant 87; John Carroll U; Med.

MALYS, ANN; Venango Christian HS; Rouseville, PA; (4); 1/36; Rep Frsh Cls; Rep Soph Cls; Rep Stu Cncl; Var Bsktbl; Var Vllybl; NHS; NEDT Awd; Val; U Of NC; Marine Bio.

MAMARY, CHRISTINE MICHELE; Central York SR HS; York, PA; (4); 22/212; Sec Art Clb; Church Yth Grp; Sec French Clb; Stage Crew; Nwsp Ed-Chief; Nwsp Stf; Stat Bsktbl; Mgr(s); High Hon Roll; Prsdntl Acdmc Ftnss Awd 87; York Coll Of PA; Rtlng Mrchnds.

MAMMARELLA, CHRIS; Brandywine Heights HS; Mertztown, PA; (2); Band; Concert Band; Mrchg Band; JV Golf; Tennis; Trk; NHS; Doctor.

MAMMARELLI, VINCENT; St Josephs Prep; Collingswood, NJ; (4); 6/249; Church Yth Grp; Cmnty Wkr; Computer Clb; German Clb; Library Aide; Math Tm; Science Clb; NHS; High Hon Roll; Oscar Mayer Schlrshp 87; Gold Medl Engl, Germn 87; Drexel U; Engrng.

MAMULA, LORI; Chartiers-Houston HS; Washington, PA; (3); Church Yth Grp; Drama Clb; Girl Scts; Mu Alpha Theta; Spanish Clb; Concert Band; Drill Tm; Score Keeper; High Hon Roll; NHS; Edinboro U; Engnrng.

MANACK, KELLY; Belle Vernon Area HS; Belle Vernon, PA; (3); Dance Clb; NFL; Ski Clb; Mrchg Band; Pres Jr Cls; Rep Stu Cncl; Twrlr; Cit Awd; Hon Roll; NHS.

MANACK, RANDOLPH E; Belle Vernon Area HS; Belle Vernon, PA; (3); JV Bsbl; Hon Roll; Envrnmntl Engrng.

MANARCHUCK, NELLIE; Carbondale Area JR SR HS; Carbondale, PA; (4); Art Clb; Computer Clb; FBLA; Science Clb; Ski Clb; Spanish Clb; Chorus; Nwsp Stf; Yrbk Ed-Chief; Sec Sr Cls; Pres Phys Fitness Awd 82 & 87; Schlstc Art Awd, PTA Reflctns Art Awd 86; Bloomsburg U; Nrsng.

MANBECK, TRACY L; Oley Valley HS; Fleetwood, PA; (3); Debate Tm; Quiz Bowl; Color Guard; Nwsp Rptr; Yrbk Ed-Chief; Im Bowling; NHS; Hugh O Brian Yth Ldrshp Smnr Ambssdr 86; PA ST Smmr Intnsv Lang Inst Schlrshp-Chinese 87; Frgn Langs.

MANCE, MICHAEL; Montour HS; Coraopolis, PA; (3); 20/277; Boy Scts; Exploring; Band; Mrchg Band; High Hon Roll; Hon Roll; Eagle Scout 87; U Pittsburgh; Engrng.

MANCINI, DANIEL; Montour HS; Coraopolis, PA; (3); Cmnty Wkr; Letterman Clb; SADD; Varsity Clb; Var Bsktbl; Var L Crs Cntry; Var L Trk; High Hon Roll; Hon Roll; Educ.

MANCINI, SHERI A; West Allegheny HS; Oakdale, PA; (3); 3/180; Intnl Clb; Spanish Clb; Y-Teens; Chorus; Church Choir; School Play; JV Sftbl; High Hon Roll; NHS; Awd Making Hnr Roll 3 9-Wk Periods In A Row; Pre-Med Pgm.

MANCINO, BARB; Corry Area HS; Corry, PA; (4); Civic Clb; French Clb; Color Guard; Variety Show; Rep Jr Cls; VP Sr Cls; Rep Stu Cncl; Hon Roll; Pres Schlr; Rennerr Merit Schlrshp-Bethany Coll 87; Bethany Coll; French.

MANCUSO, DALE; Washington HS; Washington, PA; (4); 29/147; Pres FBLA; Key Clb; Library Aide; Pres Ski Clb; Spanish Clb; Sec Jr Cls; VP Sr Cls; Rep Stu Cncl; Capt Socr; High Hon Roll; Stu Mnth 86; Acctng Hnrs 87; Mercyhurst Coll; Bus.

MANCUSO, MARK; Holy Name HS; Wyomissing, PA; (3); 2/125; Camera Clb; VP JA; SADD; School Play; Nwsp Ed-Chief; Bowling; Socr; Trk; Hon Roll; NHS; 1st Pl PJAS Lcl & ST Lvl 85 & 87; Schlrshp Dale Carnegie Crs 87.

MANCUSO, SUSAN; Valley View HS; Archbald, PA; (4); Trs French Clb; Yrbk Ed-Chief; Yrbk Phtg; Yrbk Stf; Sec Soph Cls; Trs Stu Cncl; Vllybl; Hon Roll; NHS; Church Yth Grp; Lckwnna Cnty Drg & Alchl Essy Wnnr 86; Cert Merit Frnch 87; Presdntl Schlrshp 87; U Of Scranton; Cmmnctns.

MANCUSO, TANYA; Greensburg Central Catholic HS; Greensburg, PA; (3); German Clb; Hosp Aide; Pep Clb; Ski Clb; Powder Puff Ftbl; High Hon Roll; Hon Roll; Ntl Merit Ltr; Variety Show; Lit Mag; Phrmcy.

MANDALAS, GLENN; Conneaut Valley HS; Conneautville, PA; (3); 7/75; Pres Church Yth Grp; Sec Band; Sec Concert Band; Sec Mrchg Band; Nwsp Stf; Yrbk Stf; Pres Stu Cncl; Var Vllybl; Sec High Hon Roll; NHS; Nvl Arch.

MANDARINO, SCOTT; Yough HS; W Newton, PA; (3); 25/236; Church Yth Grp; Computer Clb; Pep Clb; VP Spanish Clb; Chorus; Yrbk Stf; Bsktbl; Var L Ftbl; Powder Puff Ftbl; Var L Trk; U Of Pittsburgh; Phys Thrpst.

MANDEL, TERI; West Branch HS; Kylertown, PA; (3); 8/130; Drama Clb; Science Clb; Spanish Clb; Varsity Clb; Mrchg Band; Stu Cncl; Bsktbl; High Hon Roll; Hon Roll; NHS; Phy Thrpst.

MANDELKER, SIGAL; Taylor-Alderdice HS; Pittsburgh, PA; (2); Cmnty Wkr; Hosp Aide; Key Clb; NFL; Ski Clb; Trs VP Temple Yth Grp; High Hon Roll; Math Clb; Nwsp Rptr; Nwsp Stf.

MANDIK, LAURA; Spring-Ford HS; Schwenksville, PA; (2); 1/289; German Clb; Math Clb; Concert Band; Mrchg Band; JV Bsktbl; JV Sftbl; High Hon Roll; NHS; Band; Wrtr Of Yr 85-86; Sectn Wrtr Of Yr 87.

MANDLOWITZ, TRACY; Phoenixville Area HS; Phoenixville, PA; (3); VP Key Clb; SADD; School Musical; VP Soph Cls; VP Soph Cls; Rep Stu Cncl; Var Capt Cheerleading; Hon Roll; Jr NHS; NHS; Dogwood Qn 87; Comms.

MANDROS, CHRISTOPHER; Penn Hills HS; Pittsburgh, PA; (3); Ski Clb; Spanish Clb; Varsity Clb; Stage Crew; Var L Socr; Var L Swmmng; High Hon Roll; Hon Roll; Prfct Atten Awd; Pres Schlr; U Of Pittsburgh; Engrng.

MANENDO, HEATHER; St Benedict Acad; Erie, PA; (3); 4/53; 4-H; Q&S; Yrbk Stf; Lit Mag; Rep Frsh Cls; Trs Soph Cls; Rep Jr Cls; Pres Sr Cls; Stu Cncl; JV Var Bsktbl; Sci Awd Hghst Sci Avg 86-87; Yrbk Awds 85-86; Zoolgy.

MANES, MONICA; St Paul Cathedral HS; Pittsburgh, PA; (3); 3/53; Drama Clb; Chorus; Church Choir; School Musical; Ed Nwsp Stf; Pres Jr Cls; High Hon Roll; NHS; Red Cross Aide; Alpine Lodge; Stu Advsry Bd; Ambssdr; Voice.

MANEVAL, STACY; South Williamsport Area JR S HS; S Williamsport, PA; (3); Aud/Vis; Drama Clb; FHA; Ski Clb; School Play; Stage Crew; Vet Asst.

MANGAN, LU ANNE; Sacred Heart HS; Pittsburgh, PA; (3); 30/139; Cmnty Wkr; Exploring; Hosp Aide; Pep Clb; Spanish Clb; Chorus; Var Trk; Im Vllybl; Hon Roll; NHS; Early Chldhd Ed.

MANGAN, MICHAEL; Jeannette SR HS; Jeannette, PA; (3); Var L Ftbl; Var Trk; Var L Wrstlng; Slippery Rock; Tchng.

MANGANELLA, JENNIFER; Tunkhannock Area HS; Tunkhannock, PA; (3); Sec Art Clb; French Clb; Rep Jr Cls; Tennis; Cit Awd; High Hon Roll; NHS; Rep Frsh Cls; Rep Soph Cls; Gold Key-Schltc Art Awd 85; Hrbl Mntn-SMR Mem Art Cntst 86; Cert Of Merit-Natl Frnch Cntst 86; Art.

MANGES, AMY; Conemaugh Valley HS; Johnstown, PA; (3); 6/104; Church Yth Grp; Band; Church Choir; Concert Band; Drm Mjr(t); Mrchg Band; Stat Bsktbl; Hon Roll; Jr NHS; NHS; Cambria Rowe Bus Coll.

MANGES, APRYL; North Star HS; Hooversville, PA; (3); #23 In Class; FCA; 4-H; Varsity Clb; Yrbk Stf; Sec Jr Cls; Var L Bsktbl; Var L Sftbl; Cit Awd; 4-H Awd; Hon Roll.

MANGES, BOBBI J; Chestnut Ridge SR HS; New Paris, PA; (4); SADD; Teachers Aide; Nwsp Ed-Chief; Nwsp Stf; Lit Mag; Stat Bsbl; Stat Bsktbl; Hon Roll; NHS; Prfct Atten Awd; CREAA Teacher Schlrshp 87; Lock Haven U; Elem Educ.

MANGES, KHRISTY; Bishop Mc Cort HS; Holsapple, PA; (3); 17/178; Mu Alpha Theta; Ski Clb; Spanish Clb; Chorus; Yrbk Stf; L Var Vllybl; High Hon Roll; NHS; Spanish NHS; Sci Olympd Dstnctn Awd 85; Med.

MANGIN, MICHAEL; Hickory HS; Hermitage, PA; (3); Pres Latin Clb; Acpl Chr; Drm Mjr(t); Jazz Band; Mrchg Band; Orch; School Musical; Nwsp Stf; NHS; Ntl Merit Ltr; Physical Therapy.

MANGINE, RALPH; West Catholic HS; Philadelphia, PA; (3); 20/286; Hon Roll.

MANGOL, PAM; Cumberland Valley HS; Mechanicsburg, PA; (3); Spanish Clb; Band; Chorus; Color Guard; Mrchg Band; Symp Band; Hon Roll; Ntl Merit Ltr; Ldr Nrsng Hm Awd 87; Hnrbl Mntn Arts Fest 87; 2 Awds Excllnc Music 85-86; Penn ST; Music.

MANGUS, JEFFREY; Leechburg Area HS; Leechburg, PA; (3); Church Yth Grp; Drama Clb; Band; Chorus; Church Choir; Concert Band; Mrchg Band; Pep Band; School Play; Stage Crew; Arts Cmnctns.

MANGUS, TINA; Bradford Area HS; Bradford, PA; (4); Exploring; Library Aide; Pep Clb; Crs Cntry; Gym; Trk; Vllybl; Hon Roll; Prfct Atten Awd; Stu Cncl Schlrshp 87; Kendall/Amalie Schlrshp 87; Brian Lechner Schlrshp 87; U Of Pittsburgh; Nrsng.

MANHARDT, ERIKA; Gateway SR HS; Monroeville, PA; (3); 82/477; Drama Clb; Exploring; NFL; Political Wkr; Science Clb; Y-Teens; Nwsp Stf; Trk; Hon Roll; Med.

MANIFOLD, SHARON L; Hempfield HS; E Petersburg, PA; (3); 6/450; Church Yth Grp; Exploring; Science Clb; Orch; Lit Mag; Rep Soph Cls; JV Var Fld Hcky; High Hon Roll; NHS; Schltc Wrtg Awd 87; Phys Ther.

MANION, JEFFREY E; Nativity B V M HS; St Clair, PA; (2); 2/80; Latin Clb; NFL; Ski Clb; Off Frsh Cls; Off Soph Cls; JV Bsktbl; L Var Crs Cntry; High Hon Roll; NHS; Prfct Atten Awd; Gold Mdl Natl Latin Tst.

MANION, JOHN; Charleroi HS; Charleroi, PA; (3); Church Yth Grp; Science Clb; Varsity Clb; Stu Cncl; JV Bsktbl; Var Capt Ftbl; High Hon Roll; Hon Roll; NHS; Arch.

MANION, MATTHEW; Msgr Bonner HS; Upper Darby, PA; (3); 3/258; Civic Clb; Math Clb; Service Clb; Nwsp Rptr; Yrbk Rptr; Trs Jr Cls; Var Crs Cntry; Var Trk; High Hon Roll; NHS.

MANKAMYER, KELLY; Somerset Area SR HS; Somerset, PA; (3); 2/230; Art Clb; Pres Church Yth Grp; English Clb; VP 4-H; Mu Alpha Theta; Rep Stu Cncl; Var L Socr; Gov Hon Prg Awd; NHS; Exploring; Gnnon U Poetry Cntst-Hnrbl Mntn 87; Agrcltr.

MANKEVICH, SHARYL; Seneca Valley HS; Mars, PA; (4); Drama Clb; Pep Clb; Trs VP Thesps; Madrigals; School Musical; School Play; Stage Crew; Nwsp Rptr; High Hon Roll; Hon Roll; Hnrs Chorus-Wstmnstr Coll 86-87; Dist Chorus-Hrmtg PA 86-87; Prfrmd, Bass, Beautyshp Qrtet 85-87; Comms.

MANKEY, BRETT P; Mc Guffey HS; Claysville, PA; (3); Letterman Clb; Spanish Clb; Off Jr Cls; Var Bsbl; Var Bsktbl; VP Ftbl; High Hon Roll; Hon Roll; NHS; Pre Med.

MANKO, GERARD; Our Lady Of The Sacred Heart HS; Ambridge, PA; (4); 5/57; Exploring; School Play; Stage Crew; High Hon Roll; Pres Schlr; Im Bowling; Frnch IV Acadc Awd 86-87; Comp Sci 272 Acadc Awd 85-86; St Bonaventure U; Comp Sci.

MANKO, MELISSA; The Acad Of Notre Dame; Newtown Square, PA; (3); Art Clb; Cmnty Wkr; Computer Clb; GAA; Chorus; Yrbk Stf; Rep Soph Cls; JV Var Lcrss; JV Tennis; Hon Roll; Natl Merit Recog 87; Psyclgy.

MANLEY, LORI; Northampton Area SR HS; Bath, PA; (4); 4/459; Trs AFS; Trs Leo Clb; Ski Clb; Nwsp Ed-Chief; Capt L Fld Hcky; High Hon Roll; NHS; Ntl Merit Ltr; Voice Dem Awd; HS Stud Of Month 86; Syracuse U; Pre-Law.

MANN, ALICIA; Leechburg Area HS; Leechburg, PA; (2); Chorus; Drm Mjr(t); Twrlr; Hon Roll; Penn ST; Med.

MANN, BETSY; Yough SR HS; Herminie, PA; (3); Church Yth Grp; FBLA; Hon Roll; 1st Pl Stenogrphr I FBLA Rgnl Ldrshp Conf 87; 3rd Pl Stenogrphr I FBLA ST Ldrshp Conf 87; Computer Sys Inst; Paralgl.

MANN, CARLA; Sayre Area HS; Athens, PA; (3); Pres Church Yth Grp; Chorus; Twrlr.

MANN, DANA; West Branch Area HS; Kylertown, PA; (4); 9/128; VP Science Clb; Trs Ski Clb; SADD; Varsity Clb; Band; Nwsp Stf; Yrbk Stf; VP Stu Cncl; Capt Cheerleading; Hon Roll; Outstndng Achvmnt In Russian II 85-86; Stu Mnth Sep 86; Penn ST U; Psych.

MANN, JAMES S; York Suburban SR HS; York, PA; (4); 19/187; Concert Band; Mrchg Band; Rep Soph Cls; Rep Jr Cls; VP Sr Cls; Var Capt Crs Cntry; Var Trk; High Hon Roll; Hon Roll; Ntl Merit Ltr; Lehigh U; Engrng.

MANN, JENNIFER; Wm Allen HS; Allentown, PA; (4); Debate Tm; Key Clb; Model UN; Yrbk Stf; Pres Sr Cls; Rep Stu Cncl; Tennis; Hon Roll; American U; Politcl Sci.

MANN, KELLY; South Park JR SR HS; Library, PA; (4); 19/190; French Clb; Teachers Aide; Y-Teens; High Hon Roll; NHS; Carlon Coll Presdntl Schlrshp 87; Duquense Educ & Cmpt Schlrshp 87; Duquense U; Elem Educ.

MANN, LETITIA; Reading HS; Reading, PA; (3); 41/740; Girl Scts; Teachers Aide; Band; Chorus; Stu Cncl; Bsktbl; Vllybl; Hon Roll; Med.

MANN, MALENA; Stroudsburg HS; Stroudsburg, PA; (3); 30/250; 4-H; Spanish Clb; Chorus; Hon Roll; Jr NHS; NHS; PA ST U; Med.

MANN, MICHAEL; Wellsboro HS; Wellsboro, PA; (3); 5/150; Ski Clb; Band; Sec Frsh Cls; Rep Soph Cls; Rep Jr Cls; Var Capt Bsktbl; Var L Golf; Var L Trk; NHS; Bus Admin.

MANN, NIKKI; W Branch Area HS; Kylertown, PA; (2); Drama Clb; Spanish Clb; Varsity Clb; Band; Concert Band; Mrchg Band; Stage Crew; Sec Soph Cls; Rep Stu Cncl; JV Var Bsktbl; Typing Outstndng Achvt 86-87; Bsktbl Defnsv Plyr Of Year 86-87; Business.

MANN, PATRICIA; Altoona Area HS; Altoona, PA; (4); 11/718; Chess Clb; VP French Clb; Science Clb; School Musical; Nwsp Rptr; Rep Jr Cls; Hon Roll; Jr NHS; Ntl Merit Ltr; NEDT Awd; PSU; Phrmcy.

MANN, RHONDA; Exeter HS; Reading, PA; (4); 8/214; Drama Clb; Temple Yth Grp; Y-Teens; Band; Concert Band; Symp Band; Yrbk Stf; Stu Cncl; High Hon Roll; NHS; Bnai Brith Yth Orgnztn Vp 86-87; Berks Cty Bnd 84 86-87; Rcvd Distngshd Hnrs 83-86; Rutgers U; Commnctns.

MANN, RUDOLPH; Monongahela Valley Catholic HS; Monongahela, PA; (3); 6/102; Spanish Clb; JV Bsbl; JV Ftbl; Var L Golf; Wt Lftg; Hon Roll; NHS; Spanish NHS; Diploma Merit Spn I, II, III 85-87; U Pittsburgh; Engrng.

MANN, TANYA; Reading HS; Reading, PA; (4); Chorus; VP Sr Cls; Rep Stu Cncl; Var Capt Bsktbl; Var Crs Cntry; Var Trk; JV Var Vllybl; Hon Roll; NHS; Girl Scts; Rutgers U; Nrsng.

MANNARINO, DONNA; Bishop Conwell HS; Bristol, PA; (3); Rep Jr Cls; JV Mat Maids; Hon Roll; Holy Family; Bus Adm.

MANNING, DENISE; Gateway SR HS; Monroeville, PA; (2); Ski Clb; Hon Roll; Hnr Roll 85-87; UCLA.

MANNING, SCOTT; S Williamsport Area JR/Sr HS; S Williamsport, PA; (3); 4/98; Trs Soph Cls; JV Var Bsktbl; Var Ftbl; Im Wt Lftg; Cit Awd; High Hon Roll; Hon Roll; NHS; Gftd Stu Pgm 84-87.

MANNING, STEPHEN; Warren Area HS; Warren, PA; (3); 7/270; Drama Clb; Pres Spanish Clb; School Play; Rep Stu Cncl; Var Diving; Var Swmmng; Var Tennis; High Hon Roll; Jr NHS; NHS; Mathmtcs.

MANNINO, JENNIFER; Bishop Conwell HS; Bensalem, PA; (3); 23/298; Church Yth Grp; Drama Clb; Office Aide; PAVAS; School Musical; School Play; Yrbk Stf; Trk; High Hon Roll; Hon Roll; 1st Awd Rgnl & 3rd Awd St PJAS 86; AF Outstndg Awd-Trenton Sci Fair 86; Marine Outstndg Awd Sci Fair; PA ST U; Genetc Engrng.

MANNO, JAMES; Elk County Christian Schl; Ridgway, PA; (4); 17/82; Key Clb; Political Wkr; Ski Clb; SADD; Stu Cncl; Trk; Hon Roll; Kiwanis Awd; NHS; Ntl Merit Schol; Penn ST U; AE.

MANNO, JILL; Elk County Christian HS; Ridgway, PA; (3); Aud/Vis; Model UN; Ski Clb; Nwsp Bus Mgr; Yrbk Phtg; Cheerleading; Trk; High Hon Roll; NEDT Awd; Ntl Ldrshp Merit Awd 86-87.

MANOLANGAS, GEORGE; Canon Mc Millan SR HS; Canonsburg, PA; (3); 10/349; Church Yth Grp; Cmnty Wkr; Science Clb; Variety Show; Nwsp Rptr; Nwsp Stf; Yrbk Ed-Chief; High Hon Roll; Spanish NHS; Duquesne U; Pharm.

MANSBERGER, ANN; Middletown Area HS; Middletown, PA; (3); Hosp Aide; Band; Concert Band; Drm & Bgl; Jazz Band; Mrchg Band; Orch; Hon Roll; Prfct Atten Awd; Nrsng.

MANSBERGER, JAMES; Mount Union Area HS; Calvin, PA; (4); Boy Scts; Model UN; Band; Chorus; School Musical; Nwsp Stf; Bowling; Hon Roll; NHS; Pres Acdmc Fitness & Harold Mc Callips Memorial Awds 87; Penn ST U; Vet.

MANSELL, EDWARD; Wilmington Area HS; New Wilmington, PA; (4); 1/112; Concert Band; Jazz Band; Mrchg Band; Nwsp Stf; Yrbk Stf; NHS; Ntl Merit SF; Pres Schlr; Rotary Awd; Val; Westminster Coll; Physcs.

MANSFIELD, BRIAN; West York Area HS; York, PA; (4); 8/195; Boy Scts; Pres Sec Spanish Clb; Stat Mgr Ftbl; Var Trk; God Cntry Awd; High Hon Roll; NHS; Opt Clb Awd; Eagle Sct 85; West York Exchng Clb Stu Yr 87; Lafayette Coll; Engrng.

MANSFIELD, DONALD; Lock Haven SR HS; Lock Haven, PA; (3); 35/250; Chorus; Variety Show; Nwsp Rptr; Var Capt Ftbl; L Trk; Wt Lftg; Hon Roll; Lock Haven U Upward Bound Trphy 87; Marine Sci Consrtm Cert 87; Gettysburg Coll; Phys Ed.

MANSFIELD III, FREDERICK; Susquehanna Township HS; Harrisburg, PA; (4); 38/155; Rep Frsh Cls; Rep Stu Cncl; Var JV Bsktbl; Var JV Ftbl; Hon Roll; Rotary Awd; Blmsbrg U; Law.

MANSFIELD, KEVIN W; Mountain View HS; Gibson, PA; (3); 14/105; Camera Clb; Chess Clb; Trs Church Yth Grp; Var L Socr; Var L Trk; Var Rptr Vllybl; Prfct Atten Awd; Ldrs Rtry Clb 86; PA ST Schlrs Smnrs 86-87; Mntn Vw Stu Mnth 86-87; Elec Engr.

MANTZ, ERIKA; William Allen HS; Allentown, PA; (3); Trs German Clb; JCL; Ski Clb; SADD; Concert Band; Mrchg Band; Nwsp Rptr; Lit Mag; Trk; NHS; Mc Cormick Bk Awds & Natl Latin Exam Hnrb Merit 87; Comms.

MANTZ, SHELLEY; Brandywine Heights HS; Macungie, PA; (4); 14/121; Band; Concert Band; Mrchg Band; Pep Band; Hon Roll; Lion Awd; NHS; Cnty Band 86-87; PA ST U; Med.

MANTZELL, BRADLEY; Maplewood HS; Guys Mills, PA; (4); 10/125; Church Yth Grp; Ski Clb; Chorus; Pres Sr Cls; Rep Stu Cncl; Bsktbl; Hon Roll; Pres NHS; Grove City Coll; Dentist.

MANUBANY, JEANNE; Reading HS; Reading, PA; (3); 7/710; Exploring; Hosp Aide; Key Clb; Chorus; Orch; Hon Roll; NHS; Horace Custer Awd 85; Supt Schlstc Recgntn Awd 87; Berks Sci & Engr Fair 3rd Pl Zoolgy 85; Med.

MANUEL, BARB; Seneca Valley HS; Mars, PA; (3); Dance Clb; JA; Ski Clb; Varsity Clb; School Play; Yrbk Bus Mgr; Yrbk Rptr; Yrbk Stf; Rep Stu Cncl; Cheerleading.

MANUPPELLI, MARK; Penn Hills SR HS; Pittsburgh, PA; (3); Letterman Clb; Ftbl; Wrstlng; High Hon Roll; Hon Roll; Law.

MANZINI, COLLEEN; Yough HS; W Newton, PA; (3); 80/237; Pep Clb; Spanish Clb; Chorus; Yrbk Stf; Rep Stu Cncl; JV Var Cheerleading; Golf; Powder Puff Ftbl; Hon Roll; Prfct Atten Awd.

MANZONI, ALFRED; Lake-Lehman HS; Dallas, PA; (2); Exploring; 4-H; L Var Socr; L Var Trk; Hon Roll; Jr NHS; Rotary Awd; PA ST; Engrng.

MAPES, LINDA; Wyalusing Valley HS; Wyalusing, PA; (4); 37/134; Spanish Clb; Church Choir; Mrchg Band; School Musical; Cheerleading; Mat Maids; Twrlr; Hon Roll; Prfct Atten Awd; Outstndng Wrstlng Chrldr 87; Bloomsbrg U; Psych.

MARAGULIA, KELLY; Notre Dame HS; Easton, PA; (1); Am Leg Aux Girls St; Cheerleading; Sftbl; High Hon Roll; Hon Roll; Ivy League; Law.

MARAKOVITS, THOMAS; Northampton Area SR HS; Northampton, PA; (4); 12/450; DECA; Capt Scholastic Bowl; Rep Frsh Cls; Off Jr Cls; Off Sr Cls; Pres Stu Cncl; JV Var Ftbl; JV Var Wt Lftg; Cit Awd; DAR Awd; Stu Mnth Exch Club 86; Dist Wnnr DECA 1st Pl Finance 87; ST Wnnr DECA Interview 2nd Pl 87; PA ST U; Acctng.

MARAKOWSKI, KRISTA; Villa Maria Acad; Philadelphia, PA; (3); 5/98; Church Yth Grp; SADD; Ed Yrbk Stf; Lit Mag; Sec French Hon Soc; High Hon Roll; NHS; Villa Maria Acad 4 Yr Tuition Schlrshp 84-88; Thlgy Awd 87; Frnch Awd 85.

MARANKI, JOANN; Bishop Hafey HS; Freeland, PA; (4); 4/126; French Clb; Service Clb; VP Chorus; School Play; Yrbk Stf; French Hon Soc; High Hon Roll; VP NHS; Prfct Atten Awd; Wilkes Coll; Bio.

MARASCO, MATTHEW; Dubois Area HS; Dubois, PA; (2); 35/250; Pres Jr Cls; Vet.

MARASCO, MELISSA; Ambridge Area HS; Baden, PA; (4); 34/267; French Clb; Pres JA; Pep Clb; Red Cross Aide; Off Sr Cls; Score Keeper; High Hon Roll; Hon Roll; NHS; Schlrshp To PA Free Entrprs Wk 86; ADJAC-JR Achiev 87; Marietta Coll; Intl Bus.

MARAVICH, KEITH; Aliquippa HS; Aliquippa, PA; (3); #7 In Class; Church Yth Grp; Drama Clb; Exploring; French Clb; School Play; Variety Show; JV Bsktbl; Var Trk; High Hon Roll; Hon Roll.

MARAVICH, NICOLE; Center HS; Aliquippa, PA; (2); Spanish Clb; Varsity Clb; Stu Cncl; Bowling; Var Cheerleading; Coach Actv; Powder Puff Ftbl; Sftbl.

MARBURGER, KEITH A; Upper Merion Area HS; Wayne, PA; (4); 4/320; Aud/Vis; Church Yth Grp; Computer Clb; Math Tm; Chorus; Yrbk Stf; Soph Cls; Ntl Merit SF; Crs Cntry; Hon Roll; Gen Elect Town Meetng Tomorrow 85; Elect Engr.

MARBURGER, TINA; Seneca Valley HS; Evans Cty, PA; (2); Sec Church Yth Grp; Hon Roll; 1st Pl Pres Acadmc Games & 1st Pl Ovrll Histry & 3rd Amer 87; Acadmc Games 1st Pl Equasians 87; Accntng.

MARCELLA, SANDRA J; Trinity HS; APO Miami, FL; (3); 27/139; Cmnty Wkr; Model UN; Spanish Clb; Band; Concert Band; Mrchg Band; Trk; Hon Roll; Spanish NHS; Schlstc Wrtng Awds-Cert Merit 84-85; Vrsty Ltr Band 86-87; Law.

MARCH, CHERYL; C A S HS; Glenmoore, PA; (3); 147/517; French Clb; Hosp Aide; Leo Clb; Ski Clb; Band; Chorus; Color Guard; Off Jr Cls; JV Tennis; Hon Roll; Dntl Hygnst.

MARCH, MELISSA; Franklin Regional HS; Delmont, PA; (3); AFS; Computer Clb; Pres Girl Scts; SADD; Chorus; School Musical; Swing Chorus; Yrbk Stf; Hon Roll; Slvr Awd-Grl Scts 85; Slvr Ldrshp-Grl Scts 85; Messiah; Med.

MARCHALL, HARRY; Elk County Christian HS; St Marys, PA; (3); 13/72; Cmnty Wkr; Letterman Clb; Var Ftbl; Var Capt Wrstlng; High Hon Roll; Hon Roll; Acadc All Amer 86-87; 1st Pl Dist Amer Lgn Axlry Esy Cntst 87; 1st Pl Allegany Wrstlng Trnmnt 86; Mech Engr.

MARCHESE, NADINE; Hazleton HS; Hazleton, PA; (3); 5/445; Cmnty Wkr; Drama Clb; JA; Leo Clb; Office Aide; Pep Clb; Science Clb; SADD; Chorus; School Play; Pres Acad Fit Awd 85; JR Acad Sci 87; Penn ST U; RN.

MARCHETTA, NICK; West Catholic High Schl For Boys; Philadelphia, PA; (3); Prfct Atten Awd; Commnctns.

MARCHETTI, DANIELLE; Bishop Hafey HS; Hazleton, PA; (4); 15/129; Spanish Clb; Y-Teens; Bsktbl; Trk; High Hon Roll; NHS; Spanish NHS; Mst Career Pts Track 84-87; Phila Coll Phrmcy & Sci; Phrmcy.

MARCHETTI, SAMANTHA; Hazleton HS; Hazleton, PA; (3); 122/455; Drama Clb; FBLA; Office Aide; Pep Clb; Ski Clb; Y-Teens; Band; Chorus; Concert Band; Mrchg Band; Chrldng Squad Co-Capt 84-85; Cadette Clb 85-87; Hnr Rll 85-86; Bloomburg U; CPA.

MARCHEWSKI, JENNIFER; Nazareth Acad; Phila, PA; (3); Church Yth Grp; Cmnty Wkr; Color Guard; Flag Corp; Lit Mag; Sec Frsh Cls; VP Soph Cls; VP Jr Cls; Pom Pon; Hon Roll; Pom Pon Squad Awds 85-86; Hahnemann U; Nrsng.

MARCHI, MICHELE; South Side Beaver HS; Clinton, PA; (3); Library Aide; SADD; Varsity Clb; NHS; VP Jr Cls; Powder Puff Ftbl; Var L Trk; High Hon Roll; Hon Roll; Jr NHS.

MARCHIONDA, KIMBERLY; Aliquippa SR HS; Aliquippa, PA; (2); Sec French Clb; Band; Concert Band; Mrchg Band; Pep Band; Hon Roll; Church Yth Grp; Computer Clb; JV Capt Cheerleading; Score Keeper; Beaver Cnty Hnrs Band 86-87.

MARCHIONE, DANIELLE J; Villa Maria Acad; West Chester, PA; (4); 1/110; Capt Math Tm; Pres Mu Alpha Theta; Pres Quiz Bowl; Lit Mag; Bowling; Mu Alpha Theta Awd; NCTE Awd; NHS; Ntl Merit SF; VP Spanish NHS; Bio Engrng.

MARCHO, AMY; Mountain View HS; South Gibson, PA; (3); Ski Clb; Band; Concert Band; Mrchg Band; School Musical; School Play; Pres Soph Cls; Pres Jr Cls; Off Stu Cncl; Cheerleading; Thtr Arts.

MARCI, CARL; Parkland SR HS; Allentown, PA; (4); 5/459; Var Capt Bsktbl; Var Trk; High Hon Roll; Pres NHS; E PA Cnfrnc All-Star Tm Trck & Fld 86; Larc Classic All Star Tm Bsktbl 87; Acad Excllnc Awd 86; Bioengrng.

MARCIN, JAMES; Panther Valley HS; Lansford, PA; (3); Aud/Vis; Drama Clb; Library Aide; School Play; Nwsp Stf; Rep Soph Cls; Bsbl; Ftbl; Golf; Mgr(s); Bus Mgmnt.

MARCINIAK, STANLEY; North Catholic HS; Pittsburgh, PA; (3); 110/333; Ski Clb; SADD; Rep Frsh Cls; VP Soph Cls; Rep Jr Cls; Off Stu Cncl; Ftbl; Var JV Wt Lftg; Pep Clb; Chiro.

MARCINKEVICH, FRANK; Mid Valley HS; Dickson City, PA; (4); Boy Scts; Drama Clb; Scholastic Bowl; Nwsp Ed-Chief; VP Frsh Cls; Rep Jr Cls; Pres Stu Cncl; High Hon Roll; VP NHS; Eagle Scout 84; U Of Scranton; Atty.

MARCINKO, CARRALEE; Windber Area HS; Windber, PA; (3); Sec Drama Clb; French Clb; Hosp Aide; Math Clb; Band; Color Guard; Concert Band; Mrchg Band; School Play; Hon Roll; Stu Of Mnth; U Of Pittsburgh; Elem Educ.

MARCINKOWSKI, SANDRA; John S Fine HS; Nanticoke, PA; (3); 27/259; FBLA; Hosp Aide; Ski Clb; Sec Frsh Cls; Sec Soph Cls; Sec Soph Cls; JV Bsktbl; Var Mgr(s); JV Vllybl; Accntng.

MARCINOWSKI, JEFFREY; St Josephs Prep; Philadelphia, PA; (4); 6/225; Chess Clb; Debate Tm; Library Aide; Science Clb; Yrbk Phtg; Yrbk Rptr; Yrbk Stf; High Hon Roll; NHS; Ntl Merit Ltr; Prep Schlr; MI Annl Gvng Schlrshp; U Of MI; Engrng.

MARCO, CHRISTOPHER EUGENE; Leechburg Area HS; Leechburg, PA; (4); 15/82; VP Frsh Cls; VP Soph Cls; Rep Stu Cncl; Capt Bsbl; Var Bsktbl; U Of Pittsburgh; Engrng.

MARCON, LARA; William Allen HS; Allentown, PA; (4); 7/560; Am Leg Aux Girls St; Key Clb; Letterman Clb; Model UN; SADD; VP Stu Cncl; Diving; DAR Awd; High Hon Roll; NHS; PIAA Dist XI Diving Champ 85-87; Smith Coll.

MARCONI, TRACEY; Penn Cambria SR HS; Gallitzin, PA; (3); Camera Clb; Spanish Clb; Hon Roll.

MARCOZ, TAMARA; Penn Trafford HS; Level Green, PA; (3); 7/301; JCL; Latin Clb; Rep Frsh Cls; Trs Soph Cls; Trs Jr Cls; Trs Sr Cls; Var Cheerleading; Trk; High Hon Roll; NHS; Seton Hll Wmns Ldrshp Smnr 86.

MARCUS, ROSLYN; Plymouth Whitemarsh HS; Norristown, PA; (3); Hosp Aide; Band; Concert Band; Drill Tm; Mrchg Band; Yrbk Bus Mgr; Yrbk Stf; Hon Roll; Jr NHS; Genetcs.

MARCY, MELISSA; Montrose Area JR/Sr HS; Hallstead, PA; (3); Church Yth Grp; Spanish Clb; SADD; Varsity Clb; Nwsp Stf; Yrbk Ed-Chief; Yrbk Stf; Stu Cncl; Stat Fld Hcky; Mgr(s).

MARCZINKO, MARIA; Steel Valley HS; Munhall, PA; (4); 18/201; Church Yth Grp; Teachers Aide; Yrbk Stf; High Hon Roll; Hon Roll; NHS; Bus Adm.

MARCZINKO, SARI; Steel Valley SR HS; Munhall, PA; (3); 5/209; Yrbk Stf; Var Mat Maids; Var Tennis; High Hon Roll; Hon Roll; NHS.

MARDER, JEFFREY I; Council Rock HS; Richboro, PA; (4); Temple Yth Grp; Band; Concert Band; Jazz Band; Orch; School Musical; Symp Band; Hon Roll; Bart Pitman Memrl Schlrshp 87; Ruth Kieth Schlrshp 87; Simon-Ford Music Schlrshp 87; Temple U; Jazz Ed.

MARDIS, BRENDA; Connellsville SR High East; Connellsville, PA; (3); FBLA; French Hon Soc; High Hon Roll; Hon Roll; NHS; Bradford; Bus.

MAREK, TAMMY; Uniontown Area HS; Uniontown, PA; (4); JA; Latin Clb; Spanish Clb; Sec Soph Cls; High Hon Roll; Hon Roll; Helen Bryce Schlrshp 87; Leichliter Schlrshp 87; St Vincent Coll; Biology.

MARENDT, ERIC; Meadville HS; Meadville, PA; (2); Church Yth Grp; Var Crs Cntry; Var Trk; Hon Roll; Military.

MARENGO, BRIAN G; Conestoga HS; Berwyn, PA; (4); 89/454; Service Clb; SADD; Nwsp Phtg; JV Var Bsbl; Hon Roll; Elec Engrng.

MARFINETZ, JOHN; Brownsville Area HS; Allison, PA; (4); 15/200; Drama Clb; Ski Clb; SADD; Yrbk Stf; Pres Jr Cls; High Hon Roll; Hon Roll; PA ST U; Admn Of Jstc.

MARFLAK, EDWARD; Bethel Parh HS; Bethel Pk, PA; (4); Church Yth Grp; Computer Clb; Political Wkr; Gov Hon Prg Awd; Hon Roll; Penn ST; Engr.

MARGIOTTA, GINA; Sacred Heart HS; Pittsburgh, PA; (3); VP Spanish Clb; High Hon Roll; Hon Roll; NHS; VP Frsh Cls; Trs Soph Cls; VP Jr Cls; VP Sr Cls; Stu Cncl; Pntng Chsn-Shwn Hrns Wndw-3 Rvrs Arts Fstvl 87; Art.

MARGO, DAVID; Shaler HS; Glenshaw, PA; (2); 15/512; Ski Clb; Socr; High Hon Roll; NHS; Spanish NHS; Ntl Sci Olympd 87; Acctng.

MARHEFKA, DANIELLE; South Allegheny HS; Port Vue, PA; (3); Exploring; FNA; German Clb; VP JA; Office Aide; Chorus; Color Guard; Nwsp Stf; Bsktbl; Hon Roll; Engnrng.

MARHEFKA, ROBIN; Shanksville-Stonycreek HS; Central City, PA; (4); 5/37; VP Ski Clb; Pres Band; VP Chorus; Drm Mjr(t); Pres Sr Cls; Pres Stu Cncl; Capt Cheerleading; Vllybl; NHS; Spanish NHS; Swng Awd; 3rd Pl JR Miss; Cmnty Ldrs Of Amer; U Ptsbrg; Comp Sci.

MARHEFKA, RONNA; Central Cambria HS; Mineral Pt, PA; (3); 14/210; Library Aide; Color Guard; Hon Roll; U Pittsburgh; Elem Ed.

MARHEFKA, SUSAN; Upper Dublin HS; Maple Glen, PA; (4); 5/318; Pres Aud/Vis; Cmnty Wkr; Pres Radio Clb; Nwsp Rptr; Hon Roll; NHS; Prfct Atten Awd; Frnch Awd 87; Frgn Exchng Stu 86; Ntl Merit Fnlst 87; U Of Notre Dame; Engr.

MARIA, JAY; Wyoming Area HS; West Wyoming, PA; (3); VP Church Yth Grp; Computer Clb; French Clb; Key Clb; Ski Clb; Nwsp Rptr; Nwsp Sprt Ed; Nwsp Stf; Bus Admin.

MARIANI, CARMELA; Taylor Allderdice HS; Pittsburgh, PA; (2); Church Yth Grp; Cmnty Wkr; Ski Clb; Varsity Clb; Var Crs Cntry; Var Trk; High Hon Roll; NHS.

MARIANO, CHRISTINE; Notre Dame HS; Easton, PA; (3); 8/96; Hosp Aide; Ski Clb; Chorus; School Musical; School Play; Nwsp Ed-Chief; Nwsp Stf; Yrbk Stf; JV Cheerleading; Coach Actv; Dstngshd Hnrs-Grds Abv 93 87; Acdmc All-Amrcn 86; Intl Frgn Lang Awd 85; Catholic U; Nrsng.

MARIANO, MARIELLE; Bensalem HS; Bensalem, PA; (2); Key Clb; Spanish Clb; SADD; Nwsp Stf; Fld Hcky; Cit Awd; Gov Hon Prg Awd; High Hon Roll; NHS; Chem Engrng.

MARIANO, MICHAEL; The Haverford School; Byrn Mawr, PA; (3); Capt Var Bsktbl; Var Lcrss; Capt Var Socr; Hon Roll; Bus.

MARIETTA, CHERYL; Connellsville Area HS; Acme, PA; (3); 69/530; Church Yth Grp; German Clb; Chorus; Mrchg Band; Symp Band; High Hon Roll; NHS; Prfct Atten Awd; Grm Hnr Soc 87.

MARINACCIO, KATHLEEN P; Delaware Valley HS; Milford, PA; (4); 48/135; Varsity Clb; Band; Concert Band; Mrchg Band; School Musical; Yrbk Stf; Var Capt Cheerleading; High Hon Roll; Hon Roll; Pop Warner Ftbll Leag Schlrshp 87; Polanis/Laizure Mem Trphy Outstndg Chrldr 87; Amer Lgn Pst 139 87; Pratt Inst; Fine Arts.

MARINAK, GLENN; Bellwood-Antis HS; Bellwood, PA; (3); 2/115; Badmtn; Var L Bsbl; JV Var Bsktbl; Vllybl; High Hon Roll; Hon Roll; JC Awd; Prfct Atten Awd; Mst Acad Sbjst High Grd Pnt Avrg 85-87; Cmptr Engr.

MARINELLI, CORINNE; Northeastern HS; York Haven, PA; (3); 50/200; Church Yth Grp; Drama Clb; SADD; Thesps; Pres Y-Teens; Chorus; Nwsp Rptr; Tennis; Hon Roll; Vrsty Lttr In Tnns & Trphy 86-87; Lebanon Vly Coll Ldrshp Cert 85-86; Pol Sci.

MARINELLI, KATHY; Scranton Tech; Scranton, PA; (4); FBLA; Letterman Clb; Q&S; Band; Orch; Nwsp Stf; Yrbk Stf; Co-Capt Cheerleading; Sftbl; Bus.

MARINES, AARON; Blacklick Valley JR SR HS; Vintondale, PA; (2); VP Church Yth Grp; NFL; Ski Clb; Church Choir; Nwsp Rptr; Stu Cncl; JV Bsktbl; Var Ftbl; Var Trk; High Hon Roll; Natl Acad All Amer 85-86; 3rd Pl Intl Teen Invlvd Wrd Of Life Comp 86; Engrng.

MARINKO, CHRISTINE; Bishop Hafey HS; Hazleton, PA; (3); Church Yth Grp; Cmnty Wkr; Hosp Aide; Key Clb; Pep Clb; Spanish Clb; Y-Teens; Yrbk Stf; Trk; Bus.

MARINKO, DENISE P; Bishop Hafey HS; Hazleton, PA; (1); Y-Teens.

MARINO III, ARTHUR J; Central Catholic HS; Pittsburgh, PA; (4); Church Yth Grp; Drama Clb; School Play; Rep Frsh Cls; Rep Jr Cls; Rep Sr Cls; Rep Stu Cncl; Bowling; Hon Roll; Newspaper Carrier Of Yr Awed 85; Duqesne U; Comms.

MARINO, CATHERINA; York Catholic HS; York, PA; (2); 8/200; Camera Clb; French Clb; Model UN; Ski Clb; Chorus; School Musical; Yrbk Stf; Var Fld Hcky; Var Tennis; JV Trk; Engrng.

MARINO, DANA; Plum SR HS; Pittsburgh, PA; (4); Dance Clb; French Clb; School Musical; Nwsp Sprt Ed; Coach Actv; Hon Roll; NEDT Awd; AFS; Ski Clb; Variety Show; Pres Schlrshp Kent ST U 87; Frnch Awd 87; Comp Figure Sktng 83-87; Kent ST U; Pre-Bus.

MARINO, KIMBERLY; St Maria Goretti HS; Philadelphia, PA; (3); French Clb; Phys.

MARINO, LISA L; Bishop Kenrick HS; Center Square, PA; (3); 98/330; GAA; JV Stat Bsktbl; JV Fld Hcky; Stat Mgr(s); Score Keeper; JV Trk; Var Powder Puff Ftbl; Bus.

MARINO, MARK J; Penn Trafford HS; Irwin, PA; (3); AFS; Pres Chess Clb; Hosp Aide; Pres Trs JCL; Latin Clb; Math Clb; Varsity Clb; Swing Chorus; Var L Wrstlng; Jr NHS; PA ST U; Pre-Med.

MARINO, PHILLIP; Greensburg Central Catholic HS; Greensburg, PA; (3); Ftbl; High Hon Roll; NHS; Acad All Amer 87; Crng-Mln U; Comp Systms Anlyst.

MARINOS, ROBIN; Monessen HS; Monessen, PA; (3); French Clb; Drm Mjr(t); Stage Crew; Yrbk Stf; Twrlr; High Hon Roll; Hon Roll; NHS; PRIDE Std 84-88; Advrstg.

MARINUCCI, JEFFREY J; Archbishop Ryan High Schl For Boys; Philadelphia, PA; (4); 10/485; Church Yth Grp; JA; Lit Mag; JV Bsbl; Hon Roll; NHS; Prfct Atten Awd; Western Civilization Awd; Span Awd; Prncpls Awd Hons; PA ST U; Accounting.

MARISON, KERRY; Waynesburg Central HS; Waynesburg, PA; (3); 1/250; Church Yth Grp; VP Letterman Clb; Ski Clb; Spanish Clb; SADD; Bsbl; Capt Bsktbl; Crs Cntry; NHS; NEDT Awd; Eng Awd; Spnsh Awd; Bus.

MARK, HEATHER; Tulpehochen HS; Myerstown, PA; (4); 6/115; Office Aide; Hon Roll; Schlr Awd 86; Trjn Prd Stu-Oct 86; Sec.

MARK, JUDY; Philadelphia HS For Girls; Philadelphia, PA; (3); 30/405; Teachers Aide; Stage Crew; Yrbk Stf; Hon Roll; Hnr Cert Merit Schlstc Achvt 86-87; U Of PA; Bus.

MARK, JULIE; Belle Fonte HS; Howard, PA; (4); 20/237; Drama Clb; 4-H; Hosp Aide; Spanish Clb; SADD; Band; Chorus; Mrchg Band; School Musical; Semper Fidelis Awd 87; Frank I & Elizabeth A Wetzler Mem Awd 87; All ST Band 87; Lock Haven U; Occ Therapy.

MARK, KIMBERLY; Philadelphia Montgomery Chrstn Acad; Philadelphia, PA; (3); Art Clb; Church Yth Grp; Chorus; School Play; JV Var Fld Hcky; JV Var Sftbl; Hon Roll; BFA; Art.

MARK, NOAH P; Cedar Cliff HS; Mechanicsburg, PA; (2); 5/286; Church Yth Grp; JCL; Latin Clb; Bowling; High Hon Roll; Latin Hnr Soc 87; Cum Laude In Natl Latn Exam 86-87.

MARK, PETER; Radnor HS; Wayne, PA; (3); Chess Clb; Exploring; Science Clb; Rep Soph Cls; Rep Jr Cls; Im Bsktbl; Var Golf; Im Vllybl; Atlantic Pacific Awd 84-85; Cmptn Dsgn Awd 84; Drexel U; Engr.

MARK, SIERRA; State College Area SR HS; Huntingdon, PA; (3); Key Clb; SADD; Yrbk Phtg; Var Fld Hcky; Var Powder Puff Ftbl; Var Trk; Im Vllybl; IN U PA; Psych.

MARK, TODD; Annville-Cleona HS; Annville, PA; (4); 7/112; VP Frsh Cls; VP Soph Cls; VP Jr Cls; VP Sr Cls; Trs Stu Cncl; Var L Socr; Var L Wrstlng; Dnfth Awd; Hon Roll; VP Pres NHS; Shippensburg U; Elem Ed.

MARK, WAYNE; Central HS Of Phila; Philadelphia, PA; (4); 39/296; Church Yth Grp; Im Bsktbl; Barnwell Awd 84-86; Drexel U; Comp Sci.

MARKARIAN, ELIZABETH; Pennsburg HS; Yardley, PA; (3); Dance Clb; Drama Clb; Chorus; School Musical; School Play; Variety Show; Yrbk Stf; High Hon Roll; Hon Roll; Cert Cmmndtn-Chem 87; Ntl Leag Amer Pen Wmn-Shrt Stry Cntst 83; Jrnlsm.

MARKATOS, ANGELO; Upper Darby SR HS; Upr Darby, PA; (3); JV Tennis; High Hon Roll; Hon Roll; U PA; Engrng.

MARKEL, DWAYNE; Central Dauphin HS; Harrisburg, PA; (3); Church Yth Grp; Band; Concert Band; Jazz Band; Mrchg Band; Hon Roll; Comp Sci.

MARKER, STACY; Dallastown Area HS; Dallastown, PA; (3); 41/330; Church Yth Grp; Concert Band; Jazz Band; Mrchg Band; Nwsp Rptr; Nwsp Stf; High Hon Roll; Library Aide; Band; Pep Band; 5.1 GPA Hghr Prvlg Pass 85-87; 2nd Pl Bhvrl Sci Catg Sci Fair 85; Peer Tutor-Alg & Bio 86-87; Wake Forest U; Psych.

MARKER, WANDA; Mt Pleasant HS; Mt Pleasant, PA; (3); Church Yth Grp; Varsity Clb; VICA; Chorus; Church Choir; JV Crs Cntry; Im Mat Maids; JV Im Trk; Hon Roll; Prfct Atten Awd; Cnty Dist Chorus 85; Pres Chorus 85; Secy Yth Grp 86-87; PBA; Csmtlgy.

MARKET, PATRICK S; Mohawk Area JR/Sr HS; New Castle, PA; (4); 29/141; School Musical; School Play; Stage Crew; Cmnty Wkr; Hon Roll; Frnch & Stg Crw Excllnc Awds 84-87; Rutgers; Mtrlgy.

MARKEY, MONIQUE; Wyomissing Area HS; West Lawn, PA; (3); 3/145; Church Yth Grp; Intnl Clb; Latin Clb; Spanish Clb; Nwsp Stf; Yrbk Stf; Trs Stu Cncl; JV Fld Hcky; High Hon Roll; Jr NHS; Schl Rep Freedom Week 85; Engr.

MARKHAM, DAVID; Beth Center HS; Marianna, PA; (3); JV Ftbl; Hon Roll; Hstry.

MARKHAM, JEFFREY; Dieruff HS; Allentown, PA; (2); Church Yth Grp; Debate Tm; JA; ROTC; Chorus; Church Choir; Hon Roll; Prfct Atten Awd; Law.

MARKHAM, STACEY; Moon Area HS; Coraopolis, PA; (3); 67/322; Hosp Aide; Band; Concert Band; Mrchg Band; Nwsp Stf; Yrbk Stf; Stu Cncl; Var Swmmng; Hon Roll; Psych.

MARKIEWICH, CARLA; Carmichaels Area HS; Carmichaels, PA; (4); 8/100; French Clb; Library Aide; Pep Clb; Ski Clb; High Hon Roll; Hon Roll; NHS; IN U PA; Fash Merch.

MARKIEWICZ, MISSY; West Mifflin Area HS; W Mifflin, PA; (3); 78/302; Key Clb; Office Aide; Pep Clb; Ski Clb; Teachers Aide; Drill Tm; Stu Cncl; Capt Cheerleading; Trk; Wt Lftg; Clairon U; Spch.

MARKLE, CHRISTINE; South Western HS; Hanover, PA; (2); 56/251; Varsity Clb; Stat Bsktbl; L Mgr(s); High Hon Roll; Hon Roll.

MARKLE, DONNA; Yough HS; Smithton, PA; (3); Church Yth Grp; Dance Clb; Library Aide; Office Aide; Pep Clb; Ski Clb; Spanish Clb; SADD; Boy Scts; Chorus; W PA Nursing Schl; Nursing.

MARKLE, JEFF; Hanover HS; Hanover, PA; (4); Letterman Clb; Bsbl; Ftbl; Am Legion Basebll 85-87; Towson ST; Phys Ed.

MARKLE, JENNIFER; Yough SR HS; W Newton, PA; (3); 26/236; Rep French Clb; Trs Band; Chorus; Concert Band; Jazz Band; Mrchg Band; Yrbk Stf; High Hon Roll; Hon Roll; NHS.

MARKLE, JULIE; Eastern York JR-SR HS; Hellam, PA; (2); 7/144; Church Yth Grp; Concert Band; Mrchg Band; School Musical; Band; Church Choir; High Hon Roll; Jr NHS; PA Ambssdrs Music Tr Of Eurp 87; Hstry & Frnch Dept Awds 87; Natl Piano Plyng Adtns-Dist Lvl 87; HSTRY.

MARKLE, MICHELLE; Trinity HS; Washington, PA; (2); Art Clb; German Clb; Color Guard; Flag Corp; Mrchg Band; Ed Lit Mag; High Hon Roll; Chmst.

MARKLEY, CHRISTOPHER M; Hempfield HS; Lancaster, PA; (3); 140/490; Church Yth Grp; Hosp Aide; Key Clb; Red Cross Aide; Pres Frsh Cls; Stu Cncl; Var L FHA; Var L Tennis; Elks Awd; Prfct Atten Awd; 2nd Tm All Leag Ftbl 85fdoubles Champ Fennis 87; Comm.

MARKLEY, NICOLE; Hempfield HS; Mountville, PA; (3); Cmnty Wkr; Exploring; Varsity Clb; Stat Bsktbl; Var JV Fld Hcky; Var L Trk; High Hon Roll; Hon Roll; Jr NHS; NHS; Juniata; Psych.

MARKLEY, SCOTT; Palmeton Area HS; Bowmanstown, PA; (3); 6/173; Am Leg Boys St; L Bsktbl; Var L Crs Cntry; Var L Trk; High Hon Roll; Hon Roll; 5 Acadc Awds.

MARKO, CARL; Readinga Rea HS; Reading, PA; (3); 73/710; Debate Tm; Exploring; Mrchg Band; Ftbl; High Hon Roll; Hon Roll; Band; Ind Arts Awd 87; 1st Prz-Wood Block Awd 87; Lehi U; Engrng.

MARKO, JENNIFER; Hazleton HS; Hazleton, PA; (3); 39/450; FNA; Pep Clb; Service Clb; Spanish Clb; Y-Teens; L Var Bsktbl; L Var Sftbl; High Hon Roll; Prfct Atten Awd; Ken Pollock Awd 87.

MARKO, MELISSA; Hazleton SR HS; Hazleton, PA; (2); French Clb; FNA; Hosp Aide; Pep Clb; Service Clb; Y-Teens; Yrbk Stf; Bsktbl; Var L Trk; Hon Roll; Psychology.

MARKOTAN, THOMAS; Elizabeth Forward HS; Elizabeth, PA; (3); 40/340; French Clb; JA; High Hon Roll; Hon Roll; NHS; Acad All-Amer Schlr Awd 87; Penn ST; Sci.

MARKOWSKI, ANNETTE; Conrad Weisser HS; St Johns, PA; (4); 27/187; Debate Tm; Drama Clb; GAA; JCL; Key Clb; SADD; Teachers Aide; Varsity Clb; Sec Chorus; School Musical; Key Clbbr Mnth 85; Jr Wmns Clb Girl Mnth 87; Penn ST U; Pre Law.

MARKOWSKI, LYNN ANN; Seneca Valley HS; Zelienople, PA; (4); 7/347; Aud/Vis; Church Yth Grp; Thesps; School Play; Stage Crew; Symp Band; High Hon Roll; NHS; Cmnty Wkr; Hosp Aide; Hnr Thspn 87; Hstss Of Read To Me TV Show 87; U Of Pittsburgh; Theatre Arts.

MARKS, AARON; William Allen HS; Allentown, PA; (3); Pres Computer Clb; Ski Clb; Bryant U; Comp Sci.

MARKS, ERIC; Downingtown SR HS; Exton, PA; (3); 58/648; German Clb; Letterman Clb; Band; Wrstlng; Hon Roll; NHS; PA Free Enterprise Wk Schlrshp 87; Bucknell; Finance.

MARKS, FRED; Nativity Bum HS; Minersville, PA; (4); 42/99; Computer Clb; Ski Clb; Spanish Clb; JV Bsbl; Var Bsktbl; Var Ice Hcky; PA ST U; Med.

MARKS, KRISTIN; Allentown Central Catholic HS; Northampton, PA; (3); 27/241; German Clb; Key Clb; Math Tm; Pep Clb; Service Clb; Yrbk Stf; Lit Mag; High Hon Roll; NHS; Principals Awd 85; PA ST U; Mrktg.

MARKS, LORI; Tunkhannock HS; Tunkhannock, PA; (4); Drama Clb; French Clb; Key Clb; Latin Clb; School Musical; School Play; Yrbk Stf; Var Cheerleading; Hon Roll; NHS; U Of NC.

MARKS, MARY ANN; Sto-Rox HS; Mckees Rocks, PA; (2); 9/130; Band; Concert Band; Mrchg Band; JV Bsktbl; Var Sftbl; High Hon Roll; Hon Roll; Mech Engrng.

MARKS, PHIL; Warwick HS; Lititz, PA; (3); 1/270; Im Bsktbl; Ftbl; Im Vllybl; Wt Lftg; Wrstlng; High Hon Roll; Engr.

MARKS, SEAN; Elizabeth-Forward HS; Mc Keesport, PA; (3); Spanish Clb; SADD; Bsktbl; Ftbl; Hon Roll; NHS; Acdmc All Amer 87; Athl Trng.

MARKWOOD, SUSAN; Elizabeth Forward HS; Elizabeth, PA; (3); 21/345; Church Yth Grp; Exploring; Latin Clb; Sec Leo Clb; Band; Concert Band; Jazz Band; Mrchg Band; High Hon Roll; Hon Roll; Pre-Law.

MARMAGIN, JOELLE; Ambridge Area HS; Baden, PA; (4); VP JA; Office Aide; School Play; Off Jr Cls; Off Sr Cls; Stu Cncl; Capt Cheerleading; Pom Pon; Trk; Hon Roll; Boyd Career Schl; Travel.

MARMOL, ERIC J; Fairchance Georges HS; Uniontown, PA; (3); Church Yth Grp; Concert Band; Mrchg Band; Hon Roll; NHS; PA ST U; Engrng.

MARMON, JONATHAN; Lowel Moreland HS; Huntingdon Valley, PA; (4); 70/202; FBLA; Key Clb; Office Aide; VP Mrchg Band; Im Bsktbl; Hon Roll; PA ST U; Pre Law.

MARNELL, ELAINE; Hazleton HS; Hazleton, PA; (3); 2/445; FNA; Spanish Clb; Y-Teens; Hon Roll; Sal; Kngs Coll Natl Spnsh Cntst Lvl 3 87; Kngs Coll Natl Spnsh Cntst Lvl 2 86; Pres Acad Ftns Awd 85; Intrntl Bus.

MARNELL, MARY; Greensburg Central Catholic HS; Greensburg, PA; (4); Cmnty Wkr; French Clb; Political Wkr; Ski Clb; Teachers Aide; Chorus; School Play; Lit Mag; Powder Puff Ftbl; L Stat Tennis; PSU; Pre-Law.

MAROFSKY, BRIAN; Mercyhurst Prep; Erie, PA; (4); Rep Stu Cncl; Var JV Socr; Penn ST; Manag.

MARONE, TINA; Windber Area HS; Windber, PA; (4); 1/130; Office Aide; Color Guard; Mrchg Band; Nwsp Ed-Chief; Nwsp Stf; Yrbk Stf; Sec Sr Cls; Capt Twrlr; High Hon Roll; Jr NHS; Robert Byrd Scholar 87; Windber PTO Scholar 87; Stu Mnth 87; U Pittsburgh; Phrmcy.

MARONEY, AMY; Sun Valley HS; Brookhaven, PA; (4); 2/311; Red Cross Aide; Sec SADD; Hst Band; School Musical; Yrbk Stf; JV Sftbl; High Hon Roll; Lion Awd; Trs NHS; Ntl Merit Ltr; Stu Of Mnth 86-87; Wdnr Sci Enrchmnt Pgm 86-87.

MAROSEK, JOHN; Phoenixville Area HS; Phoenixville, PA; (2); Hon Roll; MI U; Accntng.

MAROSKI, CALENE; Northampton HS; Bath, PA; (4); FBLA; SADD; High Hon Roll; Hon Roll; Bus Ldrs Of Amer Rgnl Comp 4th Bus Engl 87; Upward Bound Smmr Prog Cert Of Merit Career Ed 86; Penn ST U; Comp Sci.

MAROTTA, EDDIE; Waynesburg Central HS; Waynesburg, PA; (4); Art Clb; Letterman Clb; Band; Nwsp Rptr; Var Bsbl; Var Golf; Var Trk; Var L Wrstlng; Hon Roll; Washington/Jefferson Coll; Med.

MAROUCHOC, JIM; Freedom HS; Allentown, PA; (4); 49/439; Var L Bsbl; Capt Var Ftbl; Im Wt Lftg; Hon Roll; John W Butler Awd Most Outstndg Lnmn 85; US Army Rsrv Natl Schlr Athlt Awd 87; Moravian Coll; Acctg.

MARQUARDT, DONNA; Council Rock HS; Newtown, PA; (4); 3/860; Sec Church Yth Grp; Drama Clb; Hosp Aide; Band; Mrchg Band; Symp Band; NHS; Ntl Merit Ltr; Phila Coll/Bible; Scndry Educ.

MARQUES, DANZILIA MARIA; S Phuiladelphia HS; Philadelphia, PA; (4); 3/450; JA; Library Aide; Acpl Chr; Chorus; Color Guard; Rep Sr Cls; Socr; Hon Roll; Prfct Atten Awd; Ntl Hnr Soc 87; Spanish Ntl Hnr 86; Ntl Yng Ldrs Of Amer Conf 87; Philadelphia CC; Arch.

MARQUET, JAMES; Cardinal O Hara HS; Media, PA; (3); 109/710; Var L Ftbl.

MARQUETTE, KAREN; Pottstown SR HS; Pottstown, PA; (3); 41/155; Art Clb; Key Clb; Spanish Clb; SADD; Concert Band; Mrchg Band; Yrbk Stf; JV Sftbl; Hon Roll; Physics.

MARQUIS, JILL; Eisenhower HS; Warren, PA; (3); 1/119; Church Yth Grp; Hosp Aide; Office Aide; Chorus; Stage Crew; Stat Bsktbl; L Sftbl; High Hon Roll; VP Trs Jr NHS; VP NHS.

MARRA, BRIAN; Valley View HS; Eynon, PA; (4); 3/195; Church Yth Grp; Computer Clb; Math Tm; Spanish Clb; JV Var Crs Cntry; Var Trk; Im Capt Vllybl; DAR Awd; NHS; Ntl Merit SF; Math League Cert Merit 86; Cert Merit Spnsh 84-86; Ntl Merit Ltr Commendtn 86; Engrng.

MARRA, CATHY; St Maria Goretti HS; Philadelphia, PA; (4); 54/387; Cmnty Wkr; Dance Clb; GAA; Spanish Clb; Off Soph Cls; High Hon Roll; Pres Acad Ftns Awd 86-87; Temple U.

MARRANGONI, NICHOLAS; Kennedy Christian HS; New Castle, PA; (3); Church Yth Grp; Science Clb; Spanish Clb; High Hon Roll; Hon Roll; Jr NHS; Headmasters Incentv Scholar Awd 84-85; 1st Cath Slovak Ladies Assn HS Schlr 86-87; 90 Pct NEDT; Bus.

MARRERO, JAVIER; William Penn SR HS; York, PA; (3); 56/296; Church Yth Grp; Spanish Clb; Trk; Hon Roll; Boy Of The Month 83-84; US Air Force; Air Trffc Cntrll.

MARRERO, JEANETTE; City Center Acad; Philadelphia, PA; (3); Art Clb; Pres Church Yth Grp; Computer Clb; Drama Clb; Pep Clb; School Play; Stage Crew; Pres Jr Cls; Emma Chmpn Awd 85; Acctng.

MARRERO, MAYRA; Little Flower HS; Philadelphia, PA; (3); 68/365; Church Yth Grp; Cmnty Wkr; JA; Band; Chorus; Drill Tm; Drm Mjr(t); Flag Corp; Mrchg Band; Orch.

MARRIGGI, MARIE; Pittston Area SR HS; Avoca, PA; (3); 31/305; Church Yth Grp; Cmnty Wkr; Ski Clb; Chorus; School Musical; Swmmng; Trk; High Hon Roll; Hon Roll; NHS; Boston Coll; Tchr.

MARROMATES, NICKOLAOS; West-York HS; York, PA; (3); 42/186; Am Leg Boys St; Church Yth Grp; CAP; Varsity Clb; Ftbl; US Military Acad.

MARRONE, ANDREW; Lebanon Catholic HS; Palmyra, PA; (4); Computer Clb; Band; Chorus; Concert Band; Jazz Band; Mrchg Band; Variety Show; Hon Roll; Exclince In Comp Prgmng & Psych, Brwn Blt Isshin Ryu Karate; Ithaca Coll; Music.

MARSDEN, AMY; Villa Maria Acad; Erie, PA; (3); Cmnty Wkr; Pep Clb; Science Clb; VP Spanish Clb; Var Bsktbl; Var Capt Socr; Hon Roll; Hlth Fld.

MARSH, BRENDA; Mercer JR SR HS; Mercer, PA; (4); 3/135; Band; Concert Band; Mrchg Band; School Play; Rep Stu Cncl; JV Stat Bsktbl; Mgr(s); Elks Awd; Hon Roll; NHS; Schltc Awd 87; OH Northern U; Phrmcy.

MARSH, DANA P; State College Area SR HS; State College, PA; (4); 101/575; Red Cross Aide; Lit Mag; Rep Soph Cls; Rep Jr Cls; Rep Sr Cls; Rep Stu Cncl; Powder Puff Ftbl; JV Vllybl; Hon Roll; Power Of The Paws 84-87; PA ST U; Psych.

MARSH, DAVE; Elizabethtown Area HS; Elizabethtown, PA; (3); 24/250; Church Yth Grp; Church Choir; JV Bsktbl; Var L Golf; Var L Trk; Hon Roll; Jr NHS; NHS; Amer Lgn Awd 85; Bus Mngmnt.

MARSH, DIANE; Fairview HS; Fairview, PA; (3); 3/150; French Clb; Off Varsity Clb; Rep Stu Cncl; Var L Cheerleading; Var Crs Cntry; JV Sftbl; Var L Swmmng; High Hon Roll; NHS; Med.

MARSH, ELIZABETH; Hughesville JR/Sr HS; Hughesville, PA; (3); VP French Clb; VP Band; Concert Band; Mrchg Band; School Musical; Var Trk; Hon Roll; NHS; Anml Sci.

MARSH, GRETCHEN; Indiana Area SR HS; Indiana, PA; (3); Church Yth Grp; English Clb; French Clb; Hosp Aide; Acpl Chr; Chorus; Jazz Band; High Hon Roll; Sec Jr NHS; NEDT Awd; Rnr Up-Pennas Govs Schl For Gftd 86; Wrthy Advsr-PA Rnbw For Grls 86.

MARSH, JENNIFER; Boiling Springs HS; Gardners, PA; (2); 1/139; Hon Roll; NHS.

MARSH, KELLY; Fairview HS; Fairview, PA; (4); 1/160; Dance Clb; French Clb; Q&S; Off Varsity Clb; Nwsp Rptr; Rep Sr Cls; Var Capt Crs Cntry; Var Capt Swmmng; Var Capt Trk; High Hon Roll; US Navy Athl/Schlr Awd 87; Outstndg Crss Cntry-Trk Awd 87; All St Hnrs X-Cntry, Swmmg, Trk 86-87; Bucknell U; Pol Sci.

MARSH, MEGAN; East Pennsboro Area HS; Enola, PA; (3); 43/200; Art Clb; French Clb; Teachers Aide; Yrbk Bus Mgr; Yrbk Stf; Chrmn Stu Cncl; Cheerleading; Score Keeper; Hon Roll; Schl Rep Natl Stu Cncl Conf 87; Kutztown U; Bio.

MARSHALICK, LUBOW J; Our Lady Of Lourdes Regional HS; Shamokin, PA; (4); 7/92; VP Library Aide; Spanish Clb; Yrbk Ed-Chief; Stat Bsktbl; High Hon Roll; NHS; Spanish NHS; Bloomsburg U; Med Tech.

MARSHALL, ALISON; York Suburban SR HS; State College, PA; (3); JA; Letterman Clb; Varsity Clb; Chorus; School Musical; Nwsp Rptr; Var Bsktbl; Var Capt Sftbl; Var Capt Vllybl; High Hon Roll; William & Mary; Intl Rel.

MARSHALL, BENJAMIN; Venango Christian HS; Seneca, PA; (2); 2/42; Spanish Clb; Speech Tm; SADD; Chorus; Pres Jr Cls; Var L Bsbl; Var L Bsktbl; JV Ftbl; High Hon Roll; Masonic Awd; Schlrshp To PA Free Entrprse Wk 87; Engnrng.

MARSHALL, CONNIE; Chestnut Ridge SR HS; Imler, PA; (3); JV Bsktbl; JV Sftbl; Sprts Cstng.

MARSHALL, DARLA; Shenango HS; New Castle, PA; (4); 8/113; Hosp Aide; Math Tm; Office Aide; Teachers Aide; Flag Corp; Yrbk Stf; Bsktbl; Score Keeper; Vllybl; Hon Roll; 1st Pl Poetry Cntst Lwrnce Cnty 86; 2nd Pl Acdmc Gms 85-86; Acdmc Schlrshp Gannon 87; Gannon U; Biomed Engrng.

MARSHALL, ERIC A; Dallas Area HS; Shaverstown, PA; (3); Chess Clb; Sec Church Yth Grp; Computer Clb; Exploring; L Socr; High Hon Roll; Phy Ed Awd Outstndng Achvt 87; PA ST U; Pharm.

MARSHALL, JEFF; Waynesburg Central HS; Waynesburg, PA; (3); Spanish Clb; Var L Trk; JV Var Wrstlng; High Hon Roll; Hon Roll; Waynesburg Coll; 2ndry Ed.

MARSHALL, JENNIFER; Lincoln HS; Wampum, PA; (3); Spanish Clb; SADD; Y-Teens; Band; Concert Band; Mrchg Band; High Hon Roll; Hon Roll; Accntng.

MARSHALL, KATHLEEN; Central York SR HS; York, PA; (3); Church Yth Grp; Cmnty Wkr; Girl Scts; Yrbk Stf; Var Trk; Hon Roll; Bus.

MARSHALL, LYNITA J; Philadelphia HS For Girls; Philadelphia, PA; (3); 204/405; Church Yth Grp; Dance Clb; Office Aide; Yrbk Stf; Trphy Tap Dncng 86; Phila Pblc Schlgymnstcs Meet 83; Comp.

MARSHALL, MARLA; Langley HS; Pittsburgh, PA; (3); VP Jr Cls; Cit Awd; Hon Roll; Sawyer; Med Sec.

MARSHALL, MICHELLE; Northern Cambria HS; Barnesboro, PA; (3); 47/152; French Clb; Spanish Clb; Teachers Aide; Chorus; Color Guard; Trk; High Hon Roll; Hon Roll; Spanish NHS.

MARSHALL, MIKE; Bedford HS; Bedford, PA; (3); 12/206; Boy Scts; Church Yth Grp; Computer Clb; Letterman Clb; NAACP; Red Cross Aide; Chorus; School Musical; JV L Bsktbl; Var L Ftbl; Acad Mdl 85, 87; Trk Outstndng Sprinter 86-87; Ftbl Outstndng Rnng Back 86; Med.

MARSHALL, RICHARD; Chambersburg Area SR HS; Chambersburg, PA; (4); 20/606; Boy Scts; German Clb; Scholastic Bowl; Trs Science Clb; Chorus; Var L Trk; Var L Wrstlng; High Hon Roll; Hon Roll; NHS; PA ST U; Pre-Med.

MARSHALL, STEVEN; Notre Dame HS; Easton, PA; (3); 30/93; Church Yth Grp; Ski Clb; Spanish Clb; Band; Chorus; Concert Band; Mrchg Band; Orch; Pep Band; Stage Crew; Mst Imprvd Music Awd 85-86; Comp Pgmmng.

MARSHALL, TIA; Walter Biddle Saul HS Of Ag Sciences; Philadelphia, PA; (2); Church Yth Grp; FCA; FFA; Girl Scts; Hosp Aide; Church Choir; Sec Frsh Cls; Sec Soph Cls; Bsktbl; Proj Explore Haverford Coll, PASA Cert Achvt 86; UCLA; Med.

MARSHALL, TINA; Fairchance-Georges HS; Uniontown, PA; (3); Drama Clb; Spanish Clb; School Play; Variety Show; Pres Soph Cls; High Hon Roll; Hon Roll; Pres Jr NHS; NHS; Pres Schlr; Penn ST U; Law.

MARSICANO, JONATHAN; Hazleton HS; Hazleton, PA; (2); 8/450; Church Yth Grp; Nwsp Ed-Chief; Nwsp Stf; Yrbk Rptr; JV Var Bsktbl; Hon Roll; Amer Legion Schlstc Awd 86; Newspr Awds 86; Penn ST U; Med.

MARSICO, JOE; Valley HS; Arnold, PA; (3); Hosp Aide; Science Clb; Spanish Clb; Trk; Wt Lftg; Med.

MARSICO, PAULA; Lakeland HS; Mayfield, PA; (3); 4-H; Girl Scts; SADD; Band; Chorus; Church Choir; Mrchg Band; Stage Crew; High Hon Roll; Prfct Atten Awd; Penn ST; Ag.

MARSINI, JOSEPH; Marple Newtown SR HS; Broomall, PA; (2); 31/324; Nwsp Stf; Lcrss; Swmmng; Hon Roll.

MARSIT, JOSEPH; Hazleton HS; Hazleton, PA; (3); 10/450; Cmnty Wkr; French Clb; Latin Clb; Science Clb; Capt L Bowling; Var L Golf; Capt L Tennis; Wt Lftg; French Hon Soc; High Hon Roll; Latn Natl Hnr Socty; Anthracita Leag Tennis Champ; Corp Acctnt.

MARSTELLAR, ROBERTA; Kennedy Christian HS; Sharpsvle, PA; (2); 2/96; Latin Clb; Nwsp Rptr; Ed Nwsp Stf; Yrbk Rptr; Yrbk Stf; NEDT Awd; PA JR Acad Sci 86 & 87; Engrng.

MARSTELLER, TIM; Baldwin HS; Pittsburgh, PA; (3); 110/477; Mrchg Band; Orch; School Musical; Symp Band; Hon Roll; Prfct Atten Awd; Hnr Roll; Yth Symphony Band; Prfct Atten; U Pittsburgh; Civil Engrng.

MARTA, MONICA L; West Scranton HS; Scranton, PA; (2); #5 In Class; Spanish Clb; Band; Concert Band; Jazz Band; Mrchg Band; Orch; Stu Cncl; Pom Pon; High Hon Roll; Hon Roll; Ntl Fraternity Of Stu Musicians Dist Hnrs 82-86; 4 Intl Hnrs; Sonatina Plaque 85; Ntl Hnrs 87; U Of Scranton; Surgeon.

MARTE, JENNY; Butler Area SR HS; Butler, PA; (3); 247/705; Church Yth Grp; Exploring; Office Aide; Band; Mrchg Band; Symp Band; Yrbk Phtg; Yrbk Stf; Sftbl; Hon Roll; Clarion U Of PA; Dentst.

MARTE, KRISTINA M; Carlisle SR HS; Carlisle, PA; (4); 80/382; Art Clb; Band; Color Guard; JV Cheerleading; Ntl Merit Schol; Schlstc Art Gold Key; Hallmark Awd; Moore Coll Of Art; Graphics.

MARTENEY, KENNETH; Meyersdale Area HS; Meyersdale, PA; (3); Pres Church Yth Grp; Cmnty Wkr; French Clb; Band; Chorus; Concert Band; Mrchg Band; School Musical; School Play; Stage Crew; Hstry.

MARTIN, ALICIA MARIE; Mid-Valley Secondary Ctr; Olyphant, PA; (1); 2/24; Dance Clb; Drama Clb; School Musical; Cheerleading; Hon Roll.

MARTIN, ALIZA; Greater Works Acad; Pittsburgh, PA; (4); 6/32; Cmnty Wkr; French Clb; Service Clb; Mgr Ski Clb; Band; Yrbk Stf; L Vllybl; High Hon Roll; Hon Roll; Duquesne U; Phrmcy.

MARTIN, AMY; Jefferson-Morgan HS; Waynesburg, PA; (2); 2/109; Flag Corp; High Hon Roll.

MARTIN, AMY; Solanco HS; Drumore, PA; (2); 25/283; Church Yth Grp; 4-H; FFA; Girl Scts; Concert Band; Mrchg Band; Cit Awd; Hon Roll.

MARTIN, ANDY; Manheim Central HS; Mt Joy, PA; (4); 50/224; Var Ftbl; Hon Roll; Lancaster-Lebanon Lg All Star Tm Hnrb Mntn 85 & 86; 4-Way Test Awd; Grove City Coll; Engrng.

MARTIN, BRIAN; Abington Hts North Campus HS; Clarks Summit, PA; (3); 13/292; Scholastic Bowl; Ski Clb; Im Bsbl; Hon Roll; Ntl Merit Ltr; Kngs Coll Anual Invtnl Grmn Cont 86; Mbr Chmpn Schlstc Bowl Tm 87; Syracuse U; Civil Engrng.

MARTIN, BRIAN; Seneca Valley HS; Mars, PA; (3); Boy Scts; Church Yth Grp; Varsity Clb; Var L Ftbl; Var L Trk; Var Wt Lftg; Hon Roll; Penn ST; Pre Law.

MARTIN, BRIAN K; Trinity HS; Washington, PA; (3); 29/408; Boy Scts; Church Yth Grp; Computer Clb; Ski Clb; Band; Variety Show; Var L Ftbl; Wt Lftg; Wrstlng; Hon Roll; Physcs.

MARTIN, CARLEEN; Shalom Christian Acad; Chambersburg, PA; (3); Church Yth Grp; FHA; VP Jr Cls; Fld Hcky; Trk; Vllybl; High Hon Roll; Hon Roll; Spanish NHS.

MARTIN, CHERIE; Living Word Acad; Ephrata, PA; (1); Church Yth Grp; Band; School Musical; Rep Stu Cncl; Var Bsktbl; Var Trk; Hon Roll; Character Hnr Roll 86.

MARTIN, CHRISTOPHER L; Cocalico HS; Reinholds, PA; (2); Church Yth Grp; 4-H; Band; Concert Band; Jazz Band; Mrchg Band; Crs Cntry; Trk; 4-H Awd; Hon Roll; Pres Phys Fitness Awd 84-85; Holds Schl Track Record In 800 Meter Run 87; Anml Sci.

MARTIN, CYNTHIA; West Scranton HS; Scranton, PA; (2); French Clb; Pom Pon; Hon Roll; Lackawanna JC; Med Sec.

MARTIN, DAN; Lower Merion HS; Wynnewood, PA; (3); Boy Scts; French Clb; Band; JV Tennis; Var Wrstlng; French Hon Soc; High Hon Roll; Ntl Merit Ltr; Math Schlrshp Awd 85; JV Awd Tnns 85; Wrstlng Awd 85; Stanford U; Bus.

MARTIN, DARREL; Loyalsock Township HS; Williamsport, PA; (3); German Clb; Speech Tm; SADD; Stage Crew; Yrbk Ed-Chief; Socr; Trk; Hon Roll; Sys Anlys.

MARTIN, DAVID; Danville HS; Danville, PA; (4); Church Yth Grp; Exploring; Key Clb; Letterman Clb; Ski Clb; Spanish Clb; VP Jr Cls; VP Sr Cls; Var L Socr; Var L Wrstlng; PA ST U.

MARTIN, DAVID; Millville HS; Millville, PA; (4); 12/75; Chess Clb; Var Bsbl; Var Bsktbl; Var Socr; Elks Awd; Hon Roll; NEDT Awd; C Seymore Stere Almn Schlrshp 87; AAA Achvmnt Awd 86; Prsdntl Ftnss Awd; Penn ST Hazleton; Engrng.

MARTIN, DEBORAH; Archbishop Ryan Girls HS; Philadelphia, PA; (3); 2/530; French Clb; Office Aide; Science Clb; School Musical; Nwsp Rptr; French Hon Soc; High Hon Roll; NHS; Prfct Atten Awd; Drama Clb; Algbr I & Ii Awds 85 & 86; Bio Awd 85; French Ii Awd 86; Sci.

MARTIN, DEBORAH; North Allegheny HS; Pittsburgh, PA; (4); 77/660; Church Yth Grp; Debate Tm; Chorus; Drill Tm; School Musical; Lit Mag; Hon Roll; Jr NHS; NHS; Mount Holyoke; Chld Psych.

MARTIN, DEL RAY; Greencastle Antrim HS; Greencastle, PA; (3); 19/188; Church Yth Grp; Hon Roll; Shippensburg U; Bus Mgmt.

MARTIN, DENISE; Tunkhannock HS; Falls, PA; (4); 25/280; Art Clb; Key Clb; Spanish Clb; Hon Roll; NHS; Kings Coll; Bus.

MARTIN II, DONALD C; Hershey HS; Hershey, PA; (3); Ski Clb; Nwsp Rptr; Hon Roll; Sports Schlrshp 87; Murray ST U; Bus Admin.

MARTIN, DUSTY; Chambersburg SR HS; Chambersburg, PA; (3); 4-H; Spanish Clb; Color Guard; Yrbk Ed-Chief; Var L Sftbl; JV Vllybl; Hon Roll; Vrsty Lttrs 22 Cal Rifle Team 85-87; Cptn 22 Cal Rifle Team 87-88; Physics.

MARTIN, ELDRED CHAD; Charleroi Area HS; Stockdale, PA; (4); Boy Scts; Church Yth Grp; Cmnty Wkr; Science Clb; Ski Clb; Spanish Clb; Varsity Clb; L Ftbl; L Trk; Hon Roll; NAMES 86; Recog Awd-Vlntrng-Chldrns Hosp 85; Waynesburg Coll; Physics.

MARTIN, ELIZABETH; Mifflinburg HS; Laurelton, PA; (1); Spanish Clb; Chorus; School Musical; Rep Stu Cncl; JV Bsktbl; JV Fld Hcky; High Hon Roll; Bloomsburg U; Nrsng.

MARTIN, ERIC; Neshannock HS; New Castle, PA; (3); 5/110; NFL; Pres Science Clb; Band; Mrchg Band; Var L Tennis; Hon Roll; NHS; JR Acad Of Sci-1st Pl Lcl, 2nd Pl ST; Eclgy Meet-1st Pl; ST Frnscs Meet-6th Pl.

MARTIN, ERIN K; Lower Dauphin HS; Hummelstown, PA; (3); 18/273; Am Leg Aux Girls St; Cmnty Wkr; Thesps; Chorus; Orch; School Musical; Rep Jr Cls; Hon Roll; NHS; Pltcl Sci.

MARTIN, GEORGE; Central Catholic HS; Pittsburgh, PA; (3); Im Bsbl; Im Fld Hcky; Im Ftbl; Var Trk; Var L Wrstlng; Engr.

MARTIN, GINA; Monongahela Valley Catholic HS; Monongahela, PA; (3); Teachers Aide; School Musical; School Play; Yrbk Stf; Mgr Ftbl; Mgr(s); Im Powder Puff Ftbl; Spanish NHS; Library Aide; Spanish Clb; U Pittsburgh; Nrsng.

MARTIN, GRACE; Carlisle HS; Carlisle, PA; (3); Debate Tm; Speech Tm; Ed Lit Mag; Hon Roll; NHS; Schlrshp Wake Frst Smr Debate Wrkshp 85; Pltcs.

MARTIN, GREG; Cocalico HS; Steven, PA; (3); Bsbl; Bsktbl; Prfct Atten Awd; Stu Mnth 87; Ath Wk Ephrata Review 87; Phys Ed.

MARTIN, GREG; Upp Dublin HS; Dresher, PA; (4); 5/316; Church Yth Grp; Math Tm; Ski Clb; Im Bsktbl; JV Golf; Im Vllybl; NHS; Im Ice Hcky; Im Wt Lftg; Schlrshp To Wall Street Smnr 86; Harold S Maynard Meml Schlrshp-PTA 87; Pres Acad Ftnss Awd 87; Purdue U; Elec Engrng.

MARTIN, JAMES; Garden Spot HS; E Earl, PA; (2); Church Yth Grp; Chorus; Rep Soph Cls; JV Bsbl; Bus.

MARTIN, JAMES; Pine Grove Area HS; Pine Grove, PA; (2); Church Yth Grp; Wrstlng; Const Wrk.

MARTIN, JILL; West Perry HS; Loysville, PA; (4); 4/182; French Clb; Chorus; Church Choir; Lit Mag; Hon Roll; NHS; Messiah Coll; Hist.

MARTIN, JODI; Waynesboro Area SR HS; Waynesboro, PA; (4); Sec Pres Church Yth Grp; Chorus; Yrbk Phtg; Yrbk Stf; Rep Frsh Cls; High Hon Roll; Hon Roll; NHS; Intl Forgn Lang Awd 85-86; Acctng.

MARTIN, JONATHAN; William Allen HS; Allentown, PA; (3); 38/659; Church Yth Grp; Exploring; German Clb; Intnl Clb; Church Choir; Hon Roll; Jr NHS; NHS; Ntl Merit Ltr; Bio.

MARTIN, JOSEPHINE; Little Flower Catholic HS For Girls; Philadelphia, PA; (3); 170/326; Church Yth Grp; Chorus; Church Choir; School Musical; School Play; Cert Awd Vocal Music 87; Katharine Gibbs; Lgl Secy.

MARTIN, JULIE; Meadville Area SR HS; Meadville, PA; (4); 35/270; Art Clb; Church Yth Grp; Hosp Aide; SADD; Orch; Yrbk Stf; Hon Roll; Meadville Schltc Hnr Soc 87; Pres Fit SR Merit 86; Painting Leg Art Exhibit 87; Gannon U; Elem Ed.

MARTIN, KATHLEEN; St Hubert HS For Girls; Philadelphia, PA; (3); 4/421; French Clb; Hosp Aide; Math Clb; Nwsp Stf; Lit Mag; Swmmng; High Hon Roll; Jr NHS; NHS; Prfct Atten Awd; All Cathlc Swmmr 86-87; Amer Chem Soc Awd Chem 87; Swm Tm Rcrds 85-87; Nrsng.

MARTIN, KIMBERLY; Neshaminy HS; Langhorne, PA; (3); 82/824; Church Yth Grp; SADD; Chorus; Church Choir; School Musical; Sec Sr Cls; Stu Cncl; Fld Hcky; Mgr(s); Score Keeper; Elem Educ.

MARTIN, LARRY; Garden Spot HS; New Holland, PA; (2); Aud/Vis; JV Church Yth Grp; Drama Clb; Chorus; Church Choir; School Play; Stage Crew; Rep Frsh Cls; Rep Soph Cls; Bus Exec.

MARTIN, LISA; Blue Mt Acad; Natick, MA; (2); Off Frsh Cls; Gym; High Hon Roll; Hon Roll; Outdr Clb, Theta Kappa Gamma Clb 86-87; Atlantic Union Coll.

MARTIN, LISA; St Hubert HS; Philadelphia, PA; (2); 115/368; Cmnty Wkr; Penn ST; Engr.

MARTIN, LORI J; Ephrata SR HS; Ephrata, PA; (4); 39/257; Rep Soph Cls; Rep Jr Cls; Rep Sr Cls; Var Bsktbl; Im Fld Hcky; Var Sftbl; Hon Roll; Ephrata Area Ed Assn 87; 4 Harry Hibshmn Schlrshp 87; Sftbl All Str Hnbl Mntn 87; IN U Of PA; Erly Chldhd Ed.

MARTIN, MELANIE; Engineering And Science HS; Philadelphia, PA; (3); 58/190; Church Yth Grp; Cmnty Wkr; Office Aide; SADD; Church Choir; Rep Frsh Cls; Rep Soph Cls; Var Bsktbl; Im Tennis; Hon Roll; Philadelphia Zoo Smmr Stud 85; Hahnemann U Mnrty Rsrch Pgm 87; U Of PA Acad Achvt Pgm 86-87; Bio.

MARTIN, MELINDA; Dallstown Area HS; York, PA; (4); 112/353; Church Yth Grp; Church Choir; Orch; Im Bsktbl; Im Fld Hcky; Im Sftbl; Im Vllybl; Hon Roll; NHS; Music Awd 87; York Coll; Special Ed.

MARTIN, MELISSA A; Pamlyra HS; Palmyra, PA; (4); 27/187; Art Clb; French Clb; Stat Swmmng; Var Capt Tennis; Hon Roll; Rotary Awd; VFW Awd; Francis Larkin Mc Common & Herman H Eisenhauer Family Schlrshp & Franklin & Marshall Bk Prz 87; Savannah Coll Of Art & Dsgn.

MARTIN, MICHAEL; Governor Mifflin SR HS; Mohnton, PA; (3); 58/328; Boy Scts; Church Yth Grp; Sec Exploring; Stage Crew; Nwsp Ed-Chief; Hon Roll; Prfct Atten Awd; Natl Sci Olympd Physcs Awd 86-87; Chem Eng.

MARTIN, MICHELE; Quigley HS; Sewickley, PA; (3); 24/79; Aud/Vis; Math Tm; Service Clb; Nwsp Stf; Yrbk Ed-Chief; Rep Stu Cncl; Var Coach Actv; Var Mgr(s); L Stat Trk; Hon Roll; Extra Effrt Awd, Svc Awd Mnstry Tm 86-87; Outstndng Yrbk Stff 87; Duquesne; Psych.

ARTIN, MICHELLE; Greencastle-Antrim HS; Greencastle, PA; (3); rbk Stf; Var JV Cheerleading; Lawyer.

ARTIN, MICHELLE; West Scranton HS; Scranton, PA; (3); 14/262; panish Clb; Orch; Sec Sr Cls; Var Cheerleading; Var Tennis; Hon Roll; HS; Compu Sci.

ARTIN, MICHIKO; Red Land HS; New Cumberland, PA; (4); 1/286; ebate Tm; Red Cross Aide; Yrbk Ed-Chief; Pres Stu Cncl; Vllybl; NHS; al; Church Yth Grp; Cmnty Wkr; Spanish Clb; Natl Hnr Soc Schlrshp 87; icknsn Coll, PA Smmr Schlrshp 86; Appt US Militry Acad 87; US Naval cad; Poltcl Sci.

ARTIN, MIKE; Mt Pleasant Area SR HS; Mt Pleasant, PA; (4); 7/246; ki Clb; Spanish Clb; Bsbl; Bsktbl; Bausch & Lomb Sci Awd; High Hon oll; NHS; Spanish NHS; Stu Of The Wk 86; PA JR Acad Of Sci 85; Chem ngr.

ARTIN, QUINTO; Greensburg Salem SR HS; Greensburg, PA; (3); Art b; Exploring; Pep Clb; Ski Clb; Spanish Clb; Ed Nwsp Stf; Lit Mag; Rep rsh Cls; Bsbl; Ftbl; 4th Pl Art Shw Wstmrlnd CC 87; Seton Hll Coll Art hw 86; Endinboro ST Coll Art Shw 86; Ltr Ftbl 84; Parsons Schl Of esign; Grphc.

ARTIN, ROBERT; Northeast Catholic HS; Philadelphia, PA; (2); 122/ 53; Boys Clb Am; Accntng.

ARTIN, ROBERT; St John Neumann HS; Philadelphia, PA; (3); 106/ 49; Yrbk Phtg; Im Bsktbl; VP L Tennis; FL ST; Phot.

ARTIN, ROBERT; Sun Valley HS; Aston, PA; (3); 71/285; ROTC; olor Guard; Drill Tm; JV Bsktbl; JV Socr; Cit Awd; Hon Roll; SAR Awd; FW Awd; Hghst JROTC Cadet Cmmndr Lt Col 87; Penn ST U; Bus.

ARTIN, ROBIN; Octorara Area HS; Parkesburg, PA; (3); 9/157; Trs horus; Church Choir; School Musical; School Play; Stage Crew; Tennis; rk; High Hon Roll; Hon Roll; Music.

ARTIN, RONALD; Downingtown SR HS; West Chester, PA; (4); 112/ 55; Boy Scts; 4-H; Spanish Clb; 4-H Awd; God Cntry Awd; Hon Roll; agle Scout BSA 87; Biochmstry.

ARTIN, SCOTT; South Fayette JR SR HS; Bridgeville, PA; (3); 1/94; rt Clb; Aud/Vis; Computer Clb; Drama Clb; Ski Clb; Variety Show; High on Roll; Jr NHS; NHS; Pres Schlr.

ARTIN, SHERRI; Charleroi Area HS; Stockdale, PA; (4); 20/162; VP rench Clb; Science Clb; SADD; Varsity Clb; Yrbk Ed-Chief; Rep Sr Cls; ep Stu Cncl; Var Capt Cheerleading; NHS; Pres Schlr; Robert C Byrd onors Schlrshp 87; Charthene Club Girl Mnth 87; PA ST U; Engr.

ARTIN, SHERRY L; Warwick HS; Lititz, PA; (4); FBLA; Office Aide; and; Concert Band; Mrchg Band; Nwsp Stf; JV Tennis; Hon Roll; Goldey eacon Coll; Admn.

ARTIN, STEPHEN; Riverview HS; Oakmont, PA; (4); 3/120; VP AFS; rama Clb; Ski Clb; Jazz Band; School Play; Ed Yrbk Phtg; Var Crs ntry; Var Trk; NHS; Natl Merit Finalist 87; Williams Coll.

ARTIN, TAMMY L; Garden Spot HS; New Holland, PA; (4); Church th Grp; Drama Clb; Sec FFA; Spanish Clb; Stage Crew; PA Kystn Frmr gree 87; Grsslnd Chapt Frmr Dgree 85; 1st Plc Lncstr Co FFA Pblc Spkg ntst 84; Agri.

ARTIN, TERESA; Bethlehem Catholic HS; Bethlehem, PA; (3); hurch Yth Grp; Key Clb; Science Clb; Stage Crew; High Hon Roll; Hon oll; Penn ST; Engrng.

ARTIN, TINA MARIE; Bradford Area HS; Bradford, PA; (3); Am Leg ux Girls St; Drama Clb; Ski Clb; VP Frsh Cls; Pres Soph Cls; Pres Jr Cls; res Stu Cncl; Cheerleading; L Trk; French Clb; Outstndng Soc Stds Stu 4-85; Mansfield Ready Wrtrs Cntst 86-87; Pltcl Sci.

ARTIN, TODD; Wilmington Area HS; Volant, PA; (4); 13/112; Church th Grp; Drama Clb; Band; Concert Band; Mrchg Band; Pep Band; Mgr tage Crew; L Var Golf; JP Sousa Awd; NHS; Pres Acdmc Ftnss Awd 6-87; PA ST U; Engrng.

ARTIN, TRACY; Meadville Area SR HS; Meadville, PA; (3); 62/375; rench Clb; Pep Clb; Science Clb; Varsity Clb; School Play; Stage Crew; ep Stu Cncl; Swmmng; Trk; Hon Roll; AF Acad; Flight.

ARTIN, VALERIE; Sharon SR HS; Sharon, PA; (3); 30/180; French lb; Band; Concert Band; Mrchg Band; JV Var Bsktbl; Var Crs Cntry; on Roll; Med.

ARTIN, WENDY; Cocalico HS; Stevens, PA; (3); 30/163; Church Yth rp; 4-H; Yrbk Stf; Hon Roll; Bank.

ARTIN, WENDY; Juniata HS; Thompsontown, PA; (3); Church Yth rp; 4-H; FHA; SADD; Varsity Clb; Var Cheerleading; JV Sftbl; 4-H Awd; HS.

ARTINAK, LORI; Belle Vernon Area HS; Fayette, PA; (4); Ski Clb; and; Drm Mjr(t); Yrbk Stf; Stu Cncl; Powder Puff Ftbl; Sftbl; NHS; ashngtn & Jefferson Coll; Chem.

ARTINAK, MICHAEL; Belle Vernon Area HS; Fayette City, PA; (3); ki Clb; Stu Cncl; Ftbl; Wt Lftg; Wrstlng; Cit Awd; Hon Roll; Nclr Med.

ARTINAK, TRINA LOUISE; Frazier HS; Perryopolis, PA; (2); 1/116; ance Clb; Red Cross Aide; Yrbk Stf; Hon Roll; Church Yth Grp; Drama lb; 4-H; Ski Clb; School Play; Stage Crew; JR Miss Estrn Swthrt Tlnt nnr 1st Pl 86; Connellsvl Scuba Clb 84-87; Stu Dnc Indstrctr 87; Penn T U; Pilot.

ARTINAZZI, MARIA; Bishop Carroll HS; Nanty Glo, PA; (3); Church th Grp; Cmnty Wkr; Ski Clb; Spanish Clb; SADD; Rep Stu Cncl; Trk; on Roll; Psychlgy.

ARTINEK, GREGORY; Portage Area HS; Portage, PA; (3); 11/110; hurch Yth Grp; French Clb; JV Bsktbl; Hon Roll; NHS; U Of Pittsburgh; led.

ARTINEZ, ELIZABETH; Bethlehem Catholic HS; Miami, FL; (3); 14/ 00; Boulder CO; Spcl Educ.

ARTINEZ, LISA; Olney HS; Philadelphia, PA; (4); 2/701; CAP; French lb; Math Tm; Var Bsktbl; Var Fld Hcky; Var Capt Sftbl; Cit Awd; High on Roll; Pres NHS; Prfct Atten Awd; French Honor Scty 83-87; Temple ; Comm.

ARTINI JR, CHARLES C; Monsignour Bonneir HS; Havertown, PA;); 9/303; Church Yth Grp; Cmnty Wkr; Quiz Bowl; Nwsp Rptr; Yrbk d-Chief; High Hon Roll; NHS; Villanova U; Bus Field.

ARTINI, CHRIS; Emmaus HS; Wescosville, PA; (4); 92/473; Model N; Political Wkr; Band; Mrchg Band; Pres Frsh Cls; JV Var Bsktbl; JV apt Ftbl; Hon Roll; Lehigh U; Bus.

ARTINI, KRISTA; Homer Center HS; Homer City, PA; (3); Teachers ide; Drill Tm; Yrbk Stf; Trs Frsh Cls; Hst Sr Cls; Stu Cncl; Var JV heerleading; Hon Roll; Jr NHS; Supts Advsry Cncl 86-87; Jrnlsm.

ARTINI, RENA MICHELLE; Homer Center HS; Homer City, PA; (4); /92; Church Yth Grp; Varsity Clb; Drill Tm; School Musical; Yrbk d-Chief; Hst Sr Cls; Vllybl; High Hon Roll; Jr NHS; NHS; Sons Of Itly 70 Schlrshp 87; SR Of Mnth 87; Presdntl Acadmc Ftns Awd 87; Penn ST ; Advrtsng.

MARTINI, WASILYNN; West Hazleton HS; Hazleton, PA; (3); 8/235; High Hon Roll; Hon Roll; Presdntl Acadc Ftns Awd 85; Temple U; Psych.

MARTINIE, JOHN; Devon Prep Schl; Exton, PA; (4); 5/47; Nwsp Rptr; Rep Frsh Cls; Sec Stu Cncl; Var Capt Bsktbl; Im Ftbl; Var Capt Socr; Var Trk; High Hon Roll; Hon Roll; NEDT Awd; Devon Prep Book Awd Math 84-86; All Bcntnl Lg Sccr Tm 86; Duke; Blgy.

MARTINIS, TRACY; South Allegheny JR SR HS; Port Vue, PA; (4); 65/ 177; Spanish Clb; Yrbk Stf; Var L Bsbl; Hon Roll; Office Aide; Y-Teens; Powder Puff Ftbl; Trk; Sons Itly Glssprt Schlrshp 87; Hmcmng Ct, Chrstms Ct, & Prom Ct 86-87; CC Allegheny Cnty; Stwrdss.

MARTINO, DINO; Center Area HS; Aliquippa, PA; (3); Am Leg Boys St; Pres Camera Clb; Chess Clb; German Clb; Letterman Clb; Library Aide; Varsity Clb; School Play; Stage Crew; Variety Show; 3 Yr 4.0 Avg German Stud 87; US Marines Cert Of Apprctn 85; Certfd Lab Tech For 1 Hr Photo 87; Comp Engrng.

MARTINO, LISA; Faith Christian HS; Turtle Crk, PA; (2); Band; High Hon Roll; Hon Roll; Bus Mgmt.

MARTINSEN, DANA; Bensalem HS; Bensalem, PA; (4); 86/500; Teachers Aide; Band; Concert Band; Mrchg Band; Pep Band; Var Stat Diving; Var Stat Swmmng; Hon Roll; Cnty Orch 85; R C Struble Schlrshp 87; W Chester U; Ed Mth.

MARTINSON, GEORGE; Henderson HS; West Chester, PA; (3); 120/ 370; Boy Scts; JCL; Ski Clb; Pres Frsh Cls; Rep Stu Cncl; Var Socr; JV Tennis.

MARTOCCI, LISA; Pleasant Valley HS; Brodheadsville, PA; (2); Drama Clb; Ski Clb; SADD; Teachers Aide; Mrchg Band; Rep Stu Cncl; Twrlr; High Hon Roll; Hon Roll; Elem Tchng.

MARTOCCI, ROBERT; Archbishop Carroll HS; Bala Cynwyd, PA; (4); 11/367; Cmnty Wkr; Dance Clb; Quiz Bowl; School Musical; NHS; Drama Clb; Pres Acad Fit Awd 87; Cert Merit 87; Math Awds; George Mason U; Comp Sci.

MARTON, REBECA; Gateway SR HS; Monroeville, PA; (3); Aud/Vis; FBLA; JA; Office Aide; Pep Clb; Ski Clb; Yrbk Stf; Hon Roll; Intl Stds.

MARTORANA, CHARLES R; William Penn SR HS; York, PA; (3); 33/ 498; Church Yth Grp; SADD; Band; Jazz Band; Mrchg Band; Orch; School Musical; Symp Band; Hon Roll; VP NHS; Arspc Enrgnr.

MARTOS, JUSTIN; Allen HS; Allentown, PA; (3); 15/651; Boy Scts; Capt Debate Tm; Key Clb; Latin Clb; Ski Clb; Rep Stu Cncl; Var L Socr; Hon Roll; Jr NHS; Trs NHS; Pre Med.

MARTUCCIO, MICHELLE; Hickory HS; Hermitage, PA; (3); Art Clb; Varsity Clb; Yrbk Stf; Pres Soph Cls; Pres Jr Cls; Stat Bsktbl; JV Cheerleading; Var L Gym; Sftbl; Im Vllybl; HOBV Ambass 85-86; Cert Of Merit For Achvmnt In Sci & Engineering 87; Penn ST; Engineering.

MARTYAK, MONICA; Bishop Hafey HS; Hazleton, PA; (1); Aud/Vis; Latin Clb; Service Clb; Y-Teens; Chorus; JR Acad Sci 1st Awd Regnl 87.

MARTZ, BOB; Mt Pleasant Area SR HS; Mt Pleasant, PA; (4); Boy Scts; Church Yth Grp; Var Mgr(s); Var Wt Lftg; Var Wrstlng; High Hon Roll; Hon Roll; Prfct Atten Awd; Schlrshp Joseph E Silvis 87; CA U Of PA; Psych.

MARTZ, CHRISTINE; Cocalico HS; Denver, PA; (3); Art Clb; Camera Clb; Church Yth Grp; Rep Stu Cncl; JV Var Bsktbl; JV Var Fld Hcky; Var L Sftbl; Hon Roll; Art.

MARTZ, JIM; Jeanette SR HS; Jeannette, PA; (3); Band; Concert Band; Jazz Band; Mrchg Band; Symp Band; Hon Roll; Electrncs.

MARTZ JR, PHILIP; Berlin Brothersvalley HS; Berlin, PA; (3); FFA; Spanish Clb; SADD; Band; Concert Band; Jazz Band; School Play; Hon Roll; NHS; Ag.

MARTZALL, TANA; Lancaster Mennonite HS; Narvon, PA; (3); 37/155; Sec Church Yth Grp; Spanish Clb; Chorus; Hon Roll; Elem Ed.

MARTZEN, MELISSA; Marion Catholic HS; Mc Adoo, PA; (3); 13/104; Service Clb; Acpl Chr; Drill Tm; Yrbk Stf; French Hon Soc; High Hon Roll; NHS.

MARUCA, KRISTEN; Laurel Highlands HS; Uniontown, PA; (2); Nwsp Rptr; Nwsp Stf; Yrbk Rptr; Yrbk Stf; VP Soph Cls; High Hon Roll; Bus.

MARUCA, MELISSA; Bishop Caroll HS; Ashville, PA; (3); 3/128; Church Yth Grp; Pep Clb; Ski Clb; Sec Soph Cls; Sec Jr Cls; Cheerleading; High Hon Roll; Hon Roll; NHS; IUP; Nrsng.

MARUSKIN, LYNN; Ringgold HS; Monongahela, PA; (4); Sec Church Yth Grp; Civic Clb; Hosp Aide; JA; Ski Clb; Concert Band; Sec Mrchg Band; Hon Roll; Sec NHS; Carroll Twnshp Fire Dept Schlrshp 87; Clarion U; Elem Ed.

MARVENKO, KEN; Littlestown SR HS; Gettysburg, PA; (3); Letterman Clb; Varsity Clb; Chorus; Stage Crew; Swing Chorus; JV Bsktbl; Var L Tennis; Hon Roll; Natl Sci Olympiad Dist Hnrs 87; Advrstng.

MARVIN, DEANA; Uniontown Area SR HS; Waltersburg, PA; (3); VP JA; Spanish Clb; Band; Concert Band; Flag Corp; Mrchg Band; Nwsp Rptr; Yrbk Stf; Mgr Swmmng; Hon Roll; JA Grp Hghst Sellg Awd 87; CA U PA; Jrnlsm.

MARVIN, WILLIAM; The Episcopal Acad; Wynnewood, PA; (4); Cmnty Wkr; FCA; Letterman Clb; Pep Clb; Varsity Clb; Jazz Band; Pep Band; Var Golf; Var L Socr; SAR Awd.

MARZZACCO, ANTHONY; South Williamsport HS; S Williamsport, PA; (4); VP Soph Cls; VP Jr Cls; Pres Sr Cls; Stu Cncl; Capt Bsktbl; Trk; Hon Roll; NHS; Yrbk Rptr; Yrbk Stf; Exchng Clb Yth Yr Awd, & Am Lgn Awd 87; Lock Haven U; Socl Sci.

MASALONIS, ANTHONY J; Wyoming Valley West HS; Kingston, PA; (4); 101/397; Key Clb; Radio Clb; Var Trk; Hon Roll; Ntl Merit SF; Language Awd; Lib Arts.

MASCHAK, JEANNINE; United HS; Seward, PA; (3); Drama Clb; French Clb; SADD; Band; Chorus; Concert Band; Mrchg Band; School Musical; School Play; Powder Puff Ftbl; Med.

MASCHERINO, JOSEPH A; Coatesville Area SR HS; Coatesville, PA; (3); 43/517; Church Yth Grp; French Clb; Leo Clb; Ski Clb; Concert Band; Jazz Band; Mrchg Band; Pep Band; NHS; Presdntl Acadc Ftns Awd 86.

MASCI, VALERIE; St Maria Goretti HS; Philadelphia, PA; (4); 150/385; Hosp Aide; Library Aide; Office Aide; Cit Awd; Hon Roll; White Williams Schlrshps Fndtn 84-87; Temple U; Nrs.

MASCIANTONIO, GINA; Jeanette SR HS; Jeannette, PA; (3); 52/130; Ski Clb; Band; Color Guard; Concert Band; Mrchg Band; Hon Roll; Bus Adm.

MASCIARELLI, TAMMY; Waynesburg Central HS; Spraggs, PA; (4); French Clb; VICA; Yrbk Stf; High Hon Roll; Nrsng.

MASCILLI, BRIAN; Valley HS; Arnold, PA; (3); Key Clb; Spanish Clb; Ftbl; CA U.

MASCILLI, SCOTT; Valley HS; Arnold, PA; (4); 84/245; Chess Clb; Drama Clb; Pres FBLA; VP JA; Key Clb; Spanish Clb; Band; Mgr Mrchg Band; Bsktbl; Hon Roll; Mr Future Bus Ldr Of Amer Dist Wnnr 86-87; IN U Of PA; Acctg.

MASCIOLI, DANA; Wyoming Valley West HS; Swoyersville, PA; (4); Cmnty Wkr; Girl Scts; Key Clb; Library Aide; Ski Clb; Chorus; School Musical; School Play; Lit Mag; Hon Roll; Susquehanna U; Bus Adm.

MASCIOLI, JENIFER; Notre Dame Acad; West Chester, PA; (3); Art Clb; Church Yth Grp; Cmnty Wkr; Hosp Aide; Intnl Clb; Model UN; Pep Clb; Yrbk Stf; Lit Mag; Cheerleading; Our Mother Good Cnsl Awd; Ntl Spnsh Cntst; Cert Apprctn Coop Soc Svc; Nrsng.

MASCOLA, JENNIFER; Lansdale Catholic HS; Hatfield, PA; (3); #32 In Class; Cmnty Wkr; Drama Clb; SADD; Chorus; School Musical; Stage Crew; Hon Roll; Excllnc Stdy Of Amrcn Cltrs 86-87; Psychlgy.

MASCUILLI, MONICA; Coatesville Area SR HS; Coatesville, PA; (3); 147/517; Leo Clb; Ski Clb; Spanish Clb; Color Guard; Flag Corp; Mrchg Band; Off Jr Cls; Cheerleading; Sftbl; Hon Roll; Dntl Asst.

MASELLA, LISA; Geibel HS; Uniontown, PA; (3); Church Yth Grp; JV Capt Cheerleading; High Hon Roll; NHS; NEDT Awd; Prfct Atten Awd; Spanish NHS; Pres Phys Fit Awd 86.

MASH, VALERIE; Jeannette SR HS; Jeannette, PA; (3); #5 In Class; French Clb; Ski Clb; Color Guard; Jazz Band; Mrchg Band; Stu Cncl; High Hon Roll; JC Awd; NHS; Concert Band; Seton Hill Coll Ldrshp Schlrshp 86; Point Park Coll; Fshn Mrchndsng.

MASHACK, JANET; Nativity B V M; St Clair, PA; (2); 11/94; Drama Clb; Variety Show; Twrlr; God Cntry Awd; Hon Roll.

MASIEJCZYK, EDMUND; Father Judge HS; Philadelphia, PA; (3); 36/ 402; Boys Clb Am; Boy Scts; Church Yth Grp; Exploring; Office Aide; Cit Awd; High Hon Roll; Hon Roll; Prosthetists.

MASISAK, LISA; Elk County Christian HS; Ridgway, PA; (3); 6/72; SADD; Sec Stu Cncl; Bowling; Cheerleading; Hon Roll; Intl Bus.

MASKAS, JULIE; Highlands SR HS; Natrona Hts, PA; (3); DECA; FNA; Teachers Aide; Chorus; Color Guard; Flag Corp; Mrchg Band; Rep Stu Cncl; Var Trk; Schlstc Achvt Awd 84-87; Pres Phys Fit Awd 86; Bus.

MASKREY, KRIS; Plum SR HS; Pittsburgh, PA; (4); Art Clb; Dance Clb; School Musical; School Play; Stage Crew; Ed Nwsp Bus Mgr; Lit Mag; Sftbl; Trk; CC Awd; US Archery Tm, YMCA Outstndng Schlr Athl Frm All-Sprts Bnqt 87; AZ ST U.

MASLOWSKI, JO ANN; Wyoming Valley West HS; Kingston, PA; (2); Aud/Vis; Hosp Aide; Chorus; High Hon Roll; Hon Roll; NHS; Anthrct Brnch 288 Cert Recog 85-86; Frgn Lang Cert Achvt 86-87; Excllnt Atten Awd 85-86; Penn ST U; Psych.

MASLYK, LOUIE; New Castle SR HS; New Castle, PA; (3); Band; Concert Band; Jazz Band; Mrchg Band; Pep Band; Clarion; Hstry.

MASNERI, DAVID; California HS; California, PA; (3); Church Yth Grp; Drama Clb; Pep Clb; School Musical; School Play; Var Bsktbl; Var Ftbl.

MASON, ANNMARIE; Little Flower Catholic HS; Philadelphia, PA; (3); 40/350; Office Aide; Teachers Aide; Nwsp Rptr; Nwsp Stf; Yrbk Rptr; Yrbk Stf; Lit Mag; Rep Frsh Cls; Rep Soph Cls; Stu Cncl; Certs Tutoring 85-87; La Salle U; Jrnlsm.

MASON, DAVID A; Muncy HS; Muncy, PA; (3); French Clb; Hon Roll; NHS; Ntl Merit SF.

MASON, JAMIE; Wallenpaupack HS; White Mills, PA; (3); 19/154; Cmnty Wkr; 4-H; Science Clb; Church Choir; Yrbk Stf; High Hon Roll; NHS; Vet.

MASON, KELLI; Schenley HS; Pittsburgh, PA; (4); School Play; Mgr Stage Crew; Pres Sr Cls; Sec Stu Cncl; Swmmng; DAR Awd; High Hon Roll; Pres NHS; Prfct Atten Awd.

MASON, KIMBERLY; Hopewell HS; Aliquippa, PA; (3); 82/265; German Clb; Chorus; School Play; L Var Bsktbl; Capt Var Trk; Elks Awd; High Hon Roll; Hon Roll; Masonic Awd; CC Allegehny Cnty; Culnary.

MASON, LYNNE; Moon SR HS; Coraopolis, PA; (3); Church Yth Grp; Hosp Aide; Office Aide; Teachers Aide; Hon Roll; Indiana U Of PA; Tchr.

MASON, NICOLE; Cecilian Acad; Philadelphia, PA; (2); Church Yth Grp; Drama Clb; Service Clb; Chorus; Church Choir; Nwsp Rptr; Rep Frsh Cls; Rep Soph Cls; Rep Stu Cncl; Hon Roll; Cecilian Acad Schlrshp 85; Natl Sci Olympd 86; Cum Laude Natl Lat Exam 87; Med.

MASON, PAMELA; Cardinal O Hara HS; Glenolden, PA; (4); Service Clb; SADD; Yrbk Stf; French Hon Soc; Hon Roll; NCTE Awd; NHS; Dance Clb; 1st Pl Cathlc Dghtrs Amer Essy Cntst 87; Cert Merit Natl Frnch Cntst 86; Pres Acdmc Fit Awd 87; Mktg.

MASON JR, PERRY G; Purchase Line HS; Commodore, PA; (4); French Clb; Letterman Clb; Pep Clb; Varsity Clb; Chorus; Stage Crew; Bsktbl; Ftbl; Trk; Hon Roll; Acad All Amer NSE Cncl Dir 87; Purchase Lines Dragon Awd Outstndng Ath Achvt 87; Military.

MASOTTI, CHRISTOPHER; Hickory HS; Hermitage, PA; (4); 6/180; Cmnty Wkr; Latin Clb; Pres Letterman Clb; Spanish Clb; Pres Varsity Clb; Acpl Chr; Band; Chorus; Concert Band; Mrchg Band; Accntnt.

MASSA, BRENDA LEE; Hazleton SR HS; Hazleton, PA; (3); Drama Clb; FBLA; German Clb; Pep Clb; Band; Chorus; Concert Band; Mrchg Band; Pep Band; High Hon Roll.

MASSARI, JOHN; Kiski Area HS; Vandergrift, PA; (3); JV Sftbl; High Hon Roll; Hon Roll; Penn ST.

MASSARI, LOUIS; Ringgold HS; Finleyville, PA; (4); Stu Cncl; Var Bsktbl; Var Ftbl; Var Trk; Im Vllybl; Engrng.

MASSARO, CYNTHIA; Abington SR HS; Abington, PA; (4); Church Yth Grp; French Clb; Hosp Aide; Sec Latin Clb; Library Aide; Chorus; Church Choir; Yrbk Stf; JV Cheerleading; Natl JR Clsscl Leag Maxima Cum Laude Natl Ltn Exam 86; Hlth Careers Clb Sec & Pres 85-87; Temple U; Occuptnl Ther.

MASSARO, MARGERET; Bishop Conwell HS; Yardley, PA; (3); 27/277; Church Yth Grp; Science Clb; SADD; Teachers Aide; Capt Tennis; High Hon Roll; Hon Roll; NHS; 1st Prz PA Free Entrprse 86; Hghst Avg Socl Stds 86; Cert Spnsh 86; U Of Pittsburgh; Dntstry.

MASSELLI, CARMELLA; Philadelphia HS For Girls; Philadelphia, PA; (3); 53/490; Church Yth Grp; Cmnty Wkr; Latin Clb; Library Aide; Office Aide; Teachers Aide; Rep Frsh Cls; Rep Soph Cls; Rep Jr Cls; Hon Roll; 1st Pl Schl Cnty Fair 86; La Salle U; Bus Admin.

MASSENBURG, LISA; W Catholic Girls HS; Philadelphia, PA; (3); 134/ 250; Art Clb; Girl Scts; Latin Clb; Office Aide; Science Clb; Spanish Clb; Nwsp Stf; JV Bsktbl; Im Tennis; Im Vllybl; U Of PA; Pre Med.

MASSENGILL, CORRELL; Churchill HS; Braddock, PA; (2); 45/220; Hosp Aide; Spanish Clb; Bsbl; Bsktbl; Law.

MASSENGILL, DANIEL; Burgettstown Area JR-SR HS; Slovan, PA; (3); Science Clb; Spanish Clb; JV L Bsktbl; JV Var Ftbl; Hon Roll; Bus Mgmt.

MASSENGILL, DENNIS; Burgettstown Area JR-SR HS; Slovan, PA; (3); Science Clb; Spanish Clb; JV L Bsktbl; JV L Ftbl; Hon Roll; Bus Mgmt.

MASSENGILL, PAULA; Burgettstown Area JR SR HS; Langeloth, PA; (3); Library Aide; Spanish Clb; High Hon Roll; Hon Roll; NHS; Libry Club 84-85; Child Psych.

MASSEY, CYNTHIA; Greater Latrobe SR HS; Greensburg, PA; (4); 9/406; Am Leg Aux Girls St; Church Yth Grp; FCA; Letterman Clb; Pep Clb; Ski Clb; Cheerleading; High Hon Roll; NHS; Pres Schlr; Acdmc All Amer 87; PA ST U; Bus Admin.

MASSEY, ELIZABETH; Villa Maria HS; New Castle, PA; (4); 11/60; French Clb; Thesps; Chorus; Madrigals; School Musical; Rep Sr Cls; French Hon Soc; NHS; NEDT Awd; Pres Schlr; Dist & Regl Chorus & Solo 86-87; Outstndng Chorl Awd 87; Outstndng Thespn Awd 87; Bard Coll.

MASSEY, MARC; Daniel Boone HS; Douglassville, PA; (2); 7/166; Chess Clb; German Clb; Band; Concert Band; Mrchg Band; JV Bsktbl; Hon Roll; Med.

MASSEY, MELISSA; Belle Vernon Area HS; Belle Vernon, PA; (3); Church Yth Grp; Drama Clb; Pep Clb; High Hon Roll.

MASSEY, SONIA; West Phila Catholic Girls HS; Philadelphia, PA; (3); Latin Clb; Library Aide; School Musical; School Play; Nwsp Rptr; Hon Roll; Cmmtte Wrtr Anl W Cthlc Day Shw 86-87; Flg Bearer Grad Cls 86-87; Shalom 84-85; Cornell; Htl Mgmt.

MASSICCI, JULIA; Canevin HS; Pittsburgh, PA; (3); 37/185; FBLA; Chorus; Drill Tm; School Musical; Yrbk Stf; Rep Frsh Cls; Rep Sr Cls; Hon Roll; Buhl Sci Ctr-H J Heinz Co Awd 86; Pittsburgh; Theater Arts.

MASSIE, MARY; Peabody HS; Pittsburgh, PA; (4); 8/292; Pres Soph Cls; Pres Jr Cls; Pres Stu Cncl; Capt Bsktbl; Capt Vllybl; High Hon Roll; Jr NHS; Pres NHS; Prfct Atten Awd; All-Amrcn Schlr Awd 85-86; PA ST U; Bio-Chem.

MASSIMINI, LYNNA; Woodland Hills HS; Rankin, PA; (2); 42/193; Art Clb; Lit Mag; Hon Roll; Art.

MASSING, CINDY; Mc Dowell Intermediate HS; Erie, PA; (2); 20/629; Exploring; German Clb; Chorus; JV Capt Socr; Trk; High Hon Roll; Med.

MASSING, KEITH; Commodore Perry HS; Greenville, PA; (4); 2/63; Church Yth Grp; Math Tm; Stage Crew; Nwsp Sprt Ed; Yrbk Phtg; Crs Cntry; Hon Roll; NHS; Voice Dem Awd; Ambssdr Awd Crss Cntry 85; Panthr Mnth 85; Hnr Rll 6 Tms 86; Behrend.

MASSON, TRACY ANN; New Castle SR HS; New Castle, PA; (4); 2/235; Church Yth Grp; Computer Clb; Scholastic Bowl; Rep Band; Stu Cncl; High Hon Roll; NHS; Cmnty Wkr; Math Tm; Schlstc Achvmnt 86; Ntl Acadmc Games 3rd Pl Lang Arts 85; Chem Engr.

MASSOUD, CHRISTINE; Hopewell SR HS; Aliquippa, PA; (2); Church Yth Grp; French Clb; Pep Clb; Color Guard; Drill Tm; Flag Corp; Mrchg Band; Hon Roll; Beaver Cnty Bar Assn Explrs Post 86-87; Crmnl Law.

MAST, BRIAN; Tunkhannock Area HS; Tunkhannock, PA; (4); 9/310; Church Yth Grp; FCA; Letterman Clb; Ski Clb; Var Ftbl; Var Trk; Wt Lftg; High Hon Roll; NHS; Pre-Med.

MAST, BRITTA; Reading SR HS; Reading, PA; (3); 1/740; Trs Church Yth Grp; Pres JA; Scholastic Bowl; Chorus; School Musical; Rep Stu Cncl; Diving; Gym; Hon Roll; NHS; U Of DE; Mrn Sci.

MASTANTUONO, MICHELE; Cardinal O Hara HS; Springfield, PA; (3); 137/710; Cmnty Wkr; SADD; Art.

MASTELLER, CHERYL; Bald Eagle Area HS; Bellefonte, PA; (4); Valley Forge Christian Coll.

MASTELLER, TRACIE L; Brandywine Heights HS; Fleetwood, PA; (3); 40/117; 4-H; Nwsp Rptr; Nwsp Stf; Var L Sftbl; Twrlr; 4-H Awd; 4-H Achvt Cert 85; Acad Achvt Cert Engl 85; Acad Achvt Cert Geom 86; West Chester Coll; Bus Mngmnt.

MASTER, MELISSA; Reading HS; Reading, PA; (3); 80/710; Pres Trs Church Yth Grp; Concert Band; Jazz Band; Mrchg Band; Orch; Pep Band; School Musical; Zeswitz Music Awd 85; Amer Music Abroad Eorpn Tour Symphnc Band 87; Music Ed.

MASTERS, MICHELLE; Mt View HS; Hop Bottom, PA; (3); Aud/Vis; Church Yth Grp; Hosp Aide; Stage Crew; Fld Hcky; Trk; Frgn Lngs.

MASTERS, NANCY A; Quigley HS; Midland, PA; (3); 3/80; Dance Clb; Letterman Clb; Math Tm; Spanish Clb; Trs Jr Cls; Rep Stu Cncl; Var L Cheerleading; High Hon Roll; Ntl Merit Ltr; Trs Soph Cls; Hstry Awd 85; Spansh II Awd 86; Engrng.

MASTERS, SHERRIE; Norwin SR HS; N Huntingdon, PA; (3); Church Yth Grp; Girl Scts; SADD; Chorus; Church Choir; Sftbl; Hon Roll; Elem Spcl Ed Tchr.

MASTERSON, JOHN; Ephrata SR HS; Akron, PA; (4); 120/253; Boy Scts; Camera Clb; JA; Letterman Clb; Ski Clb; Varsity Clb; Drm & Bgl; Mrchg Band; Socr; Hon Roll; Penn ST; Arch Engrng.

MASTERSON, KRISSY; Fort Cherry HS; Mc Donald, PA; (4); 5/111; Pres Chorus; School Play; Nwsp Ed-Chief; Yrbk Stf; Lit Mag; Pres Soph Cls; Var Cheerleading; Var Capt Vllybl; NHS; Computer Clb; Syracuse U; Cmmnctns.

MASTERSON, TAMMY; Elizabethtown Area HS; Elizabethtown, PA; (4); 66/223; JV Tennis; French Hon Soc; Widener U; Fshn Mrchndsng.

MASTILLO, CANDACE; North Star HS; Holsopple, PA; (3); 20/140; Art Clb; Church Yth Grp; FCA; Nwsp Stf; Yrbk Stf; Pres Frsh Cls; Var L Cheerleading; Trk; Cit Awd; Hon Roll; Comm.

MASTIN, ALLEN; Wilmington Area HS; Volant, PA; (3); Computer Clb; FBLA; Band; Chorus; Concert Band; Jazz Band; Mrchg Band; Pep Band; Socr; Hon Roll; Jzz Band Pin 86; Brdcstng.

MASTOLLER, RACHAEL; North Star HS; Boswell, PA; (2); 13/135; FCA; Sec Trs 4-H; Rep Stu Cncl; Stat Bsktbl; Mat Maids; Score Keeper; Timer; 4-H Awd; Hon Roll; Pres Schlr; West VA U; Anml Productn.

MASTRAMICO, PHILIP; Hopewell HS; Aliquippa, PA; (4); 12/254; Spanish Clb; Chorus; JV Var Bsbl; JV Im Bsktbl; Im Sftbl; High Hon Roll; U Of Pittsburgh; Pre Law.

MASTRANGELO, DEBBIE; New Castle SR HS; New Castle, PA; (2); 7/220; Church Yth Grp; Concert Band; Drill Tm; Jazz Band; Mrchg Band; Nwsp Stf; Stu Cncl; Vllybl; Hon Roll; NHS; Acdmc Game Awds; Med.

MASTRANGELO, LUANN; New Castle SR HS; New Castle, PA; (3); 7/293; Church Yth Grp; Spanish Clb; Band; Concert Band; Drill Tm; Mrchg Band; Pep Band; Stu Cncl; Hon Roll; Yrbk Sls Rep 86-87.

MASTRANGELO, MARIA; Gwynedd Mercy Acad; Plymouth, PA; (2); Cmnty Wkr; Pep Clb; Service Clb; Ski Clb; Thesps; Church Choir; Var Fld Hcky; JV Sftbl; Var Swmmng.

MASTRICOLO, MICHAEL; Central Bucks HS West; Chalfont, PA; (4); 6/473; FBLA; Golf; Vllybl; High Hon Roll; Jr NHS; Ntl Merit Ltr; USAF Rcrtng Srvc Awd Schlstc Achvt Math & Sci, Mst Outstndng Bus Stu Accntng, Pres Acdmc Ftnss 87; Clarkson U; Math.

MASTRILLI, DONNA; Plymouth-Whitemarsh HS; Plymoth Mtg, PA; (3); JV Vllybl; NHS; German Awd; Schlstic Hnrs 87; Phila Coll; Intr Decrtr.

MASTROCOLA, ELIZABETH; Haverford HS; Ardmore, PA; (2); 42/389; Latin Clb; Rep Frsh Cls; Rep Soph Cls; JV Fld Hcky; Var L Lcrss; Hon Roll; Syracuse; Comm.

MASTROGIOVANNI, JEFFREY; St John Neumann HS; Philadelphia, PA; (2); 17/351; Church Yth Grp; Math Tm; Yrbk Phtg; Rep Frsh Cls; Rep Soph Cls; Rep Stu Cncl; High Hon Roll; Drexel; Engrng.

MASTROIANNI, ANGELA; Bishop Hannan HS; Scranton, PA; (4); 12/123; Speech Tm; Orch; Rep Frsh Cls; Rep Soph Cls; Off Jr Cls; Off Sr Cls; Stu Cncl; Tennis; Hon Roll; Pres NHS; Cls Awd Mst Likely To Succeed 87; Schl Rep Discplnry Brd 87; Career Awrnss Explrer 84-86; U Scranton; Humnties.

MASTROIANNI, MARIO; West Scranton SR HS; Scranton, PA; (3); Boys Clb Am; Church Yth Grp; Letterman Clb; Trs Sr Cls; Stu Cncl; Bsbl; JV Bsktbl; L Ftbl; JV Trk; High Hon Roll.

MASUGA, JEANNETTE; North Allegheny HS; Pittsburgh, PA; (2); 268/649; Art Clb; Church Yth Grp; Var Swmmng; Var Wt Lftg; Hon Roll; Artist Residence Pgm 84 & 86.

MASULLO, JEFFREY D; Bellefonte SR HS; Bellefonte, PA; (4); 50/243; L Crs Cntry; L Wrstlng; Hon Roll; Williamsport CC; Carpntry.

MATALIK, CHRISTOPHER; Burgettstown Area JR/SR HS; Burgettstown, PA; (3); JV Bsbl; JV Bsktbl; Var Ftbl; Im Wt Lftg; Hon Roll; NHS; Lock Haven; Sports Med.

MATALIK, MICHELLE L; Burgettstown Area JR Sr HS; Burgettstown, PA; (3); Drama Clb; Ski Clb; Spanish Clb; Yrbk Stf; Hon Roll; NHS; Acctng.

MATARRESE, KIM; Kiski Area HS; Vandergrift, PA; (3); Sec Church Yth Grp; FBLA; Pep Clb; Boy Scts; Mrchg Band; Symp Band; High Hon Roll; Hon Roll; Robert Morris U; Exec Secy.

MATCHAK, MARLA; Hickory HS; Sharpsville, PA; (3); Church Yth Grp; Service Clb; Chorus; Drill Tm; School Musical; Yrbk Stf; Rep Sec Jr Cls; Cheerleading; NHS; Spanish NHS; Elem Educ.

MATCHETT, JASON; Hempfield Area HS; Jeannette, PA; (2); Church Yth Grp; Computer Clb; Drama Clb; Ski Clb; Band; Church Choir; Concert Band; Drm Mjr(t); Jazz Band; Mrchg Band; Arch.

MATCHICKA, NICOLE; Reading SR HS; Reading, PA; (4); 7/563; Trs German Clb; Rep Stu Cncl; Var Tennis; Var Vllybl; Hon Roll; NHS; Superintndnts Schlrst Reg Awd 85-86; U Of Scranton; Phy Thrpy.

MATCHIK JR, JOHN R; Windber Area HS; Windber, PA; (3); Chess Clb; Church Yth Grp; Math Clb; Var Bsbl; JV Bsktbl; Var Golf; Hon Roll; NHS; U Of Pittsburgh; Pre-Med.

MATEJA, KATHERINE; Methacton HS; Norristown, PA; (3); 45/381; Acpl Chr; Chorus; School Musical; Swing Chorus; High Hon Roll; NHS; PMEA Dist 11 Chorus 87; Scl Wrk.

MATHE, CHRIS; Girard HS; W Grove, PA; (3); Aud/Vis; Library Aide; Ski Clb; High Hon Roll; Hon Roll; 4th Pl Chmstry Awd 87; U Of DE; Engrng.

MATHER, MARK; Palmyra HS; Mt Gretna, PA; (4); 9/186; French Clb; Band; Chorus; Concert Band; Jazz Band; Mrchg Band; Capt Crs Cntry; Capt Trk; High Hon Roll; NHS; Penn ST.

MATHER, MELISSA; Strong Vincent HS; Erie, PA; (4); 2/160; VP Sec French Clb; Nwsp Rptr; Ed Lit Mag; Var Cheerleading; Hon Roll; Sec NHS; Pres Schlr; Sal; Sec Debate Tm; Intnl Clb; PTA Schlr Awd 87; Jrnlstc Srv Awd 87; Gannon U; Comms.

MATHES, CRISTA; Marple Newtown HS; Newtown Square, PA; (2); 21/324; Church Yth Grp; French Clb; SADD; Stu Cncl; JV Bsktbl; JV Fld Hcky; Var Lcrss; JR VP Interact Clb.

MATHEW, ABRAHAM; Central HS; Philadelphia, PA; (2); Wt Lftg.

MATHEW, BOBBY P; Simon Grantz HS; Philadelphia, PA; (4); Chess Clb; Church Yth Grp; Computer Clb; Math Clb; Math Tm; Office Aide; SADD; Church Choir; High Hon Roll; Hon Roll; Wht Wllms Schlrshp Dr Rth Hyr Schlrshp 85-87; Bst Offc Aide Scl Svc; Bst Math Stu; Drexel U; Elec Engrngn.

MATHEW, SAJINI; Philadelphia HS; Philadelphia, PA; (3); 12/405; VP Church Yth Grp; Orch; High Hon Roll; Young Artists Awd 87.

MATHEWS, FAITH; West Branch HS; Lanse, PA; (2); Drama Clb; Science Clb; Spanish Clb; Band; Concert Band; Mrchg Band; Stage Crew; Im Sftbl; Hon Roll; Prfct Atten Awd; JR Hgh Sftbl Awd 86.

MATHEWS, JEFF; J P Mc Caskey HS; Lancaster, PA; (3); 26/515; VP AFS; Am Leg Boys St; Drama Clb; Radio Clb; Chorus; Nwsp Stf; Sec Jr Cls; Trs Stu Cncl; Hon Roll; Capt Coach Actv; Keystone Boys ST Schlrshp 86-87.

MATHEWS, MARLA; Abraham Lincoln HS; Philadelphia, PA; (3); 29/500; Drama Clb; School Musical; School Play; Variety Show; Nwsp Stf; Yrbk Stf; Lit Mag; Hon Roll; Wrtng Awd-Essay Constitutn 87; Brdcst Jrnlsm.

MATHIANAS, MELISSA; Brownsville Area HS; Brownsville, PA; (3); Drama Clb; Hosp Aide; Math Clb; Math Tm; SADD; Band; Chorus; School Musical; Var Co-Capt Cheerleading; Hon Roll.

MATHIAS, BELINDA; Hempfield HS; Columbia, PA; (2); 87/442; Computer Clb; Hon Roll; Psychtrst.

MATHIAS, CHRISTOPHER; Boyertown HS; Gilbertsville, PA; (1); Church Yth Grp; Library Aide; Teachers Aide; Varsity Clb; Chorus; Church Choir; School Musical; Im Bsktbl; High Hon Roll; Hon Roll; Cul Art.

MATHIAS, DENISE; Spring Grove SR HS; Spring Grove, PA; (4); 64/279; Drill Tm; Mrchg Band; Rep Stu Cncl; Stat Bsktbl; Var Cheerleading; High Hon Roll; Hon Roll; Economists Awd 87; Bus.

MATIANSKI, JACKIE; Charleroi Area HS; Monongahela, PA; (4); 26/162; French Clb; Varsity Clb; Sftbl; Swmmng; Hon Roll; NHS; Vrsty Awd 87; IN U Of PA.

MATIASH, CHRISTINE; Quigley HS; Aliquippa, PA; (3); 42/90; Drama Clb; Library Aide; Color Guard; Drm Mjr(t); Mrchg Band; School Play; Var Capt Cheerleading; Mgr(s); L Trk; Var L Twrlr; Pblc Relations.

MATIJEVICH, JAMES; Burgettstown Area JR SR HS; Burgettstown, PA; (2); Church Yth Grp; Band; Concert Band; Symp Band; Rep Soph Cls; Capt Bsktbl; Var Ftbl; Var Wt Lftg; Hon Roll; NHS; Engrng.

MATIS, MELISSA; Butler Area SR HS; Butler, PA; (3); Church Yth Grp; French Clb; Hosp Aide; Band; Chorus; Drill Tm; School Musical; Pom Pon; High Hon Roll; Hon Roll; Ed.

MATISAK, CHRISTOPHER; Bishop Hafey HS; Hazleton, PA; (3); 11/113; Ski Clb; SADD; Chorus; School Musical; Yrbk Stf; Rep Stu Cncl; Var L Ftbl; Var Trk; Dnfth Awd; God Cntry Awd; Hugh O Brian Ldrshp Sem 86; PA Sci Tlnt Srch Awd 87; U Of Notre Dame; Pre-Med.

MATLACK III, R ALLYN; North Allegheny HS; Pittsburgh, PA; (3); Intnl Clb; Capt ROTC; Rep Jr Cls; Rep Stu Cncl; L Trk; Hon Roll; Ntl Merit SF; Rep Frsh Cls; Rep Soph Cls; Outstdndng Cadet AFJROTC 85; Offcrs Assn Awd 87; PA St Stu Cncl Bd 87; Intl Affairs.

MATLOCK, KELLEE; Pius X HS; Nazerath, PA; (4); 20/34; Letterman Clb; Pep Clb; Varsity Clb; Chorus; School Musical; Nwsp Stf; Yrbk Stf; Rep Frsh Cls; Rep Sr Cls; Capt Var Bsktbl; JV Sftbl; Bngr Police Acad-Outstndng Drvr Awd 87; Northampton Area CC; Rdlgc Tec.

MATOS, JEANNETTE; Reading HS; Reading, PA; (3); 47/710; Concert Band; Mrchg Band; Orch; Pep Band; Hon Roll; Penn ST U; Comp.

MATOUS, CYNDI; Penns Manor HS; Penn Run, PA; (3); Camera Clb; Church Yth Grp; Library Aide; SADD; Chorus; Church Choir; Hon Roll; IUP; Music.

MATOUSHEK, KIMBERLY; Western Wayne HS; Waymart, PA; (2); Band; Concert Band; Mrchg Band; School Musical; School Play; Hon Roll; Msc Thrpy.

MATOUSHEK, SUSAN; Western Wayne HS; Waymart, PA; (4); SADD; Var JV Bsktbl; Capt Var Cheerleading; High Hon Roll; Hon Roll; NHS; Empire Beauty Schl; Csmtlgy.

MATRAZZO, KELLY L; New Brighton HS; New Brighton, PA; (4); 8/177; Am Leg Aux Girls St; Drama Clb; GAA; Letterman Clb; Varsity Clb; Chorus; School Play; Nwsp Rptr; Nwsp Stf; Yrbk Ed-Chief; Am Leg Awd 84-85; Yrbk Sem Awds 87; WVU; Elem Ed.

MATRICCINO, KELLY; Hazleton HS; Hazleton, PA; (3); French Clb; German Clb; Stu Cncl; French Hon Soc; High Hon Roll; Hon Roll; 3rd Pl Natl Frnch Cont 85; Hnrbl Mntn Natl Frnch Cont 86 & 87; Temple U; Intl Langs.

MATRICIAN, CHRISTINE; Palmerton Area HS; Palmerton, PA; (3); 21/173; FBLA; Hosp Aide; Drill Tm; Yrbk Stf; Tennis; Hon Roll; Allentown Bus Schl; Legal Sec.

MATSCHERZ, KATHRYN; West Greene Middle SR HS; Prosperity, PA; (3); 32/108; Cmnty Wkr; FHA; Ski Clb; Color Guard; Mrchg Band; Stage Crew; Nwsp Rptr; Nwsp Stf; Yrbk Rptr; Yrbk Stf; NY U; Jrnslm.

MATSCHNER, TRACEY; Ambridge Area HS; Baden, PA; (3); French Clb; Hosp Aide; Office Aide; Pep Clb; Red Cross Aide; Chorus; Rep Soph Cls; Rep Jr Cls; JV Crs Cntry; JV Trk; Schl Of Radiography; Rdlgc Tech.

MATSON, MICHEAL; Technical Memorial HS; Erie, PA; (3); German Clb; Var L Socr; Hon Roll; PA ST; Comp.

MATSUMOTO, SARAH; Marple Newtown SR HS; Newtown Square, PA; (3); Church Yth Grp; Ski Clb; SADD; Band; Concert Band; Mrchg Band; Orch; Sec Sr Cls; Var Diving; Var Trk; Intl Bus.

MATTEI JR, RAFAEL; St Francis Prep; Frederick, MD; (1); 1/14; Generl Acad Excllnce 86-87; Music.

MATTEI, RENEE; Lakeland HS; Olyphant, PA; (4); 8/150; VP Girl Scts; Pres JA; Band; Yrbk Stf; Rep Stu Cncl; L Sftbl; High Hon Roll; NHS; Pres Schlr; Amer Assoc Physics Tchrs Awd Outstndg Stu Yr 87; Kings Coll.

MATTEO, JERRY; Bishop Haffey HS; Hazleton, PA; (3); Chess Clb; Church Yth Grp; Cmnty Wkr; Math Clb; Ski Clb; Spanish Clb; Bowling; Crs Cntry; Golf; L Tennis; Medical-Dntl Fld.

MATTEO, JIM; Hazelton HS; Hazleton, PA; (4); Scholastic Bowl; Bsktbl; High Hon Roll; Pres Schlr; Andy Fierro Memrl Awd 87; Bloomsburg U; Educ.

MATTEO, JOHN; Hazleton HS; Hazleton, PA; (2); VP Stu Cncl; JV Bsktbl; Hon Roll; Pres Acad Ftns Awd 86; Sci.

MATTEO, MARY ANNE; Hershey HS; Hershey, PA; (4); 41/199; Spanish Clb; Teachers Aide; Chorus; Stat Bsktbl; Var Cheerleading; Powder Puff Ftbl; Wt Lftg; Hon Roll; Girl Of Mth; Hm Ecs Awd; Shippensburg U; Scndry Ed.

MATTER, SANDRA; East Juniata HS; Millerstown, PA; (3); 11/100; Chess Clb; Trs Church Yth Grp; Pres 4-H; High Hon Roll; Hon Roll; Bible Quiz Hgh Score Awd 87; Missions.

MATTER, TRACY; Millersburg Area HS; Millersburg, PA; (3); Color Guard; Mrchg Band; Powder Puff Ftbl; Hon Roll; Consrvtn Clb 86-87; Schl Nwspaper Head Typst 87-88; Med Sec.

MATTERN, JENNIFER; Saint Basil Acad; Philadelphia, PA; (3); 10/85; Drama Clb; French Clb; Thesps; Stage Crew; Variety Show; Rep Frsh Cls; Rep Stu Cncl; St Basil Acad Scholar 84; Natl Engl Merit Awd 87; Soc Distngshd Amer HS Stu 87; Fordham U; Theatre Arts.

MATTERN, JERRY; East Pennsboro HS; Camp Hill, PA; (3); 34/195; Spanish Clb; Varsity Clb; School Musical; School Play; JV Bsktbl; Var Ftbl; Trk; High Hon Roll; VP NHS; Crmnl Jstce.

MATTHEW, CAROL; Glendale JR SR HS; Fallentimber, PA; (3); 5/70; Science Clb; SADD; Yrbk Stf; VP Stu Cncl; Bsktbl; Hon Roll; NHS; Voice Dem Awd.

MATTHEWS, ANTHONY; John S Fine SR HS; Nanticoke, PA; (3); 6/240; Band; Concert Band; Drm Mjr(t); Jazz Band; Mrchg Band; Variety Show; High Hon Roll; NHS; Penn ST U; Arspc Engrng.

MATTHEWS, BRADLEY; William Penn HS; York, PA; (3); Hon Roll; Prfct Atten Awd; Bearcat Of Month Awd 85-86; Physcl Ftnss Awd 84-85; Psych.

MATTHEWS, BRIAN; Stroudsburg HS; Stroudsburg, PA; (2); 30/265; Church Yth Grp; Math Clb; Math Tm; Quiz Bowl; JV Bsbl; JV Capt Bsktbl; Hon Roll; Jr NHS; NHS; Prsdntl Acdmc Fitness Awd 85-86; West Point; Engrng.

MATTHEWS, COURTNEY; Hempfield HS; Lancaster, PA; (4); 2/425; Church Yth Grp; Q&S; Nwsp Ed-Chief; Mgr(s); Powder Puff Ftbl; NHS; Sal; Voice Dem Awd; Gould Inc Schlrshp 87; W Hmpfld Plc Acdmc & Voice Dmcrcy 2d Pl Awds 86; La Fayette Coll; Engl.

MATTHEWS, DAWN; Germantown HS; Philadelphia, PA; (4); 1/485; Yrbk Stf; Cit Awd; DAR Awd; High Hon Roll; Hon Roll; NHS; Pres Schlr; Val; Library Aide; Office Aide; Brown U Bk Awd 86; Math Awd 87; Temple U Schlrshp 87; Temple U; Corp Law.

MATTHEWS, DENISE; North Star HS; Stoystown, PA; (4); 7/130; Church Yth Grp; FCA; VP Mu Alpha Theta; Cit Awd; Hon Roll; NHS; Activities Boosters Stu Of Mnth 86; Frostburg ST Coll; Math.

MATTHEWS, DIANA; High School Of Engineering & Science; Philadelphia, PA; (3); 8/184; JA; High Hon Roll; NHS; U Penn; Chem Engr.

MATTHEWS, ESTHER J; Boyertown JR High East; Frederick, PA; (1); French Clb; Girl Scts; Library Aide; Band; Concert Band; Mrchg Band; Pep Band; Hon Roll; Prfct Atten Awd; Electrical Engineering.

MATTHEWS, JEFF; Downingtown SR HS; West Chester, PA; (3); 196/695; Boy Scts; Chess Clb; German Clb; Latin Clb; Library Aide; SADD; Yrbk Stf; Hon Roll; Sci.

MATTHEWS, LISA; Mastbaum HS; Philadelphia, PA; (3); 7/288; Bowling; Sftbl; Hon Roll; NHS.

MATTHEWS, MARK; Grove City HS; Grove City, PA; (3); 15/220; Ski Clb; Stu Cncl; Crs Cntry; L Swmmng; High Hon Roll; NHS.

MATTHEWS, MARK; John S Fine SR HS; Nanticoke, PA; (4); 27/251; Band; Concert Band; Mrchg Band; Orch; Symp Band; Variety Show; JV Bsktbl; High Hon Roll; Hon Roll; NHS; Luzerne Co CC; Hotel/Rest Mgmt.

MATTHEWS, MELISSA; Moniteau HS; Boyers, PA; (3); Drama Clb; FHA; Spanish Clb; Nwsp Stf; Yrbk Phtg; Capt JV Cheerleading; Stat Ftbl; Capt Var Vllybl; NHS; Clarion U; Scl Stds Tchr.

MATTHEWS, MICHELE; Donegal HS; Mount Joy, PA; (3); 40/179; Chorus; Color Guard; Nwsp Rptr; Yrbk Stf; Capt Var Crs Cntry; Hon Roll; Med Lab Tech.

MATTHEWS, MICHELE; Greenville SR HS; Greenville, PA; (1); French Clb; Var L Crs Cntry; Var Trk; Hon Roll; Acclrtd Courses Amer Cultures, Geom, Bio, Engl 86-87; Swimteam 86-87; Math.

MATTHEWS, MICHELE; Northeastern HS; Mt Wolf, PA; (4); 20/161; Ski Clb; Sec Trs Varsity Clb; Chorus; L Var Gym; Hon Roll; Church Yth Grp; Pres Schlr; Stu Of Mo 86; Shippensburg U; Elem Educ.

MATTHEWS, PAMELA; St Pius X HS; Schwenksville, PA; (1); 86/146; Drama Clb; Var Swmmng; Ntl Merit SF; Tri-County Swmmng Leag 86; Optimist Cluf Of Perkiomen Vly Wrtng Awd 86; Cert Of Merit For Essay 86; Engl.

MATTHEWS, TRACIE; United HS; Dilltown, PA; (3); 40/160; Sec Art Clb; Camera Clb; Church Yth Grp; Dance Clb; French Clb; Library Aide; Pep Clb; Ski Clb; Chorus; Nwsp Ed-Chief; 1st Pl Lit Awds Poetry, Prose 85-86 Gov Schl Arts Pgm IUP 86; Carnegie-Melon Smmr Stds Pgm 87; Jrnlsm.

MATTHEWS, WENDY; Downingtown SR HS; Downingtown, PA; (4); 74/523; French Clb; SADD; Band; Color Guard; Drm Mjr(t); Mrchg Band; Twrlr; High Hon Roll; NEDT Awd; Valerie Freas Memrl Awd-Twrlng 86-87; Gold Music Srvc Awd 87; U Of DE; Psych.

MATTIKO, DENNIS; Plum SR HS; Pittsburgh, PA; (3); Jazz Band; Mrchg Band; School Musical; Symp Band; High Hon Roll; NHS; Sci.

MATTIOLI, LYNN; Notre Dame HS; Easton, PA; (4); Drama Clb; Girl Scts; Key Clb; NFL; Speech Tm; Chorus; School Musical; School Play; Nwsp Rptr; Yrbk Rptr; Ntl Fed Blnd-Schlrshp 87; Scty Wmn Engrs Awd 86-87; Albright Coll; Nutrtn.

MATTIOLI, MARIA; Riverside JR SR HS; Taylor, PA; (3); Dance Clb; Pep Clb; Ski Clb; Variety Show; Var Capt Cheerleading; Capt JV Chrldrs 85-86; Miss Viking Capt Of Units 87; Nrsng.

MATTIS, DEBORAH; Windber Area HS; Windber, PA; (3); 7/128; Trs Drama Clb; JA; Concert Band; Mrchg Band; School Play; Stu Cncl; Sftbl; High Hon Roll; NHS; Dstct & Rgnl Bnd Fstvls 87.

MATTIUZ, JEFFREY MARK; St Marys Area HS; Dagus Mines, PA; (3); 29/269; Am Leg Boys St; Boys Clb Am; Var Bsbl; Im Bsktbl; Var L Ftbl; Im Sftbl; Var Wt Lftg; Hon Roll; NHS.

MATTOX, DAVID; Trinity Christian HS; Pittsburgh, PA; (4); 1/13; Chorus; Pres Jr Cls; Pres Sr Cls; High Hon Roll; NHS; Ntl Merit SF; U Of PA; Business.

MATTRESS, TINA; S Fayette HS; Bridgeville, PA; (4); 16/71; Yrbk Stf; Pres Jr Cls; Pres Sr Cls; Var Capt Bsktbl; Var Cheerleading; Var L Mgr(s); Var Capt Sftbl; Hon Roll; NHS; PA ST U; Liberal Arts.

MATTSON, JOHN A; Cash HS; Coatesville, PA; (4); 105/457; Church Yth Grp; SADD; VICA; High Hon Roll; Outstndng Plmbng Stu 86-87.

MATTUCH, BRIAN; Ambridge Area HS; Baden, PA; (3); 14/334; Am Leg Boys St; Computer Clb; French Clb; Letterman Clb; Pep Clb; Band; JV Bsktbl; Var Capt Golf; JV Capt Vllybl; Lion Awd; AISA 1st Pl ST Champ Tech Writg & 3rd Pl ST Champ Publ Spkg 87; Air Trffc Cntrl.

MATTUS, DAVID; Upper Morel.and HS; Willow Grove, PA; (3); Mrchg Band; Hon Roll.

MATTY, MARIE; Belle Vernon Area HS; Belle Vernon, PA; (3); 4-H; FBLA; Score Keeper; High Hon Roll; NHS.

MATTY, STACY; Monessen JR-SR HS; Monessen, PA; (3); Aud/Vis; Dance Clb; Drama Clb; Hosp Aide; Office Aide; PAVAS; School Play; Var Cheerleading; Profsnl Dancer.

MATUIZEK, MIKE; Highlands HS; Natrona Hts, PA; (3); DECA; Key Clb; Teachers Aide; Prfct Atten Awd; Brwn Awd 87; PA Inst Of Culinary Arts; Chef.

MATUKAITIS, MICHAEL; Southern Columbis HS; Elysburg, PA; (3); 9/107; Varsity Clb; Nwsp Stf; VP Jr Cls; L Crs Cntry; Var Trk; Var L Wrstlng; High Hon Roll; Hon Roll; NHS; Voice Dem Awd; Outstndng HS Athltc In Amer 87; Airplane Pilot.

MATULEVICH, JONATHAN; West Hazleton HS; Harwood Mines, PA; (4); 29/224; French Clb; Red Cross Aide; Ski Clb; SADD; Varsity Clb; Trs VP Stu Cncl; Var Capt Bsbl; Var Capt Ftbl; High Hon Roll; NHS; PA ST U; Engrng.

MATUNIS, DAVID; West Perry HS; Loysville, PA; (2); Art Clb; Church Yth Grp; Red Cross Aide; Band; Concert Band; Mrchg Band; Socr; Trk; Wrstlng; Hon Roll; Penn ST; Vet.

MATUNIS, REBECCA; West Perry SR HS; Loysville, PA; (3); Chrmn Church Yth Grp; Spanish Clb; Varsity Clb; Chorus; Concert Band; Jazz Band; Mrchg Band; Var Fld Hcky; Trk; Hon Roll; Cnty Band 86 & 87; Trk Awd 86; Sci Ed.

MATUSZ, KAREN; Plum SR HS; Pittsburgh, PA; (3); 6/410; Varsity Clb; Chorus; L Bsktbl; L Socr; High Hon Roll; NHS; Exploring; French Clb; Ski Clb; SADD; Civil Engnrs Soc Achvt Awd Physics 85-87; Rgnl & ST PA Jr Acad Of Sci Cmpttn 85-87; PA Tlnt Srch 87; Penn ST U; Bus.

MATUSZEWSKI, LIZA; Bishop Guilfoyle HS; Altoona, PA; (3); 2/156; Church Yth Grp; NFL; Speech Tm; SADD; Band; Chorus; Pres Jr Cls; Stu Cncl; High Hon Roll; Hon Roll; Hugh Obrian Ldrshp Awd 85; Semi-Finlst Teens Grt Mdl Srch 85-86; Govnt.

MATVEY, MICHAEL; Central Catholic HS; Pittsburgh, PA; (4); 31/260; Church Yth Grp; Dance Clb; Chorus; Vllybl; High Hon Roll; Hon Roll; NHS; Robert C Byrd Scholar 87; PA ST; Cmmnctns.

MATVEY, TERRY; West Middlesex HS; Mercer, PA; (4); 3/94; Office Aide; Spanish Clb; Mrchg Band; Gym; Trk; Capt Twrlr; High Hon Roll; Jr NHS; Sec Trs NHS; Spanish NHS; Miss Western PA Mjrt Capt 84; Natl Sci Merit Awd 83-86; Clarion U; Acctng.

MATVEY, TRACEY; W Middlesex HS; Mercer, PA; (4); 10/94; JA; Spanish Clb; Trs Jr Cls; Trs Sr Cls; Twrlr; High Hon Roll; Hon Roll; Jr NHS; NHS; Spanish NHS; Natl Sci Mrt Awd 86; Clarion U.

MATWAY, CATHY; Mary Fuller Frazier HS; Perryopolis, PA; (4); FNA; GAA; Library Aide; Varsity Clb; Band; Chorus; Flag Corp; Nwsp Rptr; Nwsp Sprt Ed; Nwsp Stf; Penn ST; Nrsg.

MATWAY, CINDY; Frazier HS; Perryopolis, PA; (3); Library Aide; Band; Chorus; Mrchg Band; Sftbl; Vllybl; Mdcl Sec.

MATZ, JENNIFER; Moniteau HS; Slippery Rock, PA; (3); 14/132; Pres Art Clb; Civic Clb; Drama Clb; Pres French Clb; Capt Science Clb; Jazz Band; Var L Trk; Var L Vllybl; Hon Roll; NHS; Natl Fdrtn Music Clbs Awd, Smmr Acad Perfrmng Arts Schlrshp 87; US Army Corps Engrs-2nd Pl Eclgy 86; Chem.

MATZ, KEITH; Moniteau HS; Slippery Rock, PA; (1); Band; Concert Band; Jazz Band; Mrchg Band; Orch; Trk; Penn ST; Accntnt.

MATZ, MARC; Upper Merion HS; King Of Prussia, PA; (3); 30/309; Math Tm.

MAUE, DAVID; Hazleton HS; Hazleton, PA; (3); 7/466; Civic Clb; Drama Clb; Leo Clb; Spanish Clb; Trs Sr Cls; High Hon Roll; Pres Schlr; Nwsp Rptr; Yrbk Rptr; Rep Stu Cncl; Hugh O Brian Yth Fndtn Cntrl PA Ldrshp Smnr & Intl Rep 86; Latin Natl Hnr Soc; Bus.

MAUERY, ANDREA; Chief Logan HS; Lewistown, PA; (4); 6/199; VP Art Clb; French Clb; Ski Clb; Varsity Clb; Sec Chorus; Yrbk Stf; Capt Crs Cntry; High Hon Roll; Trs NHS; Pres Schlr; AAL Schlrshp 87; Schlstc Art Awds Gold Key & Blue Ribbon 87; Charles Hidley Art Awd 87; IN U Of PA; Art Educ.

MAUGER, KATHLEEN; Elizabeth Forward HS; Monongahela, PA; (4); 28/293; French Clb; Library Aide; Chorus; School Musical; Co-Capt Yrbk Stf; High Hon Roll; Hon Roll; NHS; Pres Acad Ftns Awd US Dept Of Ed 87; U Of Pittsburgh; Occptnl Thrpy.

MAUGHAN, JOHN; Central Bucks HS East; Pineville, PA; (3); 38/488; Scholastic Bowl; Band; Concert Band; Mrchg Band; Orch; High Hon Roll; Hon Roll; Psych.

MAUGHLIN, BILL; Northeastern HS; Manchester, PA; (3); Boy Scts; Church Yth Grp; FBLA; German Clb; SADD; Band; Chorus; School Musical; Hon Roll; Bus Manag.

MAUK, KENDRA; Claysburg Kimmel HS; Claysburg, PA; (2); Church Yth Grp; Drama Clb; Band; Chorus; Concert Band; Mrchg Band; School Play; Stu Cncl; Cheerleading; Sftbl; Hnrs Banquet 85-87; Hnr Pins 85-87; PA ST U; Pol Sci.

MAUL, LANCE; West Forest JR-SR HS; Oil City, PA; (3); Church Yth Grp; Cmnty Wkr; NHS; Aerosp Engr.

MAUL, TRENT; Mercer HS; Mercer, PA; (3); Letterman Clb; Spanish Clb; Varsity Clb; Yrbk Stf; Rep Stu Cncl; Var Trk; Var L Wrstlng; Hon Roll; Spanish NHS; Radlgc Tech.

MAULA, ROSEMARY; East Stroudsburg HS; E Stroudsburg, PA; (3); 25/240; Church Yth Grp; Cmnty Wkr; Band; Chorus; Concert Band; Drm Mjr(t); Mrchg Band; Swing Chorus; Var JV Tennis; High Hon Roll; MVP Ten 86 & 87; Outstndng Marcher Awd 86; Home Econ Awd 86; Cmmnctn.

MAULFAIR, JAMES; Cedar Crest HS; Lebanon, PA; (3); Boy Scts; Spanish Clb; School Musical; Yrbk Bus Mgr.

MAURER, ANN; Berlin Brothers Valley HS; Fairhope, PA; (3); 11/100; Pres French Clb; Chorus; Drill Tm; School Play; Hon Roll; NHS; Marine Bio.

MAURER, ELIZABETH; Spring-Ford SR HS; Schwenksville, PA; (3); Church Yth Grp; Drama Clb; Girl Scts; Hosp Aide; Library Aide; Spanish Clb; SADD; Thesps; Chorus; School Musical; Bsktbl Awd 85; Psych.

MAURER, JODY; Susquenita HS; Marysville, PA; (3); 4/157; Quiz Bowl; Ski Clb; Spanish Clb; Band; Chorus; Nwsp Rptr; Yrbk Ed-Chief; High Hon Roll; NHS; Cert Super Prfrmnc NEDT Tst 86; Schltc Gld Key Wrtng Awd 85-86; PA JR Acad Sci 2nd Awd ST Mtng 86; Bio.

MAURER, MICHAEL C; Mifflinburg HS; New Berlin, PA; (1); Church Yth Grp; High Hon Roll; Bus.

MAURIELLO, DAVID; Upper Darby HS; Drexel Hill, PA; (3); 41/562; Lit Mag; Var Bsktbl; Var Lcrss.

MAURO, ANTHONY F; Kinggold HS; Donora, PA; (3); Church Yth Grp; Ski Clb; VP Frsh Cls; Off Soph Cls; Off Jr Cls; Stu Cncl; Var L Bsbl; L Bsktbl; JV Ftbl; Im Vllybl; Amer Legn Awd 84-85; Natl Math & Sci Hnr Socty 85-87; Bus Law.

MAUS, SHELLEY; Central Dauphin HS; Harrisburg, PA; (4); 13/367; Concert Band; Jazz Band; Mrchg Band; High Hon Roll; Hon Roll; NHS; Ntl Merit Ltr; Pres Schlr; Corinne Mnk Wahr Schlrshp 87; IN U Of PA; Frnch.

MAUSS, ROBERT L; Biglerville HS; Biglerville, PA; (3); 28/90; Yrbk Stf; Wrstlng; High Hon Roll; Hon Roll; Comp.

MAUST, GLENN; Salisbury Elk-Lick HS; Meyersdale, PA; (2); Church Yth Grp; Sec FFA; Yrbk Stf; Off Frsh Cls; Off Soph Cls; Hon Roll; Star Chapt Frmr FFA 86-87; Chapt Frmr Degree FFA 86-87; Grnhnd Degree FFA 85-86; Allegheny CC; Drftsmn.

MAUTE, ALISON; Boyertown Area SR HS; Bechtelsvl, PA; (3); 47/470; Church Yth Grp; School Play; Yrbk Stf; Rep Soph Cls; Rep Stu Cncl; Im Golf; Var L Tennis; Cit Awd; Hon Roll; NHS; Pres Acdmc Fit Awd 85; Forgn Lang.

MAUTE, TERESA M; Souderton Area HS; Telford, PA; (3); Hon Roll; Exec Secr.

MAVRICH, ANGIE; Hopewell HS; Aliquippa, PA; (4); 3/245; Church Yth Grp; Computer Clb; French Clb; Math Tm; Yrbk Sprt Ed; Pres Frsh Cls; Pres Soph Cls; Pres Jr Cls; Rep Sr Cls; Stu Cncl; Amer Lgn Awd 83; KDKA Extra Effort Awd 87; Schlr Athlete Awd 86 & 87; Washington; Math.

MAVRICH, MIRIAM; Hopewell HS; Aliquippa, PA; (2); Church Yth Grp; French Clb; Chorus; Church Choir; Pres Frsh Cls; Pres Soph Cls; Var L Chess Clb; Sftbl; Var L Trk; High Hon Roll; Phys Thrpy.

MAWHINNEY, JENNIFER; Carmichaels Area SR HS; Waynesburg, PA; (3); 1/120; Cmnty Wkr; Pres VP 4-H; Pep Clb; Ski Clb; SADD; Trs Band; Concert Band; Mrchg Band; Pep Band; Yrbk Stf; PA Jr Winner Natl Rep 85-86; PA St Blue Form Winner 87; Physical Therapy.

MAWHINNEY, SUSAN; Carmichaels Area HS; Waynesburg, PA; (1); 5/120; Pres 4-H; Band; School Play; Nwsp Rptr; JV Bsktbl; Dnfth Awd; 4-H Awd; High Hon Roll; Jr NHS; Pres Schlr; Arch.

MAWJI, ZUBINA; William Allen HS; Allentown, PA; (3); 4/610; High Hon Roll; Lion Awd; NHS; Ntl Merit Ltr; Spanish NHS; VFW Awd; Voice Dem Awd; Chess Clb; Drama Clb; Ski Clb; 2nd Pl FL Natl Spn Exam Lvl 1 85; Treas Cont Affrs Clb 87; Top 10 Natl Math Exam 87; Med.

MAXSON, MISTY; Owwayo Valley JR SR HS; Shinglehouse, PA; (3); Church Yth Grp; French Clb; Girl Scts; Library Aide; Chorus; Church Choir; DAR Awd; Prfct Atten Awd; Nrs.

MAXWELL, CONNIE; Peters Township HS; Mcmurray, PA; (2); Hosp Aide; Ski Clb; Band; Color Guard; Mrchg Band; Participation Awd For Color Guard 86; U Of Pittsburgh; Phys Therapy.

MAXWELL, DINA; Exeter SR HS; Reading, PA; (4); 21/214; Varsity Clb; Y-Teens; Band; Concert Band; Flag Corp; Off Sr Cls; Rep Stu Cncl; Var Cheerleading; Var Tennis; Trk; U DE; Mrktng.

MAXWELL, JOHN; Central Dauphin HS; Harrisburg, PA; (3); 30/369; Band; Chorus; Concert Band; Jazz Band; Mrchg Band; Orch; School Musical; Rep Stu Cncl; Hon Roll; NHS; Pre-Med.

MAXWELL, MAGDALENE; Donegal HS; Mount Joy, PA; (2); Church Yth Grp; Drama Clb; Chorus; Hon Roll; Presdntl Physcl Ftnss Awd 85-87.

MAXWELL, MARGARET; Bishop Mc Devitt HS; Glenside, PA; (3); 65/351; Church Yth Grp; Cmnty Wkr; Office Aide; Service Clb; Rep Soph Cls; Rep Jr Cls; Rep Stu Cncl; Powder Puff Ftbl; Trk; Hon Roll; Hmcmng Crt.

MAXWELL, ROBERT; Penn Manor HS; Millersville, PA; (3); Thesps; Acpl Chr; Band; Chorus; Color Guard; Jazz Band; Mrchg Band; Pep Band; School Musical; Capt Vllybl; Pegasus Awd PA Poetry Soc 87; PA ST; Arch.

MAXWELL, SHANNON; West Mifflin Area HS; W Mifflin, PA; (3); FBLA; Girl Scts; Office Aide; Pep Clb; Ski Clb; Sec Stu Cncl; Tennis; Hon Roll; Jr NHS; NHS.

MAY, BARBARA JEAN; Neshaminy HS; Penndel, PA; (3); 5/800; Hon Roll; March Dimes Walkthn Awd 86; Roger Williams Coll; Oceanogrph.

MAY, HEATHER; Lock Haven SR HS; Lock Haven, PA; (4); 31/250; Church Yth Grp; French Clb; Model UN; Spanish Clb; Chorus; Pres Concert Band; Jazz Band; Pres Mrchg Band; Orch; High Hon Roll; Meritorious Ability & Perf Music 87; PA Music Educators Assoc All-St Chorus & Rgnl Band Fest 85-87; Grove City Coll; Bio.

MAY, HEIDI; Central Dauphin HS; Harrisburg, PA; (3); 9/370; Art Clb; Church Yth Grp; German Clb; Key Clb; Ski Clb; Chorus; Church Choir; Var L Vllybl; NHS; Pres Schlr; PA ST U; Arch Engr.

MAY, JAMES; The Baptist HS; Clarks Summit, PA; (3); Church Yth Grp; Acpl Chr; Orch; Pres Stu Cncl; Prfct Atten Awd; Pres Chorus; Rep Frsh Cls; Rep Soph Cls; VP Jr Cls; L Bsktbl; 2nd Pl Natl Tlnts Christ-Brass Cmptn 87; 1st Pl Keystone Chrstn Educ Assn St Cmptn 85-87; Grnd Rapids Baptist Coll; Music.

MAY, JENNIFER; Connellsville Area HS; Connellsville, PA; (2); Girl Scts; School Musical; Nwsp Rptr; Yrbk Stf; Stu Cncl; High Hon Roll; Pre-Med.

MAY, LESLIE; Everett Area HS; Breezewood, PA; (2); #12 In Class; Drama Clb; French Clb; FHA; Chorus; Var Tennis; High Hon Roll; Hon Roll; PA ST; RN.

MAY, MICAH; Hillell Acad; Pittsburgh, PA; (3); 2/8; School Play; Stu Cncl; Var Capt Bsktbl; Var Capt Ftbl; High Hon Roll; NHS; Sal; School Musical; Stage Crew; Var Capt Sftbl; Yeshiva Univ; Med.

MAY, PHILIP; Mt Pleasant Area HS; Acme, PA; (2); FCA; German Clb; Band; Mrchg Band; Pep Band; Symp Band; Capt Wt Lftg; Hon Roll; Pres Schlr; Duquesne U Mid-Eastern Hnrs Band 87; Naval Prep Schl; Militory.

MAY, RENEE M; Palmyra Area HS; Palmyra, PA; (4); 22/190; Drama Clb; Spanish Clb; Chorus; High Hon Roll; Hon Roll; Pres Acdmc Ftns Awd 87.

MAY, TERRI; Everett Area HS; Clearville, PA; (2); Spanish Clb; Band; Concert Band; Drm Mjr(t); Mrchg Band; Off Stu Cncl; Trk; Spanish NHS; Nrsng.

MAY, TERRY; Connellsville Area HS; Mill Run, PA; (4); Cmnty Wkr; High Hon Roll; Prfct Atten Awd; Acad Excllnce Awd 83-84; Springfield Twp Vol Fireman 87.

MAY, WENDY; Scranton Prepatory Schl; Scranton, PA; (4); Band; Chorus; Church Choir; Sec Concert Band; Sec Jazz Band; Sec Orch; Sec Pep Band; Stage Crew; L Trk; Hon Roll; U Of Scranton; Med.

MAYCONICH, MARY; Center HS; Monaca, PA; (3); 46/180; Sec Camera Clb; German Clb; Sec JA; Letterman Clb; Varsity Clb; Yrbk Stf; Powder Puff Ftbl; Tennis; Trk; Hon Roll; Ldrshp Trnng Conf Corp Sec 86; Ldrshp Trnng Conf Asst Mrktng Calgon 87; Cert Grmn Cls 3.2 3 Yrs 87; Embry Riddle; Aviation.

MAYER, ANITA; Central Cambria HS; Johnstown, PA; (3); 22/210; Art Clb; IN U Of PA; Engl.

MAYER, CAROL; Chartiers Valley HS; Heidelberg, PA; (3); Pep Clb; School Musical; Nwsp Rptr; Rep Stu Cncl; U Pittsburgh; Fshn Dsgn.

MAYER, GARY; Morrisville HS; Morrisville, PA; (3); 2/85; Scholastic Bowl; Ed Yrbk Stf; High Hon Roll; Hon Roll; NHS; Exchng Stu Japan Cert Merit 87; Lwr Bucks Sci Smnr 86-87; Air Frc Acad; Aeronaut Engr.

MAYER, MARCI; Fleetwood Area HS; Fleetwood, PA; (3); 5/112; Sec Frsh Cls; Sec Soph Cls; Var Fld Hcky; Hon Roll; Jr NHS; Acdmc All AM 86-87; US Achvmnt Acdmy 86-87; Math.

MAYER, ROB; Hempfield HS; Lancaster, PA; (3); Science Clb; Ski Clb; Nwsp Stf; Mgr Bsktbl; Ice Hcky.

MAYER, STACI; Lower Moreland HS; Huntingdon Valley, PA; (2); FBLA; Pep Clb; Science Clb; SADD; Varsity Clb; JV Cheerleading; JV Crs Cntry; JV Swmmng; Var Trk; Hon Roll.

MAYERNIK, JEREMY; Chartiers Valley HS; Pittsburgh, PA; (3); Band; Concert Band; Jazz Band; Mrchg Band; School Musical; School Play; Stage Crew; Yrbk Ed-Chief; High Hon Roll; NHS; WV Hnrs Band 87.

MAYERS, CARRIE; Brownsville Area HS; Grindstone, PA; (3); Hosp Aide; SADD; Teachers Aide; Y-Teens; Band; Flag Corp; Mrchg Band; High Hon Roll; Hon Roll; Acctng.

MAYES, ANTHONY; Edward Bok HS; Philadelphia, PA; (3); Boy Scts; Chess Clb; Church Yth Grp; Computer Clb; FBLA; Science Clb; Teachers Aide; Band; Rep Frsh Cls; Stu Cncl; FBLA Schlrshp 87; Cheney ST U; Comp Pgmmr.

MAYES, JOEL; Warren County Christian Schl; Warren, PA; (4); 1/7; Church Yth Grp; Pres Chorus; School Musical; Variety Show; Yrbk Stf; Pres Stu Cncl; Var Bsktbl; Capt Socr; Christian Witness Awd 84-86; Soccer MVP 87; Clarion U; Comm Arts.

MAYHUE, ELIZABETH; Tyrone Area HS; Tyrone, PA; (3); Art Clb; French Clb; Key Clb; Office Aide; Pep Clb; Chorus; Hon Roll; Lbrl Arts.

MAYKOWSKI, LORI; Sharpsville Area HS; Sharpsville, PA; (3); Chorus; Yrbk Stf; Hon Roll; Acdmc Achvt Awd; Engl.

MAYNARD, CRYSTAL; Cornell HS; Coraopolis, PA; (3); Exploring; Key Clb; Church Choir; Mrchg Band; School Play; Nwsp Stf; Var JV Cheerleading; Var Pom Pon; JV Sftbl; Hon Roll; Norfolk ST; Bus.

MAYNARD, NATHANIEL; Cathedral Preparatory Schl; Edinboro, PA; (3); 53/238; Camera Clb; Church Yth Grp; Trs Political Wkr; Science Clb; Nwsp Phtg; Yrbk Phtg; Yrbk Stf; Bsktbl; Ftbl; Wrstlng; Full Schlrshp Cathedral Prep Schl 85-86.

MAYNARD, PATRICK; Milton SR HS; New Columbia, PA; (2); Boy Scts; Church Yth Grp; Penn ST; Meteorology.

MAYNES, SHANNON; Cardinal Dougherty HS; Philadelphia, PA; (3); 49/684; Cmnty Wkr; Hosp Aide; JV Var Bsktbl; JV Var Fld Hcky; JV Socr; JV Var Sftbl; Hon Roll; NHS; Physical Therapy.

MAYO, JANE-MARGARET; Parkland HS; Allentown, PA; (2); Pres Exploring; VP JCL; Latin Clb; Scholastic Bowl; Science Clb; Var Fld Hcky; Var Trk; High Hon Roll; Math Tm; School Musical; VP PA JR Clsscl Lg 87-88; PA Bio Olympcs Tm 87; PA Sci Olympd Regnl 87.

MAYO, SHELDON; West Mifflin Area HS; W Mifflin, PA; (3); Pres Church Yth Grp; Drama Clb; Exploring; Hosp Aide; Pres Church Choir; Nwsp Stf; Hon Roll; NHS; Penn ST Mnrty Advcd Plcmnt Pgm 87; Cmmnctns.

MAYOR, ALISA G; Council Rock HS; Holland, PA; (4); 23/848; VP FBLA; Chorus; Ed Nwsp Rptr; Ed Lit Mag; High Hon Roll; NHS; Ntl Merit SF; Brwn Univ Bk Awd 86; St Busi Englsh Ftr Busi Ldrs 85; Englsh.

MAYR, KARIN; Allentown Central Catholic HS; Allentown, PA; (4); 1/204; Am Leg Aux Girls St; Church Yth Grp; Math Clb; Math Tm; Scholastic Bowl; Lit Mag; NHS; Ntl Merit SF; Val; Amrcn Assn Physcs Tchrs Awd Outstndg Physcs Stu Of Yr 87; Soc Wmn Engnrs Awd 87; Carnegie-Mellon U; Arch.

MAYS, CHRISTOPHER L; Chartiers Valley HS; Carnegie, PA; (4); 20/300; Pres Church Yth Grp; Varsity Clb; VP Socr; VP Capt Trk; High Hon Roll; NHS; Ntl Merit SF; Pres Schlr; St Schlr; PA Cert Of Merit-Outstndng Prfrmnc On SAT 87; U Schlrshp-Duquesne U 87; Provost Schlrshp-U Of Pbgh; U Of Pittsburgh; Math.

MAYS, MISTY; Susquehannock HS; New Freedom, PA; (2); 44/243; Varsity Clb; Rep Frsh Cls; Pres Jr Cls; Var L Sftbl; Var L Vllybl; Hon Roll; USVBA S PA Vlybl Tm 87; Chld Psych.

MAYS, PAIGE; Keystone JR SR HS; Knox, PA; (3); Pep Clb; Chorus; School Musical; JV Cheerleading; Hon Roll; Ntl Travel Schl Of Pittsburgh.

MAYS, TABITHA LOVE; West Catholic Girls HS; Philadelphia, PA; (3); 82/246; Hosp Aide; Sec Latin Clb; Library Aide; Office Aide; Pep Clb; Teachers Aide; Drill Tm; Nwsp Stf; Yrbk Stf; Rep Frsh Cls; Charles Ellis Schlsrph Fund 86-88; Sci Olympiap Winnder 86; Acad Achvt In Hstry & Typing 86-87; Med.

MAYSE, KELLY; Uniontown Area SR HS; Markleysburg, PA; (4); 48/278; Spanish Clb; High Hon Roll; Hon Roll; Jr NHS; Frgn Lang Hnr Soc; Hmroom VP.

MAYSTER, EDWARD; Chartiers Valley HS; Pittsburgh, PA; (3); Boy Scts; Church Yth Grp; Cmnty Wkr; FBLA; Temple Yth Grp; Score Keeper; Hon Roll; PA ST; Bus.

MAYTAN, ROBERT; Valley HS; Arnold, PA; (3); 14/265; Science Clb; Spanish Clb; Varsity Clb; JV Bsbl; Bsktbl; JV Ftbl; High Hon Roll; Hon Roll; NHS; Amer Lgn Awd 84-85; Stu Of Mnth Awd 85; Penn ST; Mech Engr.

MAZAKAS, PETER; Nativity B V M HS; Orwigsburg, PA; (2); 33/77; Aud/Vis; JV Var Bsktbl; Prfct Atten Awd; Sprts Brdcstng.

MAZEITIS, JAMIE; Bishop O Reilly HS; Courtdale, PA; (4); Service Clb; Chorus; Yrbk Ed-Chief; Sftbl; High Hon Roll; NHS; Pro Life Clb 84-85; Wilkes; Engl.

MAZESKI, MATTHEW; Saint Puis X HS; Sanatoga, PA; (4); 1/148; Latin Clb; Math Tm; Rep Frsh Cls; Off Soph Cls; Rep Jr Cls; Off Sr Cls; High Hon Roll; Lion Awd; NHS; Val; Amer Legion Awd 87; St Piux X Excell Engl & Theology 87; Villanova U; Jrnlsm.

MAZIARZ, CHRISTOPHER; Meadville Area SR HS; Meadville, PA; (4); Church Yth Grp; Pres VP Key Clb; Ed Science Clb; SADD; Varsity Clb; School Play; Nwsp Rptr; Nwsp Stf; Rep Soph Cls; L JV Bsktbl; Schlstc Hnr Scty 87; U Of Pittsburgh; Mech Engr.

MAZIAS, JOHN; Carlisle HS; Carlisle, PA; (3); Church Yth Grp; Cmnty Wkr; Computer Clb; Science Clb; JV Var Bsktbl; Wt Lftg; Hon Roll; Prfct Atten Awd; Captl Area Sci & Engnrng Fair Hnrbl Mntn 86; PTAA AAAA ST Bsktbll Champ 87; Bio.

MAZICH, EDWARD; Danville Area HS; Danville, PA; (1); 33/233; Boy Scts; Red Cross Aide; JV Crs Cntry; JV Trk; God Cntry Awd; High Hon Roll; Hon Roll; Pres Schlr.

MAZICH, JAMES; Danville Area SR HS; Danville, PA; (3); 49/187; Boy Scts; Key Clb; Red Cross Aide; Spanish Clb; JV Crs Cntry; Var Trk; God Cntry Awd; Hon Roll; NHS; Pres Schlr; PA ST U; Engr.

MAZIEKAS, JONATHAN; Mahanoy Area HS; Mahanoy City, PA; (2); Art Clb; Boy Scts; Spanish Clb; SADD; Band; Concert Band; Mrchg Band; Nwsp Stf; Bsbl; Prfct Atten Awd; Semi Fnls Govrs Schl For Arts 86; Ad Altare Dei Awd Boy Scouts Of Amer 87; Bloomsburg U; Art.

MAZOL, BILLIE JO; Dover Area HS; Dover, PA; (3); Camera Clb; Computer Clb; Drama Clb; Varsity Clb; School Play; Var JV Bsktbl; Var Mgr(s); Millersville; Commnctns.

MAZON, MARY BETH; Gateway SR HS; Monroeville, PA; (2); VP Sec JA; Model UN; Chorus; Church Choir; Off Soph Cls; JV Vllybl; High Hon Roll; Intl Mktg.

MAZUR, CHRISTINE; Penn Cambria HS; Cresson, PA; (3); Cheerleading; Hon Roll; Accntnt.

MAZUR, MICHELLE; Ambridge HS; Baden, PA; (4); 30/265; Church Yth Grp; French Clb; Girl Scts; Pep Clb; Concert Band; Mrchg Band; Pep Band; School Musical; Symp Band; Hon Roll; GS Svlr Ldrshp Awd 83; Slvr Awd 84; Gold Ldrshp Awd 86; Beaver Castle GS Cncl Brd Of Dir Rep 86-87; CC Of Beaver Cnty; Pub Rel.

MAZUR, TRINETTE; Bishop Carroll HS; Portage, PA; (4); 23/107; Pep Clb; Ski Clb; Yrbk Stf; Var Capt Bsktbl; Powder Puff Ftbl; Var Trk; Var L Vllybl; Hon Roll; NEDT Awd; U Of Dayton; Intl Law.

MAZYCK, DAVID; Lake-Lehman HS; Harveys Lake, PA; (2); Ski Clb; Band; Concert Band; Mrchg Band; High Hon Roll; Hon Roll; Jr NHS; NHS.

MAZZA, CHRISTINA; Marple Newtown SR HS; Broomall, PA; (4); 15/324; Drm Mjr(t); Trs Mrchg Band; Orch; Symp Band; VP Sec Stu Cncl; Hon Roll; Jr NHS; Pres NHS; NEDT Awd; Frnch Edtr Frgn Lang Nwspaper; La Salle U.

MAZZAFERRI, PAULA; Kutztown Area HS; Kutztown, PA; (4); 11/147; Band; Chorus; Flag Corp; School Musical; School Play; Variety Show; Stat Bsktbl; JV Var Tennis; High Hon Roll; NHS; Pres Acadmc Ftns Awd 87; Schlr Athlt Awd 87; Acadmc Schlrshp-Loyola U Of Chgo 87; Loyola U Chgo; Cmnctns.

MAZZAFERRO, SUSAN L; Hempfield Area SR HS; Largo, FL; (4); DECA; Swmmng; Hon Roll; DECA 3rd Dist Wnnr 86-87; DECA 7th Pl Dist Wnnr 85-86; Bus Mgt.

MAZZATESTA, JENNIFER; Susquehanna Township HS; Harrisburg, PA; (4); Church Yth Grp; Girl Scts; Key Clb; Model UN; Chorus; Mrchg Band; Var Cheerleading; Hon Roll; Miss Xmas Seal Awd 87; Photography Awd 87; Penn ST U; Liberal Arts.

MAZZATTA, KEVIN; Scranton Central HS; Scranton, PA; (4); JV Wrstlng; Hon Roll; Natl Art Hnr Soc 87; Penn ST; Bus.

MAZZEI, LAURIE M; Neshannock HS; New Castle, PA; (3); Girl Scts; Ski Clb; Chorus; School Musical; JV Var Cheerleading; Sftbl; Hon Roll.

MAZZIO, VINCENT; Salesianum HS For Boys; West Chester, PA; (3); 51/268; Jazz Band; Mrchg Band; Symp Band; Im Socr; Hon Roll.

MAZZOCCO, MICHAEL; Penn Cambria HS; Cresson, PA; (3); 17/209; French Clb; Pres Frsh Cls; Pres Jr Cls; L Bsbl; L Bsktbl; L Ftbl; High Hon Roll; Hon Roll; NHS; Prfct Atten Awd.

MAZZOTTA, MARY; Burrell SR HS; Lower Burrell, PA; (3); High Hon Roll; NHS; Ltr B Swiss Lamp Knowldge 85-87; Elem Ed.

MAZZOTTA, VINCENT; Penn Trafford HS; Jeannette, PA; (2); 1/321; Chess Clb; Church Yth Grp; Varsity Clb; Crs Cntry; Var L Tennis; High Hon Roll; Prfct Atten Awd; Acad All-Amer 87; Engr.

MBONU, DOZIE; Church Farm Schl; Philadelphia, PA; (3); 1/16; Rep Soph Cls; Stu Cncl; Var Capt Bsktbl; Var Trk; Cit Awd; Hon Roll; Sec NHS; Band; Orch; Var Socr; Amer Chem Soc Awd 87; Bsktbl Spirit Awd 86-87; Bsktbl 1st Tm Keystone Athl Conf 86-87; Engr.

MC AARLAND, MICHELE; Oil City Area HS; Oil City, PA; (3); Model UN; Pep Clb; Nwsp Stf; Yrbk Stf; Var Bsktbl; Capt Cheerleading; JV Diving; Var Sftbl; Var Vllybl; Hon Roll; Cmnctns.

MC ADAMS, AMY; Saltsburg JR SR HS; New Alexandria, PA; (3); Drama Clb; Hosp Aide; Mrchg Band; Stat Vllybl; High Hon Roll; Hon Roll.

MC ADAMS, CARL; Blairsville SR HS; Blairsville, PA; (3); Military.

MC ADAMS, DAVID J; Penn Hills SR HS; Pittsburgh, PA; (3); 99/799; Am Leg Boys St; VP French Clb; Yrbk Ed-Chief; Rep Frsh Cls; Rep Soph Cls; Rep Jr Cls; Rep Stu Cncl; Vllybl; Hon Roll; Prfct Atten Awd; Red Crs Adv Life Saving 83; PA ST U; Aerontcl Engrng.

MC ADOO, JAMES; Punxsutawney Area SR HS; Glen Campbell, PA; (4); 12/246; Exploring; Math Tm; Science Clb; Trs Spanish Clb; Jazz Band; Symp Band; Variety Show; Yrbk Stf; High Hon Roll; NHS; Gannon U Acdmc Schlrshp 87; James V Colonna Band Awd 87; Gannon U; Fmly Med.

MC AFEE, AMY; Cumberland Valley HS; Camp Hill, PA; (3); 50/539; Key Clb; Latin Clb; Spanish Clb; Var Trk; High Hon Roll; NHS; Gold Key For Lit 85.

MC AFOOS, TINA; Punxsutawney Area SR HS; Punxsutawney, PA; (3); Hosp Aide; Spanish Clb; Varsity Clb; JV Var Bsktbl; Var L Tennis; Hon Roll; Stu Of Mnth 85 & 86; Pre-Law.

MC ALANIS, VICKI; Sch Haven HS; Auburn, PA; (4); English Clb; FNA; Girl Scts; Hosp Aide; Library Aide; SADD; Yrbk Stf; Pblctn 2 Poems Ntl Mgzns 86 & 87; Pblctn Poem & Cmpstn Penn St Schyl Wrtrs Bk 86 & 87; Med.

MC ALEE, CATHERINE; Cardinal O Hara HS; Springfield, PA; (3); 20/710; Dance Clb; Latin Clb; Office Aide; Service Clb; School Musical; Nwsp Stf; Ed Yrbk Stf; Hon Roll; NHS; Prfct Atten Awd; Acadc Hnrs Cnvctn 85-88; A P European Hstry Awd 86; Coll Prfsr.

MC ALEER, TRACEY; Steel Valley HS; Munhall, PA; (4); 27/201; Hosp Aide; Teachers Aide; Mat Maids; High Hon Roll; Hon Roll; NHS; Prfct Atten Awd; U Of Pittsburgh; Pre-Med.

MC ALILEY, LAUREN; Bishop Kenrick HS; Norristown, PA; (4); 92/219; Church Yth Grp; NAACP; Spanish Clb; Drill Tm; Flag Corp; School Musical; Mgr(s); Powder Puff Ftbl; Sftbl; Twigs Inc Schlrshp 87; Duquesne U; Psych.

MC ALLISTER, ANITA; West Perry HS; Shermansdale, PA; (2); 42/222; Drama Clb; French Clb; Pep Clb; Band; School Play; Sftbl; Hon Roll; Miss Amer Coed ST Fnlst PA 87; Jrnlsm.

MC ALLISTER, APRIL; Uniontown Area HS; Uniontown, PA; (2); Drama Clb; Spanish Clb; Band; Mrchg Band; Swmmng; DAR Awd; High Hon Roll; Hon Roll; Spanish NHS; Swmmng Ltr 86; Cnty Band Awds/Badge 85 & 86.

MC ALLISTER, DONNA; Steel Valley HS; W Homestead, PA; (3); 7/209; Church Yth Grp; Yrbk Stf; High Hon Roll; Hon Roll; NHS; Nutrition.

MC ALLISTER, KRISTIE; Fairchance-Georges HS; Fairchance, PA; (3); Band; Concert Band; Flag Corp; Mrchg Band; Bsktbl; Sftbl; Hon Roll.

MC ALLISTER, LENNY; Central Catholic HS; Verona, PA; (2); 70/300; Dance Clb; JV Bsbl; JV Bsktbl; JV Ftbl; Hon Roll; Hugh O Brian Yth Ldrshp Fndtn Ambssdr 87; Conf For Ldrs In F S C High Schools 87; Psych.

MC ALLISTER, NATASHA; Upper Darby HS; Upr Darby, PA; (3); 23/598; Cmnty Wkr; Pres VP German Clb; Concert Band; Mrchg Band; Rep Jr Cls; Cit Awd; High Hon Roll; Jr NHS; Opt Clb Awd; Prfct Atten Awd; Marine Bio.

MC ALPINE, MARCIA; Seneca Valley HS; Callery, PA; (3); Sec Church Yth Grp; Cmnty Wkr; Band; Mrchg Band; Symp Band; Yrbk Stf; Rep Jr Cls; Hon Roll; NHS; Elem Ed.

MC ANALLEN, ERIC; Lincoln HS; New Castle, PA; (4); 2/165; Boy Scts; Drama Clb; Spanish Clb; Chorus; School Musical; Bausch & Lomb Sci Awd; High Hon Roll; NHS; NEDT Awd; Sal; Jack Pearson Mem Scholar 87; Lions Clb Stu Of Mnth 86; Slippery Rock U Bk Awd 87; Carnegie Mellon; Appld Math.

MC ANALLEN, LAURA; Washington HS; Washington, PA; (2); Ski Clb; Spanish Clb; Stu Cncl; Cheerleading; Vllybl; High Hon Roll; Hon Roll; Notre Dame; Engrng.

MC ANDREW, DAWN; Bishop O Reilly HS; Kingston, PA; (3); Church Yth Grp; Drama Clb; Pep Clb; Red Cross Aide; Chorus; School Musical; School Play; Var JV Cheerleading; Hon Roll; NEDT Awd; Physcl Thpry.

MC ANDREW, JAY; Emmaus HS; Emmaus, PA; (3); 36/548; Crs Cntry; Wrstlng; Hon Roll; Jr NHS; NHS; Bus.

MC ANDREW, SHARON; Bishop O Hara HS; Archbald, PA; (4); 15/115; French Clb; Sec Latin Clb; Chorus; School Musical; Ed Nwsp Rptr; Sec Frsh Cls; Hon Roll; NHS; Fnlst Gov Schl Arts 85; Marywood Coll; Jrnlsm.

MC ANINCH, KELLI; Freeport Area SR HS; Sarver, PA; (3); 46/215; Mrchg Band; Stat Bsktbl; Capt Cheerleading; Hon Roll; Nsrg.

MC ANLIS, COLLEEN; Mohawk Area JR-SR HS; Enon Valley, PA; (4); 4/130; Girl Scts; Band; Concert Band; Jazz Band; Yrbk Stf; Sec Sr Cls; Score Keeper; Hon Roll; NHS; Ntl Merit Ltr; Slippery Rock St U Book Awd 87; Carolyn Knox Fndtn Schlrshp Awd 87; Carnegie Mellon U; Chemistry.

MC ANLIS, JENNIFER; Mohawk Area JR SR HS; Enon Valley, PA; (3); Girl Scts; Latin Clb; SADD; VP Band; Concert Band; Mrchg Band; Orch; School Musical; Yrbk Stf; Stu Cncl; Amr Leg Awd 85; Envrnmntl Stds.

MC ANULTY, ROBYN LYNN; Archbishop Prendergast HS; Upper Darby, PA; (4); 49/325; Church Yth Grp; Political Wkr; Teachers Aide; Orch; Yrbk Rptr; Yrbk Stf; Im Sftbl; Im Vllybl; Hon Roll; Prfct Atten Awd; W W Smith Awd 87; Cabrini Coll; Early Chldhd Ed.

MC ARDLE, BRADLEY; Jim Thorpe HS; Jim Thorpe, PA; (3); 5/90; Aud/Vis; Quiz Bowl; Scholastic Bowl; Band; Concert Band; Mrchg Band; Im Vllybl; High Hon Roll; Chem Engrng.

MC ARDLE, LAURA; West Allegheny SR HS; Imperial, PA; (2); 38/230; Hosp Aide; Spanish Clb; Y-Teens; Score Keeper; Swmmng; Hon Roll; Scl Wrkr.

MC ARDLE, LISA; Ambridge Area HS; Baden, PA; (2); French Clb; Girl Scts; Hosp Aide; Pep Clb; Teachers Aide; Band; Concert Band; Co-Capt Drill Tm; Mrchg Band; Hon Roll.

MC ARDLE, LORI; Ambridge Area HS; Baden, PA; (3); French Cl Hosp Aide; Pep Clb; Band; Concert Band; Jazz Band; Mrchg Band; Orc School Musical; Symp Band; Geneva Coll; Engrng.

MC ATEE, JENNIFER; Neshaminy HS; Langhorne, PA; (3); 30/79 Dance Clb; Service Clb; Chorus; School Musical; Nwsp Rptr; Nwsp S High Hon Roll; Hon Roll; NHS; Nwpr Entertainment Editor 86-87; Am Leg Merit Awd; Sci.

MC AVOY, JAMES; Bishop Hafey HS; Sugar Loaf, PA; (3); Ski Cl Spanish Clb.

MC AVOY, KATHLEEN; Lake-Lehman HS; Sweet Valley, PA; (3 Church Yth Grp; Girl Scts; SADD; Rep Band; Concert Band; Rep Mrc Band; Orch; Rep Symp Band; Sec Frsh Cls; Sec Soph Cls; PA All ST Ban 87; Dist & Rgnl Band 86-87; Dist & Rgnl Orch 86-87; Temple U; Pharm

MC AVOY, TIMOTHY; Hanover Area HS; Wilkes Barre, PA; (4); Ke Clb; Ski Clb; Stage Crew; Bsktbl; Crs Cntry; Trk.

MC BLAIN, JOSEPH; Monsignor Bonner HS; Aldan, PA; (3); Offi Aide; Hon Roll; Bus Adm.

MC BRAIRTY, CHRISTOPHER; Notre Dame HS; Easton, PA; (3); 2 96; Coach Actv; Var Ftbl; Wt Lftg; High Hon Roll; Bio.

MC BRIAR, MARK; Penn Hills SR HS; Penn Hills, PA; (3); Church Y Grp; Drama Clb; Science Clb; Ski Clb; Mgr Stage Crew; Rep Stu Cncl; V L Ftbl; Var Sftbl; Var Trk; Var High Hon Roll; Pony Lg Bsbl Lg Champ 84; TAC Regnl Champ 400 Yd Dash 84; Jesse Owens City Champ 400 Y Dash 84; Engrng.

MC BRIDE, JASON; Aliquippa HS; Aliquippa, PA; (3); Church Yth Gr DECA; NAACP; Var Bsktbl; Var Capt Ftbl; Var L Wt Lftg; Hon Roll.

MC BRIDE, LYNNETTE; Seneca Valley HS; Evans City, PA; (4); 2 347; JA; Ski Clb; Varsity Clb; Var Capt Bsktbl; Crs Cntry; Var Capt Tr High Hon Roll; Hon Roll; NHS; Acadmc Athltc Schlrshp 87; Trck MV 86-87; Bsktbl MVP 87; Bucknell U; Bus.

MC BRIDE, MARGRET; Marian Catholic HS; Jim Thorpe, PA; (4); 2 114; Church Yth Grp; Pep Clb; Ski Clb; SADD; School Play; Stat Ftl Sftbl; High Hon Roll; Hon Roll; Spanish NHS; E Stroudsberg U; Mgmt

MC BRIDE, PETER; Seneca HS; Erie, PA; (3); JV Var Ftbl; Var Tr Hon Roll.

MC BURNEY, JANE; Millersburg Area HS; Millersburg, PA; (4); 13/8 Church Yth Grp; Chorus; Church Choir; Nwsp Bus Mgr; Nwsp Stf; Sec S Cls; Powder Puff Ftbl; Trk; Hon Roll; NHS; Harrisburg Area CC; Bu Mgmt.

MC CABE, CAROL; Franklin Regional HS; Bowie, MD; (4); AFS; A Clb; Church Yth Grp; FHA; Yrbk Stf; Hon Roll; U Of MD; German.

MC CABE, CLIFF; Athens Area HS; Athens, PA; (3); Church Yth Gr FFA; SADD; Yrbk Rptr; Bsbl; Bsktbl; Coach Actv; Ftbl; Trk; Prfct Atte Awd; Sci.

MC CABE, JAMES P; Archbishop Ryan For Boys; Philadelphia, PA; (3 31/414; Church Yth Grp; Spanish Clb; JV L Crs Cntry; JV L Trk; Hi Hon Roll; Hon Roll.

MC CABE, LINDA; Portage Area HS; Portage, PA; (3); 40/109; Hon Ro Cake Baking Cont Hm Mkng Cls 2nd Pl 87.

MC CABE, MICHELLE; Lake Lehman HS; Harveys Lake, PA; (4); Se Church Yth Grp; SADD; School Play; High Hon Roll; Bowling; Hon Ro NHS; Susquehanna U; Mktg.

MC CAFFERTY, MALINDA; Interboro HS; Essington, PA; (4); Cmnt Wkr; Computer Clb; JCL; Latin Clb; Flag Corp; Yrbk Stf; Off Frsh Cls; O Soph Cls; Off Jr Cls; Off Sr Cls; U S Cngrssnl Page 85-86; Sctt Papr Hi Q Tm 86-87; Cum Laude-Ntl Ltn Exam 84; Georgetown U; Bio.

MC CAFFERY, ANDREW C; Danville SR HS; Danville, PA; (4); 43/19 Aud/Vis; Chess Clb; Cmnty Wkr; Exploring; Latin Clb; Red Cross Aid Rep Sr Cls; JV Wrstlng; High Hon Roll; Prfct Atten Awd; Penn S Meterolgy.

MC CAFFERY, JANE; Danville SR HS; Danville, PA; (3); Spanish Cl Trk; Hon Roll; Natl Hnr Soc 86-87; Bloomsburg U; Accntng.

MC CAFFREY, TRICIA; St Fancis Acad; Pittsburgh, PA; (2); #1 Class; High Hon Roll; NHS; Prfct Atten Awd; VFW Awd; U Of Pittsbur Med Dctr.

MC CAGUE, MARK; Riverview HS; Oakmont, PA; (4); 6/120; Dram Clb; Ski Clb; Varsity Clb; School Play; Yrbk Sprt Ed; Pres Sr Cls; Rep St Cncl; Capt Crs Cntry; JV Ftbl; Capt Trk; Natl Merit Corp Schlrshp 8 Carnegie-Mellon U; Ind Mgmt.

MC CAIN, JAMES; Meadville Area SR HS; Meadville, PA; (4); 71/32 Wt Lftg; Hon Roll; NHS; Arch.

MC CAIN, JENNIFER; Owen J Roberts HS; Pottstown, PA; (2); 11/31 Dance Clb; Key Clb; Chorus; Madrigals; Mrchg Band; Orch; Scho Musical; School Play; Var Trk; Hon Roll; Marine Bio.

MC CAIN, THOMAS; Oil City SR HS; Rouseville, PA; (3); 61/28 Camera Clb; Drama Clb; Science Clb; PA ST; Engnrg.

MC CALICHER, TRICIA; Reading SR HS; Reading, PA; (2); 69/81 Key Clb; Nwsp Stf; Bsktbl; Sftbl; Vllybl; Prfct Atten Awd; Art Aw Graphic Reproduction.

MC CALL, BRIAN; Monsignor Bonner HS; Lansdowne, PA; (3); 1/27 Debate Tm; Model UN; JV Rep NFL; Speech Tm; Yrbk Stf; Pres Frsh Cl Pres Soph Cls; Pres Jr Cls; French Hon Soc; High Hon Roll; NCLF Gran Ntl Tourn 5th Pl 86; Schrlshp Monsgnr Bonner 84-88; HOBY Foun Outstndng Stu 86; Pol Sci.

MC CALL, BRUCE; Karns City HS; Chicora, PA; (4); Church Yth Gr Exploring; FCA; Var L Crs Cntry; Var L Trk; Hon Roll; NHS; Grove Cit Coll; Math.

MC CALL, DONALD; Elizabeth-Forward HS; Elizabeth, PA; (3); Cmnt Wkr; Jazz Band; Mrchg Band; Vol & Emergncy Mdl Techn Tri Com Ambl 87; Vol Firefghtr Gallatin Sunnyside VFD 85-87; U Pittsburgh; P Med.

MC CALL, ERIN; Henderson SR HS; West Chester, PA; (3); Intnl Cl Ski Clb; SADD; Crs Cntry; Lcrss; NHS; Voice Dem Awd; Acadc Ach Awd 87; Smmr Smnr Camp Grmny 87; Penn ST; Art.

MC CALL, FLYNN; Keystone Oaks HS; Pittsburgh, PA; (3); 52/25 Capt Var Bsktbl; French Hon Soc; Hon Roll.

MC CALL, KENDRA; Pocono Mountain HS; Pocono Summit, PA; (3 Church Yth Grp; Computer Clb; Girl Scts; SADD; VICA; Capt Bowlin Hon Roll; Prfct Atten Awd; Comp.

MC CALLAN, THOMAS; Hopewell HS; Aliquippa, PA; (3); 15/25 Church Yth Grp; Latin Clb; High Hon Roll; Hon Roll; Aviation.

MC CALLUM, SHARON; Harry S Truman HS; Levittown, PA; (3); 8 599; Stage Crew; Cmrcl Art.

MC CAMEY, KAREN; Perry T A HS; Pittsburgh, PA; (4); 15/119; German Clb; Library Aide; Office Aide; Radio Clb; Teachers Aide; Chorus; Drill Tm; Nwsp Stf; High Hon Roll; NHS; Hnrs Schlrshp Boyce Campus 87; Hnr Grad 87; Cert Of Compltn Jrnslm Wrkshp Pt Park Coll 85; Boyce Coll; Jrnlsm.

MC CAMEY, RENEE; Riverview HS; Oakmont, PA; (3); Drama Clb; French Clb; Varsity Clb; Ed Yrbk Stf; Stu Cncl; Stat Bsbl; JV Var Cheerleading; Powder Puff Ftbl; High Hon Roll; Hon Roll; Pittsburgh Beauty; Csmtlgy.

MC CAMMON, DIANE; Upper Dublin HS; Ft Washington, PA; (3); 9/300; Intnl Clb; SADD; Nwsp Stf; Yrbk Bus Mgr; Rep Stu Cncl; Fld Hcky; Lcrss; Hon Roll; NHS; Math.

MC CAMMON, ELIZABETH; General Mc Lane HS; Mckean, PA; (4); Cmnty Wkr; Exploring; German Clb; Hosp Aide; Teachers Aide; Mrchg Band; Rep Stu Cncl; High Hon Roll; Hon Roll; NHS; Cndystrpng 87; Pres Acad Ftns Awd 87; Bowling Green ST U.

MC CANCE, RICHARD A; East Junrata JR SR HS; Liverpool, PA; (4); 15/90; Var Capt Bsktbl; Var Socr; Var Capt Trk; High Hon Roll; Natl Schlstc Art Awds Gold Key Awd 85-86; Carnegie-Mellon U; Arch.

MC CANDLESS, JULIE; Western Beaver JR SR HS; Pittsburgh, PA; (2); Church Yth Grp; Chorus; Symp Band; Nwsp Rptr; Yrbk Stf; Cheerleading; Trk; High Hon Roll; Hon Roll; HOBY Yth Ldrshp Awd.

MC CANDLESS, RACHEL; Slippery Rock Area HS; Prospect, PA; (4); Camera Clb; French Clb; Pep Clb; SADD; Capt Drm & Bgl; Capt Flag Corp; High Hon Roll; Pres Schlr; St Schlr; Kent ST U; Psych.

MC CANN, ANTHONY; Lansdale Catholic HS; Chalfont, PA; (3); Letterman Clb; SADD; Varsity Clb; Yrbk Rptr; Yrbk Stf; Var Bsktbl; Var L Socr; Var L Trk; Hon Roll; Pres Schlr; Bus Adm.

MC CANN, JIM; Butler Area SR HS; Butler, PA; (4); Exploring; JV Trk; Hon Roll; Pres Schlr; U Pittsburgh; Mech Engrng.

MC CANN, JOAN; Seneca Valley HS; Zelienople, PA; (3); 53/360; JA; Church Choir; Mrchg Band; Symp Band; Ed Yrbk Stf; VP Jr Cls; Sec Sr Cls; Sec Stu Cncl; High Hon Roll; Lion Awd; Westmnstr Coll Hnrs Band 86-87; PA Dist V Band 87; Butler Cnty All Str Band 85-86; Elem Ed.

MC CANN, KAREN B; Academy Of Notre Dame; King Of Prussia, PA; (4); Cmnty Wkr; Drama Clb; Hosp Aide; School Musical; School Play; Yrbk Stf; Hon Roll; Bucknell U; Psych.

MC CANN, MIKE; Parkland HS; Allentown, PA; (2); Capt JV Bsktbl; Hon Roll.

MC CANN, SCOTT; Freedom HS; Bethlehem, PA; (4); 35/435; Drama Clb; French Clb; Thesps; School Play; Stage Crew; Yrbk Phtg; Ice Hcky; Tennis; High Hon Roll; Prsdntl Acdmc Ftnss Awd 86-87; U Of Notre Dame; Arntcl Engrng.

MC CANN, STACY L; Duphin County Technical Schl; Harrisburg, PA; (3); 26/212; Cmnty Wkr; DECA; SADD; Yrbk Stf; Hon Roll; Brdcstng.

MC CANN, TRACEY; Upper Darby HS; Upper Darby, PA; (3); Band; Color Guard; Hon Roll; Physcl Thrpy.

MC CARDELL, TAMMY; Waynesboro Area SR HS; Rouzerville, PA; (3); Trs Church Yth Grp; Girl Scts; Color Guard; Score Keeper; Hon Roll; Pep Clb; Yrbk Stf; Hghst Gld Awd In Girl Sctng 86; Med Sec.

MC CARDELL, THOMAS; Solanco HS; Kirkwood, PA; (2); 8/240; Cmnty Wkr; Exploring; Pres Frsh Cls; Pres Soph Cls; Rep Stu Cncl; JV Bsbl; JV Ftbl; Im Wt Lftg; High Hon Roll; NHS; HOBY.

MC CARDLE, JENNIFER; Chief Logan HS; Yeagertown, PA; (4); 1/200; Spanish Clb; Speech Tm; Band; Chorus; Fld Hcky; High Hon Roll; NHS; Val; Church Yth Grp; French Clb; Jostons Hstry Awd 87; Yrbk Copy Edtr; Shippensburg U; Elem Tchr.

MC CARRAHER, JAMES; Cedar Grove Christian Acad; Philadelphia, PA; (4); Church Yth Grp; Drama Clb; School Play; Nwsp Rptr; Off Frsh Cls; Off Soph Cls; Off Sr Cls; High Hon Roll; Hon Roll; Acadc Hnr 87; Music Schlrshp 87; Dean Schlrshp 87; Philadelphia Coll Bible; Music.

MC CARRAHER, TAMMY; Horace C Scott HS; Pomeroy, PA; (2); Ski Clb; Spanish Clb; Var Fld Hcky; Var Sftbl; Hon Roll; Pres Schlr.

MC CARRON, MEGAN; Acad Of Notre Dame; Media, PA; (3); Cmnty Wkr; Service Clb; School Musical; School Play; Stage Crew; Yrbk Stf; Med Prfsn W/Chldrn.

MC CARTHY, BRIAN; Susquehannock HS; Glen Rock, PA; (2); 46/260; AFS; Pres Ski Clb; Teachers Aide; Rep Frsh Cls; Rep Soph Cls; Rep Jr Cls; Rep Stu Cncl; Var Crs Cntry; JV Trk; Hon Roll; USAFA; Aerontcs.

MC CARTHY, CRISTIN; Villa Mana Acad; Exton, PA; (3); 1/96; Church Yth Grp; Sec NFL; Capt Speech Tm; School Musical; Rep Soph Cls; Var Tennis; High Hon Roll; NHS; Spanish NHS; Opt Clb Awd; Numers Spkg Awds Incldg Qualf NCFL Natls 86-87; Chem Engrng.

MC CARTHY, DENINE; Mahanoy Area HS; Mahanoy Plane, PA; (3); Spanish Clb; Band; Concert Band; Jazz Band; Mrchg Band; Pep Band; Var L Trk; Hon Roll; Nursng.

MC CARTHY, DIANE; Linesville HS; Conneaut Lk, PA; (3); 8/65; FHA; Spanish Clb; Hon Roll.

MC CARTHY JR, M; N E Bradford HS; Rome, PA; (3); Boy Scts; Camera Clb; Chess Clb; Debate Tm; 4-H; Hon Roll; Engl.

MC CARTHY, MONIKA; Strath Haven HS; Swarthmore, PA; (3); French Clb; German Clb; Red Cross Aide; JV Var Sftbl; Deans List 84-87; German Acdmc Hon 85-87; Envrmntl Stds.

MC CARTNEY, CRYSTAL; Altoona Area HS; Altoona, PA; (3); 50/768; Spanish Clb; SADD; Band; Concert Band; Drm & Bgl; Mrchg Band; Orch; High Hon Roll; Hon Roll; Pblctn Dsgnd Tch JR Hgh Stu 87; Law.

MC CARTNEY, PAUL; Quigley HS; Evans City, PA; (4); 5/98; Computer Clb; JA; Math Tm; Teachers Aide; Nwsp Rptr; Trk; High Hon Roll; Hon Roll; NHS; Robert Byrd Schlrshp 87; Air Force Math &sci Awd 87; Adv Bio Awd 87; Carnegie Mellon U; Sci.

MC CARTNEY, T P; Quigley HS; Evans City, PA; (4); 9/113; Exploring; JA; Math Clb; Nwsp Stf; Trk; High Hon Roll; NHS; Sci.

MC CARTNEY, TAGG; Washington Christian Schl; Prosperity, PA; (2); Debate Tm; Trs Stu Cncl; 4-H Awd; Spanish Clb; School Play; Hon Roll; Vet.

MC CARTNEY, TERRANCE; Quigley HS; Evans City, PA; (4); 5/98; Computer Clb; JA; Math Clb; Teachers Aide; Nwsp Rptr; Trk; High Hon Roll; Hon Roll; NHS; Robert Byrd Schlrshp 87; Air Force Math & Sci Awd 87; Comp Sci II Awd 87; Carnegie Mellon U; Appld Math.

MC CARTY, THERESA; Quakertown SR HS; Quakertown, PA; (3); VP Church Yth Grp; Library Aide; Church Choir; Stat Bsbl; High Hon Roll; Hon Roll; Jr NHS; NHS; Ntl Merit Ltr; Pres Schlr; U Of IN; Astro Physcs.

MC CASLIN, KELLY; Lincoln HS; Ellwood City, PA; (3); 16/163; Church Yth Grp; Drama Clb; VP Latin Clb; Y-Teens; Chorus; School Musical; Swing Chorus; Rep Frsh Cls; Tennis; High Hon Roll; Westminster Hnrs Chorus 85.

MC CASLIN, SUSAN L; Muncy HS; Muncy, PA; (4); Pres Church Yth Grp; Pres Sec 4-H; Sec VP Spanish Clb; Band; Rep Stu Cncl; JC Awd; 4-H Awd; High Hon Roll; NHS; Spanish NHS; 4-H Keystone Wnnr Blue Frm Rcrd Bk, Pres Acdmc Ftnss Awd, & PTSA Schlrshp 87; Penn ST U; Ag.

MC CAULEY, AMY; Connellsville Area HS; S Connellsville, PA; (3); GAA; Var L Bsktbl; Mgr(s); Hon Roll; NHS; Chld Dev.

MC CAULEY, DIANNA; North Clarion HS; Fryburg, PA; (3); Sec Church Yth Grp; Pres 4-H; Spanish Clb; Color Guard; Yrbk Stf; JV Cheerleading; High Hon Roll; Hon Roll; NHS; Clarion U; RN.

MC CAULEY, LEEANN; Saint Huberts HS; Philadelphia, PA; (3); 87/421; Cmnty Wkr; Dance Clb; Pep Clb; Spanish Clb; Chorus; Chrmn Orch; School Musical; School Play; Var JV Mgr(s); Var JV Score Keeper; Temple U.

MC CAULEY, MARY; Solanco HS; Drumore, PA; (2); Church Yth Grp; Cmnty Wkr; Chorus; High Hon Roll; Hon Roll; Debate Tm; Law.

MC CAULEY, MAUREEN; Archbiship Carroll HS; Havertown, PA; (3); 120/376; Church Yth Grp; Cmnty Wkr; Lit Mag; Socr; Penn ST; Comms.

MC CAULLEY JR, RON; Blairsville-Saltzburg HS; Blairsville, PA; (1); Hon Roll; Pa ST U; Aerontcl Engr.

MC CAULLY, PAMELA ANNE; Schuylkill Valley HS; Mohrsville, PA; (3); 10/134; 4-H; Chorus; School Play; Fld Hcky; Vllybl; NHS; US Army; Linguistcs.

MC CHESNEY, TAMMI; Oswayo Valley HS; Shinglehouse, PA; (3); JA; Varsity Clb; Flag Corp; Mrchg Band; Stu Cncl; Bsktbl; Score Keeper; Stat Trk; JV Var Vllybl; Hon Roll; Edinboro; Jrnlsm.

MC CHESSNEY, DARRIN; Williamsburg HS; Williamsburg, PA; (3); 4/60; Church Yth Grp; Concert Band; Yrbk Stf; JV Var Ftbl; Wt Lftg; Hon Roll; NHS.

MC CLAFFERTY, CARRIE; Bishop Conwell HS; Levittown, PA; (3); 14/277; Rep Vllybl; Pres Sr Cls; Var Capt Socr; High Hon Roll; Hon Roll; NHS; PA JR Acad Sci Rgnl & ST Meets 1st Awds 86; All Cathlc Philadelphia Cathlc Leag Sccr 86-87; Bus.

MC CLAIN JR, GENE; Jeannette HS; Jeannette, PA; (2); Var JV Bsktbl; Var JV Ftbl; Hon Roll; Chrch Rltd Svc, Actvts; Demogrphcs.

MC CLAIN, HEATHER; Belle Vernon Area HS; Belle Vernon, PA; (3); Church Yth Grp; Band; Concert Band; Mrchg Band; Stage Crew; Powder Puff Ftbl; Stat Sftbl; Hon Roll; NHS; Acctng.

MC CLAIN, KIMBERLY; Bedford HS; Bedford, PA; (4); Church Yth Grp; Office Aide; SADD; Chorus; Trk; Hon Roll; Outstndng Achvt Awd Typng 85; Southeastern Bible Clg; Elem Ed.

MC CLAIN, RANDY; Huntingdon Area SR HS; Huntingdon, PA; (2); Chess Clb; Church Yth Grp; VICA; Comp Svc Tech.

MC CLAIN, SCOTT; Montour HS; Coraopolis, PA; (3); Church Yth Grp; Culinary Inst PA; Fd Preprtn.

MC CLAIN, STACY; Burgettstown JR SR HS; Burgettstown, PA; (4); 20/140; Ski Clb; Spanish Clb; Chorus; Stu Cncl; Cheerleading; Sftbl; Wt Lftg; High Hon Roll; Hon Roll; NHS; Diploma Merit 87; Schlrshp Cert Honor 87; Vrsty Ltr Sftbl & Chrldng 84-87; U Of Pittsburgh; Pharm.

MC CLAIN, STEPHEN D; Harrisburg High HS; Harrisburg, PA; (2); 4/256; Chess Clb; Hon Roll; 2nd Pl HS Sci Fair 85-86; Psychlgst.

MC CLANAHAN, CHRISTY; Waynesboro Area SR HS; Waynesboro, PA; (3); Band; Chorus; Concert Band; Mrchg Band; Rep Jr Cls; NHS; Comm.

MC CLARY, RAY; Tunkhannock Area HS; Tunkhannock, PA; (3); Aud/Vis; Letterman Clb; Science Clb; Crs Cntry; Trk; Hon Roll; Aerontcs.

MC CLAY, SCOTT; Mercer Area HS; Mercer, PA; (1); Church Yth Grp; Ftbl; U Of PA Slpry Rck; Math.

MC CLEARY, BRIDGOT; Du Bois Area SR HS; Rockton, PA; (2); 44/311; Dance Clb; Band; Chorus; Concert Band; Flag Corp; Mrchg Band; School Musical; Swing Chorus; Hon Roll; Prfct Atten Awd; Vocal Music.

MC CLEARY, BRYNN; Biglerville HS; Biglerville, PA; (2); 18/109; Library Aide; JV Fld Hcky; High Hon Roll; Hon Roll; Jr NHS; Cosmtlgy.

MC CLEARY, CARRIE; Seneca Valley HS; Evans Cty, PA; (2); Art Clb; VP 4-H; Ski Clb; Stat Ftbl; Hon Roll; HS 1st Yr Schlstc Awd 86-87; Engrng.

MC CLEARY, GEOFFREY; Mifflinburg Area SR HS; Mifflinburg, PA; (3); 42/173; Church Yth Grp; French Clb; Key Clb; Yrbk Phtg; High Hon Roll; Hon Roll; PA ST U; Aerospc Engrng.

MC CLEARY, MEGAN; General Mc Lane HS; Mckean, PA; (3); 36/223; German Clb; GAA; Letterman Clb; Model UN; Off Stu Cncl; Var Capt Crs Cntry; Var Trk; Hon Roll; MVP Cross Country Runner 87; All County, Dist & State In Cross Country 87; Cornell U; Bio.

MC CLEARY, MICHAEL; Brookville Area HS; Mayport, PA; (3); 76/175; Art Clb; Chess Clb; German Clb; Varsity Clb; Chorus; Var L Wrstlng.

MC CLEARY, WILLIAM; Father Judge HS; Philadelphia, PA; (3); 39/401; Art Clb; Aud/Vis; Camera Clb; Spanish Clb; Yrbk Ed-Chief; Ice Hcky; JV Trk; Hon Roll; NHS; Admtnce Natl Hnr Soc, Yrbk Awd Bst Wrk 87; Recgntn Excllnce Engl 85; Boston U; Bus Admin.

MC CLELAND, DAVE; Quakertown SR HS; Green Lane, PA; (4); 43/311; Am Leg Boys St; Church Yth Grp; VP Pres 4-H; Capt Socr; 4-H Awd; Hon Roll; Geo Wshngtn U; Law Enfrcmnt.

MC CLELLAN, CINDY; West Greene HS; Sycamore, PA; (4); 23/105; Rep Rptr DECA; FHA; Pres SADD; Pres Trs VICA; Band; VP Chorus; Color Guard; Stage Crew; Rep Stu Cncl; Hon Roll; Outstndg Stu 1st Sem Vo-Tech Mrktg 85-86; IN U Of PA; Vctnl Educ.

MC CLELLAN, LOLETTA; West Greene HS; Graysville, PA; (4); 13/105; Church Yth Grp; FHA; Church Choir; High Hon Roll; Hon Roll; NHS; Miss Upwrd Bnd; Brain Bstr Awd.

MC CLELLAN, MEREDITH; Northampton Area SR HS; Northampton, PA; (3); 75/497; DECA; Rep Frsh Cls; Rep Soph Cls; Var Capt Cheerleading; Hon Roll; 1st Pl DECA Dist Vi 87; 1st Pl Mini-Awds DECA State Conf 87; 2nd Pl DECA Dist 86; Bus.

MC CLELLAN, SHARI; Ft Le Boeuf HS; Waterford, PA; (3); 13/207; Ski Clb; Rep Soph Cls; Trs Rep Stu Cncl; Cheerleading; Score Keeper; Trk; Vllybl; High Hon Roll; NHS; Liberal Arts.

MC CLELLAN, SHELLEY; Glendale JR SR HS; Glasgow, PA; (2); Library Aide; Chorus; Stu Cncl; Stat Bsktbl; JV Cheerleading; JV Sftbl; Hon Roll; Pres Phy Ftns Awd; Nrsng.

MC CLELLAND, JAMI; Otto-Eldred HS; Rixford, PA; (3); Trs SADD; Varsity Clb; Chorus; Yrbk Stf; Sec Jr Cls; Rep Stu Cncl; Var Cheerleading; Hon Roll; Mantle Top Bus Stu 87; Bus.

MC CLELLAND, JUDITH; Sto-Rox SR HS; Mc Kees Rocks, PA; (3); 1/150; Church Yth Grp; FBLA; Hosp Aide; Letterman Clb; Chorus; Nwsp Stf; Yrbk Stf; Frsh Cls; Cheerleading; Hon Roll; Hlth.

MC CLELLAND, LAURA J; Mercer Area JR SR HS; Mercer, PA; (4); 1/140; Church Yth Grp; Service Clb; Ski Clb; School Musical; School Play; Ed Nwsp Ed-Chief; Yrbk Stf; Rep Stu Cncl; Pres NHS; SADD; Acad Games Ltr; Yth In Prtnrshp In Mission Tm Alaska Trp 85; Hugh O Brian Yth Ldrshp Sem; Intl Bus.

MC CLELLAND, LAUREL; Highlands SR HS; Natrona Hgts, PA; (3); Cmnty Wkr; SADD; Yrbk Stf; Sec Frsh Cls; Var JV Cheerleading; High Hon Roll; Jr NHS; NHS; NEDT Awd; Rachael Carson Essay Cont Awd Wnnr 87; Elem Ed.

MC CLELLAND, MICHAEL C; Pocono Mountain HS; Bartonsville, PA; (4); 40/330; Q&S; Ski Clb; Nwsp Stf; Lit Mag; Off Soph Cls; JV Bsktbl; Var Crs Cntry; JV Golf; Gym; Co-Capt Socr; Temple U; Cmmnctns.

MC CLELLAND, MICHELE; Brownsville Area HS; New Salem, PA; (4); 35/200; Drama Clb; Library Aide; Math Clb; SADD; Variety Show; Nwsp Rptr; Yrbk Stf; Rep Jr Cls; Vllybl; High Hon Roll; Penn ST U; Frgn Svc.

MC CLELLAND, MINDI; Conemaugh Township HS; Johnstown, PA; (3); Sec French Clb; Hosp Aide; Spanish Clb; School Musical; School Play; Stage Crew; Lit Mag; JV Vllybl; French Hon Soc; Spanish NHS; Spcl Educ.

MC CLENDON, MARVIN; Harrisburg HS; Harrisburg, PA; (4); 81/235; Art Clb; Band; Concert Band; Mrchg Band; JV Bsbl; Var Ftbl; Var Socr; Antonelli Schl; Commrcl Art.

MC CLIMANS, SCOTT; Moniteau JR-SR HS; West Sunbury, PA; (2); 6/143; Church Yth Grp; Band; Concert Band; Mrchg Band; Trk; Jr NHS; NHS; Bio.

MC CLINTIC, KRISTI; Center HS; Aliquippa, PA; (2); 57/200; Spanish Clb; Powder Puff Ftbl; Sftbl; Swmmng; Vllybl; Hon Roll.

MC CLINTICK, JASON; St Marys Area HS; Weedville, PA; (3); 86/290; Trs Church Yth Grp; JV Crs Cntry; Im Trk; Pre-Law.

MC CLINTOCK, GAREA; Mifflin Burgarea HS; Mifflinburg, PA; (1); French Clb; JV Bsbl; L JV Ftbl; Wrstlng; Hon Roll; Penn ST U; Tchr.

MC CLINTOCK, KEVIN LEE; Laurel Highlands SR HS; Uniontown, PA; (2); Acpl Chr; Church Choir; Yrbk Rptr; Yrbk Stf; High Hon Roll; NEDT Top Finalist 86; Psycht.

MC CLOSKEY, ALLISON; Archbishop Prendergast HS; Drexel Hill, PA; (3); 42/327; Church Yth Grp; Girl Scts; Chorus; School Play; NHS; Tri M-Modern Music Masters 85-87; Paralegal.

MC CLOSKEY, ANTHONY JOSEPH; Central Dauphin HS; Harrisburg, PA; (4); 8/366; Church Yth Grp; Science Clb; Band; Concert Band; Im Vllybl; Cit Awd; High Hon Roll; Hon Roll; Pres Jr NHS; Pres NHS; Rotary Clb Of Colonial Pk Schlrshp 87; Acadmc Stu Of Mo Sept 86; Penn ST U; Engrng.

MC CLOSKEY, BETH ANN; United HS; Homer City, PA; (3); 2/147; Church Yth Grp; French Clb; SADD; Vllybl; High Hon Roll; Hon Roll; Prfct Atten Awd; Math & Sci Enhancement Project 87.

MC CLOSKEY, KIMBERLY; Tyrone Area HS; Tyrone, PA; (2); French Clb; Key Clb; Chorus; Color Guard; PA ST U; Int Dsgn.

MC CLOSKEY, MATTHEW; Archbishop Ryan HS; Philadelphia, PA; (2); 9/352; Im Bsbl; Im Bsktbl; Var Crs Cntry; Var Trk; High Hon Roll.

MC CLOSKEY, MEGAN E; Seton-La Salle HS; Bethel Park, PA; (4); 3/260; Pres Dance Clb; Pres Pep Clb; Nwsp Rptr; Rep Frsh Cls; VP Jr Cls; Pres Stu Cncl; Var L Vllybl; High Hon Roll; NHS; Ntl Merit SF; Cert Merit PA Brd Of Ed 86; Top 1 PCT SRA PAC Tsts 84; Acadmc Achvt Rgln Hnrs Gmtry 85; Rlgn Acadmc; Englsh.

MC CLOSKEY, MELANNE; Jamestown HS; Jamestown, PA; (4); Church Yth Grp; FBLA; Band; Chorus; Church Choir; Concert Band; Mrchg Band; Pep Band; School Musical; Variety Show; Dist Chorus 86-87; Rgnl Chorus 86; Slppry Rck U; Fin.

MC CLOSKEY, SAMANTHA; Bellefonte Area HS; Bellefonte, PA; (4); 5/237; Church Yth Grp; Chorus; Rep Frsh Cls; Rep Stu Cncl; High Hon Roll; Hon Roll; Comm Awd 87; Awd For Acad Excll AAUW 86; South Hills Bus Coll; Accntng.

MC CLOSKEY, SCOTT; Charleroi Area HS; Charleroi, PA; (3); Boy Scts; Pres Church Yth Grp; Trs Ski Clb; Varsity Clb; Stu Cncl; Im Bsktbl; JV Ftbl; L Trk; Penn ST; Arch Engr.

MC CLOSKEY, SUSAN; Bellwood-Antis HS; Bellwood, PA; (4); 15/116; French Clb; Varsity Clb; Chorus; School Musical; Ed Yrbk Ed-Chief; Var VP Jr Cls; Rep Stu Cncl; Capt Fld Hcky; Hon Roll; NHS; Ambssdr Hugh O Brian Yth Fndtn Sem 85; Bus Prof Wmns Girl Of Mo 86; Slippery Rock U; Business.

MC CLURE, CRYSTAL; Norristown Area HS; Norristown, PA; (3); 67/524; Pep Clb; Band; Mrchg Band; Symp Band; Cheerleading; Hon Roll; Villanova U; Psych.

MC CLURE, DARREN; Laurel Valley HS; Bolivar, PA; (4); 2/87; Trs Stu Cncl; Bsktbl; Ftbl; High Hon Roll; VP NHS; Sal; AFS; Scholastic Bowl; Varsity Clb; Chorus; Tibune Dem Schlr Athlt, The Thoburn Fndtn For Educ Schlrshp 87; Appalachian Conf Bsktbl All Stars; Penn ST U; Engrng.

MC CLURE, NICOLE; John Harris Campus HS; Harrisburg, PA; (3); 71/265; Band; Concert Band; Mrchg Band; Sec Jr Cls; Rep Stu Cncl; Var Cheerleading; Var Sftbl; Hon Roll; Actvty Ltrs Sprts 84-87; Chrldng & Band Mdls 84-87; Penn ST; Bus Admin.

MC CLURE, RICK; Meadville Area SR HS; Meadville, PA; (2); Church Yth Grp; French Clb; Nwsp Stf; Yrbk Stf; Pres Stu Cncl; High Hon Roll; Elks Clb Stu Mnth 85-86; Schl Imprvmnt Cncl 85-87.

MC CLURE, VINCENT; Homer Center HS; Indiana, PA; (2); VICA; Ftbl; Trk; Wt Lftg; Hon Roll; PA ST Pittsburg; Engrng.

MC CLUSKEY, DANIEL; St Marys Area HS; Weedville, PA; (3); Boy Scts; Bsbl; Var Capt Ftbl; Var Capt Wt Lftg; Hon Roll; NHS; Prfct Atten Awd; Amer Lgn ST Police Yth Wk 87; PENN ST U; Bus.

MC CLUSKEY, JODI; St Marys Area HS; Benezett, PA; (4); 47/310; Hon Roll; Schlrshp Bennetts Vly Wmns Clb 87; PA Gvrnrs Schl For Agri 86; PA ST U; Envrnmntl Engnrng.

MC CLUSKEY, KARYN; St Francis Acad; Pittsburgh, PA; (4); 4/35; VP Church Yth Grp; Yrbk Rptr; Yrbk Stf; Pres Jr Cls; VP Stu Cncl; Sftbl; NHS; Drama Clb; JA; Ntl Hnr Roll Awd 86-87; Gannon U; Bus.

MC CLYMONDS, ANN; Grove City SR HS; Grove City, PA; (4); 52/199; Church Yth Grp; 4-H; FBLA; Girl Scts; Key Clb; Ski Clb; Band; Chorus; Concert Band; Mrchg Band; 2nd Dist Cont Natl Hstry Day 84; Rnnr Up Albert H Diebold Awd Chrstn Endvr 83; Slippery Rock U; Equestrn Stds.

MC CLYMONT, NEIL; Gettysburg SR HS; Gettysburg, PA; (2); Camera Clb; Computer Clb; French Clb; Y-Teens; Yrbk Phtg; Yrbk Rptr; Yrbk Stf; High Hon Roll; NHS; Engrng.

MC COACH, DOROTHY E; St Francis Acad; Bethlehem, PA; (4); 2/20; Drama Clb; Girl Scts; Service Clb; Chorus; School Musical; School Play; Nwsp Stf; Yrbk Stf; Lit Mag; Pres Stu Cncl; PA Jr Acad Sci 1st St 85&86; Prsntr PA Sci & Hmnts Symp 86; GSA Gld Lrshp Awd-Slvr Awd 85; U VA; Econ.

MC COLGAN, CHRISTINA; Abington SR HS; Glenside, PA; (4); 66/486; Library Aide; Mrchg Band; Stage Crew; Twrlr; NHS; Presdntl Acadc Ftnss Awd 87; DE Vly Coll Of Sci & Ag; Fd In.

MC COLGAN, JENNIFER; Central Bucks East HS; Warrington, PA; (4); 101/468; Church Yth Grp; Chorus; Nwsp Stf; Yrbk Stf; Var Capt Bsktbl; Var Capt Sftbl; Hon Roll; FBLA; Ski Clb; Rep Stu Cncl; All Suburban 3rd Bsmn Sftbll 87; West Chester U; Pre Med.

MC COLL, RON; Susquehanna Community HS; Union Dale, PA; (3); Scholastic Bowl; Bsbl; Crs Cntry; Wrstlng; Hon Roll.

MC COLLIM, MARCY; Bensalem HS; Bensalem, PA; (3); German Clb; Hosp Aide; Key Clb; Pep Clb; Chorus; Color Guard; Stu Cncl; Bsktbl; Frankford Hosp Schl Of Nrsng.

MC COLLOUGH, DONALD; Karns City Area HS; Chicora, PA; (3); Aud/Vis; Chorus; Stage Crew; Yrbk Stf; Rep Stu Cncl; Bsktbl; Hon Roll; Photo.

MC COLLOUGH, KATHY; Butler Area SR HS; Butler, PA; (3); Church Yth Grp; JA; Office Aide; Spanish Clb; SADD; Teachers Aide; Thesps; Trk; Hon Roll; Jr NHS; Elem Ed.

MC COLLUM, JENNIFER; Bishop Conwell HS; Levittown, PA; (3); 90/279; FTA; Office Aide; Service Clb; SADD; Band; Lit Mag; Hon Roll; Scndry Ed.

MC COLLUM, NICOLE M; Mahanoy Area HS; Bainesville, PA; (2); 9/30; Drama Clb; Ski Clb; Spanish Clb; School Play; Nwsp Stf; JV Cheerleading; JV Sftbl; Hon Roll; Pediatrtn.

MC COLLUM, STACY; West Greene HS; Holbrook, PA; (2); School Musical; School Play; Rep Stu Cncl; Vllybl; High Hon Roll; Germ Stu Awd 87; Comm Art.

MC COMBIE, BLAZE; Northern Cambria HS; Nicktown, PA; (3); 17/152; Boy Scts; Chess Clb; Church Yth Grp; Computer Clb; French Clb; ROTC; JV Trk; High Hon Roll; Hon Roll; UIP; Comp Pgmr.

MC COMBIE, WENDY; Connellsville Area HS; Connellsville, PA; (3); 7/520; Pres Pep Clb; Science Clb; Mgr Mrchg Band; Mgr School Musical; Mgr Symp Band; Mgr Nwsp Stf; Mgr Yrbk Stf; Mgr French Hon Soc; High Hon Roll; Mgr NHS; Hghst Acad Achvt.

MC CONNAUGHEY, MATTHEW; Fairview HS; Fairview, PA; (4); 33/154; Cmnty Wkr; Band; Concert Band; Jazz Band; Mrchg Band; Pep Band; School Musical; Symp Band; Ed Lit Mag; Im Vllybl; Acad All Amer 87; Scrd 5 AP Engl Test 87; Dist & Regnl Band 86-87; Instrmntl Merit Awd 86-87; Baldwin & Wallace; Engl.

MC CONNELL, BRADLEY K; Hampton HS; Allison Park, PA; (4); 10/255; Boy Scts; Pres Church Yth Grp; Spanish Clb; Rep Stu Cncl; Crs Cntry; Tennis; Trk; High Hon Roll; NHS; Pres Schlr; Penn ST U; Optemetry.

MC CONNELL, CHRISTIE; Afairview HS; Erie, PA; (4); 31/154; Ski Clb; Varsity Clb; Cheerleading; Socr; Sftbl; NHS; Yrbk Stf; Rep Frsh Cls; Rep Soph Cls; Rep Jr Cls; PA Free Entrprse Wk Schlrshp; Penn ST U; Spcl Ed.

MC CONNELL, DANA; Bishop Guilfoyle HS; Altoona, PA; (3); 15/156; Church Yth Grp; SADD; Rep Stu Cncl; Var JV Cheerleading; Hon Roll; Child Psych.

MC CONNELL, G SCOTT; Cocalico HS; Denver, PA; (2); Church Yth Grp; Concert Band; Jazz Band; Mrchg Band; Sec Jr Cls; Im Bsktbl; Im Socr; Var Trk; Im Vllybl; JV Wrstlng; Engrng.

MC CONNELL, JERRY; Pleasant Valley HS; Brodheadsville, PA; (3); Computer Clb; FBLA; Varsity Clb; Rep Frsh Cls; Rep Soph Cls; Rep Jr Cls; JV Stu Cncl; Capt JV Bsktbl; Var L Ftbl; Var L Trk; Ftbl All Area Easton Hrnb Mntn 87; Pittsburgh U; Accntng.

MC CONNELL, KRISTIN; Trinity HS; Washington, PA; (3); 25/402; French Clb; Concert Band; Mrchg Band; High Hon Roll; Hon Roll; Math.

MC CONNELL, M SCOTT; Philadelphia Mntgmry Christian Acad; Ft Washington, PA; (2); Stat Bsbl; Var L Bsktbl; High Hon Roll; Bus.

MC CONNELL, MICHAEL; Henderson HS; West Chester, PA; (3); Hon Roll; Prfct Atten Awd; West Chester U; Comp Spec.

MC CONNELL, SUSANNA; Bentworth SR HS; Bentleyville, PA; (4); 17/123; FBLA; FHA; Ski Clb; SADD; Band; Off Sr Cls; Stu Cncl; High Hon Roll; NHS; Pres Schlr; WV Wesleyan Acadmc Schlrshp 87; Mid East Musical Bnd 86-87; Cnty Bnd 87; WV Wesleyan Coll; Elem Ed.

MC CONNELL, TAMMY; Bishop Guilfoyle HS; Altoona, PA; (4); 12/120; Church Yth Grp; Library Aide; Ski Clb; Chorus; Yrbk Stf; Trs Stu Cncl; Capt Cheerleading; Wt Lftg; High Hon Roll; Hon Roll; Penn ST U; Chem.

MC CONNELL, THOMPSON; Cocalico HS; Denver, PA; (3); Pres Church Yth Grp; Off CAP; Science Clb; Chorus; Concert Band; Jazz Band; Mrchg Band; High Hon Roll; Hon Roll; Lions Club Stu Of Month 87; Engr.

MC CONVILLE, KELLY; Plum SR HS; Pittsburgh, PA; (4); 14/378; Nwsp Rptr; Twrlr; High Hon Roll; NHS; Dance Clb; Spanish Clb; SADD; Teachers Aide; Lit Mag; CA U Of PA Faclty Schlrshp 87; Acad Achvt Awd 87; Acad Xlnc 87; CA U Of PA; Jrnlsm.

MC CONVILLE, MELISSA; Freeport SR HS; Sarver, PA; (4); 1/162; Drill Tm; Rep Frsh Cls; Trs Soph Cls; Pres Schlr; Pres Sr Cls; Off Stu Cncl; L Var Sftbl; Var L Vllybl; High Hon Roll; Pres NHS; St Vincent Coll Ldrshp Schlrshp 87; St Vincent Coll Acad Schlrshp 87; US Army Reserve Natl Schlr 87; St Vincent Coll; Bio.

MC COOL, SUZANNE; St Basil Acad; Philadelphia, PA; (3); School Play; Nwsp Rptr; Yrbk Stf; Var Socr; High Hon Roll; Hon Roll; Drama Clb; French Clb; GAA; Ntl Sci Merit Awd 86-87; Ntl Englsh Merit Awd 86-87; Cmnctns.

MC COPPIN, MICHAEL; Milton Area SR HS; Milton, PA; (2); Boys Clb Am; Boy Scts; Exploring; Latin Clb; JV Ftbl; Im Vllybl; Im Wt Lftg; Karate Green Belt 86; Engr.

MC CORMACK, DOUGLAS; Hopewell SR HS; Aliquippa, PA; (3); Church Yth Grp; Pres Exploring; Political Wkr; Pres Soph Cls; Pres Jr Cls; Pres Sr Cls; Var Wrstlng; NHS; High Hon Roll; Hugh Obrien Ldrshp Awd 86; Pre Med.

MC CORMACK, JENNIFER; Faith Community Christian Schl; Pittsburgh, PA; (2); 8/40; Church Yth Grp; Drama Clb; Office Aide; Teachers Aide; Yrbk Stf; Pres Frsh Cls; Pres Soph Cls; Cheerleading; Sftbl; Vllybl; Hghst-Cvcs Cls 85-86; Grove City Coll; Hstry.

MC CORMACK, SCOTT; Bradford Central Christian HS; Bradford, PA; (3); 4/27; Computer Clb; Key Clb; Library Aide; Ski Clb; Yrbk Ed-Chief; Yrbk Stf; JV Bsbl; L Bsktbl; L Ftbl; Hon Roll; Pilot.

MC CORMICK, BRIAN; Devon Prep School; Audubon, PA; (4); Cmnty Wkr; Ski Clb; School Play; Stage Crew; Nwsp Sprt Ed; Yrbk Stf; VP Stu Cncl; Var Bsbl; JV Socr; NHS.

MC CORMICK, CYNTHIA; Danville Area HS; Danville, PA; (3); Computer Clb; Chorus; Yrbk Stf; Sci Fair Hnr Mntn Awd 84-85; Bus Mngmt.

MC CORMICK, DIANA; Mc Guffey HS; Washington, PA; (4); 16/201; Pres VP 4-H; German Clb; Pres Band; Jazz Band; Mrchg Band; Pep Band; Yrbk Stf; NHS; Pep Clb; Church Choir; Washington County Band & Mid-East Music Festival 87; Grove City Coll.

MC CORMICK, ERIN; Shippensburg Area SR HS; Orrstown, PA; (3); 26/350; Trs Camera Clb; SADD; Yrbk Stf; Rep Stu Cncl; Capt Cheerleading; Var Crs Cntry; Im Socr; Var L Trk; Hon Roll; NHS; Bus.

MC CORMICK, JODY; Hempfield HS; E Petersburg, PA; (4); 8/418; JV Bsktbl; JV Var Fld Hcky; JV Trk; Cit Awd; High Hon Roll; Hon Roll; NHS; Educ Assoc Schlrshp 87; Teen Wk 87; Stu Mnth 86; Shippensburg; Spnsh.

MC CORMICK, JULIE; New Castle SR HS; New Castle, PA; (3); 26/237; AFS; Spanish Clb; SADD; Church Choir; Nwsp Bus Mgr; Nwsp Rptr; Stu Cncl; Trk; High Hon Roll; Hon Roll; Brown U; Pre-Med.

MC CORMICK, KEVIN; Trinity HS; Washington, PA; (3); Computer Clb; Debate Tm; Math Tm; Speech Tm; Trs Stu Cncl; Crs Cntry; High Hon Roll; Med.

MC CORMICK, MAUREEN; Cumberland Valley HS; Mechanicsburg, PA; (4); Drama Clb; Office Aide; Radio Clb; Speech Tm; SADD; VP Chorus; School Musical; School Play; High Hon Roll.

MC CORMICK, MICHAEL; Waynesboro Area SR HS; Waynesboro, PA; (4); AFS; Spanish Clb; Yrbk Stf; Rep Sr Cls; NHS; Ft Rtchie Thrft Shp Schlrshp Awd 87; Johnson & Wales Coll; Chef.

MC CORMICK, PATRICK; Loyalsack Township HS; Williamsport, PA; (3); 8/120; German Clb; Key Clb; Letterman Clb; Ski Clb; Varsity Clb; School Play; Variety Show; Stu Cncl; Var L Socr; Var L Tennis; Natl Hnr Soc 87.

MC COURY, MISSY; Spring Grove Area SR HS; Thomasville, PA; (4); 26/276; Church Yth Grp; Varsity Clb; Capt Color Guard; Orch; School Musical; Rep Stu Cncl; Cheerleading; Var Powder Puff Ftbl; High Hon Roll; NHS; Swthrt Ct 85; HM Rhmyr Schlrshp & Jffrsns Lions Clb Schlrshp 87; Chrch Schlrshp 87; Penn ST York.

MC COWAN, TANYA; West Catholic For Girls; Philadelphia, PA; (4); 80/246; Church Yth Grp; French Clb; Chorus; Orch; School Musical; School Play; Variety Show; Presdntl Acad Achvt Awd 87; PA CC; Sci.

MC COY, AMY JO; Ambridge Area SR HS; Ambridge, PA; (4); 30/265; Cmnty Wkr; Pep Clb; Red Cross Aide; Spanish Clb; VICA; Church Choir; Soph Cls; Jr Cls; Sr Cls; High Hon Roll; Bond Outstndng Vo Tech Stdnt Wolvs Clb 87; Ardoms Beauty Acad Schlrshp 87; PA ST U; Elem Ed.

MC COY, CHRISTOPHER; Pocono Mountain HS; Swiftwater, PA; (2); Band; Concert Band; Mrchg Band; Off Frsh Cls; Bsbl; Bsktbl; Mgr(s); Hon Roll; Cardinal Flight Awd 85-86; OK City.

MC COY, JOHN; Pocono Mountain HS; Bartonsville, PA; (3); Bsbl; Ftbl; Wrstlng; Hnrbl Mntn All Leauge Full Back & Def End 86-87; 3rd Pl Centennial League 2nd Tm All Pocono 86-87.

MC COY, KELLEY; Hughesville HS; Hughesville, PA; (3); 9/147; Ski Clb; SADD; Off Jr Cls; Off Sr Cls; Pres Sec Stu Cncl; Bsktbl; Timer; Trk; Hon Roll; NHS; Grn & Wht Awd 87; Lycoming; Med Tech.

MC COY, KIMBERLEE D; St Marys Area HS; Kersey, PA; (4); 23/279; Sec Church Yth Grp; Library Aide; Concert Band; Jazz Band; Mrchg Band; Pep Band; Hon Roll; NHS; Outstndng Sr Fml Stu 86-87; Sr Band Awd 86-87; Clarion U Of PA; Accntng.

MC COY, MARGO; Oil City SR HS; Franklin, PA; (4); 22/232; Art Clb; Aud/Vis; Office Aide; Rep Stu Cncl; High Hon Roll; Hon Roll; NHS; Teachers Aide; Stat Wrstlng; Edinboro U Summr Acad 84; Vlntr Specl Olympc & Easter Seals 85-87; Pres Acad Fit Awd 87; Art Inst Pittsburgh; Fash Illst.

MC CRABB, KELLY; Muhlenberg HS; Laureldale, PA; (4); 10/181; Science Clb; School Play; Off Stu Cncl; Var Cheerleading; Var Trk; High Hon Roll; NHS; VA Wesleyan Coll 4 Yr Schlrshp; Soc For Acadc Achvt 87; VA Wesleyan Coll; Vet.

MC CRABB, STEPHANIE; Lampeter Strasburg HS; Willow Street, PA; (3); 29/140; VP 4-H; Mgr Bsktbl; Var Trk; Im Wt Lftg; 4-H Awd; Hon Roll; Burrowes Schlr 87; Physical Thrpy.

MC CRACKE, LYNN; Kinoch HS; Sarver, PA; (4); 2/247; Drama Clb; Orch; Pep Band; School Musical; School Play; Pom Pon; NHS; Voice Dem Awd; Grove Cty Coll.

MC CRACKEN, ALEX; St Pius X HS; Pottstown, PA; (4); 19/150; Computer Clb; Math Tm; Hon Roll; DE Valley Coll; Agrnmy.

MC CRACKEN, ANDREA; Commodore Perry HS; Hadley, PA; (4); FTA; Math Tm; Office Aide; Chorus; School Musical; Cheerleading; Score Keeper; Twrlr; High Hon Roll; NHS; NCA Chrldr All Amer 85; Ma Educ Clarion; Ed.

MC CRACKEN, CALLI; Karns City JR SR HS; Karns City, PA; (3); Am Leg Aux Girls St; Pres Church Yth Grp; Band; Chorus; Church Choir; Concert Band; Mrchg Band; Hon Roll; NHS; Butler County CC; Aviatn.

MC CRACKEN, KAREN; Homer-Center HS; Homer City, PA; (3); #2 In Class; Church Yth Grp; French Clb; Library Aide; SADD; Varsity Clb; Color Guard; Nwsp Ed-Chief; Trk; Bausch & Lomb Sci Awd; NHS; Hugh O Brian Ldrshp Awd 86.

MC CRACKEN, KIMBERLY; Bradford Area HS; Bradford, PA; (3); 8/307; AFS; Science Clb; Spanish Clb; Stu Cncl; Stat Swmmng; Var Tennis; Var Trk; High Hon Roll; Hon Roll; Off Jr Cls; Pres Acad Fit Awd 84; Biol.

MC CRACKEN, LYNN; Knoch HS; Sarver, PA; (4); 2/243; SADD; Orch; Pep Band; School Musical; School Play; Yrbk Stf; Pom Pon; NHS; Sal; Voice Dem Awd; Grove Cty Coll; Comp Sys.

MC CRACKEN, PAUL; Penn-Trafford HS; Trafford, PA; (2); 10/350; Church Yth Grp; Exploring; JV Bsktbl; Var Crs Cntry; Ftbl; Im Sftbl; High Hon Roll; PA JR Acad Of Sci 2nd Pl 85; Acad All Amer 86-87; Mech Engrng.

MC CRACKEN, ROBERT; Rochester Area HS; New Brighton, PA; (3); Pep Clb; Nwsp Phtg; Nwsp Rptr; Nwsp Sprt Ed; Nwsp Stf; Var L Bsbl; JV Bsktbl; Var Cheerleading; Var L Ftbl; Hon Roll; Chem Engr.

MC CRACKEN, SUSAN; Wilmington Area HS; New Wilmington, PA; (2); 2/140; Pres FBLA; Nwsp Stf; Stat Bsktbl; High Hon Roll; Hon Roll; NHS; 1st In Rgns Entrepreneurship Cntst 86; 2nd Rgns Bus Math Cntst 87; Business.

MC CRAY, FELICIA; Vo-Tech HS; Mc Keesport, PA; (1); Church Yth Grp; Library Aide; NAACP; Office Aide; Y-Teens; Chorus; Church Choir; Hon Roll; Amer Leg Auxiliary Certfct Schl Awd 86; Singer.

MC CREA, MICHAEL; North Hills HS; Pittsburgh, PA; (4); 35/467; Church Yth Grp; Key Clb; Var L Bsbl; Var L Bsktbl; High Hon Roll; NHS; PA ST U; Bus.

MC CREADY, DAVID O; Beaver Falls HS; Beaver Falls, PA; (3); 3/170; Boy Scts; Pres Science Clb; Spanish Clb; Band; Mrchg Band; Symp Band; Nwsp Ed-Chief; Capt Tennis; High Hon Roll; NHS; Samuel Sheffield Memrl Tnns Awd 88; U Of Pittsburgh; Law.

MC CREERY, DAN; Chestnut Ridge HS; Springfield, VA; (4); Church Yth Grp; Computer Clb; Science Clb; SADD; Nwsp Rptr; Nwsp Stf; Va Trk; Hon Roll; NHS; Prfct Atten Awd; Outstndng Frshmn Yr Trck & Fld 84; VA Tech; Engrng.

MC CUE, DENEEN; Carrick HS; Pittsburgh, PA; (2); Church Yth Grp; Girl Scts; High Hon Roll; Hon Roll; Elem Tchr.

MC CUE, KAREN; Turtle Creek HS; North Braddock, PA; (3); 4/221; Science Clb; Spanish Clb; VP Frsh Cls; Rep Soph Cls; Pres Jr Cls; Rep Stu Cncl; Powder Puff Ftbl; High Hon Roll; Prfct Atten Awd; Med.

MC CUE, LAURA; Connellsville HS; Dunbar, PA; (3); 70/550; Pep Clb; Ski Clb; Chorus; Stage Crew; Var Cheerleading; Hon Roll; Jr NHS; NHS

MC CUE, TERRY; Penn Hills HS; Pittsburgh, PA; (4); 44/616; Debate Tm; FFA; FHA; FNA; German Clb; Math Tm; Science Clb; Varsity Clb; Wrstlng; NHS; Washington; Chmcl Engrng.

MC CUEN, LORI; Cardinal O Hara HS; Broomall, PA; (3); 82/710; Church Yth Grp; Spanish Clb; SADD; School Play; Nwsp Rptr; High Hon Roll; Hon Roll; Villanova; Cmmnctns.

MC CULLA, AMY; Youngsville HS; Pittsfield, PA; (4); 1/97; Pres Church Yth Grp; French Clb; Math Tm; Off Chorus; Church Choir; School Play; JV Cheerleading; JV Vllybl; High Hon Roll; Trs NHS; Psych.

MC CULLIGAN, JENNIFER; Saint Basil Acad; Philadelphia, PA; (3); Drama Clb; GAA; Nwsp Stf; Lit Mag; Var Socr; Hnrbl Mntn Acrylc Pntng 87; All Star Awd Sccr 86; Comm.

MC CULLOUGH, HOLLY; Burgettstown JR SR HS; Burgettstown, PA; (3); French Clb; Hosp Aide; Mrchg Band; Pep Band; Symp Band; Yrbk Stf; Var Twrlr; High Hon Roll; NHS; Band.

MC CULLOUGH, JOCINDA; Bellefonte Area HS; Bellefonte, PA; (3); 9/211; Church Yth Grp; SADD; Band; Chorus; Church Choir; Color Guard; School Musical; Rep Jr Cls; High Hon Roll; NHS.

MC CULLOUGH, KELLY; Bishop Shanahan HS; West Chester, PA; (4); 19/216; Dance Clb; Service Clb; Ski Clb; School Musical; Var Cheerleading; Vllybl; Hon Roll; NHS; Drexel; Fshn Merch.

MC CULLOUGH, LORI; Deer Lakes JR SR HS; Gibsonia, PA; (4); 1/166; Band; Flag Corp; School Musical; Yrbk Stf; Stat L Trk; Pres NHS; Val; Church Yth Grp; Hosp Aide; Concert Band; Duquesne U; Pre Law.

MC CULLOUGH, MARY; E Pennsboro HS; Camp Hill, PA; (2); Dance Clb; Drama Clb; Sec French Clb; GAA; Crs Cntry; JV Var Trk; High Hon Roll; NHS; Mst Imprvd Plyr Trk 86-87; Acadc Achvt Cert Engl, Histry & Frnch 85-86.

MC CULLOUGH, ROBERT W; Northeast Catholic HS; Philadelphia, PA; (4); 17/359; Stage Crew; Nwsp Stf; NHS; Drexel U; Engr.

MC CULLOUGH, TRISHA; Christian School Of York; York, PA; (4); 4/58; Trs Church Yth Grp; Cmnty Wkr; Chorus; School Musical; Co-Capt Bsktbl; Co-Capt Sftbl; Hon Roll; Ntl Merit Ltr; Sftbl Awd 87; Cmmnwlth Christian Athltc Conf All Conf Slctn Awd 86; Pres Acad Fit Awd 87; Geneva Coll; Bus Admin.

MC CUNE III, JAMES P; Ringgold HS; Monongahela, PA; (4); 65/343; Cmnty Wkr; Pres Band; Concert Band; Jazz Band; Mrchg Band; School Musical; Cty Band 87; Music Conf 83-84; Washington-Jefferson Coll; Law.

MC CUNE, JEANNINE; Plum HS; Pittsburgh, PA; (3); 16/410; French Clb; Trs FHA; Hosp Aide; Capt Color Guard; School Musical; Symp Band; Hon Roll; Sec NHS; Duquesne U; Health Flds.

MC CURDY, AIME; Donegal HS; Mount Joy, PA; (3); Teachers Aide; Varsity Clb; Band; Concert Band; Mrchg Band; Var Bsktbl; Cheerleading; Var Fld Hcky; Im Powder Puff Ftbl; Im Sftbl; Mktg.

MC CURDY, DAWN; Shenango JR/Sr HS; New Castle, PA; (2); 8/124; Sec Church Yth Grp; French Clb; Flag Corp; Crs Cntry; Sftbl; Hon Roll; VP Jr NHS; Medcl Sci.

MC CURLEY, SCOTT; Upper Dublin HS; Ft Washington, PA; (3); 60/300; Camera Clb; Quiz Bowl; Varsity Clb; Nwsp Stf; Capt Var Swmmng; Var Trk; Im Wt Lftg; Part In PA St Swim Champs As A JR 86-87; Pre-Med.

MC CUSKER, JENNIFER; Beth Center HS; Richeyville, PA; (3); Drama Clb; GAA; JA; Pep Clb; Ski Clb; Spanish Clb; Stage Crew; Yrbk Stf; Rep Soph Cls; Var Stat Bsktbl; Sls Clb Awd For JA, Assist VP For JA For Yr Of 86-87; Physcl Thrpst.

MC CUSKER, MARY; Mc Keesport Area HS; Mckeesport, PA; (3); 6/410; AFS; Church Yth Grp; Trs German Clb; Acpl Chr; School Musical; Nwsp Rptr; High Hon Roll; NHS; Outstndng Achvt Alg 85; Yearly Hnr Rl 85 & 86; 1st Pl Chem Sci Fair 85.

MC DADE, KAREN; Penn Hills SR HS; Verona, PA; (4); 1/609; Cmnty Wkr; German Clb; Teachers Aide; Acpl Chr; Yrbk Stf; Lit Mag; Stat Ice Hcky; High Hon Roll; Val; Acdmc Fitness Awd 86-87; WPIHL AA Div Lge Statistician 86-87; Gannon U; Engr.

MC DAID, PATRICK; Archbishop Wood For Boys; Warminster, PA; (4); 11/276; Cmnty Wkr; Yrbk Stf; Rep Rptr Jr Cls; High Hon Roll; NHS; Anna M Vincent Schlrshp 87; Warminster Rtry Schlrshp 87; Chrstn Bros Grant 87; La Salle U; Bio.

MC DANIEL, JULIE; Germantown HS; Philadelphia, PA; (4); 16/362; Computer Clb; FBLA; Office Aide; Hon Roll; NHS; Prfct Atten Awd; Bonnie Wolfe Radoff Bus Educ Dept Prz 87; White-Williams Fndtn Cert Cmmndtn 87; Comp Tech.

MC DEAVITT-JONES, STACY; Slippery Rock HS; Slippery Rock, PA; (4); 4-H; FBLA; Girl Scts; Library Aide; Pep Clb; SADD; Chorus; Church Choir; 4-H Awd; Hon Roll; Homemaker.

MC DERMOTT, C LAUREN; East HS; West Chester, PA; (4); 29/405; Pep Clb; Pres SADD; Chorus; Yrbk Stf; Rep Frsh Cls; Rep Jr Cls; Trs Stu Cncl; Var Cheerleading; Lcrss; NHS; Bus.

MC DERMOTT, HEATHER; Riverview HS; Verona, PA; (3); 7/112; French Clb; Varsity Clb; Yrbk Stf; Sec Jr Cls; Off Stu Cncl; Capt Var Cheerleading; French Hon Soc; High Hon Roll; NHS; Prfct Atten Awd; Yth Ldrshp Convntn 87; Edtr Yrbk 87; Marine Bio.

MC DERMOTT, JAMES; Wyoming Area HS; Falls, PA; (3); Am Leg Boys St; Computer Clb; French Clb; Ski Clb; Nwsp Stf; L Var Bsbl; L Var Ftbl; Im Wt Lftg; Ftbl Excllnc 86; PA ST; Engrng.

MC DERMOTT, JENNIFER; Upper Moreland HS; Hatboro, PA; (2); 11/243; Key Clb; SADD; Rep Stu Cncl; JV Cheerleading; JV Lcrss; High Hon Roll; NHS; Sci.

MC DERMOTT, KATHLEEN; Carmichaels Area HS; Carmichaels, PA; (2); Girl Scts; Spanish Clb; Mrchg Band; Trs Rep Stu Cncl; Hon Roll; Jr NHS; NEDT Awd; Exploring; Nwsp Ed-Chief; DAR Awd; Hugh Obrn Yth Awd 87; Majrtt 86; Disc Jcky For Waynsbrg Coll Radio 87; Waynesburg Coll; Brdcst Jrnlsm.

MC DERMOTT, KRISTA; Blairsville SR HS; Blairsville, PA; (1); 1/118; Chess Clb; Band; Concert Band; Mrchg Band; High Hon Roll; St Vincent Coll Pgm Scholar 87; Psych.

MC DERMOTT, MARGIE; Freeport Area HS; Freeport, PA; (2); 1/198; Jazz Band; Mrchg Band; Symp Band; Stat Bsktbl; High Hon Roll; JR All Amer Hall Fame Band Hnrs 87; PA ST U; Meteorlgy.

MC DERMOTT, NICOLE; Marple-Newtown HS; Newtown Square, PA; (4); 16/362; Civic Clb; Dance Clb; Drama Clb; Math Tm; Pep Clb; Ski Clb; Spanish Clb; Speech Tm; Thesps; School Musical; 2nd Pl Natl Mth Cont 86; 1st Pl Dist Chrldng 86; UCLA; Thtr.

MC DERMOTT, STACEY; West Scranton SR HS; Scranton, PA; (2); 23/250; Cmnty Wkr; Spanish Clb; Thesps; Crs Cntry; Trk; High Hon Roll; Jr NHS; Athltc Trainer.

MC DEVITT, MARGARET; St Hubert HS; Philadelphia, PA; (3); 53/421; Cmnty Wkr; Spanish Clb; SADD; Nwsp Rptr; Nwsp Stf; Var Cheerleading; JV Trk; Hon Roll; Ntl Merit SF; Yth Trffc Sfty Cncl Awd 87; Wssnmng Athltc Awd 85; Crmnl Law.

MC DEVITT, STEPHEN; Archbishop Wood For Boys; Warminster, PA; (2); 55/276; Math Tm; Band; Concert Band; Jazz Band; School Musical; Elec Engr.

MC DONALD, ANGELA; Laurel Valley HS; Seward, PA; (4); 22/86; Sec Varsity Clb; Capt Drill Tm; JV Var Sftbl; IUP; Math.

MC DONALD, COLLEEN; Lancaster Catholic HS; Lancaster, PA; (4); Varsity Clb; School Musical; Yrbk Rptr; Yrbk Stf; Sec Frsh Cls; Sec Soph Cls; Pres Jr Cls; Rep Sr Cls; Stu Cncl; JV Capt Bsktbl; E Carolina U; Tele Comm.

MC DONALD, DAVID; Pottsville Area HS; Pt Carbon, PA; (4); 57/237; Aud/Vis; Latin Clb; Chorus; Bsktbl; Ftbl; Trk; Wrstlng; Hon Roll; Sol Lipton Schlrshp 87; Latn Clb 87; Eclgy Clb 87; Wilkes; Engr.

MC DONALD, ERICA; Lincoln HS; Ellwood City, PA; (3); Camera Clb; German Clb; Ski Clb; Y-Teens; Yrbk Phtg; Yrbk Stf; Capt Cheerleading; Powder Puff Ftbl; Var Sftbl; Nrsng.

MC DONALD, JAMES; Notre Dame G P HS; Easton, PA; (3); 30/105; Aud/Vis; Church Yth Grp; Office Aide; Teachers Aide; L Var Bsbl; L Var Bsktbl; L Var Ftbl; L Var Trk; Wt Lftg; Hon Roll; J J Gustony Awd Excllnc Ftbl, Bsktbl 87; Al-Area Hnrs Bsktbl 87; Psych.

MC DONALD, JOANNE; Cardinal Brennan HS; Girardville, PA; (4); 6/50; Spanish Clb; Yrbk Stf; Sr Cls; Capt Bsktbl; Stat Ftbl; Vllybl; Hon Roll; NHS; Spanish NHS; MVP Bsktbll 85-86; Stu Of Mo Jan 86-87; Female Schlr Athlt 86-87; Wilkes Coll; Comp Sci.

MC DONALD, KATHLEEN; West Catholic HS For Girls; Philadelphia, PA; (4); 56/252; Church Yth Grp; Cmnty Wkr; Dance Clb; French Clb; Jazz Band; School Musical; Nwsp Rptr; Rep Soph Cls; Hon Roll; Prfct Atten Awd; Presdntl Acadc Ftnss Awd 87; West Chester U; Psych.

MC DONALD, KELLY; Jamestown Area HS; Jamestown, PA; (3); 8/63; Trs 4-H; Nwsp Stf; Yrbk Stf; Rep Stu Cncl; Stat Bsktbl; Score Keeper; 4-H Awd; High Hon Roll; Hon Roll; Outstndng Schltc Achvt 85-86; Pres Phy Fitness Awd 85; Intr Design.

MC DONALD, LISA; Abington Hts HS; Clarks Summit, PA; (2); FBLA; JA; Chorus; School Musical.

MC DONALD, MARGARET; Trinity HS; Camp Hill, PA; (2); Cmnty Wkr; French Clb; Pep Clb; Rep Stu Cncl; JV Capt Cheerleading; High Hon Roll; NEDT Awd; Med.

MC DONALD, MARIA; Nativity BVM HS; New Phila, PA; (2); 37/77; Latin Clb; Chorus; Magna Cum Lauda Awd-Ntl Ltn Exam 85-86.

MC DONALD, MARIA; Purchase Line HS; Cherry Tree, PA; (4); Pres Sec 4-H; Sec Spanish Clb; Chorus; Concert Band; Drill Tm; Mrchg Band; Nwsp Rptr; 4-H Awd; High Hon Roll; NHS; Wrtg Awd IN Gaztt Edtrl Cntst; PTSA Awds Lit Cntst; IN U Of PA; Jrnlsm.

MC DONALD, MARY; Pocono Mountain HS; Albrightsville, PA; (2); Church Yth Grp; Latin Clb; Service Clb; Ski Clb; JV Dance Clb; Hon Roll; Lang Intrprtr.

MC DONALD, MARY R; Southern Lehigh HS; Coopersburg, PA; (4); 23/237; Hosp Aide; JA; Mgr Scholastic Bowl; Band; Concert Band; Orch; School Musical; Rep Stu Cncl; High Hon Roll; Magna Cum Laude Ntl Latin Exam 85; Bell Of PA/Diamond ST Tlphn Schlrshp 87; Latin Tutor 85; Mc Gill U; Med.

MC DONALD, MATT; Greencastle-Antrim HS; Greencastle, PA; (3); 22/190; Trs Jr Cls; Stu Cncl; JV Bsktbl; Var L Crs Cntry; Var L Trk; Hon Roll; ST Boys AA Crss Cntry Tm Champs 86; Boys AA ST Cham Trck Relay 86-87; All ST Hon Crss Cntry 85-86; Engr.

MC DONALD, PATRICK; Pine Forge Acad; Columbia, MD; (3); Aud/Vis; Camera Clb; Computer Clb; FCA; Math Clb; Acpl Chr; Chorus; Church Choir; School Musical; School Play; Oakwood Coll; Med.

MC DONALD, TAMMY; Belle Vernon Area HS; Belle Vernon, PA; (4); 67/270; Dance Clb; Band; Concert Band; Mrchg Band; Yrbk Ed-Chief; Powder Puff Ftbl; Stat Swmmng; Hon Roll; Art Clb; Drama Clb; U Of Pittsburgh; Phrmcy.

MC DONALD, TRACY; Windber Area HS; Windber, PA; (3); Church Yth Grp; Drama Clb; Spanish Clb; Chorus; Church Choir; Color Guard; Mrchg Band; Hon Roll; Student Of Month 86; Juniata Coll; Childcare.

MC DONELL, THOMAS; Central Catholic HS; Rankin, PA; (2); 53/298; Boy Scts; VP Church Yth Grp; Debate Tm; Drama Clb; Hosp Aide; NFL; Band; Concert Band; Mrchg Band; Cit Awd; Eagle Scout 86; Vol Svc Awd 85; 300 Hour Awd Braddock Gen Hosp 85; Duquesne Coll; Comm.

MC DONNELL, KELLY; St Basil Acad; Philadelphia, PA; (4); Drama Clb; French Clb; VP GAA; Spanish Clb; Chrmn SADD; School Play; Var Bowling; Var Fld Hcky; Stat Score Keeper; Timer; De Sales Schlrshp 87; Schlstc Wrtng Awd 84; Alntwn Coll; Actress.

MC DONNELL, PATRICK J; State College Area SR HS; State College, PA; (4); 13/580; Debate Tm; Model UN; NFL; Jazz Band; Im Lcrss; Im Socr; JETS Awd; Ntl Merit SF; Rotary Awd; Engrng.

MC DONNELL, SEAN; Pocono Central Catholic HS; Pocono Lake, PA; (3); 6/31; JV Bsbl; Var L Bsktbl; High Hon Roll; Hon Roll; Fin Spelling Bee 85; Notre Dame U; Telecmmnctns.

MC DONNELL, SEAN J; State Coll Area SR HS; State College, PA; (3); 11/533; Math Clb; Sec Model UN; Pres Service Clb; Yrbk Rptr; Rep Frsh Cls; Im Bsktbl; NEDT Awd; Prfct Atten Awd; Excllnc Sci & Engl 84-85.

MC DONNELL, STEPHEN; Eastern Montgomery County Vo-Tech; Cheltenham, PA; (4); Kiwanis Awd; Buildng Cntrctr.

MC DONOUGH, COLLEEN; Upper Darby HS; Aldan, PA; (4); 2/580; Var Bsktbl; Var Fld Hcky; Var Lcrss; High Hon Roll; Pres NHS; Ntl Merit Schol; Rotary Awd; Soc Wmn Engrs Awd 87; Outstndg Fml Athlt 87; Presdntl Acadc Ftnss Awd 87; Dartmouth Coll; Med.

MC DONOUGH, JAYME; Chartiers Valley HS; Pittsburgh, PA; (3); 70/328; Exploring; Var L Swmmng; Athletic Awd 85-87; Acctng.

MC DOUGAL, MICHAEL; Morrisville HS; Morrisville, PA; (3); #13 In Class; School Musical; JV Var Bsbl; JV Var Bsktbl; JV Var Ftbl; Hon Roll; NHS; Cmmnctns.

MC DOUGAL, SHARON; Waynesburg Central HS; Spraggs, PA; (3); Church Yth Grp; Pres 4-H; French Clb; Natl Beta Clb; Pres Jr Cls; Rep Stu Cncl; Capt L Cheerleading; Im Mgr Wt Lftg; 4-H Awd; Hon Roll; Frshmn Hmcmng Ct 84; JR Prom Crt 87; Syracuse U; Cmmnctns.

MC DOWELL, THOMAS; Cardinal Dougherty HS; Philadelphia, PA; (4); 161/696; Boy Scts; Church Yth Grp; Cmnty Wkr; Drama Clb; Band; Chorus; Concert Band; Mrchg Band; Pep Band; School Musical; Temple U; Jrnlsm.

MC ELHANEY, BRUCE; Center HS; Monaca, PA; (2); Boy Scts; Church Yth Grp; Exploring; German Clb; High Hon Roll; Hon Roll; Pres Schlr; Eagle Rank BSA 87; TX A&M; Vet Sci.

MC ELHANEY, STEVEN; Faith Community Christian Schl; Bethel Park, PA; (2); 3/39; Church Yth Grp; French Clb; Church Choir; VP Soph Cls; High Hon Roll; NEDT Awd; Geom Awd & Acdmc Chem Awd & Acdmc Engl III Awd 87; Music.

MC ELHANY, MARSHA; Tyrone Area HS; Tyrone, PA; (2); Key Clb; Chorus; Concert Band; Mrchg Band; School Play; Chrmn Soph Cls; Rep Stu Cncl; Outstndng Engl Stu Awd 85-86; Pstv Attitd & Effrt In Geom Awd 86-87; Williamsport Area CC; Dntl Hyg.

MC ELHATTAN, TAMMY; Quigley HS; Lacey, WA; (4); 35/99; Var JV Sftbl; High Hon Roll; Hon Roll; Mst Quiet Friend Awd 87; Stu Orgnzd Svc Awd 86; Health.

MC ELHENY, BETH; Penn Cambria HS; Cresson, PA; (3); Drama Clb; French Clb; SADD; Var Capt Cheerleading; Hon Roll; NHS; Psych.

MC ELHINNY, ABIGAIL; Kennedy Christian HS; Greenville, PA; (3); Church Yth Grp; Cmnty Wkr; Hosp Aide; Spanish Clb; School Play; Capt Var Swmmng; High Hon Roll; NEDT Awd; Cath Daughters Of Am ST Poetry Awd 86 & 87; Am Lgn Essy Awd 86; Respiratory.

MC ELHINNY, JULIE; Kennedy Christian HS; Linesvle, PA; (3); 1/97; Science Clb; Spanish Clb; Nwsp Rptr; Nwsp Stf; Yrbk Rptr; Yrbk Stf; DAR Awd; High Hon Roll; Ntl Merit SF; Prfct Atten Awd; Amer Chem Soc Cert Merit 87; PA Jr Acad Aci 85; Natl Rnks NEDT Test 85-86; Genetcs.

MC ELHINNY, KELLY L; Seneca Valley SR HS; Evans City, PA; (3); 96/350; Sec Trs Church Yth Grp; JA; Ski Clb; Chorus; Yrbk Bus Mgr; Yrbk Stf; Trk; Elem Educ.

MC ELHINNY, LINDA; Bishop Boyle HS; West Homestead, PA; (2); 1/38; Chorus; Nwsp Stf; Pres Frsh Cls; Pres Soph Cls; Var JV Bsktbl; Var Sftbl; Var JV Vllybl; High Hon Roll; NHS; Prfct Atten Awd; Hugh O Brian Ldrshp Awd 87.

MC ELHINNY, MARK; Linesville Conneaut Summit HS; Linesville, PA; (2); 4/65; Var Soph Cls; Var Bsbl; Var Bsktbl; JV Ftbl; Var Wt Lftg; Hon Roll.

MC ELRAVY, TERRA; Bellwood-Antis HS; Tyrone, PA; (3); 11/115; Chorus; Color Guard; Flag Corp; School Musical; Rep Stu Cncl; Im Badmtn; JV Fld Hcky; Hon Roll; NHS; Bio.

MC ELRONE, MAUREEN; Notre Dame HS; Easton, PA; (2); Church Choir; Yrbk Phtg; Yrbk Stf; Cheerleading; Trk; Church Yth Grp; NFL; Pep Clb; Chorus; Bsktbl; Marine Biologist.

MC ELROY, HELEN; William Allen HS; Allentown, PA; (3); Art Clb; Camera Clb; Church Yth Grp; Computer Clb; Drama Clb; Girl Scts; Political Wkr; SADD; Band; Chorus; Comm Svc Awd Miss Teen PA Pagnt 87; Ath Of Yr Awd 86; Comm Chrmn PA Assoc Ofs Tu Cncls 87; Visual Arts.

MC ELWAIN, ERIK; Parkland HS; Allentown, PA; (3); 34/480; Debate Tm; JA; Math Clb; Var Trk; Var Wrstlng; High Hon Roll; NHS; Ntl Merit Ltr; Chess Clb; Hosp Aide; Engrng.

MC ELWAIN, KEVIN PATRICK; Parkland HS; Allentown, PA; (4); 121/440; Debate Tm; FBLA; Pres JA; Pres Math Clb; Var L Trk; Var L Wrstlng; High Hon Roll; JC Awd; Prfct Atten Awd; Pres Schlr; Dale Carnegie Crs Schlrshp 86; Presdntl Schlrshp 87; Shppnsbrg U; Fin.

MC ELWAIN, MARK; Kennard-Dale HS; Stewartstown, PA; (2); Church Yth Grp; 4-H; Chorus; Church Choir; JV Socr; JV Trk; Hon Roll; JR Am Ctzns Cont 85; Prfrmng Arts Stu.

MC ELWAIN, PAM; Riverside HS; Ellwood City, PA; (2); 1/212; Pres Church Yth Grp; GAA; Band; Drm Mjr(t); Var Capt Bowling; Var L Trk; High Hon Roll; Concert Band; Mrchg Band; Pep Band; Outstndng Algbr II & Acad Amer Hstry Stu 86-87; Outstndng Gmtry Stu 85-86; Engrng.

MC ELWEE, CATHERINE; Chartiers Valley HS; Bridgeville, PA; (3); Church Yth Grp; School Musical; Bus.

MC EVOY, JEFFREY; Bishop Carroll HS; Nanty Glo, PA; (3); Ski Clb; Chorus; Off Frsh Cls; Bsktbl; Bowling; Crs Cntry; Ftbl; Trk; Hon Roll.

MC EWEN, DALISSA; Hatboro-Horsham SR HS; Hatboro, PA; (4); 17/230; Pep Clb; Ski Clb; SADD; Rep Frsh Cls; Rep Soph Cls; Rep Jr Cls; Rep Sr Cls; Rep Sr Cls; JV Var Cheerleading; Var Powder Puff Ftbl; 1st Pl Schlstc Art Awd Comp 87; Chmpns Learning Art Awd 87; Art.

MC EWEN, HEIDI; Canon Mc Millan HS; Eighty Four, PA; (4); 37/355; Chess Clb; French Clb; Office Aide; Varsity Clb; Chorus; Nwsp Stf; Stu Cncl; Var Capt Cheerleading; High Hon Roll; Hon Roll; CA U Of PA.

MC FADDEN, KEVIN; Central Cathloic Of Allentwn; Allentown, PA; (3); JA; JV Var Ftbl; Hon Roll; Ntl Merit Ltr; Stu Govt Day-Le High County Cmmssnr 87; Dusquene U-Pittsburgh; Phrmcy.

MC FADDEN, LAURIE; Mechanicsburg Area HS; Mechanicsburg, PA; (3); 86/338; Church Yth Grp; Cmnty Wkr; JV Var Bsktbl; Var Fld Hcky; Var Sftbl; Keystone St Games Schlstc Fameal Soccer Tm For Region III PA 85-87; Cert Soccer Referee; Health Sci.

MC FADDEN, MICHAEL; Saint John Neumann HS; Philadelphia, PA; (3); 1/350; Church Yth Grp; Math Tm; Science Clb; Varsity Clb; Lit Mag; Rep Jr Cls; Im Bsktbl; JV Ftbl; NHS; Neumann Activities Awd 86-87; 1st Pl Math Comptn Wnnr 85-86; Engl Challng 2nd Pl 84-85; Drexel U; Engrng.

MC FADDEN, ROBERT; E L Meyers HS; Wilkes Barre, PA; (4); Church Yth Grp; Ski Clb; SADD; Capt Crs Cntry; L Trk; Capt Wrstlng; Hon Roll; Jr NHS; NHS; Spanish NHS; PIAA Athlt-Schlr Awd 87; Bucknell.

MC FADDEN, TONY; Garden Spot HS; New Holland, PA; (2); Church Yth Grp; Chorus; Rep Soph Cls; Var L Ftbl; Trk; JV Wrstlng; High Hon Roll; Hon Roll; Jr NHS.

MC FALL, CHERYL; Canton HS; Grover, PA; (4); 9/121; French Clb; Office Aide; Nwsp Ed-Chief; Nwsp Rptr; Nwsp Stf; Yrbk Rptr; Yrbk Stf; Hon Roll; NHS; Wmsprt Schl Of Cmmrc; Exec Secy.

MC FARLAND, BRENDA; Conrad Weiser HS; Robesonia, PA; (2); 15/163; Camera Clb; FFA; Sftbl; High Hon Roll; Hon Roll; Photo.

MC FARLAND, CHAD; Quaker Valley HS; Sewickley, PA; (2); Church Yth Grp; Key Clb; Ski Clb; Spanish Clb; Band; Concert Band; Mrchg Band; Pep Band; JV Var Socr; High Hon Roll; Aerosp Engr.

MC FARLAND, MICHELE; Oil City Area SR HS; Oil City, PA; (3); Hosp Aide; Latin Clb; Model UN; Pep Clb; Nwsp Rptr; Var Bsktbl; Capt Cheerleading; JV Diving; Var Sftbl; Var Vllybl; Ithaca Coll; Phys Thrpy.

MC FARLAND, WENDY; Denningtown SR HS; Downingtown, PA; (4); French Clb; Intnl Clb; Ntl Merit Ltr; NEDT Awd; Wheaton Coll Grnt 87; Wheaton Coll; Psych.

MC FARLIN, SCHEBEEKA; Blairsville SR HS; Blairsville, PA; (2); Pres Church Yth Grp; FCA; French Clb; Girl Scts; Hosp Aide; Chorus; Church Choir; JV Bsktbl; Stat Score Keeper; Bausch & Lomb Sci Awd; Pitt; Law.

MC FEELY, RICHARD P; Shippensburg Area SR HS; Shippensburg, PA; (3); Am Leg Boys St; Var Boy Scts; Band; Concert Band; Jazz Band; School Musical; School Play; Stat Crs Cntry; L Trk; Hon Roll.

MC FETRIDGE, JIM; Smethport Area HS; Smethport, PA; (2); Boy Scts; Computer Clb; Drama Clb; Exploring; French Clb; Band; NHS; NFL; Science Clb; Concert Band; Hugh O Brian Yth Fndtn Smnr 87; Eclgy Tm 87; NEDT Lcl & Ntl Hgh Plcmnt Certs 86; Mech Engrng.

MC GAHAN, AMY; Carlynton JR SR HS; Pittsburgh, PA; (3); 22/169; Art Clb; Church Yth Grp; Trs French Clb; Yrbk Stf; VP Jr Cls; Var L Swmmng; Hon Roll; Jr NHS; Pres Acdmc Ftns Awd 84-85; Crlytn Spcl Merit Awd In Acdmc Hnrs 85.

MC GANN, MICHAEL; Highlands SR HS; Natrona Hgts, PA; (3); 17/303; Pres Sr Cls; Var L Bsktbl; Var Golf; High Hon Roll; Jr NHS; NHS; U Of Notre Dame.

MC GARRY, CHRIS; Curwensville HS; Curwensville, PA; (3); Letterman Clb; Stu Cncl; Bsktbl; Ftbl; PA ST; Accntng.

MC GARRY, KATHLEEN MARIE; Pittston Area SR HS; Inkerman, PA; (4); 27/350; VP French Clb; Key Clb; Math Clb; SADD; Drill Tm; Yrbk Stf; High Hon Roll; NHS; Acadmc Schlrshp To Coll Misericordia 87-91; Coll Misericordia; Occptnl Thrp.

MC GARRY, MEGAN; Downingtown SR HS; Chester Springs, PA; (3); 42/648; French Clb; Intnl Clb; SADD; Chorus; Trk; High Hon Roll; NHS; NEDT Awd.

MC GARRY, PATRICK; Curwensville Area HS; Curwensville, PA; (4); FFA; Hon Roll; FFA Chptr Schlrshp; FFA Tree Jdgng Awd 87.

MC GARVEY, DOUGLAS; Punxsutawney Area HS; Punxsutawney, PA; (4); Ftbl; Wrstlng; Hon Roll; Edinboro U; Comp Sci.

MC GARY, MELISSA; Trinity HS; Washington, PA; (3); 4/402; Am Leg Aux Girls St; Church Yth Grp; Math Tm; Yrbk Phtg; Lit Mag; Swmmng; High Hon Roll; NHS; Ntl Merit Ltr; NEDT Awd; Bio.

MC GARY, MICHELLE; Wilmington Area HS; Volant, PA; (3); French Clb; Key Clb; Yrbk Stf; Trs Jr Cls; Powder Puff Ftbl.

MC GAUGHEY, KATHERINE; Quigley HS; Ambridge, PA; (3); Computer Clb; French Clb; Pep Clb; Chorus; Trs Frsh Cls; Hon Roll; Comp Applications Awd & Outstndng Stu Awd-Tae Kwon Do Fdrtn 87; Comp Info Systems.

MC GEARY, MATT; Newport HS; Newport, PA; (3); 18/125; Chorus; School Musical; School Play; Swing Chorus; Stu Cncl; JV Bsktbl; Im Gym; Im Vllybl; Hon Roll; Engrng.

MC GEARY, ROCKY; West Allegheny HS; Oakdale, PA; (2); Coach Actv; Var L Ftbl; Capt Trk; Var L Wrstlng; Hon Roll; 12th At Natl JR Olpmcs Trck & Fld & 2nd At Freestyle Wrstlng St 87; SPRTS Med.

MC GEARY, STACEY; Altoona Area HS; Altoona, PA; (3); DECA; French Clb; Band; Chorus; Concert Band; Mrchg Band; Orch; Cit Awd; French Hon Soc; Hon Roll; Penn ST U; Elem Ed.

MC GEARY, SUSAN L; Sewickley Acad; Sewickley, PA; (4); 3/67; NFL; Pres Band; Chorus; Church Choir; School Musical; School Play; High Hon Roll; Rep Frsh Cls; Var JV Socr; Var Sftbl; PA Govnrs Schl Art 86; Cum Laude Soc 86-87; James E Cavalier Perp Trphy Scholar Sptsmnshp Ctznshp 87; Smith Coll; Dram Art.

MC GEE, ELIZABETH; Hempfield HS; Mountville, PA; (2); 179/455; Art Clb; Church Yth Grp; Office Aide; Yrbk Stf; Coach Actv; Hon Roll; Philadelphia Inst Art; Artist.

MC GEE, KEVIN; Leechburg Area HS; Leechburg, PA; (2); Band; Concert Band; Mrchg Band; Pep Band; Yrbk Stf; Vllybl; Hotel Mgmt.

MC GEE, TOM; Baldwin HS; Pittsburgh, PA; (2); 197/481; Im Bsktbl; Hon Roll.

MC GEEHAN, KIM; Bishop Hafey HS; Hazleton, PA; (4); 27/128; Cmnty Wkr; French Clb; Intnl Clb; Ski Clb; Var JV Bsktbl; French Hon Soc; Hon Roll; Acadc Awd 87; Kings Coll; Bus.

MC GEEHAN, MICHAEL; W Hazleton HS; Hazleton, PA; (4); 43/224; FNA; FTA; Letterman Clb; Office Aide; Sec Spanish Clb; SADD; Varsity Clb; Var Capt Bsktbl; Trk; Hon Roll; USAF Acad.

MC GEEHAN, THOMAS; Bishop Hafey HS; Hazleton, PA; (2); Church Yth Grp; Debate Tm; Exploring; French Clb; Math Clb; Math Tm; Quiz Bowl; Scholastic Bowl; Science Clb; Ski Clb; Hgh Cmmltv Avg Alg I & IPS 86; U Of Miami FL; Nclr Engnr.

MC GEORGE JR, DAVID S B; State College Area Intermediat HS; Penna Furnace, PA; (1); Church Yth Grp; Concert Band; Rep Frsh Cls; Var L Swmmng; Cit Awd; Hon Roll; Power Of The Paws Awd & Swmr Of The Yr 87; Prsdntl Phys Fitness Awd 86; Brown U; Arch.

MC GILL, CAROL; Bishop Guilfoyle HS; Altoona, PA; (3); Church Yth Grp; Red Cross Aide; Spanish Clb; Tennis; Penn ST U; Bus Adv.

MC GILL, CHERYL; Pine Forge Acad; Columbus, OH; (2); 4/60; Cmnty Wkr; Chorus; VP Soph Cls; Swmmng; Cit Awd; High Hon Roll; Hon Roll; NHS; Prfct Atten Awd; Fash Desgn.

MC GILL, DANIELLE; Acad Of Notre Dame De Namur; Springfield, PA; (4); Church Yth Grp; Dance Clb; Service Clb; Nwsp Stf; Crs Cntry; Trk; High Hon Roll; Math Tm; Socr; Hon Roll; Presdntl Schlrshp Loyola Coll 87; Schlrshp CT Coll, V Wesleyan Coll; Presdntl Acadc Ftnss Awd 87; U Of Richmond; Pre Law.

MC GILL, JENNIFER; Harry S Truman HS; Levittown, PA; (4); Hon Roll; Bucks Cnty CC; Telecomm.

MC GILL, MATT; North Pocono HS; Moscow, PA; (4); 37/250; Church Yth Grp; FBLA; Ski Clb; Var L Bsbl; Var Golf; High Hon Roll; Hon Roll; NHS; Amer West Assn Cert Of Apprectn 86; PHEAA Cert Of Merit 86.

MC GILL, MICHELLE; Pien Forge Acad; Columbus, OH; (3); 8/60; High Hon Roll; Hon Roll; NHS; Howard U; Music.

MC GILL, TAMMIE; Fort Le Boeuf HS; Waterford, PA; (2); Girl Scts; Pep Clb; Cheerleading; Stat Ftbl; Trk; High Hon Roll; Hon Roll; Bus Adm.

MC GINLEY, MELISSA; Butler Area HS; Renfrew, PA; (4); Church Yth Grp; Pres VICA.

MC GINLEY, PATRICK T; Cardinal O Hara HS; Broomall, PA; (3); 18/750; Church Yth Grp; Cmnty Wkr; Computer Clb; Latin Clb; Spanish Clb; Varsity Clb; Capt Var Crs Cntry; Var Trk; High Hon Roll; NHS; Dicesan Schlrs Pgm 87; Med.

MC GINLEY, RACHEL; Abington Heights HS; Clarks Summit, PA; (2); 5/294; Concert Band; Mrchg Band; Yrbk Stf; JV Fld Hcky; Hon Roll.

MC GINN, JAMES; Central Catholic HS; Coopersburg, PA; (3); JA; Math Clb; Hon Roll; Boy Scts; Bsktbl; Crs Cntry; Ftbl; Acad Of Sci 85-86; Bus.

MC GINN, PATRICIA E; Pocono Central Catholic HS; Tannersville, PA; (4); 10/28; VP Speech Tm; Yrbk Ed-Chief; Trs Stu Cncl; Var Bsktbl; Var Fld Hcky; Capt Sftbl; Cit Awd; DAR Awd; Gov Hon Prg Awd; Rtry Ann Awd 87; Knghts Clmbs Aux Awd 87; Srptmst Good Ctzn Awd 87; West Chester U; Elem Ed.

MC GINNIS, CINDY; Commodore Perry HS; Clarks Mills, PA; (3); Church Yth Grp; Computer Clb; Trs FFA; Science Clb; VICA; Mrchg Band; Var Cheerleading; Stat Sftbl; Twrlr; Hon Roll; FFA Star Greenhand 85; Penn ST; Comptr Sci.

MC GINNIS, DONALD; Marion Center Area HS; Marion Center, PA; (3); Varsity Clb; Stu Cncl; Var L Bsbl; Var JV Bsktbl; JV Ftbl; High Hon Roll; Hon Roll; Jr NHS; NHS; IN U PA; Crmnlgy.

MC GIVERN, JAMES; Seneca Valley SR HS; Mars, PA; (3); Am Leg Boys St; VP JA; ROTC; Ntl Grd Assc PA-MLTRY Achvt Awd 87; PA Hse Reps-Cdt Mltry Awd 86; Engnrng.

MC GLINCHEY, KERRIE; Nazareth Acad; Croydon, PA; (3); Art Clb; Cmnty Wkr; Fld Hcky; Hon Roll; Cmmrcl Art.

MC GLONE, CHRISTOPHER; Henderson HS; West Chester, PA; (2); 7/335; Var Bsbl; JV Ftbl; Im Ice Hcky; Im Vllybl; French Hon Soc; High Hon Roll.

MC GLONE, JENNIFER; Scranton Prep; Scranton, PA; (3); 128/196; Church Yth Grp; Pep Clb; Service Clb; Ski Clb; Chorus; School Play; Lit Mag; Yth Rep Scranton Diocese 86-88; Catechst Instrctr 85-87; NE Yth Cncl Rep 85-87; Ithaca Coll; Comm.

MC GLYNN, JAMES; Tunkhannock HS; Tunkhannock, PA; (3); Science Clb; Ski Clb; Spanish Clb; Hon Roll; PA ST; Engr.

MC GLYNN, KELLI; Neshaminy HS; Trevose, PA; (4); 135/725; JV Bsktbl; Var Fld Hcky; Im Lcrss; Var Sftbl; Fld Hcky Plyr Yr, 1st Tm Suburb I Leag Hcky 86-87; 2nd Tm Suburb I Leag Sftbl 85-86; U Of DE; Med Tech.

MC GLYNN, MICHELE; Blacklick Valley JR-SR HS; Twin Rocks, PA; (4); 5/91; Camera Clb; Pres Sec Church Yth Grp; German Clb; Hosp Aide; Yrbk Stf; High Hon Roll; Hon Roll; NHS; PA ST U.

MC GONIGAL, HOWARD; West Branch Area HS; Karthaus, PA; (2); SADD; Varsity Clb; Var Bsbl; Hon Roll; Stu Of Mnth 87.

MC GONIGLE, DAN; Allentown Central Catholic HS; Whitehall, PA; (4); Boy Scts; Drama Clb; Exploring; JA; Chorus; School Musical; School Play; Var L Ftbl; Var L Wt Lftg; Hon Roll; U Of Shippensburg; Comp Sci.

MC GOUGH, AMY; Northgate HS; Pittsburgh, PA; (4); 1/132; Math Tm; Q&S; Ed Yrbk Stf; Trs Sr Cls; Capt Var Cheerleading; Var Trk; JV Stat Vllybl; Cit Awd; Lion Awd; Val; Jack Brice Awd 86; N Boroughs Yth Awd 86; Duquesne U; Phrmcy.

MC GOUGH, KATHLEEN; West Scranton HS; Scranton, PA; (3); 23/260; Letterman Clb; VP Spanish Clb; Nwsp Stf; Rep Stu Cncl; JV Var Bsktbl; JV Var Cheerleading; Tennis; Jr NHS; NHS; Physcl Thrpy.

MC GOULDRICK, ROSEMARY; Bethlehem Catholic HS; Bethlehem, PA; (3); 71/193; Library Aide; High Hon Roll; Bus.

MC GOVERN, EDWARD C; Pine Grove Area HS; Pine Grove, PA; (3); Am Leg Boys St; Cmnty Wkr; Exploring; ROTC; Teachers Aide; VICA; Ftbl; Wrstlng; Hon Roll; JR Frmn Yr 85; Spcl Awd All Arnd Otstndng Svc 86; Hnr Acad Excllnc Scl Stds 86-87; Elec Engr.

MC GOVERN IV, FRANK J; Msgr Bonner HS; Drexel Hill, PA; (4); 15/331; Boy Scts; Chess Clb; Church Yth Grp; Exploring; Letterman Clb; Library Aide; Pep Clb; Quiz Bowl; Pres Radio Clb; Rep Red Cross Aide; U PA; Cmnctns.

MC GOVERN, JILL; Crestwood HS; Mt Top, PA; (1); 32/208; Cheerleading; JV Mgr(s); Sftbl; Hon Roll.

MC GOVERN, NICOLE; Carrick HS; Pittsburgh, PA; (3); Art Clb; Hosp Aide; Q&S; Ski Clb; Spanish Clb; Stage Crew; Nwsp Stf; Hon Roll; Opthamology.

MC GOVERN, SEAN; Bishop O Reilly HS; Dallas, PA; (3); Capt L Bsbl; Capt L Bsktbl; Math.

MC GOVERN, SUZANNE; Pottsville Area HS; Pottsville, PA; (4); 14/242; Cmnty Wkr; Hosp Aide; Pres Latin Clb; Ski Clb; Var L Bsktbl; Hon Roll; NHS; Pres Schlr; Elizabethtown Coll.

MC GOWAN, BRIAN; Fort Le Boeut HS; Erie, PA; (4); 2/164; FCA; Rep Jr Cls; Rep Sr Cls; Var L Bsktbl; Var L Ftbl; Var L Trk; High Hon Roll; VP NHS; Sal; Pres Acad Fit Awd 87; Westminster Coll.

MC GOWAN, EILEEN; Hopewell SR HS; Aliquippa, PA; (3); Pres VP Art Clb; Church Yth Grp; Cmnty Wkr; Dance Clb; Spanish Clb; Drill Tm; Off Stu Cncl; L Swmmng; Hon Roll; Chorus; Dnc Mstrs Of Amer 1st Pl Ntl 85; Checcetti Schlrshp 3rd Pl Dnc 86; Sec Educ.

MC GOWAN, GERTRUDE C; Bishop Hoban HS; Ashley, PA; (3); FBLA; Hosp Aide; Latin Clb; Mu Alpha Theta; Yrbk Rptr; High Hon Roll; NHS; NEDT Awd; Corporate Lwyr.

MC GOWAN, JILL; Montour HS; Mckees Rocks, PA; (3); 46/277; Rep SADD; Rep Stu Cncl; JV Var Cheerleading; Powder Puff Ftbl; Var Trk; High Hon Roll; Hon Roll; Stu Cncl Treas 87-88; Accntng.

MC GOWAN, JOHN; Coughlin HS; Wilkes Barre, PA; (3); 5/362; VP Church Yth Grp; Band; Concert Band; Jazz Band; Var L Tennis; Jr NHS; NHS; NEDT Awd; Letterman Clb; Orch; Natl Cncl On Yth Ldrshp & Coaches To NE Tennis All Star Tm 87; Pres Acdmc Fitness Awd 85; Kings Coll; Comp Info System.

MC GOWAN, KELLIE; Chichester SR HS; Boothwyn, PA; (4); 17/276; Hosp Aide; Band; Yrbk Stf; Rep Stu Cncl; Var Fld Hcky; Var Lcrss; Hon Roll; NHS; Rotary Awd; Sec Spanish NHS; Sacred Heart Med & Dentl Staff Hlth Career Awd 87; Acad Scholar Elizabethtown Coll 87; Rotary Scholar; Elizabethtown Coll; Occ Thrpy.

MC GOWAN, KIMBERLY L; The Christian Acad; Media, PA; (4); 5/65; Church Yth Grp; Drama Clb; FCA; Hosp Aide; Library Aide; Sec Jr Cls; Capt Cheerleading; High Hon Roll; Widener U; Acctng.

MC GOWAN, MEG; Cardinal O Hara HS; Newtown Square, PA; (3); Dance Clb; Drama Clb; School Play; Nwsp Stf; Bsktbl; Powder Puff Ftbl; Trk; Var Capt Vllybl; Hon Roll.

MC GOWAN, SHERI; Fort Le Boeuf HS; Erie, PA; (2); 98/210; Church Yth Grp; Teachers Aide; Score Keeper; Hon Roll.

MC GOWAN, TAMMY; Cocalico HS; Stevens, PA; (2); #55 In Class; Var Co-Capt Cheerleading; JV Fld Hcky; Im Vllybl; Hon Roll; Prfct Atten Awd; Iu Elem Tchr.

MC GRADY, BRIAN; Carrick HS; Pittsburgh, PA; (4); 79/340; Q&S; Ski Clb; School Play; Stage Crew; Nwsp Rptr Ed; Nwsp Stf; Sec Jr Cls; Trs Sr Cls; L Tennis; Hon Roll; Clarion U; Comms.

MC GRANAHAN, DEVIN; Warren Area HS; Warren, PA; (4); 2/340; Art Clb; Camera Clb; Dance Clb; Math Tm; Ski Clb; Pres Spanish Clb; Varsity Clb; Jazz Band; Yrbk Phtg; Stu Cncl; Amer Chem Soc Outstndng Chem Stdnt 87; Warren Area HS Apprctn Awd 87; Outstndng Debater 87; U Of PA; Engrng.

MC GRANN, BERNARD; Lancaster Catholic HS; Lancaster, PA; (3); 6/200; Drama Clb; Model UN; Speech Tm; School Musical; School Play; Variety Show; NHS; Schl Schlstc Wrtng Awds Hon Men 84; 3rd & 1st Pl Lcl Hist Day Cmpttn Grp Prfrmnc 86-87; Lbrl Arts.

MC GRATH, CHRISTOPHER A; North East HS; North East, PA; (4); 3/137; Boy Scts; Model UN; Quiz Bowl; Science Clb; Nwsp Rptr; High Hon Roll; JC Awd; JETS Awd; Ntl Merit SF; Gannon U Schlrshp 86; SR Sci Awd 87; Hugh Obrien Yth Fndtn Awd 84; Cornell U; Chem Engr.

MC GRATH, CRYSTAL; St Marys Area HS; St Marys, PA; (2); Church Yth Grp; Exploring; FBLA; Hosp Aide; Spanish Clb; Yrbk Stf; Score Keeper; Vllybl; Spn Triva Awd 86; Typg 87; Hnr Roll Awd 85; Polit Sci.

MC GRATH, DAVID; Belle Vernon Area HS; Belle Vernon, PA; (3); JV Vllybl; Var L Wrstlng; Hon Roll; Bio.

MC GRATH, JAMES; West Catholic HS; Philadelphia, PA; (3); 27/264; Cmnty Wkr; Intnl Clb; JA; Math Clb; Math Tm; Stu Cncl; Var JV Bsbl; Cit Awd; High Hon Roll; Amer Outstndng Names & Faces; Star Schlr; Math Clb.

MC GRATH, KATHLEEN; Riverview HS; Oakmont, PA; (3); 7/112; Pres Key Clb; Library Aide; Nwsp Stf; High Hon Roll; NHS; NEDT Awd; Ed.

MC GRATH, PADRAIC D; North East HS; North East, PA; (3); 12/150; Am Leg Boys St; Latin Clb; Q&S; ROTC; Yrbk Sprt Ed; Trs Jr Cls; Trs Stu Cncl; Ftbl; Trk; Hon Roll.

MC GRATH, STEPHANIE; York Catholic HS; York, PA; (3); 84/175; Church Yth Grp; Cmnty Wkr; Girl Scts; Library Aide; Pep Clb; SADD; Chorus; Color Guard; School Musical; School Play; Lock Haven ST U; Erly Chldhd.

MC GRATH, SUSAN; St Hubert Catholic HS For Girls; Philadelphia, PA; (3); 6/421; Service Clb; Spanish Clb; Nwsp Rptr; Rptr Nwsp Stf; Yrbk Stf; High Hon Roll; NHS; Church Yth Grp; Teachers Aide; Lit Mag; Hghst Avg Wrld Cult II 86; Hnrb Mntn Hnrs Engl III 87; Svc Awd Wrld Affrs Clb 85-87.

MC GRAW, COLEEN; Burgettstown HS; Langeloth, PA; (3); Office Aide; Ski Clb; VP Spanish Clb; Yrbk Stf; Pres Trs Stu Cncl; Hon Roll; Jr NHS; Chldhd Dvlpmnt.

MC GRAW, KRISTEN; Gateway HS; Monroeville, PA; (4); Church Yth Grp; Ski Clb; Chorus; School Play; Hon Roll; Boston Coll; Psych.

MC GRAW, LISA; South Allegheny JR- SR HS; Port Vue, PA; (3); Y-Teens; Drm Mjr(t); Powder Puff Ftbl; Hon Roll; Standard 1st Aid-CPR-1ST Pl ST & 3rd Pl Natl 87; Western Schl Of Health; Dental.

MC GREGOR, JENNIFER; Reading JR Acad; Reading, PA; (2); Church Yth Grp; Church Choir; Yrbk Stf; Pres Stu Cncl; Cit Awd; Hon Roll; Prfct Atten Awd; Psycht.

MC GREGOR, MICHELE; Somerset Area HS; Somerset, PA; (3); 3/230; Church Yth Grp; English Clb; Spanish Clb; Band; Chorus; DAR Awd; Hon Roll; NHS; Voice Dem Awd; Actg.

MC GROGAN, JENNIFER; Mt Pleasant Area HS; Mt Pleasant, PA; (3); French Clb; GAA; Red Cross Aide; Yrbk Stf; Var Tennis; Im Vllybl; High Hon Roll; Hon Roll.

MC GROGAN, KATHI; Geibel HS; E Dunbar, PA; (3); 12/100; Ski Clb; VP Sr Cls; JV Var Cheerleading; Sftbl; French Hon Soc; High Hon Roll; Hon Roll; Jr NHS; Pres Phys Ftnss Awd 85 87; Frnch Merit Awd 85-86.

MC GROGAN, KATHLEEN; Notre Dame HS; Easton, PA; (3); 11/100; Cmnty Wkr; Dance Clb; Spanish Clb; Band; Chorus; School Musical; School Play; Stage Crew; Yrbk Stf; Hon Roll; Trphys & Certs For Dncng 84-87; Moravan Coll; Bus.

MC GROGAN, RITA; Yough SR HS; W Newton, PA; (4); 17/242; French Clb; Library Aide; Office Aide; Spanish Clb; Rep Frsh Cls; Capt L Bsktbl; Powder Puff Ftbl; Var L Trk; High Hon Roll; NHS; U Of Pittsburgh; Bus.

MC GROSKY, MARK; Bethel Pk HS; Bethel Pk, PA; (4); FBLA; Letterman Clb; Ski Clb; Yrbk Stf; Capt Wrstlng; High Hon Roll; Psych.

MC GROTHER, SHAWN; Cardinal Dougherty HS; Philadelphia, PA; (3); JA; Var JV Ftbl; Physical Educ & World Cultures Proficiency Awd 87 & 85; PA ST U; Mech Engrng.

MC GROTTY, KYLE A; Upper Moreland HS; Huntingdon Vly, PA; (4); 24/254; Pres Key Clb; Pres Frsh Cls; Pres Soph Cls; Pres Jr Cls; Pres Sr Cls; Off Stu Cncl; Var Capt Bsktbl; Crs Cntry; Cit Awd; High Hon Roll; Vanderbilt U; Librl Arts.

MC GUCKIN, ALAN W; New Brighton HS; New Brighton, PA; (3); Am Leg Boys St; Nwsp Ed-Chief; Stat Bsbl; Golf; Mgr(s); Hon Roll; Prfct Atten Awd; Stud Wk 84-85; Marine Bio.

MC GUCKIN, CHRISTOPHER; Archbishop Ryan For Boys; Philadelphia, PA; (4); 36/422; Cmnty Wkr; Political Wkr; Bsbl; Wt Lftg; High Hon Roll; Prncpls Awd 86; Temple U; Accntng.

MC GUIGAN, BRENDA; St Pius X HS; Phoenixville, PA; (1); 14/148; Rep Frsh Cls; Rep Stu Cncl; JV Cheerleading; Hon Roll; Jr NHS; Prfct Atten Awd; Child Dvlpmt.

MC GUIGAN, JOHN D; Norristown Area HS; Norristown, PA; (4); 12/432; Debate Tm; FBLA; Key Clb; Pep Clb; Drm Mjr(t); School Play; Yrbk Stf; Hon Roll; NHS; Prfct Atten Awd; Pltcl Sci Awd 84; Symphnc Band Awd 85; Physcl Educ Awd 85; Accntng.

MC GUIRE, JENNIFER; Jenkintown JR SR HS; Jenkintown, PA; (4); Hosp Aide; Madrigals; Nwsp Phtg; Yrbk Phtg; Hon Roll; Ntl Merit SF; PA Cert Of Merit 86; Phys Sci.

MC GUIRE, KAREN; Fort Le Boeuf HS; Waterford, PA; (3); Church Yth Grp; Ski Clb; Chorus; School Musical; Pres Stu Cncl; Cheerleading; Sftbl; Vllybl; High Hon Roll.

MC GUIRE, LOUISE; Carrick HS; Pittsburgh, PA; (3); School Musical; Nwsp Stf; Powder Puff Ftbl; Carnegie Mellon U; Drama.

MC GUIRE, MARGARET; Moon SR HS; Coraopolis, PA; (4); 7/288; Church Yth Grp; Spanish Clb; Trs Chorus; Var Trk; NHS; Drama Clb; Sec Exploring; Key Clb; Nwsp Rptr; Nwsp Stf; Int Smnr Of Wrld Affrs, Olympcs Of The Mind-Tech Rgnl Champs 86; Olyssy Of The Mind-Chain Rctn 87; Carnegie Mellon U; Engnrng.

MC GUIRE, MICHAEL; Freeport HS; Freeport, PA; (3); 28/213; Chess Clb; Nwsp Phtg; Nwsp Stf; Mgr(s); Trk; High Hon Roll; Hon Roll; Penn ST U.

MC GUIRE, NICOLE; Linesville HS; Linesville, PA; (2); FHA; Spanish Clb; Concert Band; Yrbk Phtg; Yrbk Stf; Stat Bsktbl; Mgr(s); Score Keeper; JV Sftbl; Hon Roll; Proj Enhance Edinboro U 85-87; FCC Licensed Radio Operator 86; Duke U; Med.

MC GUIRE, PHILLIP; West Scranton HS; Scranton, PA; (3); Bsbl; Bsktbl; High Hon Roll; Jr NHS; U Of Scranton; Sprts Jrnlsm.

MC GURK, MARYANNE; St Huberx HS For Girls; Philadelphia, PA; (3); 36/421; Camp Fr Inc; Office Aide; Nwsp Phtg; Hon Roll; Hnrb Mntn Urban Stds 87; Scl Srvc.

MC HADDON, MARK; Kittanning SR HS; Worthington, PA; (3); Church Yth Grp; SADD; High Hon Roll; Hon Roll; Westminister; Psych.

MC HALE, CAROLANN; Little Flower HS; Philadelphia, PA; (3); 40/340; Computer Clb; French Clb; GAA; Math Clb; Math Tm; Rep Frsh Cls; Rep Soph Cls; Rep Jr Cls; Rep Sr Cls; Var L Fld Hcky; Sci Fair 85-88; Elk Grant Schlrshp; CSC; La Salle; Accntng.

MC HALE, COLLEEN; Reading Central Catholic HS; Reading, PA; (3); 15/128; Church Yth Grp; Spanish Clb; Teachers Aide; Flag Corp; Mrchg Band; School Musical; School Play; Variety Show; Hon Roll; NHS; Schlrshp; Frst Hnrs; Dental Hygiene.

MC HALE, JOY; Scranton Prep HS; Archbald, PA; (2); Hosp Aide; Yrbk Phtg; Yrbk Rptr; Var Capt Cheerleading; Intrior Dsgn.

MC HALE, SCOTT; Tunkhannock Area HS; Falls, PA; (4); 11/280; Letterman Clb; Science Clb; Ski Clb; Varsity Clb; Var L Crs Cntry; Var L Swmmng; Var L Trk; High Hon Roll; NHS; Dist Mdlst, ST Qulfr-Swmng; Crs Cntry 86; VA Tech; Aerspc Engrng.

MC HALE, TIMOTHY; W Seranton HS; Scranton, PA; (2); Art Clb; Boy Clb Am; Computer Clb; Latin Clb; Letterman Clb; Ski Clb; JV Var Bsktbl; JV Var Ftbl; Var JV Trk; Hon Roll; Scranton U.

MC HATTIE, KEN S; Ambridge Area HS; Ambridge, PA; (3); Church Yth Grp; Pres Trs Exploring; Hon Roll; Prfct Atten Awd; Boy Scts Ord Arrw, SR Patrol Ldr, & Gldn Poet Awd Wrld Poety 87; CC Beavery Cnty; Engl.

MC HENRY, BRIDGET; Ambridge Area HS; Baden, PA; (4); 72/265; Church Yth Grp; JA; Pep Clb; Red Cross Aide; Band; Ed Yrbk Stf; Off Soph Cls; Off Jr Cls; Off Sr Cls; Hon Roll; Sawyer Schl Bus; Trvl.

MC HENRY, JENNIFER A; Greater Latrobe SR HS; Latrobe, PA; (4); AFS; JA; Pep Clb; Sftbl; DAR Awd; High Hon Roll; Lion Awd; NCTE Awd; NHS; Spanish NHS; Westminster Coll; Bus.

MC HENRY, ROBERT; Lawrence County Vo-Tech; New Castle, PA; (3); VICA; Youngstown ST U; Adm.

MC HENRY, SAMANTHA; Waynesburg Central HS; Waynesburg, PA; (3); French Clb; Yrbk Phtg; Yrbk Rptr; Yrbk Stf; High Hon Roll; Hon Roll; Gifted Pgm 84-87; Yrbk-Assoc Editor 86-87; Yrbk-Co-Editor 85-86; Chem.

MC HUGH, CHRISTOPHER; Danville Area HS; Danville, PA; (1); JV Bsbl; Im Bsktbl; Im Ftbl; High Hon Roll; Hon Roll; Engrng.

MC HUGH, JENNIFER; Upper Dublin SR HS; Ft Washington, PA; (3); Intnl Clb; SADD; Varsity Clb; Tennis; Hon Roll; Edu.

MC HUGH, KELLI; Greensburg Central Catholic HS; Greensburg, PA; (3); 99/246; Ski Clb; SADD; Chorus; School Play; Yrbk Bus Mgr; Rep Soph Cls; Rep Cmnty Wkr; Rep Sr Cls; Stu Cncl; Powder Puff Ftbl; Nrsng.

MC HUGH, KELLI; Mid Valley HS; Throop, PA; (2); Art Clb; Drama Clb; SADD; Rep Frsh Cls; Rep Soph Cls; Rep Jr Cls; Rep Stu Cncl; Var Cheerleading; Var Sftbl; Hon Roll; Mary Lou Regan Awd-Sftbl 86; U Of Scranton; Corp Law.

MC HUGH, KELLY; Notre Dame HS; Easton, PA; (3); Yrbk Stf; Sec Stu Cncl; Var Bsktbl; Sftbl; Hon Roll; Outstndng Achvt Spn III 87; Mktng.

MC HUGH, THERESA; Cardinal Dougherty HS; Philadelphia, PA; (3); 260/670; Church Yth Grp; Office Aide; Service Clb; Stage Crew; Physcl Thrpst.

MC ILNAY, JODI; Mt Pleasant HS; Stahlstown, PA; (4); Church Yth Grp; GAA; Ski Clb; Chorus; Nwsp Stf; Stat Bsktbl; Cheerleading; Ma Maids; Var Sftbl; Vllybl; Homecoming Queen 87.

MC ILROY, THOMAS; Moon SR HS; Coraopolis, PA; (3); Acpl Chr; Chorus; Im Bsbl; Im JV Ftbl; Im Wrstlng.

MC ILVAINE, HEATHER M; Waynesburg Central HS; Waynesburg, PA; (3); French Clb; Ski Clb; Trk; Var Vllybl; Hon Roll; NHS; Med.

MC ILVAINE, JOY; Lancaster Mennonite HS; Lititz, PA; (3); 17/179; Church Yth Grp; Hosp Aide; Speech Tm; Chorus; Church Choir; Hon Roll; Mid Atlntc Chrstn Schls Assn Excel Awd 87; 3rd Rdng Intrptn Fine Art Fstvl 86; Blue Rbbn Arts/Crft 87; Bio.

MC INERNEY, KATHLEEN; Hershey HS; Hummelstown, PA; (2); Pep Clb; Ski Clb; Chorus; Stat Bsbl; JV Cheerleading; High Hon Roll; Spanish NHS; SCI.

MC INTIRE, CHRISTINE; Lenape Vo-Tech; Worthington, PA; (4); Library Aide; VICA; Band; Nwsp Stf; Trs Yrbk Stf; High Hon Roll; NHS; Accntng.

MC INTOSH, KEVIN L; Rochester Area HS; Rochester, PA; (3); Am Leg Boys St; Office Aide; Church Choir; Yrbk Stf; VP Frsh Cls; Pres Soph Cls; Pres Jr Cls; Pres Sr Cls; Stu Cncl; Ftbl; Prom Cmmtte 87; Heart Hop Court 85; Bradford; Bus.

MC INTYRE, GARY; Dunmore HS; Dunmore, PA; (3); 70/154; Am Leg Boys St; Drama Clb; Pres Acpl Chr; Pres Band; School Musical; Nwsp Phtg; Yrbk Phtg; JV Bsbl; Var Golf; Var Swmmng; PMEA Dist 9 & Rgn Iv ST Chorus 87; All-Amer Hall Of Fame Hnrs Band 86-87; Luzerne CC; Respiratory Thrpy.

MC INTYRE, KATHLEEN F; Phoenixville Area HS; Phoenixville, PA; (3); Varsity Clb; Var Tennis; S E Natl Bank Artst Of Mnth Awd 85; Exhbtr Soroptmst Art Show 85; Thomas Jefferson U Hosp Art Show 85; Bio.

MC INTYRE, KELLY ANN; St Basil Acad; Philadelphia, PA; (3); Drama Clb; French Clb; SADD; Acpl Chr; Chorus; U Of CA; Indstrl Psych.

MC INTYRE, LEE ANN; Somerset Area SR HS; Sipesville, PA; (3); 16/230; English Clb; French Clb; Q&S; School Play; Yrbk Stf; Sec Soph Cls; Rep Stu Cncl; High Hon Roll; Hon Roll; Sec NHS; Bus Admin.

MC INTYRE, TERESE; Susquehanna Community HS; Lanesboro, PA; (3); Chorus; School Play; Variety Show; Var L Cheerleading; Var Powder Puff Ftbl; Var L Score Keeper; High Hon Roll; Hon Roll; Ntl Merit Schol; Amrcn Legion Awd 83-84.

MC INTYRE, TONY; Corry Area HS; Corry, PA; (2); Church Yth Grp; JV L Ftbl; Wt Lftg; High Hon Roll; U Of Pittsburgh; Business.

MC INTYRE, TRACY; Highlands SR HS; Natrona, PA; (3); Exploring; Hosp Aide; Intnl Clb; Office Aide; Capt L Bsktbl; Jr NHS; Citizens Hosp Schl Nrsng; Nrsng.

MC ISAAC, SUZANNE; Cameron County HS; Emporium, PA; (3); Concert Band; Drm Mjr(t); Mrchg Band; Yrbk Phtg; Yrbk Stf; Rep Soph Cls; Stu Cncl; JV Co-Capt Cheerleading; L Golf; Hon Roll; Delta Epsilon Phi 87.

MC KAIN, AMY; Butler Area SR HS; Butler, PA; (3); Pres Church Yth Grp; Dance Clb; Exploring; French Clb; SADD; Thesps; Ed Nwsp Bus Mgr; Rep Stu Cncl; Hon Roll; Drama Clb; Cmmnctns.

MC KAIN, SHEILA; Donegal HS; Marietta, PA; (2); Church Yth Grp; GAA; JV Bsktbl; Mgr(s); Score Keeper; JV Sftbl; Hon Roll; Stheastrn Acad; Trvl.

MC KAY, MARY; East Pennsboro Area HS; Camp Hill, PA; (3); 40/185; GAA; Spanish Clb; Stat Bsbl; Var L Gym; Var JV Mgr(s); High Hon Roll; Hon Roll; NHS; Stat Sftbl; Athltc Trng.

MC KAY, MAUREEN; W Mifflin Area HS; West Mifflin, PA; (4); Church Yth Grp; FBLA; Office Aide; Teachers Aide; Yrbk Ed-Chief; Hon Roll; Jr NHS; NHS; Grt Amrcn Fdrl Schlrshp, WV Wesleyan Schlrahp, Mst Outstndng Studnt Sec 87; WV Wesleyan Coll; Accntnt.

MC KAY, MICHAEL; The Christian Acad; Philadelphia, PA; (3); Camera Clb; Hosp Aide; Library Aide; Nwsp Rptr; Nwsp Stf; Hon Roll; Rep Jr Cls; Rep Sr Cls; Math 85; Hnr Rl Mdl 85; Cameamn.

MC KAY, MICHELLE; Philipsburg-Osceola SR HS; Osceola Mills, PA; (3); 84/238; Church Yth Grp; Pep Clb; Church Choir; Trs Stu Cncl; Score Keeper; Stat Wrstlng; Kiwanis Sci Fair Awd 2nd Pl 85; Stdnt Cncl Awd 85; IN U Of PA.

MC KAY, MICHELLE; Tidioute HS; Tidioute, PA; (2); 3/22; Varsity Clb; Chorus; Church Choir; VP Frsh Cls; Pres Soph Cls; Rep Stu Cncl; Bsktbl; Sftbl; Vllybl; Hon Roll.

MC KEAN, AMANDA; Hatboro Horsham SR HS; Hatboro, PA; (3); 20/200; Key Clb; SADD; Color Guard; Drill Tm; Mrchg Band; Mgr(s); Hon Roll; Indoor Guard 86-87; Indoor Drumline 86-87; PA ST; Advrstng.

MC KEE, ALICIA; Hollidaysburg Area SR HS; Hollidaysburg, PA; (4); French Clb; Library Aide; Nwsp Rptr; Navy; Data Proc.

MC KEE, BONNIE KAY; Leechburg HS; Leechburg, PA; (4); 11/84; Dance Clb; Debate Tm; Hosp Aide; VP JA; Math Tm; Concert Band; School Play; Stat Bsktbl; Var L Sftbl; Var Twrlr; Ernest Mirandola Schlrshp 87; Sidney Bennett Schlrshp 87; Leechburg Mothers Club Schlrshp 87; PA ST; Frgn Svc.

MC KEE, DUANE; Seneca Valley HS; Mars, PA; (4); Bsktbl; Trk; Penn ST; Engrng.

MC KEE, KELLY; Milton SR HS; New Columbia, PA; (4); Sec Church Yth Grp; Computer Clb; German Clb; Latin Clb; Varsity Clb; Mrchg Band; Fld Hcky; Sftbl; Hon Roll; NHS; Deifuss Schlrshp; Presdntl Acadc Ftns Awd; Cntrl Susquehanna Schlrshp Spnsrd PA House; Bloomsburg U; Elem Ed.

MC KEE, LISA; Biship Hafey HS; Conyngham, PA; (2); 11/106; Drama Clb; Hosp Aide; Ski Clb; Spanish Clb; School Musical; School Play; JV Bsktbl; Var Bowling; High Hon Roll; Hon Roll; Gynecology.

MC KEE, LISA; Marion Center Area HS; Clymer, PA; (4); 14/169; FBLA; Intnl Clb; Library Aide; Q&S; Science Clb; SADD; Nwsp Rptr; High Hon Roll; Hon Roll; 1st Awd Album Rvw We Are The World 85; Penn ST; Film.

MC KEE, LYNN; Sharon HS; Sharon, PA; (3); 38/194; French Clb; GAA; Library Aide; Varsity Clb; Chorus; Church Choir; School Play; Rep Frsh Cls; Rep Soph Cls; Pres Sr Cls; Phys Ftnss Awd 85; St Fnlst 8 Mile Relay 85; St Fnlst Crss Cntry 86; Pittsburgh U; Phys Thrpy.

MC KEE, SEAN R; Du Bois Area SR HS; Du Bois, PA; (2); 64/300; JV Bsbl; Jrnlst.

MC KEEGAN, SUZANNE; Stroudsburg HS; Stroudsburg, PA; (3); FBLA; Hosp Aide; Pep Clb; Band; Chorus; Concert Band; Mrchg Band; Pep Band; Hon Roll; Clerk Typist-Rgnl Level Future Bus Ldrs Of Amer 5th Pl 87; Allentown Bus Schl; Travel.

MC KEEVER, ANNE; Panther Valley HS; Nesquehoning, PA; (3); 44/132; Camera Clb; Church Yth Grp; Library Aide; Band; Concert Band; Mrchg Band; Stage Crew; Nwsp Rptr; Nwsp Stf; Yrbk Stf; Cvl Law.

MC KEEVER, TINA MARIE; St Huberts Catholic HS; Philadelphia, PA; (2); 136/368; Church Yth Grp; Cmnty Wkr; Hosp Aide; Office Aide; Teachers Aide; Coach Actv; Gym; Score Keeper; Swmmng; Vllybl; U Of Miami; Child Development.

MC KELVIE, LEAH; Bensalem HS; Bensalem, PA; (2); JV Trk; High Hon Roll; Hon Roll; John Hopkins Tlnt Srch 84; Bryn Mawr; Engl.

MC KELVY, SONIA; HS Of Engineering And Science; Phila, PA; (3); 82/241; Yrbk Stf; Hon Roll; Acdmc Achvt U PA, Smithkline Beckmn Potentls Pgm; Chemcl Engr.

MC KENNA, MELISSA; Springdale HS; Springdale, PA; (4); 11/108; Church Yth Grp; SADD; Lib Acpl Chr; Church Choir; Yrbk Ed-Chief; High Hon Roll; NHS; Pres Schlr; Alleghney Coll Sesqucntnl & S C & E M Wasilak Memrl Schlrshps 87; Cheswick Lions Clb Stu Mnt 87; Allegheny Coll; Elem Ed.

MC KENNEY, STEVEN; Susquehanna Township HS; Harrisburg, PA; (3); Boy Scts; SADD; Band; Yrbk Stf; Trk; Hon Roll; Penn ST; Psych.

MC KENZIE, CORI; New Castle SR HS; New Castle, PA; (4); 44/228; Pres Church Yth Grp; Drill Tm; Mrchg Band; Yrbk Stf; Off Stu Cncl; Capt Cheerleading; L Gym; Var Trk; Hon Roll; Ntl Acdmc Games Olympcs 85 & 87; Rtry Intl Yth Exchng Stu-Finlnd 87; PA Prfct Teen Pgnt Cntstnt 86; IN U Of PA; Bus.

MC KENZIE, JANICE; Clearfield Area HS; Clearfield, PA; (4); 70/285; Drama Clb; Rep Spanish Clb; Score Keeper; Capt Twrlr; Hon Roll; Gannon U; Radiological Tech.

MC KENZIE, ROBBY; Berlin Brothersvalley HS; Meyersdale, PA; (4); 25/81; Church Yth Grp; French Clb; Chorus; Var JV Vllybl; French Hon Soc; Hon Roll; Lion Awd; Prfct Atten Awd; Frnch III Cert 86; Cambree-Rowe Business; CPA.

MC KERNAN, LISA; Kennedy Christian HS; Sharon, PA; (2); 9/96; Church Yth Grp; Hosp Aide; Spanish Clb; Band; Concert Band; Mrchg Band; Im Bsktbl; Var L Trk; High Hon Roll; NEDT Awd; PA ST U; Med.

MC KIERNAN, AMANDA M; Cardinal Dougherty HS; Philadelphia, PA; (2); 258/656; Cmnty Wkr; Office Aide; Chorus; School Musical; School Play; Variety Show; Hon Roll; Cert Of Acad Proficiency-Alg I 86; Cert Of Acad Profcncy-World Cultures II 87.

MC KILLIP, RONALD; United HS; New Florence, PA; (3); 24/147; Var L Wrstlng; Acctng.

MC KIM, KEVIN; De Lone Catholic HS; Hanover, PA; (4); #2 In Class; Model UN; Im Bsktbl; Im Vllybl; High Hon Roll; NHS; Sal; Penn ST U; Engrng.

MC KINLEY, CHARLOTTE S; Clarion Area HS; Clarion, PA; (3); 1/91; Concert Band; Jazz Band; Mrchg Band; Yrbk Phtg; L Bsktbl; L Trk; High Hon Roll; NHS; Chem Educ.

MC KINLEY, KRISTEN; Valley HS; Arnold, PA; (4); 5/200; Girl Scts; VP JA; Band; Rep Stu Cncl; Var L Trk; NHS; Pres Schlr; Church Yth Grp; Drama Clb; Pittsburgh Press Acad All ST Achvr 87; PTA Schlrshp 87; Local & Natl Conf JA 85-86; IN U; Elem Educ.

MC KINLEY, LORI; William Penn Vo-Tech; Harrisburg, PA; (3); 6/156; FBLA; Pep Clb; Color Guard; Mrchg Band; Off Jr Cls; JV Cheerleading; Hon Roll; NHS; Bio.

MC KINLEY, MATTHEW G; Upper Merion Area HS; King Of Prussia, PA; (3); 8/300; Math Tm; JV Bsbl; JV Im Bsktbl; JV Ftbl; High Hon Roll; NHS; Rotary Awd; Business Administration.

MC KINLEY, MEREDITH; Marple Newtown SR HS; Broomall, PA; (3); Church Yth Grp; FCA; SADD; Band; Mrchg Band; Stu Cncl; Var Capt Cheerleading; Im Sftbl; Stat Swmmng; Educ.

MC KINLEY, MICHAEL; First Baptist Church Acad; Du Bois, PA; (3); Chorus; Concert Band; Mrchg Band; Yrbk Ed-Chief; Yrbk Phtg; VP Stu Cncl; High Hon Roll; Hon Roll; Church Yth Grp; Quiz Bowl; Learn Systems Inc 1800 Clb Read Awd.

MC KINLEY, YVONNE; Franklin HS; Clintonville, PA; (2); Var L Tennis; Sch Directors Awd 86-87; Ed.

MC KINNEY, DAVID; Mohawk HS; New Galilee, PA; (3); French Clb; Hst FFA; JV Bsktbl; Var Trk; High Hon Roll; Hon Roll; NHS.

MC KINNEY, DEBRA; Pine Forge Acad; Albuquerque, NM; (3); Church Yth Grp; Hosp Aide; Teachers Aide; Chorus; Sec Frsh Cls; Rep Soph Cls; VP Jr Cls; Bsktbl; Cit Awd; Hon Roll; Oakwood Coll; Accntng.

MC KINNEY, JACALYN; Mohawk Area HS; Enon Valley, PA; (3); 7/135; VP Sec French Clb; Concert Band; Mrchg Band; Var L Bsktbl; Im Powder Puff Ftbl; L Trk; High Hon Roll; Hon Roll; NHS; Hnrbl Mntn Sctn XVI AA Bsktbll 86; 2nd Tm All Star Sctn XVI AA Bsktbll 87; Elem Educ.

MC KINNEY, JANICE; Pine Forge Acad; Albuquerque, NM; (4); 7/79; NAACP; Chorus; Nwsp Rptr; Pres Sr Cls; Var Cheerleading; Bausch & Lomb Sci Awd; High Hon Roll; Ntl Merit Schol; U Of NM; Nrlgst.

MC KINNEY, JILL; Biglerville HS; Bendersville, PA; (3); 31/90; Art Clb; FCA; German Clb; Varsity Clb; Hst Frsh Cls; Hst Soph Cls; Hst Jr Cls; Rep Stu Cncl; Capt Cheerleading; Hon Roll.

MC KINNEY, JOSEPH; United HS; Robinson, PA; (3); Boy Scts; Band; High Hon Roll; Hon Roll; Military.

MC KINNEY, LINDA; Tyrone Area HS; Tyrone, PA; (2); Key Clb; Spanish Clb; Chorus; Color Guard; Mrchg Band; Stage Crew; Hon Roll; Tchng.

MC KINNEY, ROBERT; Marple-Newtown SR HS; Broomall, PA; (3); 150/323; Yrbk Phtg; Yrbk Stf; Off Stu Cncl; Trk; Hon Roll.

MC KINNEY, TERRIANN; Knoch JR SR HS; Cabot, PA; (4); Chorus; Drill Tm; Stat Bsktbl; Crs Cntry; Pom Pon; Score Keeper; Trk; Wt Lftg; High Hon Roll; NHS; Cert Merit Outstndg Hlth 85; Edinboro U; Dietcn.

MC KINSEY, SHAYNE; Springside Schl; Oreland, PA; (3); Dance Clb; GAA; Nwsp Rptr; Nwsp Stf; Pres Frsh Cls; JV Bsktbl; JV Var Fld Hcky; JV Var Lcrss; French Hon Soc; Hon Roll; Natl Frnch Cntst Wnnr 85; Natl Lat Cntst Wnnr 87; Psych.

MC KITO, JANET L; Ringgold HS; Donora, PA; (3); Chorus; Hon Roll; Jr NHS; NHS; Bus.

MC KITTEN, CARLA; Villa Maria HS; Chicora, PA; (4); 2/52; Cmnty Wkr; Drama Clb; Key Clb; Pep Clb; Science Clb; Ski Clb; Spanish Clb; Thesps; School Play; Rep Sr Cls; PA JR Acad Sci 1st Regnl & ST 85; John Carroll; Med.

MC KLVEEN, CHRIS; Mt Pleasant Area HS; Latrobe, PA; (2); Boy Scts; Church Yth Grp; Computer Clb; Ski Clb; Ftbl; Trk; Wt Lftg; Hon Roll.

MC KNIGHT, ERIC; Schenley HS; Pittsburgh, PA; (3); Aud/Vis; French Clb; JA; School Musical; VP Stu Cncl; Crs Cntry; High Hon Roll; Hon Roll; VP NHS; Prfct Atten Awd; Pre Law.

MC KNIGHT, KATHARINE; Quaker Valley HS; Sewickley, PA; (1); Chorus; Nwsp Stf; Var L Socr; Var L Trk; High Hon Roll; Pres Acad Ftnss Awds Prgm 86-87.

MC KNIGHT, MELISSA K; Central HS; E Freedom, PA; (3); Church Yth Grp; SADD; JV Var Bsktbl; JV Var Vllybl; Socl Work.

MC KOSKY, TRACY LYNN; Frazier JR SR HS; Perryopolis, PA; (3); Drama Clb; Spanish Clb; Chorus; Cheerleading; Hon Roll; Jr Vrrsty Cheerldng Squad; CA U Of PA; Elem Educ.

MC KRUIT, DE ANNA; Shenango JR SR HS; New Castle, PA; (3); 8/125; French Clb; Hosp Aide; Library Aide; Office Aide; Yrbk Stf; High Hon Roll; Hon Roll; Jr NHS; Arch.

MC KULA, PATRICK; Mt Pleasant Area HS; Acme, PA; (3); German Clb; VP Jr Cls; Var L Bsbl; Ftbl; Hon Roll; Pres Schlr; Acad All Amer 85; Schl Tchr.

MC LAIN, KELLY; Exeter Township HS; Reading, PA; (3); 21/241; Church Yth Grp; Drama Clb; Teachers Aide; Band; Concert Band; Mrchg Band; School Play; High Hon Roll; Hon Roll; NHS; Elem Educ.

MC LAIN, TODD; Exeter Township HS; Reading, PA; (3); 60/245; Boy Scts; Church Yth Grp; Band; Mrchg Band; Comp Prog.

MC LAUGHLIN, ANNE; Carbondale Area HS; Carbondale, PA; (3); Church Yth Grp; FBLA; Letterman Clb; Rep Jr Cls; Capt Var Bsktbl; Var Fld Hcky; Hon Roll.

MC LAUGHLIN II, CHARLES W; Ringgold HS; Donora, PA; (4); Boy Scts; Band; Concert Band; Jazz Band; Mrchg Band; Hon Roll; Penn ST U; Biomed Equip Tech.

MC LAUGHLIN, CORY; Hamburg Area HS; Bernville, PA; (3); Boy Scts; Church Yth Grp; 4-H; Im Bsktbl; Var L Crs Cntry; JV Var Trk; 4-H Awd; Hon Roll; PA ST U; Arch.

MC LAUGHLIN, DIANE; Manheim Township HS; Lancaster, PA; (2); 40/330; Church Yth Grp; FBLA; Key Clb; Spanish Clb; Varsity Clb; Band; Var L Crs Cntry; Var L Trk; High Hon Roll; Church Choir; Hugh O Brian Ldrshp Conf 87; Dirctrs Awd Band Ldrshp; Mayors Yth Ldrshp Smnr 87; Sci.

MC LAUGHLIN, GINA; Kennard-Dale HS; Delta, PA; (3); Drama Clb; Ski Clb; Church Choir; School Musical; School Play; Yrbk Stf; VP Soph Cls; VP Jr Cls; Rep Stu Cncl; JV Vllybl.

MC LAUGHLIN, GRANT REED; North Hills HS; Pittsburgh, PA; (4); 155/480; AFS; Exploring; JA; Key Clb; Ski Clb; Band; Nwsp Rptr; Yrbk Stf; Sec Frsh Cls; Sec Jr Cls; Hnr Rll 86-87; Bethany U; Cmmnctns.

MC LAUGHLIN, JANET; Reynolds HS; Greenville, PA; (3); 11/145; Latin Clb; Spanish Clb; Color Guard; Capt Drill Tm; Mrchg Band; Mat Maids; NHS; NEDT Awd; Pre Med.

MC LAUGHLIN, KELLY; Avon Grove HS; Landenberg, PA; (3); 5/215; Drama Clb; Sec SADD; Band; Chorus; Concert Band; Mrchg Band; School Musical; School Play; Variety Show; Stu Cncl; Dstrct Chorus 87; Cmnctns.

MC LAUGHLIN, KYLE; Cathedral Prep Schl; Erie, PA; (3); 3/204; Latin Clb; Model UN; Nwsp Rptr; Nwsp Stf; Yrbk Rptr; Yrbk Stf; L Swmmng; High Hon Roll; Hon Roll; Ntl Merit Ltr; Latin Hon Soc 84-87; All City Water Polo Tm Hon Ment & 1st Tm 85-87; Duke U; Med.

MC LAUGHLIN, LAURA; Manheim Township HS; Lancaster, PA; (4); 8/325; Church Yth Grp; Key Clb; Science Clb; Band; Lit Mag; Var L Diving; Var L Trk; High Hon Roll; Ntl Merit Schol; Drama Clb; PA Govnrs Schl Art 86; Robert Byrd Scholar ABWA Scholar & PSU Scholar 87; Cngrssnl Page Apointee 86; Penn ST U; Biol.

MC LAUGHLIN, LISA; Bishop Conwell HS; Levittown, PA; (3); 31/277; Girl Scts; Service Clb; Cheerleading; Hon Roll; NHS; Engl Awd 85-86; Spnsh Awd 86-87; Comp Sci.

MC LAUGHLIN, MARA; Bishop Makey HS; Harleigh, PA; (3); 58/119; Cmnty Wkr; Dance Clb; Girl Scts; Latin Clb; Spanish Clb; Y-Teens; Hon Roll; Spanish NHS; St Francis Allentown; Socl Wrk.

MC LAUGHLIN, PATRICK; Abington HS; Jenkintown, PA; (3); Latin Clb; VICA; Chorus; School Musical; Electrncs.

MC LAUGHLIN, PAUL; Burrell SR HS; Lower Burrell, PA; (3); Church Yth Grp; Concert Band; Jazz Band; Trs Frsh Cls; Trs Stu Cncl; L Tennis; High Hon Roll; Jr NHS; NHS; Rotary Awd; Notre Dame; Bus Admin.

MC LAUGHLIN, SHANNON; Bishop Mc Cory HS; Johnstown, PA; (3); 7/178; JCL; Pres Latin Clb; Mu Alpha Theta; Speech Tm; Chorus; Yrbk Stf; Sec Jr Cls; Rep Stu Cncl; High Hon Roll; NHS.

MC LAURIN, KATHLEEN; Riverview HS; Oakmont, PA; (2); 5/104; French Clb; Key Clb; Ski Clb; Band; Chorus; Concert Band; Jazz Band; Mrchg Band; Yrbk Stf; Hon Roll; Bus Admin.

MC LEAN, ALYSON; Archbishop Carroll HS; Gladwyne, PA; (4); 121/347; French Clb; Intnl Clb; SADD; Yrbk Rptr; Hon Roll; Temple U; Jrnlsm.

MC LEAN, CHERYL; Philadelphia H S For Girls; Philadelphia, PA; (3); 22/405; Church Yth Grp; Cmnty Wkr; Dance Clb; Office Aide; Pep Clb; Service Clb; School Musical; Stage Crew; Off Sr Cls; Cheerleading; Rcvd Hnr In Natl Frnch Cmptn 86; Rcvd Bond From All-Cncrnd Black Men Inc 87; Rcvd Keys Dstnghsd Stud; Howard Univ; Elec Engnrng.

MC LEAN, DENISE; Bald Eagle Nittany HS; Mill Hall, PA; (2); 10/135; Drama Clb; Spanish Clb; Band; Color Guard; Mrchg Band; School Musical; School Play; Stu Cncl; Hon Roll; NHS; Rifle Capt 87.

MC LEAN, KERRIE; Southmorlenad SR HS; Scottdale, PA; (3); Latin Clb; Library Aide; Nwsp Stf; Yrbk Stf; Lit Mag; Ntl Merit Ltr; Fashn Dsgn.

MC LEAN, KRISTEN; Schuylkill Valley HS; Leesport, PA; (3); 34/140; Rep FBLA; Pep Clb; SADD; Chorus; Capt Color Guard; Mrchg Band; School Musical; Yrbk Stf; Rep Stu Cncl; Bsktbl; Busi.

MC LEAN, MICHAEL; Council Rock HS; Richboro, PA; (2); JV Bsbl; JV Capt Ftbl; Im Lcrss; JV Capt Wrstlng; Hon Roll; Prfct Atten Awd; Avtn.

MC LEAN, PAMELA; HS Of Engineering & Science; Philladelphia, PA; (3); 5/250; Trs Church Yth Grp; Dance Clb; Girl Scts; JA; Drill Tm; Variety Show; High Hon Roll; NHS; Engrng.

MC LEAN, SARAH L; Garden Spot HS; New Holland, PA; (2); 60/225; Drama Clb; 4-H; Chorus; Jazz Band; School Play; Hon Roll; Church Yth Grp; Church Choir; School Musical; Hon Roll; Hugh O Brian Yth Fndtn 87.

MC LEE, ANDREA; Little Flower Catholie HS For Girls; Philadelphia, PA; (3); Trk; Hon Roll; Black Stu Leag; Trach Awd; Accntng.

MC LELLAND, SANDRA; Springside Schl; Philadelphia, PA; (3); Church Yth Grp; Church Choir; Lit Mag; VP Soph Cls; VP Sr Cls; Rep Stu Cncl; Fld Hcky; JV Score Keeper; High Hon Roll; Hon Roll.

MC LISTER, DENNIS; Butler HS; Butler, PA; (3); 24/800; Church Yth Grp; School Musical; Yrbk Ed-Chief; Sec Soph Cls; Rep Stu Cncl; Im Bsktbl; Var Ftbl; Var Trk; Im Wt Lftg; High Hon Roll; Finance.

MC LOUGHLIN, HEATHER L; Creative & Performing Arts HS; Philadelphia, PA; (4); 2/125; High Hon Roll; Hon Roll; Jr NHS; NHS; Closed Prof Divisn Penna-Ballet 80-87; Dance Inthe Nutcrakcer With Pa Ballet 83-87; Phila Art Awd 84; Dancer.

MC LOVICH, DARLA; Blue Mountain HS; Orwigsburg, PA; (3); 1/200; Church Yth Grp; SADD; Sec Trs Chorus; School Musical; School Play; Ed Nwsp Rptr; Trs Rep Stu Cncl; Co-Capt Cheerleading; Trk; NEDT Awd; High Hnr Rl 84-86; Pre-Law.

MC MAHAN, KAREN; Baldwin HS; Pittsburgh, PA; (4); 61/533; Church Yth Grp; Girl Scts; Key Clb; Concert Band; Mrchg Band; School Musical; Yrbk Stf; L Bsktbl; High Hon Roll; NHS; Sesquicentennial Schlrshp Of Allegheny Coll 87; Grad With Hghst Hnrs 87; Worthy Advsr White Hls 85-87; Allegheny Coll; Bio.

MC MAHAN, MARK; Marion Center Area HS; Marion Center, PA; (3); 51/153; Boy Scts; Church Yth Grp; Intnl Clb; Varsity Clb; VP Band; Concert Band; Mrchg Band; Var Bsbl; Var Swmmng; Hon Roll; Eagle Scout Awd 86.

MC MAHON, PATRICIA; Boyertown SR HS; Green Lane, PA; (4); Pres 4-H; French Clb; Spanish Clb; Chorus; School Musical; School Play; Cit Awd; 4-H Awd; Wildner U; Hotel Mngmnt.

MC MAHON, SEAN; Mohawk JR/Sr HS; Enon Valley, PA; (3); Boys Clb Am; Boy Scts; Church Yth Grp; Computer Clb; Exploring; French Clb; JA; Office Aide; Ski Clb; Speech Tm; Cert Of Achvt Ftbl 86; PA ST U; Elec Engr.

MC MANAMA, MAUREEN; Montour HS; Mckees Rocks, PA; (4); Church Yth Grp; Hosp Aide; SADD; Im Sftbl; Var L Swmmng; Var L Trk; Hon Roll; Apprctn Awd Yth Grp/Christn Mthrs 87; Apalacha Wrk Camp 86; OH Vly Schl Nrsng; RN.

MC MANN, HEATHER; Lock Haven SR HS; Lock Haven, PA; (3); Church Yth Grp; French Clb; SADD; Chorus; Color Guard; Mrchg Band; Variety Show; Rep Stu Cncl; Var L Twrlr; Hon Roll; Bloomsburg; Soc.

MC MANN, SAMANTHA; Harbor Creek HS; Erie, PA; (4); 32/225; Office Aide; Chorus; Variety Show; Rep Jr Cls; Powder Puff Ftbl; L Trk; Hon Roll; NHS; Erie Bus Ctr; Med Asst.

MC MANUS, SHERRY; Beth Center SR HS; Clarksville, PA; (4); Art Clb; Church Yth Grp; Dance Clb; Spanish Clb; L Bsktbl; L Sftbl; Hon Roll; CA U.

MC MARTIN, LEIANNE; Northern Lebanon JR/Sr HS; Jonestown, PA; (4); 12/166; Church Yth Grp; Cmnty Wkr; Math Tm; Model UN; Nwsp Rptr; Var Fld Hcky; Kiwanis Awd; NHS; Art Clb; Drama Clb; Olympcs Of Mind Tm Capt 86-87; Tchng Schlrshp 87; Lycoming Coll; Math.

MC MASTER, CYNTHIA; Delone Catholic HS; Hanover, PA; (3); 32/158; FBLA; JV Var Cheerleading; Hon Roll; NHS; Top 10 Pct Clss 86; Excllnc Span 86.

MC MASTER, GARY; Somerset Area SR HS; Somerset, PA; (4); 10/232; English Clb; French Clb; JA; Mu Alpha Theta; Varsity Clb; Var L Bsbl; Var L Bsktbl; High Hon Roll; JC Awd; NHS; Carnegie Mellon; Engrng.

MC MASTER, LINDA; Centre County Christian Acad; Mingoville, PA; (3); Church Yth Grp; Drama Clb; French Clb; FBLA; Teachers Aide; Chorus; Church Choir; Cheerleading; Hon Roll; Prfct Atten Awd; PA ST U; Legal Sec.

MC MASTER, SCOTT; Seneca Valley SR HS; Zelienople, PA; (3); 13/350; Thesps; Jazz Band; Mrchg Band; School Musical; School Play; Symp Band; Trk; High Hon Roll; Lion Awd; NHS; Chem Engr.

MC MENAMIN, DEIRDRE; W B Saul HS; Philadelphia, PA; (1); FFA; Im Socr; Im Tennis; Im Vllybl; 1st Prize Bio, Outstndng Studnt Awd FFA, Maine Island Ecology Prog Schlrshp 87; Coll Of The Atlantic; Bio.

MC MICHAEL, ELLEN; Oxford Area HS; Oxford, PA; (3); Pres Church Yth Grp; Trs FTA; Ski Clb; SADD; VP Chorus; Church Choir; Co-Capt Color Guard; School Musical; High Hon Roll; Ed.

MC MILLAN, DANNY; Center Area HS; Aliquippa, PA; (2); Church Yth Grp; Spanish Clb; Chorus; School Musical; Bowling; Hon Roll; Prfct Atten Awd; U Pittsburgh; Dntstry.

MC MILLAN, MAXINE; Abraham Lincoln HS; Philadelphia, PA; (3); Cmnty Wkr; Varsity Clb; Variety Show; Yrbk Stf; Pres Jr Cls; Rep Stu Cncl; Cheerleading; Pom Pon; Capt Trk; Hon Roll; PSBA St Conf Offcl Stu Delg 86; Spelman; Philosophy.

MC MILLEN, BARBARA; Saltsburg JR SR HS; Saltsburg, PA; (3); Hosp Aide; SADD; Varsity Clb; Yrbk Stf; Trs Jr Cls; Stu Cncl; Var Capt Cheerleading; Gym; Powder Puff Ftbl; Hon Roll; Sweater Hop Escrt 85; Bradford Bus Schl; Sec.

MC MILLEN, DIANE; Marion Center Area HS; Creekside, PA; (3); 24/149; Aud/Vis; FNA; Latin Clb; Science Clb; Varsity Clb; Chorus; Yrbk Stf; Var Stat Sftbl; Hon Roll; County Chorus 86-87; Eng.

MC MILLEN, JANET; Mapletown JR SR HS; Greensboro, PA; (3); Church Yth Grp; Cmnty Wkr; Red Cross Aide; High Hon Roll; Hon Roll; Pres Phys Ftnss Awd 86-87; Sec.

MC MILLEN, KRISTI; West Perry SR HS; Loysville, PA; (2); 20/231; Church Yth Grp; French Clb; Band; Chorus; Concert Band; Jazz Band; Mrchg Band; JV Bsktbl; Hon Roll; Amer Musical Fndtn Band Hnr 87; Cnty Band 86-87; Cnty Chorus 87; Crmnl Just.

MC MULLEN, KELLIE; Meyersdale Area HS; Meyersdale, PA; (3); Trs Library Aide; Yrbk Stf; NHS; Art.

MC MULLEN, KIMBERLY; Altoona Area HS; Altoona, PA; (3); Church Yth Grp; French Clb; Rep Jr Cls; Hon Roll; Prfct Atten Awd; Law.

MC MULLEN, ROBERT; Cambria Heights HS; Ashville, PA; (3); 77/182; 4-H; ROTC; Hon Roll; Williamsport Area Comm Coll.

MC MULLEN, SHAWN; Blacklick Valley HS; Nanty Glo, PA; (3); Church Yth Grp; Cmnty Wkr; Mgr Bsktbl; Hon Roll; U Of Pittsburgh-Johnstwn; Engrg.

MC MULLEN, SHERRIE; Bensalem SR HS; Bensalem, PA; (3); Office Aide; Teachers Aide; Off Stu Cncl; Cheerleading; Var Trk; Hon Roll; Retail Buyer.

MC MULLIN, ELISE; Plum SR HS; Pittsburgh, PA; (3); AFS; 4-H; French Clb; Acpl Chr; School Musical; Symp Band; Nwsp Stf; Yrbk Stf; 4-H Awd; NEDT Awd; Counslr For 4-H Week At PA ST U 87; Natl Merit Hnr.

MC MUNN, PATTY; Conneaut Lake HS; Conneaut Lake, PA; (3); GAA; Girl Scts; Office Aide; Spanish Clb; SADD; Varsity Clb; Var Capt Bsktbl; Var Vllybl; Hon Roll; NHS; Lttrmn Frshmn Yr Bsktbl Capt JV 85; Hon Roll 84-87; All Star Tm Bsktbl Camp 86; Nurse.

MC MURRAY, WENDY; Clearfield HS; Clearfield, PA; (4); Cmnty Wkr; Drama Clb; Hosp Aide; Spanish Clb; Chorus; Mrchg Band; School Musical; Variety Show; Pres Stu Cncl; High Hon Roll; Slpry Rck U; Physcl Thrpy.

MC MURRY, SUSAN; Shikellamy HS; Sunbury, PA; (3); 1/310; Debate Tm; Sec French Clb; Speech Tm; Hst Chorus; School Musical; Lit Mag; French Hon Soc; NHS; Drama Clb; Quiz Bowl; US Senate Schlrshp Smmr Japan 87; Hnrs Lincoln Douglas Debt Natl Qualf 85-87; Frnch II-IV Awd 85-87; Lib Arts.

MC MURTRIE, JASON; Bellefonte HS; Bellefonte, PA; (3); 10/207; Drama Clb; Pres French Clb; Pres Model UN; Yrbk Rptr; Pres Frsh Cls; Pres Soph Cls; Rep Jr Cls; Pres Sr Cls; Rep Stu Cncl; Hugh Obrian Yth Fndtn 85-86; U Of Southern CA; Pre Med.

MC NAB, TAMMY; Hazleton HS; Hazleton, PA; (4); Drama Clb; Red Cross Aide; Varsity Clb; School Musical; Nwsp Ed-Chief; Capt Trk; Mdrn Miss PA ST Fnls Spch Wnnr 86; Mdrn Miss Bst Thank You Ltr 86; Cert Aprctn-A Chlds Wsh Come True; Phys Thrpy.

MC NABB, BARBARA; Villa Maria Acad; Malvern, PA; (3); 33/98; Church Yth Grp; Service Clb; Im Bsktbl; Im Fld Hcky; Hon Roll; Bus.

MC NALLY, KELLEY; Sharon HS; Sharon, PA; (3); 22/186; French Clb; FTA; Latin Clb; Teachers Aide; Yrbk Stf; Capt Cheerleading; High Hon Roll; Slippery Rock U; Ath Training.

MC NAMARA, CHRISTINE; Abington HS; Roslyn, PA; (3); 117/507; Varsity Clb; Var Fld Hcky; Var Sftbl; Prfct Atten Awd; Arch.

MC NAMARA, THOMAS; Father Judge HS; Philadelphia, PA; (3); 15/402; Cmnty Wkr; Drama Clb; School Musical; School Play; Yrbk Rptr; Hon Roll; NHS; Pres Sacristans; Svc Awds.

MC NAMARA, TOM; Governor Mifflin HS; Shillington, PA; (3); 78/350; Varsity Clb; Socr; Wrstlng; Hon Roll; Bus.

MC NAMEE, MARLENE; Nazareth Acad; Phila, PA; (3); French Clb; Service Clb; Off Soph Cls; Off Jr Cls; Pres Stu Cncl; Cheerleading; Var Fld Hcky; Var Sftbl; Hon Roll; NHS; Hugh O Brian Yth Fndtn Ldrshp Smnr 86; Torresdale Yth Clb Girl Of Yr 87; JR Peer Cnslr 87; Philadelphia U; Finance.

MC NAVAGE, JOHN; Shaler SR HS; Glenshaw, PA; (4); Boy Scts; Ski Clb; Im Bsbl; Im Bsktbl; JV Tennis; Var Wrstlng; Elks Awd; Lion Awd; Egl Sct 85; Ad Attre Del Awd 85; Pope Pius XII Awd 87; PA ST U.

MC NEELY, LORI; Burgettstown JR/Sr Pa; Avella, PA; (3); Drama Clb; Spanish Clb; Sec Band; Chorus; Mrchg Band; School Musical; County Band 86-87; Pittsburgh U Mc Donalds Band 86; Arch.

MC NEFF, JACKIE; Upper Moreland HS; Hatboro, PA; (4); 60/262; Key Clb; SADD; Rep Frsh Cls; Rep Soph Cls; Rep Jr Cls; Rep Sr Cls; Stat Bsktbl; Var Lcrss; High Hon Roll; Hon Roll; Pres V Schlrshp U Scrantn 87; U Of Scranton.

MC NEIL, LISA; Engineering & Science HS; Philadelphia, PA; (4); Variety Show; Var Bsktbl; Jr NHS; Natl So Phi Delta Kapp Inc 83-87; St Josephs U; Bus Adm.

MC NEIL, ONTONJIA; Central HS; Philadelphia, PA; (4); 70/308; Cmnty Wkr; Yrbk Stf; Lit Mag; Spanish NHS; Humanitarian Awd 87; NY U; Bus Admin.

MC NEIL, TASHIA E; Easton Area HS; Easton, PA; (2); 8/474; Trs Church Yth Grp; Debate Tm; Math Tm; Pres NAACP; Chorus; Pres Church Choir; Off Soph Cls; High Hon Roll; Hon Roll; Jr NHS; Bus Awd Hghst Av Cls 85-86; Spnsh II Awd Mst Comprhnsv & Hghst Av 85-86; Temple U; Photo.

MC NELIS III, ANDREW W; Central Catholic HS; Pittsburgh, PA; (3); Church Yth Grp; Drama Clb; JA; School Musical; School Play; Bowling; Ftbl; Hon Roll; Crmnlgy.

MC NELLIE, JODI; Venango Christian HS; Oil City, PA; (4); 6/36; SADD; Variety Show; Rep Frsh Cls; Rep Soph Cls; JV Var Cheerleading; Var Score Keeper; JV Var Vllybl; NHS; Prom Queen 87; Exclnc Engl Awd 87; Pres Acadmc Ftns Awd 87; Gannon U; Hlth & Phys Ed.

MC NEMAR, PAUL; William Allen HS; Allentown, PA; (3); 66/609; Art Clb; Drama Clb; Service Clb; SADD; School Musical; School Play; Pres Stage Crew; Variety Show; Lit Mag; Rep Stu Cncl.

MC NICHOL, CHARLES G; Norristown Area HS; Norristown, PA; (3); 60/524; Computer Clb; Intnl Clb; Nwsp Rptr; Hon Roll; Prfct Atten Awd; Comp Sci.

MC NICHOL, CHRIS; Msgr Bonner HS; Drexel Hill, PA; (3); 5/258; Nwsp Ed-Chief; Sec Frsh Cls; Sec Soph Cls; Sec Jr Cls; Var Bsktbl; Hon Roll; NHS; Acad Awd In Thlgy 85; Svc Awd To Clss 85-86; Law.

MC NICHOLAS, MARYBETH; Ridley SR HS; Ridley Park, PA; (3); 19/423; Spanish Clb; Varsity Clb; Var L Cheerleading; Var L Fld Hcky; Var L Gym; Var L Lcrss; Hon Roll; NHS; 3rd Pl PIAA Advncd St Chmpnshps 86; 4th Pl All Arnd PIAA Dist Chmpnshps 87; Daily Tms Athltc Hnr Rl.

MC NULTY, JENNIFER; West Perry SR HS; Green Park, PA; (4); 10/200; Sec Computer Clb; Math Clb; Spanish Clb; Varsity Clb; Nwsp Stf; Pres Jr Cls; JV Var Cheerleading; Var L Trk; High Hon Roll; NHS; Comp Excllnc Awd 86; Sci Excllnc Awd-Coll Oriendtd Bio, Physcs 87; Juniata Coll; Pre-Med.

MC NULTY, PAUL; Saint Clair HS; St Clair, PA; (4); Boy Scts; Exploring; Hon Roll; NHS; Bloomsburg U; Hstry Tchr.

MC NULTY, TRACIE; Pittston Area SR HS; Pittston, PA; (3); French Clb; FNA; Var Cheerleading; JV Trk; High Hon Roll; NHS; Plq Hon Soc 86; Vrsty Lttr Chrldng 86; Trck Mdl 85; Pharmacy.

MC NUTT, CARLA; Franklin HS; Franklin, PA; (4); Teachers Aide; Var Capt Cheerleading; Hon Roll; Schl Dirctrs Awd; Clarion U Of PA; Paralegal.

MC OWEN, DAVID; Archbishop Wood High Schl For Boys; Warminster, PA; (3); 31/235; Drama Clb; School Musical; School Play; Stage Crew; JV Crs Cntry; JV Trk; High Hon Roll; Hon Roll; Ntl Merit Ltr; 1st Pl Bucks Cnty Sci Fair Engr 87; Aero Engr.

MC OWEN, PATRICK; Lansdale Catholic HS; Hatfield, PA; (3); Nwsp Rptr; Nwsp Stf; Communications.

MC PAUL, KELLY; Elizabeth Forward HS; Mc Keesport, PA; (3); 31/330; Chorus; Yrbk Phtg; Yrbk Stf; High Hon Roll; Hon Roll; Duquesne U; Phrmcy.

MC PEAK, TERESE; Freeport Area HS; Freeport, PA; (4); FBLA; OEA; Pres Chorus; Stage Crew; Nwsp Stf; Yrbk Stf; Hon Roll; Outstdng Choral Std Awd 87; Indiana U Of PA; Elem Ed.

MC PHERSON, CHRIS; East Pennsboro HS; Enola, PA; (4); Church Yth Grp; VICA; JV Bsktbl; Hon Roll; Schlrshp Hair Masters 87; Csmtlgy.

MC PHERSON, HEATHER L; Seneca Valley SR HS; Evans City, PA; (4); 99/340; Thesps; Chorus; L Madrigals; School Play; Stage Crew; Hon Roll; Cvc Lght Opera Schlrshp 87; PA Gvrnrs Schl Arts Alt Actng 85-85; Point Park Coll; Musical Theatr.

MC POLAND, KURT V; Ligonier Valley SR HS; Rector, PA; (4); 5/154; VP AFS; Library Aide; Scholastic Bowl; Science Clb; School Play; Rep Stu Cncl; Var L Golf; High Hon Roll; NHS; Ntl Merit SF; Chem Engineering.

MC QUATE, CINDY; Northern Lebanon HS; Lebanon, PA; (4); Art Clb; Varsity Clb; Stat Bsbl; Capt Var Cheerleading; Powder Puff Ftbl; Trk; Keystone JC; Trvl.

MC QUEEN, CHRIS; Meadville Area SR HS; Meadville, PA; (4); SADD; Band; Concert Band; Jazz Band; Mrchg Band; Pep Band; Chris Mc Queen; Elem Educ.

MC QUEEN, JULIE; C A S HS; Fayetteville, PA; (4); 39/606; AFS; Church Yth Grp; German Clb; Ski Clb; Yrbk Stf; Var L Socr; Hon Roll; NHS; Acad Schlrshp LEAD Thrift Shop 87; Acad Awd Acctng Chbg Downton Merchnts 87; Millersville U; CPA.

MC QUILLEN, CLARE ANN; Peters Township HS; Mc Murray, PA; (2); Ski Clb; Spanish Clb; Varsity Clb; Tennis; Spanish NHS; Seton Hall U; Sports Med.

MC QUILLIN, PATRICIA; Dwynedd Mercy Acad; Chalfont, PA; (2); Hosp Aide; Yrbk Stf; Stu Cncl; Im Bsktbl; Bowling; Coach Actv; High Hon Roll; Cmnty Wkr; Office Aide; SADD; Hghst Gen Avg Typwrtng 87; Top 10% Bio 87; Natl Latn Awd 86; Med.

MC QUISTON, APRIL; Franklin JR SR HS; Harrisville, PA; (4); 33/212; Church Yth Grp; Sec Trs 4-H; Spanish Clb; 4-H Awd; High Hon Roll; Hon Roll; NHS; Prfct Atten Awd; Wilma Boyd Career Schl; Trvl.

MC QUISTON, JULEE; Corry Area HS; Corry, PA; (4); Sec Trs Y-Teens; Yrbk Ed-Chief; Yrbk Stf; Rep Jr Cls; Rep Stu Cncl; High Hon Roll; Hon Roll; French Clb; Office Aide; Mrchg Band; Bus & Prfssnl Wmns Clb Grl Of Mnth 87; HS Almn Assn Schlrshp 87; Bus & Prfssnl Wmns Clb Grl Of Yr 87; Allegheny Coll.

MC QUOWN, STEPHEN G; Williamsport Area HS; Cogan Station, PA; (4); 3/518; Boy Scts; Key Clb; Concert Band; Jazz Band; Mrchg Band; Yrbk Phtg; Yrbk Sprt Ed; Hon Roll; VP NHS; Ntl Merit SF; Sci.

MC RAE, HEATHER; Lock Haven SR HS; Lock Haven, PA; (3); Art Clb; Hosp Aide; Spanish Clb; Hon Roll; NHS; Acad All-Amer Awd 87; Home Ec Awd 85; Fshn Dsgn.

MC REDMOND, MICHAEL T; Central Dauphin HS; Harrisburg, PA; (3); 35/369; Hosp Aide; Nwsp Rptr; Var L Swmmng; Hon Roll; JETS Awd; Jr NHS; NHS; People To People HS Stu Ambsdr Pgm 85; Engrng.

MC ROBERTS, COLLEEN; Beaver Area JR SR HS; Beaver, PA; (4); 33/200; Church Yth Grp; Pres FNA; JCL; Latin Clb; VP Pep Clb; SADD; Band; Concert Band; Mrchg Band; Yrbk Stf; PA ST U; Nrsng.

MC ROY, TIFFANY; Pine Forge HS; Leavenworth, KS; (3); Art Clb; Church Yth Grp; Computer Clb; Quiz Bowl; Spanish Clb; Church Choir; Score Keeper; Oakwood; Hist.

MC SPARRAN, VICKI; Elizabethtown Area HS; Elizabethtown, PA; (4); 45/237; Church Yth Grp; Model UN; Church Choir; Im Powder Puff Ftbl; Var Score Keeper; Var Swmmng; Var Trk; Im Wt Lftg; Penn ST U.

MC SPARREN, BOBBY; Oil City SR HS; Rouseville, PA; (3); 84/192; Letterman Clb; Teachers Aide; Varsity Clb; Im Bsktbl; Var Capt Ftbl; Im Vllybl; Var Wt Lftg; Hon Roll; Prfct Atten Awd; Im Socr; Lock Haven U; Sprts Med.

MC TAVISH, LORI; Clearfield HS; W Decatur, PA; (4); 130/400; Pres Church Yth Grp; Hosp Aide; Pres SADD; Chorus; Church Choir; Im Badmtn; Im Vllybl; High Hon Roll; Hon Roll; Prfct Atten Awd; Slippery Rock U; Elem Ed.

MC TEAR, AMY; Villa Maria Acad; St Peters, PA; (4); Lcrss; Gov Hon Prg Awd; Hon Roll; Art Clb; Yrbk Stf; Lit Mag; Excllnce Art Awd 85-87; Coll Scholar MD Inst Art & Moore Coll Art 87; 2nd Prz Art Exhibit Wmns Clb 87; MD Inst; Vis Comm.

MC TIGHE, MARY ANNE; Greensburg Central Catholic HS; Jeannette, PA; (3); 30/200; Church Yth Grp; Pres 4-H; JCL; Latin Clb; SADD; Chorus; Color Guard; Var Swmmng; Var Trk; 4-H Awd; 4-H Awd-Pblc Spkng, 2nd ST, 1st Dist & 1st Rgn 86; 4-H Awd-Dmnstrtn, 1st Dist & Rgn & 1st ST 85; Med.

MC TIGUE, MELISSA; Bishop Guilfoyle HS; Duncansville, PA; (3); Chorus; Rep Frsh Cls; Rep Soph Cls; Rep Stu Cncl; Vllybl; Hon Roll; Indian Schl Of PA; Psychlgy.

MC TIGUE, MICHAEL; Father Judge HS For Boys; Philadelphia, PA; (3); 15/306; Yrbk Stf; Trk; NHS; U Of Scranton; Bnkng.

MC VAY, BRYAN; Washington HS; Washington, PA; (2); Chess Clb; Spanish Clb; SADD; Pres Frsh Cls; Pres Soph Cls; High Hon Roll; Hon Roll; Rhino Clb 86-877; Pigs In Wldrns 86-87; Accntng.

MC VAY, LYNN; Trinity HS; Amity, PA; (3); Art Clb; Church Yth Grp; Dance Clb; Girl Scts; Color Guard; Pep Band; Crs Cntry; Sftbl; Trk; YWCA Art 1st Pl Awd 86.

MC VEIGH, KEVIN; Cardinal O Hara HS; Clifton Heights, PA; (3); 107/715; Boys Clb Am; Im Bowling; Hon Roll; Drexel U; Econ.

MC VERRY, BRYAN; Mt Lebanon HS; Pittsburgh, PA; (3); 7/485; Art Clb; Church Yth Grp; German Clb; JV Var Golf; JV Socr; High Hon Roll; SAR Awd; Rotary Yth Ldrshp Conf 87; Stu Curriculum Advsry Cncl 84-87; Three Rivers Arts Fest/Banner 86; Pre Med.

MC VERRY, ERIN; Mt Lebanbon SR HS; Pittsburgh, PA; (4); 17/530; Church Yth Grp; SADD; Rep Sr Cls; Rep Stu Cncl; Var L Vllybl; High Hon Roll; NHS; Ntl Merit SF; Church Yth Grp; Boston Coll.

MC VEY, DAVID; Blair County Christian HS; Duncansville, PA; (3); 1/17; Church Yth Grp; Debate Tm; Chorus; Off Soph Cls; Var Bsbl; Var L Bsktbl; Var L Socr; Var Trk; High Hon Roll; Cedarville; Tchr.

MC VEY, SUSAN; Blair County Christian Schl; Duncansville, PA; (1); 1/25; Church Yth Grp; FTA; Teachers Aide; Band; Chorus; Yrbk Stf; Trs Frsh Cls; High Hon Roll; Keystone Christian Ed Assn Engl Hnr 87; Bob Jones U; Tchg.

MC VICKER, JENNIFER; Fort Cherry HS; Mcdonald, PA; (4); 30/112; Church Yth Grp; FNA; Math Clb; Science Clb; Ski Clb; Spanish Clb; Varsity Clb; Chorus; Church Choir; Capt Var Bsktbl; Athltc Schlrshp Bsktbl Awd 87; Slippery Rock U.

MC VICKER, KIMBERLY; Faith Christian Schl; Saylorsburg, PA; (3); 5/15; Church Yth Grp; Office Aide; Band; Chorus; Concert Band; Variety Show; Yrbk Bus Mgr; Off Jr Cls; Stu Cncl; Cheerleading; Busnss Admin.

MC VICKER, LAUREN J; Owen J Roberts HS; Pottstown, PA; (2); Spanish Clb; Chorus; School Musical; Stu Cncl; Bsktbl; Swmmng; Med.

MC VICKER, LYCERCIA; Red Lion Area HS; Felton, PA; (3); Church Yth Grp; Cmnty Wkr; Chorus; High Hon Roll; Hnr Roll 4 Qtrs 85-86; Hnr Roll 3 Qtrs 86-87; Miss Lineboro Fire Prevntn Qn 2nd Rnnr Up 86-87; Cedarcrest Coll; Paralegal.

MC VICKER, STACY; North Star HS; Friedens, PA; (4); FCA; Mu Alpha Theta; Band; Chorus; Church Choir; Mrchg Band; Cit Awd; Hon Roll; Cnty Band & Cnty Chorus 84-87; Bio.

MC WATTERS, TRACI; Lewistown Area HS; Lewistown, PA; (3); AFS; Key Clb; SADD; Varsity Clb; Chorus; Rep Jr Cls; Rep Sr Cls; Var L Fld Hcky; Var L Trk; Hon Roll; PA Fld Hcky Kystn Games 87; USA Olympc Fld Hcky Camp 86 & 87; Physcl Thrpy.

MC WHITE, FELTON; Frankford HS; Philadelphia, PA; (3); PA ST; Cmmnctns.

MC WILLIAMS, BELINDA; Yough SR HS; Irwin, PA; (3); 4-H; FBLA; Ski Clb; Bsktbl; Powder Puff Ftbl; Trk; Vllybl; Hon Roll; Sawyer Schl; Sec.

MC WILLIAMS, BETSY; Waynesburg Central HS; Fremont, CA; (3); Drama Clb; French Clb; Natl Beta Clb; Pep Clb; Ski Clb; SADD; Variety Show; Swmmng; Trk; Hon Roll; Law.

MC WILLIAMS, DOUG; Red Lion Area SR HS; Red Lion, PA; (3); 60/342; Boy Scts; Church Yth Grp; 4-H; Var Golf; Hon Roll; PA ST; Engrng.

MC WILLIAMS, ERIC; Red Lion Area SR HS; Red Lion, PA; (2); 51/344; Boy Scts; Band; Concert Band; Mrchg Band; U Of PA; Vet Med.

MC WILLIAMS, JOHN L; Grove City HS; Grove City, PA; (4); 4/200; Church Yth Grp; Science Clb; Stage Crew; Var Wt Lftg; Elks Awd; High Hon Roll; NHS; Ntl Merit Ltr; Certf Of Merit From PA Hghr Educ Assist Agncy 87; Lafayette Coll; Elec Engr.

MC WILLIAMS, SEAN; Norristown Area HS; Norristown, PA; (4); 50/500; DECA; Exploring; FBLA; JA; Socr; JV Var Tennis; Hon Roll; Dstrbtn Educ Clbs Amer-Chptr Pres, ST Rep, Bst Rnkd Bus Stu Cls; 86-87; Cngrssmn S Medal Merit 87; Phila Coll Txtls & Sci; Mrktng.

MC WILLIAMS, SHERRY; Hopewell SR HS; Aliquippa, PA; (3); 35/255; Church Yth Grp; French Clb; Chorus; School Musical; Variety Show; Rep Stu Cncl; Var Bowling; High Hon Roll; Hon Roll; NHS; Childhood Develop.

MC WILLIAMS, TRACY; Pocono Mountain HS; Cresco, PA; (2); Chorus; JV Cheerleading; Hon Roll; Hnrs Cert 86-87; Frgn Lang.

MC WREATH, LU ANNE; Trinity HS; Washington, PA; (3); 69/381; Concert Band; Mrchg Band; High Hon Roll; Hon Roll.

MCGRATH, SHAWN; Frankford HS; Philadelphia, PA; (3); Hon Roll.

MEACHAM III, ROGER H; Henderson SR HS; Exton, PA; (4); Art Clb; PAVAS; Red Cross Aide; SADD; Stage Crew; JV Var Lcrss; JV Socr; Philadelphia Coll; Illustrn Art.

MEAD, JENNIFER; Dowington SR HS; Downington, PA; (3); French Clb; GAA; Ski Clb; SADD; Chorus; JV Var Cheerleading; Hon Roll; Dental.

MEAD, KEVIN; Tunkhannock HS; Falls, PA; (3); 36/365; Art Clb; Letterman Clb; Varsity Clb; Wt Lftg; Wrstlng; Gntc Enrng.

MEADE, ELAINE; Mahanoy Area HS; Mahanoy Plaine, PA; (3); Church Yth Grp; Drama Clb; FHA; Spanish Clb; Band; Flag Corp; School Play; Variety Show; Nwsp Stf; Yrbk Stf; Law.

MEADE, LEONARD; Aliquippa HS; Aliquippa, PA; (4); 14/136; Church Yth Grp; French Clb; Sr Cls; Hon Roll; NHS; Ntl Merit SF; Aliquippa Branch NAACP Schltc Achvt 86; Scholar PA ST MAPP Pgm; Engrng.

MEADE, SCOTT; Belle Vernon Area HS; Belle Vernon, PA; (3); Art Clb; Ski Clb; Concert Band; Mrchg Band; Yrbk Phtg; Socr; Hon Roll; NHS; Prfct Atten Awd; U Of Pittsburgh; Bio.

MEADOWS, DAN; Cathedral Prep; Erie, PA; (4); Ftbl; Wt Lftg; Wrstlng; Robert Morris Coll; Bus.

MEADOWS, DON; Peters Township HS; Mcmurray, PA; (3); 5/240; Church Yth Grp; Computer Clb; Church Choir; Var JV Bsbl; Im Ftbl; JV Golf; High Hon Roll; Prfct Atten Awd; Top Engl, Amer Hstry Stu 84-85; Top Bio II Stu 85-86; Pre-Med.

MEALS, CHRIS; East Pennsboro HS; Camp Hill, PA; (3); French Clb; Varsity Clb; JV Var Bsbl; JV Var Bsktbl; Im Ftbl; Hon Roll; NHS.

MEALS, KEVIN; Ridgway HS; Ridgway, PA; (4); 12/110; Golf; VP Capt Tennis; Amer Chem Soc-Outstndg Achvt In Chem 85; JR Golf Chmpn Of Elk Cnty Cntry Clb 83-86; PA ST U.

MEANOR, MARK; Ambridge Area SR HS; Freedom, PA; (3); Trs French Clb; Chorus; School Musical; JV Var Socr; Penn ST U; Elec Engrng.

MEANS, DEBRA; Uniontown HS; Uniontown, PA; (4); 89/290; Church Yth Grp; Pres JA; Spanish Clb; Band; Concert Band; Drill Tm; School Play; Sec Jr Cls; Stu Cncl; Pom Pon; JA Sls Awd 85-86; Laurel Bus Inst; Banking.

MEANS, PAUL; Connellsville Area HS; Connellsville, PA; (4); 32/550; VP Sr Cls; High Hon Roll; NHS; Acadc Excllnc 86-87; Cls King 86-87; Washington & Jefferson; Pre-Med.

MEANS, ROBERT; Punxsutawney Area HS; Punxsutawney, PA; (2); Church Yth Grp; French Clb; Trk; Hon Roll; Clarion Univ Upwrd Bnd Prog Hnr Stud 85-87.

MEANS, STEVE; Keystone HS; Knox, PA; (3); 38/145; Aud/Vis; Boy Scts; Model UN; Varsity Clb; Concert Band; Jazz Band; Stage Crew; JV Bsktbl; Var Capt Ftbl; Ftbl Most Imprvd Plyr 87; U AK; Fisheries Sci.

MEARKLE, JAMES; Everett Area HS; Clearville, PA; (2); 6/150; Church Yth Grp; Spanish Clb; Band; Jazz Band; Pep Band; Stu Cncl; High Hon Roll; Hon Roll; Acad All-Amer 85-86; Natl Hstry & Gvnt Awd 85-86.

MEASE, JERRY; Monongahela Valley Catholic HS; Coal Center, PA; (2); 7/77; Boy Scts; FBLA; VP JA; Science Clb; Band; School Play; Var Ftbl; Wt Lftg; High Hon Roll; NAJAC Awd 87; JA Dist Best Slsprsn 87; CMU; Phycology.

MEASLEY, MICHAEL; Dover Area HS; Dover, PA; (3); 2/260; Church Yth Grp; Quiz Bowl; Band; Jazz Band; Mrchg Band; Stage Crew; High Hon Roll; NHS; Outstndng Sci Awd 87; Comp Sci.

MECCARIELLO, LORENZA; Phoenixville Area HS; Phoenixville, PA; (3); Key Clb; School Play; Hon Roll; NHS; Spnsh Awd 86; Htl/Rstrnt Mgr.

MECK, JUDY; Lower Dauphin HS; Palmyra, PA; (3); Church Yth Grp; Ski Clb; Im Bsktbl; Tennis; Hon Roll; Vet.

MECKLER, LAURA; Bethlehem Catholic HS; Bethlehem, PA; (3); 72/192; Key Clb; Band; Chorus; Concert Band; Jazz Band; L Mrchg Band; School Musical; High Hon Roll; Hon Roll; Schl Ltr Band 86; Music.

MECKLEY, ANN MARGARET; Chambersburg Area SR HS; Chambersburg, PA; (4); Am Leg Aux Girls St; Trs Debate Tm; English Clb; NFL; Spanish Clb; Yrbk Ed-Chief; Rep Jr Cls; High Hon Roll; Hon Roll; NHS; HOBY Lrdshp Ambsdr 85; Ltr Kenney Thrift Shop Schlrshp 87; Span Club Awd 85; U Pittsburgh; Behavioral Neuro.

MECKLEY, ERIN; Hempfield HS; Greensburg, PA; (2); Church Yth Grp; Hosp Aide; Ski Clb; Spanish Clb; Hon Roll; Jr NHS; Med.

MECKLEY III, JOHN; Milton Area HS; Milton, PA; (3); Boy Scts; FBLA; Key Clb; Nwsp Ed-Chief; Pres Jr Cls; Pres Sr Cls; Rep Stu Cncl; High Hon Roll; Pres NHS; Hugh O Brien Yth Fndtn; Pre-Law.

MECKLEY, SUZANNE; Cocalico HS; Stevens, PA; (4); Camera Clb; GAA; Yrbk Sprt Ed; Im Badmtn; Capt Tennis; Im Vllybl; High Hon Roll; Hon Roll; Yrbk Stf; Athltcs Schlrshp 87; MVP Tnns 87; Readng Hosp Med Ctr; Radiolgy.

MECKWOOD, DONNA MARIE; Scranton Technical HS; Scranton, PA; (3); Dance Clb; SADD; VICA; Drill Tm; Off Sr Cls; Bsktbl; Pom Pon; Score Keeper; Sftbl; Tennis; Csmtlgy Awd 86; Wilfred Bty Acad; Csmtlgy.

MEDIATE, ANGELA; East Allegheny HS; East Mc Keesport, PA; (2); French Clb; JA; Ski Clb; Yrbk Stf; Timer; Stat Trk; Hon Roll; PA ST; Indstrl Engr.

MEDICI, AMY V; North Pocono HS; Lake Ariel, PA; (2); 23/246; Ski Clb; Chorus; Orch; Yrbk Stf; Tennis; High Hon Roll; Hon Roll; NHS; Flag Corp; Natl Piano Guild, Project Bus Cert & NE Yth Cncl Brd 86; Engl.

MEDICO, KARIM; Scranton Preparatory Schl; Wilkes-Barre, PA; (2); 64/190; Church Yth Grp; 4-H; Pep Clb; Ski Clb; Cheerleading; Hon Roll; Psych.

MEDIE, NEIL; Moon SR HS; Coraopolis, PA; (3); Chorus; School Musical; Pres Frsh Cls; Rep Stu Cncl; Var L Bsbl; Im JV Bsktbl; Var L Ftbl; Wt Lftg; Hon Roll; Penn ST; Pre Med.

MEDINA, BETSY; HS Engineering & Science; Philadelphia, PA; (3); Drama Clb; Exploring; Chorus; Church Choir; Drill Tm; School Musical; Variety Show; Art Awd; Princeton Coll; Physics.

MEDINA, SCOTT A; Strath Haven HS; Wallingford, PA; (4); Ski Clb; School Musical; Variety Show; Nwsp Ed-Chief; High Hon Roll; Pres Schlr; Dlwr Cnty Tms Wrtng Cntst Wnnr 86; Hamilton Coll; Engl.

MEDIVITZ, MICHELLE; Bishop O Reilly HS; Kingston, PA; (3); Rep Frsh Cls; Fld Hcky; Presdntl Acadc Ftns Awd 87; Wilkes Coll; Elem Tchr.

MEDRICK, LINDA; Meadville Area SR HS; Meadville, PA; (4); 26/310; French Clb; Key Clb; Pep Clb; Spanish Clb; SADD; Y-Teens; High Hon Roll; Slippery Rock U; Bus.

MEDSGER, CARL; Yough SR HS; W Newton, PA; (3); Boy Scts; Exploring; French Clb.

MEDVITZ JR, DAVID; West Allegheny HS; Imperial, PA; (2); 25/212; Boy Scts; Church Yth Grp; Band; Chorus; Concert Band; Jazz Band; Mrchg Band; Pep Band; High Hon Roll; Hon Roll; Comp Sci.

MEEHAN, CHRISTOPHER; Cardinal O Hara HS; Newtown Sq, PA; (3); 144/710; Band; Concert Band; Mrchg Band; School Play; Jr All Amer Hall Fame Band Hnrs 87; Bus.

MEEHAN, JOE; Maplewood HS; Philadelphia, PA; (3).

MEEHAN, TERRY; Plum HS; Verona, PA; (3); Letterman Clb; Varsity Clb; Im Bsbl; JV Bsktbl; Var Capt Ftbl; Var Capt Trk; Hon Roll; Math.

MEEK, JEFFREY; Beaver Area JR-SR HS; Beaver, PA; (3); 32/215; Church Yth Grp; German Clb; SADD; Rep Sr Cls; Var L Golf; High Hon Roll; Hon Roll; Letterman Clb; Varsity Clb; JV Bsktbl; Comm.

MEEK, JOHN; Greencastle-Antrim HS; Greencastle, PA; (3); Var L Bsbl; Var L Bsktbl; Wt Lftg; Hon Roll; Voice Dem Awd; Crim Just.

MEEKER II, C ALLEN; Union HS; Rimersburg, PA; (3); 10/110; FCA; SADD; Pres Frsh Cls; Pres Jr Cls; L Capt Bsktbl; L Capt Ftbl; Var L Trk; Var Wt Lftg; Jr NHS; NHS; Natl Stu Ldrshp & Srv Awd 85; Acad All Amer Schlr 85; PA ST; Cmnctns.

MEEKER, STACIE; Fairview HS; Fairview, PA; (4); 58/154; French Clb; Sftbl; High Hon Roll; Hon Roll; Art Wrk Edinboro HS Art Comptn; Hon Mtn Pntd Cngrssmn Ridges Art Comptn; Art Awd 87; Kent ST U; Interior Dsgn.

MEEKER, WENDY; Boyertown SR HS; Gilbertsville, PA; (2); 117/471; Chorus; Church Choir; Variety Show; Lcrss; Trk; Hon Roll; Acctg.

MEEKINS, KELLY; Chichester SR HS; Aston, PA; (3); 12/350; Hosp Aide; SADD; Flag Corp; Var Lcrss; JV Mgr(s); JV Score Keeper; Stat Wrstlng; Hon Roll; NHS; Spanish NHS; Recording Sec Of Span Antl Hnr Soc; Paralegal.

MEERDO, ANDREW; Burgettstown Area JR SR HS; Burgettstown, PA; (2); Bsktbl; Wt Lftg; Hon Roll; Hon Mntn 86-87.

MEFFORD, JUDY; Waynesburg Central HS; Waynesburg, PA; (4); Pres FHA; VICA; Chorus; Hon Roll; Johnson & Whales; Fd Serv.

MEGGETT, MARCUS K; Central HS; Philadelphia, PA; (4); 90/300; Var L Bsktbl; Var L Trk; Hon Roll; Cncrnd Blck Men Inc Cmnty Actvty Awd 87; Duval Imprvmt Assoc Schlrshp 87; Ursinus Coll; Bus Admin.

MEHALLO, CHRIS; West Hazelton HS; Hazleton, PA; (4); 24/224; Art Clb; French Clb; Library Aide; Ski Clb; VICA; VP Sr Cls; High Hon Roll; NHS; Employee Mnth 87; Lehigh U; Mech Engrng.

MEHEGAN, KELLY; Villa Maria Acad; Erie, PA; (3); 14/150; Model UN; Science Clb; Ski Clb; SADD; Stage Crew; Nwsp Rptr; Rep Pres Stu Cncl; JV Var Cheerleading; High Hon Roll; NHS; Stu Rep For Erie County On Drug & Alch Comm 86-87; PA Assoc Stu Councils Dist I Secty 87-88; Public Relations.

MEHOLICK, JEFFREY PATRICK; Du Bois Area HS; Reynoldsville, PA; (4); 88/270; Varsity Clb; Bsktbl; Hon Roll; Clarion U.

MEHTA, AMISH; Parkland SR HS; Allentown, PA; (2); JA; Scholastic Bowl; Var JV Bsbl; Var JV Bsktbl; High Hon Roll; Prfct Atten Awd; Pres Schlr.

MEIER, ALFRED G; Council Rock HS; Richboro, PA; (4); 10/848; Chess Clb; Math Tm; Orch; Mgr(s); Hon Roll; Ntl Merit SF; Penn ST U; Math.

MEIER, AMY; Penn-Trafford HS; Irwin, PA; (2); AFS; Drama Clb; JV Var Bsktbl; Var Trk; JV Vllybl; High Hon Roll.

MEIER, CHRISTINE; Penn Trafford HS; Irwin, PA; (3); AFS; Drama Clb; FBLA; German Clb; Chorus; Bsktbl; Vllybl; High Hon Roll; NHS; U Of PA; Psychology.

MEIER, GWEN; Mc Guffey SR HS; W Alexander, PA; (4); 2/196; German Clb; Model UN; Yrbk Stf; Off Jr Cls; Gov Hon Prg Awd; High Hon Roll; NHS; Congress-Bundestag Schlrshp 86-87; Macalester Coll; Lang.

MEIER, KARYN; Pequea Valley HS; Paradise, PA; (4); 3/109; AFS; FBLA; Color Guard; Capt Drill Tm; Stage Crew; Yrbk Stf; Mgr(s); High Hon Roll; NHS; Pres Schlr; Lanco Srtma-Ctzn Schlrshp Awd 87; Amrstrng Sci Awd 87; Eshlmn Chem Awd 87; Math & Engl Dept Awds 87; Temple U; Phrmcy.

MEIER, KRISTEN; Pequea Valley HS; Paradise, PA; (3); 17/125; Sec AFS; Church Yth Grp; Drama Clb; SADD; Band; Church Choir; Concert Band; Mrchg Band; Stage Crew; Rep Frsh Cls; Bloomsburg U; Spch Thrpy.

MEIER, MICHAEL; Franklin Regional HS; Export, PA; (3); 107/329; Church Yth Grp; SADD; Im Bsbl; Im Bsktbl; L Ftbl; Im Socr; L Trk; Wt Lftg; Wrstlng; Hon Roll; All Conf Tm-All Schlstc Tm 86; Plyr Of Wk-Achvr Of Wk 86; Acdmc All Amer 87.

MEIER, PATRICIA; Thayer SR HS; Pittsburgh, PA; (4); GAA; JA; Sftbl; Wt Lftg; Wrstlng; High Hon Roll.

MEIER, SHANA; Tunkhannock HS; Tunkhannock, PA; (4); 51/262; Art Clb; French Clb; Color Guard; Flag Corp; School Play; Yrbk Stf; Hon Roll; NHS; Pres Scholar 87-88; Commuter Scholar Art 87-88; Schltc Cert Merit Art Awds 87; Keystone JC; Fash Illus.

MEINERT, LINDA; Quigley HS; Ambridge, PA; (4); 14/102; Math Clb; Yrbk Stf; Powder Puff Ftbl; Tennis; High Hon Roll; Hon Roll; Jr NHS; NHS; Finance.

MEISER, CHRISTY; East Juniata HS; Richfield, PA; (3); 1/100; Church Yth Grp; Chorus; Church Choir; Concert Band; Mrchg Band; School Musical; School Play; Yrbk Stf; High Hon Roll; NHS; PMEA Dstrct Bnd & Chorus Fstvl 86 & 87; Piano Tchr.

MEISER, KURT; Penncrest HS; Media, PA; (3); 91/320; Boys Clb Am; Boy Scts; Cmnty Wkr; Variety Show; Bsktbl; Im Ftbl; Var Lcrss; Var Swmmng; Im Hon Roll.

MEISER, LESLIE; East Junita HS; Mcalisterville, PA; (3); 1/100; Concert Band; Mrchg Band; Pep Band; School Musical; School Play; Yrbk Stf; Rep Stu Cncl; JV Var Fld Hcky; High Hon Roll; NHS; Marketing.

MEISLIK, MICHELLE; Seneca Valley HS; Mars, PA; (4); 91/372; Drama Clb; JA; Ski Clb; Varsity Clb; Drill Tm; School Musical; School Play; Nwsp Stf; Stu Cncl; Pom Pon; Pom Pon Of The Yr Awd 87; Wrld Affairs Conf Rotary 87; Edinboro U Of PA; Med Tech.

MEIXSELL, LYNN; Pen Argyl HS; Pen Argyl, PA; (2); Church Yth Grp; Leo Clb; Orch; Rep Stu Cncl; Cheerleading; High Hon Roll; Prfct Atten Awd; Mdcl Rsrch.

MEIXSELL, STEPHANIE; Nazareth Area SR HS; Nazareth, PA; (3); Church Yth Grp; Drama Clb; Key Clb; Ski Clb; Church Choir; Nwsp Rptr; Nwsp Stf; Intl Rltns.

MEKOLICHICK, JEANNE T; Warwick HS; Lititz, PA; (2); Computer Clb; Varsity Clb; Rep Stu Cncl; JV Bsktbl; JV Fld Hcky; Var Trk; High Hon Roll; Advtg.

MEKOLICHICK, SHARON; Hazleton SR HS; Sugarloaf, PA; (3); 32/445; Hon Roll.

MELARAGNO, MICHAEL; Cathedral Prep Schl; Erie, PA; (3); Mgr(s); Stat Swmmng; Penn ST; Engr.

MELBER, TRACY; Wm Allen HS; Allentown, PA; (3); German Clb; Band; Concert Band; Mrchg Band; Pep Band; Hon Roll; Jr NHS; Bus Admin.

MELBY, LEIGH ANN; Conneaut Lake HS; Conneaut Lake, PA; (4); 3/84; Band; Jazz Band; Mrchg Band; Nwsp Rptr; Stu Cncl; Capt Vllybl; High Hon Roll; JP Sousa Awd; NHS; Pres Schlr; All ST Band PA, Gerry Hughes Memrl Schlrshp, Mst Career Srvng Points Vlybl 679 87; George Washington U; Sys Anlyst.

MELCHER, KELLY; Conrad Weiser HS; Robesonia, PA; (2); 21/163; Drama Clb; JCL; Chorus; Color Guard; School Musical; Nwsp Stf; Var JV Cheerleading; JV L Fld Hcky; JV Trk; Hon Roll; Most Improved Cheerleader Awd 86-87; Leading Role In Fresh Musical 85-86; Arch Design.

MELCHIORRE, ALLISON; East HS; W Chester, PA; (3); FBLA; JCL; Office Aide; Yrbk Stf; JV Fld Hcky; Penn ST; Accntng.

MELCHIORRE, AMY; New Castle HS; New Castle, PA; (4); Church Yth Grp; Cmnty Wkr; Hosp Aide; Office Aide; High Hon Roll; Hon Roll; Pres Schlr; U Of Pittsburgh.

MELENYZER, KIMBERLY; Belle Vernon Area HS; Belle Vernon, PA; (3); Trs NFL; Band; Concert Band; Mrchg Band; Im Powder Puff Ftbl; Var Trk; Hon Roll; Voice Dem Awd; Pre-Med.

MELLARKEY, SHERI; N Pocono HS; Moscow, PA; (4); Church Yth Grp; Dance Clb; FBLA; Chorus; Church Choir; High Hon Roll; Hon Roll; NHS; Prnt, Tchr, Stu Assc Schlrshp 87; Kngs Coll Schlrshp 87; Kings Coll; Crtv Wrtng.

MELLINGER, CHRISTINA; Hempfield HS; Landisville, PA; (4); 11/415; Chorus; Orch; L Var Crs Cntry; Capt L Trk; Cit Awd; Dnfth Awd; Hon Roll; NHS; Pres Schlr; Kids Saving Kids Anti Drg Alch Grp; Millersville U; Pol Sci.

MELLINGER, ESTHER; Pequea Valley HS; Paradise, PA; (3); AFS; Church Yth Grp; Drama Clb; GAA; Sec Chorus; Color Guard; School Musical; JV Bsktbl; High Hon Roll; NHS; Psych.

MELLINGER, HEATHER; Eastern York HS; York, PA; (4); 35/167; Drama Clb; Girl Scts; Chorus; Capt Flag Corp; Mrchg Band; School Musical; Variety Show; Nwsp Rptr; Yrbk Stf; Hon Roll; Dist Chorus 87; Helen Weiser Ziegler Memrl Schlrshp 87; Lester E Loucks Memrl Awd 87; IN U Of PA; Elem Ed.

MELLINGER, J MICHAEL; Solanco SR HS; Peach Bottom, PA; (2); 68/283; Church Yth Grp; FFA; JV Socr; Hon Roll; Penn ST U; Wldlfe-Cnsrvtn Tech.

MELLOR, LISA; St Huberts HS; Philadelphia, PA; (3); Camp Fr Inc; Dance Clb; FBLA; Library Aide; Red Cross Aide; SADD; Nwsp Bus Mgr; Manor JC; Bus Admin.

MELLOTT, ANDY; Southern Fulton HS; Needmore, PA; (3); FFA; Trk; Hon Roll; FFA Beef & Sheep Prod Awds 87; FFA Pub Spkng Awd 87; Diesel Inst Amer; Diesel Mech.

MELLOTT, DWAYNE; Chief Logan HS; Lewistown, PA; (3); 52/184; Church Yth Grp; Cmnty Wkr; Computer Clb; Spanish Clb; Varsity Clb; Concert Band; Bsbl; Ftbl; Wt Lftg; Wrstlng; V Lttr In Wrstlng 87; V Lttr In Ftbll 86-87; Accntng.

MELLOTT, TRAVIS; Lock Haven SR HS; Fleminton, PA; (3); FBLA; Spanish Clb; Ftbl; Trk; Wt Lftg; FBLA PA ST Chpt 3rd Pl Entrprnrshp 87; Ofc Job Trng Awds 87; Acctng.

MELLOTT, WENDY; Pottstown HS; Pottstown, PA; (3); 10/155; Church Yth Grp; Key Clb; Nwsp Stf; Rep Frsh Cls; Rep Soph Cls; Rep Jr Cls; Rep Sr Cls; High Hon Roll; NHS; Prfct Atten Awd; Comp Prog.

MELMAN, JONATHAN; Haverford Twp SR HS; Havertown, PA; (3); 30/423; Boy Scts; School Play; Var Crs Cntry; Trk; Hon Roll.

MELMED, EDEN; Neshaminy HS; Levittown, PA; (3); 8/800; Church Yth Grp; Girl Scts; Teachers Aide; Var Gym; High Hon Roll; Hon Roll; NHS; Ntl Merit Schol; Prfct Atten Awd; Pres Schlr; Diplomatic Corps.

MELNICHUK, THERESA; Saint Hubert HS; Philadelphia, PA; (4); 146/364; Cmnty Wkr; Dance Clb; Office Aide; Chorus; Prfct Atten Awd; Merit Hnr; Commnctns.

MELNICK, JAMES; Archbishop Wood HS For Boys; Southampton, PA; (2); 14/264; Var Golf; JV Ice Hcky; JV Socr; High Hon Roll.

MELNICK, JASON; Oil City Area SR HS; Oil City, PA; (3); 58/230; Letterman Clb; Varsity Clb; Chorus; Stu Cncl; Bsktbl; Var Capt Crs Cntry; L Trk; Hon Roll; NHS; Prfct Atten Awd; Arch Engrng.

MELNICK, JENNIFER; Belle Vernon Area HS; Belle Vernon, PA; (3); NFL; Ski Clb; SADD; Band; Nwsp Rptr; VP Sr Cls; VP Stu Cncl; NHS; Voice Dem Awd; Concert Band; Amer Lgn Awd 84; Wrthy Advsr Natl Ordr Rainbow Girls 85-86; Washington Jeffersn; Pre Law.

MELOVICH, SUZANNE; Pennsbury HS; Levittown, PA; (4); 220/777; Spanish Clb; SADD; Rep Stu Cncl; Capt Swmmng; PA Miss Teen Pgnt Cntstnt 86; Olympir Trials Competitor 84; JR Olympc Natls Synchrnzd Swmmg Cmptn 86; Temple U; Radio TV.

MELTER, DEBORAH; Villa Maria Acad; Erie, PA; (3); Exploring; Science Clb; SADD; Bowling; Hon Roll; Gannon U; Nrs.

MELTON, CHRISTINA; Brookville Area JR SR HS; Brookville, PA; (3); Cmnty Wkr; French Clb; Varsity Clb; Band; Chorus; Mrchg Band; Swing Chorus; Var L Sftbl; Var L Vllybl; High Hon Roll; Pes Phys Ftns Awd 86-87; Chem Engrng.

MELTON, MELISSA M; Pottsgrove HS; Pottstown, PA; (4); 14/226; Science Clb; Varsity Clb; Chorus; Pres Concert Band; Pres Mrchg Band; Rep Stu Cncl; Capt Bsktbl; Sftbl; Hon Roll; VP NHS; Bsktbl Hnrb Mntn Pac-8 Lg 87; MVP Sftbl 87; Pottsgrove Fed Tchrs Scholar 87; Drexel U; Engrng.

MELTSCH, TAMI; Central Catholic HS; Northampton, PA; (3); Key Clb; Math Clb; Math Tm; Capt Flag Corp; Ed Yrbk Stf; High Hon Roll; Elec Engr.

MELUCCI, MICHELE; St Francis Acad; Pittsburgh, PA; (4); Red Cross Aide; Band; Rosemont Coll.

MELUSKEY, MICHAEL; Cardinal O Hara HS; Media, PA; (3); 45/710; Church Yth Grp; JA; Rep Frsh Cls; Rep Soph Cls; Rep Jr Cls; Off Sr Cls; Off Stu Cncl; Var L Ftbl; Var L Tennis; Hon Roll; 2nd Pl Math DE Cnty Sci Fair 87; Hon Mntn DE Vly Sci Fair Math 87; Bus.

MELVIN, DENISE; Archbihop Ryan For Girls; Phila, PA; (3); Cmnty Wkr; French Clb; Red Cross Aide; Band; Swmmng; Soph Yr Engl Awd; La Salle Coll; Acctg.

MELWSKY, SHERRY; Minersville Area HS; Minersville, PA; (3); 16/110; Art Clb; Pep Clb; Ski Clb; Spanish Clb; Flag Corp; Yrbk Stf; Stu Cncl; JV Sftbl; Var JV Vllybl; Hon Roll; IN U; Pre-Med.

MEMOLO, MISSY; Abington Heights South Campus; Clarks Green, PA; (1); Chorus; Mrchg Band; School Musical; Yrbk Stf; Rep Frsh Cls; Cheerleading; L Swmmng; Hon Roll; Band; Concert Band; Ldrshp Awd Stu Cncl 87; 2nd Pl Jr Acad Sci 87; All Star Sftbl Tm 87; Law.

MENAND, CHRISTINE; Beaver Area HS; Beaver, PA; (3); Church Yth Grp; JCL; Latin Clb; Ski Clb; SADD; Band; Color Guard; Concert Band; Flag Corp; Mrchg Band; Acad Awd 85-87.

MENAPACE, SHARON; Mt Carmel Area JR SR HS; Atlas, PA; (4); 20/159; Key Clb; Pep Clb; Q&S; Ski Clb; Spanish Clb; School Musical; Nwsp Rptr; Hon Roll; NHS; Wittiest Stu 87; Bloomsburg U Of PA; Spch Path.

MENCER III, MARION; Marion Center Area HS; Indiana, PA; (3); Boy Scts; Intnl Clb; JV Crs Cntry; JV Trk; Hon Roll; NHS; Eagle Scout 85; Penn-St; Cvl Eltrcl Engnr.

MENDELSOHN, SETH; Susquehanna Township HS; Harrisburg, PA; (3); 37/150; AFS; Exploring; Model UN; Political Wkr; Trs Frsh Cls; Trs Soph Cls; Trs Jr Cls; Stu Cncl; Hon Roll; Rotary Awd; Rtry Intl Ldrshp Conf 87; Mock Trl Compttn 87; Law.

MENDOLA, EDWARD; Charleroi Area HS; Charleroi, PA; (4); 9/162; FBLA; Varsity Clb; Rep Soph Cls; Rep Jr Cls; Rep Sr Cls; Ftbl; High Hon Roll; Lion Awd; NHS; PA ST U; Bus.

MENDOLA, ERIC; Charleroi HS; Charleroi, PA; (3); Church Yth Grp; FBLA; Varsity Clb; Rep Soph Cls; Rep Jr Cls; Im Bsktbl; Im Coach Actv; Var Ftbl; Hon Roll; NHS; Chmps Schlstc Awd.

MENDOZA, GLADYS; Jules Mastbaum Vo-Tech HS; Philadelphia, PA; (4); FBLA; Spanish Clb; Band; Yrbk Rptr; Yrbk Stf; Vllybl; Prfct Atten Awd; Brandywine Coll; Travel.

MENEFEE, TODD; Harrisburg HS; Steelton, PA; (4); 27/367; Computer Clb; Band; Concert Band; Drm Mjr(t); Jazz Band; Mrchg Band; Pep Band; Hon Roll; Boy Scts; Omega Psi Phi Stu Yr; Omega Psi Phi Schlrshp; Penn St U; Aero Engr.

MENGEL, ROBIN; Exeter SR HS; Birdsboro, PA; (3); Pres Church Yth Grp; Leo Clb; VP SADD; Varsity Clb; Flag Corp; Nwsp Stf; Rep Jr Cls; Rep Stu Cncl; Cheerleading; NHS; 2nd Pl Spch-Miss PA TEEN 87.

MENGEL, SHELLEY; Kutztown Area HS; Kutztown, PA; (3); 54/167; Pres Church Yth Grp; Band; Chorus; Concert Band; Mrchg Band; Pep Band; School Musical; Swing Chorus; Yrbk Bus Mgr; Var Sftbl; John Philip Sousa Natl Hnrs Band 87; Comp Oper.

MENGEL, TODD; Northern Lehigh HS; Slatington, PA; (3); 22/166; Computer Clb; Band; Concert Band; Jazz Band; Mrchg Band; Pep Band; High Hon Roll; Prfct Atten Awd; Schl Ltr 86-87; Comp Sci.

MENGLE, TERRY; Middleburg HS; Mt Pleasant Mls, PA; (4); 19/120; Key Clb; Chorus; Concert Band; Mrchg Band; Nwsp Stf; Yrbk Stf; VP Sr Cls; Var L Fld Hcky; Prfct Atten Awd; Pres Schlr.

MENICHETTI, TRACY; Valley View HS; Peckville, PA; (2); Church Yth Grp; Spanish Clb; School Musical; Capt Vllybl; Hon Roll.

MENIST, TINA; Meadville Area SR HS; Meadville, PA; (2); Church Yth Grp; Spanish Clb; JV Cheerleading; DAR Awd; High Hon Roll; Hon Roll; Hstry Awd On Liberty 1st Pl 87.

MENON, VIKAS; Fairview HS; Erie, PA; (4); 24/153; Debate Tm; Model UN; Q&S; Nwsp Stf; Lit Mag; L Trk; Hon Roll; Ntl Merit Ltr; 1st Pl Review Gannan Tri-St Jrnlsm Cntst87; Engl Dept Awd 87; 1st Pl Feature Gannan Tri-St Jrnlsm 86; Penn ST U.

MENTCH, JARROD; Danville Area HS; Danville, PA; (1); Ski Clb; JV Bsbl; JV Ftbl; High Hon Roll; Pres Schlr; Pres Acad Ftnss Awd 87; PA ST U; Arch.

MENTCH, RON; Hempfield HS; Lancaster, PA; (2); 112/450; Key Clb; JV Socr; Vet Med.

MENTZER, TODD; Waynesboro Area SR HS; Waynesboro, PA; (4); 50/390; Church Yth Grp; Band; Chorus; Concert Band; Drm Mjr(t); Jazz Band; Mrchg Band; Swing Chorus; Crs Cntry; Trk; Lbn Vly Coll; Msc.

MENYO, MELISSA; Marple Newton SR HS; Broomall, PA; (4); 74/307; Hosp Aide; Lit Mag; Var L Vllybl; Villanova U.

MENZ, BETH; Penn Trafford HS; Trafford, PA; (4); AFS; FBLA; Latin Clb; SADD; Hon Roll; U Of Pittsburgh; Acctg.

MENZEL, KARIN; Mercyhurst Preparatory Schl; Erie, PA; (4); 49/155; Hosp Aide; Spanish Clb; Off Jr Cls; JV Sftbl; Capt Var Swmmng; Hon Roll; PA ST, Behrend; Elem Ed.

MEO, JEANNINE; Lansdale Catholic HS; Chalfont, PA; (3); 29/250; Drama Clb; Exploring; 4-H; Service Clb; Yrbk Stf; Hon Roll; Bus.

MERANTE, BILLY; Beaver Area HS; Beaver, PA; (2); French Clb; Band; Concert Band; Jazz Band; Mrchg Band; School Play.

MERANTI, ANN MARIE; Riverside JR SR HS; Taylor, PA; (3); JV Var Cheerleading; Trk; Dntl Hygnst.

MERCANTE, DEBRA; Archbishop Prendergast HS; Collingdale, PA; (4); Church Yth Grp; Cmnty Wkr; Intnl Clb; Office Aide; Spanish Clb; Stage Crew; Nwsp Rptr; Ultrasound.

MERCATORIS, ADELE; Meadville Area SR HS; Meadville, PA; (3); 60/328; Trs Key Clb; Letterman Clb; Math Clb; SADD; Varsity Clb; Hon Roll; Var L Diving; Var L Golf; Var L Swmmng; 16 Ntn Dvng 85; 1st YMCA STS Dvng 85-86; 3rd HS STS 85, 6th 86; Aviation.

MERCER, MATT; Highlands HS; Natrona Hgts, PA; (3); 43/303; JA; Key Clb; SADD; Concert Band; Jazz Band; Mrchg Band; Trk; Hon Roll; Jr NHS; NHS; OH U; Civl Engrng.

MERCER, NATHAN; Cranberry HS; Seneca, PA; (3); 11/144; Varsity Clb; Capt Golf; High Hon Roll; Hon Roll; French Clb; FBLA; Letterman Clb; Var Bsbl; JV Bsktbl; JV Timer; IN U Of Pa; Accntng.

MERCHANT, ELIZABETH; North Penn HS; Lansdale, PA; (3); 33/699; Ski Clb; Rep Jr Cls; Var Cheerleading; Powder Puff Ftbl; Tennis; Hon Roll; Amer Lgn Aux Mdl Awd 84; Hnb Ment Amer Assoc Of Univ Women Writing Cntst 86; N P HS Rep 86; Villanova U; Mrktng.

MERCOLINI, DANIELLE; West Allegheny HS; Coraopolis, PA; (3); Exploring; High Hon Roll; Jr NHS; NHS; Grmn Awd 84-85; Bus.

MEREDITH, AMY; Mechanicsburg Area SR HS; Mechanicsburg, PA; (4); 2/303; NFL; Ski Clb; Drm Mjr(t); Yrbk Ed-Chief; High Hon Roll; NHS; Ntl Merit Ltr; Sal; Church Yth Grp; Speech Tm; Harrisburg Patriot News Journlsm Achvt Awd 87; Exch Club Harrisburg Yth Of Month 86; Hall Foundtn Schl; PA ST U; Bus Admin.

MERENICH, MICHAEL J; Freeland HS; Freeland, PA; (2); 4/87; Church Yth Grp; JV Bsktbl; High Hon Roll; Jr NHS; Penn ST U; Elctrcl Engr.

MERGET, AMY S; Reading HS; Reading, PA; (3); 25/710; Key Clb; Library Aide; Chorus; Swing Chorus; Masonic Awd; NHS; Acdmc All-Amer Schlr 85; Merit Roll 82-87; Hnrb Mntn Berk Cnty Essay Contest 87; Frgn Lang-Spnsh.

MERICLE, JENNIFER; Wyoming Valley West HS; Kingston, PA; (3); 11/416; Key Clb; Chorus; Rep Stu Cncl; Im Sftbl; JV Trk; Var Im Vllybl; High Hon Roll; NHS; NEDT Awd; Prfct Atten Awd; Leigh Dickinson U; Marine Bio.

MERISKO, JEANNE; Steel Valley HS; Munhall, PA; (3); 2/218; Church Yth Grp; Key Clb; Teachers Aide; Band; Concert Band; Mrchg Band; Stu Cncl; Mat Maids; High Hon Roll; NHS; Penn ST U; Elem Educ.

MERKEL, DONNA; Governor Mifflin HS; Shillington, PA; (4); 28/300; GAA; School Musical; Off Sr Cls; Stu Cncl; Var Capt Cheerleading; Var Powder Puff Ftbl; Var Capt Swmmng; Cit Awd; Hon Roll; Jr NHS; Mst Schl Spirited 87; Girl Mnth 87; Sportsmnshp Awd 87; U MD; Phys Thrpy.

MERKEL, MALISSA; Kutztown Area HS; Lenhartsville, PA; (3); Church Yth Grp; FHA; Intnl Clb; High Hon Roll; Hon Roll; NHS; Pre Med.

MERKEL, STEPHANIE; William Allen HS; Allentown, PA; (4); 52/560; Leo Clb; Ed Yrbk Stf; Hon Roll; Jr NHS; NHS; Pres Acad Ftns Awd 87; Temple U; Advrtsng.

MERKT, DAVID; Hamburg Area HS; Hamburg, PA; (3); Boy Scts; German Clb; Var Socr; Var Trk; High Hon Roll; Hon Roll; Pres Schlr; Ldg Chf Kittatinny Ldg No 5 86-87; Stu German Natl Hon Soc 86; Eagle Scout Hghst Rank 85; Penn ST; Engrng.

MERLIN, LISA MARIE; Greensburg Central Catholic HS; Greensburg, PA; (3); Church Yth Grp; Hosp Aide; Ski Clb; Yrbk Stf; Var Powder Puff Ftbl; Im Sftbl; Var JV Vllybl; High Hon Roll; PA ST U; Architecture.

MERLOT, KRISTIN; Riverview HS; Oakmont, PA; (3); French Clb; Ski Clb; Band; Concert Band; Mrchg Band; Off Sr Cls; Stu Cncl; Powder Puff Ftbl; Tennis; Twrlr; Elem Ed.

MEROLA, JILL AMY; Freedom HS; Bethlehem, PA; (4); 76/446; Science Clb; VP Ski Clb; Orch; Capt L Cheerleading; Hon Roll; Chrldng MVP 86-87; PA ST U.

MERRBACH, STEVEN; Meyersdale Area HS; Garrett, PA; (2); Yrbk Sprt Ed; Capt Var Bsktbl; Var Trk; High Hon Roll; Prfct Atten Awd; Ltrd Vrsty Bsktbl & Trck 86-87; Prehstrc Life.

MERRELL, CLAYTON F; Franklin Regional HS; Murrysville, PA; (4); NHS; Ntl Merit SF; AFS; Boy Scts; Church Yth Grp; Drama Clb; Ski Clb; Thesps; School Play; Stage Crew; Full Schlrshp PA Govnrs Schl Arts 86; Bst Shw 86; Boy Scts Of Amer Eagle Sct Palms 84-85; Arch.

MERRIAM, MICHAEL; Montour HS; Pittsburgh, PA; (3); Exploring; High Hon Roll; NHS; Prfct Atten Awd; Rep Frsh Cls; Rep Soph Cls; Rep Jr Cls; Rep Sr Cls; Var L Bowling; Im Trk; U Of Pittsburgh; Chem Engrng.

MERRIFIELD, W DOUGLAS; Palmyra HS; Campbelltown, PA; (4); Band; Concert Band; Orch; Pres Schlr; Elizabethtown Coll; Acctngn.

MERRIGAN, CARL; Carbondale Area HS; Simpson, PA; (3); FBLA; Ski Clb; Bsktbl; Hon Roll; Accntng.

MERRILL, DAWN; Susquehannock HS; New Freedom, PA; (2); 52/242; Church Yth Grp; Var Cheerleading; Mgmt.

MERRILL, N GAI; The Haverford Schl; Ardmore, PA; (3); 15/87; Boy Scts; Pres VP Church Yth Grp; Cmnty Wkr; Sec Church Choir; Lit Mag; Var L Bsktbl; Var L Trk; Hon Roll; Ntl Merit Ltr; 7th Pl Sci Fair/Zoology 84-85; Engrng.

MERRILL, RANDY; Berlin Brothers Valley HS; Berlin, PA; (3); 7/89; Am Leg Boys St; Ski Clb; Spanish Clb; SADD; School Play; Trk; Hon Roll; Pres NHS; Officer.

MERRIMAN, SHANE F; Cambria Heights HS; Ashville, PA; (4); 20/189; Off ROTC; Var Capt Crs Cntry; L Swmmng; L Trk; High Hon Roll; NHS; NEDT Awd; VFW Awd; Air Force Schlrshp, Acadmc All Amrcn 87; PA ST U; Electrcl Engrng.

MERRING, SHEILA; Pine Grove Area HS; Pine Grove, PA; (3); SADD; Varsity Clb; Yrbk Stf; Pres Stu Cncl; Sec Bsktbl; Var Cheerleading; Hon Roll; NHS; JR Achvt Awd In Math 84; Elem Educ.

MERRITT, BETTY; West Branch Area JR SR HS; Winburne, PA; (4); 4/128; Church Yth Grp; VP Drama Clb; Science Clb; Band; School Play; Nwsp Rptr; Pres Sr Cls; Score Keeper; High Hon Roll; Sec NHS; District Band 85-87; Penn ST U; Ed.

MERRITT, HEIDI; Athens HS; Athens, PA; (3); Var Sftbl; Var Vllybl; Sftbl-Ltr 85-86; Vllybl-Ltr 86-87; Sftbl Pin & Trphy MVP 86-87.

MERRITT, JOELLE; Northwestern HS; Albion, PA; (3); 7/150; Drama Clb; Model UN; Spanish Clb; Stu Cncl; Stat Bsktbl; Cheerleading; Stat Ftbl; Var Powder Puff Ftbl; Sftbl; JV Trk; Emeliha Earhart Ldrshp Awd 87; Shppensbrg All Grls ST 87; Chrprsn JR-SR Prom 87; Med.

MERRITT, SARA; West Branch Area HS; Winburne, PA; (2); #3 In Class; Drama Clb; Science Clb; Spanish Clb; SADD; Mgr(s); Hon Roll; NHS; Penn ST U; Biolgst.

MERRITTS, STEFANY; Bellwood-Antis HS; Tyrone, PA; (4); Chorus; Trs Mrchg Band; School Musical; Capt Twrlr; Hon Roll; Hostler Mem Schlrshp 87; Slippery Rock U; Scndry Ed.

MERRYMAN, AUDRA; Northwestern HS; Albion, PA; (4); 11/145; Science Clb; Concert Band; Flag Corp; Trs Stu Cncl; Capt Cheerleading; Powder Puff Ftbl; Sftbl; Hon Roll; NHS; U S Chrldr Achvmnt Awd 87; U Of Pittsburgh; Physcl Thrpy.

MERRYMAN, GEORGIE; Karns City HS; Petrolia, PA; (3); Church Yth Grp; Color Guard; Concert Band; Drill Tm; Drm & Bgl; Drm Mjr(t); Pom Pon; Radiology.

MERRYMAN, GREY; Central Dauphin HS; Harrisburg, PA; (2); 25/405; Church Yth Grp; Pres Ski Clb; Band; Concert Band; Jazz Band; Mrchg Band; Orch; Pres Soph Cls; Rep Stu Cncl; Crs Cntry; PASC Exec Brd Rgnl Rep 86; Schlrshp-NASC Annl Conf-Schl Brd 87; Bus Adm.

MERRYMAN, SAMUEL; Union HS; Sligo, PA; (3); Boy Scts; Church Yth Grp; Cmnty Wkr; Computer Clb; Drama Clb; FCA; Pep Clb; Speech Tm; Acpl Chr; Band; Co Chrs 85-87; Dist Chrs 85-87.

MERSHON, JAMES; Penn Wood HS; Lansdowne, PA; (2); 12/350; Boy Scts; Church Yth Grp; Debate Tm; Science Clb; Lit Mag; JV Crs Cntry; JV Mgr Trk; Hon Roll; Math Prob Of The Week Awd 85-86; Pres Acadmc Ftns Awd 85-86; Natl Math Exam 2nd Pl Schl 87; Engrng.

MERTSOCK, JOHN; Oswayo Valley HS; Shinglehouse, PA; (4); 4/61; Varsity Clb; Ed Nwsp Ed-Chief; Pres Frsh Cls; Pres Soph Cls; Pres Jr Cls; Pres Sr Cls; Rep Stu Cncl; Var L Crs Cntry; Var L Trk; NCTE Awd; Edinboro U.

MERTZ, CHARLIE; Council Rock HS; Holland, PA; (1); JV Bsbl; Annapolis Naval Acad.

MERTZ, COLLESCE; Danville SR HS; Danville, PA; (1); Church Yth Grp; 4-H; Nwsp Rptr; 4-H Awd; High Hon Roll; Sci Fair Awd, Keystone & ST 4-H Wnnr, & Pres Acdc Ftnss Awd 87; Grphc Art.

MERTZ, GRETCHEN; Bishop Mc Devitt HS; Harrisburg, PA; (3); 13/245; Q&S; Service Clb; Acpl Chr; Chorus; Nwsp Sprt Ed; Nwsp Stf; Yrbk Stf; Var Cheerleading; Hon Roll; NHS; Hghst Avg Awds Sci, Rlgn & Engl 85-86; 3rd Pl Sci Fr 85; Vrsty Ltr Chrldng 86; Coll Pharmacy; Phrmcy.

MERTZ, HEATHER; Beaver HS; Beaver, PA; (4); 5/202; Off Church Yth Grp; French Clb; JCL; Key Clb; Drill Tm; Var L Swmmng; Var Trk; NHS; Pres Schlr; Acdmc Awds 85-87; Geneva Coll; Chem.

MERTZ, JEREMY; Cedar Crest HS; Cornwall, PA; (2); Var JV Ftbl.

MERTZ, JOLENE; Danville HS; Danville, PA; (3); Latin Clb; Ski Clb; Spanish Clb; Yrbk Stf; Sec Soph Cls; Rep Stu Cncl; Cheerleading; Powder Puff Ftbl; High Hon Roll; NHS; Graham F Stephens Mem Awd 85; Chld Dvlpmnt.

MERULLI, WENDY; Center HS; Monaca, PA; (2); Hosp Aide; Office Aide; Spanish Clb; Varsity Clb; Sec Soph Cls; Pres Jr Cls; Stu Cncl; Var L Cheerleading; Hon Roll; Camera Clb; Stu Forum Of Beaver Cnty 87.

MERY, PAMELA; Northampton SR HS; Danielsville, PA; (3); 2/494; Drama Clb; Exploring; VP Sec 4-H; Church Choir; Orch; School Musical; School Play; High Hon Roll; Jr NHS; NHS; Medicine.

MESAROS III, JOHN M; Wyoming Valley West HS; Edwardsville, PA; (4); 21/397; Church Yth Grp; Varsity Clb; Im Bsktbl; Var Girl Scts; Im Var Vllybl; High Hon Roll; Hon Roll; NHS; Pres Schlr; Highest Spnsh Avg 85; Phldlphia Coll Of Phrmcy & Sci.

MESAROS, MARY ANN; Bishop O Reilly HS; Forty Fort, PA; (3); Church Yth Grp; Ski Clb; Chorus; School Musical; School Play; NHS; Spanish NHS; NEDT Cert 84-85; Bloomsburg U; Psych.

MESAROS, RONALD; Waynesboro Area SR HS; Waynesboro, PA; (3); Var Capt Ftbl; Var L Trk; Cit Awd; High Hon Roll; NHS.

MESEROLE, STEPHEN; Otto-Eldred JR-SR HS; Duke Center, PA; (4); Nwsp Stf; Stat Bsktbl; Hon Roll; NHS; Pres Schlr; Pnzl Schlrshp 87; Pres Schlrshp 87; Advncd Bio Awd 87; U Ptsbrg/Brdfrd; Chmstry.

MESHANKO, TRACY; Karns City HS; Chicora, PA; (2); Library Aide; Spanish Clb; Chorus; Hon Roll; Zoolgst.

MESHEY, TAMMY; Conestoga Valley HS; Ronks, PA; (4); 68/255; VP Art Clb; Girl Scts; Band; Concert Band; Mrchg Band; Stage Crew; Yrbk Stf; Mgr(s); Hon Roll; Score Keeper; Legal Scrtry.

MESICH, BETH ANN; Albert Gallatin SR HS; Masontown, PA; (4); Ski Clb; Varsity Clb; Chorus; Stu Cncl; Capt Cheerleading; Cit Awd; High Hon Roll; Gnrl Vldctrn 87; WV U; Elem Ed.

MESIN, BOBBI; Kennedy Christian HS; Farrell, PA; (3); 10/97; Church Yth Grp; Dance Clb; FBLA; Spanish Clb; Nwsp Rptr; Nwsp Stf; Yrbk Stf; High Hon Roll; U Of Pittsburgh; Bus Adm.

MESLEY, DEBORAH; Meadville Area HS; Meadville, PA; (3); 6/328; Church Yth Grp; Drama Clb; French Clb; Hosp Aide; School Play; High Hon Roll.

MESMER, SARA; Warren Area HS; Warren, PA; (3); Art Clb; Church Yth Grp; Pep Clb; Ski Clb; Spanish Clb; Varsity Clb; Acpl Chr; Chorus; Church Choir; School Musical.

MESNAR, GINGER; Highlands SR HS; Tarentum, PA; (4); 47/329; Church Yth Grp; Cmnty Wkr; Key Clb; Office Aide; Scholastic Bowl; SADD; Band; Drm Mjr(t); Yrbk Stf; Rep Soph Cls; Health Occupations St Competition 1st Place 87; 3rd Runnerup Miss Natl Teen 87; Physics Sci Fair 87; Pittsburgh U; Med.

MESO, WENDY; Valley HS; Arnold, PA; (2); Drama Clb; Hosp Aide; Office Aide; Acpl Chr; School Play; DAR Awd; Hon Roll; Sci Med.

MESSAM, WINSOME; Blue Mountain Acad; Laurelton, NY; (3); FCA; Office Aide; Teachers Aide; Varsity Clb; Drill Tm; Bsktbl; Gym; Trk; Prfct Atten Awd; Prncpls Lst 85-86; Andrews; Acctnt.

MESSENLEHNER, MARY LOUISE; Nazareth Area SR HS; Nazareth, PA; (1); 2/245; Ski Clb; Yrbk Stf; Cheerleading; Mat Maids; High Hon Roll; NHS; Dance Clb; Top Ten AAPHER Yth Phy Fit Test 85; JR Miss Pagnt 86; CF Martin Co Math Awd 87; E Stroudsburg Fclty; East Stroudsburg U.

MESSER, AMY; Carlynton HS; Crafton, PA; (4); 14/154; Pres Sec Church Yth Grp; Cmnty Wkr; Drama Clb; Pres Sec German Clb; Girl Scts; Capt Drill Tm; Nwsp Stf; Rep Frsh Cls; Rep Soph Cls; Rep Jr Cls; Slippery Rock U; Psych.

MESSER, JEFF; Upper Moreland HS; Hatboro, PA; (3); 36/285; VP Church Yth Grp; Key Clb; Rep Jr Cls; JV Trk; High Hon Roll; NHS; French Clb; Rep Soph Cls; Var Mgr(s); JV Socr; Corporate Law.

MESSINA, DAWN; Frankford HS; Philadelphia, PA; (3); 48/600; Drama Clb; GAA; Variety Show; Nwsp Stf; Yrbk Stf; JV Fld Hcky; Capt Var Tennis; Psych.

MESSINA, JAMES; Kennedy Christian HS; Burtonsville, MD; (4); 36/93; Letterman Clb; Ski Clb; Spanish Clb; Bsbl; Bsktbl; Tennis; Wt Lftg; High Hon Roll; Hon Roll; NHS; MD U; Pre-Med.

MESSINGER, ANGELA; Greater Works Acad; Pittsburgh, PA; (4); 1/32; Ski Clb; Pres Jazz Band; Stage Crew; Nwsp Ed-Chief; Yrbk Stf; VP Stu Cncl; Var Capt Bsktbl; Vllybl; Air Force ROTC 87; Army ROTC 87; Miami U Full Schlrshp 87; PA ST; Engrng.

MESSINGER, CHARLENE J; William Allen HS; Allentown, PA; (4); Girl Scts; Hosp Aide; Chorus; Church Choir; Color Guard; School Musical; Lit Mag; Ntl Merit SF; Interior Decortng.

MESSINGER JR, GARY; Northern Lebanon Schl Dist; Fredericksburg, PA; (4); 16/166; Church Yth Grp; Quiz Bowl; Varsity Clb; Church Choir; School Play; Nwsp Sprt Ed; Var Bsbl; Var Bsktbl; Var Ftbl; Hon Roll; Outstndng Cls Boy, Outstndng Mle Athl Yr 87; Mle Athl Yr Central Penn Chptr Sprts Hll Fme 87; Coll Of Wm & Mary; Math Tchr.

MESSINGER, MATTHEW; Milton Area SR HS; Milton, PA; (2); Boy Scts; Spanish Clb; Band; Chorus; Concert Band; Mrchg Band; Nwsp Stf; Rep Stu Cncl; Hon Roll; Pres Acadc Ftns Awd 85-86; Law.

MESSINGER, MEREDITH; Penncrest HS; Media, PA; (3); Office Aide; Rep Jr Cls; JV Var Cheerleading; Var Diving; JV Var Sftbl; JV Swmmng; Hon Roll; Prfct Atten Awd; Physcl Thrpy.

MESSINGER, TOMMY; Pen Argyl HS; Pen Argyl, PA; (3); 22/165; Band; Concert Band; Jazz Band; Mrchg Band; Orch; School Play; Boy Scts; Church Yth Grp; Spanish Clb; Stu Cncl; Mst Imprvd Percssnst Awd 87; Musicn.

MESSNER, JILL; Penn Manor HS; Lancaster, PA; (3); 122/370; Church Yth Grp; Library Aide; Ski Clb; SADD; Band; Chorus; School Musical; Stage Crew; Var Cheerleading; Var Ice Hcky.

MESSNER, TRACEY; Tri-Valley HS; Valley View, PA; (2); 24/85; Church Yth Grp; Drama Clb; Ski Clb; Band; Chorus; Concert Band; Mrchg Band; School Musical; School Play; Hon Roll; Natl Lng Arts Olympiad W/ Distnctn 84-85; Outstndg Newspr Carrier Of The Year Runner Up Sr Div 86; Elem Educ.

MESTISHEN, LORETTA A; Pottsville Area HS; Pottsville, PA; (4); 19/238; VP Art Clb; Drama Clb; Chorus; Concert Band; Drm Mjr(t); Mrchg Band; Nwsp Ed-Chief; Hon Roll; Ntl Merit Ltr; NEDT Awd; Schlstc Art Awd 85-87; Rosemont Coll.

MESURE, WILLIAM; Archbishop Wood For Boys HS; Warrington, PA; (2); 97/256; Church Yth Grp; JV Socr; Im Vllybl.

META, JEFFREY; Lakeland HS; Jermyn, PA; (3); 83/195; Letterman Clb; SADD; Varsity Clb; Variety Show; VP Jr Cls; Rep Stu Cncl; JV Var Bsbl; Var Bsktbl; Capt Var Ftbl; Wt Lftg; Criminal Justice.

METALONIS, CHERYL; Philipsburg-Osceola Area HS; Philipsburg, PA; (4); 80/234; Church Yth Grp; Pep Clb; SADD; Chorus; School Musical; School Play; Stage Crew; Stu Cncl; Stat Bsktbl; Hon Roll; Penn ST U.

METCALF, FRED; Northern Potter HS; Westfield, PA; (1); Church Yth Grp; Cmnty Wkr; 4-H; High Hon Roll; Hon Roll; Ntl Merit Ltr; Dsgnd-Pttr Cnty Fair Bttn 87; US Army.

METCALF, WENDY; Saltsburg JR/SR HS; Saltsburg, PA; (4); 2/90; Camera Clb; Church Yth Grp; Pres Ski Clb; Varsity Clb; Flag Corp; School Musical; Variety Show; Ed Lit Mag; Sec Frsh Cls; Var L Bsktbl; Marine Sci Consortium Hnr 85; IN U PA Mentorshp Physics Hnr 86; Pres Phys Fit Awd 86; Purdue U; Engrng.

METCALFE, LYNDA; Seneca Valley SR HS; Harmony, PA; (4); 58/340; Church Yth Grp; SADD; S W Butler Cnty Ed Assn Schlrshp 87; Butler Cnty CC; Elem Ed.

METCALFE, SUSAN; Hempfield HS; Lancaster, PA; (4); 6/418; Aud/Vis; Cmnty Wkr; Dance Clb; Drama Clb; English Clb; Exploring; Office Aide; PAVAS; Political Wkr; Radio Clb; Alpha Lambda Delta & Mdrn Lang Awd, Outstndng Coll Frshmn Yr & Deans Lst 87; Amrcn Lgn Ctznshp Awd 84; Elizabethtown Coll; Engl.

METEER, MICHAEL R; Wyalusing Valley HS; Wyalusing, PA; (3); 1/150; Am Leg Boys St; Boy Scts; Letterman Clb; Spanish Clb; Pres Sr Cls; Rep Stu Cncl; Var L Bsktbl; Var L Trk; Cit Awd; NHS; Engrng.

METELSKY, GEORGE; Ambridge Area HS; Ambridge, PA; (4); 14/265; Am Leg Boys St; Church Yth Grp; German Clb; Math Clb; VICA; L Golf; High Hon Roll; Lion Awd; NHS; Prfct Atten Awd; U Of Pittsburgh; Comp Sci.

METHENY, AMBER; Calvary Baptist Christian Acad; Meadville, PA; (3); 1/14; Church Yth Grp; Chorus; School Play; Sec Soph Cls; L Var Bsktbl; L Sftbl; Var L Vllybl; Amer Assoc Chrstn Schls Hnr Scty 85-86.

METRO, MICHAEL; Marian Catholic HS; Lansford, PA; (4); 20/109; Band; Chorus; Concert Band; Mrchg Band; Orch; School Musical; School Play; Hon Roll; St Chrls Borromeo Semnry; Theo.

METRO, MICHAEL J; Chartiers Valley HS; Pittsburgh, PA; (3); 1/300; Ski Clb; Varsity Clb; Rep Frsh Cls; Rep Soph Cls; Var JV Bsbl; Bsktbl; Var L Socr; Gov Hon Prg Awd; High Hon Roll; Hon Roll; Pittsburgh U; Pre Med.

METRO, SUSAN; Chartiers Valley HS; Pittsburgh, PA; (3); 29/328; Dance Clb; Ski Clb; Spanish Clb; Thesps; Chorus; Drill Tm; School Musical; School Play; VP Sr Cls; Rep Stu Cncl; Cmmnctns.

METROCAVAGE, MARIA; Our Lady Of Lourdes Regional HS; Shamokin, PA; (3); 1/89; Spanish Clb; Yrbk Stf; Trs Frsh Cls; Rep Soph Cls; Trs Jr Cls; Bsktbl; Score Keeper; Hon Roll; Trs NHS; Spanish NHS; 2 Hnrb Mntns In Spnsh II & III/Ntl Spnsh Exam 86 & 87.

METSGER, LORI; Connellsville SR HS; Connellsville, PA; (3); 1/520; Pres Church Yth Grp; Church Choir; Jazz Band; Mrchg Band; School Musical; Nwsp Ed-Chief; French Hon Soc; High Hon Roll; NHS; Office Aide; Mst Outstndng Stu Awd, Acdmc Excllnce Awd, Mst Studius Awd 85; 2ndry Ed.

METTEE, ANN; Kennard-Dale HS; Airville, PA; (3); Girl Scts; Band; Chorus; Concert Band; Nwsp Stf; Mgr(s); Score Keeper; Timer; JV Vllybl; Hon Roll; Cert Of Apprctn Wrkng With Hrng Imprd Chldrn 86; Frgn Lang.

METTS, CLAUDIA; Elizabeth Forward HS; Mckeesport, PA; (2); French Clb; Pep Clb; VP Chorus; Color Guard; Yrbk Stf; Capt Cheerleading; Coach Actv; Hon Roll; U WV; Dance Tchr.

METZ, CORRINE; West Middlesex JR SR HS; West Middlesex, PA; (2); 1/109; Pres French Clb; Hosp Aide; Chorus; Nwsp Rptr; Yrbk Stf; Sec Stu Cncl; Var Cheerleading; NHS; Hugh Obrn Yth Fndtn Ambssdr 87.

METZ, DIANA; Bedford HS; Bedford, PA; (3); 45/204; Church Yth Grp; Rptr FBLA; Chorus; Church Choir; Trk; Hon Roll; Exec Sec.

METZ, KATHY; Bensalem HS; Bensalem, PA; (4); 22/499; FBLA; Color Guard; Socr; High Hon Roll; NHS; Pres Schlr; Sal; Bucks CC Scholar; Provident Natl Bank Awd; Bucks CC; CPA.

METZ, LISA; Hamburg Area HS; Hamburg, PA; (4); 29/141; French Clb; Library Aide; Ski Clb; Spanish Clb; SADD; Concert Band; Mrchg Band; Stu Cncl; Hon Roll; NHS; York Coll PA; Crimnl Justice.

METZGER, ANNISSA; Canton Area JR/SR HS; Canton, PA; (4); 2/122; Scholastic Bowl; School Play; Bausch & Lomb Sci Awd; Hon Roll; NHS; Pres Schlr; Sal; AFS; Drama Clb; Letterman Clb; Duke U.

METZGER, BRENDA; Milton SR HS; New Columbia, PA; (3); Computer Clb; Spanish Clb; Varsity Clb; Rep Frsh Cls; Bsktbl; Fld Hcky; Sftbl; Hon Roll; Amer Lgn Auxilary Awd 85; Vet.

METZGER, DIRK; Milton HS; West Milton, PA; (2); VP Latin Clb; JV Ftbl; JV Trk; Hon Roll; Pres Schlr; Latin Hnr Soc 85-87; PA ST; Wildlife Mgnt.

METZGER, ELAINE; Central HS; Roaring Spring, PA; (3); FCA; GAA; Ski Clb; Varsity Clb; Sec Soph Cls; Sec Jr Cls; JV Bsktbl; Var Cheerleading; Var Trk; Hon Roll.

METZGER, ELDON; Beaver Area JR SR HS; Beaver, PA; (3); 33/215; Art Clb; Chess Clb; FCA; German Clb; Letterman Clb; Math Tm; Ski Clb; SADD; Varsity Clb; Bsbl; AZ ST; Electrcl Engr.

METZGER, JESSICA; Bethlehem Catholic HS; Bethlehem, PA; (3); 85/200; Church Yth Grp; Band; Color Guard; Mrchg Band; Twrlr; Hon Roll; Bus Mgmt.

METZGER, MATTHEW; Nazareth Area HS; Bethlehem, PA; (3); 187/265; Band; Concert Band; Jazz Band; Mrchg Band; School Musical; School Play; Stage Crew; Music.

METZGER, ROBERT; Berks Christian Schl; Fleetwood, PA; (3); 6/23; Church Yth Grp; Computer Clb; Band; Concert Band; Yrbk Rptr; Yrbk Stf; Bsktbl; Socr; Trk; Hon Roll; Bsktbl, Sccr & Track 85-86 & 86 & 87; Albright Coll; Bus Admin.

METZGER, WENDY; Danville SR HS; Danville, PA; (3); 65/195; Spanish Clb; Band; Mrchg Band; Symp Band; Yrbk Stf; Var L Fld Hcky; Var L Trk; Hon Roll; NHS; Church Yth Grp; Pres Acad Awd 85; Phys Thrpy.

METZLER, SARAH E; Solanco HS; New Providence, PA; (4); 42/200; Art Clb; Exploring; Ski Clb; Band; Concert Band; Mrchg Band; Orch; Pep Band; School Musical; Symp Band; Region Band 87; Dist Band 87; Ladies Aux Awd 87; Indiana U-PA; Music Tchr.

MEWHIRTER, DOUGLAS R; Fox Chapel Area HS; Pittsburgh, PA; (4); 26/322; Ski Clb; Vllybl; High Hon Roll; NHS; Ntl Merit SF; US Naval Acad; Naval Offcr.

MEYER, CHRIS; Archbishop Wood For Boys; Willow Grove, PA; (3); 52/235; Chess Clb; SADD; Im Bsktbl; Hon Roll; NHS; Bus Admin.

MEYER, CHRISTINE; Saint Basil Acad; Philadelphia, PA; (4); Cmnty Wkr; Latin Clb; Scholastic Bowl; Pres Science Clb; Yrbk Sprt Ed; Im Bsktbl; Im Trk; High Hon Roll; NHS; Envrmntl Clb Pres; Campus Mnstry Bd; Ursinus Col6; Bio.

MEYER, CHRISTOPHER; Penns Valley Area HS; Rebersburg, PA; (3); Varsity Clb; Var L Bsbl; Var L Ftbl; Ctrl PA Bsbl League All Star Awd 87; Athltc Trng.

MEYER, DAVID; Wyoming Seminary; Kingston, PA; (2); Intnl Clb; Math Clb; Math Tm; Scholastic Bowl; Temple Yth Grp; Yrbk Rptr; Yrbk Stf; Off Frsh Cls; Off Soph Cls; Tennis; Wnnr Essy Cont Cmmnrtng 200th Yr Of Constitution 87; Ntl Advsry Brd To Coll Brd 87; Doctor.

MEYER, DAVID J; The Baptist HS; Clarks Summit, PA; (4); 2/16; Church Yth Grp; Drama Clb; Chorus; School Play; Bsktbl; L Socr; Cit Awd; High Hon Roll; Sal; US Snte Exch Schlrshp 86; Amer Assoc Chrstn Schls Natl Cmptntn 86; 1st Pl Pblc Spkng 86; Drew U; Rssn Area Stds.

MEYER, DAWN; Cumberland Valley HS; Carlisle, PA; (3); 123/595; Sec Church Yth Grp; Pres 4-H; French Clb; Church Choir; Color Guard; Yrbk Stf; 4-H Awd; High Hon Roll; Miss Hidden Valley 86; ST 4-H Speech Awd 86; Teacher.

MEYER, DONNA; Gateway SR HS; Monroeville, PA; (3); Hosp Aide; Model UN; VP NFL; Science Clb; Orch; Nwsp Ed-Chief; Off Church Yth Grp; High Hon Roll; VP NHS; Historian Med Club 86-87; ST Orch 87; ST Forn Trnmnt 86; Pol Sci.

MEYER, HEIDI; North East HS; North East, PA; (4); 1/138; Sec AFS; Pres Trs Church Yth Grp; Pres Q&S; Trs Concert Band; Sec Sr Cls; Var Capt Vllybl; Bausch & Lomb Sci Awd; Sec NHS; Val; Latin Clb; North East Exchng Clb & Lk Erie Dist Exchng Clb Stu Yr Awds 87; Aid Assn Lutherans Schlrshp 87-91; Mercyhurst Coll.

MEYER, HEIDI M; Owen J Roberts HS; Pottstown, PA; (2); 1/311; Key Clb; SADD; Chorus; School Musical; Variety Show; Rep Stu Cncl; JV Bsktbl; Var Tennis; Sci.

MEYER, KIMBERLY; Plum SR HS; Pittsburgh, PA; (3); Camera Clb; Church Yth Grp; FTA; Library Aide; Jazz Band; Mrchg Band; Symp Band; Hon Roll; Valparaiso U; Polit Sci.

MEYER, KRISTEN M; Canon Mc Millan SR HS; Canonsburg, PA; (4); Church Yth Grp; Letterman Clb; Varsity Clb; Swmmng; Trk; In U Of PA; Elem Educ.

MEYER, KRISTIN; Hatboro Horsham HS; Hatboro, PA; (3); Political Wkr; Cheerleading; Fld Hcky; Powder Puff Ftbl; Swmmng; High Hon Roll; NHS; Lcrss.

MEYER, MELISSA M; North Schuylkill JR SR HS; Ashland, PA; (3); Rep Stu Cncl; Var Cheerleading; Voice Dem Awd; Millersville U; Spcl Educ.

MEYER, PAUL; Upper Dublin HS; Maple Glen, PA; (3); 23/295; Sec Science Clb; SADD; Variety Show; Stu Cncl; Im Capt Bsktbl; JV Socr; Hon Roll; NHS; Church Yth Grp; Intnl Clb; Free Enterprise Bus Pgm 87; Rotary Intl Ldrshp Camp 87; Bio.

MEYER, REBECCA; Gateway SR HS; Monroeville, PA; (3); FBLA; NFL; Ski Clb; Orch; Cheerleading; Crs Cntry; Trk; Hon Roll.

MEYER, REBECCA; Lewisburg Area HS; Lewisburg, PA; (4); Band; Chorus; Church Choir; Concert Band; Mrchg Band; Orch; School Musical; Lit Mag; Hon Roll; Arion Music Awd 86; IN U Of PA; Music.

MEYER, REED; Central Dauphin HS; Hummelstown, PA; (2); 5/400; Pres Computer Clb; Orch; School Musical; Nwsp Stf; High Hon Roll; Jr NHS; Capital Area Clsscs Fstvl Latin-2 1st Pl Awds, 2 3rd Pls 85 & 86; Rgn IV-V PMEA Orchestra 87; Engrng.

MEYER, STEVEN; Seneca Valley SR HS; Mars, PA; (3); 1/333; Math Tm; Ski Clb; High Hon Roll; Hon Roll; PA ST; Engrng.

MEYERS, ALISA; Somerset Area SR HS; Somerset, PA; (4); 66/239; Art Clb; French Clb; GAA; JA; Band; Chorus; Yrbk Stf; Stu Cncl; Cheerleading; Vllybl; 5 Art Awds Best Show Outstndng Achvt 86-87; Frostburg; Art Ed.

MEYERS, ALLISON; West Side Area Vo Tech Schl; Luzerne, PA; (3); Chorus; Variety Show; High Hon Roll; Cosmtlgst.

MEYERS, CHRISTOPHER; Warren Area HS; Warren, PA; (3); SADD; Varsity Clb; Var L Bsbl; JV Bsktbl; Var L Ftbl; Wt Lftg; Hon Roll; Jr NHS; NHS; Rtry Yth Ldrshp Awd 87; U Of PA; Chem Engrng.

MEYERS, DESIREE; John Harris HS; Harrisburg, PA; (3); 100/305; Chorus; Church Choir; Orch; Off Jr Cls; JV Trk; High Hon Roll; Hamilton U; Bus Admin.

MEYERS, JONATHAN; Central Bucks High School East; Doylestown, PA; (3); 85/505; Ski Clb; Var Socr; Var Trk; Hon Roll; Engr.

MEYERS, KELLIE; Seneca HS; Union City, PA; (4); 29/147; Pres VP Church Yth Grp; Church Choir; Color Guard; School Musical; Pres Sec Stage Crew; Nwsp Rptr; Yrbk Rptr; Stat Bsktbl; Var Trk; Hon Roll; Edinboro U; Scl Wrk.

MEYERS, KENNETH; Souderton Area HS; Souderton, PA; (3); 93/423; Church Yth Grp; Office Aide; Quiz Bowl; Spanish Clb; Band; Hon Roll; Prfct Atten Awd; Southeastern Acad; Htl Mgmt.

MEYERS, KENT; Chambersburg Area SR HS; Chambersburg, PA; (3); Pres Church Yth Grp; Cmnty Wkr; Letterman Clb; Red Cross Aide; SADD; Varsity Clb; Chorus; Church Choir; L Capt Bsktbl; Hon Roll; RIT; Elec Engr.

MEYERS, LARRY; Newport HS; Newport, PA; (2); Church Yth Grp; JV Bsbl; Ftbl; JV Wrstlng; High Hon Roll; Hon Roll; Algebr I Awd 86; Arch.

MEYERS, LISA; Bishop Mc Cort HS; Stoystown, PA; (4); Dance Clb; Pep Clb; Band; Chorus; Orch; Nwsp Stf; High Hon Roll; Hon Roll; FCA; Hosp Aide; Acdmc All-Amer, Annncr Allegheney Rgnl Band-WJAC TV 6 87; U Of Pittsburgh; Sclgy.

MEYERS, LORI; Conemaugh Township Area HS; Hollsopple, PA; (3); 9/121; Art Clb; Pres Church Yth Grp; Drama Clb; Pres Intnl Clb; Pep Clb; Trs Ski Clb; Spanish Clb; Chorus; Capt Cheerleading; Sftbl; Hugh O Brien Youth Fndtn 86; Rotary Youth Ldrshp Smnr 87; Somerset-Cambria Jr Miss Fnlst 87; Elem Educ.

MEYERS, TRACY; Seneca Valley SR HS; Harmony, PA; (2); Church Yth Grp; JA; Sec Soph Cls; Var L Cheerleading; Var L Mgr(s); Hon Roll; Ski Clb; Church Choir; School Musical; Symp Band; Bus Admn.

MEZAN, JACQUELINE; Belle Vernon Area HS; Belle Vernon, PA; (3); Stat Bsktbl; High Hon Roll; NHS; Mc Donalds Feb Crew Mmbr 87.

MIAZGA, JIM; The Christian Acad; Upland, PA; (3); German Clb; Acpl Chr; Var L Bsbl; Hon Roll; PA Inst Of Tech; Jet Mechnc.

MICCICHE, MELISSA; Dunmore HS; Dunmore, PA; (3); French Clb; Girl Scts; Letterman Clb; Pres Ski Clb; School Play; Nwsp Rptr; Yrbk Stf; Var Capt Cheerleading; Var Trk; Hon Roll; Cmmnctns.

MICCO, GARY; New Castle SR HS; New Castle, PA; (3); Bus.

MICCO, TAMMY; Neshannock HS; New Castle, PA; (3); 6/114; Church Yth Grp; Math Tm; Speech Tm; SADD; Teachers Aide; Nwsp Sprt Ed; Nwsp Stf; NHS; NEDT Awd; Band; Pres Acdmc Ftns Awd 85; U Of Pittsbrgh; Ed.

MICELI, CHRISTINE; Bishop Mc Devitt HS; Dauphin, PA; (3); 32/240; Service Clb; Nwsp Rptr; Yrbk Sprt Ed; Sftbl; Swmmng; Hon Roll; Ed.

MICHAEL, BIERLY; Du Bois Area SR HS; Reynoldsville, PA; (3); Boy Scts; Church Yth Grp; Hon Roll; Penn ST U; Gentc Engrng.

MICHAEL, CONNIE; Little Flower Catholic HS; Philadelphia, PA; (3); 48/322; Camera Clb; Church Yth Grp; German Clb; Office Aide; Yrbk Stf; Hon Roll; Philadelphia CC; Acctng.

MICHAEL, KEN; Butler HS; Butler, PA; (4); Church Yth Grp; Exploring; Im Ftbl; High Hon Roll; Hon Roll; Grove City Coll; Elect Engr.

MICHAEL, MARK; Center Area HS; Aliquippa, PA; (4); Boy Scts; FFA; Vllybl; Dgr Of Grnhnd FFA 86; Tri Cnty Vllybl FFA 87; Nrsry/Lndscp Sprng Rndup Cmmtte FFA 87; Lndscpng.

MICHAEL, MARK; New Castle HS; New Castle, PA; (3); 6/250; Church Yth Grp; Var Trk; High Hon Roll; Hon Roll; NHS; Acdmc Gms Awd 85-87; Engnrng.

MICHAEL, THOMAS; Tri-Valley HS; Mc Clellandtown, PA; (3); Church Yth Grp; Nwsp Rptr; Nwsp Stf; Yrbk Stf; Bsbl; Bsktbl; Ftbl; Hon Roll; Sprts Broadcasting.

MICHAEL, VICKI; Northern Lebanon HS; Jonestown, PA; (4); 4/170; Church Yth Grp; Drama Clb; Chorus; Mrchg Band; Pep Band; School Musical; Dnfth Awd; High Hon Roll; NHS; Ntl Merit SF; Ft Wayne Bible Coll; Mission.

MICHAELS, CHRIS; Ligonier Valley S HS; Ligonier, PA; (3); 1/155; AFS; Pres Church Yth Grp; Yrbk Stf; Rep Sr Cls; VP Rep Stu Cncl; Var Bsktbl; High Hon Roll; Pres Jr NHS; Pres NHS; Ntl Merit Ltr; Chmstry.

MICHAELS, JEFFREY; Southern Columbia Area HS; Catawissa, PA; (3); Varsity Clb; Nwsp Sprt Ed; Var L Bsktbl; Var L Crs Cntry; Var L Trk; High Hon Roll; NHS; Hugh O Brian Yth Ldrshp Smnr 86; Principals Cncl 87.

MICHAELS, KAREN; Taylor Allderdice HS; Pittsburgh, PA; (2); Drama Clb; Ski Clb; Chorus; High Hon Roll; Jr NHS; NHS.

MICHAELS, ROB; Lake-Lehman HS; Dallas, PA; (2); Aud/Vis; Var L Bsbl; Var L Bsktbl; Var L Ftbl; Hon Roll; Jr NHS.

MICHAJLUK, SUSAN M; Greencastle Antrim HS; Greencastle, PA; (3); Church Yth Grp; Teachers Aide; Chorus; Yrbk Stf; High Hon Roll; Hon Roll; NHS; Prfct Atten Awd; Peer Advct Spprt Group 87.

MICHALEK, RICHARD; Carbondale Area HS; Carbondale, PA; (3); 54/119; Aud/Vis; Ski Clb; Spanish Clb; Chorus; Stage Crew; Variety Show; JV Ftbl; Williamsport CC; Clnry Arts.

MICHALEK, STEPHANIE; Lake-Lehman HS; Hunlock Crk, PA; (3); 11/220; Library Aide; Office Aide; Teachers Aide; Hon Roll; Jr NHS; NHS; Kings Coll; Ed Fld.

MICHALIK, CAROL; Shenandoah Valley JR SR HS; Shenandoah, PA; (3); Library Aide; Pep Clb; SADD; Chorus; Nwsp Stf; Yrbk Stf; Rep Soph Cls; Stu Cncl; Stat Crs Cntry; Stat Trk; Brdcst Jrnlsm.

MICHALSKI, ANTHONY; Coughlin HS; Wilkes Barre, PA; (2); 1/400; Chess Clb; Computer Clb; Drama Clb; German Clb; Math Clb; Science Clb; School Play; Variety Show; Stu Cncl; High Hon Roll; Engl, Grmn , Sci, Geom Awds; Chrch Lector Acolyte; Physics.

MICHALSKI, CATHERINE ANNE; St Basil Acad; Philadelphia, PA; (3); 10/82; French Clb; German Clb; Girl Scts; Nwsp Bus Mgr; Nwsp Stf; Yrbk Stf; JV Socr; JV Swmmng; Ukrainian Clb Treas 86-87 & Pres 87-88; Lang.

MICHALSKI, MARK; Cathedral Prep HS; Erie, PA; (3); 69/193; Boy Scts; Church Yth Grp; Exploring; Bio.

MICHALSKI, MARY; Vincentian HS; Gibsonia, PA; (1); Church Yth Grp; Girl Scts; Church Choir; School Musical; High Hon Roll; Hon Roll; Pilot.

MICHEL, JENNIFER; Our Lady Of The Sacred Heart HS; Aliquippa, PA; (3); 10/65; Church Yth Grp; Rep Stu Cncl; Im Bsktbl; Var Crs Cntry; Im Ice Hcky; Im Socr; JV Sftbl; Outstndng Achvt Awd East West Cvlztn 84-85; Outstndng Achvt Awd Coll Bnd Rdng 86-87; Poltcl Sci.

MICHEL, JOHN; Greensburg Central Catholic HS; Manor, PA; (3); Chess Clb; Church Yth Grp; Letterman Clb; NFL; Ski Clb; Var L Bsbl; Im Bsktbl; Var L Golf; Im Capt Vllybl; High Hon Roll; Math.

MICHEL, STEPHANIE; Lancaster Christian HS; Lancaster, PA; (4); 3/26; Church Yth Grp; Yrbk Ed-Chief; Yrbk Stf; VP Frsh Cls; Rep Sec Stu Cncl; Var Capt Bsktbl; Var L Fld Hcky; Var Capt Sftbl; High Hon Roll; Soc Distngshd Chrstn HS Stu 85-86; Millersville U; Ed.

MICHELE, JOSEPH; Marion Ctr; Rochester Mills, PA; (3); Intnl Clb; Ski Clb; Hon Roll; Engrng.

MICHELS, MICHELLE; Shady Side Acad; Pittsburbh, PA; (3); Hosp Aide; Chorus; Mgr Ftbl; Mgr(s); Sftbl; High Hon Roll; Hon Roll; Georgetown U; Bus Admin.

MICHELS, TRICIA K; Laurel HS; New Castle, PA; (4); SADD; Sec Trs Band; Chorus; Concert Band; Sec Trs Jazz Band; Sec Trs Mrchg Band; Sec Trs Pep Band; Ed Yrbk Ed-Chief; Trk; Hon Roll; HS Stu Cncl Actvts Awd 87; New Castle Music Clb Vcl Awd 87; Penn ST; Cmmnctns.

MICHELSON, ROGER A; Susquehanna Twp HS; Harrisburg, PA; (3); 26/152; AFS; Computer Clb; Drama Clb; Model UN; Teachers Aide; Temple Yth Grp; Chorus; Orch; School Musical; Yrbk Stf; Aerospace Engnrng.

MICHRINA, MARIA; Canon-Mcmillan JHS At Cecil; Muse, PA; (1); Yrbk Stf; High Hon Roll; Hon Roll; Law.

MICHUCK, RONNA; Brockway Area HS; Brockway, PA; (4); 8/88; Drama Clb; Thesps; Band; Concert Band; Jazz Band; Mrchg Band; Pep Band; School Musical; Stu Cncl; Hon Roll; Bloomsburg U; Pre-Med.

MICKLEY, CHAD; South Western HS; Hanover, PA; (2); Key Clb; Varsity Clb; Ftbl; Trk; Wt Lftg; Hon Roll; Ftbl Lttr-Grd 9 & 10; Trck Lttr 10; Sprt Brdcstg.

MICOTRA, CHRISTA; North Catholic HS; Allison Pk, PA; (3); Church Yth Grp; Church Choir; School Play; Rep Soph Cls; Sftbl; Tennis; US Stu Cncl Awd 86; Ntl Ldrshp & Svc Awd 86; Acadc All Am 86; Duquensne U; Dntl.

MIDDLEBROUGH, CAROL; Monessen HS; Monessen, PA; (3); 29/115; Girl Scts; Church Choir; Hon Roll.

MIDDLETON, LINDA ANNE; Sun Valley HS; Brookhaven, PA; (4); 23/311; Teachers Aide; Band; Concert Band; Mrchg Band; Variety Show; Cheerleading; Lcrss; Mgr(s); High Hon Roll; Hon Roll; Philadelphia Coll; Physcl Thrpy.

MIELE, ANDREA; Mt Pleasant Area SR HS; Mt Pleasant, PA; (2); 1/245; GAA; Pep Clb; Concert Band; Mrchg Band; Ed Yrbk Stf; Rep Frsh Cls; Trs Soph Cls; High Hon Roll; Cntyh Band Fest 85-86; Dist Band Fest 85-86; Pre Med.

MIERNICKI, JOHN; Nazareth Area HS; Nazareth, PA; (4); 22/241; Var L Bsbl; Var Ftbl; Im Wt Lftg; High Hon Roll; Hon Roll; Pres Schlr; Fulton Fncl Corp Schlrshp 87; Penn ST U; Bus Admin.

MIERS, SUSAN; Dallas SR HS; Dallas, PA; (3); Stage Crew; Yrbk Stf; Trs Sr Cls; Sec Rep Stu Cncl; Hon Roll; NEDT Awd; Strng Cmmtte; Drama Constr & Make-Up Crew; Gifted Cls; Georgetown; Intl Rltns.

MIERZEJEWSKI, LYNN; St Basil Acad; Philadelphia, PA; (4); 14/97; French Clb; VP FBLA; Acpl Chr; Chorus; Madrigals; High Hon Roll; Hon Roll; NHS; Sci Fair Proj Awd For Hnrbl Men 84-85; Acctng.

MIETH, ALFRED J; Northgate JRSR HS; Pittsburgh, PA; (3); 7/157; Debate Tm; Math Clb; Math Tm; Nwsp Rptr; Lit Mag; JV Crs Cntry; High Hon Roll; NEDT Awd; Prfct Atten Awd; PA JR Acdmy Sci 86; Physics.

MIGATULSKI, JOHN; Mount Union Area HS; Huntingdon, PA; (3); 35/152; Boy Scts; York Coll Of PA; Law Enfrcmnt.

MIGLIARINO, SONIA; Merion Mercy Acad; Phila, PA; (4); 11/73; French Clb; Library Aide; Scholastic Bowl; Science Clb; Service Clb; Im Bsktbl; Im Vllybl; High Hon Roll; Prfct Atten Awd; Natl Hnr Soc 86-87; Villanova U; Nrsng.

MIGLIOSI, ROBERT; Wyoming Area SR HS; Exeter, PA; (4); 31/250; Computer Clb; French Clb; Pep Clb; Red Cross Aide; Nwsp Stf; Yrbk Stf; Bowling; Coach Actv; Vllybl; NHS; Kings Coll; Psych.

MIGNOGNA, KAREN; Bishop Conwell HS; Levittown, PA; (3); 2/292; Cmnty Wkr; French Clb; Latin Clb; Library Aide; Office Aide; Hon Roll; NHS; Acad All-Amer 85-86; Diocesan Schlrs Prg 87; Search Of Ldrs 87; Comp Engrng.

MIGYANKO, JOSEPH; Fairchance-Georges SR HS; Uniontown, PA; (3); Band; School Play; Variety Show; Var L Ftbl; Var L Wrstlng; High Hon Roll; Hon Roll; Jr NHS; NHS; All Conf Ftbl 85; Sect Rnnr Up Wrstlng 85; WV U.

MIHALAK, JANE M; Seton Catholic HS; Moosic, PA; (3); 11/88; Church Yth Grp; Pres Drama Clb; School Musical; School Play; Nwsp Stf; Crs Cntry; Fld Hcky; Vllybl; NHS; Natl Sci Merit Awd 86; Natl Honor Roll 87; Magna Cum Laude 85; Kings; Bio.

MIHALEK, WILLIAM J; Bentworth HS; Ellsworth, PA; (3); 3/115; NHS; Elec Engrng.

MIHALIC, MELISSA; Mc Keesport Area SR HS; Mc Keesport, PA; (1); Pep Clb; Nwsp Stf; Cheerleading; Vllybl; Penn ST; Psych.

MIHALKO, ANNA MARIE; Uniontown Area SR HS; Uniontown, PA; (3); Church Yth Grp; Cmnty Wkr; Letterman Clb; Library Aide; Band; Chorus; Church Choir; Concert Band; Mrchg Band; Swing Chorus; Music.

MIHALKO, CHRISTINA; Wyoming Valley West HS; Larksville, PA; (2); Church Yth Grp; French Clb; Band; Church Choir; Concert Band; Drm Mjr(t); Mrchg Band; Orch; School Musical; Hon Roll.

MIHALKO, KRISTEN; Yough HS; Lowber, PA; (3); VP French Clb; Band; Chorus; Mrchg Band; Nwsp Stf; Yrbk Stf; Off Stu Cncl; Mgr(s); Hon Roll; Sec NHS.

MIHALKO, TARAS; Wyoming Valley West HS; Larksville, PA; (4); Band; Concert Band; Mrchg Band; Hon Roll; Wilkes Coll; Mech Engr.

MIHALO, MISSY; Moon SR HS; Coraopolis, PA; (3); 35/328; Church Yth Grp; DECA; High Hon Roll; Hon Roll; NHS.

MIHELIC, MICHELENE; Aliquippa HS; West Aliquippa, PA; (2); French Clb; Library Aide; Yrbk Stf; Hon Roll; Sports Med.

MIHLFRIED, RUTH ANN; Neshannock HS; Neshannock, PA; (3); SADD; Band; Mrchg Band; Orch; Pep Band; School Musical; JV Var Bsktbl; JV Var Mgr(s); JV Var Score Keeper; Svc Awd 85-86; Counselor.

MIHNESKI, MICHAEL; J S Fine HS; Nanticoke, PA; (2); Boy Scts; Chorus; Mrchg Band; Var Swmmng; JV Vllybl; High Hon Roll; Ltrmn Swm Tm 85-87; Sci Data Prcssng.

MIKAN, SUSAN; Shaler Area HS; Glenshaw, PA; (4); 70/509; Camp Fr Inc; Band; Hon Roll; Spanish NHS; La Roche Coll; Accounting.

MIKE, DAVID; Aliquippa HS; Aliquippa, PA; (2); 25/150; Church Yth Grp; Drama Clb; French Clb; School Play; Var Bsktbl; L Ftbl; Hon Roll; Merit Awd Math Cncl 86; Bus.

MIKESELL, NICOLE; Punxsutawney HS; Rossiter, PA; (4); 127/247; Girl Scts; Varsity Clb; Variety Show; Cheerleading; Crs Cntry; Sftbl; Trk; IUP; Bus.

MIKITKA, JOHN; Bethelhem Catholic HS; Bethlehem, PA; (3); 4/220; Math Tm; Scholastic Bowl; SADD; School Musical; School Play; Stage Crew; High Hon Roll; Jr NHS; VP NHS; Ntl Merit Ltr; Lehigh U; Engrng.

MIKLAVIC, JEFF; South Fayette HS; Bridgeville, PA; (4); 5/71; VP Band; Concert Band; Jazz Band; Mrchg Band; High Hon Roll; Hon Roll; NHS; Mid East Instrmntl Music Conf 85-87; PA ST U; Psych.

MIKLAVIC, MELISSA; Seneca Valley SR HS; Mars, PA; (3); Art Clb; Color Guard; Yrbk Stf; Hon Roll; Bus.

MIKLOS, PETER; Lancaster Catholic HS; Bainbridge, PA; (3); Boys Clb Am; Church Yth Grp; Varsity Clb; Im Bsktbl; L Ftbl; JV Trk; Var Wt Lftg; Bus.

MIKOLENKO, YURI; Northeast HS; Philadelphia, PA; (3); 1/370; Chess Clb; Computer Clb; Library Aide; Political Wkr; French Hon Soc; High Hon Roll; Hon Roll; White Williams Fndtn Schlrshp 85-87; Penn ST U; Banking.

MIKOLIC, CAROLYN; Greater Johnstown HS; Johnstown, PA; (3); Art Clb; Church Yth Grp; Key Clb; Church Choir; Color Guard; Yrbk Stf; Rep Jr Cls; Pres Physcl Ftnss Awd 86-87; Accntng.

MIKOVCH, ERIC; Northwestern HS; Cranesville, PA; (4); 2/165; Model UN; Madrigals; Stu Cncl; Bsbl; Var Capt Bsktbl; Var Capt Ftbl; High Hon Roll; Rotary Awd; Sal; SAR Awd; All Cnty Qrtrbck Erie Cnty Lg 86; 2nd Tm All Cnty Bsktbll Erie Cnty Lg 86; MVP Ftbll 86; Ivy League U; Lawyer.

MIKULA, ERIC; Altoona Area HS; Altoona, PA; (4); German Clb; Yrbk Phtg; Yrbk Stf; Rep Frsh Cls; Im Bsktbl; JV Crs Cntry; JV VP Ftbl; JV Trk; Im Vllybl; High Hon Roll; WV U; Chem Engrng.

MIKULA, KEITH; Altoona Area HS; Altoona, PA; (3); Church Yth Grp; Political Wkr; Band; Concert Band; Mrchg Band; Pep Band; Variety Show; Hon Roll; Prfct Atten Awd; IN U-Penna; Math.

MIKULA, MICHAEL; Aliquippa HS; Aliquippa, PA; (2); Band; Concert Band; Mrchg Band; Pep Band; High Hon Roll; Hon Roll.

MIKULAK JR, MICHAEL; Carbondale Area JR SR HS; Carbondale, PA; (3); French Clb; Ski Clb; Trk; Wt Lftg.

MIKULAK, ROSHELLE; West Scranton HS; Scranton, PA; (2); Cheerleading; Tennis; Hon Roll; NHS; Child Dvlpmnt.

MIKULKA, MILISSA; Tunkhannock Area HS; Tunkhannock, PA; (3); Church Yth Grp; Letterman Clb; Spanish Clb; SADD; Score Keeper; Var L Trk; Var Stat Vllybl; Cmptr Sci.

MIKULSKI, LISA; Christian Acad; Aston, PA; (3); Chorus; Church Choir; School Play; Lit Mag; Stu Cncl; Fld Hcky; Hon Roll.

MILAN, JENNIFER K; Hempfield Area HS; Greensburg, PA; (2); Chess Clb; Pres Church Yth Grp; Computer Clb; Library Aide; Spanish Clb; School Play; High Hon Roll; Hon Roll; Jr NHS; Lion Awd; Pres Acad Ftnss 86; Corp Law.

MILANKOW, BARBARA; Susquehannck HS; New Freedom, PA; (2); 14/243; Sec Trs Church Yth Grp; Hon Roll; NHS; Frnch Acadc Awd 87; Vet.

MILANO, JEFFREY C; Arch Bishop Ryan H S For Boys; Philadelphia, PA; (3); 36/419; High Hon Roll; Hon Roll; Engl I Outstndng Achvmnt Awd 84-85; Wstrn Cvlztnb Outstndng Achvt Awd 84-85; Mdrn Wrld Outstndng Achvt; Stmfltrs Loc Union #2.

MILARSKY, MELISSA; Lincoln HS; Philadelphia, PA; (3); 227/500; Red Cross Aide; Rep Jr Cls; Swmmng; Tennis; Hon Roll; Temple U.

MILAZZO, CHARLES; Wyoming Area HS; West Wyoming, PA; (3); French Clb; Key Clb; Ski Clb; Ftbl; Trk; Wt Lftg; Hon Roll; Wilkes Coll; Phrmctcl Chem.

MILAZZO II, JOSEPH S; Blairsville SR HS; Blairsville, PA; (3); 3/109; Chess Clb; Computer Clb; Var Crs Cntry; Var Trk; High Hon Roll; NHS; Ntl Merit Ltr; French Clb; Bsktbl; Socr; Pttsbrgh Post-Gazette Rndtbl Wrtr; 1st Awd ST Compttn PA JR Acad Sci; Pttsbrgh Wrld Affrs Cncl Delg; Comp Engrng.

MILBOURNE, KAREN E; Agnes Irwin Schl; Strafford, PA; (3); Art Clb; Church Yth Grp; Cmnty Wkr; Debate Tm; Hosp Aide; Model UN; Political Wkr; SADD; Teachers Aide; Nwsp Stf; Natl Frnch Cont 84; PA Math Cont 85; All AP & Hnrs Courses; Psych.

MILDREW, MICHELLE; Elk County Christian HS; St Marys, PA; (2); 1/90; Hosp Aide; SADD; Church Choir; Color Guard; Concert Band; Nwsp Rptr; Off Stu Cncl; Var JV Cheerleading; High Hon Roll; NEDT Awd; Fine Arts.

MILES, AMY; Archbishop Ryan-Girls HS; Philadelphia, PA; (3); 9/512; Church Yth Grp; Science Clb; Service Clb; Spanish Clb; Concert Band; Mrchg Band; Pep Band; High Hon Roll; NHS; Prfct Atten Awd; Engl Awd 86; Hstry Awd 86; Hnbl Mntn Engl 85; Schlr Mnth Awd 86.

MILES, BRANDON; Chestnut Ridge SR HS; New Paris, PA; (3); Aud/Vis; SADD; Ftbl; Wt Lftg; Hon Roll; Prfct Atten Awd; Penn ST; Arch.

MILES, CHRISTIAN; West Scranton HS; Scranton, PA; (2); 14/350; Boys Clb Am; Bsktbl; Crs Cntry; Trk; Wrstlng; High Hon Roll; Jr NHS; Bys Clb Yth Yr Pgm 87; Hmntrn Awd Rotary Ldrshp Cmp 87; MI U; Pre Med.

MILES, CRYSTAL; Quaker Valley HS; Leetsdale, PA; (2); Church Yth Grp; Spanish Clb; Chorus; Hon Roll; Schlstc Achvt Awd 85-86; Christian Coll; Psych.

MILES, DONALD; United HS; Blairsville, PA; (3); Aud/Vis; Camera Clb; Church Yth Grp; Drama Clb; French Clb; Ski Clb; Chorus; School Play; Stage Crew; Off Stu Cncl; IN U Mntrshp 85-86; Prncpls Advsry Comm 86-87.

MILES, JOHN R; York Catholic HS; York, PA; (3); 24/154; Debate Tm; Hosp Aide; Nwsp Sprt Ed; Rep Frsh Cls; Var Capt Crs Cntry; Var L Trk; High Hon Roll; Hon Roll; Boy Scts; Church Yth Grp; All Cnty, 13th Dist, 38th St Cross Cntry Tm Champ 85-86; All Cnty, 9th Dist, 29th St Crss Cntry 86-87.

MILES, RICH; Bellefonte Area SR HS; Bellefonte, PA; (3); Boy Scts; Im Vllybl; Hon Roll.

MILES, RICK; Cowansque HS; Westfield, PA; (4); 30/85; French Clb; FFA; Chorus; School Musical; School Play; Yrbk Phtg; Ftbl; Trk; Wrstlng; Hon Roll; FFA Chptr Sls & Svc Prfcncy Awd 87; ST Ptrl.

MILEY, JEFF; Carbondale Area HS; Carbondale, PA; (3); 14/119; FBLA; Trs German Clb; JA; Ski Clb; Band; High Hon Roll; Hon Roll; Trs Soph Cls; Pres Jr Cls; Pres Physcl Ftnss Awd 86; Avation.

MILIER, MICHELE; Holy Name HS; Wyomissing, PA; (3); 5/119; French Clb; Pep Clb; Nwsp Rptr; Bsktbl; Bowling; Fld Hcky; Sftbl; Hon Roll; NHS; All Div Sftbl-Outfldr 87; V Lttr Wnnr-Bsktbl, Sftbl, Hcky 84-87; Latn & Frnch Awd-Hghst Avg 87 & 86.

MILINOVICH, JIM; Waynesburg Central HS; Waynesburg, PA; (3); Boy Scts; Church Yth Grp; French Clb; Pres Band; Pres Concert Band; Pres Jazz Band; Pres Mrchg Band; Hon Roll; NHS; Duquesne U; Law.

MILIOS, HELEN; Upper Darby HS; Upper Darby, PA; (4); 142/590; Dance Clb; JA; Library Aide; Office Aide; Yrbk Bus Mgr; Yrbk Stf; Rep Sr Cls; Rep Stu Cncl; Hon Roll; Distngsh Hnr Rll 87; Hnr Rll 86-87; Drexel U; Accntng.

MILISAVIC, BONNIE; Cedar Cliff HS; Camp Hill, PA; (3); 89/320; French Clb; GAA; Girl Scts; Ski Clb; Nwsp Rptr; Nwsp Stf; Stu Cncl; Var L Sftbl; Var Trk; Var Vllybl; Publc Svcs.

MILITO, ERIK; Highlands HS; Natrona, PA; (3); 20/303; VP Sr Cls; Rep Stu Cncl; Var Ftbl; Var Tennis; High Hon Roll; Pres NHS; Prfct Atten Awd; Rotary Awd; Sci Olympd Awds 87; Notre Dame.

MILKE, DANA; Cumberland Valley HS; Mechanicsburg, PA; (4); 186/540; Girl Scts; Key Clb; Ski Clb; Band; Nwsp Ed-Chief; Nwsp Rptr; Nwsp Stf; Ed Lit Mag; Sec Soph Cls; Rep Jr Cls; Natl Hnr Quill & Scroll For Outstndng Achvts Schl Nwsppr & Pblctns 87; Rosemont Coll; Bus Mgmt.

MILKENT, HEATHER; Belle Vernon Area HS; Belle Vernon, PA; (4); 65/270; Ski Clb; Band; Mrchg Band; Yrbk Stf; Powder Puff Ftbl; L Swmmng; Hon Roll; Washington & Jefferson.

MILKO, GINA; Northern Cambria HS; Barnesboro, PA; (2); 2/144; Civic Clb; French Clb; Band; Concert Band; Mrchg Band; Pep Band; Variety Show; High Hon Roll; Penn ST U; Physics.

MILKOVICH, AMY; Westmont Hilltop HS; Johnstown, PA; (4); 12/160; Sec Y-Teens; Capt Color Guard; Concert Band; Jazz Band; Orch; NHS; Pres Schlr; Rotary Awd; Westmnt Hilltp Band Bstrs Awd 87; Dist 6 & Rgn 3 Band 87; U Pittsburgh Johnstown; Psych.

MILLAR, ROBERT; Danville Area HS; Riverside, PA; (3); JV Bsbl; Var Bsktbl; Var L Ftbl; Var Trk.

MILLER, ABIGAIL; Southern Lehigh HS; Emmaus, PA; (4); 3/221; Office Aide; Pres Varsity Clb; Yrbk Sprt Ed; Rep Jr Cls; Var Tennis; Jr NHS; NHS; Ntl Sci Mrt Awd Wnnr 87; PA ST U; Arch.

MILLER, ALAN; Pennsbury HS; Yardley, PA; (2); Band; Concert Band; Jazz Band; Mrchg Band; Pep Band; Rep Stu Cncl; Im Bowling; Im Vllybl; High Hon Roll; Straight A In Geom, Bio & German III 86 & 87; Best Trombone Awds Pennsbury Concert Jazz Band 87.

MILLER, ALLY-KAREN D; Oil City Area SR HS; Cooperstown, PA; (3); AFS; CAP; German Clb; Girl Scts; Political Wkr; Sec Concert Band; Cit Awd; Church Yth Grp; Cmnty Wkr; Computer Clb; Grl Sct Gld Awd, SR Ldrshp Dev 87; PAGE-PA Gftd Ed Pgm 79-87; Natl Grl Sct Cnvtndelg Frm PA 87; Allegheny Coll; Med.

MILLER, AMY; Boyertown SR HS; Boyertown, PA; (3); Church Yth Grp; Chorus; Variety Show; Fshn Merch.

MILLER, AMY; Catasauqua HS; Catasauqua, PA; (2); 3/160; SADD; Rep Frsh Cls; Stu Cncl; JV Bsktbl; JV Fld Hcky; JV Sftbl; Hon Roll.

MILLER, AMY JO; Northern Bedford County HS; Everett, PA; (3); Trs 4-H; Trs 4-H; SADD; Band; Chorus; Church Choir; Cheerleading; Score Keeper; 4-H Awd; Hon Roll; Dentl Hyg.

MILLER, ANDREA; Pequea Valley HS; Paradise, PA; (3); 12/144; Drama Clb; Varsity Clb; Capt Drill Tm; Var Fld Hcky; High Hon Roll; Hon Roll; NHS; AFS; GAA; Chorus; Stu Of Mnth Paradise Rtry Clb 87; Poetry Bk Pblshd 87; Comm.

MILLER, ANDREW; Lincoln HS; Ellwood City, PA; (4); 44/169; Church Yth Grp; Computer Clb; Drama Clb; Pres Key Clb; School Musical; Yrbk Stf; Stu Cncl; Tennis; Kiwanis Awd; Key Club Schlrshp 87; Clarion U; Bus Admin.

MILLER, ANDREW; William Penn SR HS; York, PA; (3); 81/462; JA; Orch; Socr; Mltry Plc.

MILLER, ANGELA; West Allegheny SR HS; Imperial, PA; (3); 29/196; VP Church Yth Grp; Teachers Aide; Band; Chorus; Jazz Band; Mrchg Band; Pep Band; High Hon Roll; Cmnty Wkr; Girl Scts; Mid-E Msc Fest 84-87; Hnrs Bnd 84; Duquesne Univ; Msc Ed.

MILLER, ANGIE; Mahanoy Area HS; Mahanoy City, PA; (3); Am Leg Aux Girls St; Church Yth Grp; Drama Clb; FHA; Sec Spanish Clb; Flag Corp; School Play; Variety Show; Nwsp Stf; Trk; West Chester U; Acctg.

MILLER, ANN; Pine Grove Area HS; Schuylkill Haven, PA; (4); 22/111; Chorus; Hon Roll; Prfct Atten Awd; Home Econ Awd 86; Bus.

MILLER, ANN; Stroudsburg HS; Stroudburg, PA; (2); Church Yth Grp; GAA; Varsity Clb; Stu Cncl; Var Gym; Var Score Keeper; JV Sftbl; Var Trk; Hon Roll.

MILLER, ANN MARIE; Williams Vly HS; Lykens, PA; (4); 16/100; Church Yth Grp; Teachers Aide; Chorus; School Musical; Yrbk Bus Mgr; Yrbk Ed-Chief; Yrbk Stf; Cheerleading; Ftbl; NHS; Marine Yth Phys Ftnss 86-87; Stu Mnth Rotry 87; Peer Educ Grp 85-87; Penn ST; Elem Ed.

MILLER, ANNETTE; Somerset Area HS; Friedens, PA; (4); VP JA; NFL; Q&S; Spanish Clb; Chorus; School Play; Capt Stu Cncl; Var L Trk; High Hon Roll; Hon Roll; IN U Of PA; Psychlgy.

MILLER, ARTHUR; Meyersdale Area HS; Meyersdale, PA; (3); Church Yth Grp; Math Tm; Church Choir; NHS; Comp Tech.

MILLER, BARB; Bethel Christian Schl; Erie, PA; (4); 2/12; Church Yth Grp; Drama Clb; Band; Chorus; Church Choir; Concert Band; School Musical; School Play; Stage Crew; Variety Show; Bst Actrss Awd 84 & 86; Bst Supprtng Actrss 85; Bob Jones U; Broadcasting.

MILLER, BETH; Donegal HS; Columbia, PA; (2); Church Yth Grp; Varsity Clb; Band; Chorus; Concert Band; Jazz Band; Mrchg Band; Tennis; Hon Roll; Spanish NHS.

MILLER, BETH; Kiski Area HS; New Kensington, PA; (3); Church Yth Grp; Spanish Clb; Church Choir; Concert Band; Yrbk Stf; Stu Cncl; Cheerleading; Swmmng; High Hon Roll; Hon Roll; Shop Clb 84-85; Top Ten 84-85; Penn ST; Acctg.

MILLER, BOBBIJO; Elizabeth Forward HS; Mckeesport, PA; (3); 28/332; French Clb; Pep Clb; Trs Jr Cls; Var L Bsktbl; Capt L Crs Cntry; Var L Trk; Wt Lftg; High Hon Roll; Hon Roll; Prfct Atten Awd; Golden Poet Awd 85; Silver Poet Awd 86; Jrnlsm.

MILLER, BRAD; Altoona HS; Altoona, PA; (3); VICA; Ftbl; Wrstlng; Lock Haven U; Gm Wrdn.

MILLER, BRADLEY; Wilmington Area HS; Edinburg, PA; (3); 5/115; Pres Church Yth Grp; Computer Clb; Rptr 4-H; Nwsp Rptr; Vllybl; 4-H Awd; High Hon Roll; Hon Roll; Achvt Awd 84; PA ST Sun Sch Assn Poetry Wnnr 83.

MILLER, BRANDON; Halifax Area HS; Halifax, PA; (2); FFA; Varsity Clb; Lit Mag; Rep Frsh Cls; VP Soph Cls; JV Ftbl; Wt Lftg; Var Wrstlng; Hon Roll; Kiwanis Awd; Bus.

MILLER, BRIAN; Greater Johnstown Voc-Tech Schl; Portage, PA; (3); 24/365; Art Clb; Church Yth Grp; Computer Clb; Debate Tm; VP JA; Key Clb; Nwsp Stf; Im Bsktbl; Im Ftbl; Hon Roll; Ntl Yth Marine Ftnss Awd, Vctnl-Tech Achvt Awd & Awd Of Emplyblty 85-86 & 86-87; Penn ST.

MILLER, BRIAN; Lincoln HS; Ellwood City, PA; (3); VP Drama Clb; French Clb; German Clb; SADD; School Play; Rep Stu Cncl; Socr; Let In Drama 85-87; Let In Stu Cncl 86-87; Theater.

MILLER, BRIAN; Moon Area SR HS; Glenwillard, PA; (3); 83/304; Band; Concert Band; Mrchg Band; Hon Roll; Chem.

MILLER, BRIAN; Muhlenberg HS; Reading, PA; (3); Computer Clb; Debate Tm; Pres Model UN; Chorus; Concert Band; Drm Mjr(t); Jazz Band; Mrchg Band; School Play; Nwsp Rptr; Math Tchr.

MILLER, BRIAN; St Marys Area HS; Saint Marys, PA; (4); Capt Var Bsktbl; Capt Var Crs Cntry; Trk; IN U Of PA; Accntng.

MILLER, BUFFY; Cumberland Valley HS; Mechanicsburg, PA; (3); 194/578; German Clb; Pre Dntstry.

MILLER, CAMELA; Central Dauphin East HS; Dauphin, PA; (4); 34/237; Nwsp Ed-Chief; Crs Cntry; Diving; Trk; Hon Roll; NHS; Band; Chorus; Swmmng; People-People HS Ambssdr Pgm 86; Athltc Schlrshp X-Cntry Amrcn U 87; Amrcn Wmns Bus Assn Schlrshp 87; The American U; Cmmnctns.

MILLER, CARL; Jeannette SR HS; Jeannette, PA; (3); Am Leg Boys St; Spanish Clb; Band; Concert Band; Jazz Band; Mrchg Band; Var L Bsbl; Var Golf; Hon Roll; Accntng.

MILLER, CAROL; Cedar Grove Christian Acad; Philadelphia, PA; (4); 1/44; Church Yth Grp; JA; Chorus; High Hon Roll; NHS; Prfct Atten Awd; Val; Acctng, Shrthnd, Ofc Prctc & Spch Excel Awds 87; BEAP 3rd Acctng II 87; Bst Of Cls 87; Exec Sec.

MILLER, CAROLINE; Upper Moreland HS; Willow Grove, PA; (3); Church Yth Grp; Trs Key Clb; SADD; Var Bsktbl; Var Trk; High Hon Roll; NHS; Frgn Lang Pgm Scholar Ursinus Coll 87; Fit Awd 87; Biol.

MILLER, CARRIE; Christian Schl Of York; Thomasville, PA; (2); 11/68; Sec Church Yth Grp; Church Choir; Fld Hcky; Sftbl; JA; Library Aide; Spanish Clb; Chorus; Score Keeper; High Hon Roll; Geneva; Spch Pathlgy.

MILLER, CHAD; Louis E Dieruff HS; Allentown, PA; (3); ROTC; Varsity Clb; Var JV Bsbl; Var JV Ftbl; Var JV Wt Lftg; Hon Roll; Dstrct XI Bsbl W/Dvsn Chmps 87; Physcl Thrpst.

MILLER, CHRIS; West Greene HS; Sycamore, PA; (2); Ski Clb; Band; Chorus; Color Guard; Yrbk Stf; Mgr Sftbl; Trk; Hon Roll; Spllng Bee Awd 86; Duffs; Acct.

MILLER, CHRISTINE; Frankford HS; Philadelphia, PA; (3); #19 In Class; JV Bsktbl; Var L Cheerleading; Var Coach Actv; JV Var Fld Hcky; Var Vllybl; Hon Roll; Schlrshp Awd; Jefferson U; Nrsng.

MILLER, CHRISTINE E; Altoona Area HS; Altoona, PA; (4); 6/718; VP Sec Chess Clb; Pres Sec Church Yth Grp; Spanish Clb; Var Capt Swmmng; Bausch & Lomb Sci Awd; NHS; Pres Schlr; Math Clb; Math Tm; Chorus; Judy Patt Schlr/Athl Mem Schlrshp 87; Rensselaer Awd 86; Susan Heaton Mem Schlrshp 87; Millersville U; Bio-Chem.

MILLER, CHRISTINE E; North Pocono HS; Moscow, PA; (3); 12/250; Church Yth Grp; Drama Clb; FBLA; JA; Varsity Clb; Flag Corp; Rep Frsh Cls; High Hon Roll; NHS; Ms PA Co-Ed Pgnt St Spch Wnr 87; Diploma Awd Barbizon Mdlng Schl 87; Prin List 85; Am Coll Applied Arts; Intr Dsgn.

MILLER, CHRISTOPHER; Emmaus HS; Allentown, PA; (3); 17/548; Spanish Clb; Var L Bsbl; High Hon Roll; Hon Roll; Jr NHS; NHS; Prfct Atten Awd; Comp Sci.

MILLER, CHRISTOPHER ALLAN; West Mifflin Area HS; West Mifflin, PA; (4); Key Clb; VP Ski Clb; Varsity Clb; Bsbl; Coach Actv; Var Ftbl; Var Capt Socr; Sftbl; Var Wrstlng; Hon Roll; MVP Soccer Tm 87; U S Army Class Of 87-Most Valuble Soccr Plyr 87.

MILLER, CHRISTY; Peters Township HS; Washington, PA; (4); Church Yth Grp; Cmnty Wkr; Teachers Aide; Nwsp Bus Mgr; Nwsp Phtg; Nwsp Rptr; Nwsp Stf; Yrbk Phtg; Yrbk Stf; Stu Cncl; Mcmurray Rotary Clb Chld Dvlpmnt Tchng Awd 86-87; Kent ST U; Elem Ed.

MILLER, CHRITIAN; Bansor Area HS; Bangor, PA; (3); Boy Scts; Chess Clb; Library Aide; Varsity Clb; Im Bsbl; JV Var Bsktbl; Hon Roll; Hnr Roll 86; MIP Bsktbl 87; Lbrl Arts.

MILLER, CINDY; Calvary Baptist Christian Schl; Reinholds, PA; (4); Church Yth Grp; Quiz Bowl; Band; Chorus; School Musical; School Play; Var L Bsktbl; Var L Cheerleading; Var L Vllybl; High Hon Roll; Maronatha Baptist; Secndry Mth.

MILLER, CORY; Lehighton Area SR HS; Lehighton, PA; (3); 32/234; Boys Clb Am; Boy Scts; Chess Clb; Church Yth Grp; Debate Tm; Scholastic Bowl; Stage Crew; Hon Roll; PA ST; Lawyer.

MILLER, CRAIG; Mohawk Area HS; Wampum, PA; (3); Church Yth Grp; French Clb; Varsity Clb; Var Bsbl; Var Bsktbl; Var Ftbl; Powder Puff Ftbl; Hon Roll; Hon Roll Awd 86-87; IUP.

MILLER, CURTIS; Exeter HS; Reading, PA; (3); Aud/Vis; Camera Clb; Key Clb; Band; Concert Band; Mrchg Band; School Musical; School Play; Stage Crew; Jr NHS; Elec Engr.

MILLER, CYNTHIA; Seneca HS; Erie, PA; (3); 5/166; Drama Clb; Q&S; High Hon Roll; NHS; PA Soc Of Professional Engrs Cert Of Merit & Academic All-Amer 86; JETS Academic Games Cmptn 87; English.

MILLER, DALE; Aliu Vippa JR SR HS; Aliquippa, PA; (4); VICA; High Hon Roll; Hon Roll; NHS; U S Navy; Aviation Mech.

MILLER, DANA; Liberty JR SR HS; Liberty, PA; (4); 6/45; German Clb; Chorus; School Musical; Rep Stu Cncl; Stat Bsktbl; Var Cheerleading; Cit Awd; Hon Roll; NHS; PTO Schlrshp 87; Grad Hnrs 87; Lycoming Coll; Mass Cmmnctns.

MILLER, DANELLE; Villa Maria Acad; Erie, PA; (3); 10/168; Church Yth Grp; Drama Clb; PAVAS; SADD; Thesps; Church Choir; School Musical; School Play; Variety Show; Var Cheerleading; Theresa Burns Schlrshp 84-85.

MILLER, DANIEL W; John Harris Campus; Harrisburg, PA; (1); ROTC.

MILLER, DARYL; Hershey SR HS; Hummelstown, PA; (3); Band; Chorus; Jazz Band; Mrchg Band; Orch; School Musical; School Play; Stage Crew; High Hon Roll; PA All ST Lions Band 87; Amer Music Abrd 86; Engrng.

MILLER, DAVID; Leechburg Area HS; Leechburg, PA; (3); Math Tm; Yrbk Phtg; High Hon Roll; Hon Roll; NHS; Elec Engrng.

MILLER, DAVID; Pen Argyl Area HS; Wind Gap, PA; (3); 60/160; Leo Clb; Concert Band; Mrchg Band; Squad Of Yr 87; Intl Rltns.

MILLER, DAVID; The Hill Schl; Chester Spg, PA; (3); Drama Clb; English Clb; Latin Clb; Ski Clb; Sec Spanish Clb; Varsity Clb; Lit Mag; Var Bsktbl; JV Tennis; High Hon Roll; Literature.

MILLER, DEANNA; Forest Hills SR HS; South Fork, PA; (3); 9/170; Pep Clb; Ski Clb; Chorus; Im Sftbl; L Trk; L Vllybl; Grls Athltcs Awd 84-85; Penn ST U.

MILLER, DEBBIE; Springdale HS; Cheswick, PA; (3); 19/128; Pres FBLA; VP JA; Teachers Aide; Band; Chorus; Madrigals; Mrchg Band; Sftbl; Hon Roll; Prfct Atten Awd; Outstndng Achvt Awds-Bus Math, Typing II, Trnscptn 86-87; Ms FBLA Trphy 86-87; Exec Wmn Intl Pgm; Saddelback Coll; Exec Sec.

MILLER, DENISE; Chestnut Ridge HS; New Paris, PA; (4); 11/137; Church Yth Grp; SADD; Band; Sec Frsh Cls; Sec Soph Cls; Sec Sr Cls; Rep Stu Cncl; JV Var Sftbl; JV Var Vllybl; Dnfth Awd; Chestnut Ridge Alumni Schlrshp 87; Bedford Hosp Med Schlrshp 87; CA U Of PA; Med Tech.

MILLER, DIANE; Danville HS; Danville, PA; (2); Drama Clb; Hosp Aide; Concert Band; Jazz Band; Mrchg Band; NEDT Awd; Pres Acadc Ftnss Awd 86.

MILLER, DIANE; Greensburg Central Catholic HS; Jeannette, PA; (3); 32/231; AFS; Sec Art Clb; Church Yth Grp; JCL; NFL; High Hon Roll; NHS; Arch.

MILLER, DONNA; Cambridge Sprionga HS; Saegertown, PA; (4); 13/103; Trs Church Yth Grp; VP 4-H; Trs Chorus; Mrchg Band; Yrbk Stf; Sec Jr Cls; Stu Cncl; Pom Pon; 4-H Awd; Hon Roll; Crawford Co Vo-Tech; Med Sec.

MILLER, DONNA; Nazareth Area SR HS; Bethlehem, PA; (3); Church Yth Grp; Computer Clb; French Clb; Chorus; Church Choir; Swing Chorus; Rep Stu Cncl; Var L Fld Hcky; Var L Sftbl; Hon Roll; Microbio.

MILLER, DONNA; University City HS; Philadelphia, PA; (3); Debate Tm; Girl Scts; Teachers Aide; Chorus; School Play; Trk; Cit Awd; Hon Roll; Prfct Atten Awd; Spanish NHS; Villanova; Comp Engr.

MILLER, DOUGLAS; Somerset Area SR HS; Somerset, PA; (3); English Clb; French Clb; JA; Varsity Clb; Stu Cncl; Bsbl; Bsktbl; Tennis; Physcl Thrpy.

MILLER, ED; Connellsville Area HS; Connellsville, PA; (2); Church Yth Grp; Chorus; Stage Crew; Swmmng; Trk; Hon Roll.

MILLER, ELAINE; Big Spring HS; Carlisle, PA; (3); Pres Church Yth Grp; Var Sftbl; Var JV Vllybl; Outstndng Sprtsmnshp Awd-Sftbll 87.

MILLER, ELISABETH; Harriton HS; Villanova, PA; (3); Cmnty Wkr; Pep Clb; Pres Service Clb; SADD; Yrbk Stf; Co-Capt Cheerleading; Var L Trk; Hon Roll; NHS; Prfct Atten Awd; Principals Awd; Wellesley Book; Pres Phy Ftns Awd.

MILLER, ELIZABETH; Hollidaysburg Area SR HS; Duncansville, PA; (3); 10/385; Latin Clb; Band; Chorus; Church Choir; School Musical; Hon Roll; Prfct Atten Awd; Concert Band; Mrchg Band; Acadmc Achvt Awd 86; Penn ST U; Elem Tchr.

MILLER, ERIC; Avon Grove HS; Lincoln Univ, PA; (3); VP FTA; SADD; School Play; Ed Yrbk Phtg; Hst Jr Cls; Hst Sr Cls; Tennis; Hon Roll; NHS; Prfct Atten Awd; Outstndng Stu Awd Avon Grove Yth Ed Assn 85.

MILLER, FRANK; Dover Area HS; Dover, PA; (3); 10/300; Hosp Aide; Rep Jr Cls; Rep Stu Cncl; Tennis; Hon Roll; NHS; Gftd Mnrs Prog; Engrng.

MILLER, FRANK PATRICK; Sto-Rox SR HS; Mckees Rocks, PA; (3); Boys Clb Am; VP Trk; High Hon Roll; Hon Roll.

MILLER, FRED; Tyrone Area HS; Tyrone, PA; (3); Am Leg Boys St; VP Key Clb; Pres Science Clb; Yrbk Rptr; JV Var Bsktbl; Im Vllybl; High Hon Roll; NHS; Pres Clssrm 87; Bus.

MILLER, GAIL; Tunkhannock HS; Dalton, PA; (2); Art Clb; Church Yth Grp; Spanish Clb; SADD; JV Vllybl; Hon Roll.

MILLER JR, GARY A; Williamsburg HS; Williamsburg, PA; (4); 3/68; Boy Scts; Church Yth Grp; Exploring; Ed Nwsp Rptr; Yrbk Stf; Stat Bsktbl; Mgr(s); High Hon Roll; NHS; Pres Schlr; Religious Scouting Awd, David L Gutshell Soc Stud Awd, Am Leg Aux Essay Awd 87; Penn ST.

MILLER, GERALD; Conemaugh Township Area HS; Hollsopple, PA; (3); 16/120; Cmnty Wkr; Pres Sr Cls; Rep Stu Cncl; Var Ftbl; Var Trk; Im Wt Lftg; Var L Wrstlng; Hon Roll; All-Cnty Ftbll-1st Tm 85-86; USKF Rgnl Ntl Freestyle Wrstng Champ 86; USKF Grnd Natl Freestyle 86; Cvl Eng.

MILLER, GINA; Mon Valley Catholic HS; Charleroi, PA; (3); Rptr Church Yth Grp; Ski Clb; Chorus; Sec Church Choir; School Musical; School Play; Nwsp Stf; JV Cheerleading; French Hon Soc; Hon Roll; Dstrct 2 Hnrs Choir 86; Phys Ther.

MILLER, GINGER; Council Rock HS; Richboro, PA; (2); SE Assembley Of God; Yth Pstr.

MILLER, GREGORY; Jeannette SR HS; Jeannette, PA; (4); Pres Church Yth Grp; Pres Computer Clb; Math Tm; Science Clb; Bausch & Lomb Sci Awd; High Hon Roll; NHS; NEDT Awd; Pres Schlr; Rotary Awd; Royal Rangers Gold Medal Of Achvt 87; Natl Sci Fair Cmptn 86; U Of Pittsburgh; Engr.

MILLER, GUS; West Mifflin Area HS; West Mifflin, PA; (2); Pres Aud/Vis; Pres Chess Clb; German Clb; Concert Band; Jazz Band; Mrchg Band; Orch; Stage Crew; High Hon Roll; Hon Roll; Outstndng Chess 85-86; U Of Pittsburgh; Engl.

MILLER, GWENYTH; Penn Hills HS; Pittsburgh, PA; (3); German Clb; Office Aide; Band; Off Stu Cncl; Hon Roll; Mellon U; Intr Dcrtr.

MILLER, H ERIC; St Pius X HS; Pottstown, PA; (1); 77/146; SADD; Bsktbl; Socr; Tennis; Penn ST; Forstry.

MILLER, H JERROLD; Methacton HS; Trooper, PA; (3); 61/381; Boy Scts; Band; Chorus; Jazz Band; Mrchg Band; School Musical; Rep Jr Cls; Var Socr; JV Tennis; JV Trk; Chem Sci Olympd Awd 86-87.

MILLER, HEATHER; Central HS; Martinsburg, PA; (4); 32/190; Church Yth Grp; FCA; Ski Clb; Varsity Clb; Acpl Chr; Chorus; Trs Jr Cls; Stu Cncl; Capt Cheerleading; Wt Lftg; Bus & Prfssnl Wmns Clb Grl Mnth 87; Past Grnd Chrty Intl Order Rnbw Grls 86-87; Juniata Coll; Pre Med.

MILLER, HEATHER A; Whitehall-Coplay HS; Coplay, PA; (3); 155/300; Am Leg Aux Girls St; Leo Clb; Bsktbl; Cit Awd; Voice Dem Awd; Phys Thrpst.

MILLER, HOLLY; New Oxford HS; New Oxford, PA; (2); Sec FFA; PA ST; Vet.

MILLER, HOLLY; Tulpehocken HS; Bethel, PA; (4); 12/119; Sec Church Yth Grp; Spanish Clb; Teachers Aide; Variety Show; Hnr Rl Awd 86; Stu Recgntn Schlr Awd 86.

MILLER, HOWARD; Parkland SR HS; Allentown, PA; (2); Art Clb; Computer Clb.

MILLER, J DOUGLAS; York County Area Vo Tech; Felton, PA; (2); 11/413; SADD; VICA; Color Guard; Stage Crew; Hon Roll.

MILLER, JACQUELYNN ELINE; Freedom SR HS; Bethlehem, PA; (3); 183/486; Church Yth Grp; 4-H; Band; Church Choir; 4-H Awd; Hon Roll; Mrchg Band; Orch; Yng Peopls Phlhrmnc-Lhigh Vly 85-88; Hstrc Bthlhm Inc 85-87; Tchr-Violin 86-88; Bloomsburg ST U; Math.

MILLER, JAMES; Aliquippa SR HS; Aliquippa, PA; (2); Computer Clb; Band; Concert Band; Drm Mjr(t); Jazz Band; Mrchg Band; Pep Band; Nwsp Rptr; Hon Roll; Arch.

MILLER, JAMES; Central Catholic HS; Pittsburgh, PA; (4); VP Sec JA; Im Ftbl; Im Ice Hcky; Hon Roll; Juniata Coll; Bus.

MILLER, JAMES; Cumberland Valley HS; Mechanicsburg, PA; (4); 46/519; Ski Clb; Church Choir; Concert Band; Orch; Symp Band; Var Crs Cntry; Var Trk; Hon Roll; NHS; NCTE Awd; Latin Cert Of Achvt 85-87; U Of Richmond.

MILLER II, JAMES W; Penn Manor HS; Lancaster, PA; (3); #98 In Class; Hon Roll; Indus Arts-Tech Educ Achvt Awd 86; Elec.

MILLER, JAMIE; North Star HS; Chattanooga, TN; (3); 1/132; Church Yth Grp; Math Tm; Var JV Ftbl; Cit Awd; Hon Roll; NHS; Sci & Soc Stds Awd 87; Prsdntl Physcl Ftnss Awd 85; Le Tourneau Coll; Mech Engnrng.

MILLER, JANELLE; Warwick HS; Lititz, PA; (2); 35/325; Girl Scts; Stu Cncl; JV Fld Hcky; High Hon Roll; Hon Roll; Curator.

MILLER, JANET; Ambridge Area HS; Ambridge, PA; (2); French Clb; Pep Clb; Band; Concert Band; Mrchg Band; Symp Band; Prfct Atten Awd; Slippery Rock U; Tchr.

MILLER, JANINE; Sharpsville HS; Sharpsville, PA; (3); 1/100; Chess Clb; Hosp Aide; Band; Concert Band; Mrchg Band; Pep Band; Nwsp Stf; Yrbk Stf; Hon Roll; NHS; Hugh O Brian Yth Fndtn Awd 86; JR All-Amer Hall Of Fame Band Hnrs 86; Acad Achvt Awd 85 & 86; Grove City Coll; Ed.

MILLER, JASON; Mechanicsburg Area SR HS; Mechanicsburg, PA; (4); 63/301; Quiz Bowl; Scholastic Bowl; Stage Crew; Im Bowling; High Hon Roll; Hon Roll; Jr NHS; NHS; Natl Def Cadet Corps 83-84; Albright Coll; Alpha Pgm.

MILLER, JASON; North Star HS; Chattanooga, TN; (2); 1/134; Church Yth Grp; Math Tm; Var JV Ftbl; Im Var Socr; Var Vllybl; Hon Roll; Presdntl Physcl Ftns Awd 85; Le Tourneau Coll; Avtn Technlgy.

MILLER, JASON J; Thomas Jefferson HS; Jefferson Boro, PA; (4); Boy Scts; Chess Clb; Cmnty Wkr; Computer Clb; Exploring; French Clb; Band; Concert Band; Jazz Band; Orch; Marine Bio.

MILLER, JAYSON; Red Lion Area SR HS; Red Lion, PA; (3); 57/342; Am Leg Boys St; Boy Scts; JA; Science Clb; Trs Jr Cls; Rep Stu Cncl; Hon Roll; York Cnty Envir-Olymp 1st Forestry 87; Civil Engr.

MILLER, JEANNE; Brandywine Heights HS; Topton, PA; (2); Hosp Aide; Chorus; Var Vllybl; Prfct Atten Awd; Retail Buyer.

MILLER, JEFF; Coatesville Area SR HS; Coatesville, PA; (3); 66/450; Capt Tennis; Hnr Roll 86-87.

MILLER, JEFF; Mechanicsburg HS; Grantham, PA; (2); 18/309; Church Yth Grp; Concert Band; JV Capt Socr; Var L Trk; Law.

MILLER, JEFFREY; Cedar Crest HS; Lebanon, PA; (4); 36/360; Crs Cntry; Ftbl; Trk; Hon Roll; Pres Schlr; Alcoa Foundtn Schlrshp 87; Penn ST U Main; Comp Sci.

MILLER, JEFFREY; Conrad Weiser HS; Wernersville, PA; (3); 49/189; Church Yth Grp; Chorus; Church Choir; Concert Band; Jazz Band; Mrchg Band; School Musical; Socr; Outstndng Rhythm Awd & Best Rythm Soloist-Jazz Fest 85 & 87; Music.

MILLER, JENNIFER; Abington SR HS; Rydal, PA; (3); 71/502; French Clb; Latin Clb; SADD; Yrbk Ed-Chief; Ed Yrbk Stf; Lcrss; NHS.

MILLER, JENNIFER; Cedar Crest HS; Lebanon, PA; (3); Church Yth Grp; French Clb; FBLA; FTA; Pep Clb; Teachers Aide; Bsktbl; Elem Educ.

MILLER, JENNIFER; Conneaut Lake HS; Durham, NC; (4); 24/80; Spanish Clb; SADD; Band; Concert Band; Mrchg Band; Mgr Ftbl; Mgr(s); Hon Roll.

MILLER, JENNIFER; Exeter HS; Reading, PA; (4); 9/215; Church Yth Grp; German Clb; Quiz Bowl; Teachers Aide; Band; Jazz Band; Orch; DAR Awd; High Hon Roll; NHS; Cnty Band 84-87; Dist Orch 86-87; Messiah Coll; Music Ed.

MILLER, JENNIFER; Lower Merion HS; Bala Cynwyd, PA; (3); VP Intnl Clb; Service Clb; Spanish Clb; SADD; Yrbk Stf; Off Jr Cls; Trk; Hon Roll; Rotary Awd; Spanish NHS.

MILLER, JENNIFER; Nativity B V M HS; Branchdale, PA; (3); 14/86; Art Clb; Flag Corp; Nwsp Stf; JV Bsktbl; Var Crs Cntry; Var Sftbl; Hon Roll; Drama Clb; Ski Clb; French II Highest Achvt Awd, Presidntl Phys Fitness Awd & Sci Fair Hnrbl Mntn 85-86; Arch.

MILLER, JENNIFER L; Dallastown HS; Seven Valleys, PA; (4); Hosp Aide; Chorus; School Musical; School Play; Rep Stu Cncl; Cheerleading; Trk; High Hon Roll; NHS; PA Gvrnrs Schl Arts Fnlst, Wnnr Stblt Sfty Pstr Cont 86; Stu Mnth 83; Temple U; Theatre.

MILLER, JILL; South Allegheny HS; Elizabeth, PA; (2); JA; School Musical; School Play; Gym; Swmmng; Hon Roll; Prfct Atten Awd; Marine Bio.

MILLER, JILL MARIE; Kennedy Christian HS; Grenville, PA; (2); 3/96; Drama Clb; German Clb; Ski Clb; Spanish Clb; Chorus; Church Choir; School Play; Var Trk; Im Mgr Vllybl; High Hon Roll; Engl.

MILLER, JO ELLEN; Pine Grove Area HS; Pine Grove, PA; (3); Off ROTC; SADD; Varsity Clb; Drill Tm; Yrbk Stf; Trs Stu Cncl; Var L Vllybl; Hon Roll; NHS; Prfct Atten Awd; Schlstc Achvt Awd, Hgh Achvt Awd Frnch, Engl, Socl Stds & Sci 86-87; Nrsng.

MILLER, JOCELYN; Conrad Weiser HS; Robesonia, PA; (3); 6/179; Church Yth Grp; Sec Pres 4-H; Sec Pres Key Clb; Teachers Aide; Chorus; School Musical; Yrbk Stf; Var Capt Fld Hcky; High Hon Roll; NHS; Penn ST.

MILLER, JODY; Eisenhower HS; Russell, PA; (3); 15/116; Key Clb; Office Aide; Spanish Clb; Chorus; Nwsp Stf; Yrbk Sprt Ed; Yrbk Stf; Trs Soph Cls; Rep Stu Cncl; Stat Bsktbl.

MILLER, JODY; Spring Grove Area SR HS; Spring Grove, PA; (3); 17/301; Pres Church Yth Grp; Acpl Chr; Church Choir; Madrigals; School Play; 4-H Awd; High Hon Roll; NHS; Elizabethtwn Hnrs Choir 87; Pres Acad Fit Awd 85; Music Ed.

MILLER, JOHN; Shaler Area HS; Allison Pk, PA; (4); 63/510; Church Yth Grp; Band; Mrchg Band; School Musical; Variety Show; Hon Roll; Pres Acdmc Fit Awd 87; Penn ST; Engrng.

MILLER III, JOHN; Hyndman Middle SR HS; Hyndman, PA; (3); Church Yth Grp; Spanish Clb; Varsity Clb; Var L Bsbl; High Hon Roll; Hon Roll; Sec Trs NHS; Ag.

MILLER JR, JOHN GREGG; The Haverford School; St Davids, PA; (3); 13/87; Rep Frsh Cls; Rep Soph Cls; Rep Jr Cls; Rep Stu Cncl; Var Ftbl; Var Lcrss; JV Wrstlng; Hon Roll; Cecil B Jarvis Awd; Wm G Warden II Mem Prize.

MILLER, JONATHAN; Williams Valley JR SR HS; Williamstown, PA; (1); Band; Chorus; Church Choir; Mrchg Band; Pep Band; School Musical; Symp Band; Yrbk Stf; Stu Cncl; Hon Roll; Bus Adm.

MILLER, JOSHUA ANDREW; Reading SR HS; Reading, PA; (3); 22/720; Chess Clb; Trs Debate Tm; German Clb; Trs Model UN; Var L Socr; Cit Awd; Hon Roll; NHS; Bowdoin; Law.

MILLER, JOSHUA J; Bermudian Springs HS; York Spgs, PA; (3); 4/126; Church Yth Grp; Chorus; Concert Band; Jazz Band; Madrigals; Mrchg Band; School Musical; High Hon Roll; Chess Clb; Acpl Chr; Marine Bio.

MILLER, JUDY; Chestnut Ridge HS; New Paris, PA; (3); Church Yth Grp; Teachers Aide; Band; Church Choir; Concert Band; Stu Cncl; Var Vllybl; Sec NHS; JV Bsktbl; JV Trk; Elem Ed.

MILLER, JULIE; Wilson Christian Acad; Mckeesport, PA; (3); 4/12; Art Clb; Church Yth Grp; School Play; Capt L Bsktbl; Im Socr; Capt Sftbl; Vllybl; Hon Roll; Prfct Atten Awd; CCAC.

MILLER, KAREN; Conemaugh Valley JR SR HS; Johnstown, PA; (4); Pep Clb; Varsity Clb; L Sftbl; High Hon Roll; NHS; Wm Salem Mem Schlrshp Awd 87; U Pittsburgh Johnstown; Chem.

MILLER, KAREN; Emmaus HS; Allentown, PA; (3); 61/518; JA; Latin Clb; Spanish Clb; Hon Roll; Jr NHS; NHS; Prfct Atten Awd; Pres Schlr.

MILLER, KAREN; Kennard-Dale HS; Stewartstown, PA; (2); 2/167; FNA; Hosp Aide; Chorus; High Hon Roll; Chorus Awd, & York Hosp JR Vol Awd 87; Sci.

MILLER, KAREN; Mechanicsburg SR HS; Mechanicsburg, PA; (4); Chorus; Mrchg Band; VP Orch; Symp Band; Yrbk Stf; High Hon Roll; Dist 7 Uppr PMEA Band 87; Cmbnd Intl Schlrshp; Cumberland Cnty Band 84-87; Chorus & Orchester 87; Penn ST U; Lbrl Arts.

MILLER, KAREN; Neshaminy HS; Penndel, PA; (4); 34/694; Aud/Vis; Trs Church Yth Grp; Sec Service Clb; SADD; Concert Band; Nwsp Bus Mgr; NHS; Prfct Atten Awd; Var Trk; Hon Roll; Girl Scout Gold Awd 87; Ed Assoc Bk Schlrshp 87; Outstndng Svc To Schl Awd 87; Syracuse U; Comm.

MILLER, KAREN; Schuylkill Valley HS; Shoemakersville, PA; (4); 5/130; Quiz Bowl; Scholastic Bowl; SADD; Chorus; Nwsp Ed-Chief; Nwsp Phtg; Yrbk Phtg; High Hon Roll; NHS; Ntl Merit Ltr; Ursinus Coll; Engl.

MILLER, KATHLEEN; Quigley HS; St Peters, MO; (4); French Clb; GAA; Girl Scts; Letterman Clb; Pep Clb; SADD; Varsity Clb; Chorus; Church Choir; Mgr Bsktbl; T J Fitzgerald Awd-Outstndng Wmn Athlt 86-87; MVP-VLYBL 86; MVP-SFTBL 87; Duquesne U; Sec Ed.

MILLER, KATHY; Keystone SR HS; Shippenville, PA; (3); Church Yth Grp; FBLA; Office Aide; Chorus; Rep Stu Cncl; Hon Roll; Prfct Atten Awd.

MILLER, KEITH; Tech Memorial HS; Erie, PA; (4); 78/324; Art Clb; Boy Scts; Yrbk Ed-Chief; Hon Roll; Eagle Scout Awd 87; Columbus Coll; Advstng.

MILLER, KEN; Bellefonte Area HS; Mingoville, PA; (3); Trs Jr Cls; Fld Hcky; Ice Hcky; Penn ST U; Auto.

MILLER, KENNEDY; North Hills SR HS; Pittsburgh, PA; (4); Pep Clb; Mrchg Band; Orch; Pep Band; Symp Band; High Hon Roll; NHS; Prfrmnc Mdls From Solo & Ensmbl Fstvl 84; Coll Of Wooster; Intl Bus.

MILLER, KENNETH; Conemaugh Township Area HS; Holsapple, PA; (4); 4/101; Pres Church Yth Grp; Drama Clb; Speech Tm; Band; Drm Mjr(t); Mrchg Band; School Musical; Hon Roll; NHS; Rotary Awd; Jerome PTO Schlrshp 87; Conemaugh Twp Band Schlrshp 87; U Of Pittsburgh; Engr.

MILLER, KENNETH; Jeannett SR HS; Jeannette, PA; (3); Am Leg Boys St; Spanish Clb; Band; Concert Band; Jazz Band; Mrchg Band; Var L Bsbl; Var Golf; Hon Roll; Accntng.

MILLER, KERRI; Scranton Technical HS; Scranton, PA; (4); FBLA; Letterman Clb; Pep Clb; Yrbk Stf; Stu Cncl; Capt Cheerleading; Wt Lftg; Capt Ftbl & Bsktbl Chrldng.

MILLER, KERRY L; John Harris Campus HS; Harrisburg, PA; (2); 41/356; Hon Roll; 2nd Honors 86-87; Bus.

MILLER, KEVIN; Conemaugh Valley HS; Johnstown, PA; (4); Computer Clb; Library Aide; Pep Clb; Service Clb; High Hon Roll; NHS; Rotary Awd; Conemaugh Valley Math Dept Awd 87; U Of Pittsburg; Chem Engr.

MILLER, KEVIN; West Catholic HS For Boys; Philadelphia, PA; (2); 45/248; Cmnty Wkr; Varsity Clb; Off Jr Cls; Stu Cncl; Ftbl; Wt Lftg; Lion Awd; Fine Coop & Prfct Cndct Awd, Advncd Plcmnt Sci & Math; Notre Dame; Med.

MILLER, KIM; Barmudian Springs HS; Idaville, PA; (3); 8/128; Chorus; Flag Corp; Madrigals; Mrchg Band; School Musical; School Play; Capt Cheerleading; L Mgr(s); Sec L Trk; Hon Roll.

MILLER, KIM; Marion Ctr; Shelocta, PA; (3); FHA; Hon Roll; IUP; Early Chldhd Ed.

MILLER, KIMBERLY; Northeastern HS; York Haven, PA; (3); Pep Clb; Chorus; Color Guard; Mrchg Band; Yrbk Stf; Trk; Hon Roll.

MILLER, KIMBERLY; Sacred Heart HS; Pittsburgh, PA; (4); 7/140; Cmnty Wkr; Drama Clb; Exploring; Math Clb; Science Clb; Stage Crew; High Hon Roll; NHS; Pres Schlr; Silver E Awd Ldrshp Exploring 87; Special Nalt Merit Schlrshp Consolidation Coal Company 87; Grove City Coll; Elect Engrngb.

MILLER, KIMM; Governor Mifflin HS; Mohnton, PA; (3); 42/326; Church Yth Grp; Var L Cheerleading; Coach Actv; Var L Diving; Var L Trk; Hon Roll; NHS; Pres Schlr; Art Clb; All Leag Dvng Cntrl PA Leag 85-87; All T Dvng 3rd Pl 87; All ST Hon Mntn Dvng 85.

MILLER, KRIS; Belle Vernon Area HS; Belle Vernon, PA; (3); FBLA; Band; Hon Roll; CA U PA; Accntng.

MILLER, KRISTA; Lancaster Mennonite HS; Willow St, PA; (3); 9/179; Pres Church Yth Grp; Girl Scts; Yrbk Phtg; High Hon Roll; Hon Roll; Comp Sci.

MILLER, KRISTEN; Northern Bedford County HS; Woodbury, PA; (3); Church Yth Grp; SADD; Varsity Clb; Chorus; School Musical; Yrbk Stf; Var Cheerleading; Var Socr; Var Trk; Hon Roll; Bedford Cnty Champ 100 & 200 M Dash 86; Outstndng Feml Athl Awd 86; Hgh Schl Outstndng Trck Awd 86; Sprts Med.

MILLER, KRISTEN; Sun Valley HS; Aston, PA; (4); 30/311; Pres SADD; Sec Band; Mrchg Band; Trs School Musical; Variety Show; Var Mgr(s); Var Trk; Hon Roll; NHS; Natl Ldrshp & Svc Awds 87; Acad All Amer Schlr Awd 86; Bloomsburg U; Elem Ed.

MILLER, KRISTI; Berks Christian Schl; Boyertown, PA; (3); Church Yth Grp; Chorus; Church Choir; School Musical; Rep Stu Cncl; Bsktbl; Trk; Capt Vllybl; Hon Roll; Kutztown U; RN.

MILLER, KRISTI; Connellsville Area SR HS; Connellsville, PA; (1); Church Yth Grp; Office Aide; SADD; Acpl Chr; Chorus; Mgr Drill Tm; Cheerleading; Vllybl; Valentine Ct 87; 2 Frshmn Awds Most Schl Spirit & Best Smile 87; Rifle Squad 87; U Of Pittsburgh; Dentistry.

MILLER, KRISTIN; Eisenhower HS; Russell, PA; (3); 13/113; VP Church Yth Grp; GAA; Girl Scts; Office Aide; Speech Tm; Chorus; Score Keeper; Sftbl; Vllybl; High Hon Roll; Pre Law.

MILLER, KRISTINE; Bellwood-Antis HS; Bellwood, PA; (4); 1/118; Trs Varsity Clb; Pres Sr Cls; Var Co-Capt Bsktbl; L Trk; Cit Awd; High Hon Roll; Pres NHS; Ntl Merit Ltr; Acad All-Amrcn 85-86; Juniata Vly Lg 86; Chem Engr.

MILLER, KYLENE; Oley Valley HS; Fleetwood, PA; (3); 20/147; Camp Fr Inc; Cmnty Wkr; Sec JA; Teachers Aide; Chorus; Color Guard; Nwsp Ed-Chief; Co-Capt Cheerleading; Hon Roll; NHS; Presdntl Ftns Awd; Cnty Chorus; PA ST Berks Campus; Spch Pthl.

MILLER, LAINIE; Kennedy Christian HS; Wheatland, PA; (2); 39/96; Girl Scts; Hosp Aide; Latin Clb; Church Choir; Cheerleading; Coach Actv; Swmmng; Trk; Pres Schlr; Med.

MILLER, LARA; Philadelphia HS For Girls; Philadelphia, PA; (3); 180/400; VP Church Yth Grp; Mgr Band; Concert Band; Jazz Band; Mrchg Band; Orch; School Musical; German Hnr Soc 86-87; Music Ed.

MILLER, LARRY; Greater Johnstown Vo Tech; Johnstown, PA; (2); Church Yth Grp; 4-H; Ski Clb; Auto Mech.

MILLER JR, LARRY E; Mifflinburg Area HS; Mifflinburg, PA; (3); FFA; School Musical; Hon Roll; Prfct Atten Awd; US Navy; Avtn.

MILLER, LAURA; Eisenhower HS; Russell, PA; (4); 5/115; Pres Church Yth Grp; Var VP Bsktbl; VP L Sftbl; High Hon Roll; Jr NHS; NHS; Sal; Chorus; Yrbk Stf; SR Mthmtcs Awd 87; JETS Tm 85 & 87; Grove City Coll; Elec Engrng.

MILLER, LEE; Tri-Valley SR HS; Fairchance, PA; (3); Math Clb; Spanish Clb; High Hon Roll; Hon Roll; Jr NHS; NHS; Physcs.

MILLER, LENNY; Harry S Truman HS; Levittown, PA; (3); Band; JV Bsbl; JV Socr; Hon Roll; Pres Fit Awd 85-86; Penn ST; Electrncs.

MILLER, LESLEY; Tyrone Area HS; Tyrone, PA; (4); 34/180; Varsity Clb; Chorus; Church Choir; Var Bsktbl; Coach Actv; Im Powder Puff Ftbl; Score Keeper; Var Sftbl; Timer; High Hon Roll; PTO Tchng Schlrshp 87; Chrch Schlrshp 87; 1st Tm All Str Sftbl Outfld Slctn 87; Lock Haven U; Spcl Educ.

MILLER III, LEWIS H; William Penn SR HS; York, PA; (3); 20/365; Boy Scts; Computer Clb; FBLA; JA; Red Cross Aide; Bsbl; Trk; Hon Roll; NHS; Prfct Atten Awd; USAF Acad; Cmmrcl Plt.

MILLER, LINDA A; Hopewell HS; Aliquippa, PA; (3); 16/256; Drama Clb; Exploring; French Clb; JA; Latin Clb; Service Clb; School Play; High Hon Roll; Gifted & Talented Pgm 85-87; U Of Pittsburgh; Premed.

MILLER, LISA; Central Cambria HS; Ebensburg, PA; (2); NFL; Rep Frsh Cls; Im Bowling; Hon Roll.

MILLER, LISA; Lower Moreland HS; Huntingdon Valley, PA; (3); Debate Tm; FBLA; Key Clb; Science Clb; JV Capt Cheerleading; JV Lcrss; Pre-Law.

MILLER, LISA; Shamokin Area HS; Paxinos, PA; (4); 10/213; Church Yth Grp; Pres Science Clb; Chorus; School Musical; Rep Stu Cncl; Capt Twrlr; High Hon Roll; NHS; Cmnty Wkr; Drama Clb; PTA Ctznshp Awd 87; Slvtn Army Comm Wrk Schlrshp 87; Sci Olympc Tm 86-87; Juniata Coll; Educ.

MILLER, LISA; St Marys Area HS; St Marys, PA; (3); Hon Roll; Bus Hnrs Soc 87; Vllybl Clb 84-85; Accntnt.

MILLER, LISA; Taylor Allderdice HS; Pittsburgh, PA; (2); Hosp Aide; Ski Clb; Nwsp Stf; Trs Soph Cls; Crs Cntry; Hon Roll; Bus.

MILLER, LORAN; Rockwood HS; Somerset, PA; (2); Church Yth Grp; 4-H; Var L Bsbl; High Hon Roll; Hon Roll; Schltc Awd 85-86; Engrng.

MILLER, LORRAINE; Claysburg-Kimmel HS; Queen, PA; (3); 1/70; Speech Tm; SADD; Band; Concert Band; Jazz Band; Mrchg Band; Yrbk Ed-Chief; Rep Stu Cncl; Bsktbl; Hon Roll; PA ST Summer Intensive Lang Inst Schlrshp 87; Lbrl Arts.

MILLER, LUCINDA; Conrad Weiser HS; Womelsdorf, PA; (3); Chess Clb; Church Yth Grp; Girl Scts; Spanish Clb; Chorus; Stu Cncl; Bsktbl; Hon Roll; Internatl Bus.

MILLER, LUCY; Cranberry Area HS; Seneca, PA; (2); Aud/Vis; GAA; Pep Clb; Science Clb; Spanish Clb; SADD; Chorus; Score Keeper; Sftbl; High Hon Roll.

MILLER, MARCI; Berlin Brothersvalley HS; Berlin, PA; (2); GAA; NFL; Spanish Clb; SADD; Band; Concert Band; Mrchg Band; Sec Frsh Cls; Sec Soph Cls; Bsktbl; HOBY Ldrshp Smnr 87; Psych.

MILLER, MARGARET; James M Coughlin HS; Wilkes Barre, PA; (3); 37/374; Church Yth Grp; Key Clb; Chorus; Yrbk Stf; Stat Bsktbl; Stat Fld Hcky; JV Var Sftbl; Jr NHS; NHS; NEDT Awd; Yng Schlr Pgm At Wilkes Coll 87-88; USAF Acad; Comp Sci.

MILLER, MARJORIE; Northwestern HS; E Springfield, PA; (3); Art Clb; Sec 4-H; Hon Roll; Dietetics.

MILLER, MARK; Leechburg HS; Leechburg, PA; (4); 9/82; Band; Mrchg Band; Pep Band; Yrbk Bus Mgr; Yrbk Stf; VP Jr Cls; Pres Schlr; IUP Metorship Pgm 87; PA ST; Mech Eng.

MILLER, MARSHA; Western Beaver HS; Industry, PA; (4); Church Yth Grp; Computer Clb; Band; Chorus; Drill Tm; Jazz Band; Yrbk Stf; Stu Cncl; Pom Pon; Hon Roll.

MILLER, MARY; Williamsburg HS; Williamsburg, PA; (3); Band; Chorus; Flag Corp; Mrchg Band; VP Frsh Cls; Rep Soph Cls; Var Cheerleading; JV Var Vllybl; Im Wt Lftg; Most Valuable Ply Vllybl 85-86; Sports Med.

MILLER, MATT; Liberty HS; Bethlehem, PA; (3); 43/400; Church Yth Grp; Church Choir; Bsktbl; Trk; High Hon Roll; Hon Roll; Carrier Mnth Lcl Nwspapr Awd 86.

MILLER, MATTHEW; Butler SR HS; Butler, PA; (3); French Clb; JA; Office Aide; Yrbk Stf; Rep Stu Cncl; Im Bsktbl; Im Ftbl; High Hon Roll; Hon Roll; Jr NHS; Yth Ldrshp Awd Natl Yng Ldrs Cnfrnc 87.

MILLER, MATTHEW; Central Cambrig HS; Mineral Point, PA; (3); Var L Trk; Im Wt Lftg; U Fo Pittsburgh; Phys Thrpy.

MILLER, MATTHEW L; Shikellamy HS; Northumberland, PA; (3); 10/330; Am Leg Boys St; Boys Clb Am; German Clb; Nwsp Stf; Lit Mag; Tennis; Hon Roll; NHS; VP Church Yth Grp; Conservation Ldrshp Schl & German Hnr Soc 87; Wildlife Sci.

MILLER, MELINDA; North Star HS; Stoystown, PA; (3); 13/148; Church Yth Grp; FCA; Varsity Clb; Band; Yrbk Stf; Var L Bsktbl; Var L Sftbl; Var JV Vllybl; Hon Roll; Sec Frsh Cls; Enrichmt Pgm-Gftd 8 Yrs 83-86; Bus Admin.

MILLER, MELISSA; Greencastle Antrim HS; Greencastle, PA; (3); Cmnty Wkr; Computer Clb; Key Clb; Library Aide; Spanish Clb; Band; Concert Band; Mrchg Band; Spanish NHS; Psych.

MILLER, MELISSA; Northeastern HS; Mt Wolf, PA; (4); 1/162; Band; Nwsp Ed-Chief; Sec Jr Cls; Rep Sr Cls; Stu Cncl; High Hon Roll; NHS; Rotary Awd; Val; Mrchg Band; Epco Sci Awd; PA ST U; Chem Engnrng.

MILLER, MELISSA ANN; Northeastern HS; Manchester, PA; (3); French Clb; Var L Bsktbl; Im Sftbl; Var L Tennis; Im JV Vllybl; Hon Roll; Child Psych.

MILLER, MICHAEL; Bensalem HS; Bensalem, PA; (4); 14/500; FBLA; Band; Golf; Trk; Wrstlng; High Hon Roll; Hon Roll; NHS; Acad All Amer 87; Dstngshd Achvt In Johns Hopkins Tlnt Srch 83; Chris Gabriel-Mc Donalds Schlrshp 87; Lehigh U; Stckbrkr.

MILLER, MICHAEL; Lehighton Area HS; Lehighton, PA; (3); Stage Crew; Golf; Ice Hcky; Wt Lftg; Mgr Bsbl; Mgr(s); Prfct Attend Awd 85-86; Military Pilot.

MILLER, MICHAEL; Marple Newtown SR HS; Newtown Square, PA; (4); 33/330; Cmnty Wkr; JV Bsbl; JV Bsktbl; Var Socr; Var Tennis; High Hon Roll; Hon Roll; NHS; Pres Schlr; Outstndng Serv-Stu Cncl 86-87; Dickinson Coll; Med.

MILLER, MICHAEL; West Hazleton JR SR HS; Hazleton, PA; (3); 6/217; Science Clb; Ski Clb; Var Tennis; Bausch & Lomb Sci Awd; Ntl Merit Ltr; French Clb; Nwsp Stf; Hon Roll.

MILLER, MICHAEL; William Penn HS; York, PA; (3); 15/500; VP JA; Band; Concert Band; Mrchg Band; Symp Band; Frsh Cls; Var L Bsbl; Im Vllybl; Hon Roll; NHS; Chem Engrng.

MILLER, MICHAEL T; Chambersburg Area SR HS; Chambersburg, PA; (3); 29/689; Am Leg Boys St; German Clb; JV Ftbl; Var JV Golf; High Hon Roll; Hon Roll; NHS; Church Yth Grp; JV Bsbl; MS Bnd Area Educ Agncy Yng Wrtrs Conf 85; IA Ftr Prblm Slvng Bwl 86; HOBY Fndtn Oustndng Yth 86; Bus Econ.

MILLER, MICHELE; Butler SR HS; Butler, PA; (3); Church Yth Grp; Girl Scts; Library Aide; Spanish Clb; Chorus; Hon Roll.

MILLER, MICHELE; Ford City JR SR HS; Ford Cliff, PA; (3); Church Yth Grp; Hosp Aide; Spanish Clb; Chorus; Off Jr Cls; Stu Cncl; VP L Tennis; NHS; Psych.

MILLER, MICHELLE; Butler Intermediate HS; Butler, PA; (2); Spanish Clb; SADD; Teachers Aide; Hon Roll; Slippery Rock; Education.

MILLER, MICHELLE; Central Dauphin HS; Harrisburg, PA; (3); French Clb; Key Clb; Teachers Aide; Chorus; Var Cheerleading; Var Diving; Var Trk; Var JV Vllybl; Hon Roll; NHS; Publc Reltns.

MILLER, MICHELLE; Conrad Weiser HS; Sinking Spring, PA; (3); 13/179; Church Yth Grp; Cmnty Wkr; Dance Clb; German Clb; Key Clb; Service Clb; Teachers Aide; Chorus; School Play; Cit Awd; Beaver Coll; Physical Therapy.

MILLER, MICHELLE; Fort Cherry HS; Midway, PA; (4); 17/112; Pres Sec Church Yth Grp; French Clb; Math Clb; Chorus; Co-Capt Drill Tm; Yrbk Stf; Var L Sftbl; Var L Tennis; High Hon Roll; NHS; OH Northern Deans Scholar 87-88; OH Northern U; Intl Stud.

MILLER, MICHELLE; Tunkhannock Area HS; Tunkhannock, PA; (2); 4/300; French Clb; Key Clb; Var L Bsktbl; Var L Vllybl; Hon Roll; SR Grls Sftbl ST Fnlst 86.

MILLER, MICHELLE M; State College Area HS; State College, PA; (2); 27/536; Spanish Clb; Band; Chorus; JV Cheerleading; High Hon Roll; Prfct Atten Awd; Acad Achvt Awd 87; Elem Ed.

MILLER, MICHELLE M; York Area Vo-Tech; Airville, PA; (3); 7/456; Am Leg Aux Girls St; Church Yth Grp; 4-H; Library Aide; Teachers Aide; 4-H Awd; High Hon Roll; NHS; Dntl Hygnst.

MILLER, MITCHELL; Kennard-Dale HS; Stewartstown, PA; (3); Chorus; Orch; Bsbl; Bsktbl; Socr; Wt Lftg; Hon Roll; Elec Engr.

MILLER, MOLLY; Elmer L Meyers HS; Wilkes Barre, PA; (3); 27/198; French Clb; Ski Clb; Chorus; Concert Band; Mrchg Band; Orch; Hon Roll; Jr NHS; NHS; NEDT Awd; Advanced Amer Hstry Plcmnt 86-87; Hlth Care.

MILLER, MYRA JONAI; Harrisburg HS; Harrisburg, PA; (4); Cmnty Wkr; French Clb; Girl Scts; Hosp Aide; Latin Clb; Science Clb; Color Guard; Lit Mag; Off Sr Cls; Cit Awd; John Hall Fndtn & Brd Gvrnrs Schlrshps 87-88; Bloomsburg U; Nrsng.

MILLER, NOELLE; Hickory HS; Shaprsville, PA; (2); Hosp Aide; Latin Clb; Office Aide; Teachers Aide; Chorus; Hon Roll; U Of Pittsburgh; Chem.

MILLER, PAM; Hempfield Area SR HS; Jeannette, PA; (3); GAA; Pep Clb; Spanish Clb; Chorus; Trk; Hmnts Day At Pitt Of Greensburg 87; Gannon Univ Dept Of Engl 3rd Pl Ptry 87; IN Univ Of PAFINTR Dsgn.

MILLER, PAMELLA SUE; Pennsburg HS; Fairless Hills, PA; (4); Dance Clb; Drama Clb; Chorus; Concert Band; Mrchg Band; Orch; School Musical; School Play; Swing Chorus; Hon Roll; Crtc Awd Exclinc Actng Bcks Cnty Playhse 85; Hnr Cert Drama 87; Bucks Cnty CC; Music Tchr.

MILLER, PATRICIA; Central Dauphin HS; Harrisbrg, PA; (2); High Hon Roll.

MILLER, PATTI; Forest Hills HS; South Fork, PA; (4); 12/154; Pep Clb; Var Cheerleading; Var Trk; High Hon Roll; Hon Roll; Jr NHS; Spanish NHS; IN U At PA; Acctng.

MILLER, PAUL; Beaver Area SR HS; Beaver, PA; (3); Church Yth Grp; VP JCL; Science Clb; Nwsp Stf; L Crs Cntry; L Swmmng; L Trk; High Hon Roll; NHS; Ntl Merit SF; Elec Engrng.

MILLER, PAUL; North Allegheny SR HS; Allison Pk, PA; (3); 161/649; Jazz Band; Mrchg Band; Pep Band; Symp Band; Allghny Vly Hnrs Band 83-85; Carnegie Mellon Solo Compttn 1st Pl 85; Opthlmlgy.

MILLER, PENNY; Avonworth SR HS; Pittsburgh, PA; (4); AFS; Trs Soph Cls; Score Keeper; Socr; Sftbl; Hon Roll; Sawyer Schl; Travel.

MILLER, PETER; Liberty JR SR HS; Trout Run, PA; (3); Rptr FFA; Var JV Bsktbl; Ftbl; Wmsport Area CC; Hvy Eqpmnt.

MILLER, RACHEL; Central HS; Philadelphia, PA; (3); Drama Clb; Band; Mrchg Band; Orch; School Musical; School Play; VP Frsh Cls; Hon Roll; NHS; Orthdntst.

MILLER, REBECCA; Spring Grove Area HS; Spring Grove, PA; (3); 11/301; Ski Clb; Church Choir; Jazz Band; Orch; School Musical; Nwsp Stf; High Hon Roll; Hon Roll; Trs NHS; Presdntl Academic Fitness Awd & Outstndng Spnsh Stu Awd 85; Schlstc Achvt Awd 86; U Of Pittsburgh; Pharmacy.

MILLER, RICHARD; Northern Lebanon HS; Grantville, PA; (3); 37/213; Chess Clb; Computer Clb; Science Clb; Im Vllybl; Hon Roll; Engrng.

MILLER, ROBERT; Chartiers Valley HS; Bridgeville, PA; (3); Varsity Clb; Nwsp Rptr; Ftbl; Wrstlng; High Hon Roll; NHS; Sports Med.

MILLER, ROBERT; Tech Memorial HS; Erie, PA; (3); 22/330; Yrbk Rptr; Var Capt Socr; Var Capt Wrstlng; Hon Roll; Athltc Hnr Soc 85-87; Amrcn HS Math Exam 85-86; Ldrshp Cnfrnc 86; U Of HI; Mrn Bio.

MILLER JR, ROBERT; Penn-Trafford HS; Level Green, PA; (3); 17/301; Drama Clb; JCL; Off Band; Jazz Band; Nwsp Rptr; JV Bsktbl; High Hon Roll; NHS; Chess Clb; Purdue; Chem Engrng.

MILLER, ROBERT B; Stroudsburg HS; Stroudsburg, PA; (3); 20/250; Am Leg Boys St; German Clb; Letterman Clb; Varsity Clb; JV Ftbl; Im Wt Lftg; JV Var Wrstlng; Hon Roll; NHS; Rotary Clb Ldrs Camp 86; La Fayette; Polit Sci.

MILLER, ROBERTA F; St Pius X HS; Pottstown, PA; (4); 16/148; Hosp Aide; Service Clb; Tennis; Hon Roll; NHS; Prfct Atten Awd; Schlrshp-Dcknsn Coll 87-88; Merit Awd-Cntry 87; 4 Yr Frfct Atten Awd; Dickinson Coll; Law.

MILLER, ROLLIN; Pleasant Valley HS; Effort, PA; (2); Boy Scts; Church Yth Grp; Civic Clb; Math Tm; Ski Clb; Ftbl; JV Socr; L Trk; God Cntry Awd; Hon Roll; Eagle Scout 85; PA ST; Engrng.

MILLER, ROXANNE; Lock Haven SR HS; Castanea, PA; (4); 29/247; German Clb; Keywanettes; SADD; Chorus; Church Choir; Concert Band; Jazz Band; Mrchg Band; Variety Show; Off Stu Cncl; Outstndng Vocl Perf 87; Dist 4 Chorus 86-87; Regnl Chorus 86; Lock Haven U PA; Bio.

MILLER, RUSSELL; Connellsville Area SR HS; Connellsville, PA; (2); Church Yth Grp; Civic Clb; Cmnty Wkr; Computer Clb; Dance Clb; Political Wkr; Var Crs Cntry; Var L Trk; Crmnlgy.

MILLER, RYAN; Fort Cherry HS; Midway, PA; (2); Church Yth Grp; Math Clb; Science Clb; Spanish Clb; Varsity Clb; Chorus; L Bsbl; Var Ftbl; Var L Wrstlng; Hon Roll; Aeronautics.

MILLER, SANDRA; Windber Area HS; Windber, PA; (3); Drama Clb; Concert Band; Drm Mjr(t); Mrchg Band; Yrbk Bus Mgr; High Hon Roll; NHS; Pres Schlr; Band; School Play; IN U PA Hnrs Band; Dist & Regnl Band; Human Physlgy Awd; U Pittsburgh; Phrmcy.

MILLER, SHANNON; Crestwood HS; Wapwallopen, PA; (1); Church Yth Grp; Girl Scts; Var Cheerleading; Var Trk; Hon Roll; Fshn Mrchndsng.

MILLER, SHARI; Kiski Area HS; Vandergrift, PA; (4); Varsity Clb; Acpl Chr; Chorus; Church Choir; Swing Chorus; Variety Show; Var L Trk; Church Yth Grp; Cmnty Wkr; Computer Clb; Outstndng Vocal Musician Awd 87; CMU Schlrshp 87; Cnty, Dist & Rgn Choir; Carnegie-Mellon U; Music.

MILLER, SHAWN; Millville HS; Millville, PA; (4); Chess Clb; Church Yth Grp; FBLA; JV Bsbl; Var JV Bsktbl; Var JV Socr; Wt Lftg; Elks Awd; Hon Roll; Physical Educ Awd 87; Bloomsburg U; Math Educ.

MILLER, SHAWNA; Cocalico HS; Denver, PA; (2); Sec Church Yth Grp; Dance Clb; Chorus; Church Choir; Nwsp Stf; Yrbk Rptr; Hon Roll; 1st Pl-Chrch Spnsrd Dist Tlnt Shw 86; Ambassador Coll.

MILLER, STACEY; Central Cambria HS; Vintondale, PA; (3); 70/210; Art Clb; Church Yth Grp; FHA; JA; Chorus; Prfct Atten Awd; Chorus Ltr 85-86; Art.

MILLER, STACY; Liberty JR SR HS; Liberty, PA; (2); 5/54; FHA; Sec German Clb; Band; Chorus; Mrchg Band; School Musical; Rep Stu Cncl; Capt Cheerleading; Trk; Hon Roll; Hlth.

MILLER, STEPHEN; Boiling Springs HS; Carlisle, PA; (3); Letterman Clb; Var L Ftbl; Var L Trk; Wt Lftg; Var L Wrstlng; High Hon Roll; Hon Roll; NHS; Bucknell U; Engrng.

MILLER, STEPHEN D; Spring Grove Area SR HS; Codorus, PA; (3); VP Church Yth Grp; Letterman Clb; Varsity Clb; Band; Concert Band; Mrchg Band; JV Bsktbl; Var L Ftbl; Var L Trk; Rptr Jr Cls; Hstry.

MILLER, STEPHEN R; Spring-Ford SR HS; Royersford, PA; (3); 23/256; FBLA; German Clb; Math Clb; Hon Roll; 2nd Pl Awd Acctng I FBLA Rgnl Fnls, St Fnls 86; 2nd Pl Acctng II FBLA Rgnl Fnls 87; Acctng.

MILLER, SUE; Hillside Christian Acad; Mifflinburg, PA; (3); Art Clb; Church Yth Grp; Chorus; Capt Cheerleading; Sftbl; Capt Vllybl; Hon Roll; Highest Math Av Awd 87; Pensacola Christian; Juv Dlnqcy.

MILLER, SUSAN; Frazier HS; Fayette City, PA; (1); Dance Clb; Nwsp Stf; Capt Cheerleading; Gym; Hon Roll; Elem Schl Tchr.

MILLER, SUZANNE; Waynesboro Area SR HS; Waynesboro, PA; (4); 3/354; Ski Clb; Capt Var Crs Cntry; Var Trk; Cit Awd; High Hon Roll; NHS; Ntl Merit SF; Mt Holyoke Coll; Med Rsrch.

MILLER, SUZANNE ELIZABETH; Hempfield HS; Lancaster, PA; (4); 10/415; Am Leg Aux Girls St; Varsity Clb; Chorus; Var Swmmng; High Hon Roll; NHS; Pres Schlr; Socl Stds Deptmntl Awd 87; Top 10 Acdmc Stu Awd 87; Wellesley Coll; Pol Sci.

MILLER, TAMARA; Homer Center HS; Homer City, PA; (3); Sec Computer Clb; VP Library Aide; Bsktbl; Twrlr; High Hon Roll; Jr NHS; NHS; IN U Of PA; Spch Pthlgy.

MILLER, TAMMY; Athens HS; Athens, PA; (3); Hosp Aide; Mrchg Band; Crs Cntry; Trk; Ltr Trk 84 & 85; Ltr X-Country 85.

MILLER, TAMMY; Catasauqua HS; Catasauqua, PA; (4); 3/130; SADD; Varsity Clb; Hst Soph Cls; Hst Jr Cls; Hst Sr Cls; Off Stu Cncl; Capt Bsktbl; Capt Fld Hcky; Sftbl; High Hon Roll; Natl Sci Awd, Natl Hnr Soc Awd 86; Schlr Athltc; Soc Wmns Engrs; Leonard Carlton Peckitt Schlrshp 87; PA ST U; Bus Admin.

MILLER, TAMMY; Lower Dauphin HS; Hummelstown, PA; (3); JA; Teachers Aide; Band; Chorus; Church Choir; Mrchg Band; School Musical; Variety Show; Pres Frsh Cls; Cheerleading; Indoor Twrlng Chmpns 87; Otstndng German Awd 87; Westpoint Acad; Nurse.

MILLER, TANYA; Southmoreland HS; Scottdale, PA; (3); 28/224; Church Yth Grp; FBLA; Latin Clb; Chorus; Church Choir; WCCC; Scrtry.

MILLER, TERI; Mt Pleasant Area HS; Mt Pleasant, PA; (4); Color Guard; Nwsp Ed-Chief; Off Frsh Cls; Off Jr Cls; Cit Awd; High Hon Roll; Yth Educ Assn Schlrshp, & CMC Employees Schlrshp 87; Edinboro U PA; Psych.

MILLER, THERESA; Saltsburg JR-SR HS; Saltsburg, PA; (4); 9/90; Camera Clb; Ski Clb; Varsity Clb; Band; Lit Mag; Trk; Vllybl; High Hon Roll; NHS; Church Yth Grp; IN Cnty JR Miss Fnlst 87; Mst Artstc SR Persnlty 86-87; Duquesne U; Intl Corp Lwyr.

MILLER, TINA; Brandywine Heights HS; Alburtis, PA; (3); 12/117; FBLA; Nwsp Bus Mgr; Nwsp Rptr; Nwsp Sprt Ed; Vllybl; Hon Roll; Cmmnctns.

MILLER, TINA; Homer Center HS; Homer City, PA; (2); Pres FHA; Sec VICA; Band; Concert Band; Drill Tm; Mrchg Band; Bsktbl; Hon Roll; Prfct Atten Awd; Outstndng Hm Ec Ofcr 86-87; Pittsburgh Bty Acad; Cosmtlgst.

MILLER, TONIA; Bellefonte Area HS; Howard, PA; (4); 46/236; Hon Roll; PA ST U; Bus Mgmt.

MILLER, TONIA; William Penn SR HS; York, PA; (3); 16/452; PAVAS; Ski Clb; SADD; Tennis; Twrlr; Hon Roll; NHS; Phldpha Acad Thtrcl Arts Schlrshp Awd 85; Cntrl Pa Am Intrntl Grl Mdl 84-85; Teen Yrk Cnty Mdl 85-86.

MILLER, TRACEY ANN; Curwensville Area HS; Curwensville, PA; (3); Church Yth Grp; FBLA; Spanish Clb; Chorus; Church Choir; Bsktbl; Mat Maids; Vllybl; Wt Lftg; JC Awd; 1st Pl Stngrphr I Awd Rgnls In FBLA 87; Top Ten In ST Stngrphr I 87; Acad All Amer Awd 87; Med Scrtry.

MILLER, TRACEY L; Louis E Dieruff HS; Allentown, PA; (3); 40/322; Pres FBLA; JA; VP Key Clb; Ski Clb; Powder Puff Ftbl; Hon Roll; Prfct Atten Awd; Bloomsburg ST Coll; Bus Admin.

MILLER, TRACY; Rocky Grove JR SR HS; Franklin, PA; (4); 11/90; Drama Clb; Sec SADD; Chorus; Variety Show; Yrbk Sprt Ed; Rep Jr Cls; Rep Stu Cncl; Hon Roll; NHS; Pres Schlr; Acdmc Hnr Awd 85 & 87; Music Ltr, Plaque, Cert & Pins 84-87; Clarion U Of PA; Elem Educ.

MILLER, TREVOR S; Chartiers Valley HS; Carnegie, PA; (3); Culinary Arts Inst; Chef.

MILLER, TRINA; Bedford HS; Bedford, PA; (4); 41/176; Church Yth Grp; Chorus; Trs Frsh Cls; Trs Soph Cls; Trs Jr Cls; Trs Sr Cls; Rep Stu Cncl; Cheerleading; Trk; Hon Roll; Homecoming Queen 86-87; Fall Foliage 85-86; Allegheny Comm Coll.

MILLER, TRISHA; William Allen HS; Allentown, PA; (3); 70/659; Pres Church Yth Grp; Girl Scts; SADD; Pres Band; NHS; VP Drama Clb; Leo Clb; Church Choir; Pres Concert Band; Madrigals; PA Govs Schl For Arts-Music & ST Speakers Trnmnt Wnnr PA 87; Allentown Cncl Yth 85; Music.

MILLER, WADE T; Connellsville Area SR HS; Connellsville, PA; (3); 113/523; Art Clb; Church Yth Grp; Exploring; Band; Jazz Band; Mrchg Band; Pep Band; Stage Crew; Symp Band; Hon Roll; Slctd Rgnl Cnty Band 85; Mrchng Bnd Ldrshp Awd 86; Accntng.

MILLER, WENDY; Conemaugh Township HS; Jerome, PA; (4); 20/102; Drama Clb; Hosp Aide; JA; Band; School Musical; School Play; Yrbk Stf; Score Keeper; Vllybl; Hon Roll; Vrsty C Plq Fr Prtcptng Schl Sprts 86-87; CMVH Schl Nursing; Nrsng.

MILLER, WENDY; Williams Valley HS; Tower City, PA; (4); 11/97; Chorus; Var L Bsktbl; Var Capt Sftbl; High Hon Roll; Hon Roll; NHS; Prfct Atten Awd; Church Yth Grp; Girl Scts; Feml Schlr Athl 87; Chosn Ply Bsktbl All Str Gm 87; MVP Sftbl 87; Thompson Inst; Med Asst.

MILLER, WENDY SUE; Wm Allen HS; Allentown, PA; (3); 60/659; Leo Clb; SADD; Color Guard; Flag Corp; School Play; Yrbk Stf; Hon Roll; Jr NHS; NHS; Mc Cormick Bk Awd 87; Secy Explrer Post 86-87; PA ST U; Acctg.

MILLER, WILLIAM; Northern Bedford County HS; Loysburg, PA; (4); FFA; Bsbl; Bsktbl; Ftbl; Frstry.

MILLER, WILLIAM; Tunkhannock Area HS; Factoryville, PA; (3); 11/330; Key Clb; Bsktbl; Ftbl; JV Trk; High Hon Roll; Rotary Intl Ldrshp Camp Alt 86; Pre-Med.

MILLER, WILLIAM; Uniontown Area HS; Chalk Hill, PA; (2); French Clb; JV Ftbl; Wt Lftg; High Hon Roll; PA ST; Crimnlgy.

MILLER, YVETTE; Neshaminy HS; Penndel, PA; (3); Church Yth Grp; Chorus; School Musical; JV Var Bsktbl; Hon Roll.

MILLERO, MOLLIE A; Commodore Perry HS; Hadley, PA; (3); Sec FTA; Math Tm; Chorus; Capt Cheerleading; Var Crs Cntry; Mgr(s); Hon Roll; NHS; Bus Adm.

MILLHAM, MARY P; Bishop Oreilly HS; Shavertown, PA; (2); Church Yth Grp; Cmnty Wkr; Spanish Clb; Chorus; Fld Hcky; Photo Jrnlsm.

MILLHOUSE, BRIAN STACY; Solanco HS; Drumore, PA; (4); Boy Scts; Church Yth Grp; Ski Clb; Lit Mag; Im Bsbl; Im Bsktbl; JV Ftbl; Im Sftbl; God Cntry Awd; Hon Roll; Blue Belt In Mos Duk Kwan Karate 86; Penn ST; Bus Admin.

MILLICK, JULIE; Trinity HS; Washington, PA; (3); German Clb; Key Clb; Pep Clb; SADD; Yrbk Rptr; Yrbk Stf; Trs Frsh Cls; Rep Soph Cls; Trs Jr Cls; Rep Sr Cls; JR Hmcmng Attndnt 86; U Pittsburg; Nrsng.

MILLIGAN, CATHY; Beaver Area SR HS; Beaver, PA; (4); 12/200; Pres VP 4-H; JCL; Drm & Bgl; Jazz Band; Mrchg Band; Symp Band; High Hon Roll; NHS; Pres Schlr; PA Sci Olympics 1st Pl Msrmnt 87; 2nd Pl Physics Team 87; Geneva Coll Early Coll Pgm 86-87; Carnegie Mellon U; Chem.

MILLIGAN, MIKE; Strath Haven HS; Media, PA; (3); Intnl Clb; JV Var Bsbl; JV Var Ftbl; Wrstlng; High Hon Roll; Hon Roll; Pre-Law.

MILLIGAN, WILLIAM; Montrose Area HS; Montrose, PA; (3); Aud/Vis; Church Yth Grp; Latin Clb; Chorus; Church Choir; Madrigals; School Musical; School Play; Nwsp Rptr; Var Socr.

MILLIKEN, AUTUMN; North Hills HS; Pittsburgh, PA; (4); 30/475; Cmnty Wkr; Pres Key Clb; Math Tm; Ski Clb; Lit Mag; Var Bsktbl; High Hon Roll; NHS; Ntl Merit SF; Princeton U; Chemcl Engrng.

MILLIKEN, LORI; Coatesville Area SR HS; Coatesville, PA; (3); 53/509; Church Yth Grp; Spanish Clb; Band; Chorus; Church Choir; Color Guard; Concert Band; Var Swmmng; Hon Roll; Swmng MVP 85-87; Sumng Rcrd Hldr 100 Free Style 87; Accntng.

MILLIRON, JOHANNA; Otto-Eldred JR SR HS; Eldred, PA; (2); 1/90; Church Yth Grp; SADD; Varsity Clb; Chorus; Church Choir; Yrbk Ed-Chief; Var JV Cheerleading; Var JV Vllybl; High Hon Roll; Hon Roll.

MILLS, ANNE; Commodore Perry HS; Greenville, PA; (4); 10/64; FBLA; Office Aide; Hon Roll; Yth Ed Assn 84-86; Mercer Cnty Vo Tech Data Proc PM Pres 86-87; U Pittsburgh; Acctng.

MILLS, CARRIE; Northeastern SR HS; Manchester, PA; (3); 2/185; Concert Band; Mrchg Band; Orch; Rep Jr Cls; Var Stu Cncl; Var L Fld Hcky; L Trk; High Hon Roll; NHS; Rotary Awd; Lebanon Vly Coll Yth Schlrs Inst In Chem 87; Penn ST U; Chem.

MILLS, GLENDA; Belle Vernon Area HS; Belle Vernon, PA; (4); 33/270; Drama Clb; FBLA; NFL; Ski Clb; Band; Concert Band; Mrchg Band; Trk; High Hon Roll; NHS; FBLA Frnsc Trphy 87; U Of Pittsburgh; Spch Cmmnctns.

MILLS, GREGORY; Montour HS; Pittsburgh, PA; (3); 5/286; L Var Socr; High Hon Roll; NHS; Ntl Merit SF; Wnng Reg Sci Olympd 87; MIT; Aerospc Engrng.

MILLS, HOLLY; Southern Huntingdon Co HS; Rockhill Furnace, PA; (3); 1/150; VP Pres GAA; Trs SADD; Band; Chorus; Drm Mjr(t); Nwsp Rptr; Capt L Bsktbl; Var L Fld Hcky; Dnfth Awd; High Hon Roll; Phys Ed.

MILLS, JEFFREY M; Grove City Area HS; Grove City, PA; (3); 12/214; Am Leg Boys St; VP Science Clb; Pres Frsh Cls; VP Soph Cls; VP Jr Cls; Pres VP Stu Cncl; NHS; Hugh O Brian ILS Ambssdr 86; PA Free Enterprise Wk 87.

MILLS, JENNIFER; Hezleton HS; Hazleton, PA; (3); Drama Clb; Girl Scts; VICA; Chorus; School Play; Lackawanna JC; Early Chldhd Ed.

MILLS, JENNIFER; Pennsbury HS; Yardley, PA; (4); 13/777; French Clb; Orch; Hon Roll; Jr NHS; NHS; Wake Forest U.

MILLS, JENY; Lake Lehman HS; Lehman, PA; (3); JV Capt Fld Hcky; High Hon Roll; Hon Roll; Jr NHS; NHS; Cert Profcncy Century 21 Typewrtng 87; Exec Sec.

MILLS, JULIANNE; Shanksville-Stonycreek HS; Friedens, PA; (4); 4/37; Church Yth Grp; CAP; Spanish Clb; Band; Chorus; Concert Band; Mrchg Band; School Play; Symp Band; Yrbk Stf; PA ST U; Aerontcl Engr.

MILLS, KATHRYN; Lampeter-Strasburg HS; Strasburg, PA; (3); 30/140; Church Yth Grp; GAA; Chorus; School Musical; Ed Yrbk Stf; Var JV Cheerleading; Mgr(s); Var JV Sftbl; Elem Ed.

MILLS, KELLY; Belle Vernon Area HS; Belle Vernon, PA; (3); Band; Concert Band; Mrchg Band; Pep Band; Powder Puff Ftbl; Trk; Hon Roll; Scndry Educ.

MILLS, KIM; Garnet Valley JRSR HS; Glen Mills, PA; (3); 56/174; French Clb; FBLA; JA; Office Aide; Ski Clb; Varsity Clb; Rep Stu Cncl; Var L Fld Hcky; Var L Lcrss; Rotary Awd; 1st Tm All Lgu Field Hockey 86; 1st Tm All Lgu La Crosse 87; 2nd Tm All DE Cnty La Crosse 87.

MILLS, LORI; Hopewell SR HS; Aliquippa, PA; (3); Art Clb; Exploring; French Clb; Hon Roll; Psych.

MILLS, LORRI; Pocono Mountain HS; Mt Pocono, PA; (3); NFL; Q&S; Chorus; School Musical; Swing Chorus; Lit Mag; High Hon Roll; NHS; Ntl Merit Ltr; Opt Clb Awd; Monroe Cnty Law Day Essy Cntst 1st Pl 87; Hofstra U; Theatre Arts.

MILLS, MARCIE JO; Punxsutawney Area HS; Punxsutawney, PA; (4); 74/265; Band; Concert Band; Drill Tm; Mrchg Band; Variety Show; Twrlr; Hon Roll.

MILLS, MICHELE; Bishop Shanahan HS; W Chester, PA; (4); 24/215; Cmnty Wkr; Dance Clb; Hosp Aide; School Play; Var Fld Hcky; Var Swmmng; High Hon Roll; Hon Roll; NHS; Pres Schlr; Rosemont Trustee Schlrshp 87; Altnt For Josephine C Connelly Schlrshp 87; Rosemont Coll; Bus Admin.

MILLS, RHONDA; Du Bois Area SR HS; Punxsutawney, PA; (3); SADD; School Musical; Hon Roll; Nice Kid Awd 85-86; Rtl Mgr.

MILLS, ROBERT E; Richland SR HS; Johnstown, PA; (3); 37/139; Pres Trs Church Yth Grp; JA; Key Clb; Library Aide; Math Clb; Chorus; Church Choir; School Musical; Hon Roll; Dale Carnegie Course Scholar JA 86; Dale Carnegie Book Awd 87; Robert Morris Coll; Bus Adm.

MILLS, SEAN; Tunkhannock Area HS; Mehoopany, PA; (4); 18/270; Church Yth Grp; Spanish Clb; School Musical; JV Crs Cntry; Var Socr; Var Tennis; Cit Awd; NHS; Computer Clb; Ski Clb; PA Govrs Schl-Arts; NMTA Gld Audtn Stu; NMTA Cmptn Piano-ST Lvl.

MILLS, STACY; Chambersburg Area SR HS; Marion, PA; (4); Pres Church Yth Grp; Pep Clb; Spanish Clb; Band; Chorus; Church Choir; Concert Band; Mrchg Band; Nwsp Stf; Slippery Rock U; Elem Educ.

MILLS, TAMARA; Solanco HS; Quarryville, PA; (3); Church Yth Grp; Varsity Clb; Band; Chorus; Church Choir; Concert Band; Drm Mjr(t); Mrchg Band; School Musical; School Play; Outstndg Vocal Awd 87.

MILLS, TERRY; Phila HS For Girls; Philadelphia, PA; (3); 11/405; Dance Clb; Office Aide; Church Choir; Rep Jr Cls; JV Bsktbl; Bowling; Hon Roll; Spanish NHS; Psych.

MILLSAP, MONIQUE; Valley HS; New Kensington, PA; (2); Church Yth Grp; French Clb; Library Aide; Church Choir; High Hon Roll; Hon Roll; Prsdntl Acad Achvt Awd 85-86; Ped.

MILNE, RICHARD; Uniontown HS; Uniontown, PA; (3); 24/318; Boy Scts; Church Yth Grp; Spanish Clb; Concert Band; Mrchg Band; God Cntry Awd; High Hon Roll; Jr NHS; NHS; Prfct Atten Awd; WVU; Elec Engrng.

MILNER, MICHAEL; Tunkhannock Area HS; Tunkhannock, PA; (3); JV Bsktbl; Var Trk; Wt Lftg; High Hon Roll.

MILO, MARY; Lakeland HS; Carbondale, PA; (3); Church Yth Grp; Hosp Aide; JA; Trs Band; Concert Band; Mrchg Band; School Musical; Nwsp Stf; Acadmc All Amer 87.

MILOSER, MICHAEL; Lincoln HS; Wampum, PA; (4); 55/165; Boy Scts; Church Yth Grp; Computer Clb; French Clb; Band; Church Choir; Concert Band; Jazz Band; Mrchg Band; Orch; Penn ST; Music Educ.

MILOSH, KATHY; Meadville Area SR HS; Conneaut Lake, PA; (4); 110/344; French Clb; Sec Ski Clb; Spanish Clb; JV Var Bsktbl; Var Sftbl; Hon Roll; Edinboro U Of PA; Bus Admin.

MILOT, LISA; Northwestern Lehigh HS; Orefield, PA; (3); Debate Tm; Nwsp Phtg; Nwsp Rptr; Yrbk Ed-Chief; Sec Trs Frsh Cls; Sec Trs Soph Cls; Sec Trs Jr Cls; Sec Trs Sr Cls; Stu Cncl; NHS; St Prst Rd Race Time Trl Chmpnshps 87.

MILSHAW, SUZANNE; Reading HS; Reading, PA; (3); 23/720; Exploring; German Clb; Key Clb; Sec Library Aide; Model UN; Service Clb; Pres SADD; Chorus; Stage Crew; Hon Roll; Army Awd In Rdng Berks Sci Fair 87; Ldrshp Awd Kiwanis Svc In SADD 87; Hostess & Sec Knight Life 86-7; Amer Univ; Diplomatic Corps.

MILSLAGLE, JANET; Elk County Christian HS; St Marys, PA; (3); Art Clb; Ski Clb; Yrbk Stf; JV Var Cheerleading; Stat Ftbl; Timer; Bausch & Lomb Sci Awd; Gov Hon Prg Awd; High Hon Roll; Hon Roll; Advrtsng.

MILTENBERGER, LEE; Nazareth Area SR HS; Nazareth, PA; (3); Church Yth Grp; Chorus; Crs Cntry; Trk; Meterologist.

MILTON, BOBBI JO; Bellefonte Area HS; Bellefonte, PA; (3); Church Yth Grp; Church Choir; Dance Clb; Hon Roll; Sth Hlls Bus Schl; Bus.

MILTON, SHARON; Punxsutawney Area HS; Punxsutawney, PA; (3); French Clb; Varsity Clb; Var L Cheerleading; Stat Vllybl; Hon Roll; Natl Champ Coed Cheerleading Squad 87; Basketeers 85-87; PA ST U; Corp Law.

MILTZ, DON; Bentworth HS; Bentleyville, PA; (4); Hon Roll; Waynesburg Coll; Chmcl Engr.

MILZ, STEVEN; Hanover Area HS; Ashley, PA; (4); 7/160; Key Clb; Yrbk Stf; L Trk; High Hon Roll; NHS; Pres Awd Hghst Acdmc Avg Sprts, Stu Mnth 87; Penn ST; Comp Sci.

MINARDI, THERESA; Charleroi Area JR-SR HS; Charleroi, PA; (3); Church Yth Grp; Civic Clb; FBLA; Color Guard; Concert Band; Mrchg Band; Nwsp Rptr; Stu Cncl; Hon Roll; Secy.

MINCEMOYER, MICHAEL; Milton Area HS; Montandon, PA; (3); German Clb; Varsity Clb; Var Capt Crs Cntry; Var Capt Trk; Trs NHS; Mech Engr.

MINDER, MARTIN; Bishop Kenrick HS; Norristown, PA; (4); 28/285; Ski Clb; Var Bowling; Var Ftbl; Hon Roll; NHS; Ftbl Plyr Of Wk & All-Catholic-Ftbl 87; Penn ST U; Engrng.

MINDER, MELISSA; Solanco SR HS; Quarryville, PA; (3); Ski Clb; Teachers Aide; Varsity Clb; Off Soph Cls; Stu Cncl; Bsktbl; Capt Fld Hcky; Gym; Powder Puff Ftbl; Sftbl; Reading Tutors 86-87.

MINDISH, ERIKA; Bishop Mc Cort HS; Johnstown, PA; (2); Hosp Aide; Pep Clb; Ski Clb; Spanish Clb; Var L Crs Cntry; Hon Roll; Phys Thrpy.

MINEARD, TARA A; New Brighton HS; New Brighton, PA; (3); #5 In Class; Am Leg Aux Girls St; GAA; Hosp Aide; Chorus; Trs Sr Cls; JV Bsktbl; JV Cheerleading; High Hon Roll; Acadc Achvt Awd 85-87; Duquesne U; Phrmcy.

MINECCI, LISA; Plymouth Whitemarsh HS; Conshohocken, PA; (3); 20/350; Stage Crew; Rep Frsh Cls; Rep Soph Cls; Jr Cls; Sr Cls; Var Sftbl; Var Swmmng; Var Vllybl; High Hon Roll; Jr NHS; Law.

MINECH, LAURA R; Moon Area HS; Coraopolis, PA; (4); 5/296; Church Yth Grp; Drama Clb; French Clb; Flag Corp; Mrchg Band; School Play; CC Awd; High Hon Roll; Hon Roll; NHS; Merit Schlrshp 87; CAFE Schlrshp 87; Robt Byrd Schlrshp 87; Wshngtn-Jffrsn Coll; Bus.

MINELLA, MARIA; North Pocono HS; Moscow, PA; (4); 21/250; Dance Clb; 4-H; Yrbk Stf; High Hon Roll; Hon Roll; NHS; Prfct Atten Awd; Pres Schlr; Hnr Grad 87; Anthony B Ritter Schlrshp 87; Marywood Schlrshp 87; Marywood Coll; Nrsng.

MINEO, ANDREA M; Mt Pleasnt Area HS; Mt Pleasant, PA; (4); Girl Scts; Letterman Clb; Red Cross Aide; Ski Clb; SADD; Varsity Clb; Nwsp Sprt Ed; Yrbk Stf; Sftbl; Vllybl; Sftbl Awd 87; Mst Athltc Awd 84; Thiel Coll; Phys Educ.

MINER, BRENDA; Tunkhannock HS; Mehoopany, PA; (4); 62/282; Letterman Clb; Spanish Clb; VP Frsh Cls; VP Soph Cls; VP Jr Cls; Var Capt Fld Hcky; Var Swmmng; Var Capt Trk; Hon Roll; NHS; Tnkhnnck Bus & Prfssnl Wmns Clb Schlrshp, Mst Outstndng Offnsv Plyr Awd Fld Hcky; Blmsbrg U; Accntng.

MINER, LAURA; Tunkhannock HS; Mehoopany, PA; (3); Church Yth Grp; JV Bsktbl; Var Fld Hcky; Hon Roll; Bsktbl Most Dedctd Plyr 85; Hnrbl Ment Essay For Peace 86; Chem.

MINER, SHERRY; Montrose Area HS; Friendsville, PA; (3); VP Church Yth Grp; SADD; Chorus; Church Choir; Nwsp Stf; Rep Stu Cncl; Var Cheerleading; Spanish Clb; School Musical; Stat Crs Cntry; Bloomburg U; Erly Chldhd Ed.

MINERD, COLLEEN; Connellsville SR HS; Connellsville, PA; (3); 30/550; SADD; Band; Mrchg Band; Symp Band; Nwsp Rptr; Pres Trs Stu Cncl; High Hon Roll; Hon Roll; NHS; Spanish NHS; Upwrd Bnd; CA U PA; Sec Educ.

MINERD, DONNA; Carmichaels Area HS; Carmichaels, PA; (4); 12/101; Trs French Clb; Office Aide; Pep Clb; Ski Clb; SADD; Yrbk Rptr; Stu Cncl; High Hon Roll; NHS; Acad All-Amer 86; IN U Of PA; Accntng.

MINERD, MICHAEL; Connellsville SR HS; Connellsville, PA; (4); 11/520; Trs Aud/Vis; Drama Clb; Prfct Atten Awd; Actr.

MINGLE, CYNTHIA; Plymouth White Marsh HS; Norristown, PA; (3); Swmmng; Trk; RI Schl Of Design; Commrcl Art.

MINGLE, MICHELLE; Bensalem HS; Bensalem, PA; (4); 105/499; Office Aide; Color Guard; Mrchg Band; Im Gym; Im Swmmng; Im Tennis; Var Trk; Im Vllybl; High Hon Roll; Hon Roll; Bucks Cnty CC; Chem Lab Tech.

MINICH, CINDY; Brookville Area HS; Brookville, PA; (3); Church Yth Grp; French Clb; FHA; Chorus.

MINICH, LORI; Butler SR HS; Butler, PA; (3); Exploring; VP JA; Ski Clb; VP SADD; Thesps; Rep Stu Cncl; JV Capt Cheerleading; Var Pom Pon; Var L Tennis; Jr NHS; Bus.

MINICH, SHERRI; Brookville Area HS; Sigel, PA; (3); German Clb; Pep Clb; Chorus; School Musical; Hon Roll; Jr NHS; NHS; IN U.

MINICH, STEVEN; Boiling Springs HS; Carlisle, PA; (2); 1/140; Im Wt Lftg; High Hon Roll; Hon Roll; NHS.

MINIOTAS, MIKE; North Catholic HS; Pittsburgh, PA; (3); 35/285; Church Yth Grp; German Clb; Var Bsktbl; Var Ftbl; Wt Lftg; Hon Roll; NHS; Bus.

MINISSALE, ANGELA; Country Day Schl Of The Sacred Heart; Gladwyne, PA; (4); 5/39; Cmnty Wkr; Hosp Aide; Office Aide; Political Wkr; Hon Roll; Pres Schlr; JR Cls Awd Dilignc 86; Psych.

MINK, DAVE; Central Dauphin HS; Harrisburg, PA; (2); Church Yth Grp; Band; Concert Band; Jazz Band; Mrchg Band; MD; Comp Pgmmr.

MINNICH, AMY; Northampton HS; Bath, PA; (3); 54/492; Pres Church Yth Grp; Hosp Aide; Pres SADD; Chorus; Nwsp Stf; Rep Stu Cncl; Co-Capt Twrlr; Hon Roll; Response Team 85-88; Nrsng.

MINNICH, ANDREA; Bangor Area SR HS; Bangor, PA; (2); Computer Clb; Ski Clb; Teachers Aide; Varsity Clb; Co-Capt Cheerleading; Trk; Hon Roll; U Pittsburgh; Law.

MINNICH, BRENDA; Solanco HS; Quarryville, PA; (2); 20/286; Church Yth Grp; Stat Bsktbl; Mgr(s); Score Keeper; JV Trk; High Hon Roll; Hon Roll; Jr NHS; NHS; Solanco Bus Schlr 85-86.

MINNICH, DAWN; Williams Valley HS; Williamstown, PA; (3); 1/90; Chorus; Sec Yrbk Stf; Sec Soph Cls; Stat Bsktbl; Var L Cheerleading; High Hon Roll; Pres NHS; NEDT Awd; Wrld Hstry Awd Woodman 84-85; Bio.

MINNICH, JEFFERSON; Cedar Crest HS; Mt Gretna, PA; (3); Cmnty Wkr; French Clb; Pep Clb; Swmmng; Tennis; Vllybl; NHS.

MINNICH, KANDI; Red Lion SR HS; Brogue, PA; (4); 94/350; Church Yth Grp; German Clb; Yrbk Stf; Var Tennis; Hon Roll; 1st Fed Chptr Schlrshp 87; York Coll; Legl Secy.

MINNICH, MELISSA; Northern Lebanon HS; Lebanon, PA; (2); 15/87; Chorus; Im Vllybl; Hon Roll; NHS; Zoologist.

MINNICK, ANNETTE; Bloomsburg Christian Schl; Catawissa, PA; (3); Church Yth Grp; VP Sec 4-H; School Play; 4-H Awd; Hon Roll; Brnz Mdl 5K Race 86.

MINNICK, LAURA; Bishop Hafey HS; Hazleton, PA; (2); Hosp Aide; Yrbk Stf; Stat Mgr(s); Stat Score Keeper; Hon Roll; Spnsh Cont Part Awd 86; Valentines Day Crt 87; Temple Univ; Psych.

MINNICK, MARCINDA; Bloomsburg Christian Schl; Catawissa, PA; (2); Church Yth Grp; Sec 4-H; Yrbk Stf; 4-H Awd; Hon Roll.

MINNUCCI, ALISA; Lansdale Catholic HS; Doylestown, PA; (3); Art Clb; SADD; VP Frsh Cls; Pres Soph Cls; VP Jr Cls; Var Cheerleading; Pom Pon; Natl Chrldng Compttn 10th In Nation 86; Tyler; Grphc Dsgn.

MINOTTE, MICHELLE; Pius V HS; Pen Argyl, PA; (1); #4 In Class; Dance Clb; Drama Clb; Pep Clb; Varsity Clb; Chorus; Church Choir; School Musical; Yrbk Stf; Rep Frsh Cls; Stu Cncl.

MINSKEY, RENEE; Beth-Center SR HS; Fredericktown, PA; (2); 24/156; Church Yth Grp; Band; Concert Band; Mrchg Band; Pep Band; Hon Roll; Penn ST; Nursing.

MINTEER, AMY; Kittanning SR HS; Worthington, PA; (3); 11/226; Church Yth Grp; Hosp Aide; Mgr(s); High Hon Roll; Hon Roll; VP NHS; Phys Thrpy.

MINTMIER, EILEEN; United HS; New Florence, PA; (3); French Clb; Hosp Aide; Ski Clb; Chorus; Concert Band; Mrchg Band; Trk; Hon Roll; Prfct Atten Awd; Powder Puff Ftbl; Cnty Chorus 87; Psych.

MINTO, JANET; Purchase Line HS; Cherry Tree, PA; (3); 15/98; FBLA; Chorus; Concert Band; Mrchg Band; Stage Crew; Nwsp Phtg; Nwsp Rptr; Pres Jr Cls; 4-H Awd; Hon Roll; Bus.

MIODUSKI, EDWARD; Burgettstown Area JR-SR HS; Burgettstown, PA; (3); 30/190; Church Yth Grp; Sec VP Stu Cncl; Bsbl; Bsktbl; Golf; Wt Lftg; Hon Roll; NHS; Std Forum Pres 87; Southern Coll; Elem Ed.

MIOFF, MICHELLE; Central Dauphin HS; Harrisburg, PA; (2); Drama Clb; Exploring; Ski Clb; Chorus; Church Choir; School Musical; Yrbk Stf; Hon Roll; Jr NHS; Hstry.

MIONE, JASON; Williams Valley JR SR HS; Tower City, PA; (3); 23/96; Church Yth Grp; Band; Concert Band; Jazz Band; Mrchg Band; Symp Band; JV Ftbl; Marine Physcl Ftns Awd 85-87; USC Penn ST; Sports Med.

MIORELLI, DENISE; Portage Area HS; Portage, PA; (3); 10/110; 4-H; Rep Stu Cncl; Trk; 4-H Awd; Hon Roll; NHS; PA ST U.

MIORELLI, GINA; Penn Cambria HS; Lilly, PA; (3); Drama Clb; Speech Tm; SADD; Nwsp Rptr; Nwsp Stf; Rep Frsh Cls; Rep Stu Cncl; JV Cheerleading; Hon Roll; Scl Wkr.

MIORELLI, PAUL; West Hazleton HS; Conyngham, PA; (4); 19/220; Ski Clb; Thesps; Varsity Clb; Chorus; School Musical; School Play; Rep Sr Cls; Var L Crs Cntry; Var L Trk; NHS; Elecl Engnrng.

MIORIN, TODD; Susquehanna Twp HS; Harrisburg, PA; (2); Church Yth Grp; Ski Clb; Hon Roll; Engr.

MIRANDA, BRIGITTA; Hempfield HS; Greensburg, PA; (4); 10/693; Am Leg Aux Girls St; NFL; Pep Clb; Spanish Clb; School Play; Yrbk Phtg; Powder Puff Ftbl; Hon Roll; NHS; Spanish NHS; 1st Pl Spnsh Recitations Comp 86; Schlrshp To Gannon U 86; George Mason In VA; Intl Rel.

MIRICH-GAINES, TARA; Burgettstown Area JR SR HS; Burgettstown, PA; (3); 9/164; FNA; Ski Clb; Spanish Clb; SADD; Drill Tm; Yrbk Stf; High Hon Roll; Hon Roll; Jr NHS; NHS; Shadyside Hosp Schl Nrsng; Nrsn.

MISAVAGE, MICHELLE; Sharon HS; Sharon, PA; (3); 2/200; Hosp Aide; Latin Clb; Varsity Clb; Yrbk Stf; L Crs Cntry; Swmmng; Stat Trk; NHS; :Pre Vet.

MISCANNON JR, JOSEPH S; Shenandoah Valley JR- SR HS; Shenandoah, PA; (3); 24/79; Library Aide; Stage Crew; Aud/Vis; Church Yth Grp; Computer Clb; Hon Roll; Prfct Atten Awd; Penn ST; Geol Sci.

MISCHISSIN, MARY BETH; M M I Preparatory Schl; Freeland, PA; (3); Church Yth Grp; SADD; Var Capt Bowling; Var Capt Cheerleading; Var L Sftbl; Hnrb Mntn Awd-Spnsh Cntst 85 & 86; Bus Adm.

MISCHLER, MICHAEL FORREST; Cathedral Prep Schl; Erie, PA; (4); 90/212; Cmnty Wkr; French Clb; Letterman Clb; Service Clb; Nwsp Ed-Chief; Nwsp Rptr; Nwsp Sprt Ed; Im Bsktbl; Cheerleading; Var L Ftbl; All Metro Ftbl Tckl All Cty; Dist Ten Chmpn; E J Wilwohl Mem Awd; Coll Of William & Mary; Pre Law.

MISCIO, DENA M; Immaculate Conception HS; Washington, PA; (4); 14/52; Church Yth Grp; Cmnty Wkr; Hosp Aide; Nwsp Ed-Chief; Yrbk Phtg; Yrbk Stf; Rep Stu Cncl; Hon Roll; NHS; Duquesne U Prsh Hnr Schlrshp 87; Duquesne U; Jrnlsm.

MISH, LORI; Conemaugh TWP Area HS; Davidsville, PA; (4); 8/101; Sec VP 4-H; VP JA; NFL; Ed Nwsp Stf; Yrbk Phtg; Pres Stu Cncl; JV Var Cheerleading; NHS; Church Yth Grp; Drama Clb; Hugh O Brian Yth Fndtn Ldrshp Smnr 85; Cambria-Somerset Jr Miss Fnlst 86-87; Vet Med.

MISHLER, CHRISTINA; Blue Mountain Acad; Rockwood, PA; (3); Art Clb; Church Yth Grp; Cmnty Wkr; Drama Clb; VP FHA; GAA; Girl Scts; Library Aide; Speech Tm; Varsity Clb; Mdl In Sftbl 88; Rbns For Trck 83-86; Andrws U MI; Elem Tchr.

MISHOCK, JOHN; Penn Cambria SR HS; Gallitzin, PA; (3); Am Leg Boys St; Church Yth Grp; Band; Var L Bsbl; Var Bsktbl.

MISHORICH, JO ANNA; Conneaut Lake HS; Hartstown, PA; (3); Drama Clb; Spanish Clb; SADD; Chorus; Mrchg Band; Nwsp Ed-Chief; Yrbk Phtg; Off Stu Cncl; Var Cheerleading; Var Vllybl; Int Dsgnr.

MISHRA, VIJOY; Waynesburg Central HS; Waynesburg, PA; (3); 1/200; Pres Chess Clb; French Clb; Concert Band; Jazz Band; VP Mrchg Band; High Hon Roll; NHS; NEDT Awd; Algebra III, Trig, French II, French I Awds 85-86; Carnegie Mellon U; Chem Eng.

MISHRELL, SHERRIE; Fort Le Boeuf HS; Waterford, PA; (4); 50/167; Capt Varsity Clb; Band; Concert Band; Mrchg Band; Var Capt Bsktbl; Var Capt Sftbl; Hon Roll; Mercy Hurst Coll.

MISIEWICZ, SUSAN; Cardinal Brennan HS; Ashland, PA; (3); 2/58; Band; Chorus; Pres Concert Band; Pres Mrchg Band; School Musical; Rep Frsh Cls; Rep Soph Cls; Rep Jr Cls; Rep Stu Cncl; Stat Bsbl; Hghst Hnr Role 85-87; Bus.

MISIOLEK, SUSAN; Red Lion HS; York, PA; (4); 60/330; Latin Clb; SADD; Varsity Clb; Off Rep Stu Cncl; JV Var Cheerleading; Towson ST U; Math.

MISKE, ANITA; Rochester JR SR HS; Rochester, PA; (3); 2/110; Sec Drama Clb; French Clb; Teachers Aide; Chorus; High Hon Roll; NHS; Prfct Atten Awd; Pres Schlr; Elem Ed.

MISKE, CHRISTINA MARIE; Rochester Area Schl Dist; Rochester, PA; (4); 1/95; School Musical; Nwsp Ed-Chief; Yrbk Phtg; Pres Stu Cncl; L Cheerleading; Capt Powder Puff Ftbl; L Tennis; Bausch & Lomb Sci Awd; Pres NHS; Val; Qull & Scrll 86&87; Lions Clb Awd 87; Wlvs Clb Awd 87; Cornell U; Bio.

MISKO, HOLLY; Nazareth Acad; Philadelphia, PA; (3); German Clb; Hosp Aide; Hon Roll; NE Hosp Nursng Schl; Nrsng.

MISKO, KEVIN; Cathedral Prep; Fairview, PA; (3); 19/193; Art Clb; Church Yth Grp; FCA; Pep Clb; Ski Clb; Yrbk Phtg; Rep Stu Cncl; Im JV Bsktbl; Im Ftbl; Im Golf.

MISLEVY, PAMELA; Tunkhannock Area HS; Tunkhannock, PA; (3); 25/360; Ski Clb; Band; Concert Band; Mrchg Band; Var Fld Hcky; Var Sftbl; Var Swmmng; Hon Roll; NHS; Engr.

MISSIMER, BARBARA; William Allen HS; Allentown, PA; (3); 26/600; Color Guard; Yrbk Stf; Twrlr; Hon Roll; Jr NHS; NHS; Natl Hnr Scty-Hnr Lttr & Awd 87; Cmmnctns.

MISTAL, KRISTY; West Hazleton HS; W Hazleton, PA; (2); 17/225; Scholastic Bowl; Ski Clb; Varsity Clb; Chorus; Ed Yrbk Ed-Chief; VP Trs Stu Cncl; Stat Bsktbl; Cheerleading; Var L Crs Cntry; Var L Trk; Bucknell U; Elem Educ.

MISTRETTA, SHANNON; Homer Center JR SR HS; Homer City, PA; (3); #1 In Class; Color Guard; Ed Nwsp Ed-Chief; VP Jr Cls; L Var Sftbl; Var Vllybl; NHS; Intl Frgn Lang Awd 85; Arin Mntrshp Pgm 86-87; Hghst GPA 86; Accntng.

MISTYSYN, MARK J; Nativity BVM HS; Pottsville, PA; (1); Variety Show; Nwsp Rptr; Nwsp Stf; JV Bsbl; Bsktbl; Hon Roll; Jrnlsm.

MITCEHLL, DAWN; Harry S Truman HS; Levittown, PA; (3); 164/599; Church Yth Grp; Girl Scts; Pep Clb; SADD; Church Choir; Flag Corp; Mrchg Band; Yrbk Stf; JV Bsktbl; Var Fld Hcky; Bloomsburg; Elem Educ.

MITCHELL, ANDREA; Central Dauphin HS; Harrisburg, PA; (4); Church Yth Grp; Girl Scts; Red Cross Aide; SADD; Band; Chorus; Concert Band; Madrigals; Mrchg Band; Yrbk Stf; Citation From Senator Shuemaker 84-85; Presdntl Acad Fit Awds Prog 86-8m; Elizabethtown; Lawyer.

MITCHELL, ANISSA; Norristown Area HS; Norristown, PA; (3); 41/524; Church Yth Grp; Trk; Vllybl; Wt Lftg; Cit Awd; High Hon Roll; Citizen Of Mnth Awd 84; Golden Key Spanish Awd 84; Track 85; Elec Engr.

MITCHELL, CHRISTOPHER H; Carmichaels Area JR SR HS; Rices Landing, PA; (4); 10/101; Drama Clb; VP Spanish Clb; Rep Jr Cls; Rep Sr Cls; Rep Stu Cncl; L Bsbl; L Golf; Pres NHS; NEDT 90 Prcntl 84; Olympc Of Minds St Fnlst 86; Physics.

MITCHELL, CHRISTOPHER J; Nativity BVM HS; Port Carbon, PA; (1); 14/94; Boy Scts; Church Yth Grp; Computer Clb; Nwsp Rptr; Nwsp Stf; Hon Roll; 3rd Pl Sci Fair Awd 87; Comp Sci.

MITCHELL, CINDY; Marion Center HS; Indiana, PA; (4); Pres Church Yth Grp; Intnl Clb; Q&S; Science Clb; SADD; Capt Flag Corp; Nwsp Bus Mgr; Rep Stu Cncl; Var Sftbl; VP NHS; Indiana U Of PA; Frnch Educ.

MITCHELL, COREY; Hempfield HS; Manheim, PA; (4); 16/415; Math Tm; Quiz Bowl; Im Bsktbl; High Hon Roll; NHS; Ntl Merit Ltr; Pres Schlr; AHSME 86-87; IUP Physics Test 87; Penn ST; Math.

MITCHELL, CYNTHIA JEAN; Peters Twp HS; Mc Murray, PA; (4); Church Yth Grp; Computer Clb; FBLA; Intl Clb; Key Clb; Library Aide; Mrchg Band; Yrbk Stf; Lit Mag; L Sftbl; Waynesburg Coll; Acctng.

MITCHELL, DAVID W; Mercyhurst Prep Schl; Erie, PA; (4); 80/155; Drama Clb; Spanish Clb; Pres Thesps; Chorus; School Musical; School Play; Stage Crew; Variety Show; Rep Stu Cncl; Hon Roll; Hnr Thspn; Bst Thspn; Edinboro U PA; Art.

MITCHELL, DIANE; Clearfield Area HS; Clearfield, PA; (4); 2/292; French Clb; Band; Chorus; Drm Mjr(t); Orch; Nwsp Ed-Chief; Yrbk Ed-Chief; High Hon Roll; NHS; Sal; Charles Vogelsong Memrl & Womans Clb Schlrshps 87; Penn ST U; Aerospc Engrng.

MITCHELL, DONALD; Council Rock HS; Churchville, PA; (4); 45/850; Boy Scts; Im Ice Hcky; Im Socr; Im Vllybl; Hon Roll; NHS; Lafayette Coll; Elec Engrng.

MITCHELL, ERIKA; Sattsburg JR SR HS; Saltsburg, PA; (3); 13/62; Drama Clb; FTA; SADD; Varsity Clb; Yrbk Stf; Powder Puff Ftbl; Score Keeper; Trk; High Hon Roll; Hon Roll; Pres Physcl Ftnss Awd 86-87.

MITCHELL, GLENN; Bensalem SR HS; Bensalem, PA; (2); Science Clb; Stage Crew; High Hon Roll; NHS; Acad Excellence Awd 86-87; Penn St Sci Olympd Awd Exclince 87; Penn ST; Astrophysicist.

MITCHELL, JENNIFER; Laurel Highlands SR HS; Hopwood, PA; (3); 48/535; Church Yth Grp; Exploring; Teachers Aide; Color Guard; Flag Corp; Nwsp Stf; Vllybl; High Hon Roll; Hon Roll; Prfct Atten Awd; U Of Pittsburgh; Sci.

MITCHELL, JONATHAN; Dallas Senior HS; Dallas, PA; (3); Boy Scts; Chess Clb; Exploring; Hon Roll; NEDT Awd; Engr.

MITCHELL, KIM; Linesville HS; Linesville, PA; (4); 2/87; Keywanettes; Mu Alpha Theta; Pep Clb; SADD; Chorus; Score Keeper; High Hon Roll; NHS; Pres Schlr; Sal; Hlth Occup Stu Of Amer 86; PA ST U; Pre-Med.

MITCHELL, KIM; Northwestern HS; Edinboro, PA; (2); 16/145; Church Yth Grp; Pres 4-H; Rep Stu Cncl; Var L Bsktbl; Var L Trk; Var L Vllybl; Hon Roll; Acdmc All Amer Alg II 9th Grd 86; Penn ST; Sprts Med.

MITCHELL, KIMBERLY; William Allen HS; Allentown, PA; (3); 141/610; Key Clb; Leo Clb; Nwsp Stf; Rep Stu Cncl; Bowling; Powder Puff Ftbl; Hon Roll; Jr NHS; Clinical Psych.

MITCHELL, LAURIE R; Burrell HS; Lower Burrell, PA; (4); 1/203; JA; Spanish Clb; Nwsp Phtg; Yrbk Phtg; Capt Var Bsktbl; High Hon Roll; NHS; Pres Schlr; Rotary Awd; Hon Roll; Bnfcl Fndtn E T Higgins Schlrshp, C E Marker Schlr-Athlt Awd, US Marine Corps Disting Athlt Awd 87; U Of Pittsburg; Phys Thrpy.

MITCHELL, LEANNE M; Hershey SR HS; Hershey, PA; (4); 26/178; Church Yth Grp; Hosp Aide; Model UN; Pep Clb; Ski Clb; Spanish Clb; Stage Crew; Variety Show; Nwsp Rptr; Yrbk Rptr; PA ST U; Advrtsng Communctns.

MITCHELL, LORI; Burgettstown HS; Eldersville, PA; (4); 6/150; Ski Clb; Pres Band; Concert Band; Mrchg Band; Jr NHS; NHS; Nrsng.

MITCHELL, MARSHALL; Central HS; Philadelphia, PA; (3); Boy Scts; Cmnty Wkr; NAACP; Political Wkr; Nwsp Rptr; Nwsp Stf; VP Jr Cls; Var Tennis; Georgetown; Polit Sci.

MITCHELL, MARY; North Catholic HS; Pgh, PA; (3); 63/240; Hosp Aide; Bsktbl; Hon Roll; St Margarets Schl/Nrsng; Nrs.

MITCHELL, MATT; Fort Le Boeuf HS; Waterford, PA; (3); 4-H; JV Ftbl; 4-H Awd; Hon Roll.

MITCHELL, MICHAEL; Bishop Mc Cort HS; Johnstown, PA; (3); 25/155; Var JV Bsktbl; Var L Trk; High Hon Roll; NHS; Acad All Amer 87; VP Natl Hnr Scty 87; Engr.

MITCHELL, MILTON H; Wyoming Smnry; Dallas, PA; (4); 3/99; Computer Clb; Political Wkr; Jazz Band; Orch; Symp Band; Yrbk Ed-Chief; Var L Socr; Var Tennis; High Hon Roll; NHS; Ntl Merit SF; Cum Laude Socty.

MITCHELL, REBECCA; Meyersdale Area HS; Meyersdale, PA; (3); 1/111; Am Leg Aux Girls St; Pres Church Yth Grp; Sec Spanish Clb; VP Chorus; Church Choir; School Musical; Off Stu Cncl; Var L Cheerleading; Dnfth Awd; High Hon Roll; Spcl Ed.

MITCHELL, SHANNON L; Fort Le Boeuf HS; Waterford, PA; (3); Art Clb; Score Keeper; Stat Trk; Stat Wrstlng; Hon Roll; Fnlst In Govrs Schl Of The Arts 87; Cmmrcl Arts.

MITCHELL, SHERRY; Chartiers-Houston HS; Houston, PA; (4); 20/120; Church Yth Grp; Drama Clb; FCA; French Clb; GAA; Pep Clb; PAVAS; Science Clb; Varsity Clb; Acpl Chr; Jrnlsm Acdmc Awd 87; Westminster Coll; Microbio.

MITCHELL, STEPHANIE; Solanco HS; Quarryville, PA; (4); Teachers Aide; Hon Roll; Prfct Atten Awd.

MITCHEM, PAM; East Pennsboro HS; W Fairview, PA; (2); 29/189; Drama Clb; French Clb; Hosp Aide; Band; Chorus; Concert Band; Drill Tm; Mrchg Band; Pep Band; School Musical; U Of CT; Radiology.

MITRE, EDWARD E S; Shady Side Acad; Pittsburgh, PA; (4); Chess Clb; Debate Tm; Drama Clb; School Play; Nwsp Ed-Chief; Nwsp Rptr; JV Socr; Var Trk; Ntl Merit SF; Spanish NHS; Pres Prize 87; Columbia Coll; Molecular Bio.

MITRUS, VICTORIA; Bishop Mc Cort HS; Johnstown, PA; (3); 33/155; Church Yth Grp; Drama Clb; JA; Spanish Clb; Chorus; Church Choir; Hon Roll; Spanish NHS; Spnsh Natl Hnr Scty 85-86; Spclzd Nrsng.

MITSCH, LINDA; South Park HS; Library, PA; (3); Drama Clb; Thesps; Concert Band; Mrchg Band; School Musical; School Play; Stage Crew; High Hon Roll; Hon Roll; NHS; NEDT Awd; Pharm.

MITSCH, WILLIAM; Montour HS; Pittsburgh, PA; (4); 23/302; Ftbl; Trk; Hon Roll; NHS; WV Wesleyan; Engrng.

MITSTIFER, SAMANTHA A; Liberty JR/SR HS; Troutrun, PA; (2); Pres 4-H; FHA; German Clb; Bsktbl; HOBY 86-87; Pblc Rltns.

MITTS, DARLA; Connellsville Area SR HS; Connellsville, PA; (3); 75/500; Drama Clb; Band; Chorus; Church Choir; Mrchg Band; Orch; School Musical; Symp Band; Tennis; High Hon Roll; Point Park Coll; Pub Rel.

MITURA, JOSEPH; St Josephs Prep HS; Philadelphia, PA; (4); 60/224; Boy Scts; Science Clb; Yrbk Stf; Im Bsktbl; Im Ftbl; Im Ice Hcky; Hon Roll; NHS; U Harftof Schlrhsp 87; Eagle Scout Awd 84; U Hartford; Engrng.

MITZEL, THERESA; Red Lion HS; Red Lion, PA; (3); 35/342; Varsity Clb; Yrbk Stf; Var Trk; Var Vllybl; Hon Roll; USVBA Jr Olympcs 85-87; Hnrbl Mntn Yrk Dsptch Vlybl 86-87; All Trnmt Tm All Star Vlybl 86; Psych.

MIVILLE, JEFF; Montgomery Area HS; Watsontown, PA; (3); Computer Clb; French Clb; Stage Crew; JV L Ftbl; Var L Trk; Var L Wrstlng; High Hon Roll; Hon Roll; NHS; Typng Awd 85-86; Comp Prg.

MIX, STEVEN L; Butler HS; Butler, PA; (3); Boy Scts; Spanish Clb; Var Bowling; Hon Roll; Cvl Engr.

MIX, THEODORE; Oswayo Valley JRSR HS; Shinglehouse, PA; (3); Yrbk Sprt Ed; JV Capt Bsbl; JV Bsktbl; Var Socr; Hon Roll.

MIZELLE, TERRI; Center HS; Aliquippa, PA; (3); German Clb; Band; Concert Band; Mrchg Band; Stu Cncl; Powder Puff Ftbl; Vllybl; Fash Dsgn.

MIZENKO, CHERYL; Bishop O Reilly HS; Swoyersville, PA; (2); Hosp Aide; Spanish Clb; Trs Jr Cls; Rep Rep Stu Cncl; Var Pom Pon; Hon Roll; Prfct Atten Awd; Med.

MLODZINSKI, PAUL; Cardinal Dougherty HS; Philadelphia, PA; (4); 4/704; Off Boy Scts; Latin Clb; Golf; Cit Awd; NHS; Advncd Career Trnng Pgm Philadlphia Cncl C Of C Schl 86; Archdiocese Phila Ofc Cath Ed Schlr 87; La Salle U; Geol.

MLYNARSKI, KIMBERLY ANNE; Nazareth Acad; Philadelphia, PA; (3); 23/125; Cmnty Wkr; Hosp Aide; Q&S; Nwsp Ed-Chief; Pres Jr Cls; Off Stu Cncl; Bowling; NHS; Philadelphia Dicoesan Schlr 87; Nazareth Acad Alunmae Assn Tuition Grant 87-88; Villanova U; Attorney.

MOATS, BRIAN; Sharpsville Area HS; Clark, PA; (4); 13/123; Math Clb; Science Clb; Spanish Clb; School Play; Hon Roll; NHS; Pres Schlr; Indiana U Of PA; Bus.

MOATS, DARLA; Fairchance-Georges HS; Smithfield, PA; (3); Drama Clb; FHA; School Play; Stage Crew; Nwsp Stf; Hon Roll; Scrtry.

MOATS, EDWARD; Fairchance-Georges SR HS; Fairchance, PA; (3); FHA; Hon Roll; NHS; Outstndng Parent Awd Dept Voctnl Hmmkng 85; Marine Bio.

MOATZ, MONICA L; Moravian Acad; Emmaus, PA; (4); Art Clb; Computer Clb; Ski Clb; Chorus; School Musical; Variety Show; Nwsp Stf; Yrbk Stf; Mgr Bsktbl; Lcrss; U Of Miami; Grphc Dsgn.

MOCK, ANDREA; Eastern Lebanon County HS; Myerstown, PA; (3); 36/146; SADD; Band; Chorus; Drm Mjr(t); Jazz Band; Mrchg Band; Trs Stu Cncl; Stat Bsktbl; JV Var Sftbl; NHS; Acctng.

MOCK, CHERI; Claysburg-Kimmel HS; Imler, PA; (3); 4/76; Pres Church Yth Grp; VICA; Band; Rep Frsh Cls; Rep Soph Cls; VP Jr Cls; Co-Capt Twrlr; High Hon Roll; Sec NHS; Prfct Atten Awd; Hghst Acad Avg Voc Currclm 87; Dntl Asstnt.

MOCK, CHERYL; Claysburg Kimmel HS; Claysburgh, PA; (2); 5/97; Band; Color Guard; Mrchg Band; Hon Roll; Psychlgy.

MOCK, JASON; Keystone HS; Shippenville, PA; (3); SADD; Chorus; Nwsp Phtg; Nwsp Rptr; Stu Cncl; High Hon Roll; Aviator.

MOCK, MATTHEW; Keystone HS; Shippenville, PA; (4); 9/125; French Clb; Band; Chorus; Concert Band; Mrchg Band; School Musical; Nwsp Ed-Chief; High Hon Roll; Prfct Atten Awd; Clrn U Of PA-SMMR Acad-Comm 86; Penn ST; Arspc Engr.

MOCNIAK, JUDI; Mapletown JR SR HS; Garards Fort, PA; (4); 20/75; Drama Clb; GAA; Ski Clb; School Play; Yrbk Phtg; Rep Sr Cls; Im Vllybl; High Hon Roll; Hon Roll; Nwsp Phtg; Stdnt Mnth Mar 87; Waynesburg; Nrsg.

MODAR, ANNETTE; Greensburg Central Catholic HS; Jeannette, PA; (3); Church Yth Grp; Pep Clb; Chorus; High Hon Roll; Bus.

MODESITT, KEITH; Center HS; Aliquippa, PA; (4); German Clb; Varsity Clb; Bsbl; Bowling; L Trk; Hon Roll; Rgn II JR Olympc Wnnr Trk/Fld 87; Eastern MI U; Forestry Mgmt.

MODESTO, LISA; Danville Area HS; Danville, PA; (2); 4/165; Church Yth Grp; Exploring; French Clb; Hosp Aide; Key Clb; NFL; Var JV Cheerleading; JV Tennis; Gov Hon Prg Awd; High Hon Roll; Grhm F Stvns Crtsy Awd 86; Hgh Avg-Sci & Alg II 86; Prsdntl Acdmc Ftnss Awd 86; Med.

MODRESKY, MICHALENE; James M Coughlin HS; Wilkes Barre, PA; (3); Church Yth Grp; Drama Clb; Math Tm; School Play; Yrbk Stf; Var L Bsktbl; Hon Roll; NHS; Pre Med.

MODY, BHAVANA G; Frankford HS; Philadelphia, PA; (4); Drama Clb; Hosp Aide; JA; Office Aide; School Play; Nwsp Bus Mgr; Yrbk Rptr; Badmtn; Vllybl; Hon Roll; Natl Schl Schlrshp For Med Sec 87-88; Cosmpoltn Awd Saving Bond 87; Natl Schl; Med Sec.

MOE, RACHEL; Western Wayne HS; Lake Ariel, PA; (3); 37/200; Hosp Aide; Spanish Clb; Im Trk; Hon Roll; Millersvl U; Marine Bio.

MOECKEL, MARK; Dunmore HS; Dunmore, PA; (3); 17/148; French Clb; Science Clb; Spanish Clb; Nwsp Rptr; Yrbk Rptr; High Hon Roll; Hon Roll; Jr NHS; NHS; Comms.

MOEHLER, MICHELLE; Windber Area HS; Windber, PA; (4); Art Clb; FTA; Library Aide; Ski Clb; Yrbk Stf; High Hon Roll; Stu Mnth Awds 83-87; Acad Achvt Awds Art II & III 85-87; Acad Excell Art Awd 87; Kent ST U; Grphc Dsgn.

MOELLENBROCK, BONNY; Penns Valley Area HS; Centre Hall, PA; (3); 1/160; Trs SADD; Varsity Clb; Chorus; Concert Band; Mrchg Band; Yrbk Ed-Chief; Var L Crs Cntry; Var L Trk; High Hon Roll; NHS; Prtcptd PMEA Dist & Rgnl Chorus 87.

MOELLENBROCK, JENNIFER; Seneca Valley SR HS; Mars, PA; (3); 50/400; Church Yth Grp; Ski Clb; Varsity Clb; JV Bsktbl; Var L Sftbl; Var L Tennis; JV Trk; High Hon Roll; Hon Roll; NHS; Penn ST U; Sports Med.

MOERDER, DAVID; Tamaqua HS; Andreas, PA; (3); Chess Clb; French Clb; Nwsp Rptr; Nwsp Stf; French Hon Soc; Hon Roll; Engrng.

MOFFAT, TERESA; Delaware Valley HS; Matamoras, PA; (4); 16/143; Teachers Aide; Band; Concert Band; JV Stat Bsktbl; High Hon Roll; Hon Roll; NHS; Phys Fitness Awd 87; Susquehanna U; Elem Ed.

MOFFATT, CHUCK; Union City HS; Union City, PA; (4); 6/82; Boy Scts; Varsity Clb; Capt Var Bsbl; JV Trk; Var JV Wrstlng; Hon Roll; Pres Schlr; Pres Physcl Ftns Awd 87; All Cnty Bsbl 86-87; U Of WY; Educ.

MOFFATT, ELIZABETH; West Perry SR HS; Millerstown, PA; (4); 18/188; Pres Chorus; Concert Band; Drm Mjr(t); Jazz Band; Sec Mrchg Band; Nwsp Rptr; Yrbk Ed-Chief; Sec Trs Lit Mag; Pres Church Yth Grp; Sec Drama Clb; Outstndng Drum Major 84; Outstndng Music Stu 83-87; County Band 83-86; U Pittsburgh; Med.

MOFFETT, LISA; Bangor Area SR HS; Bangor, PA; (3); Pep Clb; Ski Clb; Concert Band; Drill Tm; Rep Stu Cncl; Mgr Bsktbl; Mgr Tennis; Trk; Hon Roll; Stu Gov Awd 2 Yrs Off 87; Natl Merit Awd Mjrtts 86; HS JR Miss Pgnt 87; Trvl.

MOFFETT, MARK; Upper Merion Area HS; King Of Prussia, PA; (3); Boy Scts; Ftbl; Lcrss; Swmmng; Wt Lftg; Wrstlng; Drexel U; Arch.

MOFFITT, AMY; Notre Dame HS; Bethlehem, PA; (3); 24/90; French Clb; Math Clb; Pep Clb; Nwsp Sprt Ed; Nwsp Stf; Yrbk Stf; Trs Soph Cls; Trs Jr Cls; Var Cheerleading; Var Trk; Engl.

MOFFITT, MELISSA; St Basil Acad; Philadelphia, PA; (3); 6/88; Chorus; Yrbk Stf; High Hon Roll; Spanish NHS; Natl Eng Mrt Awd 86-87; Natl Sci Mrt Awd 86-87; Bucknell U; Biochem.

MOFFITT, MICHELE; Wallenpaupack HS; Paupack, PA; (3); 13/157; Am Leg Aux Girls St; Drama Clb; School Play; VP Stu Cncl; JV Var Fld Hcky; Var Trk; High Hon Roll; VP NHS; Most Improved Rnnr Track; ST Stu Cncl Conf Wrkshp; Advrtsng.

MOFFITT, SUSAN; Peters Twp HS; Mcmurray, PA; (3); 12/216; Church Yth Grp; Cmnty Wkr; Debate Tm; Key Clb; Spanish Clb; Yrbk Ed-Chief; Yrbk Stf; Socr; NHS; Spanish NHS; Occptnl Thrpst.

MOGLE, TONYA A; Southmoreland HS; Alverton, PA; (2); Drama Clb; Sec Exploring; French Clb; Ski Clb; Color Guard; Concert Band; Mrchg Band; Jr NHS; Distric Band & Chorus & Cnty Chorus 86; Med.

MOHALLATEE, MICHAEL; Allen Hig HS; Allentown, PA; (4); 33/585; Chess Clb; Exploring; Science Clb; Ski Clb; Yrbk Phtg; Yrbk Stf; High Hon Roll; Hon Roll; NHS; Pres Schlr; Physcs Olympcs; Chss Trnmnts; U Of Pitt; Engrng.

MOHAMMAD, JENIFER; Wilkinsburg JR/Sr HS; Pittsburgh, PA; (4); French Clb; Office Aide; Acpl Chr; Chorus; Yrbk Stf; Off Sr Cls; Bsktbl; Hon Roll; Jr NHS; NHS; Bus.

MOHAMMED, BONNIE; William Penn HS; York, PA; (3); Teachers Aide; Nrsry Schl Tchr.

MOHAN, DANIEL; Kennedy Christian HS; Clark, PA; (2); 12/100; Boy Scts; Spanish Clb; Stu Cncl; Var JV Bsktbl; Ftbl; Vllybl; High Hon Roll; NEDT Awd; Med.

MOHL, CAROL; Hatboro-Horsham HS; Hatboro, PA; (3); Church Yth Grp; Key Clb; Library Aide; SADD; Var Capt Crs Cntry; Var Trk; All Suburban I 2 Team Crss Cntry 86-87; Bob Jones U.

MOHLER, LIZABETH M; William Penn SR HS; York, PA; (3); 50/500; VP JA; Chorus; Color Guard; Mrchg Band; Nwsp Ed-Chief; Nwsp Rptr; Nwsp Stf; Hon Roll; Jr NHS; NHS; Med Tech.

MOHLER, ROBERT; Penn Manor HS; Pequea, PA; (3); 54/317; Boy Scts; Pres Church Yth Grp; Exploring; Varsity Clb; L Var Crs Cntry; Lit Mag; 1st Pl York Tech Drftg Cntst 86; FL Inst Of Tech; Aerosp Engrng.

MOHN, CYNTHIA; Pine Grove Area HS; Donaldson, PA; (4); 24/116; Am Leg Aux Girls St; Varsity Clb; Band; Chorus; Concert Band; Mrchg Band; School Musical; JV Var Bsktbl; Stat Sftbl; Im Tennis; Kutztown U; Specl Educ.

MOHN, MARK; Governor Mifflin SR HS; Mohnton, PA; (3); 85/300; Boy Scts; Church Yth Grp; Key Clb; Acpl Chr; School Musical; Swing Chorus; Hon Roll; Prfct Atten Awd; 2nd V Chf Kittatinny Ldg, Ordr Of Arrow 87; Ltn Awd 85; Millersville U; Marine Bio.

MOHN, MICHAEL; Cedar Crest HS; Lebanon, PA; (2); 33/345; Church Yth Grp; German Clb; Pep Clb; Hon Roll; Prfct Atten Awd; Hnrs Banquet Medal For B Avg All Yr 86-87; Lebanon Vly Coll; Tchr.

MOHN, ROBERT; Cedar Cliff HS; New Cumberland, PA; (2); 44/288; Computer Clb; Ski Clb; Band; Concert Band; Crs Cntry; Trk; High Hon Roll; Prfct Atten Awd; Arntcl Engrng.

MOHNEY, GLENN; Du Bois Area HS; Reynoldsville, PA; (3); Church Yth Grp; Exploring; Hon Roll; Engrng.

MOHNEY, KEN; Mt Pleasant Area HS; Mount Pleasant, PA; (4); Church Yth Grp; Latin Clb; Hon Roll; U Of Pittsburgh; Psych.

MOHNKERN, JULIE S; Norm East HS; North East, PA; (4); 5/141; AFS; Camera Clb; Church Yth Grp; Girl Scts; Hosp Aide; Latin Clb; Sec Q&S; Trs Chorus; Church Choir; School Musical; 1st Pl PA Schl Press Assn 85; 2nd Pl Wmns Club Art Cont & Schl Schlrshp 87; Westminster Coll.

MOHR, BECKY; Northern Bedford County HS; Bakers Summit, PA; (4); 5/92; Band; Chorus; School Musical; High Hon Roll; Hon Roll; JP Sousa Awd; NHS; Trs 4-H; FTA; SADD; Music Awd 50 Dollar Svngs Bond 87; Penn ST U; Music Ed.

MOHR, BRIAN; Solanco HS; Kirkwood, PA; (2); Bsbl; Socr; Hon Roll; NHS; Temple U; Engr.

MOHR, RHONDA; Boyertown Area SR HS; New Berlinvl, PA; (4); 12/437; Math Tm; Band; Chorus; Church Choir; Jazz Band; Orch; High Hon Roll; VP NHS; Pres VP Church Yth Grp; Girl Scts; Arlen R Saylor Schlrhsp Awd 87; Presdntl Acad Fit Awd 8m; Slipper Rock U; Music Therapy.

MOHR, SHARON; Milton Area SR HS; Lewisburg, PA; (3); Cmnty Wkr; Trs FTA; Trs Pres German Clb; Teachers Aide; Bsktbl; Coach Actv; Fld Hcky; Powder Puff Ftbl; Sftbl; Trk; Bloomsburg U; Scndry Ed.

MOHUTSKY, TONY; Cardinal Brennan HS; Frackville, PA; (3); 9/58; Nwsp Sprt Ed; Yrbk Stf; Rep Jr Cls; Rep Sr Cls; Rep Stu Cncl; Var Bsktbl; High Hon Roll; Hon Roll; NHS; Ntl Merit Schol.

MOHUTSKY, VALERIE; Cardinal Brennan HS; Shenandoah, PA; (3); Band; Chorus; Concert Band; Drm Mjr(t); Rptr Yrbk Rptr; Stu Cncl; Stat Bsktbl; Score Keeper; Outstndg Achvt Am Cultures 86; Outstndg Achvt Bio 86; Outstndg Achvt Engl 86.

MOIST, CINDY; Lewistown Area HS; Mc Veytown, PA; (2); AFS; French Clb; Ski Clb; Band; Concert Band; Mrchg Band; JV Fld Hcky; Mgr(s); Score Keeper; Stat Trk; Penn ST U; Athltc Trnr.

MOIST, KEVIN; Chief Logan HS; Lewistown, PA; (4); 13/197; French Clb; Band; Chorus; Concert Band; Jazz Band; High Hon Roll; Ntl Merit SF; Pres Schlr; Penn ST U; Journlsm.

MOJICA, EMILY; Bethlehem Catholic HS; Bethlehem, PA; (3); 104/202; Hosp Aide; Rep Jr Cls; Stu Cncl; Fld Hcky; Hon Roll.

MOJOCK JR, DAVID; New Castle HS; New Castle, PA; (3); Letterman Clb; Rep Frsh Cls; Rep Soph Cls; Rep Sr Cls; Rep Stu Cncl; Var JV Bsktbl; Var Capt Crs Cntry; Var Trk; High Hon Roll; Hon Roll; Air Force ROTC; Physcs.

MOLCHAN, ERIC; James Buchanan HS; Fort Loudon, PA; (3); Varsity Clb; L Crs Cntry; L Wrstlng; Hon Roll; Christman Tourney Champ Wrestling 85-86; 2nd Sectional Champ Wrestling 85-87.

MOLCHAN, JAMES E; Gateway HS; Pitcairn, PA; (3); Am Leg Boys St; Church Yth Grp; Computer Clb; Science Clb; Chorus; Yrbk Stf; Off Frsh Cls; Off Soph Cls; Off Jr Cls; High Hon Roll; Chem.

MOLCHAN, JIM; Gateway HS; Pitcairn, PA; (3); Am Leg Boys St; Church Yth Grp; Computer Clb; Science Clb; Chorus; Yrbk Stf; Off Frsh Cls; Off Soph Cls; Jr Cls; High Hon Roll; Chmcl Engrng.

MOLCHEN, GREGORY CARL; Ambridge Area HS; Ambridge, PA; (3); Exploring; Ski Clb; Y-Teens; Band; Jazz Band; Mrchg Band; Symp Band; Church Yth Grp; Dance Clb; French Clb; Gftd & Tlntd Prgm 84-88; Cmnctns-Coll Presp Englsh 84-88; U MI; Marine Bio.

MOLDOVAN, AMY; Lincoln HS; Ellwood City, PA; (3); 74/162; Spanish Clb; Y-Teens; Chorus; Powder Puff Ftbl; Hon Roll.

MOLDOVAN, TONY; Hickory HS; Sharpsville, PA; (3); DECA; Band; Jazz Band; Mrchg Band; Pep Band; PA Free Entrprse Wk, 1 Wk Schlrshp 87; DECA Dist 1 VP 86-87.

MOLER, CHARLES; Carlisle HS; Woodbridge, VA; (4); 8/398; Camera Clb; Church Yth Grp; Model UN; Teachers Aide; Varsity Clb; Pres Soph Cls; JV Bsktbl; Var Ftbl; Socr; NHS; All Europe Ftbl Puntr, All Conf Qtrbck & Kckr 85; All Conf Bsktbl & All Star Tm 86; Gene Evans Awd 87; VA Polytechnic Inst; Engrng.

MOLINARI, GLORIA; Saint Maria Goretti HS; Philadelphia, PA; (4); 3/384; Capt Math Tm; Yrbk Ed-Chief; High Hon Roll; NHS; Prfct Atten Awd; Wms Aux Of Cmmnwlth Ldg Sns Of Italy Schlrshp 87; Philadelphia City Schlrshp 87; Drexel U; Chem Engr.

MOLINARI, TONY; West Mifflin Area HS; W Mifflin, PA; (3); Boy Scts; Ski Clb; Varsity Clb; Rep Stu Cncl; JV Bsbl; JV Bsktbl; Var Socr; Var Trk; Hon Roll; Off Plyr Yr Soccr 84-85 & 85-86; ACE Pgm 77-87; Pre-Law.

MOLINARO, KAREN; Washington HS; Washington, PA; (3); Band; Concert Band; Jazz Band; Mrchg Band; Symp Band; Yrbk Stf.

MOLINO, CHRISTOPHER; South Williamsport HS; S Wmspt, PA; (4); Leo Clb; Pres Rep Stu Cncl; Var L Ftbl; Var L Trk; Var L Wrstlng; Hon Roll; All Leag Ftbl All Star 84-85 & 86-87; All Leag Trk/Dist Trk 83-85; Athl Awds 87; Lycoming Coll; Elem Tchr.

MOLISH, STACEY; Jefferson-Morgan HS; Rices Landing, PA; (3); 17/72; Church Yth Grp; Cmnty Wkr; Library Aide; Nwsp Rptr; Nwsp Stf; Yrbk Stf; Hon Roll.

MOLISHUS, JEFFREY F; Archbishop Ryan HS For Boys; Philadelphia, PA; (3); 24/427; Lit Mag; Rep Frsh Cls; JV Var Socr; JV Trk; Hon Roll; NHS; Penn ST; Aerospace Engrng.

MOLITIERNO, JOSEPH; Punxsutawney Area HS; Punxsutawney, PA; (2); Boy Scts; Math Tm; Var JV Ftbl; Var Trk; Im Wt Lftg; JV Wrstlng; Hon Roll; Stu Of Month 86; Med.

MOLL, SUSAN; Fleetwood HS; Kutztown, PA; (3); VICA; Hon Roll; NHS; Stu Qtr Voc Tech Schl Csmtlgy 85-87; Pedtrcs.

MOLL, TRACEY; Reading HS; Reading, PA; (2); 89/815; German Clb; Hosp Aide; Key Clb; Band; Chorus; Concert Band; Mrchg Band; Orch; Pep Band; Crs Cntry; Comms.

MOLLICA, KORY; South Allegheny HS; Glassport, PA; (3); U Of Pittsburgh; Med.

MOLLICHELLA, STEPEHN; Msgr Bonner HS; Glenolden, PA; (3); 36/255; Dance Clb; Im Ftbl; High Hon Roll; Hon Roll.

MOLLO, BENJAMIN; Blairsville SR HS; Blairsville, PA; (4); Yrbk Stf; Var Ftbl; Var Trk; Var Capt Wrstlng; Hon Roll; Tri-Cnty Wrstlr Yr, PA ST Wrstlng Trnmnt 6th Pl, & PA ST Trk/Fld Meet 5th Pl Hrdls 87; Wshngtn & Jeffersn Coll; Physcs.

MOLLOIE, DANIEL; Church Farm HS; Audubon, NJ; (3); 4/16; Aud/Vis; Church Yth Grp; Cmnty Wkr; Computer Clb; Drama Clb; Library Aide; Office Aide; Chorus; Nwsp Ed-Chief; Yrbk Stf; Shoby Organization Ambassador 86; Greatest Schl Svc 87; Stu Vestry 86-88; Psych.

MOLLURA, RHONDA; West Branch JR & SR HS; Morrisdale, PA; (2); Drama Clb; Spanish Clb; SADD; Varsity Clb; Yrbk Stf; Var JV Bsktbl; Cheerleading; Wt Lftg; Hon Roll; Russian Awd 86-87; Air Force.

MOLNAR, KATRINA; Newport HS; Newport, PA; (1); 1/126; Girl Scts; Band; Chorus; Jazz Band; Mrchg Band; School Musical; Rep Frsh Cls; High Hon Roll; Susquehanna U; Geo Chem.

MOLNAR, MELISSA; Northampton Area SR HS; Northampton, PA; (4); 15/445; AFS; Computer Clb; Leo Clb; Var Fld Hcky; Powder Puff Ftbl; Var Capt Sftbl; High Hon Roll; Hon Roll; NHS; Pres Schlr; Rotary Clb Hnrs Awd 87; E PA Cnfrnc 1st Team All-Stars 86; Temple U; Phys Thrpy.

MOLONEY, COLLEEN; Bishop Guilfoyle HS; Altoona, PA; (4); 5/123; Red Cross Aide; Pres Science Clb; Chorus; Sec Jr Cls; JV Var Cheerleading; High Hon Roll; Hon Roll; Jr NHS; NHS; Natl Sci Merit Awd 85; U Of Pgh; Pharmacy.

MOLTER, THOMAS; Danville SR HS; Danville, PA; (3); Boy Scts; Exploring; Im Ftbl; Chem.

MOLTZ, MARIANNE; Venango Christian HS; Oil City, PA; (4); 14/36; Dance Clb; GAA; Variety Show; Bsktbl; Cheerleading; Sftbl; Hon Roll; NHS; Prfct Atten Awd; Hgh Obrn Yth Fndtn Ldrshp Awd 85; US Army Rsrv Natl Schlr Athl Awd 87; Pres Acdmcc Ftnss Awd 87; Clarion U; Comm.

MOLYNEAUX, KELLY; Mount Alvernia HS; Verona, PA; (3); 2/54; Drama Clb; French Clb; JA; School Musical; Nwsp Rptr; Var L Bsktbl; High Hon Roll; NHS; Elem Math.

MONACH, CHERYL; Quigley HS; Midland, PA; (3); 9/80; Letterman Clb; Math Tm; Spanish Clb; Chorus; Cheerleading; Hon Roll.

MONACO, STEVEN; Peters Township HS; Mc Murray, PA; (4); 3/242; Pres Computer Clb; Science Clb; Var L Ftbl; Bausch & Lomb Sci Awd; CC Awd; High Hon Roll; NHS; Ntl Merit SF; Pres Schlr; Rotary Awd; Westinghouse Sci Hnrs Inst 87; Natl Young Ldrs Conf Was DC 87; Dravo Corportn Schlrshp 87; Carnegie-Mellon U; Engr.

MONAHAN, TAWNYA; Connellsville Area Jr High West; Connellsville, PA; (1); Teachers Aide; Band; Jazz Band; Nwsp Ed-Chief; Yrbk Stf; Mgr(s); Score Keeper; High Hon Roll; VP Jr NHS; Prfct Atten Awd; Frnch Recgntn Awd 86; Entrmnt.

MONAHAN, THOMAS; Glendale JR SR HS; Blandburg, PA; (2); Church Yth Grp; Chorus; School Play; Hon Roll; Pre-Law.

MONASKY, ANN; Upper Dublin SR HS; Ambler, PA; (3); 50/284; Concert Band; Jazz Band; Mrchg Band; Pep Band; Var L Sftbl; NHS; PA ST U; Aerospc Engrng.

MONCMAN, TIMOTHY; Freedom HS; Bethlehem, PA; (3); 45/510; VP Frsh Cls; VP Soph Cls; VP Jr Cls; VP Sr Cls; Rep Stu Cncl; Var L Bsbl; Var Capt Ftbl; Hon Roll; Jr NHS; NHS; Bsbl MVP 86-87; Ftbl Defns MVP 86-87; Acctnt.

MONCRIEF, MATTHEW; Bishop Shanahan HS; W Chester, PA; (4); 33/213; Drama Clb; Band; Chorus; Concert Band; Jazz Band; School Musical; Nwsp Rptr; Exclncy Instrumntl Music & Accptnce Archdioceson Hnrs Bnd 85-87; Jacksonville U; Marine Sci.

MONDAY, TROY; Mifflinburg HS; New Berlin, PA; (2); French Clb; JV Bsktbl; High Hon Roll.

MONDE, TODD; Heritage Christian Acad; Erie, PA; (1); 1/9; Church Yth Grp; Drama Clb; Var Crs Cntry; Var JV Socr; Hon Roll; Edinboro U; Tchr-Math.

MONDY III, MICHAEL; Everett Area HS; Everett, PA; (3); 11/113; French Clb; Varsity Clb; Band; Chorus; Drm Mjr(t); L Var Tennis; French Hon Soc; Hon Roll; Woodmn Wrld Lf Ins Socty Awd Outstndng Schlstc Achvt Amer Hstry 86.

MONGEON, SHARON; Freedom SR HS; Bethlehem, PA; (3); 170/486; Church Yth Grp; Cmnty Wkr; Ski Clb; Chorus; Church Choir; Orch; Hon Roll; Part In Nacel Cultural Excng Prog 87; Psych.

MONIOT, DAVE; Seneca Valley HS; Mars, PA; (3); 35/333; Pep Clb; Ski Clb; Band; Concert Band; Jazz Band; Mrchg Band; Pep Band; School Play; Symp Band; Hon Roll; Pitt; Chem Engrng.

MONIT, BROOKE; Beaver Area JR-SR HS; Beaver, PA; (2); Church Yth Grp; French Clb; Hosp Aide; SADD; School Musical; Rep Stu Cncl; Trk; Hon Roll; Ltr Of Dstngshd Ctzshp 86.

MONLEY, ROBERT; Greensburg Central Catholic HS; Murrysville, PA; (2); Ski Clb; JV Ftbl; Im Vllybl; Hon Roll; Elec Engnrng.

MONRO, MARY ANN; Belle Vernon Area HS; Belle Vernon, PA; (3); Aud/Vis; JA; Pep Clb; Band; Concert Band; Mrchg Band; Pep Band; Stage Crew; JV Var Vllybl; Hon Roll; Arch.

MONROE, BETHANY; Galeton JR SR HS; Galeton, PA; (3); 5/42; French Clb; Hosp Aide; Chorus; School Play; Var Bsktbl; Var Vllybl; NHS; Chem Awd 86-87; Nrsng.

MONROE, JASON S; Plymouth HS; Plymouth Meeting, PA; (4); Computer Clb; Political Wkr; Scholastic Bowl; Temple Yth Grp; Band; Jazz Band; Orch; School Musical; Nwsp Rptr; Stu Cncl; Natl Socty Prfssnl Engrs Schlrshp 87; Suma Cum Laud Grad 87; Color Photo 2nd Pl St Wmns Clb Amer 87; Drexel U; Chemcl Engrng.

MONSTROLA, DEANNA; Jeannette SR HS; Jeannette, PA; (3); VICA; Band; Chorus; Color Guard; Concert Band; Mrchg Band; Sftbl; Hon Roll; WCCC; Vet.

MONTAGNA, GREG; Brownsville Area HS; Cardale, PA; (4); 3/216; Drama Clb; Math Tm; Ski Clb; Nwsp Rptr; Wrstlng; High Hon Roll; NHS; Prfct Atten Awd; DAR Good Citiz Awd 87; U Of Pittsburg Provost Schlrshp Awd 87; Hirim Coll-Garfield Schlrshp 87; U Of Pittsburgh; Astrophysics.

MONTALBANO, LORI S; Bishop O Hara HS; Dunmore, PA; (3); 13/96; French Clb; Hosp Aide; Latin Clb; Science Clb; Service Clb; Chorus; Stage Crew; Nwsp Stf; VP Jr Cls; Phrmcy.

MONTALTO, ANTHONY; Monsignor Bonner HS; Upper Darby, PA; (3); 80/283; Hon Roll; DE Cnty CC; Comp Tech.

MONTANARO, ANGELO; Northern Cambria HS; Barnesboro, PA; (4); 6/130; French Clb; Trs Soph Cls; Trs Jr Cls; Trs Sr Cls; Rep Stu Cncl; L Bsbl; Capt L Bsktbl; L Ftbl; L Trk; NHS; Schlr-Athlt Awd 87; MVP Awd Bsktbl, Trk 87; IN U Of PA; Acctng.

MONTANTE, MELISSA; Wyoming Area HS; West Pittston, PA; (3); 150/385; French Clb; L Var Swmmng; JV Var Trk; Lttr Swmmng 86-87; Elem Ed.

MONTANTE, STEVEN; Scranton Prep; West Pittston, PA; (4); 23/190; Drama Clb; Chorus; School Musical; School Play; Nwsp Stf; Yrbk Stf; Swmmng; High Hon Roll; NHS; Scl Stds Gold Medal & Prsdntl Acdmc Fitness Awd 86-87; Natl Greek Exam 85-86; U Of Scranton; Med.

MONTE, CHRISTOPHER; Devon Prep; Westchester, PA; (3); 13/45; Camera Clb; Computer Clb; Math Clb; Math Tm; Nwsp Rptr; Yrbk Stf; Off Jr Cls; Var Crs Cntry; Var Trk; NHS; Bio Awd 85; Rlgn Awd 87.

MONTE, KRISTINE; Bishop Conwell HS; Bristol, PA; (3); 57/277; Church Yth Grp; Cmnty Wkr; Girl Scts; Office Aide; SADD; Teachers Aide; Hon Roll; Crtfct Of Cmmndtn Bus Educ Curriculum Cmmtt 87.

MONTECINOS, GUILLERMO P; Devon Prep Schl; Audubon, PA; (1); High Hon Roll; Latin Awd 84-86; Engrng.

MONTELLO, SHARON; Our Lady Of The Sacred Heart HS; Coraopolis, PA; (3); 13/65; Off Church Yth Grp; Drama Clb; School Play; Yrbk Phtg; Rptr Yrbk Rptr; Yrbk Stf; VP Soph Cls; JV Cheerleading; Hon Roll; Natl Hstry Awd 84-85; Sci Awd 84-85; PA Jr Acad Of Sci 85-87; Advrtsng.

MONTEVERDE, LAURA; Liberty HS; Bethlehem, PA; (3); Art Clb; French Clb; GAA; Nwsp Rptr; Nwsp Stf; Trk; Hon Roll; Hnrs Awd Engl, Soc Stud, Engl Frsncs 86-87; Navy; Law.

MONTGOMERY, BRIDGETTE; Mc Keesport SR HS; Mckeesport, PA; (4); 83/335; GAA; Bsktbl; Trk; Cit Awd; Hon Roll; Robert Morris Coll; Accntng.

MONTGOMERY, DONNA; Clarion Area HS; Sligo, PA; (4); Chorus; Color Guard; School Musical; Swing Chorus; Variety Show; Yrbk Stf; Stat Crs Cntry; High Hon Roll; Hon Roll; Drma.

MONTGOMERY, JENNIFER; Freeport Area SR HS; Freeport, PA; (2); FBLA; Hon Roll; 3rd Pl Bus Math FBLA Region 13 Regl Comptn March 87; Bus.

MONTGOMERY, JOHN; Freeport Area SR HS; Freeport, PA; (3); Optomtry.

MONTGOMERY, KIMBERLY G; West Greene Middle SR HS; New Freeport, PA; (4); 4-H; Letterman Clb; Varsity Clb; Chorus; Rep Stu Cncl; Var Co-Capt Cheerleading; Vrsty Chrldrs IOCC Fnlsts 85-86, WVU Smmr Cmp Grnd Chmpns 85, Green Cntys Chmpns 87; W Penn Hosp Schl Nrsng; RN.

MONTGOMERY, LORA; Towanda Area HS; Wysox, PA; (4); Trs Church Yth Grp; Cmnty Wkr; Drama Clb; Sec Trs FTA; SADD; Teachers Aide; Band; Church Choir; Concert Band; School Play; Csrcrd Coll; Scndry Ed.

MONTGOMERY, MELISSA A; Norristown Area HS; Norristown, PA; (3); 18/400; Capt Drill Tm; Mrchg Band; Lit Mag; High Hon Roll; Hon Roll; Lawyer.

MONTINI, CHARLES; Aliquippa HS; Aliquippa, PA; (3); DECA; French Clb; Yrbk Stf; Rep Jr Cls; Hon Roll; Engr.

MONTROSS, WILLIAM; Tunkhannock HS; Dallas, PA; (2); Boy Scts; Church Yth Grp; French Clb; Band; Church Choir; Concert Band; Jazz Band; Mrchg Band; School Musical; Stage Crew; Chem Engr.

MOODY, BRENDA; Canon Mc Millan HS; Canonsburg, PA; (3); 130/349; Church Yth Grp; Office Aide; Varsity Clb; Var L Sftbl; L Tennis; Hon Roll; CA U; Hlth Admin.

MOODY, BRYAN; Red Land HS; Etters, PA; (3); 12/306; Am Leg Boys St; Pres Church Yth Grp; Co-Capt Debate Tm; Letterman Clb; SADD; Church Choir; Off Frsh Cls; Rep Stu Cncl; High Hon Roll; NHS; Bucknell U; Pre Law.

MOODY, JOHN; Shamokin Area HS; Paxinos, PA; (4); 2/250; Am Leg Boys St; Boy Scts; Chess Clb; German Clb; Varsity Clb; Orch; L Golf; Var Trk; High Hon Roll; Sal; Egl Sct 85; Juniata Coll; Chmst.

MOODY, KELLY; Hempfield HS; Irwin, PA; (3); Art Clb; Pep Clb; Rep Stu Cncl; Stat Bsktbl; Stat Trk; Cit Awd; High Hon Roll; Fshn Mrchndsng.

MOODY, LISA; Shamokin HS; Paxinos, PA; (2); 12/252; Hst Art Clb; Girl Scts; SADD; Varsity Clb; Orch; Var L Sftbl; Var L Vllybl; Yth Fllwshp Pres 86-87; Dist Orch 86; Sting Ensmbl 85-87; Crmnlgy.

MOODY, MELISSA; Farrell Area HS; Farrell, PA; (4); 6/87; Pres Drama Clb; French Clb; Letterman Clb; Spanish Clb; Chorus; Capt Diving; Capt Swmmng; Hon Roll; Sec NHS; Pres Schlr; Amer Bus Womens Assoc Schlrshp 87; Wolves Schlrshp 87; Mimi Bonier Ath Schlrshp 87; Allegheny Coll; Forgn Lang.

MOODY, NATALIE; Cecil JR HS; Muse, PA; (1); Chorus; Mrchg Band; Nwsp Ed-Chief; Twrlr; High Hon Roll; Math.

MOOK, BRAD; Meadville Area HS; Meadville, PA; (3); Rep Jr Cls; VP Bsbl; VP Bsktbl; Hon Roll.

MOON, RENE; Elizabeth-Forward HS; Mckeesport, PA; (2); Dance Clb; French Clb; Pep Clb; Chorus; Yrbk Stf; Rep Frsh Cls; Rep Soph Cls; Cheerleading; Coach Actv; High Hon Roll.

MOON, SUNG; Abington SR HS; Hunt Valley, PA; (3); 40/508; Spanish Clb; Nwsp Rptr; JV Ftbl; Var Lcrss; Hon Roll; Jr NHS; NHS.

MOONEY, ANDREA; Upper Dublin HS; Ambler, PA; (4); 61/308; Hosp Aide; Sec JA; Socr; Sftbl; Tennis; Vllybl; NHS; Pres Schlr; Loyola Coll; Spch Thrpy.

MOONEY, EDWARD; Devon Preparatory Schl; Wayne, PA; (3); 25/43; Ski Clb; Rep Frsh Cls; Var Crs Cntry; Var Trk; Hon Roll; NEDT Awd; Prom Cmmttee Chrmn 87-88; Al-Leag Slctn Crss-Cntry 87; Navy ROTC; Finance.

MOONEY, KEITH; Reading SR HS; Reading, PA; (4); 56/571; Boys Clb Am; Im Bsktbl; Var L Ftbl; Im Vllybl; Ntl Merit SF; Acadmc All Berks Football 86-87; U Of DE Merit Schlrshp 87; U Of DE; Political Sci.

MOONEY, LISA; Chambersburg Area SR HS; Chambersburg, PA; (2); Art Clb; 4-H; Hosp Aide; JCL; Soph Cls; Stu Cncl; 4-H Awd; High Hon Roll; Hon Roll; Hosp Volntr Awd 86.

MOONEY, MARTY; Nativity BVM HS; St Clair, PA; (3); 30/96; Art Clb; Church Yth Grp; Computer Clb; Red Cross Aide; Nwsp Phtg; JV L Bsktbl; Var L Ftbl; Var L Trk; Im Wt Lftg; Hon Roll; Penn ST U; Accntng.

MOONEY, PATRICIA; St Basil Acad; Philadelphia, PA; (3); Drama Clb; GAA; Spanish Clb; Thesps; Chorus; School Musical; School Play; Stage Crew; Variety Show; Sftbl; Natl Hnr Roll & Natl Ldrshp Awd 87.

MOONEY, STEPHANIE; Villa Maria Acad; Erie, PA; (3); PAVAS; Quiz Bowl; SADD; School Musical; School Play; Hon Roll; NHS; Elec Engrng.

MOORE, ALLEN; Meadville Area SR HS; Meadville, PA; (2); Church Yth Grp; SADD; Band; Chorus; Concert Band; Mrchg Band; Edinboro ST Coll; Chrprctr.

MOORE, ALYSSA; Downingtown HS; Downington, PA; (3); Cmnty Wkr; GAA; Latin Clb; Band; Chorus; Color Guard; Flag Corp; Mrchg Band; Yrbk Stf; Coach Actv; Pathways Prgm Marywood Coll 87; Advncd Lfsvg & Water Sfty 86; Fshn Mrchndsg.

MOORE, AMY; Yough SR HS; Herminie, PA; (3); Library Aide; Pep Clb; Ski Clb; VICA; Band; Concert Band; Mrchg Band; Symp Band; Hon Roll; Csmtlgy.

MOORE, BETSY; Fort Cherry HS; Mcdonald, PA; (2); Church Yth Grp; Math Clb; Ski Clb; Spanish Clb; Rep Stu Cncl; Stat Bsktbl; Stat Mgr(s); Stat Score Keeper; High Hon Roll; Phy Ftns Awd 86-87; Accntng.

MOORE, BILL; Sun Valley HS; Aston, PA; (4); 45/308; Cmnty Wkr; Exploring; Hosp Aide; SADD; Var L Bsktbl; Var Trk; Hon Roll; Lebanon Valley Coll; Acctg.

MOORE, BRIAN; Cedar Crest HS; Lebanon, PA; (1); Church Yth Grp; German Clb; Key Clb; Library Aide; Pep Clb; Im Ftbl; Engrng.

MOORE, BRIAN; Solanco HS; Quarryville, PA; (2); Art Clb; Trs Church Yth Grp; Trk; Hon Roll; Zoology.

MOORE, BRIAN; Spring Grove Area SR HS; York, PA; (3); CAP; Trs Band; Sec Chorus; Concert Band; Mrchg Band; Pep Band; Pres Jr Cls; Var Trk; Hon Roll; VA Militry Inst; Bus Adm.

MOORE, BRYAN; Governor Mifflin SR HS; Shillington, PA; (3); 10/300; Exploring; Q&S; Band; Concert Band; Jazz Band; Mrchg Band; School Musical; Stage Crew; Nwsp Ed-Chief; Nwsp Stf; Comms.

MOORE, CHARLES; St John Neumann HS; Philadelphia, PA; (3); 24/349; Band; Jr NHS; NHS; Military Law.

MOORE, CHERYL; North Pocono HS; Lake Ariel, PA; (3); 6/237; School Musical; Mrchg Band; Orch; Yrbk Phtg; Yrbk Stf; Gov Hon Prg Awd; High Hon Roll; NHS; Ntl Merit SF.

MOORE, CHRIS; Brandywine Heights HS; Fleetwood, PA; (2); Church Yth Grp; JV Trk; Var Wrstlng; Hon Roll; NHS; Rotary Awd.

MOORE, CHRISTOPHER; Susquehannock HS; Glen Rock, PA; (3); 25/243; Ski Clb; Var L Crs Cntry; Var Trk; Hon Roll; Cnty Ind Arts Awd Power Tech 1st Pl 87; Best Show Power Tech Fine Arts Fair 87; Engr.

MOORE, CHRISTOPHER; West Branch Area HS; Morrisdale, PA; (2); Hon Roll; Vet Sci.

MOORE, DAMION; Westinghouse HS; Poughkeepsie, PA; (3); Exploring; Cit Awd; High Hon Roll; Hon Roll; Prfct Atten Awd; Outstndng Ldrshp & Acad Awd 86; Videocamera Man Awd 87; Acctng.

MOORE, DAWN; Bethlehem Cntr HS; Marianna, PA; (3); 26/156; Drama Clb; Spanish Clb; Concert Band; Mrchg Band; Pep Band; Yrbk Stf; Stu Cncl; Twrlr; Hon Roll; Prfct Atten Awd; Am Leg Awd 85-86; Chld Psych.

MOORE, DAWN P; Neshaminy HS; Langhorne, PA; (3); 194/800; Girl Scts; Office Aide; Stu Cncl; Mgr(s); Hon Roll; Amer Hstry.

MOORE, DEBORAH; Cathedral HS; Pittsburgh, PA; (3); 5/54; Cmnty Wkr; Drama Clb; Library Aide; Red Cross Aide; VP Spanish Clb; Chorus; School Play; Stage Crew; Stu Cncl; High Hon Roll; Congrssnl Yth Ldrshp Cncl 86; Outstndg Achvt Biol I 85-86; Outstndg Achvt Span II 85-86; Cmmnctns.

MOORE, DERRICK; West Catholic For Boys; Philadelphia, PA; (3); JV Im Bsktbl; Hon Roll; Conduct Awd 84-85.

MOORE, DOROTHY; Strawberry Mansion HS; Phila, PA; (3); 3/130; Cmnty Wkr; Model UN; Office Aide; Teachers Aide; Temple Yth Grp; Stage Crew; Yrbk Bus Mgr; Yrbk Stf; Off Soph Cls; Off Jr Cls; Bio Med Sci Pgm Templ U 84-85; Upwrd Bnd Pgm U Of PA 85-86; Prfct Attndnc Awds 84-87; Lincoln; Psych.

MOORE, ED; Seneca Valley HS; Mars, PA; (3); 83/350; Letterman Clb; Ski Clb; Varsity Clb; Rep Stu Cncl; Var L Bsbl; Var L Ftbl; Var Wt Lftg; JV Wrstlng; Hon Roll; Kent ST; Arch.

MOORE, FRANK JAMES; Neshaminy HS; Levittown, PA; (3); 112/768; Church Yth Grp; Cmnty Wkr; Computer Clb; JV Wrstlng; Hon Roll; Prfct Atten Awd; Comp.

MOORE, GAYLE; York County Vo-Tech HS; Lancaster, PA; (3); 1/465; Pres Church Yth Grp; FFA; Rep Stu Cncl; Var JV Vllybl; High Hon Roll; PA ST FFA Nrsry & Lndscp, 3rd Pl Awd 87; Wht Rose Chptr FFA Schlrshp Awd 87; Landscp Dsgn.

MOORE, GERALD; Bishop Mc Devitt HS; Philadelphia, PA; (3); Ftbl; Wt Lftg; DE ST; Accntng.

MOORE, GERI; Bishop Mc Devitt HS; Harrisburg, PA; (3); Office Aide; Teachers Aide; Band; Concert Band; Mrchg Band; Cert Merit Outstndng Perf Chrstn Morality 87; Acctng.

MOORE, GLORIA; Meadville Area SR HS; Meadville, PA; (3); Church Yth Grp; Pep Clb; Sec Spanish Clb; Nwsp Stf; Yrbk Stf; Rep Frsh Cls; Rep Jr Cls; JV Cheerleading; Hon Roll; Psychlgy.

MOORE, J CHAD; Hughesville HS; Picture Rocks, PA; (3); Band; Chorus; Church Choir; School Musical; Nwsp Ed-Chief; Tennis; Hon Roll; NHS; Ntl Merit Ltr.

MOORE, JEFFREY; Bensalem HS; Bensalem, PA; (2); Boy Scts; Concert Band; Mrchg Band; Rep Stu Cncl; JV Tennis; Hon Roll; Music.

MOORE, JERRY; Octorara HS; Coatesville, PA; (3); 12/157; Cmnty Wkr; Radio Clb; Red Cross Aide; Service Clb; Nwsp Sprt Ed; Yrbk Stf; JV Bsbl; JV Tennis; Hon Roll; NHS; Lions Club Schlrshp Amer Red Cross Ldrshp Devlpmnt Conf 86.

MOORE, JODI; Ft Cherry HS; Bulger, PA; (4); Church Yth Grp; Drama Clb; Letterman Clb; Math Clb; Science Clb; Ski Clb; Spanish Clb; Varsity Clb; Band; Chorus.

MOORE, KERRY; Carmichaels HS; Carmichaels, PA; (4); 8/100; Pep Clb; Ski Clb; Spanish Clb; SADD; Color Guard; Cit Awd; DAR Awd; High Hon Roll; NHS; Prfct Atten Awd; Spnsh Awds 85-86; Jrnlsm.

MOORE, KIM; Yough SR HS; Ruffsdale, PA; (3); 36/239; Cmnty Wkr; French Clb; Hosp Aide; Library Aide; Office Aide; Band; Chorus; Mrchg Band; Var Twrlr; Hon Roll; Wstmrlnd CC; Nrsng.

MOORE, KIMBERLEA; Harbor Creek HS; Harbor Creek, PA; (4); 17/228; ROTC; Teachers Aide; Concert Band; L Mrchg Band; Sec Pep Band; Var L Trk; Hon Roll; U S Navy; Ofcr.

MOORE II, LAWRENCE E; Natiyity B Y M HS; Pottsville, PA; (1); 10/94; Boy Scts; Speech Tm; JV Ftbl; JV Trk; Hon Roll; Ad Altare Dei-Boy Scout Religious Awd 86; Diocese Of Allentown HS Schlrshp 86; Mech Engrng.

MOORE, LISA; Yough SR HS; Herminite, PA; (4); Ski Clb; VICA; Band; Chorus; Concert Band; Jazz Band; Stage Crew; Symp Band; Hon Roll; Cnty Band 84-85; Dntl Hygnst.

MOORE, LORI; Bethlehem-Center HS; Clarksville, PA; (4); 26/156; 4-H; Spanish Clb; Varsity Clb; Nwsp Stf; Rep Sr Cls; JV Var Bsktbl; Hon Roll; 3rd Sfty Cncl Auto Sfty 86; Cmptr Mgmnt.

MOORE, LUCINDA; N Hills HS; Pittsburgh, PA; (4); Ski Clb; Band; Mrchg Band; Orch; NHS.

MOORE, LYNDA; Baldwin HS; Pittsburgh, PA; (3); 240/465; GAA; Girl Scts; JA; Band; Concert Band; Orch; Variety Show; JV Var Bsktbl; JV Var Sftbl; Var JV Vllybl; CPA.

MOORE, MARGIE; Shaler Area HS; Glenshaw, PA; (3); 69/493; Hosp Aide; Office Aide; Ski Clb; Yrbk Stf; Cheerleading; Score Keeper; DAR Awd; High Hon Roll; Hon Roll; Chld Psych.

MOORE, MARK; Williams Valley HS; Tower City, PA; (3); 17/98; Chess Clb; Church Yth Grp; SADD; Yrbk Phtg; JV Golf; High Hon Roll; Hon Roll.

MOORE, MELINDA; Northeast Bradford JR SR HS; Warren Center, PA; (3); Church Yth Grp; Band; Chorus; Concert Band; Mrchg Band; Sec Frsh Cls; Trs Stu Cncl; Cheerleading; Hon Roll; Trs NHS; Slvr Schlstc Plq 85-87; Vsty Ltr Chrldng 86-87; Fshn Inst Of Phila; Fshn Merch.

MOORE, MELISSA; Altoona Area HS; Altoona, PA; (3); 59/792; Trs Church Yth Grp; Band; Chorus; Mrchg Band; Orch; Swing Chorus; Variety Show; Rep Stu Cncl; Capt Swmmng; IN U PA; Elem Ed.

MOORE, MELISSA; Mohawk JR-SR HS; Wampum, PA; (3); FBLA; FHA; SADD; Chorus; Powder Puff Ftbl; High Hon Roll; Hon Roll; Bus.

MOORE, MICHAEL; Shaler Area HS; Glenshaw, PA; (3); Cmnty Wkr; Exploring; Ski Clb; VP Sr Cls; VP Stu Cncl; JV Bsbl; JV Ftbl; Mgr(s); Score Keeper; JV Wrstlng; Pol Sci.

MOORE, MICHELE; Bishop Mc Devitt HS; Harrisburg, PA; (3); 70/216; FBLA; Pep Clb; Chorus; Bowling; Civic Clb; Mgr(s); Tennis; Bus Admin.

MOORE, MICHELE; Bugettstown Area JR SR HS; Burgettstown, PA; (3); Church Yth Grp; Drama Clb; Office Aide; Science Clb; Ski Clb; Yrbk Stf; High Hon Roll; Hon Roll; NHS; U Of Pittsburg; Law.

MOORE, MICHELLE; Horner Center JR-SR HS; Homer City, PA; (3); 6/118; French Clb; Speech Tm; Color Guard; High Hon Roll; Hon Roll; Jr NHS; NHS; Frgn Lang Awd 85-86; IUP; Psych.

MOORE, MIKE; E L Meyers HS; Wilkes Barre, PA; (4); 26/154; Boy Scts; Church Yth Grp; Office Aide; School Musical; School Play; Stage Crew; Variety Show; Wrstlng; Hon Roll; Jr NHS; Bishops Awd For Yth Mnstry 87; Kings Coll; Comm.

MOORE, NICOLE; Hamburg Area HS; Shoemakersville, PA; (3); Church Yth Grp; German Clb; SADD; Band; Chorus; Stage Crew; Capt Twrlr; Hon Roll; German Natl Hnr Soc 86-87; Nurs.

MOORE, NICOLE; Monessen JR-SR HS; Monessen, PA; (3); FBLA; Key Clb; Var Mgr(s); Hon Roll; Opt Clb Awd; Sawyer Schl Bus; Trvl Agncy.

MOORE, PAULA; Central York SR HS; York, PA; (4); 17/203; Jazz Band; Mrchg Band; Orch; Symp Band; Yrbk Stf; Tennis; CC Awd; Hon Roll; Lion Awd; NHS; JR Miss Fnlst York Cnty 86; Outstndng SR Musician Awd 87; Temple U; Jrnlsm.

MOORE, RHONDA; Clarion Area HS; Clarion, PA; (3); FCA; Science Clb; Teachers Aide; Chorus; Yrbk Stf; Var L Bsktbl; Stat Ftbl; Var L Trk; Var L Vllybl; Hon Roll.

MOORE, RHONDA; Lewistown Area HS; Lewistown, PA; (2); Church Yth Grp; High Hon Roll; Hyles-Anderson; Missionary.

MOORE, ROBIN; East Pennsboro Area HS; Enola, PA; (2); 32/189; Church Yth Grp; Latin Clb; Band; Church Choir; Concert Band; Mrchg Band; Pep Band; School Musical; Var Gym; Radiology.

MOORE, SHARON; William Penn SR HS; York, PA; (3); Church Yth Grp; JA; Band; Chorus; Church Choir; Color Guard; Mrchg Band; Orch; Vllybl; Prfct Atten Awd; Music Awd-Orch, Mrchng Band, Chorus 84-86, 85-87, 86-87; Comm.

MOORE, STACEY; Belle Vernon Area HS; Belle Vernon, PA; (4); 2/270; Pres Art Clb; Band; Ed Yrbk Stf; Rep Jr Cls; Off Stu Cncl; High Hon Roll; NHS; Sal; Natl Marine Corps Schlrshp 87; WA & Jefferson Eagle Schlrshp 87; WA & Jffrsn Coll; Entrprnrl.

MOORE, STANFORD; Warren Area HS; Warren, PA; (3); 26/287; High Hon Roll; Math.

MOORE, SUSAN; Littlestown SR HS; Littlestown, PA; (4); 1/118; L Speech Tm; Varsity Clb; School Play; Swing Chorus; Yrbk Stf; Sec Stu Cncl; L Crs Cntry; Voice Dem Awd; Scholastic Bowl; Chorus; Hugh O Breian Yth Fndtn Ldrshp Awd.

MOORE, THEOLA; Brownsville Area HS; Republic, PA; (3); SADD; Nwsp Stf; JV Var Mgr(s); Var Vllybl; High Hon Roll; Hon Roll; Howard U; Comp Sci.

MOORE, TRACY; Brownsville Area HS; E Millsboro, PA; (3); #29 In Class; Hosp Aide; Library Aide; Church Choir; Lit Mag; High Hon Roll; Hon Roll; 1st Pl Bible Quiz 85 & 86; 1st Pl Bible Sword Drill 85 & 86; Penn ST U; Accntng.

MOORE, WENDY; Du Bois HS; Reynoldsville, PA; (4); 18/269; Science Clb; NHS; Ntl Merit Ltr; Brockway Inc Schlrshp 87; PA ST U; Bio.

MOORHATCH, STEVE; Delaware County Christian Schl; Paoli, PA; (4); 14/78; Church Yth Grp; Math Tm; Chorus; School Play; Var L Socr; Capt Trk; High Hon Roll; NHS; Ntl Merit Ltr; ACSI Distngshd Christian HS Stu 86; Drexel U; Mech Engr.

MOORS, JENIFER; Gateway SR HS; Monroeville, PA; (3); 1/400; Model UN; NFL; PAVAS; Red Cross Aide; Nwsp Ed-Chief; Ntl Merit SF; Girl Scts; Nwsp Bus Mgr; Nwsp Rptr; Nwsp Stf; Schlrshp To Duquesne U Smmr Hon Prog 86; Schlrshp To PSU Smmr Lang Prog Arabic 87; 1st Pl Poetry 87; Intl Rltns.

MOOSBRUGGER, STEPHEN; Neshaminy HS; Levittown, PA; (3); Var Socr; Hon Roll; Ntl Merit SF.

MOOSE, CRISTY; Sto-Rox SR HS; Mckees Rocks, PA; (2); Boys Clb Am; JA; Office Aide; Chorus; Yrbk Stf; JV Cheerleading; Hon Roll; Jrnlsm.

MORA, PAMELA; Cranberry HS; Oil City, PA; (3); 20/140; Rep FHA; Pep Clb; Science Clb; Spanish Clb; SADD; Drill Tm; Rep Stu Cncl; Var JV Cheerleading; High Hon Roll; Hon Roll.

MORA, PATRICIA; Central SR HS; York, PA; (3); FHA; Science Clb; Spanish Clb; Chorus; Drill Tm; Hon Roll.

MORAD, KIMBERLY A; Fort Le Boeuf HS; Erie, PA; (3); 29/215; Dance Clb; Var L Bsktbl; Var L Trk; Im Vllybl; High Hon Roll; Hon Roll; Engrng.

MORALES, ESTEBAN; Solanco SR HS; New Providence, PA; (3); Var JV Ftbl; Wt Lftg; Cit Awd; High Hon Roll; Hon Roll; Jr NHS; Rotary Awd; Schlr For World Cultures & Spnsh 85-86; Chem.

MORALES, PAULA; Coatesville Area HS; Coatesville, PA; (3); Church Yth Grp; Hosp Aide; Spanish Clb; Band; Pres Chorus; Church Choir; Color Guard; Rep Frsh Cls; Rep Soph Cls; Rep Jr Cls; Brandywine Schl Nrsng; RN.

MORAN, JOHN; Sacred Heart HS; Carbondale, PA; (3); 6/49; Am Leg Boys St; Computer Clb; JCL; Latin Clb; Ski Clb; SADD; School Play; Var Bsbl; JV Bsktbl; Capt Golf; Temple U; Phrmcy.

MORAN, LEANNE; West Scranton HS; Scranton, PA; (2); Swmmng; PA ST U.

MORAN, MARY; West Scranton SR HS; Scranton, PA; (4); 12/250; High Hon Roll; Hon Roll; Jr NHS; NHS; Acdmc All Am 86-87; PA ST U; Comp Sci.

MORAN JR, MICHAEL F; West Scranton HS; Scranton, PA; (3); 68/263; Boys Clb Am; Ski Clb; JV Ftbl; Var Golf; Var Trk; Hon Roll; Drexel U; Arch.

MORAN, MIKE; Mountain View HS; Clifford, PA; (2); 11/96; Boy Scts; Ski Clb; Chorus; School Musical; Pres Soph Cls; Hon Roll; Med.

MORAN, SHARON; Chartiers Valley HS; Pittsburgh, PA; (3); Civic Clb; Drama Clb; Ski Clb; Nwsp Stf; Stu Cncl; Bsktbl; Score Keeper; Trk; Hon Roll; U Dayton; Fash Merch.

MORAN, SUEZAN; Jeannette SR HS; Jeannette, PA; (3); Church Yth Grp; Sftbl; Hon Roll; Prfct Atten Awd; Bradford Schl; Bus Mgmt.

MORAN, THOMAS; Conemaugh Valley HS; Conemaugh, PA; (3); Pep Clb; Varsity Clb; Ftbl; Mgr(s); High Hon Roll; VP Jr NHS; NHS; Prfct Atten Awd; Outstndng Stu Yr P A History 85; U Pittsburgh Johnstown; Chem.

MORANDUZZO, LISA; Conemaugh Twp Area HS; Davidsville, PA; (4); 4/101; Trs Spanish Clb; Ed Lit Mag; Rep Stu Cncl; Stat Bsktbl; Capt Var Cheerleading; Capt Var Sftbl; Hon Roll; NHS; Acad All-Amer 86; Tri Democrat Schlr Athlete Awd 87; Central PTA Schlrshp 87; IN U Of PA; Respiratry Thrpy.

MORCOM, JENNIFER; Lakeland JR/Sr HS; Jermyn, PA; (4); Dance Clb; Girl Scts; Spanish Clb; Drill Tm; Yrbk Stf; Rep Stu Cncl; Var Sftbl; Hon Roll; Keystone JC Acdmc Schlrshp 87; U S Bus Ed Awd 87; NE Inst Ed; Acctg.

MORDAN, BOB; Danville Area SR HS; Danville, PA; (4); 29/202; Church Yth Grp; Key Clb; Ski Clb; Var L Bsbl; Var Capt Bsktbl; Var L Ftbl; High Hon Roll; Hon Roll; NHS; Prfct Atten Awd; Penn ST U; Liberal Arts.

MORDAN, JOHN; Danville HS; Danville, PA; (2); 26/159; Computer Clb; Key Clb; VP Frsh Cls; VP Soph Cls; VP Jr Cls; JV Var Ftbl; Var Trk; High Hon Roll; Kiwanis Awd; Advertising.

MORDENTE, MICHELE; Old Forge HS; Old Forge, PA; (3); High Hon Roll; NHS; Intl Frgn Lang Awd Spnsh 86-87.

MORDER, VINCENT; Huntingdon Area HS; Huntingdon, PA; (3); 1/228; Pres Frsh Cls; Pres Soph Cls; Pres Jr Cls; Trs Stu Cncl; Var Capt Crs Cntry; Var Capt Trk; High Hon Roll; Masonic Awd; NHS; Opt Clb Awd; Councilmen Yr Fin 85-86; Juniata Coll; Engrng.

MORE, GINA; Central Bucks West HS; Doylestown, PA; (3); 38/481; Church Yth Grp; Band; Concert Band; Mrchg Band; Bsktbl; Fld Hcky; Sftbl; Hon Roll; Jr NHS; Pres Schlr; Presdntl Physcl Ftnss; Elect Engrng.

MOREAU, ROBERT; Fort Cherry HS; Mc Donald, PA; (4); Church Yth Grp; Cmnty Wkr; FFA; High Hon Roll; Hon Roll; Firefighter.

MOREIRA, CARLOS F; Archbishop Ryan HS For Boys; Philadelphia, PA; (4); 40/430; Cmnty Wkr; Intnl Clb; Political Wkr; High Hon Roll; Hon Roll; Drexel U; Bus Adm.

MORELLI, CRISTINA; New Castle HS; New Castle, PA; (4); AFS; Gym; Hon Roll; Lang.

MORELLI, RICHARD; Hazleton HS; Mcadoo, PA; (2); FBLA; Ski Clb; SADD; Stu Cncl; Var Bsbl; JV Bsktbl; Var Ftbl; Wt Lftg; Hon Roll; Med.

MORELLO, DINO; North Hills HS; Pittsburgh, PA; (3); 2/493; Church Yth Grp; Cmnty Wkr; Debate Tm; Mrchg Band; School Musical; Symp Band; Bsbl; High Hon Roll; NHS; Prfct Atten Awd; Carnegie Mellon U; Chemcl Rsrch.

MOREY, DAWN MARIE; Nazareth Academy HS; Philadelphia, PA; (3); Cmnty Wkr; Hosp Aide; Math Clb; Math Tm; Pep Clb; Chorus; School Play; Nwsp Rptr; Nwsp Stf; Bowling; Comp Sci.

MORGAN, AMY; Canton Area JR SR HS; Canton, PA; (4); 13/115; Rptr FBLA; Letterman Clb; Concert Band; Drm Mjr(t); Mrchg Band; Trs Sr Cls; JV Var Vllybl; Mgr Wrstlng; High Hon Roll; Williamsport Schl Commrc; Bus.

MORGAN, ANDREA; St Hubert Catholic HS; Philadelphia, PA; (3); Office Aide; Coach Actv; Swmmng; Nrsng.

MORGAN, BRETT; Connellsville Area HS; Connellsville, PA; (3); 126/550; Church Yth Grp; Band; Trk; Wt Lftg; High Hon Roll; Hon Roll; NHS; 1st Pl Wgt Lft-155 Lb Cls 86-87; 2nd Pl Strng Man Awd 86-87.

MORGAN, BRIAN; Clearfield Area HS; Clearfield, PA; (4); 67/287; French Clb; Key Clb; Science Clb; Bsktbl; Bowling; Hon Roll; Marjorie Keast Bell Memrl Schlrshp 87; Penn ST U; Comp Sci.

MORGAN, CAZ; Danville SR HS; Danville, PA; (3); Church Yth Grp; Exploring; Band; Concert Band; Jazz Band; Mrchg Band; Pep Band; Hon Roll.

MORGAN, CHERI; Claysburg-Kimmel HS; Sproul, PA; (2); 13/97; Ski Clb; Band; Chorus; Concert Band; Capt Flag Corp; Mrchg Band; High Hon Roll; Hon Roll; Allegheny CC; Law.

MORGAN, DAVID; Hanover Area HS; Ashley, PA; (4); 16/166; Key Clb; Ski Clb; Var L Crs Cntry; Var L Trk; High Hon Roll; Hon Roll; Jr NHS; Trs NHS; NEDT Awd; Penn ST U; Mrktng.

MORGAN, DEB; Danville HS; Danville, PA; (3); FHA; Spanish Clb; 1st & 2nd Cake Decrtng Bloom Fair 86-87, 3rd Pl Sewing Items 85-87, 4th Pl Sewing Cont 85-86; US Army; Photogrphy.

MORGAN, DEBBIE; Oxford Area HS; Oxford, PA; (3); Art Clb; Church Yth Grp; Civic Clb; High Hon Roll; Hon Roll; 1st Pl Oxford Research Clb Gen Div 85; Outstndng Under Clsmn Awd Home Ec Clthng Dept 86; Fashion Dsgn.

MORGAN, ESI M; Germantown Friends Schl; Philadelphia, PA; (4); Chorus; Nwsp Stf; Rep Jr Cls; Var JV Bsktbl; Var Capt Crs Cntry; Var Trk; Bausch & Lomb Sci Awd; Ntl Merit SF; Harvard Awd 86; LEAD Pgm 86.

MORGAN, HEATHER; Peters Township HS; Mcmurray, PA; (2); NFL; SADD; Thesps; Varsity Clb; School Play; Yrbk Phtg; Yrbk Stf; Stu Cncl; Var JV Cheerleading; Swmmng; Ntl Hstry Day 3rd On Prjct; PTA Cultrl Arts Wnnr; Cmmnctns.

MORGAN, HOLLY; Southern Huntingdon County HS; Saltillo, PA; (3); SADD; Varsity Clb; Band; Chorus; School Musical; Var L Bsktbl; Powder Puff Ftbl; Var L Sftbl; Hon Roll; NHS; Natl Sci & Frnch Mrt Awds 85 & 86; Math.

MORGAN, HOPE; Mahanoy Area HS; Mahanoy City, PA; (3); FHA; Trs Library Aide; SADD; Yrbk Stf; JV Bsktbl; Var Sftbl; Hon Roll; NHS; Wst End Fre & Rsce; Dcn 1st Prbytrn Chrch; Mc Canns Schl Of Bus; Accntng.

MORGAN, JOHN; Wm Allen HS; Allentown, PA; (4); 75/574; Letterman Clb; Varsity Clb; Var Bsbl; Var Ftbl; Var Wt Lftg; Hon Roll; Pres Schlr; Schlr Athlt 86-87; Est PA Conf 1st Tm 86-87; Lehigh Vly All Star Ftbl Clsc 86-87; Muhlenberg Coll; Phrmcy.

MORGAN, JOSEPH; Father Judge HS; Philadelphia, PA; (3); 16/402; Boys Clb Am; Church Yth Grp; Rep Frsh Cls; Rep Soph Cls; Sec Jr Cls; Sec Sr Cls; Stu Cncl; Var L Bsbl; Var JV Bsktbl; Cit Awd; Ptchd Crpntr Cup Cath All Stars Vet Stad 87.

MORGAN, KATHLEEN; Harry S Truman HS; Levittown, PA; (3); 146/600; Drama Clb; VP Service Clb; Spanish Clb; School Musical; Rep Soph Cls; Hst Jr Cls; VP Sr Cls; Stu Cncl; JV Fld Hcky; Var L Socr; Most Team Spirit Soccer Team 87; Theatre.

MORGAN, KELLY; Pine Grove Area HS; Donaldson, PA; (3); Quiz Bowl; Varsity Clb; Concert Band; Mrchg Band; Sec Frsh Cls; Sec Soph Cls; Sec Jr Cls; Rep Stu Cncl; Bsktbl; Cheerleading.

MORGAN, KIMBERLY D; The Baldwin Schl; Villanova, PA; (4); Pres Debate Tm; French Clb; Intnl Clb; Latin Clb; Model UN; Political Wkr; Pres SADD; Sec Frsh Cls; Pres Soph Cls; Pres Stu Cncl; Yngr Schlrs Rsrch Grnt-NEH 86; Wellsley Coll Bk Awd 86; Govt.

MORGAN, KIRK; General Mc Lane HS; Waterford, PA; (4); 48/234; 4-H; VP Pres FFA; Var JV Wrstlng; 4-H Awd; Hon Roll; Pres Church Yth Grp; Keystone St Farmer Degree 87; Erie County Fair Fund Schlrshp 87; Comp Ag Awd 87; OH Diesel Tech Inst; Diesel.

MORGAN, KRISTEN; Freedom HS; Bethlehem, PA; (3); 160/509; Church Yth Grp; French Clb; Ski Clb; Var JV Fld Hcky; Hon Roll; Mrktng.

MORGAN, LA RON; Perry Traditional Acad; Pittsburgh, PA; (3); Aud/Vis; Camp Fr Inc; Church Yth Grp; Debate Tm; Drama Clb; JA; Letterman Clb; Office Aide; Pep Clb; Varsity Clb; Doctor.

MORGAN, MARCIA; Nativity B V M HS; Orwigsburg, PA; (3); 16/87; French Clb; Chorus; School Musical; Yrbk Stf; Var Cheerleading; JV Vllybl; Hon Roll; NHS; Math.

MORGAN, MARGARET; Warren Area HS; Warren, PA; (3); 1/300; Church Yth Grp; Math Tm; French Clb; Acpl Chr; Nwsp Rptr; Ski Clb; Trs Jr Cls; Sftbl; High Hon Roll; Pres Jr NHS; Beaty Englsh Awd 85; Schlstc Lttr 86; Schlrshp To Chautaugua Inst 85.

MORGAN, MICHELE; Curwensville HS; Curwensville, PA; (3); Sec French Clb; Ski Clb; Chorus; Capt Flag Corp; Stage Crew; Nwsp Rptr; Yrbk Stf; High Hon Roll; NHS; Acad All Am 86-87.

MORGAN, MICHELE; Wilmington Area HS; Grove City, PA; (3); 10/115; Church Yth Grp; Sec Chorus; Concert Band; Drm Mjr(t); Jazz Band; Pep Band; Hon Roll; Office Aide; Teachers Aide; Band; Hnrs Chorus 86; Hnrs Band 85-86; Regnl Band PMEA & Regnl Chorus 86; Music.

MORGAN, MICHELLE; Connellsville Area HS; Connellsville, PA; (2); Church Yth Grp; Band; Concert Band; Mrchg Band; Symp Band; High Hon Roll; Hon Roll; Med.

MORGAN, SARAH C; Pennsbury HS; Yardley, PA; (4); Pres Church Yth Grp; Intnl Clb; Pep Clb; SADD; Capt L Swmmng; High Hon Roll; NHS; Service Clb; Chorus; School Musical; Wk Schlrshp PA Free Entrprs Wk 86; Comp Lab Asst Gld Pin Awd 87; Outstndg Swmmr Yr Vrsty Tm 87; Southern CT ST U; Bus Admin.

MORGAN, SCOTT; Jamestown Area HS; Jamestown, PA; (4); Computer Clb; Math Clb; VP Frsh Cls; Pres Sr Cls; Im Vllybl; Thiel Coll; Elec Engnrng.

MORGAN, TAMMEY; Sayre HS; Waverly, NY; (3); Church Yth Grp; SADD; Flag Corp; Mrchg Band; School Play; Yrbk Stf; Pres Frsh Cls; Stu Cncl; Im Cheerleading; Bus.

MORGAN, TARA; Lutheran HS; Philadelphia, PA; (3); 2/20; Church Choir; Cheerleading; High Hon Roll; VFW Awd; Voice Dem Awd; Voice Dmcrcy 87; Hgh Hnr Rl 87; Chrldng 87; Cmmnctns.

MORGAN, TINA; Line Mountain HS; Trevorton, PA; (4); 42/131; Church Yth Grp; Key Clb; Band; Concert Band; Mrchg Band; Stage Crew; JV Var Score Keeper; Prfct Atten Awd; Eucharistic Mnstr 86-87; Band Vrsty Ltr & Pins 85-87; Hlth Career Club Awd 87; Cmmnty Gen Hosp; X-Ray Tech.

MORGAN, TRACY; Hopewell SR HS; Aliquippa, PA; (3); 52/255; Church Yth Grp; Trs French Clb; Church Choir; Bowling; Mgr(s); Hon Roll; NHS; Elem Educ.

MORGANO, VIOLA; Sacred Heart HS; Pittsburgh, PA; (4); 4/135; Church Yth Grp; Math Clb; Mu Alpha Theta; Pres Spanish Clb; Chorus; Stage Crew; Variety Show; High Hon Roll; Hon Roll; VP NHS; U Of Pittsburgh; Engrng.

MORGANOSKY, JANICE; Fairchance-Georges SR HS; Mcclellandtown, PA; (3); Church Yth Grp; Drama Clb; Hosp Aide; Pres Schlr; School Play; Hon Roll; Jr NHS; Early Chldhd Educ.

MORGANTI, RITA; Wyoming Area HS; West Pittston, PA; (4); 52/247; Art Clb; Ski Clb; Spanish Clb; VP Frsh Cls; Pres Soph Cls; Pres Sr Cls; Cheerleading; Trk; Prncpls Awd-Ldrshp 87; Cum Laude Hnrs 87; Kings Coll; Bus.

MORGANTINI, KELLIE; Wyoming Area SR HS; W Pittston, PA; (3); Drama Clb; French Clb; Girl Scts; Cheerleading; Gym; Trk; Vllybl.

MORGUES, STACEY; Parkland HS; Allentown, PA; (3); 85/483; Art Clb; Key Clb; SADD; Stu Cncl; Var Tennis; Hon Roll; 1st Pl Janet West Rosen Memorial Art Contest 85-86; Penn ST; Architectural Engrng.

MORI, TARA LIN; Hempfield SR HS; Greensburg, PA; (3); French Clb; Pep Clb; Ski Clb; School Musical; Nwsp Stf; Yrbk Stf; Trs Jr Cls; Sec Stu Cncl; Cheerleading; Powder Puff Ftbl; Schlrshp Phila Acad Theatrcl Arts 86; Bronze Awd Solo Jazz Dance 87; Awd Grp Jazz Dance 87; Cmmnctns.

MORIARTY, MELISSA; Penn Manor HS; Millersvlle, PA; (4); AFS; Cmnty Wkr; JA; Stage Crew; Ed Yrbk Stf; Rep Sr Cls; JV Fld Hcky; Var Powder Puff Ftbl; Hon Roll; Presdntl Ftns Awd 86; Outstndng Contrbtns-Trumpeter-Yrbk 87; Tourst Indstry.

MORINIERE, MARCUS A; Northeast HS; Philadelphia, PA; (4); 30/690; Church Yth Grp; Computer Clb; FCA; Yrbk Stf; Trs Sr Cls; Bsktbl; Ftbl; Hon Roll; Howard U; Comp Engrng.

MORLEY, JOHN; Dover Area HS; Dover, PA; (3); 135/260; Varsity Clb; Band; Ftbl; Swmmng; Trk; Im Wt Lftg; 5th Pl Discus-St Trk & Fld Chmpnshps 87; Frstry.

MORNINGSTAR, AMBER; South Western HS; Brodbecks, PA; (2); JA; Office Aide; Nwsp Stf; Yrbk Stf; JV Bsktbl; Poli Sci.

MORNINGSTAR, SHERRY; Northeastern HS; Manchester, PA; (3); Pep Clb; Color Guard; Var Cheerleading; Hon Roll; Psych.

MOROSKIE, LARISSA; Shamokin Area HS; Shamokin, PA; (2); 37/250; Hosp Aide; Key Clb; Pep Clb; SADD; Cheerleading; High Hon Roll; Physical Thrpst.

MOROUSE, ANTHONY; South Park HS; Pittsburgh, PA; (3); 5/238; Drama Clb; Thesps; Band; Chorus; Concert Band; Mrchg Band; School Musical; School Play; Socr; High Hon Roll.

MORPHY, HEATHER; North Hills HS; Pittsburgh, PA; (3); Church Yth Grp; Hosp Aide; Ski Clb; Mrchg Band; Symp Band; High Hon Roll; NHS.

MORREALE, NICOLE; Pittston Area SR HS; Pittston, PA; (4); 23/348; Drama Clb; Science Clb; Yrbk Stf; High Hon Roll; Hon Roll; Jr NHS; NHS; Biol.

MORREN, BEVERLY; GAR HS; Wilkes-Barre, PA; (3); 31/153; Church Yth Grp; Library Aide; Chorus; Flag Corp; Stu Cncl; Sftbl; Vllybl; French Hon Soc; Hon Roll; NHS; Crmnl Jstc.

MORRET, TRACI; Mechanicsburg Area SR HS; Mechanicsburg, PA; (4); 12/306; Chorus; Nwsp Rptr; Var Crs Cntry; Var Sftbl; Var Co-Capt Swmmng; Hon Roll; NHS; Pres Schlr; Army Rsve Natl Schlr Athltc Awd 87; Drexel U; Engrng.

MORRIS, ALICIA; Millville HS; Millville, PA; (4); 30/73; Camera Clb; Drama Clb; Pres 4-H; Trs Band; Chorus; School Play; Yrbk Stf; 4-H Awd; NEDT Awd; PA ST Rsrv Plsr Hrs Chmp 86; Bloomsburg U; Bus Ed.

MORRIS, CAROLINE; Neshaminy HS; Levittown, PA; (3); 123/780; Computer Clb; Ski Clb; Im Lcrss; Im Sftbl; High Hon Roll; Hon Roll; Dist Hnr Roll 86-87; Dequenses; Chem.

MORRIS, CARRIE; Waynesburg Central HS; Waynesburg, PA; (3); Church Yth Grp; Drama Clb; Sec Mu Alpha Theta; Spanish Clb; School Musical; Stu Cncl; Cheerleading; Trk; High Hon Roll; Top 10 Chrldrs Tri-ST 86.

MORRIS, CHRIS; Kennedy Christian HS; Brookfield, OH; (4); Aud/Vis; French Clb; Library Aide; Service Clb; Hon Roll; Kent ST U; Tchr.

MORRIS, CHRISTY; Pocono Mountain SR HS; Tannersville, PA; (2); Church Yth Grp; Pep Clb; Band; Var L Cheerleading; Trk; Hon Roll; Crmnl Law.

MORRIS, CRAIG E; Monaca JR SR HS; Monaca, PA; (3); 2/90; Am Leg Boys St; Quiz Bowl; Concert Band; Mrchg Band; Pep Band; Stage Crew; Stu Cncl; Ntl Merit Ltr; Sal; HOBY Schl Rep 86.

MORRIS, DAVID; Dallas SR HS; Trucksville, PA; (3); 18/220; Bsbl; Socr; Hon Roll; NEDT Awd; JR Cls Math Awd 86-87; Engrng.

MORRIS, DAWN M; Fox Chapel Area HS; Pittsburgh, PA; (3); Church Yth Grp; Red Cross Aide; Chorus; Capt Color Guard; High Hon Roll; Hon Roll; Art Awd 87; Commrcl Dsgn.

MORRIS, EMILY S; Waynesburg Central HS; Waynesburg, PA; (3); AFS; Church Yth Grp; VP Drama Clb; French Clb; Trs Natl Beta Clb; Pres Stu Cncl; Var L Sftbl; Var L Vllybl; Hon Roll; Quiz Bowl; Hugh O Brian Yth Fndtn Outstndng Clsmn 86; Messiah Coll.

MORRIS III, HARRIS L; Penncrest HS; Media, PA; (4); 44/329; Intnl Clb; Trs Ski Clb; SADD; Variety Show; Off Sr Cls; Var Capt Socr; Var Capt Trk; High Hon Roll; Hon Roll; NHS; West Point; Ofcr.

MORRIS, HEATHER; Cambridge Springs Joint HS; Cambridge Spg, PA; (3); 4/98; Debate Tm; Sec French Clb; SADD; Concert Band; Mrchg Band; Nwsp Stf; Rep Stu Cncl; Var Cheerleading; Hon Roll; H O Brian Yth Ldrshp Ambsdr 86; Gannon U SAT Schlrshp 87; Bus Mgmt.

MORRIS, JEFFREY S; Pennridge HS; Dublin, PA; (3); Am Leg Boys St; Trs Church Yth Grp; JV Stat Bsktbl; High Hon Roll; NHS; Prfct Atten Awd; Bsktbl Coaches Awd 87; U PA; Comp Sci.

MORRIS, JENNIFER; Upper Merion HS; King Of Prussia, PA; (4); Hosp Aide; Math Tm; Spanish Clb; Nwsp Stf; Yrbk Stf; Crs Cntry; Hon Roll; Acad Ftns Awd 87; PA ST.

MORRIS, KENNETH; Otto-Eldred JR & SR HS; Eldred, PA; (3); 17/89; Pres Church Yth Grp; Spanish Clb; Y-Teens; Church Choir; Hon Roll; Comp Pgmmng.

MORRIS, KYMBERLY; Phoenixville HS; Phoenixville, PA; (3); SADD; Varsity Clb; Crs Cntry; Trk; High Hon Roll; Hon Roll; Jr NHS; NHS; Pres Schlr; PA Gov Schl Ag Schlrshp Pgm 86; Vet Med.

MORRIS, LAURIE; Susquenita HS; Marysville, PA; (3); 11/157; Church Yth Grp; Leo Clb; Letterman Clb; Spanish Clb; Yrbk Stf; Stat Bsktbl; L Crs Cntry; Mgr(s); Trk; Hon Roll; Gov Energy Awd; Ltrmn; Sci Fair 1st Pl; Aerontcl Engr.

MORRIS, MARTINA; Schuylkill Haven HS; Sch Haven, PA; (2); 45/101; Church Yth Grp; FNA; Library Aide; Pep Clb; SADD; Var JV Bsktbl; Hon Roll; Penn ST U; Nrsng.

MORRIS, MARYELLEN; Archbishop Prendergast HS; Aldan, PA; (3); 140/327; Office Aide; Var Bsktbl; Im Bowling; Im Sftbl; Sprts Med.

MORRIS, MELANIE; Palmerton Area HS; Bowmanstown, PA; (3); 22/175; Pep Clb; Y-Teens; Nwsp Stf; Yrbk Stf; Var L Crs Cntry; Var L Gym; Var L Trk; Hon Roll; Danc.

MORRIS, MICHAEL; Center Area HS; Aliquippa, PA; (3); 13/188; Latin Clb; Temple Yth Grp; Band; Concert Band; Drm Mjr(t); Jazz Band; Mrchg Band; School Musical; School Play; Ftbl; PA All-ST Bnd 87; U S All-East Hnrs Bnd 87; Westminster Hnrs Bnd 85-87.

MORRIS, MICHELLE; Curwensville Area HS; Curwensville, PA; (3); Drama Clb; French Clb; Ski Clb; Thesps; Varsity Clb; Yrbk Stf; Sec Frsh Cls; Cheerleading.

MORRIS, MICHELLE D; Forest Hills SR HS; Beaverdale, PA; (3); 1/154; Am Leg Aux Girls St; Art Clb; Trs Church Yth Grp; Drama Clb; Library Aide; NFL; Scholastic Bowl; Lib Band; School Musical; Nwsp Stf; Bus Admin.

MORRIS, NICOLE; Shenandoah Valley JR SR HS; Shenandoah, PA; (3); 21/80; SADD; Chorus; Nwsp Stf; Pres Frsh Cls; Pres Soph Cls; Pres Jr Cls; Sec Sr Cls; Stu Cncl; Var Bsktbl; Gym; Schuylkill Cnty Chorus 86-87; Exec Brnch Of Stu Cncl 86-87; Jrnlsm.

MORRIS, REBECCA; Ligonier Valley SR HS; Ligonier, PA; (3); 2/157; Office Aide; Red Cross Aide; Swing Chorus; Yrbk Stf; Stat Bsktbl; Mgr(s); Score Keeper; Vllybl; High Hon Roll; Jr NHS; 1st Pl Chem Olympcs At Pitt 87; 2nd Pl Sci Day At U Of Pitt-Greensburg 87; Outstndng Achiev In Bio 85; Chem.

MORRIS, RICHARD MALIK; Westinghouse HS; Pittsburgh, PA; (3); JA; Letterman Clb; Varsity Clb; Pres Stu Cncl; Capt Ftbl; Trk; Wt Lftg; High Hon Roll; NHS; Hampton U; Bus Admin.

MORRIS, SHARON; Pittston Area SR HS; Pittston, PA; (4); 27/348; Rep French Clb; Key Clb; Pres SADD; Nwsp Ed-Chief; Var Socr; Var Capt Swmmng; Hon Roll; Pres NHS; Soc Distngushd Am Stu 86.

MORRIS, SUZANNE; Danville SR HS; Danville, PA; (2); Church Yth Grp; Key Clb; Ski Clb; Stu Cncl; Var Cheerleading; Im Socr; Tennis; Trk; High Hon Roll; Pres Acad Ftns Awd 86; Kystn ST Games Rgnl Sccr Tm 87; Dr.

MORRIS, TAMMY; Pittston Area HS; Duryea, PA; (3); Key Clb; Chorus; Color Guard; Accntng.

MORRISON, AMY; Central Columbia HS; Bloomsburg, PA; (4); 96/170; Pres DECA; FBLA; FHA; Library Aide; DECA ST Awd Cert 86-87; Schl Store Regntn 86; Accntng.

MORRISON, ARTRESE; Reading SR HS; Reading, PA; (3); 12/710; Cmnty Wkr; Color Guard; Nwsp Stf; Yrbk Ed-Chief; Yrbk Stf; Trk; Cit Awd; Hon Roll; Pres Jr NHS; NHS; Pre Law.

MORRISON, BOB; Valley View HS; Carbondale, PA; (3); Church Yth Grp; French Clb; Bsbl; Bsktbl; Golf; Freeck Keen Sprtsmnshp Awd Bsbll 83; Engnrng.

MORRISON, CARRIE; Freeport HS; Freeport, PA; (2); Girl Scts; Office Aide; Chorus; Color Guard; Stage Crew; Hon Roll; Chef.

MORRISON, COLETTE; Warren Area HS; Warren, PA; (4); Pres Church Yth Grp; French Clb; School Play; Var JV Cheerleading; Stat Trk; Cit Awd; High Hon Roll; Hon Roll; Sec Jr NHS; George Mason U; Bus.

MORRISON, DANIEL; Mechanicsburg Area SR HS; Mechanicsburg, PA; (3); 4/338; Church Yth Grp; Cmnty Wkr; Church Choir; School Play; Yrbk Rptr; Rep Stu Cncl; JV L Golf; Var L Swmmng; Var L Trk; High Hon Roll; Gordon Coll; Med Engr.

MORRISON, DANIELLE; Northampton SR HS; Nazareth, PA; (2); Church Yth Grp; Pep Clb; Chorus; Church Choir; Rep Soph Cls; Var Diving; JV Fld Hcky; Im Gym; JV Sftbl; Hon Roll; Phys Ther.

MORRISON, DAVID; Connellsville Area HS; Dunbar, PA; (3); 125/550; Cmnty Wkr; Sec Soph Cls; Var Bsbl; Var Bsktbl; Var Trk; High Hon Roll; Hon Roll; NHS.

MORRISON, HEATHER; Tyrone Area JR/Sr HS; Tyrone, PA; (3); 13/209; Am Leg Aux Girls St; Key Clb; Spanish Clb; SADD; Varsity Clb; Chorus; Yrbk Bus Mgr; Stu Cncl; Var Capt Cheerleading; Powder Puff Ftbl; Altrnt Armcn Lgn Axlry Grl ST 87; US Nvl Acad; Acngrphr.

MORRISON, MATTHEW; Boiling Springs HS; Carlisle, PA; (2); Aud/Vis; Mrchg Band; Stage Crew; Var L Socr; Var L Swmmng; Church Yth Grp; Spanish Clb; Band; Concert Band; VP Soph Cls.

MORRISON, MELISSA A; Mt Pleasant SR HS; Mt Pleasant, PA; (4); Church Yth Grp; Computer Clb; GAA; Intnl Clb; Latin Clb; Ski Clb; Concert Band; Mrchg Band; Hon Roll; Psych Clb 87; Duquesne U; Mngmnt.

MORRISON JR, RAYMOND G; Eisenhower HS; Pittsfield, PA; (4); 5/116; Computer Clb; Mrchg Band; Yrbk Phtg; Rep Stu Cncl; High Hon Roll; NHS; Sal; Prsdntl Acdmc Ftnss Awd 87; PA ST U; Aerospc Engrng.

MORRISON, ROBERT; Central Bucks HS West; New Britain, PA; (3); 77/492; Cmnty Wkr; Ski Clb; Stu Cncl; Golf; Socr; Vllybl; Hon Roll; Jr NHS; Fnc.

MORRISON, ROBERT; Frankford HS; Philadelphia, PA; (3); Boy Scts; Band; Mrchg Band; Orch; Nwsp Phtg; Nwsp Rptr; Nwsp Sprt Ed; Nwsp Stf; Rotary Awd; Rnnr Up Clmbs Day Essy Cntst 85-86; Advncd Plcmnt Pgrm Mbr 86-87; Temple; Jrnlsm.

MORRONE, KIM; Marion Ctr; Clymer, PA; (3); 81/149; FBLA; FHA; FNA; Hosp Aide; Library Aide; Red Cross Aide; Flag Corp; Mrchg Band; Yrbk Stf; Hon Roll; Bradford Schl Bus; Retal Mgmt.

MORRONI, KATHLEEN; Moshannon Valley HS; Smithmill, PA; (3); 11/112; Spanish Clb; VP SADD; Chorus; School Play; Nwsp Stf; Stat Bsktbl; High Hon Roll; Hon Roll; Trs NHS; Aud/Vis; Psychlgy.

MORROW, JEFF; Pennsbury HS; Yardley, PA; (4); 32/769; Intnl Clb; Spanish Clb; Tennis; Vllybl; Wrstlng; High Hon Roll; NHS; Pres Schlr; Pres Schlrshp Loyola Coll 87; U Of DE; Sci.

MORROW, MEGAN; Freeport Area SR HS; Freeport, PA; (4); 1/165; Concert Band; Jazz Band; Mrchg Band; Pep Band; Symp Band; Rep Stu Cncl; High Hon Roll; NHS; PA ST U; Sci.

MORROW, MICHAEL; Karns City JR- SR HS; Karns City, PA; (3); 29/99; Art Clb; Aud/Vis; Spanish Clb; Chorus; School Musical; School Play; Stage Crew; Var Golf; Var Trk; Foundtn Free Enterprise Educ Schlrshp 87; Air Force Tech Schl; Pilot.

MORROW, RICHARD; South Side Area HS; Hookstown, PA; (3); 8/135; JV Bsktbl; Im Cheerleading; Var Ftbl; Var Trk; High Hon Roll; Hon Roll; NHS; Ntl Merit Ltr; Chem Olympcs U Pittsburgh 86 & 87; CC Beaver Cnty H S Enrchmnt Scholar 87; IN ST U; Pilot.

MORROW, TARA; Lower Dauphin HS; Grantville, PA; (3); Am Leg Aux Girls St; CAP; Library Aide; Office Aide; Aud/Vis; Color Guard; Coach Actv; Mgr(s); Hon Roll; VFW Awd; Law.

MORSE, BENJAMIN; Henderson HS; Exton, PA; (3); 47/350; JCL; Latin Clb; Chorus; Lit Mag; Trs Soph Cls; Sec Jr Cls; Stu Cncl; Socr; Latin Hnr Soc 86-87; Philosophy.

MORSE, LORRIE; Everett HS; Everett, PA; (3); 7/133; Art Clb; Pres Church Yth Grp; Drama Clb; Library Aide; Spanish Clb; Chorus; School Play; Stage Crew; Off Stu Cncl; High Hon Roll.

MORT IV, DARE W; New Castle SR HS; New Castle, PA; (3); Hon Roll; Clarion U; Pre Law.

MORT, MARK E; United HS; Seward, PA; (4); 14/157; Mu Alpha Theta; Trs Ski Clb; Trs Jr Cls; Trs Sr Cls; Stat Bsktbl; Stat Ftbl; Mu Alpha Theta Awd; NHS; Natl Yth Ldrshp Conf 86; PA ST; Engrng.

MORT, SUSAN; Fairfield HS; Fairfield, PA; (3); Art Clb; Camera Clb; Cmnty Wkr; 4-H; French Clb; FFA; FHA; Library Aide; Chorus; School Play; Computer Prgrmr.

MORT, TAMMY; United HS; Armagh, PA; (4); 47/157; Camera Clb; Church Yth Grp; VP FNA; Girl Scts; Hosp Aide; Ski Clb; Hon Roll; Hosp Vlntrng Awds 84 & 85; Conemaugh Vly Memrl Hosp; RN.

MORTENSEN, MELISSA; Cambria Heights HS; Hasting, PA; (3); Drama Clb; 4-H; FHA; Library Aide; Teachers Aide; Nwsp Stf; Yrbk Rptr; Yrbk Stf; Sftbl; Hon Roll; ICM; Bus Tchr.

MORTIMER, CYNTHIA; Ambridge Area HS; Freedom, PA; (4); 45/265; Trs French Clb; Rep Pep Clb; Off Soph Cls; Drug & Alcohol Cmmtte Chrprsn 86-87; Carlow Coll Schlrshp 87-88; Carlow Coll; Nrsng.

MORTIMER III, LEO F; Ambridge HS; Freedom, PA; (4); 38/265; French Clb; Pep Band; High Hon Roll; Hon Roll; Elizabeth Steward Schlrshp 87; Passavant Schlrshp 87; Thiel Coll; Bio.

MORTON, CARRIEJEAN; Central Dauphin HS; Harrisburg, PA; (3); 100/326; Church Yth Grp; Band; Chorus; Concert Band; Mrchg Band; Orch; Pep Band; Stage Crew; Hon Roll; Jr NHS; HACC; Bus.

MORTON, CHAD; Bucktail Area HS; Renovo, PA; (2); Letterman Clb; Varsity Clb; VP Soph Cls; VP Stu Cncl; Var Wrstlng; High Hon Roll; Hon Roll; Sci, Language Arts & Hist Awds 87; Physical Achvt Awd 87; Med.

MORTON, JENNIFER; Nazareth Acad; Philadelphia, PA; (3); Sec NFL; Pep Clb; Sec Speech Tm; Chorus; Stage Crew; Nwsp Phtg; Lit Mag; Mgr Fld Hcky; 2nd City Cathlc Frnscs Leag 87; 1st W Cathlc Spch Trnmnt 87; Art Hstry.

MORTON, JOHN; Biglerville HS; Biglerville, PA; (2); 19/116; Boy Scts; Church Yth Grp; 4-H; Science Clb; Chorus; Mgr(s); Tennis; 4-H Awd; High Hon Roll; Jr NHS; Eagle Scout 87; PA ST; FBI Agent.

MORTON, TALISA; Penn Hills HS; Pittsburgh, PA; (3); Church Yth Grp; Pep Clb; Spanish Clb; Off Soph Cls; Off Jr Cls; VP Stu Cncl; Hon Roll; May Qn Allgheny Union Baptist Assoc 85; U Of Pittsburgh; Acctng.

MORY, DUANE; Parkland HS; Coplay, PA; (3); 173/503; DECA; Pres DECA Chptr 86-87; Dist Rep PA ST DECA 87-88; Dist Wnr Comp 6th Pl 86; Mktg.

MORZE, STACY; Nazareth Acad; Phila, PA; (3); Dance Clb; French Clb; Spanish Clb; School Musical; School Play; Yrbk Stf; VP Frsh Cls; Pres Soph Cls; Stu Cncl; Cmnty Wkr; Amer Legion Assn Ldrshp Awd 84; Psychlgy.

MOSACK, LYNN; Kiski Area HS; Apollo, PA; (4); Pep Clb; Spanish Clb; Varsity Clb; Yrbk Stf; Rep Frsh Cls; Stat Bsbl; Co-Capt Cheerleading; Mgr(s); Score Keeper; High Hon Roll; Duquesne U; Bio.

MOSBACHER, DEBBIE; Meadville Area HS; Meadville, PA; (3); 91/363; Church Yth Grp; 4-H; Girl Scts; Hosp Aide; JA; Spanish Clb; Speech Tm; SADD; Chorus; School Play; Communctn.

MOSBACHER, ERIC; Ft Le Boeuf HS; Erie, PA; (3); 33/220; Church Yth Grp; Var Bsbl; Var Ftbl; Im Vllybl; High Hon Roll.

MOSBACHER, KEVIN; Meadville Area SR HS; Meadville, PA; (4); Varsity Clb; Var Bsktbl; Var Capt Socr; Var Vllybl; Church Yth Grp; Nwsp Stf; High Hon Roll; Hon Roll; NHS; Penn ST.

MOSCHGAT, ERIN; Bishop Mc Cort HS; Windber, PA; (2); German Clb; Hosp Aide; Band; Chorus; Concert Band; Mrchg Band; Orch; Pep Band; Symp Band; Var L Swmmng; IN U PA Hnrs Band 85 & 86; Rgnl Band 87; Dist Band, Orchstra 86; Music Ed.

MOSCHGAT, ROBERT; Forest Hills HS; Elton, PA; (3); FBLA; School Play; Variety Show; Nwsp Stf; Pres Jr Cls; Capt JV Bsktbl; Capt Var Ftbl; Capt Var Trk; Hon Roll; CA U; Sprts Med.

MOSCO, MICHAEL; Blairsville SR HS; Blairsville, PA; (1); Church Yth Grp; Computer Clb; French Clb; SADD; Chorus; Bowling; Swmmng; Tennis; High Hon Roll; Hon Roll; Penn ST; Math.

MOSELY, MARIA; Monessen JR & SR HS; Monessen, PA; (4); 12/93; Drama Clb; Model UN; Trs OEA; Concert Band; Nwsp Ed-Chief; Nwsp Sprt Ed; Yrbk Ed-Chief; JV Var Bsktbl; High Hon Roll; NHS; St Paul Coll Presdntl Schlrshp 87; Mdrn Miss Pgnt ST Fnlst PA 86; St Pauls Coll; Poli Sci.

MOSENG, EDWIN; Phil-Mont Christian Acad; Hatboro, PA; (4); 1/35; Stat Bsbl; High Hon Roll; NHS; Math.

MOSER, CAROL; Springdale HS; Cheswick, PA; (3); Church Yth Grp; Drama Clb; Exploring; Spanish Clb; SADD; Band; Color Guard; Mrchg Band; Stage Crew; Yrbk Stf; Hlth Sci.

MOSER, CRISTIE; Knoch HS; Cabot, PA; (3); Trs Church Yth Grp; SADD; Trs Band; Concert Band; Mrchg Band; Pep Band; School Play; Symp Band; High Hon Roll; NHS; Grove City Coll; Cmmnctns.

MOSER, DANIEL; Milton HS; New Columbia, PA; (3); Varsity Clb; Capt Ftbl; Im Wt Lftg; Var L Wrstlng; Mst Outstndng Wrstlr 86-87; 1st Team Of Cntrl Susquehanna Cnfrnc All Star Team In Ftbl 86.

MOSER, JAMES D; Hershey SR HS; Hershey, PA; (3); 27/209; Computer Clb; Band; Chorus; Jazz Band; Mrchg Band; School Musical; School Play; Swing Chorus; Variety Show; NHS; Dist/Rgnl Chorus 87; Comp Pgmr.

MOSER, MATTHEW; Highlands HS; Natrona Hgts, PA; (3); Var Capt Bsktbl; Var L Ftbl; Var Jr NHS.

MOSER, MELISSA; Notre Dame HS; Easton, PA; (3); 14/89; Pep Clb; Yrbk Stf; Rep Soph Cls; Sec Jr Cls; Var Cheerleading; Mgr(s); High Hon Roll; Hon Roll; Lwyr.

MOSER, RONALD; Morrisville HS; Morrisville, PA; (3); 21/92; Var JV Bsbl; Var JV Ftbl; Var JV Wt Lftg; Hon Roll; Jr NHS; NHS; Prfct Atten Awd.

MOSER, SHEILA; Weatherly HS; Weatherly, PA; (4); 4/66; Bsktbl; Crs Cntry; Score Keeper; Sftbl; Hon Roll; Pres Schlr; Acdmc Achvt Awd 87; Pres Acdmc Fit Awd 87; Outstndng Typg Achvt 87; Bridgewater; Physlgy.

MOSER, SONYA; Conemaugh Township HS; Hollsopple, PA; (3); 26/119; Church Yth Grp; Hosp Aide; Band; Church Choir; Jazz Band; Mrchg Band; School Musical; Hon Roll; Estrn Mennonite Coll; Nrsng.

MOSES, CHEREL; University City HS; Philadelphia, PA; (3); 5/23; Aud/Vis; Cmnty Wkr; Science Clb; Lit Mag; Hon Roll; Prfct Atten Awd; Crisis Intervention Network & Urban Gdng Awd 87; Temple U; Med.

MOSES, ERIC; Central Catholic HS; Sewickley, PA; (3); Band; Concert Band; Mrchg Band; Rep Frsh Cls; JV Crs Cntry; Trk; Bell Acres Boro JR Vlntr Fire Dptmnt 87.

MOSES, KESHA; Pine Forge Acad; Randallstown, MD; (3); 5/60; Office Aide; Teachers Aide; Chorus; School Play; Yrbk Stf; Trs Soph Cls; Rep Stu Cncl; Co-Capt Socr; High Hon Roll; Sal; Princeton U; Comp Prgmmr.

MOSES, MOLLY; Rockwood Area HS; Rockwood, PA; (3); 3/82; Band; Drill Tm; Mrchg Band; VP Frsh Cls; Pres Soph Cls; VP Jr Cls; VP Stu Cncl; Var Sftbl; JV Var Vllybl; High Hon Roll; Math.

MOSEY, JOE; Central Dauphin HS; Harrisburg, PA; (3); Teachers Aide; Stu Cncl; Bsbl; Bsktbl; Ftbl; Golf; Wt Lftg; Dale Carnegie Awd 85; Dentstry.

MOSHOLDER, KRISTINA; Somerset Area SR HS; Somerset, PA; (3); 26/250; 4-H; French Clb; Red Cross Aide; Ski Clb; L Mrchg Band; Yrbk Stf; Rep Stu Cncl; L Cheerleading; L Trk; L High Hon Roll; Penn ST; Vet Med.

MOSHOLDER, SHAWN; Rockwood Area HS; Rockwood, PA; (4); 21/98; Pres Church Yth Grp; Cmnty Wkr; Chorus; Trk; High Hon Roll; Hon Roll.

MOSIER, BARBARA; St Marys Area HS; Kersey, PA; (4); 33/275; Girl Scts; Hosp Aide; Church Choir; Jr NHS; NHS; Spnsh Awd 87; Ntl Hnr Scty 87; WV U; Scl Wrkr.

MOSIER, LYNNE; Trinity HS; Washington, PA; (3); 78/402; Church Yth Grp; French Clb; Hosp Aide; Pep Clb; Nwsp Stf; Yrbk Bus Mgr; Yrbk Stf; Trs Sr Cls; VP L Tennis; Hon Roll; Nrsng.

MOSIER, RANDY; Trinity HS; Washington, PA; (2); German Clb; Jazz Band; JV Bsktbl; High Hon Roll; Hon Roll; Duquesne U; Phrmcy.

MOSIER, VALERIE; Northwestern HS; Albion, PA; (3); 42/136; Chorus; Drill Tm; Flag Corp; Yrbk Stf; Twrlr; Hon Roll; Accntng.

MOSKAL, VALISSA; Fairfield HS; Orrtanna, PA; (3); Ski Clb; Nwsp Rptr; Nwsp Stf; Yrbk Stf; Hst Stu Cncl; Var L Cheerleading; JV Fld Hcky; Var Trk; Church Yth Grp; Band; Art Awd-Hon Mntn/Gvrnrs Cmte-Emplymnt Of The Handicapped 86; Penn Fed Of Sportsmens Clb 87; Travel Industry.

MOSLE III, WILLIAM; Shady Side Acad; Pittsburgh, PA; (3); Camera Clb; Chess Clb; Debate Tm; Drama Clb; French Clb; Intnl Clb; Math Tm; Science Clb; Ski Clb; Spanish Clb; Keewaydin Gigitowin 87; Amer Chem Soc Outstndng Stu Awd 86; Photography Clb Pres & Founder 84-87; Duke U; Engrng.

MOSLEY, CINDY; Coughlin HS; Wilkes Barre, PA; (3); Art Clb; Church Yth Grp; Library Aide; Band; Nwsp Rptr; Nwsp Stf; Trs Frsh Cls; Rep Stu Cncl; Var Vllybl; Hon Roll; Valley Forge Chrstn Coll; Sci.

MOSLEY, NICHOLAS; Scotland Schl For Vetrans Children; Philadelphia, PA; (3); ROTC; Varsity Clb; Band; Concert Band; Jazz Band; Mrchg Band; Pep Band; Symp Band; Var Ftbl; Var Trk; Voctnl Achvt Awd Excllnc Prnt; Instrmntlst Mag Merit Awd Music; Arch.

MOSLOCK, SUSAN; Danville SR HS; Danville, PA; (1); Sec Trs 4-H; JV Fld Hcky; JV Trk; 4-H Awd; High Hon Roll; Hon Roll; Pres Acdmc Ftnss Awd 87.

MOSS, BILL; W Middlesex HS; W Middlesex, PA; (4); 13/97; L Bsbl; L Ftbl; Wt Lftg; Hon Roll; Spanish NHS; Youngstown U; Army ROTC.

MOSS, CHUCK; Seneca Valley SR HS; Evans City, PA; (3); Speech Tm; High Hon Roll; Hon Roll; Schlstc Achvt Awd 86 & 87; Sci Tchr.

MOSS, DANIEL; Lower Moreland HS; Huntingdon Valley, PA; (2); FBLA; Spanish Clb; Rep Frsh Cls; Stu Cncl; Var Bsbl; Var JV Bsktbl.

MOSS, ELLEN; Bethel Park SR HS; Bethel Park, PA; (4); 26/519; Band; Concert Band; Drill Tm; Mrchg Band; Orch; School Musical; Symp Band; High Hon Roll; NHS; Penn ST U; Educ.

MOSS, ERIC; Central HS; Philadelphia, PA; (4); Teachers Aide; Hon Roll; Barnwell Hnr Awd; PA St U; Arch Engr.

MOSS, JOSETTA; Chester HS; Brook Haven, PA; (3); Spanish Clb; Chorus; Church Choir; Sec Soph Cls; VP Stu Cncl; Hon Roll; Prfct Atten Awd; Music.

MOSS, KEITH; Neshaminy HS; Trevose, PA; (3); 115/788; Var Bsbl; Var Bowling; Var Ftbl; Hon Roll; Capt Powder Puff Ftbl.

MOSS, KENNETH; North Pocono HS; Moscow, PA; (4); 37/242; Am Leg Boys St; Rep Church Yth Grp; VP FBLA; Ski Clb; Church Choir; Variety Show; Nwsp Sprt Ed; JV Vllybl; Hon Roll; NHS; PTSA Schlrshp Awd 87; U Of Scranton; Pre Med.

MOSS, NATALEE; Nazareth Area SR HS; Nazareth, PA; (4); 41/230; Key Clb; Letterman Clb; Red Cross Aide; Ski Clb; Pres Soph Cls; Pres Jr Cls; Pres Sr Cls; Trs Stu Cncl; Cheerleading; Kiwanis Awd; 2nd Pl Crfts Awd 87; Bloomsburg U; Accntng.

MOSS, PAM; West Scranton HS; Scranton, PA; (4); Ski Clb; Spanish Clb; Yrbk Stf; Cheerleading; Hon Roll; NHS; Acad All Amer 87; Penn ST; Social Wrk.

MOSSER, BRENT; Panther Valley HS; Nesquehoning, PA; (2); 9/120; Church Yth Grp; Drama Clb; School Play; Var Trk; High Hon Roll; Hon Roll; Pre-Med.

MOSSER, DARRICK O; Bald Eagle Wittany HS; Mill Hall, PA; (3); Pres Key Clb; Varsity Clb; Chorus; School Play; Var Ftbl.

MOSSER, ERIC; Panther Valley HS; Nesquehoning, PA; (1); 39/127; Art Clb; Church Yth Grp; German Clb; Bsktbl; Trk; Hon Roll; Prfct Atten Awd.

MOSTELLER, DOUGLAS C; Henderson HS; Wdst Chester, PA; (3); 26/360; Church Yth Grp; Spanish Clb; Yrbk Stf; Stu Cncl; Var Crs Cntry; Swmmng; Im Vllybl; Hon Roll; NHS; Spanish NHS; YMCA Swim Natls; Chem Engrng.

MOSTOLLER, MELISSA; North Star HS; Boswell, PA; (2); 2/130; Church Yth Grp; FCA; Ski Clb; SADD; Rep Stu Cncl; Twrlr; Hon Roll; Stu Mth; Med.

MOSTOLLER, TROY; Somerset Area SR HS; Somerset, PA; (3); Boy Scts; Bsktbl; Penn ST U; Arch.

MOSTOWY, KARA; Karns City Area HS; Bruin, PA; (3); Spanish Clb; SADD; Thesps; Band; Concert Band; Mrchg Band; Pep Band; School Play; Stage Crew; Yrbk Stf; Joanne Bly Ltr Merit; Robert Morris; Paralegal.

MOTEL, DIANE; Hazleton HS; Hazleton, PA; (3); 55/450; Cmnty Wkr; FBLA; Chorus; Color Guard; Nwsp Rptr; Hon Roll.

MOTEN, ROBYN; John Harris Campus HS; Harrisburg, PA; (4); 6/235; Intnl Clb; VP Science Clb; Chorus; High Hon Roll; Hon Roll; Sec NHS; VFW Awd; U S Ambsdr To Frnc Frgn Exch Stu 84; Prsrvnc Awd For Acad Of Sci 83-87; IN U Of Pnyslvna; Chmstry.

MOTIL, GLEN ERIC; W Hazleton HS; Oneida, PA; (4); 59/228; Church Yth Grp; Civic Clb; Pres Sr Cls; Rep Stu Cncl; Elks Awd; High Hon Roll; Hon Roll; NHS; U S Marines; Cmnctns.

MOTISKO, LYNNETT; Valley View JR/Sr HS; Eynon, PA; (2); Art Clb; Latin Clb; Rep Soph Cls; Pres Jr Cls; Rep Stu Cncl; Stat Bsktbl; Vllybl; High Hon Roll; Hon Roll; Amer Coll Of Musicns-Natl Piano Plyng Adtns 80-87; Natl Sec Ed Cncl Schlr Prog 86; Acad Excel 85-86; U Of Scranton; Hlth.

MOTLEY, LINDA; Minersville Area HS; Pottsville, PA; (3); #11 In Class; Exploring; Sec FBLA; Ski Clb; Spanish Clb; Yrbk Stf; High Hon Roll; NHS; JR Garland Group 87; Typng II & Acctng Awd 8m; Bus.

MOTT, MICHAEL; Penn Manor HS; Elizabethtown, PA; (3); Boys Clb Am; Boy Scts; Cmnty Wkr; Exploring; FFA; Ski Clb; Life Scout & Jr Ldr 84; Outward Bound; Wldrns Srvl Grad; Boys Clubs Vol Cnslr; Forest Fire Crew; Ag Mech.

MOTTA, KRISTINA; Steel Valley HS; Munhall, PA; (3); Church Yth Grp; Nwsp Stf; Vllybl; Wt Lftg; Amer Legn Awd Annl Vet Day Essy Cntst 86-87; Cmnctns.

MOTTER, TRAVIS; South Western HS; Hanover, PA; (2); Chess Clb; Ski Clb; Ftbl; Hon Roll; Shippnesburg Coll.

MOTTO, ANNE-MARIE; Lourdes Regional HS; Excelsior, PA; (4); 4/96; Pres Library Aide; Pep Clb; Sec PAVAS; Service Clb; Sec Spanish Clb; Thesps; Chorus; School Play; NHS; Spanish NHS; Drew U; Pol Sci.

MOTTO, CHRIS; Mifflinburg Area HS; Mifflinburg, PA; (1); Boy Scts; German Clb; Key Clb; Bsktbl; Ftbl; Cit Awd; High Hon Roll; Hon Roll; JC Awd; Syracuse; Commerical Pilot.

MOTUK, TRACEE; Minersville Area HS; Pottsville, PA; (3); 21/102; French Clb; Flag Corp; Jr NHS; French Hon Soc; Hon Roll; Empire Beauty Schl; Btcn.

MOTZ, KATHERINE; Waynesboro SR HS; Waynesboro, PA; (3); AFS; Color Guard; Yrbk Stf; Var Cheerleading; Hon Roll.

MOTZ, LEON; Tamaqua SR HS; Tamaqua, PA; (3); Church Yth Grp; Science Clb; JV Wrstlng; Hon Roll; Pre Law.

MOTZ, SUZANN MICHELL; Lower Dauphin HS; Hershey, PA; (4); 4/240; Capt Church Yth Grp; Debate Tm; Concert Band; Drm Mjr(t); Jazz Band; Mrchg Band; Orch; Trk; JP Sousa Awd; NHS; U Of Rochester; Optical Engrng.

MOUGHAN, MEGAN; Cardinal O Hara HS; Media, PA; (3); 189/710; Church Yth Grp; Cmnty Wkr; JA; Service Clb; SADD; School Musical; School Play; Yrbk Stf; Im Bsktbl; Var Socr; Fshn Dsgn.

MOUKOULIS, JOANN; Phoenixville Area SR HS; Phoenixville, PA; (3); Church Yth Grp; Pep Clb; Spanish Clb; Trs Chorus; Jr NHS; NHS; Pres Schlr; Outstndng Stu Chem Awd 87; Maids Athena Pres 87; Dogwood Pgnt 87; Biochem.

MOUL, JON; Red Lion SR HS; York, PA; (3); 42/348; Varsity Clb; Var Bsktbl; Var Crs Cntry; Var Trk; Wt Lftg; Natl Hnr History Awd 87; Med.

MOUL, TODD; Big Spring HS; Plainfield, PA; (3); Boy Scts; Pres Church Yth Grp; Ski Clb; Varsity Clb; Band; Concert Band; Var Crs Cntry; Var Trk; Crmnlgy.

MOULD, DANIEL W; Lackawanna Trail HS; Factoryville, PA; (4); 19/84; Church Yth Grp; JA; Concert Band; Jazz Band; Madrigals; Mrchg Band; School Musical; Wt Lftg; Hon Roll; Ski Clb; Keystone JC; Bus Mgmt.

MOULDER, ERICH; Coatesville HS; Parkesburg, PA; (2); Boy Scts; CAP; ROTC; Varsity Clb; JV Ftbl; Var Wrstlng; God Cntry Awd; Hon Roll; Prfct Atten Awd; SAR Awd; Outstndng Cadet Awd 87; USAF Acad; Fghtr Pilot.

MOUNTAIN, COLLEEN; Wellsboro Area HS; Wellsboro, PA; (4); Pres Church Yth Grp; Pres Trs French Clb; Pep Clb; Concert Band; Mrchg Band; Rep Stu Cncl; Var L Tennis; JV Stat Trk; Hon Roll; NHS; Packer Fndtn Schlrshp 87; St Bonaventure U; Micro-Bio.

MOUNTS, LESLIE; Mc Guffey HS; Claysville, PA; (3); 12/250; 4-H; Pep Clb; Spanish Clb; Trs Band; Color Guard; Flag Corp; Mrchg Band; Stat Trk; Capt Twrlr; NHS; Nrsng.

MOUNTS, RHONDA; New Castle SR HS; New Castle, PA; (4); AFS; Pres Church Yth Grp; Office Aide; Pep Clb; Spanish Clb; SADD; Teachers Aide; Band; Church Choir; Yrbk Phtg; Typng Awd 85; Miss Yth Cmp 86; Lee Coll.

MOUTSOS, KIM; Meadville Area SR HS; Meadville, PA; (4); 9/304; VP Church Yth Grp; German Clb; Sec Key Clb; Church Choir; Variety Show; Rep Sr Cls; High Hon Roll.

MOVINSKY, JAMES; Purchase Line HS; Barnesboro, PA; (4); VICA; Hon Roll; Wllmsprt Area CC; Diesel Mech.

MOWAD, NICOLE; Danville SR HS; Danville, PA; (3); VP Church Yth Grp; Debate Tm; Drama Clb; French Clb; GAA; Hosp Aide; Pres Keywanettes; Latin Clb; NFL; Ski Clb; HOBY Ldrshp Ambssdr 86-87; Lt Gvrnr Div 14 Key Clb Intl 87-88; Yth Rep Mntour Cnty Athrty Brd 87-88; Bus.

MOWEN, K MICHAEL; James Buchanan HS; Mercersburg, PA; (3); FBLA; VICA; Chorus; Rep Frsh Cls; Ldrshp Ctznshp Skills Cert 86; Comp.

MOWEN, MARVIN; Greencastle-Antrim HS; Greencastle, PA; (3); Chorus; Sftbl; IN Inst Tech; Acctg.

MOWER, BETH; Waynesboro Area HS; Waynesboro, PA; (3); 110/369; Band; Chorus; Concert Band; Jazz Band; Mrchg Band; Nwsp Sprt Ed; Bsktbl; Var Trk; Hon Roll; Shippensburg U; Tch Biol.

MOWER, CINDY; Boyertown Area HS; Boyertown, PA; (3); Chorus; Cit Awd; High Hon Roll; Hon Roll; Prfct Atten Awd; Real Estate Agnt.

MOWERY, CHRIS; Pottstown SR HS; Pottstown, PA; (3); 33/155; French Clb; Key Clb; Ski Clb; Nwsp Rptr; Nwsp Sprt Ed; Nwsp Stf; Yrbk Stf; JV Var Bsbl; Var Golf; Hon Roll; Bus Adm.

MOWERY, JODY; Southern Columbia Area HS; Elysburg, PA; (3); 24/107; FBLA; Spanish Clb; Chorus; Color Guard; Flag Corp; Mrchg Band; JV Bsktbl; JV Var Mgr(s); Var Score Keeper; Hon Roll; Offc Wrk.

MOWREY, BRIAN; First Baptist Church Acad; Sykesville, PA; (3); 4/13; Chorus; Var Bsktbl; Socr; DAR Awd; VFW Awd; Church Yth Grp; Church Choir; Concert Band; School Musical; Hon Roll; Sccr-MVP & All-Leag Tm 85-87; Bus Mgmt.

MOWREY, KELLY; Yough SR HS; Herminie, PA; (4); Office Aide; Spanish Clb; Teachers Aide; Chorus; Mrchg Band; Yrbk Bus Mgr; Yrbk Ed-Chief; Jr NHS; NHS; IN U Of PA; Elem Ed.

MOWRIS, JENNIFER; Meadville HS; Meadville, PA; (4); 29/304; Church Yth Grp; Varsity Clb; Rep Sr Cls; Var Capt Bsktbl; Var Capt Sftbl; High Hon Roll; NHS; Acctng.

MOWRY, BRADLEY; Clarion Area HS; Shippenville, PA; (3); Pres AFS; VP FCA; Yrbk Phtg; Rep Stu Cncl; Var L Bsktbl; Var L Ftbl; Im Vllybl; Var Wt Lftg; Hugh O Brien Outstndg Soph Awd 86; Ed.

MOWRY, CANDI; Connellsville Area SR HS; Mill Run, PA; (3); Trs VICA; Hon Roll; Dirctrs List-Nrth Fayette AVTS 85-87; 3rd Pl-Opning & Clsng Cont-VICA 86-87.

MOWRY, JERRY; Chestnut Ridge HS; Schellsburg, PA; (3); 34/144; Chorus; Bsbl; Ftbl.

MOWRY, MICHELE; Elk Lake HS; Meshoppen, PA; (3); 28/109; Art Clb; 4-H; Ski Clb; SADD; VICA; Var Bsktbl; Var Fld Hcky; Var Tennis; Var Trk; Church Yth Grp; Pres Physical Ftnss Awd 85-87; Air Force.

MOXIE, KARA; Highlands SR HS; Natrona Hts, PA; (4); 48/280; Hosp Aide; SADD; Yrbk Stf; Pres Soph Cls; Pres Jr Cls; Rep Stu Cncl; JV Var Cheerleading; Var Swmmng; Hon Roll; NHS; Athl Schlrshp Pitt U 87; Pittsburgh U; Educ.

MOY, ELIZABETH; Cardinal O Hara HS; Broomall, PA; (3); 13/739; Cmnty Wkr; 4-H; Hosp Aide; Spanish Clb; Rep Stu Cncl; High Hon Roll; Pres NHS; Latin Clb; Service Clb; Rep Frsh Cls; PA Jr Acad Sci 1st Rgn, 1st St 86; Intrgrp Cncl Prmts Bttr Rltns In Schl Awd 87; Diocesan Schlr 87-88; Lbrl Arts.

MOYAR, GINA; Canon Mc Millan SR HS; Canonsburg, PA; (4); 72/355; Hosp Aide; Library Aide; Science Clb; Ski Clb; Spanish Clb; VP Band; Concert Band; VP Mrchg Band; High Hon Roll; Hon Roll; Bst Rank Awd Mrchng Band 84-86; Ntl Hnr Roll Soc 85-86; Chatham Coll; Bio Chem.

MOYER, BRENT; Perkiomen Valley HS; Harleysville, PA; (3); Church Yth Grp; Ski Clb; Church Choir; Bsbl; Bsktbl; Socr; Hon Roll; NHS; Rotary Awd; Bus Mgmt.

MOYER, CHRIS; Springford HS; Schwenksville, PA; (3); 36/268; Spanish Clb; Var Bsbl; High Hon Roll; Hon Roll; Ursinus Coll; Med.

MOYER, DAVE; Quakertown HS; Quakertown, PA; (3); 13/313; Church Yth Grp; German Clb; Intnl Clb; Ski Clb; Varsity Clb; Trs Frsh Cls; Sec Soph Cls; Sec Jr Cls; Sec Sr Cls; Var Crs Cntry; 1st Team All Leag Wrstlng 85-86; Hon Ment Pole Vault 87; Med.

MOYER, DAVID; Northern Bedford HS; Woodbury, PA; (3); Pres Church Yth Grp; FFA; Letterman Clb; SADD; Varsity Clb; Var L Ftbl; Hon Roll; NHS.

MOYER, ELIZABETH; Blue Mountain HS; Auburn, PA; (3); Mu Alpha Theta; Chorus; Crs Cntry; Trk; French Hon Soc; High Hon Roll; Hon Roll; NHS; Trck Ltrs 85-86; Intl French Contst Hnr Mntn 86; French.

MOYER, GRANT; Nothern Lebanon HS; Jonestown, PA; (3); Boy Scts; Ski Clb; Socr; Tennis; Hon Roll; Engrng.

MOYER, JANET; Susquenita HS; Duncannon, PA; (3); Chorus; Concert Band; Drm Mjr(t); Mrchg Band; School Musical; School Play; Nwsp Rptr; Rep Soph Cls; Rep Stu Cncl; Hon Roll; Hnrs Choir; West Side Singers Intl Music Fest.

MOYER, JENNIFER; Northern York HS; Dillsburg, PA; (3); Var Cheerleading; Fshn Merch.

MOYER, JENNIFER; Pleasant Valley HS; Brodheadsville, PA; (3); 5/240; Pres Church Yth Grp; Pres 4-H; Math Tm; Var L Cheerleading; Var L Crs Cntry; Var L Trk; Hon Roll; NHS; Acad All Amercn 86; Ldrshp All Amercn 87; Med.

MOYER, JENNIFER L; Quakertown HS; Trumbauersville, PA; (2); 23/359; Cmnty Wkr; Ski Clb; Varsity Clb; Stat Bsbl; L Var Cheerleading; Mgr(s); Score Keeper; JV Var Sftbl; Timer; L Var Vllybl; Prsdntl Physcl & Acdmc Ftnss Awds 86; U Of NC Chapel Hill; Scndry Ed.

MOYER, JENNY; Quakertown Comm SR HS; Quakertown, PA; (3); Hosp Aide; Ski Clb; Off Jr Cls; Mgr Fld Hcky; JV Tennis; Mgr Trk; High Hon Roll; Hon Roll; Jr NHS; NHS; Outstndng Schlstc Achvt & Acdmc Achvt Awd 84-85; Elem Ed.

MOYER, JULIE; Northwestern HS; Albion, PA; (3); 4/150; Chorus; Yrbk Stf; Rep Stu Cncl; Hon Roll; Prfct Atten Awd; Upwrd Bnd Prfct Atten Awd 84-87; Trphy-Rnng Trk Mt 84-85; Cert Of Merit-PA Soc Prfsnl Engrs 86-87; Phrmcy.

MOYER, KRISTI; Eastern York HS; York, PA; (3); FHA; JA; Library Aide; Math Clb; SADD; Vllybl; Hon Roll; Jr NHS; Comm Art.

MOYER, LANCE; Northwestern Lehigh HS; Germansville, PA; (3); Boys Clb Am; Boy Scts; Exploring; Rep Frsh Cls; Rep Soph Cls; Rep Jr Cls; Rep Sr Cls; VP Stu Cncl; Var Bsbl; Var Socr; Aero Engrng.

MOYER, LOU; Jim Thorpe Area HS; Jim Thorpe, PA; (2); Quiz Bowl; Scholastic Bowl; Thesps; Chorus; Nwsp Rptr; Rep Stu Cncl; Var Bsbl; JV Bsktbl; JV Ftbl; Wt Lftg; Hstry.

MOYER, MELINDA; Quakertown HS; Quakertown, PA; (2); French Clb; Ski Clb; Y-Teens; Off Frsh Cls; Off Soph Cls; Stu Cncl; Cheerleading; Pom Pon; Tennis; High Hon Roll; Bio.

MOYER, MELODY; Mifflinburg Area HS; Mifflinburg, PA; (3); French Clb; Key Clb; Mrchg Band; Rep Frsh Cls; Rep Soph Cls; JV Fld Hcky; High Hon Roll; Hon Roll; Band; Chorus; Miss TEEN Schlrshp & Rcgntn Pgnt 86; Frshmn Dance Qn & Hmcmng Crt 84; Phys Thrpst Asst.

MOYER, MICHELE; St Marys Area HS; Kersey, PA; (3); 31/290; Office Aide; Var JV Cheerleading; Hon Roll; NHS.

MOYER, PAUL; Huntingdon Area HS; Huntingdon, PA; (3); 4/224; Art Clb; Chess Clb; School Play; Yrbk Stf; High Hon Roll; Hon Roll; NHS; Pres Schlr.

MOYER, RICKY; Palmerton HS; Palmerton, PA; (3); 31/170; Pres Church Yth Grp; Computer Clb; Yrbk Phtg; Yrbk Stf; Bsktbl; Crs Cntry; L Trk; Acad Awd Pre-Calc 86-87; Math.

MOYER, SCOTT; Reading SR HS; Reading, PA; (2); 23/851; Chess Clb; Debate Tm; Math Tm; Model UN; Quiz Bowl; Yrbk Rptr; Yrbk Stf; Ftbl; Mgr(s); Var Trk; John Hopkins U; Sports Med.

MOYER, SHARON; Hazelton HS; Hazleton, PA; (4); FBLA; Office Aide; Pep Clb; Ski Clb; Chorus; Yrbk Stf; JV Capt Cheerleading; High Hon Roll; Hon Roll; PA ST U; Hosp Admin.

MOYER, SHEILA; Juniata HS; Thompsontown, PA; (3); Sec Church Yth Grp; 4-H; FHA; SADD; Chorus; Yrbk Stf; JV Sftbl; Im Vllybl; Hon Roll; NHS; Erly Chldhd Ed.

MOYER, STEVEN; Valley Forge Military Acad; Denver, PA; (4); 3/145; German Clb; ROTC; Concert Band; Mrchg Band; Var Swmmng; Hon Roll; NHS; Emigh Mdl-Hghst Grd Physcs 87; PA All ST Band & Orchstra 86-87; AM Chmcl Soc Awd 86; PA ST U; Nclr Engnrng.

MOYER, THOMAS; Greensburg Salem SR HS; Greensburg, PA; (2); Boy Scts; Church Yth Grp; German Clb; High Hon Roll; Hon Roll; Carnegie Mellon U; Physcs.

MOYER, TRACEY; Schuylkill Haven HS; Auburn, PA; (4); 42/86; Cmnty Wkr; English Clb; FNA; Science Clb; Spanish Clb; Soph Cls; Stu Cncl; Hon Roll; E Stroudsburg; Psych.

MOYERS, JASON; Henderson SR HS; Exton, PA; (3); 13/330; Science Clb; Spanish Clb; Band; Chorus; Concert Band; Jazz Band; Mrchg Band; Orch; School Musical; Sec Sr Cls; Chester Cnty Bar Assn Law Day Essay Cntst 1st Pl 85 & 87; Frgn Lang Assn PA Poster Cntst 86-87; U VA; Pltcl Sci.

MOYLAN, BILL; Abington Heights HS; Clarks Summit, PA; (3); Cmnty Wkr; Ski Clb; Bsbl; Bsktbl; Ftbl; Trk; Wt Lftg; U Of Pittsburgh; Bus Admin.

MOYLE, SCOTT; Lewistown Area HS; Lewistown, PA; (3); Church Yth Grp; Wrstlng; Hon Roll; Penn ST; Aerospc Engr.

MOZES, EMILY; Harry S Truman HS; Levittown, PA; (3); Art Clb; Church Yth Grp; French Clb; Rep Stu Cncl; Badmtn; Vllybl; Human Svcs.

MOZINA, SAMANTHA; Cambria Heights HS; Patton, PA; (4); Q&S; Pres SADD; Jazz Band; Nwsp Rptr; Yrbk Ed-Chief; Var L Cheerleading; Var L Trk; Var L Twrlr; NHS; Ntl Merit Ltr; Acad All Amer 87; Grad Spkr 87; Dist Forn 6th Pl Fnlst 84; Penn ST U; Engrng.

MOZINGO, REBECCA J; Shippensburg SR HS; Newsburg, PA; (4); 54/220; Pres Camera Clb; GAA; Office Aide; SADD; Rep Soph Cls; Im Fld Hcky; Im Socr; Var Sftbl; Var Swmmng; Hon Roll; Shippensburg Art Lge $200 87; Kutztown U; Art Ed.

MOZZACHIO, ALICIA; Nazareth Acad; Philadelphia, PA; (3); 26/124; Cmnty Wkr; VP Chorus; VP Church Choir; School Musical; Trs Soph Cls; High Hon Roll; NHS; Prfct Atten Awd; School Play; Sci Rsrch.

MOZZOCIO, CATHRYN; New Castle SR HS; West Pittsburgh, PA; (4); 2/263; French Clb; Stu Cncl; Var Cheerleading; Bausch & Lomb Sci Awd; High Hon Roll; NHS; Ntl Merit Ltr; Duquesne U; Phrmcy.

MRAZ, KIMBERLY; New Castle SR HS; New Castle, PA; (4); 15/232; Church Yth Grp; Nwsp Rptr; Yrbk Stf; Rep Stu Cncl; Vllybl; Cit Awd; Hon Roll; Jr NHS; NHS; Ldrshp Merit Awds 85 & 86; Slippery Rock U; Elem Ed.

MRAZIK, JUDITH; St Paul Cathedral HS; Pittsburgh, PA; (3); 9/65; Hosp Aide; School Play; Stage Crew; Variety Show; Nwsp Stf; Gym; Vllybl; High Hon Roll; Hon Roll; Prfct Atten Awd; Acad All Amer Spnsh II 86; Bus.

MRAZIK, LYNN; St Paul Cathedral HS; Pittsburgh, PA; (3); 6/65; FBLA; Hosp Aide; Nwsp Rptr; Nwsp Stf; Gym; Vllybl; High Hon Roll; Hon Roll; Prfct Atten Awd; Outstndng Span Stu Medal 86-87; Schltc All Amercn Stu 86-87.

MRKICH, KATHLEEN; Peters Township HS; Mc Murray, PA; (4); 20/248; Computer Clb; FBLA; NFL; Thesps; Drm Mjr(t); Mrchg Band; Nwsp Bus Mgr; Off Stu Cncl; NHS; Voice Dem Awd; CA U; Math.

MRKICH, SHANNON; Bishop Mc Cort HS; Johnstown, PA; (2); 2/142; NFL; Ski Clb; Yrbk Stf; VP Stu Cncl; Bsktbl; L Trk; High Hon Roll; NHS; Pre-Med.

MROZEK, CONNIE; Portage Area HS; Portage, PA; (4); French Clb; Chorus; Mrchg Band; Pep Band; School Musical; Variety Show; Sec Jr Cls; Sec Sr Cls; Stat Bsktbl; Hon Roll; Presdntl Phy Ftns Awd 87; Secy Band 87; ICM Bus Schl; Mdcl Offc Asst.

MROZEK, ERIC; New Castle SR HS; New Castle, PA; (4); AFS; Y-Teens; Band; Concert Band; Mrchg Band; Rep Stu Cncl; Im Vllybl; High Hon Roll; NHS; PA ST U; Engrng.

MROZEK, TODD; Mohawk HS; New Castle, PA; (3); French Clb; VP Soph Cls; Trs Jr Cls; Var L Bsbl; Var L Bsktbl; High Hon Roll; Hon Roll; Jr NHS; NHS; Prfct Atten Awd; Natl Hnr Soc 87; 2 Yrs Prfct Atten 86-87; Vrsty Bsktbl & Bsbl 86.

MRVOS, MARC; Mckeesport SR HS; Mckeesport, PA; (4); 80/373; Boys Clb Am; Church Yth Grp; Civic Clb; Cmnty Wkr; Office Aide; Stage Crew; L Capt Bsbl; L Capt Ftbl; Trk; Wt Lftg; MVP Daily News 86; All Conf WPIAL 86; WPIAL All STAR 86; IN U Of PA.

MUCCIOLO, JOE; North Pocono HS; Moscow, PA; (3); 30/260; Boy Scts; Church Yth Grp; Ski Clb; Ftbl; Tennis; Wt Lftg; High Hon Roll; NHS; Prfct Atten Awd; U Of Scranton; Med.

MUCHA, STANLEY W; Central Bucks East HS; Doylestown, PA; (4); 21/468; Aud/Vis; Computer Clb; Chorus; High Hon Roll; Hon Roll; Jr NHS; Prsdntl Acdmc Fitness Awd 87; DE Vly Coll; Vet Med.

MUCHA, STEPHEN; Cathedral Prep; Erie, PA; (4); Im Vllybl; U MI; Engrng.

MUCHICKA, LORI; Bethel Park HS; Bethel Park, PA; (4); 55/519; Chorus; Drill Tm; Mrchg Band; School Musical; Swing Chorus; Variety Show; Pom Pon; High Hon Roll; NHS; Pres Schlr; Kent ST U; Journlsm.

MUCKEY, WESLEY; Conrad Weiser HS; Wernersville, PA; (3); 29/179; German Clb; Band; Rep Stu Cncl; Var Bsktbl; Var Ftbl; Var Trk; Var Wt Lftg; Art.

MUCKINHAUPT, MICHAEL; Cambridge Springs HS; Cambridge Spgs, PA; (2); 24/103; Church Yth Grp; Hon Roll; Penn ST U; Archtctr.

MUDRAK, VINCENT; Penns Valley HS; Centre Hall, PA; (3); Camera Clb; Nwsp Phtg; Yrbk Phtg; Var Golf; JV Var Trk; Im Wrstlng; Penn ST U; Bus.

MUELLER, ERIN; Carrick HS; Pittsburgh, PA; (3); Am Leg Aux Girls St; FHA; Q&S; Nwsp Stf; Yrbk Stf; Rep Stu Cncl; JV Capt Cheerleading; Powder Puff Ftbl; DAR Awd; High Hon Roll; Acad Ltr Acad Achvt 86; Typng Awd 86; Ftns Merit 85-86; CMU; Jrnlsm.

MUELLER, JASON; Immaculate Conception HS; Mc Donald, PA; (2); 1/35; Boy Scts; Radio Clb; High Hon Roll; U Pittsburgh; Elec Engr.

MUELLER, JENNIFER; Cedar Cliff HS; Mechanicsburg, PA; (3); 87/304; Trs French Clb; Hosp Aide; Concert Band; Mrchg Band; Var Trk; Hon Roll; Vrsty Ltr Trk Hghjmp 85-87; PIAA Dist III Trk/Fld Chmpnshp 3rd Pl Hgh Jmp, ST 6th Pl Hgh Jmp 87; Pre Med.

MUELLER, MARY; Mercyhurst Prepatory HS; Erie, PA; (3); Church Yth Grp; Chorus; Madrigals; School Musical; Var Socr; Hon Roll; PA ST U.

MUFFLY, MIKE; West Middlesex HS; W Middlesex, PA; (2); Church Yth Grp; Office Aide; VP Science Clb; Spanish Clb; Band; L Bsbl; L Bsktbl; L Ftbl; U Of NC; Sci Ed.

MUHA, TERESA ANN; West Mifflin Area HS; W Mifflin, PA; (4); 10/332; Key Clb; Teachers Aide; Chorus; Yrbk Ed-Chief; Trk; High Hon Roll; Sec NHS; Pres Schlr; Gannon U; Engrng.

MUHAIMIN, LAILA; Sister Clara Muhammad HS; Philadelphia, PA; (2); Art Clb; Cmnty Wkr; Debate Tm; Office Aide; Science Clb; Teachers Aide; School Play; Cit Awd; High Hon Roll; Sci Awd 1st Pl 86; Princeton; Archtctr.

MUHAMMAD, KEISHA; Sis Clara Muhammad Schl; Philadelphia, PA; (3); 1/11; Girl Scts; Science Clb; Off Frsh Cls; Vllybl; Hon Roll; Prfct Atten Awd; Awd For All A & Bs 85; Awd For Supr Achiev & Excell Of Perf In Arabic 85; Awd For Sci Achiev Sci Fair; Temple Univ; Bus Law.

MUHLENKAMP, WENDY S; North Allegheny SR HS; Bradford Woods, PA; (4); 3/650; Sec Church Yth Grp; Cmnty Wkr; Teachers Aide; Band; Vllybl; Jr NHS; NHS; Ntl Merit SF; Smith Bk Awd.

MUIR, COLLEEN; George Washington HS; Philadelphia, PA; (1); 73/746; Church Yth Grp; Y-Teens; Band; Concert Band; Mrchg Band; School Play; Stage Crew; High Hon Roll; Hon Roll; Dance Clb; Messiah Coll; Sci.

MUIR, MARK; Corry Area HS; Corry, PA; (2); Church Yth Grp; Drama Clb; Library Aide; PAVAS; Thesps; School Musical; School Play; Stage Crew; Nwsp Stf; Artist.

MUIR, NANCY; Connellsville Area HS; S Connellsville, PA; (4); AFS; Art Clb; Church Yth Grp; Girl Scts; Office Aide; Ski Clb; SADD; Chorus; Church Choir; School Musical; Mercyhurst Coll; Intr Dsgn.

MUIR, RITA; United JR SR HS; Blairsville, PA; (4); 62/157; Library Aide; Pep Clb; Ski Clb; Chorus; Lit Mag; Var Capt Bsktbl; Powder Puff Ftbl; Score Keeper; Var L Sftbl; Hon Roll; Secy Penn View Mt Hunting Club 85-86; Range Secy 83-85; Coral Ensmbls 86-87; Bradford Schl; Secy.

MUIR, SCOTT; Burrell HS; Lower Burrell, PA; (3); Boy Scts; French Clb; Spanish Clb; SADD; Band; High Hon Roll; Hon Roll; Jr NHS; Prfct Atten Awd; Natl Sci Olympd Awd 84-85; BYEA 86-87; Acad Ltr 87; PA ST; Bus Adm.

MUIRHEAD, CHARLES; Moon SR HS; Coraopolis, PA; (3); Trs Key Clb; Rep Soph Cls; Rep Jr Cls; Rep Stu Cncl; Hon Roll; Im Bsktbl.

MULANEY, LUANN; Millville HS; Benton, PA; (3); Camera Clb; Church Yth Grp; Cmnty Wkr; Drama Clb; VP 4-H; FBLA; JA; Library Aide; Pep Clb; Band; KY Natls Comptng Team Demon 85; Cosmtlgy.

MULCAHY, DENISE; Pocono Central Catholic HS; Newfoundland, PA; (3); 3/30; Art Clb; Church Yth Grp; Chorus; High Hon Roll; Hon Roll; NHS; Technel Schl; Sec.

MULHAIR, KEVIN; Bethel Park SR HS; Bethel Park, PA; (4); 26/519; JA; Letterman Clb; Varsity Clb; Var L Ftbl; High Hon Roll; NHS; Pres Schlr; Naval 4 Yr ROTC Schlrshp 87; U Of Notre Dame; Engrng.

MULHEARN, RICHARD; Monsignor Bonner HS; Havertown, PA; (4); 32/302; Boy Scts; Hon Roll; School Play; Nwsp Stf; Temple U; Cmnctns.

MULHERN, ANNE C; The Baldwin Schl; Ardmore, PA; (4); Math Tm; Socr; Sftbl; Ntl Merit SF; Govrnrs Schl Interntl Studs 86; Engrng.

MULHERN, CAECILIA M; Lower Merion HS; Ardmore, PA; (4); 63/370; Church Yth Grp; Sec Spanish Clb; Hon Roll; Ntl Merit SF; Pres Schlr; Pa Hghr Edctn Assstnc Agcy 86; Princeton; Mechncl Engr.

MULHOLLAND, JOSEPH; Holy Ghost Prep; Philadelphia, PA; (4); 9/81; Camera Clb; Latin Clb; Teachers Aide; Concert Band; Nwsp Stf; High Hon Roll; NHS; Pres Schlr; Aud/Vis; Library Aide; Wnnr Scl Stds Awd 86; Grad Summa Cum Laude 87; Wnnr Tlnt Shw 86 & 87; Ursinus Coll; Pre-Med.

MULHOLLAND, KATHLEEN; Waynesburg Central HS; Waynesburg, PA; (4); Church Yth Grp; Dance Clb; FHA; Library Aide; Office Aide; Ski Clb; Spanish Clb; Capt Vllybl; Cit Awd; Hon Roll; Mrtha Mxn Essy Schlrshp 87; NEDT Awd 83; WV U; Sec Educ.

MULL, BARBARA; Steelton-Highspire HS; Steelton, PA; (3); 4/102; Band; Concert Band; Mrchg Band; School Musical; Yrbk Stf; High Hon Roll; Hon Roll; NHS.

MULL, DAVID; Central Dauphin HS; Harrisburg, PA; (3); 16/369; Var Capt Crs Cntry; Var L Trk; Im Vllybl; Hon Roll; Jr NHS; NHS; Bus Admin.

MULL, HEATHER; Conrad Weiser HS; Sinking Spring, PA; (3); 32/179; FBLA; Hst German Clb; Capt Color Guard; Typng Awd 87; Nrsng.

MULL, RONDA; Milton SR HS; Milton, PA; (3); Computer Clb; Latin Clb; Band; Chorus; Church Choir; Concert Band; Drm Mjr(t); Mrchg Band; Williamsport Paramedic; Paramed.

MULL, SHELLY; Coatesville Area SR HS; Parkesburg, PA; (4); 72/460; Spanish Clb; Mrchg Band; Symp Band; Off Sr Cls; Rep Stu Cncl; Hon Roll; Congenlty Awd 87; Stu Cncl Awd 87; Wm Donohue Music Awd 87; West Chester U; Nrsng.

MULLEN, ANNE; Bishop O Hara HS; Jessup, PA; (4); 6/114; Art Clb; Spanish Clb; Chorus; Nwsp Stf; Yrbk Ed-Chief; Sec Sr Cls; Stu Cncl; High Hon Roll; High Hon Roll; NHS; Art Awds; Marywood Coll; Deaf Educ.

MULLEN, DANIEL; Cardinal O Hara HS; Broomall, PA; (3); 21/719; Church Yth Grp; Math Tm; Quiz Bowl; Spanish Clb; Nwsp Sprt Ed; Yrbk Rptr; Lit Mag; Var Tennis; High Hon Roll; Acadmc Convocatn 85-87; Diocesan Schlrs Pgm Schlrshp 87.

MULLEN, DEIRDRE; Wellsboro HS; Wellsboro, PA; (4); Art Clb; Trs Drama Clb; Chorus; School Musical; Yrbk Stf; Bowling; Hon Roll; Skidmore Schlrshp 87; Hnrb Mntn World Of Ptry Cont 87; Amer Ptry Anthology 86; Skidmore Coll; Anthrplgy.

MULLEN, ERICA; Bishop Conwell HS; Morrisville, PA; (3); 7/277; Latin Clb; Office Aide; Scholastic Bowl; Church Choir; Concert Band; Ed Nwsp Rptr; Lit Mag; High Hon Roll; Hon Roll; NHS; PA Jr Acad Of Sci 3rd Awd 85; Lat Awd 85-86; Bio.

MULLEN, JAMES A; Eastern York HS; Wrightsville, PA; (3); 40/177; Varsity Clb; JV Var Socr; Im Vllybl; Im Wt Lftg; High Hon Roll; Hon Roll; NC ST U; Comp Prog.

MULLEN, JENNIFER; Karns City Area JR SR HS; Chicora, PA; (3); 5/91; Art Clb; Church Yth Grp; Concert Band; High Hon Roll; Hon Roll; NHS; Ntl Merit Ltr; Chem.

MULLEN, JODIE; Rocky Grove JR/Sr HS; Franklin, PA; (4); Pres 4-H; VP SADD; JV Bsktbl; Capt Bowling; JV Vllybl; 4-H Awd; High Hon Roll; Hon Roll; Acad Excllnce 84-85.

MULLEN, KELLY; Valley View HS; Eynon, PA; (4); 21/195; French Clb; Drill Tm; French Hon Soc; Hon Roll; U Scranton; Social Work.

MULLEN, KELLY; West Scranton HS; Scranton, PA; (4); 27/265; Pres FNA; Latin Clb; Letterman Clb; Red Cross Aide; Nwsp Rptr; Yrbk Phtg; Cheerleading; Trk; High Hon Roll; NHS; PA ST U; Math Tchr.

MULLEN, LEAH; Crestwood HS; Mountaintop, PA; (3); 4-H; School Play; Yrbk Rptr; Yrbk Stf; Mgr(s); Score Keeper; Timer; Vllybl; 4-H Awd; High Hon Roll; Vet Med.

MULLEN, LISA; North Penn HS; Hatfield, PA; (3); CAP; Math Tm; Chorus; Im Powder Puff Ftbl; JV Trk; Hon Roll; Lit Mag; Im Bowling; Im Vllybl; Im Wt Lftg; Mont Cnty CC Bus Math Symposium 87; Lit Hon Mntn 86; Temple U; Crmnl Jstc.

MULLEN, NATALIE; Newport HS; Newport, PA; (1); Chorus; Swing Chorus; Twrlr; Hon Roll; Jrnlsm.

MULLEN, SUSAN; Lock Haven SR HS; Lock Haven, PA; (3); Art Clb; FHA; Keywanettes; Spanish Clb; SADD; Chorus; Variety Show; Nwsp Rptr; Nwsp Stf; JV Bsktbl; Lock Haven U; Bio.

MULLER, KATHRYN P; Northeast HS; Philadelphia, PA; (4); 30/600; Church Yth Grp; Var Crs Cntry; Var Trk; Hon Roll; PA Jr Acad Of Sci Rgnl 84-86 & ST Mtng 1st Pl Awds 85-86; PA Sci Tlnt Srch Jr Awd 86; PA ST U; Psych.

MULLER, SANDRA; West Phila Catholic Girls HS; Philadelphia, PA; (3); 95/246; Sec Church Yth Grp; Hosp Aide; Library Aide; Service Clb; Chorus; Church Choir; Concert Band; Hon Roll; Prfct Atten Awd; Nrs.

MULLETT, MATTHEW; Blairsville SR HS; Coral, PA; (1); 12/116; Band; Concert Band; Mrchg Band; School Musical; High Hon Roll; Hon Roll; Prfct Atten Awd.

MULLIGAN, CAROL; Marian Catholic HS; Jim Thorpe, PA; (3); 20/106; Church Yth Grp; French Clb; Office Aide; Pep Clb; Chorus; JV Sftbl; Capt Trk; Twrlr; Nrsng.

MULLIGAN, MARY KAY; Allentown Central Catholic HS; Allentown, PA; (3); Church Yth Grp; Exploring; French Clb; Key Clb; Crs Cntry; Powder Puff Ftbl; NHS; Presdntl Clsrm Young Americans 87; Rcvd 3rd Pl Awd Law Day USA Essy Cntst 87; Hnrd Allentown Jycs 87.

MULLIGAN, PATTI; Meadville Area SR HS; Meadville, PA; (3); 56/375; Church Yth Grp; Nwsp Rptr; High Hon Roll; Hon Roll; Arch Engr.

MULLIN, SUSAN; Hampton HS; Allison Pk, PA; (2); Hosp Aide; Spanish Clb; Band; Concert Band; Powder Puff Ftbl; Var Swmmng; JV Var Vllybl; High Hon Roll; Opthamology.

MULLINS, MIKE; Avon Grove HS; Landenberg, PA; (3); 18/205; FBLA; School Play; VP Jr Cls; Var Socr; Var Tennis; Var Wrstlng; High Hon Roll; NHS; Off Stu Cncl; Im Ftbl; Phys Ed Awd 86; Outstndng Wrstlr Awd 85 87; Bus.

MULLNER, JAMES; Butler Area SR HS; Butler, PA; (4); Boy Scts; Cmnty Wkr; Golf; PA ST U; Engineering.

MULRANEY, RENAE; Cambria Heights SR HS; Elmora, PA; (3); SADD; Sec.

MULROY, JOHN; York Catholic HS; York, PA; (3); Camera Clb; French Clb; Service Clb; Ski Clb; Varsity Clb; Nwsp Phtg; Yrbk Phtg; Ftbl; Rotary Awd; Area Spch Semi-Fnlst 87; IN U PA; Govt.

MULVIN, JENNIFER; Harbor Creek HS; Erie, PA; (4); 13/220; VP Church Yth Grp; Model UN; Variety Show; Yrbk Bus Mgr; Var L Bsktbl; Var L Crs Cntry; Var L Trk; High Hon Roll; NHS; Rotary Awd; Yth Trienium 86; Grove City; Sec Ed.

MUMAU, STACY E; Iroquois HS; Erie, PA; (3); 7/125; Am Leg Aux Girls St; Aud/Vis; Church Yth Grp; Chorus; Flag Corp; Nwsp Ed-Chief; Capt Bowling; Hon Roll; NHS; PA Schl Press Assn 2nd Pl Shrt Stry 86; PA Schl Press Assn 2nd Pl Indepth News 86; Jrnlsm.

MUMAW, KIMBERLY; Council Rock HS; Newtown, PA; (4); 101/848; Church Yth Grp; Concert Band; Mrchg Band; Symp Band; High Hon Roll; Hon Roll; NHS; Silver Awd Girl Scouts 86; Ann Lynn Connolly Mem Schlrshp 87; Bloomsburg U PA; Bus.

MUMAW, LAURIE; Hazleton HS; Hazleton, PA; (3); #164 In Class; Drama Clb; FBLA; FHA; Pep Clb; Acctg.

MUMAW, SHANNON; West Hazleton HS; W Hazleton, PA; (2); GAA; Latin Clb; Pep Clb; Ski Clb; SADD; Var L Bsktbl; Trk; High Hon Roll.

MUMFORD, FRANK; Chester HS; Chester, PA; (3); Spanish Clb; Yrbk Stf; Hon Roll; Outstndng Hon In Spanish 85-87; Theatre.

MUMMA, AMY JO; Lower Dauphin HS; Hummelstown, PA; (3); 29/276; Aud/Vis; Library Aide; Ski Clb; Stage Crew; Hon Roll; JETS Awd; Elec Engrng.

MUMMA, JOYCE; Waynesboro Area SR HS; Waynesboro, PA; (4); Girl Scts; Ski Clb; Band; Chorus; Concert Band; Mrchg Band; Bsktbl; Fld Hcky; Trk; Vllybl; IN U; Bus Admin.

MUMMERT, ANGELA; Hanover SR HS; Hanover, PA; (3); Pres Church Yth Grp; Hosp Aide; Chorus; Church Choir; JV Vllybl; High Hon Roll; Hon Roll; Prfct Atten Awd; Bus.

MUMMERT, BRENDA; Northern York County HS; Wellsville, PA; (3); 6/232; Church Yth Grp; Band; Concert Band; Mrchg Band; French Hon Soc; Phys Ther.

MUMMERT, BRENDA; Spring Grove SR HS; Thomasville, PA; (3); Art Clb; Church Yth Grp; Chorus; Church Choir; School Musical; Hon Roll; 100 Pt Pin 87; Merit Cert AAA Poster Cont 87; Beautcn.

MUMMERT, GEORGE; Coatesville Area SR HS; Thorndale, PA; (3); Church Yth Grp; Spanish Clb; Chorus; Concert Band; School Musical; School Play; Bowling; Hon Roll; Forestry.

MUMMERT, HALLIE; Sayre Area HS; Athens, PA; (3); Church Yth Grp; Key Clb; Varsity Clb; Yrbk Phtg; Yrbk Rptr; Lit Mag; Var L Trk; JV Capt Vllybl; Hon Roll; NEDT Awd; Cmmnctns.

MUMMERT, PAULINE; Spring Grove Area SR HS; Thomasville, PA; (3); Pres VP Church Yth Grp; Chorus; Orch; School Musical; School Play; High Hon Roll; Hon Roll; NHS; Pres Schlr; Drama Clb; Dist & Regnl Chrs; Fnlst JR Miss Pagnt York Cnty; Dist Yth Pres S PA Dist; Shenandoah Coll; Music Ther.

MUMMERT, RHONDA; Southwestern HS; Hanover, PA; (2); Pep Clb; Band; Concert Band; Jazz Band; Mrchg Band; Pep Band; Symp Band; High Hon Roll; Hon Roll.

MUMMERT, STEPHANIE; West York Area SR HS; York, PA; (3); 11/190; Pres Sec Church Yth Grp; Yrbk Stf; Rep Frsh Cls; Rep Soph Cls; Rep Jr Cls; Rep Sr Cls; Im Bsktbl; JV Var Cheerleading; High Hon Roll; Hon Roll; Peer Tutor; Accntng.

MUNCH, KIMBERLY; St Paul Cathedral HS; Munhall, PA; (2); Church Yth Grp; Cmnty Wkr; Girl Scts; JA; Nwsp Rptr; Nwsp Stf; JV VP Cheerleading; Var JV Vllybl; High Hon Roll; Hon Roll; Catholic Yth Cncl Of &A & Pittsburgh Diocesean Yth Cncl 87-89; Criminology.

MUNDIS, KERRI; Northeastern HS; Mt Wolf, PA; (3); 29/189; Teachers Aide; Vllybl; Hon Roll; Grphc Comm.

MUNGER, GARETH TORREY; Hershey HS; Hershey, PA; (2); Boy Scts; Cmnty Wkr; Computer Clb; Hosp Aide; Math Tm; Science Clb; JV Crs Cntry; Var Trk; Im Wt Lftg; Hon Roll; St & Ntl Sci Olympd 87; Biophycs.

MUNION, CHRISTINE; Norristown Area HS; Norristown, PA; (4); 2/457; Ski Clb; Symp Band; Nwsp Rptr; Yrbk Sprt Ed; Var Capt Bsktbl; JV Socr; Sftbl; Tennis; NHS; Rotary Awd; Bio Awd 84-85; Prfct Atten Awd 83-85; Bio.

MUNION, JEAN M; Norristown Area HS; Norristown, PA; (4); 1/450; Ski Clb; Symp Band; Yrbk Stf; Var Diving; JV Var Fld Hcky; Var Lcrss; High Hon Roll; NHS; Rotary Awd; Val; Hrvrd Clb Of Phila Awd 86; Brwn U Awd 86; Frnch Awd 86; Rtrys Stu Of Mnth 86; Arch.

MUNIZ II, NICHOLAS A; Palmerton Area HS; Palmerton, PA; (3); Am Leg Boys St; Church Yth Grp; Capt Scholastic Bowl; Nwsp Rptr; Yrbk Ed-Chief; Yrbk Phtg; Yrbk Sprt Ed; Off Stu Cncl; Mgr Bsktbl; Tennis; Spnsh & Engl Acdmc Awds 85; Physics Acdmc Awd 87.

MUNLEY, DAN; Valley View HS; Jessup, PA; (3); 63/193; Computer Clb; Im Vllybl; Var Wrstlng; Spanish NHS; Elec Engr.

MUNLEY, JANICE; Valey View HS; Archbald, PA; (4); Latin Clb; Hon Roll; Pres Hlth Ocptn Stu Amer; Outstndng Dntl Assist; Outstndng Achvt Hlth Assist; Luzerne Cnty CC; Dntl Hygn.

MUNLEY, JASON; Tunkhannock Area HS; Tunkhannock, PA; (2); 11/330; Key Clb; Spanish Clb; Wrstlng; High Hon Roll; Hon Baquet 85-86.

MUNLEY, SHANNON; Tunkhannock HS; Tunkhannock, PA; (3); 97/315; Drama Clb; GAA; Letterman Clb; Capt Pep Clb; Acpl Chr; Chorus; School Play; Swing Chorus; Variety Show; Sec Sr Cls; Occupational Therapy.

MUNNELL, MICHELLE L; Mc Guffey HS; Claysville, PA; (4); 1/201; Pres JA; Model UN; Spanish Clb; Stu Cncl; Gov Hon Prg Awd; Pres NHS; Ntl Merit SF; Rotary Awd; Pres Wash Dist Cncl On Yth Mnstrs 86-87 W PA Brd Of Chrch & Scty Comm On Peace & Wrld Order 86-87; Boston U; Pre-Med.

MUNNELLY, ALICE; Archbishop Ryan HS For Girls; Philadelphia, PA; (4); 7/491; Dance Clb; Math Tm; Q&S; Yrbk Rptr; Yrbk Stf; Im Bowling; High Hon Roll; NHS; Span Awd 85; Intro Phys Sci Awd 84; Wrld Cultures II Awd 86; Aerospace Engrng.

MUNRO, JOYCE L; J P Mc Caskey HS; Lancaster, PA; (4); 17/400; Trs AFS; Pres Church Yth Grp; Sec Exploring; JCL; Math Clb; Red Cross Aide; VP Service Clb; Concert Band; Jazz Band; Lib Mrchg Band; Monroe Sloyer Awd 87; JR Lg Outstndng Yth Vlntr Of Yr 86; Ntl Ltn Hnr Soc; Duke U; Econ.

MUNSELL, JILL; Cameron County HS; Emporium, PA; (2); Spanish Clb; Hon Roll; Pres Acadc Ftns Awd 85-86.

MUPHY, TERI; Hazleton HS; Drums, PA; (3); 152/460; Church Yth Grp; Girl Scts; Band; Chorus; Concert Band; Mrchg Band; God Cntry Awd; PFA Yth Rep 87; German Camp Rep 87; Millersville U; Elem Ed.

MURAD, SCOTT; Central Dauphin HS; Harrisburg, PA; (2); French Clb; JA; Took SAT Test At John Hopkins U 85; Designs.

MURANO, MICHELE; Carlynton HS; Carnegie, PA; (4); 34/151; FBLA; Sec Band; Concert Band; Jazz Band; Mrchg Band; Symp Band; High Hon Roll; Hon Roll; Robert Morris Coll; Bus.

MURARO, NICOLE; Salisbury HS; Allentown, PA; (3); 40/150; Nwsp Stf; Trs Soph Cls; Trs Jr Cls; L Crs Cntry; L Diving; L Swmmng; L Tennis; L Trk; Hon Roll; Key Clb; MVP Trck & Fld 85-87; Clnl Leag Tnns Chmpn 86-87; 6th Pl St Comptn Hgh Jmp 85-86; Cmmntns.

MURAWSKI, RICHARD; Moshannon Valley HS; Houtzdale, PA; (3); 5/115; Spanish Clb; Band; Concert Band; Mrchg Band; Pep Band; High Hon Roll; NHS.

MURCKO, MEGAN; Kennedy Christian HS; Fedonia, PA; (2); 33/96; Ski Clb; Spanish Clb; Flag Corp; Nwsp Stf; Yrbk Stf; Sec Jr Cls; Mat Maids; Hon Roll; Pep Clb.

MURCKO, THOMAS; North Hills HS; Pittsburgh, PA; (3); 26/498; Chess Clb; Exploring; JA; Letterman Clb; Ski Clb; Nwsp Rptr; Yrbk Stf; Var L Tennis; High Hon Roll; NHS; Ecnmcs.

MURDICK, JUDY; Homer Center HS; Homer City, PA; (3); DECA; SADD; 2 Gold Mdls-Top 3 On 2 Wrttn Tst/Slsmnshp 87; Rtl Mgmt.

MURDICK, WILLIAM; Butler HS; Butler, PA; (2); Church Yth Grp; Chorus; Church Choir; Swing Chorus; Cit Awd; Hon Roll; CPA.

MURDOCCA, ROBERT; Mechanicsburg Area SR HS; Shiremanstown, PA; (4); 4/303; Church Yth Grp; Cmnty Wkr; VP SADD; Yrbk Stf; Rep Frsh Cls; Rep Soph Cls; Rep Jr Cls; Rep Sr Cls; JV Bsktbl; Var L Ftbl; Dfns Actvts Fed Crdt Union Schlrshp 87-88; Amer Mltry Soc Of Cmptrllrs 87-88; Amer Cmptv Sys Awd 87; U Of PA; Bus.

MURDOCH, MICHAEL; St Piux X HS; Gilbertsville, PA; (1); 28/146; Boy Scts; JV Ftbl; JV Trk; JV Wt Lftg; God Cntry Awd; Hon Roll; Gttysburg Hstrc Trl Awd 87.

MURDOCK, DANA; Brookville Area HS; Brookville, PA; (3); 30/179; Sec FTA; Trs Key Clb; Pres SADD; Varsity Clb; Sec Chorus; Stu Cncl; French Clb; Pep Clb; Coach Actv; High Hon Roll; Pres Physcl Ftns Awd 86-87; MVP Clarion U Bsktbl Cmp 84-85; 9th Grd Prty Queen; Elem Ed.

MURDOCK, TAMI; Conneaut Lake Area HS; Conneaut Lake, PA; (4); 12/80; Church Yth Grp; Pres Trs 4-H; Office Aide; Nwsp Ed-Chief; Yrbk Rptr; Stat Ftbl; Score Keeper; 4-H Awd; Hon Roll; VICA; Crawford Cnty Firemans Schlrshp 87; Jameson Mem Schl; Nrsng.

MURETTA, DAVID; Notre Dame HS; Easton, PA; (3); Church Yth Grp; NFL; Band; Chorus; Concert Band; Mrchg Band; School Musical; School Play; JV Ftbl; Hon Roll; JV Ltr; Shoprite Baking Cont SF Awd & Bond; PA ST; Vet.

MURICEAK, JEFFREY A; Hollidaysburg Area SR HS; Altoona, PA; (4); 5/330; Latin Clb; Service Clb; Ski Clb; Sec Jr Cls; Sec Sr Cls; Stu Cncl; Var Golf; Im Vllybl; High Hon Roll; NHS; Judge Thomas Baldridge Awd 86-87; Juniata Coll.

MURKENS, HEATHER; Meadville SR HS; Meadville, PA; (3); Church Yth Grp; Chorus; School Play; Nwsp Rptr; Nwsp Stf; Yrbk Stf; Capt Bsktbl; JV Vllybl; Hon Roll; Cmnty Wkr; Prsdnts Physcl Ftnss Awd 86; Elem Educ.

MURLING, JACKI; Bangor Area SR HS; Bangor, PA; (3); 11/227; Girl Scts; Chorus; Concert Band; Jazz Band; Mrchg Band; School Musical; Yrbk Stf; High Hon Roll; Jr NHS; NHS; Rainbow Girls Grand Lecturer Dist 87,Grand Cross Color 85; Natl Engl Merit Awd 85; Corp Law.

MURLO, LORIE; Panther Valley HS; Lansford, PA; (3); 34/132; Am Leg Aux Girls St; Office Aide; Red Cross Aide; ROTC; VICA; Yrbk Stf; JV Bsktbl; Hon Roll; Carbon Cnty Vo-Tech; Cosmetlgst.

MURNYACK, TAMMY; Bald Eagle Area HS; Clarence, PA; (4); 21/187; Hosp Aide; Chorus; Yrbk Sprt Ed; Yrbk Stf; Trs Sr Cls; Stu Cncl; Capt Cheerleading; High Hon Roll; Hon Roll; French Clb; Centre Cnty JR Miss Finalist 86; PA ST U; Eng Educ.

MUROSKI, TOM; Johnsonburg Area HS; Johnsonburg, PA; (4); 4/62; VP Sr Cls; L Bsktbl; Hon Roll; L Tennis; NHS; Engineering.

MURPHEY, MELISSA; North Star HS; Boswell, PA; (4); 6/130; Church Yth Grp; FCA; Mu Alpha Theta; VP Band; Chorus; Concert Band; Drm & Bgl; Mrchg Band; School Play; High Hon Roll; Cnty Band 84-87; Dist & Rgn III Band 86-87; Allegheny Hearthland Rgnl Band 84-87; Albright Coll; Psych.

MURPHY, AMY; Central York SR HS; York, PA; (4); 52/214; Dance Clb; French Clb; Intnl Clb; Ski Clb; Flag Corp; Yrbk Bus Mgr; Rep Sr Cls; Stu Cncl; Hon Roll; Piano Cncrt Awds; Shippensburg U; Film.

MURPHY, BARBARA; Elk County Christian HS; Ridgway, PA; (4); 8/79; Model UN; Varsity Clb; Yrbk Stf; VP Soph Cls; VP Jr Cls; VP Sr Cls; Stat Bsktbl; Var L Crs Cntry; Var L Trk; High Hon Roll; Psych.

MURPHY, CHRISTOPHER; Penn Hills SR HS; Pittsburgh, PA; (4); German Clb; Spanish Clb; Varsity Clb; JV Var Ftbl; Var Capt Ice Hcky; Hon Roll; Prfct Atten Awd; Syracuse U; Mass Comms.

MURPHY, CINDY; Central Cambria HS; Colver, PA; (4); 16/204; Nwsp Stf; Yrbk Stf; Hon Roll; NHS; Art Clb; Ski Clb; Church Choir; JV Bsktbl; L Crs Cntry; JV Trk; IN U Of Pennsylvania.

MURPHY, COLLEEN; William Accen HS; Allentown, PA; (2); Church Yth Grp; Sec Trs Exploring; German Clb; ROTC; Color Guard; Drill Tm; Hon Roll; Jr NHS; Dstngshed Cadet, Acad Achvt 87.

MURPHY, DANIELLE; Nazareth Acad; Bensalem, PA; (3); Cmnty Wkr; Hosp Aide; JCL; Latin Clb; Band; Drm Mjr(t); VP Orch; School Musical; School Play; Lit Mag; Nrs.

MURPHY, DAVID; Westmont Hilltop HS; Johnstown, PA; (2); Var L Ice Hcky; Var L Trk; Hon Roll; Ldrng Scr Westmont Vrsty Hockey Team 86-87; Keystone ST Games Ice Hcky 86-87; Dist Trk 86-87; Real Estate.

MURPHY, DENISE; Riverside HS; Fombell, PA; (2); Band; Color Guard; Concert Band; Flag Corp; Mrchg Band; Stu Cncl; High Hon Roll; NEDT Awd; Bio II Awd 86-87; Hist Awd 85-86.

MURPHY, DONNA; Johnstown Vo-Tech HS; South Fork, PA; (4); 5/258; Art Clb; Debate Tm; SADD; VICA; Flag Corp; High Hon Roll; Jr NHS; NHS; Art Hnr Soc 85-87; St Francis Coll; Psych.

MURPHY, ELLEN; Bethlehem Catholic HS; Hellertown, PA; (3); 16/200; Letterman Clb; Ski Clb; Color Guard; Mrchg Band; Rep Frsh Cls; Rep Soph Cls; Stu Cncl; Capt Twrlr; High Hon Roll; NHS; Diocesan Acad Schlrshp 84; PA ST; Frgn Lang.

MURPHY, JAMES; Coatesville Area SR HS; Thorndale, PA; (3); French Clb; Ski Clb; Food Prep.

MURPHY, JENNIFER; Elizabeth Forward HS; Elizabeth, PA; (3); AFS; Trs Church Yth Grp; French Clb; Pep Clb; Chorus; School Musical; Yrbk Stf; Cheerleading; High Hon Roll; NHS; Drama.

MURPHY, JENNIFER; Scranton Central HS; Scranton, PA; (3); Art Clb; French Clb; Ski Clb; Var Crs Cntry; Var Trk; Ntl Art Hnr Soc Prlmntrn 87-88; Misericordia Coll; Psych.

MURPHY, JENNIFER A; Archbishop Ryan For Girls; Philadelphia, PA; (3); SADD; Teachers Aide; Rep Frsh Cls; Rep Jr Cls; Hon Roll; Lbrl Arts.

MURPHY, JESS A; Jefferson-Morgan JR SR HS; Waynesburg, PA; (3); 4/75; Boy Scts; Church Yth Grp; Teachers Aide; Var Bsbl; High Hon Roll; NEDT Awd; Waynesburg Coll Sci Fair 86; Outstndng Frgn Lang Stu Yr Spansh 85; Intl Day Spansh Cert 85; Electrncs.

MURPHY, JOHANNA; Bishop Mc Devitt HS; Harrisburg, PA; (3); 63/200; Art Clb; Church Yth Grp; Drama Clb; Band; Concert Band; Mrchg Band; School Musical; School Play; Stage Crew; Nwsp Rptr; 1st Pl Talent Show 87; Engl.

MURPHY, JOHN; Cardinal Dougherty HS; Philadelphia, PA; (4); FBLA; Nwsp Rptr; NHS; U Of CA.

MURPHY, KAREN; Bermudian Springs HS; York Spgs, PA; (3); Church Yth Grp; Pres Drama Clb; Pres FNA; Girl Scts; Pres Speech Tm; SADD; Varsity Clb; Band; Concert Band; Mrchg Band; Gannon U; Nrs.

MURPHY, KIM; Yough HS; W Newton, PA; (3); Girl Scts; Pep Clb; Spanish Clb; Band; Chorus; Concert Band; Jazz Band; Mrchg Band; Pep Band; Symp Band.

MURPHY, LONA; Beth Center SR HS; Marianna, PA; (3); Art Clb; Computer Clb; FBLA; Spanish Clb; Varsity Clb; Nwsp Stf; Yrbk Stf; Off Jr Cls; Trk; Bus Adm Mgmt.

MURPHY, MARIANNE; West Hazleton HS; W Hazleton, PA; (3); Letterman Clb; Pep Clb; L Var Sftbl; Hon Roll.

MURPHY, MICHAEL; Athens HS; Athens, PA; (3); JV Ftbl; Bausch & Lomb Sci Awd; High Hon Roll; NHS; PA ST U; Engr.

MURPHY, MICHAEL; Quaker Valley HS; Sewickley, PA; (1); Church Yth Grp; Ski Clb; Y-Teens; Bsktbl; JV Socr; Hon Roll; Schlsrhp Awd Cert 86-87.

MURPHY, MICHAEL A; Mechanicsburg Area SR HS; Mechanicsburg, PA; (3); 140/338; Cmnty Wkr; Tennis; Hon Roll; Bus Mgmt.

MURPHY, MICHAEL S; Northeastern HS; Mt Wolf, PA; (4); 9/120; Aud/Vis; Jazz Band; Stage Crew; Yrbk Phtg; Yrbk Stf; Im Bsktbl; Im JV Vllybl; High Hon Roll; Hon Roll; Mgr NHS; Hnr Awd Outstndng Acad Achvt 87; PA ST U; Elec Engrng.

MURPHY, PAUL; Red Lion Area SR HS; Red Lion, PA; (3); 84/353; Exploring; Library Aide; School Play; Shppensburg U Spring Lang Cont 86; Accntng.

MURPHY, SUSAN; Gateway SR HS; Monroeville, PA; (2); 106/452; Service Clb; Color Guard; Jazz Band; Hon Roll; Bus.

MURPHY, SUSAN; Seneca HS; Wattsburg, PA; (3); Pres Church Yth Grp; Drama Clb; Chorus; Church Choir; Hon Roll; Crwnd Hnr Str Mssntt Pgm 84; Miss Cngnlty Wattsburg Fr Qn Cntst 86; SE Coll; Mssns.

MURPHY, TERI; Hazelton HS; Drums, PA; (3); 120/500; Sec Church Yth Grp; German Clb; Girl Scts; Chorus; Mrchg Band; Swmmng; God Cntry Awd; Luzerne Cnty PFA Rep & HS Rep For M Illersville German Camp 87; Girl Scout Silver Awd 85; Millersville U; Elem Tchr.

MURPHY, THERESA; Shade-Central City HS; Cairnbrk, PA; (3); Pres Varsity Clb; Chorus; Nwsp Stf; Yrbk Ed-Chief; Sec Stu Cncl; JV Var Bsktbl; Var L Trk; JV Var Vllybl; Hon Roll; Cmnty Wkr; Cambria-Somerset Jr Miss Finalist 87-88; Journalism.

MURPHY, THOMAS; Blairsville SR HS; Blairsville, PA; (3); Church Yth Grp; Cmnty Wkr; Spanish Clb; SADD; Varsity Clb; Stu Cncl; Var JV Bsktbl; L Var Golf; Wt Lftg; High Hon Roll; Elec Engr.

MURPHY, THOMAS; Quaker Valley HS; Sewickley, PA; (1); Boy Scts; Church Yth Grp; JA; Chorus; Nwsp Stf; Tennis; High Hon Roll; Hon Roll.

MURPHY, TIM; Penn Hills SR HS; Verona, PA; (3); Key Clb; Spanish Clb; Hon Roll; Pres Acdmc Fit Awd 85; Acdmc All Amer Awd 85; Comp Prgrmg.

MURPHY, VIRGINIA; Minersville Area HS; Minersville, PA; (3); 13/95; Computer Clb; FBLA; Library Aide; Pep Clb; Ski Clb; Spanish Clb; SADD; Flag Corp; Rep Stu Cncl; Hon Roll; Phy Thrpy.

MURPHY, WILLIAM; High Point Baptist Acad; Elverson, PA; (4); Spanish Clb; Yrbk Bus Mgr; Hon Roll; Ntl Merit Ltr; Arch.

MURRAY, AMY; Abraham Lincoln HS; Philadelphia, PA; (3); 3/450; French Clb; Ed Nwsp Stf; Rptr Yrbk Stf; Swmmng; High Hon Roll; Fleet Reserve Assoc Essay Awd 1st Pl 86-87; Sons Of Italy Essay Awd-Hnrbl Mntn 86-87; Engrng.

MURRAY, AMY; Boiling Springs HS; Carlisle, PA; (2); Var L Sftbl; Im Vllybl; High Hon Roll; Hon Roll; Spnsh Achvt Awd 86-87.

MURRAY, APRIL; Mohawk HS; Pulaski, PA; (3); Latin Clb; SADD; Chorus; Flag Corp; Im Powder Puff Ftbl; Var Trk; Im Wt Lftg; Hon Roll; Prfct Atten Awd; Art 85-87; Pittsburg Art Inst; Cmmrcl Arts.

MURRAY II, AUSTIN P; The Haverford Schl; Narberth, PA; (4); 1/84; Im Bsktbl; Var L Lcrss; Var L Socr; High Hon Roll; Ntl Merit SF; Highr Educ Certf Merit 86; US Squash Racqts Assoc 85-86.

MURRAY, DAVID C; Archbishop Ryan HS For Boys HS; Philadelphia, PA; (3); 10/427; Church Yth Grp; Spanish Clb; JV Trk; NHS; Prncpls Awd 86; Crtfct Hnr Chem 86; Crtfct Hnr 85; Lafayette Coll.

MURRAY, EILEEN; Norristown HS; Audubon, PA; (4); 8/416; Key Clb; Sec SADD; Mrchg Band; Ed Lit Mag; Sec Stu Cncl; Capt Cheerleading; Lcrss; NHS; Tchrs Club Awd 84-86; Ursinus; Physics.

MURRAY, GREG; Deer Lakes HS; Gibsonia, PA; (4); 1/170; Scholastic Bowl; High Hon Roll; NHS; NEDT Awd; Opt Clb Awd; Prfct Atten Awd; Pres Schlr; French Clb; Lrnt $1000 Memrl Schlrshp 87; Rbrt Krlnd Memrl Schlrshp 87; Allghny Schlr 87; Allegheny Coll; Pre-Med.

MURRAY, JEFFREY; Milton Area SR HS; Montandon, PA; (3); 1/210; Boy Scts; Key Clb; Concert Band; Mrchg Band; Yrbk Stf; Rep Stu Cncl; High Hon Roll; NHS; Ntl Merit Ltr; Church Yth Grp; PA Gvrnrs Schl For Sci 87; Engnrng.

MURRAY, JENNIFER; Punxsutawney Area HS; Punxsutawney, PA; (4); 2/246; French Clb; Math Tm; Science Clb; Spanish Clb; High Hon Roll; VP NHS; Ntl Merit Ltr; Sal; Earth Sci.

MURRAY, LYDIA; Girls HS; Philadelphia, PA; (1); Math Clb; Math Tm; Teachers Aide; School Play; Nwsp Stf; Off Frsh Cls; Penn ST; Law.

MURRAY, MAUREEN; Blairsville SR HS; Blairsville, PA; (4); 14/137; Office Aide; SADD; High Hon Roll; Hon Roll; NHS; Prfct Atten Awd; All Amer Acdmc Awd 86-87; IN U; Bus Mngmt.

MURRAY, MICHAEL W; Spring Grove Area HS; York, PA; (4); 28/289; Am Leg Boys St; Band; Concert Band; Jazz Band; Mrchg Band; Pep Band; High Hon Roll; Hon Roll; NHS; Bst Trmpt Solost Awd Wm Penn Jazz Fstvl 86; Sctn Ldr-Jazz Band, Marchng Band & Concrt Band 87; PA ST U; Pre-Med.

MURRAY, RAWNETTE; Laurel Highlands JR HS; Uniontown, PA; (2); 30/343; VP JA; Spanish Clb; SADD; Pres Church Choir; Nwsp Rptr; Stat Trk; High Hon Roll; NEDT Awd; Med.

MURRAY, REGINA; Ambridge HS; Ambridge, PA; (3); Church Yth Grp; Spanish Clb; Church Choir; Var Bsktbl; Elem Ed.

MURRAY, RESHEMMA; Ridley SR HS; Woodlyn, PA; (3); 61/131; Church Yth Grp; 4-H; Girl Scts; Office Aide; Chorus; Church Choir; Stat Bsktbl; Mgr(s); Stat Trk; Hon Roll; Temple U; Acctng.

MURRAY, ROBERT; Carlisle SR HS; Carlisle, PA; (4); Chess Clb; Church Yth Grp; Computer Clb; JV Crs Cntry; JV Socr; Trk; Hon Roll; Gld Mdl 400 Mtr Hrdles, Keystone St Gms 86, 5th Mlr Rly Tm, Dist 86; Trk Lttr 85; PSU; Engrng.

MURRAY, ROSIE; Pottsville Area HS; Pottsville, PA; (3); 22/263; Church Yth Grp; French Clb; Service Clb; Chorus; Mrchg Band; VP Soph Cls; VP Jr Cls; Stu Cncl; JV Var Cheerleading; L Trk; Penn ST U; Phys Thrpy.

MURRAY, SHERRY; Peters Township HS; Mc Murray, PA; (4); CAP; Girl Scts; Thesps; School Play; Variety Show; Nwsp Stf; Yrbk Stf; Sec Frsh Cls; Vllybl; Rotary Awd; U Of SC; Bus Admn.

MURRAY, TRACI; North Allegheny SR HS; Bradfordwoods, PA; (4); Aud/Vis; Church Yth Grp; Pres Thesps; School Play; Ed Lit Mag; Rep Soph Cls; Stu Cncl; L Cheerleading; Hon Roll; NHS; Harbison Walker Schlrshp 87; JR Natl Hnr Socty 84-85; Miami U Of OH; Mass Cmmnctns.

MURRAY, WILLIAM VANN; Shalom Christian Acad; Hagerstown, MD; (4); Church Yth Grp; Cmnty Wkr; Teachers Aide; Chorus; Hon Roll; Dstngshd Christian HS Awd-ACSI 85-86; Oral Roberts U; Comm.

MURRELL, SHAWN; South Phila HS Motvtn; Philadelphia, PA; (4); Cmnty Wkr; Drama Clb; French Clb; Lit Mag; Im Bsktbl; Prfct Atten Awd; Poetry Mnth Rctn Philadelphia 87; Army.

MURREN, JENNY; Delone Catholic HS; Hanover, PA; (3); 6/175; Spanish Clb; Color Guard; Var Cheerleading; Hon Roll; NHS; Natl Sci Merit Awds 86-87; Natl Spn Merit Awds 85-87; Doctor.

MURRHY, COLLEEN; William Allen HS; Allentown, PA; (2); Church Yth Grp; Sec Trs Exploring; German Clb; ROTC; Color Guard; Drill Tm; Hon Roll; Jr NHS.

MURRY, SHANE; Hempfield HS; Columbia, PA; (4); 50/426; Boy Scts; Exploring; VICA; L Wrstlng; Cit Awd; 4-H Awd; High Hon Roll; Hon Roll; Egl Sct 86; Outstndng Drftsmn 87; Penn ST U; Mech Engrng.

MURTHA, EILEEN; St Hubert HS For Girls; Philadelphia, PA; (3); 76/421; Dance Clb; Exploring; Spanish Clb; Stage Crew; Nwsp Stf; Fld Hcky; Mgr(s); Score Keeper; Hon Roll; Htl Mgmt.

MURTI, SRINIVAS; Middletown Area HS; Middletown, PA; (3); #16 In Class; Radio Clb; Var Cmnty Wkr; Hon Roll; PA ST U; Cmnctns.

MUSCARA, DOMINIC; Pottsville Area HS; Pottsville, PA; (4); 2/250; Sec Latin Clb; Quiz Bowl; Scholastic Bowl; Ski Clb; Pres Stu Cncl; Golf; Rotary Awd; DAR Awd; NHS; Sal; US Senate Yth Pgm-ST Alt 86-87; Rensselaer Polytech Inst; Arch.

MUSCH, SCOTT; Bradford SR HS; Bradford, PA; (4); 1/267; Church Yth Grp; Debate Tm; Trs Key Clb; Trs Rep Stu Cncl; Var Capt Swmmng; High Hon Roll; Lion Awd; NHS; Val; Var Crs Cntry; US Army Rsrv Natl Schlr Athl Awd 87; Timothy S Eyssen & Mary Mottey Mem Awds 87; Schlr Athl Awd 87; U PA; Econmcs.

MUSCHLLTZ, GREG; Neshaminy HS; Levittown, PA; (3); 36/780; Band; Jazz Band; Mrchg Band; Symp Band; Var Trk; Hon Roll; NHS; Aerontcl Engrng.

MUSE, GARNETT; Central HS; Philadelphia, PA; (2); Church Yth Grp; Cmnty Wkr; Debate Tm; Girl Scts; JA; Math Tm; Spanish Clb; Church Choir; Rep Frsh Cls; Swmmng; U PA; Engrng.

MUSGROVE, ELIZABETH; Pocono Mountain HS; Mt Pocono, PA; (3); 88/320; Church Yth Grp; VICA; Bowling; Hon Roll; Bus.

MUSHALKO, KRISTINA; Mt Carmel JR- SR HS; Elysburg, PA; (2); French Clb; Chorus; Color Guard; Hon Roll.

MUSHINSKI, VICKI; Seneca Valley HS; Harmony, PA; (3); 147/347; Ski Clb; Rep Frsh Cls; Diving; Gym; Swmmng; Wt Lftg; Cmrcl Pilot.

MUSHINSKY, BOB; Vincentian HS; Pittsburgh, PA; (2); Cmnty Wkr; Hosp Aide; Nwsp Rptr; High Hon Roll; Hon Roll; Stu Rep Pgh Catholic 86-87; All Am Awd 87; Duquense; Jrnlsm.

MUSHINSKY, RUSSELL; James M Coughlin HS; Wilkes Barre, PA; (3); Latin Clb; Letterman Clb; Math Clb; Var L Bsbl; Var L Bsktbl; Var L Ftbl; High Hon Roll; Hon Roll; Jr NHS; NHS; All Schltc-Bsbl-All Schltc-Bsktbl 86-87; Nestor Chylak Mem Awd 86; PA St Games 87; Sprts Med.

MUSHOLT, ABIGAIL; Sharon SR HS; Sharon, PA; (3); 1/179; VP Y-Teens; Orch; Nwsp Stf; Rep Stu Cncl; Bausch & Lomb Sci Awd; CC Awd; High Hon Roll; NHS; Rotary Awd; Cmnty Wkr; OH Mdls Cnvntn Top Fml Mdl 85; YSU Engl Fstvl Compstn Awds 85-87; 2ndry Ed.

MUSIAL, KRISTI; Hickory HS; Hermitage, PA; (2); Spanish Clb; Sftbl; JV Vllybl; Spanish NHS.

MUSIAL II, THOMAS; Central Catholic District HS; Pittsburgh, PA; (4); Boy Scts; VP JA; Band; Concert Band; Jazz Band; Mrchg Band; School Musical; School Play; Ed Lit Mag; Socr; Stu Mnth 86-87; Charles Schmidt Scholar 86-87; Carnegie-Mellon U; Writing.

MUSICO, BILL; Trinity HS; New Cumberland, PA; (2); 30/139; Debate Tm; Nwsp Phtg; Nwsp Stf; Ftbl; Socr; Trk; Wt Lftg; High Hon Roll; Hon Roll; Engrng.

MUSIKE, SHAWN; Freedom HS; Easton, PA; (4); 165/446; Boy Scts; Hon Roll; Electrcn.

MUSSELMAN, CATHY; Claysburg-Kimmel HS; Claysburg, PA; (3); 3/80; Band; School Musical; VP Soph Cls; Pres Stu Cncl; JV Capt Bsktbl; Var Cheerleading; Var Sftbl; Hon Roll; NHS; All Star Awd Claysburg Chrstms Tourn 86; PA ST; Elect Engrng.

MUSSELMAN JR, CHARLES; Altoona Area HS; Altoona, PA; (3); 70/796; Pres Chess Clb; Key Clb; Math Tm; Spanish Clb; Crs Cntry; Swmmng; Tennis; Hon Roll; Jr NHS; NEDT Awd; Engrng.

MUSSELMAN, DEBRA; Claysburg-Kimmel HS; Claysburg, PA; (4); 2/52; Sec Church Yth Grp; Sec Trs Girl Scts; Library Aide; Sec SADD; Band; Ed Yrbk Stf; Stat Bsbl; Stat Bsktbl; Hon Roll; NHS; Mst Likely Succeed 86-87; PA ST U; Elem Educ.

MUSSELMAN, JAMES; Claysburg-Kimmel HS; E Freedom, PA; (3); 33/97; Camera Clb; FBLA; Band; Concert Band; Jazz Band; Mrchg Band; School Play; Rep Stu Cncl; Hon Roll; NHS.

MUSSER, BRIAN; Chambersburg Area SR HS; Newburg, PA; (4); Church Yth Grp; FFA; De Kalb Awd 86; Holstn Awd 85.

MUSSER, DARYL; Garden Spot HS; East Earl, PA; (3); Church Yth Grp; FBLA; High Hon Roll; Hon Roll; 4th Pl Bus Math Rgnl Conf Future Bus Ldrs Am 84; Lincoln Tech Schl; Drftng.

MUSSER, DENISE; Lancaster Mennonite HS; Mohnton, PA; (3); Church Yth Grp; Acpl Chr; Chorus; Hon Roll; Sal.

MUSSER, GWEN; Lancaster Mennonite HS; Mechanicsburg, PA; (4); 11/142; Church Yth Grp; Chorus; Concert Band; Orch; School Play; High Hon Roll; NHS; Dist Band 86; Cert Merit 86; Messiah Coll; Cmmnctns.

MUSSER, JERRY; Grace Christian Schl; Manheim, PA; (3); 5/22; Church Yth Grp; Yrbk Stf; Bsbl; Bsktbl; Ftbl; Socr; Trk; Wt Lftg.

MUSSER, JOHN EVANS; Mt Pleasant Area HS; Somerset, PA; (4); German Clb; Ski Clb; SADD; Var Tennis; High Hon Roll; Hon Roll; U UT; Physics.

MUSSER, KELLI; Penns Valley HS; Aaronsburg, PA; (3); 72/130; Cmnty Wkr; 4-H; French Clb; Pep Clb; Band; Concert Band; Jazz Band; Mrchg Band; Pep Band; Yrbk Stf; Miss TEEN Pagnt 86; Schlrshp Barbazon Beauty Schl Phila 86; Mrch Dimes TEEN Walk 86.

MUSSER, KELLY SUE; Cocalico HS; Denver, PA; (3); 52/163; Art Clb; Camera Clb; Pres Sec FBLA; Varsity Clb; JV Var Fld Hcky; JV Var Sftbl; Hon Roll; Bryland Schl Of Cosmtlgy; Csmtl.

MUSSER, LANCE; East Juniata HS; Mc Alisterville, PA; (3); 13/100; Church Yth Grp; Sec Trs Stu Cncl; JV Bsbl; Var Bsktbl; Var Capt Socr; Var Trk; Im Vllybl; Hon Roll; NHS; Messiah Coll.

MUSSER, PAUL S; Harrisburg HS; Harrisburg, PA; (3); 23/350; Library Aide; ROTC; Church Choir; Color Guard; Var Bsbl; Im Bowling; Var Socr; Im Swmmng; Im Vllybl; Ntl Merit Schol; Dist Hnr Cadet & Outstndng Cadet ROTC 85-86:Sci Fair 1st Pl 84-85; Hnr Roll 84-86.

MUSSER, STEPHEN J; Solanco HS; New Prvidence, PA; (4); 1/240; Aud/Vis; Boys Clb Am; Boy Scts; Chess Clb; Pres Church Yth Grp; FBLA; Math Tm; Science Clb; Teachers Aide; Varsity Clb; Messiah Coll; Accntng.

MUSSER, TRICIA; Elizabethtown Area HS; Elizabethtown, PA; (4); Church Yth Grp; Pres 4-H; FFA; Office Aide; Chorus; Fld Hcky; Tennis; Trk; 4-H Awd; PA ST U; Bus Adm.

MUSSO, MICHELLE; Scranton Central HS; Scranton, PA; (4); 55/307; Aud/Vis; Church Yth Grp; Dance Clb; Hon Roll; NHS; PA ST U; Lbrl Arts.

MUSTELLO, MARCI; Butler HS; Butler, PA; (3); AFS; Spanish Clb; Mrchg Band; Rep Stu Cncl; L Tennis; Thesps; Band; Concert Band; Jazz Band; Orch; Psych.

MUSTO, DENISE; Northampton Area SR HS; Bethlehem, PA; (4); AFS; Drama Clb; French Clb; Leo Clb; Model UN; SADD; Chorus; Drill Tm; Mrchg Band; Nwsp Stf; Empire Beauty Schl Schlrshp 87; Pom Pon Sqad Ltr 87; PA ST U; Molecular Bio.

MUTCH, MICHAEL; West Mifflin Area HS; W Mifflin, PA; (4); 37/350; Ski Clb; Varsity Clb; Golf; Socr; Trk; High Hon Roll; Hon Roll; Jr NHS; NHS; Pres Ftns Awd 87; U Of Pittsburgh Hnrs Coll 87; U Of Pittsburgh; Engr.

MUTCHLER, THOMAS; Stroudsburg HS; E Stroudsburg, PA; (2); 4/302; Boy Scts; Church Yth Grp; Concert Band; Mrchg Band; High Hon Roll; NHS; Gld Mdl PA Sci Olympd, 1st Pl Rgn 2nd Pl St Acad Sci 87; Rensselaer Polytech Inst; Engr.

MUTHLER, ANNA M; Bald Eagle Nittany HS; Mill Hall, PA; (4); 3/115; French Clb; Hosp Aide; VP Trs Band; Color Guard; School Musical; High Hon Roll; Hon Roll; Trs NHS; Model UN; Concert Band; Semper Fidelis Awd, PTO Frnch Awd, Prsdntl Acdmc Ftnss Awd 87; Lock Haven U; Elem Educ.

MUTHLER, THOMAS; Northern Bedford County HS; New Enterprise, PA; (3); Church Yth Grp; Math Clb; SADD; Varsity Clb; Chorus; Nwsp Rptr; Nwsp Sprt Ed; Yrbk Rptr; Bsbl; Bsktbl; Defnsve Awd Bsktbl, Hnbl Mntn All County Bsktbl 87; County All Star Ftbl & Bsbl 86-87.

MUTSCHELLER, MELISSA; Quigley HS; Beaver Falls, PA; (3); 11/80; Church Yth Grp; Math Tm; Pres Soph Cls; Pres Jr Cls; Stat Bsktbl; L Trk; Wt Lftg; High Hon Roll; Hon Roll; Chorus; Physical Therapy.

MUY, SOPHONG; William Penn SR HS; York, PA; (3); 21/452; Pep Clb; Ski Clb; Chorus; Mrchg Band; Orch; School Play; Yrbk Stf; Trk; Acctnt.

MUZYDLA, TRACY; Waynesburg Central HS; Waynesburg, PA; (3); French Clb; Natl Beta Clb; Pep Clb; Band; Concert Band; Mrchg Band; Pep Band; Vllybl; High Hon Roll; Hon Roll; Hi Hnrs & Hnr Roll 84-87; MBA Fnls Partcptn Awds 86; Physcl Thrpy.

MUZYKA JR, JOSEPH F; Archbishop Ryan For Boys HS; Philadelphia, PA; (4); 100/424; Church Yth Grp; Dance Clb; Office Aide; Bsbl; Ftbl; Swmmng; Hon Roll; Temple U; Engrng.

MYER, GWENDOLYN R; Lancaster Christian Schl; Lititz, PA; (3); Church Yth Grp; Drama Clb; 4-H; Church Choir; VP Jr Cls; Rep Stu Cncl; Var L Bsktbl; Var Capt Fld Hcky; Hon Roll; All Star Hockey Tm SIAC Lge 85-86; Nrsng.

MYER, JENNA; Wilson HS; Sinking Spring, PA; (3); 18/304; Church Yth Grp; French Clb; Pres Spanish Clb; Off Stu Cncl; Mgr Bsktbl; Mgr(s); Mgr Trk; High Hon Roll; Hon Roll; NHS; Tp Lang Stu 86; 1st Pl Cert D Honneur Cncrs Ntl De Frncs 86.

MYER, KRISTELLE; Warwick HS; Lititz, PA; (3); 25/300; Church Yth Grp; 4-H; High Hon Roll; NHS; Yrk Coll PA; Accntng.

MYER, RONALD; Solanco SR HS; Quarryville, PA; (4); 10/235; Church Yth Grp; Varsity Clb; Var Bsbl; Capt Var Bsktbl; Var Golf; High Hon Roll; NHS; Pres Schlr; Schlr Athlt Awd Army 87; Pres Ftns Awd 87; Bio Stu Yr 84; U Scranton; Bus Mngmnt.

MYERS, AIMEE M; Lancaster Mennonite HS; Elverson, PA; (3); 10/165; Church Yth Grp; Cmnty Wkr; Drama Clb; Quiz Bowl; Acpl Chr; Chorus; Orch; School Play; High Hon Roll; Hon Roll; Music Mdl, Plaque; Outstndng Tst Achvt Schlstc Tsts; Dist 7 Orch, Amer Christian Yth Chorale; Messiah Coll; Music.

MYERS, AMY; Phil-Mont Christian Acad; Glenside, PA; (3); Hosp Aide; Trs Jr Cls; JV Tennis; Var Trk; High Hon Roll; Hon Roll; NHS; Bus.

MYERS, ANDREW; MMI Prep Schl; Mountaintop, PA; (4); Mgr(s); Var Tennis; High Hon Roll; Hon Roll; NEDT Awd; PHEAA Cert Of Merit 87; Penn ST Univ; Hist.

MYERS, ANGELA K; South Western HS; Hanover, PA; (4); 10/201; AFS; Church Yth Grp; Band; Chorus; Church Choir; Concert Band; School Musical; Capt JV Vllybl; High Hon Roll; Hon Roll; Fin Christa Mc Auliffe Scholar 87; Bloomsburg U; Deaf Ed.

MYERS, BARRY E; Northeastern HS; York Haven, PA; (4); Art Clb; Camera Clb; Lit Mag; JV Var Tennis; Hon Roll; Art Wrk Dsplyd York Art Assn 87; PA Schl Art; Comm Art.

MYERS, BETHANN; Lock Haven SR HS; Lock Haven, PA; (4); Spanish Clb; SADD; Yrbk Stf; Stu Cncl; Trk; Lock Haven U; Elem Ed.

MYERS, CAROLYN Y; James Buchanan HS; Ft Loudon, PA; (3); Chrmn AFS; Cmnty Wkr; Capt Debate Tm; Drama Clb; Ski Clb; School Play; Stage Crew; Rep Soph Cls; Rep Stu Cncl; Hon Roll; Temple U; Anthrplgy.

MYERS, CHRISTA; Eastern York HS; Windsor, PA; (2); Am Leg Aux Girls St; Political Wkr; SADD; Chorus; Nwsp Stf; Rep Stu Cncl; Bsktbl; Sftbl; Trk; Vllybl; Drug Conf 86-87; Penn ST; Police Sci.

MYERS, CHRISTY; Hempfield HS; Lancaster, PA; (3); Dance Clb; Drama Clb; Chorus; Nwsp Stf; Off Sr Cls; Stu Cncl; Crs Cntry; Hon Roll; People To People 86; French Awd 87; Psych.

MYERS, CLINTON; Danville SR HS; Danville, PA; (3); Boy Scts; Spanish Clb; Var Crs Cntry; Var Trk; High Hon Roll; NHS.

MYERS, COREY; Eastern York HS; York, PA; (3); Hon Roll; Millersville U; Marine Bio.

MYERS, DAVE; Blue Mountain HS; Schuylkill Haven, PA; (4); Boy Scts; School Play; JV Wrstlng; PA ST; Aerospc Engrng.

MYERS, DAVID; Aliquippa HS; Aliquippa, PA; (2); Church Yth Grp; Church Choir; Trk; Capt L Wrstlng; Hon Roll; Acctng.

MYERS, DENISE; B Reed Henderson HS; West Chester, PA; (4); 7/335; Ski Clb; Band; Mrchg Band; JV Sftbl; JV Vllybl; French Hon Soc; Hon Roll; Sec NHS; Engrng.

MYERS, GREGORY; Northeastern HS; Mt Wolf, PA; (4); 11/162; Aud/Vis; Teachers Aide; School Musical; School Play; Stage Crew; Bsktbl; Var L Vllybl; High Hon Roll; Hon Roll; NHS; Dstngshd Hnr Roll 87; Navy; Elect.

MYERS, HANNAH; Chambersburg Area SR HS; Fayetteville, PA; (2); Computer Clb; Drama Clb; French Clb; Trs Hosp Aide; Chorus; Stage Crew; Nwsp Stf; Rep Frsh Cls; Rep Soph Cls; Hon Roll; Psych Thrpy.

MYERS, JACQUELINE; Muncy JR-SR HS; Muncy, PA; (4); 2/87; Sec Church Yth Grp; Trs French Clb; Varsity Clb; Pres Band; Concert Band; Mrchg Band; Yrbk Stf; Socr; NHS; Sal; Bryan Acad Schlrshp 86; Muncy HS Stu Of The Yr 84-86; Acad All Amer 86; Med.

MYERS, JASON; Uniontown Area HS; Markleysburg, PA; (3); 17/318; JA; Math Tm; Spanish Clb; Mgr(s); Score Keeper; CC Awd; High Hon Roll; NHS; Engrng.

MYERS, JEFF; Laurel Highlands HS; Lemont Furnace, PA; (2); 4/349; Chess Clb; Church Yth Grp; Exploring; FCA; Math Tm; Var L Diving; High Hon Roll; Penn ST; Chem Engr.

MYERS, JEFFREY; Wm Penn SR HS; York, PA; (3); 11/490; Boy Scts; Concert Band; Mrchg Band; Orch; Symp Band; Var Bsbl; Var Swmmng; Hon Roll; NHS; Mth.

MYERS, JEFFREY L; Mt Zion Christian Acad; Mt Pleasant, PA; (4); 1/5; Camera Clb; Pres Church Yth Grp; Yrbk Ed-Chief; Pres Sr Cls; Rep Stu Cncl; High Hon Roll; Hon Roll; Val; Penn ST U; Elec Engr.

MYERS, JENNIFER; Mount Union HS; Mt Union, PA; (3); Church Yth Grp; French Clb; GAA; SADD; Band; Church Choir; Concert Band; Mrchg Band; Stage Crew; JV Sftbl; Mst Athletic Grl Chrch Camp 85; Penn ST; Air Force.

MYERS, JEREMY; Warren Area HS; Warren, PA; (3); Church Yth Grp; French Clb; Ski Clb; Spanish Clb; Varsity Clb; School Play; Var L Wrstlng; Hon Roll; Accntng.

MYERS, JOANN; Tamaqua Area SR HS; Tamaqua, PA; (3); 51/234; Pres Church Yth Grp; Pep Clb; Mrchg Band; Yrbk Stf; VP Frsh Cls; Rep Soph Cls; VP Jr Cls; VP Sr Cls; Rep Stu Cncl; Cheerleading.

MYERS, JODY; Northeastern HS; Mt Wolf, PA; (3); Bsbl; Bsktbl; Vllybl; Athl Trainer.

MYERS, JOHN; Pine Grove Area HS; Tremont, PA; (3); ROTC; Varsity Clb; Hon Roll; Archery Vrsty 84-86; Drftng Achvt Awd 87; Archtchl Engr.

MYERS, KAREN; Leechburg Area HS; Leechburg, PA; (4); 2/82; Cmnty Wkr; Math Tm; Band; Chorus; Yrbk Ed-Chief; Sec Jr Cls; High Hon Roll; Trs NHS; Sal; JA; All-Star Achvt Awd-Pittsburgh Press 87; Penn ST; Mech Engrng.

MYERS, KEVIN; Big Spring HS; Newville, PA; (3); 15/258; Church Yth Grp; Computer Clb; School Musical; High Hon Roll; Hon Roll.

MYERS, LAURIE; Mc Keesport Area HS; Mckeesport, PA; (3); 52/426; Sec AFS; Pres Church Yth Grp; Hosp Aide; NFL; Acpl Chr; Band; Church Choir; Orch; School Musical; Hon Roll; U Of Pittsburgh; Physcl Thrpy.

MYERS, LISA; Biglerville HS; Biglerville, PA; (3); 1/105; Hosp Aide; Band; Chorus; Concert Band; Jazz Band; Pep Band; School Musical; Var Tennis; Hon Roll; Jr NHS.

MYERS, LISA; Wm Penn SR HS; York, PA; (3); 29/490; Church Yth Grp; Jazz Band; Mrchg Band; Orch; School Musical; Symp Band; Sftbl; Var Vllybl; Hon Roll; ST Teachers Coll; Elem Ed.

MYERS, MELISSA; Spring-Ford HS; Royersford, PA; (3); 11/256; Trs Church Yth Grp; Spanish Clb; SADD; Co-Capt Flag Corp; Mrchg Band; Yrbk Stf; Rep Frsh Cls; Rep Soph Cls; Rep Jr Cls; NHS; Psych.

MYERS, MICHAEL; Freeport Area HS; Freeport, PA; (3); 1/200; Band; Church Choir; Concert Band; Mrchg Band; Pep Band; School Musical; Trk; High Hon Roll; Law.

MYERS, MICHELLE; Northern Cambria HS; Barnesboro, PA; (4); 39/124; Computer Clb; Math Tm; SADD; Chorus; Nwsp Stf; Yrbk Stf; Tennis; Vllybl; Hon Roll; Prfct Atten Awd; Cecilia & Pius Miller Loan Fnd Awd; Typng Cert; Steno Cert; Mount Aloysius Coll; Accntng.

MYERS, NATHAN; Philipsburg Osceola Area HS; Osceola Mills, PA; (4); 8/234; Chess Clb; Band; Concert Band; Mrchg Band; Pep Band; Yrbk Stf; Hon Roll; NHS; Prfct Atten Awd; Rotary Awd; Provost Schlrshp U Of Pittsbgh 86; Accptnc To U Hnrs Coll Of U Of Pitt 86; The Semper Fidelis Awd 87; U Of Pittsbgh; Pharmacy.

MYERS, NICOLE; Newport HS; Newport, PA; (4); 13/93; Am Leg Aux Girls St; Pep Clb; Quiz Bowl; Hst Varsity Clb; Chorus; School Musical; School Play; Nwsp Rptr; Yrbk Phtg; Yrbk Sprt Ed; Mayors Awd For Bst Fml Athlt 86; Hmcmng Queen 87; Duke U; Pre-Med.

MYERS, PAMELA; Central Catholic HS; Coplay, PA; (3); Church Yth Grp; Exploring; Key Clb; Spanish Clb; Var JV Bsktbl; JV L Fld Hcky; Im Powder Puff Ftbl; High Hon Roll; Hon Roll; Penn ST U; Bus.

MYERS, PATRICK; Lancaster Mennonite HS; Akron, PA; (3); Chess Clb; Trs Church Yth Grp; Quiz Bowl; Orch; Crs Cntry.

MYERS, PAUL; Canevin HS; Pgh, PA; (3); 100/192; Slippery Rock.

MYERS, PAUL; Mt Pleasant Area HS; Greensburg, PA; (3); 19/250; Latin Clb; Yrbk Stf; Var JV Bsktbl; Capt Stat Vllybl; High Hon Roll; Hon Roll; 3rd Pl-Latin Recttn Humanities Day 85; Math.

MYERS, REGINA; Scranton Prep HS; Scranton, PA; (2); 52/190; JV Cheerleading; Gym; High Hon Roll; Hon Roll; Penn ST U; Pre-Law.

MYERS, RICHARD; Northwestern HS; W Springfield, PA; (4); Chess Clb; Church Yth Grp; Computer Clb; Model UN; Quiz Bowl; Gym; Wt Lftg; Hon Roll; Gannon Comp Sci Schlrshp 87; Scl Study Awd 87; Math Awd 87; IN U Of PA; Comp Sci.

MYERS, RONALD; Roman Catholic HS; Philadelphia, PA; (4); NAACP; Y-Teens; Hon Roll; NHS; Pres Schlr; Penn ST U; Comp Eng.

MYERS, SAM; Chambersburg Area SR HS; Newburg, PA; (2); Med.

MYERS, SEAN; Fairchance-Georges HS; Hopwood, PA; (4); 2/150; Drama Clb; School Play; Nwsp Rptr; JV Ftbl; Hon Roll; Jr NHS; NHS; Sal; Full Scshlrshp Penn St-Fayette, Pres Acad Ftns Awd Pgm 87; Penn T Fayette; Educ.

MYERS, SHAWN; Yough HS; Irwin, PA; (3); 20/236; Ski Clb; Spanish Clb; Ftbl; Wt Lftg; NHS.

MYERS, STEPHANIE M; Red Land HS; Lewisberry, PA; (3); 37/306; Am Leg Aux Girls St; Cmnty Wkr; Capt Debate Tm; Hosp Aide; Speech Tm; Chrmn SADD; Orch; High Hon Roll; Hon Roll; V Lttr Debate 84-85; V Pin Debate, Wrtng Cert Merit, Distrct Champs Debate 85-86; Wdmn Wrld Hstry Awd; Bio.

MYERS, STEVEN R; Mount Union Area HS; Mt Union, PA; (4); 20/180; Church Yth Grp; Spanish Clb; L Bsktbl; L Trk; Wrstlng; NHS; Shippensbury U; Acctg.

MYERS, TAMARA; Ford City HS; Ford City, PA; (4); Church Yth Grp; GAA; Key Clb; Chorus; Variety Show; Yrbk Stf; Var L Sftbl; Var L Tennis; Hon Roll; NHS; Clarion U PA.

MYERS, TIM; Hanover SR HS; Hanover, PA; (3); 20/126; Chess Clb; VP Church Yth Grp; Chorus; Church Choir; JV Bsbl; Hon Roll; Prfct Atten Awd; NEDT Awd 85; PSAT Hgh Scorg Awd 86; Millesville; Acctg.

MYERS, TINA; Carlisle SR HS; Carlisle, PA; (3); VP Church Yth Grp; Drama Clb; Sec Pres 4-H; Key Clb; Band; Chorus; Color Guard; School Musical; Stu Cncl; 4-H Awd; Hnrb Mntn Ast 4-H Poster Cont 85; Mdlng.

MYERS, TOBY; Donegal HS; Mt Joy, PA; (2); Church Yth Grp; Variety Show; JV Crs Cntry; JV Wrstlng; High Hon Roll; Hon Roll; Bennington; Law.

MYERS, TRACEY; Bermudian Springs HS; E Berlin, PA; (3); SADD; Varsity Clb; Band; Color Guard; Concert Band; Mrchg Band; VP Stu Cncl; Bsktbl; Sftbl; Vllybl; PA Sprts Hall Fame Bsktbl, & Hanover Evening Sun All Star Tm Bsktbl 87; Elem Ed.

MYERS, TRACY; Daniel Boone HS; Birdsboro, PA; (3); 53/172; JA; VP Service Clb; Spanish Clb; SADD; Yrbk Stf; Stat Bsktbl; Mgr(s); Var Trk; Hon Roll; Psych.

MYERS, TRICIA; Eastern York HS; York, PA; (4); Varsity Clb; Var JV Bsktbl; Var JV Vllybl; Hon Roll; Jr NHS; NHS; Hosp Aide; Central PA Bus Schl; Trvl.

MYERS, TRINA; Chambersburg Area SR HS; Orrstown, PA; (3); 41/697; JCL; Pep Clb; Chorus; Rep Stu Cncl; Var Cheerleading; Hon Roll; Ntl Ltn Exm Slvr Mdl 84; PA ST U; Ad Exec.

MYERS, TRUDY; Huntingdon Area HS; Allensville, PA; (2); 6/193; Fld Hcky; High Hon Roll; NHS; Sci Stu Month Awd Chem 87; Shippensburg U; Acctng.

MYERS, WILLIAM D; Mercer Area JR/Sr HS; New Wilmington, PA; (3); Am Leg Boys St; Pres Computer Clb; Jazz Band; Mrchg Band; School Musical; School Play; Swing Chorus; Church Yth Grp; Library Aide; Math Tm; Dist V Chorus 86-87; Dist V Band 87; Regn I Band 87; Physcs.

MYERS JR, WILLIAM R; Lincoln JR SR HS; Ellwood City, PA; (3); 49/170; German Clb; Stage Crew; High Hon Roll; Hon Roll; NEDT Awd; Cert Merit Outstndng Schlstc Achvt 87; Penn ST; Chem Engrng.

MYFORD, DONNA; Grove City HS; Grove City, PA; (4); 20/163; Key Clb; Sec Jr Cls; Var L Bsktbl; Elks Awd; High Hon Roll; NHS; All-Am Acadc Stu 85-87; Mercer Cnty Hll Fm Acadc & Athltc Awd 86-87; Jiggs Wolford Athltc Awd 86-87; Coll Wooster; Bus Econ.

MYFORD, MEGAN; Freeport Area HS; Sarver, PA; (3); 38/186; Church Yth Grp; Chorus; Drill Tm.

MYLAN, LORI; Jefferson-Morgan HS; Clarksville, PA; (3); Letterman Clb; Spanish Clb; Varsity Clb; Color Guard; Yrbk Stf; Pres Frsh Cls; VP Pres Stu Cncl; Var L Bsktbl; Var L Sftbl; Hon Roll; Slpry Rock; Physcl Ed Coach.

MYRO, BERNARD; Nativity BUM HS; New Phila, PA; (3); 27/87; Art Clb; Church Yth Grp; Computer Clb; Nwsp Phtg; Nwsp Rptr; JV Var Trk; Wt Lftg; Hon Roll; Spanish NHS; Hghst Spnsh, Am Cltrs & Wrld Cltrs; Elec Engr.

NACCARATI, MICHELLE; Turtle Creek HS; Pittsburgh, PA; (3); 18/221; German Clb; Science Clb; SADD; Concert Band; Mrchg Band; Ed Yrbk Stf; Pres Frsh Cls; Pres Soph Cls; Off Stu Cncl; Mgr(s); Hugh O Brian Yth Ldrshp Awd 86; Med.

NACCARATO, DIANA; Shaler Area SR HS; Glenshaw, PA; (4); Pep Clb; Ski Clb; SADD; Flag Corp; Mrchg Band; School Musical; Symp Band; Variety Show; Nwsp Stf; Im Bowling; 4 Yr Ltrmn-Mrchng Band 87; Kent ST Flg Corp Schlrshp 87; Kent ST U; Intrior Dsgn.

NACCARATO, VICKI; Elizabeth Forward HS; Mc Keesport, PA; (4); 4/293; French Clb; Mrchg Band; Nwsp Stf; Rep Frsh Cls; Rep Soph Cls; Twrlr; High Hon Roll; Jr NHS; NHS; Pres Acadmc Ftns Awd; Kent ST U; Bus.

NACE, EMILY; Greenwood HS; Millerstown, PA; (2); 5/69; Church Yth Grp; GAA; Chorus; VP Soph Cls; Rep Stu Cncl; JV Bsktbl; JV Fld Hcky; Var Sftbl; High Hon Roll; NHS.

NACE, KRISTI; Susquenita HS; Duncannon, PA; (3); 4/200; Quiz Bowl; Nwsp Stf; VP Soph Cls; Pres Jr Cls; Pres Sr Cls; Bsktbl; Capt Cheerleading; 4-H Awd; NHS; Sec 4-H Awd 84-85; Amer Legn Essay Awd 85; Hghst Ranking Freshmn Girl 84-85; U Pittsburgh; Child Psychlgy.

NACE, KRISTY; Beaver Area HS; Beaver, PA; (2); 1/257; Church Yth Grp; JCL; Latin Clb; Pep Clb; VP Soph Cls; VP Jr Cls; Var L Bsktbl; Var L Vllybl; High Hon Roll; Hugh Obrien Ldrshp Awd 86-87; AAU JR Olympic Natl Chmpshp Bsktbll Tm 86-87; Med.

NACE, MICHELE; Mifflinburg Area HS; Mifflinburg, PA; (1); VP FFA; JV Sftbl; Hon Roll; Penn ST; Comp Sci.

NACHBAR, KARI; Hempfield HS; Manheim, PA; (3); Pres Church Yth Grp; Dance Clb; Sec 4-H; Varsity Clb; Drill Tm; Pep Band; JV Crs Cntry; Var Trk; 4-H Awd; Opt Clb Awd; CA ST U; Law Enfrcmnt.

NACHMAN, MICHAEL; Lower Merion HS; Wynnewood, PA; (4); Nwsp Rptr; Nwsp Sprt Ed; Nwsp Stf; Yrbk Rptr; Rep Jr Cls; Rep Stu Cncl; JV Socr; Var Capt Tennis; High Hon Roll; Spanish NHS; Capt Ten Tm 87 & 88; Edtr Feat Page Schl Paper 87-88; U MI; Comm.

NACHSIN, RYAN; Council Rock HS; Holland, PA; (2); Boy Scts; Key Clb; Rep Soph Cls; JV Wrstlng; Hon Roll; Hon Roll 8 Mrkng Periods 85-87; Law.

NACOPOULOS, JOANNA; Fairview HS; Erie, PA; (3); Pres Church Yth Grp; Dance Clb; Drama Clb; French Clb; Q&S; Thesps; Ed Lit Mag; Cit Awd; High Hon Roll; NHS; Ed.

NADEL, JULI; Danville HS; Danville, PA; (1); 27/322; Pres Church Yth Grp; Ski Clb; Temple Yth Grp; Socr; Tennis; Trk; High Hon Roll; Hon Roll; Presdntl Acad Fit Awd 86-8m; Law.

NADEL, MITCH; Danville Area HS; Danville, PA; (2); 41/162; Ski Clb; Band; Concert Band; Mrchg Band; Pep Band; Var L Golf; Capt Tennis; High Hon Roll; NEDT Awd; Penn ST; Aerospce.

NADOLNY, MICHELLE; Corry Area HS; Corry, PA; (4); Church Yth Grp; Mgr VP Bsktbl; Capt Mgr Vllybl; Joan Kolaja Schlrshp 87; Outstndng Grl Athlt La June Wms Awd 87; All Cnty 1st Tm Vllybl 87; Slippery Rock U; Math.

NADOLSKY, MARIE; Penn Cambria SR HS; Lilly, PA; (4); 14/200; Drama Clb; Speech Tm; SADD; School Play; Yrbk Stf; Stat Trk; Hon Roll; Schlstc Prfrmnc Awd 87; Commutr Schlrshp 87; St Francis Coll; Elem Ed.

NADOLSKY, SAN DEE; Penn Cambria SR HS; Lilly, PA; (4); Drama Clb; SADD; High Hon Roll; Hon Roll.

NADZADY, JOSEPH; Homer Center HS; Coral, PA; (3); 11/120; Debate Tm; French Clb; Library Aide; Varsity Clb; School Musical; Stu Cncl; Ftbl; Hon Roll; Jr NHS; NHS; IN U Of PA.

NADZAM, MARGARET; North Hills HS; Pittsburgh, PA; (3); 45/488; Church Yth Grp; Keywanettes; Band; Flag Corp; Mrchg Band; High Hon Roll; Hon Roll; NHS.

NADZAM, VICTORIA; Sacred Heart HS; W Homestead, PA; (3); Church Yth Grp; Hosp Aide; Rep Sr Cls; Var L Bsktbl; JV Crs Cntry; Med.

NAEHR, NANCY; St Hubert HS; Philadelphia, PA; (3); 47/421; Cmnty Wkr; Hosp Aide; Office Aide; Spanish Clb; Stage Crew; Nwsp Rptr; Nwsp Stf; Rep Stu Cncl; Var Fld Hcky; NHS; Mktg.

NAGEL IV, SIMON; Methactan SR HS; Audubon, PA; (3); 20/400; Boy Scts; High Hon Roll; Opt Clb Awd; Nwsp Rptr; Cornell U; Aerontcl Engrng.

NAGI, LYNNETTE; St Marys HS; St Marys, PA; (3); Yrbk Stf; Trs Jr Cls; JV Cheerleading; Var Coach Actv; Var JV Mgr(s); Ftbll Ltrs-Stats; Villia Maria; Nurse.

NAGLE, CHRISTINA; Cambria Heights HS; Patton, PA; (3); 13/180; Chorus; Var L Cheerleading; Hon Roll; NHS; Ski Clb; Nwsp Rptr; Yrbk Stf; Vllybl; Nrs.

NAGLE, CHRISTINE; Altoona Area HS; Altoona, PA; (3); 46/890; Ski Clb; Band; Concert Band; Jazz Band; Mrchg Band; Orch; Symp Band; Variety Show; Var L Bsktbl; Var L Sftbl; Altoona Prd Awd 87; IN U Of PA; Elem Tchr.

NAGLE, CHRISTOPHER C; Warwick HS; Lititz, PA; (3); 31/325; Am Leg Boys St; Band; Chorus; Orch; School Musical; School Play; High Hon Roll; NHS; Hnbl Mntn Lancaster Sci & Engrng Fair 87; Cnty And Dist Chrses 87; Warwick Schlr For Vcl Music 87; Engl.

NAGLE, CLAUDINE; Northern Cambria HS; Barnesboro, PA; (4); Drama Clb; Band; Chorus; School Play; Yrbk Stf; Stu Cncl; Bsktbl; Sftbl; High Hon Roll; NHS; U S Army Rsrve Natl Schlr Ath Awd 86-87.

NAGLE, DANIEL; Pine Grove Area HS; Pine Grove, PA; (3); Boy Scts; Church Yth Grp; ROTC; Rep Jr Cls; Var Ftbl; JV Wrstlng; High Hon Roll; Hon Roll; Engl Awd 87; Soc Stud Awd 87; Math Awd 87.

NAGLE, DONNA; Cambria Heights HS; Patton, PA; (3); 28/197; FHA; Q&S; SADD; Chorus; School Musical; Yrbk Rptr; Yrbk Stf; High Hon Roll; Hon Roll; NHS; Hosp Admin.

NAGLE, DOUGLAS; Mercer Area HS; Sharon, PA; (3); Rep Stu Cncl; Var L Bsktbl; Var L Trk; High Hon Roll; NHS; Prfct Atten Awd; Pre Med.

NAGLE, JOHN; Sayre Area HS; Sayre, PA; (3); Boy Scts; Spanish Clb; Varsity Clb; School Play; Pres Stu Cncl; Var Bsktbl; Capt Var Crs Cntry; Var Capt Trk; High Hon Roll; NHS; Pres Stu Gvrnmnt Assc-Brdfrd Cnty 88; Rtry Ldrshp Dlgt 86; Aerospc Engr.

NAGLE, KELLY; Pine Grove Area HS; Pine Grove, PA; (3); Yrbk Stf; Rep Stu Cncl; JV Bsktbl; JV Vllybl; High Hon Roll; Hon Roll; NHS; Engl Achvt Awd 86-87; Socl Studs Achvt Awd 86-87; Bus Educ Achvt Awd 87; Secy.

NAGLIERI, LYNELL; Central York SR HS; York, PA; (3); Pep Clb; Varsity Clb; Nwsp Stf; Yrbk Stf; Cheerleading; Trk; Hon Roll; Bus.

NAGRANT, RENATA; Schenley HS; Pittsburgh, PA; (4); German Clb; Math Tm; Yrbk Stf; High Hon Roll.

NAGY, DONNA J; Freeport Area SR HS; Freeport, PA; (4); Art Clb; FBLA; Hosp Aide; Model UN; Hon Roll; Prfct Atten Awd; FBLA Rgnl Awd 4th Pl-Prlmntry Procdrs 87; Alghny Vly Hosp Vlnteer Awd 86-87; Median Schl Allied Hlth Career.

NAGY, ELAINE; Mt Pleasant Area HS; Mt Pleasant, PA; (2); Sec Ski Clb; Rep Frsh Cls; Stu Cncl; Hon Roll; Pres Acad Fit Awd 85; Pharmacy.

NAGY, GEORGE; Southern Lehigh HS; Coopersburg, PA; (3); 3/243; Boy Scts; Quiz Bowl; Chorus; School Musical; Nwsp Rptr; Trs Stu Cncl; Hon Roll; NHS; PA ST U PA Cncl Tchrs Engl Essy Fnlst 85; US Nvl Acad Smmr Sem 87; Aerospace Engrng.

NAGY, LYN; Moon HS; Coraopolis, PA; (2); Church Yth Grp; French Clb; Chorus; School Musical; Rep Soph Cls; Hon Roll; Biolgcl Sci.

NAGY, MICHELLE; Blairsville SR HS; Blairsville, PA; (4); 35/110; Church Yth Grp; Drama Clb; Band; Chorus; Church Choir; Concert Band; Mrchg Band; School Musical; School Play; Vllybl; Dist Chorus, Band & Cnty Chorus & Band; Phy Fitness; IN U; Music.

NAGY, SHEILA; Avon Grove HS; Landenberg, PA; (3); 12/209; FBLA; Nwsp Stf; High Hon Roll; Hon Roll; Alg A Awd 85; Alg B Awd Spnsh II Awd Health Awd 86; Engl Chem Acctng II & Art Awds 87; Westchester U; Acctng.

NAGY, TODD; Manheim Township HS; Lancaster, PA; (4); Var Capt Wrstlng; Gov Hon Prg Awd; Hon Roll; Ntl Merit Ltr; Carnegie Mellon U; Bio.

NAIDOFF, LISA; Neshaminy HS; Langhorne, PA; (3); 140/800; Aud/Vis; Chorus; School Musical; Bsktbl; Fld Hcky; Sftbl; Tennis; Hon Roll; NHS; Occup Ther.

NAILOR, CYNTHIA; Dover Area HS; Dillsburg, PA; (3); Novelist.

NAIR, HARI A; Cathedral Prep Schl; Mc Kean, PA; (4); 1/215; German Clb; Model UN; Capt Scholastic Bowl; Science Clb; Spanish Clb; VP Frsh Cls; VP Soph Cls; High Hon Roll; Ntl Merit SF; Rensselaer Polytech Awd 86; Engr.

NAJDA, SUSAN; Shenandoah Valley HS; Shenandoah, PA; (4); 9/103; Dance Clb; Pep Clb; Nwsp Stf; Yrbk Ed-Chief; Stat Bsktbl; Capt Cheerleading; Capt Pom Pon; Hon Roll; NHS; Pres Schlr; Acad All Amer 85-87; Fred G Smith 87; Bloomsburg U; Accntng.

NALE, DEANNA; E Juniata HS; Mcalisterville, PA; (3); 6/100; Camera Clb; Girl Scts; SADD; School Musical; School Play; Variety Show; Yrbk Stf; High Hon Roll; NHS.

NALEPA, ANDY; Mc Keesport Area HS; White Oak, PA; (3); 42/420; High Hon Roll; Hon Roll; Pa ST U Mc Keesport; Comp Tec.

NALESNIK JR, BERNARD J; Palmerton Area HS; Palmerton, PA; (4); 1/140; Am Leg Boys St; Debate Tm; Quiz Bowl; Var Capt Bsbl; JV Capt Bsktbl; Var Capt Ftbl; Var Wrstlng; Bausch & Lomb Sci Awd; High Hon Roll; NHS; 19 In All Schltc Areas; Sci.

NALESNIK, CATHY; Palmerton Area HS; Palmerton, PA; (3); #1 In Class; Am Leg Aux Girls St; Church Yth Grp; Debate Tm; Hosp Aide; Scholastic Bowl; Var L Bsktbl; Bausch & Lomb Sci Awd; Cit Awd; High Hon Roll; NHS; Math.

NALEVANKO, KATHRYN; Abington Heights HS; Dalton, PA; (3); Ski Clb; Chorus; School Musical; Sec Stu Cncl; Tennis; Most Comptve Tennis Plyr Trphy 85; Booster Club Awd Tennis 87; Dist II Doubles Champ 87.

NALITZ, JENNIFER; Wayne S Burg Central HS; Waynesburg, PA; (3); French Clb; Concert Band; Jazz Band; Mrchg Band; Var Trk; JV Vllybl; High Hon Roll; NHS; NEDT Awd; Law.

NALL, NANCY L; Brookville Area HS; Brookville, PA; (3); Art Clb; Church Yth Grp; Drama Clb; FNA; Key Clb; Varsity Clb; School Musical; Bsktbl; Var Cheerleading; Var Score Keeper; Nrsng.

NALOR, TIM; Biglerville HS; Biglerville, PA; (2); Latin Clb; Trs Varsity Clb; Var L Bsktbl; Bowling; L Trk; Im Wrstlng; High Hon Roll; Hon Roll; NHS; MVP Bsktbl 86-87; Al-Times Bsktbl Tm 86-87; Top 6 Undrclsmn Bsktbl Rgn 86-87.

NAM, JAE; Marple Newtown SR HS; Broomall, PA; (2); 4/325; Debate Tm; Nwsp Rptr; JV Crs Cntry; Wrstlng; High Hon Roll; Engrng.

NAMADAN, JEFF; Western Beaver JR- SR HS; Industry, PA; (3); JA; Chorus; Nwsp Rptr; Bsktbl; Im Bowling; Var Trk; High Hon Roll; Hon Roll; NHS.

NAMATKA, FRANK P; Abington Heights HS; Clarks Summit, PA; (3); 70/300; Ski Clb; Band; Concert Band; Mrchg Band; Var L Ftbl; Hon Roll; Engrng.

NAMESNIK, ERIC; Butler SR HS; Butler, PA; (3); Church Yth Grp; Cmnty Wkr; Exploring; French Clb; SADD; Band; Orch; JV Crs Cntry; Var Swmmng; NHS; HS ST & YMCA Dist, ST, & Natl Swmmng Champ 87; Pre-Dntl.

NANNI, MARY BETH; Marion Center Area HS; Creekside, PA; (4); VP Church Yth Grp; VP Intnl Clb; Capt Flag Corp; Trs Soph Cls; Trs Jr Cls; Trs Sr Cls; Rep Stu Cncl; DAR Awd; NHS; HOBY Ambass Marion Ctr 85; Homecomg Court 86; Elem Ed.

NAPARSTECK, SAMANTHA; Dallas SR HS; Dallas, PA; (3); Church Yth Grp; Girl Scts; Church Choir; Nwsp Rptr; Nwsp Stf; Hon Roll; NEDT Awd; PA ST U; Psych.

NAPE, MARNA; Bishop Hannan HS; Scranton, PA; (4); School Play; VP Jr Cls; Capt Cheerleading; Golf; Sftbl; High Hon Roll; Hon Roll; Jr NHS; NHS; Pres Fit Awd 87; Temple U; Bus Law.

NAPIERALSKI, JAY; Lake Lehman HS; Shavertown, PA; (4); 40/155; Church Yth Grp; SADD; School Play; Var Tennis; Hon Roll; Bshps Awd For Rlgs Ed/Yth Mnstry 87; Kings Coll; Comp Info Systms.

NAPIERALSKI, LAURA; Lake-Lehman HS; Shavertown, PA; (2); Art Clb; JA; Spanish Clb; Varsity Clb; Fld Hcky; Trk; Hon Roll; Jr NHS; S M Rosetti Art Awd 87; Mrcy Hosp 5 Ml Rn 86; Kings Coll.

NAPLES, ANGELA; Cedar Crest HS; Lebanon, PA; (3); 37/340; French Clb; Latin Clb; Pep Clb; Science Clb; Var Cheerleading; JV Fld Hcky; Var L Sftbl; Im Vllybl; Hon Roll; NHS; Law.

NAPOLEON, MICHELLE; Southmoreland HS; Scottdale, PA; (3); Church Yth Grp; VP Exploring; French Clb; Girl Scts; Hosp Aide; Latin Clb; Ski Clb; Teachers Aide; Rep Stu Cncl; Powder Puff Ftbl; Nursing.

NAPOLETANO, MARIO; Downingtown HS; Downingtown, PA; (4); Intnl Clb; Ski Clb; Spanish Clb; Teachers Aide; Lcrss; Socr; Trk; Vllybl; High Hon Roll; NHS; Boston U; Pre-Med.

NAPOLI, MARIA; Cardinal O Hara HS; Springfield, PA; (3); 96/710; Cmnty Wkr; French Clb; SADD; Chorus; Lit Mag; High Hon Roll; Hon Roll; Art & Frnch Schlstc Awds 85-87; Prncpls Awd Acad Excell 84-87; Moor Coll Art Sat Art Cls Schlrshp 87; Grphc Design.

NAPOVANIC, NOELLE A; Mononhahela Valley Catholic HS; Donora, PA; (4); 14/80; Pep Clb; Band; Chorus; Concert Band; Drm Mjr(t); Flag Corp; Mrchg Band; School Musical; Yrbk Bus Mgr; Powder Puff Ftbl; Prsdntl Acad Achvt Awd 87; U Of Pittsburgh; Chem Engr.

NAPSON, THERESA; West Catholic Girls HS; Philadelphia, PA; (4); 6/246; Pres Debate Tm; NFL; Pres Speech Tm; Nwsp Bus Mgr; Rep Soph Cls; Rep Jr Cls; NHS; Hon Roll; Drama Clb; French Clb; Schlrshp To LEAD Prog 87; WDAS-FM Radio Assy Cont Finalst 84; ST Semi-Finlst In Speech Comp 87; English.

NARBY, LYNNE; Villa Marie Acad; Erie, PA; (3); Hosp Aide; Model UN; Science Clb; Service Clb; SADD; Nwsp Rptr; Hon Roll; NHS; Outstndng Svc Awd-Campus Mnstry 87; Cmmnctns.

NARCISI, STEPHANIE; Solanco HS; Oxford, PA; (3); Art Clb; Computer Clb; Spanish Clb; Bowling; Hon Roll; 3rd Plc Sci Fair Rewrd 85; Comp Prcssr.

NARDA, GREG; St John Neumann HS; Philadelphia, PA; (3); 99/354; Intnl Clb; La Salle U; Bus Admin.

NARDELL, CARL A; Wyoming Valley West HS; Swoyersville, PA; (3); Pres Ski Clb; SADD; Band; Chorus; Church Choir; Jazz Band; Mrchg Band; Orch; School Musical; Hon Roll; Natl Hstry Day Dist 5 85; Embry-Riddle Aeronautical U.

NARDIS, STACEY; West Greene HS; Wind Ridge, PA; (4); 11/105; Drama Clb; Letterman Clb; Library Aide; School Musical; Var L Cheerleading; Trk; High Hon Roll; NHS; Concert Band; Yrbk Stf; Recvd Outstndng Chrldr WVU Chrldng Cmp; Intl Open Chrldng Chmpnshps 1-A; Nshvll TN-15TH In Ntn; U Of Pittsburgh; Scl Wrk.

NARDONE, JAMES ALBERT; Pittston Area SR HS; Pittston, PA; (4); French Clb; Chorus; Im Bsktbl; Im Sftbl; High Hon Roll; Hon Roll; NHS; 4.0 Avg Cert Comp Pgmmng 86-87; Luzerne Cnty CC; Comp Sci.

NARKUNSKI, JESSICA; Creative & Performing Arts HS; Philadelphia, PA; (4); 2/140; Rep Stu Cncl; High Hon Roll; Hon Roll; NHS; Holocaust Awareness Cont 1st Prize Painting 87; Philadelphia Greeting Card Cont 3rd Prize Painting 85; Parsons Schl Design; Fash Desgn.

NARSAVAGE, PETER A; Scranton Prep Schl; Moscow, PA; (4); 41/191; Scholastic Bowl; Acpl Chr; Chorus; Concert Band; Orch; Pres Pep Band; School Play; High Hon Roll; NHS; Ntl Merit SF; MIT; Chem Engr.

NARTATEZ, AMY; Philipsburg-Osceola Area HS; Philipsburg, PA; (4); 12/230; Am Leg Aux Girls St; Church Yth Grp; FCA; Letterman Clb; Pep Clb; Ski Clb; Varsity Clb; Sec Band; Mrchg Band; Nwsp Stf; IN U Of PA; Bus Admin.

NARUSHOFF, CHRIS; Faith Christian HS; Monroeville, PA; (2); Church Yth Grp; Drama Clb; Chorus; Nwsp Rptr; Yrbk Stf; JV Bsktbl; High Hon Roll.

NARVETT, LORRAINE; Beaver Area JR SR HS; Beaver, PA; (3); 15/215; JCL; Ski Clb; Trs Soph Cls; Trs Jr Cls; Trs Sr Cls; JV Var Cheerleading; Powder Puff Ftbl; Var L Swmmng; High Hon Roll; NHS; Acad Achvt 86-87; PA ST; Aero Engrng.

NARZISI, CHRISTINE; Liberty HS; Bethlehem, PA; (3); 45/445; Exploring; Hosp Aide; Model UN; Political Wkr; Spanish Clb; SADD; Band; Concert Band; Mrchg Band; Hon Roll; Chem Engnrng.

NARZISI, ROBERT; Council Rock HS; Newtown, PA; (3); Church Yth Grp; Trk; Hon Roll.

NASEEM, SHAWN; Gateway HS; Monroeville, PA; (3); Intnl Clb; Ski Clb; Chorus; Bsktbl; Vllybl; Wt Lftg; French Hon Soc; Hon Roll; Blackbelt Karate 85; U Of Pittsburgh; Phy.

NASER, DAVID; Trinity HS; Washington, PA; (3); 76/402; Church Yth Grp; Pres 4-H; Im Coach Actv; Var L Socr; Var L Wrstlng; 4-H Awd; Hon Roll; AIJCA Outstndng JR 84; Bus Adm.

NASER, HOWARD; Washington HS; Washington, PA; (3); 15/153; Letterman Clb; Spanish Clb; Yrbk Stf; Rep Frsh Cls; Rep Stu Cncl; Var L Bsbl; Var L Ftbl; Var L Wrstlng; High Hon Roll; NHS; Crimnlgy.

NASH, LORI; Butler SR HS; Butler, PA; (3); Church Yth Grp; Office Aide; Chorus; Drm Mjr(t); Hon Roll; Speed Achvmt Shorthand I Cert 87; Proficiency Typing I Cert 86; Bradford U; Secy.

NASH, MARILYN; Lebanon Catholic HS; Lebanon, PA; (3); 9/72; German Clb; Pres Service Clb; Chorus; Church Choir; Nwsp Ed-Chief; Sec Stu Cncl; NHS; Ntl Merit Ltr; Rotary Awd; School Play; 1st Pl Women Rotary Int Essay Cont 87; Educ.

NASH, THOMAS; North Catholic HS; Pittsburgh, PA; (3); Var L Bsbl; Im Bsktbl; High Hon Roll; NHS; U Of Pttsbrgh.

NASH, YOLANDA; Philadelphia Christian Acad; Philadelphia, PA; (4); Latin Clb; Church Choir; Yrbk Stf; Off Sr Cls; Hon Roll; Sec Church Yth Grp; Capt Debate Tm; Rep Stu Cncl; Val; CC Philadelphia; Psych.

NASKI, KIMBERLY; Strath Haven HS; Wallingford, PA; (3); Art Clb; Cmnty Wkr; FBLA; GAA; Chrmn Red Cross Aide; Ski Clb; Spanish Clb; Yrbk Stf; L Var Swmmng; Hon Roll; Stu Actvts Cncl; Wallingfrd Swim/Rcqut Clb Vrsty; DE Bus Smnr U Of DE 87; Bus.

NASMAN, SHAUN; Warren Area HS; Russell, PA; (3); 4-H; German Clb; SADD; Pittsburgh; Engrng.

NASPINSKI, ED; Wyalusing Valley HS; New Albany, PA; (4); 1/135; Am Leg Boys St; Chorus; Jazz Band; VP Stu Cncl; Var Capt Crs Cntry; Var Capt Trk; Bausch & Lomb Sci Awd; NHS; Pres Schlr; Val; Half Tutn Schlrshp Penn ST 87-88; Penn ST U; Elec Engr.

NASS, CHRISTINE M; St Basil Acad; Philadelphia, PA; (3); Church Yth Grp; Computer Clb; Drama Clb; GAA; Spanish Clb; SADD; Chorus; Church Choir; Madrigals; Natl Hnr Roll 87; Teen Spirit Awd 87; Miss PA US Teen Pagent 87; Temple U; Music.

NASSIF, ROBERT; Altoona Area HS; Altoona, PA; (3); Key Clb; NFL; Political Wkr; Spanish Clb; VP Jr Cls; VP Sr Cls; Swmmng; NHS; Ntl Merit SF; Pres Schlr; Penn ST; Pltcl Sci.

NAST, HOWARD; Roman Catholic HS; Philadelphia, PA; (3); 33/121; ROTC; Nwsp Stf; Bsbl; Fld Hcky; Ice Hcky; Swmmng; Tennis; Wt Lftg; High Hon Roll; NHS; Bst Sprtsmn Of Yr 82; Athltc Awd 81 & 82; Bsbl Awd 83 & 84; Military; Pilot.

NATAL, ADA; Bodine HSIA HS; Philadelphia, PA; (3); 21/110; Church Yth Grp; Dance Clb; Spanish Clb; Stage Crew; Stu Cncl; Spirit Comm 86-87; Fashn Shw Comm Actvts 86-87; JR Clss Ofcr Secy 86-87; Secy.

NATALE, BETH ANN; New Castle HS; New Castle, PA; (4); 8/263; Var Capt Bsktbl; Var Capt Tennis; Hon Roll; NHS; Prfct Atten Awd; Elem Ed.

NATALE, NICHOLAS; Salisbury HS; Allentown, PA; (3); Var L Wrstlng; Hon Roll; Embry Riddle.

NATALE, SHANNON; Cedar Crest HS; Lebanon, PA; (3); Church Yth Grp; French Clb; FTA; Hosp Aide; Pep Clb; Church Choir; Concert Band; Orch.

NATH, RITIKA; Mt Lebanon HS; Pittsburgh, PA; (4); 10/537; French Clb; Hosp Aide; Ski Clb; Varsity Clb; Drill Tm; Sec Frsh Cls; VP Soph Cls; Pres Jr Cls; Pres Sr Cls; Gym; Carnegie Mellon U; Medicine.

NATHAN, HORACE; Simon Gratz HS; Philadelphia, PA; (4); Church Yth Grp; Math Clb; VICA; Bsktbl; Cert Merit E Washington Rhodes Schl Sci Dept, Cert Srvc E W Rhodes Schl 82; Comp Sci.

NATHANSON, ELINOR; Taylor Allderdice HS; Pittsburgh, PA; (3); Math Clb; Ski Clb; Temple Yth Grp; Nwsp Ed-Chief; High Hon Roll; Jr NHS; NHS.

NATION, RUSSEL; West Allegheny SR HS; Sturgeon, PA; (3); Aud/Vis; Computer Clb; High Hon Roll; Hon Roll; Penn Tech Inst; Elec Tech.

NATT, SUSAN; Wyoming Area HS; Pittston, PA; (3); Spanish Clb; SADD; High Hon Roll; Hon Roll; Rep Stu Cncl.

NATTRASS, AMY; James M Coughlin HS; Wilkes Barre, PA; (3); 6/374; Pres Church Yth Grp; Drama Clb; German Clb; Hosp Aide; Key Clb; Math Clb; Chorus; Concert Band; Off Stu Cncl; NHS; Hugh O Brian Ldrshp Awd 86; Luzerne Cnty Sci Tchrs Assn Awd 85; U Of IL; Med.

NAUGHTON, SCOTT; South Williamsport SR HS; Williamsport, PA; (3); 21/111; Stu Cncl; Ftbl; Wrstlng; Hon Mntn Wst Brnch Conf Def Tckle, Plc Kckr 86.

NAUGLE, BARBARA; New Castle SR HS; New Castle, PA; (4); 5/279; Pres Church Yth Grp; Pres French Clb; Hosp Aide; SADD; Band; Nwsp Sprt Ed; Var Ftbl; Mgr(s); L Trk; High Hon Roll; Soc Dstngshd Amer HS Stu 86; Prfct Atten Awd; Ithaca Coll NY; Phys Ther.

NAUGLE, JOANNA; High Point Baptist Acad; Fleetwood, PA; (3); 5/32; Church Yth Grp; Cmnty Wkr; Church Choir; High Hon Roll; Hon Roll; American Chrstn Hnr Soc 87.

NAUGLE, RICHARD; Greensburg Central Catholic HS; Jeannette, PA; (3); Ski Clb; Var L Ice Hcky; Hon Roll; Med.

NAUMANN, LISA M; Oley Valley HS; Oley, PA; (4); 1/152; Pep Clb; SADD; Teachers Aide; Nwsp Rptr; Nwsp Stf; High Hon Roll; NHS; Rotary Awd; Val; Hon Roll; Grk Cncl Schlrshp Mllrsvll U Acdmc & Extracrrclr Achvmnts; Dengler Schlrshp; Outstndg Acctg Stu Cntywd; Millersville U PA; Elem Educ.

NAUSE, JEFFREY; Hazleton SR HS; Drums, PA; (3); 17/465; Leo Clb; Quiz Bowl; Ski Clb; Teachers Aide; Pres Sr Cls; Stu Cncl; Cit Awd; French Hon Soc; High Hon Roll; French Clb; Acadc Al-Amer 87; PA JR Acad Sci 1st Pl ST Div 87; Dist Comp Cntst Wnnr 1st Pl; PA ST U; Comp Engr.

NAVARRO, EFREN; Central York SR HS; York, PA; (4); 11/218; Mrchg Band; Orch; School Musical; Symp Band; CC Awd; Lion Awd; NHS; George Washington U Trustees Engrng Schlrshp, Prsdntl Acdmc Fitness Awd & Math Awd 87; George Washington U; Elec Engr.

NAVAS, LAURIE; Canevin Catholic HS; Pittsburgh, PA; (3); Aud/Vis; Chorus; Drill Tm; Yrbk Stf; Rep Frsh Cls; Rep Soph Cls; Rep Stu Cncl; Powder Puff Ftbl; Vllybl; Hon Roll; ST Fnlst Miss American Coed 86-87; Comms.

NAVAZIO, MICHELLE R; St Maria Goretti HS; Philadelphia, PA; (4); 44/384; Cmnty Wkr; Nwsp Rptr; Lit Mag; Rep Frsh Cls; Rep Jr Cls; Schlrshp Frm Tmstrs Lcl 850 87; Prsdntl Acdmc Awd 87; PA Coll Of Pharmacy & Sci.

NAVEH, SHARON; Parkland HS; Allentown, PA; (3); Chess Clb; Exploring; Library Aide; Quiz Bowl; Science Clb; Sec Temple Yth Grp; Yrbk Ed-Chief; Lit Mag; High Hon Roll; NHS; Schlr Awd 86; Regnl Hstry Fair 85; Comptn Smmr Sci Enrchmnt Prog 86; Bio.

NAVRATIL, HEIDI; Pocono Mountain HS; Tobyhanna, PA; (3); 39/300; SADD; Band; Trs Concert Band; Trs Mrchg Band; Bowling; Swmmng; Tennis; Trk; Vllybl; Hon Roll; Bus.

NAWROCKI, ALICIA; Leechburg Area HS; Leechburg, PA; (3); 27/87; Art Clb; VP Church Yth Grp; Drama Clb; Math Tm; Speech Tm; Band; Chorus; Church Choir; Nwsp Rptr; Vllybl; Westminster; Law.

NAWROCKI, CHRISTOPHER; Nativity BVM HS; New Philadelphi, PA; (3); 28/86; Math Clb; VP Spanish Clb; Crs Cntry; JV Capt Ftbl; Hon Roll; Bloomsburg U; Econ Finance.

NAWROCKI, ELDENA; Pocono Central Catholic HS; Gouldsboro, PA; (3); 8/33; Art Clb; French Clb; Pep Clb; Chorus; School Musical; School Play; Rep Stu Cncl; Var Capt Sftbl; Hon Roll; Prfct Atten Awd; Artist.

NAWROCKI, JOHN; Cathedral Prep; Erie, PA; (3); 2/194; Church Yth Grp; Cmnty Wkr; German Clb; Service Clb; VP Jr Cls; Rep Stu Cncl; Var L Bsbl; Im Bsktbl; Hon Roll; Ntl Merit Ltr; Rensselaer Polytech Inst Mdl For Excel In Mth & Sci 86-87.

NAWROCKI, LAURA W; Susquehanna Twnshp HS; Harrisburg, PA; (4); 2/155; Am Leg Aux Girls St; Drama Clb; Math Tm; Model UN; Chorus; School Musical; Nwsp Stf; High Hon Roll; NHS; Ntl Merit SF; Outstndng Spnsh III Stud 85-86; Intl Stdies.

NAYLON, CAROL; West Hazleton HS; Conyngham, PA; (4); 55/224; Church Yth Grp; Spanish Clb; Varsity Clb; Yrbk Rptr; Yrbk Sprt Ed; Yrbk Stf; Var Bsktbl; Var Sftbl; Hon Roll; NHS; Geisinger Med Ctr; Rad.

NAYLOR, DEBRA; Northeastern HS; Manchester, PA; (3); 12/195; Varsity Clb; Jr Cls; Var Trk; Var Vllybl; High Hon Roll; Hon Roll; NHS; Ski Clb; Chorus; Flag Corp; York Dispatch All Stars 85-86; York Daily Record All Team 85; Sports Med.

NAYLOR, HEATHER; Tyrone Area HS; Tyrone, PA; (2); VP Pres Church Yth Grp; Spanish Clb; Pres SADD; Chorus; Church Choir; Color Guard; Mrchg Band; Stage Crew; Var Trk; Hon Roll; Fash Mrchndsr.

NAYLOR, HOLLY; West Perry SR HS; Landisburg, PA; (4); 16/188; VP Computer Clb; Varsity Clb; Yrbk Sprt Ed; VP Sr Cls; Rep Stu Cncl; Var Capt Fld Hcky; NHS; Red Cross Aide; Spanish Clb; Yrbk Rptr; Coaches Awd Hcky 87; Comp Awd 87; Hmcmng Qn 86-87; Shippensburg U; Comp Sci.

NAZWORTH, MIKA; Aliquippa SR HS; Aliquippa, PA; (3); VICA; Med.

NAZZARIO, JANINE; Cardinal O Hara HS; Springfield, PA; (3); 137/710; Boys Clb Am; Trs VP Church Yth Grp; Cmnty Wkr; SADD; Yrbk Stf.

NAZZARO, MARY-NICOLE; Bensalem HS; Bensalem, PA; (2); Debate Tm; Science Clb; SADD; Concert Band; Jazz Band; Madrigals; Mrchg Band; JV Crs Cntry; Drama Clb; Band; PA Music Educators Assn Dstrct XI & Rgn VI Band & PMEA Dstrct VI & All-St Chorus 87; Aerospace Engrng.

NEAL, BARBARA; Central York SR HS; York, PA; (4); 9/210; Church Choir; Mrchg Band; School Musical; Swing Chorus; Symp Band; Yrbk Ed-Chief; Lion Awd; NHS; Pres Schlr; Cntl York Educ Assoc Teachers Schlrshp, Robert C Bird Schlrshp, & Natl Schl Choral Awd 87; Penn ST U; Elem Educ.

NEAL, DODY; Jeannette SR HS; Jeannette, PA; (2); 4/130; Church Yth Grp; Drama Clb; Ski Clb; Spanish Clb; High Hon Roll; Engrng.

NEAL, LARA; Steelton Highspire HS; Steelton, PA; (3); 17/102; Pep Clb; Spanish Clb; Cheerleading; High Hon Roll; Hacc; Accntng.

NEAL, MATTHEW; St Plus X HS; Douglassville, PA; (1); 13/146; JV Bsbl; High Hon Roll; Prfct Atten Awd; Pres Schlr; Band; Stage Crew; Schlrshp To Pius 86-87; Computer Programming.

NEAL, MICHAEL; Donegal HS; Marietta, PA; (3); 27/178; Church Yth Grp; Stage Crew; L Var Bsbl; L Var Bsktbl; L Var Ftbl; Wt Lftg; Hon Roll; Co-Capt Ftbl 87-88; Keystone Gms Bsbl, All-Cnty Bsbl & Ftbl 87.

NEAL, MICHELLE; Penn-Trafford HS; Irwin, PA; (3); 10/301; AFS; Hosp Aide; JCL; Ski Clb; Chorus; Stu Cncl; Var L Trk; Var L Vllybl; NHS; Ntl Merit Ltr; Outstndng Asn Pcfc Amer Hrtg Stu Awd 87; PA Free Entrprs Wk Schlrshp 87; Kystn Grls ST Schlrshp 86; Arch.

NEAL, RENEE; West Perry SR HS; Shermansdale, PA; (3); Nwsp Rptr; Nwsp Stf; Mgr(s); Mat Maids; Hon Roll; HACC; Exec Secy.

NEAL, ROBIN LYNN; Franklin JR/Sr HS; Polk, PA; (4); 18/208; French Clb; Library Aide; Math Tm; JV Vllybl; High Hon Roll; Hon Roll; NHS; Acadc Schlrshp Gannon U 87-88; Schl Brd Dir Awd 84-87; Gannon U; Pre Med.

NEALEN, BARBARA; Cambria Heights HS; Carrolltown, PA; (3); Church Yth Grp; FHA; Library Aide; ROTC; Teachers Aide; Color Guard; Drill Tm; Nwsp Rptr; Hon Roll; VFW Awd; Various Awds ROTC Longevity I, II, III 84-87; EXEC Secy.

NEALMAN, STEPHANIE; Norristown Area HS; Norristown, PA; (2); 46/521; Church Yth Grp; GAA; Intnl Clb; SADD; Rep Frsh Cls; Rep Soph Cls; Rep Stu Cncl; Mgr(s); Var Sftbl; Hon Roll; Bus Awd Outstndng Secr 87; Crmnl Jstc.

NEALON, KARIN; Tunkhannock Area HS; Falls, PA; (2); 2/322; Drama Clb; Pres German Clb; Key Clb; Ski Clb; Concert Band; Mrchg Band; School Play; Stat Wrstlng; High Hon Roll; Band; Hnrd Annl Schlrshp Bnqt-Basedon Clss Rnk 86; Psych.

NEALON, MARY BETH; West Scranton HS; Scranton, PA; (2); #11 In Class; Aud/Vis; Drama Clb; Latin Clb; Speech Tm; Chorus; Hon Roll; Cosmotology.

NEARHOOD, KRISTA; West Branch Area HS; Kylertown, PA; (3); 56/110; Drama Clb; Spanish Clb; SADD; Chorus; Color Guard; Stage Crew; Twrlr; Accntng.

NEARHOOF, SHARON; Tyrone Area HS; Warriors Mark, PA; (4); Key Clb; Office Aide; SADD; Color Guard; Co-Capt Flag Corp; Yrbk Rptr; Score Keeper; Elks Awd; Alumni Merit Schlrshp 87-88; Juniata Coll; Bio.

NEARY, COLEEN; Henderson HS; Exton, PA; (2); 15/330; Office Aide; Lcrss; High Hon Roll; Spanish NHS; 2nd Pl Upper Main Line Piano Tchrs Fest 86-87; Acctng.

NEAS, CHERYL A; Emmaus HS; Emmaus, PA; (3); 2/550; Model UN; Q&S; Scholastic Bowl; Spanish Clb; Lib Mrchg Band; Ed Lit Mag; Gov Hon Prg Awd; High Hon Roll; NHS; Chorus; Intl Rltns.

NEASE, MATTHEW; Blairsville HS; Blairsville, PA; (4); Varsity Clb; Ftbl; NHS; Pres Schlr; W Sec Ed Coun Acad All-Amer Schlr 86-87; U Of Pittsbgh; Elec Engnrng.

NEBGEN, ELLEN; Tyrone Area HS; Altoona, PA; (4); 4-H; French Clb; Thesps; Chorus; Mrchg Band; Swing Chorus; 4-H Awd; Hon Roll; Prfct Atten Awd; Band; U Of Pittsburgh; Phrmcy.

NEDEROSTEK, DOUGLAS; Castasauqua HS; Catasauqua, PA; (3); 2/140; Boy Scts; VP Debate Tm; Pres Exploring; Hosp Aide; Capt Scholastic Bowl; Ed Lit Mag; Pres NHS; Voice Dem Awd; Altrnt PA Gvrnrs Schl For Sci 87; Eastern PA Hugh O Brian Ldrshp Intl Smnr 86; Bio.

NEDRICH, TARA; Blacklick Valley HS; Ebensburg, PA; (3); 4/100; Library Aide; Varsity Clb; Pres Jr Cls; Var JV Bsktbl; Var Trk; High Hon Roll; HOBY Ambassador 86; Law.

NEDRICH, TRAVIS; Blacklick Valley HS; Ebensburg, PA; (2); 8/105; NFL; Varsity Clb; Var JV Ftbl; Var Trk.

NEDROW, RICHELLE; Hempfield SR HS; New Stanton, PA; (4); 63/693; Pep Clb; Ski Clb; Off Stu Cncl; JV Cheerleading; NHS; Spanish NHS; Exploring; Spanish Clb; Powder Puff Ftbl; JV Vllybl; U Of Pittsburgh; Phrmcy.

NEDZESKY, ANTHONY; Seton La Salle Regional HS; Pittsburgh, PA; (3); 71/248; Drama Clb; Math Tm; NFL; Spanish Clb; School Musical; Stage Crew; Variety Show; Var Trk; Engnrng.

NEE, MICHELE; Greensburg Central Catholic HS; Irwin, PA; (3); 27/231; Var L Bsktbl; Var L Crs Cntry; Var L Trk; Var L Vllybl; High Hon Roll; NHS; Section IX Honorable Mention-Bsktbll 87; All Tournament Team 87.

NEE, SHAWN; Old Forge HS; Old Forge, PA; (3); 31/123; Ski Clb; Nwsp Stf; JV Var Crs Cntry; Hon Roll; NHS; U Of Miami; Marine Ecology.

NEEL, HEATHER; Jefferson-Morgan HS; Jefferson, PA; (4); 1/97; Science Clb; Pres Service Clb; Chorus; School Play; Rep Stu Cncl; Var Sftbl; DAR Awd; Sec NHS; Val; Washington & Jefferson Coll.

NEELY, BELINDA; Purchase Line HS; Cherry Tree, PA; (3); French Clb; SADD; Chorus; Nwsp Rptr; Sftbl; High Hon Roll; Hon Roll.

NEELY, JONATHAN; Butler Area SR HS; Butler, PA; (3); VP German Clb; Sec Latin Clb; Varsity Clb; Rep Frsh Cls; Im Bsktbl; Var Capt Socr; Jr NHS; Ntl Merit SF; Soccer Dfnsv MVP & Mens All-Star Team 86-87; Bus Admin.

NEELY, LORI; Greensburg Central Catholic HS; Bloomington, IL; (2); Rep Frsh Cls; Cit Awd; High Hon Roll; Hon Roll; NHS; Pres Schlr; Bus Mgmt.

NEELY, MICHAEL; Butler JR HS; Butler, PA; (3); Exploring; Spanish Clb; Jazz Band; Mrchg Band; Pres Stu Cncl; Gym; Var L Trk; High Hon Roll; VP Jr NHS; NHS; Most Active Jr Awd 86-87.

NEENAN, MARY; Liberty HS; Liberty, PA; (2); German Clb; Concert Band; Mrchg Band; School Musical; JV Bsktbl; Var Trk; Bus Mgmt.

NEENAN, PAT; Liberty JR-SR HS; Liberty, PA; (2); Computer Clb; German Clb; Bsktbl; Score Keeper; Aerntcl Engrng.

NEENHOLD, JAMIE C; Archbishop Ryan HS; Philadelphia, PA; (2); 16/360; Var Crs Cntry; Var Trk; High Hon Roll; Hon Roll; Prfct Atten Awd; Pres Schlr; US Naval Acad; Aerospace Engr.

NEFF, CYNTHIA; Butler Area SR HS; Chicora, PA; (4); 44/699; Office Aide; Color Guard; Drill Tm; School Musical; Jr NHS; NHS; Gannon U; Optometry.

NEFF, EMILIE; Abington SR HS; Abington, PA; (3); 6/502; SADD; Varsity Clb; Church Choir; Symp Band; Rep Jr Cls; Rep Stu Cncl; Var Fld Hcky; Var Lcrss; DAR Awd; High Hon Roll.

NEFF, ERIN; Liberty HS; Bethlehem, PA; (3); 65/496; Sec German Clb; SADD; Nwsp Bus Mgr; Nwsp Stf; Yrbk Sprt Ed; Lit Mag; Rep Stu Cncl; Var L Bsktbl; Stat Socr; Hon Roll; Merit Awd Mayor For German Exch 87; Engl.

NEFF, KATIE; Hershey HS; Hummelstown, PA; (3); 18/210; Model UN; High Hon Roll; NHS; Schltc Wrtng Awds 2nd Awd 86-87.

NEFF, REBECCA K; Butler Area SR HS; Chicora, PA; (4); 60/755; Church Yth Grp; DECA; Office Aide; Teachers Aide; Hon Roll; DECA Stu Of Yr Awd, Acdmc Achvt Awd & Schlrshp For Butler Coll 87; Butler Cnry CC; Bus Mgmt.

NEFF, TARLA KAY; Curwensville Avera HS; Curwensville, PA; (3); Church Yth Grp; Ski Clb; Spanish Clb; Y-Teens; Chorus; Nwsp Stf; Yrbk Stf; Rep Frsh Cls; Rep Stu Cncl; Stat Bsktbl; MVP Chrldng Awd 86; Penn ST; Law.

NEFF, TINA; Butler SR HS; Butler, PA; (3); Hosp Aide; JA; Library Aide; Office Aide; Spanish Clb; VP Sr Cls; Rep Stu Cncl; Gold Cert Awd 3.6 QPA Or Better 87; Acctg.

NEFF, TONYA; Garden Spot HS; New Holland, PA; (2); Church Yth Grp; Chorus; Flag Corp; School Musical; Sec Frsh Cls; Sec Soph Cls; Sec Jr Cls; Capt Var Trk; High Hon Roll; NHS; Chorus Awd 86.

NEGLER, JENNIFER; Cedar Cliff HS; Camp Hill, PA; (3); Camera Clb; Key Clb; Ski Clb; Spanish Clb; Teachers Aide; School Musical; Nwsp Rptr; Nwsp Stf; Yrbk Stf; Stu Cncl.

NEGLEY, BECKY; Saltsburg JR/SR HS; Clarksburg, PA; (1); Var L Cheerleading; Var Gym; Var L Trk; Hon Roll; Presdntl Phys Ftns Awd 87; Smi Fnlst-Mdrn Miss 87; IUP; Engr.

NEGLEY, KELLY; Knoch SR HS; Butler, PA; (4); 35/245; 4-H; FBLA; SADD; Orch; School Musical; 4-H Awd; Hon Roll; NHS; Ntl Schl Orchestra Awd 87; Acad Achvmnt Awd 87; Knights Of Knowledge Awd 87; Butler CC; Accntng.

NEGVESKY, MARIA E; Central Columbia HS; Bloomsburg, PA; (3); Church Yth Grp; Cmnty Wkr; Hosp Aide; Math Tm; Spanish Clb; Crs Cntry; Socr; Tennis; Trk; Hon Roll; Natl Piano Auditions 82-87; Natl Piano Roll 84-87; Bus Admin.

NEHILLA, TOM; Ringgold HS; Finleyville, PA; (3); Intnl Clb; Math Clb; Science Clb; Ski Clb; Speech Tm; Ftbl; Cit Awd; Hon Roll; Trs NHS; U Of Pittsburgh; Law.

NEIBERT, JILL; Mechanisburg SR HS; Mechanicsburg, PA; (3); 101/338; VP Church Yth Grp; Girl Scts; Band; Chorus; Concert Band; Mrchg Band; School Play; Im Bsktbl; Prfct Atten Awd; Peer Advoctae; Tv Cmnctns.

NEIDERHISER, JULIANE; Ligonier Valley SR HS; Ligonier, PA; (3); Sec Band; Var Trk; Hon Roll; Jr NHS.

NEIDIGH, DUANE; Palmyra HS; Annville, PA; (4); 36/201; Band; Concert Band; Mrchg Band; Capt Bsbl; Capt Golf; High Hon Roll; Hon Roll; Prfct Atten Awd; Ind Arts Awd 86-87; Lycoming Coll.

NEIGH, MATTHEW; Butler HS; Butler, PA; (2); Church Yth Grp; French Clb; SADD; Rep Frsh Cls; Sec CAP; Sec Stu Cncl; Var Crs Cntry; JV Var Trk; Hon Roll; PA ST U; Bus.

NEIL, EDWARD; Hollidaysburg Area SR HS; Hollidaysburg, PA; (3); #68 In Class; Boy Scts; Band; Concert Band; Jazz Band; Mrchg Band; Hollidaysburg Blue Band Svc Awd 86; Bio.

NEILL, JOHN; Portersville HS; Zelienople, PA; (3); Boy Scts; Yrbk Bus Mgr; JV Var Bsktbl; PA JR Acad Sci 2nd Pl 86-87; Bsktbl Mst Imprvd Plyr Awd 86; Manuba Swm Chmp 87; Geneva Coll; Bus Admin.

NEIMAN, MICHELE; Central Dauphin HS; Harirsburg, PA; (2); High Hon Roll; Jr NHS; Pres Schlr; PTA Awd For Exc In Frnch 86; Math.

NEIMAN, SHELBI A; Quakertown Community SR HS; Quakertown, PA; (2); 117/359; Varsity Clb; Concert Band; Mrchg Band; Var L Fld Hcky; Jr NHS; Resolution Fld Hcky Tm Co-Champ Amer Conf Lbrty Div 86; Ltr ST Rep Sub 1 Co-Champ Fld Hcky 87; Elem Ed.

NEIMEYER, SHEILA; Brandywine Hts HS; Mertztown, PA; (4); 5/120; Am Leg Aux Girls St; Q&S; Yrbk Ed-Chief; Pres Sr Cls; Var Capt Sftbl; Var Capt Tennis; NHS; Stu Athlt Awd 87; Glen Reifinger Mem Schlrhsp 87; Fink Trexler Mem Awd Sftbl 87; Penn ST U; Bus Adm.

NEIPERT, RENEE L; Pocono Mountain HS; Tobyhanna, PA; (4); 30/280; Cmnty Wkr; Pep Clb; SADD; Im Powder Puff Ftbl; Trk; Hon Roll; Peer Spprt Vlntrs 86-87; Northampton Cnty CC; Lab Tech.

NEISWONGER, KEVIN; Mercer JR SR HS; Mercer, PA; (3); Boy Scts; NFL; Speech Tm; Band; Concert Band; Jazz Band; Mrchg Band; School Musical; School Play; Hon Roll; Sci.

NEISWORTH, HEATHER; Quigley HS; Ambridge, PA; (4); 28/105; French Clb; Ski Clb; SADD; Chorus; Nwsp Rptr; Yrbk Rptr; Yrbk Stf; Bsktbl; Tennis; Hon Roll; Cortez Peters Chmpnshp Awd 87; Tnns Ltr 85-87; U Of Pitt; Intl Bus.

NEITZ, KIMBERLEE; Shikellamy HS; Northumberland, PA; (3); Pres Church Yth Grp; French Clb; German Clb; Teachers Aide; Yrbk Rptr; Hon Roll; Intl Reltns.

NEKORANIK, PAUL; Pennsbury HS; Yardley, PA; (2); 1/800; Dance Clb; Chorus; Im Bowling; Im Trk; High Hon Roll; Danc Mstrs Of Amer-Teen Mr Danc Of NY 87; Johns Hopkins U Cty Pgm 87; Bucks Cnty Music Fstvl 3rd 87; Physcs.

NEKUZA, TIMOTHY A; Elk County Christian HS; St Marys, PA; (3); 17/81; Band; Concert Band; Jazz Band; Mrchg Band; Pep Band; Symp Band; Hon Roll; JV Trk; Comms.

NELKO, MATTHEW J; Ambridge Area HS; Baden, PA; (4); Trs Church Yth Grp; French Clb; Math Clb; Pep Clb; Jazz Band; Mrchg Band; Symp Band; Rep Soph Cls; Rep Sr Cls; Hon Roll; Pittsburgh U; English.

NELMES, BRIAN; Hazleton SR HS; Hazleton, PA; (3); Church Yth Grp; Cmnty Wkr; Capt Debate Tm; Hosp Aide; Quiz Bowl; VICA; Chorus; Variety Show; Hon Roll; Rotary Awd.

NELSON, ADAM; Neshaminy HS; Langhorne, PA; (3); Debate Tm; Hosp Aide; SADD; Temple Yth Grp; Stage Crew; Nwsp Phtg; Nwsp Stf; Yrbk Phtg; Yrbk Stf; Off Jr Cls; Neshaminy Schl Dist Awd Rcgntn 86; Brd Of Ed Serv Awd 87; Chldrns Hosp Phila Cert Of Rcgntn 86; Pre Med.

NELSON, AIMEE; Coudersport Area HS; Coudersport, PA; (4); French Clb; Band; Chorus; Mrchg Band; Yrbk Stf; Stat Bsktbl; Score Keeper; Trk; Hon Roll; NHS; Lock Haven U; Socl Wrk.

NELSON, AMY; Keystone Oaks HS; Pittsburgh, PA; (3); 34/285; Variety Show; Yrbk Stf; Var L Cheerleading; Coach Actv; Vllybl; Hon Roll; Elem Ed.

NELSON, BRIDGET; Corry Area HS; Corry, PA; (2); Church Yth Grp; French Clb; Yrbk Stf; Vllybl; High Hon Roll.

NELSON, CAROL; Harbor Creek HS; Erie, PA; (4); 19/218; Model UN; Band; Concert Band; Mrchg Band; Pres Pep Band; Variety Show; Hon Roll; NHS; PA ST Grape Qn Ms Congnlty 87; Grove City Coll; Bus Admin.

NELSON, CHRISTINE; East Stroudsburg HS; East Stroudsburg, PA; (1); 3/239; Church Yth Grp; Girl Scts; Band; Chorus; Church Choir; Color Guard; Concert Band; Jazz Band; JV Fld Hcky; High Hon Roll; FL Inst Tech; Marine Bio.

NELSON, CHRISTOPHER; Cumberland Valley HS; Mechanicsburg, PA; (2); Church Yth Grp; Church Choir; Bowling; Comp Engrng.

NELSON, CRAIG; West Branch Area HS; Grassflat, PA; (2); Science Clb; Spanish Clb; Varsity Clb; L Bsktbl; JV Crs Cntry; Hon Roll.

NELSON, DON; Central Dauphin HS; Harrisburg, PA; (3); 10/370; Key Clb; Yrbk Phtg; Wrstlng; Cit Awd; High Hon Roll; Hon Roll; NHS; Pres Schlr; Trs Church Yth Grp; Wt Lftg; Plntrm Asst Clb; Sci Olympd; Sci Awd; Bell Choir.

NELSON, EDWARD; Warren Area HS; Warren, PA; (3); Church Yth Grp; French Clb; Spanish Clb; Golf; High Hon Roll; Hon Roll.

NELSON, EMILY; Marple Newtown SR HS; Newtown Square, PA; (3); 31/322; Ski Clb; Sec SADD; School Musical; Yrbk Stf; Stu Cncl; Var Tennis; JV Trk; Hon Roll; NHS; Voice Dem Awd; Amer Lgn; HS Exchng Prog China 86.

NELSON, HAIKEEM; Sister Clara Muhammad HS; Philadelphia, PA; (3); Computer Clb; Science Clb; Nwsp Stf; Prfct Atten Awd; AFNA Schlr 85-87; Bus.

NELSON, JACQUELINE; Northern Cambria HS; Nicktown, PA; (3); 37/152; Drama Clb; Ski Clb; Chorus; JV Cheerleading; High Hon Roll; Hon Roll; Nrsng.

NELSON, KIMBERLY; Sun Valley HS; Aston, PA; (3); 62/270; Nwsp Stf; Yrbk Stf; Score Keeper; Stat Wrstlng; Hon Roll; West-Chester; Early Chldhd Ed.

NELSON, LISA; Northern Cambria HS; Barnesboro, PA; (3); 34/152; Girl Scts; High Hon Roll; Hon Roll; Girl Scout Slvr Ldrshp Awd 86; Altoona Schl Nursing; Nrsng.

NELSON, LUKE; Sharon HS; Hermitage, PA; (3); 30/179; Art Clb; Church Yth Grp; French Clb; Letterman Clb; Varsity Clb; Crs Cntry; Trk; Wrstlng; Hon Roll.

NELSON, MICHAEL; Chichester SR HS; Marcus Hook, PA; (3); 52/297; JV Bsbl; Hon Roll; Aero Clb PA Flyng Schlrshp 87; Crusdrs Sprtsmnshp Awd 85; Embry-Riddle; Profssnl Aviation.

NELSON, MICHAEL G; B Reed Henderson SR HS; West Chester, PA; (3); 54/366; French Clb; Intnl Clb; JCL; SADD; Yrbk Stf; French Hon Soc; Hon Roll; NHS; Boy Scts; Debate Tm; Slvr Cum Laude On Natl Lat Exam 87-88.

NELSON, MIKE; Annville-Cleona HS; Cleona, PA; (4); Pres Church Yth Grp; Varsity Clb; Band; Concert Band; Mrchg Band; Orch; School Musical; JV Bsbl; Var Capt Ftbl; JV Trk; Rotry Boy Mnth 87; Stu Govt Maintence Supervsr 87; Williamsport Area CC; Const.

NELSON, PENNY; High Point Baptist Acad; Elverson, PA; (4); 6/34; Church Yth Grp; Chorus; Yrbk Stf; Var L Cheerleading; High Hon Roll; Hon Roll; Intl Frgn Lang Awd 85; Ntl Hnr Roll 86; Comp Sci.

NELSON, SANDY; Calvary Baptist Christian Acad; Meadville, PA; (4); 1/2; Church Yth Grp; Chorus; School Play; Capt L Cheerleading; L JV Vllybl; NHS; Val; Band; School Musical; Yrbk Stf; 1st Pl In ST Engl Comp 85-87; MVP Vllybl 85; 1st Pl Rgnl Engl & Essy Comp 84-87; U Of Pittsburgh; Phy Thrpy.

NELSON, SCOT; Hatboro-Horsham HS; Hatboro, PA; (3); 12/295; Y-Teens; Socr; Wrstlng; Arch.

NELSON, SCOTT P; Franklin Regional SR HS; Murrysville, PA; (3); Church Yth Grp; Ski Clb; Pres Spanish Clb; Chorus; Concert Band; Jazz Band; Mrchg Band; School Play; High Hon Roll; NHS; Acctng.

NELSON, SUE; South Western HS; Hanover, PA; (3); Band; Concert Band; Mrchg Band; School Musical; Symp Band; Hon Roll; NHS; Acctng.

NELSON, TODD; Penn Trafford HS; Irwin, PA; (2); Boy Scts; Church Yth Grp; Band; Concert Band; Jazz Band; Mrchg Band; Pep Band; School Musical; High Hon Roll; Westmoreland Yth Symph Orch 86-87; Cnty Band 85-86; IN U Of PA Hnrs Band 86.

NELSON, TRACI; Dover Area HS; Dillsburg, PA; (4); 37/235; Cmnty Wkr; Spanish Clb; Teachers Aide; Color Guard; Mrchg Band; Nwsp Rptr; Nwsp Stf; High Hon Roll; Hon Roll; Trvl.

NEMEC, REBECCA; Vough SR HS; Smithton, PA; (3); Computer Clb; Pep Clb; Ski Clb; Spanish Clb; Chorus; Yrbk Stf; Im Golf; Im Powder Puff Ftbl; High Hon Roll; NHS.

NEMETH, PHYLANN; Towanda HS; Wysox, PA; (3); 26/140; Am Leg Aux Girls St; Camera Clb; Cmnty Wkr; Pres FBLA; SADD; High Hon Roll; NHS; Lgl Secr.

NENTWIG, AMY; Donegal HS; Mount Joy, PA; (2); Drama Clb; Pep Clb; Rep Stu Cncl; Hon Roll; Millersville U; Child Pshyclgy.

NENTWIG, MICHAEL; Donegal HS; Mt Joy, PA; (3); JV Bsbl; Hon Roll; Arch Engr.

NEPOMUCENO, RANDY RAY; Saint Josephs Prep Schl; Jenkintown, PA; (4); 40/240; Rep Sr Cls; JV Wrstlng; High Hon Roll; NHS; Ntl Merit Ltr; Pres Schlr; Camera Clb; French Clb; Hosp Aide; Intnl Clb; PA Hghr Educ Asst Agency Cert Merit 86-87; 1st Pl City Novice Tourn Wrstlng 84-85; Edtr-Chf Yrbk 86; U Of PA; Pre-Med.

NERAL, MELISSA; Penn Trafford HS; Irwin, PA; (2); Sec Drama Clb; Chorus; Church Choir; School Musical; School Play; Variety Show; High Hon Roll; Sweet 16 Sngng & Dncng Grp 86-87; Hnrs Chr Seton Hill Coll 86-87; Slct Chr 86-87; Cmmnctns.

NERI, CYNTHIA; North Star HS; Boswell, PA; (2); Trs Church Yth Grp; FCA; VP Trs 4-H; Band; Concert Band; Mrchg Band; Yrbk Phtg; Yrbk Stf; Cit Awd; 4-H Awd.

NERI, JOHN; Neshaminy Longhorne HS; Feasterville, PA; (3); 136/788; FCA; Var L Bsbl; Var L Bsktbl; Var L Ftbl; Wt Lftg; High Hon Roll; Hon Roll; Ski Clb; JV Socr; Prfct Atten Awd; Sbrbn 1 All Leag 1st Tm-Bsbl 87; 3-D Awd-Ftbll 87; Tm Ldng Screr-Bsktbl 87; Bus.

NERI, JOHN; North Star HS; Jennerstown, PA; (3); #20 In Class; Aud/Vis; Chess Clb; FCA; Chorus; Concert Band; Jazz Band; Mrchg Band; Rep Stu Cncl; Golf; Hon Roll; Geolgy.

NERO, ALLYSON; New Castle HS; New Castle, PA; (2); SADD; Chorus; School Musical; Variety Show.

NERO, PAMELA; New Castle SR HS; New Castle, PA; (4); 14/232; Exploring; Chorus; Drill Tm; Hon Roll; Jr NHS; NHS; Lab Tech.

NESBELLA, JENNIFER; Big Spring HS; Carlisle, PA; (3); 1/257; Quiz Bowl; Band; Chorus; Mrchg Band; School Musical; School Play; Stu Cncl; Swmmng; Sec NHS; Ntl Merit Ltr; Intl Bus.

NESBIT, BRENDA; Punxsutawney SR HS; Marchand, PA; (2); Church Yth Grp; FFA; SADD; 4-H; Band; Concert Band; Jazz Band; Mrchg Band; Pep Band; IUP Indiana PA.

NESBITT, JILL; Archbishop Carroll HS; King Of Prussia, PA; (3); 124/388; Church Yth Grp; Service Clb; SADD; Hon Roll.

NESBITT, JULIA; Marple Newtown HS; Broomall, PA; (4); 9/330; GAA; Var VP Sftbl; Var VP Vllybl; Bausch & Lomb Sci Awd; Cit Awd; Hon Roll; NHS; Opt Clb Awd; Church Yth Grp; Band; Math, Sci & Future Tchr Awds 87; Amer Chem Scty Awd 85; MVP Sftbl 85 & 87; Slippery Rock U; Phys Educ Tchr.

NESBITT, SUSAN; Ambridge Area HS; Ambridge, PA; (3); Band; Concert Band; Mrchg Band; Symp Band; CC Beaver County; Engl.

NESS, ANISSA; Christian Schl Of York; Dallastown, PA; (2); Varsity Clb; Var JV Bsktbl; Var Score Keeper; Var L Sftbl; Hon Roll; Shippensburg; Sprts Med.

NESS, CAROL; Lancaster Mennonite HS; Lancaster, PA; (4); Church Yth Grp; Drama Clb; Acpl Chr; Band; Chorus; Church Choir; Concert Band; Orch; School Play; Stage Crew; Dist 7 Band 85-86; Natl Phy Fit Awd 83-86; Slvr Cert In Fine Arts Fest 85-86.

NESSELROAD, TERESA; Claysburg-Kimmel HS; Claysburg, PA; (1); 1/17; Y-Teens; High Hon Roll; Lawyr.

NESTER, CHRISTINE; Spring-Ford SR HS; Royersford, PA; (3); 81/256; Spanish Clb; SADD; Chorus; Church Choir; Stage Crew; Yrbk Stf; Rep Frsh Cls; Rep Soph Cls; Hon Roll; Outstndng Wrtr; Nrsng.

NESTER, JOSEPH; Hazleton SR HS; Audanried, PA; (2); French Clb; Yrbk Stf; Hon Roll.

NESTERUK, THOMAS; Valley HS; New Kensington, PA; (3); French Clb; FBLA; Leo Clb; Ski Clb; VP Jr Cls; Pres Sr Cls; Wt Lftg; French Hon Soc; High Hon Roll; NHS; Acctng.

NESTOR, ADAM; Blacklick Valley JR-SR HS; Nanty Glo, PA; (3); Ski Clb; Speech Tm; Varsity Clb; Band; Concert Band; Mrchg Band; Trk; Hon Roll; NHS; Pres Schlr; Acadc Al-Amer 86; VISTO.

NESTOR, JULIE; Richland HS; Mars, PA; (3); 17/151; Cmnty Wkr; Debate Tm; Chorus; Color Guard; School Musical; School Play; Yrbk Stf; Rep Stu Cncl; High Hon Roll; NHS; Mst Imprvd Sftbl Plyr 86; Marchng Band Lttr 87; Pre Law.

NETT, MICHELLE; Gettysburg SR HS; Gettysburg, PA; (2); Chorus; Swing Chorus; Hon Roll; Schlstc Art Awd 86; USAF; Aviator.

NETTERBLADE, JEANNINE; West Branch Area JR-SR HS; Lanse, PA; (3); 10/130; Science Clb; Trs Spanish Clb; Band; Hon Roll; NHS; PA ST U; Math.

NETTLES JR, JAMES A; Minersville Area HS; Pottsville, PA; (4); 15/114; Ski Clb; Spanish Clb; Stage Crew; Yrbk Stf; Var L Bsbl; Var L Bsktbl; Im Fld Hcky; Ftbl; Im Lcrss; Im Socr; Acad Exc In Spnsh; Blmsbrg U; Engrng.

NEUER, DARRIN; Hempfield HS; Mountville, PA; (3).

NEUGEBAUER, JOHN; North Catholic HS; Pittsburgh, PA; (2); 99/232; Art Clb; German Clb; Hon Roll; Bus.

NEUHARD, TODD; Milton HS; Milton, PA; (3); 23/242; Trs Varsity Clb; Trs Frsh Cls; Ftbl; Wrstlng; Hon Roll; Larry Barlett Mem Awd 84; Secndry Educ.

NEUIN, LISA MARIE; Schuykill Haven HS; Schuylkill Haven, PA; (4); 25/90; Am Leg Aux Girls St; Library Aide; SADD; Teachers Aide; Band; Chorus; School Musical; School Play; Stage Crew; Hon Roll; Hnr Grd 86; Cnty Chrs 84 & 87; Twin Valley Bnd 87; Kuztown; Ed.

NEULIGHT, HEATHER; Council Park HS; Churchville, PA; (2); Church Yth Grp; Hon Roll.

NEUMAN, JENNIFER; Pennsbury HS; Levittown, PA; (2); Am Leg Aux Girls St; 4-H; GAA; Teachers Aide; Band; Rep Frsh Cls; JV Bsktbl; JV Fld Hcky; Im Sftbl; Im Vllybl; Stu Of Yr 85-86; Amer Lgn Awd 86-87; Zoology.

NEUMANN, DANA; Beaver Falls HS; Beaver Falls, PA; (1); 6/222; Computer Clb; Dance Clb; Spanish Clb; Drill Tm; Flag Corp; Pom Pon; High Hon Roll; Hon Roll; Boston U; Comp Sci.

NEUMANN, JENNIFER; Mt Union Area HS; Mt Union, PA; (3); 30/161; Church Yth Grp; Drama Clb; FBLA; GAA; Spanish Clb; SADD; Band; Concert Band; Flag Corp; Mrchg Band; FBLA Regn 14 Comptn Ust Pl Impromptu Spkng 87; Psych.

NEUMANN, SERINA; Northern Lehigh HS; Slatington, PA; (3); 8/166; Boys Clb Am; Debate Tm; Exploring; Ski Clb; Chorus; Color Guard; Trk; High Hon Roll; Mrchg Band; Pres Acdmc Ftnss Awd 85; Cnty Chorus 87; Pre Med.

NEUMYER, TODD M; Central Dauphin E HS; Harrisburg, PA; (4); 29/274; Boy Scts; Cmnty Wkr; Exploring; Letterman Clb; Red Cross Aide; SADD; Teachers Aide; Varsity Clb; Acpl Chr; Chorus; Capt Wrstlng Tm 85-87; Mst Outstndng Male Athl Awd 86-87; Rotary Clb Stu Mnth 86; Eagle Sct 83; PA ST U; Med.

NEUREUTER, JEANNE; Lackawanna Trail HS; Factoryville, PA; (2); Art Clb; Ski Clb; JV Fld Hcky; Var L Sftbl; Hon Roll; NHS; Nursng.

NEUREUTER, PAUL; Lackawanna Trail HS; Factoryville, PA; (3); Boy Scts; Ski Clb; French Hon Soc; High Hon Roll; Hon Roll; NHS; Engr.

NEUSTADTER, AMY; Hempfield HS; Lancaster, PA; (3); 55/393; Church Yth Grp; Drama Clb; School Play; Rep Stu Cncl; Capt Twrlr; High Hon Roll; NHS; Vrsty Ltr-Twrlng 87; Fshn Mrchndsng.

NEVEL, MICHAEL; Berwick Area SR HS; Berwick, PA; (4); Spanish Clb; Yrbk Stf; Off Stu Cncl; Hon Roll; NHS; Prfct Atten Awd; 14th Street Alumni Awd 87; Bloomsburg U; Bus Admin.

NEVILLE, FRANCESCA; Trinity HS; Camp Hill, PA; (2); 24/139; French Clb; GAA; Pep Clb; Thesps; Yrbk Stf; Trk; Hon Roll; NEDT Awd; 1st Pl Fstvl Of The Arts For Drmtc Prsntn 87; Actress.

NEVIUS, GREGORY; Danville SR HS; Danville, PA; (2); Drama Clb; Latin Clb; Speech Tm; Thesps; School Play; Nwsp Stf; High Hon Roll; Lion Awd; Im Bsbl; Im Bsktbl; Various Forensics Tournaments 86-87; Bloomsburg U; Advertising Art.

NEVRINCEAN, BETH; Oxford Area HS; Oxford, PA; (3); Hosp Aide; SADD; Chorus; Pep Band; Mrchg Band; Stage Crew; Ed Nwsp Phtg; Yrbk Phtg; Brdcstr Edtrs Awd 87; RI Schl Of Phtgrphy; Phtgrphr.

NEWBALL, ALBERT; Blue Mt Acad; East Patchogue, NY; (4); Church Yth Grp; Scholastic Bowl; Church Choir; Stage Crew; Trs Jr Cls; Off Stu Cncl; Bsktbl; Sftbl; Vllybl; High Hon Roll; Mens Clb Pres 86-87; Walla Walla Coll; Engnrng.

NEWBALL, NANCY; Blue Mountain Acad; East Patchogue, NY; (3); Church Yth Grp; Chorus; Church Choir; Nwsp Rptr; Soph Cls; VP Jr Cls; High Hon Roll; Hon Roll; Prfct Atten Awd; Yth Understndg Intl Exchg Cert Merit 86.

NEWCAMP, JAMES; Mercy Hurst Prep; Erie, PA; (2); Chorus; Pep Band; School Musical; Im Bowling; JV Crs Cntry; Hon Roll; Therese Burns Acad Scholar 85-86.

NEWCASTER, JAYANNE; Butler SR HS; Butler, PA; (4); Hosp Aide; VP Spanish Clb; SADD; Variety Show; Rep Stu Cncl; Pom Pon; Jr NHS; NHS; Pres Acad Fit Awd 87; PA ST U.

NEWCOMB, KRIS; Bethel Christian HS; Erie, PA; (3); 1/16; Church Yth Grp; Cmnty Wkr; FCA; Chorus; Variety Show; Var Capt Bsktbl; Var Sftbl; Var Capt Vllybl; High Hon Roll; Prfct Atten Awd; Acad Achvmnt Awd 86; ST Fnlst Miss Natl Tngr Pgnt 86; Med.

NEWCOME, JULIE; Brookville Area HS; Brookville, PA; (3); 10/175; Drama Clb; 4-H; French Clb; Chorus; Orch; School Musical; Rep Soph Cls; Stu Cncl; Vllybl; NHS; Western MI U; PR.

NEWCOMER, BRAD; Red Lion Area SR HS; Red Lion, PA; (3); 100/450; Church Yth Grp; French Clb; SADD; Wt Lftg; Hon Roll.

NEWCOMER, BRYAN; Oil City Area SR HS; Oil City, PA; (3); German Clb; Acpl Chr; Chorus; Church Choir; Rep Stu Cncl; Hon Roll; Engr.

NEWCOMER, EMILY; Pennsbury HS; Yardley, PA; (2); Church Yth Grp; Hosp Aide; Concert Band; Rep Stu Cncl; Var Fld Hcky; Var Gym; Var Sftbl; High Hon Roll; Fshn Merch.

NEWELL, KIM; St Marys Area HS; Saint Marys, PA; (4); 9/300; Church Yth Grp; SADD; Band; Church Choir; Drm & Bgl; Jazz Band; Mrchg Band; Stat Trk; Hon Roll; NHS; Semper Fidelis Awd Music 87; U MI; Music Prfrmnc.

NEWELL, MIKE; West Allegheny HS; Jacksonville, FL; (2); 20/270; FCA; Pep Clb; Spanish Clb; Varsity Clb; Acpl Chr; Chorus; Stu Cncl; Var Bsbl; Var Bsktbl; Var Ftbl.

NEWELL, SHELLEY; John S Fine HS; Nanticoke, PA; (2); 36/250; Church Yth Grp; Key Clb; Chorus; Church Choir; Var JV Cheerleading; Im Powder Puff Ftbl; L Swmmng; High Hon Roll; NHS; Pediatrician.

NEWHAMS, COLLEEN; Sacred Heart HS; Pittsburgh, PA; (3); Church Yth Grp; Library Aide; Chorus; Church Choir; School Musical; Im Bowling; Var Trk; Im Vllybl; High Hon Roll; Hon Roll; MA Inst Of Tech; Astrntcl Engr.

NEWHARD, CATHY; Nazareth Area SR HS; Nazareth, PA; (3); 14/265; Exploring; Girl Scts; VICA; High Hon Roll; Hon Roll; Dsl Mech.

NEWHART, BRIAN; Millville HS; Bloomsburg, PA; (3); Boy Scts; Pres Church Yth Grp; Drama Clb; Pres Exploring; FBLA; School Musical; School Play; God Cntry Awd; Hon Roll; Camera Clb; AF; Air Trfc Cntrl.

NEWHART, MARCY; Elk Lake HS; Meshoppen, PA; (2); SADD; Swmmng; French Clb; Band; Mrchg Band; Yrbk Stf; Cheerleading; Score Keeper; Vllybl; Natl Fraternity Of Stu Musicians 84-86; Temple U; Music Ed.

NEWHART, RAYMOND; Elk Lake HS; Montrose, PA; (2); 4-H; French Clb; Ski Clb; SADD; Nwsp Stf; Yrbk Sprt Ed; JV Var Bsbl; Bsktbl; Wt Lftg; Hon Roll.

NEWLIN, DONNA; Homer Center JR SR HS; Coral, PA; (3); 13/120; French Clb; FNA; SADD; Chorus; Capt Color Guard; High Hon Roll; Hon Roll; NHS; Prfct Atten Awd; Nrsng.

NEWMAN, AMY; Pennsbury HS; Yardley, PA; (4); 39/770; Hosp Aide; Spanish Clb; Chorus; Tennis; Hon Roll; NHS; Rep Stu Cncl; Pres Acad Ftns Awd 87; PA ST; Acctng.

NEWMAN, ANDREW; The Haverford Schl; Bryn Mawr, PA; (2); 10/83; Service Clb; Church Choir; Nwsp Sprt Ed; JV Bsbl; JV Bsktbl; Capt Var Socr; Wt Lftg; High Hon Roll; Hon Roll; Vrsty Ltr 86; Orthopdc Srgn.

NEWMAN, JAMIE; Littlestown HS; Littlestown, PA; (3); Varsity Clb; Band; Chorus; Church Choir; Concert Band; Mrchg Band; Swing Chorus; Yrbk Stf; Fld Hcky; Hon Roll; PA ST U; Sprts Med.

NEWMAN, MICHAEL; W Greene HS; Rogersville, PA; (4); 5/108; French Clb; NHS; Embry Riddle Aero U; Aero Engr.

NEWMAN, TASHA A; Council Rock HS; Newtown, PA; (4); Intnl Clb; Key Clb; Office Aide; Red Cross Aide; Stage Crew; Yrbk Stf; Fld Hcky; Sftbl; Swmmng; Kiwanis Awd; Buck Co CC Trenton; Spch Path.

NEWMAN, TODD; Chambersburg Area SR HS; Chambersburg, PA; (2); Shippensburg U; Geography.

NEWMYER, CHRISTOPHER; Lower Dauphin HS; Hummelstown, PA; (1); JV Bsbl; JV Bsktbl; Engrng.

NEWRUCK, JEAN; Galeton Area HS; Gaines, PA; (3); Church Yth Grp; Chorus; Color Guard; Yrbk Stf; Rep Stu Cncl; Stat Bsktbl; Tennis; High Hon Roll; NHS; Acad Ftnss Awd; Intr Dsgn.

NEWTON, ANN; Greenwood HS; Liverpool, PA; (3); 10/64; Church Yth Grp; VP FBLA; GAA; Varsity Clb; Chorus; Bsktbl; Fld Hcky; Sftbl; Hon Roll; NHS; Sec.

NEWTON, LONA; Bishop Guilfoyle HS; Altoona, PA; (3); Church Yth Grp; Chorus; Off Jr Cls; Hon Roll; Penn ST; Bus Adm.

NEWTON, SCOTT; Marian HS; Nesquehoning, PA; (3); 30/104; Var L Bsbl; Var JV Ftbl; Wt Lftg; Hon Roll; Babe Ruth Bsbl Lg RBI Trophy All Star Select 85-86; Pitching Trophy & Golden Glove Awd Shortstop 86.

NEY, YVETTE; Columbia Montour Area Vo Tech Schl; Berwick, PA; (3); SADD; Nwsp Ed-Chief; High Hon Roll; Hon Roll; Jr NHS; NHS; Prfct Atten Awd; French Awd 84-85; Graphic Arts.

NEYE, JENNIFER; Tri-Valley HS; Klingerstown, PA; (2); 27/85; Church Yth Grp; Drama Clb; German Clb; Ski Clb; Band; Chorus; Concert Band; Mrchg Band; School Musical; Continental Math Lge 86.

NEYER, KYLE; Daniel Boone HS; Douglassville, PA; (2); 37/161; Church Yth Grp; German Clb; Intnl Clb; Model UN; Var Socr; Var JV Trk; JV Wrstlng; Temple U; Phys Thrpst.

NEYHARD, LAUREL; Bloomsburg SR HS; Bloomsburg, PA; (4); 50/135; Drama Clb; Pep Clb; Thesps; Varsity Clb; Acpl Chr; Church Choir; School Musical; School Play; Stage Crew; Variety Show; Most Outstndg Supprtng Actress 85; Penn ST U; Psych.

NEZNESKI, PATRICE; Portage Area HS; Portage, PA; (4); Ski Clb; Thesps; Band; Chorus; Drm Mjr(t); School Musical; Capt Trk; Capt Twrlr; Var Im Vllybl; Pres NHS; Cnty Dist Rgnl Chorus & Band 86-87; Dusquene; Phrmcy.

NG, MINDY O M; North Allegheny SR HS; Pittsburgh, PA; (3); Hon Roll.

NG, VICTOR; The Hill Schl; Pottstown, PA; (4); 3/133; Camera Clb; German Clb; Nwsp Phtg; Yrbk Phtg; Lit Mag; Badmtn; Im Tennis; Trk; High Hon Roll; U Of PA; Med.

NGUYEN, ANH; York Catholic HS; York, PA; (2); 14/150; Boys Clb Am; Church Yth Grp; Var Trk; Hon Roll; Opt Clb Awd; U IL; Med.

NGUYEN, ANH-THU; United HS; Robinson, PA; (3); 7/147; Sec Camera Clb; Church Yth Grp; Mu Alpha Theta; Ski Clb; Chorus; Church Choir; Yrbk Stf; Sec Jr Cls; Var Cheerleading; Gov Hon Prg Awd; Summer Happenings 86; U Of Pittsburgh; Pre-Med.

NGUYEN, CHINH; Lancaster Country Day HS; Lancaster, PA; (2); Boys Clb Am; Var Bsktbl; Var Socr; Var Tennis; Coach Awds-Tnns, Bsktbl 86-87.

NGUYEN, CUONG; Roman Catholic HS; Philadelphia, PA; (3); 21/121; Intnl Clb; Band; Im Bsktbl; Prfct Atten Awd; 2nd Pl NAACP 87; Temple U; Bus.

NGUYEN, CUONG; Trinity HS; Mechanicsburg, PA; (2); 26/139; Ed Lit Mag; Ftbl; Trk; NEDT Awd; Gld Key & Blue Rbbn Ptriot Nws Schltc Art Awd 87; Arch.

NGUYEN, DANH; Harrisburg High-John Marric; Harrisburg, PA; (3); 15/274; Chess Clb; Math Clb; Science Clb; Yrbk Ed-Chief; Swmmng; Vllybl; High Hon Roll; Hon Roll; NHS; Ntl Merit Schol; Penn St; Architecture.

NGUYEN, DIEM SUONG; Hempfield HS; Landisville, PA; (3); 1/550; Computer Clb; Drama Clb; Science Clb; Nwsp Stf; Im Fld Hcky; French Hon Soc; High Hon Roll; Hon Roll; Jr NHS; NHS; Peace Essy Cntst-Hnrbl Mntn 85-86; Sci Fair-1st Envrnmntl Sci 85 & 2nd Bio 86; Med.

NGUYEN, DUNG; Mechanicsburg Area SR HS; Mechanicsburg, PA; (2); Church Yth Grp; Cmnty Wkr; Computer Clb; Library Aide; Church Choir; Hon Roll; Messiah Coll; Lab Tech.

NGUYEN, HA; St Josephs Prep; Philadelphia, PA; (4); Cmnty Wkr; Intnl Clb; Varsity Clb; Band; Concert Band; Var Mgr(s); Var Socr; Prfct Atten Awd; Phila Coll Phrm & Sci; Phrmcy.

NGUYEN, HIEU; Marple Newtown SR HS; Broomall, PA; (4); 19/330; Pres Computer Clb; Trs Math Clb; Co-Capt Math Tm; Trs Science Clb; Stage Crew; Socr; Hon Roll; Prfct Atten Awd; Rotary Awd; Amer HS Math Exam Hnr Roll 86; VA Tech; Elec Engr.

NGUYEN, HIEU; York Catholic HS; York, PA; (3); Church Yth Grp; Exploring; German Clb; JV Ftbl; Im Socr; PA ST York; Pharmacy.

NGUYEN, KIM M H; Harrisburg HS; Harrisburg, PA; (3); 16/274; Science Clb; Jr Cls; Tennis; Hon Roll; NHS; PA ST U; Acctg.

NGUYEN, LINH; Central Dauphin HS; Harrisburg, PA; (4); Chorus; Color Guard; Crs Cntry; Ftbl; Cit Awd; High Hon Roll; Jr NHS; NHS; Pres Schlr; Math Awd 83; Stu Mnth Awd 86; Maryann Corbett Mem Commencemnt Awd 87; Franklin & Marshall; Pre-Med.

NGUYEN, LOAN; Bishop Mc Devitt HS; Harrisburg, PA; (3); Awds Math, Comp 86-87; PA ST U; Comp Sci.

NGUYEN, MAC-PHUONG; United HS; Robinson, PA; (4); 5/155; Aud/Vis; Camera Clb; Ski Clb; Mgr Trk; Gov Hon Prg Awd; Hon Roll; Trs NHS; Prfct Atten Awd; Summer Happenings 86; PA ST Park; Bio.

NGUYEN, MINH T; West York HS; York, PA; (4); VP Dance Clb; Drama Clb; Sec French Clb; Hosp Aide; Library Aide; Chorus; School Play; Ed Yrbk Stf; Hon Roll; Prfct Atten Awd; Walter C & Grace M & Russell H Howe Schlrshp 87; York Hosp Recog Vlntr Awd 87; Penn ST U; Bio-Chem.

NGUYEN, PHAN ANH; Bishop Hoban HS; Wilkes-Barre, PA; (2); 1/229; French Clb; Math Clb; Mu Alpha Theta; High Hon Roll; Mu Alpha Theta Awd; NEDT Awd; Natl Frnch Cntst Awd 86-87; MAO Rsrch Awd 87; Penn ST U; Med.

NGUYEN, PHONG Q; Msgr Bonner HS; Upper Darby, PA; (3); Cmnty Wkr; Computer Clb; Latin Clb; Library Aide; Yrbk Stf; Stat Bsktbl; Im Ftbl; Var Socr; Hon Roll; NHS; U Of PA; Electcl Engnrng.

NGUYEN, PHUONG; West York SR HS; York, PA; (4); 7/197; Drama Clb; French Clb; Hosp Aide; Library Aide; Chorus; School Play; Ed Yrbk Stf; High Hon Roll; NHS; Opt Clb Awd; Srptmst Intl Yth Ctznshp Awd 87; Yrk Hsptl Vlntr Rcgntn Awd 87; Elzbth Yng Mem Schlrhsp 87; Penn ST U; Phrmcy.

NGUYEN, TAM; W Catholic Boys HS; Philadelphia, PA; (3); 3/247; Math Tm; Cmnty Wkr; German Clb; Math Clb; Science Clb; Service Clb; Nwsp Stf; Yrbk Stf; Socr; Tennis; Chem Awd 87; Bio Awd 86; Diocesan Schlr Prgm 87; U Of Penn; Comp-Sci.

NGUYEN, TRUNG; Chambersburg SR HS; Chambersburg, PA; (2); Chess Clb; Tennis; Hon Roll; Phy Ftns Awd 85-86; Penn ST; Comp Engr.

NGUYEN, XUANTHAO; Girls HS; Philadelphia, PA; (3); Library Aide; Hon Roll; Temple; Phar.

NICE, KAREN LYNN; Little Flower Catholic HS For Girls; Philadelphia, PA; (3); 60/325; Cmnty Wkr; Hosp Aide; Office Aide; Service Clb; Nwsp Bus Mgr; Nwsp Rptr; Var Mgr(s); Var Trk; Hon Roll; NHS; Mdcl Tchnlgy.

NICELY, ELISA; Carlisle HS; Carlisle, PA; (3); Ski Clb; Band; Drm & Bgl; Mrchg Band; Stage Crew; Trk; Hon Roll; PJAS Sci Fair 2nd Pl; Art Hnr Soc; Yth & Government Rep.

NICEWONGER, ROBERT; Altoona Area HS; Altoona, PA; (3); Computer Clb; Math Clb; Math Tm; Varsity Clb; Band; Jazz Band; Nwsp Ed-Chief; Nwsp Rptr; Var Bsktbl; High Hon Roll; Engrg.

NICHOLAS, CRYSTAL; Northampton SR HS; Walnutport, PA; (2); High Hon Roll; Hon Roll; Kutztown U; Cmmrcl Artist.

NICHOLAS, JAN THOMAS; Milton HS; Milton, PA; (3); 20/229; Computer Clb; VP Key Clb; Band; Chorus; JV Var Trk; Concert Band; Drm & Bgl; Mrchg Band; School Musical; Mgr(s); Rgnl St Orchestra Fest 87; Rgnl St Band Fest 87; Chem Engrng.

NICHOLAS, ORISHA; Chester HS; Chester, PA; (4); #1 In Class; Art Clb; Science Clb; Spanish Clb; Chorus; Church Choir; Nwsp Ed-Chief; Nwsp Stf; Cit Awd; Elks Awd; NHS; NAACP Acad Achvmnt Awd 86; Hghst Avg Spnsh II & III Awds 84-86; People Against Drugs & Alchol 86; Elec Engrng.

NICHOLAS, SPERO; North Hills HS; Pittsburgh, PA; (3); 2/493; Exploring; Math Tm; Quiz Bowl; Scholastic Bowl; Ski Clb; L Socr; High Hon Roll; NHS; Sci.

NICHOLAS, SUSAN; Archbishop Wood HS For Girls; Warrington, PA; (3); 53/239; Office Aide; Capt Color Guard; Drill Tm; Flag Corp; L Mrchg Band; Stage Crew; Twrlr; Hon Roll; HS Schlrshp 84; 3rd Pl Sci Fair 85; Acctng.

NICHOLLS, HEATHER; Solanco HS; Quarryville, PA; (3); 59/273; Church Yth Grp; Drama Clb; Pep Clb; Chorus; Church Choir; School Musical; School Play; Var Cheerleading; Hon Roll; Jr NHS; Comm.

NICHOLS, BEN; Beaver Area HS; Beaver, PA; (2); 28/256; Church Yth Grp; JCL; Latin Clb; Bsbl; Bsktbl; Ftbl; Cit Awd; High Hon Roll.

NICHOLS, DEAN; Fox Chapel SR HS; Pittsbg, PA; (4); Church Yth Grp; Band; Concert Band; L Mrchg Band; Stage Crew; Symp Band; High Hon Roll; NHS; Pres Schlr; Hnrs Band 86-87; U Of Pittsburgh; Elec Engr.

NICHOLS, JILL; Philadelphia HS For Girls; Philadelphia, PA; (3); 82/405; Church Yth Grp; Service Clb; Teachers Aide; Chorus; Church Choir; Rep Jr Cls; Rep Stu Cncl; Hon Roll; Ntl Merit Ltr; Howard U; Engrng.

NICHOLS, JOHN GRAYSON; Slippery Rock Area HS; Slippery Rock, PA; (4); 1/172; Rep Am Leg Boys St; Pres Latin Clb; VP Thesps; School Play; Nwsp Ed-Chief; Pres Schlr; Sal; Rep Stu Cncl; Robert C Byrd Hnrs Schlrshp 87; U Of Richmond Schlr Awd 87; Elks Acad Schlr Of Yr 87; U Richmond.

NICHOLS, KIMBERLY; Monessen JR SR HS; Monessen, PA; (3); Church Yth Grp; Band; Chorus; Mrchg Band; Swing Chorus; Twrlr; Hon Roll; Sawyer Schl Pittsbrgh; Exec Sec.

NICHOLS, MICHAEL; Wm Allen HS; Allentown, PA; (3); Boy Scts; Trs Church Yth Grp; Exploring; German Clb; SADD; Hon Roll; NHS; Intl Bus.

NICHOLS, MIKE; Marple Newtown HS; Newtown Sq, PA; (4); Intnl Clb; Variety Show; Stu Cncl; Crs Cntry; Ftbl; Trk; Wt Lftg; High Hon Roll; Hon Roll; NHS; Capt Indr, Outdr Trck 86-87; Varty Show MC 87; Pres Acadmc Ftnss Awd 87; Lehigh U; Fin.

NICHOLS, PATRICIA; Sayre HS; Sayre, PA; (3); FHA; Hosp Aide; Hon Roll; Mst Likely To Succeed Food Indstry 86-87; Best Atten 86-87.

NICHOLS, PHILIP; Seneca Valley HS; Mars, PA; (3); 13/333; Math Tm; Scholastic Bowl; High Hon Roll; Hon Roll; Ntl Merit Ltr; ST Trnmt 1st Pl Mr Pres Tm, 1st Pl Propaganda Tm Coords Awd 86-87; Natl Trnmt 1st Pl Mrs Pres Tm; Grove City Coll; Pre-Law.

NICHOLS, SHARON; Williamsport Area HS; Williamsport, PA; (4); Key Clb; Chorus; Church Choir; School Musical; Swing Chorus; Variety Show; Rep Sr Cls; Var Capt Cheerleading; Var L Sftbl; High Hon Roll; Hnr Roll; Bucknell; Arts.

NICHOLS, SHARON L; Calvary Baptist Schls; Hatfield, PA; (4); Band; Chorus; Church Choir; Yrbk Stf; Rep Soph Cls; Ntl Merit SF; Natl Ldrshp & Svc Awd 86; Acad All-Amer 85; Pre-Med.

NICHOLS, STEPHEN D; Maplewood HS; Titusville, PA; (4); 2/125; French Clb; Varsity Clb; VP Stu Cncl; Var Capt Bsbl; Var L Ftbl; Vllybl; Wt Lftg; Var Wrstlng; NHS; Sal; PA ST U; Math.

NICHOLS, THOMAS ROSS; Greenville SR HS; Greenville, PA; (4); 1/124; JCL; VP Latin Clb; Chorus; French Clb; Var L Tennis; NHS; Ntl Merit Schol; Val; Gibson Awd 87; Amer Chem Soc Awd 85-86; Carnegie Mellon U; Chem.

NICHOLSON, ANGELA; Blairsville SR HS; Blairsville, PA; (1); Chess Clb; Pres 4-H; French Clb; Ski Clb; Chorus; Concert Band; Mrchg Band; High Hon Roll; Hon Roll; Thrpst.

NICHOLSON, BRIAN; Carmichaels Area HS; Carmichaels, PA; (4); 49/101; Spanish Clb; SADD.

NICHOLSON, CHRISTY; Moon SR HS; Corapolis, PA; (3); 88/296; Church Yth Grp; French Clb; Hosp Aide; Key Clb; Pep Clb; Chorus; Mgr(s); Score Keeper; Timer; Pre Law.

NICHOLSON, GREGG; Wyoming Area HS; Exeter, PA; (3); French Clb; Var Trk.

NICHOLSON, JEFFREY; Meadville Area SR HS; Meadville, PA; (3); Church Yth Grp; French Clb; JV Var Socr; Trk; Hon Roll; JV Ltr Socr 84; Vrsty Ltr Socr 86.

NICHOLSON, KIMBERLY; Downingtown SR HS; Exton, PA; (3); Spanish Clb; SADD; Acpl Chr; Band; Chorus; Church Choir; Concert Band; Flag Corp; Madrigals; Mrchg Band; Outstndng Voclst 85.

NICHOLSON, MARK; Somerset Area HS; Somerset, PA; (3); 58/236; Chorus; Wt Lftg; High Hon Roll; Hon Roll; Shippensburg U; Hstry Tchr.

NICHOLSON, MARY LOU; Carmichaels JR SR HS; Carmichaels, PA; (4); 40/101; Am Leg Boys St; DECA; Hosp Aide; Math Tm; Office Aide; Pep Clb; SADD; VICA; Color Guard; Mrchg Band; 4th Genrl Merchnds Master Emply 84-85 & 2nd Pl 86-87; Bradford Coll; Retail Mgmnt.

NICHOLSON JR, P GEOFFREY; Kennard Dale HS; Delta, PA; (3); Church Yth Grp; Cmnty Wkr; Varsity Clb; School Musical; JV Bsktbl; JV Var Ftbl; Var Trk; High Hon Roll; NHS; Prfct Atten Awd; Morturary Sci.

NICHOLSON, ROBIN; Pocono Mt SR HS; Tobyhanna, PA; (2); Pep Clb; JV Cheerleading; Hon Roll; PA ST; Law.

NICHOLSON, SHELLY; Connellsville SR HS; Mill Run, PA; (3); 34/500; Pres FBLA; Library Aide; Chorus; Nwsp Stf; Rep Stu Cncl; High Hon Roll; Hon Roll; NHS; Bus Educ.

NICKEL, CHERYL; Sharpsville Area HS; Sharpsville, PA; (3); 4-H; Library Aide; Drill Tm; Nwsp Stf; Yrbk Stf; Rep Stu Cncl; Pom Pon; 4-H Awd; Hon Roll; NHS; ST 4-H Fshn Review 85; Acadc Ltr 85; Slvr Acadc Bar 86; Kent ST U; Fshn Merch.

NICKEL, MICHELLE; West Perry SR HS; Landisburg, PA; (3); L Var Sftbl; Hon Roll; Achvt Awd 86-87; Statue Of Lbrty Hnr Rl 86; Penn ST.

NICKELS, JACK; Lansdale Catholic HS; Chalfont, PA; (3); SADD; Socr; Wrstlng; Hon Roll; Pres Schlr; PA ST; Bus.

NICKELSON, ERIN; Connellsville Area SR HS; Connellsville, PA; (2); Sec Band; Concert Band; Mrchg Band; Symp Band; Pres Frsh Cls; Pres Soph Cls; Off Stu Cncl; Hon Roll; Wntr Sprts Qn Ct 86-87.

NICKELSON, RAYMOND E; Milton Area SR HS; New Columbia, PA; (4); 8/206; Computer Clb; Key Clb; Spanish Clb; NHS; Pres Acdmc Ftnss Awds Pgm 87; Dreifuss Schlrshp 87; Rtry Frgn Exchng Stu; Bucknell U; Pre-Med.

NICKEY, LISA; Donegal HS; Marietta, PA; (2); Church Yth Grp; Girl Scts; Band; Concert Band; Jazz Band; Mrchg Band; JV Fld Hcky; Im Gym; Im Sftbl; Sociology.

NICKLAS, KYLE LEWIS; Warren Area HS; Warren, PA; (4); 15/300; French Clb; Math Tm; Ski Clb; JV Wrstlng; High Hon Roll; Hon Roll; Jr NHS; NHS; Pres Schlr; Art Clb; Silver B 84; Alfred U Pres Schlrshp 87; Alfred U; Mech Engrng.

NICKLAUS, KAREN; Lancaster Catholic HS; Lancaster, PA; (3); 30/200; Chrmn Church Yth Grp; Pep Clb; Service Clb; SADD; JV Fld Hcky; Bus Admin.

NICKLES, MICHELE; Central Catholic HS; Catasauqua, PA; (3); Church Yth Grp; GAA; Key Clb; Service Clb; Im Var Bsktbl; Im Powder Puff Ftbl; Wt Lftg; High Hon Roll; Hon Roll; Psych.

NICKLIS II, FRED; Cumberland Valley HS; Mechanicsburg, PA; (3); Church Yth Grp; Computer Clb; FBLA; Wt Lftg; Hon Roll; NHS; Penn ST; Bus Admin.

NICKLOW, JOHN; Berlin Brothers Valley HS; Berlin, PA; (3); 2/98; 4-H; Spanish Clb; Band; Yrbk Stf; 4-H Awd; Hon Roll; NHS; Var Bsktbl; Var Ftbl; Engnrng.

NICKLOW, KAREN; Connellsville HS; W Leisenring, PA; (1); Office Aide; Church Choir; Bsktbl; W VA Career Coll; Secy.

NICKOL, MICHAEL; Southwestern HS; Hanover, PA; (3); 15/233; Computer Clb; Band; Jazz Band; Mrchg Band; Pep Band; Stage Crew; Symp Band; JV Wrstlng; High Hon Roll; Hon Roll; Accntng.

NICKS JR, GERALD; Iroquois JR SR HS; Erie, PA; (4); 17/132; Boy Scts; Cmnty Wkr; Exploring; Concert Band; Mrchg Band; High Hon Roll; NHS; Engrng Explrs Projct Comp 86 & 87; PA ST U; Aerospace Designing.

NICODEMUS, KELLY; Bedford HS; Manns Choice, PA; (3); 56/204; Pres Church Yth Grp; SADD; Chorus; Concert Band; Flag Corp; Jazz Band; Mrchg Band; Hon Roll; Prfct Atten Awd; Yrbk Stf; Yth Delg United Meth Conf 84-86; New Coll Sthrn FL; Pre-Med.

NICODEMUS, SUSAN C; Central Dauphin HS; Harrisburg, PA; (4); Band; Chorus; Church Choir; School Musical; School Play; Gov Hon Prg Awd; High Hon Roll; Lion Awd; Voice Dem Awd; Alpha Phi Omega Talent Hunt 86-87; Telethon Perf 86-87; Arts Magnet Schl 86-87; Philadelphia Coll Arts; Theater.

NICOL, DAVID; Beaver Area SR HS; Beaver, PA; (3); FCA; Spanish Clb; Var Bsbl; Var Bsktbl; Var Ftbl; Var Trk; Wt Lftg; High Hon Roll; Hon Roll; 3-AA 1st Tm All Sctn Ftbl.

NICOLAZZO, MICHAEL; Springdale HS; Harwick, PA; (3); Aud/Vis; Hon Roll; Outstndng Achvt In Spanish & Geometry; Sci Field.

NICOLO, LISA; Cameron County HS; Emporium, PA; (1); German Clb; Sec Soph Cls; Stu Cncl; Cheerleading; Pom Pon; High Hon Roll; Hon Roll; Natl Art Hnr Soc 87; Delta Epsilon Phi 87; 1st Pl Awd Republcn Party Poster Cont 87; Comm Art.

NICOLO, SHERRY; Connellsville SR HS; Connellsville, PA; (3); Cmnty Wkr; 4-H; FNA; Girl Scts; Hosp Aide; Red Cross Aide; VICA; Rep Frsh Cls; Rep Stu Cncl; 4-H Awd; RN.

NICOTERA, SALLY; Mount Pleasant Area HS; Mt Pleasant, PA; (4); French Clb; GAA; Ski Clb; Band; Concert Band; Mrchg Band; Nwsp Stf; Mat Maids; Vllybl; Hon Roll; CA U Of PA; Elem Ed.

NICOTRA, BEVERLY; North Catholic HS; Pittsburgh, PA; (3); 71/285; German Clb; Stat Socr; Hon Roll; Pre Med.

NIEBISCH, STEFANIE; Hatboro-Horsham HS; Hatboro, PA; (4); 1/270; Cmnty Wkr; Model UN; Trs Service Clb; Capt Tennis; High Hon Roll; NHS; Ntl Merit SF; PA Gvrnrs Schl Intl Stds 85; Rnsslr Mdl Math & Sci 86; Htboro-Hrshm Poet Laureate 86; Intl Stds.

NIEDZIELKA, AMY L; Seton-La Salle HS; Pittsburgh, PA; (4); 1/270; Math Tm; SADD; Nwsp Sprt Ed; Capt Bsktbl; Powder Puff Ftbl; Sftbl; Vllybl; High Hon Roll; VP NHS; Ntl Merit SF; U Of Pittsburgh Prvst Day Math Cmptn 3rd Rank In Fnls 85-86; Engrng.

NIEDZIELKA, MINDY S; Seton-La Salle HS; Pittsburgh, PA; (4); 2/270; Math Tm; SADD; Variety Show; Nwsp Ed-Chief; High Hon Roll; NCTE Awd; Pres NHS; Ntl Merit Ltr; Sal; Schlrshp Ballet Stu 85; Schlrshp Wnr In U Of Pittsburgh Prvst Day Math Cmptn 86; Engrng.

NIEDZWIECKI, JOHN; Nativity B V M HS; Orwigsburg, PA; (3); Boy Scts; Church Yth Grp; Computer Clb; French Clb; Var Crs Cntry; Hon Roll; PA Soc Engrs Sci Fair Awd 87; Audubon Soc Awd 86; Captl Area Sci Fair 85-87; Shppnsbrg U; Comp Sci.

NIEFER, DOLORES; Marple Newtown HS; Broomall, PA; (4); Cmnty Wkr; Hosp Aide; Intnl Clb; SADD; Yrbk Ed-Chief; Swmmng; Hon Roll; NHS; Lock Haven U; Soc Wrk.

NIEHAUS, AMY; Wyomissing Area HS; Wyomissing, PA; (4); 7/100; Church Yth Grp; JA; Ski Clb; Yrbk Ed-Chief; Trs Rep Stu Cncl; Var Cheerleading; Var Capt Tennis; High Hon Roll; NHS; Cmnty Wkr; HOBY Awd 85; Villanova; Pre Med.

NIELSEN III, KENNETH; Susquehannock HS; Shrewsbury, PA; (2); 12/243; Teachers Aide; JV Vllybl; High Hon Roll; Penn ST U; Med.

NIEMAN, GEORGE; Central Catholic HS; Pittsburgh, PA; (3); 88/270; Am Leg Boys St; VP Church Yth Grp; Dance Clb; VP JA; Var L Bsbl; JV Im Ftbl; High Hon Roll; Hon Roll; Rotary Awd; Im Bsktbl; W PA Hugh O Brian Ldrshp Semnr 86; Duquesne U; Journalsm.

NIEMCZAK, STANLEY J; Archbishop Ryan For Boys; Philadelphia, PA; (2); 15/367; German Clb; Var Crs Cntry; Var Trk; High Hon Roll; Outstndng Math Awd 85; Engrng.

NIEMEYER, DARLENE; Fort Le Boeuf HS; Waterford, PA; (4); Art Clb; Cmnty Wkr; GAA; Ski Clb; Church Choir; Bsktbl; Sftbl; Swmmng; Hon Roll; Church Yth Grp; U Of AL; Socl Wrk.

NIER, TAMARA; Plymouth Whitemarsh HS; Plymouth Meeting, PA; (3); Computer Clb; German Clb; Science Clb; SADD; JV Diving; Swmmng; Trk; High Hon Roll; Hon Roll; Jr NHS; Grmn II Awd Hghst Grd Stndrzd Tst 85-86; Physics Olympcis Champs 87; Math.

NIERODA, CHRISTINE; Norht Pocono HS; Moscow, PA; (3); 1/231; FBLA; JA; Ski Clb; Capt Color Guard; High Hon Roll; NHS; Nrsng.

NIEZGODA, KIM; Lake Lehman HS; Dallas, PA; (2); 46/192; Hosp Aide; Library Aide; Office Aide; Teachers Aide; Chorus; Yrbk Stf; JV Vllybl; Hon Roll; Villanova; Bio.

NIGGEL, DAVID; Hempfield HS; E Petersburg, PA; (4); 142/465; Hon Roll; Millersville U; Accntng.

NIGUT, BRYAN; Penn Trafford HS; Irwin, PA; (2); JCL; Latin Clb; JV Bsbl; L Socr; Med.

NIKOLISHEN, DAVID; Tech Memorial HS; Erie, PA; (3); CAP; Computer Clb; SADD; Hon Roll; Gannon; Data Prcsng.

NIKOLISHEN, KATE; Central Cambria HS; Ebensburg, PA; (4); 13/204; Girl Scts; Var L Trk; Var L Vllybl; NHS; ST Champ Mock Trl Tm Attorney 87; Penn ST U; Pre Law.

NIKOLOPOULOS, PEGGY; St Basil Acad; Philadelphia, PA; (3); Sec Church Yth Grp; French Clb; Pres Science Clb; Church Choir; Orch; Yrbk Stf; Hon Roll; NHS; Acad All-American Awd Sci; Hnrb Mntn Sci Fair Proj; Temple U; Pharmacy.

NILAN, KATIE; Penn Hills SR HS; Pittsburgh, PA; (3); French Clb; Spanish Clb; Color Guard; Off Stu Cncl; High Hon Roll; Hon Roll; NHS; Lamp Of Knowledge Awd 85-87; Penn ST U; Frnch Trnsltr.

NILL, FREDERICK; Valley Forge Military Acad; W Chester, PA; (3); VP Drama Clb; ROTC; Ski Clb; Thesps; Varsity Clb; Chorus; Var L Socr; Hon Roll; German Clb; Church Choir.

NILSON, SONJA; Rocky Grove HS; Franklin, PA; (4); 15/89; Church Yth Grp; Science Clb; Band; Pep Band; Vllybl; Hon Roll; Kiwanis Awd; Sec NHS; Hosp Aide; Pep Clb; Dist & Rgnl Bnd 86-87; Clarion U PA; Elem Ed.

NIPPLE, ANGELA; Middleburg HS; Liverpool, PA; (3); Band; Concert Band; Jazz Band; Mrchg Band; Yrbk Stf; Key Clb; Ski Clb; Pep Band; Nwsp Stf; Yrbk Phtg; York Coll Of PA; Bus Admin.

NIPPLE, JOY; Greenwood HS; Liverpool, PA; (3); 16/77; Varsity Clb; JV Var Cheerleading; Hon Roll; NHS; Bus Clb 85-87; Accntng.

NISHIK, SUSAN; Quigley HS; Zelienople, PA; (4); Pep Clb; Hnr Roll/Dstctn 85-86; Awd Of Prsnl Exllnc In JR Rlgn 85-86; La Roche.

NISSLEY, GIL; Souderton Area HS; Telford, PA; (4); Aud/Vis; Boy Scts; VICA; High Hon Roll; NHS; Eagle Sct 87; Outstndng Stu In Mth 87; Outstndng Stu In Elec Tech 87; U S Air Force; Elecs.

NISSLEY, JANE; Bishop Mc Devitt HS; Harrisburg, PA; (3); 87/240; Art Clb; Church Yth Grp; Cmnty Wkr; Key Clb; Office Aide; Service Clb; Spanish Clb; Church Choir; Im Bsktbl; Im Bowling.

NISSLEY, KRISTIN; Bishop Mcdevitt HS; Harrisburg, PA; (4); #47 In Class; Church Yth Grp; Drama Clb; Office Aide; Spanish Clb; Capt Color Guard; Capt Flag Corp; Bsktbl; NHS; Rotary Awd; Occptnl Thrpy.

NISSLEY, MARK; Lancaster Mennonite HS; Mt Joy, PA; (3); Drama Clb; Model UN; School Play; Yrbk Phtg; Yrbk Rptr; Yrbk Stf; Im Bsktbl; Im Socr; Wt Lftg; Hon Roll; Rugby Team 84-86; Bus.

NISSLY, SHARON L; Donegal HS; Mt Joy, PA; (4); 12/161; Cmnty Wkr; Girl Scts; JV Fld Hcky; Ftbl; Hon Roll; NHS; VFW Awd; Girl Sct Gld Awd 86; Mt Joy Bus & Pro Wmns Schlrshp 87; Mt Joy Wlcm Wgn Cmnty Svc Awd 87; St Joseph Hosp Schl Nrsng; RN.

NITTERHOUSE, JODI; Chambersburg Area SR HS; Chambersburg, PA; (4); French Clb; Office Aide; Teachers Aide; Chorus; Off Stu Cncl; Hon Roll; ST Chmpn In Olympia Typing Cont, Typing 100 WPM, Ida E Heller Awd 87; SECY.

NITTINGER, JENNY; Sayre Area HS; Sayre, PA; (3); French Clb; Red Cross Aide; Ski Clb; Stu Cncl; Bsktbl; Cheerleading; High Hon Roll; Lbrl Arts.

NIX, JAMES; Mt Lebanon HS; Pittsburgh, PA; (4); VP AFS; Art Clb; Chess Clb; Ski Clb; Spanish Clb; Swmmng; Var Tennis; High Hon Roll; Natl Hispanic Merit Semi-Finalist 87; Cornell U; Mechncl Engrng.

NIXDORF, DIANE; Warwick HS; Lititz, PA; (3); 8/280; Varsity Clb; Stu Cncl; Var Cheerleading; Var Crs Cntry; Var Trk; Im Vllybl; High Hon Roll; Pres NHS.

NIXON, JENNIFER; Downingtown SR HS; Downingtown, PA; (3); Art Clb; Church Yth Grp; GAA; Ski Clb; Spanish Clb; Varsity Clb; Chorus; Var Cheerleading; Var Mgr(s); Var Trk; Congressmns Medal Merit Art 87; Studio Art.

NIXON, SEAN; Upper Merion HS; King Of Prussia, PA; (3); 52/305; Boy Scts; Var Bsbl; Im Bsktbl; Var Ftbl; Im Vllybl; Hon Roll; Prfct Atten Awd; Med.

NIXON, TARA; Edward Bok AVT; Philadelphia, PA; (3); Computer Clb; Dance Clb; FBLA; Drill Tm; Yrbk Stf; Stu Cncl; Bsktbl; Cheerleading; Vllybl; Wt Lftg; Pierce JC; Wrd Prcssg.

NIZICH, RENEE; Wyoming Area HS; West Pittston, PA; (4); 70/249; Church Yth Grp; German Clb; SADD; Marywood Coll; Spec Ed.

NOBEL, YVONNE; Mahoanoy Area HS; Barnesville, PA; (3); Church Yth Grp; FHA; Spanish Clb; SADD; Chorus; Nwsp Rptr; Var Trk; High Hon Roll.

NOBLE, AMY; Spring Grove SR HS; Spring Grove, PA; (3); 39/306; Chorus; Orch; School Musical; Nwsp Rptr; Var Tennis; Hon Roll; NHS; Bloomsburg; Cmmnctns.

NOBLE, ANGELA; West Perry SR HS; Blain, PA; (2); 8/224; FHA; Pep Clb; Hon Roll; Elem Tchr.

NOBLE, ERIC; Penn-Trafford HS; Harrison City, PA; (2); Letterman Clb; Bsbl; Ftbl; Wrstlng; Hon Roll.

NOBLE, HOLLY; Fort Le Boeuf HS; Waterford, PA; (4); Art Clb; Dance Clb; Concert Band; Mrchg Band; Trs Soph Cls; Stat Bsbl; Capt Cheerleading; Var Sftbl; High Hon Roll; NHS; Edinboro U PA; Bus Adm.

NOBLE, REBECCA S; Everett Area HS; Everett, PA; (3); 2/133; Drama Clb; Color Guard; Flag Corp; Stage Crew; Hon Roll; Spanish NHS; Acadmc All Amercn 86; Central PA Bus Schl; Adm Asst.

NOBLE, SEAN P; Methacton HS; Audubon, PA; (4); 5/360; Pres Debate Tm; Math Tm; Lit Mag; VP Jr Cls; Crs Cntry; High Hon Roll; NHS; Ntl Merit SF; Rotary Awd; Natl Yng Ldrs Conf 86; Elec Engrng.

NOBLE, TRICIA M; Owen J Roberts HS; Pottstown, PA; (3); 30/299; Chorus; Concert Band; Mrchg Band; School Musical; Yrbk Stf; Im Tennis; Im Vllybl; High Hon Roll; Hon Roll; NHS; Music.

NOBLE, WILLIAM; Penn Trafford HS; Harrison Cty, PA; (4); Cmnty Wkr; JCL; Latin Clb; Ski Clb; Var JV Ftbl; Var Trk; Hon Roll; Edinboro U; Crmnl Just.

NOBLEJAS, ANNA L; Morrisville HS; Morrisville, PA; (4); 16/95; Chorus; Stage Crew; Yrbk Stf; Vllybl; Hon Roll; NHS; PA ST; Child Psych.

NOCCHI, DAVE; Freeland HS; Freeland, PA; (3); 2/85; VP FBLA; Pep Clb; Scholastic Bowl; Band; Concert Band; VP Soph Cls; VP Jr Cls; Stu Cncl; Hon Roll; Jr NHS; Outstndng Band 87; Pre-Med.

NOCEK, CATHY; Wyoming Area HS; West Wyoming, PA; (3); Pres Church Yth Grp; French Clb; FHA; Hosp Aide; Spanish Clb; SADD; Teachers Aide; Band; Church Choir; Concert Band; Kings; Acctnt.

NOCHE, CONRAD; Uniontown Area HS; Uniontown, PA; (3); Spanish Clb; Im Bsktbl; CC Awd; High Hon Roll; Hon Roll; NHS; Acctg.

NOCK, BOB; Avonworth HS; Pittsbg, PA; (4); Teachers Aide; Nwsp Rptr; Trs Frsh Cls; Pres Soph Cls; Pres Jr Cls; Pres Sr Cls; Bsbl; Bsktbl; Cit Awd; High Hon Roll; Hutchison Awd 87; Law Day Essay Awd 86; Schlr Athlt 87; PA ST U; Bus.

NODERER, ELLEN; Upper Moreland HS; Hatboro, PA; (2); 65/250; Key Clb; Ski Clb; Fld Hcky; Lcrss; Score Keeper; Nwsp Stf; Yrbk Rptr; PA ST; Arch.

NOE, HEATHER; Avella Area JR SR HS; Avella, PA; (3); Trs Art Clb; Computer Clb; Letterman Clb; Chorus; Capt Color Guard; Capt Flag Corp; Mrchg Band; School Play; Off Stu Cncl; Score Keeper; Psych.

NOEL, JIM; Altoona Area HS; Altoona, PA; (3); 76/1200; Boy Scts; Church Yth Grp; Cmnty Wkr; German Clb; Chorus; Church Choir; Swing Chorus; High Hon Roll; Hon Roll; Computer Clb; 6 Years Paperboy 81-87; PA ST U.

NOEL, JOANNE; Penn Cambria HS; Ashville, PA; (3); French Clb; NFL; Speech Tm; Vllybl; High Hon Roll; Hon Roll; NHS; Elem Ed.

NOEL, JONATHAN; The Episcopel Acad; Bryn Mawr, PA; (2); Chorus; JV L Bsktbl; JV Ftbl; Var L Lcrss; Hon Roll; Vestry Schl Chapel Svcs 86-89; Acad Blues Mens Chorus 86-89.

NOEL, KELLEY; Danville SR HS; Danville, PA; (4); Church Yth Grp; FBLA; FHA; SADD; Chorus; Color Guard; JV Bsktbl; JV Bowling; Trk; Hon Roll; Shrthnd Theory, Trnscrptn & Speed 85-87; Typng Awd Top Clss 84; Sec.

NOEL, MARK; Athens HS; Sayre, PA; (3); Boy Scts; Band; Chorus; Concert Band; Mrchg Band; Orch; JV Crs Cntry; Bus Mngmnt.

NOEL, MICHAEL; Outler Area SR HS; Butler, PA; (3); French Clb; Im Bsktbl; Im Ftbl; Crng Mln U; Mech Engr.

NOEL, MICHELLE; Bellwood-Antis HS; Bellwood, PA; (4); 23/115; Pres SADD; Chorus; School Musical; VP Sr Cls; Pres Stu Cncl; Hon Roll; Trs NHS; Princess Of Ftbl 83; Stu Of Week 86; Cngrssnl Yth Ldrshp Cncl; Csmtlgy.

NOEL, SEAN; Cambria Heights SR HS; Patton, PA; (3); 8/182; ROTC; Ski Clb; Var L Bsbl; Var Ftbl; Hon Roll; NHS; NEDT Awd; Air Force Assoc Awd 87; Military Order Of World Wars Awd 85; Engrng.

NOEL, SHELLY; Beaver Falls SR HS; Beaver Falls, PA; (3); 41/171; Church Yth Grp; Cmnty Wkr; Q&S; Spanish Clb; Stage Crew; Yrbk Ed-Chief; Yrbk Stf; High Hon Roll; Hon Roll; Radlgy.

NOEL, TERESA; Tyrone Area HS; Altoona, PA; (3); Pres 4-H; Key Clb; Library Aide; Office Aide; SADD; Band; Yrbk Phtg; Stat Trk; High Hon Roll; Hon Roll; Englsh Positive Attitude Awd 86-87; Indiana U PA; Cnslng Teengrs.

NOGA, ANITA; Burgettstown JR SR HS; Burgettstown, PA; (4); 33/139; Hosp Aide; Office Aide; Science Clb; Chorus; Yrbk Stf; Hon Roll; NHS; Schlrshp ICM Schl Bus, Secr Hlth Careers Clb, VP Med Explrs 86-87; ICM Schl Of Business; Med Asst.

NOGA, SUZANNE; Saint Maria Goretti HS; Philadelphia, PA; (4); 36/384; Cmnty Wkr; Dance Clb; GAA; Intnl Clb; Off Sr Cls; High Hon Roll; Jr NHS; VP NHS; Pres Schlr; VP Natl Hnr Soc 87; Pres Acdmc Ftnss Awd 87; Drexel U; Bus Admin.

NOGAST, MELISSA; Hazleton SR HS; Hazleton, PA; (2); Church Yth Grp; Pep Clb; Y-Teens; Color Guard; High Hon Roll; Hon Roll; Pres Acdmc Ftnss Awd 85-86; Chld Psych.

NOGGLE, CHRISTINA; Carlisle SR HS; Carlisle, PA; (3); 64/450; Church Yth Grp; Chorus; Hon Roll; Engl.

NOGLE, JAMES; Danville HS; Danville, PA; (2); French Clb; Ski Clb; Band; Concert Band; Mrchg Band; JV Bsbl; JV Bsktbl; JV Golf; Band Stu Awd; Arch.

NOLAN, BRYAN; Huntingdon Area HS; Hesston, PA; (4); Boy Scts; Band; Chorus; Concert Band; Mrchg Band; Var Tennis; JV Wrstlng; Hon Roll; Pres Schlr; PA ST U; Aerospc Engrng.

NOLAN, CHRIS; Ambridge Area HS; Freedom, PA; (3); Var Capt Socr; Penn ST; Arch.

NOLAN III, WILLIAM A; Oliver HS; Pittsburgh, PA; (4); 4/238; Chess Clb; Computer Clb; Sec Math Clb; Math Tm; Mu Alpha Theta; Science Clb; Teachers Aide; Score Keeper; High Hon Roll; NHS; U Pittsburgh; Elec Engrg.

NOLE, KIM; Dunmore HS; Dunmore, PA; (4); 24/145; French Clb; Letterman Clb; Ski Clb; Spanish Clb; Yrbk Phtg; Var JV Bsktbl; Capt Var Sftbl; Hon Roll; Hlth Crs Clb 83-87; PA ST U; Elem Ed.

NOLF, LORI; Punxsutawney SR HS; Sprankle Mills, PA; (3); FNA; Office Aide; Spanish Clb; Hon Roll; Nrsg.

NOLL, BRIAN; Greenwood HS; Millerstown, PA; (4); 7/63; Stage Crew; Nwsp Stf; Yrbk Stf; Hon Roll; JC Awd; NHS; Millersville Univ; Comp Sci.

NOLL, CHRISTOPHER; Newport HS; Newport, PA; (3); 27/125; Varsity Clb; Nwsp Phtg; Nwsp Stf; Hst Soph Cls; Var Bsbl; Var Ftbl; Var Wrstlng; Hon Roll; Tri-Vly Leag All Str 1st Bsmn JR.

NOLL, DENISE; Moon SR HS; Coraopolis, PA; (3); Church Yth Grp; Sec German Clb; JA; Key Clb; Varsity Clb; L Var Bsktbl; L Var Tennis; High Hon Roll; Hon Roll; Jr NHS; Aummer Pgm-Georgetown U 87; Intl Bus.

NOLL, JAMES; West Mifflin Area HS; W Mifflin, PA; (4); 3/300; Boy Scts; High Hon Roll; NHS; Thiel Coll; Chem Engrng.

NOLL, JENNIFER; Bishop Mc Devitt HS; Harrisburg, PA; (4); 1/176; Computer Clb; Office Aide; Red Cross Aide; Science Clb; Service Clb; Drill Tm; Mgr Mrchg Band; Yrbk Bus Mgr; Hon Roll; NHS; Holy Crss Bk Awd; Chem Engrng.

NOLL, MELISSA; Center Area HS; Monaca, PA; (2); Church Yth Grp; Spanish Clb; Band; Drill Tm; Mrchg Band; Orch; Var Pom Pon; Hon Roll; Accntnt.

NOLL, MICHELLE; Reynolds HS; Greenville, PA; (4); 14/147; German Clb; Math Clb; Varsity Clb; Yrbk Stf; Stu Cncl; Bsktbl; Score Keeper; Hon Roll; NHS; SR Of Wk For Lcl Nwspr 87; Emplye Of Mo Mc Donalds 86; Clarion U.

NOLL, THOMAS; Scranton Tech HS; Scranton, PA; (4); 7/230; Boys Clb Am; VICA; Band; Jazz Band; Mrchg Band; Bsktbl; Hon Roll; NHS; U S Army Rsrve.

NOLL, TIM; Danville Area HS; Danville, PA; (3); Church Yth Grp; Ski Clb; Spanish Clb; Band; Drm & Bgl; Jazz Band; Mrchg Band; Symp Band; JV Tennis; Hon Roll; Bucknell; Acctng.

NOLT, DAVID; Manheim Central HS; Manheim, PA; (3); Pres Church Yth Grp; Rptr FFA; Chorus; Socr; 4-H Awd.

NOLT, KRISTIN; Hempfeild HS; Lancaster, PA; (3); 59/420; Boys Clb Am; Chorus; School Musical; Rep Frsh Cls; Sec Soph Cls; Sec Jr Cls; Sec Sr Cls; Var Cheerleading; Hon Roll; NHS.

NOLT, MATTHEW; Elizabethtown Area HS; Elizabethtown, PA; (3); 26/259; Church Yth Grp; Letterman Clb; Ski Clb; Socr; Tennis; NHS.

NOLT, TIMOTHY; Hempfield HS; Lancaster, PA; (4); 17/420; Church Yth Grp; Computer Clb; Ski Clb; School Musical; School Play; Var L Socr; Var L Trk; Hon Roll; NHS; Police Awd Schlrshp Svc, Ctznshp 87; Lehigh U; Engr.

NONEVSKI, TANIA; Lincoln HS; Ellwood City, PA; (3); 20/168; Trs Camera Clb; French Clb; Key Clb; Ski Clb; Y-Teens; Chorus; Powder Puff Ftbl; High Hon Roll; Hon Roll; NHS; Washngtn & Jeffrsn Coll; Chem.

NOON, MELISSA; Chestnut Ridge SR HS; Imler, PA; (4); 6/132; SADD; Chorus; Mrchg Band; Nwsp Rptr; Stu Cncl; High Hon Roll; Trs NHS; VP Spanish Clb; Cnty, Dist, Rgnl & State Choruses 84-85; Cnty, Dist, & Rgnl Choruses 85-86; Dist Rgnl, St Chorus 86-87; W Chester U; Music Ed.

NOONAN, KATHY; Cumberland Valley HS; Mechanicsburg, PA; (3); 108/578; Cmnty Wkr; GAA; Hosp Aide; Key Clb; Latin Clb; Spanish Clb; Rep Stu Cncl; Hon Roll; Ntl Hnr Rl 87; Phy Thrpy.

NOONAN, PHILIP; Archbishop Wood HS; Warminster, PA; (2); 54/266; Church Yth Grp; JV Bsktbl; JV Socr; JV Vllybl; Prfct Atten Awd.

NOONE, KELLEY; New Hope-Solebury HS; New Hope, PA; (4); 10/80; Political Wkr; Ski Clb; Chorus; Rep Stu Cncl; Bsktbl; Hon Roll; VFW Awd; Poltcl Sci.

NORFLEET, CLAUDIA; Chestermiah HS; Chester, PA; (3); Art Clb; Computer Clb; Drama Clb; 4-H; Math Clb; Spanish Clb.

NORFOLK, DAVID; Technical Memorial HS; Erie, PA; (3); 22/311; Boy Scts; Exploring; Navy Schls; Engnrng.

NORMAN, DAVE; Pennsbury HS; Yardley, PA; (3); Aud/Vis; Drama Clb; Thesps; Band; Concert Band; Jazz Band; School Musical; School Play; Var JV Socr; NHS; Sci.

NORMAN, HELEN; Liberty JR SR HS; Liberty, PA; (3); Sec Trs FFA; FHA; Chorus; School Musical; Sec Jr Cls; JP Sousa Awd; NHS; Dist & Rgnl Bnd Fstvls 86-87; PA Lions All-ST Bnd 86; Music Ed.

NORMAN, JOHN; St Pius X HS; Pottstown, PA; (1); 88/148; Im Bowling; PA ST; Engrng.

NORMAN III, JOHN W; Central Catholic HS; N Braddock, PA; (2); 78/300; Boy Scts; Church Yth Grp; Hon Roll; Am Legion Awd 85.

NORMAN, THOMAS; Northern Chester County Tech Schl; Phoenixville, PA; (4); 8/120; Boy Scts; Spanish Clb; Im Ftbl; JV Tennis; High Hon Roll; Hon Roll; NHS; William J Passavant Schlrshp 87-88; Thiel Coll; Comp Engrng.

NORNHOLD, RICHARD; Donegal HS; Mount Joy, PA; (3); Chess Clb; CAP; Stage Crew; Nwsp Sprt Ed; Rep Frsh Cls; Rep Soph Cls; Rep Jr Cls; Ftbl; Trk; Aero Engrng.

NORR, RONDA; Conneaut Valley HS; Springboro, PA; (3); FFA; Leo Clb; Drama Clb; German Clb; Pep Clb; Band; Chorus; Concert Band; Mrchg Band; Pep Band; Firefighter.

NORRIS, BRINN; York County Area Vo-Tech Schl; York, PA; (2); Church Yth Grp; SADD; Church Choir; Var JV Fld Hcky; Temple U; Dental Lab Tech.

NORRIS, HELEN; Lincoln HS; Ellwood City, PA; (3); Drama Clb; Hosp Aide; SADD; Y-Teens; Chorus; School Musical; Hon Roll; New Castle Bus Schl; Accntng.

NORRIS, KERRY ANNE; Beaver Area JR SR HS; Beaver, PA; (2); Church Yth Grp; French Clb; Mrchg Band; School Musical; High Hon Roll; Hon Roll; Pep Clb; Church Choir; Concert Band; Pep Band; Jrnlsm.

NORRIS, NATHAN; Seneca Valley SR HS; Evans Cty, PA; (2); JA; Ski Clb; Var Tennis; High Hon Roll; Cert Merit-Erie Cnty Chptr PA Soc Prfssnl Engrs 86-87.

NORRIS, RUTHANNA; Curwensville Area HS; Curwensville, PA; (3); Cmnty Wkr; Dance Clb; Drama Clb; 4-H; French Clb; FHA; FTA; Chorus; Rep Stu Cncl; L Cheerleading; Penn ST; Ed.

NORRIS, TRACY; Moon SR HS; Coraopolis, PA; (4); JA; Key Clb; Acpl Chr; Chorus; School Musical; School Play; Swing Chorus; Variety Show; Off Stu Cncl; Var L Cheerleading; Washington.

NORRIS, TRUDY ELLEN; Greencastle-Antrim HS; Greencastle, PA; (3); 35/167; Church Yth Grp; Band; Concert Band; Mrchg Band; Fld Hcky; Trk; Vllybl; Hon Roll; Sci Fair Hnrb Mntn 86 & 87; Messiah Coll; Comp Sci.

NORTH, JASON; Garnet Valley HS; Glen Mills, PA; (4); 53/149; Church Yth Grp; Intnl Clb; Varsity Clb; Variety Show; Var Bsbl; JV Ftbl; Tennis; Trk; Hon Roll; Rotary Awd; Prfct Atten 85-86; JV Ltr Bsbl 86; Stu Of Mnth 86; U Of Cntrl FL; Aerontcl Engrng.

NORTH, MICHAEL D; Penncrest HS; Brookhaven, PA; (3); 6/344; Boys Clb Am; SADD; Variety Show; Var Capt Bsbl; Var Capt Socr; JC Awd; Jr NHS; Math.

NORTHROP, RONALD; Johnsonburg Area HS; Wilcox, PA; (3); Camera Clb; Rep Jr Cls; Hon Roll; Prfct Atten Awd; Acdmc All-Amrcn Awd 86; U S Air Force Acad; Comp Sci.

NORTON, ALISA; Avon Grove HS; West Grove, PA; (4); 22/187; Drama Clb; SADD; Band; Concert Band; Mrchg Band; School Play; Stage Crew; Var Cheerleading; NHS; Cnty Jr Miss Fnlst 86; Cmmndtn Plays 85-86; U Of DE; Med Tech.

NORTON, KELLY; Eisenhower HS; Russell, PA; (3); 7/120; Church Yth Grp; Hosp Aide; Acpl Chr; Chorus; Church Choir; Yrbk Phtg; Pres Frsh Cls; Rep Stu Cncl; Sftbl; High Hon Roll; Ltrd Sftbl 86-87; Spec Ed.

NORTON, MATT; Carlisle SR HS; Carlisle, PA; (3); 32/467; Political Wkr; School Musical; School Play; JV L Socr; Var L Wrstlng; High Hon Roll; Hon Roll; VP NHS; Chess Clb; JA; Spcl Awd 3 Mile Islnd Nclr Plnt-Wrk On Rdn Gas Prblm In S Cntrl PA 87; Pltcl Sci.

NORTON, NIKKI; Corry Area HS; Spartansburg, PA; (3); Drama Clb; Office Aide; Spanish Clb; Band; Mrchg Band; Pep Band; Nwsp Stf; Al-Erie Cnty Mc Donalds HS Band 86-87; Edinboro U Of PA; Cmnctns.

NORWICH, MICHELLE; Bishop Mc Devitt HS; Harrisburg, PA; (3); Church Yth Grp; Cmnty Wkr; FBLA; Girl Scts; Library Aide; Pep Clb; Service Clb; Spanish Clb; Chorus; School Play; Accntng.

NORWOOD, CHRISTOPHER O NEIL; Coatesville Area SR HS; Coatesville, PA; (3); French Clb; Leo Clb; Ski Clb; Acpl Chr; Chorus; School Musical; Yrbk Stf; Rep Jr Cls; Rep Sr Cls; Rep Stu Cncl; U Of Pittsburg; Elec Engrng.

NORWOOD, DAVID; Downingtown SR HS; Exton, PA; (3); 171/656; Church Yth Grp; Ski Clb; VICA; Chorus; School Musical; Stage Crew; Pres Sr Cls; Im Lcrss; Var Socr; Var Trk; Carpntry.

NORWOOD, KATIE; Council Rock HS; Churchville, PA; (3); Church Yth Grp; Drama Clb; Acpl Chr; Chorus; School Musical; School Play; Variety Show; Hon Roll; All-Cnty Chorus 85-86; Child Psych.

NORWOOD, RUTH; Freedom HS; Bethlehem, PA; (4); 47/446; Sec French Clb; Band; Mrchg Band; Hon Roll; Boston U; Pre-Dent.

NOSZKA, MICHAEL; Central Catholic HS; Pittsburgh, PA; (3); 58/300; Rep Jr Cls; JV Bsktbl; Hon Roll; NHS; Notre Dame; Brdcstr.

NOTARIANNI, STEPHANIE; Cardinal O Hara HS; Havertown, PA; (2); 484/648; Dance Clb; Var Bowling.

NOTTINGHAM, SHEILA; Edward Bok A V T HS; Philadelphia, PA; (3); VICA; Yrbk Stf; PA ST; Scl Wrkr.

NOTTO, TRICIA L; Norristown Area HS; Norristown, PA; (3); 61/491; Church Yth Grp; DECA; Exploring; SADD; Mgr(s); Hon Roll; Mktg.

NOULLET, SCOTT; Peters Twp HS; Venetia, PA; (3); Boy Scts; Church Yth Grp; Computer Clb; Exploring; SADD; Stage Crew; Wt Lftg; Eagle Scout Awd 86; Vigil In Order Of Arrow Boy Scts Amer 86; Engrng.

NOURIAN, BEN; North Polono HS; Moscow, PA; (3); 21/231; Letterman Clb; Capt Bsktbl; Capt Tennis; High Hon Roll; NHS; Ntl Merit Ltr; Voice Dem Awd; PA Amer Lgn ST Plc Yth Wk 87; Otstndng Stud Awd 84; Columbia Prss Assoc 1st Pl Ftr Stry 83; Syracuse Univ; Jrnlsm.

NOUSE, STACIE; Dover Area HS; Dover, PA; (3); Teachers Aide; Nwsp Rptr; Rep Frsh Cls; Rep Soph Cls; Rep Jr Cls; Diving; Hon Roll; York Coll; Nrsng.

NOUSE, SUSAN; Middletown Area HS; Middletown, PA; (3); 1/193; Band; Chorus; Concert Band; Drm Mjr(t); Jazz Band; Mrchg Band; Orch; Swing Chorus; Sec Stu Cncl; Lion Awd; Scndry Ed.

NOVACK, TAMMY LOUISE; Pittston Area SR HS; Avoca, PA; (3); Art Clb; FNA; JA; Math Clb; JV Trk; NHS; Phrmcy.

NOVAJOSKY, PAUL; Scranton Tech; Scranton, PA; (3); Drama Clb; Letterman Clb; Ski Clb; SADD; School Play; Nwsp Rptr; Nwsp Stf; Var Bsbl; Var Ftbl; Wt Lftg; Educ.

NOVAK, ANDREA; Bishop O Hara HS; Olyphant, PA; (2); 1/127; Latin Clb; Spanish Clb; Church Choir; Nwsp Stf; Trs Soph Cls; High Hon Roll; Lion Awd; Penn ST; Med.

NOVAK, CASSIE; Beth-Center SR HS; Marianna, PA; (3); Church Yth Grp; Cmnty Wkr; Drama Clb; Spanish Clb; Varsity Clb; Chorus; Church Choir; School Play; Stage Crew; Nwsp Stf; WA Cnty Choir Fstvl 85-87; Psych.

NOVAK, CHRISTINA; Bishop O Hara HS; Dickson City, PA; (4); 23/115; Cmnty Wkr; Chorus; Sec Soph Cls; Trs Sr Cls; High Hon Roll; NHS; Poderewski Gold Mdl-Natl Piano Guild 86.

NOVAK, CHRISTINE; Ringgold HS; Finleyville, PA; (1); 44/343; JA; Math Clb; Science Clb; Band; Concert Band; Mrchg Band; School Musical; Variety Show; Pom Pon; Hon Roll; Amercn Legn Auxllry Awd Outstndng Stu 84; Pharmacy.

NOVAK, DON; Monessen JR SR HS; Monessen, PA; (3); VICA; Hon Roll; Prfct Atten Awd; Triangle Tech; Crpntry.

NOVAK, JANETTE; North Catholic HS; Allison Park, PA; (3); 3/285; German Clb; Hosp Aide; NFL; Service Clb; Speech Tm; High Hon Roll; Hon Roll; NHS; NEDT Awd; Bio Sci.

NOVAK, JOSEPH; Ford City HS; Ford City, PA; (3); Spanish Clb; Var Golf; Trk.

NOVAK, JOSEPH M; Baldwin High HS; Pittsburgh, PA; (4); 36/535; Boy Scts; Cmnty Wkr; Math Clb; Math Tm; Science Clb; Rep Frsh Cls; High Hon Roll; Ntl Merit Schol; Boy Scouts-Life Rank 85; Math Leag-AHSME 86; Carnegie Mellon Natl Merit Semi-Fnlst Schlrshp 86; Carnegie Mellon U; Biochem.

NOVAK, KAREN; Marian Catholic HS; Mc Adoo, PA; (4); 7/109; Pep Clb; Chorus; Drill Tm; School Musical; Rep Soph Cls; Rep Jr Cls; Rep Sr Cls; High Hon Roll; NHS; Spanish NHS; Pres Acdmc Fit Awd 87; Bloomsburg U; Elem U.

NOVAK, KERRY; Downingtown Senior HS; Downingtown, PA; (3); 103/640; Dance Clb; VP GAA; Pep Clb; Spanish Clb; SADD; Teachers Aide; Chorus; Rep Frsh Cls; Var Lcrss; Hon Roll.

NOVAK, KIM; Brockway Area HS; Brockport, PA; (3); Art Clb; VP Church Yth Grp; Ski Clb; Varsity Clb; Band; Concert Band; Jazz Band; Mrchg Band; Pep Band; Capt Bsktbl; MVP Sftbll 86-87; All Tourney Tm Bsktbll 85-86; All Star Sftbll 83-84; Athltc Trnng.

NOVAK, MATT; Vincentian HS; Pittsburgh, PA; (1); Boy Scts; Frsh Cls; Hon Roll.

NOVAK, NICOLE; Vincentian HS; Pittsburgh, PA; (1); Rep Frsh Cls; JV Cheerleading; Hon Roll.

NOVAK, PAUL; Southwestern HS; Hanover, PA; (3); Varsity Clb; Var Ftbl; Im Socr; Var Trk; Im Wt Lftg; Var Wrstlng; Hon Roll; Sprts Med.

NOVAK, SHELLY; United JR SR HS; Blairsville, PA; (3); Camera Clb; VP Pres 4-H; Mu Alpha Theta; Var L Bsktbl; Im Powder Puff Ftbl; Var L Trk; 4-H Awd; Hon Roll; Appalachn Conf Track All Star 85-86; IN CO Gazette Track All Stars 84-85 & 85-86; Wilson Coll; Physcl Thrpy.

NOVAK, SONYA; Nazareth Acad; Phila, PA; (2); 15/125; Spanish Clb; Speech Tm; Chorus; Church Choir; Orch; School Musical; Rep Stu Cncl; Hon Roll; NHS; Opt Clb Awd; Archdiocesan Schlr Pgm 87; H O Brien Ldrshp Cntst 86; Educ.

NOVAK, TERESA; Bishop O Hara HS; Olyphant, PA; (3); 1/95; Latin Clb; Spanish Clb; Nwsp Rptr; Trs Soph Cls; Trs Jr Cls; High Hon Roll; Lion Awd; NHS; Educ.

NOVAKOSKI, SHARON; Valley SR HS; New Kensington, PA; (3); 41/225; Drama Clb; French Clb; JA; Key Clb; Varsity Clb; Chorus; Mrchg Band; JV Tennis; High Hon Roll; Stu Mnth 85; IN U Of PA; Elem Educ.

NOVALESI, SHARI L; Riverside HS; Ellwood City, PA; (4); #11 In Class; Pres Band; Chorus; Jazz Band; Variety Show; Nwsp Rptr; Off Stu Cncl; Sftbl; High Hon Roll; Lion Awd; NHS; Westminster Hnrs Chorus 84; Bearer Vlly Invt Band 84-85; Dist & Rgnl Chours 85-87; Mendelssohm Choir 87; Comm.

NOVELLA, DIANNE; Northern Cambria HS; Spangler, PA; (3); 11/152; Hosp Aide; Ski Clb; Sec Spanish Clb; SADD; Chorus; Capt Cheerleading; High Hon Roll; NHS; VP Spanish NHS; Acctng.

NOVELLO, JAY C; Henderson HS; W Chester, PA; (3); Pres Art Clb; Church Yth Grp; SADD; Variety Show; Lit Mag; Gov Hon Prg Awd; Cmmrcl Arts.

NOVICENSKIE, WENDY E; Bishop Hoban HS; Laflin, PA; (2); 4/229; Church Yth Grp; Drama Clb; Mu Alpha Theta; SADD; Chorus; Church Choir; School Musical; School Play; Swing Chorus; Variety Show; Med.

NOVICK, CHRIS A; Fort Cherry HS; Hickory, PA; (4); Boy Scts; Church Yth Grp; Science Clb; Ski Clb; Band; Mrchg Band; Pep Band; Wrstlng; Hon Roll; Penn ST.

NOVIELLO, MARIA; New Castle SR HS; New Castle, PA; (4); Church Yth Grp; Dance Clb; SADD; Band; Concert Band; Drill Tm; Jazz Band; Mrchg Band; Orch; Yrbk Stf; Acdmc All AM Schlr 87; Drill Tm Squad Rdr; Clarion U; Educ.

NOVINGER, LARA; Millersburg Area HS; Millersburg, PA; (3); Pres Sec Church Yth Grp; French Clb; Sec Spanish Clb; Yrbk Stf; Stu Cncl; Var Capt Cheerleading; Powder Puff Ftbl; Trk; Hon Roll; Amer Lgn Awd Wnnr 2nd Pl Essay Contest 86-87; Lang.

NOVITSKY, EDWARD; Dallas SR HS; Wyoming, PA; (3); 5/230; Chess Clb; Band; Jazz Band; Mrchg Band; Pep Band; School Musical; High Hon Roll; Hon Roll; NHS; NEDT Awd; Elec Engrng.

NOVITSKY, JOYCE; Mid Valley HS; Dickson City, PA; (4); 18/75; Ski Clb; Band; Drill Tm; Mrchg Band; Off Frsh Cls; Crs Cntry; High Hon Roll; Hon Roll; Pres Acdmc Fit Awd 87; Marywood Coll; Fshn Merch.

NOVOBILSKI, PATRICIA; Carbondale Area HS; Simpson, PA; (3); Church Yth Grp; VP German Clb; Girl Scts; Ski Clb; Band; Chorus; Concert Band; Mrchg Band; School Musical; Variety Show; Marywood Hnrs Band 84-85; Dist Band 86; Ger Cult Test 2nd Pl Awd 86.

NOVOTNE, JODY; Shenango JR SR HS; New Castle, PA; (3); 9/110; Church Yth Grp; French Clb; Math Tm; NFL; Band; Concert Band; Drill Tm; Pom Pon; Vllybl; High Hon Roll; Grove City Coll; Math.

NOVOTNY, LANCE; Bishop Hafey HS; Hazleton, PA; (3); Ski Clb; Spanish Clb; JV Ftbl; Hon Roll; Hnr Stu 85 & 86; Mech Engr.

NOVROCKI, MICHAEL; Wyoming Valley West HS; Larksville, PA; (2); 3/450; Church Yth Grp; Chorus; Nwsp Rptr; Rep Stu Cncl; Var Trk; Cit Awd; High Hon Roll; NHS; Science Clb; Nwsp Stf; 1st Pl Dist Hstry Day Compttn 87; Publ Piano Rectl 86; Hnrbl Mntn Kings Coll Spnsh Exam 86; Jrnlsm.

NOWACKI, MARIA; Nazareth Acad; Philadelphia, PA; (4); Cmnty Wkr; Red Cross Aide; Spanish Clb; Orch; School Play; Sec Jr Cls; Rep Stu Cncl; JV Capt Cheerleading; NHS; Holy Family Coll; Nrsng.

NOWAK, SALLY; Gwynedd Mercy Acad; Lafayette Hill, PA; (2); Cmnty Wkr; Service Clb; Variety Show; Im Bsktbl; JV Fld Hcky; JV Sftbl; Acdmc Schlrshps Gwyndd Mrcy Acad & Mnt St Josephs Acad 86; Ed.

NOWAKOWSKI, MARIA; Pittston Area SR HS; Duryea, PA; (3); Nrsng.

NOWOTARSKI, SUSAN; Exeter SR HS; Reading, PA; (4); Pep Clb; Varsity Clb; Y-Teens; Mrchg Band; Variety Show; Stu Cncl; Var Cheerleading; Harcum JC; Med Asst.

NOYE, MELANIE; Williamsburg HS; Williamsburg, PA; (3); Camera Clb; 4-H; FBLA; Teachers Aide; Band; Nwsp Rptr; Nwsp Stf; Yrbk Stf; Vllybl; Hon Roll.

NOYER, CAROL; Iroquois HS; Erie, PA; (4); Am Leg Aux Girls St; Debate Tm; Drama Clb; Ski Clb; Pep Band; Yrbk Stf; Sec Jr Cls; Trs Sr Cls; Var Capt Cheerleading; NHS; Duquesne U; Phrmcy.

NOYES, MARK; Souderton Area HS; Schwenkville, PA; (3); Church Yth Grp; Band; Jazz Band; Im Bsbl; JV Bsktbl; Var L Golf; Im Socr; Var L Tennis; High Hon Roll; Hon Roll; Bus.

NUCCI, TERRI; Charleroi Area HS; Stockdale, PA; (3); Church Yth Grp; Spanish Clb; Varsity Clb; Chorus; Yrbk Stf; Var Co-Capt Cheerleading; Powder Puff Ftbl; Im Vllybl; Hon Roll; Career Clb 86-88; IN U PA; Bus.

NUDY, LISA; Conestoga SR HS; Berwyn, PA; (3); 76/423; Pres Natl Beta Clb; Rep Jr Cls; Rep Stu Cncl; Var Fld Hcky; Var Trk; Computer Clb; Orch; Lit Mag; Rep Frsh Cls; Rep Soph Cls; TEMPO Instrmntlst Yr 85; Pres Acad Fit Awd 85; T-E Stu Mnth 84; DE Cnty Yth Orch Awd 86 & 87.

NUGENT, MARY; Council Rock HS; Wash Corss, PA; (3); 220/941; Debate Tm; FBLA; Intnl Clb; Key Clb; Nwsp Stf; Yrbk Stf; Stu Cncl; Cheerleading; Powder Puff Ftbl; Hon Roll.

NUHFER, MARTHA; Cranberry HS; Seneca, PA; (3); 9/148; Church Yth Grp; Hosp Aide; Letterman Clb; Pep Clb; Science Clb; Spanish Clb; Varsity Clb; Chorus; Church Choir; School Musical; U Of Pittsburg-Titusville; Spns.

NUJOMA, YVONNE; Central HS; Philadelphia, PA; (2); High Hon Roll; Prfct Atten Awd; Hnr Rl 87; Beaver Coll; Med.

NULPH, MICHELLE; Mohawk Area JR-SR HS; New Galilee, PA; (3); Drama Clb; FBLA; FHA; Hosp Aide; Office Aide; SADD; Teachers Aide; Yrbk Stf; Mgr(s); Powder Puff Ftbl; Home Ec Acad Awd 87; Culinary Inst Pittsburgh; Chef.

NULTY, AMY; Nazareth Acad; Philadelphia, PA; (4); 3/117; VP German Clb; Library Aide; Model UN; NFL; Q&S; Yrbk Ed-Chief; Stu Cncl; Bsktbl; Hon Roll; NHS; Leonardine Checchio Achvt Awd Jrnlsm 87; Quill & Scrll 87; Holy Family Coll; Orthdntst.

NULTY, LESLIE; Nazareth Acad; Philadelphia, PA; (4); 2/117; Library Aide; NFL; Q&S; Spanish Clb; Yrbk Ed-Chief; Rep Stu Cncl; Bsktbl; Cit Awd; Hon Roll; NHS; Frances Weston Good Ctznshp Awd 87; Holy Family Coll; Pre Med.

NUNAMAKER, DEBBIE; St Marys Area HS; St Marys, PA; (2); Church Yth Grp; JV Trk; Hon Roll.

NUNAMAKER, JUNE; Dayton JR/Sr HS; Templeton, PA; (3); Church Yth Grp; Band; Chorus; Color Guard; Mrchg Band; Pep Band; School Musical; :Secretarial.

NUNAMAKER, TONY; Elk County Christian HS; St Marys, PA; (3); 39/72; Boys Clb Am; JV Bsktbl; Var L Ftbl; Var L Trk; Hon Roll.

NUNEMAKER, STEVEN; Octorara HS; Parkesburg, PA; (3); 82/157; Aud/Vis; Boy Scts; FFA; Variety Show; Score Keeper; Socr; Ag Schlrshp Awd 85-86; Star Greenhnd Awd 84-85; Ag Mechncs 86-87; Audio Engrng.

NURSS, LEANNE; Wilson Christian Acad; Mckeesport, PA; (3); 1/11; Church Yth Grp; Exploring; Yrbk Stf; Sec Soph Cls; Sec Jr. Cls; Var Stu Cncl; Score Keeper; High Hon Roll; NHS; 3rd Pl Wnnr Buhl Sci Fair 85; PA St U; Chmcl Engnrng.

NUSS, CATRINA L; Boyertown Area HS; Bechtelsville, PA; (3); 13/461; Am Leg Aux Girls St; Chorus; Church Choir; Yrbk Bus Mgr; JV Var Bsktbl; Var L Sftbl; High Hon Roll; NHS; Prfct Atten Awd; Pres Schlr; Paralegl Studies.

NUSS, HEATHER; Pocono Mountain HS; Pocono Lk, PA; (4); 58/250; Pep Clb; Ski Clb; Rep Sr Cls; Hon Roll; JC Awd; Schlrshp Mem Studio Art 87; Kutztown U; Cmnctn Dsgn.

NUSSBAUMER, JILL; Connellsville Area HS; Connellsville, PA; (3); 19/535; Sftbl; Vllybl; High Hon Roll; NHS.

NUTTER, SCOTT; Christian School Of York; Wrightsville, PA; (4); Trs Sr Cls; Bsbl; Bsktbl; L Socr; Assn Chrstn Schls Intl Distngshd Stdnt 86-87; Grace Coll; Bus.

NUZZO, JODY; Corry Area HS; Corry, PA; (4); 10/200; Cmnty Wkr; Political Wkr; Concert Band; Jazz Band; Mrchg Band; Trs Sr Cls; L Trk; High Hon Roll; Pres Schlr; Sheen Scholar Pre-Med Stu 87; Geneva Coll Hnr Schlr; Geneva Coll; Physicn.

NUZZO, MICHAEL M; Bethel Park SR HS; Bethel Park, PA; (3); 8/530; Am Leg Boys St; Pres Church Yth Grp; Debate Tm; VP JA; NFL; Off Frsh Cls; JV Bsbl; NHS; Am Lgn Oratorical Cont 87; JR Achvt Wstrn PA Co Yr 87; Kenyon Coll; Corp Law.

NUZZOLO, DAVID; Pennsbury HS; Yardley, PA; (2); Church Yth Grp; Teachers Aide; Im Bsktbl; Im Vllybl; Cit Awd; High Hon Roll; Hon Roll; Prfct Atten Awd; La Salle U; Marine Bio.

NYCE, DREW; Central Bucks West HS; Chalfont, PA; (3); 13/491; Aud/Vis; Var Bsbl; High Hon Roll; Hon Roll; Jr NHS; Street Hcky 86-87; Acdmcs Ftnss Awd 85; Bst Art Avg 85; Sprts Phys.

NYCE, LORI; Central Dauphin East HS; Harrisburg, PA; (3); French Clb; Acpl Chr; Band; Chorus; Concert Band; Mrchg Band; High Hon Roll; Jr NHS; NHS; Pres Schlr; Frnch Tchr.

NYE, LES; Eastern HS; York, PA; (4); 3/168; Chess Clb; Church Yth Grp; Cit Awd; High Hon Roll; Jr NHS; NHS; Am Leg Awd 84; Deans List Ps/Y 86; Penn ST Main; Comp Sci.

NYE, LISA; Bishop Mc Devitt HS; Harrisburg, PA; (3); FBLA; SADD; Chorus; Yrbk Stf; Bus Admin.

NYE, PAMELA; Donegal HS; Maytown, PA; (4); Girl Scts; Spanish Clb; Chorus; Nwsp Stf; Yrbk Stf; JV Sftbl; High Hon Roll; Hon Roll; Secy.

NYGA, BETH; Highlands SR HS; Natrona Hts, PA; (4); Exploring; JA; Key Clb; Stage Crew; Nwsp Rptr; Tennis; Jr NHS; NHS; Prfct Atten Awd; Brown & Gld Awds 85-87; U Of Pittsburgh; Psych.

NYKAZA, LISA; Riverside JR SR HS; Taylor, PA; (4); 4/175; Church Yth Grp; German Clb; Scholastic Bowl; Ski Clb; Nwsp Stf; Yrbk Stf; Stu Cncl; High Hon Roll; NHS; All Amer Acad Awd 85-87; Gov Schlr Perf Arts 86; U Of Scranton Pres Schlrshp 87; U Of Scranton; Bio-Chem.

NYKOLUK, MIA; Lower Dauphin SR HS; Hershey, PA; (3); Band; School Play; Stat Score Keeper; JV Im Vllybl; Hon Roll; Cmp Cnsllr 84-87; Emplyd-Ctrer & Gft Sllr 86 & 87; Mrn Bio.

NYMAN, LEANNE; North Allegheny SR HS; Pittsburgh, PA; (3); 49/649; JA; Hon Roll; NHS; Sci Distngshd Achvmt Awd 87.

NYPAVER, PATTY; Springdale HS; Harwick, PA; (4); 7/108; Church Yth Grp; GAA; SADD; Band; Mrchg Band; Yrbk Ed-Chief; Yrbk Rptr; Yrbk Sprt Ed; Yrbk Stf; Capt Vllybl; Pace U; Psych.

NYQUIST, KURT; St Marys Area HS; Kersey, PA; (4); 38/278; Am Leg Boys St; Im Bsbl; JV Var Bsktbl; Stat Ftbl; Im Sftbl; Im Tennis; Cit Awd; NHS; Grove City Coll; Accntng.

NYQUIST, POLLY; Unionville HS; Chadds Ford, PA; (4); 4/316; AFS; Church Yth Grp; Mu Alpha Theta; Chorus; School Musical; Swing Chorus; Nwsp Bus Mgr; Mgr Sftbl; NHS; Ntl Merit SF.

NYSSE, JOHN D; Pennsbury HS; Levittown, PA; (4); 43/770; Lit Mag; Rep Stu Cncl; Im Bsktbl; Hon Roll; Pres Acdmc Ftns Awd 86-87; Trntn ST Coll; Art.

NYZIO, KAREN; J W Hallahan HS; Philadelphia, PA; (3); 39/298; Cmnty Wkr; Chorus; Nwsp Rptr; Nwsp Stf; Yrbk Rptr; Yrbk Stf; High Hon Roll; Hon Roll; Outstndng Achvt Phys Sci 85; Outstndng Perf Chorus 87; Elem Ed.

O BARTO, WENDY; South Allegheny HS; Glassport, PA; (4); 3/184; Pres Church Yth Grp; Rptr FBLA; Y-Teens; Nwsp Ed-Chief; Powder Puff Ftbl; High Hon Roll; Hon Roll; Bradford Schl Of Bus; Accntng.

O BOYLE, BRYEN; Chichester SR HS; Aston, PA; (3); Church Yth Grp; Drama Clb; Band; Chorus; Concert Band; Jazz Band; Mrchg Band; School Musical; Rep Stu Cncl; Var L Wrstlng; Teens N Talent Dist Piano Comptn 1st Pl 86; Teens N Talent Regl Piano Comptn 4th Pl 87; Musician.

O BOYLE, JOSEPH; Pittston Area HS; Dupont, PA; (3); Church Yth Grp; Computer Clb; Key Clb; Var Bsktbl; Var Trk; High Hon Roll; NHS; NEDT Cert 84-85; U Scranton; Comp Sci.

O BOYLE, LAURA BETH; Pocono Central Catholic HS; Pocono Summit, PA; (3); 2/32; Ski Clb; Chorus; Trs Jr Cls; JV Var Cheerleading; JV Sftbl; DAR Awd; High Hon Roll; NHS; Voice Dem Awd; Law.

O BOYLE, STEVEN M; Pittston Area HS; Avoca, PA; (4); Church Yth Grp; Math Clb; Spanish Clb; Chorus; Capt JV Bsktbl; L Crs Cntry; Var Capt Trk; High Hon Roll; VP NHS; Rotary Awd; Moravian Coll.

O BRIEN, ANDREW; Tyrone Area HS; Tyrone, PA; (3); Spanish Clb; Varsity Clb; Wrstlng; High Hon Roll; NHS; Outstndng Stu Engl 86-87; Penn St U; Htl Mgmt.

O BRIEN, ANNE; North Hills HS; Pittsburgh, PA; (3); Drama Clb; Thesps; Band; School Musical; School Play; Stage Crew; Lit Mag; High Hon Roll; NHS; Med Resrch.

O BRIEN, DANIEL; Pocono Central Catholic HS; Mt Pocono, PA; (4); 4/32; Pep Clb; Scholastic Bowl; Ski Clb; Var Bsbl; Var Bsktbl; Var Capt Socr; Im Vllybl; Hon Roll; Pres NHS; Irish Way Pgm 86; Hugh O Brian Yth Leadrshp Semnr 85; Villanova U; Economics.

O BRIEN, DEBRA; Connellsville SR HS; S Connellsville, PA; (3); Drama Clb; Var Tennis; JV Bsktbl; Bus.

O BRIEN, ERIN; Northwestern HS; Albion, PA; (4); 39/145; Am Leg Aux Girls St; Sec Thesps; Concert Band; Drm Mjr(t); Madrigals; School Musical; Var Capt Cheerleading; Var Trk; JP Sousa Awd; Edinboro U; Elem Ed.

O BRIEN, KELLY; Minersville Area HS; Minersville, PA; (3); Spanish Clb; Wrstlng; Achvt Awd 86-87; Bus.

O BRIEN, KELLY; Rockwood HS; Markleton, PA; (3); #12 In Class; NFL; ROTC; Speech Tm; Band; School Play; Nwsp Stf; Stu Cncl; Cheerleading; Sftbl; High Hon Roll; Eng Awd 86; Natl Hnr Roll 86-87; Intl Forgn Lang Awd 86-87; Creative Wrtng.

O BRIEN, KEVIN E; Bethlehem Catholic HS; Allentown, PA; (3); 54/206; VP Jr Cls; Rep Stu Cncl; L Ftbl; Wt Lftg; PA ST; Mech Engrng.

O BRIEN, NANCY; Nazareth Acad; Philadelphia, PA; (3); 1/125; Chorus; School Musical; Nwsp Rptr; Rep Soph Cls; Rep Jr Cls; Rep Stu Cncl; VP NHS; Pfull Schlrshp To Nazareth Acad 84; Half Schlrshp To Mt St Josephs 84; Dstgshd Cert Of Merit 84-87.

O BRIEN, PHILIP; Pittston Area HS; Inkerman, PA; (2); Church Yth Grp; Ski Clb; Band; Concert Band; Jazz Band; Mrchg Band; Swmmng; High Hon Roll; U Of Scranton; Medicine.

O BRIEN, RENEE; Aliquippa HS; Aliquippa, PA; (4); Math Tm; Yrbk Ed-Chief; Yrbk Stf; Hon Roll; NHS; Gftd Tlntd Prgrm 84-87; Fshn Mrchndsng.

O BRIEN, TANYA; Rockwood Area HS; Somerset, PA; (2); Computer Clb; VP 4-H; Band; Chorus; Mrchg Band; Var JV Bsktbl; High Hon Roll; Hon Roll; Vet Asst.

O BRIEN, THOMAS J; Archbishop Wood HS; Warminster, PA; (4); 99/285; Aud/Vis; Chess Clb; Computer Clb; Drama Clb; Science Clb; Band; Concert Band; Mrchg Band; School Musical; School Play; IEEE Awd Bst Engrng Prjct 87; Archbshp Wood Sci Fair, DE Valley Sci Fair 1st ,K; Drexel U; Elec Engrng.

O BRIEN, TRISH; Jenkintown HS; Jenkintown, PA; (3); 4/37; Varsity Clb; Chorus; Nwsp Stf; Capt Bsktbl; Var Fld Hcky; Var Lcrss; French Hon Soc; Hon Roll; Jr NHS; NHS.

O CILKA, ANGELA; Mars Area SR HS; Valencia, PA; (4); 10/141; Sec German Clb; GAA; Thesps; Varsity Clb; Chorus; School Musical; Yrbk Stf; Off Soph Cls; High Hon Roll; NHS; PA ST U; Business.

O CONNELL, BRENT; Johnsonburg Area HS; Wilcox, PA; (4); Cmnty Wkr; Varsity Clb; Var Trk; Var Wt Lftg; Hon Roll; Accntng.

O CONNELL, SHAUN; Notre Dame HS; Easton, PA; (3); Church Yth Grp; VP Exploring; Political Wkr; Yrbk Stf; Rep Stu Cncl; Var L Ftbl; Wt Lftg; Var L Wrstlng; High Hon Roll; Hon Roll; Pres Acad Fit Awd 85; Thfology III Outstndng Effort Awd 87; Perfect Attend Awd 86.

O CONNELL, THOMAS; Central Catholic HS; Pittsburgh, PA; (2); 69/302; JV Bsktbl; Var Crs Cntry; Var Trk; Hon Roll.

O CONNOR, CHRIS; St James H S For Boys; Brookhaven, PA; (4); 4/130; Aud/Vis; VP Church Yth Grp; Var Crs Cntry; Var Golf; Var Trk; Var Wrstlng; High Hon Roll; NHS; $2000 Mrnst Schlrsthp To St James 83; Drftng Awd 85; Acdmc All Amer Awd 85; U DE; Cvl Engrng.

O CONNOR, JENNY; Petes Township HS; Mc Murray, PA; (3); AFS; Key Clb; Math Tm; Rep Frsh Cls; JV Var Cheerleading; Powder Puff Ftbl; JV Trk; High Hon Roll; Hon Roll; Giftd Pgm 84-86; Lwyr.

O CONNOR, KEVIN FRANCIS; St James Catholic HS; Brookhaven, PA; (4); 6/130; Im Bsktbl; Var Crs Cntry; JV Golf; Var Trk; JV Wrstlng; High Hon Roll; Hon Roll; NHS; Soc Marianists Scholar 83-87; Villanova; Civl Engrng.

O CONNOR, MICHAEL B; Trinity HS; Washington, PA; (3); 14/402; Church Yth Grp; French Clb; Letterman Clb; Var L Bsktbl; JV Golf; High Hon Roll; NHS; Vrsty Bsktbll Tm Asst Ldr 85-87; Bus.

O CONNOR, STACEY; Central York SR HS; York, PA; (3); 4-H; PAVAS; Band; Chorus; Mrchg Band; School Musical; JV Fld Hcky; 4-H Awd; Hon Roll; Elem Ed.

O DEA, TERRI; Tunkhannock Area HS; Tunkhannock, PA; (3); Letterman Clb; Pep Clb; Spanish Clb; Varsity Clb; Yrbk Stf; Capt Cheerleading; JV Fld Hcky; Var Sftbl; Hon Roll; NHS; U Of Pittsburgh; Physcl Thrpy.

O DELL, COLLEEN; North Hills HS; Pittsburgh, PA; (3); 29/493; Church Yth Grp; Cmnty Wkr; Key Clb; JV Sftbl; Var L Swmmng; High Hon Roll; Hon Roll; NHS; Bus.

O DONALD, RICHARD; Bellefonte SR HS; Bellefonte, PA; (3); 41/215; Model UN; Yrbk Phtg; VP Frsh Cls; VP Soph Cls; JV Ftbl; Hon Roll; PA ST U; Arch.

O DONNELL, ADAM; Girard Coll; Philadelphia, PA; (3); #1 In Class; Boy Scts; Varsity Clb; Band; Chorus; Pres Soph Cls; Var Capt Crs Cntry; Var Capt Swmmng; Var L Twrlr; High Hon Roll; NHS; Eagle Scout Awd 87; George H Dunkle Awd Outstndg Boy Scout Ideas 86; 7th Pl Bus Awd 87; Air Force Acad; Aerospace Engrn.

O DONNELL, ALICEN; Scranton Preparatory Schl; Dunmore, PA; (2); Church Yth Grp; Dance Clb; Hosp Aide; JA; Latin Clb; Pep Clb; Ski Clb; Nwsp Phtg; Yrbk Phtg; Var Cheerleading; PA ST U; Law.

O DONNELL, CAROLE; St Francis Acad; Pittsburgh, PA; (4); 8/34; VP Church Yth Grp; Cmnty Wkr; Hosp Aide; Pep Clb; VP Red Cross Aide; SADD; Nwsp Stf; High Hon Roll; Hon Roll; NHS; Pres Ftns Awd; Acadmc All Amer; Penn ST Mckeesprt; Bio.

O DONNELL, HEATHER; Mid-Valley Secondary HS; Dickson City, PA; (3); Dance Clb; Drama Clb; SADD; School Musical; School Play; Stage Crew; Nwsp Stf; Fshn Dsgn.

O DONNELL, JENIFFER; Lincoln HS; Ellwood City, PA; (3); Spanish Clb; Y-Teens; Chorus; JV Bsktbl; Powder Puff Ftbl; Trk; Beaver Cnty CC.

O DONNELL, JIM; Father Judge HS; Philadelphia, PA; (3); 89/452; Church Yth Grp; Cmnty Wkr; Im Bsbl; Var Bowling; Im Fld Hcky; Im Ftbl; Hon Roll; La Salle Coll; Accntnt.

O DONNELL, MARY; Brookville Area HS; Sigel, PA; (3); 65/175; Art Clb; FNA; Chorus; Capt Drill Tm; Arch.

O DONNELL, MEGHAN; Quaker Valley HS; Sewickley, PA; (2); Hon Roll; Stu Cncl Awd; Hnr Roll Awd; Cmnctns.

O DONNELL, MICHAEL; Archbishop Wood For Boys; Southampton, PA; (4); 23/279; Church Yth Grp; SADD; Yrbk Stf; Var Bsbl; JV Crs Cntry; Var Trk; Var High Hon Roll; NHS; Math Hghst Grd Cmltv For Yr 86-87; Schlrshp Wth Hnrs 86-87; PA ST U; Engnrng.

O DONNELL, MIKE; Daniel Boone Area Schl; Earlville, PA; (2); 18/166; German Clb; Ski Clb; Varsity Clb; VP Frsh Cls; VP Soph Cls; JV Crs Cntry; Trk; Wrstlng; Cit Awd; Hon Roll; Millersville U; Med.

O DONNELL, ROBERT; Towanda Area HS; Towanda, PA; (3); Boy Scts; Church Yth Grp; Letterman Clb; Model UN; Ski Clb; Ftbl; Trk; Hon Roll; 2 Slvr Mdls Natl Jr Olympic Trk 85-86; Rtry Ldrshp Trnng Keystone Coll 86; Arch.

O DONOHUE, LINDA; Bishop Mc Devitt HS; Dresher, PA; (2); 63/345; Drill Tm; Mrchg Band; JV Trk; High Hon Roll; Hon Roll; NCTE Awd; Natl Cncl Of Teachrs Algebra Awd 86-87.

O GRADY, MICHAEL; Devon Prep Schl; Newtown Sq, PA; (3); 12/43; School Musical; School Play; Lit Mag; Trs Soph Cls; Rep Stu Cncl; JV Socr; Hon Roll; Ntl Merit Ltr; La Salle U; Engl.

O HARA, JOHN; Purchase Line HS; Clymer, PA; (2); Stat Bsktbl; Im Ftbl; Ftbl Ltr 85-86; Air Frc CC; Arch.

O HARAH, DANIELLE; Harbor Creek HS; Harbor Creek, PA; (4); 52/213; Band; School Play; Variety Show; Stu Cncl; Pom Pon; Powder Puff Ftbl; Trk; Hon Roll; NHS; Mercy Hurst; Intr Desgn.

O KEEFE, KEVIN P; Archbishop Ryan High School For Boys; Philadelphia, PA; (2); 2/352; High Hon Roll; Univ Of PA; Merch Eng.

O KEEFE, SIOBHAN; St Basil Acad; Philadelphia, PA; (3); Computer Clb; Pres Drama Clb; French Clb; SADD; Pres Thesps; School Musical; School Play; Stage Crew; Yrbk Stf; Hon Roll; Natl Hnrs Hstry, Govt & Sci 87; Prncpls Awd Chem 87; Bus Admin.

O LARE, CHRISSY; North Allegheny HS; Pittsburgh, PA; (2); 9/630; Church Yth Grp; Exploring; Hosp Aide; JV Socr; Hon Roll; Jr NHS.

O LEARY, CAROL; Claysburg-Kimmel HS; Portage, PA; (3); Sec Trs Church Yth Grp; Speech Tm; SADD; Band; Chorus; Church Choir; Hon Roll; NHS; German Clb; Ski Clb; Mid-East All Str Band 86; Dist Chorus Fstvl 85; Erly Chldhd Educ.

O LEARY, JOSEPH; Bishop Mc Devitt HS; Steelton, PA; (3); 40/250; Debate Tm; Drama Clb; Nwsp Ed-Chief; Rep Soph Cls; Rep Jr Cls; Trs Sr Cls; Trs Stu Cncl; NHS; Voice Dem Awd; Peer Cnslr 86-88; Law.

O MAHEN, COLLEEN; Hickory SR HS; Hermitage, PA; (4); 5/190; Service Clb; Varsity Clb; Chorus; School Musical; JV Var Bsktbl; Capt Crs Cntry; Capt Trk; NHS; Spanish NHS; Math.

O MALLEY, CHRISTA; Bishop O Hara HS; Dickson City, PA; (3); 4/99; French Clb; Hosp Aide; Latin Clb; Ski Clb; Stage Crew; High Hon Roll; NHS; Arch Engnr.

O MALLEY, DAVID; Cardinal O Hara HS; Springfield, PA; (3); Church Yth Grp; Debate Tm; JA; Service Clb; Nwsp Rptr; Nwsp Stf; Lit Mag; Bsbl; Pre Law.

O MALLEY, LUCY; Scranton Prep; Scranton, PA; (4); 9/190; Church Yth Grp; Cmnty Wkr; Pep Clb; Political Wkr; Quiz Bowl; Scholastic Bowl; School Play; Cheerleading; Trk; Gov Hon Prg Awd; Cngrssnl Schlr 86; U Of PA.

O MEARA, AMY K; Mount St Joseph Acad; Huntingdon Valley, PA; (4); Church Yth Grp; Cmnty Wkr; Drama Clb; Latin Clb; Science Clb; Spanish Clb; Chorus; School Musical; School Play; Stage Crew; Snasa/NSTA Spac Shuttle Stu Invlvmnt Pgm Natl Wnnr 84-85; PA Jr Acad Sci Del AAAS Natl Cnvtn 87; Bio.

O MEARA, TARA; Pennsbury HS; Morrisville, PA; (3); Computer Clb; German Clb; Intnl Clb; Spanish Clb; Church Choir; Rptr Nwsp Rptr; Nwsp Stf; Hon Roll; NHS.

O NEAL, ERICA; Connellsville Area HS; Vanderbilt, PA; (2); 185/575; Office Aide; Radio Clb; Flag Corp; Stage Crew; VP Soph Cls; Hon Roll; Prfct Atten Awd; Psychlgy.

O NEAL, KELLEY E; Henderson HS; West Chester, PA; (3); 44/376; Church Yth Grp; Hosp Aide; Intnl Clb; Sec Jr Civitan Int; Ski Clb; SADD; School Musical; Yrbk Stf; Var Trk; Hon Roll.

O NEIL, SHANNON; Cedar Crest HS; Lebanon, PA; (3); 31/342; Church Yth Grp; Pep Clb; Spanish Clb; SADD; Chorus; High Hon Roll; Hon Roll; Radiolgy.

O NEIL, TERESA; Keystoone HS; Knox, PA; (3); Church Yth Grp; Pep Clb; Red Cross Aide; SADD; VICA; Chorus; Hon Roll; Sec Keystone Yth Ed Assoc 87-88; 1st & 3rd Pl Voctnl Indstrl Clubs Amer Cont 87; Nrsng.

O NEILL, BRIAN; Cumberland Valley HS; Mechanicsburg, PA; (3); L Ftbl; L Trk; Hon Roll; Spanish NHS.

O NEILL, LISA M; Ambridge Area HS; Ambridge, PA; (4); 35/265; Hosp Aide; Library Aide; Pep Clb; Off Frsh Cls; Off Soph Cls; Off Jr Cls; Sec Sr Cls; Bradford Schl; Scrtrl.

O NEILL, NOREEN; Clarion Area HS; Clarion, PA; (3); Art Clb; Hon Roll; Edinboro U; Comms.

O NEILL, PATRICK; Bishop Hafey HS; White Haven, PA; (4); Sec Chess Clb; Teachers Aide; L Var Socr; High Hon Roll; Hon Roll; Wstrn ST Coll Acad Schlrshp, Mc Cann Schl Of Bus Outstndng Stu Awd 87; CPA.

O NEILL, SCOTT; Penn Cambria HS; Cresson, PA; (2); Boy Scts; Exploring; Im Bsbl; Im Bsktbl; Im Vllybl; Am Leg Awd 85.

O ROURKE, CANDACE J; Danville Area HS; Danville, PA; (3); 40/200; Sec Church Yth Grp; Hosp Aide; Key Clb; Ski Clb; Var Fld Hcky; High Hon Roll; NHS; NEDT Awd; Pres Schlr.

O ROURKE, PATRICK; Olney HS; Philadelphia, PA; (2); Teachers Aide; Temple U; Phys Ther.

O SHEA, AMY; Carlynton HS; Pittsburgh, PA; (4); 5/161; Sec Letterman Clb; Ski Clb; Spanish Clb; Trs Jr Cls; Trs Sr Cls; Stat Bsbl; L Capt Swmmng; L Tennis; CC Awd; High Hon Roll; Schlr Ath 87; John Carroll U; Math.

O SHEA, ELIZABETH; W Philadelphia Catholic Girls HS; Philadelphia, PA; (3); 1/246; Nwsp Rptr; Nwsp Stf; Hon Roll; NHS; Prfct Atten Awd; Comm.

O SHEA, PATRICK; Beaver Area JR SR HS; Beaver, PA; (2); Church Yth Grp; Band; Concert Band; Jazz Band; Mrchg Band; Pep Band; Hon Roll; Penn ST U; Cvl Engrng.

O SHEA, SHEILA; Bedford HS; Bedford, PA; (3); Pres Church Yth Grp; Chorus; Sec Frsh Cls; Sec Soph Cls; Sec Jr Cls; Sec Sr Cls; Sec Stu Cncl; Var Bsktbl; Var Sftbl; Var Vllybl; Chld Psych.

O SHELL, TODD; Harmony HS; Cherry Tree, PA; (4); 14/50; Yrbk Phtg; VP Sr Cls; Var L Bsbl; Var L Bsktbl; Dnfth Awd; NHS; Ski Clb; Band; Concert Band; US Army Rsrv Schlr/Athl Awd 87; NEC Acad All-Amer 87; United Elec Corp Ldrshp Awd 87; Slippery Rock U; Comm.

O TOOLE, CHANTELLE L; Pittston Area HS; Pittston, PA; (3); Dance Clb; French Clb; FNA; Ski Clb; Chorus; High Hon Roll; Hon Roll; Behavrl Sci.

O TOOLE, JOSEPH; Central Catholic HS; Pittsburgh, PA; (3); 20/272; JCL; Chorus; Stu Cncl; Socr; Swmmng; Trk; High Hon Roll; NHS; Latn Hnr Socty 86-87.

O TOOLE, MARGARET; Sacred Heart HS; Pittsburgh, PA; (4); 5/140; Computer Clb; Dance Clb; Hosp Aide; Math Clb; Off Ski Clb; Capt Crs Cntry; Capt Trk; High Hon Roll; Bsktbl; Gym; Westinghouse Sci Honors Inst 86-87; Medallion Ball 86; Boston Coll; Bus.

OAKES, DUANE M; Downingtown SR HS; Exton, PA; (4); 8/551; German Clb; Letterman Clb; Ski Clb; Pres Chorus; Rep Stu Cncl; Var L Socr; High Hon Roll; NHS; Hnbl Mntn Sccr 86-87; Downgtwn Rotry Stdnt Mnth 86-87; Engrng.

OAKES, LORI; Hollidaysburg SR HS; Hollidaysburg, PA; (3); Drama Clb; Pres 4-H; Chorus; School Musical; School Play; Rep Stu Cncl; Mgr(s); Mgr Swmmng; Hon Roll; Ntl Merit Ltr; Duke U; Mktg.

OAKES, MIKE; Pocono Mtn HS; Tobyhanna, PA; (2); Art Clb; Aud/Vis; Aud/Vis; Spanish Clb; Rep Frsh Cls; Ftbl; Trk; JV Ftbl Ltr 86-87; Cnstrctn.

OAKILL, GREGG; Minersville Area HS; Pottsville, PA; (3); Crs Cntry; Wrstlng; PA ST; Comp.

OAKLEY, ANDREA; Lower Dauphin HS; Middletown, PA; (3); 109/276; Im Bsktbl; Var L Fld Hcky; Stat Wrstlng; Bus.

OAKLEY, BRYAN; Chartiers-Houston HS; Houston, PA; (4); 11/120; Church Yth Grp; Mu Alpha Theta; NAACP; Varsity Clb; Church Choir; Rep Stu Cncl; Var Capt Bsktbl; Var Capt Ftbl; Wt Lftg; Hon Roll; Latin Achvt Awd 87; Deans Schlrshp U SC 87-88; Gftd & Tlntd Schlr 83-87; U Of Southern CA; Biolgcl Sci.

OAKLEY, ESTHER; Athens HS; Sayre, PA; (3); 1/135; VP Pres SADD; Chorus; Color Guard; Trs Jr Cls; VP Sr Cls; Var JV Bsktbl; JV L Sftbl; Var JV Vllybl; NHS; Var Ntl Merit Ltr; Pre Med.

OAKS, CINDY; Harmony HS; Westover, PA; (3); 3/51; Pres Trs Church Yth Grp; Library Aide; Ski Clb; Chorus; Color Guard; Mrchg Band; Yrbk Ed-Chief; Trs Soph Cls; Im Stat Bsktbl; Var Score Keeper.

OATES, MICHELLE; Linesville HS; Linesville, PA; (2); 23/76; Art Clb; Church Yth Grp; Ski Clb; Var Crs Cntry; Spanish Clb; Band; Concert Band; Drill Tm; Mrchg Band; School Musical.

OBARA, DANIEL; Greensburg Central Catholic HS; Irwin, PA; (3); 22/246; Chess Clb; Church Yth Grp; Cmnty Wkr; Ftbl; Trk; Wt Lftg; High Hon Roll; NHS; Outstndng Nwspr Carrier Yr 84; Penn ST; Aerospc Engrng.

OBELDOBEL, ROSEANN; Carrick HS; Pittsburgh, PA; (3); Yrbk Stf; Crs Cntry; Swmmng; Trk; High Hon Roll; 1st Plc Frgn Lang Pstr 87; Robert Morris Coll; Acctg.

OBENREDER, CHRISTINE; Harbor Creek HS; Erie, PA; (4); Political Wkr; Color Guard; School Play; Nwsp Rptr; Ed Yrbk Phtg; Rep Stu Cncl; Tennis; Hon Roll; NHS; Ntl Hnr Soc Jrnlsts 86-87; Drmtcs Awd 87; PA ST U; Thtr Arts.

OBER, GERALDINE; Hopewell HS; Aliquippa, PA; (3); 13/255; Pres Exploring; German Clb; Math Tm; Pep Clb; Chorus; Drill Tm; School Musical; Pom Pon; High Hon Roll; Acdmc All Am 87; Chld Psych.

OBER, SCOTT; Elizabethtown Area HS; Elizabethtown, PA; (3); Church Yth Grp; JV Bsbl; Schlstc Art Awds Merit Cert 87; Photogrphy Dir.

OBER JR, TERRY R; Donegal HS; Mount Joy, PA; (2); Church Yth Grp; Im Ftbl; Im JV Wrstlng.

OBER, TRACY; Yough SR HS; Irwin, PA; (3); 65/242; FBLA; High Hon Roll; FBLA Rgnl Ldrshp Conf 3rd Pl 87; Bradford Bus Schl; Law.

OBERDICK, GREGORY; William Penn SR HS; York, PA; (3); 35/465; Cmnty Wkr; FBLA; JA; SADD; Chorus; School Musical; Im Swmmng; Im Wt Lftg; Hon Roll; Jr NHS; Bucknelle; Comp Prog.

OBERDORF, ERIC; Leechburg Area HS; Leechburg, PA; (3); Yrbk Stf; L Bsbl; L Ftbl; Im Vllybl.

OBERDORF, JOSEPH; Danville SR HS; Riverside, PA; (2); Church Yth Grp; Computer Clb; Hon Roll; Prfct Atten Awd; Comp Prgmng.

OBERDORF, LISA; Mifflinburg HS; Lewisburg, PA; (1); French Clb; Key Clb; Bsktbl; High Hon Roll; Hon Roll; Pol Sci.

OBERHARDT, MATTHEW; Trinity HS; Camp Hill, PA; (2); 3/139; Model UN; Red Cross Aide; School Play; Rep Stu Cncl; Var L Crs Cntry; Var L Trk; High Hon Roll; NHS; Church Yth Grp; Cmnty Wkr; Jr Div Grand Chmpn At Capitol Area Sci & Engrng Fair 86; Achvt Cert For Poetry 86; Bioengrng.

OBERHOLTZER, BETH; Hempfield HS; E Petersburg, PA; (3); 34/396; Sec Church Yth Grp; Chorus; School Musical; Variety Show; Hon Roll; NHS.

OBERLANDER, MIKE; Fort Le Boeuf HS; Waterford, PA; (3); 32/236; Church Yth Grp; 4-H; Science Clb; Wrstlng; High Hon Roll; Mchncl Engrng.

OBERMAN, JAMES; Liberty HS; Bethlehem, PA; (3); 8/460; Model UN; School Play; Nwsp Rptr; Yrbk Bus Mgr; Lit Mag; Pres Frsh Cls; Pres Soph Cls; Rep Stu Cncl; Var L Swmmng; NHS; NHS Recog Awd 86-87; Schl Rep Rotary Spnsrd Ldrshp Conf 87; St Cult Exch Scholar Japan 87; Med.

OBERMEIER, JOSEPH; Meadville Area SR HS; Meadville, PA; (3); 45/328; Church Yth Grp; French Clb; Trk; Penn St; Aero Engr.

OBERT, RALPH; Union City Area HS; Union City, PA; (3); 2/120; Ski Clb; Varsity Clb; Band; Chorus; Concert Band; School Musical; Bsktbl; Ftbl; Trk; Wt Lftg.

OBES, NICOLE; John S Fine HS; Nanticoke, PA; (3); 26/228; Cheerleading; Fld Hcky; High Hon Roll; Ski Clb; Variety Show.

OBITKO, RENEE; Ringgold HS; Monongahela, PA; (3); French Clb; Stat Bsktbl; JV Vllybl; French Hon Soc; Bus.

OBLICK, SUE; Liberty SR HS; Bethlehem, PA; (3); 89/429; VICA; Nrthamptn Cnty Area CC; Comp.

OBRAN, KELLY; Bethlehem Catholic HS; Bethlehem, PA; (3); 44/210; Church Yth Grp; Science Clb; Im Vllybl; High Hon Roll; Northamptor Area CC; Med Tech.

OBRANOVICH, VICKI; Elizabeth Forward HS; Mckeesport, PA; (2); French Clb; Hon Roll; U Pittsburgh; Engr.

OBRIEN, KELLY; Mahoney Area HS; Mahonoy City, PA; (3); Drama Clb; FHA; Ski Clb; Spanish Clb; Variety Show; Nwsp Rptr; Nwsp Stf; Yrbk Stf; Trk; Educ.

OBUCHOWSKI, JODI; Mt Lebanon HS; Mt Lebanon, PA; (4); Cmnty Wkr; German Clb; Hosp Aide; Ski Clb; School Play; Variety Show; Pres Frsh Cls; VP Pres CAP; Pres VP Jr Cls; Stu Cncl; Medallion Ball 86; Schlrshp Coll Wooster 87; Coll Wooster.

OCAMPO, BETH; Hempfield HS; Mountville, PA; (3); MD Art Inst; Intr Dsgn.

OCCHIPINTI, MICHELE; Riverside HS; Taylor, PA; (4); Art Clb; Drama Clb; Chorus; School Musical; School Play; Off Stu Cncl; JV Var Cheerleading; Hon Roll; East Stroudsburg; Psych.

OCEPEK, BRIAN; Greensburg Central Ctholic HS; Greensburg, PA; (3); 26/240; VP Soph Cls; Rep Jr Cls; Rep Stu Cncl; Mgr Bsbl; Mgr Ftbl; Mgr(s); Im Sftbl; Trk; Im Vllybl; High Hon Roll.

OCHS, EDITH MARIE; Brookville Area HS; Brookville, PA; (3); Drama Clb; French Clb; Ski Clb; Band; Chorus; Concert Band; Jazz Band; Mrchg Band; Pep Band; School Musical; Mrktng.

OCHS, SUZANNE; North Clarion JR-SR HS; Lucinda, PA; (3); 1/110; VP Chorus; Yrbk Stf; VP Jr Cls; Stu Cncl; Stat Bsktbl; Stat Socr; Var L Trk; High Hon Roll; Hon Roll; NHS; Co Athr & Co Edtr JR Hstrns 87-88; Hstry.

OCKELMANN-LO BELLO, LISA; Western Wayne HS; Lake Ariel, PA; (3); Spanish Clb; Rep Stu Cncl; Mgr(s); Var Sftbl; Trk; Berkeley Bus Schl; Fshn Mrktng.

OCONNELL, JAYNE; Williamsport Area HS; Williamsport, PA; (4); Teachers Aide; Chorus; Church Choir; Kiwanis Awd; Martha C Thatcher Prize, Valerie M Aponick Schlrshp & Yth Fellowship Awd 87; Lycoming Coll; Accntng.

OCONNELL, KELLY; Cardinal Brennan HS; Frackville, PA; (3); 8/57; Color Guard; Rep Frsh Cls; Rep Soph Cls; Rep Jr Cls; Rep Sr Cls; Rep Stu Cncl; L Cheerleading; High Hon Roll; Hon Roll; NHS; Hghst Hnrs Spncs 84-87; Phys Thrpy.

OCONNER, MIKE; Towanda Area HS; Monroeton, PA; (4); FFA; Lion Awd.

OCONNOR, KELLY; Monaca HS; Monaca, PA; (3); 15/83; French Clb; Pep Clb; Capt Drill Tm; Trs Jr Cls; Stu Cncl; Cheerleading; Score Keeper; Sftbl; Tennis; Hon Roll; IN U Of PA; Bus Mgmt.

OCONNOR, TED; Conestoga HS; Berwyn, PA; (3); 56/400; Lit Mag; Crs Cntry; Trk; Engl.

OCWIEJA, SUE; West Scranton HS; Scranton, PA; (2); Girl Scts; Letterman Clb; Spanish Clb; Orch; Var Bsktbl; Var Trk; Twrlr; Chld Care Svc.

ODATO, DON; Plum SR HS; Pittsburgh, PA; (3); 283/410; Am Leg Boys St; Church Yth Grp; Teachers Aide; Varsity Clb; Bsbl; Bsktbl; Diving; Ftbl; Wt Lftg; Hon Roll; IN U Of PA; Bus.

ODELL, SUSAN; Harry S Truman HS; Levittown, PA; (3); Debate Tm; Drama Clb; Girl Scts; NFL; Speech Tm; Band; Chorus; Mrchg Band; School Musical; School Play; Arch.

ODELLI, TERRY; Yough HS; Smithton, PA; (4); French Clb; Spanish Clb; L Var Bsbl; JV Bsktbl; L Var Ftbl; NHS; Schlstc Awd 86-87; Washington & Jefferson; Bus.

ODOM, BARBARA; Little Flower Catholic HS For Girls; Philadelphia, PA; (4); Art Clb; Church Yth Grp; Cmnty Wkr; Drama Clb; Hosp Aide; Political Wkr; Church Choir; School Musical; Stage Crew; Variety Show; Bible Camp Volntr Of Yr Awd 84; Ellis Charles Grant Schlrshp 86-87; Drama Schlrshp 86-87; Bio.

ODONNELL, DONALD; Bishop Mc Cort HS; Johnstown, PA; (3); German Clb; Var Golf; NHS; Engrng.

ODOR, TAURA; Bethlehem Catholic HS; Bethlehem, PA; (3); 123/210; Red Cross Aide; Band; Color Guard; Drm Mjr(t); Mrchg Band; Accntng.

ODOSEY, NICHOLAS; Archbishop Wood HS; Oakford, PA; (2); 147/254; SADD; JV Swmmng; Sci.

ODOSKI, KATHLEEN; Duquesne HS; Duquesne, PA; (4); VICA; Band; Concert Band; Drill Tm; Jazz Band; Mrchg Band; Pep Band; Stu Cncl; Hon Roll; NHS; CSMTLGST.

OELER, PAULA; William Allen HS; Allentown, PA; (3); 18/609; Varsity Clb; Nwsp Stf; Lit Mag; Stu Cncl; Var L Swmmng; NHS; SADD; Nwsp Rptr; Stat Mgr(s); Hon Roll.

OELER, ROLF; William Allen HS; Allentown, PA; (4); Nwsp Sprt Ed; Nwsp Stf; VP Soph Cls; Socr.

OELSCHLAGER, HOLLY; Hopewell SR HS; Aliquippa, PA; (3); 7/255; Art Clb; Church Yth Grp; Cmnty Wkr; German Clb; High Hon Roll; NHS; Cnsrvtn Clb Chpln 86-87; Cnsrvtn Clb Pblc Rltns Ofc 87-88; Elem Educ.

OERTHER, JANINE; Pottsville Area HS; Pottsville, PA; (2); FBLA; Ski Clb; Teachers Aide; Stu Cncl; Bsktbl; Cheerleading; Vllybl; Wt Lftg; Wrstlng; Hon Roll; Presdntl Physcl Ftnss Awd 85; Hnrb Mntn-Art 85; Achvt Awd-Physcl Ftnss 87; Empire Beauty Schl; Csmtlgy.

OESTERLING, DIANNE; Butler Area SR HS; Butler, PA; (4); Chorus; Hon Roll; Btlr Cnty Area Vo-Tch Schl Crt Grphc Art Dpt 87; Hnr Awds-Btlr Cnty Area Vo-Tch Grphcs Art Dpt 85-87; Butler Cnty CC; Elec Educ.

OFFMAN, SONJA; Portage Area HS; Portage, PA; (3); Church Yth Grp; Dance Clb; French Clb; SADD; School Play; Variety Show; Off Stu Cncl; Cheerleading; Trk; Wt Lftg; Amer Lgn Essy Dist & Cnty 85.

OFFSHACK, KRISTINE; Plymouth-Whitemarsh HS; Norristown, PA; (3); Spanish Clb; Concert Band; Off Frsh Cls; Off Soph Cls; Jr Cls; Sftbl; Swmmng; Vllybl; High Hon Roll; NHS; Acad Exclince Awd 86; All Lgue Awds Vllbyl & Sftbl 85-86; Bio.

OFMAN, PAMELA; United HS; New Florence, PA; (3); 6/147; Camera Clb; VP 4-H; Yrbk Stf; Var Powder Puff Ftbl; Var Trk; Hon Roll; Jr NHS; NHS; FBLA; 4-H Awd; Outstndng SR 4-H Horse Mbr 86; Bio Tchr.

OFNER, STEVEN; Southmoreland HS; Ruffsdale, PA; (2); Computer Clb; German Clb; Var Tennis; Im Vllybl; Hon Roll; German Natl Hnr Scty 86-87; Comp.

OGBORN, JAMES; Council Rock HS; Wash Cross, PA; (3); 121/908; Church Yth Grp; Cmnty Wkr; FBLA; Ski Clb; JV Var Bsbl; JV Im Bsktbl; Im Tennis; Im Vllybl; Hon Roll; NHS; Bus Admin.

OGBURN, VALERIE; Berlin Brothers Valley HS; Glencoe, PA; (3); Am Leg Aux Girls St; Church Yth Grp; Drama Clb; 4-H; French Clb; NFL; Spanish Clb; Speech Tm; Band; Mrchg Band; Outstndng Spkr 87; Amer Hist Awd 87; Drama.

OGDEN, ADRIENNE; Hamburg Area HS; Hamburg, PA; (3); French Clb; Ski Clb; Trs Spanish Clb; Off Frsh Cls; Off Soph Cls; Off Jr Cls; VP Sr Cls; Cheerleading; Trk; Hon Roll.

OGDEN, JOHN; St Marys Area HS; St Marys, PA; (2); 56/301; Hon Roll.

OGLESBY, TAMICA; Northeast Prep; Philadelphia, PA; (4); Church Yth Grp; Church Choir; Hon Roll; World Affairs Cncl 83-87; CC Of Philadelphia; Accntng.

OGLEVEE, STEFAN; Somerset Area SR HS; Somerset, PA; (3); 11/230; Church Yth Grp; English Clb; French Clb; JA; Model UN; Mu Alpha Theta; Ski Clb; Varsity Clb; Var L Socr; NHS; Comm Airline Pilot.

OGLINE, AMY; Somerset SR HS; Somerset, PA; (4); 11/239; NFL; Q&S; Red Cross Aide; School Play; Yrbk Stf; Stu Cncl; Var L Cheerleading; High Hon Roll; NHS; Pres Schlr; Penn ST U; Ecnmcs.

OGOZALY, LAURA; Carbondale Area JR SR HS; Carbondale, PA; (3); 7/119; Sec Trs Church Yth Grp; Trs FBLA; German Clb; Chorus; High Hon Roll; Hon Roll; NHS; Essay Contst Awd 82-83; Sectry.

OH, DANNY; Stroudsburg HS; Stroudsburg, PA; (2); French Clb; FBLA; Scholastic Bowl; Nwsp Stf; Ftbl; High Hon Roll; Susquentenial Art Shw 2nd Pl 86; Mall Art Shw 2nd Pl 87; Jr Acad Of Sci 2nd Awd 87; Wharton Schl Of Bus; Fin.

OH, JOHN; William Allen HS; Allentown, PA; (3); Chess Clb; Debate Tm; German Clb; JA; Key Clb; Math Tm; Ski Clb; Varsity Clb; Rep Jr Cls; Chrmn Stu Cncl; Full Schlrshp PA Gov Schl Sci, Pgm West Point Smmr 87.

OHARA, TIM; Archbishop Wood For Boys; Warminster, PA; (3); 26/254; Church Yth Grp; Rep Stu Cncl; Capt Bsbl; JV Crs Cntry; JV Socr; High Hon Roll; Hon Roll; NHS.

OHARAH, DANIEL; Du Bois Area HS; Reynoldsville, PA; (3); 40/309; Church Yth Grp; German Clb; Band; Concert Band; Mrchg Band; Engnrng.

OHL, TODD; Northampton Area SR HS; Bath, PA; (4); Drama Clb; Art Clb; Thesps; School Musical; School Play; Hon Roll; Penn ST; Theatre Arts.

OHLER, LAURA; Berlin Brothers Valley HS; Berlin, PA; (2); GAA; Spanish Clb; SADD; Color Guard; Mrchg Band; Var Bsktbl; Var Sftbl; JV Vllybl; Hon Roll; Pre Med.

OHLER, TRACY; North Star HS; Stoystown, PA; (2); Pres Sec Church Yth Grp; FCA; Nwsp Stf; Stu Cncl; Hon Roll; Westmoreland Cnty CC; Secy Sci.

OHLINGER, MARK; Conrad Weiser Area HS; Robesonia, PA; (3); 20/178; Church Yth Grp; Drama Clb; Spanish Clb; Band; Chorus; Concert Band; Jazz Band; Mrchg Band; School Musical; School Play; Lock Haven U; Intl Stds.

OHLINGER, RAY; Wilmington Area HS; Pulaski, PA; (3); Band; Concert Band; Mrchg Band; Pep Band; Hon Roll; Math.

OHLRICH, CHRISTINA; Technical Memorial HS; Erie, PA; (4); 33/324; VICA; Chorus; Sec Stu Cncl; Score Keeper; Trk; NHS; Edinboro U.

OHMER, GRACE; Northwestern HS; Albion, PA; (3); 27/147; Drama Clb; Chorus; Yrbk Stf; Am Leg Aux Essay Cont Wnnr 85; Engl.

OHNHAUS, LORI; Carrick HS; Pittsburgh, PA; (3); 23/391; School Play; Var Tennis; Hon Roll; U Of Pittsburgh; Phrmcy.

OHNHAUS, WILLIAM CHARLES; Plum SR HS; Pittsburgh, PA; (4); 12/368; Office Aide; Chorus; Ice Hcky; NHS; St Schlr; U Of Pittsburgh; Elec Engr.

OHREL, ALEXANDRA; Christian School Of York; Columbia, PA; (2); Church Yth Grp; Chorus; Church Choir; Sec Frsh Cls; Sec Soph Cls; JV Fld Hcky; Var Sftbl; High Hon Roll; Ntl Merit Schol.

OHRUM, PATTY; Northern York County HS; Dillsburg, PA; (3); 28/232; SADD; Chorus; Color Guard; Concert Band; Drill Tm; Mrchg Band; School Musical; Powder Puff Ftbl; High Hon Roll; Hon Roll; Miss PA US Teen Pgnt 87; Doc.

OKAMOTO, NEIL E; Council Rock HS; Holland, PA; (4); 1/845; Computer Clb; Jazz Band; Capt Mrchg Band; Symp Band; High Hon Roll; Lion Awd; Pres NHS; Ntl Merit SF; PA Dist II Band 85; Germn Soc PA Hnrb Mntn 86; Bucks County Music Fest 83-85; Engrng.

OKEN, EMILY; Lower Merion HS; Bala Cynwyd, PA; (4); 1/370; French Clb; JCL; Yrbk Stf; JV Var Sftbl; JV Swmmng; Hon Roll; Ntl Merit SF; Cum Laude In Exam Of Jr 86; 1st Pl In Dist Comp Of Natl Hist Day 85; Commendatn For Prfmnc Natl Frnch; Math.

OKEY, JENNY; Beaver Area JR SR HS; Beaver, PA; (2); JCL; Latin Clb; Office Aide; Ski Clb; Spanish Clb; Swmmng; Timer; High Hon Roll; Hon Roll; Gannon U; Pre-Med.

OKONSKI, CHRIS; Wyoming Valley West HS; Swoyersville, PA; (4); French Clb; Ski Clb; Chorus; Yrbk Phtg; Yrbk Stf; Lit Mag; Sec Rep Frsh Cls; Rep Soph Cls; Rep Jr Cls; Rep Sr Cls; Hnrb Mntn Awd Ntl Frnch Cntst; U Ptsbrg; Frnch.

OKRESIK, ROBERT; Hickory HS; W Middlesex, PA; (3); 40/170; Spanish Clb; Varsity Clb; Chorus; Im Bsktbl; Var L Ftbl; Im Sftbl; Hstry Tchr.

OLACZ, TOM; Shenango HS; New Castle, PA; (3); 10/125; High Hon Roll; Hon Roll; NHS.

OLAH, KIMBERLY; Shenandoah Valley HS; Shenandoah, PA; (3); 24/79; Library Aide; Sec Mrchg Band; Sec Frsh Cls; Trs Soph Cls; Sec Jr Cls; Stu Cncl; Stat Trk; Hon Roll; Rep To Hugh O Brien Ldrshp Smnr 86; Frng Langs.

OLBRICH, ERIC P; Lewistown Area HS; Lewistown, PA; (4); 65/244; AFS; Boy Scts; Ski Clb; Acpl Chr; Band; Chorus; Concert Band; Mrchg Band; School Musical; God Cntry Awd; Eagle Scout Awd 87; Susquehanna U; Bus.

OLCZAK, LAURA; Mc Guffey HS; Prosperity, PA; (3); 46/250; Camera Clb; Trs 4-H; Trs German Clb; Hosp Aide; Office Aide; Varsity Clb; Var L Bsktbl; L Trk; 4-H Awd; Hon Roll; Phys Thrpy.

OLDANI, ANN; Ridgway Area HS; Ridgway, PA; (4); 1/104; Chorus; Yrbk Phtg; Yrbk Sprt Ed; Yrbk Stf; Stu Cncl; Var L Bsktbl; Var L Trk; Var L Vllybl; High Hon Roll; NHS; PA St U; Admn Of Justice.

OLDHAM, KEVIN; Chestnut Ridge HS; New Paris, PA; (3); 6/137; Pres Trs Church Yth Grp; Band; Concert Band; Mrchg Band; Pep Band; JV Bsktbl; Hon Roll; Jr NHS; NHS.

OLDT, SHELLY; Middleburg HS; M Iddleburg, PA; (3); Key Clb; Ski Clb; Concert Band; Mrchg Band; Nwsp Bus Mgr; Nwsp Stf; Cheerleading; Fld Hcky; Sftbl; Hon Roll; Dstrct & Regnl Bnd 86; MVP Sftbl 86; Bloomsburg; Acctng.

OLEARY, KATHLEEN; Cambria Heights SR HS; Patton, PA; (3); 73/182; DECA; Color Guard; Mrchg Band; Trk; Financing.

OLEJAR, MICHAEL; Hazleton SR HS; Hazleton, PA; (3); Church Yth Grp; Leo Clb; Hon Roll; Pres Acad Fit Awd 84-85.

OLENER, AMY; Pennsbury HS; Yardley, PA; (3); Cmnty Wkr; Political Wkr; Spanish Clb; Teachers Aide; Chorus; School Play; Hon Roll; NHS; Ntl Merit Ltr; Valdctrn 86; 1st Dist Wide Spnsh Cmptn 87; Cmmndtn Excel Wrk Camp Jr Cnslr 86; Intl Stds.

OLENIC, KRISTEN; Butler HS; Butler, PA; (2); French Clb; Hosp Aide; SADD; Chorus; Church Choir; Swing Chorus; Hon Roll; Jr NHS; Acadc Ltr 87; Med.

OLENIK, BRYAN; South Allegheny JR SR HS; Glassport, PA; (4); 1/177; Church Yth Grp; French Clb; Math Tm; Quiz Bowl; Pres Soph Cls; Rep Stu Cncl; High Hon Roll; Pres NHS; U Pittsburgh; Math.

OLENWINE, LORI; William Allen HS; Allentown, PA; (2); JA; Off Stu Cncl; Powder Puff Ftbl; Hon Roll; UCLA.

OLESH, BETH; Connellsville Area SR HS; S Connellsville, PA; (2); Y-Teens; Drm & Bgl; Yrbk Stf; High Hon Roll; Hon Roll; Spanish NHS; Acadmc Excllnc 85-86.

OLESKI, MICHELLE; Mercyhurst Prep; Erie, PA; (3); 26/179; Church Yth Grp; Cmnty Wkr; Ski Clb; SADD; Y-Teens; Yrbk Stf; Hon Roll; PA JR Acad Sci Awd 85; Cert Apprctn Outstndng Vol Svc Bnftng Comm 87.

OLEWILER, KENNETH; Spring Grove Area SR HS; York, PA; (2); 13/373; Art Clb; Church Yth Grp; School Play; Nwsp Rptr; Yrbk Stf; High Hon Roll; NHS; Pres Schlr; Drama Clb; AAA Pstr Cont Grnd Prz Wnnr Yrk Cnty 87; Organ Schlrshp 86-87; Grphc Dsgn.

OLEY, JOHN S; Lake Lehman HS; Hunlock Creek, PA; (3); 4-H; Rep Frsh Cls; Rep Soph Cls; Hon Roll; Hstry Tchr.

OLEY, RICHARD; James M Coughlin HS; Plainsville, PA; (3); 18/397; Boy Scts; Key Clb; Chorus; Jazz Band; Mrchg Band; Orch; Var Socr; NHS; Computer Clb; Ski Clb; Natl Yth Ldrshp Amer Awd 87; WY Vly Yth Salute 87; Wilkes Coll Yng Schlrs Pgm 87; U Of Scranton; Pre Med.

OLIM, MATTHEW L; Germantown Acad; Ambler, PA; (4); Math Clb; Yrbk Ed-Chief; Hon Roll; Ntl Merit SF; Var Crs Cntry; Schlrshp PA Gov Schlr Sci 85; Math.

OLIVER, APRIL; Washington HS; Washington, PA; (3); Church Yth Grp; Spanish Clb; Trk; Hon Roll.

OLIVER, JILL; Pittston Area HS; Pittston, PA; (4); 7/340; Art Clb; Church Yth Grp; Drama Clb; Key Clb; Math Clb; Spanish Clb; SADD; Chorus; NHS; Moreau Schlrshp 87; Kings Coll; Mth.

OLIVER, KARIN; Strong Vincent HS; Erie, PA; (4); 24/160; Church Yth Grp; Chorus; Church Choir; Pensacola Christian Col; Bible.

OLIVER, LISA; West Middlesex HS; West Middlesex, PA; (4); 14/95; Chorus; Mrchg Band; Nwsp Ed-Chief; Yrbk Stf; Var Capt Bsktbl; L Var Trk; Prfct Atten Awd; PTA Schlrshp Awd, 2nd Tm All Mercer Cnty Grls Bsktbl Stars, & Cum Laude Grad 87; Westminster Coll; Elem Ed.

OLIVER, MARK; North Allegheny HS; Pittsburgh, PA; (2); 1/612; Math Tm; Band; Concert Band; Mrchg Band; Symp Band; JV Bsktbl; Var L Trk; High Hon Roll; Hon Roll; Jr NHS.

OLIVERI, MARK; Mifflinburg HS; Mifflinburg, PA; (1); Church Yth Grp; French Clb; JV Socr; High Hon Roll; Hon Roll; Prfct Atten Awd.

OLIVERIA, TERESA; Parkland HS; Schnecksville, PA; (2); Mrchg Band; Var Trk; Var Twrlr; Pres Acdmc Ftnss Awd 85-86.

OLIVERIO, JOHN S; South Park HS; Pittsburgh, PA; (4); 10/192; Exploring; Yrbk Stf; Trs Stu Cncl; High Hon Roll; NHS; Prfct Atten Awd; U Of Pittsburgh; Bus Mgmt.

OLIVIERI, BRIAN; Old Forge HS; Old Forge, PA; (3); VP Jr Cls; Var Bsbl; Var Bsktbl; Var Ftbl; High Hon Roll; Hon Roll; NHS; Cvl Engrng.

OLLEY, MARY ANNE; Cedar Cliff HS; New Cumberland, PA; (3); 37/309; Camera Clb; Trs Key Clb; Spanish Clb; Color Guard; Mrchg Band; Trk; Bus Mngt.

OLLIVER, JEANNE; Central Bucks West HS; Doylestown, PA; (3); 52/486; Band; Yrbk Phtg; L Swmmng; L Tennis; L Trk; High Hon Roll; Hon Roll; Jr NHS; Prfct Atten Awd; Rotary Awd; Frnch III Awd 86; Photo Awd 85; Englnd Schl Exchnge 85; Sci.

OLMSTEAD, ELLIOT; Helshey HS; Hershey, PA; (4); 19/206; Chess Clb; Math Tm; Spanish Clb; Chorus; Lit Mag; Crs Cntry; Trk; High Hon Roll; NHS; Spanish NHS; Ntl Yth Ldrshp Cncl 87; PA ST U; Arspc Engr.

OLOSKY, CHRISTI; Du Bois Area SR HS; Du Bois, PA; (2); #12 In Class; German Clb; Band; Concert Band; Mrchg Band; School Musical; Hon Roll; NHS; Vet Sci.

OLOSKY, COLEEN; Curwensville HS; Curwensville, PA; (3); Church Yth Grp; Drama Clb; Ski Clb; Var L Cheerleading; Gym; Hon Roll; NHS; Acad All Amer 86-87; Bus.

OLSEN, ERIK S; Boyertown JR HS East; Frederick, PA; (1); Rep Frsh Cls; Var Socr; Var Trk; High Hon Roll; Hon Roll; PA ST; Arntcl Engrng.

OLSEN, LISA; Interboro HS; Norwood, PA; (4); AFS; Art Clb; Spanish Clb; Hon Roll; NHS; Susquehanna U; Accntng.

OLSEN, MICHELE LYN; Stroudsburg Area HS; Stroudsburg, PA; (3); French Clb; FBLA; Color Guard; Mrchg Band; Bowling; Twrlr; Hon Roll; Allentown Bus Schl; Bus Ed.

OLSHANSKY, DANIEL; Leechburg Area HS; Leechburg, PA; (3); 1/90; Math Tm; VP Frsh Cls; Pres Soph Cls; Pres Jr Cls; VP Stu Cncl; Bsbl; L Ftbl; Cit Awd; High Hon Roll; Hon Roll; Math.

OLSOMMER, DIANN; John S Fine HS; Wapwallopen, PA; (2); Cmnty Wkr; Exploring; Chorus; Hon Roll; Penn ST; Archtct.

OLSON, DEAN; Lakeview HS; Stonesboro, PA; (4); 12/128; Church Yth Grp; Varsity Clb; Band; Chorus; Drm Mjr(t); School Play; Yrbk Bus Mgr; L Bsktbl; L Trk; Pres NHS; Engrng.

OLSON, GRETA; Linden Hall HS; Lititz, PA; (2); 1/18; High Hon Roll; U Of NC; Med Prfssn.

OLSON, JENNIFER; Canon-Mc Millan HS; Mc Donald, PA; (1); Art Clb; Chorus; High Hon Roll; Pres Schlr; Literary Appreciation Awd 86.

OLSON, JOANNE; Somerset Area SR HS; Somerset, PA; (3); 65/230; Pres Church Yth Grp; English Clb; FHA; JA; Spanish Clb; Chorus; Church Choir; Yrbk Stf; Tennis; NHS; Grove Cty Coll; Educ.

OLSON, JOHN; Arch Bishop Wood HS For Boys; Hatboro, PA; (2); 51/254; Church Yth Grp; German Clb; SADD; Teachers Aide; Hon Roll; Frnkln Inst Awd Outstndng Achvt 86, & DE Vly Sci Fair 1st Pl Physics 86; Enrgy Ed Advsry Cncl 87; PA ST U; Engrng.

OLSZANSKI, DOUGLAS; Fairview HS; Bay Village, OH; (4); 2/154; Debate Tm; Model UN; Ski Clb; Varsity Clb; Var L Socr; Var L Trk; NHS; Sal; MI Alumni Schlrshp; U Of MI; Med.

OLSZEWSKI, CORINNE A; John S Fine HS; Nanticoke, PA; (4); Yrbk Stf; Hon Roll; LCCC; Drama.

OLSZEWSKI, LISA; Portage Area HS; Portage, PA; (3); 39/106; Church Yth Grp; 4-H; Church Choir; Var JV Cheerleading; Flght Attndnt.

OLSZEWSKI, MARY; E L Meyers HS; Wilkes-Barre, PA; (4); Key Clb; Ski Clb; Chorus; Yrbk Stf; Fld Hcky; Sftbl; Hon Roll; Jr NHS; NHS; PA ST U; Chld Psychlgy.

OLSZEWSKI, RENEE; Emmaus HS; Macungie, PA; (3); 36/530; Rep Stu Cncl; Var Bsktbl; JV Sftbl; Var Capt Vllybl; High Hon Roll; NHS; Mktg.

OLVER, JENNIFER; John S Fine HS; Nanticoke, PA; (4); 29/251; Key Clb; Yrbk Stf; Mgr Ftbl; High Hon Roll; NHS; NEDT Awd; Intl Bus.

OMALLEY, RICHELLE; West Allegheny HS; Coraopolis, PA; (2); 8/210; Drama Clb; Yrbk Stf; Lit Mag; Rep Stu Cncl; High Hon Roll; Intl Soc Sci Pgm 87-88; U Of Pittsburgh; Elem Educ.

OMALLEY, WAYNE; Central HS; Scranton, PA; (2); Boys Clb Am; Bsktbl; Ftbl; Wt Lftg.

OMAN, STACEY; Du Bois Area HS; Dubois, PA; (2); 87/250; Band; Concert Band; Jazz Band; Mrchg Band; Tchr.

OMAN, SUSAN G; Bloomsburg Christian Schl; Bloomsburg, PA; (4); 2/8; Church Yth Grp; Drama Clb; 4-H; Spanish Clb; Chorus; Sec Jr Cls; VP Sr Cls; 4-H Awd; High Hon Roll; Hon Roll; Wilson Coll; Vet Med Tech.

OMLOR, STEPHEN; Millville HS; Millville, PA; (4); School Play; VP Sr Cls; Stu Cncl; Bsbl; Capt Var Wrstlng; Kiwanis Awd; Lotalty Awd 87; Mst Imprvd Wrstler & Coaches Awd 87; Prom King & Jim Berry Mem Awd 87; West Chester U; Bio Chem.

OMSTEAD, KRISTIE; Seneca Valley SR HS; Zelienople, PA; (3); 52/333; Church Yth Grp; Pep Clb; ROTC; Thesps; Band; Chorus; Drill Tm; School Play; Symp Band; Gntcst.

ONCAY, REBECCA KATHERINE; Wyoming Valley West HS; Swoyersville, PA; (4); Church Yth Grp; Exploring; Ski Clb; Band; Concert Band; Mrchg Band; Orch; Coll Misericordia; Radiolgy.

ONDER, SHARON; Portage JR SR HS; Portage, PA; (4); 9/118; NFL; Varsity Clb; Pres Band; Chorus; Concert Band; Mrchg Band; NHS; Aud/Vis; Pep Band; Hugh O Brian Outstndng Soph Ldrshp Awd 85; Amvets Portage, PA Amer Essay Awd 84; Penn ST; Vet.

ONDISH, MIKE; Norwin SR HS; N Huntingdon, PA; (4); 91/527; Computer Clb; German Clb; Var Capt Socr; Hon Roll; MVP Sccr 85-86; Sectn 1 Sccr All-Stars 86-87; Electronics Clb VP 86-87; Penn ST; Elec Engrng.

ONDO, AL; West Mifflin Area HS; West Mifflin, PA; (2); Church Yth Grp; Exploring; High Hon Roll; Hon Roll; NHS; Engrng.

ONDO, ERIC; Homer Center HS; Homer City, PA; (3); French Clb; Varsity Clb; Bsktbl; Trk; Hon Roll; Jr NHS.

ONDREJCA, RON; Northampton SR HS; Northampton, PA; (3); Rep Frsh Cls; Rep Soph Cls; Rep Stu Cncl; Var L Bsktbl; Var Ftbl; Var L Socr; Wt Lftg; Hon Roll; Bsbll All Est PA Cnfrnc Tm 87; Pre Med.

ONDRIEZEK, CAROL; Central Cambria HS; Mineral Pt, PA; (2); JA; Key Clb; Chorus; Hon Roll; Socl Wrk.

ONEIL, TERESA; Keystone HS; Knox, PA; (3); Church Yth Grp; Hosp Aide; Office Aide; Pep Clb; Red Cross Aide; Spanish Clb; SADD; VICA; Chorus; Hon Roll; Vo Indus Clbs Am 1st Pl Cont 86-87; VICA Degree Awd 87; Sec Kystn Yth Ed Assoc 88; Nrsng.

ONEILL, COLLEEN; W B Saul HS; Philadelphia, PA; (2); FFA; Hon Roll; Prfct Atten Awd; Outstndng Stu Awd 86-87.

ONEILL, EDWARD; Purchase Line HS; Commodore, PA; (3); Chess Clb; Library Aide; Radio Clb; IVP; Comp Sci.

ONEILL, MICHAEL; Cardinal O Hara HS; Springfield, PA; (3); 170/710; Cmnty Wkr; Computer Clb; FBLA; JA; Office Aide; OEA; Service Clb; SADD; Varsity Clb; Nwsp Sprt Ed; Mrktng.

ONEILL, REBECCA; Jenkintown HS; Jenkintown, PA; (3); 11/37; Band; Stage Crew; Symp Band; Nwsp Rptr; Yrbk Ed-Chief; Rep Stu Cncl; JV Capt Fld Hcky; Hon Roll; Drama Clb; French Clb; Hnrb Mntn Montgomery Cnty Sci Fair 86; 1st Pl Jenkintown Sci Fair 85-86.

ONELANGSY, SOMXAY; Harrisburg HS; Harrisburg, PA; (4); 16/235; Church Yth Grp; Teachers Aide; Socr; Swmmng; Vllybl; Hon Roll; Eastern Mennonite Coll; Bus Adm.

ONG, ALBERT; Carlisle SR HS; Carlisle, PA; (3); 9/467; Science Clb; Orch; Var Swmmng; High Hon Roll; NHS; Ntl Merit SF; Computer Clb; German Clb; JV Trk; Hon Roll; Most Dist Bio Stu 84-85; Var Sci Fair Awds 85 & 87; 2nd Pl Schl Essay Cont 86-87; Mech Engr.

ONIMUS, MELISSA; Nazareth Acad; Philadelphia, PA; (3); VP Church Yth Grp; Cmnty Wkr; Hosp Aide; Math Clb; NFL; Service Clb; Speech Tm; Church Choir; Drill Tm; Im Vllybl; Brhm Amblnc-Mst Imprvd Atten 86; ST Certfd-Emrgncy Med Tech 87; Frankford Nursing Schl; Nrsng.

ONUSCHECK, MARK; Peters Township HS; Mcmurray, PA; (4); 50/242; Church Yth Grp; Key Clb; Pres VP Thesps; Pres Lib Chorus; Church Choir; School Musical; School Play; Stu Cncl; Hon Roll; Rotary Awd; Thspn Hall Of Fm 86; Chr Ldrshp Awd 87; Allegheny Coll; Pre Law.

ONUSKA, LISA; Beaver HS; Beaver, PA; (3); 67/198; JA; Spanish Clb; Powder Puff Ftbl; Trk; Vllybl; Hon Roll.

OPANEL, CHERYL; Shenandoah Valley JR-SR HS; Frackville, PA; (4); 16/103; Dance Clb; Library Aide; Pep Clb; Mrchg Band; Nwsp Bus Mgr; Yrbk Stf; Rep Sr Cls; Cheerleading; Crs Cntry; Hon Roll; Acad All-Amer 86-87.

OPEL, KATHY; Brownsville Area HS; W Brownsville, PA; (3); VP Church Yth Grp; FBLA; Girl Scts; Office Aide; Band; High Hon Roll; Hon Roll; WVU; Acctnt.

OPELLA, NADINE; Mahanoy Area HS; Mahanoy City, PA; (2); Spanish Clb; Variety Show; Var Cheerleading; Trk; Hon Roll.

OPHER, DORIT R; Akiba Hebrew Acad; Havertown, PA; (4); Science Clb; Sec SADD; Rep Stu Cncl; Var Mgr Bsktbl; Mgr Socr; U Of PA; Nrsng.

OPOLSKY, PATRICIA; Mahanoy Area HS; Barnesville, PA; (2); Drama Clb; Exploring; Spanish Clb; Variety Show; Bsktbl; York Coll; Lab Technology.

OPPERMAN, SHARON B; Brandywine Heights HS; Fleetwood, PA; (2); Drama Clb; Band; Concert Band; Mrchg Band; Var L Sftbl; Church Yth Grp; School Play; Hon Roll; Penn ST; Htl/Rstrnt Mgmt.

OPREY, DONNIE; Tri-Valley HS; Pitman, PA; (2); 21/85; JV Var Bsktbl; JV Var Ftbl; Wt Lftg; Hon Roll; Am Hstry Awd-Woodmens Ins 87; Engrng.

OPSITNIK, LEAH; General Mc Lane HS; Edinboo, PA; (4); 9/187; Letterman Clb; Model UN; Radio Clb; Mrchg Band; Orch; Symp Band; Nwsp Stf; High Hon Roll; NHS; Pres Schlr; Westminster Coll; Mlclr Bio.

OPST, JODI; Geibel HS; Dunbar, PA; (3); Pep Clb; Yrbk Stf; JV Stat Bsktbl; Var L Sftbl; Var L Vllybl; High Hon Roll; Hon Roll; NHS; Frnch Merit Awd 86-87; Educ.

OQUENDO, MILDRED; Little Flower HS; Philadelphia, PA; (4); 33/454; Latin Clb; Teachers Aide; Band; Jazz Band; Orch; School Musical; School Play; Symp Band; NHS; Prfct Atten Awd; 1st Chr Music; Engl Awd; Cert Merit Music; Manor JC; Hmn Svcs.

ORANGE, KELLIE C; Penn Trafford HS; Jeannette, PA; (4); Church Yth Grp; FBLA; Trs Spanish Clb; Color Guard; Yrbk Stf; Twrlr; Hon Roll; St Vincents Coll; Med Tech.

ORAVITZ, AMY; West Allegheny HS; Oakdale, PA; (4); 41/202; FBLA; Office Aide; Teachers Aide; Color Guard; Mrchg Band; Powder Puff Ftbl; High Hon Roll; Hon Roll; Outstndng Bus Stu; Duffs Bus Inst; Secr Fnshng.

ORAZI, JANELLE; Connellsville HS; Lemont Furnace, PA; (3); Art Clb; Church Yth Grp; Drama Clb; Office Aide; Pep Clb; Chorus; School Musical; Nwsp Stf; Yrbk Stf; Sec Frsh Cls; Stu Mst Initiative; Psychtry.

ORAZI, JOHN; Connellsville Area HS; Lemont Furn, PA; (1); Art Clb; Office Aide; Sec Frsh Cls; Sec Stu Cncl; JV Bsbl; JV Bsktbl; High Hon Roll; Jr NHS; Prfct Atten Awd.

ORBAN, ALYSSA; Franklin Regional SR HS; Murrysville, PA; (3); Church Yth Grp; FHA; Office Aide; Spanish Clb; Im Fld Hcky; Vllybl; NHS; Ambassador Coll; Nutrtnst.

ORBAN, KELLY; Bethelem Catholic HS; Bethlehem, PA; (3); 42/225; Church Yth Grp; Science Clb; Nwsp Stf; Im Vllybl; High Hon Roll; Muhlenburg Coll; Med Tech.

ORBIN, MICHAEL; West Hazelton HS; Conyngham, PA; (3); 43/227; Boys Clb Am; Chess Clb; Sec Trs Church Yth Grp; Computer Clb; Office Aide; Ski Clb; Spanish Clb; Church Choir; School Play; Mktg.

ORBIN, PAUL; Waynesburg Central HS; Waynesburg, PA; (4); 42/200; Boy Scts; Spanish Clb; Trs Band; Trs Concert Band; Jazz Band; Trs Mrchg Band; Var L Bsktbl; Hon Roll; Cnty Band 84-87; Boy Mnth 86; IN U PA; Cmmnctns.

ORDWAY, BARBARA; Troy SR HS; Troy, PA; (1); Computer Clb; 4-H; Girl Scts; SADD; Bowling; JV Trk; Prfct Atten Awd; Modern Miss 87; Bowling Hgh Avg 86-87; Comp Sci.

ORDY, KAREN; Butler Area SR HS; Butler, PA; (3); Church Yth Grp; Cmnty Wkr; Spanish Clb; SADD; Band; Concert Band; Mrchg Band; Pep Band; Symp Band; Im Bsktbl; Acad Achvt Awd 86-87; Butler Cnty All Star Cncrt Band 85; Ntl JR Hon Soc Cert 85; PA ST U; Psych.

OREKAR, ERIN; Council Rock HS; Washington, PA; (2); Band; Drill Tm; Flag Corp; Stu Cncl; Mgr Bsktbl; Hon Roll; Bus.

OREM, LYNN; Nazareth Area SR HS; Tatamy, PA; (3); 9/266; Sec Church Yth Grp; Drama Clb; Key Clb; SADD; Church Choir; School Musical; School Play; Yrbk Stf; High Hon Roll; NHS; Top 20 Cls Awd 87; Psych.

ORFANOPOULOS, MICHAEL; Penn Hills SR HS; Pittsburgh, PA; (3); JV Bsbl; JV Socr; High Hon Roll; Hon Roll.

ORGAN, JODI; Punxsutawney SR HS; Punxsutawney, PA; (2); Science Clb; Spanish Clb; Nwsp Phtg; Nwsp Rptr; Nwsp Stf; Rep Frsh Cls; Off Soph Cls; Off Stu Cncl; JV Tennis; Hon Roll.

ORGANIS, JEANANN; Hazleton HS; Hazleton, PA; (2); Church Yth Grp; Leo Clb; Pep Clb; Political Wkr; Var Trk; Hon Roll; Psycht.

ORLANDI, KATHERINE; St Huberts HS; Philadelphia, PA; (3); 127/436; Cmnty Wkr; Computer Clb; Dance Clb; Drama Clb; Hosp Aide; Office Aide; Teachers Aide; School Musical; School Play; Swing Chorus; Temple U; Accntng.

ORLANDI, LISA; Sharon HS; Sharon, PA; (4); 7/159; Latin Clb; Science Clb; Spanish Clb; SADD; Hon Roll; NHS; Opt Clb Awd; Pres Schlr; U Of Pittsburgh; Physcl Thrpy.

ORLANDO, DANIELLE; Villa Maria Acad; Erie, PA; (3); Science Clb; SADD; Mgr(s); Swmmng; Hon Roll.

ORLANDO, LESA; Villa Maria Acad; Erie, PA; (3); High Hon Roll; NHS; 1st Awd In Regnl PA JR Acad Of Sci 84-85; Hnrs In Latin 85-86; Gannon U; Health Scis.

ORLANDO, SHERRY; Chichester SR HS; Boothwyn, PA; (3); 31/293; French Clb; Office Aide; Hon Roll.

ORLANDO, TRACY; Lakeland HS; Mayfield, PA; (3); 28/176; Art Clb; French Clb; Hosp Aide; Pep Clb; Teachers Aide; Rep Stu Cncl; Var L Cheerleading; High Hon Roll; Hon Roll; NHS; Med Sci.

ORLICK, CHRISTOHER; Neshaminy HS; Langhorne, PA; (3); Ski Clb; JV Ftbl; JV Trk; Hon Roll; Engrng.

ORLOFF, ERICA A; Nativity BVM HS; Cumbola, PA; (2); 1/94; High Hon Roll.

ORLOWSKI, JAMES; Ambridge Area HS; Ambridge, PA; (3); Aud/Vis; Boy Scts; Camera Clb; Church Yth Grp; Computer Clb; Spanish Clb; Church Choir; School Play; Nwsp Phtg; Hon Roll; Comm.

ORMOND, VALDAMIR; Father Judge HS; Philadelphia, PA; (4); 12/356; Cmnty Wkr; Yrbk Stf; Im Bsktbl; Var L Ftbl; High Hon Roll; NHS; Pres Schlr; All Star Ftbl Gm Schlr/Athl Awd 87; Disabld Amer Vets Schlrshp 87; Mayors Cty Of Phila Schlrshp 87; Carnegie-Mellon U; Indstrl Mgmt.

ORNDORF, BRIAN; Mifflinburg Area SR HS; Mifflinburg, PA; (1); Church Yth Grp; German Clb; Key Clb; Var Capt Wrstlng; High Hon Roll; Prfct Atten Awd.

ORNDORFF, KAREN; Littlestown SR HS; Gettysburg, PA; (4); 6/117; Church Yth Grp; Pres 4-H; SADD; Band; Chorus; Church Choir; Color Guard; Concert Band; Mrchg Band; Pep Band; Frat Order Eagles Scholar 87; Williamsport Area CC; Dntl Hyg.

ORNDORFF, ROBBIE; Connellsville Area HS; Mill Run, PA; (4); Church Yth Grp; Rep Stu Cncl; Var Capt Bsbl; French Hon Soc; High Hon Roll; NHS; Bsbl Schlrshp Liberty U VA 87-88; 1st Tm All Sect Bsbl & MVP 87; T J Piasecki Mem Awd 87; Liberty U; Phys Ed.

ORNDORFF, TIFFANY; Gettysburg SR HS; Gettysburg, PA; (2); French Clb; Varsity Clb; Band; Mrchg Band; JV Fld Hcky; L Var Sftbl; Hon Roll; Nrs.

ORNER, MELISSA K; Oxford Area HS; Oxford, PA; (3); Art Clb; Church Yth Grp; Scholastic Bowl; SADD; Co-Capt Flag Corp; Nwsp Stf; Rptr Yrbk Stf; High Hon Roll; Hon Roll; NHS; T E Gillingham Awd For Excllnc In Art 87; Art Proficiency Awds 85-87; Awd For A P Amer Hstry 87; Kutztown U Of PA; Cmrcl Arts.

OROBONO, MICHAEL; Downingtown SR HS; West Chester, PA; (3); Church Yth Grp; VICA; Band; Church Choir; Mrchg Band; Hon Roll; JV Trk; 1st Pl Auto Mech Comp In VICA 86-87; Prod Dirctr Singer Of Cont Christian Rock Group 86-87; Aircraft Mech Schl; Counselor.

OROZCO, MISSIE; Emmaus HS; Trexlertown, PA; (4); 113/468; Sec Church Yth Grp; Exploring; Spanish Clb; Drill Tm; Rep Sr Cls; Var L Cheerleading; Var L Trk; Hon Roll.

ORR, JAMIE; Connelsville Area SR HS; Dawson, PA; (2); Church Yth Grp; Band; Chorus; Concert Band; Mrchg Band; Stage Crew; Nwsp Stf; Stat Ftbl; Hon Roll; NHS; Psych.

ORR, MIKE; Fort Le Boeuf HS; Waterford, PA; (3); 23/225; Pep Clb; Nwsp Rptr; Nwsp Stf; Rep Soph Cls; JV Bsbl; High Hon Roll; Hon Roll; Engrng.

ORR, ROSALYNN; Pine Forge Acad; Cleveland, OH; (4); 5/79; Pep Clb; Acpl Chr; Chorus; Off Frsh Cls; Trs Soph Cls; Trs Jr Cls; Off Stu Cncl; Cheerleading; High Hon Roll; Hon Roll; Cleveland ST U; Comps.

ORRIS, JOSEPH; Valley HS; New Kensington, PA; (3); 30/220; Chess Clb; French Clb; JA; Chorus; Ftbl; High Hon Roll; Hon Roll; NHS; Prfct Atten Awd; Rotary Awd; Cnty Chorus 86; Frshmn Cnty Chorus 85; Stu Mont 85; USC; Law.

ORRIS, LEANN; Springdale HS; Harwick, PA; (2); Drama Clb; GAA; Spanish Clb; Var Cheerleading; Stat Sftbl; Hnr Mntn Rbbn Freeport Art Exhbt 87; 4th Pl Rbbn Sprngdle Art Shw 87; Mdrn Miss Pgnt ST Fnlst 87; Med.

ORRIS, TERRI; Valley HS; Arnold, PA; (3); Art Clb; Science Clb; Ski Clb; Varsity Clb; Chorus; Sec Soph Cls; Sec Jr Cls; Var Cheerleading; JV Vllybl; NHS; Intl Forgn Lang Awd 86-87.

ORSAG, JAMES; Rochester HS; Rochester, PA; (3); 3/107; Am Leg Boys St; Pres Drama Clb; Quiz Bowl; Chorus; School Musical; Nwsp Ed-Chief; Var L Tennis; High Hon Roll; NHS; Ntl Merit Ltr; Brdcst Jrnlsm.

ORSICH, WENDY; Du Bois Area HS; Du Bois, PA; (3); 31/365; Church Yth Grp; Cmnty Wkr; Letterman Clb; Varsity Clb; Chorus; Var L Bsktbl; Var L Sftbl; L Trk; Hon Roll; Psychtry.

ORSIN, JO; Bald Eagle-Nittany HS; Lamar, PA; (2); 5/136; French Clb; Key Clb; Stat Bsktbl; Hon Roll; U PA; Law.

ORSINO, TINA M; Cranberry Are HS; Franklin, PA; (4); 7/118; FBLA; Girl Scts; Pep Clb; Science Clb; Trs Spanish Clb; SADD; Co-Capt Drill Tm; Hon Roll; Lion Awd; NHS; U Of Pittsburh; Phys Therapy.

ORT, SHAWN; Northeastern SR HS; Dover, PA; (4); Comp Pgmmr.

ORT, TRACY; Northeastern HS; York Haven, PA; (3); Pep Clb; Teachers Aide; Chorus; Yrbk Stf; JV Bsktbl; JV Vllybl; Hon Roll; Dntl Asst.

ORTH, LISA; Wyomissing Area HS; Wyomissing, PA; (4); 19/99; Church Yth Grp; French Clb; JA; Chorus; Capt Var Flag Corp; Capt Var Mrchg Band; Var Bowling; Im Sftbl; High Hon Roll; Hon Roll; Millersville U; Math Tchr.

ORTIGOZA, BRENDA; Gateway HS; Monroeville, PA; (3); 11/452; Church Yth Grp; Capt Hosp Aide; Model UN; Church Choir; Drill Tm; Mrchg Band; Gov Hon Prg Awd; High Hon Roll; Sec NHS; Hmnts Apprtcshp 87-88; Intntl Studies.

ORTIZ, MITCHELL; Carlisle HS; Carlisle, PA; (3); Cmnty Wkr; Dance Clb; JA; Office Aide; Nwsp Rptr; Bsktbl; Ftbl; Trk; IN U Of PA; Accounting.

ORTIZ, MYRA; Little Flower HS; Philadelphia, PA; (4); 58/384; Spanish Clb; Orch; School Musical; School Play; High Hon Roll; Prfct Atten Awd; Camera Clb; Exploring; Pep Band; Hon Roll; Phila Job Incntv Awd Outstndng Emplyee 86; Merit Bus Educ Curr Spllng, Typist Cert 87; Immaculata Coll; Bus Admin.

ORTMAN, SHAWN; Pennsbury HS; Yardley, PA; (3); Cmnty Wkr; Service Clb; Varsity Clb; Var L Bsbl; Var L Bsktbl; Var L Ftbl; Wt Lftg; Hon Roll; Hnrbl Mntn Cnty Def Bck 86-87; 3rd Awd Wnr Vrsty Bsktbll 86-87; Nmd Natl Hnr Rll 86-87; Sci.

ORTZ, JEANIE; Brockway Area HS; Reynoldsville, PA; (3); 13/110; Trs Church Yth Grp; Trs Chorus; Sec Jr Cls; JV Bsktbl; Var Twrlr; Hon Roll; Drama Clb; Thesps; Concert Band; Cmmnctns.

ORUOSH, CHRISTINE; Saltsburg JR SR HS; Saltsburg, PA; (2); 32/97; SADD; Band; Concert Band; Mrchg Band; School Musical; Rep Stu Cncl; Sftbl; Co-Capt Twrlr; Vllybl; High Hon Roll; Twrlts Trphy Jckt Bonds; 1st Pl Mjrt Sqd Cmptn 86.

ORVOSH, CHRISTINE; Saltsburg JR- SR HS; Saltsburg, PA; (2); 32/97; SADD; Band; Concert Band; Mrchg Band; School Musical; Rep Stu Cncl; Sftbl; Co-Capt Twrlr; Vllybl; High Hon Roll; Saltsburg Twrltts Trphys, Jckts, Bands 74-86; 1st Pl Mjrtt Compttn 86.

ORVOSH, LA RAYNE; Kiski Area HS; Saltsburg, PA; (3); Drama Clb; FBLA; Library Aide; Ski Clb; Teachers Aide; Concert Band; Stu Cncl; Tennis; Twrlr; Hon Roll; ICM Bus Schl; Accntng.

OSBORN, MICHAEL; West Allegheny HS; Coraopolis, PA; (4); Band; Chorus; JV Var Bsbl; Bsktbl; Coach Actv; Crs Cntry; Ftbl; High Hon Roll; Hon Roll; NHS; Acad All Amer Awd 85; Ldrshp Svc Awd 86; W Minister Coll; Econ.

OSBORNE, CHRIS; Wilmington Area HS; W Wilmington, PA; (3); Spanish Clb; Varsity Clb; Variety Show; Yrbk Sprt Ed; Rep Frsh Cls; Capt Bsbl; Bsktbl; Coach Actv; Capt Ftbl; Powder Puff Ftbl; All St Hnrb Mntn Ftbl, 1st Tm All Sec 85; Ftbl Unmous Choice 1st Tm 86; Bsbl 1st Tm All Sec 85-86.

OSBORNE, DAVID; Sharpsville HS; Sharpsville, PA; (4); 6/122; Church Yth Grp; Band; Church Choir; Mrchg Band; Bsktbl; Ftbl; Score Keeper; Trk; NHS; Pres Schlr; US Steelworkers Schlrshp 87; Gannon U Acdmc Schlrshp 87; Pres Schlr 87; Gannon U; Family Med Pgm.

OSBORNE, DEBBIE; Reynolds HS; Fredonia, PA; (4); 1/144; Church Yth Grp; Chorus; Var L Cheerleading; Var L Trk; JV Capt Vllybl; NHS; VFW Awd; Latin Clb; Letterman Clb; Library Aide; Pres Acad Ftnss Awd 87; Mercer Cnty Hall Of Fame Acad All-Star Awd 87; Schlrshp Awd Val 87; Grove City Coll; Pre-Med.

OSBORNE, JASON; Charleroi Area SR HS; Charleroi, PA; (3); French Clb; Science Clb; Ski Clb; Mrchg Band; Orch; School Musical; Stage Crew; Symp Band; Hon Roll; NHS; Fisheries Sci.

OSBORNE, JEFF; Trinity HS; Washington, PA; (4); 20/350; Var L Bsbl; Var Bsktbl; Var Ftbl; High Hon Roll; Hon Roll; WV U; Engrng.

OSBORNE, JENNIFER; Solanco HS; Quarryville, PA; (2); Church Yth Grp; Varsity Clb; Band; Concert Band; Mrchg Band; Crs Cntry; Trk.

OSBORNE, JILL; Trinity HS; Washington, PA; (3); Band; Phy Thrpst.

OSCHE, MICHAEL; North Catholic HS; Pittsburgh, PA; (2); Band; Concert Band; Mrchg Band; JV Bsktbl; Var Tennis; High Hon Roll; Hon Roll; NHS; Elec Engr.

OSCHWALD, ARIANE; Methacton HS; Collegeville, PA; (4); 14/375; Math Tm; Var Powder Puff Ftbl; JV Sftbl; High Hon Roll; NHS; Prkmn Vlly Frndsd & Nghbrs Awd 87; Mth.

OSHALL JR, WILLIAM H; Glendale JR SR HS; Fallentimber, PA; (4); 3/98; Yrbk Bus Mgr; Var L Wrstlng; NHS; Pres Schlr; Science Clb; Yrbk Stf; Hon Roll; Voice Dem Awd; PA ST U; Cvl Engrng.

OSHEA, ERIC; Moshannon Valley HS; Houtzdale, PA; (3); 6/120; Boy Scts; Varsity Clb; School Play; Var L Ftbl; Var L Wrstlng; High Hon Roll; NHS; U Of Pittsburgh; Physical Thrpy.

OSIECKI, KRISTEN; Villa Maria Acad; Erie, PA; (3); 11/151; Church Yth Grp; Dance Clb; Drama Clb; PAVAS; Chorus; School Musical; Rep Stu Cncl; Swmmng; Hon Roll; NHS; Schl Schlrshp Achvt Spnsh 87; Marn Bio.

OSIKA, DAVE; Dieruff HS; Allentown, PA; (2); JV Bsbl; Var Socr; JV Wrstlng; Hon Roll; Acctg.

OSKIN, AMY; East Allegheny HS; North Versailles, PA; (3); 34/217; Ski Clb; Chorus; School Musical; School Play; VP Soph Cls; VP Jr Cls; Stu Cncl; High Hon Roll; Hon Roll; NHS; Bus.

OSKIN, JEFF; Penn-Trafford HS; Irwin, PA; (3); 25/300; Chess Clb; Computer Clb; JCL; Latin Clb; Var L Bsbl; JV Bsktbl; JV Var Socr; High Hon Roll; Hon Roll; NHS; Engrng.

OSKOWSKI, JONATHAN; Hopewell HS; Aliquippa, PA; (4); 100/247; Church Yth Grp; Exploring; JA; Spanish Clb; Band; Concert Band; Jazz Band; Mrchg Band; Yrbk Phtg; Yrbk Stf; US Marines; Avncs.

OSMAN, JENNIFER; Monaca JR/Sr HS; Monaca, PA; (4); 14/89; Sec Pep Clb; Concert Band; Capt Drill Tm; Mrchg Band; Yrbk Stf; Tennis; Hon Roll; NHS; Red Cross Aide; Ski Clb; Elmer & Clara Fisher Memrl Schlrshp 87; Elctd May Qn 87; Gannon U; Acctng.

OSMAN, TODD; Montour HS; Coraopolis, PA; (4); SADD; Jazz Band; Mrchg Band; Tennis; Trk; NHS; Pres Schlr; Westinghouse Sci Hnrs Inst PA JR Acad Of Sci 86-87; Carnegie Musuem Hist Natl Sci Week 86; Cent II; Case Western Reserve U; Engrng.

OSMANSKI, MICHELLE; Beaver Area HS; Beaver, PA; (2); 1/242; Hosp Aide; VP JA; Spanish Clb; School Play; Nwsp Rptr; Yrbk Stf; Rep Stu Cncl; JV Tennis; Var Trk; High Hon Roll; Awd Excel Acad Achvt 86-87.

OSMERS, CATHY D; Central Bucks East HS; Doylestown, PA; (3); 39/491; Am Leg Aux Girls St; Chorus; Var Bsktbl; Var Fld Hcky; Lcrss; Var Sftbl; Cit Awd; DAR Awd; High Hon Roll; NHS; Hnrbl All Amer La Crosse 87; JR Olympcs Fld Hcky 86.

OSMOLINSKI, TAMMY; Bishop Guilfo/Yle HS; Altoona, PA; (3); Spanish Clb; SADD; Chorus; Off Stu Cncl; Var JV Cheerleading; Wt Lftg; Hon Roll; NHS; Natl Hnr Scty 87; Allegheny Comm Coll; Dntl Hyg.

OSOSKI, MELISSA; Cardinal O Hara HS; Milmont Park, PA; (3); 10/710; Service Clb; Band; Concert Band; Drm Mjr(t); Mrchg Band; French Hon Soc; High Hon Roll; Hon Roll; NHS; Prfct Atten Awd; JR All Amer Hall Fame Music 87; Principals Awd Acad Excell 85-87; Intl Stds.

OSSELBURN, KRISTIN; Somerset SR HS; Somerset, PA; (4); 18/231; English Clb; French Clb; Chorus; Gym; Mat Maids; Sftbl; High Hon Roll; NHS.

OSTEEN, RANDY; Conestoga HS; Berwyn, PA; (3); 24/405; Model UN; Ed Nwsp Stf; DAR Awd; Hon Roll; NHS; Ntl Merit SF; Law.

OSTER, WENDY; Coatesville Area SR HS; Coatesville, PA; (3); 80/577; French Clb; Ski Clb; Chorus; Stu Cncl; Hon Roll; Millersville U; Zoolgy.

OSTERBERG, KRISTEN; Red Lion Area Sr HS; Felton, PA; (3); 34/342; VP Pres Church Yth Grp; Band; Concert Band; Mrchg Band; Pep Band; School Musical; Symp Band; Yrbk Ed-Chief; Stu Cncl; Hon Roll.

OSTERGARD, KERRY; Warren Area HS; Warren, PA; (4); French Clb; Acpl Chr; School Play; High Hon Roll; Hon Roll; Jr NHS; NHS; IN U; Elem Ed.

OSTERRIED, ROBERT; Keystone JR SR HS; Marble, PA; (1); Boy Scts; French Hon Soc; High Hon Roll; Acdmc All AM 86-87.

OSTERRIEDER, SCOTT E; Richland HS; Gibsonia, PA; (2); Computer Clb; Stage Crew; Yrbk Phtg; Yrbk Stf; Crs Cntry; Golf; Trk; Hon Roll; Penn ST; Interior Desgn.

OSTMAN, HENRY; Trinity HS; Enola, PA; (2); Boy Scts; Ski Clb; Hon Roll.

OSTOVIC, SARAH; Washington HS; Washington, PA; (4); Cmnty Wkr; Drama Clb; Letterman Clb; Pres SADD; Nwsp Bus Mgr; Nwsp Rptr; Rep Stu Cncl; JV Var Cheerleading; L Tennis; Hon Roll; Mercyhurst Coll; Law.

OSTOYICH, JENNIFER; Council Rock HS; Holland, PA; (2); Drama Clb; Girl Scts; Band; Flag Corp; Mrchg Band; Orch; School Musical; School Play; Stage Crew; Hon Roll; All Bucks Cnty Chorus 85; All Bucks Cnty Orch 87; Bucks Cnty Music Educ Assos 86-8m; Musician.

OSTRANDER JR, JOSEPH L; Lebanon Catholic HS; Lebanon, PA; (4); Chess Clb; Church Yth Grp; Key Clb; Science Clb; Ski Clb; Chorus; Church Choir; School Play; Stage Crew; Swing Chorus; Excllnc-Foods & Ntrtn 86-87; Kutztown U; Marine Bio.

OSTRASKY, LORI; Cashs HS; Chambersburg, PA; (2); French Clb; Color Guard; Flag Corp; Mrchg Band; Penn ST; Fshn Merch.

OSTROSKI, LORI; Bishop Hafey HS; West Hazleton, PA; (3); 17/120; Church Yth Grp; Leo Clb; Spanish Clb; SADD; Drill Tm; Rep Stu Cncl; Var Cheerleading; High Hon Roll; Hon Roll; NHS; Amer Leg Awd 85; Dstngshd Amer HS Stu 87; Accntng.

OSTROSKI, LORI ANN; Reading SR HS; Reading, PA; (3); 103/710; Hon Roll; Nrsng.

OSTROVECKY, ROBERT; Highlands SR HS; Natrona Hgts, PA; (3); 36/303; Key Clb; Band; Concert Band; Jazz Band; Mrchg Band; School Musical; Symp Band; Var Bsbl; Trk; NHS; Penn ST; Comp Sci.

OSTROWSKI, DAVID; Cathedral Prep; Erie, PA; (3); French Clb; Trk; WV U; Physcl Thrpy.

OSTROWSKI, EDWARD; Bishop O Reilly HS; Forty Fort, PA; (3); Spanish Clb; Var JV Bsktbl; L Crs Cntry; Im Vllybl; Penn ST Coll; Engrng.

OSTROWSKI, LORI; Pittston Area HS; Pittston, PA; (4); Art Clb; Church Yth Grp; French Clb; Ski Clb; Chorus; Wilkes Coll; Sec Ed.

OSTRUM, TAMMY; Bradford Area HS; Bradford, PA; (4); Church Yth Grp; Cmnty Wkr; Concert Band; Mrchg Band; Rep Frsh Cls; Rep Soph Cls; Rep Sr Cls; Stu Cncl; Swmmng; Jr NHS; Conservation Camp Head Counselor; Slippery Rock U; Bio.

OSULLIVAN, MAUREEN; Elk Lake HS; Laceyville, PA; (4); 4/104; Art Clb; French Clb; Band; Concert Band; Jazz Band; Rep Stu Cncl; Var Cheerleading; Mgr Trk; Hon Roll.

OSWALD, BRENDA L; Huntingdon Area HS; Huntingdon, PA; (3); 14/224; Key Clb; VP Soroptimist; Band; Chorus; Color Guard; Concert Band; Mrchg Band; Yrbk Phtg; Rep Soph Cls; Sftbl.

OSWALD, JAMES; Brandywine Heights HS; Mertztown, PA; (4); 13/124; FBLA; Trk; Vllybl; Hon Roll; NHS; Pres Acdmc Fit Awd; Penn ST; Engrng.

OSWALD, JAMIE; Westmont Hilltop HS; Johnstown, PA; (4); 17/158; Hosp Aide; Key Clb; Chorus; School Musical; High Hon Roll; Hon Roll; NHS; Westmont Hilltop Memrl Awd 87; IUP; Nrsng.

OSWALD, JOSEPH; Cumberland Valley HS; Mechanicsburg, PA; (3); 8/578; Math Tm; Quiz Bowl; Concert Band; Mrchg Band; Symp Band; Lit Mag; Hon Roll; NHS; Ntl Merit SF; Rnsslr Plytchnc Inst Mdl-Outstndng Math & Sci Stu 87; Sci.

OSWALD, LORI; Fleetwood HS; Fleetwood, PA; (3); 25/104; Church Yth Grp; Drill Tm; Mrchg Band; Yrbk Stf; Vllybl; Hon Roll; Empire Beauty; Cosmtlgy.

OSWALD, NICOLE; Brandywine Heights HS; Topton, PA; (2); Chorus; Trs Soph Cls; Rep Stu Cncl; Hon Roll; Outstndng Intro To Bus Soph 87.

OSWALD, ROBERTA; Lower Merion HS; Bala Cynwyd, PA; (3); Sec Church Yth Grp; Rep Stu Cncl; Homecoming Ct 86; Ceramics Cls At Cmnty Clg Of Philadelphia & Received A B 87; Arch.

OSWALT, JULIE ANN; Homer-Center HS; Homer City, PA; (3); 3/110; French Clb; VP Band; Sec Chorus; Jazz Band; Sec Frsh Cls; Hst Sr Cls; Trs Dance Clb; Var JV Cheerleading; High Hon Roll; Hon Roll; Jr Miss Fnlst 87; Summer Happenings 87; Methodist Youth Chorale 86; Music Prfmnc.

OTERI, CORINNE; Northeast Prep HS; Philadelphia, PA; (3); Dance Clb; Library Aide; Office Aide; Hon Roll; Haidresser.

OTIS, GARY; Wyalusing Valley HS; Wyalusing, PA; (3); 1/156; Boy Scts; German Clb; VP Jr Cls; VP Sr Cls; Var Capt Ftbl; Var L Trk; Var L Wrstlng; Cit Awd; High Hon Roll; Hon Roll; HOBY Ldrshp Sem 85-86; 1st Tm All Star Ftbl 86-87; Vet Sci.

OTOOLE, KELLY; West Allegheny HS; Oakdale, PA; (3); 18/198; Sec Art Clb; Computer Clb; German Clb; Var L Bsktbl; Capt Powder Puff Ftbl; Score Keeper; Stat Socr; Var L Sftbl; High Hon Roll; Hon Roll.

OTOOLE, MAUREEN; Steel Valley HS; Homestead, PA; (3); Church Yth Grp; Var JV Cheerleading; Hon Roll; NHS; Arch.

OTOOLE, MIKE; Chariers Valley HS; Bridgeville, PA; (3); 88/328; Computer Clb; Mgr Bsktbl; Hon Roll; Jacksonville U; Infrmtn Sys.

OTOOLE, PATRICK; Kennedy Christian HS; Brookfld, OH; (2); 57/97; Aud/Vis; JA; Ski Clb; Spanish Clb; L Golf; Hon Roll; Hotel Mgmt.

OTT, DAN; Punxsutawney Area SR HS; Big Run, PA; (4); Science Clb; Pres Spanish Clb; Variety Show; Ftbl; Trk; Capt L Wrstlng; BYU; Anthropology.

OTT, DANA; Abington Heights HS; Chinchilla, PA; (3); 14/292; Concert Band; Mrchg Band; Orch; School Musical; Lit Mag; Rep Stu Cncl; Hon Roll; NHS; Dist Band 86-87; Regional Band 87.

OTT, DANIEL; Central HS; Newry, PA; (3); 3/187; Computer Clb; Science Clb; Ski Clb; Im Vllybl; Im Wt Lftg; Cit Awd; High Hon Roll; Hon Roll; Pres Schlr; Prsdntl Acdmc Ftnss Awd 85; Acdmc Awd 85; Hnr Soc Awd 87; PA ST U; Engrng.

OTT, GARY; Du Bois Area HS; Du Bois, PA; (3); #90 In Class; Church Yth Grp; Letterman Clb; Varsity Clb; Wrstlng; Hon Roll; Med.

OTT, KATHY; Saint Benedict Acad; Erie, PA; (3); 7/53; Q&S; School Play; Yrbk Stf; Sec Soph Cls; Rep Stu Cncl; Var L Golf; NHS; Art Clb; High Hon Roll; Trs Frsh Cls; Gld Key Art Awd 87; PA Jr Acad Of Sci 86; Stu Cncl Schlrshp For Cmnty Svc & Sprt 87; PA ST.

OTT, RON; Meadville Area SR HS; Meadville, PA; (2); Var L Ice Hcky; Hon Roll; Hnr Rl Awd 86.

OTT, WENDY; West Hazleton HS; West Hazleton, PA; (3); Pep Clb; Chorus; School Musical.

OTTAVIANI, FRED; Highlands SR HS; Natrona Hts, PA; (3); Art Clb; Off Jr Cls; Bsbl; Wt Lftg; Pitt U; Phrmcst.

OTTENA, MICHAEL; Jefferson Morgan JR SR HS; Clarksville, PA; (3); /73; Church Yth Grp; Band; Hon Roll.

OTTERBEIN, LISA; Bishop Hafey HS; Hazleton, PA; (1); Library Aide; High Hon Roll.

OTTERMAN, AMY; East Allegheny HS; N Versailles, PA; (4); 19/217; Exploring; French Clb; Girl Scts; Hosp Aide; Pep Clb; Ski Clb; Chorus; School Musical; Yrbk Stf; Soph Cls; IN U Of PA; Erly Chldhd Educ.

OTTEY, KRISTA; Harry S Truman HS; Bristol, PA; (3); 8/650; GAA; NFL; Office Aide; Speech Tm; SADD; Im L Bsktbl; L Sftbl; Hon Roll; Trs NHS; Prfct Atten Awd; Chld Psych.

OTTINGER, TRINA M; Haverford SR HS; Havertown, PA; (3); 119/423; Band; Concert Band; Mrchg Band; Symp Band; Sftbl; Lawyr.

OTTO, BILLIEJO A; Penn-Trafford HS; Penn, PA; (3); AFS; Church Yth Grp; Drama Clb; Hosp Aide; Trs Chorus; School Musical; School Play; Swing Chorus; NHS; Eng.

OTTO, BOBBI; St Marys Area HS; St Marys, PA; (3); VP 4-H; Office Aide; Pep Clb; Teachers Aide; Co-Capt Cheerleading; Hon Roll; NHS; Legl Sec.

OTTO, GREGORY; HS Of Engineering & Science; Philadelphia, PA; (3); Im Bsktbl; Im Ftbl; Im Swmmng; Comp Sci.

OTTO, JENNIFER; Biglerville HS; Gardners, PA; (2); 36/109; 4-H; Chorus; Concert Band; Mrchg Band; School Musical; Stage Crew; Cit Awd; Hon Roll; Jr NHS; Harrisburg Area CC; Accntng.

OTTO, ROSEANNE; Scotland Schl For Veterans Children; Aldan, PA; (4); 6/35; Pres Art Clb; Drm & Bgl; Capt Flag Corp; Nwsp Ed-Chief; Yrbk Stf; Lit Mag; DAR Awd; Hon Roll; VFW Awd; Voice Dem Awd; VFW Schl Awd 85-86; VFW Schlrshp & Onyx Schlrshp; Bnd Frnt Awd 84-85; Cdr Crst Coll; Nrsng.

OVER, KELLY; Northern Bedford County HS; Woodbury, PA; (3); VP Church Yth Grp; Math Clb; Chorus; Church Choir; School Musical; Pres Frsh Cls; Off Stu Cncl; JV Bsbl; JV Bsktbl; JV Ftbl; Amer HS Math Exam Awd 87.

OVERBAUGH, DAWN; Littlestown HS; Gettysburg, PA; (3); 6/150; Varsity Clb; School Musical; School Play; Yrbk Ed-Chief; Yrbk Stf; Var L Tennis; High Hon Roll; Hon Roll; NHS; Voice Dem Awd; Phys Thrpy.

OVERBAUGH, MATTHEW; Hempfield HS; Lancaster, PA; (2); 100/450; Science Clb; Varsity Clb; Var Bsktbl; JV Ftbl; Var Trk; Hon Roll; Jr Cls Steering Cmmttee 87-88; Villanova; Pre Med.

OVERBERG, KERRI; Methacton SR HS; Collegeville, PA; (3); FBLA; Office Aide; Teachers Aide; Chorus; Rep Frsh Cls; 2nd Pl Methacton Comm Writng Cntst 87; Stu Wrtr Mo 86; Journ.

OVERDORFF, ROCHELLE; Purchase Line HS; Cherry Tree, PA; (2); Church Yth Grp; French Clb; Pep Clb; SADD; Chorus; Church Choir; Off Frsh Cls; JV Bsktbl; High Hon Roll.

OVERHOLTZER, KAREN L; Boyertown JR HS East Ctr; Gilbertsville, PA; (1); Art Clb; Aud/Vis; Church Yth Grp; Band; Concert Band; Mrchg Band; Orch; Var Fld Hcky; Lcrss; High Hon Roll.

OVERLY, PATTI; Punxsutawney Area HS; Punxsutawney, PA; (4); 33/250; FNA; Letterman Clb; Office Aide; Chorus; Variety Show; Yrbk Phtg; Yrbk Stf; Var Capt Cheerleading; High Hon Roll; Hon Roll; Prncpls Awd 84; Stu Mnth 84; IN U Of PA; Psych.

OVERLY, TRACI; Connellsville HS; Cville, PA; (3); 18/550; Library Aide; Chorus; Drm & Bgl; Stage Crew; Pres Soph Cls; VP Jr Cls; Stat Bsktbl; High Hon Roll; Spanish NHS.

OVERMILLER, ANGEL; Eastern York HS; York, PA; (2); Nwsp Stf; Swmmng; Hon Roll; Systms Anlyst.

OVERMOYER, BRIAN; Linesville HS; Linesville, PA; (2); 1/75; Chess Clb; Church Yth Grp; Trs 4-H; Trs FFA; Trs Soph Cls; JV Ftbl; High Hon Roll; NHS; Ski Clb; Star Chptr Frmr 86-87; Preprd Publ Spkg 10th ST 87; Ecnmcs.

OVITSKY, ERIC; Hempfield Area HS; Greensburg, PA; (4); 125/695; AFS; Art Clb; Church Yth Grp; Debate Tm; NFL; Spanish Clb; Speech Tm; Orch; Nwsp Ed-Chief; Ntl Merit SF; Miami U; Arch.

OWCZAREK, JENNIFER; Liberty HS; Bethlehem, PA; (3); 82/429; JV Var Cheerleading; Var Trk; Hon Roll; Art Awd 85-86; Lehigh U.

OWEN, DENA; Northern Lehigh HS; Slatington, PA; (3); 18/166; Debate Tm; Drill Tm; School Musical; Yrbk Stf; L Fld Hcky; High Hon Roll; Flbrl Arts.

OWEN, KATHLEEN; Trinity Christian HS; Pittsburgh, PA; (1); Church Yth Grp; Quiz Bowl; Chorus; School Play; Ed Yrbk Stf; JV Socr; High Hon Roll; Hon Roll; Jr NHS; NEDT Awd; Vet Med.

OWEN, RUTH; Penn Hills SR HS; Pittsburgh, PA; (4); 1/616; Aud/Vis; Church Yth Grp; German Clb; Orch; High Hon Roll; NHS; Ntl Merit SF; Val; AFS; School Musical; Amer HS Math Exam Hnr Roll 86; Rensselaer Medal 86.

OWEN, VANESSA; Lewistown AREA HS; Lewistown, PA; (2); Sec AFS; German Clb; Church Choir; Yrbk Phtg; Yrbk Rptr; Yrbk Stf; JV Bsktbl; PA ST U; Chmcl Engr.

OWENS, BRIAN; Clearfield HS; Clearfield, PA; (4); 87/300; Var Crs Cntry; Wt Lftg; Var Wrstlng; Art Weiss Schlrshp Awd 87; Lock Haven U; Comp Sci.

OWENS, DANIELLE MARIE; Carlisle SR HS; Carlisle, PA; (3); 94/400; Pres Sec Church Yth Grp; Chorus; Church Choir; Mgr Bsktbl; Var Mgr(s); Hon Roll; Lebanon Vly Coll; Music Ed.

OWENS, LORI; Belle Vernon Area HS; Belle Vernon, PA; (3); Art Clb; FBLA; NFL; Pep Clb; Ski Clb; Swmmng; Hon Roll; Bradford Schl Off Bus; Mgmt.

OWENS, NICHELLE D; Cecilian Academy HS; Philadelphia, PA; (3); 5/36; Cmnty Wkr; Debate Tm; Red Cross Aide; Nwsp Stf; Yrbk Stf; Stu Cncl; NHS; Pep Clb; Variety Show; Yrbk Phtg; Magna Cum Laude Phila Clsscl Latin Scty 85-87; Cert Of Prtcptn Cncrnd Black Men Yth Of Yr Cntst 86-87; Math.

OWENS, SARA; Clearfield Area HS; Frenchville, PA; (4); Church Yth Grp; Rep DECA; French Clb; Trs SADD; Hon Roll; Prfct Atten Awd; Awd For Hardest Co-Op Wrkr 86-87; Hnr Fair Queen 2nd Pl 85-86; Clearfield Cnty Vo-Tech; Nrsng.

OWENS, SHANNON; York Catholic HS; York, PA; (3); 5/180; Church Yth Grp; Spanish Clb; Varsity Clb; Im JV Bsktbl; Var Vllybl; High Hon Roll; NHS; 1st In Cls 86-87; Chem.

OWENS, STEPHEN; Hempfield HS; Mountville, PA; (3); Mrchg Band; Im JV Bsbl; Im Coach Actv; Im JV Ftbl; Im Vllybl; Im Wt Lftg; All Section 2nd Base 87; Sci Rsrch.

OWENS, THERESIA; East Stroudsburg SR HS; E Stroudsburg, PA; (1); 26/238; Pep Clb; Chorus; School Musical; Variety Show; Cheerleading; High Hon Roll; Jr NHS; U Of Miami; Psych.

OWINGS, HARVA; Newport JR SR HS; Newport, PA; (4); 8/95; Art Clb; Yrbk Stf; High Hon Roll; NHS; Lgsltv Awd-Artwrk Entrd Cntst 86; Mssh Coll Cert Of Merit-Piece In Cntst 87; Head Hntrs Acad/Csmtlgy; Btcn.

OWINGS, HEIDI; Biglerville HS; Biglerville, PA; (3); FCA; Varsity Clb; Pres Frsh Cls; VP Soph Cls; Rep Jr Cls; Trs Sr Cls; Rep Stu Cncl; Var Bsktbl; Capt Var Cheerleading; Capt Var Trk; Rookie Of Yr In Trck 85; Mst Dedictiated In Trck 87; PA ST; Physcl Ed.

OYASKI, CYNTHIA; Bishop Carroll HS; Ebensburg, PA; (3); 7/128; Church Yth Grp; Pep Clb; Spanish Clb; Yrbk Sprt Ed; Yrbk Stf; Stu Cncl; Bsktbl; Trk; Vllybl; NHS; Penn ST U; Arch Engr.

OYLER, JENNIFER; Altoona Area HS; Altoona, PA; (3); Church Yth Grp; German Clb; PAVAS; VP SADD; Acpl Chr; Chorus; Church Choir; School Musical; School Play; Swing Chorus; Vocal Music Awd-Stu Vocal Awd 85; PA ST U; Educ.

OYLER, VICKI; Windber HS; Windber, PA; (3); Church Yth Grp; French Clb; Bsktbl; Sftbl; Hon Roll; Honors Night 87; Occptnl Thrpy.

PACAK, ROBERT S; Monessen HS; Monessen, PA; (4); 7/97; PAVAS; Stage Crew; Pres Soph Cls; Stu Cncl; Capt Bsktbl; Capt Golf; High Hon Roll; NHS; Stu Trainer 87; Washington & Jefferson Coll; Med.

PACE, TINA M; Rochester Area HS; Rochester, PA; (3); 11/115; Service Clb; Ski Clb; Co-Capt Drill Tm; Nwsp Stf; Yrbk Ed-Chief; Var L Cheerleading; Powder Puff Ftbl; Var Tennis; Var Trk; High Hon Roll; Ntl Hnr Rll 87; Beaver Cnty Tms Acdmc All-Str 85-87; Geneva Coll Exprmntl Bio Pgm 87; Penn ST; Biomed Engnrng.

PACELLA, NICOLE; Peters Township HS; Bridgeville, PA; (3); Church Yth Grp; Thesps; Stage Crew; Nwsp Stf; Yrbk Stf; Rep Frsh Cls; DAR Awd; U Pittsburgh; Psych.

PACHARIS, MICHAEL; Berks Christian HS; Birdsboro, PA; (3); Capt Var Bsktbl.

PACHARIS, MONICA; Oley Valley HS; Reading, PA; (3); 7/142; Drama Clb; Chorus; School Musical; School Play; Nwsp Stf; Stu Cncl; Co-Capt Cheerleading; High Hon Roll; NHS; Govs Schl For Arts 86; Point Pk Coll; Jrnlsm.

PACHELLA, SAMANTHA; C H Boehm HS; Yardley, PA; (2); Church Yth Grp; Cmnty Wkr; Variety Show; JV Cheerleading; JV Socr; Hon Roll; German I,Ii 85-87; Phys Educ 85-87; Intl Bus.

PACHENCE, DINA; Hazleton HS; Hazleton, PA; (3); 92/445; Drama Clb; French Clb; Leo Clb; Ski Clb; Y-Teens; Var Cheerleading; Tennis; High Hon Roll; Hon Roll; Chorus; Natl Frnch Hon 80-86; U Of MD; Lbrl Arts.

PACIFICO, MARK; Reading HS; Reading, PA; (3); Chess Clb; Debate Tm; Exploring; German Clb; Key Clb; Library Aide; Model UN; Pep Clb; SADD; School Play; Socl Stds Ed.

PACKARD, JAMIE; Millersburg Area HS; Millersburg, PA; (4); 23/76; Library Aide; Spanish Clb; Pres SADD; Capt Drill Tm; Stu Cncl; Var Capt Bsktbl; Powder Puff Ftbl; Hon Roll; NHS; Pres Fit Awd 87; Bloomsburg U; Biol.

PACKARD, TERRI; Troy HS; Troy, PA; (2); 2/200; Church Yth Grp; VP 4-H; Church Choir; Concert Band; Mrchg Band; Pres Frsh Cls; Pres Soph Cls; JV Bsktbl; 4-H Awd; High Hon Roll; Attnd PAFC Smmr Inst, PA JR Holstn Assoc Exec Commtte, Bradford Cnty 4-H Cnty Cncl 86; PA ST U.

PACKER, DAVID; Central HS; Philadelphia, PA; (3); 2/530; Math Clb; Math Tm; Science Clb; Nwsp Rptr; Harvard Bk Awd 86-87; Krause Math Awd 86-87; Swarthmore Coll; Math.

PACKER, MARY B; Tunkhannock HS; Dalton, PA; (4); 30/290; Am Leg Aux Girls St; Church Yth Grp; Drama Clb; Office Aide; Trs Spanish Clb; Teachers Aide; Band; Concert Band; Jazz Band; Mrchg Band; PA Music Tchrs Assoc Blue Ribbon 84; Tunk Womens Clb 85; U Of Scranton; Sec Educ.

PACOE, ELIZABETH; Sacred Heart HS; Pittsburgh, PA; (3); 14/140; Cmnty Wkr; NFL; Speech Tm; Trs Sr Cls; Var Sftbl; Var Trk; Im Vllybl; High Hon Roll; Hon Roll; Med.

PACZEK, PAUL; Windber Area HS; Windber, PA; (3); Boy Scts; Church Yth Grp; Library Aide; Math Clb; Spanish Clb; Var Bsbl; Im Bsktbl; ST Policeman.

PADE, BRADLEY; Plum HS; Pittsburgh, PA; (3); Exploring; Band; Jazz Band; Mrchg Band; Symp Band; JV Bsktbl; Capt Bowling; Hon Roll.

PADEN, CLINT; Mohawk HS; New Castle, PA; (3); Boy Scts; Ski Clb; Var L Ftbl; Im Sftbl; Var L Trk; Wt Lftg; Hon Roll; Acad Excell & Achvt In Industral Arts 87.

PADGETT, ALEKSONDRICK D; York Catholic HS; York, PA; (2); 110/146; Boys Clb Am; Boy Scts; Church Yth Grp; FCA; French Clb; Speech Tm; Church Choir; JV Bsbl; Ftbl; JV Wrstlng; Dickinson; Lwyr.

PADGETT, DENISE; Delaware Valley HS; Mill Rift, PA; (3); 14/150; Hosp Aide; SADD; High Hon Roll; Hon Roll; Prfct Atten Awd.

PADGETT, JEFF; Henderson SR HS; West Chester, PA; (3); 38/400; Church Yth Grp; Crs Cntry; Trk; Wrstlng; Hon Roll; NHS; Spanish NHS; Engrng.

PADGETT, MALIK CHEVEZ; York Catholic HS; York, PA; (1); 90/146; Boys Clb Am; Boy Scts; Church Yth Grp; JA; Speech Tm; Chorus; Church Choir; School Musical; School Play; Variety Show; Scholar ENC Comm Sklls; Check & Trphy Yorks TV Talent 86; Hnr Trphies 80 & 81; ENC; Lwyr.

PADILLA, ANTHONY; Bethlehem Catholic HS; Bethlehem, PA; (4); Key Clb; Rep Soph Cls; Rep Jr Cls; Rep Sr Cls; Off Stu Cncl; L Crs Cntry; Var Capt Wrstlng; Hon Roll; 5th Pl PA ST Wrstlng Trnmnt 87; Bernie J Gallagher Schlrshp Wnnr 87; Hawthorne Coll; Aero Sci.

PADISAK, JACQUELINE; West Branch HS; Grassflat, PA; (3); 18/103; Drama Clb; Office Aide; Science Clb; Spanish Clb; SADD; Teachers Aide; Chorus; Co-Capt Drm Mjr(t); Hon Roll; Shrthnd II Awd 87; Bus.

PADJEN, MARY; Freedom HS; Bethlehem, PA; (3); 50/486; Intnl Clb; Church Choir; Cheerleading; Hon Roll; NHS; Le High U; Accntnt.

PAFF, KRISTINE; Wyoming Area HS; Harding, PA; (4); Art Clb; Computer Clb; Drama Clb; German Clb; Vllybl; Dvlpmnt Of PA Hnrs Test 87; U Of Scranton; Bio.

PAGAN, HARRY A; Allentown Central Catholic HS; Allentown, PA; (4); Chorus; School Musical; Nwsp Rptr; Nwsp Stf; Smmr Schlrshp PA Govs Sch Of Art 86; Hnrbl Mntn In Arts & Rcgntn Tlnt Srch 87; E Allentwn Nghbd Schlr; PA ST U; Theatre.

PAGANO, SANDRA; Greensburg Central Catholic HS; New Stanton, PA; (4); 90/265; AFS; Band; Concert Band; Mrchg Band; Ftbl; Mgr Socr; High Hon Roll; Hon Roll; U Of Pittsburgh; Phys Ther.

PAGE, BECKY; Conemaugh Township Area HS; Hollsopple, PA; (3); 17/122; Drama Clb; Trs French Clb; Band; Concert Band; Mrchg Band; School Musical; Educ.

PAGE, JOHN; Greensburg Salem SR HS; Greensburg, PA; (2); German Clb; Ski Clb; Var JV Bsktbl; Pres Physcl Ftns Awd 85-86; Ftbl Athlt Awd 85-86.

PAGLIA, ANTHONY M; Cardinal O Hara HS; Aston, PA; (3); 278/715; Ftbl; Score Keeper; Timer; Wt Lftg; JV Wrstlng; Bsbl & Ftbl Trphs & Awds 80-86; Wrstlng Ltr Schl; Law.

PAGLIARO, SUSANNA F; Strath Haven HS; Swartmore, PA; (4); Hosp Aide; Var Gym; Central Lg Gym Champs 85 & 86; Var Ltr Gym 84-87; Strath Haven ST Champ Girls Gym Mgr 87; Goucher Coll.

PAGLIOTTI, CHARLES; Bishop Saint John Neuman HS; Philadelphia, PA; (2); 9/355; Boy Scts; Computer Clb; Latin Clb; Science Clb; Band; High Hon Roll; Hon Roll; Am Legion Awd 85; Math Poster Cont 86; Math Comp Awd 86; U Of PA; Comp Prog.

PAGNINI, JENNIFER; Cardnal O Hara HS; Drexel Hill, PA; (3); 229/710; Cmnty Wkr; Service Clb; Stage Crew; Var Capt Bsktbl; Var JV Socr; Schlstc Art Awd 87; All Delco Bsktbl Hnrb Mntn 87; DE Cnty Sci Fair 1st 86; Phila Coll Of Arts; Grphc Dsgn.

PAGOTTO, CHRISTOPHER; Northampton Area JR HS; Northampton, PA; (1); Church Yth Grp; Band; Concert Band; Jazz Band; Mrchg Band; Orch; Symp Band; Hon Roll; Pres Acdmc Ftnss Awd 86-87.

PAHL, JEFF; Reading HS; Reading, PA; (3); 26/710; German Clb; Band; Orch; Var Capt Bowling; Hon Roll; NHS; MVP Bwlg Tm 86; Penn ST U; Comp Sci.

PAICH, ROBYN; Center HS; Monaca, PA; (3); 19/186; Church Yth Grp; Hosp Aide; Latin Clb; Band; Church Choir; Concert Band; Mrchg Band; Stu Cncl; High Hon Roll; Hon Roll; Acad Awd Achvng Staight A Whole Yr 86-87; Lat Awd A Average 86-87; Stu Council Awd 86-87.

PAIDA, DOUGLAS; Bishop Shanahan HS; W Chester, PA; (4); 15/215; Church Yth Grp; Math Tm; Quiz Bowl; Nwsp Stf; High Hon Roll; Hon Roll; NHS; Ametek Fndtn Natl Merit Spcl Schlrshp 87; Geom Awd 85; Alg 2 Awd 86; Drexel U; Chemical Engrng.

PAINTER, DAWNE; Manheim Central SR HS; Manheim, PA; (4); Teachers Aide; Pres Ftns Awd 87; Goldey Beacom; Med Secy.

PAINTER, PAIGE; Warren Area HS; Warren, PA; (3); 33/300; Art Clb; Church Yth Grp; French Clb; Office Aide; SADD; Chorus; Church Choir; Nwsp Rptr; Sec Soph Cls; Stu Cncl; Newspaper Artcl Awd 84-85; Sec Ed.

PAINTER JR, RUSS; Highlands HS; Tarentum, PA; (3); Aud/Vis; Computer Clb; DECA; FBLA; Stage Crew; Hon Roll; Jr NHS; NHS; Natl Sci Merit Awd 87; Acadmc All Amer 87; Mr Future Bus Ldr :Fbla 2nd Pl Regnl 86; Penn ST; Comp Interfacing.

PAINTER, TIFFANY; Seneca Valley SR HS; Evans City, PA; (4); 27/350; Sec Art Clb; FTA; SADD; Mgr School Musical; Lit Mag; Mgr(s); Var Sftbl; High Hon Roll; Hon Roll; Rotary Awd; Zelienople Bus & Prof Wmn Schlrshp 87; Campus Exec Schrshp 87; Beaver Campus Schlrshp 87; PA ST U; Educ.

PAINTON, STERLING; Moon SR HS; Coraopolis, PA; (2); Mgr(s); Score Keeper; Vllybl; High Hon Roll; Hon Roll; NHS; Cmmrcl Art.

PAISLEY, JANET L; Tamaqua Area HS; Tamaqua, PA; (3); 24/208; VP Sec Drama Clb; Band; Rep Chorus; Drm Mjr(t); School Musical; School Play; Nwsp Phtg; French Hon Soc; Hon Roll; Cnty Chrs 86 & 87; Wrthy Advsr, Rnbw Grls 85; E Stroudsburg; Elem Ed.

PAJAK, JO ELLEN; Hopewell HS; Aliquippa, PA; (3); 85/266; Trs Church Yth Grp; Hosp Aide; Pres Trs Spanish Clb; Var Bowling; Mgr Socr; JV Vllybl; Polt Sci.

PAJAK, JOAN; Saint Basil Acad; Philadelphia, PA; (4); Church Yth Grp; French Clb; Math Clb; Science Clb; Chorus; Stage Crew; Variety Show; High Hon Roll; Hon Roll; Prfct Atten Awd; Goldn Petry Awd Wrld Poetry 85; Slvr Poet Awd Wrld Poetry 86; Gwynedd Mercy Schlrshp 87-88; Gwynedd-Mercy Coll; Elem Ed.

PAJAKINAS, TONY; Marian HS; Coaldale, PA; (3); 67/110; Church Yth Grp; Ski Clb; SADD; Var Bsbl; JV Ftbl; Bloomsburg U; Bus Mngmnt.

PAJOVICH, GEORGE; West Hazleton SR HS; W Hazleton, PA; (3); Church Yth Grp; Cmnty Wkr; Capt Scholastic Bowl; VP Thesps; Varsity Clb; Pres Sr Cls; Stu Cncl; L Tennis; Hon Roll; PA Sci Tlnt Srch Awd Wnnr 87; Marine Bio.

PALACZ, JOHN; Lourdes Regional HS; Paxinos, PA; (3); 22/89; Pep Clb; Sr Cls; VP Stu Cncl; Var Bsktbl; Accntng.

PALADINO, ELYSIA; Mount Pleasant Area SR HS; Mount Pleasant, PA; (3); 1/244; Ski Clb; Spanish Clb; Band; Drm Mjr(t); Mrchg Band; Nwsp Ed-Chief; Yrbk Stf; VP Frsh Cls; Diving; High Hon Roll; Cty Band Festvl; Dist Band; Mid East All Star Band Festvl; U CA; Fine Arts.

PALADINO, JUDITH; Owen J Roberts HS; Spring City, PA; (4); Church Yth Grp; Drama Clb; Exploring; Band; School Musical; School Play; Var JV Bsktbl; Stat Fld Hcky; JV Capt Socr; Im Vllybl; Ursinus Coll; Intl Bus.

PALAIA, LAURIE; Nazareth Acad; Philadelphia, PA; (3); Church Yth Grp; Dance Clb; Drama Clb; Political Wkr; Thesps; Chorus; Church Choir; School Musical; Stage Crew; Variety Show; Prfct Atten Awd; Glee Clb Awd; Tnns Awd; Music.

PALANSKY, LISA MARIE; Central Catholic HS; Allentown, PA; (4); 20/207; Civic Clb; Pep Clb; Service Clb; Spanish Clb; SADD; Nwsp Stf; Stu Cncl; Var L Crs Cntry; High Hon Roll; Church Yth Grp; Intl Stu Ldrshp Inst 86; U Scrntn OH; Crmnl Jstc.

PALASTRO, GREGG; Chartiers Valley HS; Carnegie, PA; (3); 69/328; Church Yth Grp; Cmnty Wkr; Library Aide; Rep Band; Jazz Band; Mrchg Band; Orch; Pep Band; School Musical; School Play; Music Fest 84-86; Dist Roch 84-85; Yng Peoples Orch 84-86; Dist Band 85-87; Honors & Regnl Band 86-87; Purdue U; Pre-Med.

PALAZZETTI, JENNIFER; Bradford Central Christian HS; Bradford, PA; (2); Computer Clb; Math Clb; Pep Clb; SADD; VP Soph Cls; High Hon Roll; NHS; Cert Merit Schlstc Achvt Sci 87; Outstndng Acdmc Achvt 87; Gannon; RN.

PALCZEWSKI, ROXANNE; John S Fine HS; Nanticoke, PA; (3); FBLA; Library Aide; Spanish Clb; Color Guard; Yrbk Stf; Trk; High Hon Roll; Bus.

PALDAN, KAREN; Owen J Roberts HS; St Peters, PA; (2); 27/311; Mgr(s); Score Keeper; Vllybl; Hon Roll; Law.

PALENIK, PATRICIA; Conemaugh Twp Area HS; Davidsville, PA; (3); Church Yth Grp; French Clb; Spanish Clb; Trk; Spnsh Awd 85-87; Frnch Awd 87; Lang.

PALEOS, JOHN; Ambridge Area SR HS; Ambridge, PA; (4); Pep Clb; SADD; Off Sr Cls; Hon Roll; U Of Pittsburgh; Elec Engr.

PALERINO, JODI; Pottsville Area HS; Pottsville, PA; (4); 18/242; Cmnty Wkr; Drama Clb; Latin Clb; Mrchg Band; Rep Stu Cncl; Cheerleading; Swmmng; High Hon Roll; Hon Roll; La Salle U; Lib Art.

PALERMO, MARYANN; MMI Preparatory Schl; Hazleton, PA; (3); Hosp Aide; Ski Clb; Sec Jr Cls; Var L Bowling; Var L Cheerleading; Var L Sftbl; Hon Roll; Spanish NHS; Church Yth Grp; Political Wkr; PA Jr Acad Of Sci 1st Dist & 2nd St 85; Kings Coll Spnsh Cntst 3rd Pl 86; Athlete Of Yr 85; Sprts Med.

PALERMO, PAMELA; Kiski Area HS; Vandergrift, PA; (2); Band; Hon Roll; Duffs Schl Of Bus; Stenography.

PALESTRA, GAIL; Plum HS; Pittsburgh, PA; (3); AFS; Drill Tm; Rep Sr Cls; Stat Bsktbl; Im Cheerleading; Var L Vllybl; Allghny Cnty Apprctn Awd SADD 87.

PALETSKI, MARLA ANN; Bishop Hafey HS; Hazleton, PA; (3); 15/113; PAVAS; Spanish Clb; Yrbk Bus Mgr; Hon Roll; NHS; Church Yth Grp; Girl Scts; Key Clb; Math Clb; Science Clb; Slvr Awd Grl Scts 84-87; SR Excllnce Awd Btny PA JR Acad Of Sci 87; 2nd Pl Awd PA JR Acad 85-86; U Of Scranton; Pharm.

PALETTA, JOHN; Peabody HS; Pittsburgh, PA; (4); 30/297; JCL; Latin Clb; Trs Jr Cls; Trs Sr Cls; Ftbl; Socr; Hon Roll; NHS; Prfct Atten Awd; U Of Pittsburgh; Premed.

PALFEY, MICHAEL; Yough SR HS; Rillton, PA; (3); Ski Clb; Spanish Clb; High Hon Roll; Hon Roll; Distngshd Hnr Rl.

PALFEY, TOM; Hanover Area HS; Wilkes Barre, PA; (3); 13/194; Church Yth Grp; Church Choir; Off Stu Cncl; Var L Bsbl; JV Bsktbl; Var L Ftbl; Wt Lftg; High Hon Roll; Hon Roll; Jr NHS; Yth Ldrshp Awd 87; Yth Rep Askam Un Mthdst Chrch 84-87; Engnrng.

PALIANI, LORI; Ambridge Area HS; Ambridge, PA; (3); Pep Clb; Off Soph Cls; Off Jr Cls; Off Sr Cls; Capt Cheerleading; Gym; High Hon Roll; Hon Roll; Psych.

PALIPCHAK, TONY; New Castle HS; W Pittsburg, PA; (2); Art Clb; Aud/Vis; Computer Clb; Exploring; Science Clb; SADD; Nwsp Bus Mgr; Swmmng; Capt Vllybl; High Hon Roll; Gvnrs Hnr Prgm 88; Bus.

PALKA, JOHN; West Chester East HS; Westtown, PA; (3); Intnl Clb; Concert Band; Jazz Band; School Play; Ftbl; Socr; Sftbl; Crmnl Jstc.

PALKO, ERIN; Valley HS; New Kensington, PA; (2); 38/237; Art Clb; Varsity Clb; Chorus; Concert Band; Mrchg Band; Yrbk Sprt Ed; Var Sftbl; Var Swmmng; JV Vllybl.

PALKO, JOSEPH; Dunmore HS; Dunmore, PA; (3); Computer Clb; Letterman Clb; Ski Clb; SADD; Ftbl; Trk; Wt Lftg; Hon Roll; Accntng.

PALKO, MARGARET; Central HS; Martinsburg, PA; (3); Drama Clb; FBLA; Band; High Hon Roll; NHS; 1st Pl Bgng Bkkpng Williamsport PA 87; Acctng.

PALLADINI, KELLY ANN; Ambridge Area HS; Freedom, PA; (4); 90/265; Church Yth Grp; Pep Clb; Spanish Clb; Band; Concert Band; Mrchg Band; Rep Frsh Cls; Rep Soph Cls; Rep Jr Cls; Rep Sr Cls; Slippery Rock U; Elem Ed.

PALLADINO, ROCHELLE M; New Castle SR HS; New Castle, PA; (3); SADD; Nwsp Rptr; JV Var Cheerleading; Var L Gym; Hon Roll; AFS; Nwsp Bus Mgr; Rep Stu Cncl; Trk; JR Acad Sci Regnl 1st & ST 1st 86-87; Italian Club Rep 86-87; Boston Coll; Bio.

PALLAS, DENISE; Hampton HS; Gibsonia, PA; (2).

PALLASH, ATTWOOD; Shamokin Area HS; Shamokin, PA; (3); 20/225; Cmnty Wkr; Computer Clb; Key Clb; Letterman Clb; ROTC; Science Clb; Spanish Clb; Varsity Clb; Bsktbl; Ftbl; Penn ST.

PALLO, FRANK; West Branch JR SR HS; Hawk Run, PA; (3); Spanish Clb; SADD; Varsity Clb; Var Ftbl; Im Wt Lftg; JV Wrstlng; Outstndng Achvt Comp Grphcs Tchrs Awd 86-87; Comp Grphcs.

PALM, BRENDA; Union HS; Sligo, PA; (3); 13/104; SADD; Band; Chorus; Color Guard; Hon Roll; NHS; Clarion U Of PA; Chld Psychlgy.

PALM, JEFF; Carlisle SR HS; Carlisle, PA; (4); 50/382; Band; Concert Band; Jazz Band; Mrchg Band; Hon Roll; Evng Sentnl Newspr Carrier Schlrshp 87; Awd Schltc Achvt 87; Shippensburg U.

PALM, MICHAEL; Charleroi Area HS; Charleroi, PA; (3); Art Clb; Varsity Clb; Stu Cncl; JV L Ftbl; L Trk; Hon Roll; Art.

PALMA, SCOTT; Lower Moreland HS; Huntingdon Valley, PA; (3); Office Aide; Science Clb; SADD; Teachers Aide; Off Frsh Cls; Off Soph Cls; Off Jr Cls; Var Ftbl; High Hon Roll; Hon Roll; Med.

PALMER, BRADLEY J; Calvary Christian Acad; Huntingdon, PA; (3); 2/11; Church Yth Grp; 4-H; Church Choir; Yrbk Stf; Var L Bsktbl; Var L Socr; Var L Trk; 4-H Awd; Hon Roll; Soccer MVP 85; Sprtsmnshp Awd-Bsktbl & Soccer 86.

PALMER, DAVE; Upper Moreland HS; Willow Gr, PA; (3); #157 In Class; Boy Scts; Ski Clb; Rep Stu Cncl; Var Trk; Hon Roll; Ofcl Stu Of Shawnee Boy Sct Patrol 84; Music Cmpstn.

PALMER, DAVID; Conestoga HS; Berwyn, PA; (3); 37/400; Natl Beta Clb; Varsity Clb; Nwsp Rptr; Nwsp Stf; Capt Golf; Lcrss; Hon Roll; NHS.

PALMER, DAVID; Mc Keesport Area HS; White Oak, PA; (1); Art Clb; Spanish Clb; SADD; Off Frsh Cls; Bsbl; Bsktbl; Swmmng; Trk; Hon Roll.

PALMER, ELLEN; Donegal HS; Maytown, PA; (2); Church Yth Grp; Rep Frsh Cls; JV Var Fld Hcky; Var Trk; Hon Roll; Presdntl Awd 85-87; Lawyer.

PALMER, ERIC; Parkland HS; Schnecksville, PA; (2); Boy Scts; Chess Clb; Computer Clb; Exploring; Band; Concert Band; Jazz Band; Mrchg Band; Symp Band; JV Bsbl; Aerospc Engr.

PALMER, GAIL; Carlisle SR HS; Carlisle, PA; (3); Church Yth Grp; Drama Clb; GAA; Office Aide; Church Choir; Drill Tm; Cheerleading; Trk; Hon Roll; Norfolk; Bus Mgmt.

PALMER, JON; Corry Area HS; Corry, PA; (2); Church Yth Grp; FCA; 4-H; Chorus; Rep Frsh Cls; Rep Soph Cls; Var L Ftbl; Var L Wrstlng; High Hon Roll; NHS; Delta Epsilon Phi 86; Med.

PALMER, MARY; Salisbury HS; Allentown, PA; (4); 10/128; Church Yth Grp; Cmnty Wkr; Exploring; Hosp Aide; Key Clb; Service Clb; School Musical; JV Fld Hcky; High Hon Roll; Hon Roll; Bloomsburg U; Nrsng.

PALMER, RICKY; Oxford Area HS; Oxford, PA; (3); 6/196; Var Crs Cntry; Var Trk; High Hon Roll; Hon Roll; NHS; Engrng.

PALMER, STACY; Knoch HS; Saxonburg, PA; (3); French Clb; Hst FHA; Pep Clb; SADD; Teachers Aide; Chorus; High Hon Roll; NHS; Penn ST; Mngmnt.

PALMER, TERESA; South Fayette HS; Mc Donald, PA; (4); 2/70; Drama Clb; Sec Chorus; School Play; Yrbk Stf; Sec Sr Cls; Cheerleading; Hon Roll; VP NHS; French Clb; Key Clb; Natl Hnr Soc Schlrshp 87; 2nd Pl Commnctns Bowl 86; Kent ST U; Telecomm.

PALMETER, BETH; Montoursville HS; Montoursville, PA; (3); 75/185; Church Yth Grp; FBLA; German Clb; Band; Chorus; Color Guard; School Musical; Bsktbl; Socr; Var L Sftbl; Secy Stds.

PALMIERI, LORI; Gateway SR HS; Monroeville, PA; (4); 27/484; Ed Yrbk Stf; High Hon Roll; Trs NHS; Pres Schlr; FHA; Teachers Aide; Swmmng; Ld Hnrs Frnch V 87; All Star Achvrs 87; Acadc Ldrshp Schlrshp 87; St Vincent Coll; Acctng.

PALMIERO, ALLISON; Meadville HS; Meadville, PA; (3); 43/363; Aud/Vis; Church Yth Grp; Dance Clb; French Clb; VP Rep Stu Cncl; Stat Ftbl; Tennis; Hon Roll; Bus Mgt.

PALMISANO, LISA; Montour HS; Mckees Rocks, PA; (3); Church Yth Grp; SADD; Yrbk Stf; Rep Jr Cls; Var Cheerleading; High Hon Roll; AHSME 85-87; 1st Yr Alg Tst 85; Intl Tn Ms Western PA Pagnt 86; Comp.

PALOMBI, SUE; Carlynton HS; Carnegie, PA; (4); French Clb; Color Guard; Drill Tm; Mrchg Band; Sec Stu Cncl; Co-Capt Twrlr; Hmcmnt Ct 3rd Rnnr Up 86-87fstu Advsry Bd 86-87; U Of Pittsburgh; Psych.

PALOMBO, MARIANN; Aliquippa JR SR HS; Aliquippa, PA; (4); 2/130; Church Yth Grp; Drama Clb; Sec French Clb; Church Choir; Concert Band; Mrchg Band; Pep Band; Yrbk Ed-Chief; Sec Jr Cls; Sec Sr Cls; Bst Actrs Awd Pittsbrgh Plyhs Comptn 87; Seton Hill Coll; Music Educ.

PALOVICH, LEIGH; Elizabeth Forward HS; Elizabeth, PA; (3); 15/343; Var L Bsktbl; Var L Sftbl; Var L Vllybl; High Hon Roll; NHS; Acad All Amer 87; Prom Crt 87; Sci.

PALUCHAK, JOSEPH; Bishop Mc Cort HS; Johnstown, PA; (2); JA; Var Bsbl; Var L Ice Hcky; Hon Roll; Prsdntl Schlrshp 87.

PALUCK, JAMES J; Panther Valley HS; Nesquehoning, PA; (3); 33/134; Church Yth Grp; Rep Soph Cls; Bsbl; Capt Bsktbl; Ftbl; Trk; 1st Tm SIAL Dfnsv Back Ftbl 86-87; Eastern ST Fnslts Bsktbl 86-86; USMC Dstngshd Athlt 86-87; Science.

PALUMBO, JOHN; Hempfield HS; Lancaster, PA; (3); Boy Scts; Diving; Hon Roll; Penn ST; Bus.

PALUMBO, KELLY; Neshannock HS; New Castle, PA; (4); 1/114; FBLA; Drill Tm; Nwsp Bus Mgr; Nwsp Ed-Chief; High Hon Roll; NHS; Ntl Merit SF; Pres Schlr; Val; Slippery Rock U Bk Awd 87; Best Cls Awd 87; Cornell U; Pre-Med.

PALUMBO, KRISTIE; Cardinal Ohara HS; Broomall, PA; (3); 26/710; Cmnty Wkr; Pep Clb; Political Wkr; SADD; School Play; Nwsp Stf; Yrbk Stf; Mgr(s); French Hon Soc; Hon Roll; Prncpls Awd Acadmc Excllnc 84-87; French Schlstc Awd 87; Sci Fair Chem 2nd Pl 87; Med.

PALUMBO, LYNN; Vincentian HS; Pittsburgh, PA; (2); 7/66; Hosp Aide; Library Aide; Service Clb; Chorus; Church Choir; Rep Frsh Cls; Stat Bsktbl; Mgr(s); Hon Roll; John Carroll U; Pre Med.

PALUSELLI, AMY LYNN; Greensburg Central Catholic HS; Delmont, PA; (4); 19/222; AFS; Pres Church Yth Grp; Yrbk Ed-Chief; High Hon Roll; Lion Awd; VP NHS; Ntl Merit Ltr; Stage Crew; Hugh O Brian Youth Fndn Ldrshp Awd 85; St Vincent Acad Schlrshp & Ldrshp Schlrshp; St Vincent Coll; Accounting.

PALUSELLI, ANDY; North Allegheny HS; Pittsburgh, PA; (3); Capt Dance Clb; Thesps; School Musical; School Play; Yrbk Phtg; Lit Mag; Rep Stu Cncl; Var L Diving; JV Ftbl; Gym; Theatr Apprntcshp Gftd Pgm 87; Comm.

PALUSO, CYNTHIA L; Mc Guffey HS; Washington, PA; (4); 2/203; Office Aide; Trs Spanish Clb; Color Guard; Mgr Stage Crew; Yrbk Bus Mgr; Stat L Ftbl; Mgr L Wrstlng; High Hon Roll; NHS.

PALYO, LISA; Elizabeth Forward HS; Monongahela, PA; (3); 34/328; Chorus; School Musical; Hon Roll; Kent ST U; Anthrplgy.

PAMBIANCO, AMY; Valley View HS; Peckville, PA; (4); 26/198; French Clb; Pres SADD; Lib Chorus; VP Sr Cls; Pres Stu Cncl; Capt Cheerleading; Vllybl; French Hon Soc; High Hon Roll; Pres NHS; Stu Cncl Awd For Svc To Stu Cncl 87; Penn ST U; Acctng.

PAMPENO, SHERYL; Ford City HS; Ford City, PA; (4); AFS; FBLA; Rep SADD; Rep Chorus; Nwsp Rptr; Yrbk Rptr; Rep Sr Cls; High Hon Roll; Hon Roll; FBLA Reg Cmptn Awd 87; Stu Actvts Awd 87; New Kensington Co Schl; Acctnt.

PAMPHILE, ROSE ELLEN; Schenley HS; Pittsburgh, PA; (2); Church Yth Grp; French Clb; Hosp Aide; Church Choir; Stu Cncl; Sftbl; Trk; DAR Awd; Hon Roll; Prfct Atten Awd; Rcvd 2nd Pl Project Jr Acad Sci Competition 85; Obstetritian.

PAMULA, CHRISTINE; Saint Benedict Acad; Erie, PA; (4); Office Aide; Pres Chorus; Color Guard; Mrchg Band; Variety Show; Cheerleading; Var Capt Socr; Hon Roll; Excllnc Music Awd 85-87; Best Defensv Plyr Sccr 86-87; Erie Bus Schl; Med Asst.

PANACKAL, ANIL; Central HS; Philadelphia, PA; (3); 1/511; Church Yth Grp; French Clb; Math Clb; Office Aide; Band; Church Choir; Concert Band; Nwsp Rptr; Nwsp Stf; Bsbl; U Of PA Book Awd 86-87; Merit Awd 84-85; Spector Sci Fair Awd 85-86; U Of PA; Med.

PANAGOS, PERIKLIS; Chambersburg Area SR HS; Chambersburg, PA; (3); Hon Roll; Shpnsbrg U Dstrct Hstry Day 86; Shpnsbrg U; Bus.

PANAIA, LORRI W; Indiana Area SR HS; Indiana, PA; (4); Drm Mjr(t); School Musical; Yrbk Ed-Chief; Rep Stu Cncl; High Hon Roll; NHS; Opt Clb Awd; Church Yth Grp; Cmnty Wkr; Dance Clb; JR Wmns Cvc Clbs Girl Of Mth 87; Patti Hurley Mem Schlrshp 87; Amer Lgn Axlry Awd 84; PA ST U; Engl.

PANASCI, KATHY; Greater Johnstown HS; Johnstown, PA; (4); 76/306; Pep Clb; Spanish Clb; SADD; School Musical; Nwsp Rptr; Off Jr Cls; Stu Cncl; Var Cheerleading; Hon Roll; Passavant Schlrshp Awd 87; Thiel Coll; Cmmnctns.

PANAYOTOFF, LARA; Bangor Area HS; Bangor, PA; (3); 7/213; Varsity Clb; Chorus; Jazz Band; Rep Mrchg Band; School Play; Stage Crew; Var Sftbl; Var Tennis; NHS.

PANCOAST, JO BETH; Owen J Roberts SR HS; Spring City, PA; (3); 9/299; Trs Key Clb; Letterman Clb; School Musical; Rep Frsh Cls; Pres Jr Cls; Var Cheerleading; High Hon Roll; Hon Roll; NHS; Hugh Obrien Yth Fndtn Ldrshp Semnr Awd 86; CPA.

PANCU, DIANA; Philadelphia High School For Girls; Philadelphia, PA; (4); 5/365; GAA; Nwsp Stf; Fld Hcky; Capt Tennis; Gov Hon Prg Awd; High Hon Roll; Jr NHS; NHS; Spanish NHS; Val; Eleanor & Arthur Stranstrom Awd 87; Briggs Constable Schlrshp 87; U Of Penn; Biochem.

PANCZAK, CHRISTINA; Northern Cambria HS; Ebensburg, PA; (3); 1/152; Trs Drama Clb; NFL; Ski Clb; Band; Chorus; Color Guard; Mrchg Band; High Hon Roll; NHS; Pres Spanish NHS; U Pittsburgh; Secndry Ed.

PANDICH, JENNIFER; Susquehanna Community HS; Susquehanna, PA; (4); 9/84; Library Aide; Scholastic Bowl; Ski Clb; SADD; School Play; Nwsp Ed-Chief; Nwsp Phtg; Nwsp Rptr; Hon Roll; Drama Clb; Stu Press Corps 86; Laurel St Theatr Brd 85-86; Jrnlsm.

PANE, BETSY; Bishop Ohara HS; Dunmore, PA; (2); 15/125; Drama Clb; Latin Clb; Spanish Clb; Wrstlng; High Hon Roll; Hon Roll.

PANEK, CHRISTOPHER; Ambridge Area HS; Baden, PA; (2); Exploring; Pep Clb; Spanish Clb; Chorus; Rep Soph Cls; JV Bsktbl; Var L Golf; Var L Tennis; Hon Roll; Im Socr; Hugh O Brien Ldrshp Ambsdr-Soph Cls 86-87.

PANEK, HEATHER; North Pocono HS; Moscow, PA; (4); 5/250; Band; Chorus; Concert Band; Orch; Var L Tennis; Bausch & Lomb Sci Awd; High Hon Roll; NHS; Ntl Sci Merit Awd 83-85; Pre-Med.

PANEK, KATHLEEN; Bishop Mc Cort HS; Johnstown, PA; (3); NFL; Spanish Clb; Speech Tm; JV Var Cheerleading; L Var Trk; High Hon Roll; Hon Roll; Mu Alpha Theta Awd; NHS; Spanish NHS; Crmnl Justice.

PANEK, SUZANNE; Bishop Carroll HS; Lilly, PA; (3); 43/128; Office Aide; Pep Clb; Spanish Clb; Im L Bsktbl; Im Powder Puff Ftbl; Var L Trk; Hon Roll; AAU Jr Olympc Bsktbl Team 87; St Chmpn Bsktbl Team 86-87; Altoona Mirror Bsktbl Plyr Of Yr 86-87; Ed.

'ANGANIBAN, ZSANDRA; Bishop Neumann HS; Montoursville, PA; 2); Cmnty Wkr; Model UN; Chorus; Cheerleading; High Hon Roll; Hon Roll; NHS; Rotary Awd; Bus.

'ANGONIS, TRESSA; Indiana Area SR HS; Indiana, PA; (3); Church 'th Grp; Pep Clb; Red Cross Aide; SADD; Orch; JV Vllybl; Cit Awd; High Hon Roll; Hon Roll; IUP; Medcl.

'ANICHELLA, MARK; Greensburg Salem SR HS; Greensburg, PA; (3); Church Yth Grp; French Clb; Yrbk Stf; French Hon Soc; Hon Roll; Humanities Day Awd For Frnch Poetry 86.

'ANICO, ANGELA M; Lansdale Catholic HS; Lansdale, PA; (4); 50/220; mnty Wkr; Drama Clb; Pep Clb; SADD; School Musical; School Play; ariety Show; Nwsp Stf; Yrbk Stf; Pres Sr Cls; Spirit Awd, Stu Cncl Pres wd, Angla Markno Awd Stu Exm Schl Svc 87; Villanova U; Fnnce.

'ANKAKE, SHEILA; Lower Dauphin HS; Grantville, PA; (3); 30/276; Church Yth Grp; Band; Concert Band; Mrchg Band; Rep Frsh Cls; Rep oph Cls; Rep Jr Cls; Hon Roll; NHS; Prfct Atten Awd; Bloomsburg U; Med-Nrsng.

'ANKEY, MICHAELE; W Catholic HS For Girls; Philadelphia, PA; (3); Church Yth Grp; Bsktbl; Hon Roll; Temple U; Law.

'ANNEBAKKER, LYNN; Abraham Lincoln HS; Philadelphia, PA; (4); 5 In Class; Church Yth Grp; Drama Clb; Spanish Clb; Varsity Clb; JV ar Bsktbl; JV Sftbl; Var Tennis; High Hon Roll; Hon Roll; VP NHS; strict C Gates Schlrshp 87; Cokestates Schlrshp 87; Outstndng Schlrshp wd Yarn Kits Inc 87; IU PA; Vet.

ANSSITI, TRACI; Tyrone Area HS; Tyrone, PA; (2); Key Clb; Chorus; V Cheerleading; High Hon Roll; Hon Roll; Jr NHS; Fshn Merch.

'ANTALEO, KIM; Hopewell HS; Aliquippa, PA; (4); 75/245; Church Yth rp; Capt Dance Clb; Sec Exploring; Teachers Aide; Capt Drill Tm; Yrbk tf; Gym; Capt Pom Pon; High Hon Roll; Hon Roll.

ANTLE, LORI; Lake Lehman HS; Sweet Valley, PA; (4); 47/155; Sec Jr ls; Var Cheerleading; Var Fld Hcky; Var Sftbl; Hon Roll; Jr NHS; llentown Coll; Crmnl Jstce.

ANZETTA, JOSEPH J; Radnor HS; Wayne, PA; (4); Pres Drama Clb; chool Play; Variety Show; Pres Sr Cls; Stu Cncl; Gym; Lcrss; Cit Awd; AR Awd; Gov Hon Prg Awd; Marquette AMUW Scholar Theatr Art 87; uke Teehan Mem Scholar 87; Actors Wrkshp Aawd Theatre 87; arquette U; Theatre.

AOLINO, FOSTINA; South Park HS; Library, PA; (3); 52/300; Drama lb; German Clb; JV Vllybl; High Hon Roll; Hon Roll; Pittsburgh U; Civil ngr.

AOLINO, KARLA; Schenley HS; Pittsburgh, PA; (3); French Clb; heerleading; Trk; High Hon Roll; Hon Roll; Prfct Atten Awd; Athltc Awd 5; NY U; Prelaw.

AONE, DAN; Interboro HS; Prospect Park, PA; (3); French Clb; horus; Concert Band; Jazz Band; Mrchg Band; Stage Crew; Nwsp Stf; igh Hon Roll; NHS; Scott Hi-Q 85-87.

AONE, JOSEPH A; Archbishop Ryan For Boys; Philadelphia, PA; (3); 414; Off Lit Mag; Im Bsktbl; L Var Crs Cntry; L Var Trk; Hon Roll; HS; Outstndg Acad Achvt Engl I 85; Outstndg Acad Achvt Alg II Tri & P Europ Hstry 86.

APACOSMA, S JASON; Governor Mifflin HS; Reading, PA; (3); 7/325; rs French Clb; Nwsp Stf; Bsktbl; Socr; Tennis; Trk; Wt Lftg; High Hon oll; NHS.

APEIKA, MICHELLE B; Nativity BVM HS; Port Carbon, PA; (3); 7/ 3; Church Yth Grp; Exploring; Latin Clb; Ski Clb; Drm Mjr(t); Variety ow; Rep Frsh Cls; Rep Soph Cls; High Hon Roll; NHS; Latin & Religion old Engl Awds 86; Bio.

API, ANDREW; Bellwood-Antis HS; Tyrone, PA; (4); 33/203; High Hon oll; Hon Roll; Indian Creek Schlrs Prog 86; Alter Boy 85; De Vry Inst Of ech; Elec Engr.

APOUTSIS, DIANE; South Western HS; Hanover, PA; (3); 8/233; hurch Yth Grp; Yrbk Stf; High Hon Roll; NHS; NEDT Awd; Prfct Atten wd; Bible Clb; Phy.

APP, ALLEN; Upper Moreland SR HS; Hatboro, PA; (4); 67/254; Ski lb; Trk; High Hon Roll; Hon Roll; Mech Engrng.

APP, LORI; Pottstown SR HS; Pottstown, PA; (3); 42/155; Key Clb; wsp Stf; Var Cheerleading; Var Lcrss; Hon Roll; NHS; Bus Adm.

APP, SUSAN; Spring-Ford SR HS; Limerick, PA; (4); 12/237; Church h Grp; Trs 4-H; Camera Clb; Camp Fr Inc; Chess Clb; JV Bsktbl; Var d Hcky; JV Lcrss; Var Trk; 4-H Awd; Sel Stds Excel Awd 87; ring-Ford Hnr Scty Schlrshps 87; Qlfd For St Fnls In 4-H Hrose Comp ; Old Dominion Univ; Pol Sci.

APPALARDO, KATHLEEN; Stroudsburg HS; Stroudsburg, PA; (2); ADD; JV Fld Hcky; JV Sftbl.

APPAS, GEORGE; East Stroudsburg HS; E Stroudsburg, PA; (3); 19/ 0; Am Leg Boys St; Boy Scts; French Clb; German Clb; Spanish Clb; gh Hon Roll; Hon Roll; Acad Schlrshp Awd; Kensington U; Econ.

APPAS, IDA; Avonworth HS; Pittsbg, PA; (4); 18/100; AFS; Debate Tm; ench Clb; Varsity Clb; Pres Chorus; Church Choir; School Musical; hool Play; Nwsp Rptr; Yrbk Rptr; All Estrn Choir-Jr Mndllshn oir-Dist & Rgn Choir 87; Dqvsn Comp & Acdmc Schlrshp 87; Duquesne ; Music.

APPAS, K; Carlisle SR HS; Carlisle, PA; (3); 96/460; Church Yth Grp; nnty Wkr; Varsity Clb; Rep Jr Cls; JV Var Crs Cntry; Bus.

APPAS, PAMELA; Riverview HS; Verona, PA; (3); 1/112; Pres Trs urch Yth Grp; Key Clb; Speech Tm; Orch; Nwsp Rptr; Yrbk Stf; Rep u Cncl; L Tennis; Var L Vllybl; NHS; Hgh Hnr Roll 84-87; Hosp Aide 85 86; Natl Ed Dvlpmnt Test Awd 85; Phrmclgy.

AQUET, KAREN; Interboro HS; Prospect Park, PA; (4); 8/287; French b; Key Clb; Teachers Aide; Rep Soph Cls; Rep Jr Cls; Rep Stu Cncl; lb; Cheerleading; Mgr Ftbl; Sftbl; Lafayette Coll; Ecnmcs.

ARADIS, MARC; Archbishop Wood Boys HS; Doylestown, PA; (3); 60/ 0; Var Ftbl.

ARDI, CAROLYN M; Greater Latrobe HS; Latrobe, PA; (4); Exploring; erman Clb; Girl Scts; Library Aide; Pep Clb; Ski Clb; Chorus; Yrbk l-Chief; Stat Mat Maids; DAR Awd; Pre-Law.

ARDO, BETHANNE; Bethlehem Catholic HS; Bethlehem, PA; (3); 78/ 0; Office Aide; Teachers Aide; School Musical; School Play; Yrbk Stf; p Frsh Cls; Rep Soph Cls; Rep Stu Cncl; Var Cheerleading; High Hon ll; Bthlhm Sokols Qn 87; Htl Mgmt.

ARDO, MARIA ELENA A; St Maria Goretti HS; Philadelphia, PA; (4); 6/384; Camera Clb; Cmnty Wkr; Nwsp Phtg; Spanish Clb; Teachers de; Chorus; School Musical; Rochester Inst Tech Schlrshp 87; iladelphia Coll Art Awd 86; Moore Coll Art Awd 85; Rochester Inst Of ch; Photo.

ARDUE, MICHELLE; Center Area HS; Monaca, PA; (3); 42/186; Latin b; Library Aide; Spanish Clb; Hon Roll; Lang Achvt Awd Spnsh 87; arine Bio.

PARENT, DAWN; St Pius X HS; Pottstown, PA; (4); Art Clb; Cmnty Wkr; French Clb; FNA; Scholastic Bowl; Service Clb; Ski Clb; CA U PA; Soc Wrk.

PARENTE, BETTY; Liberty HS; Bethlehem, PA; (4); 16/390; Cmnty Wkr; Hosp Aide; High Hon Roll; Prfct Atten Awd; UNICO Chptr Schlrshp 87; Lehigh U; Engr.

PARESA, LEINAALA; Hazleton HS; Drums, PA; (3); Intnl Clb; JA; Spanish Clb; Orch; High Hon Roll; Sons Of Italy In Amrca 87; PA Gvrnrs Schl For Intl Stds 87; U Of Pittsburgh; Intl Affrs.

PARIKH, CRYSTAL; Daniel Boone JR-SR HS; Birdsboro, PA; (3); 9/ 172; Sec Girl Scts; Model UN; Quiz Bowl; Pres Service Clb; Nwsp Stf; Yrbk Stf; Stat Wrstlng; High Hon Roll; NHS; Slvr Awd In Glr Sctng 85; Cmmnd Stu In PSAT/NMSQT 87; Law.

PARIKH, SUSHRUT; Daniel Boone HS; Birdsboro, PA; (2); 26/166; Chess Clb; French Clb; Library Aide; Model UN; JV Bsktbl; Hon Roll; Pres Schlr; Chem.

PARINISI, ANDREA; West Scranton HS; Scranton, PA; (4); 15/240; Dance Clb; Ski Clb; Spanish Clb; Yrbk Stf; Crs Cntry; Trk; High Hon Roll; Hon Roll; Jr NHS; NHS; Pittsburgh U; Phrmcy.

PARIS, NICOLE; Central HS; Scranton, PA; (1); 2/293; French Clb; Ski Clb; Yrbk Phtg; Yrbk Stf; Hon Roll; St Josephs U; Soc Sci.

PARISE, JENNIFER; Scranton Central HS; Scranton, PA; (2); Girl Scts; Ski Clb; Spanish Clb; Cheerleading; U Of Scranton; Educ.

PARISE, MELISSA; First Baptist Acad; Walston, PA; (2); Church Yth Grp; Chorus; Church Choir; Color Guard; Rep Stu Cncl; Var Cheerleading; Var Socr; Hon Roll; Psych.

PARISELLA, JILL; Bradford Area HS; Bradford, PA; (4); Pres Church Yth Grp; Ski Clb; Acpl Chr; Pres Chorus; Variety Show; VP Stu Cncl; Capt Cheerleading; L Trk; Hon Roll; Jr NHS; Miss Mc Kean Cnty Fair Queen 86-87; Dstrct & Rgnl Chrl Fstvl Soloist 85-87; Ithaca Coll; Spch Pthlgy.

PARISH, BRIAN; Center HS; Aliquippa, PA; (2); Band; Concert Band; Jazz Band; Mrchg Band; Pep Band; Hon Roll; Westminster Hnrs Band 87; Music.

PARK, ERIC R; St Marys Area HS; St Marys, PA; (3).

PARK, JAE; Engineering & Science HS; Philadelphia, PA; (3); 13/241; Model UN; High Hon Roll; Hon Roll; NHS; Crisis Intrvntn Ntwrk Awd 87; Elec Engrng.

PARK, JEAN; Elizabeth Forward SR HS; Mc Keesport, PA; (3); 1/350; Sec Church Yth Grp; Exploring; Hosp Aide; Leo Clb; Q&S; School Musical; Nwsp Rptr; Yrbk Stf; High Hon Roll; NHS; Attnd Rotary Clb Yth Ldrshp Conf 87; Acadmc All Am 87; Pre-Med.

PARK, JEANNE S; Upper St Clair HS; Pittsburgh, PA; (4); 28/382; Sec AFS; Sec French Clb; Q&S; Sec Mrchg Band; Yrbk Sprt Ed; High Hon Roll; NHS; Ntl Merit SF; Westnghs Sci Hnrs Inst Prgm 86-87; Amer Yth Symphnc Bnd 85; Med Dctr.

PARK, JOANNE; Blue Mountain Acad; Pottsville, PA; (3); Band; Church Choir; Nwsp Rptr; Pres Jr Cls; High Hon Roll; NHS; Prfct Atten Awd; Loma Linda Med Schl; Med.

PARK, JUDY; North Penn HS; North Wales, PA; (4); 29/705; Pres Church Yth Grp; 4-H; Key Clb; Ski Clb; Acpl Chr; Band; Chorus; Church Choir; Jazz Band; Madrigals; N Penn Area Schlrshp 84; All-St Fshn Revue Wnnr 85-86; Miss Korea-NY 1st Pl 87; PA St U; Mech Engnrng.

PARK, LISA; Radnor HS; Newtown Square, PA; (4); 2/297; VP Sec Church Yth Grp; Math Tm; Service Clb; Orch; Lit Mag; Gov Hon Prg Awd; Ntl Merit Schol; Pres Schlr; Sal; Ntl Cncl On Yth Ldrshp Schlrshp; PTSA Math & Sci Awd; Hrvr Bk Prz; Rnslr Poly Tech Inst Awd Math/Sci; Hrvrd U; Med.

PARK, LORI; State College Area SR HS; State College, PA; (4); VP Camp Fr Inc; Church Yth Grp; Dance Clb; Variety Show; Towson St U; Bio.

PARK, OHN; Cheltenham HS; Elkins Pk, PA; (4); 8/360; Cmnty Wkr; Intnl Clb; Math Tm; Model UN; Science Clb; Orch; School Musical; Nwsp Stf; Trs Stu Cncl; Capt Bowling; Commonwlth PA Cert Merit 86-87; Frnch Cert Merit.

PARK, SHERRI; Greencastle-Antrim HS; Waynesboro, PA; (3); 12/180; Church Yth Grp; Rep Stu Cncl; Var L Fld Hcky; Hon Roll; NHS; Intl Rltns.

PARKE, ALISON; Moon SR HS; Coraopolis, PA; (2); Church Yth Grp; Band; Church Choir; Mrchg Band; Symp Band; Var Capt Cheerleading; Hon Roll; Flute Accompanist Dist Chorus 86; Spnsh Bus.

PARKE, AMY; Kiski Area HS; Apollo, PA; (4); 1/358; Church Yth Grp; Math Tm; Sec SADD; Mrchg Band; Symp Band; Capt Swmmng; Cit Awd; High Hon Roll; Pres NHS; Val; Westinghouse Fmly Schlrshp; Frgn Lng Schlrshp; Gov Schl Intrnl Stds; Johns Hopkins U; Intrl Rltns.

PARKER, BETH; Sun Valley HS; Brookhaven, PA; (4); 24/320; Drama Clb; Teachers Aide; Band; Chorus; Drm Mjr(t); School Musical; Variety Show; Hon Roll; Jr NHS; NHS; Atlantic Coast Tournmt Of Bands-Best Drum Mjr 85; Penn ST U.

PARKER, DEAN W; Central HS; Philadelphia, PA; (4); 48/309; Boy Scts; Computer Clb; English Clb; Math Clb; Math Tm; Science Clb; Nwsp Bus Mgr; Yrbk Stf; Lit Mag; Var Bsktbl; Rensselaer Polytech Inst; Engr.

PARKER, GEORGE; Yough HS; W Newton, PA; (4); Boy Scts; Hon Roll; NHS; Penn ST U.

PARKER, JODI; Danville Area JR HS; Washingtonville, PA; (1); Church Yth Grp; Cmnty Wkr; Hosp Aide; High Hon Roll; Prfct Atten Awd; Prsdntl Acad Fitness Awd 86-87.

PARKER, KAREN D; Mohawk JR SR HS; Wampum, PA; (3); Church Yth Grp; FBLA; FHA; Hosp Aide; Latin Clb; Stage Crew; Powder Puff Ftbl; Trk.

PARKER, KARL; Bishop Neumann HS; Lock Haven, PA; (2); 2/48; Sec VP Model UN; Pep Clb; SADD; Nwsp Rptr; Yrbk Rptr; Yrbk Stf; High Hon Roll; Pres NHS; Rcgntn Acad Achvt 86-87; Harvard Model Cngrss Bst Delg 86-87; Frnch Awd 86-87; Med.

PARKER, KRISTA; Williamson HS; Tioga, PA; (3); CAP; Yrbk Phtg; Yrbk Rptr; Var L Trk; High Hon Roll; Computer Clb; JV Bsktbl; Hon Roll; Jr NHS; NHS; Embry-Riddle Aero U; Pilot.

PARKER, KRISTI; Linesville Conneaut Summit HS; Conneaut Lk, PA; (2); 11/74; Spanish Clb; Chorus; Drm Mjr(t); Co-Capt Flag Corp; JV Cheerleading; Golf; Hon Roll; Bus.

PARKER, LESLIE RENE; Bensalem HS; Trevose, PA; (3); Church Yth Grp; Cmnty Wkr; Pres Intnl Clb; Chorus; Church Choir; Stat Bsktbl; JV Fld Hcky; Var JV Mgr(s); Var JV Score Keeper; Opt Clb Awd; 1st Pl Dist Lvl Optmst Intrct/Oratcl Cont 87; Ldrshp Conf 87; Rotry Clb 87; Syracuse U; Jrnlsm.

PARKER, MELISSA; Crestwood HS; Mountaintop, PA; (3); Math Clb; Mu Alpha Theta; Ski Clb; School Play; Trk; High Hon Roll; Jr NHS; NHS; PA JR Acad Sci 1st Regnls & ST 86, 1st Regnls 2nd ST 87; Pre-Dent.

PARKER, RAVI K; Central HS; Philadelphia, PA; (4); Art Clb; Office Aide; Yrbk Stf; Stat Im Bsktbl; JV Bowling; Im Score Keeper; Im Vllybl; Im Wt Lftg; Var Ntl Merit SF; Var Prfct Atten Awd; Bio.

PARKER, SHERRY; Fairchance Georges JR SR HS; Union Town, PA; (4); Church Yth Grp; French Clb; Girl Scts; Ski Clb; Church Choir; Concert Band; Mrchg Band; Mgr(s); Hon Roll; Penn ST U; Med.

PARKHURST, DONANNE; Hempfield Area SR HS; Manor, PA; (3); Am Leg Aux Girls St; Pres Church Yth Grp; JCL; Latin Clb; Pep Clb; Ski Clb; Spanish Clb; Chorus; Church Choir; School Musical; 2nd Pl Spansh Poetry-Pitt U Humanities Day 87; 1st Pl Tm-Conf Bible Quizzing 87; U Of HI.

PARKS, AMY; Tyrone Area HS; Tyrone, PA; (2); Art Clb; VP Church Yth Grp; Key Clb; Office Aide; Spanish Clb; Varsity Clb; Crs Cntry; Trk; Vllybl; Hon Roll; Pres Phys Ftns Awd 83-85; Art.

PARKS, ERIC; Kittanning SR HS; Worthington, PA; (4); 7/228; Church Yth Grp; French Clb; Office Aide; High Hon Roll; NHS; Pres Schlr; PA JR Acad Of Sci 10-1st Pl Awds 84-87; All Star Achvr 87; Bio & Chmstry Awds 85-86; IN U Of PA; Comp Sci.

PARKS, JO L; New Brighton Area SR HS; New Brighton, PA; (4); 4/146; Pres Computer Clb; Girl Scts; Concert Band; Mrchg Band; School Play; Nwsp Stf; Ntl Merit SF; Drama Clb; Library Aide; PA Nwsppr Publshrs Assn Hnr Carrier; Westmnstr Hnrs Band; Pre-Law.

PARKS, MICHAEL; Hughesville HS; Unityville, PA; (2); High Hon Roll; Hon Roll; Grn & Wht Awd 86-87; Pre-Med.

PARKS, MICHELLE; Conemaugh Township HS; Jerome, PA; (3); 13/ 121; Spanish Clb; Nwsp Rptr; Nwsp Stf; Var Trk; Hon Roll; Spnsh Hnr Awd 85-87; U Of Pittsburgh Johnstown; Nrs.

PARLETT, MICHAEL; Kennard Dale HS; Stewartstown, PA; (3); 6/165; Pres Trs Church Yth Grp; German Clb; Pres Library Aide; School Musical; School Play; Yrbk Stf; God Cntry Awd; High Hon Roll; Hon Roll; NHS; Chmstry.

PARLIER, REBECCA; Christian Life Acad; West Pittston, PA; (3); Church Yth Grp; Quiz Bowl; Teachers Aide; School Play; Variety Show; Nwsp Rptr; High Hon Roll; Hon Roll; Sec Frsh Cls; Pres Soph Cls; Stu Yr 84-85; Hghst Mth Avg 85-86; Jrnlsm.

PARNELL, DANA; Mercer Area JR SR HS; Mercer, PA; (1); NFL; Speech Tm; Cheerleading; Trk; Degree Mrt Dgree Hnr 86-87.

PARONISH, FRANCIS; Altoona Area HS; Altoona, PA; (4); 163/718; Boy Scts; Library Aide; Science Clb; Band; Concert Band; Mrchg Band; Pep Band; Off Sr Cls; IN U Of PA; Forensic Sci.

PAROSKY, LEAH; Bishop Hafey HS; Hazleton, PA; (4); Church Yth Grp; Orch; Hon Roll; Shldng Jcksn Coll Schlrshp 87-88; Shldn Jckson Coll; Aquatc Resrc.

PARR, DAVID; Richland HS; Valencia, PA; (3); Debate Tm; Drama Clb; English Clb; French Clb; Math Tm; NFL; Quiz Bowl; Speech Tm; SADD; Nwsp Rptr; OH ST U; Jrnlst.

PARR, GUY; Elk Lake HS; Meshoppen, PA; (1); Boy Scts; 4-H; Spanish Clb; SADD; Stage Crew; Socr; 4-H Awd; Hon Roll; Prfct Atten Awd; PA ST U; Chem.

PARRISH, CAROL A; Ephrata SR HS; Akron, PA; (4); Pres Drama Clb; Pres Chorus; Concert Band; Jazz Band; Orch; School Musical; School Play; Rep Stu Cncl; Powder Puff Ftbl; Hon Roll; Natl Schl Chrl Awd Lancaster-Lebanon Music Ed Assn 87; Wmns Symph Assn Music Awd 87; Temple U Pres Awd; Temple U.

PARRISH, MARK; Notre Dame HS; Easton, PA; (3); Cmnty Wkr; Pres Computer Clb; Pres Exploring; Yrbk Sprt Ed; VP Jr Cls; Pres Stu Cncl; JV Ftbl; Var Tennis; Hon Roll; Prfct Atten Awd; Cmndtn PA St Univ & PA Cncl/Tchrs Englsh For Writing Ability 84; Prtcptn Awd Natl Spnsh Cont 86; Elec Engrng.

PARRISH, STEPHEN; Allentown Central Catholic HS; Whitehall, PA; (3); 50/250; Aud/Vis; Trs Church Yth Grp; Drama Clb; School Musical; School Play; Nwsp Ed-Chief; Var Crs Cntry; Hon Roll; PA JR Acad Sci ST Sympsm 1st Pl; Opt Clb Ortrcl Cont 2nd Pl; Natl Sci Merit Awd; NY U; Cmmnctns.

PARROTTO, JOSEPH; North Catholic HS; Allison Park, PA; (3); Model UN; Spanish Clb; SADD; High Hon Roll; Hon Roll; Natl Hnr Roll 87; Hnr Roll 85; Congrsnl Yth Ldrshp Cncl 87; Pre-Med.

PARRY, AMY; Du Bois Area HS; Du Bois, PA; (2); German Clb; Library Aide; Hon Roll; PA ST U.

PARRY, JENNIFER; Scranton Prep; Peckville, PA; (3); 50/190; Pep Clb; Service Clb; Chorus; School Musical; Stage Crew; Var Cheerleading; Var L Trk; Hon Roll; Law.

PARRY, KIMBERLY; Nazareth Area SR HS; Nazareth, PA; (3); Art Clb; Drama Clb; Key Clb; Teachers Aide; Chorus; School Musical; Nwsp Ed-Chief; Nwsp Phtg; Cheerleading; Hon Roll; 2nd Pl Feature Photo 87; 1st Pl Ovrall Art 85; Grphc Dsgn.

PARRY, MICHELLE; Western Wayne HS; Moscow, PA; (3); 9/192; Church Yth Grp; Spanish Clb; Bsktbl; Mgr(s); High Hon Roll; Hon Roll; NHS; Rep Natl Hon Soc 87; Elec VP SR Yr 87; U Of Scraton; Pre Med.

PARRY, PRUDENCE; Lake-Lehman SR HS; Dallas, PA; (2); 4-H; JV Fld Hcky; Hon Roll; Jr NHS.

PARRY, SHARON; Butler Intermediate HS; Butler, PA; (2); Church Yth Grp; French Clb; Hosp Aide; Drm & Bgl; Orch; Hon Roll; Jr NHS; U Of Pittsburgh; Phys Thrpy.

PARRY, TAMI; West Greene HS; Graysville, PA; (3); 18/97; Trs FHA; SADD; VICA; Band; Capt Drill Tm; Drm Mjr(t); Mrchg Band; Stu Cncl; Twrlr; High Hon Roll; Hlth Occptn Stu Amer VP; Ntl Voc Tech Hnr Soc VP; Hlth Asst Advsry Comm; Dntl Hygnst.

PARSCH JR, JOHN C; Hollidaysburg Area HS; Hollidaysburg, PA; (3); Computer Clb; Trs German Clb; Im Vllybl; Hon Roll; Ntl Merit Ltr; Prfct Atten Awd; Outstndng Germ II Stu 87.

PARSON, LORNA; West Allegheny HS; Imperial, PA; (4); 20/201; VP Trs Church Yth Grp; VP Band; Sec Chorus; Church Choir; Drm Mjr(t); Mrchg Band; JV Bsktbl; Var L Trk; High Hon Roll; Jr NHS; U Of Pittsburgh.

PARSON, SHELLY; Saltsburg JR SR HS; Saltsburg, PA; (2); Drama Clb; SADD; Chorus; Bsktbl; Cheerleading; Mgr(s); Sftbl; Hon Roll; Indiana U-PA; Phys Thrpy.

PARSON, TIM; West Greene HS; Windridge, PA; (2); FFA; Ftbl; Trk; Wt Lftg; Hon Roll.

PARSONS, BRENDA; Wellsboro SR HS; Wellsboro, PA; (4); Pres Art Clb; French Clb; Pep Clb; Nwsp Rptr; Yrbk Stf; Capt Cheerleading; Mgr(s); Hon Roll; Bus Law Awd 87; Art Clb Activities Awd 87; IN U Of PA.

PARSONS, BRIAN; Juniata HS; Port Royal, PA; (4); 3/142; Pres Drama Clb; Mrchg Band; School Musical; School Play; Yrbk Stf; Hst Sr Cls; Cit Awd; High Hon Roll; VP NHS; Pres Schlr; Math Awd 87; Drama Awd 87; Distgnshd Hnr Stu Awd 87; Penn ST U; Elec Engr.

PARSONS, GAIL; William Allen HS; Allentown, PA; (3); 10/610; Church Yth Grp; Hosp Aide; SADD; Mgr Chorus; Church Choir; Nwsp Stf; Rep Soph Cls; Rep Jr Cls; High Hon Roll; NHS; Mgna Cm Ld Phila Clsscl Soc Annl Ltn Wk Cmptn 88; Mxma Cm Ld Natl Ltn Exm 88; Pblshd Ltry Mgzn 88; Finance.

PARSONS, JAMES; Ringgold HS; Monongahela, PA; (2); Church Yth Grp; Spanish Clb; Speech Tm; SADD; Bsbl; Hon Roll; Pharmacy.

PARSONS, STEPHANIE; Hazelton HS; Drums, PA; (4); 34/376; Drama Clb; French Clb; Leo Clb; Ski Clb; Chorus; Capt Color Guard; French Hon Soc; Hon Roll; NHS; Office Aide; Pres Acad Ftns Awd 87; Kings Coll; Bio.

PARSONS, TRICIA; Beaver Area HS; Beaver, PA; (3); 56/215; FCA; Pep Clb; Ski Clb; Sec Spanish Clb; Yrbk Stf; Sec Soph Cls; Var JV Cheerleading; Powder Puff Ftbl; JV Trk; High Hon Roll; JR Miss 87; Yth Ftnss Awd; Dietcn.

PARSONS, TROY S; Frobes Road HS; Hustontown, PA; (4); 3/47; Boy Scts; Church Yth Grp; French Clb; Varsity Clb; Pres Soph Cls; Pres Jr Cls; Pres Sr Cls; VP Pres Stu Cncl; Var L Bsbl; JV Var Bsktbl; Beta Sigma Phi Awd 87; Pres Acad Fit Awd 87; Duquesne U; Phrmcy.

PARTILLA, PATRICIA; Gar-Memorial HS; Wilkes-Barre, PA; (3); 14/152; French Clb; Chorus; Color Guard; Drill Tm; Fld Hcky; Hon Roll; Jr NHS; NHS; Ltr Fld Hcky 84-86; Bus Mgmt.

PARTINGTON, MEGAN; Seneca Valley HS; Zelienople, PA; (3); Church Yth Grp; JA; Ski Clb; Band; Chorus; Church Choir; Jazz Band; Mrchg Band; School Musical; School Play; Miami U Of OH; Optom.

PARTSCH, DAVID; Conemaugh Valley JR SR HS; Johnstown, PA; (3); 2/110; Boy Scts; Chess Clb; Computer Clb; Exploring; Letterman Clb; Pep Clb; Quiz Bowl; Scholastic Bowl; Varsity Clb; Pres Soph Cls; Pharm.

PARTSCH, MATTHEW; Conemaugh Valley HS; Johnstown, PA; (3); 4-H; Pep Clb; Ftbl; Mgr(s); Jr NHS; NHS; Engrng.

PARTSCH, PATRICK; Conemaugh Valley HS; Johnstown, PA; (4); 8/125; Boy Scts; Computer Clb; Drama Clb; JA; Scholastic Bowl; Speech Tm; Varsity Clb; Capt Ftbl; NHS; Exploring; US Army Schlr-Ath Awd 87; Penn ST; Engrng.

PARUSO, LESLIE A; Brockway Area HS; Falls Creek, PA; (3); 20/115; Art Clb; Varsity Clb; Band; Mrchg Band; Yrbk Stf; Sec Frsh Cls; Stu Cncl; Var Cheerleading; Sftbl; Var Capt Vllybl; Dist Band; PA ST; Physcl Ed.

PARZANESE, MARIA; St Maria Goretti HS; Philadelphia, PA; (4); 2/384; Church Yth Grp; French Clb; Math Clb; School Musical; Nwsp Rptr; Rep Jr Cls; High Hon Roll; NHS; Sal; Sons Of Italy Schlrshp 87; Drexel U; Arch Engrng.

PASCARELLA, MIKE; Richland HS; Wexford, PA; (3); Aud/Vis; Church Yth Grp; Band; Church Choir; Concert Band; Jazz Band; Mrchg Band; Orch; Pep Band; School Musical; OH ST; Accntng.

PASCAVAGE, JILL; Eastern York HS; Wrightsville, PA; (3); Drama Clb; Girl Scts; SADD; Concert Band; School Musical; Yrbk Stf; Hst Frsh Cls; Stu Cncl; Cheerleading; Sftbl; Bloomsburg; Educ.

PASCHALL, KAREN E; Carlisle SR HS; Carlisle, PA; (4); Church Yth Grp; Pres Stu Cncl; Var L Tennis; NHS; Red Cross Aide; School Play; Nwsp Stf; Rep Jr Cls; High Hon Roll; Exchng Clb Stu Yr 86-87; Offcrs Wvs Clb Achvt Schlrshp 86-87.

PASCONE III, ROY J; Northeast Catholic HS; Philadelphia, PA; (3); Aud/Vis; Drama Clb; School Musical; School Play; Stage Crew; Drexel U; Bus.

PASCUZZI, JOSEPH; Muhlenberg HS; Reading, PA; (4); 62/184; Aud/Vis; Band; Concert Band; Jazz Band; Mrchg Band; Pep Band; School Musical; School Play; Stage Crew; Variety Show; PA ST U; Mech Engr.

PASCUZZO, LINDA; Carmichaels Area HS; Carmichaels, PA; (4); Office Aide; Pep Clb; Ski Clb; Spanish Clb; SADD; School Play; Sr Cls; Score Keeper; DAR Awd; High Hon Roll; Pittsburgh Beauty Acad; Cosmtgy.

PASH, JOHN; Lakeland HS; Jermyn, PA; (3); Ski Clb; JV Bsbl; Var Bsktbl; Var Golf; JV Trk.

PASH, MARY; York Catholic HS; York, PA; (2); 12/171; GAA; Rep Jr Cls; Var JV Cheerleading; Timer; JV Trk; High Hon Roll; Hon Roll; NC ST; Chld Psych.

PASHCHUK, KATHY; Mountain View HS; Nicholson, PA; (3); Ski Clb; Chorus; School Musical; School Play; Cheerleading; Gym; Grphc Cmmnctns.

PASHEL JR, ROBERT; Peabody HS; Pittsburgh, PA; (4); 33/273; Computer Clb; Band; Var Crs Cntry; JV Socr; High Hon Roll; Hon Roll; NHS; Prfct Atten Awd; De Vry Inst; Comp Tech.

PASI, DAVD; Elk County Christian HS; St Marys, PA; (2); 11/90; JV Bsktbl; JV Ftbl; Wt Lftg; High Hon Roll; NEDT Awd; H S Schlrp 85; Elks PA St Hoop Shoot Champ 84.

PASICH, STEPHEN; Marian HS; Haddock, PA; (3); 3/104; Scholastic Bowl; Nwsp Stf; NHS; Spanish NHS.

PASKELL, ANNE MARIE; York Catholic HS; York, PA; (3); 8/152; VP Pep Clb; Spanish Clb; Chorus; School Musical; Stage Crew; Yrbk Stf; Hon Roll; Sec NHS; Opt Clb Awd; Church Yth Grp; Chem.

PASKER, STEPHEN; Warwick HS; Lititz, PA; (3); 78/250; Boy Scts; Chess Clb; Chorus; High Hon Roll; Hon Roll; Order Of The Arrow Boy Scouts 84; Soc Stud.

PASKO, RITA; Mc Keesport Area HS; Mckeesport, PA; (3); 13/200; AFS; Cmnty Wkr; Exploring; German Clb; Hon Roll; NHS; Most Outstndg Eng Lit Stu 86-87; Most Outstndg Psych Stu 86-87; Med.

PASQUALIN, KRISSY; Hopewell HS; Aliquippa, PA; (4); 17/447; Pres Latin Clb; Band; Chorus; School Musical; Yrbk Stf; Off Stu Cncl; Bsktbl; Bowling; NHS; Carnegie Mellon; Engrng.

PASQUALINI, CHRISTINA; Archbishop Kennedy HS; Conshohocken, PA; (4); 24/170; Cmnty Wkr; FTA; Teachers Aide; Var Vllybl; Hon Roll; Pres Acdmc Ftnss Awd 87; Vrsty Vlybl Ltr 87; Anthny Di Pallo Schlrshp Awd 87; Cabrini Coll.

PASQUARELLI, VINCE; Peters Township HS; Mcmurray, PA; (3); 24/239; Intnl Clb; Spanish Clb; Var Crs Cntry; JV Trk; High Hon Roll; Hon Roll; Prfct Atten Awd; U Of Pittsburgh.

PASQUARELLO, LISA; Villa Maria Acad; Glenmoore, PA; (3); Quiz Bowl; Science Clb; SADD; Chorus; Stage Crew; Yrbk Sprt Ed; Bsktbl; Sftbl; Trk; High Hon Roll; Math Sci Bwl Tourn Tm 1st Pl 86; U PA; Biol.

PASQUENELLI, KRISTEN; Richland HS; Gibsonia, PA; (2); Art Clb; Chorus; School Musical; Variety Show; Sec Jr Cls; Rep Stu Cncl; Cheerleading.

PASQUINELLI, AMY; Elk County Christian HS; St Marys, PA; (2); 4-H; GAA; Intnl Clb; Nwsp Stf; JV Bsktbl; Tennis; 4-H Awd; High Hon Roll; NEDT Awd; Med.

PASQUINELLI, PAULA; St Marys Area HS; Saint Marys, PA; (4); 50/302; High Hon Roll; Natl Hnr Rll 86-87; Yth Ldrshp Bst Spkr Awd 85-86; Hal Garvin Schl Dnc 84-87; PA ST; Stockbrkr.

PASQUINELLI, STEVE; North Hills HS; Glenshaw, PA; (3); Band.

PASQUINO, JENNIFER; Altoona Area HS; Altoona, PA; (4); 125/717; Dance Clb; Hosp Aide; Key Clb; Spanish Clb; School Play; Pom Pon; Prsdntl Ftnss Awd 84; Mount Aloysius; Med Lab Tech.

PASSE, LISA; Bangor Area HS; Mt Bethel, PA; (3); 22/240; Band; Concert Band; Jazz Band; Mrchg Band; Trk; High Hon Roll; Hon Roll; NHS; Vet.

PASSELL, MARCI; West Branch Area HS; Grassflat, PA; (3); 7/125; Church Yth Grp; Drama Clb; Office Aide; Ski Clb; Band; Concert Band; Yrbk Phtg; Rep Stu Cncl; JV Cheerleading; Hon Roll; U Of Pittsburgh; Russia Trnlstg.

PASSIO, LORI; St Maria Goretti HS; Philadelphia, PA; (4); 22/384; Church Yth Grp; Cmnty Wkr; French Clb; Math Clb; Science Clb; Rep Frsh Cls; High Hon Roll; Hon Roll; Jr NHS; Trs NHS; Pres Acad Fit Awd 87; Achvt Awd Natl Soc Studs Olympd 86; Merit Awd Yth & The Poltcl Sys Sem 86; Philadelphia Coll; Phrmcy.

PASSMORE, D SHAWN; Du Bois Area HS; Du Bois, PA; (2); 49/305; Varsity Clb; JV Bsbl; JV Ftbl; JV Wrstlng; Hon Roll; Law/Bus.

PASSMORE, MATTHEW; Curwensville Area HS; Curwensville, PA; (3); Boy Scts; FFA; JV Ftbl; Hon Roll; Grhnd Degr FFA Ag Mech 85; Triangle Tech Du Bois; Crptr.

PASTERICK, GENE; Belle Vernon Area HS; Belle Vernon, PA; (4); 28/267; Church Yth Grp; Var L Bsbl; Var L Ftbl; Var Wt Lftg; High Hon Roll; Jr NHS; NHS; Rotary Awd; Hmrm Trsr 87; Trsr NHS 87; Cmptv Schlrshp 87; Duquesne U; Accntng.

PASTERICK, KELLY; Belle Vernon Area HS; Belle Vernon, PA; (3); Ski Clb; Cheerleading; Powder Puff Ftbl; Hon Roll.

PASTERNAK, DAVID; Bishop Boyle HS; Pittsburgh, PA; (3); 6/62; Yrbk Stf; Trs Jr Cls; Hon Roll; NHS; Acdmc All-Amrcn Spnsh 85-86; Intl Bus.

PASTIR, BETH; Saucon Valley SR HS; Hellertown, PA; (1); Dance Clb; Office Aide; Band; Chorus; Concert Band; School Musical; VP Stu Cncl; Var L Cheerleading; Var L Swmmng; Pres Schlr; PA ST U; Marine Bio.

PASTOR JR, FRANK; North Hills HS; Pittsburgh, PA; (4); 13/467; Church Yth Grp; Nwsp Sprt Ed; Im Bsktbl; Ftbl; Var L Socr; Im Sftbl; High Hon Roll; Hon Roll; NHS; Elec Engrng.

PASTOR, SAMUEL; Duquesne HS; Duquesne, PA; (4); 28/95; Letterman Clb; Varsity Clb; Variety Show; Yrbk Sprt Ed; Pres Soph Cls; Stu Cncl; Var L Bsbl; Var L Bsktbl; Var L Ftbl; Hon Roll; Tm MVP Bsbll 87; All-Sect 13 Tm Bsbll 87; Led Bsbll Tm .421 Bttg Avg Hghst In Lg 87; U Of SC; Crmnl Jstc.

PASTORS, JENNIFER; Geibel HS; Connellsville, PA; (3); Church Yth Grp; Pep Clb; Service Clb; Yrbk Stf; Rep Jr Cls; JV Var Cheerleading; Vllybl; French Hon Soc; High Hon Roll; Hon Roll; 3rd Pl Humanities Day Awds 87; Penn ST; Nrs Ansthtst.

PASTUSZEK, TARA; Cardinal O Hara HS; Media, PA; (4); 145/771; Off Aud/Vis; Camera Clb; Lit Mag; Im Bsktbl; Im Vllybl; Hon Roll; NY U Schlarhp 87; Emerson Coll Schlrshp 87; Ithaca Coll; Cmmnctns.

PATCHES, ROBERT; Northern Lebanon HS; Jonestown, PA; (2); JV Bsbl; Var Socr.

PATEL, ALPESH; Bishop O Hara HS; Scranton, PA; (1); Am Leg Boys St; Boy Scts; Camera Clb; Ski Clb; Bowling; Crs Cntry; Swmmng; Trk; Hon Roll; Prfct Atten Awd; Clinical Psych.

PATEL, AMIT; Neshannock HS; Neshannock, PA; (3); Camera Clb; Science Clb; SADD; Varsity Clb; Nwsp Phtg; Nwsp Rptr; Nwsp Sprt Ed; Bsktbl; Comp Engr.

PATEL, CHHAYA; Donegal HS; Marietta, PA; (3); 10/180; Drama Clb; Bausch & Lomb Sci Awd; High Hon Roll; Hon Roll; NHS; Bausch & Lomb Sci Awd 86-87; Sci.

PATEL, KETUL J; Bishop Mc Cort HS; Johnstown, PA; (3); French Clb; Latin Clb; Math Tm; Mu Alpha Theta; Ski Clb; VP Stu Cncl; Tennis; High Hon Roll; Mu Alpha Theta Awd; NHS; Medicine.

PATEL, MANISHA; Pocono Mountain HS; Canadensis, PA; (3); Pep Clb; Service Clb; SADD; Yrbk Stf; Bio.

PATEL, MEDHA; Taylor Allderdice HS; Pittsburgh, PA; (2); Drama Clb; Ski Clb; Cit Awd; DAR Awd; High Hon Roll; Hon Roll; Jr NHS; NHS; Pres Schlr; Archit.

PATEL, NURPESH; Central HS; Scranton, PA; (2); French Clb; Ski Clb; Mrchg Band; Hon Roll; NHS; PA ST; Phrmcst.

PATEL, PARESH; Trinity HS; Mechanicsburg, PA; (2); French Clb; Ski Clb; Yrbk Stf; Golf; Socr; High Hon Roll; Congrssnl Yth Ldr Cncl WA DC 87; Acctng.

PATEL, PERRY; Danville HS; Danville, PA; (1); 13/231; Ski Clb; JV Socr; JV Tennis; High Hon Roll; Key Clb Awd 87; Pres Acad Ftnss Awd 87; Doc.

PATEL, PRATIK; Harry S Truman HS; Bristol, PA; (3); Cmnty Wkr; Computer Clb; Quiz Bowl; Science Clb; Hon Roll; Comp Engr.

PATEL, RACHANA; West York HS; York, PA; (2); Drama Clb; Hosp Aide; JA; Library Aide; Spanish Clb; Temple Yth Grp; Band; Chorus; Concert Band; Mrchg Band; Prfct Attndnc Awd 85-87; Hnr Rll 86 & 87; Bus Mrktng.

PATEL, RUPAL; Bensalem HS; Bensalem, PA; (3); Dance Clb; Office Aide; SADD; Rep Stu Cncl; High Hon Roll; Hon Roll; Nrsng.

PATETE, DANA; Hollidaysburg Area HS; Duncansville, PA; (3); 16/401; Intnl Clb; Latin Clb; Office Aide; SADD; Varsity Clb; Var L Bsktbl; Var L Sftbl; Hon Roll; NHS; Bio.

PATMON, DAUGHN LA RAE; Canon Mc Millan HS; Canonsburg, PA; (3); Dance Clb; FBLA; Drill Tm; Gym; Pom Pon; High Hon Roll; Hon Roll; Psych.

PATNIK, SUSAN; Plum SR HS; Pittsburgh, PA; (2); Art Clb; DECA; French Clb; Varsity Clb; Chorus; JV Var Cheerleading.

PATRENE, DANA; Peters Township HS; Mc Murray, PA; (4); 62/265; GAA; Varsity Clb; Stu Cncl; Bsktbl; Cheerleading; Powder Puff Ftbl; Trk; Hon Roll; Hmcng Ct SR Yr 86-87; Capt Chrldng & Bsktbl Vrsty 86-87; Fashn Merchdsng.

PATRICK, JAMES; Lincoln HS; Ellwood City, PA; (3); Ski Clb; Var JV Bsbl; Im Bsktbl; JV Var Ftbl; Var Trk; High Hon Roll; Hon Roll.

PATRICK, JULIA; Harverford SR HS; Havertown, PA; (3); 48/430; Church Yth Grp; Spanish Clb; Nwsp Rptr; Lit Mag; Rep Jr Cls; Rep Sr Cls; Var Crs Cntry; Var Trk; Hon Roll; Schl Brd Rep 86-88.

PATRICK, JULIE; Jefferson Morgan HS; Rices Landing, PA; (2); 6/120; Intnl Clb; Band; Chorus; Church Choir; Concert Band; Drm Mjr(t); Mrchg Band; School Play; High Hon Roll; PMEA JR Hgh Dist Band Awd 86; Music.

PATRICK, KELLIE; Johnsonburg Area HS; Wilcox, PA; (3); Camera Clb; Yrbk Stf; VP Frsh Cls; Rep Stu Cncl; Stat Bsktbl; High Hon Roll; Hon Roll; NCTE Awd; PA ST U; Jrnlsm.

PATRICK, LYNN; Chapel Christian Schl; Belle Vernon, PA; (4); 1/5 Band; Mrchg Band; Yrbk Ed-Chief; Yrbk Stf; Sec Soph Cls; Var Capt Cheerleading; High Hon Roll; Val; Natl Ldrshp & Svc Awd 84-85 Extraordinary Christina Stu Of US 86-87; Miss Metro Pittsburgh Nat 86-7; Thiel; Crmnlgy.

PATRICK, PAULA S; Greensburg Central Catholic HS; Greensburg, PA (3); 39/246; Pres Church Yth Grp; French Clb; Girl Scts; Chorus; Sec Church Choir; High Hon Roll; Hon Roll; NHS; Co-Fndr Yth Mnstry 86 Prsdntl Acdmc Ftnss Awd 85.

PATRICK, SEAN; Southern Columbia Area HS; Shamokin, PA; (3); Key Clb; Letterman Clb; Varsity Clb; Sec Jr Cls; Var L Bsbl; Var L Bsktbl; Var L Ftbl; Wt Lftg; Hon Roll.

PATRICO, MICHELE; Blue Mountain Acad; Uniontown, PA; (3) Church Yth Grp; Church Choir; Orch; Yrbk Stf; Score Keeper; Sftbl Vllybl; MD U; Psych.

PATRINOS, NYA; Central HS; Philadelphia, PA; (4); 31/350; French Clb; Math Clb; School Play; Yrbk Sprt Ed; Ed Lit Mag; Var Crs Cntry; Var Swmmng; Hon Roll; Ntl Merit Ltr; Pres Schlr; Natl Achvt Fin 87; RI Schl Design; Artist.

PATRINOS, RANDY; Chartiers Valley HS; Pittsburgh, PA; (3); Service Clb; Ski Clb; Y-Teens; Nwsp Bus Mgr; Nwsp Rptr; Wrstlng; NHS; Rotary Awd; U Pittsburgh; Bus.

PATRONE, MICHELE; Saint Maria Goretti HS; Philadelphia, PA; (4) 90/384; Camera Clb; Cmnty Wkr; GAA; SADD; Chorus; School Musical Nwsp Phtg; Nwsp Stf; Hon Roll; Prfct Atten Awd; Natl Schl Chrl Awd 87 Hgh Hnr Rll 83; St Josephs U; Law.

PATRONIE, KIMBERLY; Canon-Mc Millan HS; Canonsburg, PA; (4) Latin Clb; High Hon Roll; Hon Roll; Duquesne U; Bus Admn.

PATT, LISA; Montoursville Area HS; Montoursville, PA; (3); 30/185 French Clb; Rep Frsh Cls; Rep Soph Cls; Stu Cncl; Hon Roll.

PATTE, PATRICK; James M Coughlin HS; Wilkes Barre, PA; (3); 68/362; Letterman Clb; SADD; Ftbl; Wt Lftg; High Hon Roll; Jr NHS; Acad All-Am 87; Sci.

PATTERSON, BARBARA; Penn Cambria HS; Cresson, PA; (3); 19/201 FBLA; SADD; Band; Chorus; Color Guard; Concert Band; Mrchg Band Rep Frsh Cls; Trk; Altoona Schl Of Commerce.

PATTERSON, BRANDON; Mt Pleasant Area HS; Mt Pleasant, PA; (2) Boy Scts; German Clb; Var Golf; Hon Roll; SAR Awd.

PATTERSON, BRENDA; West Greene HS; Graysville, PA; (2); Sec FTA; Pres Frsh Cls; Pres Soph Cls; JV Cheerleading; High Hon Roll; Hon Roll; Opt Clb Awd; FHA; Chorus; Color Guard; Natl Engl Merit Awd 84-85; JR Acad Sci 2nd Pl Awd 86-87; Upwrd Bnd 84-87; HOBY 86-87 Penn ST; Law.

PATTERSON, CARLA; Purchase Line HS; Clymer, PA; (4); 3/104 Church Yth Grp; FBLA; Teachers Aide; High Hon Roll; NCTE Awd NHS; PA FBLA Schlrshp 87; Bradford Schl Bus; Bus.

PATTERSON, CHRISTOPHER; Father Judge HS; Philadelphia, PA (3); 1/403; NFL; School Play; Nwsp Rptr; Lit Mag; Var Tennis; High Hon Roll; NHS; Debate Tm; Drama Clb; Speech Tm; Philadelphia Inquirer Schlrshp Asst Awd, Lincoln-Dougls Delegate 1st Pl & Frnscs Natl Finl 32nd 87; Poltcl Sci.

PATTERSON, DAVID; Central Bucks HS West; Chalfont, PA; (3); 125/525; Pres Church Yth Grp; SADD; Drm Mjr(t); Yrbk Stf; Trs Jr Cls; Tr Sr Cls; Pres Stu Cncl; Cit Awd; Rotary Awd; CC Awd; Bus.

PATTERSON, DAWN; Penn Trafford HS; Irwin, PA; (4); 85/344 Church Yth Grp; Acpl Chr; Chorus; Church Choir; Stat Bsbl; Stat Bowling Mgr(s); Score Keeper; Sftbl; Hon Roll; Slippery Rock U; Athletc Trainr.

PATTERSON, DORCAS A; Avon Grove SR HS; West Grove, PA; (4) 32/168; Computer Clb; Sec FBLA; Bsktbl; Var Crs Cntry; Var Trk; Hon Roll; NHS; Ursinus Coll; Bus Adm.

PATTERSON, DOUGLAS; Mechanicsburg Area SR HS Mechanicsburg, PA; (2); Art Clb; Boy Scts; Church Yth Grp; Chorus Church Choir; Stage Crew; Variety Show; Hon Roll; Natl Art Hnr Soc 86 Enrchmnt/Gftd Pgm 85; Musician.

PATTERSON, ERIC V; Cardinal Dougherty HS; Philadelphia, PA; (4) 189/695; Band; Concert Band; Drm Mjr(t); Jazz Band; Mrchg Band; Orch School Musical; Hon Roll; William F Quilty Awd 87; MI ST U; Scl Sci.

PATTERSON, JASON; Penn Manor HS; Millersville, PA; (3); Ski Clb Stu Cncl; Crs Cntry; Socr; Tennis; Trk; Bus.

PATTERSON, KATHY; Little Flower HS; Philadelphia, PA; (3); Church Yth Grp; VP SADD; Chorus; School Musical; School Play.

PATTERSON, KENNETH; Marion Center HS; Indiana, PA; (4); Varsity Clb; VICA; Wrstlng; High Hon Roll; Hon Roll; Indiana Co Vo-Tec Sch Shop Pres 85-87; 2nd Pl St VICA Compttn & Mjr Applnc Rpr 85; Applnc Techncn.

PATTERSON, LAURIE; Kennedy Christian HS; Sharon, PA; (3); 28/97 French Clb; Pep Clb; Ski Clb; Drill Tm; Crs Cntry; Hon Roll; Chld Psych.

PATTERSON, LOIS SUE; Wyalusing Valley JR SR HS; Wyalusing, PA (4); 11/133; 4-H; Pep Clb; Spanish Clb; School Musical; Sec Sr Cls; Capt L Cheerleading; Var L Trk; Cit Awd; High Hon Roll; NHS; Outstndg Chrldr Awd 85; Jr Miss Kraft Awd 86; Most Ded Girl-Trk 87; Penn ST U Med.

PATTERSON, LORI; Hanover SR HS; Hanover, PA; (3); Varsity Clb Band; Chorus; Concert Band; Mrchg Band; Variety Show; Var Capt Bsktbl; Var Tennis; Elks Awd; Hon Roll; Tnns-Yrk Dsptch Athlt Of Wk 86-87; Awd-Undftd Seasn-Tnns 85-86; Tnns Schlrshp-Mrymnt VA Coll 85-86; Indiana U Of PA; Elem Ed.

PATTERSON, MARY JO; Wyoming Area SR HS; West Pittston, PA (3); 31/250; Hosp Aide; Library Aide; Spanish Clb; Var Trk; High Hon Roll; Hon Roll; NHS; Child Psych.

PATTERSON, RANDY; Fort Le Boeuf HS; Erie, PA; (2); Drama Clb Spanish Clb; School Musical; Yrbk Stf; Im Bsktbl; Im Golf; Pres Acad Ftns Awd; 1 Thtr Stu Awd; NC U; Intl Bus.

PATTERSON, STEPHANIE; Washington HS; Washington, PA; (2) Church Yth Grp; Cmnty Wkr; Computer Clb; French Clb; Chorus; JV Var Score Keeper; Cit Awd; Hon Roll; Emory U; Crmnl Law.

PATTERSON, TAMARA; South Williamsport Area HS; S Williamsport PA; (4); 12/140; Library Aide; Spanish Clb; Chorus; Nwsp Rptr; Nwsp Stf Yrbk Rptr; Yrbk Stf; Var L Tennis; Im Vllybl; NHS; Ntl Yng Ldrs Conf 86; Hnrbl Mntn-Grt Amer Poetry Cont 87; Goldn Poet Awd 87 Shippensburg U; Marine Bio.

PATTERSON, VALERIE; Coatesville Area SR HS; Coatesville, PA; (4) 71/467; Girl Scts; Sr Cls; Hon Roll; Prfct Atten Awd; Hnr Soc 87.

PATTI, NINA; Strath Haven HS; Wallingford, PA; (3); Library Aide Teachers Aide; High Hon Roll; Hon Roll; Elem Ed.

PATTON, BRADLEY; Wyoming Valley West HS; Luzerne, PA; (4); French Clb; Radio Clb; Red Cross Aide; School Musical; Stage Crew; Nwsp Stf; High Hon Roll; Hon Roll; NHS; Pres Acad Ftnss Awd 86-87; Kings Coll; Mass Cmmnctns.

PATTON, CARL; Lebanon Catholic HS; Lebanon, PA; (3); 4/65; Spanish Clb; JV Bsktbl; Var Ftbl; Im Wt Lftg; Parish Alter Boy Awd 84; Embry Rddle; Aeronaut.

PATTON, CHRISTINA; Red Lion Area SR HS; Brogue, PA; (3); 53/342; Church Yth Grp; Science Clb; Prfct Atten Awd; Samuel H Shply Dstngshd Achvt Awd 87; JR Yng Rdr Awd US Drssg Fed 86; Brnz Mdl Intl Eqstrn Orgzntn.

PATTON, CINDI; Northwestern SR HS; E Springfield, PA; (3); 5/135; Math Clb; Spanish Clb; Band; Mrchg Band; Stage Crew; Var L Sftbl; Hon Roll; Ntl Merit Schol; English Clb; Math.

PATTON, DONNA; Butler Area SR HS; Prospect, PA; (3); Office Aide; FNA; Hon Roll; Nrsg.

PATTON, HEATHER; Mohawk Area JR-SR HS; Edinburg, PA; (3); Church Yth Grp; FBLA; FHA; Hosp Aide; Teachers Aide; Nwsp Stf; Rep Jr Cls; Stu Cncl; Stat Ftbl; High Hon Roll; Acctng.

PATTON, PATTI; Ambridge Area HS; Baden, PA; (2); Church Yth Grp; Sec 4-H; German Clb; Pep Clb; Band; Concert Band; Mrchg Band; Var Socr; High Hon Roll; Hon Roll; 1st Pl In 4-H Cnty Horse Show 87; Jdgng & Training Horses.

PATTON, STEVE; Plum SR HS; Pittsburgh, PA; (2); Im Var Bsktbl; Var Im Ftbl; Im Trk; Im Wt Lftg; Hon Roll; Sci.

PATTON, VAUGHN; Ford City HS; Ford City, PA; (4); 31/152; Church Yth Grp; Rep FBLA; Hosp Aide; Rep Spanish Clb; Rep Chorus; Rep Nwsp Stf; Rep Frsh Cls; Rep Soph Cls; Rep Jr Cls; Rep Sr Cls; Outstndng Acctng Stu 87; Stu Acvitivities Stu Cncl 87; New Kensington; Acctng.

PAUCKE, JON; Williamsport Area HS; Williamsport, PA; (4); 60/470; Key Clb; Letterman Clb; Var L Bsbl; JV Golf; Var Swmmng; Hon Roll; PA ST U; Bus.

PAUKSTIS, DEANNA; Nativity B V M HS; New Philadelphia, PA; (2); 14/78; Hosp Aide; Spanish Clb; Chorus; Drill Tm; High Hon Roll; AM Cltr Awd, Physcl Sci & Rlgn Awd 86; Nrsng.

PAUL, CHRISTINE M; Mount St Joseph Acad; Dresher, PA; (4); Cmnty Wkr; French Clb; Intnl Clb; Math Tm; Model UN; Service Clb; Lit Mag; NHS; Ntl Merit SF; JCL; Ntl Latin Hnr Scty; Awd Merit In Study Of French; Alumnae Schlrshp; Georgetown U; Pol Sci.

PAUL, DAVID; Yough HS; W Newton, PA; (3); Yrbk Stf; Swmmng; Hon Roll; Penn ST U; Engrng.

PAUL, DEBORAH; Berklin Brothers Valley HS; Berlin, PA; (3); 2/90; Church Yth Grp; Band; Yrbk Stf; Trs Frsh Cls; Pres Jr Cls; Trs Stu Cncl; Co-Capt Cheerleading; Hon Roll; NHS; Acctg.

PAUL, ELAINE; Tri-Valley HS; Sacramento, PA; (3); 19/76; Pres Church Yth Grp; Drama Clb; Band; Chorus; Church Choir; Concert Band; Mrchg Band; School Musical; Yrbk Stf; Stat Vllybl; Great Bks Pgm 86-87; Rep Rotry Yth Exchng Pgm 86; Lock Haven U; Tchng.

PAUL, JASON; Wilson Christian Acad; Munhall, PA; (3); 4/10; Pres Jr Cls; Wt Lftg; Hon Roll; PA ST U; Nutrition.

PAUL, MELISSA; Bishop Mc Cort HS; Johnstown, PA; (2); Church Yth Grp; Church Choir; Bsktbl; JV Lib Cheerleading; Hon Roll; Guid Cnslr.

PAUL, MIKE; Bethlehem Center SR HS; Marianna, PA; (4); 4-H; Ski Clb; VICA; Aviation.

PAUL, MITCHELL; Lower Moreland HS; Huntingdon Valley, PA; (4); 44/201; FBLA; Key Clb; SADD; JV Bsbl; Var JV Bsktbl; JV Diving; JV Ftbl; Hon Roll; NHS; Pres Schlr; Penn ST Univ; Bus.

PAUL, NICHOLE; Trinity HS; Washington, PA; (2); Spanish Clb; JV Vllybl; High Hon Roll; Sci.

PAUL, RENU; Archbishop Prendergast HS; Upper Darby, PA; (3); 4/329; Aud/Vis; Intnl Clb; Library Aide; Nwsp Rptr; Hon Roll; NHS; Prfct Atten Awd; Spanish NHS; Cert Achvt Bio, Engl, Spnsh 87; Schl Splling Bee Champ 83 & 84; 1st Chrch Essay Comp 86; U Of PA; Engl.

PAUL, STEPHANIE; Upper Dauphin Area HS; Lykens, PA; (4); 7/101; Church Yth Grp; Drama Clb; Band; Concert Band; Jazz Band; Mrchg Band; School Play; JV Bsktbl; JV Capt Sftbl; Swmmng; Pres Fit Awd 87; 1st Pl Annual HS Math Exam 87; Purdue; Engrng.

PAUL, TINA; Mt Carmel Area JR SR HS; Mt Carmel, PA; (4); Hst FTA; Key Clb; Pep Clb; Chorus; Concert Band; Mrchg Band; JV Bsktbl; Var L Cheerleading; Var L Swmmng; Var L Trk; Lgsltive Cmnty Svc Awd 86; Bloomsburg U; Spcl Ed.

PAUL JR, TOM; E L Meyers HS; Wilkes-Barre, PA; (3); 47/187; Letterman Clb; Pep Clb; SADD; Chorus; Yrbk Stf; Var L Ftbl; Var L Trk; Im Vllybl; Var Wt Lftg; Hon Roll; VA Mltry Inst; Law.

PAULETICH, CINNAMON L; Franklin Regional SR HS; Export, PA; (4); 1/338; Pres French Clb; Sec Trs Chorus; Variety Show; Sec Jr Cls; Rep Stu Cncl; High Hon Roll; NHS; Ntl Merit SF; Schlrshp U Of Pittsbrgh 86; Cert Pa Hghr Ed Asst 86; Pennsylvania ST U; French.

PAULEY, GARRY; Ringgold HS; Monongahela, PA; (3); Im JV Bsbl; JV Bsktbl; Math & Sci Hnr Soc 86-87; Acctng.

PAULIN, JAMIE LYNN; Hopewell HS; Aliquippa, PA; (4); 20/245; Sec French Clb; Chorus; Sec Drill Tm; School Musical; Yrbk Phtg; Stu Cncl; Sec Pom Pon; Trk; High Hon Roll; NHS; Kent ST U; Chem.

PAULINA, MARIA; Cardinal O Hara HS; Havertown, PA; (3); 4/710; Church Yth Grp; Office Aide; Service Clb; School Musical; Nwsp Stf; Yrbk Stf; Vllybl; High Hon Roll; NHS; Prfct Atten Awd; Sci Fair Awds 85-87; PA Free Enterprs Wk Schlrshp 86; Acad Convctns 85-87; Relgn & Latin Awds 85; Psych.

PAULING, WILLIAM; Watsontow Christian Acad; Montgomery, PA; (3); 1/11; Church Yth Grp; 4-H; Yrbk Phtg; Yrbk Stf; Bsktbl; Socr; High Hon Roll; Hon Roll.

PAULL, SUSAN; Northeastern HS; Manchester, PA; (3); Ski Clb; Band; Chorus; Church Choir; Concert Band; Mrchg Band; Orch; Pep Band; School Musical; Hon Roll.

PAULOVICH, DANIELLE; Western Beaver HS; Midland, PA; (4); Pres JA; Teachers Aide; Band; Chorus; Concert Band; Mrchg Band; Symp Band; Cheerleading; Mgr(s); Score Keeper; U Pittsburgh; Chld Psych.

PAULSHOCK, ANN M; Bishop Hafey HS; Freeland, PA; (3); 61/116; FNA; Drill Tm; School Play; Cheerleading; Pom Pon; Bloomsburg U; Nrsng.

PAULSHOCK, BRYAN; West Hazelton HS; Sugarloaf, PA; (2); 11/110; Aud/Vis; SADD; High Hon Roll; Hon Roll; Penn ST U.

PAULSON, CARLISE; Tunkhannock Area HS; Tunkhannock, PA; (3); 5/320; Sec Trs Church Yth Grp; VP Jr Cls; Rep Stu Cncl; JV Bsktbl; Var Fld Hcky; Var Trk; Cit Awd; Hon Roll; NHS; HOBY Rep 86; Ctznshp Awd 85; Hnrs Banquet Awd 85 & 86.

PAULSON, JESICA ANN; Fairview HS; Fairview, PA; (3); 54/162; Church Yth Grp; German Clb; Model UN; Q&S; Teachers Aide; Varsity Clb; Yrbk Ed-Chief; Yrbk Phtg; Yrbk Rptr; L Sftbl; Jrnlsm.

PAULSON, TIMOTHY; Tunkhannock Area HS; Tunkhannock, PA; (4); 9/270; Church Yth Grp; Spanish Clb; JV Bsktbl; Var L Golf; Hon Roll; NHS.

PAUSTENBACH, KERRY; Immaculate Conception HS; Washington, PA; (3); 10/42; Art Clb; Camera Clb; Church Yth Grp; Cmnty Wkr; Dance Clb; Debate Tm; Drama Clb; French Clb; Hosp Aide; Key Clb; Bus.

PAUSTENBACH, MEGAN; Burrell JR HS; Lower Burrell, PA; (3); AFS; Cmnty Wkr; Spanish Clb; Yrbk Stf; Var Sftbl; Var Capt Tennis; U Of S FL; Srgcl Nrs.

PAUTZ, DONALD; Cowanesque Valley HS; Westfield, PA; (4); Boy Scts; Church Yth Grp; Drama Clb; German Clb; Letterman Clb; Science Clb; Band; School Play; Bsktbl; Capt Ftbl; All Conf In Ftbl 86; All Dist In Ftbl 86; All Regn In Ftbl 86; Eagle Scout 85; Schlr Athlt Awds 86; Elecl Engrng.

PAUTZ, JOSEPH; Lebanon Catholic HS; Lebanon, PA; (3); German Clb; Stage Crew; Var Bowling; Stu Mnth Awd 86-87; US Air Frc.

PAVALONE, PAMELA SUE; Carbondale Area JR/Sr HS; Carbondale, PA; (2); Art Clb; Church Yth Grp; Ski Clb; Spanish Clb; Chorus; Color Guard; Trk; Hon Roll; Hosp Aide; School Musical; Penn ST; Law.

PAVELETZ, SHARON; John S Fine HS; Nanticoke, PA; (3); 13/228; High Hon Roll; NHS; Bloomsburg U; Elem Tchr.

PAVELIK, ERIC; Scott Intermediate HS; Coatesville, PA; (2); Ski Clb; Chorus; Rep Frsh Cls; Rep Stu Cncl; JV Bsbl; JV Socr; Hon Roll; Pres Phys Fit Awd 86-87; Natl Ed Dev Tst Awd 86-87; Med.

PAVIA, DEBRA; New Castle SR HS; New Castle, PA; (4); 30/228; AFS; Computer Clb; Office Aide; SADD; Im Vllybl; Hon Roll; NHS; Acadmc All-Amer 87; Edinboro U; Psychlgy.

PAVICK, HELEN; Waynesburg Central HS; Waynesburg, PA; (4); French Clb; Hosp Aide; Intnl Clb; Natl Beta Clb; Trk; Hon Roll; Commnctns.

PAVILLIAN, SUSAN; Franklin Regional SR HS; Murrysville, PA; (3); 1/329; Service Clb; Spanish Clb; SADD; Band; Color Guard; Concert Band; Mrchg Band; School Musical; High Hon Roll; NHS; Acad Exclnce Awd 85 & 86.

PAVINA, STEPHANIE; Brownsville Area HS; Republic, PA; (3); Nrsng.

PAVLASKY, JONI; North Catholic HS; Pittsburgh, PA; (3); 39/294; Am Leg Aux Girls St; Church Yth Grp; FCA; Spanish Clb; SADD; Rep Stu Cncl; JV Var Bsktbl; DAR Awd; High Hon Roll; Hon Roll.

PAVLICK, DAWN; Lake-Lehman SR HS; Hunlock Crk, PA; (3); Aud/Vis; Drama Clb; Ski Clb; Speech Tm; School Play; Variety Show; Stu Cncl; Var Cheerleading; Coach Actv; Var Trk; Mini Ftbl Coaching Awd 86-87; Air Force; Pilot.

PAVLICK, KIMBERLY; M M I Preparatory Schl; Freeland, PA; (3); 8/39; Sec Debate Tm; Hosp Aide; Pep Clb; Nwsp Rptr; Var Cheerleading; Crs Cntry; Cit Awd; Elks Awd; High Hon Roll; HOBY Fndtn Intl Ambssdr 86; 3rd Rnnr Up Miss Teen USA PA 85; German NHS 85-86; Med.

PAVLICK, ROBYN; Lake Lehman HS; Hunlock Creek, PA; (1); 4-H; Drill Tm; Trs Frsh Cls; Cheerleading; Cit Awd; 4-H Awd; High Hon Roll; Hon Roll; Jr NHS; Equine Stds.

PAVLIK, EUGENE; Lehighton Area HS; Lehighton, PA; (3); 30/245; Boy Scts; Chess Clb; Ski Clb; School Play; Stu Cncl; Var Golf; Var Trk; Var Wrstlng; Hon Roll.

PAVLIK, GREG; Highlands HS; Natrona, PA; (3); Aud/Vis; Camera Clb; Computer Clb; German Clb; Intnl Clb; Trk; Jr NHS; Prfct Atten Awd; PA ST U.

PAVLIK, HOLLY; Bethel Park HS; Bethel Park, PA; (4); Church Yth Grp; Debate Tm; DECA; Drama Clb; Stu Cncl; DAR Awd; Bethany Coll; Econ.

PAVLIK, WALTER; Hazelton HS; Hazleton, PA; (3); #42 In Class; Church Yth Grp; Letterman Clb; Pep Clb; Scholastic Bowl; Varsity Clb; Golf; Trk; Hon Roll; Jr NHS; Penn ST; Acctng.

PAVLOCAK, JEFF; Mt Pleasant HS; Mt Pleasant, PA; (4); German Clb; Letterman Clb; Red Cross Aide; Ski Clb; Band; Concert Band; Jazz Band; Mrchg Band; Pep Band; Variety Show; Comp Sys Inst; Comp Sys Anlyst.

PAVLOCK, MELISSA; Johnsonburg Area HS; Johnsonburg, PA; (4); Church Yth Grp; Girl Scts; SADD; Varsity Clb; Band; Yrbk Stf; Rep Stu Cncl; Tennis; High Hon Roll; NHS; Ptrlm Engr.

PAVOLKO, JACKIE; Northwestern SR HS; Albion, PA; (3); Drama Clb; Spanish Clb; Thesps; Chorus; Stage Crew; Rep Jr Cls; Bsktbl; Ftbl; NHS; St Vincent Schl Of Nrsng; Nrs.

PAVOLONIS, PAULA; Bishop O Reilly HS; Luzerne, PA; (2); Ski Clb; Spanish Clb; Chorus; School Play; Sec Soph Cls; JV Cheerleading; High Hon Roll; NHS; Prfct Atten Awd; Spanish NHS; Law.

PAVONCELLO JR, RICHARD A; Mechanicsburg Area SR HS; Mechanicsburg, PA; (3); 17/338; Band; Concert Band; Mrchg Band; Symp Band; Yrbk Stf; Ftbl; Hon Roll; JETS Awd; Engrng.

PAVTIS, LAURIE; Belle Vernon Area HS; Belle Vernon, PA; (4); 49/267; Church Yth Grp; Girl Scts; Pep Clb; Drm & Bgl; Mrchg Band; Variety Show; VP Soph Cls; Rep Sr Cls; Sec Stu Cncl; Stat Bsktbl; U Pitt Greensburg; Physcl Ther.

PAWLAK, MELISSA; Muncy HS; Muncy, PA; (1); Stu Cncl; Var Cheerleading; Hon Roll; Mgr Var Fld Hcky; Sftbl; Empire Beauty Schl; Hairstylist.

PAWLAK, PAM; Mount Alvernia HS; Pittsburgh, PA; (3); 16/54; Drama Clb; Chorus; School Play; JV Capt Bsktbl; Var Sftbl; Hon Roll; Jr NHS; NHS; Rotary Awd; Bus Hnr Socty 86-87.

PAWLOSKI, JAMES; Plum SR HS; Pittsburgh, PA; (3); Chorus; High Hon Roll; PA ST U; Arspc Engr.

PAWLOWICZ, JERRY T; Knoch HS; Butler, PA; (3); 24/224; Am Leg Boys St; SADD; Varsity Clb; Nwsp Stf; Trs Frsh Cls; Stu Cncl; Var L Bsktbl; Var Capt Golf; NHS; High Hon Roll; HOBY Awd 86.

PAWLOWSKI, KATHERINE; John S Fine SR HS; Nanticoke, PA; (4); 30/270; Library Aide; Band; Pres Chorus; Concert Band; Mrchg Band; Yrbk Stf; High Hon Roll; NHS; Dist Chorus 85-87; PA ST U.

PAXSON, KIMBERLY; Solanco HS; Nottingham, PA; (2); Chorus; Flag Corp; Rep Stu Cncl; JV Im Bsktbl; JV Fld Hcky; JV Sftbl; Hon Roll; Prfct Atten Awd; Phys Thrpy.

PAYNE, ADRIENNE; Garden Spot HS; Bowmansville, PA; (3); 30/196; Chess Clb; FFA; Chorus; Nwsp Rptr; Nwsp Stf; Hon Roll; Alt PA Gov Schl Agri 87; Jrnlsm.

PAYNE, DIANNA; Hempfield HS; Landisville, PA; (3); Church Yth Grp; Nwsp Stf; Var Bsktbl; Var Sftbl; Hon Roll; 4-H; Chorus; 4-H Awd; Schl Art Shw Hon Mntn Mech Drwng I 86-87; Arch.

PAYNE, GLENN; Mc Keesport SR HS; Mckeesport, PA; (3); Boys Clb Am; Hon Roll; AF.

PAYNE, RHONDA; Rochester Area JR SR HS; Rochester, PA; (3); 12/130; Pres Church Yth Grp; French Clb; Office Aide; Teachers Aide; Chorus; Church Choir; Trk; Hon Roll; NHS; Penn ST; Psych.

PAYNE, TWILA; Mt Union Area HS; Mt Union, PA; (3); 18/160; Church Yth Grp; French Clb; Chorus; Stage Crew; Hon Roll.

PAYNE, URSULA; Union Area JR SR HS; New Castle, PA; (4); 8/66; Church Yth Grp; Dance Clb; Drama Clb; NAACP; Pep Clb; SADD; Band; Chorus; Church Choir; Concert Band; 1st Rnnr Up Jr Miss Schlrshp Pgnt 86-87; US Rsv Ntl Schlr/Athltc Awd 87; Athltc Of Yr 86-87; Slippery Rock U; Math.

PAZDERSKI, HOLLY; Warren Area HS; Warren, PA; (4); Camera Clb; Church Yth Grp; Cmnty Wkr; French Clb; Hosp Aide; Office Aide; Chorus; Stage Crew; Timer; Jr NHS.

PAZDZIORKO, KIMBERLY; Wyoming Area SR HS; Exeter, PA; (3); Aud/Vis; Civic Clb; Drama Clb; German Clb; Intnl Clb; Office Aide; Red Cross Aide; SADD; Nwsp Rptr; Rotary Awd; Psychtry.

PAZGAN, DAVID; Hickory HS; Hermitage, PA; (3); 15/190; German Clb; Chorus; Crs Cntry; Swmmng; Trk.

PAZIN, JOHN G; North Allegheny SR HS; Pittsburgh, PA; (3); 4/649; Am Leg Boys St; VP Church Yth Grp; Orch; Rep Stu Cncl; Bausch & Lomb Sci Awd; High Hon Roll; Jr NHS; NHS; Ntl Merit SF; James R Wall Humanitarian Awd 86; Walter Strycula Math Awd 86; Med.

PCHOLINSKY, LYNN; Sacred Heart HS; Pittsburgh, PA; (4); 37/142; Church Yth Grp; Pep Clb; Spanish Clb; Var Capt Cheerleading; High Hon Roll; Hon Roll; Duguesne U; Pre-Law.

PCOLINSKY, MICHELE; Hazleton HS; Hazleton, PA; (3); 28/450; Pep Clb; Spanish Clb; Chorus; Var Swmmng; Hon Roll; Bus Mgmt.

PEACE, CINDY; Purchase Line HS; Mahaffey, PA; (3); FBLA; Library Aide; Pep Clb; Spanish Clb; Yrbk Stf; High Hon Roll; Hon Roll.

PEACE, THERESA M; Plymouth Whitemarsh HS; Norristown, PA; (3); 4-H; 4-H Awd; Scholastic Hon 86-87; Gen Study.

PEACE, TRACY; Dubois Area HS; Dubois, PA; (4); Church Yth Grp; Chorus; JV Capt Cheerleading; Edinboro ST U; Nrsng.

PEACHEY, CHARLENE; Mifflinburg HS; Mifflinburg, PA; (3); Church Yth Grp; Drama Clb; French Clb; Hosp Aide; Acpl Chr; Band; Chorus; Concert Band; Mrchg Band; School Play; E Mennonite Coll; Educ.

PEACHEY, GWENDOLYN K; Kishacoquillas JR/Sr HS; Belleville, PA; (4); 17/140; Sec Church Yth Grp; Pres FNA; Teachers Aide; Band; Chorus; School Play; Variety Show; Im Vllybl; Cit Awd; High Hon Roll; Stu Of Mo 86-87; Civic Clb Schlrshp; Eastern Mennonite Coll; Nrsng.

PEACHEY, SHERRI; Juniata HS; Pt Royal, PA; (3); Sec Church Yth Grp; SADD; Varsity Clb; Concert Band; Mrchg Band; Sec Jr Cls; Off Stu Cncl; JV Var Fld Hcky; High Hon Roll; NHS; Nrsng.

PEACOCK, BRADLEY S; North Allegheny SR HS; Wexford, PA; (4); VP Church Yth Grp; Church Choir; Lit Mag; Var L Swmmng; Hon Roll; Depauw U.

PEACOCK, STERLING; W B Saul HS Of Agriculture & Science; Philadelphia, PA; (3); FFA; Im Bsktbl; Im Sftbl; Gov Hon Prg Awd; Hon Roll; NHS; Vet.

PEAHL, JONATHAN; Red Land HS; New Cumberland, PA; (3); 40/300; VP Church Yth Grp; Quiz Bowl; Orch; Nwsp Rptr; Sr Cls; Var L Crs Cntry; Var L Trk; Hon Roll; U Of NV-LAS Vegas; Htl Mgmt.

PEAK, SAMUEL; New Castle SR HS; New Castle, PA; (4); 10/232; Church Yth Grp; Cmnty Wkr; Spanish Clb; SADD; Band; Concert Band; Mrchg Band; Trk; Vllybl; High Hon Roll; PA Free Entrprs Wk Schlrshp 86; Pres Schlrshp Tomrrw Ldrs 87; CPA.

PEAK, SHELLEY; New Castle SR HS; New Castle, PA; (4); 20/242; AFS; Church Yth Grp; Office Aide; Spanish Clb; Rep Stu Cncl; Hon Roll; Sec NHS; Westminster; Elem Ed.

PEARCE, ANNIE; North Star HS; Boswell, PA; (2); 1/133; Mu Alpha Theta; Band; Chorus; Church Choir; Orch; High Hon Roll; Pres Schlr; Church Yth Grp; FCA; Concert Band; Acdmc Math Curric Awd 86; WJAC-TV Super Stu 87; Actvts Booster Stu Of Mnth 86; Instrmntl Music Prfrmnc.

PEARCE, GREGORY; Punxsutawney HS; Rossiter, PA; (3); JV Ftbl; Hon Roll; Paralegal.

PEARCE, SHEILA; Punxsutawney Area HS; Rossiter, PA; (4); 16/246; Church Yth Grp; French Clb; Hosp Aide; Science Clb; Variety Show; Hon Roll; NHS; Fren Foreign Lang Awd 87; IN U.

PEARL, BENJAMIN J; Central Dauphin East 081987 HS; Harrisburg, PA; (3); 14/297; Am Leg Boys St; Debate Tm; French Clb; Ski Clb; JV Ftbl; Var Golf; Var Trk; JV Var Wrstlng; NHS; Penn ST; Engrng.

PEARN, DEANA; Northampton SR HS; Northampton, PA; (4); Cmnty Wkr; Girl Scts; Leo Clb; Color Guard; Mrchg Band; Nwsp Bus Mgr; Nwsp Stf; Sftbl; High Hon Roll; NHS; Kutztown U; Scndry Math.

PEARSALL, BETH; Penn Wood HS; Lansdowne, PA; (4); 22/346; VP Church Yth Grp; GAA; Yrbk Stf; Sec Jr Cls; Chrmn Sr Cls; Fld Hcky; Lcrss; Cit Awd; Hon Roll; Pres Schlr; Pres Schlrshp Awd 87; 1st Pl Penn Wood Art Shw 85-86; Eva Jay Rogers Ctznshp Awd 87; Dickinson Coll; Art Psych.

PEARSE, KAREN; Downingtown SR HS; Exton, PA; (3); 14/648; Ski Clb; SADD; Chorus; Color Guard; Mrchg Band; School Musical; Stage Crew; Bowling; High Hon Roll; NHS; Biochem.

PEARSON, CRYSTAL; Dover Area HS; Dover, PA; (3); French Clb; Color Guard; Mrchg Band; Hon Roll; Silks Capt 86-88; Empire Bty Schl; Cosmtlgy.

PEARSON, KRISTINA M; Oil City SR HS; Oil City, PA; (4); Varsity Clb; Acpl Chr; Band; Drill Tm; Drm Mjr(t); Mrchg Band; Variety Show; Yrbk Stf; Lit Mag; Swmmng; Misericordia; Jrnlsm.

PEARSON, LISA; Bishop Mc Devitt HS; Harrisburg, PA; (3); 43/210; Art Clb; Ski Clb; Yrbk Stf; Im Bowling; JV Mgr(s); Hon Roll; NHS; 1st Pl Art Awd 84; 2nd Pl Art Awd 87; Religious Awd 87; Elem Educ.

PEARSON, LORI; Benton JR SR HS; Orangeville, PA; (4); 12/49; Church Yth Grp; FTA; Keywanettes; Ski Clb; Soroptimist; Yrbk Stf; Sftbl; High Hon Roll; NHS; Pres Schlr; Oral Roberts U; Anthrplgy.

PEARSON, MARGARET; Lewistown Area HS; Lewistown, PA; (3); AFS; German Clb; Key Clb; Ski Clb; Speech Tm; Varsity Clb; Trs Jr Cls; Stu Cncl; Co-Capt Fld Hcky; Hon Roll.

PEARSON, SCOTT; Eisenhower HS; Russell, PA; (4); 21/116; Band; Orch; Variety Show; Im Badmtn; Var L Bsktbl; Var L Golf; Im Vllybl; High Hon Roll; Hon Roll; NHS; OH St Mandolin Chmpnshps 86; OH St Gutr Chmpn 85; 2nd Pl Phtgrphy Cntst 85; Slippery Rock U; Bus.

PEAVY, JENNIFER; Downingtown SR HS; Downingtown, PA; (3); 15/648; French Clb; Ski Clb; Band; Color Guard; Concert Band; Mrchg Band; Bowling; High Hon Roll; Hon Roll; NHS; Engrng.

PECCI, BRUCE; Plum SR HS; Pittsburgh, PA; (3); Exploring; FTA; Capt Math Tm; Varsity Clb; Nwsp Stf; Yrbk Stf; Capt Var Crs Cntry; Var L Trk; Var L Wrstlng; High Hon Roll; MIT; Elec Engrng.

PECHA, VICTORIA L; Panther Valley HS; Nesquehoning, PA; (4); 4/105; FHA; Stage Crew; Nwsp Stf; Trs Frsh Cls; Capt Cheerleading; Trk; Cit Awd; High Hon Roll; NHS; Pres Schlr; Womens Clb Schlrshp 87; Amer Assoc Rtrd Prsns Schlrshp 87; 1st Pl Pstr PP&L Cntst 87; Antonelli Inst; Cmmrcl Art.

PECHART, DEBORAH; Northern SR HS; Dillsburg, PA; (3); 3/232; Church Yth Grp; Quiz Bowl; Powder Puff Ftbl; Bausch & Lomb Sci Awd; French Hon Soc; High Hon Roll; NHS; Acdmc Achvt Awd 86 & 87.

PECHATSKO, VICTORIA; Fairchance/Georges HS; Uniontown, PA; (4); 23/137; Drama Clb; Hosp Aide; Spanish Clb; School Play; Stage Crew; High Hon Roll; Hon Roll; Sal; ICM Schl Bus; Comp Mgmt.

PECHIN, G KEITH; Oxford Area HS; Oxford, PA; (3); 29/197; Boy Scts; Ski Clb; Ed Yrbk Phtg; Yrbk Stf; Var L Ftbl; JV L Socr; Var L Trk; High Hon Roll; Hon Roll; NHS; 2nd Pl Pole Vaulting 87; Boy Scouts-Order Of Arrow 85; Air Force Acad; Pilot.

PECHTER, STEVEN; Bensalem HS; Bensalem, PA; (2); Stu Cncl; Trk; Hon Roll; PA ST U; Arch.

PECIULIS, LORI; Knoch JR SR HS; Sarver, PA; (3); 1/250; Am Leg Aux Girls St; Hosp Aide; Trs Chorus; Church Choir; Drill Tm; Madrigals; School Musical; School Play; Pom Pon; High Hon Roll; JR Miss Cont Butler Cnty 87; Usherette Grad 87; IUP; Nrsng.

PECK, ANGELA; Mechanicsburg HS; Shiremanstown, PA; (3); Rep Church Yth Grp; Teachers Aide; JV L Bsktbl; Bus Admin.

PECK, DONNA; Juniata HS; Mifflintown, PA; (4); Chorus; Flag Corp; Mrchg Band; School Musical; School Play; Yrbk Stf; High Hon Roll; Hon Roll; NHS; Prfct Atten Awd; PA ST U; Hmn Dvlpmnt.

PECK, KRISTAL M; Northern SR HS; Lewisberry, PA; (4); 70/200; VP DECA; Pep Clb; Chorus; Nwsp Stf; Yrbk Stf; Cheerleading; Pom Pon; Powder Puff Ftbl; Score Keeper; Hon Roll; Camp Hill PA; Comp Oper.

PECK, MICHAEL; Juniata HS; Mifflintown, PA; (3); Drama Clb; Chorus; Concert Band; Jazz Band; Mrchg Band; School Play; Variety Show; Yrbk Stf; High Hon Roll; NHS; PA ST U.

PECK, MICHAEL; Susquenita HS; Duncannon, PA; (3); Spanish Clb; Hon Roll.

PECK, MICHELE; Ambridge Area HS; Freedom, PA; (2); Church Yth Grp; JA; Pep Clb; Spanish Clb; Drill Tm; Mrchg Band; School Musical; School Play; Yrbk Stf; Soph Cls; Rgnl Chmpn, Natl Chmpn, Wrld Fnlst Dance Compttn 86; Slippery Rck; Nrsng.

PECKYNO, ROBERT; Monessen HS; Monessen, PA; (4); 3/93; Boy Scts; French Clb; JA; Nwsp Stf; Yrbk Stf; Tennis; Cit Awd; High Hon Roll; Amer Lgn; Hugh O Brian; Hnr Scty; Monessh JR Tamburitzans; Duquesne U; Pharm.

PECORARO, TERRI; Burrell HS; Lower Burrell, PA; (4); JA; Library Aide; Radio Clb; Spanish Clb; Chorus; Co-Capt Color Guard; Nwsp Rptr; Nwsp Stf; Lit Mag; Gym; WV U; Jrnlsm.

PECUCH, NICOLE; Old Forge HS; Old Forge, PA; (3); JA; Ski Clb; JV Bsktbl; Var Sftbl; Hon Roll; Jr NHS; NHS; La Salle; Sci.

PEDANO, MONICA A; Merion Mercy Acad; Merion, PA; (4); 36/75; French Clb; Pres GAA; Chorus; Var Capt Fld Hcky; Im Var Mgr(s); Var Capt Sftbl; Im Capt Tennis; Im Var Vllybl; Hon Roll; Stu Athltc Of Yr 86-87; Svc Awd 86-87; Rugers Coll; Bus Admin.

PEDATELLA, LORI; Valley HS; New Kensington, PA; (2); Art Clb; Church Yth Grp; FBLA; Hosp Aide; Key Clb; Band; Color Guard; Concert Band; Mrchg Band; JV Mgr(s); Bus.

PEDERSEN, JENNIFER; Pocono Mountain HS; Tannersville, PA; (3); Trs Church Yth Grp; Pep Clb; SADD; Cheerleading; Sftbl; Hon Roll; NHS; Teaching.

PEDLEY, DAWN; Hempfield SR HS; Manor, PA; (3); FBLA; IN U Of PA; CPA.

PEDMO, HOLLY; Moshannon Valley HS; Houtzdale, PA; (3); Bus Adm.

PEDONE, BETH; Meadville Area SR HS; Meadville, PA; (3); 48/363; Church Yth Grp; French Clb; Letterman Clb; Stage Crew; Stu Cncl; Score Keeper; Var L Socr; Var L Swmmng; Var Trk; Hon Roll.

PEDRAZZOLI, JOSEPH; Greater Latrobe HS; Greensburg, PA; (4); 7/407; Boy Scts; Pres German Clb; Letterman Clb; Pres Jr Cls; Rep Stu Cncl; L Bsbl; JV Bsktbl; Var Score Keeper; DAR Awd; Pres NHS; Engrng.

PEDUZZI, TRINA; Quaker Valley HS; Sewickley, PA; (1); Church Yth Grp; Latin Clb; Service Clb; Band; Concert Band; Symp Band; Rptr Nwsp Rptr; Var Trk; High Hon Roll; Amrcn Rd Crss Cmmnty Svc Awd, Pres Acdmc Ftns Awd, Mid East Band Fstvl 86-87.

PEEL, DIANE; Purchase Line HS; Cherry Tree, PA; (3); Sec FBLA; Color Guard; Mrchg Band; Stage Crew; Yrbk Stf; Hon Roll; Otstndng Bus Stu 86; Scrtrl.

PEET, DEBBIE; The Baptist HS; Nicholson, PA; (4); VP Church Yth Grp; Yrbk Stf; Bsktbl; Hon Roll; Schrlshp 1st Pl Talents Christ Piano Comptn 87; Grad Hon 87; Hghst Avg Bus Comm Animal Sci 87; Baptist Bible C; Physcl Ed Tchr.

PEETERS, SHELLEY; Bermudian Springs HS; York Spgs, PA; (3); 31/110; Church Yth Grp; FNA; SADD; JV Fld Hcky; Psychlgy.

PEFFER, BONNIE; Mt Pleasant Area HS; Norvelt, PA; (4); French Clb; GAA; Math Clb; Red Cross Aide; Ski Clb; Band; Concert Band; Mrchg Band; Nwsp Bus Mgr; Nwsp Rptr; Slippery Rock U; Spec Ed.

PEFFLEY, AMMON; Mechanicsburg Area HS; Mechanicsburg, PA; (3); 16/311; Bsbl; Bsktbl; Socr; High Hon Roll; NHS; Pres Schlr; Altruism Awd 87; USA Rsrv Ntl Schlr/Ath Awd 87; PA ST U; Engrng.

PEFFLEY, ANDREA; Governor Mifflin SR HS; Shillington, PA; (3); 16/350; Band; Chorus; Concert Band; Drm Mjr(t); Mrchg Band; Hon Roll; Govnr Mifflin Hnr Soc 87; The Arts.

PEFFLEY, MIKE; Lebanon HS; Lebanon, PA; (4); 8/279; Key Clb; German Clb; Ski Clb; Sec Varsity Clb; Ed Yrbk Ed-Chief; Rep Sr Cls; Capt Bsktbl; Tennis; Hon Roll; Kiwanis Awd; Laudermilch Trust Fund Schlrshp 87; Army Schlr Athlete Awd 87; Coaches Awd In Bsktbll; Rensselaer Polytech Inst-Biol.

PEGLOW, KIM; West Allegheny HS; Coraopolis, PA; (3); 18/199; German Clb; VP JA; Bsktbl; Powder Puff Ftbl; Score Keeper; Sftbl; High Hon Roll; Hon Roll; Chem Olympcs 86; Hgh Achvt Grm Awds 85-87; Physcs.

PEGNETTER, JOE; Dubois Area HS; Reynoldsville, PA; (3); 41/320; Church Yth Grp; Varsity Clb; JV Ftbl; Var Trk; Vllybl; Wt Lftg; Hon Roll.

PEGULA, CHRISTOPHER; Bishop Ohara HS; Olyphant, PA; (2); 11/127; 4-H; French Clb; Latin Clb; Ski Clb; Chorus; School Musical; School Play; High Hon Roll; VP Soph Cls; Rep Stu Cncl; Art Awd 85-86; Vet Med.

PEICH, BRENT; Henderson HS; West Chester, PA; (3); 9/369; Debate Tm; JCL; Political Wkr; Science Clb; Chorus; Orch; School Musical; Hon Roll; Voice Dem Awd; Pres Clssrm 87; Pltcl Sci.

PEIFER, JEN; Lancaster Mennonite HS; Manheim, PA; (3); 19/155; Rep Church Yth Grp; Cmnty Wkr; Trs Exploring; VP JA; Acpl Chr; Chorus; Yrbk Ed-Chief; Hon Roll; NHS; Med.

PEIFER, LAUREL; Milton Area SR HS; Milton, PA; (2); Sec Church Yth Grp; Spanish Clb; Band; Chorus; Concert Band; Mrchg Band; Prfct Atten Awd; Susquehanna Vly Band 87.

PEIFFER, ANISSA; Cedar Crest HS; Lebanon, PA; (3); German Clb; Pep Clb; Hon Roll; Prfct Atten Awd; Acad Merit Awd 86-87; Clarion U; Psych.

PEIFFER, CHARLENE; Northern Lebanon JR SR HS; Annville, PA; (3); 11/200; French Clb; German Clb; Model UN; School Play; Tennis; Hon Roll.

PEIFFER, JODIE; Cedar Crest HS; Lebanon, PA; (3); 97/342; French Clb; FTA; Pep Clb; SADD; Teachers Aide; Color Guard; Mrchg Band; Yrbk Stf; Lit Mag; Hon Roll; Elem Educ.

PEIFFER, MARGIE; Towanda Area HS; Wysox, PA; (4); 4/136; VP Church Yth Grp; Drama Clb; FTA; Model UN; SADD; Band; Mrchg Band; Yrbk Stf; Stat Bsktbl; Ntl Merit Ltr; Eng.

PEIRCE, FRANCIS R; Bishop Egan HS; Philadelphia, PA; (3); French Clb; Office Aide; Variety Show; Bsktbl; Hon Roll; Math Achvt Awd; Lawyer.

PEIRILLO, KATHLEEN; Jeannette SR HS; Jeannette, PA; (3); Art Clb; Drama Clb; Office Aide; Ski Clb; Spanish Clb; Stu Cncl; Hon Roll; JC Awd; U Of Pittsburgh.

PEIRITSCH, MELANIE; Nazareth Acad; Philadelphia, PA; (3); Math Clb; Stage Crew; Yrbk Stf; Bowling; Hnr Cert Of Attendance 85-86; Bus.

PEIRSON, EDWARD; South Western HS; Hanover, PA; (3); Church Yth Grp; Key Clb; School Play; Rep Jr Cls; JV L Bsktbl; Hon Roll; Penn ST; Fghtr Pilot.

PEKALA, BARBARA M; Windber Area HS; Windber, PA; (3); Cmnty Wkr; FTA; Hosp Aide; Math Clb; Red Cross Aide; Spanish Clb; Var Capt Bsktbl; High Hon Roll; Hon Roll; Jr NHS; Stu Mth 85-87; Presdntl Phy Ftns Awd 84-87; U Of Pittsburgh; Bio.

PEKAREK, DONNA M; Donegal HS; Mt Joy, PA; (4); 37/160; Church Yth Grp; Hon Roll; Millersville U; Acctng.

PEKARSKI, JO RENEE; Coudersport JR/Srt HS; Coudersport, PA; (4); 26/88; Church Yth Grp; FTA; Teachers Aide; Varsity Clb; Band; Chorus; Stu Cncl; Vllybl; Hon Roll; NHS; Lock Haven U; Elem Ed.

PEKICH, CHRISTINA; East Allegheny HS; Wilmerding, PA; (2); Boy Scts; French Clb; Ski Clb; Concert Band; Mrchg Band; Orch; School Musical; Yrbk Stf; High Hon Roll; NHS; Phrmcst.

PEKOVSKY, JASON; Northeast HS; Philadelphia, PA; (4); 32/690; Aud/Vis; Drama Clb; Ski Clb; Chorus; School Play; Stage Crew; Yrbk Stf; UC Irvine.

PEKURNY, CHRIS; Lehighton Area HS; Lehighton, PA; (4); Yrbk Stf; Var Bsbl; JV Golf; Var Wrstlng; MVP Bsbl 87; Mansfield U; Rsprtry Thrpy.

PELISSERO, BRANDON; Ringgold HS; Eighty-Four, PA; (3); JA; Library Aide; Ski Clb; Stu Cncl; Im Bsktbl; Im Vllybl; High Hon Roll; Hon Roll; Part In JR Hgh Amer Lgn Essay 84-85; Bus Adv.

PELKOFER III, FRANK; Moniteau JR SR HS; Karns City, PA; (1); Dance Clb; Exploring; Spanish Clb; Band; Concert Band; Mrchg Band; Swing Chorus; Trk; High Hon Roll; Jr NHS; Air Frc Acad; Miltry Nvgtr.

PELL, MARY ANNE; Archbishop Carroll HS; Norristown, PA; (3); 174/376; Ski Clb; SADD; Lit Mag; Var Gym; NHS; Saint Josephs U; Intl Rltns.

PELLE, MICHELLE; Beaver Area HS; Beaver, PA; (2); Church Yth Grp; French Clb; Letterman Clb; Library Aide; Ski Clb; JV Var Cheerleading; Var L Trk; High Hon Roll; Prsdntl Acdmc Ftnss Awd 86-87.

PELLEGRINO, BRIAN; Butler SR HS; Butler, PA; (3); Spanish Clb; Var L Socr; Hon Roll; Sprts Med.

PELLEGRINO, DANIELLE; Pocono Mountain HS; Tannersville, PA; (2); Pep Clb; Chorus; JV Cheerleading; Hon Roll.

PELLEGRINO, PATRICK; Archbishop Wood HS; Holland, PA; (2); 33/257; JV Ftbl; Var Swmmng; Bus Mgmt.

PELLEGRINO, RUSSELL; Shenandoah Valley JR SR HS; Shenandoah, PA; (3); 3/79; Library Aide; L JV Bsktbl; Im Crs Cntry; Score Keeper; Var JV Trk; High Hon Roll; NHS; Acdmc All Amer 85-87; Hstry.

PELLEGRINO, VALERIE A; Exeter Twp SR HS; Birdsboro, PA; (4); 4/214; Drama Clb; Chorus; Jazz Band; School Musical; School Play; High Hon Roll; Jr NHS; NHS; Pres Schlr; Hosp Aide; PA All ST Chorus 87; Cnty, Dist, Regnl Chorus 84-87; American U; Pre-Law.

PELLOT, EDWIN; Roman Catholic HS; Philadelphia, PA; (3); 26/117; Rep Jr Cls; Rep Stu Cncl; Var Capt Bsbl; Var Capt Ftbl; Hon Roll; Hnrs Physcl Sci, Wrld Cltrs, 84-85; 2nd Hnrs 1st Sem 84-85; Cert Athltc Accmplshmnt Mrn Crps Lg 86-87; Brdcst Tech.

PELOTTE, MICHAEL; Downingtown SR HS; Chester Springs, PA; (3); Church Yth Grp; Ski Clb; Band; Mrchg Band; School Musical; Im Bowling; Im Vllybl; High Hon Roll; Hon Roll; Amer Music Abrd 87.

PELTON, MELANIE; West Branch HS; Lanse, PA; (2); Church Yth Grp; Spanish Clb; Church Choir; Flag Corp; Rep Stu Cncl; Hon Roll; NHS.

PELTON, MICHELE; Northeast Bradford JR SR HS; Rome, PA; (3); Camera Clb; Dance Clb; Drama Clb; Band; Sec Stu Cncl; Mgr Sftbl; FHA; Hon Roll; Prfct Atten Awd; Mst Likely Sccd Culinary Wrld 85-86; Mst Outstndng Stu 86-87; Trsm.

PELTON, TRACY; Northeast Bradford HS; Ulster, PA; (1); Art Clb; Camera Clb; Dance Clb; Exploring; FFA; DECA; Concert Band; Nwsp Stf; Im Vllybl; Prfct Atten Awd; Penn ST; Art.

PELUZZO, CHRISTINA; St Basil Acad; Philadelphia, PA; (4); 33/97; Spanish Clb; SADD; School Play; Yrbk Stf; Lit Mag; Im Bsktbl; Drexel U; Engrng.

PENA, ERNEST; Cedar Cliff HS; Mechanicsburg, PA; (2); 11/286; Computer Clb; Debate Tm; JCL; VP Latin Clb; Math Tm; Quiz Bowl; Im Vllybl; Wrstlng; High Hon Roll; Prfct Atten Awd; Magna Cum Laude Natl Latin Exm 85-87; 2nd Pl Debte Tm Dist VII Trnmt 87; Cert Achvt Cvcs Geom & Chem; MIT; Aerospc Engrng.

PENA, JANET; Ohney HS; Philadelphia, PA; (2); Penn ST; Med.

PENATZER, JOHN; Lancaster Cath3lic HS; Strasburg, PA; (3); 31/194; Boy Scts; Pep Clb; Varsity Clb; School Musical; Stage Crew; Rep Jr Cls; Var Capt Cheerleading; Hon Roll; Med.

PENCE, ANDY; Calvary Baptist Christian Acad; Altoona, PA; (4); Church Yth Grp; Drama Clb; Bsbl; Var Bsktbl; Score Keeper; Var Socr; Var Trk; High Hon Roll; NHS.

PENCEK, MARK; Abington Heights HS; Clarks Summit, PA; (3); 110/292; Church Yth Grp; L Capt Bsbl; Var L Bsktbl; Hghst Battng Avg-Bsbl 86; Crmnl Jstc.

PENCEK, MATTHEW; Tunkhannock HS; Tunkhannock, PA; (4); 30/320; Church Yth Grp; Drama Clb; School Musical; School Play; Nwsp Sprt Ed; JV Bsktbl; Var Golf; Var Tennis; Hon Roll; NHS; Pres Acdmc Ftnss Awd 87; Penn ST U; Comms.

PENDERGRASS, WENDY; Meadville Area SR HS; Meadville, PA; (3); GAA; Key Clb; Ski Clb; Spanish Clb; Im Coach Actv; L Var Socr; UMA; Archeolgy.

PENECALE, GINA; Upper Moreland HS; Hatboro, PA; (4); 85/254; Key Clb; Pres SADD; Color Guard; VP Mrchg Band; Var Cheerleading; Var Trk; Cit Awd; Kiwanis Awd; Chorus; Lit Mag; Stu Of Mon 87; White Rlty & Wllm Gbsn Mem Schlrshp 87; Manor JC; Lgl Secr.

PENKO, JANICE; Ridley HS; Woodlyn, PA; (3); 10/423; Girl Scts; Ski Clb; Spanish Clb; Band; Chorus; Church Choir; Concert Band; Mrchg Band; JV Lcrss; JV Swmmng; Brown Book Awd Brown U 87; Scott Paper Co Cert Scotts Hi-Q Tm 87-88; Psych.

PENKROT, AMY; Lake-Lehman HS; Shavertown, PA; (4); 13/161; French Clb; Key Clb; Ski Clb; Yrbk Stf; Capt Cheerleading; Hon Roll; Villinova U; Accntng.

PENLAND, MICHELE; Archbishop Carroll HS; Wayne, PA; (3); 96/376; Math Tm; Cheerleading; Mgr(s); Score Keeper; Timer; Engl Awd Rcgntn For Achvmnt.

PENN, MICHAEL C; West Perry SR HS; Loysville, PA; (3); 1/236; Yrbk Ed-Chief; Yrbk Phtg; Yrbk Rptr; Yrbk Stf; Stu Cncl; High Hon Roll; Hon Roll; VP NHS; Rotary Awd; French Clb; Rtry Intl Ldrshp Cnfrnc 87; Sphmr & JR Hnr Stu Awds 86 & 87; Pre Med.

PENNELLA, BETHANN; Susquehannock HS; Shrewsbury, PA; (2); 31/243; AFS; Church Yth Grp; SADD; Chorus; Church Choir; Rep Soph Cls; Var Mgr(s); JV Vllybl; Hon Roll.

PENNELLA, JAMES; Old Forge HS; Scranton, PA; (3); #4 In Class; L Var Bsbl; High Hon Roll; VP NHS; Spnsh Awd 86-87; Engrng.

PENNEY, LAUREL; Hampton HS; Allison Park, PA; (3); Co-Capt Church Yth Grp; Girl Scts; Church Choir; Co-Capt Color Guard; Mrchg Band; School Musical; Symp Band; High Hon Roll; NHS; Tri-M Music Hnr Scty; Elem Educ.

PENNI, LEWIS; Saltsburg JR SR HS; Saltsburg, PA; (2); 1/93; Varsity Clb; Stage Crew; Pres Frsh Cls; JV Bsktbl; JV Ftbl; High Hon Roll; Pres Schlr.

PENNICK, KELLY; Penn Center Acad; Philadelphia, PA; (3); Library Aide; Teachers Aide; School Play; Stage Crew; Yrbk Stf; Pres Frsh Cls; Pres Off Stu Cncl; High Hon Roll; Prfct Atten Awd; Jr Cls; Ellis Grant 85-88; Courtesy Queen 84-85; Stu Mnth 86-87; Libry Asst; Tchrs Aide; Perfect Attndng Awd; Bus Admin.

PENNINGTON, BARBARA; John Bartram HS; Philadelphia, PA; (4); 4/650; JA; Office Aide; Yrbk Stf; Rep Soph Cls; Rep Jr Cls; Off Stu Cncl; Stfbl; High Hon Roll; JC Awd; NHS; Acad All Star 86-87; All Star 85-87.

PENNYPACKER, JENNIFER; St Pius X HS; Graterford, PA; (1); 9/146; Rep Frsh Cls; JV Bsktbl; Hon Roll; Prfct Atten Awd; Cert Of Hnrb Mntn Natl Latin Exam 87.

PENNYPACKER, LISA; Emmaus HS; Macungie, PA; (4); Art Clb; Teachers Aide; Chorus; School Musical; Yrbk Stf; JV Bsktbl; Var Cheerleading; L Fld Hcky; Var Trk; High Hon Roll; Kutztown U; Fine Arts.

PENROD, CORY; North Star HS; Boswell, PA; (3); Pres Church Yth Grp; FCA; Chorus; Church Choir; Mrchg Band; Yrbk Sprt Ed; Yrbk Stf; Stu Cncl; Hon Roll.

PENROD, LISA; Warwick HS; Lititz, PA; (3); 118/300; FBLA; Spanish Clb; Band; Mrchg Band; Im Badmtn; Im Bsktbl; Im Bowling; JV Sftbl; Im Vllybl; Im Wt Lftg; SOCIALOLGY.

PENROSE, ROBERT; United JR SR HS; New Florence, PA; (4); 39/153; Church Yth Grp; Chorus; Church Choir; Concert Band; Lit Mag; L Capt Ftbl; L Trk; Hon Roll; NHS; Ntl Merit Ltr; IN Of Of PA; Pre-Med.

PENSIS, BOBBI; Charleroi Area JR SR HS; Charleroi, PA; (4); 14/169; French Clb; Office Aide; Ski Clb; SADD; School Musical; Nwsp Rptr; Yrbk Stf; Stu Cncl; Powder Puff Ftbl; NHS; WVU; Intl Econ.

PENTECOST, JENNIFER; Bensalem HS; Bensalem, PA; (2); Computer Clb; GAA; Girl Scts; Office Aide; Teachers Aide; Varsity Clb; Yrbk Stf; Rep Frsh Cls; JV Bsktbl; JV Fld Hcky; Sftbl Awd-Determntn, Dedicatn 87; Penn ST; Phy Ed.

PENTZ, MONICA; York Co Voc- Tech; Dover, PA; (4); VICA; Rep Sr Cls; Var Bsktbl; CC Awd; Cit Awd; DAR Awd; Hon Roll; NHS; York Mfg Assoc Gold Watch 87; Drafting.

PEOPLES, BRENDA; Perkiomen Valley SR HS; Harleysville, PA; (4); 9/170; VP Science Clb; Spanish Clb; Trs Varsity Clb; JV Fld Hcky; JV Lcrss; Var Swmmng; Hon Roll; Lion Awd; NHS; Opt Clb Awd; Margaret B Bunn Schlrshp Hartwick Coll, Outstndng SR Awd, Natl Army Rsrv Athl/Schlr Awd 87; Hartwick Coll; Nrsng.

PEOPLES, DIONNE; Milton HS; Milton, PA; (3); Band; Color Guard; Drm & Bgl; School Play; Nwsp Stf; Hon Roll; Library Aide; Spanish Clb; Chorus; Church Choir; West Chester U; Scl Wrk.

PEORIA, MATTHEW; Hempfield SR HS; Youngwood, PA; (4); 195/697; AFS; CAP; Yrbk Stf; Var Swmmng; Im Wt Lftg; Hon Roll; Penn ST; Engrng.

PEPE, DAVID; Wyoming Area SR HS; West Pittston, PA; (4); 9/250; Church Yth Grp; Computer Clb; Math Clb; Math Tm; Science Clb; Spanish Clb; Var Bsbl; High Hon Roll; NHS; West Pittston Lions Club Schlrshp 87; Rotry Intl Ldrshp Camp 85; Schls Sci & Math Teams 87; Lehigh U; Engrng.

PEPE, JOSEPH C; State College Area HS; Boalsburg, PA; (4); 163/541; Art Clb; Cmnty Wkr; Spanish Clb; Nwsp Stf; Yrbk Phtg; Yrbk Stf; Lit Mag; Tennis; Gov Hon Prg Awd; Hon Roll; Pratt Inst Natl Talnt Srch 3rd Pl Wnnr 86-87; Schlstc Art Awds 1 Gold Key 2 Blue Rbns 87; Pratt Inst; Indstrl Dsgn.

PEPER, SARAH; Downingtown SR HS; Dowingtown, PA; (3); 1/648; Church Yth Grp; GAA; Teachers Aide; Chorus; Church Choir; Orch; Rep Stu Cncl; Var L Trk; NHS; Spanish Clb; Natl Merit High Scorer 87.

PEPERAK, CYNTHIA D; Connellsville Area SR HS; Connellsville, PA; (4); 7/500; Pres GAA; Library Aide; Stu Cncl; Capt L Bsktbl; L Var Sftbl; L Var Vllybl; French Hon Soc; High Hon Roll; Trs NHS.

PEPIN, SUSAN; Seneca Valley HS; Mars, PA; (4); Office Aide; OEA; Chorus; High Hon Roll; Hon Roll; Bradford; Acctng.

PEPKE, ALEXANDER; Ringgold HS; Elrama, PA; (3); Math Clb; Office Aide; Science Clb; Hon Roll; Prfct Atten Awd; Duquesne U; Priest.

PEPPER, SARAH; Downington HS; Downingtown, PA; (3); 1/648; Church Yth Grp; Sec Spanish Clb; Chorus; Church Choir; Orch; Rep Stu Cncl; Trk; High Hon Roll; NHS; NEDT Awd 85-86; Allied Hlth.

PEPPETTI, JON; Bishop Carroll HS; Cresson, PA; (3); 14/128; Ski Clb; Stage Crew; Var Capt Golf; Var Trk; Hon Roll; Bus.

PEPSIN, PAUL; Old Forge HS; Old Forge, PA; (3); Hon Roll; U Scranton; Bus Admin.

PEQUIGNOT, KELLY; Liberty JR/Sr HS; Liberty, PA; (2); L Exploring; FHA; German Clb; Rep Stu Cncl; JV Var Bsktbl; Sec Score Keeper; JV Trk; JV Capt Vllybl; Hon Roll; JV Bsktbll MVP 85-86; Physcl Ed.

PERANICH, MELISSA; West Scranton HS; Scranton, PA; (3); Hosp Aide; Spanish Clb; Thesps; Yrbk Stf; Stu Cncl; Pom Pon; Cltrl Arts Cont-Lit Div-1st Pl Dist Awd, 1st Pl Rgnl Awd 86, 87; Nrsng.

PERCHERKE, JAMES; North Star HS; Boswell, PA; (4); 1/129; Mu Alpha Theta; Quiz Bowl; Ski Clb; Varsity Clb; VP Stu Cncl; Ftbl; Golf; Hon Roll; NHS; Val; Yth Exchng Clb Stu Of Mnth 86; Mu Alpha Theta Pres 86-87; Sci Merit Awd 86-87; MD U; Chem Engr.

PERCHINSKY, MARGARET; Monongahela Valley Catholic HS; Bentleyville, PA; (2); 4-H; Science Clb; Ski Clb; Band; Concert Band; Mrchg Band; St Schlr; Mstr Lmb Shwmn WA Cnty Fair 83; Lmb Fttr WA Cnty Fair 82; Phys Thrpy.

PERCOSKY, KATHY; Forest Hills SR HS; Windber, PA; (4); 4/158; FBLA; Y-Teens; Chorus; Nwsp Rptr; Var JV Bsktbl; Jr NHS; NHS; Pres Schlr; Rotary Awd; VP Spanish NHS; Schlrs & Socl Stds Awds 87; U Of Pittss-Johnstown; Bio.

PERCOSKY, RENEE; West Hazleton HS; W Hazleton, PA; (4); 60/224; Church Yth Grp; Pep Clb; Spanish Clb; Nwsp Rptr; Yrbk Bus Mgr; Yrbk Phtg; Yrbk Rptr; Yrbk Stf; Gym; Mat Maids; Philadelphia Coll Pharm & Sci.

PERCY, ELAINE M; Grove City SR HS; Volant, PA; (4); 7/175; FBLA; Key Clb; Concert Band; Mrchg Band; Pep Band; School Musical; High Hon Roll; NHS; Pres Schlr; Coll Club Of Sharon English Awd 87.

PEREIRA, LEONARDO; Lower Merion HS; Merion, PA; (4); 16/360; Boy Scts; Civic Clb; Exploring; 4-H; Trs French Clb; Sr Cls; JV Ftbl; Trs French Hon Soc; Hon Roll; School Play; Rwng Team Vrsty Lttrs 85-86; Mid Yr Grad 87; Rwng Cty, Rgnl, Natl Champ 86; Columbia U; Peace Corps.

PERETIN, JEFFREY; Baldwin HS; Pittsburgh, PA; (3); Church Yth Grp; Rep Frsh Cls; Rep Soph Cls; Rep Jr Cls; Im JV Bsktbl; Mgr(s); Im Wt Lftg; High Hon Roll; Hon Roll; Engr.

PERETIN, JOE; Baldwin HS; Pittsburgh, PA; (4); 134/535; Church Yth Grp; Var L Bsktbl; Mgr(s); Score Keeper; High Hon Roll; Hon Roll; Grad With Hnrs 87; Clarion U; Bus.

PEREZ, DEBBIE; Little Flower Catholic HS; Philadelphia, PA; (3); 98/322; Hon Roll; Prfct Atten Awd; Boyd Airline/Trvl Schl; Agnt.

PEREZ, GEMMA; Geibel HS; Connellsville, PA; (4); Drama Clb; Hosp Aide; Pep Clb; Ski Clb; SADD; School Musical; Lit Mag; Rep Soph Cls; Sec Jr Cls; VP Sr Cls; Svc Awd 87; Duquesne U.

PEREZ, MARIA ANGELICA D; Pius X HS; Bangor, PA; (4); Art Clb; Trs Church Yth Grp; Drama Clb; Acpl Chr; Chorus; Church Choir; School Musical; School Play; Nwsp Ed-Chief; Nwsp Rptr; Kevin Colahan Mem Awd 87; Gerry Roxas Awd Outstndng Ldrshp 84; Dclmtn & Ortrcl Cntst Wnnr 81 & 83; Poli Sci.

PERFETTI, MIKE; East Stroudsburg HS; E Stroudsburg, PA; (3); 61/302; Church Yth Grp; Var JV Golf; Var Wrstlng; Hon Roll; 1st Pl 132 Lbs Cntnnl Wrstlng 87; Outstndng Grphc & Ind Arts 87; Art.

PERHACH JR, ANDREW J; Schenley HS; Pittsburgh, PA; (3); Computer Clb; Schlrshp Pin 85; Schlrshp Grd Pin 86; U S Navy.

PERHALLA, JANICE; Pittston Area SR HS; Duryea, PA; (2); Drill Tm; High Hon Roll.

PERILLI, JOSEPH; Panther Valley HS; Summit Hill, PA; (1); Church Yth Grp; Pres Frsh Cls; Rep Stu Cncl; Bsbl; JV Bsktbl; Capt Ftbl; Var Trk; Var Wt Lftg; Hon Roll; Pres Schlr; Amer Legn Awd Wnnr 86; John Hopkins Tlnt Srch 85.

PERINI, KENDRA SUE; Lebanon Catholic HS; Lebanon, PA; (4); 20/74; Civic Clb; Service Clb; Spanish Clb; Yrbk Ed-Chief; Trs Stu Cncl; L Bowling; Cheerleading; Hon Roll; Stdnt Mnth Rotry; Grl Mnth JR Womns Clb Lebanon.

PERISH, SHARON; Pennsbury HS; Yardley, PA; (2); Chorus; Church Choir; Drill Tm; Fld Hcky; Hon Roll; PA ST U; Psychtrst.

PERKINS, BONNIE; Nazareth Acad; Philadelphia, PA; (4); 27/117; Church Yth Grp; Pres Latin Clb; Lit Mag; Rep Soph Cls; High Hon Roll; E Stroudsburg U; Nrsg.

PERKINS, DEBRA; Saint Hubert HS; Philadelphia, PA; (3); 67/421; Church Yth Grp; Cmnty Wkr; Science Clb; Service Clb; Spanish Clb; High Hon Roll; Prfct Atten Awd; Gwynedd-Mercy Coll; Nrsng.

PERKINS, MELISSA; Hempfield Area HS; Greensburg, PA; (4); Capt Color Guard; Nwsp Rptr; Var L Swmmng; Prfct Atten Awd; Edinboro U; Psychlgy.

PERKINS, PAMELA M; Bishop Hoban HS; Mountaintop, PA; (3); 13/194; Mu Alpha Theta; Ski Clb; Spanish Clb; SADD; Color Guard; Yrbk Stf; High Hon Roll; NHS; Annl Math Awd Hghst Avg 85-86; Mu Alph Theta Math Rsrch Awd 87; Philadelphia Schl Pharm; Pharm.

PERKINS, RICHARD; Shady Side Acad; Oakmont, PA; (3); Ski Clb; Nwsp Stf; Capt Var Bsbl; JV Bsktbl; Im Vllybl; High Hon Roll; Hon Roll.

PERKINS, TIMOTHY; Archbishop Ryan HS For Boys; Philadelphia, PA; (2); 73/349; Var JV Ftbl; Hon Roll; Prfct Atten Awd.

PERKINSON, JACOB; Central HS; Philadelphia, PA; (3); 200/564; Teachers Aide; Varsity Clb; Band; Jazz Band; Mrchg Band; Orch; Rep Frsh Cls; Rep Soph Cls; Rep Jr Cls; Socr; JV Soccr Ltr 84; Var Soccr Ltr 85 & 86; Philosphy.

PERKOSKY, JOHN; Shaler Area HS; Pittsburgh, PA; (4); 33/509; SADD; Stage Crew; Nwsp Stf; Rep Jr Cls; Rep Sr Cls; Rep Stu Cncl; Var Capt Wrstlng; Hon Roll; Bucknell U.

PERLA, ANTHONY; Central Catholic HS; Pittsburgh, PA; (3); Ski Clb; Im Bsktbl; Im Crs Cntry; Im Ftbl; Hon Roll; Intl Bus.

PERLMAN, ADAM; Bensalem HS; Bensalem, PA; (2); Model UN; JV L Trk; Hon Roll; Archtctr.

PERLMUTTER, DAVID; Lower Merion HS; Ardmore, PA; (4); 55/377; Computer Clb; Drama Clb; SADD; Off Stu Cncl; Golf; Tennis; High Hon Roll; Jr NHS; NHS; Ntl Merit Ltr; Sci Dept Hnrs 87; Muhlenberg; Pre Med.

PERLOFF, ILYSE; Neshaminy HS; Langhorne, PA; (3); 7/799; Church Yth Grp; VP Service Clb; Chorus; Jazz Band; Im Lcrss; Var Mgr(s); Stat Trk; High Hon Roll; NHS; Freedom Fndtn Ldrshp Conf, & PA Free Enterprise Wk 87.

PERMAN, RACHELLE; Hickory HS; Sharpsville, PA; (4); 2/175; Chorus; Concert Band; Drm Mjr(t); Orch; School Musical; Var L Bsktbl; Var L Trk; Bausch & Lomb Sci Awd; DAR Awd; Trs NHS; Outstndndg Achvt Sci 86; Chem Engr.

PERNA, TRISH; Bishop Kenrick HS; Norristown, PA; (3); 2nd Hnrs 87.

PERO, KELLY; Meadville SR HS; Meadville, PA; (3); 48/361; Aud/Vis; Church Yth Grp; Dance Clb; Sec Frsh Cls; Stu Cncl; Sftbl; Trk; Elks Awd; Hon Roll; Gov-Sec 84-85; Sftbl 84-86; Chrch Yth Grp 84-88; Med.

PERON, KYLE; Council Rock HS; Chuchville, PA; (3); Art Clb; Church Yth Grp; Band; Concert Band; High Hon Roll; Hon Roll; Prfct Atten Awd; Grphc Dsgn.

PEROSE, ROBERT; William Allen HS; Allentown, PA; (3); 145/659; Ski Clb; Var L Golf; Hon Roll; Jr NHS; Jerome Schneider Golf Awd 86; Accntng.

PERRI, ROSEMARY; St Basil Acad; Rockledge, PA; (3); 23/88; Church Yth Grp; Dance Clb; Drama Clb; Hosp Aide; Spanish Clb; SADD; Stage Crew; Var Capt Cheerleading; Socr; Nursing.

PERRICONE, CARRIE; Brandywine Heights Area HS; Alburtis, PA; (3); Church Yth Grp; Stat Bsktbl; Mgr(s); Mgr Trk; Capt Twrlr; Var Vllybl; Hon Roll; NHS; Pblc Rltns.

PERRIER, GARY; Central York SR HS; York, PA; (3); High Hon Roll; Hon Roll; IN U Of PA; Comp Engrng.

PERRIN, JIM; Lincoln High 081987 HS; Ellwood City, PA; (3); French Clb; JV Bsktbl; Im JV Ftbl; Sprts Mgr.

PERRINE, BRADLEY; Conneaut Lake Area HS; Conneaut Lk, PA; (3); Spanish Clb; SADD; L Crs Cntry; Wt Lftg; High Hon Roll; Hon Roll.

PERRINE, JENNIFER; Moon SR HS; Coraopolis, PA; (2); Church Yth Grp; Band; Concert Band; Mrchg Band; Pep Band; Symp Band; Hon Roll; Dir Smmr Fun Trk Meet 87; Photo.

PERRINS, GERALD; Pittston Area HS; Pittston, PA; (4); 21/348; Key Clb; SADD; Trs Frsh Cls; Off Soph Cls; VP Sr Cls; Ftbl; Trk; NHS; Rotary Awd; Stu Athl Yr Awd 87; Kings Coll; Bio.

PERRONE III, DOMINIC; Greensburg Central Catholic HS; Gbg, PA; (3); Letterman Clb; Ski Clb; Varsity Clb; Ice Hcky; IUP; Law.

PERROTTA, ROSANNE; New Castle HS; New Castle, PA; (3); Chorus; Trk; Bus.

PERROTTI, ANTHONY; Greenville HS; Greenville, PA; (4); 5/142; French Clb; Bsbl; JV Ftbl; NHS; Clarion U; Accntnt.

PERROTTI, MICHAEL; Warren Area HS; Warren, PA; (3); Church Yth Grp; Red Cross Aide; Ski Clb; Spanish Clb; Varsity Clb; School Play; JV Bsbl; Var L Golf; High Hon Roll; Hon Roll; ASSE 86; U CO; Med.

PERRY, ABBY; Freedom HS; Bethlehem, PA; (4); 135/446; Hon Roll; Artwrk Bethlehems Kemmerer Musuem 87; Tyler Schl Of Art; Comm Art.

PERRY, ADAM C; Stroudsburg HS; East Stroudsburg, PA; (3); #11 In Class; Nwsp Sprt Ed; Pres Frsh Cls; Pres Stu Cncl; Var Ftbl; Var Trk; High Hon Roll; NHS.

PERRY, ALYSON; Shady-Side Acad; Pittsburgh, PA; (3); French Clb; Girl Scts; Intnl Clb; Letterman Clb; Ski Clb; School Musical; Var Bsktbl; Var Cheerleading; JV Var Fld Hcky; Var Socr; Acdmc Schlrshp Shady Side Acad 87-88; Pre-Med.

PERRY, AMY; Everett Area HS; Everett, PA; (3); 4/133; Trs Drama Clb; Band; Concert Band; Jazz Band; Mrchg Band; Pep Band; School Play; Var L Tennis; French Hon Soc; Hon Roll; Bedford Cnty Band 87; Dist VI Band 87; IN U; Music.

PERRY, BETH; Chambersburg HS; Fayetteville, PA; (2); French Clb; Hosp Aide; French Hon Soc; Hon Roll; Fren Awd 86; Shippensburg U; Social Relation.

PERRY, CAROL; Big Spring HS; Newville, PA; (4); Pres 4-H; Teachers Aide; Nwsp Bus Mgr; Nwsp Rptr; Trs Sr Cls; Var L Crs Cntry; Mgr(s); Stat Trk; 4-H Awd; Hon Roll; Pres Phys Fit Awd 85-86; Newville Wmns Club Stu Mnth 86; Shippensburg U; Ed.

PERRY, CLARA; Sayre Area HS; Sayre, PA; (3); Spanish Clb; SADD; School Play; Yrbk Stf; VP Frsh Cls; Stu Cncl; JV Cheerleading; Var Sftbl; Var Vllybl; Hon Roll; Bus Admin.

PERRY, DEANNA; Riverside HS; Ellwood City, PA; (3); 6/169; Varsity Clb; Cheerleading; Hon Roll; NHS; Engrng.

PERRY, JAMES; Waynesboro Area SR HS; Waynesboro, PA; (3); 4/400; Chess Clb; JCL; Ski Clb; Band; Jazz Band; Rep Soph Cls; JV Trk; High Hon Roll; NHS; Presdntl Acadc Ftns Awd 85; Cnty Band 85-87; PA ST Prep Prog 87; PA ST U; Fin.

PERRY, JULIE; Coatesville Area SR HS; Coatesville, PA; (3); 71/530; Trs German Clb; JV Fld Hcky; Mgr(s); Var Trk; Hon Roll; Minority Advance Placement Prog 87; Usher Sr Cls Cmmncmnt 87; Temple; Phrmcy.

PERRY, KIMBERLY; Lakeland JR SR HS; Mayfield, PA; (3); 24/148; French Clb; FHA; Nwsp Stf; JV Var Cheerleading; Hon Roll; Pedtrcn.

PERRY, MARK; Montour HS; Pittsburgh, PA; (2); Church Yth Grp; Trk; High Hon Roll; Hon Roll; 2nd Degree Red Blt Karate 87; Penn ST U; Arch Engr.

PERRY, MICHAEL; Northampton Area SR HS; Walnutport, PA; (4); AFS; Boy Scts; Leo Clb; Capt L Crs Cntry; L Trk; High Hon Roll; VP NHS; Rotary Awd; Stu Of Month 86; PA ST U; Animal Sci.

PERRY, NICHOLAS; Lincoln HS; Ellwood City, PA; (3); 45/162; Spanish Clb; VP Stu Cncl; L Bsbl; L Ftbl; High Hon Roll; Hon Roll; Am Lgn Awd 83-84; Ftbl All Conf Dfnsv Back 86-87; Bsbl All Conf Ctchr 86-87; Law.

PERRY, ROBERT; Central Dauphin HS; Harrisburg, PA; (2); Bsktbl; Ftbl; Trk; Vllybl; Wt Lftg; Wake Forest; Law.

PERRY, SONYA RAINE; Coastesville Area SR HS; Coatesville, PA; (2); 33/439; Var Bsktbl; Coach Actv; Var Fld Hcky; Var Trk; High Hon Roll; 2nd Tm All Chestmont Fld Hcky 86-87; Pres Acad Ftns Awd 86-87; Temple U; Med.

PERRY, SUSAN; Seneca Valley SR HS; Harmony, PA; (3); Church Yth Grp; Ski Clb; Swmmng; Hm Ec.

PERRY, TIM; Moshannon Valley HS; Houtzdale, PA; (3); Varsity Clb; JV Var Bsktbl; Mgr(s); Im Vllybl.

PERSHING, JOHN; Northern Cambria HS; Barnesboro, PA; (3); 22/152; Spanish Clb; Var L Ftbl; Var L Trk; Wt Lftg; High Hon Roll; Penn ST; Comp Drftg.

PERSI, MICHAEL; Aliquippa HS; Aliquippa, PA; (3); 1/120; Trs Chess Clb; Church Yth Grp; Trs Exploring; Math Tm; Band; Concert Band; Mrchg Band; Pep Band; Off Jr Cls; High Hon Roll; Elec Engrng.

PERSI, NINA; Ambridge Area HS; Baden, PA; (3); Pep Clb; Spanish Clb; Band; Concert Band; Mrchg Band; Pep Band; Symp Band; Off Jr Cls; Stu Cncl; Hon Roll; Slippery Rock U.

PERSI, RENEE; Western Beaver HS; Industry, PA; (3); Yrbk Stf; Sec Soph Cls; Sec Jr Cls; Off Stu Cncl; Bowling; Co-Capt Var Cheerleading; Sftbl; Wt Lftg; High Hon Roll; NHS; Prm Qn 86-87; Cvl Engrng.

PERSIO, CHRISTIAN; Central Cambria HS; Ebensburg, PA; (3); Ski Clb; Ftbl; Trk; Wt Lftg.

PERSUDA, JANET; Charleroi Area HS; Charleroi, PA; (4); 16/165; Chorus; Color Guard; Jazz Band; School Musical; Nwsp Stf; Hon Roll; NHS; Pres Schlr; Mary Noss Frshmn Schlrshp 87; Frank F Paterra Vocal Music Awd 87; Stu Tutor 87; CA U Of PA; Acctg.

PERSUN, SHERRY; Highlands SR HS; Tarentum, PA; (4); 8/277; Ftbl; SADD; High Hon Roll; Hon Roll; Jr NHS; NHS; Pres Schlr; Robert Byrd Scholar 87; U Pittsburgh; Chiroprctr.

PERTILE, CHERYL; Lincoln HS; Ellwood City, PA; (3); 67/162; AFS; Camera Clb; Girl Scts; Hosp Aide; Ski Clb; Spanish Clb; Y-Teens; Chorus; Powder Puff Ftbl; JV Trk; Early Chldhd.

PERTZOG, ERIC; Hempfield SR HS; Jeannette, PA; (3); Art Clb; Off Church Yth Grp; Cmnty Wkr; Computer Clb; Pep Clb; Ski Clb; Spanish Clb; Hon Roll; Adv.

PERUGINI, SAM; Holy Ghost Prep; Philadelphia, PA; (4); Pres Latin Clb; Band; School Play; Variety Show; Nwsp Rptr; High Hon Roll; NHS; Pres Schlr; Science Clb; Aud/Vis; Excllnc-Adv Lvl Latin 85-87; Offcl Schl Wthr Frcstr 86-87; Hurrcn Frcstr Asst 86-87; Penn ST U; Meteorlgy.

PESCI, LORI; Freeport SR HS; Freeport, PA; (3); Yrbk Stf; Trk; High Hon Roll; Phldpha Coll Arts; Graphic Art.

PESENSON, MICHAEL; Abington SR HS; Meadowbrook, PA; (4); 29/486; Chess Clb; Exploring; French Clb; Cit Awd; High Hon Roll; Hon Roll; NHS; Gen Elec Star Awd, Oak Lane Shakespeare Clb Awd, Prsdntl Acdmc Ftnss Awd 87; U Of PA; Med.

PESI, CHRIS; Frazier HS; Star Junction, PA; (4); Drama Clb; Library Aide; Spanish Clb; Band; Color Guard; Mrchg Band; Pep Band; School Play; Nwsp Stf; Yrbk Stf; St Vincent; Elem Educ.

PESKE, HEATHER G; Mc Dowell HS; Erie, PA; (3); 25/598; Am Leg Aux Girls St; Church Yth Grp; Cmnty Wkr; French Clb; Hosp Aide; Model UN; Ski Clb; Pres Stu Cncl; Tennis; DAR Awd; Pol Sci.

PESTA, DANIEL; Council Rock HS; Newtown, PA; (3); 145/408; Chess Clb; School Play; Trk; Vllybl; Wrstlng; Hon Roll; Austrian Embssy Book Awd 86.

PETA, DOUGLAS M; Henderson HS; West Chester, PA; (4); 10/336; JCL; Nwsp Rptr; Lit Mag; Rep Soph Cls; Rep Jr Cls; Rep Sr Cls; JV Bsbl; Im Bsktbl; Im Socr; Im Vllybl; Magna Cum Ld Natl Latn Exm 86; PA Cert Merit Prfrmnc SAT 86; U Of VA; Finc.

PETAK, TAMARA; Carbondale Area JR SR HS; Simpson, PA; (2); Computer Clb; Ski Clb; Spanish Clb; Pres Soph Cls; Stu Cncl; Var Cheerleading; High Hon Roll; HOBY Fndtn Sem For Soph 87.

PETE, CAROLYN; Lebanon Catholic HS; Lebanon, PA; (3); Library Aide; Spanish Clb; School Play; Commercial Art.

PETE, JAMES; Owen J Roberts SR HS; Spring City, PA; (4); German Clb; Band; Mrchg Band; Symp Band; Hon Roll; Temple U; Bus Mgmt.

PETEK, BOB; Ringgold HS; Finleyville, PA; (3); Boy Scts; Church Yth Grp; Drama Clb; Rep Frsh Cls; Rep Soph Cls.

PETENBRINK, SHANNON; Meyersdale Area HS; Garrett, PA; (4); Spanish Clb; Band; Mrchg Band; School Musical; Var L Bsktbl; High Hon Roll; NHS; Clarion U; Bus Admin.

PETERMAN, CORINNE; Danville HS; Danville, PA; (1); 3/233; High Hon Roll; Bus.

PETERMAN, RENEE; Morrisville HS; Morrisville, PA; (3); Sec FBLA; Capt Color Guard; Free Enterprise Wk, Wk At Lock Haven Univ Schlrshp 87; Achvt Awd Sociology, Engl, & Rcrdkpng 87; U Of PA; Bus Admin.

PETERMAN, SHARI; Hughesville HS; Benton, PA; (4); 12/134; French Clb; Key Clb; Chorus; Cit Awd; Hon Roll; NHS; Green & Wht Awd 84-87; Cmmnwlth Bk Bus Mgmt Schlrshp 87; Lock Haven U; Elem Ed.

PETERS, ABBY; Red Lion SR HS; York, PA; (3); 21/342; Pres VP Church Yth Grp; Yrbk Stf; High Hon Roll; Hon Roll; Messiah Coll; Christian Cnslr.

PETERS, BRETT; Somerset Area HS; Somerset, PA; (4); English Clb; German Clb; Mu Alpha Theta; Spanish Clb; Hon Roll; Kwns Boy Of Mon 87; Indiana U Of PA; Accntng.

PETERS, BRONSON; Northwestern Le HS; Germansville, PA; (4); Church Yth Grp; Computer Clb; Letterman Clb; Science Clb; School Play; Stage Crew; Capt L Crs Cntry; Capt L Trk; Capt L Wrstlng; Hon Roll; Leag & Dist Qlfr Crs Cntry & Trk 85-86; N W 2nd Pl Wrstlng Trnmnt 86; 3rd Pl Mdl Wnnr Rly L & D 87; Penn ST U; Engrng.

PETERS, CHARLES; Abington SR HS; Abington, PA; (3); 63/502; Latin Clb; Spanish Clb; Varsity Clb; Im Bsktbl; Var Golf; Var Lcrss; Hon Roll; Jr NHS; NHS; Pres Schlr; Pa Free Enterprise 86; Bus.

PETERS, CHRIS; Emmaus HS; Wescosville, PA; (4); 40/458; JV VP Bsbl; High Hon Roll; Hon Roll; Jr NHS; NHS; Ntl Merit Ltr; Pres Schlr; Lafayette Coll; Engr.

PETERS, DAN; Ft Le Boeuf HS; Waterford, PA; (4); Exploring; Band; Mrchg Band; Im Capt Vllybl; High Hon Roll; NHS; Pres Schlr; Debate Tm; Pep Clb; Nwsp Rptr; Stnly-Proto Tl Indus Arts Schlrshp Cntst 1st Pl 86-87; Hnr Rll Awd 84-87; Outstndg Sr Awd Ind Arts 87; Penn ST Erie; Engrng.

PETERS, DAVID; Highlands SR HS; Tarentum, PA; (3); Art Clb; DECA; 2 Brown Awds 85-86; Pittsburgh Art Inst; Comm Art.

PETERS, DEANNE; Nazareth Area SR HS; Nazareth, PA; (3); Art Clb; Church Yth Grp; Letterman Clb; Stage Crew; Capt Crs Cntry; Trk; Hon Roll; Kiwanis Awd; Drama Clb; Varsity Clb; Ltr Awd Trck, Cross Cntry 85-87; Art.

PETERS, DEBRA L; Commodore Perry HS; Greenville, PA; (4); 3/60; FBLA; Math Tm; School Play; Yrbk Stf; Sec Frsh Cls; Sec Soph Cls; Rep Stu Cncl; NHS; Drama Clb; FHA; PA ST Univ; Bus Adm.

PETERS, DONNA; Little Flower Catholic HS For Girls; Philadelphia, PA; (2); Var Trk; JV Vllybl; Cmnty Svc Corps 85-87; La Salle Coll; Comp Prgmmr.

PETERS, ERIC; Bermudian Springs HS; Gardners, PA; (4); 2/126; Pres 4-H; Pres Chorus; Concert Band; Jazz Band; Mrchg Band; School Musical; High Hon Roll; Ntl Merit SF; Band; Church Choir; Drama Awd 86; Patriot News Wrtg Awd 86fnatl Piano Gld Awd 84; Tv Prod.

PETERS, FRANK; Harborcreek HS; Harbor Creek, PA; (4); 9/213; Cmnty Wkr; DAR Awd; NHS; High Hon Roll; Hon Roll; Hrbrcrk Fire Dept 83-87; Emrgncy Med Tech 86-87; Penn ST; Engrng.

PETERS, GERALD; Central HS; Philadelphia, PA; (3); Art Clb; Church Yth Grp; Cmnty Wkr; Dance Clb; FCA; Math Tm; Church Choir; Im Bsktbl; Elec Engr.

PETERS, JENNIFER; Jeannette SR HS; Jeannette, PA; (3); 17/124; French Clb; FBLA; Office Aide; Spanish Clb; Band; Color Guard; Concert Band; Jazz Band; Mrchg Band; Hon Roll; Dist & Rgnl Band, FBLA Rgnl Cont 3rd Pl Typng II 87; U Of Miami; Frgn Lang.

PETERS, JENNIFER; Monessen HS; Monessen, PA; (3); 10/115; FBLA; Teachers Aide; Nwsp Rptr; Nwsp Stf; Yrbk Bus Mgr; Yrbk Stf; Stu Cncl; High Hon Roll; NHS; French Clb; Monessen Yth Educ Assn; Elem Educ.

PETERS, JENNIFER; Monongahela Valley Catholic HS; Brownsville, PA; (3); 5/97; Church Yth Grp; Yrbk Bus Mgr; Trs Frsh Cls; Trs Soph Cls; Trs Jr Cls; Trs Sr Cls; JV Var Bsktbl; French Hon Soc; High Hon Roll; NHS; PA JR Acad Sci 1st Awd Regn & ST Comptn 85; Cert Merit Gannon U Outstndng Sci Stu 86; Med.

PETERS, KATHLEEN; Central York SR HS; York, PA; (3); Band; Church Choir; Concert Band; Jazz Band; Mrchg Band; Bsktbl; Trk; High Hon Roll; Hon Roll; Finlst PA Govnrs Schl Arts 86; Sci Olympiad Team 86-87; Art.

PETERS, KELLIE; Fort Le Boeuf HS; Waterford, PA; (4); 25/162; Pres Stu Cncl; Hon Roll; Acad Scholar Gannon U 87-88; Homecoming 86; Stu Cncl Achvt Awd 86-87; Gannon U; Lwyrs Asst.

PETERS, KIMBERLY S; Mon Valley Catholic HS; Brownsville, PA; (4); Church Yth Grp; Science Clb; Nwsp Stf; Yrbk Stf; Stu Cncl; Cheerleading; Hon Roll; NHS; Spanish NHS; Alt PA Govrnrs Schl The Sci 86; Pre Med.

PETERS, LEILANI; Warwick HS; Lititz, PA; (3); 76/270; Office Aide; Yrbk Stf; High Hon Roll; Hon Roll; Lancaster Gen Hosp Schl Of Nrs.

PETERS, MARIANN; Susquenita HS; Duncannon, PA; (3); Am Leg Aux Girls St; Leo Clb; Spanish Clb; Ed Nwsp Stf; VP Jr Cls; Trs VP Stu Cncl; Fld Hcky; Trk; Hon Roll; PA JR Acad Of Sci STS Awd 85-87; Cptl Area Sci & Engrng Fair Awd 85-87; Perry Cnty Anti Drunk Drvng; Psych.

PETERS, MARISSA; Scranton Prep; Moscow, PA; (3); 7/190; Political Wkr; Chorus; School Play; Yrbk Phtg; Rep Soph Cls; Rep Jr Cls; Stu Cncl; Cheerleading; Trk; High Hon Roll; Lwyr.

PETERS, MARY; Sharpsville Area HS; Sharpsville, PA; (3); Chess Clb; Office Aide; Spanish Clb; SADD; Chorus; School Musical; Nwsp Stf; Yrbk Rptr; VP Frsh Cls; Stu Cncl; Acadmc Achvt Awd; Bio.

PETERS, MELISSA; Mid Valley HS; Dickson City, PA; (4); 2/88; High Hon Roll; Lion Awd; Lackawanna JC; Acctng.

PETERS, MICHELLE; Otto-Eldred HS; Eldred, PA; (3); 6/87; Cmnty Wkr; Chorus; School Musical; Var JV Mgr(s); Hon Roll; Hlth Awd 87; Wheeling Coll; RN.

PETERS, ROBERT; Red Lion Area SR HS; Red Lion, PA; (3); 76/342; Band; Concert Band; Jazz Band; Mrchg Band; Orch; Pep Band; Symp Band; Im Crs Cntry; JV Tennis; Hon Roll; Engrng.

PETERS, STEPHANIE CAROLINE; Quigley Catholic HS; Freedom, PA; (4); Am Leg Aux Girls St; Camera Clb; Church Yth Grp; Sec Trs 4-H; Model UN; Band; Concert Band; Mrchg Band; Mgr(s); Powder Puff Ftbl.

PETERS, TAMI; Solanco SR HS; Quarryville, PA; (3); 62/287; Art Clb; CAP; Exploring; FTA; GAA; Crs Cntry; Trk; Wt Lftg; Office Aide; Pep Clb; Mst Imprvd Rnnr 86-87; Air Force; Law Enfrcmnt.

PETERS JR, WILLIAM; Montgomery Area JR-SR HS; Montgomery, PA; (3); French Clb; Thesps; Chorus; School Musical; School Play; Stage Crew; Bsktbl; Bowling; Ftbl; Mgr(s); Jr County Choir 84-85; Chem.

PETERSEN, DAVID; Exeter SR HS; Reading, PA; (3); #22 In Class; Boy Scts; Church Yth Grp; Drama Clb; School Musical; School Play; Variety Show; High Hon Roll; Lwyr.

PETERSEN, MARGARET; Grosse Pointe South HS; Newtown Square, PA; (3); 24/265; Rep Frsh Cls; Rep Soph Cls; Rep Jr Cls; Var Tennis; NHS; French Clb; SADD; Variety Show; JV Capt Bsktbl; JV Sftbl; Hgh Hnr Roll & Hntl Hnr Soc 86 & 87; Tnns Tm ST Chmpn & Fnlst 85 & 86; Stu Gvrnmnt 84-87; Law.

PETERSHEIM, TERRY; Lancaster Mennonite HS; Paradise, PA; (4); 19/151; Pres Church Yth Grp; Drama Clb; Acpl Chr; Chorus; Rep Soph Cls; Rep Sr Cls; High Hon Roll; NHS; Rotary Awd; JV Socr; MVP Chss Tm 86; Cert Of Hnr Mscl Perf 86; EMC; Yt Pstr.

PETERSON, BRETT; Cambridge Springs HS; Cambridge Spgs, PA; (2); 29/96; SADD; Variety Show; JV Var Bsktbl; JV Var Vllybl; Wt Lftg; Hon Roll.

PETERSON, BRYAN; Cranberry Area HS; Seneca, PA; (2); SADD; Hon Roll; Millers Speed Sktng Team.

PETERSON, CHRIS ANN; Mc Keesport HS; White Oak, PA; (4); 27/335; AFS; Concert Band; Jazz Band; Mrchg Band; Symp Band; JV Bsktbl; Powder Puff Ftbl; High Hon Roll; Jr NHS; NHS; Wumodausis Schlrshp 87; Crawford Schlrshp 87; Rtry Hnr Stu 87; Penn ST; Nrsng.

PETERSON, JENNIFER; Fannett-Metal HS; Dry Run, PA; (4); 3/41; Drama Clb; Hosp Aide; Band; Chorus; Concert Band; Drm Mjr(t); Mrchg Band; School Play; Yrbk Stf; Hon Roll; York Coll Of PA; Nrsg.

PETERSON, KARYN; Rockwood Area HS; Rockwood, PA; (4); 6/96; Intnl Clb; Spanish Clb; Band; Chorus; Concert Band; Mrchg Band; School Play; Rep Stu Cncl; Stat Bsktbl; Var Cheerleading; IN U Pennsylvania; Span.

PETERSON, KAY; Glendale JR-SR HS; Irvona, PA; (3); FBLA; Science Clb; Band; Mrchg Band; JV Bsktbl; NHS.

PETERSON, KEITH; Seneca HS; Erie, PA; (4); Computer Clb; Pep Clb; Hon Roll; NHS; PA ST Behrend; Engnrng.

PETERSON, KRISTA; Wellsboro SR HS; Wellsboro, PA; (4); 6/122; Band; Capt Bsktbl; Capt Trk; High Hon Roll; NHS; U S Army Reserve Schlr/Ath Awd 87; Shelley Taynton Mem Scholar Awd 87; Owlett Mem Scholar Soc Stud 87; Susquehanna U; Intl Stud.

PETERSON, KRISTIN; Parkland HS; Orefield, PA; (3); Church Yth Grp; Cmnty Wkr; German Clb; Key Clb; Library Aide; Band; Stage Crew; Nwsp Stf; Bsktbl; Hon Roll; Vrsty Lttr Bsktbl 85-86; Lvd Abrd In Grmny For 1 Yr With Fmly 85-86; Kutztown U; Education.

PETERSON, MELISSA; Southern Huntingdon HS; Shade Gap, PA; (3); FBLA; FHA; SADD; Varsity Clb; Band; Var L Fld Hcky; Powder Puff Ftbl; Var L Sftbl; Twrlr; NHS; Rtl Mgmt.

PETERSON, MICHELE; Meadville SR HS; Meadville, PA; (3); 49/350; Y-Teens; Orch; Hon Roll; Strght A In Hstry 85; Secr.

PETERSON, RENE; Hickory HS; Sharpsville, PA; (3); 10/183; Art Clb; Church Yth Grp; Exploring; Latin Clb; Varsity Clb; Var L Crs Cntry; Var L Trk; NHS; Spanish NHS; Acad All Amer 87; Pre-Med.

PETERSON, RHONDA; Jamestown HS; Jamestown, PA; (3); 3/65; Church Yth Grp; Drama Clb; VP French Clb; Sec FHA; Flag Corp; Yrbk Stf; High Hon Roll; Hon Roll; NHS; Med.

PETERSON, ROBERT; Glendale JR/Sr HS; Irvona, PA; (3); Science Clb; Yrbk Stf; Stu Cncl; JV Bsktbl; JV Var Ftbl; Hon Roll.

PETERSON, SHARON; Fannett-Metal HS; Spring Run, PA; (4); Church Yth Grp; Drama Clb; Teachers Aide; Varsity Clb; VICA; Color Guard; Flag Corp; School Play; Trs Frsh Cls; Trs Soph Cls; 1st Pl Wnnr VICA Comptn 84-85; Cosmtlgy.

PETERSON, STACY; North Allegheny SR HS; Wexford, PA; (3); 282/649; Off Soph Cls; Off Jr Cls; Off Stu Cncl; JV Bsktbl; JV Cheerleading; Off Sftbl; Var Trk; Shrt Stry Publshd N Alleghenys Lit Mag 87; Vrsty Lttr & Pin Trk 86-87; Jrnlsm.

PETEY, SHERYL; Center Area HS; Monaca, PA; (3); 29/186; Church Yth Grp; Exploring; Hosp Aide; Spanish Clb; Drill Tm; Mrchg Band; Stu Cncl; Co-Capt Twrlr; Hon Roll; NHS; Dplma De Merito Excel Spnsh Lang 84-87; Stu Cncl Awd 86-87; PA ST U; Elem Educ.

PETHERICK, KIMBERLY; Lackawanna Trail HS; Dalton, PA; (4); 11/86; Church Yth Grp; Cmnty Wkr; Office Aide; Scholastic Bowl; High Hon Roll; Hon Roll; NHS; Dept Schlrshp-Marywd Coll 87; LTEA Schlrshp, Da Hn Wmns Clb Schlrshp 87; Prsdntl Acdmc Ftnss Awd 87; Marywood Coll; Math.

PETICCA, LEANNE; Oxford Area HS; Oxford, PA; (3); Sec VP Church Yth Grp; Band; Chorus; Sec Concert Band; Sec Mrchg Band; Var Capt Tennis; Var Trk; High Hon Roll; NHS; Profcncy Awd Alg II & Trig 85 & 87; Profcncy Awd Band 87; All Star Ath Awd Tennis 86-87; Math.

PETITJEAN, BETH; Governor Mifflin HS; Shillington, PA; (4); 36/257; School Musical; Stage Crew; Nwsp Rptr; Yrbk Stf; Lit Mag; Hon Roll; Lion Awd; Aud/Vis; Exploring; Hosp Aide; Joseph Pleuyak Mem Scholar 87; Allentown Coll Talent Scholar 86; Richard Caron Fndtn Awd 87; Allentown Coll; Tech Theatre.

PETITO, ANITA; Saucon Valley HS; Bethlehem, PA; (3); 19/156; Spanish Clb; Chorus; School Play; Var L Cheerleading; Gym; Swmmng; High Hon Roll; NHS; Awd Excllnc Natl Chrldrs Asso Clnc 86.

PETKA, WENDY; Burgettstown JR/SR HS; Avella, PA; (3); 1/175; French Clb; Science Clb; Ski Clb; Drill Tm; Mrchg Band; VP Jr Cls; VP Stu Cncl; Capt Coach Actv; High Hon Roll; VP Jr NHS; Ntl Acadmc All Amer & Sci Merit Schlr Awd 86; Genetic Engr.

PETO, CHRISTI; Greensburg Salem SR HS; Slickville, PA; (3); Church Yth Grp; Ski Clb; Spanish Clb; Band; Concert Band; Mrchg Band; School Musical; Trk; High Hon Roll; Hon Roll; 1st Pl Medal Trck Relay 86; Sci.

PETONAK, PAUL; Bishop O Reilly HS; Exeter, PA; (4); Debate Tm; Ski Clb; Chorus; Stage Crew; Nwsp Sprt Ed; Yrbk Bus Mgr; Yrbk Stf; High Hon Roll; Ntl Merit Ltr; Acad All Amer; U Penn; Psych.

PETRARCA, APRIL; Blairsville SR HS; Blairsville, PA; (1); VP Church Yth Grp; Girl Scts; SADD; Band; Church Choir; Concert Band; Mrchg Band; JV Sftbl; Hon Roll; County Band 87; IUP; Music.

PETRASEK, MARIA; Bishop O Reilly HS; Forty Fort, PA; (3); Ski Clb; Chorus; JV Cheerleading; Var Crs Cntry; Sftbl; Math.

PETRASIC, KATHY; Bishop Mc Devitt HS; Harrisburg, PA; (2); 79/230; Art Clb; Service Clb; Yrbk Stf; Cheerleading; Mgr(s).

PETRATUS, JUDITH; Carmichaels Area HS; Rices Landing, PA; (4); 2/101; French Clb; Library Aide; Office Aide; Pep Clb; Ski Clb; Cheerleading; Hon Roll; NHS; Womans Cvc Clb Oct Girl Of Month 86; Nclrphysics Clb 86-87; Psycht.

PETRAVICH, ALAN; Pine Grove Area HS; Pine Grove, PA; (4); 7/112; Drama Clb; Chorus; Church Choir; School Musical; Rep Jr Cls; Rep Sr Cls; Rep Stu Cncl; Cit Awd; Hon Roll; NHS; Penn ST U; Bio.

PETRELLA, CARLA; Monaca JR SR HS; Monaca, PA; (3); 27/90; Church Yth Grp; Pres French Clb; Girl Scts; JA; Pres VP Red Cross Aide; Sec Band; Sec Mrchg Band; Pep Band; School Musical; Yrbk Stf; PA ST U; Engl.

PETRELLA, CHRISTINE; Beaver Area JR-SR HS; Beaver, PA; (3); Cmnty Wkr; French Clb; German Clb; Hosp Aide; JA; Pep Clb; Socr; Hon Roll; Acctg.

PETRELLA, HEATHER; St Hubert HS; Philadelphia, PA; (3); 26/421; French Clb; Hosp Aide; High Hon Roll; Hon Roll; Acad All-Amer 87; Frgn Langs.

PETRI, ANGELA; Moon SR HS; Coraopolis, PA; (3); 89/307; Drama Clb; JA; School Play; Stage Crew; Yrbk Stf; Var L Trk; Hon Roll; Trk Awd 86-87; Physcl Thrpy.

PETRI, KIMM; General Mc Lane HS; Fairview, PA; (3); 2/218; Chess Clb; French Clb; Model UN; Pep Band; Nwsp Stf; Lit Mag; High Hon Roll; Hon Roll; Ntl Merit Ltr; German Clb; Bio.

PETRICK, BRENT; Cambridge Springs Joint HS; Cambridge Spg, PA; (3); 20/98; Camera Clb; Yrbk Phtg; Coach Actv; Wt Lftg; Hon Roll; Phys Therapist.

PETRICK, ROBERT A; West Perry HS; Loysville, PA; (2); 2/205; Spanish Clb; Varsity Clb; Rep Stu Cncl; Var JV Bsktbl; Var Trk; High Hon Roll; US Naval Acad.

PETRICKO, JENNIFER; West Allegheny SR HS; Oakdale, PA; (3); 35/210; Sec Drama Clb; VP JA; Pres Band; Pres Chorus; Trs Frsh Cls; VP Jr Cls; Civic Clb; Masonic Awd; Rotary Awd; Church Yth Grp; HOBY Awd; Grnd Rep New South Wales Australia; 2ndry Engl Ed.

PETRILAK, ANNE; Central Dauphin HS; Harrisburg, PA; (2); Key Clb; Chorus; Twrlr; Hon Roll; Jr NHS.

PETRILAK, JOHN; Pen Argyl HS; Pen Argyl, PA; (4); 25/117; Ski Clb; School Play; Frsh Cls; Stu Cncl; Im Bsbl; Var Ftbl; Var Trk; Cit Awd; Hon Roll; PA ST; Engrng.

PETRILLI, DENISE; St Marys Area HS; Saint Marys, PA; (4); Sec Frsh Cls; Sec Soph Cls; L Stat Bsktbl; Var L Cheerleading; Var L Sftbl; Brooks Coll; Fash Merch.

PETRILLO, AMANDA; Pocono Mountain HS; Swiftwater, PA; (3); SADD; Stat Crs Cntry; Stat Trk; Hon Roll; Prfct Atten Awd; E Stroudsburg U; Psych.

PETRILLO, BAMBI; Daniel Boone HS; Birdsboro, PA; (3); 19/168; German Clb; Girl Scts; Yrbk Stf; Trs Soph Cls; Trs Jr Cls; Mgr(s); Mgr Wrstlng; Hon Roll; Elem Ed.

PETRILLO, DENISE M; South Allegheny JR SR HS; Glassport, PA; (4); Sec Camera Clb; Sec Church Yth Grp; French Clb; JA; Office Aide; Y-Teens; Chorus; Var Powder Puff Ftbl; Var Trk; Waynesburg Coll; Acctng.

PETRILLO, MATTHEW; Elmer L Meyers HS; Wilkes Barre, PA; (4); Letterman Clb; Red Cross Aide; SADD; Chorus; L Swmmng; Im Vllybl; Cngrssnl Schlr Natl Yng Ldrs Conf 87; Gettysburg Coll.

PETRINI, DONNA; Carbondale Area HS; Carbondale, PA; (2); 8/126; FBLA; Spanish Clb; Band; Rep Stu Cncl; High Hon Roll; Hon Roll; Marywood Coll Music Awd 85-86; Law.

PETRINI, MARCIA; Kennedy Christian HS; Sharon, PA; (2); 1/96; Cmnty Wkr; Hosp Aide; Latin Clb; Service Clb; Co-Capt Flag Corp; Var Trk; High Hon Roll; Hon Roll; NEDT Cert 85-87.

PETRISIN JR, GERALD J; Clairton HS; Clairton, PA; (4); Am Leg Boys St; Hon Roll; Wllm A Pssvnt Awd 87; Thiel Coll; Pltcl Sci.

PETRITUS, ROSEMARIE E; Bishop Hannan HS; Scranton, PA; (4); Art Clb; Drama Clb; Hosp Aide; Chorus; Off Frsh Cls; Hon Roll; Art Talent Scholar Marywood Coll 87; Mercy Hosp Teen Vlntr Scholar 87; Summer Art Scholar IN U PA 86; Marywood Coll; Art.

PETRO, CHRISTINE; Ringgold HS; Donora, PA; (4); 4/330; Ski Clb; Pres Stu Cncl; Gym; Hon Roll; NHS; Church Yth Grp; Diving; Sci-Mth Hnr Soc; SR Activities Comm; Gifted Ed.

PETRO, KENNETH E; Peters Township HS; Mc Murray, PA; (3); 75/242; Church Yth Grp; Exploring; Science Clb; Stage Crew; Wrstlng; Hon Roll; Assctnl Wnnr-Spkrs Trnmnt 86; Med.

PETRO, MISSY; Mc Keesport Area HS; White Oak, PA; (4); 26/354; AFS; Office Aide; Pep Clb; Yrbk Ed-Chief; Yrbk Stf; Sec Stu Cncl; High Hon Roll; Hon Roll; NHS; Pres Schlr; Rotary Hnr Stu 87; Penn ST U; Nrsng.

PETROCELLI, DOMENIC; Monsignor Bonner HS; Aldan, PA; (3); 125/255; Var L Ice Hcky.

PETROF, KARL; Glendale JR SR HS; Flinton, PA; (3); 1/78; Art Clb; Letterman Clb; Varsity Clb; Var L Ftbl; Var L Wrstlng; Bausch & Lomb Sci Awd; NHS.

PETROFF, RON; Ambridge Area HS; Ambridge, PA; (3); Am Leg Boys St; Pep Clb; Spanish Clb; Band; Concert Band; Jazz Band; Mrchg Band; Pep Band; Symp Band; Stu Cncl; Most Outstndg Jazz Soloist 87; WV U; Law.

PETROSKE, JENNIFER; Ringgold HS; Donora, PA; (4); FNA; Chorus; Nwsp Stf; Yrbk Ed-Chief; Hon Roll; Jrnlsm Awd 87; W Penn Hosp Schl; Nrsng.

PETROSKEY, NICK; Ringgold HS; Monongahela, PA; (2); Ftbl; Var Trk; Var Wt Lftg; Pitt-PA ST; Chiroprctr.

PETROSKI, ANDREJ; Coudersport JR- SR HS; Coudersport, PA; (3); 31/79; Church Yth Grp; Cmnty Wkr; Varsity Clb; Chorus; Nwsp Rptr; Var JV Bsktbl; Var JV Ftbl; Var Trk; Hon Roll; Pierce JC Philadelphia; Bus.

PETROSKI, CYNTHIA; Wyoming Area SR HS; Wyoming, PA; (2); Hosp Aide; Spanish Clb; Marywood Coll; Elem Ed.

PETROSKI, FRANCIS WILLIAM; Wyoming Valley West HS; Dallas, PA; (3); Latin Clb; Science Clb; JV Ftbl; Var Capt Sftbl; High Hon Roll; Hon Roll; Yth Grp Treas 86 & 87; Scranton U; Dentistry.

PETROSKY, AMY; Greater Latrobe SR HS; Latrobe, PA; (3); AFS; Debate Tm; Sec German Clb; Pep Clb; Science Clb; SADD; Symp Band; JV Cheerleading; High Hon Roll; Schlrshp To St Vincent Coll Chllng Prog 84; Gld Cup Rep 6 Consec Supr Rtngs In Natl Fed Of Msc 85.

PETROSKY, PAMELA; Old Forge HS; Old Forge, PA; (3); School Musical; High Hon Roll; NHS; Acdmc All Amer 85; PA ST U; Bus Adm.

PETROVIA, TRACEY; Neshaminy SR HS; Langhorne, PA; (3); Boy Scts; Church Yth Grp; DECA; FNA; Girl Scts; Hosp Aide; PAVAS; Red Cross Aide; SADD; Nwsp Stf; Bucks Cnty CC; Xray Techncn.

PETROVICH, LAURIE; Saucon Valley HS; Hellertown, PA; (2); Band; Concert Band; Stat Bsbl; Var Cheerleading; High Hon Roll; Hon Roll; Nrsng.

PETROVICH, LISA; Our Lady Of Lourdes Regional HS; Marion Hts, PA; (3); 51/89; Pep Clb; SADD; Rep Stu Cncl; Sftbl; Drama Clb; French Clb; Lgl Asst.

PETRUCCI, WILLIAM; Wyoming Area HS; Exeter, PA; (3); 40/260; Church Yth Grp; Civic Clb; Computer Clb; Spanish Clb; JV Var Bsktbl; High Hon Roll; Hon Roll; NHS.

PETRUCELLI, JASON; Coughlin HS; Wilkes Barre, PA; (4); JV Bsbl; JV Bsktbl; Var Ftbl; Hon Roll; Jr NHS; Pre-Law.

PETRUSIC, ALLEN; Johnstown HS; Johnstown, PA; (3); Hst German Clb; Ski Clb; SADD; Chorus; Concert Band; Jazz Band; Mrchg Band; Pep Band; School Musical; Rep Jr Cls; Electrical Engineering.

PETRUSKA, JEFF; Monsignor Bonner HS; Lansdowne, PA; (3); 21/234; Service Clb; Var Socr; Var Trk; High Hon Roll; Hon Roll; NHS; 2nd Tm All Cathlic Trk 86; 4th Pl Mdlst US Jr Olympcs Anchor Leg Natl Lvl 86; US Military Acad W Point; Bus.

PETRUSKA, LISA; Lake Lehman HS; Hunlock Crk, PA; (2); Var Bsktbl; JV Sftbl; L Vllybl; High Hon Roll; Hon Roll; Jr NHS; NEDT Awd; Sci.

PETRUSKY, ANDREW; Baldwin HS; Pittsburgh, PA; (3); Church Yth Grp; Var L Trk; Vllybl; Bus Mgmt.

PETRUSKY, JOSEPH; Seton-La Salle HS; Pittsburgh, PA; (4); FBLA; Ski Clb; Ftbl; Wt Lftg; U Of Pittsburgh; Bus Mgmt.

PETRUSO, POLLY; Meadville Area SR HS; Meadville, PA; (3); French Clb; Key Clb; Varsity Clb; Stu Cncl; JV Var Cheerleading; Hon Roll.

PETRUZZELLO, ANDREA; South Western HS; Hanover, PA; (3); VP 4-H; Key Clb; Sec Rep Stu Cncl; 4-H Awd; 4-H Awd 85.

PETRY, GREGORY; Bishop Shanahan HS; Cochranville, PA; (4); 62/215; Boy Scts; Chorus; School Play; Hon Roll; Var L Crs Cntry; Var L Trk; Drexel U; Cvl Engrng.

PETTENATI, ANGELA; Blair County Christian HS; Ashville, PA; (2); 5/15; Church Yth Grp; Debate Tm; Chorus; Sec Soph Cls; Var L Bsktbl; Var L Cheerleading; Score Keeper; Var Sftbl; Trk; High Hon Roll; Physcl Thrpy.

PETTINE, DANIELLE ANITA; Plymouth-Whitemarsh HS; Conshohocken, PA; (3); 25/375; Science Clb; School Musical; Sec Frsh Cls; Sec Soph Cls; Var JV Fld Hcky; Var L Swmmng; NHS; High Hon Roll; Acdmc Excllnc Awd 85-87; All-Leag Hnrs 200 M Mdly Rly, Achvt Awd Sci Olympiad Tm-Estrn Rgnl Chmpns 87; Bio Sci.

PETTIT, ALANNA K; Reading Central Catholic HS; Reading, PA; (3); 30/129; Letterman Clb; Office Aide; Spanish Clb; Varsity Clb; School Play; Rep Soph Cls; Cheerleading; Var Swmmng; Hon Roll; Hgh Achvt In Hstry; Sped Ed.

PETTIT, CINDY; West Greene HS; Holbrook, PA; (2); Church Yth Grp; 4-H; Pres FFA; SADD; Chorus; Church Choir; High Hon Roll; Penn ST; Vo-Ag Educ.

PETTIT, TANIA; Nazareth Area SR HS; Nazareth, PA; (3); 17/270; Exploring; Pres Hosp Aide; Key Clb; Yrbk Stf; High Hon Roll; Hon Roll; Pres JR Axlry Muhlenberg Hosp 86; Vlntr Spec Olympcs 85-87; Acadc Achvt Awd Top 20 Cls 87; T Jefferson Coll; Cytchnlgy.

PETTY, DAVID; Mt Lebanon HS; Pittsburgh, PA; (4); Computer Clb; Orch; School Musical; Hon Roll; Pres Acad Ftnss Awd 86-87; Hnrs Band PA Dist I 85-87; Gftd & Tlntd Pgm 84-87; U Of Pittsburgh; Math.

PETTY, KELLY; Reading SR HS; Reading, PA; (4); 93/563; Boys Clb Am; Im Bsktbl; Var Ftbl; Im Vllybl; Kiwanis Awd; Sir Thomas J Lipton Boys Clb Sprtsmnshp Awd 84; Cvl Engrng.

PETUCCI, CHRISTOPHER; Altoona Area HS; Altoona, PA; (3); Chess Clb; Exploring; Spanish Clb; Band; Concert Band; Mrchg Band; Orch; Juniata Coll; Pre-Med.

PETUSKY, MIKE; Scranton Prep Schl; Scranton, PA; (4); 57/190; Am Leg Boys St; Boys Clb Am; Cmnty Wkr; Political Wkr; Varsity Clb; Yrbk Rptr; Var Capt Bsbl; High Hon Roll; Hon Roll; NHS; Cavalier Awd 3 Yrs Vrsty Bsbll 87; U Of Richmond; Finance.

PETYK, STEPHEN; Conestoga SR HS; Berwyn, PA; (3); 147/472; Aud/Vis; Camera Clb; Latin Clb; Office Aide; Ski Clb; Varsity Clb; Band; Chorus; Concert Band; Stage Crew; Northeastern U; Law.

PEWTERBAUGH, CHRISTOPHER; Garnet Valley JR SR HS; Boothwyn, PA; (4); 12/150; Cmnty Wkr; FBLA; Office Aide; Spanish Clb; Hon Roll; NHS; Cert Of Mrt In Peer Cnslng 84; Clemson U; Arch.

PEYTON, SHELLEY; West Allegheny SR HS; Mcdonald, PA; (4); 6/201; Pres VP Church Yth Grp; VP SADD; VP Chorus; Church Choir; Capt Color Guard; Concert Band; Powder Puff Ftbl; High Hon Roll; NHS; Ntl Merit Ltr; Gifted Pgm 85-86; PA ST U; Pre Med.

PEZZI, JULIANNE; Lincoln HS; Wampum, PA; (3); AFS; Art Clb; Church Yth Grp; Y-Teens; Yrbk Stf; Cheerleading; Powder Puff Ftbl; Trk; High Hon Roll; Hon Roll; Notre Dame; Psychlgy.

PFAFF, CRAIG; Neshaminy HS; Levittown, PA; (4); Gym; Socr; Elks Awd; U Of Pittsburg; Psych.

PFAFF, JILL; Elk County Christian HS; St Marys, PA; (4); Cmnty Wkr; Letterman Clb; Yrbk Stf; Stu Cncl; Var Co-Capt Cheerleading; Hon Roll; NHS; St Bonaventure U; Psych.

PFAFF, JUNE; Elk Coiunty Christian HS; St Marys, PA; (3); 29/72; Art Clb; Ski Clb; Varsity Clb; Trs Stu Cncl; Cheerleading; Tennis; Stat Wrstlng; Hon Roll; Var Ltr Ten 86; Graphic Art.

PFAFF, SERENA; Lock Haven HS; Lock Haven, PA; (3); Sec FHA; Girl Scts; SADD; Band; Color Guard; Mrchg Band; Bsktbl; Prfct Atten Awd.

PFAU, STEPHEN K; Archbishop Wood HS; Warminster, PA; (2); 55/254; Church Yth Grp; German Clb; Ice Hcky; Hon Roll; Bus.

PFAUTZ, ANNE L; Owen J Roberts HS; Glenmoore, PA; (2); 18/311; Band; Mrchg Band; School Musical; Symp Band; Var Lcrss; JV Trk; Hon Roll; District Band 87.

PFEFFER, TAMMY; Christian Schl Of York; York, PA; (3); Art Clb; Hosp Aide; Spanish Clb; Chorus; Mgr(s); Stat Trk; Hon Roll; Prfct Atten Awd; Sci & Engrng Fair Awd 86; 1st Pl Fine Arts Art Awd 85; Nrsng.

PFEIFER, DENISE; Seneca Valley SR HS; Mars, PA; (3); Art Clb; Ski Clb; Off Soph Cls; Off Jr Cls; Bsktbl; Chld Psych.

PFEIFER, MARC; Butler HS; Butler, PA; (2); German Clb; Band; Concert Band; Mrchg Band; Symp Band; JV Trk; Hon Roll; Yng Musician Note 86; Musician.

PFEIFER, SHARON; Hempfield Area SR HS; Greensburg, PA; (2); French Clb; Nwsp Phtg; Nwsp Rptr; Nwsp Stf; Yrbk Stf; Cheerleading; Mat Maids; Nrsng.

PFEIFER, TRACEY; Butler Area HS; Butler, PA; (2); Church Yth Grp; French Clb; Chorus; Church Choir; Hon Roll; Jr NHS; WVU; Phys Thrpy.

PFEIFFER, DEBBY; Marion Center Area HS; Marion Ctr, PA; (4); FBLA; Sec Pres FNA; Science Clb; Band; Concert Band; Mrchg Band; VP Soph Cls; Trs Stu Cncl; Var Capt Swmmng; Hon Roll.

PFEIFFER JR, JOHN B; Emmaus HS; Wescosville, PA; (3); 60/535; German Clb; Pres Key Clb; SADD; Chorus; School Play; Nwsp Ed-Chief; Pres Soph Cls; Pres Stu Cncl; Cheerleading; VP NHS; Howard A Eyer Awd Excllnc; Natl Hstry Day 85; Locl 1st Pl Indvl Prfrmnc; Optmst Clb Oratrcl Cntst 1st; Intl Rel.

PFEIFFER, JULIE C; Bethlehem Catholic HS; Northampton, PA; (3); 36/210; Hosp Aide; SADD; Rep Jr Cls; JV Capt Bsktbl; Hon Roll; MVP JV Bsktbl 85-86; Amer Diabetes Assn Teen Spprt Grp 83-87; Bus.

PFEIL, JAMIE; Bishop Mc Cart HS; Johnstown, PA; (3); Pep Clb; Varsity Clb; Chorus; School Musical; Cheerleading; Hon Roll; Bus.

PFENDER, AMY; Montour HS; Mckees Rocks, PA; (2); Church Yth Grp; Hosp Aide; Teachers Aide; Hon Roll; Nrsng.

PFERDEHIRT, AMY; Seneca Valley HS; Evans Cty, PA; (4); 8/350; Pres Ski Clb; Madrigals; Sec Jr Cls; Pres Sr Cls; Trs Stu Cncl; L Capt Crs Cntry; L Trk; DAR Awd; Sec NHS; Rotary Awd; Murray Athl Schl Awd 87; Jostens Ldrshp Awd 87; Delke-Ryan Schlrshp 87; Grove City Coll; Engrng.

PFEUFER, JILL; Elk County Christian HS; St Marys, PA; (3); 2/72; Ski Clb; Var JV Bsktbl; JV Cheerleading; Var JV Crs Cntry; Var Trk; High Hon Roll; Hon Roll; NHS.

PFEUFER, KELLY; Elk County Christian HS; St Marys, PA; (4); 20/80; Letterman Clb; Varsity Clb; Off Soph Cls; Off Jr Cls; Sec Sr Cls; Tennis; Trk; Hon Roll; NHS; St Francis Coll; Soclgy.

PFIRMAN, DAVID; South Williamsport HS; Williamsport, PA; (3); Art Clb; Camera Clb; Key Clb; Ski Clb; Band; Concert Band; Drm & Bgl; Jazz Band; Mrchg Band; Pep Band; Millersville U; Marine Bio.

PFIRMAN, PAM; Mifflinburg Area HS; Mifflinburg, PA; (2); Drama Clb; French Clb; Key Clb; Chorus; School Musical; Var L Gym; High Hon Roll; Hon Roll; Arch.

PFISTER, SARA; York Catholic HS; York, PA; (3); Church Yth Grp; Drama Clb; French Clb; Chorus; Rep Frsh Cls; Sec Stu Cncl; Capt Cheerleading; Mgr(s); Hon Roll; NHS; Messiah Coll.

PFIZENMAYER, AMY; Bensalem HS; Bensalem, PA; (3); Science Clb; Spanish Clb; SADD; Concert Band; Jazz Band; Mrchg Band; School Musical; High Hon Roll; NHS; Ntl Merit Ltr.

PFLEIGER, DENNIS; Quakertown Community HS; Quakertown, PA; (3); 66/313; Church Yth Grp; Cmnty Wkr; Hosp Aide; Ski Clb; Church Choir; JV Ftbl; Hon Roll; Temple U; Phrmcy.

PFLIEGLER, SCOTT; Freedom HS; Bethlehem, PA; (4); Northampton Cnty CC.

PFLUEGER, JESSICA; Ft Le Boeuf HS; Waterford, PA; (3); Yrbk Stf; JV Bsktbl; High Hon Roll; NHS.

PFLUGLER, LAURIE; Nazareth Area SR HS; Nazareth, PA; (3); 7/271; Sec Key Clb; Library Aide; SADD; Teachers Aide; Nwsp Rptr; Mat Maids; High Hon Roll; Hon Roll; NHS; Peer Cnslr; Elem Spcl Ed.

PFLUM, JOAN; Peabody HS; Pittsburgh, PA; (4); DECA; Office Aide; Color Guard; Sec Sr Cls; Stu Cncl; High Hon Roll; NHS; Accntnt.

PFUELLER, STEPHANIE M; Neshaminy HS; Langhorne, PA; (3); 28/785; Church Yth Grp; Intnl Clb; Library Aide; Red Cross Aide; Scholastic Bowl; Yrbk Stf; High Hon Roll; Hon Roll; NHS; Amer U; Intl Rltns.

PFUHL, NANCY; G R Johnstown HS; Johnstown, PA; (4); 2/31; Ski Clb; Band; Nwsp Rptr; Nwsp Stf; Trs Jr Cls; Sec Sr Cls; L Tennis; High Hon Roll; NHS; French Clb; Am Leg Aux Schl Mdl Awd 84; U Pittsburgh.

PHAM, ANN; Carlisle HS; Carlisle, PA; (3); Computer Clb; German Clb; Hon Roll; Acctnt.

PHAM, CHIEU; Manheim Twp HS; Lancaster, PA; (4); Church Yth Grp; Science Clb; Yrbk Phtg; Yrbk Stf; Trk; Vllybl; Wt Lftg; High Hon Roll; Hon Roll; NHS; Stu Of Mon 84; Mr Upwrd Bnd-Mllrsvll U 86; Schlstc Art Awds 87; Drexel U; Elctrnc Engnrng.

PHAM, NGA; West Catholic Girls HS; Philadelphia, PA; (3); Art Prz 86; Biochem.

PHAM, THIEP; Kutztown Area HS; Kutztown, PA; (4); Sec Computer Clb; Trs Science Clb; Band; Concert Band; Mrchg Band; Pep Band; Nwsp Stf; Var Trk; High Hon Roll; AT&T Sci Fair Awd-1st Pl 86-87, 3rd Pl 85-86; Athl Awd-V Trk & Fld 83-87; Kutztown U; Comp.

PHAN, NINI; HS For Creative Performing Arts; Philadelphia, PA; (4); Art Clb; 1st Hnrs All Sbjcts 84-85; Gimbl Awd 85; Awd Achvt Outstndng Contrbtn 85; Berkley Coll Of Music; Music.

PHANOR, GILBERTE; Bishop Conwell HS; Bensalem, PA; (3); 85/277; Rep Soph Cls; VP Stu Cncl; Art Clb; Drama Clb; Girl Scts; Model UN; Office Aide; PAVAS; Acpl Chr; Chorus; Exclnc Chrs 87; Guidance Rep 87; Psychtry.

PHARES, MICHELE; Lake Lehman HS; Hunlock Creek, PA; (2); Cmnty Wkr; Band; Church Choir; Concert Band; Mrchg Band; Vllybl; High Hon Roll; Jr NHS; NHS; Pres Schlr; Dist Band 87.

PHATUROS, WILLIAM; Riverview HS; Oakmont, PA; (3); 34/112; Varsity Clb; Capt Bsbl; Capt Ftbl; Capt Wrstlng; Phys Thrpy.

PHEASANT, SCOTT M; Academy HS; Erie, PA; (3); 1/226; Boy Scts; Band; Concert Band; Mrchg Band; High Hon Roll; Jr NHS; NHS; Eagle Sct Awd 86; Bst Clrnst Awd 84-87; Penn ST U; Elec Engnrng.

PHELAN, KATIE; Franklin Regional HS; Murrysville, PA; (4); 25/336; AFS; Pres Spanish Clb; SADD; Chorus; School Musical; JV Cheerleading; Var Pom Pon; High Hon Roll; NHS; Rotary Awd; PA ST U; Intl Rltns.

PHELAN, MATTHEW; Monsignor Bonner HS; Drexel Hill, PA; (3); 15/255; Intnl Clb; Stage Crew; Nwsp Ed-Chief; Nwsp Rptr; Nwsp Stf; Yrbk Stf; High Hon Roll; Hon Roll; NHS; Prtl Schlrshp HS 84; Diocesan Schlr-Clses Cabrini Coll 87; Comms.

PHELAN, PAULA; Saegertown HS; Meadville, PA; (4); 9/107; GAA; Letterman Clb; Spanish Clb; SADD; Varsity Clb; Stat Bsktbl; Var JV Sftbl; Var JV Vllybl; Hon Roll; Jr NHS; 3rd Pl-ST-SGRTWN Vrsty Vllybl-IN U Of PA 86; Gannon U; Lgl Asst.

PHELPS, DEANNA; Meadville Area SR HS; Meadville, PA; (2); Church Yth Grp; Latin Clb; Spanish Clb; Concert Band; Mrchg Band; Mgr(s); High Hon Roll; Hon Roll; Prfct Atten Awd; 2nd Rgnl Hstry Day 87; Cnty Band At Alleghany Coll 87.

PHELPS, SAM; Mc Keesport Area HS; Mc Keesport, PA; (4); Band; Mrchg Band; Trk; Amer Lgn Schl Awd 82-83; CA ST; Med.

PHENNEGER, STEPHEN; Coatesville Area SR HS; Coatesville, PA; (2); 25/550; Church Yth Grp; Drama Clb; Ski Clb; Chorus; School Musical; School Play; Rep Soph Cls; Rep Stu Cncl; Var Swmmng; NHS.

PHILIPS, CURT; Karns City HS; Chicora, PA; (4); 5/116; Exploring; Golf; Hon Roll; Butler CC Brd Trustees Acad Schlrshp Cert Acad Excllnce 87; Pres Acad Ftns Awd 87; Butler County CC; Arch.

PHILLIPPI, AMY JO; Seneca Valley HS; Zelienople, PA; (3); 4/331; Church Yth Grp; Cmnty Wkr; Chorus; High Hon Roll; Hon Roll.

PHILLIPPI, KEVIN; Rockwood Area HS; Rockwood, PA; (3); Computer Clb; Yrbk Stf; Wrstlng; Hon Roll; Art.

PHILLIPPI, LE ANNE; Hopewell SR HS; Aliquippa, PA; (3); 8/255; Latin Clb; Math Clb; Chorus; Church Choir; Flag Corp; Jazz Band; High Hon Roll; NHS; Church Yth Grp; Girl Scts; Marian Medal Awd 85; Acad All Am Awd 87; Pharmacy.

PHILLIPS, ALICIA; Downingtown SR HS; Downingtown, PA; (3); Library Aide; Chorus; Nwsp Stf; High Hon Roll; Hon Roll; Paramdc.

PHILLIPS, AMY; North Pocono HS; Lake Ariel, PA; (1); Church Yth Grp; Dance Clb; Ski Clb; Orch; Var Pom Pon; Gftd Pgm 86-87; Acclrtd Pgm 86-87; Physcl Thrpy.

PHILLIPS, AMY; Trinity Area HS; Washington, PA; (2); Off Civic Clb; Cmnty Wkr; Hosp Aide; Key Clb; Spanish Clb; Band; Concert Band; Mrchg Band; Orch; Symp Band; West Point; Bus Admin.

PHILLIPS, ANDREW JOHN; Punxsutawney Area HS; Rochester Mills, PA; (4); 81/246; Art Clb; Church Yth Grp; French Clb; Science Clb; Varsity Clb; Variety Show; Var L Bsbl; Var L Ftbl; Hon Roll; Rotary Awd; Gannon U; Bio.

PHILLIPS, ANNELEZE; Bethlehem Center SR HS; Vestaburg, PA; (2); Pep Clb; Varsity Clb; Sec Band; Concert Band; Mrchg Band; Pres Frsh Cls; Rep Soph Cls; Stu Cncl; Var Cheerleading; Hon Roll.

PHILLIPS, BARRY; Montoursville HS; Montoursville, PA; (3); German Clb; Key Clb; Band; Concert Band; Mrchg Band; Pep Band; Variety Show; Bus.

PHILLIPS, CAROLYN J; Butler SR HS; West Sunbury, PA; (4); DECA; Exploring; FNA; Girl Scts; Library Aide; Teachers Aide; Band; Concert Band; Drm & Bgl; Mrchg Band; Edinboro U Of PA; Med.

PHILLIPS, CHARLES; Moshannon Valley HS; Houtzdale, PA; (3); Chess Clb; Debate Tm; Latin Clb; Math Clb; Spanish Clb; Hon Roll; Math Tm.

PHILLIPS, CHERYL; Elizabeth Forward HS; Elizabeth, PA; (4); 11/297; Dance Clb; 4-H; Ski Clb; Spanish Clb; Nwsp Stf; Yrbk Stf; 4-H Awd; High Hon Roll; NHS; Spanish NHS; Womens Clb Of Elizabeth Schlrhp 87; PA ST U.

PHILLIPS, CHRISTIAN; Purchase Line HS; Cherry Tree, PA; (3); Band; Concert Band; Mrchg Band; School Play; Hon Roll; Prfct Atten Awd; Engr.

PHILLIPS, DANA; Carlynton HS; Pittsburgh, PA; (3); Drama Clb; JA; Nwsp Ed-Chief; Trk; Spanish Clb; Pom Pon; Powder Puff Ftbl; Swmmng; Hon Roll; Prfct Atten Awd; JA Top Slsprsn Awd 86-87; Sheldon Calvry Cmp Mrksmnshp Qualf Awd 86-87; Cert Merit Awd Engl 86-87; Elem Tchg.

PHILLIPS, DAVID; Pennsbury HS; Levittown, PA; (3); Computer Clb; Exploring; Stage Crew; Im Bsktbl; JV Ftbl; Elec Engrng.

PHILLIPS, DAWN; Tunkhannock Area HS; Tunkhannock, PA; (4); Letterman Clb; Ski Clb; Spanish Clb; Color Guard; Var Bsktbl; Stat Ftbl; Var Trk; Hon Roll; Presdntl Acad Ftns Awd 87; Penn ST U; Cmmnctns.

PHILLIPS, DEAN; Ambridge Area HS; Baden, PA; (3); Boy Scts; Pep Clb; Band; Concert Band; Mrchg Band; Var Socr; Var Tennis; Hon Roll; Church Yth Grp; Symp Band; Soccer Team Defnsv MVP Awd 86; Eagle Scout 87; Penn ST U; Engr.

PHILLIPS, DEBORAH; Hempfield HS; Landisville, PA; (3); Church Yth Grp; Dance Clb; Chorus; Rep Soph Cls; Rep Jr Cls; Rep Sr Cls; Rep Stu Cncl; JV Var Fld Hcky; Hon Roll; Intr Dcrtr.

PHILLIPS, DONALD; Brownsville HS; Grindstone, PA; (4); 9/200; VICA; Wrstlng; Hon Roll; DECA; VICA Clb-Cntstnt 3rd Pl Dsel Mech 86; OH Diesel Tech Inst; Dsl Mech.

PHILLIPS, ERIN; Penn Ftrafford HS; Irwin, PA; (3); 30/301; JCL; Latin Clb; Service Clb; Color Guard; Mrchg Band; Yrbk Stf; Twrlr; High Hon Roll; NHS; Ski Clb; Hnrs Coll Summer Pgm Arch Ball ST U 87; PA ST; Arch.

PHILLIPS, GARY; Danville HS; Riverside, PA; (4); Boy Scts; Drama Clb; Spanish Clb; School Play; Nwsp Rptr; JV Bowling; Eagle Scout 84; Amrcn Lgn Good Citznshp Citatn, PA House Of Reps Good Citznshp Citatn 85; Penn ST U; Law.

PHILLIPS, GLORIANN M; West Catholic HS; Philadelphia, PA; (3); Yrbk Rptr; High Hon Roll; Hon Roll; Lion Awd.

PHILLIPS, GREG; Waynesburg Central HS; Waynesburg, PA; (3); Chess Clb; Sec Trs Spanish Clb; Crs Cntry; Ftbl; Wrstlng; High Hon Roll; NHS.

PHILLIPS, HARMONY KAY; Shikellamy HS; Danville, PA; (3); 4/319; Pres German Clb; Speech Tm; Rep Mrchg Band; Nwsp Ed-Chief; Ed Yrbk Stf; Rep Jr Cls; Stu Cncl; Var Trk; Bausch & Lomb Sci Awd; NHS; German Natl Hnr Soc; PA Jr Acad Of Sci 1st Pl; Acdmc All-Amer; Rice; Med.

PHILLIPS, JACQUELYN; Harry S Truman HS; Levittown, PA; (4); 21/600; Church Yth Grp; Color Guard; Mrchg Band; Rep Stu Cncl; Var Trk; Hon Roll; NHS; Prfct Atten Awd; Grad Natl Hnrs Soc, Tmple U 87; Temple U Ambler; Psych.

PHILLIPS, JAMES; Arch Bishop Ryan HS For Boys; Philadelphia, PA; (2); 83/349; Civic Clb; JV Bsktbl; Hons 86-87; Accntng.

PHILLIPS, JAMES; Archbishop Wood HS For Boys; Warrington, PA; (3); Computer Clb; French Clb; Capt Math Tm; Office Aide; Scholastic Bowl; Nwsp Rptr; Bowling; Mgr(s); Trk; NHS; Sci Fair 1st Pl DE Vly Sci Fair Math 86, 3rd Pl 87; Top Awd Alg II 86; U PA; Actrl Sci.

PHILLIPS III, JOHN SCOTT; Abington Heights HS; Clarks Summit, PA; (3); 65/300; Boy Scts; Church Yth Grp; SADD; Rep Jr Cls; Var Swmmng; All Amer-100 Yd Brststrk 87; Pre-Med.

PHILLIPS, KARLENE; Ringgold HS; Eighty Four, PA; (2); Sec Pres 4-H; Ski Clb; Chorus; School Musical; Trs Sec Stu Cncl; Hon Roll; NHS; Washington & Jefferson; Advrtsg.

PHILLIPS, KATRINA; Oxford Area HS; Oxford, PA; (4); 4/197; Church Yth Grp; Chorus; Color Guard; Flag Corp; Nwsp Rptr; Crs Cntry; Trk; High Hon Roll; NHS; Law Enfrcmnt.

PHILLIPS, KRIS; Combria Hts HS; St Boniface, PA; (3); 55/180; Ski Clb; Chorus; VP Frsh Cls; VP Soph Cls; Hon Roll; Penn ST U; Civil Engr.

PHILLIPS, KRISTIN; Hanover SR HS; Hanover, PA; (3); Band; Chorus; Concert Band; Mrchg Band; School Musical; School Play; Swing Chorus; Nwsp Stf; Lit Mag; Bsktbl; Creative Wrtng.

PHILLIPS, LARRY; Western Beaver JR SR HS; Midland, PA; (3); Church Yth Grp; VP JA; Chorus; Nwsp Rptr; Yrbk Stf; Rep Jr Cls; Trs Stu Cncl; JV VP Bsktbl; Im Bowling; VP Trk; Achiever Awd 86-87; Adv.

PHILLIPS, LEEANN; Penn Cambria HS; Cresson, PA; (4); 7/206; Drama Clb; Soroptimist; Spanish Clb; SADD; Yrbk Stf; VP Frsh Cls; Stat Bsktbl; Co-Capt Cheerleading; Var JV Vllybl; High Hon Roll; Hi Schltc Achvt Awd 87; IN U Of PA; Acctng.

PHILLIPS, LISA; Fleetwood Area HS; Fleetwood, PA; (3); 31/118; VICA; Var JV Bsktbl; Var L Sftbl; Var L Tennis; Dntl Lab Tech.

PHILLIPS, LORETTA; Lake Lehman HS; Hunlock Creek, PA; (3); Golf; Hon Roll; Jr NHS; Odd Fllws Pilgrimage Yth 87; Med.

PHILLIPS, LORRAINE; Quakertown HS; Quakertown, PA; (3); 53/330; Ski Clb; SADD; Rep Soph Cls; VP Var Cheerleading; Mgr(s); Hon Roll; NHS; Anti-Smoking Comm 85-87; Trvl.

PHILLIPS, LYNN; Windber Area HS; Windber, PA; (4); 28/128; Church Yth Grp; JA; Math Clb; Band; Var JV Bsktbl; Var Capt Sftbl; Var JV Vllybl; High Hon Roll; Tri-Cnty Bsktbl Leag All-Star Tm, Hgh Acdmc/Athlt Awd US Army 86-87; X-Ray Tech.

PHILLIPS, RACHEL; Franklin Learning Center; Philadelphia, PA; (3); Exploring; Service Clb; Teachers Aide; Church Choir; Variety Show; Hon Roll; CC Of Phila; Nrsng.

PHILLIPS, RICKY; Philipsburg-Osceola HS; West Decatur, PA; (4); 72/234; French Clb; Crs Cntry; Wt Lftg; Wrstlng; God Cntry Awd; Goshin Jutsu Purple Belt 84-85; Wrstlng Ltrs; Penn ST; Ofcr.

PHILLIPS, ROBIN; W Middlesex JR SR HS; W Middlesex, PA; (3); 11/101; Spanish Clb; Band; Chorus; Mrchg Band; Stu Cncl; Cheerleading; Hon Roll; Jr NHS; NHS.

PHILLIPS, RONALD; Plymouth Whitemarsh SR HS; Conshohocken, PA; (3); Var Crs Cntry.

PHILLIPS, SCOTT; Shamokin Area HS; Shamokin, PA; (2); 48/250; Art Clb; Camera Clb; SADD; Ftbl.

PHILLIPS, SHAWN; South Williamsport Area HS; S Williamsport, PA; (3); 37/111; Band; Concert Band; Mrchg Band; School Musical; Symp Band; Yrbk Stf; Sec Stu Cncl; Bsktbl; Sftbl; Trk; Cnty Band 84-86; Rcrtnl Thrpy.

PHILLIPS, SYLVIA; St Marys Area HS; St Marys, PA; (3); 129/269; Art Clb; Church Yth Grp; Dance Clb.

PHILLIPS, TIM; Central HS; Martinsburg, PA; (3); Computer Clb; Debate Tm; Math Tm; Speech Tm; Varsity Clb; Trk; Wt Lftg; Wrstlng; PA ST; Aero Engr.

PHILLIPS, TODD K; East Lycoming JR & SR HS; Muncy, PA; (4); Spanish Clb; Bsbl; Bsktbl; High Hon Roll; Hon Roll; NHS; Grn & Wht Awd Wnnr 84-86; Lgn Pst 601 Schlrshp Awd 87; Grdtd Hghst Hnrs 87; PA ST U; Lbrl Arts.

PHILLIPS, TOM; Belle Vernon Area HS; Belle Vernon, PA; (3); Concert Band; Powder Puff Ftbl; Socr; Hon Roll; Acad America 84; Accntng.

PHILLIPS, TONIA; Minersville Area HS; Pottsville, PA; (3); FBLA; Ski Clb; Spanish Clb; SADD; Chorus; School Musical; Co-Capt Cheerleading; High Hon Roll; SBI; Secr.

PHIPPS, CHRISTINE; Archbishop Ryan For Girls; Philadelphia, PA; (3); 9/40; Cmnty Wkr; French Clb; Latin Clb; Science Clb; Band; Church Choir; Concert Band; Mrchg Band; NHS; Westchester U; Vet.

PHOENIX, HARVEY; West Catholic HS; Philadelphia, PA; (4); Church Yth Grp; Cmnty Wkr; SADD; Y-Teens; JV Bsktbl; Serra Intl-Serra Club Altar Server Awd 87; Medicine.

PHOENIX, TARA; Central Dauphin HS; Harrisburg, PA; (3); Church Yth Grp; Civic Clb; Exploring; Latin Clb; Pep Clb; Spanish Clb; Teachers Aide; Varsity Clb; Stage Crew; Nwsp Stf; Vrsty Athlt 85-86; Pres Dauphin Co Bar Assoc 87-88; Mock Trl Comp Law Explrs 86; U PA; Law.

PHU, LE VAN; Creative & Performing Arts HS; Philadelphia, PA; (3); Art Clb; Poster Awd 86; Energy Pstr Awd 85; Hnr Roll 84; Art.

PIANKA, KAREN E; Chambersburg Area HS; Chambersburg, PA; (4); 2/606; Church Yth Grp; German Clb; Chorus; Church Choir; Jazz Band; Orch; School Musical; High Hon Roll; NHS; Ntl Merit SF; PA Govs Schl Arts 86.

PIATT, HOWARD SCOTT; Lock Haven HS; Lock Haven, PA; (4); 15/242; Church Yth Grp; Model UN; Teachers Aide; Socr; Hon Roll; NHS; Lock Haven U; Scndry Ed Engl.

PICARDI, MICHAEL; St John Neumann HS; Philadelphia, PA; (2); 23/360; Computer Clb; Latin Clb; Math Tm; Q&S; Lit Mag; Ftbl; High Hon Roll; Top Algebra Stu Awd 85-87; Latin Fluency Awd 86-87; Penn ST U; Law.

PICARELLO, JOSEPH; Roman Catholic HS; Philadelphia, PA; (3); 16/121; SADD; Yrbk Stf; Hon Roll; NHS; Al Tegler Schlrshp 86 & 87; Serra Clb/Phila Awd-Altr Boy Soc 85; St Josephs U; Med.

PICARRO, MICHELE; New Castle HS; New Castle, PA; (2); Church Yth Grp; Cmnty Wkr; Hosp Aide; Red Cross Aide; Trk; Sec.

PICCIANO, VALERIE; Marple Newtown SR HS; Broomall, PA; (3); 15/324; Pres Church Yth Grp; VP SADD; Chorus; Orch; School Play; Nwsp Rptr; Mgr(s); NHS; Ntl Merit Ltr; French Clb; Grnd Lctrer Dist 46 Intl Order Rainbw Grls 86; ; Sec Interact Clb 87; Awd Excll Natl Hstry Day 86; Law.

PICCIONI, JENNIFER; Aliquippa HS; Aliquippa, PA; (2); Church Yth Grp; French Clb; Cheerleading; DAR Awd; Hon Roll.

PICCIRILLI, JOHN; Sharpsville Area HS; Sharpsville, PA; (3); Chess Clb; Math Clb; Science Clb; Chorus; JV Var Bsktbl; Hon Roll; NHS; Acctng.

PICCIRILLI, RHEA; Wyoming Area HS; Pittston, PA; (3); 59/250; Church Yth Grp; Drama Clb; Hosp Aide; Spanish Clb; Chorus; Pres Church Choir; Var L Sftbl; Var L Swmmng; Lycoming; Accntng.

PICCIRILLI, ROSANNA; Our Lady Of The Sacred Heart HS; Coraopolis, PA; (3); Hst Soph Cls; Hst Jr Cls; JV Cheerleading; L JV Vllybl; Hon Roll; Bus Adm.

PICCOLI, ALBERT; HS Of Engineering & Science; Phila, PA; (3); Am Leg Boys St; Teachers Aide; School Play; Stage Crew; Variety Show; Var Bsbl; Var Bsktbl; Var Socr; All Pblc Bsbl, Pblc Leag All-Star Tm Bsebl 87; Engrng.

PICCOLO, BRONWYN; St Marys Area HS; Saint Marys, PA; (4); 52/280; Hosp Aide; Office Aide; Red Cross Aide; Band; Concert Band; Mrchg Band; Stu Cncl; L Mgr(s); Timer; L Trk; Clarion U; Elem Educ.

PICCOLOMINI, MARLA; Laurel Highlands HS; Uniontown, PA; (4); 64/317; Cmnty Wkr; French Clb; Office Aide; Pep Clb; Nwsp Rptr; Var Sftbl; Im Vllybl; DAR Awd; Hon Roll; Jr NHS; Clemson U; Fncl Mng.

PICHECO, GARY; Northwestern HS; Albion, PA; (3); Computer Clb; FBLA; Varsity Clb; Bsbl; Bowling; Golf; Swmmng; Wt Lftg; Lion Awd; All-Cnty Ftbl Plyr 86; Most Outstndng Dfnsv Lnmn 86; Dayton; Bus Admn.

PICHER, AMANDA; Garnet Valley HS; Glen Mills, PA; (3); French Clb; Intnl Clb; Concert Band; Orch; School Musical; School Play; Lit Mag; NHS; Science Clb; High Hon Roll; Frnch Awd 85 & 87; 4th Pl In PA Jrnlsm Cntst Spnsrd By Govrs Cmmtte On Emplymnt Of Handicppd 87; Psych.

PICHIARELLO, MARY B; Bishop O Hara HS; Dunmore, PA; (4); 1/113; Computer Clb; French Clb; Latin Clb; Scholastic Bowl; Ed Nwsp Stf; Bausch & Lomb Sci Awd; High Hon Roll; Pres NHS; Hugh O Brien Yth Found 85; U Of Scranton; Law.

PICHLER, LINDA; Bethlehem Catholic HS; Bethlehem, PA; (3); 66/210; Pres Key Clb; SADD; Church Choir; Score Keeper; Hon Roll; Kiwanis Awd; Accntng.

PICKAR, ELIZABETH; St Pius X HS; Douglassvile, PA; (1); 35/146; Cmnty Wkr; Service Clb; SADD; Bsktbl; Hon Roll; Prfct Atten Awd; Bsktbl Svngs Bnd For Athlt Of Yr 86; Westchester U; Engl.

PICKELL, LISA; Spring Grove SR HS; Codorus, PA; (3); 49/301; VP Church Yth Grp; French Clb; Stage Crew; Nwsp Stf; Hon Roll; 200 Pt Pin Awd 85-86; Empire Beauty Schl.

PICKENHEIM, MARK; North Pocono HS; Moscow, PA; (3); 5/220; Ski Clb; Rep Stu Cncl; Trk; High Hon Roll; NHS; Trea Natl Hnr Soc 86-87.

PICKENS, JENNIFER; Northampton SR HS; Nazareth, PA; (3); Drama Clb; Girl Scts; Pep Clb; Spanish Clb; Swmmng; Rgnls Dance Cmpttn 1st Pl 86; Nation Dance Cmpttn 86; Exec Sec.

PICKETT, DEBORAH; Wyalusing Valley HS; Laceyville, PA; (4); 9/132; FBLA; Ski Clb; Spanish Clb; SADD; Yrbk Stf; Var Capt Bsktbl; Im Bowling; Var Capt Cheerleading; Var Sftbl; Var Vllybl; Outstndng Ltrmn, Outstndng SR Feml Athl 87; US Army Resrv Natl Schlr Athl Awd 87; Bloomsbrg U; Chem Tchr.

PIDGEON, KATE; Lakeland HS; Jermyn, PA; (3); 10/140; Trs Frsh Cls; Off Soph Cls; Off Jr Cls; Off Sr Cls; Rep Stu Cncl; L JV Bsktbl; Cheerleading; L JV Sftbl; Hon Roll; NHS; Med.

PIDRO, BRIAN; New Castle SR HS; New Castle, PA; (3); Yrbk Sprt Ed; Yrbk Stf; Var L Bsbl; Im Vllybl; NHS; Itln Clb Cls Rep 85-87; Engrng.

PIDRO, SAM; New Castle SR HS; New Castle, PA; (4); Library Aide; Vllybl; Pres Schlr; Pres Acdmcs Ftnss Awd 87; Doquesne U.

PIE, MARK A; Geibel HS; Connellsville, PA; (4); 24/81; Boy Scts; Church Yth Grp; French Clb; Math Tm; Science Clb; Ski Clb; Capt L Ftbl; Wt Lftg; French Hon Soc; Hon Roll; Air Force; Cardiovsclr Med.

PIECHNICK, CRAIG; Canon Mc Millan HS; Canonsburg, PA; (4); French Clb; Varsity Clb; Yrbk Stf; VP Stu Cncl; Bsbl; Ftbl; Wrstlng; High Hon Roll; NHS; Pres Schlr; US Naval Acad; Engrng.

PIECHOCKI, KRISTEN; Wyoming Area HS; Larksville, PA; (3); Art Clb; Key Clb; Var Socr; Hon Roll; Outstndng Schlstc Achvt; Ithaca NY; Art.

PIECK, MICHAEL; James M Coughlin HS; Plains, PA; (3); #6 In Class; Church Yth Grp; Drama Clb; Key Clb; Band; Chorus; Orch; Crs Cntry; High Hon Roll; NHS; Elec Engrng.

PIECKNICK, LORI; Trinity HS; Washington, PA; (3); 24/402; Sec Trs Exploring; French Clb; Trs Hosp Aide; Pep Clb; Ski Clb; Speech Tm; Yrbk Stf; Rep VP Stu Cncl; Cheerleading; High Hon Roll; Intl Law.

PIEHOTA, TANYA; Bishop Hafey HS; Hazleton, PA; (2); #2 In Class; Church Yth Grp; Pep Clb; Ski Clb; Rep Soph Cls; Rep Stu Cncl; JV Bsktbl; Sftbl; CC Awd; Elks Awd; High Hon Roll; Social Work.

PIENKOWSKA, ANNA; John W Hallahan HS; Philadelphia, PA; (3); 32/292; VP Church Yth Grp; Cmnty Wkr; Library Aide; Math Tm; School Musical; Yrbk Stf; High Hon Roll; Hon Roll; NHS; Ellis Grant 85-88; Mech Engrng.

PIERCE, BETH; Union Area Middle HS; New Castle, PA; (4); 16/67; Library Aide; SADD; Concert Band; Jazz Band; Mrchg Band; Pep Band; Yrbk Stf; Stat Trk; Hon Roll; NHS; Top 10 Percent Of Cls; Gannon U; Respiratory Thrpy.

PIERCE, CRAIG; Moniteau HS; Harrisville, PA; (3); Church Yth Grp; Drama Clb; Var L Ftbl; Var L Trk; Hon Roll.

PIERCE, DANIEL; Ft Le Boeuf HS; Waterford, PA; (3); Church Yth Grp; Computer Clb; Exploring; Am Leg Boys St; Vllybl; Hon Roll; Elec Engrng.

PIERCE, KARLA; Cumberland Valley HS; Mechanicsburg, PA; (3); Sec Church Yth Grp; Dance Clb; Girl Scts; Thesps; Orch; Hon Roll; Spanish NHS; Cmnty Wkr; Red Cross Aide; Spanish Clb; Soviet Am Peace Child Tour 86; Harrisburg Arts Magnet Schl 85-88; GS Slvr Awd For Ldrshp Cmny Svc 84; UCLA; Theatre.

PIERCE, LISA; Solanco HS; Kirkwood, PA; (2); Radio Clb; Spanish Clb; SADD; Teachers Aide; Cit Awd; Hon Roll; Prncpls Awd Bus Mth 87; Pre-Med.

PIERCE, MATT; Wilmington Area HS; New Wilmington, PA; (3); Church Yth Grp; Drama Clb; Band; Chorus; Church Choir; Concert Band; Jazz Band; Mrchg Band; Pep Band; School Play; Westminister Coll Hnrs Band 87; 2nd Pl Rnnr Up Regnl Speech Comptn 87; Clarion U; Music Professor.

PIERCE, MIKE; Cameron County HS; Emporium, PA; (2); 1/120; Church Yth Grp; Computer Clb; German Clb; Library Aide; Spanish Clb; Crs Cntry; Trk; Wrstlng; High Hon Roll; Hon Roll; Germ Hnr Scty 86-87; Natl Sci Olympiad 85-86; Mansfield U Wrtng Cont 87; Pre Med.

PIERCE, OLIVIA; Cedar Crest HS; Lebanon, PA; (4); 68/306; Church Yth Grp; Drama Clb; French Clb; Pep Clb; SADD; Concert Band; Mrchg Band; Vllybl; Hon Roll; Elizabethtown Coll; Bus.

PIERCE, RICHARD; Mercer HS; Hermitage, PA; (4); Boys Clb Am; Church Yth Grp; Ski Clb; Bsktbl; Golf; Socr; Hon Roll; Asset Mgmt.

PIERCE, SHERRI; W Mifflin Area HS; W Mifflin, PA; (4); 18/338; Exploring; Hosp Aide; Office Aide; Concert Band; Mrchg Band; Mat Maids; Score Keeper; High Hon Roll; NHS; Pres Schlr; Edinboro U; Elem/Spcl Educ.

PIERLOTT, MARYANN BILLIG; South Side HS; Clinton, PA; (3); Church Yth Grp; Ski Clb; Chorus; School Play; Variety Show; Powder Puff Ftbl; Trk; Vllybl; Hnovr Sftbl Leag All Stars 85; Penn ST; Accntng.

PIERMATTEO, VICTORIA; Upper Merion Area HS; King Of Prussia, PA; (4); 24/273; Computer Clb; Sec VP German Clb; Intnl Clb; Model UN; Chorus; School Musical; Nwsp Stf; Rep Stu Cncl; Ftbl; Im Vllybl; Pres Acadc Ftns & Temple U Pres Awds 87; Temple U; Finance.

PIEROSH, ROBERT; Harry S Truman HS; Levittown, PA; (4); Art Clb; School Musical; Rep Stu Cncl; FL Inst Tech; Advrtsng.

PIERRARD, DANA; West Allegheny HS; Mc Donald, PA; (2); VP FBLA; Color Guard; High Hon Roll; Hon Roll; 2nd Pl Entrepreneuship I 87; Fshn Mrchndsng.

PIERSON, DANIELA J; Central HS; Philadelphia, PA; (4); 10/330; Debate Tm; Chorus; Madrigals; Orch; School Musical; Trs Soph Cls; Hon Roll; NHS; Ntl Merit SF; 1st Pl In PA NATSP 84; 1st Pl Rgn NATSP 85; Most Acadmclly Promising Stu 84; U Of PA.

PIERSON, DUANE; Wilson Area HS; West Easton, PA; (4); 23/123; Boy Scts; Church Yth Grp; Debate Tm; Drama Clb; Model UN; Pres Band; Chorus; Church Choir; Concert Band; Pres Drm Mjr(t); P W Filer Schlrshp 87; Wilson Police Dept Schlrshp 87; Wilson Elem Schlrshp 87; U Of Scranton; Scl Sci.

PIERSON, THERESA; Nazareth Acad; Phila, PA; (3); Cmnty Wkr; Chorus; School Musical; Stage Crew; Lit Mag; Hon Roll; Bus Admn.

PIESESKI, KRISTIN; Penn Trafford HS; Levelgreen, PA; (3); 42/296; Drama Clb; JCL; Latin Clb; Varsity Clb; Chorus; Var L Swmmng; Var Trk; JV Vllybl; High Hon Roll; Hon Roll; Rookie Of Yr Swm Team 84-85; Mst Dedctd Swim Team 86-87; Law.

PIETROCINI, LISA; Allentown Central Catholic HS; Allentown, PA; (3); 50/266; Exploring; Hosp Aide; Math Clb; Pep Clb; Stu Cncl; Var L Bsktbl; Var Vllybl; Medical.

PIETROPAOLO, RENEE; Plum SR HS; Pittsburgh, PA; (3); Pres FTA; Mrchg Band; School Musical; School Play; Sec Trs Symp Band; Nwsp Stf; Yrbk Ed-Chief; NHS; Ntl Merit Ltr; AFS; 1st Pl Cltrl Arts Musical Comp 85-86; 2nd Pl JR Acad Sci 86-87.

PIETSCHMANN, CAROL; Avon Grove HS; Lincoln Univ, PA; (3); Chorus; Penn ST.

PIGMAN, MATTHEW MACKIE; Peterstwp HS; Bridgeville, PA; (4); Church Yth Grp; Cmnty Wkr; Letterman Clb; Varsity Clb; Lit Mag; Ice Hcky; Tennis; Regnl Wnnr Cult Art Cont 86-87; Yng Repub Clb; Hnr Grad; Bucknell U; Pre-Law.

PIKE, BRADLEY A; Altoona Area HS; Altoona, PA; (4); 68/716; Art Clb; Computer Clb; French Clb; Science Clb; Lit Mag; Rep Soph Cls; Rep Jr Cls; Rep Sr Cls; Stu Cncl; PA ST U; Comp Sci.

PIKULSKY, RICHELLE; Uniontown SR HS; Uniontown, PA; (4); 9/290; VP JA; Capt Drill Tm; Trs Jr Cls; Trs Sr Cls; Stu Cncl; High Hon Roll; Pres NHS; Pres Schlr; U Schlrs Schlrshp 87; Strght A-S Awd 87; Duquesne U; Phrmcy.

PILARCIK, FRANK; Frazier HS; Perryopolis, PA; (3); Var L Ftbl; Wt Lftg; Pittsburgh; Civil Engrng Tech.

PILARSKI, LORRAINE; Mercy Vocational HS; Philadelphia, PA; (4); 7/133; Nwsp Ed-Chief; Ed Nwsp Rptr; Hon Roll; Budd Employee Exch Schlrshp 87; 2nd Hnrs 87; Bus Ed Awd 87; CC Philadelphia; Jstc.

PILCAVAGE, MATTHEW; Meyers HS; Wilkes Barre, PA; (2); Ski Clb; Hon Roll; Bus.

PILEGGI, DENISE; Upper Moreland HS; Willow Grove, PA; (3); 80/276; Church Yth Grp; Stu Cncl; Var Bsktbl; Var Fld Hcky; Im Socr; Var Sftbl; Hon Roll.

PILLAR, SAMANTHA R; Saint Francis Acad; Allentown, PA; (4); Church Yth Grp; Drama Clb; Chorus; School Musical; Yrbk Stf; Trs Stu Cncl; Hon Roll; Pres Schlr; Schltc Pblctns Awd 87; 1st Pl Rgnl, 2nd Pl ST PA Jr Acad Sci 86; Mary Wshngtn Coll; Hstrc Prsrvt.

PILLAY, KAMALA; Wilmington Area HS; New Castle, PA; (3); Dance Clb; Drill Tm; Variety Show; Var Gym; Var Powder Puff Ftbl; Tennis; Hon Roll.

PILLUS, MELISSA; Pottsville Area HS; Pottsville, PA; (3); 90/230; Aud/Vis; Cmnty Wkr; Hosp Aide; Latin Clb; Ski Clb; Spanish Clb; Band; Cheerleading; Swmmng; Hon Roll; Kutztown U; Art Educ.

PILSTON, REBECCA; Highlands SR HS; Tarentum, PA; (4); 21/281; Intnl Clb; Trs Key Clb; Office Aide; Band; Color Guard; Mrchg Band; Stat Swmmng; NHS; Pres Schlr; Rotary Club Schlrshp 87; U Pittsburgh; Pre-Law.

PILTZ, MICHAEL D; Brandywine Heights Area HS; Mertztown, PA; (3); Pres Aud/Vis; Quiz Bowl; School Play; Stage Crew; Var Tennis; Var Vllybl; High Hon Roll; NHS; Ntl Merit Ltr; Cert Of Acad Excllnc-Earth Sci & Engl; Cert Outstndg Achvt-Ntl Engrng Aptd Tst; Cert Achvt Amer Cltrs; PA ST; Telecmmnctns.

PINARDI, MARIO; Laurel Highlands SR HS; Uniontown, PA; (3); 19/250; Drama Clb; Band; Concert Band; Mrchg Band; School Play; Nwsp Ed-Chief; Nwsp Rptr; Yrbk Stf; High Hon Roll; NHS; Advsry Bd OU H S Publctns Wrkshp 87; Provosts Day Fnlst U Of Ptsbrgh 87; Lead Pole Mck Const Cvn 87; OH U; Jrnlsm.

PINCHOT, DANIEL; Ambridge Area HS; Freedom, PA; (4); 90/240; Pep Clb; Political Wkr; Red Cross Aide; Spanish Clb; Thesps; Band; VP Chorus; School Musical; Swing Chorus; Variety Show; M Wilson Awd 87; Dist V Dist & Hnrs Chorus Fstvl 85-87; PA ST U; Cmnctns.

PINCHOTTI, CHRISTINA; Monaca JR SR HS; Monaca, PA; (3); Pres Jr Cls; Hon Roll; Pep Clb; Ski Clb; Sec Spanish Clb; Trs Frsh Cls; Stat Bsktbl; Var Cheerleading; Var Vllybl; Pittsburg U; Psych.

PINCHOTTI, STEVE; Beaver Area HS; Beaver, PA; (2); French Clb; Ski Clb; Socr; High Hon Roll; Hon Roll; Sccr Ltr 86-87; Comp Tech.

PINE, AMY; Chambersburg Area SR HS; Marion, PA; (3); 28/697; Hosp Aide; Spanish Clb; Band; Concert Band; Mrchg Band; Pep Band; Hon Roll; Hlth Occptns Stu Of Amer Rprtr 86-87; Hlth.

PINE, RAYMOND; Northeast Catholic HS; Philadelphia, PA; (3); 51/400; Chess Clb; Band; Concert Band; Jazz Band; Mrchg Band; Trk; Hon Roll; NHS; Prfct Atten Awd; Musc Schlrshp 86; Sci.

PINER, CHERYL; Northeast HS; Philadelphia, PA; (4); #189 In Class; Girl Scts; Library Aide; Hon Roll; Outstndng Prtcptn In Drexel Univ Upward Bound Pgm 84-87; Temple Univ; Med Tech.

PINES, NOAH; Haverford HS; Havertown, PA; (3); Nwsp Rptr; Nwsp Stf; Yrbk Stf; Capt Ice Hcky; French Hon Soc; High Hon Roll; NHS; Law.

PINKERTON, ANDRE LEE; Williams Valley JR/Sr HS; Tower City, PA; (4); 21/97; Trs Art Clb; Ski Clb; Bowling; High Hon Roll; Hon Roll; Academic All American Student 84-85 & 85-86.

PINKERTON, OWEN J; Cumberland Valley HS; Camp Hill, PA; (3); 109/578; Boy Scts; Church Yth Grp; Debate Tm; Latin Clb; Model UN; Ski Clb; Im Bsktbl; Im Socr; JV Var Trk; Hon Roll; Psych.

PINKETTI, PAULA; W Chester East HS; West Chester, PA; (3); 26/429; Church Yth Grp; Rep Frsh Cls; VP Soph Cls; Off Stu Cncl; JV Bsktbl; Im Sftbl; DAR Awd; French Hon Soc; High Hon Roll; Hon Roll.

PINKHAM, TODD; Somerset Area SR HS; Somerset, PA; (4); 31/239; Off Art Clb; VP JA; Q&S; Trs Spanish Clb; School Play; Tennis; Gov Hon Prg Awd; Hon Roll; NHS; VFW Awd; IN U PA Dstngshd Achvr Schlrshp Awd 87; Smrst Cnty Art Assoc Awd 87; Millie Mtthws Mem Art Awd 82-84; IN U PA; Art.

PINKNEY, TODD; Bishop Mc Devitt HS; Harrisburg, PA; (3); Boy Scts; Ski Clb; Band; Concert Band; Jazz Band; Mrchg Band; School Musical; Variety Show; Ftbl; Var L Tennis; Keystone Boys St Grad 87; Penn ST; Music.

PINKOS, STEVE; Peters Township HS; Mcmurray, PA; (3); 39/241; Church Yth Grp; Political Wkr; Varsity Clb; Var Ftbl; Wt Lftg; Ski Clb; JV Var Bsbl; JV Var Bsktbl; French Hon Soc; Hon Roll; Poetry Cntst Wnnr 86; Pltcl Sci.

PINKOVSKY, LYNN; Duquesne HS; Duquesne, PA; (4); 4/84; Office Aide; Band; Color Guard; DAR Awd; High Hon Roll; Hon Roll; NHS; Offcr Cmrcl Bus Clb 86-87; Hmcmng Ct 86-87.

PINOLA, STEPHANIE; Gwynedd Mercy Acad; Blue Bell, PA; (2); Art Clb; Drama Clb; Stu Cncl; Var Tennis; JV Trk; Camera Clb; Stage Crew; Rep Soph Cls; JV Bsktbl; JV Crs Cntry; ST & Regnl Racquetball Champn 81-87; Natl Racquetball Champn 84-87; Art & Wrld Hist Awd 86-87; Art.

PINTI, KIM; Sharon HS; Sharon, PA; (4); 55/158; Exploring; French Clb; Hosp Aide; School Play; Cheerleading; Gym; Swmmng; Hon Roll; Penn St U; Pre-Med.

PINTO, CHRISTINE; Western Wayne HS; Lake Ariel, PA; (3); Church Yth Grp; FBLA; Flag Corp; Hon Roll; Intl Stu Ldrshp Inst 85; Advrtsng.

PINTO, YVONNE; Archbishop Prendergast HS; Yeadon, PA; (3); 38/327; Aud/Vis; Church Yth Grp; Church Choir; Gym; Hon Roll; Prfct Atten Awd; Second Hnrs; Excllnc Chm Awd.

PIOCQUIDIO, LISA; Aliquippa HS; Aliquippa, PA; (4); 8/150; Aud/Vis; French Clb; Hosp Aide; Band; Concert Band; Drm Mjr(t); Mrchg Band; Pep Band; Yrbk Rptr; Yrbk Stf; Penn St U; Cmmnctns.

PIONTEK, CHRIS; St Pius X HS; Pottstown, PA; (1); 41/148; JV Bsktbl; Var Golf; Hon Roll; Am Leg Awd 85-86; Bucciaglia Mem Awd 85-86.

PIONTKOWSKI, KAREN; John S Fine HS; Nanticoke, PA; (4); 34/242; FBLA; Drill Tm; Nwsp Stf; Stat Bsktbl; High Hon Roll; NHS; Acadmc All Amercn 86; Luzerne County CC; Mdcl Sec.

PIOTROWSKI, CARI-LYNN; Allentown Central Catholic HS; Allentown, PA; (3); Church Yth Grp; Key Clb; Sec Frsh Cls; Sec Soph Cls; Sec Jr Cls; Sec Sr Cls; Var Capt Bsktbl; Var Capt Crs Cntry; Var Capt Sftbl; Hon Roll; 3 Vrsty Ltrs Bsktbl, Sftbl & X Cntry 84-85; ST Champs Bsktbl Tm Capt 87; Dist XI All Star Tm 86-87; Elementary Education.

PIOTROWSKI, MICHAEL; Northeast Catholic HS; Philadelphia, PA; (3); Science Clb; Teachers Aide; Yrbk Stf; Im Trk; Hon Roll; NHS; Mst Imprvd Oarsmn Awd Rowng 85; All Cathlc Rowing 87; FL Inst Tech; Marine Bio.

PIPA, ANNE; Southern Columbia Area HS; Elysburg, PA; (3); Pres SADD; Varsity Clb; Band; Chorus; Concert Band; Jazz Band; School Play; Stat Bsktbl; Var L Crs Cntry; Var L Trk; Drm Tchr.

PIPER, CARMEL; Ligonier Valley HS; Latrobe, PA; (4); 1/154; Pres Church Yth Grp; Trs NFL; Pres Science Clb; Pres Band; School Musical; Ed Yrbk Stf; Trk; NHS; Ntl Merit Ltr; Art Clb; Natl Elks Fndtn Schlrshp 86-87; Natl Hnr Soc Schlrshp 86-87; Chnnl II Tp Of Clss 86-87; PA ST U; Arch Engnrng.

PIPER, DIXIE; Hollidaysburg Area SR HS; Duncansville, PA; (3); Latin Clb; Science Clb; Chorus; Orch; Hon Roll; NHS; Educ.

PIPER, JILLIAN; Neshannock HS; New Castle, PA; (3); 9/102; School Play; Nwsp Bus Mgr; Nwsp Ed-Chief; Nwsp Rptr; Yrbk Ed-Chief; VP Jr Cls; Hon Roll; Sec NHS; Cmnty Wkr; Drama Clb; Pres Acad Fit Awd 85; Hnr Roll 85 & 87; PA JR Acad Of Sci Awd 86; PA ST U; Jrnlsm.

PIPER, LEE; West Greene Middle/SR HS; Waynesburg, PA; (3); 14/130; Varsity Clb; Nwsp Stf; Var Bsbl; JV Var Bsktbl; Var Ftbl; High Hon Roll; Gftd/Tlntd Acadmc Stdy 84-86; Ldng Scorermst Hts Bsbl-Penn WPIAL 86; Schl Rcrd Batting Avg 86; Phrmcy.

PIPER, THOMAS; Juniata HS; Pt Royal, PA; (3); Varsity Clb; Var L Ftbl; JV Wrstlng; Hon Roll.

PIPHER, KRISTY; Cumberland Valley HS; Mecahnicsburg, PA; (3); 193/587; Church Yth Grp; Latin Clb; SADD; Chorus; Mrchg Band; School Musical; Nwsp Rptr; Nwsp Stf; Key Clb; Color Guard; Crew Mbr Of Mon-Mcdnlds 87; Educ.

PIPICH, KIMBERLY M; Elizabeth-Forward HS; Mc Keesport, PA; (3); 19/345; Exploring; French Clb; Sec Girl Scts; Hosp Aide; Jazz Band; Sec Mrchg Band; Hon Roll; NHS; St Elizabeth Ann Seton Awd 85; Radlgc Technlgy.

PIPPIS, ELLENI; Liberty SR HS; Bethlehem, PA; (3); 21/429; Church Yth Grp; Hosp Aide; Model UN; Chorus; Church Choir; Orch; Yrbk Stf; High Hon Roll; Hon Roll; NHS; Rookie Of Yr Awd-Mst Hrs Vlntrd-Smmr 85; Med.

PIRAINO, LEE; Lakeland JR SR HS; Jermyn, PA; (4); French Clb; FHA; Yrbk Stf; Hon Roll; NHS; Prsdntl Acdmc Ftnss Awd 87; Marywood Coll; Scl Wrkr.

PIREAUX, KELLIE; Charleroi Area JR SR HS; N Charleroi, PA; (4); 2/160; French Clb; Office Aide; SADD; Varsity Clb; Rep Sr Cls; Powder Puff Ftbl; Dnfth Awd; High Hon Roll; NHS; Sal; N Charleroi Tst Strs Outstndng Stu 87; Frgn Lang Awd 87; Pres Acdmc Ftnss Awd 87; PA ST U.

PIRO, FRANK S; Upper Dublin HS; Ambler, PA; (3); 9/303; Aud/Vis; Drama Clb; FBLA; Intnl Clb; Radio Clb; Science Clb; Trs SADD; School Musical; Rep Frsh Cls; Trs Soph Cls; PJAS Sci Fair-Regionals-1st Pl 85-86; PJAS Sci Fair-State-2nd Pl 85; Monco Sci Fair-Hon Mention 85; Comm.

PIROCH, JOSEPH; Meadville Area SR HS; Meadville, PA; (4); 5/280; Debate Tm; French Clb; German Clb; JCL; Latin Clb; Math Tm; NFL; Speech Tm; Im Bsbll; Im Bsktbl; John Marshall Schlr 87; Franklin Coll.

PIROLLO, ROBERT; Downingtown SR HS; Downingtown, PA; (3); 286/648; Church Yth Grp; Spanish Clb; Band; Church Choir; Concert Band; Jazz Band; Mrchg Band; Im Tennis; Intl Bus.

PIROLLO, SALVATORE; St John Neuman HS; Philadelphia, PA; (4); 140/390; Teachers Aide; Ftbl; Humane Soc Awd 84; Bus.

PIRRELLO, MICHAEL G; Waynesboro Area SR HS; Waynesboro, PA; (4); 1/382; Art Clb; Library Aide; School Musical; Yrbk Stf; Lit Mag; Cit Awd; High Hon Roll; NHS; Ntl Merit SF; Citiz Of Mth Waynesboro Area SR HS 86; PHEAA Cert Of Mrt 86; PA Gvrnrs Schl For Sci Cert Of Attndn.

PIRRELLO, SUSAN; Waynesboro Area SR HS; Waynesboro, PA; (3); Pres Trs Art Clb; Intnl Clb; Library Aide; Chorus; Stage Crew; Yrbk Phtg; Yrbk Stf; High Hon Roll; Hon Roll; NHS; Vsl Art Wrkshp La Grange Coll 87; Cmmrcl Art.

PIRRIS, JOHN; Central Catholic HS; Washington, PA; (3); 9/300; Ski Clb; Ftbl; Socr; JV Var Wrstlng; High Hon Roll; NHS.

PIRROTTA, KATHRYN ANN COLETTE; Peters Township HS; Mc Murray, PA; (4); 1/242; VP Intnl Clb; Rep Key Clb; Pres Speech Tm; Mrchg Band; Yrbk Stf; NHS; Ntl Merit SF; Church Yth Grp; Debate Tm; NFL; Double Ruby Awd Ntl Fornsc Leag 86; 2nd Pl Allegany Singer Resrch Inst Sci Comp 86; Yale U; Chem Engr.

PISANO, KAREN; Warwick HS; Lititz, PA; (3); 62/300; Drama Clb; Thesps; Capt Band; Chorus; Mrchg Band; School Musical; School Play; Stat Trk; Im Vllybl; High Hon Roll; Vol Svc Awd 84-87; Drama Cmpttns Bst Mnlgue 87; 2nd Pl ST Wmns Clb Drama Cmpttns 87; Mount Holyoke; Intl Bus.

PISANO, MICHAEL; Nwe Brighton SR HS; New Brighton, PA; (3); 19/161; Am Leg Boys St; Church Yth Grp; Computer Clb; Chorus; Church Choir; L Tennis; Hon Roll; Engrng.

PISARCHICK, MICHAEL; Brockway Area HS; Brockway, PA; (3); 7/89; Var L Ftbl; Var L Wrstlng; Hon Roll; Little 12 All Cnfrnc 86; Dist 9 Wrstlng Chmp 86; Brockway Inc Essy Wnnr 85; Sprts Med.

PISARCHICK, TAMMY; Lynesville HS; Linesville, PA; (4); 60/89; DECA; Pep Clb; Trs SADD; Mgr(s); JV Vllybl; 3rd Pl DECA Shadow Box Cmptn 87.

PISARCIK, MARK; Fort Cherry HS; Hickory, PA; (3); Drama Clb; French Clb; Math Clb; Science Clb; Ski Clb; School Play; Stu Cncl; Bsbl; Bsktbl; High Hon Roll.

PISAREK, THERESA; St Paul Cathedral HS; Pittsburgh, PA; (4); 12/56; Church Yth Grp; VP FBLA; Nwsp Sprt Ed; Nwsp Stf; Yrbk Stf; Rep Frsh Cls; Stu Cncl; Var Cheerleading; High Hon Roll; NHS; 1st Pl FBLA Rgn 24 Stengrphr I 86; IN U Pennsylvania; Rsprtry Thr.

PISCIONERI, DINA; Penns Hills SR HS; Pittsburgh, PA; (3); Church Yth Grp; Exploring; Spanish Clb; Drill Tm; School Musical; School Play; Yrbk Stf; VP Soph Cls; Rep Jr Cls; Rep Sr Cls; Hnr Roll Typing Awd 86-87; Gregg Short Hand Theory Awd 86-87; Athlt Awd 86; Prlgl Secy.

PISIECZKO, FRANCINE; St Huberts HS For Girls; Philadelphia, PA; (3); 267/421; Church Yth Grp; Cmnty Wkr; Exploring; Pres FNA; Hosp Aide; Office Aide; Red Cross Aide; SADD; Stage Crew; Swmmng; Millersville U; Rsptry Thrpy.

PISKAI, RACHANEE; Villa Maria Acad; Exton, PA; (3); 5/98; VP Trs Church Yth Grp; Debate Tm; Mu Alpha Theta; School Musical; Ed Yrbk Rptr; Im Fld Hcky; JV Tennis; High Hon Roll; Ntl Merit SF; Math Tm; Hgh Obrn Ldrshp Semnr Ambsdr 86; Physics Awd 87.

PISKURA, KIM; Bishop Mc Cort HS; Johnstown, PA; (4); Pep Clb; Chorus; Nwsp Ed-Chief; Nwsp Rptr; Nwsp Stf; Yrbk Phtg; Yrbk Stf; High Hon Roll; Rotary Awd; German Clb; Tribune Democrat Schlstc Journlst Awd 87; California U Of PA; Cmmnctns.

PISKURICH, KAREN; North Catholic HS; Pittsburgh, PA; (3); High Hon Roll; NHS.

PISTON, EDWARD; Wyoming Valley West HS; Plymouth, PA; (4); 2/397; Math Clb; Rep Stu Cncl; Capt Vllybl; Cit Awd; JETS Awd; Pres NHS; NEDT Awd; Sal; J P Peeler Chem & William Garnet Math Awds 87; Penn ST; Elec Engrng.

PISTORIA, LISA; Deer Lakes JR-SR HS; Gibsonia, PA; (4); 25/193; Computer Clb; Drama Clb; French Clb; Girl Scts; Office Aide; Ski Clb; Varsity Clb; School Musical; School Play; Rep Stu Cncl; Physcl Educ Awd-$50 U S Bond 87; Clarion U; Intl Bus.

PITCAVAGE, HOLLY; Dallas SR HS; Shavertown, PA; (3); 1/211; Chorus; Capt Flag Corp; Madrigals; Stage Crew; Yrbk Stf; Off Soph Cls; Off Stu Cncl; High Hon Roll; NHS; NEDT Awd; Luzerne Co Math Teachers Assoc Cntst 87; Wellesley Book Awd 87; Dallas HS Math Awd, Sci Awd 86 & 87; Sci.

PITKOW, STEPHANIE; Bensalem HS; Bensalem, PA; (2); Key Clb; Math Tm; SADD; Nwsp Stf; Tennis; Trk; High Hon Roll; Hon Roll; NHS.

PITT, RICHARD N; W B Saul H S Of Ag Sciences; Philadelphia, PA; (4); 3/151; Church Yth Grp; Debate Tm; Exploring; FFA; Church Choir; Nwsp Sprt Ed; VP Sr Cls; Im Socr; Im Vllybl; High Hon Roll; Black Achvt Awd $1000 87; NROTC Schlrshp 87; PA ST U; Micro.

PITTA, GINA; Carlisle HS; Carlisle, PA; (4); 80/400; Church Yth Grp; Pep Clb; Ski Clb; Spanish Clb; Band; Color Guard; Mrchg Band; Sftbl; Swmmng; Trk; Clemson U; Med.

PITTERLE, DENISE; Greensburg Central Catholic HS; Greensburg, PA; (3); 3/231; Trs AFS; Trs Church Yth Grp; Ed Yrbk Stf; Rep Soph Cls; Rep Jr Cls; VP Sr Cls; L Im Sftbl; L Im Vllybl; High Hon Roll; Sec NHS; Bus Mgmt.

PITTMAN, CARRIE; Carrick HS; Pittsburgh, PA; (3); Sec Church Yth Grp; Q&S; Ski Clb; Spanish Clb; Nwsp Stf; Stu Cncl; Cheerleading; Powder Puff Ftbl; Hon Roll.

PITTMAN, DANA; Simon Gratz HS; Philadelphia, PA; (4); 10/300; Church Yth Grp; Teachers Aide; VP Church Choir; Hon Roll; Bus Admin.

PITTMAN, DONALD; Simon Gratz HS; Philadelphia, PA; (3); Debate Tm; JA; Ftbl; Hon Roll; Ntl Merit Schol; Prfct Atten Awd; VP Frsh Cls; Off Jr Cls; Off Sr Cls; Schl Svc Awd 87; Law Prjct Cmpltn Awd 86; Pres/Stu Rep At Temple U 87; Temple; Corp Law.

PITTMAN, EXELEE; Burgettstown Area JR SR HS; Burgettstown, PA; (3); 4-H; French Clb; Ski Clb; Drill Tm; Hon Roll; SR Jazz Co 85-86; Rock-N-Roll Court 86; Dance.

PITTMAN, JUDI; Greencastle Antrim HS; Greencastle, PA; (3); Church Yth Grp; Band; Chorus; Church Choir; Color Guard; Concert Band; Mrchg Band; Twrlr; RN.

PITTS, ISAAC R; Mastbaum Voc Tech HS; Philadelphia, PA; (3); VICA; Prfct Atten Awd; MVP Awd Cmnty Vllybl Tm 85 & 86; Drexel U; Elec Engrng.

PITUS, KRISTIN; Forest City Regional HS; Browndale, PA; (3); #7 In Class; German Clb; Hosp Aide; Letterman Clb; Stu Cncl; Var Capt Bsktbl; Var Capt Crs Cntry; NHS; Art Clb; Cmnty Wkr; Drama Clb; Natl Sci Merit Awds Chem, Bio 87, 86; Natl Ldrshp & Svc Awd 87; Occuptnl Thrpy.

PITZER, JEFFREY; New Castle SR HS; New Castle, PA; (4); 19/240; AFS; VP Church Yth Grp; Computer Clb; Math Tm; Quiz Bowl; Stat Bsktbl; Var Bowling; Var Tennis; Hon Roll; NHS; Finc.

PITZER, KEVIN; New Castle SR HS; New Castle, PA; (4); 12/232; Computer Clb; Spanish Clb; Mgr(s); Trk; Wt Lftg; JV Wrstlng; NHS; Prfct Atten Awd; Anesthesia.

PITZER, MICHELE; Wilmington Area HS; New Wilmington, PA; (4); Dance Clb; Drill Tm; Sec Soph Cls; Sec Jr Cls; Sec Sr Cls; JV Gym; JV Var Powder Puff Ftbl; Hon Roll; Drama Clb; Library Aide; Hmcmng Queen 87; Queen-Sr Prom 87; Kent ST U; Real Est.

PIVETZ, TIMOTHY R; Mount Lebanon HS; Pittsburgh, PA; (4); 15/537; Church Yth Grp; Exploring; Latin Clb; Rep Stu Cncl; JV Bsbl; Im Bsktbl; Im Ftbl; High Hon Roll; Ntl Merit SF; Prfct Atten Awd; Math.

PIVOVARNIK, JEFF; Abington Heights HS; Clarks Summit, PA; (3); 31/292; Boy Scts; Church Yth Grp; Latin Clb; Var L Bsktbl; JV Var Ftbl; Cit Awd; Hon Roll; NHS; Rotary Awd; MIP Bsktbl 86-87; Vly Vw Rndbl Tourn MVP Bsktbl 87; Law.

PIXLEY, TRACY; Pleasant Valley HS; Kresgeville, PA; (3); Math Tm; OEA; SADD; Teachers Aide; Varsity Clb; Trs Frsh Cls; Trs Soph Cls; Stu Cncl; Var Cheerleading; Trk; U AZ; Pol Sci.

PIZANO, JOS; Wyoming Area HS; Wyoming, PA; (3); Chess Clb; Spanish Clb; JV Trk; Var Vllybl; Hon Roll; Spnsh.

PIZARRO, SHELLY; Philadelphia HS For Girls; Philadelphia, PA; (4); 28/365; Church Yth Grp; French Clb; Yrbk Stf; JV Vllybl; French Hon Soc; Hon Roll; Mrktng.

PIZER, STEPHANIE; Indiana Area HS; Indiana, PA; (1); 126/310; Key Clb; Yrbk Stf; Hon Roll; Vrsty Ltr Rifle Team 86-87; IUP; Intr Decoration.

PIZII, GEOFF; Henderson HS; W Chester, PA; (3); Rep Frsh Cls; Rep Stu Cncl; Var Capt Socr; Temple U; Cmnctns.

PIZUR, RICK; North Pocono HS; Moscow, PA; (3); Ski Clb; High Hon Roll; NHS; Eng.

PIZZELLA, JUSTIN; Springdale HS; Cheswick, PA; (4); 5/125; Art Clb; Spanish Clb; Nwsp Rptr; Off Frsh Cls; Off Soph Cls; Off Jr Cls; Off Sr Cls; Off Stu Cncl; Var Capt Socr; High Hon Roll; All WPIAL 85-86; USSF Referee 83-86; High Hnr Roll; Engrng.

PIZZI, JENNIFER; Washington HS; Washington, PA; (2); Key Clb; Ski Clb; Spanish Clb; Band; Concert Band; Mrchg Band; Symp Band; JV Var Cheerleading; Tennis; Trk.

PIZZI, MARK; Arch Bishop Carroll HS; Havertown, PA; (4); 90/400; Math Clb; Ski Clb; Stage Crew; Yrbk Phtg; Rep Sr Cls; Im Bsktbl; JV Ftbl; Var Trk; Im Wt Lftg; Var Wrstlng; Drexell U; Bus.

PIZZUTO, ROSAMARIA; West Catholic Girls HS; Philadelphia, PA; (3); 40/246; Hosp Aide; Office Aide; Yrbk Stf; Hon Roll; Ital II Awd 85-86; Med.

PLACE, JENNIFER; Bradford Central Christian HS; Bradford, PA; (2); Church Yth Grp; Computer Clb; Drama Clb; French Clb; Pep Clb; SADD; Nwsp Rptr; Nwsp Stf; Natl Gld Of Piano Plyrs-NFSM 84-85; Natl Gld Of Piano Plyrs-Natl 82-83; Natl Gld Of Piano Plyrs-St; Kent ST U; Jrnlsm.

PLACE, KEVIN; East Stroudsburg Area HS; E Stroudsburg, PA; (3); 4/260; Boy Scts; Church Yth Grp; French Clb; Math Tm; Model UN; Trk; High Hon Roll; NHS; Rfle Tm 86-87; Srvyng Engr.

PLACEK, TRACY; Our Lady Of The Sacred Heart HS; Coraopolis, PA; (4); 10/57; Church Choir; School Musical; Mgr Bsktbl; Bowling; Coach Actv; Gym; Pres Schlr; Hnrs Schlrshp Edinboro U 87; Grad Top 10 Hgh Hnrs 87; Edinboros Hnrs Pgm 87; Edinboro U; Med Tech.

PLACK, MATTHEW; Susquehanna Township HS; Harrisburg, PA; (4); Letterman Clb; Model UN; Political Wkr; Quiz Bowl; Yrbk Sprt Ed; Hon Roll; Ntl Merit Ltr; Pres Sr Cls; Var Capt Crs Cntry; Var Trk; Pres Natl Hnr Soc 87; Western MD Coll; Pltcl Sci.

PLANK, RUSS; Upper Merion SR HS; King Of Prussia, PA; (3); 5/295; Math Tm; Spanish Clb; Rep Soph Cls; Rep Jr Cls; JV Bsbl; Im Bsktbl; Var Capt Socr; Im Vllybl; High Hon Roll; NHS.

PLANK, SONJA; Newport JR SR HS; Newport, PA; (3); 8/117; Church Yth Grp; Pres 4-H; Chorus; Church Choir; Mrchg Band; School Musical; School Play; Swing Chorus; JV Sftbl; 4-H Awd; Prfct Atten Awd 84-85; Hnr Roll 84-86; Intrmrl Vllybl 85-86; PA ST; Acctng.

PLAPPERT, MICHAEL; Old Forge HS; Old Forge, PA; (3); Ski Clb; Hon Roll; NHS.

PLASHA, BARBARA A; Garnet Valley SR HS; Glen Mills, PA; (2); 23/169; German Clb; Model UN; Office Aide; Ski Clb; Off Frsh Cls; Off Soph Cls; Rep Stu Cncl; Fld Hcky; Lcrss; Mgr(s); Close Up Club 86-89.

PLASHA, WAYNE; Lower Moreland HS; Huntingdon Valley, PA; (4); Capt Debate Tm; German Clb; NFL; Science Clb; Nwsp Stf; Yrbk Ed-Chief; Lit Mag; Wrld Affrs Cncl VP 86-87; Govs Schl Intl Stds 86-87; Wrtng.

PLASSIO, SHELLY; Yough SR HS; Irwin, PA; (4); FBLA; Var Sftbl; SR Athltc Awd 86-87; Bus.

PLATEK, PAULA; Montour HS; Mckees Rocks, PA; (2); SADD; Chorus; Var Swmmng; High Hon Roll; Hon Roll; Nrsng.

PLATSKY, STEPHANIE; E L Meyers HS; Wilkes Barre, PA; (4); Drama Clb; Pres French Clb; Hosp Aide; JA; Key Clb; Pep Clb; Ski Clb; SADD; Temple Yth Grp; Chorus; Phys Thrpy.

PLATT, ERIKA; Indiana Area SR HS; Indiana, PA; (4); 10/325; Cmnty Wkr; Debate Tm; Off Latin Clb; Model UN; NFL; Ed Nwsp Stf; Ed Lit Mag; High Hon Roll; NHS; Ntl Merit SF; Rotary Clb Dist Lttrs For Peace 1st Pl 86; 1st Edtrl IN Gazette Cntst 86; Georgetown U; Frgn Lang.

PLATT, JODEE; Du Bois Area HS; Du Bois, PA; (3); Stat Mat Maids; Var Sftbl; Hon Roll; NHS; Du Bois Bus Coll; Acct.

PLATT, KATHLEEN; Gettysburg SR HS; Gettysburg, PA; (2); 32/262; Art Clb; Girl Scts; Office Aide; Pep Clb; Varsity Clb; Orch; Cheerleading; Lcrss; Hon Roll; Coach Actv; Pres Acdmc Fit Awd 85-86; Phy Thrpst.

PLATT, LANCE; West Mifflin Area HS; West Mifflin, PA; (3); L Crs Cntry; JV Swmmng; L Trk; Scrty & Invstmnt.

PLATT, LISA; Berlin Brothers Valley HS; Berlin, PA; (4); French Clb; Co-Capt Color Guard; Concert Band; Yrbk Stf; Co-Capt Var Cheerleading; Stat Wrstlng; Hon Roll; Acdmc All Amer Schlrshp Awd 85; Fashn Ins Pittsburgh; Fshn Merc.

PLATZ, CHERYL; Fairview HS; Fairview, PA; (3); 17/162; Trs Sec Church Yth Grp; German Clb; Model UN; Teachers Aide; Varsity Clb; Yrbk Stf; Mgr(s); Var L Trk; Var L Vllybl; NHS.

PLATZ, DEAN; Fairview HS; Fairview, PA; (4); 6/150; Boy Scts; Church Yth Grp; Debate Tm; Varsity Clb; Var Bsbl; Var Capt Ftbl; Var Trk; Var Capt Wrstlng; High Hon Roll; NHS; US Army Resrv Acadmc Athlt Excllnc 87; All Cnty Ftbl 87; Outstndng Athl Trck Wrstlng 87; Grove City Coll; Math Educ.

PLAUSCHINAT, SUZETTE; Plymouth Whitemarsh HS; Norristown, PA; (3); Yrbk Rptr; Yrbk Stf; JV Capt Bsktbl; Fld Hcky; Hon Roll; Phys Ther.

PLEBAN, CHRIS; Weatherly Area HS; Weatherly, PA; (4); 2/65; Am Leg Boys St; FBLA; Letterman Clb; Rep Stu Cncl; Bsbl; Golf; CC Awd; High Hon Roll; NHS; Penn ST U Engl Merit Awd; Embry Riddle U; Arntcl Sci.

PLETCHER, AMY; West Allegheny SR HS; Oakdale, PA; (3); Drama Clb; FBLA; Nwsp Rptr; Nwsp Stf; Rep Stu Cncl; Var Powder Puff Ftbl; High Hon Roll; Hon Roll; German.

PLETCHER, DAWN; Rockwood JR SR HS; Rockwood, PA; (4); 4/116; Hosp Aide; Spanish Clb; School Play; Nwsp Rptr; Nwsp Stf; High Hon Roll; Hon Roll; NHS; Prfct Atten Awd; Pharm.

PLETCHER, KRISTA; Mifflinburg HS; Mifflinburg, PA; (3); Am Leg Aux Girls St; Yrbk Stf; Rep Jr Cls; Rep Sr Cls; Var Bsktbl; Capt Fld Hcky; Var Sftbl; High Hon Roll; NHS; 4-H; Hugh O Brian Ldrshp Semnr 86; 2nd Tm All-Star Field Hcky 87; Sci.

PLETCHER, PATTI; Rockwood Area HS; Rockwood, PA; (2); NFL; Speech Tm; Band; Drm Mjr(t); Mrchg Band; School Play; Sec Soph Cls; JV Capt Cheerleading; High Hon Roll; Hon Roll; Natl Forensic League Dist Tourn Fnlst 86; Rockwood Spch Team Best Spkr Awd 86; Comm.

PLETCHER, SHAWN L; Rockwood Area HS; Rockwood, PA; (4); 9/116; Spanish Clb; Yrbk Stf; High Hon Roll; NHS; PA ST U; Aerospace Engr.

PLETCHER, SHELBY; Rockwood HS; Rockwood, PA; (2); Debate Tm; NFL; Speech Tm; Band; Chorus; Drm & Bgl; Mrchg Band; School Play; Nwsp Rptr; Nwsp Stf; Ldrshp Svc Awd 84-85; Penn ST U; Law.

PLEVER, MICHELE; Highianas SR HS; Natrona Hts, PA; (3); Church Yth Grp; Dance Clb; Office Aide; Var Gym; Btty Crckr Awd; Prfct Atten Awd; Penn ST; Bus.

PLISKANER, ANNE; Perry Traditional Acad; Pittsburgh, PA; (3); 4/190; Chorus; Var Swmmng; Hon Roll; NHS; Vet.

PLISKO, LYNN; Connellsville Area HS; Connellsville, PA; (3); 130/510; Library Aide; Office Aide; Pres Pep Clb; Ski Clb; Chorus; Church Choir; Flag Corp; School Musical; Stat Ftbl; Hon Roll; Psych.

PLITNICK, CHRISTOPHER; Bishop Hafey HS; Sugarloaf, PA; (3); 3/113; Debate Tm; Math Clb; Quiz Bowl; Scholastic Bowl; Science Clb; Speech Tm; Orch; Rep Stu Cncl; Var Socr; Trk; Math Awd 84; Kings Coll; Acctg.

PLOCINIK, LYNDA; Rochester Area HS; Rochester, PA; (4); 18/89; Girl Scts; VP JA; Off Concert Band; Jazz Band; Off Mrchg Band; Orch; Powder Puff Ftbl; Var L Trk; Hon Roll; NHS; PMEA Dist 5 Band 85-87; Beaver Cnty Hnrs Band 85-87; Outstndg SR Awd Instrmntl Music 87; Westminster Coll; Telecomm.

PLONSKI, LAURA; Carbondale Area HS; Carbondale, PA; (4); 8/144; Computer Clb; FBLA; Ski Clb; Spanish Clb; Band; Concert Band; Mrchg Band; High Hon Roll; NHS; U Of Scranton; Accntng.

PLOSS, KRISTINA; Archibishop Ryan For Girls; Philadelphia, PA; (4); 80/490; Church Yth Grp; French Clb; Hosp Aide; Office Aide; Service Clb; Hon Roll; Temple U.

PLOTZ, CINDY L; Baldwin HS; Pittsburgh, PA; (2); 39/481; Chorus; School Musical; High Hon Roll; Hon Roll; Bus Manag.

PLOUMAKER, MISSY; Riverside HS; Beaver Fls, PA; (3); Church Yth Grp; GAA; Girl Scts; Letterman Clb; Service Clb; Chorus; Var Trk; High Hon Roll; Hon Roll; NHS; U Of Pittsburgh; Med.

PLOWFIELD, MICHAEL; Warwick HS; Lititz, PA; (3); Boy Scts; Concert Band; Jazz Band; Mrchg Band; Orch; Nwsp Stf; Hon Roll; Model UN; Eagl Sct Awd; Band Distngshd Svc Awd; U S Navy.

PLUBELL, ALICE; West Branch HS; Karthaus, PA; (2); Science Clb; Chorus; Hon Roll; PA ST; Psych.

PLUBELL, JILL; Clarfield Aren HS; Frenchville, PA; (3); 52/329; Sec Exploring; VICA; Yrbk Phtg; Yrbk Stf; JV Cheerleading; High Hon Roll; Hon Roll; Hon Roll Date Prcssng CLFD Vo-Tech 86; Attnd VICA Comp For Job Intrvw 87; ICM Schl Of Bus; Med Scrtry.

PLUCINSKY, AMY; Lancaster Country Day Schl; Wyomissing Hills, PA; (3); Church Yth Grp; Sec Trs Drama Clb; Girl Scts; Model UN; Nwsp Phtg; Nwsp Stf; Yrbk Phtg; Yrbk Stf; Fld Hcky; Mgr(s); Med.

PLUKO, JON; Northeast Bradford Jr/Sr HS; Rome, PA; (3); Art Clb; Church Yth Grp; Cmnty Wkr; Church Choir; Hon Roll; Peer Helper 86-87; Bio Chem.

PLUM, JEFFREY ALAN; Liberty HS; Bethlehem, PA; (4); 105/421; Art Clb; Boy Scts; Church Yth Grp; Hon Roll; Williamsport Area CC; Elec Tch.

PLUMER, PETER; Venango Christia; Oil City, PA; (1); Boy Scts; Chorus; School Play; Var Bsktbl; Var Ftbl; High Hon Roll; Prfct Atten Awd; Ntl Rifle Assn Expert Rflmn 86; US Military Acad; Military.

PLUMLEY, KELLY; Council Rock HS; Newtown, PA; (3); 128/900; Church Yth Grp; Rep Frsh Cls; Rep Soph Cls; Rep Jr Cls; Stu Cncl; JV Var Cheerleading; Hon Roll; Busnss.

PLUMMER, HELEN BARBARA; Faith Community Christian Schl; Pittsburgh, PA; (3); 12/27; Church Yth Grp; JA; Ski Clb; Spanish Clb; Nwsp Stf; Yrbk Stf; Sec Jr Cls; VP Sr Cls; VP Sec Stu Cncl; Var Sftbl; Bus Adm.

PLUMMER, JEAN M; Conrad Weiser HS; Robesonia, PA; (4); 5/184; Drama Clb; Ed JCL; VP Key Clb; Yrbk Ed-Chief; Ed Lit Mag; NHS; Ntl Merit Ltr; Pres Schlr; Trs Church Yth Grp; Computer Clb; Lebanon Daily News Jrnlsm Awd 87; Key Clbbr Of Mnth Awd 85-86; Robesonia Womens Club Girl Of Mnth 86; Loyola; Engl.

PLUMMER, TARA; Lewistown Area HS; Lewistown, PA; (2); Art Clb; Spanish Clb; Mrchg Band; JV Bsktbl; Var Crs Cntry; Trk; NHS.

PLUNKETT, PATRICK; Arch Bisoph Ryan For Boys HS; Philadelphia, PA; (3); 79/349; Am Leg Boys St; Boy Scts; Church Yth Grp; Cmnty Wkr; Computer Clb; Debate Tm; English Clb; Intnl Clb; Teachers Aide; Y-Teens; Engl Spn 86-87; Hstry 87; Lwyr.

PLYLER, BONNIE; Punxsutawney Area SR HS; Punxsutawney, PA; (4); 26/245; Church Yth Grp; FBLA; Band; Church Choir; Concert Band; Mrchg Band; Pep Band; Variety Show; Hon Roll; Prfct Atten Awd; Top Bus Typg Awd 87.

POCHAN, DARRIN; N Hills HS; Pittsburgh, PA; (3); Pres Church Yth Grp; Chorus; Church Choir; Var L Crs Cntry; Var L Trk; High Hon Roll; Trs NHS.

POCHINSKY, ANN; Mt Pleasant Area HS; Latrobe, PA; (3); French Clb; GAA; Nwsp Ed-Chief; Tennis; Bausch & Lomb Sci Awd; High Hon Roll; NHS; Ntl Merit Ltr; Prfct Atten Awd; Psych.

PODBIELSKI, DANIELLE; Downingtown SR HS; Exton, PA; (3); Hon Roll; Brandywine Coll; Bus Educ.

PODLASKI, STEVEN; Mercer JR/Sr HS; Mercer, PA; (3); Church Yth Grp; Var L Bsktbl; Capt Var Crs Cntry; Var L Trk; Hon Roll; NHS; Comp Pgrmr.

PODLESNY, CHRISTINE; Manheim Central HS; Manheim, PA; (4); Capt Flag Corp; Mrchg Band; Variety Show; VP Jr Cls; VP Church Yth Grp; JV Capt Cheerleading; Coach Actv; Powder Puff Ftbl; Hon Roll; Rotary Awd; RCA Career Schlrshp 87; Bauder Fash Coll; Fash Merch.

PODOLSKY, MICHA; Freedom HS; Bethlehem, PA; (3); 42/486; Church Yth Grp; Cmnty Wkr; Drama Clb; French Clb; Chorus; School Play; High Hon Roll; NHS; PA Gov Schl For Arts Schlrshp 86; NY U; Dnc.

PODRAZA, IAN; York Suburban HS; York, PA; (3); 48/177; Boy Scts; Band; Jazz Band; Mrchg Band; School Musical; Symp Band; Nwsp Rptr; Lit Mag; Hon Roll; Prfct Atten Awd; Cmmnctns.

POE, AUDREY; Peters Township HS; Finleyville, PA; (4); Spanish Clb; Lit Mag; High Hon Roll; Hon Roll; NHS; Rotary Awd; Spanish NHS; Stnly Gldn Hmmr Awd Indstrl Arts 86-87; Cntry Clb Achvmnt Awd 86-87; Pittsburgh Tech Inst; Drftg.

POE, BRANDON; Mechanicsburg Area HS; Mechanicsburg, PA; (4); 32/303; Orch; Yrbk Stf; Var Capt Socr; Var Trk; Var Wrstlng; High Hon Roll; Hon Roll; NHS; Bucknell U; Bus.

POET, ROBBY; Northeastern HS; Mt Wolf, PA; (3); Varsity Clb; Rep Frsh Cls; VP Soph Cls; Off Jr Cls; Off Sr Cls; Rep Stu Cncl; Var Capt Socr; Var Trk; High Hon Roll; Voice Dem Awd; Law.

POFF, MICHELLE; Milton SR HS; Milton, PA; (3); Church Yth Grp; FHA; Intnl Clb; Library Aide; NHS; Cntrl PA Bus Schl; Paralgl.

POFF, SUSANNE J; Eastern Lebanon County HS; Lebanon, PA; (3); 1/190; Trs VP Church Yth Grp; Band; Chorus; Swing Chorus; Soph Cls; Jr Cls; JV Capt Fld Hcky; High Hon Roll; NHS; NEDT Awd; Honor Attndnt Cmmncmnt 87; MVP Fld Hcky 86-87; Hugh O Brian Yth Fndtn Amb 86; Math.

POFF, TONI ANNE; Beaver Area JR SR HS; Beaver, PA; (2); FCA; JCL; Pep Clb; Ski Clb; Orch; School Play; Var L Sftbl; L Swmmng; Var L Vllybl.

POFFEL, ANGELA; Vincentian HS; Allison Park, PA; (4); 4/58; Service Clb; School Play; Ed Yrbk Stf; Stu Cncl; High Hon Roll; NHS; Pres Acad Fitness Awd 87; Congrsnl Schlr 86-87; Clemson U; Psych.

POFI, SUSAN; Penn Hills HS; Pittsburgh, PA; (4); 27/609; French Clb; Drill Tm; Mrchg Band; Crs Cntry; Pom Pon; Swmmng; Trk; DAR Awd; High Hon Roll; NHS; Schlr Athl Yr 87; Penn ST U; Htl/Mtl Mgmt.

POGOZELEC, TERESA; Lincoln HS; Wampum, PA; (4); 28/165; Trs Band; Concert Band; Mrchg Band; Orch; Bowling; Powder Puff Ftbl; Trk; Prfct Atten Awd; Bus & Prfsnl Wmns Clb Schlrshp 87; Outstndgn Bus Stu 2(Accntng II 87; Bradford Bus Schl; Accntng.

POGOZELSKI, MARK D; Turtle Creek HS; Pittsburgh, PA; (4); 3/202; Computer Clb; German Clb; Math Tm; Scholastic Bowl; Nwsp Stf; Im Bsktbl; High Hon Roll; Ntl Merit SF; Natl Mrt Smfnlst 86; Engr.

POHL, ROBERT; Pius X HS; Columbia, NJ; (3); 9/28; Boy Scts; Chess Clb; Scholastic Bowl; Varsity Clb; School Musical; Yrbk Stf; JV L Bsbl; JV L Bsktbl; JV Ftbl; Egl By Sct 87; Ad Altare Dei Rlgs Awd 85; Comp Sci.

POHLOT, MARYLOU; Bentworth SR HS; Bentleyville, PA; (4); Dance Clb; FHA; Drill Tm; Yrbk Phtg; Yrbk Stf; Gym; Hon Roll; Outstndng Amer Stu 85-86; CA U Of PA; Nrsng.

POINDEXTER, JAMES; Bethlehem-Center SR HS; Denbo, PA; (3); 3/160; Concert Band; Mrchg Band; NHS; Amer Legn Awd 84-85.

POINELLI, JENNIFER; Du Bois Area HS; Penfield, PA; (4); 12/273; Cmnty Wkr; Chorus; Color Guard; School Musical; Hon Roll; Kiwanis Awd; Hst NHS; Pres Schlr; Voice Dem Awd; 4th Pl Courier Express Chrstms Essay 86; IN U.

POIRIER, NOEL; Warwick HS; Lititz, PA; (3); 141/280; Library Aide; VP Model UN; Lit Mag; Var Tennis; Hstry.

POIST, SUSAN; Southwestern HS; Brodbecks, PA; (3); 3/250; Orch; Nwsp Rptr; High Hon Roll; NHS; NEDT Awd; Catholic U; Soc Wrkr.

POJUNIS, DEBBIE; Hanover Area HS; Wilkes Barre, PA; (3); Key Clb; Sec Jr Cls; Stu Cncl; Var Cheerleading; Hon Roll; VP Jr NHS; NHS; Bus.

POKRIFKA, ANN; Clarion-Limestone HS; Strattanville, PA; (3); FHA; SADD; Nwsp Rptr; Nwsp Stf; Sec Jr Cls; Var Cheerleading; Hon Roll; Typng Prfcncy Awd 85; Bus Excptnl Achvt Awd 85; Shrthnd Dctn Awd 86; Secy.

POKRIFKA, ANNETTE; Steel Valley HS; Munhall, PA; (4); 13/201; Dance Clb; Teachers Aide; Nwsp Stf; Mat Maids; Twrlr; Wt Lftg; High Hon Roll; Church Yth Grp; NHS; Amer Lgn Cert Apprctn Essay 86; Exec Sec.

POLACONIS, JOANN; Shenandoah Valley JR-SR HS; Shenandoah, PA; (3); 10/79; Library Aide; Variety Show; Rep Frsh Cls; VP Soph Cls; Rep Jr Cls; Rep Stu Cncl; JV Bsktbl; JV Trk; JV L Vllybl; High Hon Roll; Teaching.

POLASKI, JILL; Mc Dowell HS; Erie, PA; (2); Dance Clb; Color Guard; Mrchg Band; L Trk; Bus.

POLCZYNSKI, DONNA; St Josephs HS; Natrona Hgts, PA; (3); Church Yth Grp; Dance Clb; Girl Scts; Intnl Clb; Soroptimist; Boy Scts; Jazz Band; School Musical; Swing Chorus; Nwsp Rptr; PA Free Entrprs Wk Schlrshp 86; Pres Phys Ftns Awd 86; Law.

POLCZYNSKI, ERIC; Freeport Area HS; Sarver, PA; (2); 29/202; Bsbl; Trk.

POLECHKO, TODD; Greensburg Central Catholic HS; Greensburg, PA; (3); Boy Scts; NFL; Ski Clb; School Play; Pres Jr Cls; JV Ftbl; Var Trk; L Wrstlng; Vgl Hnr, Ordr Of Arrw, Boy Scts 86; Intl Law.

POLEDNAK, MICHAEL; Lakeland HS; Mayfield, PA; (3); Off Boy Scts; Church Yth Grp; Cmnty Wkr; Red Cross Aide; Band; Concert Band; Mrchg Band; Var Golf; God Cntry Awd; School Musical; Eagle Scout 87; Emrgncy Med Tech 87.

POLEY, KENNY; Springford HS; Spring City, PA; (3); 48/256; Var Bsbl; Var Wrstlng; Elec Engr.

POLEY, KRISTINA; Middletown Area HS; Middletown, PA; (3); 13/193; Band; Chorus; Color Guard; Mrchg Band; School Musical; School Play; Swing Chorus; Variety Show; Twrlr; Hon Roll; Psych.

POLGREAN, JOHN; Hazleton HS; Hazleton, PA; (3); 18/445; JV Bsbl; High Hon Roll; Hon Roll; Pres Acad Fit Awd 85; PA ST U; Pre-Med.

POLICINSKI, ALICIA; Marple-Newtown SR HS; Newtown Square, PA; (3); Key Clb; Mu Alpha Theta; SADD; Swmmng; Tennis; Mgr Trk; Hon Roll; NHS; Church Yth Grp; French Clb; Schlry Athlt 86-87; Vtrns Svc Awd 86-87.

POLICZ, MICHELLE; Jefferson-Morgan HS; Rices Landing, PA; (3); 6/77; Pres Exploring; Intnl Clb; Nwsp Rptr; Nwsp Stf; Rep Stu Cncl; Twrlr; High Hon Roll; Hon Roll; Acad All-Amer Awd 87; Phrmcy.

POLILLO, SUZANN; Mechanicsburg Area SR HS; Mechanicsburg, PA; (3); 31/341; Chorus; Mrchg Band; Cmmnctns.

POLIS, ADAM; Central Bucks High Schl East; Warrington, PA; (4); Yrbk Sprt Ed; Yrbk Stf; Rep Frsh Cls; Rep Soph Cls; Rep Jr Cls; Rep Sr Cls; Off Stu Cncl; Ftbl; Hon Roll; NHS; U Of DE; Biochem.

POLITES, ANN; Lourdes Regional HS; Mt Carmel, PA; (3); 17/92; Cmnty Wkr; SADD; Chorus; Church Choir; Off Stu Cncl; Var L Bsktbl; Mgr(s); Var Sftbl; Sign Lang Class 1st Grad 87; Notre Dame Ldrshp Conf 86; Bloomsburg U; Educ.

POLITZ, MICHAEL; Bensalem HS; Bensalem, PA; (2); Var L Aud/Vis; JV Bsbl; High Hon Roll; Hon Roll; Prfct Atten Awd.

POLIZZI, ROSARIA; Elizabethtown Area HS; Elizabethtown, PA; (4); Church Yth Grp; FFA; Teachers Aide; Nwsp Rptr; Nwsp Stf; Hon Roll; Harrisburg Area CC; Bus Mngmnt.

POLLACK, ANNE; Bishop Hafey HS; Freeland, PA; (4); NAACP; Church Yth Grp; Cmnty Wkr; 4-H; Science Clb; Varsity Clb; Band; Yrbk Stf; Bowling; Sftbl; Ladies Of Unico $250 Acad Schlrshp 86-87; PASU; Bus Comm.

POLLACK, CHRISTOPHER; Central Dauphin HS; Harrisburg, PA; (2); 4/405; Church Yth Grp; Ski Clb; Orch; School Musical; JV Ftbl; L Trk; Jr NHS; PA Dist 7 Orch 86-87; PA Govrs Schl For Arts Schlrshp 87-88; Stu Of Mnth Feb 87-88.

POLLACK, KIM; Mc Keesport SR HS; Mckeesport, PA; (4); 70/344; Church Yth Grp; Exploring; Hosp Aide; Pep Clb; VICA; Nwsp Rptr; Var JV Bsktbl; Var Mgr(s); Var Score Keeper; Var Timer; Hnrbl Mntn Cake Dcrtng 86-87; Dietician.

POLLACK, LISA; Great Valley HS; Malvern, PA; (3); 1/265; JCL; Scholastic Bowl; Yrbk Stf; Lit Mag; NHS; Ntl Merit Ltr; Prfct Atten Awd; Rep Stu Cncl; JV Crs Cntry; JV Sftbl; Rensslr Mdl, Cum Laude Natl Latn Exm 87; Yth Schlr Lebnon Vly Coll 86; Mt Holyoke; Chem.

POLLAK, BRIAN M; Elizabeth Forward HS; Elizabeth, PA; (3); 4/345; Boy Scts; Cmnty Wkr; Crs Cntry; Trk; High Hon Roll; NHS; Pre-Med.

POLLAK, HOPE; Kiski Area HS; Murrysville, PA; (3); SADD; Chorus; Nwsp Stf; High Hon Roll; Hon Roll; Library Aide; Pep Clb; School Play; Stage Crew; Rep Stu Cncl; Jazz Rock Ensemble 86-88; Physcl Ftns Awd 85-87; Educ.

POLLAK, KEITH W; Elizabeth Forfward HS; Elizabeth, PA; (3); Boy Scts; Computer Clb; Crs Cntry; Trk; God Cntry Awd; High Hon Roll; NHS; Eagle Scout & Jr Sci Acad 86; Engrng.

POLLAK, SARA; Downingtown SR HS; Exton, PA; (3); 121/628; Library Aide; Ski Clb; Spanish Clb; SADD; Temple Yth Grp; Chorus; Flag Corp; Madrigals; School Musical; Swing Chorus.

POLLARD, ANN; Fairview HS; Erie, PA; (3); German Clb; Model UN; Q&S; Ski Clb; Jazz Band; School Play; Nwsp Rptr; Nwsp Stf; Ed Lit Mag; Hon Roll; Physcl Thrpy.

POLLARD, NAOMI; Neshaminy HS; Levittown, PA; (3); 113/837; Church Yth Grp; SADD; Church Choir; Nwsp Rptr; JV Cheerleading; Im Gym; Im Wt Lftg; High Hon Roll; Hon Roll; Nrsng.

POLLARD, STACEY; Philadelphia HS For Girls; Philadelphia, PA; (2); Camera Clb; Church Yth Grp; Computer Clb; Library Aide; Church Choir; Drill Tm; Trs Soph Cls; Cheerleading; Cit Awd; Prfct Atten Awd; Army; Comp Procssr.

POLLARD, TRACY C; East HS; West Chester, PA; (4); 3/409; JCL; SADD; Chorus; School Musical; Variety Show; Nwsp Rptr; Yrbk Rptr; Lit Mag; French Hon Soc; NHS; PA Gvnrs Schl For The Arts 85; Awd For Excllnc In Lnge Stdy-NE Cnfrnce On Tchng Of Frng Lngs 87; NY U; Theatre.

POLLARD, WILLIAM; Martin Luther King HS; Philadelphia, PA; (1); 3/33; English Clb; French Clb; Science Clb; Off Frsh Cls; Var Bsbl; Var Ftbl; Vllybl; Hon Roll; Ntl Merit Ltr; Arch.

POLLI, CYNTHIA; West Hazleton HS; W Hazleton, PA; (4); 75/224; Pep Clb; Nwsp Rptr; Nwsp Stf; Yrbk Stf; Hon Roll; Temple U; Radio,Tv,Film.

POLLICK, MICHELLE; Tunkhannock Area HS; Tunkhannock, PA; (3); Spanish Clb; Flag Corp; Cheerleading; Hon Roll; Educ.

POLLINS, SCOTT; Manheim Township HS; Lancaster, PA; (4); 12/325; Exploring; VP JA; Key Clb; Nwsp Sprt Ed; Lit Mag; Im Bsktbl; Var L Crs Cntry; Var L Trk; High Hon Roll; NHS; Studnt Of Mnth 86; Sales Club 86-87; Exec Awd JR Achvt 87; Bucknell U; Law.

POLLOCK, AMY; Penn Hills HS; Pittsburgh, PA; (3); French Clb; Varsity Clb; Cheerleading; Hon Roll; Elem Tchr.

POLLOCK, BOB; Pottstown HS; Pottstown, PA; (3); 14/261; Rep Stu Cncl; Var Bsktbl; Var L Ftbl; High Hon Roll; Jr NHS; Penn ST; Bus Adm.

POLLOCK, JENNIFER; Monongahela Valley Catholic HS; Monongahela, PA; (2); Drama Clb; Hosp Aide; Ski Clb; SADD; Chorus; Yrbk Stf; Off Jr Cls; JV Bsktbl; JV Var Cheerleading; Swmmng; PA ST U; Accntng.

POLLOCK, MELISSA; Portage Area HS; Portage, PA; (3); Varsity Clb; Band; Concert Band; Jazz Band; Mrchg Band; Pep Band; Var JV Bsktbl; Var JV Vllybl; Hon Roll.

POLLOCK, PATRICIA; Coatesville Area SR HS; Coatesville, PA; (3); 165/517; Ski Clb; Spanish Clb; Band; Mrchg Band; Art Clb; Aud/Vis; FBLA; Leo Clb; Radio Clb; Color Guard; Bus.

POLOGRUTO, PATRICIA M; Mt Pleasant SR HS; Mt Pleasant, PA; (2); Pep Clb; Ski Clb; Band; Rep Stu Cncl; High Hon Roll; Hon Roll; German Clb; GAA; Concert Band; Mat Maids; Presdntl Acadc Ftns Awd 86; Indstrl Psychlgy.

POLOKA, JACQUELINE; Carlynton JR SR HS; Pittsburgh, PA; (3); 18/167; Camera Clb; Dance Clb; Ski Clb; Capt Color Guard; Yrbk Stf; Twrlr; High Hon Roll; Hon Roll; Jr NHS; Prfct Atten Awd.

POLONS, KELLY; Hanover JR SR HS; Ashley, PA; (3); 8/152; Key Clb; Ski Clb; LCCC; Nrsng.

POLOYAC, SAM; Conemaugh Valley HS; Johnstown, PA; (3); 7/110; Computer Clb; Ski Clb; Band; Concert Band; Mrchg Band; Yrbk Stf; High Hon Roll; Hon Roll; NHS; Pre-Med.

POLSENBERG, LISAROSE; Lebanon Catholic HS; Palmyra, PA; (4); Key Clb; Library Aide; Ski Clb; SADD; Chorus; School Play; Stage Crew; Yrbk Phtg; Yrbk Stf; Lebanon Rotary Clb,Catholics Stu Mnth & Catholics Peer Cnslng Clb Tres 86-87; Shippensburg U; Elem Ed.

POLSKY, CANDICE; Haverford HS; Havertown, PA; (4); 12/447; Drama Clb; French Clb; Sec Scholastic Bowl; Temple Yth Grp; Band; Drill Tm; Orch; Pres Stu Cncl; Ntl Merit Ltr; Stu Snt Schlrshp 87; Duke U; Lwyr.

POLT, MONICA; Archbishop Ryan H S For Girls; Philadelphia, PA; (4); 8/490; Church Yth Grp; German Clb; Hosp Aide; Science Clb; High Hon Roll; Hon Roll; NHS; Schlrshp Awd 85; German Awd 84-86; Bio Awd 85; Penn ST; Bus Adm.

POLTRACK, SEAN; Westmont Hilltop HS; Johnstown, PA; (2); French Clb; JA; Ski Clb; Im Bsktbl; JV Ftbl; Var Trk; Wt Lftg; JV Wrstlng; US Naval Acad.

POLYMENAKOS, NICHOLAS; Upper Darby HS; Upr Darby, PA; (3); 5/584; Band; Concert Band; Jazz Band; Mrchg Band; Ice Hcky; High Hon Roll; Hon Roll; Jr NHS; NHS; Amer Lgn Schl Awd 87; La Salle U PA; Jrnlsm.

POLYMENAKOS, WILLIAM; Upper Darby HS; Upr Darby, PA; (3); #1 In Class; Church Yth Grp; Computer Clb; Library Aide; Quiz Bowl; High Hon Roll; Opt Clb Awd; Harvard Book Clb Awd 87; A P Comp Sci Awd Advncd Plcmnt 87; Engl Advncd Plcmnt Awd 87; Comp Sci.

POMARICO, KELLY; Mt Pleasant Area HS; Mt Pleasant, PA; (3); 34/250; French Clb; Rep GAA; Science Clb; SADD; Band; Yrbk Stf; Var L Sftbl; Im Vllybl; High Hon Roll; Duquesne; Phrmcy.

POMAYBO, AMY; Highlands SR HS; Natrona Hgts, PA; (3); Band; Concert Band; Mrchg Band; Variety Show; Stu Cncl; Var Capt Bsktbl; Var L Sftbl; Var L Swmmng; High Hon Roll; NHS; Engrng.

POMFRET, ELLEN; Country Day Schl Of The Sacred Heart; Devon, PA; (4); 1/39; School Play; Pres Stu Cncl; Var Bsktbl; Var Fld Hcky; Var Capt Lcrss; NHS; Val; Duke U; Bio.

POMPE, MICHELLE D; Burgettstown Area JR SR HS; Burgettstown, PA; (4); 52/137; Church Yth Grp; VP French Clb; Office Aide; Pres Ski Clb; Yrbk Stf; Pres Soph Cls; VP Jr Cls; Pres Sr Cls; Rep Stu Cncl; Var JV Cheerleading; Socl Wrk.

POMPONI, CRISTINA; Central Catholic HS; Temple, PA; (3); 15/130; Office Aide; Pep Clb; Spanish Clb; Varsity Clb; Pep Band; School Musical; Var Capt Cheerleading; Vllybl; Hon Roll; Prfct Atten Awd; Exeter HS All-Star Chrldng Sqd 86.

POMROY, THERESA; Nazareth Acad; Phila, PA; (3); 32/125; Orch; School Musical; Accntng.

PONCHERI, DANIELLE; Hazleton HS; Hazleton, PA; (3); French Clb; French Hon Soc; High Hon Roll; Hon Roll; 1st Pl Ntl French Cntst 87; Gold Key Awd 87; Hnr Mntn 87; Philadelphia Coll; Graphic Art.

POND, DONALD; Athens HS; Athens, PA; (3); FFA; SADD; JV Ftbl; Wt Lftg; Var Wrstlng; Hon Roll; Bryant; Bus.

PONESS, MICHELE; Chartiers-Houston HS; Houston, PA; (4); 6/120; French Clb; Drill Tm; Vllybl; Hon Roll; W Liberty; Bus Educ.

PONGRAZZI, LORI; West Hazleton HS; Nuremberg, PA; (2); VP Church Yth Grp; Pep Clb; Ski Clb; Mgr Bsktbl; Im Sftbl; Im Vllybl; Hon Roll.

PONIST, SHERRY; Pen Argyl Area HS; Easton, PA; (3); 37/160; Cmnty Wkr; Drama Clb; Girl Scts; Leo Clb; Concert Band; Mrchg Band; Nwsp Stf; Yrbk Stf; L Sftbl; Capt Var Twrlr; Mjrt Capt Trphy 87 & 88; Tchng.

PONKEVITCH, LAURA; Riverside JR SR HS; Taylor, PA; (4); 1/170; Art Clb; Drama Clb; Scholastic Bowl; School Musical; Yrbk Ed-Chief; Off Stu Cncl; Tennis; NHS; Val; Drexels Prsdnts Frshmn Schlrshp 87; Drexel U; Comp Engrng.

PONKO, AME; John S Fine HS; Nanticoke, PA; (2); 17/243; Church Yth Grp; Band; Concert Band; Flag Corp; Mrchg Band; Pep Band; NHS; Flag Corps 5 Mdls 86; Bnd Mdl 86; Penn St; Med Exmnr.

PONTICELLO, LAURIEANN; Lansdale Catholic HS; Lansdale, PA; (3); 18/268; Drama Clb; Hosp Aide; Mgr(s); Sftbl; Vllybl; NHS; Docesan Schlrs Pgm 87-88; Villanova; Pediatrician.

PONTIUS, STEPHANIE; Hillside Christian Acad; Mifflinburg, PA; (3); Church Yth Grp; 4-H; Hosp Aide; Library Aide; Church Choir; Bowling; Cheerleading; Gym; Sftbl; Vllybl; Pensacola Chrstn Coll; Csmtlgy.

PONTZ, JENNIFER; Lancaster Country Day Schl; Lancaster, PA; (2); Orch; School Play; Yrbk Stf; Rep Soph Cls; Stu Cncl; JV Fld Hcky; Hon Roll; PMEA Dist Band 7 87; Church Orch 86-87.

PONTZER, ALICIA; Elk County Christian HS; St Marys, PA; (3); 18/73; Girl Scts; Hosp Aide; Ski Clb; Varsity Clb; Yrbk Stf; Var Crs Cntry; Var Trk; Hon Roll; Sci.

PONTZER, MELISSA; St Marys Area HS; Kersey, PA; (4); Camera Clb; Cmnty Wkr; Girl Scts; Hosp Aide; Hon Roll; Jr NHS; NHS; Duquesne U; Pharmacy.

POOLE, AMY; Purchase Line HS; Lajose, PA; (3); 9/98; Pres VP Pep Clb; Pres Spanish Clb; VP Frsh Cls; Sec Soph Cls; Var Capt Cheerleading; High Hon Roll; Hon Roll; Acad All-Amer 87; Natl Ldrshp & Svc Awds 87; Intl Foreign Lang Awds 87; Aerospc Engrng.

POORE, VICTORIA; Huntingdon Area HS; Huntingdon, PA; (2); 1/200; Trs Church Yth Grp; Key Clb; Sec Soroptimist; SADD; Chorus; Church Choir; School Musical; High Hon Roll; NEDT Awd; Sci Stu Mnth Awd 86; Prsdntl Physcl Ftnss Awd 86-87; Prvsnl-Natl Hnr Soc 87; Bio Sci.

POORMAN, DARLA; Elizabeth Forward HS; Monongahela, PA; (3); Teachers Aide; High Hon Roll; Hon Roll; NHS.

POPADAK, STEFANIE J; Villa Maria HS; Erie, PA; (3); Dance Clb; Var Golf; Hon Roll; Golf Leag Awd 86; Amnesty Intl Treas 86-87; Rcqtbl Club 86-87; Bus.

POPE, ADRIAN; Farrell Area HS; Farrell, PA; (3); 23/108; Church Yth Grp; Computer Clb; Drama Clb; French Clb; Key Clb; Pep Clb; Political Wkr; SADD; Teachers Aide; Chorus; Kent ST; Htl Mgmt.

POPE, KIMBERLY DEE; Methaeton HS; Audubon, PA; (4); 21/375; Off Soph Cls; Off Jr Cls; Off Sr Cls; Stu Cncl; JV Var Lcrss; High Hon Roll; NHS; Dance Clb; French Clb; Off Frsh Cls; Hmcmg Qn 86-87; PA Hmcmg Qn ST Fnlst 87; Outstndng Acmdc Achvt Pres Acmdc Fit Awds Prog 87.

POPE, TAWNYA; Westinghouse HS; Pittsburgh, PA; (2); Church Yth Grp; Natl Beta Clb; Church Choir; Yrbk Stf; Bsktbl; Ftbl; Sftbl; Im Swmmng; Hon Roll; NHS.

POPE, WILLIAM; Elizabeth Forward HS; Elizabeth, PA; (3); 4/331; Boy Scts; Im Bsbl; Var Crs Cntry; Var Trk; Cit Awd; God Cntry Awd; High Hon Roll; Jr NHS; NHS; Eagle Sct 86; Penn ST For Arch; Arch.

POPECK, LISA M; Nativity B V M HS; Pottsville, PA; (3); 3/86; NFL; Co-Capt Drill Tm; Nwsp Rptr; Bsktbl; Vllybl; High Hon Roll; Hon Roll; NHS; Acadmc All Amercn 87; Sci Fair Awds 85086; Frnsc Awd 86; Hlth.

POPIELARZ, BARBARA; Merion Mercy Acad; Phila, PA; (4); Camera Clb; Spanish Clb; Variety Show; Hon Roll; Villanova U; Commnctns.

POPIS, ANNE; West Scranton HS; Scranton, PA; (2); Hosp Aide; Pep Clb; Spanish Clb; JV Var Cheerleading; Hon Roll; Jr NHS; PA ST; Med.

POPKY, JENNY; The Springside Schl; Philadelphia, PA; (3); Chorus; School Musical; School Play; Stage Crew; Nwsp Phtg; Yrbk Phtg; Yrbk Stf; Lit Mag; Score Keeper; Hon Roll.

POPKY, JUDITH; Wyoming Valley West HS; Kingston, PA; (3); 22/416; Cmnty Wkr; Hosp Aide; VP Temple Yth Grp; Flag Corp; Mrchg Band; Nwsp Stf; High Hon Roll; Hon Roll; NHS; NEDT Awd; Natl Hstry Day Dist 1st Pl Wnnr 86; Comms.

POPLOSKIE, GEORGE; Southern Columbia HS; Elysburg, PA; (3); 19/90; Nwsp Stf; High Hon Roll; Hon Roll; NHS; VFW Awd; Voice Dem Awd; Comp Math Outstndng Achvt Awd 86; Cert Excllc Math Advncd Math 87; Comp Sci.

POPOLOW, BRETT; The Hill Schl; Pottstown, PA; (3); Model UN; Spanish Clb; Nwsp Rptr; Lit Mag; JV Var Ftbl; Var Trk; High Hon Roll; Spnsh 6 Hon Przs 85-87.

POPOVICH, BRIAN; New Castle SR HS; New Castle, PA; (2); Band; Concert Band; Jazz Band; Rep Stu Cncl; Bsbl; Ftbl; Wt Lftg; Hon Roll.

POPOVICH, MICHAEL; Penn-Trafford HS; Irwin, PA; (2); 14/346; Chess Clb; Spanish Clb; High Hon Roll; Pres Schlr; Spnsh Drwng 2nd Pl Humanities Day U Of Psstbrgh 87; Outstndng Achvt Awd Chem 87; Math.

POPOWITZ, RACHELLE; Mc Keesport Area HS; Mc Keesport, PA; (1); Church Yth Grp; Nwsp Stf; Hon Roll; Georgetown U; Law.

POPPER, DAWNE; North Pocono HS; Moscow, PA; (3); 16/236; FBLA; Trk; Vllybl; High Hon Roll; Hon Roll; NHS; Math.

POPRIK, DAN; Highlands HS; Brackenridge, PA; (4); 18/284; Am Leg Boys St; Church Yth Grp; Key Clb; Nwsp Rptr; Capt Crs Cntry; Capt Tennis; High Hon Roll; Jr NHS; NHS; Pres Schlr; PA ST U; Engrng.

POPSON, HEATHER; West York Area HS; York, PA; (3); Spanish Clb; Varsity Clb; VP Frsh Cls; VP Soph Cls; JV Bsktbl; Bowling; Capt Cheerleading; Var Vllybl; IUP; Tchr.

PORADA, DEANNE; New Castle SR HS; New Castle, PA; (3); Church Yth Grp; Cmnty Wkr; 4-H; SADD; Var Trk; Im Vllybl; Hon Roll; Chllng Plus Pgm Penn ST 85 & 86; Bio.

PORADA, LYNDA; Punxsutawney Area SR HS; Punxsutawney, PA; (2); French Clb; Varsity Clb; Rep Frsh Cls; Off Soph Cls; Stu Cncl; Cheerleading.

PORNELUZI, KEVIN; Butler SR HS; Butler, PA; (3); Boy Scts; French Clb; Im Bsktbl; Var Ftbl; Var Trk; Bio.

PORODA, JAY; Ringgold HS; Monongahela, PA; (4); Drama Clb; JA; Hon Roll; Interact Clb 86; Outdoor Ed Clb 85; SR Actvts Comm 86; Lockhaven; Physcl Thrpy.

PORRECA, STEPHANIE A; Boyertown JR High East; Barto, PA; (1); Mgr(s); Score Keeper; High Hon Roll; Intr Dsgn.

PORRECCA, S STEPHEN; Upper Merion Area HS; King Of Prussia, PA; (4); 31/277; Math Tm; Spanish Clb; Var Badmtn; Im Bsktbl; Var Socr; Im Vllybl; Hon Roll; Swarthmore Coll; Engrng.

PORRECCA, STEVE; Upper Merion Area HS; King Of Prussa, PA; (4); 31/277; Math Tm; Spanish Clb; Var Bsbl; Im Bsktbl; Var Socr; Im Vllybl; Hon Roll; Swarthmore Coll; Elec Engrng.

PORT, CHAS; Huntingdon Area HS; Huntingdon, PA; (3); 34/224; Boy Scts; Trs Jr Cls; Var Ftbl; Var Wrstlng; Hon Roll; Engrng.

PORTA, CAROLYN; Trionity HS; Mechanicsburg, PA; (3); 70/140; Girl Scts; Ski Clb; Spanish Clb; Band; Concert Band; Mrchg Band; Yrbk Stf; Bsktbl; Trk; Harrisburg Area CC; Bus.

PORTER, BRIAN NELSON; Trinity HS; Washington, PA; (3); 1/402; German Clb; Crs Cntry; L Trk; High Hon Roll; VP NHS; Ntl Merit Ltr; Rotary Awd; Pgh Marathn Yngst Prsn 86-87; 5th Degr Grn Belt Tai Kwon Do Karate 87; 10 K Rd Races Mdls 84-87; Harvard Med Schl; Sprts Med.

PORTER, BRYAN; Unionville HS; Kennett Sq, PA; (4); 12/319; Church Yth Grp; FBLA; Acpl Chr; Band; Chorus; Church Choir; Concert Band; Jazz Band; Mrchg Band; Orch; Unionville Cmmnty Scholar Wnnr 87; HOBY Rep Regnl 85; Instrmntl Awd 87; VA Tech; Bio.

PORTER, CHRIS; Clearfield Area HS; Hyde, PA; (4); Chorus; Ftbl; Wt Lftg; Hon Roll; Masonic Awd; US Nvy.

PORTER, DAVID; Spring-Ford HS; Royersford, PA; (3); 40/256; Boy Scts; Church Yth Grp; VP Exploring; Church Choir; L Ftbl; Hon Roll; Eastern Nazarene Coll; Minstry.

PORTER, DIANNA; Mary Fuller Frazier Memorial HS; Dawson, PA; (4); Church Yth Grp; FNA; Hosp Aide; VICA; Variety Show; Sftbl; Vllybl; High Hon Roll; Hon Roll; HOSA Parlmntrn 86-87; Stu Mth 86; 2nd Pl Wnnr HOSA Bwl Cmptn 86; Uniontown Hosp Schl Of Nrsng.

PORTER, ERIC; Penn Trafford HS; Irwin, PA; (2); JCL; Latin Clb; Socr; High Hon Roll.

PORTER, GENEVIEVE; Nazareth Acad; Yardley, PA; (4); Debate Tm; Latin Clb; Math Clb; NFL; Speech Tm; Band; Orch; Im Bsktbl; Opt Clb Awd; Voice Dem Awd; Philadephia Coll; Phrmcy.

PORTER, JAMES; Butler Area SR HS; Butler, PA; (3); Latin Clb; Math Tm; Nwsp Stf; High Hon Roll; Jr NHS; NHS; PA Math Leag Cert Merit 86-87; Math.

PORTER, JENNIFER; Pleasant Valley HS; Kunkletown, PA; (2); Church Yth Grp; Drama Clb; Math Tm; Ski Clb; Chorus; Flag Corp; Stat Bsktbl; High Hon Roll; Jr NHS; Mgr(s); Top Math Stu 86-87; Brigham Young U.

PORTER, KELLI; Oxford Area HS; Oxford, PA; (4); Church Yth Grp; FBLA; Hosp Aide; Library Aide; Church Choir; Stage Crew; High Hon Roll; Hon Roll; Bwlng Trphy 87; Bio Awd 85; Photo.

PORTER, KRISTA; Southmoreland HS; Scottdale, PA; (3); 20/222; Aud/Vis; Church Yth Grp; French Clb; Stage Crew; Var Mgr(s); Var Mat Maids; French Hon Soc; Nrsng.

PORTER, MALIKKA; Allderdice HS; Pittsburgh, PA; (3); Drama Clb; Pep Clb; SADD; High Hon Roll; Hon Roll; Camp Fr Inc; Dance Clb; Cheerleading; Sftbl; Trk; High Hnrs 82-84; Bus Admin.

PORTER, ROBERT; Lancaster Country Day Schl; Lancaster, PA; (2); Nwsp Sprt Ed; Nwsp Stf; Var L Bsktbl; Score Keeper; Var L Socr; High Hon Roll; Elizabeth Ross Wrtng Awd 86-87; Dept Hnrs Art 86-87; Cert Of Merit-Natl Schltc Art Awds 86-87; Artist.

PORTER, ROSEMARIE; Lenape AVTS HS; Ford City, PA; (4); Library Aide; Spanish Clb; VICA; Nwsp Rptr; Nwsp Stf; Yrbk Stf; High Hon Roll; Hon Roll; NHS; Lcl VICA Wnnr Comp Sci 87; Comp.

PORTER, SUSAN; Freeport SR HS; Freeport, PA; (4); 1/163; FBLA; Band; Drm Mjr(t); VP Frsh Cls; VP Soph Cls; Stu Cncl; Var L Bsktbl; Trk; High Hon Roll; NHS; Acad Schlrshp 87; Ldrshp Schlrshp 87; Girl Yr Awd 87; St Vincent Coll; Accntng.

PORTER, SUZANNE; Connellsville Area SR HS; Connellsville, PA; (3); Office Aide; Var Trk; French Hon Soc; High Hon Roll; NHS.

PORTER, WENDY; Williamson JR SR HS; Millerton, PA; (2); Ski Clb; Spanish Clb; SADD; Nwsp Stf; Yrbk Phtg; Yrbk Rptr; Yrbk Stf; Pres Trs Stu Cncl; Hon Roll; Nrs.

PORTER II, WILLIAM E; Taylor Alderdice HS; Pittsburgh, PA; (4); 50/403; Acpl Chr; Band; Chorus; Church Choir; Jazz Band; School Musical; High Hon Roll; NHS; Ntl Arts Rcgntn & Tlnt Srch 87; Carnegie Mellon U; Musical Thre.

PORTERFIELD, BARBARA; Franklin Regional HS; Trafford, PA; (4); 53/350; AFS; French Clb; Ski Clb; SADD; School Musical; Yrbk Sprt Ed; Socr; High Hon Roll; NHS; Natl Hispanic Schlrshp 86; Concours Natl De Francais 85; PA ST Univ; Law.

PORTUGALLO II, NATHAN; Lincoln HS; Ellwood City, PA; (3); Spanish Clb; Pres Jr Cls; Var L Bsktbl; High Hon Roll; Rotary Awd; Schlstc Athl Hnr Rll Bvr Cnty 87; Pre Law.

POSEY, BRIAN; Waynesboro Area SR HS; Waynesboro, PA; (3); 15/399; Pres Church Yth Grp; Band; Concert Band; Jazz Band; Mrchg Band; Rep Frsh Cls; Rep Soph Cls; Bsktbl; VP NHS; Pres Schlr; Comm.

POSEY, SCOTT; Benton HS; Orangeville, PA; (3); Church Yth Grp; Hon Roll; Pilot.

POSEY, SHAWN; Slippery Rock HS; Butler, PA; (4); 60/170; Am Leg Boys St; Letterman Clb; Pep Clb; Ski Clb; Varsity Clb; Var Bsbl; Var L Ftbl; Powder Puff Ftbl; Wt Lftg; Hnr Mntn All Conf Def Tckle 85; Plyr Wk; Marietta Coll; Petroleum Engrng.

POSKA, GREGORY; Carlisle HS; Carlisle, PA; (3); 64/467; Chess Clb; Church Yth Grp; Im Bsbl; JV Var Ftbl; Im Tennis; Hon Roll; Acdmc Excllnc 86-87; Chem Engrng.

POSSESSKY, LAURA; Bethel Park SR HS; Bethel Park, PA; (4); 6/519; Church Yth Grp; Pres Drama Clb; Pres Thesps; Chorus; School Musical; School Play; Swing Chorus; Yrbk Phtg; Yrbk Stf; Rep Jr Cls; U Pittsburgh Prvost Day Compttn Sem Fnlst 86; Westnghse Fmly Schlrshp Fnlts 87; U Of PA; Intl Rltns.

POST, RENEE; Trinity HS; Camp Hill, PA; (2); French Clb; Pep Clb; Ski Clb; Yrbk Stf; Stu Cncl; Cheerleading; Vllybl; Hon Roll; Capital Area Sci & Engr Fair 3rd Pl Zoology 86; Schlstc Wrtng Compt Cert Merit 86; Sci Fair Hon Men 87; Psych.

POST, VICKIE; Seneca HS; Union City, PA; (4); 27/157; Church Yth Grp; FBLA; Yrbk Ed-Chief; Yrbk Stf; Var Cheerleading; Im Sftbl; Hon Roll; PTSU Schlrshp 87; 1st Pl Shrthnd Cmptn At Erie Bus Ctr 87; Hmcmng Queen 86; R Morris Bus Coll; Bus Ed.

POSTENS, TARA; Danville SR HS; Danville, PA; (2); 31/165; Key Clb; Ski Clb; Spanish Clb; Color Guard; Stage Crew; Trk; High Hon Roll; Occptnl Thrpy.

POSTICK, MICHAEL; Minersville Area HS; Pottsville, PA; (4); 3/114; Exploring; Pep Clb; Spanish Clb; Stage Crew; Yrbk Sprt Ed; Var L Wrstlng; High Hon Roll; NHS; Schlstc Achvmnt Awd 84-87; Rotry Intl Schlrshp 87; PA Sent Good Ctznshp Awd 87; PA ST U; Engrng.

POSTIE, DESIREE; Marian Catholic HS; Delano, PA; (4); 40/110; Art Clb; Office Aide; SADD; School Musical; School Play; Nwsp Stf; Allentown Bus Schl; Med Asst.

POSTLETHWAIT, TERESA; Central Christian HS; Rockton, PA; (3); Debate Tm; Drama Clb; Ski Clb; Varsity Clb; Stu Cncl; Crs Cntry; Co-Capt Socr; Sftbl; High Hon Roll; NHS; Ldrshp Awd-Sccr 86-87; MVP-X-CNTRY 85-87; Educ.

POTAK, LYNN; Wyoming Valley West HS; Edwardsville, PA; (3); Cmnty Wkr; Key Clb; Library Aide; Ski Clb; Mrchg Band; Twrlr; High Hon Roll; Hon Roll; NHS; Phy Thrpy.

POTASH, SCOTT; Bishop Hafey HS; Beaver Meadows, PA; (3); Science Clb; Ski Clb; Hon Roll; Jr Acad Of Sci 2nd Pl Awd 85; Lincoln Tech Inst; Elect Engrng.

POTEAT, DAVID; Cedar Grove Christian Acad; Philadelphia, PA; (3); Chess Clb; Pres Church Yth Grp; Band; Concert Band; Orch; Pep Band; Variety Show; Nwsp Phtg; Nwsp Rptr; Yrbk Phtg; Stu Of The Mnth 86; Teenager Of The Wk 86; Mst Likely To Succeed 86.

POTERO, TIMOTHY; St Josephs Prep; Philadelphia, PA; (4); 50/225; Cmnty Wkr; Nwsp Rptr; Yrbk Rptr; Rep Soph Cls; Stu Cncl; Var L Golf; JV Socr; Var Trk; High Hon Roll; Hon Roll; Army ROTC Schlrshp 87; Yth/The Amer Pol Sys Rep 86; Marquette U Hnr Awd 87; Syracuse U; Law.

POTH, ROB; North Hills HS; Pittsburgh, PA; (3); Boy Scts; High Hon Roll; Hon Roll; Edinboro U Of PA; Pre-Med.

POTLAS, MICHELLE; Kiski Area SR HS; Apollo, PA; (3); Computer Clb; Debate Tm; Pep Clb; Spanish Clb; SADD; Varsity Clb; Chorus; School Musical; Var L Vllybl; Hon Roll; IUP; Jrnlsm.

POTOKA, DOUG; Mt Pleasant Area HS; Mt Pleasant, PA; (4); 1/250; Latin Clb; Varsity Clb; Var L Ftbl; Var L Wrstlng; High Hon Roll; Engr.

POTTEIGER, CHAD; Chambersburg Area SR HS; Chambersburg, PA; (2); Art Clb; Golf; Spllng Bee Drawing 82-83; Air Force.

POTTEIGER, MICHELLE; Central Dauphin HS; Harrisburg, PA; (3); 42/369; Ski Clb; Chorus; Nwsp Ed-Chief; Nwsp Stf; Rep Frsh Cls; Rep Soph Cls; Rep Jr Cls; High Hon Roll; Hon Roll; Jr NHS; Mktg.

POTTER, BRENDA L; Mt Pleasant Area HS; Acme, PA; (3); SADD; Bus Mngmt.

POTTER, CHRISTOPHER; South Williamsport Area HS; S Williamsport, PA; (3); 17/100; Red Cross Aide; Ski Clb; Varsity Clb; Var L Ftbl; Var L Trk; Capt Wrstlng; Pre Law.

POTTER, DAVID; Oswayo Valley HS; Oswayo, PA; (3); VP Jr Cls; VP Trk; High Hon Roll; Hon Roll; NHS.

POTTER, EDYTHE; Jamestown Area HS; Jamestown, PA; (4); 4/54; Service Clb; Pres Spanish Clb; Stage Crew; Rep Stu Cncl; Stat Bsbl; Stat Wrstlng; High Hon Roll; NHS; Pres Schlr; PA ST U; Psych.

POTTER, ERIN; Farview HS; Marlboro, MA; (4); 17/154; Sec French Clb; Ski Clb; Var L Crs Cntry; Hon Roll; U NH; French.

POTTER, JULIE; Villa Maria Acad; Erie, PA; (3); Art Clb; Church Yth Grp; Cmnty Wkr; FCA; PAVAS; Spanish Clb; Var Bsktbl; Retailing Mngmnt.

POTTINGER, DARLENE J; Penn Trafford HS; Jeannette, PA; (3); 10/286; Am Leg Aux Girls St; Drama Clb; GAA; High Hon Roll; NHS; Prfct Atten Awd; Acadc Al-Amer 87; U Of Pittsburgh; Hgh Fin.

POTTS, DEBORAH; Donegal HS; Mount Joy, PA; (2); Exploring; Color Guard; Hon Roll; Vet.

POTTS, JODI; Schuylkill Haven Area HS; Sch Haven, PA; (3); 25/80; Library Aide; Pep Clb; Science Clb; SADD; Church Choir; Mat Maids; JV Sftbl; Hon Roll; Hnr Guard 87; Tchr.

POTTS, KATHLEEN; Vincetian HS; Glenshaw, PA; (3); 3/73; Church Yth Grp; JV Fld Hcky; High Hon Roll; Hon Roll; Dusquene U; Psych.

POTTS, LISA; Clairton HS; Clairton, PA; (3); Hosp Aide; Drm Mjr(t); Fashion.

POTTS, REBECCA; Clearfield Area HS; Clearfield, PA; (4); Key Clb; Spanish Clb; Capt Var Cheerleading; L Trk; Cit Awd; Hon Roll; NCA All-Amer Chrldr 86; Indiana U Of PA.

POTTS, STACY; Cocalico HS; Denver, PA; (3); 1/176; Computer Clb; Drama Clb; Soph Cls; Sec Jr Cls; JV Var Cheerleading; Tennis; High Hon Roll; NHS; Acad Achvt Awds 82-84.

POTTS, WENDY; Mc Keesport Area HS; Mc Keesport, PA; (2); Powder Puff Ftbl; Sftbl; Am Leg Awd 85; Robert Morris; Acctng.

POUCH, ANDREA SHONDELL; Northern Lebanon HS; Fredericksburg, PA; (3); 6/230; Sec Church Yth Grp; Model UN; Pep Clb; Varsity Clb; Bsktbl; Fld Hcky; Key Clb; Wt Lftg; Hon Roll; NHS.

POULOS, JAMES; Plum HS; Pittsburgh, PA; (3); Church Yth Grp; Band; Concert Band; Jazz Band; Mrchg Band; Orch; School Musical; Symp Band; Hon Roll; Aeronaut Engr.

POULOS, KRIS; Catasauqua HS; Catasauqua, PA; (3); 8/150; Office Aide; SADD; Varsity Clb; VP Stu Cncl; Var Fld Hcky; Var Sftbl; High Hon Roll; NHS.

POULSON, BENITA; Philadelphia HS For Girls; Philadelphia, PA; (2); GAA; JV Sftbl.

POULTER, KATHLEEN LYNN; Indiana SR HS; Indiana, PA; (4); 23/325; Debate Tm; NFL; SADD; Off Stu Cncl; Bsktbl; Trs Cheerleading; Sftbl; Trk; High Hon Roll; NEDT Awd; Natl Frnsc Leag Awd 87; U Of KY; Acctng.

POUND, REBECCA; Chambersburg Area SR HS; Fayetteville, PA; (2); Church Yth Grp; Drama Clb; German Clb; Band; Chorus; Church Choir; Concert Band; Mrchg Band; JV Crs Cntry; Var Trk.

POUPARD III, ARTHUR R; Archbishop Ryan HS For Boys; Philadelphia, PA; (2); 20/356; Band; Chorus; Concert Band; Drm & Bgl; Jazz Band; Mrchg Band; School Musical; School Play; Hon Roll; Med.

POUST, KRISTINA; Hughesville HS; Muncy, PA; (3); 11/140; Sec Church Yth Grp; Sec FTA; Key Clb; Pres Spanish Clb; SADD; Teachers Aide; Im Vllybl; High Hon Roll; Hon Roll; NHS; Elem Ed.

POVICH, JAISON; Ringgold HS; New Eagle, PA; (2); JV Socr; Hon Roll; Sprts Med.

POW, PAULA; Beaver Area JR SR HS; Beaver, PA; (3); 16/215; JCL; Ski Clb; Band; Color Guard; Mrchg Band; Symp Band; High Hon Roll; Hon Roll; Ntl Merit Ltr; Acad Exc Awd 86; Alghny Coll; Wrtng.

POWELL, BRYAN; Lake Lehman HS; Hunlock Creek, PA; (3); 27/214; Ski Clb; Var Capt Crs Cntry; Var L Trk; JV Wrstlng; PA ST Jr Doubles Champ Trapshooting 87; X-Cntry All Stars 86; PA Jr Trapshooting Tm 85 & 86.

POWELL, CHARLES M; Council Rock HS; Holland, PA; (4); 9/848; Rep Frsh Cls; High Hon Roll; NHS; Ntl Merit Schol; Hon Roll; Drexel U Pres Scholar 87; Rolling Hills Alumni Scholar 87; Amer Math Assn Awd 87; Drexel U; Elec Engrng.

POWELL, CHRISTINA; Western Wayne HS; Lake Ariel, PA; (4); #12 In Class; SADD; Ed Yrbk Stf; Trs Jr Cls; Sftbl; Tennis; Vllybl; Hon Roll; NHS; SUNY Binghamton; Psych.

POWELL, DAVE; Baldwin HS; Pittsburgh, PA; (2); 78/481; Ski Clb; Var Swmmng; Emery Riddle; Pilot.

POWELL, DAVID; John S Fine HS; Nanticoke, PA; (4); Teachers Aide; High Hon Roll; Lion Awd; Prfct Atten Awd; Sr Sec Awd, Olympia Intl Awd & Bus Law Awd 86-87; LCCC; Bus.

POWELL, DREW; Northampton SR HS; Walnutport, PA; (2); Ski Clb.

POWELL, JAMES; Pittston Area SR HS; Pittston, PA; (3); 1/305; Ski Clb; Crs Cntry; Trk; High Hon Roll; NHS; Rotary Awd; Penn ST; Acctng.

POWELL, JEFFREY; East Juniataq HS; Richfield, PA; (3); Church Yth Grp; Computer Clb; 4-H; SADD; Bsktbl; 4-H Awd; Hon Roll; Prfct Atten Awd; Elec Cmptr.

POWELL, JEFFREY; Grtr Nanticoke Area J S Fine HS; Nanticoke, PA; (2); 16/243; High Hon Roll; NHS.

POWELL, JEFFREY; St John Newmann HS; Philadelphia, PA; (3); 50/375; JA; Speech Tm; VP Jr Cls; VP Sr Cls; Stu Cncl; Var Ftbl; Var Trk; Var Wt Lftg; NHS; Carver Explrtr Proj Wrkr Yr 86; Ftbl Scholar 87; Towson ST U; Bus Adm.

POWELL, JOHN; S Park HS; Library, PA; (3); 39/227; L Ice Hcky; Hon Roll; Outstndng Def Ice Hcky 85; Accntng.

POWELL, KRISTAN; Jefferson-Morgan HS; Jefferson, PA; (4); 10/100; Rep Am Leg Aux Girls St; Varsity Clb; Nwsp Stf; Pres Frsh Cls; Sec VP Stu Cncl; Var Capt Cheerleading; Trk; Hon Roll; Span Awd 84-86; Homcmng Ct 83 & 85; Dental Hygenist.

POWELL, MICHAEL; Center Area HS; Aliquippa, PA; (3); 50/186; Art Clb; Letterman Clb; Spanish Clb; Varsity Clb; Yrbk Stf; Bsktbl; Trk; Hon Roll; Edenboro; Art.

POWELL, MICHELLE; Northwest Area HS; Huntington Mills, PA; (3); Yrbk Ed-Chief; Pres Soph Cls; Var Cheerleading; Var Fld Hcky; Var Trk; Hon Roll.

POWELL, RALPH G; East Allegheny HS; North Versailles, PA; (3); Am Leg Boys St; Pres Church Yth Grp; Nwsp Sprt Ed; Yrbk Rptr; Var L Bsbl; Var L Bsktbl; Var L Ftbl; Prfct Atten Awd; Vrsty Bsbl-2nd Tm All-Conf Dsgntd Hitter 87; Jrnlsm.

POWELL, STACEY; Elizabeth Forward HS; Buena Vista, PA; (2); Church Yth Grp; Dance Clb; French Clb; GAA; Girl Scts; JA; Chorus; Color Guard; Hon Roll; Save-A-Life Swm For Cncr 85-86; Mrn Bio.

POWELL, TERRI; Purchase Ling HS; Commodore, PA; (2); Chess Clb; FBLA; Library Aide; Pep Clb; Teachers Aide; Chorus; Rep Frsh Cls; Bsktbl; Sftbl; Vllybl.

POWELL, TODD; Huntingdon Area HS; Huntingdon, PA; (3); 73/221; Boy Scts; Chorus; Concert Band; Mrchg Band; Im Bsktbl; Mgr(s); Crmnlgy.

POWELL, TRACEY; Quaker Valley SR HS; Fair Oaks, PA; (4); 2/157; VP German Clb; Math Tm; Trs Chorus; School Musical; Variety Show; Yrbk Rptr; Yrbk Stf; Pres Stu Cncl; High Hon Roll; Jr NHS; Harold S Irons Scholar 87; Patricia Lynn Papinchak Grant 87; Hnrb Mntn Pittsburgh Press Acad All Star; PA ST U; Med.

POWELL, WILLIAM; Carbondale Area JR SR HS; Carbondale, PA; (3); Art Clb; Boy Scts; 4-H; German Clb; Ski Clb; Spanish Clb; Band; Chorus; Stage Crew; Capt L Golf; Physcl Ftnss Awd 85-86; Air Force; Aviatn.

POWELL, YVONNE; Fairchance-Georges HS; Smithfield, PA; (3); Pres Frsh Cls; High Hon Roll; Hon Roll; Jr NHS; 3 Typng Cert 86-87; Mrn Bio.

POWER, GINA; Bethlehem Ctr; Vestaburg, PA; (3); 40/165; Am Leg Aux Girls St; Drama Clb; Stu Cncl; JV Capt Cheerleading; Hon Roll; Hmcmg Qns Attndnt 85; Hmcmg Qn 86; Ntrl Hlprs Pgm 85-88; Pittsburgh Beauty Acad; Csmtlgy.

POWER, MICHAEL; State College HS; State College, PA; (2); 68/554; Concert Band; Jazz Band; Mrchg Band; Pep Band; Symp Band; Rep Frsh Cls; Rep Soph Cls; JV Vllybl; Hon Roll.

POWER, TAMMY; Belle Vernon Area HS; Belle Vernon, PA; (3); Exploring; JA; NFL; Ski Clb; Color Guard; Mrchg Band; Yrbk Stf; Pres Frsh Cls; Pres Soph Cls; Trs Jr Cls; Math Awd 85; Phy Thrpy.

POWERS, BILL; Coudersport JR SR HS; Coudersport, PA; (3); FFA; Im Ftbl.

POWERS, BRANDON C; Camp Hill HS; Camp Hill, PA; (2); 33/90; Boy Scts; Church Yth Grp; Model UN; Chorus; Var Ftbl; Swmmng; Im Wt Lftg; Var Wrstlng; God Cntry Awd; Hon Roll; Naval Acad; Engrng.

POWERS, COREENA; Kennard-Dale HS; Delta, PA; (2); Drama Clb; Hon Roll; Comp Prog.

POWERS JR, EDWARD J; Cumberland Valley HS; Mechanicsburg, PA; (3); 15/542; Boy Scts; Debate Tm; Math Tm; Speech Tm; School Musical; Hon Roll; NHS; PA Govs Schl Intl Studies 87; West Point Acdmc Wrkshp 87.

POWERS, JAMES W; Archbishop Ryan H S For Boys; Philadelphia, PA; (3); 36/414; Bsktbl; JV Ftbl; Golf; Hon Roll; 1st Hnrs; 2nd Hnrs; USC; Electrncs Engrng Tech.

POWERS, ROBERT; Bermudian Springs HS; E Berlin, PA; (3); FFA.

POWERS, SHERRY; North Easter SR HS; York Haven, PA; (3); VP Girl Scts; Teachers Aide; Chorus; Vllybl; Hon Roll; Central Penn; Retl Sls Mgr.

POWLIS, KEITA; Lower Merion HS; Merion, PA; (3); French Clb; Intnl Clb; Service Clb; SADD; Yrbk Stf; Trk; French Hon Soc; Hon Roll.

POWNALL, LEA; Solanco SR HS; Quarryville, PA; (2); FFA; Teachers Aide; JV Trk; Cit Awd; Hon Roll; Ag.

POZZA, JACQUELINE E; Hazleton SR HS; Hazleton, PA; (2); Drama Clb; French Clb; Girl Scts; Ski Clb; Band; Chorus; Concert Band; Mrchg Band; Pep Band; Swing Chorus; U Of Pittsburgh; Phys Thrpy.

PRAISACH, DALE RONALD; Penn Hills HS; Verona, PA; (3); Church Yth Grp; German Clb; Hon Roll; De Molay Jr Counselor 87; ROTC; Translator.

PRASAD, SAPNA; Girls HS; Philadelphia, PA; (2); Civic Clb; Intnl Clb; Band; Variety Show; High Hon Roll; U Of PA; Med.

PRASCHAK, PAULA; Riverside JR SR HS; Taylor, PA; (4); VP Drama Clb; School Musical; School Play; Variety Show; Yrbk Stf; JV Capt Cheerleading; Hon Roll; Cntry Clb Nrs Schlrshp Awd 87; Miss Vikng 86-87; Dncng 83-87; Lancaster Gen Hosp Schl Nrsng.

PRASKO, ELENA; Hopewell HS; Aliquippa, PA; (3); 29/256; VP GAA; JA; Math Clb; Pres Thesps; Band; School Musical; School Play; Capt Tennis; High Hon Roll; Sec NHS; Bst Thespian Of Yr 87; Math.

PRATER, LISA MICHELLE; Meadowbrook Crhsitian Schl; Lewisburg, PA; (4); Church Yth Grp; Drama Clb; Church Choir; Nwsp Ed-Chief; Sec Jr Cls; Off Sr Cls; Hon Roll; KCEA Engl Comptn 1st Pl 86; Hstry Awd 86; Delg Electn 84 Yth Inaugrl Conf Wash DC 85; Messiah Coll; Psych.

PRATER, NATHAN C; Calvary Christian Acad; Kirkwood, PA; (4); Church Yth Grp; Teachers Aide; Band; School Play; Yrbk Ed-Chief; High Hon Roll; Val; Amer Christian Hnr Soc 86; Cert Merit PA 86.

PRATHER, MICHAEL; Valley Forge Military Acad; Vauxhall, NJ; (2); 8/200; Stage Crew; Nwsp Rptr; Nwsp Stf; Im Bsktbl; Im Sftbl; Im Vllybl; Hon Roll; Anthony Wayne Legion Guard 87; Supt Awd 87; JR ROTC Awd 87; Harvard; Bus.

PRATT, CHRISTOPHER; Wilmington Area HS; Pulaski, PA; (3); 6/115; Aud/Vis; Computer Clb; Var L Ftbl; Wt Lftg; High Hon Roll; Hon Roll; Acdmc Acvt Awd 85-86; 6 Yr Partcptn Awd 86; U S Pre Indr Tenns Ballprsn 84-86; Artcls Publshd Comp Clb; Math.

PRATT, DAWN; Phila HS For Girls; Philadelphia, PA; (1); Church Yth Grp; Rep Frsh Cls; U Of PA; Dctr.

PRATT, JEFF; Hanover SR HS; Hanover, PA; (4); 11/104; Varsity Clb; Variety Show; JV Bsbl; L Ftbl; L Trk; Hon Roll; NEDT Awd; Rotary Awd; U Of AZ; Geoglc Engr.

PRATT, KRISTY; Danville HS; Danville, PA; (3); Church Yth Grp; Chorus; Color Guard; Mrchg Band; School Musical; Nwsp Stf.

PRATT, MARK; Troy HS; Granville Summit, PA; (3); Pres Church Yth Grp; 4-H; Quiz Bowl; 4-H Awd; Electd 4-H Ldrshp Congrss ST PA 86; Pres Sprtmns Clb 86; Lock Haven U; Physcl Ed.

PRATT, SARA; Conemaugh Township Area HS; Hollsopple, PA; (3); 1/118; Ski Clb; Nwsp Phtg; Nwsp Sprt Ed; Lit Mag; Var L Vllybl; Bausch & Lomb Sci Awd; High Hon Roll; Sec NHS; Ntl Merit Ltr; Quiz Bowl; Spnsh Awds 85-87; Yth Trffc Sfty Cncl 86-87.

PRATT, SHARON; Burgettstown JR/Sr HS; Burgettstown, PA; (4); 27/139; 4-H; SADD; Chorus; Concert Band; Mrchg Band; School Musical; Symp Band; 4-H Awd; NHS; Pres Schlr; Tarkio Coll MO; Acctg.

PRATT, THOMAS; Gerbel HS; Connellsville, PA; (4); 20/79; Lit Mag; Rep Jr Cls; VP Stu Cncl; Co-Capt Bsbl; Co-Capt Bsktbl; Stat Vllybl; DAR Awd; High Hon Roll; Hon Roll; Rotary Awd; Phil Foley Mem Schlrshp, US Army Rsrv Schlr Athlt 87; Bishop Connare Awd, Svc Awd 87; St Vincents Coll; Eductnl.

PRAUL, SUSAN; Bishop Conwell HS; Croydon, PA; (3); 60/277; Church Yth Grp; French Clb; Nwsp Rptr; Nwsp Stf; Hon Roll; PA Free Enterprise Wk Schlrshp 86; Bus.

PRAVE, MARC; Curwensville Area HS; Curwensville, PA; (3); Church Yth Grp; English Clb; Letterman Clb; Varsity Clb; Ftbl; Wt Lftg; Wrstlng; IUP; Bus.

PREATE, DON; Scranton Prep Schl; Waverly, PA; (4); 11/190; Boys Clb Am; Cmnty Wkr; Drama Clb; Chorus; School Musical; Rep Jr Cls; Rep Sr Cls; Rep Stu Cncl; L Bowling; JV Ftbl; Hgh Hnrs Natl Grk Exm 86; Pres Acadc Ftnss Awd 87; Hnr Cert & Mdls 83-87; U Of Scranton; Pre Med.

PREAUX, CHERYL ELIZABETH; Canon-Mc Millan HS; Cecil, PA; (4); French Clb; FBLA; Library Aide; Chorus; Nwsp Bus Mgr; Tennis; Sawyer Schl Of Bus; Accntng.

PREDAJNA, DEBORAH; Yough HS; West Newton, PA; (3); 9/239; Church Yth Grp; French Clb; Concert Band; Mrchg Band; Yrbk Bus Mgr; JV Bsktbl; High Hon Roll; NHS; Natl Engl Merit Awd 87.

PREISING, BARRY; Garnet Valley HS; Thornton, PA; (3); Art Clb; Computer Clb; German Clb; Varsity Clb; Chorus; Lit Mag; JV Bsktbl; JV Ftbl; Tennis; Hon Roll; Chem Engrng.

PREISLER, VICTORIA JO; Freedom HS; Bethlehem, PA; (4); 27/446; Art Clb; Pep Clb; Spanish Clb; Church Choir; Var Mgr Ftbl; Var Capt Sftbl; Var Vllybl; High Hon Roll; NHS; Pres Schlr; Prfct Atten 82; Penn ST; Vet.

PRELETZ, NICOLE; Bathlehem Catholic HS; Bethlehem, PA; (3); Key Clb; Latin Clb; Im Badmtn; Im Bsktbl; Hon Roll; 100 Hr Svc Awd Vlntrng St Lukes Hosp 86; Chld Care.

PRELLWITZ, JOHN; Quigley HS; Conway, PA; (3); 33/88; Church Yth Grp; SADD; Bsbl; Ftbl; J Bobish & N Istanok Mem Schlrshp 84; Intl Affairs.

PRENDERGAST, DEBRA; South Side HS; Hookstown, PA; (3); FBLA; Varsity Clb; Yrbk Stf; Mgr(s); Var Sftbl; Vllybl; Hon Roll; Clerk Typist I Rgnl Conf 2nd Pl 87; Bus.

PRENDERGAST, JILL; Archbishop Kennedy HS; Philadelphia, PA; (4); 7/178; Aud/Vis; Service Clb; Nwsp Rptr; Capt Var Crs Cntry; Co-Capt Var Trk; Cit Awd; Church Yth Grp; Dance Clb; Drama Clb; La Salle U Christian Brothers Schlrshp 87; La Salle U Athltc Schlrshp 87; La Salle U; Comm.

PRENNI, LEW; Saltsburg JR SR HS; Saltsburg, PA; (2); 1/100; Boy Scts; Ski Clb; Pres Frsh Cls; JV Capt Bsktbl; JV Capt Ftbl; Wt Lftg; High Hon Roll; Pres Schlr.

PRENNI, MARK; Saltsburg JR SR HS; Clarksburg, PA; (3); 9/80; Varsity Clb; Nwsp Stf; Pres Frsh Cls; VP Stu Cncl; Ftbl; Trk; Wt Lftg; Wrstlng; High Hon Roll; Hon Roll.

PRENNI, TRACY; Saltsburg JR SR HS; Saltsburg, PA; (4); 7/89; Yrbk Ed-Chief; Sec Jr Cls; Sec Sr Cls; Pres Stu Cncl; Capt Cheerleading; Capt Sftbl; DAR Awd; NHS; Aud/Vis; Camera Clb; Alpha Delta Kappa Schlrshp 87; BSEA Schlrshp 87; Sftbl Chmpns 84-87; IN U Of PA; Bio Educ.

PRENTICE, KARA KATHLEEN; Belle Vernon Area HS; West Newton, PA; (4); 4/267; Girl Scts; Trs Concert Band; Trs Mrchg Band; Nwsp Stf; Var L Bsktbl; Powder Puff Ftbl; Var L Sftbl; Var L Vllybl; High Hon Roll; NHS; Robert Byrd Schlrshp 87; Pres Schlr 87; Marietta Coll; Chem.

PRESANT, JANET E; Council Rock HS; Churchville, PA; (4); 161/848; Church Yth Grp; Drama Clb; SADD; Teachers Aide; Church Choir; School Musical; Mgr(s); Swmmng; Hon Roll; Prfct Atten Awd; Millersville; Spcl Educ.

PRESBRUCH, RACHEL; Middletown Area HS; Middletown, PA; (3); Chorus; Yrbk Stf; Harrisburg Area CC; Bus.

PRESCOTT, MICHELLE L; North Catholic HS; Pittsburgh, PA; (3); Church Yth Grp; Drama Clb; School Musical; Variety Show; Lit Mag; Rep Jr Cls; Trs Sr Cls; Im Stu Cncl; Im Bsktbl; Hon Roll; Marine Biol.

PRESHAK, AMY; Johnsonburg Area HS; Johnsonburg, PA; (3); Girl Scts; Varsity Clb; Bsktbl; Sftbl; Vllybl; Hon Roll; Prfct Atten Awd; Acadmc All Amercn.

PRESOGNA, CHRISTINE; Villa Maria Acad; Erie, PA; (4); Hosp Aide; Villa Maria Coll; Prof Nrsng.

PRESOGNA, DAWN M; North East HS; North East, PA; (2); Latin Clb; Spanish Clb; Rep Stu Cncl; L Golf; Var Sftbl; Hon Roll; Med.

PRESSLER, MELISSA A; State College Area SR HS; Port Matilda, PA; (4); 56/567; Church Yth Grp; Hosp Aide; Political Wkr; Acpl Chr; Church Choir; Mrchg Band; Yrbk Stf; Socr; High Hon Roll; Ntl Merit SF; PA ST U; Pltcl Sci.

PRESTON, A J; Maplewood HS; Centerville, PA; (4); 5/140; Pres Church Yth Grp; Pres 4-H; Varsity Clb; Trs Jr Cls; Trs Sr Cls; Capt Bsbl; Capt Ftbl; Wt Lftg; JETS Awd; NHS; Grove City Coll; Engrng.

PRESTON, BRETT; Conrad Weiser HS; Wernersville, PA; (3); 5/179; JCL; Band; Concert Band; Mrchg Band; School Musical; Yrbk Stf; Hon Roll; NHS; Im Bowling; Var Tennis; Bus Mgnt.

PRESTON, HEATHER; Kennard Dale HS; Fawn Grove, PA; (3); 13/140; French Clb; Hosp Aide; Varsity Clb; Chorus; Stage Crew; Yrbk Stf; Crs Cntry; Trk; Hon Roll; Lion Awd; Elem Ed.

PRETE, TODD; Plum Boro HS; Pittsburgh, PA; (4); Var L Ftbl; Var L Trk; Church Yth Grp; Letterman Clb; Office Aide; Varsity Clb; Variety Show; Im Bsktbl; Im Socr; Var Wt Lftg; IVP Ftbl Schlrshp, 1st Fed MVP, All-Dist Trib Rvw, All-Conf Gatewy Prss & Prss East All Star 87; IN U-Pittsburgh; Mgmt Info Sys.

PREVADE, CRAIG; South Fayette JR SR HS; Cuddy, PA; (3); 6/88; Ski Clb; Band; Jazz Band; Mrchg Band; School Play; Hon Roll; NHS.

PREVENSLIK, LISA A; Greenburg Central Catholic HS; Youngwood, PA; (3); Pres AFS; Hosp Aide; Pres NFL; School Play; Nwsp Sprt Ed; Swmmng; High Hon Roll; NHS; Japanese Studs U Pittsburgh 87; Summr Pgm Japan Intl Christian U 87; Georgetown U; Intl Rltns.

PREVENSLIK, MICHAEL; Mt Pleasant Area SR HS; Mt Pleasant, PA; (2); Church Yth Grp; Bsktbl; Vllybl; Wt Lftg; Pittsburgh; Comm.

PREVITE, ANTHONY; Bishop Shanahan HS; Coatesville, PA; (4); 34/215; High Hon Roll; Hon Roll; NHS; Villanova; Mech Engnrng.

PREVITE, CHRIS; Blacklick Valley HS; Nanty Glo, PA; (3); 25/100; Aud/Vis; German Clb; De Vry; Data Systems Repair.

PREVOZNIK, JEAN; Upper Darby HS; Drexel Hl, PA; (3); Church Yth Grp; Dance Clb; Thesps; Chorus; School Musical; Variety Show; Cheerleading; Erly Chldhd Educ.

PREVOZNIK, MARK; Kutztown Area HS; Lenhartsville, PA; (3); Boy Scts; JV Bsbl; Var L Ftbl; Wt Lftg; High Hon Roll; Hon Roll; Navy; Diver.

PREZIOSO, MICHAEL; Seton-La Salle HS; Canonsburg, PA; (3); 69/271; Boy Scts; Church Yth Grp; Library Aide; Ski Clb; Rep Frsh Cls; Var L Crs Cntry; Var L Trk; High Hon Roll; Hon Roll; Nwsp Stf; Boy Scout Eagle Awd 86; Penn ST.

PREZIUSO, MONICA; Chichester HS; Twin Oaks, PA; (3); 4/296; Yrbk Stf; Stat Bsbl; Twrlr; High Hon Roll; Jr NHS; Trs NHS; Prfct Atten Awd; Spanish NHS; Top Math & Sci Awds 85; Paralgl.

PRIBISH, DAVID; West Mifflin Area HS; W Mifflin, PA; (2); Orch; Rep Frsh Cls; JV Crs Cntry; Trk; Hon Roll; Jr NHS; Pres Acad Fit Awd 86; Orch Fest Dist 1 86; Metallrgcl Engrng.

PRIBULA, RAEANN; Wyoming Area HS; Exeter, PA; (3); 15/244; Drama Clb; Spanish Clb; Chorus; Yrbk Stf; Var L Swmmng; High Hon Roll; Debate Tm; Comm.

PRIBULSKY, JAYCEE; Mechanicsburg SR HS; Mechanicsburg, PA; (2); 23/309; NFL; Speech Tm; Chorus; Mgr(s); Socr.

PRICE, ALEXANDRA; MMI Preparatory Schl; Conyngham, PA; (3); Aud/Vis; Pep Clb; VP Frsh Cls; Rep Stu Cncl; JV Var Cheerleading; High Hon Roll; NHS; Spanish NHS; Hon Roll; Var Crs Cntry; Pa Jr Acdmy Sci 2nd Pl State 85; Kings Coll Spanish Exam 3rd Pl 86; Cert Of Ed Dvlpmnt Ntl 85-86; Marine Bio.

PRICE, ANGELA; Everett Area HS; Everett, PA; (3); 10/126; VP Pres Church Yth Grp; Sec FHA; GAA; Library Aide; Spanish Clb; SADD; Chorus; Rep Stu Cncl; Hon Roll; NHS; Sec.

PRICE, BECKY; Slippery Rock Areia HS; Portersville, PA; (4); 17/172; Trs Church Yth Grp; Intnl Clb; Political Wkr; Chorus; Stage Crew; Stu Cncl; Hon Roll; NHS; JCL; Pep Clb; Olivet Nazarene U Almni Schlrshp, Presdntl Schlrshp 87; Olivet Nazarene U; Elem Ed.

PRICE, BETH; Ligoner Valley HS; Ligonier, PA; (3); Pres AFS; Pres French Clb; Hosp Aide; Rep SADD; Band; Mrchg Band; Stat Bsktbl; Hon Roll; NHS; Pres Clssrm Yng Amrcns, AFS Frgn Exchng Stu 87; PA Free Entrprs Wk 86; Crmnl Law.

PRICE, CARRIE; Butler SR HS; Herman, PA; (3); French Clb; FBLA; JA; Spanish Clb; Band; Hon Roll; Jr NHS; NHS.

PRICE, DAVID; Mountain View HS; Nicholson, PA; (3); 8/103; Chess Clb; 4-H; Hon Roll; Voice Dem Awd; Rotary Ldrshp Camp 86; Schl Brd 87; Penn ST Schlr 86-87; Bus Mgmt.

PRICE, DENISE; Ambridge Area HS; Sewickley, PA; (3); Church Yth Grp; French Clb; Girl Scts; Hosp Aide; Pep Clb; Red Cross Aide; Band; Mrchg Band; Pep Band; Symp Band.

PRICE, ERIC; Bethlelehm Catholic HS; Hellertown, PA; (3); 64/202; Stu Cncl; Var Bsktbl; Var L Ftbl; Score Keeper; Wt Lftg; High Hon Roll; Medical Careers Club 86-87; Bus.

PRICE, GRETCHEN; Coatesville Area HS; Coatesville, PA; (2); GAA; Ski Clb; Chorus; School Musical; Stu Cncl; Var L Tennis; Hon Roll; MVP Ten 86-87; Jwlry Dsgn.

PRICE, HEATHER; Canon Mc Millan HS; Canonsburg, PA; (4); 42/370; Latin Clb; Ski Clb; Varsity Clb; Sftbl; Swmmng; High Hon Roll; Hon Roll; CA U Of PA; Pre-Med.

PRICE, HOLLY; Central Dauphin HS; Harrisburg, PA; (4); 18/373; Exploring; Orch; Nwsp Bus Mgr; Yrbk Bus Mgr; Off Sr Cls; Off Stu Cncl; Tennis; Im Vllybl; NHS; ACES Hnr Essay Awd 87; Pres Acad Fit Awd 87; U Richmond.

PRICE, JENNIFER; Everett Area HS; Everett, PA; (2); Pres Church Yth Grp; Spanish Clb; Band; Concert Band; Jazz Band; Mrchg Band; Stu Cncl; Golf; Hon Roll; Prfct Atten Awd; Natl Hstry & Govt Awd 86; PA ST U.

PRICE, KENNETH; Mechanicsburg SR HS; Mechanicsburg, PA; (3); 100/309; Church Yth Grp; Nwsp Stf; Lit Mag; Hon Roll; Teen Bible Quiz Pgm 87; PA Wrtrs 86; Cmrcl Artst.

PRICE, LAURA; Westmont Hilltop HS; Johnstown, PA; (3); Art Clb; Church Yth Grp; Girl Scts; Key Clb; Spanish Clb; Band; Chorus; Concert Band; Mrchg Band; Stage Crew; Forgn Bus.

PRICE, MARIE; Carbondale Area HS; Carbondale, PA; (3); Church Yth Grp; FBLA; Pres German Clb; Ski Clb; Stu Cncl; Bsktbl; Fld Hcky; High Hon Roll; German Clb High Hnrs 85; Penn ST U; Ed.

PRICE, REBECCA; Wyalusing Valley HS; Dushore, PA; (3); Pres Trs 4-H; Spanish Clb; Band; Pres Frsh Cls; Rep Stu Cncl; Bsktbl; Sftbl; Vllybl; 4-H Awd; Hon Roll; Boyd Business Schl; Travel.

PRICE, ROBERT H; Perkiomen Valley HS; Collegeville, PA; (4); Am Leg Boys St; Yrbk Stf; VP Frsh Cls; Trs Soph Cls; Rep Jr Cls; Rep Sr Cls; Rep Stu Cncl; Hon Roll; NHS; Schwenksville Cmnty Schlrshp, & Ursinus Coll Stu Tchr Schlrshp 87; Ursinus Coll; Accntng.

PRICE, SAMUEL; Blacklick Valley HS; Nanty-Glo, PA; (3); 13/105; German Clb; Red Cross Aide; Varsity Clb; Im Bsktbl; Var L Ftbl; Var Trk; High Hon Roll; Hon Roll; Pres Schlr; Optmtry.

PRICE, STEPHANIE; Philipsburg Osceola SR HS; Sandy Ridge, PA; (4); 90/234; SADD; Band; Chorus; Mrchg Band; Stage Crew; Nwsp Rptr; Nwsp Stf; Bsktbl; Sftbl; Frnch.

PRICE, TINA; Cambridge Springs HS; Saegertown, PA; (3); JA; Spanish Clb; Rep Jr Cls; Stat Ftbl; Sftbl; RN.

PRICE, VICTORIA; Bishop Hafey HS; Conyngham, PA; (4); 15/126; Cmnty Wkr; French Clb; Ski Clb; Band; Stage Crew; Yrbk Stf; French Hon Soc; Hon Roll; Denison U; Psych.

PRICHARD, JILL; Harbor Creek HS; Erie, PA; (4); 2/213; Pres 4-H; Model UN; Sec Concert Band; Sec Mrchg Band; School Play; Variety Show; Rep Stu Cncl; Capt L Swmmng; Sec NHS; Sal; Acad Scholar 87-91; Mercyhurst Coll; Fash Merch.

PRICKETT, JOHN; Steelton-Highspire HS; Highspire, PA; (3); Quiz Bowl; Band; Concert Band; Jazz Band; Mrchg Band; School Musical; Ftbl; Trk; Hon Roll; PA ST U; Biochem.

PRIDE JR, ALAN R; East Stroudsburg HS; East Stroudsburg, PA; (3); 26/280; Stu Cncl; Crs Cntry; Socr; Trk; High Hon Roll; Hon Roll; Intl Frgn Lang Awd 87; Frnch.

PRIEBE, KRISTEN; Upper Darby HS; Drexel Hill, PA; (4); Church Yth Grp; Dance Clb; Hosp Aide; Color Guard; Drill Tm; Flag Corp; Mrchg Band; Lcrss; High Hon Roll; Hon Roll; Widener U; Nrsng.

PRIEST, JO ANNE M; Philadelphia HS For Girls; Philadelphia, PA; (2); Church Yth Grp; GAA; Service Clb; Stage Crew; Var Bowling; Var Sftbl; Hon Roll; Hghst Avg Sci; Acdmc Hnrs; Vrsty Ltr; Med.

PRIESTER, KURT; S R U HS; E Smithfield, PA; (2); Camera Clb; Pres Drama Clb; SADD; Teachers Aide; School Play; Rep Stu Cncl; Cit Awd; Hon Roll; NHS; Prfct Atten Awd; Citznshp Awd Senate PA 86; Cert Merit Arnot Art Museum 86; PA Govrns Schl Semi Fnlst 87; Art.

PRIGG, LAURA; Laurel Highlands HS; Uniontown, PA; (2); SADD; Sec Frsh Cls; VP Soph Cls; Cheerleading; L Diving; Swmmng; Trk; Im Vllybl; High Hon Roll; Pres Phys Ftns Awd 86; Pre Med.

PRIMAK, NATALIE; Juniata HS; Mifflintown, PA; (4); Quiz Bowl; School Musical; School Play; Nwsp Stf; Yrbk Sprt Ed; JV Trk; Hon Roll; NHS; Voice Dem Awd; Charles De Lauter Schlrshp 87; Susquehana U; Poltcl Sci.

PRIMATIC, LISA; Elmer L Meyers HS; Wilkes-Barre, PA; (3); SADD; Chorus; Church Choir; Concert Band; Mrchg Band; Orch; School Musical; High Hon Roll; Jr NHS; NEDT Awd; Dist & Regn Choruses 86; Dist Band 86; Dist & Regn Bands 87; Wilkes Coll; Music.

PRIMAVERA, VINCENT; Conemaugh Township HS; Hollsopple, PA; (3); Church Yth Grp; Spanish Clb; Band; Mrchg Band; Bsbl; Bsktbl; Dentistry.

PRIMEAUX, ANDRE; City Center Acad; Philadelphia, PA; (3); Art Clb; Chess Clb; Church Yth Grp; Computer Clb; Debate Tm; Latin Clb; Church Choir; School Play; JV Bsktbl; Morris Brown; Pre-Med.

PRIMERANO, DAVID; Mastbaum AVTS HS; Philadelphia, PA; (2); Elec.

PRIMERANO, MICHAEL; Lincoln HS; Ellwood City, PA; (3); Chorus; JV Ftbl; Hon Roll; Perfect Atten 84-86; Comms.

PRIMM, DANIEL; Central Catholic HS; Pittsburgh, PA; (3); 67/260; JV Var Socr; Hon Roll; NHS; CA ST U PA; Athl Trng.

PRIMO, MICHELLE; Monaca JR SR HS; Monaca, PA; (4); 18/90; Am Leg Aux Girls St; Exploring; Pres Library Aide; Sec Red Cross Aide; Spanish Clb; Church Choir; School Musical; JV Sftbl; Hon Roll; NHS; Parent Tchrs Assn Schlrshp 87; Ntl Assn Of The Wolves Grant 87; Monaca Wmns Club Gril Of Mth 87; Gannon U; Bio.

PRINCE, DIANE; Oswayo Valley JR-SR HS; Shinglehouse, PA; (3); 1/72; Sec 4-H; VP French Clb; Varsity Clb; Sec Stu Cncl; Var Capt Cheerleading; Var L Crs Cntry; Var Trk; JV Im Vllybl; 4-H Awd; High Hon Roll; Hugh O Brian Yth Fndtn Ldrshp Smnr Rep 86; Pre Med.

PRINCE, LYNNE MARIE; Mt Pleasant Area HS; Mt Pleasant, PA; (3); 35/250; Chrmn DECA; SADD; Ed Nwsp Stf; Rep Soph Cls; Rep Jr Cls; Rep Sr Cls; Rep Stu Cncl; L Swmmng; High Hon Roll; Sec NHS; Pre-Law.

PRINCE, PHOEBE; Hopewell HS; Aliquippa, PA; (3); Exploring; French Clb; Rptr FFA; Band; Concert Band; Mrchg Band; Pep Band; Hon Roll; FFA Awds-2nd Pl Rgnl Lndscp/Nrsry Comptn & Achvt Awd Nrsry Oprtns 87; Floricltr.

PRINCIOTTA, KIM; Upper Darby HS; Clifton Hts, PA; (3); Philadelphia Art Inst; Dcrtng.

PRINGLE, JARED; Danville SR HS; Danville, PA; (1); Boy Scts; Exploring; JV Ftbl; JV Trk; Hon Roll; Pres Acad Ftns Awd 87; Engrng.

PRINKEY, GEORGIA; Southmoreland HS; Scottdale, PA; (4); 49/222; Pep Clb; VICA; Chorus; Church Choir; Hon Roll; Prfct Atten Awd; Pres Acdmc Ftnss Awd 86-87; Median Schl; Dntl Asstng.

PRINKEY, PAUL; Connellsville SR HS; Connellsville, PA; (3); VICA; Band; Chorus; Church Choir; Concert Band; Mrchg Band; Hstry Tchr.

PRINTY, LORI; Cardinal Brennan HS; Shenandoah, PA; (3); German Clb; School Musical; JV Var Cheerleading; Bus Admin.

PRINTZ, STEVEN; Tulpehocken HS; Bethel, PA; (2); Stage Crew; Nwsp Stf; Jrnlsm.

PRIORI, JEANNA; Coatesville Area SR HS; Coatesville, PA; (3); 45/540; Leo Clb; Ski Clb; Spanish Clb; Band; Concert Band; Flag Corp; Mrchg Band; Yrbk Stf; Off Jr Cls; Hon Roll; Phys Thrpy.

PRISTASH, DAWN; Spring-Ford SR HS; Mont Clare, PA; (4); 19/237; Sec Spanish Clb; Hon Roll; NHS; Pres Schlr; Buckwalter Schlrshp 87; Warren Y Francis Awd Excllnce Span 87; Schlrshp Awd 87; W Chester U; Psych.

PRISTASH, MICHELLE; West Branch Area HS; Philipsburg, PA; (2); Pres Church Yth Grp; Spanish Clb; Band; Concert Band; Mrchg Band; Hon Roll; Bus Admin.

PRITCHARD, CATHERINE M; North Catholic HS; Pittsburgh, PA; (4); 2/238; Church Yth Grp; Debate Tm; Hosp Aide; NFL; Science Clb; Speech Tm; Nwsp Ed-Chief; Yrbk Ed-Chief; NHS; Sal; Mellwood Schlrshp; Sheffield Exch Stu; N Hills Bus & Professionl Wmns Stu Of Nov 86; Notre Dame; Journalism.

PRITCHETT, LISA; Jeannette SR HS; Jeannette, PA; (3); Drama Clb; French Clb; Spanish Clb; Teachers Aide; Hon Roll; Seton Hill; Vet Med.

PRITTS, KANDI; Connesville Area SR HS; Indian Head, PA; (3); 23/550; Am Leg Aux Girls St; Office Aide; Chorus; Rep Stu Cncl; High Hon Roll; Jr NHS; NHS; Prfct Atten Awd; Spanish NHS; Pittsburgh U; Radiologic Tech.

PRITTS, KRISTA; Rockwood Area HS; Garrett, PA; (3); Church Yth Grp; Band; Mrchg Band; VP Stu Cncl; Stat Sftbl; L Vllybl; High Hon Roll; Stu Schl Bd Dir 86-87; Frshmn Salutatorian; Acad All Amer Schlr 85-86; Lwyr.

PRITTS, MELISSA; Rockwood Area HS; Rockwood, PA; (2); Hosp Aide; Chorus; JV Cheerleading; Hon Roll.

PRIVETTE, THADDIOUS D; Pine Forge Acad; Moorestown, NJ; (2); Band; Church Choir; Concert Band; Orch; Bsktbl; Sftbl; Swmmng; Trk; Hon Roll; Oak Wood Coll; Zoolgst.

PRIZNIAK, JENNIFER; John S Fine HS; Nanticoke, PA; (3); 52/256; FBLA; Hosp Aide; Spanish Clb; Band; Chorus; Concert Band; Jazz Band; Mrchg Band; Pep Band; Variety Show; Gloria Honabach Awd 84; Dist Band Wnnr & Chorus 86-87; Natl Piano Wnnr 79-88; Misercordia; Music.

PROBST, BRIAN; Senior HS; North Bend, PA; (2); 1/56; Letterman Clb; Varsity Clb; Stu Cncl; Ftbl; Wt Lftg; Wrstlng; DAR Awd; French Hon Soc; High Hon Roll; Hon Roll; PA ST Coll; Law.

PROBST, MOLLY; Northern Vork County HS; Dillsburg, PA; (4); 32/207; Chorus; Off Concert Band; Mrchg Band; Orch; School Musical; Hon Roll; Church Yth Grp; French Clb; Off Band; Church Choir; Prsdntl Acdmc Ftnss Awds Pgm 87; Tri-M Natl Music Hnrs Soc 86-87; Dist & Rgnl Band & Orchestra 85-87; Temple U; Music Prfrmnc.

PROBST, SCOTT; Mercer Area HS; Mercer, PA; (4); 2/143; Speech Tm; Concert Band; Jazz Band; School Play; Off Stu Cncl; Capt Ftbl; Elks Awd; NHS; Opt Clb Awd; Sal; L B Armstrong Jazz Awd 86; PA Free Entrprs Wk Schlrshp 86; Mercer Cnty All-Star Jazz Bnd 86; PA ST U; Engnrng.

PROCHNAU, TIMOTHY; William Allen HS; Allentown, PA; (4); 20/550; German Clb; Band; Concert Band; Mrchg Band; Orch; Stage Crew; High Hon Roll; Hon Roll; Jr NHS; NHS; Pres Acad Fit Awd 87; Moravion Coll; Mech Engrng.

PROCKO, SCOTT; Monongahela Valley Catholic HS; Charleroi, PA; (2); 4/75; Church Yth Grp; Band; Concert Band; Mrchg Band; Yrbk Ed-Chief; French Hon Soc; Hon Roll; Jrnlsm.

PROCOPIO JR, ALFREDO; St John Neumann HS; Philadelphia, PA; (3); Math Clb; Math Tm; High Hon Roll; Hon Roll; Jr NHS; NHS; Cnstrctn.

PROCOPIO, MICHAEL; Northwestern Lehigh HS; Kempton, PA; (4); 33/158; Scholastic Bowl; School Musical; School Play; Var L Crs Cntry; L Capt Trk; Hon Roll; NEDT Awd; Exploring; Teachers Aide; Yrbk Stf; Physics Tstng Comptn Wnnr 86; E Stroudsburg U Hnrs Comm Schlrshp 87; Outstndng Sr Trk 87; E Stroudsburg U; Comp Sci.

PROCTOR, ERIC; Beaver Area HS; Beaver, PA; (3); Cmnty Wkr; Chrmn French Clb; Capt Socr; Var JV Tennis; JV Trk; Hon Roll; Goalkeeper On Pittsburgh Select Sccr Tm 87; Section Ldng Goalkeeper HS 86; Sprts Med.

PROCTOR, JOSEPH; Harrisburg HS; Harrisburg, PA; (4); 9/235; Boys Clb Am; Model UN; Pep Clb; Var JV Bsktbl; Var JV Ftbl; High Hon Roll; Hon Roll; Kiwanis Awd; NHS; Ntl Merit Ltr; Chllng Grnt 87; Ray S Shoemkr Schlrshp 87; Mst Lkly Sccd, Mst Ldrshp Ablty 87; U Of Pittsburgh; Bus Mngmt.

PROCTOR, KELLEE; Penn-Trafford HS; Levelgreen, PA; (3); 15/368; Am Leg Aux Girls St; Church Yth Grp; Drama Clb; SADD; Church Choir; High Hon Roll; NHS; Acad All Amer By Ntl Sec Ed Cncl 87; Boston U; Enr.

PROFFITT, JENNIFER; Seton-La Salle HS; Pittsburgh, PA; (2); 27/250; Dance Clb; Spanish Clb; SADD; Nwsp Stf; High Hon Roll; Acadmc All Amrcn 87-88; Poetry Form 87; PA ST; Phrmcst.

PROFFITT, STEVEN; Garden Spot HS; Narvon, PA; (2); Ftbl; Wt Lftg; High Hon Roll; Hon Roll; NHS.

PROFIT, ANGELA; Mt Carmel Area HS; Mt Carmel, PA; (4); 11/164; Cmnty Wkr; Key Clb; Latin Clb; Math Tm; Pep Clb; Q&S; Ski Clb; Spanish Clb; Chorus; School Musical; Albright Coll; Bio.

PROIETTO, DENISE; Pittston Area HS; Dupont, PA; (4); 19/326; FBLA; Science Clb; VICA; High Hon Roll; Hon Roll; NHS; Kings Coll Acadc Schlrshp 87; Kings Coll; Fin.

PROKOP, MARLENE; Shanksville Stonycreek HS; Shanksville, PA; (3); 2/34; Hosp Aide; Library Aide; Band; Concert Band; Mrchg Band; Nwsp Rptr; Nwsp Stf; Pres Frsh Cls; High Hon Roll; NHS; Comp.

PROKOP, MICHAEL T; Archbishop Kennedy HS; Plymouth Meeting, PA; (4); 15/170; Boy Scts; Church Yth Grp; Cmnty Wkr; French Clb; Science Clb; Stu Cncl; Trk; High Hon Roll; Hon Roll; SAR Awd; Amer Legion Awd 84; JR Stu Of Yr Awd Karate 85; Schlrshp Phila Coll Of Sci & Pharm 87; Drexel U; Bio Chem.

PROLA, MONICA; Blairsville SR HS; Blairsville, PA; (3); Church Yth Grp; Drama Clb; Trs SADD; Chorus; Capt Color Guard; Concert Band; School Musical; High Hon Roll; NHS; Distngshd Hnr Rll 86-87.

PROM, ERIC; Perry Traditional Acad; Pittsburgh, PA; (3); 14/300; Debate Tm; German Clb; Variety Show; Var Ftbl; Swmmng; Wt Lftg; Hon Roll; Sci.

PROPER, AARON; Oil City SR HS; Tituville, PA; (3); #8 In Class; Boy Scts; German Clb; Nwsp Phtg; Nwsp Rptr; Im Bsktbl; Im Vllybl; NHS.

PROPER, ALLEN; Corry Area HS; Spartansburg, PA; (2); AFS; Spanish Clb; Crs Cntry; Hon Roll; Math Tchr.

PROPER, ERIK S; Titusville HS; Titusville, PA; (3); 63/255; Am Leg Boys St; Church Yth Grp; German Clb; Varsity Clb; Var L Golf; Hon Roll; Mgr(s); Presdntl Acad Fitness Awd 85; Penn ST; Aerospace Engrng.

PROPER, HEATHER; Maplewood HS; Titusville, PA; (3); DECA; SADD; Yrbk Stf; Gym; Swmmng; Wrstlng; Hon Roll; Church Yth Grp; Computer Clb; French Clb; Bus Mgmt.

PROPHET, KRISTEN; Middletown Area HS; Middletown, PA; (3); 6/193; Chorus; Color Guard; Mrchg Band; Var Fld Hcky; Var Gym; Var Trk; Var Twrlr; Im Vllybl; Hon Roll.

PROPHET, WILLIAM; Fairfield HS; Orrtanna, PA; (3); 10/84; Spanish Clb; Band; School Play; Off Bsbl; L Bsktbl; L Socr; High Hon Roll; Hon Roll; NHS; CA ST U Long Beach.

PROROK, JEFF; Downingtown SR HS; Downingtown, PA; (3); 200/560; Ski Clb; Chorus; Var L Trk; Im Vllybl; JV Var Wrstlng; Hon Roll.

PROSKE, NICOLE; Elk County Christian HS; Ridgway, PA; (4); 1/80; Art Clb; Ski Clb; Varsity Clb; Nwsp Stf; Yrbk Ed-Chief; Cheerleading; Var L Tennis; Bausch & Lomb Sci Awd; High Hon Roll; NEDT Awd; Duquesne U; Phrmcy.

PROSKIN, GARY; Penn-Trafford HS; Irwin, PA; (3); 46/301; JCL; Latin Clb; VP Frsh Cls; VP Soph Cls; Ftbl; Socr; Wrstlng; High Hon Roll; Hon Roll; Sccr Ltr 86 & 87; Wrstlng Ltr 87; Slippery Rock Coll; Chiroprctc.

PROSPERI, ANNE; Greensburg Central Catholic HS; Latrobe, PA; (3); 1/225; AFS; Church Yth Grp; Cmnty Wkr; Exploring; Ski Clb; Band; Concert Band; Mrchg Band; JV Var Crs Cntry; JV Trk; Pre-Med.

PROSSER, KEVIN; Newport HS; Newport, PA; (3); Pres 4-H; Var Ftbl; Var Wt Lftg; 4-H Awd; Pre Law.

PROSTKO, ERIC; Freedom HS; Bethlehem, PA; (3); 90/550; Boy Scts; Concert Band; Mrchg Band; Ntl Merit Ltr; Aero Engr.

PROUDFIT, JULIE A; Washington HS; Washington, PA; (3); 4/160; Am Leg Aux Girls St; Cmnty Wkr; Key Clb; Letterman Clb; Library Aide; Political Wkr; Q&S; Sec Spanish Clb; Nwsp Stf; Off Frsh Cls; Chem Engrng.

PROUGH, JASON; Elizabethtown Area HS; Elizabehtown, PA; (3); 128/224; Office Aide; Ski Clb; School Play; VP Soph Cls; Golf; Trk; Bus.

PROVENCHER, STACY; Chambersburg Area SR HS; Chambersburg, PA; (2); 32/740; Pres Church Yth Grp; French Clb; SADD; Band; Chorus; Concert Band; Mrchg Band; Rep Soph Cls; Rep Stu Cncl; Med Fld.

PROVENZANO, MARC; Valley Forge Military Acad; Mt Laurel, NJ; (2); 2/156; Art Clb; Camera Clb; French Clb; Chorus; School Musical; Lit Mag; High Hon Roll; NHS; Pres Schlr; Golden Sword 87; Engl & Sci Awd 87; Georgetown U; Law.

PROVIANO, THOMAS; Ringgold HS; Finleyville, PA; (3); Bsbl; Hon Roll; NHS; Mth, Sci Hnr Soc 86-87; Penn ST U.

PROWELL, MICHAEL; West York Area SR HS; York, PA; (3); 12/189; Spanish Clb; Varsity Clb; Var Bsktbl; Var Trk; NHS; Sprts Med.

PROWISOR, JOSHUA; Engineering & Science HS; Philadelphia, PA; (3); Camera Clb; JA; Radio Clb; Science Clb; Ski Clb; Yrbk Phtg; Yrbk Stf; Badmtn; Swmmng; Wt Lftg; Chinese Pgm Awd Aid 84-86; Meritorious Acddmc Achvt Awd & Sci & Art-Exclnnc Awds 83; Rensalaer Ply Inst; Chem Engrng.

PROZZOLY, DEAN; Keystone Oaks HS; Carnegie, PA; (3); 62/287; Spanish Clb; Var JV Bsbl; JV Golf; Wt Lftg; U Of Pgh; Pilot.

PRUCE, ROBERT; Canon Mc Millan SR HS; Canonsburg, PA; (3); 88/367; Boy Scts; Band; Concert Band; Mrchg Band; Hon Roll.

PRUGH IV, EDWIN N; Waynesburg Central HS; Mt Morris, PA; (3); Aud/Vis; 4-H; French Clb; Stage Crew; Score Keeper; Hon Roll; Voice Dem Awd; Anne Meighen Wrld Hist Awd 86; Stu Of The Wk Awd 87; Audio Commnctns.

PRUITT, MATTHEW SHANE; Downingtown HS; Exton, PA; (3); Letterman Clb; Ski Clb; Spanish Clb; SADD; Var JV Socr; JV Tennis; High Hon Roll; NHS; Key Clb; Acdmc Cmpttn Team 86-87.

PRUM, PISET ANG; Lebanon SR HS; Lebanon, PA; (4); Drama Clb; French Clb; Latin Clb; Spanish Clb; Speech Tm; Teachers Aide; Nwsp Ed-Chief; Yrbk Stf; Tennis; Hon Roll; Drexel U; Fshn Dsgn.

PRUSHINSKI, BOB; Wyoming Valley West HS; Larksville, PA; (3); Cmnty Wkr; Math Clb; Nwsp Stf; Yrbk Rptr; Var L Bsktbl; Im Vllybl; Im Wt Lftg; High Hon Roll; NHS; Ntl Merit SF; Rotary Intl Ldrshp Camp 86; Hstry Clb 86-88; WUW Bsktbl Acad Achvt Awd 86 & 87; Law.

PRUSS, MARY; Shade HS; Cenral City, PA; (2); Color Guard; Spanish Clb; Chorus; Flag Corp; Nwsp Stf; Hon Roll; 1st Pl Duet Prfrmnc 86; Clrs Schl Dsgn.

PRUSS, MATTHEW; Tunkhannock Area HS; Tunkhannock, PA; (2); JV Bsbl; Var Golf; Hon Roll; Ntl Frnch Cont 86; PA ST U; Astrnmy.

PRUSZENSKI, ANTHONY; Quigley HS; Ambridge, PA; (3); Yrbk Bus Mgr; Yrbk Stf; Var L Crs Cntry; Var L Trk; Var L Wrstlng; Wrstlng Sec 10 Champ 86-87; Top 100 Wrstlrs Of PA 85-86; Elec Engrng.

PRUTZMAN, SHANNON; Mifflinburg HS; Mifflinburg, PA; (1); French Clb; Bsktbl; Ftbl; Socr; Hon Roll; Annapolis Naval Acad; Offcr.

PRUYNE, PATRICIA; Northeast Bradford JR-SR HS; Towanda, PA; (3); 20/102; Pres Church Yth Grp; Cmnty Wkr; FHA; Girl Scts; SADD; VICA; Chorus; Nwsp Stf; High Hon Roll; Hon Roll; Mst Cooprtv In Cls-Brdfrd Cnty Area Vo-Tech Schl 85-86; Slvr Schlr Awd 85-87; Culnry Arts.

PRY, JULIE; Downingtown SR HS; Downingtown, PA; (3); Church Yth Grp; French Clb; GAA; Band; Chorus; Var Cheerleading; Var Lcrss; Im Sftbl; Var Trk; High Hon Roll; DE Coll; Phys Thrpy.

PRYAL, SHANE; North Star HS; Stoystown, PA; (2); FCA; Mu Alpha Theta; JV Bsktbl; Mgr(s); Cit Awd; Hon Roll; Stu Of The Mnth Awd 87.

PRYBICIEN, MICHAEL; Lakeland JR SR HS; Mayfield, PA; (3); 38/145; Church Yth Grp; SADD; Yrbk Stf; JV Bsbl; Var L Ftbl; JV Trk; Im Wt Lftg; Hon Roll; Prfct Atten Awd; Med.

PRYDE, CARRIE A; Philipsburg-Osceola HS; Philipsburg, PA; (4); 53/250; Ski Clb; SADD; Chorus; Flag Corp; School Play; Nwsp Ed-Chief; Nwsp Phtg; Nwsp Rptr; Nwsp Stf; Yrbk Stf; Emerson Coll; Jrnlsm.

PRYNDA, MICHELE; Carbondale JR SR HS; Simpson, PA; (4); 30/144; Church Yth Grp; Computer Clb; English Clb; Ski Clb; Spanish Clb; Yrbk Stf; Var Cheerleading; Gym; Var L Trk; Hon Roll; Phys Ftns Awds 81-86; Mst Spiritd Chrldr 86; Gymnstcs Awd 79-85; Penn ST; Acctng.

PRYOR, LISA; Kiski Area HS; Apollo, PA; (3); FBLA; FHA; Office Aide; Teachers Aide; Band; Mgr Bsbl; Cheerleading; Stat Ftbl; Mgr(s); Timer; 1st Pie Baking Cntst 86; IN U PA; CPA.

PRYOR, SARAH; Waynesboro Area SR HS; Blue Ridge Smt, PA; (4); 185/355; Camera Clb; Church Yth Grp; Hosp Aide; Chorus; Yrbk Stf; High Hon Roll; Hon Roll; Cedar Crest Coll; Nrsng.

PRYOR, WILLIAM; Henderson SR HS; W Chester, PA; (3); Church Yth Grp; Ski Clb; Var L Ftbl; Var L Trk; Physcl Thrpy.

PRZYBYCIEN, PAMELA; Fort Le Boeuf HS; Waterford, PA; (2); 21/221; Drama Clb; Pep Clb; Spanish Clb; Chorus; Trk; High Hon Roll; Hon Roll; Pres Schlr; Church Choir; Chrmn Spirit Day Club 87; Educ.

PRZYBYLKOWSKI, SANDY; Western Wayne HS; Lake Ariel, PA; (3); 31/190; SADD; Band; Concert Band; Mrchg Band; Sec VP Stu Cncl; Bsbl; Cheerleading; Vllybl; High Hon Roll; Hon Roll; Elem Educ.

PSARROS, TOM; Freedom HS; Bethlehem, PA; (3); 76/555; Capt Socr; Hon Roll.

PSZCZOLKOWSKI, DEBRA; Freeport SR HS; Sarver, PA; (3); 48/210; Church Yth Grp; Stage Crew; Yrbk Stf; JV Bsktbl; L Var Trk; Capt L Vllybl; High Hon Roll; Hon Roll.

PUCHAK, AMY; Pocono Mountain HS; Tannersville, PA; (2); 1/370; Church Yth Grp; Nwsp Stf; Trs Frsh Cls; Im JV Bsktbl; High Hon Roll; Hon Roll; NHS; Amrcn Lgn Aux Mdl Awd Post 922, Prsdntl Acdmc Ftnss Awd, Stu Mnth 85-86.

PUCKERIN, CHRISTAL; Lutheran HS; Philadelphia, PA; (3); #4 In Class; Church Yth Grp; Debate Tm; Teachers Aide; Church Choir; Var Bsktbl; Var Trk; Jr NHS; Outstndng Spn 87; Outstndng Debate 86; Pedtrcn.

PUCKETT, JOSIE; Solanco HS; Quarryville, PA; (3); Pep Clb; Teachers Aide; Varsity Clb; Band; Concert Band; Var Capt Cheerleading; Gym; Powder Puff Ftbl; JV Sftbl; JV Trk; Millersville U; Teaching.

PUCKEY, STEVE; Yough SR HS; W Newton, PA; (4); Pres Church Yth Grp; French Clb; Ski Clb; JV Var Bsbl; NHS; Indiana U PA; Lbrl Arts.

PUDLOWSKI, HEATHER ANNE; Lower Dauphin HS; Grantville, PA; (4); Camera Clb; Dance Clb; Thesps; Capt Color Guard; School Play; Lit Mag; Hon Roll; NHS; Cmnty Wkr; Girl Scts; Jack Woolf Awd 87; Pres Pyscl Ftns Awd 83-86; Mst Outstndng Gurd Awd 86; Harrisburg Area CC; Mass Comm.

PUFFENBERGER, BRETT; Rockwood Area HS; Somerset, PA; (2); Chess Clb; Computer Clb; NFL; Trs Ski Clb; Speech Tm; School Play; L Golf; L Socr; Var Trk; Comp Prog.

PUGH, ALAN; Neshannock HS; Neshannock, PA; (3); Drama Clb; Chorus; School Musical; Stage Crew; L Ftbl; L Trk; Prfct Atten Awd; Srvc Awd 86-87; Gftd Prgm 84-88; Penn ST; Sprts Medcne.

PUGH, BERNARD; Cardinal Dougherty HS; Philadelphia, PA; (2); Dance Clb; Math Clb; Science Clb; Chorus; Yrbk Phtg; Crs Cntry; Ftbl; Trk; Prfct Atten Awd; Acad Prof Wad Phys Sci 85-86.

PUGH, KELLY; North Star HS; Jenners, PA; (3); 2/141; FCA; Mu Alpha Theta; Teachers Aide; Band; Concert Band; Mrchg Band; JV Cheerleading; Hon Roll; Hghst GPA Awd Mth 84-85; Hghst GPA Awd Engl 85-86; Elem Ed.

PUGH, REBECCA; Fannett-Metal HS; Spring Run, PA; (4); 5/40; Trs Art Clb; Pres Church Yth Grp; Trs Drama Clb; Pres Chorus; School Play; Pres Swing Chorus; Sec Nwsp Stf; Cheerleading; Hon Roll; French Awd 86; Scndry Ed.

PUGLIANO, TONY; Ambridge Area HS; Baden, PA; (3); German Clb; Yrbk Stf; Stu Cncl; Var Socr; Var Tennis; Var Trk; Im Vllybl; Hon Roll; Keystone Boys Clb 87; Radio.

PUGLIESE, CATERINA; Dunmore HS; Dunmore, PA; (4); 11/150; French Clb; Letterman Clb; Yrbk Sprt Ed; Trs Jr Cls; Trs Sr Cls; Stu Cncl; Var Bsktbl; Var Cheerleading; Jr NHS; NHS; Wmns Clb Schlrshp 87; Widener U.

PUGLIESE, LISA; Freeport Area HS; Sarver, PA; (2); 35/202; Chorus; Var JV Trk; Hon Roll; Law.

PUGLIESE, MICHELLE; Williams Valley JR/Sr HS; Tower City, PA; (3); 10/108; Office Aide; Drill Tm; Mrchg Band; Nwsp Stf; Yrbk Stf; VP Frsh Cls; Stu Cncl; Var VP Cheerleading; High Hon Roll; Hon Roll; Fshn.

PUGNE, KAREN; Seneca Valley HS; Mars, PA; (3); #14 In Class; Ski Clb; Yrbk Stf; High Hon Roll; Hon Roll.

PUHALLA, KAREN; Scranton Central HS; Scranton, PA; (2); Spanish Clb; Orch; School Musical; Rep Stu Cncl; Dist Orch 87; Nrsng.

PUKACH, JENNIFER; Quigley HS; Aliquippa, PA; (4); 17/101; Hosp Aide; Math Clb; Band; Nwsp Stf; Yrbk Stf; High Hon Roll; Hon Roll; NHS; Concert Band; Dist Band 86-87; Cert Of Merit Schlrshp Duquesne 87; Band Sec Ldr Awd 85-86; Duquesne U; Bus Adm.

PULASKI, LEANNE M; Bentworth SR HS; Bentleyville, PA; (3); 1/115; Am Leg Aux Girls St; Ski Clb; SADD; Varsity Clb; Drill Tm; VP Jr Cls; VP Sr Cls; Rep Stu Cncl; Stat Bsktbl; Vllybl; Child Psych.

PULITI, ANGELA; Red Land HS; New Cumberland, PA; (4); 37/275; Red Cross Aide; SADD; Rep Frsh Cls; Rep Soph Cls; Rep Jr Cls; Rep Sr Cls; Rep Stu Cncl; Capt Cheerleading; Capt Swmmng; Hon Roll; Natl Chrldng Champ Fnlsts 87; U Of PA; Exercise Sci.

PULLEASE, CINDY; Maplewood HS; Guys Mills, PA; (3); Pep Clb; SADD; Color Guard; Mrchg Band; Rep Frsh Cls; Rep Soph Cls; Mgr(s); JH Thompson Bus Acad; Med Sec.

PULLIN, PATRICIA; Interboro HS; Norwood, PA; (4); French Clb; Latin Clb; Yrbk Stf; Rep Soph Cls; Rep Jr Cls; Rep Sr Cls; High Hon Roll; NHS.

PULLO, MELISSA; Pius X HS; Roseto, PA; (4); 3/32; Library Aide; School Musical; Sftbl; High Hon Roll; Lion Awd; NHS; Pres Schlr; Fr Ducci Schlrhsp 87; Drlene Lee Mem Schlrhsp 87; Bloomsburg U; Offc Admin.

PULTZ, SHANNON; Seneca Valley HS; Mars, PA; (2); Art Clb; Ski Clb; Varsity Clb; Band; Rep Frsh Cls; Rep Soph Cls; Cheerleading; Diving; Trk; Hon Roll; Schlrshp Carnegie Mellon U, Pre-Coll Art Pgm 87-88; Schlrshp Gvrnrs Schl PA-ARTS 87; Gftd Pgm; Art.

PULVINO, DENNISE; Harbor Creek SR HS; Erie, PA; (3); Nwsp Rptr; Stu Cncl; Var Cheerleading; Powder Puff Ftbl; Hon Roll; Elem Ed.

PUMO, VICTOR; Council Rock HS; Washington Cros, PA; (4); 58/848; L Socr; Trk; Hon Roll; NHS; Makefield PTA Schlrshp & Busmns Assn Schlrshp; Villanova U; Bus.

PUMPHREY, PATRICIA; Chester HS; Brookhaven, PA; (3); Rep Frsh Cls; Rep Soph Cls; Off Jr Cls; Off Sr Cls; Stu Cncl; Stat Ftbl; Var Sftbl; Var Trk; Howard U; Cmmnctns.

PUNCHELLO, CATHARINE; Pennsbury HS; Morrisville, PA; (4); 71/771; Exploring; Hon Roll; NHS; Pres Schlr; Dance Clb; French Clb; Chorus; Yrbk Stf; Stu Cncl; Bowling; Natl Lw Enfrcmnt Explr Acad Wash DC 87; Pnnsbry Schlrshp Fndtn Schlrshp 87; King Coll; Crmnl Jstc.

PUNIA, SURINDER; Warren Area HS; Warren, PA; (3); Chess Clb; French Clb; Tennis; Trk; High Hon Roll; Hon Roll; Gannon U; Med.

PUPA, LISA; Pittston Area SR HS; Pittston, PA; (3); Art Clb; Church Yth Grp; French Clb; FNA; Girl Scts; Hosp Aide; Key Clb; SADD; Chorus; Hon Roll; Bloomsburg U; Nrsng.

PUPI, ROBERT; Monaca HS; Monaca, PA; (4); 1/90; Exploring; School Musical; Var L Bsktbl; Var L Ftbl; Bausch & Lomb Sci Awd; High Hon Roll; Pres NHS; Prfct Atten Awd; Val; Schlr Athlete Ftbl & Bsktbl; OH Vly Cnfrence Sctn 2-A 2nd Team Rcvr; Bio.

PUPO, MARY B; Penn Cambria SR HS; Cresson, PA; (4); 4/196; Pres Church Yth Grp; Trs Girl Scts; SADD; Chorus; Color Guard; Yrbk Phtg; Off Stu Cncl; Var L Vllybl; Hon Roll; NHS; Outstndng Frnch Stu 83; PA ST U; Engr.

PURBAUGH, BARBARA; Meyersdale HS; Garrett, PA; (4); FFA; Hon Roll; FFA Greenhand Awd 85; FFA Chap Farmer Awd 86; Pres Acadmc Ftns Awd 86; Writer.

PURCELL, CHRISTI; Cocalico SR HS; Denver, PA; (4); Church Yth Grp; Hosp Aide; Trs Soph Cls; Trs Jr Cls; Trs Sr Cls; Pres Stu Cncl; Var Tennis; Hon Roll; Stdnt Mnth 86; Intl Pol.

PURCELL, JOSEPH; Minersville Area HS; Minersville, PA; (3); 37/105; German Clb; VP Leo Clb; Letterman Clb; Pep Clb; Ski Clb; Varsity Clb; Var L Ftbl; Wt Lftg; Law Enfrcmnt.

PURCELL, NICOLE; Schuylkill Haven Area HS; Sch Haven, PA; (2); 7/107; FNA; German Clb; Pep Clb; SADD; Band; Chorus; Sec Frsh Cls; VP Soph Cls; Rep Stu Cncl; JV Cheerleading; Pre Med.

PURDY, CAROL L; Harrisburg HS; Harrisburg, PA; (1); 28/468; Chorus; Bsktbl; Fld Hcky; Trk; DE ST Coll; Med.

PURDY, TERI; Lackawanna Trail HS; Factoryville, PA; (4); 3/86; 4-H; FHA; Girl Scts; SADD; Chorus; Church Choir; Drill Tm; Hon Roll; NHS; Pres Schlr; Bloomsburg U; Imaging.

PURNELL, KELSEY; Henderson HS; West Chester, PA; (3); Church Yth Grp; Hosp Aide; Intnl Clb; Library Aide; Lit Mag; Var Crs Cntry; Var Trk; Hon Roll; PIAA ST Chmpn Trck Team 88; Scndry Ed.

PURTA, LORI; North Pocono HS; Moscow, PA; (4); 11/240; Pep Clb; Ski Clb; Spanish Clb; Var Capt Trk; High Hon Roll; NHS; Marywood Schlrshp 87-88; Hnr Grad 87; Marywood Coll; Span.

PURTELL, MATTHEW; Montrose Area HS; Little Meadows, PA; (3); Boy Scts; Church Yth Grp; Spanish Clb; Chorus; Golf; Socr; Wt Lftg; Susquehanna Cnty Invit Bus Ed Cont 87; Acctg.

PURTELL, SEAN; South Park HS; Library, PA; (3); 47/227; JV Bsbl; Var Ftbl; Var Trk; Var Wt Lftg; Hon Roll; Prfct Atten Awd; Bus Manag.

PURUCKER, MICHAEL; Shaler Area SR HS; Pittsburgh, PA; (3); 1/486; Var JV Bsbl; Capt Var Bsktbl; Bausch & Lomb Sci Awd; French Hon Soc; High Hon Roll; NHS; Ntl Merit Ltr; NEDT Awd; Band; Natl Sci Olympd Chem 1st Pl; PA Math Leag 1st Pl; Fnlst Prvsts Schlrshp U Pittsbrgh.

PURVIS, GREGORY J; Allentown Central Catholic HS; Whitehall, PA; (4); AFS; Math Clb; Ski Clb; Im Fld Hcky; Var Capt Tennis; Hon Roll; MVP Ten 86-87; PSU Allentown; Engr.

PURVIS, JENNIFER; Seneca Valley HS; Evans City, PA; (4); Church Yth Grp; Thesps; Acpl Chr; Chorus; Church Choir; Madrigals; School Musical; School Play; Stage Crew; Swing Chorus; Wesminster Hnrs Chorus 85-87; ST Chorus 86; Eastern Seaboard Choir 86-87; Slippery Rock U; Music Thrpy.

PURYEAR, AKI; Wilkinsburg JR/Sr HS; Pittsburgh, PA; (3); JA; Spanish Clb; Band; Drm Mjr(t); Mrchg Band; Rep Stu Cncl; Ftbl; High Hon Roll; Hon Roll; NHS; Rensselar Outstndg Math & Sci Achvt Awd 87; USAA Span Awd 86-87; Elect Engr.

PUSCHNIGG, GREG; Ligonier Valley SR HS; Latrobe, PA; (3); 1/154; Am Leg Boys St; Church Yth Grp; Computer Clb; Ftbl; Wt Lftg; Wrstlng; High Hon Roll; Hon Roll; Urch Mem Wrstlng Awd 87; Arspc Engnrng.

PUSKAR, ERIK; Springdale HS; Springdale, PA; (3); Church Yth Grp; Sec Exploring; Key Clb; Spanish Clb; SADD; Varsity Clb; JV Var Ftbl; Wt Lftg; Prfct Atten Awd; Spnsh Hnrs 87; Educ.

PUSKAR JR, JOSEPH; Highlands SR HS; Brackenridge, PA; (2); Pres Aud/Vis; Intnl Clb; Trs Key Clb; Band; Concert Band; Mrchg Band; Schlstc Achvt Awds 84-87; PA ST; Engr.

PUSKAR, LORI; Hazleton SR HS; Hazleton, PA; (2); Drama Clb; FBLA; Pep Clb; Y-Teens; JV Cheerleading; Im Gym; Hon Roll; Penn ST; Chrprctc.

PUSKAR, PHILIP; Mt Pleasant Area HS; Mt Pleasant, PA; (4); German Clb; Bsktbl; Hon Roll; Johnson & Wales Coll; Motel Mgt.

PUSKARIC, ROSEMARY; Elizabeth Forward SR HS; Buena Vista, PA; (2); Art Clb; French Clb; Library Aide; Ski Clb; Teachers Aide; Color Guard; Mrchg Band; Badmtn; High Hon Roll; Hon Roll.

PUSKARICH, PENNY D; Trinity HS; Washington, PA; (3); 7/402; Church Yth Grp; Cmnty Wkr; Debate Tm; Math Tm; Yrbk Sprt Ed; High Hon Roll; Hon Roll; Essay Medal M L King 86; Cert Hgh Scores NEDT Test 85; Psych.

PUSKAS II, FRANCIS J; Pocono Mountain HS; Pocono Lake, PA; (3); French Clb; SADD; Rep Frsh Cls; Rep Jr Cls; Off Sr Cls; Pres Stu Cncl; High Hon Roll; Hon Roll; NHS; Pocono Mtn Stu Gov Svc Awd 86-87; Acad All-Amer Awd 86-87; Corp Law.

PUTNAM, ELLEN; Warren Area HS; Warren, PA; (4); Ski Clb; Acpl Chr; Madrigals; School Musical; School Play; Yrbk Stf; Var Trk; DAR Awd; NHS; Pres Schlr; PA Govnrs Schl For The Arts/Crtv Wrgng 86; C B Spade Eglsh/Crtv Wrtng Awd 87; CT Coll; Archlgy.

PUTNEY, SEAN; Meadville Area SR HS; Meadville, PA; (3); 100/365; Church Yth Grp; French Clb; Letterman Clb; Varsity Clb; Church Choir; Im Badmtn; L Var Bsbl; L Var Ftbl; L Var Ice Hcky; Im Wt Lftg; Phy Thrpy.

PUTT, KAREN; Lower Dauphin HS; Hummelstown, PA; (3); 49/237; Ski Clb; Color Guard; Drm Mjr(t); Flag Corp; Twrlr; Hon Roll; Ed.

PUZ, BRIAN; Burrell HS; Lower Burrell, PA; (3); 27/176; Chess Clb; Church Yth Grp; Tennis; Penn ST U; Engr.

PYLE, JOSEPH; Downington SR HS; Exton, PA; (4); 4/551; JA; Quiz Bowl; Scholastic Bowl; Ski Clb; Spanish Clb; Teachers Aide; Acpl Chr; Band; Chorus; Concert Band; PA ST Acad Excllnc Awd 87-91; PA ST U; Geosci.

PYLE, SUZANNE; Heritage Christian Acad; Erie, PA; (2); 1/13; Office Aide; Ski Clb; Yrbk Stf; Bsktbl; Sftbl; Vllybl; Hon Roll; NHS.

PYNE, PATRICK; Central Catholic HS; Dubois, PA; (2).

PYSHER, TODD; Conrad Weiser HS; Wernersville, PA; (3); 30/179; Computer Clb; Spanish Clb; Bsbl; Bsktbl; Socr; Vllybl; Hon Roll; NHS; Arch.

PYTASH, FAITH; Blacklick Valley JR-SR HS; Vintondale, PA; (2); #1 In Class; Library Aide; NFL; Spanish Clb; Speech Tm; Varsity Clb; Stage Crew; Yrbk Rptr; Yrbk Stf; Off Frsh Cls; Stu Cncl; Acad All-Amer 85-86; Pres Acad Awd 85-86; Bradford Pttsbrgh Pa; Mngmnt.

QUACKENBUSH, APRIL; Du Bois Area HS; Dubois, PA; (3); Church Yth Grp; Nrsg.

QUACKENBUSH, SUSANNE; St Marys Area HS; St Marys, PA; (2); Band; Concert Band; Drm Mjr(t); Jazz Band; Mrchg Band; Pep Band; Hon Roll; Lwyr.

QUAGLIERI, LISA; Gateway SR HS; Monroeville, PA; (4); 151/501; Church Yth Grp; Ski Clb; Teachers Aide; Chorus; Yrbk Stf; JV Var Cheerleading; Score Keeper; Trk; IN U Of PA; Resprtry Therapy.

QUARLES, ATASHA; The Cecilian Acad; Philadelphia, PA; (2); Chorus; School Musical; Prfct Atten Awd; Math Acctnt.

QUARRY, KRISTIE; Altoona Area HS; Altoona, PA; (3); Pres FTA; Sec SADD; Teachers Aide; Hon Roll; German Clb; Stage Crew; Crs Cntry; Trk; Pres Phys Fit Awd 84-85; Tchng.

QUATTRO, JASON; Oil City SR HS; Oil City, PA; (3); 40/250; Dance Clb; Letterman Clb; Varsity Clb; Jazz Band; Pep Band; Variety Show; Yrbk Stf; Var JV Bsktbl; JV Var Crs Cntry; Var JV Trk; MIP Bsktbl V 86-87; Music.

QUATTRO, ROB; Garnet Valley HS; Glen Mills, PA; (3); Art Clb; German Clb; Model UN; PAVAS; Ski Clb; Yrbk Stf; Trk; Tyler Art Schl PA; Cmmrcl Art.

QUAY, SCOTT; Altoona Area HS; Altoona, PA; (3); Drama Clb; Spanish Clb; Chorus; School Musical; School Play; High Hon Roll; Art Clb; Computer Clb; PAVAS; Thesps; Lead Vocalist Rock Bnd-Necracedia 87; Music.

QUEEN, DANIEL; Parkland SR HS; Coplay, PA; (3); 150/500; Church Yth Grp; Trs German Clb; Ski Clb; Band; Trs Stu Cncl; JV Bsbl; Elec Engrng.

QUEER, FENNA; Rockwood Area SR HS; Rockwood, PA; (4); 19/94; Ski Clb; Spanish Clb; Drm Mjr(t); Yrbk Stf; Rep Jr Cls; Rep Stu Cncl; JV Var Cheerleading; Stat Sftbl; JV Var Vllybl; Hon Roll; Math Awd 82-83; Vntr Clb Applcnt 86-87; Wilma Boyd Career Schl; Trvl.

QUEER, SHAWN; Connellsville Area SR HS; Dunbar, PA; (2); VICA; Stage Crew; Hon Roll; Law.

QUEER, TALESA; Rockwood Area HS; Rockwood, PA; (3); Ski Clb; Band; Chorus; Church Choir; Drm Mjr(t); Mrchg Band; Trs Frsh Cls; Cheerleading; Socr; Sftbl; Schlstc Awd 84-85; Hnr Roll Awd; Wilma Boyd Career Schl; Scrtry.

QUEER, TRINA; Laurel Highlands HS; Uniontown, PA; (3); Church Yth Grp; JA; SADD; Yrbk Stf; JV Cheerleading; Im Vllybl; High Hon Roll; Hon Roll; Psych.

QUERIO, ANDREA M; Highlands SR HS; Brackenridge, PA; (4); 93/277; Art Clb; Church Yth Grp; FBLA; FHA; Yrbk Stf; Jr NHS; Prsdntl Physcl Ftns Awd 84; Edinboro; Art.

QUESINBERRY, ANITA; Bermudian Springs HS; Gardners, PA; (3); Library Aide; Spanish Clb; Nwsp Stf; Yrbk Stf; Hon Roll; Radlgy.

QUIACHON, DIVINE; S Philadelphia HS; Philadelphia, PA; (3); Math Clb; School Musical; Variety Show; Score Keeper; Var Tennis; Var Vllybl; Hon Roll; Charles Ellis Schlrshp Grnt 87-88; Colmbus Essy Cert 86-87; Cert Gd Perfrmnc 85-86; Orthdntstry.

QUICK, JOEY; State College Area HS; State College, PA; (4); Drama Clb; Hosp Aide; Office Aide; Teachers Aide; Thesps; Chorus; School Musical; School Play; Stage Crew; Hon Roll; Penn ST; Spec Ed.

QUIGG, COLLEEN; Parkland HS; Allentown, PA; (2); Church Yth Grp; Exploring; Key Clb; Library Aide; Nwsp Phtg; Nwsp Stf; Yrbk Phtg; Bsktbl; Swmmng; Trk; Med.

QUIGLEY, ALICIA; Phoenixville Area HS; Phoenixville, PA; (4); 7/202; Church Yth Grp; SADD; School Play; Nwsp Rptr; Trs Sr Cls; Rep Stu Cncl; NHS; Ntl Merit Ltr; Key Clb; Library Aide; Trustee Schlrshp NY U 87; Top 10 Outstndng Schlr Awd 87; NY U; Flm Dir.

QUIGLEY, COLLEEN; St Basil Acad; Philadelphia, PA; (3); Church Yth Grp; Drama Clb; Spanish Clb; SADD; Variety Show; Acadc All Amercn 86-87; Nrsng.

QUIGLEY, HEATHER; Quigley HS; Sewickley, PA; (3); 7/89; Church Yth Grp; Math Tm; Teachers Aide; High Hon Roll; Hon Roll; Alg I Awd 85; Extra Effrt Awd 86.

QUIGLEY, JASON; Beth Ctr; Scenery Hill, PA; (3); Art Clb; Spanish Clb; Amer Lgn Awd 82.

QUIGLEY, JULIE; Mechanicsburg Area SR HS; Mechanicsburg, PA; (3); 130/365; Ski Clb; JV Var Bsktbl; JV Sftbl; JV Var Trk; Var Capt Vllybl.

QUIGLEY, TODD; Northeastern HS; Mt Wolf, PA; (3); Cmnty Wkr; Drama Clb; Ski Clb; Band; Concert Band; Mrchg Band; Bsbl; Bsktbl; High Hon Roll; Hon Roll; Elec Engnrng.

QUINIO, JUDD; Highlands SR HS; Natrona Hgts, PA; (3); Intnl Clb; Var JV Golf; Var JV Trk; Jr NHS; Acad Awds 84-85/85-86/86-87.

QUINLAN, GERARD; Monsignor Bonner HS; Havertown, PA; (4); 8/338; Church Yth Grp; Civic Clb; Nwsp Stf; NHS; Opt Clb Awd; Excllnc US Hstry Awd 86; U Of Notre Dame; Finc.

QUINLIVAN, KRISTA; Ringgold HS; Monongahela, PA; (2); 13/410; Church Yth Grp; Math Clb; Science Clb; Ski Clb; Chorus; Trs Soph Cls; Rep Stu Cncl; Var Cheerleading; Var L Trk; High Hon Roll; Hgh Hnr Outstndng Achvt Hon Soc 86; Hnrbl Mntn PTSA Ltrture Cont 86; 2 Bronze Mtls Big 10 Conf Trk Mt; Med Fld.

QUINN, ANGELA; Upper Merion HS; King Of Prussia, PA; (3); 53/297; Spanish Clb; Hon Roll; Math/Engrng.

QUINN, BILL; Kennedy Christian HS; W Middlesex, PA; (4); 18/93; Science Clb; Ski Clb; Spanish Clb; Varsity Clb; Band; Concert Band; Jazz Band; Mrchg Band; School Musical; Stu Cncl; 1st Pl Regionals & ST PA JR Acad Of Sci 84-85; Susquehanna U; Intl Bus.

QUINN, DAN; St John Neumann HS; Philadelphia, PA; (3); 90/350; Computer Clb; Pep Band; Im Bsktbl; Im Fld Hcky; Elec.

QUINN, DARLENE; Marrisville HS; Morrisville, PA; (4); 15/96; Church Yth Grp; School Musical; Nwsp Rptr; Yrbk Stf; Pres Soph Cls; Var Capt Cheerleading; Sftbl; Hon Roll; Pres Jr NHS; Ntl Merit Ltr; Outstndng Achvt Engl, Media Arts, Pblc Spkng 86; SR Sptlght 87; Rnnr Up JR Mss Dance US 83; Commnctns.

QUINN, DENISE; Archbishop Prendergast HS; Lansdowne, PA; (3); 28/327; Church Yth Grp; GAA; Latin Clb; JV Socr; Var Vllybl; Hon Roll; Psych.

QUINN, HEATHER; Freeport HS; Sarver, PA; (4); 1/178; Band; School Musical; Off Stu Cncl; Var JV Bsktbl; Capt L Trk; Wt Lftg; High Hon Roll; NHS; Hrb Mc Crkn Awd 87; Al Abrhms Gldn Tringl Hnr 87; Prsdntl Ftnss Awd; Shppensburg U; Psychlgy.

QUINN, KELLY; Souderton Area HS; Souderton, PA; (3); Church Yth Grp; 4-H; Band; Concert Band; Mrchg Band; Pep Band; School Musical; Symp Band; Off Soph Cls; Math.

QUINN, LISA; Butler SR HS; Butler, PA; (4); 75/750; Chorus; Hon Roll; Pres Schlr.

QUINN, LIZ; Gwynedd Mercy Acad; Huntingdon Vly, PA; (2); Church Yth Grp; Church Choir; Im Vllybl.

QUINN, MATTHEW; St Josephs Preparatory Schl; W Trenton, NJ; (4); Spanish Clb; Yrbk Ed-Chief; Diving; Swmmng; Wt Lftg; St Josephs U; Engl.

QUINN, PATRICK; Valley HS; New Kensington, PA; (3); 2/221; Chess Clb; Church Yth Grp; Math Tm; Science Clb; Spanish Clb; Var Bsbl; Im Ftbl; High Hon Roll; NHS; Math & Sci Awd Rensselaer Polytech Inst 87; Chem Engrng.

QUINN, THOMAS; Seneca Valley HS; Mars, PA; (3); Ski Clb; SADD; Varsity Clb; Bsktbl; Crs Cntry; Trk; High Hon Roll; Hon Roll; Top Stu Trk Athl 86-87; Law.

QUINTER, CATHY; Reading SR HS; Reading, PA; (1); Cmnty Wkr; Teachers Aide; Band; Concert Band; Mrchg Band; Orch; School Musical; School Play; Nwsp Rptr; Hon Roll; Modern Miss 87; Slippery Rock U; Med.

QUIRK, KEVIN; Cumberland Valley HS; Mechanicsburg, PA; (3); 27/546; Computer Clb; Pres Debate Tm; Drama Clb; Exploring; Key Clb; Latin Clb; Model UN; Speech Tm; NHS; Ntl Merit Ltr.

QUIRK, LEIGH; Downingtown SR HS; Exton, PA; (3); 150/648; Ski Clb; Spanish Clb; Band; Color Guard; Mrchg Band; School Musical; Hon Roll; NEDT Awd; Bus.

QUIRK, MEGHAN; Central Bucks East HS; Furlong, PA; (3); 155/488; Library Aide; Chorus; Hon Roll.

QUORESIMO, CATHERINE; Saegertown HS; Meadville, PA; (4); 14/107; Key Clb; Letterman Clb; SADD; Varsity Clb; Variety Show; Stat Bsktbl; Score Keeper; Stat Vllybl; Hon Roll; Edinboro U.

QURESHI, AMNA; Bensalem HS; Bensalem, PA; (3); Key Clb; Spanish Clb; Chorus; Nwsp Stf; Hon Roll; Co Curricular Awd 86-87; Med Technlgy.

RA, CHRISTINE; Upper Darby HS; Upr Darby, PA; (3); Church Yth Grp; Office Aide; Chorus; Hon Roll; Optmtry.

RAAB, CHERYL; Northhampton Area SR HS; Walnutport, PA; (3); 6/424; AFS; Pres Drama Clb; Chorus; School Musical; School Play; Stage Crew; Var Capt Tennis; God Cntry Awd; High Hon Roll; NHS; ST Fnlst Natl Hstry Day 85; BPW Jan Grl Mnth, Rotary Hnrs Rcgntn Top 30 Stu 87; Mary Washington Coll; Elem Educ.

RAAB, GREGG E; Carlisle SR HS; Carlisle, PA; (3); 2/454; Am Leg Boys St; Model UN; NFL; Quiz Bowl; Stu Cncl; Var Capt Ftbl; NHS; Debate Tm; Speech Tm; JV Bsktbl; Outstndng Sntr Model US Senate 86; 3rd Pl Stu Cngrs Debate PA HS Chmpnshps 87; Wdmn Wrld Life Ins; Law.

RAABE, JAMES; Tyrone Area HS; Tyrone, PA; (3); Key Clb; Band; Chorus; Hon Roll; IN Inst Of Tech; Elec Engrng.

RAASCH, JESSICA; Maplewood HS; Townville, PA; (3); 26/170; Sec Church Yth Grp; French Clb; Pep Clb; Ski Clb; Varsity Clb; Yrbk Stf; Cheerleading; Hon Roll; Bio.

RABEL, KELLY; Mid-Valley HS; Olyphant, PA; (3); Trs Frsh Cls; Trs Stu Cncl; JV Bsktbl; JV Cheerleading; Var Crs Cntry; Var Sftbl; High Hon Roll; Ntl Merit Ltr.

RABENA, ANDREA; Bishop Conwell HS; Bensalem, PA; (3); FNA; GAA; Nwsp Rptr; Var Crs Cntry; Var Trk; All Area Wntr Trck 87; Vrsty Ltrs, Crss Cntry, Wntr Trck, Sprng Trck 87; Hlth.

RABINO, MARIETTA C; Trinity HS; Mechanicsburg, PA; (3); Church Yth Grp; French Clb; Pep Clb; Chorus; School Musical; Rep Stu Cncl; Hon Roll; Natl Latin Exam-Cum Laude 85; Capital Area Music Fest-Superior & Excllnt 85 & 86; Arch Engrng.

RABISH, JEFFREY M; Penn Cambria HS; Gallitzin, PA; (2); Am Leg Boys St; Boy Scts; Camera Clb; Church Yth Grp; Spanish Clb; Speech Tm; SADD; Chorus; Concert Band; Mrchg Band; Boy Sct Eagle Rnk 85; Jr Asst Sctmstr 86; US Coast Guard Acad; Math.

RABITS, JENNIFER; Bishop Guilfoyle HS; Altoona, PA; (4); 35/117; Art Clb; Church Yth Grp; Dance Clb; Hosp Aide; Science Clb; Ski Clb; SADD; Y-Teens; Church Choir; Mrchg Band; Penn ST; Nrsng.

RABOLD, RONALD; Mercer HS; Mercer, PA; (4); FFA; Penn ST; Farming.

RABOLD, SHARI; Mercer HS; Mercer, PA; (2); Cmnty Wkr; 4-H; FFA; Hon Roll; PA ST U; Elem Ed.

RABUTINO, DAWN; St Maria Goretti HS; Philadelphia, PA; (4); 16/391; Math Tm; Nwsp Stf; Ed Yrbk Stf; Rep Sr Cls; High Hon Roll; NHS; Art Clb; Aud/Vis; Church Yth Grp; Dance Clb; Mayors Schlrshp U PA 87; Presdntl Outstndng Acad Achvt Awd 87; U PA; Pre Med.

RACE, WALTER; Elk Lake HS; Meshoppen, PA; (3); Church Yth Grp; FCA; VP 4-H; SADD; Band; JV Trk; Auto Mech.

RACHAEL, MELINDA; So Williamsport Area HS; Williamsport, PA; (3); Stu Cncl; Gym; L Trk; Fash Merch.

RACHFORD, TOBIN; Cumberland Valley HS; Mechanicsburg, PA; (3); 15/600; Var Crs Cntry; Var Trk; NHS; Ntl Merit Ltr; Service Clb; Orch; Hon Roll; Penn ST; Ntrl Sci.

RACHO, JEFF; MMI Prep; Hazleton, PA; (4); Computer Clb; School Play; Yrbk Phtg; Pres Frsh Cls; Var Bsbl; Hon Roll; NHS; Ntl Merit Ltr; NEDT Awd; Pep Clb; Prtcptd US Mltry Acdmy Acdmc Wrkshp 86.

RACHO, MARIA; West Hazleton HS; Conyngham, PA; (4); 53/223; Ski Clb; VP Spanish Clb; Capt Color Guard; Mrchg Band; Nwsp Stf; Co-Capt Yrbk Stf; Hon Roll; NHS; Statue Lbrty Drill Team NY 86; HS Column Hazleton Stndrd Spkr Newspr 86-87; IN U; Mrktng,Advrtsng.

RACHO, MARY JANE; Hazleton HS; Hazleton, PA; (3); 157/450; FBLA; Cheerleading; Hon Roll; Phys Ther.

RACICOT, ARTHUR; Carson Long Military Inst; Drayton Plains, MI; (4); 6/38; ROTC; Varsity Clb; Rep Stu Cncl; Socr; Tennis; High Hon Roll; Hon Roll; Lt Eugene E Koen Mdl 87; Brgdr Gnl Frank Tressler Prz 87; MI ST U; Cvl Engnrng.

RACINE, BRIAN; Hamburg Area HS; Hamburg, PA; (4); 9/144; Pres French Clb; Library Aide; Ski Clb; Teachers Aide; Yrbk Stf; Stu Cncl; Socr; Tennis; High Hon Roll; NHS; SICO Fndtn Schlrshp 87; Luth Brthrhd Schlrshp 87; Bio, Alg II, Geom Calc Acdmc Ltrs 84-87; Millrsvl U; Math.

RACITI, LINDA; Bishop Kenrick HS; Norristown, PA; (4); 11/290; Church Yth Grp; Drama Clb; Pep Clb; PAVAS; Science Clb; Chorus; Church Choir; School Play; Variety Show; Yrbk Rptr; U Of Scranton; Bio.

RACK, DOROTHY; Abraham Lincoln HS; Philadelphia, PA; (2); Library Aide; Rep Soph Cls; Hon Roll; Jump Rope For Heart Assoc 82; Comp Prgmmg.

RACKE, TAMMIE; Kiski Area HS; Apollo, PA; (2); High Hon Roll; Hon Roll; Trvl Agnt.

RADACK, LORI; Oil City SR HS; Rouseville, PA; (4); 9/200; AFS; German Clb; GAA; Varsity Clb; Var Bsktbl; Var Crs Cntry; Var Am Leg Aux Girls St.

RADAKER, JOHN JOSEPH; Butler SR HS; Butler, PA; (3); Church Yth Grp; Spanish Clb; Thesps; Chorus; Church Choir; School Musical; Swing Chorus; Nwsp Phtg; Nwsp Rptr; Nwsp Stf; Amer Intercultural Stu Exch 86; St Paul Yth Natl Conventn 85; Stubenville U; Teaching.

RADAKER, SHAWN; Mc Keesport HS; Mckeesport, PA; (3); Boy Scts; Cmnty Wkr; FBLA; Rep Frsh Cls; Rep Soph Cls; Sec Jr Cls; Stu Cncl; Im JV Ftbl; JV Trk; Hon Roll; PA ST U; Accntng.

RADANOVICH, STEVE; Ambridge Area HS; South Heights, PA; (3); German Clb; Hon Roll; PA ST U; Arch.

RADASZEWSKI, DAVID A; Gar Memorial HS; Wilkes-Barre, PA; (3); 5/125; Band; Chorus; Jazz Band; Mrchg Band; Orch; Bsbl; Golf; Jr NHS; NHS; Rep To Rotary Club Ldrshp Camp 86; Dist Band 86; Dentistry.

RADER, BRIAN; Keystone HS; Knox, PA; (4); 9/122; Aud/Vis; Spanish Clb; Trs Band; Concert Band; Jazz Band; Mrchg Band; Pep Band; Hon Roll; NHS; Hugh O Brien Ldrshp 85; Gannon U; Elctrcl Engrng.

RADER, CHRISTOPHER; Riverside Of Beaver County HS; Beaver Falls, PA; (2); Debate Tm; Trs NFL; PAVAS; Speech Tm; Pres SADD; Concert Band; Jazz Band; Mrchg Band; School Play; Hon Roll; Veaver Vly Hnrs Band 86; Westmnstr Hnrs Band 87; Beaver Vly Hnrs Band 87; USAF Acad; Arspc.

RADER, DAVE; Liberty HS; Bethlehem, PA; (4); 12/390; Math Tm; High Hon Roll; U Of Richmond; Math.

RADER, JONATHAN; West Allegheny HS; Corapolis, PA; (2); 13/202; Aud/Vis; JA; Stage Crew; Ftbl; Hon Roll; Jr NHS; Air Force Acad; Pilot.

RADFORD, LESLIE; Sharpsville Area HS; Sharpsville, PA; (3); VICA; Chorus; School Musical; Nwsp Ed-Chief; Nwsp Phtg; Nwsp Rptr; Vllybl; Hon Roll; Achvt Awd 84-87; Comms.

RADO, MARK; Homer Center JR SR HS; Homer City, PA; (3); 18/120; Church Yth Grp; French Clb; Varsity Clb; Concert Band; Jazz Band; Nwsp Stf; Var Ftbl; Var Trk; Hon Roll; NHS; Commrcl Airlinr Pilot.

RADOCAY, RONALD; Springdale HS; Harwick, PA; (3); Pres Church Yth Grp; Computer Clb; JA; Spanish Clb; Band; Mrchg Band; Nwsp Rptr; Hon Roll; U Pittsburgh; Chem.

RADOVICH, MICHELLE; Springdale HS; Springdale, PA; (4); 3/108; Trs Art Clb; Key Clb; Spanish Clb; Yrbk Stf; JV Capt Vllybl; DAR Awd; High Hon Roll; Prfct Atten Awd; Pres Schlr; New Knsngtn Plc Dept Trning Awd 86 & 87; Edinboro; Crmnl Jstc.

RADTKE, WILLIAM; Archbishop Ryan Boys HS; Philadelphia, PA; (2); 104/349; Church Yth Grp; Intnl Clb; Hon Roll; Penn ST U; Bus.

RADY, NOELLE; Our Lady Of The Sacred Heart HS; Aliquippa, PA; (4); Model UN; Pep Clb; Church Choir; School Play; L Cheerleading; Var L Crs Cntry; La Roche Coll; Intr Dsgn.

RADY, STEPHANIE; St Clair Area HS; St Clair, PA; (4); 3/77; Pres Drama Clb; Mu Alpha Theta; Ski Clb; Yrbk Stf; DAR Awd; Kiwanis Awd; Trs NHS; Am Leg Aux Girls St; Computer Clb; French Clb; Miss X-Mas Seal Rep St Clair Area 86-87; St Clair Area Schl Dist Scholar 87; Kutztown U Scholar 87; Kutztown U; Math.

RADZIEWICZ, SCOTT; Nativity B V M HS; Port Carbon, PA; (3); Church Yth Grp; Pres Computer Clb; Ski Clb; Nwsp Rptr; Var Crs Cntry; Var Trk; Hon Roll; Stu Mnth 87; 7 Hghst Achvt Awds 86-87; Chem Engrng.

RAE, BRYAN; Downingtown HS; Downingtown, PA; (3); 203/648; Computer Clb; Ski Clb; Spanish Clb; Stu Cncl; Bowling; Var Golf; Hon Roll; Arch.

RAE, DEBRA; West Middlesex HS; West Middlesex, PA; (3); #5 In Class; French Clb; Band; Chorus; Concert Band; Stu Cncl; Bsktbl; NHS; Pres Schlr; WV Music Camp Schlrshp 85; Regnl Band 87; Hnrs Band 87; Music Educ.

RAE, JOSEPH; Tunkhennock Area HS; Harveys Lake, PA; (1); 7/304; Boy Scts; Computer Clb; Hon Roll; Comp Sci.

RAEBIGER, JAMES W; Plymouth-Whitemarsh HS; Ft Washington, PA; (3); 20/350; Chess Clb; FCA; Math Clb; Trs Stu Cncl; Stat Bsktbl; Hon Roll; Jr NHS; NHS; Top Jr PW Penn ST Math League Comptns 86-87.

RAEZER, KARA; Marple Newtown HS; Newtown Square, PA; (4); 3/309; Drama Clb; Thesps; School Play; Nwsp Stf; Lit Mag; VP Stu Cncl; Trk; High Hon Roll; Lion Awd; NHS; Almni Hmcmg Qn 87; Cmmncmnt Spkr 87; U Of PA; Cmmnctns.

RAFALLI, LESLIE; Hazleton HS; Hazleton, PA; (2); Church Yth Grp; Drama Clb; French Clb; Hosp Aide; Concert Band; L Cheerleading; Gym; Hon Roll; Law.

RAFFEINNER, TIM; St Marys Area HS; Kersey, PA; (4); 4/276; Debate Tm; JA; High Hon Roll; NHS; Pres Acdmc Ftnss Awd 87.

RAFFERTY, EMMETT; Beth-Center HS; Vestaburg, PA; (4); 15/159; Church Yth Grp; Civic Clb; Drama Clb; School Play; Nwsp Ed-Chief; Nwsp Rptr; Nwsp Stf; High Hon Roll; Hon Roll; US Coast Guard Acad; Engrng.

RAFFERTY, ERIN; Blue Ridge HS; Hallstead, PA; (3); Hosp Aide; Pep Clb; Spanish Clb; Band; Color Guard; Mrchg Band; Rep Stu Cncl; Capt Cheerleading; Swmmng; Trk.

RAFFERTY, KELLY; Mahanoy Area HS; Gilberton, PA; (3); Ski Clb; Trs Spanish Clb; Y-Teens; Drill Tm; Variety Show; Nwsp Stf; Sec Stu Cncl; Mgr(s); Swmmng; L Trk; Psych.

RAFFERTY, MARY PAT; St Maria Goretti HS; Philadelphia, PA; (3); GAA; Spanish Clb; Orch; Rep Soph Cls; Rep Jr Cls; Sec Sr Cls; Sec Stu Cncl; Bsktbl; Sftbl; Hon Roll; 2nd Hnrs 84-87.

RAFFERTY, ROBERT D; Marian Catholic HS; Nesquehoning, PA; (1); 29/113; Church Yth Grp; French Clb; SADD; Y-Teens; Rep Frsh Cls; Rep Soph Cls; Rep Stu Cncl; Bsktbl; JV Var Ftbl; Tennis; Cert Merit 86-87; 93% Tst Achvt Profcncy 87; Law.

RAGAN, BEVERLY; Slippery Rock Area HS; Prospect, PA; (4); FBLA; Intnl Clb; Pep Clb; High Hon Roll; Hon Roll; NHS; Presdntl Acad Fit Awd; Bus.

RAGAN, KELLY; Hazleton HS; Hazelton, PA; (3); Drama Clb; FBLA; Girl Scts; PA ST U; Real Est.

RAGER, DAWN; Penn-Trafford HS; Irwin, PA; (2); Hosp Aide; JCL; Latin Clb; SADD; Nwsp Rptr; Nwsp Stf; Vllybl; Hon Roll; Med.

RAGER, DENNIS; Lewistown Area HS; Lewistown, PA; (4); Art Clb; Church Yth Grp; VICA; Concert Band; Wrstlng; High Hon Roll; Hon Roll; Elctrncs Engr.

RAGER, JENNY; Central HS; Martinsburg, PA; (3); 58/185; Library Aide; SADD; Chorus; Color Guard; Stage Crew; Mgr(s).

RAGNELLI, DINA; Northwestern Lehigh HS; Germansvile, PA; (4); 5/160; SADD; Sec Stu Cncl; Capt Twrlr; High Hon Roll; Masonic Awd; NHS; Prfct Atten Awd; Pres Schlr; Lee Taccoca Ldrshp Awd 87; Bandfront Scholar 87; Shrthnd Awd & Grange Awd 87; PA ST.

RAGO JR, ROBERT V; St John Neumann HS; Philadelphia, PA; (4); 139/331; Chorus; Im Bsktbl; Pierce JC; Acctng.

RAGO, SHERRY; Penn Hills SR HS; Pittsburgh, PA; (4); 27/609; Exploring; Hosp Aide; VP Pres Science Clb; Ski Clb; Spanish Clb; Mrchg Band; School Musical; Stu Cncl; High Hon Roll; NHS; Jr Natl Hnr Scty 84-85; Attndnc Awd 83-87; U Of Pittsburgh; Pre-Med.

RAHM, BRENDA; Bishop Guilfoyle HS; Altoona, PA; (4); 82/117; L GAA; Stu Cncl; JV Var Bsktbl; Score Keeper; Var Sftbl; Timer; Wt Lftg; Hon Roll; Prfct Atten Awd; Natl Phy Ed Awd 87; Grls Bsktbl Westrn Champ 84 & 87; Grls Bsktbl Dist VI Champ 84-87; Penn ST U; Bus Adm.

RAHM, DANIEL; Bishop Guilfoyle HS; Altoona, PA; (3); Art Clb; Church Yth Grp; German Clb; Ski Clb; Chorus; Tennis; Govt Schl For Art-Semifnlst 85; IUP; Art.

RAHN, DEBRA L; Muhlenberg HS; Reading, PA; (4); 16/186; Chorus; Ed Yrbk Stf; Rep Stu Cncl; Capt Cheerleading; Var L Trk; Hon Roll; NHS; Pres Schlr; Aud/Vis; School Musical; Soc For Acad Achvt 86-87; Pennsylvanias Gvrnrs Schl Arts-Dance 85; Shippensburg U.

RAHN, TINA; Waynesboro SR HS; Waynesboro, PA; (4); Girl Scts; Ski Clb; Band; Concert Band; Mrchg Band; Rep Jr Cls; Rep Sr Cls; Girl Scout Slvr Ldrshp Awd 84; Girl Scout Slvr Awd 86; Elizabethtown Coll; Phy Thrpy.

RAHN, VICKIE L; Muhlenberg HS; Reading, PA; (4); 3/183; Sec Band; Drm Mjr(t); Mrchg Band; Sec School Musical; Sec School Play; Yrbk Stf; Var Capt Bsktbl; Var Capt Sftbl; Var Tennis; Bausch & Lomb Sci Awd; Outstndg Math Stu; Outstndg Engl Stu; U Of Rochester; Math.

RAIBLE JR, ROBERT; Bald Eagle Nittany HS; Mill Hall, PA; (4); German Clb; Key Clb; Model UN; Ski Clb; Varsity Clb; Rep Stu Cncl; Bsktbl; Capt Ftbl; Bausch & Lomb Sci Awd; High Hon Roll; Nittany Ftbl Brnch 1st Tm All-Conf Offnsv Grd 86; Pre-Med.

RAICH, ANTOINETTE; Greater Johnstown HS; Johnstown, PA; (4); 13/297; Ski Clb; Pres Spanish Clb; Pres Band; Pres Mrchg Band; Orch; Yrbk Stf; Rep Stu Cncl; Var Capt Vllybl; High Hon Roll; NHS; U Of Pittsburgh; Hmnts.

RAIDA, CHRIS; Shaler Area HS; Glenshaw, PA; (3); 52/492; Color Guard; High Hon Roll; Hon Roll; Spanish NHS; Phrmcy.

RAIFSNIDER, TUCKER; Elizabethtown Area HS; Elizabethtown, PA; (3); 55/280; Var L Bsktbl; Var L Ftbl; Var L Wt Lftg; Def Plyr Wk 85; PA ST; Acctng.

RAIMONDO, KIMBERLY; Kimberly Raimondo HS; Mckees Rocks, PA; (3); 51/163; FBLA; Library Aide; Office Aide; Hon Roll; Point Park Coll; Jrnlsm.

RAIN, KIMBERLY; Penn-Trafford HS; Irwin, PA; (3); 23/301; Cmnty Wkr; JCL; Latin Clb; Varsity Clb; L Bsktbl; L Sftbl; Capt L Vllybl; High Hon Roll; NHS; Acad All Amer Schlr Awd 87; Engrng.

RAINEY, BRENDA; Lock Haven HS; Woolrich, PA; (3); German Clb; Service Clb; SADD; Acpl Chr; Band; Chorus; Orch; Variety Show; Bsktbl; Hon Roll; 2nd Pl Schlrshp PA ST JR Bwlng Trnmnt 86; Lock Haven U; Educ.

RAINEY, KRISTIN; Purchase Line HS; Mahaffey, PA; (3); SADD; Band; Mrchg Band; Nwsp Phtg; Nwsp Stf; Twrlr; High Hon Roll; NHS; Cert For Superior Achvt ARIN Mentorshp Pgm 86; PLHS Hon Clb Cert 86; The IN Gazette HS Stu Cert 86.

RAINEY, LISA; Purchase Line HS; Hillsdale, PA; (4); 4/111; Sec 4-H; FBLA; Pep Clb; Mrchg Band; School Play; Twrlr; High Hon Roll; Jr NHS; Rptr NHS; Ntl Merit Ltr; IN U Of PA; Bus Admin.

RAINSBERGER, HEATHER; Hampton HS; Allison Park, PA; (4); Sec Church Yth Grp; Dance Clb; French Clb; Girl Scts; Drill Tm; JV Cheerleading; Var Pom Pon; Socr; High Hon Roll; Hon Roll; Mt Union Coll; Elem Ed.

RAIRIAH, JUDITH; Purchase Ine HS; Hillsdale, PA; (3); 7/99; French Clb; SADD; Band; Chorus; Nwsp Bus Mgr; JV Sftbl; High Hon Roll; Hon Roll; NHS; 1st Pl-Dist Prnt Tchr Stu Assn PTSA 86-87; Bus.

RAIRIGH, JUDY; Purchase Line JR SR HS; Hillsdale, PA; (3); 7/94; French Clb; SADD; Chorus; Concert Band; Nwsp Bus Mgr; Nwsp Phtg; Nwsp Stf; JV Sftbl; Hon Roll; NHS; PA ST; Bus Adm.

RAISNER, MELISSA; Bangor Area SR HS; E Bangor, PA; (3); Church Yth Grp; Pep Clb; Capt Drill Tm; Yrbk Stf; Capt Twrlr; Hon Roll; Jr NHS; Natl Engl Merit Awd 85; Interior Dsgn.

RAJARATNAM, EMILIE; Phil-Mont Christian Acad; Philadelphia, PA; (3); 1/48; Church Yth Grp; Cmnty Wkr; Chorus; Tennis; High Hon Roll; NHS; Stwrdshp Awd-Tns 85-86; Jrnlsm.

RAJCHEL, GREG; Butler Area SR HS; Butler, PA; (3); Office Aide; JV Bsbl; Var L Bsktbl; Im Ftbl; Bus Admin.

RAK, LINDA; Vincentian HS; Glenshaw, PA; (4); Church Yth Grp; School Musical; Rep Jr Cls; Rep Sr Cls; Im Badmtn; Im Fld Hcky; Im Vllybl; Hon Roll; CC Allegheny Cnty; Comp Draft.

RAKACZEWSKI, MICHAEL T; Bishop Hoban HS; Wilkes-Barre, PA; (2); 8/292; Church Yth Grp; Latin Clb; Mu Alpha Theta; High Hon Roll; Mu Alpha Theta Awd; NEDT Awd; Hon Roll; Purple Belt Washin Ryu Style Karate 86; Harvard Law Coll; Law.

RAKE, ELIZABETH; Danville SR HS; Danville, PA; (3); Exploring; Spanish Clb; Yrbk Stf; JV Fld Hcky; Gym; Socr; JV Sftbl; Hon Roll.

RAKE, JENNY; Montgomery Area HS; Montgomery, PA; (3); Rep FBLA; Band; Co-Capt Color Guard; Rep Yrbk Stf; Pres Jr Cls; Pres Sr Cls; Rep Stu Cncl; Mgr(s); Trk; NHS; Tchr.

RAKER, CELESTE; Liberty JR SR HS; Liberty, PA; (2); Exploring; FHA; German Clb; Hosp Aide; Band; Chorus; School Musical; Cheerleading; Trk; Hon Roll; Penn ST U; Med.

RAKER, ROBERT; South Park HS; Library, PA; (4); Church Yth Grp; Exploring; French Clb; SADD; Teachers Aide; Band; Variety Show; High Hon Roll; Hon Roll; Johnson & Wales Coll; Chef.

RAKOWSKI, JIM; Highland SR HS; Natrona Hts, PA; (3); Exploring; Tennis; NHS; Ntl Merit Ltr.

RAKOWSKI, PAUL; Central Catholic HS; Allison Pk, PA; (3); 70/250; Church Yth Grp; Pres Debate Tm; Exploring; NFL; Pres Speech Tm; Hon Roll; Amer Legn Schl Awd 83-84; ST Debt Champ 86-87; Ecnmcs.

RALEY, SARAH; Carlisle SR HS; Carlisle, PA; (3); Church Yth Grp; Drama Clb; Exploring; Radio Clb; Ski Clb; Stage Crew; Nwsp Stf; Off Frsh Cls; Trs Soph Cls; Off Jr Cls; Acad Schlrshp Coll Enrchmnt Prgm 87; Allegheny Coll; Engl.

RALL, MERI; Mid-Valley HS; Olyphant, PA; (3); Art Clb; Computer Clb; Hosp Aide; JA; Mgr(s); Score Keeper; High Hon Roll; Hon Roll; Psych.

RALLIS, STACY; Stroudsburg HS; Stroudsburg, PA; (3); French Clb; FBLA; Tennis; Trk; Northampton CC; Bus.

RALLY, JULIE; Hopewell SR HS; Aliquippa, PA; (2); 46/270; Church Yth Grp; School Musical; School Play; Hon Roll; 1st Pl Intl Dance Cmptn 86.

RALSTON, AMY; Penncrest HS; Glen Mills, PA; (4); Band; Mrchg Band; Var Lcrss; JV Socr; High Hon Roll; Hon Roll; NHS; Ntl Merit Ltr; MVP JV Sccr 85; Wellesley Coll; Engnrng.

RALSTON, TERI JO; Susquehanna Community JR SR HS; Susquehanna, PA; (2); Girl Scts; Spanish Clb; Chorus; Capt Color Guard; Off Stu Cncl; Bowling; Capt Cheerleading; Crs Cntry; Trk; Hon Roll; USSCA 86.

RALSTON, THOMAS J; Old Forge HS; Old Forge, PA; (4); Aud/Vis; PAVAS; Mgr Concert Band; Mgr Mrchg Band; Mgr School Musical; Mgr School Play; Mgr Stage Crew; Variety Show; Stat Bsktbl; Var Golf; Penn ST U; Elect Engrng.

RALSTON, WILLIAM; Westinghouse HS; Pittsburgh, PA; (3); Church Yth Grp; Off Jr Cls; Bsktbl; Ft Valley ST; Acctg.

RAMALEY, BRIAN; Coatesville Area SR HS; Coatesville, PA; (4); 73/457; Leo Clb; Pep Clb; Ski Clb; Spanish Clb; Band; Rep Sr Cls; Var Golf; Var Wrstlng; Hon Roll; Michael A Hemlock Memrl Golf Awd 87; U Of DE; Chem Engrng.

RAMBO, DENISE; Ambridge Area HS; Baden, PA; (4); 87/265; Church Yth Grp; Office Aide; Pep Clb; Spanish Clb; SADD; Sec Chorus; School Musical; Swing Chorus; Variety Show; Hon Roll; Baden Lions Club Schlrshp 87; Messiah Coll; Acctng.

RAMBO, MEREDITH L; Nazareth Acad; Feasterville, PA; (2); Pres Church Yth Grp; Sec VP Girl Scts; Spanish Clb; Chorus; Church Choir; School Musical; Swing Chorus; Nwsp Rptr; Rptr Nwsp Stf; Var Cheerleading; Girl Sct Slvr Ldrshp Awd & Slver Awd 84-85; Girl Sct Gold Ldrshp Awd 85-86; Bus Adm.

RAMEAS, AMY E; Waynesburg Central HS; Waynesburg, PA; (3); Church Yth Grp; French Clb; Letterman Clb; Var L Bsktbl; Var L Sftbl; High Hon Roll; NHS; Band; JV Golf; JV Vllybl; Ideal Squad Sftbl 86-87; Top Girl In JR Cls 86-87; Med.

RAMELLA, LISA; Lincoln HS; Ellwood City, PA; (3); 36/163; Ski Clb; Spanish Clb; Y-Teens; Stu Cncl; Co-Capt Var Cheerleading; Powder Puff Ftbl; Accntng.

RAMEY, KRISTIN; Fairview HS; Erie, PA; (3); Cmnty Wkr; PAVAS; Spanish Clb; Chorus; School Musical; High Hon Roll; Hon Roll; NHS; Teachers Aide; Stage Crew; Outstanding Chorus Stu Awd 84-86; Young Life Christian Youth Org Member 84-87; Humanities.

RAMEY, ROBIN; Ringgold HS; Monagahela, PA; (4); Office Aide; Pres Band; Pres Church Choir; Yrbk Ed-Chief; Rep Frsh Cls; Rep Soph Cls; Rep Sr Cls; Var Cheerleading; Cit Awd; Hon Roll; Homecmng Ct 86; Physcl Thrpy.

RAMEY, TINA; Brookville Area HS; Brookville, PA; (3); 50/175; Church Yth Grp; Pres FBLA; SADD; VP Band; VP Pep Band; School Musical; Sec Frsh Cls; Stu Cncl; Stat Vllybl; Hon Roll; Bradford Bus Schl; Bus.

RAMIREZ, KATHY; Blue Mountain Acad; Philadelphia, PA; (3); Capt Church Yth Grp; Office Aide; Teachers Aide; Capt Drill Tm; Bsbl; Bsktbl; Im Trk; Im Vllybl; Im Wt Lftg; Prfct Atten Awd; Awd Phila Art Cont 84; Nova U; Engrng.

RAMIREZ, TERRI; Norwin SR HS; N Versailles, PA; (4); 137/557; Computer Clb; Letterman Clb; Trk; Capt Vllybl; Vllybll Schlrshp Slippery Rock 87; Sst Chmpns Vllybll 86.

RAMIREZ, TONY; Mc Keesport HS; Mc Keesport, PA; (2); German Clb; Trk; Hon Roll; Prfct Atten Awd; Gaitor Inst Tech; Rock Star.

RAMOS, AMELIA; Thomas A Edison HS; Philadelphia, PA; (4); 3/300; Church Yth Grp; Math Clb; Church Choir; Yrbk Stf; Lit Mag; Hon Roll; NHS; Drexel U; Mech Engrng.

RAMOS, CARMEN; Biglerville HS; Aspers, PA; (2); 21/109; Spanish Clb; High Hon Roll; Hon Roll; Jr NHS; NHS.

RAMSAY, SCOTT; Pius X HS; Bangor, PA; (2); Varsity Clb; Bsbl; Ftbl; Wt Lftg; Wrstlng; Hon Roll; NHS; Accnt.

RAMSDEN, BRANDON; Blairsville SR HS; Blairsville, PA; (1); Church Yth Grp; Band; Concert Band; Mrchg Band; Crs Cntry; Trk; High Hon Roll; PA ST.

RAMSEUR, MICHAEL; Clairton HS; Clairton, PA; (3); 4/101; Boys Clb Am; Band; Concert Band; Jazz Band; Mrchg Band; Var Capt Bsktbl; Ftbl; High Hon Roll; NHS; Acad All-Amer 86; Engnrng.

RAMSEY, AMY M; Beaver Area HS; Beaver, PA; (3); 139/197; DECA; German Clb; JA; Office Aide; Teachers Aide; Mktng.

RAMSEY, ELIZABETH; Union HS; Rimersburg, PA; (3); 25/104; Church Yth Grp; Dance Clb; Pep Clb; SADD; Chorus; Church Choir; School Musical; Variety Show; Yrbk Stf; Sec Stu Cncl.

RAMSEY, KELLY; Coudersport Jr Sr HS; Coudersport, PA; (3); 2/79; Am Leg Aux Girls St; Church Yth Grp; Drama Clb; Chorus; Church Choir; Concert Band; Yrbk Stf; Score Keeper; High Hon Roll; NHS; Nyack Coll; Missions.

RAMSEY, KIMBERLY; Allegheny Clarion Valley HS; Emlenton, PA; (4); 26/90; Trs FHA; Mrchg Band; IN U Penn; Dietetics.

RAMSEY, REBECCA; Daniel Boone HS; Douglassville, PA; (3); 62/172; French Clb; FBLA; Color Guard; Nwsp Stf; Htl/Rstrnt Mgmt.

RAMSEY, STACEY; Everett Area HS; Breezewood, PA; (3); Office Aide; SADD; Pres Frsh Cls; Pres Soph Cls; Pres Jr Cls; Pres Sr Cls; Rep Stu Cncl; Im Cheerleading; JV Score Keeper; Im Twrlr; Dntl Hygnst.

RANCIER, KAITLIN; Abington Heights HS; Dalton, PA; (3); Church Yth Grp; Drama Clb; Hosp Aide; Ski Clb; Chorus; School Musical; School Play; Yrbk Phtg; Yrbk Stf; Var JV Tennis.

RANCK, PAMELA; Lancaster Mennonite HS; Johns Isl, SC; (3); 5/177; Church Yth Grp; Latin Clb; Teachers Aide; High Hon Roll; Jr NHS; NHS; E Mennonite Coll; Elem Ed.

RANCK, SHARON; Pennsbury-Medial Bair HS; Fairless Hls, PA; (1); Library Aide; Teachers Aide; Chorus; Flag Corp; Mrchg Band; School Musical; Off Stu Cncl; Bsktbl; Fld Hcky; Mgr(s).

RANCK, STEPHEN; Mechanicsburg Area SR HS; Mechanicsburg, PA; (2); 1/309; Church Yth Grp; JV Bsbl; JV Bsktbl; High Hon Roll; NHS; Acclds Wrtng Awd 87; PA ST U; Arch.

RANCK, TRACY; Danville Area SR HS; Milton, PA; (2); Band; Concert Band; Mrchg Band; Mat Maids; High Hon Roll.

RANDALL, BECKY; Coudersport JR SR HS; Coudersport, PA; (4); 4/87; VP Church Yth Grp; Varsity Clb; Band; Chorus; Sec Soph Cls; VP Sr Cls; Var Bsktbl; Var Trk; Var Vllybl; Pres NHS; Kolat Music Awd 87; Messiah Coll; Music.

RANDALL, CONNIE; Northeast Bradford HS; Wysox, PA; (3); Art Clb; Computer Clb; Debate Tm; Trs 4-H; FHA; Hosp Aide; SADD; Chorus; Hon Roll; Prfct Atten Awd; Cntrl PA Bus Schl; Paralgl.

RANDALL, DAVID; Coudersport JR-SR HS; Coudersport, PA; (3); Boy Scts; Church Yth Grp; Church Choir; Elctrcn.

RANDALL, JEFFREY TODD; Garden Spot HS; Narvon, PA; (4); 8/218; Boy Scts; Church Yth Grp; Chorus; Church Choir; School Musical; School Play; Stage Crew; Capt Trk; Ntl Merit Ltr; U WI; Sci.

RANDALL, KEITH; Upper Dublin HS; Ft Washington, PA; (2); 8/283; Pres Computer Clb; VP Math Tm; Science Clb; Var Crs Cntry; JV Trk; PA Math Lg 1st Pl 86-87; PA JR Acad Sci 1st Pl Comp Sci 85-86; Math.

RANDALL, KELLI; Meadville Area SR HS; Meadville, PA; (3); French Clb; Varsity Clb; Stu Cncl; Trk; Vllybl; High Hon Roll; Hon Roll; Yth Fit Achvt Awd 86-87; TCAC Vllybl All Star Tm 2nd Tm 86; Vrsty Ltr Trk 84-85, Vllybl 85-87; Phys Ther.

RANDALL, PAUL; Upper Dublin SR HS; Ft Washington, PA; (3); 62/295; Computer Clb; Science Clb; Var Crs Cntry; Im Lcrss; NHS; PA JR Acad Sci Cnty 1st Pl 87; PA JR Acad Sci ST Comp 1st Pl 87; Cnty PA Sci Rsrch Comp 2nd Pl; Chem Engrng.

RANDALL, TANYA D; Phila HS For Girls; Philadelphia, PA; (3); Hosp Aide; Soph Cls; Trs Jr Cls; Bsktbl; Jr NHS; Engrng.

RANDALL, WADE; Northwestern HS; Cranesville, PA; (3); French Clb; Model UN; Scholastic Bowl; Yrbk Stf; JV Ftbl; Var L Wrstlng; Hon Roll; Penn ST; Engr.

RANDIG, SHARYN; South Allegheny HS; Elizabeth, PA; (4); 9/177; Exploring; Pres Girl Scts; Y-Teens; Chorus; Powder Puff Ftbl; Hon Roll; NHS; Prfct Atten Awd; Robert Morris Coll; Bus Mgmt.

RANDLER, TAMMY; Cocalico HS; Denver, PA; (3); Church Yth Grp; GAA; VP Frsh Cls; Rep Stu Cncl; Im Badmtn; JV Bsktbl; Var Fld Hcky; Im Lcrss; Im Socr; Im Sftbl; PA Fnlst Ms Am Coed Pgnt 87; Bus Adm.

RANDOLPH, DAVID; Henderson HS; Downingtown, PA; (3); 90/375; Art Clb; Ski Clb; Lit Mag; Stu Cncl; JV Tennis; Spanish NHS; Penn ST; Advrtsng.

RANDOLPH, NICOLE; William Penn HS; Philadelphia, PA; (3); 10/200; $50 Bond-Bst Grds 85; Temple U; Comp Pgmmng.

RANDOLPH, THOMAS; Northern Cambria HS; Marsteller, PA; (3); Church Yth Grp; Gov Hon Prg Awd; High Hon Roll; Marine Bio.

RANDOUR, ELISE; Fort Cherry HS; Mc Donald, PA; (3); 19/147; FTA; Math Clb; Science Clb; Varsity Clb; Chorus; Lit Mag; L Bsktbl; Cheerleading; High Hon Roll; NHS; Teacher.

RANDT, DAVID; Fairfield HS; Carroll Valley, PA; (3); 14/40; Spanish Clb; Jazz Band; Variety Show; Capt JV Socr; L Trk; Hon Roll; Shippensburg; Radio Comm.

RANGEL, VICTOR; Lincoln HS; Ellwood City, PA; (4); VP Church Yth Grp; Spanish Clb; Pres SADD; Var L Bsbl; Capt L Socr; IN U Of PA; Optmtry.

RANIERI, ROBERT; Trinity HS; Camp Hill, PA; (2); Church Yth Grp; Cmnty Wkr; Var L Crs Cntry; Var L Trk; Hon Roll; Cert NEDT 87; Engr.

RANKIN, JAMES; Union HS; Rimersburg, PA; (3); 2/100; Nwsp Stf; L Bsktbl; L Ftbl; Var Trk; Hon Roll; NHS; Prfct Atten Awd; PA Gov Schl Sci 87.

RANKIN, JANET; Punxsutawney Area HS; Punxsutawney, PA; (4); 88/245; French Clb; Varsity Clb; Var Cheerleading; Hon Roll; Slippery Rock U Of PA; Phy Ed.

RANKIN, RACHEL; California Area HS; Calif, PA; (4); 1/101; Pres Drama Clb; Pep Clb; Science Clb; School Play; Nwsp Ed-Chief; Nwsp Stf; Pres Soph Cls; VP Jr Cls; Score Keeper; Tennis; La Fayette Coll; Engnrng.

RANKIN, STACIE; Penn Manor HS; Millersville, PA; (3); 37/317; Sec Pres Church Yth Grp; SADD; Sec Concert Band; Sec Mrchg Band; Pep Band; Symp Band; Nwsp Stf; Sec Stu Cncl; Hon Roll; Lion Awd; Millersville U; Elem Ed.

RANKIN, TAMMY; Blacklick Valley JR-SR HS; Ebensburg, PA; (3); Camera Clb; Ski Clb; Speech Tm; Varsity Clb; Nwsp Stf; Yrbk Stf; Bsktbl; Mgr(s); Score Keeper; Crmnlgy.

RANONE, KELLY; Center HS; Monaca, PA; (4); Trs Church Yth Grp; Exploring; German Clb; Concert Band; Mrchg Band; Stu Cncl; Hon Roll; NHS; Prfct Atten Awd; Pres Schlr; U Of Pittsburgh; Phrmcy.

RANSBOTTOM, JAMES M; Punxsutawney Area HS; Punxsutawney, PA; (3); Am Leg Boys St; French Clb; German Clb; Math Tm; Science Clb; JV Socr; Var Trk; Hon Roll; NHS; Prfct Atten Awd; Comp Sci.

RANSOM, CYNTHIA; Jamestown HS; Westford, PA; (3); 14/63; Trs Church Yth Grp; Sec Spanish Clb; Varsity Clb; Band; Chorus; Variety Show; L Var Cheerleading; L Var Vllybl; Hon Roll; Prsdntl Phys Ftnss Awd; Bus Manag.

RANSOM, DONNA; Notre Dame HS; E Stroudsburg, PA; (3); 3/45; Hosp Aide; Yrbk Stf; Trs Soph Cls; JV Var Cheerleading; High Hon Roll; NHS; Prfct Atten Awd; Latin Hnr Soc; Nrsng.

RANSOM, SHEILA; Faith Community Christian Schl; Bethel Park, PA; (2); 1/38; Church Yth Grp; Var Bsktbl; Var Sftbl; Var Vllybl; High Hon Roll; NHS; Duquesne U; Law.

RAO, ANAND; Fairview HS; Fairview, PA; (3); Trs French Clb; Model UN; Speech Tm; Varsity Clb; Trs Sr Cls; Var L Swmmng; Var Tennis; Hon Roll; NHS; VP HS JR Stsmn Am 87-88; Schlrshp To PA Free Entrprs Wk 87; Med.

RAO, ISHU; North Hills HS; Glenshaw, PA; (3); 9/493; Scholastic Bowl; Ski Clb; Temple Yth Grp; Nwsp Stf; Yrbk Stf; Gov Hon Prg Awd; High Hon Roll; NHS; Exploring; Quiz Bowl; 1st Awd PA JR Acad Of Sci 85-8l; U Of Miami; Med.

RAO, KISHOR; Gateway HS; Monroeville, PA; (3); 35/452; Camera Clb; Pres Computer Clb; Science Clb; Chrmn Temple Yth Grp; Hon Roll; PA ST; Comp Sci.

RAO, SHUBHRA; E Stroudsburg HS; East Stroudsburg, PA; (3); 4/300; Art Clb; Intnl Clb; Band; Chorus; Jazz Band; Yrbk Stf; High Hon Roll; Concert Band; Mrchg Band; Pep Band; Rgn II PA JR Acad Of Sci 3rd Awd; Frshmn Math Awd; Frshmn Music Awd.

RAO, VANI; Mechanicsburg Area SR HS; Mechanicsburg, PA; (4); 2/303; High Hon Roll; Hon Roll; NHS; Irving Coll Schlrshp 87; Pres Acad Fit Awd 87; 1st Schlstc Awd Pin 87; PA ST U; Bus Admin.

RAO, VEENA V; Upper Merion HS; King Of Prussia, PA; (3); Drama Clb; Intnl Clb; Library Aide; Math Clb; Chorus; Color Guard; School Musical; School Play; Yrbk Stf; Mgr(s); Law.

RAO, VIVEK; Gateway SR HS; Monroeville, PA; (3); 2/478; Pres Chess Clb; Exploring; Math Clb; Math Tm; NFL; High Hon Roll; NHS; Ntl Merit SF; Prfct Atten Awd; Sal; PA Govrnrs Schl Bus Stu 87; Schlrshp Computer Camp Stanford 87; Natl HS Chess Champn 87-86; Harvard; Physics.

RAPACUK, MISSY; Ft Cherry HS; Mc Donald, PA; (2); Church Yth Grp; Math Clb; Science Clb; Ski Clb; Spanish Clb; Chorus; Cheerleading; Mgr(s); High Hon Roll; Med.

RAPCHAK, ANDREA; Brownsville Area HS; Grindstone, PA; (3); FBLA; Office Aide; Ski Clb; Trs Frsh Cls; Trs Soph Cls; Stu Cncl; Hon Roll.

RAPE, LISA A; Seneca Valley HS; Zelienople, PA; (4); Camera Clb; Dance Clb; Red Cross Aide; Medical Careers Clb; Robert Morris Coll; Accntng.

RAPONE, WILLIAM J; Arch Ryan HS For Boys; Philadelphia, PA; (2); 8/368; Church Yth Grp; Civic Clb; Office Aide; Political Wkr; JV Ftbl; Var L Swmmng; High Hon Roll; Prfct Atten Awd; Mst Imprvd Soph Awd Swim Tm 87; Prncpls Awd For Distgshd Hnrs 86; USMA West Point; Engrng.

RAPP, KAREN; Bishop Conwell HS; Morrisville, PA; (3); 59/277; Hon Roll; Cert Excel Outstndng Achvt Frnch Lang 84-87; Litrtr.

RAPP, LORI; Donegal HS; Marietta, PA; (3); 37/377; Spanish NHS; Law.

RAPP, MARTIN; Middleburg HS; Kreamer, PA; (3); 26/129; Chess Clb; Drama Clb; School Musical; Hon Roll; Hnrd-Cert Of Acadc Excllnc-HS 87; Penn ST; Law.

RAPP, MEREDITH; Downingtown SR HS; Downingtown, PA; (3); 145/648; Pres 4-H; French Clb; Political Wkr; Ski Clb; Concert Band; Mrchg Band; 4-H Awd; High Hon Roll; Hon Roll; 4-H Shephrdss Yr Awd 86; Vet Sci.

RAPPAPORT, LOUIS; Pennsbury HS; Yardley, PA; (3); 72/770; Cmnty Wkr; Math Clb; Temple Yth Grp; Concert Band; Drm Mjr(t); Jazz Band; Mrchg Band; Orch; High Hon Roll; NHS; U Of Penn; Fin.

RAPPAPORT, SHARYN; Wyoming Valley West HS; Kingston, PA; (3); 65/416; Key Clb; Sec Temple Yth Grp; Flag Corp; Mrchg Band; Mgr(s); High Hon Roll; Hon Roll; NHS; Comp.

RARDIN, CHARLES R; Germantown Friends Schl; Philadelphia, PA; (4); Church Yth Grp; Pres Acpl Chr; Chorus; School Musical; Variety Show; JV Bsbl; Ntl Merit SF; Spaeth Msc Awd & Davis H Forsythe Schlrshp Gen Acad 86; Geore W Emlen Hist Awd 85flatin II Awd 84; Willams Coll; Breeder.

RARICK, SUSAN; Tamaqua Area SR HS; Tamaqua, PA; (4); 5/178; Drama Clb; Concert Band; Capt Mrchg Band; Yrbk Ed-Chief; Pres Stu Cncl; High Hon Roll; Sec NHS; Pres Schlr; VP Spanish NHS; Scty Dstngshd AM HS Stu 86-87; Bwmnn Ashe Schlrshp 87-88; Chrstn Essy-1st Pl 87; U Of Miami; Psychlgy.

RARIG, LAURA; Bloomsburg HS; Bloomsburg, PA; (3); Pep Clb; Varsity Clb; School Play; Sec Jr Cls; Var Bsktbl; Im JV Cheerleading; JV Var Powder Puff Ftbl; Im JV Sftbl; Elem Ed.

RASCHKE, MATTHEW A; J P Mc Caskey HS; Lancaster, PA; (3); 3/517; Boy Scts; Pep Clb; Cit Awd; High Hon Roll; NHS; Penn ST; Envrnmntl Bio.

RASEL, JARETT; Bethlehem Center SR HS; Amity, PA; (2); Ski Clb; JV Ftbl; Hon Roll; Elec Engrng.

RASHID, FAISAL; Blue Mountain HS; Orwigsburg, PA; (3); 1/220; Quiz Bowl; Scholastic Bowl; Nwsp Rptr; Nwsp Stf; Yrbk Rptr; Yrbk Stf; Var Tennis; High Hon Roll; U Of PA; Srgn.

RASKAUSKAS, DIANE; Seneca Valley HS; Mars, PA; (3); Nwsp Stf; Lit Mag; Hon Roll; Phys Thrpy.

RASMUS, DENISE; John S Fine HS; Plymouth, PA; (2); Spanish Clb; VICA; High Hon Roll; NHS; Nrsng.

RASSNER, ILISSA; Charles H Boehm HS; Yardley, PA; (2); Computer Clb; Teachers Aide; Band; Concert Band; Mrchg Band; High Hon Roll; Prfct Atten Awd; Std Of Mnth 86; Geom, French II Grade Hnrs 85-86; Bio, French III, Algebra II Grade Hnrs 86-87; Math.

RATAJCZAK, KELLY; Northwestern SR HS; E Springfield, PA; (3); 1/169; Computer Clb; French Clb; Math Tm; Thesps; L Mrchg Band; School Musical; Hst Jr Cls; JV Trk; High Hon Roll; NHS; Nacel Exchnge Studnt 86; Wake Forest U; Law.

RATAY, LORENE; Penns Manor Area HS; Penn Run, PA; (3); 25/104; Camera Clb; Pres Chess Clb; VP 4-H; Chorus; School Musical; Yrbk Stf; Rep Trs Stu Cncl; Stat Bsktbl; Hon Roll; NEDT Awd; IN U Of PA.

RATCHFORD, DANYIEL; Bishop Guilfoyle HS; Altoona, PA; (3); 2/150; Church Yth Grp; French Clb; Red Cross Aide; Ski Clb; SADD; Chorus; Ballet Clss; Piano Lsns; Gutr Lssns; PA ST U; Bus.

RATCHFORD, MARK; Bishop Carroll HS; Ebensburg, PA; (3); 11/128; Church Yth Grp; 4-H; Pres Soph Cls; L Bsbl; Var Bsktbl; 4-H Awd; Hon Roll; NHS.

RATHBUN, DARIN L; Troy SR HS; Columbia Cross Ro, PA; (3); 22/184; Am Leg Boys St; Letterman Clb; JV Var Bsbl; JV Var Ftbl; Im Wt Lftg; NHS; Vrsty Ftbl 2nd Team Ntl 86-87; Achvr Week 85-86; Arch Engr.

RATHBURN, CHRIS; Fort Le Boeuf HS; Erie, PA; (2); Var L Ftbl; Var L Trk; Hon Roll; Gold Medal 1st Pl In AAU-USA Jr Olympics 200 & 100 Meter Dash 85; Electrician.

RATHFON, STEPHANIE; Butler SR HS; Butler, PA; (3); Cmnty Wkr; Hosp Aide; Drill Tm; School Musical; Variety Show; Rep Soph Cls; Rep Jr Cls; Stu Cncl; Hon Roll; Jr NHS; U Pittsburgh; Psychology.

RATHKE, JEFFREY D; Hampton HS; Gibsonia, PA; (4); 1/255; VP L Socr; KDKA TV Extra Effrt Awd; ACS Chem Olympcs; Westnghouse Sci Hnrs Inst; Engrng.

RATHMAN, KELLY; Cocalico HS; Stevens, PA; (3); Rep Stu Cncl; JV Capt Cheerleading; JV Capt Fld Hcky; Hon Roll; Law.

RATHWAY, RONNA; Belle Vernon Area HS; Perryopolis, PA; (3); Pres Pep Clb; Ski Clb; Church Choir; Pres Frsh Cls; Rep Soph Cls; Rep Jr Cls; Trs Sr Cls; Pres Stu Cncl; Hon Roll; Nrsng.

RATJAVONG, SAYSAVATH; Pequea Valley HS; Gordonville, PA; (4); Art Clb; Church Yth Grp; Computer Clb; School Play; Variety Show; Rep Frsh Cls; Hon Roll; Prfct Atten Awd; Aud/Vis; Drama Clb; Dale C Mallory Mem 87; Art Awd 87; PA ST; Arch.

RATLEY, DELLANE; Oliver HS; Pittsburgh, PA; (1); Cit Awd; Gov Hon Prg Awd; Hon Roll; Prfct Atten Awd; Slipery Rock U; Poli Sci.

RATNAPARKHI, ADWAIT; Bensalem HS; Trevose, PA; (3); Debate Tm; Intnl Clb; Math Tm; Concert Band; Jazz Band; Mrchg Band; Bausch & Lomb Sci Awd; High Hon Roll; NHS; Scholastic Bowl; PA Gov Schl For Mth & Sci 87; Comp Sci.

RAUB, DEVLYN; Souderton Area HS; Tylersport, PA; (4); Chorus; Capt Color Guard; Mrchg Band; Rep Stu Cncl; Var JV Score Keeper; High Hon Roll; Hon Roll; Jr NHS; NHS; Prfct Atten Awd; Pres Acdmc Ftnss Awd 87; Outstndng Rifle Awd 87; German Awd 87; Allentown Bus Schl; Fin.

RAUCH, DEANNA; Souderton Area HS; Telford, PA; (3); Aud/Vis; Church Yth Grp; FCA; Stu Cncl; Var Fld Hcky; Var Lcrss; Hon Roll.

RAUCH, STARR; Northwestern Lehigh HS; New Tripoli, PA; (4); Church Yth Grp; Pres Capt Drill Tm; Yrbk Stf; Capt Twrlr; High Hon Roll; NHS; Pres Schlr; Nrthwstrn Lehgh Schlrshp 87; Theme Wrtng & Coll Math Awds 87; Kutztown U; Speech.

RAUCH, TAMMY; Jim Thorpe Area HS; Jim Thorpe, PA; (3); Camera Clb; Scholastic Bowl; Ski Clb; Chorus; Color Guard; Flag Corp; Nwsp Stf; Hon Roll; Comp Infrmtn Sys.

RAUDABAUGH, MICHAEL; Big Spring HS; Newville, PA; (3); Math Tm; Mgr Band; Concert Band; Jazz Band; Mrchg Band; JV Bsbl; Hon Roll; Cnty Band; Comp Sci.

RAUP, JOSEPH; Southern Columbia HS; Catawissa, PA; (3); 53/90; ROTC; Stage Crew; Bsbl; Bowling; Ftbl; Ice Hcky; Sftbl; Wt Lftg; Prfct Atten Awd; VFW Awd; Construction.

RAUPP, JEFFREY; Plymouth Whitewarsh HS; Lafayette Hill, PA; (4); 39/332; Math Clb; Mu Alpha Theta; JV Bsbl; Im Bsktbl; Capt L Swmmng; High Hon Roll; Ntl Merit Ltr; Pres Schlr; William Boulton Dixon Amer Lgn Math Awd 87; DE U; Mech Engr.

RAUSCHER, SANDRA; Baldwin HS; Pittsburgh, PA; (3); 53/477; Drama Clb; Pres French Clb; VP JA; Acpl Chr; Chorus; School Musical; Rep Frsh Cls; Rep Soph Cls; Rep Jr Cls; High Hon Roll; Duquesne U; Spch Pthlgy.

RAVENZAHN, HEIDI; Fleetwood HS; Kutztown, PA; (3); Drill Tm; School Musical; Golf; Var JV Sftbl; Cert Achvt 86; Recog Night 87; Elizabethtown Coll; Biol.

RAVITZ, TOVAH RENEE; Blue Mountain HS; Schuylkill Haven, PA; (4); 40/215; Trs VP SADD; School Play; Yrbk Ed-Chief; Pres Frsh Cls; Pres Soph Cls; Pres Sr Cls; Rep Stu Cncl; Var L Trk; Boy Scts; Cmnty Wkr; Century III Ldrshp Awd; PA Leglstv Art Awd; Schltc Art Awd Cert Of Merit; Pltcl Sci.

RAVOIRA, HEATHER; The University Schl; Washington, PA; (3); Camera Clb; Debate Tm; Exploring; Office Aide; Ski Clb; SADD; Teachers Aide; Y-Teens; Hon Roll; Scndry Engl Tchr.

RAVOTTI, LISA; Freeport SR HS; Freeport, PA; (2); Library Aide; Chorus; Mrchg Band; JV Stat Bsktbl; Mgr(s); Stat Trk; Hon Roll; Optomtry.

RAWHOUSER, TINA; West York SR HS; York, PA; (3); 19/185; Church Yth Grp; Drama Clb; Girl Scts; JA; Varsity Clb; School Play; Fld Hcky; Trk; High Hon Roll; Hon Roll; PA House Of Rep Guest 86; Broadcast Jrnlsm.

RAWICZ, DAVID; York Catholic HS; York, PA; (3); 11/156; Boys Clb Am; Church Yth Grp; Latin Clb; Ski Clb; Spanish Clb; Varsity Clb; JV Bsbl; JV Bsktbl; Var Ftbl; Hon Roll; Med.

RAWSKI, FREDERICK; Cardinal O Hara HS; Media, PA; (3); 35/719; Aud/Vis; Orch; School Musical; Lit Mag; Hon Roll; DE Vly Sci Fair 86-87; PA Free Entrprs Wk Schlrshp 86.

RAWSON, ELENA; Gwynedd Mercy Acad; Wyndmoor, PA; (2); Cmnty Wkr; 4-H; Hosp Aide; Office Aide; Ski Clb; Rep Soph Cls; Rep Jr Cls; Bsktbl; Fld Hcky; Lcrss; Mst Imprvd Plyr 87; Hghst Scrng JV Lacrss Plyr 86; Hghst Scrng Vrsty Plyr 87.

RAWSON, JUDY; Clarion-Limestone HS; Strattanville, PA; (3); Sec Church Yth Grp; Chorus; Church Choir; Sec & Trea JR Vol Fire Dept 85-87; Bus Adm.

RAY, ASHTON; Riversid Beaver County HS; Beaver Falls, PA; (2); Computer Clb; SADD; PA ST U; Nclr Engr.

RAY, HOLLY; Sharpsville HS; Greenville, PA; (3); 6/102; Church Yth Grp; Hosp Aide; Acpl Chr; Chorus; Church Choir; Drill Tm; Nwsp Stf; Yrbk Stf; High Hon Roll; NHS; Acadc Achvt Awd; Hnrs Bio, Mth Sci Pgm; Vet Med.

RAY, JACK; Northern York County HS; Wellsville, PA; (3); Boy Scts; Chess Clb; Concert Band; Jazz Band; Mrchg Band; French Hon Soc; Aerosp.

RAY, JONNA; Moniteau HS; West Sunbury, PA; (4); 24/133; Church Yth Grp; Girl Scts; Chorus; Concert Band; Jazz Band; Mrchg Band; Score Keeper; Hon Roll; NHS; Btlr Cnty JR Miss Fnlst 87; Best Mrchr Awd 86; Butler Comm Coll; Mtrlgy.

RAY, MARGO; Farrell HS; Farrell, PA; (4); 12/90; Sec Computer Clb; French Clb; Key Clb; Letterman Clb; Pres Varsity Clb; Capt Vllybl; Elks Awd; Hon Roll; VP NHS; Epsiln Mu Omega Schlrshp 87; Alturst Gld Awd 87; Ernest Truesdale Awd 87; Syracuse U; Corp Law.

RAY, MELISSA; Rockwood Area HS; Rockwood, PA; (2); 46/107; Hosp Aide; Band; Chorus; Concert Band; Mrchg Band; Stu Cncl; Hon Roll; Comptuers.

RAY, MICHELE; Solanco HS; Quarryville, PA; (2); 52/285; Church Yth Grp; Band; Chorus; Church Choir; Concert Band; Mrchg Band; Pep Band; JV Trk; Cit Awd; Hon Roll; Med.

RAYBUCK, DORILEE; Keystone JR-SR HS; Knox, PA; (3); VP Pres FBLA; SADD; Teachers Aide; Ed Nwsp Rptr; VP Jr Cls; Rep Stu Cncl; Var Capt Cheerleading; Hon Roll; Pep Clb; Varsity Clb; 4th Entrepenuership I Sprng Rgnl FBLA Conf 86; 1st Bus Law Sprng Rgnl FBLA Conf 87.

RAYCA, RICHARD; Father Judge HS; Philadelphia, PA; (3); 29/402; Cmnty Wkr; Math Tm; Yrbk Stf; JV Ftbl; NHS.

RAYER, THOMAS J; Marple-Newtown HS; Broomall, PA; (4); Capt Chess Clb; Computer Clb; Intnl Clb; Im Bsktbl; Im Ice Hcky; Rugby All-Star Team & Babe Truth Sprtsmnshp 85-86; Prsdntl Acdmc Awd 87; Penn ST; Aerospace Engrng.

RAYFORD, LISA; Methacton HS; Eagleville, PA; (3); 82/381; SADD; Band; Chorus; Church Choir; Concert Band; Mrchg Band; Orch; School Musical; Rep Soph Cls; Rep Jr Cls; Psych.

RAYHA, KRISTI; Bishop Mc Cort HS; Johnstown, PA; (3); Hosp Aide; Pep Clb; Chorus; Trk; NHS; Pharm.

RAYMAN, HEATHER; Wyoming Valley West HS; Edwardsville, PA; (3); Sec Church Yth Grp; Key Clb; Yrbk Stf; Sec Frsh Cls; Stu Cncl; Hon Roll; Comm.

RAYMOND, JOHN; Bellefonte HS; Bellefonte, PA; (3); Pres Drama Clb; Chorus; Church Choir; Color Guard; Concert Band; Drm Mjr(t); Mrchg Band; School Musical; Yrbk Stf.

RAYMOND, KEN; Northwestern SR HS; Albion, PA; (4); Pres Church Yth Grp; Nwsp Rptr; Nwsp Stf; Bsktbl; Hon Roll; Russell M Wood Acctg Schlrshp 87; Voted Most Arrogant By Cls Of 87; Edinboro U Of PA; Bus Admin.

RAYMOND, MATTHEW; Valley HS; New Kensington, PA; (3); Drama Clb; Ski Clb; Spanish Clb; Band; Pres Chorus; Concert Band; Mrchg Band; Stu Cncl; Bsbl; Golf; PA ST; Bus.

RAYMONT, DOREEN; Lenape Vo Tech School; Ford City, PA; (4); Hosp Aide; Office Aide; Spanish Clb; VICA; Rep Stu Cncl; High Hon Roll; Hon Roll; NHS; IN U; Nrsng.

RAYMUNDO, JOSE; Seneca Valley HS; Harmony, PA; (2); JA; Ski Clb; Capt Tennis; Hon Roll.

RAZZI III, LARRY; Upper Darby HS; Upper Darby, PA; (3); Varsity Clb; Rep Stu Cncl; Bsbl; Ftbl; High Hon Roll; Hon Roll; Lawyer.

REA, TIM; Upper Perkiomen HS; Pennsburg, PA; (4); 14/225; Computer Clb; Pres Band; Var L Socr; High Hon Roll; Lion Awd; NHS; Pres Schlr; Rotary Awd; Ntl Hnr Soc Schlrshp 87; Golack Schlrshp 87; Drexel U; Elec Engr.

READ, JAMES E; Twin Valley Bible Acad; Narvon, PA; (4); 1/12; Quiz Bowl; Chorus; School Play; Yrbk Stf; Pres Jr Cls; Pres Sr Cls; Rep Stu Cncl; L Socr; Hon Roll; Ntl Merit SF; Hnr Society 82-86.

READER, WILLIAM; Danville SR HS; Danville, PA; (3); Ski Clb; Spanish Clb; Nwsp Rptr; Nwsp Stf; Var JV Socr; Var JV Trk; High Hon Roll; Hon Roll; Wildlife Sci.

READING, JEFFREY; Schuylkill Haven HS; Sch Haven, PA; (3); 30/86; Church Yth Grp; FCA; Library Aide; Spanish Clb; SADD; Var L Bsbl; Var Bsktbl; Var Ftbl; Hon Roll; JR Hnr Grd Escrtng Grad SR 87; Shippenburg; Accntng.

READSHAW, MEGAN; Corrick HS; Pittsburgh, PA; (3); 32/434; Q&S; SADD; School Musical; Nwsp Bus Mgr; Yrbk Stf; Pres Jr Cls; Var L Swmmng; Var L Vllybl; Hon Roll; Church Yth Grp; Stu Athltc Trainer Ftbll & Bsbll.

REAGAN, BRIAN; Upper Merion Area HS; King Of Prussia, PA; (3); 30/320; Aud/Vis; Church Yth Grp; Math Tm; Model UN; Yrbk Stf; Stu Cncl; JV Bsktbl; Var Tennis; Hon Roll; NHS; MVP Vrsty Tnns Tm 87; Awd Peace Treaty I Pssd Mdl UN 87; Awd Quality Prfrmnc Math Tm 86-87; Rutger U; Lawyers.

REAGLE, DOUGLAS; Franklin HS; Franklin, PA; (4); Boy Scts; Church Yth Grp; German Clb; SADD; Varsity Clb; Band; Concert Band; Bsbl; Bsktbl; Ftbl; Allegheney Coll; Pre-Med.

REAGLE, GRETCHEN; Eisenhower HS; Russell, PA; (3); GAA; Office Aide; SADD; Band; Concert Band; Mrchg Band; Co-Capt Cheerleading; Trk; High Hon Roll; Hon Roll; Jr Instrmntlst Of Yr 87; Gftd Prog; Elem Ed.

REAGLE, SCOTT; Mercert Jt Consolidated HS; Mercer, PA; (3); Church Yth Grp; Cmnty Wkr; Library Aide; Red Cross Aide; Chorus; School Play; CA St; Engrg.

REAGOSO, NICOLE; Upper Darby HS; Drexel Hill, PA; (3); Chorus; Rep Frsh Cls; Rep Soph Cls; Var VP Cheerleading; Trk; Hon Roll.

REAM, CHERIE; Greater Johnstown Area Vo Tech Schl; Johnstown, PA; (3); 32/185; Hosp Aide; SADD; VICA; Chorus; Yrbk Stf; JV Cheerleading; Var Pom Pon; Hon Roll; Awd Emplyblty 86 & 87; Awd Rcgntn For Csmtlgy 87.

REAM, DESIREE; Mechanicsburg HS; Mechanicsburg, PA; (2); 10/309; Church Yth Grp; Speech Tm; Orch; VP Jr Cls; Stu Cncl; Stat Bsktbl; Var L Fld Hcky; Var L Trk; High Hon Roll; NHS; Penn ST; Engrng.

REAM, KIMBERLY; Central Douphin HS; Harrisburg, PA; (3); 11/369; Church Yth Grp; Chorus; Concert Band; Mrchg Band; School Musical; Rep Stu Cncl; Cit Awd; Hon Roll; Jr NHS; NHS.

REAM, MARK A; Sun Valley HS; Brookhaven, PA; (3); 39/284; Am Leg Boys St; Church Yth Grp; Cmnty Wkr; Teachers Aide; Acpl Chr; Band; Chorus; Church Choir; Concert Band; Jazz Band; PA ST; Bus.

REAM, MICHAEL; Rockwood HS; Markleton, PA; (2); Computer Clb; Pres 4-H; Ski Clb; Band; Concert Band; Mrchg Band; Crs Cntry; Trk; Hon Roll; Comp Engrng.

REAM, SUSAN; Rockwood Area HS; Rockwood, PA; (2); 3/107; VP Church Yth Grp; Computer Clb; Rptr 4-H; NFL; Speech Tm; Band; Mrchg Band; School Play; Vllybl; High Hon Roll; Med.

REAMER, JESSIE; Hempfield HS; Irwin, PA; (3); Church Yth Grp; Sec German Clb; NFL; Chorus; Church Choir; Nwsp Stf; Mat Maids; High Hon Roll; Hon Roll.

REAMER, TODD; Yough SR HS; Madison, PA; (3); 28/239; Church Yth Grp; Ski Clb; Spanish Clb; Off Frsh Cls; Rep Stu Cncl; High Hon Roll; NHS; Westmoreland Chptr De Molay 85-87; Penn ST; Engrng.

REAP, ELIZABETH A; Smithport Area HS; Smethport 1, PA; (4); 3/100; Debate Tm; Varsity Clb; Chorus; Church Choir; Yrbk Stf; Pres Frsh Cls; Pres Soph Cls; Pres Jr Cls; Pres Sr Cls; Trs Stu Cncl; PA Gvrnrs Schl Arts 86; Jastens Fndtn Natl Schlrshp 87; Knights Columbus Englsh Awd 87; Syracuse; Advrtsng.

REARDEN, JENNIFER; Mt Penn HS; Reading, PA; (2); Church Yth Grp; Spanish Clb; Y-Teens; Trs Soph Cls; Bsktbl; Sftbl; High Hon Roll; Hon Roll; Pres Schlr.

REARDON, MARIANNE; Downingtown SR HS; Exton, PA; (3); GAA; Spanish Clb; JV Cheerleading; Mgr(s); Millerville; Lbrl Arts.

REARICK, TODD; Ft Le Boeuf HS; Waterford, PA; (3); Computer Clb; Ski Clb; High Hon Roll; Hon Roll; PA Free Entrprs Wk; Case Wstrn Rsrv U Smmr Sympsm; Elctrcl Engrng.

REASER, AMY; Milton Area SR HS; Milton, PA; (3); 11/243; Camera Clb; Varsity Clb; Yrbk Stf; Hst Soph Cls; Hst Jr Cls; Hst Sr Cls; Hst Stu Cncl; Var Fld Hcky; Powder Puff Ftbl; NHS; Elem Educ.

REASH, LOUIS; Conneaut Lake HS; Harstown, PA; (3); Church Yth Grp; 4-H; Spanish Clb; SADD; Band; Chorus; Concert Band; Mrchg Band; Orch; Pep Band.

REASNER, RONDA; South Williamsport HS; S Wmspt, PA; (4); Hosp Aide; Key Clb; Pres Leo Clb; Quiz Bowl; Varsity Clb; Color Guard; Var Cheerleading; Var L Trk; Hon Roll; NHS; Dists Trck 87; Schlrshp Daemen 87; Daemen Coll; Physcl Thrpy.

REBER, MYFANIE; Gettysburg SR HS; Gettysburg, PA; (2); 73/262; Church Yth Grp; Pep Clb; Ski Clb; Spanish Clb; Cheerleading; Vllybl; Hon Roll; Band; Chorus; Concert Band; Pres Acad Achvt Awd 85-86; Psych.

REBERT, BETH; Wilson HS; Reading, PA; (2); Church Yth Grp; Hosp Aide; Teachers Aide; Orch; School Musical; Hon Roll; Bible Quiz Tm; Choir Harvey Cedrs Bible Conf; Staff HCBC.

REBERT, LAURA; Littlestown SR HS; Hanover, PA; (3); Hosp Aide; Varsity Clb; Band; Concert Band; Jazz Band; Mrchg Band; L Fld Hcky; L Sftbl; Rdlgy.

REBERT, MICHELLE; Hanover SR HS; Hanover, PA; (3); GAA; Letterman Clb; Q&S; Varsity Clb; School Play; Yrbk Stf; Coach Actv; Var Vllybl; Hon Roll; Prfct Atten Awd; Central Penn Bus Schl; Travel.

REBUCK, CRAIG; Line Mountain HS; Klingerstown, PA; (4); 26/121; FBLA; Band; Concert Band; Mrchg Band; Stage Crew; JV Var Bsktbl; All Am Hll Fm Band Hnr 85-87; Twn Vly SR Band Fstvl 86-87; Am Lgn Cert Schl Awd 87; Bloomsburg U; Accntng.

RECCEK, ANTHONY; Saucon Valley SR HS; Hellertown, PA; (4); 22/144; Natl Sci Olypd Life Sci 83-84; Natl SS Olympd SS II 83-84; Natl Sci Olympd Bio 86-87; Allentown Coll; Bio.

RECCEK, SHERRY; Northampton Area SR HS; Northampton, PA; (3); 66/494; Cmnty Wkr; Leo Clb; SADD; Pres Jr Cls; Rep Stu Cncl; Mgr(s); Mat Maids; Sftbl; Hon Roll; Pres Schlr; PA ST U; Publc Rltns.

RECH, DEBBIE; Strath Haven HS; Wallingford, PA; (3); Spanish Clb; Nwsp Rptr; Rep Stu Cncl; Var Bsktbl; Var Trk; Hon Roll; Liberal Arts.

RECHENBERG, RICHARD; Geibel HS; Dunbar, PA; (3); Pres Church Yth Grp; Drama Clb; Pep Clb; Ski Clb; Y-Teens; Church Choir; School Play; Rep Soph Cls; Trs VP Stu Cncl; Score Keeper; Geibel Yth Mnstry; Penn ST U; Bus Adm.

RECHTORIK, TANYA; Carrick HS; Pittsburgh, PA; (2); Rep Frsh Cls; High Hon Roll; Hon Roll; U Of Pittsburgh; Pharm.

RECIO, R MATTHEW; Central Catholic HS; Pittsburgh, PA; (3); Dance Clb; Pep Clb; Ed Yrbk Stf; Hon Roll; NHS.

RECKHART, JODY; Freeport SR HS; Sarver, PA; (3); Church Yth Grp; FBLA; Office Aide; SADD; Chorus; Swing Chorus; Hon Roll; Yth Educ Assc Pres 86-88; Schl Of Performing Arts; Music.

RECKNER, CYNTHIA; Rockwood Area HS; Rockwood, PA; (3); Church Yth Grp; FBLA; Office Aide; Var Sftbl; High Hon Roll; Jr NHS; Outstndng Soph Bus Stu 86; Outstndng Schltc Achvt 85-86; Cambria-Rowe Bus Schl.

RECKTENWALD, REBECCA; Burgettstown Area JR SR HS; Burgettstown, PA; (4); 20/165; Cmnty Wkr; Hosp Aide; Library Aide; Office Aide; Science Clb; Teachers Aide; Y-Teens; Color Guard; High Hon Roll; Hon Roll.

RECORD, ANDREA; Penn Hills SR HS; Pittsburgh, PA; (3); Trs Jr Cls; Trs Sr Cls; Office Aide; Spanish Clb; School Play; Rep Frsh Cls; Rep Soph Cls; Rep Stu Cncl; Hon Roll; Spanish NHS; Lamp Of Knowledge Awd 86-87; Psych.

RECTOR, INGRID S; Lawrence County Vo-Tech HS; New Castle, PA; (4); 33/216; VP Computer Clb; Pres 4-H; Trs VICA; Mrchg Band; Hon Roll; Rotary Awd; Church Yth Grp; Cmnty Wkr; French Clb; Library Aide; Lawrnce Cnty Vo Tech Chrstms Qn 86-87; Crwn Trphy/Bnnr Outstndng Miss Amer Co Ed Pgnt, Mst Anglc 87; Robert Morris Coll; Bus Admin.

RED, MISTY; Bishop Hafey HS; Weston, PA; (3); Cmnty Wkr; Drama Clb; Pep Clb; SADD; Trs Y-Teens; Sec Chorus; Color Guard; School Musical; School Play; Stage Crew; Natl Coun Of Tchrs Math 87; Natl Sec Stu Olympiad Am Hist Comptn 87; Cmmnctns.

REDCAY, SHARON; Garden Spot HS; Denver, PA; (2); Church Yth Grp; Drama Clb; Chorus; Church Choir; School Musical; Yrbk Stf; Sftbl; High Hon Roll; Hon Roll; Psych.

REDCAY, TERI; Solanco HS; Quarryville, PA; (3); Church Yth Grp; Office Aide; Ski Clb; Teachers Aide; Varsity Clb; Yrbk Stf; Rep Stu Cncl; Var Bsktbl; Powder Puff Ftbl; JV Trk; Bus Adm.

REDDEN, IRA; Chichester SR HS; Boothwyn, PA; (2); Art Clb; FBLA; Pep Clb; Varsity Clb; Bsbl; Coach Actv; Ftbl; Wt Lftg; Wrstlng; Widenor Coll; Archtctrl Dsgn.

REDDIG, SCOTT; Cocalico HS; Reamstown, PA; (2); 1/221; Church Yth Grp; Var JV Bsktbl; High Hon Roll; Cmnty Wkr.

REDDING, DAVID; Cumberland Valley Christian Schl; Chambersburg, PA; (4); 1/11; Church Yth Grp; Varsity Clb; Yrbk Stf; Pres Sr Cls; Var Capt Socr; High Hon Roll; NHS; Val; Liberty U; Bio.

REDDING, MARK ANTHONY; Hanover SR HS; Hanover, PA; (4); 18/107; Chess Clb; Computer Clb; Political Wkr; Stat Bsktbl; Score Keeper; DAR Awd; Hon Roll; Ntl Merit Ltr; Cngrsnl Yth Ldrshp Cncl Rep 87; Cntry III Ldr 86; York Cnty Acadc All-Str 87; G Washington U; Frgn Svc Offcr.

REDDINGER, VERONICA DEE; Center HS; Monaca, PA; (3); 26/186; Girl Scts; Hosp Aide; Latin Clb; Chorus; School Musical; Swing Chorus; Hon Roll; Grl Sct Slvr Awd & Ldrshp 84; Philadelphia Coll; Physcl Thrpy.

REDDINGTON, ED; Clearfield Area HS; Clearfield, PA; (4); 11/300; Off Stu Cncl; Ftbl; Wt Lftg; Wrstlng; High Hon Roll; NHS; Yth Cncl Ldrshp 87; Appntd US Military Acad 86-87; West Point; Pol Sci.

REDDINGTON, SHARON; Uniontown Area SR HS; Pittsburgh, PA; (4); Spanish Clb; Hon Roll; Spanish NHS; Duffs Bus Inst; Bus Mngmnt.

REDDY, DAVID; Carrick HS; Pittsburgh, PA; (4); 132/341; Church Yth Grp; Ski Clb; Pres Frsh Cls; Pres Soph Cls; Pres Jr Cls; Pres Sr Cls; Bsbl; Bsktbl; Ftbl; Prfct Atten Awd; Bus Ad Acctg.

REDINGER, SHELBY; Everett Area HS; Everett, PA; (3); French Clb; GAA; Pep Clb; Varsity Clb; Band; Concert Band; Mrchg Band; Pep Band; Stu Cncl; Bsktbl; Bedford Cnty Fl Flg Qn Rnnr Up 86; Nrsng.

REDINGTON II, ROBERT M; Lancaster Catholic HS; Lancaster, PA; (3); 73/230; Model UN; Band; Concert Band; Mrchg Band; Pep Band; School Musical; Penn ST; Elec.

REDLICH, ALLISON D; Norristown Area HS; Norristown, PA; (3); 4/524; DECA; Math Clb; Sec VP Temple Yth Grp; Lit Mag; Rep Frsh Cls; Rep Soph Cls; Var L Diving; High Hon Roll; Hon Roll; NHS; Hugh Obrian Yth Fndtn Ldrshp Awd.

REDMAN, DENISE; Athens HS; Athens, PA; (3); Sec Art Clb; Ski Clb; SADD; JV Bsktbl; Var JV Cheerleading; Var L Sftbl; Var JV Vllybl; Hon Roll; Commrcl Art.

REDMOND, CHRISTINE; Harbor Creek HS; Erie, PA; (4); 6/222; Color Guard; School Play; Nwsp Ed-Chief; Ed Yrbk Stf; Sec Stu Cncl; Powder Puff Ftbl; Stat L Sftbl; High Hon Roll; NHS; Jrnlsm & Englsh Awd At Grad 87; Penn ST; Jrnlsm.

REDMOND, MICHELE; Our Lady Of The Sacred Heart HS; Pittsburgh, PA; (3); Cmnty Wkr; Computer Clb; GAA; Hosp Aide; Stage Crew; Yrbk Phtg; Yrbk Stf; Off Stu Cncl; Var L Bsktbl; Var L Sftbl; Hghst Acadmc Scres Frnch II & III; Sftbl MIP; Sftbl MVP; UC Davis; Psych.

REDUZZI, TRACY; Peb Argyl Area HS; Pen Argyl, PA; (3); 9/113; Ski Clb; Varsity Clb; Sec Jr Cls; Sec Sr Cls; Var Stu Cncl; Var Cheerleading; High Hon Roll; Hon Roll; Soc Of Wmns Engrs Awd Hghst Achvt In Math & Sci 87; Pres Acad Ftns Awd 87; Pen Argyl JR Wmns Clb Awd; Muhlenberg Coll; Pol Sci.

REDZENSKY, CAROL; Moshannon Valley HS; Ramey, PA; (4); 1/120; Girl Scts; Pres Spanish Clb; Band; Chorus; Concert Band; Capt Flag Corp; Mrchg Band; School Play; Bausch & Lomb Sci Awd; DAR Awd; Rensselaer Medl For Math & Sci 86; Top Music Stu 87; Juniata Coll; Pre-Phrmcy.

REECE, LAUREN; Pine Forge Acad; N Bayshore, NY; (3); Church Yth Grp; Drama Clb; Library Aide; Teachers Aide; Chorus; Church Choir; Rep Frsh Cls; Sec Soph Cls; Jr Cls; Rep Stu Cncl; Oakwood Coll; Psych.

REED, ANDY; Manheim Central HS; Manheim, PA; (2); Concert Band; Var L Crs Cntry; Trk.

REED, ANJELA; Elizabethtown Area HS; Elizabethtown, PA; (3); 12/260; Chrmn Model UN; Red Cross Aide; Sec Thesps; Chorus; School Musical; School Play; Stage Crew; NHS; Prtcptn-Close Up Pgm; Hmn Rltns Clb-VP; Elem Ed.

REED, CHERYL; B Reed Henderson HS; W Chester, PA; (4); 4/349; Spanish Clb; JV Var Cheerleading; Hon Roll; NHS; Spanish NHS; Natl Achvt Schlrshp Fnlst 87; U Of DE; Chemcl Engr.

REED, CHRISTINA; Du Bois SR HS; Reynoldsville, PA; (2); 4-H; Girl Scts; Library Aide; Nice Kid Awd 87; Secy.

REED, DINA; West Mifflin Area HS; W Mifflin, PA; (3); Drama Clb; Ski Clb; School Play; Mgr Trk; High Hon Roll; Hon Roll; Trs NHS; Penn ST; Bus.

REED, ERICKA; Oxford Area HS; Oxford, PA; (2); NAACP; Spanish Clb; Band; Chorus; Yrbk Bus Mgr; Frsh Cls; Soph Cls; Stu Cncl; Cheerleading; Hon Roll; Spelman Coll; Frgn Lang.

REED, ERIKA; Harrisburg HS; Harrisburg, PA; (3); 39/265; Pep Clb; Chorus; Comp Prog.

REED, JENNIFER L; Gwynedd Mercy Acad; North Wales, PA; (4); 2/102; Pres Band; Chorus; Orch; School Musical; School Play; Nwsp Stf; Hon Roll; NHS; Ntl Merit SF; Natl JR Clsscl Leag Lat Exam Slvr Medal 85; Bio.

REED, JENNIFER L; Upper Perkiomen HS; Red Hill, PA; (3); 11/244; Am Leg Aux Girls St; Chorus; VP Frsh Cls; VP Soph Cls; VP Jr Cls; Pres Sr Cls; VP Stu Cncl; Fld Hcky; Lcrss; Powder Puff Ftbl; All PAC 8 Hockey & Lacrsse 86-87; Mktng.

REED, JOHN; Greencastle-Antrim HS; Greencastle, PA; (3); Church Yth Grp; DECA; JV Var Ftbl; Var Wt Lftg; Militry.

REED, JUDITH; Monessen HS; Monessen, PA; (3); 1/108; Drama Clb; VP FBLA; Pres FNA; Trs Band; Chorus; School Play; Stage Crew; Nwsp Rptr; Yrbk Rptr; NHS; Amrcn Lgn Awd 85; Chrch God Natl Bible Rdng Rnnr Up 86; Rensselear Awd 87; Carnegie-Mellon U; Chem Engrng.

REED, KEVIN; Mid Valley HS; Olyphant, PA; (4); 6/130; Church Yth Grp; Drama Clb; School Play; Stage Crew; Rep Frsh Cls; Rep Soph Cls; Pres Jr Cls; Rep Stu Cncl; Var Crs Cntry; Var Ftbl; PA Coll Phrmcy & Sci; Phrmcy.

REED, KRISTIN; Unionville HS; Kennett Sq, PA; (4); Yrbk Stf; Hon Roll; VA Tech; Comm.

REED, KURT E; Allegheny-Clarion Valley HS; Volant, PA; (2); Am Leg Boys St; Exploring; French Clb; Stat Bsktbl; Ftbl; Trk; High Hon Roll; Engrng.

REED, LINDA; Cedar Crest HS; Lebanon, PA; (1); Church Yth Grp; Cmnty Wkr; German Clb; Hosp Aide; High Hon Roll; Hon Roll; Prfct Atten Awd; Med.

REED, LORI; Central Dauphin HS; Harrisburg, PA; (2); 14/405; Key Clb; Ski Clb; Chorus; Yrbk Stf; Mat Maids; JV Tennis; High Hon Roll; Hon Roll; Jr NHS; NHS; Engrng.

REED, MICHAEL; Gateway HS; Monroeville, PA; (3); 12/450; VP Chess Clb; Capt Debate Tm; Math Clb; Math Tm; NFL; PAVAS; Chorus; Madrigals; Nwsp Rptr; NHS; Ust Tm PHSSL Debt Qlfr 86; 1st Tm PA Math Leag 86; Alt 1st Tm Allegheny Intmdte Math Leag 87; Carnegie-Mellon U; Engrng.

REED, REBECCA; Wyoming Valley West HS; Edwardsville, PA; (2); Political Wkr; High Hon Roll; Hon Roll; NHS; Prfct Atten Awd; 3rd Pl Dist Wnnr Natl Hstry Day 86-87; Hstry Day Club 86-87; Hghst Avg Latin III Cls Awd 86-87; NYU; Med.

REED, ROBIN; Wilson Christian Acad; Mc Keesport, PA; (4); #3 In Class; Church Yth Grp; Girl Scts; JA; Swing Chorus; Yrbk Stf; Var Bsktbl; L Sftbl; L Vllybl; NHS; VFW Awd; Wilson Christian Acad & Prnt Tchrs Fllwshp Schlrshp 87; Mc Keesport Bus & Profsnl Wmn Clb Schlrshp 87; Penn ST U; Accntng.

REED, SCOTT; Riverside HS; Beaver Falls, PA; (2); 15/203; L Bsktbl; L Trk; High Hon Roll; Hon Roll.

REED, SHANNON; Westinghouse HS; Poughkeepsie, PA; (2); School Musical; Cit Awd; High Hon Roll; Hon Roll.

REED, SHELLEY; St Marys Area HS; Kersey, PA; (3); Library Aide; Band; Chorus; Church Choir; Concert Band; Drm Mjr(t); Mrchg Band; Hon Roll; Scl Sci.

REED, SHELLEY; Taylor Allderdice HS; Pittsburgh, PA; (2); Church Yth Grp; JA; Ski Clb; Var L Sftbl; High Hon Roll; NHS; Acadc Ltr 85-86; Artstc Excel Awd 86-87; Art.

REED, STACEY E; Geibel HS; Connellsville, PA; (3); 9/103; Church Yth Grp; French Clb; Political Wkr; Yrbk Phtg; French Hon Soc; High Hon Roll; NHS; NEDT Awd; Voice Dem Awd; Intl Studies.

REED, STEPHANIE; Allegheny-Clarion Valley HS; Volant, PA; (4); 7/97; 4-H; VP Varsity Clb; Drm Mjr(t); VP Stu Cncl; Var L Bsktbl; Var L Cheerleading; Var L Trk; NHS; French Clb; Band; HOBY 85; Clarion-Venango Cnty Dairy Prncss 86; ST PA Assn Frmr Coop Smnr 85; U NC Chapel Hill; Math.

REED, TAMMY; Hanover HS; Hanover, PA; (3); Church Yth Grp; Varsity Clb; Yrbk Stf; Mgr Fld Hcky; JV Var Mgr(s); JV Var Timer.

REED, TOM; Highlands HS; Natrona Hgts, PA; (3); 23/303; L Var Bsktbl; L Var Golf; Jr NHS; NHS; Bus.

REED, WILEY; Cathedral Prep HS; Erie, PA; (4); 53/212; Pres Church Yth Grp; Debate Tm; French Clb; Ski Clb; Church Choir; Socr; Hon Roll; Lat Hnr Soc 85; Wake Forest U; Bus.

REED, WILLIAM; Central HS; Philadelphia, PA; (3); 22/540; Hon Roll; Jr NHS; Prfct Atten Awd; Barnwell Hnr Pins 85-86; Engr.

REEDER, BETH; Lewistown Area HS; Lewistown, PA; (2); AFS; Church Yth Grp; German Clb; Ski Clb; Band; Chorus; Concert Band; Mrchg Band; Im Bsktbl; High Hon Roll; Nrsng.

REEDER, MIKE; Lampeter-Strasburg HS; Strasburg, PA; (4); Stage Crew; Aud/Vis; Boy Scts; Church Yth Grp; Cmnty Wkr; FBLA; Library Aide; Varsity Clb; Crs Cntry; Trk; Gallaudet U; Hist.

REEDY, LA RUE; Mifflinburg Area HS; Mifflinburg, PA; (1); Church Yth Grp; FCA; Library Aide; Spanish Clb; Hon Roll; Prfct Atten Awd; Lincoln Tech Inst; Drftng.

REEDY, PENNY; Keystone JR/Sr HS; Knox, PA; (3); 4-H; FBLA; Girl Scts; Office Aide; Chorus; School Musical; High Hon Roll; Accntng.

REEGER, WENDY; Kiski Area HS; Apollo, PA; (3); Ski Clb; Chorus; High Hon Roll; Hon Roll.

REEHER, JONNA; New Brighton Area HS; New Brighton, PA; (3); Sec DECA; Off Stu Cncl; JV Cheerleading; Hon Roll; Bradford Schl; Bus Mngt.

REENAN, LORI; Pennsbury HS; Fairless Hls, PA; (3); Chorus; Hon Roll; Debate Tm; Nrsng.

REENAN, NEAL J; Archbishop Ryan HS Boys; Huntingdon Valley, PA; (2); 3/360; Yrbk Stf; Hon Roll; PA Gvrnr Schl Schlrshp 87; Hugh O Brien Yth Fndtn Schl Ambssdr 87; Assn Cthlc Tchrs Schlrshp 86; Biology.

REEPING, JEFFREY; Somerset Area HS; Somersert, PA; (3); 73/200; Church Yth Grp; Rep Frsh Cls; Var L Bsktbl; JV L Ftbl; Var L Tennis; JV L Trk; Hon Roll.

REES, DAWNA; New Castle SR HS; New Castle, PA; (3); 36/263; Spanish Clb; Speech Tm; VP SADD; Mrchg Band; Stage Crew; Nwsp Stf; Rep Soph Cls; Vllybl; Hon Roll; Church Yth Grp; 2nd Pl Imprmtu Essy-Engl Fstvl 85; Wrtng Cntst-Ntl Cncl Of Tchrs Engl 87; Engl.

REES, WALTER; Oho Eldred JR SR HS; Eldred, PA; (4); Varsity Clb; Yrbk Sprt Ed; Yrbk Stf; Chorus; Ftbl; Trk; Wt Lftg; Hon Roll; George Washington U; Engnrng.

REESE, BRIAN; Governor Mifflin HS; Reading, PA; (4); 13/257; Church Yth Grp; Concert Band; Jazz Band; Mrchg Band; Orch; Pep Band; School Musical; JV Trk; High Hon Roll; NHS; J J Foley Awd Acadc Excllnc 87; Presdntl Acadc Ftnss Awd 87; Unfd Pnt Awds 85-87; Penn ST; Cvl Engrng.

REESE, CHRIS; Scranton Tech; Scranton, PA; (2); Boy Scts; Drama Clb; Ski Clb; Chorus; School Musical; School Play; Swing Chorus; Variety Show; Ftbl; Wrstlng; US Navy.

REESE, COLLEEN; Hollidaysburg Area SR HS; Hollidaysburg, PA; (3); 32/385; Church Yth Grp; Hosp Aide; Latin Clb; Band; Concert Band; Mrchg Band; Symp Band; Var Trk; Hon Roll; Acad Awd 86; Lock Haven U; Athltc Trng.

REESE, ERIK; Penn Cambria HS; Lilly, PA; (3); Var L Ftbl; Golf; Var L Wt Lftg; Wrstlng; Hon Roll.

REESE, KELLY; Spring-Ford HS; Mont Clare, PA; (4); 1/239; Math Clb; Spanish Clb; Var Capt Bsktbl; L Fld Hcky; Var Capt Sftbl; Pres NHS; Ntl Merit Ltr; Val; Presdntl Acad Fit Awd 87; U PA; :Bio.

REESE, KIMBERLY; Wyoming Valley West HS; Kingston, PA; (4); French Clb; Key Clb; Ski Clb; Yrbk Stf; Lit Mag; Stu Cncl; L Var Cheerleading; Gym; Im Vllybl; Hon Roll; Wilkes Coll; Bus Admin.

REESE, RANDY; Jim Thorpe SR HS; Jim Thorpe, PA; (3); 6/87; Boy Scts; Ski Clb; Var L Ftbl; Var L Wrstlng; High Hon Roll; NHS; PA ST; Educ.

REESE, RANDY; Mt Pleasant Area HS; Acme, PA; (3); 96/250; VICA; Thaddeus Stevens PA; Carpntry.

REEVE, JOCELYN; Council Rock HS; Holland, PA; (4); 143/843; Church Yth Grp; Hosp Aide; Church Choir; Concert Band; Mrchg Band; Symp Band; Hon Roll; Hlth Ed Awd 87; IUP; RN.

REEVES, DACIA; North East HS; Philladelphia, PA; (2); FNA; Church Choir; Pom Pon; Nursing.

REEVES, JENNIFER; Harry S Truman HS; Levittown, PA; (3); Drama Clb; French Clb; NFL; Speech Tm; School Musical; School Play; French Hon Soc; High Hon Roll; NHS; Dist & Rgnl Dramma Champ 86; NCFL Natl Forensic Trnmt 87; Theatre.

REFFNER, COREY; Everett HS; Everett, PA; (1); Church Yth Grp; Pres Frsh Cls; VP Stu Cncl; Var L Bsbl; L Capt Ftbl; L Capt Wrstlng; Hon Roll.

REFFORD, MICHELLE; Downingtown SR HS; Downingtown, PA; (3); 235/648; Church Yth Grp; French Clb; Library Aide; SADD; Chorus; Variety Show; Yrbk Stf; Rep Soph Cls; Im Vllybl; Hon Roll; Cert Prtcptn Tlnt Shw 85; Cert Apprctn Brians Run 86; Rep Sri Lanka Untd Ntns Clb 87; Hstry.

REFSIN, SHARON; Lower Moreland HS; Huntingdon Valley, PA; (3); Science Clb; Nwsp Rptr; Ed Lit Mag; High Hon Roll; NHS; US Natl Ldrshp Merit Awd 86-87; Outstndng Achvt Am Hstry 85-86; Outstndng Achvt Spnsh 86-87.

REGA, NATALIE; Mount Pleasant Area HS; Mount Pleasant, PA; (3); 10/244; Latin Clb; Ski Clb; Band; Nwsp Stf; Yrbk Stf; Stu Cncl; Cheerleading; High Hon Roll; Prfct Atten Awd; Seal Gftd Prgrm 84-87.

REGAL, SHANE; Northern HS; Lewisberry, PA; (4); 48/200; Church Yth Grp; Chorus; School Musical; JV Bsbl; JV Ftbl; Var L Wrstlng; High Hon Roll; Hon Roll; NHS; York Coll; Bus Admin.

REGAN, KAY; Tunkhannock Area HS; Tunkhannock, PA; (3); Art Clb; Spanish Clb; SADD; Rep Frsh Cls; Rep Soph Cls; Rep Jr Cls; Var Swmmng; JV Stat Trk; Pol Sci.

REGEC, JONATHAN; Dubois HS; Dubois, PA; (3); 39/412; German Clb; Church Choir; Nwsp Rptr; Lit Mag; High Hon Roll; PA T U; Pre-Med.

REGEL, SHARON; Belelfonte Area HS; Pleasant Gap, PA; (3); 19/210; Drama Clb; Ski Clb; SADD; Band; Concert Band; Jazz Band; Mrchg Band; School Musical; School Play; Sftbl; PA ST U.

REGGIE, JOSEPH; Pittston Area HS; Duryea, PA; (3); Ski Clb; Gym; Im Sftbl; Var Trk; Var Capt Wrstlng; Hon Roll; Psych.

REGINA, LISA; Donegal HS; Mount Joy, PA; (2); 4-H; Girl Scts; Band; Concert Band; Mrchg Band; Stat Bsktbl; Mgr(s); Stat Trk; Med.

REGITZ, GRETA; Penn-Trafford HS; Jeannette, PA; (4); AFS; Library Aide; Spanish Clb; VICA; Nwsp Rptr; Seton Hill Coll; Engl Ed.

REGULE, DAVID; Hickory HS; Hermitage, PA; (3); Art Clb; Latin Clb; Concert Band; Mrchg Band; Pep Band; Nwsp Rptr; Crs Cntry; Trk; Wt Lftg; NHS; Ntl Latin Hnr Soc 86-87; Cert Merit Ntl Soc Prof Engr 87; Cong Schlr Ntl Young Leadrs Conf 87; Arch.

REHKUGLER, CYNTHIA A; Solanco HS; New Providence, PA; (2); 7/252; Girl Scts; Varsity Clb; Nwsp Rptr; Var L Mgr(s); High Hon Roll; Hon Roll; NHS; Asstng Nwspaper Ed; Ftbl, Indoor/Outdoor Trk, & Sccr Athl Trainer; Pre Med.

REHNER, ROBERTA; Hickory HS; Sharpsville, PA; (3); Dance Clb; Drama Clb; French Clb; Hosp Aide; Band; Chorus; Church Choir; Concert Band; Drill Tm; Madrigals; Bus Admin.

REHRIG, HEATHER; Jim Thorpe SR HS; Jim Thorpe, PA; (3); 10/100; GAA; Color Guard; Yrbk Bus Mgr; Yrbk Stf; Var JV Bsktbl; Gym; Var JV Vllybl; High Hon Roll; Hon Roll; NHS.

REIBER, AMBER; New Wilmington Area HS; New Wilmington, PA; (2); Var L Trk; Var Capt Vllybl; Hon Roll; Acadmc Achvt Awd 86; Athlts Of Wk Vlybl Tm 87; Phys Ed.

REIBER, RICHARD; West York Area HS; York, PA; (3); Boy Scts; Varsity Clb; Band; Concert Band; Jazz Band; Mrchg Band; JV Ftbl; Im Socr; Var Trk; Penn ST; Engrng.

REIBER, STACY; Panther Valley HS; Summit Hill, PA; (1); 31/127; Band; Concert Band; Mrchg Band; Var Mgr(s); Var Score Keeper; Law.

REIBER, TRICIA; Wilmington Area HS; Volant, PA; (2); Nwsp Stf; Bsktbl; Powder Puff Ftbl; Sftbl; Hon Roll; Restrnt Mngmt.

REIBOLD, MARC; Peters Township HS; Mcmurray, PA; (3); Socr; L Swmmng; Trk; Ivp.

REIBOLD, ROBERT L; Bethel Park SR HS; Bethel Park, PA; (3); Am Leg Boys St; Art Clb; Key Clb; NFL; Rep Stu Cncl; High Hon Roll; NHS; Ntl Merit Ltr; Computer Clb; Drama Clb; Natl Assn Stu Cncls Conf 87; Natl Catholic Forensic League Tourney 87; Comm.

REIBSANE, DAWN; Williams Valley JR SR HS; Tower City, PA; (1); 2/119; Church Yth Grp; Office Aide; Spanish Clb; Chorus; Madrigals; Mrchg Band; Pep Band; Symp Band; High Hon Roll; NEDT Awd; Psychtrst.

REIBSON, CHRISTY; Sullivan County HS; Forksville, PA; (4); Drama Clb; Vllybl; Hon Roll; NHS.

REICH, CELINA; Tunkhannock Area HS; Tunkhannock, PA; (3); 63/310; Spanish Clb; Capt Flag Corp; Hon Roll; Psych.

REICH, DONNA; Southern Lehigh HS; Coopersburg, PA; (4); 8/230; Hosp Aide; Sec Key Clb; Scholastic Bowl; Ski Clb; Rep Jr Cls; High Hon Roll; Hon Roll; NHS; Natl Sci Mrt Awd 87; Sltd For Schl Sci Tm 87; Bio.

REICH, HEATHER; Cocalico HS; Ephrata, PA; (3); Band; Concert Band; Mrchg Band; High Hon Roll; Psych.

REICH, MICHAEL; Du Bois Area HS; Dubois, PA; (3); Church Yth Grp; Hon Roll; Arch.

REICHARD, AMY; Mifflinburg Area HS; Mifflinburg, PA; (1); Church Yth Grp; FHA; German Clb; Hosp Aide; Dnstry.

REICHARD, DIANNE; Reynolds HS; Greenville, PA; (4); 4/147; Pres Latin Clb; Varsity Clb; Chorus; Pres Frsh Cls; VP Stu Cncl; Var Capt Vllybl; High Hon Roll; Trs NHS; Stat Bsktbl; Acdmc All Amer 86; Spkr Grad 87; Grove City Coll; Math.

REICHENBACH, TANDI; East Juniata HS; Mc Alisterville, PA; (4); Camera Clb; Chess Clb; FHA; Chorus; School Musical; Var Capt Cheerleading; Twrlr; Hon Roll; Lancaster Genl Hosp; Rad Tech.

REICHERT, JEREMY; Harrisburg Christian Acad; Harrisburg, PA; (2); Boy Scts; Church Yth Grp; Soph Cls; Ftbl; Hon Roll; Med.

REICHERT, MISSI; Spring-Ford HS; Collegeville, PA; (2); 4-H; Hon Roll; Para Legal Sec.

REICHLEY, TAMI; Quakertown SR HS; Quakertown, PA; (2); 55/333; Letterman Clb; Varsity Clb; Sec Frsh Cls; Rep Soph Cls; Bsktbl; JV Capt Sftbl; Tennis; Cit Awd; High Hon Roll; Jr NHS; Amer Legion Outstndg Stu Awd 86.

REICHMAN, DIANE; Wallenpaupack Area HS; Greentown, PA; (3); 2/154; Am Leg Aux Girls St; Science Clb; Chorus; Mrchg Band; Orch; Trk; Bausch & Lomb Sci Awd; High Hon Roll; Hon Roll; NHS; USNA; Chem Engrng.

REICHMAN, LYNNE MARIE; Wallenpaupack Area HS; Greentown, PA; (4); 7/142; Am Leg Aux Girls St; Science Clb; Concert Band; Mrchg Band; High Hon Roll; NHS; Church Yth Grp; Debate Tm; NFL; Speech Tm; Band Arion Awd, Rgnl/County/Dist Band, Stu Mnth, Fine Arts Stu Mnth 87; Johnson & Wales Coll; Hotel Fd.

REID, AMY; Vincentian HS; Pittsburgh, PA; (4); 10/63; Computer Clb; Dance Clb; Drama Clb; Library Aide; Office Aide; Teachers Aide; Chorus; School Musical; School Play; Stage Crew; Duquesne U; Mgmt Info Sci.

REID, GWEN; Plymouth Whitemarsh HS; Lafayette Hill, PA; (3); DECA; Math Clb; Yrbk Stf; Stu Cncl; Cheerleading; Powder Puff Ftbl; Sftbl; Swmmng; Hon Roll; Hnr Roll 87; Bus.

REID, LESLEY D; Boyertown Junior High East; Bechtelsville, PA; (1); Art Clb; French Clb; High Hon Roll; Heavy Mtl Music.

REID, MARK; Pottstown HS; Pottstown, PA; (3); Boy Scts; Letterman Clb; Spanish Clb; Bsbl; Bsktbl; Ftbl; Wt Lftg; High Hon Roll; Hon Roll; Prfct Atten Awd; Vrsty Ftbl Awd 87; Bsktbl Awd 85; U Of CA-SAN Diego; Elec Engrng.

REID, MARY; Liberty JR-SR HS; Liberty, PA; (3); Pres 4-H; Band; Chorus; Concert Band; Mrchg Band; Trs Jr Cls; Dnfth Awd; 4-H Awd; Hon Roll; PMEA Dist 8 Band 87; PMEA Regnl Band 87; Journlsm.

REID, SHAUN; Downingtown SR HS; Downingtown, PA; (3); Ski Clb; Band; Rep Jr Cls; Im Lcrss; Var Socr; Hon Roll; Lvng Arts Awd Mech Drwngs; Drexel U; Arch Engrng.

REID, SHERI; William Allen HS; Allentown, PA; (3); 30/659; Art Clb; Key Clb; Yrbk Stf; Lit Mag; Capt Cheerleading; Hon Roll; Jr NHS; NHS; Oratrcl Cntst Wnnr 86; Art Cntst Fnlst 87; Grphc.

REID, WAYNE; New Castle SR HS; W Pittsburg, PA; (3); 1/417; Church Yth Grp; Chorus; JV Crs Cntry; Im Vllybl; High Hon Roll; Ntl Merit Ltr; Val; Variety Show; PA ST Sndy Schl Assoc 86; Italian Clb Offcr 86-87; Acad Gms Cmptn 83-84; Law.

REIDELL, JEANNETTE; Mifflinburg Area HS; Mifflinburg, PA; (2); 3/200; Drama Clb; French Clb; Key Clb; School Play; Stage Crew; Yrbk Phtg; High Hon Roll; NHS; Pres Schlr; School Musical; Am Assoc French Prof-Concours Natl 86; Intl Stud.

REIDENBAUGH, STACIE; Hempfield HS; East Petersburg, PA; (2); 25/442; Pres Church Yth Grp; Office Aide; Chorus; Church Choir; Nwsp Rptr; Nwsp Stf; Var L Gym; Var Trk; Hon Roll; Pre-Med.

REIDER, CAMERON; York County Vocational Tech; Dover, PA; (2); JA; VICA; JV Bsbl.

REIDER, TAMI; Garden Spot HS; Terre Hill, PA; (3); Var Crs Cntry; Powder Puff Ftbl; Var Trk; Mgr Wrstlng; Hon Roll; Trck Hgh Pnt Screr 86-87; Gvmnt Schl Arts Fnalst 87; Hnrd Schl Clndr & Yrbk Dsgns 86-87; Hnrb Mntn Ltho; Comm Artst.

REIDINGER, DAVID; Archbishop HS For Boys; Warrington, PA; (2); 1/260; FBLA; School Play; Nwsp Bus Mgr; Nwsp Ed-Chief; Rep Soph Cls; Stu Cncl; Gov Hon Prg Awd; High Hon Roll; Church Yth Grp; Drama Clb; PA Gov Schl Bus Schlrshp 87; Bst Fair DE Vly Sci Fair 86-87; Corp Law.

REIDLER, JEANNETTE; Bethlehem Catholic HS; Upr Black Eddy, PA; (4); Var JV Mgr(s); Hon Roll; Allentown Bus; Trvl Agnt.

REIDLER, LORI; Nativity B V M HS; Orwigsburg, PA; (2); Chorus; Drill Tm; Spec Tchr.

REIFF, MICHELLE; Warren Area HS; Warren, PA; (3); Hosp Aide; Pres Art Clb; French Clb; Ski Clb; SADD; Yrbk Stf; JV Trk; High Hon Roll; Jr NHS; NHS; Case Wstrn Rsrv U; Engrng.

REIGEL, MIKE; Shamokin Area HS; Shamokin, PA; (3); 28/204; Sec Camera Clb; Key Clb; SADD; Var Golf; Var Swmmng; NHS; Drama Clb; German Clb; Science Clb; Pres Phys Ftnss Awd 87; Photo Cont Wnnr 84; Coast Guard Acad; Helicptr Pilt.

REIGH, GINGER; Bellefonte Area HS; Bellefonte, PA; (3); 7/236; Church Yth Grp; Spanish Clb; Yrbk Rptr; Ed Yrbk Stf; Rep Frsh Cls; Rep Soph Cls; Im Vllybl; DAR Awd; High Hon Roll; Hon Roll; Comp Prgrmg.

REIGH, PAMELA; Algoona Area HS; Altoona, PA; (4); 32/720; Trs Drama Clb; Trs Key Clb; Science Clb; Ski Clb; Band; Chorus; Flag Corp; Trs Sec Jr Cls; High Hon Roll; NHS; Penn ST U; Bio.

REIGHARD, JULIE; Parkland SR HS; Allentown, PA; (2); Key Clb; Chorus; School Musical; Swing Chorus; Vet.

REIGHARD, TRICIA; Forest Hills HS; Sidman, PA; (4); 1/152; Chorus; Nwsp Rptr; Yrbk Rptr; Trs Stu Cncl; Bausch & Lomb Sci Awd; Jr NHS; NHS; Pres Schlr; Spanish NHS; Val; Heffley Memrl Schlrshp-U Pittsbrgh Johnstwn 87; Schl Dir Awd 87; U Of Pittsburgh; Mdcl Technlgy.

REIGLE, JENNIFER; Newport HS; Newport, PA; (1); Concert Band; Mrchg Band; Swing Chorus; JV Capt Cheerleading; Im Gym; Hon Roll; Hnbl Ment Capital Area Sci & Engrng Fair 87.

REIGLE, NICHOLE; Shamokin HS; Shamokin, PA; (2); 47/258; Art Clb; Drama Clb; Key Clb; NFL; Pep Clb; Ski Clb; SADD; School Musical; School Play; Voice Dem Awd; Drama.

REIGLEMAN, RACHELLE; Jamestown HS; Jamestown, PA; (3); 1/65; Church Yth Grp; Band; Chorus; Mrchg Band; School Musical; Rep Stu Cncl; Var Bsktbl; High Hon Roll; NHS; French Clb; Outstndng Musicianship Awd 84-85; Dist Band 86-87; Hnrs Chorus 85-86; Grove City; Med.

REIHART, MICHELLE; Juniata Valley HS; Huntingdon, PA; (4); Am Leg Aux Girls St; Sec Trs FHA; Hosp Aide; Library Aide; Speech Tm; Chorus; Nwsp Rptr; Rep Stu Cncl; JV Cheerleading; Voice Dem Awd.

REILEY JR, DAVID; Somerset Area HS; Somerset, PA; (4); 1/237; Trs French Clb; Jazz Band; Pres Orch; Trs Stu Cncl; Gov Hon Prg Awd; Pres NHS; Ntl Merit Schol; English Clb; VP JA; Math Tm; U S Dept Of Enrgy HS Hnrs Pgm Fermilb 87; Natl Hnr Soc Schlrshp 87; All-Eastrn Orchstra 87; Princeton U; Physcs.

REILLEY, PATRICK; Cardinal Brennan HS; Elysburg, PA; (3); Aud/Vis; Boy Scts; Chess Clb; Library Aide; Ski Clb; Stage Crew; Wt Lftg; Hon Roll; Penn ST; Arch.

REILLY, BRUCE; Claysburg-Kimmel HS; Claysburg, PA; (2); 6/97; Drama Clb; Spanish Clb; Varsity Clb; Band; Rep Stu Cncl; Var L Bsktbl; Var L Ftbl; High Hon Roll; Church Yth Grp; German Clb; Ntl Affairs Conf 85-6; Pre-Med.

REILLY, DAVID; Towanda Area HS; Towanda, PA; (3); Boy Scts; Church Yth Grp; Drama Clb; Letterman Clb; Ski Clb; School Play; Yrbk Stf; Var L Ftbl; Var L Trk; JV Wrstlng.

REILLY, HEATHER A; Gwynedd Mercy Acad; Colmar, PA; (4); 1/105; Model UN; Band; Chorus; Church Choir; School Musical; Ed Nwsp Stf; VP NHS; Ntl Merit SF; Intl Rel.

REILLY, JOHN; Notre Dame HS; Hellertown, PA; (3); 10/89; Exploring; German Clb; Trs Soph Cls; Rep Jr Cls; Stu Cncl; Ftbl; Vllybl; High Hon Roll; NHS; 2nd Tm Cntnnl Leag Lnbck Ftbl 86; Mst Outstndng Lnmn Ftbl 86; Wghtlftng 2nd Ntl Bnch Prs Cntst 87; Med.

REILLY, KATHLEEN; Bishop Mc Devitt HS; Elkins Park, PA; (3); 100/350; Drama Clb; French Clb; PAVAS; Service Clb; SADD; Chorus; School Musical; School Play; Yrbk Stf; Coach Actv.

REILLY, KERRI; Freedom SR HS; Bethlehem, PA; (4); 14/433; Cmnty Wkr; Intnl Clb; Pep Clb; Trs Spanish Clb; Color Guard; Orch; Im Swmmng; High Hon Roll; VP NHS; Pres Schlr; Keystone Svings Assn Awd $25 87; Acad Awds Sweater; Gettysburg Coll; Pol Sci.

REILLY, MARYBETH; Central Christian HS; Dubois, PA; (2); Drama Clb; Ski Clb; Cheerleading; Pom Pon; Sftbl; Vllybl; Physicians Assistance.

REILLY, MICHELE; Ridley HS; Folsom, PA; (2); 63/417; Spanish Clb.

REILLY, PATRICK J; Malvem Prep Schl; Exton, PA; (4); 1/98; Boy Scts; Pres Math Tm; Ed Nwsp Stf; Ed Lit Mag; Var Trk; High Hon Roll; NHS; Ntl Merit Ltr; God Cntry Awd; NEDT Awd; Full Tuition Schlrshp Malvern Prep Schl 83-87; Full Tuition Schlrshp Fordham U 87-91; Fordham U; Cmmnctns.

REILLY, ROBERT L; Bishop Hoban HS; Ashley, PA; (2); 5/207; Debate Tm; Latin Clb; Math Clb; Mu Alpha Theta; JV Bsktbl; High Hon Roll; Mu Alpha Theta Awd; Pres Schlr; Penn ST U; Atty.

REILLY, SUSAN; Greensburg Central Catholic HS; Ruffs Dale, PA; (3); Dance Clb; Pres 4-H; Pep Clb; Quiz Bowl; Ski Clb; Chorus; School Musical; Sec VP Cheerleading; JV Coach Actv; 4-H Awd; Chrstn Athlt Of Yr 84; Miss Westmoreland Cnty Hmsphr Bty, Model, Photognc 87; U Of Pittsburgh; Corp Law.

REILLY, THERESA; Saint Basil Acad; Philadelphia, PA; (3); 1/84; Nwsp Stf; Lit Mag; Rep Frsh Cls; Trs Soph Cls; Fld Hcky; High Hon Roll; Science Clb; Spanish Clb; SADD; Montgomery Cnty Sci Fair 85; 4 Yr Acad Schlrshp ST Basil Acad 84-88; HOBY 86; Notre Dame; Chem Engrng.

REIM, KARYN; Villa Maria Acad; Fairview, PA; (3); Hosp Aide; Science Clb; School Musical; JV Crs Cntry; JV Trk; High Hon Roll; Hon Roll; Pres NHS; PA ST U; Physical Therapy.

REIM, MEG; Villa Maria Acad; Fairview, PA; (4); 24/130; Hosp Aide; Ski Clb; SADD; Rep Stu Cncl; Var Crs Cntry; Trk; High Hon Roll; Hon Roll; NHS; Pres Schlr; Recogntn Awd Peer Jury Pgm 86-87; PA ST U; Bus Adm.

REIMANN, GLENN W; Council Rock HS; Holland, PA; (3); 150/908; FBLA; Honor Roll 85-86; Pol Sci.

REIMER, KAREN; Northampton SR HS; Walnutport, PA; (3); 185/487; Nwsp Bus Mgr; Nwsp Rptr; Nwsp Stf; Yrbk Stf; Fld Hcky; Sftbl; Wt Lftg; Hon Roll; 1st Pl Sports Wrtng-PA Prss Clb 86; Mdcl Technlgy.

REIMER, MICHAEL; Bangor Area SR HS; Bangor, PA; (3); 19/220; Church Yth Grp; Computer Clb; Band; Church Choir; VP Concert Band; VP Jazz Band; VP Mrchg Band; Var Tennis; Hon Roll; NHS; Air Force.

REIMER, MIKE; Cedar Cliff HS; Camp Hill, PA; (2); 63/286; Concert Band; Crs Cntry; Trk; Hon Roll; Ski Clb; Fnlst SR Div,Patriot News Otstndng Carrier Cmptn 86; 1st Rnnr Up JR Div,Patriot News Otstndng 85; Math.

REIMER, STACY; Northampton SR HS; Northampton, PA; (3); VICA; Hon Roll; Hghst Grade Avg Trophy Csmtlgy 87; 1st Pl Shampoo Blow Dry Styles 87; 2nd Pl Rqsts Csmtlgy Svcs 87; Csmtlgy.

REIMERT, JENNY; Mt Penn JR SR HS; Mt Penn, PA; (2); 4/60; FTA; Spanish Clb; Y-Teens; Chorus; Sec Soph Cls; JV Bsktbl; JV Var Sftbl; High Hon Roll; Jr NHS; Natl Sci Merit Awds, Intl Frgn Lang Awds 86; Prsdntl Acdmc Ftnss Awds 87; Kutztown U; Elem Educ.

REIMILLER, LAURA; Tunkhannock Area HS; Tunkhannock, PA; (3); Aud/Vis; FCA; Stage Crew; Yrbk Stf; Crs Cntry; Score Keeper; Bus Admin.

REINARD, BRIAN; Cumberland Valley HS; Carlisle, PA; (2); Im Badmtn; Im Bsbl; Trk; Vllybl; Wrstlng; Pres Acad Ftns Awd 85; PA ST; Engrng.

REINBOTH, WENDY; Council Rock HS; Richboro, PA; (3); Church Yth Grp; Rep Soph Cls; Figure Skating Silver Medal 84,Gold Medal 85; Elem Ed.

REINDOLLAR, DENISE; Southwestern HS; Hanover, PA; (4); 18/201; AFS; Var Capt Cheerleading; High Hon Roll; Hon Roll; Pres Acad Ftnss Awd 87; NEDT Awd 85; OH U; Cmmnctns.

REINECKER, VICKIE; Christian Schl Of York; Dover, PA; (3); Chorus; Church Choir; School Play; Child Psychlgy.

REINER, DENISE; Line Mountain HS; Leck Kill, PA; (4); 42/121; Sec VP Church Yth Grp; Sec VP 4-H; Key Clb; Varsity Clb; Var Capt Bsktbl; Var Capt Fld Hcky; Var Capt Sftbl; Ski Clb; Stage Crew; Im Ftbl; All Star Fld Hcky 86; E Stroudsburg U Of PA; Educ.

REINER, MICHAEL D; Line Mountain HS; Rebuck, PA; (1); 1/129; Rptr FBLA; VP Soph Cls; VP Jr Cls; Pres Sr Cls; Pres Stu Cncl; Var L Bsktbl; Var L Crs Cntry; Dnfth Awd; 4-H Awd; Ntl Merit SF; Air Force Acad; Astrntcl Engr.

REINER, RENEE; Williams Valley HS; Muir, PA; (3); 15/98; Church Yth Grp; Drama Clb; Chorus; Church Choir; Mrchg Band; Twrlr; Hon Roll; Schl Sngrs Orgnztn; JR & SR Prom Commttee; Hlth.

REINERT, CONNIE; Boyertown SR HS; Boyertown, PA; (2); Cmnty Wkr; Dance Clb; Girl Scts; Library Aide; Office Aide; Teachers Aide; Color Guard; Mrchg Band; Cit Awd; Prfct Atten Awd; Lansdale Schl Of Bus; Lgl Sec.

REINERT, MATTHEW ERIC; Lake-Lehman HS; Shavertown, PA; (3); School Play; Var Capt Socr; JV Trk; Var L Wrstlng; High Hon Roll; Jr NHS; NHS; NEDT Awd; Stage Crew; Hugh O Brien Yth Ldrshp Smnrs 86; Rtry Clb Ldrshp Camp 86.

REINHARD, JENNIFER; Linden Hall HS; Lititz, PA; (2); 2/18; VP Soph Cls; Hon Roll; Linden Hall Tour Guide 86-87; Psych.

REINHARD, REBECCA; Central Dauphin HS; Harrisburg, PA; (3); Church Yth Grp; Key Clb; Band; Chorus; Jazz Band; Mrchg Band; School Musical; Elem Educ.

REINHARD, TERRI; William Allen HS; Allentown, PA; (2); Drama Clb; Ski Clb; Color Guard; Bloomsburg; Pedtrcn.

REINHARDT, GREG; Lower Dauphin HS; Hummelstown, PA; (3); 36/327; Boy Scts; Chorus; Drm & Bgl; Drm Mjr(t); Jazz Band; Mrchg Band; JV Socr; Var Trk; Hon Roll; NHS; Eagl Sct Awd 87; Bst Drum Mjr Trnmt Music Fstvl Williamsbrg VA 87; Air Frc Pilot.

REINHARDT, SUSAN; Bangor Area HS; Mt Bethel, PA; (3); Girl Scts; Hon Roll; Accntng.

REINHART, ANGELA; Perkiomen Valley HS; Collegeville, PA; (3); Cmnty Wkr; Office Aide; Acpl Chr; Chorus; Yrbk Phtg; Yrbk Rptr; Yrbk Stf; Stat Lcrss; Mgr(s); Hon Roll; Activity Awd 87; Vrsty Let And Cert Of Sprts 86-87; Mrktng.

REINHART, KATHY; Marlan HS; Jim Thorpe, PA; (4); 17/109; Chorus; School Play; Nwsp Rptr; Yrbk Stf; Sftbl; Hon Roll; NHS; Trs Spanish NHS; Helen S Noonan Mem Schlrshp 87; Acad Schlrshp 87; Kutztown U.

REINHART, MARK; Hempfield HS; Landisville, PA; (3); 90/472; Letterman Clb; Varsity Clb; Chorus; School Musical; Bsbl; Bsktbl; Ftbl; Wt Lftg; Hon Roll.

REINHART, NICOLE; Central Dauphin HS; Harrisburg, PA; (2); Church Yth Grp; Ski Clb; Nwsp Stf; Yrbk Stf; Rep Frsh Cls; Sec Soph Cls; Sec Jr Cls; Var Capt Cheerleading; Trk; Im Vllybl; Chld Psych.

REINMILLER, KURT; West Hazleton HS; Sybertsville, PA; (3); 39/220; Chess Clb; Teachers Aide; Var Golf; Hon Roll; Penn ST U; Mtrlgy.

REINSEL, KRISTI; Hampton HS; Allison Pk, PA; (4); 35/255; Church Yth Grp; Cmnty Wkr; Latin Clb; NFL; Political Wkr; Yrbk Stf; Stu Cncl; Trk; High Hon Roll; Pres Schlr; 2nd Dist Natl Hstry Day Cmptn 84-85; Outstndng Acad Achvt Awd 83-85; Dickinson Coll.

REIS, STEVEN; Mt Penn HS; Reading, PA; (4); 2/60; Church Yth Grp; Pres FTA; Yrbk Stf; JV Bsktbl; VP NHS; Vllybl; Bausch & Lomb Sci Awd; High Hon Roll; Sal; Natl Merit Schlrshp Corp Commended Stu 86; Alfred U Presdntl Schlrshp 87; Alfred U; Ceramic Engrng.

REISENWEAVER, KEVIN; Greater Latrobe HS; Greensburg, PA; (3); 4/386; German Clb; Letterman Clb; Varsity Clb; Bsktbl; Golf; Hon Roll; NHS; Rotary Awd; Bus Adm.

REISER, ELLI M; Allegheny Clarion Valley HS; Emlenton, PA; (4); 28/91; Art Clb; DECA; 4-H; FHA; Spanish Clb; Chorus; Trk; 4-H Awd; Hon Roll; DECA Cmpttns 4th Pl Rest Mgmt 87; National Guard; Psych.

REISER, JENNIFER; West Allegheny HS; Coraopolis, PA; (3); 5/200; JA; Spanish Clb; Chorus; Var Trk; High Hon Roll; Pres NHS; Provost Day Schlr 87; Communctns.

REISER, KELLI; Lakeview HS; Stoneboro, PA; (4); 13/129; Varsity Clb; School Play; Yrbk Stf; JV Var Bsktbl; Trk; NHS; Church Yth Grp; Drama Clb; Intnl Clb; Letterman Clb; Wrthy Advsr Intl Ordr Rainbow Girls 84-85; Presby Yth Trienium-Purdue U 86; VP Med Explr Post 85-86; U Of Pittsburgh Ttsvl; Phy Ther.

REISER, KURT; Knoch HS; Renfrew, PA; (2); JV Bsktbl; JV Ftbl; Trk; High Hon Roll; US Naval Acad; Aerontcl Engr.

REISH, STEPHANIE; Milton Area HS; New Columbia, PA; (2); Library Aide; Spanish Clb; JV Trk; Hon Roll; NAVY; Bio.

REISINGER, BETH; Ringgold HS; Charleroi, PA; (3); JA; Pep Clb; Ski Clb; Band; Mgr(s); L Pom Pon; Trk; High Hon Roll; Math & Sci Hnr Soc; Pre-Med.

REISINGER, EDWARD; Eastern York HS; Wrightsville, PA; (3); VP Stu Cncl; Var L Bsktbl; JV L Socr; Var Hon Roll; Poli Sci.

REISINGER, GREG; West Perry HS; Ickesburg, PA; (3); Spanish Clb; JV Bsbl; JV Bsktbl; Var Ftbl; Vllybl; Wt Lftg; Hon Roll; Penn ST; Accntng.

REISINGER, LAURA; Kennard Dale HS; Stewartstown, PA; (3); Varsity Clb; Chorus; Church Choir; Color Guard; Crs Cntry; Trk; 4-H Awd; High Hon Roll; Hon Roll; Lion Awd; Dist Wnnr & ST Rnnr Up Crss Cntry Tm 86; 2nd Pl Fnshr Mile & 2 Mile 87; 3rd Pl Fnshr 2 Mile Dist 87; Journlsm.

REISINGER, SAMUEL; West Perry SR HS; Elliottsburg, PA; (2); 28/222; Cmnty Wkr; Math Tm; JV Ftbl; JV Wrstlng; Hon Roll; PA Math Leag 86-87; Law.

REISINGER, SUSAN R; Lakeview HS; Jackson Center, PA; (2); Sec 4-H; Intnl Clb; Band; Concert Band; Mrchg Band; Stu Cncl; Cheerleading; Acad All Amer Awd 86-87; Comm.

REISNAUER, MICHELE; Elizabeth Forward HS; Elizabeth, PA; (3); Sec AFS; Rep Church Yth Grp; Exploring; Sec 4-H; French Clb; Pep Clb; Stage Crew; Rep Soph Cls; Rep Jr Cls; Var L Bsktbl; Maycrowning Court At Chrch 87; Presdntl Phy Fit Awd 83-85; WPIAL Trck 86; Nrsng.

REISNER, DANNY; Moravian Acad; Allentown, PA; (4); 2/67; Model UN; Ski Clb; Nwsp Ed-Chief; Pres Stu Cncl; Var Crs Cntry; DAR Awd; High Hon Roll; Ntl Merit Ltr; Amrcn Assn Physcs Tchrs 87; Cum Laude Hnr Soc, Wllm E Dstr Awd Super Achvt Engl 86; Wesleyan U; Ecnmcs.

REISS, ROBIN; Northampton SR HS; Northampton, PA; (4); Leo Clb; SADD; Band; Mrchg Band; Stu Cncl; Cheerleading; Mgr(s); Pom Pon; Hon Roll; Girl Scts; Le High Twp Lions Scholar 87; Le High Twp Elem PTA Scholar 87; PTA Scholar 87; Kutztown U; Elem Ed.

REIST, JOEL; Southmoreland HS; Scottdale, PA; (3); German Clb; Band; Concert Band; Jazz Band; Orch; Symp Band; Variety Show; Yrbk Phtg; Socr; Ger NHS; Profssnl Bassist.

REITA, DIANNE; Hempfield SR HS; Greensburg, PA; (2); Drama Clb; GAA; Hosp Aide; Pep Clb; Ski Clb; Spanish Clb; School Play; High Hon Roll; Hon Roll; Pres Schlr.

REITANO, ANNETTE; Neshaminy HS; Levittown, PA; (4); 37/720; SADD; Concert Band; Drm Mjr(t); Mrchg Band; School Musical; Sec Stu Cncl; High Hon Roll; Hon Roll; NHS; Drama Clb; Outstndg Stu Ldrshp 85-87; Stu Rep Schl Bd 87; Outstndg Svc To Schl 86&87; PA ST U; Chem Engnrng.

REITER, ANGEL; West Branch Area HS; Morrisdale, PA; (3); 11/124; Science Clb; SADD; Chorus; Hon Roll; Mdcl Technlgy.

REITER, DAVE; Marion Center Area HS; Marion Center, PA; (4); 1/170; Pres Church Yth Grp; Trs Band; Chorus; Church Choir; Stage Crew; Rep Stu Cncl; Stat Bsktbl; Stat Ftbl; Var Trk; NHS; Mcdnlds All Am Bnd 86; Dstct & Rgnl Bnd 86; Orgnst Marion Ctr HS Cmmncmnt 84-86; Grove City; Bnkng.

REITER, NANCY; Taylor Allderale HS; Pittsburgh, PA; (3); French Clb; Model UN; Band; Trs Soph Cls; Rep Stu Cncl; Swmmng; High Hon Roll; NHS; ACS Chem Comp; IUP Physics Olympcs.

REITER, STEVE; Pine Grove Area HS; Pine Grove, PA; (4); Am Leg Boys St; Church Yth Grp; Varsity Clb; Concert Band; Mrchg Band; School Play; Stage Crew; JV Bsktbl; Var Ftbl; Hon Roll; Millersville U; Bus Admin.

REITH, SALLY; Upper Darby HS; Drexel Hl, PA; (3); Library Aide; Band; Concert Band; Jazz Band; Mrchg Band; Orch; School Musical; Mgr(s); High Hon Roll; Math.

REITLER, EDWARD; Ford City HS; Ford City, PA; (3); 31/163; AFS; Pres German Clb; Chorus; JV Bsbl; High Hon Roll; Hon Roll; NHS; Physcl Sci Tchr.

REITMEYER, KRISTEN; Bishop Hafey HS; Nuremberg, PA; (4); Drama Clb; Ski Clb; Bloomsburg U; Mass Cmnctns.

REITZ, DOUG; State College Area SR HS; State College, PA; (4); French Clb; Science Clb; Hon Roll; Prfct Atten Awd; Penn ST U; Elec Engr.

REITZ, JOHN; Union HS; Sligo, PA; (3); VICA; L Trk; Wt Lftg; Sprts Awds 85-87; St Plc.

REITZ, MELISSA; Solanco SR HS; New Providence, PA; (2); Church Yth Grp; Band; Concert Band; Jazz Band; Mrchg Band; Orch; School Musical; JV Bsktbl; High Hon Roll; Hon Roll; Music.

REKLAITIS, MATT; Pittston Area SR HS; Pittston, PA; (2); English Clb; Math Tm; Science Clb; Nwsp Stf; Var Tennis; JV Trk; High Hon Roll; JETS Awd; NHS; NEDT Awd; 2nd Pl Am Chem Soc Tst, & 1st Pl Marywood Math Exam 87; 1st Pl Marywood Math Exam 86; Syracuse; Chem.

REKUS, PAMELA; Central Dauphin HS; Harrisburg, PA; (4); 25/388; Dance Clb; Teachers Aide; Chorus; Flag Corp; Madrigals; Orch; School Musical; NHS; Pres Schlr; Girl Scts; Parnt Tchr Assoc Awd Excllnc Frnch 84; Dist 7 Choir Stu 87; Shippensburg U; Ecnmcs.

REMALEY, CHRISTOPHER; Allderdice HS; Pittsburgh, PA; (3); Boys Clb Am; Nwsp Stf; JV Ftbl; JV Trk; Var L Vllybl; High Hon Roll; Hon Roll; Ntl Merit Ltr.

REMALY, KIMBERLY; Northampton Area SR HS; Bath, PA; (3); Church Yth Grp; Girl Scts; Hosp Aide; Office Aide; Band; Chorus; Church Choir; Concert Band; Drm Mjr(t); Mrchg Band; Nurse.

REMENTER, RICHARD; Neshaminy HS; Penndel, PA; (3); 100/818; Var Crs Cntry; Var Ftbl; L Var Trk; Hon Roll; Prfct Atten Awd; Prjct Bus 85; Suburbn I All Leag Trk 86; Accntnt.

REMICH, NICOLE; Sheffield HS; Clarendon, PA; (4); 4/75; SADD; Drm Mjr(t); Jazz Band; Mrchg Band; School Musical; Symp Band; Cheerleading; High Hon Roll; VP NHS; Voice Dem Awd; Semper Fidelis Awd Musical Excllnce 87; Hnr Stu Top 10 Cls 87; Acad Ltr Awd 87; Clarion U; Mktg.

REMICK, VICKI; Valley View JR SR HS; Peckville, PA; (3); Chorus; Vllybl; High Hon Roll; Hon Roll; Lackawanna JC; Accntng.

REMINGTON, BRENDA; Wyalusing Valley HS; Wyalusing, PA; (3); Church Yth Grp; Library Aide; Spanish Clb; Teachers Aide; Chorus; Church Choir; School Musical; School Play; Stage Crew; Mgr(s); Mst Imprtnt Sftbl Plyr Troph 84-85; Hnbl Mntn Bradford Cnty Consrvtn Postr Cntst 86-87; Art Ed.

REMINGTON, RICHARD S; Warrior Run HS; Turbotville, PA; (3); 6/180; VP AFS; Am Leg Boys St; Pres Spanish Clb; Chorus; School Musical; Rep Stu Cncl; High Hon Roll; Hon Roll; NHS; Trs Church Yth Grp; Spnsh Stu Yr 85-86; Law.

REMISH, SHAWN; Montgomery Area HS; Montgomery, PA; (3); Thesps; Band; Chorus; Mrchg Band; Trk; Var Capt Wrstlng; High Hon Roll; Hon Roll; Jr NHS; NHS; Mst Valuble Wrstlr 86-87; Forestry.

REMLEY, AMY; Benton Area JR SR HS; Benton, PA; (3); Art Clb; Church Yth Grp; Cmnty Wkr; Drama Clb; Trs 4-H; Keywanettes; Library Aide; Band; Chorus; Mrchg Band; Chld Dvlpmnt.

RENALDO, CARLA; Pen Argyl HS; Pen Argyl, PA; (3); 10/160; AFS; German Clb; Band; Orch; Nwsp Rptr; JV Bsktbl; Var JV Tennis; Var Trk; High Hon Roll; Hon Roll; Psych.

RENDOS, KAREN M; Ambridge Area HS; Baden, PA; (4); 13/265; Computer Clb; Pep Clb; VP Sec Spanish Clb; Capt Drill Tm; Mrchg Band; Off Sr Cls; Pres Stu Cncl; Capt Pom Pon; High Hon Roll; NHS; Grl Mnth Ecnmy Boro Cvcs Clb 86; Ambrdge Area Chmbr Cmmrce Schlrshp, Pres Acdmc Ftns Awd 87; U Of Pittsburgh; Math.

RENGERS, STEPHEN; Seneca Valley HS; Evans Cty, PA; (2); 1/410; Math Tm; High Hon Roll; Ntl Acdmc Gms 3rd Pl In Scl Stdys 87; PA Scty Prfsnl Engrs Cert Of Merit 87; PA Math League 87.

RENN, CHRISTOPHER; Danville HS; Danville, PA; (1); French Hon Soc; High Hon Roll; Pres Schlr; Alg II Awd 87; Graham F Stephens Awd 87; Sci.

RENN, JAMIE; Jeanette SR HS; Jeannette, PA; (2); 27/130; Drama Clb; VP French Clb; Mrchg Band; Rep Frsh Cls; Rep Soph Cls; Var Cheerleading; Hon Roll; Ski Clb; Pom Pon; Miss Teenge PA NCHA 87; Schlstc Achvt Awd 85; Stu Advsry Brd 86; PA ST U; Elem Ed.

RENN, STACY; Shamokin HS; Shamokin, PA; (3); Drama Clb; 4-H; German Clb; Red Cross Aide; Science Clb; Orch; Rep Jr Cls; 4-H Awd; Stu Recgntn 85-87.

RENN, TARA; Red Lion HS; York, PA; (4); Am Leg Aux Girls St; SADD; Varsity Clb; Trs Frsh Cls; Rep Soph Cls; VP Jr Cls; Rep Sr Cls; Off Stu Cncl; Var Capt Cheerleading; Im Powder Puff Ftbl; WV U; Pblc Rltns.

RENN JR, WILLIAM; Danville HS; Danville, PA; (3); Computer Clb; Band; Mrchg Band; Symp Band; Hon Roll; NHS; Prfct Atten Awd; Comp Sci.

RENNING, RUTH; Punxsutawney Area HS; Punxsutawney, PA; (4); 9/245; Trs Drama Clb; Math Tm; Science Clb; Band; School Musical; Variety Show; Yrbk Stf; NHS; Mary Ann Irvng Schlrshp, Hetrick Memrl Schlrshp 87; IA ST U; Indstrl Engrng.

RENNINGER, DAN; Clarion-Limestone HS; Strattanville, PA; (3); 10/78; FFA; Spanish Clb; Chorus; Pres Sr Cls; Rep Stu Cncl; L Trk; Hon Roll; NHS; Clarion U; Broadcstng.

RENNINGER, HEIDI; Juniata HS; Mifflintown, PA; (3); Camera Clb; Drama Clb; 4-H; FFA; FHA; SADD; School Play; Yrbk Stf; 4-H Awd.

RENO, KERR; HS For Engineering & Sci; Phila, PA; (3); 34/240; Computer Clb; JA; Math Clb; Model UN; Yrbk Bus Mgr; Yrbk Stf; Hon Roll; NHS; Cmptr Bowl Tm 87; APEA Smr Prgrm Carnegie Mellon 87; NROTC Fnlst 87; Engr.

RENO, MICHELLE; South Park HS; Library, PA; (3); Church Yth Grp; Pres FBLA; Hosp Aide; JA; Red Cross Aide; JV Bsktbl; JV Mgr(s); Score Keeper; 3rd Pl Shrthnd FBLA Rgnls 87; Law.

RENSHAW, LINDA; Pequea Valley HS; Gap, PA; (3); 54/121; Dance Clb; FBLA; Hon Roll; FBLA Typng I St Fnls Awd 87; Bus.

RENTNER, AMY; Montrose JR SR HS; Montrose, PA; (3); German Clb; Latin Clb; Chorus; School Musical; Nwsp Stf; Rep Stu Cncl; JV Stat Fld Hcky; High Hon Roll; Hon Roll; NHS; Vrsty Lttr Fld Hcky Mgr 85; Franklin & Marshall; Pre Med.

RENTSCHLER, RHONDA; Norther Chester County Vo-Tech; Spg City, PA; (3); 24/124; Church Yth Grp; FBLA; Yrbk Stf; Swmmng; Hon Roll; Empr Schl Bty; Csmtlgy.

RENTZEL, AMY ELIZABETH; West York Area SR HS; York, PA; (4); 11/185; Church Yth Grp; VP JA; VP SADD; Church Choir; Mrchg Band; Symp Band; Yrbk Stf; High Hon Roll; Hon Roll; NHS; Modern Music Masters 87; Supr Plus Ratg Natl Piano Play Aud 87; Dist Lower Band Fstvl 87; BYU; Anthro.

RENWICK, TERRI; St Marys Area HS; Kersey, PA; (3); 4-H; Hon Roll; NHS; Veterinarian.

RENYE, MARK; Father Judge HS; Philadelphia, PA; (3); 140/465; Chess Clb; Computer Clb; Nwsp Stf; Lit Mag; Bowling; Ice Hcky; Trk; Genetics.

RENZO, DAVALA; Rochester Area Schl Dist; Rochester, PA; (4); 14/89; DECA; Q&S; Service Clb; Ski Clb; Drill Tm; Nwsp Ed-Chief; Nwsp Stf; Stu Cncl; Trk; NHS; Outstndng Awd In Jrnlsm; Pres Acad Ftns Awd; Gannon U; Cmnctns.

REOLA, DENEE; Springdale HS; Cheswick, PA; (3); Church Yth Grp; Cmnty Wkr; Political Wkr; Band; Color Guard; Concert Band; Trs Jr Cls; Stat Bsktbl; High Hon Roll; Hon Roll.

REPAK, RIK; Ford City HS; Ford City, PA; (3); Var L Ftbl; Var L Trk; Hon Roll; Arch.

REPASH, DONNA; Archbishop Ryan For Girls; Phila, PA; (3); JA; Office Aide; Ski Clb; Spanish Clb; Penn ST; Medical.

REPINE, LYDIA; Living Word Acad; Lancaster, PA; (2); Church Yth Grp; Chorus; Yrbk Stf; Rep Stu Cncl; Var Bsktbl; Var Fld Hcky; Hon Roll; Var Trk; Pres Physcl Ftnes Awd 85-86; ACSI Sci Fair Proj 1st Pl Life Sci 86; Chrctr Hnr Roll 85-86; Messiah Coll; Bus.

REPKO, ROBERT; Bangor Area SR HS; Bangor, PA; (3); 15/206; Concert Band; Mrchg Band; School Play; Rep Soph Cls; Rep Jr Cls; High Hon Roll; Jr NHS; NHS; Ntl Merit Ltr; Navy; Aviation Tech.

REPLOGLE, ALLEN; Northern Bedford County HS; New Enterprise, PA; (4); Church Yth Grp; Math Tm; SADD; Band; Chorus; Jazz Band; School Musical; Swing Chorus; Nwsp Stf; Yrbk Stf; Pres Phy Fitness Awd 85-87; Triangle Tech; Draftsman.

REPLOGLE, LORI; Central HS; Martinsburg, PA; (3); Church Yth Grp; Chorus; Church Choir.

REPOSKY, DAWN; Brownsville HS; Brownsville, PA; (3); Drama Clb; FBLA; Office Aide; Ski Clb; Nwsp Stf; Trs Rep Stu Cncl; Capt Var Cheerleading; Gym; Sftbl; Hon Roll; Miss All Am Cheerldr Pgnt 87; Comp.

REPPERT, ANGELA; Allentown Central Catholic HS; Northampton, PA; (4); 83/208; Chorus; Color Guard; Mrchg Band; Capt Twrlr; Hon Roll; Kings Coll; Psych.

REPPERT, GREG; Cedar Crest HS; Lebanon, PA; (3); 20/306; German Clb; Pep Clb; Hon Roll; Chem.

REPPERT, GREGORY; Wm Allen HS; Allentown, PA; (2); Chess Clb; Hosp Aide; Nwsp Stf; Lit Mag; Ice Hcky; High Hon Roll; Hon Roll; Jr NHS; Prfct Atten Awd; Math.

REPPERT, MELISSA; William Allen HS; Allentown, PA; (4); 27/550; GAA; Key Clb; Varsity Clb; Stu Cncl; Capt Crs Cntry; Capt Gym; Capt Trk; High Hon Roll; Jr NHS; NHS; PHEAA Cert Merit, AHS Aprtsmnshp Awd 87; AHS Summo Cum Honore Schlrshp Awd 86; Penn ST U; Sprts Med.

REPPERT, TURIE; Harnburg Area HS; Shoemakersville, PA; (3); 37/170; 4-H; Girl Scts; Library Aide; Spanish Clb; SADD; Var L Bsktbl; Gym; Var Trk; Hon Roll; Intl Frgn Lang Awds 86; Acadc All Am At Lrg Div 86; Acadc Hnrs Spnsh II 87; Slippery Rock U; Psych.

RESAVAGE, LAURA; Bethel Park HS; Bethel Park, PA; (3); Church Yth Grp; Cmnty Wkr; VP FBLA; Pres Intnl Clb; Red Cross Aide; Nwsp Stf; Hon Roll; Cert Of Superb Fshn Modeling-Barbizon 86; Bus Admin.

RESCHER, MARK A; Central Catholic HS; Pittsburgh, PA; (4); 8/264; Dance Clb; Latin Clb; School Play; Stage Crew; Rep Stu Cncl; High Hon Roll; Hon Roll; Ntl Merit SF; Rotary Awd; Stu Affrs Cncl 86-87; Washington Wrkshps I 86; Cornell Univ Smmr Coll 86; Georgetown; Intl Rel.

RESELE, RON; Conneaut Lake HS; Hartstown, PA; (2); Church Yth Grp; Cmnty Wkr; Spanish Clb; Frsh Cls; Soph Cls; Var L Wrstlng; Elks Awd; High Hon Roll; NHS; Sci Field.

RESER, ANDREW; Wallenpaupack Area HS; Hawley, PA; (3); 24/154; Church Yth Grp; Computer Clb; Science Clb; Ski Clb; Band; Concert Band; Mrchg Band; Var L Bsbl; JV Bsktbl; Var L Socr; PA ST U; Comm.

RESH, JASON; South Western HS; Hanover, PA; (3); 32/233; Varsity Clb; Band; Concert Band; Mrchg Band; Stage Crew; Symp Band; Nwsp Stf; Var Swmmng; Hon Roll; NHS; Art.

RESICK, CHRIS; Bishop Carroll HS; South Fork, PA; (3); Letterman Clb; Ski Clb; JV Var Ftbl; Var L Trk; Im Wt Lftg; Chrch Altr Svr, Chrch CCD Instrctr; Acctng.

RESKOVAC, RENEE; Riverside HS; New Brighton, PA; (3); 22/169; Church Yth Grp; Hosp Aide; SADD; Band; Chorus; Flag Corp; Yrbk Stf; High Hon Roll; Hon Roll; 4-H; Gifted Ed; U WV.

RESS, TRICIA; Frazier Memorial JR SR HS; Fayette City, PA; (3); Church Yth Grp; Drama Clb; FNA; Ski Clb; Drm Mjr(t); Yrbk Bus Mgr; Rep Stu Cncl; Twrlr; Elem Ed.

RESSLER, JASON; Conrad Weiser HS; Robesonia, PA; (3); 24/182; Church Yth Grp; German Clb; Latin Clb; Var Bsbl; Var Bsktbl; Var Socr; Hon Roll; Elctrcl Engr.

RESSLER JR, RICHARD; Azreth Area SR HS; Nazareth, PA; (3); 32/275; Computer Clb; Band; Concert Band; Drm & Bgl; Jazz Band; Mrchg Band; School Musical; Cit Awd; Hon Roll; Dstct Bnd 86-87; Rgn V & Iv Ochrstr 86; Aero Engr.

RESTA, LYNN; Western Beaver HS; Industry, PA; (4); 11/75; Chorus; Church Choir; Orch; Nwsp Ed-Chief; Stat Sftbl; Co-Capt Vllybl; NHS; Pres Schlr; Trs Church Yth Grp; FHA; Beaver Cnty Times Stu/Ath Schlr 86-87; 2nd Team All-Stars Vlybl 86-87; CC Beaver Cnty; Word Proc.

RESTAINO, GERRY; Center HS; Monaca, PA; (2); Spanish Clb; Stage Crew; PA ST; Engrng.

RESTUCCIA, NADINE; Pittston Area HS; Pittston, PA; (4); FBLA; FNA; Key Clb; Ski Clb; SADD; Yrbk Stf; Pres Jr Cls; Pres Sr Cls; NHS; Misericordia Coll; Bio.

RESURRECCION, ZITA; Lower Moreland HS; Huntingdon Valley, PA; (3); Key Clb; Science Clb; SADD; Chorus; Concert Band; Orch; Rep Soph Cls; Crs Cntry; Trk; School Musical; MVP Winter Track 85-86; Stu Forum Rep 86-87.

RETORT, MICHAEL; Highlands SR HS; Natrona Hts, PA; (3); German Clb; Rep Stu Cncl; Bsbl; Bsktbl; Ftbl; Trk; Wt Lftg; Plyr Game TV 3 Ftbl 85; Brown Awd Schltc Achvt 86-87; Crim Just.

RETTER, CYNTHIA MARIE; Kiski Area HS; Vandergrift, PA; (4); FBLA; JA; Teachers Aide; Chorus; High Hon Roll; Hon Roll; Bus Stu Of Mon 87; Oakbridge Acad; Med Asst.

RETTER, HEIDI; Northeast Bradford HS; Warren Center, PA; (4); 2/74; Band; Chorus; Hst Sr Cls; Pres VP Stu Cncl; Var Cheerleading; Bausch & Lomb Sci Awd; VP NHS; Sal; Am Leg Aux Girls St; Church Yth Grp; Presdntl Acad Fit Awd 87; Natl Schl Choral Awd 87; JR Miss Schltc Achvt Awd 86; PA ST U; Pre Med.

RETTEW, STACY; Donegal HS; Marietta, PA; (3); 56/173; Stat Bsbl; Mgr(s); Score Keeper.

RETTGER, LU ANN; St Marys Area HS; St Marys, PA; (3); Cmnty Wkr; Hosp Aide; JV Cheerleading; Hon Roll; NHS; Med.

REULBACH, MICHAEL; Bishop Guilfoyle HS; Altoona, PA; (3); Quiz Bowl; Speech Tm; Ctznshp Awd 84-85; Bus Admin.

REUSCHER, NANCY; Elk County Christian HS; St Marys, PA; (2); 8/89; Church Choir; Sec Frsh Cls; Trs Soph Cls; Trk; High Hon Roll; Notre Dame; Math.

REUSCHER, TANYA; Elk County Christian HS; St Marys, PA; (3); 35/72; Hosp Aide; Service Clb; Ski Clb; Yrbk Stf; Stat Bsktbl; Cheerleading; Stat Trk; Hon Roll; Fshn Merch.

REUSS, LAURA; Upper Darby HS; Upr Darby, PA; (4); 15/590; Band; Concert Band; Mrchg Band; Orch; JV L Sftbl; Cit Awd; High Hon Roll; Hon Roll; NHS; Pres Schlr; Shandler-Berman Awd Outstndng Achvt In Amercanism 87; U Of DE; Bio.

REUTHER, GARY; North Pocono HS; Moscow, PA; (3); 2/240; Pres Church Yth Grp; Band; Mrchg Band; Pres Orch; L Golf; High Hon Roll; NHS; Sal.

REUWER, EDITH; J P Mc Caskey HS; Lancaster, PA; (3); 105/517; Chorus; School Play; Variety Show; Hon Roll; Prfct Atten Awd; 1st Pl NOW Essay Cntst 85; Creative Wrtng.

REVELT, KATHLEEN; Southmoreland SR HS; Ruffsdale, PA; (3); 6/222; Church Yth Grp; French Clb; Math Clb; Pep Clb; Teachers Aide; Nwsp Stf; Lit Mag; JV L Bsktbl; French Hon Soc; NHS; Biol.

REVERON, DANIEL A; Mc Caskey HS; Lancaster, PA; (3); Boys Clb Am; Boy Scts; CAP; Radio Clb; Spanish Clb; VICA; Nwsp Phtg; Nwsp Rptr; Off Sr Cls; Bsktbl; Art Awd 85; Mltry Polc.

REVIELLO, KEITH; Scranton Prep; Scranton, PA; (4); Computer Clb; Service Clb; Spanish Clb; SADD; Stage Crew; Ftbl; PA ST U; Arch Engrng.

REVILAK, STEVE; North Pocono HS; Moscow, PA; (3); 36/231; Boy Scts; Orch; NHS; Computer Clb; Variety Show; High Hon Roll; Hon Roll; Eagle Scout Troop 132 84; Brnz & Gold Palms 85; Silver Palm 87; Berklee Schl Of Music; Music.

REX, JENNIFER; Carmichaels Area JR/Sr HS; Carmichaels, PA; (2); 5/130; AFS; Church Yth Grp; French Clb; Concert Band; Drm Mjr(t); Mrchg Band; Rep Stu Cncl; High Hon Roll; Jr NHS; Church Yth Grp; Cngrss Bundestag Exchng Pgm Alt 87; Yale; Law.

REXROTH, JAMES; Eastern York HS; Windsor, PA; (3); 9/190; Am Leg Boys St; Church Yth Grp; 4-H; SADD; Teachers Aide; Pres Jr Cls; Pres Sr Cls; Rep Stu Cncl; Var Ftbl; Wt Lftg; Acad Lttr For Being In Top 10 87; Ag.

REYNAR, JEFFREY; Abington SR HS; Abington, PA; (4); 32/486; Church Yth Grp; Church Choir; Hon Roll; NHS; Ntl Merit Ltr; U Of DE; Elec Engrng.

REYNARD, MICHELLE; Parkland HS; Breinigsville, PA; (4); 43/459; Sec Church Yth Grp; VP 4-H; Leo Clb; Flag Corp; 4-H Awd; High Hon Roll; Hon Roll; NHS; Kutztown U; Schl Psych.

REYNOLDS, AIMEE; Cedar Cliff HS; New Cumberland, PA; (2); 65/286; Church Yth Grp; French Clb; Key Clb; Church Choir; Hon Roll; Spcl Ed.

REYNOLDS, ALEXA; Lakeview HS; Sandy Lake, PA; (3); Aud/Vis; 4-H; FHA; Library Aide; VICA; Band; Color Guard; Concert Band; Mrchg Band; 4-H Awd; Inter Cnty Hrsmns Assoc Champn 86; 14-17 Yrs Sddl St Eqtatn; Penn ST; Drafting.

REYNOLDS, DANIEL; Bishop O Reilly HS; Dallas, PA; (4); 9/110; Debate Tm; Ski Clb; Thesps; Chorus; School Musical; School Play; Trs Stu Cncl; Capt Socr; NHS; Sec Church Yth Grp; Lawyr-Luzerne Cnty Mock Law Trial; St Josephs U; Fd Mktg.

REYNOLDS, JENNIFER; Yough SR HS; Herminie, PA; (3); Trs Band; Chorus; Concert Band; Jazz Band; Mrchg Band; Nwsp Stf; Powder Puff Ftbl; Wstmrlnd Cnty Bnd Fstvl 84-87; Dist I Rgn I Bnd Fstvls 87; Natl Engl Merit Awd 87; Penn ST U; Pltcl Sci.

REYNOLDS, KATHY; Central HS; Martinsburg, PA; (4); 11/190; GAA; Pres Girl Scts; Library Aide; Ski Clb; Yrbk Stf; Hon Roll; NHS; NEDT Awd; Acdmc All Amer 87; PA ST U; Microbio.

REYNOLDS, KEVIN; Peabody HS; Pittsburgh, PA; (4); 29/292; Church Yth Grp; FHA; Acpl Chr; Chorus; Church Choir; School Musical; Variety Show; Pres Frsh Cls; VP Soph Cls; Crs Cntry; Future Homemakers Of Amer 85-86; Smmr Yth Emplymnt 85-86; Merit Awd 84-85; CMU; Vocal & Foods.

REYNOLDS, MARTY; Bishop O Reilly HS; Dallas, PA; (2); Boy Scts; Church Yth Grp; Ski Clb; Varsity Clb; Chorus; Church Choir; School Musical; School Play; Stage Crew; Bsktbl; Chld Care.

REYNOLDS, MICHELLE; Kiski Area HS; Salina, PA; (3); German Clb; Nwsp Stf; High Hon Roll; Hon Roll; Pres Schlr; FHA; Band; Color Guard; Concert Band; Mrchg Band; Edinboro U; Secndry Ed.

REYNOLDS, MICHELLE; Maplewood HS; Guys Mills, PA; (4); 7/136; French Clb; Chorus; Color Guard; Mrchg Band; Sec Sr Cls; Rep Stu Cncl; JV Var Bsktbl; Var L Sftbl; Hon Roll; Trs NHS; Behrend Coll; Math.

REYNOLDS II, RICHARD L; South Hills Christian Schl; Bethel Park, PA; (4); 1/8; Church Yth Grp; Computer Clb; Chorus; School Play; Nwsp Ed-Chief; Pres Sr Cls; Capt Bsktbl; Var Coach Actv; Dnfth Awd; Val; Comp Engrng.

REYNOLDS, ROBIN; Warwick HS; Lititz, PA; (3); 57/250; Exploring; Chorus; Concert Band; School Musical; Ed Lit Mag; Bio.

REYNOLDS, RONALD; Schenley HS; Pittsburgh, PA; (3); Chess Clb; German Clb; High Hon Roll; Hon Roll; Jr NHS; Pres Schlr; SAR Awd; Military.

REYNOLDS, THERESA; Downingtown HS; Downington, PA; (3); 124/648; Church Yth Grp; Ski Clb; Spanish Clb; SADD; JV Bsktbl; Im Vllybl; High Hon Roll; Hon Roll; Bus.

REYNOLDS, THOMAS; North Allegheny SR HS; Allison Pk, PA; (3); 57/649; VP JA; SADD; Yrbk Phtg; Lit Mag; Rep Soph Cls; Trs Jr Cls; Rep Sr Cls; Rep Stu Cncl; Jr NHS; NHS; Bus.

REYNOLDS, TRACI; Uniontown Area SR HS; Uniontown, PA; (3); 13/286; Letterman Clb; Yrbk Stf; Sec Stu Cncl; L Swmmng; French Hon Soc; High Hon Roll; NHS; French Clb; Chorus; Yrbk Rptr; Bio.

REYNOLDS, TRENEICE; Bensalem SR HS; Bensalem, PA; (2); Drama Clb; Key Clb; Chorus; School Play; Stage Crew; High Hon Roll; Prfct Atten Awd; Morehouse Coll; Jrnlsm.

REZNICK, MELISSA; Hazleton SR HS; Hazleton, PA; (4); Drama Clb; Spanish Clb; Color Guard; Orch; Stage Crew; Lit Mag; High Hon Roll; Hon Roll; NHS; Spanish NHS; Vrsty Ltr Clrgrd Slk 84; Hnrbl Mntn Natl Spnsh Cntst 84-85; Lackawann JC.

REZNIK, SHELLY; Beaver Area SR HS; Beaver, PA; (2); Church Yth Grp; Cmnty Wkr; French Clb; Ski Clb; SADD; Nwsp Stf; Cheerleading; Coach Actv; Sftbl; Var L Trk; U Pittsburgh; Accntng.

RHEA, HEATHER; Purchase Line HS; Dixonville, PA; (4); 21/104; SADD; Drm Mjr(t); Mrchg Band; Stage Crew; Yrbk Stf; VP Frsh Cls; VP Soph Cls; VP Jr Cls; VP Sr Cls; Hon Roll; U Of Pittsburgh; Pre-Vet.

RHEA, LAURA; Clarion Area HS; Clarion, PA; (2); FHA; Bsktbl; Vllybl; Wt Lftg; NHS; Prfct Atten Awd.

RHEASANT, JANELLE M; Juniata Valley HS; Alexandria, PA; (4); 9/70; Pres FHA; Pres Chorus; Trs Sr Cls; Stu Cncl; High Hon Roll; Hon Roll; Sec NHS; Church Yth Grp; Speech Tm; Solo Allegheny Ballet Co 83-87; PA Govrnschl Arts 85; Schlrshp Joffrey Ballet Smmr Prog 86; Shenandoah Coll; Ballet.

RHINE, BARBARA; Penns Manor HS; Strongstown, PA; (3); 24/97; FBLA; Girl Scts; SADD; Nwsp Stf; Yrbk Stf; Hon Roll; Psych.

RHINES, AMANDA; Hopewell SR HS; Aliquippa, PA; (4); 20/240; German Clb; Girl Scts; Band; Chorus; Jazz Band; Variety Show; Yrbk Stf; Rep Frsh Cls; Rep Soph Cls; Rep Jr Cls; GS Gld Awd 86; Grmn Hnr Awd 87; Lockhaven; Intl Stds.

RHOADES, ANDREW; Tyrone Area HS; Tyrone, PA; (2); Science Clb; Bsbl; Bsktbl; Trk; Wt Lftg; High Hon Roll; Hon Roll; PA ST U; Elec Engnrng.

RHOADES, KEITH; Blairsville HS; Blairsville, PA; (1); AFS; Civic Clb; Cmnty Wkr; 4-H; FFA; FHA; Letterman Clb; Radio Clb; ROTC; Varsity Clb; Greenhand Awd; Armed Svcs.

RHOADES, ROBERTA; Big Spring HS; Newville, PA; (3); 61/258; Pres Sec Church Yth Grp; Sec Concert Band; Jazz Band; Mrchg Band; Pres Stu Cncl; Mgr(s); Powder Puff Ftbl; Hon Roll; Outstndng Studnt Cncl Mbr 85-87; Wmns Club Awd 87; Tchr.

RHOADES, SCOTT; Wesleyan Holiness Acad; Nanty-Glo, PA; (4); 1/2; Boy Scts; Church Yth Grp; Cmnty Wkr; Exploring; Red Cross Aide; Band; Chorus; Church Choir; Drill Tm; School Musical; NASA-NSTA Space Shttl Stu Invlvmnt Proj 84-86; Explr Sct Grwth Awd 86; Bible Awd 85-86; PA ST U; Emrgncy Med.

RHOADES, SEMBER; Keystone JR SR HS; Knox, PA; (3); Trs FBLA; Office Aide; Trs Pep Clb; SADD; Chorus; Rep Stu Cncl; Erie Bus Center; Acctg.

RHOADES, TAMMY; Wilson Christian Acad; W Newton, PA; (4); 1/14; Yrbk Stf; Swmmng; High Hon Roll; NCTE Awd; NHS; Sal; English & Communications Awd 87; Economics Awd 86; Waynesburg Coll; Elem Educ.

RHOADS, EDWARD; Northern Lebanon JR SR HS; Lebanon, PA; (3); 19/213; Church Yth Grp; Math Tm; Quiz Bowl; School Play; Var JV Ftbl; Var Trk; Im Wrstlng; High Hon Roll; Church Yth Grp; Med.

RHOADS, PAULA; Shanksville-Stonycreek HS; Friedens, PA; (3); 6/34; Church Yth Grp; 4-H; Ski Clb; Mrchg Band; Nwsp Stf; Pres Frsh Cls; Pres Soph Cls; Pres Jr Cls; Stu Cncl; Capt Var Bsktbl; Pres Physcl Ftnss Awd 86; Am Leg Essay Awd 85; Dntstry.

RHOADS, ROBERT; Palmyra HS; Palmyra, PA; (4); Church Yth Grp; Hosp Aide; JV Bsbl; JV Ftbl; Cit Awd; High Hon Roll; Hon Roll; Harrisburg Area CC; Radlgy.

RHODES, JENNIFER; Hollidaysburg Area SR HS; Hollidaysburg, PA; (4); JA; Latin Clb; Chorus; PA ST U; Psychology.

RHODES, JULIE; Tyrone Area HS; Tyrone, PA; (4); FBLA; Key Clb; Chorus; Cheerleading; High Hon Roll; Hon Roll; Jr NHS; Prfct Atten Awd; Won Rgnl Shrthnd Cmptn 87; Outstndng Shrthnd Awd 87; Advtsng.

RHODES, RHONDA; Shippensburg Area SR HS; Shippensburg, PA; (4); 28/219; Church Yth Grp; GAA; Chorus; Orch; L Var Fld Hcky; Trk; Hon Roll; NHS; Central PA Bus Schl; Crt Rprtg.

RHODES, ROBERT; Roxborough HS; Philadelphia, PA; (4); 5/250; Aud/Vis; Computer Clb; Bowling; Bausch & Lomb Sci Awd; High Hon Roll; NHS; Roxborough Alumni Schlrshp 87; Physcs Awd 87; Penn ST; Comp Sci.

RHODES, RUTH; General Mc Lane HS; Edinboro, PA; (3); 18/256; Drama Clb; Model UN; Quiz Bowl; Band; Mrchg Band; School Play; Nwsp Stf; Pres Stu Cncl; JV Sftbl; NHS; Yth Gov YMCA Yth/Govt 87.

RHODES, SARA; Berlin Brothersvalley HS; Berlin, PA; (2); Church Yth Grp; NFL; Spanish Clb; SADD; Band; Capt Color Guard; Mrchg Band; Hon Roll; Marine Bio.

RHODES, TAMMY; Vough SR HS; Ruffsdale, PA; (3); 44/250; FBLA; Chorus; Church Choir; Color Guard; Concert Band; Jazz Band; Nwsp Ed-Chief; Hon Roll; NHS; Prfct Atten Awd; WCMEA Cnty Chorus 86; Westmoreland Cnty CC; Sec Sci.

RHODES, TERRI; Bethlehem-Center HS; Fredericktown, PA; (3); 21/168; Art Clb; Ski Clb; Varsity Clb; Yrbk Stf; L Var Sftbl; Capt Var Vllybl; Hon Roll.

RHODESIDE, DEBORAH; George Washington HS; Philadelphia, PA; (4); 120/800; Dance Clb; SADD; School Play; Yrbk Stf; Sec Jr Cls; Sec Sr Cls; Gym; High Hon Roll; NHS; Val; Volunteers Svcs Awd 87; PA ST U; Elem Educ.

RHODY, HILLARY; Loyalsock Township HS; Williamsport, PA; (3); 48/117; JA; Spanish Clb; Chorus; Co-Capt Cheerleading; Tennis; Hon Roll; Bus Mgmt.

RHONE, LEANNE; Susquehanna Community HS; Starrucca, PA; (4); Church Yth Grp; 4-H; Girl Scts; Ski Clb; Concert Band; Mrchg Band; Yrbk Stf; Cheerleading; Crs Cntry; Trk; Art Awd 87; Kutztown U; Art Educ.

RHUDY, KIM; Hanover SR HS; Hanover, PA; (4); 5/104; Art Clb; Church Yth Grp; Chorus; Yrbk Stf; Hon Roll; Pres Schlr; Rotary Awd; Pep Clb; Church Choir; Pres Schlrshp $14000 Bridgewater; York Cnty Acdmc All Star 87; Bridgewater Coll; Art.

RHYDER, KAREN; Lehighton Area HS; Lehighton, PA; (3); 18/246; Am Leg Aux Girls St; FBLA; SADD; Chorus; Stage Crew; Yrbk Ed-Chief; Yrbk Stf; Stu Cncl; Fld Hcky; Mgr(s); Attnd Presdntl Clsrm Washington DC 87; Bus.

RHYMESTINE, GEORGE D; Moshannon Valley HS; Madera, PA; (3); Ski Clb; Varsity Clb; Band; Bsbl; Ftbl; Wrstlng; Penn ST U; Bus Mgmt.

RHYU, JAMES; Lower Moreland HS; Huntingdon Valley, PA; (4); 12/201; Church Yth Grp; School Musical; Yrbk Bus Mgr; VP Jr Cls; VP Sr Cls; Capt Socr; Trk; Wrstlng; Hon Roll; NHS.

RIBAR, EDWARD; Gateway SR HS; Monroeville, PA; (3); 69/467; Boy Scts; Drm Mjr(t); Jazz Band; Mrchg Band; Symp Band; Stu Cncl; Hon Roll; PMEA Dstrct Bnd 84 & 86; PMEA Rgnl Bn 85 & 87; IUP Hnrs Bnd 86.

RIBORTELLA, EVELYN ANN; Western Wayne HS; Moscow, PA; (3); Aud/Vis; Office Aide; Spanish Clb; Teachers Aide; Mrchg Band; Hon Roll; Psych.

RICCHE, KERRY; Bishop Guilfoyle HS; Altoona, PA; (3); 9/140; German Clb; Science Clb; SADD; Yrbk Stf; VP Frsh Cls; VP Soph Cls; Off Stu Cncl; Vllybl; High Hon Roll; NHS; Princeton U; Frgn Rltns.

RICCI, LISA; Hanover Area HS; Wilkes Barre, PA; (3); 8/194; Cmnty Wkr; Key Clb; Stage Crew; Yrbk Stf; Stu Cncl; Cheerleading; High Hon Roll; Jr NHS; NHS; Prfct Atten Awd; Phrmcy.

RICCI, MARK; Ringgold HS; New Eagle, PA; (4); 17/350; Soph Cls; Jr Cls; Sr Cls; Stu Cncl; L Golf; Cit Awd; Hon Roll; Trs NHS; Stu Rep Schl Brd 85-86 & 86-87; Sci Mth Hnr Soc Chrmn 84-87; Carnegie-Mellon U; Chem Engr.

RICCI, PAUL; Bishop Mc Cort HS; Johnstown, PA; (3); 40/155; Sec Church Yth Grp; NFL; Speech Tm; Thesps; School Play; Nwsp Rptr; Im Bsktbl; High Hon Roll; Hon Roll; Natl Sci Olympiad Top 10 Bio/Chem 86-87; Juniata Coll; Pre-Law.

RICCIARDI, JEFF; Ambridge HS; Freedom, PA; (3); German Clb; Jazz Band; School Musical; School Play; Variety Show; Jr Cls; Wrstlng; Hon Roll; Prfct Atten Awd; U Of PA ST; Elec Engrng.

RICCIARDI, SANDRA; Upper Darby HS; Clifton Hts, PA; (3); 51/550; Office Aide; Chorus; Rep Frsh Cls; Rep Soph Cls; Rep Jr Cls; Rep Stu Cncl; Mgr(s); Vllybl; High Hon Roll; Hon Roll; Amer Stds Awd 86-87; Vlybl Lttr 84-87.

RICCINI, LESLIE; Scranton Central HS; Scranton, PA; (2); Trs Church Yth Grp; Spanish Clb; SADD; Band; Church Choir; Concert Band; Mrchg Band; Pep Band; Rep Stu Cncl.

RICCITELLI, ANTHONY; Center HS; Monaca, PA; (3); Spanish Clb; VP Bsbl; Im Bsktbl; Maryland U; Mrktng.

RICE, AMY; Nazareth Area SR HS; Nazareth, PA; (3); Church Yth Grp; Yrbk Stf; Badmtn; Mgr(s); Stat Score Keeper; Hon Roll; Church Choir; Colossians Awd Private Schl 84.

RICE, ANITA; Wyoming Area HS; W Wyoming, PA; (2); Art Clb; Ski Clb; Spanish Clb; Var L Crs Cntry; Var L Trk; High Hon Roll; NHS.

RICE, GEORGE; Avon Grove HS; Cochranville, PA; (3); Computer Clb; Concert Band; Mrchg Band; School Musical; Var JV Crs Cntry; Swmmng; Wt Lftg; Var JV Wrstlng; Hon Roll; Chem.

RICE, JEFF; Haverford SR HS; Havertown, PA; (3); Church Yth Grp; FCA; German Clb; Red Cross Aide; Band; Mrchg Band; Pep Band; Symp Band; Nwsp Stf; Var Ftbl; Vrsty Ftbl Awd 86-87; Vrsty Swmmng Awd 86-87.

RICE, JENNIFER; Ephrata SR HS; Ephrata, PA; (4); Pres Trs Church Yth Grp; Exploring; Spanish Clb; Concert Band; Var L Sftbl; Var L Tennis; Hon Roll; Pres Schlr; J Harry Hibsman Schlrshp 87; U S Army Rsrv Natl Schl/Athlt Awd 87; Phil Coll Of Phrmcy; Phrmcst.

RICE, JENNIFER; Rocky Grove HS; Cooperstown, PA; (3); 11/81; VP Church Yth Grp; Cmnty Wkr; Hosp Aide; Service Clb; SADD; Yrbk Bus Mgr; Yrbk Ed-Chief; Drama Clb; Library Aide; Chorus; HOBY Ldrshp Awd 85-86; Cert Awd Cnsqtv Acdmc Excllnc 86; Plq Acdmc Excllnc 86; CPA.

RICE, JODIE; Peters Township HS; Mcmurray, PA; (3); Yrbk Stf.

RICE, JOHN; Peters Township HS; Mcmurray, PA; (4); JV Var Ftbl; U Pittsburgh; Bus.

RICE, KARLA; Bishop Conwell HS; Penndel, PA; (4); 2/263; Spanish Clb; Stage Crew; High Hon Roll; NHS; Prfct Atten Awd; Soroptomists Intl Merit Awd 87; Awd Excel Soc Studies 87; Cert Archdcsn Acadc Hnr 87; Holy Family; Elem Ed.

RICE, LARA; Seneca Valley HS; Harmony, PA; (3); GAA; JV Sftbl; Hon Roll; Advertising.

RICE, MARK; Susquenita HS; Duncannon, PA; (3); 1/200; Pres Spanish Clb; Var L Bsbl; JV L Socr; Cit Awd; High Hon Roll; Pres NHS; VFW Awd; Mid Penn III All ST Ptchr 87; Pltcl Sci.

RICE, MICHAEL Z; Ferndale HS; Johnstown, PA; (3); 3/90; Am Leg Boys St; Computer Clb; VP Ski Clb; Band; Yrbk Phtg; Rep Stu Cncl; Bsbl; Stat Bsktbl; High Hon Roll; NHS; Coached Little Lgu Bsbl Won Champshp 85; Pittsburgh U; Pre Dentstry.

RICE, NANCE; Pocono Mountain SR HS; Tobyhanna, PA; (4); 40/350; SADD; JV Var Powder Puff Ftbl; Hon Roll; Acad Excllnc 85-6; Acad Achvt 83-4 & 86-7; Lackawanna JC; Radio Comm.

RICE, RENEE; Freeland HS; Freeland, PA; (3); Church Yth Grp; Pep Clb; Chorus; School Musical; Nwsp Rptr; Yrbk Stf; Rep Soph Cls; Stu Cncl; Capt Cheerleading; Coach Actv; Med Tech.

RICE JR, REX P; Beaver Area HS; Beaver, PA; (2); Art Clb; Trs Church Yth Grp; French Clb; Im Bsktbl; JV Ftbl; JV Trk; Im Wt Lftg; AF.

RICE JR, RICHARD; Portage Area HS; Portage, PA; (3); 4/109; Pres Jr Cls; Rep Stu Cncl; JV Bsktbl; JV Ftbl; Diving; Hon Roll.

RICE, RUSSELL; Pennsbury HS; Yardley, PA; (4); 181/777; Boy Scts; Church Yth Grp; Stage Crew; Var Bowling; Bloomsburg U; Acctng.

RICE, SHARON; South Side HS; Georgetown, PA; (3); 16/140; FBLA; Teachers Aide; Varsity Clb; Yrbk Rptr; Yrbk Stf; L Vllybl; High Hon Roll; NHS.

RICE, STANLEY G; Mon Valley Catholic HS; Monongahela, PA; (3); 30/100; French Hon Soc; Hon Roll; Scndry Ed.

RICE, WENDY JO; Elizabethtown Area HS; Elizabethtown, PA; (3); 35/224; French Clb; Natl Sci Olympiad Awd 87; Bus.

RICH, DAVID S; Akiba Hebrew Acad; Philadelphia, PA; (4); Temple Yth Grp; Nwsp Rptr; Var Capt Crs Cntry; Var Capt Wrstlng; High Hon Roll; Ntl Merit SF; Harvard Alumni Assn Bk Awd 85; Crss Cntry Mst Valuable Rnnr 85-86; Rnnr Up PA Jersey Crss Cntry Chmpn; Liberal Arts.

RICH, JOSEPH; Notre Dame HS; Easton, PA; (3); 30/98; Var Bsbl; Im Bsktbl; Var Ftbl; Im Swmmng; Im Wt Lftg; Hon Roll; Outstndg Efrt Bio 85-86; Outstndg Efrt Spnsh II 86-87; East Stroudsburg ST; Bio Educ.

RICH, SONJA; Lock Haven SR HS; Woolrich, PA; (3); Church Yth Grp; Spanish Clb; Sec Band; Sec Chorus; Cheerleading; Sftbl; Trk; Beta Sigma Phi Awd Mst Dsrvng 9th Grd Grl 84-85; Physcl Thrpy.

RICH, WENDY JEAN; Lewisburg Area HS; Lewisburg, PA; (4); 3/155; Church Yth Grp; Acpl Chr; Chorus; School Musical; School Play; Ed Lit Mag; Var JV Cheerleading; Hon Roll; NHS; Am Leg Aux Girls St; PA Govrns Schl For Arts & Theater 86; Rotary Stu 86; Lorraine Grenoble Awd For Theatre 87; Amherst Coll; Eng.

RICHARD, KATIE; Newport HS; Wila, PA; (4); 16/93; Pres Church Yth Grp; Sec 4-H; Concert Band; Mrchg Band; Pep Band; School Play; Ed Yrbk Stf; Sftbl; Hon Roll; Tri-M Modern Music Mastrs Hist 86-87; PYEA VP 85-87; IN U; Cmmcntns.

RICHARD, MELISSA; Crestwood JR/Sr HS; White Haven, PA; (4); FBLA; Key Clb; SADD; Chorus; Mgr(s); Score Keeper; High Hon Roll; Hon Roll; NEDT Awd; Pres Acad Ftns Awd 87; Avtn.

RICHARDI, DANIELLE; William Allen HS; Allentown, PA; (3); Church Yth Grp; SADD; Chorus; Flag Corp; Mrchg Band; Orch; Twrlr; Hon Roll; NHS.

RICHARDS, AMY; Beaver Area HS; Beaver, PA; (3); JCL; Key Clb; Chorus; Church Choir; High Hon Roll; Acadc Hnr Awd 86-87; Nrsng.

RICHARDS, BRIAN; Milton Area SR HS; Milton, PA; (2); Boy Scts; Latin Clb; Band; Concert Band; Drm & Bgl; Mrchg Band; Pep Band; God Cntry Awd; Hon Roll; Natl Lat Hnr Soc 86-87; Math.

RICHARDS, CRAIG; Bald Eagle Area HS; Howard, PA; (4); Boy Scts; Church Yth Grp; Church Choir; Trk; Wrstlng; Hon Roll; PA DE Dist Yth Schl & Royal Ranger Assn Commander 87; Vly Forge Christian Coll; Pstrl.

RICHARDS, DANIEL; Brockway Area HS; Brockport, PA; (3); 2/110; Math Tm; Varsity Clb; Var Bsbl; Var Capt Golf; Hon Roll; NHS; PA Free Enterprise Wk 87; JR Marshall Cmmncmnt 87; Penn ST; Math.

RICHARDS, DAVID; Loyalsock Township HS; Montoursville, PA; (3); Church Yth Grp; Nwsp Rptr; Nwsp Sprt Ed; JV Bsktbl; Im Bowling; Var L Golf; High Hon Roll; Hon Roll; Gifted Pgm; PA ST; Mass Cmmnctns.

RICHARDS, DOUG; Trinity HS; Eighty Four, PA; (3); French Clb; Band; Drill Tm; Mrchg Band; MBA Cls AA 1st Pl Akron OH 85; WVU; Psych.

RICHARDS, JENNIFER; Methacton HS; Audubon, PA; (3); Church Yth Grp; Debate Tm; Key Clb; SADD; Varsity Clb; Chorus; Yrbk Sprt Ed; Yrbk Stf; Off Frsh Cls; Off Soph Cls; Engrng.

RICHARDS, JENNIFER; Wyoming Valley West HS; Kingston, PA; (3); 12/416; Church Yth Grp; Key Clb; Ski Clb; Cit Awd; High Hon Roll; NHS; NEDT Awd; Sftbl; Var Swmmng; Var Trk; Psych.

RICHARDS, JODI; South Park HS; Library, PA; (3); 17/223; Political Wkr; Concert Band; Mrchg Band; Nwsp Rptr; Socr; High Hon Roll; Hon Roll; NHS; Cmnty Wkr; GAA; Outstndng Acad Achvt Scholar Awd 86; Amer Red Crs Vlntr Svc Yth Pgm 85; Pitt-Allegheny Cty 1st Aid; PA ST; Elec Engrng.

RICHARDS, KAREN F; Peters Township HS; Venetia, PA; (2); Trs Church Yth Grp; L Color Guard; Yrbk Phtg; Trs Stu Cncl; L Mgr(s); Timer; High Hon Roll; Hon Roll; Spanish NHS; Spirit Awd-Silks Sqd-Hghst Awd 86-87; Intl Law.

RICHARDS, KIRK; Kennedy Christian HS; Farrell, PA; (3); 30/97; Boy Scts; Church Yth Grp; NAACP; Pep Clb; Spanish Clb; Chorus; Concert Band; Im Bsktbl; Im Bowling; Var L Ftbl; Comp.

RICHARDS, MARK; Laurel Valley HS; New Florence, PA; (4); AFS; Varsity Clb; Chorus; Trs Sr Cls; Off Stu Cncl; Var L Bsbl; Var L Bsktbl; Var L Ftbl; Powder Puff Ftbl; Im Vllybl; USMC Dstngshd Athl Awd 87; IN U PA; Comp Sci.

RICHARDS, MICHAEL H; Bishop Mc Devitt HS; Harrisburg, PA; (3); Science Clb; Yrbk Stf; Var Socr; Swmmng; Hstry Day Awd 86; Frgn Lang Inst Schlrshp 87; Marine Phys Ftnss Team 84-87; Sci Fair Awds 85-86; Penn ST U; Med.

RICHARDS, MICHELLE; Middletown Area HS; Middletown, PA; (3); 24/193; Office Aide; Im Vllybl; Hon Roll; Dntl Hygenist.

RICHARDS, NICOLE; Bradford Central Christian HS; Bradford, PA; (3); 2/26; Computer Clb; French Clb; Letterman Clb; Pep Clb; Ski Clb; VP Stu Cncl; Var Bsktbl; Var Sftbl; High Hon Roll; Jr NHS; US Stdnt Cncl Awd, Ntl Merit Awd Sci 86; Hugh O Brien Ldrshp Awd 85; Bus.

RICHARDS, RAHN; Tri-Valley JR-SR HS; Hegins, PA; (4); 30/74; Boy Scts; Cmnty Wkr; Red Cross Aide; Chorus; School Musical; Hst Jr Cls; Hst Sr Cls; Var L Ftbl; Hon Roll; NEDT Awd; All Star Twin Vly Tm Ftbl 85; Temple U; Pre-Med.

RICHARDS, STACY; Hempfield HS; Lancaster, PA; (3); 119/393; Dance Clb; Variety Show; Rep Frsh Cls; Rep Soph Cls; Hst Jr Cls; Rep Sr Cls; Var Capt Cheerleading; High Hon Roll; Schlstc Art Awd; Mss Tn PA Hmsphr 86-87.

RICHARDSON, AMY; Uniontown Area HS; Smock, PA; (3); 25/385; Cmnty Wkr; JA; VP Ski Clb; Spanish Clb; Band; Yrbk Stf; High Hon Roll; NHS; Spanish NHS; Outstdng 4-H Awd 85; Pitt U; Physcl Thrpy.

RICHARDSON, CHRIS; West Middlesex Area JR/Sr HS; West Middlesex, PA; (4); Office Aide; Stu Cncl; Var Bsktbl; Hon Roll; Jr NHS; VP NHS; Spanish NHS; Degree Of Hnr Schlrshp 87; Pres Schlrshp Kent ST 87-91; Kent ST U; Aerospac Flght Tech.

RICHARDSON, CRYSTAL; Cardinal Ohara HS; Chester, PA; (2); 209/647; Office Aide; Spanish Clb; Church Choir; Hon Roll; Med Dr.

RICHARDSON, DAWN; Marion Center Area HS; Rochester Mills, PA; (3); Trs 4-H; FBLA; Girl Scts; Bus Mngmnt.

RICHARDSON, DAWN; West Middlesex HS; West Middlesex, PA; (3); 23/108; Sec French Clb; JA; Band; Chorus; Church Choir; Concert Band; Mrchg Band; Pep Band; Sftbl; Trk; Ntl Hnr Rll 86; Kent ST U; Tchng.

RICHARDSON, DORI; South Allegheny HS; Mckeesport, PA; (3); Church Yth Grp; JA; Library Aide; Office Aide; Pres Chorus; School Play; Cheerleading; Powder Puff Ftbl; NHS; Hon Choir 87; 1st Pl Talent Show Singing 87; Bus Adm.

RICHARDSON, ERIC A; Bishop Kenrick HS; Collegeville, PA; (4); 6/287; Rep Frsh Cls; Rep Soph Cls; Rep Jr Cls; Pres Sr Cls; Pres Stu Cncl; Var Capt Swmmng; Var Capt Tennis; Bausch & Lomb Sci Awd; NHS; Prfct Atten Awd; Century III Ldrs Schl Wnnr 86; Norristown Exchg Club Yth Of Yr Awd 85, Rotary Club Ldrshp Camp 86; William & Mary; Finance.

RICHARDSON, JAMES; Haverford SR HS; Havertown, PA; (3); 25/423; Boy Scts; Chess Clb; Church Yth Grp; Cmnty Wkr; Ski Clb; Orch; Bsbl; Crs Cntry; Trk; NHS.

RICHARDSON, JENNIFER L; Christian School Of York; Manchester, MD; (3); Chorus; Yrbk Stf; Trs Frsh Cls; Trs Soph Cls; L Cheerleading; Hon Roll; W MD Coll; Pol Sci.

RICHARDSON, JOHN; Lampeter-Strasburg HS; Lampeter, PA; (3); 9/148; Boy Scts; Varsity Clb; Band; Concert Band; Mrchg Band; Pres Stu Cncl; Var Socr; Var Wrstlng; NHS; Engrng.

RICHARDSON, LISA; Henderson HS; West Chester, PA; (3); 7/377; Church Yth Grp; Ski Clb; Crs Cntry; Fld Hcky; Sftbl; French Hon Soc; High Hon Roll.

RICHARDSON, PATRICK; Central Bucks West HS; Chalfont, PA; (3); 7/481; Boy Scts; Math Tm; Science Clb; Bausch & Lomb Sci Awd; High Hon Roll; Ntl Merit SF; Pres Schlr; Contntl Math Leag 84-85; Ntl Sci Olympiad-Physcs & Chem 86-87; Engrng.

RICHARDSON, TAMARA; Harrisburg HS; Harrisburg, PA; (3); 46/265; ROTC; Chorus; Concert Band; Mrchg Band; Rep Stu Cncl; Hon Roll; Shppnsburg U; Accntng.

RICHARDSON, THOMAS; Emmaus HS; Emmaus, PA; (3); 16/548; German Clb; Key Clb; Latin Clb; Rep Soph Cls; Swmmng; NHS; Trk; High Hon Roll; Jr NHS; Opt Clb Awd; Med.

RICHARDSON, WORENA; West Middlesex HS; West Middlesex, PA; (2); Church Yth Grp; Hosp Aide; Spanish Clb; Band; Concert Band; Mrchg Band; Pep Band; Bsktbl; Trk; High Hon Roll; Bus.

RICHARDSON, YVETTE; Bishop Mc Devitt HS; Harrisburg, PA; (2); Hosp Aide; Church Choir; Cheerleading; Cornell U; OB Gyn.

RICHART, KAREN LYNN; Muncy JR/Sr HS; Muncy, PA; (2); Art Clb; Dance Clb; VP French Clb; Hosp Aide; Varsity Clb; Band; Stu Cncl; Bsktbl; JV Capt Cheerleading; Hon Roll; U Pittsburgh; Phy Thrpy.

RICHART, MICHAEL; Milton SR HS; Milton, PA; (3); Church Yth Grp; Drama Clb; Spanish Clb; Stu Cncl; Hon Roll; Southeastern Bible Coll; Pastrl.

RICHART, MICHELLE; Muncy HS; Muncy, PA; (4); Spanish Clb; Varsity Clb; Concert Band; Mrchg Band; School Play; Yrbk Stf; Stu Cncl; Bsktbl; Co-Capt Cheerleading; Off Spanish NHS; US Air Force.

RICHE, CHERYL; Warren Area HS; Warren, PA; (3); Church Yth Grp; Drama Clb; Spanish Clb; Chorus; School Play; Hon Roll; Cmnctns.

RICHELL, DANA; West Allegheny HS; Oakdale, PA; (2); 4/210; Church Yth Grp; JA; Spanish Clb; Color Guard; Lit Mag; Off Stu Cncl; High Hon Roll; Lbrl Arts.

RICHET JR, CURTIS L; Norristown Area HS; Norristown, PA; (4); Pres Church Yth Grp; Intnl Clb; Math Clb; Stu Cncl; Var Bsktbl; Hon Roll; NHS; Teachers Awd 85; Engrng.

RICHETTA, KERRI; Crestwood HS; Mountain Top, PA; (3); Ski Clb; Sec Soph Cls; Rep Stu Cncl; Var Cheerleading; Sftbl; High Hon Roll; Hon Roll; Bus.

RICHEY, ALISON; Ringgold HS; Monongahela, PA; (3); Church Yth Grp; Drama Clb; JA; Office Aide; Chorus; School Musical; Yrbk Phtg; Yrbk Stf; Off Soph Cls; Hon Roll; WVU; Bus.

RICHEY, NICOLE; Leechburg Area HS; Leechburg, PA; (3); Art Clb; Hon Roll; Hnbl Mntn In Art Cntst 85; Comp Sci.

RICHEY, VICKY; Gateway SR HS; Monroeville, PA; (2); Orch; Hon Roll; Pastry Chef.

RICHIE, RAMI; Parkland HS; Easton, PA; (3); Church Yth Grp; JCL; Latin Clb; JV Ftbl; JV Var Wrstlng; Hon Roll; Pres Church Teen Orgnztn 87-88; Chem Engr.

RICHMOND, CHRISTINE; Jim Thorpe Area HS; Jim Thorpe, PA; (3); 13/106; FHA; German Clb; Ski Clb; Chorus; Nwsp Stf; Yrbk Stf; Cheerleading; High Hon Roll; Hon Roll; Law.

RICHMOND, DEBORAH; Tunkhannock HS; Tunkhannock, PA; (3); 93/310; JA; Spanish Clb; Capt Flag Corp; Rep Jr Cls; Hon Roll; USAF; Pblc Rltns.

RICHMOND, JAY; Mc Guffey HS; Claysville, PA; (4); 11/201; Boy Scts; Model UN; Pep Clb; VP Spanish Clb; Golf; High Hon Roll; Hon Roll; NHS; Acad All Amer Awd 85-86; Cert Of Acad Exclinc 85-86.

RICHMOND, KELLY; Nazareth Acad; Phila, PA; (3); Alumni Assn Schlrshp 84-86; Natl Chmpnshp Arabian Hrs Shw 86; U Of DE; Vet.

RICHNAFSKY, LISA; Clairton HS; Clairton, PA; (3); 18/110; Dance Clb; Hosp Aide; Drm Mjr(t); Twrlr; High Hon Roll; Hon Roll; NHS; Physcl Thrpy.

RICHNER, JEFF; Centre County Christian Acad; Bellefonte, PA; (4); 2/11; Church Yth Grp; Drama Clb; Teachers Aide; Church Choir; School Play; VP Sr Cls; Var Socr; Sal; Roll Hnr 86-87; Pres Awd 86-87; Phil Coll Of Bible; Educ.

RICHTER, ADAM; Reading SR HS; Reading, PA; (3); 41/720; Aud/Vis; Var Debate Tm; Model UN; Quiz Bowl; Nwsp Rptr; Yrbk Stf; Jrnlst.

RICHTER, AMY; Connellsville Area SR HS; Normalville, PA; (3); Church Yth Grp; German Clb; Teachers Aide; Band; Swmmng; DAR Awd; Hon Roll; Germn Hnr Soc 86-87; Med.

RICHTER, MARK; Meadville Area SR HS; Meadville, PA; (2); German Clb; Latin Clb; Radio Clb; Science Clb; Hon Roll; Frgn Lang Comp Awd Ger 87; Oral Comprhnsn Ger Culture 87; Allegheny Coll; Meteorlgy.

RICHWALSKI, LISA; Pleasant Valley HS; Brodheadsville, PA; (3); Math Tm; High Hon Roll; Hon Roll; Sec NHS; Top Acad Avg Cls 84-86; Elem Ed.

RICHWINE, MARK; Northern York County HS; Dillsburg, PA; (4); 10/210; VP Band; VP Chorus; Jazz Band; Orch; School Musical; Tennis; NHS; Ntl Merit SF; Pres Schlr; Church Yth Grp; Music Hnr Soc VP 86-87; IN U; Music Perf.

RICHWINE, TINA; Carlisle SR HS; Gardners, PA; (3); 12/467; Pep Clb; Band; Concert Band; Mrchg Band; School Musical; Swing Chorus; High Hon Roll; Hon Roll; NHS; Cmmnctns.

RICK II, DAVID T; Hamburg Area HS; Hamburg, PA; (4); 40/144; Rep Latin Clb; VP Spanish Clb; Rep Sr Cls; VP Stu Cncl; JV Var Bowling; JV Im Socr; Hon Roll; JC Awd; NHS; Acad Ltr Awds Worlt Cultures & Amer Hist 85-86; Most Spirit SR John W Ebling Mem Awd 86-87; Shippensburg U; Soc Stud.

RICKARD, KIMBERLY; Glendale HS; Blandburg, PA; (3); 24/73; Sec Pres Church Yth Grp; Drama Clb; Library Aide; Science Clb; SADD; Band; Chorus; Nwsp Stf; Hon Roll; Legl Sec.

RICKARD, LANCE; Clarion Area HS; Sligo, PA; (3); Church Yth Grp; FCA; Var L Ftbl; Wt Lftg; Rotary Awd.

RICKARD, NANCY; Churchill HS; Braddock, PA; (2); 43/222; Acpl Chr; Chorus; School Musical; Hon Roll; Gifted Prog 85.

RICKENBACH, HEATHER; Cumberland Valley HS; Mechanicsburg, PA; (3); Model UN; Band; Mrchg Band; Symp Band; Trs Frsh Cls; VP Soph Cls; VP Jr Cls; Rep Sr Cls; VP Stu Cncl; JV Fld Hcky; U Of TN; Bus Admin.

RICKER, PAUL M; Mt Lebanon SR HS; Mt Lebanon, PA; (4); 1/500; Computer Clb; NFL; Science Clb; Lit Mag; High Hon Roll; Ntl Merit SF; Spanish NHS; Val; PA Gvrnrs Schl For Sci 85; 1st Awd PA JR Acad Of Sci 86; Wstnghse Sci Hnrs Inst 86-87; Cornell U; Astrphyscs.

RICKERT, AMY SUE; Schuylkill Valley HS; Mohrsville, PA; (4); 15/132; Church Yth Grp; FTA; Teachers Aide; Chorus; Capt Flag Corp; School Play; Yrbk Stf; Var Trk; Hon Roll; NHS; O S Rothenberger Mem Awd 87; Santilli Oil Co Spnsh Awd 87; Presdntl Acadc Ftns Awd 87; Millersville U; Spnsh Ed.

RICKERT, ANDREW P; Phil-Mont Christian Acad; Ardsley, PA; (2); Church Yth Grp; CAP; Sec Frsh Cls; JV Socr; High Hon Roll; Hon Roll; Temple U.

RICKERT, JILL MARIE; Meadville Area SR HS; Meadville, PA; (4); 143/290; Chorus; JV Var Socr; Hon Roll; Dist Chorus Fest 84-87; Regnl Chorus Fest 85-87; Acad All Amer Awd 85-86; Natl Choral Awd 86-87; Point Park Coll; Bus Mgmt.

RICKERT, SCOTT; Daniel Boone HS; Douglassville, PA; (2); Boy Scts; Church Yth Grp; French Clb; VP SADD; Chorus; Church Choir; Mrchg Band; Nwsp Bus Mgr; Off Stu Cncl; God Cntry Awd; Outstndng Vocalist Awd 83; Frnch Cmpttn 1st Pl 86; Music.

RICKETTS, CONSTANCE; Moshannon Valley HS; Irvona, PA; (4); Hosp Aide; Spanish Clb; SADD; Chorus; School Play; Cntrl PA Schl Nrsng; Nrsng.

RICKETTS, JULIA; Sacred Heart HS; Pittsburgh, PA; (3); High Hon Roll; NHS; Cmnty Wkr; French Clb; Dnfth Awd; Ntl Merit Ltr; Time Magazine-Natl Stu Editorial Cntst-Fnlst Awd & Carnegie Mellon U Art Pgm Schlrshp 87; Fine Arts.

RICKETTS, LAURA; North Hills HS; Pittsburgh, PA; (3); 9/488; Church Yth Grp; Debate Tm; Drama Clb; French Clb; Hosp Aide; Keywanettes; Thesps; School Play; High Hon Roll; NHS.

RICKRODE JR, STEVEN; Cumberland Valley HS; Mechanicsburg, PA; (3); 106/575; Church Yth Grp; Color Guard; Concert Band; Drm Mjr(t); Jazz Band; Mrchg Band; School Play; Symp Band; Lit Mag; High Hon Roll; Hon Mntn Schlstc Wrtng Awds 87; Air Force.

RICKRODE, TRACY; Carlisle SR HS; Carlisle, PA; (3); JA; VP Key Clb; Color Guard; Mrchg Band; Hon Roll; Art Hnr Soc 86-88; Elem Educ.

RIDALL, GINA; Tunkhannock HS; Mehoopany, PA; (3); Church Yth Grp; Cmnty Wkr; FHA; JA; Office Aide; Spanish Clb; SADD; Hon Roll; Key Degr FHA 85; Trvl Agnt.

RIDDELL, SHERRI; Montgomery Area JR SR HS; Allenwood, PA; (4); 7/63; Church Yth Grp; French Clb; Library Aide; Band; Church Choir; Nwsp Stf; L Bsktbl; Hon Roll; JC Awd; NHS; Band Parents Awd 87; Lack Haven U; Scndry Math.

RIDDERHOFF, AMY; Sch Haven Area HS; Sch Haven, PA; (2); 8/102; Chorus; Concert Band; Mrchg Band; Yrbk Phtg; Yrbk Sprt Ed; Crs Cntry; Diving; Swmmng; Trk; Hon Roll; All Stars Tm Crs Cntry Awd 86-87; Leag Meet Crs Cntry Medallion Awd 86-87; 2nd Rnnrup Nwsp Car 86-87.

RIDDLE, DEBORAH; Villa Maria Acad; Erie, PA; (3); Church Yth Grp; Cmnty Wkr; Science Clb; Church Choir; JV Trk; Hon Roll; Accntng.

RIDDLE, JAMES; St John Neumann HS; Philadelphia, PA; (3); 3/350; Var L Ftbl; Var Trk; Var Wt Lftg; High Hon Roll; Hon Roll; NHS; Prfct Atten Awd; Norbetine Schlrshp 84-88; Engr.

RIDER, CLINT; Bellefonte HS; Pleasant Gap, PA; (4); 22/232; German Clb; Tennis; High Hon Roll; Bus Admin Fin Awd 87; Pres Acad Ftns Awd 87; Bloomsburg ST U; Accntng.

RIDER, LINETTA; Juniata HS; Mifflintown, PA; (4); Church Yth Grp; Sec Chorus; School Musical; Stu Cncl; Vllybl; High Hon Roll; NHS; Pres Schlr; Voice Dem Awd; Girl Scts; Juniata Cnty Educ Assn Eductn Awd 87; Schlstc J 85-87; Lock Haven U; Elem Educ.

RIDER, WILLIAM; Bishop Neumann HS; Williamsport, PA; (3); Art Clb; Pres Church Yth Grp; Drama Clb; FBLA; Model UN; NFL; School Musical; School Play; Hon Roll; Rotary Awd; Chrmn Crdntr Rcgntn Annctn Yth Grp 85; Old Dmncn Mdl UN 87; Harvard U Mdl Cngrss 87; Arch Engrng.

RIDGLEY, TROY; Ambridge Area HS; Baden, PA; (3); FCA; German Clb; Pep Clb; Var Capt Ftbl; Var Capt Wrstlng; Hon Roll; Army Rsrv All Amer Tm-Ftbl 87; FCA Pres 87; Schlrshp-Notre Dame, Ftbl 87; Notre Dame; Med.

RIDLEHOOVER, MELISSA C; Downingtown Area SR HS; Chester Spgs, PA; (3); Church Yth Grp; French Clb; Teachers Aide; Im Vllybl; NEDT Awd; Engr.

RIDRIGUEZ, TIMOTHY J; Mon Valley Catholic HS; Belle Vernon, PA; (4); Letterman Clb; Spanish Clb; Teachers Aide; Varsity Clb; Variety Show; Var Bsbl; Var Bsktbl; L Var Golf; Powder Puff Ftbl; NHS; Hugh O Brien Awd 84; Bushnell Sci Awd 86; Engrng.

RIDZON, ROCHELLE; Crestwood HS; Wapwallopen, PA; (3); High Hon Roll; Hon Roll; Perfect Attnd 76-84; Advncd Coll Prep; Teacher.

RIECK, AMY; Chambersburg Area HS; Fayetteville, PA; (2); 13/735; VP Church Yth Grp; JCL; Latin Clb; SADD; Chorus; Church Choir; Orch; Off Stu Cncl; Var Cheerleading; Hon Roll; Dnstry.

RIECKS, SHANNON; Bethlehem Center SR HS; Clarksville, PA; (4); 25/165; Church Yth Grp; Drama Clb; Spanish Clb; Stage Crew; Socr; Wrstlng; Hon Roll; Waynesburg Coll; Chem Engr.

RIEDE, TREENA; Cumberland Valley HS; Mechanicsburg, PA; (3); Chorus; Hon Roll; Trvl Agnt.

RIEDE, VICCI L; Grove City HS; Grove City, PA; (4); 5/199; Church Yth Grp; Sec Key Clb; Pres Science Clb; Ski Clb; Band; Concert Band; Mrchg Band; School Play; Yrbk Stf; VP Frsh Cls; Hmcmng Crt 86-87; Wntrfstvl Crt 85-86; La Roche; Intr Dsgn.

RIEDEL, RICHARD; W B Saul HS; Philadelphia, PA; (4); 97/143; Boy Scts; FFA; Red Cross Aide; Ice Hcky; Wt Lftg; Eagle Sct 85; Temple U; Envrnmntl Sci.

RIEDEL, SEAN; J P Mc Caskey HS; Lancaster, PA; (4); 10/400; Pres FBLA; Rep Sr Cls; Rep Stu Cncl; Hon Roll; NHS; Pres Schlr; Frnkln & Marshll Coll; Sck Brkr.

RIEG, VICKI; Du Bois Area HS; Dubois, PA; (3); Library Aide; SADD; L Trk; Acctg.

RIEGNER, DOUGLAS; Seton La Salle HS; Pittsburgh, PA; (2); Church Yth Grp; Cmnty Wkr; Exploring; Ski Clb; Bsktbl; JV Ftbl; Mgr(s); Score Keeper; Coaches Bsktbll Awd 85; Lw Enfrcmnt.

RIEGNER, MICHELLE; Northwestern Lehigh HS; Germansville, PA; (3); 15/139; Debate Tm; School Musical; School Play; High Hon Roll; Hon Roll; Accntng I Rcgntn Awd 86-87; Vrsty Ltr-Shcl Plays 86-87; Law.

RIEHL, GARY; Hamburg Area HS; Strausstown, PA; (4); 63/144; Hon Roll; Stu Of The Quarter-Berks Vo Tech 86-87; Penn ST U; Engrng.

RIEK, MICHAEL; Bishop Mc Cort HS; Johnstown, PA; (3); Aud/Vis; Latin Clb; Chorus; Church Choir; School Musical; Stage Crew; JV Ftbl; Im Vllybl.

RIEKER, MICHAEL; Annville Cleona HS; Cleona, PA; (4); CAP; German Clb; Hosp Aide; Latin Clb; Red Cross Aide; JV Crs Cntry; Kiwanis Awd; Stage Crew; JV Trk; Im Vllybl; Hugh O Brian Ldrshp Awd; Natl Ldrshp & Svc Awd; Latin Excell Awd; Penn ST U; Nrsng Admin.

RIEPPEL, KIM; Cowanesque Valley HS; Cowanesque, PA; (4); 3/80; Quiz Bowl; SADD; Yrbk Rptr; Yrbk Stf; Stat Bsktbl; Capt Tennis; High Hon Roll; Hon Roll; NHS; Acad Ltr, Pin & Cert; Lycoming Coll; Accntng.

RIES, CATHYANN; Nazareth Acad; Philadelphia, PA; (4); German Clb; VP Girl Scts; Math Clb; Math Tm; Model UN; NFL; Speech Tm; Mgr Stage Crew; Im Vllybl; NHS; La Salle U Full Schlrshp 87; Kings Coll Partial Schlrshp 87; Girl Scout Silver, Ldrshp Awds 87; La Salle U; Bio.

RIESER, SUSAN; Burrell SR HS; Lower Burrell, PA; (3); Camera Clb; Church Yth Grp; Cmnty Wkr; French Clb; School Play; Ed Nwsp Ed-Chief; Yrbk Phtg; Ed Lit Mag; Trk; Jr NHS; Jrnlsm.

RIFE, JULIE; Chambersburg Area SR HS; Chambersburg, PA; (3); 93/697; AFS; Spanish Clb; Nwsp Stf; Hon Roll; Prtcptd Smmr AFS Prog Swtzrland 87.

RIFE, JULIE; Eastern York HS; Wrightsvlle, PA; (2); Latin Clb; Varsity Clb; Sec Soph Cls; Var Cheerleading; Var Gym; JV Sftbl; Var JV Vllybl; Hon Roll; Vet Asst.

RIFFANY, MICHELE; Hallstead Christian Acad; Hallstead, PA; (3); 1/3; Yrbk Bus Mgr; Yrbk Ed-Chief; Var L Bsktbl; Var Capt Cheerleading; Var L Vllybl; High Hon Roll; Drama Clb; Chorus; School Play; Yrbk Stf; Secndry Educ.

RIFKIN, STACEY; Wyoming Valley West HS; Kingston, PA; (4); 16/397; FBLA; Key Clb; Library Aide; Pep Clb; Ski Clb; VP Temple Yth Grp; Chorus; Lit Mag; JV Var Cheerleading; Var L Tennis; Natl Cncl Yth Ldrshp 85-86; U Of Scranton; Pre Med.

RIGATTI, RHEA; St Francis Acad; Bethel Park, PA; (2); 1/50; Hosp Aide; Pep Clb; Service Clb; School Musical; School Play; Rep Stu Cncl; Cheerleading; Gym; Hon Roll; Schl Sci Awd 86; Chem Engrng.

RIGBY, LAUREL; Corry Area HS; Spring Creek, PA; (4); 5/193; French Clb; Band; Concert Band; Mrchg Band; Pep Band; Rep Sr Cls; Rep Stu Cncl; High Hon Roll; Hon Roll; Bus & Prfsnl Wmns Grl Mnth 86; Fisher Allen Schlrshp 87; Barbara Wojcienhowski Schlrshp 87; Bradford Bus Schl; Accntng.

RIGBY, MIKE; North Pocano HS; Moscow, PA; (3); 11/260; Ski Clb; Variety Show; Nwsp Stf; Capt Vllybl; NHS; Physics.

RIGGIN, BETH; Connellsville Area HS; Dawson, PA; (4); Church Yth Grp; FBLA; FTA; Office Aide; Chorus; School Play; Yrbk Stf; High Hon Roll; NHS; Seton Hill Coll; Elem Tchg.

RIGGIN, JULIE; Uniontown Area SR HS; Chalk Hill, PA; (3); French Clb; Latin Clb; Letterman Clb; SADD; Concert Band; Mrchg Band; Pres Jr Cls; Var L Sftbl; Capt Twrlr; High Hon Roll; Wrtng Awd Hrld Stndrd Nwspaper 86; Psych.

RIGGIN, MARCIA; Connellsville SR HS; Dawson, PA; (1); Church Yth Grp; Pep Clb; Chorus; Church Choir; Rep Stu Cncl; Klorth Fayette; Mgr.

RIGGLE, CARRIE L; Leechburg Area HS; Leechburg, PA; (4); 14/84; Drama Clb; JA; Office Aide; Band; School Play; Nwsp Rptr; Nwsp Stf; Yrbk Stf; JV Var Cheerleading; Pres Schlr; Grove City Coll; Psych.

RIGGS, DENNIS; Mc Guffey HS; Washington, PA; (4); 91/214; Boy Scts; Church Yth Grp; German Clb; Ski Clb; Chorus; School Musical; School Play; Stage Crew; Crs Cntry; Trk; Army; Nuclr Engr.

RIGGS, LINDA RAE; North Allegheny HS; Bradford Woods, PA; (3); Cmnty Wkr; Sec VICA; School Musical; School Play; Prfct Atten Awd.

RIGGS, STEPHANIE J; Warriar Run HS; Turbotville, PA; (4); 4/160; Concert Band; Mrchg Band; Orch; School Musical; Nwsp Stf; Yrbk Stf; NHS; Ntl Merit SF; FNA; Acad All-Amer 87; Messiah Coll; Nrsng.

RIGHTER, REBECCA; Blue Mountain Acad; Hamburg, PA; (2); Library Aide; Teachers Aide; Band; Concert Band; High Hon Roll; Hon Roll; Andrews U; Nrsg.

RIHEL, KRISTINE; Harborcreek JR SR HS; Erie, PA; (3); 8/236; Girl Scts; Model UN; ROTC; Band; Mrchg Band; Pep Band; Variety Show; Swmmng; Hon Roll; Yrbk Stf; Regionl Schl Excellnce Envirnmntl Sci 87; Biomed Sci.

RIKER, CANDACE; Upper Dublin HS; Maple Glenn, PA; (4); 27/318; Aud/Vis; FBLA; Radio Clb; JV Lcrss; JV Tennis; NHS; Pres Schlr; Intnl Clb; Drxls Pres Frshmn Schlrshp 87; Brnhrst Awd 87; Prmsng Wrtr Awd 87; Drexel U; Int Dsgn.

RIKER, JULIE P; Cumberland Valley HS; Mechanicsburg, PA; (4); 56/516; VP Orch; NHS; Art Clb; Church Yth Grp; Key Clb; Spanish Clb; Chorus; Mrchg Band; School Musical; Hon Roll; PA All ST Orchstr 87; All Estrn Div Orchstr 87; PA Govrn Schl Arts 85; Natl Art Hon Soc 85-87; PA Coll Of The Arts; Illstrtn.

RIKER, LEANNE L; Corry Area HS; Corry, PA; (3); Drama Clb; German Clb; Office Aide; Band; Concert Band; Mrchg Band; Pep Band; Communications.

RILEY, CHERYL; Greenville HS; Greenville, PA; (1); 1/160; Church Yth Grp; French Clb; Hosp Aide; Office Aide; Chorus; Church Choir; Hon Roll; Acad Gms 86-87; Piano Accmpnst Schl Chr 86-87; Bus.

RILEY, DAN; Jenkintown HS; Jenkintown, PA; (3); 9/36; Drexel U; Engrng.

RILEY III, JAMES; South Philadelphia HS; Philadelphia, PA; (4); 4/775; Teachers Aide; Acpl Chr; Stage Crew; Yrbk Stf; Hon Roll; Comp Prgrmmng.

RILEY, JENNIFER; Elizabethtown Area HS; Elizabethtown, PA; (3); 3/230; Band; Chorus; Concert Band; Mrchg Band; Orch; School Musical; NHS; Math.

RILEY, JOSEPH; Msgr Bonner HS; Lansdowne, PA; (3); 4/282; Pres Church Yth Grp; Var Socr; High Hon Roll; Jr NHS; Prtl Schlrshp Msgr Bnnr HS 84-88; Acad Excllnc Awd AP Erpn Hstry Rlgn II 86; Boston Coll; Busi.

RILEY, KEVIN; Pocono Central Catholic HS; Scotrun, PA; (4); Am Leg Boys St; Church Yth Grp; Ski Clb; Spanish Clb; School Play; Yrbk Bus Mgr; Pres Frsh Cls; Rep Soph Cls; Pres Jr Cls; Rep Sr Cls; Knights Of Columbus John F Kennedy Schlrshp Awd 87; All-Conf Soccer Plyr Awd 87; MVP Soccer 87; St Josephs U; Acctg.

RILEY, KIM; Waynesburg Central HS; Waynesburg, PA; (4); 21/190; French Clb; Natl Beta Clb; Pep Clb; Pres Chorus; Swing Chorus; High Hon Roll; NHS; Natl Schl Choral Awd 87; Waynesburg Coll; Elem Educ.

RILEY, LYNDA; Notre Dame Acad; Villanova, PA; (4); Debate Tm; Drama Clb; SADD; Chorus; School Play; Variety Show; Nwsp Stf; Yrbk Stf; Pres Soph Cls; Pres Jr Cls; Govr Schl For Prfmng Arts Fnlst; PAL Tlnt Srch Wnr; Tlnt Amer Wnr; Theater.

RILEY, SHANNON; Exeter Twp SR HS; Reading, PA; (3); 27/250; Varsity Clb; Y-Teens; School Musical; School Play; Sec Stu Cncl; L Cheerleading; Powder Puff Ftbl; L Trk; High Hon Roll; NHS; Forgn Reltns.

RILEY, SUSAN; Athens HS; Athens, PA; (3); Chorus; High Hon Roll; Prfct Atten Awd; Civics 85; Engl 9 85; Penn ST U; Clncl Bio.

RILEY, TERRI; Karns City HS; Chicora, PA; (3); SADD; Chorus; Yrbk Stf; Sec Pres Stu Cncl; Var Capt Cheerleading; Trk; Hon Roll; Btlr Cnty Jr Mss Fnlst 87; Hmcmng Jr Attndnt 86-87; Comms.

RIM, EDWIN; Cedar Crest HS; Lebanon, PA; (2); 20/350; German Clb; Pep Clb; Orch; School Musical; Hon Roll; NHS.

RIM, REBECCA; Watsontown Christian Acad; Hughesville, PA; (1); 1/11; Church Yth Grp; Chorus; Church Choir; Sec Frsh Cls; Var Socr; Hon Roll.

RIMBEY, JANET; Chartiers Valley HS; Carnegie, PA; (3); Trs Church Yth Grp; Drama Clb; GAA; Girl Scts; School Play; Ed Yrbk Stf; NHS; Elem Ed.

RIMBY, STEVE; Exeter Twp SR HS; Reading, PA; (4); Aud/Vis; Boy Scts; Drama Clb; Varsity Clb; Band; Concert Band; Mrchg Band; School Play; Stage Crew; Lit Mag; Eagl Sct 87; Outstndng Cmnty Svc 87; Milersville U; Brdcstng.

RIMEL, CHRIS; Mt Pleasant Area HS; Acme, PA; (4); 15/240; Letterman Clb; SADD; Varsity Clb; Yrbk Ed-Chief; Rep Frsh Cls; VP Soph Cls; VP Jr Cls; Pres Sr Cls; Rep Stu Cncl; L Bsktbl; St Vincent Coll; Pre-Med.

RIMER, DAVID; Hershey HS; Hummelstown, PA; (3); 107/205; French Clb; Math Tm; School Play; Stage Crew; High Hon Roll; Hon Roll; JV Trk.

RIMER, SHAWNA; Johnsonburg Area HS; Johnsonburg, PA; (3); JV Capt Cheerleading; Prfct Atten Awd; Acadmc All Am 86.

RIMM, JOHN M; Stroudsburg HS; Stroudsburg, PA; (2); 60/317; FBLA; JV Bsktbl; Ftbl; Var Capt Golf; High Hon Roll; Hon Roll.

RIMMEY, SUSAN; Bellefonte Area SR HS; Mingoville, PA; (4); 4/237; Trs Church Yth Grp; Im Vllybl; Hon Roll; Bookpng Prof Awd 87; Sr Acadmc Achvt Awd 87; Marion-Walker Excellnc Awd 87; Centre Cnty Vo-Tech; Nursingt.

RINALDI, MARISA; Scranton Prep Schl; Moscow, PA; (1); 14/176; Dance Clb; Capt Cheerleading; Coach Actv; Var Trk; High Hon Roll; Law.

RINDOCK, PAMELA; Allentown Central Catholic HS; Allentown, PA; (3); 91/232; Drama Clb; Girl Scts; Band; Concert Band; Mrchg Band; Pep Band; Yrbk Stf; Hon Roll; Church Yth Grp; Camera Clb; Grl Sct Slvr Awd 85; Ntl Hnr Rl Bk 87; Music.

RINE, KIMBERLY A; Lower Dauphin HS; Hummelstown, PA; (3); Hosp Aide; Spanish Clb; Chorus; Church Choir; Lit Mag; Stat Mgr(s); Score Keeper; County Chorus 84-85; English.

RINE, MICHELE M; Bald Eagle-Nittany HS; Mill Hall, PA; (4); 2/115; Trs Drama Clb; Trs French Clb; Key Clb; Varsity Clb; Sec Band; Chorus; Concert Band; Madrigals; Mrchg Band; School Musical; Frnch Club Awd 86-87; Bloomsburg U; Mass Cmncatns.

RINE, STEVEN; Wallenpanpack Area HS; Hawley, PA; (3); 3/156; Church Yth Grp; Quiz Bowl; Scholastic Bowl; Science Clb; Church Choir; Bowling; Trk; High Hon Roll; Jr NHS; NHS; 1st Pl Sci Olympd Trpgrphc Maps In ST, 3rd In Ntls 86; Pai Govnrs Schl Intl Studies 87; Social Sci.

RINEHAMER, LAURIE; John S Fine HS; Wanamie, PA; (1); Pres Church Yth Grp; Hosp Aide; Chorus; Luzerne Cnty CC.

RINEHART, CHRISTINE; Great Hope Baptist HS; Shermansdale, PA; (4); 1/4; Teachers Aide; Yrbk Bus Mgr; Val; JV Cheerleading; Var Vllybl; Bible Engl & Hstry 87; Awd For Cnstncy In Grds 87; Palmer; Sec Sci.

RINEHART, JENNIFER; Biglerville HS; Gettysburg, PA; (3); 8/101; Varsity Clb; Yrbk Sprt Ed; Trs Soph Cls; VP Jr Cls; Sec Sr Cls; Rep Stu Cncl; Var Bsktbl; Var Trk; Hon Roll; Jr NHS; Physcl Thrpy.

RINEHART, TAMMY; Susquehannock HS; Shrewsbury, PA; (2); 11/243; AFS; Varsity Clb; School Play; Var Cheerleading; Var Mgr(s); Hon Roll; NHS; Prfct Atten Awd; Art Awd & Acdmc Letter 87.

RINGER, KAREN; Plum SR HS; Pittsburgh, PA; (4); Exploring; French Clb; Band; Concert Band; Jazz Band; Mrchg Band; Symp Band; Hon Roll; NHS; NEDT Awd; Prsdntl Acad Fitness Awd 87; Cert Acad Achvt 87; Clssrm Achvt Awd Band 86; Median Schl/Pittsburgh; Vet Ast.

RINGER, LISA; Fort Cherry HS; Mcdonald, PA; (2); Church Yth Grp; High Hon Roll; Exploring; Math Clb; Ski Clb; Chorus; Yrbk Stf; High Hon Roll; Acad Achvt Awd; Medicine.

RINGER, MICHELLE; Rockwood Area HS; Rockwood, PA; (3); VP 4-H; Band; Chorus; Mrchg Band; Nwsp Stf; Yrbk Stf; Rep Stu Cncl; Stat Bsktbl; Score Keeper; Hon Roll.

RINGHOLM, MEREDITH; William Allen HS; Allentown, PA; (3); Church Yth Grp; GAA; Letterman Clb; Ski Clb; Var L Bsktbl; Var L Fld Hcky; Var L Sftbl; Hon Roll; 1st Tm E PA Div II Sftbl Tm 87; Holiday Trnmnt All-Star Bsktbl 86.

RINGLABEN, PATRICIA; West Hazleton HS; W Hazelton, PA; (4); Sec FBLA; Office Aide; SADD; Hon Roll; Typng Awd 86; Acctng Awd 85; Exec Secy.

RINKER, MICHAEL; Dover Area HS; Dover, PA; (3); Bsbl; Capt Bsktbl; Capt Ftbl; Law Enfrcmnt.

RIORDAN, ERIN; Meadville Area SR HS; Meadville, PA; (3); 38/363; French Clb; High Hon Roll; Hon Roll; Arch.

RIORDAN, RITA; West Philadelphia Catholic Girls; Philadelphia, PA; (4); 102/233; Art Clb; School Play; Yrbk Stf; Sftbl; Prfct Atten Awd; Pres Acad Achvt Awd Phys Ftns 87; Med Sec.

RIOS, RICHARD LEE; J P Mc Caskey HS; Lancaster, PA; (3); Chorus; Church Choir; Rep Stu Cncl; Trk; High Hon Roll; Hon Roll; Jr NHS; Opt Clb Awd; Rotary Awd; Air Force; Elctrncs.

RIPA, MELISSA; Wyoming Area SR HS; Pittston, PA; (3); Church Yth Grp; Ski Clb; Spanish Clb; Band; Concert Band; Pres Mrchg Band; Var Capt Sftbl; Hon Roll; NHS.

RIPLEY, MATT; Pennridge HS; Perkasie, PA; (4); Church Yth Grp; 4-H; Rep Frsh Cls; Rep Soph Cls; Var Crs Cntry; Var Trk; Var Wrstlng; Kutztown U; Physcs.

RIPPARD, DARREN; North East HS; North East, PA; (3); 4-H; Band; Bowling; Var L Crs Cntry; JV L Trk; 4-H Awd; Hon Roll; Chem.

RIPPEON, JACQUELINE E; Littlestown HS; Littlestown, PA; (4); 7/117; Church Yth Grp; FBLA; Yrbk Stf; Hon Roll; Bus Awd 87; York Coll; Bus Mgmt.

RIPPLE, RICHARD; Claysburg-Kimmel HS; Claysburg, PA; (2); 32/97; Ftbl; Wt Lftg; Bus.

RIPPOLE, CRAIG; Sto-Rox SR HS; Mckees Rocks, PA; (2); 10/143; Am Leg Boys St; Chess Clb; Church Yth Grp; Pres FBLA; JA; Letterman Clb; Nwsp Sprt Ed; Yrbk Stf; Stu Cncl; Var L Bsktbl; Acadc Al-Amer; MVP Dfns Ftbl; US Nvl Acad; Militry Sci.

RISBON, PATRICIA; Cambria Heights HS; Patton, PA; (4); ROTC; Yrbk Stf; Hon Roll; Cert For Work On Yrbk 86-87; Mount Aloysius JC; Trvl.

RISCH, FREDERICK JOHN; Wyoming Area SR HS; Harding, PA; (4); 26/249; Cmnty Wkr; Debate Tm; German Clb; Scholastic Bowl; Trs Sr Cls; High Hon Roll; Hon Roll; NHS; Penn ST U; Finnce.

RISER, SHELLEY; Connellsville Area SR HS; Connellsville, PA; (3); 63/481; GAA; Office Aide; Pres Frsh Cls; VP Soph Cls; Pres Jr Cls; Stu Cncl; Stat Bsktbl; Var Vllybl; High Hon Roll; NHS; U Of Pittsburgh; Nrsng.

RISH, PATTI; Lake-Lehman HS; Dallas, PA; (4); 64/157; 4-H; SADD; Sec Soph Cls; Stat Ftbl; JV Var Sftbl; Var Trk; Hon Roll; Jr NHS; Vrsty Trck Ltr; CA ST U; Advrtsng.

RISHEL, ADAM; Central York HS; York, PA; (3); Church Yth Grp; German Clb; SADD; Yrbk Stf; JV Ftbl; Var Trk; High Hon Roll; Hon Roll; NHS; PA Gov Schl Ag 86; PA ST; Engrng.

RISHEL, DAWN; Mifflinburg Area HS; Mifflinburg, PA; (1); Trs 4-H; FHA; Spanish Clb; Var Trk; 4-H Awd; Hon Roll.

RISHEL, KIMBERLY K; Shaler Area SR HS; Glenshaw, PA; (3); 24/486; Church Yth Grp; Cmnty Wkr; Band; Trs Mrchg Band; Yrbk Stf; High Hon Roll; NHS; Prfct Atten Awd; Spanish NHS; Spanish Clb; Mid-East Music Fstvl 85-87; Bio.

RISHEL, MARY ANNE; Greencastle Antrim HS; Greencastle, PA; (4); 2/176; Hst Band; Concert Band; Jazz Band; Mrchg Band; Trs Jr Cls; Var JV Bsktbl; Var JV Fld Hcky; Var L Sftbl; Elks Awd; High Hon Roll; U Of MI; Archaelgy.

RISHELL, CHRISTY; Laurel Valley HS; New Florence, PA; (2); 48/131; FCA; FBLA; Chorus; Nwsp Stf; Im Vllybl; Hon Roll; Lgl Sec.

RISHER, BRIEN; Central Catholic HS; Pittsburgh, PA; (2); JV Bsktbl; Score Keeper; JV Socr; JV Var Trk; Hon Roll; Prfct Atten Awd; Pres Fitness Awd 85-86; Silver Medal At Area Track Championships 85-86; Math.

RISHFORTH, BRYAN; Wm Penn SR HS; York, PA; (4); 5/373; Debate Tm; Ski Clb; Symp Band; Sec Rep Stu Cncl; JV Var Socr; Var Capt Tennis; High Hon Roll; Jr NHS; NHS; Rotary Awd; Lebanon Vly Clg Uth Schlrs Inst Schlrshp 86; Engrng.

RISHKO, CHERYL; Wyoming Area HS; Wyoming, PA; (3); Art Clb; Church Yth Grp; Drama Clb; French Clb; Thesps; Rep Stu Cncl; Brandywine; Travel.

RISHKO, TARA; Allentown Central Catholic HS; Allentown, PA; (4); 2/204; Am Leg Aux Girls St; Math Clb; School Play; Var Cheerleading; High Hon Roll; NHS; Ntl Merit Ltr; Sal; Lehigh Cnty Jr Miss 87; Purdue U; Aerospace Engrng.

RISKO, GARY; Penn Cambria HS; Lilly, PA; (3); Boy Scts; Scholastic Bowl; Speech Tm; SADD; Hon Roll; Egl Sct 85; Premed.

RISSER, BRIAN; Elizabethtown Area HS; Elizabethtown, PA; (4); 4/229; Teachers Aide; Varsity Clb; Bsbl; Ftbl; Wrstlng; High Hon Roll; Kiwanis Awd; NHS; Rotary Awd; Hghst GPA-MATH 87; Gettysburg Coll; Bus Mgmt.

RISSER, RANDY; Solanco HS; Holtwood, PA; (4); 5/235; VP Church Yth Grp; VP FFA; Teachers Aide; High Hon Roll; VFW Awd; Gov Schl Ag VP 86; FFA Pub Spkng Cntst 86; Solonco Schlr 86; Ag.

RISSLER, QUENTIN D; Garden Spot HS; Denver, PA; (3); 7/200; Chess Clb; Trs Church Yth Grp; Computer Clb; VP Spanish Clb; Rep Jr Cls; Rep Stu Cncl; High Hon Roll; NHS; Prfct Atten Awd; Bible Quizzing Champ Tm 87; Eng.

RISSMILLER, AMY; Stroudsburg HS; Stroudsburg, PA; (3); Cmnty Wkr; Scholastic Bowl; Spanish Clb; Chorus; Ed Nwsp Ed-Chief; High Hon Roll; NHS; Schlstc Tm Ltr; Jrnlsm.

RIST, EDDY; Trinity HS; New Cumberland, PA; (2); Church Yth Grp; CAP; ROTC; JV Bsktbl; JV Socr; Hon Roll; Aud/Vis; Chess Clb; Pep Clb; Color Guard; West Point; Hstry.

RITA, KRISTEN; Tamaqua Area HS; Tamaqua, PA; (3); 53/226; Church Yth Grp; Civic Clb; Drama Clb; French Clb; Science Clb; Mrchg Band; Yrbk Stf; Cheerleading; Trk; French Hon Soc; Fshn Merch.

RITCHEY, PETER; Northern Bedford County HS; Martinsburg, PA; (3); 2/100; Math Clb; Trs Band; Chorus; Jazz Band; School Musical; Nwsp Ed-Chief; Var Bsktbl; Trk; High Hon Roll; Pres NHS; Indstrl Engr.

RITCHEY, REBECCA L; Hollidaysburg Area HS; Hollidaysburg, PA; (4); French Clb; Library Aide; Office Aide; Im Vllybl; Gov Hon Prg Awd; High Hon Roll; Hon Roll; NHS; U Of Pgh; Pre Med.

RITCHEY, TAMMY S; Dover Area HS; Dover, PA; (3); Church Yth Grp; Varsity Clb; Band; Mrchg Band; School Play; Nwsp Sprt Ed; Nwsp Stf; Sec Stu Cncl; Var Crs Cntry; Var Swmmng; Art.

RITCHEY, TERA; Blair County Christian Schl; Duncansville, PA; (2); 6/15; Church Yth Grp; Debate Tm; Chorus; Yrbk Sprt Ed; Rep Soph Cls; Stu Cncl; Var L Cheerleading; Var Trk; High Hon Roll; Hon Roll.

RITCHIE JR, BARRY W; Belle Vernon Area HS; Belle Vernon, PA; (3); 30/290; Trs Jr Cls; Var Socr; Var Wrstlng; Cit Awd; High Hon Roll; NHS; Prfct Atten Awd; Church Yth Grp; Cmnty Wkr; Penn ST U; Elec Engr.

RITCHIE, LISA D; Eisenhower HS; Warren, PA; (3); Art Clb; Church Yth Grp; Key Clb; Office Aide; Spanish Clb; Speech Tm; Teachers Aide; Band; Concert Band; Mrchg Band; Varrious Ribbons, Letters, Pins & Money Awds; Cmmrcl Art.

RITCHIE, PEGGY; Shikellamy HS; Sunbury, PA; (3); Chorus; Lit Mag; Hon Roll; NHS; Bloomsburg U; Math 2nd Educ.

RITENOUR, SCOTT; Belle Vernon Area HS; Belle Vernon, PA; (3); Pres Debate Tm; NFL; Ski Clb; Band; Mrchg Band; Stu Cncl; Golf; High Hon Roll; NHS; Amer Legn Oratrcl Comptn 1st Runr Up 87; Penn ST; Engrng.

RITO, RICH; Cambria Heights HS; Patton, PA; (3); 40/182; Drama Clb; JV Bsktbl; Hon Roll; Optometrist.

RITTENHOUSE, KRISTI; Lewistown Area HS; Mc Veytown, PA; (2); Art Clb; French Clb; Ski Clb; VP Frsh Cls; VP Soph Cls; Rep Stu Cncl; Cheerleading; Swmmng; High Hon Roll; NHS; Rgnl Schltc Art Awd 87; Acadc All Amercn Assn 86; Occptnl Thrpy.

RITTER, BRIAN; Salisbury HS; Allentown, PA; (4); 17/142; Aud/Vis; Church Yth Grp; Cmnty Wkr; Computer Clb; Exploring; Red Cross Aide; Im Bsktbl; JV Socr; Hon Roll; Nations 3rd Hghst Series Bwlg 87; Hghst Avg AABPA Trvlg Lg Bwlg 86-87; JR Bwlrs Tour Champ 87; Le High County CC; Comp Tech.

RITTER, CANDY; Fairfield HS; Fairfield, PA; (3); 2/72; VP Church Yth Grp; Hosp Aide; SADD; Sec Chorus; Swing Chorus; Var Bsktbl; Var Fld Hcky; Var Sftbl; Sec NHS; FHA; Schl Bd Rep; Mt St Marys U; Preschl Tchr.

RITTER, DENISE; West Perry HS; Loysville, PA; (4); 3/180; Girl Scts; Varsity Clb; Church Choir; Var L Bsktbl; High Hon Roll; Hon Roll; Jr NHS; NHS; Prfct Atten Awd; HACC; System Analyst.

RITTER, JEANNE; Tamaqua HS; Quakake, PA; (3); 30/224; Church Yth Grp; Drama Clb; 4-H; Science Clb; Flag Corp; Mrchg Band; Ed Yrbk Phtg; Yrbk Stf; Hon Roll; Lehigh CC; Bus Admin.

RITTER, KARI; South Western HS; Hanover, PA; (3); 60/233; Political Wkr; Nwsp Rptr; Nwsp Stf; Rep Frsh Cls; Rep Soph Cls; Rep Jr Cls; Var L Cheerleading; Hon Roll; PA Schl Prss Awds 86; Intl Rltns.

RITTER, MELODY; Harry S Truman HS; Bristol, PA; (3); Girl Scts; Concert Band; Hon Roll; Accntng.

RITTER, MIKE; Harry S Truman HS; Levittown, PA; (3); Pep Clb; Scholastic Bowl; Spanish Clb; SADD; Varsity Clb; Yrbk Stf; Var L Bsbl; Var L Ftbl; Im Vllybl; Im Var Wt Lftg.

RITTER, STACY; Milton Area HS; Milton, PA; (3); 11/300; Church Yth Grp; Letterman Clb; Spanish Clb; Varsity Clb; Chorus; Color Guard; Flag Corp; Mrchg Band; Yrbk Stf; Stu Cncl.

RITTER, TAMMY; B Reed Henderson HS; Exton, PA; (4); 12/340; Church Yth Grp; JCL; Latin Clb; Var Bsktbl; Var Vllybl; French Hon Soc; Hon Roll; NHS; Ntl Latin Ex Maxima Cum Laude 86; Acad Achvt Awd 86; Ed.

RITTS, DAVE; Archbishop Wood HS; Warminster, PA; (3); 80/235; Rep Frsh Cls; JV Bsbl; JV Ice Hcky; Var Socr; Mst Imprvd Plyr Sccr Vrsty 86-87.

RITZ, NICHOLAS; Mt Pleasant Area HS; Mt Pleasant, PA; (3); 32/250; German Clb; ROTC; Ski Clb; Concert Band; Yrbk Stf; Rep Stu Cncl; Ftbl; Wt Lftg; NHS; USNA; Aero Engrng.

RITZ, PATRICK; Moniteau HS; Boyers, PA; (3); 30/130; Boy Scts; Jazz Band; Mrchg Band; Exploring; Spanish Clb; Concert Band; Hon Roll; Eagle Scout 86; Grove City Coll; Mech Engrng.

RITZ, RODNEY; Southmoreland SR HS; Mt Pleasant, PA; (3); 37/224; Letterman Clb; Office Aide; Spanish Clb; Concert Band; Jazz Band; Mrchg Band; Var L Trk; Mid-East Hnrs Band, WV Hnrs Band, Westmoreland Co Hnrs Band 87; Comp Pgmr.

RITZEL, JIM; Fort Le Boeuf HS; Erie, PA; (3); 94/213; Rep Soph Cls; Var L Bsbl; Var L Bsktbl; Im Coach Actv; Ftbl; Im Vllybl; Hon Roll; All Cnty Bsktbll 86-87.

RITZMAN, CHRISTINE; Pequea Valley HS; Paradise, PA; (4); Church Yth Grp; Varsity Clb; Chorus; Concert Band; Mrchg Band; School Musical; Symp Band; Crs Cntry; NHS; Cnty Chorus 85; Philadelphia Coll Bible; Cosmet.

RIVALTA, MIA; Upper Merion HS; King Of Prussia, PA; (3); 64/290; Cmnty Wkr; DECA; SADD; Mrchg Band; JV Bsktbl; Var Fld Hcky; Var Capt Lcrss; Im Vllybl; Hon Roll; Prfct Atten Awd; PHYS Educ.

RIVENBARK III, HARRY L; Maplewood HS; Norristown, PA; (3); 60/151; Debate Tm; 4-H; Var Bsbl; Var Golf; Sftbl; 4-H Awd; Hon Roll; Prfct Atten Awd; Phys Ed Awd-Outstndng Achvt 85; Achvt Awd 85; Armed Forces.

RIVENBURGH, LINDA; Susquehanna Community HS; Thompson, PA; (4); 2/84; Ski Clb; Band; Chorus; Concert Band; Drm Mjr(t); Mrchg Band; Stu Cncl; Powder Puff Ftbl; Hon Roll; NHS; Admn Assis.

RIVENBURGH, THOMAS; Susquehanna Community HS; Thompson, PA; (3); 1/82; Ski Clb; Band; Concert Band; Mrchg Band; Var Vllybl; Wrstlng; Hon Roll.

RIVERA, ARLENE; Northwestern Lehigh HS; New Tripoli, PA; (3); 6/139; Trs Am Leg Aux Girls St; Debate Tm; Trs SADD; Nwsp Ed-Chief; Ed Yrbk Rptr; Rep Stu Cncl; Dnfth Awd; High Hon Roll; Lion Awd; Sec NHS; Acad All Amer; Jrnlsm.

RIVERA, MAGGIE; Oxford Area HS; Lincoln Univ, PA; (3); Cmnty Wkr; FFA; Spanish Clb; Hon Roll; FFA Greenhand & Chptr Frmr Degree 86; Outstndng Accmplshmnts Awd Smmr Yth Trngn Prog 86; Farming.

RIVERA, RAMON; Carlisle SR HS; Carlisle, PA; (4); 24/397; Church Yth Grp; Rep Stu Cncl; Timer; L Trk; Cit Awd; High Hon Roll; Hon Roll; La Salle U; Bio.

RIVERA, REBECCA; Stephen Watts Kearny HS; Philadelphia, PA; (4); 134/314; Trs DECA; Sec Drama Clb; Office Aide; Band; Flag Corp; School Play; Nwsp Stf; Yrbk Stf; U Of CA San Diego; Entrpnr.

RIVERA, RUBEN; Olney HS; Philadelphia, PA; (2); Boys Clb Am; Boy Scts; Church Yth Grp; Cmnty Wkr; Red Cross Aide; Teachers Aide; School Play; Soph Cls; Bsbl; Bsktbl; East Stroudesburg; Drftng.

RIVERS, SCOTT; Butler SR HS; Butler, PA; (3); Boy Scts; Church Yth Grp; Exploring; VP Spanish Clb; JV Socr; Hon Roll; Jr NHS; NHS; Engineering.

RIVERS, SHARON; Coatesville Area SR HS; Coatesville, PA; (3); FBLA; Hosp Aide; SADD; Chorus; Rep Jr Cls; Hon Roll; Prfct Atten Awd; Church Yth Grp; Spanish Clb; Church Choir; Trk 84; Pre Law.

RIXMAN, TODD; Bangor Area SR HS; E Bangor, PA; (3); Leo Clb; Var Tennis; High Hon Roll; NHS; Physics.

RIZEN, MICHAEL; Lower Moreland HS; Huntingdon Vly, PA; (4); 3/201; SADD; School Musical; Lit Mag; VP Soph Cls; Var L Diving; Var L Socr; JV Trk; Bausch & Lomb Sci Awd; High Hon Roll; VP NHS; Rensselaer Mdl 85-86; Jean Sthrlnd Mem Awd 86-87; Hntngdn Vly Jr Wmns Clb Schlrshp 86-87; MA Inst Tech; Chem.

RIZOR, BILL; West Allegheny HS; Imperial, PA; (4); 8/201; Math Tm; Science Clb; Var L Ftbl; Var L Trk; Wt Lftg; High Hon Roll; Lion Awd; NHS; Ntl Merit Ltr; Broke Natl Teen Weightlifting Record With Deadlift Of 550 LBS 87; U Of Pittsburgh Provost Schlrshp; U Of Pittsburgh; Medicine.

RIZOR, MELISSA; West Greene HS; New Freeport, PA; (3); Dance Clb; French Clb; GAA; Quiz Bowl; Science Clb; Ski Clb; Drill Tm; Mrchg Band; Stu Cncl; Cheerleading; Prfmng Arts.

RIZOR, RANETTE; West Greene HS; Graysville, PA; (3); 3/103; Church Yth Grp; 4-H; Science Clb; Nwsp Stf; Stat Bsktbl; Im Coach Actv; L Sftbl; JV Vllybl; DAR Awd; 4-H Awd; 1st Rgnl St Wnnr PA Jr Acad Of Sci 86; Top Acad Frshmn/Soph Stu 84-86; DAR Essay Wnnr 84; Hlth.

RIZZARDI, PAUL; Pocono Mountain HS; Swiftwater, PA; (4); 13/329; Var Socr; NHS; Natl Sci Olympiad In Bio 85; Ball ST U; Arch.

RIZZO, COURTNEY P; Peters Township HS; Venetia, PA; (4); Varsity Clb; Yrbk Stf; Stu Cncl; JV Cheerleading; Powder Puff Ftbl; Trk; Hon Roll; Art Inst Of Pittsburg; Intr Des.

RIZZO, DANA; Westmont Hilltop HS; Johnstown, PA; (2); 45/145; Church Yth Grp; Hosp Aide; Ski Clb; SADD; Chorus; Church Choir; Nwsp Rptr; Nwsp Stf; Hon Roll.

RIZZO, RACHELLE; Winchester Thurston HS; Pittsburgh, PA; (4); AFS; Church Yth Grp; GAA; Ski Clb; School Play; Rep Stu Cncl; Var Sftbl; Var Tennis; John Carroll U; Intl Bus.

RIZZO, RAMONA; James M Coughlin HS; Wilkes Barre, PA; (3); 61/362; Key Clb; Math Clb; Office Aide; Ski Clb; Chorus; Concert Band; Mrchg Band; Orch; Hon Roll; Jr NHS; Wlks-Barre All Area Orchstr 85-87; Hnrs Band 85; Prsdntl Acdmc Ftnss Awd 85; Wilkes Coll; Accntng.

RIZZO, TONI M; Norwin SR HS; N Huntingdon, PA; (3); FBLA; Library Aide; Pep Clb; SADD; Color Guard; Rep Stu Cncl; Twrlr; Bus.

ROACH, CHRISTINA; Saint Hubert HS For Girls; Philadelphia, PA; (3); 106/421; Church Yth Grp; Cmnty Wkr; Girl Scts; Office Aide; Spanish Clb; SADD; School Musical; Nwsp Rptr; Nwsp Stf; Prfct Atten Awd; Grl Sct Slvr & Slvr Ldrshp Awds 85; Svc Awd-Cmmnty Svc Corps 86-87; Svc Awd-Schl Nwsp 86; Comm.

ROACH, PATRICK; Western Beaver JR-SR HS; Industry, PA; (2); Church Yth Grp; Computer Clb; Letterman Clb; Bsbl; Bsktbl; Ftbl; Wt Lftg; Hon Roll; Prfct Atten Awd; Crmnl Just.

ROACH, TAMARA; Franklin HS; Franklin, PA; (3); Drama Clb; Model UN; Radio Clb; Acpl Chr; Chorus; Madrigals; VP Rep Soph Cls; Hon Roll; French Clb; Cmmnctns.

ROACH, TERESA; Grove City SR HS; Grove City, PA; (4); 40/185; Pres VP Church Yth Grp; Pres Trs Ski Clb; Band; Ed Yrbk Ed-Chief; Sec Soph Cls; Capt L Cheerleading; Stat Powder Puff Ftbl; L Var Trk; Capt L Vllybl; OH ST U; Vsl Comms.

ROACHE, MICHELE; Kiski Area HS; Apollo, PA; (2); Library Aide; Spanish Clb; Mgr(s); Hon Roll; Robert Morris Coll; Flght Atten.

ROADES, VICTORIA; Shady Side Acad; Pittsburgh, PA; (3); Chorus; Orch; Variety Show; Yrbk Phtg; Yrbk Sprt Ed; Yrbk Stf; Rep Soph Cls; JV Fld Hcky; Lcrss; Swmmng; Schlrshp Pgh Plyhs Smmr Arts 87; C'sn Dnc Apprntcshp Gifted Studs Pgm 87-88; Psych.

ROADMAN, LORI; Mt Pleasant Area HS; Acme, PA; (4); 15/248; Church Yth Grp; Latin Clb; Band; Church Choir; Concert Band; Mrchg Band; Yrbk Stf; High Hon Roll; Jr NHS; NHS; Penn ST Educ Assc Schlrshp 87; Grove City Coll; Educ.

ROADMAN, SAM; Avella Area JR SR HS; Avella, PA; (3); Computer Clb; French Clb; Concert Band; Jazz Band; Mrchg Band; Off Stu Cncl; High Hon Roll; NHS; Pres Schlr; SAR Awd; Chem Achvt Awd 86-87; Geom Achvt, Bio Achtvt Awd 85-86; Carnegie Mellon; Chem Engrng.

ROBACKER, KRISTEN; Freedom SR HS; Bethlehem, PA; (4); 92/489; Trs Drama Clb; VP SADD; School Play; Nwsp Stf; Trs Stu Cncl; Capt L Fld Hcky; Hon Roll; French Clb; German Clb; JA; Cngrsmn D Ritter Awd Outstndng Ctznshp 87; SR All Star Tm Fld Hcky 87; Villanova U.

ROBATISIN, DONNA; Hopewell HS; Aliquippa, PA; (3); 26/360; Church Yth Grp; Trs German Clb; Service Clb; Band; Concert Band; Mrchg Band; Yrbk Stf; JV Trk; High Hon Roll; NHS.

ROBB, BRIAN; Mt Pleasant Area HS; Acme, PA; (2); Boy Scts; Debate Tm; German Clb; Pres Soph Cls; Pres Jr Cls; Rep Stu Cncl; Capt Bsktbl; High Hon Roll; Hon Roll; Bst Schlr Awd 86; Carnegie Mellon U; Chem Engrng.

ROBB, JANINE; Kiski Area HS; Vandergrift, PA; (4); French Clb; Pep Clb; Chorus; Yrbk Stf; Stu Cncl; High Hon Roll; Pres Schlr; Gradtd Wth Hnrs-Hnr Chrd 87; Top Ten Awd 84; Acdmc Ltrs 84-87; Penn ST U; Accntng.

ROBB, KATHY; Manheim Twp HS; Lancaster, PA; (4); 65/328; Service Clb; Chorus; School Musical; School Play; Swing Chorus; Lit Mag; Coach Actv; High Hon Roll; Hon Roll; NHS; Manheim Twp Ed Assoc Schlrshp 87; Sychrnzd Swmmng Clb Soloist 86-87; U Of DE; Elem Ed.

ROBB, SAMUEL J; Serra Catholic HS; Mc Keesport, PA; (4); 5/165; JA; Library Aide; Math Clb; Math Tm; Q&S; Nwsp Sprt Ed; JV Var Trk; High Hon Roll; NHS; Ntl Merit SF; Engrng.

ROBBA, J DAVID; Fairchance Georges SR HS; Smithfield, PA; (3); Aud/Vis; Stage Crew; Var L Ftbl; Wt Lftg; Var L Wrstlng; Hon Roll; Jr NHS.

ROBBINS, ELIZABETH; Youngsville HS; Bear Lake, PA; (4); Nwsp Stf; Yrbk Stf; Ed Lit Mag; L Mgr(s); Stat Vllybl; High Hon Roll; NHS; ROTC Schlrshp Army 87; U Of Tampa Schrslhp 87; U Tampa; Psych.

ROBBINS, LUCINDA; Connellsville Area HS; Dunbar, PA; (2); Office Aide; Band; Chorus; Concert Band; Mrchg Band; School Musical; Nwsp Ed-Chief; Yrbk Stf; High Hon Roll; Gifted Prog 85-87.

ROBBINS, MOLLIE; Pennsbury HS; Yardley, PA; (3); Church Yth Grp; Yrbk Stf; Rep Frsh Cls; Rep Soph Cls; Var JV Cheerleading; Im Gym.

ROBBINS, PAUL; Cambridge Springs Joint HS; Cambridge Springs, PA; (3); Spanish Clb; SADD; JV L Bsktbl; Hon Roll; Comp Drftng & Dsgn.

ROBBINS, SHERRY; Benton Area HS; Stillwater, PA; (3); Art Clb; NHS; Century 2u Accntng Cert 87; Century 21 Typewrtng Cert 86; Accntng.

ROBERSON, BONNIE; Central HS; Philadelphia, PA; (2); Hon Roll; Jr NHS; U Of PA; Vet.

ROBERTS, AMY; Jefferson-Morgan HS; Rices Landing, PA; (2); 1/80; Pres Intnl Clb; Library Aide; Capt Color Guard; Nwsp Rptr; High Hon Roll; NHS; NEDT Awd; Acad All-Amer 86-87.

ROBERTS, ANGELA; Parkland HS; Fogelsville, PA; (3); 80/495; FBLA; Band; High Hon Roll; Hon Roll; NHS; Dental Asst.

ROBERTS, ANYEKA; West Catholic Girls HS; Philadelphia, PA; (3); Intnl Clb; Latin Clb; Spanish Clb; Hon Roll; Ntl Merit Ltr; Prfct Attndnc Awd 85-86; Prfct Condct Awd 85-87; 2nd Hnrs 86-87; Temple U Phila; Bilinguist.

ROBERTS, BRENDA; Everett Area HS; Everett, PA; (1); Camera Clb; Church Yth Grp; French Clb; GAA; Chorus; Stu Cncl; Trk; Vllybl; High Hon Roll; Hon Roll; Nrsng.

ROBERTS, BRIAN; Dover Area HS; Dover, PA; (3); 19/260; Church Yth Grp; Pres Band; Chorus; Concert Band; Mrchg Band; Rep Jr Cls; Rep Stu Cncl; L Trk; Capt Wrstlng; NHS; Hnr Rll 85-87; Penn ST; Aeronautcl Engrng.

ROBERTS, BRIAN; John S Fine HS; Plymouth, PA; (3); Science Clb; Yrbk Stf; Wrstlng; Natl Eductn Devlpmnt Test Cert 85 & 86; Acadmc All Amer 84; Penn ST; Astronmcl Research.

ROBERTS, CHRIS; Harriton HS; Wynnewood, PA; (3); Debate Tm; Drama Clb; Math Tm; Band; Jazz Band; Mrchg Band; School Play; Lit Mag; JV Wrstlng; Hon Roll; Schlstc Wrtng Awd Hnrbl Mntn 85; 3rd Pl-Mn Ln Wmns Strk Peace Essy Cont 86; Outstndng Instru Music 87.

ROBERTS, ELAINE; Charleroi Area SR HS; N Charleroi, PA; (4); Spanish Clb; SADD; Band; Mrchg Band; IN U Of PA; Hmnts.

ROBERTS, GEORGIANA; Corry Area HS; Corry, PA; (3); 86/224; Var JV Vllybl; High Hon Roll; Hon Roll.

ROBERTS JR, JAMES; Sacred Heart HS; Carbondale, PA; (3); Church Yth Grp; Ski Clb; Pres Stu Cncl; Bsbl; US Navy; Cryptlgc.

ROBERTS, JENNIFER; Charleroi Area HS; N Charleroi, PA; (3); Concert Band; Hero Clb 84-86; Elem Ed.

ROBERTS, KAREN; Bensalem HS; Bensalem, PA; (2); Spanish Clb; Var Swmmng; Im Wt Lftg; Hon Roll; Cmp Cnslr 85-87; Asst Swim Inst 85-87; Sccr Asst Coach 87; Coast Guard Acad.

ROBERTS, KATHLEEN; Parkland SR HS; Allentown, PA; (3); 35/483; Church Yth Grp; Drama Clb; Band; Chorus; Stage Crew; High Hon Roll; Jr NHS; PA ST; Trvl.

ROBERTS, LAURIE; Danville SR HS; Danville, PA; (3); Pres Church Yth Grp; Rep FHA; Chorus; Church Choir; School Musical; Hon Roll; Crmnlgy.

ROBERTS, LEIGH; Lower Moreland HS; Huntingdon Valley, PA; (4); 21/201; Exploring; Key Clb; Science Clb; SADD; Stat Swmmng; Var Tennis; Hon Roll; Trs NHS; Ntl Merit Ltr; Med.

ROBERTS, LYNN; Wyoming Valley West HS; Swoyersville, PA; (3); 1/416; Chorus; Trs Frsh Cls; Off Stu Cncl; Var L Cheerleading; Var L Sftbl; Cit Awd; High Hon Roll; NHS; NEDT Awd; Prfct Atten Awd; Hghst Acad Avg; ST Hist Day Wnnr; Intl Foreign Lang Awd; Orthodntst.

ROBERTS, MARY BETH; Hopewell Area SR HS; Aliquippa, PA; (4); 18/240; Exploring; Trs Latin Clb; Rep Trs Band; Jazz Band; Rep Mrchg Band; Rep Sr Cls; Capt Var Bsktbl; Capt Var Sftbl; High Hon Roll; NHS; Cmptv Schlrshp For Duquesne U 87-88; Schlr Athlt Awd 83-87; Bronze Mdl Of Achvt In Music 86; Duquesne U; Phrmcy.

ROBERTS, MELISSA S; Beaver Area JR/Sr HS; Beaver, PA; (3); DECA; Yrbk Bus Mgr; Stu Cncl; Hon Roll; Church Yth Grp; JCL; Latin Clb; Pep Clb; Ski Clb; Powder Puff Ftbl; 4th DECA Comptn 87; Top 10 Mag Sales 86-87; Robert Morris Coll; Buyer.

ROBERTS, MICHAEL; Dover Area HS; Dover, PA; (3); 13/260; Band; Chorus; Concert Band; Mrchg Band; School Play; VP Sr Cls; JV Trk; Var Wrstlng; Hon Roll; NHS; Aerospace Engr.

ROBERTS, MICHAEL; Gateway SR HS; Monroeville, PA; (3); 20/490; Math Clb; Math Tm; SADD; Var Capt Tennis; Hon Roll; NHS; Georgetown; Ecnmcs.

ROBERTS, MICHAEL L; Twin Valley HS; Birdsboro, PA; (3); 14/142; Am Leg Boys St; Spanish Clb; Drm & Bgl; Rep Stu Cncl; Var Bsbl; Var Bsktbl; Var Golf; Hon Roll; NHS; NROTC; Nvl Aviator.

ROBERTS, NATALIE; North Allegheny HS; Wexford, PA; (2); 92/630; Church Yth Grp; GAA; Var JV Sftbl; Hon Roll; Alg II Awd 87; U Of South FL; Bus.

ROBERTS, PAUL; St John Neumann HS; Philadelphia, PA; (2); 90/351; Rep Frsh Cls; Rep Soph Cls.

ROBERTS, RAYMOND; Port Allegany HS; Roulette, PA; (3); Art Clb; Cmnty Wkr; SADD; Varsity Clb; Yrbk Phtg; Bsbl; Bsktbl; Trk; Wt Lftg; Prfct Atten Awd; Math.

ROBERTS, SHERRY; Cedar Crest HS; Lebanon, PA; (3); 109/342; Pep Clb; Spanish Clb; SADD; Var Swmmng; Var Trk; Hon Roll; Math.

ROBERTS, TERRANCE; Jeannette HS; Jeannette, PA; (3); 8/130; Art Clb; Chess Clb; Spanish Clb; Yrbk Stf; Wt Lftg; High Hon Roll; NHS; Engrng.

ROBERTS, TOM; Beaver Area JR SR HS; Beaver, PA; (4); 16/200; FCA; JCL; VP Jr Cls; VP Sr Cls; Var L Ftbl; Var L Trk; Dnfth Awd; NHS; Church Yth Grp; German Clb; Kay Lewis Awd 87; Hgh Hons Grp 86-87; 2 Gld Mdls Trojan Trck Clssc Invttnl 87; U Of Pittsburgh; Phys Thrpy.

ROBERTSON, ALBERT; Taylor Allderdice HS; Pittsburgh, PA; (2); Math Clb; Math Tm; Cit Awd; High Hon Roll; NHS; Ntl Merit Ltr; MA Inst Tech; Robtcs Engrng.

ROBERTSON, BRYAN; Burgettstown Area JR SR HS; Burgettstown, PA; (3); 4/164; Church Yth Grp; Cmnty Wkr; Exploring; Spanish Clb; JV Bsbl; Var Bsktbl; High Hon Roll; Hon Roll; NHS; Drg & Alchl Awrns Prg; Chem.

ROBERTSON, CHRISTOPHER; Owen J Roberts HS; Chester Springs, PA; (2); 18/311; Jazz Band; Mrchg Band; Symp Band; Im Wt Lftg; JV Wrstlng; Hon Roll; Profsnl Muscn.

ROBERTSON, CLINTON; Meadville Area SR HS; Cochranton, PA; (3); Art Clb; Aud/Vis; Chess Clb; CAP; JA; Radio Clb; Bowling; Swmmng; Vllybl; Hon Roll; Radio Cmmnctns.

ROBERTSON, JAMES; Center HS; Monaca, PA; (3); Bowling; Hon Roll; PA ST; Aero Engr.

ROBERTSON, JIM; East Alleghany HS; N Versailles, PA; (4); 2/220; Capt Chess Clb; Math Tm; Science Clb; Yrbk Stf; Lit Mag; Var L Crs Cntry; Var Trk; NHS; Opt Clb Awd; Sal; Chrmn Brd Dir Soc Studs Sem 86-87; U Pittsburgh; Lawyer.

ROBERTSON, MICHELLE; Somerset Area SR HS; Sipesville, PA; (3); 23/230; English Clb; SADD; Yrbk Stf; High Hon Roll; NHS; Comm.

ROBERTSON, PAUL; St Marys Area HS; St Marys, PA; (3); 3/269; Boys Clb Am; Cmnty Wkr; JV L Bsktbl; Var L Crs Cntry; Var L Trk; High Hon Roll; NHS; Erie Cnty Chptr PA Scty Prof Engrs 87; Comp Sci.

ROBERTSON, TINA; Meyersdale Area HS; Meyersdale, PA; (3); Exploring; Pres French Clb; Chorus; School Musical; Yrbk Ed-Chief; Yrbk Stf; JV Var Bsktbl; High Hon Roll; Hon Roll; NHS; Wilson; Pre-Med.

ROBERTSON, TRACY; Du Bois Area HS; Reynoldsville, PA; (3); 21/321; Church Yth Grp; Teachers Aide; Varsity Clb; Chorus; Stu Cncl; Capt Bsktbl; Var L Cheerleading; Var L Crs Cntry; Hon Roll; Penn ST; Bus.

ROBERTUCCI, ANNE; Connellsville Area SR HS; S Connellsville, PA; (3); Am Leg Aux Girls St; Girl Scts; Leo Clb; Chorus; Sec Swmmng; JV Var Trk; Hon Roll.

ROBICH, JENNIFER; Plum SR HS; Pittsburgh, PA; (3); AFS; Church Yth Grp; DECA; Color Guard; Hon Roll; Bus.

ROBIDOUX, RAYMOND A; Milton Hershey Schl; Manchester, NH; (4); 5/125; Am Leg Boys St; Library Aide; Service Clb; Yrbk Ed-Chief; Ed Lit Mag; Rep Stu Cncl; High Hon Roll; NHS; Rotary Awd; Mgr Stat Bsktbl; Stu Ldrshp Soc 85-87; Stu Mo Mar 87; Sports Writer Hummelstown Sun Newsp; St Anselm Coll; Comp Sci.

ROBINETT, RITA; Franklin Regional HS; Murrysville, PA; (4); 1/338; AFS; Church Yth Grp; French Clb; JA; SADD; Golf; High Hon Roll; NHS; Ntl Merit SF; Pol Sci.

ROBINS, DALE; Cardinal O Hara HS; Secane, PA; (3); 351/719; Penn ST; Elem Educ.

ROBINSON, ALAN; Pius X HS; Pen Argyl, PA; (3); Boy Scts; Varsity Clb; Rep Stu Cncl; Var Bsbl; Var Bsktbl; Var Ftbl; Wt Lftg; High Hon Roll; NHS; Diocese Of Allentown Schlrshp 84-85.

ROBINSON, ANTHONY; Forest City Regional HS; Pleasant Mount, PA; (3); Boy Scts; 4-H; Letterman Clb; Ski Clb; Spanish Clb; 4-H Awd; Hon Roll; NHS; Rep Stu Cncl; Var Crs Cntry; Engr.

ROBINSON, ARMINTIA; West Catholic Girls HS; Philadelphia, PA; (3); French Clb; Service Clb; Band; Chorus; Orch; School Musical; Trk; Hon Roll; Drexel U; Comp Sci.

ROBINSON, CHRISTY; Penn-Trafford HS; Trafford, PA; (2); Church Yth Grp; Chorus; Im Sftbl; Var Tennis; Tchng.

ROBINSON, COREY; Butler HS; Butler, PA; (2); Church Yth Grp; French Clb; Ski Clb; SADD; Band; Church Choir; Mrchg Band; Socr; Swmmng; Tennis.

ROBINSON, DERRECK; Germantown Friends HS; Philadelphia, PA; (2); Church Yth Grp; Computer Clb; English Clb; FFA; Nwsp Rptr; JV Bsktbl; Cit Awd; Hon Roll; NHS; Full Schlrshp 86; Drexel U; Engrng.

ROBINSON, IZELLA; Cardinal O Hara HS; Chester, PA; (2); Church Yth Grp; Dance Clb; 4-H; FBLA; Office Aide; Red Cross Aide; VICA; Church Choir; Hon Roll; Bst Achvd Religion 86; Bst Achvd Bio 87; Sec.

ROBINSON, JANEE; Mechanicsburg Area SR HS; Mechanicsburg, PA; (3); 13/34; Church Yth Grp; Debate Tm; GAA; NFL; Chorus; Church Choir; High Hon Roll; NHS; Intrprtr Frnch.

ROBINSON, JEANNE; Lawrence County Vo-Tech; New Castle, PA; (3); Church Yth Grp; FFA; FHA; VICA; Chorus; Church Choir; Variety Show; Hon Roll; Bus Admin.

ROBINSON, JOANNE; Archbishop John Carroll HS; Philadelphia, PA; (3); 122/376; Intnl Clb; SADD; Teachers Aide; Church Choir; School Musical; Rep Frsh Cls; Im Cheerleading; Trk; Hon Roll; Prfct Atten Awd; Trk Awds Plcng 2nd Natnwde, JV Ltrs 84-85; Howard U; Bio.

ROBINSON, KAREN ELIZABETH; Phil-Mont Christian Acad; Philadlephia, PA; (3); Chorus; Church Choir; JV Var Sftbl; Hon Roll.

ROBINSON, KEINO; John Bartram HS; Philadelphia, PA; (4); 7/900; Church Yth Grp; JA; Chorus; Yrbk Rptr; Pres Stu Cncl; Var Bowling; Var Crs Cntry; Ftbl; Trk; High Hon Roll; Bus.

ROBINSON, KELLY; Jefferson Morgan HS; Waynesburg, PA; (3); 9/77; Varsity Clb; Capt Cheerleading; DAR Awd; Hon Roll; HOB Rep 86; Interact Clb Trea; WV U; Pre-Law.

ROBINSON, KELLY; Merion Mercy Acad; Phila, PA; (4); 9/72; French Clb; Intnl Clb; Latin Clb; Math Clb; Math Tm; NAACP; NFL; Science Clb; Chorus; Nwsp Phtg; Cum Lande Latin Cont 84; Svc Awd 87; Amherst Coll; Med.

ROBINSON, KENNETH; Burrell SR HS; New Kensington, PA; (3); Boy Scts; Capt Math Tm; Concert Band; Mrchg Band; Pep Band; Nwsp Stf; High Hon Roll; Sec NHS; Church Yth Grp; Exploring; U S Naval Acad; Aerosp Engrng.

ROBINSON, LEE DIANE; Altoona Area HS; Altoona, PA; (3); Church Yth Grp; Band; Concert Band; Mrchg Band; Orch; High Hon Roll; Hon Roll; Elem Ed.

ROBINSON, MARYANN; Shikellamy HS; Northumberland, PA; (3); Sec German Clb; Mrchg Band; Rep Stu Cncl; Hon Roll; NHS; Grmn Awd 85-87; Intl Stdys.

ROBINSON, MATTHEW; Fort Le Boeuf HS; Erie, PA; (4); 6/167; Model UN; Var Bsbl; Var Bsktbl; Coach Actv; High Hon Roll; NHS; Smmt Lns Clb Schlrshp 87; Otstndng SR Sci Stu 87; Allegheny Coll; Bio.

ROBINSON, MICHELE; Northeast Bradford HS; Rome, PA; (3); Church Yth Grp; Varsity Clb; Chorus; Pres Stu Cncl; Cheerleading; Sftbl; VP NHS.

ROBINSON, MICHELLE; Cecilian Acad; Philadelphia, PA; (2); Church Yth Grp; Science Clb; Church Choir; Schlrshp For Schl 85-89; Pre-Med.

ROBINSON, NADINE; Milton Area SR HS; Milton, PA; (2); FTA; Band; Chorus; Church Choir; Concert Band; Mrchg Band; Voice.

ROBINSON, ROCHELLE; Samuel P Langley SR HS; Pittsburgh, PA; (3); Pep Clb; Nwsp Stf; Yrbk Stf; Rep Stu Cncl; Mgr(s); Score Keeper; Var Capt Vllybl; Cit Awd; DAR Awd; Hon Roll; Outstndng Feml Athlt; Ctr Advncd Stdy; Pittsburgh Schlrs Pgm; Penn ST; Engrng.

ROBINSON, SERENA; Strath Haven HS; Wallingford, PA; (1); Church Yth Grp; NAACP; Church Choir; Symp Band; Bsktbl; Trk; Vllybl; Hon Roll; Band; Concert Band; Law.

ROBINSON, SHELLEY; Western Wayne HS; Lake Ariel, PA; (4); 7/140; FBLA; SADD; Band; Concert Band; Jazz Band; Mrchg Band; School Musical; Hon Roll; NHS; Mansfield Schlrs Awd 87; Natl Band Awd 86; Pres Acad Fit Awd 87; Mansfield U; Pre-Law.

ROBINSON, TALITHA G; Wilson HS; West Lawn, PA; (4); 5/321; Church Yth Grp; Quiz Bowl; Rep Stu Cncl; L Var Crs Cntry; L Var Tennis; L Var Trk; DAR Awd; VP NHS; Ntl Merit SF; Leo Clb; Sci Mjr.

ROBINSON, SHERRY; Hollidaysburg SR HS; Duncansville, PA; (4); Pres Church Yth Grp; Cmnty Wkr; Ski Clb; Spanish Clb; Varsity Clb; Church Choir; JV Var Bsktbl; JV Var Sftbl; Im Vllybl; Prfct Atten Awd; Penn ST; Bus Adm.

ROBITZ, LISA; Center HS; Monaca, PA; (4); 16/186; Church Yth Grp; Hosp Aide; Latin Clb; Chorus; Church Choir; School Musical; Swing Chorus; Rep Stu Cncl; High Hon Roll; Hon Roll; Music.

ROBL, SHEILA; East Allegheny HS; North Versailles, PA; (3); JA; Ski Clb; Band; Concert Band; Mrchg Band; Orch; School Musical; Symp Band; Sftbl; Swmmng; 2nd Pl Mon-Yough Sci Fair 84; IN U; Bus.

ROBLES, MAXINE; New Castle HS; New Castle, PA; (3); 28/260; Hosp Aide; Spanish Clb; Drill Tm; Yrbk Ed-Chief; Yrbk Stf; Rep Jr Cls; Stu Cncl; Hon Roll; NHS; Prfct Atten Awd; U Of Pittsburgh; Phys Ther.

ROBOVITSKY, JOHN; West Catholic HS For Boys; Philadelphia, PA; (3); 67/264; Band; Mrchg Band; JV Wt Lftg; High Hon Roll; Hon Roll; DE ST; Pre-Med.

ROBY, BETH; Connellsville Area HS; Cnlvle, PA; (3); German Clb; GAA; Girl Scts; Band; Chorus; Concert Band; Sec Frsh Cls; Stat Mgr(s); Score Keeper; Var Sftbl; Crmnlgy.

ROCCASANO, VICTORIA; Pennhills SR HS; Verona, PA; (3); Band; Chorus; Color Guard; Drill Tm; Mrchg Band; Var Pom Pon; High Hon Roll; Hon Roll; Robert Morris Coll; Accntng.

ROCCHI, ROCHELLE; Archbishop Ryan HS; Philadelphia, PA; (4); 208/490; Pres Art Clb; Church Yth Grp; Dance Clb; Variety Show; Rep Frsh Cls; Rep Soph Cls; Rep Sr Cls; Rep Stu Cncl; Trk; Hon Roll; Excptnl Perf Adv Art 85-86; Prtl Schlrshp-Moore Coll-Art 87; Excllnc Awd-Still Lf Drwg 86; Moore Coll Of Art.

ROCCI, EDWARD; Garnet Valley HS; Goen Mills, PA; (2); German Clb; Chorus; School Musical; Ftbl; Wrstlng; Frgn Exchng Clb; U Of PA; Stck Invstmt.

ROCCO, MICHELENA; Saltsburg JR SR HS; Saltsburg, PA; (3); DECA; Drama Clb; SADD; Varsity Clb; Bsktbl; Mgr(s); Vllybl; NHS; Pres Acadc Ftnss Awd 85.

ROCCO, MIKE; Bald Eagle Nittany HS; Mill Hall, PA; (3); #2 In Class; Key Clb; Rep Stu Cncl; Ftbl; Wrstlng; Hon Roll; NHS; Most Dedicated Wrstlr Awd 85.

ROCCO, TIFFANY; Saltsburg JR SR HS; Saltsburg, PA; (1); JV Bsktbl; Stat Vllybl; Med Tech.

ROCCOGRANDI, MARIA; Bishop O Reilly HS; Forty Fort, PA; (4); 4/116; Pres French Clb; Chorus; Stage Crew; Yrbk Stf; Trs Jr Cls; Fld Hcky; Pres French Hon Soc; High Hon Roll; NHS; NEDT Awd; Mrn Bio.

ROCERETA, LEE ANN; Monessen HS; Monessen, PA; (3); Dance Clb; French Clb; Hosp Aide; VP Sr Cls; Hon Roll; U Of Pittsburgh; Bio Chem.

ROCHE, PAMELA; Landsale Catholic HS; Lansdale, PA; (4); Dance Clb; Nwsp Rptr; Nwsp Stf; Yrbk Stf; Hon Roll.

ROCHELLE, JINADA; Cedar Crest HS; Lebanon, PA; (2); Church Yth Grp; FBLA; Pep Clb; Spanish Clb; Band; Mrchg Band; Trk; Hon Roll; USC; Corp Law.

ROCHELLE, YOUNGKIN; Lehighton Area HS; Lehighton, PA; (3); 28/254; Church Yth Grp; FHA; SADD; Church Choir; Var L Crs Cntry; Var L Trk; Chrch Sftbl Tm,Centnnl Leag Trck Mt 3rd Pl-100 M Hrdls 86-87; Phys Thrpy.

ROCHESTER, SHANEA; John Bartram HS; Philadelphia, PA; (3); Computer Clb; Math Tm; Office Aide; Teachers Aide; Score Keeper; Hon Roll; NHS; Acadmc All Star Awd 86; CES Acammc Prog; Comp Engr.

ROCK, ANGIE; Greencastle Antrim HS; Shady Grove, PA; (3); 14/179; Church Yth Grp; Band; Chorus; Concert Band; Mrchg Band; Pep Band; Hon Roll; Bus.

ROCK, CATHY; Lock Haven SR HS; Lock Haven, PA; (3); FHA; Key Clb; Spanish Clb; SADD; Chorus; Color Guard; Mrchg Band; Hon Roll; Prfct Atten Awd; Lock Haven U.

ROCK, JEFF; James M Coughlin HS; Wilkes Barre, PA; (3); 30/374; L Ftbl; Jr NHS; NHS; Dentstry.

ROCKEY, CRYSTAL; Penns Valley Area JR/Sr HS; Millheim, PA; (3); 1/150; Drama Clb; French Clb; VP SADD; School Play; Nwsp Rptr; Ed Yrbk Stf; Im JV Trk; High Hon Roll; NHS; Math Clb; PA Govnrs Schl Of Bus 87; Enrchmnt Prog 85-87; Chmcl Engrng.

ROCKEY, DANA; Lock Haven SR HS; Lock Haven, PA; (3); Sec Drama Clb; Sec Pres Spanish Clb; School Musical; School Play; Nwsp Rptr; Var L Cheerleading; Var L Trk; Hon Roll; NHS; NEDT Awd; Caroline Garthoff Kalmback Awd Chem 87; Tck Most Imprvd Of Yr 86; Trck Outstndng JR Of Yr 87; Forgn Lang.

ROCKEY, HEATHER; State College Area HS; State College, PA; (2); Powder Puff Ftbl; Var Trk; Penn ST U.

ROCKEY, JENNIFER; Mechanicsburg SR HS; Mechanicsburg, PA; (3); Speech Tm; Chorus; Psych.

ROCKEY, LISA; Hughesville HS; Hughesville, PA; (4); 12/139; Trs Key Clb; Ski Clb; VP Band; Drm Mjr(t); School Musical; Trk; NHS; Church Yth Grp; Concert Band; Mrchg Band; Hghst Avg Sci 87; Penn ST Erie; Biochem.

ROCKOVICH, BRIAN; Hazleton HS; Hazleton, PA; (4); Drama Clb; FBLA; Scholastic Bowl; Stage Crew; Hon Roll; Natl Eng Merit Awd 85; Hnrs Soc 86-87; Bloomsburg U; Accntng.

ROCKWELL, BRIAN; Bethlehem Center HS; Brownsville, PA; (2); 50/157; Camera Clb; Computer Clb; Rep Soph Cls; JV Bsbl; Wt Lftg; Hon Roll; Army Offcr.

ROCKWELL, DAVID; Susquehanna Community JR/SR HS; Susquehanna, PA; (3); 3/110; Computer Clb; Latin Clb; Quiz Bowl; Ski Clb; Spanish Clb; SADD; Bsbl; Hon Roll; NHS.

ROCKWOOD, CHRIS; Trinity HS; Carlisle, PA; (4); 26/144; Church Yth Grp; School Musical; Rep Stu Cncl; Capt L Bsktbl; Capt L Socr; L Var Trk; Hon Roll; French Clb; School Play; Stage Crew; Univ Schlrshp To St Josephs Univ 87; MVP Trck & Field 86-87; St Josephs Univ; Psych.

ROCUSKIE, KIM; Marian HS; Tamaqua, PA; (3); 45/104; Pep Clb; SADD; Rep Frsh Cls; Rep Soph Cls; Rep Stu Cncl; Var Bsktbl; Var L Sftbl; Office Aide; Peer Facltr; Pres Phy Ftnss Awd.

RODDY, JUNE; Mt Pleasant SR HS; Mt Pleasant, PA; (3); 40/250; Pres Church Yth Grp; Library Aide; Ski Clb; Chorus; Church Choir; Nwsp Stf; Var Tennis; High Hon Roll; Hon Roll; NHS; Law.

RODE, DEANNA; Northeastern HS; Mount Wolf, PA; (2); 74/210; VP Sec Church Yth Grp; Teachers Aide; Chorus; Var L Trk; JV Vllybl; Hon Roll; Diag Med Sonogrphy.

RODE, ERICA; Central SR HS; York, PA; (3); Chorus; Stage Crew; Yrbk Stf; High Hon Roll; Hon Roll; Ntl Merit Ltr; Psych.

RODEGHIERO, ERIC; Pittston Area HS; Wilkes Barre, PA; (2); Ski Clb; Tennis; High Hon Roll; JETS Awd; NHS; NEDT Awd; Rotary Awd; Sal; Boy Scts; Church Yth Grp; Amer Cham Soc 1st Pl 87; Jets Cmptn 2nd Pl 87.

RODENBAUGH, PATRICIA; Kennedy Christian HS; Hermitage, PA; (2); 47/98; Church Yth Grp; Latin Clb; Pep Clb; Im Vllybl; Hon Roll; Miami U Of FL; Marine Bio.

RODENBERG, ERIK; Montour HS; Pittsburgh, PA; (3); Boy Scts; Chess Clb; JA; Rep Frsh Cls; Rep Soph Cls; Rep Jr Cls; Rep Sr Cls; Rep Stu Cncl; Ftbl; Powder Puff Ftbl; Acdmc Achvt Awd 87; JR Olympc Trck Mbr 86; Penn ST; Mrktng.

RODENHAVER, JAMES; Danville Area HS; Danville, PA; (2); 34/160; Church Yth Grp; Var JV Crs Cntry; Var Trk; High Hon Roll; Hon Roll; Presdntl Acad Fit Awd; Annapolis.

RODENHAVER, TAMMY; Danville Area HS; Danville, PA; (3); Latin Clb; Ski Clb; Yrbk Stf; Bsktbl; Mat Maids; Sftbl.

RODGERS, BRENDA; Cranberry HS; Cranberry, PA; (3); 30/150; Computer Clb; DECA; Sec FBLA; SADD; Drill Tm; Nwsp Stf; Hon Roll; Masonic Awd; Church Yth Grp; Girl Scts; ST Fnlst Bwlg; Miss Teen PA Cont; Psych.

RODGERS, BRUCE; Wilmington Area Schls; New Wilmington, PA; (4); 4/132; Aud/Vis; Trs Church Yth Grp; Drama Clb; Math Tm; Spanish Clb; Band; Concert Band; Mrchg Band; Pep Band; School Play; Grove City Coll; Math.

RODGERS, COLLEEN; West Hazleton HS; W Hazleton, PA; (4); Cmnty Wkr; Ski Clb; Nwsp Stf; Yrbk Ed-Chief; Stu Cncl; JV Bsktbl; Var Sftbl; Im Swmmng; Hon Roll; Penn ST U; Elem Ed.

RODGERS, ERINN; Trinity HS; Mechanicsburg, PA; (2); 41/139; Exploring; Library Aide; Pep Clb; Spanish Clb; Band; Mrchg Band; Yrbk Stf; JV Cheerleading; Hon Roll; NEDT Awd; Brdcstg Jrnlsm.

RODGERS, JOANNA; Knoch JR SR HS; Butler, PA; (2); JA; SADD; Chorus; Madrigals; Mrchg Band; School Musical; Variety Show; Mgr(s); Var Pom Pon; Score Keeper; Dr.

RODGERS, JOHN; Hazleton HS; Hazleton, PA; (2); Scholastic Bowl; Var Bsktbl; Hon Roll.

RODGERS, KEIRSTEN; Parkland HS; Allentown, PA; (4); Sec Debate Tm; Exploring; Rep Key Clb; SADD; Yrbk Rptr; Rep Stu Cncl; Stat L Bsbl; Mgr Ftbl; Capt L Twrlr; Lehigh Cnty JR Miss-Poise & Apprnc Awd 87; 2nd Pl Ntl Hstry Day-Rgnl 84; JR Prom Queen 86; Kutztown U; Geo-Physcs.

RODGERS, LANCE; Franklin HS; Cochranton, PA; (2); Church Yth Grp; Golf; Swmmng; Hon Roll.

RODGERS, MARY KATHRYN; Kennedy Christian HS; Hermitage, PA; (2); 10/96; Latin Clb; Library Aide; Chorus; School Play; Nwsp Stf; High Hon Roll; NEDT Awd; Gldn Eagle Acdmc Schlrshp 85-86; Cathlc Dghtrs Amer 1st Pl Poetry Awd 85-86; Law.

RODGERS, SHANNON; Upper Dublin HS; Ft Washington, PA; (3); Church Yth Grp; Varsity Clb; Orch; JV Capt Bsktbl; Stat Ftbl; Powder Puff Ftbl; Var L Sftbl; Chem Engrng.

RODGERS, SUSAN; Grove City HS; Grove City, PA; (4); 43/176; Hosp Aide; Key Clb; Science Clb; Concert Band; Mrchg Band; JV Var Cheerleading; Im Tennis; Hon Roll; U Of CA; Elem Tchr.

RODGERS, TAMMI K; Rocky Grove HS; Reno, PA; (4); 9/89; Hosp Aide; Band; Chorus; Pep Band; High Hon Roll; Hon Roll; Acad Excllnc Awd 83-87; Williams Schlrshp 87; Gannon U; Phys Asst.

RODGERS, TRACEY; Northern SR HS; Wellsville, PA; (3); 68/232; SADD; Acpl Chr; Band; Chorus; Concert Band; Drill Tm; Mrchg Band; School Musical; School Play; Stage Crew; Dist & Rgnl Choruses 85-86; Chosen For Arts Magnet Schl 87-88; Film Prdctn.

RODGERS, TUESDAE; Franklin HS; Cochranton, PA; (4); 19/212; Church Yth Grp; German Clb; Radio Clb; Pres Service Clb; Stu Cncl; Capt Swmmng; High Hon Roll; Hon Roll; NHS; Pres Schlr; Schl Bd Dir Awd 85-87; Acad Schlrshp 87-88; Westminstor; Psych.

RODICHOK, JOSEPH; Williams Valley HS; Williamstown, PA; (4); 6/108; Ski Clb; Band; Chorus; Jazz Band; Bsktbl; Ftbl; Wt Lftg; Hon Roll; NHS; Hofstra U; Aerospc Engrng.

RODINO, CHRISTOPHER; Hazleton HS; Hazleton, PA; (2); French Clb; Leo Clb; Spanish Clb; Orch; Crs Cntry; Trk; Hon Roll; Aerontcs.

RODLAND, JEFF; Harbor Creek HS; Erie, PA; (4); 46/218; Model UN; Chorus; Variety Show; Nwsp Ed-Chief; Yrbk Ed-Chief; Rep Sr Cls; Hon Roll; NHS; Natl Hnr Soc Jrnlsts 87; Lock Haven U; Elem Ed.

RODLI, KARI; Huntingdon Area HS; Huntingdon, PA; (2); Pres Church Yth Grp; Sec 4-H; Key Clb; Ski Clb; Soroptimist; Chorus; JV Fld Hcky; Var L Trk; Hon Roll; NHS; Lib Arts.

RODOCHA, REGINA; Allen HS; Allentown, PA; (3); 59/610; Cmnty Wkr; Stu Cncl; Bsktbl; Sftbl; Trk; Vllybl; Wt Lftg; Hon Roll; Jr NHS; NHS; Psych.

RODOWICZ, CHRISTOPHER; Arch Bishop Wood For Boys; Iuyland, PA; (2); 48/260; JV Crs Cntry; JV Socr; JV Trk; Var Hon Roll.

RODOWICZ, KEVIN; Archbishop Wood HS; Ivyland, PA; (3); 15/250; Cmnty Wkr; Var Math Tm; Scholastic Bowl; Service Clb; Yrbk Stf; Var Crs Cntry; JV Socr; Var Trk; High Hon Roll; Trs NHS; Gld Mdl Buck Cnty Sci Fair 8l; Engrng.

RODRIGUEZ, CRISTINA; Philadelphia HS For Girls; Philadelphia, PA; (3); Teachers Aide; Band; Concert Band; Jazz Band; Mrchg Band; Orch; VP Stage Crew; NHS; Aerospc Tech.

RODRIGUEZ, DMAYDA; Little Flower HS; Philadelphia, PA; (3); Library Aide; Chorus; School Play; Church Yth Grp; Latin Clb; Church Choir; Mrchg Band; Hon Roll; Ind Hnr 86 & 87; NRS.

RODRIGUEZ, GLADYS; Mastbaum Voc Tech HS; Philadelphia, PA; (4); 14/288; Church Yth Grp; Dance Clb; FBLA; Math Tm; Rep Sr Cls; High Hon Roll; Pres Schlr; 4-H; Church Choir; Yrbk Stf; Pres Ftns Awd, Top Stu Chem Awd, Acdmc Achvt Awd 87; Temple U; Phys Thrpy.

RODRIGUEZ, GREGORY; Devon Preparatory Schl; Philadelphia, PA; (3); Church Yth Grp; Dance Clb; Drama Clb; French Clb; JA; Latin Clb; Radio Clb; Church Choir; School Play; Stage Crew; Inmclt Coll Awd Essy 87; Frnch Awd JR Cls 87; Sci.

RODRIGUEZ, IRENE; Reading HS; Reading, PA; (3); 131/710; Pres Church Yth Grp; VP FCA; JA; Library Aide; Office Aide; Hon Roll; Lab Tech.

RODRIGUEZ, JOEL; Christian Schl Of York; York, PA; (2); Church Yth Grp; Bsktbl; Hon Roll.

RODWELL, CLIFF; East HS; West Chester, PA; (3); Pep Clb; Ski Clb; Yrbk Stf; Tennis; Hon Roll; Prfct Atten Awd.

RODZINAK, VANESSA; Lake-Lehman HS; Hunlock Creek, PA; (4); 5/155; Ski Clb; Hon Roll; NHS; Grl Mnth Harveys Lake Womns Svc Clb 87; Robert C Byrd Schlrshp 87; Kings Coll; Bio.

ROE, CHERYL; Susquehanna Community HS; Susquehanna, PA; (3); 8/84; Church Yth Grp; Computer Clb; Girl Scts; Church Choir; Hon Roll; Misercordia; Acctg.

ROE, RHONDA; Penn-Trafford HS; Trafford, PA; (4); Pres AFS; 4-H; Hosp Aide; VP JA; Math Clb; Pres Chorus; Lit Mag; Var Diving; High Hon Roll; Aud/Vis; PA St Capitl Page 86; IN U PA Smmr Schl Arts 86; Westmoreld Cnty 4-H Brd Dir 86-87; PA ST U; Arch Engr.

ROEDER, CHARLES; Pine Grove Area HS; Tremont, PA; (3); Stu Cncl; Var L Bsktbl; JV Ftbl.

ROEHM, BRANDEN; Chichester SR HS; Marcus Hook, PA; (3); 3/375; Model UN; Spanish Clb; Wt Lftg; High Hon Roll; NHS; Spanish NHS; Dudas Dive Schl; Profsnl Scuba.

ROESCH, MAUREEN; Bishop Guilfoyle HS; Altoona, PA; (4); 4/129; Art Clb; Church Yth Grp; Cmnty Wkr; German Clb; Mrchg Band; Yrbk Stf; Trs Jr Cls; Trs Sr Cls; Rep Stu Cncl; Bsktbl; PA ST U; Bus.

ROESCH, MICHELLE; Bishop Guilfoyle HS; Altoona, PA; (4); 14/117; Cmnty Wkr; Science Clb; Mrchg Band; Yrbk Stf; Rep Soph Cls; Trs Jr Cls; Sec Sr Cls; Var JV Bsktbl; Cit Awd; Hon Roll; PA ST U; Bus.

ROETHER, DENISE; Ephrata SR HS; Stevens, PA; (3); Off FBLA; Im Trk; Hon Roll; Sec.

ROGAL, JESSICA; Pennsbury HS; Morrisville, PA; (3); French Clb; Political Wkr; Chorus; Yrbk Stf; Var Crs Cntry; JV Fld Hcky; Var Trk; Hon Roll; NHS; Subrbn All Leag Grl Vrsty Crss Cntry 86-87; Stu Mnth 85; Schlstc Awd Excllnc Vrsty Athltcs 87; Poltcl Sci.

ROGALEWICZ, JUDITH; West Scranton SR HS; Scranton, PA; (3); FNA; Hon Roll; NHS; JR Acad Sci 84; Natl JR Hnr Soc 84; Intr Dcrtng.

ROGALSKI, LYNNE; Old Forge HS; Old Forge, PA; (3); Cmnty Wkr; Hosp Aide; Pep Clb; Color Guard; School Play; Stage Crew; Hon Roll; NHS.

ROGAN, KELLI; Trinity HS; Carlisle, PA; (4); 4/140; Drama Clb; French Clb; School Musical; Ed Yrbk Stf; Gym; Trk; NHS; Pep Clb; Ski Clb; Stage Crew; Am Lgn Aux Dept Schl Awd 87; Slvr Mdl Excllnc Math 87; Brnz Mdl Excllnc Frnch 87; Clemson U; Pre Med.

ROGEL, RENA; Northern Cambria HS; Barnesboro, PA; (3); 13/158; French Clb; Ski Clb; Color Guard; Concert Band; Yrbk Ed-Chief; High Hon Roll; NHS; Dist & ST Hstry Day 86; Pre Law.

ROGERS, DANA; Penn-Trafford HS; Irwin, PA; (2); Hon Roll; Dntstry.

ROGERS, EVALENA; Oil City SR HS; Oil City, PA; (3); 11/250; Trs FBLA; Pres Girl Scts; Capt Color Guard; Variety Show; Nwsp Stf; High Hon Roll; Hon Roll; Prfct Atten Awd; 3rd Pl Clerk Typist I FBLA Conf 85-86; Silver Awd & Silver Ldrshp Awd-Girl Scouts 84; Bus Educ.

ROGERS, GREGORY; Bensalem HS; Bensalem, PA; (2); Bsktbl; Ftbl; Trk; Hon Roll; Penn ST U.

ROGERS, HEATHER L; Waynesburg Central HS; Blacksville, WV; (3); French Clb; Natl Beta Clb; Ski Clb; Band; Color Guard; Mrchg Band; High Hon Roll; Sec NHS.

ROGERS, JANA; Penn Wood HS; Lansdowne, PA; (3); VICA; Yrbk Phtg; Yrbk Stf; Var Cheerleading; JV Var Mgr(s); Var Stat Vllybl; High Hon Roll; Hon Roll; Prfct Atten Awd; Spcl Recgntn Geom 86-87; Hair Stylst.

ROGERS, JENNIFER; Susquehannock HS; New Freedom, PA; (4); Church Yth Grp; Office Aide; Chorus; Yrbk Rptr; Var Mgr(s); Var Sftbl; Mgr Vllybl; Hon Roll; NHS; Loyola Coll; Adv.

ROGERS, KIMBERLY ANNE; Shippensburg Area SR HS; Shippensburg, PA; (4); 2/220; Am Leg Aux Girls St; Girl Scts; SADD; Varsity Clb; Band; Chorus; School Musical; School Play; Stu Cncl; Fld Hcky; Century III Ldrshp Awd 86; Hugh O Brian Yth Ldrshp Seminar 84; Rotary Club Schlrshp 87; Gettysburg Coll.

ROGERS, LINDA; Jefferson-Morgan HS; Jefferson, PA; (3); 16/69; Intnl Clb; Library Aide; Red Cross Aide; Spanish Clb; Teachers Aide; Nwsp Rptr; Sec Sr Cls; Co-Capt Twrlr; Hon Roll; Spanish NHS; Waynesburg Coll; Nrsng.

ROGERS, LORI; Lake Lehman HS; Lehman, PA; (3); 2/231; Pres Key Clb; SADD; Color Guard; Mrchg Band; Yrbk Stf; Twrlr; High Hon Roll; Jr NHS; NHS; NEDT Awd; Research.

ROGERS, ROBERT; Council Rock HS; Newtown, PA; (3); 31/908; Orch; Var Crs Cntry; Var Trk; NHS; Chem.

ROGOVIN, MICHAEL; St Pius X HS; Obelisk, PA; (1); 31/148; SADD; Ftbl; Wt Lftg; Hon Roll; Jr NHS; St Pius X Schlrshp 86.

ROGOZINSKI, RONALD; Allentown Central Catholic HS; Coopersburg, PA; (3); Concert Band; Jazz Band; Mrchg Band; Orch; Ed Nwsp Phtg; Var Crs Cntry; Hon Roll; NHS; Rep Frsh Cls; PA Jr Acad Of Sci-ST 2nd Pl 85; Diocesan Band; Accntng.

ROHAL, TODD; Avella JR SR HS; W Middletown, PA; (4); Pres Art Clb; French Clb; Math Tm; Nwsp Stf; Pres Frsh Cls; VP Rep Stu Cncl; Hon Roll; VP Jr Cls; Acdmc Schlrshp 87; Westminster Coll PA.

ROHALL, MICHAEL; Churchill HS; Pittsburgh, PA; (2); 14/222; Ski Clb; JV Bsbl; High Hon Roll; Hon Roll; Engrng.

ROHAN, JOEL; Cathedral Prep; Erie, PA; (3); 30/194; Model UN; Im Bsktbl; Hon Roll; Phy Thrpy.

ROHANNA, KELLY; Waynesburg Central HS; Waynesburg, PA; (3); Mu Alpha Theta; VP Natl Beta Clb; Spanish Clb; Stu Cncl; Bus.

ROHLAND JR, JACK WADE; Freeport Area HS; Sarver, PA; (4); 17/170; Var Capt Ftbl; Var Trk; High Hon Roll; NHS; Opt Clb Awd; Pres Schlr; Freeport Area HS Schlstc Ltr 87; US Marine Corps Stu Athlt Awd 87; U Of Pittsburgh; Pharm.

ROHLER, SHARON; Mercyhurst Prep Schl; Erie, PA; (3); Spanish Clb; Yrbk Stf; Lit Mag; Hon Roll; NHS.

ROHLFING, DENISE; Lehighton Area HS; Lehighton, PA; (3); 23/240; Art Clb; SADD; Chorus; Stage Crew; Hon Roll; NHS; Top Acad Awd 87; Elem Educ.

ROHLFING, MARK; Central Bucks HS West; Chalfont, PA; (3); 44/481; Var Crs Cntry; Var L Trk; High Hon Roll; Hon Roll; Prfct Atten Awd; Natl Sci Olympiad-Chemistry 86-7; Bio Sci.

ROHLIN, RICHARD J; Eisenhower HS; Russell, PA; (3); 4/112; Math Tm; VP Soph Cls; Pres Jr Cls; Pres Sr Cls; Var Bsbl; Var L Bsktbl; Var L Golf; High Hon Roll; Jr NHS; NHS.

ROHM, KEVIN; Connellsville Area HS; Connellsville, PA; (3); 54/530; Computer Clb; Band; Mrchg Band; Stu Cncl; French Hon Soc; Hon Roll; Jr NHS; NHS; Prfct Atten Awd; Acctng.

ROHRBACH, JENNIFER DEBRA; Brandywine Heights HS; Fleetwood, PA; (2); 32/140; Band; Chorus; Color Guard; Concert Band; Flag Corp; Sec Soph Cls; Sec Stu Cncl; Var Cheerleading; Hon Roll; Rotary Awd; Kutztown U; Bus Mgmt.

ROHRBAUGH, MARY; Bermudian Springs HS; Dillsburg, PA; (3); Dance Clb; Band; Chorus; Church Choir; Co-Capt Color Guard; Concert Band; Drill Tm; Madrigals; Mrchg Band; School Musical; Empire Beauty Schl; Csmtlgy.

ROHRER, LONNA; Pequea Valley HS; Paradise, PA; (3); 16/141; Sec Church Yth Grp; GAA; Thesps; Sec Varsity Clb; Acpl Chr; Chorus; Church Choir; Madrigals; School Musical; School Play.

ROHRER, MICHELE; Manheim Central HS; Lititz, PA; (4); 3/217; Trs Church Yth Grp; 4-H; Band; Chorus; School Musical; Yrbk Ed-Chief; Tennis; NHS; Ntl Merit Ltr; Messiah Coll; Social Work.

ROHRER, TIFFANY; Oxford Area HS; Nottingham, PA; (3); Sec Church Yth Grp; Sec 4-H; Sec FFA; Nwsp Ed-Chief; Var Bsktbl; Sftbl; 4-H Awd; High Hon Roll; NHS; Scholastic Bowl; Hugh O Brian Smnr Schl Rep 85-86; Pre Vet.

ROHRHIRSCH, RHONDA; Bishop Guilfoyle HS; Altoona, PA; (3); Art Clb; Girl Scts; Var Tennis; Penn ST U; Psych.

ROKE, LISA; John S Fine HS; Glen Lyon, PA; (4); Am Leg Aux Girls St; Key Clb; Library Aide; Model UN; Speech Tm; Chorus; Hon Roll; Unsung Heros Awd-Spch 87; SR Awd-Spch 87; 3rd Pl Spch Tm Awd 87; Penn ST; Comp Sci.

ROKICKA, KIMBERLY; Avon Grove HS; West Grove, PA; (3); Church Yth Grp; FBLA; Library Aide; SADD; Chorus; Church Choir; Var Capt Cheerleading; Im Wt Lftg; Cit Awd; Elected Prlmentrn Of Locl Chapt FBLA 86; Elected Rgn 9 Rcrdng Sec For FBLA 87; 2nd Pl Rgn Wrstlng Ch; Glassboro ST Coll; Pre-Law.

ROLAND, CHRISTINA; Greensburg Salem SR HS; Greensburg, PA; (3); 75/302; French Clb; Library Aide; Office Aide; Red Cross Aide; Chorus; Mat Maids; High Hon Roll; Hon Roll; Pre-Schl Child Care.

ROLAND, JENNIFER; West York Area SR HS; York, PA; (2); Trs French Clb; Chorus; Swing Chorus; Sec Frsh Cls; Sec Soph Cls; Rep Stu Cncl; JV Cheerleading; Naval Acad.

ROLAND, KEVIN; Our Lady Of The Sacred Heart HS; Pittsburgh, PA; (4); 1/57; Computer Clb; School Play; Stage Crew; Bowling; Socr; Cit Awd; DAR Awd; High Hon Roll; Pres NHS; Pres Schlr; MVP Soccer Team,Capt 87; DAR Good Citizen Awd 87; Econ,Calculus,Physcs,Comp Sci Awds 87; Rensselaer Polytech Inst; Engr.

ROLAND, KRISTIN; Conrad Weiser HS; Robesonia, PA; (3); 11/179; German Clb; Key Clb; Chorus; School Musical; Variety Show; Nwsp Sprt Ed; Yrbk Sprt Ed; Lit Mag; Pres Stu Cncl; Bsktbl; Berks Cnty Girls Golf Champnshp 1st Pl 85-86; Dist 3 Golf Champnshp 6th Pl 86; PA ST Grls Golf Finls; Bio.

ROLES, CHRISTA; Blacklick Valley JR SR HS; Strongstown, PA; (2); 5/105; Church Yth Grp; Library Aide; NFL; Varsity Clb; Yrbk Stf; Stu Cncl; Trk; Hon Roll; Acad All Amrcn Schlr 85-86; Prsdntl Acad Ftnss Awd 85-86.

ROLF, ANN; Kiski Area HS; New Kensington, PA; (3); Hosp Aide; Ski Clb; Band; Concert Band; Mrchg Band; Symp Band; Yrbk Stf; Rep Stu Cncl; High Hon Roll; Hon Roll; Hnrs Band 85; Mrtkg.

ROLKO, MICHELE; East Pennsboro HS; Enola, PA; (3); Camera Clb; Girl Scts; Latin Clb; Yrbk Phtg; Var Bsktbl; JV Fld Hcky; Var Sftbl; Hon Roll.

ROLLESTON, HOWARD; The Chrisitan Acad; Glen Mills, PA; (3); French Clb; Letterman Clb; Chorus; Pres Soph Cls; Var Crs Cntry; JV Trk; Hon Roll.

ROLLINS, JULI; North Hills SR HS; Pittsburgh, PA; (3); AFS; Drama Clb; French Clb; NFL; Pres Pep Clb; Speech Tm; Rep Stu Cncl; Cheerleading; High Hon Roll; Church Yth Grp; WV ST Frnscs Champ Declamtn 86; U Pittsburgh; Frgn Lang.

ROLLINSON, THOMAS; Hermitage School District; Hermitage, PA; (3); 47/167; Dance Clb; German Clb; Letterman Clb; JV Var Ftbl; Im Vllybl; Grove City Coll; Mech Engr.

ROLLS, HEATHER; Lower Moreland HS; Huntingdon Valley, PA; (3); Church Yth Grp; FBLA; Science Clb; Off Stu Cncl; Score Keeper; L JV Sftbl; Stat JV Wrstlng; High Hon Roll; Hon Roll; Math Ed.

ROLSTON, MICHELLE; Newport JR-SR HS; Newport, PA; (2); 6/130; Chorus; School Play; Sec Frsh Cls; Pres Soph Cls; Rep Stu Cncl; Bsktbl; Fld Hcky; Sftbl; Vllybl; Wt Lftg; Acad All Amer Schlr Pgm 84; Headhunters; Beautcian.

ROMAN, DEBRA; Chichester HS; Trainer, PA; (3); 22/293; Spanish Clb; Band; Stu Cncl; Var Cheerleading; Var Lcrss; JV Sftbl; Twrlr; Hon Roll; Prfct Atten Awd; Spanish NHS; Neumann Coll; RN.

ROMAN, JEANNE; Lansdale Catholic HS; Lansdale, PA; (3); Chess Clb; Dance Clb; Stage Crew; Variety Show; Bowling; Hon Roll; Chem.

ROMAN, JILL; Greensburg Central Catholic HS; Greensburg, PA; (3); Cmnty Wkr; Trs Exploring; Hosp Aide; Pep Clb; Ski Clb; School Musical; Nwsp Ed-Chief; Im Vllybl; High Hon Roll; NHS; Med.

ROMAN, KYMM; Nazareth Acad; Phila, PA; (3); Boys Clb Am; Church Yth Grp; 4-H; Spanish Clb; Variety Show; Var Socr; Hon Roll; Athltc Awds 85-87; Phila Natl Sccr Sprtsmnshp Awd 84-85; La Salle U; Bus Admin.

ROMAN, MAUREEN; Little Flower Catholic HS For Girls; Philadelphia, PA; (3); Office Aide; Rep Frsh Cls; Rep Soph Cls; Rep Jr Cls; Rep Sr Cls; Rep Stu Cncl; Im Bsktbl; Im Powder Puff Ftbl; Schl Cnslr.

ROMAN, MELANIE; West Middlesex JR SR HS; West Middlesex, PA; (2); Sec Church Yth Grp; Sec French Clb; Service Clb; Band; Mrchg Band; Wt Lftg; Hon Roll.

ROMAN, MELISSA; West Middlesex HS; West Middlesex, PA; (2); Library Aide; Office Aide; Spanish Clb; Sec Frsh Cls; Var Capt Cheerleading; Hon Roll; NHS; Stu Schvrs Accntng I 87; Tchr.

ROMAN, RICHARD; Dunmore HS; Dunmore, PA; (3); French Clb; Ski Clb; Y-Teens; Variety Show; Nwsp Rptr; Trs Sr Cls; Ftbl; Swmmng; Trk; Hon Roll; Penn ST; Htl/Rest Mgt.

ROMANCE, JANNETTE; Western Wayne HS; Aldenville, PA; (4); 14/140; Pres Church Yth Grp; Pres 4-H; FBLA; Pres SADD; Church Choir; Mrchg Band; Rep Frsh Cls; VP Soph Cls; Pres Jr Cls; Pres Sr Cls; Amer Red Cross Rep Brd Dir 85-87; Nrsng.

ROMANIA, GREG; Southern Columbia HS; Catawissa, PA; (3); Exploring; Ski Clb; Bsktbl; Trk; Wt Lftg; Elecrncs.

ROMANIC, MARY LYNNE; St Marys Area HS; Byrnedale, PA; (4); 8/279; Girl Scts; Sec Stu Cncl; Capt Trk; Hon Roll; Lion Awd; NHS; ICM Schl Bus; Trvl.

ROMANIE, MATTHEW; Homer Center JR SR HS; Homer City, PA; (3); French Clb; SADD; Band; Concert Band; Jazz Band; Nwsp Bus Mgr; Yrbk Stf; NHS; 1st Pl Grtr PA Bwlng Schlrshp Tourn 86; Gannon U; Med.

ROMANIK, CHARLENE L; Emmaus HS; Emmaus, PA; (4); 16/461; Am Leg Aux Girls St; Band; Chorus; Rep Frsh Cls; High Hon Roll; Jr NHS; NHS; Prfct Atten Awd; Pres Schlr; Spanish NHS; JR Wmns Clb & Wmns Clb Schlrshp 87; Penn ST U; Intl Reltns.

ROMANISKO, JULIE; Jim Thrope HS; Jim Thorpe, PA; (3); 4/90; Chorus; Nwsp Stf; Var Cheerleading; High Hon Roll; NHS; Pharm.

ROMANO, AMELIA; Pocono Mountain HS; Tobyhanna, PA; (4); 136/291; Church Yth Grp; Cmnty Wkr; Hosp Aide; Library Aide; Science Clb; Hon Roll; Hnr Rl; Awd Lib Asst; E Stroudsburg; Nrsng.

ROMANO, JOE; Mc Guffey HS; Washington, PA; (2); 3/227; Var L Bsbl; Var L Bsktbl; High Hon Roll; Stu Rcgntn Awd 85-86; Stu Rcgntn Awd 86-87.

ROMANO, JOHN; Deer Lakes JR SR HS; Gibsonia, PA; (3); Drama Clb; Varsity Clb; JV Var Ftbl; Var Capt Vllybl; Hon Roll; Acctng.

ROMANO, KIMBERLY; Old Forge HS; Old Forge, PA; (3); 3/30; Stu Cncl; High Hon Roll; NHS; Art Clb; Ski Clb; Spanish Clb; School Play; NEIU.

ROMANO, NICOLE; Wyoming Seminary HS; Weatherly, PA; (3); Art Clb; 4-H; GAA; SADD; Varsity Clb; Band; Chorus; Concert Band; Mrchg Band; Pep Band; Mst Vlbl Swmmr 86-87; Rsdnts Asst 87-88; Phys Thrpy.

ROMANOFSKY, KAREN; Steelton-Highspire HS; Steelton, PA; (3); 12/102; Band; Concert Band; Jazz Band; Mrchg Band; Pep Band; School Musical; Stage Crew; Yrbk Stf; High Hon Roll; NHS.

ROMANOWSKI, PATTY; Wyoming Area SR HS; W Pittston, PA; (2); Spanish Clb; SADD.

ROMANSKI, MARIBETH; Holy Name HS; Reading, PA; (3); 20/119; Church Yth Grp; Capt Flag Corp; School Musical; School Play; Var Score Keeper; Hon Roll; NHS; Exploring; Band; Hghst Grd Alge/Trgnmtry & Music Theory 86-87; Var Let Music 86-87; Math.

ROMANUSKI, CONNIE; Shenandoah Valley JR/Sr HS; Shenandoah, PA; (3); Band; Var JV Bsktbl; Mgr Crs Cntry; JV Trk; Co-Capt Twrlr; Hon Roll; Penn ST U; Social Wrkr.

ROMBERGER, JENNIFER; Central Dauphin HS HS; Harrisburg, PA; (3); 23/369; Dance Clb; Chorus; Madrigals; School Musical; School Play; Im Vllybl; High Hon Roll; Hon Roll; NHS; Pres Schlr; Pres Acad Fitness Awd 85; GFWC PA Fdtn Wmnc Club Awd 87; Harrisburg Cmnty Theatre Schl Awd 84-85; IN U; Mgmt.

ROMBERGER, LEE ANN; Williams Valley JR-SR HS; Williamstown, PA; (3); 18/101; Office Aide; Chorus; Co-Capt Drill Tm; School Musical; Yrbk Stf; Sec Jr Cls; Rep Stu Cncl; Stat Bsktbl; Capt Ftbl; Mgr Wrstlng; Bloomsburg; Scndry Educ.

ROMBOLD, JOHN; Sharon HS; Sharon, PA; (3); 18/182; Church Yth Grp; French Clb; Variety Show; Nwsp Rptr; Nwsp Sprt Ed; Rep Stu Cncl; Var Ftbl; Var L Trk; Var L Wrstlng; Hon Roll.

ROME, MARIANNE; St Francis HS; West Mifflin, PA; (2); 3/58; NFL; Pep Clb; Service Clb; SADD; High Hon Roll; Bradford U; Bus.

ROMEO, ANITA; Center HS; Monaca, PA; (4); 28/186; Spanish Clb; Band; Concert Band; Drm Mjr(t); Mrchg Band; School Musical; Hon Roll; NHS; Sewickley Symph Orch 84-87; Beaver Cnty Hnrs Band 87; Clarion U; Med Tech.

ROMEO, MICHAEL; St John Neumann HS; Philadelphia, PA; (2); 40/350; Exploring; Band; Concert Band; Drm & Bgl; Pep Band; Hon Roll.

ROMEO, RONALD; Center HS; Monaca, PA; (2); Spanish Clb; Varsity Clb; Band; Concert Band; Jazz Band; Mrchg Band; Symp Band; Crs Cntry; Trk; Hon Roll; Westminster Hnrs Band 86 & 87; Beaver Cnty Hnrs Band 87.

ROMICH, TAMMY; Scranton Central HS; Scranton, PA; (4); 149/306; Church Yth Grp; French Clb; JA; SADD; Band; Church Choir; Concert Band; Mrchg Band; Gold Awd Band-4 Yr 87; Pinebrook JC; Chld Psych.

ROMIG, CYNTHIA; Owen J Roberts HS; Pottstown, PA; (2); 9/311; Church Yth Grp; Library Aide; Chorus; Church Choir; Flag Corp; School Musical; Stu Cncl; High Hon Roll; Mem Of Owen J Roberts Chptr Of Amnsty Intl; Mem Of Stud Advsry.

ROMIGH, KELLY M; Sewickley Acad; Beaver, PA; (4); French Clb; Chorus; School Play; Nwsp Ed-Chief; Ed Nwsp Stf; Off Lit Mag; Sec Stu Cncl; High Hon Roll; Hon Roll; Geo Washington U; Cmnctns.

ROMINSKI, CAROL; Hanover Area JR SR HS; Wilkes Barre, PA; (3); Color Guard; Drill Tm; Mrchg Band; Trk; Tsunmi Blue Indr Guard Ntl Jdgs Assc Chmpnshp Guard 85 & 87; Phys Thrpst.

ROMITO, CARRIE; Garnet Valley HS; Glen Mills, PA; (2); 14/169; French Clb; Ski Clb; Teachers Aide; Varsity Clb; Off Frsh Cls; Off Soph Cls; Stu Cncl; Fld Hcky; Lcrss; Score Keeper; Comp Engr.

RONAN, DANA; Bishop Guilfoyle HS; Altoona, PA; (4); 11/123; Church Yth Grp; Dance Clb; Red Cross Aide; Y-Teens; Trs Frsh Cls; Rep Jr Cls; Stu Cncl; Cheerleading; High Hon Roll; Hon Roll; Hmcmng Ct 85-86; Physics Club 86-87; PA ST U; Optometry.

RONAN, TIMOTHY; Moshannon Valley HS; Houtzdale, PA; (3); 8/120; Math Clb; Pep Clb; Ski Clb; Spanish Clb; Varsity Clb; JV Bsbl; Bsktbl; JV Ftbl; Wrstlng; NHS.

RONCHI, JILL; Valley View HS; Peckville, PA; (2); Art Clb; French Clb; Rep Sec Stu Cncl; Var Cheerleading; Var Trk; Var Vllybl; Hon Roll.

RONCHI, MARK; Valley View HS; Peckville, PA; (3); 27/197; Latin Clb; Ftbl; Trk; Wt Lftg; Sprts Med.

RONEY, TODD; Danville Area HS; Danville, PA; (2); Ski Clb; Varsity Clb; Rep Frsh Cls; Hst Soph Cls; JV Bsktbl; Var Ftbl; Var Trk; DE; Therapist.

RONEY, WILLIAM; East HS; West Chester, PA; (2); Socr; Comp Engr.

RONGAUS, LEE; Mon Valley Catholic HS; Donora, PA; (2); French Clb; Ski Clb; Rep Soph Cls; JV Bsktbl; L Ftbl; L Socr; US Naval Acad.

RONGHI, ANNE MARIE; Hopewell HS; Aliquippa, PA; (3); Church Yth Grp; Drama Clb; Hosp Aide; Library Aide; Band; Chorus; Concert Band; Mrchg Band; Variety Show; Yrbk Stf; Cathlc Yth Mnsty Yth Cncl Rep 86-88; Smmr Theater Co 87; Music.

ROOF, REGINA; Cedar Crest HS; Lebanon, PA; (4); Am Leg Aux Girls St; Drama Clb; 4-H; German Clb; Key Clb; SADD; Chorus; Cit Awd; 4-H Awd; Hon Roll; Messiah Coll; Psych.

ROOFNER, FRANKLIN; Leechburg Area HS; Vandergrift, PA; (4); VP JA; Band; Concert Band; Mrchg Band; Pep Band; Stage Crew; Yrbk Stf; Trs Jr Cls; Capt Vllybl; Upr Burrel Shamrcks Mrchng Grp/Natl VFW Chmpns, ST Amer Lgn Chmpns Hershey PA, ST VFW Chmpns 84; Thiel Coll.

ROOK, MICHELLE; Butler Area SR HS; Butler, PA; (4); Church Yth Grp; FBLA; Office Aide; School Musical; Swing Chorus; Rep Stu Cncl; Var L Gym; Var L Socr; Cmnty Wkr; Chorus; Pres Of Ushers Clb 86-87; Sccr Coach For YMCA 86; Acad Schlrshp To Franciscan U Of Steubenville 87; Franciscan U Steubenville; Bus.

ROOKEY, AUSTIN; Oil City HS; Oil City, PA; (3); Church Yth Grp; German Clb; Science Clb; VP Y-Teens; Acpl Chr; VP Chorus; Var Drill Tm; Drm Mjr(t); School Musical; School Play; Rotary German Exchange & Jr Olympics 87; Law.

ROONEY, BECKY CHRISS; Central Dauphin East HS; Dauphin, PA; (3); 15/290; Am Leg Aux Girls St; Band; Capt Flag Corp; Yrbk Stf; Sec Soph Cls; Sec Jr Cls; Var Swmmng; Hon Roll; Jr NHS; VP NHS; Pres Acad Ftnss Awd 85; Psych.

ROONEY, KELLY; Bishop Hannan HS; Scranton, PA; (3); Spanish Clb; Yrbk Rptr; Rep Frsh Cls; Sec Jr Cls; Rep Sr Cls; Rep Stu Cncl; Var Capt Cheerleading; Sftbl; Hon Roll; NHS; Physcl Ther.

ROONEY, ROB A; Phoenixville Area HS; Phoenixville, PA; (2); Ed Lit Mag; VP Frsh Cls; Rep Soph Cls; Var Socr; JV Tennis; Emerson Coll; Film.

ROONEY, TIMOTHY; Central Catholic HS; Pittsburgh, PA; (3); 33/260; Boy Scts; Exploring; Ski Clb; Spanish Clb; Stage Crew; Crs Cntry; Trk; Hon Roll; NHS; Spanish NHS; U VA; Pre Med.

ROONEY, WILLIAM; Faith Community Christian Schl; Pittsburgh, PA; (4); 3/24; Capt Aud/Vis; Church Yth Grp; Computer Clb; Capt Stage Crew; Ftbl; Dnfth Awd; High Hon Roll; NEDT Awd; Elec Engrng.

ROOSA, MICHELE; Downingtown SR HS; Downingtown, PA; (3); Church Yth Grp; Dance Clb; Exploring; SADD; School Play; Hon Roll; Flght Attendnt.

ROOSE, TRACY; Yough SR HS; Hutchinson, PA; (3); Church Yth Grp; Library Aide; Pep Clb; Ski Clb; Spanish Clb; Teachers Aide; Band; Chorus; Hon Roll.

ROOT, DAN; East Pennsboro HS; Enola, PA; (2); 29/190; VP Church Yth Grp; Spanish Clb; Chorus; Church Choir; JV Socr; High Hon Roll; Hon Roll; Messiah Coll; Comp Pgmmr.

ROOT, JAMES; Athens HS; Athens, PA; (3); Church Yth Grp; Ski Clb; Var Bsbl; Var Crs Cntry; Capt L Swmmng; Hon Roll; Prfct Atten Awd; Mst Outstndng Swmmr 86; Mst Outstndng Swmmr & Swmmr/Rly Tm, Chem Awd 87; Engrng.

ROOT, MARK; North Catholic HS; Pittsburgh, PA; (3); 105/305; Church Yth Grp; Exploring; French Clb; Stage Crew; Var Bsktbl; Var Ftbl; Hon Roll.

ROOTE, DENISE; John S Fine HS; Nanticoke, PA; (2); 16/243; Band; Concert Band; Mrchg Band; Pep Band; High Hon Roll; Hon Roll; Sci Mdl 85; Awds Math & Readg 85; Math.

ROPER, TRACY; Perry Traditional Acad; Pittsburgh, PA; (3); 24/170; Camera Clb; FHA; Ski Clb; Yrbk Stf; Coach Actv; Cit Awd; High Hon Roll; Hon Roll; Carnegie Mellon U; Ilstrtv Art.

ROPIETSKI, JOSEPH; Hanover HS; Wilkes Barre, PA; (3); 30/195; Variety Show; Stu Cncl; Capt Bsbl; Capt Ftbl; Capt Wrstlng; Hon Roll; All-Schlstc Bsbl, Ftbl; Dist Wrstlng 3rd Pl; Chem.

ROPON, KARRIE; Quigley HS; Fair Oaks, PA; (4); Camera Clb; Church Yth Grp; Cmnty Wkr; Var JV Cheerleading; Mgr(s); L Pom Pon; Powder Puff Ftbl; Concert Band; Mrchg Band; Yrbk Phtg; Spd & Accrcy Typg Awd 86; Troph Chrldg Ftbl Seasn & Quigley Clssc 86-87; Geneva Coll; Elem Ed.

ROPSKI, SANDRA; Interboro HS; Prospect Park, PA; (3); VP Church Yth Grp; Intnl Clb; SADD; Drill Tm; Mrchg Band; Nwsp Rptr; Nwsp Stf; Yrbk Stf; Lit Mag; Mat Maids; Stuart Hall Essay Schlrshp Cont 84; Acad All-Amer 86; Drexel U; Informtn Studies.

ROSADO, TOMAS; Louis E Dieruff HS; Allentown, PA; (3); Cmnty Wkr; Hosp Aide; JA; Latin Clb; Bsktbl; Socr; Sftbl; Wt Lftg; Allentown Bus Schl.

ROSAGE, LAURA; Bishop Mc Cort HS; Johnstown, PA; (3); Sec Latin Clb; Math Tm; Mu Alpha Theta; Band; Chorus; Concert Band; Mrchg Band; Orch; High Hon Roll; NHS; Bus Adm.

ROSAGE, LISA; Bishop Mc Cort HS; Johnstown, PA; (4); 11/133; Dance Clb; JCL; Latin Clb; Mu Alpha Theta; Pep Clb; Teachers Aide; Band; Chorus; Drm Mjr(t); NHS; Latin Awd 87; Drctrs Awd 87; Ntl Merit Ldrshp Awd 86; Indiana U Of PA; Educ.

ROSAK, JO ANN; South Side HS; Georgetown, PA; (3); 6/150; Am Leg Aux Girls St; Sec Church Yth Grp; 4-H; Varsity Clb; Church Choir; Stat Bsbl; Var Bsktbl; Co-Capt Pom Pon; NHS; Lang.

ROSARIO, YOLANDA; Mastbaum Area Vo Tech; Philadelphia, PA; (2); DECA; Chorus; Hon Roll; Ntl Merit Awd 1st Hnrs 86-87; Pierce JC.

ROSATO, LEE V; Hazleton SR HS; Mc Adoo, PA; (3); Pres Church Yth Grp; Cmnty Wkr; Hosp Aide; Im Bsbl; Pres Ftbl; Im Diving; Im Swmmng; Im Wt Lftg; Hazleton SR H S Athletic Awd 84-86; Cert Of Achvmnt Awd 83; Emergency Med.

ROSATO, MARIA; St Maria Goretti HS; Philadelphia, PA; (4); 53/384; VP Church Yth Grp; Cmnty Wkr; French Clb; GAA; Math Clb; Stage Crew; Hon Roll; Sec NHS; Prfct Atten Awd; Pres Schlr; Cert Apprctn CYO 85-86; Knghts Clmbs Essy Cntst Wnnr 86; Temple U; Bus Admin.

ROSBACH, MICHELLE; St Basil Acad; Philadelphia, PA; (3); 19/84; Church Yth Grp; Sec Drama Clb; French Clb; SADD; Thesps; Chorus; School Play; Yrbk Stf; Im Sftbl; Im Vllybl; Bus Admin.

ROSBOROUGH, VICKIE; Monessen HS; Monessen, PA; (4); 8/93; VP JA; PAVAS; Teachers Aide; Sec Band; Drm Mjr(t); School Play; Nwsp Stf; Yrbk Stf; High Hon Roll; Sec NHS; SR Awd Special Seniors 87; Band Scholar 87; Slippery Rock U; Elem Ed.

ROSCIOLI, STEVE; Wilson Area HS; Easton, PA; (4); 11/129; Church Yth Grp; Pres Soph Cls; Rep Stu Cncl; Capt Var Ftbl; Capt Var Wrstlng; High Hon Roll; Hon Roll; Lion Awd; NHS; Rotary Awd; Sclr-Athlt Ftbl 87; U Of Pittsburg; Pharm.

ROSCOE, B; Reynolds HS; Transfer, PA; (3); 26/160; Latin Clb; Var Letterman Clb; Band; Concert Band; Nwsp Rptr; Pres Sr Cls; Rep Stu Cncl; Capt Var Ftbl; Trk; Wt Lftg; 1st Tm All Conf For Off & Def 86; All ST Hnrbl Mntn 86; Art.

ROSCOE, KATHLEEN; Elizabeth Forward HS; Elizabeth, PA; (3); AFS; Church Yth Grp; Hosp Aide; Color Guard; Nwsp Rptr; Nwsp Stf; Ed Yrbk Stf; High Hon Roll; Hon Roll; NHS; Penn ST U; Elem Educ.

ROSE, CHRISSA; Lewistown Area HS; Lewistown, PA; (2); AFS; German Clb; Yrbk Phtg; Yrbk Rptr; Yrbk Stf; Fld Hcky; High Hon Roll; NHS; Schlrshp PA Govnrs Schl Ag, Acadmc Star 87; Acdmc Ltr 86; PA ST U; Vet Sci.

ROSE, ERIC; Rockwood Avera HS; Somerset, PA; (3); 20/82; Trs FFA; Stage Crew; Trs Soph Cls; Hon Roll; Outstndng Begng Forestr 85; Greenhand Degree FFA 85; Natl Harwood Lmbr Grdng; Forsty.

ROSE, JENNIFER; Seneca HS; Erie, PA; (3); 10/160; Art Clb; School Musical; Nwsp Bus Mgr; Nwsp Rptr; Yrbk Phtg; Rep Stu Cncl; L Var Trk; L Var Twrlr; High Hon Roll; Hon Roll; Pres Phys Ftnss Awd, Hon Mntn Dist Shrt Stry Cont, & Schlrshp Lockhaven-Free Entrprs Wk 87; Envrnmntl Rsrc Mgmt.

ROSE, JILL; Immaculate Conception HS; Claysville, PA; (3); 1/52; Art Clb; Church Yth Grp; Letterman Clb; Math Tm; Sec Pres Stu Cncl; Co-Capt Cheerleading; High Hon Roll; NHS; Otstndng Stu In Alg III,Trio & US Hstry 86-87; Brown U; Corporate Law.

ROSE, KIM; Carlisle HS; Carlisle, PA; (3); Hosp Aide; JA; Var L Gym; Bus.

ROSE, LAUREN; Jenkintown HS; Huntingdon Vly, PA; (3); #10 In Class; Art Clb; Key Clb; Nwsp Phtg; Nwsp Stf; Yrbk Phtg; Yrbk Stf; Rep Frsh Cls; Rep Jr Cls; Rep Sr Cls; Var JV Mgr(s); Psych.

ROSE, MELISSA; Lawrence County Vo-Tech; New Castle, PA; (3); 18/296; Church Yth Grp; FBLA; Library Aide; Nwsp Rptr; Yrbk Stf; Trs Soph Cls; Pres Jr Cls; Stu Cncl; Hon Roll; Prfct Atten Awd; Voctnl Excllnce Awd 86-87; Child Psych.

ROSE, SHARON; Harbor Creek HS; Erie, PA; (4); 1/216; Church Yth Grp; Trs Model UN; Trs Band; Mrchg Band; Pep Band; Trs Sr Cls; Var Bsktbl; Gov Hon Prg Awd; Trs NHS; Rotary Yth Ldrshp Conf, PA Humnts & Sci Sympsm 86; Richard M Simpson Schlrshp Juniata Coll 87; Juniata Coll; Bio.

ROSE, STEPHEN; Father Judge HS; Philadelphia, PA; (3); 4/402; Cmnty Wkr; Hosp Aide; Lit Mag; Var Crs Cntry; Var Tennis; JV Trk; High Hon Roll; Hon Roll; Jr NHS; NHS; La Salle U; Bus.

ROSE, SUSAN E; Greensburg Salem HS; Greensburg, PA; (3); 72/300; Church Yth Grp; German Clb; Office Aide; Chorus; Church Choir; High Hon Roll; Hon Roll; 3rd Pl Music Grmn Mt Pleasnt Humants Day 85; Cmnty Actn Pgm 85-86; Grmn.

ROSE, TAMMY; Central Cambria HS; Portage, PA; (4); 10/214; Art Clb; French Clb; Trs FBLA; Color Guard; Mgr(s); Score Keeper; Swmmng; Hon Roll; Acctg.

ROSE, TRICIA; Southmoreland SR HS; Mt Pleasant, PA; (3); 34/228; Church Yth Grp; Exploring; Latin Clb; Letterman Clb; Ski Clb; Sec Jr Cls; Sec Sr Cls; Rep Stu Cncl; Var L Bsktbl; Var Powder Puff Ftbl; Mdcl.

ROSE, VEDA; Athens HS; Athens, PA; (3); 12/120; French Clb; FHA; Girl Scts; Teachers Aide; High Hon Roll; Hon Roll; Prfct Atten Awd; Alge/Trig Awd, Geo Awd & French Awd Being An A Stu 85-87; CA U; Math.

ROSEBERRY, ERIN; Chambersburg Area SR HS; Marion, PA; (4); Yrbk Stf; IUP; Intl Stud.

ROSEBERRY, TRICIA; Curwensville Area HS; Clearfield, PA; (3); Church Yth Grp; French Clb; Band; Chorus; Church Choir; Concert Band; Mrchg Band; Yrbk Stf; Empire Beauty Schl; Csmtlgy.

ROSEBORO, MELISSA; Cocalico HS; Denver, PA; (3); 1/176; Radio Clb; Pres Jr Cls; Off Stu Cncl; JV Var Cheerleading; Var L Tennis; High Hon Roll; NHS; Church Yth Grp; Cmnty Wkr; Pres Frsh Cls; Stu Plnning Cmmtte; Outstndng Achvt & Ldrshp-Scl Stds; Psychlgy.

ROSEBOROUGH, ROBERT; Plymouth Whitemarsh HS; Conshohocken, PA; (2); Var JV Ftbl; Var JV Wt Lftg; Hon Roll; Bus.

ROSELLI, PAMELA; Pleasant Valley HS; Saylorsburg, PA; (2); Nwsp Rptr; Nwsp Stf; Lit Mag; Rep Frsh Cls; Rep Soph Cls; Rep Stu Cncl; JV Var Bsktbl; JV Var Sftbl; Hon Roll; Jrnlsm.

ROSEMEIER, RANDAL G; Monongahela Valley Catholic HS; Cokeburg, PA; (4); 6/78; Trs Frsh Cls; Trs Soph Cls; Trs Jr Cls; Trs Sr Cls; Var L Bsbl; Var L Bsktbl; Powder Puff Ftbl; NHS; Spanish NHS; Eucharistic Minister; USAF Acad; Aerospc Engrng.

ROSEN, JOEL; Bensalem HS; Bensalem, PA; (4); 31/471; Computer Clb; Stu Cncl; Var Bsktbl; Var Score Keeper; Var Wt Lftg; High Hon Roll; Hon Roll; Pres Schlr; Beaver Coll; Comp Sci.

ROSENAU, IRA; Plymouth-Whitemarsh HS; Norristown, PA; (3); 16/384; Aud/Vis; Temple Yth Grp; Nwsp Rptr; Nwsp Sprt Ed; Yrbk Stf; Lit Mag; JV Bsbl; Socr; High Hon Roll; Jr NHS; Liberal Arts.

ROSENBAUM, RONALD; Bishop Mc Cort HS; Johnstown, PA; (3); Church Yth Grp; French Clb; Mu Alpha Theta; Chorus; Mu Alpha Theta Awd; NHS; Chemstry.

ROSENBERGER, BRIAN; Souderton HS; Telford, PA; (4); 62/340; Ski Clb; Y-Teens; Nwsp Stf; Co-Capt Var Socr; Hon Roll; Dickinson Coll; Bus.

ROSENBERGER, DEBRA; Susquenita HS; Duncannon, PA; (4); 7/150; Acpl Chr; Concert Band; Drm Mjr(t); Mrchg Band; School Musical; Yrbk Stf; Cit Awd; High Hon Roll; NHS; Grnd Chmpn Sci Fair 86; Schlrshp Compstn What Christ Means To Me Cont 87; Central Bible Coll; Missions.

ROSENBERGER, HEATHER; Northern York County HS; Dillsburg, PA; (3); Cmnty Wkr; Girl Scts; Ski Clb; SADD; Band; Color Guard; Drill Tm; Mrchg Band; Rep Frsh Cls; Rep Soph Cls.

ROSENBERGER, JULIA; Marion Center Area HS; Home, PA; (4); 27/165; VP FNA; Intnl Clb; Science Clb; Concert Band; Mrchg Band; Sec Jr Cls; Sec Sr Cls; Trs Stu Cncl; Hon Roll; NHS; Clarion U Of PA; Educ.

ROSENBERGER, MARY; Chartiers Valley HS; Pittsburgh, PA; (3); Church Yth Grp; Drama Clb; Intnl Clb; Library Aide; School Play; NHS; Ntl Merit Ltr; Pep Clb; Spanish Clb; Thesps; Garnegie Area Revitalztn Effrt Essy Contst Wnnr 87; Carnegie-Mellon U; Engrng.

ROSENBERGER, MELISSA; Central Bucks West HS; Chalfont, PA; (4); 10/473; Church Yth Grp; Band; Var L Cheerleading; Var L Fld Hcky; Var L Mgr(s); High Hon Roll; Jr NHS; Amer Assoc Of U Wmn Schlrhsp; Grls ST Alt; Latin II Awd; Presdntl Acad Fit Awd; James Madison U; Intl Bus.

ROSENBERGER, RAYMOND A; Quakertown SR HS; Quakertown, PA; (4); 8/290; Capt Scholastic Bowl; Pres Stu Cncl; High Hon Roll; NCTE Awd; NHS; Ntl Merit SF; Art Clb; French Clb; Nwsp Rptr; Rep Soph Cls; PA Gov Schl Arts 86; Rep Yth Conf 86; Eng.

ROSENBERRY, CHRISTOPHER; West Perry HS; New Bloomfield, PA; (3); 6/221; Var Bsbl; Var L Ftbl; Wt Lftg; High Hon Roll; Hon Roll; NHS; All-Conf Ftbl 86.

ROSENBERRY, LINN; Greencastle-Antrim HS; Greencastle, PA; (3); 26/179; Boy Scts; Pres VP Exploring; Var Capt Ftbl; Var L Trk; Wt Lftg; Hon Roll; Ntl Athltc Merit Endrsmnt Svr 86-87; Wght Lftng Clb & Eclgy Clb; Physcl Thrpy.

ROSENBERRY, TAMI; Connellsville SR HS; Normalville, PA; (4); 40/520; Church Yth Grp; Chorus; School Musical; French Hon Soc; High Hon Roll; NHS; Natl Bible Quizzing 86; Nurses Aide 83-87; Westmoreland Cnty CC; Sec Sci.

ROSENBLOOM, HEATHER; Marple Newtown HS; Broomall, PA; (3); 5/330; Intnl Clb; School Play; Yrbk Stf; Stu Cncl; Mgr(s); Co-Capt Vllybl; High Hon Roll; NHS; Ntl Merit Ltr; Opt Clb Awd; PA Gov Schl Bus Schlrshp 87; Natl Hist Day 1st Dist,2nd ST 86; Wrld Constitution Proj 87; U Of PA.

ROSENBLUM, CHARLES; Shady Side Acad; Stevebenville, OH; (3); VP Debate Tm; Drama Clb; Pres FHA; Church Choir; Lit Mag; Rep Stu Cncl; JV Bsktbl; Var Crs Cntry; JV Socr; Var Tennis; Ntl French Cont 5th & 7th Pl 86-87; Stanford; Econ.

ROSENELLA, DEBORAH; Dunmore HS; Dunmore, PA; (4); 5/150; Drama Clb; French Clb; Sec Letterman Clb; Yrbk Sprt Ed; Var Bsktbl; Var Capt Trk; High Hon Roll; Sec NHS; William Ruddy Memrl Schlrshp 87; Fran Massaro Memrl Awd Grls Trck 87; U S Army Rsrvs Ntl Schlr Athl 87; Bloomsburg U; Elem Ed.

ROSENSKI II, FRANK G; Pittston Area HS; Avoca, PA; (3); Boy Scts; Computer Clb; Ski Clb; Bsktbl; Var L Socr; PA ST U; Cermc Engrng.

ROSENSTEEL, CHRISTOPHER; Altoona HS; Altoona, PA; (3); Boy Scts; Church Yth Grp; Ski Clb; Trk.

ROSENSTEEL, MONICA; Warwick HS; Lititz, PA; (2); 28/310; AFS; Church Yth Grp; SADD; Var L Tennis; High Hon Roll; Mentorship Gftd Prog; Math.

ROSENTEL, ERIC; Dallas SR HS; Dallas, PA; (3); 3/230; Chess Clb; Var L Socr; High Hon Roll; Hon Roll; NHS; Prfct Atten Awd; NEDT; Engineering.

ROSENTHAL, HOLLY; Fort Le Boeuf HS; Waterford, PA; (2); 66/210; Girl Scts; Yrbk Stf; High Hon Roll; Hon Roll.

ROSENTHAL, MICHAEL; Lower Moreland HS; Huntingdon Valley, PA; (4); 46/201; Drama Clb; FBLA; Key Clb; Pres SADD; School Musical; Yrbk Stf; JV Bsbl; Var Socr; Hon Roll.

ROSENTRAUCH, ERIK; Central Dauphin HS; Harrisburg, PA; (3); Boy Scts; Computer Clb; Science Clb; Yrbk Bus Mgr; Yrbk Phtg; Var Socr; Var Trk; 2nd Pl Mdls ST Sci Olympiad, 3rd Pl Cnty PTA Photo, & 1st Pl Awd Cntrl PA Mock Trials 87; Bus Admin.

ROSENZWEIG, JENNIFER; Nazareth Acad; Phila, PA; (3); Art Clb; Cmnty Wkr; Hon Roll; Art.

ROSFELD, MARGARET; Penn Hills SR HS; Verona, PA; (3); AFS; Off Church Yth Grp; Off Cmnty Wkr; Drama Clb; Capt Girl Scts; JA; Spanish Clb; Chorus; Church Choir; Color Guard; Penn ST; Psych.

ROSH, SHARON; Sayre Area HS; Sayre, PA; (4); 21/110; Spanish Clb; High Hon Roll; Hon Roll; Prfct Atten Awd; Baton Twrlg 83-86; Dancing 83; Elmira Coll; Acctg.

ROSIAK, JON; Lackawanna Trail HS; Nicholson, PA; (4); Ski Clb; Var L Bsbl; Var L Ftbl; Hon Roll; E Stroudsburg U; Engl.

ROSIEK, STEVEN G; Seneca Valley HS; Mars, PA; (4); Boy Scts; Chess Clb; High Hon Roll; Acdmc Awd Gannon U 87, & Lone Star Schlrshp 87; Gannon U; Mech Engrng.

ROSING, MARCI; Dallas SR HS; Dallas, PA; (3); Drama Clb; Pres Temple Yth Grp; Capt Mrchg Band; Stage Crew; Stu Cncl; High Hon Roll; Hon Roll; Bus.

ROSKOS, RAYMOND; Monessen HS; Monessen, PA; (3); 24/108; Stage Crew; Bsbl; Bsktbl; Ftbl; Acdmc All Amer 86 & 87; Phys Thrpy.

ROSLER, SEAN; Carbondale Area HS; Carbondale, PA; (3); Cmnty Wkr; German Clb; Letterman Clb; Varsity Clb; Var L Drama Clb; Var Capt Bsktbl; Var L Ftbl; High Hon Roll; Hon Roll; Church Yth Grp; John Caporali Sprtsmnshp Awd 86; Comp Sci.

ROSNER, MICHELE; Louis E Dieruff HS; Allentown, PA; (2); Church Yth Grp; Ski Clb; Band; Concert Band; Mrchg Band; Pep Band; Yrbk Stf; Trs Frsh Cls; Rep Stu Cncl; Hon Roll; Educ.

ROSS, ANGELA; Conneaut Valley HS; Albion, PA; (3); Art Clb; Letterman Clb; Pep Clb; VP Varsity Clb; Sec Jr Cls; Var Capt Cheerleading; Sftbl; Hon Roll; MIP Softball 87; Bus.

ROSS, CHERYL; Academy Of Notre Dame De Namur; Philadelphia, PA; (3); Art Clb; Camera Clb; Math Clb; Service Clb; Yrbk Stf; Lit Mag; Hon Roll; 3rd Awd Acad Of Notre Dame Phtgrphy Cont 87; Awd Distnctn Natl Sci Olympiad Physics Cont 87; Archtctrl Engrng.

ROSS, DANA; Shenango HS; New Castle, PA; (4); 6/112; Capt Drill Tm; VP Sr Cls; Trs Stu Cncl; JV Capt Cheerleading; Gym; Cit Awd; NHS; Rotary Awd; Trs Church Yth Grp; Varsity Clb; Sci Merit Awd 86; Chem Awd 86; Physcl Thrpy.

ROSS, DAWN; Eastern HS; York, PA; (2); 59/155; Church Yth Grp; SADD; Varsity Clb; Band; Concert Band; Nwsp Rptr; Nwsp Stf; Var JV Cheerleading; Prfct Atten Awd; Psycl Thrpy.

ROSS, DEBBY; Marple Newtown HS; Broomall, PA; (4); 64/330; Drama Clb; Service Clb; SADD; School Play; Nwsp Stf; Ed Yrbk Stf; Frsh Cls; Soph Cls; Jr Cls; VP Stu Cncl; Hnr Schlrshp With Spec Tlnt Per Yr 87; Eckerd Coll; Crmnl Justc.

ROSS, ERIK; West Hazleton HS; Drums, PA; (3); 3/217; Cmnty Wkr; Letterman Clb; Var L Ftbl; Var Trk; Var L Wrstlng; Rotary Awd; PA Free Enterprise Wk 87; I Dare You Ldrshp Awd 87; Acad All Amer 87; Bus Finance.

ROSS, JAMES; Elk County Christian HS; St Marys, PA; (4); 1/83; Letterman Clb; Ski Clb; Bowling; L Crs Cntry; L Trk; PA ST; Mech Engr.

ROSS, JAMES; Mountain View HS; Nicholson, PA; (3); Stage Crew; Im Bsbl; Im Bsktbl; Im Socr; Im Sftbl; Im Vllybl; Hon Roll; Comp Sci.

ROSS, JENNIFER; Central Dauphin HS; Harrisburg, PA; (2); Ski Clb; Band; Concert Band; Mrchg Band; Orch; School Play; Var Crs Cntry; Var Trk; Hon Roll.

ROSS, JENNIFER; West Scranton HS; Clarks Summit, PA; (4); 24/240; VP French Clb; Letterman Clb; Yrbk Stf; Cheerleading; Crs Cntry; Mat Maids; Trk; Hon Roll; Jr NHS; NHS; West Scranton Lions Clb Schlrshp 87; Lockhaven U.

ROSS, JILL; Canon-Mc Millan HS; Canonsburg, PA; (3); Sec Varsity Clb; Rep Frsh Cls; Rep Stu Cncl; Var L Crs Cntry; Var L Swmmng; Var L Trk; Wt Lftg; High Hon Roll; NHS; Jr NHS.

ROSS, JOHN; Brownsville Area HS; Brownsville, PA; (3); Church Yth Grp; Ski Clb; Im Bsktbl; Im Vllybl; CA U; Cmmnctns.

ROSS, JOSEPH; Allderdice HS; Pittsburgh, PA; (3); Church Yth Grp; Latin Clb; Nwsp Sprt Ed; Nwsp Stf; Boy Scts; Yrbk Sprt Ed; Yrbk Stf; Ftbl; Wt Lftg; Wrstlng; U Of Pittsburgh; Acad.

ROSS, KATRINA; Carmichaels HS; Carmichaels, PA; (4); Library Aide; Office Aide; Pep Clb; Ski Clb; Spanish Clb; Stu Cncl; High Hon Roll; Hon Roll; Jr NHS; NHS; Law.

ROSS, LISA; Bellwood Antis HS; Bellwood, PA; (3); 10/115; Pres Church Yth Grp; Pres 4-H; Pres FHA; SADD; Varsity Clb; Nwsp Sprt Ed; Yrbk Stf; Var L Fld Hcky; High Hon Roll; NHS; Preveterinary Med.

ROSS, LISA; SR HS; Butler, PA; (3); Teachers Aide; Band; Color Guard; Mrchg Band; Badmtn; Hon Roll; Acdmc Achvt Awd 86-87; Penn ST U; Chld Psych.

ROSS, LOU ANN; Connellsville Area SR HS; Dunbar, PA; (3); 27/580; Library Aide; SADD; Chorus; Yrbk Stf; Jr NHS; NHS; Spanish NHS; English Nannies Schl Inc; Nanny.

ROSS, MATTHEW; Downingtown SR HS; Downingtown, PA; (3); 1/648; Letterman Clb; Ski Clb; Spanish Clb; SADD; Concert Band; Mrchg Band; Stu Cncl; Tennis; High Hon Roll; All Ches Mont Tnns Team 4th Sngle 86; US Naval Acad; Arntcl Engrng.

ROSS, MICHAEL; Marple-Newtown SR HS; Broomall, PA; (3); Church Yth Grp; School Musical; School Play; VP Stage Crew; Variety Show; Rep Soph Cls; Off Stu Cncl; Var JV Lcrss; Var L Swmmng; Hon Roll.

ROSS, MICHAEL; Northern York HS; Dillsburg, PA; (3); 87/232; FFA; Nwsp Stf; Rptr Jr Cls; Hon Roll; Chptr Schlstc Achvt Awd 87.

ROSS, MICHAEL; Trinity HS; Washington, PA; (4); 8/322; Debate Tm; Math Tm; NFL; Spanish Clb; JV Bsktbl; Im Ftbl; Var L Tennis; High Hon Roll; NHS; Ntl Art Hnr Soc; Carnegie-Mellon U; Arch.

ROSS, MICHELE RAE; Troy SR HS; Troy, PA; (4); 42/149; Am Leg Aux Girls St; Letterman Clb; Pep Clb; Ski Clb; Band; Mrchg Band; Cheerleading; Sftbl; Twrlr; NHS; Ellen Ross Memrl Awd Featr Twrlr 87; Alfred ST Coll; Rtl Bus Mgmt.

ROSS, MONICA; Philadelphia HS For Girls; Philadelphia, PA; (3); Camera Clb; Church Yth Grp; VP Exploring; Hosp Aide; Teachers Aide; Chorus; Stu Cncl; Trk; High Hon Roll; Pre-Med.

ROSS, PAM; Rocky Grove HS; Franklin, PA; (3); 6/87; Church Yth Grp; Band; Chorus; Concert Band; Jazz Band; Pep Band; Rep Jr Cls; Rep Stu Cncl; Var Sftbl; NHS; Acdmc Excllnc Awd Plaq 84-85; Musicl Awds 84-87; Comm.

ROSS, ROBERT; Central Dauphin HS; Harrisburg, PA; (2); 92/405; Aud/Vis; Trk; Engrng.

ROSS, TAMMY; Leechburg Area HS; Leechburg, PA; (4); 10/82; Church Yth Grp; JA; Band; Chorus; Pres Concert Band; Mrchg Band; Pep Band; Yrbk Sprt Ed; Yrbk Stf; Hon Roll; Rgnl Band 85 & 87; Dstrct Band 85-87; Cnty Chorus 87; IN U Of PA; Music Ed.

ROSS, VICKI; Trinity HS; Carlisle, PA; (2); Hon Roll; Comp Learning Ctr; Comp Oper.

ROSS, VICTOR; Neshannock HS; New Castle, PA; (3); 27/112; Aud/Vis; Camera Clb; Drama Clb; School Musical; Nwsp Phtg; Var L Crs Cntry; Var L Trk; Svc Awd 86; Hnr Awd 87; Marine Bio.

ROSSELL, SHELLEY M; Saucon Valley SR HS; Bethlehem, PA; (3); 7/170; Am Leg Aux Girls St; 4-H; Hosp Aide; Model UN; Jazz Band; School Musical; Nwsp Stf; Sec Stu Cncl; Tennis; NHS; Adv.

ROSSER, AMY; Pittston Area HS; Avoca, PA; (3); Church Yth Grp; Girl Scts; Hosp Aide; Key Clb; Med.

ROSSER, HEATHER; Williamsburg HS; Williamsburg, PA; (3); Church Yth Grp; Band; Concert Band; Mrchg Band; Cnsrvtn Awd 85.

ROSSETTI, TIMOTHY; Carbondale Area HS; Carbondale, PA; (3); Aud/Vis; Boy Scts; FBLA; German Clb; Letterman Clb; SADD; Varsity Clb; Chorus; Stage Crew; JV Bsktbl.

ROSSETTI, TRACY L; Pann Hills SR HS; Verona, PA; (4); 16/610; Church Yth Grp; French Clb; Spanish Clb; Varsity Clb; Nwsp Ed-Chief; Sftbl; Tennis; High Hon Roll; NHS; Shenandoah PTA Scholar 87; Shrt Stry Publshd Yng American Mag 87; Grove City Coll; Intl Bus.

ROSSEY, RE NAE; Clarion-Limestone HS; Corsica, PA; (4); 3/61; Church Yth Grp; FFA; High Hon Roll; Hon Roll; NHS; Prfct Atten Awd; Clarion-Limeston HS Outstndng Sr 86-87; U Of PA; Bus.

ROSSI, AMY; Bellwood Antis HS; Tyrone, PA; (1); Church Yth Grp; Chorus; School Musical; Cheerleading; Fld Hcky; Hon Roll; Penn ST; Bus.

ROSSI, EILEEN; Villa Maria Acad; Erie, PA; (3); Church Yth Grp; PAVAS; Political Wkr; SADD; School Musical; Stage Crew; Nwsp Rptr; Var Cheerleading; Hon Roll; NHS; Math.

ROSSI, ELIZABETH ANN; Easton Area HS; Easton, PA; (4); 9/447; Am Leg Aux Girls St; Church Yth Grp; Ski Clb; Color Guard; Orch; Var Crs Cntry; Var Trk; NHS; Rotary Awd; PA Gvrnrs Schl Arts 86; Rtry Exchnge Stu Schlrshp Fnlnd 87-88; Smith Coll.

ROSSI, JAUDIE; Greensburg Central Catholic HS; Jeannette, PA; (4); AFS; Ski Clb; Crs Cntry; Hon Roll; NHS; Trk; The American U; Law.

ROSSI, JODI; Greensburg Central Catholic HS; Jeannette, PA; (4); 37/222; French Clb; Ski Clb; Crs Cntry; Socr; Trk; Chess Clb; Hon Roll; NHS; Powder Puff Ftbl; Chick Fil A Schlrshp 87; American U; Intl Law.

ROSSI, LEAH; Bentworth HS; Bentleyville, PA; (4); Drama Clb; Letterman Clb; Pep Clb; Ski Clb; Varsity Clb; School Play; Stu Cncl; Cheerleading; Vllybl; High Hon Roll; Bradford Bus Schl; Accntng.

ROSSI, MICHAEL; Bishop Hafey HS; Hazleton, PA; (3); Chess Clb; Ski Clb.

ROSSI, TERESA; Hopewell SR HS; Aliquippa, PA; (4); Church Yth Grp; French Clb; Hosp Aide; Library Aide; Spanish Clb; Mgr(s); Mgr Socr; Im Trk; JV Vllybl; Hon Roll; WV U; Intl Stds.

ROSSINI, MELANIE; Geibel HS; Masontown, PA; (3); Ed Yrbk Stf; French Hon Soc; High Hon Roll; Prfct Atten Awd; Humanities Day Wnr-2nd Pl Frnch Poetry 87; CA U Of PA; Elem Ed.

ROSSINO, JEANETTE; Marian Catholic HS; Jim Thorpe, PA; (4); Church Yth Grp; Science Clb; SADD; Chorus; Church Choir; School Musical; Nwsp Stf; Off Stu Cncl; Stat Ftbl; High Hon Roll; St Davids Socty Vocl Schlrshp 87; Carbon Tamaqua Area JR Miss & Tlnt Wnnr PA ST Fnls 87; Allentown Coll St Francis; Bio.

ROSSO, ANTHONY; Morrisville HS; Morrisville, PA; (3); 5/100; Var Bsbl; Var Bowling; Hon Roll; Elect Engr.

ROTCHFORD, JENNIFER; Mt St Joseph Acad; Hatboro, PA; (3); Pres Church Yth Grp; VP Science Clb; Chrmn Service Clb; Lit Mag; Bausch & Lomb Sci Awd; High Hon Roll; NHS; NEDT Awd; JCL; Latin Clb; Arch Diocesan Schlr 87-88; 2nd Pl DE Vly Sci Comp 86-87; Eagle Of Crs Awd Archdiocese Of Phila 87; Biotech.

ROTERING, CHRISTINE D; Mifflinburg Area HS; Kutztown, PA; (4); 12/154; Am Leg Aux Girls St; French Clb; Hosp Aide; High Hon Roll; NHS; Presdntl Acadc Ftns Awd 87; Athaneum Clb Awd 87; Kutztown U; Marine Sci.

ROTH, ANDREA; Kiski Area HS; Saltsburg, PA; (3); VP Trs 4-H; Varsity Clb; Chorus; Var L Crs Cntry; Var L Trk; 4-H Awd; High Hon Roll; Hon Roll; Prfct Atten Awd; Outstndng Athltc Achvt Awd 85-87; Trck & Crs Cntry MVP 85-87; Brdfrd Schl; Bus Scrtry.

ROTH, ANDREW; Owen J Roberts HS; Pottstown, PA; (2); 22/311; Boy Scts; Church Yth Grp; Band; Concert Band; Jazz Band; Mrchg Band; School Musical; Symp Band; Yrbk Stf; Socr.

ROTH, BRYAN; State College Area HS; Pine Grove Mil, PA; (2); Boy Scts; Church Yth Grp; Ski Clb; Im Lcrss; Hon Roll; Pwr Of Paws Awd 87; Engr.

ROTH, FERNE; Council Rock HS; Newtown, PA; (4); 210/848; Office Aide; Teachers Aide; Temple Yth Grp; Rep Badmtn; Var Cheerleading; Var Tennis; Hon Roll; Prfct Atten Awd; U Pittsburgh; Arts & Sci.

ROTH, JAMES; Baldwin-Whitehall HS; Pittsburgh, PA; (3); 90/477; Church Yth Grp; Hon Roll; U Pittsburgh.

ROTH, JENNIFER; Quakertown Community HS; Quakertown, PA; (3); VP Church Yth Grp; Church Choir; Rep Soph Cls; Pres Jr Cls; Rep Stu Cncl; JV Var Bsktbl; JV Var Fld Hcky; High Hon Roll; Hon Roll; NHS; Fld Hcky Team 2nd ST Silver Medal 86; Elem Ed.

ROTH, LISA; Garden Spot HS; New Holland, PA; (4); Drama Clb; PAVAS; Chorus; Church Choir; School Musical; School Play; Stage Crew; High Hon Roll; Church Yth Grp; German Clb; PA Governors Schl Of Arts Altrnt 86; Hnr Soloist 86; Best Supprtng Actrss In Perfrmng Arts 87; Perfrmng Arts.

ROTH, MARCIA; West Middlesex HS; Pulaski, PA; (1); 4-H; Hon Roll; Ed.

ROTH, MICHAEL Q; Pen Argyl HS; Nazareth, PA; (3); 1/160; Am Leg Boys St; Church Yth Grp; Scholastic Bowl; Chorus; Jazz Band; Mrchg Band; Ed Yrbk Stf; High Hon Roll; Lion Awd; NHS; HOBY Outstndng Stu Awd 85-86; Hstry Day Compttn Awds 1st Pl, 3rd Pl & 1st Pl 84-87; Hstry.

ROTH, MICHELE; Methacton SR HS; Collegeville, PA; (3); Cmnty Wkr; VP 4-H; VICA; 4-H Awd; Hon Roll.

ROTH, MIKE; Penn Hills HS; Pittsburgh, PA; (4); Computer Clb; Science Clb; Spanish Clb; Nwsp Stf; High Hon Roll; NHS; Grove City Coll; Comp Sys.

ROTH, RAMONA; Bellefonte Area HS; Pleasant Gap, PA; (3); 12/211; Girl Scts; Hosp Aide; Ski Clb; Spanish Clb; SADD; Band; Concert Band; Mrchg Band; NHS; Rptr Soph Cls; Stu Agnst Drnk Drvng Vp 86-87; Stu Rprtr For WBLF 86-87; Hlth Careers Clb 85-86; PA ST U.

ROTH, SANDRA; Richland HS; Johnstown, PA; (4); 1/153; Mu Alpha Theta; Trs Ski Clb; Band; Sec Jr Cls; Stu Cncl; AF ROTC Schlrshp 87; Johnstown Exchng Clb Yth Of Yr 87; U Of Notre Dame; Mathematics.

ROTHENBACH, TRICIA; Germantown Acad; Hatboro, PA; (4); Sec Soph Cls; Crs Cntry; Fld Hcky; Sftbl; Swmmng; NHS; All-Amer Swmmng 86; Swmmng Schlrshp 86-87; Sthrn IL U; Pre-Med.

ROTHERMEL, AMY; Oley Valley HS; Oley, PA; (3); Drama Clb; Key Clb; Pep Clb; School Musical; Nwsp Rptr; Sec Soph Cls; Sec Sr Cls; Var JV Cheerleading; Fld Hcky; Var L Trk; Pre Law.

ROTHERMEL, BRETT; Shikellamy HS; Sunbury, PA; (3); Church Yth Grp; Hon Roll; Bloomsburg U; Psych.

ROTHERMEL, ELAINE; Mechanicsburg Area SR HS; Mechanicsburg, PA; (4); Church Yth Grp; GAA; Girl Scts; Variety Show; Sec Sr Cls; Fld Hcky; Penn ST U; Sports Med.

ROTHERMEL, JEFF; Danville HS; Danville, PA; (3); 6/198; Boy Scts; Debate Tm; Key Clb; NFL; Speech Tm; Band; Lit Mag; VP Golf; NHS; Eagle Scout 86; PA ST U; Aerospace Engrng.

ROTHERMEL, KIMBERLY; Millersburg Area HS; Millersburg, PA; (3); Church Yth Grp; Chorus; Mrchg Band; Nwsp Rptr; Nwsp Stf; Yrbk Phtg; Yrbk Rptr; Yrbk Stf; JV Bsktbl; Mgr Trk; 3rd Pl Amer Lgn Essy 87; Gregg Shrthnd Awd 87; HACC; Engl.

ROTHERMEL, RICHELLE; Shikellamy HS; Sunbury, PA; (3); 15/351; Spanish Clb; Rep Stu Cncl; Var Cheerleading; Trk; Hon Roll; Jr NHS; Penn ST; Phys Thrpy.

ROTHERMEL, TAMMY; Millersburg Area HS; Millersburg, PA; (3); Cmnty Wkr; Spanish Clb; Band; Chorus; Concert Band; Var Sftbl; High Hon Roll; Hon Roll; NEDT Awd; Val; Acad All-Amrcn 86; US Natl Ldrshp Mrt Awd 86; Pstl Wrkr.

ROTHMAN, MARK; Meadville Area SR HS; Meadville, PA; (3); 26/300; Church Yth Grp; Band; Orch; U Pittsburgh; Psych.

ROTHROCK, MICHAEL; Palmerton HS; Palmerton, PA; (3); JV Var Bsbl; JV Var Bsktbl; Hon Roll; German Awd, Earth/Space Sci Awd.

ROTHROCK, RICHARD; South Western HS; Hanover, PA; (2); Key Clb; JV Trk; Prfct Atten Awd.

ROTHSTEIN, ANDREW D; Pennridge HS; Hatfield, PA; (4); 2/423; Science Clb; Rep Stu Cncl; Var Mgr(s); Var Socr; Var L Tennis; High Hon Roll; NHS; Ntl Merit SF; Boy Scts; Quiz Bowl; Alterded The PA Cvrnrs Schl For The Sci 86; MA Inst Of Tech; Physcs.

ROTOLO, CARISSA; Belle Vernon Area HS; Belle Vernon, PA; (3); Church Yth Grp; Library Aide; Band; High Hon Roll; Hon Roll; Pst Wrthy Advsr Rnbw Grls 85-86; Csmtlgy.

ROTONDO, NADINE; Upper Merion HS; Bridgeport, PA; (4); 60/263; Nwsp Stf; VP Frsh Cls; VP Soph Cls; VP Jr Cls; Stu Cncl; Fld Hcky; Capt Lcrss; Powder Puff Ftbl; Trk; Widener U; Pre-Law.

ROTTENBERG, MARK; Abington HS; Huntington Valley, PA; (3); 140/503; French Clb; Orch; Rep Jr Cls; Rep Stu Cncl; Ice Hcky; Tennis; Hon Roll; Jr NHS; Med.

ROTUNA, RAY; Quigley HS; Ambridge, PA; (3); Church Yth Grp; Spanish Clb; Var Bsbl; JV Bsktbl; L Var Golf; Amer Lgn Awd 84; Acdmc All-Amer Schlrs 87; Optmtry.

ROTUNDO, GABBIE; Cocalico HS; Denver, PA; (3); 32/168; Drama Clb; FTA; GAA; School Play; Stage Crew; VP Sr Cls; JV Cheerleading; Im Vllybl; High Hon Roll; Hon Roll; Psych.

ROUCE, JOHN; North Allegheny SR HS; Pittsburgh, PA; (3); Church Yth Grp; FBLA; JA; Chorus; Hon Roll; Jr NHS; Johnnie Wlkr Intl Hole-In-One Awd 85; Accntng.

ROUDA, KIM; Du Bois Area HS; Du Bois, PA; (3); 74/312; Sec Girl Scts; SADD; Chorus; Concert Band; Drm Mjr(t); Mrchg Band; Stage Crew; Hon Roll; Grl Sct Slvr Awd 85; Physcl Thrpy.

ROUGHT, CHRIS; Lachawanna Trail HS; Nicholson, PA; (3); Church Yth Grp; Chorus; JV Var Bsktbl; Hon Roll; Navy.

ROUGHT, KRISTI; Westy Scranton HS; Scranton, PA; (3); Camera Clb; Latin Clb; Ski Clb; Crs Cntry; Trk; Math Awd 85; Typg Awd 87; Vet.

ROUGHT, TODD; Tunkhannock Area HS; Falls, PA; (3); Church Yth Grp; Cmnty Wkr; Hon Roll; Penn ST U; Elec Engrng.

ROULE, LORA; Brownsville Area HS; Brownsville, PA; (3); Drama Clb; Akron U; Word Proc.

ROUNANIK, LESLEE; Burrell HS; Lower Burrell, PA; (4); 83/199; AFS; Dance Clb; Ski Clb; Spanish Clb; Drm Mjr(t); Mrchg Band; Yrbk Stf; Rep Frsh Cls; Rep Soph Cls; Rep Jr Cls; Hd Myrtt 86-87; Duffs Bus Insti; Merch.

ROUNCE, ROBERT; Seneca Valley HS; Zelienople, PA; (3); Chess Clb; Letterman Clb; ROTC; Ski Clb; Varsity Clb; Var JV Ftbl; Var Wt Lftg; US Navy.

ROUNDTREE, KRYSTAL; Engineering & Science HS; Philadelphia, PA; (3); Church Yth Grp; Hosp Aide; Political Wkr; Yrbk Stf; Rep Frsh Cls; Rep Jr Cls; Rep Stu Cncl; Var Cheerleading; Hon Roll; Operatn Understndng 87; Miss March Alpha Kappa Alpha Sorority Scholar 87; Georgetown U; Med.

ROUNSVILLE, DAWN; Bradford Area HS; Lewis Run, PA; (3); Computer Clb; Band; Mrchg Band; Yrbk Bus Mgr; Yrbk Ed-Chief; Yrbk Phtg; Yrbk Rptr; Yrbk Stf; Hon Roll; Accntng.

ROUPP, LORI; Liberty JR-SR HS; Liberty, PA; (3); 3/40; Trs FHA; Band; Chorus; Church Choir; School Musical; Trs Stu Cncl; Capt Cheerleading; Hon Roll; Dist, Rgnl, St Chorus 87; Dance Amer Natl Fnlst 86; Fred Waring US Chorus 87; Pblc Rltns.

ROUPP, MELISSA; Canton HS; Ralston, PA; (4); 3/115; AFS; Pres VP French Clb; Scholastic Bowl; Stage Crew; Yrbk Stf; Hon Roll; Sec NHS; Pres Schlr; 3rd Hgh Hnrs Grad; Hghst Avg French IV Awd; U Scranton; Crimnl Justc.

ROUSCHER, AARON; Dover Area HS; Dover, PA; (3); High Hon Roll; PA Dist 4 Bwlng Chmpns 87; PA ST Chmpnshp Rnnr-Up Bwlng 87; Rc Car Drvr.

ROUSE, BONNIE; Pocono Mountain SR HS; Albrightsville, PA; (2); Music.

ROUSER, MARILYN; Lawrence County AVTS HS; New Castle, PA; (3); 17/280; FBLA; Chorus; Drill Tm; VP Soph Cls; VP Jr Cls; VP Sr Cls; Cheerleading; Gym; Trk; Hon Roll; Acad & Voctnl Excllnc Awd 86-87; FBLA Awds 85-87; Christmas Ct JR Rep 86-87; Bradford Schl Of Bus; Med Sec.

ROUSH, MELISSA; West Middlesex HS; Mercer, PA; (1); Spanish Clb; Band; Mrchg Band; Hon Roll; Typing Awd 87; Penn ST; Elem Ed.

ROUTE, DENNY; Canton HS; Ralston, PA; (4); 23/117; French Clb; Letterman Clb; SADD; VP Soph Cls; Var L Ftbl; Capt Var Wrstlng; Civic Clb Awd-Most Outstndng Wrestler 87; 5th Pl ST Wrstlng Champnshps 87; Lycoming Coll; Accntng.

ROUZER, TAMI; Central Cambria HS; Johnstown, PA; (3); FHA; Key Clb; Mrchg Band; Nwsp Stf; Yrbk Stf; Stat Crs Cntry; Twrlr; Hon Roll; Dntstry.

ROVINSKY, GREGG; Plymouth-Whitemarsh HS; Plymouth Mtg, PA; (3); 29/365; Chess Clb; Computer Clb; Math Clb; Scholastic Bowl; Var Bsktbl; High Hon Roll; Jr NHS; Comp Sci.

ROVITO, LORI; Norther SR HS; Dillsburg, PA; (4); 24/204; Drama Clb; Teachers Aide; JV Var Cheerleading; Powder Puff Ftbl; Var Trk; High Hon Roll; Hon Roll; Pres Schlr; PA ST U; Vet Med.

ROWAN, DAVID; Parkland HS; Allentown, PA; (3); 31/481; Chess Clb; Debate Tm; JA; JV Bsktbl; Im Vllybl; High Hon Roll; NHS; Ntl Merit SF; Bio Med Engrng.

ROWAN, GABRIELLE; Spring-Ford HS; Collegville, PA; (3); 146/256; French Clb; Trs Thesps; Chorus; School Musical; School Play; Stage Crew; Nwsp Rptr; Wrtr Yr 86.

ROWAN, KERRY JILL; Trinity HS; Mechanicsburg, PA; (3); 12/138; Church Yth Grp; French Clb; Model UN; Red Cross Aide; Ski Clb; Mrchg Band; Yrbk Ed-Chief; Rep Stu Cncl; Hon Roll; NHS.

ROWE, ANGIE; Kennedy Christian HS; W Middlesex, PA; (2); 17/97; Spanish Clb; Pres Frsh Cls; Sec Soph Cls; Stu Cncl; Var Bsktbl; Crs Cntry; Mat Maids; Sftbl; Trk; Vllybl; Vet.

ROWE, BRIAN; Dover Area HS; Dover, PA; (3); Computer Clb; Hon Roll; Ntl Merit Ltr; Cert Of Outstndng Achvmnt In Grmn Class 84-85; Engrng.

ROWE, CORL; Elizabeth Forward HS; Elizabeth, PA; (3); Church Yth Grp; Girl Scts; JA; Chorus; Timer; Hon Roll; Acctng.

ROWE, DARA; Big Spring HS; Carlisle, PA; (4); 7/181; Church Yth Grp; Yrbk Stf; Rep Sr Cls; Mgr Crs Cntry; Mgr Swmmng; Trk; Elks Awd; High Hon Roll; Lion Awd; Trs NHS; PA ST U; Bus Admin.

ROWE, DEANNA; Marple Newtown HS; Broomall, PA; (3); 27/322; Cmnty Wkr; SADD; Stu Cncl; JV Fld Hcky; JV Lcrss; Hon Roll; Phys Thrpst.

ROWE, KAREN; Marple Newtown SR HS; Broomall, PA; (4); Rep Stu Cncl; Hon Roll; Prfct Atten Awd; Eckerd Coll; Intl Mktg.

ROWE, KIMBERLY; Hopewell HS; Aliquippa, PA; (4); 18/245; Cmnty Wkr; Latin Clb; Concert Band; Jazz Band; Mrchg Band; Stage Crew; Jr NHS; NHS; Exploring; Pep Band; Alghny Coll; Chmstry Tchr.

ROWE, LISA; Valley HS; New Kensington, PA; (3); 19/250; Boys Clb Am; Trs Exploring; FBLA; Varsity Clb; Band; Color Guard; Concert Band; Mrchg Band; Hon Roll; NHS; US Bus Educ Awd 87; Howard U; Secretarial Sci.

ROWE, MICHAEL; Elk Lake HS; Meshoppen, PA; (2); Art Clb; Band; Off Soph Cls; Johnson Tech Trde Schl; Elec.

ROWE, NANCY; Perkiomen Valley HS; Perkiomenville, PA; (3); Church Yth Grp; Church Choir; Concert Band; Drm Mjr(t); Mrchg Band; School Musical; Rep Stu Cncl; Var Diving; Hon Roll; NHS; Bux-Mnt Cnty Band 86 & 87; Dist Band 87; Intl Rltns.

ROWE, RONALD; Kennedy Christian HS; W Middlesex, PA; (3); Rep Stu Cncl; Science Clb; Spanish Clb; Var Bsbl; Var Crs Cntry; Var Wrstlng; NEDT Awd; Pharm.

ROWE, SUSANNE; Brookville Area HS; Brookville, PA; (3); 14/175; Church Yth Grp; Library Aide; Pep Clb; Band; Concert Band; Mrchg Band; Yrbk Stf; High Hon Roll; Hon Roll; NHS.

ROWE, TARA; Western Beaver HS; Industry, PA; (3); Sec Church Yth Grp; Pres 4-H; Band; Chorus; Capt Color Guard; Nwsp Rptr; Sec Stu Cncl; 4-H Awd; Hon Roll; Rainbow Girls-Wrthy Adv 87.

ROWELL, CYNTHIA; Henderson HS; Exton, PA; (3); 5/377; Cmnty Wkr; Intnl Clb; School Musical; Yrbk Stf; Lit Mag; French Hon Soc; Hon Roll; Cert Ntl Frnch Tst 85; Cmmnctns.

ROWELL, TRACY; Lancaster Catholic HS; Lancaster, PA; (3); Mgr Band; Drill Tm; Nwsp Stf; Trk; Med.

ROWLAND, AMY; Big Spring HS; Carlisle, PA; (4); 3/189; Nwsp Rptr; Yrbk Ed-Chief; Capt Powder Puff Ftbl; Stat Socr; Var Capt Swmmng; High Hon Roll; Lion Awd; NHS; Sec Frsh Cls; Pep Clb; Stu Of Mnth 86; Central College Schlrshp 87; Central Coll-Pella; Frgn Lang.

ROWLAND, AMY; Laurel Valley HS; New Florence, PA; (1); AFS; Debate Tm; GAA; Varsity Clb; Chorus; VP Frsh Cls; Var L Bsktbl; Var L Sftbl; Var L Vllybl; High Hon Roll; Amer Legn Awd 86.

ROWLAND, SIOBHAN; Unionville HS; Kennett Sq, PA; (4); 75/316; Chorus; Mrchg Band; School Musical; Nwsp Stf; Trk; Hon Roll; Marywood Coll; Med Tech.

ROWLANDS, MELISSA; The Baptist HS; Falls, PA; (4); Chorus; Church Choir; Rep Soph Cls; Pres Sr Cls; Rep Stu Cncl; Stat Bsktbl; Var L Cheerleading; Var Capt Socr; Ldrshp Awd-Sccr 86-87; Good Condct-Ldrshp Awd 86-87; Christn Educ.

ROWLES, GEO; Clearfield Area HS; Clearfield, PA; (4); 186/297; Aud/Vis; Church Yth Grp; Cmnty Wkr; Computer Clb; Debate Tm; Drama Clb; Key Clb; Ski Clb; Spanish Clb; Speech Tm; Theology.

ROWLES, KRISTINE; Wallenpaupack Area HS; White Mills, PA; (3); Church Yth Grp; Pep Clb; PAVAS; Red Cross Aide; Ski Clb; Chorus; Church Choir; Capt Cheerleading; Mgr(s); Stat Sftbl.

ROWLES, RAY; Brockway Area HS; Brockport, PA; (4); 2/87; Church Yth Grp; Math Tm; Varsity Clb; VP Jr Cls; Trs Sr Cls; Ftbl; High Hon Roll; Hst NHS; Sal; US Military Acad; Engrng.

ROWLEY, CHARLOTTE; Simon Gratz HS; Philadelphia, PA; (3); 18/200; Computer Clb; Office Aide; Yrbk Stf; Sftbl; Hon Roll.

ROWLEY, LISA A; Bishop Hoban HS; Wilkes-Barre, PA; (3); Computer Clb; Math Clb; Mu Alpha Theta; Hon Roll; NHS; NEDT Awd.

ROY, STEPHANE A; Boyertown JR High East; Perkiomenville, PA; (1); Computer Clb; Math Clb; Mrchg Band; High Hon Roll; Prfct Atten Awd; Hon Roll; Band; Concert Band; Pep Band; Art Clb; MIT; Comp Pgmng.

ROYAL, BILLY; Aliquippa HS; Aliquippa, PA; (3); Var Ftbl; Var Wt Lftg; Hon Roll; Bus.

ROYAL, JAMES JOHN; E L Meyers HS; Wilkes-Barre, PA; (4); 30/161; Church Yth Grp; Key Clb; Trs SADD; Chorus; Nwsp Sprt Ed; Rep Stu Cncl; Var Bsbl; VP Capt Ftbl; High Hon Roll; Rotary Awd; Dist 741 Rotary Interntl Leader 85; Sunday Indepdnt/Times Ldr All Schlstc Ftbl 86; Pre-Dental.

ROYCROFT, BECKY; Fairchance Georges JR/Sr HS; Fairchance, PA; (4); Church Yth Grp; Drama Clb; FHA; Spanish Clb; School Play; Stage Crew; Trs Jr Cls; Civic Clb; High Hon Roll; Hon Roll; IMC Schl Bus; Comp Mgmt.

ROYE, DONNA; The Lutheran HS Of Phila HS; Philadelphia, PA; (3); Church Yth Grp; Cmnty Wkr; Computer Clb; Capt Debate Tm; Hosp Aide; JA; Library Aide; Political Wkr; Chorus; Yrbk Stf; Chapel Svc Awds 84-87; Hghst Hnrs Sci Awd 85; Good Sprtsmnshp & Part Awds 84-87; Spelman Coll; Pre-Law.

ROYER, ALEX; Quigley HS; Baden, PA; (4); 6/99; Math Tm; Var L Ftbl; Trk; Var Capt Wrstlng; NHS; MVP Wrstlng & Ftbl 86; Bus.

ROYER, BETSEY A; Cocalico HS; Stevens, PA; (4); Church Yth Grp; 4-H; Hosp Aide; Trs Stu Cncl; Var Cheerleading; JV Fld Hcky; 4-H Awd; Hon Roll; Penn ST; Liberal Arts.

ROYER, CHERI; Oley Valley HS; Fleetwood, PA; (3); Dance Clb; FBLA; JA; Library Aide; Pep Clb; Color Guard; Cheerleading; Prfct Atten Awd; Katherin Gibbs Sec Of Future Hnry Awd 87.

ROYER, CHRISTIAN; Danville HS; Danville, PA; (3); Computer Clb; Debate Tm; Exploring; Key Clb; Letterman Clb; NFL; Spanish Clb; Speech Tm; Off Jr Cls; Off Sr Cls; Pre-Law.

ROYER, DAVID; Red Lion Area HS; Brogue, PA; (3); 89/342; Church Yth Grp; Band; Concert Band; Jazz Band; Mrchg Band; Orch; School Musical; Symp Band; JV Var Bsbl; Hon Roll.

ROYER, GWYNETH ANNE; Danville Area HS; Danville, PA; (2); Church Yth Grp; Cmnty Wkr; Drama Clb; Exploring; Hosp Aide; Key Clb; Latin Clb; NFL; Ski Clb; Speech Tm; Natl Hnr Soc Ltn, Natl Ltn Exam-Cum Laude Cert 87; Med.

ROYER, HEATHER; Middletown Area HS; Middletown, PA; (3); Bsktbl; Var L Tennis; Var L Trk; Im Vllybl; High Hon Roll; Hon Roll.

ROYER, JENNIFER; Bethlehem Catholic HS; Bethlehem, PA; (3); 67/193; Red Cross Aide; SADD; Chorus; Yrbk Phtg; High Hon Roll; Hon Roll; Ralph J Romano Key Clbr Mnth Awds 85-87; Bio Chem.

ROYER, KRISTI; Northern Lebanon HS; Fredericksbur, PA; (2); 13/208; Church Yth Grp; Varsity Clb; Chorus; Church Choir; Color Guard; Mrchg Band; Bsktbl; Fld Hcky; Sftbl; Twrlr; Dist Field Hockey Rnnr Up 86; Vrsty Ltr In Fld Hockey 86; Dntl Hygn.

ROYER, MARK; Northern Lebanon HS; Jonestown, PA; (3); 44/201; VP Trs Church Yth Grp; Ski Clb; Church Choir; Var JV Bsktbl; Var Golf; Var Tennis; Hon Roll; Elec Schl Tech; Comp Rprmn.

ROYER, RHONDA; Lock Haven SR HS; Lock Haven, PA; (3); Church Yth Grp; Drama Clb; 4-H; Bsktbl; Mgr(s); Tennis; Trk; 4-H Awd; Bus.

ROZANSKI, STEPHEN; Cardinal Dougherty JR/Sr HS; Philadelphia, PA; (4); Church Yth Grp; Teachers Aide; Advance Plcmnt Math 85-87; Math.

ROZETAR, JOHN G; Minersville Area JR-SR HS; Pottsville, PA; (4); VICA; High Hon Roll; Williamsport Area CC; Toolmkng.

ROZGONY, DAVID; Laurel Highlands HS; Uniontown, PA; (2); Science Clb; Ski Clb; Var Crs Cntry; Var Socr; Var Trk; Ntl Merit Ltr; Carnegie Mellon U; Physcs.

ROZMAN, JOHN; West Allegheny HS; Oakdale, PA; (4); 60/201; Spanish Clb; Chorus; Var JV Bsbl; S Hlls Area Schl Dist Assc Awd 86; IUP; Manag Info Systms.

ROZYCKI, RAY; Frazier JR SR Memorial HS; Dawson, PA; (3); Math Tm; Off Soph Cls; Jr Cls; Var L Bsbl; Capt L Bsktbl; Wt Lftg; High Hon Roll; NHS; Penn ST; Math.

RUBENSTEIN, DAVID; Upper Dublin HS; Ambler, PA; (3); 37/296; Camera Clb; FBLA; Intnl Clb; Tennis; Hon Roll; NHS; Prfct Atten Awd; Law.

RUBENSTEIN, ROBERT; Upper Dublin HS; Roslyn, PA; (3); 98/250; FBLA; Intnl Clb; Letterman Clb; Varsity Clb; Rep Frsh Cls; Rep Soph Cls; JV Bsbl; Im Bsktbl; Var Socr; Hon Roll; Sprts Med.

RUBERT, AMY; Upper Merion SR HS; King Of Prussia, PA; (3); Spanish Clb; Bsktbl; Socr; Vllybl; Hon Roll; Cmmntcns.

RUBIN, BENJAMIN; Cheltenham HS; Elkins Pk, PA; (4); 36/360; Jazz Band; Mrchg Band; Orch; Pep Band; School Musical; Symp Band; Pres Stu Cncl; Var Lcrss; JP Sousa Awd; Ntl Merit SF; Ntl Hnrs Soc-86-87; Cornell U; Htl Mgmt.

RUBIN, JENNY; Plymouth-Whitemarsh HS; Lafayette Hill, PA; (3); 26/365; Cheerleading; Lcrss; Powder Puff Ftbl; Tennis; Vllybl; High Hon Roll; B Nai Brith Yth Orgnztn, ST Fnlst Miss PA US Teen Pgnt 86-87.

RUBIN, LISA; Taylor Allderdice HS; Pittsburgh, PA; (2).

RUBINCAN, DAWN; Coatesville Area SR HS; Coatesville, PA; (4); 103/487; French Clb; Leo Clb; Ski Clb; Chorus; Off Jr Cls; Off Sr Cls; Stu Cncl; Swmmng; Tennis; Lion Awd; West Chester U; Sclgy.

RUBINI, LOREDANA; Bodine HS For Intl Affairs; Philadelphia, PA; (4); 1/94; Debate Tm; Latin Clb; Library Aide; Yrbk Ed-Chief; Bowling; Sftbl; Hon Roll; Jr NHS; NHS; Natl Young Ldrs Conf Tchrs Schlrshp 86; Hugh Obrien Yth Fndtn Schl Rep 85; Drexel U; Pltcl Sci.

RUBINO, MARY JO; Wyoming Area HS; Wyoming, PA; (4); 6/249; Drama Clb; French Clb; Key Clb; Chorus; Color Guard; High Hon Roll; NHS; R S Capin Schlrshp 87; Suprntndnts Achvt Awd 87; Wilkes Coll; Acctng.

RUBINO, NANCY; St Marys Area Public HS; Saint Marys, PA; (4); Art Inst Pittsburgh; Intr Dsgn.

RUBINO, TONY; Beaver JR SR HS; Beaver, PA; (4); Church Yth Grp; Sec JCL; Ski Clb; School Musical; Yrbk Bus Mgr; VP Soph Cls; Pres Stu Cncl; JV Ftbl; Var Tennis; WA & Jefferson Coll; Optmtry.

RUBNER, RAY; Abington Heights HS; Clarks Summit, PA; (3); 3/292; Yrbk Sprt Ed; Lit Mag; L Ftbl; Var Trk; Wt Lftg; Bausch & Lomb Sci Awd; High Hon Roll; Ntl Merit SF; Rotary Ldrshp Comp 86; Amer Free Pwrlftng Assoc Meet Best 17 Yr Old 87; Albington Pwrlftng 1st Pl 87; Pre-Med.

RUBRIGHT, RANDY; Norwin SR HS; N Huntingdon, PA; (3); 4-H; VICA; Chorus; 4-H Awd; Pwrline Const.

RUBY, EDEN; Faith Christian HS; Turtle Crk, PA; (2); Church Yth Grp; Drama Clb; Chorus; School Play; Yrbk Bus Mgr; Yrbk Rptr; Stu Cncl; Var Bsktbl; Var Vllybl; High Hon Roll; U PTSBRG; Elem Ed.

RUBY, MONICA LYNN; Indiana Area SR HS; Indiana, PA; (4); Hosp Aide; Key Clb; Pep Clb; Band; Chorus; Color Guard; Nwsp Rptr; Hon Roll; PA JR Acad Of Sci; PA ST U; CPA.

RUCH, KIMBERLY; Salisbury HS; Allentown, PA; (3); 38/153; Drama Clb; Key Clb; JV Bsktbl; Var L Fld Hcky; L Swmmng; Hon Roll; Bio Chem.

RUCH, KURT A; Bishop O Reilly HS; Swoyersville, PA; (3); Am Leg Boys St; Cmnty Wkr; Rep Jr Cls; Var Bsbl; Var Bsktbl; Var Crs Cntry; Var Wt Lftg; Prfct Atten Awd; Inds Arts Awd 87; Bus Admin.

RUCHAK, JOSEPH; Bishop O Hara HS; Dunmore, PA; (2); Church Yth Grp; Computer Clb; Drama Clb; Pep Clb; Ski Clb; Spanish Clb; Chorus; School Musical; School Play; Stage Crew; Penn ST; Bus.

RUCINSKI, DEBORAH; Du Bois Area HS; Penfield, PA; (3); 29/312; Varsity Clb; Sec Frsh Cls; Sec Soph Cls; Sec Jr Cls; Pres Sr Cls; Stat Bsbl; Var Capt Cheerleading; Outstndng Stu Cncl Prsn Awd 85; Adm.

RUCK, KELLY; Central SR HS; York, PA; (3); FBLA; FHA; Mrchg Band; Twrlr; Hon Roll; York Coll Of PA; Stenographer.

RUCK, KENNETH; Archbishop Wood HS For Boys; Hatboro, PA; (4); 54/276; Model UN; Service Clb; SADD; Rep Frsh Cls; Var Crs Cntry; Var Trk; Hon Roll; NHS; PA Dept Envrnmtl Resources Awd Outstndng Achvt Sci 85; US Marine Awd Outstndng Achvt Envrnmntl Sci; U Of DE; Bio.

RUCK, LORI; Ambridge Area SR HS; Baden, PA; (3); German Clb; Pep Clb; SADD; Sec VICA; Rep Stu Cncl; High Hon Roll; Hon Roll; Beaver Cnty Tms Hnr Carrier 86; Penn Tech Inst; Elec Engrng.

RUCKER, SARA; New Castle SR HS; New Castle, PA; (4); 15/253; Spanish Clb; Trk; Hon Roll; NHS; Bus.

RUCKERT, CRAIG; Center HS; Monaca, PA; (3); 34/189; Am Leg Boys St; Spanish Clb; Varsity Clb; Var Bsktbl; Var L Trk; Hon Roll; Penn ST; Aerospc Engrng.

RUCKI, AMY; St Marys Area HS; St Marys, PA; (2); Art Clb; Dance Clb; Hosp Aide; JV Var Gym; Hon Roll; Duquane U; Phrmcy.

RUCZHAK, JEANNE; Octorara Area HS; Christiana, PA; (4); 42/152; Church Yth Grp; FTA; Library Aide; Service Clb; SADD; Teachers Aide; Nwsp Rptr; Nwsp Stf; Lit Mag; Hon Roll; Lock Haven U; Specl Elem Ed.

RUDA, JOHNINE; North Allegheny SR HS; Wexford, PA; (4); 150/660; Dance Clb; Ski Clb; Band; Drill Tm; School Musical; Yrbk Stf; Hon Roll; Spanish NHS; Acadc All Am 84-85; 1st HS Fml Rwng Tm Allegheny Cnty 87; De Pauw U.

RUDA, MARY; Lake-Lehman HS; Hunlock Creek, PA; (4); SADD; Cheerleading; Trk; Vllybl; Hon Roll; Jr NHS; NHS; Luzerne Cnty CC; Med Secr.

RUDACILLE, BRIAN; Red Lion Area SR HS; Brogue, PA; (3); 87/342; Hon Roll; Navy; Elec Tech.

RUDAR, HEATHER; Peters Township HS; Venetia, PA; (3); 30/300; Drama Clb; GAA; Intnl Clb; Key Clb; Library Aide; NFL; PAVAS; Spanish Clb; SADD; Thesps; Thespn Theatr Awd Bst Ply 87; Pres Fit Awd 85; Purdue U; Prof Cmmrcl Plot.

RUDD-SAFRAN, KELLY; Penn Wood HS; Yeadon, PA; (3); 18/300; Church Yth Grp; Variety Show; Cheerleading; JV Lcrss; High Hon Roll; NHS.

RUDDOCK, SHARON; Acad Notre Dame De Namur; Newtown Square, PA; (3); Math Tm; SADD; Var Bsktbl; Var Socr; Var Capt Sftbl; High Hon Roll; Hon Roll; Engr.

RUDDY, LISA; Carlynton HS; Carnegie, PA; (3); Art Clb; French Clb; Yrbk Stf; PA ST U; Bus.

RUDDY, REMA; Carbondale Area HS; Carbondale, PA; (3); Art Clb; French Clb; FBLA; JA; Ski Clb; School Play; Rep Soph Cls; Sec Jr Cls; Bsktbl; Crs Cntry.

RUDEK, RAYMOND; Moon HS; Coraopolis, PA; (4); 19/300; Trs Key Clb; Q&S; Yrbk Phtg; Yrbk Sprt Ed; Var L Socr; Var L Swmmng; L Trk; Hon Roll; Trs Kiwanis Awd; NHS; Soc Autmtv Engrs-Rgnl Sci Fair 86; Schl Stu Athlt Schlrshp 87; Lions Clb Stu Of Mnth-Jan 87; Purdue U; Chem Engrng.

RUDIGER, CHRISTINE; Peters Twp HS; West Chester, PA; (3); Art Clb; Ski Clb; Varsity Clb; Color Guard; Concert Band; Mrchg Band; Yrbk Stf; Var L Cheerleading; Var L Trk; High Hon Roll; Graphic Art.

RUDISLL, ANN; Mt Carmel Area JR-SR HS; Mt Carmel, PA; (4); 14/170; Key Clb; Latin Clb; NFL; Pep Clb; Pres Q&S; Spanish Clb; Chorus; School Musical; Nwsp Ed-Chief; Off Stu Cncl; Amy Vanderbilt Awd 87; Laurel Queen 87; J P Deppen Schlrshp 87; Bucknell U.

RUDMAN, SCOT; Carlynton JR SR HS; Pittsburgh, PA; (3); Boys Clb Am; Var L Socr; U Of Miami; Marine Bio.

RUDNIK, MICHAEL; Hempfield Area HS; Jeannette, PA; (4); 211/693; German Clb; High Hon Roll; Hon Roll; U Of Pittsburgh; Psych.

RUDOCK, CHRIS; Solanco HS; Nottingham, PA; (4); 58/240; Teachers Aide; Cit Awd; High Hon Roll; Hon Roll; Amer Stds Awd 86; Prncpls Awd Math 87; Mltry US Navy.

RUDOLPH, DAWN; Quakertown Community HS; Quakertown, PA; (3); Church Yth Grp; SADD; Varsity Clb; Chorus; Nwsp Stf; Crs Cntry; Trk; NHS; VFW Awd; Voice Dem Awd; Phy Ed-Hlth.

RUDOLPH, LARA; Rocky Grove JR SR HS; Franklin, PA; (4); 6/88; VP Church Yth Grp; French Clb; Library Aide; Office Aide; SADD; Chorus; School Musical; Sec Jr Cls; Pres Stu Cncl; Var JV Cheerleading; Clarion U; Psychlgy.

RUDOLPH, SHELBY; Sheffield JR SR HS; Sheffield, PA; (4); Pep Clb; VP SADD; Varsity Clb; Trs Soph Cls; Trs Sr Cls; Stu Cncl; VP Cheerleading; Stat Trk; Hon Roll; Hmcmng Queen 86-87; Hmcmng Clss Attndnt 84-86; Penn ST U; Wldlf Sci.

RUDOLPH, THEODORE; Cardinal O Hara HS; Springfield, PA; (4); Ski Clb; Stage Crew; Hon Roll; Opt Clb Awd; U S Army Sci & Engrng Awd 87; Best Of DE County Sci Fair Awd 87; IEEE Special Excllnc Awd 85; Drexel U; Comp Engrng.

RUDOWSKY, MICHAEL; West Mifflin Area HS; W Mifflin, PA; (4); 5/338; Sec Science Clb; Band; Concert Band; Drm Mjr(t); Mrchg Band; Pep Band; High Hon Roll; NHS; Pres Schlr; PA ST U; Cmptr Sci.

RUDOY, CAROLINE; Abington HS; Huntingdon Valley, PA; (3); French Clb; Hosp Aide; Temple Yth Grp; Nwsp Ed-Chief; Nwsp Rptr; Nwsp Stf; Yrbk Rptr; Yrbk Stf; Rep Stu Cncl; Hon Roll; Giftd Prgm 85-87; U Of PA Pre Coll Pgm 87; Psychlgy.

RUDY, AMY; South Middleton HS; Boiling Spgs, PA; (2); Ski Clb; Var Fld Hcky; Var Trk; Lonnie R Whitcomb Frshmn Athlt 85-86; Chld Psych.

RUDY, KRISTIN; Danville SR HS; Danville, PA; (3); Key Clb; Spanish Clb; SADD; Yrbk Phtg; Yrbk Stf; Sec Frsh Cls; Sec Jr Cls; Sec Sr Cls; Rep Stu Cncl; Var Cheerleading.

RUDY, TAMMY; Danville SR HS; Danville, PA; (3); Church Yth Grp; Girl Scts; Latin Clb; Var Bowling; High Hon Roll; NHS; Natl Latin Hnr Soc 86-87; Bloomsburg U; Nrsng.

RUDY, TINA; Central Dauphin HS; Harrisburg, PA; (3); 67/369; Dance Clb; Library Aide; Chorus; School Musical; Stat Bsktbl; Mgr Ftbl; Sftbl; Im Vllybl; Hon Roll; Jr NHS; Advrtsng Dsgn.

RUDZKI, JILL; North Catholic HS; Pgh, PA; (3); 83/303; Red Cross Aide; Ski Clb; Nwsp Rptr; Bsktbl; Comm.

RUEFLE, GREGORY; Plum Boro SR HS; Pittsburgh, PA; (3); Band; Ftbl; Trk; Wrstlng; Hon Roll; Orthdntstry.

RUEV, CASSANDRA; Ringgold HS; Donora, PA; (4); 84/344; Band; Swing Chorus; Var JV Vllybl; Hon Roll; Church Yth Grp; Hosp Aide; Chorus; Concert Band; Mrchg Band; Variety Show; Guest Spkr Rotary Clb 86-87; Outdr Educ Clb 84-87; Chrmn For Toys For Tots 86-87; Douglas Schl Of Bus; Exec Sec.

RUFF, CARL; Red Lion Area SR HS; Felton, PA; (2); 48/344; Church Yth Grp; Concert Band; Jazz Band; Mrchg Band; Symp Band; Prfct Atten Awd.

RUFF, CHRISTINE; Bethel Park SR HS; Pittsburgh, PA; (4); 7/519; Church Yth Grp; FHA; Key Clb; Im Bsktbl; JV Cheerleading; JV Mgr(s); Pom Pon; JV Powder Puff Ftbl; Score Keeper; Im Sftbl; Charles L Scharfe Memrl Schlrshp 87; U Of Pittsburgh; Occptn Thrpy.

RUFF, JENNIFER A; Lower Moreland HS; Huntingdon Valley, PA; (4); Acpl Chr; Chorus; Concert Band; Mrchg Band; Orch; School Musical; School Play; NHS; Ntl Merit SF; High Hnr Achvt Soc Of Engrs 86; Ntl Merit Semi-Fnlst 86; U Of PA; Sci.

RUFF, STEPHANIE JANE; Shippensburg Area SR HS; Shippensburg, PA; (4); 6/219; Band; Jazz Band; Orch; School Musical; School Play; High Hon Roll; NHS; Art Clb; Chorus; Concert Band; Cert Merit Schlstc Wrtng Awd 82,83 & 85; Civic Club Stu Mnth 86; Wayland Rhoads Mem Schlrshp 87; U Of KY; Anml Sci.

RUFFALO, AARON; New Brighton Area HS; New Brighton, PA; (3); Aud/Vis; Boy Scts; JA; Red Cross Aide; Spanish Clb; Stage Crew; Hon Roll; Prfct Atten Awd; Amer Red Crss Excptnl Vlntr Awd 85; Rsprtry Thrpst.

RUFFIN, JANENE; ABP Carroll HS; Wayne, PA; (4); Cmnty Wkr; Library Aide; Office Aide; Pep Clb; Service Clb; SADD; Lit Mag; Rep Soph Cls; Pres Sr Cls; Stu Cncl; U Of VA; Psych.

RUFFNER, ALAN; Greater Latrobe HS; Latrobe, PA; (4); 5/420; German Clb; Letterman Clb; Var L Swmmng; High Hon Roll; NHS; Penn ST; Aerosp Engrng.

RUFFNER, JACQUELYN A; Penn-Trafford HS; Harrison City, PA; (4); Drama Clb; Math Clb; Spanish Clb; School Musical; Ed Lit Mag; Hon Roll; NHS; U Of Southern CA Donrs Schlrshp 87; U Of Southern CA; Screenwrtr.

RUGANI, ROY; Sto-Rox SR HS; Mckees Rocks, PA; (3); 2/180; Boy Scts; Chorus; Yrbk Stf; Trk; God Cntry Awd; Hon Roll; Prfct Atten Awd; Comp Sci.

RUGGERI, DAVID M; Norwin HS; N Huntingdon, PA; (4); 170/570; Pres DECA; Ski Clb; Nwsp Rptr; JV Bsbl; JV Ftbl; Trk; Hon Roll; 2nd Pl DECA Dist Cmptn Rstrnt Mrktng And 4th Pl In 87; 3rd Pl DECA Cmptn Finane & Credit 87; Robert Morris Coll; Bus.

RUGGIERO, LEE; Hazleton HS; Hazleton, PA; (3); 42/445; Scholastic Bowl; Off Stu Cncl; JV Var Bsktbl; Hon Roll; Pre Med.

RUGGIERO, TRICIA; Bishop Hafey HS; Sugarloaf, PA; (4); 26/127; Cmnty Wkr; French Clb; Hosp Aide; Thesps; School Musical; School Play; French Hon Soc; French Exchng 86; Nrthestrn U; Finance.

RUGGLES, DIANE; Central HS; East Freedom, PA; (3); 69/189; Church Yth Grp; Cmnty Wkr; Drama Clb; FBLA; Office Aide; School Musical; FBLA Regnls 4th Pl Entrprnrshp 86; VISTOS Awd 87; Central Penn; Bus Mgmt.

RUGH, KELLI; Nativity BVM HS; Orwigsburg, PA; (2); 13/78; French Clb; Chorus; Var Cheerleading; Crs Cntry; Hon Roll; Pres Phys Ftnss Awd.

RUGH, KRISTA; Jeannette SR HS; Jeannette, PA; (3); 8/135; Trs Church Yth Grp; Sec FBLA; Spanish Clb; Trs Chorus; Var JV Bsktbl; JV Sftbl; High Hon Roll; Hon Roll; JC Awd; NHS; Cnty Juvenel Justice Essay Cntst 1st Pl 86; Jaycees Stu Of Mnth 86; Rotary Yth Ldrshp Awds Conf 87; Grove City Coll.

RUGH, KRISTINA A; Jeannette SR HS; Jeannette, PA; (3); 3/130; Church Yth Grp; VP FBLA; Spanish Clb; Chorus; Church Choir; JV Var Bsktbl; Var Sftbl; High Hon Roll; Hon Roll; NHS; 2nd Pl FBLA Rgnl Spkng 87; Seton Hill Coll Ldrshp Conf 86; Rotry Yth Ldrshp Awd Conf 87; Grove City Coll.

RUGOLA, AMY; Brownsville Area HS; Allison, PA; (4); 15/220; Drama Clb; SADD; Band; Mrchg Band; Pep Band; Variety Show; Vllybl; High Hon Roll; Hon Roll; Jr NHS; U Of Pittsburgh; Math Ed.

RUHE, HEATHER; Mt Penn JR/Sr HS; Reading, PA; (3); FTA; Science Clb; Sec Y-Teens; Variety Show; Yrbk Stf; Var Fld Hcky; Var Sftbl; Hon Roll; Presdntl Acadc Ftns Awd 87; Comm.

RUHL, ANN; Villa Maria Acad; West Chester, PA; (3); 9/98; Church Yth Grp; Quiz Bowl; Scholastic Bowl; Science Clb; Spanish Clb; Im Bsktbl; High Hon Roll; NHS; Prfct Atten Awd; Spanish NHS; Part With Distinction In Natl Lang Arts Olympiad 85; 1st Prz Main Line Stu Peace Essay Cont 86; Chemistry.

RUHL, ERIC C; Hershey HS; Palmyra, PA; (3); Boy Scts; Cmnty Wkr; Exploring; School Play; Ftbl; Wrstlng; Eagle Scout 87; Bus.

RUHL, JENNIFER A; Spring-Ford HS; Royersford, PA; (3); 71/256; German Clb; Rep Frsh Cls; Rep Soph Cls; Rep Jr Cls; JV Fld Hcky; Var Sftbl; Im Vllybl; Hon Roll; Crim Just.

RUHL, LARRY J; Pennsbury HS; Levittown, PA; (1); Church Yth Grp; Drama Clb; Chorus; Church Choir; School Musical; School Play; Hon Roll; Law.

RUHL, MICHAEL; Cedar Crest HS; Lebanon, PA; (1); 103/350; German Clb; Pep Clb; Trk; Wt Lftg; Hon Roll; Hstry Awd 84; Penn ST U.

RUIA, MONYC P; Owen J Roberts HS; Spring, PA; (3); 3/330; Rep Stu Cncl; JV Fld Hcky; JV Lcrss; High Hon Roll; Hon Roll; Rep NHS; Rep Frsh Cls; Rep Soph Cls; Im Vllybl; U Of PA; Frgn Bus.

RULLO, CHRISTINE; Ringgold HS; Monongahela, PA; (4); 28/327; Church Yth Grp; Girl Scts; Ski Clb; Nwsp Stf; Yrbk Ed-Chief; Sr Jrnlsm Awd 87; Penn St.

RULLO, GINA M; Marple Newtown HS; Broomall, PA; (3); Drama Clb; SADD; School Musical; School Play; Variety Show; Nwsp Stf; Yrbk Stf; Sec Soph Cls; Sec Stu Cncl; Var Cheerleading; Teaching.

RUMBAUGH, STEVEN; Knoch HS; Cabot, PA; (3); Church Yth Grp; Chorus; Mgr(s); Butler Co CC; Gnrl Stu.

RUMBERGER, KIRSTEN; Berks Christian Schl; Oley, PA; (3); Chorus; Yrbk Stf; Trs Jr Cls; Capt Cheerleading; Trk; High Hon Roll; NHS; Marine Bio.

RUMBLE, BETH; Brandywine Heights HS; Mertztown, PA; (4); 10/121; Church Yth Grp; Band; Concert Band; Jazz Band; Mrchg Band; Pep Band; High Hon Roll; NHS; Rotary Awd; Kutztown U; Elem Ed.

RUMMEL, JULIE; Everett Christian Acad; Everett, PA; (4); Church Yth Grp; Debate Tm; Chorus; Church Choir; Concert Band; School Musical; Pres Jr Cls; Pres Sr Cls; VP Stu Cncl; Capt Bsktbl; Acdmc Excllnc 85; Hghst Overall Avg 85; Schlstc Achvmnt 86; Lee Coll; Gen Bus.

RUMMEL, KURTIS; Central Cambria HS; Revloc, PA; (3); 40/200; Church Yth Grp; Computer Clb; 4-H; ROTC; Cntrl Cambria Comp Tm Awd 87; Aeronautical Engrng.

RUMMEL JR, LARRY L; South Western HS; Brodbecks, PA; (3); Im Bsktbl; Hon Roll; Med.

RUMNEY, JOHN; Marion Center Area HS; Rossiter, PA; (4); 25/159; Church Yth Grp; Latin Clb; Science Clb; Chorus; Off Stu Cncl; Var Bsbl; High Hon Roll; Hon Roll; Congrssnl Yth Ldrshp Cncl 87; Slippery Rock U; Med.

RUMPH, JENNIFER; South Park HS; Library, PA; (4); Church Yth Grp; Drama Clb; Girl Scts; Thesps; Capt Color Guard; Mrchg Band; School Play; Stage Crew; Rep Frsh Cls; NHS; Deg Wrld Affairs Cncl Of Pgh 86; Alg Intr Unit Soc Sci 86; Giftd & Tlntd Enrchmnt Prog GATE 83-87; Intl Stud.

RUMSEY, CURT; Christian School Of York; York, PA; (2); Church Yth Grp; Cmnty Wkr; JA; Rep Stu Cncl; Var L Bsbl; Var L Sftbl; Hon Roll; Mech Engrng.

RUMSKEY, CHERIE L; Waynesburg Ctl HS; Waynesburg, PA; (4); 18/200; Church Yth Grp; Letterman Clb; Office Aide; Stage Crew; Capt Var Cheerleading; Trk; High Hon Roll; Lion Awd; NHS; Girl Yr 87; Waynesburg Coll Hnr Scholar 87; Waynesburg Coll.

RUNDLE, BRIAN; Lancaster Country Day HS; Reading, PA; (3); Pres Church Yth Grp; Pres Dance Clb; Intnl Clb; Model UN; Rep Jr Cls; Rep Stu Cncl; Var Tennis; Hon Roll; Ntl Merit SF; Stud Cncl Awd; PA Math Leag Cont.

RUNDLE, SCOTT; Waynesboro Area SR HS; Waynesboro, PA; (4); 12/383; Church Yth Grp; Chorus; Church Choir; Concert Band; Jazz Band; Mrchg Band; School Musical; High Hon Roll; JP Sousa Awd; NHS; Wynsboro Tchrs Assoc Schlrshp 87; Penn ST U; Educ.

RUNK, DAVID; Coatesville HS; Coatesville, PA; (3); 34/509; Church Yth Grp; French Clb; Ski Clb; Chorus; Rep Stu Cncl; Hon Roll; NHS; Prfct Atten Awd; Vet Med.

RUNK, KARENA; Fannett-Metal HS; Willow Hill, PA; (4); VP DECA; Drama Clb; Sec Varsity Clb; Color Guard; VP Stu Cncl; Capt Bsktbl; Capt Sftbl; Hon Roll; NHS; Acad All-Amer 86-87.

RUNK, KATHRYN; Cumberland Valley HS; Mechanicsburg, PA; (3); Drama Clb; Quiz Bowl; Varsity Clb; Chorus; School Musical; Trk; Wt Lftg; Hon Roll; Ntl Merit SF; Penn ST; Med.

RUNKEL, ZOE; Northern Lebanon JR-SR HS; Lebanon, PA; (3); 2/213; Computer Clb; Science Clb; Chorus; School Play; JV Socr; High Hon Roll; Marine Bio.

RUNKLE, CHRIS; Hollidaysburg Area Senior HS; Hollidaysburg, PA; (3); Church Yth Grp; SADD; Varsity Clb; Sec Soph Cls; Rep Stu Cncl; Bsktbl; L Ftbl; Golf; L Trk; Vllybl; Engrng.

RUNKLE, LISA; Mechanicsburg SR HS; Mechanicsburg, PA; (3); 90/338; Ski Clb; Chorus; Yrbk Stf; Rep Soph Cls; Sec Jr Cls; Pres Sr Cls; Diving; Natl Art Hnr Soc 85-87; Natl Art Hnr Soc Secy, Pres 86-87; Art.

RUNKLE, REBECCA; Kennard Dale HS; Felton, PA; (3); 24/167; Church Yth Grp; Hosp Aide; Chorus; Church Choir; School Musical; School Play; Nwsp Ed-Chief; High Hon Roll; Hon Roll; NHS; String Quartet 85-88; K-Dettes 85-88; Soloist Company Praise 85; Music Thrpy.

RUNNELS, JOHN W; Hempfield HS; Mountville, PA; (2); Cmnty Wkr; Drama Clb; Rep Stu Cncl; Var Trk; Hon Roll; Variety Show; JV Ftbl; Rider Coll; Accntng.

RUPERT, AMY; Montour HS; Coraopolis, PA; (3); Debate Tm; SADD; Variety Show; Nwsp Phtg; Nwsp Rptr; Nwsp Stf; Htl Mngmnt.

RUPERT, JOYCE; Hughesville HS; Hughesville, PA; (4); 9/136; Key Clb; Library Aide; Teachers Aide; Hon Roll; NHS; Green & White Awd 85; Lock Haven U; Sec Educ.

RUPERT, NICOLE; Bishop Guilfoyle HS; Altoona, PA; (3); Church Yth Grp; Hosp Aide; Ski Clb; SADD; Chorus; Yrbk Stf; Pom Pon; PA ST; Phys Thrpy.

RUPERT, THERESA; Fred City JR SR HS; Ford City, PA; (4); 17/156; Church Yth Grp; FBLA; Pep Clb; Spanish Clb; Teachers Aide; Chorus; NHS; High Hon Roll; Hon Roll; Outstndng Sec Stu Awd 87; Army; Comp.

RUPP, JESSICA; Ephrata SR HS; Ephrata, PA; (4); 105/257; Camera Clb; German Clb; Pep Clb; Rep Frsh Cls; Rep Jr Cls; Stu Cncl; Bsktbl; Hon Roll; Lancaster Schl Of Cosmetlgy.

RUPP III, LOUIS; Palisades HS; Kintnersville, PA; (4); 17/179; Trs Jr Cls; Pres Stu Cncl; Var Socr; Var Tennis; High Hon Roll; Jr NHS; NHS; Rotary Awd; AFS; JV Bsktbl; Sccr Schlr Athlt 86; Schl Brd Rep, IV Rep 85-87; U Of Pittsburgh; Mchncl Engr.

RUPP, MELISSA; Carbondale Area HS; Simpson, PA; (3); Art Clb; French Clb; Spanish Clb; High Hon Roll; NHS; Spanish NHS; Ed.

RUPPEL, JENNIFER; S Fayette JR Ssr HS; Bridgeville, PA; (3); Art Clb; Church Yth Grp; Drama Clb; Ski Clb; School Play; JV Cheerleading; High Hon Roll; Hon Roll; NHS; Cmmrcl Art.

RUPPEL, KARA; Turkeyfoot Valley Area HS; Confluence, PA; (4); 3/57; Q&S; Ski Clb; Varsity Clb; Chorus; Nwsp Rptr; Yrbk Stf; Sec VP Stu Cncl; Var Capt Cheerleading; High Hon Roll; Pres NHS; Phys Ed Awd; Coll Prep Eng Awd; Bio Awd; U MD; Phys Ther.

RUPPERT, KIMBERLY; Dover Area HS; Dover, PA; (4); 36/247; Girl Scts; Hosp Aide; Color Guard; L Mrchg Band; Stat L Bsbl; Hon Roll; Forgn Exch Clb 85-87; Millersville U; Elem Ed.

RUPSKY, DIANNE; Tunkhannock Area HS; Tunkhannock, PA; (2); Spanish Clb; Bsktbl; Crs Cntry; Sftbl; Hon Roll.

RUSAK, ERIC; Valley HS; New Kensington, PA; (3); Science Clb; Spanish Clb; Rep Soph Cls; Rep Jr Cls; Var Capt Swmmng; Var Wrstlng; High Hon Roll; NHS; Engrng.

RUSCH, WENDI; Greater Works Acad; Pittsburgh, PA; (3); 3/35; Church Yth Grp; Ski Clb; Band; Nwsp Stf; Rep Stu Cncl; Sftbl; Trk; Vllybl; High Hon Roll; 2nd Pl Sci Fair 85 & 86; Pres Phys Fit Awd 85-87; Svc & Ministry Munich W Germany 85; Engrng.

RUSCILLE, CHRISTOPHER; New Castle SR HS; New Castle, PA; (3); 3/293; Spanish Clb; High Hon Roll; Hon Roll.

RUSCITTO, JASON; Mon Valley Catholic HS; Scenery Hill, PA; (3); 40/140; Art Clb; Church Yth Grp; JA; Letterman Clb; Ski Clb; Yrbk Rptr; Bsbl; Ftbl; Tennis; Ftbl-All Conf, All Cnty 86; 4 Yr Lttrmn 84-88; Arch.

RUSCITTO, MARC; Peters Township HS; Venetia, PA; (3); 20/241; Church Yth Grp; Cmnty Wkr; Computer Clb; French Clb; Letterman Clb; Ski Clb; Varsity Clb; Yrbk Stf; Tennis; Hon Roll; Bus.

RUSEK, JEANNE; Archbishop Prendergast HS; Secane, PA; (3); 188/327; Office Aide; PA ST; Acctng.

RUSH, BECKY; Waynesburg Central HS; Waynesburg, PA; (3); Church Yth Grp; 4-H; French Clb; Mu Alpha Theta; Natl Beta Clb; VP Stu Cncl; Dnfth Awd; Hon Roll; NHS; U Of SC.

RUSH, CHRISTOPHER; Liberty HS; Bethlehem, PA; (3); 35/429; Church Yth Grp; German Clb; Band; Chorus; Church Choir; Mrchg Band; JV Var Bsktbl; YWCA Bsktbll Spirit Awd Church Lge 85; Jr Vrsty Coaches Awd Bsktbll 85-86.

RUSH, KAREN; Cumberland Valley HS; Camp Hill, PA; (4); 105/522; Key Clb; Nwsp Rptr; Sec Frsh Cls; VP Soph Cls; Rep Stu Cncl; Var Cheerleading; Hon Roll; Ski Clb; Church Choir; Nwsp Stf; Pinebrook Civic Assoc Awd 87; New Cumberland Army Depot Thrft Shp Awd 87; JR Prom Rep 86; OH U-Athens; Fashn Merch.

RUSH, KELLY; Carmichaels Area HS; Carmichaels, PA; (4); 8/101; Ski Clb; Spanish Clb; Color Guard; Concert Band; Trs Jr Cls; Trs Sr Cls; High Hon Roll; NHS; Ntl Merit Ltr; CA U; Acctng.

RUSH, KELLY; Vincentian HS; Pittsburgh, PA; (3); 1/63; Service Clb; Pres Frsh Cls; Pres Soph Cls; Var Capt Bsktbl; JV Var Fld Hcky; Var Im Sftbl; High Hon Roll; NHS; Office Aide; Teachers Aide; Hugh O Brien Ldrshp Awd 86; 23rd Annl PA JR Sci 86; PA JR Acad Sci 1st Pl Awd 85 & 86; Med.

RUSH, KRISTIE; Connellsville Area SR HS; Connellsville, PA; (3); Church Yth Grp; Computer Clb; Office Aide; Yrbk Stf; Hon Roll; Comp Engrng.

RUSH, MATTHEW; Mc Guffey HS; Claysville, PA; (2); Church Yth Grp; German Clb; Bsktbl; Golf; Tennis; High Hon Roll; Pres Schlr; Engrng.

RUSH, ROBIN L; Keystone HS; Woodbridge, VA; (3); French Clb; Model UN; Pep Clb; VP SADD; Stu Cncl; JV Bsktbl; L Cheerleading; Hon Roll; Church Yth Grp; Rep FBLA; George Washington; Prim Ed.

RUSHANAN, MARIE THERESE; Nativity B V M HS; Minersville, PA; (2); 31/77; Church Yth Grp; Spanish Clb; Variety Show; Cheerleading; Hon Roll; Hghst Achvt Amer Lit 87; Ftnss All Amer 86-87; Bus.

RUSHTON, JOHN; West Perry SR HS; Duncannon, PA; (2); Art Clb; Boys Clb Am; French Clb; Drm & Bgl; Bsbl; Tennis; High Hon Roll; Hon Roll; Penn ST Wrtng Comptn 85-86; Harrisburg CC; Cosmotolgy.

RUSILOSKI, AMY; Crestwood HS; Mountain Top, PA; (3); 1/203; Sec Mu Alpha Theta; NHS; Ntl Merit Ltr; Cmnty Wkr; 4-H; Hosp Aide; Key Clb; Math Clb; Science Clb; Service Clb; PA Dist II Champ 800m, 1600m, 3200m, Crss Cntry 85-87; PA Gvrnrs Schl Sci Schlrs 87; Pre-Med.

RUSILOSKI, BETSY; Crestwood HS; Mountaintop, PA; (2); Cmnty Wkr; Pep Clb; Varsity Clb; Sec Frsh Cls; Rep Soph Cls; Var L Cheerleading; Var L Crs Cntry; Var L Trk; Hon Roll.

RUSIN, TINA; Montour HS; Coraopolis, PA; (3); Church Yth Grp; Dance Clb; Exploring; Nwsp Stf; Stu Cncl; Robert Morris; Bus Mgmt.

RUSINCHAK, ANDY; Wyoming Area HS; W Wyoming, PA; (2); 45/250; Scholastic Bowl; Ski Clb; Spanish Clb; Bsbl; Bsktbl; Ftbl; Golf; Tennis; Wrstlng; Dentstry.

RUSINKO, JOSEPH VINCENT; East Allegheny HS; North Versailles, PA; (2); Church Yth Grp; French Clb; Science Clb; Ski Clb; Spanish Clb; School Musical; Rep Soph Cls; Var L Trk; Var Wt Lftg; High Hon Roll; Bio Engr.

RUSKIN, CATHY; Ambridge Area HS; Baden, PA; (3); Pep Clb; Red Cross Aide; VICA; Off Soph Cls; Off Jr Cls; Hon Roll; Pittsburgh Beauty Acad; Csmtlgy.

RUSKIN, REMY; Shadyside Acad; Pittsburgh, PA; (3); Dance Clb; Hosp Aide; Nwsp Rptr; Yrbk Stf; Var JV Fld Hcky; Lcrss; Cmmnctns.

RUSNOCK, PAULA; West Mifflin Area HS; W Mifflin, PA; (3); Hon Roll; Vet Med.

RUSS, AMY; Mc Keesport Area HS; Mc Keesport, PA; (4); Q&S; Trs Band; Mrchg Band; Orch; School Musical; Symp Band; Powder Puff Ftbl; High Hon Roll; NHS; Rtry Hnr Stu 86; Duquesne U; Phrmcy.

RUSS, DAWN; Rockwood Area JR SR HS; Stoystown, PA; (4); 17/92; Trs FHA; Trs VICA; Chorus; Stage Crew; High Hon Roll; Hon Roll; Ntl Merit Ltr; Pittsburg Beauty Acad; Hair Dsn.

RUSSEL, KARIN; Benton Area JR SR HS; Benton, PA; (2); Drama Clb; French Clb; Sec Trs Library Aide; Chorus; Nwsp Stf; Hon Roll.

RUSSELL, ALEXANDER; George Washington Ctr H S Engr Sci; Philadelphia, PA; (4); 3/229; Computer Clb; Math Clb; Scholastic Bowl; Mrchg Band; High Hon Roll; Hon Roll; NHS; St Schlr; PA JR Acad Sci 1st Prz Regnl 86-87, 1st Prz ST 86; 2nd Pl Geo WA Carver Sci Fair 86; Comp Sci.

RUSSELL, BRENDA; The Ellis Schl; Pittsburgh, PA; (3); JCL; Latin Clb; Im Badmtn; 4 Yr Acdmc Schlrshp-Ellis 84; Accptnc Vet Sci Apprntcshp Pgm, Sec/Treas Yth Cry-Peace Orgnztn 87; Duke; Vet Med.

RUSSELL, BRIAN; Pleasant Valley HS; Brodheadsville, PA; (3); AFS; Church Yth Grp; German Clb; Scholastic Bowl; JV Crs Cntry; JV Wrstlng; Hon Roll; Ntl Merit Ltr; Johns Hopkins CTY Pgm 84-85; Music.

RUSSELL, CHERYL; Frazier HS; Perryopolis, PA; (3); Cmnty Wkr; GAA; Girl Scts; Hosp Aide; Pep Clb; Band; Chorus; Concert Band; Jazz Band; Mrchg Band; Bradford Bus Schl; Med Secy.

RUSSELL, CHRIS; Purchase Line HS; Commodore, PA; (3); Varsity Clb; Chorus; Nwsp Stf; VP Jr Cls; Bsktbl; Var L Ftbl; Var L Trk; Im Wt Lftg; Hon Roll; Indiana U Of PA; Crmnlgy.

RUSSELL, CHRIS; Shikellamy HS; Sunbury, PA; (3); 79/319; Boy Scts; VP Church Yth Grp; Trs German Clb; Wrstlng; Hon Roll; Bus Adm.

RUSSELL, COLLEEN; Pennsbury HS; Yardley, PA; (3); #47 In Class; Art Clb; Cmnty Wkr; French Clb; Intnl Clb; Political Wkr; School Musical; Yrbk Stf; Rep Jr Cls; Var L Cheerleading; Var Cmnty Wkr.

RUSSELL, DINA; Phila HS For Girls; Philadelphia, PA; (3); 136/405; Church Yth Grp; Cmnty Wkr; Dance Clb; German Clb; Library Aide; Office Aide; Service Clb; Teachers Aide; Church Choir; Drill Tm; Veterinary Med.

RUSSELL, ERIKA; Quaker Valley HS; Sewickley, PA; (3); Service Clb; Chorus; Yrbk Stf; Trk.

RUSSELL, GREGORY; Geibel HS; Uniontown, PA; (3); Band; School Musical; Crs Cntry; French Hon Soc; High Hon Roll; Prfct Atten Awd; Musicl Prfrmnce.

RUSSELL, HARRISON SCOTT; Neshaminy HS; Langhorne, PA; (3); Boy Scts; Church Yth Grp; Band; Church Choir; Concert Band; Jazz Band; Mrchg Band; Orch; Symp Band; Nwsp Rptr; Air Force.

RUSSELL, JEANINE; Mt Pleasant Area SR HS; Mt Pleasant, PA; (4); 3/246; Sec Church Yth Grp; GAA; Pres Band; Pres Concert Band; Jazz Band; Pres Mrchg Band; Yrbk Phtg; Sec NHS; High Hon Roll; Prncpls Awd 84; Acdmc Exc Awd 85-86; Cnty & Dstrct Hnrs Bnd Fstvls 83-86; Kent ST; Archtctr.

RUSSELL, JENNIFER; Charleroi Area JR SR HS; Charleroi, PA; (3); Church Yth Grp; FBLA; Science Clb; Spanish Clb; SADD; Yrbk Stf; VP Rep Jr Cls; Capt Socr; Hon Roll; NHS; WPIAL All Conf Tm Sccr 85-86; Advncd Qualfrs Trk 86-87; Sprts Med.

RUSSELL, JON D; Troy SR HS; Towanda, PA; (3); 21/184; Am Leg Boys St; Boy Scts; Im JV Bsktbl; Var L Ftbl; Im Wt Lftg; Hon Roll; NHS; Phrmcy.

RUSSELL, JULIA; Mercer JR SR HS; Mercer, PA; (4); 9/144; Ski Clb; Nwsp Ed-Chief; Nwsp Rptr; Yrbk Stf; Trs Jr Cls; Trs Sr Cls; Rep Stu Cncl; Var L Bsktbl; VP NHS; Indiana U Of PA; Math Educ.

RUSSELL, JULIE; Otto-Edred HS; Eldred, PA; (3); Spanish Clb; Varsity Clb; Chorus; Sec Soph Cls; Pres Jr Cls; Cheerleading; Trk; Hon Roll; NHS; Surgcl Nrse.

RUSSELL, KAREN M; North Penn HS; Lansdale, PA; (3); 120/699; 4-H; Key Clb; Flag Corp; Orch; Rep Soph Cls; Trk; Hon Roll; Mth.

RUSSELL, KRISTIN; Highlands SR HS; Pittsburgh, PA; (4); 28/288; Church Yth Grp; Hosp Aide; Intnl Clb; Key Clb; Office Aide; SADD; Teachers Aide; Band; Color Guard; Concert Band; 1st Pl At Canadas Wndrlnd For Best Overall Band Front 87; Untd Mthds Mnstrl Schlrshp 87-88; Music Fest; Otterbein Coll; Phys Thrpy.

RUSSELL, LINCOLN; Northeast Bradford HS; Rome, PA; (3); Church Yth Grp; Computer Clb; Office Aide; Teachers Aide; Varsity Clb; Rep Jr Cls; Rep Sr Cls; Stu Cncl; Bsktbl; Hon Roll; Edu.

RUSSELL, MICHELE; Solanco HS; Quarryville, PA; (2); 36/286; Church Yth Grp; Acpl Chr; Chorus; Church Choir; School Musical; Stat Mgr(s); Stat Score Keeper; Cit Awd; High Hon Roll; Hon Roll; Prncpls Awd Grmn 86-87; Nrsng.

RUSSELL, NICHOLAS; West Hazleton HS; West Hazleton, PA; (4); 14/224; Computer Clb; Math Tm; Ski Clb; Band; Mrchg Band; Bowling; High Hon Roll; Hon Roll; NHS; Ntl Merit Ltr; 1st Pl Awd Schl Dist Compu Cntst 86; 2nd Pl Awds PA Jr Acad Sci Cmpttn 85-86; 3rd Degree Brwn Blt 87; PA ST U; Compu Sci.

RUSSELL, ROBERT L; Curwensville HS; Grampian, PA; (4); Art Clb; Chess Clb; 4-H; FFA; Red Cross Aide; Swmmng; Wt Lftg; 4-H Awd; Farming.

RUSSELL, STEVEN; Old Forge HS; Old Forge, PA; (3); Drama Clb; Band; Drm Mjr(t); Mrchg Band; School Musical; School Play; Twrlr; Hon Roll; Bus Adm.

RUSSELL, VANESSA; St Marys Area HS; Byrnedale, PA; (2); Trs Soph Cls; Cheerleading; Im Sftbl; Var L Tennis; Var Trk; Im Vllybl; Hon Roll.

RUSSIN, MICHAEL; New Castle SR HS; New Castle, PA; (1); 6/232; AFS; VP French Clb; SADD; Jazz Band; Mrchg Band; Pep Band; Capt Cheerleading; High Hon Roll; Trs NHS; Penn ST U; Chem.

RUSSO, ANGELA; Lock Haven HS; Lock Haven, PA; (3); Cmnty Wkr; German Clb; Band; Chorus; Concert Band; Mrchg Band; Pep Band; Variety Show; Twrlr; Hon Roll; Pharmacy.

RUSSO, BARBARA; St Maria Goretti HS; Philadelphia, PA; (3); 19/350; Math Clb; School Play; Stage Crew; Nwsp Rptr; Var Bowling; Score Keeper; High Hon Roll; Hon Roll; Prfct Atten Awd; Cmmnctns.

RUSSO, DOMINICK; Lincoln HS; Ellwood City, PA; (3); Var L Socr; US Army.

RUSSO, DOUGLAS; Quigley HS; Baden, PA; (3); 1/82; Camera Clb; VP Church Yth Grp; German Clb; Math Clb; Chorus; Yrbk Stf; High Hon Roll; Rlgn & Grmn Awds; Law.

RUSSO, GINA; Bishop Kenrick HS; Norristown, PA; (3); 6/355; GAA; Math Tm; Service Clb; Stu Cncl; Fld Hcky; Sftbl; High Hon Roll; Hon Roll; NHS; Prfct Atten Awd; Outstndng Teengr Awd 86; Hugh O Brian Ldrshp Schlrshp Semnr 86; Math Medl; Acctg.

RUSSO, JAMIE; Academy HS; Erie, PA; (3); 83/226; German Clb; Concert Band; Mrchg Band; Orch; School Musical; Rep Stu Cncl; Crs Cntry; Boy Scts; Red Cross Aide; Band; Yrbk Rep 84-87; Section Ldr Of Drumline 87-88; Presdntl Phy Awd 84-85; IN U; Law.

RUSSO, LISA; Quaker Valley HS; Sewickley, PA; (4); 16/165; German Clb; Latin Clb; Band; Stage Crew; Lit Mag; Var Bowling; Var Socr; Var Sftbl; Grmn Exchng Pgm 86; Prom Cmte 86-87; Westchester U; Forensic Chem.

RUSSO, LYNN; Methacton HS; Audubon, PA; (3); 34/380; Church Yth Grp; Cmnty Wkr; Key Clb; Red Cross Aide; SADD; Church Choir; Off Frsh Cls; Off Soph Cls; Off Jr Cls; Off Sr Cls; Acad Achvt Awd 87; Intl Rltns.

RUSSO, MARCY; Wyoming Area SR HS; Exeter, PA; (3); 25/250; Church Yth Grp; Drama Clb; Key Clb; Spanish Clb; Capt Flag Corp; Nwsp Stf; VP Stu Cncl; High Hon Roll; Hon Roll; NHS; Math.

RUSSO, NICK; Bishop O Reilly HS; Swoyersville, PA; (3); Spanish Clb; Hon Roll; NHS; Spanish NHS; 2nd Pl NE PA Chptr Natl Spn Cont 87; Archit.

RUSSO, NICOLE; Peters Township HS; Venetia, PA; (3); 108/265; Dance Clb; French Clb; Ski Clb; Drill Tm; Mrchg Band; Yrbk Stf; Lit Mag; Gym; Pom Pon; Prfct Mrchr Awd 87; Pdtrtn.

RUSSO, RON; West Scranton HS; Scranton, PA; (3); 93/250; Letterman Clb; Pep Clb; Ski Clb; Spanish Clb; Rep Stu Cncl; JV Var Ftbl; Im Wt Lftg; NHS; SADD; Rep Frsh Cls; Ski Team; Hlth Careers Club; Palmer Coll; Chiropractor.

RUSSO, SHAWN; Karns City JR SR HS; Parker, PA; (4); 38/112; Letterman Clb; Spanish Clb; Varsity Clb; Stage Crew; Nwsp Stf; Rep Stu Cncl; Var L Trk; Hon Roll; US Army; Chiroprctc.

RUSSO, THOMAS P; Archbishop John Carroll HS; Wayne, PA; (4); 42/365; Band; Concert Band; Nwsp Stf; Im Ftbl; Var Tennis; Hon Roll; NHS; Nwspr Page Edtr 86-87sctts Hi-Q Tm 84-87; Loyola Coll; Finnce.

RUSYNYK, JULIA; Central Dauphin HS; Harrisburg, PA; (4); Band; Concert Band; Drill Tm; Mrchg Band; NHS; Millersville U.

RUTAN, DAWN; Mc Guffey HS; Washington, PA; (3); 61/250; French Clb; Ski Clb; Powder Puff Ftbl; Tennis; Trk; Hon Roll; Acctng.

RUTAN, DENISE; West Greene HS; Sycamore, PA; (3); 4/103; Pres 4-H; Nwsp Stf; Sec Soph Cls; Stu Cncl; Var Capt Cheerleading; Trk; 4-H Awd; High Hon Roll; Hon Roll; Ski Clb; Frank P Ross Cash Awd 83-84; 5th Pl Indiv Chrldg Comp 85; Chiropretr.

RUTAN, ERICA; Waynesburg Central HS; Waynesburg, PA; (3); Art Clb; Pep Clb; Spanish Clb; Band; Concert Band; Sftbl; Tennis; Elem Ed.

RUTH, CHRIS; Hempfield HS; Mt Joy, PA; (3); Camera Clb; Science Clb; Chorus; Church Choir; High Hon Roll; Hon Roll; Chef.

RUTH, LAURIE; Donegal HS; Mt Joy, PA; (3); Pep Clb; Band; Jazz Band; Mrchg Band; Rep Stu Cncl; Cheerleading; Powder Puff Ftbl; Hon Roll; Newspr Editor-Artwrk 86-87; County Band 86-87; Honor Band 86-87; Psych.

RUTH, MONTIKA; William Penn SR HS; York, PA; (4); Dance Clb; Drama Clb; Thesps; Chorus; Church Choir; School Musical; Cheerleading; Hon Roll; NHS; Prfct Atten Awd; Dance.

RUTHERFORD, SHANON; Bishop Conwell HS; Langhorne, PA; (3); 19/278; French Clb; Latin Clb; Church Choir; French Hon Soc; High Hon Roll; Hon Roll; NHS.

RUTHERFORD, TRACY; Freedom HS; Bethlehem, PA; (3); 120/515; Church Yth Grp; FCA; Capt Gym; French Hon Soc; Hon Roll; PIAA ST Champnshp Gym Tm 87; Keystone ST Games Gym Tm 87; U FL; Sports Psych.

RUTKOWSKI, LISA; Forest City Regional HS; Forest City, PA; (4); 11/56; Sec Letterman Clb; Ski Clb; Pres Sec Band; Pres Jazz Band; Sec Jr Cls; Sec Sr Cls; Sec Stu Cncl; Capt Var Sftbl; Capt Var Vllybl; Hon Roll; Schlrshp Penn Demctrc Wmn 87; All Str Tm Vlybl, Sftbl 86-87; Ltrs/Hnrs Vlybl, Sftbl, Bsktbl Stats 87; Bloomsburg U Of PA; Med Tech.

RUTKOWSKI, TERESA; Fort Le Boeuf HS; Waterford, PA; (3); 12/215; Band; Concert Band; Mrchg Band; School Musical; High Hon Roll; Edinboro U Of PA; Bus Adm.

RUTKOWSKI, TRACY; John S Fine SR HS; Nanticoke, PA; (2); 37/250; Church Yth Grp; Hosp Aide; Library Aide; Ski Clb; Chorus; Drill Tm; Mrchg Band; Yrbk Stf; Bsktbl; Powder Puff Ftbl; Pl 2nd Pwdr Puff Ftbll 85; Pl 11th Mrchng Bnd 86; Pharm.

RUTKOWSKY, SUSAN; Saint Basil Acad; Philadelphia, PA; (3); 5/85; Drama Clb; French Clb; Science Clb; Yrbk Rptr; Hon Roll; Ntl Merit Ltr; Sci Fair Awd 84-85; Acad All Am 86-87; Med.

RUTLEDGE, DOUGLAS; Bishop Mccort HS; Johnstown, PA; (2); JV Bsktbl; Var Golf; Hon Roll; NHS; Engrng.

RUTT, JAMIE; Mt Calvary Christian Schl; Hummelstown, PA; (4); Chess Clb; Church Yth Grp; Chorus; School Play; Stage Crew; Pres Jr Cls; VP Sr Cls; Rep Stu Cncl; L Bsbl; Var Capt Bsktbl; Bus Adm.

RUTZMOSER, CHRISTINA; Phil Mont Christian Acad; Huntingdon Valley, PA; (3); Church Yth Grp; Drama Clb; Chorus; School Play; Sec Soph Cls; Sec Jr Cls; JV Bsktbl; Hon Roll; Red Cross Advanced Life Saving 87; Stewardship Awd JV Bsktbl 86; Kings Coll; Elem Educ.

RUUD, KELLY; Cedar Crest HS; Lebanon, PA; (2); 92/365; Church Yth Grp; GAA; Key Clb; Pep Clb; Spanish Clb; Church Choir; L Var Cheerleading; Socr; Psych.

RUVOLO, LISA; Middletown Area HS; Middletown, PA; (4); Key Clb; Ski Clb; Varsity Clb; Concert Band; Mrchg Band; Yrbk Stf; Var Socr; Var Sftbl; Im Vllybl; Hon Roll; U Of DE; Mktg.

RUZANIC, MARHEA; North Allegheny HS; Allison Pk, PA; (3); 32/649; Church Yth Grp; Cmnty Wkr; Hosp Aide; Ski Clb; Church Choir; Rptr Soph Cls; Var L Tennis; Var Trk; High Hon Roll; Jr NHS; Frnch Acad Awd 85; Partial Schlrshp To Ellis Schl 84; Intl Banking.

RUZZI, VINCENT J; Strath Haven HS; Princeton Jct, NJ; (4); Aud/Vis; Church Yth Grp; Cmnty Wkr; Computer Clb; Science Clb; Wrstlng; Hon Roll; Natl Yth Physcl Ftnss Awd Mrn Corp Leag 84-85; Gordon Coll; Bus.

RYAN, ANNE MARIE; Clearfield Area HS; Clearfield, PA; (4); Church Yth Grp; French Clb; Nwsp Stf; Sec Frsh Cls; Sec Soph Cls; Var Capt Bsktbl; Var L Sftbl; Bloomsburg U; Fin.

RYAN, CARLEEN; Elizabeth Forward HS; Buena Vista, PA; (3); 8/345; Exploring; Q&S; Band; Concert Band; Jazz Band; Mrchg Band; Nwsp Rptr; High Hon Roll; Hon Roll; NHS; U Pittsburgh; Phys Ther.

RYAN, CELESTE; Blue Mountain Acad; E Branch, NY; (3); Band; Chorus; Church Choir; Nwsp Rptr; JV Var Bsktbl; JV Var Sftbl; Hon Roll; NHS; Computer Clb; Girl Scts; Grls Clb Theta Kappa Gamma Treas 86-87; Gld Music Awd Excllnc In Choir 85-86; Psychlgy.

RYAN, CHRISTINA; Technical HS; Scranton, PA; (4); Art Clb; Letterman Clb; Ski Clb; Stage Crew; Yrbk Stf; Cheerleading; Sftbl; Swmmng; Trk; Amer Ed Wk 2nd Pl Drwg 84; Red & White Awd Sftbl & Art Club 87; Miss Sftbl Awd 87; NE Inst Of Ed; Mgmt.

RYAN, CONNIE; Norwin HS; N Huntingdon, PA; (3); Pres AFS; French Clb; Library Aide; Hon Roll; Jr NHS; Cmmnctns.

RYAN, DANIEL M; West Scranton HS; Scranton, PA; (3); 100/250; Letterman Clb; Ski Clb; Var L Ftbl; Var Trk; Wt Lftg.

RYAN, DEBBIE E; Central SR HS; York, PA; (4); 7/202; Cmnty Wkr; Political Wkr; Yrbk Stf; Mgr(s); CC Awd; Lion Awd; Masonic Awd; Sec NHS; Pres Schlr; Heff Jones Schlr Awd 87; George Washington U; Intl Rltns.

RYAN, DESMOND; St Josephs Prep For Boys; Narberth, PA; (4); 69/225; Church Yth Grp; CAP; Drama Clb; Hosp Aide; Service Clb; School Play; Yrbk Phtg; High Hon Roll; Ntl Merit SF; AP Bio Awd 87; Boston Coll; Med.

RYAN, FRANK; Meyersdale Area HS; Meyersdale, PA; (4); French Clb; Q&S; Nwsp Rptr; Nwsp Stf; Yrbk Rptr; Yrbk Stf; Var L Bsbl; Hon Roll; Church Choir; Rep Sr Cls; Cert Of Merit The Repblc Nwspr & Raider Review Sprts Rptr 87; Frostburg ST U; Cmnctns.

RYAN, JENNIFER; Cocalico HS; Denver, PA; (3); 16/168; Camera Clb; Girl Scts; Band; Concert Band; Jazz Band; Mrchg Band; Pep Band; Hon Roll; Art,Thrpy.

RYAN, KELLY; Shaler Area HS; Allison Pk, PA; (4); 79/510; French Clb; Girl Scts; Hosp Aide; Pep Clb; Rep SADD; Chorus; Flag Corp; School Musical; School Play; Nwsp Stf; Allegheny Coll.

RYAN, KEVIN; Perkiomen Valley HS; Collegeville, PA; (3); Leo Clb; SADD; Varsity Clb; Bsbl; Capt Bsktbl; Var Ftbl; Hon Roll; Church Yth Grp; Cmnty Wkr; FBLA; Vrsty Ftbl 85-87; Vrsty Bsktbl Capt 85-87; Hnr Roll 86-87; Bus Adm.

RYAN, KYRAN; Nativity BVM; St Clair, PA; (3); Rep Jr Cls; Var Crs Cntry; High Hon Roll; Hon Roll; JV Bsktbl; Trk; JV Vllybl; Presdnl Fit Awd 85-87; Philadelphia Coll; Pharmcy.

RYAN, LORIE; William Penn SR HS; York, PA; (3); Church Yth Grp; Concert Band; Mrchg Band; Symp Band; Hon Roll.

RYAN, LORRI; Springdale HS; Cheswick, PA; (3); GAA; Spanish Clb; SADD; Cheerleading; Sftbl; Vllybl; High Hon Roll; Hon Roll; NHS; Art Clb; Natl Acadc Games Qulfr; Advncd Hnrs Cls; Marine Bio.

RYAN, MARIE L; Turtle Creek HS; N Braddock, PA; (4); 5/180; Library Aide; Pep Clb; Science Clb; Spanish Clb; Nwsp Rptr; High Hon Roll; Spnsh, Acad Schlrshps 87; Gannon U; Pre Med.

RYAN, MICHAEL; Altoona Area HS; Altoona, PA; (3); 61/796; Chess Clb; Church Yth Grp; French Clb; Key Clb; Math Tm; Var Crs Cntry; Var Timer; Trk; Hon Roll; Bus.

RYAN, MIKE; Danville HS; Danville, PA; (2); JV Var Socr; High Hon Roll; Hon Roll; Bus Law.

RYAN, NICOLE; Little Flower HS; Philadelphia, PA; (2); 48/497; GAA; Science Clb; Chorus; School Musical; School Play; Var Socr; Hon Roll; Sci Fair Awd 3rd Pz 86; Sci Fair Awd Hnrbl Mention 87; Laboratory Technician.

RYAN, SEAN; St Josephs Predatory Schl; Philadelphia, PA; (4); Cmnty Wkr; French Clb; Varsity Clb; Rep Soph Cls; Rep Jr Cls; Rep Stu Cncl; Var L Bsktbl; JV Diving; Mgr(s); NHS; JR Natl Crew Tm 86-87; S Josephs Prep Schlr 85-87; Stotesbvry Cup Champ Heavwight Vrsty Eight Crew; Penn U; Pre Med.

RYAN, THOMAS; Somerset Area SR HS; Somerset, PA; (3); 68/230; Am Leg Boys St; JA; Model UN; Q&S; VP Ski Clb; Nwsp Phtg; Pres Stu Cncl; Ftbl; Wt Lftg; Hon Roll.

RYAN, TRACEY; Indiana SR HS; Indiana, PA; (3); 31/322; Key Clb; Red Cross Aide; SADD; Nwsp Phtg; Yrbk Phtg; Var L Sftbl; High Hon Roll; Jr NHS; Kiwanis Awd; Prfct Atten Awd.

RYBARCZYK, GENE; Bishop Hafey HS; Freeland, PA; (4); Aud/Vis; Chess Clb; Var L Socr; Prfct Atten Awd; Arch.

RYDER, RICK; Greencastle Antrim HS; Greencastle, PA; (3); Pres Church Yth Grp; JV Socr; Hon Roll.

RYDER, SEAN; Knoch JR/Sr HS; Butler, PA; (2); Bsktbl; Ftbl; Trk; US Naval Acad; Avtn.

RYDZESKI, CINDY; Shikellamy HS; Northumberland, PA; (1); Spanish Clb; Off Frsh Cls; Cheerleading; Sftbl; Trk; Hon Roll; Math Tchr.

RYDZIK, JOSEPH; Carbondale Area HS; Simpson, PA; (2); Ski Clb; Spanish Clb; Hon Roll.

RYEN, ANGIE; Clearfield HS; Woodland, PA; (1); Var Cheerleading; Sftbl; Hon Roll.

RYEN, CHERYL; Marion Center HS; Rochester Mills, PA; (3); 1/168; Trs Girl Scts; Mgr Intnl Clb; Mgr Q&S; Sec Varsity Clb; Stu Cncl; Capt Var Swmmng; Var Trk; Mgr NHS; Mgr Jr NHS; Distngshd Soc Amer HS Stu 84-87; Acad All Amer 87; Sci.

RYEN JR, WILLIAM L; West Branch Area HS; Morrisdale, PA; (3); Church Yth Grp; Varsity Clb; Var JV Bsktbl; Var JV Ftbl; Wt Lftg; Keystone JC; Comp Sci.

RYLKE, PATRICE; Bishop Carroll HS; Portage, PA; (3); Ski Clb; Spanish Clb; Stat Bsbl; L Bsktbl; L Trk; L Vllybl; Hon Roll; Startg Pt Grd Bishp Cntrl Lady Huskies PA ST Champs 87; Keystn Gms Bsktbl Subrgnls 87.

RYND, ANNIE; Mercer JR SR HS; Mercer, PA; (3); Pres 4-H; German Clb; Chorus; School Play; Stage Crew; Swing Chorus; Var Cheerleading; 4-H Awd; Hon Roll; 4-H Buckeye Schlrshp-Outstndng Intermediate Camp Counslr 86; Jr All-Amer Holstein 4yr Old Cow 86; PA ST U; Dairy Mgmt.

RYNKIEWICZ, SHARON; John S Fine HS; Nanticoke, PA; (3); 21/228; Color Guard; High Hon Roll; Med.

RYOO, NANCY; Moon HS; Coraopolis, PA; (3); Cmnty Wkr; Key Clb; Office Aide; Yrbk Bus Mgr; Yrbk Stf; Rep Frsh Cls; Rep Soph Cls; Rep Jr Cls; Rep Stu Cncl; Pitt U; Early Chld Educ.

RYWAK, NANCY L; Valley HS; New Kensington, PA; (3); 31/250; French Clb; Science Clb; Ski Clb; Band; Chorus; Rep Stu Cncl; JV Var Cheerleading; Vllybl; High Hon Roll; Hon Roll; Bus.

RZESZOTARSKI, TRACEY M; Sullivan County HS; Dushore, PA; (4); VP FBLA; Yrbk Bus Mgr; Pres Frsh Cls; Capt Cheerleading; Key Clb; Band; Color Guard; Mrchg Band; Yrbk Stf; Rep Stu Cncl; Stu Mnth 87; Hmcmng Queen 86-87; Williamsport Schl; Exec Sec.

RZODKIEWICZ, TINA; Bethel Christian Schl; Erie, PA; (2); Church Yth Grp; Teachers Aide; Band; Chorus; Church Choir; Variety Show; Yrbk Stf; Sec Frsh Cls; Var Bsktbl; L Sftbl; All Cnfrnc All Str Vllybll 86-87; Horse Show Ribbions 86-87; Liberty U; Pre-Med.

SAALBACH, GRETCHEN; Upper Merion Area HS; Swedesburg, PA; (3); 9/297; Pres Church Yth Grp; Sec Math Tm; Acpl Chr; Chorus; Mrchg Band; Trs Orch; School Musical; Hon Roll; NHS; Ntl Merit Ltr; German Lang Cmpttn Montgomery Cnty Assn Frgn Lang Tchrs 2nd Pl 86; Smmr Schlrshp Ursinus Grmn Lang 87; Robotic Engr.

SAALFRANK, AMY; Upper Moreland HS; Willow Gr, PA; (3); Hosp Aide; Band; Chorus; Concert Band; Mrchg Band; Orch; School Musical; Symp Band; Lit Mag; Bowling; Music Appreciation As Librarian 85-87; Elem Educ.

SABA, CAROLINE A; Penncrest HS; Lima, PA; (3); Church Yth Grp; Intnl Clb; SADD; Chorus; Variety Show; Yrbk Stf; Lit Mag; High Hon Roll; Hon Roll; NHS.

SABA, CINDY; Hanover Area HS; Wilkes Barre, PA; (3); Church Yth Grp; JA; Red Cross Aide; Ski Clb; Varsity Clb; Rep Jr Cls; Crs Cntry; Vllybl; Hon Roll; Ntl Merit Ltr; Ntl Poetry Awd-Hnrb Mntn 87; Wilkes Coll; Psychlgy.

SABA, STEVEN; Council Rock HS; Holland, PA; (2); JV Gym; Villanova U; Law.

SABADISH, MIKE; Bishop O Reilly HS; Swoyersville, PA; (2); Ski Clb; Spanish Clb; Pres Frsh Cls; Pres Jr Cls; Rep Stu Cncl; JV Ftbl; High Hon Roll; NHS; NEDT Awd; Spanish NHS.

SABADOS, LANCE; Shaler Area HS; Allison Pk, PA; (4); 55/509; Rep Frsh Cls; Rep Soph Cls; Rep Jr Cls; Rep Sr Cls; Rep Sr Cls; Rep Stu Cncl; Var L Bsbl; L Capt Socr; High Hon Roll; Hon Roll; Ntl Sci Olympd Tst-Hnrbl Mntn 85-86; Grove City Coll; Elctrcl Engr.

SABAT, MICHELLE; Plum SR HS; Pittsburgh, PA; (3); Church Yth Grp; Trs DECA; French Clb; FHA; Sec SADD; Band; Hon Roll; 1st Pl Slsmnshp DECA ST Comptn 87; Acctng.

SABATASSO, JANET; Seton-La Salle HS; Pittsburgh, PA; (2); Bsktbl; Swmmng; Trk; Cit Awd; Hon Roll; Hnr Of Beingan Acadmc All Amer 87; Schl Poetry Forum 87; Arts Apprntcshp Poetry 87; Penn ST Coll; Bus.

SABATELLE, KAREN; Old Forge HS; Old Forge, PA; (3); Ski Clb; Nwsp Stf; Yrbk Stf; Bsktbl; Hon Roll; NHS.

SABATINI, CARLO; Wyoming Seminary; Dallas, PA; (3); Ski Clb; Yrbk Ed-Chief; Socr; High Hon Roll; Jr NHS; Lion Awd; Yng Schlrs Pgm 87; Bus Admin.

SABATINO, DENISE; Boiling Springs HS; Boiling Spgs, PA; (3); Pres Band; Chorus; Drm Mjr(t); Nwsp Stf; Sec Pres Stu Cncl; Fld Hcky; Swmmng; Hon Roll; NHS; Hugh O Brian Yth Ldrshp Smnr 86; Bio.

SABATINO, PHILIP; St John Neumann HS; Philadelphia, PA; (2); 2/350; French Clb; Math Tm; JV Bowling; High Hon Roll; Math Cmptn Wnnr 86-87; Engl Cmptn Wnnr 87HS Schlrshp 85; Bus.

SABATULA, DARLA; Laurel Highlands SR HS; Uniontown, PA; (3); 16/365; Office Aide; Flag Corp; Mrchg Band; Nwsp Stf; Trk; High Hon Roll; NHS; Indiana U Of PA; Accntng.

SABINO, HEATHER; Ambridge HS; Ambridge, PA; (2); Church Yth Grp; Pep Clb; Church Choir; Hon Roll; BUS.

SABINO, MARC; Sharon HS; Sharon, PA; (3); 20/186; Varsity Clb; Band; Concert Band; Mrchg Band; Var L Golf; Hon Roll; NEDT Awd; Bus Adm.

SABO, JOHN; Central Catholic HS; Verona, PA; (2); L Vllybl; French Hon Soc; High Hon Roll.

SABO, MELISSA; Chestnut Ridge SR HS; Bedford, PA; (3); Lit Mag; Dance Clb; French Clb; Orch; PA Acad Of Cosmetology-Csmtlg.

SABO, WENDY; West Middlesex HS; Mercer, PA; (1); Spanish Clb; High Hon Roll; Hon Roll; Jr NHS; Merit Awd Gen Bus 87; Merit Awd Enthusium 87; Law.

SABOL, CHRISTY; Carmichaels Area HS; Carmichaels, PA; (4); GAA; Office Aide; Pep Clb; Ski Clb; Varsity Clb; Band; Concert Band; Mrchg Band; VP Stu Cncl; JV Capt Cheerleading; CA U; Elem Ed.

SABOL, KELLY; Ambridge Area HS; Ambridge, PA; (3); Church Yth Grp; Rep Soph Cls; Var L Bsktbl; Var L Sftbl; Var L Tennis; Sctn II Tnns Sngls Chmpn 86; Al-Star Bsktbl Tm 87; Rnnr-Up Mdwstrn Athltc Conf Tnns Trnmt 85.

SABOL, LORI; Bishop Hafey HS; Lattimer, PA; (3); 11/121; French Clb; Ski Clb; Spanish Clb; Band; Yrbk Stf; Lit Mag; Stat Socr; Trk; High Hon Roll; NHS; Villanova U; Law.

SABOL, PATRICIA; Marian Catholic HS; Nesquehoning, PA; (4); 1/110; Nwsp Ed-Chief; Nwsp Stf; DAR Awd; French Hon Soc; High Hon Roll; Trs NHS; Ntl Merit Ltr; Val; Amer Assn Of Teachrs NE PA Chptr-3rd Prz Natl French Contst 85; 3rd Prz-Math/Sci Bowl 86; Poltcl Sci.

SABOTTA, CHRISTIAN; Downingtown SR HS; Downingtown, PA; (4); 35/551; Sec Church Yth Grp; German Clb; Teachers Aide; Chorus; Lit Mag; Var Socr; Cit Awd; High Hon Roll; NHS; Ski Clb; Ntl Chrl Awd 84; Valpraiso U; Mech Engr.

SABOURIN, PAUL; Pennsbury HS; Morrisville, PA; (4); 25/771; Am Leg Boys St; Thesps; Chorus; Concert Band; Jazz Band; Mrchg Band; Pep Band; Symp Band; Cit Awd; NHS; Lead Trumpet Pa All State Jazz Band 87; Penn ST; Psych.

SABY, RACHEL; Parkland SR HS; Allentown, PA; (2); Library Aide; Office Aide; Nwsp Stf; Yrbk Stf; Gym; Mat Maids; High Hon Roll; NHS; Penn ST; Med.

SACANE, JOSEPH; Charleroi Area HS; Charleroi, PA; (4); 48/165; Boy Scts; Church Yth Grp; Pres Exploring; FBLA; JA; Eagle Scout 86; FBLA 1st Pl Bus Law Regnl Cmptn 87; CA U Of PA; Math.

SACCO, MARY JILL; Hazleton HS; Hazleton, PA; (3); FBLA; Csmtlgy.

SACCO, SHARON; Butler SR HS; Butler, PA; (4); 97/699; Exploring; Latin Clb; Library Aide; Chorus; Stu Cncl; Var L Gym; Acadc Achvt Awd 87; IN U; Law.

SACCO, TERRI; South Fayette HS; Bridgeville, PA; (3); 3/90; Ski Clb; Sec Soph Cls; Sec Jr Cls; Cheerleading; High Hon Roll; Hon Roll; Pres NHS; Prfct Atten Awd.

SACCO, TODD; Moon SR HS; Coraopolis, PA; (4); 23/294; Boy Scts; CAP; Jazz Band; Mrchg Band; Symp Band; Stu Cncl; Var Trk; Var L Wrstlng; NHS; Ntl Merit Ltr; Allegheny Cmptv Exm Fnlst 87; Sesquicntnl Schlrshp 87-91; Allegheny Coll; Intl Rltns.

SACCO, VINCENT; Riverview HS; Verona, PA; (3); JV Ftbl; Awana-Timothy Awd Wnnr 84; Volntr-Lcl Nrsg Hm 87; Taught Sunday Schl 87; Cincinnati Bible Coll; Pastor.

SACHERICH, AMY; Shenango Area JR SR HS; New Castle, PA; (3); 2/122; Camera Clb; Drama Clb; Girl Scts; Library Aide; Spanish Clb; Speech Tm; Y-Teens; School Play; High Hon Roll; NHS.

SACHS, WILLIAM; Arch Bishop Ryan HS; Philadelphia, PA; (2); Church Yth Grp; Cmnty Wkr; Bsktbl; Ftbl; Golf; Hon Roll; Phrmcst.

SACKETT, KERRIE; Kiski Area HS; Apollo, PA; (3); Library Aide; Office Aide; Teachers Aide; L Band; L Concert Band; Sec Jazz Band; VP Mrchg Band; L Symp Band; High Hon Roll; Hon Roll; Accntng.

SACKS, AMIE; Bethlehem Ctr; Fredericktown, PA; (3); 7/165; Drama Clb; Exploring; Girl Scts; Spanish Clb; Band; Concert Band; Mrchg Band; Stage Crew; High Hon Roll; NHS; Duquesne U; Phrmcy.

SADAKA, RANDA E; Abington Heights HS; Clarks Summit, PA; (4); 24/260; Cmnty Wkr; Dance Clb; Quiz Bowl; Stage Crew; Nwsp Stf; Lit Mag; Soph Cls; Rep Jr Cls; Trs Sr Cls; Stu Cncl; Byrd Schlrshp 87; Friedman Awd 87; Pres Natl Honors Scty Awd 86-87; U Of Scranton; Bio.

SADAVAGE, JEFFERY; Mid-Valley HS; Olyphant, PA; (4); 8/126; Capt Bsbl; Bsktbl; Capt Ftbl; Wt Lftg; High Hon Roll; NHS; Outstndng HS Athltcs Amer 84-86; Acad All Amer 84-86; Ptchr & 1st Bs All Star Bsbl 87; U Of Scranton; Pre Law.

SADDIC, KIMBERLY; Henderson SR HS; West Chester, PA; (3); 13/367; Rep Frsh Cls; Rep Soph Cls; Stu Cncl; Capt Crs Cntry; Trk; High Hon Roll; Hon Roll; Spanish NHS.

SADLER, GLENN; South Western HS; Hanover, PA; (2); JV Bsktbl; JV Bowling; JV Ftbl; Air Force; Pilot.

SADLER, MARK; Donegal HS; Marietta, PA; (3); 15/177; Aud/Vis; Camera Clb; Var Bsbl; Bsktbl; Capt Ftbl; Powder Puff Ftbl; Score Keeper; High Hon Roll; Lion Awd; NHS.

SADLER, NANNETTE A; Monongahela Valley HS; Charleroi, PA; (4); 8/75; Church Yth Grp; Trs FBLA; Pep Clb; Spanish Clb; SADD; Chorus; Nwsp Stf; Yrbk Stf; Rep Sr Cls; High Hon Roll; Natl Physcl Ed Awd 86-87; CA U PA; Mth & Comp Sci.

SADLER, ROBERT; Wilmington Area HS; Volant, PA; (4); 22/112; Drama Clb; Spanish Clb; School Play; Stage Crew; Bsktbl; Golf; Trk; Hon Roll; Golf & Track Ltrs 83-87; PA ST; Engrng.

SADLOWSKI, CYNTHIA; Holy Name HS; West Lawn, PA; (4); 26/111; Pep Clb; JV Var Cheerleading; Mgr(s); Jr Miss Rep 87; Phila Coll Textile & Sci; Fshn.

SADOWSKI, JACQUELINE; Pittston Area HS; Pittston, PA; (3); FBLA; Hon Roll; Mc Cann Bus Schl; Sectrl.

SADOWSKI, JENNFIER; Abraham Lincoln HS; Philadelphia, PA; (3); 3/700; Aud/Vis; Computer Clb; French Clb; Nwsp Rptr; Ed Nwsp Stf; Yrbk Stf; Lit Mag; Var JV Score Keeper; High Hon Roll; Hon Roll; Soc Jstc & Law Esy Cont 4th Pl 87; Acadc All Am 85-87; Temple U; Tchr.

SADOWSKI, JOHN P; Northwestern HS; Kutztown, PA; (3); 5/153; Nwsp Stf; Yrbk Stf; JV Bsbl; JV Bsktbl; Var L Crs Cntry; Trk; High Hon Roll; Hon Roll; Lion Awd; NHS; Grmn Awd; Engl Awd; Muhlenberg U; Dntstry.

SADOWSKI, SHEILA; Freedom HS; Bethlehem, PA; (4); 141/446; Dance Clb; Drama Clb; French Clb; Pep Clb; Ski Clb; Chorus; Mrchg Band; Cheerleading; Powder Puff Ftbl; Twrlr; PA Dnce Mstrs Of AM-1ST Pl 86 & 4th Rnnr Up 87; 3rd Pl DEA Ntls 87; Temple U; Comms.

SADVARI, LAURIE; Windber Area HS; Windber, PA; (3); Cmnty Wkr; Drama Clb; French Clb; Hosp Aide; Library Aide; Chorus; Nwsp Stf; High Hon Roll; NHS; Pres Acdmc Ftnss Awd 85; Art Inst Of Pittsburgh; Photo.

SAEGER, JENNIFER; Emmaus HS; Allentown, PA; (3); 41/530; Exploring; JA; Spanish Clb; Yrbk Stf; Stu Cncl; Hon Roll; Jr NHS; NHS; Cedar Crest Coll; Gntc Engrng.

SAFFORD, SHAWN; Annville-Cleona HS; Annville, PA; (1); Camera Clb; Model UN; VP SADD; Nwsp Rptr; Yrbk Phtg; Stu Cncl; Trs Jr NHS; NHS; Yth For Undrstndg Exch Stu Norway 86-87; Washington Wrkshps 86; Med Sci.

SAFKA, SCOTT; J S Fine SR HS; Nanticoke, PA; (4); Boy Scts; Letterman Clb; Ski Clb; SADD; L Band; Concert Band; Mrchg Band; Orch; Variety Show; L Golf; Kings Coll Acdmc Awd 87; Kings Coll.

SAFKO, STEPHEN; Sto-Rox HS; Mckees Rocks, PA; (3); 2/167; Boy Scts; Computer Clb; Exploring; Math Tm; Quiz Bowl; Chorus; Variety Show; L Bsbl; Var Ftbl; Hon Roll; Eagle Scout 85; All Star Tm Bsbll 81-86; Systms Anlyst.

SAFRAN, LESLIE; Hempfield HS; Lancaster, PA; (2); 16/424; Church Yth Grp; Ski Clb; Spanish Clb; Speech Tm; JV Bsktbl; L Var Sftbl; L Var Vllybl; High Hon Roll; Outstndng Schlstc Achvt Awd Spnsh 87; Law.

SAFRAN, REBECCA; Ambridge Area HS; Ambridge, PA; (3); Office Aide; Pep Clb; Red Cross Aide; School Musical; Swing Chorus; Off Jr Cls; Stu Cncl; Var L Golf; High Hon Roll; NHS; Med.

SAGANOWICH, DAN; Northwestern Lehigh HS; Germansville, PA; (3); 36/170; Varsity Clb; JV Bsbl; Capt L Bsktbl; JV Crs Cntry; Im Vllybl; Im Wt Lftg; Hon Roll; Lion Awd; Comp Sci.

SAGATH, KIMBERLY; Penn Trafford HS; Irwin, PA; (3); Pres VP AFS; Church Yth Grp; Hosp Aide; Red Cross Aide; Band; Chorus; Church Choir; Concert Band; Mrchg Band; Pep Band; Culnry Arts.

SAGE, MEGAN; Owen J Roberts HS; Pottstown, PA; (3); 8/299; GAA; Letterman Clb; Rep Stu Cncl; Var L Bsktbl; Var L Fld Hcky; Var L Lcrss; Hon Roll; NHS; Stu Rep Schl Brd 86-87; Fld Hcky All Cnesmnt 1st Tm 86-87; Bus.

SAGER, GARRET; Palmyra Area SR HS; Annville, PA; (3); Boys Clb Am; Computer Clb; Chorus; School Play; Nwsp Phtg; Nwsp Rptr; Nwsp Stf; Yrbk Phtg; Hon Roll; Prfct Atten Awd; Aero Engr.

SAGGIOMO, MARYBETH; Nazareth Acad; Phila, PA; (3); Trs Latin Clb; Var Bsktbl; Var Socr; Var Sftbl; All Star Bsktbl Scor & Sftbl 86-87; All Tourn Tm Bsktbl 85-86; Philadelphia Inquirers Ath Of Wk Sftbl; Bus.

SAHAYDA, JOANN; Wyoming Area SR HS; West Wyoming, PA; (3); Sec Art Clb; Church Yth Grp; Drama Clb; Key Clb; Spanish Clb; High Hon Roll; NHS; Spec Merit Awd Socl Stds 86-87; Comm Arts.

SAHM, SHANNON; Cocalico HS; Denver, PA; (3); Church Yth Grp; Band; Concert Band; Jazz Band; Mrchg Band; Pep Band; Vllybl; Hon Roll; County Band 87; Stevens Trade; Cabinet Maker.

SAHNI, JODY; Fox Chapel Area HS; Pittsburgh, PA; (3); Exploring; NFL; Science Clb; Temple Yth Grp; Nwsp Stf; High Hon Roll; NHS; Ntl Merit Ltr; Summa Cum Laud Gld Mdl Outstndng Prfrmnc Natl Latn Exm 87; Med.

SAHONICK, TONY; Mt Carmel Area HS; Mt Carmel, PA; (2); Key Clb; Spanish Clb; Band; Concert Band; Mrchg Band; School Musical; Hon Roll; U PA; Orthodontics.

SAIDT, SUSAN; North Penn HS; Lansdale, PA; (3); 50/650; Dance Clb; Variety Show; Var JV Cheerleading; Var L Sftbl; High Hon Roll; Hon Roll; Sec NHS; Ski Clb; Rep Soph Cls; Rep Jr Cls; Cert Acad Excllnc 86; Spnsh Cert Highest Avg 85; 1st Pl Sftbl Home Run Derby-Hitting & Throwing 85; Chem.

SAIENNI, MARY; Avon Grove HS; W Grove, PA; (3); 16/219; Hosp Aide; Sec OEA; Sec Service Clb; Band; Concert Band; Mrchg Band; Rep Stu Cncl; JV Bsktbl; High Hon Roll; NHS; Janet Loughlin Scholar Comm Svc 87; Nrsng.

SAIENNI, MARY; Benton Area JR SR HS; Stillwater, PA; (2); Drama Clb; Trs 4-H; Chorus; School Musical; Nwsp Rptr; Sec Frsh Cls; Var Capt Cheerleading; Var Sftbl; Var Twrlr; Hon Roll; Scrtrl.

SAIERS, RICH; Bellefonte HS; Howard, PA; (3); 26/212; Library Aide; Jr Cls; Hon Roll; S Hills Business Schl; Business.

SAIN, ARLENE; Brookville Are HS; Brookville, PA; (4); 10/123; Key Clb; Trs Varsity Clb; Nwsp Rptr; Stu Cncl; Var Capt Swmmng; Var Capt Trk; Var Vllybl; DAR Awd; VP NHS; SADD; Us Marine Corps Dstngshd Athlte 85-87; BAHS Undrclssmn And Swimmer Yr 86-87; Penn ST U ; Landscape Arch.

SAJNANI, RAVI; Catasaugua HS; Catasauqua, PA; (4); Boy Scts; Penn ST U; Comp Sci.

SAKS, SCOTT; Southern Lehigh HS; Coopersburg, PA; (4); 33/230; Key Clb; Ski Clb; Jr Cls; Sr Cls; Hon Roll; Ntl Merit Ltr; Bio.

SALA, PETE; Strong Vincent HS; Erie, PA; (4); 3/160; Nwsp Rptr; Yrbk Rptr; Stu Cncl; Bsbl; Bsktbl; Ftbl; High Hon Roll; Pres Schlr; Acad Schlrshp; Wolves Clb Schlrshp; Gannon U; Pre Law.

SALAC, TRACEY; St Paul Cathedral HS; Pittsburgh, PA; (3); Art Clb; Church Yth Grp; Computer Clb; FBLA; Sec Intnl Clb; Vllybl; CMU Hist Day 86; Penn ST U; Accntng.

SALADNA, ANTOINETTE; Monon Gahela Valley Catholic HS; Belle Vernon, PA; (3); Cmnty Wkr; Chorus; School Musical; Rep Jr Cls; Var Capt Cheerleading; Var Sftbl; French Hon Soc; High Hon Roll; NHS; Jr Cthlc Dghtrs Of Amer 85-87; PA ST U; Tele Cmnctns.

SALAK, GARY; Western Wayne HS; Waymart, PA; (3); 11/200; Church Yth Grp; FBLA; Office Aide; Pres Stu Cncl; L Tennis; High Hon Roll; Hon Roll; Trs NHS; Prfct Atten Awd; Rotary Awd; Sci.

SALAK, MIKE; Western Wayne HS; Waymart, PA; (4); 10/140; Trs FBLA; Pres Frsh Cls; Rep Trs Stu Cncl; L Tennis; Cit Awd; DAR Awd; High Hon Roll; NHS; Prfct Atten Awd; Rotary Awd; Stu Yr 86-87; Mr FBL Region 22 86-87; Kings Coll; Acctg.

SALAMONE, DANA; Perkiomen Valley HS; Collegeville, PA; (4); 38/158; Office Aide; School Musical; School Play; Rep Frsh Cls; Rep Soph Cls; Off Jr Cls; Off Jr Cls; Stu Cncl; JV Var Cheerleading; Hon Roll; ST U Of NY; Poli Sci.

SALAMONE, LYNETTE; Villa Maria Acad; Erie, PA; (3); Science Clb; SADD; Hon Roll; Gannon U; Bus.

SALANICK, KIMBERLY; Laurel Highlands SR HS; Uniontown, PA; (2); Hon Roll; Csmtlgy.

SALASKI, CHRIS; Freedom HS; Bethlehem, PA; (3); 5/486; Math Tm; Trs Frsh Cls; Trs Soph Cls; Trs Jr Cls; Trs Sr Cls; Rep Stu Cncl; Var JV Bsbl; L Bsktbl; High Hon Roll; NHS; MVP Awd Vrsty Bsktbl 86-87.

SALATA, CHRISTINE; Bishop Hafey HS; Hazleton, PA; (4); 3/127; Ski Clb; Spanish Clb; Y-Teens; Rep Stu Cncl; Var L Cheerleading; High Hon Roll; NHS; Spanish NHS.

SALAZER, DENISE; Bishop Hafey HS; Hazleton, PA; (4); Church Yth Grp; Spanish Clb; Y-Teens; Mgr(s); Score Keeper; Stat Sftbl; Hon Roll; Jr NHS; NHS; Century II Typing Awd 86; Awd Hghst Avg Agl II 86; Penn St; Business.

SALDIVAR, MADELAINE; Gwynedd-Mercy Acad; Hatfield, PA; (2); Service Clb; Chorus; School Musical; Nwsp Stf; Yrbk Rptr; Yrbk Stf; Maxima Cum Laude Natl Ltn Exam 86; Med.

SALDUTTI, ANTHONY; Lansdale Catholic HS; Lansdale, PA; (3); CC Awd; Hon Roll; Achvt Awd Chem 87; Elec Tech.

SALEEM-UGDAH, NAJLA; Sis Clara Muhammad HS; Philadelphia, PA; (4); Trs Computer Clb; Debate Tm; Pres Science Clb; Nwsp Rptr; Yrbk Rptr; Rep Frsh Cls; Stu Cncl; Cit Awd; High Hon Roll; Nwsp Stf; Acad Achvt Awd 86-87; Stu Mnth 85; Temple Univ; Phrmcy.

SALERNO, AMY; Old Forge HS; Old Forge, PA; (3); Empire Beauty Schl; Cosmetlgy.

SALFI, KARL; Bensalem HS; Bensalem, PA; (3); Elec Engr.

SALIBA, GERRY; Uniontown Area HS; Uniontown, PA; (2); Letterman Clb; Spanish Clb; Var L Bsbl; JV Bsktbl; Ftbl; OH ST U; Dntstry.

SALIBURY, PAIGE; Lock Haven SR HS; Castanea, PA; (3); Church Yth Grp; Cmnty Wkr; Spanish Clb; SADD; Chorus; Color Guard; Drm Mjr(t); Variety Show; Yrbk Stf; JV Cheerleading; Lock Haven U; Rprtr.

SALINGER, CHRISTINE; Methacton HS; Audubon, PA; (3); 72/381; Key Clb; Red Cross Aide; SADD; Band; Chorus; Off Frsh Cls; Off Soph Cls; Off Jr Cls; JV Bsktbl; JV Fld Hcky; Nrsng.

SALISBURY, BRENT; Northwestern HS; E Springfield, PA; (3); 6/160; Rep Stu Cncl; Var L Bsbl; Rotary Yth Ldrshp Awd 87; Ltr Wnnr Acad 87; Gannon U; Pharm.

SALKO, HEATHER; Lake-Lehman HS; Shavertown, PA; (1); Church Yth Grp; High Hon Roll; Jr NHS; Stdnt Wk 85-86.

SALLAVANTI, ARMANDO; Old Forge HS; Old Forge, PA; (3); 5/120; Var Capt Bsbl; Var Capt Bsktbl; Var L Ftbl; High Hon Roll; NHS; 3rd Tm All Schltc Bsktbl Point Guard 87; 2nd Tm All Schltc Def Bk Ftbl 87; U Scranton; Pre-Dent.

SALLIS, ROXANNE; Western Beaver HS; Industry, PA; (4); Drama Clb; FHA; Library Aide; Speech Tm; Chorus; Nwsp Stf; Bowling; Trk; Capt L Vllybl; Gov Acamdc Schlrshp 87; James H Morrison Schlrshp 87; Slippery Rck U; Econ.

SALLMEN, JANETTE; New Wilmington Area HS; Pulaski, PA; (3); Rep Church Yth Grp; VP Latin Clb; Pres Spanish Clb; Band; Concert Band; JV Vllybl; Mst Imprvd Vllybl Plyr 84; 1st Pl Trio Sngng & Drwng Chrch 85; Yth Pstr.

SALLMEN JR, ROBERT; Wilmington Area HS; Pulaski, PA; (3); 11/121; Chorus; Rep Stu Cncl; JV Ftbl.

SALMON, REBECCA; Mc Dowell HS; Erie, PA; (4); 12/600; Sec Church Yth Grp; Chorus; Orch; Yrbk Ed-Chief; Sec Stu Cncl; Var Capt Trk; Hon Roll; Kiwanis Awd; NHS; Ntl Merit Ltr; Outstndg Distnc Rnnr 85-87; US Army Rsrv Schlr/Athl Awd 87; Actvtys Medl 87; IU Bloomington; Math Tchr.

SALONE, MICHAEL; Souderton Area HS; Telford, PA; (3); Camera Clb; Computer Clb; Nwsp Rptr; Ftbl; Wrstlng; High Hon Roll; NHS; Pre-Med.

SALOOM, CHARLENE R; Mt Pleasant Area SR HS; Mount Pleasant, PA; (4); 8/249; Sec Trs 4-H; Latin Clb; Concert Band; Drm Mjr(t); Jazz Band; Mrchg Band; Yrbk Stf; High Hon Roll; NHS; Bowman Ashe Schlrshp U Of Miami 87; Mid-Est Msc Fstvl 86-87; Stu Of Week 87; U Of Miami.

SALOPEK, EDWARD J; Norwin HS; N Huntingdon, PA; (4); 7/557; VP Art Clb; Spanish Clb; School Play; Yrbk Stf; High Hon Roll; NHS; Ntl Merit SF; Pre Med.

SALOTTO, STEVEN P; Monsignor Bonner HS; Upper Darby, PA; (4); 32/304; Church Yth Grp; Pres Debate Tm; Drama Clb; Pres NFL; Pres Speech Tm; School Musical; School Play; Nwsp Stf; Im Ftbl; Im Trk; Govrs Schl For The Arts 86; Allentown Coll; Theatre.

SALOVAY, MICHAEL; Parkland HS; Allentown, PA; (2); Church Yth Grp; JA; JV Bsbl; JV Bsktbl; Hon Roll; U Of Pittsburgh; Engrng.

SALPECK, ROCCO; Quigley HS; Baden, PA; (3); Church Yth Grp; Letterman Clb; Math Clb; L Bsbl; Bsktbl; L Ftbl; Ice Hcky; Trk; Hon Roll; Natl Athltc Merit Endrsmnt Svc 87; U Pittsburgh.

SALSGIVER, MELISSA; Purchase Line HS; Glen Campbell, PA; (3); SADD; Band; Chorus; Concert Band; Mrchg Band; Nwsp Phtg; Nwsp Stf; Stu Cncl; High Hon Roll; NHS.

SALTZ, WESLEY; Wyoming Area SR HS; W Wyoming, PA; (3); 65/250; Pres Church Yth Grp; Cmnty Wkr; Ski Clb; Concert Band; Capt Mrchg Band; VP Soph Cls; JV Bsbl; Spnsh Cont 86; Comp Tech.

SALTZBURG, STACY; Susquenita HS; Duncannon, PA; (3); Pres Church Yth Grp; Trs French Clb; SADD; Nwsp Stf; Stu Cncl; JV Bsktbl; Engrng.

SALTZMAN, KELLY; Hempfield HS; Jeannette, PA; (2); Art Clb; Pep Clb; Ski Clb; Spanish Clb; Nwsp Stf; Rep Stu Cncl; Var Swmmng; Ntl Merit Ltr; R Shaw Arts Fr Awd 86; Art Inst; Art.

SALUS, DAVE; Wyoming Valley West HS; Swoyersville, PA; (4); 113/385; Church Yth Grp; Rep Sr Cls; Off Civic Clb; Cmnty Wkr; Ski Clb; Varsity Clb; JV Bsbl; Var Ftbl; Wt Lftg; Hon Roll; Lttrmn 86-87; PA ST U; Engrng.

SALUS, THOMAS; Couglin HS; Plains, PA; (3); 45/352; Spanish Clb; Stat Bsktbl; Var Capt Crs Cntry; Var L Trk; NHS; Toxicology.

SALVA, ELIZABETH; Dunmore HS; Dunmore, PA; (3); Science Clb; Chorus; Color Guard; Swing Chorus; Nwsp Phtg; Nwsp Rptr; Yrbk Stf; High Hon Roll; NHS; Health Prof.

SALVAGGIO, SUZIE A; Parkland HS; Allentown, PA; (4); 28/481; Rep Stu Cncl; Var L Bsktbl; Var L Tennis; Var L Trk; NHS; Dist Track Plcmnt 5th In 1/2 Mile 87; PA ST U; Bus.

SALVANISH, MELISSA; Bellefonte Area SR HS; Howard, PA; (3); 20/217; Church Yth Grp; Drama Clb; Political Wkr; Ski Clb; Chorus; Concert Band; Mrchg Band; Vllybl; High Hon Roll; PA ST U.

SALVATO, CLAUDINE; Bishop Conwell HS; Hulmeville, PA; (3); 45/277; Chorus; Madrigals; School Musical; School Play; Variety Show; Hon Roll; Music Vocal & Spnsh Awd; Aerospc Engrng.

SALVIA, ELISE; Villa Maria Acad; Erie, PA; (4); Art Clb; Church Yth Grp; Dance Clb; PAVAS; Ski Clb; Coach Actv; Gym; Socr; High Hon Roll; NHS; Cert Recgntn An Artstc Discvry 87; Wnnr Dwntwn Now 87; Sprgburst 87; PA ST U; Art.

SALVIA, JACQUELINE; Pennsbury HS; Yardley, PA; (4); Varsity Clb; Chorus; Rep Jr Cls; Co-Capt Swmmng; Middle Atlantic Duet Cham& 85-87; PA ST Champ Tm & Duet 84-86; Jr Assoc Solo Cham& 87; OH ST U; Physcl Thrpy.

SALVINO, TRACY; Upper Moreland HS; Willow Grove, PA; (3); 8/242; Nwsp Stf; Var Capt Gym; High Hon Roll; NHS; Subrbn I All Arnd Gymnstcs Chmpn 87.

SALVO, ANGE; Union HS; Rimersburg, PA; (2); Church Yth Grp; Chorus; Church Choir; School Musical; School Play; Variety Show; Bsktbl; Ftbl; Trk; Hon Roll; Cnty Chorus 86-87; Dist Chorus 86-87; Lector At St Richards Catholic Church 85-87; PA ST; Aviation Pilot.

SALVUCCI, DEAN; West Mifflin Area HS; W Mifflin, PA; (3); 35/300; Church Yth Grp; Ski Clb; Wt Lftg; Wrstlng; Hon Roll; NHS; Penn ST U; Pltcl Sci.

SALVUCCI, RICHARD; West Catholic HS; Philadelphia, PA; (2); 7/248; Church Yth Grp; Cmnty Wkr; High Hon Roll; Hon Roll.

SALZMAN, FREDERICK M; Eastern York HS; Wrightsville, PA; (3); Am Leg Boys St; SADD; Rep Pres Stu Cncl; JV Bsktbl; Var L Ftbl; Im Wt Lftg; High Hon Roll; Hon Roll; Med.

SALZMAN, KELLIE; Ringgold SR HS; Monongahela, PA; (3); Office Aide; Yrbk Stf; Vllybl; Pittsburgh Beauty Acad; Csmtlgy.

SAM, MICHELLE; Windber Area HS; Windber, PA; (3); 2/128; Drama Clb; French Clb; Ski Clb; Trs Capt Speech Tm; Nwsp Rptr; Var Cheerleading; High Hon Roll; NHS; Ntl Merit Ltr; Pres Schlr; HOBY Ldrshp Awd 86; Fnlst Cambria-Somerst JR Miss Pgm 87; Rotry Yth Ldrshp Assmbly 87; WA & Jefferson U; Poltcl Sci.

SAMCHUCK, MICHAEL; Beaver Area HS; Beaver, PA; (2); Church Yth Grp; Spanish Clb; JV Bsktbl; High Hon Roll; Schlstc Achvt Awd 86-87; U Of VA; Engrng.

SAMEC, TIMOTHY; West Hazleton HS; Tresckow, PA; (3); 33/221; Boy Scts; Letterman Clb; Varsity Clb; Stu Cncl; Var L Ftbl; Wt Lftg; Var Capt Wrstlng; Hon Roll; NHS; Wldlf Sci.

SAMELKO, STEPHANIE; N Schuylkill JR SR HS; Ashland, PA; (3); 69/206; Church Yth Grp; Girl Scts; Chorus; Church Choir; Rep Jr Cls; Stu Cncl; Var L Cheerleading; Stat Ftbl; Hon Roll; Bio.

SAMLES, LONI; Montrose Jr/Sr HS; S Montrose, PA; (3); Church Yth Grp; French Clb; Hosp Aide; Latin Clb; Ski Clb; SADD; Band; Church Choir; Concert Band; Jazz Band; Tm Spirit Awd Track 87; Physcl Thrpy.

SAMPEY, BETH; Connellsville Area SR HS; Connellsville, PA; (2); Church Yth Grp; SADD; Teachers Aide; Chorus; Mrchg Band; School Musical; Symp Band; Yrbk Stf; Hon Roll; Masonic Awd; Elem Ed.

SAMPLE, KIRSTIN; Fairview HS; Fairview, PA; (3); 14/169; Speech Tm; Band; Pres Chorus; Church Choir; Color Guard; Concert Band; Church Yth Grp; Thesps; Jazz Band; Mrchg Band; Pre-Law.

SAMPSELL, BELINDA; Milton SR HS; Selinsgrove, PA; (4); Sec FFA; Office Aide; Chorus; Foods Awd 87; Empire Beauty Schl; Csmtlgy.

SAMPSON, MICHELLE; Frankford HS; Philadelphia, PA; (3); Capt Math Clb; Capt Math Tm; Teachers Aide; Rep Frsh Cls; Hon Roll; Temple U; Child Dvlpmnt.

SAMPSON JR, ROBERT; Center HS; Monaca, PA; (4); German Clb; Letterman Clb; Political Wkr; Varsity Clb; Stage Crew; Im Bsktbl; Var L Trk; Slippery Rock ST U; Polt Sci.

SAMUDA, KAREN HERMA-MARIE; Strawberry Mansion HS; Phila, PA; (3); 5/170; Church Choir; Yrbk Stf; Rep Frsh Cls; Pres Soph Cls; Pres Jr Cls; Cheerleading; Trk; Hon Roll; NHS; Prfct Atten Awd; Obstrcn.

SAMUEL, BRENDA; West Scranton HS; Scranton, PA; (4); 57/260; Aud/Vis; Dance Clb; Hon Roll; NHS; West Side Lions Clb Schlrshp 87; Penn ST; Comp Sci.

SAMUEL, ROBERT E; Abington Hts HS; Clarks Summit, PA; (4); Boy Scts; Church Yth Grp; Pres Radio Clb; Red Cross Aide; Yrbk Phtg; L Wrstlng; Hon Roll; NHS; Im Golf; Im Tennis; Eagle Sct 86; Pat Calvey Ldrshp Awd/Schlrshp 87; Radio Clb Awd 87; Widener U; Engrng.

SAMUELS, KARI; Plymouth-Whitemarsh HS; Lafayette Hill, PA; (3); 17/356; School Musical; Off Frsh Cls; Off Soph Cls; Off Jr Cls; Var Cheerleading; JV Sftbl; High Hon Roll; Jr NHS; Law.

SANCHEZ, SABY; Lancaster Catholic HS; Lancaster, PA; (3); 27/192; Church Yth Grp; Sec JA; Pres Service Clb; Rep Soph Cls; Rep Jr Cls; Sec Sr Cls; Sec Stu Cncl; Bsktbl; JV Fld Hcky; Ftbl; Hghst Avg Spnsh III 86; Hghst Avg Spnsh IV 87; Cathlc Alumnae Awd 84-85; Bio.

SANDBERG, KARI; East Stroudsburg Area HS; E Stroudsburg, PA; (3); 44/241; Church Yth Grp; SADD; Concert Band; Mrchg Band; Off Stu Cncl; Law.

SANDER, JENNIFER; William Allen HS; Allentown, PA; (2); Church Yth Grp; Exploring; German Clb; Hosp Aide; Ski Clb; SADD; Flag Corp; High Hon Roll; Hon Roll; Prfct Atten Awd; Villanova; Nrsng.

SANDER, TAMMY; Wilmington Area HS; Pulaski, PA; (3); 9/115; Drama Clb; French Clb; Hosp Aide; VP Key Clb; Hon Roll; NHS; Nrsng.

SANDERS, BLAKE; Franklin Regional SR HS; Murrysville, PA; (4); Sec AFS; VP Thesps; Chorus; Stage Crew; Swing Chorus; High Hon Roll; NHS; Best Thespian 87; PA ST U; Engrng.

SANDERS, GIDEON; Henderson HS; W Chester, PA; (3); 83/377; Church Yth Grp; Cmnty Wkr; VP Intnl Clb; JCL; Science Clb; Spanish Clb; School Musical; School Play; Variety Show; Yrbk Phtg; Med.

SANDERS, JANINE M; James Buchanan HS; Mercersburg, PA; (4); French Clb; Hosp Aide; SADD; Band; Drm Mjr(t); Orch; Powder Puff Ftbl; Hon Roll; Prfct Atten Awd; Concert Band; Mc Donalds All-Amer Band 86; Excell Scl Stds 87; Harrisburg Area CC; Med Lab Tc.

SANDERS, JENNIFER L; Penn Trafford HS; Export, PA; (2); Chess Clb; Church Yth Grp; Spanish Clb; Band; Concert Band; Mrchg Band; Im Vllybl; Hon Roll; CA Achvt Tst Top 7% Cls, Top 10% Natnwde 86-87.

SANDERS, LAURA; Carlisle SR HS; Carlisle, PA; (3); 15/456; Church Yth Grp; Concert Band; Mrchg Band; Off Stu Cncl; High Hon Roll; Hon Roll; NHS; Nrsng.

SANDERS, MARGARET; Cedar Crest HS; Lebanon, PA; (4); 18/306; French Clb; Girl Scts; Pep Clb; Band; Concert Band; Mrchg Band; Pep Band; Hon Roll; NHS; Ntl Merit SF; Drew Schlrs Schlrshp, Pres Acdmc Ftns Awd 87; Drew U; Anthrplgy.

SANDERS, MICHAEL; Mifflinburg Area HS; Mifflinburg, PA; (1); Bsktbl; Socr; Sci.

SANDERS, REBECCA; Bensalem HS; Bensalem, PA; (2); French Clb; Key Clb; SADD; Rep Soph Cls; JV Fld Hcky; Var Swmmng; High Hon Roll; NHS; Art.

SANDERS, SANDRA RENEE; Kennedy Christian HS; Wheatland, PA; (4); 5/93; Nwsp Ed-Chief; Yrbk Ed-Chief; Stu Cncl; Vllybl; NCTE Awd; NHS; Pres Schlr; Church Yth Grp; Computer Clb; Hosp Aide; U Of Ptsbrg Chllng Schlrshp 87; U Of MI Schlrshp 87; Mercer Cnty Hall Of Fame All-Star Awd 87; U Of Pittsburgh; Phrmcy.

SANDERS, SHANNON; Montrose Area HS; Brackney, PA; (3); Sec Church Yth Grp; Church Choir; Color Guard; Mrchg Band; Var Trk; Accntng.

SANDERSON, JOY; Carlisle HS; Carlisle, PA; (3); Pep Clb; Hon Roll; Natl Art Soc 86-87; U S Air Force.

SANDERSON, KAREN; West Perry HS; New Bloomfield, PA; (3); 2/221; French Clb; Ski Clb; Band; Chorus; School Play; Trs Stu Cncl; JV Fld Hcky; Var Trk; High Hon Roll; Trs NHS; Allegheny; Vet.

SANDERSON, TAMMY; Greater Latrobe SR HS; Latrobe, PA; (2); Church Yth Grp; 4-H; German Clb; Library Aide; 4-H Awd; Hon Roll; Amer Coll Appld Arts; Comm Art.

SANDHERR, JENNY; Abington Heights HS; Waverly, PA; (2); 57/305; Church Yth Grp; Ski Clb; SADD; Chorus; Orch; Fld Hcky; Trk; Hon Roll; Prfct Atten Awd; FNA; Bishops Awd 85; Nrs.

SANDIN, ANN MARGARET; Lower Moreland HS; Huntingdon Valley, PA; (4); 9/201; Exploring; German Clb; Rep Stu Cncl; JV L Crs Cntry; Capt Var Sftbl; High Hon Roll; Hon Roll; Chrmn NHS; Ntl Merit Ltr; Bio-Med.

SANDLER, JOY; Blue Mountain HS; Auburn, PA; (3); 8/216; Mu Alpha Theta; Trs Frsh Cls; Pres Soph Cls; Pres Jr Cls; Rep Stu Cncl; L Bsktbl; L Trk; L Vllybl; NEDT Awd; Bio-Engrng.

SANDMAN, BRAD; Council Rock HS; Holland, PA; (4); 83/845; Spanish Clb; Mrchg Band; Hon Roll; NHS; Drexel U; Mech Engrng.

SANDMEYER, EDIE; Belle Vernon Area HS; W Newton, PA; (3); Church Yth Grp; Pep Clb; VICA; Hon Roll; Fash Inst Pitts; Cosmetlgy.

SANDOE, SEAN; Pequea Valley HS; New Holland, PA; (3); 2/130; Acpl Chr; Chorus; Concert Band; Drm Mjr(t); Jazz Band; Mrchg Band; School Musical; School Play; NHS; Rotary Awd; All Estrn US Chorus 87; PA All ST Chorus 87; Mst Outstndng Drum Mjr 86; PA ST; Music.

SANDOE, TRACY; Lancaster Catholic HS; Lancaster, PA; (3); Cmnty Wkr; Hosp Aide; Office Aide; Red Cross Aide; Chorus; Nwsp Rptr; Bsktbl; Crs Cntry; Fld Hcky; Score Keeper; Awds Fld Hcky, Vlybl, Crss Cntry; Awds Schl Nwsp; Comms.

SANDS, KIM; Dallas SR HS; Wyoming, PA; (3); Church Yth Grp; Computer Clb; Hosp Aide; Key Clb; Political Wkr; U Of Pgh; Spnsh.

SANDS, KIMBERLY; Shenandoah Valley HS; Shenandoah, PA; (4); Library Aide; Chorus; Color Guard; Variety Show; Nwsp Stf; Yrbk Stf; Capt Crs Cntry; Sftbl; Capt Trk; Hon Roll; Millersvl U; Elem Educ.

SANDS IV, WILLIAM; Upper Perklomen HS; Pennsburg, PA; (4); 4/225; VP Trs Church Yth Grp; VP Debate Tm; Pres Radio Clb; Chorus; Mrchg Band; Var Socr; Trs NHS; Pres Schlr; Aud/Vis; Computer Clb; Sci Fair 1st Pl 83-85; HOBY 2nd Male E PA 85; Rotary Ldrshp Camp 86; Carnegie Mellon U; Elect Engrng.

SANDVIK, HOLLY; Hollidaysburg SR HS; Duncansville, PA; (3); 30/371; Cmnty Wkr; Intnl Clb; Band; Concert Band; Mrchg Band; Orch; Variety Show; Rep Stu Cncl; Hon Roll; NHS; Intl Rltns.

SANDY, AMY; Homer Center HS; Lucerne Mines, PA; (4); French Clb; SADD; Band; Chorus; Mrchg Band; School Play; Swing Chorus; Stu Cncl; Hon Roll; IUP.

SANDY, DENISE MARIE; Quaker Town Community HS; Quakertown, PA; (4); 16/290; German Clb; Hosp Aide; Library Aide; JV Bsktbl; Var L Sftbl; High Hon Roll; Hon Roll; Kiwanis Awd; NHS; Opt Clb Awd; Hofstra U; Poltcl Sci.

SANDY, LAURA; Red Lion HS; Red Lion, PA; (3); 55/342; Church Yth Grp; Cmnty Wkr; Varsity Clb; Chorus; Concert Band; School Musical; Cheerleading; Hon Roll; Mdrn Music Mstrs Hnr Soc 87; Pblcty Secr Cncrt Choir 87-88; Secr Yth Grp 85-86; Chld Daycare.

SANDY, MARY GRACE; West Scranton HS; Scranton, PA; (2); #15 In Class; Orch; Twrlr; High Hon Roll; Jr NHS; U Scranton; Med Tech.

SANDZIMIER, JASON; Mt Pleasant HS; Mt Pleasant, PA; (3); 7/250; Church Yth Grp; German Clb; JV Var Bsktbl; Ftbl; Golf; High Hon Roll; NHS; Engrng.

SANER, ARLEN; Juniata HS; Mifflin, PA; (3); Drama Clb; Chorus; Stage Crew; Eastern Mennonite Coll; Educ.

SANFORD, KRISTEN; Downingtown SR HS; Downingtown, PA; (3); 1/648; Church Yth Grp; Drama Clb; Scholastic Bowl; Band; Chorus; High Hon Roll; NHS; Ntl Merit SF; NEDT Awd; Voice Dem Awd; Gld Mdl Russn Olympd 85; 3rd Pl Natl Spnsh Exam 86; Optmst Clb Ortry Awd 85.

SANFORD, MICHAEL G; Mc Dowell HS; Erie, PA; (4); 22/599; Am Leg Boys St; Boy Scts; Church Yth Grp; German Clb; Spanish Clb; Ftbl; Cit Awd; High Hon Roll; NHS; Acdmc All Am 85; Eagle Sct Awd 87; Schlrshp Grv Cty Coll 87; Grove Cty Coll; Engrng.

SANFORD, PENNY; Heritage Christian Acad; Erie, PA; (2); Church Yth Grp; Hosp Aide; Office Aide; Church Choir; Cheerleading; Sftbl; Trk.

SANFORD, SHEILA; Heritage Christian Acad; Erie, PA; (4); 1/5; Sec Church Yth Grp; Hosp Aide; Office Aide; Teachers Aide; Church Choir; Nwsp Ed-Chief; Yrbk Ed-Chief; Hon Roll; NHS; Val; Anderson Coll; Jrnlsm.

SANGER, PAMELA; Christian Schl Of York; Manchester, PA; (3); Art Clb; Church Yth Grp; Spanish Clb; Chorus; School Play; Hon Roll; Hon Ment CSY Sci Fair 86; Mid-Atl Chrstn Schl Assoc Excell Rtng Phtgrphy & Prntmkng 86; Liberty U; Accntng.

SANGER, SHARON; Lebanon HS; Lebanon, PA; (4); 2/266; Sec Latin Clb; Sec Trs Spanish Clb; Chorus; Nwsp Ed-Chief; Yrbk Stf; Pres Sr Cls; Sec Stu Cncl; Pres NHS; Pres Spanish NHS; Pres Schlr; Womns Club Grl Of Yr 87; Ortrcl Cntst Wnnr 86 & 87; Outstndng Musicn Of Yr 87; Messiah Coll; Math.

SANGERMANO, MARIA; Ambridge HS; Ambridge, PA; (2); Church Yth Grp; Hosp Aide; Pep Clb; Hon Roll; Off Frsh Cls; Rep Soph Cls; Cheerleading; Gym; Slipper Rock U; Rgstrd Nurse.

SANGREY, ROBERT; Tyrone Area HS; Tyrone, PA; (3); Pres Church Yth Grp; VP FFA; Elks Awd; NHS; Ag.

SANGUINITO, MICHELE; Pen Argy Area HS; Pen Argyl, PA; (3); Drama Clb; FBLA; Math Clb; Ski Clb; Varsity Clb; Chorus; Nwsp Rptr; Stu Cncl; Cheerleading; Bus.

SANKARAN, VEDAVALLI; Altoona Area HS; Altoona, PA; (3); Speech Tm; Chorus; Orch; High Hon Roll; NHS; NEDT Awd; Engl Lit.

SANKEY, SHAWN; Bishop Gbuilfoyle HS; Altoona, PA; (3); 22/156; JV Var Bsktbl; Hon Roll; Penn ST.

SANNER, JEFFREY; Fairview HS; Erie, PA; (3); German Clb; Varsity Clb; L Var Socr; Wt Lftg; Hon Roll; NHS; Pharmacy.

SANNER, KRISTIN NOELLE; Penns Valley HS; Spring Mills, PA; (4); Pres French Clb; Concert Band; Mrchg Band; Pep Band; School Musical; Nwsp Stf; Yrbk Ed-Chief; Yrbk Stf; DAR Awd; Elks Awd; Chatham Coll Div Schlrshp Modern Lang 87; Chatham Coll; Intl Bus.

SANNER, SHELLEY; Penns Valley Area HS; Spring Mills, PA; (3); 16/150; Sec French Clb; Chorus; Concert Band; Jazz Band; Mrchg Band; Pep Band; Nwsp Stf; Yrbk Sprt Ed; Trk; High Hon Roll; HRB Sngr Corp Smmr Sci Stdt 87; Lit Magzn Wrtr; Elem Ed.

SANOSKI, CINDY; Sharpsville Area HS; Sharpsville, PA; (3); 1/97; Pres Chess Clb; Hosp Aide; Chorus; Concert Band; Mrchg Band; Nwsp Rptr; Yrbk Stf; Hon Roll; NHS; Westminster Hnrs Band 86; PMEA Dist V Band 87; PMEA Regnl I Band 87; Duquesne U; Phrmcy.

SANSIG, BRENDA; Connellsville HS; Dunbar, PA; (4); 15/521; Chorus; Concert Band; Drm Mjr(t); Jazz Band; Mrchg Band; School Musical; Symp Band; Var Bsktbl; French Hon Soc; High Hon Roll; Govrs Schl Of Music 86; PMEA Hnrs Band & Dist Band 83-85; Pitt Engrng Schlrshp & Military Awd 86-87; Muscn.

SANSOM, VERONICA; Mercyhurst Preparatory Schl; Erie, PA; (3); 45/172; Varsity Clb; Var L Bsktbl; Im Coach Actv; Var L Socr; Var L Sftbl; Im Vllybl; Kystn ST Gms 86-87; All Trny Tm-Bsktbl 85-86; All Str Tms-Sftbl, Socr, Bsktbl 85-86; Rec Ldrshp.

SANSONI, GREGORY; Bishop Hafey HS; Hazleton, PA; (1); High Hon Roll; $50,000 Bond For Hghst Avg At St Joseph Mem Schl 86.

SANSONI, STEPHANIE B; Knoch HS; Butler, PA; (3); 1/232; Exploring; Pep Clb; Science Clb; SADD; Drill Tm; Nwsp Bus Mgr; Nwsp Rptr; Pom Pon; Trk; NHS; NCA Superstar Drill Team 1st Pl 85; Achvt Awd Bio Olympcs 86; Alg II Achvt Awd 86; Pre-Med.

SANT, TODD; Center HS; Aliquippa, PA; (2); Letterman Clb; Spanish Clb; Varsity Clb; Var L Socr; Hon Roll; Spanish NHS; Penn ST; MD.

SANTANGELO, LAUREL; New Brighton Area HS; New Brighton, PA; (3); Computer Clb; Band; Chorus; Concert Band; Mrchg Band; Nwsp Stf; Trk; Hon Roll; Nrsng.

SANTANGINI, RICHARD; Bethlehem Catholic HS; Bethlehem, PA; (3); 77/210; Computer Clb; Hon Roll; Engrng.

SANTARELLI, DIANE; Ambridge Area HS; Ambridge, PA; (4); 16/265; Church Yth Grp; French Clb; Pep Clb; Red Cross Aide; Yrbk Ed-Chief; Off Jr Cls; Off Sr Cls; High Hon Roll; Hon Roll; NHS; Aprl Grl Of Mnth 87; Ambridge Wmns Clb Schlrshp 87; Pres Acad Ftns Awd 87; IN U Of PA; Elem Educ.

SANTARELLI, RAYMOND; St Josephs Preparatory HS; Philadelphia, PA; (4); 28/240; Spanish Clb; Nwsp Rptr; Im Bsktbl; Im Ftbl; High Hon Roll; NHS; Prfct Atten Awd; Gold Mtl European Hstry 86-87; Phldlpha City Schlrshp 87-88; Villanova U; Bus.

SANTARSIERO, ROBERT; Dunmore HS; Dunmore, PA; (3); 56/146; Cmnty Wkr; Drama Clb; JA; Spanish Clb; SADD; School Play; Nwsp Phtg; Yrbk Phtg; Var Tennis; High Hon Roll; Penn ST U; Bus.

SANTAVICCA, TIFFANY MARIE; Archbishop John Carroll HS; Bala Cynwyd, PA; (3); 18/376; Church Yth Grp; Key Clb; Math Tm; Science Clb; Spanish Clb; Golf; Sftbl; High Hon Roll; NHS; Ntl Merit Ltr; Chem Awd Hghst Avg 86-87.

SANTELLO, JEFFREY; Elizabeth Forward HS; Monongahela, PA; (4); 54/289; Church Yth Grp; Varsity Clb; Var Crs Cntry; Var Golf; Hon Roll; Var Golf Tm 84-87; Hnr Rl 84-87; Homerm Rep 87; PA ST U; Radlgy.

SANTIA, PATRICIA; Aliquippa HS; Aliquippa, PA; (3); VP Church Yth Grp; Drama Clb; Sec French Clb; VICA; School Musical; School Play; Stage Crew; Off Jr Cls; Hon Roll.

SANTIAGO, CANDIDA; Edison HS; Philadelphia, PA; (4); Library Aide; Office Aide; Teachers Aide; School Play; Nwsp Rptr; Yrbk Rptr; Jr Cls; High Hon Roll; Hon Roll; Prfct Atten 81-83; Outstndng Achvt 81-83; Esol Cls Awd Fastst Lrner 81; Exec Secr.

SANTIAGO, DANIEL; Lutheran HS; Philadelphia, PA; (4); 1/7; Church Yth Grp; Computer Clb; Debate Tm; Nwsp Ed-Chief; Nwsp Rptr; Nwsp Stf; Pres Sr Cls; Pres Stu Cncl; Hon Roll; Val; Temple U.

SANTIAGO, DIANA; Little Flower Catholic HS For Girls; Philadelphia, PA; (3); 189/322; Aud/Vis; Church Yth Grp; Cmnty Wkr; Highst Avrge Awd 85-86; Moore Coll; Fshn Dsnr.

SANTIAGO, KENNETH; Archbishop Wood Schl; Holland, PA; (2); 20/277; Hon Roll; UCLA; Mech Engnrng.

SANTIAGO, MICHAEL; Roman Catholic HS; Philadelphia, PA; (3); 9/122; Hon Roll; Prep Schlr 84-85; Pfrct Atten 86-87; Flght.

SANTIAGO, ODILLE; Morrisville HS; Morrisville, PA; (4); 3/96; Church Yth Grp; Drm Mjr(t); Mrchg Band; School Musical; Nwsp Ed-Chief; Nwsp Rptr; Nwsp Stf; Yrbk Stf; VP Sec Stu Cncl; Var JV Cheerleading; Schlrshp St Marys Cthdrl, Pres Acdmc Ftnss Awd, Hgh Hnrs Math & Sci 87; U Chicago; Pre Med.

SANTILLA, GEORGE; Monsignor Bonner HS; Havertown, PA; (3); 66/255; Swmmng; Trk; Hon Roll; Drexel U; Engrng.

SANTILLO, CORRI; Lincoln HS; Ellwood City, PA; (4); 60/167; Church Yth Grp; SADD; Y-Teens; Chorus; Yrbk Stf; Rep Stu Cncl; Powder Puff Ftbl; JV Var Trk; Hon Roll; Bradford Schl Bus; Rtl Mgmt.

SANTILLO, TRACI; Lincoln HS; Ellwood City, PA; (3); VP Y-Teens; Rep Frsh Cls; Sec Soph Cls; VP Jr Cls; VP Sr Cls; JV Var Powder Puff Ftbl; High Hon Roll; Hon Roll.

SANTISO, LINDA; Western Wayne HS; Lake Ariel, PA; (3); 8/199; Exploring; Red Cross Aide; Band; Concert Band; Jazz Band; Mrchg Band; School Musical; Rep Sr Cls; High Hon Roll; Rep Pres NHS; Dist 9 Band Festvl 87; U Scranton; Pre Law.

SANTOLI, LAURIE; Bishop Hannan HS; Scranton, PA; (4); 1/120; Cmnty Wkr; Capt Scholastic Bowl; Sec Trs Spanish Clb; Teachers Aide; Bausch & Lomb Sci Awd; Val; VFW Awd; Voice Dem Awd; Math Clb; Stage Crew; Presdntl III Schlrshp U Scranton 87; Math, Sci, Thlgy, Engl Mdls 87; U Of Scranton; Math.

SANTONE, PAM; Grove City HS; Grove City, PA; (4); 4/162; Church Yth Grp; VP JA; Ski Clb; Teachers Aide; Drill Tm; Im Vllybl; High Hon Roll; NHS; French Clb; Mascot Eagle Sprt 86-87; Stu For Life 86-87; Penn ST; Bio/Pre-Med.

SANTONI, THOMAS; Bishop Mc Devitt HS; Harrisburg, PA; (3); 23/248; Key Clb; Ski Clb; Rep Soph Cls; Rep Jr Cls; Var Bsbl; Bsktbl; Var L Ftbl; Tennis; Wt Lftg; Hon Roll; Ecnmcs.

SANTORA, GINA; Meadville Area SR HS; Meadville, PA; (2); Aud/Vis; Church Yth Grp; Cmnty Wkr; French Clb; Nwsp Stf; VP Soph Cls; JV Cheerleading; Golf; Marine Bio.

SANTORA, MARIA; South Philadelphia HS; Philadelphia, PA; (4); 8/650; JA; Acpl Chr; Hon Roll; NHS; Venus Beauty Schl; Cosmtlgy.

SANTORO, ANTHONY F; Archbishop Ryan HS For Boys; Philadelphia, PA; (3); 2/440; Church Yth Grp; Intnl Clb; Latin Clb; Lit Mag; Bsktbl; Socr; Hon Roll; NHS; Ntl Merit Schol; Outstndng Achvt Awd; Bio Achvt Awd; Theolgy & Latin Achvt Awd; U PA; Sci.

SANTOS, CHRIS; Notre Dame HS; Easton, PA; (3); Stage Crew; Ftbl; Wt Lftg; Wrstlng; Hon Roll; Art Awd 86-87; 2nd Prize HS Art Awd Allentown Coll 86-87; Art.

SANTOS, GERSON; Saul Agricultural HS; Philadelphia, PA; (1); FFA; Im Bsktbl; Im Ftbl; Im Sftbl; Hnr Sci Awd 87; Agronmst.

SANTOS, MARY; Punxsutawney HS; Punxsutawney, PA; (2); Art Clb; Church Yth Grp; Drama Clb; French Clb; Stat Bsbl; Bsktbl; Vllybl; Wrstlng; 4-H Awd; High Hon Roll; Pre Med.

SANTOS, NURIA LISA; Bishop Shanahan HS; West Chester, PA; (4); 65/215; Church Yth Grp; Hosp Aide; Pep Clb; Varsity Clb; Rep Jr Cls; Stu Cncl; Var Fld Hcky; Var Trk; Hon Roll; Office Aide; PHEEA Grnt 87-88; U Of Pittsburgh; Nrsng.

SANTOS, SHILLA; Dover HS; Dover, PA; (3); SADD; Varsity Clb; Yrbk Stf; VP Frsh Cls; VP Soph Cls; VP Jr Cls; Rep Stu Cncl; Var Capt Cheerleading; Physcl Thrpy.

SANZO, DAWN; Shade-Central City HS; Cairnbrook, PA; (3); 2/74; Math Tm; Spanish Clb; Chorus; Nwsp Stf; Sec Jr Cls; Var JV Cheerleading; High Hon Roll; Hon Roll; NHS; Outstndng Acad Bio 84-85; Outstndng Acad Psych 86-87; Juniata Coll; Pediatrician.

SAPERS, TAMARA; Central Bucks HS East; Warrington, PA; (4); 25/468; Ski Clb; Temple Yth Grp; Chorus; Yrbk Stf; Lit Mag; High Hon Roll; Hon Roll; Jr NHS; Pres Schlr; Penn ST U; Pre Law.

SAPIENZA, ANNE; Henderson HS; W Chester, PA; (3); 33/394; Capt CAP; Dance Clb; Drama Clb; Ski Clb; Chorus; School Musical; Variety Show; JV Cheerleading; NHS; Opt Clb Awd; Paul Giringrich Flight & Shannon Memrl Flight Schlrshps 86; Jr Miss Pageant Fnlst 87; Psych.

SAPOLIO, TRACEY; Peters Township HS; Bridgeville, PA; (2); Art Clb; Dance Clb; GAA; Chorus; Tennis.

SAPORITO, JAMES; Warren Area HS; Warren, PA; (3); Church Yth Grp; Drama Clb; French Clb; Acpl Chr; Chorus; Church Choir; School Play; Stage Crew; Pres Sr Cls; Im Bsbl; Golden Dragon Awd 86-87; Slippery Rock U; Bus Mngmnt.

SAPP, DEBBIE; Marion Center HS; Marion Center, PA; (4); 20/168; FHA; Pep Clb; Q&S; SADD; Yrbk Ed-Chief; Yrbk Sprt Ed; High Hon Roll; Nwsp Rptr; Yrbk Rptr; Outstndng Layout Awd 87; Hl Mntr 86; IUP; Elem Ed.

SAPP, KEVIN; Wilmington Area HS; Volant, PA; (2); Var Bsbl; Var JV Ftbl; Cit Awd; High Hon Roll; Hon Roll; NHS; SCI.

SAPP, MELISSA; Purchase Line HS; Commodore, PA; (2); Spanish Clb; High Hon Roll; Hon Roll; Med.

SAPP, THEODORE MAURICE; Northeast/Swenson Skills Center; Philadelphia, PA; (4); Chess Clb; Computer Clb; DECA; FBLA; Math Clb; Chorus; Hon Roll; Comp Engr.

SAPUTSKI, DENISE; Mount Aluernia HS; Pittsburgh, PA; (4); 6/70; Art Clb; Boys Clb Am; Computer Clb; Science Clb; High Hon Roll; Hon Roll; NHS; Sal; SAR Awd; U Of Pittsburgh; Nrs.

SARACINO, MELANIE; Parkland SR HS; Allentown, PA; (3); Hosp Aide; Key Clb; Library Aide; Ski Clb; Y-Teens; Chorus; Stage Crew; Swmmng; High Hon Roll; Hon Roll; Penn ST; Bus.

SARANTAKIS, BARBARA K; East SR HS; West Chester, PA; (4); 2/405; Church Yth Grp; Concert Band; Jazz Band; Mrchg Band; Orch; School Musical; School Play; Ed Lit Mag; NHS; Ntl Merit SF; Hgh Hnr Roll; Frnch Hnr Socty; Mdcn.

SARANTIDIS, GREGORY; Parkland SR HS; Allentown, PA; (2); Hon Roll; Engr.

SARGEANT, LESLIE; Western Beaver HS; Industry, PA; (3); Band; Chorus; Color Guard; Mrchg Band; Symp Band; Im Bowling; L Sftbl; Hon Roll; NHS.

SARGEANT, NERADA MICHELL; Harry S Truman HS; Bristol, PA; (2); Camera Clb; Church Yth Grp; Computer Clb; Dance Clb; FNA; Pep Clb; ROTC; SADD; Drill Tm; Nwsp Stf; Nrs.

SARGENT, KAREN M; Owen J Roberts HS; Pottstown, PA; (3); 12/299; Mrchg Band; Stage Crew; Symp Band; Yrbk Stf; Hon Roll; NHS; Trvl.

SARIKIANOS, PAMELA; Upper Merion Area HS; Wayne, PA; (3); Church Yth Grp; French Clb; Orch; Nwsp Stf; Rep Soph Cls; Jr Cls; Swmmng; Trk; Moore Coll Of Art Schlrshp 87; District Orchestra 86; Fashion Design.

SARISKY, BRIAN; Notre Dame HS; Easton, PA; (4); 4/85; Exploring; Quiz Bowl; Scholastic Bowl; French Hon Soc; High Hon Roll; NHS; Prfct Atten Awd; Pres Schlr; Moravian Coll; Mech Engrng.

SARISKY, TIFFANY; Pocono Mountain SR HS; Pocono Lake, PA; (2); Sec Frsh Cls; Stat Bsktbl; Hon Roll; Wrtrs Club Ptry Awd-2nd Pl 86.

SARNACKI, PAMELA G; Ambridge Area HS; Baden, PA; (3); Sec Spanish Clb; Band; Mrchg Band; School Musical; Off Jr Cls; Hon Roll; NHS; Pittsburghs 3 Rivers Yng Peoples Orch 85-88; Attndd Hnrs Bands 85-87; U Of Pittsburgh; Med Tech.

SARNECKI, KIMBERLY; James M Coughlin HS; Plains, PA; (4); 58/324; Ski Clb; SADD; Concert Band; VP Jr Cls; VP Sr Cls; Var L Bsktbl; Capt L Fld Hcky; Hon Roll; Jr NHS; NHS; Wlks Coll; Dnstry.

SARNO, DANA; Mt Lebanon HS; Mt Lebanon, PA; (2); Latin Clb; Science Clb; Varsity Clb; Stage Crew; Var Socr; 1st Pl St Sci Fair 84-87; Bio-Chemist.

SARNOWSKI, HEATHER; Langley HS; Pittsburgh, PA; (3); Drama Clb; Chorus; Drill Tm; School Musical; School Play; Stage Crew; Nwsp Rptr; Var Cheerleading; High Hon Roll; Hon Roll; Math.

SAROCKY, DENEEN; Greensburg Central Catholic HS; N Huntingdon, PA; (4); Rep Frsh Cls; Rep Stu Cncl; Im Vllybl; Penn ST U; Bus Admn.

SAROKA, KEITH WILLIAM; Harry S Truman HS; Levittown, PA; (4); 2/534; Var Coach Actv; Im Powder Puff Ftbl; Im Sftbl; Var Capt Tennis; Bausch & Lomb Sci Awd; Kiwanis Awd; NHS; Pres Schlr; Sal; Sci Achvt Awd 87; Socl Studies Awd 87; Engl Awd 85; PA ST U; Metrlgy.

SARSON, DAWN; Lehighton HS; Ashfield, PA; (1); Church Yth Grp; High Hon Roll; Hon Roll; Bio.

SARTOR, MARCI; Upper Merion HS; King Of Prussia, PA; (2); 74/301; French Clb; Red Cross Aide; Bsktbl; Var Cheerleading; Gym; Var Lcrss; Vllybl; Most Improved Cheerleader 86; Librl Arts.

SARTORI, DAVID; Burgettstown Area JR SR HS; Bulger, PA; (2); Church Yth Grp; Spanish Clb; JV Bsktbl; Hon Roll; Natl Sci Merit Awds 86-87; Airforce Acad; Pilot.

SARVER, CHRIS; Greenwood HS; Millerstown, PA; (3); 12/70; GAA; Varsity Clb; School Musical; Stage Crew; Yrbk Stf; Rep Frsh Cls; Rep Stu Cncl; Bsktbl; Fld Hcky; Sftbl; Law.

SARVER, SHANNON; Lincoln HS; Ellwood City, PA; (3); 25/163; Church Yth Grp; 4-H; Chorus; Church Choir; JV Powder Puff Ftbl; High Hon Roll; Hon Roll; Prfct Atten Awd; Accntng I Bus Stu 87.

SASFAI, CHRISTIAN; South Fayette HS; Mc Donald, PA; (3); 15/90; Ski Clb; High Hon Roll; Hon Roll; NHS; Flght Trng.

SASSAMAN, DARYL A; Cameron Cnty HS; Emporium, PA; (4); 5/85; German Clb; Mu Alpha Theta; Yrbk Phtg; Var L Ftbl; Var L Trk; Var L Wrstlng; High Hon Roll; Mu Alpha Theta Awd; NHS; Prfct Atten Awd; PIAA St Track & Wrestling 87; US Army Rsrv Schlr Athlete Awd 87; US Air Force Acad; Aerospace.

SASSAMAN, PETER; Danville SR HS; Danville, PA; (2); 46/159; Var L Crs Cntry; Var L Wrstlng; High Hon Roll.

SASSAMAN, WILLIAM K; Liberty HS; Bethlehem, PA; (4); 42/421; Computer Clb; Hon Roll; NHS; Comenius Schlrshp 87-88; Moravian Coll; Comp Sci.

SASSANI, CARLA; Our Lady Of Lourdes HS; Mount Carmel, PA; (3); 33/89; Drama Clb; French Clb; Library Aide; Pep Clb; Im Bowling; JV Sftbl; Hghst GPA-CHLD Devlpmnt 86-87; Pre-Elem Educ.

SASTOKAS, BRYAN; Kennedy Christian HS; Sharpsville, PA; (4); Boy Scts; Church Yth Grp; VP Computer Clb; Sec French Clb; Trs Science Clb; Varsity Clb; Nwsp Sprt Ed; Pres Frsh Cls; Trs Soph Cls; Rep Jr Cls; Mike Koska Mem Schlrshp Awd 87; Allegheny Coll; Pre-Med.

SATELL, GREG; Harriton HS; Narberth, PA; (4); Var Ftbl; Capt Wrstlng; Most Imprvd Wrstlng 86; Most Outstndg MVP Wrstlng 87; All Main Line, Concast & All Cnty Ftbll/Wrstlng; Lawrencville Prep; Med.

SATINSKY, AMY; Lower Moreland HS; Huntingdon Valley, PA; (4); 63/201; French Clb; FBLA; Key Clb; Yrbk Bus Mgr; Yrbk Stf; Sec Jr Cls; Sec Sr Cls; Var Capt Fld Hcky; Var Capt Lcrss; Hon Roll; Nutritn.

SATKOWSKI, BARBARA; Pittston Area HS; Avoca, PA; (4); 8/348; FBLA; Key Clb; Ski Clb; SADD; Yrbk Stf; High Hon Roll; Hon Roll; NHS; Hmcmng Queen 86-87; Acctg.

SATO, NAOMI; Southern Columbia JR SR HS; Bloomsburg, PA; (4); 10/78; Key Clb; School Play; Yrbk Stf; L Fld Hcky; Powder Puff Ftbl; Socr; Elks Awd; High Hon Roll; NHS; Voice Dem Awd; Robert C Byrd Schlrshp Rcpnt 87; 2nd Pl Awd AAUW Essay Cont 87; Pres Acad Ftnss Awd 87; Bloomsburg Univ.

SATOW, CLINTON; Emmaus HS; Allentown, PA; (3); 30/548; Church Yth Grp; JA; High Hon Roll; Hon Roll; NHS; Math.

SATTAZAHN, KIRK; Conrad Weiser HS; Womelsdorf, PA; (2); 20/157; Pres 4-H; VP FFA; Spanish Clb; 4-H Awd; Hon Roll; HOBY Yth Ldrshp Conf 87; PA ST Jr Grange Prince 86-87; 1st Pl St Creed Spkng FFA 86; Penn ST Schl Ag; Ag Bus.

SATTER, STEPHANIE; Conrad Weiser HS; Wernersville, PA; (3); 2/179; Girl Scts; Spanish Clb; Band; Concert Band; Drm Mjr(t); Mrchg Band; Yrbk Stf; Hon Roll; NHS; Bus.

SATTERLY, BRENT; Wellsboro Area HS; Wellsboro, PA; (2); Church Yth Grp; Drama Clb; 4-H; French Clb; Intnl Clb; Chorus; School Musical; 4-H Awd; Church Choir; School Play; USIA Schlrshp-Int Trvl Japan 86; Cnty Ctznshp Awd-4-H ST Comptn 85-86; VP 4-H Cnty Cncl 86; Phila Schl/Fine Arts; Drama.

SATTESON, STACY; Montgomery Area HS; Montgomery, PA; (3); Church Yth Grp; FBLA; Sec Jr Cls; JV Bsktbl; Hon Roll; NHS; Sec.

SAUDER, SHARI; Manheim Central HS; Lititz, PA; (4); 12/222; Color Guard; Yrbk Stf; Rep Jr Cls; Rep Sr Cls; Rep Stu Cncl; Cheerleading; Fld Hcky; Trk; Hon Roll; NHS; Hmcmg Ct 86; Grl Mnth 87; Schlr Athl Awd 87; Elizabethtown Coll; Elem Ed.

SAUER, DAVID; G A R Memorial HS; Wilkes-Barre, PA; (3); Chorus; Hon Roll; Jr NHS; NHS; Coast Guard.

SAUER, STACY; Conrad Weiser HS; Womelsdorf, PA; (3); 37/179; Pres Church Yth Grp; Drama Clb; FNA; Pres JCL; Band; Chorus; Church Choir; Concert Band; Drm Mjr(t); Mrchg Band; Spirit Awd 87; Bloomsburg U; Med Tech.

SAUERS, THOMAS; Mifflinburg Area HS; Lewisburg, PA; (1); FFA; Trk; Agronomy.

SAUL, PAMELA; Harry S Truman HS; Croydon, PA; (3); Debate Tm; Drama Clb; SADD; Band; School Musical; School Play; Cheerleading; Trk; Hon Roll; Hnr Of Excllnc Frnscs 85-86; PA ST; Cmmnctns.

SAULA, SUSAN; Hempfield SR HS; Madison, PA; (4); 21/693; Pres Spanish Clb; Stu Cncl; Cit Awd; High Hon Roll; Jr NHS; Kiwanis Awd; NHS; Pres Schlr; Trs Spanish NHS; Hlf Tuitn Acdmc Schlrshp Gannon U 87; Hnrd 5 Spnsh Stdnts Grad Clss 87; Hnr Grad 87; Gannon U; Spnsh.

SAULINO, MARK A; Archbishop Wood Boys HS; Warminster, PA; (4); 1/282; Nwsp Stf; Ed Yrbk Stf; Lit Mag; Rep Stu Cncl; JV Bsktbl; High Hon Roll; Sec NHS; Ntl Merit SF; Crprt Lawyer.

SAUNDERS, DANIELLE; Warren Area HS; Warren, PA; (3); Debate Tm; Drama Clb; German Clb; Hosp Aide; Color Guard; School Play; Stage Crew; Variety Show; Trk; High Hon Roll; Bst Debate Tm Cnty HS 85-86; Exchng Stu Grmny 87; Theatre Arts.

SAUNDERS, DAVID; Westinghouse HS; Pittsburgh, PA; (4); Library Aide; Mrchg Band; Tennis; Wt Lftg; Hon Roll; NHS; U Of Pittsburgh; Comp Sci.

SAUNDERS, MILTON T; Central HS; Philadelphia, PA; (4); 49/340; Camera Clb; Computer Clb; Teachers Aide; Orch; Var Crs Cntry; Powder Puff Ftbl; Var Timer; Hon Roll; Natl Achvt Fnlst 87; Barnwell Hnrs 85, 87; U DE; Mech Engrng.

SAUR, DAWN; Council Rock HS; Newtown, PA; (3); 307/906; Spanish Clb; Rep Soph Cls; Rep Jr Cls; Stat Mgr(s); Im Powder Puff Ftbl; Trs Score Keeper; Stat Swmmng; Timer; Trk; Stu Yr 81-82; MS Read-A-Thon Spr Achvt Awd 83; Temple U.

SAURITCH, PATRICK; Belle Vernon Area HS; Belle Vernon, PA; (3); Church Yth Grp; FBLA; VP L Ftbl; Wt Lftg; Hon Roll; Bus.

SAUVE, JOHN; Coudersport HS; Coudersport, PA; (3); Letterman Clb; Varsity Clb; Im Ftbl; Var L Trk; Capt L Wrstlng; High Hon Roll; Hon Roll; Triangle Tech; Comp Drftg.

SAVAGE, DEBBRA; Southern Columbia Area HS; Catawissa, PA; (3); Varsity Clb; JV Var Cheerleading; JV Fld Hcky; Hon Roll; NHS; Bus Admin.

SAVAGE, JENNIFER; Nazareth Acad; Phila, PA; (3); 12/120; Capt Dance Clb; Sec French Clb; Intnl Clb; Service Clb; School Musical; Lit Mag; Var Cheerleading; High Hon Roll; NHS; Elem Educ.

SAVAGE, JIM; Laurel Highlands SR HS; Uniontown, PA; (2); Computer Clb; Radio Clb; Science Clb; High Hon Roll; JETS Awd; PA JA Sci 1st Awd 86-87; Eclgy Clb 85-86; Bio Tm 86-87.

SAVAGE, KEITH; Butler HS; Butler, PA; (2); Im Bsktbl; High Hon Roll; Jr NHS; Penn ST U; Engr.

SAVAGE, KRISTI; Tyrone Area HS; Pt Matilda, PA; (2); French Clb; Chrmn Key Clb; Library Aide; Science Clb; Speech Tm; SADD; Chorus; High Hon Roll; Hon Roll; Jr NHS; Ambssdr To Hugh O Brien Ldrshp Smnr 87; Outstndng Frnch, Math Stu 86-87; Harvard U; Law.

SAVAGE, REBECCA L; Highlands SR HS; Brackenridge, PA; (4); 76/288; Church Yth Grp; Girl Scts; Key Clb; SADD; Band; Jazz Band; Pep Band; Symp Band; Hon Roll; Mrchg Band; Amer Hall Fame Band Hnrs 86-87; Gold Awd SR Girl Scts S W PA 85-86; Clarion U PA; Chem.

SAVAGE, STACEY; Central Bucks West HS; Doylestown, PA; (3); Church Yth Grp; Cmnty Wkr; Drama Clb; Teachers Aide; Var Socr; High Hon Roll; Hon Roll; Hnrb Mntn 86 & 87; Top Stu Scl Stds 85; Elem Ed.

SAVAKES, WENDY M; Plum SR HS; Pittsburgh, PA; (2); Drama Clb; Pep Clb; Chorus; School Play; High Hon Roll; Church Yth Grp; 4-H; Office Aide; SADD; Grls Ldrs Assoc Outstndng Svc Awd 86-87; Crwnd Miss E Suburban 86-87; Chrch Yth Nwspr Edtr Chf 85-87; Cmnctns.

SAVANT, JAMES; Tulpehocken HS; Bethel, PA; (3); Boy Scts; FFA; Trk; Var L Wrstlng; MIP In Wrestling 86-87; Lttr In J V Wrestlng 85-86; 3rd At Wrstlng Sect 86-87; Army; Auto Mech.

SAVATT, MISSY; Sto-Rox SR HS; Mc Kees Rocks, PA; (2); Church Yth Grp; JA; Library Aide; Office Aide; Yrbk Stf; Hon Roll; Elem Educ.

SAVER, JULIE; Plum SR HS; Pittsburgh, PA; (4); 16/377; French Clb; FHA; Band; Color Guard; Symp Band; Stat Socr; Stat Trk; NHS; Plum Borough Educ Assn Schlrshp 87; Natl Merit Commended Stu 85; PA ST U; Hlth Plng.

SAVIDGE, CRAIG; Lebanon HS; Lebanon, PA; (4); 16/288; Trs Church Yth Grp; Pres Computer Clb; Band; Jazz Band; Mrchg Band; Orch; Pep Band; Var Tennis; Pres Schlr; Rotary Awd; Sempter Fidels Awd 87; Penn ST U.

SAVIGNANO, ERIC; Tunkhannock HS; Tunkhannock, PA; (4); Church Yth Grp; Letterman Clb; Var Crs Cntry; Var Trk; Hon Roll; NHS; Pres Schlr; Penn ST; Elec Engrng.

SAVINA, TIM; South Side Area HS; Clinton, PA; (3); Trs Band; Trs Concert Band; Trs Mrchg Band; Orch; Pep Band; School Musical; Yrbk Stf; Hon Roll; Hnrs Clb 84-86; 1st Chair Trmptr 84-88; Psych.

SAVITSKE, JENNIFER; Saucon Valley SR HS; Hellertown, PA; (2); 35/161; Church Yth Grp; French Clb; Nwsp Phtg; Nwsp Rptr; Yrbk Rptr; Yrbk Stf; Cheerleading; Hon Roll.

SAVOKINAS, ARTHUR; Pittston Area SR HS; Pittston, PA; (2); English Clb; Nwsp Phtg; Nwsp Rptr; Nwsp Sprt Ed; Nwsp Stf; High Hon Roll; Hon Roll; NHS; Mgr Lttl Lg Bsbll Tm 86; Lttl Lg Bd Of Drctrs 86; Scranton U; Med.

SAWA, JOHN; Ringgold HS; Donora, PA; (3); Aud/Vis; SADD; Band; Concert Band; Mrchg Band; Dist Band 84-85; CA U PA; Comm.

SAWATIS, KERNIE; Ambridge Area HS; Baden, PA; (3); Church Yth Grp; French Clb; Chorus; Stage Crew; Im Vllybl; Music Prfrmnc.

SAWHILL, KENDELL; North Hills HS; Pittsburgh, PA; (3); #12 In Class; Church Yth Grp; Chorus; Flag Corp; Mrchg Band; Swing Chorus; High Hon Roll; NHS; Prfct Atten Awd; Musicl Thtr.

SAWICKI, SUSAN; Mount Carmel Area JR SR HS; Atlas, PA; (2); 15/158; FTA; Key Clb; Sftbl; Hon Roll; French Clb; Latin Clb; Bsktbl; Olympics Mind 86&87; Susquehanna U; Math.

SAWICKY, CHRISTINA IRENE; Gwynedd Mercy Acad; Ambler, PA; (2); Art Clb; GAA; Girl Scts; Pres Frsh Cls; Pres Soph Cls; Co-Capt Rep Jr Cls; Stu Cncl; Im Bsktbl; Var JV Fld Hcky; JV Lcrss; Maxima Cum Laude Natl Lat Exam 86; Outstndg Achvt Lat I 86.

SAWMELLE, GREG; Trinity HS; Washington, PA; (3); 64/400; Boy Scts; Math Tm; Ski Clb; Band; Concert Band; Jazz Band; Mrchg Band; Hon Roll; Engr.

SAWYER, DENISE; Bradford Area HS; Bradford, PA; (3); 34/207; AFS; Girl Scts; Office Aide; Spanish Clb; Chorus; Yrbk Stf; Stu Cncl; Hon Roll; Jr NHS; NHS; Sec Zonta Club 87-88; Miss BHS 87-88; Physcns Asst.

SAWYER, STACEY; Ringgold HS; Finleyville, PA; (4); 53/254; Girl Scts; Math Clb; Science Clb; Ski Clb; Band; Concert Band; Mrchg Band; School Musical; Powder Puff Ftbl; Math/Sci Hon Soc; Outdoor Ed Clb; SR Actvts Comm; Duquesne U; Pre Vet.

SAWYER JR, WILLIAM; Inverboro HS; Prospect Park, PA; (4); Aud/Vis; JA; Thesps; Nwsp Phtg; Vllybl; Hon Roll; DE County CC; Bus Admin.

SAXON, SCOTT; Penn Hills HS; Pittsburgh, PA; (3); Science Clb; High Hon Roll; Hon Roll; Amer Chmcl Soc Pttsbrg Educ Sub Grp 86-87.

SAY, BRAD; Ford City JR SR HS; Ford City, PA; (3); Cmnty Wkr; Concert Band; Mrchg Band; Pep Band; High Hon Roll; Hon Roll; Band; Prfct Atten Awd; IUP Honors Band 86; Cnty Band 86; Regl Band 87; All St Band 87; Std Activities Awd 87; Dist Band 87; Military Band.

SAYDAH, JAYNE; Methacton HS; Collegeville, PA; (3); 31/384; Church Yth Grp; Red Cross Aide; Chorus; Var Fld Hcky; Var Sftbl; Var Swmmng; High Hon Roll; NHS; Lit Mag; Dstngshd Hnr Rl Awd 86-87; Stu Athltc Trainr 85-87; Engr.

SAYER, ROBYN; Gwynedd Mercy Acad; Gwynedd Vly, PA; (2); Art Clb; Cmnty Wkr; Hosp Aide; JV Sftbl; JV Tennis; French Hon Soc; Excllnc Bio, Geo, Art 87; Bio.

SAYERS, KAREN; Philadelphia H S For Girls; Dover, DE; (4); 133/354; Sec Cmnty Wkr; Sftbl; Hon Roll; Wsly Coll; Nrsng.

SAYKO, ELIZABETH; Council Rock HS; Newtown, PA; (2); FBLA; Hon Roll; Bio.

SAYKO, KATHY; Council Rock HS; Newtown, PA; (2); FBLA; Girl Scts; Library Aide; Spanish Clb; Im Fld Hcky; Im Sftbl; Hon Roll.

SAYLOR, BRIAN; Bishop Carroll HS; Gallitzin, PA; (3); 31/140; Am Leg Boys St; Boy Scts; Spanish Clb; JV Var Ftbl; Hon Roll; PA ST U; Aero Engrng.

SAYLOR, DREU; Rockwood Area HS; Rockwood, PA; (2); Chess Clb; Cmnty Wkr; Computer Clb; 4-H; JV L Bsktbl; Hon Roll.

SAYLOR, JAMES; Bellefonte HS; Bellefonte, PA; (3); 16/230; Model UN; Band; Concert Band; Drm & Bgl; Jazz Band; Pep Band; School Musical; JV Trk; Hon Roll; Ntl Merit Ltr; Outstndng Delg Model UN 87; Outstndng Dlgtn Model UN 87; Penn ST U; Mech Engr.

SAYLOR, JENNIFER; Tunkhannock Area HS; Tunkhannock, PA; (3); Crs Cntry; Trk; Hon Roll; Criminal Psych.

SAYLOR, JON P; Bishop Carroll HS; Gallitzin, PA; (2); Am Leg Boys St; Boy Scts; Church Yth Grp; JV Var Bsktbl; Var JV Ftbl; Cit Awd; Rlgn Awd 85; Mech Engrng.

SAYLOR, KATHY; Donegal HS; Mount Joy, PA; (3); 9/177; Trs Church Yth Grp; Sec Trs Band; Pres Chorus; Concert Band; Jazz Band; Mrchg Band; Hon Roll; NHS; Spanish NHS; Lebanon Valley Coll Hnrs Band 2 Yrs 86-87; Cnty Chorus 87; Cnty Band 86-87; Landscaping.

SAYLOR, LAURA; Rockwood HS; Rockwood, PA; (2); Computer Clb; Color Guard; Hon Roll; IN U; Engl.

SAYLOR, MELINDA; Eastern York HS; Windsor, PA; (3); Rep Soph Cls; Rep Jr Cls; Rep Sr Cls; Rep Stu Cncl; Var L Trk; JV L Vllybl; Stat Wrstlng; JP Sousa Awd; Physcl Thrpy.

SAYLOR, MICHAEL; Rockwood Area HS; Rockwood, PA; (2); 3/123; Sec Church Yth Grp; 4-H; NFL; Band; School Play; Rep Stu Cncl; Var L Socr; Var Trk; High Hon Roll; 2nd Tm Bi ST Sccr 86; Cvl Engr.

SAYLOR, MICHELE; Avon Grove HS; Landenberg, PA; (3); AFS; Pres Church Yth Grp; Church Choir; Nwsp Stf; High Hon Roll; Hon Roll; Prfct Atten Awd; Art Awd 86-87; Gifted Pgm; Advrtsng.

SAYLOR, MICHELE; Gateway SR HS; Monroeville, PA; (4); 21/486; FHA; Capt Hosp Aide; Pres Service Clb; School Play; Yrbk Stf; Jr NHS; NHS; Prfct Atten Awd; Pres Schlr; Jr Cath Daughters, Duquesne Prsdntl & Robert Byrd Schlrshps 87; U Of Pittsburgh; Elem Educ.

SAYLOR, RICHIE; Blacklick Valley HS; Vintondale, PA; (3); Art Clb; Ski Clb; Spanish Clb; Varsity Clb; Var L Bsbl; Var L Ftbl; Hon Roll; Air Force; Pilot.

SAYLOR, STEPHANIE L; Red Lion Area SR HS; Felton, PA; (3); 32/342; Sec Church Yth Grp; JA; Church Choir; School Play; Hon Roll; Outstndng Spanish Stu Awd, Typwrtng Awd 55 Wrds Per Min 87; Exec Secr.

SAYLOR, TAMMIE; Rockwood Area HS; Rockwood, PA; (3); 3/80; Pres Church Yth Grp; Sec 4-H; Hosp Aide; Band; Chorus; Stu Cncl; Var L Bsktbl; Var L Vllybl; High Hon Roll; Grls Physcl Ed Awd 84-86; Phycsl Thrpy.

SAYLOR, TRICIA; Conemaugh Twp Area HS; Johnstown, PA; (4); Pres VP Stu Cncl; Var Cheerleading; Rotary Awd; Stu Cncl Awd 86-87; K Gibb Bus Schl; Lgl Secr.

SAYMAN, TINA; Montgomery Area HS; Montgomery, PA; (3); French Clb; FHA; Var Tennis; Trk; Hon Roll; Tennis Coaches Awd 87.

SAYRE, KIRK; Moniteau HS; Boyers, PA; (3); 1/139; Drama Clb; Spanish Clb; Band; Jazz Band; Mrchg Band; Hon Roll; NHS; PA Govnr Schl Intl Stds & Sci 86 & 87; PA JR Acad Sci 1st Pl 84 & 86-87; Comp Sci.

SAYSON, CLARISSA; Lebanon Catholic HS; Lebanon, PA; (3); 2/72; German Clb; Band; Chorus; Off Jazz Band; Nwsp Rptr; Stu Cncl; Gov Hon Prg Awd; High Hon Roll; NHS; Pep Clb; Cert Of Merit Amer Assoc Of Tchrs Of German Inc 86-87; PA Govr Schl Intl Studies 86; Acdmc All Amer; Itnl Rltns.

SCAFARIA, AIMEE; Academy Of Notre Dame; West Chester, PA; (3); Church Yth Grp; Cmnty Wkr; Dance Clb; School Play; Variety Show; Yrbk Stf; Cheerleading; Hon Roll; Caitlin Endeavor Awd 86; Penn ST.

SCAFF, DAVID W; Lock Haven HS; Loganton, PA; (4); 16/242; Key Clb; Model UN; Spanish Clb; VP SADD; Rep Stu Cncl; Var L Socr; Cit Awd; Hon Roll; Lion Awd; NEDT Awd; Scintfc Awd-Excllnc-Bio & Chem 87; Gannon U-Erie PA; Pre-Med.

SCAGLIOTTI, PATRICE; Bishop Ohara HS; Archbald, PA; (2); 9/126; Camera Clb; French Clb; Latin Clb; Ski Clb; Phrmcy.

SCALES, JEAN; Hopewell Area HS; Aliquippa, PA; (3); 11/250; Art Clb; Church Yth Grp; French Clb; JA; Math Clb; Trk; High Hon Roll; NHS; Acadmc All Amer 87; Engrng.

SCALET, STEVEN P; York Suburban HS; York, PA; (3); Am Leg Boys St; Drama Clb; Ski Clb; Varsity Clb; School Play; Nwsp Rptr; Nwsp Sprt Ed; Yrbk Stf; Off Frsh Cls; Off Soph Cls; YCIAA Div I All Cnty Lnbckr 87; Natl Piano Plyng Auditions 85-86.

SCALONGE, BRENDA; Wyoming Area HS; Exeter, PA; (3); French Clb; FBLA; Band; Mrchg Band; Hon Roll; Cnslr.

SCALZO, KRISTA; Loyalsock Township HS; Fort Wayne, IN; (4); 6/102; Drama Clb; Speech Tm; Varsity Clb; Trs Soph Cls; VP Jr Cls; Sec Sr Cls; Sftbl; NHS; Robt Byrd Schlrshp 87; Srptmst Yth Ctzshp Awd 87; GRIT Outstndng Yng Ctzn Awd 87; Boston U; Pre-Med.

SCAMPONE, MELISSA L; Perkiomen Valley HS; Schwenksville, PA; (4); Library Aide; SADD; Band; Chorus; School Musical; School Play; Var Vllybl; PA ST U; Lib Arts.

SCAMUFFA, ANTOINETTE; Coatesville Area HS; Coatesville, PA; (3); 37/517; FBLA; Leo Clb; Ski Clb; Spanish Clb; Mrchg Band; Jr Cls; Cheerleading; Sftbl; Twrlr; Hon Roll; Perfect Attndnc 85 & 87; Cert Accmplshmnt Shrthnd I 86-87.

SCANCELLA, JOSEPH J; Council Rock HS; Newtown, PA; (3); 62/908; Boy Scts; Rep Stu Cncl; VP Trk; Im Vllybl; Im Wrstlng; Hon Roll; NHS; Sr Little League ST Champs 85; US Coast Guard AIM Fnlst & Rotary Clb Ldrshp Camp 87; Intl Bus.

SCANDLE, MICHAEL; Shamokin Area HS; Sunbury, PA; (2); Rep Frsh Cls; Rep Stu Cncl; Im Badmtn; Im Bsktbl; Im Ftbl; Im Gym; Im Swmmng; Im Vllybl; Im Wt Lftg; JV Wrstlng; Wrstlng & Stu Cncl Achvt 85-86; WACC; Comp Repair.

SCANISH III, STEPHEN; St Marys Area HS; Kersey, PA; (3); 139/269; Sec Exploring; JV Ftbl; Triangle Tech; Mech Drftng.

SCANLAN, JENNIFER; Cardinal O Hara HS; Clifton Hgts, PA; (3); 36/710; Service Clb; French Hon Soc; Hon Roll; Office Aide; Lit Mag; Hnrb Mntn Schl Sci Fair 86; Intl Bus.

SCANLON, KERRY; North Catholic HS; Wexford, PA; (3); Drama Clb; NFL; Speech Tm; School Musical; Nwsp Rptr; Lit Mag; Var Cheerleading; Trk; Jrnlsm.

SCANLON, PATRICK BARRY; Ligonier Valley SR HS; Ligonier, PA; (3); Computer Clb; Stage Crew; JV Ftbl; Hon Roll; Jr NHS; Penn ST; Engr.

SCANLON, ROSEMARY; Northgate JR SR HS; Pittsburgh, PA; (3); Girl Scts; Ed Lit Mag; Hon Roll; Carnegie-Mellon U; Englsh.

SCANLON, SHARON; State College Area SR HS; State College, PA; (4); 19/561; Concert Band; Yrbk Stf; High Hon Roll; Ntl Merit Schol; NEDT Awd; Accu-Weather Earth Sci Awd, John Stuart Memrl Schlrshp 87; Penn ST U; Earth/Minrl Sci.

SCANNAPIECO, RAYMOND; Archbishop Carroll HS; King Of Prussia, PA; (4); 75/367; Art Clb; High Hon Roll; Jr NHS; Chmstry Awd 84-85; US Hstry Awd 85-86; Prsdntl Ftnss & Acdmc Awd 86-87; Drexel U; Engnrng.

SCARAN III, ERNEST D; Bishop Hafey HS; Hazleton, PA; (3); Church Yth Grp; Ski Clb; Spanish Clb; Teachers Aide; Ftbl.

SCARBOROUGH, ALLISON; Central Bucks HS East; Doylestown, PA; (3); Debate Tm; Political Wkr; Yrbk Bus Mgr; Yrbk Stf; Rep Stu Cncl; JV Sftbl; Var Capt Tennis; Hon Roll; Prfct Atten Awd; Cocoa Ave Plz Sngls Champ Tnns 85; Phil & Subrbn Tnns Assn Gld Cup Fnlst 85-87; Keystone ST Gms 87; Pre Med.

SCARBOROUGH, MATTHEW J; William Penn HS; York, PA; (3); Debate Tm; Drama Clb; Ski Clb; Thesps; Band; Chorus; Sec Stu Cncl; Var Socr; Var L Tennis; NHS; U VA; Pltcl Sci.

SCARCELLA, VANESSA; Hazleton HS; Hazleton, PA; (4); 14/376; Drama Clb; Exploring; Leo Clb; Pep Clb; Ski Clb; School Play; Stage Crew; Nwsp Rptr; Yrbk Stf; High Hon Roll; Penn ST; Engr.

SCARFARO, ERIN; Faith Christian HS; Roseto, PA; (3); Church Yth Grp; French Clb; Hosp Aide; Chorus; Church Choir; School Play; Ed Yrbk Stf; Sec Jr Cls; Rep Stu Cncl; Stat Bsktbl; Sign Lang Comp 1st Pl 86; Pinebrook JC; Legl Sec.

SCARFUTTI, STACY; Highlands SR HS; Natrona Hts, PA; (4); 13/280; Drama Clb; Intnl Clb; Key Clb; Office Aide; SADD; Color Guard; School Play; Rep Stu Cncl; NHS; Ntl Merit SF; Pres Acad Ftns Awd 87; Sci Olympc Tm Stu; Intrmdt Unit 2nd Pl Wnnr Dscssn Bwl 87; NC ST U; Gntcs.

SCARPINO, MARY; Villa Maria Acad; Erie, PA; (3); Church Yth Grp; Computer Clb; Exploring; Model UN; Science Clb; School Play; Im Bsktbl; Im Vllybl; Hon Roll; NHS; Med Tech.

SCARPITTI, MARION; Mc Dowell HS; Erie, PA; (2); 140/629; Yrbk Stf; Gannon U.

SCARSELLONE, ELLEN; Hopewell SR HS; Aliquippa, PA; (3); Girl Scts; Trs Library Aide; IN U PA; Law.

SCARVEL, MARISSA; Monessen HS; Monessen, PA; (3); 6/110; Church Yth Grp; VP JA; Drill Tm; Drm Mjr(t); School Play; Nwsp Rptr; Yrbk Stf; Pres Soph Cls; High Hon Roll; NHS; HOBY Yth Fndtn 85-86; Cmmnctns.

SCATTON, FRANCINE; Hazleton HS; Williamson, NY; (4); 110/350; Drama Clb; Office Aide; Chorus; Color Guard; School Play; Stage Crew; Nwsp Rptr; Trs Soph Cls; Crs Cntry; Mgr Swmmng; Hnr Roll 85; 1st Hnrs 85; HAVTS; Nrsng.

SCATTON, MICHELLE; Hazleton HS; Kelayres, PA; (4); Pres Drama Clb; Intnl Clb; Thesps; Stage Crew; Off Stu Cncl; Tennis; Hon Roll; Scolastic Art Awd 86-87; Lions Clb 1st Pl Fine Arts Awd 87; Penn ST U; Bus Admin.

SCHAACK, STEPHANIE; Northwestern HS; Albion, PA; (3); Cmnty Wkr; Debate Tm; Model UN; Color Guard; Drill Tm; Mrchg Band; Rep Stu Cncl; JV Var Pom Pon; Im Powder Puff Ftbl; JV Var Trk; Edinboro U; Publ Rel.

SCHAAD, WENDY; Peters Twp HS; Mcmurray, PA; (3); 17/237; NFL; SADD; Color Guard; NHS; Spanish NHS; Arch.

SCHAADT, JOHN; Northampton JR HS; Treichlers, PA; (1); Drama Clb; Rep Frsh Cls; Rep Stu Cncl; JV Socr; Var Trk; Hon Roll; Pres Schlr.

SCHAAF JR, JOSEPH R; Catherdral Preparatory Schl; Erie, PA; (3); 13/193; Pres Sec Debate Tm; Model UN; NFL; Mrchg Band; Yrbk Bus Mgr; Swmmng; Boy Scts; Band; Trk; Natl Jrnlsm Awd, NCFL Dist 3rd Pl Lincoln-Douglas Debate 87; 1st Pl Frshmn/Sophmr Lincoln Debate 86; Duke U.

SCHAAF, PAUL; Penn Hills SR HS; Penn Hills, PA; (4); Boy Scts; Drama Clb; VP JA; Science Clb; School Musical; School Play; Yrbk Phtg; Yrbk Stf; Hon Roll; Prfct Atten Awd; Deans Hnr Awd 87; Physics Lab Asst 87; Brnz & Gold Eagle Palms 87; Case Western Rsrv U; Physics.

SCHACH, CRYSTAL; Pine Grove Area HS; Pine Grove, PA; (4); ROTC; Varsity Clb; Sftbl; Im Vllybl; Pres Schlr; Kutztown U; Studio Art.

SCHACHTE, MICHAEL; Greensburg Central Catholic HS; United, PA; (4); 30/222; Cmnty Wkr; 4-H; High Hon Roll; NHS; Ntl Merit SF; Penn ST U; Engrng.

SCHAD, CHRISTINE; South Park HS; Library, PA; (4); 6/203; L Crs Cntry; L Tennis; L Trk; High Hon Roll; NHS; Prfct Atten Awd; Finance.

SCHAD, RON; Beaver Area HS; Beaver, PA; (3); 88/200; Ski Clb; Spanish Clb; Im Bsktbl; Var JV Ftbl; Var Swmmng; Var L Trk; Im Wt Lftg; Hon Roll; Trck Mbr Rcrd Brkng 400 Rly 87; Sprts Med.

SCHADDER, MELANIE; Hazleton HS; Hazleton, PA; (3); Hosp Aide; VICA; Band; Chorus; Mrchg Band; JV Capt Cheerleading; Hon Roll; Csmtlgy.

SCHADLER, BETH; St Pius X HS; Pottstown, PA; (1); 24/148; Hosp Aide; Med.

SCHAEBERLE, MICHAEL D; Spring Grove SR HS; Spring Grove, PA; (3); 10/310; Boy Scts; Church Yth Grp; Varsity Clb; Rep Stu Cncl; Var Socr; JV Wrstlng; Hon Roll; NHS; Eagle Scout Awd 88; Yth Schlrs Inst Chem 88; Forensic Chem.

SCHAEFER, CHRISTOPHER; Bishop Hafey HS; Hazleton, PA; (4); Pres Chess Clb; Church Yth Grp; Key Clb; Service Clb; Ski Clb; Rep Sr Cls; JV Bsktbl; JV Var Crs Cntry; JV Var Trk; Hon Roll; Engrng.

SCHAEFER, DAVID; Mohawk HS; Bessemer, PA; (4); 3/139; Sec Spanish Clb; Var Bsbl; L Capt Ftbl; Wt Lftg; High Hon Roll; Pres NHS; Ntl Merit Ltr; Grove Cty Col6; Elec Engr.

SCHAEFER, DAVID J; Blackhawk HS; Beaver Falls, PA; (4); 69/270; Chess Clb; Chorus; School Musical; School Play; Var L Socr; Var L Swmmng; Ntl Merit SF; Aud/Vis; Math Clb; Acpl Chr; Arian Awd Music 87; Dist Choir 85-87; SAT Scores 800 Math & 710 Verbal 87; Geneva Coll; Sci.

SCHAEFER, EDWARD; Pocono Mountain HS; Tobyhanna, PA; (3); 87/310; Boy Scts; Trs Church Yth Grp; Acpl Chr; Band; Chorus; Church Choir; Concert Band; Drm & Bgl; Mrchg Band; School Musical; Prnt Meda Jrnlsm.

SCHAEFER, GREG; Butler SR HS; Butler, PA; (3); Boy Scts; VP Church Yth Grp; French Clb; Im Bsktbl; Im Ftbl; Sierra Clb Essy Cntst Awd Wnnr 85.

SCHAEFER JR, JAMES; St Marys Area HS; Saint Marys, PA; (4); Pres Band; Pres Concert Band; Drm & Bgl; Drm Mjr(t); Jazz Band; Pres Mrchg Band; Orch; Pep Band; Outstndng Mscn Awd 84; US Const Bi-Cntnl MENC Msc Prog Cert 87; IN U Of PA; Msc Ed.

SCHAEFER, STEVE; Council Rock HS; Churchville, PA; (3); 102/908; Var Socr; Trk; NHS; Estrn PA Soccr Select Tm 84-86.

SCHAEFER, WILLIAM; Hazelton SR HS; Hazleton, PA; (3); 155/455; Church Yth Grp; FBLA; German Clb; Pep Clb; Scholastic Bowl; SADD; Stage Crew; Rep Stu Cncl; Var Cheerleading; Hon Roll; Psych.

SCHAEFFER, CASSIE; Ford City HS; Ford City, PA; (4); Drama Clb; Pep Clb; Spanish Clb; Chorus; Drm Mjr(t); Mrchg Band; School Play; Rep Soph Cls; Rep Sr Cls; Rep Stu Cncl; IN U Of PA; Crmnlgy.

SCHAEFFER, CRYSTAL; Souderton Area HS; Telford, PA; (3); 40/377; Band; Mgr L Bsktbl; Var L Lcrss; Mgr(s); High Hon Roll; Hon Roll; Pres Acad Fit Awd 84-85; Vet Hosp Job-Work; Vet Med.

SCHAEFFER, CYNTHIA; Boyertown Area SR HS; Boyertown, PA; (3); VICA; Chorus; Flag Corp; Stu Cncl; Cit Awd; Hon Roll; Berks Voc-Tech Schl; HOSA-REPORTER; Nrsng.

SCHAEFFER, JENNIFER; Cedar Crest HS; Lebanon, PA; (3); 126/342; German Clb; Pep Clb; Science Clb; Vllybl; Hnr Rl 86-87.

SCHAEFFER, JENNIFER; Oley Valley HS; Oley, PA; (3); 3/142; Trs Band; Concert Band; Jazz Band; Mrchg Band; Orch; Pep Band; School Musical; Yrbk Bus Mgr; Var Crs Cntry; JV Trk; Cnty,Dist,Regnl Band & Orch 84-87; ST Orch 87; Civil Engr.

SCHAEFFER, JENNIFER; Schuylkill Haven HS; Sch Haven, PA; (3); 11/82; Science Clb; Yrbk Stf; Trs Soph Cls; Trs Jr Cls; Stu Cncl; Capt JV Cheerleading; Stat Trk; Hon Roll; NHS; Nrthmptn Cnty Area CC; Dntl Hy.

SCHAEFFER, MARIA; Nativity BVM HS; Pottsville, PA; (4); 13/98; Art Clb; French Clb; Math Clb; Yrbk Ed-Chief; Off Frsh Cls; Rep Jr Cls; Sec Stu Cncl; Sftbl; NHS; Stu Of Mnth 86; Villanova; Acctg.

SCHAEFFER, MATTHEW; Episcopal Acad; Newtown Square, PA; (2); Im Bsbl; Im Ftbl; Var L Wrstlng; Pres Ftns Awd 86.

SCHAEFFER, PAM; Northern Chester County Tech HS; Phoenixville, PA; (3); 1/130; FBLA; Pep Clb; Ski Clb; VICA; Band; Concert Band; Mrchg Band; Pep Band; Rep Jr Cls; High Hon Roll; Schlstc Achvt-German I 84-85; 1st Pl Accntng I 85-86; 1st Pl Typing II 86-87.

SCHAEFFER, SCOTT; Governor Mifflin HS; Shillington, PA; (3); Band; Concert Band; Mrchg Band; Var L Bsktbl; Var L Ftbl; Var L Socr; Im Vllybl; Penn ST; Mech Engr.

SCHAFER, LISA; Central Cambria HS; Ebensburg, PA; (3); JA; Library Aide; Chorus; Kent St OH; Psych.

SCHAFER, MARISA; Penn Hills SR HS; Pittsburgh, PA; (4); 50/609; Office Aide; Spanish Clb; Teachers Aide; Yrbk Stf; Rep Sr Cls; JV Bsktbl; High Hon Roll; Hon Roll; NHS; Hnrs Scholar Allegheny CC 87; Fnlst Heinz Fndtn Scholar 87; CCAC Boyce; Hotel Mgmt.

SCHAFER, RALPH D; Lehighton HS; Lehighton, PA; (3); Chess Clb; 4-H; Concert Band; School Play; Ftbl; Golf; Mgr(s); Trk; Hon Roll; Prfct Atten Awd; Penn ST U; Engrng.

SCHAFER, RICHARD R; LAS HS; Lehighton, PA; (3); Aud/Vis; Camera Clb; Chess Clb; Church Yth Grp; Debate Tm; 4-H; Letterman Clb; Red Cross Aide; Band; Chorus; Rtry Yth Exchange Stu Schlrshp 86-87; Lehighton Womens Clb, 4-H Treas Poetry Awd 86; Penn ST U; Vet.

SCHAFER, TAMMY; Hopewell HS; Aliquippa, PA; (3); 36/243; Pres Exploring; French Clb; Hosp Aide; Pep Clb; Flag Corp; Frsh Cls; Wt Lftg; High Hon Roll; NHS; Central MI U; Bus Admin.

SCHAFER, TRICIA; Reading HS; Reading, PA; (3); 48/710; Sec Aud/Vis; VP Dance Clb; Chorus; School Musical; School Play; Var Tennis; Var Vllybl; Outstndg Music Stu Of Yr 85; Hmcmg Qn 87; Vrsty Lttr Tnns 86; Drexel U; Arch.

SCHAFFER, BILL; PA Trafford HS; Harrison Cty, PA; (3); Ski Clb; Golf; Socr; Tennis.

SCHAFFER, BRAD; Penn Trafford HS; Harrison City, PA; (2); 20/325; Ski Clb; Varsity Clb; Im Fld Hcky; L Wrstlng; High Hon Roll; PA ST; Bus.

SCHAFFER, CAROL ANN; Bishop Guilfoyle HS; Duncansville, PA; (3); Band; Concert Band; Mrchg Band; Rep Stu Cncl; JV Var Bsktbl; Score Keeper; JV Var Sftbl; Hon Roll; NHS; Duquesne U; Phrmclgy.

SCHAFFER, ERIC; Palmerton Area HS; Palmerton, PA; (3); 42/171; Bsbl; Bsktbl; Wrstlng.

SCHAFFER, ERIC; Ridley SR HS; Morton, PA; (4); 40/427; Church Yth Grp; Cmnty Wkr; Var JV Bsbl; Ftbl; Capt Var Golf; Hon Roll; NHS; Presdntl Acad Ftns Awd 87; U Of Pittsburgh.

SCHAFFER, JASON; Cardinal O Hara HS; Media, PA; (3); 23/710; Cmnty Wkr; German Clb; Lit Mag; Im Bsktbl; NHS; Ger Natl Hnr Soc 85-87; Villanova U; Intl Bus.

SCHAFFER, REBECCA; Council Rock HS; Newtown, PA; (3); 170/950; Concert Band; Rep Soph Cls; Rep Jr Cls; Pres Stu Cncl; Var Swmmng; Hon Roll; Gen Elec Town Mtng Tmrrw 86; Mst Imprvd Swmmr 84-85; Chrmn Red Crss Blood Moble 87; Jrnlsm.

SCHAIRER, SUSAN; Upper Moreland HS; Willow Grove, PA; (3); 20/276; Church Yth Grp; SADD; Rep Soph Cls; Rep Jr Cls; Rep Stu Cncl; JV Var Fld Hcky; JV Var Lcrss; Var Swmmng; High Hon Roll; NHS; Coaches Assoc Awd Vrsty Lrs JR Yr 87; Phy Therapy.

SCHALL, CHRIS; Elderton JR SR HS; Elderton, PA; (3); 13/90; Varsity Clb; Capt Bsktbl; Var JV Vllybl; High Hon Roll; Church Yth Grp; Cmnty Wkr; Girl Scts; Spanish Clb; Band; Color Guard; Bradford Schl; Retail Mgmnt.

SCHALL, HAROLD; Butler SR HS; Butler, PA; (4); 9/699; Trs JA; SADD; Im Ftbl; High Hon Roll; L Trs Jr NHS; L Trs NHS; Pres Schlr; Honor Grad 87; JA Schlrshps; Butler Cnty CC; Accntng.

SCHAMBERGER, DANIEL; Emmaus HS; Emmaus, PA; (4); 67/466; VP Exploring; German Clb; Hon Roll; Jr NHS; NHS; Athltc Trnr 85; Stck Mrkt Clb 87; Frostburg ST Coll; Wldlf Mgmt.

SCHAMRIS, JOLIE; Bishop Guilfoyle HS; Altoona, PA; (3); German Clb; Hosp Aide; Library Aide; Service Clb; Vllybl; Penn ST; Bus.

SCHANE, TAMMY; N Pocono HS; Moscow, PA; (4); 4/240; Ski Clb; Chorus; Nwsp Stf; Yrbk Ed-Chief; Yrbk Stf; Lit Mag; Rep Stu Cncl; High Hon Roll; NHS; Jrnlsm.

SCHANELY, KEVIN; Souderton Area HS; Telford, PA; (3); Church Yth Grp; Spanish Clb; Chorus; Church Choir; Orch; School Musical; School Play; Variety Show; Nwsp Stf; Hon Roll; Temple U; Televeision-Film.

SCHANK, RACHEL; Norwin SR HS; N Huntingdon, PA; (4); 196/556; Trs FHA; Lib Band; Church Choir; Concert Band; Jazz Band; Mrchg Band; Pep Band; Ltrd Band 84-87; Marching Bands Of Am 5 Mdls 8 Certs 84-87; Bradford Bus Schl; Comp Sec.

SCHANTZ, MELISSA; Emmaus HS; Wescosville, PA; (3); German Clb; Key Clb; SADD; Nwsp Rptr; Sec Jr Cls; Var L Cheerleading; Var L Trk; NHS; Pres Schlr; Mrktng.

SCHAPPELL, LISA; Hamburg Area HS; Hamburg, PA; (4); 39/154; German Clb; Sec Chorus; School Musical; Rep Jr Cls; Hon Roll; Acdmc Ltr Awd 85 & 86; Grmn Ntl Hnr Soc 86 & 87; Wldrnss Clb 84-87; Central PA Bus Schl; Trvl.

SCHAPPELL, TRICIA; Hamburg Area JR/Sr HS; Hamburg, PA; (3); 44/170; Trs Church Yth Grp; Pres VP FBLA; VP Ski Clb; Im Spanish Clb; Stu Cncl; Cheerleading; Fld Hcky; Gym; Trk; Hon Roll; Cmnctns.

SCHARBA, TRACI; Sharon SR HS; Sharon, PA; (4); 32/159; Spanish Clb; Ed Nwsp Ed-Chief; Rep Stu Cncl; Var Cheerleading; Hon Roll; Spanish NHS; Slippery Rock U.

SCHARDING, DAVID; Lewistown Area HS; Lewistown, PA; (2); Art Clb; Spanish Clb; Rptr Yrbk Stf; Off Soph Cls; Ftbl; Trk.

SCHARDT, CHRISTINE; Saltsburg JR SR HS; Saltsburg, PA; (3); DECA; Girl Scts; Hosp Aide; Chorus; High Hon Roll; Hon Roll; Zoolgst.

SCHATZ, KAREN; Elk County Christian HS; St Marys, PA; (4); Office Aide; Church Choir; Stat Bsktbl; Ftbl; JV Vllybl; Hon Roll; Howard M Keebler Schrlshp 87; Indiana U Of PA; Scndry Educ.

SCHAUB, RON; Fort Cherry HS; Washington, PA; (3); Drama Clb; Math Clb; Trs Science Clb; Ski Clb; Spanish Clb; SADD; Varsity Clb; Pres Frsh Cls; Var L Bsktbl; Var L Ftbl; Hgh Hon Roll 87; PTA Acdmc Awd 86; Hnrbl Mntn In Ftbl 86; Accntng.

SCHAUER, STACEY; Brandywine Heights HS; Topton, PA; (4); Q&S; Quiz Bowl; Band; Concert Band; Mrchg Band; Nwsp Sprt Ed; Yrbk Rptr; Fld Hcky; NHS; Hosp Aide; Pres Acad Ftns Awds Pgm Awd 87; Ursinus Coll; Intl Relations.

SCHAUFELBERGER, LYNN; Plymouth-Whitemarsh HS; Norristown, PA; (3); Aud/Vis; SADD; Nwsp Ed-Chief; Nwsp Rptr; Yrbk Stf; Powder Puff Ftbl; Hon Roll; Jrnlsm.

SCHAUPP, BILL; West Allegheny HS; Oakdale, PA; (2); 26/200; Spanish Clb; Chorus; Var Crs Cntry; Var Trk; Hon Roll; U Of Pittsburg; Vet.

SCHAUT, LUCY; St Marys HS; Saint Marys, PA; (4); Hosp Aide; Yrbk Phtg; Yrbk Stf; Cheerleading; Hon Roll; NHS; Pres Schlr; Penn ST U; Admin Just.

SCHAUT, WILLIAM; St Marys Area HS; St Marys, PA; (3); 43/248; Swmmng; Vllybl; Wt Lftg; Hon Roll; Penn ST; Physcs.

SCHEERS, JODI; West Allegheny SR HS; Oakdale, PA; (3); Quiz Bowl; Scholastic Bowl; Chorus; Color Guard; Lit Mag; Powder Puff Ftbl; Hon Roll; Jr NHS; Nrsng.

SCHEIN, ELLEN; Wyoming Seminary HS; Harrisburg, PA; (2); Red Cross Aide; Ski Clb; SADD; Temple Yth Grp; Chorus; School Musical; School Play; Rep Frsh Cls; Rep Stu Cncl; Var Cheerleading; Cnty Piano Compttn 1st 86; Music.

SCHEIRER, ERIC; Peters Township HS; Mcmurray, PA; (2); Hon Roll; CMU; Chem Engrng.

SCHEITHAUER, MARIA; Our Lady Of Lourdes Regional HS; Marion Heights, PA; (4); 26/88; AFS; Church Yth Grp; Library Aide; Pep Clb; Spanish Clb; Stage Crew; Yrbk Stf; Hon Roll; Cthlc Hgh Alumni Schlrshp 87; Lock Haven U; Early Elem Ed.

SCHELL, ELIZABETH; Clearfield Area HS; Clearfield, PA; (4); 60/292; Spanish Clb; SADD; Chorus; Concert Band; Orch; Var Stat Diving; Var Sec Mat Maids; Var Swmmng; Var Twrlr; High Hon Roll; Elizabethtown Coll.

SCHELL, ERIKA; Susquehanna Community HS; Susquehanna, PA; (3); Church Yth Grp; Band; Chorus; Drm Mjr(t); Jazz Band; Symp Band; Rep Stu Cncl; Capt Powder Puff Ftbl; Hon Roll; Drama Clb; Dist Chorus 6th Chr 86; Dist Band 86; Rgnl Band 87; Music Educ.

SCHELL, JULIE; Sharpsville HS; Clark, PA; (3); Camera Clb; Chess Clb; SADD; Nwsp Stf; Pres Jr Cls; Stu Cncl; JV Var Cheerleading; Nrs.

SCHELL, MARIA; Blue Mountain HS; Orwigsburg, PA; (1).

SCHELL, STEPHANIE; Berwick Area HS; Nescopeck, PA; (4); Drama Clb; VP Key Clb; Library Aide; Chorus; School Play; Nwsp Rptr; Nwsp Stf; Yrbk Phtg; Yrbk Stf; Var Capt Sftbl; CA U Of PA; Grpch Comm.

SCHELLHAMER, CHRIS D; Northwestern Lehigh HS; Slatington, PA; (4); 36/160; Am Leg Boys St; Capt L Bsbl; Capt L Bsktbl; L Crs Cntry; High Hon Roll; JC Awd; Jaycees-Athltc Schlrshp-Bsktbl 87; Ed Assoc-Tchr Schlrshp 87; High Hnrs-Grmn Stu 87; E Stroudsburg U; Sec Ed.

SCHELLHAMER, KAREN; Northwestern Le High HS; New Tripoli, PA; (4); 7/167; Ski Clb; Chorus; Fld Hcky; Stat Ftbl; Sftbl; High Hon Roll; NHS; Pres Schlr; NWL Schlrshp Fnd Awd 87; Pres Schlr Awd 87; Kutztown U; Med Tech.

SCHELLY, JESSICA L; Parkland HS; Allentown, PA; (3); Drama Clb; German Clb; Leo Clb; Library Aide; SADD; Stat Bsktbl; Stat Trk; Hon Roll; Graphc Desgn.

SCHELTER, DENISE; Towanda Area HS; Towanda, PA; (3); 11/175; French Clb; Band; Chorus; Concert Band; Mrchg Band; Var Swmmng; Hon Roll; NHS.

SCHEMM, JODI; West Scranton HS; Scranton, PA; (3); 62/262; Hosp Aide; Letterman Clb; Speech Tm; Thesps; Stu Cncl; L Sftbl; Hon Roll; HS Dist PTA Rflctns-4th Pl 84-85; HS Dist PTA Rflctns ST-3RD Pl 84-85; Educ.

SCHEMPP, LINDA; Abraham Lincoln HS; Philadelphia, PA; (3); Cmnty Wkr; Red Cross Aide; Service Clb; Spanish Clb; SADD; School Play; Yrbk Stf; Var Badmtn; Var Gym; Hon Roll; All Pblc Awd Gym 87; Delaware Valley Coll; Hrtcltr.

SCHENCK, BETH; Milton Area SR HS; New Columbia, PA; (4); 30/230; Pres Church Yth Grp; Latin Clb; Band; Church Choir; Color Guard; Concert Band; Mrchg Band; Yrbk Stf; Stu Cncl; Powder Puff Ftbl; Dreiffus Schlrshp 87; Geisinger Schl Nrsng; RN.

SCHENCK, GREGORY; Henderson HS; W Chester, PA; (3); Boy Scts; Nwsp Phtg; Nwsp Stf; Yrbk Phtg; Yrbk Stf; Rep Stu Cncl; JV Lcrss; JV Socr; JV Wrstlng; Hon Roll; PA ST; Frstry.

SCHENCK, TRACY; Bald Eagle Nittany HS; Mill Hall, PA; (3); Sec Trs 4-H; Variety Show; Var JV Cheerleading; Var L Sftbl; Cit Awd; 4-H Awd; Teachers Aide; Nwsp Rptr; L Bsktbl; Elctd Rep Clntn Cnty 4-H 87; USAF; Polc.

SCHENDLER, PAULA; Seneca HS; Erie, PA; (3); 1/160; Computer Clb; Drill Tm; Mrchg Band; School Musical; Pom Pon; High Hon Roll; NHS; PA Free Enterprise Wk 887; Amelia Earhart-Ldrshp Awd 87; Clemson U; Arch.

SCHENEIDER, BRETT; Upper Moreland HS; Hatboro, PA; (3); 35/300; Key Clb; Rep Stu Cncl; Var Bsbl; Var Bowling; Var Capt Socr; High Hon Roll; Med.

SCHENKE, TODD; Pequa Valley HS; Paradise, PA; (3); AFS; Drama Clb; Band; Trs Chorus; Concert Band; Mrchg Band; School Musical; School Play; Stage Crew; Yrbk Stf; Hstry.

SCHENKER, JEFFREY; Cathedral Prep; Erie, PA; (3); 55/193; Art Clb; Cmnty Wkr; Spanish Clb; Wt Lftg; Hon Roll; Penn ST; Sci.

SCHERBA, TAMMY; West Allegheny HS; Coraopolis, PA; (3); JA; Office Aide; Spanish Clb; Yrbk Stf; Powder Puff Ftbl; IUP; Travel.

SCHERER III, GORDON; Lehighton Area HS; Lehighton, PA; (4); 13/233; Boy Scts; Church Yth Grp; Chorus; School Play; Yrbk Stf; Crs Cntry; Trk; Ntl Merit Ltr; PA ST U; Elec Engr.

SCHERER, HELEN; Plymouth-Whitemarsh HS; Plymough Mtg, PA; (3); Church Yth Grp; SADD; Color Guard; Nwsp Rptr; Yrbk Stf; Hon Roll; PA Free Entrprs Wk 87.

SCHERER, KIMBERLY; Nazareth SR HS; Bethlehem, PA; (4); 25/236; Hosp Aide; Concert Band; Jazz Band; Mrchg Band; Swing Chorus; High Hon Roll; Art Clb; Church Yth Grp; Drama Clb; Stu Dir & Band Pres; Schlstc Scrmmg Tm; Dist & Rgnl Band; Dist Chorus; Indiana U Of PA; Nrsg.

SCHERER, WILLIAM; Conemaugh Vly JR SR HS; Johnstown, PA; (4); 13/118; Church Yth Grp; Drama Clb; JA; Office Aide; Church Choir; Stage Crew; Yrbk Stf; Golf; NHS; Pres Acad Fitness Awd 87; Air Force; Firefighter.

SCHERFEL, WILLIAM; Ambridge Area HS; Ambridge, PA; (2); VP Church Yth Grp; Pep Clb; Spanish Clb; SADD; Off Soph Cls; Stu Cncl; Bsbl; Bsktbl; Ftbl; Hon Roll; U Of Pittsburgh; Dnstry.

SCHERRAH, DAWN; Riverview HS; Verona, PA; (3); 9/112; Church Yth Grp; Flag Corp; Nwsp Stf; Yrbk Stf; Stat Trk; High Hon Roll; Prfct Atten Awd; Bus.

SCHEUING, RODGER; Donegal HS; Maytown, PA; (2); Band; Jazz Band; Im Socr; JV Trk; Millersville U; Drftng.

SCHEURING, LISA; Shaler HS; Pittsburgh, PA; (4); 19/495; Office Aide; Drill Tm; Mrchg Band; Symp Band; Nwsp Rptr; Stu Cncl; High Hon Roll; NHS; Pres Spanish NHS; Amer Assoctn Of Teachers Of Spanish & Portuguese-Bronze Medal 87; U Of Pittsburgh; Nrsng.

SCHIANO, JEANINE; Delaware Valley HS; Dingmans Ferry, PA; (3); 22/165; Church Yth Grp; Ski Clb; Band; Chorus; Mrchg Band; Var JV Fld Hcky; Var JV Sftbl; Law.

SCHIAVI, MICHAEL; Chartiers Valley HS; Pittsburgh, PA; (4); 1/303; Drama Clb; Library Aide; Pep Clb; Trs Thesps; School Musical; School Play; Stage Crew; High Hon Roll; NHS; Ntl Merit Ltr; Prsdntl Schlrshp Amrcn U, John Marshall Schlrshp Franklin & Marshall Coll 87; The American U; Spnsh Diplmt.

SCHICKLEY, KATHLEEN; Mt Carmel Area JR/Sr HS; Mt Carmel, PA; (3); #11 In Class; FNA; Key Clb; Pep Clb; Spanish Clb; Speech Tm; Var L Sftbl; Var L Trk; High Hon Roll; Hon Roll; NHS.

SCHICKLING, KIMBERLY; St Huberts HS; Philadelphia, PA; (3); Aud/Vis; Church Yth Grp; French Clb; Hosp Aide; Office Aide; SADD; Stage Crew; Gym; Trk; Chem.

SCHIEFER, LISA; Crestwood HS; Mountain Top, PA; (3); 8/177; Math Clb; Science Clb; Ski Clb; VP Soph Cls; Pres Jr Cls; JV Capt Cheerleading; Fld Hcky; Trk; High Hon Roll; Jr NHS.

SCHIELA, MICHELE; South Park HS; Library, PA; (3); Drama Clb; Ski Clb; Color Guard; Rep Frsh Cls; High Hon Roll; Hon Roll; Tchr.

SCHIELDS, COLLEEN; Red Lion Area SR HS; Red Lion, PA; (3); 14/342; Pres Church Yth Grp; Exploring; Hosp Aide; Concert Band; Mrchg Band; Symp Band; High Hon Roll; Hon Roll; NHS; Lebanon Vly Coll Yth Schlrs Inst 87; RN.

SCHIFANO, CHRIS; Old Forge HS; Old Forge, PA; (3); French Clb; Ski Clb; Cheerleading; Hon Roll.

SCHILDT, BETTY; Faith Christian Schl; Columbia, NJ; (3); 2/15; Art Clb; Teachers Aide; Church Choir; Trs Frsh Cls; High Hon Roll; Hon Roll; Hnr Rl 84-87; Erly Chldhd Ed.

SCHILL, VALERIE; Clarion-Limestone Area HS; Clarion, PA; (2); 1/94; Sec French Clb; Sec SADD; Chorus; Madrigals; Rep Soph Cls; Rep Stu Cncl; High Hon Roll; Hon Roll; NHS; Hgh Schltc Awd Svngs Bond 85-86; Miss PA Amer Coed Pgnt 3rd Rnnrup 87; Achvt Rbbns Sci, Socl Stds 86; Clarion U; Comp Pgmmr.

SCHILLER, ERIC; Plum SR HS; Pittsburgh, PA; (3); 26/410; Ftbl; High Hon Roll; NHS; Anthplgy.

SCHILLER, ERIN; South Park HS; Library, PA; (3); 20/200; German Clb; JA; Ski Clb; Wt Lftg; High Hon Roll; Penn St U; Bus.

SCHILLING, ALICE; Marian Catholic HS; Coaldale, PA; (4); 10/115; Service Clb; SADD; School Play; Yrbk Ed-Chief; High Hon Roll; NHS; Spanish NHS; 1st Hnrs 83-87; Susquehanna U Hnrs Prog 87; Susquehanna U; Biomed Engrng.

SCHILLING, DAWN; Blacklick Valley JR-SR HS; Belsano, PA; (3); 9/100; Library Aide; NFL; Spanish Clb; Varsity Clb; Trk; High Hon Roll; Presidential Acdmc Fitness Awd 84; Civil Engineer.

SCHIMEK, RICHARD; Valley Forge Military Acad; Lansdale, PA; (3); Aud/Vis; Chess Clb; German Clb; ROTC; Ski Clb; School Musical; School Play; Nwsp Rptr; High Hon Roll; Hon Roll; Temple; Bus.

SCHIMPF, MARIANNE; Bishop Conwell HS; Croydon, PA; (3); 54/277; French Clb; Pep Clb; Variety Show; Var Socr; Hon Roll; Mst Otstndng 86-87; Sci.

SCHINOSI, KIRK; South Park HS; Library, PA; (3); 42/223; Ski Clb; Var Capt Ftbl; Wt Lftg; Hon Roll.

SCHIPANI, ESTHER A; William Tennent S HS; Warminster, PA; (4); 38/580; Cmnty Wkr; Key Clb; Capt Scholastic Bowl; Concert Band; High Hon Roll; NHS; Rotary Awd; Voice Dem Awd; Church Yth Grp; Computer Clb; Medal Schlrshp Millersville U 87; Gould Fountn Schlrshp 87; William Tennent Natl Hnr Scty Awd 87; Millersville U; Cmmnctns.

SCHIRATO, BECKY; Central Dauphin HS; Hummelstown, PA; (3); 2/369; Church Yth Grp; Church Choir; Concert Band; Mrchg Band; High Hon Roll; NHS; Ntl Merit Ltr; PA Gov Schl Sci 87; Capital Area Sci & Engr Fair Awd 85; Pres Acad Ftns Awd 85; Sci.

SCHIRF, ANNE; Altoona Area HS; Altoona, PA; (3); VICA; Chorus; JV Crs Cntry; JV Trk; Williamsport Area CC; Food.

SCHIRF, ROBERT; Cambria Heights SR HS; Loretto, PA; (3); 13/181; Co-Capt Ftbl; Var Wt Lftg; Hon Roll; NHS; NEDT Awd; Cmnty Wkr; Chorus; JV Trk; Sci Awd Amer Chem Socty Tst 87; Sprts Med.

SCHITTLER, LINDA; Brandywine Heights HS; Alburtis, PA; (4); Hosp Aide; Pep Clb; Chorus; Color Guard; Flag Corp; Reading Hosp Schl Nrsng.

SCHIVELY, NOEL; Loyalsock Township HS; Williamsport, PA; (3); 6/120; Rep French Clb; Drm Mjr(t); VP Mrchg Band; School Musical; Nwsp Ed-Chief; Trk; NHS; Ntl Merit Ltr; Chorus; VP Concert Band; PA Gov Schl Intl Stds 87; Lewis And SR Div Ltl Leag Bsbl, Gold Key Awd & 4th Pl Natl Schlr Wrtng 85; Anthro.

SCHJODT, KIM; Chambersburg Area SR HS; Chambersburg, PA; (2); AFS; French Clb; Library Aide; Pep Clb; Band; Flag Corp; Hon Roll; PA ST U; Bus.

SCHLACK, BOBBI MARIE; Shenandoah Valley JR-SR HS; Shenandoah, PA; (4); 5/108; Debate Tm; French Clb; Office Aide; Pep Clb; Stage Crew; Variety Show; Nwsp Phtg; Nwsp Stf; Yrbk Phtg; Yrbk Stf; Mrtry Sci.

SCHLAKE, HEIDI; Nazareth Area SR HS; Nazareth, PA; (3); 8/280; Computer Clb; Key Clb; Band; Concert Band; Jazz Band; Mrchg Band; Yrbk Stf; High Hon Roll; Hon Roll; NHS.

SCHLAPPICH, SUEANN; Conrad Weiser HS; Robesonia, PA; (2); 1/163; Church Yth Grp; Drama Clb; FBLA; JCL; Key Clb; Band; Chorus; School Musical; School Play; Rep Frsh Cls; Albright Schlrshp Clg Opprtnty Engl & Math 87; Pre-Med.

SCHLECHT, THERESA; Jim Thorpe SR HS; Jim Thorpe, PA; (3); 14/92; FHA; Yrbk Sprt Ed; Rep Stu Cncl; Var Bsktbl; Var Sftbl; Var Vllybl; Hon Roll; Natl Sci Merit Awd 86; Med Tech.

SCHLEGEL, BRENDA; Oley Valley HS; Oley, PA; (3); 18/135; Camp Fr Inc; Quiz Bowl; Chorus; School Musical; Nwsp Ed-Chief; Var L Crs Cntry; JV Fld Hcky; Var L Trk; Hon Roll; NHS; Animal Hlth Tech.

SCHLEGEL, CHRISTOPHER; Devon Prep Schl; Ardmore, PA; (4); Drama Clb; Hosp Aide; Pres Chorus; School Musical; School Play; Nwsp Stf; Yrbk Stf; Rep Frsh Cls; Rep Jr Cls; Var L Bsbl; Albright Coll Trustee Schlrshp 87; Villanova Univ; Bio.

SCHLEGEL, DENISE; Cocalico SR HS; Denver, PA; (4); 3/175; Drama Clb; FTA; Quiz Bowl; Chorus; School Play; High Hon Roll; Trs NHS; Ntl Merit SF; Church Yth Grp; Computer Clb; Denver Fair Queen 86; Presdntl Dept Schlrshp York Coll 87; Reinholds Lions Club Sci Schlrshp 87; York Coll; Bio.

SCHLEGEL, EDWARD; Shamokin Area HS; Shamokin, PA; (2); Debate Tm; Drama Clb; Speech Tm; SADD; Band; Concert Band; Mrchg Band; Orch; School Play; Rep Soph Cls; Bst Actr 87; Top 10 Radio Anncr PA HS Spch Leag 87; Penn ST; Music Tchr.

SCHLEGEL, HOLLY J; Northeastern HS; Manchester, PA; (4); 5/162; Dance Clb; FBLA; Teachers Aide; Yrbk Rptr; Lit Mag; Var L Bsktbl; Var Capt Sftbl; High Hon Roll; NHS; Pres Schlr; Acad All Star 87; Outstndg Yrbk Awd 87; York Coll; Radio.

SCHLEGEL, JENNIFER; Pen Argyl Area SR HS; Nazareth, PA; (3); Cmnty Wkr; German Clb; Math Clb; Ski Clb; Orch; Pres Jr Cls; Var L Trk; Hon Roll; Acctg.

SCHLEGEL, SANDRA; Fleetwood Area HS; Fleetwood, PA; (4); 6/116; Trs Band; Chorus; Concert Band; Mrchg Band; Stage Crew; Trs Stu Cncl; JV Capt Bsktbl; Var Capt Tennis; NHS; USNLMA US Natl Ldrshp Mrt Awd Wnr 86; MVP Tnns Awd Wnnr 85-86.

SCHLEGEL, TINA; Northampton SR HS; Northampton, PA; (4); Dance Clb; Office Aide; Yrbk Stf; Pres Soph Cls; Trs Jr Cls; Trs Sr Cls; Stu Cncl; Trk; Hon Roll; Hmcmng Queen 87; Jck Frst Parade Queen 86-87; Wst Chstr U; Crmnl Jstc.

SCHLEICHER, NANCI; William Allen HS; Allentown, PA; (3); Sec Church Yth Grp; Bloomsburg Coll; Bus.

SCHLEIFER, GRETCHEN; Tunkhannock HS; Tunkhannock, PA; (3); 27/320; Drama Clb; Chorus; School Musical; School Play; Variety Show; Hon Roll; Recrdng Engr.

SCHLEIG, LISA ANN; Council Rock HS; Churchville, PA; (3); 222/985; Church Yth Grp; Drama Clb; Intnl Clb; Spanish Clb; Stage Crew; Yrbk Rptr; Yrbk Stf; Im Powder Puff Ftbl; Hon Roll; HS Sock N Buskin Clb Awd 85-86; Extnsv Invlvmnt Frgn Exchng Pgm 87; Frgn Lang.

SCHLEITER, JENNIFER; Ambridge HS; Baden, PA; (3); Church Yth Grp; German Clb; Pep Clb; Band; Chorus; Concert Band; Mrchg Band; Pep Band; Off Jr Cls; Hon Roll; Penn ST U; Secondary Educ.

SCHLENER, KIMBERLY A; Saucon Vly SR HS; Bethlehem, PA; (4); Church Yth Grp; French Clb; Hosp Aide; Red Cross Aide; Band; Church Choir; Concert Band; Mrchg Band; Hon Roll; Amrcn Lgn Awd Essay 82-83; Penn ST; Vet.

SCHLEPPY, LIZ; Stroudsburg HS; Sciota, PA; (2); Sec Pres Church Yth Grp; French Clb; Spanish Clb; Pres SADD; Varsity Clb; Sec Stu Cncl; JV Bsktbl; JV Fld Hcky; L Var Sftbl; Hon Roll; Drug/Alcohol Task Force 87; IV 20 Stu Forum 87; Fshn Mrchndsng.

SCHLIEP, MELINDA; Kennedy Christian HS; Sharon, PA; (3); 29/96; Art Clb; French Clb; Yrbk Stf; Var L Bsktbl; High Hon Roll; Mercer Cnty Ath Cnfrnc 2nd Team 86-87; Dist 10 Champ Cls A 87; NE Tourn Champ 86; Mercyhurst Coll; Fshn Mrchndsng.

SCHLIEPER, GRETCHEN; Faith Community Christian Schl; Finleyville, PA; (3); 5/28; French Clb; Pep Clb; Science Clb; Ski Clb; School Play; Rep Soph Cls; Var Cheerleading; Im Vllybl; High Hon Roll; Bio Acdmc Awd 85; PTA Art Awds 76,78,80; Awd Of Cndct & Bhvr 82,84,86; CA U Of PA; Bio.

SCHLIMM II, JOHN; Elk County Christian HS; St Marys, PA; (1); 8/84; Hosp Aide; Intnl Clb; SADD; Crs Cntry; Trk; Hon Roll; U Of CA; Mdcn.

SCHLOSS, JUDEANNE; Cardinal O Hara HS; Eddystone, PA; (4); 112/776; Computer Clb; Dance Clb; Office Aide; School Musical; School Play; Nwsp Stf; Yrbk Stf; High Hon Roll; 2nd Hnrs 85-87; Widener U; Chem Engnrng.

SCHLOSSBERG, MICHAEL; Louis E Dieruff HS; Allentown, PA; (2); Ski Clb; Music.

SCHLOSSER, DAWN; Souderton Area HS; Telford, PA; (3); Church Yth Grp; Yrbk Stf; JV Lcrss; Hon Roll; NHS; Pres Schlr; Occup Thrpy.

SCHLOSSER, DONIA; East Pennsboro HS; Mechanicsburg, PA; (3); Art Clb; Ski Clb; JV Bsktbl; Stat Trk; Hon Roll; Millersville U; Comp Sci.

SCHLOSSER, TINA; Cambridge Springs HS; Cambridge Spgs, PA; (2); 17/99; Church Yth Grp; JA; Stat Bsktbl; Score Keeper; Hon Roll; JA Company Yr Awd 87; JA Achvr Awd 87; KY Chrstn Coll; Elem Ed.

SCHLOTTER, JIM; Council Rock HS; Ivyland, PA; (2); Var Bsbl; JV Bsktbl; High Hon Roll; Hon Roll; Schlstc Awd Excel Vrsty Athltcs 87; Bucks Cnty Courier Tms Gldn 14 Bsbl 87; U Of NC; Mech Engr.

SCHLOTTER, LAUREN; East Allegheny HS; N Versailles, PA; (4); 34/213; Pres Church Yth Grp; Sec Band; Sec Concert Band; Sec Mrchg Band; Orch; School Musical; Sr Cls; Var Trk; Hon Roll; NHS; Mon-Yough Sci Awd-2nd & 3rd Pls; Boyce CC; Med.

SCHMADER, AMY; Warren Area HS; Russell, PA; (3); German Clb; Teachers Aide; Color Guard; Yrbk Stf; Bsktbl; Hon Roll; Manag.

SCHMADER, BARBARA; North Clarion HS; Lucinda, PA; (3); Spanish Clb; VP Frsh Cls; Var JV Bsktbl; L Trk; Hon Roll; Clarion U; Accntng.

SCHMADER, CASEY; North Clarion HS; Lucinda, PA; (3); Bsktbl; Socr; Hon Roll; Prfct Atten Awd; Clarion U; Comp Sci.

SCHMADER, DEANNA; North Clarion JR SR HS; Lucinda, PA; (3); Spanish Clb; Var L Bsktbl; Trk; Hon Roll; NHS; NEDT Awd; Psych.

SCHMADER, DEBBIE; North Clarion HS; Lucinda, PA; (4); 3/83; Spanish Clb; Nwsp Rptr; Nwsp Stf; Yrbk Ed-Chief; Yrbk Stf; Stat Bsktbl; Cheerleading; JV Var Trk; Hon Roll; NHS; Bus Awd Acad Excllnce Awd 87; Big E Awd 87; Clarion U; Bus.

SCHMADER, GRETTA; Clarion Area HS; Shippenville, PA; (4); 46/100; Ski Clb; Band; Chorus; Concert Band; Mrchg Band; Pep Band; Var L Bsktbl; Stat Var Trk; Vllybl; Hon Roll; Most Valuable Defensive Plyr-Bsktbl; Kent ST U; Fashion Merch.

SCHMEHL, AMY; Hempfield HS; Lancaster, PA; (3); Stat Bsktbl; JV Fld Hcky; Var Letterman Clb; Hon Roll.

SCHMELDER, MIKE; Greencastle-Antrim HS; Waynesboro, PA; (3); 15/163; CAP; Drama Clb; Math Tm; School Play; Pres Soph Cls; JV Socr; JV Trk; Hon Roll; Ntl Merit SF; Billy Mitchell Awd 86; Worchester Polytech Inst; Comp.

SCHMELZ, ERIC; Western Beaver HS; Industry, PA; (3); Band; Concert Band; Jazz Band; Mrchg Band; Pep Band; Im Ftbl; High Hon Roll; Hon Roll; NHS; Schl Beautification Awd 87; Engrng.

SCHMID, TRACEY; Knoch JR/Sr HS; Butler, PA; (4); 5/283; FBLA; Band; Jazz Band; School Musical; Stage Crew; NHS; Pres Schlr; Church Yth Grp; Drama Clb; Mrchg Band; Honors Band 85-87; Rgnl Band 86-87; Boston Coll Ex 86; Clarion U Of PA; Accntng.

SCHMIDT, BILL; Stroudsburg HS; East Stroudsburg, PA; (3); 13/266; Boys Clb Am; Scholastic Bowl; Science Clb; Varsity Clb; School Musical; Stu Cncl; Var Diving; JV Ftbl; Var Trk; High Hon Roll; Woodmen Of World Hist Awd 84; Scout Of Yr 84.

SCHMIDT, CATHY; Central Bucks HS West; Chalfont, PA; (3); 79/481; JV Bsktbl; Var Crs Cntry; High Hon Roll; Hon Roll; Crs Cntry Bux-Mont Champs 85.

SCHMIDT, DEBBIE; Fort Cherry HS; Mc Donald, PA; (4); 16/112; Computer Clb; Drama Clb; Science Clb; Ski Clb; Varsity Clb; Chorus; Drill Tm; Yrbk Phtg; NHS; Pharmacy.

SCHMIDT, DOUGLAS; Garnet Valley HS; Glen Mills, PA; (4); 1/152; Pres Church Yth Grp; Letterman Clb; Model UN; Quiz Bowl; Ski Clb; Band; JV Bsktbl; Var Socr; Hon Roll; NHS; MIT; Math.

SCHMIDT, ERIC WILLIAM; Hempfield HS; Manheim, PA; (4); 71/401; Band; Concert Band; Mrchg Band; Hon Roll; Penn ST U; Bus Admin.

SCHMIDT, ERIK; St Francis Prep HS; Larchmont, NY; (3); 2/24; Art Clb; Drama Clb; Exploring; Ski Clb; School Musical; School Play; Pres Stu Cncl; Ftbl; Socr; Wrstlng.

SCHMIDT, JAMES W; Central SR HS; York, PA; (3); Trs Exploring; Ski Clb; Mrchg Band; School Musical; School Play; Yrbk Stf; High Hon Roll; NHS; Ntl Merit Ltr; Opt Clb Awd.

SCHMIDT, JEANNINE ANNE; Cambridge Springs HS; Conneautville, PA; (4); 29/104; Church Yth Grp; 4-H; Pep Clb; Spanish Clb; SADD; Band; Church Choir; Concert Band; Mrchg Band; Pep Band; Amer Legion Hnr For Acad 84; Music Awd 87; Bishop Watson Schlrshp 87; Mercyhurst Coll; Htl Rstrnt Mgr.

SCHMIDT, JOHN; Lakeland JR/Sr HS; Clarks Summit, PA; (4); Church Yth Grp; French Clb; JA; Band; Nwsp Rptr; Var L Bsbl; Ftbl; Hon Roll; PA ST U; Commnctns.

SCHMIDT, JULIE; Lower Moreland HS; Huntingdon Valley, PA; (3); Church Yth Grp; Drama Clb; SADD; Chorus; Madrigals; School Musical; School Play; Variety Show; Stat L Bsktbl; Hon Roll.

SCHMIDT, KARIN; Upper St Clair HS; Pittsburgh, PA; (3); 16/456; Cmnty Wkr; German Clb; Q&S; Ed Yrbk Stf; High Hon Roll; Hon Roll; NHS; Pres Schlr; Magna Cum Laude Natl Latin Exam 87; Acad Fitness Awd-Lttr 87; Acad Achvt Awd In Law Studies 87.

SCHMIDT, KATHRYN; Montour HS; Mckees Rocks, PA; (2); Church Yth Grp; Library Aide; Concert Band; Mrchg Band; Yrbk Stf; High Hon Roll; Hon Roll; Jrnlsm.

SCHMIDT, KRISTEN; State Clg Area Intermediate HS; State College, PA; (1); 3/476; Church Yth Grp; Church Choir; School Musical; Var Trk; Cit Awd; High Hon Roll; Bio & German Awd 87; Arch.

SCHMIDT, KRISTINE; Greensburg Salem HS; Greensburg, PA; (2); 1/325; Art Clb; Exploring; German Clb; Hosp Aide; Ski Clb; Nwsp Stf; JV Bsktbl; Jr NHS; Nwsp Rptr; High Hon Roll; Ziskino Mem Awd For Hghst Acad Achiev 86; Dist Acad Achiev Awd 86; Math.

SCHMIDT, LORY; Freedom HS; Bethlehem, PA; (3); 118/509; Church Yth Grp; Hosp Aide; Chorus; Hon Roll; St Lukes Schl Nrsng; Nrsng.

SCHMIDT, MARISA; Upper Darby HS; Drexel Hill, PA; (4); 57/590; Cmnty Wkr; Spanish Clb; Orch; School Musical; Yrbk Rptr; Trk; Hon Roll; NHS; East Stroudsburg U; Bus.

SCHMIDT, MARK; Homer-Center HS; Coral, PA; (3); Varsity Clb; JV Ftbl; JV Wt Lftg; High Hon Roll; Hon Roll.

SCHMIDT, REBECCA ANNE; Cambridge Springs HS; Saegertown, PA; (3); 32/109; Key Clb; Pep Clb; VP Spanish Clb; SADD; VP Jr Cls; Var L Sftbl; Cit Awd; Church Yth Grp; Computer Clb; 4-H; Hmcmng Princess 86; 1st Team All-Co Vlybl Plyr 86; 2nd Team All-Co Bsktbl Plyr 86-87.

SCHMIDT, RENEE; Somerset Area SR HS; Somerset, PA; (3); 54/260; English Clb; Ski Clb; SADD; Varsity Clb; Band; Concert Band; Drm Mjr(t); Mrchg Band; Yrbk Stf; Off Stu Cncl; Pres Phy Ftns Awd 86-87; PA ST U; Liberal Arts.

SCHMIDT, ROBERT; Cambridge Springs HS; Saegertown, PA; (4); 33/100; Church Yth Grp; Computer Clb; 4-H; Pep Clb; Spanish Clb; SADD; Var Bsktbl; Var Ftbl; Var Vllybl; Im Wt Lftg; Homecoming Prince 85; All Cnty Ftbl 86; All Cnty Vllybl 87; Gannon U; Chem Engrng.

SCHMIDT, SHARON A; Cardinal Brennan HS; Ashland, PA; (3); German Clb; Chorus; Co-Capt Drill Tm; School Musical; Yrbk Stf; Bowling; Hon Roll; Varsity Letters Band, Varsity Singers 86-87; Beaver Coll; Physical Therapy.

SCHMIDT, SONNA; Warren County Christian Schl; Youngsville, PA; (2); Church Yth Grp; Chorus; Yrbk Bus Mgr; Stu Cncl; Bsktbl; Cheerleading; Crs Cntry; Sftbl; Trk; Vllybl; Educ.

SCHMIEDBERG, STEFAN; Norht Hills SR HS; Pittsburgh, PA; (3); 18/496; Debate Tm; Yrbk Ed-Chief; Rep Stu Cncl; Var L Socr; High Hon Roll; NHS; 1st Awd PA JR Acad Sci Rgnls 87; US Army Cert Achvt Sci 87; Engrng Physics.

SCHMIEG, RICK; Towanda Area HS; Towanda, PA; (4); Acpl Chr; Band; Chorus; Concert Band; Drm Mjr(t); Mrchg Band; Swing Chorus; Bowling; Towanda Music Soc Awd 87; Dir Awd In Music 86; US Navy; Comp Spclst.

SCHMITT JR, EDWARD; Corry Area HS; Corry, PA; (3); 9/223; Aud/Vis; Chess Clb; German Clb; Rep Jr Cls; High Hon Roll; German Hnr Scty; Friendship Connection; Meteorologist.

SCHMITT, ERIC; Highlands SR HS; Natrona Hts, PA; (4); 65/288; Bsktbl; Mgr(s); Score Keeper; Hon Roll; Pres Acad Awd 87; U Of Pittsburg; Engr.

SCHMITT, EUGENE V; Lancaster Catholic HS; Columbia, PA; (4); 74/190; Cmnty Wkr; OK ST U; Fire Protctn Engrng.

SCHMITT, JAMES; Father Judge HS; Philadelphia, PA; (3); 66/410; Latin Clb; Im Bsktbl; Im Ftbl; High Hon Roll; Hon Roll; Phila Clscl Soc Ltn Comp 85; Med.

SCHMITT, PAMELA; Technical Memorial HS; Erie, PA; (4); 23/324; Spanish Clb; SADD; Teachers Aide; VICA; Nwsp Phtg; Yrbk Phtg; Yrbk Rptr; Yrbk Stf; Hon Roll; Stu Mst Lkly Sccd 87; PA ST U; Rl Est.

SCHMITTLEIN, CLINTON S; Butler Area SR HS; Butler, PA; (3); Church Yth Grp; Exploring; Spanish Clb; Band; Concert Band; Mrchg Band; Symp Band; Trk; Hon Roll; Jr NHS; Physics.

SCHMITTLEIN II, KENNETH G; Butler SR HS; Butler, PA; (3); Church Yth Grp; Exploring; Spanish Clb; Band; Concert Band; Mrchg Band; Symp Band; Trk; Hon Roll; Jr NHS; Sci.

SCHMITZ, BECKIE; Trinity HS; Mechanicsburg, PA; (2); Pep Clb; Ski Clb; Spanish Clb; Stage Crew; Variety Show; Var Trk; Natl Ed Dvlpmnt Tsts Awd Super Prfrmnce 86; Psych.

SCHMITZGEBEL, JAY; Methacton HS; Collegeville, PA; (3); 29/381; Boy Scts; Spanish Clb; Pres Chorus; Pres Concert Band; Madrigals; Pres Mrchg Band; Swing Chorus; High Hon Roll; NHS.

SCHMONDIUK, RENAE; E Allegheny HS; Wall, PA; (4); 13/213; Ski Clb; Band; Yrbk Stf; Off Soph Cls; Off Jr Cls; Off Sr Cls; Off Stu Cncl; Twrlr; High Hon Roll; NHS; Washington & Jefferson; Pre-Med.

SCHMOOK, JEFFREY; Southmoreland HS; Scottdale, PA; (3); 28/224; Church Yth Grp; Letterman Clb; Spanish Clb; Rep Stu Cncl; Im Bsktbl; Ftbl; JV Golf; Im Socr; Im Vllybl; L Wrstlng; Accntng.

SCHMOUDER, LON; Liberty HS; Liberty, PA; (4); 2/42; Church Yth Grp; Pep Clb; School Musical; Stage Crew; Yrbk Stf; Var L Bsktbl; Var L Tennis; Cit Awd; DAR Awd; Hon Roll; Mansfield U.

SCHMOYER, DUANE; Middleburg HS; Middleburg, PA; (3); Chess Clb; Trs Church Yth Grp; Computer Clb; Varsity Clb; Sec Jr Cls; Pres Sr Cls; Var Socr; Var Wrstlng; Prfct Atten Awd.

SCHMOYER, JASON; Parkland HS; Allentown, PA; (3); 111/481; Chrmn Exploring; Sci.

SCHMOYER, JULIE; Emmaus HS; Emmaus, PA; (2); Dance Clb; Drama Clb; Spanish Clb; Chorus; School Musical; School Play; Variety Show; Stu Cncl; Hon Roll; Bruce Polster Talent Awd 86; Lock Ridge Park Talent Awd 86; Cmmnctns.

SCHMOYER, KIMBERLY ANNE; Liberty SR HS; Bethlehem, PA; (4); 53/434; Drama Clb; School Play; Stage Crew; Lit Mag; Hon Roll; Stage Arts Awd 87; NCACC; Phtgrphy.

SCHMOYER, ROBIN MELISSA; Lower Dauphin HS; Elizabethtown, PA; (4); 7/233; Sec Exploring; Hosp Aide; Spanish Clb; Rep Sr Cls; Stu Cncl; JV Fld Hcky; High Hon Roll; NHS; Pres Schlr; GAA; Outstndng Bus Stu Awds 85-87; M Simons Schlrshp 86-87; Goshen Coll.

SCHMUCK, BRIAN; Christian Schl Of York; Dover, PA; (2); Band; Chorus; Trs Frsh Cls; Trs Soph Cls; Var L Bsktbl; Var L Socr; Hon Roll; Communications.

SCHMUDE, ROBERT; Freeport HS; Sarver, PA; (3); 29/201; Hon Roll.

SCHMUTZLER, JEFFERY; Chambersburg Area SR HS; Chambersburg, PA; (2); Church Yth Grp; Computer Clb; Chorus; Off Stu Cncl; French Hon Soc; Hon Roll; Med.

SCHNABEL, LAURA; Peters Township HS; Bridgeville, PA; (3); Church Yth Grp; Dance Clb; Drill Tm; JV Cheerleading; Pom Pon; High Hon Roll; Hon Roll; Chld Dvlpmnt.

SCHNABEL II, RONALD; Fleetwood Area HS; Fleetwood, PA; (3); 13/104; Spanish Clb; Varsity Clb; JV Var Socr; Var L Tennis; High Hon Roll; Hon Roll; Sprtsmnshp 84-85; Rotry Cmp 87; US Naval Acad.

SCHNAITMAN, SUSAN; Western Wayne HS; Waymart, PA; (3); 20/200; Dance Clb; Drama Clb; Pep Clb; Ski Clb; Spanish Clb; School Musical; School Play; Cheerleading; Pom Pon; High Hon Roll; Sci.

SCHNALZER, MARYBETH; Bethlehem Catholic HS; Bethlehem, PA; (3); 101/236; Ski Clb; Im JV Cheerleading; Fld Hcky; Powder Puff Ftbl; Hon Roll; Bloomsburg; Bus.

SCHNECK, BRAD; Northampton SR HS; Northampton, PA; (2); Boy Scts; Church Yth Grp; DECA; Drama Clb; Exploring; Ed Nwsp Stf; 6th Pl DECA-GNRL Mrchndsng Dist Lvl 87; 2nd Pl DECA-GNRL Mrchndsng, Wrtn Knwldg, St Lvl 87; Penn ST; Bus.

SCHNECK, KURT L; Pine Grove Area HS; Pine Grove, PA; (3); 23/115; ROTC; Varsity Clb; Band; Stage Crew; Rep Frsh Cls; Rep Soph Cls; Rep Jr Cls; Ftbl; Wt Lftg; Wrstlng; 3rd Pl St Of PA Wrstlng 87; Co Cmmdr ROTC Pgm 87-88; Pres Phys Ftnss Awd 84 & 87; Advtg.

SCHNECK, TAMMY; Pine Grove Area HS; Pine Grove, PA; (3); Church Yth Grp; Ed Yrbk Stf; Hon Roll; NHS; Prfct Atten Awd; Bus Ed, Socl Stds, Hm Econ, Bio, Engl Achvt Awds 86-87.

SCHNECK, WENDY; William Allen HS; Allentown, PA; (3); 6/609; VP Church Yth Grp; German Clb; Hosp Aide; VP Band; Church Choir; Jazz Band; Orch; High Hon Roll; NHS; SADD; Amer Musical Fndtn Band Hnrs 85 & 86; Messiah Coll.

SCHNEE, KAREN; Lampeter-Strasburg HS; Lancaster, PA; (4); 12/145; Sec Church Yth Grp; Thesps; Band; Chorus; Madrigals; School Musical; Trk; Hon Roll; NHS; Pres Schlr; Pres Acad Ftns Awd 87; Cnty, Dist Chorus, Music Awds 87; Dist Bnd 87; Millersville U; Actg.

SCHNEEMAN, ANDREA; Bellefonte Area SR HS; Bellefonte, PA; (3); 1/211; Drama Clb; Model UN; School Musical; School Play; Stage Crew; Yrbk Ed-Chief; Yrbk Stf; Rep Frsh Cls; High Hon Roll; Hon Roll; Top Scorer In NEDT Test 86; PA Music Tchrs Assoc Superior Rtng ST Comp 86; Art.

SCHNEIDER, ANTHONY; Northeast Prep; Philadelphia, PA; (4); #1 In Class; Chess Clb; Math Clb; ROTC; High Hon Roll; Hon Roll; Aerosp Engrng.

SCHNEIDER, BRENDA; Springdale HS; Pittsburgh, PA; (3); 12/130; Exploring; Spanish Clb; SADD; Band; Concert Band; Drm Mjr(t); Mrchg Band; Pep Band; Capt Vllybl; High Hon Roll; Dentistry.

SCHNEIDER, CAROLYN; Cedar Crest HS; Lebanon, PA; (3); French Clb; JV Var Cheerleading; JV Fld Hcky; Hon Roll; Phy Therapy.

SCHNEIDER, GREG; St Marys Area HS; St Marys, PA; (4); 30/302; Var Bsbl; Pres Schlr; Du Bois PA ST U; Bus Admin.

SCHNEIDER, GRETCHEN; Fox Chapel Area HS; Pittsburgh, PA; (3); Church Yth Grp; Key Clb; Ski Clb; Trs Mrchg Band; Symp Band; Yrbk Ed-Chief; Var Rep Stu Cncl; Var JV Swmmng; High Hon Roll; NHS; Arch.

SCHNEIDER, HEATHER; Plymouth Whitemarsh HS; Lafayette Hill, PA; (4); 62/328; Aud/Vis; Hosp Aide; Lcrss; Twrlr; Hon Roll; Pres Schlr; Schl Brd Recgntn Cmnty Svc 87; Helen S Noonan Schlrshp 87; Prodcr/Anchr CITV Locl News 86-87; Kutztown U; Telecomms.

SCHNEIDER, LORETA J; Oil City Area SR HS; Oil City, PA; (4); 23/231; AFS; Varsity Clb; Chorus; Var L Bsktbl; Var L Crs Cntry; Var L Trk; Im Vllybl; Beverly Enterprise Schlrshp 87; Clarion U; Nrsng.

SCHNEIDER, MICHELLE; Mercyhurst Prep Schl; Harborcreek, PA; (4); 27/155; French Clb; Hosp Aide; Pres Spanish Clb; Yrbk Stf; Lit Mag; Cheerleading; Vllybl; Hon Roll; NHS; Penn ST Erie; Bus.

SCHNETZKA, TERESA; York County Area Vo Tech Schl; Brodbecks, PA; (4); 20/363; VICA; Yrbk Stf; NHS; JA; Fld Hcky; 2nd Pl Poster Cont For Handicppd 87; Rcvd Watch High Shop Grade 87; Sav Bond Commrcl Art Awd 87; Art Inst Ft Laudrdl; Vis Art.

SCHNOKE, LYNDA; Cedar Crest HS; Lebanon, PA; (4); Band; Concert Band; Jazz Band; Sec Mrchg Band; Pep Band; Indr Drmln 86-87; YEA 86-87; Astrnmy Clb 86-87; Millersville U; Engl.

SCHNORR, AMY; York Catholic HS; York, PA; (2); 1/169; Church Yth Grp; Hosp Aide; Pep Clb; Chorus; Rep Frsh Cls; Rep Soph Cls; Rep Stu Cncl; JV Capt Bsktbl; Var L Trk; High Hon Roll.

SCHNUR, JOANN; Cardinal Dougherty HS; Philadelphia, PA; (3); Church Yth Grp; JA; Stage Crew; Hon Roll; Law.

SCHOBERT, GWYN; The Alternative Program; Grand Forks, ND; (3); French Clb; German Clb; Thesps; Orch; School Musical; School Play; Stage Crew; Lit Mag; Hon Roll; Ntl Merit Ltr; Frgn Lang Olymps Frnch III & IV Schlrshp & Gold Mdl 85-86; 1st Pl Germn II ST Lang Arts Fest 85; Penn ST U; Modern Lang.

SCHOCK, CHERYL; Carlisle SR HS; Carlisle, PA; (3); 53/434; Band; Chorus; Concert Band; Mrchg Band; School Musical; Hon Roll; Prfct Atten Awd; Cert Excllnc Fedrtn Allnces 85-86.

SCHOCK, MARCINE ANN; Charleroi Area JR SR HS; N Charlaroi, PA; (4); FBLA; Library Aide; Office Aide; IN U Of PA; Accntng.

SCHOEN, ERIKA; Eastern York JR-SR HS; Wrightsville, PA; (3); Library Aide; SADD; Yrbk Rptr; Yrbk Stf; JV Vllybl; High Hon Roll; Hon Roll; Camera Clb; Computer Clb; Drama Clb; Millersville U; Bio.

SCHOENBERGER, CHRISTINE; Upper Moreland HS; Horsham, PA; (2); 58/242; Church Yth Grp; Hosp Aide; SADD; Fld Hcky; Trk; High Hon Roll; Hon Roll; Surgeon.

SCHOENEBECK, SCOTT; Council Rock HS; Newtown, PA; (3); 108/908; Im Ice Hcky; Im Lcrss; JV Socr; Var Trk; Im Capt Vllybl; Im Wt Lftg; High Hon Roll; Hon Roll; NHS; Bio.

SCHOENEBERGER, TODD; Pen Argyl HS; Wind Gap, PA; (4); 6/117; Church Yth Grp; ROTC; Ski Clb; Pres Band; Drm Mjr(t); Jazz Band; Yrbk Stf; High Hon Roll; Jr NHS; NHS; ROTC Schlrshp; Rnsslr Polytech Inst Awd For Mth & Sci 85-86; Wilkes Coll; Elec Engrng.

SCHOENEWEIS, JAMES; Moon SR HS; Coraopolis, PA; (3); 40/361; Church Yth Grp; Off Jr Cls; JV Bsbl; Var Trk; High Hon Roll; Hon Roll.

SCHOENNAGLE, SCOTT; Hazleton HS; Hazleton, PA; (3); Drama Clb; FBLA; Scholastic Bowl; SADD; Rep Stu Cncl; Bsbl; Bsktbl; Ftbl; Tennis; Wt Lftg.

SCHOFF, RICHARD; South Park HS; Library, PA; (3); 7/228; JV Bsktbl; High Hon Roll; NEDT Awd; Bst Jgglr Awd 86; U Pittsburgh; Engrng.

SCHOFFSTALL, DAMON; Bermudian Springs HS; York Spgs, PA; (3); Stage Crew; Var Ftbl; Hon Roll; Cert Awd Ftbl 84; Auto Body.

SCHOFFSTALL, JEANNETTE; Steelton Highspire HS; Steelton, PA; (4); Girl Scts; Hosp Aide; Spanish Clb; Co-Capt Color Guard; Concert Band; Ed Yrbk Stf; Hon Roll; JC Awd; NHS; Rotary Awd; HOBY Reunion Comm Sec 86; Marchng Band Sqd Ldr 83; 2nd Pl Rbn Art Drwng 83; Harrisburg Area CC; Psych.

SCHOFIELD, LORI; Hopewell Area HS; Aliquippa, PA; (3); Sec Trs Church Yth Grp; Chrmn French Clb; German Clb; Rep Band; Co-Capt Capt Flag Corp; Ed Yrbk Stf; Hon Roll; Masonic Awd; 4-H; Intl Order Of Rainbow For Girls-Worthy Advisor 86; Teaching.

SCHOFIELD, LORI; Mastbaum Area Vo-Tech; Philadelphia, PA; (3); Teachers Aide; Yrbk Stf; Prfct Atten Awd; Pierce JC; Accntng.

SCHOFIELD, ROBYN; Penns Manor Area HS; Clymer, PA; (3); Camera Clb; SADD; Acpl Chr; Chorus; Color Guard; School Musical; Yrbk Phtg; Yrbk Stf; Stu Cncl; Hon Roll; IU PA; Sec Math Tchr.

SCHOLL III, EDWIN R; Chestnut Hill Acad; Erdenheim, PA; (4); 4/46; Chorus; School Play; Nwsp Phtg; Yrbk Phtg; Bsbl; Crs Cntry; Socr; Wt Lftg; Wrstlng; High Hon Roll; Villanova; Elec Engrng.

SCHOLL, GREG J; Avonworth HS; Pittsburgh, PA; (4); 13/98; Church Yth Grp; Cmnty Wkr; JCL; VP Latin Clb; SADD; Varsity Clb; Band; Nwsp Ed-Chief; Pres Sr Cls; Capt L Ftbl; Amer Acad Achvt Goldn Scrll Awd 87; Pittsburgh Pres All Str Achvt 87; All Conf Vrsty Lnbkr Ftbl 87; Harvard U; Comp Sci.

SCHOLL, JENNY; Kutztown Area HS; Kutztown, PA; (3); FBLA; Office Aide; High Hon Roll; Hon Roll; Acctng.

SCHOLL, PATRICIA; Northern York HS; Dillsburg, PA; (3); 55/232; Church Yth Grp; Band; Concert Band; Mrchg Band; Stage Crew; Mgr(s); Capt Var Powder Puff Ftbl; Var Sftbl; Var Trk; Hon Roll; Inter-Act Soc 87-88; Millersville U; Psych.

SCHOLL, PETER; Hamburg Area HS; Hamburg, PA; (3); Art Clb; French Clb; German Clb; Hon Roll; Kutztown U; Cmmrcl Art.

SCHONER, HEATHER; Dallas SR HS; Dallas, PA; (3); Aud/Vis; Color Guard; Sec Soph Cls; Rep Stu Cncl; JV Cheerleading; Pom Pon; Trk; Hon Roll; Phrmcy.

SCHOOLEY, KIMBERLI; St Huberts Catholic HS For Girls; Philadelphia, PA; (3); 97/421; Dance Clb; French Clb; Girl Scts; Chorus; School Musical; Gym; Wt Lftg; Hon Roll.

SCHOOLS, KRISTIN; Gwynedd HS; Norristown, PA; (2); GAA; Math Clb; Pep Clb; Spanish Clb; Stage Crew; Rep Jr Cls; Var L Bsktbl; Var L Fld Hcky; Var L Sftbl; Athltc Admn.

SCHOONOVER, FRANK; Tunkhannock Area HS; Tunkhannock, PA; (2); Church Yth Grp; FFA; Spanish Clb; DAR Awd; Hon Roll; Engrng.

SCHOONOVER, PAULA J; Bucktail Area HS; Renovo, PA; (4); 1/72; Church Yth Grp; Chorus; Color Guard; Elks Awd; High Hon Roll; Hon Roll; NHS; Val; L V Dwyer Awd 87; M A Fox Schlrshp 87; Presdntl Acadc Ftns Awd 87; Bucknell U; Bio.

SCHOONOVER, STACEY; Tunkhannock Area HS; Tunkhannock, PA; (1); 2/304; Science Clb; Spanish Clb; Band; Chorus; School Musical; Hon Roll; Concert Band; Mrchg Band; Stage Crew.

SCHORK, SCOTT; Mc Keesport SR HS; Mckeesport, PA; (3); 30/432; AFS; Library Aide; Office Aide; Spanish Clb; Ftbl; Wt Lftg; High Hon Roll; Hon Roll; Mon-Yough Sci Fair 1st Pl Astrnmy 85-86; Outstndng Achvt Gov 1st Pl 85-86; Arch.

SCHORN, COLLEEN; Reading SR HS; Reading, PA; (4); 25/579; Church Yth Grp; Key Clb; Nwsp Bus Mgr; Nwsp Rptr; Stu Cncl; Capt Swmmng; Hon Roll; Pres NHS; Model UN; Pep Clb; AM Len Awd 83-84; All ST Swmmng Awd 84-86; Beaver Coll; Physcl Thrpy.

SCHORY, KERIA; East Pennsboro Area HS; Enola, PA; (3); French Clb; Capt Mrchg Band; Nwsp Stf; VP Frsh Cls; VP Soph Cls; VP Jr Cls; VP Sr Cls; Rep Stu Cncl; Capt Cheerleading; Hon Roll.

SCHOTT, ERIKA; Dover Area HS; E Berlin, PA; (3); 28/260; Church Yth Grp; Trs Jr Cls; Trs Sr Cls; Cheerleading; High Hon Roll.

SCHOTT, RYAN; Galeton Area HS; Galeton, PA; (4); Church Yth Grp; Band; Chorus; Church Choir; Bsbl; Bsktbl; Socr; Cit Awd; Hon Roll; Boy Scts; PIAA Dist 4 Bsktbl Champs 86; Natl Sci Olympd Awd 85; Philadelphia Coll Phrmcy; Phrmc.

SCHRACK, SUSAN; Northern HS; Dillsburg, PA; (4); 28/207; Art Clb; Church Yth Grp; Debate Tm; Drama Clb; Hosp Aide; VP NFL; Band; Chorus; Church Choir; Concert Band; Tri-M Natl Music Hnr Soc 87; Instrmntlst Mag Merit Awd 87; Pres Acad Fit Awd 87; Syracuse U; Cmmnctns.

SCHRADER, ERIC; Washington HS; Washington, PA; (2); Band; Jazz Band; Mrchg Band; Symp Band; Bsktbl; High Hon Roll; Hon Roll; Music Dir.

SCHRAEDER, JENNIFER; Upper Darby HS; Upper Darby, PA; (3); Church Yth Grp; Hosp Aide; Office Aide; Bsktbl; Fld Hcky; Lcrss; High Hon Roll; Hon Roll; Millersville; Psych.

SCHRAWDER, CRAIG; Northwestern HS; New Tripoli, PA; (3); Chorus; Yrbk Stf; Hon Roll; Chorus Svc Awds 82-87; Arch.

SCHRECENGAST, DIANA; Ford City JR/Sr HS; Ford Cliff, PA; (3); Spanish Clb; Chorus; Drill Tm; Rep Soph Cls; Rep Jr Cls; Rep Stu Cncl; Vllybl; Hon Roll; Tchng.

SCHRECK, KAREN; Dunmore HS; Dunmore, PA; (3); Var Bsktbl; Var Sftbl.

SCHRECONGOST, TINA; Freeport Area Joint HS; Freeport, PA; (4); 29/162; 4-H; FFA; German Clb; Pres Ski Clb; Pres SADD; VP VICA; Pres Jr Cls; Pres Sr Cls; JV Im Bsktbl; Dnfth Awd; 4-H Plt Bk Schlrshp 87; WA Ldrshp Trnng Inst Cert Natl VICA Ldr 86; Mst Imprvd Ger Stu 83-84; U Of Pittsburgh; Phrmcy.

SCHREFFLER, SHANNON; Hamburg Area HS; Hamburg, PA; (3); 49/170; Trs Church Yth Grp; Latin Clb; Library Aide; Spanish Clb; Chorus; Stage Crew; Variety Show; Var Tennis; Hon Roll; Physcl Thrpy.

SCHREFFLER, STEVEN; Hughesville HS; Hughesville, PA; (1); Boy Scts; VP Church Yth Grp; Band; Concert Band; Jazz Band; Mrchg Band; Trk; L Wrstlng; WA U; Comp Sci.

SCHREIBER, KELLY; St Marys Area HS; Kersey, PA; (3); 38/269; Art Clb; Camera Clb; Cmnty Wkr; Pep Clb; Stat Bsbl; Capt L Cheerleading; Stat Gym; Stat Wrstlng; Hon Roll; NHS.

SCHREIBER, TRACY; North Clarion HS; Marienville, PA; (3); 3/108; Drama Clb; Pres French Clb; Chorus; Church Choir; VP School Musical; School Play; JV Cheerleading; Var JV Mgr(s); JV Var Trk; High Hon Roll; Stu Mnth Hstry 85; Awd Top 5 Cls Rnk 86; Cert Merit Erie Co Chptr PA Soc Prof Engrs 87; Math.

SCHREIBER, W ROBERT; Central SR HS; York, PA; (3); Varsity Clb; Var L Golf; High Hon Roll; NHS; Engrng.

SCHREIER, JAMES; Northern SR HS; Dillsburg, PA; (3); 40/232; JV Socr; Hon Roll.

SCHREIER, MELISSA; Conemaugh Valley JR SR HS; Johnstown, PA; (4); 6/120; Drama Clb; Speech Tm; VP Band; School Play; VP Sr Cls; Var L Sftbl; Var Capt Vllybl; Cit Awd; JP Sousa Awd; VP NHS; Nicholas Stripy Schlrshp Awd 87; Woodmen Of Wrld Ins Co Histry Awd 87; Scl Studs Dept Awd 87; U Of Pittsburgh; Pharmacy.

SCHREINER, SONJA; Spring-Ford SR HS; Royersford, PA; (3); 70/256; Math Clb; Spanish Clb; Yrbk Stf; Off Frsh Cls; Off Soph Cls; Off Jr Cls; Off Sr Cls; Stu Cncl; Bsktbl; Lcrss; Yth Apprctn Wk Citatn 84; Phy Thrpy.

SCHRETZMAN, KELLY; St Hubert HS; Philadelphia, PA; (3); 150/436; Exploring; Orch; Vet.

SCHRIFT, THERESA; Penn Cambria HS; Portage, PA; (3); 30/207; Spanish Clb; Hon Roll; NHS.

SCHRIMPER, LORI; Fort Le Boeuf HS; Waterford, PA; (3); 5/207; Pep Clb; Teachers Aide; Chorus; Church Choir; School Musical; Yrbk Stf; Stat Bsktbl; Sftbl; High Hon Roll; Sec Trs NHS; Acdmc Achvt Awd 85-87; Jamestown Bus Coll; Accntng.

SCHRIVER, DOUGLAS; West Mifflin Area HS; Monroeville, PA; (3); Boy Scts; Camera Clb; Spanish Clb; Trk; Hon Roll; Med.

SCHRIVER, KIMBERLY B; Peters Township HS; Mc Murray, PA; (4); 32/240; Aud/Vis; Church Yth Grp; Cmnty Wkr; Exploring; Key Clb; Yrbk Ed-Chief; Yrbk Sprt Ed; High Hon Roll; Hon Roll; Pres Acad Fitness Awd 87; Chambr Comm Awd 87; PA ST U; Hlth Planning.

SCHRIVER, MICHAEL; Highlands SR HS; Natrona Hts, PA; (3); Intnl Clb; Key Clb; SADD; Nwsp Bus Mgr; Nwsp Ed-Chief; Lit Mag; Ice Hcky; Score Keeper; Socr; PA ST U; Cmmnctns.

SCHROCK, DALE ANN; Somerset SR HS; Somerset, PA; (3); 56/230; Sec Church Yth Grp; SADD; Band; Chorus; Color Guard; Concert Band; Drm Mjr(t); Flag Corp; Jazz Band; Mrchg Band; Performing & Visual Arts 85-87; Occuptnl Thrpy.

SCHROCK, JENNIFER; Rockwood Area HS; Rockwood, PA; (4); 7/94; Band; Chorus; Yrbk Stf; Var Sftbl; Var Vllybl; High Hon Roll; NHS; NEDT Awd; Pres Physcl Ftns Awd 81-86; PA ST U; Engrng.

SCHROCK, LOUELLA; Riverview HS; Verona, PA; (3); Girl Scts; Office Aide; Chorus; Color Guard; Vllybl; Hon Roll; Bus Mgmt.

SCHROECK, TRACY; Villa Maria Acad; Erie, PA; (2); Science Clb; High Hon Roll; Gannon U; Pre-Med.

SCHROEDER, CHRISTINE; Downingtown SR HS; Exton, PA; (4); 28/560; GAA; Intnl Clb; Orch; Rep Stu Cncl; JV L Fld Hcky; L JV Trk; NHS; High Hon Roll; Hon Roll; Church Yth Grp; Outstndng Amer Stdnt 87; Outstndng Strng Plyr 87; Alld Chem Schlrshp To Grmny 84; U Of WI; Intl Bus.

SCHROEDER, KRISTINE; Kennard Dale HS; Delta, PA; (3); Church Yth Grp; Girl Scts; Band; Chorus; Concert Band; Mrchg Band; Pep Band; School Musical; Mgr(s); Socr; Chldhd Ed.

SCHROEDER, MATT; Kennard-Dale HS; New Park, PA; (2); Church Yth Grp; JV Socr; High Hon Roll; NEDT Awd; Amrcn Hstry Awd 85-86; Engr.

SCHROEDER, SARAH; Trinity HS; Carlisle, PA; (3); Model UN; Pep Clb; Ski Clb; Teachers Aide; Ed Yrbk Stf; Stu Cncl; JV Bsktbl; L Mgr(s); Stat Socr; Law.

SCHROETTNER, ANDREA; Nazareth Area SR HS; Nazareth, PA; (4); 32/236; Aud/Vis; Church Yth Grp; GAA; Key Clb; Library Aide; Yrbk Stf; High Hon Roll; Hon Roll; Pres Acad Phys Fit Awd 87; E Stroudsburg U; Med Tech.

SCHROPP, JILL; Oley Valley HS; Oley, PA; (3); 8/142; Camp Fr Inc; Concert Band; Mrchg Band; School Musical; Pres Sr Cls; Trs Stu Cncl; JV Capt Fld Hcky; Stat Trk; High Hon Roll; NHS; Spnsh.

SCHROTH, JENNIFER; Bishop Guilfoyle HS; Altoona, PA; (3); 62/156; Red Cross Aide; SADD; Rep Frsh Cls; Rep Jr Cls; JV Cheerleading; JV Tennis; Schl Of Arts & Music; Dancer.

SCHROTH, TRACI; Butler Area SR HS; Fenelton, PA; (4); Church Yth Grp; Exploring; German Clb; Library Aide; Office Aide; ROTC; Westminster Coll; Psychlgy.

SCHRUFER, MATTHEW; Ole Valley HS; Oley, PA; (3); 32/142; Cmnty Wkr; Nwsp Rptr; Rep Stu Cncl; Var Capt Bsktbl; Var Capt Socr; Var Vllybl; Hon Roll; Key Clb; Stu Of Month 87; Berks Cnty Div I 1st Team Scr 85-86; Pres Athl Assoc 87-88; Bus Mgmt.

SCHUBERT, AMY; Shaler Area HS; Glenshaw, PA; (3); 13/489; Capt Flag Corp; School Play; Variety Show; Yrbk Phtg; Yrbk Stf; French Hon Soc; High Hon Roll; NHS; Church Yth Grp; Ski Clb; Natl Sci Olympiad Awd In Chem 87; Rsrch Editor Of Yrbk 87-88; Gftd & Tlntd Ed Prgm 85; Physician.

SCHUBERT, HEIDI; Boyertown SR HS; Boyertown, PA; (4); Office Aide; Chorus; Variety Show; JV Cheerleading; Cit Awd; Hon Roll; Lansdale Schl Of Bus; Sec Sci.

SCHUBERT, MARGARET; B Reed Henderson HS; West Chester, PA; (2); 15/325; French Clb; Ski Clb; Rep Stu Cncl; Var L Fld Hcky; L Lcrss; French Hon Soc; Hon Roll.

SCHUCHART, NEIL; South Western HS; Hanover, PA; (3); Chorus; School Musical; Nwsp Rptr; JV Golf; Hon Roll; Law.

SCHUCKER, KATHY; Kutztown HS; Kempton, PA; (4); 15/146; Band; Chorus; Color Guard; Drill Tm; Flag Corp; Jazz Band; Variety Show; High Hon Roll; NHS; Pres Schlr; Grimley Trust Schlrshp 87; Millersville U; Elem Educ.

SCHUCKER, SCOTT A; Cedar Cliff HS; Camp Hill, PA; (4); 25/243; Church Yth Grp; Cmnty Wkr; Drama Clb; German Clb; Key Clb; Ski Clb; Y-Teens; School Musical; School Play; Bowling; PA ST U; Physical Sci.

SCHUCKERS, ERIK; Do Bois Area SR HS; Luthersburg, PA; (3); 1/320; Concert Band; Jazz Band; Mrchg Band; School Musical; NHS; CAP; Val; Band; Variety Show; High Hon Roll; Attnd Govs Schl For Art Wrtng 87; Du Bois Area SR HS Sci Awd 85; Am Lgn Essy Awd 85; Journalism.

SCHUCKERS, MICHAEL; Cumberland Valley HS; Camp Hill, PA; (3); 48/578; Church Yth Grp; Latin Clb; Math Tm; JV Var Ftbl; JV Trk; Hon Roll; Trs NHS; Ntl Merit Ltr; Shippensburg Math Cntst 3rd Pl Indv 1st Pl Team 86-87.

SCHUCOLSKY, PAMELA; Peters Township HS; Mcmurray, PA; (2); Church Yth Grp; Speech Tm; Varsity Clb; Drill Tm; Yrbk Stf; Stu Cncl; Swmmng; High Hon Roll; Psych.

SCHUELLER, JOHN C; Tulpehocken Area HS; Bernville, PA; (4); Computer Clb; Band; Hon Roll; Presdntl Acadc, Physcl Ftns Awds 87; Lincoln Tech Inst Schlrshp 87; Lincoln Tech Inst; Elec Tech.

SCHUERER, DOUGLAS J; Gateway SR HS; Monroeville, PA; (4); 8/500; Boy Scts; Key Clb; Math Tm; Ski Clb; Band; Mrchg Band; Im Vllybl; High Hon Roll; NHS; Ntl Merit SF; Mth Tm Calcu-Solve Bowl 2nd Pl 84-85; Mth Tm 1st Pl Calcu-Solve Bowl 86-87; Mth Lg 1st Pl Tm 85-86; Med.

SCHUETTLER, MICHAEL; Nativity B V M HS; Pottsville, PA; (4); Camera Clb; Computer Clb; Spanish Clb; Band.

SCHULD, MICHELLE; Downingtown SR HS; Downingtown, PA; (4); Aud/Vis; Church Yth Grp; Cmnty Wkr; French Clb; Intnl Clb; Yrbk Stf; Temple U; Radio.

SCHULL, CYNTHIA; Milton Hershey Schl; San Diego, CA; (4); 21/125; Sec Drama Clb; Library Aide; Thesps; Chorus; School Play; Yrbk Stf; Lit Mag; Off Stu Cncl; Var L Trk; High Hon Roll; 3rd Pl Susquehanna Litho Cntst 87; Vrsty Ltrs Drama & Grls Chrs 87; Dsgn Inst Of San Diego; Arts.

SCHULL, JULIA; Central Bucks HS East; Doylestown, PA; (3); 40/505; Pres Church Yth Grp; Cmnty Wkr; JCL; Latin Clb; Ski Clb; SADD; Yrbk Stf; Var L Trk; Hon Roll; NHS; Cathl Yth Orgnztn Most Active Parish 87; Psych.

SCHULTE, PAULA; Clairton HS; Clairton, PA; (3); 15/94; Girl Scts; Hosp Aide; SADD; Nwsp Stf; Stu Cncl; Cheerleading; Sftbl; High Hon Roll; Jr NHS; NHS; Pt Park Coll Smmr Sci Camp 87; Allegheny Intrmdt Unit Anml Bhvr Apprntc 87; OH ST U; Jrnlsm.

SCHULTHEIS, BETH; Scranton Central HS; Scranton, PA; (4); 110/293; Church Yth Grp; SADD; Church Choir; Orch; Hon Roll; Jr NHS; Gold Awd 87; PinebrookJC; Early Chldhd Educ.

SCHULTHEIS, CHRISTINE; Kiski Area HS; Leechburg, PA; (4); Debate Tm; 4-H; Pres French Clb; Pres Spanish Clb; Rep Stu Cncl; Var L Trk; 4-H Awd; NHS; Ntl Merit Ltr; Natl Yng Ldrs Conf 86-87; Dickinson Coll; Intl Rel.

SCHULTHEIS, DARLENE; Mount Pleasant SR HS; Mt Pleasant, PA; (4); 40/149; Pres Church Yth Grp; Pep Clb; Chorus; Church Choir; High Hon Roll; Hon Roll; Westmoreland Cnty Chours; Clark Queer Mem Schlrshp; Slippery Rock U; Physcl Thrpy.

SCHULTZ, CHRISTIAN; General Mclane HS; Mc Kean, PA; (4); 22/240; Church Yth Grp; Letterman Clb; Var Capt Bsktbl; Var Ftbl; Var Capt Trk; NHS; Dist Medlst Trk 86; All Star Tm Grandvw Bsktbl Camp 84; Stu Acad Excllnce 86-87; U Of Pittsburgh; Engrng.

SCHULTZ JR, DAVID C; Nazareth Area HS; Bethlehem, PA; (4); 14/236; Key Clb; Math Tm; JV Bsbl; Var L Bsktbl; Var Ftbl; Var L Trk; Im Wt Lftg; High Hon Roll; Hon Roll; NHS; Pres Acad Ftnss Awd 86-87; Lwr Nazareth PTA Schlrshp 87; Fnlst Chryslr 1st Bsktbl Schlrshp 87; Albright Coll; Chem.

SCHULTZ, ERIC; Fort Cherry HS; Mc Donald, PA; (3); 30/130; Art Clb; Church Yth Grp; Letterman Clb; Math Clb; Science Clb; Ski Clb; Varsity Clb; Var L Bsbl; Var L Ftbl; Var L Wrstlng; Engnrng.

SCHULTZ, JEFF; Riverside HS; Taylor, PA; (3); 34/135; Art Clb; Exploring; Stage Crew; JV Bsbl; Var L Bsktbl; Hon Roll; Aerontcs Engrng.

SCHULTZ, JOHN; New Castle SR HS; New Castle, PA; (3); 20/293; Math Tm; Pep Clb; Chorus; School Play; Yrbk Stf; Hon Roll; Natl Achad Games In Eatonton GA 83-84; Math Teacher.

SCHULTZ, JOYCE; Canon-Mc Millan SR HS; Eighty Four, PA; (4); VP Sec 4-H; FBLA; JA; Office Aide; Ski Clb; SADD; Vllybl; Hon Roll; Library Aide; Chorus; Bradford Schl.

SCHULTZ, KAREN; Montoorsville Area HS; Muncy, PA; (3); Sec Computer Clb; Girl Scts; Hosp Aide; Red Cross Aide; Chorus; Trk; Grl Sct Gold Awd 86; UNC-WILLMINGTON; Marine Bio.

SCHULTZ, KARLYN; Strong Vincent HS; Erie, PA; (4); 25/168; Yrbk Stf; Sec Sr Cls; Capt Cheerleading; NHS; Syracuse U Schlrshp & Grnt 87; Syracuse U; Psych.

SCHULTZ, KENNETH; Freedom HS; Bethlehem, PA; (4); 10/435; Boy Scts; Chess Clb; German Clb; VP JA; Capt Math Tm; Model UN; Capt Scholastic Bowl; Science Clb; Rep Stu Cncl; High Hon Roll; Dale Carnegie Course Grad 86; Eagle Sct 86; PA Govrnrs Schl For Sci 86; Carnegie-Mellon U; Elect Engrng.

SCHULTZ, REBECCA; Taylor Allderdice HS; Pittsburgh, PA; (2); AFS; Drama Clb; Q&S; Ski Clb; Nwsp Rptr; High Hon Roll; Hon Roll; Jr NHS; Best New Jrnlst 86; Art.

SCHULTZ, ROGER; Bethlehem Catholic HS; Bethlehem, PA; (3); 109/210; JV Socr; Hon Roll; Math.

SCHULTZ, RYAN; Gettysburg HS; Gettysburg, PA; (2); VP Church Yth Grp; Church Choir; Orch; JV Trk; Hon Roll; Adams-Cumberland Cnty Orchestra 87; Sci.

SCHULTZ, SCOTT; Parkland HS; Breinigsville, PA; (2); Im Vllybl; Im Wt Lftg; Hon Roll; Mktng Analyst.

SCHULTZ, SHERRI; Seton-La-Salle HS; Pittsburgh, PA; (4); 42/263; Church Yth Grp; Cmnty Wkr; Dance Clb; FBLA; Stage Crew; Mat Maids; High Hon Roll; 2nd Plc FBLA Rgnls Acctg 86-87; Acctg I Awd 85-86; Chrprsn Big Sisters 86-87; Duquesne U; Acctg.

SCHULTZ, STACEY; Knoch HS; Renfrew, PA; (3); 16/222; Dance Clb; Chorus; School Musical; VP Frsh Cls; Rep Stu Cncl; Capt Var Cheerleading; Im Diving; Im Swmmng; High Hon Roll; NHS; U Of NC; Bio.

SCHULTZ, SUSAN; Ambridge Area HS; Baden, PA; (4); 18/365; 4-H; French Clb; Office Aide; Pep Clb; Red Cross Aide; Off Soph Cls; Off Jr Cls; Off Sr Cls; 4-H Awd; High Hon Roll; Penn ST; Bio.

SCHULTZ, WENDY; Richland HS; Gibsonia, PA; (2); Band; Drill Tm; Variety Show; Var L Bsktbl; L Trk; Var L Vllybl; High Hon Roll; Willow Pnd JR Olympc Vlybl Tm 86-87; Kystn ST Games Vlybl 87.

SCHULZ, LINDA F; Cheltenham HS; Glenside, PA; (4); 112/365; Capt L Color Guard; Stu Cncl; Coach Actv; Sftbl; Capt L Swmmng; Suburban I All Leag 1st Tm Grls Swmmng 87; Holden Awd 86-87; Schl Cmndtn For Outstndng Accmplsmnt 87; Gettysburg Coll; Physcl Edu.

SCHULZ, PEGGY; John Bartram HS; Philadelphia, PA; (4); 2/650; Exploring; Intnl Clb; Office Aide; Teachers Aide; JV Band; Yrbk Stf; Jr Cls; JV L Cheerleading; High Hon Roll; NHS; Hnrary Awd Hugh O Brian Yuth Fdtn 85; Acad Excel 85-86; Acad All Star Clb; Bus Mgmnt.

SCHULZE, TAMMY; Garden Spot HS; New Holland, PA; (2); Church Yth Grp; Library Aide; Spanish Clb; Legal Secy.

SCHUMACHER, DIANE; Hampton HS; Allison Pk, PA; (2); Church Yth Grp; Color Guard; Yrbk Rptr; Yrbk Stf; Swmmng; High Hon Roll; Hon Roll; Jonell Schl Fnshng; Model.

SCHUMACHER, LAUREN; Salisbury SR HS; Allentown, PA; (4); 17/128; Drama Clb; VP Key Clb; School Musical; School Play; Rep Frsh Cls; Rep Soph Cls; Rep Stu Cncl; JV Var Bsktbl; JV Var Fld Hcky; JV Var Sftbl; Future Educator Schlrshp 87; Susquehanna U; Educ.

SCHUMACHER, LINDA; Hampton HS; Allison Park, PA; (4); 20/260; Church Yth Grp; Hosp Aide; Spanish Clb; Color Guard; Powder Puff Ftbl; High Hon Roll; Ntl Merit Ltr; Pediatrician.

SCHUMACHER, LISA; Bishop Hafey HS; Milnesville, PA; (4); French Clb; Y-Teens; Hon Roll; Excllnc Bus Ed 87; Luzern Cnty CC; Accntng.

SCHUMACHER, LISA; Frazier Men JR SR HS; Perryopolis, PA; (4); GAA; Nwsp Sprt Ed; Yrbk Stf; Golf; Powder Puff Ftbl; Sftbl; Prfct Atten Awd; Robert Morris Coll; Med Tech.

SCHUMACHER, MAGGIE; Villa Maria Acad; Erie, PA; (3); Camera Clb; Church Yth Grp; Cmnty Wkr; Latin Clb; Service Clb; Ski Clb; Nwsp Phtg; Nwsp Stf; Yrbk Phtg; Yrbk Stf; Humanities.

SCHUMAKER, STEPHANIE; Hamburg Area HS; Hamburg, PA; (4); 2/143; Trs Church Yth Grp; German Clb; Pres Jr Cls; Var Bsktbl; Var Capt Fld Hcky; High Hon Roll; Trs NHS; Sal; Bausch & Lomb Sci Awd; Grmn Natl Hnr Soc Pres 86-87; Lebanon Vly Coll Pres Ldrshp Schlrshp 87-91; HOBY Awd 85; Lebanon Vly Coll; Actuarl Sci.

SCHUMAN, KYLE D; New Oxford HS; Hanover, PA; (3); 1/167; Am Leg Boys St; Aud/Vis; Drama Clb; Sec Varsity Clb; Variety Show; Trs Sr Cls; Var JV Bsktbl; Var Crs Cntry; Var Trk; High Hon Roll; Dstngshd Hnr Roll Mdl 85-87; Natl Sojourners Essay Cont 86-87; Comp Sci.

SCHUMM, DEBORAH; The Christian Acad; Chester, PA; (3); Church Yth Grp; Church Choir; Yrbk Rptr; Rep Stu Cncl; Var Capt Sftbl; Var Capt Vllybl; High Hon Roll; Hon Roll; Ntl Merit Schol; Bus Math Awd; Intl Rel.

SCHUMMER JR, JAMES; Quakertown Community HS; Quakertown, PA; (3); 37/310; Camera Clb; Band; Jazz Band; Mrchg Band; School Musical; Rep Jr Cls; High Hon Roll; Hon Roll; NHS; Ntl Merit Ltr; Mc Donalds All Amer H S Band 86-87; PA All ST Band 87; Finc.

SCHUON, KATHY; Northampton SR HS; Northampton, PA; (3); 246/400; AFS; FTA; Pep Clb; Chorus; Yrbk Phtg; Hon Roll; Bloomsburg U; Elem Educ.

SCHUPBACH, STEPHANIE; Peters Township HS; Ponca City, OK; (4); Drama Clb; FBLA; Rep NFL; Speech Tm; CC Awd; High Hon Roll; Kiwanis Awd; VP NHS; Pres Schlr; Spanish NHS; U Of OK.

SCHUR, NEIL; Cheltenham HS; Elkins Pk, PA; (4); 23/346; Capt Debate Tm; School Play; Ed Nwsp Stf; Pres Soph Cls; Sec Stu Cncl; NHS; Drama Clb; JCL; Temple Yth Grp; School Musical; Latin Dept Awd, Ben & Ceacilia Moss Svc Awd 87; Latin Summa Cum Laude Awd 86-87; U PA.

SCHURER, ANDREA; Southmoreland SR HS; Scottdale, PA; (3); Church Yth Grp; English Clb; Library Aide; Spanish Clb; High Hon Roll; Hon Roll; NEDT Awd; Spanish NHS; Bus.

SCHURER, JOSEPH; Perry Traditional Acad; Pittsburgh, PA; (3); 3/190; Boy Scts; Church Yth Grp; JA; Nwsp Stf; Yrbk Stf; Lit Mag; Var Swmmng; High Hon Roll; Hon Roll; NHS; HOBY 86; Am Lgn Ctznshp Awd 84; OAR Excllnc Hstry Awd 84; Engl.

SCHUSTER, JENNIFER; Ringgold HS; Monongahela, PA; (4); 21/325; Hon Roll; Cltrl Arts 2nd Plc PA; Chatham Coll; Bus Admin.

SCHUSTER, KEVIN M; Quakertown Community HS; E Greenville, PA; (2); School Play; JV Ftbl; Trk; Hon Roll; Jr NHS; Engr.

SCHUSTER, MARY ANN; Allegheny-Clarion Valley HS; Parker, PA; (4); 26/90; FHA; Office Aide; Spanish Clb; School Musical; Trs Soph Cls; Trs Jr Cls; Pres Sr Cls; Stu Cncl; Stat Bsktbl; Stat Trk; Clarion U; Elem Educ.

SCHUTT, BURT; Northampton Area SR HS; Northampton, PA; (3); 121/500; Church Yth Grp; Ski Clb; Spanish Clb; Wt Lftg; Med.

SCHUTTER, CYNTHIA; Pennsbury HS; Yardley, PA; (3); Band; Concert Band; Mrchg Band; NY U.

SCHUTZ, MICHELLE; St Marys Area HS; St Marys, PA; (3); Church Yth Grp; Sec Hosp Aide; Band; Concert Band.

SCHWAB, ROCHELLE; Monessen HS; Monessen, PA; (3); FBLA; VP JA; Library Aide; Stage Crew; ICM Schl Of Bus; Accntnt.

SCHWAB, WILLIAM; Fort Leboeuf HS; Waterford, PA; (4); 4/167; Rep Stu Cncl; JV Cheerleading; Var L Ftbl; Var L Trk; Var Capt Wrstlng; High Hon Roll; NHS; Ft Le Boeuf Male Athlt Of Yr 87; 1st Team All-Cnty-Ftbl,Wrstlng,Track 86-87; Team Co-MVP Ftbl 86; Princeton U; Lawyer.

SCHWALM, MICHAEL; Tri-Valley HS; Hegins, PA; (3); 18/76; VP Church Yth Grp; Rep Stu Cncl; L Bsktbl; Hon Roll; NHS; NEDT Awd.

SCHWAN, BARBARA; William Allen HS; Allentown, PA; (3); Church Yth Grp; German Clb; JCL; Latin Clb; PAVAS; Acpl Chr; Church Choir; High Hon Roll; Hon Roll; NHS; Natl Ltn Hnr Soc 86-87; Med.

SCHWARTZ, AMY; Cocalico HS; Adamstown, PA; (3); Band; Chorus; Church Choir; Concert Band; Drill Tm; Jazz Band; Mrchg Band; Pep Band; School Musical; Symp Band.

SCHWARTZ, AMY; Ft Le Boeuf HS; Erie, PA; (2); Church Yth Grp; Dance Clb; Band; Church Choir; Concert Band; Drill Tm; Flag Corp; Mrchg Band; School Musical; School Play; Communications.

SCHWARTZ, BENJAMIN; Kennard-Dale HS; Fawn Grove, PA; (2); Church Yth Grp; Ski Clb; JV L Bsbl; JV L Bsktbl; JV L Socr; Aero Engrng.

SCHWARTZ, DAVID J; Mt Penn JR SR HS; Reading, PA; (3); VICA; Var Socr; Plmbng.

SCHWARTZ, GARY; Council Rock HS; Richboro, PA; (2); Drama Clb; Temple Yth Grp; Chorus; Hon Roll.

SCHWARTZ, JEFF; Boiling Springs HS; Boiling Spgs, PA; (4); 1/107; Trs Church Yth Grp; Concert Band; Jazz Band; Var L Ftbl; Var Trk; JETS Awd; Lion Awd; Pres NHS; Rotary Awd; Val; Lehigh U; Engrng.

SCHWARTZ, JEFF; Hampton HS; Allison Park, PA; (3); 4/230; Ski Clb; Rep Soph Cls; Var JV Socr; Var Trk; High Hon Roll; Advncd Plcmnt Hist 86-87; Penn St U; Mech.

SCHWARTZ, JENNIFER; State Coll Area Intermediate HS; State College, PA; (1); Office Aide; School Musical; Yrbk Rptr; Yrbk Stf; JV Cheerleading; JV Pom Pon; Power/Paws 87; Elem Ed.

SCHWARTZ, KEVIN JAY; Lower Merion HS; Bala Cynwyd, PA; (3); Math Tm; Capt Speech Tm; Orch; Stu Cncl; Var Swmmng; French Hon Soc; High Hon Roll; NHS; Ntl Merit Ltr; Cmnty Wkr; Bst Tmpl Yth Grp Pres PA Rgn 86-87; Engrng.

SCHWARTZ, KIMBERLY; Tri-Valley HS; Hegins, PA; (2); 17/85; Church Yth Grp; Hosp Aide; Teachers Aide; Chorus; Church Choir; Drill Tm; Stage Crew; Nwsp Rptr; L Twrlr; Cit Awd; Presdntl Physcl Ftns Awd 86-87; VCS Tchr Aide Awd 86; Child Psych.

SCHWARTZ, LAURIE; Chapel Christian Acad; Pottstown, PA; (4); Church Yth Grp; Drama Clb; Library Aide; Office Aide; Pep Clb; Chorus; School Play; Yrbk Stf; Capt Cheerleading; Pres Schlr; 1st Pl At Rgnl & St Spch Cmptn KCEA 84-87; Liberty U.

SCHWARTZ, LESLIE; William Allen HS; Allentown, PA; (2); Church Yth Grp; Hosp Aide; Key Clb; Orch; Trs Frsh Cls; Trk; Hon Roll; Jr NHS; Bio.

SCHWARTZ, MARCIA; Riverview HS; Oakmont, PA; (2); French Clb; Band; Mrchg Band; Yrbk Stf; Stu Cncl; JV Bsktbl; Pom Pon; JV Tennis; Var Trk; High Hon Roll.

SCHWARTZ, MELISSA; Haverford SR HS; Havertown, PA; (3); 26/452; Church Yth Grp; Service Clb; Spanish Clb; Temple Yth Grp; Nwsp Rptr; Lit Mag; Rep Jr Cls; Var L Tennis; High Hon Roll; Hon Roll; U Of PA; Bus.

SCHWARTZ, SHARON; Schuylkill Haven HS; Sch Haven, PA; (4); 11/83; Church Yth Grp; FCA; German Clb; Pep Clb; VP SADD; Teachers Aide; Stu Cncl; Hon Roll; Ntl Merit Ltr; Hnr Guard 86; Hnr Bnqt 84-87; Century 3 Ldrshp Rep 87; Johnson & Wales; Mngmt.

SCHWARTZ, STACEY; Council Rock HS; Newtown, PA; (3); 335/908; Art Clb; Im Powder Puff Ftbl; Art.

SCHWARTZ, STEVEN; Hempfield HS; Lancaster, PA; (3); 68/425; VP Church Yth Grp; Computer Clb; Chorus; Church Choir; Var Crs Cntry; Hon Roll; Comp Fld.

SCHWARTZ, SUSAN A; Nativity BVM HS; New Philadelphia, PA; (4); 7/97; Church Yth Grp; Cmnty Wkr; Sec Spanish Clb; Chorus; Flag Corp; Variety Show; High Hon Roll; Hon Roll; NHS; Prfct Atten Awd; Awd Partcptn Pottsville Club Career Day 86; Awd Highest Achvt Span, Htlh & World Cultures 84-86; East Stroudsburg U; Htl Rest Mg.

SCHWARTZ, TAMARA; Cumberland Valley HS; Mechanicsburg, PA; (3); 14/600; Trs Key Clb; Model UN; School Musical; Ed Yrbk Stf; Stat Bsktbl; Var Mgr(s); Pom Pon; High Hon Roll; NHS.

SCHWARZ, FRANCES; Hopewell SR HS; Aliquippa, PA; (4); #87 In Class; Cmnty Wkr; DECA; Hosp Aide; Latin Clb; JV Mgr(s); Hon Roll; Beaver Cnty CC; Exec Secr.

SCHWARZ, STEPHEN D; Trinity Schl District; Washington, PA; (3); 37/402; Church Yth Grp; Cmnty Wkr; French Clb; Pep Clb; Ski Clb; Teachers Aide; Var L Ftbl; Wt Lftg; High Hon Roll; Hon Roll; Cmnty Svc Awd Thrptc Hrsbk Rdng Pgm 85; JR Deacon Lone Pine Chrstn Chrch 86-87; Law.

SCHWARZ, TODD; Central York HS; York, PA; (3); Boy Scts; Cmnty Wkr; Speech Tm; Thesps; L Ftbl; High Hon Roll; Hon Roll; NHS; ST Fnlst Persuasv Spkg 86; 1st Pl York Cnty Watr Qual Envrnmt Olympcs 87; Lf Sci.

SCHWEGEL, THERESA; Archbishop Ryan HS; Philadelphia, PA; (4); 30/490; Cmnty Wkr; Red Cross Aide; Sec Trs Science Clb; Service Clb; Rep Color Guard; Rep Mrchg Band; Variety Show; High Hon Roll; Hon Roll; Ntl Merit Ltr; Millersville U Srch Of Exclnc Schlrshp 87; Cabrini Coll Acad Schlrshp 87; Rhodes Coll Acad Schlrshp 87; Gwynedd-Mercy Coll.

SCHWEICKERT, BRIAN; Penn Trafford HS; Trafford, PA; (3); Boy Scts; Im Bsktbl; Var Crs Cntry; Im Ftbl; Im Sftbl; Var L Swmmng; Var Tennis; High Hon Roll; Hon Roll; Prfct Atten Awd; Swm Rcrd-200 Indvdl Mdly & Mdly Rly 86-87; Engrng.

SCHWEIGERT, LORI; Schuylkill Haven Area HS; Sch Haven, PA; (2); 27/104; Church Yth Grp; Band; Concert Band; Mrchg Band; Sftbl; Hon Roll; Bus.

SCHWEIGERT, SCOTT; Schuylkill Haven Area HS; Schuylkill Haven, PA; (3); 7/98; Church Yth Grp; German Clb; Science Clb; Teachers Aide; Church Choir; Stu Cncl; Frgn Lang Cmptn Bloomsburg U; Future Sci Amer; Bible Quiz Tm Co-Cap; Psychlgy.

SCHWEIKERT, SUZANNE; Avella Area HS; Avella, PA; (3); French Clb; Pep Clb; Ski Clb; Capt Cheerleading; Golf; Sftbl; Hon Roll; Ed.

SCHWEINGRUBER, ERIC; Cedar Crest HS; Lebanon, PA; (4); 3/303; French Clb; Pep Clb; Band; Church Choir; Concert Band; Jazz Band; Mrchg Band; Orch; Pep Band; School Musical; All Estrn HS Band 87; Natl Band Mstrs Hnrs Band 86; PA Gov Schl Perfrmng Arts 86; Temple U; Music Ed.

SCHWEITZER, DERRICK; Downingtown HS; Exton, PA; (3); 27/650; German Clb; Model UN; SADD; Im Lcrss; Im Vllybl; Hon Roll; Ntl Merit Ltr; NEDT Awd; Bio.

SCHWEITZER, KIRSTEN; Vincentian HS; Pittsburgh, PA; (3); 11/73; Service Clb; Nwsp Stf; Hon Roll; U Of Pittsburgh; Nrsg.

SCHWEITZER, LORI; Correy Area HS; Spartansburg, PA; (3); Church Yth Grp; Chorus; Capt Flag Corp; Mrchg Band; Rep Frsh Cls; Rep Soph Cls; Rep Stu Cncl; Im Sftbl; High Hon Roll; Hon Roll; Delta Epsilon Phi Grmn Hnr Soc 86; Dist Chrs 85; Engl.

SCHWEITZER, MICHELE; Corry Area HS; Spartansburg, PA; (3); Church Yth Grp; German Clb; Band; Concert Band; Jazz Band; Mrchg Band; School Play; Yrbk Phtg; Yrbk Stf; Spartansburg Fair Queen 86-87; JR High Dist Bnd 85; PA St; PT.

SCHWEITZER, TRACI; Central Cambria HS; Ebensburg, PA; (3); 47/210; Band; Drill Tm; Mrchg Band; Hon Roll; NHS; Art Clb; Church Yth Grp; Color Guard; IN U Of PA; Htl-Rest Mgmt.

SCHWEIZER, CHRIS; St Huberts HS; Philadelphia, PA; (2); 150/385; Church Yth Grp; Cmnty Wkr; French Clb; GAA; JV Bsktbl; JV Fld Hcky; Var Mgr(s); Var JV Sftbl; Var JV Vllybl; Hon Roll; Acctg.

SCHWEIZER, KAREN; Downingtown SR HS; Downingtown, PA; (3); 43/648; French Clb; Capt Flag Corp; Yrbk Phtg; Var L Trk; NEDT Awd; Ski Clb; SADD; Chorus; Im Bowling; High Hon Roll; Pres Acad Ftnss Awd 85; Adv.

SCHWEIZER, LISA MARIE; Ridley SR HS; Folsom, PA; (4); 46/407; FBLA; Chorus; Color Guard; Mrchg Band; Bus Awd Ridley Bus Assn 87; K Gibbs FSA 86; DE Cnty CC; Sec.

SCHWER, VICKIE; Brownsville Area HS; New Salem, PA; (3); Drama Clb; Hon Roll; Penn ST; Lab Tech.

SCHWERIN, ERIC; Cheltenham HS; Melrose Pk, PA; (4); 15/365; JCL; Temple Yth Grp; Concert Band; Yrbk Ed-Chief; NHS; Ntl Merit Ltr; NEDT Awd; Geoffrey Price Mem Awd Scl Stds, Joseph Simms Srvc Awd, Prsdntl Clssrm Prtcpnt 87; U Of PA; Lbrl Arts.

SCHWING, RONALD; Bensalem HS; Bensalem, PA; (3); Boy Scts; French Clb; Service Clb; Varsity Clb; Crs Cntry; Trk; NHS; Secy Natl Hnr Socty 86-87; Pres Natl Hnr Socty 87-88; Actvty Comm 86-87; Mech Engrng.

SCHWOEBLE, ERIC; New Castle HS; New Castle, PA; (2); High Hon Roll; Hon Roll; U Of Pittsburgh; Bus.

SCIALABBA, MERI; Butler SR HS; Butler, PA; (3); Office Aide; Thesps; Co-Capt Drill Tm; School Musical; Frsh Cls; Soph Cls; Stu Cncl; Cheerleading; Pom Pon; Sftbl; Adv.

SCIARRA, GINA; Wissahickon HS; Gwynedd, PA; (3); 75/272; Intnl Clb; Ski Clb; Lit Mag; Sftbl; Hon Roll; Opt Clb Awd; Bus.

SCIBEK, AMY; Crestwood HS; Mountaintop, PA; (1); SADD; VP Soph Cls; Stu Cncl; Cheerleading; Crs Cntry; Gym; Trk; High Hon Roll; Prfct Atten Awd; Temple U; Dentistry.

SCIBELLI, AMY; Cedar Crest HS; Lebanon, PA; (2); 57/350; Pep Clb; Spanish Clb; Bsktbl; Sftbl; High Hon Roll; Hon Roll; Brnz Mtl Hnr Rl 86-87; Phys Thrpy.

SCIBELLI, CHRIS; Cedar Crest HS; Lebanon, PA; (4); 2/312; Bsktbl; Var L Golf; Wt Lftg; High Hon Roll; Kiwanis Awd; Lion Awd; NHS; Opt Clb Awd; Pres Schlr; Sal; Herm H Eisenhauer Memrl Schlrshp 87; Booster Clb Schlrshp 87; John Tamasco Awd - Golf W/Hgst GPA 87; Franklin; Pre Healng Arts.

SCICCHITANO, LISA; Our Lady Of Lourdes Regional HS; Shamokin, PA; (3); 2/94; AFS; Drama Clb; Pep Clb; Trs Spanish Clb; School Play; Sec Frsh Cls; Rep Soph Cls; Var Capt Cheerleading; Coach Actv; Twrlr; Aerontcl Engnrng.

SCILINGO, BILL; Johnsonburg Area HS; Johnsonburg, PA; (3); Church Yth Grp; Red Cross Aide; Varsity Clb; Pres Frsh Cls; Pres Soph Cls; Pres Jr Cls; Pres Stu Cncl; Var Capt Bsktbl; L Var Tennis; Hon Roll; Intl Frgn Lang Awd 86; Ntl Acad Achvt Awd; Ntl Acad Achvt Awd 86; Engrng.

SCIOCHETTI, VICKI; Council Rock HS; Churchill, PA; (3); 149/908; Band; Concert Band; Mrchg Band; Pep Band; Symp Band; Sec Frsh Cls; Im Vllybl; Hon Roll; Bus Adm.

SCIOLA, JESSICA; Middletown Area HS; Middletown, PA; (3); Church Yth Grp; Cmnty Wkr; FBLA; Model UN; Teachers Aide; Yrbk Stf; Socl Welfare.

SCIORTINO, ANGELA RENEE; William Penn SR HS; York, PA; (3); 5/452; VP JA; Sec Ski Clb; Mrchg Band; School Musical; Symp Band; JV Golf; Var Mgr(s); Hon Roll; NHS; Prfct Atten Awd; 2nd Rnnr Up Employee Yr JA 84; Stu Mnth 85; Bus.

SCIULLO, ARMANDO; Central Catholic HS; Pittsburgh, PA; (3); 95/295; JA; JV Wrstlng; Hon Roll; Bio.

SCIULLO, NANCY; Saint Paul Cathedral HS; Pittsburgh, PA; (4); 16/54; Camera Clb; Exploring; JA; Chorus; Nwsp Stf; Yrbk Stf; Stu Cncl; U Of Pittsburgh; Dntstry.

SCLAN, RACHEL; Plymouth Whitemarsh HS; Plymouth Mtg, PA; (3); 41/356; School Musical; Off Jr Cls; Stu Cncl; Bsktbl; Powder Puff Ftbl; Swmmng; High Hon Roll; Jr NHS; Prfct Atten Awd.

SCLARSKY, KIMBERLY; Taylor Allderdice HS; Pittsburgh, PA; (2); AFS; Church Yth Grp; Hosp Aide; JA; DAR Awd; High Hon Roll; Prfct Atten Awd; PA JR Acad Sci 2nd Pl 86.

SCOBEL, PATRICIA; Valley HS; Arnold, PA; (3); 16/255; Church Yth Grp; Drama Clb; French Clb; Math Tm; Science Clb; Ski Clb; Band; Chorus; Church Choir.

SCOFF, TIMOTHY; Hickory HS; W Middlesex, PA; (2); Cmnty Wkr; Latin Clb; Band; Concert Band; Mrchg Band; Pep Band; Var Mgr(s); Stat Trk; Cert Merit Erie Cnty Chptr PA Soc Prfssnl Engrs 87; Engrng.

SCOLLICK, KEITH; Wyomissing Area HS; Shillington, PA; (4); 5/100; Chess Clb; Capt Quiz Bowl; Capt Scholastic Bowl; Capt Band; Capt Mrchg Band; School Musical; Yrbk Stf; Capt Var Bowling; NHS; French Clb; Astro.

SCOLNIK, CHRISSA J; Strath Haven HS; Wallingford, PA; (4); Co-Capt Drill Tm; School Musical; Nwsp Stf; Rep Stu Cncl; Cheerleading; High Hon Roll; Pres Schlr; Community Arts Ctr Awd 87; Temple U Pres Awd 87; Temple U; Pub Rltns.

SCOPELLITI, DEBI; Scranton Central HS; Scranton, PA; (4); 4/307; Church Yth Grp; Debate Tm; Drama Clb; Pres French Clb; NFL; Pep Clb; Speech Tm; SADD; Thesps; Stage Crew; Treverton Clark Awd; Pre-Med.

SCORAN, CATHY; Portage Area HS; Portage, PA; (4); 41/124; Chorus; Drm Mjr(t); Stage Crew; Stat Bsktbl; Trk; Nrs.

SCORZA, LARI; Charlerol SR HS; Charleroi, PA; (4); 5/162; Science Clb; SADD; Varsity Clb; Yrbk Ed-Chief; Off Sr Cls; Trs Stu Cncl; Capt Swmmng; Bausch & Lomb Sci Awd; High Hon Roll; Sec NHS; Penn ST; Pre-Med.

SCOTT, ANDREW P; Eisenhower HS; Bear Lk, PA; (3); 23/115; Pres VP 4-H; Varsity Clb; Rep Stu Cncl; Var L Bsktbl; Var L Ftbl; Var L Trk; 4-H Awd; High Hon Roll; Hon Roll; NHS.

SCOTT, ANN ELIZABETH; Conestoga SR HS; Paoli, PA; (2); Church Yth Grp; Orch; Ed Yrbk Stf; Var L Fld Hcky; Var L Lcrss; Var L Swmmng; High Hon Roll; Hon Roll; Apprctn Awd-Yrbk 86; Outstndng Acdmc Achvt & Prsdntl Acdmc Ftnss Awd Pgm 86; Outstndng Swmmr 86 & 85; Penn ST; Bus.

SCOTT, ANNETTE; Oswayo Valley HS; Shinglehouse, PA; (4); Ski Clb; Varsity Clb; Color Guard; Yrbk Stf; Trs Jr Cls; Bsktbl; Vllybl; Humn Svcs.

SCOTT, CAROLYNN; Ridley HS; Ridley Pk, PA; (2); 9/434; Pep Clb; Varsity Clb; Chorus; Trk; Vllybl; High Hon Roll; Hon Roll; Mst Imprvd Plyr Vllybl 86-87; MVP Sftbl Cmnty 86; Law.

SCOTT, CHARLES RICHARD; Coatesville Area SR HS; Coatesville, PA; (3); 36/509; Boy Scts; ROTC; Var Swmmng; God Cntry Awd; Hon Roll; NHS; Prfct Atten Awd; Eagle Sct Awd, & Cngrssmns Mdl Merit 86; Ceremnies Exec Order Arrow BSA 87.

SCOTT, CRAIG; Sharpsville Area HS; Sharpsville, PA; (3); 8/108; Ski Clb; Pres Frsh Cls; Rep Soph Cls; Trs Stu Cncl; Capt Ftbl; Wt Lftg; Wrstlng; Dnfth Awd; Hon Roll; NHS; Acdmc Achvt Ltr 84-85 & 85-86; USNMAA Awd 86; Lbrl Arts.

SCOTT, DARIELLE; Wallenpaupack HS; Hawley, PA; (3); French Clb; Hosp Aide; Office Aide; Band; Concert Band; Mrchg Band; Rep Stu Cncl; Bsktbl; Bowling; Cheerleading; Outstndng In Trk 84-85; MV Rnnr In Trk 85-87; Nrsng.

SCOTT, DEREK; Central HS Of Phldlph; Philadelphia, PA; (3); 147/520; French Clb; Hosp Aide; JV Trk; Central HS-BARNWELL Awd Bronze 86; Martin Luther King Schlrshp Awd 87; Pinceton U; Civil Engrng.

SCOTT, ELIZABETH; Churchill HS; Pittsburgh, PA; (4); 16/190; Ski Clb; Acpl Chr; Color Guard; Rep Stu Cncl; Sftbl; High Hon Roll; U Pittsburgh; Hlth.

SCOTT, GERALD; Archbishop Wood HS; Warminster, PA; (2); 23/254; Stage Crew; Rep Frsh Cls; Rep Soph Cls; JV Bsbl; JV Ftbl.

SCOTT, GREGORY; Penn-Trafford HS; Jeannette, PA; (3); 1/296; Boy Scts; Varsity Clb; Var Bsbl; L Capt Ftbl; L Capt Wrstlng; High Hon Roll; NHS; Ntl Merit Schol; Top 100 Wrstlrs 86-87; Gtwy Prss All Str Tm 86-87; USAF Acad; Elec.

SCOTT, HOLLY; Trinity HS; Washington, PA; (3); 33/389; Chorus; School Play; Stage Crew; Variety Show; Var L Bsktbl; Var L Socr; Var L Trk; High Hon Roll; Hon Roll; PA Gvnrs Schl Arts Semi-Fnlst-Drama 87; Sprts Sci.

SCOTT, JAY; Germantown HS; Philadelphia, PA; (3); Cit Awd; Hon Roll; Schl Of Comp Trng; Bus Admin.

SCOTT, JENNIFER; Trinity HS; Mechanicsburg, PA; (3); French Clb; Pep Clb; School Play; Nwsp Stf; Yrbk Stf; Rep Trs Stu Cncl; Var L Bsktbl; Stat Ftbl; Vllybl; High Hon Roll; Penn St; Lbrl Arts.

SCOTT, JOHN; Harry S Truman HS; Bristol, PA; (3); Church Yth Grp; SADD; Chorus; Jazz Band; Mrchg Band; School Musical; Hon Roll; NHS; Prfct Atten Awd; Temple U; Law.

SCOTT, JUDITH; Cambria Heights HS; Ebensburg, PA; (3); 31/180; 4-H; Band; Church Choir; Concert Band; Pep Band; Yrbk Stf; Hon Roll; IN U Of PA; Elem Education.

SCOTT, KEVIN; Cardinal O Hara HS; Broomall, PA; (3); 137/715; Church Yth Grp; Stage Crew; Im Bsktbl; Im Score Keeper; Prfct Atten Awd; Engrng.

SCOTT, KIMBERLY; Shippensburg Area SR HS; Shippensburg, PA; (3); 55/261; Art Clb; Camera Clb; SADD; Chorus; Color Guard; Hon Roll; Spanish NHS; Psychlgy.

SCOTT, KRISTIN; Hopewell Area SR HS; Aliquippa, PA; (3); 12/280; Sec Art Clb; Church Yth Grp; Exploring; Math Tm; Nwsp Stf; Var L Tennis; High Hon Roll; Pres NHS; Altrnt To PA Gov Schl Of Sci 87; Bio Rsrch Pgm At Seton Hill Coll 87; Bio.

SCOTT, LARENDA; Frankford HS; Philadelphia, PA; (3); 43/400; Library Aide; Church Choir; School Musical; Yrbk Stf; Rep Frsh Cls; Im Tennis; Var JV Vllybl; High Hon Roll; Hon Roll; Amer Lgn Awd 85; Lankaneu Hosp Of Nrsng; Nrsng.

SCOTT, LAURIE; Central Dauphin HS; Harrisburg, PA; (3); Church Yth Grp; 4-H; Girl Scts; Hosp Aide; Band; Concert Band; Mrchg Band; Trk; Hon Roll; Comp Prgrm.

SCOTT, LINDA; Ridgway Area HS; Ridgway, PA; (3); 1/105; Church Yth Grp; Girl Scts; Library Aide; Concert Band; Jazz Band; Mrchg Band; Pep Band; Var Trk; High Hon Roll; NHS; GS Gold Awd 87; SR Ldrshp Develpmnt 86; Band Capt 86-87; US Military Acad; Aeron Engr.

SCOTT, LYNN; Northern Cambria HS; Spangler, PA; (3); #8 In Class; Spanish Clb; Chorus; Color Guard; Var L Bsktbl; Var L Trk; High Hon Roll; Hon Roll; NHS; Spanish NHS; Med Tech.

SCOTT, MARCY; Penns Manor HS; Clymer, PA; (4); Camera Clb; SADD; Chorus; School Musical; High Hon Roll; Hon Roll; NHS; IN Bankers Assoc Schlrshp 87; IN U Of PA; Nrsng.

SCOTT, MARK; North Catholic HS; Pittsburgh, PA; (3); Church Yth Grp; Bsktbl; Hon Roll.

SCOTT, MARY; Slippery Rock Area HS; Slippery Rock, PA; (4); 5/183; VP Spanish Clb; School Play; Nwsp Rptr; Yrbk Bus Mgr; Yrbk Ed-Chief; Rep Stu Cncl; Capt Cheerleading; Capt Powder Puff Ftbl; High Hon Roll; NHS; Wmns Clb Schlrshp 87; Elk Stu Of Mnth 86; Butler Cnty Schlrshp 86; Pittsburgh U; Pre Med.

SCOTT, MELISSA JANE; Tunkhannock HS; Noxen, PA; (2); German Clb; Hon Roll; Pres Physcl Ftnss Awd 86; Ava Spc.

SCOTT, MICHELLE; Center HS; Aliquippa, PA; (3); Sec Church Yth Grp; Trs Spanish Clb; Varsity Clb; Sec Church Choir; Cheerleading; Mgr(s); Trk; Hon Roll; NHS; Bus.

SCOTT, MICHELLE; Loyalsock Township HS; Williamsport, PA; (3); French Clb; Sec Key Clb; Ski Clb; VP SADD; Trs Frsh Cls; Trs Soph Cls; Trs Jr Cls; Trs Stu Cncl; Var Cheerleading; Hon Roll.

SCOTT, NANCY; Warwick HS; Lititz, PA; (3); 25/267; Yrbk Phtg; Yrbk Rptr; Yrbk Stf; High Hon Roll; Womans Clb Ltry Awd 87.

SCOTT, NICOLE; Curwensville HS; Curwensville, PA; (3); Computer Clb; Trs French Clb; Pep Clb; Pres Band; Concert Band; Mrchg Band; Pep Band; VP Stu Cncl; Bsktbl; Capt Twrlr; Penn ST.

SCOTT, PEGGY; Lakeview HS; Stoneboro, PA; (4); 3/128; Pres Church Yth Grp; Science Clb; Varsity Clb; School Play; Yrbk Stf; Sec Jr Cls; Trs Stu Cncl; Stat Bsktbl; NHS; Boy Scts; Latin Schlr Awd 85; Stud Rep To Schl Brd 85-86; Pres Physcl Ftnss Awd 83-85; Math.

SCOTT, PRESTON; Marple Newtown SR HS; Newtown Square, PA; (3); 100/350; Cmnty Wkr; Ski Clb; Variety Show; Yrbk Phtg; Off Stu Cncl; Bsktbl; Ftbl; Trk; Wt Lftg; Hon Roll; Capt Indoor & Outdoor Track 86-87 & 87-88.

SCOTT, SAM; Butler Area SR HS; Butler, PA; (3); 4-H; Band; Church Choir; Concert Band; Mrchg Band.

SCOTT, SUSAN; Mechanicsburg Area SR HS; Mechanicsburg, PA; (4); 39/303; Band; Chorus; Church Choir; Concert Band; Mrchg Band; Orch; Symp Band; God Cntry Awd; High Hon Roll; Hon Roll; Penn ST Music Schlrshp; Penn ST U; Music Ed.

SCOTT, SUSAN; Tunkhannock Area HS; Tunkhannock, PA; (3); Fld Hcky; Trk; Cit Awd; Hon Roll; NHS; Pres Physcl Fit Awd 83-86; Frnch Ntl Merit Awd 84; Nrsng.

SCOTT, TELEAH V; John Harris HS; Harrisburg, PA; (3); 11/275; Church Yth Grp; Cmnty Wkr; Debate Tm; JA; Pep Clb; Speech Tm; Church Choir; Yrbk Stf; High Hon Roll; Ntl Merit Schol; Deta Sigma Theta Pag Miss Creativity, Scholar, Talent 86; Howard U; Crimnl Law.

SCOTT, TERI L; Shippensburg Area SR HS; Shippensburg, PA; (4); 37/216; Model UN; Capt Color Guard; School Musical; Sec Stu Cncl; Lion Awd; Spanish NHS; U Pittsburgh; Pol Sci.

SCOTT, WILLIAM; Juniata HS; Mifflintohn, PA; (4); Varsity Clb; Band; Concert Band; Jazz Band; Mrchg Band; Orch; Pep Band; School Musical; School Play; Var Bsbl; PA ST U; Arspc Engrng.

SCOTTI, STACEY; Bensalem HS; Bensalem, PA; (4); 101/500; GAA; Teachers Aide; Rep Sr Cls; Stu Cncl; Var JV Cheerleading; Mgr Ftbl; Mgr(s); Var Socr; High Hon Roll; Hon Roll; Scholar Awd 87; Outstndng SR Awd 87; Hnrb Mntn Suburban 1 Lg Girls Soccr Tm 84 & 87; Westchester U; Bus Mgmt.

SCOTTO, ELVIRA; Meadville Area SR HS; Meadville, PA; (3); 11/330; Church Yth Grp; Exploring; French Clb; JA; Chorus; Rep Frsh Cls; Rep Soph Cls; Mgr(s); High Hon Roll; Hon Roll; Pltcl Sci.

SCOUVART, MICHELE; Trinity Area HS; Washington, PA; (2); Art Clb; Church Yth Grp; Ski Clb; Var Score Keeper; Trk; Hon Roll; NHS; Pgh Yth Diocesan Yth Cncl 87-89; Psych.

SCRABIS, LYNN; Sto-Rox SR HS; Mc Kees Rocks, PA; (4); 1/138; Letterman Clb; Chorus; Nwsp Ed-Chief; Nwsp Rptr; Co-Capt JV Cheerleading; Bausch & Lomb Sci Awd; Hon Roll; NHS; Rotary Awd; Val; 3 Yr Hgh Schltc Av 87; Penn ST U; Comm.

SCRANTON, KAREN CELESTE; Meadville Area SR HS; Meadville, PA; (3); Church Yth Grp; FFA; German Clb; Library Aide; Church Choir; High Hon Roll; Scl Wrk.

SCRANTON, KRISTINE; Highlands HS; Natrona Heights, PA; (3); 41/311; Church Yth Grp; Chorus; Color Guard; Nwsp Rptr; Nwsp Stf; Rep Stu Cncl.

SCRIBNER, ERICA; Iroquois HS; Erie, PA; (4); 40/150; Model UN; Spanish Clb; Varsity Clb; Band; Concert Band; Jazz Band; Pep Band; Yrbk Stf; Bsktbl; Cheerleading; Ms Lawrence Pk 85-86; Athlt Yr 87-86; MVP Barringer Awd; Crozier Mem Awd Chrldr Bst Camp Awd; Behrend Coll.

SCRIP, JOE; Mon Valley Catholic HS; Monessen, PA; (3); Boy Scts; Bsbl; Bsktbl; French Hon Soc; Hon Roll; Nwspr Carrier Of Yr 84; Natl Sci Olympd 87; IN ST U; Bus.

SCRUTCHINS, JOAN ANDREA; Hopewell HS; Aliquippa, PA; (4); 15/240; Church Yth Grp; German Clb; Latin Clb; Band; Church Choir; Rep Frsh Cls; Stu Cncl; Var JV Cheerleading; High Hon Roll; NHS; Aliquippa Wmns Achvt Clb Outstndng Stu Of Yr 87; Negro Bus & Prfssnl Wmns Clb Awd Outstndng Achvt 87; Northwestern U; Pre Med.

SCULL, BARBARA; Upper Darby HS; Drexel Hill, PA; (3); Church Yth Grp; German Clb; Library Aide; Band; Concert Band; Drill Tm; Mrchg Band; Orch; Fld Hcky; Lcrss; Med.

SCULLEY, JAMES; Cathedral Prep; Erie, PA; (3); 8/193; Ntl Merit SF; Prfct Atten Awd; Mech Engr.

SCULLI, MONICA L; Cardinal O Hara HS; Springfield, PA; (4); 32/771; French Clb; Hosp Aide; Lit Mag; French Hon Soc; Hon Roll; NHS; Princpls Awd Acad Excllnce; Schltc Awd Fren IV; Drexel U; Civil Engrng.

SCURRY, BRENDA; Franklin HS; Franklin, PA; (4); Church Yth Grp; Hosp Aide; Letterman Clb; Varsity Clb; Bsktbl; Sftbl; Swmmng; Hon Roll; Brd Scchl Drcts Awd 85; Edinboro U PA; Cmmnctns.

SCUTTI, MARIA; Nazareth Acad; Phila, PA; (3); 21/125; Math Clb; Jazz Band; Orch; School Musical; Lit Mag; Jr NHS; Music Schlrshp At Sttlmnt Music Schl 86-88; JR Peer Cnslng 86-88; Music Rep 85-86; Drexel U; Music.

SCZESNIAK, EDWARD; Bishop O Hara HS; Jermyn, PA; (2); 10/127; Cmnty Wkr; JV Bsbl; JV Bsktbl; High Hon Roll.

SEABURN, SHARLET; Curwensville Area HS; Curwensville, PA; (3); Flag Corp; Off Jr Cls.

SEAGER, ERICK E; Bedford HS; Bedford, PA; (3); 88/198; Boy Scts; Church Yth Grp; Chorus; Stage Crew; Var Trk; Hon Roll; Pre Law.

SEAL, ANGIE; Oswayo Valley JR SR HS; Shinglehouse, PA; (3); 16/72; Chorus; Nwsp Rptr; Nwsp Stf; JV Bsktbl; Hon Roll; NHS; Enlsh Tchr.

SEAL, LAUREN; Marple-Newton HS; Newtown Sq, PA; (3); 49/322; Civic Clb; Office Aide; SADD; Rep Stu Cncl; JV Bsktbl; Bus.

SEALFON, ROBIN; Abington Hts HS; Clarks Summit, PA; (3); Hosp Aide; Pep Clb; Ski Clb; Temple Yth Grp; Cheerleading; Trk; Coachs Awd Chrldng 85-86; Northeastern ; Psychology.

SEALS, PETER; Quakertown Community HS; Quakertown, PA; (3); Math Clb; SADD; Stage Crew; Yrbk Stf; Var Trk; High Hon Roll; NHS; Ntl Merit Ltr; Camera Clb; Computer Clb; Acad Decathlete 87; JR Olympc Regnl Soccr Tm 85; NYU; Film Maker.

SEALS, TAWANA; Quaker Valley HS; Sewickley, PA; (2); Chorus; Hon Roll; Scholastics Awd 85-86.

SEAMAN, CHRIS; Hamburg Area HS; Hamburg, PA; (3); 9/170; Camera Clb; German Clb; Socr; High Hon Roll; Hon Roll; NHS; Grmn Natl Hnr Scty 86-87; Acad Lttr-Trig/Alg III 86-87; Acad Lttr Plane Geo 85-86; Elec Engnrng.

SEAMAN, DALE; East Juniata HS; Richfield, PA; (3); 12/83; Boy Scts; VICA; Band; Mrchg Band; JV Var Socr; Trk; Hon Roll; Order Arrow; Comp.

SEAMAN, DANIEL; East Juniata HS; Richfield, PA; (4); 11/80; Boy Scts; Band; Concert Band; Mrchg Band; Trs Jr Cls; Socr; Trk; Hon Roll; NHS; Pres Schlr; Elec Inst; Comp Tech.

SEAMAN, MARK; Sharon SR HS; Sharon, PA; (3); 8/185; Boys Clb Am; French Clb; Concert Band; Jazz Band; Mrchg Band; Pep Band; Nwsp Rptr; Stu Cncl; High Hon Roll; NHS; Rotry Holdy Yth Exchng Itly 87; Lang.

SEAMAN, PATRICK; Mc Guffey HS; Claysville, PA; (3); Boy Scts; JV Var Ftbl; Trk; Physcs.

SEAMAN, SHERYL; Peters Twp HS; Mcmurray, PA; (3); Church Yth Grp; Cmnty Wkr; FBLA; Varsity Clb; Yrbk Stf; Rep Stu Cncl; Var Bsktbl; Var Trk; Spanish NHS; Hmcmng Rep 86; Notre Dame; Bus.

SEAMAN, TARA; Quakertown SR HS; Quakertown, PA; (1); Spanish Clb; Cheerleading; Dance.

SEARER, GARY R; Hershey SR HS; Hershey, PA; (3); 2/200; Church Yth Grp; Computer Clb; Debate Tm; Quiz Bowl; Science Clb; High Hon Roll; NHS; Aud/Vis; Exploring; Mgr Bsktbl; PA Gov Schl Sci, Ag 86-87; Sci Olympd Rgnl ST Natl 13 Mdls 85-87; Engrng.

SEARFASS, MICHAEL; Parkland HS; Schnecksville, PA; (3); 14/481; Chess Clb; Exploring; Math Tm; Scholastic Bowl; Pres Science Clb; Rep Stu Cncl; Im Wt Lftg; High Hon Roll; NHS; Ntl Merit Ltr; Engr.

SEARFOSS, JOHN S; Jim Thorpe Area HS; Jim Thorpe, PA; (4); 30/90; Aud/Vis; Teachers Aide; Chorus; Stage Crew; VP Soph Cls; VP Jr Cls; VP Sr Cls; Stu Cncl; Mgr Pres Bsbl; Bsktbl; Registry For Excll In Phys Ed 87; Helbing Fllwshp Awd 87; HOBY Rep 85; E Stroudsburg U; Rec & Lei Mgt.

SEARFOSS, SUZANNE MARY; Allentown Central Catholic HS; Allentown, PA; (3); 11/235; Church Yth Grp; Trs FBLA; Sec JA; Key Clb; Math Clb; Service Clb; Spanish Clb; High Hon Roll; NHS; Natl Sci Merit Awd 85 & 86; Dale Carnegie Crs Effctv Spkng & Human Rltns 86-87.

SEARLE, SHAWN; Ringgold HS; Monongahela, PA; (1); Boy Scts; Band; Concert Band; Jazz Band; Mrchg Band; Var Crs Cntry; Var Wrstlng; Annapolis; Spc Aerontcs.

SEARLES, TERRI; Minersville Area HS; Minersville, PA; (3); 6/106; Spanish Clb; SADD; School Musical; Yrbk Stf; Stu Cncl; Var Crs Cntry; Var Sftbl; Var Vllybl; High Hon Roll; NHS; Psych.

SEARLS, COLEEN; Meadville Area SR HS; Meadville, PA; (4); 30/301; Church Yth Grp; Pres Hosp Aide; Spanish Clb; Rep Jr Cls; Rep Sr Cls; Stat Sftbl; High Hon Roll; Hon Roll; Estella Van Horne Schlrshp, Schlstc Hnr Soc 87; D Youville Coll; Phys Thrpy.

SEARS, JENNIFER; Valley HS; Arnold, PA; (2); Sec Exploring; Ski Clb; Mrchg Band; Twrlr; High Hon Roll; Bus.

SEARS, JUDITH; Little Flower Catholic HS; Philadelphia, PA; (3); 90/322; Exploring; Girl Scts; Concert Band; Jazz Band; Orch; School Musical; School Play; Nwsp Phtg; Rep Soph Cls; Rep Stu Cncl; Cert Awd Orchestra & Black Stu League 86-87; Culinary Arts.

SEASE, LESLIE; Waynesboro Area SR HS; Waynesboro, PA; (3); Church Yth Grp; Library Aide; Chorus; Mrchg Band; Nwsp Rptr; High Hon Roll; Hon Roll; NHS; Engl.

SEATON, BRYAN; Brownsville HS; New Salem, PA; (3); Boy Scts; Church Yth Grp; Drama Clb; Math Tm; Ski Clb; SADD; Band; Drm Mjr(t); Mrchg Band; Rep Frsh Cls; Penn ST; Bus.

SEAVER, MAUREEN; Panther Valley HS; Lansford, PA; (2); 35/120; Aud/Vis; Drama Clb; Library Aide; Ski Clb; Chorus; Drill Tm; Flag Corp; Mrchg Band; School Musical; Yrbk Stf; W Chester; Social Work.

SEAY, TANYA; Steelton HS; Steelton, PA; (3); 62/102; Cmnty Wkr; Computer Clb; Spanish Clb; Band; Church Choir; Mrchg Band; Yrbk Stf; Fld Hcky; Vllybl; Hon Roll; Yth Ftns Achvt Awd 83-84; Vlybl Cup 84-85; Intramurals; Bus Admin.

SEBASTIAN, BETH A; Open Door Christian Acad; Saltsburg, PA; (4); Library Aide; Quiz Bowl; Chorus; Yrbk Ed-Chief; Vllybl; Psych.

SEBASTINELLI, RONNIE; Valley View JR SR HS; Jessup, PA; (4); 50/198; Pep Clb; Spanish Clb; Yrbk Phtg; Yrbk Rptr; Yrbk Stf; Var L Ftbl; Var Capt Trk; Im Vllybl; Im Wt Lftg; Ftbl Cptn 83; Wilkes; Pltcl Sci.

SEBEK JR, RONALD J; Mount Pleasant Area HS; Mt Pleasant, PA; (3); 18/250; Church Yth Grp; Cmnty Wkr; Debate Tm; Political Wkr; Science Clb; Yrbk Stf; JV Var Bsktbl; Golf; Cit Awd; Gov Hon Prg Awd; Amer Lgn Awd 85; Prncpls Awd 85; Case Western Reserve; Engr Nuke.

SEBRING, MITCHELL CORY; Hempfield Area HS; Greensburg, PA; (2); Art Clb; Cmnty Wkr; Computer Clb; Red Cross Aide; Im Bsktbl; Im Vllybl; High Hon Roll; Jr NHS; Prfct Atten Awd; Pres Schlr; Carnegie Mellon; Elec Engrng.

SEBULSKY, RAY; Blairsville SR HS; Blairsville, PA; (1); Capt Ftbl; High Hon Roll; Engrng.

SEBURN III, JESS; West Hazleton HS; Sugarloaf, PA; (2); Chess Clb; Trs Church Yth Grp; Yrbk Bus Mgr; Var Bowling; Hon Roll; Prfct Atten Awd; Penn ST; Econ.

SECCO, JENNIFER; St Marys Area HS; Kersey, PA; (1); Capt Cheerleading; L Gym; Hon Roll; Bus.

SECHLER, JARROD; Turkeyfoot Valley HS; Addison, PA; (1); Ski Clb; Pres Frsh Cls; JV Capt Ftbl; Wt Lftg; High Hon Roll.

SECHRIST, AMBER; Susquehannock HS; Shrewsbury, PA; (3); 9/194; AFS; Church Yth Grp; School Play; Yrbk Stf; Rep Jr Cls; Rep Sr Cls; Mgr(s); High Hon Roll; Hon Roll; NHS; BYU; Law.

SECHRIST, MICHAEL; Yough HS; Ruffsdale, PA; (3); 41/249; Spanish Clb; High Hon Roll; Prfct Atten Awd; Secndry Educ.

SECKINGER, SARAH; Peabody HS; Pittsburgh, PA; (4); #1 In Class; JCL; Ski Clb; Yrbk Phtg; Var Crs Cntry; Swmmng; Trk; High Hon Roll; NHS; PA Gvrnrs Schl Sci 86; Sci.

SECKO, ELANA; Greensburg Central Catholic HS; Irwin, PA; (3); 8/246; AFS; Church Yth Grp; Exploring; Ski Clb; Var Mgr(s); JV Powder Puff Ftbl; High Hon Roll; NHS.

SECOR, LAURA; State Coll Area Intermediate HS; State College, PA; (2); 47/528; Church Yth Grp; Intnl Clb; Model UN; Nwsp Ed-Chief; Yrbk Bus Mgr; Lit Mag; Rep Soph Cls; 2nd Pl Wind In The Willows Crtv Wrtng Cont 85; Intl Rltns.

SECRISKEY, KATHY; Forest Hills HS; Sidman, PA; (4); Pep Clb; Band; Concert Band; Sec Trs Mrchg Band; Hon Roll; U Of Pittsburgh; Phys Thrpy.

SEDDON, CHERYL; Lock Haven HS; Castanea, PA; (4); German Clb; SADD; Awd For Outstndng Excllnc In Chld Care 87; Lock Haven U; Home Ec Ed.

SEDER, CHRISSY; Portage Area HS; Portage, PA; (3); 11/118; Science Clb; Varsity Clb; Stat Bsktbl; L Trk; Var L Vllybl; Hon Roll; NHS; Elctrcl Engr.

SEDERBURG JR, LOREN NEIL; Sheffield JR SR HS; Tiona, PA; (4); 2/74; Pres Computer Clb; SADD; Jazz Band; Mrchg Band; Pep Band; School Play; JETS Awd; NHS; Pres Schlr; Sal; PA ST; Elec Engrng.

SEDLAK, MARK; Belle Vernon Area HS; Belle Vernon, PA; (3); Art Clb; JA; Library Aide; Band; Trs Soph Cls; Powder Puff Ftbl; Socr; High Hon Roll; NHS; Sci Engrng.

SEDLAK, SUZANNE; Meadville Area SR HS; Meadville, PA; (4); Orch; Nwsp Stf; Ed Yrbk Stf; Rep Jr Cls; Rep Stu Cncl; Co-Capt Tennis; Hon Roll; NHS; Japan-US Schlrshp Rnnr Up 85; Natl Math Cntst 86; Edinboro Hist Day Awd 85; Allegheny Coll; Pre-Law.

SEDLMEYER, TROY; North Star HS; Holsopple, PA; (3); 1/141; Church Yth Grp; FCA; Mu Alpha Theta; Teachers Aide; Hon Roll; Spnsh Quiz Team 3rd Pl 86; Mu Alpha Theta Indctn Awd 86; Bstrs Clb Stud Mnth Awds 86; Comp Prog.

SEDOROVICH, JAMES; Hanover Area HS; Ashley, PA; (3); Church Yth Grp; FCA; SADD; Rep Frsh Cls; Rep Soph Cls; Rep Stu Cncl; JV Bsktbl; L Capt Ftbl; Var L Trk; Var Capt Wt Lftg.

SEDUSKI, EDWARD S; Du Bois Area HS; Penfield, PA; (3); 20/326; L Var Bsbl; Hon Roll; Vtrnry Med.

SEDWICK, RAYMOND; Karns City JR/Sr HS; Chicora, PA; (3); 1/140; Computer Clb; Spanish Clb; Mrchg Band; School Play; Symp Band; Golf; Cit Awd; High Hon Roll; NHS; Am Leg Boys St; PA JR Acad Sci 1st Pl ST 84-87; PA JR Acad Sci 2nd Pl Region 86; Aero.

SEEBER, JUDITH ANNE; Bishop Conwell HS; Langhorne, PA; (3); 20/277; Cmnty Wkr; Library Aide; SADD; Nwsp Rptr; Nwsp Stf; Bsktbl; Coach Actv; High Hon Roll; Hon Roll; NHS.

SEEBOLD, CINDIE; Mifflinburg Area HS; Lewisburg, PA; (1); French Clb; Key Clb; JV Cheerleading; JV Fld Hcky; Hon Roll; Bloomsburg U; Teachng.

SEEBOLD, DAWN; West Snyder HS; Troxelville, PA; (2); 4-H; VP SADD; Varsity Clb; Chorus; School Musical; Stu Cncl; Cheerleading; Int Dcrtr.

SEEDS, MEGAN; Cardinal O Hara HS; Broomall, PA; (4); 30/775; VP Church Yth Grp; Political Wkr; Chorus; Church Choir; School Play; Yrbk Ed-Chief; Hon Roll; NHS; Philadelphia Coll-Phrmcy/Sci Pres Schlrshp 87; Villanova U; Math.

SEELEY, BRENDA; Lake Lehman HS; Dallas, PA; (4); Drama Clb; Pep Clb; SADD; School Play; Var Capt Cheerleading; Var Pom Pon; Stat Trk; Hon Roll; Varsity Clb; Variety Show; Marywood Coll; Psych.

SEEM, ALAN D; Riverview HS; Oakmont, PA; (4); 1/120; Trs AFS; Boy Scts; VP Band; Jazz Band; Nwsp Bus Mgr; Var Bsktbl; Var Capt Golf; High Hon Roll; NHS; Ntl Merit SF.

SEERGAE, MELISSA; Bishop Mc Devitt HS; Harrisburg, PA; (3); FBLA; Hosp Aide; Service Clb; Chorus; Yrbk Stf; Cheerleading; Penn ST; Nrsng.

SEERY, JENNIFER; Ringgold HS; Finleyville, PA; (3); Library Aide; Speech Tm; Variety Show; Nwsp Stf; Hon Roll; Rotary Awd; Amer Lgn Hnrble Mntn 85.

SEESE, MATTHEW; Homer Center JR-SR HS; Homer City, PA; (3); Band; Concert Band; Jazz Band; Mrchg Band; Nwsp Rptr; Nwsp Stf; Wlms Port Area CC; Wldlf Tech.

SEESE, MICHAEL; Brownsville Area HS; Brownsville, PA; (4); #17 In Class; Chess Clb; Ski Clb; High Hon Roll; Elec Engr.

SEESHOLTZ, KIMBERLY; Bishop Mc Cort HS; Johnstown, PA; (4); 6/133; German Clb; Mu Alpha Theta; Spanish Clb; Chorus; Concert Band; Mrchg Band; Off Orch; High Hon Roll; NHS; Pres Schlr; Arion Awd 87; Band Dedctn Awd 87; Grl Of Mnth 86; U Of Pittsburgh; Elem Educ.

SEEWALD, JEFF; Chartiers Valley HS; Pittsburgh, PA; (3); Hosp Aide; Model UN; Service Clb; Temple Yth Grp; Nwsp Ed-Chief; NHS; Ellen Rudto Yth Schlrshp Awd 86; Chem Olympics 86-87; Engrng.

SEGAL, AMIT; Allderdice HS; Pittsburgh, PA; (2); Ski Clb; Temple Yth Grp; Orch; Hon Roll; Math & Vrbl Tlnt Srch Johns Hopkins U ST Awd 84.

SEGAL, ELLEN; Council Rock HS; Richboro, PA; (2); Cmnty Wkr; Var Crs Cntry; Var L Trk; High Hon Roll; Hon Roll; Schltc Awd 87; Cross Country League Chmps 86-87; Trk League Chmps 87; Law.

SEGAL, ELLEN; Pennsbury HS; Yardley, PA; (3); 19/770; Cmnty Wkr; Hosp Aide; Spanish Clb; VP Trs Temple Yth Grp; Yrbk Ed-Chief; Yrbk Stf; High Hon Roll; NHS; Tmrrws Ldrs Cnfrnc Rotry Intl 87; Pennsbury Smmr Schl Abrd Spain 85; Nrsng.

SEGAL, STEPHANIE; Pennsbury HS; Yardley, PA; (4); 13/770; Nwsp Rptr; Var Swmmng; Hon Roll; NHS; Time Mag Art Cover Natl Fin 87; Natl Yng Ldrs Conf 87; Pres Yng Embroiderers Amer 87; U MD; Govt.

SEGEBART, CHRIS; Millersburg Area HS; Millersburg, PA; (3); Am Leg Aux Girls St; Art Clb; Library Aide; Pep Clb; Spanish Clb; Yrbk Stf; Cheerleading; YMCA Yth Vol Yr 85; Harrisburg Area CC; Elem Ed.

SEGER, JULIE; Reynolds HS; Fredonia, PA; (3); 27/1159; Latin Clb; Chorus; Concert Band; Rep Trs Stu Cncl; Var Capt Cheerleading; Trk; Wt Lftg; Sci.

SEGER, TAMMY; Curwensville Area HS; Grampian, PA; (4); 37/114; VP DECA; Stage Crew; Nwsp Rptr; Nwsp Stf; VP Frsh Cls; VP Soph Cls; Pres Jr Cls; Pres Sr Cls; Cit Awd; Hon Roll; Prsdntl Athlt Awd 87; Du Bois Business Coll; Accntng.

SEGERMARK, SUZANNE M; Radnor HS; Wayne, PA; (4); 107/296; Chorus; Church Choir; Orch; School Musical; Latin Clb; Acpl Chr; Band; Concert Band; Mrchg Band; Natl Orchestra Awd 87; Penn ST U; Music Educ.

SEGESSENMAN, JENNIFER; Biglerville HS; Arendtsville, PA; (4); 8/79; Church Yth Grp; SADD; Concert Band; Mrchg Band; Pep Band; Yrbk Stf; JV Bsktbl; High Hon Roll; NHS; Pres Schlr; Natl Sojrnrs 86; LV Stck Sci Awd 87; Eastern Bapt Coll; Sci.

SEGRAVE-DALY, SHEILA; Villa Maria Acad; West Chester, PA; (3); 20/97; Dance Clb; High Hon Roll; Hon Roll; Girl Scts; Villanova U; Bus.

SEHULSTER, DONALD; Delaware Valley HS; Shohola, PA; (3); Drama Clb; Band; Chorus; Church Choir; School Musical; VP Soph Cls; VP Jr Cls; Var JV Bsktbl; NHS; PA Gvrnrs Schl For Arts 86; Opera.

SEIBERT, BETH; Cedar Crest HS; Lebanon, PA; (4); 53/312; Church Yth Grp; French Clb; Latin Clb; Pep Clb; Political Wkr; Band; Orch; Cheerleading; Diving; Socr; Hofstra U; Dentist.

SEIBERT, DAVID; Meadowbrook Christian HS; Milton, PA; (3); VP Church Yth Grp; Spanish Clb; Teachers Aide; Pres Frsh Cls; Pres Soph Cls; Pres Jr Cls; Pres Sr Cls; Var Capt Socr; High Hon Roll; Prfct Atten Awd; Bible Memory KCEA Comp 1st Regnls & ST 86; Chem Awd 1st 86; Hstrya Wd 1st 86; IN U PA; Alg.

SEIBERT, DIANNE STEPHANIE; Peters Township HS; Library, PA; (3); Ski Clb; Flag Corp; Mrchg Band; Yrbk Stf; Stu Cncl; Twrlr; Hon Roll; Rnnr Up Miss Loves Baby Sft Mdlng Cmptn 85; GATE Pgm ,4-88; Psych.

SEIBERT, ERIC; Spring Grove Area HS; E Berlin, PA; (3); 1/301; Church Yth Grp; Drama Clb; Band; Chorus; Church Choir; School Musical; Trk; High Hon Roll; NHS; Pres Schlr.

SEID, ALAN; Churchill HS; Pittsburgh, PA; (4); 25/193; Trs Band; Trs Concert Band; Trs Mrchg Band; Trs Orch; Stu Cncl; High Hon Roll; Womes Club Of Churchill Achvt 87; U Of Pittsburgh; Sci Engr.

SEIDEL, JOHN; Hamburg Area HS; Hamburg, PA; (3); German Clb; Military Police.

SEIDEL, MARK; Oley Valley HS; Fleetwood, PA; (3); 26/142; Band; Concert Band; Jazz Band; Mrchg Band; Pep Band; Var Crs Cntry; Hon Roll; NHS; Distingshd Expert Marksmanship Awd 85; Pre-Law.

SEIDEL, SUSAN; W Perry SR HS; Blain, PA; (3); 23/221; Church Yth Grp; French Clb; Varsity Clb; Bsktbl; Trk; Vllybl; Hon Roll; Physcl Thrpy.

SEIDEL, TED; Hamburg Area HS; Shoemakersville, PA; (3); SADD; Crs Cntry; Trk; Culinary Artst.

SEIDEL, TROY; Kutztown Area HS; Kutztown, PA; (3); Pres VP FFA; High Hon Roll; NHS; Prfct Atten Awd; FFA Schlrshp 85; FFA Outstndng Ldrshp Awd, Rotary Stu Mnth 87; Frm Mgr.

SEIDEN, JENNIFER; Upper Dublin HS; Dresher, PA; (3); Intnl Clb; Capt Pep Clb; SADD; Temple Yth Grp; Varsity Clb; Yrbk Stf; Capt Cheerleading; Hon Roll; NHS; Fshn Merch.

SEIFERT, CARLA; Austin Area Schl; Austin, PA; (3); 6/32; Sec Chorus; Nwsp Stf; Yrbk Phtg; Yrbk Stf; Soph Cls; Jr Cls; JV Bsktbl; JV Var Vllybl; Hon Roll; U Pittsburg Bradford Camp Smmr Acad Gftd & Tlntd 86; Dist Chrous Rep 87; IN U Of PA; Acctg.

SEIFRIT, DAVID WILLIAM; Garden Spot HS; Denver, PA; (2); Exploring; Stage Crew; Crs Cntry; Trk; Hon Roll; Ntl Amer Inds Arts Stu Assn 86; AIASA St 1st Pl Metric 500 Dragster Cont 87; Biochemist.

SEIGER, GREGORY; Red Land HS; Lewisberry, PA; (3); 89/329; Am Leg Boys St; Church Yth Grp; Band; Chorus; Concert Band; Mrchg Band; Orch; School Musical; Stu Cncl; Hon Roll; Tour Europe Amer Music 87; Band Pres 88; Acctng.

SEIGHMAN, ROXANN; Ringgold HS; Monongahela, PA; (4); Chorus; Hon Roll.

SEILER, DEBRA; Archbishop Prendergast HS; Drexel Hill, PA; (3); 58/327; FBLA; Intnl Clb; Trs Latin Clb; Office Aide; Spanish Clb; Rep Stu Cncl; Var Fld Hcky; Capt Sftbl; Hon Roll; 4-H; Pres Of HS CYO 87; Rep Fo Rgn On CYO Conv 84-87; Mgmt.

SEILER, TANYA; Avella Area JR & SR HS; Avella, PA; (3); Art Clb; Church Yth Grp; Girl Scts; Church Choir; Yrbk Stf; Hon Roll; Pre-Law.

SEIP, STEVEN M; Northern Lehigh HS; Walnutport, PA; (3); 3/166; Boy Scts; Rep Stu Cncl; Var L Bsbl; Var L Bsktbl; Var L Crs Cntry; JV Var Ftbl; High Hon Roll; NHS; Rotary Awd; Penn ST U; Engr.

SEISCIO, JILL; Pottsgrove HS; Pottstown, PA; (4); 5/228; Debate Tm; German Clb; Key Clb; Latin Clb; Pep Clb; Science Clb; Ski Clb; SADD; Teachers Aide; Varsity Clb; Brown Bk Awd 86; Golden Awd Vrsty Yrs Of Chrng 86; Dickinson Coll; Pre Law.

SEISS, JEFFREY; Steel Valley HS; Munhall, PA; (3); Exploring; Band; Mrchg Band; Rep Frsh Cls; Rep Soph Cls; Rep Jr Cls; Rep Sr Cls; Var Bsbl; Hon Roll; NHS.

SEITH, AMY; Faith Christian School; Southampton, PA; (2); Church Yth Grp; Drama Clb; Chorus; High Hon Roll; Hon Roll; Rep Frsh Cls; Cheerleading; Soclgy.

SEITZ, AMY; Perry Traditional Acad; Pittsburgh, PA; (3); 1/190; Church Yth Grp; Band; Concert Band; Mrchg Band; Yrbk Stf; High Hon Roll; NHS; Ed.

SEITZ, GREG; Moniteau JR SR HS; West Sunbury, PA; (1); Math Tm; Spanish Clb; Band; Concert Band; Jazz Band; Mrchg Band; Orch; Pep Band; High Hon Roll; Hon Roll.

SEITZ, LAURA; Moniteau JR SR HS; West Sunbury, PA; (3); 52/136; Drama Clb; French Clb; Library Aide; Chorus; Flag Corp; School Play; Trk; ICM Schl Of Bus; Comp Mgmt.

SEITZ, MELISSA; Elizabethtown Area HS; Elizabethtown, PA; (3); 73/224; JA; JV Var Cheerleading; Var Tennis; Accntng.

SEITZ, RENEE; Mary Fuller Frazier HS; Perryopolis, PA; (4); Ski Clb; Spanish Clb; Mrchg Band; Stat Bsktbl; Var Cheerleading; Var Powder Puff Ftbl; Hon Roll; Slippery Rock U; Comm.

SEITZINGER, KATHY; Allentown Central Catholic; Macungie, PA; (3); Cmnty Wkr; Key Clb; Pep Clb; Service Clb; Spanish Clb; Rep Frsh Cls; Rep Soph Cls; Rep Jr Cls; Hon Roll; Nrsng.

SEKELIK, DONALD S; Chartiers Valley HS; Carnegie, PA; (4); 14/299; Church Yth Grp; Var JV Bsbl; Presdntl Acad Fit Awds Prog 87; PA ST U; Math.

SEKELLICK, KRISTIN M; Boyertown Jr HS; Frederick, PA; (1); Church Yth Grp; Mrchg Band; Rep Stu Cncl; Var Fld Hcky; Var Lcrss; High Hon Roll; Spcl Rcgntn Plqs For All A 84-86; VP Pres Of Band 86-87.

SEKERA, TAMMY; Riverview HS; Verona, PA; (4); 28/120; Office Aide; Band; Capt Color Guard; Yrbk Phtg; Yrbk Stf; Off Jr Cls; Powder Puff Ftbl; Hon Roll; NEDT Awd 85; Stu Cncl Schlshrp 87; Forbes Rd E AVTS Hnrs 85-86; Robert Morris; Consmr Mktng.

SEKOL, ALLISON; Delaware Valley HS; Matamoras, PA; (3); 11/150; 4-H; Ski Clb; Chorus; Stat Bsktbl; Var L Fld Hcky; Var L Sftbl; High Hon Roll; Hon Roll; Pres NHS; Pre-Med.

SELBEL, DALE; Moon HS; Coraopolis, PA; (2); JV L Bsbl; JV Var Ftbl; Hon Roll.

SELBY, JONATHAN; Mt Lebanon HS; Pittsburgh, PA; (2); Church Yth Grp; Exploring; Ski Clb; JV Diving; Hon Roll.

SELBY, JULIE; Freedom HS; Easton, PA; (4); 94/433; Drama Clb; German Clb; JA; Pep Clb; Chorus; Nwsp Phtg; Yrbk Phtg; Mgr(s); Shippensburg U; Pblc Rltns.

SELCHER, CRAIG; Elizabethtown Area HS; Elizabethtown, PA; (3); 45/248; Drama Clb; Model UN; Thesps; Band; Concert Band; Mrchg Band; Pep Band; School Musical; School Play; Stage Crew; Poly Sci.

SELDOMRIDGE, BONNY; Brandywine Heights HS; Mertztown, PA; (4); Trs Art Clb; Sec 4-H; Band; Concert Band; Dance Awd 86; Dance Cert 87; Schl Imprvmnt Hnr Art 87; PA ST U; Lbrl Arts.

SELDOMRIDGE, BRENT; Pequea Valley HS; Gap, PA; (3); 3/125; Church Yth Grp; FFA; Varsity Clb; Var Cmnty Wkr; Bausch & Lomb Sci Awd; Hon Roll; NHS; Math.

SELEMBO, ANGELA; Ringgold HS; Eighty Four, PA; (3); 4-H; Stu Cncl; CA U; Med.

SELER, JENNIFER; West Snyder HS; Mc Clure, PA; (3); 15/142; Pep Clb; Ski Clb; Spanish Clb; Drill Tm; Flag Corp; Tennis; High Hon Roll; Hon Roll; NHS; Prfct Atten Awd; Spnsh Tchr.

SELFE, AMY; Lock Haven SR HS; Lock Haven, PA; (3); School Play; Yrbk Rptr; Sec Jr Cls; Sec Stu Cncl; Var Capt Cheerleading; Swmmng; Lock Haven U.

SELFON, DORI; York Suburban HS; York, PA; (3); VP Church Yth Grp; Girl Scts; SADD; Temple Yth Grp; School Play; Stat Socr; Var Sftbl; Fash Mdsg.

SELL, ANITA; Holy Name HS; Leesport, PA; (3); 1/122; Cmnty Wkr; Trs Exploring; JA; Q&S; Yrbk Ed-Chief; NHS; Ntl Merit SF; Val; Aud/Vis; Church Yth Grp; Gvrnr Schl Sci 87; Readg Oratrcl Cntst 1st Pl Schlrshp Rtry Clb 87; Berks Cnty Pharm Assn Awd 86; Pre-Med.

SELL, KATHLEEN; Penns Manor HS; Barnesboro, PA; (3); Camera Clb; SADD; Varsity Clb; Yrbk Stf; JV Var Bsktbl; Hon Roll; Elem Ed.

SELLARI, SUSAN; Valley HS; New Kensington, PA; (3); Drama Clb; Ski Clb; Chorus; Church Choir; Stu Cncl; JV Var Cheerleading; High Hon Roll; Hon Roll; Dramatic Arts.

SELLECK, MARK N; Clarion-Limestone HS; Clarion, PA; (4); 1/85; Am Leg Boys St; Drama Clb; Varsity Clb; Nwsp Ed-Chief; Pres Jr Cls; Rep Stu Cncl; Tennis; Trk; Val; Babson Coll; Intl Bus.

SELLERS, PAULA; Center HS; Monaca, PA; (3); Church Yth Grp; Spanish Clb; Band; Concert Band; Mrchg Band; Pep Band; Bsktbl; Prfct Atten Awd.

SELLMAN, PATRICIA M; Upper Merion Area HS; King Of Prussia, PA; (4); 34/309; Fld Hcky; Lcrss; Hon Roll; NHS; Pres Schlr; Ithaca Coll; Phys Ther.

SELSER, MICHELLE; Hatboro-Horsham HS; Horsham, PA; (3); Var Crs Cntry; Powder Puff Ftbl; Var Trk; Hon Roll; Bus Awd 85; Hnbl Mntn Subrbn I Freedm Leag Tripl Jmp 87; Comp Aid Grphcs.

SELTNER, JOSEPH; Northeast Catholic HS; Philadelphia, PA; (2); 22/363; Hon Roll; Prfct Atten Awd; Drexel U; Comp Engr.

SELTZ, JOSET; Aliquippa HS; Aliquippa, PA; (3); Church Yth Grp; Exploring; French Clb; Stat Score Keeper; Hon Roll; Psychiatrst.

SELTZER, LYNN; Benton Area JR-SR HS; Benton, PA; (4); 18/49; Keywanettes; Flag Corp; Trs Soph Cls; Trs Jr Cls; Trs Sr Cls; NHS; Rtl Clthng.

SELVERIAN, CHRISTOPHER; Marple Newton SR HS; Newtown Square, PA; (3); 82/325; Boy Scts; Church Yth Grp; Drama Clb; Ski Clb; School Play; Nwsp Stf; Trs Soph Cls; Pres Jr Cls; Rep Stu Cncl; Var Tennis; Lehigh; Finance.

SELWAY, MICHAEL; Trinity HS; Washington, PA; (4); 25/325; Letterman Clb; Bsbl; Bsktbl; Coach Actv; Ftbl; Wt Lftg; High Hon Roll; Hon Roll; Akron U; Bus.

SEMAN, RANDY; Frazier HS; Perryopolis, PA; (3); JV Bsbl; Penn ST; Comp Sci.

SEMANCHICK, STANLEY A; Nativity B V M HS; Pottsville, PA; (4); Hon Roll; Wilkes Coll; Elec Engrng.

SEMANS, KRISTI; Frazier HS; Perryopolis, PA; (3); Ski Clb; Off Jr Cls; Trs Sr Cls; Capt Powder Puff Ftbl; Hon Roll; JR Clss Treas 86-87; Prom Comm 86-87; Almst Anythg Goes 85-86; Vet.

SEMENTELLI, ARTHUR; Cathedral Prep; Erie, PA; (3); 23/193; VP Exploring; Latin Clb; L Swmmng; High Hon Roll; Hon Roll; Outdrs Clb 85-86; US Navl Acad; Chem.

SEMENZA, GINA; Old Forge HS; Old Forge, PA; (4); Yrbk Stf; Stu Cncl; JV Var Cheerleading; High Hon Roll; Hon Roll; NHS; Pharmacy.

SEMENZA, MICHELLE; Old Forge HS; Old Forge, PA; (2); Ski Clb; Spanish Clb; Cheerleading; Hon Roll.

SEMIC, BETH; Central Dauphin East HS; Harrisburg, PA; (4); Pres Church Yth Grp; Chorus; Sec Soph Cls; Sec Jr Cls; Sec Sr Cls; Capt Cheerleading; Hon Roll; NHS; VFW Awd; French Clb; VFW-VOICE Of Democracy Spch Cntst Wnnr & Svc As Sec On Cls Cncl Medal 86-87; PA ST U; Comms.

SEMINARA, CARMELO; St John Neumann HS; Philadelphia, PA; (3); 109/349; Church Yth Grp; Im Bsbl; Hon Roll; Penn ST.

SEMMELROTH, LAURA; Merion Mercy Acad; Drexel Pk, PA; (4); Camera Clb; Cmnty Wkr; French Clb; Service Clb; Stage Crew; Ed Yrbk Stf; Ntl Art Hnr Soc Membr 86,Ntl Art Hnr Soc Awd For Achvt 86-87; Moore Coll Art Schlrshp; Drexel U; Intrior Dsgn.

SEMPLE JR, EDWARD R; Mt Union Area HS; Mt Union, PA; (4); 20/162; Am Leg Boys St; FBLA; Im Bsktbl; Hon Roll; NHS; Sth Hills Bus Schl; Accntng.

SEN, CHAITALI; Pennsbury HS; Morrisville, PA; (3); French Clb; Hosp Aide; Concert Band; Yrbk Stf; Hon Roll; NHS; PA Govs Schl Of Intl Studies 86; Natl Cncl Tchrs Engl Awd 87; Bucks Co Ldrshp Acad 87; Social Science.

SENETA, WENDY; Northwestern HS; Albion, PA; (3); 43/145; Church Yth Grp; Library Aide; Chorus; Sftbl; Hon Roll; St Vincent Schl/Nrsng; RN.

SENN, MICHELLE; Hopewell HS; Aliquippa, PA; (3); Church Yth Grp; Red Cross Aide; VICA; Chorus; Church Choir; School Musical; Powder Puff Ftbl; Hon Roll; Sewickly Vly Schl; Nursing.

SENOSKI, CAROLYN; St Paul Cathedral HS; Pittsburgh, PA; (3); Cmnty Wkr; Drama Clb; French Clb; Pres Red Cross Aide; Stage Crew; Nwsp Stf; Yrbk Stf; High Hon Roll; NHS; Frnch Awd 85; Schlrshp Course Chatham Coll 86; Red Crss Awd 86; Chatham; Med.

SENSENIG, KATHLEEN A; Lancaster Mennonite HS; New Holland, PA; (3); Art Clb; Church Yth Grp; Drama Clb; Chorus; Orch; Nwsp Rptr; 1 Of Top 18 Bible Qzzng 87; Gold Key & Hnrbl Mntn In Schlstcs Art Show 87; Fine Art.

SENSER, GREGORY J; MMI Preparatory Schl; Mountaintop, PA; (4); Aud/Vis; Chess Clb; Pep Clb; Ski Clb; Variety Show; Yrbk Phtg; Yrbk Rptr; Yrbk Stf; Sec Sr Cls; Var Bsbl; PA Jr Acad Of Sci-2nd & 3rd Pl Rgnl Awds 84-85 & 86-87; St Josephs U; Bus.

SENSS, SUSAN; St Maria Goretti HS; Philadelphia, PA; (4); Church Yth Grp; Computer Clb; GAA; Science Clb; Chorus; School Musical; VP Stage Crew; Nwsp Phtg; Nwsp Rptr; High Hon Roll; West Chestern U; Bio.

SENWESKY, JOHN; Coatesville Area SR HS; Coatesville, PA; (3); French Clb; Hon Roll; Meterolgy.

SEO, DAVID; Governor Mifflin HS; Reading, PA; (3); 2/320; Chess Clb; Trs Key Clb; Model UN; Nwsp Rptr; Var Tennis; Var Trk; High Hon Roll; Hon Roll; NHS; Ntl Merit SF; Philadelphia Clsscl Leag Ltn Slvr Mdl 87; Med.

SEPHAKIS JR, THOMAS; Ambridge Area HS; Sewickley, PA; (3); Hon Roll; Penn ST U; Bus Admin.

SEPHTON, SHARLENE; St Basil Acad; Philadelphia, PA; (3); 3/89; Computer Clb; Drama Clb; Trs Science Clb; Spanish Clb; School Play; Stage Crew; Nwsp Rptr; Lit Mag; High Hon Roll; Natnl Jrnlsm Awd 87; Englsh & Sci Merit Awd 87.

SEPITKO, WAYNE; Charleroi Area JR/Sr HS; Charleroi, PA; (3); Church Yth Grp; Science Clb; Ski Clb; Spanish Clb; Nwsp Stf; Stu Cncl; Trk; Hon Roll; NHS; H O Brian Yth Ldrshp Awd 86.

SEPRISH, LISA; Bald Eagle Area HS; Snow Shoe, PA; (4); French Clb; Nwsp Stf; Yrbk Stf; Var Cheerleading; Hon Roll; Girls Ldrs; PA ST; Bus Adm.

SEQUETE, LISA; Butler SR HS; Butler, PA; (3); Church Yth Grp; Dance Clb; French Clb; Office Aide; Political Wkr; SADD; Teachers Aide; Thesps; Yrbk Stf; Pom Pon; AFS Awd 87.

SERA, KATHLEEN; Pequea Valley HS; Gap, PA; (4); 3/110; AFS; Drama Clb; Varsity Clb; Acpl Chr; Band; Chorus; Concert Band; Jazz Band; Mrchg Band; School Musical; West Chester U; Nrsng.

SERAFIN, CAROLYN; Bishop Mc Cort HS; Johnstown, PA; (4); German Clb; Mu Alpha Theta; Pep Clb; Ski Clb; Chorus; Church Choir; Vllybl; Hon Roll; Mu Alpha Theta Awd; NHS; PA ST U.

SERAFIN, JENNIFER; Cambria Heights HS; Carrolltown, PA; (3); Concert Band; Mrchg Band; Hon Roll; NHS; Band; Church Choir; Yrbk Stf; Cahbria County Band 84-86; Geogrpahy.

SERAFINI, KEVIN G; Valley HS; New Keinsington, PA; (4); 3/200; Trs Science Clb; Spanish Clb; Varsity Clb; Gov Hon Prg Awd; Ntl Merit SF; Rotary Awd; Pres Soph Cls; Pres Jr Cls; Pres Sr Cls; JV Var Bsbl; MIT; Astrnmy.

SERBAK, MICHAEL; Trinity HS; Washington, PA; (3); Boy Scts; Church Yth Grp; Exploring; VICA; High Hon Roll; Hon Roll; Luthrn Lvng Faith Awd 85; PIT; Drftng.

SERBIN, BETSY; Spring-Ford HS; Royersford, PA; (3); 19/282; 4-H; German Clb; Girl Scts; Math Clb; Pep Clb; Ski Clb; Yrbk Stf; Stu Cncl; L Fld Hcky; L Sftbl; 2nd Tm All Pioneer Ath Conf Sftbl 2nd Base 87; Wharton; Bus Adm.

SERFASS, JENNIFER; Spring Grove Area HS; Codorus, PA; (3); Varsity Clb; VP Concert Band; Jazz Band; Mrchg Band; Pres Soph Cls; Stu Cncl; Var L Trk; High Hon Roll; VP NHS; Pres Schlr; Bus Admin.

SERGI, RUTH ANN; Moon HS; Coraopolis, PA; (4); 33/307; Church Yth Grp; Spanish Clb; Mrchg Band; Symp Band; Capt Var Diving; Var Capt Socr; Lion Awd; Band; Church Choir; Ntl Schlr/Athlt Awd 87; Westminster Coll; Intl Bus.

SERISH, LISA; Burgettstown Area JR-SR HS; Burgettstown, PA; (4); 30/137; Sec Drama Clb; French Clb; Hosp Aide; SADD; Yrbk Ed-Chief; Hon Roll; Jr NHS; NHS; Chorus; Jstns Gldn Glln Awd; Stu Cncl Schlrshp; U Of Pittsburgh; Physcl Thrpy.

SERNIAK, ALAN; Sacred Heart HS; Jermyn, PA; (3); Computer Clb; Hosp Aide; Science Clb; SADD; JV Var Bsktbl; Hon Roll; Jeffery Davis Mem Schlrshp Awd $500 87; PA Jr Acad Of Sci 2nd Pl 87; U Of Scranton; Phys Therapy.

SERNIK, JILL; Reynolds HS; Greenville, PA; (4); 37/146; Pres Church Yth Grp; Latin Clb; Math Clb; Science Clb; Stat Score Keeper; NHS; NEDT Awd; Cngrsnl Art Cmptn 3rd Pl 86; Lgsltv Art Exhbt 87; Cngrsnl Art Cmptn 87; Edinboro U PA; Art Ed.

SEROKA, MIKE; Marian Catholic HS; New Ringgold, PA; (4); 19/110; 4-H; Band; Church Choir; Concert Band; School Play; 4-H Awd; NHS; Cnty 4-H Horse Bowl 86-87; Allentown Coll; Bio.

SEROTA, ALYSON; Upper Dublin HS; Dresher, PA; (3); 88/300; SADD; Nwsp Ed-Chief; Nwsp Stf; Yrbk Rptr; Yrbk Stf; Stu Cncl; JV Tennis; Edtr Schl Nwspr 87; Mgr Ice Hockey Tm; Spch Pthlgy.

SEROTTA, ANDREW H; North Penn HS; Lansdale, PA; (4); 1/650; Pres Chess Clb; Nwsp Ed-Chief; Yrbk Ed-Chief; Stu Cncl; VP NHS; Ntl Merit SF; Val; Boys Clb Am; Intnl Clb; Math Clb; PA ST HS Chess Champ 86; National Master USCF 86; Gold Medal PA Acad Decthln 86; Mth.

SEROWINSKI, BRIAN; North Pocono HS; Moscow, PA; (4); 37/248; VP Pres JA; Rep Sr Cls; Var L Golf; NHS; PA ST U; Arch Engrng.

SERSUN, DOUGLAS K; Oxford Area HS; Nottingham, PA; (4); 5/172; Boy Scts; Yrbk Stf; Pres Frsh Cls; Pres Soph Cls; Pres Jr Cls; Pres Sr Cls; Rep Stu Cncl; Capt Var Crs Cntry; Capt L Trk; High Hon Roll; X-Cntry Lg MVP; Trck Lg Chmp 800m 1600m.

SERSUN, PATRICIA; Oxford HS; Nottingham, PA; (2); Church Yth Grp; Stage Crew; Yrbk Stf; Stu Cncl; JV Var Cheerleading; Var Crs Cntry; JV Var Trk; High Hon Roll; Hon Roll; Spnsh Proficiency Awd 86; Drama.

SERVELLO, KELLY JEAN; Penn Cambira SR HS; Cresson, PA; (3); Drama Clb; Spanish Clb; Speech Tm; School Play; Stage Crew; Trk; Hon Roll; Pres Phys Fit Awd 85 & 87; Outstndng Achvt Phys Ed 86; PA ST; Cmmnctns.

SERVICE, AMY; Danville Area HS; Danville, PA; (3); 36/186; Key Clb; Ski Clb; Hst Frsh Cls; Hst Soph Cls; Hst Jr Cls; JV Var Cheerleading; Var Trk; French Hon Soc; Hon Roll; NHS.

SERVICE, JENNIFER A; Bethel Park SR HS; Bethel Park, PA; (4); 2/520; VP Sec NFL; Sec Thesps; High Hon Roll; NHS; Ntl Merit Schol; Pres Schlr; Sal; Cmnty Wkr; Drama Clb; Intnl Clb; Leads SR Cls Ply & Muscl 86-87; 12 Frnscs Trphys; Dist Frshmn Schlrshp MI ST 87; MI ST U; Chmstry.

SERWINSKI, VINCE; Blairsville SR HS; Blairsville, PA; (3); SADD; School Musical; VP Frsh Cls; Trs Soph Cls; Golf; Trk; High Hon Roll; Hon Roll; Engrng.

SERXNER, ALLYSON; Lower Merion HS; Merion, PA; (3); Debate Tm; NFL; Ed Yrbk Bus Mgr; Pres Stu Cncl; Fld Hcky; Q&S; NHS; Cmnty Wkr; French Clb; Acad All Amercn Schlr Prog 84; Natl Ldrshp & Svc Awd 85; Lawyer.

SESSAMEN, MELISSA; Tyrone Area HS; Tyrone, PA; (3); Key Clb; Varsity Clb; Chorus; Drm Mjr(t); Sec Soph Cls; Sec Jr Cls; Sec Stu Cncl; Cheerleading; Powder Puff Ftbl; Hon Roll; Phys Thrpy.

SESTI, MELISSA; Ambridge Area HS; Baden, PA; (4); 5/265; Am Leg Aux Girls St; Hosp Aide; Office Aide; Pep Clb; Sr Cls; Var Sftbl; Var L Vllybl; High Hon Roll; Trs NHS; Pres Ftns & Acadmc Awd 87; ABPW Club Grl Of Mnth 86.

SESTOCK, DOUGLAS; Mt Pleasant Area HS; Mt Pleasant, PA; (3); 98/250; Boy Scts; Church Yth Grp; Ski Clb; Yrbk Stf; Var Ftbl; God Cntry Awd; Arrow Brthrhd Dnc Tm Chrmn 84-87.

SETH, JOE; Kittanning SR HS; Worthington, PA; (3); 40/215; Band; Hon Roll.

SETON-MC COY, MARIE E A; Pocono Mountain HS; Scotrun, PA; (4); 97/300; DECA; Cit Awd; Hon Roll; Kiwanis Awd; Outstndng DECA Achvt 86; E Stroudsburg U; Mgnt.

SETTELMAIER, JIM; Seton-La Salle HS; Pittsburgh, PA; (2); 62/235; JV Bsktbl; Hon Roll; Brdcstng.

SETTEMBRINO, MARCELLO; Archbishop Ryan For Boys; Philadelphia, PA; (2); Civic Clb; JV Ftbl; JV Golf; Wt Lftg; Hon Roll; Bus.

SETTLE, TRACY; Frankford HS; Philadelphia, PA; (3); Art Clb; GAA; Bsktbl; Cheerleading; Fld Hcky; Sftbl; Hon Roll; Secy Danaides-Charity Org 87; Lwyr.

SETTLEMYER, JONATHAN; Jersey Shore SR HS; Jersey Shore, PA; (4); 34/243; Boy Scts; Band; Chorus; Jazz Band; Mrchg Band; School Musical; Swmmng; Cit Awd; NHS; Rotary Awd; Past Mstr Cnclr Tiadaghtn Elm Ordr De Molay 86; Instrmntl Music Awd 87; Grove City Coll; Bio.

SETTNEK, SUE; Gateway SR HS; Pitcairn, PA; (4); Drama Clb; Hon Roll; Model.

SEVERCOOL, BECKY; Lackawanna Trail HS; Factoryville, PA; (4); 5/89; Ski Clb; Madrigals; School Musical; Yrbk Stf; Stat Bsktbl; French Hon Soc; High Hon Roll; NHS; Pres Schlr; Hofstra U; Comm.

SEVERIN, R TYSON; William Penn HS; York, PA; (3); Church Yth Grp; Band; Chorus; Church Choir; Concert Band; Jazz Band; Orch; Symp Band; Crs Cntry; Capt Trk; Messiah Bible Coll; Chld Daycar.

SEVERINO, JAMES; Montour HS; Mckees Rocks, PA; (3); Computer Clb; Math Clb; Science Clb; SADD; Band; Nwsp Rptr; Nwsp Stf; Var Ftbl; Var Wt Lftg; High Hon Roll; Penn ST DE; Law.

SEVERSON, BRAD; Danville SR HS; Danville, PA; (3); Ski Clb; Socr; Trk; High Hon Roll; Pres Schlr; Real Est.

SEWALL, JUDY; Sharon HS; Sharon, PA; (3); 17/180; Drama Clb; French Clb; SADD; Band; Concert Band; Mrchg Band; Orch; JV Var Tennis; Var Trk; NHS; Comp Sci.

SEWELL, ANDREA; Abington SR HS; Elkins Pk, PA; (4); 23/486; Church Yth Grp; Rep Frsh Cls; Rep Jr Cls; Rep Sr Cls; Rep Stu Cncl; High Hon Roll; Hon Roll; NHS; Prfct Atten Awd; Pres Schr; Ravilla Davenport Memrl Schlrshp 87; J D Fox Ldrshp Awd 87; Temple U; Math.

SEWELL, CARLA; Westinghouse HS; Pittsburgh, PA; (3); Church Yth Grp; Hosp Aide; NAACP; Sec Church Choir; Trk; Hon Roll; Good Attndnc & Achvmnt SAT Prep Course 87; Duquesne U; Pharmclgy.

SEWELL, MARK; Conrad Weiser HS; Wernersville, PA; (2); 87/163; Band; Chorus; Jazz Band; Mrchg Band; School Musical; Socr; Tennis; Trk; USAF Acad; Engrng.

SEYBERT, CRAIG A; Columbia-Montour AVTS HS; Berwick, PA; (4); 4/180; SADD; VICA; Nwsp Phtg; Nwsp Stf; Off Stu Cncl; High Hon Roll; NHS; Grphc Arts Stu Yr, 2nd Pl ST VICA Cmpttn 86-87; Prss Oprtr.

SEYBOTH, HEATHER; Beaver Area JR SR HS; Beaver, PA; (2); Church Yth Grp; Civic Clb; Sec Cmnty Wkr; French Clb; Ski Clb; SADD; Yrbk Stf; Swmmng; Trk; Hon Roll; Bus.

SEYFERT, SUE; Hamburg Area HS; Hamburg, PA; (4); 6/144; German Clb; Ski Clb; SADD; Trs Band; Chorus; School Musical; Tennis; Hon Roll; NHS; Ntl Merit Ltr; German Hnr Soc 85-87; Cngrssnal Schlr 86; MENSA Soc 83-87; Penn ST; Engrng.

SEYMORE, PAMELA J; Bishop Guilfoyle HS; Altoona, PA; (2); Ski Clb; Rep Soph Cls; JV Vllybl; Law.

SEYMOUR, BECCA; Methacton HS; Fairview Village, PA; (3); 100/450; Church Yth Grp; Key Clb; Band; Chorus; Church Choir; Concert Band; Stat Bsbl; Capt Cheerleading; Trk; Pep Clb; Eng.

SEYMOUR, ELIZABETH; Bishop Guifoyle HS; Altoona, PA; (3); 3/156; Cmnty Wkr; Library Aide; NFL; Science Clb; Service Clb; Ski Clb; SADD; Chorus; Yrbk Stf; Rep Stu Cncl; Svc Awd Holidaysburg Vets Home 86; Catholic Daughtrs Amer Essy Awd 86; Med.

SEYMOUR, JAMES; Quaker Valley HS; Sewickley, PA; (1); 25/130; Church Yth Grp; Band; School Musical; Bsbl; Bsktbl; Golf; High Hon Roll; Mst Vlbl Athlte 87; Red Cross Ldrshp Awd; Mstr Crmns 87; Hnrs Prg.

SEYMOUR, LESLIE; Penn Cambria HS; Lilly, PA; (3); FBLA; Hon Roll; Cert Hghst Avg Am Hstry 84; PA ST U; Fmly Chld Cr.

SEYMOUR, REBEKAH; Methacton HS; Fairview Vlg, PA; (3); 107/435; Church Yth Grp; Key Clb; Chorus; Rep Jr Cls; Cheerleading; Hon Roll.

SEZERBAR, DEBBIE; Pocono Mountain HS; Scotrun, PA; (2); Pep Clb; Pres Frsh Cls; Rep Soph Cls; JV L Cheerleading; Crs Cntry; Var L Trk; Pres Phys Fit Awd 85-86; Supr Initatve & Ldrshp 86; UCLA; Law.

SFIDA, MELISSA; West Catholic Girls HS; Philadelphia, PA; (3); Cmnty Wkr; Drama Clb; Office Aide; Lit Mag; Coach Actv; Sftbl; Hon Roll; Opt Clb Awd; Charles Ellis Grant 84-87; Psych.

SFORZA, LAURA; Kiski Area HS; Vandergrift, PA; (4); FBLA; JA; Chorus; Color Guard; Hon Roll; Oakbridge Acad; Med Asst.

SFORZA, ROBERT; West Allegheny HS; Oakdale, PA; (3); 25/200; Church Yth Grp; Science Clb; Chorus; VP Jr Cls; Rep Stu Cncl; Im Bsbl; Var L Tennis; High Hon Roll; Hon Roll.

SGRO, JEANNIE; Saint Basil Acad; Philadelphia, PA; (3); Drama Clb; Pres French Clb; Trs GAA; SADD; Acpl Chr; School Musical; Yrbk Stf; Fld Hcky; Mgr(s); Sftbl; Accntng.

SGRO, NICOLE; Upper Darby SR HS; Upper Darby, PA; (3); Drama Clb; Hosp Aide; Spanish Clb; Chorus; Stage Crew; Mgr(s); Score Keeper; Trk; Hon Roll; DE Cnty Coll; Brdcstng.

SHAAK, CHRISTOPHER; Lebanon Catholic HS; Annville, PA; (4); 35/80; Boy Scts; Cmnty Wkr; German Clb; Stage Crew; Ftbl; Wt Lftg; God Cntry Awd; Cty Yth Govt Crmnl Detctv 86; Eagle Sct 84; IN U PA; Crmnlgy.

SHABAZIAN, IRENE; Athens Area HS; Athens, PA; (3); 23/119; Church Yth Grp; Red Cross Aide; SADD; Chorus; Nwsp Rptr; Lit Mag; Stu Cncl; Cheerleading; High Hon Roll; Hon Roll.

SHABLIK, JASON; Norwin SR HS; N Huntingdon, PA; (4); Pres Band; Concert Band; Jazz Band; Mrchg Band; Hon Roll; PA Dist 1 Hnrs Band 86; PMEA Dist 1 Band 1st Chair 87; PMEA Regn 1 Band 87; U Miami; Music Engrng.

SHADE, ERIC; Bishop Guilfoyle HS; Hollidaysburg, PA; (3); Cmnty Wkr; Hon Roll; Lbrl Arts.

SHADE, MARIE; Bellefonte Area HS; Pleasant Gap, PA; (3); Church Yth Grp; Thesps; Chorus; Church Choir; School Musical; School Play; Stage Crew; Rep Frsh Cls; Rep Sr Cls; Hon Roll; Vsl Arts.

SHADE, THOMAS A; Lock Haven HS; Lock Haven, PA; (1); Computer Clb; Im Bsbl; Im Ftbl; High Hon Roll; Hon Roll; Comp Prgrmr.

SHADEL, JENNIFER; East Juniata HS; Richfield, PA; (3); 1/100; Chess Clb; Concert Band; Mrchg Band; School Musical; School Play; Stage Crew; VP Jr Cls; L Var Fld Hcky; High Hon Roll; NHS; Penn ST U; Archaeolgst.

SHADLE, KELLY; Littlestown SR HS; Littlestown, PA; (4); Varsity Clb; Color Guard; Lib Concert Band; Mrchg Band; Yrbk Stf; Var L Fld Hcky; MIP Fld Hcky 87; Yrktwn Bus Inst; Scrtrl.

SHADLE, KRISTI; Williams Valley HS; Tower City, PA; (1); Spanish Clb; Band; Chorus; Jazz Band; Mrchg Band; Pep Band; School Musical; Symp Band; Hon Roll; Prfct Atten Awd; Bus Mgmt.

SHADLE, PAMELA; Watsontown Christian Acad; Winfield, PA; (2); 2/16; Hosp Aide; School Play; Yrbk Stf; Sec Trs Soph Cls; Var Bsktbl; Var Socr; Hon Roll; Chrstn Chrctr Awd 83-85; Spnsh Awd 86; Hstry Awd 86; Penn ST U; Mchncl Engr.

SHADLE, TOM; Marion Center HS; Marion Center, PA; (2); Boy Scts; Latin Clb; Band; Concert Band; Mrchg Band; JV Trk; Hon Roll; NHS; PA Jr Acad Sci 1st Pl Rgnl, St-Comp Sci 85-87; PA Learnng Resrcs Assn 1st Pl Dist, Rgnl Comp Sci 86.

SHAEFFER, THERESA; Lenape Vo-Tech; Worthington, PA; (3); Trs DECA; Tennis; High Hon Roll; Hon Roll; Bus.

SHAFER, DEBORAH; Cumberland Valley HS; Mechanicsburg, PA; (3); 85/601; Pres Church Yth Grp; German Clb; Rep Girl Scts; Key Clb; SADD; Band; Mrchg Band; Symp Band; Fld Hcky; Trk; Slvr Ldrshp Awd 86; Slvr Awd 87; Gold Ldrshp Awd 87; Intl Rel.

SHAFER, GARY; Forbes Road HS; Waterfall, PA; (3); 1/50; Computer Clb; French Clb; FFA; High Hon Roll; Hon Roll; 1st Pl Cnty Envrnmtl Olympcs Tm 86-87; Comp Sci.

SHAFER JR, JACK; Crestwood HS; Wapwallopen, PA; (4); 9/216; Math Clb; Science Clb; Ski Clb; Variety Show; Var L Bsbl; Im Bsktbl; JV Ftbl; Var L Socr; Im Tennis; Im Wt Lftg; Robert E Byrd Hnrs Schlrshp 87; PA ST U; Engrng.

SHAFFER, AMY; Cardinal O Hara HS; Springfield, PA; (4); 9/771; Church Yth Grp; Service Clb; Spanish Clb; SADD; Yrbk Stf; High Hon Roll; Lion Awd; NHS; Ntl Merit Ltr; Spanish NHS; Springfield Womens Clb Stu Of Mo 86; Lehigh U; Bus.

SHAFFER, AMY; Somerset Area Schls; Friedens, PA; (4); 20/233; Pres English Clb; Pres German Clb; Hosp Aide; JA; Pres NFL; Q&S; Spanish Clb; Yrbk Ed-Chief; Sec Stu Cncl; High Hon Roll; Dale Carnegie Scholar 87; Cls Play 87; Candy Striper Yr Awd 85; PA ST U; Intl Poltcs.

SHAFFER, BRENDA; Somerset Area HS; Somerset, PA; (4); 33/232; Art Clb; JA; Mu Alpha Theta; Band; Stu Cncl; Cheerleading; High Hon Roll; Hon Roll; English Clb; FBLA; FHA 3rd Pl Demo ST Tm Cmpttn 87; FBLA Accntng II 2nd Pl Rgnls, 10th Pl ST 86-87; IN U PA; Accntng.

SHAFFER, BRIAN; Parkland SR HS; Allentown, PA; (3); 80/481; Pres Church Yth Grp; Exploring; JV Tennis; NHS; Elctrcl Engrng.

SHAFFER, BRIAN; Western Wayne HS; Waymart, PA; (3); 42/180; Computer Clb; Spanish Clb; Var Capt Bsktbl; Var Socr; Tennis; Pre-Law.

SHAFFER, CARLA; Ligonier Valley SR HS; Ligonier, PA; (3); 2/148; Am Leg Aux Girls St; Church Yth Grp; SADD; Band; Rep Stu Cncl; High Hon Roll; Hon Roll; Prfct Atten Awd; French Clb; NFL; Cnty Band 84-86; PA Free Entrprs Wk 86; Comp Sci.

SHAFFER, CHAD; Hempfield HS; Lancaster, PA; (3); 40/400; Exploring; Band; Concert Band; Mrchg Band; Jr NHS; NHS; U Pittsburg; Geolgy.

SHAFFER, CHRISTOPHER; Sayre Area HS; S Waverly, PA; (3); Boy Scts; French Clb; Band; Concert Band; Jazz Band; Mrchg Band; Pep Band; High Hon Roll; Hon Roll; NHS; U Of NC; Pharm.

SHAFFER, DAVID; Neshaminy HS; Hulmeville, PA; (3); Bsbl; Wt Lftg.

SHAFFER, DIANA; Du Bois Area SR HS; Reynoldsville, PA; (3); SADD; Chorus; Color Guard; Nwsp Stf; Govenors Schl Of Arts Creatv Wrtng Semifnlst 87; Commnctns.

SHAFFER, DONNA; Millersburg Area HS; Millersburg, PA; (3); Cmnty Wkr; Band; Chorus; Concert Band; Mrchg Band; Sec Soph Cls; Sec Jr Cls; Hon Roll; US Music Ambsdr Hawaiian Tour 87; Fshn Mrchndsr.

SHAFFER, ED; Central Dauphin HS; Harrisburg, PA; (3); JV Wrstlng; Hon Roll; NHS; Engrng.

SHAFFER, ERIC; Dover Area HS; Dover, PA; (4); Boy Scts; Church Yth Grp; Band; Chorus; Rep Sr Cls; Socr; Trk; Concert Band; Jazz Band; Mrchg Band; Eagle Scout Awd 87; Stu Of Mnth Awd 87; York Cnty Soccer All Star Tm 86.

SHAFFER, HEATHER; Conemaugn Twp Area HS; Boswell, PA; (3); 38/108; Church Yth Grp; Drama Clb; Hosp Aide; Chorus; Church Choir; Rep Stu Cncl; Art Clb; Cmnty Wkr; FTA; Pep Clb; All Cnty Alto 2nd Chr 85, 1st Chr 86; Ed.

SHAFFER, HOLLI; Riverside SR HS; Ellwood City, PA; (2); 52/203; Church Yth Grp; Band; Chorus; Concert Band; Mrchg Band; Bowling; Trk; Hon Roll; PA ST; Comp Anlyst.

SHAFFER JR, JAMES M; Montgomery Area HS; Montgomery, PA; (4); 1/60; French Clb; High Hon Roll; NHS; Ntl Merit SF; Cert Merit PA Higher Educ Assist Agency 86; Bucknell U; Elec Engrng.

SHAFFER, JEFF; Grove City HS; Grove City, PA; (3); 6/207; Office Aide; Var Bsktbl; Im Ftbl; Var L Trk; High Hon Roll; NHS; Pres Schlr.

SHAFFER, JENNIFER; Danville SR HS; Danville, PA; (3); Art Clb; French Clb; Spanish Clb; French Hon Soc; Cmnctns.

SHAFFER, JENNIFER; Forest City Regional HS; Pleasant Mount, PA; (4); 4/56; German Clb; Scholastic Bowl; Band; Jazz Band; Yrbk Ed-Chief; VP Jr Cls; VP Sr Cls; Pres Trs Stu Cncl; VP NHS; Rotary Awd; CA U Alumn Schlrshp, Commnty Chorus Awd, Hme & Schl Assn Ldrshp Awd 87; CA U Of PA; Creatve Wrtng.

SHAFFER, JILL; Bedford HS; Bedford, PA; (3); 18/204; Church Yth Grp; JA; Ski Clb; Rep Stu Cncl; Var L Gym; Var L Trk; Hon Roll; NHS; Schltc Medl 86; Allegany CC; Math.

SHAFFER, JOHN; St Marys Area HS; St Marys, PA; (3); Am Leg Boys St; Ftbl; Var L Trk; Hon Roll; NHS; Corp Bus Mgmt.

SHAFFER, JOSHUA; Du Bois Area HS; Dubois, PA; (2); 11/374; Church Yth Grp; Dance Clb; FCA; PAVAS; Varsity Clb; School Musical; Yrbk Sprt Ed; Rep Soph Cls; Var Socr; Pres Schlr.

SHAFFER, JULIE; Marion Center Area HS; Creekside, PA; (4); Church Yth Grp; Cmnty Wkr; 4-H; Girl Scts; Office Aide; VICA; Church Choir; Yrbk Rptr; Yrbk Stf; High Hon Roll; Pittsburgh Beauty Acad Schlrshp 87; Scndry Hnr Roll Hnr Awd 87; Greensburg Beauty Acad; Mgmnt.

SHAFFER, KARLA E; Christian Liberty Acad; Forksville, PA; (4); Camera Clb; Church Yth Grp; Rep Frsh Cls; Rep Stu Cncl; JV Bsktbl; Var Wt Lftg; High Hon Roll; Jr NHS; NHS; Engl.

SHAFFER, KATHY; Central SR HS; York, PA; (3); 34/250; Art Clb; Intnl Clb; Ski Clb; Flag Corp; Nwsp Stf; Yrbk Stf; Lit Mag; Mgr(s); Tennis; Hon Roll; Natl PTA Reflections Prog 2nd 86-87; House Rep Citation Art 86; Lawyer.

SHAFFER, KERI; East Pennsboro HS; Enola, PA; (3); 44/184; Art Clb; Drama Clb; German Clb; Ski Clb; Trs SADD; Drill Tm; VP Stu Cncl; Trk; Hon Roll; NHS; Ntl Art Hnr Soc 85-86; Cert Of Merit 84-85; Delgt-Ntl Stu Cncl Conf & Wrkshp 86; Mktg.

SHAFFER, LESLIE; Warren Area HS; Warren, PA; (3); Art Clb; Church Yth Grp; Civic Clb; French Clb; Spanish Clb; Varsity Clb; Orch; JV Var Sftbl; Stat Wrstlng; Hon Roll; Intl Rltns.

SHAFFER, LISA; Frazier HS; Perryopolis, PA; (4); 11/130; Pres FNA; Hosp Aide; Color Guard; Trs Mrchg Band; Nwsp Stf; Ed Yrbk Stf; High Hon Roll; NHS; Prfct Atten Awd; Eleanor A Knox Womans Schlrshp 87; Stu Gov Schlrshp 87; Pres Ftns Awd 87; U Of Pittsburgh; Nrsng.

SHAFFER, LISA; Marion Center HS; Marion Center, PA; (3); Pres FNA; Intnl Clb; Pep Clb; Red Cross Aide; Teachers Aide; Var Sftbl; Var Vllybl; Hon Roll.

SHAFFER, LISA; North Star HS; Hooversville, PA; (2); 7/139; FCA; Mu Alpha Theta; Bsktbl; Hon Roll; Med.

SHAFFER, LISA M; Moshannon Valley JR SR HS; Houtzdale, PA; (3); Girl Scts; Hosp Aide; Varsity Clb; Chorus; Var Capt Cheerleading; IN U Of PA; Elem Ed.

SHAFFER, MARK; Blairsville SR HS; Blairsville, PA; (3); 8/150; Pres 4-H; FFA; Sec VICA; JV Wrstlng; 4-H Awd; High Hon Roll; NHS; Natl Champ-Equestrian 86; Reg Voc Ind Clbs Of Am-2nd Pl 87; PA ST; Teaching.

SHAFFER, MELISSA; Garden Spot HS; Morgantown, PA; (4); German Clb; Library Aide; Ski Clb; JV Bsktbl; High Hon Roll; Hon Roll; Jr NHS; Trustees Grnt Albright Coll; Cong Bundstg Exchng Pgm; Albright Coll; Bio.

SHAFFER, MICHAEL ALAN; Shade-Central City HS; Stoystown, PA; (3); 5/71; Scholastic Bowl; Pres Spanish Clb; Nwsp Stf; Yrbk Sprt Ed; Trs Jr Cls; Var JV Bsktbl; Var JV Ftbl; High Hon Roll; Hon Roll; NHS; Physcl Thrpst.

SHAFFER, MICHELLE; York Catholic HS; York, PA; (3); 13/152; Drama Clb; VP Exploring; Pres VP FBLA; Trs Girl Scts; Pres JA; Pres Pep Clb; Political Wkr; School Play; Yrbk Stf; High Hon Roll; Srch Of Ldrs Schlrshp-Chestnug Hill Coll 87; Presof Yr-S Cntrl Pennsylvania Jr Achvt; Accntng.

SHAFFER, NICOLE; Bald Eagle Nittany HS; Mill Hall, PA; (3); 17/148; Church Yth Grp; French Clb; SADD; Yrbk Phtg; Yrbk Rptr; Yrbk Stf; Im Vllybl; Sec Ed.

SHAFFER, NOELLE; Milton HS; Milton, PA; (2); Church Yth Grp; FTA; Intnl Clb; Sec Latin Clb; Band; Chorus; Concert Band; Mrchg Band; Var Fld Hcky; Hon Roll; Ltn Hnr Soc 87; Vrsty M Fld Hcky Awd 86 & 87; Elem Educ.

SHAFFER, PENNY; North Star HS; Hooversville, PA; (2); FCA; Girl Scts; Ski Clb; SADD; Var Mat Maids; Stat Vllybl; Cit Awd; Hon Roll.

SHAFFER, ROBERT; Fort Cherry HS; Midway, PA; (3); 58/147; Aud/Vis; Boy Scts; Computer Clb; Drama Clb; Math Clb; Ski Clb; Spanish Clb; Ftbl.

SHAFFER, RON; Jefferson Morgan HS; Jefferson, PA; (4); 3/97; Rep Frsh Cls; Pres Jr Cls; VP Sr Cls; L Bsbl; Capt Bsktbl; Bausch & Lomb Sci Awd; Lion Awd; NHS; Pres Schlrshp 87-91; Am Legion Schlrshp 87; U S Army Res Nat Athl Awd 87; Waynesburg Coll; Chem.

SHAFFER, RUTH; Grove City SR HS; Grove City, PA; (4); 15/199; Church Yth Grp; Cmnty Wkr; FNA; Key Clb; Im Tennis; Im Vllybl; High Hon Roll; Hon Roll; NHS; Grove City Coll; Soclgy.

SHAFFER, SHANDA; Everett Area HS; Everett, PA; (1); GAA; Chorus; School Musical; Off Frsh Cls; Bsktbl; Hon Roll; Most Impvd Plyr 86; Kent U VA; Pilot.

SHAFFER, SHARON; Harrisburg Christian Schl; Harrisburg, PA; (2); School Play; Sec Trs Soph Cls; Cheerleading; Hon Roll; NHS; Cmnty Wkr; Nalt Young Ldrs Conf 86; Christian Testimony Awds Cheerleading & Drama 87; Counseling.

SHAFFER, SHARON; Purchase Line HS; Clymer, PA; (3); 13/98; FBLA; Pep Clb; SADD; Chorus; Yrbk Stf; Hon Roll; St Mock Trl Cmptn Tm; KM Schl Of Bus; Acctng.

SHAFFER, SUZAN; Northampton Area SR HS; Bath, PA; (3); AFS; Aud/Vis; Exploring; Leo Clb; Ski Clb; SADD; Powder Puff Ftbl; Drama Clb; FTA; Pep Clb; Mrn Bio.

SHAFFER, TAMMY; Connellsville Area SR HS; Dawson, PA; (3); Dance Clb; 4-H; German Clb; Pep Clb; Spanish Clb; Chorus; VP Soph Cls; Var Capt Cheerleading; Gym; Vllybl; Wntr Sprts Ct Attndnt 86; Valentines Ct 84-85.

SHAFFER, TRACEY; Geibel HS; Acme, PA; (3); Church Yth Grp; Cmnty Wkr; Pep Clb; Ski Clb; SADD; Nwsp Rptr; Rep Jr Cls; Stat Bsktbl; Var L Crs Cntry; Var L Trk; PA JR Acad Of Sci 3rd Pl; MVP Awd For Cross Cntry.

SHAFFER, TROY; Hempfield SR HS; Greensburg, PA; (3); VICA; Auto Mech.

SHAFFER, WENDY; Shanksville-Stonycreek HS; Central City, PA; (4); 3/37; Band; Chorus; Nwsp Stf; Yrbk Stf; Stu Cncl; Vllybl; Hon Roll; Pres NHS; Spanish NHS; Maple Prncss 86-87; Cambria Somerset JR Mss Fnlst 86; Stu Advncd Ldrshp Trainng 86; Child Psych.

SHAFFERT, JENNIFER; Abington SR HS; Doylestown, PA; (4); 112/486; Chrmn SADD; Chorus; Madrigals; Mrchg Band; School Musical; Yrbk Stf; Off Sr Cls; Stu Cncl; JV Trk; NHS; Principals Awd 87; Stu Govt Awd 87; U Of New England; Phys Ther.

SHAFFRON, DARLENE; East Pennsboro HS; Enola, PA; (2); GAA; Latin Clb; Band; Concert Band; Mrchg Band; School Musical; Bsktbl; Fld Hcky; Sftbl; Pediatric.

SHAH, AKASH; Schenley HS; Pittsburgh, PA; (3); Spanish Clb; Bsktbl; Wt Lftg; High Hon Roll; Pilot.

SHAH, ANITA; Moon SR HS; Coraopolis, PA; (3); 3/350; French Clb; Hosp Aide; JA; Temple Yth Grp; Chorus; Off Jr Cls; High Hon Roll; Jr NHS; NHS; Prfct Atten Awd; Dstngshd Hnr Roll 84-87; Acad Excllnc Awd 85-87; Med.

SHAH, SHIRLEY; Du Bois Area HS; Dubois, PA; (3); Girl Scts; Chorus; Trs Stu Cncl; Hon Roll; Engnrng.

SHAH, SUHRUD; Cumberland Valley HS; Mechanicsburg, PA; (3); Computer Clb; Model UN; Bus.

SHAH, TALIAH; Clara Muhammad Schl; Philadelphia, PA; (2); Cmnty Wkr; Computer Clb; English Clb; Girl Scts; Library Aide; Office Aide; Science Clb; Teachers Aide; School Play; Variety Show; Amer Fndtn Negro Affairs 86; Howard U; Law.

SHAIKH, ZAKIR; Wilmington Area HS; New Wilmington, PA; (3); 6/115; JV Bsktbl; Capt Socr; Hon Roll; Acdmc Achvt 83-86; U Of Pittsburgh; Orthdntstry.

SHAKUR, AMINA; Sis Clara Muhammad Schl; Philadelphia, PA; (3); 1/10; Church Yth Grp; Cmnty Wkr; Debate Tm; Girl Scts; Teachers Aide; Yrbk Rptr; Vllybl; Cit Awd; High Hon Roll; Hon Roll; Outstndg Acad Awd 84-85; Corp Law.

SHALAYDA, STEVE; Ambridge Area HS; Baden, PA; (2); FCA; Spanish Clb; JV Bsbl; JV Ftbl; Bus.

SHALLER, ANDREA; Marian Catholic HS; Mc Adoo, PA; (3); 10/104; Church Choir; Yrbk Stf; High Hon Roll; NHS; Spanish NHS; Penn ST U; Metrlgy.

SHAM, RICHARD; North Catholic HS; Gibsonia, PA; (3); 23/267; Church Yth Grp; Math Clb; Math Tm; Spanish Clb; Band; Concert Band; Jazz Band; Yrbk Sprt Ed; Ftbl; Hon Roll; Penn ST Coll; Elec Engrng.

SHAMANY, SCOTT; Hazleton HS; Hazleton, PA; (3); 85/445; FBLA; Ski Clb; Off Stu Cncl; L Bsbl; L Bsktbl; L Ftbl; Hon Roll; Bus Admin.

SHAMBOUGH, THOMAS; Central York SR HS; York, PA; (3); Church Yth Grp; Varsity Clb; JV Crs Cntry; Var Socr; JV Wrstlng; High Hon Roll; Hon Roll; Electrncs.

SHAMITIS, NEIL; Greensburg Central Catholic HS; Hermine, PA; (2); Boy Scts; Church Yth Grp; Ski Clb; Church Choir; Hon Roll; Hosp Admin.

SHAMITIS, RENEE; Central Catholic HS; Herminie, PA; (4); 10/217; AFS; Church Yth Grp; Exploring; Hosp Aide; High Hon Roll; NHS; U Of Pittsburgh; Phrmcy.

SHAMITKO, RONALD; Trinity HS; Washington, PA; (3); 33/402; Art Clb; VICA; JV Ftbl; High Hon Roll; Hon Roll; Art Inst Pittsburgh; Comm Art.

SHAMORY, BRETT; Middlebuirg HS; Middleburg, PA; (3); 2/138; Boy Scts; Chess Clb; Church Yth Grp; Varsity Clb; Var Bsbl; Var Bsktbl; L Socr; High Hon Roll; NHS; Rensselaer Math & Sci Awd 87; Hugh O Brien Yth Fndtn Awd 86; Eagle Scout Awd 87; Penn ST U; Engr.

SHANAFELT, TERRI; Peters Township HS; Mcmurray, PA; (3); 60/241; SADD; Varsity Clb; Drill Tm; Yrbk Bus Mgr; VP Soph Cls; Rep Stu Cncl; Capt Bsktbl; Trk; Vllybl; Hon Roll; Ntl Hnr Roll 87; Bus.

SHANAHAN, THOMAS; South Park HS; Library, PA; (3); 9/228; Var Ftbl; Trk; Wt Lftg; High Hon Roll; Highest No Points Phys Ftns Test 86; US Naval Acad; Nutritional Sci.

SHANDOR, PAMELA RAE; Ringgold SR HS; Finleyville, PA; (3); Sec Drama Clb; Chorus; Church Choir; Variety Show; Rep Stu Cncl; Score Keeper; L Sftbl; L Vllybl; High Hon Roll; Hon Roll; Frgn Lang.

SHANEBROOK, SCOTT; New Oxford SR HS; Mcsherrystown, PA; (4); 20/170; Am Leg Boys St; Boys Clb Am; FBLA; FTA; JA; Political Wkr; SADD; Rep Stu Cncl; High Hon Roll; Prfct Atten Awd; Thompson Inst; Bus Admin.

SHANER, AMY; Hughesville HS; Hughesville, PA; (3); 15/140; Ski Clb; SADD; Varsity Clb; Chorus; Yrbk Rptr; Sec Soph Cls; Sec Jr Cls; Sec Stu Cncl; Var Capt Cheerleading; Hon Roll; Booster Club Chrldng Awds-Best All Around & Most Spirited 87; Booster Club Softbll Awd 86; Lycoming; Mass Comm.

SHANER, DAWN; Boyertonw Area SR HS; Gilbertsvl, PA; (4); 28/426; Stage Crew; Stu Cncl; Capt L Stu Cncl; Capt L Fld Hcky; Capt L Lcrss; Cit Awd; High Hon Roll; Hon Roll; NHS; Pres Schlr; Boyertown Area Ed Assn Scholar Awd 87; All Chestmont Fld Hcky Tm 86; West Chester U; Elem Ed.

SHANER, JOY; Galeton Area HS; Galeton, PA; (3); Spanish Clb; School Play; Hon Roll; NHS; Pres Acad Fit Awd 85; Recptnst.

SHANER, SANDRA; Ford City HS; Ford City, PA; (4); 48/140; Spanish Clb; SADD; Chorus; Color Guard; Flag Corp; Mrchg Band; Stage Crew; Variety Show; Nwsp Rptr; Nwsp Stf; Clarion U; Elem Educ.

SHANEYFELT, DEIRDRE; Fairchance Georges SR HS; Smithfield, PA; (3); High Hon Roll; Hon Roll; NHS.

SHANK, DIANA; Germantown Acad; Harleysville, PA; (3); Camera Clb; Church Yth Grp; Cmnty Wkr; 4-H; Hosp Aide; Office Aide; Service Clb; Teachers Aide; Nwsp Phtg; Yrbk Phtg; Drexel; Mktng.

SHANK, JAYNIE; Western Beaver HS; Industry, PA; (2); Chorus; Nwsp Stf; Yrbk Stf; Pres Frsh Cls; Co-Capt Cheerleading; Trk.

SHANK, LISA; Northern HS; Wellsville, PA; (3); 36/232; French Clb; Library Aide; Peer Cnslng 84-85; York Coll PA.

SHANK, LUCINDA; Windber Area HS; Windber, PA; (3); Sftbl; Trk; Hon Roll; NHS; Ntl Merit Ltr; Stu Mnth Awd 85-87; Pres Phys Ftnss Awd 86; Cambria Rowe Bus Coll; Med Secr.

SHANK, NEVIN; Lewistown Area HS; Mc Veytown, PA; (3); VP Science Clb; L Mgr(s); Bausch & Lomb Sci Awd; High Hon Roll; Biochem.

SHANK, PATRICIA; Cambria Heights HS; Carrolltown, PA; (3); Concert Band; Nwsp Rptr; Yrbk Stf; High Hon Roll; NHS; Orthdntst Asst.

SHANK, RANDALL J; Ephrata SR HS; Ephrata, PA; (4); 5/257; Computer Clb; Math Tm; Capt Quiz Bowl; Radio Clb; Nwsp Ed-Chief; Gov Hon Prg Awd; NHS; Ntl Merit SF; Rotary Awd; Aud/Vis; 4th Pl Intl Sci Fair Chem 86; Comp Sci.

SHANK, SHARON; Valley HS; New Kensington, PA; (3); DECA; Ski Clb; Chorus; New Knsngtn Cmmrcl Schl; Trvl.

SHANK, STACEY; Cumberland Valley Christian Schl; Chambersburg, PA; (4); 3/11; Pres Art Clb; Yrbk Stf; Sec Trs Frsh Cls; Sec Trs Soph Cls; Sec Trs Jr Cls; Sec Trs Sr Cls; Sftbl; Cit Awd; NHS; Bus Mgmt.

SHANK, TRACY; Henderson HS; Exton, PA; (3); 16/365; Church Yth Grp; French Clb; Hosp Aide; Y-Teens; Lcrss; Vllybl; French Hon Soc; Hon Roll; NHS; 3.5 GPA Awd 87; Genetic Engrng.

SHANK, WILMER; Fairfield Area HS; Fairfield, PA; (3); 9/73; Church Yth Grp; Band; Concert Band; Mrchg Band; Pep Band; Crs Cntry; Trk; High Hon Roll; Hon Roll; 1st Var Awd & 2nd Var Awd Track 86 & 87; Crs Cntry Var Awd 86; 3rd Pl Sci Fair Awd 87; Aviation.

SHANKLE, TAMMY; Freeport SR HS; Freeport, PA; (2); Hon Roll.

SHANKWEILER, ANN; Parkland HS; Schnecksville, PA; (2); Aud/Vis; Sec Church Yth Grp; 4-H; Office Aide; SADD; Boy Scts; Concert Band; Pres Frsh Cls; Rep Jr Cls; Rep Stu Cncl; Sports Med.

SHANKWEILER, CINDY; Allentown Central Catholic HS; Coplay, PA; (3); 12/230; VP Church Yth Grp; Girl Scts; Pep Clb; Spanish Clb; Band; Mrchg Band; Orch; Swmmng; High Hon Roll; NHS; 1st Pl PA JR Acad Sci 86; 3rd Pl Hstry Day Lehigh Cnty CC 87; Bio.

SHANKWEILER, PAULETTE; Wallenpaupack Area HS; Greentown, PA; (3); 28/155; Ski Clb; Teachers Aide; Var Trk; Wt Lftg; Hon Roll; NHS; Ntl Imprvd Plyr-Trck Tm, Rcgntn & Trphy 87; Slctd & Attnded Art Crses-Kystn JC 86; Med.

SHANLEY, EDWARD; Saegertown HS; Meadville, PA; (3); 8/124; Hosp Aide; VP JA; Pres Library Aide; Quiz Bowl; Mrchg Band; Yrbk Stf; JETS Awd; NHS; Hon Roll; Pres Aud/Vis; PA Free Enterprise Week 86; Smmr Intnsv Fgn Lang Inst 87; PSU; Intl Pol Sci.

SHANNON, BRIAN; Wilmington Area HS; New Wilmington, PA; (4); 5/121; Hosp Aide; Key Clb; Pres Soph Cls; Pres Jr Cls; Pres Sr Cls; Pres Stu Cncl; Var L Bsbl; Var Capt Bsktbl; Im Coach Actv; Var Capt Ftbl; 1st Team All ST Ftbl 86-87; Schlr & Athl Awds 86-87; Big 33 PA All Star Ftbl Team 87; U Notre Dame; Engrng.

SHANNON, COLLEEN; Brockway Area HS; Brockway, PA; (4); Art Clb; Debate Tm; Spanish Clb; Varsity Clb; Mrchg Band; Rep Stu Cncl; Mgr Socr; JV Vllybl; Hon Roll; Pres Schlr; REACH Amer 87; Voctnl Explrers; Penn ST U; Elem Ed.

SHANNON, HEATHER; Peters Township HS; Mcmurray, PA; (3); High Hon Roll; Hon Roll; Riflery Awds 85-87; Sec Tchng.

SHANROCK, JILL; Tunkhannock Area HS; Tunkhannock, PA; (2); Art Clb; Church Yth Grp; Latin Clb; Spanish Clb; SADD; Church Choir; Hon Roll; Bus Adm.

SHANTZ, GRETCHEN; Seneca Valley HS; Zelienople, PA; (3); Church Yth Grp; JA; Model UN; Ski Clb; Varsity Clb; Flag Corp; Lit Mag; VP Soph Cls; Im Socr; Var Swmmng; Pre-Med.

SHAPELLA, MICHAEL F; Nativity BVM HS; New Philadelphia, PA; (1); 13/93; Cit Awd; PA ST Coll; Pilot.

SHAPIRO, SIOUXSIE; Performing Arts Schl Of Phila; Philadelphia, PA; (4); School Play; Lit Mag; Off Frsh Cls; Off Soph Cls; Hon Roll; Psych Awd 87; Creatv Wrtng Awd 87; Shakespear Awd 87; American Acad Drama; Drama.

SHAPPELL, KAREN; Schuylkill Haven HS; Sch Haven, PA; (3); 10/88; Church Yth Grp; FCA; Pep Clb; SADD; Chorus; Yrbk Stf; Sec Jr Cls; Stu Cncl; Var Bsktbl; Var Trk; Kutztown U; Elem Ed.

SHAPPLE, DEBBIE; Liberty HS; Bethlehem, PA; (3); 9/445; German Clb; Hosp Aide; SADD; Band; Chorus; Concert Band; Mrchg Band; School Musical; School Play; Var Fld Hcky; Pre Med.

SHARAPAN, AMY; Allderdice HS; Pittsburgh, PA; (3); Cmnty Wkr; Ski Clb; Temple Yth Grp; Yrbk Stf; Trs Jr Cls; High Hon Roll; Zionist Off Am Schlrshp To Israel 87.

SHARE, SHIRLEY; West Scranton HS; Scranton, PA; (2); Orch; High Hon Roll; Hon Roll; Jr NHS; Gifted Prog; Medicine.

SHAREK, DIANE; Hopewell SR HS; Aliquippa, PA; (2); JA; Library Aide; Teachers Aide; Band; Concert Band; Mrchg Band; High Hon Roll; Prfct Atten Awd; Chem.

SHARER, ELESA; Valley SR HS; New Kensington, PA; (3); 21/255; AFS; JA; Key Clb; Varsity Clb; Band; Yrbk Stf; Sftbl; Swmmng; High Hon Roll; NHS; Grls Hgh Scorer Awd Swmmng 85-87; Nrsng.

SHARFF, BRYAN; Lower Moreland HS; Huntingdon Valley, PA; (3); FBLA; Tennis.

SHARIF, RUQAIYA; St Joseph Acad; Dover, PA; (4); 1/17; Dnfth Awd; Pres Schlr; Val; Voice Dem Awd; Walter A Brunhouse Schlshp Penn ST 87; Bishops Relgn Awd 87; SR Ldrshp Awd 87; PA ST U; Intl Rel.

SHARKEY, CHERYL ANN; West Scranton SR HS; Scranton, PA; (4); Red Cross Aide; Ski Clb; Speech Tm; Thesps; Stage Crew; Trs Stu Cncl; Hon Roll; NHS; Marywood Coll; Med Tech.

SHARKEY, KIM; Council Rock HS; Holland, PA; (3); 209/908; Dance Clb; Hosp Aide; Spanish Clb; SADD; Chorus; Color Guard; Mrchg Band; School Play; Twrlr; Hon Roll; Intl Law.

SHARKEY, VINCENT E; Stroudsburg HS; Stroudsburg, PA; (3); Boy Scts; Church Yth Grp; Cmnty Wkr; Drama Clb; FFA; VICA; Church Choir; School Musical; School Play; Nwsp Ed-Chief; Upwrd Bnd Ldrshp Awd 85-86; Schl Ltr & Pin 87; ST FFA Ldrshp Awd 87; Keystone JC; Frstry.

SHARKINS, TONY; Burrell HS; Lower Burrell, PA; (3); 7/175; Var L Bsbl; Var L Ftbl; L Swmmng; High Hon Roll; Jr NHS; NHS; Schltc Ltr 85-87; WPIAL Qlfr Swmmng-Frstyle 85-87; WPIAL AA Chmp Ftbl-SE OLB 86; Chem.

SHARP JR, ARTHUR H; Valley Forge Military Acad; S Weymouth, MA; (3); Aud/Vis; Boy Scts; Church Yth Grp; Exploring; ROTC; Color Guard; JV Bsbl; Im Bsktbl; Im Ftbl; Trk; Eagle Scout 88; Mltry Coll; Pilot.

SHARP, JEFFREY; Uniontown SR HS; Uniontown, PA; (2); Trs Church Yth Grp; VP German Clb; Letterman Clb; Im Bsktbl; Var Crs Cntry; Var L Swmmng; Var Trk; DAR Awd; High Hon Roll; Hon Roll; US Naval Acad; Aerospace Engr.

SHARP, JODI; Shikellamy HS; Sunbury, PA; (3); 58/320; French Clb; Band; Chorus; Capt Color Guard; Concert Band; Drill Tm; Mrchg Band; Hon Roll; Indoor Guard Number Yr 85-86; Med.

SHARP, MELISSA; Baldwin HS; Sylvania, OH; (4); 189/533; Camp Fr Inc; Exploring; Girl Scts; Hosp Aide; Library Aide; Chorus; Hon Roll; Typng Awd 84; Shrthnd Awd 85-86; Grad Stl Cntr Vo Tech 87; Med.

SHARP, TONYA; Lancaster Mennonite HS; New Holland, PA; (3); 9/163; Church Yth Grp; Lit Mag; Sec Frsh Cls; Trs Jr Cls; Sec Stu Cncl; JV Var Bsktbl; Var Trk; High Hon Roll; Jr NHS; NHS; Honor Pass 85; Messiah Coll; Bus.

SHARP, WILLIAM A; Franklin HS; Franklin, PA; (3); 8/215; Pres Band; Jazz Band; Mrchg Band; School Musical; Variety Show; Cit Awd; High Hon Roll; NHS; Church Yth Grp; Concert Band; Dist, Rgnl Band 87; Schl Dirctrs Awd 85-87; Mech Engr.

SHARPE, JOHN; North Catholic HS; Pittsburgh, PA; (3); Pres French Clb; Stage Crew; Rep Soph Cls; Stu Cncl; Crs Cntry; French Hon Soc; Bus Admin.

SHARPE, JUANITA; Penn Wood HS; Yeadon, PA; (3); 30/369; Church Yth Grp; Yrbk Stf; Lit Mag; Mgr(s); Socr; Vllybl; Hon Roll; Sci & Spnsh Awd 84-85; Bio.

SHARPE, KIMBERLEY; Clarion Area HS; Shippenville, PA; (4); 11/95; Church Yth Grp; Cmnty Wkr; FCA; FTA; Girl Scts; Political Wkr; Chorus; Variety Show; Yrbk Stf; Stat Trk; SUNY-BINGHAMTON; Poli Sci.

SHARPS, CHERYLE J; Aliquippa JR-SR HS; Aliquippa, PA; (3); Church Yth Grp; Pres French Clb; Band; Concert Band; Mrchg Band; Pep Band; School Play; Yrbk Stf; Stat Wrstlng; Hon Roll; Beaver County Honors Band 86-87.

SHARRAR, BRUCE; Cranberry JR SR HS; Seneca, PA; (2); Aud/Vis; Cmnty Wkr; French Clb; Intnl Clb; Pep Clb; Pep Band; Stu Cncl; Bowling; Sftbl; Wrstlng; PMEA Dist Orchestra Awd 86; Slippery Rock Orchestra Festvl Awd 84-85; US Naval Acad; Med.

SHATTEEN, TAMIKA; Coatesville Area SR HS; Coatesville Hts, PA; (3); Drama Clb; Church Choir; Capt Color Guard; Concert Band; Mrchg Band; Rep Jr Cls; JV Cheerleading; Var Trk; Hon Roll; Rotary Awd; LA ST U; Aerospce.

SHATTENBERG, CARA; Venango Christian HS; Shippenville, PA; (2); 1/45; Yrbk Stf; Trs Stu Cncl; High Hon Roll; Constitution Tv Cont 86-87; Advncd In Every On Of My Cls 86-7; Homecmng Ct-Rep Of Soph 86-87; Engr.

SHATTENBERG, PAMALA; Keystone JR/Sr HS; Shippenville, PA; (3); 14/136; Cmnty Wkr; Trs VICA; Chorus; High Hon Roll; Hon Roll; Prfct Atten Awd; 3rd Plc Opng & Clsng Ceremonies ST VICA Cmptn 87; 2nd Plc Jb Intrvw Lcl VICA Cmptn 87; Phrmcy.

SHATTO, PATRICIA; West York HS; York, PA; (3); Church Yth Grp; Spanish Clb; Church Choir; JV Bsktbl; Im Swmmng; High Hon Roll; Hon Roll; Voice Dem Awd; Pre Law.

SHATTUCK, JOHANNA T; Hershey SR HS; Hershey, PA; (3); CAP; Exploring; Girl Scts; Spanish Clb; Varsity Clb; Lit Mag; Rep Jr Cls; Bsktbl; Crs Cntry; Hon Roll; Ran The Mntrl Marathn; 2nd Airmn-Cvl Air Ptrl; Universidad De Las Americes.

SHATZ, REBECCA; Coudersport JR SR HS; Coudersport, PA; (4); 5/87; 4-H; French Clb; Ski Clb; Flag Corp; School Play; Yrbk Stf; Stat Bsktbl; 4-H Awd; High Hon Roll; NHS; Beneficial Hodson Schlrshp 87; Grand Prz Sci Fair 86; PTSA Lit Reflection Contest 2nd Pl 85; HOOD Coll; Bio.

SHATZER, STEPHANIE C; James Buchanan HS; St Thomas, PA; (2); Pep Clb; VP SADD; Teachers Aide; Hon Roll; Art Awd 84-85.

SHAUB, JOSH; Strath Haven HS; Wallingford, PA; (3); Ski Clb; Temple Yth Grp; Nwsp Rptr; Nwsp Stf; Var Socr; JV Trk; JV Wrstlng; High Hon Roll; Hon Roll; Free Enterprz Wk 87; Gov Schl Arts SF 87; Lib Arts.

SHAUB, MICHAEL; Lampeter-Strasburg HS; Lampeter, PA; (3); 15/148; Pres Church Yth Grp; Thesps; Band; Chorus; Concert Band; Madrigals; Mrchg Band; School Musical; Hon Roll; NHS; Natl Hnr Soc 87; Hon Mntn Physcs Sci Fair 87; 2nd Pl Physcs Sci Fair 86; Relgn.

SHAUBACH, ROBERT A; Pequea Valley HS; Paradise, PA; (3); 1/125; AFS; Band; Jazz Band; Madrigals; Pep Band; School Musical; NHS; Rotary Awd; Church Yth Grp; Chorus; PA All ST Chorus 86; Music Eductrs Natl Conf Estrn Div Hnr Choir 87; Millersvl U; Music Educ.

SHAUGHNESSY, AMY; Tunkhannock HS; Tunkhannock, PA; (2); 5/380; Pep Clb; Ski Clb; Spanish Clb; JV Fld Hcky; Hon Roll; Law.

SHAUGHNESSY, CHRISTINE; West Scranton HS; Scranton, PA; (4); 54/248; Boys Clb Am; Dance Clb; Debate Tm; FNA; Girl Scts; NFL; Ski Clb; Boys Clb Am; Speech Tm; Yrbk Stf; PA Fnlst Yth Of Yr Boys Clb Of Am 87; Pres Keystone Clb 87; Presdntl Acadmc Ftns Awd 87; Penn ST; Education.

SHAUGHNESSY, MICHAEL; Shady Side Acad; Pittsburgh, PA; (3); Ski Clb; Spanish Clb; L Var Ice Hcky; Capt Var Lcrss; Bus Mngmt.

SHAULIS, ANGELA; Berlin Brothers Valley HS; Berlin, PA; (3); 1/95; Church Yth Grp; Spanish Clb; SADD; Chorus; School Play; Rep Stu Cncl; Hon Roll; NHS; Algbr II Awd 85-86.

SHAULIS, KRISTIE; Saltsburg JR SR HS; Saltsburg, PA; (2); 21/95; Church Yth Grp; SADD; Drm & Bgl; Mrchg Band; School Musical; Capt JV Bsktbl; Var Twrlr; Capt JV Vllybl; Hon Roll.

SHAULIS, LORELEE; Butler Area SR HS; Butler, PA; (3); Sec Church Yth Grp; Sec Hosp Aide; Color Guard; Lit Mag; Rep Frsh Cls; Rep Soph Cls; Hon Roll; Jr NHS; French Clb; Office Aide; Acdmc Lttr, JR Natl Hnr Soc 86; White Awd 3.0 & Hghr 87; Grove City Coll; Engl.

SHAULL, JEFF; Red Lion Area SR HS; Brogue, PA; (2); 35/344; Band; Church Choir; Concert Band; Jazz Band; Mrchg Band; Orch; Pep Band; School Musical; Symp Band; Hon Roll; Chrch Orgnst 83; Dir-Cond Chrch Orchstra Band 86; Music Ed.

SHAW, AMANDA; Quaker Valley SR HS; Sewickley, PA; (1); Latin Clb; Pep Clb; Service Clb; Band; Concert Band; Mrchg Band; Orch; Swmmng; Trk; High Hon Roll.

SHAW, AMBRA; Northeast Prep; Philadelphia, PA; (4); 1/65; French Clb; VP Intnl Clb; Stage Crew; Sec Yrbk Stf; Rep Sr Cls; Trk; Hon Roll; Opt Clb Awd; Val; Intl Mrktng.

SHAW, ANDREW; Huntingdon Area HS; Huntingdon, PA; (4); 19/227; Pres Frsh Cls; VP Soph Cls; Pres Jr Cls; Pres Sr Cls; Rep Stu Cncl; Capt Ftbl; Im Wt Lftg; USMA; Miltry Acad.

SHAW, ANNE MARIE; Kennard-Dale HS; Stewartstown, PA; (2); Church Yth Grp; German Clb; Band; Chorus; Concert Band; Mrchg Band; Sec Orch; Pep Band; School Musical; Hon Roll.

SHAW, ANTHONY; Red Lion HS; Red Lion, PA; (3); 30/342; JCL; Science Clb; Varsity Clb; Jazz Band; Mrchg Band; School Musical; Symp Band; Var L Trk; High Hon Roll; Band; Ntl Latin Soc 87; Trim Music Soc 87; Sci.

SHAW, BEVERLY; Northwestern Lehigh HS; Fogelsville, PA; (3); 1/139; Church Yth Grp; Trs Exploring; SADD; School Musical; School Play; Trk; High Hon Roll; NHS; Vet Med.

SHAW, BRIAN; Philipsburg-Osceola HS; West Decatur, PA; (4); 72/250; Am Leg Boys St; Letterman Clb; Scholastic Bowl; Band; Concert Band; Yrbk Stf; Stu Cncl; L Co-Capt Ftbl; Wt Lftg; NEDT Awd; Penn ST U; Bus Admin.

SHAW, BRIAN; South Allegheny HS; Liberty Boro, PA; (4); 3/177; German Clb; Scholastic Bowl; Sec Trs Science Clb; Ed Yrbk Stf; Trk; High Hon Roll; Hon Roll; NHS; PA Gvrnrs Schl For The Arts 86; Gftd & Tlntd Enrchmnt 84-86; Allegheny Sngr Rsrch Inst Sci Comp 86; Yale Univ; Art.

SHAW, CAROL; Ridgway Area HS; Ridgway, PA; (4); 17/107; Church Yth Grp; Ski Clb; Nwsp Rptr; Nwsp Stf; Yrbk Stf; Stu Cncl; Var L Crs Cntry; L Trk; High Hon Roll; Hon Roll; Chrldng Awd Mst Spirited 85-86; Big 30 Ftbl Classic Chrldr 87; Edinboro U; Elem Ed.

SHAW, CHARLENE; Engineering And Sci HS; Phila, PA; (3); Church Yth Grp; Exploring; Variety Show; Yrbk Stf; Charles Ellis Schlrshp-Acad Achvt Pgm 86-87; C Ellis Schlrshp-Cmpltn Of PUP Pgm 87; U Of Pittsburgh; Elec Engrng.

SHAW, CHRISTINE; Cambria Heights HS; Patton, PA; (3); 52/182; FHA; SADD; Church Choir; Nwsp Stf; Hon Roll; FHA HERO Awd 85; FHA HERO ST Postr Comptn Tm 2nd Pl 87; Gregg Shrthd Achvt Awd 87; Secy.

SHAW, DAWN; Hempfield Area SR HS; Irwin, PA; (4); 141/693; Drama Clb; Exploring; VP Chorus; Church Choir; School Musical; Stage Crew; Cit Awd; Jr NHS; Dist I Hnrs Choir 86; ICM; Trvl.

SHAW, HEATHER; Portersville Christian Schl; Mars, PA; (4); Chorus; Church Choir; Variety Show; Capt Cheerleading; Wt Lftg; Hon Roll; NHS; Clarissa Schl; Apprl Tech.

SHAW, HEIDI; Beaver Area JR SR HS; Beaver, PA; (3); German Clb; Hosp Aide; Chorus; Color Guard; JV Powder Puff Ftbl; Hon Roll; Med Asst.

SHAW, JAMES; Upper Dublin HS; Ft Washington, PA; (3); 68/295; Church Yth Grp; JA; Engl.

SHAW, JENNY; Frazier HS; Perryopolis, PA; (4); High Hon Roll; Hon Roll; John D Mihm Mem Schlrshp 87; Peer Tutoring Awd 87; Top 10 Of Clss Awd 87; Laurel Bus Inst Inc; Accntng.

SHAW, KELLI; Central HS; E Freedom, PA; (4); 83/187; Church Yth Grp; VP FBLA; FNA; GAA; Varsity Clb; Chorus; Yrbk Stf; Stu Cncl; Score Keeper; Sftbl.

SHAW, KERRY; Hollidaysburg Area SR HS; Duncansville, PA; (3); 11/385; Civic Clb; Latin Clb; Gov Hon Prg Awd; High Hon Roll; Pre-Law.

SHAW, KEVIN; Wilmington Area HS; New Wilmington, PA; (3); 4-H; Ftbl; Trk; Slippery Rock U; Physcl Thrpy.

SHAW, MELINDA; General Mc Lane HS; Edinboro, PA; (4); 54/187; Office Aide; Spanish Clb; Teachers Aide; Yrbk Stf; High Hon Roll; Hon Roll; Army; Personnel Mgmt.

SHAW, MICHELLE; Juniata HS; Honey Grove, PA; (3); 4-H; FHA; SADD; Concert Band; Mrchg Band; Stage Crew; Nwsp Stf; JV Sftbl; Hon Roll; Radiolgy.

SHAW, SETH; Marheim Central HS; Penryn, PA; (4); 51/227; Bsktbl; Coach Actv; Trk; Vllybl; Wt Lftg; Drexel; Comp Sci.

SHAW, TRENDA; West Mifflin Area HS; W Mifflin, PA; (3); Church Yth Grp; Hosp Aide; Pep Clb; Co-Capt Drm Mjr(t); Orch; Co-Capt Twrlr; Hon Roll; Jr NHS; Nrs.

SHAW, VIRGINIA; Cardinal O Hara HS; Springfield, PA; (4); 91/776; Church Yth Grp; JA; Latin Clb; Band; Mrchg Band; Pep Band; Off Sr Cls; High Hon Roll; Hon Roll; Rotary Awd; Rtry Tech Schlrshp Awd 87; Grdn Phllps Cnslrs Schlrshp 87; Gordon Phillips Beauty Schl.

SHAWARYN, MARLA; St Basil Acad; Philadelphia, PA; (4); 4/97; Cmnty Wkr; French Clb; Science Clb; Madrigals; Yrbk Sprt Ed; Var Bsktbl; Var Sftbl; Var Capt Tennis; Vllybl; High Hon Roll; Schlrshp 4 Yrs; 1st Pl Sci Fair; Georgetown U; Psych.

SHAWLEY, ERICKA; Yough SR HS; Herminie, PA; (3); Pep Clb; Band; Chorus; Stat Trk; PBA; Hair Drsr.

SHAY, HEATHER; Cedar Crest HS; Lebanon, PA; (3); German Clb; Pep Clb; Band; Concert Band; Mrchg Band; Diving; Sftbl; Capt Swmmng; Hon Roll; Hnrs Banquet; Penn St.

SHAY, MICHAEL; Nativity BVM; Pottsville, PA; (2); Boy Scts; Church Yth Grp; Latin Clb; Hon Roll; Maxima Cum Laude 86; Hghst Achvt Awd Wrld Cult 87; Ad Altare Dei 85; Penn ST U; Ed.

SHAY, PATRICIA; Villa Maria Acad; Media, PA; (3); 13/98; Hosp Aide; Lit Mag; Var Lcrss; High Hon Roll; NHS; Spanish NHS; Tri-M Music Hnr Soc VP 87-88; Music Minstry Ldr 87-88; Physcl Thrpy.

SHAZER, NINA; Sto-Rox SR HS; Mckees Rocks, PA; (3); 5/170; Girl Scts; Office Aide; Sec Frsh Cls; Sec Soph Cls; JV Var Mgr(s); Hon Roll; Robert Morris; CPA.

SHEA, ANDREA; Country Day School; Wynnewood, PA; (4); 5/40; Drama Clb; Chorus; Yrbk Stf; Var Fld Hcky; Var Lcrss; Hon Roll; NHS; Dickinson Coll; Liberal Arts.

SHEA, CHARLES B; Hempfield Area SR HS; Greensburg, PA; (4); 8/693; Boy Scts; Nwsp Sprt Ed; Var L Crs Cntry; Var Trk; High Hon Roll; NHS; Ntl Merit SF; Outstndng Acdmc Achvmnt 84-86; Cert Of Merit 86; Engr.

SHEA, DANIEL; Pocono Mountain HS; Mt Pocono, PA; (1); Band; Im Bsbl; Im Bsktbl; JV Ftbl; Im Golf; Im Socr; Var Trk; Im Vllybl; Im Wt Lftg.

SHEA JR, JAMES A; Mountain View HS; South Gibson, PA; (3); Letterman Clb; Ski Clb; Varsity Clb; Nwsp Rptr; Var L Crs Cntry; Var L Trk; Var L Wrstlng; Hon Roll; MVP All Str Crss Cntry 85-86; MVP All Str Trck 86; Lock Haven U; Phy Thrpy.

SHEA, KERI; Canon Mc Millan HS; Mc Donald, PA; (1); Pres Band; Concert Band; Mrchg Band; Bsktbl; Cheerleading; Hon Roll; Picked For Grtr Latrobe Dist Bnd 87; PA ST; Math Tchr.

SHEA, LIA; Cambersburg Area SR HS; Chambersburg, PA; (2); 12/786; Orch; Trk; Hon Roll; Jr NHS; Cert Of Acht For Exc In Englsh 85-86; PA ST; Gntcs.

SHEA, TAMMY; Tunkhannock HS; Tunkhannock, PA; (3); Ski Clb; JV Crs Cntry; Trk; Hon Roll; Crs Cntry All Stars 84; Crs Cntry States 84; Bus Mgmt.

SHEADER, SCOTT; Sto-Rox SR HS; Mc Kees Rocks, PA; (4); Art Clb; Boys Clb Am; Boy Scts; Exploring; Letterman Clb; School Play; Stage Crew; Nwsp Stf; Yrbk Stf; Ftbl; Gold Pin; Hghst Avg Art; Penn ST U; Elec Engrng.

SHEAFFER, ANITA; Lampeter-Strasburg HS; Lancaster, PA; (3); AFS; Art Clb; Church Yth Grp; Drama Clb; Thesps; Band; Chorus; Color Guard; School Musical; Yrbk Stf; Internatl Thespian Soc 87; West Chester; Pltcl Sci.

SHEAFFER, ANNMARIE; Owen J Roberts HS; Elverson, PA; (4); 101/176; Church Yth Grp; Drama Clb; French Clb; Pep Clb; SADD; School Musical; Var Cheerleading; High Hon Roll; Computer Clb; Band; Miss Ntl Teen Ager Fnlst Trphy 85-86; Metro Phila Miss Hsptlty Teenager 85-86; Elizabethtown; Occptnl Thrpy.

SHEAFFER, DEAN; West Perry HS; Shermansdale, PA; (3); 10/221; Varsity Clb; Var L Bsbl; NHS; Ntl Merit SF; Acad All Amer 87; PA ST U; Comp Sci.

SHEAFFER, JAMIE; Big Spring HS; Newville, PA; (3); 60/270; Stu Cncl; Var Capt Bsktbl; Var L Crs Cntry; Var JV Fld Hcky; Powder Puff Ftbl; Var L Sftbl; Var L Trk; Hon Roll; Mid-Penn Div III All Star Bsktbll Team 86-87; Sports Hall Of Fame Bsktbll 87; MVP Girls Bkstbl 86-87; Ed.

SHEAFFER, JANET; Middletown Area HS; Middletown, PA; (3); 28/161; Cmnty Wkr; Library Aide; Model UN; Chorus; Stage Crew; Nwsp Stf; Yrbk Stf; Hon Roll; Prfct Atten Awd; Jrnlsm.

SHEAFFER, JEANNETTE; West Perry SR HS; New Bloomfield, PA; (3); 9/216; Pep Clb; Spanish Clb; Band; Chorus; Concert Band; Mrchg Band; Rep Stu Cncl; Score Keeper; Hon Roll; NHS; Amer Musicl Fndtn Band Hnrs 87; Acdmc All Amer 86; Tchg.

SHEAFFER, JENNIFER; Greenwood HS; Millerstown, PA; (4); 3/67; Political Wkr; Teachers Aide; Chorus; School Musical; School Play; Yrbk Ed-Chief; Cheerleading; Trk; High Hon Roll; NHS; H O Brian Ldrshp Awd 85; PA ST U.

SHEAFFER, KIMBERLY; Solanco HS; Drumore, PA; (3); 24/273; VP Church Yth Grp; Drama Clb; Exploring; Girl Scts; Spanish Clb; Hon Roll; Biology Awd; Drivers Ed Awd High Grade Point Avg; Anatomy, Physiology Citznshp Awd; Elem Educ.

SHEAFFER, LAURA; Carlisle HS; Carlisle, PA; (4); 44/400; Church Yth Grp; Pep Clb; Ski Clb; Color Guard; Nwsp Ed-Chief; Nwsp Stf; Hon Roll; Outstndg Sr Awd 87; Roanoke Coll; Psychlgy.

SHEARER, CHRISTINE; Hazleton SR HS; Hazleton, PA; (3); 33/425; Drama Clb; Ed Exploring; Nwsp Ed-Chief; Nwsp Rptr; Nwsp Stf; Yrbk Stf; Hon Roll; Prfct Atten Awd; Pres Acad Fit Awd 85; Point Park Coll; Jrnlsm.

SHEARER, GWEN; Faith Mennonite HS; Lancaster, PA; (4); Church Yth Grp; Library Aide; Math Tm; Acpl Chr; Nwsp Ed-Chief; Sec Frsh Cls; Rep Soph Cls; Trs Sr Cls; Hon Roll; Character Awd; Millersville U; Social Wk.

SHEARER, HOPE; Connelsville SR HS; Mill Run, PA; (3); VP Church Yth Grp; 4-H; Trs VICA; Nwsp Stf; Hon Roll; Dir List 86 & 87; Uniontown Beauty Acad; Csmtlgst.

SHEARER, JILL; Leechburg Area HS; Leechburg, PA; (2); Math Tm; Spanish Clb; Chorus; Cheerleading; Hon Roll.

SHEARER, JUD; E L Meyers HS; Wilkes-Barre, PA; (4); Ski Clb; SADD; Chorus; Yrbk Stf; Pres Jr Cls; Pres Sr Cls; Stu Cncl; L Crs Cntry; L Trk; NHS.

SHEARER, LAURABETH; Liberty HS; Ono, PA; (3); 9/550; Pres Church Yth Grp; VP German Clb; Model UN; Church Choir; Stu Cncl; Hon Roll; NHS; Girl Scout Silver Awd 87; PMTA Natl Piano Plyng Aud 87; Liberal Arts.

SHEARER, MARJORIE; Juniata HS; Pt Royal, PA; (3); Drama Clb; 4-H; VP FFA; Yrbk Stf; JV Sftbl; JV Trk; Hon Roll; NHS.

SHEARER, MARK J; Red Land HS; Etters, PA; (4); 17/254; Acpl Chr; Chorus; School Musical; Capt Ftbl; Wt Lftg; French Hon Soc; Kiwanis Awd; NHS; Acad All-Amer 86; Amos Alonzo Stagg Awd 86; Le High U; Mech Engr.

SHEARER, MICHELLE; Waynesboro Area HS; Waynesboro, PA; (3); Hosp Aide; Intnl Clb; Nwsp Stf; High Hon Roll; Hon Roll; NHS; Bus Clb Hstrn 86-87; Bus.

SHEARER, PETER W; Belle Vernon Area HS; Belle Vernon, PA; (4); 67/274; Capt Bsktbl; Capt Var Ftbl; Hon Roll; SAR Awd; All Trnmnt Team Charleroiholiday Bsktbll Tourn 86; U Pittsburgh; Commnctns.

SHEARER, RAY; Freeport SR HS; Sarver, PA; (3); Distnguishd Hnr Rl 85-86; Penn ST; Physics.

SHEARER, RICHELE; Northern HS; Dillsburg, PA; (3); 54/253; Dance Clb; SADD; Band; Color Guard; Pres Sr Cls; Rep Stu Cncl; Var Trk; Capt Var Twrlr; High Hon Roll; Prfct Atten Awd; Miami U; Bio Sci.

SHEARER, VALERIE; Big Spring HS; Newville, PA; (3); 20/280; Chorus; Church Choir; School Musical; School Play; Trs Jr Cls; Trs Sr Cls; Swmmng; Trk; Hon Roll; NHS; JR Womens Clb Stu Of Mnth 87; ;Pltcl Sci.

SHEARLDS, KHALIL; Penn Wood HS; Lansdowne, PA; (3); Church Yth Grp; Yrbk Stf; Ftbl; Trk; Hon Roll; Prfct Atten Awd; Pres Acadc Ftnss Awd 85; Outstndng Achvt Awd In Bus Law.

SHEARMAN, SCOTT; Windber Area HS; Windber, PA; (4); FTA; Math Clb; Yrbk Stf; Trs Frsh Cls; Bsbl; Bsktbl; Hon Roll; Prfct Atten Awd; Stud Mnths 86-87; Pittsburgh Tech Inst; Sys Oper.

SHEBA, DAN; Laurel Highlands SR HS; Uniontown, PA; (2); Science Clb; JV Var Golf; Hon Roll; Engr.

SHEBBY, WM; Our Lady Of Lourdes Regional HS; Mount Carmel, PA; (3); 46/89; Art Clb; Trs Sr Cls; JV Ftbl; Wt Lftg; VP L Wrstlng; Key Clb; Letterman Clb; Variety Show; Hon Roll; Gold Key Awd In Art 84; Mech Engrng.

SHECKLER, CRAIG D; Southern Lehigh HS; Coopersburg, PA; (4); 2/230; Chess Clb; Trs Church Yth Grp; Math Tm; Jazz Band; Orch; Yrbk Stf; High Hon Roll; NHS; Im Vllybl; Franklin & Marshall Awd 86; Gold Mdl Summa Cum Laude Latn Exm 86; Comp Engrng.

SHEDD, HEATHER; Faith Christian School; Blairstown, NJ; (3); 9/16; Church Yth Grp; Yrbk Ed-Chief; Pres Frsh Cls; Pres Jr Cls; Sftbl; Vllybl; Rhema Bible Trng Ctr.

SHEDLOCK, DENISE; Moshannon Valley HS; Ramey, PA; (4); Cmnty Wkr; Hosp Aide; Pep Clb; Red Cross Aide; Spanish Clb; Band; Chorus; Concert Band; Mrchg Band; Pep Band; Central PA Schl Nrsng.

SHEEDER, DAMON; Curwensville HS; Curwensville, PA; (3); Letterman Clb; Ski Clb; JV Var Bsbl; JV Var Ftbl.

SHEEHAN, AMY; Kennedy Christian HS; Brookfield, OH; (4); 19/97; Civic Clb; Pep Clb; Spanish Clb; Band; Concert Band; Mrchg Band; Pep Band; Im Vllybl; High Hon Roll; PA ST U; Ed.

SHEEHAN, CHRISTA; Cardinal O Hara HS; Springfield, PA; (4); 8/790; SADD; Band; Concert Band; Orch; School Musical; Ed Nwsp Phtg; French Hon Soc; High Hon Roll; NHS; Rotary Awd; Slv Mdlst-Natl Ltn Exm 86; Dickinson Coll; Intl Studies.

SHEEHAN, STACEY; Central Cambria HS; Ebensburg, PA; (2); Key Clb; Stu Cncl; Var Bsktbl; Trk; Psychtry.

SHEELEY, STACEY; Waynesboro Area SR HS; Waynesboro, PA; (3); Am Leg Aux Girls St; Art Clb; Church Yth Grp; Stu Cncl; Var Bsktbl; Var Trk; Var Vllybl; Cit Awd; High Hon Roll; NHS; Penn ST; Elem Ed.

SHEELY, KATHRYN; Mechanicsburg Area SR HS; Mechanicsburg, PA; (3); 19/309; Pres Church Yth Grp; Chorus; Church Choir; Var L Swmmng; High Hon Roll; NHS.

SHEERAN, DIANA; Avon Grove HS; Landenberg, PA; (3); Service Clb; Mrchg Band; Variety Show; JV Fld Hcky; Var Trk; Twrlr; Hon Roll; Prfct Atten Awd; Lg Chmps Dist Trck 85-87; Fshn Mechndsng.

SHEESLEY, SUSAN L; Penns Manor HS; Clymer, PA; (3); 8/105; NAACP; Pep Clb; Spanish Clb; SADD; Stu Cncl; Cheerleading; High Hon Roll; Hon Roll; Jr NHS; Spanish NHS; PA US Teen Pgnt 87; Arin Intrmdt Clss 87; Ntl Yth Ldrshp Cncl 87; IN U Of PA; Physcl Thrpy.

SHEETS, ANGELA; Hughesville HS; Hughesville, PA; (2); Key Clb; Band; Concert Band; Mrchg Band; Variety Show; Yrbk Stf; Trk; Green/White Awd 85-86.

SHEETS, ERIN; Saegertown HS; Meadville, PA; (4); 1/109; VP Church Yth Grp; VP Pres 4-H; Concert Band; Jazz Band; Pres Mrchg Band; Yrbk Ed-Chief; L Mgr(s); JP Sousa Awd; Val; Letterman Clb; Band Arion Awd 87; Estella Van Horne Schlrshp 87; Math & Sci Awds 87; Juniata Coll; Chem.

SHEETS, JENIFER; Beth-Center HS; Beallsville, PA; (3); 15/165; Art Clb; Ski Clb; Spanish Clb; Varsity Clb; Stat Bsktbl; L Var Sftbl; Capt L Vllybl; Hon Roll.

SHEETS, LISA A; Burrell SR HS; Lower Burrell, PA; (3); Church Yth Grp; SADD; Church Choir; Stage Crew; Var Trk; Hon Roll; Biotech.

SHEETZ, KELLY; Penn Manor HS; Mountville, PA; (3); 29/323; Trs Church Yth Grp; Hon Roll; Psych.

SHEETZ, RANDY S; Cumberland Valley HS; Mechanicsburg, PA; (4); Widener U; Htl/Rest Mgmt.

SHEFFIELD, ARTHUR; Montour HS; Mckees Rocks, PA; (2); JA; Stu Cncl; Bsktbl; Ftbl; Trk; Hon Roll; Prfct Atten Awd; Med.

SHEFFY, TODD; Northern Lebanon HS; Jonestown, PA; (3); 22/212; FCA; Model UN; Band; Mrchg Band; Pep Band; VP Soph Cls; VP Jr Cls; Pres Stu Cncl; Var Ftbl; Hon Roll; Comp Sci.

SHEFTIC, MICHAEL; North Star HS; Stoystown, PA; (2); 8/140; Aud/Vis; FCA; Mu Alpha Theta; Stage Crew; Bsbl; Bsktbl; Wt Lftg; Hon Roll; U Of FL Gainsvl; Aerntcl Engr.

SHEIBLEY, ADRIANE; West Perry HS; Landisburg, PA; (2); 23/220; Church Yth Grp; Red Cross Aide; Spanish Clb; Church Choir; Off Stu Cncl; JV Fld Hcky; JV Stat Trk; Prfct Atten Awd; Accntng.

SHEISS, DONALD; Greencastle Antrim HS; Chambersburg, PA; (3); Pres Sec 4-H; 4-H Awd; Anml Prdctn.

SHELBY, MICHELE MARIE; West Hazleton HS; Hazleton, PA; (4); 22/224; Pep Clb; Spanish Clb; Thesps; Drm Mjr(t); School Play; Hon Roll; NHS; PA JR Acad Sci 85; Selctv Plnng Resrchng Careers 85-87; PA Free Entrprs Wk 86; Bloomsburg U; Math.

SHELDON, JEFFRY; Susquehanna Community HS; Thompson, PA; (3); Church Yth Grp; Cmnty Wkr; Ski Clb; Hon Roll; US Natl Art Awd 85; Natl Ldrshp & Srvc Awds 85 & 86; Acdmc All-Amer, US Natl Ldrshp Mert Awds Sci 84; Penn ST; Engrng.

SHELEY, STACI; Brookville Area HS; Reynoldsville, PA; (3); Church Yth Grp; Band; Concert Band; Mrchg Band; Pep Band; Hon Roll; Prsdntl Physcl Ftnss Awd 84-87; Air Force; Secr.

SHELHAMER, PAULA; Seneca HS; Erie, PA; (3); 6/150; Church Yth Grp; 4-H; Teachers Aide; Band; Var Bsktbl; Var Crs Cntry; Var Trk; 4-H Awd; High Hon Roll; NHS; 110% Awd Bsktbl 85-86; Triple Crwn 86-87; Memorandm Statue Liberty 84-85; Slippery Rock; Crrctv Ther.

SHELHAMER, TONI; Seneca HS; Waterford, PA; (3); Computer Clb; VP Pep Clb; Yrbk Stf; JV Cheerleading; Hon Roll; Ped Nrsng.

SHELLENBERGER, DIANE; West York Area HS; York, PA; (2); 2/209; Church Yth Grp; Sec Drama Clb; German Clb; Varsity Clb; Trs Jr Cls; Stu Cncl; Tennis; High Hon Roll; Voice Dem Awd.

SHELLENBERGER, PARRISH; Juniata Joint HS; Port Royal, PA; (4); Variety Show; Trk; Vllybl; Wrstlng; Hon Roll; JR Golden Hammer Awd 85; Inds Arts Awds 87; Lincoln Tech; Drftng.

SHELLENBERGER, SCOTT; Milton Area SR HS; Milton, PA; (2); Varsity Clb; JV Bsbl; Var Golf; JV Wrstlng; Golf Mgmt.

SHELLENHAMER, STACY; Palmyra HS; Palmyra, PA; (4); 13/195; Hosp Aide; Math Tm; Mrchg Band; Twrlr; High Hon Roll; NHS; Pres Schlr; Math Awd, SR Hnrs Dnnr; Westchester Nrsng Schl; Nrs.

SHELLEY, JENNIFER; Taylor Allderdice HS; Pittsburgh, PA; (4); 34/430; Hosp Aide; Lit Mag; High Hon Roll; Hon Roll; Jr NHS; Ntl Merit Ltr; ST Cmmndtn Perf SAT 86; Bio.

SHELLEY, LISA; Pen Argyl Area HS; Pen Argyl, PA; (3); FBLA; Color Guard; Mrchg Band; Hon Roll; Mst Imprvd Band Front 87; Bnkng.

SHELLITO, DEANNA; Aliquippa HS; Aliquippa, PA; (3); 21/150; Church Yth Grp; Pep Clb; Hon Roll; Child Psych.

SHELP, LISA; Mifflinburg Area HS; Mifflinburg, PA; (3); Computer Clb; Pep Clb; Spanish Clb; Yrbk Stf; JV Bsktbl; Var Trk; Bsktbl Awd 85; Vrsty Trk Ltr 85; Brsty Trk Pin 86; Elem Ed.

SHELTON, CYNTHIA; B Reed Henderson HS; Exton, PA; (3); 88/367; Intnl Clb; Yrbk Stf; Lit Mag; Hon Roll; Millersville U PA; Amer Hstry.

SHELTON, SCOTT M; William Penn SR HS; York, PA; (4); 9/373; School Play; Rep Soph Cls; Rep Jr Cls; Pres Stu Cncl; Var L Wrstlng; Hon Roll; Jr NHS; NHS; Prfct Atten Awd; Sectnl Champ Wrstlng 86; US Naval Acad; Engrng.

SHELVEY, JAMES; Meadville Area SR HS; Meadville, PA; (4); 70/285; Hon Roll; Hnr Scty 87; Pitt At Titusville; CAS.

SHEMER, DENISE; Quigley HS; Aliquippa, PA; (3); 8/88; French Clb; Math Tm; VP Soph Cls; VP Jr Cls; Rep Stu Cncl; Var L Cheerleading; High Hon Roll; Hon Roll; Ntl Merit Ltr; Frnch I Awd 85; Frnch II Awd 86; Phrmcy.

SHENAL, JOHN; Brownsville Area HS; Smock, PA; (4); Chess Clb; Ski Clb; Bsbl; High Hon Roll; NHS; Penn ST; Eng.

SHENCK, JONI; Cedar Cliff HS; New Cumberland, PA; (4); 95/247; German Clb; Key Clb; Pres Pep Clb; Spanish Clb; SADD; Yrbk Phtg; Cheerleading; Crs Cntry; Capt Trk; Pres Schlr; E Stroudsburg U; Phys Ed.

SHENK, DELAINE; Penn Manor HS; Conestoga, PA; (3); #49 In Class; Art Clb; Camera Clb; Hon Roll.

SHENK, PAM; Hempfield HS; Lancaster, PA; (3); Var Fld Hcky; Var Powder Puff Ftbl; Hon Roll; Dance Clb; Variety Show; Graphic Arts.

SHENK, TIMOTHY; Lancaster Mennonite HS; Mountville, PA; (3); Pres Church Yth Grp; Chorus; Nwsp Rptr; Var Capt Socr; Im Vllybl; Im Wt Lftg; Hon Roll; Math.

SHEPARD, HOLLY; Penn Trafford HS; Jeannette, PA; (2); Chorus; Nwsp Stf; Lit Mag; Im Sftbl; Hon Roll; Prfct Atten Awd; Trnsltr.

SHEPARD, TARA; Western Wayne HS; Lake Ariel, PA; (3); Church Yth Grp; Flag Corp; Hon Roll.

SHEPHARD, GRETCHEN; Farrell HS; Farrell, PA; (4); 13/87; Computer Clb; Varsity Clb; Band; Chorus; Church Choir; School Play; Stat Swmmng; Trk; NHS; Dist Chorus 87; PA Anncr 87; Penn ST U; Pol Sci.

SHEPHARD, KIMBERLY; Corry Area HS; Corry, PA; (4); 19/193; French Clb; Trs SADD; Co-Capt Drm Mjr(t); Yrbk Ed-Chief; Cheerleading; Hon Roll; Trs Y-Teens; Fisher Allen Scholar 87; Mc Innes Steel Scholar Grant 87; Acad Achvt Awd 87; Edinboro U; Spec Ed.

SHEPHERD, DANIELLE; Tunkhannock HS; Tunkhannock, PA; (3); 48/330; Church Yth Grp; French Clb; Hosp Aide; Letterman Clb; Ski Clb; Spanish Clb; JV Mgr(s); JV Var Swmmng; Sec Trk; Hon Roll; Mrn Bio.

SHEPHERD, DEREK D; Chester HS; Chester, PA; (3); Boy Scts; Church Yth Grp; Cmnty Wkr; Dance Clb; VP Pres SADD; NAACP; Red Cross Aide; Science Clb; Spanish Clb; Church Choir; Mst Imprvd Spn Stu Awd 86-87; Swath More Coll Upward Bound Acad Achvt Awd 86-87; Aerospc Engr.

SHEPHERD, RONDA; Oxford Area HS; Lincoln Univ, PA; (3); 2/85; Church Yth Grp; FTA; Hosp Aide; Church Choir; Yrbk Stf; High Hon Roll; Hon Roll; Millresville F&M; Psych.

SHEPLEY, HAROLD; North Star HS; Stoystown, PA; (3); 6/141; VP Church Yth Grp; FCA; Math Clb; Mu Alpha Theta; Quiz Bowl; Band; Chorus; Church Choir; Concert Band; Mrchg Band; Stud Of The Mnth 84; Tble Tnns Chmpshp 85-86; Dugueshe; Law.

SHEPLEY, NICOLE; Millersburg Area HS; Millersburg, PA; (3); 8/72; Art Clb; French Clb; Band; Concert Band; Mrchg Band; Nwsp Stf; High Hon Roll; Hon Roll; Hnr Roll Awd Plaque 84-86.

SHEPPARD, CHERYL; Penn-Trafford HS; Jeannette, PA; (2); Church Yth Grp; Drama Clb; German Clb; GAA; Hosp Aide; Chorus; School Musical; Im Sftbl; High Hon Roll; Im Vllybl; Slct Choir 86-87.

SHEPPARD, ELIZABETH; Lancaster Catholic HS; Leola, PA; (4); Band; Concert Band; Mrchg Band; Chld Dvlpmnt Awd 87; Millersville U; Elem Ed.

SHEPPARD, KIM; Moniteau HS; Butler, PA; (4); Church Yth Grp; Drama Clb; French Clb; Band; Chorus; Concert Band; Mrchg Band; Nwsp Rptr; Nwsp Stf; Lit Mag; Slippery Rock U; Psych.

SHEPPARD, SUZANNE; Charters Valley SR HS; Heidelberg, PA; (3); Church Yth Grp; German Clb; Pep Clb; Rotary Awd; Accntng.

SHEPPELA, JOHN; Ambridge Area HS; Baden, PA; (3); German Clb; SADD; Band; Concert Band; Mrchg Band; Pep Band; Symp Band; Var L Bsbl; Hon Roll; Boy Scts; Outstndng Bsbl Achvt Awd 86.

SHEPTAK, TRISHA; Forest City Regional HS; Uniondale, PA; (3); Ski Clb; Spanish Clb; Sftbl; High Hon Roll; Sec NHS; Finance.

SHER, JAMES; Oley Valley HS; Fleetwood, PA; (3); Boy Scts; Pres JA; Yrbk Stf; Var Crs Cntry; JV Trk; JA Schlrshp 85; JA Achvt Awd 87; Archt.

SHERAW, NICHOLLE; Connellsville Area HS; Dickerson, PA; (1); Chorus; Flag Corp.

SHERAW, SCOTT; Union HS; Sligo, PA; (2); Church Yth Grp; SADD; Trs Stu Cncl; JV Bsktbl; JV Ftbl; Var Trk; Hon Roll.

SHERBINE, ERIC; Portage Area HS; Portage, PA; (4); 19/120; Trs Varsity Clb; Trs Soph Cls; Trs Jr Cls; Trs Sr Cls; Var L Ftbl; Var L Wrstlng; High Hon Roll; NHS; Great IX Conf Ftbl All-Star 86; PASU; Mgmt Info Systems.

SHERBINE, ROBERT; Portage Area HS; Portage, PA; (3); Pres Church Yth Grp; Church Choir; Hon Roll; Awana Meritrs Awd 86; Awana Schlrshp Camp Merit Awd 86.

SHERIDAN, JOHN; Hershey HS; Hummelstown, PA; (4); 10/192; Math Tm; VP Pres Spanish Clb; Band; Mgr Stage Crew; NHS; Rotary Awd; VP Spanish NHS; Church Yth Grp; Ski Clb; Concert Band; Hershey Educ Assoc Schlrshp & Treva Dise Schlrshp 87; Rensselaer Polytechnic Inst Math & Sci Awd 86; Penn ST U; Engrng.

SHERIFF, CHERYL; Great Hope Baptist Schl; Carlisle, PA; (3); Teachers Aide; Chorus; Church Choir; School Musical; School Play; Stage Crew; Yrbk Stf; L Cheerleading; Var Vllybl; Hon Roll; Elem Ed.

SHERIFF, CHRIS; Minersville Area HS; Minersville, PA; (4); Im Bsktbl; Var JV Ftbl; Var JV Wt Lftg; Pres Schlr; Outstndng Acad Achvt 82; Cnty Educ Assn 3rd Anl Studnt Art Exhbt 83; Presdntl Acad Ftns Awd 87; Penn ST U; Hnotel Mngt.

SHERIFF, HEATHER; Easthern York JR/Sr HS; York, PA; (4); 15/160; Varsity Clb; Pres Sec Band; Drm Mjr(t); Trs Frsh Cls; Trs Jr Cls; Trs Sr Cls; Capt Var Bsktbl; Capt Var Trk; DAR Awd; JP Sousa Awd; Stu Of Mnth 87; Rotry Ldrshp Conf 86; Susquehanna U; Bio.

SHERIFF, LIZ; West Perry HS; Shermansdale, PA; (2); Drama Clb; French Clb; Concert Band; School Play; Var JV Fld Hcky; Trk; Hon Roll; Dickenson Schl Of Law; Law.

SHERKNESS, MARY; Marian Catholic HS; Mcadoo, PA; (3); 22/104; Church Yth Grp; Hosp Aide; Math Clb; Office Aide; Pep Clb; Ski Clb; Chorus; JV Var Cheerleading; JV Var Sftbl; Hon Roll.

SHERLOCK, DAWN; Morrisville HS; Morrisville, PA; (3); 35/92; FBLA; School Musical; Yrbk Stf; Cheerleading; Hon Roll; Bus.

SHERLOCK, DENISE LYNN; Cardinal O Hara HS; Clifton Heights, PA; (4); 21/771; Dance Clb; French Clb; School Musical; French Hon Soc; High Hon Roll; Sec NHS; Pres Schlr; Stu Of Month 86; St Josephs U; Education.

SHERLOCK, JENNIFER; Huntingdon Area HS; Huntingdon, PA; (4); 40/220; Chrmn Key Clb; Teachers Aide; Yrbk Stf; JV Fld Hcky; L JV Sftbl; Var L Vllybl; Hon Roll; NEDT Awd; Sch Spirit Awd 86-87; Rotary Club Schlrshp 87; Penn ST; Polymer Sci.

SHERMAN, BRETT A; Carlisle SR HS; Carlisle, PA; (3); DECA; Library Aide; ROTC; L Ftbl; Wt Lftg; Wrstlng; Hon Roll; 4th Pl DECA Dist Conf 86-87; FL ST U; Advrtsng.

SHERMAN, BRIAN; Wellsboro HS; Wellsboro, PA; (4); 2/130; Pres 4-H; Pres Band; Chorus; Concert Band; Jazz Band; Mrchg Band; Rep Stu Cncl; 4-H Awd; High Hon Roll; NHS; District Band 87; Music Ed.

SHERMAN JR, C RICHARD; West Scranton HS; Scranton, PA; (2); Hon Roll; Jr NHS.

SHERMAN, JAMES; Northern Potter HS; Westfield, PA; (4); 1/80; German Clb; Math Tm; Bowling; Socr; Trk; Gov Hon Prg Awd; High Hon Roll; NHS; Val; YABA Bwlng Schlrshp 87; Penn ST Comp Sci.

SHERMAN, KIMBERLY; Brookville Area HS; Brookville, PA; (4); 22/125; Church Yth Grp; French Clb; Key Clb; SADD; Varsity Clb; School Musical; Pres Jr Cls; Trs Sr Cls; Cheerleading; NHS; U Of Pittsburgh; Physcl Thrpy.

SHERMAN, MARY ANNE; Central Christian HS; Du Bois, PA; (4); 4/40; Church Yth Grp; Cmnty Wkr; Exploring; SADD; Chorus; School Play; Nwsp Phtg; Var L Crs Cntry; High Hon Roll; Hon Roll; Gold Key Awd For Music Chorus 87; Acad Fitness 87; INDIANA U Of PA; Pre-Schl.

SHERMAN, STEPHEN T; Exeter Township HS; Reading, PA; (3); 36/241; Varsity Clb; Band; Concert Band; Jazz Band; Mrchg Band; Orch; Pep Band; Rep Jr Cls; Rep Stu Cncl; Var Crs Cntry; Dist Band 87; Cnty Band 86-87; Bus.

SHERMAN, VIVI; George Washington HS; Philadelphia, PA; (4); 51/800; SADD; Teachers Aide; Temple Yth Grp; Chorus; School Musical; School Play; Nwsp Rptr; Yrbk Stf; Hon Roll; NHS; Jewish Heritage Awd 87; Jewish Educ Cert Tchrs Diploma 86; Jewish Culture Awd 84-87; Drexel U; Cmmnctns.

SHERNISKY, DIANE; Mon Valley Catholic HS; Belle Vernon, PA; (4); FBLA; Girl Scts; Pep Clb; Band; Mrchg Band; Yrbk Bus Mgr; Stat Bsktbl; Score Keeper; Hon Roll; Fl Schlrshp Coll Pittsburgh Bty Acad 87; Pittsburgh Bty Acad; Csmtlgy.

SHERNISKY, JAMES; Monon Gahela Valley Catholic HS; Belle Vernon, PA; (2); 20/76; Boy Scts; Band; Concert Band; Mrchg Band; JV Var Bsktbl; Hon Roll; Eagle Scout Awd In Boy Sctng 87.

SHERO, BECKY; Cambria Heights HS; Carrolltown, PA; (3); 19/181; French Clb; FHA; SADD; Chorus; Nwsp Phtg; Nwsp Rptr; Yrbk Rptr; Yrbk Stf; Hon Roll; Enrchmnt Cls 84-87; Cambria Somerst JR Miss Semi Fnlst 86-87; Elem Educ.

SHERRETTS, CATHY; Sharon HS; Sharon, PA; (4); 32/159; French Clb; Latin Clb; Color Guard; Sftbl; Penn ST.

SHERROD, ROBIN M; John W Hallahan HS; Philadelphia, PA; (4); 76/299; Stage Crew; Crs Cntry; Mgr(s); Trk; Prfct Atten Awd; 2nd Hnrs 83-86; Brnz Penn Rely Mdls 85-87; PA ST U; Pre-Med.

SHERROW, RANDALL; Oxford Area HS; Oxford, PA; (3); 32/198; FFA; High Hon Roll; Hon Roll; Star Grnhand 84-85; Beef Prdctn 84-85; Chptr VP FFA 88; Vo Ag Shp Awd; PA ST; Engr.

SHERRY, ANGELA K; North Allegheny HS; Pittsburg, CA; (4); 188/660; Church Yth Grp; Cmnty Wkr; Exploring; FBLA; Political Wkr; Church Choir; School Musical; High Hon Roll; Hon Roll; Jr NHS; Brghm Yng U; Psych.

SHERRY, DAWN; William Allen HS; Allentown, PA; (3); Key Clb; Ski Clb; VP Frsh Cls; Rep Stu Cncl; Var Crs Cntry; Var Swmmng; Var Trk; Hon Roll; Jr NHS; NHS; Rep Soph Cls; MVP Trck Awd; Elem Ed.

SHERRY, DEBBIE; Cambria Heights HS; Carrolltown, PA; (3); Art Clb; Chorus; Stat Bsktbl; Sftbl; L Trk; Elem Ed.

SHERRY, LORI; Cambria Heights HS; Ashville, PA; (3); Cmnty Wkr; High Hon Roll; Hon Roll; Altoona Schl Commrce; Med Secr.

SHERRY, LYNN; Bishop Carroll HS; Ebensburg, PA; (3); 19/128; 4-H; NFL; Trs Sec SADD; Rep Soph Cls; VP Jr Cls; Hon Roll; NHS; Optometrist.

SHERRY, MICHAEL; Trinity HS; Mechanicsburg, PA; (3); Pres Aud/Vis; Church Yth Grp; Cmnty Wkr; Speech Tm; Chorus; School Musical; School Play; Pres Stage Crew; Wt Lftg; Cit Awd; Outstndg Svc Awd JR Theol Ed 85-87; Acctg.

SHERRY, TARA; Northern Cambria HS; Barnesboro, PA; (3); Spanish Clb; Band; Color Guard; Concert Band; Nwsp Stf; L Trk; JV Vllybl; Hon Roll; NHS; Spanish NHS; VFW Schlrshp; Educ.

SHERTZER, JERE; Lancaster Christian HS; Lancaster, PA; (4); Church Yth Grp; 4-H; Stage Crew; Pres Soph Cls; Var Bsbl; Var Socr; 4-H Awd; High Hon Roll; Hon Roll; ACSI Chrstn HS Stu 85-86; Lancaster Blb Coll; Aviation.

SHERWIN, HEATHER; Bishop Carroll HS; Cherry Tree, PA; (4); 17/107; Pep Clb; Ski Clb; Band; Concert Band; Jazz Band; Mrchg Band; Pep Band; Hon Roll; NHS; NEDT Awd; Acctng.

SHERWIN, JOE; Council Rock HS; Churchville, PA; (4); 78/836; Hon Roll; PHEAA Cert Merit Outstndng Perfrmnc SAT Hnrs Test 87; Cert Rcgntn Devlpmnt PA 87; Penn ST U; Physics.

SHERWIN, LLOYD; Purchase Line HS; Mahaffey, PA; (3); Chess Clb; Church Yth Grp; Computer Clb; Band; Chorus; Hon Roll; Arch.

SHERWOOD, DEIDRE; Crestwood HS; Mountaintop, PA; (4); FBLA; FHA; Hosp Aide; Yrbk Stf; Hon Roll; Bloomsburg U.

SHERWOOD, SCOTT; Wilkinsburgh JR/Sr HS; Pittsburgh, PA; (3); Spanish Clb; Acpl Chr; Band; Madrigals; Nwsp Rptr; Stu Cncl; NHS; Ntl Merit Ltr; Rotary Awd; HOBY Yth Fndtn ST Semnr 86; Civil Engr.

SHETTEL, BRIAN; Red Lion HS; York, PA; (3); Church Yth Grp; JA; Spanish Clb; Im Bsktbl; Im Vllybl; Im Wt Lftg; High Hon Roll; Hon Roll; Spanish NHS; Clemson; Poltcs.

SHETTERLY, DEBRA; Millersburg Area HS; Millersburg, PA; (3); 17/69; Church Yth Grp; 4-H; Quiz Bowl; Band; Concert Band; Mrchg Band; ROTC; Hon Roll; NHS; Word Proc.

SHETTERLY, STEVEN; Millersburg Area HS; Millersburg, PA; (4); Church Yth Grp; Pres 4-H; Band; Concert Band; Mrchg Band; Hon Roll; NHS; Vet.

SHETZLINE, JESSICA; Harry S Truman HS; Bristol, PA; (4); French Clb; Library Aide; Pep Clb; SADD; Yrbk Stf; Im Golf; Hon Roll; Prfct Atten Awd; Fshn Merch.

SHEVLIN, ANN MARIE; Wyoming Area HS; Exeter, PA; (3); 40/244; Church Yth Grp; Key Clb; Ski Clb; Spanish Clb; Trk; Twrlr; NHS; High Hnr & Hnr Roll 2 Yrs.

SHEWAN, KATE; Saint Benedict Acad; Erie, PA; (4); 41/60; Band; VP Chorus; Color Guard; Concert Band; Mrchg Band; School Musical; Variety Show; Var Socr; Hon Roll; Mst Imprvd SR Sccr 87; Music Awd Chrs 87; Slippery Rock U; Spcl Ed.

SHICK, EDWARD; Roman Catholic HS; Philadelphia, PA; (3); 5/155; Chess Clb; Computer Clb; Library Aide; Teachers Aide; High Hon Roll; Hon Roll; NHS; Prfct Atten Awd; White Williams Schlrshp 86-87; U Of PA; Bus.

SHICK, SHANIN; Union HS; Rimersburg, PA; (3); Hosp Aide; VICA; Rep Stu Cncl; Hon Roll; Prfct Atten Awd; Dirctrs Lst & VP-CLARION Cnty Area Vo Tech Schl-Csmtlgy 86-87; Csmtlgy.

SHIDEMANTLE, JENNIFER; Butler Area SR HS; Butler, PA; (3); Church Yth Grp; SADD; Church Choir; Mrchg Band; School Musical; Var L Gym; Hon Roll; L Jr NHS; 1st Chair Sphmr II Hnr Chorus & Rgnl Chorus 87; Music.

SHIDERLY, RONALD; Mohawk HS; New Castle, PA; (4); Church Yth Grp; French Clb; Im Bsktbl; Var L Ftbl; Var Capt Trk; Hon Roll; NHS; Acad All Amer 86-87; Geneva Coll; Sci.

SHIELDS, ERIC; Altoona Area HS; Altoona, PA; (4); 250/718; VP Church Yth Grp; Drama Clb; JA; Speech Tm; School Play; Nwsp Rptr; Stu Cncl; Prfct Atten Awd; Sprt Awd 87; Cert Excllnc-Dmly Rtl 87; Indiana U Of PA; Accntng.

SHIELDS, ERIN; Valley View JR/Sr HS; Archbald, PA; (2); Cmnty Wkr; Spanish Clb; SADD; Sec Frsh Cls; Sec Soph Cls; Sec Jr Cls; Rep Stu Cncl; Var Score Keeper; Var Trk; Pres Dist PA Assoc Stud Cncls 87-88; U Of Scranton; Law.

SHIELDS, JENNIFER; Brookville Area HS; Summerville, PA; (4); 4/140; Church Yth Grp; Drama Clb; FTA; Sec Trs German Clb; Band; Pres Jazz Band; School Musical; Nwsp Ed-Chief; NHS; Ntl Merit SF; Grmn-Amrcn Prtnr Pgm 87; Alt Dairy Princess Jefferson County 86-87; Clarion U; Chem.

SHIELDS, KIMBERLY; Nativity BVM; Branchdale, PA; (2); 6/78; Girl Scts; Office Aide; Chorus; Variety Show; Rep Frsh Cls; Rep Soph Cls; Var Cheerleading; Crs Cntry; Cit Awd; High Hon Roll; 1st Pl PJAS Regionals 87; 1st Pl Schl Sci Fair 86; 3rd Pl Capital Area ST Sci Fair 86; Med.

SHIELDS, KRISTY; Lancaster Christian HS; Lancaster, PA; (4); 9/26; Church Yth Grp; 4-H; Red Cross Aide; Band; Chorus; Cheerleading; Sftbl; Hon Roll; Exclnt Span Cert 86; Hrs Shwng Trphs & Rbbns 83-87; Lancaster Bible; Msnry.

SHIELDS, LISA; Steelton-Highspire HS; Highspire, PA; (3); Church Yth Grp; GAA; Girl Scts; Spanish Clb; Teachers Aide; Co-Capt Mrchg Band; Stage Crew; Yrbk Stf; Capt Var Bsktbl; Var Sftbl; Dstngshd Athl Awd 86-87; All Star Sftbl 86-87; Hnr Mntn Sftbl 84-85.

SHIELDS, LORIANNE; Pittston Area SR HS; Hughestown, PA; (4); Church Yth Grp; Computer Clb; Drama Clb; FBLA; Girl Scts; Key Clb; Ski Clb; Yrbk Stf; Hon Roll; Rehbltn Schlrshp Penn ST 87; Penn ST U; Phrmcy.

SHIELDS, MARK; Kittanning SR HS; Worthington, PA; (2); L Bsktbl; Hon Roll; Chem.

SHIELDS, SEAN; Pocono Mountain HS; Mountainhome, PA; (2); JV Bsktbl; JV Socr; Hon Roll; Opt Clb Awd.

SHIELDS, STEPHANIE; Punxsutawney Area HS; Punxsutawney, PA; (3); Hosp Aide; Varsity Clb; Cheerleading; Hon Roll.

SHIELDS, VICTORIA L; Harrisburg HS; Harrisburg, PA; (4); 22/235; Pep Clb; Speech Tm; Chorus; Mrchg Band; Fld Hcky; Mgr(s); Swmmng; Trk; Hon Roll; NHS; Tmeple U; Athletic Training.

SHIFKO, WILLIAM; Jeannette SR HS; Jeannette, PA; (3); Am Leg Boys St; Church Yth Grp; Ski Clb; Spanish Clb; Ftbl; Trk; High Hon Roll; Hon Roll; JC Awd; NHS; Phrmcy.

SHILEY, PEGGY; Northwestern SR HS; Albion, PA; (3); Sec Church Yth Grp; JV Sftbl; Hon Roll; Crmnl Justc.

SHILLABEER, KAREN; Pittston Area HS; Pittston, PA; (3); FNA; Trk; Hon Roll; Wilkes Coll; Nrsng.

SHILLING, CAROLE; Waynesboro HS; Waynesboro, PA; (4); 24/355; Church Yth Grp; Yrbk Stf; Sec Sr Cls; Rep Stu Cncl; Fld Hcky; Trk; Var Capt Vllybl; Cit Awd; High Hon Roll; NHS; Hagerstown JC; Phy Ed.

SHILLING, CHARITY; Chief Logan HS; Lewistown, PA; (3); 48/182; Hosp Aide; Spanish Clb; High Hon Roll; Hon Roll; Equine Studies.

SHILLING, DARLENE; Waynesboro SR HS; Waynesboro, PA; (3); 26/379; Church Yth Grp; Pres Soph Cls; VP Jr Cls; Pres Sr Cls; Rep VP Stu Cncl; Capt Var Bsktbl; Var Vllybl; Cit Awd; High Hon Roll; NHS; E JR Hgh Ctzn Yr 84-85; Dentl Hyg.

SHILLING, STEVE; Conneaot Valley HS; Conneautville, PA; (2); VP German Clb; Letterman Clb; Science Clb; Varsity Clb; Rep Stu Cncl; Var L Bsbl; Elks Awd; High Hon Roll; JETS Awd; NHS; All-Frnch Crk Vly Conf Bsbl 1st Tm.

SHILLINGER, TRACY; Gateway HS; Monroeville, PA; (4); FBLA; High Hon Roll; Hon Roll; Bradford Bus Schl; Accntng.

SHILLINGFORD, FRANK; Monsignor Bonner HS; Drexel Hill, PA; (3); 9/255; Camera Clb; Chess Clb; Church Yth Grp; Cmnty Wkr; Computer Clb; School Musical; High Hon Roll; Ntl Merit Ltr; Drexel U; Elec Engrng.

SHILLOW, CHRISTINE; Lancaster Catholic HS; Columbia, PA; (3); 19/198; Chorus; Nwsp Bus Mgr; High Hon Roll; Hon Roll; Jr NHS; NHS; Modrn Chem,Ecnmcs & Am Cultrs Awds 85-87.

SHIMADA, AKI; Lower Merion HS; Penn Wynne, PA; (3); German Clb; Chorus; Mrchg Band; Orch; Rep Frsh Cls; Trs Soph Cls; Socr; Cit Awd; Hon Roll; Hon Roll; Eagle Awd 85; PA House Reps Citation 85; PMEA Dist 12 Cert Awd 87.

SHIMCHOCK, FRANCINE; Curwensville Area HS; Olanta, PA; (4); 24/114; Camera Clb; French Clb; Pres FBLA; Nwsp Stf; Hon Roll; NHS; Air Force.

SHIMEL, TINA; Curwensville Area HS; Curwensville, PA; (4); 16/114; Church Yth Grp; Sec FBLA; Varsity Clb; Church Choir; Var JV Sftbl; Hon Roll; NHS; Du Bois Bus Coll; Exec Sec.

SHIMKO, THERESA; Wyoming Area HS; West Pittston, PA; (3); 21/255; Church Yth Grp; Rep Stu Cncl; Var L Swmmng; Var L Trk; High Hon Roll; Hon Roll; NHS; Sci.

SHIMKUS, ALICIA; Nazareth Area HS; Nazareth, PA; (3); 13/260; Key Clb; Sec Band; Concert Band; Jazz Band; Mrchg Band; Orch; Pep Band; School Musical; Symp Band; High Hon Roll; Acad Sweater 87; Band Ltr 87; Music Therapy.

SHIMON, SHELLEY; Burgettstown JR SR HS; Bulger, PA; (3); 15/175; French Clb; Ski Clb; Drill Tm; Yrbk Stf; High Hon Roll; NHS; PA ST U; Engrng.

SHIMP, LORA; Carlisle SR HS; Carlisle, PA; (3); 16/455; Pres VP Church Yth Grp; Drama Clb; Intnl Clb; Stage Crew; Nwsp Rptr; Lit Mag; VP Soph Cls; Rep Jr Cls; Rep Sr Cls; JV Capt Fld Hcky; Art Hnr Soc 87; Intl Rltns.

SHIN, DAVID; Beaver Area JR SR HS; Beaver, PA; (3); #1 In Class; Pres German Clb; Q&S; Nwsp Ed-Chief; High Hon Roll; Acadmc Excel Awd 86-87.

SHIN, SANDRA; Villa Maria Acad; Erie, PA; (3); French Clb; Science Clb; Ski Clb; Hon Roll; NHS; Gannon U; Pre Med.

SHINDEL, GLEN; Lebanon SR HS; Lebanon, PA; (4); Aud/Vis; VICA; Stage Crew; Hon Roll; Electronis Inst; Elec Engrng.

SHINDLE, ELAINE; Coatesville Area SR HS; Coatesville, PA; (3); 107/520; JV Fld Hcky; JV Var Sftbl; Hon Roll; Secy.

SHINDLE, JACK; Montrose Area HS; Montrose, PA; (3); Boy Scts; German Clb; Ski Clb; Band; Concert Band; Jazz Band; Mrchg Band; Golf; Aerospc Engnrng.

SHINDLER, ALANA L; Garden Spot HS; New Holland, PA; (4); Var Sftbl; Hon Roll; Consldtd Bus Schl Lancaster.

SHINE, HOLLY; Jamestown HS; Jamestown, PA; (2); 1/53; 4-H; French Clb; Varsity Clb; Stu Cncl; Var Bsktbl; 4-H Awd; High Hon Roll; NHS; Pres Schlr; Sci Math Frnch I 85-86; 4-H Keystone Interview 85-86; Pres Phys Fit 86-87; PA ST U; Vet.

SHINER, DAMIAN P; Eastern Lebanon County HS; Myerstown, PA; (4); 8/178; Pres Church Yth Grp; Pres 4-H; FBLA; School Musical; Nwsp Rptr; Rep Stu Cncl; Socr; Var Trk; 4-H Awd; NHS; Srptmst Yth Ctznshp Awd 87; Amer Lgn Ortrcl Cntst PA ST Wnnr 87; PA Outstndng 4-Hr Wshngtn Conf 86; U Of Notre Dame; Grphc Dsgn.

SHINGLE, BRYAN; Northern Cambria HS; Barnesboro, PA; (3); 24/152; Pres Drama Clb; Pres NFL; Pres Speech Tm; School Play; Rep Stu Cncl; Mgr Bsbl; Mgr Bsktbl; Mgr Ftbl; Mgr(s); High Hon Roll; 1st Pl IUP Dist Hstry Day 86; Penn ST Hstry Day 86; Optomtry.

SHINHAM, LISA; State College Intermed; State College, PA; (2); 338/536; Church Yth Grp; Hosp Aide; Office Aide; Frsh Cls; Soph Cls; JV Vllybl; Bus Ed Awd 86-87; Soph Senate 86-87; Power Of The Paws Awd 86-87; Juniata Coll; Elem Ed.

SHINN, ROBYN; Lewisburg Area HS; Winfield, PA; (3); Sec Spanish Clb; Chorus; School Musical; Trs Sr Cls; Var Trk; NHS; Spanish NHS; Band; Church Choir; Concert Band.

SHINNAMON, HEATHER; Beaver Area HS; Beaver, PA; (2); Band; High Hon Roll; Math Tm; Concert Band; Mrchg Band; Pep Band; Acdmc Achvt Awd 87; Acdmc All Am Schlr Pgm 86; Psych.

SHINSKY, COLEEN; Canon Mcmillan SR HS; Canonsburg, PA; (4); Art Clb; Hosp Aide; Library Aide; Band; Mrchg Band; School Play; Mgr(s); Twrlr; Hon Roll; Prfct Atten Awd; Let Trophy Majorette 86-87; California U Of PA; Bus Adm.

SHIPANGA, DENEENE N; Germantown HS; Philadelphia, PA; (4); 7/362; Boys Clb Am; Church Yth Grp; Dance Clb; Hosp Aide; Library Aide; Political Wkr; Chorus; Yrbk Stf; High Hon Roll; Hon Roll; Physcs, S Knx Hrpr Mem Schlrshp & Blck Incntv Grnt Awds 87; Penn ST U; Nrsng.

SHIPE, ANDREW; Shikellamy HS; Sunbury, PA; (4); 3/301; Am Leg Boys St; Pres Sr Cls; Var Wrstlng; Hon Roll; NHS; West Point; Elec Engr.

SHIPE, DIANE; Knoch JR-SR HS; Saxonbug, PA; (4); 43/243; Rptr Church Yth Grp; Rptr FBLA; Band; Concert Band; Mrchg Band; Orch; Pep Band; School Musical; High Hon Roll; Hon Roll; Girl Yr Awd 87; FBLA Shrthnd Awd 87; Pittsburgh Pirate Cntnl Honors Band 87; Butler Cnty CC; Legal Secy.

SHIPLEY, STEPHANIE; Kennard Dale HS; Stewartstown, PA; (3); 13/176; Art Clb; Exploring; Ski Clb; Varsity Clb; Chorus; Rep Sec Stu Cncl; JV L Bsktbl; Var L Fld Hcky; Var L Trk; High Hon Roll; Pltcl Sci.

SHIPLEY, TRACY; Mary Fuller Frazier JR- SR HS; Grindstone, PA; (3); Church Yth Grp; Yrbk Stf; High Hon Roll; NHS; PA Free Enterprise Week 87; Accntng.

SHIPMAN, CINDY; West Scranton HS; Scranton, PA; (3); 59/276; Debate Tm; Drama Clb; French Clb; FBLA; Pres JA; Spanish Clb; Stage Crew; Hon Roll; Elem Ed.

SHIPMAN, PATRICIA; Loyalsock Township HS; Montoursville, PA; (3); 5/120; French Clb; Hosp Aide; Latin Clb; Model UN; Band; Chorus; Stage Crew; Yrbk Rptr; Hon Roll; NHS; Loyalsock Squire Awd Frnch 85-86; Loyalsock Knight Awd Comp Math 86-87; Bio.

SHIRER, JOSEPH; Connellsville HS; Connellsville, PA; (2); 48/500; Boy Scts; Church Yth Grp; CAP; Band; Color Guard; Drill Tm; Symp Band; High Hon Roll; Hon Roll; WCC Coll Certs 84-87; Air Frc Acad CO Spgs; Pilot.

SHIREY, ANDREW M; Daniel Boon Area School District; Douglassville, PA; (3); 18/180; Church Yth Grp; Rep Jr Cls; JV Var Bsbl; Im Var Ftbl; Var Capt Sftbl; Var L Vllybl; Im Var Wt Lftg; Hon Roll; De Vry; Comp Tech.

SHIREY, ANITA; United JR-SR HS; Robinson, PA; (4); 64/150; Art Clb; French Clb; Library Aide; Ski Clb; SADD; JV Var Vllybl; Marquerite Werner Falk Schlrshp 87; Let Vllybll 87; Seton Hill Coll; Med Lab Tech.

SHIREY, GINA; Freeport SR HS; Sarver, PA; (4); 1/147; Church Yth Grp; Drm Mjr(t); Mrchg Band; Symp Band; Yrbk Stf; L Bsktbl; L Trk; High Hon Roll; NHS; Pres Schlr; Westminster Coll.

SHIREY, JONATHAN; Freeport Area SR HS; Sarver, PA; (2); Band; Var Bsktbl; Var L Ftbl; Var L Trk; High Hon Roll.

SHIREY, TODD; Mechanicsburg HS; Mechanicsburg, PA; (2); 25/309; Church Yth Grp; Var L Bsbl; Im L Bsktbl; Var L Ftbl; High Hon Roll; Hon Roll; Auto Engrng.

SHIRING, STEVE; Western Beaver HS; Beaver, PA; (4); 4/87; Am Leg Boys St; Concert Band; Drm Mjr(t); Mrchg Band; VP Soph Cls; Trs Jr Cls; Pres Stu Cncl; Var Capt Bsktbl; Golf; High Hon Roll; Naval ROTC Scholar U Notre Dame 87-91; Pres Acad Fit Awd 87; U Notre Dame; Elec Engrng.

SHIRK, JAMES; Garden Spot-Elanco School Dist; E Earl, PA; (3); 1/196; Chess Clb; Church Yth Grp; Exploring; FFA; Chorus; Orch; School Musical; Var Bsbl; High Hon Roll; NHS; FFA BOAC Achvt Vlntrsm PA Wnnr 86; FFA BOAC Achvt Vlntrsm Ntl Fnlst 86.

SHIRK, JOHN; Garden Spot HS; E Earl, PA; (2); Boy Scts; Church Yth Grp; Ftbl; Tennis; Wt Lftg; High Hon Roll; Hon Roll; Jr NHS; NHS; Engr.

SHIRK, KAREN; Garden Spot HS; Martindale, PA; (4); 45/218; Church Yth Grp; JV Fld Hcky; Powder Puff Ftbl; Hon Roll; Jr NHS; Lancaster Cnty Vo-Tech; Nrsng.

SHIRK, MATTHEW; Fleetwood Area HS; Blandon, PA; (3); Boy Scts; Chess Clb; Scholastic Bowl; Chorus; Jazz Band; School Musical; Stu Cncl; Golf; High Hon Roll; Swing Chorus; Fleetwood Schlr 87; Albright Coll; Prof.

SHIRK, MICHAEL; Cocalico HS; Reinholds, PA; (3); 3/163; Chess Clb; Sec Church Yth Grp; CAP; Science Clb; Color Guard; Drill Tm; Trk; High Hon Roll; Trs NHS; Mitchell Awd; Earhart Awd Civial Air Patrol 86-87; Church Organist Plyd Keyboards 10 Yrs 87; Chem.

SHIRK, ROSEANNE; Donegal HS; Maytown, PA; (4); Varsity Clb; Var L Bsktbl; Var L Sftbl; Spec Ed.

SHIRLEY, BRENDA; Saltsburg JR SR HS; Saltsburg, PA; (2); 1/95; Church Yth Grp; Rptr 4-H; FTA; Concert Band; Mrchg Band; 4-H Awd; High Hon Roll; Stat Vllybl; Band; School Musical; Pres Acadmc Ftns Awd 85-86; IN Cnty Bnd 86-87; PMEA Dist 3 Bnd Fstvl 87.

SHIRLEY, JENNIFER; Connellsville Area SR HS; Connellsville, PA; (3); 10/550; Office Aide; School Musical; Rep Stu Cncl; Var Capt Cheerleading; Stat Trk; High Hon Roll; NHS; Spanish NHS; VP Soph Cls; Pres Jr Cls; Math.

SHIRVINSKI, JOSEPH; Mahanoy Area HS; Barnesville, PA; (3); Art Clb; Spanish Clb; School Play; Variety Show; Nwsp Sprt Ed; Yrbk Stf; Swmmng; Trk; Wt Lftg; Ftbl; Kutztown U; Scndry Ed.

SHISSLER, DAVID LOREN; Shalom Christian Acad; Newburg, PA; (4); 1/26; Church Yth Grp; Chorus; School Musical; Val; Acad Schlrshp 87; 4th Pl Bible Qzng Team 87; Oral Roberts U; Bus Admin.

SHIVELY, MICHAEL; Mechanicsburg HS; Mechanicsburg, PA; (2); 91/309; Band; Jazz Band; Mrchg Band; Symp Band; Im Bsktbl; Penn ST; Architect.

SHIVELY, NICOLE; Milton Area HS; Milton, PA; (4); 50/236; Girl Scts; Varsity Clb; Drill Tm; Mrchg Band; Yrbk Stf; Sec Stu Cncl; Capt Cheerleading; Powder Puff Ftbl; CC Awd; Trs Rotary Awd; WACC Bus Symp Awd 84-87; Outstndng Stu Cncl Awd 86-87; Wilma Boyd; Trvl Indstry.

SHMIDHEISER, JAMIE; Lower Moreland HS; Huntingdon Valley, PA; (2); German Clb; Trk; Commnctns.

SHOAF, RHONDA; Shenango HS; New Castle, PA; (2); Church Yth Grp; Drill Tm; 4-H; Girl Scts; Office Aide; Hon Roll; Jr NHS.

SHOAFF, DEBBIE; Lawrence County Vo-Tech HS; New Castle, PA; (3); DECA; Quiz Bowl; SADD; Chorus; Hon Roll; Mktng.

SHOAFF, KEVIN; Hatboro-Horsham HS; Hatboro, PA; (3); Key Clb; Ski Clb; Concert Band; Mrchg Band; Var Wrstlng; Penn ST U; Military.

SHOBER, J; Panther Valley HS; Nesquehoning, PA; (1); 25/127; Church Yth Grp; Cmnty Wkr; 4-H; German Clb; Math Clb; Math Tm; Political Wkr; School Play; Trs Frsh Cls; Trs Soph Cls; John Hopkins Achvt Aptitude Test 85; Notre Dame; Med.

SHOBER, MARK; High Point Baptist Acad; Geigertown, PA; (3); Church Yth Grp; Drama Clb; School Play; JV Var Bsktbl; JV Var Socr; Hon Roll; Spanish NHS; Arch.

SHOBER, THEODORE; Panther Valley HS; Nesquehoning, PA; (3); 23/132; Church Yth Grp; Cmnty Wkr; 4-H; German Clb; JA; Political Wkr; Bsbl; Bsktbl; Fld Hcky; Ftbl; IA U; Med.

SHOBERT, KIMBERLY; Danville Area SR HS; Danville, PA; (3); 16/187; Drama Clb; Spanish Clb; Band; Concert Band; Mrchg Band; School Musical; Fld Hcky; NHS; Psychology.

SHOCH, BARBARA; Shikellamy HS; Sunbury, PA; (4); 25/305; Pres Church Yth Grp; Sec French Clb; Teachers Aide; Sec Hst Band; Chorus; Church Choir; Capt Color Guard; Concert Band; Capt Mrchg Band; School Musical; Dist Chr; Snr Of Mnth-Dec-Rtry Clb; Bloomsburg U; Elem Schl Tchr.

SHOCKET, GLENN; N E Prep; Bensalem, PA; (3); Boy Scts; Computer Clb; Office Aide; Hon Roll; Chess Clb; Temple U; Comp Sci.

SHOCKEY, JODI; Portersville Christian Schl; Butler, PA; (4); 4/15; Drama Clb; Speech Tm; Chorus; Capt Bsktbl; Var L Vllybl; High Hon Roll; NHS; Geneva Coll; Second Educ.

SHOCKEY, NIKKI; Greencastle-Antrim HS; Greencastle, PA; (3); 5/176; Band; Chorus; Concert Band; Jazz Band; Mrchg Band; VP Jr Cls; Off Stu Cncl; High Hon Roll; NHS; Prfct Atten Awd; Music.

SHODI, SAMUEL; Leechburg Area HS; Leechburg, PA; (2); Pres Frsh Cls; Pres Soph Cls; Var Bsbl; JV Bsktbl; Var Ftbl; High Hon Roll.

SHOEMAKER, BARRY RAY; Dover Area HS; Dover, PA; (4); 21/236; Church Yth Grp; Chorus; Church Choir; School Musical; Var Socr; Hon Roll; NHS; Renaissance 85-87; SICO Fndtn Scholar Awd 87; Shippensburg U; Chem.

SHOEMAKER, KIMBERLY; Salisbury Elk Lick HS; Springs, PA; (3); 8/28; Pres Church Yth Grp; Pres 4-H; Band; Chorus; Church Choir; School Play; Nwsp Rptr; Nwsp Stf; Cheerleading; Hon Roll; Elem Educ.

SHOEMAKER, LYNNE A; Philipsburg-Osceola HS; Philipsburg, PA; (4); 11/245; Pep Clb; Ski Clb; Band; Concert Band; Mrchg Band; Pep Band; Btty Crckr Awd; NHS; Prfct Atten Awd; Clairon U; Elem Educ.

SHOEMAKER, MARK; Greater Latrobe HS; Latrobe, PA; (4); French Clb; Var JV Socr; French Hon Soc; High Hon Roll; Hon Roll; Prfct Atten Awd; Indiana U Of PA; Sec Educ.

SHOEMAKER, MATT; Lewistown Area HS; Lewistown, PA; (2); Church Yth Grp; Spanish Clb; Pres Soph Cls; Rep Stu Cncl; Var Bsbl; JV Bsktbl; L Golf; High Hon Roll; NHS; Acad Ltr 86 & 87; Pres Acad Ftns Awd 85.

SHOEMAKER, MELISSA; Sayre Area HS; Athens, PA; (3); Band; Chorus; Concert Band; Jazz Band; Mrchg Band; Hon Roll; Prfct Atten Awd.

SHOEMAKER, NICOLE; Lock Haven SR HS; Lock Haven, PA; (3); 200/250; Library Aide; SADD; Band; Concert Band; Mrchg Band; Pep Band; School Musical; School Play; Stage Crew; Powder Puff Ftbl; Outstndng Band Stu Hnr 84-85; Lock Haven U; Crminlgy.

SHOEMAKER, ROBBY; Tunkhannock Area HS; Mehoopany, PA; (2); 46/310; Bsbl; Ftbl; Wt Lftg.

SHOEMAKER, ROBERT; Chambersburg Area SR HS; Orrstown, PA; (2); Hon Roll; Prfct Atten Awd; 3rd Pl Trnng Field Of Firefightng 85; Pres Physcl Ftns Awd 86-84; Shippensburg U; Comp.

SHOEMAKER, ROBERT; Somerset Area HS; Somerset, PA; (3); 49/231; Church Yth Grp; English Clb; German Clb; Letterman Clb; Red Cross Aide; Varsity Clb; Var L Socr; Var Trk; Hon Roll; Towson ST U; Athltc Trng.

SHOEMAKER, TARA L; Millville Area HS; Millville, PA; (4); 1/74; Pres Band; Chorus; Drm Mjr(t); Ed Yrbk Ed-Chief; Ed Lit Mag; Pres Jr Cls; Co-Capt Cheerleading; Gov Hon Prg Awd; Pres NHS; Val; Daughters Of Amer Rvltn Good Ctzn Rgnl Wnnr 86; Duke.

SHOEMAKER, THERESA; Bishop Guilfoyle HS; Duncansville, PA; (4); Cmnty Wkr; Science Clb; Sec Soph Cls; Rep Jr Cls; Stu Cncl; Var Capt Cheerleading; Hon Roll; Hmcmng Queen 86; PA ST U; Bus Mngmnt.

SHOEMAKER, TIMOTHY; Tamaqua Area HS; Tamaqua, PA; (3); #22 In Class; Boy Scts; French Hon Soc; Comp Sci.

SHOENER, HOLLY; Pine Grove Area HS; Pine Grove, PA; (2); Pres 4-H; Varsity Clb; Band; Cheerleading; 4-H Awd; Hon Roll; Pres Schlr; 3rd Pl ST Gettysbrg Add 85; Algbr Awd 87; 9th Grd Sci Awd 86; Pres Fit Awd 87; Penn ST U; Anml Bio Sci.

SHOENFELT, SUSAN; Bishop Guilfoyle HS; Altoona, PA; (4); 22/123; Cmnty Wkr; Girl Scts; Red Cross Aide; Science Clb; Service Clb; Capt Flag Corp; Off Jr Cls; High Hon Roll; Hon Roll; Ntl Sci Merit Awd; Gld Ldrshp Awd; PA ST U.

SHOENTHAL, NINA; Northampton SR HS; Northampton, PA; (2); AFS; Pep Clb; Ski Clb; Hon Roll; John Hopkins Qualifier 83-84; Psych.

SHOFF, DAVID; Big Spring HS; Newville, PA; (3); 8/266; Math Tm; JV Var Bsbl; JV Var Ftbl; Im Sftbl; JV Var Wt Lftg; High Hon Roll; Hon Roll; Dcknsn Coll Smmr Schlrshp Pgm 87; Shppnsbrg U Math Sci Day Schlrshp 87; Archaeolgst.

SHOFRAN, SARAH; Marian Catholic HS; Weatherly, PA; (3); 11/104; Sec Church Yth Grp; Quiz Bowl; Scholastic Bowl; Yrbk Stf; JV Cheerleading; High Hon Roll; Spanish NHS.

SHOLLENBERGER, AMY; Pottsville Area HS; Pottsville, PA; (3); 2/263; Church Yth Grp; Q&S; Yrbk Stf; JV Bsktbl; High Hon Roll; Jr NHS.

SHOLLEY, AARON; Watsontown Christian Acad; Hartleton, PA; (4); 2/13; Church Yth Grp; Drama Clb; Yrbk Ed-Chief; VP Sr Cls; Rep Stu Cncl; Var Bsktbl; Var Socr; Cit Awd; High Hon Roll; Sal; Christian Character Awd & High Sci Avrg Awd 83-84; Penn ST U; Comp Engrng.

SHOLLY, JOHN; East Pennsboro HS; Enola, PA; (3); Church Yth Grp; French Clb; Varsity Clb; Bsbl; Ftbl; Wt Lftg; Wrstlng; High Hon Roll; Hon Roll.

SHOLLY, NICOLE; Cedar Crest HS; Lebanon, PA; (3); 58/342; Sec Trs Art Clb; Camera Clb; French Clb; Pep Clb; Yrbk Phtg; L Mgr(s); Im Socr; Im Vllybl; NHS; Church Yth Grp; Fashion Design.

SHOLTIS, ROBERT; Connellsville HS; Vanderbilt, PA; (1); Church Yth Grp; Computer Clb; Pep Clb; Science Clb; Chorus; Church Choir; School Musical; School Play; Nwsp Stf; Trk.

SHOLTZ, ROBERT; Bishop Guilfoyle HS; Altoona, PA; (3); 47/110; Church Yth Grp; Chorus; Im Socr; Var Tennis; Im Vllybl; Hon Roll; Bus.

SHOMO, PEGGY; United HS; Robinson, PA; (3); Ski Clb; Spanish Clb; Yrbk Stf; JV Cheerleading; Powder Puff Ftbl; JV Sftbl; High Hon Roll; Hon Roll; Prfct Atten Awd; Natl Hnr Roll 87; CVMH Schl Of Nrsng; Nursing.

SHOMPER, BRIAN; Williams Valley HS; Tower City, PA; (2); Im Bsbl; JV Bsktbl; JV Ftbl; Stevens Tech; Machnst.

SHOMPER, JACQUELINE; Upper Dauphin Area HS; Elizabethville, PA; (3); #13 In Class; Pres Church Yth Grp; Varsity Clb; Rep Stu Cncl; JV Var Bsktbl; Sftbl; Hon Roll; Phys Ftns Awd 87; Fshn Dsgn.

SHOMPER, THOMAS; York Suburban HS; York, PA; (3); Letterman Clb; Varsity Clb; Band; Concert Band; Mrchg Band; Nwsp Stf; Var L Swmmng; JV Im Vllybl; Im Wrstlng; Comp Sci.

SHONBORN, KAREN M; Baldwin HS; Pittsburgh, PA; (3); 96/477; French Clb; Key Clb; Math Clb; Band; Mrchg Band; Hon Roll; Bus Mgmt.

SHONDECK JR, MICHAEL; Valley HS; New Kensington, PA; (2); 2/237; Math Clb; Math Tm; Science Clb; Ski Clb; Rep Soph Cls; Rep Stu Cncl; High Hon Roll.

SHONK, STEVE; Ephrata HS; Ephrata, PA; (4); 44/253; Exploring; Trs FBLA; Trs JA; Score Keeper; High Hon Roll; Hon Roll; NHS; Hibshman Schlrshp 87; Lancaster Cnty Bnkrs Assoc Schlrshp 87; Pres Acad Ftns Awd 87; Millersville U; Accntng.

SHOOK, KIMBERLY; West Mifflin Area HS; W Mifflin, PA; (3); 56/310; Pres Church Yth Grp; Hosp Aide; Teachers Aide; Band; Capt Color Guard; Mrchg Band; Stu Cncl; Hon Roll; Nrsng.

SHOOK, LORI; Nazareth Area HS; Nazareth, PA; (3); 26/238; Computer Clb; Exploring; Key Clb; Chorus; Nwsp Rptr; Nwsp Stf; Im JV Cheerleading; Im Coach Actv; Im JV Sftbl; Hon Roll; Grmn Tchr.

SHOOP, KATHY; Saegertown HS; Meadville, PA; (4); 4/107; Church Yth Grp; Key Clb; Hon Roll; G Davey Memrl Awd 87; Indiana U Of PA.

SHOOP, TRICIA; Halifax HS; Halifax, PA; (4); Hosp Aide; SADD; Chorus; Cheerleading; Twrlr; High Hon Roll; Hon Roll; Wsly Coll; Marine Bio.

SHOOP, WANDA; Marion Center HS; Home, PA; (3); 52/162; FBLA; FNA; Latin Clb; Red Cross Aide; Varsity Clb; Chorus; Church Choir; Sec Soph Cls; Stat Sftbl; Stat Trk; Bradford Bus Schl; Med Secy.

SHOPE, DEBRA; South Side HS; Clinton, PA; (3); 35/135; Church Yth Grp; Lib Band; Concert Band; Mrchg Band; Orch; Pep Band; Rep Stu Cncl; Hon Roll; School Musical; Honors Club 84-87; Music Edu.

SHOPE, LYNN; Bishop Carroll HS; Summerhill, PA; (3); 4-H; Pep Clb; Ski Clb; Spanish Clb; SADD; Chorus; Rep Stu Cncl; Cheerleading; Trk; Hon Roll.

SHOPE, SANDY; East Juniata HS; Liverpool, PA; (3); 46/100; Church Yth Grp; FHA; JV Var Bsktbl; Var Cheerleading; JV Var Sftbl; Lancaster Gen Hosp Schl; Nrsng.

SHOPF, TRICIA; Penn Manor HS; Conestoga, PA; (3); Church Yth Grp; Church Choir.

SHORE, AMY; Mechanicsburg Area SR HS; Mechanicsburg, PA; (2); 51/309; Speech Tm; Chorus; Concert Band; Mrchg Band; Crs Cntry; Swmmng; Trk; Hon Roll; Vrsty Ltr Wnnr X-Country, Swmmng, & Trck 85-86 & 86-87; Dist Champ Informative Spkng 86-87; Boston Coll; Corp Lawyer.

SHORE, CASEY; Lewistown Area HS; Lewistown, PA; (2); Pres Church Yth Grp; Spanish Clb; Varsity Clb; Rep Soph Cls; Var L Bsbl; JV Var Bsktbl; Var L Ftbl; NHS; Prfct Atten Awd.

SHORE, ERIC; Marple Newtown HS; Broomall, PA; (4); Service Clb; Temple Yth Grp; Stu Cncl; Hon Roll; Jr NHS; NEDT Awd; Pres Schlr; Emory U.

SHORT, BRIAN; Marion Center Area HS; Home, PA; (4); 25/167; Church Yth Grp; 4-H; FFA; Band; Concert Band; Keystone Farmer Awd 86-87; Star Argi-Bus Awd 86-87; Watson Lingenfelter Memorial Schlrshp 86-87; PA ST U; Bus Mngmnt.

SHORT, JENNIFER; Phoenixville Area HS; Phoenixville, PA; (2); Drama Clb; Pep Clb; School Musical; School Play; Hon Roll; Jr NHS; Pres Schlr; IN U Of PA; Int Dsgn.

SHORT, JENNIFER; Salisbury Elk-Lick HS; Salisbury, PA; (2); Var Cheerleading; JV Bsktbl; VP Soph Cls; Sec Frsh Cls; Mrchg Band; Concert Band; Chorus; Prfct Atten Awd; Band; Cosmetology.

SHORT, KAILY; Bucktail JR SR HS; Renovo, PA; (2); 3/65; Church Yth Grp; Letterman Clb; Pep Clb; Concert Band; Mrchg Band; School Musical; Stage Crew; JV Bsktbl; Hon Roll; Kiwanis Awd; T Jffrsn U; Phys Thrpy.

SHORT, KIMBERLY; Loyalsock Twp SR HS; Williamsport, PA; (3); Key Clb; Im Twrlr; Bus Admin.

SHORT, LISA; Upper Moreland HS; Willow Grove, PA; (2); 22/242; Church Yth Grp; Church Choir; School Musical; Yrbk Stf; High Hon Roll; Smmr Missnry Guatemala Cntrl Amer 86; Smmr Minstry Juvnl Delinquents Lkside Schl 87; Christian Psychlgy.

SHORTENCARRIER, GARY; Cambria Heights SR HS; Elmora, PA; (3); Comp Sci.

SHORTENCARRIER, LEA; Northern Cambria HS; Barnesboro, PA; (3); 28/153; Ski Clb; Band; Concert Band; Jazz Band; Mrchg Band; Rep Frsh Cls; Rep Jr Cls; Bsktbl; Sftbl; High Hon Roll; IUP; Elem Tchr.

SHOSTEK, AMY; Chartiers Valley HS; Carnegie, PA; (4); 10/303; Cmnty Wkr; Ski Clb; Spanish Clb; Varsity Clb; Crs Cntry; Tennis; Trk; NHS; Clarion U; Spec Educ.

SHOSTEK, BRIAN; Bishop Mc Cort HS; Johnstown, PA; (2); French Clb; Chorus; Orch; High Hon Roll; NHS; Aerospc Engrng.

SHOTKO, KRISTIN J; North Pocono HS; Moscow, PA; (3); Art Clb; Cmnty Wkr; Drama Clb; FBLA; Variety Show; Pres Soph Cls; Pres Jr Cls; Stu Cncl; Cheerleading; Gym; Hugh O Brien Yth Fndtn; Bio.

SHOTWELL, DIANA; Elizabeth Forward HS; Elizabeth, PA; (4); Exploring; Spanish Clb; SADD; Color Guard; Flag Corp; Nwsp Stf; Yrbk Stf; Hon Roll; Employed Biddle Chrprctc Clinic 85-7; Schlrshp Med Asstng 87; Med.

SHOULDIS, THERESA C; Wiliam Tennent SR HS; Warminster, PA; (4); 10/676; Math Tm; Scholastic Bowl; Band; Chorus; Concert Band; Mgr Jazz Band; Madrigals; Mrchg Band; Orch; School Musical; PMEA Dist XI Chrs 86 & 87; PMEA Rgn IV Chrs Rnk 1st 86; Art & Engl Awd 84; Lehigh U; Cvl Engrng.

SHOUP, CAROLINE; Millville Area HS; Orangeville, PA; (4); Pres Church Yth Grp; VP 4-H; Chorus; School Musical; Nwsp Stf; Yrbk Stf; Var Sftbl; Capt Twrlr; Sec NHS; Drama Clb; Darwin Strausser Mem Scholar 87; Mansfield U; Socl Wrk.

SHOUPE, DENISE; Kiski Area HS; Avonmore, PA; (4); Church Yth Grp; Pep Clb; Spanish Clb; Varsity Clb; Var Capt Bsktbl; Var Capt Vllybl; High Hon Roll; Hon Roll; Ntl Merit Ltr; Pres Schlr; Bell Avon Almni Assn Schlrshp 87; Penn ST New Kensington; Nrsng.

SHOVLIN, JIM; Bishop Hasey HS; Hazleton, PA; (3); Chorus; Orch; L Bowling; L Trk; Hon Roll; Physcl Thrpy.

SHOVLIN, LORI; Bishop Hafey HS; Freeland, PA; (3); Church Yth Grp; French Clb; Chorus; Church Choir; Orch; Hon Roll; Computers.

SHOVLIN, SHARON; Quigley HS; Midland, PA; (3); #5 In Class; Math Clb; Math Tm; Spanish Clb; Powder Puff Ftbl; High Hon Roll; CD Of A Awd 84; Prom Comm 86; Hmcmng Comm 86; Chem Engrng.

SHOW, MELISSA; Rockwood Area JR SR HS; Rockwood, PA; (2); 14/107; Pres Church Yth Grp; Computer Clb; 4-H; Band; Chorus; Church Choir; Concert Band; Mrchg Band; High Hon Roll; Hon Roll; Med.

SHOW, MICHAEL; The Baptist HS; Factoryville, PA; (4); Church Yth Grp; Teachers Aide; VP Sr Cls; Var L Bsbl; Var L Bsktbl; Var L Crs Cntry; Var L Socr; PHY Ed.

SHOWAKER, RONALD; Biglerville HS; Biglerville, PA; (3); 22/110; Computer Clb; Varsity Clb; Var L Bsbl; Var L Bsktbl; Hon Roll; Jr NHS; Acctnt.

SHOWERS, HOPE; St Marys Area HS; Benezett, PA; (3); 65/269; VP Frsh Cls; VP Soph Cls; Stat Bsktbl; Hon Roll; IN U Of PA.

SHOWERS, JAMES; Milton Area HS; Milton, PA; (2); Pres Church Yth Grp; Varsity Clb; VICA; Var Crs Cntry; Var Trk; Penn ST U; Mech Engrng.

SHOWERS, LENA; Biglerville HS; Gardners, PA; (2); 14/109; Art Clb; Aud/Vis; Sec Church Yth Grp; Computer Clb; Spanish Clb; Co-Capt ROTC; School Play; Var Cheerleading; Var Tennis; Hon Roll; Acctng.

SHOWERS, TONIA; Williams Valley HS; Williamstown, PA; (3); Ski Clb; Chorus; Concert Band; Mrchg Band; VP Pres Stu Cncl; Var L Bsktbl; Im Powder Puff Ftbl; Var L Sftbl; NHS; Hugh O Brian Outstndng 86; Unsung Hero Sftbl 87; Engrng.

SHOWERS, TRACEY; Bald Eagle Nittany HS; Mill Hall, PA; (2); 12/126; Band; Color Guard; Mrchg Band; Variety Show; Im Vllybl; Hon Roll; Prfct Atten Awd.

SHOWERS, TRACI; Milton HS; Milton, PA; (2); 21/254; Church Yth Grp; FTA; German Clb; Intnl Clb; Varsity Clb; Color Guard; Bsktbl; Fld Hcky; Sftbl; Hon Roll; Preschl Tchng.

SHPON, ARETA O; Villa Maria Acad; Erie, PA; (4); #2 In Class; Model UN; PAVAS; Ski Clb; Hon Roll; NHS; Ntl Merit SF; Ntl Ldrshp & Ser Awd 84; Ntl Sci Mrt Awd 84; Acdmc All AM 85; Med.

SHRADER, CARL W; Norristown Area HS; Norristown, PA; (4); 58/478; Key Clb; Yrbk Stf; Rep Sr Cls; L JV Bsbl; L Var Ftbl; Hon Roll; NHS.

SHRAWDER, ADRIENNE; W Middlesex JR SR HS; W Middlesex, PA; (3); 6/109; Pres FBLA; Library Aide; Office Aide; VP Spanish Clb; Nwsp Stf; Yrbk Bus Mgr; Stat Ftbl; High Hon Roll; Jr NHS; NHS; Accntng.

SHRAWDER, NICOLE; Millersburg HS; Millersburg, PA; (4); 10/78; Pres French Clb; Varsity Clb; Ed Yrbk Stf; Off Stu Cncl; Capt Cheerleading; Trk; High Hon Roll; NHS; Voice Dem Awd; Princeton U; Arch.

SHRECENGOST, JACKI; Punxutawney Area SR HS; Mayport, PA; (2); Math Tm; Speech Tm; SADD; Band; Concert Band; Mrchg Band; Pep Band; Nwsp Stf; Hon Roll; Engl.

SHRECENGOST, JASON; Redbank Valley HS; New Bethlehem, PA; (2); FFA; Star Green Hand Awd 86; AF.

SHREFFLER, CINDY; Keystone HS; Knox, PA; (3); Church Yth Grp; Pep Clb; Varsity Clb; JV Var Vllybl; Var Letter Vllybll 86-87; Bus Adm.

SHREIBER, DAVID; Central Bucks HS East; Warrington, PA; (4); 1/452; Cmnty Wkr; Computer Clb; Capt Scholastic Bowl; Science Clb; Band; Rep Stu Cncl; Var Golf; Gov Hon Prg Awd; High Hon Roll; Hon Roll; Ntl Soc Prfsnl Engrs Dist Schlrshp 87; Betz Labs Schlrshp 87; Robert C Byrd Schlrshp 87; Cornell U; Bio Med Engrng.

SHREINER JR, HARRY I; Downingtown SR HS; Exton, PA; (4); 13/600; Boy Scts; Ski Clb; Jazz Band; School Musical; L Bsbl; Im Lcrss; High Hon Roll; Lion Awd; NHS; Rotary Awd; Penn ST U; Civil Engrng.

SHREINER, SAUNDRA; James Buchanan HS; Chambersburg, PA; (2); 83/279; Hosp Aide; Concert Band; Mrchg Band; Stage Crew; Tn Vlntr Chmbrsbrg Hosp 85-87; Psych.

SHREVE, LAUREN; Corry Area HS; Corry, PA; (3); Rep Frsh Cls; Rep Jr Cls; Rep Stu Cncl; JV Ftbl; Wt Lftg; Aud/Vis; Church Yth Grp; JA; Model UN; Radio Clb; 1st Pl Corry Country Club Jr Invtnl 85; Communctns.

SHREVE, LINDA; G A R Memorial HS; Wilkes-Barre, PA; (4); 1/172; Church Yth Grp; Computer Clb; FBLA; Nwsp Stf; Stu Cncl; High Hon Roll; Hon Roll; Jr NHS; NHS; Cert Typg I 85; Cert Typg II & Shrthd I 86; Bus.

SHREVE, PATRICIA A; Conneaut Valley HS; Springboro, PA; (3); Camera Clb; Church Yth Grp; Pep Clb; Ski Clb; Spanish Clb; SADD; Varsity Clb; Var JV Bsktbl; Powder Puff Ftbl; Var JV Cmnty Wkr; MVP Bsktbl 86-87; Outstndng Offnsv Vllybl 86; Bst Dfnsv Plyr Bsktbl 85-86.

SHRINER, KAREN; Gettysburg HS; Gettysburg, PA; (4); Pep Clb; Teachers Aide; Sec Pres Frsh Cls; Pres Soph Cls; Rep Sr Cls; Rep Stu Cncl; Capt Cheerleading; High Hon Roll; Hon Roll; NHS; Outstndng Gen Bus Awd 84; Penn ST U; Bus.

SHRIVER, MICHELLE A; Trinity HS; Mechanicsburg, PA; (4); 51/139; Church Yth Grp; Drama Clb; Pep Clb; Chorus; Church Choir; School Musical; School Play; Nwsp Rptr; Yrbk Stf; Hon Roll; Medls-Diocesan Chorus 85 & 86; 1st Pl Dist-One Act Play Cmptn 86; St Genesius Medl-3 Yrs Svc To Drama; West Chester U PA; Cmmnctns.

SHROYER, VICKIE; Connellsville SR HS; Connellsville, PA; (3); 91/591; Mrchg Band; School Musical; School Play; Symp Band; Nwsp Rptr; Swmmng; Trk; Hon Roll; Jr NHS; NHS; IUP; Med.

SHRUM, BRENT; Keystone JR SR HS; Knox, PA; (3); Chess Clb; Nwsp Phtg; Nwsp Rptr; Hon Roll; Ntl Merit Ltr; Pitt U Provosts Day Fin 86-87; 1st Pl Spspa Photogrphy Cont 86-87.

SHU, JOHN W; Loyalsock Township HS; Montoursville, PA; (3); Debate Tm; Sec Band; Sec Chorus; Lit Mag; Gov Hon Prg Awd; Hon Roll; Jr NHS; Drama Clb; 4-H; Hosp Aide; PMEA All ST Chrs Fstvl 87; All ST Yth & Govt Outstndg Senator 86-87; Wnnr JR Div Symph Yth Comp; Harvard U; Physcn.

SHUBER, MICHAEL; Norwin HS; N Huntingdon, PA; (4); Church Yth Grp; Computer Clb; Debate Tm; Math Tm; NFL; VP VICA; JC Awd; Kiwanis Awd; Prfct Atten Awd; Rotary Awd; PTA Schlrshp 87; VICA Outstndng Awd 87; 3rd Pl ST Lvl Spch Cntst VICA 87; Indiana U Of PA; Crmnlgy.

SHUBLE, MICHAEL J; Fort Cherry HS; Mc Donald, PA; (3); Church Yth Grp; Drama Clb; French Clb; Math Clb; Science Clb; Ski Clb; Varsity Clb; JV Bsbl; JV Bsktbl; L Ftbl.

SHUBZDA, MARIA; Pittston Area HS; Wilkes-Barre, PA; (3); 6/310; FNA; Drill Tm; High Hon Roll; NHS; Pharmacy.

SHUCAVAGE, SHAWN; Emmaus HS; Macungie, PA; (3); Church Yth Grp; Latin Clb; Ski Clb; Crs Cntry; Socr; High Hon Roll.

SHUCHAT, STEVE; Plymouth-Whitemarsh HS; Lafayette Hill, PA; (3); 12/362; Church Yth Grp; Intnl Clb; Model UN; School Musical; Yrbk Ed-Chief; VP Jr Cls; VP Sr Cls; Var Swmmng; High Hon Roll; NHS; Intl Bus.

SHUCK, STEVEN; Lehigh Christian Acad; Bethlehem, PA; (3); Computer Clb; Varsity Clb; Band; Chorus; Concert Band; Jazz Band; School Musical; Stage Crew; Yrbk Phtg; Yrbk Rptr; All Conf Ftbl Socr & Sftbl 83-87; MVP Sftbl 87; MVP Ftbl 83; Messiah Coll; Biol.

SHUCKERS, JULIE; Brookville Area HS; Brookville, PA; (3); Church Yth Grp; Pep Clb; Varsity Clb; Yrbk Stf; Rep Frsh Cls; VP Soph Cls; Rep Jr Cls; Rep Stu Cncl; Var Cheerleading; PA ST Dubois; Elem Ed.

SHUDA, KELLY; Cardinal O Hara HS; Drexel Hill, PA; (3); 98/723; Church Yth Grp; Hosp Aide; Office Aide; Var Sftbl; Hon Roll; Prfct Atten Awd; Fldng Awd Sftbll 85; Nursing.

SHUE, AMY L; York Suburban HS; York, PA; (3); 63/176; Cmnty Wkr; Band; Concert Band; Mrchg Band; Orch; Mgr Swmmng; Var Trk; High Hon Roll; Hon Roll; Unsung Hero Trphy Vrsty Trck 87; PA Ambssdrs Of Music Tr Of Europe 87.

SHUEY, BILL; Central Dauphin East HS; Harrisburg, PA; (4); Ski Clb; Varsity Clb; Pres Stu Cncl; Golf; Vllybl; Hon Roll; Jr NHS; NHS; Outstndg Accntng Stud 86-87; Vrsty Ltr Awds 86-87; Shippensburg; Bus Admin.

SHUEY, JENNIFER; Bellefonte Area HS; Pleasant Gap, PA; (4); 1/232; Model UN; SADD; Varsity Clb; Pres Chorus; Yrbk Stf; Rep Frsh Cls; Rep Soph Cls; Rep Jr Cls; Rep Sr Cls; Capt Bsktbl; Elks Teen Mnth 86; UNC Chapel Hill; Phys Thrpy.

SHUEY, MICHELLE; Lebanon Christian Acad; Ono, PA; (4); 1/10; Sec Church Yth Grp; Drama Clb; Hosp Aide; Chorus; Church Choir; School Play; Yrbk Ed-Chief; Yrbk Stf; Pres Frsh Cls; Pres Soph Cls; Rsrch Paper Awd 86; Chrstn Ldrshp Awd 87; Sci & Math Awds; IN U; Pre Med.

SHUFRAN, DONALD; Bradford Area HS; Bradford, PA; (4); 2/265; School Play; Nwsp Stf; Trs Soph Cls; JV Golf; Capt Tennis; Lion Awd; Sal; Chess Clb; Church Yth Grp; Debate Tm; Rotry Awd 86; Amer Chem Soc Awd 86; Air Force Math/Sci Awd 87; Allegheny Coll.

SHUGARTS, DOUGLAS; Ponxsutawney Area HS; Punxsutawney, PA; (3); Camera Clb; French Clb; Math Tm; Science Clb; Band; Concert Band; Jazz Band; Mrchg Band; Pep Band; School Musical; Allegheny Coll; Econ.

SHUGDINIS, CHERYL; Wyoming Area HS; W Pittston, PA; (3); French Clb; Office Aide; Rep Ski Clb; SADD; Band; Chorus; Concert Band; Mrchg Band; JV Var Diving; Var Trk; Temple U; Nrsg.

SHUKWIT, KIMBERLY; Pennsbury HS; Levittown, PA; (3); Capt Var Bsktbl; Sftbl; Vllybl; Hon Roll; Math Awd; Nrsng.

SHULDINER, SARIT; Hillel Acad; Pittsburgh, PA; (4); 1/8; Hosp Aide; Chorus; School Play; Yrbk Bus Mgr; Yrbk Stf; VP Stu Cncl; High Hon Roll; Hon Roll; Acad All Am 84; Commuty Wide Essay Cntst Wnnr 86; Stern Coll; Med.

SHULER, ANN; Northeastern SR HS; Mount Wolf, PA; (3); 11/190; FBLA; Spanish Clb; Chorus; Rep Stu Cncl; High Hon Roll; Hon Roll; NHS; Accntng.

SHULER, CHRISTINE; Danville SR HS; Danville, PA; (2); 4-H; Key Clb; Latin Clb; Red Cross Aide; Ski Clb; JV Fld Hcky; Im Socr; Var Sftbl; Penn ST; Sci.

SHULER, HALLIE; Muncy HS; Muncy, PA; (4); 2/72; French Clb; Varsity Clb; Yrbk Rptr; Pres Jr Cls; Rep Stu Cncl; Var JV Bsktbl; Capt L Tennis; High Hon Roll; NHS; Sal; Hopwood Smmr Acad Schlrshp 86; Chem Awd 87; Richard Mays II Mem Schlrshp 87; Bio Awd 85; Albright Coll; Bio.

SHULER, STACEY; Solanco HS; New Providence, PA; (3); 160/176; Church Yth Grp; Cmnty Wkr; Drama Clb; Office Aide; Radio Clb; Speech Tm; Teachers Aide; Chorus; Church Choir; Flag Corp; Outstndng Support Assoc For Retared Ctznshp 85-86; Pblc Rltns.

SHULIN, KEN; Montour HS; Coraopolis, PA; (2); Computer Clb; Ftbl; Comp.

SHULL, BETHANY; Lancaster Mennonite HS; Denver, PA; (3); 19/179; Drama Clb; Red Cross Aide; Chorus; Orch; Mgr Crs Cntry; High Hon Roll; Ntl Merit Ltr; Music Medal 87; NEDT Tst Cert 85; Elem Ed.

SHULL, JANET; Neshaminy HS; Levittown, PA; (3); Church Yth Grp; Spanish Clb; Trk; Hon Roll; Prfct Atten Awd; Lttrd Sprng Trck 87; Hotel Mgmt.

SHULMAN, IVY; Council Rock HS; Holland, PA; (4); Chorus; Hon Roll; NHS; Walton Acdmc Schlrshp 88-89; Albright Coll.

SHULTZ II, ALBERT; Aliquippa HS; Aliquippa, PA; (2); VP Church Yth Grp; Band; Concert Band; Jazz Band; Mrchg Band; Pep Band; Wrstlng; Prfct Atten Awd; Pre-Med.

SHULTZ, JENNIFER; Lancaster Country Day Schl; Reading, PA; (3); French Clb; Model UN; Ski Clb; Hon Roll; Yrbk Stf; Fld Hcky; Sftbl; Tennis; MVP Grls Tnns Tm 87.

SHULTZ, JODIE; Pequea Valley HS; Kinzers, PA; (3); 89/121; FBLA; Teachers Aide; Stage Crew; Central Penn Bus Schl; Retl Mgm.

SHULTZ, LINDA; Hazelton SR HS; Drums, PA; (3); #54 In Class; Drama Clb; Girl Scts; Band; Chorus; Church Choir; Mrchg Band; School Musical; Swmmng; French Hon Soc; Chess Clb; Grl Sct Yr Awd 87; Vrsty Ltrs Swmg 86-87; Millersville U; Ed.

SHULTZ, LISA; Bermudian Springs HS; York Spgs, PA; (3); English Clb; Rptr 4-H; Chorus; School Musical; Nwsp Rptr; Im Bsktbl; JV Trk; Im Vllybl; Hon Roll; Govrs Schl Of Arts-Alt 87; Wrtng.

SHULTZ, LORI; Rockwood Area HS; Rockwood, PA; (3); FBLA; Church Choir; High Hon Roll; Hon Roll; Cambria Rowe; Accntng.

SHULTZ, MIKE; York County Vo-Tech; York Haven, PA; (4); 32/358; Church Yth Grp; VICA; Var L Ftbl; Hon Roll; Diesel Mech.

SHULTZ, ROBERT J; Upper Moreland HS; Willow Grove, PA; (3); Key Clb; Ski Clb; SADD; Frsh Cls; Soph Cls; Jr Cls; Var Socr; Trk; Phys Ther.

SHULTZ, SHANNON; Waynesburg Central HS; Waynesburg, PA; (3); Church Yth Grp; French Clb; Mu Alpha Theta; Natl Beta Clb; Church Choir; Hon Roll; WVU; Bus Adm.

SHULTZ, TAMMY; Connellsville SR HS; Normalville, PA; (2); Church Yth Grp; Girl Scts; VICA; Concert Band; Mrchg Band; Off Soph Cls; High Hon Roll; Hon Roll.

SHULTZ, TRACIE; Connellsville Area HS; Connellsville, PA; (2); Pres Church Yth Grp; L Sftbl; Hon Roll; Secndry Ed.

SHULTZ, TRACY; Connellsville Area SR HS; Dunbar, PA; (2); Chorus; School Musical; Rep Stu Cncl; High Hon Roll; Hon Roll; Jr NHS; Hghst Prfrmnc Cvcs, Coll Prep, Loc Hist 87; Psychtrst.

SHULTZ, TRAVIS; Waynesburg Central HS; Waynesburg, PA; (3); Spanish Clb; L Ftbl; L Wrstlng; High Hon Roll; NHS; Ntl Merit Ltr; NEDT Awd; Engrng.

SHULUGA, BRENDA; Mohawk JR SR HS; Hillsville, PA; (3); FBLA; FHA; Latin Clb; Hon Roll; NHS; Nrs.

SHUMA, CHRISTINE; Cambria Heights SR HS; Ebensburg, PA; (3); 6/200; NFL; Speech Tm; Band; Chorus; Concert Band; Mrchg Band; Pep Band; Nwsp Stf; Hon Roll; NHS; Forensics 3rd Pl Invitational Comp & 5th Pl At Dist Comp 87; Mathematics.

SHUMAKER, JACQUELINE; North Clarion HS; Leeper, PA; (3); VP Church Yth Grp; Drama Clb; Hosp Aide; Spanish Clb; School Musical; School Play; JV Cheerleading; Stat Socr; Var Trk; Jr NHS; Nursing.

SHUMAKER, JENNIFER; West Greene Middle SR HS; Sycamore, PA; (4); 2/108; Drama Clb; Sec French Clb; Library Aide; Ski Clb; Capt Chorus; School Musical; School Play; Yrbk Stf; Stat L Trk; NHS; PA Govnrs Schl Of Arts 86.

SHUMAKER, SUSAN; Berlin Brothers Valley HS; Berlin, PA; (2); 13/89; Church Yth Grp; Drama Clb; 4-H; Spanish Clb; Speech Tm; SADD; Band; Concert Band; Mrchg Band; 4-H Awd.

SHUMAN, ALAN; Lewisburg Area HS; Lewisburg, PA; (4); 45/144; Chess Clb; Exploring; French Clb; Pres Science Clb; School Play; Crs Cntry; Capt Trk; Hon Roll; Walter & Esther Sauvain Trst Fnd Schlrshp 87; Silvr Medl-St Sci Olympiad 85; V Lttrs-Trk 86 & 87; PA ST U.

SHUMAN, JOEL LEE; Lower Dauphin HS; Hershey, PA; (4); Chorus; Var L Crs Cntry; Var L Trk; JV Wrstlng; Hon Roll; Ntl Merit Ltr; Gld Key Wrtng 87; Pres Acad Ftnss Awd 87; Reg Of Excel Outstndng Ind Arts 87; PA ST U; Ag.

SHUMAN, LARRY; Wyoming Valley West HS; Kingston, PA; (4); Boy Scts; Radio Clb; Varsity Clb; Coach Actv; Var L Socr; JV Trk; Morris & Kitty Nelson Awd 87; B J Lean Awd 87; U Pittsburgh; Pre-Law.

SHUMSKI, MARY ELIZABETH; Sacred Heart HS; Carbondale, PA; (3); 5/42; Church Yth Grp; Computer Clb; Drama Clb; SADD; Stage Crew; Nwsp Ed-Chief; JV Var Bsktbl; Var Sftbl; High Hon Roll; NHS; Psych.

SHUNK, BRIAN; St Piux X HS; Pottstown, PA; (2); 6/148; Boy Scts; Golf; Swmmng; Jr NHS; Arntcl Engrng.

SHURGOTT, SAMUEL; Ringgold HS; Monongahela, PA; (3); Aud/Vis; Church Yth Grp; Pres JA; Model UN; Service Clb; Ski Clb; Chorus; Nwsp Stf; L Trk; JR Achvmt Sls Clbs 86; J A Prfct Atten Sls Clbs Asst VP Mktg 87; Mktng.

SHUTA, VINCENT J; Bishop O Hara HS; Olyphant, PA; (2); Stat JV Bsktbl; Score Keeper; Schlrshp To Bishop Ohara 85; U Of Scranton; Comp Engrng.

SHUTT, ANDREA; Pine Grove HS; Pine Grove, PA; (3); 13/110; Art Clb; Sec Leo Clb; Pres Soph Cls; Pres Jr Cls; JV Bsktbl; JV Sftbl; Cit Awd; High Hon Roll; Hon Roll; NHS; Kutztown U; Art.

SHUTT, KELLEY ANN; Elizabethtown Area HS; Elizabethtown, PA; (3); 73/300; Church Yth Grp; Drama Clb; FCA; Office Aide; SADD; Hon Roll; Northern Atlantic Achvt Comptn 86-87; Northern Atlantic Achvt Comptn Gold Mdl & 1st Pl 87; Nrs.

SHUTT, KERRI; Hempfield SR HS; Bovard, PA; (4); Art Clb; Aud/Vis; Ski Clb; Bsktbl; Cheerleading; Mgr(s); Powder Puff Ftbl; Sftbl; Vllybl; Wt Lftg; X-Ray Tech.

SHUTT, MICHELLE; Newport HS; Newport, PA; (2); Hon Roll; Stu Orgnztns Amercn Rlf 85-87; Schl Bffls Awrnss Clb-Drgs & Drnkng 84-85; Bus.

SHUTT, STACIE; Donegal HS; Mount Joy, PA; (2); Church Yth Grp; Drama Clb; Girl Scts; Color Guard; Rep Frsh Cls; Rep Soph Cls; Stu Cncl; Fld Hcky; Gym; Mgr(s); Millersville U; Psych.

SHUTTLEWORTH, ANNE; Lawrence Co Vo Tech; Ellwood City, PA; (3); 47/250; Church Yth Grp; Spanish Clb; Pres VICA; Y-Teens; Rep Stu Cncl; Var L Bsktbl; Im Bowling; Im Powder Puff Ftbl; Im Score Keeper.

SHUTTLEWORTH, GARY; Trinity SR HS; Washington, PA; (2); Computer Clb; German Clb; VP JA; Ski Clb; Spanish Clb; Thesps; Chorus; Stage Crew; Golf; Socr; Bnkr Of Yr Jr Achvt 86-87; Pre Med.

SHUTTLEWORTH, STACY; Conestoga Valley HS; Leola, PA; (4); 13/246; Art Clb; Service Clb; Stage Crew; Yrbk Stf; Hon Roll; Pres Schlr; 2 Natl Schlstc Gld Key Art Awds 86; 1 Schlstc Gld Key Art Awd; Peopl To Peopl Stdnt Ambssdr 86; Parsons Schl Desgn; Art.

SHWALLON, CHUCK; Bethlehem-Center SR HS; Richeyville, PA; (2); 50/150; Boy Scts; Church Yth Grp; Yrbk Stf; JV Bsbl; JV Bsktbl; Hon Roll; Army.

SHYK, TODD; Central Dauphin East HS; Harrisburg, PA; (4); Art Clb; Camera Clb; Debate Tm; Drama Clb; Acpl Chr; Band; Chorus; Concert Band; Jazz Band; Mrchg Band; Shippensburg U; Sec Ed.

SIANO, ROBERT; Moshannon Valley JR/Sr HS; Morann, PA; (3); 31/112; Church Yth Grp; Spanish Clb; Band; Concert Band; Mrchg Band; Pep Band; Im Bsktbl; Im Ftbl; Im Vllybl; Hon Roll; Devry Inst Of Tech; Comp.

SIAR, KIM; Shaler Area HS; Glenshaw, PA; (3); 48/486; Pep Clb; Ski Clb; SADD; Nwsp Stf; Capt Twrlr; High Hon Roll; Nrsng.

SIBETO, JACQUELINE; New Castle SR HS; New Castle, PA; (4); AFS; Church Yth Grp; Office Aide; High Hon Roll; Hon Roll; Jr NHS; NHS; Acctng.

SIBISKI, GERALD; Bethlehem Catholic HS; Bath, PA; (3); 17/220; Boys Clb Am; Var JV Socr; NHS; Elec Engrng.

SIBOLE, KEARY; Villa Maria Acad; Pohstown, PA; (3); 24/98; Library Aide; Service Clb; Yrbk Stf; Ed Lit Mag; Fld Hcky; Lcrss; Med.

SICCHITANO, HEATHER; Lock Haven JR SR HS; Woolrich, PA; (3); Keywanettes; Spanish Clb; SADD; Chorus; Var JV Bsktbl; Var L Trk; Twrlr; High Hon Roll; Hon Roll; NHS; Acad All Amer 86-87; Astrnmy.

SICILIA, TERESA; Little Flower HS; Philadelphia, PA; (3); 32/322; Church Yth Grp; Nwsp Rptr; Nwsp Stf; Rep Frsh Cls; Stu Cncl; Hon Roll; Prfct Atten Awd; CSC 85-86; CYO 85-86; Sci Fair 85-86; Accntng.

SICKLE, JOHN T; Easton Area HS; Easton, PA; (3); 24/485; Am Leg Boys St; VP Frsh Cls; Var Bsktbl; Var Vllybl; High Hon Roll; Hon Roll; Jr NHS; NHS; Acdmc All Amer; Natl Ldrshp & Srvc Awd; Engrng.

SICKLER, LUCY; Wyoming Area HS; West Pittston, PA; (3); Church Yth Grp; VP FHA; Girl Scts; Key Clb; Service Clb; Church Choir; Mrchg Band; High Hon Roll; NHS; PA Free Entrprs Schlrshp 87; Hofstra U; Law.

SICKLER, MELISSA; Bangor SR HS; Bangor, PA; (3); FFA; Pep Clb; Cheerleading; Powder Puff Ftbl; Trk; Csmtlgy.

SICKLER, TED M; Wyalusing Valley HS; Wyalusing, PA; (4); 6/135; Cmnty Wkr; Library Aide; Scholastic Bowl; Band; Chorus; Church Choir; Mrchg Band; Orch; School Musical; Rep Stu Cncl; Prctr-N-Gmbl Schlrshp 87; DAR Gd Ctzn 87; Pres Acad Ftns Awd 87; PA ST U; Jrnlsm.

SIDERIS, ANGELIQUE; Liberty HS; Bethlehem, PA; (3); 12/429; French Clb; Chorus; NHS.

SIDHU, SONYA M; Gateway SR HS; Monroeville, PA; (4); Hosp Aide; NFL; Pres Science Clb; Temple Yth Grp; Chorus; Nwsp Ed-Chief; Yrbk Sprt Ed; Ntl Merit SF; Exploring; Math Clb; Rep PMEA Hnrs Choir & Dist Chorus 86-87; Editor Of Religious Nwslttr Tri St Sikh Cultrl Soc 86-87; Case Wstrn Rsrve U; Med.

SIDLOSKI, STEVEN; G A R Memorial HS; Wilkes-Barre, PA; (3); Church Yth Grp; Bsbl; Im Bsktbl; High Hon Roll; Hon Roll; Jr NHS; NHS; Altar Svc Awd 83; Keystone Coll; Cmrcl Arts.

SIDNEY, DAEL; Towanda Area HS; Towanda, PA; (3); Church Yth Grp; Hosp Aide; Chorus; Church Choir; Cheerleading; Sftbl; Var Hon Roll; Karate 1st Degree Belt Black 87; Bradford/Sullivan Cnty JR Miss Fin 87.

SIDON, NICKI; Carlynton HS; Carnegie, PA; (3); Drama Clb; High Hon Roll; Hon Roll.

SIEBER, KATHLEEN; Cardinal Dougherty HS; Philadelphia, PA; (2); 392/656; Photo.

SIEBER, SHELBY; East Juniata HS; Mcalisterville, PA; (4); 8/83; Church Yth Grp; Church Choir; Var Ftbl; Im Vllybl; High Hon Roll; Hon Roll; NHS; Stu Of Mnth 87; Pres Acad Ftnss Awd 87; Juniata Coll; Chem.

SIEBERT, KATHLEEN; Nazareth Acad; Philadelphia, PA; (3); Camp Fr Inc; Exploring; Hosp Aide; Q&S; Spanish Clb; Church Choir; Yrbk Stf; Var JV Fld Hcky; Var Tennis; Im Vllybl; Part Schl Scholar 84; Vet Med.

SIECK, FRANK; Mahanoy Area HS; Mahanoy City, PA; (4); 40/110; Church Yth Grp; School Musical; School Play; Stage Crew; Variety Show; Var JV Bsktbl; JV Im Bsktbl; PA ST U; Finance.

SIECK, WINSTON; Franklin Regional HS; Export, PA; (4); Computer Clb; German Clb; Ski Clb; School Play; Var L Ice Hcky; High Hon Roll; Tri ST Amtur Hcky Assc Awd-Acdmc Excllnc 85-87; Dfnsv Plyr Of Yr-Hcky 83-84 & 86-87; U Of CO-BOULDER; Pilot.

SIECKO, LORI ANN; Berwick Area SR HS; Berwick, PA; (4); Drama Clb; Yrbk Ed-Chief; Stu Cncl; Var L Trk; DAR Awd; NHS; Voice Dem Awd; Exploring; Key Clb; Ski Clb; Prsdntlphyscl Ftnss Awds 85-87; Stu Of Mnth 87; Prsdntl Acdmc Ftnss Wd 87; Dickinson Coll; Law.

SIEDLECKI, PATRICIA; Carlynton HS; Carnegie, PA; (4); 16/170; German Clb; Trk; High Hon Roll; Hon Roll; NHS; Waynesburg Hnr Schlrshp 87; Carnegie Cvc Clb Schlrshp 87; Waynesburg; Nrsng.

SIEFRING, LEO; Valley View JR SR HS; Peckville, PA; (4); VP Science Clb; Trs Band; Trs Concert Band; Trs Jazz Band; Trs Mrchg Band; Lucille Mckane Music Achvt Awd 87; Dist Chorus 87; Best Soloist,Outstndng Achvt 87; Marywood Coll; Psych.

SIEGEL, ALEXANDER; Manheim Central HS; Manheim, PA; (4); Church Yth Grp; Cmnty Wkr; Library Aide; Band; Concert Band; Orch; Symp Band; Vllybl; Libr Awd 87; LLMEA Cnty Orch Awd 87; Cncrt Band Recog 86 & 87; Hstry.

SIEGEL, ANGIE; North Clarion HS; Tionesta, PA; (4); 50/83; Varsity Clb; Var Capt Trk; Hon Roll; Prfct Atten Awd; District Track 84-87; St Track Alternate 84-87; St Track Champ 1st Pl 3200 Meter Relay 87.

SIEGEL, BRAD; North Clarion HS; Tylersburg, PA; (3); Rep Stu Cncl; L Socr; Var L Trk.

SIEGFRIED, CHRIS; West Hazleton HS; Drums, PA; (4); 89/223; Var L Ftbl; Var Capt Wrstlng; Letterman Clb; Im Badmtn; Im Bsbl; Im Bsktbl; Im Sftbl; Im Tennis; Var L Trk; Im Vllybl; All Area 1st Tm Slctn Ftbl 86-87; Thomas Cronin Mem Awd 87; Frank Bill Pursell Mem Awd 87; Millersville U; Bus.

SIEGFRIED, CHRISTINE; Nazareth Area SR HS; Bethlehem, PA; (3); Var Bsktbl; Capt Sftbl; Var Vllybl; Hon Roll.

SIEGFRIED, DEANA; Shikelamy HS; Sunbury, PA; (2); Church Yth Grp; Debate Tm; Key Clb; Spanish Clb; Speech Tm; Church Choir; School Musical; School Play; Susquehanna U; Elem Schl.

SIEGFRIED, JANET; Unionville HS; West Chester, PA; (4); 20/316; Rep Soph Cls; Rep Jr Cls; Rep Sr Cls; Rep Stu Cncl; Var Bsktbl; Var Sftbl; Var Vllybl; High Hon Roll; Hon Roll; NHS; Unionville-Chadds Ford Cmnty Schlrshp, Army Schlr-Athlt Awd, Chester Cnty Press Schlr-Athlt Awd 87; Guilford Coll; Lbrl Arts.

SIEGRIST, KRISTEN; Northern Lebanon HS; Jonestown, PA; (4); 13/166; Church Yth Grp; Sec Varsity Clb; VP Jr Cls; VP Sr Cls; Rep Stu Cncl; Fld Hcky; Hon Roll; Lion Awd; Sec NHS; Boyd Career Schl; Travel.

SIEGRIST, RHONDA; Lampeter-Strasburg HS; Ronks, PA; (3); 7/130; Trs Church Yth Grp; Pres FBLA; Quiz Bowl; Chorus; Ed Lit Mag; High Hon Roll; NHS; FHA; 3rd Natls Pub Spkng 87; Bus Burrowes Schlrs 87; Bus.

SIEGWORTH, DAVE; Steel Valley SR HS; Munhall, PA; (3); Church Yth Grp; Swmmng; Natl Yth Phys Ftns Pgm Marine Corps Leag Awd 87; Phrmcy.

SIEH, HUBERT; Central HS; Philadelphia, PA; (3); 35/550; Math Clb; Math Tm; Science Clb; Prfct Atten Awd.

SIEMANIS, JENNY; Minersville Area HS; Minersville, PA; (3); JA; Latin Clb; Pep Clb; Ski Clb; Spanish Clb; SADD; Varsity Clb; School Musical; Stage Crew; Var L Bsktbl; Mrn Bio.

SIEMINSKI, ROBB; Coughlin HS; Laflin, PA; (3); Chess Clb; German Clb; Ski Clb; Bsbl; Ftbl; Wt Lftg; Hon Roll; PA ST; Mtrlgy.

SIEMONS, MICHAEL; Cumberland Valley HS; Mechanicsburg, PA; (3); German Clb; Key Clb; Ski Clb; Socr.

SIEPMANN, ADAM; Marple Newtown HS; Marple, PA; (3); Nwsp Rptr; Nwsp Stf; Lit Mag; Crs Cntry; Trk; CA U Of PA; Crtv Wrtg.

SIERZENSKI, PAUL; Father Judge HS; Philadelphia, PA; (3); 2/402; German Clb; Math Tm; VP Red Cross Aide; Yrbk Sprt Ed; Im Bowling; High Hon Roll; NHS; Im Bsktbl; Gov Hon Prg Awd; La Salle U Archdcsn Schlrshp 87-88; La Salle U; Plstc Srgn.

SIEW, PEARL; Upper Merion Area SR HS; King Of Prussia, PA; (3); Hosp Aide; Math Tm; Model UN; Pres Science Clb; Chorus; Jazz Band; Mrchg Band; Orch; Twrlr; Hon Roll; PA JR Acad Sci 84-85; Tri-Cnty Music Awd 85-86; Drexel U Music Awd 85-86; U Of PA; Pre-Med.

SIGAL, IVAN; Schuylkill Valley HS; Reading, PA; (4); 6/131; Quiz Bowl; Pres Ski Clb; School Musical; Nwsp Stf; Yrbk Phtg; Var L Swmmng; Var L Trk; Hon Roll; Var Pres NHS; Ntl Merit Ltr.

SIGLER, SUSAN; Bishop Mc Devitt HS; Dauphin, PA; (3); 29/209; Office Aide; Service Clb; Ski Clb; Chorus; Var Capt Cheerleading; High Hon Roll; Hon Roll; Jr NHS; Band; Htl Mgmt.

SIGNES, HEIDE; Liberty HS; Bethlehem, PA; (3); 30/450; Drama Clb; Red Cross Aide; Band; Concert Band; Mrchg Band; Orch; Pep Band; School Play; Stage Crew; Lit Mag; Special Ed.

SIGNOR, STEPHEN R; Mechanicsburg SR HS; Mechanicsburg, PA; (3); 41/338; Am Leg Boys St; Band; Stu Cncl; JV L Bsbl; JV L Ftbl; Capt Ice Hcky; JV L Wrstlng; High Hon Roll; Concert Band; Symp Band; Hugh O Brien Ldrshp Smnr 85; Captlzg Ldrshp In Amer Smnr 86; Hmrm Pres.

SIGNORE, KATE; New Brighton HS; New Brighton, PA; (3); Art Clb; Rep DECA; GAA; Library Aide; Varsity Clb; Mgr Bsktbl; Sftbl; Tennis; Hon Roll; Meritorious Awd 85-86; Bus.

SIGNORE, PATRICK H; Penn Hills HS; Verona, PA; (4); Political Wkr; Teachers Aide; Hon Roll; Lamp Knwldg Awd 85-87; Pittsburgh Tech Ins; Archtch.

SIKET, MELISSA; Abington Heights HS; Clarks Summit, PA; (4); 121/272; Letterman Clb; Ski Clb; Stu Cncl; Var L Cheerleading; Ltr-Chrldng 85-87; Mary Mt Coll; Intl Bus.

SIKINA, KIM; Brownsville HS; Cardale, PA; (3); FBLA; Hosp Aide; Intnl Clb; Office Aide; Nwsp Rptr; Nwsp Stf; Vllybl; Hon Roll; PA ST; Teacher.

SIKINA, KRISSIE; Brownsville HS; Cardale, PA; (3); Drama Clb; Hosp Aide; Nwsp Rptr; Nwsp Stf; Mgr Vllybl; Hon Roll; Candy Strpng 100 Hr Awd 84; FBLA 85-86; Intrct 86-87; PA ST; Physcl Thrpy.

SIKLAS, EVANGELIA; Mount Penn HS; Reading, PA; (4); 9/63; Trs Church Yth Grp; GAA; VP Intnl Clb; Scholastic Bowl; VP Science Clb; Mrchg Band; Twrlr; JV Fld Hcky; High Hon Roll; NHS; Youth Group Oraorical Fest Awd 85f; Millersville U; Interntl Law.

SIKORA, CRAIG; West Mifflin Area HS; W Mifflin, PA; (3); 4/300; Key Clb; Varsity Clb; Pres Frsh Cls; Var Capt Ftbl; Trk; Wt Lftg; High Hon Roll; Jr NHS; NHS; Ntl Merit Ltr; WA Wrkshp Model Congress 87.

SIKORA, MARK; Steel Valley HS; Homestead, PA; (3); L Diving; Var Swmmng; Hon Roll; U S Navy; Comp Sci.

SIKORA, TRACY; Owen J Roberts HS; Pottstown, PA; (2); 8/311; Church Yth Grp; Concert Band; Mrchg Band; School Musical; Rep Stu Cncl; Lcrss; Swmmng; Hon Roll; PA ST U; Law.

SIKORSKI, ANN MARIE; South Allegheny HS; Liberty Boro, PA; (4); Church Yth Grp; Drama Clb; French Clb; FNA; Hosp Aide; JA; SADD; Y-Teens; Band; Chorus; Hugh O Brian Yth Fndnt Ldrshp Awd; Natl Chrl Awd; Robert Morris Coll; Rdlgst.

SIKORSKI JR, WILLIAM H; Ambridge Area HS; Baden, PA; (3); Am Leg Aux Girls St; German Clb; Spanish Clb; L Crs Cntry; L Trk; Bausch & Lomb Sci Awd; Gov Hon Prg Awd; High Hon Roll; Jr NHS; Ntl Merit SF; USAF Math & Sci Awd 87; Acad All Amer 87.

SIKOWITZ, JACKIE; Bensalem HS; Bensalem, PA; (2); Spanish Clb; SADD; Temple Yth Grp; Chorus; School Musical; Rep Soph Cls; Hon Roll; Color Guard; School Play; Swing Chorus; Ida Smith Mem Awd 87; 2nd Pl Assn Jewish Orthdx Tchrs Essay Cont 87; 3rd Pl PA JR Acad Sci Cmptn 87; Comm.

SILBAUGH, SHEILA; United HS; Homer City, PA; (3); 68/147; Camera Clb; Church Yth Grp; Drama Clb; Pep Clb; Ski Clb; Spanish Clb; Drill Tm; Yrbk Stf; JV Bsktbl; JV Var Sftbl; Elem Ed.

SILBERMAN, MICHAEL; Abington HS; Elkins Pk, PA; (3); 25/520; Intnl Clb; Model UN; Spanish Clb; Rep Frsh Cls; Rep Soph Cls; Rep Jr Cls; Rep Stu Cncl; JV Socr; JV Trk; High Hon Roll.

SILDRA, DANIELLE; Aliquippa SR HS; Aliquippa, PA; (4); 8/120; Church Yth Grp; Hosp Aide; Concert Band; Jazz Band; Mrchg Band; Yrbk Stf; Off Sr Cls; Lion Awd; NHS; Grove City Coll; Pre-Med.

SILDRA, DELLA MARIE; Aliquippa JR/SR HS; Aliquippa, PA; (2); 1/120; Trs Church Yth Grp; Sec Computer Clb; Exploring; Trs French Clb; Band; Concert Band; Mrchg Band; Pep Band; Yrbk Stf; High Hon Roll; Beaver County Hnrs Band 86 & 87; Pre-Med.

SILEO, TRACEY; Dunmore HS; Dunmore, PA; (3); 11/150; Church Yth Grp; Computer Clb; Letterman Clb; Spanish Clb; Chorus; Church Choir; Yrbk Stf; Var Swmmng; High Hon Roll; NHS; Teen Tlnt Vocal Ensmbl Wnnr 86 & 87; Evangel Coll; Med Tech.

SILHANEK, ALISON; Liberty HS; Bethlehem, PA; (3); 31/450; Cmnty Wkr; Hosp Aide; Band; Concert Band; Mrchg Band; Orch; Hon Roll; NHS; Dist Orch & Regnl Orch 86-87; Bio.

SILK, APRIL; Du Bois Area HS; Du Bois, PA; (2); 150/330; Chorus; Mrchg Band; School Musical; School Play; Swing Chorus; Penn ST; Pub Rel.

SILLAMAN, JENNIFER; Hempfield SR HS; Hunker, PA; (2); Exploring; French Clb; Pep Clb; Ski Clb; Mgr(s); Med.

SILLERS, AMY; Carlynton JR/SR HS; Pittsburgh, PA; (4); 14/161; Church Yth Grp; French Clb; Girl Scts; Church Choir; Concert Band; Mrchg Band; High Hon Roll; Hon Roll; NHS; SHASPA Awd 87; L Beck 2nd Pl Schlrshp 87; Westminster Coll; Bio.

SILLHART, STEPHEN; Conrad Weiser HS; Wernersville, PA; (3); 14/181; German Clb; Stage Crew; Trs Stu Cncl; Capt Crs Cntry; Var L Trk; Hon Roll; Aerosp Engrng.

SILLIMAN, ANN MARIE; Bishop Hafey HS; New Coxeville, PA; (3); French Clb; Key Clb; VP Stu Cncl; Capt Bsktbl; Hon Roll; NHS; Psych.

SILLO III, JOSEPH C; St John Neumann HS; Philadelphia, PA; (2); 7/357; Boy Scts; Exploring; Ftbl; Wt Lftg; DAR Awd; SAR Awd; Union League Good Citznshp Awd 86; Merit Awd For Lit Competition At Natl Scout Jamboree 85.

SILVA, DINA M; Olney HS; Philadelphia, PA; (4); 1/700; French Clb; Library Aide; Teachers Aide; French Hon Soc; High Hon Roll; Kiwanis Awd; NHS; Meritorius Awds 84-87; Cert Allianc Frncs 86.

SILVA, KATRINA; Strath Haven HS; Wallingford, PA; (3); Church Yth Grp; Ski Clb; JV Bsktbl; Var Fld Hcky; Var Lcrss; Hon Roll; Natl HS Showcase La Crosse Team 87; Field Hcky Alt Keystone ST Games 87; Med Tech.

SILVA, MELISSA; Archbishop Ryan-Girls HS; Philadelphia, PA; (4); 148/490; Library Aide; Office Aide; Spanish Clb; School Play; Cheerleading; Hnrb J E Coleman Awd; PA ST U; Bus Adm.

SILVA, NIDIA M; Olney HS; Philadelphia, PA; (4); 3/700; French Clb; Teachers Aide; French Hon Soc; High Hon Roll; NHS; Stu Mnth 87; Cert Apprectn Am Cancer Soc 86.

SILVANO, DENEEN; Biship Shanahan HS; W Chester, PA; (4); 47/215; Service Clb; Teachers Aide; Outstndng Bus Stu 86-87; Outstndng Engl 87; Westchester U; Bus.

SILVASI, LORI; West Hazleton JR- SR HS; W Hazleton, PA; (3); 52/225; Dance Clb; Office Aide; SADD; Thesps; Chorus; Mgr(s); Hon Roll; Schl Spirt Awd 84-85; Hlth.

SILVER, JENNIFER; Susquehanna Township HS; Harrisburg, PA; (3); Church Yth Grp; Teachers Aide; Chorus; School Musical; School Play; Yrbk Stf; Var Capt Cheerleading; Hon Roll; NHS; Schlstc Writing Awd 86; Cert Merit French 86; Marketing.

SILVER, JOAN MELISSA; HS For Creative & Performing Arts; Philadelphia, PA; (4); 1/126; Vllybl; High Hon Roll; NHS; Val; William Smith Coll.

SILVER, JOSEPH A III; Carlisle SR HS; Carlisle, PA; (3); Am Leg Boys St; Chess Clb; Exploring; JA; JR Achvt S Cntrl PA VP Mrktng 87; Patriot-News Hnr Crrier Svc Excllnc Awd 86; Bus Admin.

SILVER, LYNDA; Penn Wood HS; Darby, PA; (4); 4-H; Girl Scts; Teachers Aide; Chorus; Flag Corp; Mrchg Band; School Musical; Hon Roll; Comp Oprtns.

SILVER, SARAH; Parkland HS; Allentown, PA; (3); 80/420; Exploring; Math Tm; Science Clb; SADD; Concert Band; Rep Stu Cncl; L Diving; L Trk; Hon Roll; Church Yth Grp; Mannes Yth Phys Ftnss Pgm-Tm Natl Champs & Indiv 9th Pl Natl 86-87; Med.

SILVER, STEVEN E; Northeast HS; Philadelphia, PA; (3); 1/700; Band; Concert Band; Mrchg Band; Orch; Pep Band; School Musical; High Hon Roll; Jr NHS; NHS; Philadelphia Coll; Phrmcy.

SILVERMAN, AMANDA; Upper Merion HS; King Of Prussia, PA; (3); 40/300; Spanish Clb; JV Fld Hcky; Mgr(s); High Hon Roll; Hon Roll; Prfct Atten Awd; 2nd Pl-PA JR Acad Of Sci Cmptn 85; Bus Adm.

SILVERMAN, KAREN; Plymouth Whitemarsh HS; Plymouth Meeting, PA; (2); JV Var Mgr(s); Hon Roll; Med.

SILVERSTEIN, DAN; Allderdice HS; Pittsburgh, PA; (3); Boy Scts; Ski Clb; Chorus; Im Bsktbl; JV Ftbl; Var Tennis; JV Trk; Hon Roll; MVP Tennis Tm 86-87; FSU; Law.

SILVERSTRIM, CHRISTINE T; Sullivan County HS; Dushore, PA; (4); 2/83; Key Clb; Nwsp Rptr; Var L Bsktbl; Im Capt Socr; Var L Sftbl; Var L Vllybl; High Hon Roll; Sec NHS; Sal; 4-H; Prctr/Gmbl Outstndng Acdmc Awd, Am Lgn Ldies Aux Pst 996 Amrcnsm Awd, & HS Mem Awd 87; PA ST; Chem Engrng.

SILVERSTRIM, THOMAS; Tunkhannock Area HS; Tunkhannock, PA; (2); 7/365; Drama Clb; School Play; VP German Clb; Im Bsbl; Hon Roll; NHS; Marine Sci Clb 85-86 & 86-87.

SILVESTER, DAVID; Richland HS; Gibsonia, PA; (4); 1/183; NFL; Band; School Musical; Variety Show; Nwsp Ed-Chief; Pres Sr Cls; NHS; Ntl Merit Ltr; Val; Debate Tm; Andrew Carnegie Schlrshp 87; Brwn Bk Awd 86; PA ST Sci Sympsm Dlgt 86; Carnegie Mellon U; Info Sys.

SILVESTRI, CHRIS; Downington SR HS; Downingtown, PA; (3); 72/600; French Clb; Letterman Clb; JV Var Socr; Trk; High Hon Roll; Hon Roll; NHS; Jrnlsm.

SILVIS, BRIAN; Mc Dowell HS; Erie, PA; (2); 220/629; Church Yth Grp; German Clb; JV Trk; Wt Lftg; JV Wrstlng; Comp Pgmng.

SIM, MICHAEL NORMAN; Camp Hill HS; Camp Hill, PA; (4); 8/62; Hon Roll; Kiwanis Awd; Lion Awd; NHS; NEDT Awd; Boy Scts; Nwsp Stf; Var L Crs Cntry; Var L Trk; JV Wrstlng; Bell Telephone Schlrshp Awd 87; Cross Cntry Reed Ernst Awd-Ldrshp/Schlrshp 84; Grove City Coll; Math Accntng.

SIMAKASKI, MARK; Scranton Prep Schl; Moosic, PA; (2); 45/210; Boy Scts; Church Yth Grp; Cmnty Wkr; JA; Pep Clb; Ski Clb; Band; Concert Band; Jazz Band; Orch.

SIMANSKI, AMY; Bishop Guilfoyle HS; Altoona, PA; (3); Cmnty Wkr; SADD; Chorus; Im Bsktbl; Occu Ther.

SIMARI, DEBRA J; Mohawk JR SR HS; Hillsville, PA; (4); 23/273; JCL; Latin Clb; Band; Drill Tm; Mrchg Band; Sec Jr Cls; Var Capt Cheerleading; Powder Puff Ftbl; Hon Roll; NHS; U Of Pittsburgh; Hlth Sci.

SIMCHOCK, TARA; Hazleton HS; Hazleton, PA; (3); Drama Clb; Pep Clb; School Play; Stage Crew; Hon Roll; Psychlgy.

SIMCOX, CHRISTINE; Lock Haven SR HS; Lock Haven, PA; (3); VP FBLA; Spanish Clb; SADD; Stu Cncl; Hon Roll; NHS; Williamsport Schl Of Commrce.

SIMKISS, COLLEEN T; Saint Basil Acad; Richboro, PA; (4); 8/97; Art Clb; Spanish Clb; SADD; Chorus; Rep Frsh Cls; VP Soph Cls; VP Jr Cls; VP Sr Cls; VP Stu Cncl; Hon Roll; Spnsh Cntst Wnnr 3rd Plc 87; Prsdntl Awd 87; Hussian Schl Of Art; Advrtsng.

SIMKO, STEPHEN; Baldwin HS; Pittsburgh, PA; (2); Church Yth Grp; Computer Clb; French Clb; JA; Concert Band; Mrchg Band; Symp Band; Wrstlng; High Hon Roll.

SIMKOVIC, JERRY; Jefferson-Morgan HS; Clarksville, PA; (4); Letterman Clb; Varsity Clb; Nwsp Sprt Ed; Yrbk Phtg; Yrbk Sprt Ed; Var Capt Bsbl; Var Capt Bsktbl; Var Capt Ftbl; Hon Roll; Var Bsebl & Bsktbl Awds 87; Prince Chrmng 87; Mr J-M 87; Most Rep 87; Amer Athl 86; US Navy; Elec.

SIMKOVICH, ERIC; Belle Vernon Area HS; Belle Vernon, PA; (3); JA; JV Ftbl; Var L Vllybl; Hon Roll.

SIMMEL, KLINT; Beaver Falls HS; Beaver Falls, PA; (3); 40/170; Church Yth Grp; Letterman Clb; Rep Sec Frsh Cls; Rep Sec Soph Cls; Pres Jr Cls; Capt Ftbl; Hon Roll.

SIMMERS, HOLLY; Fort Lebouef HS; Erie, PA; (2); 43/213; Computer Clb; Dance Clb; Flag Corp; Mrchg Band; JV Cheerleading; Var L Sftbl; Hon Roll; Geriatrcs.

SIMMERS, MARK; Coatesville Area SR HS; Coatesville, PA; (3); 63/518; Spanish Clb; JV Wrstlng; Hon Roll; NHS; Bus Mgmt.

SIMMERS, SHAWN; Central Cambria HS; Ebensburg, PA; (2); Bsbl; Bsktbl; Golf; Hon Roll.

SIMMONS, APRIL; HS For Creative & Performing Arts; Philadelphia, PA; (4); 13/127; Church Yth Grp; Dance Clb; Church Choir; Hon Roll; Young Artists Civic Cntr Art Show 85 & 86; Moore Coll Art Scholar 87; Moore Coll Art; Graphic Desgnr.

SIMMONS, BRENDA; Punxsutawney Area SR HS; Punxsutawney, PA; (4); 49/245; Art Clb; Math Tm; Varsity Clb; Variety Show; Var Capt Cheerleading; Var Tennis; Var Trk; Hon Roll; John W Jenks Mem Fund Schlrshp, Mary Ann Irvin Schlrshp 87; Penn ST Univ Pk; Comp Sci.

SIMMONS, GERALD; Blacklick Valley JR SR HS; Nanty-Glo, PA; (2); Ftbl; Trk; Hon Roll; Pres Schlr; Acdmc All Am 85.

SIMMONS, HEATHER; Merion Mercy Acd; Phila, PA; (4); French Clb; Intnl Clb; Pres Spanish Clb; Chorus; Nwsp Ed-Chief; French Hon Soc; High Hon Roll; JV Var NHS; Ntl Merit Ltr; Spanish NHS; Presdntl Schlrshp St Josephs U 87; 1st Pl Level II NATSP 87; WPVU Tv Best Of Cls 87; St Joseph U; Intl Reltns.

SIMMONS, JEFF; Montour HS; Pittsburgh, PA; (3); Stu Cncl; High Hon Roll; Hon Roll; NHS; Prfct Atten Awd; U Of Pittsburgh; Med.

SIMMONS, JOANNE; Uniontown SR HS; Uniontown, PA; (4); JA; Spanish Clb; SADD; Penn ST; Psych.

SIMMONS, LAUREN; Pen Argyl Area HS; Easton, PA; (3); 14/160; Church Yth Grp; Exploring; Chorus; Color Guard; Nwsp Stf; Yrbk Stf; Hon Roll; Clrgrd Capt 86-87; Natl Hstry Day Cmptn 1st Pl 84-87; Law.

SIMMONS, MIKE; Williamsburg HS; Williamsburg, PA; (3); Camera Clb; FNA; Yrbk Stf; Rep Stu Cncl; JV Ftbl; Capt Wt Lftg; High Hon Roll; NHS; Prfct Atten Awd; Sci.

SIMMONS, RYAN; Lock Haven SR HS; Blanchard, PA; (3); Math Tm; Pres Orch; Im Var Bsktbl; JV Ftbl; High Hon Roll; Hon Roll; NHS; Ntl Merit Ltr; Lock Haven Music Clb 1st Pl Awd 87; Luis L Raff Memrl Awd-Excellence In Physics 87; Exclnc In Chem 86; IN U Of PA; Music Educ.

SIMMONS, TINA; Cowanesque Valley HS; Knoxville, PA; (4); 17/76; Letterman Clb; Cheerleading; Vllybl; Hon Roll; NHS; Athltc Schlr 85-87; Elmira Bus Inst; Sec.

SIMMONS, TRACY; Chambersburg Area SR HS; Chambersburg, PA; (2); Church Yth Grp; Cmnty Wkr; French Clb; Band; Church Choir; Flag Corp; JV Trk; Hon Roll; Isbl Knld Art Awd 86; Art.

SIMMS, PAMELA; Faith Community HS; Elizabeth, PA; (4); 4/29; Church Yth Grp; Dance Clb; French Clb; Hosp Aide; School Play; Yrbk Stf; Im Cheerleading; Im Gym; JV Tennis; High Hon Roll; Free Lance Photo.

SIMMS, SUSAN; Upper Darby HS; Drexel Hl, PA; (4); Var L Bsktbl; Var L Fld Hcky; Var L Sftbl; Hon Roll; Kiwanis Awd; Sftbl All-Cntrl, All-Star Tm 85 & 87; MVP JV Bsktbl 84-85; West Chester U; Hlth Ed.

SIMON, ADRIENNE; Nazareth Acad; Phila, PA; (3); 6/125; French Clb; German Clb; NFL; Service Clb; Lit Mag; JV Fld Hcky; High Hon Roll; NHS; Intntl Finance.

SIMON, ANGIE; Franklin Learning Ctr; Philadelphia, PA; (3); Exploring; Hosp Aide; Red Cross Aide; Church Choir; Pep Band; School Play; Variety Show; Trs Soph Cls; Sec Jr Cls; L Tennis; IN U; Nrs.

SIMON, DAN; Ambridge Area HS; Ambridge, PA; (3); School Play; Stat Bsktbl; JV Ftbl; Wt Lftg; Prfct Atten 84-87; Penn ST; Archit.

SIMON, DEBBIE; West Scranton HS; Scranton, PA; (4); French Clb; Thesps; Chorus; School Musical; Variety Show; Stu Cncl; Var Capt Cheerleading; Tennis; High Hon Roll; NHS; Acadc All Amer Hnr Awd 87; Phrmcst.

SIMON, DENEAN; Oley Valley HS; Temple, PA; (3); 51/153; Art Clb; Camp Fr Inc; Pep Clb; Rep Stu Cncl; JV Fld Hcky; Score Keeper; Stat Wrstlng; Hon Roll; BCIU Enrichment Pgm-Kutztown U 86; Philadelphia Art Inst; Commcl.

SIMON, JEANNINE; Connellsville Area HS; Vanderbilt, PA; (4); Pres Church Yth Grp; Q&S; Church Choir; School Play; Nwsp Ed-Chief; Nwsp Stf; Yrbk Stf; High Hon Roll; NHS; Germn Natl Hnr Scty; PA ST; Pltcl Sci.

SIMON, JEFFREY; Lower Moreland HS; Meadowbrook, PA; (3); Key Clb; Science Clb; Temple Yth Grp; Yrbk Stf; Rep Stu Cncl; Var JV Socr; JV Tennis; Hon Roll.

SIMON, JERUSHA RUTH; Avon Grove HS; Lincoln Univ, PA; (3); 27/208; Church Yth Grp; DECA; FBLA; Hosp Aide; Chorus; Church Choir; Flag Corp; School Play; High Hon Roll; NHS; Shrthnd I Acad Awd 87; Bnd Svc Awd 87; Cntrl PA Bus Schl; Crt Rptr.

SIMON, KIM; Valley View HS; Archbald, PA; (3); 50/192; Church Yth Grp; Hosp Aide; Latin Clb; Library Aide; Red Cross Aide; Church Choir; Var Score Keeper; Var Trk; Prfct Atten Awd; RN.

SIMON, MARCI; Liberty HS; Bethlehem, PA; (4); 19/400; French Clb; Key Clb; Library Aide; Temple Yth Grp; Rep Soph Cls; Rep Sr Cls; Sec Stu Cncl; Mgr(s); Hon Roll; NHS; Frnch Awd 87; Futgers U; Lbrl Arts.

SIMON, NOAH; Central HS; Philadelphia, PA; (3); Cmnty Wkr; Band; Concert Band; Drm Mjr(t); Jazz Band; Orch; Crs Cntry; Hon Roll; Prfct Atten Awd; Music Ed.

SIMON, ROBERT; Kennedy Christian HS; New Castle, PA; (2); 15/96; Spanish Clb; Ftbl; Cit Awd; High Hon Roll; Jr NHS; Presdntl Acad Fit Awd 85; Cert Of Acad Achvt Joseph Baldwin Acad 85; Contnl Math League 85.

SIMON, SHAWN A; Center Area HS; Monaca, PA; (4); 6/185; Pres German Clb; School Musical; Ed Nwsp Ed-Chief; Pres Sr Cls; Var L Bsbl; Im Capt Bowling; NHS; Ntl Merit Schol; Am Leg Boys St; School Musical; Pres Acad Fitness Awd 87; Air Force ROTC 4 Yr Schlrshp 87; VA Plytechnc Inst; Aerospace E.

SIMONDALE, ELIZABETH; Tyrone Area HS; Tyrone, PA; (3); FBLA; Spanish Clb; Chorus; School Play; Powder Puff Ftbl; Sftbl; High Hon Roll; Hon Roll; NHS; Acctng I 87; Creative Cooking 87; Altoona Schl-Commerce; Med Secr.

SIMONETTI, NINA; Acad Of The New Church; Bryn Athyn, PA; (3); 3/45; Chorus; Madrigals; School Musical; Stage Crew; Yrbk Stf; Var L Fld Hcky; Vllybl; NHS; Songldr & Arthead Alpha Kappa Mu 86-88; Arch.

SIMONS, BRIAN; Philadelphia HS For Performng Arts; Philadelphia, PA; (4); 5/123; Drama Clb; Thesps; School Play; Rep Stu Cncl; High Hon Roll; NHS; Schlrshp PA Govrns Schl Arts 86; Cert Merit Perfrmnce A Soldiers Play 85; Schlrshp Tisch Schl Arts; NY U; Acting.

SIMONS, JASON; Carlisle HS; Carlisle, PA; (3); Var Swmmng; Church Yth Grp; Hon Roll; Bus.

SIMONS, JAY; Cumberland Valley HS; Mechanicsburg, PA; (3); Ski Clb; Im Badmtn; JV Var Bsbl; Im Bsktbl; JV Var Ftbl; Im Sftbl; Im Swmmng; Im Tennis; Im Wt Lftg; Comp Sci.

SIMONS, KARA; Fairview HS; Erie, PA; (4); 35/154; Hosp Aide; Orch; School Musical; Hon Roll; NHS; Natl Schl Orch Awd 87; Fairview Music Bstr Awd Fr Mscl Excllnc 87; Elizabethtown Msc Dept Schlrshp 87; Elezabethtown Coll; Occptnl.

SIMONS, KEVIN; Honesdale HS; Honesdale, PA; (4); 72/238; Boy Scts; French Clb; Letterman Clb; Band; Mrchg Band; Stage Crew; Off Stu Cncl; Var JV Crs Cntry; Var L Trk; Hon Roll; Dstngshd Srvc Awd 87; Bloomsburg U Of PA; Mass Comms.

SIMONS, KIM; Spring Ford HS; Royersford, PA; (3); 50/287; Church Yth Grp; Cmnty Wkr; Trs French Clb; FBLA; Pep Clb; Ski Clb; Var JV Cheerleading; Var Lcrss; Hon Roll; West Chester U; Bus Admin.

SIMONS, STEPHEN; Archbishop Ryan HS For Boys; Philadelphia, PA; (4); 15/423; Pres JA; Key Clb; Political Wkr; Spanish Clb; Nwsp Stf; Yrbk Ed-Chief; Lit Mag; Im Bsktbl; Var Golf; High Hon Roll; Spn Awd 83-87; Engl Awd 85; Marquette U; Pol Sci.

SIMONS, THOMAS; Avella Area JR SR HS; Avella, PA; (3); 15/99; Am Leg Boys St; Cmnty Wkr; Letterman Clb; Rep Soph Cls; Rep Jr Cls; Pres Stu Cncl; Var Capt Bsktbl; Var Capt Ftbl; Im Wt Lftg; Hon Roll; Comp Sci.

SIMONSEN, HEIDI; Mt Carmel Christian HS; Scottdale, PA; (4); 1/15; Chorus; School Play; Pres Sr Cls; Stu Cncl; Capt Vllybl; High Hon Roll; Ntl Merit Ltr; Val; Keystne Chrstn Ed Assn; MVP Vlybl; Grove City; Math.

SIMPKINS, LANE; Avon Grove HS; Landenberg, PA; (4); 4/215; Quiz Bowl; Service Clb; Varsity Clb; Band; Color Guard; Concert Band; Capt Flag Corp; Mrchg Band; School Musical; School Play; Acclrtd Engl Awd 85; Adv Engl Awd 87; Band Qtrmstr 85.

SIMPKINS, NANCI; Reynolds HS; Transfer, PA; (3); 1/145; Latin Clb; Varsity Clb; Chorus; Church Choir; Drill Tm; Drm Mjr(t); Mrchg Band; Yrbk Stf; Sec Stu Cncl; L Trk; Med.

SIMPSON, ALLYSON; Washington HS; Washington, PA; (4); 12/150; French Clb; Letterman Clb; Library Aide; Spanish Clb; Nwsp Ed-Chief; Rep Frsh Cls; Rep Soph Cls; Rep Jr Cls; Rep Sr Cls; Stu Cncl; Bus Prof Womens Assoc Awd 86-87; Stu Mnth 86-87; Pres Acad Ftns Awd 86-87; U Of MA; Nrsng.

SIMPSON, AMY; Lebanon Catholic HS; Lebanon, PA; (3); 24/72; Church Yth Grp; German Clb; Girl Scts; Pep Clb; Rep Stu Cncl; Var L Sftbl; Prfct Atten Awd; Ed.

SIMPSON, AMY; Methacton SR HS; Norristown, PA; (4); 103/375; Church Yth Grp; Hosp Aide; SADD; Frsh Cls; Soph Cls; Jr Cls; Sr Cls; Stu Cncl; Var Cheerleading; Var Lcrss; Hmcmng Ct 86; Hula Bowl 87; Unisys Awd Excell 87; Kutztown U; Art.

SIMPSON, BRIAN; Cameron County HS; Emporium, PA; (4); 15/93; Church Yth Grp; German Clb; Science Clb; Band; Concert Band; Drm & Bgl; Mrchg Band; Orch; Pep Band; Symp Band; Excllnce Music 86; Semper Fidelis Awd Music 87; IN U; Music.

SIMPSON, CHRISTINA; Gettysburg SR HS; Gettysburg, PA; (2); 21/250; Drama Clb; Ski Clb; School Musical; School Play; Crs Cntry; Trk; High Hon Roll; Ltr Cross-Cntry & Track 85-87; Pres Adadc Ftns Awd; Law.

SIMPSON, GREG; Brockway Area HS; Brockport, PA; (3); Letterman Clb; Varsity Clb; L Var Bsbl; L Var Ftbl; Wt Lftg; All Conf RB Ftbl 86.

SIMPSON, HEATHER; Monaca JR SR HS; Monaca, PA; (4); 13/90; JA; Library Aide; Pep Clb; Band; School Musical; Yrbk Stf; High Hon Roll; Hon Roll; NHS; Mjrtt Sqd; Hd Mrjtt; JR Mss Pgnt Fnlst; Prsdntl Physcl Ftnss Awd; Gannon U; Pre-Med.

SIMPSON, JESSICA; Lebanon Catholic HS; Lebanon, PA; (3); 11/72; Cmnty Wkr; Dance Clb; German Clb; Pep Clb; Wt Lftg; Hon Roll; NHS; Phys Educ.

SIMPSON, KELLY; Moniteau JR/ SR HS; W Sunbury, PA; (4); Exploring; Red Cross Aide; Y-Teens; Band; Chorus; Concert Band; Jazz Band; Ftbl; Hon Roll; Butter CC; Nrsng.

SIMPSON, LESLEY; New Castle HS; New Castle, PA; (2); French Clb; Nwsp Stf; Yrbk Stf; Stu Cncl; Cheerleading; L Tennis; French Hon Soc; Hon Roll.

SIMPSON, LORI; James M Coughlin HS; Wilkes Barre, PA; (4); Drama Clb; Chorus; Drill Tm; Orch; Pom Pon; High Hon Roll; Jr NHS; NHS; NEDT Awd; Ldrshp Ltr 87; Dir Orchestra Awd 87; PA ST U; Elem Ed.

SIMPSON, LORIE; Saint Hubert HS; Philadelphia, PA; (3); 13/421; Computer Clb; Band; Color Guard; Drill Tm; Flag Corp; Mrchg Band; Orch; Jr NHS; NHS; Ellis Grnt 86-88; Law.

SIMPSON, MICHELE; Mc Guffey HS; Prosperity, PA; (4); Church Yth Grp; Pep Clb; Spanish Clb; Tennis; Westminster Coll; Psych.

SIMPSON, PAMELA; Mc Guffey HS; Washington, PA; (3); 1/200; VP Church Yth Grp; French Clb; Pep Clb; Concert Band; Mrchg Band; Ed Yrbk Stf; High Hon Roll; NHS; Engl.

SIMPSON, RICHARD; Cumberland Valley HS; Mechanicsburg, PA; (3); Computer Clb; Spanish Clb; Im Bsktbl; Im Lcrss; Im Vllybl; Vrsty Rifle Tm 85-87; Drexel; Chem.

SIMPSON, ROSEMARIE; St Maria Goretti HS; Philadelphia, PA; (4); 85/392; Pres Church Yth Grp; GAA; Math Clb; La Salle U; Accntng.

SIMPSON, SAMUEL; Pine Forge Acad; Brooklyn, NY; (4); 16/79; Church Choir; Mrchg Band; Stu Cncl; Bsbl; Socr; Sftbl; Swmmng; Vllybl; Cit Awd; Hon Roll; Monmouth Coll; Chem.

SIMPSON, SHAWN; Highlands SR HS; Tarentum, PA; (3); 50/300; VP Art Clb; DECA; Teachers Aide; Stage Crew; Capt Jr Cls; Bsktbl; Hon Roll; Prfct Atten Awd; Decor Chrmn JR Cls Prom 86-87; Art Ed.

SIMPSON, SHEILA; Biglerville HS; Biglerville, PA; (3); 13/125; Computer Clb; Varsity Clb; Sec Frsh Cls; Stu Cncl; Bsktbl; Bowling; Trk; High Hon Roll; Jr NHS; Sr Natl Hnr Soc 86-87; Dentl Hygnst.

SIMPSON, TIM; West Middlesex HS; Pulaski, PA; (3); 4/105; French Clb; Trk; Wt Lftg; NHS.

SIMPSON, TRICIA; Wallenpaupack Area HS; Hawley, PA; (3); 32/157; Church Yth Grp; Chorus; School Musical; Rep Frsh Cls; Rep Soph Cls; Rep Jr Cls; Rep Sr Cls; Gov Hon Prg Awd; Hon Roll; Jr NHS; Social Wrk.

SIMS, DAVID; York Co Vo Tech; Red Lion, PA; (3); Church Yth Grp; Cmnty Wkr; Machinist.

SIMS, JACK; East SR HS; West Chester, PA; (3); VICA; Off Soph Cls; Off Jr Cls; Trk; Stu Cncerns Cmnty 85-87; Blck Stu Union 85-87; CA Coll; Robotcs.

SIMS, JACQUELINE; Solanco SR HS; Quarryville, PA; (3); Church Yth Grp; Varsity Clb; Fld Hcky; Sftbl; Hon Roll; Powder Puff Ftbl; Tchr.

SIMS, SEIJUN HIRASAWA; Taylor Allderdice HS; Pittsburgh, PA; (4); Boys Clb Am; Camera Clb; Cit Awd; High Hon Roll; Hon Roll; Ntl Merit Ltr; Pres Soc Studs Cls 83; Mst Valuable Stu 84; Fulfillment Reqrmnts Acad Curriculum Awd 87; PITT; Engrng.

SIMS, SUZANNE E; Portage Area HS; Portage, PA; (3); Varsity Clb; Stu Cncl; Bsktbl; Bowling; Trk; Vllybl; Hon Roll; NHS; Adlgst.

SINACORE, SUZANNE; East Stroudsburg Area HS; East Stroudsburg, PA; (4); 25/201; Art Clb; Dance Clb; Drama Clb; FNA; Hosp Aide; Library Aide; SADD; Teachers Aide; Chorus; NHS; E Stroudsburg U; Comp Sci.

SINCLAIR, DAVID; Butler Area HS; Renfrew, PA; (3); Debate Tm; French Clb; Math Tm; Orch; School Musical; Lit Mag; Gov Hon Prg Awd; Jr NHS; NHS; Ntl Merit SF; PA Music Ed Assn ST Orch 85-87; PA ST String Quartet Camp 85-87; Eastman Schl Music; Music.

SINCLAIR, MICHELLE; Glendla JR SR HS; Coalport, PA; (3); 24/75; Pres Church Yth Grp; Science Clb; Capt Rptr Mrchg Band; Yrbk Stf; Var Stat Score Keeper; Rep Jr Cls; Accntng.

SINCLAIR, TERRY; Saltsburg JR-SR HS; Saltsburg, PA; (2); 20/96; FTA; Band; Concert Band; Mrchg Band; Hon Roll; Flm & Tv.

SINCO, STEFAN; Crestwood HS; Mountaintop, PA; (3); 7/190; Pres Sr Cls; Rep Stu Cncl; L Bsbl; Var L Ftbl; High Hon Roll; Jr NHS; NHS; NEDT Awd; Elsa Baker Awd Acadc Excllnce 86; Amer Chem Awd, Membr Of Yth Salute 87; Med.

SINDACO, MARIO; G A R Memorial HS; Wilkes-Barre, PA; (3); French Clb; Chorus; L Var Ftbl; Capt Var Trk; High Hon Roll; Hon Roll; NHS; Church Yth Grp; Ski Clb; Church Choir; Soph Ambssdr Hugh O Brian Yth Ldrshp ST Sem 86; Dist Chorus 85-86; Ftbl All Schltc All Star 86; Surgery.

SINES, KIMBERLY; North Star HS; Gray, PA; (2); 35/139; Pres Church Yth Grp; FCA; Nwsp Stf; JV Var Bsktbl; Yng Amer Crtv Ptrtc Art Awd 86-87; Bus.

SINGAL, RACHNA; Hempfield HS; E Petersburg, PA; (3); 4/425; Exploring; Drill Tm; Mrchg Band; School Play; Nwsp Stf; Yrbk Stf; Rep Jr Cls; High Hon Roll; VP NHS; Ntl Merit Ltr.

SINGER, ANDREW; Marple Newtown HS; Broomall, PA; (3); 13/322; Model UN; SADD; Nwsp Rptr; Nwsp Stf; Bsbl; High Hon Roll; Hon Roll; Ntl Merit SF; St Fnlst Ntl Hstry Day-Hstrcl Rsch Ppr 86; Pol Sci.

SINGER, GREGORY; Radnor HS; Villanova, PA; (4); 5/297; Boy Scts; Pres Debate Tm; Model UN; NFL; Quiz Bowl; Speech Tm; High Hon Roll; NHS; Ntl Merit SF; U Of PA; Comp Sci.

SINGER, STEPHEN; Roman Catholic HS; Philadelphia, PA; (3); 10/123; JA; Spanish Clb; SADD; Rep Frsh Cls; JV Bsbl; JV Ftbl; High Hon Roll; NHS; Spanish NHS; Pharm.

SINGER, TIMOTHY; Father Judge HS For Boys; Philadelphia, PA; (3); 14/403; Debate Tm; Yrbk Stf; Cmmnty Svc Corpse; Phila Archdiocisan Schlr; Economics.

SINGER, VALERIE; Freeport Area HS; Freeport, PA; (2); Stage Crew; Nwsp Rptr; Nwsp Stf; Rep Frsh Cls; Stu Cncl; JV Capt Cheerleading; High Hon Roll; Hon Roll; Bio Chem.

SINGH, VINAY; Dover Area HS; Dover, PA; (3); 27/300; Church Yth Grp; FBLA; German Clb; Nwsp Rptr; Yrbk Rptr; Yrbk Stf; Lit Mag; Stu Cncl; Bsktbl; Tennis; CMU; Finance.

SINGLETARY, NICOLE; Aliquippa HS; Aliquippa, PA; (4); French Clb; Band; Concert Band; Mrchg Band; Pep Band; Cheerleading; Trk; Hon Roll; INDIANA U Of PA.

SINGLETON, KIRSTEN LEIGH; Penn Hills HS; Pittsburgh, PA; (4); 83/700; Church Yth Grp; French Clb; Hosp Aide; Drm Mjr(t); Mrchg Band; Stu Cncl; Co-Capt Swmmng; Hon Roll; Prfct Atten Awd; PA ST U; Lbrl Arts.

SINGLETON, MARYLOU; Butler Area HS; Butler, PA; (3); 76/710; Sec Debate Tm; Exploring; Latin Clb; NFL; Sec Speech Tm; Nwsp Ed-Chief; Nwsp Rptr; Ed Lit Mag; Jr NHS; Ntl Merit Ltr; 2 Vrsty Lttrs Spch & Dbte 85-86; Pittsburgh Diocesan Yth Cncl 86; Grinnell Coll; Psych.

SINGLETON, SHAUNA; Jules E Mastbaum Voc/Tech Area; Philadelphia, PA; (2); Girl Scts; SADD; Variety Show; Bsktbl; Trk; Hon Roll; Prfct Atten Awd; 1st Pl Typng I 87.

SINGLETON, VICKY; West Perry SR HS; Ickesburg, PA; (3); 3/221; Band; Concert Band; High Hon Roll; Hon Roll; NHS; Acad All-Amer Stud 87; HACC; Ins Agent.

SINICKI, KAREN; Seneca Valley HS; Mars, PA; (4); 72/340; Pres Church Yth Grp; Cmnty Wkr; SADD; Mrchg Band; School Musical; Yrbk Stf; High Hon Roll; Kiwanis Awd; Lion Awd; Cranberry Jr Wmns Clb Schlrshp 87; Edinboro U; Soc Wrk.

SINICKI, SANDY; Seneca Valley SR HS; Mars, PA; (2); Sec Church Yth Grp; Cmnty Wkr; Pep Clb; JV Var Crs Cntry; JV Var Trk; Hon Roll; Bus.

SINKO, MIKE; Shamokin Area HS; Paxinos, PA; (2); Art Clb; Boy Scts; Camera Clb; Science Clb; Band; Concert Band; Jazz Band; Mrchg Band; Pep Band; Trk; Art Awd 87; Actvts Awd 85-87; Bio Chem.

SINKOVICH, MIKE; Nativity B V M HS; Minersville, PA; (3); 21/87; Boy Scts; Cmnty Wkr; Im JV Bsktbl; Var L Ftbl; Var Im Trk; Im Wt Lftg; High Hon Roll; Hon Roll; Math.

SINNOTT, TINA M; Bloomsburg HS; Bloomsburg, PA; (2); Church Yth Grp; Hosp Aide; Church Choir; Flag Corp; Variety Show; JV Var Cheerleading; JV Tennis; Hon Roll; Bloomsburg U; Elem Ed.

SINOPOLI, TRACY; Hickory HS; Sharpsville, PA; (2); Hosp Aide; Latin Clb; Cmnty Wkr; FHA; Var Swmmng; Latin Hnr Soc, Stu Rep Chrch Cncl, Treas Hm Ec Clb 86-87; RN.

SINYAK, IGOR; Carver HS Of Engineering & Science; Philadelphia, PA; (3); 4/241; Math Tm; High Hon Roll; NHS; PA JR Acad Sci 1st Awd 85-87; Cmptr Bwl Tm 1st Pl 87; Smithkline Beckman Math Cont 1st Pl 86; Elec Engr.

SION, ANN; Ringgold HS; Monongahela, PA; (3); Varsity Clb; Bsktbl; Socr; Sftbl; Trk; Med.

SIPE, KELLY; Plum HS; Verona, PA; (3); 11/433; Dance Clb; Hosp Aide; Varsity Clb; Chorus; Nwsp Stf; Rep Jr Cls; Var JV Cheerleading; L Trk; High Hon Roll; NHS; Chrldng Co Capt 87; Gymnstcs Cert 85-87; Prom Crt 87; Phys Sci.

SIPE, MAXINE; Shade Central City HS; Central, PA; (3); FBLA; Spanish Clb; Sec Varsity Clb; Variety Show; Var L English Clb; Var L Sftbl; JV Vllybl; Hon Roll; Prfct Atten Awd; SECTY.

SIPES, DEBRA; Central York SR HS; York, PA; (3); Ski Clb; Varsity Clb; Mrchg Band; Symp Band; Yrbk Sprt Ed; Var L Sftbl; Var L Vllybl; High Hon Roll; NHS; Bio.

SIPES, KENNY; Mount Union Area HS; Shirleysburg, PA; (3); VICA; Im Bsktbl; JV Trk; Hon Roll; Electrcn.

SIPLE, DUANE; Punxsutawney Area HS; Punxsutawney, PA; (3); Art Clb; French Clb; Science Clb; Stu Cncl; Hon Roll.

SIPLING, COLIN; Hanover SR HS; Hanover, PA; (3); Boy Scts; Chess Clb; Computer Clb; Exploring; Radio Clb; Bsktbl; Hon Roll; Army.

SIPOWICZ, PHILLIP; Pocono Mountain HS; Stroudsburg, PA; (3); 9/300; Lit Mag; Rep Frsh Cls; Rep Soph Cls; Rep Jr Cls; Var Bsktbl; Var L Ftbl; Var L Trk; Rotary Awd; Acad All Amer 86 & 87.

SIPPEL, BARBARA; Mastbaum Area Vo-Tech; Philadelphia, PA; (2); VICA; Stu Cncl; Sftbl; Vllybl; Ntl Merit Ltr; Prfct Atten Awd; Math Student Of The Month 86; Csmtlgsts.

SIPPOS, AMY; Elizabeth Forward HS; Elizabeth, PA; (3); 25/345; Hosp Aide; Nwsp Rptr; Yrbk Ed-Chief; Hon Roll; NHS; Pres Schlr; Allegheny Intrmdt Unit Rgnl Art Exhbt 87; Carnegie Mellon; Gphc Dsgnr.

SIPPY, KINTA; Saegertown HS; Saegertown, PA; (4); 2/107; Church Yth Grp; VP Key Clb; Ski Clb; Spanish Clb; Hon Roll; Jr NHS; NHS; Sal; Frgn Lng Awd 87; Amer Legion Awd 87; Pres Acadmc Ftns Awd 87; Coll Of Wooster.

SIRNEY, CAROL; Moon HS; Coraopolis, PA; (3); Acpl Chr; Chorus; Church Choir; School Musical; High Hon Roll; Hon Roll; NHS.

SISAK, CASEY; Homer Center JR SR HS; Homer City, PA; (3); French Clb; VP Band; Concert Band; Stu Cncl; Bsktbl; Trk; High Hon Roll; Hon Roll; Pres Jr NHS; NHS.

SISAK, PATRICIA; Blairsville SR HS; Blairsville, PA; (1); School Musical; Sec Frsh Cls; Sec Soph Cls; Rep Stu Cncl; Swmmng; Psycht.

SISCO, MARIA; North Pocono HS; Moscow, PA; (1); 4-H; Teachers Aide; Var Cheerleading; Var Pom Pon; Twrlr; Ms Est Cst Pgnt 2nd Rnnr Up 86; 1st Pl Ms Mjrette Mnth 87; Norice Queen Twrlng 86; Tchr.

SISK, DOREEN; Wyoming Area HS; Pittston, PA; (4); 18/249; French Clb; Key Clb; Math Clb; Math Tm; Ski Clb; Color Guard; Nwsp Stf; Stu Cncl; High Hon Roll; NHS; Awd Prtcptn PA Hnrs Tst 87; Merit Awd 20th Century Govt 87; Penn ST U; Engrng.

SISOCK, STEPHEN; Bishop Hafey HS; Hazleton, PA; (3); Quiz Bowl; Science Clb; JV Bsbl; Hon Roll; Prfct Atten Awd; PA ST Univ; Hist.

SISTO, NIKKI; CAS HS; Fayetteville, PA; (3); Drama Clb; German Clb; Band; Chorus; Capt Flag Corp; School Play; Stage Crew; Off Jr Cls; Trk; Photo.

SITAR, LUCIA; Bishop O Reilly HS; Dallas, PA; (2); Church Yth Grp; Ski Clb; Spanish Clb; Chorus; Hon Roll; Top Ten Prcntl In NEDT Test 85; Child Dvlpmnt.

SITAR, SHAWN; Abington Heights HS; Clarks Green, PA; (4); 27/260; Exploring; Var L Swmmng; Var L Trk; High Hon Roll; Hon Roll; NHS; Pres Schlr; Natl Hnr Soc Schlrshp 87; 1st Pl Jr Acad Sci Brny & 3rd ST 87; Bstr Clb Awd Swmmng & MI Awd 86-87; Rochester Inst Tech; Bio.

SITES, DANA; Carrick HS; Pittsburgh, PA; (2); Hosp Aide; Stage Crew; Hon Roll; Robel Morris Coll; Admin Asst.

SITES, DORRIEANN B; Carrick HS; Pittsburgh, PA; (4); 58/350; Exploring; Office Aide; Q&S; SADD; Stage Crew; Nwsp Ed-Chief; Var Powder Puff Ftbl; Var Sftbl; Hon Roll; Outstndnd Spanish Stu 87; Robert Morris Coll; Mktg.

SITES, DYLAN; Donegal HS; Mount Joy, PA; (2); Civic Clb; Band; Concert Band; Jazz Band; Mrchg Band; Ftbl; Wt Lftg; Hon Roll.

SITKOWSKI, MONICA; Wyoming Area HS; West Pittston, PA; (3); 10/250; Church Yth Grp; Spanish Clb; SADD; Yrbk Stf; Score Keeper; Mgr Trk; High Hon Roll; Hon Roll; NHS; Marn Bio.

SITLER, PAUL; Christian School Of York; Wrightsville, PA; (2); Church Yth Grp; Band; Bsktbl.

SITLINGER, MARK; Upper Dauphin Area HS; Lykens, PA; (3); 9/125; Letterman Clb; Varsity Clb; VP Soph Cls; Rep Stu Cncl; Var L Bsbl; Var L Bsktbl; Var L Ftbl; Hon Roll; NHS; Rotary Awd; AHSME Math Cntst 85-86; Accntng.

SIUNIAK, STEPHANIE; Blacklick Valley JR & SR HS; Nanty Glo, PA; (4); 21/94; Camera Clb; Library Aide; Ski Clb; Cheerleading; Sftbl; Hon Roll; Penn ST U; Elem Ed.

SIVIK, MICHELLE; Meadville Area SR HS; Meadville, PA; (2); Church Yth Grp; Latin Clb; Stat Bsktbl; JV Vllybl; Hon Roll.

SIWICKI, RENEE; Shaler Area SR HS; Pittsburgh, PA; (3); 55/500; Ski Clb; SADD; Rep Frsh Cls; Rep Stu Cncl; Im Sftbl; JV Vllybl; High Hon Roll; Hon Roll; Hnr Rl Stu 84-87; Clemson; Elec Engrng.

SIWINSKI, DENISE; Archbishop Ryan High Schl For Girls; Philadelphia, PA; (4); 1/490; Am Leg Aux Girls St; Church Yth Grp; Office Aide; Q&S; VP Science Clb; Spanish Clb; Nwsp Stf; Capt Crs Cntry; Capt Trk; NHS; Cmmltv Rnk Of 1/Hghst Gen Avg Awds 84-87; Scty Of Wmn Engnrns Awd 86; Ldrshp Smnrs 85-86; Bio.

SIWULA, MICHAEL; Connellsville Area HS; Connellsville, PA; (3); Concert Band; Mrchg Band; Symp Band; Bsbl; Ftbl; Sftbl; Duquesne U; Phrmcy.

SKALA, BETH; Conemaugh Twp HS; Johnstown, PA; (4); 4/101; Drama Clb; Band; Color Guard; School Musical; School Play; Nwsp Stf; Stu Cncl; Dnfth Awd; Hon Roll; NHS; Seton Hill Coll; Soc Wrk.

SKALAMERA, TINA; St Maria Goretti HS; Philadelphia, PA; (4); 31/390; Church Yth Grp; GAA; Math Clb; Spanish Clb; Teachers Aide; High Hon Roll; Hon Roll; Jr NHS; NHS; Pres Awd Acad Achvt 87; St Josephs U; Food Mktg.

SKANDERSON, HELEN ANN; Springdale HS; Springdale, PA; (3); Art Clb; GAA; Spanish Clb; Band; Concert Band; Drm Mjr(t); Mrchg Band; Var Capt Bsktbl; JV Cheerleading; Stat Ftbl; Bus.

SKANE, DEBBIE; East SR HS; West Chester, PA; (4); 99/422; SADD; Chorus; School Musical; Nwsp Stf; Yrbk Stf; Rep Stu Cncl; JV Cheerleading; Sftbl; Tennis; High Hon Roll; Amer Music Abroad Tour Eurpoe 1st Soprano 85-86; Elem Ed.

SKARIOT, SUSAN; Trinity HS; Washington, PA; (4); Art Clb; Church Yth Grp; Exploring; French Clb; Hosp Aide; Key Clb; Office Aide; Pep Clb; Ski Clb; Hon Roll; Nrsg.

SKAROSI III, STEPHEN; Kennedy Christian HS; Burghill, OH; (2); 26/96; French Clb; Ski Clb; Bsbl; Ftbl; Vllybl; Hon Roll; Penn ST; CPA.

SKARUPSKI, MICHELE; Strong Vincent HS; Erie, PA; (3); #1 In Class; Church Yth Grp; Debate Tm; French Clb; Trs Model UN; Quiz Bowl; Yrbk Ed-Chief; Trs Stu Cncl; NHS; Ntl Merit Ltr; Zonta II Intl Amelia Earhart Awd; Med.

SKAVINSKY, MARINA; Minersville Area HS; Minersville, PA; (3); 3/108; German Clb; Lib Band; Concert Band; Mrchg Band; Orch; Pep Band; School Musical; High Hon Roll; NHS; Acdmc Achvmnt Cert Schl Dist Awd 85-86; Elem Tchr.

SKEEBA, SANDRA; Hazelton SR HS; Hazleton, PA; (3); Drama Clb; Color Guard; Mrchg Band; Stage Crew; Hon Roll; Hazleton St Jos Med Ctr; X-Ray.

SKEHAN, SHELLI; Central Christian HS; Dubois, PA; (2); Computer Clb; French Clb; Hosp Aide; Ski Clb; Chorus; School Musical; Trs Jr Cls; JV Var Cheerleading; High Hon Roll; Hon Roll; Law.

SKELLEY, DAVID; Bishop Guilfoyle HS; Altoona, PA; (3); Chorus; Bsktbl; Ftbl; Hon Roll; Physcl Thrpy.

SKELLEY II, PATRICK J; Westmont Hilltop HS; Johnstown, PA; (3); Boy Scts; Scholastic Bowl; Jazz Band; Mrchg Band; Trs Jr Cls; Var L Trk; Trs NHS; French Clb; Quiz Bowl; Science Clb; 3 Gld & 2 Brnz Mdls ST Sci Olympd 85-87; Spcl Regntn Rgnl Envrlympcs Compttn 86; Hghst Acdmc Hnr Rl; WA; Pre Med.

SKELTON, MICHELLE; Waynesburg Central HS; Waynesburg, PA; (4); AFS; Church Yth Grp; French Clb; Natl Beta Clb; Pep Clb; Ski Clb; Sec Jr Cls; Stat Bsktbl; Im Wt Lftg; Hon Roll; Fash Merch.

SKERLONG, JODI; Shaler Area SR HS; Glenshaw, PA; (3); 78/486; Church Yth Grp; Pep Clb; SADD; Drill Tm; High Hon Roll; Hon Roll; NEDT Awd; Lawyer.

SKEVA, JENNIFER; Oliver HS; Pittsburgh, PA; (3); Church Yth Grp; Cit Awd; Hon Roll; Prfct Atten Awd.

SKIBA, APRIL; Susquehanna Community HS; Susquehanna, PA; (2); SADD; Chorus; Capt Color Guard; Var Cheerleading; Var Crs Cntry; Var Trk; Hon Roll; Law.

SKIBINSKI, GREG; Wyoming Area HS; West Wyoming, PA; (4); 26/249; Church Yth Grp; Computer Clb; Dance Clb; Math Clb; Rep Stu Cncl; JV Bsktbl; Var Trk; High Hon Roll; Hon Roll; Lion Awd; Penn ST; Elctrl Eng.

SKIBINSKI, GREG; Wyoming Area SR HS; W Wyoming, PA; (4); 28/249; Chess Clb; Church Yth Grp; Computer Clb; Rep Stu Cncl; JV Bsktbl; Var Trk; Im Wt Lftg; Lion Awd; Grad-Magna Cum Laude; Penn ST; Mech Engr.

SKIBO, CHARLES; United HS; Robinson, PA; (4); Pres Art Clb; Band; Concert Band; Jazz Band; Mrchg Band; Pep Band; VP Stu Cncl; JV Bsktbl; Var L Trk; Music.

SKIENDZIELEWSKI, JENNIFER; Danville Area HS; Danville, PA; (2); 1/165; Girl Scts; Hosp Aide; NFL; Speech Tm; Color Guard; Jazz Band; Rep Frsh Cls; JV Sftbl; High Hon Roll; NEDT Awd.

SKIES, SHARON; Bishop O Hara HS; Blakely, PA; (2); 4/127; French Clb; Latin Clb; JV Cheerleading; Im Sftbl; Hugh O Brien Yth Fndtn 87; MA Coll; Phrmcst.

SKINDELL, GARRETT; Cathedral Prep; Erie, PA; (3); Nwsp Bus Mgr; Pres Jr Cls; Pres Sr Cls; Im Bsktbl; Var L Ftbl; Im Vllybl; Managing Edtrs Awd 86-87; 1st Hnr Tstmnl 85-86; 2nd Hnr Tstmnl 84-85; Temple U; Cmnctns.

SKINNER, AMY; Montrose Area HS; Montrose, PA; (3); Trs 4-H; French Clb; SADD; Band; Jazz Band; Mrchg Band; Nwsp Stf; JV Fld Hcky; Bus.

SKINNER, NANCI; Philadelphia HS For Girls; Philadelphia, PA; (2); Church Yth Grp; Girl Scts; Office Aide; Church Choir; Off Jr Cls; High Hon Roll; Prfct Atten Awd; Philadelphia Regnl Spelling Bee Fnlst 85; Temple U; Med.

SKINNER, TAMMY; Southern Huntingdon County HS; Three Spgs, PA; (2); Church Yth Grp; French Clb; SADD; Chorus; Mgr(s); Score Keeper; Stat Sftbl; Natl Ldrshp & Svc Awd 85; Intl Frgn & Lang Awds 85 & 87.

SKIRPAN, TONYA; Cannon-Mc Millan HS; Eighty Four, PA; (3); Church Yth Grp; Office Aide; Varsity Clb; Band; Sec Chorus; Swmmng; Tennis; Hon Roll; NHS; Acad All-Amer Large Div 87; Accntng.

SKLADZIEN, VANESSA; Nazareth Acad; Phila, PA; (3); Church Yth Grp; Intnl Clb; Service Clb; Chorus; Church Choir; School Musical; Hon Roll; Holy Family Coll; Elem Educ.

SKOCIK, DONNA; Belle Vernon Area HS; Belle Vernon, PA; (3); FBLA; Band; High Hon Roll; NHS; Outstndg Hlth Awd 85.

SKOLETSKY, MELISSA; Council Rock HS; Holland, PA; (3); 109/908; Varsity Clb; Off Stu Cncl; Var Fld Hcky; Mgr(s); Powder Puff Ftbl; Score Keeper; Hon Roll; NHS; Intl Bus.

SKONICKI, BRIDGET; West Allegheny SR HS; Imperial, PA; (2); 10/235; Pres Chorus; Madrigals; Nwsp Phtg; Yrbk Phtg; Lit Mag; Rep Stu Cncl; Var Swmmng; High Hon Roll; Jr NHS; PA ST U; Pre Med.

SKOROPOWSKI, JULIE; Upper Dublin SR HS; Maple Glen, PA; (3); SADD; Varsity Clb; Sec Jr Cls; Sec Sr Cls; JV Var Bsktbl; Var Sftbl; Hon Roll; People-To-People Stu Ambass Trvl USSR Finland Sweden Denmrck Germny Nthrlnds & Germny 87; Archit.

SKORUPSKI, VICKY; Downingtown SR HS; Downington, PA; (3); 216/648; GAA; SADD; Acpl Chr; Chorus; Stage Crew; Var JV Cheerleading; High Hon Roll; Hon Roll; Vrsty Ltr Chrldng 88-87; Bio Sci.

SKOURONSKY, KAREN; Tunkhannock Area HS; Tunkhannock, PA; (3); Letterman Clb; Sec Frsh Cls; Sec Soph Cls; Sec Jr Cls; Rep Stu Cncl; Capt L Cheerleading; Var L Fld Hcky; Var L Trk; Hon Roll; NHS; Bus Advtsng.

SKRIBA, JENNIFER; Plum SR HS; Pittsburgh, PA; (3); 78/410; AFS; French Clb; Library Aide; Band; Co-Capt Drill Tm; Mrchg Band; U Of Pittsburgh; Psychgly.

SKRZAT, HEIDI; Allentown Central Catholic HS; East Greenville, PA; (3); 80/235; Am Leg Aux Girls St; Art Clb; Camera Clb; Debate Tm; Drama Clb; JA; SADD; Off Chorus; Jazz Band; Swing Chorus; Mock Trial Team; Jr Acad Sci; Art Ther.

SKRZYPEK, WALTER; Central Christian HS; Dubois, PA; (2); Computer Clb; Science Clb; Ski Clb; Band; Crs Cntry.

SKURSKY, ROBERT; Bishop O Reilly HS; Wyoming, PA; (3); Boy Scts; Latin Clb; Ski Clb; Jazz Band; VP Soph Cls; Var L Ftbl; Pharmacy.

SKUTLIN, WENDY; Elizabethtown Area HS; Elizabethtown, PA; (3); 16/260; Church Yth Grp; Band; Chorus; Concert Band; Jazz Band; Mrchg Band; Hon Roll; NHS; Rotary Awd; Intl Stds.

SKWERES, JEFF; West Mifflin Area HS; West Mifflin, PA; (4); 40/358; Exploring; Var Bsbl; Var L Ftbl; Hon Roll; Jr NHS; NHS; Pittsburgh U; Elec Engrng.

SLABY, STACY; Shamokin Area HS; Shamokin, PA; (4); 20/235; Drama Clb; German Clb; Key Clb; Pep Clb; Science Clb; Ski Clb; Yrbk Stf; Trs Jr Cls; Cheerleading; Pom Pon; PA ST U; Pre-Law.

SLACK, EDWARD D; Penn-Trafford HS; Trafford, PA; (3); Chess Clb; Church Yth Grp; Spanish Clb; Var Bsktbl; Var Socr; Var L Tennis; High Hon Roll; NHS.

SLACK, GREG; Henderson HS; West Chester, PA; (2); 91/334; Letterman Clb; Ski Clb; SADD; Varsity Clb; Coach Actv; Lcrss; Socr; Hon Roll; U DE; Finance.

SLACK, JEFF; Henderson HS; West Chester, PA; (2); 88/334; Letterman Clb; Ski Clb; SADD; Varsity Clb; Coach Actv; Lcrss; Socr; Hon Roll; Penn ST U; Sports Med.

SLACKTISH, JENNIFER; Lakeland JR SR HS; Jermyn, PA; (2); 4-H; FHA; Var Cheerleading; Var L Trk; 4-H Awd; Band; Mrchg Band; School Play; Var Crs Cntry; Hon Roll; 1st Pl FHA/HERO ST Ldrshp Conf 87; Engrng.

SLADE, ROBERT; Upper Dublin HS; Dresher, PA; (3); Church Yth Grp; SADD; VP Varsity Clb; Rep Frsh Cls; Rep Soph Cls; Rep Jr Cls; Trs Stu Cncl; JV Bsbl; JV Bsktbl; Var Capt Socr; Rtry Ldrshp Awd 87; Envrnmntl Engrng.

SLADE, WILLIE; Steelton-Highspire HS; Steelton, PA; (3); 28/102; Model UN; Quiz Bowl; Yrbk Stf; Rep Stu Cncl; Var Bsbl; Im Bsktbl; Var Ftbl; Wt Lftg; High Hon Roll; Hon Roll.

SLADEK, MICHAEL; Red Lion Area SR HS; Felton, PA; (2); 18/344; Latin Clb; Stage Crew; High Hon Roll; Hon Roll; Cum L Aude Awd For Tkng Ntl Latin Exam 86; Towson ST U; Social Studies.

SLAFKA, JOEL; Elizabeth Forward HS; Elizabeth, PA; (3); Art Clb; Crs Cntry; Trk; Wt Lftg; JV Wrstlng; Hon Roll; CA ST U.

SLAGLE, BARBARA; Ford City HS; Ford Cliff, PA; (3); 20/160; Sec Church Yth Grp; Computer Clb; GAA; Spanish Clb; Chorus; Church Choir; Rep Jr Cls; Rep Stu Cncl; Var L Tennis; NHS; U Of Pgh; Psych.

SLAGLE, ELIZABETH; Lower Dauphin HS; Hummelstown, PA; (3); Library Aide; Ski Clb; Color Guard; Mrchg Band; Orch; Stat Bsktbl; Stat Trk; Hon Roll; Prfct Atten Awd.

SLAGLE, SUSAN; Blair County Christian Schl; Altoona, PA; (1); 2/25; Church Yth Grp; Chorus; Var Bsktbl; Capt JV Cheerleading; Var Sftbl; High Hon Roll; Cedarville; Ed.

SLANE, WENDY; Blue Mountain HS; Pottsville, PA; (4); Yrbk Stf; Off Stu Cncl; Var L Cheerleading; Var L Diving; High Hon Roll; Hon Roll; Ltn Hnr Soc 85-87; Penn ST U; Comp Sci.

SLANEY, ERIN; Montour HS; Pittsburgh, PA; (3); Cmnty Wkr; Y-Teens; Powder Puff Ftbl; L Swmmng; High Hon Roll; Hon Roll; St Schlr; GATE Schlr Pgm 83-88; Arntcl Sci.

SLAPPO, JERRY; Ambridge HS; Sewickley, PA; (3); Hon Roll; Outstndg Achvmnt Scl Stds 85; Acdmc Achvmnt B Avg 84; Penn ST; Scl Stds.

SLAPPY, ROLAND; The Christian Acad; Brookhaven, PA; (3); Art Clb; Chess Clb; Church Yth Grp; Pep Clb; Church Choir; School Play; Stage Crew; Hon Roll; U Of PA; Biochem.

SLATER, CRAIG; Lakeview HS; Stoneboro, PA; (4); 36/126; Boy Scts; Pres Church Yth Grp; Pres Computer Clb; DECA; FBLA; Pres Intnl Clb; Library Aide; Pres Ski Clb; SADD; VP VICA; Associated Schls; Travel Agt.

SLATER, DAVID; Taylor Allderdice HS; Pittsburgh, PA; (3); Church Yth Grp; Ski Clb; Nwsp Stf; Socr; High Hon Roll; Hon Roll; NHS; Summer Trip Israel Scholar 87; Wstrn PA ST Yth Soccr Assn Coaching License 85; U PA; Bus.

SLATER, JENNIFER; Saint Huberts HS For Girls; Philadelphia, PA; (3); Boys Clb Am; Church Yth Grp; GAA; Varsity Clb; Rep Frsh Cls; Im Bsktbl; Var Sftbl; Hon Roll; Prfct Atten Awd; Letterman Clb; Am Leg Awd 84-85; PA ST; Radlgy.

SLATER, WENDEY; Danville SR HS; Danville, PA; (3); Art Clb; Exploring; Latin Clb; Ski Clb; Spanish Clb; Yrbk Stf; Rep Stu Cncl; Powder Puff Ftbl; Hon Roll.

SLATON, ERIC; Methacton SR HS; Worcester, PA; (3); 48/381; Ski Clb; Off Jr Cls; Stu Cncl; Ftbl; Trk; High Hon Roll; Distngsh Hnrs 86-87; Meritorious Hnrs 85-86; Bio.

SLATTERY, HEATHER; Penn Hills SR HS; Pittsburgh, PA; (3); Spanish Clb; Stat Bsktbl; High Hon Roll; Hon Roll; U Of Pittsburgh; Med.

SLAUGENHAUPT, JANET; Big Spring HS; Newville, PA; (2); Church Yth Grp; Pep Clb; Color Guard; Concert Band; Mrchg Band; Var Mgr Sftbl; Var Swmmng; Hon Roll; NHS; Jeff Finkenbinder Awd 87; Psych.

SLAVIC, FRANCES; Uniontown HS; New Salem, PA; (3); French Clb; JA; VP Soph Cls; Sec Jr Cls; High Hon Roll; Hon Roll; Banking.

SLAVICK, TAMMIE; Conervaugh Valley HS; Johnstown, PA; (4); 10/118; French Clb; Pep Clb; Varsity Clb; L Capt Bsktbl; Stat Ftbl; Capt L Sftbl; L Vllybl; High Hon Roll; Lou Salem Schlrshp Awd 87; Army Schlr/Athlt Awd 87; U Of Pittsburg Johnstwn; Acctng.

SLAVIK, FRANCINE; Bellwood-Antis HS; Bellwood, PA; (1); Chorus; School Musical; Nwsp Stf; High Hon Roll; Hon Roll.

SLAVIK, ROBERT; Bellwood-Antis HS; Bellwood, PA; (3); 3/115; High Hon Roll; Hon Roll.

SLAVIK, STEPHANIE; Bishop Carroll HS; Barnesboro, PA; (3); #20 In Class; Cmnty Wkr; NFL; Band; Chorus; Concert Band; Score Keeper; Vllybl; Hon Roll; St Frances; Bus Mgt.

SLAVIN, JAMES; West Catholic HS; Philadelphia, PA; (3); Cmnty Wkr; Red Cross Aide; Yrbk Phtg; Off Frsh Cls; Off Soph Cls; Off Jr Cls; Off Sr Cls; Stu Cncl; Cit Awd; Hon Roll; Air Frc Acad; Photo.

SLAVIN, MICHELLE; Nazareth Acad; Phila, PA; (3); Intnl Clb; NFL; Spanish Clb; Chorus; School Musical; Im Bsktbl; Pre-Law.

SLAVISH, CHARLA; G A R Memorial HS; Wilkes-Barre, PA; (4); 13/172; Library Aide; SADD; Chorus; Yrbk Stf; Capt Cheerleading; Hon Roll; Jr NHS; NHS.

SLAVITSKO, DAVID; E L Meyers HS; Wilkes-Barre, PA; (4); 16/161; Letterman Clb; Red Cross Aide; SADD; Varsity Clb; Chorus; School Musical; Yrbk Stf; Var Capt Ftbl; Im Vllybl; Wt Lftg; PA ST U; Engrng.

SLAYMAKER, MICHAEL; Lampeter Strasburg HS; Strasburg, PA; (4); 1/143; Pres Thesps; Band; School Musical; Pres Sr Cls; VP Stu Cncl; Capt Ftbl; DAR Awd; High Hon Roll; NHS; Val; Ntl Hnr Soc Schlrshp 87; Penn St; Elec Engr.

SLAZINSKI, KELLY; Mercer Area HS; Mercer, PA; (3); Trs Band; Trs Concert Band; Trs Mrchg Band; School Musical; Swing Chorus; Hon Roll; Westminster Coll Honrs Band 87; Occuptnl Therapy.

SLEBODA, AMY; Hamburg Area JR/Sr HS; Hamburg, PA; (3); French Clb; FBLA; Library Aide; SADD; Band; Chorus; Concert Band; Mrchg Band; School Musical; Hon Roll; Alg II Acadc Awd 85-86; Northampton CC; Dntl Hygne.

SLEEGER, DANIKA; Northeastern HS; York, PA; (3); 13/158; Camera Clb; Church Yth Grp; Acpl Chr; Chorus; Church Choir; Rep Sr Cls; Mgr(s); Stat Socr; Hon Roll; NHS; Arch.

SLENCAK II, ROBERT J; Cambridge Springs HS; Edinboro, PA; (3); Aud/Vis; Spanish Clb; Stage Crew; Pres Jr Cls; JV Bsktbl; God Cntry Awd; Hon Roll; Gannon U; Med.

SLENKER, SHAWN; Central HS; York, PA; (3); Varsity Clb; L Bsbl; JV Bsktbl; High Hon Roll; NHS; Chem Engrng.

SLEUTARIS, RICK; Upper Moreland HS; Hatboro, PA; (3); 18/276; Church Yth Grp; Intnl Clb; Key Clb; SADD; School Musical; School Play; Var Swmmng; High Hon Roll; NHS; Hghst Score In Annual Amer HS Math Exam 87; U Of PA.

SLEZAK, BRIAN; Hickory HS; Hermitage, PA; (3); 19/181; Boy Scts; Drama Clb; German Clb; Varsity Clb; Chorus; Stage Crew; Bsktbl; Crs Cntry; VP NHS; Physics.

SLICHTER, CHANDA; Hamburg Area HS; Shoemakersville, PA; (4); 7/150; Trs Sec Ski Clb; Spanish Clb; SADD; School Musical; Trs Soph Cls; Rep Stu Cncl; Capt Var Cheerleading; High Hon Roll; NHS; JV Var Sftbl; Hambrg Rtry Schlrshp 87; Acdmc Awd Psych & Geom 86; PA ST U; Psych.

SLICK, CHERYL; Susquehanna Community HS; Union Dale, PA; (3); Church Yth Grp; Cmnty Wkr; Girl Scts; SADD; Chorus; Powder Puff Ftbl; Hon Roll; Chldhd Educ.

SLICK, KRISTINA L; J P Mc Caskey HS; Lancaster, PA; (3); 11/517; Am Leg Aux Girls St; Radio Clb; Nwsp Ed-Chief; Rep Stu Cncl; Var Fld Hcky; Var Trk; High Hon Roll; NHS; Spanish NHS; AFS; Stu Rep To Schl Bd 87-88; Cmnctns.

SLICK, STEPHANIE; Butler Area SR HS; Butler, PA; (3); Band; Stage Crew; Hon Roll; Piano Guild Cert 83-86; Vet Med.

SLIFKO, BARBARA; Moshannon Valley JR SR HS; Morann, PA; (3); Varsity Clb; Band; Color Guard; Mrchg Band; Nwsp Stf; JV Var Cheerleading; Hon Roll.

SLIKE, JILL; Bradford Central Christian HS; Bradford, PA; (2); Computer Clb; Pep Clb; Pres Soph Cls; JV Bsktbl; High Hon Roll; NHS; Med.

SLIMICK, JILL RENAE; Highlands SR HS; Tarentum, PA; (4); Exploring; Hosp Aide; VP JA; Office Aide; SADD; Stu Cncl; NHS; Natl Sci Merit Awd Wnnr 84 & 87; Natl Ldrshp & Svc Awd Wnnr 85; Acadc All Am 87; U Of Pittsburgh; Phrmcy.

SLIPKO, KRISTINA; Hopewell HS; Aliquippa, PA; (4); 47/245; Church Yth Grp; Dance Clb; GAA; JA; Spanish Clb; Drill Tm; School Musical; Yrbk Ed-Chief; Trk; Pres Schlr; U Of Pgh; Aeronaut Engrng.

SLIWINSKI, JANICE; Montour HS; Mckees Rocks, PA; (4); 17/300; Church Yth Grp; Band; Church Choir; Mrchg Band; JV Mgr(s); Trk; High Hon Roll; Jr NHS; NHS; Gannon U; Nrsng.

SLOAD, STEVE; Donegal HS; Marietta, PA; (2); Church Yth Grp; German Clb; JV Bsktbl; Hon Roll; Millersville; Pilot.

SLOAN, GARY; Central Cambria HS; Ebensburg, PA; (3); 8/211; VP Computer Clb; JA; Var L Crs Cntry; Var L Trk; Hon Roll; Ntl Math Awd 85-87; Accntng.

SLOAN, HOWARD; Union Area HS; Edinburg, PA; (4); 3/66; Dance Clb; Varsity Clb; Chorus; Madrigals; School Musical; Nwsp Rptr; Stat Bsktbl; Mgr(s); Hon Roll; NHS; Slippery Rock U; Sec Ed.

SLOAN, MELISSA; Moniteau HS; Eau Claire, PA; (4); Drama Clb; Exploring; Radio Clb; Spanish Clb; Nwsp Rptr; Yrbk Stf; Lit Mag; Stat Trk; Hon Roll; NHS; Butler Co CC Acad Achvmnt Schlrshp 87; Butler Co CC; Arch Dftng.

SLOAN, SCOTT; Bethlehem Center HS; Fredericktown, PA; (3); Boy Scts; Ski Clb; Varsity Clb; Bsbl; Socr; JV Trk; Var Wrstlng; Hon Roll; Amer Legion Aux Mdl Awd 84-85; Penn ST U; Elec Engr.

SLOAN, TIMOTHY H; Grove City SR HS; Grove City, PA; (4); 3/199; Pres Church Yth Grp; VP French Clb; Key Clb; Band; Chorus; Jazz Band; Swing Chorus; Var Trk; High Hon Roll; NHS; Grove City Coll; Math.

SLOAN, WILLIAM L; Waynesburg-Central HS; Waynesburg, PA; (3); Ski Clb; Spanish Clb; Socr; Wrstlng; Hon Roll; NEDT Awd; Bus.

SLOANE, KELLY; Harrisburg HS; Harrisburg, PA; (3); 59/360; Aud/Vis; Cmnty Wkr; School Play; Trs Stu Cncl; JV Var Cheerleading; Trk; Hon Roll; Hnrbl Mntn Wrtng Comp 87; Achvmnt Awd Arts Magnet Sch 87; Hnrs PA St YMCA; Syracuse; Cmnctns.

SLOANE, TAWNEY; Norwin HS; Mc Keesport, PA; (4); Church Yth Grp; Office Aide; Band; Chorus; Concert Band; Jazz Band; Mrchg Band; Hnrs Choir, Cnty Choir 86; Duquesne; Music Thrpy.

SLOCUM, SUSIE; Lake-Lehman HS; Dallas, PA; (4); Letterman Clb; PAVAS; SADD; Band; Bsktbl; Fld Hcky; Sftbl; High Hon Roll; NHS; Color Guard; MVP All Stars Game 86-87; All-Star Tms Cnfrence Field Hockey & Sftbll 85-87; Bloomsburg; Educ.

SLOGOFF, FREDERICK; Lower Merion HS; Bala Cynwyd, PA; (3); JCL; Nwsp Rptr; Yrbk Rptr; Rep Jr Cls; Rep Stu Cncl; Var Bsbl; JV Socr; Hon Roll; NHS; Ntl Merit Ltr.

SLOMSKI, PATRICIA; St Basil Acad; Philadelphia, PA; (3); Drama Clb; French Clb; Science Clb; Spanish Clb; SADD; Yrbk Stf; Rep Frsh Cls; Im Sftbl; Im Vllybl; Ntl Merit Ltr.

SLONAKER, JEAN ELIZABETH; Phila HS Gor Girls; Philadelphia, PA; (2); Church Yth Grp; Library Aide; Office Aide; Teachers Aide; Varsity Clb; Stage Crew; Off Frsh Cls; Fld Hcky; Var JV Sftbl; Cit Awd; Sftbll JV Lttr 87; Photo.

SLOPE, BRIAN D; Berlin Brothers Valley HS; Berlin, PA; (4); 1/83; Var Bsbl; JV Var Bsktbl; Lion Awd; NHS; Ntl Merit Ltr; Val; Spanish Clb; Speech Tm; Varsity Clb; Band; HOBY Ldrshp Ambassador; Highest Schltc Soph Awd; Phy Awd; PA ST U; Aero Engrng.

SLOUSKEY, JENNIFER; William Tennent HS; Southampton, PA; (3); 61/566; Key Clb; SADD; Yrbk Stf; Var Bsktbl; Mgr(s); Hon Roll; Bus Admin.

SLOVICK, JANE; South Fayette JR SR HS; Bridgeville, PA; (4); 3/71; Quiz Bowl; Ski Clb; Chorus; Pres Frsh Cls; Sec Soph Cls; VP Jr Cls; Capt Cheerleading; High Hon Roll; Hon Roll; NHS; PA ST Univ; Elec Engrng.

SLOWICK, KIMBERLY; HS Of Engineering & Science; Philadelphia, PA; (3); 44/250; GAA; Var Bsktbl; Var Sftbl; Early Entry Prog Temple U 87-88; Engr.

SLOZAT, DAVE; Linesville HS; Espyville, PA; (2); Exploring; Pep Clb; Ski Clb; Var JV Bsktbl; Var L Crs Cntry; High Hon Roll; Sprts.

SLUDER JR, ROBERT; Freedom Area SR HS; New Brighton, PA; (2); German Clb; Math Clb; Trk; High Hon Roll; Jr NHS; Germn I 86; Germn II, Bio I, 1st Yr Trck Ltrd 87; Natl Sci Olympd Bio 87.

SLUPE, AMY; Spring Grove Area SR HS; York, PA; (3); 27/301; JA; SADD; Color Guard; Mrchg Band; High Hon Roll; Hon Roll; Sec NHS; Pres Acdmc Fitness Awd 85; Schlstc Achvt Awd 87; Psych.

SLUPE, KELLY; Butler SR HS; Lyndora, PA; (3); French Clb; SADD; Chorus; Hon Roll.

SLUSARICK, AMY; Brownsville Area HS; Brownsville, PA; (3); Dance Clb; Drama Clb; FBLA; Office Aide; Ski Clb; SADD; Band; Concert Band; Flag Corp; Mrchg Band.

SLUSSER, CHRIS; West Hazleton HS; W Hazleton, PA; (2); Cmnty Wkr; Political Wkr; Golf; Hon Roll; Schltc Art Awd 84; Engrng.

SLUSSER, CYNTHIA; Tunkhannock Area HS; Tunkhannock, PA; (3); 23/330; Art Clb; Trs Church Yth Grp; Key Clb; Cit Awd; Hon Roll; NHS; Schltc Arts Awd-2 Gld Keys 86; SM Rossetti Mem Art Cntst-1st 2nd Hrbl Mntn 86; Grphc Arts.

SLUZELE, JENNIFER; Pittston Area HS; Inkerman, PA; (3); 1/305; Art Clb; French Clb; FNA; Key Clb; Rep SADD; Hon Roll; ; Law.

SLYE, TAMMY; Corry Area HS; Corry, PA; (3); French Clb; Girl Scts; Chorus; School Musical; Yrbk Phtg; Yrbk Rptr; Yrbk Stf; Rep Jr Cls; Cheerleading; JV Var Vllybl; Marn Bio.

SLYHOFF, KIM; Council Rock HS; Churchville, PA; (4); Capt Swmmng; Prfct Atten Awd; Ruth Keith Schlrshp 87; Capt Grls Vsty Swim Tm 87; Widener U; Htl-Rstrnt Mgmt.

SMAGIEL, JENNIFER; Lebanon Catholic HS; Cleona, PA; (3); Cmnty Wkr; German Clb; Key Clb; Office Aide; SADD; Chorus; Church Choir; School Play; Nwsp Rptr; Yrbk Rptr; Psych Excel 87; Chestnut Hill Coll; Intl Pol.

SMAGLINSKI, DENISE; Oley Valley HS; Oley, PA; (3); 24/142; Camp Fr Inc; Pep Clb; School Play; Nwsp Rptr; Var Cheerleading; Hon Roll; Smmr Intl Stds Pgm 87; Mdrn Langs.

SMAKULA, PHILIP; Conemaugh Township Area HS; Holsopple, PA; (4); Spanish Clb; Varsity Clb; VP Capt Bsbl; Var L Ftbl; Hon Roll; Rotary Awd; Clarion U; Bus.

SMALARA, STACEY; Springdale HS; Cheswick, PA; (3); 7/130; Church Yth Grp; Rep FHA; GAA; Hosp Aide; JA; Key Clb; Spanish Clb; SADD; Nwsp Stf; Yrbk Stf; Cert Apprctn For Lyl Volunteer Svcs 86; Outstndng Prfrmnc & Clssrm Awds Chem,Geomtry 85-86; U Of Pittsburgh; Bio.

SMALL, DANICA L; Pocono Mountain HS; Mountainhome, PA; (3); Art Clb; DECA; Chorus; Prfct Atten Awd; ST & Dist Compttn 86-87; Allentown Bus Schl; Mrktng.

SMALL, GRAHAM; Trinity SR HS; Washington, PA; (2); German Clb; Chorus; Bus Mgmt.

SMALL, KIMSU; Perkiomen Prep Schl; E Greenville, PA; (3); 2/55; Thesps; Varsity Clb; Chorus; Yrbk Phtg; VP Soph Cls; VP Jr Cls; Fld Hcky; Lcrss; Bausch & Lomb Sci Awd; High Hon Roll; Rensselaer Polytech Inst Mdl 87; Dr Gunard O Carlson Awd 87; Gold Acdmc Key; Sci.

SMALL, MICHAEL T; Cashs HS; Chambersburg, PA; (3); 72/697; Church Yth Grp; Computer Clb; Bsktbl; Hon Roll; NHS; Liberty; Acctng.

SMALLER, MONIQUE; Bodine HS For Intl Affairs; Philadelphia, PA; (4); Church Yth Grp; Sec Church Choir; Yrbk Stf; Lit Mag; Capt Bowling; Score Keeper; Hon Roll; NHS; Nwsp Stf; Hnr Semnr Terrorism 86; Hnr Rll 4 Semstrs Strght 86-87; PA ST U; Lib Arts.

SMALLEY, MICHELE; Quakertown HS; Quakertown, PA; (3); Church Yth Grp; SADD; Teachers Aide; Sftbl; NHS; Ski Clb; Off Frsh Cls; Vllybl; Wt Lftg; Hon Roll; Hnrbl Mntn Sftbl 86; 2nd Pl VFW Voice Of Demrcy Cntst 87; Pres Acadmc Ftns Awd 85; Math.

SMALLWOOD, SOLITA; William Penn SR HS; York, PA; (4); 22/373; FBLA; Hosp Aide; JA; Pep Clb; Science Clb; VP Jr Cls; VP Stu Cncl; Var L Cheerleading; Hon Roll; NHS.

SMAR, MICHELLE; Old Forge HS; Old Forge, PA; (3); Ski Clb; VP Sftbl; High Hon Roll; NHS; Intl Forgn Lang Awds 87; Pharm.

SMARGIASSI JR, WILLIAM J; Valley View JR SR HS; Peckville, PA; (3); 38/193; Capt Scholastic Bowl; Boy Scts; Ski Clb; Spanish Clb; Yrbk Stf; JV Var Wrstlng; Hon Roll; JETS Awd; Ntl Merit Ltr; Engrng.

SMARSH, JONATHAN; Bishop Hafey HS; Hazleton, PA; (3); Key Clb; Ski Clb; Ftbl; Hon Roll; Comp Engnrng.

SMARSH, REBECCA; Greater Johnston Vo-Tech; Johnstown, PA; (3); 2/300; VP Key Clb; VICA; High Hon Roll; NHS; Exploring; German Clb; JA; NFL; Yrbk Stf; Hon Roll; PA ST; Med Tech.

SMARTO, CARRIE; Council Rock HS; Wrightstown, PA; (3); 47/908; Drama Clb; Intnl Clb; Political Wkr; Chorus; Mrchg Band; School Musical; School Play; Stage Crew; Variety Show; Hon Roll; Intl Bus.

SMARTS, SARAH; Peabody HS; Pittsburgh, PA; (4); 6/294; Spanish Clb; Yrbk Ed-Chief; High Hon Roll; NHS; Acad All-Amer 86.

SMATHERS, DONALD; Saltsburg HS; Clarksburg, PA; (3); 26/55; IN U Of PA; Bio.

SMATHERS, GEOFFREY; Richland HS; Gibsonia, PA; (3); 54/186; Boys Clb Am; Trs Sr Cls; Rep Stu Cncl; Var Bsbl; Var Capt Golf; Wt Lftg; Ecnmcs.

SMATHERS, JEFF; United JR SR HS; Homer City, PA; (3); Camera Clb; Var JV Ftbl; Hon Roll; Arch.

SMAY, HEATHER; Spring Grove Area SR HS; York, PA; (3); 6/303; Sec Trs Exploring; Ski Clb; Color Guard; School Play; Var Crs Cntry; Im Socr; Stat Vllybl; High Hon Roll; NHS; Church Yth Grp; Presdntl Acadc Ftns Awd 85; Frnch Awd 85; 300 Pt Schltc Achvt Awd 86.

SMEDLEY, KATIE; Bishop O Reilly HS; Kingston, PA; (3); Church Yth Grp; Model UN; NFL; Ski Clb; Spanish Clb; Chorus; Drill Tm; Pres Soph Cls; VP Stu Cncl; Bsktbl; VP-STU Cncl 86-87; Ntl Yth Salute 87; Marywood Coll.

SMEDLEY, REBECCA; Agnes Irwin Schl; Haverford, PA; (3); Church Yth Grp; Cmnty Wkr; Debate Tm; Drama Clb; Chorus; School Musical; Nwsp Stf; Lcrss; Tennis; Hon Roll; Bst Latin Stu Awd 86; Plyng Piano 8 Yrs.

SMELKO, KAREN; Punxsutawney HS; Reynoldsville, PA; (4); 40/265; French Clb; Variety Show; Yrbk Stf; Stat Vllybl; Hon Roll; Indiana U PA; Fshn Merchndzng.

SMELL, LINDA; Carmichaels Area SR HS; Carmichaels, PA; (2); 7/127; Computer Clb; French Clb; Pep Clb; Yrbk Stf; High Hon Roll; Jr NHS; Comp Sci.

SMELTZ, ADAM; Oley Valley HS; Fleetwood, PA; (3); 9/142; Chess Clb; Sec Debate Tm; Stat Bsbl; Var L Socr; JV Vllybl; High Hon Roll; Hon Roll; NHS; Library Aide; Stat Bsktbl; Liensed USSF Soccer Referee 86-87; Local Ldrshp Camp 87; Usher At Jr Class Musical 87; Math.

SMELTZ, ANDREW W; Upper Dauphin Area HS; Lykens, PA; (2); FFA; Hon Roll.

SMELTZ, KANE; Line Mountain HS; Dornsife, PA; (4); Church Yth Grp; Computer Clb; Key Clb; Varsity Clb; Sec Soph Cls; Ftbl; Im Wt Lftg; Var Capt Wrstlng; Hon Roll; Enrchmnt Pgm 83-87; Shippensburg U; Bus Admin.

SMELTZ, LARRY L; Upper Dauphin Area HS; Lykens, PA; (2); Church Yth Grp; FFA; Hon Roll; Prfct Atten Awd; Star Grnhnd 85-86.

SMELTZ, RHONDA; Williams Valley HS; Wiconisco, PA; (1); Pres Spanish Clb; Band; VP Chorus; Jazz Band; Mrchg Band; School Musical; Symp Band; Powder Puff Ftbl; High Hon Roll; Hon Roll; Med.

SMELTZ, STEPHANIE; Williams Valley HS; Wiconisco, PA; (1); Spanish Clb; Chorus; Jazz Band; Mrchg Band; School Musical; Powder Puff Ftbl; High Hon Roll; Hon Roll; SR Twin Vly Bank 87; Med.

SMELTZER, AMIE; Penn Cambria HS; Cresson, PA; (4); Church Yth Grp; Drama Clb; French Clb; Ski Clb; School Play; Variety Show; Hon Roll; U Pittsburgh; Elem Ed.

SMELTZER, SHELLEY; Marion Center HS; Creekside, PA; (3); FBLA; Teachers Aide; Hon Roll; Accntng.

SMERECZNIAK, JEFF; Jefferson-Morgan HS; Clarksville, PA; (2); 4-H; Teachers Aide; Varsity Clb; Band; Concert Band; Yrbk Stf; Bsbl; JV L Ftbl; Hon Roll; Forensic Pathlgst.

SMERECZNIAK, SCOTT; Jefferson-Morgan HS; Clarksville, PA; (4); 2/98; Art Clb; Teachers Aide; Band; Yrbk Phtg; Bsbl; Trk; High Hon Roll; NHS; U Of Miami; Arch.

SMEREKAR, MICHELE; Penn Trafford HS; Trafford, PA; (3); JCL; Latin Clb; Color Guard; Mrchg Band; Nutritionist.

SMERKER, HEATHER; Baldwin HS; Pittsburgh, PA; (3); Cosmtlgy.

SMETAK, DEANNA; Mt Pleasant Area HS; Mt Pleasant, PA; (3); Church Yth Grp; Cmnty Wkr; German Clb; Ski Clb; Band; Concert Band; Mrchg Band; Stage Crew; Trs Soph Cls; Rep Sr Cls; Hon Roll; Psych.

SMETHURST, MIKE; B Reed Henderson SR HS; West Chester, PA; (3); Boy Scts; Ski Clb; JV Ftbl; JV Trk; Bus Admin.

SMICHNICK, SUZANNE; Cedar Crest HS; Lebanon, PA; (2); Church Yth Grp; Pep Clb; Spanish Clb; Band; Concert Band; Mrchg Band; Pep Band; Symp Band; L Var Swmmng; Trk; Natl JR Hnr Soc 85; Ed.

SMIGELSKI, AMY L; St Basil Acad; Philadelphia, PA; (3); 14/85; French Clb; Hosp Aide; Science Clb; Service Clb; SADD; Im Vllybl; Bio.

SMIGO, LENORE; Pottsville Area HS; Pottsville, PA; (4); Art Clb; Chorus; Hon Roll; 1st Pl Pottsville Areas Art Shw 87; Penn ST; Psych.

SMILEK, MELISSA; Western Beaver HS; Midland, PA; (3); Cmnty Wkr; Band; Chorus; VP Jr Cls; Var Cheerleading; Var L Sftbl; Var L Vllybl; Hon Roll; NHS; Ntl Merit Ltr; Wrld Affrs Smnr Schlrshp-Rotary 86.

SMILEY, DAVE; Steel Valley HS; Munhall, PA; (4); Church Yth Grp; Ftbl; Wt Lftg; Hon Roll; Natl Yth Physcl Ftns Cert Of Athlt Acmplshmnt 87; IN U Of PA; Fnc.

SMILEY, KRISSY; Indiana Area SR HS; Indiana, PA; (2); Church Yth Grp; Orch; Stage Crew; High Hon Roll; Jr NHS; Prfct Atten Awd; Pres Acdmc Ftns Awd, Outstnndg Part Orch, Pit Orch Schl Mus Flute 86; Duquesne U; Pharm.

SMILEY, WILLIAM; Pleasant Valley HS; Saylorsburg, PA; (2); JV Bsktbl; High Hon Roll; Hon Roll; Top 20 In Cls 85-87; De Paul.

SMILKO, KAREN; Nativity Bum HS; Pottsville, PA; (2); 51/96; Spanish Clb; Variety Show; Cheerleading.

SMINDAK JR, RICHARD; Portage Area HS; Portage, PA; (3); 66/108; Boy Scts; Stage Crew; Variety Show; Hon Roll; OH Diesel-Gas Inst; Diesl Mech.

SMINK, ED; Shamokin Area HS; Shamokin, PA; (4); Key Clb; Varsity Clb; Rep Frsh Cls; Rep Soph Cls; Rep Jr Cls; Rep Sr Cls; Trs Stu Cncl; L Bsbl; L Bsktbl; L Crs Cntry; Drexel U; Bus.

SMITH, AARON; State College Area HS; Boalsburg, PA; (2); Church Yth Grp; Ski Clb; Band; Concert Band; Jazz Band; Mrchg Band; Symp Band; Var Golf; Hon Roll; 3 Pwr Of PAWS 86-87; Cert Mrt Sci 86-87; Engrng.

SMITH, ADRIENNE; Johnsonburg HS; Johnsonburg, PA; (4); 5/65; Camera Clb; Sec Trs Varsity Clb; Yrbk Bus Mgr; Trs Sr Cls; Stu Cncl; Stat Bsktbl; Var Trk; Var Vllybl; High Hon Roll; Pres NHS; Century III Ldr Awd 86-87; Hugh O Brian Yth Ldrshp Ambssdr 85; Acad All-Amer Awd 85-86; Penn St U; Engrng.

SMITH, ALISON; Cedar Crest HS; Quentin, PA; (3); Pres Church Yth Grp; Pep Clb; SADD; Hon Roll; Yth Fellowship Pres 86-87; Perfect Atten Awds 85-87.

SMITH, AMANDA; Abington Heights HS; Clarks Summit, PA; (3); 55/295; Latin Clb; Ski Clb; Band; Concert Band; Mrchg Band; Lit Mag; Fld Hcky; Swmmng; Hon Roll; NHS; 2nd Pl Jr Acad Of Sci 85; Amer Hist Day Exclnt Rtng 85; Cum Laude ACL 85; Penn ST; Vet.

SMITH, AMANDA; Butler Area SR HS; Butler, PA; (3); Church Yth Grp; Library Aide; Office Aide; Spanish Clb; Band; Concert Band; Mrchg Band; Hon Roll; Jr NHS; PA Coll; Hlth Fld.

SMITH, AME; Greencastle-Antrim HS; Greencastle, PA; (3); Trs Soph Cls; Pres Jr Cls; Var Cheerleading; Var Vllybl; Hon Roll; Central Penn; Sec.

SMITH, AMEE; Hopewell HS; Aliquippa, PA; (3); Trs Art Clb; Church Yth Grp; Exploring; French Clb; SADD; Capt L Tennis; Wt Lftg; Chrmn NHS; Voice Dem Awd; Arch Engrng.

SMITH, AMY; Brownsville Area HS; Brownsville, PA; (3); 20/250; Church Yth Grp; Drama Clb; FBLA; Girl Scts; Hosp Aide; Math Clb; Sec Ski Clb; SADD; Chorus; Church Choir; HOBY Outstndng Stu 85-86; Natl Ldrshp & Sci Awd 87; U Of Pittsburgh; Dntstry.

SMITH, AMY; Canon-Mc Millan HS; Mcdonald, PA; (4); 186/371; FBLA; Sec JA; Office Aide; Spanish Clb; Teachers Aide; Hon Roll; Bradford Schl; Rtl Mgmt.

SMITH, AMY; Central HS; Roaring Spring, PA; (3); Church Yth Grp; FNA; FTA; Spanish Clb; Teachers Aide; Chorus; Church Choir; High Hon Roll; Hon Roll; PA ST U; Engl.

SMITH, AMY; Monessen SR HS; Monessen, PA; (3); Drama Clb; Hosp Aide; Cheerleading; High Hon Roll; Hon Roll; Hlth Admin.

SMITH, AMY; Mt Union Area JR SR HS; Mt Union, PA; (4); 32/172; Church Yth Grp; French Clb; FBLA; GAA; SADD; Stage Crew; Im Bowling; Mgr Sftbl; Stat Vllybl; Elizabethtown Coll; Bus Educ.

SMITH, ANDREA; Gwynedd Mercy Acad; Center Sq, PA; (2); GAA; Stage Crew; JV Fld Hcky; JV Sftbl; Im Vllybl; Hon Roll; Dist Art Awds 87; Criminal Law.

SMITH, ANDREW; Lampeter Strasburg HS; Lancaster, PA; (3); Art Clb; SADD; Varsity Clb; VP Jr Cls; Rep Stu Cncl; Ftbl; Gov Hon Prg Awd; Pres Schlr; Tennis; Trk; Borrows Schlr Awd-Art 86-87; Gftd Art Cls-Franklin & Marshall Coll 85-87; VA Tech; Arch.

SMITH, ANDY; Daniel Boone HS; Douglassville, PA; (3); 4/160; Model UN; Quiz Bowl; Var Swmmng; High Hon Roll; Ntl Merit SF; Liberal Arts.

SMITH, ANGELA; Oxford Area HS; Nottingham, PA; (3); Spanish Clb; Capt JV Cheerleading; High Hon Roll; Hon Roll.

SMITH, ANNETTE; Annville-Cleona HS; Cleona, PA; (4); VP FBLA; Office Aide; Chorus; Nwsp Stf; Yrbk Stf; Lit Mag; Hon Roll; Kiwanis Awd; NHS; Annville-Cleonas Outstndng Bus Stu 86-87; Med Sec.

SMITH, APRIL; Red Lion Area HS; Windsor, PA; (3); Varsity Clb; Yrbk Stf; Rep Stu Cncl; Tennis; Hon Roll; Church Yth Grp; GAA; Letterman Clb; Library Aide; Nwsp Stf.

SMITH, BARB; Manheim Central HS; Manheim, PA; (4); 51/237; Library Aide; Pres Jr Cls; Pres Sr Cls; Off Stu Cncl; Var Capt Bsktbl; Var Capt Sftbl; JV Tennis; Var Trk; Hon Roll; MVP Bsktbl 87; 4 Way Tst Awd 86; Rookie Yr Sftbl 86; Bloomsburg U; Mgmt.

SMITH, BELINDA; Canton JR-SR HS; Canton, PA; (4); FBLA; Letterman Clb; Office Aide; Cheerleading; Williamsport Area CC Comp Inf.

SMITH, BETH; Fairfield Area HS; Fairfield, PA; (4); 33/73; School Musical; Nwsp Stf; Yrbk Phtg; Yrbk Stf; Bsktbl; Capt Fld Hcky; Hon Roll; 3rd Pl Wldlf Intrprtns Env Olympcs 86; 4th Pl Frst Rsrcs Env Olympcs 86; 5th Pl Land Jdgng Env Olympcs; Photo Jrnlst.

SMITH, BETSY; E L Meyers HS; Wilkes-Barre, PA; (4); JA; Trs Key Clb; Chorus; Yrbk Stf; Trs Jr Cls; Trs Sr Cls; Rep Stu Cncl; Capt Fld Hcky; Var L Sftbl; Cit Awd; Fld Hcky Schlrhp Misericordia Coll 87; Misericordia; Elem Educ.

SMITH, BOBBI SUE; Bethel Park HS; Bethel Park, PA; (4); 89/519; French Clb; Capt L Crs Cntry; Hon Roll; U Of DE; Phy Thrpy.

SMITH, BRENDA; Ambridge Area HS; Sewickley, PA; (3); French Clb; Pep Clb; Red Cross Aide; Nwsp Bus Mgr; Nwsp Rptr; Frsh Cls; Soph Cls; Jr Cls; Sr Cls; Hon Roll; Psych.

SMITH, BRIAN; North Star HS; Jennerstown, PA; (2); 3/130; Aud/Vis; FCA; Varsity Clb; Stage Crew; Pres Frsh Cls; Var L Bsbl; JV L Bsktbl; Var JV Ftbl; Hon Roll; Marine Bio.

SMITH, BRYAN DAVID; Spring-Ford SR HS; Royersford, PA; (4); 5/253; Boy Scts; German Clb; Radio Clb; VP Concert Band; Drm Mjr(t); VP Jazz Band; VP Mrchg Band; Var L Trk; Cit Awd; Hon Roll; U S Air Force Acad; Aerontcl.

SMITH, CARL; Wyalusing Valley HS; New Albany, PA; (4); Boy Scts; Pres Computer Clb; German Clb; Mgr Stage Crew; Hon Roll; NHS; 1st Pl On-Line-Basic Programing Bus Symposium Williamsport Area CC 87; Bloomsburg U; Bus Comp.

SMITH, CATHY; Everett Area HS; Breezewood, PA; (4); Church Yth Grp; Cmnty Wkr; GAA; Spanish Clb; Mrchg Band; Trs Varsity Clb; Chorus; Cheerleading; Spanish NHS.

SMITH, CHAD; Mifflinburg Area HS; Mifflinburg, PA; (1); Church Yth Grp; German Clb; Key Clb; JV Bsktbl; JV Ftbl; Im Vllybl; Im Wt Lftg; Im Wrstlng; Cit Awd; High Hon Roll; Elect Engrng.

SMITH, CHARLES; E L Meyers HS; Wilkes-Barre, PA; (4); 14/141; Key Clb; Pep Clb; SADD; Chorus; Yrbk Stf; Rep Stu Cncl; Capt L Ftbl; Capt L Swmmng; NHS; Hon Roll; Cert Of Mrt Top 5000 SAT Scrs In PA 86.

SMITH JR, CHARLES G; Gateway Senior HS; Monroeville, PA; (3); 21/452; Chorus; Pres Frsh Cls; Soph Cls; Jr Cls; Sr Cls; Stu Cncl; Var L Swmmng; Im Capt Vllybl; High Hon Roll; NHS; Outstndg Swmmr Awd 85-87; AIM 85-87; Engrng.

SMITH, CHERYL; Red Lion Area SR HS; Red Lion, PA; (2); 100/344; Library Aide; Band; Concert Band; Mrchg Band; High Hon Roll; Hon Roll; Vet.

SMITH, CHERYL LYNN; E L Meyers HS; Wilkes-Barre, PA; (4); Pres Church Yth Grp; Ski Clb; SADD; Church Choir; Concert Band; Jazz Band; Mrchg Band; Orch; Nwsp Ed-Chief; Rep Stu Cncl; Slvr Crs Chrch Svc 87; Marywood Coll; Educ.

SMITH, CHRISLYN; Emmaus HS; Allentown, PA; (2); 35/495; Hosp Aide; JA; Key Clb; Yrbk Stf; Stu Cncl; Trk; Hon Roll; Jr NHS; NHS; B Nai Brith Essay Writing Cont 87; Med.

SMITH, CHRISTINA; Susquehannock HS; New Freedom, PA; (2); 51/243; Rep Frsh Cls; Comp.

SMITH, CHRISTINE; Leechburg Area HS; Leechburg, PA; (3); Art Clb; Pres FBLA; Girl Scts; Office Aide; Pep Clb; Band; Mrchg Band; Pep Band; Vllybl; Natl Stu Ldrshp Svc Awd 85; Bus.

SMITH, COLLEEN; Pocono Mountain HS; Freeland, PA; (4); 21/325; Camp Fr Inc; Library Aide; SADD; Im Powder Puff Ftbl; JV Sftbl; Hon Roll; Hnr Recgntn Plq Recvd 83-85; PA ST U.

SMITH, CONNIE; Bedford HS; Everett, PA; (3); Cmnty Wkr; Sec FBLA; Chorus; Drill Tm; Mrchg Band; Var Sftbl; Hon Roll; SADD; Pre-Teen Sftbl Coach & Sftbl Mst Imprvd Plyr 87; Go-Kart Racing 84; Comp.

SMITH, CRAIG; Otto-Eldred HS; Eldred, PA; (4); SADD; Pres Band; Concert Band; Drm Mjr(t); Mrchg Band; Pep Band; Trk; Hon Roll; Prfct Atten Awd; De Vry Inst Of Tech; Elctrncs.

SMITH, CYDNEY; Clairton HS; Clairton, PA; (3); 9/99; Chorus; Church Choir; JV Var Bsktbl; Hon Roll; NHS.

SMITH, DALE; Reynolds HS; Jamestown, PA; (3); 24/160; 4-H; Band; Concert Band; Jazz Band; Mrchg Band; Pep Band; Stage Crew; 4-H Awd; Hon Roll; PA Govs Schl For Agri 86; Farm Credit Record Kpng Awd 86; Agri.

SMITH, DANA; CAS HS; Modena, PA; (3); 121/519; JA; SADD; Pep Band; Yrbk Stf; Sr Cls; Stu Cncl; Im Bsktbl; Trk; Hon Roll.

SMITH, DAVID; Bermudian Springs HS; York Spgs, PA; (3); 1/125; Pres Church Yth Grp; Pres VP 4-H; Chorus; VP Concert Band; Jazz Band; Madrigals; VP Mrchg Band; School Musical; Dnfth Awd; High Hon Roll; Math.

SMITH, DAVID; Scranton Central HS; Scranton, PA; (3); 59/300; Hon Roll; NHS; Bio.

SMITH, DAVID T; Phoenixville Area HS; Phoenixville, PA; (4); 1/200; Boy Scts; Key Clb; Scholastic Bowl; Sec Varsity Clb; School Play; Rep Sr Cls; Var Capt Wrstlng; Pres NHS; Ntl Merit SF; High Hon Roll; Acadmc All Amer; Genl Elec Town Mtg On Tommrw; Harvrd Bk Prz; Chem Engr.

SMITH, DAWN; Cheltenham HS; Laverock, PA; (4); 88/365; Church Yth Grp; FBLA; Hosp Aide; Church Choir; Color Guard; Lit Mag; Stu Cncl; Masonic Awd; Ntl Merit Schol; SPS Tech Bus Ed Awd 87; Concrnd Parents Jrnlst; Loree P Owens Awd; Georgetown U; Accntng.

SMITH, DAWN; Conestoga SR HS; Wayne, PA; (2); AFS; Church Yth Grp; Flag Corp; Yrbk Phtg; Var Vllybl.

SMITH, DAWN; Lake Lenman HS; Wilkes-Barre, PA; (4); 45/154; Office Aide; High Hon Roll; Hon Roll; Kiwanis Awd; NHS; Pres Sr Cls; Capt Var Fld Hcky; JV Sftbl; Hockey All Star Mdl 86; Cntry 21 Typing Cert 86-87; 1st All Star Tm Sunday Independent 86; Wilkes Coll; Accntnt.

SMITH, DAYNA; Central Columbia HS; Bloomsburg, PA; (3); DECA; Chorus; Church Choir; Swing Chorus; Yrbk Stf; Stu Cncl; Diving; Hon Roll; Dist & Rgnl Chorus 87; Deca Dist 5th In Apparel & Accesories 87; Towson ST U; Bus.

SMITH, DEANNA; Juniata HS; Pt Royal, PA; (3); SADD; Band; Chorus; Mrchg Band; Orch; School Play; Yrbk Stf; Fld Hcky; Trk; Twrlr.

SMITH, DEANNA; Kennard-Dale HS; Delta, PA; (3); Church Yth Grp; Girl Scts; Hosp Aide; Library Aide; Church Choir; Var Sftbl; Stat Trk; JV Vllybl; Nanny.

SMITH, DEBORAH; Jamestown HS; Jamestown, PA; (3); 1/65; Drama Clb; VP French Clb; Varsity Clb; Band; Chorus; School Play; Nwsp Stf; Trs Jr Cls; Stat Bsbl; Var Bsktbl; Law.

SMITH, DEBORAH; Wilmington Area HS; New Wilmington, PA; (3); 22/114; Church Yth Grp; Drama Clb; Band; Church Choir; Concert Band; Jazz Band; Mrchg Band; Pep Band; Hon Roll.

SMITH, DEBRA; Susquenita HS; Marysville, PA; (3); 10/136; Church Yth Grp; Var Capt Crs Cntry; High Hon Roll; Trs NHS; French Clb; Rep Stu Cncl; JV Stat Bsktbl; Var L Trk; Hon Roll; Various Awds In Crss Cntry 86 & Trk 85 & 86; Interior Design.

SMITH, DEIRDRE; Southmoreland SR HS; Everson, PA; (3); Sec Church Yth Grp; French Clb; Letterman Clb; Powder Puff Ftbl; Score Keeper; Var L Sftbl; US Bus Ed Awd Wnnr 85; Sec.

SMITH, DENISE; Lehighton Area HS; Weissport, PA; (3); 18/254; FBLA; FHA; FNA; Sftbl; Trk; High Hon Roll; Hon Roll; NHS; RN.

SMITH, DENISE; Spring Grove Area SR HS; Spring Grove, PA; (3); 138/311; Camera Clb; Yrbk Stf; Rep Stu Cncl; Stat Ftbl; Mat Maids; Powder Puff Ftbl; Stat Trk; Stat Vllybl; Stat Wrstlng; Hon Roll; Schltc Achvt Awd 86; Travel.

SMITH, DEREK; Peteas Township HS; Mc Murray, PA; (3); Nwsp Phtg; Penn ST U.

SMITH, DIANE; Wilson HS; Reading, PA; (4); Art Clb; Hosp Aide; Rep Soph Cls; Rep Stu Cncl; Var Cheerleading; Var JV Score Keeper; JV Trk; Hon Roll; Penn ST Berks Campus; Nrsng.

SMITH, DONALD; Marion Center Area HS; Indiana, PA; (3); 47/153; Church Yth Grp; Latin Clb; Varsity Clb; Band; Chorus; Concert Band; Mrchg Band; Pep Band; JV Swmmng; Var Trk; PA ST U; Engrng.

SMITH, DONNA; Palmerton Area HS; Palmertown, PA; (3); FBLA; Stu Cncl; High Hon Roll; Hon Roll; Acad Awd Amer Cultures I 85; Acad Awds Hm Ecnmcs & Alg II 86; Acad Awd Engl 87; Clnry Arts.

SMITH, DORINE; High Point Baptist Acad; Mohnton, PA; (4); Teachers Aide; VP Jr Cls; VP Sr Cls; Capt Cheerleading; Co-Capt Vllybl; Home Ec.

SMITH, DOUG; Mc Keesport Area SR HS; Mckeesport, PA; (3); 14/425; Pres Church Yth Grp; NFL; SADD; VP Sr Cls; Pres Stu Cncl; JV Ftbl; JV Trk; L Var Wrstlng; High Hon Roll; Hon Roll; Corp Law.

SMITH, DOUG; Northampton Area SR HS; Bath, PA; (3); Boy Scts; Band; Concert Band; Jazz Band; Mrchg Band; School Musical; Stage Crew; Hon Roll; Aeronautical Engrng.

SMITH, DOUGLAS J; Bloomsburg SR HS; Bloomsburg, PA; (3); 10/124; Am Leg Boys St; Pres Pep Clb; Yrbk Phtg; Yrbk Stf; VP Stu Cncl; Var Bsbl; Im Vllybl; High Hon Roll; NHS; Stu Delgt-PA Schl Brds Assn Conf 86; Bloomsburg U; Bus Admin.

SMITH, DWIGHT; Dayton HS; Smicksburg, PA; (3); 6/52; Aud/Vis; Chess Clb; Computer Clb; Spanish Clb; Chorus; School Musical; Hon Roll; Comp Sci.

SMITH, E ALEXANDRA; Chaltanham HS; Wyncote, PA; (2); 77/355; Church Yth Grp; Band; Concert Band; Orch; Crs Cntry; Trk; U Of PA; Sci.

SMITH, EARL; Cedar Grove Acad; Philadelphia, PA; (4); Drama Clb; VP JA; Teachers Aide; Variety Show; Nwsp Ed-Chief; Nwsp Stf; Yrbk Stf; VP Soph Cls; VP Stu Cncl; Trk; Penn ST Wilkes-Barre; Bio.

SMITH, ELIZABETH; W Philadelphis Univ City HS; Philadelphia, PA; (3); Debate Tm; Drama Clb; Spanish Clb; SADD; Church Choir; Color Guard; Lit Mag; Off Sr Cls; Cit Awd; Spanish NHS; Cheyney USOCIOLOGY.

SMITH, ERIC; Red Lion Area SR HS; Brogue, PA; (3); School Play.

SMITH, ERIC; Waynesburg Central HS; Waynesburg, PA; (3); 1/200; Letterman Clb; Pres Spanish Clb; Var L Bsktbl; Var Capt Socr; Var L Trk; High Hon Roll; NHS; U Of Pittsburgh.

SMITH, ERIC J; Pen Argyl Area HS; Wind Gap, PA; (3); 2/160; Capt Scholastic Bowl; Concert Band; Jazz Band; Trs Mrchg Band; Orch; Ed Yrbk Ed-Chief; High Hon Roll; NHS; Ntl Merit Ltr; Pep Band; Renselaer Mdl Math & Sci 87; Math Ed.

SMITH, ERIKA; Lakeland JR SR HS; Jermyn, PA; (4); FHA; Cheerleading; Hon Roll; Marywood Coll; Comm.

SMITH, ERIN; Big Spring HS; Newville, PA; (3); 34/258; Church Yth Grp; Ski Clb; Band; Chorus; Rep Stu Cncl; Var Crs Cntry; Var Powder Puff Ftbl; Var Swmmng; Var Trk; Hon Roll; William & Mary Coll; Pre-Law.

SMITH, EVAN; Lower Moreland HS; Huntingdon Valley, PA; (2); FBLA; SADD; Temple Yth Grp; Band; Concert Band; Jazz Band; Orch; School Musical; Tennis; Hon Roll.

SMITH, FRANCES; Yough HS; Jacobs Creek, PA; (3); #40 In Class; Sec Church Yth Grp; Computer Clb; Ski Clb; Sec SADD; Chorus; Concert Band; Powder Puff Ftbl; Score Keeper; High Hon Roll; NHS; Nrsng.

SMITH, FRANCIS; Ambridge Area SR HS; Ambridge, PA; (3); Office Aide; Spanish Clb; SADD; Chorus; Bsktbl; Trk; Pittsburgh Art Inst; Advrtsng.

SMITH, GAYLE; Quakertown Community HS; Quakertown, PA; (3); 20/313; Trs Church Yth Grp; Varsity Clb; Off Jr Cls; Var Fld Hcky; Var Trk; Var JV Vllybl; High Hon Roll; Hon Roll; Jr NHS; NHS; Phys Thrpy.

SMITH, GILLIAN; Acad Of The New Church; Huntingdon Valley, PA; (2); Church Yth Grp; Debate Tm; Rep GAA; Yrbk Stf; Im Bsktbl; Im Gym; Im Lcrss; Im Socr; Var Trk; JV Vllybl; Gold Mdl Awd Phy Ed 86-87; Psychlgst.

SMITH, GREGORY; New Church Acad; Freeport, PA; (3); 2/40; Chess Clb; Church Yth Grp; VP 4-H; School Musical; JV Crs Cntry; JV Ice Hcky; JV Trk; High Hon Roll; Hon Roll; Penn ST U; Engr.

SMITH, GREGORY D; Ambridge Area HS; Baden, PA; (4); 3/265; Am Leg Boys St; Boy Scts; Pres VP Church Yth Grp; Trs German Clb; School Play; VP Stu Cncl; Capt L Trk; God Cntry Awd; NHS; SAR Awd; Grove City Coll; Mech Engrng.

SMITH, HEATHER; Blair County Christian Schl; Newry, PA; (1); 3/25; Church Yth Grp; FTA; Teachers Aide; Chorus; Yrbk Stf; Sec Frsh Cls; JV Cheerleading; High Hon Roll; Bob Jones U; Elem Ed.

SMITH, HEATHER; Du Bois SR HS; Du Bois, PA; (4); Church Yth Grp; German Clb; Color Guard; Mrchg Band; School Musical; Swmmng; Hon Roll; NHS; Nice Kid Awd 87; Swim Ltr 87; PA ST; Engrng.

SMITH, HEATHER; Pleasant Valley HS; Saylorsburg, PA; (2); 4-H; Pep Clb; Ski Clb; Yrbk Bus Mgr; Stu Cncl; Var Cheerleading; Var Trk; Hon Roll; Intr Dsgnr.

SMITH, HEATHER; Vincentian HS; Bradford Woods, PA; (4); 8/64; Math Clb; Science Clb; Sec Service Clb; SADD; Rep Frsh Cls; Capt JV Cheerleading; Hon Roll; NHS; Pres Schlr; Bucknell U; Pre Med.

SMITH, HEATHER; Waynesburg Central HS; Waynesburg, PA; (3); Pep Clb; Ski Clb; Spanish Clb; SADD; High Hon Roll; Hon Roll; Waynesburg Coll; Htl Mgmt.

SMITH, HEIDI; Commodore Perry HS; Hadley, PA; (4); 2/64; Pres Band; Pres Concert Band; Drm Mjr(t); Pres Jazz Band; Pres Mrchg Band; Pres Pep Band; School Play; VP Jr Cls; VP Sr Cls; NHS; Rotary Yth Ldrshp Awd 86; Natl Hnr Roll 86; Med Lab Tech.

SMITH, HEIDI; Hickory HS; W Middlesex, PA; (4); Spanish Clb; Chorus; Drill Tm; Rep Frsh Cls; Rep Jr Cls; Sec Sr Cls; Rep Stu Cncl; Jr NHS; NHS; Spanish NHS; IUP.

SMITH, HOLLY; Belle Vernon Area HS; Belle Vernon, PA; (3); Church Yth Grp; Debate Tm; Pep Clb; Band; Rep Stu Cncl; Var Cheerleading; Powder Puff Ftbl; Sftbl; Hon Roll; Acadc All Amer Schlr 85; Prom Cmmtte 87; Sr Cmmtte 87-88.

SMITH, J BONNIE; Peters Township HS; Mc Murray, PA; (3); 22/237; Church Yth Grp; Intnl Clb; Rep Key Clb; Hst NFL; Capt Sec Mrchg Band; Im Tennis; Hon Roll; Voice Dem Awd; JV Trk; School Musical; HOBY Rep; Pres Clssrm Schlr; Ruby Pin Forensics; Intl Law.

SMITH, JAMES PAUL; George Washington HS; Philadelphia, PA; (3); 47/850; Art Clb; Mu Alpha Theta; Var L Crs Cntry; Var L Trk; Bausch & Lomb Sci Awd; High Hon Roll; NHS; Ntl Merit SF; Boy Scts; Math Clb; Franklin Inst Sci Awd Physics 87; Smith, Kline, Beckman Math Awds 86; Fnlst For Drexel Rsrch Tlnt 87; Physics.

SMITH, JAMI; Du Bois Area HS; Brockway, PA; (4); 113/270; Hon Roll.

SMITH, JANE E; Central Catholic HS; Temple, PA; (3); 7/135; Church Yth Grp; Scholastic Bowl; Spanish Clb; Varsity Clb; School Musical; Ed Yrbk Stf; Var Bsktbl; Var JV Cheerleading; Swmmng; Hon Roll; JR Acad Of Sci 85; Pre Med.

SMITH, JANICE; Bishop Mc Devitt HS; Steelton, PA; (3); 79/250; Ski Clb; SADD; Chorus; Drill Tm; L Flag Corp; Yrbk Stf; L Twrlr; HACC; Bus Adm.

SMITH, JARETT; Academy Of The New Church; Freeport, PA; (4); 1/37; Pres Trs 4-H; School Musical; Pres Sr Cls; Capt Crs Cntry; L Trk; High Hon Roll; NHS; Val; Aud/Vis; Church Yth Grp; Sons Of Acad Mdl 87; MVP Crss Cntry 85-86; 4 Acad Subj Awds 87; Carnegie Mellon; Engrng.

SMITH, JASON E; Archbishop Ryan HS For Boys; Philadelphia, PA; (3); 30/420; Political Wkr; Spanish Clb; Ftbl; Trk; Drexel; Engr.

SMITH, JAYE; Kennard-Dale HS; Delta, PA; (3); French Clb; German Clb; Ski Clb; Varsity Clb; Yrbk Stf; Crs Cntry; Trk; Outstndng Achvt Typng 87; LPN.

SMITH, JEFFERY; Milton SR HS; Milton, PA; (2); VP 4-H; Bsktbl; Hon Roll; Presdntl Acadc Ftnss Awd 85-86; Penn ST; Ag.

SMITH, JEFFREY; Pruchase Line HS; Commodore, PA; (2); 21/180; Quiz Bowl; Scholastic Bowl; Varsity Clb; Band; Chorus; Stage Crew; Nwsp Rptr; Im Bsbl; JV Var Bsktbl; Var Ftbl; Class Pres 86-87; 2nd Pl Purch Line Bsktbl Tourn 86; U Of NC; Law.

SMITH, JENNIE; Newport HS; Newport, PA; (1); Pep Clb; Nwsp Stf; Rep Frsh Cls; Bsktbl; Fld Hcky; Sftbl; Wt Lftg; High Hon Roll; Hon Roll; Partcpt In Gifted Pgm 82-86.

SMITH, JENNIFER; Donegal HS; Mt Joy, PA; (3); 47/167; Cmnty Wkr; L JV Fld Hcky; JV L Trk; Hon Roll; Lancaster Gen Hosp Schl; Rdlgy.

SMITH, JENNIFER; Henderson HS; West Chester, PA; (3); 33/367; Church Yth Grp; Dance Clb; Ski Clb; Speech Tm; Y-Teens; Rep Soph Cls; Rep Jr Cls; Stu Cncl; Var Tennis; French Hon Soc; Cmmnctns.

SMITH, JENNIFER; Jeannette SR HS; Jeannette, PA; (2); Church Yth Grp; French Clb; Hosp Aide; Ski Clb; Teachers Aide; JV Var Cheerleading; Im Tennis; Hon Roll; Radlgst.

SMITH, JENNIFER; Plum SR HS; Pittsburgh, PA; (4); 108/368; Church Yth Grp; FBLA; Spanish Clb; SADD; Hon Roll; 3rd Pl Ec FBLA Rgnls 87; Clsrm Awd Brtsh Lit, Alg III & Gym 87; W Liberty ST Coll; Math.

SMITH, JENNIFER; Ringgold HS; Monongahela, PA; (3); Science Clb; Am Leg Aux Girls St; Color Guard; School Musical; School Play; Sec Soph Cls; Sec Jr Cls; Stu Cncl; Cheerleading; High Hon Roll; Am Legn Awd 84-85; HOBY Fndtn 85-86; Washington & Jefferson; Prelaw.

SMITH, JENNIFER ANNE; Hickory HS; Hermitage, PA; (3); Drama Clb; Acpl Chr; Chorus; Capt Flag Corp; School Musical; Stage Crew; Nwsp Rptr; Rep Stu Cncl; High Hon Roll; NHS; Acadc All Am Schlr 85-86; U Of Pittsburgh; Sci.

SMITH, JENNY; Waynesburg Central HS; Waynesburg, PA; (4); 8/186; Natl Beta Clb; Spanish Clb; Chorus; Nwsp Stf; Off Stu Cncl; Stat Trk; Lion Awd; NHS; NEDT Awd; Spanish NHS; JR High Dist Choir Awd 84; Waynesburg Coll; Bus.

SMITH, JEREMY; William Allen HS; Allentown, PA; (2); 1/723; L Var Ftbl; Var L Trk; Nwsp Stf; High Hon Roll; Hon Roll; Amer Assn Tchrs Grmn 4 Wk Schlrshp To Grmny To Stdy 87; Med.

SMITH, JESSE; Meyersdale Area HS; Meyersdale, PA; (3); Var Trk; Pres Phy Fit Merit Awd 86; One Of Writer In Schl Bk We Write 87; WVU.

SMITH, JESSIE; Wyoming Valley West HS; Forty Fort, PA; (4); Key Clb; Band; Concert Band; Mrchg Band; Lit Mag; Rep Stu Cncl; Swmmng; Prfct Atten Awd; Pres Schlr; VFW Awd; U Of PA; Lbrl Arts.

SMITH, JILL; Union HS; Rimersburg, PA; (3); Church Yth Grp; FCA; SADD; Yrbk Stf; Hon Roll; Clarion U Of PA; Accntng.

SMITH, JILL; West Perry HS; Blain, PA; (2); Sec Church Yth Grp; Gym; Hon Roll; Am Allnc Hlth, Phy Ed, & Rcrtn & Dnc Achv Awd; Harrisburg Area CC; Dance.

SMITH, JIM; Connellsville Area HS; Dunbar, PA; (2); 97/580; Aud/Vis; Band; Concert Band; Mrchg Band; High Hon Roll; Hon Roll; Jr NHS; Cranegie-Mellon; Engrng.

SMITH, JODEEN; Blair County Christian HS; Duncansville, PA; (4); 1/4; Church Yth Grp; Chorus; Yrbk Phtg; Trs Frsh Cls; Trs Soph Cls; Trs Jr Cls; Sec Sr Cls; Rep Stu Cncl; Var Trk; High Hon Roll; Hstry Ed.

SMITH, JODI; Clarion Area HS; Shippenville, PA; (3); FCA; Pep Clb; Acpl Chr; Ed Yrbk Stf; Trs Jr Cls; Pres Sec Stu Cncl; Bsktbl; Capt Trk; Vllybl; Hon Roll; Sci Fair 2nd Pl 87; Psychlgy.

SMITH, JODI; Mt Union Area HS; Mapleton Depot, PA; (3); Church Yth Grp; 4-H; Chorus; Hon Roll; Clncl Psych.

SMITH, JOHN; Annville-Cleona HS; Cleona, PA; (3); 2/127; Church Yth Grp; Math Tm; Quiz Bowl; Chorus; Church Choir; Concert Band; Madrigals; Mrchg Band; School Musical; High Hon Roll; PA Govr Schl Sci 86; Research Sci Inst 87; 1st Pl Shippensburg U Math Cont 87; Comp Sci.

SMITH, JOHN; HS For Engineering & Science; Philadelphia, PA; (3); Church Yth Grp; SADD; High Hon Roll; Hon Roll; Stu Awd Shlds Grn Chptr John Brwn Mem Assn Inc 82; Morehouse Coll; Pre-Med.

SMITH, JOHN S; Thomas Jefferson HS; Pittsburgh, PA; (4); 15/280; Am Leg Boys St; Sec JCL; Band; Nwsp Ed-Chief; JV Var Bsktbl; Var L Trk; High Hon Roll; NHS; Ntl Merit SF; AFS; US Mltry Acad Admtnc 87-91; ROTC Schlrshp; West Point; Military.

SMITH, JONATHAN; York Suburban HS; York, PA; (3); 46/176; Church Yth Grp; Cmnty Wkr; Science Clb; Varsity Clb; Concert Band; Jazz Band; Mrchg Band; Var Swmmng; Hon Roll; Band; 2nd Pl PA Jr Acadm Sci 86; Dist Band 86; PA ST U; Marine Bio.

SMITH, JULIA; Strath Haven HS; Swarthmore, PA; (4); Sftbl; Hon Roll; Bus Ed Awd 87; Sccr Mgr 83; Homecmng Float Cmmttee 84; WV U; Bus.

SMITH, JULIE; Brockway Area HS; Brockport, PA; (4); 10/90; FBLA; Band; Concert Band; Co-Capt Flag Corp; Mrchg Band; Pep Band; Hon Roll; Du Bois Bus Coll; Med Sec.

SMITH, K LEITA; Pine Forge Acad; Albany, NY; (1); Ski Clb; Band; Chorus; Church Choir; Sec Frsh Cls; Stat Vllybl; Hon Roll; Reg Rep Os Step; Loma Linda; Cmptr Sci.

SMITH, KAREN; Athens Area HS; Athens, PA; (3); FHA; Flag Corp; JV Var Sftbl; Hon Roll; Church Yth Grp; SADD; Stu Cncl; Prfct Atten Awd; Vrsty Lttr In Sftbl, Acad Awd For British Lit 87; Homer Cert For Date Mate Or Wait II & Crafts 86; Secr.

SMITH, KAREN; Central HS Of Phila; Philadelphia, PA; (4); Church Yth Grp; Church Choir; Yrbk Stf; Sec Stu Cncl; Var Capt Swmmng; Im Vllybl; Hon Roll; Prfct Atten Awd; Sct A Mann Mem Awd 86-87; Opthlmlgy.

SMITH, KAREN; Nazareth Acad; Bensalem, PA; (3); Art Clb; VP Orch; School Musical; Lit Mag; Sec Soph Cls; Var Bsktbl; JV Sftbl; Im Mgr Vllybl; AACA Al-Star Bsktbl 86-87; Crmnlgy.

SMITH, KAREN; Parkland HS; Schnecksville, PA; (3); Sec Church Yth Grp; Pres 4-H; VICA; Band; Church Choir; Color Guard; Im Bsktbl; Im Fld Hcky; Im Sftbl; Wt Lftg; Cosmetology.

SMITH, KATHY; Baldwin HS; Pittsburgh, PA; (2); Church Yth Grp; Flag Corp; Mrchg Band; VP Soph Cls; Hon Roll; Prfct Atten Awd.

SMITH, KATHY; Carlynton HS; Pittsburgh, PA; (4); 13/161; Ski Clb; Drill Tm; Yrbk Stf; Rep Civic Clb; Rep Jr Cls; VP Sr Cls; Rep Stu Cncl; Im Vllybl; High Hon Roll; Hon Roll; Chartiers Bus & Prof Womens Clb Schlrshp 87; Homcmng Semi-Fnlst 86; IN U Of PA; Math Educ.

SMITH, KATHY; Gettyburg SR HS; Orrtanna, PA; (2); 1/250; Church Yth Grp; Girl Scts; Chorus; Swing Chorus; Var L Crs Cntry; Var L Trk; Wrstlng; High Hon Roll; Hghst Yearly Avg Typg I & II 87; PA ST U; Elem Ed.

SMITH, KATHY; Octorara HS; Christiana, PA; (3); 33/157; SADD; Hon Roll; Acadc All Am Awd 87.

SMITH, KATY; West York Area HS; York, PA; (3); 3/186; JA; Spanish Clb; Varsity Clb; Tennis; NHS; Key Awd Elmira Coll Acad Awd 87.

SMITH, KEL; Cumberland Valley HS; Mechanicsburg, PA; (4); Camera Clb; Lit Mag; Ntl Art Hnr Soc 85-87; Fanny B Thalheimer Schlrshp 87; PA Govrnrs Schl For Arts 86; MD Inst; Photo.

SMITH, KELLI; Strath Haven HS; Wallingford, PA; (4); Church Yth Grp; Hosp Aide; Office Aide; Ski Clb; Swmmng; Mgr Vllybl; High Hon Roll; NHS; Pres Acad Ftns Awd 87; Swmmng Ltr 84 & 86,Vlybl 84-86; IN U Of PA; Spec Ed Tchr.

SMITH, KELLY; Center SR HS; Monaca, PA; (2); German Clb; Latin Clb; Office Aide; Pep Clb; Hon Roll; Wrthy Advsr Rochester Rnbw Asmbly 86; Psych.

SMITH, KELLY; Lock Haven HS; Lock Haven, PA; (3); Cmnty Wkr; Hosp Aide; Spanish Clb; SADD; Chorus; Variety Show; Bsbl; Mgr(s); Score Keeper; Tennis; Lock Haven U; Elem Educ.

SMITH, KELLY; St Huberts HS; Philadelphia, PA; (3); 20/421; Cmnty Wkr; Intnl Clb; Math Clb; Math Tm; Diocsn Schlr 87-88; Arch.

SMITH, KERRY; Liberty HS; Bethlehem, PA; (3); 97/429; Pres Spanish Clb; SADD; Stage Crew; Lit Mag; Rep Stu Cncl; Var L Fld Hcky; Cit Awd; Hon Roll; Prfct Atten Awd; Art Clb; Hugh O Brien Yth Ldrshp Smnr Rep 86; Outstndng Stu; Bus.

SMITH, KEVIN; Mohawk JR SR HS; Bessemer, PA; (3); Church Yth Grp; Spanish Clb; Nwsp Stf; Rep Stu Cncl; Bowling; NHS; Acad All American 86; Intl Foreign Lang Awd Winner 86; Youngstown ST U; Elec Engrng.

SMITH, KIMBERLEY; Bethlehem Center SR HS; Vestaburg, PA; (4); 10/153; Spanish Clb; High Hon Roll; Hon Roll; Trs NHS; ICM; Travel.

SMITH, KIMBERLY; Hickory HS; Hermitage, PA; (3); 73/167; VP Pres DECA; Art Clb; German Clb; Library Aide; Office Aide; Yrbk Phtg; Rep Jr Cls; DECA Comp Dist 1-2nd Pl Apparel & Accessories 87; Bradford; Fashion Merch.

SMITH, KIMBERLY; Northern Bedford HS; Hopewell, PA; (3); Trs Church Yth Grp; FTA; SADD; Varsity Clb; Band; Concert Band; Mrchg Band; Yrbk Stf; Sftbl; Hon Roll; Comp Sci.

SMITH, KIMBERLY; Punxsutawney Area HS; Punxsutawney, PA; (2); Rep CAP; Stat Wrstlng; Hon Roll.

SMITH, KIMBERLY A; Lampeter-Strasburg HS; Strasburg, PA; (4); 34/145; Varsity Clb; Chorus; Church Choir; School Musical; Fld Hcky; Sftbl; Voice Dem Awd; Outstndng Stu Awd 87; Bloomsburg U; Elem Ed.

SMITH, KRISTEN; Pleasant Valley HS; Saylorsburg, PA; (4); 4-H; Vllybl; Wt Lftg; 4-H Awd; Envrmntl Sci Aid Hnr Awd 87; Northampton CC; Interior Dsgn.

SMITH, KRISTIAN L; Susquehannock HS; New Freedom, PA; (3); 53/194; AFS; French Clb; Ski Clb; Spanish Clb; SADD; School Play; Yrbk Stf; Off Jr Cls; Off Sr Cls; Exploring; American U; Intl Rltns.

SMITH, KRISTIN; Upper Moreland HS; Willow Grove, PA; (3); 40/275; Rep Frsh Cls; Rep Rep Soph Cls; Rep Jr Cls; Var JV Cheerleading; Var JV Fld Hcky; Var Trk; High Hon Roll; Hon Roll; Montgomery Cnty Intermdte Unit Summer Intensv; U Miami; Marine Bio.

SMITH, KRISTINE; Acad Of Notre Dame; Downingtown, PA; (3); Church Yth Grp; Debate Tm; Hosp Aide; Model UN; Stage Crew; Nwsp Stf; Yrbk Stf; Lit Mag; Socr; Tennis; Acdmc Schlrshp HS 85-88; Pre Coll Pgm Carnegie-Mellon; Bio.

SMITH, KRISTINE; Donegal HS; Mount Joy, PA; (3); 39/160; Church Yth Grp; Library Aide; Band; Church Choir; Jazz Band; Mrchg Band; School Play; Nwsp Sprt Ed; Rep Frsh Cls; Mgr(s); Natl Hist & Gov Awd 85-86; Acad All Amer Schlr Awd 86-87; Rotary Intl Ldrs Conf 87; Comp Sci.

SMITH, KRYSTAL; Lancaster Catholic HS; Columbia, PA; (3); 89/206; Church Yth Grp; Pep Clb; Service Clb; Varsity Clb; Chorus; School Musical; Stage Crew; Variety Show; Var Cheerleading; Hon Roll; Hstry Day Awd 86; Lockhaven; Soclgst.

SMITH, KURT; James M Coughlin HS; Plains, PA; (3); 9/362; Trs Key Clb; Jazz Band; Mrchg Band; Orch; Symp Band; Yrbk Ed-Chief; Rep Frsh Cls; Rep Stu Cncl; JETS Awd; NHS; Wm Proach Mem Awd Hghst Acdmc Av 85; Rtry Ldrshp Camp Dist 741 86; Natl Yth Salute 87; Chem Engrng.

SMITH, LAURA; Bedford HS; Bedford, PA; (3); FBLA; Band; Chorus; Concert Band; Mrchg Band; Pep Band; Hon Roll; Var L Bsktbl; Var L Sftbl; Central Penn; Ct Rprtg.

SMITH, LAURA; Meadville Area SR HS; Meadville, PA; (4); Hosp Aide; Office Aide; Ski Clb; Nwsp Stf; Yrbk Stf; Rep Sr Cls; Rep Stu Cncl; High Hon Roll; Hon Roll; NHS; Penn ST U; Nrsng.

SMITH, LAURA; Northern York HS; Dillsburg, PA; (3); 94/232; SADD; JV Mgr(s); Hon Roll; Church Yth Grp; Spanish Clb; Ed Yrbk Stf; Cheerleading; Stat Socr; Harrisburg CC 87-88; Harrisburg CC; Dancing.

SMITH, LAURIE S; Central HS; Martinsburg, PA; (4); 13/190; FNA; GAA; Pres JA; Chorus; Cit Awd; NHS; Church Yth Grp; Hon Roll; NEDT Awd; Roaring Spring BPW Grl Of Mnth 87; Blair Cnty Dairy Princss 86-87; PA Gvrnrs Schl Ag 86; IN U Of PA; Nrsng.

SMITH, LEAH; Conemaugh Valley HS; Conemaugh, PA; (3); 15/109; Church Yth Grp; Pep Clb; Band; Concert Band; Mrchg Band; Rep Stu Cncl; JV Var Bsktbl; JV Var Vllybl; Jr NHS; NHS; Tribune-Democrat Newspaper Carrier Of Month 86; Spch Thrpy.

SMITH, LEIGH ANN; Fort Le Boeuf HS; Waterford, PA; (3); 20/220; Church Yth Grp; Dance Clb; Church Choir; Concert Band; Flag Corp; Mrchg Band; School Musical; Yrbk Stf; Var Trk; High Hon Roll; Acad Ahct Awd 85; Edinboro U Of PA; Nrsg.

SMITH, LESA; Red Lion SR HS; Red Lion, PA; (3); 17/342; Church Yth Grp; Hosp Aide; Chorus; Flag Corp; Mrchg Band; School Musical; Hon Roll; Natl Music Hnr Soc 87; Ed.

SMITH, LESLIE; Chambersburg Area SR HS; Fayetteville, PA; (4); 97/553; Red Cross Aide; Variety Show; Yrbk Bus Mgr; Sec Soph Cls; Sec Jr Cls; Sec Sr Cls; Pres Stu Cncl; Var Capt Cheerleading; Hon Roll; Voice Dem Awd; Marymount U Of VI; Comms Arts.

SMITH, LESLIE; Fannett-Metal HS; East Waterford, PA; (3); Varsity Clb; Yrbk Stf; Sftbl; Hon Roll; Comp.

SMITH JR, LESLIE V; Brockway Area HS; Brockport, PA; (4); 4/89; Pres Church Yth Grp; Drama Clb; Thesps; Varsity Clb; Pres Band; Pres Sr Cls; L Bsktbl; DAR Awd; High Hon Roll; VP NHS; PTA Teachers Schlrshp 87; Clarion U.

SMITH, LEWIS; Western Wayne HS; Waymart, PA; (3); Boy Scts; Church Yth Grp; FFA; Im Bowling; JV Ftbl; JV Mgr(s); FFA Bowling Trophy 2nd Pl 150 Avg 86; Lackawanna Bus Schl; Bus.

SMITH, LINDA; Bald Eagle Area HS; Howard, PA; (4); French Clb; SADD; Rptr Nwsp Rptr; Ed Nwsp Stf; Hon Roll; Chorus; Otstndng Acctng Stu Awd 87; SR Exctv Cmmtte 87; Fctly Hnr Schlrshp 87; Acctng.

SMITH, LISA; Blairsville SR HS; Blairsville, PA; (3); FNA; Girl Scts; Red Cross Aide; Stu Cncl; Sftbl; Trk; Hon Roll; US Air Force; Law Enfrcmnt.

SMITH, LISA; Somerset Area SR HS; Somerset, PA; (3); 27/231; Church Yth Grp; English Clb; French Clb; SADD; Band; Color Guard; Concert Band; Mrchg Band; JV Vllybl; Hon Roll; Vrsty S Ltr Band 85-86; JV S Ltr Vllybl 86; Vrsty S Ltr Hnr Roll 87; UPJ; Nrsng.

SMITH, LISA MARIE; Hampton HS; Allison Park, PA; (3); Cmnty Wkr; Ski Clb; Spanish Clb; Powder Puff Ftbl; High Hon Roll; Hon Roll.

SMITH, LORI; Venango Christian HS; Oil City, PA; (4); 7/36; Model UN; Yrbk Stf; Rep Frsh Cls; Rep Soph Cls; VP Sr Cls; Rep Stu Cncl; JV Bsktbl; Var Sftbl; Hon Roll; Pennzoil Schlrshp 87; Old Dominion U.

SMITH, LORI ANN; Clearfield Area HS; Clearfield, PA; (2); Key Clb; Varsity Clb; Band; Chorus; Concert Band; Mrchg Band; Var JV Cheerleading; Im Gym; Var JV Pom Pon; Im Socr; Physcl Ftns Awd 85-87; All Amer Chrldr Fnlst 86; PA ST U; Accntng.

SMITH, LURINDA; South Side HS; Georgetown, PA; (3); Trs Church Yth Grp; Cmnty Wkr; 4-H; Lib Band; Pep Band; School Musical; 4-H Awd; Hon Roll; Pltcl Sci.

SMITH, LYNN; Connellsville Area SR HS; Vanderbilt, PA; (2); Church Yth Grp; Computer Clb; Office Aide; Teachers Aide; Chorus; School Musical; Stage Crew; Pres Soph Cls; Rep Stu Cncl; Hon Roll; Yng Astrnt Prg 85-86; Spnsh.

SMITH, MARCIA S; Owen J Roberts HS; Pottstown, PA; (2); Key Clb; Hon Roll.

SMITH, MARGARET; Beaver Falls SR HS; Darlington, PA; (3); 35/170; Church Yth Grp; Drama Clb; French Clb; Q&S; Thesps; Chorus; Madrigals; Stage Crew; Yrbk Stf; Trk; Comp Tech.

SMITH, MARIA; Eastern York HS; York, PA; (4); Chorus; Yrbk Rptr; Yrbk Stf; Drm Mjr(t); Rep Stu Cncl; JV Capt Cheerleading; Im Gym; Var Mgr(s); High Hon Roll; Hon Roll; Acctng.

SMITH, MARK; Donegal HS; Maytown, PA; (2); Band; Concert Band; Jazz Band; Mrchg Band; Nwsp Stf; Hon Roll; Hnrbl Mntn-Earth & Envrnmntl Sci-Sci & Engrng Fair 87; Phys Ther.

SMITH, MARK; Southern Huntingdon County HS; Rockhill Furnace, PA; (4); 6/120; Varsity Clb; Bsbl; Co-Capt Ftbl; Powder Puff Ftbl; Wt Lftg; Bausch & Lomb Sci Awd; Dnfth Awd; NHS; Ntl Merit Ltr; Natl Ldrshp & Svc Awd 85-86; Mid-Penn Ftbl Schlrshp & Distngshd Athl Awd 87; Grove City Coll; Elec Engrng.

SMITH, MARTY E; Union HS; Parker, PA; (3); 6/94; Aud/Vis; Sec Church Yth Grp; Library Aide; SADD; Capt Color Guard; Mrchg Band; Hon Roll; Prfct Atten Awd; Rural Elec Yth Tour Washington DC 87; PAFC Smmr Inst 87; Acctng.

SMITH, MATT; Ft Le Boeuf HS; Waterford, PA; (2); High Hon Roll; Hon Roll.

SMITH, MATT; Octorara Area HS; Christiana, PA; (3); 5/162; FFA; VICA; Stage Crew; Nwsp Stf; Trs Jr Cls; Rep Stu Cncl; High Hon Roll; NHS.

SMITH, MATT; Valley HS; New Kensington, PA; (3); 1/255; Chess Clb; Pres Church Yth Grp; VP JA; Math Tm; VP Science Clb; Trs Chorus; High Hon Roll; NHS; Rotary Awd; Exploring; LEAPS Sci Prgm Buhl Sci Cntr Pittsbrgh PA 86; Aerospc Engrng.

SMITH, MELISSA; Bishop Guilfoyle HS; Altoona, PA; (3); Church Yth Grp; SADD; Lib Band; Lib Chorus; Church Choir; Concert Band; Mrchg Band; Music.

SMITH, MICHAEL; Bald Eagle-Nittany HS; Mill Hall, PA; (3); 1/148; Model UN; Pres Frsh Cls; Rep Stu Cncl; Var Bsbl; Var Bsktbl; Hon Roll; VP NHS; NEDT Awd; French Clb; Varsity Clb; Outstndng 8th Grade Boy 84; Cntrl PA Hugh O Brian Ldrshp Smnr 86.

SMITH, MICHAEL; Hempfield Area SR HS; Irwin, PA; (3); Art Clb; Church Yth Grp; Cmnty Wkr; Computer Clb; Pep Clb; Ski Clb; Cit Awd; Prfct Atten Awd; U Of Pittsburgh; Engrng.

SMITH, MICHAEL; Middleburg HS; Middleburg, PA; (3); Aud/Vis; Church Yth Grp; Computer Clb; German Clb; Bsbl; High Hon Roll; Hon Roll; Williamsport CC; Elec Lab Tech.

SMITH, MICHAEL; Neshaminy HS; Levittown, PA; (2); 345/875; Dance Clb; Pep Clb; Ski Clb; Chorus; Stage Crew; Diving; Gym; Trk; Vllybl; Wt Lftg; Auto Engr.

SMITH, MICHAEL; Peabody HS; Pittsburgh, PA; (4); 7/292; FCA; French Clb; Sec Frsh Cls; VP Soph Cls; Trs Jr Cls; Var L Ftbl; High Hon Roll; NHS; Prfct Atten Awd; Acad All Amer 85-86; Engrng.

SMITH, MICHAEL D; York Suburban SR HS; York, PA; (4); 4/187; Church Yth Grp; Concert Band; Mrchg Band; School Musical; Yrbk Stf; Hon Roll; JETS Awd; Sec NHS; Ntl Merit Ltr; Acadc Awd 84-87; York Sbrbn Acadc Mdl Wnr 87; Chmbr Cmmrc Dstgshd Acadc Hnrs Awd 87; Cornell U; Engr.

SMITH, MICHAEL P; Archbishop Ryan HS For Boys; Philadelphia, PA; (3); 7/414; Church Yth Grp; VP Civic Clb; Computer Clb; Spanish Clb; Lit Mag; JV Trk; High Hon Roll; NHS; Hugh O Brian Yth Fndtn Ldrshp Awd 86.

SMITH, MICHELE; Bishop Neumann HS; Jersey Shore, PA; (3); 5/41; FBLA; Model UN; High Hon Roll; Hon Roll; Hghst Avg Alb III, Trig, Accl Eng III & Frnch III; Hnrb Mntn Frnch Cont; Penn Qstr Prjct Hsty Rsrch; U Of PA; Fin.

SMITH, MICHELE LYNN; Canon Mc Millan SR HS; Canonsburg, PA; (3); Art Clb; Sec Trs Church Yth Grp; Office Aide; Ski Clb; Band; Co-Capt Color Guard; School Musical; Nwsp Stf; Hon Roll; Peer Cnslg 86-87; Advrtsg.

SMITH, MICHELLE; Annville-Cleona HS; Annville, PA; (3); 16/127; Church Yth Grp; Chorus; JV Fld Hcky; JV Sftbl; NHS; English Essay Cont; Equine.

SMITH, MICHELLE; Conemaugh Twp HS; Hollsopple, PA; (3); 15/121; Pres Sec Church Yth Grp; Trs Spanish Clb; Concert Band; Mrchg Band; Im Socr; Hon Roll; School Musical; Schlrshp Pin 84-85; Spnsh Awd 84-85.

SMITH, MICHELLE; Hempfield SR HS; Youngwood, PA; (3); Office Aide; Pep Clb; Science Clb; Spanish Clb; VICA; High Hon Roll; Hon Roll; Pittsburg Beaty Acad; Cosmtlgy.

SMITH, MICHELLE; Jefferson County Vocatnl Tech Schl; Reynoldsville, PA; (3); Rep Church Yth Grp; Pres DECA; 4-H; Girl Scts; Chorus; Church Choir; School Musical; Yrbk Stf; Pres Soph Cls; Pres Jr Cls; Early Chldhd Dvlpmnt.

SMITH, MICHELLE JEAN; Chartiers Valley HS; Bridgeville, PA; (4); 47/297; Pres Church Yth Grp; SADD; Thesps; Varsity Clb; Concert Band; Jazz Band; Mrchg Band; Ed Lit Mag; Var Capt Golf; Hon Roll; WV U; Math.

SMITH, MIKE; Penns Valley Area HS; Spring Mills, PA; (3); Chess Clb; FFA; SADD; Teachers Aide; Band; Concert Band; Mrchg Band; Pep Band; School Musical; Stage Crew; Farmng.

SMITH, MINDY; Red Lion Area SR HS; Brogue, PA; (3); Church Yth Grp; Library Aide; Sec Jr Cls; Rep Stu Cncl; JV Bsktbl; JV Trk; JV Var Vllybl; Hon Roll; Central PA Bus Coll; Med Secty.

SMITH, MISSIE; Spring-Ford SR HS; Royersford, PA; (3); 46/256; Church Yth Grp; German Clb; Band; Church Choir; Concert Band; Jazz Band; Mrchg Band; Orch; Pep Band; Mgr(s); Mntl Hlth.

SMITH, NICOLE; Quaker Valley HS; Sewickley, PA; (2); JA; Office Aide; Service Clb; Chorus; School Musical; Yrbk Rptr; Yrbk Stf; Cheerleading; Hon Roll; Special Merit Awd Svc Clb.

SMITH, NICOLE; Seton La Salle HS; Pittsburgh, PA; (3); High Hon Roll; Hon Roll; Robert Morris Coll; Bus Adm.

SMITH, NIKKI; Hershey SR HS; Hershey, PA; (3); 6/209; Church Yth Grp; FNA; Chorus; L Capt Bsktbl; L Capt Fld Hcky; L Capt Sftbl; Cit Awd; High Hon Roll; NHS; Model UN; Am Lgn Aux Dstngshd Achvt 84 & 85; Ndl Wnnr Both PA & Natl Sci Olympiad 85.

SMITH III, OTIS CHARLES; Cathedral Prep; Erie, PA; (3); 80/193; Im Bsktbl; Var L Ftbl; Var Trk; Var Wt Lftg; Hon Roll; 2nd Hnrs Awd 84-85; Bus.

SMITH, PAMELA; Moon HS; Coraopolis, PA; (4); Key Clb; Sec Trs Q&S; Nwsp Phtg; Yrbk Ed-Chief; Yrbk Phtg; Hon Roll; NHS; Photo Apprenticeship 86; Jrnlsm Awd 85; OH U; Photo.

SMITH, PAMELA; Southallegheny JR SR HS; Elizabeth, PA; (4); 2/183; Y-Teens; Trs Band; Lib Concert Band; Jazz Band; Mrchg Band; Pep Band; Powder Puff Ftbl; High Hon Roll; Prfct Atten Awd; Ofc Adm.

SMITH, PATTY; Cedar Cliff HS; Camp Hill, PA; (2); 48/292; French Hon Soc; Hon Roll.

SMITH, PAUL; High Point Baptist Acad; Mohnton, PA; (3); Church Yth Grp; Bsbl; Bsktbl; Socr; Hon Roll; Comp.

SMITH, PROMISE; G A R Memorial HS; Wilkes-Barre, PA; (4); French Clb; Hosp Aide; Office Aide; Ski Clb; SADD; Chorus; Stage Crew; Var L Cheerleading; Bausch & Lomb Sci Awd; God Cntry Awd.

SMITH, RANDALL; Pottstown HS; Pottstown, PA; (3); 4/155; French Clb; Pres Key Clb; Ski Clb; Nwsp Rptr; Nwsp Stf; Yrbk Stf; JV Bsbl; High Hon Roll; NHS; PA ST U; Elec Engrng.

SMITH, REBECCA; Altoona Area HS; Roaring Spring, PA; (4); 199/618; Office Aide; Spanish Clb; Rep Stu Cncl; Var Gym; Var Swmmng; U Of Pgh; Pre Med.

SMITH, REBECCA; G A R Memorial HS; Wilkes-Barre, PA; (4); Ski Clb; Sftbl; Hon Roll; NHS.

SMITH, REBECCA; St Marys Area HS; Saint Marys, PA; (4); 5/303; Hosp Aide; Band; Concert Band; Mrchg Band; Rep Stu Cncl; Var L Crs Cntry; Var L Trk; Gov Hon Prg Awd; Hon Roll; NHS; PA Govrs Schl For Intl Stud 86; Franklin/Marshall Coll; Pre-Med.

SMITH, REBECCA; Wyoming Area HS; West Pittston, PA; (3); 21/250; Aud/Vis; Church Yth Grp; Drama Clb; Trs French Clb; Key Clb; School Play; Stage Crew; French Hon Soc; High Hon Roll; NHS; Penn St Engl Awd 85; NY U; Theatre Arts.

SMITH, REGINA; Freeland HS; White Haven, PA; (3); 11/80; FBLA; Pep Clb; Spanish Clb; Band; Yrbk Stf; Bsktbl; Var JV Cheerleading; Ftbl; Hon Roll; Jr NHS; RN.

SMITH, RENEE; Central Cambria HS; Ebensburg, PA; (2); Art Clb; Church Yth Grp; JA; Concert Band; Drm Mjr(t); Mrchg Band; Pep Band; Var Sftbl; L Swmmng; Hon Roll.

SMITH, RENEE; Holy Name HS; Reading, PA; (3); 31/119; Church Yth Grp; FBLA; Hon Roll; Bus Admn.

SMITH, RENEE; Meadville Area SR HS; Meadville, PA; (2); Church Yth Grp; Rep Stu Cncl; JV Cheerleading; Hon Roll; Cmnty Wkr; Concert Band; Phys Ed Hnr Stu 86; Yth Ftnss Achvt Awd 87; Dntl Hygnst.

SMITH, RENEE M; Penn Cambria HS; Gallitzin, PA; (4); 33/209; PAVAS; Spanish Clb; SADD; Variety Show; Capt Cheerleading; Hon Roll; Pres Phys Ftns Awd 84-87; Stu Mnth 87; Phys Ftns, Poise, Apprnc Awds Jr Miss Schlrshp Pgm 86; IN U Of PA; Hlth Educ.

SMITH, RHONDA; Parkland HS; Allentown, PA; (2); Band; Concert Band; High Hon Roll; Hon Roll; Pres Schlr; Principals List 85-87; Areronticl Engr.

SMITH, RICHARD; Brownsville Area HS; Brownsville, PA; (3); VP Sec Church Yth Grp; Trs FBLA; Library Aide; Variety Show; High Hon Roll; Hon Roll; FBLA Bus Math Rgn 1st Pl, PA St 6th Pl 86; Eastern Nazarene Coll; Acctng.

SMITH, RICHARD; Northwestern Lehigh HS; Germansville, PA; (3); SADD; Concert Band; Stu Cncl; JV Ftbl; JV Trk; Var Wrstlng; Hon Roll; Trs NHS; ST Stud Cncl Conf 86; Camp Ladore 87; Area Stud Forums 87; Med.

SMITH, ROBERT; Churchill HS; Pittsburgh, PA; (4); 26/192; Pres Orch; High Hon Roll; JP Sousa Awd; VP Band; VP Concert Band; VP Mrchg Band; Mgr Stage Crew; Penn ST; Engrng.

SMITH, ROBERT; Girard College; Philadelphia, PA; (3); 16/32; Boy Scts; Chess Clb; Computer Clb; Exploring; Ski Clb; Im Bowling; JV Socr; Var L Tennis; Im Vllybl; Hon Roll; Ltr; Morehouse; Tele Comms.

SMITH JR, ROBERT J; Lower Dauphin HS; Hummelstown, PA; (3); Teachers Aide; School Play; Variety Show; Nwsp Stf; Yrbk Stf; Lit Mag; Pres Soph Cls; JV Var Bsktbl; High Hon Roll; Church Yth Grp; Hghst Achvt Awd Math, Engl & Drama 85, Math Engl, Music & Hstry 86; 1st Pl Sci Fair 86; Brdcstng.

SMITH, RONALD; Lakeland JR SR HS; Jermyn, PA; (4); French Clb; Capt Ftbl; Wt Lftg; Hon Roll; Spring Garden Coll; Arch.

SMITH, RUTHANNE; Leechburg HS; Leechburg, PA; (3); Hon Roll; New Len Commercial; Bus.

SMITH, RYAN D; Exeter Township HS; Reading, PA; (2); French Clb; Var L Bsbl; Var L Ftbl; Hon Roll; Bsbl Achvt Plque 87; Robotics Engr.

SMITH, SABINA; Oswayo Valley HS; Shinglehouse, PA; (3); AFS; French Clb; Ski Clb; Varsity Clb; Band; Concert Band; Mrchg Band; Yrbk Stf; Var Stat Bsktbl; Var JV Cheerleading; Bus Mgmt.

SMITH, SANDRA; Butler Area SR HS; Butler, PA; (3); French Clb; SADD; Band; Mrchg Band; Orch; School Musical; Jr NHS; Westminster Hnrs Band & Acdmc Achvt Awd 87; Schltc Awd 86; Math.

SMITH, SARAH C; Little Flower Catholic HS; Philadelphia, PA; (3); 134/322; Church Yth Grp; Chorus; Church Choir; School Musical; School Play; Stage Crew; Sec Frsh Cls; Im Bsktbl; Vllybl; Spnsr-A-Stu Knghts Columbus 86-88; Bio.

SMITH, SCOTT; Lebanon Catholic HS; Jonestown, PA; (3); Chess Clb; German Clb; Science Clb; Var L Bsbl; Bsktbl; Ftbl; Penn St; Elctrcl Engnrng.

SMITH, SEAN; E L Meyers HS; Wilkes Barre, PA; (3); Boy Scts; Exploring; Band; Concert Band; Jazz Band; Mrchg Band; Var Swmmng; High Hon Roll; JETS Awd; Jr NHS; Egl Sct Awd 87; Elec Engr.

SMITH, SEAN R; Exeter HS; Birdsboro, PA; (3); Boy Scts; Band; Concert Band; Jazz Band; Mrchg Band; Pep Band; JV Trk; JV Wrstlng; Music Ed.

SMITH, SHANI; Beth-Center SR HS; Marianna, PA; (2); Band; Concert Band; Mrchg Band; Socr; Sftbl; Vllybl; Med.

SMITH, SHANNON; Penncrest HS; Media, PA; (3); Church Yth Grp; NAACP; JV Bsktbl; JV Fld Hcky; Var Trk; Var Vllybl; Yth Svc Awd 86; Vrsty Ltr Vllybl 84; Untd Negro Coll Fund Cert Of Apprctn 86; W Chester U; Bus Admin.

SMITH, SHANNON; Sacred Heart HS; Jermyn, PA; (4); FFA; Spanish Clb; Chorus; School Play; Yrbk Stf; Rep Jr Cls; High Hon Roll; NHS; PA ST U; Cmnctns.

SMITH, SHARON; Columbia-Montour AVTS; Drums, PA; (3); VP 4-H; Letterman Clb; Yrbk Stf; Var L Cheerleading; L Stat Ftbl; Trk; 4-H Awd.

SMITH, SHARON; Interboro SR HS; Prospect Park, PA; (3); 4/300; Pres AFS; Spanish Clb; Band; Lcrss; Swmmng; High Hon Roll; Hon Roll; NHS; Voice Dem Awd; Nwsp Stf; Hi Q Tm 86-87; Chem.

SMITH, SHARON; Nazareth Area SR HS; Nazareth, PA; (3); 5/270; Church Yth Grp; Hosp Aide; Chorus; High Hon Roll; NHS; Acad Awd 87; Mrt Ctfct Prtcptn 87; Physcl Thrpy.

SMITH, SHAWN; Nazareth Area SR HS; Nazareth, PA; (2); Camera Clb; Church Yth Grp; Ski Clb; JV Var Bsbl; Metrlgy.

SMITH, SHAWN; W B Saul Agricultural HS; Philadelphia, PA; (3); FFA; Sec Stu Cncl; DE U; Med Tchnlgst.

SMITH, SHAWNA M; Chapel Christian Schl; West Newton, PA; (3); Church Yth Grp; Office Aide; Spanish Clb; Chorus; Mrchg Band; Symp Band; Yrbk Ed-Chief; Rep Stu Cncl; Co-Capt Cheerleading; Hon Roll; Bus Admin.

SMITH, SHERI; Biglerville HS; York Spgs, PA; (2); 15/108; Computer Clb; Spanish Clb; Bsktbl; Hon Roll; NHS.

SMITH, SHERRY Y; Chester HS; Chester, PA; (4); 16/398; Church Yth Grp; Pep Clb; Varsity Clb; Chorus; Church Choir; Nwsp Stf; Yrbk Stf; Capt Crs Cntry; Fld Hcky; Sftbl; MVP Trk Awd 87; Outstndng Effrts Alg II 86; Hero Bwl-Mile Rely 87; W Chester U; RN.

SMITH, SHIRLEY; Little Flower C G HS; Philadelphia, PA; (3); 5/331; Church Yth Grp; Sec Cmnty Wkr; Pres Computer Clb; French Clb; Girl Scts; Sec Math Tm; Nwsp Stf; Yrbk Stf; High Hon Roll; NHS; Avs Hghst Schl Scr Am HS Math Tst 87; Lttl Flwr 1st Alumnae Schlrshp 87; Villanova; Aerontcl Engrng.

SMITH, STACEY; Fairfield Area SR HS; Fairfield, PA; (3); Red Cross Aide; Ski Clb; Yrbk Stf; Stat Bsktbl; JV Trk; Var Vllybl; Hon Roll; Mst Outstndng Achvt Yrbk Stf 87; Stu Advsry Cncl SADD 87; Yrbk Bus Stff 86-87; Bus Mngmt.

SMITH, STACI; Ford City JR/Sr HS; Ford City, PA; (3); 12/160; Art Clb; Key Clb; Band; Chorus; Concert Band; Mrchg Band; Rep Frsh Cls; Rep Soph Cls; Rep Stu Cncl; PA Free Entrprs Schlrshp 87; Psych.

SMITH, STACY; Perkiomen Valley HS; Collegeville, PA; (3); Church Yth Grp; Ski Clb; Spanish Clb; SADD; Band; Stu Cncl; Cheerleading; Tennis; Hon Roll; NHS; Biol.

SMITH, STEPHANIE; Academy Of The New Church; Bryn Athyn, PA; (3); 10/30; Drama Clb; Ski Clb; Church Choir; Madrigals; Orch; School Musical; Yrbk Phtg; Yrbk Stf; Tennis; Trs NHS; Northeastern U; Bio.

SMITH, STEPHANIE; Bellefonte Area HS; Bellefonte, PA; (3); 69/200; Spanish Clb; Band; Mrchg Band; Rep Soph Cls; Rep Jr Cls; Rep Stu Cncl; Cheerleading; Mgr(s); Hon Roll; Penn ST; Soclgy.

SMITH, STEPHEN; Monsignor Bonner HS; Upper Darby, PA; (3); 12/255; Drama Clb; NFL; Nwsp Stf; Hon Roll; NHS; Trk; Latin Clb; School Play.

SMITH, SUSAN; Milton Area SR HS; New Columbia, PA; (3); 17/247; Mrchg Band; Nwsp Stf; VP Jr Cls; VP Sr Cls; Sec Stu Cncl; Var Bsktbl; Capt Crs Cntry; Powder Puff Ftbl; Trk; NHS.

SMITH, SUSAN; St Paul Cathedral HS; Pittsburgh, PA; (4); 10/56; FBLA; Library Aide; NFL; Science Clb; School Play; Stage Crew; Nwsp Rptr; Yrbk Stf; Hon Roll; NHS.

SMITH, SUZANNE; Dallas SR HS; Wyoming, PA; (3); 29/123; Nwsp Rptr; Nwsp Stf; Law.

SMITH, SYLVIA; Marion Center HS; Creekside, PA; (3); Intnl Clb; Latin Clb; Ski Clb; Varsity Clb; Concert Band; Mrchg Band; Pres Jr Cls; Capt Cheerleading; Trk; NHS; Dist Trk 85-86; USCA Tp Ten Awd Chrldng 86; Penn ST; Pre Med.

SMITH, TAMMY; Punxsy Area HS; Punxsutawney, PA; (4); Church Yth Grp; Math Tm; Spanish Clb; Variety Show; Hon Roll; IN U PA.

SMITH, TAMMY; Shenango HS; New Castle, PA; (2); Church Yth Grp; French Clb; Yrbk Stf; JV Var Sftbl; JV Var Vllybl; Jr NHS; Comp.

SMITH, TAMMY; Waynesburg Central HS; Waynesburg, PA; (3); French Clb; Color Guard; Mrchg Band; Capt Twrlr; Hon Roll.

SMITH, TERRI; Fort Cherry HS; Mc Donald, PA; (2); French Clb; FNA; Math Clb; Science Clb; Ski Clb; Mgr(s); Airlines.

SMITH, TERRY; Bethel Park HS; Bethel Park, PA; (4); Concert Band; JV Ftbl; Hon Roll; Duquesne U Schl Of Music; Music.

SMITH, TIFFANI; Montoursville HS; Montoursville, PA; (3); German Clb; Acpl Chr; Pres Chorus; Madrigals; School Musical; Rep Frsh Cls; Rep Soph Cls; Rep Jr Cls; Im Trk; Hon Roll; Lycoming Coll; Music.

SMITH, TIM; Hampton HS; Allison Pk, PA; (3); Ski Clb; Im Bowling; Hon Roll.

SMITH, TIM; Shippensburg SR; Shippensburg, PA; (3); Chess Clb; Church Yth Grp; 4-H; FFA; Im Wt Lftg; Var Wrstlng; Hon Roll; Dairy Husbndry.

SMITH, TIMOTHY; Louis E Dieruff HS; Allentown, PA; (1); 16/286; Cmnty Wkr; Debate Tm; Pres Drama Clb; Model UN; Scholastic Bowl; Band; Concert Band; Jazz Band; NCTE Awd; NHS; Wnr Socl Stud Dept Awd 86; Schlrshp Presdntl Clssrms 85; Hstry.

SMITH, TINA M; Brandywine Heights HS; Mertztown, PA; (4); 1/120; Pres VP FBLA; Trs Band; Concert Band; Mrchg Band; High Hon Roll; Trs NHS; Val; Church Yth Grp; Pep Band; Prfct Atten Awd; County Band & Dist Band Bass Clarinet 86-87; Pres Acad Ftnss Awd 87; Bloomsburg U; Accntng.

SMITH, TOM; Mc Dowell HS; Erie, PA; (2); 200/620; Debate Tm; FBLA; Letterman Clb; Ski Clb; Varsity Clb; Var Crs Cntry; Var Diving; Var Trk; IN U PA; Bus.

SMITH, TRACEY; Punxsutawney Area HS; Punxsutawney, PA; (4); French Clb; FNA; Hosp Aide; Band; Flag Corp; Variety Show; Yrbk Stf; High Hon Roll; Penn ST U; Intl Bus.

SMITH, TRACY; Central Dauphin HS; Harrisburg, PA; (3); 62/369; Church Yth Grp; Trs Exploring; SADD; Chorus; Church Choir; Madrigals; Var JV Bsktbl; Mgr(s); Vllybl; Hon Roll; Slvr Str Awd Grl Scts 84-85; IN U Of PA; Phrmcst.

SMITH, TRAVIS; Corry Area HS; Corry, PA; (2); L Ftbl; Engrng.

SMITH, TRICIA; Chestnut Ridge HS; New Paris, PA; (4); 10/137; FBLA; SADD; Pres Band; Pres Stu Cncl; Var Twrlr; Cit Awd; NHS; Concert Band; Mrchg Band; Variety Show; U S Army Rsrve Natl Schlr-Ath Awd 87; Vllybl Outstndg Ath Awd 87; Sftbl Outstndg Ath Awd 86 & 87.

SMITH, TRUDY; Senior HS; Mapleton, PA; (3); 1/67; DECA; Jr Cls; Rep Stu Cncl; Bsktbl; Score Keeper; Socr; Sftbl; Trk; Vllybl; Hon Roll.

SMITH, VERNITA C; Plymouth-Whitemarsh HS; Conshohocken, PA; (3); 78/356; Chorus; Drill Tm; Lit Mag; JV Trk; High Hon Roll; Hon Roll; Jrnlsm.

SMITH, VICKIE; Mt Pleasant HS; Mt Pleasant, PA; (4); SADD; Teachers Aide; VP Frsh Cls; Rep Soph Cls; Sec Jr Cls; Pres Sr Cls; Pres Stu Cncl; Var Cheerleading; DAR Awd; Hon Roll; Pres Classroom Hnr; Stu Forum Hnr; St Vincent; Teaching.

SMITH, VIRGINIA; Moon SR HS; Coraopolis, PA; (3); DECA; FBLA; Chorus; Flag Corp; Sec Frsh Cls; High Hon Roll; Hon Roll; Howard U; Bus Admin.

SMITH III, WARREN; Brownsville Area HS; East Millsboro, PA; (3); Am Leg Boys St; Church Yth Grp; Ski Clb; SADD; JV Wrstlng; High Hon Roll; Med.

SMITH, WENDI; Delone Catholic HS; Gettysburg, PA; (3); 9/167; School Musical; Nwsp Stf; Lit Mag; Cheerleading; Hon Roll; NHS; Spnsh Awd; Bus Mngt.

SMITH, WENDY; Pleasant Valley HS; Kunkletown, PA; (4); 1/173; Math Tm; Pep Clb; Ski Clb; Varsity Clb; Nwsp Stf; Rep Frsh Cls; Rep Soph Cls; Rep Jr Cls; Rep Sr Cls; Rep Stu Cncl; Top Sci & Hstry 84-85; Top Engl & German III 85-86; Top 20 Cls 83-87; FL Inst Of Tech; Aerospc Engr.

SMITH, WILLIAM; Greater Johnstown HS; Johnstown, PA; (4); #124 In Class; Hon Roll; Cambria Rowe Bus Coll; Bus.

SMITH, WILLIAM; Jeannette HS; Jeannette, PA; (3); 45/135; French Clb; Var Bsbl; Var Bsktbl; Var Golf; Hon Roll.

SMITH, WILLIAM; Lampeter Strasburg HS; Lancaster, PA; (3); 2/148; AFS; Church Yth Grp; FBLA; Band; Nwsp Sprt Ed; Nwsp Stf; Hon Roll; NHS; Lang Arts, German & Social Studies Schlr Awds & PA Governors Bus Schl Alternate 87; Mathmetics.

SMITH, YVONNE; The Baptist HS; Dalton, PA; (4); VP Sec Church Yth Grp; Yrbk Bus Mgr; Yrbk Ed-Chief; Yrbk Rptr; Yrbk Stf; Var Bsktbl; Var Cheerleading; Hnr Choir 85-87; Choir 1st Pl St 84-86; Art 1st Pl Regional 84; U Of Miami.

SMITH, ZANETTA; Philadelphia HS For Girls; Philadelphia, PA; (1); Church Yth Grp; Orch; Stage Crew; Tennis; Prfct Atten Awd; Stu Of Mntlly Gftd Pgm 86-87; Howard U; Psych.

SMITHMYER, ANN; Bishop Carroll HS; Loreho, PA; (4); 13/107; Pep Clb; Ski Clb; SADD; Pres Stu Cncl; Stat Bsktbl; L Crs Cntry; L Trk; DAR Awd; Hon Roll; VP NHS; Hugh O Brian Ldrshp Awd 84; Nrsng.

SMITHNOSKY, BRENDA; Connellsville Are SR HS; Mtpleasant, PA; (3); 16/550; Am Leg Aux Girls St; Dance Clb; VP Pres Pep Clb; Chorus; School Musical; Capt Cheerleading; High Hon Roll; Jr NHS; Rep Stu Cncl.

SMITLEY, JULIE; Mt Pleasant Area HS; Mt Pleasant, PA; (3); English Clb; German Clb; Ski Clb; Band; Color Guard; Concert Band; Mrchg Band; Nwsp Stf; Yrbk Stf; Capt Twrlr.

SMITRESKI, ROSEANN; Wm Allen HS; Allentown, PA; (2); Church Yth Grp; Drama Clb; Girl Scts; JA; Leo Clb; Hon Roll.

SMOKER, CAROL A; Pequea Valley HS; Intercourse, PA; (4); AFS; FBLA; GAA; Varsity Clb; Color Guard; Mrchg Band; Bsbl; Capt Bsktbl; Var Fld Hcky; Golf; Prfct Atten 84-85; 4th Pl Typg Cmptn W/FBLA 86; Bank Of Lanc Co Schlrshp, PSI Schlrshp 87; Central PA; Admin Asstnt.

SMOKER, LONNIE; Lancaster Mennonite HS; Intercourse, PA; (3); 25/150; Trs Church Yth Grp; JV Bsktbl; JV Mgr(s); Hon Roll; Ntl Merit Ltr; Eastern Momonite & Drexel; Engr.

SMOKER, REBECCA; Central SR HS; York, PA; (2); Chorus; Flag Corp; Mrchg Band; School Musical; School Play; Stage Crew; Hon Roll; Prfct Atten Awd; High Hon Roll; PA U; Med Rltd.

SMOKOVICH, ROBERT; Richland HS; Gibsonia, PA; (2); Red Cross Aide; Concert Band; Jazz Band; Mrchg Band; Orch; Trs Frsh Cls; Var L Crs Cntry; Amer Red Crss Ldrshp Ctr Stf 87; Cmnctns.

SMOLA, TARA; Penn Hills SR HS; Pittsburgh, PA; (3); Spanish Clb; Varsity Clb; L Var Gym; Hon Roll; Prfct Atten Awd; Psych.

SMOLAK, ANDREA; Stroudsburg HS; Delaware Wtr Gap, PA; (2); 7/310; French Clb; FBLA; Band; Concert Band; Mrchg Band; JV Fld Hcky; Var Swmmng; Var Trk; High Hon Roll; NHS; 1st Pl Awd Bus Math 86; Upper 10 Pct Cls 85-86 & 86-87; Crimnl Justc.

SMOLEN, RENEE; Hazleton SR HS; Hazleton, PA; (2); Am Leg Aux Girls St; Dance Clb; French Clb; Pep Clb; Y-Teens; Nwsp Rptr; Cheerleading; Gym; Hon Roll; Pres Schlr; Drama.

SMOLKE, HEATHER; Our Lady Of Lourdes Regional HS; Shamokin, PA; (4); 16/92; AFS; Drama Clb; Library Aide; Pep Clb; Spanish Clb; SADD; School Play; Variety Show; Var Capt Cheerleading; Hon Roll; Awd 2nd Pl Acctng SR Yr; 1st Pl Awd Child Develpomnt SR Yr; Elizabethtown Coll; Pre Law.

SMOLKO, TOM; Red Land HS; New Cumberland, PA; (4); 2/265; Church Yth Grp; Quiz Bowl; Spanish Clb; SADD; Nwsp Stf; Pres Sr Cls; JC Awd; NHS; Ntl Merit Ltr; Sal.

SMOLSKIS, KAREN; Minersville Area HS; Pottsville, PA; (4); 6/112; German Clb; Pep Clb; Stage Crew; Yrbk Stf; Sec Jr Cls; Var L Bsktbl; Var L Crs Cntry; Var L Sftbl; High Hon Roll; VP NHS; Jr Garland Grp-Sr Garland Grp 86-87; Bsktbl Awd; Bucknell; Engrng.

SMOOT, ANN E; The Agnes Irwin Schl; Devon, PA; (4); Church Yth Grp; Cmnty Wkr; Chorus; Church Choir; Madrigals; Teachers Aide; Thesps; Stu Cncl; French Hon Soc; High Hon Roll; Clsscs Prz 85 & 86; Frnch Prz 86; Hghst Genrl Avg Awd 84-86.

SMOUSE, JEFF; Kittanning SR HS; Worthington, PA; (3); 24/226; L Ice Hcky; High Hon Roll; Hon Roll; NHS; Accntnt.

SMOYER, DIANE; Cumberland Valley HS; Camp Hill, PA; (3); 24/484; AFS; Church Yth Grp; Cmnty Wkr; Intnl Clb; Key Clb; Latin Clb; Political Wkr; Speech Tm; Nwsp Ed-Chief; Lit Mag; Awd Outstndg Svc To Yth Understanding Exchg Pgm 86; Awd Excllnc Langs Frnch & Latin; Natl Yng Ldrs Cnf; Smith Coll; Intl Relations.

SMUCK, DAVID; Elizabethtown Area HS; Elizabethtown, PA; (3); 37/224; Church Yth Grp; Thesps; Church Choir; Concert Band; Drm Mjr(t); Jazz Band; Mrchg Band; School Musical; School Play; Stage Crew; Penn ST; Aerospace Engrng.

SMULLER, ROSEMARY; Exeter SR HS; Reading, PA; (3); 48/241; Leo Clb; Spanish Clb; Band; Orch; Hon Roll.

SMUTKO, ANN; Wyoming Area HS; Exeter, PA; (3); Art Clb; Church Yth Grp; Key Clb; Ski Clb; Spanish Clb; Commrcl Art.

SMYDO, JOE; Bentworth HS; Scenery Hill, PA; (4); 13/133; PAVAS; Ski Clb; Yrbk Ed-Chief; Pres Sr Cls; Stu Cncl; DAR Awd; High Hon Roll; NHS; Pres Schlr; Pittsburgh Prss All Str Achvrs, Hse Rep Excllnce Demcrcy 87; Prm Kng 86; Washington; Jrnlsm.

SMYERS, BERTRAND; North Catholic HS; Glenshaw, PA; (4); 15/242; Art Clb; Church Yth Grp; Drama Clb; FCA; Pres German Clb; Chorus; School Play; Rep Frsh Cls; Var Capt Bsbl; Var L Bsktbl; KDKA-TV Extra Effrt Awd-Acadmc Athltc 86; Al Abrams YMCA Al-Sprts Awd-Acadc Athltc 87; Harvard U.

SMYERS, DAVID C; Huntingdon Area HS; Huntingdon, PA; (4); 7/225; Am Leg Boys St; Ski Clb; Var L Trk; JV Wrstlng; High Hon Roll; NHS; John & Elizabeth Holmes Treas Schlrshp 87-88; Deans Schlrshp 87-88; Pres Acda Ftns Awd; PA ST; Petrlm Engrng.

SMYERS, GREGORY; North Catholic HS; Glenshaw, PA; (2); Church Yth Grp; Pres Frsh Cls; Pres Soph Cls; JV Bsktbl; JV Ftbl; Hustle Awd, Al-Star Tm Westminster Coll Smr Bsktbl Schl 86.

SMYKAL, CHRISTINE; Mount Alvernia HS; Pittsburgh, PA; (3); Cmnty Wkr; Red Cross Aide; Teachers Aide; Chorus; High Hon Roll; Hon Roll; NHS; Bus Hnr Soc 87-88; Alleg CC; Nrsng.

SMYTH, KAREN; Upper Darby HS; Drexel Hill, PA; (3); French Clb; Office Aide; Rep Soph Cls; Cheerleading; Lcrss; High Hon Roll; Hon Roll; Frsh Ltr Chrldng 84-85; Vrsty Ltr Chrldng 85-86; Bus Adm.

SMYTH, MITCH; Moniteau HS; Harrisville, PA; (3); 8/140; Letterman Clb; Spanish Clb; JV Var Ftbl; Var Trk; Im Vllybl; Im Wt Lftg; Jr NHS; NHS.

SMYTH, THOMAS; Father Judge HS; Philadelphia, PA; (3); 74/402; Church Yth Grp; Cmnty Wkr; German Clb; Im Bsktbl; Im Ftbl; Med.

SNAPP, JODI; Henderson HS; Downingtown, PA; (3); 44/377; Art Clb; Computer Clb; Pres French Clb; Drill Tm; Intnl Clb; Scholastic Bowl; NHS; Physcl Thrpy.

SNAPP, KRISTI; Carry Area HS; Spartansburg, PA; (2); Sec Trs 4-H; 4-H Awd; Hon Roll.

SNARE, LORI; Hollidaysburg HS; Duncansville, PA; (4); Church Yth Grp; Science Clb; Spanish Clb; SADD; Chorus; School Musical; Im Vllybl; Flght Attndnt.

SNARE, ROBERT; Tussey Mountain HS; Saxton, PA; (4); FBLA; Nwsp Stf; Yrbk Stf; L Capt Ftbl; L Trk; Hon Roll; Jrnlsm Awd, & Pres Ftnss Awd 87; Air Force; Scrty Spclst.

SNATCHKO, JODI; Burgettstown HS; Mcdonald, PA; (3); Church Yth Grp; Library Aide; Ski Clb; Spanish Clb; Teachers Aide; Chorus; Drill Tm; Yrbk Stf; Hon Roll; Jr NHS; Chld Psych.

SNAVELY, RICHANDA; Williamsburg HS; Williamsburg, PA; (3); Church Yth Grp; VP Sec FNA; Trs Chorus; Flag Corp; Nwsp Rptr; Yrbk Stf; Rep Frsh Cls; Rep Jr Cls; Stu Cncl; JV Var Cheerleading.

SNEDEKER, WENDY L; Canon Mc Millan SR HS; Eighty Four, PA; (4); Chess Clb; Church Yth Grp; GAA; SADD; Varsity Clb; Yrbk Stf; Var L Sftbl; Im Vllybl; High Hon Roll; Hon Roll; Slippery Rock U; Educ.

SNEE, JAMES; Mid Valley HS; Olyphant, PA; (4); 12/116; Church Yth Grp; Capt L Bsktbl; Capt L Golf; Vllybl; Wt Lftg; Hon Roll; All Str Tm Strtr Bsktbl 86-87; Lady Lbrty Essy Cntst 86; Acadmc Ftns Awd 87; U Of Scranton; Acctng.

SNEERINGER, PAUL; Delone Catholic HS; Mc Sherrystown, PA; (4); 3/158; Boy Scts; Drama Clb; NFL; Band; Chorus; Yrbk Ed-Chief; Bausch & Lomb Sci Awd; JC Awd; NHS; Eagle Sct 87; Penn ST U; Sci.

SNELICK, LAURA; St Marys Area HS; St Marys, PA; (4); 7/323; Elizabethtown Acad Schlrshp 87; Pres Acad Fit Awd 87; Elizabethtown Coll; Thrpy.

SNELL, DAN; Southern Fulton HS; Needmore, PA; (3); VP Art Clb; Church Yth Grp; Cmnty Wkr; Spanish Clb; Chorus; Lit Mag; Im Bsktbl; Hon Roll; Natl Pk Srvc.

SNELL, PAUL; Southern Fulton HS; Needmore, PA; (2); Art Clb; Church Yth Grp; Spanish Clb; Im Bsktbl; Im Vllybl; High Hon Roll; Hon Roll; 2nd Pl Smmt Cnty Pblc Schls PTA Art Shw 87; Natl Pk Svc.

SNELL, SEAN; Peabody HS; Pittsburgh, PA; (4); #51 In Class; Ftbl; Cit Awd; Hon Roll; NHS; Pitt.

SNIDER, AMY; Peabody HS; Pittsburgh, PA; (4); 10/292; Exploring; Yrbk Rptr; Yrbk Stf; High Hon Roll; NHS; Prfct Atten Awd; Acad All Amer Schlr 85-87; Law.

SNISKY, GENE; Panther Valley HS; Nesquehoning, PA; (3); 47/132; Bsbl; Capt Bsktbl; Ftbl; Wt Lftg; Pottsville Area All Star Ftbl Tm 86; Hazleton Area All Star Ftbl Tm 86; Rotary All Star Bsktbl Tm 86.

SNOCK, CINDY; South Philadelphia HS; Philadelphia, PA; (3); Computer Clb; Drama Clb; Library Aide; Math Clb; Office Aide; Nwsp Stf; Hon Roll; Sons Of Italy Awd-Essy Socl Just 87.

SNODGRASS, ROSS; Sun Valley HS; Aston, PA; (3); Church Yth Grp; Exploring; SADD; Teachers Aide; Varsity Clb; Variety Show; Socr; Tennis; National Wldlf Scty; Sierra Club; Mt Alta U; Frstry.

SNODGRASS, SUSAN; Bucktail Area HS; North Bend, PA; (2); Church Yth Grp; 4-H; FHA; Hosp Aide; Letterman Clb; Varsity Clb; Y-Teens; Band; Concert Band; Mrchg Band; Williamsport Schl Cmrc; Med Sec.

SNOHA, BETH; Panther Valley HS; Summit Hill, PA; (1); 20/127; French Clb; Varsity Clb; Mrchg Band; Pep Band; Var Mgr(s); Var Score Keeper; Var Twrlr; Cit Awd; High Hon Roll; Hon Roll.

SNOKE, CARLA; Big Spring HS; Shippensburg, PA; (3); Church Yth Grp; 4-H; Band; Concert Band; Jazz Band; Mrchg Band; Powder Puff Ftbl; Var Trk; Wt Lftg; Hon Roll; Bis Spring Womens Clb Jr Of Month 86.

SNOOK, BRYAN; West Snyder HS; Beaver Spring, PA; (4); 1/95; Rep Am Leg Boys St; Boy Scts; Pres Rep Sr Cls; Rep Stu Cncl; Var L Socr; Var Capt Wrstlng; Dnfth Awd; Pres NHS; NEDT Awd; Val; Prs Scholar 87; AAL Scholar 87; Eagle Sct BSA 87; Phila Coll Phrmcy; Phrmcy.

SNOOK, PAULA; Chief Logan HS; Lewistown, PA; (3); 58/182; Computer Clb; French Clb; Library Aide; Speech Tm; Varsity Clb; Yrbk Stf; Trk; Hon Roll; Prfct Atten Awd; Cntrl PA Bus Schl; Exec Assist.

SNOW, DONNETTE C; Philadelphia High School For Girls; Philadelphia, PA; (2); Dance Clb; Hosp Aide; Office Aide; Teachers Aide; Temple U.

SNOW, HEATHER BREEN; South Park HS; Library, PA; (3); Church Yth Grp; Cmnty Wkr; Drama Clb; Thesps; Chorus; School Musical; School Play; Variety Show; Timer; Hon Roll; Psychlgy.

SNOW, JAMIE; Butler SR HS; Butler, PA; (3); Church Yth Grp; Debate Tm; Trs Latin Clb; NFL; Speech Tm; Band; Mrchg Band; Orch; School Play; Nwsp Rptr; Pre Law-Bus.

SNOW, JODY; Peters Township HS; Venetia, PA; (4); Church Yth Grp; FBLA; Thesps; Varsity Clb; Church Choir; School Play; Stage Crew; Cheerleading; Powder Puff Ftbl; Trk; Mrktng.

SNOWDON, BRENT; Dallas HS; Dallas, PA; (3); 1/270; Aud/Vis; Drama Clb; School Musical; School Play; Socr; Var Capt Tennis; High Hon Roll; Hon Roll; NHS; H O Brian Yth Ldrshp Awd 86.

SNYDER, AMY; Eastern York HS; York, PA; (3); Exploring; Hosp Aide; SADD; Chorus; Mrchg Band; Yrbk Ed-Chief; Yrbk Stf; Twrlr; Hon Roll; Geisnger Med Ctr; Nrsng.

SNYDER, AMY; Milton Area HS; Milton, PA; (4); VP Pres Spanish Clb; Varsity Clb; Yrbk Stf; Trs Jr Cls; Trs Sr Cls; Bsktbl; Cheerleading; Powder Puff Ftbl; Trk; Hon Roll; Hmcmng Qn 86; Laurel Fstvl Rep 87; PA ST; Bus Admin.

SNYDER, AMY; Phil-Mont Christian Acad; Horsham, PA; (4); Church Yth Grp; Hosp Aide; Chorus; School Play; Var Fld Hcky; Hon Roll; NHS; Samuel & Ethel Parker Mem Awd 87; Sci & Inflnc Awd 87; Natl Hon Soc 86; Soc Dstngshd Amer Stu 86; Geneva Coll; Nrsng.

SNYDER, BOBBY; Lancaster Mennonite HS; Ephrata, PA; (3); Church Yth Grp; 4-H; German Clb; Band; Rep Soph Cls; Rep Jr Cls; Rep Sr Cls; JV Socr; 4-H Awd; Hon Roll.

SNYDER, BRAD; Hampton HS; Allison Park, PA; (3); 17/221; Church Yth Grp; JA; Latin Clb; Ski Clb; Bsbl; Hon Roll; NHS.

SNYDER, BRETT; Reading Central Catholic HS; Reading, PA; (3); Boy Scts; Church Yth Grp; German Clb; Quiz Bowl; Ski Clb; Spanish Clb; School Musical; Yrbk Stf; Wrstlng; NHS; Chem.

SNYDER, BRYAN; Salisbury HS; Bethlehem, PA; (4); Key Clb; School Musical; Stage Crew; Rep Stu Cncl; Var Ftbl; Var Trk; Var Wrstlng; Hon Roll; Ftbl Schlr-Athlete 86; Congrsnl Schlr Appointment 87; Jr Acad Of Sci 3rd Pl Bio 86-87; Muhlenberg Coll; Bio.

SNYDER, CHAD; Central York HS; York, PA; (3); JA; Varsity Clb; Var L Bsbl; Var L Bsktbl; Var L Socr; High Hon Roll; Hon Roll; NHS; Rotary Awd; USNA; Engrng.

SNYDER, CHERYL A; Northern Lehigh HS; Slatedale, PA; (4); 5/136; Pres Church Yth Grp; Cmnty Wkr; School Musical; Hst Sr Cls; Stu Cncl; Hst Sr Cls; Stu Cncl; Sec Jr NHS; Pres Schlr; Cmnty Wkr; All-Schl Spllng Bee Chmpn 84; Soc Of Women Engrs Math & Sci High Hnr 87; N Lehigh Ed Assoc Schlrshp 87; Penn ST U; Education.

SNYDER, CHRIS; Brookville Area HS; Brookville, PA; (3); German Clb; Varsity Clb; Bsktbl; Ftbl; DAR Awd; Hon Roll; Engrng.

SNYDER, CHRIS; Forbes Road HS; Wells Tannery, PA; (3); Art Clb; Computer Clb; French Clb; Band; Concert Band; Jazz Band; Mrchg Band; Stage Crew; Hon Roll; Bio-Chem.

SNYDER, CHRISTINA; New Freedom Christian HS; Dallastown, PA; (3); 4/9; Church Yth Grp; Yrbk Phtg; Chorus; Hon Roll; Stu Of The Mnth Dec 85; Alg Awd For Hghst GPA 84; Maranatha Baptist Bible; Elem.

SNYDER, CHRISTINE; John S Fine HS; Nanticoke, PA; (2); FBLA; SADD; Yrbk Stf.

SNYDER, CHRISTINE; Pocono Mountain HS; Tannersville, PA; (2); Nwsp Stf; Sec Frsh Cls; Im Bsktbl; Hon Roll; E Stroudsburg U; Nrs.

SNYDER, CHRISTOPH; Mifflinburg Area HS; Lewisburg, PA; (1); Boy Scts; Church Yth Grp; German Clb; Chorus; Church Choir; God Cntry Awd; High Hon Roll; Pres Acadc Ftnss Awd 86; Engrng.

SNYDER, CINDRA; Rockwood Area HS; Rockwood, PA; (3); 4-H; SADD; Color Guard; Drill Tm; Mrchg Band; Stu Cncl; L Var Bsktbl; 4-H Awd; High Hon Roll; NHS; Outstdng Bus Stu 86-87; 3rd Pl Typng II Awd 86-87; Ntl Lang Arts Awd 84-85; Cambria-Rose Schl Of Business.

SNYDER, COLIN; Wyoming Valley West HS; Kingston, PA; (3); Ski Clb; Rep Soph Cls; Rep Jr Cls; JV Var Bsbl; Im Bsktbl; Wt Lftg; Lib Arts.

SNYDER, CRAIG; Bethel Park HS; Bethel Park, PA; (4); 142/519; Band; Jazz Band; Mrchg Band; Orch; School Musical; Symp Band; Variety Show; Yrbk Stf; PMEA Dstrct 1 Hnrs Band 85 & 86; Pmea Dstrct & Rgnl Bands 87; Penn ST; Economics.

SNYDER, DAVID; Otto Eldred JR SR HS; Duke Center, PA; (3); #3 In Class; SADD; Rptr Nwsp Stf; Stu Cncl; Bsktbl; Bausch & Lomb Sci Awd; High Hon Roll; NHS; Debate Tm; Spanish Clb; Variety Show; Sci.

SNYDER, DAVID W; Windber Area HS; Windber, PA; (3); 42/128; Chess Clb; Drama Clb; Math Clb; Spanish Clb; Speech Tm; Band; Concert Band; Mrchg Band; Hon Roll; Stu Mth 87; Psych.

SNYDER, DAWN; Bald Eagle-Nittany HS; Mill Hall, PA; (2); 29/139; Key Clb; Spanish Clb; SADD; Church Choir; Rep Stu Cncl; VP Capt Cheerleading; Prfct Atten Awd; Im Tennis; Lock Haven U; Occptnl Thrpy.

SNYDER, DAWN; Bethlehem Catholic HS; Bethlehem, PA; (3); 47/225; Ski Clb; Rep Frsh Cls; Rep Soph Cls; Rep Stu Cncl; JV Cheerleading; Var Crs Cntry; High Hon Roll; Hon Roll; Med.

SNYDER, DAWN; Hollidaysburg Area SR HS; Hollidaysburg, PA; (3); Trs Church Yth Grp; Church Choir; Stage Crew; Yrbk Stf; Lit Mag; Score Keeper; Sftbl; JV Var Vllybl; Photogrphy.

SNYDER, DEBORAH J; Elizabethtown Area HS; Elizabethtown, PA; (3); Hosp Aide; JA; JV Tennis; Gld Key Wnnr Schlstc Art Cmptn 87; RN.

SNYDER, DIANE; William Allen HS; Allentown, PA; (3); Drama Clb; JCL; School Musical; School Play; Nwsp Rptr; Nwsp Sprt Ed; Lit Mag; Hon Roll; NHS; Library Aide; Ntl Ltn Exm Awd 87; Jrnlsm.

SNYDER, DONNA; Millersburg Area HS; Millersburg, PA; (4); 8/77; Church Yth Grp; French Clb; Spanish Clb; Church Choir; Yrbk Stf; High Hon Roll; US Achvt Acad Awd 84-86fscty Of Distngshd Amer HS Stu 86; Intl Frgn Lang Awd 85; Penn State U; Frnch.

SNYDER, ELENA; Emmaus HS; Emmaus, PA; (3); 101/548; Girl Scts; Key Clb; Pep Clb; SADD; Stu Cncl; Var L Cheerleading; JV L Mgr(s); Var L Pom Pon; Hon Roll; Bus Mngmnt.

SNYDER, ELIZABETH; High Point Baptist Acad; Phoenixvl, PA; (3); 11/33; Yrbk Stf; JV Bsktbl; Var Cheerleading; Var Sftbl; Hon Roll; Intl Frgn Lang Awd 85; Rgnl & ST Art Awds 85-87; Art.

SNYDER, FRANK; Shade HS; Stoystown, PA; (2); Spanish Clb; Band; Prfct Atten Awd; Machine Shop.

SNYDER, JASON; Tunkhannock Area HS; Tunkhannock, PA; (1); 3/312; Church Yth Grp; JA; Ski Clb; Engrng.

SNYDER, JAY; Nazareth Area HS; Wind Gap, PA; (3); 13/270; Math Tm; Chorus; JV Var Bsbl; Hon Roll; Sci.

SNYDER, JENNIFER; Meadville Area SR HS; Meadville, PA; (4); 13/306; Church Yth Grp; Hosp Aide; Trs Ski Clb; Chorus; Church Choir; Concert Band; Var Socr; NHS; High Hon Roll; Vrsty Ltr Acad 84; Vrsty Ltr Girls Vrsty Socr 85; U VA; Fin.

SNYDER, JOANNA; Blair County Christian Schl; Duncansville, PA; (1); 4/25; Church Yth Grp; FTA; Teachers Aide; Chorus; Yrbk Rptr; Yrbk Stf; VP Frsh Cls; Sec Stu Cncl; Trk; High Hon Roll.

SNYDER, JOYCE; Nazareth SR HS; Stockertown, PA; (4); Church Yth Grp; Sec Band; Concert Band; Pres Jazz Band; Sec Mrchg Band; Orch; Pep Band; School Musical; Hon Roll; U Of Pittsburgh.

SNYDER, KARLA; Mifflinburg Area HS; New Berlin, PA; (1); French Clb; Key Clb; Cheerleading; Photo.

SNYDER, KATHY; Ford City HS; Ford City, PA; (4); 6/148; Computer Clb; FBLA; Spanish Clb; SADD; Teachers Aide; Rep Jr Cls; Rep Sr Cls; High Hon Roll; Sec NHS; 1st & 2nd Awds-PA JR Acdmy Sci-Cmptr Sci, Rngls & Cmptr Sci, ST Lvl 84, 85 & 86; Indiana U Of PA; Accntng.

SNYDER, KELLEY M; Northgate HS; Pittsburgh, PA; (4); 30/120; Q&S; SADD; Color Guard; Yrbk Bus Mgr; Yrbk Ed-Chief; Rep Stu Cncl; JV Cheerleading; Timer; Hon Roll; Principals Awd & N Boroughs Distngshd Yth Awd 87; U Of Pittsburgh; Elem Educ.

SNYDER, KELLI; Coudersport JR-SR HS; Coudersport, PA; (3); 4/85; Drama Clb; Co-Capt Ski Clb; School Play; Rep Frsh Cls; Rep Soph Cls; Sec Jr Cls; Stu Cncl; L Golf; Hon Roll; NHS; Make Up Artst.

SNYDER, KIM; Bishop Carroll HS; Ebensburg, PA; (3); 22/128; Pep Clb; Ski Clb; Spanish Clb; SADD; Var Cheerleading; Var Trk; Hon Roll; Med.

SNYDER, KRISTEN; Ford City JR SR HS; Ford City, PA; (3); 11/160; Hosp Aide; Band; Concert Band; Mrchg Band; Rep Frsh Cls; Var JV Sftbl; Var JV Vllybl; VP Church Yth Grp; PA Free Enterprise Week Of Cock Haven Univ 87; Comp Sci 1st Pl 85; Grove City Coll; Comp Sci.

SNYDER, LESLIE; Brookville Area HS; Brookville, PA; (3); Orch; School Musical; Symp Band; Dist Orch 86-87; Rgnl Orch 86-87; Bus Mgmt.

SNYDER, LISA; Nazareth Area HS; Tatamy, PA; (3); Church Yth Grp; Cmnty Wkr; Drama Clb; Library Aide; Band; Chorus; Church Choir; Concert Band; Drill Tm; Jazz Band; Honor Acad Band Awd 87; Northampton Area CC; Dnstry.

SNYDER, LORA; William Allen HS; Allentown, PA; (3); 190/659; JA; SADD; Rep Soph Cls; Rep Jr Cls; Var JV Bsktbl; Im Bowling; Var Powder Puff Ftbl; Hon Roll; Jr NHS; JR Bwlng Awd 87; Lehigh Cnty CC; Comp Sci.

SNYDER, LORI; Spring Grove SR HS; York, PA; (4); 40/279; Church Yth Grp; Nwsp Ed-Chief; Nwsp Rptr; Hon Roll; NHS; Mansfield U; Travel-Tourism.

SNYDER, MARCIE; West Mifflin Area HS; W Mifflin, PA; (3); 24/301; Art Clb; Pep Clb; Drill Tm; Yrbk Stf; Powder Puff Ftbl; Trk; Stat Vllybl; High Hon Roll; Hon Roll; NHS; Hnrs-Spnsh 85-87; HS PTA Phot 87-88; Stu Of PTSA; Tchr.

SNYDER, MARK; Central York SR HS; York, PA; (3); Varsity Clb; Yrbk Stf; Var L Socr; High Hon Roll; Hon Roll; L Trk; Natl Art Hnr Soc; Indr Sccr Vrsty; Acdmc Lttr; Elec Engnrng.

SNYDER, MATTHEW; Northern Bedford County HS; New Enterprise, PA; (3); Pres Church Yth Grp; Rptr FFA; Math Clb; Chorus; School Musical; Rep Stu Cncl; JV Bsktbl; JV Ftbl; Hon Roll; NHS; Penn ST U; Russian Lang.

SNYDER, MATTHEW; Pen Argyl Area HS; Pen Argyl, PA; (3); Exploring; Scholastic Bowl; Ski Clb; Concert Band; Mrchg Band; Stage Crew; Var Trk.

SNYDER, MATTHEW; West Allegheny HS; Clinton, PA; (2); Computer Clb; Science Clb; High Hon Roll; Hon Roll; C Bowmans Archry Clb 86-87; Trphy-Outstndng Stu Of Yr-AMAA 86; Yth Grp Hebrom Chrch 85-87; Carnegie Mellon U; Comp Engrng.

SNYDER, MELISSA; Tri-Valley HS; Hegins, PA; (3); 3/76; Church Yth Grp; SADD; School Musical; Yrbk Ed-Chief; Rep Trs Stu Cncl; Vllybl; High Hon Roll; Hon Roll; NHS; Carrier Yr JR Div 84; Carrier Yr SR Div 85; Math Educ.

SNYDER, MELISSA; Windber Area HS; Windber, PA; (3); Sec Church Yth Grp; French Clb; Chorus; Church Choir; Mrchg Band; JV Var Twrlr; High Hon Roll; NHS; Pres Schlr; Awd Highest Avg In French III 87; Stu Of Month 85-87; 1st Pl Majorette Squad 87.

SNYDER, MICHELLE; Parkland HS; Allentown, PA; (2); Exploring; Ski Clb; Stage Crew; JV Sftbl; Hon Roll; Elem Ed.

SNYDER, MICHELLE A; Elizabethtown Area HS; Elizabethtown, PA; (2); Spanish Clb; Nwsp Rptr; Lit Mag; Rep Jr Cls; Rep Stu Cncl; Fld Hcky; Stat Trk; Hon Roll; Reach Amer 87; Human Rltns Clb Pres 87.

SNYDER, MONICA; Lebanon Catholic HS; Lebanon, PA; (3); Church Yth Grp; Drama Clb; Science Clb; Spanish Clb; School Play; Yrbk Stf; High Hon Roll; Hon Roll; Prfct Atten Awd.

SNYDER, NANCY; Purchase Line HS; Mahaffey, PA; (4); Art Clb; Church Yth Grp; French Clb; Pep Clb; School Play; Nwsp Stf; Pres Soph Cls; Stu Cncl; High Hon Roll.

SNYDER, NANCY E; Bishop Hoban HS; Wilkes-Barre, PA; (3); FBLA; Mu Alpha Theta; Ski Clb; Concert Band; Sec Stu Cncl; Co-Capt Cheerleading; Sftbl; High Hon Roll; NHS.

SNYDER III, NELSON B; Bishop Oreilly HS; Harvey Lake, PA; (4); 3/116; Ski Clb; Band; School Play; Pres Stu Cncl; French Hon Soc; High Hon Roll; JP Sousa Awd; NHS; Ntl Merit Ltr; NEDT Awd; Hugh Obrien Ldrshp Semnr 85; Natl Yng Ldrs Conf 86; Space Sci.

SNYDER, NICOLE; Mifflinburg Area HS; Mifflinburg, PA; (1); French Clb; FHA.

SNYDER, NORA JEAN; Northwestern Lehigh HS; Slatington, PA; (3); Church Yth Grp; FFA; Hon Roll; Hortcltr.

SNYDER, PAMELA; Avon Grove HS; West Grove, PA; (3); 30/217; Hosp Aide; Teachers Aide; School Musical; Yrbk Stf; JV Vllybl; Hon Roll; Spanish Awd 85; Penn ST; Bus.

SNYDER, PATRICIA; Solanco HS; Quarryville, PA; (4); 14/241; Art Clb; Capt Pep Clb; Ski Clb; Varsity Clb; Nwsp Rptr; Var Capt Cheerleading; Powder Puff Ftbl; Hon Roll; NHS; Pres Schlr; Cngrsnl Schlr, Chalala Family Schlrshp 87; Western Civilization Awd 85; PA ST U; Elctrnc Engrng.

SNYDER, PAUL; Louis E Dieruff HS; Allentown, PA; (2); ROTC; Nwsp Phtg; Hon Roll; Jr NHS; Prfct Atten Awd.

SNYDER, PAULA; Cedar Crest HS; Lebanon, PA; (2); 43/345; Church Yth Grp; FHA; Pep Clb; Spanish Clb; JV Socr; Hon Roll; NHS; Acadc Merit Mdln Bstr Clb 85-87; Chld Care.

SNYDER, PHILLIP; Jeannette SR HS; Jeannette, PA; (3); High Hon Roll; Hon Roll; St Vincent; Vet.

SNYDER, RICHARD; Blair County Christian Schl; Duncansville, PA; (2); #3 In Class; Church Yth Grp; Debate Tm; Chorus; Yrbk Phtg; Yrbk Stf; Pres Soph Cls; Stu Cncl; L Bsktbl; Var L Socr; Trk; Keystone Christian Ed Assoc Hnrs For Art 86-87; Aacs Ntl Art Hnrs 87.

SNYDER, RICHARD; Northern Lebaron HS; Jonestown, PA; (3); JV Bsbl; Hon Roll; Elec Tech.

SNYDER, ROBERTA; Purchase Line HS; Mahaffey, PA; (2); 26/142; Church Yth Grp; Pep Clb; Scholastic Bowl; Spanish Clb; SADD; Stat Trk; High Hon Roll; Hon Roll; Prfct Atten Awd; Messiah Coll; Phys Therapy.

SNYDER, ROBIN; Bensalem HS; Bensalem, PA; (3); French Clb; JA; Radio Clb; Ski Clb; Mgr Swmmng; Hon Roll; Early Admssn Accptnce Bucks Cnty CC 87; Bucks Cnty CC.

SNYDER, RONALD; Louis E Dieruff HS; Allentown, PA; (3); 9/322; Church Yth Grp; Church Choir; Hon Roll; Jr NHS; NHS; Prfct Atten Awd; Sheet Metl Wrkr.

SNYDER, ROSEMARIE; Philadelphia HS For Girls; Philadelphia, PA; (3); 18/405; Var L Fld Hcky; Im Lcrss; Var Trk; High Hon Roll; NHS; PA Jr Acad Sci 1st Pl Regnl,2nd Pl ST 85; Beaver Coll Schlrshp 85; Arch.

SNYDER, RYAN; Palmerton Area HS; Palmerton, PA; (3); 4/170; Debate Tm; Band; Concert Band; Jazz Band; Mrchg Band; Pep Band; Var Stat Bsktbl; Var L Golf; Hon Roll; NHS; Outstndng Musician 85 & 86; Dist & Co Bands, Lions Clb Band 85-87; Gold Mdl Glf 86; Comp Sci.

SNYDER, SAMANTHA; Pleasant Valley HS; Brodheadsville, PA; (2); 22/190; Drama Clb; Ski Clb; Stage Crew; Hon Roll; Acdmc Hnr Awd 86.

SNYDER, SCOTT; William Allen HS; Allentown, PA; (3); 7/600; Pres Church Yth Grp; Acpl Chr; Chorus; Church Choir; Jazz Band; Nwsp Ed-Chief; High Hon Roll; Hon Roll; NHS; Ntl Merit Ltr; Jrnlsm.

SNYDER, SHANE; Red Lion HS; Felton, PA; (4); Computer Clb; German Clb; JA; Science Clb; Nwsp Rptr; Hon Roll; Yor Coll Of PA; Med Tech.

SNYDER, SHANNON M; Juniata Valley HS; Huntington, PA; (3); 9/86; SADD; Chorus; Concert Band; Mrchg Band; Variety Show; Trs Sr Cls; Rep Stu Cncl; JV Cheerleading; Hon Roll; NHS; Navy; Cmmnctns.

SNYDER, SUSAN; Williams Valley HS; Williamstown, PA; (3); 8/100; Chorus; Mrchg Band; VP Jr Cls; Capt Twrlr; High Hon Roll; Hon Roll; VP NHS.

SNYDER, SUSAN LEE; Salisbury SR HS; Bethlehem, PA; (3); 3/157; Cmnty Wkr; Drama Clb; Girl Scts; Hosp Aide; Key Clb; Church Choir; Mgr Fld Hcky; Var L Swmmng; High Hon Roll; NHS; Muhlenberg Coll; Bio.

SNYDER, TAMMY; Blue Mountain HS; Friedensburg, PA; (4); Pres DECA; Hon Roll; 3rd Pl ST Comp Rstrnt Mktng 86; Bus Mktng.

SNYDER, TRACY; East Juniata HS; Richfield, PA; (3); Church Yth Grp; SADD; Concert Band; Mrchg Band; School Musical; Var Sftbl; Mdrn Music Mstr 85-86; RN.

SNYDER, VANESSA; Millersburg Area HS; Millersburg, PA; (3); Cmnty Wkr; Exploring; Library Aide; Band; Yrbk Stf; Powder Puff Ftbl; Trk; Hon Roll; NEDT Awd; Ntl Merit Awd For Ldrshp 85 & 86; Ntl Merit Awd For Bio 84; Penn ST U; Sci.

SNYDER, WENDY; Dover Area HS; Dover, PA; (3); 23/270; Pres Church Yth Grp; Teachers Aide; Varsity Clb; Chorus; School Musical; Rep Frsh Cls; Var Cheerleading; High Hon Roll; Hon Roll; NHS; Shippensburg U; Acctg.

SNYDER III, WILLIAM E; Hanover Area JR/ SR HS; Ashley, PA; (3); 4/195; Boy Scts; Church Yth Grp; Model UN; School Musical; Yrbk Ed-Chief; Var L Wrstlng; Bausch & Lomb Sci Awd; Hon Roll; NHS; NEDT Awd; Chem Engrng.

SNYDER III, WILLIAM R; Milton Area SR HS; Milton, PA; (3); Am Leg Boys St; Varsity Clb; Rep Stu Cncl; Bsbl; Var Crs Cntry; Var Ftbl; Im Vllybl; Im Wt Lftg; Var Wrstlng; Crmnlgy.

SOBCZAK, KELLY; Bethel Park HS; Bethel Park, PA; (4); 48/519; Cmnty Wkr; Drama Clb; Sec FBLA; Hosp Aide; Sec JA; Office Aide; School Musical; Capt Powder Puff Ftbl; High Hon Roll; Hon Roll; Leag Wmn Schlrshp 87; St Adalberts Almn Assoc Schlrshp 87; Intern Smithsonian Inst 87; Allegheny Coll; Frnch.

SOBER, RAEANN; Leechburg Area HS; Leechburg, PA; (3); Trs Bsbl; Chorus; School Musical; School Play; Nwsp Stf; Yrbk Stf; Sec Jr Cls; Var Cheerleading; Hon Roll; NHS; High Acad Achvt Awd 86-87; Jrnlsm.

SOBIERALSKI, CASONDRA; North Acad; Pittsburgh, PA; (2); 34/630; Hon Roll; Jr NHS; Amer & European Hstry 86; Wlrd Cultures & Art 87; Art.

SOBIERALSKI, TARA; Butler Area SR HS; Butler, PA; (3); Church Yth Grp; Office Aide; Spanish Clb; JV Cheerleading; Hon Roll; Acdmc Achvmnt Awd 86-87.

SOBJAK, MICHELLE; Boyertown JR High East; Bally, PA; (1); Chorus; High Hon Roll; Hon Roll.

SOBOLEWSKI, ANGELIC; Berwick HS; Berwick, PA; (4); Key Clb; Library Aide; Chorus; Color Guard; Yrbk Bus Mgr; Nrsg.

SOBON, DANNA; Avonworth HS; Pittsburgh, PA; (1); 7/98; AFS; VP French Clb; Band; Concert Band; High Hon Roll; NHS; Ntl Merit SF; French Awd 87; Pres Acad Fit Awd 87.

SOBUS, LAURIE; Governor Mifflin SR HS; Mohnton, PA; (3); #38 In Class; Hosp Aide; JA; Y-Teens; Chorus; Cit Awd; High Hon Roll; Hon Roll; Prfct Atten Awd.

SOCCIO, MATTHEW; Lewistown Area HS; Lewistown, PA; (2); Spanish Clb; Swmmng; High Hon Roll; Acdmc Lttr Star 87; Med.

SOCHOR, JACKI; Center HS; Monaca, PA; (2); Spanish Clb; Stu Cncl; Im Bowling; JV Cheerleading; Powder Puff Ftbl; Hon Roll; Med.

SOCK, JEFFREY; Southern Columbia Area HS; Shamokin, PA; (3); 4/100; Nwsp Rptr; Stat Sftbl; High Hon Roll; NHS; Church Yth Grp; Geo & Advncd Math Awds 86-87; Acctng.

SOCKO, DENISE; Southern Columbia Area HS; Catawissa, PA; (4); 16/77; Hosp Aide; Chorus; Church Choir; School Play; Yrbk Phtg; Ed Yrbk Stf; Elks Awd; Hon Roll; NHS; Voice Dem Awd; Cert Achvmnt Comp Mth 86; Prsdntl Acdmc Ftnss Awd 87; Gregg Typng Awds 87; Bloomsburg U PA; Acctng.

SODERBERG, DAWN; Fairview HS; Fairview, PA; (4); 17/154; French Clb; Varsity Clb; Var L Crs Cntry; Var L Trk; High Hon Roll; Hon Roll; NHS; Founders Mem Fund Scholar Amer Sterilizer 87; Zonta Club II Scholar 87; IN U PA; Psych.

SODERGREN, JEFF; Grove City HS; Grove City, PA; (3); 5/202; Drama Clb; Thesps; Chorus; Mrchg Band; School Musical; School Play; Stage Crew; Swing Chorus; Pres VP NHS; Ntl Merit SF; Grove City Coll; Pre-Law.

SOETHE, SANDRA; Yough SR HS; W Newton, PA; (3); 34/236; Library Aide; VICA; Chorus; Color Guard; Mrchg Band; Hon Roll; NHS; Data Proc.

SOFFA, MELISSA; Bethlehem Catholic HS; Bethlehem, PA; (4); 3/195; Hosp Aide; Key Clb; Red Cross Aide; SADD; High Hon Roll; Kiwanis Awd; NHS; Soc Wmn Engrs Awd, German Awd 87; U Of PA; Psych.

SOFFRONOFF, MELISSA; Piux X HS; Pon Argyl, PA; (3); Letterman Clb; Pep Clb; Varsity Clb; Chorus; Church Choir; School Musical; Yrbk Ed-Chief; Yrbk Stf; Cheerleading; Powder Puff Ftbl; Moravian Coll; Elem Ed.

SOHNS, LORI J; Lakeland JR/Sr HS; Olyphant, PA; (4); 2/146; Drama Clb; Girl Scts; VP JA; Capt Scholastic Bowl; Pres VP Band; Rep Stu Cncl; NHS; Sal; U Schlrs Pgm U Of Richmond VA 87; Walter Scully Keklak Mem Awd 87; Scott Twnshp Ctzshp Awd 87; U Of Richmond VA; Indust Psych.

SOIKA, JOHN; Connellsville Area HS; Connellsville, PA; (3); Boy Scts; Cmnty Wkr; Pep Clb; Chorus; School Play; Trs Frsh Cls; Im Ftbl; Hon Roll; Crimnlgy.

SOKAC, DANIEL; Montour HS; Mckees Rocks, PA; (3); 132/277; PAVAS; Art Inst Of Pittsburgh; Vsl Art.

SOKOL, FRANK; Burrell HS; Lower Burrell, PA; (3); 8/176; Socr; High Hon Roll; Trs NHS; Prfct Atten Awd; Natl Sci Olympiad Awd 85; Co Capt & Ldng Scer Of BLADES Strt Hcky Tm 86-87; Trivia Clb 85-86; Penn ST; Engineering.

SOKOL, JENNIFER; Uniontown SR HS; Uniontown, PA; (3); 8/350; French Clb; Letterman Clb; Math Tm; VP Soph Cls; VP Jr Cls; VP Sr Cls; Stu Cncl; Cheerleading; Var L Trk; NHS; Physical Therapy.

SOKOL, KENNY; Western Beaver JR-JR HS; Industry, PA; (3); Church Yth Grp; Church Choir; Stage Crew; Var Bsbl; Ftbl; Hon Roll; NHS; U Of Pittsburgh; Dntstry.

SOKOL, SCOTT; Belle Vernon Area HS; Belle Vernon, PA; (3); Ski Clb; Pres Frsh Cls; Pres Soph Cls; Var L Golf; Penn ST; Engr.

SOKOLOSKI, PAUL; Lakeland HS; Olyphant, PA; (3); Boy Scts; Church Yth Grp; Ski Clb; SADD; Variety Show; Rep Stu Cncl; Drama Clb; JV Var Bsktbl; JV Var Ftbl; JV Var Trk; Comp Sci.

SOKOLOWSKI, DNESE; William Allen HS; Allentown, PA; (3); 1/610; Exploring; VP German Clb; JA; Ski Clb; Band; Orch; High Hon Roll; NHS; Ntl Merit Ltr; Band Awd 87; Med.

SOKOLOWSKI, MELISSA; Western Beaver HS; Midland, PA; (3); Pres Exploring; Girl Scts; Mrchg Band; Symp Band; Yrbk Stf; Cit Awd; Hon Roll; NHS; Drama Clb; Band; Fnlst Beaver Cnty Times Carrier Of Yr 866; Poltcl Sci.

SOLDAN, ALEXANDER; Montgomery Area HS; Montgomery, PA; (4); Math Tm; Yrbk Phtg; Yrbk Stf; JV Var Bsktbl; Var Trk; High Hon Roll; Hon Roll.

SOLENSKY, GINA; Hazleton HS; Hazleton, PA; (3); 12/450; Church Yth Grp; Cmnty Wkr; Hosp Aide; Leo Clb; Science Clb; Tennis; High Hon Roll; JC Awd; NHS; Pep Clb; Pres Acad Awd 84-85; Hon Ment Kings Coll Spnsh Cont 85; Bio.

SOLER, LISA; Saltsburgh JR SR HS; Clarksburg, PA; (3); Camera Clb; Drama Clb; School Play; Yrbk Stf; Off Soph Cls; Off Stu Cncl; Stat Bsktbl; Gym; JV Powder Puff Ftbl; JV Sftbl; Optmtry.

SOLI, MICHAEL; Mercyhurst Prep; Erie, PA; (4); 20/180; Church Yth Grp; Drama Clb; English Clb; PAVAS; Spanish Clb; Thesps; Acpl Chr; Band; Chorus; Church Choir; U Pittsburgh; Eng.

SOLINSKI, KELLY ANN; Lehman HS; Dallas, PA; (3); FCA; Pep Clb; Ski Clb; Bsktbl; Cheerleading; Fld Hcky; Hon Roll; Marine Bio.

SOLLENBENGEL, JOE; Cumberland Valley HS; Enola, PA; (3); 4-H; French Clb; FHA; SADD; Rep VICA; Jr Cls; Badmtn; Bsktbl; Ftbl; Sftbl; Stu Qrtr 86; Bus.

SOLLENBERGER, KIM; Big Spring HS; Newville, PA; (3); 32/258; L Band; Concert Band; Co-Capt Drill Tm; Jazz Band; Mrchg Band; VP Jr Cls; Rep Stu Cncl; JV Powder Puff Ftbl; JV L Trk; L High Hon Roll; JR Mnth Jan-Wmns Clb Big Sprg, Hnr Rll Pin A- Avg 87; Presdntl Phys Ftnss Awd 84-87; Phys Thrpy.

SOLLENBERGER, LYNELLE; Lancaster Mennonite HS; Strasburg, PA; (3); Church Yth Grp; Drama Clb; Office Aide; Speech Tm; Chorus; Orch; JV Fld Hcky; JV Var Sftbl; Hon Roll.

SOLLIE, KYLE; Phil-Mont Christian Acad; Flourtown, PA; (2); 1/55; Church Yth Grp; Band; Chorus; Stat Bsktbl; Tennis; High Hon Roll; U Of PA; Bus-Law & Admin.

SOLMAN, KELLY SUE; Bishop Boyle HS; Munhall, PA; (4); Art Clb; Dance Clb; Drama Clb; French Clb; VP Frsh Cls; Pres Jr Cls; Rep Stu Cncl; High Hon Roll; VP NHS; NEDT Awd; Prestigious Century III Schlrshp 87.

SOLOCK, SANDY; Hickory HS; Sharpsville, PA; (3); 15/180; Library Aide; Spanish Clb; Varsity Clb; Chorus; Var Bsktbl; Var Crs Cntry; Sftbl; Var Trk; Hon Roll; Phy Thrpy.

SOLOMON, AARON; Clarion Area HS; Clarion, PA; (4); 19/97; Debate Tm; Letterman Clb; ROTC; Science Clb; Pres SADD; Drill Tm; Rep Soph Cls; Ftbl; Var Wrstlng; Hon Roll; U Of MO Rolla; Aero Engrng.

SOLOMON, ANDREA; Taylor Allderdice HS; Pittsburgh, PA; (3); Art Clb; Cmnty Wkr; Computer Clb; Ski Clb; SADD; Yrbk Phtg; Fld Hcky; Hon Roll; American U; Bus.

SOLOMON, CHARLINA; Cecilian Academy HS; Philadelphia, PA; (3); Dance Clb; Drama Clb; Office Aide; Science Clb; School Musical; Prfct Atten Awd; Natl Lat Awd 86-87; Temple Coll; Sprts Med.

SOLOMON, MARTI; Norwin SR HS; N Huntingdon, PA; (3); 217/576; Church Yth Grp; Pep Clb; Spanish Clb; SADD; Chorus; Rep Stu Cncl; Var Capt Cheerleading; L Var Gym; Fnlst At All Amer Chrldr Pgnt Awd 87; NC St; Med.

SOLOMON, MONIQUE; Westinghouse HS; Pittsburgh, PA; (2); Office Aide; Political Wkr; Teachers Aide; Mrchg Band; Nwsp Bus Mgr; Bsktbl; Gov Hon Prg Awd; Hon Roll; Pres Schlr; St Schlr.

SOLOMON, PAUL; Mifflinburg HS; Millmont, PA; (1); Art Clb; Church Yth Grp; French Clb; FFA; Chorus; Church Choir; JV Bsbl; Vllybl; Hon Roll; Prfct Atten Awd; Grn Hnd Awd FFA 86-87; Jimmy Swaggarts Coll; Prchng.

SOLOMON JR, ROBERT L; Central HS; Philadelphia, PA; (4); 61/383; Boys Clb Am; Church Yth Grp; Drama Clb; Church Choir; Yrbk Stf; Stu Cncl; JV Bsktbl; Hamtpon U; Bus.

SOLOMON, TRICIA; York Catholic HS; New Freedom, PA; (3); 12/154; Drama Clb; French Clb; Latin Clb; Pep Clb; Chorus; School Musical; Nwsp Stf; Yrbk Stf; Im Bsktbl; High Hon Roll; Engl.

SOLOMON, WILLIAM E; Jim Thorpe HS; Jim Thorpe, PA; (3); 12/92; Ftbl; Wt Lftg; Hon Roll; Bio.

SOLON, DAVID W; Cumberland Valley HS; Camp Hill, PA; (4); Camera Clb; Latin Clb; PAVAS; Gov Hon Prg Awd; Gld Key Achlstc Art Awd Photo 86-87; Awd Excel Photo 86-87; Rochester Inst Tech; Photo.

SOLONOSKI III, ANDREW; Hazelton HS; Hazleton, PA; (3); 161/465; Crs Cntry; Ftbl; Trk; Wt Lftg; Wrstlng; E Stroudsburg; Physcl Thrpy.

SOLOVEY, ELIZABETH; Northeastern SR HS; Mt Wolf, PA; (2); 1/214; Chorus; School Musical; Sec Trs Stu Cncl; JV Bsktbl; L Var Trk; Var JV Vllybl; High Hon Roll; NHS; Stu Mnth, Trk Awd Mst Prmsng Prfrmr 86; Vlybl Awd Tm Spirt Awd 86-87; Trk Awd Outstndng Prfrmr 87; Med.

SOLSMAN, MARK; Abington Heights HS; Clarks Summit, PA; (2); Aud/Vis; Computer Clb; Dance Clb; Office Aide; Radio Clb; Ski Clb; Concert Band; Mrchg Band; Orch; Stage Crew; Rotary Intl Altrnt 87; Comp Sci.

SOLT, AUDREY; Brandywine Heights HS; Mertztown, PA; (4); 15/125; Band; Chorus; School Play; Sec Frsh Cls; Sec Soph Cls; Sec Jr Cls; Sec Sr Cls; Rep Stu Cncl; Var Capt Tennis; NHS; Cnty, Dist & Rgnl Chorus; Cnty Band & Orchstr; West Chester U; Music Ed.

SOLYAK, KIMBERLY ANNE; Mt Penn HS; Pennside, PA; (2); 4/65; Church Yth Grp; Cmnty Wkr; Hosp Aide; Intnl Clb; Model UN; Quiz Bowl; Science Clb; Y-Teens; Band; Chorus; HOBY Ldrshp Awd 87; Saratona Club Hstry Essay 86; U Pittsburgh; Pre-Med.

SOMA, EILEEN; Bishop Hannan HS; Scranton, PA; (4); 18/122; Church Yth Grp; Drama Clb; Chorus; Church Choir; Orch; School Musical; VP NHS; Prsdntl Acdmc Ftnss Awd 87; Music Hnrs 84-87; U Of Scranton; Med.

SOMMER, ANN C; Meadville Area SR HS; Meadville, PA; (4); 160/306; Chrmn Church Yth Grp; Key Clb; NFL; Office Aide; Pep Clb; Science Clb; Speech Tm; Chorus; Rep Stu Cncl; Hon Roll; Pre-Elem Ed.

SOMMERS, LE ANNA M; Waynesburg Central HS; Waynesburg, PA; (3); Drama Clb; French Clb; Ski Clb; Color Guard; Nwsp Stf; Twrlr; High Hon Roll; NHS; Frnch III Awd 87; Stu Of Wk 87.

SOMMERS, MICHELLE; Conneaut Lake HS; Cochranton, PA; (3); Church Yth Grp; GAA; Spanish Clb; SADD; Nwsp Rptr; Sftbl; Vllybl; High Hon Roll; Hon Roll; 2nd Rnnr Up Jr Clss Snwbll Pgnt 86; Prm Attndnt 86; Jamestown Bus Coll; Accntng.

SOMMERS, RICHARD D; Pottstown SR HS; Pottstown, PA; (4); 1/181; Key Clb; Pres Spanish Clb; Nwsp Ed-Chief; Yrbk Stf; Elks Awd; Lion Awd; NHS; Ntl Merit Ltr; Val; Temple U.

SOMOGY, STEPHEN; Troy SR HS; Troy, PA; (3); 29/184; Chess Clb; Computer Clb; Ski Clb; Bsbl; Bowling; Trk; NHS; Mech Engrng.

SON, JACQUELINE; Shady Side Acad; Monroeville, PA; (3); Cmnty Wkr; French Clb; SADD; Orch; Yrbk Stf; JV Fld Hcky; Var L Sftbl; Hon Roll; Jr NHS; Ntl Merit Ltr.

SONHLEITNER, TERESA; Central SR HS; York, PA; (3); Church Yth Grp; GAA; Im Sftbl; JV Vllybl; High Hon Roll; Crmnl Jstc.

SONNEBORN, KELLY; Waynesburg Central HS; Waynesburg, PA; (3); Drama Clb; French Clb; Key Clb; Ski Clb; SADD; Stu Cncl; Golf; Timer; Trk; High Hon Roll; Fresh Hmcmng Attendnt 85; Soph Sweethrt 86; Hnrary Stu Cncl 87; Elem Educ.

SONNEN, BECKY; Conrad Weiser HS; Richland, PA; (3); 10/179; VP 4-H; Pres FFA; Band; Concert Band; Mrchg Band; Nwsp Stf; 4-H Awd; High Hon Roll; Hon Roll; NHS; FFA 1st Pl Extemp Spkng Cntst St PA 87; Cmnctns.

SONNEN, DAVID; Conrad Weiser HS; Richland, PA; (4); 12/189; Church Yth Grp; 4-H; JCL; Key Clb; Chorus; Church Choir; School Musical; 4-H Awd; High Hon Roll; Hon Roll; Penn Quester Scholar 84; Daniel Boone Americansm Awd & Scholar 87; Millersville U; Biol.

SONNER, HEATHER; Hazleton HS; Hazleton, PA; (3); 72/435; FBLA; Pep Clb; SADD; JV Cheerleading; Hon Roll.

SONNETT, JOHN; Hampton HS; Gibsonia, PA; (4); 16/255; Church Yth Grp; Ski Clb; Spanish Clb; High Hon Roll; Rotary Awd; Westinghouse Sci Honrs Inst Awd 86-87; PA ST U; Engrng.

SONNLEITNER, WENDY; Bishop Guilfayle HS; Altoona, PA; (3); Church Yth Grp; German Clb; Color Guard; Bus.

SONON, ANDREW E; Penn Hills HS; Pittsburgh, PA; (4); 97/616; Am Leg Boys St; Boy Scts; Computer Clb; JA; Science Clb; Band; Concert Band; Mrchg Band; Off Stu Cncl; Hon Roll; Eagle Sct 86; Stu Srch Off Semi-Fnlst 85-86; IN U Of PA.

SONON, JASON; Reading HS; Reading, PA; (3); 85/709; Aud/Vis; Sec Chess Clb; Pres Computer Clb; Trs Debate Tm; Exploring; Boy Scts; Key Clb; Model UN; Penn ST U; Softwre.

SONTHEIMER, LORI; Hughesville HS; Muncy, PA; (3); Pres FNA; Key Clb; Ski Clb; Spanish Clb; Rptr Nwsp Rptr; Rptr Yrbk Rptr; Yrbk Stf; Rep Soph Cls; Hon Roll; NHS; Green & White Awd 85-87; Hlth Prof.

SOPATA, JANINE; South Park HS; Library, PA; (3); 19/238; Church Yth Grp; Mrchg Band; JV Bsktbl; Var L Sftbl; Trk; Vllybl; High Hon Roll; NHS; NEDT Awd; Lions Clb Intl Yth Exchng Finland 86; Bst 9th Grd Artst; PA ST U.

SOPKO, BETH; Ambridge Area HS; Baden, PA; (4); 71/265; Pep Clb; Spanish Clb; Band; Concert Band; Mrchg Band; Pep Band; Symp Band; Soph Cls; Jr Cls; Sr Cls; Bradford Schol; Acctg.

SOPKO, KIMBERLY; John S Fine HS; Nanticoke, PA; (2); Swmmng; High Hon Roll; NHS; Cert Of Achvt Rdng 85; Csmtlgy.

SOPP, MATTHEW; Old Forge HS; Old Forge, PA; (3); Var Bsbl; Pre Med.

SORBER, LEESA; Lake-Lehman HS; Harveys Lk, PA; (2); Ski Clb; JV Bsktbl; JV Fld Hcky; JV Sftbl; Var L Trk; Hon Roll; Jr NHS; WY Vly Conf Fld Hcky Chmpns 86; Marine Bio.

SORBER, LISA A; Lake Lehman HS; Hunlock Creek, PA; (3); 38/214; Sec Key Clb; Office Aide; Chorus; Hon Roll; Outstndng Key Club Secretary Cert 85-87; Poetry Awd From WY Valley Poetry Soc Contst 87; Education.

SORBIN, BILLIE J; Saltsburg JR-SR HS; Saltsburg, PA; (3); SADD; Mgr(s); JV Vllybl; High Hon Roll; Hon Roll; Pres Acad Fitns Awd 86.

SORBO, DAWNYA; Laurel HS; New Castle, PA; (3); Church Yth Grp; Cmnty Wkr; French Clb; Library Aide; Chorus; Church Choir; Mrchg Band; Hon Roll; Elem Ed.

SORENSEN, MARY; Hazleton HS; Drums, PA; (3); 31/450; French Clb; FBLA; Leo Clb; Pep Clb; Cheerleading; Crs Cntry; Trk; French Hon Soc; Hon Roll; Law.

SORENSON, JEFF; Fort Le Boeuf HS; Waterford, PA; (3); 32/208; Letterman Clb; Bsbl; Ftbl; Wt Lftg; Wrstlng; High Hon Roll; Hon Roll; Lion Awd; PA ST Coll; Sprts Med.

SORICK, GRETCHEN; Pacona Central Catholic HS; Canadensis, PA; (4); 3/28; Teachers Aide; Yrbk Stf; Sec Soph Cls; Sec Sr Cls; Capt Cheerleading; Sftbl; High Hon Roll; Sec NHS; Voice Dem Awd; Elizabeth Seton Schlrshp 87; MVP Awd Chrldg 85; Cannaught Lab Schlrshp 87; West Chester U; Nrsg.

SORRENTI, ELYSIA; Notre Dame HS; Stroudsburg, PA; (3); Camera Clb; Drama Clb; Varsity Clb; Yrbk Stf; Jr Cls; Stu Cncl; Fld Hcky; Sftbl; Tennis; Spanish NHS; Spnsh, Sftbl, Fld Hcky Awds.

SORRENTINO, MARTHA; Linden Hall HS; Lititz, PA; (3); 2/40; Dance Clb; Quiz Bowl; Chorus; Drm Mjr(t); School Musical; School Play; Rptr Nwsp Rptr; VP Frsh Cls; Cheerleading; High Hon Roll.

SORRENTIONO, MARTHA; Linden Hall HS; Lancaster, PA; (3); Dance Clb; Q&S; Quiz Bowl; School Musical; School Play; Variety Show; Nwsp Rptr; VP Frsh Cls; Cheerleading; High Hon Roll; Awd 1 Best Jr Term Papers 87; Awd Hghst Grd Hist 87.

SORTINO JR, JAMES; Devon Preparatory Schl; Audubon, PA; (3); 7/40; Nwsp Rptr; Pres Soph Cls; Var Bsbl; JV Socr; High Hon Roll; NHS; Ntl Merit Ltr; NEDT Awd; Ecnmcs Awd; Law.

SOSKO, JEFF; Mt Pleasant Area HS; Mt Pleasant, PA; (4); 30/250; Var L Ftbl; Wt Lftg; Var L Wrstlng.

SOSNOWSKI, MATT; Beaver Area HS; Beaver, PA; (3); 20/215; Trs French Clb; Math Tm; Scholastic Bowl; Capt Socr; High Hon Roll; Hon Roll; PA ST U; Engrng.

SOTACK, SCOTT; West Hazleton HS; Hazleton, PA; (2); 16/225; SADD; JV Bsktbl; JV Ftbl; High Hon Roll; Pres Schlr; Law.

SOTAK, AMY L; Bethlehem Ctr; Brownsville, PA; (4); 2/154; Drama Clb; Spanish Clb; Varsity Clb; School Play; Yrbk Ed-Chief; Var L Bsktbl; Var L Vllybl; Lion Awd; NHS; Sal; Bxtr Trvnl Fndtn Schlrshp 87; Old Trails Bus & Prof Wmn Schlrshp 87; Army Rsv Ntl Schlr/Athlt Awd 87; IN U Bloomington; Sprts Mrktng.

SOTIS, DENISE; Downington SR HS; Downingtown, PA; (2); GAA; Ski Clb; Spanish Clb; Capt Var Fld Hcky; Capt Var Lcrss; Sftbl; High Hon Roll; Hon Roll; NHS; Am Lgn Awd 85; Engl.

SOTOS, HELEN; Reading SR HS; Reading, PA; (4); 42/465; Church Yth Grp; Debate Tm; Hosp Aide; Key Clb; VP Y-Teens; Ed Yrbk Ed-Chief; Stu Cncl; Mgr(s); Capt Vllybl; NHS; 2nd Pl Hgst German Cls Avg 84; 3rd Pl Hgst Eng Cls Avg 84; West Chester U; Pol Sci.

SOTTUNG, ROBERT L; Bensalem HS; Bensalem, PA; (3); Church Yth Grp; Exploring; Var Crs Cntry; JV Socr; Var Swmmng; Var Trk; High Hon Roll; Hon Roll; NHS; Engrng.

SOUBIK, KRISTINA; Our Lady Of Lourdes HS; Kulpmont, PA; (4); 20/92; Leo Clb; Spanish Clb; Chorus; Nwsp Rptr; Nwsp Stf; Yrbk Stf; Hon Roll; Prfct Atten Awd; Spanish NHS; PTO Schlrshp Nrsng 87; Lourdes Alumni Schlrhsp 87; Pottsville Schl Of Nrsng; Nrsng.

SOUCHAK, JOANN; Mahanoy Area HS; Mahanoy City, PA; (3); Drama Clb; Spanish Clb; Variety Show; Rep Frsh Cls; Sec Jr Cls; Stu Cncl; Var Cheerleading; Hon Roll; NHS; Nursing.

SOUDERS, BETTY JO; Pequed Valley HS; Narvon, PA; (3); 15/141; AFS; Chess Clb; FBLA; Girl Scts; Stage Crew; Yrbk Stf; Hon Roll; NHS; Law.

SOUDERS, MICHAEL; Chambersburg Area SR HS; Chambersburg, PA; (2); Church Yth Grp; Band; Chorus; Church Choir; Concert Band; Jazz Band; Mrchg Band; Orch; Symp Band; Variety Show; Music Prfrmnc.

SOUKUP, DAVID; Greensburg Central Catholic HS; Derry, PA; (4); Art Clb; Stage Crew; Im Capt Vllybl; Electronic Inst; Elctrnc Tech.

SOUN, SAVETH; William Allen HS; Allentown, PA; (2); 45/634; Drama Clb; Intnl Clb; Ski Clb; School Play; Hon Roll; Jr NHS; Fnlst In City Spelling Bee 87; NYIT; Arch.

SOUSA, CHRISTINE; Cambria Heights HS; Carrolltown, PA; (3); Q&S; Ski Clb; Concert Band; Mrchg Band; Yrbk Stf; Hon Roll; NHS.

SOUSA, TOM; Our Lady Of The Sacred Heart HS; Mc Kees Rocks, PA; (3); Boy Scts; Cmnty Wkr; Var L Bsbl; Var L Socr; Eagle Sct 84; Wrld Consrvtn Awd Boy Scts Am 84; Athl Cmte.

SOUTAR, TODD; Fairview HS; Erie, PA; (4); Ski Clb; JV Bsbl; JV Ftbl; JV Ice Hcky; Mgr(s); High Hon Roll; Hon Roll; Karate 86-87; Penn ST; Aerospace Engrng.

SOUTHARD, STEPHANIE; Beaver Area JR SR HS; Beaver, PA; (2); Church Yth Grp; Spanish Clb; Socr; JV Var Trk; High Hon Roll; Nrsng.

SOUTHWICK, AMMIE; Hampton HS; Allison Park, PA; (3); Civic Clb; Ski Clb; SADD; Color Guard; School Musical; Stage Crew; Yrbk Stf; Swmmng; Hon Roll.

SOUTHWICK, ANDREW; Hampton HS; Allison Park, PA; (2); 1/175; Church Yth Grp; Computer Clb; Ski Clb; SADD; Trs Frsh Cls; Rep Stu Cncl; Tennis; High Hon Roll; Hon Roll; Comptr Sci.

SOWA, MATTHEW; John S Fine HS; Nanticoke, PA; (2); 22/226; Church Yth Grp; Cmnty Wkr; Rep Soph Cls; JV Bsktbl; Trk; NHS; NEDT Awd; Sci.

SOWALLA, JASON; Northern Cambria HS; Cherry Tree, PA; (3); NFL; Ski Clb; Var Im Bsktbl; Var L Ftbl; Var L Trk; High Hon Roll; Hon Roll; NHS; Ntl Merit Ltr; Chem Engr.

SOWASH, MARLENE; Grove City Area HS; Grove City, PA; (4); 17/162; Sec FBLA; Thesps; Jazz Band; Mrchg Band; Pep Band; School Musical; School Play; Stage Crew; High Hon Roll; NHS; Grove City Coll; Accntng.

SOWERS, ANN; Springside Schl; Philadelphia, PA; (3); Church Yth Grp; Hosp Aide; Acpl Chr; Chorus; Sec Sr Cls; Im Fld Hcky; Im Vllybl; Hon Roll; Specl Recgntn Music Dept 86 & 87; 300 Vlntr Hrs Recgntn 84-86.

SOWERS, JENNIFER; Beth Center HS; Marianna, PA; (3); 62/200; Church Yth Grp; Dance Clb; Spanish Clb; Drill Tm; Flag Corp; Variety Show; Hon Roll; MENC Natl Hnr Bnd Cntst 87.

SOWERS, LISA M; Grove City HS; Grove City, PA; (4); 5/198; VP Jr Civitan Int; Yrbk Stf; Ed Sr Cls; Cheerleading; Elks Awd; NHS; Opt Clb Awd; Powder Puff Ftbl; High Hon Roll; Hon Roll; Natl Cngrssnl Yth Ldrshp Awd 86; Rotary Yth Ldrshp Awd 86; Hmcmng Ct 86; Penn ST U.

SOWERS, MATTHEW; Pequea Valley HS; Paradise, PA; (4); 5/114; School Musical; Nwsp Stf; Im Vllybl; High Hon Roll; Hon Roll; NHS; Church Yth Grp; Science Clb; Stage Crew; Outstndng Physics Stu Yr Awd; Cum Laude; Pres Acad Fit Awd; Drexel U; Physics.

SOWERS, MIKE; Northeastern HS; Mount Wolf, PA; (3); 49/188; Boy Scts; Drama Clb; Band; Mrchg Band; Rep Jr Cls; Bsktbl; Crs Cntry; Socr; L Trk; Hon Roll; Eagle Sct 86; Sprts Med.

SOWERS, SHAWN; Grove City HS; Grove City, PA; (3); 36/209; Nwsp Sprt Ed; Im Bsktbl; Var Golf; Var Tennis; Hon Roll; Golf Ltrmn; Ten Ltrmn; Cmmnctns.

SOWERS, SUSANNE; Northeastern HS; Manchester, PA; (3); 3/185; Acpl Chr; Band; Concert Band; Mrchg Band; Orch; School Musical; Rep Stu Cncl; JV Fld Hcky; High Hon Roll; NHS; Dist Band 86-87; JR Miss Pgnt 87; Engrng.

SOWGA, ROBERT; Dallas SR HS; Shaverstown, PA; (3); Chess Clb; Computer Clb; Ski Clb; Band; Concert Band; Jazz Band; Mrchg Band; Pep Band; School Musical; JV Var Bsbl.

SOWINSKI, DAWN; Freeport Area SR HS; Sarver, PA; (3); 9/213; Library Aide; Var Capt Bsktbl; L Trk; High Hon Roll; Hon Roll; Bio.

SOWKO, ROBERT; South Allegheny HS; Glassport, PA; (4); 13/167; Aud/Vis; Boy Scts; Church Yth Grp; Exploring; French Clb; Teachers Aide; Swmmng; Trk; High Hon Roll; NHS; Gilbert Solar Schlrshp Awd 87; Glassport/Glarion Rotary Club Schlrshp & Awd 87; Liberty Vet Assoc Awd; U Pittsburgh; Sci.

SOXMAN, ALAN; Plum SR HS; New Kensington, PA; (4); Pres JA; Science Clb; High Hon Roll; Jr NHS; NHS; Pres Schlr; Sls Awd JR Achvt 85; Penn ST; Aerntcl Engr.

SPADA, MICHAEL; Northern Lebanon HS; Lebanon, PA; (3); 15/200; Model UN; Quiz Bowl; Pres Spanish Clb; School Play; JV Ftbl; Var Trk; Hon Roll; NHS; Acctng.

SPADAFORA, KEITH; Mon Valley Catholic HS; Monongahela, PA; (1); 3/60; Spanish Clb; Band; Mrchg Band; Symp Band; Spanish NHS; Carnegie Mellon; Music.

SPADARO, DEANNA; Franklin Regional SR HS; Murrysville, PA; (3); Church Yth Grp; Spanish Clb; Nwsp Stf; Rep Stu Cncl; Var L Bsktbl; Var L Golf; Var L Sftbl; High Hon Roll; Hon Roll; NHS; Pres Phys Fit Awd 7 Yrs.

SPADE, ANGELA; Fairchange-Georges SR HS; Uniontown, PA; (3); FHA; Pres Jr Cls; JV Var Bsktbl; High Hon Roll; Hon Roll; NHS; Camp Fr Inc; Secr.

SPADE, CYNTHIA; Bishop Conwell HS; Fairless Hls, PA; (3); 1/277; Pres French Clb; Latin Clb; Math Tm; Science Clb; Nwsp Stf; Yrbk Stf; High Hon Roll; NHS; Gen Excllnc; 1st Pl Phildlphia Elec Rsrcn Enrgy Essy Cmpttn; Diocesn Schlr; Drexel U; Sci.

SPADEA, NICK V; St James HS; Folcroft, PA; (3); 52/176; Im Bsbl; Im Bsktbl; JV Wrstlng; Med.

SPAEDER, DEBORAH; Greensburg Central Cath HS; Greensburg, PA; (3); AFS; JCL; NFL; Pep Clb; Ski Clb; Yrbk Stf; Powder Puff Ftbl; Im Vllybl; Stat Wrstlng; High Hon Roll; Intl Rltns.

SPAFFORD, KEN; Fort Le Boeuf HS; Erie, PA; (2); Boy Scts; Chess Clb; Concert Band; Mrchg Band; School Musical; Nwsp Stf; Penn ST; Chem.

SPAHR, DAMION; Hanover SR HS; Hanover, PA; (4); 4/108; Aud/Vis; Camera Clb; JA; Scholastic Bowl; SADD; School Musical; School Play; Stage Crew; Variety Show; Nwsp Rptr; Elks Stu Of Yr 87; Pres Acad Awd 87; PA ST U; Aerosp Engrng.

SPAHR, JONATHAN; Danville SR HS; Danville, PA; (1); Church Yth Grp; Ski Clb; Band; Concert Band; Mrchg Band; JV Crs Cntry; L Tennis; High Hon Roll; Kiwanis Awd; Prfct Atten Awd; Band Awd 87.

SPAHR, TRACEY; Trinity HS; Mechanicsburg, PA; (3); 10/138; Model UN; NFL; Pep Clb; Ski Clb; Spanish Clb; Speech Tm; School Musical; Nwsp Stf; Yrbk Rptr; Var Capt Cheerleading; Cmnctns.

SPAIDE, LYNN; Bishop Hafey HS; Hazleton, PA; (3); Church Yth Grp; FNA; Key Clb; Service Clb; Ski Clb; Y-Teens; Yrbk Stf; Rep Stu Cncl; Var Bsktbl; L Trk; Early Chldhood Dvlpmnt.

SPAITS, COLLEEN; Allentown Central Catholic HS; Northampton, PA; (4); Church Yth Grp; Exploring; Pres 4-H; Hosp Aide; Mgr(s); Powder Puff Ftbl; Score Keeper; 4-H Awd; Westchester; Elem Ed.

SPAK, ANN; Punxsutawney Area SR HS; Reynoldsville, PA; (4); 69/245; French Clb; FBLA; Hosp Aide; Teachers Aide; Band; Concert Band; Mrchg Band; Variety Show; Mary Ann Irvin Schlrshp 87-88; Penn ST U; Frnch Ed.

SPANARD, RICK; Montour HS; Mckees Rocks, PA; (3); Church Yth Grp; Ftbl; Vllybl; Comp Grphcs.

SPANGLER, DAWN; Rockwood Area HS; Rockwood, PA; (4); Office Aide; High Hon Roll; Hon Roll; Sectry.

SPANGLER, HOLLY; Spring Grove SR HS; York, PA; (3); Church Yth Grp; Drama Clb; Girl Scts; Color Guard; Drill Tm; Orch; Nwsp Rptr; Var Swmmng; Hon Roll; Masonic Awd; Tall Cedars Partcptn Awd 85; Schltc Awd 100 Pt Pin 85; Yrk Drl Tm Awd 85; Wrthy Advsr Ordr Rainbow 87; Dntstry.

SPANGLER JR, JEFFREY; West York HS; York, PA; (2); High Hon Roll; JV Bsbl; JV Golf; Engrng.

SPANGLER, JOHNA; Rockwood Area HS; Rockwood, PA; (2); Church Yth Grp; Library Aide; Office Aide; Chorus; High Hon Roll; Hon Roll.

SPANGLER, KATHLEEN; William Penn SR HS; York, PA; (4); Hosp Aide; Chorus; Color Guard; School Musical; Rep Jr Cls; Hon Roll; NHS; Edinboro U Smmr Prog Gftd Stud 84-86; Guest Page In HRH 85; Bio.

SPANGLER, KELLY; Susquehannock HS; New Freedom, PA; (2); 84/243; Church Yth Grp; SADD; School Play; Mgr(s); Graphic Arts.

SPANGLER, LISA; Rockwood Area HS; Rockwood, PA; (4); 2/95; Band; Chorus; Church Choir; School Play; Yrbk Stf; Sec Sr Cls; Co-Capt Cheerleading; High Hon Roll; NHS; Pres Phy Fit Awd 85-87; Amer Yth Ldrshp Conf 86; OH Northern U; Pharm.

SPANGLER, MISHON; Millersburg Area HS; Millersburg, PA; (3); Art Clb; French Clb; Ed Nwsp Stf; Yrbk Stf; Off Stu Cncl; Var Trs Cheerleading; High Hon Roll; Woodmn Awd Outstndng Achvt Am Hstry 85-86; Schltc Art Awd Gld Key Prntmkng 85-86; Comrcl Dsgn.

SPANGLER, SANDY; Pen Argyl Area HS; Nazareth, PA; (3); Church Yth Grp; Leo Clb; Chorus; Church Choir; Mrchg Band; Variety Show; JV Var Twrlr; Hon Roll; Mst Imprv Band Frnt Awd 86-87; Northampton Cnty CC; Chld Care.

SPANGLER, TIFFANY; Central SR HS; York, PA; (3); Ski Clb; Band; Drill Tm; Flag Corp; Mrchg Band; Nwsp Stf; Yrbk Stf; Mgr(s).

SPANGLER, TONYA; North Star HS; Stoystown, PA; (2); VP Church Yth Grp; FCA; Nwsp Stf; Yrbk Stf; Var Cheerleading; Mat Maids; Acctng.

SPANGLER, TRACY; Clarion-Limestone HS; Strattanville, PA; (3); Church Yth Grp; French Clb; SADD; Chorus; Drill Tm; Mssnry.

SPANIER, CHRISTINE; Council Rock HS; Churchville, PA; (3); 155/908; Dance Clb; German Clb; German Am Partnershp Prog 86; German.

SPANIK, CHRIS; Glendale JR SR HS; Blandburg, PA; (3); Science Clb; Yrbk Stf; Var Ftbl; Pres Phys Fit Awd 85-87; Drftsmn.

SPANIK, KRISTEN; Ambridge Area HS; Ambridge, PA; (3); French Clb; Pep Clb; SADD; Drill Tm; Frsh Cls; Soph Cls; Jr Cls; High Hon Roll; Hon Roll; Cmmnctns.

SPANIK, LOREN; Highlands SR HS; Brackenridge, PA; (4); 11/277; Exploring; Hosp Aide; Key Clb; Library Aide; Office Aide; SADD; Nwsp Rptr; JV Sftbl; High Hon Roll; Jr NHS; PA ST U; Nrsng.

SPANOS, CHRIS; Northampton SR HS; Northampton, PA; (4); Civic Clb; Computer Clb; VFW Awd 86; Ebry Riddle; Aero Engrng.

SPARBANIE, CHRIS; Sto-Rox HS; Mc Kees Rocks, PA; (2); Boys Clb Am; Chorus; Yrbk Stf; Rep Soph Cls; Var Bsbl; Stat Bsktbl; Hon Roll.

SPARGUR, TODD; Connellsville Area SR HS; Normalville, PA; (3); Computer Clb; FFA; Ski Clb; VICA; High Hon Roll; Hon Roll; US Air Frc.

SPARICH, SALVATORE; Marian Catholic HS; Weatherly, PA; (3); 5/104; Math Clb; Scholastic Bowl; Var Bsktbl; L Trk; High Hon Roll; NHS; Spanish NHS; Peer Conselor; Pre-Med.

SPARKLER, CARLA; Strath Haven HS; Wallingford, PA; (3); Church Yth Grp; French Clb; GAA; Ski Clb; Spanish Clb; Varsity Clb; Rep Jr Cls; Tennis; Hon Roll; MVP-TENNIS 85 & 86.

SPARKS, AIMEE; Connellsville Area HS; Indian Head, PA; (3); Dance Clb; Office Aide; Mrchg Band; Variety Show; Nwsp Stf; Capt Twrlr; Vllybl; DAR Awd; High Hon Roll; Math Educ.

SPARKS, DIANNE; East Juniata HS; Thompsontown, PA; (3); 12/100; Chess Clb; Trs Jr Cls; Var JV Bsktbl; Var JV Fld Hcky; Var L Trk; Hon Roll; NHS.

SPARR, KAREN; York Catholic HS; New Freedom, PA; (3); French Clb; FBLA; Ski Clb; Im Bsktbl; JV Socr; Hon Roll; Bus.

SPARROW, DONNA; Uniontown SR HS; Smock, PA; (3); Church Yth Grp; Cmnty Wkr; Letterman Clb; Spanish Clb; Teachers Aide; Yrbk Stf; Var L Sftbl; Var L Tennis; High Hon Roll; Paramdc.

SPATARO, NICOLE; Avella HS; Avella, PA; (3); GAA; Letterman Clb; Ski Clb; Varsity Clb; Var Bsktbl; Var Sftbl; Var Vllybl; High Hon Roll; NHS; Observer-Reporter Grls Bsktbl All Star Tm 86-87; Awdsd Outstndng Acad Wkr Speech 86-87; Accntnt.

SPATZ, STERLING W; Twin Valley HS; Birdsboro, PA; (4); 2/118; Aud/Vis; Church Yth Grp; Drama Clb; German Clb; Quiz Bowl; Scholastic Bowl; Chorus; School Musical; Swing Chorus; Nwsp Rptr; Lutheran Brthrhd Schlrshp 87; Lehigh U; Comp Engrng.

SPAUGY JR, HAROLD; Connellsville Area HS; Connellsville, PA; (3); 69/481; High Hon Roll; Hon Roll; NHS; Air Force.

SPAYD, LINDA; Penns Valley Area HS; Centre Hall, PA; (3); 25/154; Church Yth Grp; Pep Clb; Band; Chorus; Concert Band; Jazz Band; Mrchg Band; Stage Crew; Hon Roll; Penn ST; Mech Engrng.

SPAZIANI, MARY; Ambridge Area HS; Baden, PA; (3); FBLA; Pep Clb; SADD; Band; Concert Band; Mrchg Band; Pep Band; Symp Band; Off Sr Cls; Hon Roll; Photo.

SPEAKMAN, KAREN; Oxford Area HS; Oxford, PA; (3); 20/197; Band; Chorus; Concert Band; Jazz Band; Mrchg Band; Yrbk Stf; Trk; Vllybl; High Hon Roll; NHS; Ordr Rainbw Grls; Marn Bio.

SPEAR JR, JO-WALTER; Plymouth White Marsh HS; Plymouth Meeting, PA; (4); Chess Clb; Church Yth Grp; Latin Clb; Math Clb; Math Tm; Band; Concert Band; Jazz Band; Mrchg Band; Pep Band; Cert Of Schlstc Achvmnt 87; IA U; Mech Biomed Engrng.

SPEARMAN, JAMES; Penn Hills SR HS; Penn Hills, PA; (3); VP JA; NAACP; Band; Bsktbl; Ftbl; Hon Roll; Med.

SPEARY, ROBERT; Central County Christian Acad; Bellefonte, PA; (4); Church Yth Grp; Chorus; School Play; Pres Frsh Cls; Pres Soph Cls; Pres Jr Cls; Pres Sr Cls; Var L Bsbl; Var Capt Socr; Cit Awd; Soccero MVP 84-85; Dan Horner Mem Acd Scr All Star 85-86; PA Math Leag Awd 86-87; Bob Jones U; Law.

SPEASE, CHRISTY; Saint Cyril Acad; Bloomsburg, PA; (2); Church Yth Grp; Drama Clb; Exploring; French Clb; Key Clb; Spanish Clb; Chorus; School Play; VP Frsh Cls; Hgh O Brn Yth Fndtn Smnrs Future Ldrs 87; Spnsh Natl Exm Test Cert 86; 1st Plc Sci Fair 87; Poly Sci.

SPECE, BERNADETTE; Nativity BVM HS; Pottsville, PA; (2); 22/77; Church Yth Grp; Cmnty Wkr; French Clb; Hosp Aide; Color Guard; Rep Frsh Cls; Twrlr; Hon Roll; Peer Cnslr 86-87; Med.

SPECHT, CAROL; Mt Pleasant Area HS; Acme, PA; (3); German Clb; Stage Crew; Yrbk Ed-Chief; Yrbk Phtg; Yrbk Stf; Var L Mgr(s); Var L Score Keeper; Sftbl; Var Swmmng; Rotary Exchng Stu-Jpn 87-88; Engrng.

SPECK, ANDREW; Carlisle HS; Burke, VA; (3); 10/487; Church Yth Grp; SADD; Band; Concert Band; Jazz Band; Mrchg Band; Orch; Pep Band; Capt Ftbl; Trk; Stu Of Mnth 85; Marching Bnd Awd 86; Aerospc Engr.

SPECK, KAREN L; Carlisle HS; Carlisle, PA; (2); 75/445; Church Yth Grp; Church Choir; Concert Band; Mrchg Band; Hon Roll; Presdntl Acadmc Ftnss Awd 86-87; Accntng.

SPECK, LISA; Northern Lebanon HS; Lebanon, PA; (3); French Clb; Band; Chorus; Concert Band; School Play; Tennis; Fshn Dsgn.

SPECK, ROBERT; Dubois Area HS; Dubois, PA; (2); Hon Roll; Envrnmntl Rsrcs.

SPECTOR, BONNIE; Lower Merion HS; Wynnewood, PA; (3); French Clb; Intnl Clb; Service Clb; SADD; Yrbk Stf; Tennis; French Hon Soc.

SPECTOR, JILL; Springfield Township HS; Wyndmoor, PA; (4); 33/129; Aud/Vis; Library Aide; Sec Political Wkr; Spanish Clb; Temple Yth Grp; Chorus; Stu Cncl; Hon Roll; U Of DE; Psych.

SPEECE, SUSAN; Churchill HS; Pittsburgh, PA; (2); 22/222; AFS; Church Yth Grp; Color Guard; Concert Band; Mrchg Band; School Musical; High Hon Roll; Rifle Team Vrsty.

SPEELMAN, VERONICA; Connellsville Area HS; Connellsville, PA; (4); Trs Camera Clb; Sec Computer Clb; Office Aide; SADD; Chorus; School Play; Nwsp Stf; Ed Yrbk Stf; Rep Stu Cncl; High Hon Roll; Sawyer Schl Of Bus; Bus.

SPEERHAS, TRACY; Western Beaver HS; Midland, PA; (3); Church Choir; Concert Band; Mrchg Band; Symp Band; Yrbk Stf; Rep Stu Cncl; Im Bowling; Var Sftbl; Hon Roll; NHS; Bus.

SPEES, GINA; Oswayo Valley JR SR HS; Shinglehouse, PA; (2); 2/85; AFS; Debate Tm; 4-H; French Clb; German Clb; Stat Bsktbl; Stat Var Vllybl; 4-H Awd; High Hon Roll; Hon Roll; Cornell; Intl Rltns.

SPEICHER, MARIANNE; Northeastern SR HS; Manchester, PA; (2); 7/250; Art Clb; Chess Clb; Chorus; Im Vllybl; High Hon Roll; Hon Roll; Pres Acad Fit Awd 85-87; Outstndng Frnch Awd 85-87; Arch.

SPEICHER, MICHELLE; West Hazleton HS; Conyngham, PA; (2); 11/200; Church Yth Grp; Cmnty Wkr; Spanish Clb; Thesps; School Play; Yrbk Stf; Pres Stu Cncl; Bsktbl; Vllybl; Hon Roll; Prncpls Awd 85-86; Fclty Hnr Mdl 85-86; Cert Of Merit Span Cntst 85-86.

SPEICHER, NICOLE; Kiski HS; Apollo, PA; (3); Exploring; FBLA; Teachers Aide; Sftbl; Cmnty Wkr; Hon Roll.

SPELGATTI, CHERYL; Elizabethtown Area HS; Elizabethtown, PA; (4); 9/240; Church Yth Grp; Girl Scts; Chorus; Var Cheerleading; Powder Puff Ftbl; Vllybl; Hon Roll; Kiwanis Awd; NHS; Pres Schlr; Armstrong Sci Awd 87; Wilson Coll; Bio.

SPELL, KIMBERLY; Shaler Area HS; Pittsburgh, PA; (3); 23/486; Library Aide; Pep Clb; Yrbk Stf; High Hon Roll; Hon Roll; Cert Of Achvt Bio Olympics Slippery Rock U 87; Typng Accuracy Hnr Roll 87; Bradford Schl; Bus.

SPENARD, JOYCE; Forest City Regional HS; Forest City, PA; (3); 18/60; Girl Scts; Hosp Aide; Letterman Clb; Spanish Clb; Var L Bsktbl; Var L Crs Cntry; Var L Sftbl; Var Vllybl; Hon Roll; NHS; Law.

SPENCE, BRADLEY; Wilmington Area HS; Pulaski, PA; (3); Boy Scts; Church Yth Grp; Computer Clb; Latin Clb; Spanish Clb; Chorus; Church Choir; Var L Ftbl; Var Trk; Hon Roll; Pharmclgy.

SPENCE, JESSE; Donegal HS; Mount Joy, PA; (2); JV Bsbl; JV Wrstlng; Bus.

SPENCE, MELANIE; Oil City HS; Oil City, PA; (3); 20/217; Acpl Chr; Capt Drill Tm; VP Mrchg Band; School Musical; Variety Show; Yrbk Phtg; Rep Stu Cncl; Hon Roll; Masonic Awd; NHS; Bus.

SPENCE, SAMUEL; Chester HS; Chester, PA; (3); 68/458; English Clb; German Clb; Bsktbl; Hon Roll; Voice Dem Awd; Morris Brown Coll; Scl Sci.

SPENCER, AMY; York Catholic HS; York, PA; (4); 4/168; Debate Tm; VP French Clb; Ski Clb; School Play; Nwsp Bus Mgr; L Trk; NHS; Ntl Merit Ltr; Acad All Str 87; Rev William Fitzpatrick Mrl Schlrshp 87; Mdl Excllnc Frnch 87; Villanova U; Mech Engr.

SPENCER, ANN; Haverford HS; Havertown, PA; (4); Var Bsktbl; Var Capt Fld Hcky; Var Capt Lcrss; Hon Roll; Ethel David Awd 86-87; Towson ST U; Phy Educ.

SPENCER, ELIZABETH; Lake Lehman HS; Noxen, PA; (3); 14/219; VP Key Clb; Hon Roll; Jr NHS; NHS; NEDT Awd; Bio.

SPENCER, FRANK; Bishop O Reilly HS; Dallas, PA; (3); Acpl Chr; Chorus; Church Choir; Concert Band; School Musical; Var Golf; NHS; NEDT Awd; Spanish NHS; Dist, Regnl, St Chorus 85-87; Penn ST; Agronomy.

SPENCER, HENRY; Elizabeth Forward SR HS; Mckeesport, PA; (2); French Clb; Crs Cntry; Trk; Air Force Pilot.

SPENCER, MELISSA; Blue Mountain Acad; Glenmoore, PA; (2); Church Yth Grp; Drama Clb; Band; Trs Soph Cls; Gym; Im Vllybl; High Hon Roll.

SPENCER, REGINA; Chester HS; Chester, PA; (4); 7/398; Key Clb; Spanish Clb; Pres Church Choir; Nwsp Stf; Fld Hcky; Excel Ltr 84; Math & Chem Awds 86; Temple U; Comp Sci.

SPENCER JR, ROBERT RAND; Wyoming Area HS; Falls, PA; (3); 50/245; French Clb; VP Key Clb; Ski Clb; L Bsbl; L Ftbl; Im Wt Lftg; Hon Roll.

SPENCER, SEAN D; Harrisbug HS John Harris Campus; Harrisburg, PA; (2); 34/356; Church Yth Grp; Off Soph Cls; Score Keeper; Stat Socr; Var Tennis; Hon Roll; PA Gvnrs Schl Bus 87; 3rd Pl Sci Fair 85-86.

SPERLING, JILL; Jenkintown HS; Jenkintown, PA; (2); Chorus; Var Bsktbl; Sftbl; Var Tennis; Hon Roll; Sci Fair Awd 86-87; Vet.

SPERTZEL, TAMMY; Bermudian Springs HS; Gardners, PA; (3); Trs Pres FNA; SADD; Color Guard; Yrbk Stf; Miss PA Teen Ldrshp Awd 87; Cntrl Penn Bus Schl; Lgl Asst.

SPICHER, SUSAN; Millersburg Area HS; Millersburg, PA; (3); Aud/Vis; Cmnty Wkr; FHA; Service Clb; Powder Puff Ftbl; Hon Roll; Fshn Dsgnr.

SPICKLER, GAIL; Donegal HS; Mount Joy, PA; (2); VP Church Yth Grp; Band; Church Choir; Concert Band; Mrchg Band; Im Fld Hcky; JV Tennis; Hon Roll; Intr Dsgn.

SPIECE, KAREN; West Hazelton HS; Zion Grove, PA; (3); 54/227; Church Yth Grp; Cmnty Wkr; FNA; Chorus; Church Choir; High Hon Roll; Hon Roll; PA JR Acad Sci Reg Cmptn 1st & 2nd Pl 87; Mst Outstndng Chrs Stu 85; PA ST U; Sci.

SPIEGEL, SUNNY; Washington HS; Washington, PA; (2); 3/193; Library Aide; Ski Clb; Spanish Clb; Rep Frsh Cls; Pres Soph Cls; JV Co-Capt Cheerleading; High Hon Roll; Lbry Aide Awd 85.

SPIEGLE, KAREN; St Hubert HS For Girls; Philadelphia, PA; (3); 87/421; Nwsp Rptr; Nwsp Sprt Ed; Nwsp Stf; Hon Roll; U Of Pittsburgh; Pharmacy.

SPIERING, AMY LYNN; Burnell SR HS; New Kensington, PA; (3); Library Aide; Chorus; Stage Crew; Hon Roll; Prfct Atten Awd; Rotary Awd; Csmtlgst.

SPILA, TIMOTHY P; Shippensburg Area SR HS; Shippensburg, PA; (3); 8/280; Am Leg Boys St; Trs Chess Clb; Band; Mrchg Band; School Musical; Stage Crew; Var L Crs Cntry; Var Trk; VP NHS; Physcs.

SPILDE, LISA; Shuylkill Valley HS; Reading, PA; (3); 9/140; JA; Pep Clb; Chorus; Concert Band; Mrchg Band; School Play; Nwsp Ed-Chief; Yrbk Stf; VP Stu Cncl.

SPILLMAN, SUE; Hatboro-Horsham SR HS; Hatboro, PA; (4); 21/267; Var Fld Hcky; Var Sftbl; Cit Awd; High Hon Roll; NHS; Pres Schlr; HOBY 84-85; U Of CT; Grafc Dsgn.

SPILSBURY, THEODORE; Danville HS; Danville, PA; (3); Band; Concert Band; Jazz Band; Mrchg Band; School Musical; JV Bowling; JV Golf; Hon Roll; Ssqhnna Vly Conf Bwlng Hgh Gm Awd 87; Dnvll Sctch Dbls Sr Div Bwlng Awd 86.

SPINALE, JOHN; Montour HS; Coraopolis, PA; (4); 9/302; Math Tm; Scholastic Bowl; Science Clb; Powder Puff Ftbl; Socr; Tennis; Vllybl; Bausch & Lomb Sci Awd; High Hon Roll; NHS; Attend Westinghouse Sci Hnrs Inst 86-87; PA Jr Acad Of Sci 86; Perfect 800 In Math SAT 87; Yale; Med.

SPINDLER, ANGIE; Brookville Area HS; Sigel, PA; (3); Pep Clb; Orch; Yrbk Stf; Rep Frsh Cls; Rep Soph Cls; Sftbl; Hon Roll; Amer Gvrnmnt Awd Schlrshp 86.

SPINELLI, JENNIFER; Highlands HS; Natrona Hts, PA; (3); 2/276; Intnl Clb; Key Clb; Office Aide; SADD; Mrchg Band; DAR Awd; High Hon Roll; VP NHS; Pres Schlr; Sal; Natl Yng Ldrs Conf 86; Natl Sci Olympd, Acdmc Triathln 87; U Of Pittsburg; Phrmcy.

SPITALIK, JOHN; Blairsville SR HS; Blairsville, PA; (3); Art Clb; English Clb; Q&S; Nwsp Rptr; Lit Mag; Stu Cncl; Hon Roll; Temple U; Jrnlsm.

SPITKO, KAREN; Chichester HS; Aston, PA; (3); 5/296; Church Yth Grp; Model UN; Sec SADD; Trs Sr Cls; Var Crs Cntry; Var Sftbl; Var Trk; Var Capt Vllybl; Hon Roll; NHS; Shippensburg U; Bus Admin.

SPITZER, LORI; Northampton SR HS; Northampton, PA; (4); 51/430; AFS; Exploring; FBLA; Girl Scts; Leo Clb; Nwsp Stf; Yrbk Stf; High Hon Roll; Hon Roll; Prfct Atten Awd; Sec.

SPIVAK, ROBERT; Carlynton HS; Carnegie, PA; (2); Spanish Clb; High Hon Roll; Hon Roll; Jr NHS; Pres Schlr; MAPS; Hlth Reltd Profssn.

SPIVEY, SHANNA; Seneca HS; Erie, PA; (3); 24/150; Church Yth Grp; Drama Clb; Pres FBLA; Intnl Clb; Concert Band; School Play; Yrbk Stf; Cheerleading; Crs Cntry; Twrlr; Wattsburg-Erie Cnty Fair Qn 86-87; U Of AL; Intl Bus.

SPIZER, BETH; Abington Heights HS; Clarks Green, PA; (3); Scholastic Bowl; Temple Yth Grp; Band; Mrchg Band; School Musical; School Play; Stu Cncl; Hon Roll; Lead Rls-Yth Grp Plys 85 & 87; Asst Tchr-Schl 86-87; Dncng-10 Yrs & Piano 6 Yrs; Emerson U; Brdcst Jrnlsm.

SPLITT, LISA; Danville SR HS; Danville, PA; (3); 30/200; Art Clb; Varsity Clb; Yrbk Sprt Ed; Var Capt Cheerleading; Var Capt Crs Cntry; Swmmng; Var Capt Trk; High Hon Roll; NHS.

SPOHN, JULIE; Upper St Clair HS; Pittsburgh, PA; (3); 71/240; Orch; School Musical; Yrbk Rptr; NHS; Q&S; Church Choir; High Hon Roll; Psych.

SPOHN, KENNETH ROBERT; West Perry SR HS; Shermans Dale, PA; (3); Computer Clb; Hon Roll; Princeton U; Physcs.

SPONG, CHRISSY; Honesdale HS; Equinunk, PA; (3); French Clb; Library Aide; SADD; French Hon Soc; Hon Roll; Intl Forgn Lang Awd; Intl Bus.

SPONSKY, CRAIG; Bishop Carroll HS; Ebensburg, PA; (3); 56/138; Pep Clb; Var L Bsbl; JV Bsktbl; Var L Ftbl; Wt Lftg; Hon Roll.

SPONSLER, TROY; Millersburg Area HS; Millersburg, PA; (3); Spanish Clb; Yrbk Stf; JV Bsbl; Var JV Ftbl; Wt Lftg; Hon Roll.

SPOONER, ELIZABETH; Hanover HS; Hanover, PA; (3); Band; Concert Band; Jazz Band; Mrchg Band; Orch; School Musical; School Play; Yrbk Stf; Lit Mag; NEDT Awd; District Band 86-87; Linguistics.

SPOOR, JAMES; Blue Ridge HS; Susquehanna, PA; (3); 21/98; Boy Scts; Church Yth Grp; Exploring; Library Aide; Drm & Bgl; Rep Stu Cncl; Var Crs Cntry; Var Trk; Marine Sci.

SPORE, RACHEL ALICIA; Youngsville HS; Youngsville, PA; (4); 3/97; Pres Church Yth Grp; Pres Chorus; VP Concert Band; Mrchg Band; School Play; Yrbk Stf; NHS; French Clb; Math Tm; VP Band; Dist, Regnl, All ST & All Estrn Chr 86-87; Rnkd 2nd ST 1st Alto 86-8m; Vcl Prfrmnc.

SPORER, CHRISTINE; West Scranton SR HS; Scranton, PA; (3); Latin Clb; Red Cross Aide; Hon Roll; Hlth Careers Clb; Psych.

SPORER, JULIE; Rocky Grove JR SR HS; Franklin, PA; (4); 3/89; Library Aide; SADD; Yrbk Stf; Var Golf; Stat Sftbl; JV Vllybl; High Hon Roll; Kiwanis Awd; NHS; Joy Emplys Fnd Schlrshp 87; Dist & ST Grls Glf Qlfr 83-86; Dist X Grls Glf Chmpn 84-86; Grove City Coll; Bus Admin.

SPORER, LAURA; North Clarion HS; Marble, PA; (3); Library Aide; Acctng.

SPORNER, DIANE; Elk County Christian HS; St Marys, PA; (4); 13/79; Cmnty Wkr; Hosp Aide; Library Aide; Office Aide; Trs SADD; Church Choir; Yrbk Bus Mgr; Yrbk Stf; Jr Cls; Stu Cncl; J H Thompson Acadc; Dntl Assist.

SPOSATO, BRIAN; Thomas Jefferson HS; Finleyville, PA; (4); 14/260; Church Yth Grp; Computer Clb; Exploring; Band; Ftbl; Wt Lftg; High Hon Roll; NHS; Pres Schlr; MSOE Acad Achvt 87; Penn ST; Aero Engrng.

SPOTTS, HOLLI; Penns Valley Area HS; Centre Hall, PA; (3); 15/150; Church Yth Grp; 4-H; Girl Scts; Ski Clb; SADD; Varsity Clb; Church Choir; Cheerleading; Gym; High Hon Roll; USAF.

SPOTTS, MARCI; Plymouth-Whitemarsh HS; Norristown, PA; (3); Camera Clb; Church Yth Grp; Chorus; Church Choir; Drill Tm; Mgr(s); Score Keeper; Hon Roll; Prfct Atten Awd; Psych.

SPOTTS, MARY; West Perry SR HS; New Bloomfield, PA; (2); 4/222; Chorus; Concert Band; Drm Mjr(t); Mrchg Band; JV Bsktbl; Var JV Fld Hcky; JV Capt Sftbl; High Hon Roll; Hon Roll; Church Yth Grp; Amercn Musicl Fndtn Band Hnrs 87; Dist 1 Uppr Band Fstvl 87; Cnty Band & Cnty Chrs 86, 87; Arch.

SPOTTS, VINCENT J; Seneca Valley HS; Renfrew, PA; (4); 4/347; Am Leg Boys St; Art Clb; Drm & Bgl; L Var Bsbl; High Hon Roll; Hon Roll; NHS; Schlstc Awd Acadc Achvt 85-87; Physcs Olympcs 87; PA Math Leag 86-87; U Of Pittsburgh; Engrng.

SPOTTS, VIRGINIA; Penns Manor HS; Penn Run, PA; (3); 3/113; Trs Camera Clb; Chess Clb; Chorus; Concert Band; Jazz Band; Mrchg Band; Trk; Vllybl; High Hon Roll; NHS; Bio.

SPRAGUE, MELISSA; Du Bois Area HS; Reynoldsville, PA; (3); 4-H; Chorus; Concert Band; Mrchg Band; Rep Stu Cncl; Hon Roll; Du Bois Bus Coll; Med Secr.

SPRANDO, CHRIS; Burgettstown HS; Langeloth, PA; (3); #20 In Class; French Clb; Band; Concert Band; Jazz Band; Mrchg Band; Orch; Pep Band; School Musical; Symp Band; Yrbk Phtg; Band Pres 87-88; Outstndng Music Awd 86-87; Math Awd 84-85.

SPRANKLE, DANE; Penns Manor HS; Penn Run, PA; (4); Varsity Clb; Stage Crew; Ftbl; Trk; High Hon Roll; Hon Roll; Chess Clb; School Musical; Applchn Cnfrnc Mntn Ftbll 86; Applchn Cnfrnc All Strs Trck 87; Cert Rcgntn Prtcptn PA Hrns Tst; IN U Of PA; Engnrng.

SPRANKLE, ROBERT; South Side HS; Georgetown, PA; (3); 3/135; Im Bsktbl; JV Golf; High Hon Roll; NHS; Aerospc Engrng.

SPRENGEL, SCOTT; Carlisle SR HS; Carlisle, PA; (4); 2/382; Concert Band; Jazz Band; Mrchg Band; Orch; High Hon Roll; JP Sousa Awd; NHS; Sal; Boy Scouts Amer Eagle Scout; Pit Orch Schl Musical; Carnegie Mellon; Arch.

SPRENKLE, LISA S; Northeastern HS; Manchester, PA; (4); 16/162; Ski Clb; Color Guard; Trs Jr Cls; Off Sr Cls; High Hon Roll; Hon Roll; NHS; Ntl Merit Schol; Amer Bus Womens Assoc Schlrshp 87; Ordr PTO Schlrshp 87; York Coll; Med Tech.

SPRENKLE, LLOYD; Spring Grove Area SR HS; York, PA; (3); Computer Clb; German Clb; Im Bsktbl; Im Ftbl; Var Socr; Im Sftbl; Var Trk; High Hon Roll; Hon Roll; 100 Pnt Schlstc Pin 85; 200 Pnt Schlstc Pin 86; PA ST U; Bio Chem.

SPRESSER, REBECCA; Mc Keesport Area HS; Mckeesport, PA; (4); 6/339; AFS; Church Yth Grp; Orch; School Musical; High Hon Roll; NHS; Ntl Merit Ltr; Rotary Schlr 86-87; Alleghemy Coll; Med.

SPRINGER, ANDREW V; Bishop Mc Devitt HS; N Hills, PA; (4); 21/357; Pres Drama Clb; Pres Spanish Clb; Yrbk Bus Mgr; Var Wt Lftg; Var Hon Roll; NHS; Pres Schlr; St Josephs U Schlrshp 87; Schlrshp-Cabrini Coll 87; 2nd Pl Awd Essy Cont Immaculata Coll 87; St Josephs U; Engl.

SPRINGER, CHRISTOPHER; Lancaster Catholic HS; Ephrata, PA; (3); 2/200; Trk; High Hon Roll; Hon Roll; NHS; Partcpnt Cnty ST Natl Lvls Natl Hstry 87; Wnnr IN U PA Physics Tst 87; 3rd Pl Lancaster Bar Assn 87; Elec Engr.

SPRINGER, CLAYTON; Norristown Area HS; Jeffersonville, PA; (4); 18/450; Computer Clb; Latin Clb; Math Clb; Science Clb; Nwsp Stf; Yrbk Stf; Im Crs Cntry; JV Ftbl; JV Socr; Var Tennis; Renssealer Mdl; Math Assoc Amer; Excel Math.

SPRINGER, COLLEEN; Bishop O Reilly HS; Wilkes Barre, PA; (2); Church Yth Grp; Cmnty Wkr; Sec Jr Cls; Bsktbl; Socr; Sftbl; High Hon Roll; Hon Roll; Vet.

SPRINGER, KENNETH; Spring Grove SR HS; Seven Valleys, PA; (3); 2/303; VP Trs Church Yth Grp; Pres Computer Clb; Band; Concert Band; Jazz Band; Cit Awd; High Hon Roll; NHS; Ntl Merit Ltr; VFW Awd; U Of PA; Bus Admin.

SPRINGER, KRISTINE; Bishop O Reilly HS; Wilkes-Barre, PA; (3); Church Yth Grp; Cmnty Wkr; GAA; Var Bsktbl; Socr; Var Sftbl; High Hon Roll; Hon Roll; Bst Dfns Plyr Bsktbl Jsph Yonviak Mem Awd 87; Interior Dsgn.

SPRINGER, PATTY; Rocky Grove HS; Franklin, PA; (3); Library Aide; Rep Jr Cls; Var Cheerleading; JV Crs Cntry; Im Vllybl; Hon Roll; Pres Phy Ftnss Awd 86-87; Soc Wrk.

SPRINGER, SHERRY; Laurel Valley HS; Bolivar, PA; (3); AFS; Pres VP 4-H; Library Aide; Pep Clb; Ski Clb; Varsity Clb; Var Cheerleading; 4-H Awd; Hon Roll; 4-H Kystn ST Wnnr 87; PAHA Merit Awd 84; JHSC Hgh Pnt Awd Hrse Shw 85; Pre Dntstry.

SPROAT, KIMBERLY; Haverford SR HS; Havertown, PA; (3); Rep Frsh Cls; JV Cheerleading; Hon Roll; Psych.

SPROUL, LESLIE; Seneca Valley SR HS; Harmony, PA; (3); Cmnty Wkr; FNA; Hosp Aide; SADD; Yrbk Ed-Chief; Church Yth Grp; Girl Scts; JA; Letterman Clb; Office Aide; Waynesburg; Pediatric Nurse Prc.

SPROULL, KEVIN; Freeport HS; Sarver, PA; (2); Bsbl; High Hon Roll.

SPROULL, NADINE; Punxsutawney Area HS; Punxsutawney, PA; (4); 35/245; Church Yth Grp; Band; Church Choir; Jazz Band; Mrchg Band; Pep Band; Variety Show; Yrbk Stf; Trk; Hon Roll; Mary Ann Irvin Schlrshp 87; PAFA Schlrshp 87; Janles V Colonna Bnd Awd 87; IN U Of PA; Speech Therapy.

SPROUSE, AMY M; Bishop Guilfoyle HS; Altoona, PA; (3); Service Clb; SADD; Band; Church Choir; Concert Band; Mrchg Band; Yrbk Stf; High Hon Roll; NHS.

SPROUSE, WENDY; Warren Area HS; Warren, PA; (3); German Clb; Girl Scts; Chorus; Concert Band; Mrchg Band; Bsktbl; Bowling; Hon Roll; Prfct Atten Awd; Johnson & Wales; Hotel Mgt.

SPROW, MICHAEL; Governor Mifflin HS; Shillington, PA; (4); 12/266; Teachers Aide; Varsity Clb; JV Im Bsktbl; Var Capt Socr; Var Trk; High Hon Roll; Hon Roll; Lion Awd; NHS; Pres Schlr; Presdntl Ftns Awd 87; SR Soc Stud Awd 87; Unfd Achvt Awd 86-87; Gettysburg Coll; Hstry.

SPROWLS, PAULA L; Mc Guffey HS; Washington, PA; (3); 11/250; Am Leg Aux Girls St; Church Yth Grp; French Clb; Pep Clb; Spanish Clb; Chorus; School Musical; High Hon Roll; Hon Roll; NHS; Stu Recgntn Awd 85 87; Outstndng Prfrmnc Awd 86; Natl Hnr Soc Tutrng 87; Brigham Young U.

SPRUILL, DIONNE; Steelton Highspire HS; Steelton, PA; (3); FBLA; GAA; Varsity Clb; Band; Concert Band; Drm Mjr(t); Jazz Band; Mrchg Band; Yrbk Stf; Var Capt Bsktbl; Lock Haven; Bus.

SPRUMONT, MARIE; Steel Valley HS; Munhall, PA; (4); 9/208; Church Yth Grp; Girl Scts; JCL; Pres Key Clb; Sec Band; Rep Concert Band; Jazz Band; Mrchg Band; Yrbk Ed-Chief; High Hon Roll; Amvest Legion Awd 87; Penn ST; Acctng.

SPURGEON, DAVID L; Mc Keesport SR HS; Mc Keesport, PA; (2); Band; Concert Band; Mrchg Band; Orch; School Musical; Symp Band; Hon Roll; Law.

SPYCHALSKI, MICHAEL; Strath Haven HS; Wallingford, PA; (3); Boy Scts; Rep Church Yth Grp; Red Cross Aide; Spanish Clb; Yrbk Stf; Rep Stu Cncl; L Bsktbl; Capt Ftbl; L Trk; Hon Roll; Boy Scts Eagle; Capt Ftbl; Rep Stu Cncl; Bus.

SPYRA, DAVID; South Allegheny HS; Elizabeth, PA; (3); 2/188; Spanish Clb; Yrbk Stf; Off Soph Cls; Off Jr Cls; Off Stu Cncl; Bsbl; Bsktbl; Vllybl; High Hon Roll; NHS; Aerospace Engr.

SQUEGLIA, JENNIFER; Villa Maria Acad; Erie, PA; (3); Science Clb; Spanish Clb; SADD; Im Socr; Im Vllybl; Hon Roll; NHS; PA ST U.

SQUILLANTE, ROXANNE; Mc Keesport HS; N Huningdon, PA; (3); Debate Tm; Speech Tm; School Play; Nwsp Rptr; Nwsp Sprt Ed; Rep Soph Cls; Trs Stu Cncl; L Cheerleading; Powder Puff Ftbl; NHS; Hnr Rl 86; Natl Fornsc Leag 2nd Degr Hnr 87.

SQUIRES, EILEEN; Bradford Area SR HS; Bradford, PA; (3); Rep AFS; Library Aide; Science Clb; Spanish Clb; SADD; Capt Bowling; Var Swmmng; Var Trk; Capt Vllybl; Hon Roll; Brain D Lechner Memrl Awd 87-88; Delgado CC; Culnry Arts.

SRADOMSKI, ERIN; Ambridge SR HS; Ambridge, PA; (3); Pep Clb; Color Guard; Drill Tm; Mrchg Band; Stat Bsktbl; Stat Wrstlng; Hon Roll.

SREDENSCHEK, JEFF; Forest City Regional HS; Vandling, PA; (3); 12/66; Letterman Clb; Spanish Clb; Var Capt Bsbl; Var JV Bsktbl; Var Crs Cntry; High Hon Roll; Hon Roll; NHS; Natl Sci Merit Awd 87; U Of Scranton; Criminal Justice.

SREEDHARAN, SHIJU; Upper Darby HS; Upper Darby, PA; (3); Library Aide; High Hon Roll; Hon Roll; Ntl Merit Ltr; Comp Sci.

SRIDHARAN, KARTHIK K; Norristown Area HS; Norristown, PA; (3); Computer Clb; Comp Sci.

ST AMANT, KELLY; Rocky Grove HS; Franklin, PA; (4); 16/92; Sec Drama Clb; SADD; Band; Pep Band; School Play; Yrbk Ed-Chief; Rep Sr Cls; Trs Stu Cncl; Var L Vllybl; High Hon Roll; Penn ST U; Hstry.

ST CLAIR, CHRISTA; Schuylkill Haven HS; Orwigsburg, PA; (3); Church Yth Grp; Library Aide; Spanish Clb; Teachers Aide; Off Frsh Cls; Trs Stu Cncl; JV Bsktbl; JV Vllybl; Hnr Grd 87; Elizabeth Town Coll; Thrpst.

ST CLAIR, MARK A; Bellefonte Area HS; Bellefonte, PA; (3); Model UN; Stu Cncl; JV Crs Cntry; Var Trk; Hon Roll; Penn ST U.

ST CLAIR JR, RICHARD; Frankford HS; Philadelphia, PA; (4); 1/395; High Hon Roll; NHS; Val; Rtry Clb Awd 87; Drexel U; Comp Sci.

ST PIERRE, AMY; West Hazleton HS; Conyngham, PA; (2); French Clb; Scholastic Bowl; Ski Clb; Stage Crew; Trs Stu Cncl; JV Var Bsktbl; Cheerleading; Trk; High Hon Roll; Pres Schlr; 5th Pl Le Concours Natl De Francais 86; Med.

ST PIERRE, JON; Bishop Carroll HS; Ebensburg, PA; (3); Church Yth Grp; Band; Flag Corp; Mrchg Band; Dance Clb; JV Ftbl; Mgr(s); Score Keeper; Stat Trk; Teens Encntr Christ 87; Mrchng, Stage, Flag Corp Band 86-87; U Of Pgh; Pre Law.

STAAB, BRIAN; Butler Area SR HS; Butler, PA; (3); German Clb; Latin Clb; Im Bsktbl; Im Ftbl; JV Socr; Mech Engrng.

STAAB, DOUGLAS; Butler SR HS; Butler, PA; (3); Church Yth Grp; Exploring; German Clb; Latin Clb; Socr; IN U; Crmnlgy.

STABILE, JONATHAN; Highlands HS; Natrona Hgts, PA; (3); Off Jr Cls; JV Bsbl; JV Var Ftbl; Var Trk; Im Wt Lftg; High Hon Roll; Trs NHS; Engrng.

STABILE, PAUL; Canon Mc Millan HS; Canonsburg, PA; (4); Drama Clb; Spanish Clb; Varsity Clb; School Play; L Swmmng; L Tennis; L Wrstlng; High Hon Roll; Hon Roll; Pres Schlr; Duquesne U; Cmmnctns.

STABINSKI, ALEX; Upper Darby HS; Clifton Hts, PA; (3); Boy Scts; Concert Band; Orch; Hon Roll; Art.

STABULIS, CHERYL; Ridley HS; Eddystone, PA; (3); 7/423; Exploring; Spanish Clb; Varsity Clb; JV Bsktbl; L Mgr(s); Var Sftbl; Capt L Trk; NHS; Pres Acad Fit Awd 85; Excllnce Scholar Mdl 85; Phys Thrpy.

STACEY, JENNIFER; Mt Lebanon HS; Pittsburgh, PA; (3); 56/506; AFS; Church Yth Grp; German Clb; Latin Clb; SADD; Drill Tm; Orch; School Musical; Score Keeper; JV Vllybl; Spcl Achvt Awd Miss TEEN Pgnt 86; PA ST U; Elem Educ.

STACEY, JOHN; Central Catholic HS; Pittsburgh, PA; (3); 32/265; Exploring; Math Clb; Ski Clb; Concert Band; Jazz Band; Mrchg Band; Im Bsktbl; Im Bowling; Var Capt Golf; High Hon Roll; Mech Engrng.

STACEY, ROBERT; Ahoona Area HS; Altoona, PA; (4); 14/718; VP Q&S; Nwsp Ed-Chief; Lit Mag; Pres Crs Cntry; Trk; NHS; Ntl Merit Ltr; NEDT Awd; Mildred Brennan Memrl Schlrshp 87; PA; Pre-Law.

STACHEL, WENDY LEE; Scranton Central HS; Scranton, PA; (4); 88/307; Pres VP Church Yth Grp; Pres VP Girl Scts; Office Aide; Pep Clb; Spanish Clb; SADD; Concert Band; Mrchg Band; Yrbk Stf; Score Keeper; Girl Scout Gld Awd 87; Bloomsburg U; Finance.

STACHOKUS, JOSEPH; Pittston Area SR HS; Pittston, PA; (3); Art Clb; Computer Clb; Key Clb; Ski Clb; JV Var Bsbl; JV Var Ftbl; JV Trk; High Hon Roll; Prfct Atten Awd; Penn ST; Arch.

STACK, JOHN; Washington HS; Washington, PA; (3); 18/156; Am Leg Boys St; Church Yth Grp; Letterman Clb; Spanish Clb; Sec Dance Clb; L Var Ftbl; L Var Trk; Var Wrstlng; High Hon Roll; NHS.

STACKHOUSE, BRENDA; Benton Area JR-SR HS; Benton, PA; (3); Chorus; Co-Capt Color Guard; Hon Roll; NHS; Century 21 Typng Awd 87; Century 21 Accntng I Cert 87; Secy.

STACKHOUSE, BRIAN; Williamsport Area HS; Williamsport, PA; (3); Church Yth Grp; Key Clb; Band; Concert Band; Jazz Band; Mrchg Band; JV Ftbl; Var Trk; Cnty Band 85 & 87; Pre-Med.

STACKPOLE, JULIE; Central Bucks East HS; Furlong, PA; (4); Band; High Hon Roll; Bloomsburg Univ; Nrsng.

STACY, BARBARA; West Allegheny SR HS; Oakdale, PA; (2); FBLA; JA; Teachers Aide; Color Guard; Hon Roll; 5th Pl Bus Math FBLA Ldrshp Conf 87; Bus.

STACY, HEATHER; Beaver Area HS; Beaver, PA; (2); Church Yth Grp; FCA; French Clb; Pep Clb; Ski Clb; Color Guard; Mrchg Band; Yrbk Stf; Var Crs Cntry; Var Socr; Law.

STADLER, NICHOLAS; Scranton Central HS; Scranton, PA; (2); Art Clb; Art Hnr Scty 86-87; Art.

STADLER, RENEE; Lancaster Catholic HS; Lancaster, PA; (3); 5/200; Cmnty Wkr; Concert Band; Mrchg Band; Nwsp Rptr; Rep Soph Cls; Rep Jr Cls; Rep Sr Cls; JV Trk; Hon Roll; NHS; HOBY Ambassador Catholic High 86; Scry Lanc Ctys Ldrshp Wrkshps 87; 2nd Pl Lanc Cty Sci Fair Envrnmnt; Drexel U; Industrial Engrng.

STADLER, VALERIE; Couick/Pghs Creative/Prfmng Arts; Pittsburgh, PA; (2); Cmnty Wkr; Dance Clb; Drama Clb; Chorus; School Musical; School Play; Stage Crew; Swing Chorus; Variety Show; Hon Roll; Myr Calliguris Inngrtn & Theatre Arts Ctr 86; Classical Vclst.

STADTMUELLER, TERESA; Harborcreek HS; Erie, PA; (4); 8/213; Model UN; Mrchg Band; Pep Band; School Play; Variety Show; Hon Roll; NHS; 4 Yr Schlrshp To U Of Pitts; Social Studies Awd At Commencement 87; U Of Pittsbgh; Politcl Sci.

STAFFEN, KEITH; Blairsville SR HS; Blairsville, PA; (1); Church Yth Grp; Golf; Trk; High Hon Roll; IN U Of PA; Sci.

STAFFEN, RICHARD; Blairsville SR HS; Blairsville, PA; (1); Church Yth Grp; Stu Cncl; Bsktbl; Golf; Hon Roll; Indiana U Of PA; Sprts Med.

STAFFER, THOMAS; Daniel Boone Area HS; Birdsboro, PA; (3); Boy Scts; Ftbl; Comp Sci.

STAFFORD, LIANA; Cambridge Springs Joint HS; Edinboro, PA; (3); Church Yth Grp; Cmnty Wkr; Red Cross Aide; Spanish Clb; SADD; Phys Ftnss Awd 85; Edinboro U PA; Elem Educ.

STAFFORD, MELINDA; Sharon HS; Sharon, PA; (3); 14/175; Latin Clb; Varsity Clb; School Musical; Ed Nwsp Stf; Pres Soph Cls; Var JV Bsktbl; Var Cheerleading; Var L Trk; Var L Vllybl; Hon Roll; PA ST U; Med.

STAFFORD, SHAWN; Uniontown Area HS; Uniontown, PA; (3); Math Clb; Science Clb; Spanish Clb; Trs Jr Cls; Var Wrstlng; High Hon Roll; NHS; Natl Math Test 86-87; 3rd Pl Spnsh Vocab Comp At Cal U 86; Engrng Med.

STAFFORD, TANYA; Northern Cambria HS; Spangler, PA; (3); 28/152; Computer Clb; French Clb; Girl Scts; Concert Band; Mrchg Band; Yrbk Stf; Var Trk; High Hon Roll; Hon Roll; NHS; Socl Wrkr.

STAGG, MICHAEL; Bishop Hafey HS; Conyngham, PA; (1); 5/100; JV Bsktbl.

STAGGERS, KELLY; Laurel Highlands HS; Lemont Furnace, PA; (3); 78/375; SADD; Hon Roll.

STAGGERS, MARCY LYNN; Southmoreland HS; Alverton, PA; (4); 29/240; Church Yth Grp; French Clb; Office Aide; Ski Clb; Church Choir; Nwsp Stf; Lit Mag; Schlstc Awd Jrnlsm 87; Stud Cncl Schlrshp 87; PA Anncr 87; U Of Pittsburgh; Bus Mgmt.

STAGI, PATRICK; West Branch Area JR SR HS; Philipsburg, PA; (3); Church Yth Grp; Spanish Clb; Varsity Clb; VICA; Stu Cncl; Var Ftbl; Var Wt Lftg; Hon Roll; JV Socr; Williamsport CC; Elctrnc Engr.

STAHL, AMY; Milton Area SR HS; Milton, PA; (2); Latin Clb; Mrchg Band; Hon Roll; Church Yth Grp; Band; Concert Band; Lat Hnrs Soc 86-87; Lat Cert 85-86; Hnr Crd 86-87; Geisinger; Nrsng.

STAHL, DIAHANNA; St Huberts HS For Girls; Philadelphia, PA; (3); 6/420; FBLA; Office Aide; Lit Mag; High Hon Roll; Hon Roll; Ldrshp Awd 86-87; Natl Hon Soc Banquet Svc 84-85; Awd Stengrphy & Typng Acdmc Merit 86-87; Temple U; Journlsm.

STAHL, JESSICA; Meyersdale Area HS; Meyersdale, PA; (4); Am Leg Aux Girls St; Trs Spanish Clb; Pres Sr Cls; Sec Stu Cncl; Stat Ftbl; Var L Sftbl; Var L Vllybl; Stat Wrstlng; Hon Roll; Sec NHS; All Cnty Sftbll Tm 84-86; Hmcmng Soph Attndnt 84-85; Penn ST U; Cmmnctns.

STAHL, KATHERINE; Meyersdale Area HS; Meyersdale, PA; (3); Spanish Clb; VP Band; School Musical; Stu Cncl; Var Capt Cheerleading; High Hon Roll; NHS; VFW Awd; Voice Dem Awd; Cmnty Wkr; Local & Cnty 1st Pl Amer Auxiliary Essay; Public Rltns.

STAHL, LORI; Christian School Of York; Shiremanstown, PA; (2); Church Yth Grp; Library Aide; Chorus; High Hon Roll; Hon Roll; Liberty U; Lbry Sci.

STAHL, STEVEN G; Owen J Roberts HS; Birchrunville, PA; (2); 15/311; Stu Cncl; Bsbl; Socr; Hon Roll; Temple Univ.

STAHL, SUE; Somerset Area SR HS; Somerset, PA; (4); 72/244; Church Yth Grp; English Clb; Q&S; Trs Spanish Clb; School Play; Yrbk Stf; Stu Cncl; Bsktbl; Hon Roll; Duquesne U; Comm.

STAHL, TERRY; Mt Pleasant Area HS; Acme, PA; (4); Chess Clb; Church Yth Grp; French Clb; Library Aide; Hon Roll; Ambassador Coll; Data Prcsng.

STAHL, WAYNE; Mt Pleasant Area HS; Acme, PA; (2); Chess Clb; Church Yth Grp; German Clb; Band; Concert Band.

STAHL, WESLEY; Penn View Christian Acad; Ickesburg, PA; (2); Church Yth Grp; Church Choir; Off Stu Cncl; Hon Roll; NHS; PA View.

STAHLE, RACHEL S; Dallastown Area HS; Dallastown, PA; (4); 28/356; Am Leg Aux Girls St; Art Clb; Church Choir; Nwsp Ed-Chief; Lit Mag; High Hon Roll; Hon Roll; NCTE Awd; Church Yth Grp; Cmnty Wkr; PA Cncl Tchrs Engl Awd Wrtng; Stu Mnth Nov 85; Indiana U Of PA; Engl Educ.

STAHLER, HOLLY; Bishop O Reilly HS; Wyoming, PA; (3); Exploring; Spanish Clb; Hon Roll; Spanish NHS; Med.

STAHLER, LAURA; New Freedom Christian HS; New Freedom, PA; (4); 2/9; Church Yth Grp; German Clb; Acpl Chr; School Play; Yrbk Ed-Chief; Score Keeper; Var Sftbl; Capt Vllybl; Hon Roll; Sci Fair Awd 85-86; Grmn Awd 85-86; Wrld Hstry Awd 84-85; Bob Jones U.

STAHLEY, ERIC; Wyoming Area HS; Wyoming, PA; (2); Art Clb; Church Yth Grp; Service Clb; Engrng.

STAHLEY, SHERRY; Jim Thorpe Area HS; Weatherly, PA; (3); Computer Clb; German Clb; Scholastic Bowl; Ski Clb; Nwsp Stf; Yrbk Stf; High Hon Roll; Hon Roll; Bio.

STAHLMAN, DANIEL; Punxsutawney Area HS; Punxsutawney, PA; (4); 8/245; Church Yth Grp; CAP; French Clb; Math Tm; Science Clb; Variety Show; Var Golf; Hon Roll; NHS; J Clifford Doney Math Awd 87; Penn ST U; Comp Sci.

STAHLMAN, JOANNA; Clarion Limestone HS; Clarion, PA; (3); Band; Chorus; School Musical; JV Bsktbl.

STAHLMAN, STACY; Punxsutawney Area HS; Rossiter, PA; (3); Civic Clb; PAVAS; Radio Clb; SADD; Mgr(s); Hon Roll; Secy.

STAHLSMITH, JULIE; Freeport Area SR HS; Ashville, NY; (4); Church Yth Grp; Hosp Aide; School Musical; School Play; Nwsp Stf; Yrbk Stf; High Hon Roll; NHS; Prsdntl Acdmc Ftnss Awds Pgm 87; Grove City Coll; Elem Educ.

STAHURSKI, NEIL E; Elizabeth-Forward HS; Mc Keesport, PA; (4); 40/293; Acpl Chr; Band; Church Choir; Concert Band; Drm Mjr(t); Jazz Band; Mrchg Band; Pep Band; School Musical; Hon Roll; Music Schlrshp Awd 87; Acad All Amer 86; Music/Acad Schlrshps 87; Duquesne U; Music.

STAIKIDES, MEG; Avon Grove HS; West Grove, PA; (3); Hosp Aide; Concert Band; Mrchg Band; School Musical; Rep Stu Cncl; JV Vllybl; Hon Roll; VP NHS; Dist Band 87; Avon Grv Uth Ed Assoc Secy 87-88; Am Red Cross Ldrshp Dvlpmnt Ctr 87.

STAINBROOK, TIM; Mercer Area SR JR HS; Mercer, PA; (1); Church Yth Grp; Ftbl; Trk; Penn ST; Football Mgmt.

STAINS, MIKE; East Pennsboro Area HS; Camp Hill, PA; (2); 21/194; Church Yth Grp; Latin Clb; JV Bsbl; JV Var Socr; High Hon Roll; Acad Achvt Cert Earth Space Sci 85-86, Hstry 85-87, Health 86-87; Arch Desgn.

STAIR, JUDY; South Western HS; Hanover, PA; (3); Church Yth Grp; VP Hst Band; Concert Band; Drm Mjr(t); Mrchg Band; Pep Band; Stage Crew; Symp Band; Cheerleading; Hon Roll; Bus Mgmt.

STAIRS, ANN; Hempfield HS; Monheim, PA; (4) Church Yth Grp; 4-H; Sec Varsity Clb; Yrbk Phtg; Var Capt Crs Cntry; Var L Trk; Rep Frsh Cls; Hst Soph Cls; Hst Jr Cls; Hst Sr Cls; HOBY Ldrshp Fndtn 85; PA ST.

STAKE, BRAD; Chambersburg Area SR HS; Chambersburg, PA; (4); 15/550; Orch; Symp Band; L Tennis; High Hon Roll; Hon Roll; Jr NHS; NHS; Shpnsbrg U; Bus Adm.

STAKER, ELIZABETH; Middletown HS; Middletown, PA; (3); 17/193; Model UN; Varsity Clb; Chorus; Capt Color Guard; Mrchg Band; Nwsp Rptr; Ed Nwsp Stf; JV Gym; Var Trk; Hon Roll; Elks Histrcl Essay Cont 84; Vet Med.

STALGAITIS, KAREN; Marian Catholic HS; Mcadoo, PA; (3); 22/115; Church Yth Grp; Exploring; Girl Scts; Pep Clb; Scholastic Bowl; SADD; Chorus; Nwsp Rptr; Var JV Cheerleading; Hon Roll; Marian Medal Awd 85; Immaculata Coll; Chem.

STALLONE, KAREN ANN; E L Meyers HS; Wilkes-Barre, PA; (4); 1/140; French Clb; SADD; Chorus; Nwsp Rptr; Bausch & Lomb Sci Awd; Jr NHS; NHS; Ntl Merit Ltr; NEDT Awd; Val; Ntl Frnch Cntst 2nd Pl 85; Engrng.

STALNAKER, ANN; West Greene HS; New Freeport, PA; (4); Pres Art Clb; SADD; Nwsp Stf; Ed Yrbk Stf; Trk; Wt Lftg; High Hon Roll; Hon Roll; PA ST U; Eng.

STALSKY, PETE; Mercyhurst Preparatory School; Erie, PA; (3); Cmnty Wkr; Socr; Hon Roll; NHS; Mercyhurst.

STAMAN, MATTHEW W; Warrior Run HS; Turbotville, PA; (3); 3/179; Var Am Leg Boys St; Pres Service Clb; Trs Chorus; Nwsp Bus Mgr; Ed Yrbk Stf; Trs Stu Cncl; Cit Awd; NHS; Trs AFS; Trs Church Yth Grp; Woodmen Or Wrld Amer Hstry Awd 87; PA Gov Schl Of Arts 87.

STAMBAUGH, DEBBIE; Purchase Line HS; Arcadia, PA; (2); 23/156; French Clb; Band; Concert Band; Drm Mjr(t); Mrchg Band; Pep Band; Hon Roll.

STAMBAUGH, DENISE; Hatboro-Horsham HS; Hatboro, PA; (4); Trs Key Clb; Band; Concert Band; Jazz Band; Mrchg Band; Mgr(s); Millersville U; Bio.

STAMBAUGH, DIANE; West Middlesex Area JR-SR HS; Mercer, PA; (2); 4-H; Trs French Clb; Hosp Aide; High Hon Roll; Jr NHS; NHS; Natl Sci Merit Awd 85-86; Schl Stu Achvrs Merit Awd 87; Nrsng.

STAMBAUGH, ERIC; Northern York County HS; Wellsville, PA; (4); 20/200; Chorus; School Musical; Stage Crew; Swing Chorus; Nwsp Stf; Var L Socr; French Hon Soc; Hon Roll; Pres Acdmc Fit Awd 87; PA ST U.

STAMBAUGH, ERIC; Spring Grove SR HS; Spring Grove, PA; (3); Aud/Vis; Letterman Clb; Varsity Clb; Var L Bsbl; JV Bsktbl; Var L Ftbl; Hon Roll; Bus.

STAMBAUGH, KAREN; York Catholic HS; Dover, PA; (4); 13/167; Spanish Clb; Varsity Clb; Chorus; School Musical; Stage Crew; Var Trk; JV Var Vllybl; Hon Roll; NHS; Drama Clb; Cathlc Wmns Clb Awd 87; Elem Educ.

STAMBOOLIAN, KRISTIN; Henderson SR HS; West Chester, PA; (3); Church Yth Grp; Exploring; Hosp Aide; JCL; Red Cross Aide; Acpl Chr; Concert Band; School Musical; Yrbk Stf; Var Fld Hcky; Schlrshp Red Crss Yth Ldrshp Dvlpmnt Ctr 86; Intl Bus.

STAMETS, DAWN; Elkland Area HS; Osceola, PA; (4); Church Yth Grp; Cmnty Wkr; Dance Clb; 4-H; French Clb; SADD; Yrbk Stf; 4-H Awd; NHS; Trs Girl Scts; Tioga Cty Altrnte Dairy Princess 86-87; Vet Sci.

STAMM, BECKI; Danville Area HS; Riverside, PA; (3); 34/187; Church Yth Grp; Cmnty Wkr; Debate Tm; Key Clb; NFL; Spanish Clb; Var Cheerleading; Hon Roll; NHS; Psych.

STAMM, TAMMY; Milton Area SR HS; Milton, PA; (4); Trs Computer Clb; Intnl Clb; Hst Service Clb; Varsity Clb; School Musical; Yrbk Stf; Off Jr Cls; Rep Stu Cncl; Var Cheerleading; JV Fld Hcky; Thomas Wards Memorial Booster Clb Awd 86-87; Susquebanne U; Accntng.

STAMP, KELLY; Lakeview HS; Stoneboro, PA; (4); 8/130; VP Church Yth Grp; Sec Science Clb; Band; School Play; Nwsp Ed-Chief; Trs Soph Cls; VP Sr Cls; Capt Cheerleading; NHS; Intnl Clb; Rotary Yth Ldrshp Awd RYLA 86; Bus Admn.

STAMPER, ANITA; Red Lion Area SR HS; Brogue, PA; (3); Sec Church Yth Grp; Cmnty Wkr; JA; Service Clb; SADD; Church Choir; Nwsp Rptr; Hon Roll; PA ST U; Psych.

STANAKIS, MARK; Mahanoy Area HS; Mahanoy, PA; (3); Spanish Clb; Stage Crew; Var L Bsbl; JV Var Bsktbl; Var L Ftbl.

STANAVAGE, JENNIFER; Hazleton HS; Mc Adoo, PA; (2); Dance Clb; Drama Clb; FBLA; Girl Scts; Pep Clb; School Play; Variety Show; JV Cheerleading; Gym; Hon Roll; Philadelphia Acad Thrtcl Arts Schlrshp Awd 86; Dance.

STANBACK, GREGORY; Aliquippa HS; Aliquippa, PA; (3); Church Yth Grp; Rep VICA; Band; School Play; Stu Cncl; Capt Bsktbl; JV Ftbl; Capt Socr; VP Trk; Hon Roll; U Of Pittsburgh; Phys Thpry.

STANCAMPIANO, JIM; Moon SR HS; Coraopolis, PA; (3); 82/306; Boy Scts; Church Yth Grp; Computer Clb; German Clb; Scholastic Bowl; Nwsp Rptr; Im Golf; Im Swmmng; Var L Tennis; Hon Roll; PA ST U; Chem.

STANCAVAGE, ROBINANNE; Mt Carmel Area JR/Sr HS; Mt Carmel, PA; (4); 9/159; Q&S; Var L Bsktbl; Var Capt Sftbl; Var L Trk; High Hon Roll; NHS; Ntl Merit Ltr; Cmnty Wkr; FTA; Key Clb; Co MVP Sftbl Tm; Ntl Athltc Hnr Soc Secr; N B Ottaway Schlrshp; MA Inst Tech; Biomed.

STANCHINA, C JOHN; Downingtown HS; Downingtown, PA; (4); 39/563; VP French Clb; Pep Clb; Pres Ski Clb; Off Stu Cncl; High Hon Roll; 2nd Pl US Cyclng Fed Snctnd Time Trail 85; USAA Ntl Awd Math & Sci 84 & 83; USAA; Aerospc Engnrng.

STANCZAK, KIMBERLY; Pittston Area SR HS; Inkerman, PA; (4); 51/365; French Clb; Key Clb; Yrbk Stf; CAP; High Hon Roll; Hon Roll; EKG Study.

STANCZYK, LOUISE; Valley View JR SR HS; Jessup, PA; (1); 1/175; French Clb; High Hon Roll; Natl Frnch Cont Cert Hnr 86; Amer Mth Comptn 1st Pl 86; U Scranton; Med.

STANDEN, COLLEEN; Upper Darby SR HS; Upper Darby, PA; (3); 84/598; German Clb; Library Aide; Chorus; Yrbk Stf; High Hon Roll; Hon Roll.

STANDISH, JEFF; Strath Haven HS; Wallingford, PA; (3); FBLA; Ski Clb; Teachers Aide; Yrbk Phtg; Yrbk Stf; Capt Socr; Tennis; Hon Roll; MVP Socr 84-85; Wrtg Asst Prgm 86-88; Start Forwrd ST Champ Socr Tm 86-87; Geol.

STANEK, JENNIFER; Hazleton HS; Drums, PA; (3); Church Yth Grp; FNA; Varsity Clb; Yrbk Stf; Rep Stu Cncl; Var L Cheerleading; Gym; High Hon Roll; Sec Cadette Club 87-88; Var Chrldr 85-86; Bloomsburg U; Surgcl Nrsng.

STANEK, ROBERT; Valley HS; New Kensington, PA; (2); Drama Clb; FBLA; Spanish Clb; Prfct Atten Awd; St Vincent Coll; Disc Jockey.

STANEK, ROSS; Farrell Area SR HS; Farrell, PA; (4); 5/87; Aud/Vis; Computer Clb; English Clb; French Clb; Library Aide; Science Clb; Varsity Clb; Stage Crew; Yrbk Stf; Bsktbl; Al Abrams All Sprts Awd 87; Mercer Co Hl Fame Awd 87; Army Schlr Athl Awd 87; David Kostka Meml Awd 87; Penn ST; Comp Sci.

STANFIELD, RIKKI; Penn Hills SR HS; Verona, PA; (3); Hosp Aide; Spanish Clb; VP Church Choir; Mrchg Band; Rep Jr Cls; Rep Stu Cncl; JV Var Trk; JV Vllybl; Hon Roll; Prfct Atten Awd; Spch Pthlgst.

STANFORD, HEATHER; West Middlesex HS JR-SR HS; West Middlesex, PA; (3); 9/107; Office Aide; Spanish Clb; Sec Trs Chorus; Concert Band; Mrchg Band; Var Cheerleading; Sftbl; Hon Roll; NHS; Elem Ed.

STANFORD, KEITH; Meadville Area SR HS; Meadville, PA; (4); 8/306; Key Clb; Letterman Clb; Science Clb; Varsity Clb; Pres Frsh Cls; Rep Jr Cls; Rep Sr Cls; Rep Stu Cncl; L Var Socr; Capt L Wrstlng.

STANG, KURT; Tunkhannock Area HS; Meshoppen, PA; (3); Church Yth Grp; Computer Clb; Cit Awd; Hon Roll; Elec Engrng.

STANGE, JEFF; Connellsville SR HS; Connellsville, PA; (3); Library Aide; Sec Soph Cls; Ftbl; Wt Lftg; US Army; Elec.

STANGE, REBECCA; Clarion-Limestone HS; Strattanville, PA; (4); 3/70; Pres SADD; Sec Band; School Play; Nwsp Stf; Sec Jr Cls; Pres Sr Cls; Capt Cheerleading; NHS; Ntl Merit SF; Pres Schlr; Rotary Scholar 87; Jaycees Scholar 87; Clarion U.

STANGE, SHARON; Ambridge Area HS; Freedom, PA; (3); Church Yth Grp; German Clb; Pep Clb; SADD; Drill Tm; Off Soph Cls; Off Jr Cls; Hon Roll; Sewickley Hosp Schl Nrsng; Nrsn.

STANICKYJ, LISA; St Basil Acad; Philadelphia, PA; (4); 22/97; German Clb; Chorus; Im Bsktbl; Hon Roll; Ntl Merit Ltr; Philedelphia Coll-Phrmcy & Sci.

STANISZEWSKI, JOSEPH B; Abington SR HS; Roslyn, PA; (3); 86/502; Hosp Aide; Intnl Clb; Radio Clb; Band; Jazz Band; School Musical; School Play; Stage Crew; Symp Band; Bowling; Pres Acad Fit Awd 84-85; Pre-Med.

STANKAN, ALBERT; Conemaugh Township Area HS; Boswell, PA; (3); Boy Scts; Yrbk Stf; Var Crs Cntry; JV Ftbl; Var Wrstlng; Pre-Occptnl.

STANKO, BRIAN; Kittanning SR HS; Adrian, PA; (3); 20/226; CAP; JV Var Ftbl; High Hon Roll; Hon Roll; NHS; Pres Schlr; Aviation.

STANKO, RANDI; Highlands SR HS; Tarentum, PA; (3); 28/303; Intnl Clb; Science Clb; SADD; Varsity Clb; Rep Stu Cncl; Gym; Swmmng; Trk; High Hon Roll; NHS; 1st Pl Awd Physc Olympc Comptn 86; Gymnstcs Awds 85-87; Marine Bio Gate Prog 87; Bio.

STANKO, SEAN; North Star HS; Hooversville, PA; (3); FCA; Var Bsbl; Var Bsktbl; Cit Awd; N Star Bstrs Stu Mnth Nov 86.

STANKU, ALEXANDER; Jules E Mastbaum A V T S HS; Philadelphia, PA; (4); 30/350; JV Ftbl; Im Vllybl; Var Pres Schlr; U Miami; Mech Engrng.

STANLEY, CRISTY; Nazareth SR HS; Nazareth, PA; (3); 14/270; Key Clb; Math Tm; Yrbk Stf; Stu Cncl; Trk; High Hon Roll; Hon Roll; NHS; Bio-Chem.

STANLEY, JYLENE; Allentown Central Catholic HS; Allentown, PA; (3); Church Yth Grp; Library Aide; Rep Frsh Cls; Var Bsktbl; Var Sftbl; Hon Roll; Nrsng.

STANLEY, KIM; Riverside HS; Fombell, PA; (3); AFS; DECA; DECA Shplftng & Prvntn Prjct 4th In Ntn 86; 2nd Pl PA DECA Gen Mktg & 1st Pl Free Entrprs Prjct 87; Law Enfrcmnt.

STANLEY, SHEILA; St Pius X HS; Royersford, PA; (4); 29/148; French Clb; Service Clb; Nwsp Rptr; Rep Frsh Cls; Var Cheerleading; High Hon Roll; Hon Roll; NHS; Alvernia; Bus Admn.

STANLEY, TRACY; Oxford Area HS; Nottingham, PA; (3); Church Yth Grp; Library Aide; SADD; Hon Roll.

STANSFIELD, CRYSTAL; Big Spring HS; Newville, PA; (3); 7/258; Powder Puff Ftbl; Swmmng; Trk; Hon Roll.

STANSFIELD, LEANNE; E Pennsboro HS; Enola, PA; (3); Cmnty Wkr; Spanish Clb; Church Choir; Concert Band; School Musical; Yrbk Stf; Sec Jr Cls; Sec Sr Cls; Var L Bsktbl; Var L Fld Hcky; Elem Educ.

STANTON II, LUTHER; Wilson Area HS; Easton, PA; (4); 1/124; Computer Clb; Debate Tm; Exploring; Model UN; Scholastic Bowl; Chorus; Ed Nwsp Stf; Ed Yrbk Stf; High Hon Roll; VP NHS; Lehigh U; Elec Engrng.

STANTON, MELONY; Meyersdale Area HS; Meyersdale, PA; (3); Cmnty Wkr; Spanish Clb; Band; Drm Mjr(t); Twrlr; High Hon Roll; Hon Roll; NHS; Concert Band; Mrchg Band; Spch Pthlgy.

STANTON, MICHELLE; West Middlesex HS; Pulaski, PA; (2); Office Aide; Spanish Clb; Band; Mrchg Band; Stat Bsktbl; Coach Actv; Var L Trk; Var L Vllybl; Gov Hon Prg Awd; High Hon Roll; New Image Clb 84-86; Emplyd Hogans Heros 87; PA ST; Chld Psych.

STANTON, TRACY; Philadelphia High School For Girls; Philadelphia, PA; (3); Office Aide; Teachers Aide; Drill Tm; Score Keeper; Bus Admin.

STANWOOD, GREGG D; Archbishop Kennedy HS; Conshohocken, PA; (4); 4/170; Trk; Wt Lftg; High Hon Roll; NHS; Temple U-Outstndng Achvt Schlrshp 87; Bloomsbrg U-Mitrani Schlrshp 87; Temple U.

STAPE, SANDRA N; North Penn HS; Lansdale, PA; (4); 25/655; Church Yth Grp; Ski Clb; Soph Cls; Jr Cls; Sr Cls; Stu Cncl; Cheerleading; Lcrss; High Hon Roll; Hon Roll; Slvr Mdl Ntl Latn Exam; N Penn H S Hnr Awd Acadm Excllnce; Distg Hnr Roll; Bucknell U; Law.

STAPINSKI, CARYN; John S Fine HS; Nanticoke, PA; (2); 25/243; Key Clb; Chorus; Swmmng; High Hon Roll; NHS.

STAPINSKI, KRISTINA; Valley HS; New Kensington, PA; (2); 47/237; AFS; French Clb; Ski Clb; SADD; Rep Stu Cncl; Hon Roll.

STAPLES, JUDD; Strath Haven HS; Wallingford, PA; (3); Aud/Vis; Dance Clb; Drama Clb; Ski Clb; School Play; Stage Crew; Yrbk Phtg; Yrbk Stf; Rep Sr Cls; JV Socr; Engrng.

STAPLETON, BARBARA; Saltsburg JR SR HS; Saltsburg, PA; (2); 7/95; SADD; Drm & Bgl; School Musical; Rep Stu Cncl; Capt Twrlr; Stat Vllybl; High Hon Roll; Pres Schlr; Tchr.

STAPLETON, MAUREEN; Central Bucks East HS; Doylestown, PA; (4); Church Yth Grp; Nwsp Rptr; Nwsp Stf; Lit Mag; VP Sr Cls; Rep Stu Cncl; Var Capt Crs Cntry; Var Trk; High Hon Roll; Villanova U.

STARANKO, SCOTT; Charleroi Area JR-SR HS; Charleroi, PA; (3); VP Sec Church Yth Grp; Trs French Clb; Letterman Clb; Science Clb; Ski Clb; Varsity Clb; Bsktbl; Var Capt Ftbl; Powder Puff Ftbl; Hon Roll; Bishps Awd Diocs Pittsburgh 87; Socty Distngshd Amer HS Stdnts 87; De Molay Relgn & Athltcs Awd 85; Pre-Law.

STARASINIC, GARRETT; Bishop Mc Devitt HS; Oberlin, PA; (3); 2/218; Am Leg Boys St; Off Science Clb; Concert Band; Jazz Band; Off Mrchg Band; Pep Band; Wt Lftg; Dance Clb; NHS; NEDT Awd; US Military Acad; Engrng.

STARASINICH, JOSEPH; Beaver Area JR SR HS; Beaver, PA; (2); 25/242; Church Yth Grp; Spanish Clb; Trk.

STARCHVILLE, SHELLY; Windber Area HS; Windber, PA; (3); #1 In Class; French Clb; JA; Ski Clb; Band; Concert Band; Jazz Band; Mrchg Band; Yrbk Stf; High Hon Roll; Pres NHS; Pres Acdmc Ftnss Awd 85; Cls Awds 86-87; Penn ST; Math.

STARE, LYNNETTE; Penn Hills SR HS; Pittsburgh, PA; (3); Camera Clb; German Clb; Ski Clb; Stu Cncl; Bowling; Hon Roll; Engrng.

STARK, ALISON; Ringgold HS; Eighty Four, PA; (2); 27/396; Drama Clb; Hosp Aide; Ski Clb; School Musical; Nwsp Rptr; Yrbk Stf; Stat Vllybl; High Hon Roll; NHS; Frnsc.

STARK, BRIDGET; Turkeyfoot Valley Area HS; Confluence, PA; (3); Church Yth Grp; Hosp Aide; Q&S; Band; Chorus; Nwsp Stf; Yrbk Stf; High Hon Roll; NHS; Rep Stu Cncl; Nrsg.

STARK, KELLI; Monessen HS; Monessen, PA; (3); 11/115; Church Yth Grp; French Clb; Stage Crew; Yrbk Stf; Rep Frsh Cls; Trs Soph Cls; Trs Jr Cls; Twrlr; High Hon Roll; Hon Roll; Nwspr Carr Yr Awd 85; Cmmnctns.

STARK, KURT; Meadville Area SR HS; Meadville, PA; (4); 46/295; Church Yth Grp; Science Clb; Pres Frsh Cls; L Im Bsktbl; Var L Socr; Var L Trk; Wt Lftg; Hon Roll; Intl Bro Elec Wkrs Lcl 712 Schlrshp 87-90; U Of Pittsburgh; Law.

STARK, TODD; General Mc Lane HS; Edinboro, PA; (4); Boy Scts; Church Yth Grp; Ski Clb; Spanish Clb; Pres Chorus; School Musical; Swing Chorus; Var Swmmng; Hon Roll; NHS; Attnd Dist Chrs 86 & 87; Nrmn W Schrs Awd 87; Music Hnr Awd 87; PA ST U; Elctrcl Engrng.

STARK, TODD; Tyrone Area HS; Pt Matilda, PA; (3); 22/209; Yrbk Stf; Im Bsktbl; Im Coach Actv; Var L Ftbl; JV Trk; Im Wt Lftg; JV Wrstlng; Penn ST U; Arch.

STARMAN, BECKI; Spring-Ford HS; Royersford, PA; (3); 20/256; Pep Clb; Spanish Clb; Band; Concert Band; Mrchg Band; Stu Cncl; Cheerleading; Sftbl; High Hon Roll; Hon Roll; Writer Mnth 86; Elem Ed.

STARNER, THAD E; Dallastown Area HS; Dallastown, PA; (4); 2/353; Trs Church Choir; High Hon Roll; NHS; Ntl Merit SF; Opt Clb Awd; PA Govrnrs Schl Sci 86; Intl Sci Engrng Fair 3rd Pl Comp 86; Publctn Grphc Pgm Comp Mag 85; MA Inst Tech; Artfcl Intellgnc.

STAROBIN, JENNIFER; East Pennsboro Area HS; Camp Hill, PA; (2); 21/189; French Clb; Ski Clb; Band; Concert Band; Mrchg Band; School Musical; Yrbk Stf; Stu Cncl; NHS; Drama Clb; Cert Achvt Band 86-87,Engl & Hist 85-86; Law.

STAROLIS, SUE; Dallas SR HS; Wyoming, PA; (3); 140/211; Church Yth Grp; L Capt Bsktbl; Im Gym; Var Trk; Hon Roll; MVP & Mst Vlbl Sprntr In Trck 87; Med.

STAROSCHUCK, SCOTT; Canevin HS; Mckees Rocks, PA; (3); 44/192; FBLA; Hon Roll; 3rd Pl SR Physics Sci Fair 86-87.

STARR, BRENDA; Port Allegany HS; Port Allegany, PA; (3); 34/121; French Clb; FTA; Chorus; Var JV Cheerleading; Prfct Atten Awd; Elem Ed.

STARR, CHRISSY; Brockway Area HS; Brockway, PA; (4); 15/90; Exploring; Color Guard; Ed Nwsp Stf; Hon Roll; Cert Prfncy Accntng 86; Hnr Chorus 87; Clarion U PA; Accntng.

STARR, DANNY; Elizabeth Forward HS; Elizabeth, PA; (3); 13/345; Spanish Clb; Teachers Aide; High Hon Roll; Hon Roll; NHS; Ntl Merit Ltr; ASTRONAUTICS.

STARR, GREGORY; Central Christian HS; Brockway, PA; (3); Camera Clb; Drama Clb; Ski Clb; School Play; Stage Crew; Nwsp Phtg; Nwsp Sprt Ed; Nwsp Stf; Yrbk Phtg; Yrbk Sprt Ed; PA Free Enterprise Week Lock Haven U 87; Bus.

STARR, TINA; Brookville Area HS; Brookville, PA; (3); Pres Church Yth Grp; French Clb; Chorus; Lit Mag; Hon Roll; Jr NHS; Messiah Coll; Accntnt.

STARRY, AMY; United HS; New Florence, PA; (3); Camera Clb; Drama Clb; French Clb; Pep Clb; Ski Clb; Band; Concert Band; Drill Tm; School Play; Symp Band; IN Cnty Band 87; Bio-Med.

STASA, NICOLE; Sto-Rox SR HS; Mckees Rocks, PA; (2); Boys Clb Am; Office Aide; Chorus; Yrbk Stf; Hon Roll; Stewrdss.

STASH, JAMIE; Connellsville Area HS; Dunbar, PA; (1); GAA; Office Aide; Pep Clb; Ski Clb; Spanish Clb; Teachers Aide; Chorus; Nwsp Phtg; Nwsp Stf; Yrbk Phtg; Mst Athletic 87; MVP Vllybl, Bkstbl, Pep Club 87; Stu Sec 87; IN U PA; Elem Ed.

STASH, SUSANNE; Lake Lehman HS; Shavertown, PA; (4); 14/161; Cmnty Wkr; Key Clb; SADD; School Play; Yrbk Stf; L Fld Hcky; Score Keeper; Stat Vllybl; Hon Roll; NHS; Kings Coll; Bus.

STASIK, MARK; Carrick HS; Pittsburgh, PA; (2); Boy Scts; Civic Clb; High Hon Roll; Hon Roll; Music.

STASSEL, DEBBIE; West Catholic Girls HS; Philadelphia, PA; (4); 34/235; JA; Pep Clb; Spanish Clb; School Play; Var Cheerleading; Var Pom Pon; Hon Roll; Pres Acad Fitness Awd 87; Temple U; Bus Admn.

STASSEN, NICOLE; Conestoga SR HS; Berwyn, PA; (4); 57/454; AFS; Pep Clb; Chorus; Var Crs Cntry; Var Trk; Hon Roll.

STASZEWSKI, CHERYL; Seneca HS; Erie, PA; (3); 25/160; Computer Clb; Yrbk Stf; Capt Var Bsktbl; Var Crs Cntry; Var Trk; Hon Roll; Prfct Atten Awd; Mercy Hurst Col; Hlth.

STATES, ALYSON; Ambridge Area HS; Baden, PA; (3); Church Yth Grp; DECA; French Clb; 2nd Plc DECA Dist 2 Wrhs Comp 86; Tp 20 Sls Demo ST Lvl DECA 87; Bradford Business Schl; Mktg.

STATES, TRACY; Brownsville SR HS; Grindstone, PA; (3); VICA; Comp.

STATLER, CHAD; Chambersburg Area HS; Chambersburg, PA; (2); 10/800; German Clb; L Bsbl; High Hon Roll; :Sci.

STATLER, ELIZABETH; Chambersburg Area SR HS; Chambersburg, PA; (2); Church Yth Grp; French Clb; Ski Clb; Chorus; Tennis.

STATON, WENDY M; Philadelphia H S For Girls; Philadelphia, PA; (4); 61/365; Church Yth Grp; Cmnty Wkr; Math Tm; Model UN; Office Aide; Pres Service Clb; Teachers Aide; Concert Band; Jazz Band; Mrchg Band; Exprmnt Intl Lvng Smmr Abroad Schlrshp 86; Ntl Achvmnt Cmmndtn 86; Wndws Into Sci Enrchmnt 85; Columbia Coll.

STATTON JR, JIM; Bald Eagle Nittany HS; Mill Hall, PA; (2); 2/136; Key Clb; High Hon Roll; Hon Roll; Prfct Atten Awd.

STAUB, D DEETTE; Delone Catholic HS; Hanover, PA; (4); 21/165; Debate Tm; Hosp Aide; Library Aide; Red Cross Aide; Sec Jr Cls; Sec Sr Cls; Var L Cheerleading; Hon Roll; NHS; York Coll; Nrsng.

STAUB, ELISA; South Western HS; Hanover, PA; (3); 34/216; Varsity Clb; Var L Swmmng; Var L Tennis; Var L Trk; NHS; Bio.

STAUB, JOHN; Fort Cherry HS; Imperial, PA; (2); Church Yth Grp; Computer Clb; Math Clb; Spanish Clb; Chorus; Nwsp Rptr; Nwsp Stf; High Hon Roll.

STAUB, LORI; Southwestern HS; Hanover, PA; (2); 47/212; Key Clb; Letterman Clb; Red Cross Aide; Varsity Clb; Var L Fld Hcky; Var L Swmmng; Tennis; Var L Trk; Hon Roll; Bio.

STAUB, PATRICK; York Catholic HS; York, PA; (2); 28/186; German Clb; Latin Clb; Chorus; Off Soph Cls; Off Jr Cls; Off Stu Cncl; Bsbl; Ftbl; Trk; NHS; US Naval Acad; Aviator.

STAUCH, MATTHEW; Northeastern HS; Manchester, PA; (3); 42/195; Aud/Vis; Pres Ski Clb; VP Chorus; Concert Band; Drm Mjr(t); Pres Soph Cls; Off Jr Cls; Off Sr Cls; JV Socr; PA Ambassdr-Music 87; Law.

STAUFFER, CHERI; Cedar Crest HS; Lebanon, PA; (3); Church Yth Grp; Pep Clb; Spanish Clb; Color Guard; Mrchg Band; Var Capt Cheerleading; Var Sftbl; Im Vllybl; Hon Roll; Misericordia; Thrpy.

STAUFFER, CYNTHIA; Warwick HS; Lititz, PA; (3); 53/283; Mgr(s); Stetson U; Fshn Merch.

STAUFFER, JAMIE; Connellsville Area HS; Connellsville, PA; (3); 124/491; Office Aide; School Musical; Nwsp Stf; Stu Cncl; Stat Ftbl; L Sftbl; L Tennis; JV Capt Vllybl; Hon Roll; Prfct Atten Awd; Indiana U Of PA; Nrsng.

STAUFFER, JENNIFER; Mc Keesport Area HS; Mckeesport, PA; (3); #22 In Class; German Clb; Hosp Aide; Sec Concert Band; Sec Mrchg Band; Orch; School Musical; Capt Swmmng; Hon Roll; NHS; Prfct Atten Awd; Rotary Ltr Peace Cntst 2nd City 85-86; Swmmng Ltr, WPIAL Champs 85-87; Jr Dist Band 85.

STAUFFER, KEITH A; Warwick HS; Lititz, PA; (4); 30/250; Varsity Clb; Bsktbl; Mgr(s); Tennis; Wt Lftg; High Hon Roll; Hon Roll; Purdue U; Engrng.

STAUFFER, KRIS; Solanco SR HS; Quarryville, PA; (2); VP Church Yth Grp; Church Choir; Mrchg Band; Rep Stu Cncl; JV Bsktbl; Cheerleading; JV Fld Hcky; JV Sftbl; High Hon Roll; NHS; Outstndng Stu Of Mrkng Period In Span 87, Bus 87; Awd For Hghst Cls Avrg In Span 87; Bus.

STAUFFER, MARCY L; Boyertown Area JR High East; Gilbertsville, PA; (1); Am Leg Aux Girls St; Aud/Vis; Church Yth Grp; Cmnty Wkr; Dance Clb; Trs Chorus; Yrbk Ed-Chief; Capt Cheerleading; Hon Roll; Holds PA ST & Natl Rgnl Rythmic Gymnstc Titles 87.

STAUFFER, MELISSA; St Marys Area HS; St Marys, PA; (3); Trk; Stat Wrstlng.

STAUFFER, MICHELE; Garden Spot HS; Terre Hill, PA; (2); Chorus; Trs Soph Cls; JV Var Bsktbl; Powder Puff Ftbl; High Hon Roll; Hon Roll; GSHS Grls JV Bsktbll Chchs Awd 85-86; Co Hd Chrprsn 87-88; JR-SR Prm 87; Hmn Svcs.

STAUFFER, RICHARD; Cocalico HS; Denver, PA; (3); 25/175; Var Wrstlng; High Hon Roll; Hon Roll.

STAUFFER JR, RICHARD; Boyertown Area SR HS; Boyertown, PA; (3); Aud/Vis; JV Var Ftbl; Var Trk; Var Wrstlng; Pres Schlr; Tchng.

STAUFFER, SCOTT; Northern Cambria HS; Spangler, PA; (2); 7/144; Art Clb; NFL; Trs Frsh Cls; Trs Soph Cls; Rep Stu Cncl; JV Ftbl; Var Trk; High Hon Roll.

STAUFFER, SHARON; Upper Moreland HS; Hatboro, PA; (3); 54/275; Mrchg Band; Symp Band; High Hon Roll; Hon Roll; Amer Music Abrd 87; Abngtn Schl Nrsng; Nrsng.

STAUFFER, TIMOTHY M; Upper Moreland SR HS; Hatboro, PA; (4); 2/253; Boy Scts; Church Yth Grp; Var L Socr; Cit Awd; DAR Awd; God Cntry Awd; Pres NHS; Cmnty Wkr; Key Clb; VP Science Clb; Yth Ldrshp Amerca Awd 85; Rotary Tomrws Ldrs Campr 86; Congressn Yth Ldrs Confrnce 86; Engnrng.

STAUFFER, TRACY; Emmaus HS; Emmaus, PA; (4); 21/466; French Clb; Chorus; Bsktbl; Fld Hcky; Sftbl; Trk; High Hon Roll; Hon Roll; Jr NHS; NHS; Pa ST U.

STAUNCH, FRED; Sharpsville HS; Sharpsville, PA; (3); Church Yth Grp; Letterman Clb; Bsbl; L Bsktbl; High Hon Roll; Bsktbll & Acdmc Ltr 87 & 85-87.

STAUNTON, PETER J; Archbishop Ryan For Boys; Philadelphia, PA; (3); 22/414; Church Yth Grp; Civic Clb; Pres Spanish Clb; SADD; Nwsp Rptr; High Hon Roll; Hon Roll; NHS; Spn Awd Theol 85; Engl Theol Biol Spn 86.

STAVAS, MYLES; Bishop Mc Cort HS; Johnstown, PA; (3); Exploring; Latin Clb; Yrbk Phtg; Yrbk Stf; Hon Roll; Ntl Merit Ltr; Natl Sci Olympiad Dist 87; Homeroom Treas 84-85; Aerial Photo; Aero Commander; Work L Robert Kimball; Corp Pilot.

STAVISH, KIM; Uniontown Area HS; New Salem, PA; (3); Exploring; French Clb; Color Guard; Mrchg Band; Twrlr; French Hon Soc; Physcl Thrpy.

STAYMATES, MERI; Kiski Area HS; Export, PA; (4); 2/351; Pres Church Yth Grp; Math Tm; Pep Clb; SADD; Varsity Clb; Var Capt Sftbl; Var Capt Vllybl; High Hon Roll; NHS; Pres Schlr; U S Army Rsve Natl Schlr Athltc Awd 87; WA Twnshp Alumni Assn Schlrshp 87; U S Marine Athltc Awd 87; Penn ST U; Pre-Med.

STEADLE, ROBINN; Lake Lehman HS; Wilkes-Barre, PA; (4); 27/155; Band; Concert Band; Mrchg Band; Symp Band; Yrbk Stf; Stat Socr; Mgr Wrstlng; High Hon Roll; NHS; Dist Band 86; Scranton U.

STEADMAN, MEL; Butler SR HS; Butler, PA; (3); Boy Scts; Exploring; JA; Teachers Aide; Band; Concert Band; Mrchg Band; Orch; Symp Band; Blk Belt In Tae-Kwon-Do 83; IN U Of PA; Crmnl Jstc.

STEALS, TYRONE T; Aliquippa JR SR HS; Aliquippa, PA; (4); Var Capt Bsktbl; Hon Roll; Athltc Bsktbl Schlrshp Robert Morris 87; Dapper Dan Rndbl Plyr 87; MVP Sectn 12 Bsktbl 87; Robert Morris; Bus.

STEAR, ROGER; Wallenpaupack Area HS; Hawley, PA; (3); 11/154; German Clb; Letterman Clb; Science Clb; Ski Clb; Varsity Clb; VP Stu Cncl; Var Bowling; Var L Tennis; High Hon Roll; Jr NHS; Penn ST; Mech Engrng.

STEAR, SHERRI; Marion Center Area HS; Home, PA; (4); 60/166; Trs Church Yth Grp; Hosp Aide; Sec Latin Clb; SADD; Varsity Clb; School Play; Dance Clb; Var L Sftbl; Var L Trk; Hon Roll; PA Schl Brd Assoc Rep 86-87; May S Raybuck Educ Schrlshp 86-87; IN U Of PA; Elem Educ.

STEARNS, KRISTINA; Conneaut Lake HS; Conneaut Lake, PA; (4); Church Yth Grp; Spanish Clb; Concert Band; Mrchg Band; Pep Band; JV Sftbl; Var Hon Roll; VP & Pres Cncrt Band 85-87; Sqd Ldr Mrchng Band 86-87; 1st & 2nd Pl Trphs Bwlng 85-87; Penn St Behrend; Soc Wrkr.

STEBBINS, SHERRI; Mercyhurst Prep; Erie, PA; (3); Church Yth Grp; Hosp Aide; Model UN; Thesps; School Musical; Trs Soph Cls; Stu Cncl; Trk; Hon Roll; NHS; Psychol.

STEBELSKI, MARY BETH E; Bethlehem Catholic HS; Bethlehem, PA; (4); 7/196; Key Clb; Yrbk Stf; Mgr Bsktbl; High Hon Roll; NHS; Pres Schlr; Retreat Tm; Le High U; Chemcl Engrng.

STEC, HEATHER; Scranton Preparatory Schl; Dalton, PA; (1); 7/176; JV Cheerleading; Var Trk; High Hon Roll; Honorary Schlrshp To Scranton Prep 86; Sci.

STECH, TIMOTHY; Bethel Park SR HS; Bethel Park, PA; (4); Boys Clb Am; Science Clb; JV Bsbl; Bsktbl; JV Ftbl; JV Mgr(s); Ntl Merit SF; Pres Schlrshp 87; Hiram Coll; Engr.

STECHER, LAURA; Chambersburg Area SR HS; Chambersburg, PA; (2); Band; Mrchg Band; Bsktbl.

STECHER, SHELLY; Avon Grove HS; Landenberg, PA; (3); Church Yth Grp; JA; Office Aide; Stage Crew; Hon Roll; Hon Stu-Home Ec Awd 85-86; Teaching.

STECK, STACY; Wyoming Valley West HS; Swoyersville, PA; (3); Sec Key Clb; Ski Clb; Hon Roll; Anthropolgy.

STECK, TAMARA LEE; Norwin SR HS; N Huntingdon, PA; (4); 66/557; FBLA; Chorus; Color Guard; Var JV Bsktbl; Var Sftbl; High Hon Roll; Hon Roll; NHS; 2nd Plc Steno II FBLA Rgn 11 Cnfrnc 87; SR Hmrm Secty 86-87; Cert Achvmnt Natl Sftbll Lg 84; Westmoreland Cnty CC; Crt Rprt.

STECKEL JR, BRAD; Pleasant Valley HS; Brodheadsville, PA; (2); Computer Clb; Ski Clb; JV Bsbl; JV Bsktbl; High Hon Roll; Hon Roll; Jr NHS.

STECKEL, MARC; Allentown Central Catholic HS; Slatington, PA; (3); 45/233; Math Clb; Math Tm; SADD; Im Wt Lftg; JV Wrstlng; High Hon Roll; Hon Roll; PA Math Leag 86-87; Amer H S Math Exm 87; Jaycs Govt Day Le High Cnty Cntrllr 87.

STECKER, ROBERT; Hatboro-Horsham HS; Hatboro, PA; (3); Boy Scts; Church Yth Grp; Crs Cntry; Trk; Prfct Atten Awd; Westchester U; Arch.

STECYK, KATHLEEN; B Reed Henderson HS; W Chester, PA; (3); 39/369; Var L Bsktbl; Var L Sftbl; Var L Vllybl; Hon Roll; NHS; Acad Achvt Cert 87; Wdgwd Swm Team Sprt Trphy 86 & 87; Wdgwd Swm Team Slv Mdl For Prtcptn 86.

STECZ, LAURA; Plum SR HS; Pittsburgh, PA; (2); Church Yth Grp; Teachers Aide; Varsity Clb; Yrbk Stf; Im Bsktbl; Score Keeper; Im Socr; Im Sftbl; JV Vllybl; Prfct Atten Awd; U Of Pittsburgh; Phy Thrpy.

STEDINA, DANIEL C; Blackhawk HS; Beaver Falls, PA; (4); 28/268; Exploring; JV Bsktbl; Var Socr; Capt Swmmng; L Trk; High Hon Roll; Hon Roll; NHS; Stu Of Mnth 86; Hnr Schlrshp WV U 87; WV U; Engr.

STEEBER, GREG; Belle Vernon Area HS; Belle Vernon, PA; (3); Church Yth Grp; Letterman Clb; Ski Clb; Pres Frsh Cls; Var L Bsbl; Var L Bsktbl; Var L Ftbl; Var L Trk; Hon Roll.

STEELE, BRIAN; Moon Area SR HS; Coraopolis, PA; (2); Ftbl; Wt Lftg; Hon Roll.

STEELE, BRIAN; Youngsville HS; Pittsfield, PA; (4); Var Bsktbl; Var Crs Cntry; U Of Pittsburgh.

STEELE, COREY; Reading HS; Reading, PA; (3); 83/710; Computer Clb; JV Var Bsktbl; JV Ftbl; Hon Roll; Stu Of Qrtr Comp Clss 86-87; Howard U; Engrng.

STEELE, LU ANN; Central Dauphin HS; Harrisburg, PA; (4); 36/367; L Fld Hcky; L Gym; Hon Roll; Jr NHS; NHS; Pres Schlr; MENSA 86-88; Dickinson Coll; Liberal Arts.

STEELE, MARTHA JANE; Central SR HS; York, PA; (3); 8/248; Hosp Aide; Chorus; Jazz Band; Mrchg Band; School Musical; School Play; Symp Band; Yrbk Ed-Chief; High Hon Roll; NHS; Law.

STEELE, STACY; Shamokin Area HS; Shamokin, PA; (2); 3/250; Art Clb; Pep Clb; Science Clb; Yrbk Stf; JV Stat Bsbl; Var JV Cheerleading; High Hon Roll; PA Free Enterprise Wk Schlrshp Awd.

STEELE, SUSAN; Lock Haven SR HS; Castanea, PA; (4); 4/242; French Clb; Model UN; SADD; Chorus; Variety Show; Stat Bsktbl; Var L Socr; High Hon Roll; NHS; Natl Hstry/Govt Awd 86; Franklin Coll; Biochem.

STEELE, TAMMY; Trinity HS; Washington, PA; (3); 5/100; Drama Clb; Key Clb; Model UN; School Musical; VP Frsh Cls; Off Stu Cncl; Var Cheerleading; Trk; Hon Roll; NHS; Acdmc All-Amer 85-86; Penn U; Lawyer.

STEELE, TERESA; Punxsutawney Area HS; Punxsutawney, PA; (4); 53/249; French Clb; FBLA; Math Tm; Yrbk Stf; Tennis; Trk; Hon Roll; Mary Ann Irving Schlrshp & Bus & Prof Womens Girl Of Month 87; IN U Of PA; Elem Educ.

STEELE, TIMOTHY; United JR SR HS; Seward, PA; (3); Boy Scts; Church Yth Grp; Ski Clb; Bsbl; Bsktbl; Ftbl; Score Keeper; Trk; Wt Lftg; Hon Roll; Med.

STEELE, TOM; Souderton Area HS; Souderton, PA; (3); Computer Clb; Ski Clb; Var Bsbl; Var Ftbl; Var Wrstlng; Cit Awd; Hon Roll; Jr NHS; PA ST.

STEELEY, JAMES; Hempfield Area SR HS; Greensburg, PA; (3); Letterman Clb; Yrbk Rptr; Yrbk Sprt Ed; Yrbk Stf; JV Bsktbl; Im Coach Actv; Var L Ftbl; Var Trk; High Hon Roll; Hon Roll; Ed.

STEEN, MARK; Hickory HS; Hermitage, PA; (3); 40/182; Latin Clb; Letterman Clb; Varsity Clb; Yrbk Stf; Ftbl; Wrstlng.

STEEN, ROSEMARY; Mt Lebanon HS; Mt Lebanon, PA; (3); 13/512; Am Leg Aux Girls St; Pep Clb; Sec Frsh Cls; VP Jr Cls; Capt Var Cheerleading; Hon Roll; Girls ST Ctzn 86, Cnslr 87; Chrldg Frshmn, JV, Capt Of V 84-88; VP Hmrm JR Yr.

STEENSON, DONALD; Hickory HS; Hermitage, PA; (3); 2/177; Exploring; German Clb; Letterman Clb; Varsity Clb; Var L Crs Cntry; Var L Swmmng; Var L Trk; NHS; Prfct Atten Awd; YMCA ST Swmg Champ 86-87; Microbio.

STEES, DAVID; Greenwood HS; Millerstown, PA; (3); Varsity Clb; Band; Chorus; School Musical; Bsbl; Bsktbl; Socr; Hon Roll; NHS.

STEFANAK, DANA; West Middlesex HS; Mercer, PA; (2); Trs Spanish Clb; Band; Concert Band; Drill Tm; Jr NHS; NHS; Spanish NHS; Stu Achvmnt Awd 87.

STEFANEC, CHRISTIAN; Hanover JR SR HS; Wilkes Barre, PA; (3); 1/150; Science Clb; High Hon Roll; Jr NHS; NHS; PA Jr Sci Talent Search Awd 87; Luzurne Cnty Sci Teachers Admin Awd 85; Exclinc Bio Statewide 86; Telecomms.

STEFANICK, JON; Belle Vernon Area HS; Belle Vernon, PA; (3); Band; High Hon Roll; NHS; Prfct Atten Awd; Frgn Lang Comp Spnsh 2nd Pl; PTO Exmplry Stu Intrvw; Engr.

STEFANIK, KEVIN; West Allegheny HS; Oakdale, PA; (2); 1/222; Boy Scts; Exploring; German Clb; Scholastic Bowl; Band; Mrchg Band; Orch; Var Socr; High Hon Roll; Carnegie Mellon U; Engrng.

STEFANIW, MATTHEW; Harriton HS; Villanova, PA; (4); Var Socr; Var Trk; High Hon Roll; Hon Roll; GA Tech; Aerosp Engrng.

STEFANOWICZ, JOHN; Our Lady Of Lourdes Regional HS; Shamokin, PA; (3); 15/89; Computer Clb; Key Clb; Spanish Clb; Varsity Clb; Stage Crew; Rep Frsh Cls; Im Bsktbl; Var JV Ftbl; Var Wrstlng; Hon Roll; U Pittsburgh; Pre Med.

STEFANOWICZ, KATHRYN; Lake Lehman HS; Harveys Lake, PA; (3); 10/219; Var L Cheerleading; Var L Vllybl; Hon Roll; NHS; Phrmcy.

STEFFE, JOYCE; Reading HS; Reading, PA; (3); 190/710; Spanish Clb; Stu Of Month 85-86; Stu Of Quarter 87; Writer.

STEFFEN, RODERICK D; Oley Valley HS; Boyertown, PA; (4); 8/151; Concert Band; Mrchg Band; Pep Band; Stage Crew; Var Capt Socr; Trk; High Hon Roll; Hon Roll; Pres NHS; Ntl Merit SF; Honrbl Mntn Cnty Sccr 86; Cnty Band 85; Engr.

STEFFEY, ADAM; Highlands SR HS; Natrona Heights, PA; (3); Band; Brown Awd 87; Pittsburg Aviation; Auto Mech.

STEFFEY, JENNIFER; North Allegheny HS; Bradford Woods, PA; (3); French Clb; JV Sftbl; Comm Art.

STEFFISH, RUDOLPH; Marion Center JR SR HS; Creekside, PA; (3); 16/154; Boy Scts; Latin Clb; Intl Law.

STEFFY, ANN; Cedar Crest HS; Lebanon, PA; (4); Art Clb; Drama Clb; Pep Clb; Socr; Vllybl; Hon Roll; NHS; Carnigie Mellon U; Bus Admin.

STEFFY, DANA; Punxsutawney Area HS; Punxsutawney, PA; (4); 90/245; Art Clb; FBLA; Variety Show; Nwsp Phtg; Nwsp Rptr; Bsbl; Bsktbl; Trk; Wrstlng; Hon Roll; Mary Anne Irving Schlrshp 87; IUP; Soclgy.

STEFFY, DEBORAH; Punxsutawney Area HS; Punxsutawney, PA; (2); Church Yth Grp; Cheerleading; Trk; Hon Roll.

STEGENGA II, DAVID I; Charters-Houston HS; Houston, PA; (4); French Clb; Varsity Clb; Band; Concert Band; Jazz Band; Mrchg Band; Bsbl; French Hon Soc; Hon Roll; WA & Jefferson; Bio.

STEGER, MARK A; Hempfield HS; Lancaster, PA; (3); 5/410; Am Leg Boys St; Varsity Clb; Nwsp Rptr; Pres Stu Cncl; L Var Bsktbl; L Var Socr; L Var Civic Clb; High Hon Roll; NHS; Ntl Merit Ltr; Hnrbl Mntn Lancaster Co Sci Fair-Bio 86; US Air Force Acad; Engr.

STEGMAN, RICHARD; Hampton HS; Allison Pk, PA; (4); Chess Clb; Concert Band; Mrchg Band; Pep Band; Stage Crew; Symp Band; High Hon Roll; NHS; Ntl Merit Ltr; Pres Schlr; J Behnk Mem Schlrshp 87; Westinghouse Sci Hnrs Inst 86-87; Physcs.

STEHR, ANGELA K; Tri-Valley HS; Pitman, PA; (3); Computer Clb; Spanish Clb; Yrbk Stf; Var Capt Cheerleading; Hon Roll; 2nd Pl Comp Cntst 85; Schuylkill Cnty Cnsrvtn Dist Pstr Cntst 2nd & 3rd Pl 85-86; Penn ST; Elem Ed.

STEHR, BLAKE; Millersburg Area HS; Millersburg, PA; (3); Church Yth Grp; French Clb; Bsbl; High Hon Roll; Hon Roll; Ntl Sci Merit Awd 86; Ntl Hnr Rll 85; Shippensburg U; Cmptr Sci.

STEHR, JOHN; Shamokin Area HS; Shamokin, PA; (2); 3/250; Boy Scts; SADD; Rep Soph Cls; High Hon Roll; Pres Schlr; Pres Church Yth Grp; Var Mgr(s); PA ST U; Arch.

STEIDEL, JASON; Louis E Dieruff HS; Allentown, PA; (4); 28/298; Camera Clb; Church Yth Grp; Yrbk Ed-Chief; Yrbk Phtg; Yrbk Rptr; Hon Roll; NHS; Prfct Atten Awd; Hotel Mngmnt.

STEIER, KRISTIN; Northampton HS; Treichlers, PA; (3); 52/494; AFS; Leo Clb; SADD; Trs Jr Cls; Stu Cncl; Var Mat Maids; Var Trk; Hon Roll; Pres Schlr; Chld Psych.

STEIGER, KATHERINE; Greensburg Central Catholic HS; Greensburg, PA; (3); AFS; Drama Clb; Ski Clb; SADD; Chorus; School Musical; Nwsp Rptr; Hon Roll; Psych.

STEIGER, KIMBERLY; Mt Penn HS; Reading, PA; (4); 19/70; Y-Teens; Yrbk Bus Mgr; Trs Soph Cls; Trs Jr Cls; Trs Sr Cls; Stu Cncl; Stat Bsbl; Capt Fld Hcky; Trs NHS; Stu Forum Berks Cnty SAB Rep 86-87; Albright Coll; Bus Admn.

STEIGERWALT, AMY; Red Land HS; New Cumberland, PA; (4); 37/255; Church Yth Grp; Latin Clb; Concert Band; Jazz Band; Mrchg Band; Orch; Symp Band; Swmmng; Trk; Vllybl; Ofc Vctnl Rehbltn OVR; York Coll Of PA; Bus Admin.

STEIMEL, KIRK R; Owen J Roberts HS; Pottstown, PA; (4); 15/291; JA; Band; Chorus; School Musical; School Play; Swing Chorus; Hon Roll; NHS; Math.

STEIMINGER, AMY; Burgettstown JR SR HS; Burgettstown, PA; (3); Church Yth Grp; Drama Clb; Science Clb; Spanish Clb; SADD; Yrbk Stf; Hon Roll; Jr NHS; CA U PA; Math Tchr.

STEIN, BRAD; Red Lion Area HS; Red Lion, PA; (3); French Clb; Rep Stu Cncl; Var Bsktbl; Im Coach Actv; Var Tennis; Var Trk; Htl-Rest Mgmt.

STEIN, BRIAN; Bensalem HS; Bensalem, PA; (4); 62/400; Cmnty Wkr; Letterman Clb; Temple Yth Grp; Varsity Clb; Socr; NHS; CC Awd; Chamber Of Commerce Schlrshp 87; All Leag Socr Hon Mntn 87; Emergcy Med Tech 87; Ursinus Coll; Med.

STEIN, CAROLINE; Hazleton HS; Hazleton, PA; (2); 22/436; Church Yth Grp; French Clb; Girl Scts; Pep Clb; Ski Clb; Chorus; Church Choir; Swmmng; Trk; High Hon Roll; Principals Acdmc Excllnc Awd & Prsdntl Acdmc Fitness Awd 86; Bloomsburg U; Child Psych.

STEIN, JEANNE; Meadville Arena SR HS; Meadville, PA; (4); 10/306; French Clb; Chorus; Pres Jr Cls; Pres Stu Cncl; Bsktbl; Vllybl; Elks Awd; High Hon Roll; Hon Roll; All-Eastern Chorus 87; Prof Opera Sngr.

STEIN, JOHN; Red Lion SR HS; Red Lion, PA; (2); 50/422; French Clb; Air Force; Aviation.

STEIN, KAREN; Vincentian HS; Bradfordwds, PA; (1); Church Yth Grp; Girl Scts; Church Choir; Variety Show; JV Bsktbl; High Hon Roll; Pres Acad Fit Awd 85-86.

STEIN, MATTHEW S; Hillel Academy Of Pittsburgh HS; Pittsburgh, PA; (3); Aud/Vis; Temple Yth Grp; School Play; Nwsp Phtg; Nwsp Sprt Ed; Nwsp Stf; Rep Stu Cncl; Bsktbl; Ftbl; Sftbl.

STEIN, MELISSA; Bishop Conwell HS; Levittown, PA; (3); 4/277; Am Leg Aux Girls St; Math Tm; Scholastic Bowl; Yrbk Stf; Var Swmmng; NHS; Prfct Atten Awd; Diocesan Schlr 87-88; Hnrbl Mntn Geom Awd 85-86; Hnrbl Mntn Fren Awd 85-87; Engr.

STEIN, MELISSA S; Upper Dublin HS; Dresher, PA; (4); 6/320; Camera Clb; Intnl Clb; Radio Clb; Yrbk Ed-Chief; Yrbk Phtg; Lit Mag; Stu Cncl; NHS; Ntl Merit SF; Prfct Atten Awd; Engl.

STEIN, RANDEE; Bensalem HS; Bensalem, PA; (2); Model UN; Temple Yth Grp; Acpl Chr; Chorus; Score Keeper; Timer; Mgr Trk; High Hon Roll; Hon Roll; NHS.

STEIN, TRACY; Purchase Line HS; Cherry Tree, PA; (3); Church Yth Grp; FBLA; Pep Clb; Nwsp Stf; VP Frsh Cls; Var Cheerleading; Trk; Hon Roll; Mst Outstdng Bus Std 86, 87; Impromptu Spkng Awd 87; PA ST U; Law.

STEIN, WADE; Red Lion Area SR HS; Red Lion, PA; (4); 69/333; Varsity Clb; Im Ftbl; Var JV Mgr(s); Hon Roll; Penn ST York; Comp Sci.

STEINBACH, RAE; St Marys Area HS; St Marys, PA; (3); 4-H; Bio.

STEINBERG, JEFFREY H; Germantown Acad; Meadowbrook, PA; (4); Ski Clb; Nwsp Stf; Capt L Lcrss; Capt L Socr; High Hon Roll; Ntl Merit SF; Cum Laude Soc 86.

STEINBERG, REBECCA; Plymouth Whitemarsh HS; Norristown, PA; (4); 38/336; Hosp Aide; Math Clb; Mu Alpha Theta; Temple Yth Grp; Band; Color Guard; Concert Band; Mrchg Band; Rep Stu Cncl; Var Lcrss; Yth Edctn Assoc-Pbl Rltns Chrmn 85-87; NW Inst 87; Boston U; Physcl Thrpy.

STEINBERGER, REBECCA; Wyoming Area HS; West Pittston, PA; (3); Art Clb; Sec Drama Clb; Exploring; Jazz Band; Mrchg Band; School Play; Off Stu Cncl; High Hon Roll; Hon Roll; NHS; Stu Cncl Pin Awd/Commtmnt & Invlvmnt 85-86; Law.

STEINBRING, MICHELE LEA; Greater Johnstown HS; Johnstown, PA; (4); 12/293; German Clb; Chorus; Yrbk Rptr; VP Jr Cls; Pres Sr Cls; Trs Stu Cncl; Vllybl; High Hon Roll; Lion Awd; Sec NHS; Lions Clb, Stu Mnth & Stu Yr 87; Edinboro U PA; Nrs.

STEINBROOK, JENNIFER; Springside School; Philadelphia, PA; (4); 4/44; Teachers Aide; Yrbk Phtg; Trs Sr Cls; Capt Var Bsktbl; Fld Hcky; Co-Capt Var Socr; Var Capt Sftbl; Hon Roll; Cum Laude Soc 86; Phyllis M Vare Awd 87; Caroline Susan Jones Pin 87; Bucknell U; Chldhd Ed.

STEINER, FRANCIS G; Archbishop Ryan HS For Boys; Philadelphia, PA; (4); 10/432; Cmnty Wkr; German Clb; Nwsp Stf; Yrbk Ed-Chief; Lit Mag; Rep Soph Cls; Rep Stu Cncl; Im Bsktbl; Var L Swmmng; Im Wt Lftg; Christian Bros La Salle Scholar 87; Engl Hnrs Convoctn Awd 84; La Salle U; Cmmnctns.

STEINER, JILL; Karns City HS; Chicora, PA; (3); Chorus; Yrbk Stf; Capt Pom Pon; Trk; JV Vllybl; Hon Roll; Cosmetology Teacher.

STEINER, LAURIE; Belle Vernon Area HS; Belle Vernon, PA; (3); Art Clb; FBLA; Ski Clb; Band; Var Stu Cncl; Sftbl; Swmmng; Hon Roll; Swim Ltr 85-86; Acad Hnr Awd 85-86; IUP; Bio.

STEINER, MARGIE; Franzier JR/SR HS; Newell, PA; (3); FNA; Ski Clb; SADD; Cheerleading; Gym; Powder Puff Ftbl; Sftbl; Hon Roll; Phys Thrpst.

STEINER, SONJIA; Corry Area HS; Corry, PA; (4); Drama Clb; Library Aide; Spanish Clb; Nwsp Rptr; Nwsp Stf; Bsktbl; Hiram Coll; Bio.

STEINER, STEPHEN; Coatesville Area SR HS; Coatesville, PA; (3); 40/509; Ftbl; Hon Roll; NHS; Prfct Atten Awd; Hnr Soc 85-88; Presdntl Phys Ftns Awd 86; Engrng.

STEINER, VAL; Belle Vernon Area HS; Fayette City, PA; (3); Church Yth Grp; Library Aide; Pep Clb; Trk; Hon Roll; CA U Of PA; Tchng.

STEINGRABER, BRENDA A; Montrose Area HS; Montrose, PA; (3); Yrbk Stf; Model.

STEINHOFF, GIDGET; Fairchance-Georges JR-SR HS; Uniontown, PA; (3); Hosp Aide; Office Aide; Spanish Clb; Yrbk Stf; Var Capt Cheerleading; High Hon Roll; Hon Roll; Jr NHS; Pres Schlr.

STEININGER, VALARIE; Northeastern HS; Manchester, PA; (4); Ski Clb; Chorus; Color Guard; Rep Jr Cls; Sec Sr Cls; Var JV Bsktbl; Im Sftbl; Hon Roll; NHS; Voice Dem Awd; Dr James Keller Memorial Schlrshp 87; West Chester U; Nrsng.

STEINLY, TINA; Hamburg Area HS; Mohrsville, PA; (3); Trs Church Yth Grp; German Clb; Office Aide; Teachers Aide; Chorus; Church Choir; School Musical; School Play; Stage Crew; Variety Show; Acad Cert Achvt Wrld Cltrs 86; Chrs Lttr 86; Acctng.

STEINMAN, MICHELE LEE; Spring-Ford SR HS; Royersford, PA; (3); 10/270; French Clb; Rep Soph Cls; Rep Jr Cls; Capt Fld Hcky; Hon Roll; NHS; Girl Scts; Pep Clb; Ath Trainer Bsbl Tm; Writer Yr; Anchor Club Sec; Bus Mgmt.

STEINMETZ, DAWN; Monessen JR SR HS; Monessen, PA; (3); Drama Clb; Girl Scts; Band; Concert Band; Mrchg Band; School Play; Variety Show; Nwsp Stf; High Hon Roll; NHS; Sci Day 4th Pl Psychology Games 87; PTA Relection Arts Cmpttn Hnrb Mntn 85-86; Commercial Art.

STEINPICK, ERIK; Methacton HS; Audubon, PA; (3); Church Yth Grp; JV Crs Cntry; Var Trk; JV Wrstlng; Comp.

STEINRUCK, LARA; Benton Area HS; Benton, PA; (3); Cmnty Wkr; Key Clb; Chorus; Color Guard; School Play; Sftbl; High Hon Roll; NHS; FTA; Cntry 21 Accntng 94% Awd 87; Cntry 21 Typwrtng 93% Awd 87; Central Penn Bus Schl; Acntnt.

STELL, MATT; Red Lion HS; Red Lion, PA; (3); 2/342; Varsity Clb; Bsktbl; Capt Var Swmmng; Var Trk; Wt Lftg; High Hon Roll; Aerontcl Engrng.

STELLA, LISA; Pittston Area SR HS; Pittston, PA; (3); Key Clb; Ski Clb; Var L Swmmng; Hon Roll.

STELLA, NICHOLE; Abington SR HS; Abington, PA; (3); Art Clb; Cmnty Wkr; SADD; Band; Concert Band; Jazz Band; Mrchg Band; Orch; Symp Band; Nwsp Stf; Art Therapy.

STELLING, ROBERT; Methacton HS; Audubon, PA; (3); 14/383; Church Yth Grp; Math Tm; Science Clb; Ski Clb; Rep Jr Cls; Var Ftbl; Var Trk; Im Wt Lftg; High Hon Roll; NHS; M Awd Acdmc Excllnc, Acdmc Ftnss Awd 86-87; 1st Pl Achvt Awd Math Anlys 87.

STELMA, DEBRA; Pittston Area HS; Hughestown, PA; (3); 19/305; Key Clb; Math Clb; Ski Clb; Chorus; Concert Band; Jazz Band; Mrchg Band; High Hon Roll; NHS; All Amercn Acadmc Stu Awd 86; Coll Misericordia; X-Ray Tech.

STELMA, WALTER; Mon Valley Catholic HS; Charleroi, PA; (2); Church Yth Grp; Cmnty Wkr; Band; Concert Band; Drm & Bgl; Mrchg Band; Var Bsbl; JV Var Bsktbl; Var L Ftbl; Var Wt Lftg; Arch.

STELTER, LAURA; Shenango HS; New Castle, PA; (3); 4/110; GAA; Hosp Aide; Library Aide; Concert Band; JV Var Bsktbl; Var Sftbl; Var JV Vllybl; High Hon Roll; Hon Roll; NHS; Hnr Rl 85-86; Sftbl Lg 82-83; Blgcl Dctr.

STELTZ, WENDY MONICA; Upper Perkiomen HS; Pennsburg, PA; (4); 65/225; Am Leg Aux Girls St; Hosp Aide; Teachers Aide; Concert Band; Co-Capt Flag Corp; Variety Show; Stat Swmmng; Hon Roll; BPW June Girl Of Mnth 87; Kutztown U; Elem Ed.

STELTZER, LYNNE; Susquehannock HS; Shrewsbury, PA; (3); 30/214; Church Yth Grp; French Clb; Ski Clb; School Play; Nwsp Stf; Rep Jr Cls; Mgr Socr; High Hon Roll; NHS; Short Story Awd 1st Pl 86; Various Art Cntst Awds 1st, 2nd & Hnrb Mntn 87; Comm.

STEM, BARBARA; East Stroudsburg Area HS; East Stroudsburg, PA; (4); 6/215; Pres Intnl Clb; Model UN; Yrbk Phtg; VP Frsh Cls; Pres Soph Cls; Rep Jr Cls; Rep Sr Cls; Stat Wrstlng; High Hon Roll; NHS; Exchng Clb Stu Of Mnth 86-87; Frgn Lang Awd 85-86; Scl Stds Awd 83-84; Frnch.

STEMPIN, LORI; Bishop O Reilly HS; West Wyoming, PA; (4); French Clb; Chorus; Stu Cncl; Cheerleading; French Hon Soc; Hon Roll; NHS; Bloomsburg; Nrsng.

STEMPLESKI, PAMELA; E L Meyers HS; Wilkes-Barre, PA; (4); Pres Church Yth Grp; Cmnty Wkr; Key Clb; Office Aide; Spanish Clb; Chorus; Church Choir; Variety Show; Nwsp Rptr; Nwsp Stf; ATP; Cabrini Clg; Psych.

STEN, SUSAN; Mifflinburg HS; Millmont, PA; (1); Spanish Clb; Chorus; Prfct Atten Awd; Coll Prep.

STENCIK, MARK; Coughlin HS; Plains, PA; (3); 38/374; Drama Clb; Math Tm; Ski Clb; School Play; JV Bsbl; Var L Bsktbl; Im Vllybl; Sec NHS; Hon Roll; Penn ST; Engrng.

STENDEROWICZ, MICHAEL; Archbishop Wood For Boys HS; Holland, PA; (3); 96/235; Var Swmmng; Prfct Atten Awd; Engrng.

STENGER, HEIDI; Avella HS; Avella, PA; (3); Yrbk Stf; VP Soph Cls; Trs Jr Cls; Cheerleading; Sftbl; Tennis; Hon Roll; NHS; Chrng Sqd Capt 86-87, Co-Capt 87-88; Phys Thrpy.

STENSON, KATHLEEN; Cardinal O Hara HS; Springfield, PA; (3); JA; Off Jr Cls; Cheerleading; Gym; Tennis; Hon Roll; Srch Ldrs Schlrshp Chstnt Hl Coll 87; PA ST U; Cmmnctns.

STENZEL, KIM; Chartiers Valley HS; Bridgeville, PA; (4); 49/297; Dance Clb; GAA; School Musical; Hon Roll; IN U Of PA; Mth.

STEPANIC, JOSEPH R; Greater Latrobe SR HS; Latrobe, PA; (3); 83/355; Am Leg Boys St; VP Church Yth Grp; VP JA; Ski Clb; Lit Mag; Rep Frsh Cls; Rep Soph Cls; Rep Jr Cls; Pres Sr Cls; Stu Cncl; Comms.

STEPANSKI, CATHERINE; Northeast Bradford HS; Rome, PA; (3); #2 In Class; Band; Chorus; Pres Frsh Cls; Pres Soph Cls; Sec Stu Cncl; Var L Cheerleading; Cit Awd; High Hon Roll; JP Sousa Awd; NHS; PREA Youth Tour Essay Wnnr 87.

STEPHAN, KATHY; Avon Grove HS; Landenberg, PA; (3); 3/210; Church Yth Grp; Band; School Musical; Lit Mag; Var Cheerleading; JV Trk; Var Vllybl; High Hon Roll; NHS; Prfct Atten Awd; Geo & Spnsh Awd 84-85; Archt Drftng 85-86; Engrng.

STEPHAN, SHERRI ANN; Pleasant Valley HS; Brodheadsville, PA; (3); 51/232; Pep Clb; Sec Chorus; School Musical; Rep Stu Cncl; Var Capt Cheerleading; Gym; Hon Roll; Rep Frsh Cls; Rep Soph Cls.

STEPHANO, NICOLE; Bishop Shanahan HS; Media, PA; (3); 51/200; Sec Church Yth Grp; Var Cheerleading; Var Crs Cntry; Var Socr; Var Trk; Hon Roll; Psychlgy.

STEPHENS, BRADEY; Lewistown Area HS; Lewistown, PA; (2); Computer Clb; Ski Clb; Band; Concert Band; Jazz Band; Mrchg Band; NHS; Ntl Merit Ltr; Penn ST U Smmr Cls 87; US Air Frc Acad; Electrnc Engr.

STEPHENS, CHAD; Greenwood HS; Liverpool, PA; (2); Church Yth Grp; Band; Chorus; Concert Band; Mrchg Band; School Musical; Var Bsktbl; Var Socr; Var Trk; Mdrn Music Mstrs 87; Grnwd Athltc Assoc 87; Demly 84; Naval Offcr.

STEPHENS, DAN; Trinity HS; Washington, PA; (4); 8/361; Math Tm; Ski Clb; Band; Jazz Band; Mrchg Band; Symp Band; Tennis; High Hon Roll; Hon Roll; NHS; 3 Yr Army ROTC Schlrshp 87; Penn ST U; Elec Engrng.

STEPHENS, JILL DIANE; Blacklick Valley HS; Nanty Glo, PA; (2); 5/105; German Clb; NFL; Varsity Clb; Band; Concert Band; Mrchg Band; Pep Band; Yrbk Stf; Sftbl; Hon Roll; Young Astronauts Of Amer 85-86.

STEPHENS, MELANIE; Penncrest HS; Media, PA; (3); 92/344; Church Yth Grp; SADD; Variety Show; Yrbk Stf; Capt JV Socr; Sftbl; Var Trk; Vllybl; Hon Roll; MVP Tri-County All Star Soccer 84-87; St Select Tm Soccer 86-87; Radford U; Nrsng.

STEPHENS, RANDY; Conemaugh Valley HS; Conemaugh, PA; (4); 14/120; Drama Clb; French Clb; Office Aide; Pep Clb; Varsity Clb; Mrchg Band; School Play; Stu Cncl; Capt Bsktbl; Ftbl; IN U Of PA; Fnnce.

STEPHENS, SCOTT; Blacklick Valley HS; Nicktown, PA; (2); Pres Church Yth Grp; NFL; Ski Clb; Varsity Clb; Rep Stu Cncl; JV Ftbl; Var Trk; Hon Roll; Pres Acad Ftns Awd; Tchng.

STEPHENS, SHARON; Tyrone Area HS; Tyrone, PA; (3); Computer Clb; Key Clb; Nwsp Bus Mgr; Prfct Atten Awd; DECA; Chorus; School Play; High Hon Roll; Hon Roll; NHS; Mst Outstndng Grl 86; Accntng.

STEPHENSON, ROBERT; Penn Wood SR HS; Yeadon, PA; (3); 47/388; Varsity Clb; Var Bsktbl; Var Trk; Penn ST; Engr.

STEPLER, SHELLY; Mechanicsburg Area SR HS; Mechanicsburg, PA; (3); 3/13; Band; Capt Drill Tm; Capt Mrchg Band; Var Socr; Var Sftbl; High Hon Roll; NHS; James Madison; Wildlife Bio.

STEPP, KATHLEEN; Monessen JR SR HS; Monessen, PA; (3); Girl Scts; Band; Chorus; Concert Band; Jazz Band; Mrchg Band; Symp Band; Yrbk Stf; JV Var Bsktbl; Var Socr.

STEPPE, KAREN; South Williamsport JR/Sr HS; Nisbet, PA; (3); 20/113; 4-H; Key Clb; Spanish Clb; Chorus; Var Trk; Phys Ther.

STEPSUS, LYNN; Shenandoah Valley HS; Shenandoah, PA; (4); 1/102; Pep Clb; Chorus; Color Guard; Nwsp Stf; Yrbk Sprt Ed; Trs Soph Cls; Sec Sr Cls; Sec Stu Cncl; JV Bsktbl; NHS; Acad All-Amer 83-87; SV Schl Bd Acad Achvt Awd 86; Pres Acad Achvt Awd 86; Pltcl Sci.

STEPTOE, VERONICA; The Christian Acad; Philadelphia, PA; (3); VP Church Yth Grp; Drama Clb; VP Church Choir; School Play; Nwsp Rptr; Nwsp Stf; Yrbk Stf; Lit Mag; VP Soph Cls; Rep Stu Cncl; NY U; Drama.

STERANKO, MICHAEL; Chartiers Valley HS; Carnegie, PA; (4); 9/303; Church Yth Grp; Ski Clb; Varsity Clb; Bsbl; Bsktbl; Crs Cntry; Trk; High Hon Roll; Hon Roll; NHS; Penn St; Engrng.

STERENBERG, AMY; Spring Grove Area HS; Spring Grove, PA; (3); Church Yth Grp; Cmnty Wkr; VP Drama Clb; Ski Clb; Varsity Clb; Chorus; Color Guard; School Musical; School Play; Variety Show; Thrtr Actress.

STERLING, DAWN; Northwestern SR HS; Albion, PA; (3); 13/144; Sec Church Yth Grp; Pep Clb; Band; Concert Band; Mrchg Band; Pep Band; Hon Roll; Grove City Coll; Elem Educ.

STERLING, SHANNON; Saegertown Area HS; Saegertown, PA; (4); 11/105; Am Leg Aux Girls St; VP SADD; Varsity Clb; Flag Corp; Stu Cncl; L Mgr(s); JV Vllybl; High Hon Roll; NHS; Pres Phy Fit Awd; Secy.

STERLING, THEODORE; Wyoming Valley West HS; Kingston, PA; (3); Chess Clb; Exploring; Math Clb; Var L Crs Cntry; Var Trk; Hon Roll; NHS; 11th Congrssnl Dist Consttnl Essay Cont 2nd 87; Engrng.

STERLING, TRACEY; West Greene HS; Holbrook, PA; (4); Sec Trs Band; Sec Trs Concert Band; Sec Trs Mrchg Band; Nwsp Rptr; Nwsp Stf; Rep Stu Cncl; JV Var Bsktbl; Var Sftbl; High Hon Roll; NHS; Fairmont ST Coll; Arch.

STERMER, ANNETTE; Cowanesque Valley HS; Knoxville, PA; (4); 6/86; Drama Clb; French Clb; Ski Clb; School Play; Bsktbl; Trk; Vllybl; High Hon Roll; NHS; Natl Schlr Athlete Awd 86; Accntng.

STERN, BARRY; Somerset Area SR HS; Somerset, PA; (3); 86/231; Boy Scts; FCA; SADD; Chorus; Stu Cncl; Ftbl; Wt Lftg; DAR Awd; Hon Roll; Millie Mathews Mem Art Awd 84; Project Business Awd 85; Pres Physcl Ftns Awd 84-86; WVU; Bus Mgmt.

STERN, CATHIE; Connellsville Area SR HS; Connellsville, PA; (3); Civic Clb; SADD; Capt Flag Corp; Hon Roll; NHS; Spanish NHS; Phys Ther.

STERN, CHERI; Mechanicsburg Area SR HS; Mechanicsburg, PA; (2); Church Yth Grp; Cmnty Wkr; GAA; VP Key Clb; Library Aide; Service Clb; Church Choir; Orch; Vllybl; High Hon Roll; Trphy-Cmmnty Grls Sftbll League 86; Nrsng.

STERN, STEVEN W; Carlisle Area HS; Carlisle, PA; (3); Computer Clb; DECA; FHA; JA; Band; Concert Band; Mrchg Band; Orch; Pep Band; JV Bsktbl; CO Coll; Psych.

STERNBERG, KIMBERLY; Blue Ridge HS; Hallstead, PA; (3); 2/90; Chorus; Concert Band; Jazz Band; Mrchg Band; Var Crs Cntry; Var Trk; High Hon Roll; Hon Roll; Stu Mnth 84-85; Var Ltrs Track 85-86 & 86-87, Crs Cnty & Band 86-87; Zoology.

STERNER, BRONSTON; Eastern York HS; Windsor, PA; (3); Band; Concert Band; Drm Mjr(t); Jazz Band; Mrchg Band; JV Bsktbl; Var Trk; Hon Roll; Jr NHS; Prsdntl Physcl Ftnss Awd 86; Marine Bio.

STERNER, CHRISTINE; Neshaminy HS; Langhorne, PA; (3); Church Yth Grp; SADD; Chorus; Stage Crew; Stu Cncl; JV Im Fld Hcky; Var Sec Mgr(s); High Hon Roll; Hon Roll; NHS; Rider; Actrl Sci.

STERNER, CRAIG; Red Lion Area SR HS; York, PA; (3); 9/342; Varsity Clb; L Var Bsbl; Var JV Bsktbl; L Var Socr; DECA; Distngshd Hnr Rll 84-87; Govt Awd 85; Ldrshp & Svc Awd 85; Chem Engrng.

STERNER, KIMBERLY; Southwestern HS; Hanover, PA; (2); Church Yth Grp; Key Clb; Golf; Swmmng; Swmmng; Tennis; Hon Roll; NEDT Awd.

STERNER, LINDA; Brandywine Hgts HS; Fleetwood, PA; (2); Band; Concert Band; Jazz Band; Mrchg Band; School Play; Hon Roll; NHS; Pep Band; Pres Acdmc Ftnss Awd 84-85; Acdmc Achvt Spnsh I 85-86; Outstndng Acdmc Achvt Spnsh II 86-87; Penn ST U; ST Dept.

STERNER, LINDA; Cardinal Brennan HS; Shenandoan, PA; (3); German Clb; JV Cheerleading; Twrlr; Hon Roll.

STERNER, LYNN; Spring Grove Area SR HS; Spring Grove, PA; (3); 16/301; Drama Clb; Chorus; School Play; Nwsp Phtg; Nwsp Stf; Fld Hcky; Hon Roll; NHS; Pres Acad Ftnss Awd 84-85; Tourism.

STERNER, MICHELE; Rockwood Area HS; Rockwood, PA; (3); VICA; Pres Jr Cls; High Hon Roll; Hon Roll; FHA; Yrbk Phtg; Typng Awd; Jhnsn & Wales Coll; Fshn Merch.

STERNER, RICHARD; Pen Argyle Area HS; Wind Gap, PA; (3); 57/160; Chess Clb; Math Clb; Spanish Clb; L JV Bsbl; Var L Ftbl; Var L Trk; Var L Wrstlng; 1st Team All Colonial Leag RB 2nd Team All ST Ftbl 86; Dist & Regnl Champn 6th Pl ST Wrstlng 87; Engrng.

STERNER, SUSY; Greencastle-Antrim HS; Greencastle, PA; (3); Church Yth Grp; Band; Church Choir; Concert Band; Stu Cncl; Var L Bsktbl; Var L Crs Cntry; L Trk; Bausch & Lomb Sci Awd; High Hon Roll; 3rd Pl-Sci Fair, Trig & Chmstry Awds, 1st Chr Flute & AM Chmcl Soc Cert 87; 2nd Pl-Sci Fair 86; Engnrng.

STEROWSKI, SHARON JULIA; Benton Area JR SR HS; Stillwater, PA; (4); 6/48; Sec Drama Clb; Teachers Aide; Hst Chorus; Co-Capt Color Guard; School Musical; L School Play; Ed Nwsp Ed-Chief; Nwsp Rptr; Yrbk Stf; NHS; Cntry 21 Typng Awd 85; Cntry 3 Ldrs Awd 87.

STERRETT, ANDY; St Marys Area HS; Kersey, PA; (4); Boys Clb Am; JV Bsktbl; Var Trk; Wt Lftg; Hon Roll; NHS; Ntl Merit Ltr; Prsdntl Acdmc Ftnss Awd 87; PA ST U; Engrng.

STESER, MELISSA; Moon Area HS; Coraopolis, PA; (3); 53/305; JV Bsktbl; Var Sftbl; Hon Roll; 1st Tm All-Sect 86; 1st Tm All-Sec 87; Aero Engrng.

STETKA, SCOT; Fleetwood HS; Fleetwood, PA; (3); 17/117; Boy Scts; Church Yth Grp; Quiz Bowl; Band; Chorus; Church Choir; Concert Band; Mrchg Band; Pep Band; School Musical; Socl Sci.

STETTNER, KATHLEEN; Parkland HS; Allentown, PA; (2); Church Yth Grp; Drama Clb; Office Aide; School Play; Vllybl; High Hon Roll; Hon Roll; Prfct Atten Awd; Pres Schlr; Schlstc Art Awds 86; Art.

STETZLAR, WENDY A; Hamburg Area HS; Hamburg, PA; (4); Hst FBLA; Library Aide; Chorus; Off Stu Cncl; Trk; High Hon Roll; Hon Roll; Reading Area CC; Exec Secy.

STEUCEK, ANNA; John Piersol Mccaskey HS; Millersville, PA; (3); AFS; Q&S; Lit Mag; Hon Roll; NHS; Amrcn Assoc Of Tchrs Of German Awd 87; Lancaster Peace Essay Cntst Hnr Mntn 87.

STEVANNS, SAMUEL; Salisbury Elk-Lick HS; Salisbury, PA; (3); Church Yth Grp; FFA; Band; Concert Band; Mrchg Band; Stage Crew; Bsbl; Bsktbl; Socr; Hon Roll; Mech Engr.

STEVE, T MATTHEW; Indiana Area SR HS; Indiana, PA; (2); Church Yth Grp; Computer Clb; Key Clb; Math Tm; Rep Frsh Cls; Rep Stu Cncl; JV Bsktbl; Var Golf; High Hon Roll; Jr NHS; Mgmt Info Systms.

STEVENS, AMANDA; Mt Pleasant Area SR HS; Latrobe, PA; (3); Church Yth Grp; Computer Clb; GAA; Hosp Aide; Intnl Clb; Office Aide; Ski Clb; VICA; Swmmng; Science Clb; Amer Tae Wondo Assoc 86; Blue Shirts 86; Ltrd In Swmng 85-86; Data Prcsng.

STEVENS, DANIELLE P; Octorara HS; Coatesville, PA; (4); 92/165; Service Clb; Chorus; School Musical; Variety Show; Hon Roll; Choral Awds Exclinc Perfrmnc, Svc To Chorus 87; Arts Rcgntn Tlnt Srch Pgm 86-87; W Chester U; Musical Thrpst.

STEVENS, JAMIE; Brownsville Area HS; Brownsville, PA; (3); Cmnty Wkr; Drama Clb; Hosp Aide; Office Aide; OEA; Ski Clb; SADD; Concert Band; Mrchg Band; Nwsp Stf; Elem Ed.

STEVENS, JENNIFER; West Scranton HS; Scranton, PA; (3); Church Yth Grp; FNA; Letterman Clb; Ski Clb; Spanish Clb; Crs Cntry; Swmmng; Trk; Hon Roll; Jr NHS.

STEVENS, KIM; Penn Cambria HS; Ashville, PA; (3); Spanish Clb; Prfct Atten Awd; Spanish NHS; IFLA Awd 87; Cngrssnl Yth Ldrshp Cncl 87; NSEC Ldrshp Awd 87; Psych.

STEVENS, LEIGH; State College Area HS; Boalsburg, PA; (4); Church Yth Grp; French Clb; Hosp Aide; Office Aide; Ski Clb; Acpl Chr; Rep Frsh Cls; Rep Soph Cls; Rep Jr Cls; Stu Cncl; PA ST U; Lbrl Arts.

STEVENS, LENORE; Center HS; Aliquippa, PA; (4); Church Yth Grp; Exploring; Spanish Clb; Pres Rep Stu Cncl; Mgr Ftbl; NHS; Hmcmng Ct 86; May Ct 87; Cntr Area Ftbl Mthrs Schlrshp 87; Penn ST U; Sec Educ.

STEVENS, MARK; Meadville Area SR HS; Meadville, PA; (3); 70/360; Church Yth Grp; Latin Clb; Letterman Clb; Ski Clb; Varsity Clb; Socr; Var L Vllybl; High Hon Roll; Hon Roll; JCL; Psych.

STEVENS, MICHELE; North Pocono SR HS; Lake Ariel, PA; (4); 32/235; Trs VP Church Yth Grp; Concert Band; Mrchg Band; Orch; NHS; Med.

STEVENS, SARAH; Reynolds HS; Greenville, PA; (3); 8/165; Latin Clb; Letterman Clb; SADD; Yrbk Stf; Rep Stu Cncl; Var Cheerleading; Var Trk; Hon Roll; Church Yth Grp; Spanish Clb; Fndtn Free Enrprs Educ 87; Amer Legn Awd 84; Mount Union; Law.

STEVENS, TODD; Eastern York HS; Wrightsville, PA; (3); CAP; Stu Cncl; Hon Roll; Genetics.

STEVENS, TRUDY; Waynesboro Area SR HS; Waynesboro, PA; (2); Church Yth Grp; Chorus; Hon Roll; Secy.

STEVENSON, AMANDA; Lincoln HS; Ellwood City, PA; (3); 30/162; Pres Drama Clb; French Clb; Church Choir; Mrchg Band; School Musical; Ed Nwsp Stf; Yrbk Rptr; Trs Jr Cls; NHS; Essay Cont 84-85 Sponsored By PA ST U & The PA Cncl Of Tchrs 84-85; Point Park Coll; Journlsm.

STEVENSON, DIANE; Valley HS; Arnold, PA; (3); 4/225; Drama Clb; Exploring; JA; Math Tm; Science Clb; Spanish Clb; Yrbk Stf; Mgr Bsktbl; Vllybl; High Hon Roll; Chem.

STEVENSON, JOHN; Cocalico HS; Denver, PA; (2); Boy Scts; Ski Clb; VP Frsh Cls; Im Bsktbl; Im Sftbl; Var Im Vllybl; High Hon Roll; Hon Roll; Law.

STEVENSON, KEVIN; Wallenpaupack HS; New Foundland, PA; (3); 24/150; Cmnty Wkr; PAVAS; Scholastic Bowl; Science Clb; Chorus; School Play; Yrbk Ed-Chief; Yrbk Phtg; Yrbk Rptr; Yrbk Stf; Art.

STEVENSON, KRISTEN; Yough HS; Ruffs Dale, PA; (3); 64/270; Cmnty Wkr; French Clb; Pep Clb; Ski Clb; Band; Chorus; Concert Band; Yrbk Stf; Rep Frsh Cls; Rep Stu Cncl; Presdntl Clss Rm Young Amer 87.

STEVENSON, LA SHAE; Connellsville Area SR HS; Connellsville, PA; (3); VICA; Hon Roll; Pres Physcl Ftns Awd; Hghst Avrg Hstry Cls Awd; Las Vegas Coll; Vet Assist.

STEVERSON, ELIZABETH; Taylor Allderdice HS; Pittsburgh, PA; (3); Pres Girl Scts; VP JA; SADD; Band; Flag Corp; Mrchg Band; Var Co-Capt Crs Cntry; Var Capt Mat Maids; High Hon Roll; Church Yth Grp; Grl Sct Gold & Silver Awds 86-87.

STEVES, PATRICIA M; Millville HS; Millville, PA; (3); 5/71; Am Leg Aux Girls St; Drama Clb; FBLA; SADD; Chorus; Capt Flag Corp; School Musical; School Play; Stage Crew; Nwsp Stf; Presdntl Physcl Ftnss Awd 87; Peer Cnnctn 87; Stu Tutrng Pgm 87; Bloomsburg U; Acctng.

STEWART, ANDREW; Lower Moreland HS; Huntingdon Valley, PA; (2); German Clb; Band; Concert Band; Bsktbl; Hon Roll.

STEWART, ANGELA; Karns City HS; Bruin, PA; (4); 3/112; Church Yth Grp; Trs FCA; SADD; Teachers Aide; School Play; Var L Bsktbl; DAR Awd; NHS; Camera Clb; Drama Clb; Pres Acad Athl Awd 87; Physcs Awd 87; Butler Cnty JR Miss Fnlst 86-87; Grove City Coll; Pre-Med.

STEWART, BEN; Valley Forge Military HS; Lansdale, PA; (1); Debate Tm; ROTC; Spanish Clb; Rep Trk; L Hon Roll; L NHS; Harvey Awd Highest Aver In Math 86-87; Red Stars Conting B Aver 86-87.

STEWART, CARLA; Kittanning HS; Worthington, PA; (3); DECA; Pep Clb; SADD; High Hon Roll; Hon Roll.

STEWART, CRYSTAL; West Greene SR HS; Holbrook, PA; (2); Church Yth Grp; Cmnty Wkr; Dance Clb; SADD; School Musical; School Play; Variety Show; Nwsp Stf; Stu Cncl; Hon Roll; WV U.

STEWART, DANIEL; Ford City JR-SR HS; Ford City, PA; (3); Computer Clb; Key Clb; VP Spanish Clb; Nwsp Stf; High Hon Roll; Hon Roll; Jrnlsm.

STEWART, DANIEL; Northern York HS; Wellsville, PA; (4); 16/200; French Clb; Acpl Chr; Chorus; Church Choir; School Musical; Nwsp Rptr; Nwsp Stf; Var L Bsktbl; Var L Ftbl; Var Capt Socr; Amer Schl Choral Awd 87; Dist & Rgnl Chorus 85-87; Drew U.

STEWART, DAPHNE A; Central Dauphin East HS; Dauphin, PA; (4); Chorus; Capt Flag Corp; Orch; School Musical; School Play; Yrbk Stf; Twrlr; Hon Roll; NHS; Presdntl Acad Fit Awd 87; Drexel U; Chem Engrng.

STEWART, DAVID; Canon Mc Millan HS; Canonsburg, PA; (4); 61/375; Church Yth Grp; Exploring; Latin Clb; Science Clb; Ski Clb; Trk; High Hon Roll; Hon Roll; Penn Tech Inst; Electrncs Tech.

STEWART, DAVID; Central SR HS; York, PA; (3); 175/200; Letterman Clb; Ski Clb; Varsity Clb; Var Crs Cntry; Var Socr; Var Trk; Im Wt Lftg; High Hon Roll; Hon Roll; Drexel; Physcs.

STEWART, DIANA; West Greene Mid SR HS; New Freeport, PA; (4); 1/107; Science Clb; Pres Band; Yrbk Ed-Chief; Yrbk Stf; DAR Awd; Lion Awd; Pres NHS; Val; German Intro I II Awds; All Cnty Band; Waynesburg Coll; Bus Adm.

STEWART, ERIC J; Fort Le Boeuf HS; Erie, PA; (4); 26/167; Chess Clb; Church Yth Grp; Computer Clb; Debate Tm; Nwsp Rptr; Nwsp Stf; High Hon Roll; Hon Roll; Ntl Merit SF; St Schlr; PA ST; Astrnt.

STEWART, FRANCES; Trinity HS; Carlisle, PA; (2); Trs Church Yth Grp; Cmnty Wkr; NFL; Pep Clb; School Musical; School Play; Yrbk Stf; High Hon Roll; NHS; Dance Clb; Bronze 3rd Mdl In Casef Sci Fair 86; Lbrl Arts.

STEWART, JACQUELINE; Waynesburg Central HS; Waynesburg, PA; (4); 54/197; Hosp Aide; Library Aide; Teachers Aide; Color Guard; Mrchg Band; Capt Twrlr; Hon Roll; Mst Outstndng Colorgrd-Rifle 86-87; Waynesburg Coll; Accntng.

STEWART, JAMES; Hamburg Area HS; Hamburg, PA; (3); Boy Scts; German Clb; SADD; Var Bsbl; Var L Golf; Var Trk; Im Wt Lftg; Hon Roll.

STEWART, JEFF; Hampton HS; Allison Park, PA; (3); 1/200; Quiz Bowl; JV Socr; Var Trk; High Hon Roll; Advncd Plcmnt Hist 86-87; Law.

STEWART, JOSEPH; East HS; Erie, PA; (3); 15/180; Boy Scts; Cmnty Wkr; Var Socr; Hon Roll; Comm.

STEWART, KAREN; Souderton Area HS; Harleysville, PA; (3); Church Yth Grp; Cmnty Wkr; Band; Chorus; Concert Band; Mrchg Band; School Musical; Sftbl; Hon Roll; Montgomery Cnty CC; Ocptnl Thr.

STEWART, KELLI; Homer-Center HS; Homer City, PA; (3); 11/102; Drm Mjr(t); VP Frsh Cls; Sec Soph Cls; Sec Jr Cls; Sec Sr Cls; L Vllybl; High Hon Roll; Hon Roll; Jr NHS; NHS; FBLA 4th Pl Pblc Spkng Awd 87; Sftbl 3 Yr Lttrmn 85-87; Band Mbr Mth, Oct 86; Radiolgy.

STEWART JR, KENNETH F; Connellsville SR HS; Connellsville, PA; (2); 167/575; FHA; Chorus; Stage Crew; Yrbk Rptr; Yrbk Stf; Rep Frsh Cls; Sec Soph Cls; Rep Stu Cncl; JV Swmmng; Hon Roll; Johnson & Wales; Rstrnt Mgr.

STEWART, KERRY; Carlynton JR SR HS; Pittsburgh, PA; (2); Camera Clb; JA; Letterman Clb; Ski Clb; Spanish Clb; L Bsktbl; Capt Trk; Hon Roll; Washington & Jefferson.

STEWART, KEVIN; United HS; Homer City, PA; (4); 4/160; Aud/Vis; Chess Clb; Drama Clb; Acpl Chr; Chorus; School Musical; High Hon Roll; Hon Roll; Jr NHS; NHS; ARTN Marine Bio Quest 86; Comp Engr.

STEWART, KIMBERLY; Plymouth-Whitemarsh HS; Conshohocken, PA; (2); 25/250; Office Aide; SADD; Color Guard; Orch; Rep Soph Cls; Rep Stu Cncl; Cheerleading; Swmmng; High Hon Roll; Prfct Atten Awd; Bio.

STEWART, LA DAWN; Engineering & Science HS; Philadelphia, PA; (3); Drill Tm; Cheerleading; Trk; Howard U; Psych.

STEWART, LEAH; Carlisle HS; Carlisle, PA; (3); 148/454; Ski Clb; Tennis; Trk; Carlisle Cvc Clb Art Awd.

STEWART, MARK; Meadville Area SR HS; Meadville, PA; (4); Church Yth Grp; Spanish Clb; Im Socr; High Hon Roll; Hon Roll; Schlstc Hnr Soc 87; John Carroll U Pres Hnr Awd, Schlrshp 87; John Carroll U; Bus Admin.

STEWART, MARY JO; Knoch JR-SR HS; Saxonburg, PA; (4); 89/248; Trs Debate Tm; Library Aide; Pep Clb; Speech Tm; Band; Concert Band; Mrchg Band; Pep Band; Nwsp Stf; Voice Dem Awd; Band Cert 85-86; Villa Maria Coll; Nursing.

STEWART, MICHELLE; Fort Le Boeuf HS; Waterford, PA; (3); 44/215; Church Yth Grp; Nwsp Stf; Stat Bsktbl; Var Trk; Var Vllybl; High Hon Roll; Hon Roll; Bus.

STEWART, SHERI; Meadville Area SR HS; Meadville, PA; (3); Ski Clb; Off Frsh Cls; Off Soph Cls; JV Cheerleading; Hon Roll; Nrsng.

STEWART, STACEY; Shenango HS; New Castle, PA; (3); 11/125; Church Yth Grp; Exploring; Rep Frsh Cls; Rep Soph Cls; Rep Stu Cncl; JV Var Cheerleading; Hon Roll; Jr NHS; NHS; Ntl Merit Schol; Hmcmg Ct; Psych.

STEWART, STACY; Marion Center Area HS; Marion Ctr, PA; (4); FBLA; FHA; Chorus; Capt Color Guard; Service Clb; Teachers Aide; Nwsp Stf; Pres Stu Cncl; IN U Of PA; Bus Educ.

STIADLE, MICHAEL; Montgomery Area HS; Montgomery, PA; (3); French Clb; Chorus; Concert Band; Mrchg Band; Var L Trk; NHS; PA Govrnrs Schl Arts 86; All ST Chorus 86-87; All East Chorus 87; Music Ed.

STIADLE, PATRICK; Montgomery Area HS; Montgomery, PA; (4); French Clb; Thesps; Acpl Chr; Chorus; Church Choir; JV Bsktbl; Var L Trk; High Hon Roll; NHS; Pres Schlr; Reg IV Chorus Medl 86-87; Slmni Assn Awd, Robert G More Schlrshp 87; Susquehanna U; Bio.

STICH, CATHERINE; Penn Cambria SR HS; Loretto, PA; (4); Var L Bsktbl; Var Capt Sftbl; Hon Roll; Mst Outstndng Athlt 87; St Francis Coll; Elem Educ.

STICKER, MARISA; Forest City Regional HS; Pleasant Mt, PA; (4); 5/54; German Clb; Scholastic Bowl; Hon Roll; NHS; Ntl Merit Schol; Presdntl Acad Ftnss Awd 87; U Of Scranton; Intl Studies.

STICKLE, JEFF; Mc Guffey HS; Prosperity, PA; (3); JA; Spanish Clb; Band; Chorus; Mgr Color Guard; Mrchg Band; School Musical; Stage Crew; Bsbl; Hon Roll; Cmmnctns.

STICKLER, CATHY; Northern Lebanon HS; Jonestown, PA; (3); 14/221; Girl Scts; Pep Clb; Varsity Clb; Band; Rep Frsh Cls; Rep Soph Cls; Rep Jr Cls; Stu Cncl; Var Bsktbl; Var Cheerleading; Secretary.

STICKLER, CYNTHIA; Northern Lebanon HS; Jonestown, PA; (4); 33/166; Art Clb; Pep Clb; Varsity Clb; Color Guard; VP Soph Cls; Sec Sr Cls; Rep Stu Cncl; Var Cheerleading; Hon Roll; NHS; Prfsnl Sec Int Schlrshp Awd; Sr Outstndng Stngrphc Stu; Cntrl Penn Bus Schl; Trvl.

STICKLES, DUSTY; Butler Intermediate HS; Butler, PA; (2); 112/699; Church Yth Grp; 4-H; French Clb; Chorus; 4-H Awd; Hon Roll; Jr NHS; Lakeview Ice Sktng Tm Rcvd 1st & 2nd Pl Cmpttn 86-87; 4-H Cert Merit Prtcptn Rgnl 86; Home Ec.

STICKLES, STEVEN A; Hopewell HS; Aliquippa, PA; (3); 35/270; Boy Scts; Pres VP Exploring; Trs Sr Cls; Bsktbl; L Ftbl; Trk; Wt Lftg; High Hon Roll; Hon Roll; Schlr Athl Awd 87; USC; Law.

STICKLIN, DANIELLE; Danville Area HS; Danville, PA; (4); 18/199; Key Clb; Sec Sr Cls; Var Crs Cntry; Mat Maids; Var Capt Trk; Hon Roll; Trs NHS; SADD; Sec Soph Cls; Schlr Ath Awd 87; Soropt Intl Montour Cnty Dorothy Bonawitz Awd 87; Deutsch Fmly Mem Scholar Awd 87; Dickinson Coll; Physcs.

STICKLIN, PAUL J; Danville SR HS; Danville, PA; (3); Am Leg Boys St; Church Yth Grp; Computer Clb; Drama Clb; NFL; Ski Clb; School Play; VP Frsh Cls; Rep Soph Cls; Var Socr; Conservatory Performing Arts.

STIEFEL, CINDY; Wallenpaupack Area HS; Hawley, PA; (3); 13/156; Quiz Bowl; Scholastic Bowl; Science Clb; Ski Clb; Sec Soph Cls; Sec Jr Cls; Sec Sr Cls; Stat Bsktbl; High Hon Roll; NHS; 1st Pl Grmn Lng Cntst 85-86; Pre-Vet.

STIEFEL, DIANE; Riverside HS; Beaver Falls, PA; (3); Rptr DECA; Apprl & Accssrs Mrktng-Wrttn-5th 87; Vhcl-Ptrlm Mrktng-Dist-1st, ST-3RD 86-87; Bradford Bus Schl; Rtl Mgmt.

STIEFFENHOFER, HEIDI; Abington SR HS; Glenside, PA; (3); 85/502; Art Clb; Church Yth Grp; Pres Trs Girl Scts; Band; Church Choir; Concert Band; Bsktbl; Fld Hcky; Mgr(s); Score Keeper; Beaver Coll; Sec Educ.

STIEHM, LOLA; Upper St Clair HS; Pittsburgh, PA; (4); 21/386; AFS; Church Yth Grp; Q&S; Nwsp Ed-Chief; Ed Lit Mag; High Hon Roll; Hon Roll; NHS; Ntl Merit SF.

STIELY, COREY; Tri-Valley HS; Klingerstown, PA; (3); Art Clb; Church Yth Grp; Ski Clb; VICA; Rep Jr Cls; Rep Stu Cncl; JV Var Ftbl; Hon Roll; NEDT Awd; Contntl Math Leag 84-85; Pres Athltc Ftnss Awd 85-86; Automtv Engr.

STIELY, ERIC; Upper Dauphin Area HS; Elizabethville, PA; (3); 34/124; Var Bsbl; Var Ftbl; Acctng.

STIFF, DERON; Brandywine Heights HS; Topton, PA; (2); Trs Church Yth Grp; FBLA; SADD; JV Bsbl; Stat Wrstlng; High Hon Roll; NHS; Acctng.

STIFFEY, BRIAN; Hempfield Area HS; Greensburg, PA; (4); Letterman Clb; Pep Clb; Ski Clb; L Ftbl; L Wt Lftg; L Wrstlng; St Vincent Seminary.

STIFFLER, KAROLYN; Central HS; Martinsburg, PA; (4); 54/187; Cmnty Wkr; FBLA; JA; Red Cross Aide; Chorus; School Musical; Hon Roll; MEDICAL Secty.

STIFFLER, KIMBERLY; Purchase Line HS; Marion Center, PA; (2); 5/156; FBLA; Band; Concert Band; VP Mrchg Band; Pep Band; High Hon Roll; Prfct Atten Awd; FBLA ST Parlmntrn 87; Dist & Reg Bnd 87; IN U Of PA; Reading Tchr.

STIFFLER, KRISTINE; Quigley HS; Aliquippa, PA; (4); 28/98; Band; Chorus; Concert Band; Drm Mjr(t); Mrchg Band; Var Cheerleading; Var Powder Puff Ftbl; Hon Roll; Acctng Awd 87; Tstmstrs Am Awd 85; Cortez Peters Typng Hnr Rl & Awd 86; R Morris Coll; Acctng.

STIFFLER, MARK; Southern Huntingdon County HS; Orbisonia, PA; (3); 2/155; Speech Tm; Band; Chorus; School Musical; Var Trk; God Cntry Awd; High Hon Roll; NHS; Rep Stu Cncl; Nwsp Stf; Eagle Scout, Boy Scouts Of Amer 84; FBLA Rgn 14 Mr FBL & Daily News Reporter Of Yr 87; Bio.

STIFFLER, SHANNON; Susquehannock HS; Shrewsbury, PA; (2); 8/243; Hon Roll; NHS; Acdmc Ltr 87; Brdcstg.

STIGLIANO, MELISSA; Sharpsville Area SR HS; Transfer, PA; (3); Art Clb; Camera Clb; German Clb; SADD; Chorus; Nwsp Phtg; Yrbk Phtg; Hon Roll; NHS; Acadmc Achvt Awd 84-85; Acadmc Achvt Awd/Bar 85-86; Jrnlsm.

STILES, CAROL; Penns Manor HS; Clymer, PA; (4); 6/91; Church Yth Grp; Band; Chorus; Jazz Band; Mrchg Band; School Musical; High Hon Roll; Sec NHS; Prfct Atten Awd; Dist Band 86 & 87; Rgnl Band 87; Presdntl Acadmc Fitness Awd 87; IN U Of PA; Medical Tech.

STILES, GREGORY; Waynesburg Central HS; Waynesburg, PA; (3); Church Yth Grp; Cmnty Wkr; Letterman Clb; Ftbl; Ice Hcky; Wt Lftg; Wrstlng; Hon Roll; Bus.

STILES, IVA; West York Area HS; York, PA; (2); Church Yth Grp; Hosp Aide; Chorus; Hon Roll; Music Perfrmnc Vocal.

STILES, JAMES; York Suburban HS; York, PA; (3); 77/176; Cmnty Wkr; Letterman Clb; School Musical; Rep Jr Cls; Swmmng; Trk; Hon Roll; YCIAA 1st Team All Star Swmmng Awd 87.

STILES, JENNIFER; Bangor SR HS; Bangor, PA; (3); 7/200; Church Yth Grp; Leo Clb; Varsity Clb; Church Choir; Sec Trs Stu Cncl; Stat Bsbl; JV Bsktbl; JV Fld Hcky; High Hon Roll; NHS; Crim Just.

STILES, JODI; Homer Ctr; Homer City, PA; (3); 12/108; FBLA; Pres Trs Girl Scts; Intnl Clb; SADD; Church Choir; Concert Band; Mrchg Band; Cit Awd; Hon Roll; NHS; Girl Scout Gold Awd 87; IN U PA; Acctng.

STILL, ROBERT; Cumberland Valley HS; Boiling Spgs, PA; (3); Hon Roll.

STILLIONS, JERRY LEE; Kiski Area HS; E Vandergrift, PA; (4); High Hon Roll; Hon Roll.

STILLO, MICHELLE LYNN; Pocono Mountain HS; Stroudsburg, PA; (2); French Clb; Gym; Sftbl; Trk; Dancing.

STILLWAGON, SHANNON; Seneca Valley HS; Mars, PA; (2); Sec Trs Art Clb; VP JA; Chorus; Var Tennis; High Hon Roll; Hon Roll; NHS; Schltc Awd 86-87; Art.

STILO, COLLEEN; Archbishop Ryan HS For Girls; Philadelphia, PA; (3); Camp Fr Inc; Q&S; Teachers Aide; Yrbk Stf; High Hon Roll; White Williams Schlrshp Awd 87-88; 1st Pl Phila Annl Bus Cntst Steno I 86-87; Secr Stds.

STILPHEN, SCOTT; Wyoming Area SR HS; Pittston, PA; (3); Boy Scts; Computer Clb; Hosp Aide; Kings Coll; Comp Sci.

STIMAKER, JEFFERI; Belle Vernon Area HS; Belle Vernon, PA; (3); Color Guard; Stu Cncl; High Hon Roll; U Pittsburgh.

STIMELING, TINA; East Pennsboro HS; Enola, PA; (2); Spanish Clb; Band; Color Guard; Concert Band; Mrchg Band; Hon Roll; Boston Coll; Law.

STIMELING, VALERIE; Spring-Ford Lower Lewis HS; Royersford, PA; (3); 53/256; SADD; Hon Roll; Penn ST; Chemist.

STIMMEL, BRIAN; Shaler Area SR HS; Glenshaw, PA; (3); 298/486; Church Yth Grp; Office Aide; Ski Clb; Socr; Wt Lftg; Hon Roll; Prfct Atten Awd; Pres Phys Ftnss Awd 83-84; JV Sccr Lttr 83-84; FL Southern; Bus Mgmt.

STIMMEL, ICEY; Frazier HS; Dawson, PA; (3); Hlth Occptn Stu Amer; Nrsng.

STIMPSON, STEPHANIE; Meadville Area SR HS; Meadville, PA; (2); Church Yth Grp; Drama Clb; Girl Scts; Spanish Clb; Concert Band; School Play; High Hon Roll; Prfct Atten Awd; Amer Frgn Lang Stu 87; Acadmc Ltrmn 86; Sci.

STINEDURF, SHAWN; West Middlesex HS; New Wilmington, PA; (4); 14/92; Office Aide; Pep Clb; Bsktbl; Sftbl; Vllybl; Wt Lftg; High Hon Roll; Hon Roll; Chem Field.

STINSON, JEFF; Northwestern SR HS; Albion, PA; (3); Pres VP Church Yth Grp; VP French Clb; Band; Concert Band; Mrchg Band; Pep Band; School Musical; School Play; Rep Stu Cncl; Hon Roll; Tri-M Music Natl Hnr Soc 87; Hotel Mngmnt.

STINSON, KERRI; Huntingdon Area HS; Hesston, PA; (2); 17/200; Key Clb; Soroptimist; Chorus; School Musical; Hon Roll; Merit Awd Latin 87; Pharmacist.

STINSON, NELLIE; United HS; Seward, PA; (3); Aud/Vis; Hosp Aide; Mu Alpha Theta; Yrbk Stf; Rep Stu Cncl; Var L Bsktbl; Var L Sftbl; Hon Roll; Jr NHS; NHS; Hugh Obrien Yth Fndtn Ambassador 86; RIT; Cinemtgrphr.

STINSON, RENITA; Trinity HS; Pittsburgh, PA; (4); Church Yth Grp; Girl Scts; NAACP; SADD; Drill Tm; School Play; Rep Sr Cls; Rep Stu Cncl; Capt Trk; Cit Awd; Prsdntl Phys Ftns Awd 86-87; Outstndng Awd Fine Arts, AUBA Cngrss Chrstn Educ Schlrshp 87; CA U Of PA; Sclgy.

STIRLING, THOMAS DAVID; MMI Prep Schl; Sugarloaf, PA; (3); Pres Computer Clb; Math Clb; Teachers Aide; School Play; Stat Bsktbl; Score Keeper; Timer; Advncd 1st Aid & Emerncy Medcl Techn 86-87; 1st, 2nd & 3rd Pl Open House Prog 85-87; Ambul & Exec Comm; Engrng.

STIRRAT, JENNY; Athens HS; Athens, PA; (3); 35/120; Cmnty Wkr; Hosp Aide; Band; Mrchg Band; Jr Cls; Bowling; Cheerleading; Crs Cntry; Trk; Ltr & Pin Trck, Crss Cntry 82-87; Mansfield; Fshn Dsgn.

STITELER, AMY; Du Bois Area SR HS; Dubois, PA; (3); 4-H; Art Clb; German Clb; Office Aide; Ski Clb; Hon Roll; Real Est Agnt.

STITELER, TRACEY; Marion Center Area HS; Indiana, PA; (4); FBLA; FHA; Latin Clb; Office Aide; Pep Clb; Science Clb; SADD; Concert Band; Mrchg Band; Stu Cncl; Med.

STITH, JOHN; Walter Biddle Saul HS; Philadelphia, PA; (3); FFA; Quiz Bowl; Spanish Clb; Off Frsh Cls; Off Soph Cls; Off Jr Cls; Off Sr Cls; Im Bsktbl; Im Ftbl; Im Golf; Greenhand Degree 85; Lab Animal Clb 86-87; Ed.

STITLEY, JULIE; Shikellamy HS; Sunbury, PA; (4); 6/300; Hosp Aide; VP Spanish Clb; Band; Chorus; Concert Band; Jazz Band; Mrchg Band; Hon Roll; VP NHS; Spanish NHS; Yng Am 87; Elizabethtwn Coll; Occptnl Ther.

STITLEY, ROBERT; Dover Area HS; Dover, PA; (3); Art Clb; Church Yth Grp; Varsity Clb; School Musical; School Play; Stage Crew; Var L Swmmng; Var Trk; VP Stu Cncl; Hon Roll; Comm Artst.

STITT, GRETCHEN; Clarion-Limeston HS; Clarion, PA; (3); 6/86; Girl Scts; Hosp Aide; SADD; Chorus; Sec Drill Tm; Flag Corp; School Play; Cheerleading; Hon Roll; NHS; PA Free Enterpise Wk Schlrshp 86; Rotary Yth Ldrshp Awds 87; Westminister Coll; Marketing.

STITZENBERG, KEVIN; Our Lady Of The Sacred Heart HS; Mc Kees Rocks, PA; (3); Var L Bsbl; Im Socr; Im Vllybl; Arch Engr.

STOBACK, JAMES; Athens HS; Sayre, PA; (4); 3/120; Church Yth Grp; Scholastic Bowl; Ski Clb; Swmmng; High Hon Roll; NHS; VFW Awd; Pennsylvania U; Bio.

STOCK, DINA; Wissahickon HS; Blue Bell, PA; (4); 6/278; Library Aide; Ski Clb; SADD; Band; Variety Show; Nwsp Ed-Chief; Nwsp Phtg; Nwsp Stf; Yrbk Stf; Lit Mag; Rutgers Coll Of Pharm; Pharm.

STOCK, JAMES; Shenango JR SR HS; New Castle, PA; (4); #4 In Class; Am Leg Boys St; Varsity Clb; Bsbl; Bsktbl; Ftbl; High Hon Roll; Hon Roll; Jr NHS; Lion Awd; NHS; Natl Mrt Sci Awd 85-86; Natl Mrt Math Awd 85-86; Penn ST U; Engr.

STOCK, MIKE; Central HS; E Freedom, PA; (3); Boy Scts; VP Church Yth Grp; Dance Clb; Pres Library Aide; Red Cross Aide; Band; Chorus; School Musical; School Play; Nwsp Rptr; UCLA.

STOCK, THOMAS MICHAEL; Bishop Carroll HS; Nanty-Glo, PA; (3); 57/126; SADD; Rep Frsh Cls; Rep Soph Cls; Stu Cncl; Var Bsbl; JV Bsktbl; Bowling; Var JV Ftbl; L Golf; L Trk; IN U Of PA; Crmnlgy.

STOCKDALE, HOLLY; Jefferson-Morgan JR SR HS; Jefferson, PA; (4); 23/97; Art Clb; Computer Clb; Office Aide; OEA; Spanish Clb; Band; Color Guard; Concert Band; Drm Mjr(t); Rep Frsh Cls; Waynesburg Coll; Bus Adm.

STOCKHAM, ANN J; Bermudian Springs HS; New Oxford, PA; (3); 16/126; Church Yth Grp; Lib Band; Concert Band; Mrchg Band; Hon Roll; Pep Band; Adams Cnty Band 87; Yng Womnhd Recog Awd 87; YWMIA Cmpcrftr Cert Awd 86; Bus Adm.

STOCKHAUSEN, DONALD; Western Beaver HS; Industry, PA; (2); Rep Am Leg Boys St; Sec Sr Cls; High Hon Roll; NHS; Var L Bsbl; JV Bsktbl; Im Bowling; PA ST U; Chem Engrng.

STODDARD, AMY; Corry Area HS; Corry, PA; (3); 13/223; Church Yth Grp; 4-H; French Clb; Band; Yrbk Stf; JV Vllybl; 4-H Awd; High Hon Roll; Hon Roll; Horse Shows 85-86; Cnty Horse Shows 86; Bio Sci.

STODDARD, DOUGLAS; Western Wayne HS; Waymart, PA; (2); Chess Clb; JV Socr; Hon Roll; PA ST U; Aerosp Engrng.

STODDART, JOHN; Blue Mountain Acad; Philadelphia, PA; (3); Church Yth Grp; Library Aide; Acpl Chr; Band; Chorus; Church Choir; Concert Band; Off Stu Cncl; Var Bsktbl; Var Vllybl; Andrews U; Bus Adm.

STODDART, STEPHANIE; Carlisle SR HS; Selfridge Ang, MI; (3); Band; Mrchg Band; Stat Ftbl; Var L Swmmng; High Hon Roll; NHS; Mst Val Swmmr 85-86; U MI; Engrng.

STOECKEL, HOLLY; William Allen HS; Allentown, PA; (3); Church Yth Grp; Girl Scts; JCL; Chorus; Var L Bsktbl; Var L Trk; Capt Twrlr; Var L Vllybl; Hon Roll; NHS; Bus Mgmt.

STOFFA, CHARLES; MMI Prep Schl; White Haven, PA; (3); 4/39; Math Tm; Ski Clb; Pres Jr Cls; Rep Stu Cncl; Var L Bsbl; Var L Bsktbl; Im Vllybl; High Hon Roll; NHS; NEDT Awd; Engrng.

STOFFA, GEORGE; Jim Thorpe Area SR HS; Jim Thorpe, PA; (2); Chorus; Hon Roll; Military Acad; Pilot.

STOFFEY, JANINE; Bishop Ohara HS; Peckville, PA; (2); 5/127; Latin Clb; Spanish Clb; Church Choir; Nwsp Stf; High Hon Roll; U Of Scranton; Law.

STOFFEY, SCOTT; Marian HS; Tamaqua, PA; (3); 29/104; Rep Jr Cls; Rep Stu Cncl; Var Bsktbl; Var Ftbl; Var Wt Lftg; Hon Roll.

STOFIK, SCOTT; South Park HS; Library, PA; (3); 22/228; Boy Scts; Pres Trs FBLA; JV Bsbl; High Hon Roll; Hon Roll; NHS.

STOHON, HEIDI; Bishop Carroll HS; Ebensburg, PA; (3); L Trk; Var Vllybl; Child Psychlgst.

STOKER, GEOFFREY M; Forest City Regional HS; Uniondale, PA; (3); Drama Clb; German Clb; Letterman Clb; Band; Chorus; Jazz Band; Mrchg Band; Pres Stu Cncl; Var L Bsktbl; Var L Crs Cntry; 1st Tm Leag All Star Vlybl; Soc Of Dstngshd Amer HS Stu; Attnd Dist Band & Chrs Fstvls.

STOKES, BRIAN; Greensburg Salem SR HS; Delmont, PA; (2); Spanish Clb; Bsktbl; Hon Roll; Hstry Tchr.

STOKES, BRIAN J; Carlynton HS; Crafton, PA; (4); 6/172; Church Choir; School Musical; Diving; Capt L Socr; High Hon Roll; NHS; Ntl Merit SF; Am Legn Awd 84.

STOKES, GLORIA; Chester HS; Chester, PA; (3); Girl Scts; Band; Yrbk Stf; Hon Roll; Engr.

STOKES, SHARON; Dallas SR HS; Trucksville, PA; (4); Hosp Aide; Chorus; Yrbk Stf; Hon Roll; Misericordia Coll; Nrsng.

STOKLOSA, JACKIE; Blairsville SR HS; Blairsville, PA; (1); Church Yth Grp; Girl Scts; Band; Church Choir; Concert Band; Mrchg Band; Socl Wk.

STOKLOSA, STACIE; Blairsville SR HS; Blairsville, PA; (3); 37/110; Church Yth Grp; Hosp Aide; SADD; Band; Chorus; Church Choir; Color Guard; Concert Band; Drill Tm; Mrchg Band; Nrsng.

STOLL, ROBERT A; Hempfield HS; Mountville, PA; (3); 10/400; Am Leg Boys St; Chess Clb; Var Capt Crs Cntry; Var L Trk; High Hon Roll; Hon Roll; NHS; Math.

STOLLAR, LAUREL; Mc Guffey HS; West Alexander, PA; (3); 5/220; Am Leg Aux Girls St; German Clb; Pep Clb; Chorus; School Musical; Var L Bsktbl; L Trk; NHS; IN U; Med.

STOLLAR, MARK; Trinity HS; Washington, PA; (3); Hon Roll; Triangle Tech; Drafting.

STOLTZ, CHRISTINE; Jeannette SR HS; Jeannette, PA; (3); Church Yth Grp; Ski Clb; Spanish Clb; Capt Twrlr; Hon Roll; Sec NHS.

STOLTZ, JEFF; Neshaminy HS; Levittown, PA; (3); 18/799; Band; Concert Band; Jazz Band; Mrchg Band; Orch; Pep Band; Symp Band; High Hon Roll; Hon Roll; Prfct Atten Awd; Pres Acdmc Ftnss Awd 84-85; Comp Sci.

STOLTZ, KELLIE; Altoona Area HS; Altoona, PA; (3); SADD; Orch; Variety Show; High Hon Roll; Hon Roll; NEDT Awd; Pres Schlr; Bus Admin.

STOLTZ, LAUREN; Jeannette SR HS; Jeannette, PA; (2); Church Yth Grp; Hosp Aide; Ski Clb; Spanish Clb; Cheerleading; High Hon Roll.

STOLTZ, ROBERT; Bishop Guilfoyle HS; Altoona, PA; (3); 47/156; Church Yth Grp; Band; Var Tennis; Hon Roll; Chmstry Clb 86-87; Penn State; Advrtsng.

STOLTZ, SCOTT; Bishop Guilfoyle HS; Altoona, PA; (4); 27/117; Chess Clb; VP German Clb; Letterman Clb; Chorus; Rep Stu Cncl; Var Capt Bsbl; JV Bsktbl; Var L Golf; Leo J Wechter Mem Schlrhsp 87; PA ST U; Hotel Mgmt.

STOLTZ, TODD; Cedar Crest HS; Myerstown, PA; (2); Church Yth Grp; Exploring; Pep Clb; Spanish Clb; High Hon Roll; Hon Roll; NHS; Prfct Atten Awd; Penn ST; Mdcl Fld.

STOLTZFUS, CHERRY; Pequea Valley HS; Gap, PA; (3); Church Yth Grp; FBLA; Girl Scts; Spanish Clb; Yrbk Stf; Bsktbl; Fld Hcky; Sftbl; High Hon Roll; NHS; Bus.

STOLTZFUS, EILEEN; Lancaster Mennonite HS; Morgantown, PA; (3); Church Yth Grp; Chorus; Im Gym; Atlntc Cst Conf Bible Qzzng 3rd Pl 87; Psych.

STOLTZFUS, JEFF; Christian School Of York; York, PA; (3); Band; Chorus; Church Choir; Stage Crew; Ntl Merit Schol; Radio.

STOLZ, MARTIN; Moravian Acad; Bethlehem, PA; (3); Model UN; Chorus; School Musical; Nwsp Stf; Rep Stu Cncl; Var Crs Cntry; Gov Hon Prg Awd; Hon Roll; Rotary Awd; Lit Mag; Rotary Intl Fellowship-Agentina 87-88; PA Govs Schl For Intl Stds 86; WA Workshop Schlrshp 87; Law.

STOLZ, TRACEY; Bishop Conwell HS; Fairless Hills, PA; (3); 24/278; Am Leg Aux Girls St; Dance Clb; Hon Roll; Clss I Gymnst Will Moor Gym Clb NJ 84-87; Nrsng.

STONE, BRENDA; Montrose Area HS; Montrose, PA; (3); Ski Clb; Spanish Clb; Varsity Clb; Band; Church Choir; Concert Band; Mrchg Band; Mgr(s); Score Keeper.

STONE, CHRISTOPHER; State Clg Area Intermediate HS; State College, PA; (1); Church Yth Grp; Math Clb; Band; Nwsp Stf; Hon Roll; JETS Awd; Prfct Atten Awd; ST Coll Area Schl Dist Commendtn 86-87; PA Math League Cert Merit 86-87; Math Assoc Amer Cert 86-87; Elec Engrng.

STONE, DEANNA; New Castle SR HS; New Castle, PA; (4); FBLA; SADD; Band; Vllybl; Slippery Rock U; Bus Mgmt.

STONE, DONALD; Tunkhannock Area HS; Tunkhannock, PA; (2); German Clb; Cit Awd; Hon Roll; AFROTC; Aero Engrng.

STONE, GINNY; Norwin HS; N Huntingdon, PA; (4); 101/545; German Clb; Office Aide; SADD; Yrbk Stf; Stu Cncl; Trk; Masonic Awd; ST Treas Intl Order Rainbow Girls 85-86, Grand Rep 86-87; Shippensburg U PA; Elem Ed.

STONE, MATTHEW; William Allen HS; Allentown, PA; (2); 9/700; JA; JCL; Latin Clb; Letterman Clb; Varsity Clb; Nwsp Rptr; Lit Mag; Stu Cncl; JV Crs Cntry; Var L Wrstlng; 1st Pl Robesonia Latn Convntn Certamen 86; Summa Cum Laude Lat I Nat Exm 86; Magna Cum Laude Latin II; MI; Genetic Engineering.

STONE, PETER; William Allen HS; Allentown, PA; (3); 8/600; Church Yth Grp; Nwsp Rptr; VP Soph Cls; Trs Jr Cls; Rep Sr Cls; Var L Crs Cntry; Var L Wrstlng; Civic Clb; Debate Tm; JA; Ltn, Natl, ST Smma Cm Ld Exm 85-87; WA DC Stu For Wk Pres Clsrm 87; Pblc Rltns Chrmn 86-87; Harvard U; Pltcl Sci.

STONE, STEPHEN C; Mt Lebanon SR HS; Pittsburgh, PA; (4); 1/537; VP Church Yth Grp; Exploring; German Clb; Pres Service Clb; Band; Mrchg Band; Symp Band; Lit Mag; High Hon Roll; Ntl Merit SF; Otstndng Frshmn 84; Otstndng Sphmr 85; Otstndng JR 86; Psychtry.

STONE JR, THOMAS; Shalom Christian Acad; Sharpsburg, MD; (3); Church Yth Grp; Computer Clb; French Clb; Bsktbl.

STONEBRAKER, STACIE; Hopewell HS; Aliquippa, PA; (3); 36/250; Latin Clb; Band; Concert Band; Mrchg Band; Mgr(s); Mgr Wrstlng; Hon Roll; NHS; Bio.

STONEHOUSE, DAVID; Philadelphia Mntgmry Chrstn Acad; Roslyn, PA; (2); Orch; VP Frsh Cls; VP Soph Cls; Score Keeper; Socr; Tennis; High Hon Roll; Engrng.

STONEKING, KELLY; Fairchance Georges HS; Fairchance, PA; (3); Sec Church Yth Grp; Math Tm; Spanish Clb; Church Choir; Yrbk Stf; Sec Jr Cls; DAR Awd; High Hon Roll; Hon Roll; Jr NHS; NHS; Ed.

STONEKING, MICHELLE; Mapletown HS; Mt Morris, PA; (4); 9/75; VP Girl Scts; Ed Nwsp Stf; Yrbk Stf; Im Vllybl; Hon Roll; Salem Coll; Eqstrn Educ.

STONEMAN, GUY; Lower Merion HS; Ardmore, PA; (3); Pres Stu Cncl; L Var Bsktbl; Var L Lcrss; Ntl Merit SF; Lib Arts.

STONER, BECKY; Biglerville HS; Biglerville, PA; (4); 34/79; Chorus; Nwsp Stf; Yrbk Stf; Stat Bsktbl; Stat Ftbl; Stat Trk; Allegany CC.

STONER, CHARLES; Trinity HS; Mechanicsburg, PA; (3); 30/130; CAP; Spanish Clb; Yrbk Stf; JV Ftbl; Wt Lftg; U Of AZ; Engrng.

STONER, DANIEL P; Hershey SR HS; Hershey, PA; (3); 32/209; Church Yth Grp; Church Choir; Concert Band; Mrchg Band; School Musical; Var Golf; High Hon Roll; Penn ST; Finance.

STONER, DAWN; York Catholic HS; York, PA; (3); Library Aide; Pep Clb; SADD; Chorus; Church Choir; School Musical; Var JV Bsktbl; Mgr(s); Svc Awd Alpha Peer Cnslr 85-87; Bus Mgmt.

STONER, FRED; Greenwood HS; Millerstown, PA; (4); Varsity Clb; Band; Concert Band; Mrchg Band; School Play; Nwsp Phtg; Nwsp Stf; Yrbk Phtg; Var Bsbl; Var Bsktbl; Accntng.

STONER, JODIE; Blair County Christian HS; Ebensburg, PA; (4); 2/4; Debate Tm; Band; Chorus; Nwsp Ed-Chief; Yrbk Ed-Chief; Off Sr Cls; Off Stu Cncl; Trk; Cit Awd; High Hon Roll; Acdmc Ftnss Awd 87; U Of Pittsburgh; Elctrcl Engnrn.

STONER, JOHN; Trinity HS; Washington, PA; (3); 79/402; FCA; French Clb; Yrbk Stf; Pres Frsh Cls; Pres Soph Cls; Pres Jr Cls; Pres Sr Cls; Var L Bsbl; Var L Bsktbl; Var L Ftbl.

STONER, KELLI; Central Dauphin East HS; Dauphin, PA; (3); Am Leg Aux Girls St; Ski Clb; Varsity Clb; Chorus; Pres Soph Cls; Pres Jr Cls; Rep Stu Cncl; Var Bsktbl; Trk; Jr NHS.

STONER, MICHAEL; Biglerville HS; Biglerville, PA; (3); 2/100; Varsity Clb; Rep Stu Cncl; Var L Wrstlng; High Hon Roll; Hon Roll; Jr NHS; NHS; Elec.

STONER, ROSEANNE; Eastern York JR SR HS; York, PA; (2); 63/159; JA; Band; Concert Band; Jazz Band; Mrchg Band; Pep Band; Hon Roll; Girl Scts; Mgr(s); Score Keeper; Astronomy.

STONER, SUSAN; Altoona Area HS; Altoona, PA; (4); 8/718; French Clb; JA; Chorus; Concert Band; Rep Sr Cls; Jr NHS; NHS; Ntl Merit Ltr; NEDT Awd; Frnch Awd Bst Stu 83-84; Pdtrcn.

STONEROAD, CONNIE; Upper Dauphin Area HS; Elizabethville, PA; (3); 16/115; Church Yth Grp; German Clb; Varsity Clb; Band; Concert Band; Mrchg Band; Stage Crew; Stat Bsktbl; JV L Sftbl; Hon Roll; Acctng.

STONESIFER, LUANN; Chambersburg Area SR HS; Chambersburg, PA; (2); Trs Church Yth Grp; French Clb; Ski Clb; Band; Chorus; Concert Band; Mrchg Band; Sftbl; Vllybl; Hon Roll; Juniata Coll; Elem Ed.

STONFER, DENICE; Frazier JR SR HS; Newell, PA; (4); 6/130; Band; Mrchg Band; Yrbk Sprt Ed; Yrbk Stf; Trs Jr Cls; Capt Bsktbl; High Hon Roll; Jr NHS; NHS; All-Cnty Bsktbl 85-87; Robt C Byrd Schlrshp 87; Bsktbl, Ftbl & SR Slide Show Committees 86-87; CA U Of PA; Elem Ed.

STOOPS, SEAN; Trinity HS; Lemoore, CA; (2); Boy Scts; Church Yth Grp; Cmnty Wkr; Church Choir; Var JV Mgr(s); Var Im Socr; 2nd Pl Schl Tlnt Show Bike Freestylng 86-87; Naval Acad; Pilot.

STOOTS, WILLIAM; Connellsville Area SR HS; Connellsville, PA; (3); 180/550; Spanish Clb; Varsity Clb; Bsktbl; Var Ftbl; Var Trk; Var Wt Lftg; Daily Courier All Str 1st Tm Tght End 86-87; Cvl Engr.

STOPPO, MICHAEL; Bishop Neumann HS; Williamsport, PA; (3); #3 In Class; Model UN; Scholastic Bowl; Bsktbl; High Hon Roll; Church Yth Grp; NHS; Hghst Avg-Rlgn, Hstry, Hlth, Music & Spnsh 86-87; Awd-Ntl Sci Olympd 86-87; Merit Awd-Tutrng 86-87; Econ.

STORCH, ANNE; Cedar Crest HS; Lebanon, PA; (4); French Clb; German Clb; Model UN; School Musical; School Play; Socr; Tennis; Im Vllybl; Hon Roll; Voice Dem Awd; People To People HS Stu Ambssdr 85; American U; Intl Rltns.

STOREY, JENNIFER; Peters Township HS; Mc Murray, PA; (4); Varsity Clb; Concert Band; Drill Tm; Mrchg Band; JV Gym; Var Pom Pon; Var Powder Puff Ftbl; Var Score Keeper; JV Trk; Purdue U.

STORINO, PAM; Meadville Area SR HS; Meadville, PA; (3); 81/363; Church Yth Grp; French Clb; Sec JA; Speech Tm; SADD; School Play; Nwsp Rptr; Yrbk Rptr; Mgr(s); Hon Roll; Chrstn Ldrshp Inst 87; Cmnctns.

STOSHAK, ANDREW; Gar Memorial HS; Wilkes-Barre, PA; (3); Church Yth Grp; Ski Clb; Hon Roll; NHS; Prfct Atten Awd.

STOTKA, ANDREA; Center HS; Aliquippa, PA; (2); Spanish Clb; Variety Show; Var JV Cheerleading; Powder Puff Ftbl; Gov Hon Prg Awd; High Hon Roll; Hon Roll; Spanish NHS; Sci.

STOTSENBURGH, LORI; Bishop Conwell HS; Levittown, PA; (3); 41/277; French Clb; Office Aide; Service Clb; SADD; Rep Jr Cls; Im Bsktbl; Var Socr; Hon Roll; Phys Thrpy.

STOTSKY, CHRIS; Seneca Valley HS; Evans City, PA; (3); 30/330; Art Clb; Letterman Clb; Off Jr Cls; Off Sr Cls; Stu Cncl; Ftbl; Swmmng; Trk; Hon Roll; NHS; Swmmng Ltrs; MVP Wmnng Tm; Ftbl Ltrs; Marine Bio.

STOTT, STEPHANIE; Owen J Roberts HS; Pottstown, PA; (3); 16/299; Pres German Clb; Symp Band; Stat Bsktbl; Var Trk; High Hon Roll; Hon Roll; NHS; Cmnty Wkr; Hosp Aide; Freedoms Fndtn Ldrshp Smnr 85; V Pres Anchor Clb 86; U Of MA Amherst; Speech Thrpy.

STOUD, AMY; Shamokin Area HS; Shamokin, PA; (2); Camera Clb; Church Yth Grp; German Clb; Pep Clb; Science Clb; SADD; Band; Mrchg Band; Pom Pon; Score Keeper; Psych.

STOUDMIRE, RENATA; The Philadelphia HS For Girls; Philadelphia, PA; (2); Girl Scts; Library Aide; Band; JV Sftbl; Awd Merits Schlstc Achvt 86-87; Bus Admin.

STOUDNOUR, ERIC; Altoona HS; Altoona, PA; (3); 105/800; Computer Clb; Letterman Clb; Ski Clb; Spanish Clb; Rep Stu Cncl; Ftbl; Trk; Wt Lftg; Wrstlng; Hon Roll; Pres Phy Fit Awd 86-87; PA ST U; Sci.

STOUDT, JOSEPH N; Fleetwood HS; Fleetwood, PA; (3); 1/110; Ski Clb; Var L Socr; Var L Trk; High Hon Roll; NHS; Prfct Atten Awd; Ltn Schlr Awd, Rtry Ldrshp Camp, & Union Leag Phila Ctznshp Awd 87; Engrng.

STOUDT, LANCE; Garden Spot HS; Narvon, PA; (2); 19/226; Church Yth Grp; JV Bsktbl; JV Socr; VP Tennis; High Hon Roll; Hon Roll; Jr NHS; NHS.

STOUDT III, THOMAS J; Abington SR HS; Abington, PA; (3); 16/507; French Clb; Latin Clb; Letterman Clb; L Swmmng; Hon Roll; NHS; Prfct Atten Awd; Magna Cum Ld Natl Latn Exm 87.

STOUFFER, AMY; Chambersburg Area HS; Chambersburg, PA; (2); Church Yth Grp; French Clb; Chorus; Church Choir; High Hon Roll; Girl Scts; Swing Chorus.

STOUFFER, GINGER SUE; Chambersburg Area SR HS; Chambersburg, PA; (4); 5/552; Girl Scts; Library Aide; Red Cross Aide; Concert Band; Jazz Band; Mrchg Band; Elks Awd; High Hon Roll; NHS; Grl Sct Gld Awd 87; IN U Of Pa; Accntnt.

STOUFFER, LAWRENCE; Greater Latrobe SR HS; Latrobe, PA; (4); 43/398; Church Yth Grp; CAP; French Clb; Ski Clb; Mgr(s); DAR Awd; French Hon Soc; High Hon Roll; Amelia Earhart Awd Civil Air Patrol 86; Intl Air Cdt Exchng Great Britain Civil Air Patrol 87; U Of Pittsburgh; Mech Engrng.

STOUFFER, PHOEBE; West Perry SR HS; New Bloomfield, PA; (2); 12/222; VP French Clb; Red Cross Aide; Trs Frsh Cls; Trs Soph Cls; Var JV Fld Hcky; Var Trk; Hon Roll; Yth Ftnss Achvmnt Awd 86; Amrcn Allnc Hlth, Phy Ed, Rcrtn, & Dnc Awd 87; Hnr Stu Art 87.

STOUFFER, STACIE; Waynesboro Area SR HS; Waynesboro, PA; (3); 4-H; JV Bsktbl; JV Fld Hcky; Var Sftbl; 4-H Awd; Hon Roll; Presdntl Acadc Ftnss Awd 85; Physcl Educ.

STOUGH, JOANNA; Northeastern HS; Manchester, PA; (3); French Clb; Acpl Chr; Chorus; Church Choir; School Musical; Yrbk Stf; Hon Roll; Dist, Rgnl Chorus 86-87; Gld Music Awd 86-87.

STOUGH, MICHELLE; Dover HS; Dover, PA; (4); 67/235; Church Yth Grp; Exploring; Band; Chorus; Trs Nwsp Stf; Rep Jr Cls; Var Trk; Renaissance Choral Grp 86-87; Elzbthtwn Coll; Occptnl Thrpy.

STOUGH, NICOLLE; West York Area HS; York, PA; (3); Church Yth Grp; Spanish Clb; Varsity Clb; Rep Frsh Cls; Soph Cls; Var Bsktbl; Tennis; Hon Roll; Prfct Atten Awd; Williamsport Area CC; Dntl Hyg.

STOUGH, SCOTT; West York Area HS; York, PA; (3); 17/185; Varsity Clb; Color Guard; Drill Tm; Var L Bsbl; Var L Tennis; High Hon Roll; Hon Roll; Prfct Atten Awd; Outstndng Rifle-Al Male Colorgrd; Rifle Capt; Math.

STOUT, DEANNE; Northampton SR HS; Bath, PA; (3); AFS; Church Yth Grp; Hosp Aide; Teachers Aide; Chorus; Hon Roll; Elem Ed.

STOUT, KITTY; Mercyhurst Prep Schl; Erie, PA; (4); 4/150; Cmnty Wkr; Drama Clb; JCL; Spanish Clb; Thesps; Sec Chorus; School Musical; Hon Roll; Pres NHS; Yth Undrstndng Exch Stu Spain 86.

STOUT, KRYSTINE; Carlisle SR HS; Carlisle, PA; (3); Church Yth Grp; Rep Jr Cls; Rep Sr Cls; JV Sftbl; Var Vllybl; Hon Roll; Jrnlsm.

STOUT, TAYLORINA M; Yough SR HS; Herminie, PA; (4); Church Yth Grp; School Play; Yrbk Stf; High Hon Roll; NHS; Ntl Merit Ltr; Voice Dem Awd; Ntl Engl Merit Awd 85-86; Ntl Ldrshp, Svc & Outstndng Artst Awds 86-87; Covenant Coll; Engl.

STOVER, DAVID; Mifflinburg Area HS; Millmont, PA; (1); JV Bsktbl; Law.

STOVER, DAWN; Cocalico HS; Reinholds, PA; (3); 69/175; FTA; Teachers Aide; Im Bsktbl; Hon Roll; Prfct Atten Awd; Ldrshp Awd 85-86; Elem Ed.

STOVER, DEBRAH; Bald Eagle Nittony HS; Mill Hall, PA; (3); Church Yth Grp; Hosp Aide; Library Aide; Chorus; Im Socr; Im Vllybl; 50 Hr Pin Candy Stripng 86; Nrsng.

STOVER, LISA; West York Area SR HS; York, PA; (2); 5/209; French Clb; Varsity Clb; Band; Concert Band; Mrchg Band; Symp Band; Stat Bsktbl; High Hon Roll; Pres Schlr.

STOVER, ROBERT; Hopewell Area HS; Monaca, PA; (3); Church Yth Grp; Exploring; French Clb; Band; Mrchg Band; Pep Band; Variety Show; JV Var Ftbl; Var Wt Lftg; Hon Roll.

STOVER, SHERRY; Palmyra Area HS; Campbelltown, PA; (4); 6/195; Drill Tm; Ed Yrbk Stf; Cit Awd; High Hon Roll; Kiwanis Awd; NHS; Ntl Merit Ltr; Pres Schlr; ANPA Schlstc Jrnlst Awd 87; PA ST U; Chem.

STOWE, CASSIE; Elizabethtown Area HS; Bainbridge, PA; (1); Church Yth Grp; VP Trs FFA; Ladies Farm Soc Mst Actv Ag, & ST Degree FFA 86; Ag.

STOWERS, YVETTE; Conemaugh Township HS; Hollsopple, PA; (3); FCA; Sec 4-H; French Clb; Sec JA; Library Aide; Sec Science Clb; Chorus; School Play; Stu Cncl; JV Socr; Achvt Scrtry 87; Soccer 86; Miss US Teen St Fnlst 87; U Of Pittsburg; Math Tchr.

STOY, BILL; Somerset Area SR HS; Somerset, PA; (4); 13/232; FBLA; Mu Alpha Theta; Varsity Clb; Rep Stu Cncl; L Bsbl; L Bsktbl; High Hon Roll; JC Awd; NHS; English Clb; Leroy J Manges Awd-Ecnmcs 87; Clarion U; Bus Admn.

STOY, T SAMUEL; Bishop Carroll HS; Ebensburg, PA; (3); Drama Clb; JA; NFL; Spanish Clb; SADD; School Play; Stage Crew; Var Bsbl.

STRAIT, RICKY; Forbes Road HS; Ft Littleton, PA; (3); Church Yth Grp; Computer Clb; French Clb; Im Var Bsktbl; High Hon Roll; Hon Roll; NHS; Stu Forum 86-87; Envir Olympics 86-87; Comp.

STRALEY, SUE; Greencastle Antrim HS; Greencastle, PA; (3); Hosp Aide; Band; Swmmng; Hon Roll; Prfct Atten Awd; Hnrbl Mntn Sci Fair 85-86; Hagerstown Bus Coll; Lgl Secy.

STRALLY, TAMMY; Richland HS; Gibsonia, PA; (3); 56/151; Church Yth Grp; Drama Clb; NFL; Chorus; School Play; Nwsp Rptr; Nwsp Stf; Var L Crs Cntry; Powder Puff Ftbl; Score Keeper; Intl Bus.

STRAMANAK, BRAD; Westmont Hilltop HS; Johnstown, PA; (2); Debate Tm; Stu Cncl; Bsbl; Ftbl; Wrstlng; Hon Roll; Bus Mgt.

STRANDQUEST, MICHELE; Johnstown SR HS; Johnstown, PA; (4); 29/306; Church Yth Grp; Nwsp Rptr; Nwsp Stf; Yrbk Phtg; Yrbk Stf; High Hon Roll; Hon Roll; NHS; Rotary Awd; Spanish Clb; Alumni Schlrshp Awd 87; U Of Pittsburgh; Occptnl Thrpy.

STRANGE, JON; Dallas SR HS; Dallas, PA; (3); Chess Clb; JV Crs Cntry; JV Ftbl; JV Socr; Var L Trk; Var L Vllybl; Im Wt Lftg; Var L Wrstlng; Acdmc Achvt Awd NEDT 85-86; PIAA Dist II Trck Champ 400 M Dash 87.

STRANK, PAULA; Conemaugh Valley JR SR HS; Johnstown, PA; (4); French Clb; Library Aide; Office Aide; Pep Clb; Ed Nwsp Ed-Chief; Nwsp Rptr; Yrbk Ed-Chief; Yrbk Phtg; Trs Jr Cls; NHS; Phys Ed Awd 86; FHA Awd 84; Sec.

STRANO, STACY; Punxsutawney SR HS; Punxsutawney, PA; (3); Sec Church Yth Grp; French Clb; Sec FNA; Math Tm; Trs Science Clb; Band; Var Tennis; NHS; Exploring; Hosp Aide; Math Tm Awd 86; Natl Hnr Rll 87; Phys Therapy.

STRASISER, STACY; North Star HS; Hooversville, PA; (3); FCA; Ski Clb; Varsity Clb; Sec Sr Cls; Var L Bsktbl; Var Score Keeper; Var Score Keeper; Var L Vllybl; Cit Awd; Hon Roll; All Cnty Vllybll & Bsktbll 2nd Tms 86-87; Girls Bsktbll Tournmnt All Tourney Tm 86; Phys Thrpy.

STRASSER, DEBRA; Hempfield SR HS; Greensburg, PA; (3); Trs Pres FBLA; GAA; Pep Clb; Var Powder Puff Ftbl; Var Socr; Var Wt Lftg; DCM; Bus Mgt.

STRASSER, GARRETT; Cathedral Prep; Erie, PA; (3); 43/193; Church Yth Grp; Im Bsktbl; Hon Roll; MVP Bsktbl 87.

STRATFORD, CAROLYN; Lake-Lehman HS; Harveys Lake, PA; (3); Key Clb; Letterman Clb; Ski Clb; Var Capt Cheerleading; Var L Trk; L Stat Wrstlng; Hon Roll; Arch Drftg.

STRAUB, CYNTHIA; Danville SR HS; Danville, PA; (2); Bsktbl; Bowling; Sftbl; Hon Roll; Outstndng Plyr Of Yr Trophy-Girls Sftbll Tm 87; Phys Ed Tchr.

STRAUB, JULIE; Elk County Christian HS; St Marys, PA; (4); 1/80; Pep Clb; Varsity Clb; Yrbk Stf; Sec Soph Cls; Pres VP Stu Cncl; Var Capt Bsktbl; Crs Cntry; Trk; Vllybl; Hon Roll; Schlr/Athltc Awd 86; Ntl Army Rsrv Schlr/Athltc Awd 86; St Vincent Acad Schlrshp 86; Math.

STRAUB, LINDA; Fort Le Boeuf HS; Erie, PA; (4); Camera Clb; Hosp Aide; Model UN; Yrbk Stf; Rep Jr Cls; VP Sr Cls; Var Trk; Var Vllybl; High Hon Roll; Hon Roll; Natl Hon Roll 86-87; Chsn Spkr Baccalauriate Serv Grat 87; U Pf Pittsburgh; Oral Hygn.

STRAUB, STACEY; Tri-Valley HS; Klingerstown, PA; (3); Church Yth Grp; SADD; Band; Concert Band; Mrchg Band; Yrbk Stf; Capt Cheerleading; Var Sftbl; Pre-Med.

STRAUB, TAMMY; Elk County Christian HS; St Marys, PA; (4); 7/79; Varsity Clb; Yrbk Stf; Rep Stu Cncl; Bsktbl; Trk; NEDT Awd; Duquesne U; Pharm.

STRAUCH, ALLEN; Benton Area HS; Benton, PA; (2); Church Yth Grp; Off Stu Cncl; JV Bsbl; Var Socr; Hon Roll.

STRAUCH, RICHARD; West Scranton HS; Scranton, PA; (3); 65/273; Ski Clb; JV Bsbl; L Var Golf; Hon Roll; NHS; Penn ST; Arch.

STRAUSBAUGH, AMY JO; Manheim Central HS; Manheim, PA; (3); Sec Church Yth Grp; Pres VP 4-H; FHA; FNA; Hosp Aide; Spanish Clb; Chorus; Yrbk Stf; JV Fld Hcky; 4-H Awd; Frshmn Hm Ecs Awd 85; Med Careers Clb Awd 86; St Jsph Hsp-Schl; Neontl Spclst.

STRAUSE, STEFANIE; Oley Valley HS; Douglassville, PA; (3); 16/143; Pep Clb; Teachers Aide; School Musical; Stage Crew; Stu Cncl; Fld Hcky; Sftbl; Hon Roll; Prfct Atten Awd; Stu Exchg-To New Milford CT 87; Phy Ed.

STRAUSS, LESLIE; Northern Lebanon HS; Jonestown, PA; (4); 25/166; Sec Church Yth Grp; FCA; Pres 4-H; Model UN; Band; School Play; Nwsp Rptr; Bsktbl; Powder Puff Ftbl; Lebannon Vly Coll; Psych.

STRAUSS, MARY GRACE; Center HS; Aliquippa, PA; (4); 18/186; Latin Clb; School Musical; Yrbk Ed-Chief; Trs Soph Cls; Capt Twrlr; High Hon Roll; NHS; Cntr Cvc Wmns Clb Grl Of Mnth 87; Hnr Grad Of Cntr HS 87; Gftd & Tlntd Prog; Carnegie-Mellon U; Indstrl Mgmt.

STRAUSS, NAN; Shady Side Acad; Pittsburgh, PA; (3); Dance Clb; French Clb; SADD; Teachers Aide; Chorus; School Play; Nwsp Stf; Ed Yrbk Rptr; Lit Mag; Hon Roll; Lbrl Arts.

STRAUSS, STEVE; Panther Valley HS; Nesquehoning, PA; (1); 6/127; Church Yth Grp; Rep Frsh Cls; Var JV Bsbl; JV Bsktbl; High Hon Roll; AMVETS Awd 87.

STRAUSSER, BETH; Phoenixville Area HS; Phoenixville, PA; (4); 11/210; Key Clb; Chorus; School Musical; School Play; Swing Chorus; Mgr(s); Trk; High Hon Roll; Kiwanis Awd; NHS; Bio & Chr Awd; Plce Asso Awd; Bryn Mawr Coll; Lib Arts.

STRAUSSER, DAFFNEY K; Millville HS; Bloomsburg, PA; (4); 30/71; Church Yth Grp; Spanish Clb; Chorus; School Play; Yrbk Stf; JV Fld Hcky; High Hon Roll; Hon Roll; RN.

STRAUSSER, PAMELA; Southern Columbia Area HS; Elysburg, PA; (3); Key Clb; Ski Clb; Varsity Clb; VP Soph Cls; JV Var Cheerleading; Trk; High Hon Roll; Hon Roll; NHS; Frng Lang.

STRAW, LISA; West York SR HS; York, PA; (2); 6/209; Drama Clb; French Clb; Varsity Clb; Mrchg Band; Symp Band; Nwsp Stf; Off Soph Cls; JV L Bsktbl; Var JV Trk; High Hon Roll; Pres Acdmc Ftnss Awd 87; CTY Tlnt Srch Johns Hpkns U 86-87; Band Lttr 87.

STRAWBERRY II, DORETHEA M; Creative And Performing Arts; Philadelphia, PA; (4); #16 In Class; Debate Tm; Drama Clb; School Play; Stage Crew; Variety Show; Rep Frsh Cls; Rep Soph Cls; Rep Jr Cls; Rep Sr Cls; Trs Stu Cncl; Ath Awd Table Ten; Merit Awd Hnr Rl; Prfct Atten Awd; Stu Cncl Awd; Sftbl Club Awd; Merit Awd Hnr Rl; Edinboro U; Bus.

STRAWSER, LISA; East Juniata HS; Mcalisterville, PA; (3); VP Church Yth Grp; SADD; Band; Sec Jr Cls; Fld Hcky; Trk; High Hon Roll; NHS; Chess Clb; Varsity Clb; Mdrn Music Mstrs; Outstndng Band Stu; Sprts Med.

STRAYER, CHRISTINA; Montgomery Area JR-SR HS; Allenwood, PA; (4); 2/62; Sec Yrbk Stf; Cit Awd; High Hon Roll; NHS; Sal; Montgomery Bus & Prof Womens Civic Club Awd 86-87; Outstndg Bus Educ Stu 86-87; Scl Stds Awd 86-87; Bible Educ.

STRAYER, LANCE; Upper Dauphin Area HS; Gratz, PA; (4); 5/108; Chess Clb; Rep Frsh Cls; Hon Roll; NHS; Stu Cncl Awd 87; Pres Acad Fit Awd 87; Rensselaer Polytech; Engrng.

STRAYER, SHELLEY; Chestnut Ridge SR HS; Schellsburg, PA; (4); 15/142; Office Aide; SADD; Teachers Aide; Band; Concert Band; Mrchg Band; Pep Band; Nwsp Rptr; Nwsp Stf; Stu Cncl; U Pittsbrgh Johnstwn; Elem Ed.

STRAZDUS, PAUL; Dallas SR HS; Dallas, PA; (3); Chess Clb; Ski Clb; Band; Concert Band; Jazz Band; Mrchg Band; School Musical; Var Bsbl; JV Golf; Hon Roll; Schlrshp Kings Coll 87; Engrng.

STREATOR, STEPHEN; Du Bois Area HS; Penfield, PA; (3); 30/350; Boy Scts; Church Yth Grp; Varsity Clb; Var L Crs Cntry; Var L Trk; Hon Roll; Crntn Crt 86-87; Sprts Med.

STRECK, GARY; Lock Haven SR HS; Lock Haven, PA; (3); Computer Clb; French Clb; SADD; 2nd, 3rd Pl Rbbns Frnch Compttns 87; Comp Anlyst.

STRECKEISEN, TARA; Lawrence Cnty Vocational Tech Schl; Ellwood City, PA; (3); 17/272; Church Yth Grp; DECA; Library Aide; Teachers Aide; Y-Teens; Chorus; Church Choir; Nwsp Stf; Hon Roll; Prfct Atten Awd; Early Childhood Educ.

STREET, NANCY; Archbishop Prendergast HS; Folcroft, PA; (3); 68/327; Hosp Aide; Stage Crew; Rep Frsh Cls; Nrsg.

STREETER, ERIC; Oil City SR HS; Oil City, PA; (3); 22/218; Pres Church Yth Grp; Math Tm; Rep Stu Cncl.

STREETT, KAREN; Kennard-Dale HS; Fawn Grove, PA; (4); 8/113; Varsity Clb; Chorus; Church Choir; School Musical; Yrbk Stf; Var Capt Crs Cntry; Var L Trk; Hon Roll; Lion Awd; NHS; Crs Cntry Schlrshp IUP 87; 3rd ST Crs Cntry 86; Lioness Clb Schlrshp 87; IN U PA; Bio.

STREINER, DEENA; Hopewell Area HS; Aliquippa, PA; (3); 4/268; Exploring; French Clb; High Hon Roll; NHS; Acad All Amer, Ntl Scndry Ed Cncl 87; Intl Order Of Rnbw For Grls Wrthy Advsr 86; Dntstry.

STREIT, TRACEY; Bishop Mc Devitt HS; Philadelphia, PA; (3); 4/349; Church Yth Grp; Drama Clb; Hosp Aide; Model UN; School Play; Yrbk Stf; Hon Roll; NHS; Ntl Merit SF; Assn Catholic Teachers Scholar.

STRELECKIS, MARY; Villa Maria Acad; Exton, PA; (4); 8/98; Church Yth Grp; Science Clb; Chorus; Madrigals; School Musical; Bsktbl; JV Lcrss; Im Tennis; NHS; Diocesan Scholar; Cmnctns.

STRELECKY, BETH; Upper Perkiomen HS; Pennsburg, PA; (4); 30/229; Cmnty Wkr; Yrbk Stf; Powder Puff Ftbl; Sftbl; Hon Roll; DE Vly Sci Fair Hon Ment 85; Montgomery Sci Fair 2nd Pl 85; Perkiomen Bus & Prof Womens Club Schlrhp; Moravian Coll; Math Tchr.

STREMIC, DARLENE; Bensalem HS; Bensalem, PA; (2); Key Clb; JV Bsktbl; JV Sftbl; Hon Roll; NHS; Math.

STREMMEL, DAVID; Bishop Mc Cort HS; Johnstown, PA; (2); German Clb; Math Clb; Ski Clb; Varsity Clb; Bsktbl; Ftbl; Wt Lftg; High Hon Roll; Hon Roll; Pres Frsh Cls.

STRENK, JEFFREY; Archbishop Ryan HS For Boys; Philadelphia, PA; (2); 98/349; Civic Clb; JV Socr; Hon Roll; Hstry Acdmc Achvt Awd 86; Temple U; Cmmrcl Art.

STRENSKE, SUSAN; Belle Vernon Area HS; Belle Vernon, PA; (3); Sec 4-H; Library Aide; Pep Clb; Ski Clb; Band; Yrbk Stf; Stu Cncl; Hon Roll; NHS.

STREPPA, MARY JO; West Allegheny HS; Coraopolis, PA; (2); 1/200; VP Chorus; Church Choir; Concert Band; Jazz Band; Mrchg Band; School Play; Nwsp Rptr; Pres Soph Cls; High Hon Roll; Pres Jr NHS; Mid-Atltnc Chmpn Chrs 87; U Of Pittsburgh; Psych.

STREUBERT, LAUREN; Liberty HS; Bethlehem, PA; (3); 43/430; Trs German Clb; Band; Var Fld Hcky; Hon Roll; Hosp Aide; Ski Clb; Concert Band; Mrchg Band; Vrsty Awd For Fld Hcky 87; Bio.

STREYLE, JENNIFER; Ambridge Area HS; Freedom, PA; (3); German Clb; Band; Mrchg Band; Orch; School Musical; Symp Band; Off Jr Cls; High Hon Roll; Hon Roll; Prfct Atten Awd; Dist V Band Fest 87; Beaver Cnty Hnrs Band 87; Elem Educ.

STREZNETCKY, JEFFREY; Blue Ridge HS; New Milford, PA; (3); Bus Mgmt.

STRICKLAND, COREY; Owen J Roberts HS; Pottstown, PA; (4); 1/270; Pres Church Yth Grp; JA; Math Tm; Quiz Bowl; Band; Church Choir; Concert Band; Drm & Bgl; Mrchg Band; School Musical; Penn St U; Mlclr Bio.

STRICKLAND, CYNTHIA; Eisenhower HS; Russell, PA; (3); VP Church Yth Grp; Trs Drama Clb; Office Aide; Chorus; Stage Crew; Yrbk Stf; Trs Sr Cls; Sec Bsktbl; Hon Roll; Mst Outstndng Techncl Contrbtn 85.

STRICKLAND, ERICA; Trinity Christian HS; Murrysville, PA; (3); 4/14; Church Yth Grp; Drama Clb; 4-H; Capt Pep Clb; Chorus; School Play; Yrbk Sprt Ed; Yrbk Stf; Trs Frsh Cls; Trs Soph Cls; Arch.

STRICKLER, ERIC; Elizabethtown Area HS; Elizabethtown, PA; (3); Boy Scts; Church Yth Grp; FFA; Spanish Clb; Church Choir; 1st Pl In FFA Cnty Wldlf Cont 83; 10th Pl In FFA St Wldlf Cont 85; Messiah Coll; Bio Ed.

STRICKLER, JOYCE S; Cardinal Dougherty HS; Philadelphia, PA; (2); 129/667.

STRIEFSKY, SUSAN; Carbondale Area HS; Simpson, PA; (3); FBLA; Var Bsktbl; Hon Roll.

STRIGHT, LISA; Academy HS; Erie, PA; (3); 13/226; Cmnty Wkr; JA; Stu Cncl; Hon Roll; Penn ST; Engrng.

STRIKER, ERIK; Yough SR HS; Sutersville, PA; (3); 67/283; Spanish Clb; Hon Roll.

STRINE, JESSIE; Shikellamy HS; Sunbury, PA; (3); Church Yth Grp; SADD; Y-Teens; Band; Chorus; Mrchg Band; Yrbk Phtg; Yrbk Stf; Im Wt Lftg; Hon Roll; Psycht.

STRINE, KIRK; Northeastern HS; Dover, PA; (3); Chorus; Yrbk Stf; Trs Jr Cls; Trs Sr Cls; Var Tennis; Hon Roll; NHS; Stu Of Mnth 87; Bus.

STRINE, MARK; West York Area SR HS; York, PA; (3); Letterman Clb; Varsity Clb; Bsbl; Ftbl; Wt Lftg; Wrstlng; Hon Roll; Mst Vlbl Offnsv Lnmn 86; Chem.

STRINGER, PENNEY; Governor Mifflin HS; Reading, PA; (4); 2/260; Church Choir; Orch; Pres Jr Cls; VP Trs Stu Cncl; Bsktbl; Capt Tennis; Var Trk; High Hon Roll; Sec NHS; Ntl Merit Ltr; Wellesley Coll Awd 86; Pres Acad Ftnss Awd 87; Maximus Unified Pt Awd 87; Cornell U; Pre-Med.

STRINGERT, MICHAEL; Commodore Perry HS; Clarks Mills, PA; (4); 5/65; FTA; Acpl Chr; Chorus; School Play; Yrbk Stf; Hon Roll; Slippery Rock U; Elem Teachr.

STRINGFELLOW, BRENT E; Selinsgrove Area HS; Selinsgrove, PA; (3); 7/237; Am Leg Boys St; Stage Crew; Yrbk Ed-Chief; NHS; Nwsp Rptr; Rep Frsh Cls; Rep Soph Cls; Rep Jr Cls; Rep Sr Cls; Hon Roll; Law.

STRITTMATTER, DEANNA; Bishop Guilfoyle HS; Altoona, PA; (3); Church Yth Grp; Hon Roll; PA; Psych.

STRITTMATTER, KIM; Trinity Area HS; Eighty Four, PA; (4); Art Clb; Camera Clb; Dance Clb; Drama Clb; German Clb; Girl Scts; Pep Clb; SADD; School Play; Cheerleading; Arch.

STRITTMATTER, LESLIE; Cambria Heights HS; Patton, PA; (3); 11/187; Q&S; Ski Clb; SADD; School Play; Yrbk Ed-Chief; Sec Soph Cls; Sec Jr Cls; Hon Roll; NHS; NEDT Awd; Accntnt.

STRIZZI, JON; Bishop Mc Devitt HS; Harrisburg, PA; (3); 1/236; Am Leg Boys St; Boy Scts; Drama Clb; Band; Drm Mjr(t); School Play; Yrbk Stf; NHS; NEDT Awd; Schlstc Achvt & Cmnty Invlvmnt Holy Cross Awd & Highest Chem II Avg 87; US Army Cert Of Achvt 86; Carnegie; Aeronautical Engrng.

STROBEL, ERIC; Hempfield HS; Lancaster, PA; (3); 30/430; Trs Key Clb; Var Diving; Var Socr; Engr.

STROBEL, JOANNE; Liberty HS; Bethlehem, PA; (4); 64/520; Band; Rep Frsh Cls; Sftbl; Mgr Wrstlng; Lock Haven U; Intl Stds.

STROBEL, PATRICK DAMIAN; Butler SR HS; East Butler, PA; (3); Boys Clb Am; Boy Scts; Church Yth Grp; Civic Clb; Office Aide; Teachers Aide; Band; Church Choir; School Play; Variety Show; Daubenspect Awd-Bsbl, All Vrsty Wrstlr 84; Rcrtr Awd-Boy Scts 83; Bst Sprtsmn-Bsbl 85; USAF; Atty.

STROCKOZ, SCOTT; Pius X HS; Pen Argyl, PA; (4); 6/35; Scholastic Bowl; Varsity Clb; VP Stu Cncl; Var Capt Bsbl; Var Capt Bsktbl; Var Ftbl; Hon Roll; NHS; Ntl Merit Ltr; MVP-BSKTBL 84-86; Bloomsburg U; Pltcl Sci.

STROFFOLINO, PHILIP; Cardinal O Hara HS; Media, PA; (3); 12/719; Chess Clb; Computer Clb; German Clb; Math Tm; JV L Wrstlng; Ntl Merit SF; PA Gov Schl Sci 87; DE Vly Sci Fair 1st Pl 87; Pres Mensa Club 87; MA Inst Tech; Comp Pgrmr.

STROH, NED; West Hazleton HS; Sugarloaf, PA; (2); L Golf; High Hon Roll; Ski Clb; Stage Crew; Var Stu Cncl; Var Bsktbl; 1st Acdmc Hnrs 86-87; Vrsty Glf Tm Schulkill Leag Champs 86; Penn ST; Pharm.

STROH, REBECCA; Bensalem HS; Bensalem, PA; (3); French Clb; Office Aide; Band; Color Guard; Concert Band; Drm Mjr(t); Mrchg Band; School Musical; Diving; Swmmng; Pre-Med.

STROHECKER, LYNN; Slippery Rock Area HS; Slippery Rock, PA; (4); 17/176; Church Yth Grp; Girl Scts; Chorus; Mrchg Band; Pep Band; God Cntry Awd; Hon Roll; NHS; Presdntl Acadc Ftns Awd 87; 3rd Pl-Btlr Cnty Cnsrvtn Schl 85; Grl Sct Slvr Awd 83; Penn ST U; Sci.

STROHECKER, PHILIP; Mohawk HS; New Castle, PA; (4); 1/137; Latin Clb; Concert Band; Jazz Band; Mrchg Band; Pep Band; School Musical; High Hon Roll; NHS; Val; Band; Top Stu Of Mohwk 86; NEDT Cert Mrt 84; Wstmnster Hnrs Band Cert Of Mrt 87; Youngstown ST U; Cmptr Sci.

STROHM, TAMMIE; Altoona Area HS; Altoona, PA; (3); Key Clb; Ski Clb; Spanish Clb; SADD; Sec Jr Cls; Var Crs Cntry; Var Trk; Jr NHS; NEDT Awd.

STROHMAN, JAMES W; Hollidaysburg Area SR HS; Duncansville, PA; (4); 1/351; German Clb; Math Tm; Science Clb; Band; Jazz Band; Hon Roll; NHS; Ntl Merit SF; NEDT Awd; Rensselaer Math & Sci Awd 85-6; Engrng.

STROJEK, LESLIE; Ambridge Area HS; Ambridge, PA; (4); Pep Clb; Red Cross Aide; Spanish Clb; Band; Concert Band; Mrchg Band; Off Soph Cls; Off Jr Cls; Off Sr Cls; Hon Roll; Duquesne U; Teaching.

STROKA, CONNIE; Tunkhannock HS; Tunkhannock, PA; (4); 34/289; VP Key Clb; Ski Clb; Stat Bsktbl; Var Fld Hcky; Hon Roll; NHS; Penn ST.

STROM, JEFFREY A; Southern Lehigh HS; Center Valley, PA; (4); 13/230; Chess Clb; JA; Scholastic Bowl; Ed Yrbk Stf; Off Sr Cls; High Hon Roll; Hon Roll; NHS; Ntl Merit SF; Schltc Art Comp Hnrb Mntn 86; Physcs Olympcs 2nd Pl Tm 1st Fermi Qstns 86; Math.

STROMPLE JR, RONALD; Central Catholic HS; Pittsburgh, PA; (2); 128/331; Church Yth Grp; Dance Clb; Spanish Clb; Chorus; Concert Band; Im Bsktbl; JV Crs Cntry; Var Ice Hcky; Im Powder Puff Ftbl; JV Trk; Duquesne U; Sls Rep.

STRONG, EDWARD; Penns Manor HS; Penn Run, PA; (4); 4/93; Chess Clb; Church Yth Grp; Varsity Clb; Stage Crew; Trs Sr Cls; Trk; High Hon Roll; NHS; NEDT Awd; Pres Schlr; Well Rounded Stu Awd 87; U Pittsburgh; Pharmacy.

STRONG, KIM; Punxsutawney HS; Mahaffey, PA; (3); 5/283; Church Yth Grp; French Clb; FBLA; Band; Chorus; Concert Band; Mrchg Band; Pep Band; Stat Trk; Hon Roll; FBLA 1st Data Proc 86; Messiah Coll; Accntng.

STRONG, SCOTT; Elizabethtown Area HS; Elizabethtown, PA; (3); 14/224; Band; Concert Band; Jazz Band; Mrchg Band; Pep Band; Stage Crew; Golf; NHS; Bus.

STRONY, JENNIFER; Bishop Ohara HS; Olyphant, PA; (2); 2/127; Latin Clb; Spanish Clb; Church Choir; Rep Stu Cncl; Capt Cheerleading; Sftbl; High Hon Roll; Fl H S Schlrp 85.

STRONY, RONALD; Bishop Ohara HS; Olyphant, PA; (4); 8/119; Drama Clb; Pres Latin Clb; Ski Clb; School Musical; Rep Pres Stu Cncl; Bsbl; High Hon Roll; NHS; Acad Schlrshp Gannon U 87; Gannon U; Family Med.

STROPE, ANGIE; Jefferson-Morgan HS; Waynesburg, PA; (4); 15/95; Church Yth Grp; Cmnty Wkr; 4-H; French Clb; Intnl Clb; Color Guard; Yrbk Stf; High Hon Roll; Hon Roll; Gregg Shrthnd Awd 86; Mdn Schl Of Alld Hlth; Med Asst.

STROPE, BOB; Mc Guffey HS; Taylorstown, PA; (3); Church Yth Grp; French Clb; Ski Clb; Var L Bsktbl; Var L Ftbl; Powder Puff Ftbl; Var L Tennis; Wt Lftg; High Hon Roll; NHS; Stu Recogntn Awd 84-86.

STROPE, REBECCA; E L Meyers HS; Wiles Barre, PA; (4); Church Yth Grp; Cmnty Wkr; Drama Clb; Girl Scts; Spanish Clb; SADD; Chorus; Church Choir; Orch; School Musical; Wrtng.

STROSCIO, MARIA; Bishop Mc Cort HS; Conemaugh, PA; (2); 56/163; Cmnty Wkr; Spanish Clb; Socr; High Hon Roll; Hon Roll; Spanish NHS; Cathlc Dghtrs Amerca 86; Indiana U Of PA; Law.

STROSNIDER, CHARLENE; Mapletown JR SR HS; Dilliner, PA; (3); FHA; FNA; VICA; Nwsp Stf; Vllybl; High Hon Roll; Hon Roll; LPN.

STROUD, AMY; Burgettstown Area JR SR HS; Avella, PA; (4); 8/135; Science Clb; Ski Clb; Band; Mrchg Band; Symp Band; Yrbk Stf; High Hon Roll; NHS; Ntl Merit Schol; PA ST U; Nrsng.

STROUP, CHRISTOPHER; Williams Valley HS; Williamstown, PA; (4); 19/97; Pep Clb; Chorus; Church Choir; School Musical; School Play; Swing Chorus; Var Capt Ftbl; Score Keeper; Wt Lftg; Hon Roll; Mary Margaret Nestor Fndtn Schlrshp, John Travitz Schlrshp, Singers Awd Chorus 87; Shippensburg U; Math.

STROUP, CINDY; Middleburg HS; Richfield, PA; (3); Church Yth Grp; 4-H; FFA; Key Clb; Ski Clb; SADD; Band; Church Choir; Flag Corp; Nwsp Stf; Hmcmg Ct 86; Qn Hrts Ct 87; Sci Hghst Grd Avg Yr 84; Messiah Coll.

STROUP, HARRY; Bucktail Area HS; North Bend, PA; (2); Bsktbl; Tennis; Hon Roll.

STROUP, JEFFREY; Williams Valley JR-SR HS; Williamstown, PA; (3); 39/95; Aud/Vis; Boy Scts; Chorus; Church Choir; Mrchg Band; School Musical; Symp Band; Yrbk Ed-Chief; Yrbk Stf; Prfct Atten Awd; Accntng.

STROUP, MICHELE; Montgomery HS; Allenwood, PA; (3); Trs Church Yth Grp; 4-H; FBLA; Yrbk Stf; Im Bsktbl; L Trk; Hon Roll; Typng Awd 87; Bus.

STROUP, WENDY; Newport HS; Newport, PA; (3); 32/126; Church Yth Grp; Sec 4-H; Red Cross Aide; Band; Chorus; Concert Band; Mrchg Band; School Musical; Yrbk Stf; JV Bsktbl; Geisinger Med Ctr; Nrsng.

STROUSE, GAIL; Quaker Valley SR HS; Fair Oaks, PA; (2); Art Clb; Exploring; JA; Chorus; School Musical; Lit Mag; Hon Roll; Eqstrn Ther Handicapped Vol 86-87; Sci.

STROUSE, KENNY; Penns Valley Area HS; Centre Hall, PA; (2); Church Yth Grp; 4-H; FFA; Church Choir; JV Ftbl; 4-H Awd; Green Hand Awd & Star Green Hand Awd FFA 89; Pennsylvania ST U; Soil Anlys.

STRUCKMANN, HELEN; Ridley HS; Folsom, PA; (4); 58/407; Drama Clb; Thesps; Chorus; Mrchg Band; School Musical; School Play; Symp Band; Hon Roll; Pres Acad Fit Awd 87; Bst Actress Bucks Cnty Playhouse Comptn 87; Outstndng Versitilty Actng 87; Westchester U; Psych.

STRUZZI, MELISSA; Penn Trafford HS; Jeannette, PA; (3); Sec Cmnty Wkr; FBLA; Hosp Aide; SADD; Im Ftbl; Var JV Trk; High Hon Roll; Hon Roll; Point Park Coll; Jrnlsm.

STUART, JANELLE; Butler SR HS; Butler, PA; (4); 36/755; Library Aide; Office Aide; SADD; Im Vllybl; High Hon Roll; Hon Roll; Brd Trusts Acdmc Schlrshp Cert Acdmc Excllnc 87; Butler Cnty Cmnty Schlrshp 86-87; Butler County CC; Bus Admin.

STUBENHOFER, CHERYL; Villa Maria Acad; Erie, PA; (3); 58/148; Model UN; Pep Clb; Science Clb; Socr; Hon Roll; NHS; Lang Schlrshp 86; Academic All Amer 87; Bio.

STUCK, BETH; Carmichaels Area HS; Carmichaels, PA; (3); 9/122; Spanish Clb; Church Choir; Concert Band; Mrchg Band; Stu Cncl; Var Capt Bsktbl; Golf; High Hon Roll; NHS; Alderson-Broddus Coll; Music Ed.

STUCK III, WILLIAM; Chief Logan HS; Yeagertown, PA; (4); 40/204; Boy Scts; Varsity Clb; Variety Show; Mgr Ftbl; Var Mgr(s); Cit Awd; God Cntry Awd; High Hon Roll; Hon Roll; Jack Pap Bennet Awd 87; Millersvl U; Indstrl Arts.

STUCKEY, HEATHER; Annville-Cleona HS; Annville, PA; (4); 17/112; Pres FBLA; Office Aide; SADD; Varsity Clb; Nwsp Stf; Yrbk Stf; Var Capt Cheerleading; NHS; Church Yth Grp; Altruism Awd 87; Harrisburg CC; Exectv Sec.

STUCKEY JR, TOM; Newport HS; Newport, PA; (4); Varsity Clb; Var L Bsbl; Var L Ftbl; Im Wt Lftg; Hon Roll; Shippensburg U; Bus Mgmt.

STUDDERS, COLLEEN; James M Coughlin HS; Wilkes Barre, PA; (3); 55/374; Hosp Aide; Chorus; Hon Roll; Jr NHS; NHS; Flag Corp; PA ST U; Math Tchr.

STUDENT, JOSEPH; West Hazleton HS; West Hazleton, PA; (4); 4/224; Latin Clb; Scholastic Bowl; SADD; Nwsp Ed-Chief; Rep Sr Cls; NHS; Voice Dem Awd; High Hon Roll; Hon Roll; Prsdntl Clssrm; PA JR Acad Of Sci; Cmmnty Area Nw Dvlpmnt Orgnztn; Poly Sci.

STUEBGEN, GAYLE L; Penn Hills HS; Verona, PA; (3); Church Yth Grp; JA; Spanish Clb; Acpl Chr; Church Choir; Hon Roll; Chorus; School Musical; Nwsp Rptr; Gevena; Pre-Mnstry.

STUFFT, LAURA; North Star HS; Boswell, PA; (2); 59/135; Pres Church Yth Grp; FCA; SADD; Band; Concert Band; Mrchg Band; Yrbk Stf; VP Soph Cls; JV Capt Cheerleading; Cit Awd; Tribune Democrat Wrtg Cont 86-87; Polit Sci.

STULL, ALISON R; Central Dauphin HS; Harrisburg, PA; (3); 93/401; Am Leg Aux Girls St; SADD; Teachers Aide; Trs Chorus; Trs Jr Cls; Pres Stu Cncl; Stat Swmmng; Key Clb; School Musical; School Play; Sngrs; Albright; Corp Cmncnts.

STULL, BRIAN; Gettysburg SR HS; Gettysburg, PA; (2); Church Yth Grp; L Trk; Wt Lftg; Hon Roll; Arch.

STULL, DEBORAH; Central HS; Philadelphia, PA; (2); Hosp Aide; Latin Clb; Mrchg Band; Var L Swmmng; High Hon Roll.

STULL, GREGORY; Geibel HS; Scottdale, PA; (3); Church Yth Grp; Drama Clb; Pep Clb; Church Choir; School Musical; School Play; Lit Mag; Marine Bio.

STULL, JAY; Leechburg Area HS; Leechburg, PA; (2); Church Yth Grp; Exploring; Vllybl; Penn ST; Bus.

STULL, KIMBERLY; Leechburg Area HS; Leechburg, PA; (3); Drama Clb; Library Aide; Nwsp Stf; Cheerleading; Sftbl; High Hon Roll; Hon Roll; Prfct Atten Awd; Secy.

STULL, MONICA; Geibel HS; Scottdale, PA; (4); 6/82; Drama Clb; Pep Clb; Spanish Clb; School Musical; School Play; Stage Crew; Lit Mag; High Hon Roll; Pres Schlr; Spanish NHS; Frgn Lang Awd Natl; St Vincent Coll.

STULL, TERESA; Freeport SR HS; Freeport, PA; (3); Church Yth Grp; Drama Clb; Office Aide; Med Asst.

STUMNPF, SCOTT; Cedar Crest HS; Lebanon, PA; (3); 29/342; German Clb; Rep Jr Cls; Im Vllybl; JV Wrstlng; High Hon Roll; Hon Roll; NHS; Booster Club Awd Acad Merit 86-87; Comp Sci.

STUMP, BART; Dallastown Area HS; Dallastown, PA; (3); Boy Scts; Mrchg Band; Nwsp Stf; Yrbk Bus Mgr; Var L Trk; God Cntry Awd; Hon Roll; Aud/Vis; Exploring; Concert Band; Eagl Awd Boy Sct Amer; Bio.

STUMP, CHRISTINE; Danville SR HS; Danville, PA; (2); 42/165; Concert Band; Mrchg Band; Frsh Cls; Bsktbl; Fld Hcky; Trk; High Hon Roll; Pres Schlr; Ski Clb; Soroptimist; Ntl Wnr Piano Aud 87; Hnrs Div Am Coll Musician 86 & 87; Grnd Lctr St PA Intntl Rainbow Grls 87; Physcl Thrpy.

STUMP, DAVID; Danville Area HS; Danville, PA; (3); Boy Scts; Concert Band; Mrchg Band; Rep Frsh Cls; Rep Soph Cls; L Bsbl; JV Socr; L Wrstlng; God Cntry Awd; Millersville U; Brdcstng.

STUMP, DENINE; Bangor Area HS; Bangor, PA; (3); 9/205; Sec Church Yth Grp; Pep Clb; Color Guard; Mrchg Band; Lit Mag; Stu Cncl; High Hon Roll; Jr NHS; Sec NHS; Scrtry Eco Clb 87-88; Phys Thrpy.

STUMP, KIMBERLY A; Schuylkill Valley HS; Leesport, PA; (4); 9/132; JA; SADD; Chorus; Color Guard; School Musical; Nwsp Rptr; Yrbk Stf; Trk; Vllybl; Hon Roll; Ursinus Coll; Pediatrics.

STUMP, PAULA; Belle Vernon Area HS; Belle Vernon, PA; (3); French Clb; Concert Band; Mrchg Band; Yrbk Stf; Sec Jr Cls; JV Powder Puff Ftbl; Hon Roll; Jr NHS; Engl.

STUMP, SHARON; Octorara Area HS; Atglen, PA; (3); 28/157; Pres VP 4-H; Spanish Clb; 4-H Awd; Hon Roll; Acad All Amer 86-87.

STUMPF, BRENDA; St Paul Cathedral HS; Pittsburgh, PA; (4); Computer Clb; Drama Clb; Intnl Clb; Science Clb; Teachers Aide; School Play; Yrbk Ed-Chief; Hon Roll; Pres NHS; Most Outstndng Comptr Stu 86; Supr-Pittsburgh Piano Tchrs Piano Evaltn 85; Supr Ntl Piano Evltn 86; IUP; Music Educ.

STUMPF, KRISTY; Bensalem HS; Bensalem, PA; (2); Church Yth Grp; Teachers Aide; Chorus; Church Choir; Swmmng; High Hon Roll; Hon Roll; NHS; Sec Ed.

STUMPP, KELLY A; Nativity B V M HS; Pottsville, PA; (1); 12/94; NFL; JV Vllybl; Hon Roll; Schlrshp Fund 86; Intl Frgn Lang Awds 87; Notre Dame U; Scl Svcs.

STUPI, JANE; Mechanicsburg Area SR HS; Mechanicsburg, PA; (4); 58/303; Flag Corp; Stat Swmmng; PA ST U; Engrng.

STURDEVANT, KAMIE; Sheffield Area JR/Sr HS; Sheffield, PA; (2); SADD; Varsity Clb; Concert Band; Jazz Band; Mrchg Band; Symp Band; Var L Bsktbl; Var L Sftbl; Var L Vllybl; High Hon Roll.

STURDEVANT, SHARON; Fort Le Boeuf HS; Waterford, PA; (4); 10/167; Girl Scts; Model UN; Band; Jazz Band; School Musical; Yrbk Ed-Chief; Yrbk Stf; Sec Sr Cls; High Hon Roll; Sec NHS; Outstndng Music Stu 87; HOBY Ldrshp Sem 85; PA ST U Behrend; Lbrl Arts.

STURGILL II, ROBERT E; Solanco HS; Drumore, PA; (3); Var L Bsbl; Var L Ftbl; Varsity Clb; Hon Roll; Htl/Rstrnt Mgmt.

STURM, CHARLES J; Central Catholic HS; Pittsburgh, PA; (2); French Clb; Science Clb; Wrstlng; DAR Awd; Hon Roll; Ping Pong; PJAS 85-86; Duquesne U; Law.

STURM, KAREN; Susquehanna Township HS; Harrisburg, PA; (2); Color Guard; Concert Band; Orch.

STURM, KEN; Strath Haven HS; Swarthmore, PA; (3); Im Socr; High Hon Roll; Hon Roll.

STUTTS, CATHERINE; Canon Mc Millan HS; Canonsburg, PA; (2); 1/378; Church Yth Grp; Exploring; French Clb; School Play; Nwsp Ed-Chief; Nwsp Rptr; High Hon Roll; 1st Pl Rgnls Compttn Natl Sci Olympd Rcks & Fssls 87; Pres Acdmc Ftns Awd 86; Drama, Sci, Frnch Awd 86; Sci.

STUTZ, MATT; Butler Area HS; East Butler, PA; (2); Hon Roll; Cir Cndtng & Rfrgrtn.

STUTZMAN, BRUCE; Tri Valley HS; Hegins, PA; (3); 17/76; Computer Clb; German Clb; Math Tm; Band; Concert Band; Jazz Band; Mrchg Band; Rep Stu Cncl; Hon Roll; County Band 85, 86, & 87; Engineering.

STUZMAN, PATRICIA; Archbishop Prendergast HS; Fernwood, PA; (3); 86/327; Church Yth Grp; Girl Scts; Orch; School Musical; School Play; Advertising.

STYBORSKI, CARLA; Meadville Area SR HS; Meadville, PA; (4); Church Yth Grp; French Clb; JA; Ski Clb; Spanish Clb; Color Guard; Mrchg Band; School Play; Yrbk Stf; Hon Roll; IN U Of PA; Crmnl Jstc.

STYCHE, BRIAN; Elizabeth Forward HS; Buena Vista, PA; (3); French Clb; Var Bsbl; JV Ftbl; PA ST; Arch.

STYCHE, TRICIA; Elizabeth Forward HS; Elizabeth, PA; (4); Pep Clb; Color Guard; Stat Bsktbl; Stat Swmmng; High Hon Roll; Sec NHS; Grl Mth Elizabeth Wmns Clb 87; Bst Prsnlty 87 GATE; Edinboro U Of PA; Nutrtn.

STYER, BETSY; Danville SR HS; Danville, PA; (3); High Hon Roll; Hon Roll; Bloomsburg Coll; Tchr.

STYER, CHRISTOPHER P; Central HS; Philadelphia, PA; (4); Office Aide; Bowling; Var Swmmng; Hon Roll; Med.

STYER, KEVIN; Danville SR HS; Danville, PA; (3); 47/195; Church Yth Grp; Band; Concert Band; Jazz Band; Mrchg Band; Hon Roll; NHS; Acdmc All Amer 87; Lwr Brss Spclst.

STYER, LISA; Danville Area HS; Washingtonville, PA; (2); Drama Clb; Chorus; School Play; Stage Crew; Var Bowling; Score Keeper; Timer; Hon Roll; Pomona Grange Prncss 85-87; Grange Yth Yr 86-87.

STYER, LISA; Warwick HS; Lititz, PA; (2); 71/300; AFS; Orch; Symp Band; Sftbl; Hon Roll; Phys Thrpy.

STYER, SHERI; Warwick HS; Lititz, PA; (4); 36/232; Nwsp Stf; Lit Mag; Rep Stu Cncl; JV Var Sftbl; JV Tennis; Hon Roll; NHS; Lock Haven U; Brdcst Jrnlsm.

STYERS, BRENDA; Lock Haven SR HS; Lock Haven, PA; (4); 72/243; FBLA; Library Aide; Hon Roll; S A Painter Meml Bkkpg Awd 87; Williamsport Area CC; Acctg.

STYS, DEANNA; Trinity HS; Washington, PA; (4); 12/322; German Clb; Math Clb; Math Tm; Office Aide; Drm Mjr(t); Mrchg Band; Twrlr; High Hon Roll; NEDT Awd; Mst Outstndng Mjrtte 85-86; FL ST U; Intl Law.

SUBASIC, LORI LYNN; Hickory HS; Hermitage, PA; (4); 8/163; Acpl Chr; Concert Band; Pres Mrchg Band; Orch; School Musical; Nwsp Stf; Yrbk Stf; NHS; Pres Schlr; St Orch 87.

SUCHER, COURTNEY; Cardinal O Hara HS; Springfield, PA; (3); Elem Ed.

SUCHODOLSKI, SUSAN; Nazareth Acad; Phila, PA; (3); 66/125; French Clb; NFL; Chorus; Orch; Nwsp Stf; Lit Mag; VP Frsh Cls; Peer Counselor 86-87; NYU; Jrnlsm.

SUDA, AMY; John S Fine SR HS; Nanticoke, PA; (3); Girl Scts; Hosp Aide; Speech Tm; Chorus; Var Cheerleading; High Hon Roll; Law.

SUDANO, KELLY; Rochester Area HS; Rochester, PA; (3); FBLA; Library Aide; Teachers Aide; Band; Drill Tm; Flag Corp; School Play; Variety Show; Stu Cncl; Sawyer; Bus Admin.

SUDAR, ANDREW; Hopewell HS; Hookstown, PA; (3); 8/189; Am Leg Boys St; Letterman Clb; Spanish Clb; Varsity Clb; Capt L Bsktbl; Powder Puff Ftbl; Var L Trk; High Hon Roll; Hon Roll; NHS; Hnrbl Mntn Sect All Stars-Bsktbl 86; MVP Serbian Natl Fed Natl Bsktbl Trny 85; Hgh Jmp Recrd-Trck 87; Oper Rsch Anlyst.

SUDER, KIMBERLY; Center HS; Aliquippa, PA; (3); Latin Clb; Letterman Clb; Spanish Clb; Varsity Clb; Nwsp Stf; Yrbk Stf; Trs Stu Cncl; Var Cheerleading; High Hon Roll; NHS; Pre-Medicine.

SUDER, MARCI; Meyersdale Area HS; Meyersdale, PA; (3); #23 In Class; Pres Church Yth Grp; French Clb; Band; Chorus; Concert Band; School Musical; School Play; Yrbk Sprt Ed; Co-Capt Cheerleading; Hon Roll.

SUDIK, MELINDA; Philipsburg-Osceola Area SR HS; Philipsburg, PA; (4); 20/234; Pres Church Yth Grp; Cmnty Wkr; Trs Letterman Clb; Thesps; VP Chorus; Yrbk Phtg; Golf; Hon Roll; NHS; Voice Dem Awd; 2nd Rnnr Up-Cntr CO Jr Miss Schlrshp Pgnt 86-87; 2nd Rnnr Up-Miss PA Ntl Teen Agr Pgnt 87; Clarion U; Accntng.

SUDLER III, SAMUEL G; HS Of Engineering & Science; Philadelphia, PA; (3); Boy Scts; Computer Clb; Office Aide; ROTC; School Play; Yrbk Stf; Rep Frsh Cls; Sec Soph Cls; Rep Jr Cls; Rep Stu Cncl; Trphy 3rd Annl Radio Clsscs Theatre Co, Cert Awd CIN 6th Annl Essay Cont, & Hon Early Admssn Pgm 87; Elec Engr.

SUDMEYER, TODD; Conestoga HS; Malvern, PA; (3); Church Yth Grp; Ntl Merit Ltr; 5 Score-Amer Hist AP Exam 87; 3 Score-European Hist AP Exam 86; Socl Sci.

SUDOL, BRANDY; Danville SR HS; Danville, PA; (4); 41/202; Key Clb; Ski Clb; Rep Frsh Cls; JV Var Cheerleading; Capt Fld Hcky; Mat Maids; Powder Puff Ftbl; Var Trk; High Hon Roll; NHS; Lycoming Coll; Nrsng.

SUDOL, PATRICIA D; Dallas Senior HS; Wyoming, PA; (4); 2/246; Church Yth Grp; Stage Crew; Nwsp Stf; Yrbk Stf; JV Var Bsktbl; Im Sftbl; High Hon Roll; Hon Roll; Pres NHS; Sal; Dallas Womens Fed Bk Scshlrshp, Pres Schlr 87; Hist Awd 85; Moravian Coll; Psych.

SUEIGART, LYNNE; Central Dauphin East HS; Harrisburg, PA; (3); Church Yth Grp; French Clb; Chorus; Orch; Nwsp Stf; Yrbk Stf; Hon Roll; NHS; Educ.

SUESS, STACY; Lancaster Catholic HS; Lancaster, PA; (3); 20/200; Camera Clb; Ed Nwsp Phtg; Ed Yrbk Phtg; Im Bsktbl; Mgr Sftbl; JV Trk; NHS; Sci Fair Hnrb Mntn Cnty 86; Mock Trial Comp 87; Law.

SUGAR, THOMAS; Conestock HS; Berwyn, PA; (4); 11/454; Boy Scts; Math Tm; Band; Concert Band; Mrchg Band; Orch; High Hon Roll; NHS; Ntl Merit Schol; Sci Cncl Awd 87; Pres Acad Ftns Awd 87; Amer Chmcl Scty Awd 87; U PA; Engrng.

SUHOSKY, LISA; Forest City Regional HS; Forest City, PA; (3); German Clb; Ski Clb; Sftbl; Dntst.

SUHY, EDITH; General Mc Lane HS; Edinboro, PA; (3); 81/211; Girl Scts; Hosp Aide; Library Aide; SADD; Teachers Aide; Hon Roll.

SUJANSKY, SANDRA; Somerset Area HS; Somerset, PA; (3); 17/230; English Clb; Spanish Clb; Varsity Clb; Nwsp Ed-Chief; Nwsp Stf; High Hon Roll; Stat JV Bsktbl; Var Tennis; Var Trk; NHS.

SUJANSKY, SUSAN; Somerset Area HS; Somerset, PA; (4); 16/233; Mu Alpha Theta; Q&S; School Play; Yrbk Stf; Trs Sr Cls; Sec Stu Cncl; Capt Var Tennis; Var Trk; High Hon Roll; NHS; Pres Phys Ftns Awd; Acad Ltr; Villanova U; Elec Engr.

SUKAL, MICHAEL; Brownsville Area HS; La Belle, PA; (4); 6/225; Drama Clb; Math Tm; Ski Clb; Bsbl; Ftbl; Rotary Interact Club Pres; Yth Educ Assoc; Engrng.

SUKALY, RHONDA; North Catholic HS; Pittsburgh, PA; (3); Church Yth Grp; Cmnty Wkr; German Clb; GAA; JA; Hon Roll; Fash Dsgnr.

SUKITCH, WILLIAM; North Catholic HS; Pittsburgh, PA; (2); Trs German Clb; Model UN; Ski Clb; Nwsp Stf; Var Mgr(s); JV Socr; Law.

SUKITS, SHERRY; Perry Traditional Acad; Pittsburgh, PA; (4); 11/119; Church Yth Grp; Chorus; Nwsp Sprt Ed; Capt Swmmng; Tennis; High Hon Roll; Hon Roll; VP NHS; Prfct Atten Awd; Swmmng-MVP 83-87; Best Sprtsmn Overall 86-87; Outstndng Achiev In Phys Ed Awd 83-87; Clarion U; Elem Ed.

SUKITS, STEVE; Perry Traditional Acad; Pittsburgh, PA; (3); 10/200; Church Yth Grp; Cmnty Wkr; Var Bsbl; Var Ftbl; High Hon Roll; Pres NHS; Engrng.

SULAK, MARY; Fairchance Georges HS; Uniontown, PA; (4); Art Clb; Spanish Clb; Speech Tm; SADD; Hon Roll; PA ST U.

SULESKI, JULIE M; Villa Maria Acad; Erie, PA; (3); Pres Computer Clb; Model UN; NFL; Science Clb; Band; Concert Band; Drm Mjr(t); Jazz Band; School Musical; NHS; TX Christn U; Bus Mngmt.

SULITZ, CARLA; Washington HS; Washington, PA; (2); Church Yth Grp; Dance Clb; French Clb; Teachers Aide; Church Choir; JV Crs Cntry; Trk; Hon Roll; Al-Amer Acadc Awd 86-87; Howard U; Psych.

SULKOWSKI, JENNIFER; Villa Maria Acad; Erie, PA; (3); Church Yth Grp; Computer Clb; Science Clb; Spanish Clb; SADD; Rep Stu Cncl; JV Socr; Im Vllybl; Hon Roll; NHS; Engnrng.

SULLINGER, CHERYL; Purchase Line HS; Commodore, PA; (2); 12/158; Church Yth Grp; FBLA; Mrchg Band; Stat Bsktbl; High Hon Roll; Hon Roll; Acadmc All Amer 85; ST Comptn FBLA 6th Pl 85; ST Comptn FBLA 2nd Pl 86; IN U; Accntng.

SULLIVAN, ANDREW; The Mercersburg Acad; Hagerstown, MD; (3); 14/130; Boy Scts; Latin Clb; Ski Clb; Lcrss; Socr; Wrstlng; Elks Awd; Hon Roll; Aero.

SULLIVAN, BRIAN; Shaler Area SR HS; Pittsburgh, PA; (3); 20/490; Ski Clb; Rep Jr Cls; Var L Vllybl; NHS; Spanish NHS; Med.

SULLIVAN, BRION E; Titusville HS; Titusville, PA; (3); Camera Clb; Church Yth Grp; Nwsp Phtg; Yrbk Phtg; L Diving; Mgr Ftbl; Socr; Swmmng; Navl Sci.

SULLIVAN, CHRISTOPHER; Bellefonte Area HS; Bellefonte, PA; (3); Var JV Ftbl; Im Vllybl; Im Wt Lftg; JV Wrstlng; Math.

SULLIVAN, COLLEEN; Mahanoy Area HS; Mahanoy City, PA; (3); FHA; Spanish Clb; Drm Mjr(t); Twrlr; High Hon Roll; Hon Roll; NHS; NEDT Awd; Sec Frsh Cls; Empire Beauty Schl; Beautcn.

SULLIVAN III, JOHN B; Rochester Area HS; Rochester, PA; (3); 6/107; Am Leg Boys St; Drama Clb; High Hon Roll; NHS; Amer Leg Essay Cntst 85-86; PA ST U; Comp Engr.

SULLIVAN, KATHLEEN E; Notre Dame Of Green Pond HS; Easton, PA; (4); 5/85; French Clb; Rep Frsh Cls; VP Soph Cls; VP Sr Cls; Off Stu Cncl; Crs Cntry; Mgr(s); Trk; DAR Awd; French Hon Soc; Villanova U.

SULLIVAN, KELLEY; Chichester SR HS; Marcus Hook, PA; (3); 110/297; Office Aide; Sftbl; Trk; Penn ST.

SULLIVAN, LAURA; Plymouth-Whitemarsh HS; Lafayette Hill, PA; (3); Girl Scts; Color Guard; Jazz Band; Mrchg Band; School Musical; School Play; Stage Crew; Mrchng Band Mst Outstndng Rifle 86-87; Drftng.

SULLIVAN, LEAH; Hopewell SR HS; Aliquippa, PA; (3); 22/255; Art Clb; Church Yth Grp; VP German Clb; Sec Band; Sec Concert Band; Sec Mrchg Band; Tennis; High Hon Roll; NHS; Outstndng Athltc Awd 86.

SULLIVAN, LISA; West Scranton HS; Scranton, PA; (2); Church Yth Grp; Church Choir; High Hon Roll; Jr NHS; Nurse.

SULLIVAN, MARYANN; Quaker Valley HS; Sewickley, PA; (3); German Clb; Chorus; School Musical; School Play; Stu Cncl; Mgr(s); Trk; Vllybl.

SULLIVAN, MATTHEW M; Trinity HS; New Cumberland, PA; (3); Church Yth Grp; Spanish Clb; Rep Stu Cncl; Bsktbl; Ftbl; Wt Lftg; High Hon Roll; NHS; Engr.

SULLIVAN, NOEL; St Basil Acad; Philadelphia, PA; (3); English Clb; Sec French Clb; VP Science Clb; Church Choir; Variety Show; Off Stu Cncl; Var Socr; Im Vllybl; Mst Spirtd Awd 86; Pre Law.

SULLIVAN, SCOTT; Ridley HS; Milmont Pk, PA; (3); 26/423; Bsktbl; Ftbl; Mgr(s); Var L Tennis; Var Trk; Hon Roll; Acctnt.

SULLIVAN, SEAN; Spring-Ford HS; Royersford, PA; (3); 69/256; German Clb; Ski Clb; Var Crs Cntry; Im Swmmng; Var Trk; Im Wt Lftg; Var Wrstlng; Hon Roll; Prfct Atten Awd; Arch Engrng.

SULLIVAN, SHAWN; Crestwood HS; Mountaintop, PA; (4); 6/219; Sec Math Clb; Ski Clb; SADD; School Play; Yrbk Stf; Rep Frsh Cls; Rep Soph Cls; Rep Jr Cls; Sec Stu Cncl; Capt Cheerleading; US Chrldng Awd 85, 87; Bloomsburg U; Bio.

SULUKI, SAHAR; Sister Clara Muhammad HS; Philadelphia, PA; (4); 2/10; Dance Clb; Drama Clb; Girl Scts; School Play; Yrbk Stf; Var Badmtn; Cit Awd; High Hon Roll; Hon Roll; Prfct Atten Awd; Perf Attndnc Awd 84-85; Natl Geog Soc Awd For Partcptn 85; Schlrp To Fisk U; Hampton U; Poli Sci.

SUMBURY, CHRISTY; Biglerville HS; Biglerville, PA; (3); 32/90; Art Clb; Hosp Aide; School Play; Nwsp Rptr; JV Trk; Hon Roll; Art.

SUMMA, JENNIFER; Tunkhannock HS; Tunkhannock, PA; (2); Church Yth Grp; Spanish Clb; Mrchg Band; Cheerleading; Twrlr; Hon Roll; Pres Physcl Ftnss Awd 85-86.

SUMMA, MELISSA; Tunkhannock HS; Tunkhannock, PA; (3); Church Yth Grp; Key Clb; Spanish Clb; Band; Concert Band; Jazz Band; Hon Roll; NHS; US Natl Ldrshp Merit Awd 86; Phy Thrpy.

SUMMERS, CHARLISA; Annville Cleona HS; Annville, PA; (4); Cmnty Wkr; Rep FBLA; Pres German Clb; Model UN; VP SADD; Acpl Chr; School Musical; Yrbk Stf; Stu Cncl; NHS; U Of Pittsburg; Anthro.

SUMMERS, KATHY; Elizabethtown Area HS; Elizabethtown, PA; (4); 56/223; Office Aide; Flag Corp; JV Capt Cheerleading; Gym; JV Powder Puff Ftbl; Var Tennis; Amer Farm Wmn Scty 87; Beaver Col6; Erly Chldhd.

SUMMERS, MICHELLE; Marple Newtown HS; Newtown Square, PA; (3); 65/325; Church Yth Grp; Cmnty Wkr; JV Trk; JV Vllybl; Hon Roll; Phy Thrpy.

SUMMERS, TIMOTHY; Fairview HS; Erie, PA; (4); 54/154; Computer Clb; Exploring; Band; Pep Band; Hon Roll; Penn ST U; Comp Sci.

SUMMERVILLE, BRUCE; Union HS; Sligo, PA; (3); 25/95; Boy Scts; Stat Mgr Bsktbl; Ftbl; Trk; Hon Roll; Penn ST U; Wldlf Bio.

SUMMY, JOANNE; Marple Newtown HS; Broomall, PA; (3); 35/338; SADD; Var L Lcrss; Var L Vllybl; Hon Roll; Rotary Awd; Advrtsng.

SUMNER, MAKEBA; Cecilian Academy HS; Philadelphia, PA; (3); 17/36; Cmnty Wkr; Pep Clb; Rep Soph Cls; Rep Jr Cls; VP Sr Cls; Rep Stu Cncl; Phys Ed Awd 85-86; Century 21 Typng Cert Crdt 86-87; Ntl Ldrshp Trng Ctr 87; Phrmcy.

SUMNER, THERESA; Northwestern HS; Albion, PA; (4); 33/144; Church Yth Grp; Stage Crew; Pres Soph Cls; Pres Jr Cls; Stu Cncl; Var L Bsktbl; Var L Sftbl; Var L Vllybl; Hon Roll; All Cnty Sftbll 85-87; All Cnty Bsktbl 87; All Cnty Vllybl 87; Behrend; Hlth & Hmn Dev.

SUNDAHL, LISA; Bradford Central Christian HS; Bradford, PA; (3); Debate Tm; Drama Clb; Pep Clb; Bsktbl; Sftbl; Hon Roll; Jr NHS; Ntl Merit Schol; Bus.

SUNDARJI, KARIMA; Ephrata SR HS; Ephrata, PA; (4); 12/252; Nwsp Ed-Chief; Sec Frsh Cls; Sec Soph Cls; Sec Jr Cls; Sec Sr Cls; Rep Stu Cncl; Sec NHS; Soroptmst Yth Ldrshp Awd 86-87; NY U; Hlth Admin.

SUNDERLAND, MICHAEL; Huntingdon Area HS; Huntingdon, PA; (2); 6/189; Church Yth Grp; Latin Clb; High Hon Roll; NHS.

SUNDERLAND, TROY; Mt Union Area HS; Mcveytown, PA; (3); 7/152; Church Yth Grp; French Clb; Pres Soph Cls; Pres Jr Cls; JV Trk; Var L Wrstlng; NHS; ST Wrstlng Rnnr-Up 86; ST Wrstlng Champ 87; Engrng.

SUNDLING, KIERSTEN; Autler Area SR HS; Butler, PA; (3); Mrchg Band; Bsktbl; Trk; Hon Roll; Jr NHS; Church Yth Grp; GAA; Band; Chorus; Symp Band; Elem Ed.

SUNG, JAY; Fox Chapel Area HS; Pittsburgh, PA; (3); Chess Clb; Cmnty Wkr; Math Clb; Quiz Bowl; Ski Clb; Orch; Nwsp Stf; JV Socr; JV Vllybl; Ntl Merit Ltr; Med.

SUNICK, BILL; Sun Valley HS; Aston, PA; (4); 29/310; Drama Clb; Quiz Bowl; Band; Concert Band; Mrchg Band; Pep Band; Nwsp Stf; Swmmng; NHS; Prfct Atten Awd; Hon Roll; Sci Olympiad; Widener U Scie Enrchmnt Pgm; Drexel U; Mechanical Engr.

SUNSERI, ROSE; Cambria Heights HS; Patton, PA; (4); Band; Concert Band; Mrchg Band; Yrbk Rptr; Hon Roll; Nrs.

SUPCHAK, TERESA A; Bishop O Reilly HS; Kingston, PA; (3); 9/110; Church Yth Grp; Debate Tm; Key Clb; Library Aide; Radio Clb; Ski Clb; Spanish Clb; Chorus; Church Choir; School Musical; Dist Chorus Fstvl 85-87; St Lvl Govrnrs Schl Arts 86-87; Yth Salute 87; Marywood; Psych.

SUPER, TAMMY; Mifflinburg Area HS; Mifflinburg, PA; (3); Drama Clb; Sec 4-H; French Clb; Key Clb; School Play; Yrbk Stf; JV Fld Hcky; Hon Roll; Stage Crew; Big Brothers & Big Sisters Vnltr 87; Miss Teen & Miss Amer Co-Ed Cntst 87; Bus Mgmt.

SUPERKO, JENNIFER; Lake Lehman SR HS; Hunlock Creek, PA; (2); Fld Hcky; Jr NHS; Lang-Spnsh.

SUPERNAVAGE, WILLIAM; Cardinal Brennan HS; Shenandoah Hgts, PA; (3); 3/58; Boy Scts; NFL; Quiz Bowl; Nwsp Bus Mgr; Rep Frsh Cls; JV Bsbl; Bausch & Lomb Sci Awd; Hon Roll; NHS; Ntl Merit Ltr.

SUPERNOVICH, MICHAEL; Clairton HS; Clairton, PA; (3); Computer Clb; Band; Concert Band; Mrchg Band; Pep Band; Hon Roll; Carnegie-Mellon PA ST; Comp.

SUPPA, ANGELA; Belle Vernon Area HS; Belle Vernon, PA; (3); Church Yth Grp; Band; VP Soph Cls; VP Jr Cls; Var Co-Capt Cheerleading; Powder Puff Ftbl; Twrlr; High Hon Roll; NHS; Medcl Intrst Club 87-88; Frnch Stu Of Mon 87; Pre Med.

SUPPES, MELISSA; Westmont Hilltop HS; Johnstown, PA; (3); French Clb; Key Clb; Ski Clb; Speech Tm; Concert Band; Yrbk Stf; Tennis; Trk; High Hon Roll; NHS.

SUPPOK, DANIEL; Carmichaels Area JR SR HS; Carmichaels, PA; (1); Band; Concert Band; Mrchg Band; Nwsp Stf; High Hon Roll; Jr NHS; Prsdntl Acdmc Ftnss Awd 87; UCSD; Cmptrs.

SUPPON, VICKI; Wyoming Area SR HS; Wyoming, PA; (3); Art Clb; Church Yth Grp; Key Clb; Spanish Clb; Sec Soph Cls; Stu Cncl; High Hon Roll; Hon Roll; NHS; Engl.

SURACE, VYNETTE; Norwin SR HS; N Huntingdon, PA; (4); Pres FHA; Girl Scts; Hosp Aide; Teachers Aide; Hon Roll; NHS; Norwin Cncl PTA Scholar 87; Art Inst Pittsburgh; Intr Dsgn.

SURANOFSKY, MICHAEL; Central Catholic HS; Whitehall, PA; (3); VP Hosp Aide; High Hon Roll; NHS; Math Clb; Stage Crew; Hon Roll; Med.

SURANOFSKY, ROBERT; Nazareth Area HS; Stockertown, PA; (3); Band; Concert Band; Mrchg Band; Hon Roll; Band Ltr 86-87; Comp Sci.

SURDOVAL, SCOTT; Emmaus HS; Macungie, PA; (3); 76/548; Debate Tm; Key Clb; School Play; Rep Jr Cls; Im Socr; L Trk; Im Wt Lftg; Hon Roll; Ntl Merit Ltr; Prfct Atten Awd; Elec Engrng.

SURGEONER, NADINE; Exeter SR HS; Reading, PA; (3); 76/241; Varsity Clb; Trs Pres Y-Teens; Band; Concert Band; Drm Mjr(t); Jazz Band; Mrchg Band; School Musical; Sec Stu Cncl; Cheerleading; Elem Ed.

SURGES, SHOLOM K; Red Lion Area SR HS; Wrightsville, PA; (4); 5/337; Concert Band; School Play; Symp Band; Nwsp Ed-Chief; Nwsp Stf; High Hon Roll; Pres NHS; Ntl Merit SF; Band; Hon Roll; John Hopkins Cntr Tlntd Yth Smr Pgm 84-85; Rotary Intl Ldrshp Conf 86.

SURGINER, DONIELE; Lutheran HS; Philadelphia, PA; (3); Debate Tm; French Clb; Latin Clb; Math Clb; Cheerleading; High Hon Roll; Hon Roll; Temple U Cert Merit Mock Trial 85; Cert Merit Hghst Avg Bio 86; Hnr Mntn Tri 87; Hghst Avg Frnch I, II; Ped.

SURKOVICH, NANCY; Mashannon Valley HS; Houtzdale, PA; (4); 25/120; Ski Clb; SADD; Concert Band; Flag Corp; Mrchg Band; School Play; Nwsp Stf; Stat Bsktbl; Sftbl; Hon Roll; Alt Lebanon Vly Yth Schlr 86; Indiana U Of PA; Fshn Mrchnds.

SURMACZ, STEPHEN; Penn-Trafford HS; Trafford, PA; (3); Drama Clb; JCL; Latin Clb; Band; Jazz Band; School Musical; School Play; Stage Crew; Lit Mag; Hon Roll; U Of Pittsburgh; Bus Admin.

SUROWIEC, GERALYN; Scranton Prep; Clarks Summit, PA; (4); 6/190; Chorus; Church Choir; School Musical; Trk; High Hon Roll; NHS; Amrcn Bus Wmns Assn Schlrshp, Maxima Cum Laude Natl Latin Exm 87; Fairfield U; Accntng.

SURRENA, DAVID; Hickory HS; Hermitage, PA; (3); 38/180; Art Clb; Latin Clb; Nwsp Stf; Var Trk; Im Vllybl; Ntl Merit Ltr; Bcknl U Gvnrs Schl For The Arts 87; Natl Merit Ltr Fo PSAT 87; Arch.

SURRENA, LISA; Ft La Boeuf HS; Waterford, PA; (4); 18/162; Dance Clb; Debate Tm; Pep Clb; Varsity Clb; Y-Teens; Nwsp Rptr; Sec Soph Cls; Pres Jr Cls; Pres Sr Cls; Var Cheerleading; Prom Qn 87; Ldrshp Awd; U Of Pittsburgh; Physcl Thrpy.

SURRENA, SHANAN; Franklin HS; Grove City, PA; (4); 13/210; Office Aide; Spanish Clb; Variety Show; Off Frsh Cls; Off Soph Cls; Off Jr Cls; Off Sr Cls; JV Var Cheerleading; High Hon Roll; Kiwanis Awd; Schl Directors Awd 84-87; Slipper Rock U.

SURRETT, JEMMA; Wyalusing Valley HS; Wyalusing, PA; (3); 23/150; Sec Computer Clb; German Clb; Ski Clb; Orch; School Musical; Cheerleading; Hon Roll; U Of Pittsburgh; Comp Engr.

SUSAN, STACY; Mifflinburg HS; Mifflinburg, PA; (1); Church Yth Grp; FBLA; FHA; Chorus; Church Choir; High Hon Roll; Hon Roll; Comp.

SUSI, MICHELE E; Valley View JR SR HS; Jessup, PA; (3); 17/193; Church Yth Grp; Sftbl; Vllybl; Hon Roll; Italian Clb VP 86-87; Cmrcl Art.

SUSTRIK, ROBIN; Mc Guffey HS; W Finley, PA; (4); 56/199; Church Yth Grp; Cmnty Wkr; 4-H; FFA; 4-H Awd; Keystone Farmer Degree & Star Chptr Farmer 87; Natl WA FFA Schlrshp 86; Penn ST U; Ag.

SUTARA, SHARON; Highlands SR HS; Natrona Hgts, PA; (3); Var L Trk.

SUTCAVAGE, ALBERT; Dallas HS; Trucksville, PA; (3); Art Clb; Chess Clb; Computer Clb; Stage Crew; High Hon Roll; Hon Roll; Art Exhibit 87; Film-Directing, Producing.

SUTCH, SUZANNE; Upper Dublin HS; Ft Washington, PA; (3); 85/300; Church Yth Grp; Ski Clb; SADD; Varsity Clb; Yrbk Stf; Rep Soph Cls; Rep Sr Cls; Var Fld Hcky; Var Lcrss; PA Ski Team 86-88; PA Downhill Ski Team 86; UNH; Occuptnl Thrpy.

SUTER, KATHERINE; Carlisle SR HS; Carlisle, PA; (3); 50/454; AFS; JA; Ski Clb; Color Guard; Mrchg Band; Swing Chorus; Yrbk Stf; Stu Cncl; Fld Hcky; Hon Roll; Law.

SUTER, MARK; Fort Cherry HS; Bulger, PA; (4); 1/111; Computer Clb; Drama Clb; Math Clb; Science Clb; Ski Clb; Varsity Clb; JV Wrstlng; Pres NHS; Art Clb; Yrbk Phtg; ST JR Sci & Humanities Symposium; Forgn Lang Club; Bridge Club; Elec Engrng.

SUTER, MELISSA; Southmoreland HS; Ruffsdale, PA; (3); 13/224; Trs Sec German Clb; Math Clb; Chorus; Delta Epsiln Phi 87; Hghlndr Choir Uncle Lews Crew 86-87; Pittsburgh Inst Of Aero; Avionc.

SUTHERLAND, NANCY; North Hills HS; Pittsburgh, PA; (3); Church Yth Grp; Keywanettes; Ski Clb; Chorus; Color Guard; Stu Cncl; High Hon Roll; NHS.

SUTLEY, ALLAN; Centre County Christian Acad; Pine Grove Mills, PA; (4); Chess Clb; Church Yth Grp; Teachers Aide; School Play; Yrbk Ed-Chief; Yrbk Phtg; Yrbk Rptr; Yrbk Stf; Im Socr; PA ST U; Bio.

SUTOVICH, KEVIN; Central Dauphin HS; Harrisburg, PA; (3); 19/369; Am Leg Boys St; Quiz Bowl; Yrbk Phtg; Yrbk Stf; Var Socr; Im Vllybl; Cit Awd; Hon Roll; Trs Jr NHS; NHS; Med.

SUTPHIN, AMANDA; Springside HS; Philadelphia, PA; (3); Camera Clb; Drama Clb; Intnl Clb; Political Wkr; Spanish Clb; Nwsp Ed-Chief; Lit Mag; Trs Jr Cls; Trs Sr Cls; Wt Lftg; Intl Relations.

SUTT, LARRY; Altoona Area HS; Altoona, PA; (4); 47/718; German Clb; Trk; Hon Roll; K Pin 84; PA ST U; Engrng.

SUTTER, EDEN; Beaver Area HS; Beaver, PA; (2); Church Yth Grp; French Clb; Ski Clb; Band; Mrchg Band; Pep Band; High Hon Roll; Hon Roll; Schlstc Achvmnt Awd 87; Cornell; Engl.

SUTTON, DAVID; Burrell HS; Lower Burrell, PA; (3); 1/175; Chess Clb; Pres Church Yth Grp; Spanish Clb; Church Choir; School Play; Stu Cncl; Var L Swmmng; Var L Trk; Pres Jr NHS; VP NHS; Acdmc Ltrs 85-87; US Air Force Acad Summer Sci Smnr 87; Econ.

SUTTON, LAURA; Central Bucks East HS; New Hope, PA; (4); FBLA; Ski Clb; Yrbk Phtg; Yrbk Stf; Cheerleading; Mgr(s); Hon Roll; G Washington U; Intl Bus.

SUTTON, MIKE; Belle Vernon Area HS; Belle Vernon, PA; (3); Boy Scts; Cmnty Wkr; JA; Wt Lftg; Wrstlng; Hon Roll; Prfct Atten Awd; Eagle Scout 87; Brnz Pln BSA 87.

SUTTON, PATRICIA J; Shaler HS; Glenshaw, PA; (3); 39/483; Church Yth Grp; Cmnty Wkr; SADD; School Play; Yrbk Phtg; Hon Roll; Spanish NHS; Penn Sstg U; Intl Bus.

SUTTON, SHAWN; Canon Mc Millon SR HS; Canonsburg, PA; (3); JA; Var Golf; L Tennis; Hon Roll; Air Forc ROTC 4 Yr Schlrshp & Air Forc Acad 88; Air Force Acad; Aerosp.

SUTTON, SHAWN; West York SR HS; York, PA; (3); 27/185; Drama Clb; French Clb; Chorus; Pom Pon; Interior Dsgn.

SUTTON, TAMMY; Saegertown HS; Saegertown, PA; (3); Church Yth Grp; Dance Clb; Hosp Aide; Pep Clb; SADD; Chorus; Church Choir; Mrchg Band; Gym; Stat Score Keeper; Overall Bst Mjrt Awd 85-86; JR Dist Chorus Cert 84-85; Edinboro U; RN.

SUTTON, TODD; Maplewood HS; Centerville, PA; (3); 8/154; Chess Clb; French Clb; JA; Science Clb; Chorus; Church Choir; Hon Roll; NHS; Prfct Atten Awd; Engr.

SUTTON, TRACI; Bellwood-Antis HS; Bellwood, PA; (1); Chorus; JV Bsktbl; JV Trk; Hon Roll.

SUWAN, SARUN; Freeport SR HS; Sarver, PA; (2); 35/202; L Var Trk; Hon Roll.

SUWAN, SASI; Freeport Area SR HS; Sarver, PA; (4); 1/170; English Clb; Hosp Aide; Math Tm; Office Aide; School Play; Stage Crew; Nwsp Rptr; Yrbk Stf; Stu Cncl; Stat Bsktbl; PA Gvrnrs Schl Sci 86.

SUWOLITCH, TONYA; Marion Center HS; Dixonville, PA; (4); 59/169; Latin Clb; Library Aide; Office Aide; Q&S; SADD; School Play; Yrbk Stf; Golf; Hon Roll; IN U Of PA; Med Tech.

SUYDAM, ERIC; Hempfield HS; E Petersburg, PA; (4); Millersville U; Liberal Arts.

SUYDAM, KRISTINE; Donegal HS; Mount Joy, PA; (2); Church Yth Grp; Pres FBLA; Chorus; Pres Phys Fit Awd 86-87; USGF Class II Gymnast; Accounting.

SUYDAM, MICHELE; Donegal HS; Mount Joy, PA; (3); 16/177; Concert Band; Mrchg Band; Yrbk Stf; Rep Soph Cls; Rep Jr Cls; Rep Stu Cncl; JV Cheerleading; Stat Socr; Var Trk; Spanish NHS; Trvl Agnt.

SVALBONAS, ARVYDAS; Kennard-Dale HS; Delta, PA; (3); 42/163; Debate Tm; Drama Clb; English Clb; SADD; School Musical; School Play; Var Trk; Var Wt Lftg; Hon Roll; NEDT Awd; Univ Of DE; Marine Bio.

SVEC, KRISTEN; South Western HS; Hanover, PA; (3); 60/233; Varsity Clb; Var L Vllybl; DAR Awd; Hon Roll; Bus.

SVERCEK, LEAH; Connellsville SR HS; Mill Run, PA; (3); 88/525; Chorus; Nwsp Rptr; Nwsp Stf; High Hon Roll; NHS; Spanish NHS; U Of Pittsburgh; Nrsng.

SVIDRON, DENA; Greensburg Central Catholic HS; Latrobe, PA; (3); Church Yth Grp; Exploring; Girl Scts; Hosp Aide; Ski Clb; Chorus; Color Guard; Mrchg Band; Powder Puff Ftbl; High Hon Roll; St Vincent Coll; Pre Med.

SVRCEK JR, ANDREW; Nativity BVM HS; New Phila, PA; (3); Boy Scts; Chess Clb; Church Yth Grp; Pres Frsh Cls; Stu Cncl; JV Var Bsbl; Var Bsktbl; Var Ftbl; Golf; Wt Lftg; Elec Engrng.

SWAB, KIM; Clarion HS; Brookville, PA; (4); Spanish Clb; Varsity Clb; Drill Tm; Bsktbl; Trk; Vllybl; Clarion U; Bus.

SWAFFORD, KRISTI; Fairfield HS; Fairfield, PA; (3); 7/73; Sec SADD; Varsity Clb; Rep Stu Cncl; Capt L Bsktbl; Var L Sftbl; Var L Vllybl; High Hon Roll; Hon Roll; NHS; MVP Vllybl 86; MVP Awd Sno Belle Clsc Bsktbll Trntmt 86; Mst Otstndng Plyr Ad Bsktbll 86; Educ.

SWAILS, TRACIE; Grace Christian Acad; High Spire, PA; (4); 2/6; Church Yth Grp; Drama Clb; French Clb; Red Cross Aide; Band; Chorus; Hon Roll; Sal; Psychlgy.

SWAN, ALLISON; Hanover Area JR SR HS; Ashley, PA; (3); Band; Trs Stu Cncl; Jr NHS; NHS; Stu Council Pres 87-88; Bus.

SWAN, BRIAN; Du Bois Senior HS; Dubois, PA; (3); Art Clb; Aud/Vis; Boy Scts; Camera Clb; Computer Clb; French Clb; Hosp Aide; Library Aide; Nice Kid Awd In Sopy Yr 85-86; Penn ST U; Elem Educ.

SWAN, JENNIFER; Warwick HS; Lititz, PA; (3); 48/260; Varsity Clb; School Musical; School Play; Yrbk Stf; Rep Jr Cls; VP Sr Cls; Var Fld Hcky; Var Trk; High Hon Roll; Ltrey Mgzn Bst Ptry Awd 8; Fulton Opera Hs Prdtn Color Of The Wind 87; Cmmnctns.

SWANGER, ANDREW; Cedar Crest HS; Lebanon, PA; (3); Church Yth Grp; German Clb; Prfct Atten Awd; US Army.

SWANGER, TAMMY; Milton Area SR HS; Milton, PA; (3); Art Clb; Latin Clb; Library Aide; Latin Hnr Scty 86-87; Art.

SWANHART, MELISSA; Blacklick Valley HS; Nanty-Glo, PA; (2); 1/105; Library Aide; NFL; Ski Clb; Band; Stu Cncl; Sftbl; High Hon Roll; Prfct Atten Awd; Pres Schlr; Acad All Am 86; Med.

SWANK, BRIAN; Knoch HS; Butler, PA; (4); Science Clb; Varsity Clb; Var L Bsbl; Var L Bsktbl; Hon Roll; NHS; Pres Schlr; US Merchant Marine Acad 87; U Of Pittsburgh Merit Schlrshp 87; Pittsburgh; Pharm.

SWANK, DENISE; Cumberland Valley HS; Mechanicsburg, PA; (4); 4-H; FBLA; Office Aide; Teachers Aide; Yrbk Bus Mgr; Yrbk Stf; Harrisburg Area CC; Sec.

SWANK, JAMIE; Shamokin Area HS; Shamokin, PA; (2); 31/250; Drama Clb; Pep Clb; Science Clb; SADD; JV Var Cheerleading; JV Score Keeper; Hon Roll; PA Free Enterprise Week Schrlshp 87; Georgetown U; Comp Sci.

SWANK, KRISTINA; Slippery Rock Area HS; Butler, PA; (4); Trs German Clb; Intnl Clb; Pep Clb; Band; Drm Mjr(t); Mrchg Band; Symp Band; Nwsp Stf; Powder Puff Ftbl; High Hon Roll; Slipery Rock Univ; Msc Ed.

SWANK, LORI; Gateway SR HS; Monroeville, PA; (3); 214/455; Art Clb; GAA; Pep Clb; Chorus; Color Guard; Var Sftbl; Hon Roll; Prfct Atten Awd; Cmmnctns.

SWANKOSKY, KIMBERLY; Hazleton SR HS; Beaver Meadows, PA; (2); Drama Clb; French Clb; Hosp Aide; Pep Clb; School Musical; Capt Cheerleading.

SWANLJUNG, JOHAN; Taylor Allderdiae HS; Pittsburgh, PA; (2); Ski Clb; JV Crs Cntry; Var Trk; High Hon Roll.

SWANSON, CINDY; Seneca Valley HS; Harmony, PA; (3); 26/350; Church Yth Grp; Pep Clb; Orch; School Play; High Hon Roll; Hon Roll; Cncrt Mstrs Of Yth Symphny 86-87; Acad Schlrshp Awd 85 & 86; Rstrnt Mntmng.

SWANSON, JIM; Franklin Regional HS; Murrysville, PA; (3); 61/329; JA; Ski Clb; Stu Cncl; JV L Bsktbl; L Var Golf; L Var Tennis; High Hon Roll; Hon Roll; Mike Smith Awd-MVP Gold Awd 86 & 87; Bus.

SWANSON, JIM; Warren Area HS; Warren, PA; (4); Church Yth Grp; Ski Clb; Spanish Clb; Band; Concert Band; Drm Mjr(t); Mrchg Band; Socr; Vllybl; Wt Lftg; 1st & 3rd Pl Trphy 12 Mile Crss Cntry 85; 3 1st Pl Trphs Drum Mjr 86; U Of PA Excllnct Schlrshp 87; Navy; Offcr.

SWANSON, KERRY; Punxsutawney SR HS; Punxsutawney, PA; (4); 17/245; CAP; Nwsp Ed-Chief; Yrbk Phtg; Yrbk Stf; NHS; Rotary Awd; VFW Awd; Encampment West Hnr Cadet 86; Navy; Pilot.

SWANSON, LORI; Big Spring SR HS; Carlisle, PA; (2); School Musical; Stage Crew; Nwsp Rptr; Nwsp Stf; Mgr(s); Hon Roll.

SWANSON, PAMELA A; Warren Area HS; Warren, PA; (4); 13/285; Varsity Clb; Rep Mrchg Band; VP Cmnty Wkr; VP Sr Cls; Rep Stu Cncl; Stat Bsktbl; Cit Awd; High Hon Roll; Trs NHS; Pres Schlr; Zonta Clb Schlrshp 87; Scalise-Williams Schlrshp 87; Amer Legion Awd 83; Indiana U Of PA; Accntng.

SWANSON, ROBERT; West Perry HS; Elliottsburg, PA; (3); 5/200; Church Yth Grp; Trs Drama Clb; School Play; Off Stu Cncl; High Hon Roll; Hon Roll; NHS; Nuclear Physics.

SWARD, STACIE; Harmony HS; Westover, PA; (4); 5/50; Concert Band; Mrchg Band; Stage Crew; Yrbk Ed-Chief; Rep Stu Cncl; High Hon Roll; NHS; Outstndng Artist 87; Penn ST; Pre Law.

SWARMER, SUSAN L; Seneca HS; Wattsburg, PA; (4); 2/149; Band; Drill Tm; School Musical; School Play; Sec Stu Cncl; Pom Pon; High Hon Roll; NHS; Prfct Atten Awd; Sal; Mercyhurst Coll; Teaching.

SWARNER, CINDY; Great Hope Baptist Schl; Carlisle, PA; (3); Church Yth Grp; School Play; Yrbk Stf; Sec Jr Cls; Sftbl; Vllybl; Hon Roll.

SWARNER, LORIE; Downingtown SR HS; Downingtown, PA; (4); Church Yth Grp; Cmnty Wkr; Teachers Aide; Band; Color Guard; Jazz Band; Mrchg Band; Wrstlng; Hon Roll; Kutztown Univ; Elem Educ.

SWARTWOUT, ADAM; Butler HS; Butler, PA; (2); German Clb; Latin Clb; Im Bsktbl; Hon Roll; Jr NHS; Sprts Med.

SWARTWOUT, TOM; Butler SR HS; Butler, PA; (3); Spanish Clb; Im Bsktbl; L Crs Cntry; Ftbl; L Trk; Hon Roll; Sprts Med.

SWARTZ, AMY; Susquehanna Comm HS; Starrucca, PA; (4); Band; Concert Band; Mrchg Band; Yrbk Stf; Bsktbl; Powder Puff Ftbl; CCBI; Med Adm.

SWARTZ, ANDY; Northeastern HS; York, PA; (4); 11/167; Math Tm; Varsity Clb; Acpl Chr; Var Bsbl; Var Socr; Var Vllybl; High Hon Roll; Hon Roll; NHS; Pres Schlr; Walter Brunhouse Frshmn Schlrshp 87; Penn ST; Comp Engrng.

SWARTZ, BRENDA; Du Bois Area SR HS; Reynoldsville, PA; (3); Capt Drm Mjr(t); Yrbk Phtg; Yrbk Rptr; Yrbk Stf; Off Stu Cncl; Hon Roll; Penn ST; Nrsng.

SWARTZ, CARLA; Montgomery Area HS; Montgomery, PA; (3); French Clb; FHA; Library Aide; Sec Sr Cls; Tennis; High Hon Roll; Hon Roll; NHS; Comp Sci.

SWARTZ, CLIFFORD; Conestoga HS; Berwyn, PA; (3); 38/450; Church Yth Grp; Intnl Clb; Model UN; Service Clb; Variety Show; Yrbk Phtg; Yrbk Rptr; Yrbk Sprt Ed; Yrbk Stf; Hon Roll; Econ.

SWARTZ, CRYSTAL; E Stroudsburg HS; E Stroudsburg, PA; (1); 20/250; Model UN; NHS.

SWARTZ, DOUG; Greenville HS; Greenville, PA; (4); French Clb; German Clb; Letterman Clb; Varsity Clb; Pres Sr Cls; Im Bsktbl; Var Capt Ftbl; Im Capt Vllybl; Var Wrstlng; High Hon Roll; U Of Pittsburgh.

SWARTZ, HEATHER; Conrad Weiser HS; Wernersville, PA; (2); 54/164; Church Yth Grp; FHA; German Clb; Girl Scts; Key Clb; Var Mgr(s); Prncpl Lst 86-87.

SWARTZ, KIMBERLY; Susquenita HS; Duncannon, PA; (4); 14/174; School Play; Hon Roll; NHS; Dncn Fire Cmpny Schlrshp 87; Jhn Hll Fndtn Schlrshp 87; Presdntl Acdmc Ftns Awd 87; OH ST U; Pre-Vet Med.

SWARTZ, MARK; Cumberland Valley HS; Mechanicsburg, PA; (3); 14/592; Pres Church Yth Grp; Latin Clb; JV Crs Cntry; NHS; Penn ST; Envrnmntl Rsrc Mgmnt.

SWARTZ, PAUL J; Uniontown Area SR HS; Uniontown, PA; (3); 1/350; Letterman Clb; VP Band; VP Chorus; School Musical; Var L Bsktbl; Var L Trk; High Hon Roll; NHS; Prfct Atten Awd; Drama Clb; PA Gov Schl Ag 86.

SWARTZ, PAUL W; Strath Haven HS; Wallingford, PA; (4); Ski Clb; Spanish Clb; Varsity Clb; Variety Show; Var Ftbl; JV Lcrss; Var Capt Swmmng; Hon Roll; Hnrb Mntn Natl Wrtg Awds Schltc Mag 86; Art Recog & Talent Search 87; PA ST U; Bus Adm.

SWARTZ, STACY; Brooville Area HS; Brookville, PA; (4); 18/126; Church Yth Grp; FNA; German Clb; Band; School Musical; Var Sftbl; Hon Roll; NHS; Pres Schlr; Hnr Crds 86-87; Clarion U Yenango Cmps; Nrsng.

SWARTZ, TODD; Sheffield Area HS; Sheffield, PA; (4); SADD; JV Var Ftbl; JV Wrstlng; Hon Roll; Army.

SWARTZ, TRICIA; Sheffield Area HS; Sheffield, PA; (2); FCA; SADD; Varsity Clb; VP Soph Cls; Pres Jr Cls; JV Var Cheerleading; Mat Maids; High Hon Roll; JV Vllybl; Stu Cncl.

SWARTZENDRUBER, MARCELLA; Lancaster Mennonite HS; Ephrata, PA; (3); Church Yth Grp; Chorus; Stat Bsktbl; Im Fld Hcky; Mgr(s); Im Sftbl; Im Vllybl; Hon Roll; Goshon Coll; Scl Wrk.

SWARTZENTRUBER, HEIDI; Danville Area HS; Danville, PA; (3); Am Leg Aux Girls St; Church Yth Grp; Drama Clb; French Clb; Band; Concert Band; Mrchg Band; Symp Band; Var L Fld Hcky; Hon Roll; Bnd & Hlth Awds 85; Math.

SWARTZENTRUBER, KRISTOF; Danville HS; Danville, PA; (1); Church Yth Grp; Band; Concert Band; Mrchg Band; Symp Band; JV Socr; JV Trk; High Hon Roll; Hon Roll.

SWARTZLANDER, ANGIE; Pine Grove Area HS; Tremont, PA; (3); ROTC; Varsity Clb; Drill Tm; School Musical; Mgr(s); Im Tennis; Im Vllybl; Hon Roll; NHS; Prfct Atten Awd; Sci, Socl Stds, Bus Ed Awds 86; Socl Stds, Alg I, Bus Ed, Engl Awds 87; Free Entrprs Wk Schlrshp 87; Earth Sci.

SWATSWORTH, PAULA; Laurel Valley JR-SR HS; Seward, PA; (4); 14/87; FBLA; Color Guard; Yrbk Stf; Hon Roll; Cert Honor Ecology 87; ICM Schl Bus; Accntng.

SWAUGER, MELISSA; Salisbury Elk-Lick HS; Salisbury, PA; (3); Pres Art Clb; Spanish Clb; Band; School Play; Nwsp Rptr; Yrbk Stf; VP Frsh Cls; Sec Soph Cls; Var Cheerleading; High Hon Roll; Lwyr.

SWAUGER, VAN; Beaver Area JR/SR HS; Beaver, PA; (4); 49/203; Church Yth Grp; JCL; Latin Clb; Var Bsbl; Var Bsktbl; Hon Roll; IN U Of PA; Journalism.

SWAVELY, CAROL ANN; Jim Thorpe Area HS; Jim Thorpe, PA; (4); 4/90; Band; Chorus; Ed Nwsp Stf; Ed Yrbk Stf; Off Stu Cncl; Stat Var Bsktbl; L Var Cheerleading; Lion Awd; NHS; Rotary Awd; Lebanon Valley Coll; Chem.

SWAVELY, LORA; Boyertown Area SR HS; Boyertown, PA; (3); FBLA; Cit Awd; Hon Roll; Prfct Atten Awd; Awd Of Merit Cert-Ptry Cont 86; Gldn Poet Awd 87; ST Chptr Cert-Typng Cont 87; Sec.

SWAYNE, AILEEN M; Bellwood-Antis HS; Tyrone, PA; (3); 18/115; Church Yth Grp; Girl Scts; SADD; Flag Corp; Stat Bsbl; Fld Hcky; Wrstlng; Prfct Atten Awd.

SWEATT, TERRY SUE; Ford City JR/Sr HS; Ford City, PA; (3); 10/165; Band; Chorus; Mrchg Band; Nwsp Rptr; Yrbk Ed-Chief; Yrbk Stf; Rep Frsh Cls; Rep Stu Cncl; High Hon Roll; Pres NHS; Cnty Band & Chorus 85-87; Cmmnctns.

SWEDE, GREGORY; Cowanesque Valley HS; Sabinsville, PA; (3); Boy Scts; Letterman Clb; Var Ftbl; Var Wrstlng; Hon Roll; NHS; VP Jr Cls; Rep Stu Cncl; Mthmtcs.

SWEDE, LISA; Plymouth-Whitemarsh HS; Norristown, PA; (3); Camera Clb; Office Aide; SADD; Rep Frsh Cls; Rep Soph Cls; Sec Jr Cls; Rep Sr Cls; Rep Stu Cncl; Var Cheerleading; Mgr(s); Katherine Gibbs; Exec Secy.

SWEDER, DENISE; Sacred Heart HS; Carbondale, PA; (3); Computer Clb; Pres Latin Clb; SADD; Nwsp Stf; Trs Soph Cls; High Hon Roll; NHS.

SWEENEY, JEFF; Penn Cambria SR HS; Lilly, PA; (3); Trs SADD; Mrchg Band; Hon Roll; NHS; Corp Law.

SWEENEY, KATHE; Piux X HS; East Bangor, PA; (4); 1/34; Am Leg Aux Girls St; Dance Clb; Scholastic Bowl; Church Choir; Yrbk Ed-Chief; Pres Stu Cncl; Dnfth Awd; DAR Awd; NHS; 3rd Altrnt MISS PA U S Teen Pagnt 86; Hugh O Brian Yth Fndtn Ldrshp Semnr 85; Hofstra U; Pol Sci.

SWEENEY, LAURA; Mahanoy Area HS; Barnesville, PA; (3); FHA; Spanish Clb; Chirprctr.

SWEENEY, MICHAELE; Panther Valley HS; Nesquehoning, PA; (3); 32/132; Church Yth Grp; Dance Clb; Drama Clb; FHA; Hosp Aide; Library Aide; Ski Clb; Mrchg Band; School Musical; School Play; Econ.

SWEENEY, MIKE; Panther Valley Schl Dist; Coaldale, PA; (3); 58/135; Var JV Ftbl; Var Wrstlng; PA State; Food.

SWEENEY, NICHOLE; Greensburg Central Catholic HS; Greensburg, PA; (3); 94/276; AFS; Ski Clb; Yrbk Stf; Powder Puff Ftbl; Score Keeper; Hon Roll; Educ.

SWEENEY, SEAN; Notre Dame HS; Easton, PA; (3); Drama Clb; NFL; Chorus; School Musical; School Play; Stage Crew; Crs Cntry; Trk; Allentown Coll; Sales.

SWEENEY, SHAWN; Portage Area HS; Portage, PA; (3); Boy Scts; Sec Church Yth Grp; VP FFA; Hon Roll.

SWEENEY, TERRY; Karns City HS; Bruin, PA; (4); 25/110; Cmnty Wkr; Computer Clb; Letterman Clb; SADD; Chorus; Yrbk Bus Mgr; Hon Roll; Frzr-Bck Schlrshp 87.

SWEENEY, WILLIAM; Monsignor Bonner HS; Drexel Hill, PA; (3); Church Yth Grp; Service Clb; SADD; Yrbk Stf; VP Jr Cls; Im Ftbl; Var Mgr(s); Cls Svc Awd 85-86 & 86-87.

SWEET, JAMIE; Cowanesque Valley HS; Middlebury Ctr, PA; (3); 7/80; Boy Scts; FFA; Letterman Clb; Pres Frsh Cls; VP Soph Cls; Pres Stu Cncl; Wrstlng; NHS.

SWEET, LORI; Hazleton HS; St, PA; (2); Pep Clb; Spanish Clb; SADD; Chorus; Church Choir; Nrsng.

SWEET, MICHELLE; Lincoln HS; Portersville, PA; (3); Sec Church Yth Grp; German Clb; Office Aide; SADD; Y-Teens; Drill Tm; Flag Corp; Mrchg Band; Stage Crew; Powder Puff Ftbl; Grange-Lawrence Cnty Yth Ambassador 1st Runner Up 86-87; Occptnl Thrpst.

SWEET III, ROBERT D; Chestnut Ridge SR HS; Alum Bank, PA; (4); 18/136; Church Yth Grp; Sec SADD; Stat Bsktbl; Mgr(s); NHS; Pres Acad Fitness Awd 87; Member Of SR Six 87; IN U Of PA; Comm.

SWEETY, MELISSA; St Pius X HS; Pottstown, PA; (4); 4/148; Pep Clb; Rep Frsh Cls; Off Soph Cls; Rep Jr Cls; Sec Sr Cls; Stu Cncl; Var L Fld Hcky; Var Sftbl; High Hon Roll; NHS; Josephine C Connelly Schlrshp 87-88; Gwynedd Mercy Schlrshp 87-88; Lindback Schlrshp 87-88; Gwynedd Mercy Coll; Cardio Tech.

SWEGART, DANIEL; Cocalico HS; Stevens, PA; (3); 45/185; Boy Scts; Ski Clb; Var L Golf; Hon Roll.

SWEGER, ANGELA; Cumberland Valley HS; Carlisle, PA; (2); 399/604; Pres Church Yth Grp; Band; Church Choir; Concert Band; Mrchg Band; Hon Roll; Elem Ed.

SWEIGARD, CHERYL; Upper Dauphin Area HS; Millesburg, PA; (4); 2/110; Band; Chorus; Church Choir; Concert Band; Mrchg Band; Yrbk Ed-Chief; Yrbk Stf; NHS; Rotary Awd; Sal; Spnsh Awd 85 87; Uppr Dauphn Area Ed Assn Awd 87; Rotry Ldrshp 86; Lancaster Gen Hosp Schl Nrsng.

SWEIGARD, HOLLY ANN; William Penn SR HS; York, PA; (4); 24/373; Hosp Aide; Church Choir; Drm Mjr(t); Pres Orch; Rep Stu Cncl; Capt Swmmng; Vllybl; Jr NHS; NHS; Boys Clb Am; PA Ambssdr Of Musc 85; Stu Of Mnth 85; Hnrs Choir 86; Reading Schl Of Nrsng; Nrs.

SWEIGART, CHERYL ANN; Pequea Valley HS; Gordonville, PA; (4); Varsity Clb; Band; Chorus; Pres Frsh Cls; Pres Soph Cls; Capt Bsktbl; Capt Fld Hcky; Capt Sftbl; Hon Roll; JC Awd; Mary Feree 87; Cum Laude; Nrsng.

SWEIGART, DENNIS; Hershey HS; Hershey, PA; (2); 8/250; Ftbl; Im Wt Lftg; High Hon Roll.

SWEIGART, KIMBERLY N; Lampeter-Strasburg HS; Willow Street, PA; (4); 2/148; Am Leg Aux Girls St; Concert Band; Mrchg Band; Yrbk Stf; JV Bsktbl; Bausch & Lomb Sci Awd; NCTE Awd; VP NHS; Hon Roll; Pres Art Clb; PA Gvrnrs Schl For Sci 86; Judith Resnik Sci Schlrshp 86; Science.

SWEIGERT, DAWN; Little Flower HS; Philadelphia, PA; (3); Boys Clb Am; Cmnty Wkr; FNA; GAA; Office Aide; Teachers Aide; Varsity Clb; Jr Cls; Cheerleading; Coach Actv; Gwynedd-Mercy; Nrsng.

SWEINHART, JANET; Northern Bedford County HS; New Enterprise, PA; (3); 1/106; Cmnty Wkr; Pres VP 4-H; SADD; 4-H Awd; High Hon Roll; NHS; Ntl Merit SF; Voice Dem Awd; FTA; Library Aide; Isnt Of Food Technlgsts Frsmn Schlrshp 87; PSU Coll Of Ag Schlrshp 87; Bedford Cnty Outstndg 4-H Grl; Penn ST; Food Science.

SWEINHART, JENNIFER; Boyertown SR HS; Boyertown, PA; (4); Pres Church Yth Grp; Drama Clb; Teachers Aide; Chorus; School Musical; School Play; Variety Show; Fld Hcky; Lcrss; Hon Roll; Hood Coll; Psych.

SWEITZER, ERIC; Brookville Area HS; Brookville, PA; (3); Art Clb; German Clb; Orch; School Play; Symp Band; Var Ftbl; Hon Roll; PA ST U; Grmn Lang.

SWENN, KRIS; Meadville Area SR HS; Meadville, PA; (3); 27/338; French Clb; SADD; Varsity Clb; Nwsp Rptr; Var Socr; Var Sftbl; DAR Awd; Elks Awd; Hon Roll; 3 Yrs Ltrd Vrsty Scr 86-87; Coachs Awd 86-87; Ltrd 3 Yrs Vrsty Sftbl, Hghst Bttng Avg, Bst Def Plyr; Sci.

SWENSON JR, JOHN; Mc Dowell HS; Erie, PA; (2); Ski Clb; Rep Stu Cncl; JV Ftbl; Bus Admin.

SWENSON, JULIE; Harmony HS; Cherry Tree, PA; (4); 2/50; Office Aide; Red Cross Aide; Ski Clb; Rep Sec Stu Cncl; Cheerleading; Score Keeper; High Hon Roll; NHS; Sal; IN U Of PA.

SWENSON, LAUREL; Peabody HS; Pittsburgh, PA; (4); 2/292; Yrbk Stf; Trs Jr Cls; Stu Cncl; Cheerleading; Capt Swmmng; Tennis; High Hon Roll; Hon Roll; NHS; French Clb; Ski Clb.

SWETLAND, JAMIE; Elk Lake HS; Montrose, PA; (2); French Clb; Jazz Band; Nwsp Stf; Hon Roll; Prfct Atten Awd; Penn ST U; Elctrcl Engr.

SWETLAND, LISA; Couranesque Valley HS; Cowanesque, PA; (2); Library Aide; SADD; Band; Concert Band; Mrchg Band; Pep Band; Hon Roll.

SWETTS, LISA; Geibel HS; Star Junction, PA; (3); Drama Clb; Science Clb; Stage Crew; VP Jr Cls; Capt Cheerleading; High Hon Roll; NHS; Prfct Atten Awd; Spanish NHS; Voice Dem Awd; Sister Lucy Chem Awd 87; Dentistry.

SWIDERSKI, CHRISTINE; Southern Columbia HS; Catawissa, PA; (2); VP 4-H; French Clb; Ski Clb; Color Guard; Capt Drill Tm; Flag Corp; Nwsp Stf; 4-H Awd; Top 4-H Demnstrtr In Cnty 86; Hotel Manag.

SWIDERSKI, SUSAN; Shaler Area SR HS; Pittsburgh, PA; (3); Nwsp Rptr; Nwsp Stf; Tennis; French Hon Soc; Hon Roll; Comm.

SWIDZINSKI, CONNIE; Butler Area SR HS; Butler, PA; (4); 25/700; 4-H; FBLA; Hosp Aide; Ski Clb; Spanish Clb; Hon Roll; Jr NHS; NHS; Slippery Rock U; Elem Educ.

SWIER, TERRI L; Norristown Area HS; Norristown, PA; (4); 31/478; FBLA; Hosp Aide; Intnl Clb; SADD; Chorus; Orch; Symp Band; NHS; German Awd 86; Millersville U; German.

SWIERCZYNSKI, SHARON; Annville-Cleona HS; Annville, PA; (4); 1/112; Church Yth Grp; VP French Clb; Quiz Bowl; Sec SADD; Band; Madrigals; Lit Mag; Lion Awd; Sec NHS; Val; Amer Lgn Essay Awd 85; Hauck Mfg Math Awd 86; Wdmn Of Wrld Life Ins Hstry Awd 84 & 85; Juniata Coll; Dntstry.

SWIERINGA, SCOTT K; Hew Hope-Solebury HS; Lahaska, PA; (4); Art Clb; FBLA; Ski Clb; Teachers Aide; Variety Show; Hon Roll; Ldr Of Cls Intrctn 86; Penn ST; Bus Adm.

SWIFT, ROBERT TODD; Blue Mountain Acad; Lancaster, PA; (3); Camera Clb; Church Yth Grp; Spanish Clb; School Play; Variety Show; Bsktbl; Ftbl; Sftbl; Vllybl; Prfct Atten Awd; Franklin/Marshall Coll; Pre Law.

SWIGART, KAREN; Lenape Avis HS; Worthington, PA; (4); French Clb; VICA; Nwsp Rptr; Nwsp Stf; Yrbk Phtg; Yrbk Stf; Stu Cncl; Vllybl; High Hon Roll; Hon Roll; IN U; Mgmt Infrmtn Systms.

SWIGERT, EMILY; Big Spring HS; Carlisle, PA; (3); 24/258; Church Yth Grp; Chorus; School Musical; School Play; Stage Crew; Yrbk Stf; Rep Stu Cncl; Powder Puff Ftbl; Hon Roll; NHS; Med.

SWIGERT, SARA; Big Spring HS; Carlisle, PA; (3); 63/258; Church Yth Grp; Sec Chorus; School Musical; School Play; Stage Crew; Yrbk Stf; Rep Stu Cncl; JV Powder Puff Ftbl; JV Trk; Hon Roll; Penn ST Univ; Arch.

SWIMLEY, THOMAS; Cowangsque Valley HS; Knoxville, PA; (4); Boy Scts; Letterman Clb; Band; Ftbl; Hon Roll; NHS; Acadmc All Amercn 86; Fld Bio.

SWINDELL, IVA; Mc Connellsburg HS; Needmore, PA; (4); FHA; Yrbk Stf; Hagerstown JC; Nursing.

SWINDELL, TERESA; Huntingdon Area HS; James Creek, PA; (4); Church Yth Grp; 4-H; Chorus; Church Choir; Concert Band; Mrchg Band; Yrbk Stf; Hon Roll; St Francis Coll Schlrshp Acdmc 87; St Francis Coll.

SWINEHART, DONN RAE; South Williamsport Area HS; S Williamsport, PA; (3); 22/115; Capt Var Cheerleading; Var L Trk; Hon Roll; Computer Clb; Hst Soph Cls; Hst Jr Cls; Hst Sr Cls; Pres Phys Fit Awd 87; Airways Sci.

SWINEHART, LISA; Northern York HS; Dillsburg, PA; (4); 50/204; Church Yth Grp; Cmnty Wkr; Drama Clb; Stat Bsktbl; Intrnshp-Polc 86-87; Hnr Roll 83-84; Indianan U Of PA; Crmnlgy.

SWINGENSTEIN, ALLISON; Charters Valley HS; Pittsburgh, PA; (3); Church Yth Grp; Hosp Aide; Library Aide; Pep Clb; Orch; NHS; Grove Cty Coll; Med.

SWINGLE, FRED; Carbondale Area HS; Carbondale, PA; (4); 17/151; Computer Clb; French Clb; German Clb; Science Clb; Ski Clb; L Trk; Hon Roll; Penn ST; Elec Engr.

SWINGLER, NICOLE; Chambersburg Area SR HS; Chambersburg, PA; (2); French Clb; GAA; Mgr(s); Trk; Theater Arts.

SWINK, BUDDY; Mc Guffey HS; Washington, PA; (3); Pep Clb; Spanish Clb; Trk; Edinboro ST Coll.

SWINK, MICHAEL; Connellsville SR HS; Dawson, PA; (2); Pres Church Yth Grp; Office Aide; Sec Soph Cls; Bsbl; Bsktbl; Ftbl; Wt Lftg; High Hon Roll; Hon Roll; Jr NHS; Adminstrtv Brd Dawson Methdst Chrch 87; Plyr Week Ftbl 86-87; Phys Ther.

SWISHER, BRIAN; Waynesboro Area SR HS; Blue Ridge Smt, PA; (3); JV Wrstlng; Pilot.

SWISHER, HARRY; Hughesville JR/Sr HS; Unityville, PA; (3); 21/143; Am Leg Boys St; Chess Clb; Church Yth Grp; Office Aide; Ski Clb; Spanish Clb; SADD; Chorus; Church Choir; Nwsp Rptr; Wessley Dover DE; Acctng.

SWISHER, SUZIE; Scott Intermediate HS; Coatesville, PA; (2); 4-H; Chorus; 4-H Awd; Hon Roll; Hrs Show Awds 4-H, Pony Clb, Rgnls, Lcls 85-86; Secretary.

SWITCHETT, KIMBERLY; Simon Gratz HS; Philadelphia, PA; (3); Dance Clb; Drama Clb; Spanish Clb; Temple Yth Grp; Nwsp Rptr; Nwsp Sprt Ed; Var Bsktbl; Var Capt Cheerleading; Var Crs Cntry; Var Gym; Comms.

SWITZER, SCOTT; Oil City Area HS; Oil City, PA; (3); AFS; Chess Clb; Church Yth Grp; Varsity Clb; Stu Cncl; Bsbl; Ftbl; Swmmng; Trk; Wt Lftg; PIAA Dist 10 Swim Champ 86; Natl YMCA Swim Tm 86; Acctng.

SWITZER, VICKI; Central Columbia HS; Mifflinville, PA; (4); Key Clb; Pres Color Guard; Pres Acdmc Fit Awd 87; Amer Legn Schlrshp 87; IN U Of PA; Spch Pthlgy.

SWOBODA, JENNIFER; Conemaugh Township HS; Davidsville, PA; (3); 35/121; Drama Clb; VP JA; VP Ski Clb; Trs Chorus; School Play; Nwsp Ed-Chief; Ed Lit Mag; Stu Cncl; JV Var Bsktbl; Hon Roll; Rural Elect Yth Tour Awd; U Of MA; Pol Sci.

SWOMLEY, CHRISTOPHER; Northern York HS; Dillsburg, PA; (3); 51/232; Var Capt Socr; Hon Roll; NHS.

SWOPE, JUDI; Elizabethtown Area HS; Elizabethtown, PA; (4); 55/223; Sec Pres Church Yth Grp; Library Aide; Bus Stu Of Mon 87; Bus.

SWOPE, MICHAEL; Tussey Mt HS; Robertsdale, PA; (4); 16/116; VP Church Yth Grp; Pres FBLA; Nwsp Rptr; Yrbk Stf; Var L Bsktbl; Pres Golf; Hon Roll; FBLA Regional Champshp 5th Acctng I 87; SR Staffer Awd Schl Nwspr 87; Sewickley Vly Hosp Schl; Technl.

SWOPE, TODD; Du Bois Area HS; Luthersburg, PA; (2); 36/327; Trs Church Yth Grp; 4-H; Band; Concert Band; Jazz Band; Mrchg Band; Hon Roll; Penn ST; Comp.

SWORD, MIKE; Panther Valley HS; Nesquehoning, PA; (1); 60/127; Church Yth Grp.

SYLVESTER, JEANETTE; Everett Area HS; Everett, PA; (4); 18/104; Church Yth Grp; GAA; Spanish Clb; Varsity Clb; Band; Chorus; Rep Stu Cncl; Socr; High Hon Roll; Hon Roll; Two Ten Trust Chrty Schlrshp 87; Radford U; Nrs.

SYLVESTER, SUSAN; Everett Area HS; Everett, PA; (2); Church Yth Grp; Spanish Clb; Varsity Clb; Chorus; Stu Cncl; Var L Socr; Elem Ed.

SYLVESTER, TINA; Wyoming Area SR HS; Exeter, PA; (3); Church Yth Grp; Drama Clb; Key Clb; Spanish Clb; Chorus; Vllybl; PA ST; Photogrphr.

SYLVESTER, TOM; Center Area HS; Aliquippa, PA; (2); Church Yth Grp; SADD; VP Soph Cls; Bsktbl; Ftbl; Hon Roll.

SYMONS, SHANNON; Pine Grove Area HS; Pine Grove, PA; (3); Am Leg Aux Girls St; ROTC; Varsity Clb; Chorus; School Musical; Nwsp Rptr; Pres Frsh Cls; Pres Sr Cls; Capt Cheerleading; Cit Awd; Outstndng Chrldr; Pres Phys Ftns Awd, Hnr Roll; Bloomsburg; Psych.

SYMSEK, ALYSSA; Montour HS; Mckees Rks, PA; (3); Church Yth Grp; Color Guard; High Hon Roll; Hon Roll; Tang Soo Do Karate-Red Belt 2 Yrs; Organ 5 Yrs; Sftbll 7 Yrs.

SYNNESTVEDT, MAYA C; Acad Of The New Church; Huntingdon Valley, PA; (2); 1/15; Drama Clb; Hosp Aide; Pep Clb; Chorus; Var JV Cheerleading; Geom Awd 87; Med.

SYNOSKI, EDDIE; West Hazelton HS; Harwood Mines, PA; (3); 25/221; French Clb; Scholastic Bowl; Ski Clb; JV Bsktbl; Var Golf; Var Tennis; High Hon Roll; NHS; Pres Schlr; Stage Crew; Outstndng Acdmc Achvt Prsdntl Acdmc Ftnss Awd 85; Sprt Clb; Temple U; Biochem.

SYPECK, TRACEY; West Hazleton HS; Hazleton, PA; (2); Ski Clb; SADD; Chorus; Bsktbl; Police Acad; Criminal Justice.

SYPHARD, TRACY; Wilmington Area HS; Pulaski, PA; (3); 4/115; Dance Clb; Drama Clb; French Clb; Chorus; Drill Tm; High Hon Roll; Hon Roll.

SYPNIEWSKI, KEVIN; G A R HS; Wilkes-Barre, PA; (3); Church Yth Grp; FBLA; SADD; Stu Cncl; Var Bsbl; Var Wrstlng; Hon Roll; NHS; Banking.

SYPOLT, CYNTHIA; Liski Area HS; Apollo, PA; (4); Teachers Aide; Chorus; Church Choir; Yrbk Stf; VP Frsh Cls; Rep Jr Cls; Stu Cncl; Sftbl; High Hon Roll; Hon Roll; Robt Morris Coll; Bus Admin.

SYRES, DEREK; Girard College HS; Philadelphia, PA; (3); Chess Clb; Chorus; Var JV Bsbl; Var Capt Socr; JV Swmmng; Var JV Tennis; Cit Awd; High Hon Roll; Hon Roll; Amercn Legn Awd-Ctznshp & Schlrshp 84-85; Penn ST; Pre Med.

SZABO, JAMES; Louis E Dieruff HS; Allentown, PA; (4); 7/300; Debate Tm; Exploring; VP JA; ROTC; Ski Clb; Nwsp Rptr; Var L Crs Cntry; Var L Trk; NHS; Ntl Merit Ltr; PA Hghr Ed Asst Agncy Cert Of Merit 86; Aerosp Engrng.

SZABO, THAD P; Northampton Area SR HS; Nazareth, PA; (3); 8/494; Drama Clb; Math Clb; Math Tm; Scholastic Bowl; Chorus; School Musical; School Play; High Hon Roll; NHS; US Naval Acad Smmr Semnr, Wrkshps 87; Physics.

SZAKACH, CHERYL; Kennedy Christian HS; Sharpsville, PA; (3); 3/97; Library Aide; School Play; Stage Crew; Drama Clb; Concert Band; Mrchg Band; School Musical; Yrbk Stf; High Hon Roll; NEDT Awd; 4th Pl PMEA Dist 5 Chrs Fstvl 86; Sec Ed.

SZANYI, NEIL A; Liberty HS; Bethlehem, PA; (4); 5/400; Math Tm; Band; Church Choir; Concert Band; Mrchg Band; Orch; School Play; Lit Mag; Var L Swmmng; Ntl Merit SF; Dartmouth Clg Bk Clb Awd 86; Physcs.

SZAPACS, REBECCA; Northern Lehigh HS; Slatington, PA; (1); 18/185; Ski Clb; Varsity Clb; School Musical; Nwsp Stf; Yrbk Bus Mgr; Cheerleading; Trk; Hon Roll; JETS Awd; Pres Schlr; Pres Phys Ftnss Awd 87.

SZARKO, MARK; Oley Valley HS; Oley, PA; (3); Band; Concert Band; Jazz Band; Mrchg Band; Pep Band; Nwsp Rptr; Hon Roll.

SZCZECINA, KEVIN; Panther Valley HS; Lehighton, PA; (3); 5/132; Yrbk Stf; VP Jr Cls; VP Sr Cls; Var L Ftbl; Hon Roll; NHS; 2nd Tm All-Cnty Linebkr 1986; Pharmacy.

SZCZERBOWICZ, KATHLEEN; Shenandoah Valley HS; Shenandoah, PA; (3); 14/79; Trs Frsh Cls; Sec Soph Cls; Hst Jr Cls; Trs Sr Cls; Rep Stu Cncl; L Var Trk; Capt Twrlr; L Var Vllybl; Hon Roll; NHS; Acdmc All-Amer 87; Occptnl Thrpy.

SZCZYPIORSKI, KEVIN; Father Judge HS; Philadelphia, PA; (3); #53 In Class; Church Yth Grp; Cmnty Wkr; Drama Clb; Pep Clb; School Musical; School Play; Hon Roll; Awd Thrtr Arts Clb; Cert Hnr Acadc; Cert Awd Volntr Svc; Pre Med.

SZEKERESH, LYNN; Central Cambria HS; Johnstown, PA; (4); 14/214; Art Clb; Ski Clb; Band; Ed Nwsp Stf; Ed Yrbk Stf; Rep Stu Cncl; L Crs Cntry; Swmmng; Hon Roll; U Of Pittsburgh; Sci.

SZELES, DIANE; Bishop Mc Devitt HS; Harrisbrug, PA; (3); 74/250; Cmnty Wkr; FBLA; Hosp Aide; Office Aide; Service Clb; SADD; Chorus; Stu Cncl; Mgr(s); Tennis; Bus Admin.

SZEPESI, DENISE; Mc Keesport SR HS; White Oak, PA; (3); 12/410; Church Yth Grp; Girl Scts; Pep Clb; Acpl Chr; Chorus; Drill Tm; School Musical; School Play; Stat Bsktbl; Powder Puff Ftbl.

SZEWCZAK, CYNTHIA; Nazareth Acad; Phila, PA; (3); Hosp Aide; Sec Latin Clb; Q&S; Pres Service Clb; Nwsp Ed-Chief; Nwsp Phtg; Nwsp Rptr; Bowling; Sec NHS; Psych.

SZLAVIK, TANIA; Upper Merion Area HS; King Of Prussia, PA; (3); 47/300; Cmnty Wkr; Math Tm; Spanish Clb; School Musical; Nwsp Sprt Ed; Sec Soph Cls; Sec Jr Cls; JV Cheerleading; JV Lcrss; Var Trk; Prom Chrprsn 85-86; Princeton; Law.

SZLENER, ALEXANDER W; Norristown Area HS; Norristown, PA; (3); 51/491; German Clb; VICA; Diving; Hon Roll; Prfct Attend Awd 85-86; Genl Contrctng.

SZOLIS, LEIGH A; Richland HS; Wexford, PA; (4); 56/177; Art Clb; French Clb; Girl Scts; Hosp Aide; Nwsp Stf; Yrbk Stf; Rep Stu Cncl; Powder Puff Ftbl; Score Keeper; Hon Roll; La Roche; Fin.

SZOSZOREK, SUZANNE; Nazareth HS; Easton, PA; (3); Church Yth Grp; Debate Tm; Drama Clb; Exploring; Key Clb; Pep Clb; Political Wkr; Speech Tm; SADD; Chorus; Poltcl Sci.

SZPARAGOWSKI, GEORGE; Northeast Catholic HS; Philadelphia, PA; (2); 66/363; JV Wrstlng; Navy.

SZUBA, MICHAEL; Quaker Valley HS; Sewickley, PA; (3); 20/166; Key Clb; Var L Ftbl; Var L Trk.

SZUGYE, CHRISTINE ELIZABETH; Kennedy Christian HS; Farrell, PA; (4); 12/93; Church Yth Grp; Pep Clb; Science Clb; Spanish Clb; Im Bsktbl; Im Vllybl; High Hon Roll; Hon Roll; NHS; NEDT Awd; E A Seton Awd 83; Pres Ftnss Awd 87; Penn ST; Bus.

SZUGYE, TINA; Kennedy Christian HS; Farrell, PA; (4); 12/93; Pep Clb; Science Clb; Spanish Clb; Im Bsktbl; Im Vllybl; High Hon Roll; NHS; NEDT Awd; St Elizabeth Seton Awd 83; Penn ST; Bus.

SZUL, ANDY; Central HS; Philadelphia, PA; (3); Boys Clb Am; Boy Scts; Chess Clb; Civic Clb; Cmnty Wkr; Computer Clb; Debate Tm; Library Aide; Office Aide; Political Wkr; Advncd Plcmnt Engrng Crs 87; Pblshd Ptry In Mnthly Jrnl; Penn ST U; Law.

SZULBORSKI, JASON; Pleasant Valley HS; Effort, PA; (2); 21/250; Math Tm; Ski Clb; Var L Bsbl; Var L Ftbl; Hon Roll; Clemson U; Bsbl.

SZUSZCZEWICZ, BRENDA; Nazareth Acad; Philadelphia, PA; (4); Cmnty Wkr; Service Clb; Orch; Lit Mag; Hon Roll; Ntl Merit SF; Classrm Pres 87; Penn ST; Pltcl Sci.

SZVERRA, LISA; Selinsgrove Area HS; Selinsgrove, PA; (4); 20/210; Pres Trs 4-H; Varsity Clb; Nwsp Stf; Rep Stu Cncl; Var L Fld Hcky; Var L Trk; Dnfth Awd; 4-H Awd; Hon Roll; NHS; Bloomsburg U; Acctg.

SZYMALA, MICHELLE; Spring-Ford HS; Royersford, PA; (3); 26/256; Spanish Clb; Band; Concert Band; Mrchg Band; Pep Band; Symp Band; JV Cheerleading; High Hon Roll; Hon Roll; NHS; Vet.

SZYMANSKI, LARRY; West Allegheny HS; Oakdale, PA; (2); 20/200; Ski Clb; Spanish Clb; Var Tennis; Hon Roll; PA ST; Med Prfsn.

SZYMANSKI, PETER; Taylor Allderdice HS; Pittsburgh, PA; (3); Art Clb; Boy Scts; Cmnty Wkr; Ski Clb; Nwsp Rptr; Nwsp Stf; Im Diving; Mgr(s); Im Trk; Var Im Vllybl; Advrtsng.

SZYMKIEWICZ, MARK; Freeport Area HS; Sarver, PA; (2); Commercial Art.

SZYMKOWIAK, AARON; Hampton HS; Gibsonia, PA; (4); 7/260; Var L Bsbl; High Hon Roll; NHS; Ntl Merit Ltr; PA Hghr Ed Asstnc Agncy Cert Of Merit 87; Wstnghs Sci Hnrs Inst 86-87; Engrng.

SZYMKOWSKI, HEIDI; Kennedy Christian HS; Atlantic, PA; (3); 22/97; 4-H; Hosp Aide; Ski Clb; Spanish Clb; Yrbk Stf; Im Vllybl; 4-H Awd; Hon Roll; Rotary Awd; Dale Carnegie Crs & Grad Asstnt 86-87.

TABARRINI, RICHARD; Old Forge HS; Old Forge, PA; (3); Boy Scts; Ski Clb; Bsbl; Ftbl; Hon Roll; NHS; Pre Med.

TABARRINI, TARA; Old Forge HS; Old Forge, PA; (4); 23/104; Office Aide; Ski Clb; Yrbk Ed-Chief; High Hon Roll; Hon Roll; NHS; Typng Awd 85; PA ST; Undergrad Stu.

TABINOWSKI, KRISTIN; Seneca Valley SR HS; Mars, PA; (2); Art Clb; Sftbl; High Hon Roll; Hon Roll; Vet.

TABOR, LAURA; Council Rock HS; Newtown, PA; (3); 191/908; Church Yth Grp; Spanish Clb; Band; Concert Band; Drm Mjr(t); Mrchg Band; Pep Band; Symp Band; Hon Roll; Educ.

TABORSKI, KARIN; Fort Cherry HS; Mcdonald, PA; (2); Church Yth Grp; Drama Clb; Hosp Aide; Spanish Clb; School Play; Hon Roll.

TACELOSKY, ROBIN; Shenandoah Valley HS; Shenandoah, PA; (3); 9/80; Pep Clb; Hst Frsh Cls; Hst Soph Cls; Rep Jr Cls; Off Stu Cncl; Var Cheerleading; Stat Mgr(s); Var Sftbl; Hon Roll; NHS; U Of Pittsburgh; Med Rec Admin.

TACELOSKY, TONY; Marian HS; Mahonoy City, PA; (4); 11/110; Church Yth Grp; SADD; School Play; Stu Cncl; Co-Capt L Bsktbl; Coach Actv; L Ftbl; Trk; NHS; Spanish NHS; Elctrcl Engnrng.

TACHOVSKY, JENNIFER; Henderson HS; Kennett Square, PA; (3); 23/376; Intnl Clb; Office Aide; Ski Clb; Orch; School Musical; Yrbk Stf; Lit Mag; Trs Frsh Cls; Pres Soph Cls; Sec Stu Cncl; Acad Achvt Awd 87; Intl Bus.

TACK, DAVE; Knoch HS; Butler, PA; (2); Engr.

TACK, JENNIFER; Butter Area SR HS; Butler, PA; (3); Church Yth Grp; Band; Variety Show; Cheerleading; Gym; Hon Roll; Jr NHS; Elem Educ.

TADAJWESKI, ANN E; Easton Area HS; Easton, PA; (4); 1/460; Church Yth Grp; Exploring; Pres Key Clb; Ed Lit Mag; Var L Swmmng; Jr NHS; Pres NHS; Ntl Merit SF; Dartmouth Clb Estrn PA Bk Awd 86; Alliance Frnch Awd 85; Exchng Clb Stu Mth 86.

TADDEO, JOE; Ambridgea Area HS; Baden, PA; (4); Art Clb; AIASA 1st Plc STS Grphc Art; 2nd Plc Rgnl Grphc Art 85-86; 1st Plc Rgnl Grphc Art & 2nd ST 86-87; Indstrl Arts Tchrs.

TAFT, ERIN; Susquenita HS; Marysville, PA; (3); 20/200; French Clb; German Clb; Stage Crew; Nwsp Stf; Sec Frsh Cls; JV Var Cheerleading; JV Gym; Trk; Wt Lftg; High Hon Roll; Brdcstng.

TAGERT, STEVE; Upper Darby HS; Aldan, PA; (2); Lcrss; Socr; Swmmng; Hon Roll; High Honor Roll 83; Art Awd 85; Arch.

TAGLIABOSKI, LARIE; Bald Eagle Area HS; Bellefonte, PA; (4); 12/189; Varsity Clb; Yrbk Stf; Var L Bsktbl; L Crs Cntry; L Trk; High Hon Roll; NHS; Hghst Hnr Awd 87; James H Snyder Memrl Awd 87; US Army Rsrv Natl Schlr/Athlt Awd 87.

TAGLIENTE, DON; Clearfield Area HS; Clearfield, PA; (4); 17/296; Camera Clb; French Clb; Band; Chorus; Concert Band; Orch; Nwsp Phtg; Nwsp Rptr; Yrbk Phtg; High Hon Roll; PA ST U; Cmmnctns.

TAHAR, MICHAEL; Downingtown SR HS; Downingtown, PA; (3); Acpl Chr; Chorus; School Musical; Bowling; Vllybl; High Hon Roll; Hon Roll; Pres Schlr; PA ST; Engrng.

TAHTINEN, SHERRI; Tunkhannock HS; Tunkhannock, PA; (2); 2/340; Aud/Vis; Church Yth Grp; Dance Clb; German Clb; Key Clb; Latin Clb; Letterman Clb; Pep Clb; Ski Clb; Band.

TAHTINEN, TERRI; Tunkhannock Area HS; Tunkhannock, PA; (2); 2/340; Church Yth Grp; German Clb; Key Clb; Latin Clb; Letterman Clb; Concert Band; Mrchg Band; Mgr Stage Crew; Var Tennis; High Hon Roll.

TAIKO, KRISTIN; Mahanoy Area HS; Barnesville, PA; (4); Church Yth Grp; FHA; Spanish Clb; Chorus; Church Choir; Mc Canns Schl/Bus; Comp Sci.

TAKACH, CORA; Pottstown SR HS; Pottstown, PA; (3); 6/155; High Hon Roll; NHS.

TAKACH, SARA; Lakeland HS; Carbondale, PA; (4); 24/156; Drama Clb; FCA; FHA; Ski Clb; Band; Mrchg Band; School Musical; Nwsp Stf; Yrbk Stf; Cheerleading; Lakeland Svc Awd 87; ST Offcr FMA 86-87; Acad Fd Mrktng Schlrshp 87; St Josephs U; Food.

TAKACS, LAURE; Lincoln HS; Ellwood City, PA; (3); #43 In Class; Drama Clb; French Clb; School Play; Bowling; Tennis; High Hon Roll; Hon Roll; Cmmnctns.

TALACKA, RAYMOND; G A R Memorial HS; Wilkes-Barre, PA; (3); 2/150; Exploring; Ski Clb; Band; Jazz Band; Orch; L Golf; Trk; High Hon Roll; NEDT Awd; Natl Piano Plyng Audtns 83; Aeronatcl Engr.

TALARICO, JUDY; Canon-Mc Millan SR HS; Canonsburg, PA; (4); FBLA; Office Aide; Spanish Clb; High Hon Roll; NHS; Spanish NHS; FBLA Scholar Duffs Bus Inst 87; Duffs Bus Inst; Secy.

TALATY, MUKUL; Methacton SR HS; Audubon, PA; (3); 4/381; Math Tm; JV Golf; Var Tennis; JV Var Trk; High Hon Roll; Lion Awd; NHS; Ntl Merit Ltr; Pres Schlr; Top Score Cntnentl Calculus League, Cntnentl Comp Cont Awd & Natl Sci Olympiad Awd 86-87.

TALBAT, JULIE; Center HS; Monaca, PA; (3); 4/180; Band; Jazz Band; L Crs Cntry; Var L Trk; NHS; Educ.

TALBERT, BRUCE; Chester HS; Chester, PA; (3); 98/355; Drama Clb; French Clb; NAACP; Band; Chorus; Concert Band; Mrchg Band; School Musical; School Play; Tennis; Salisbury ST U; Bio.

TALBERT, CHRISTINE; John Bartram HS; Philadelphia, PA; (3); Church Yth Grp; Church Choir; All Stars Club 84-87; La Salle U; Psychlgst.

TALBERT, JEREMY F; Solanco HS; Holtwood, PA; (2); Chess Clb; Spanish Clb; Teachers Aide.

TALBOT, JOANNA; Oxford Area HS; Oxford, PA; (2); Ski Clb; School Play; Yrbk Stf; Stat Bsbl; Var JV Cheerleading; JV Fld Hcky; High Hon Roll; Hon Roll.

TALBOT, KIMBERLY LYN; Philadelphia-Montgomery Christ Acad; Philadelphia, PA; (4); Var Capt Fld Hcky; Var L Trk; Cit Awd; High Hon Roll; Hon Roll; Womens Track & Fld Var MVP 84-85.

TALBOT, RICHARD; Penncrest HS; Media, PA; (3); Var Bsbl; Var Bsktbl; Var Ftbl; Engrng.

TALERICO, TAMMY; Hopewell SR HS; Aliquippa, PA; (4); Church Yth Grp; Cmnty Wkr; Drama Clb; French Clb; Sec Thesps; Chorus; School Musical; Yrbk Stf; Penn ST; Ed.

TALFORD, ERIC; Reading HS; Reading, PA; (2); Art Clb; Science Clb; Off Soph Cls; Bsktbl; Ftbl; Trk; Merit Rll 86-87; Dntstry.

TALIANO JR, JOSEPH; Kennard-Dale HS; Stewartstown, PA; (2); Church Yth Grp; FBLA; Library Aide; High Hon Roll; Hon Roll; Bus Mgmt.

TALLION, LORI; Windber Area HS; Windber, PA; (3); Church Yth Grp; French Clb; Pres JA; VP Speech Tm; Concert Band; Mrchg Band; Yrbk Stf; High Hon Roll; NHS; Stu Month 85-87; AP Eng Awd Highest Grade 87; Pres Acad Fit 85; Nrsng.

TALLO, JENNY; Valley View HS; Peckville, PA; (1); Ski Clb; Spanish Clb; Chorus; School Musical; Var Swmmng; Var Trk; JV Vllybl; High Hon Roll; Phrmcst.

TALOTTA, ANGEL; St Maria Goretti HS; Philadelphia, PA; (4); 48/384; Art Clb; Pres Cmnty Wkr; Math Clb; Pres Model UN; Office Aide; Spanish Clb; Lit Mag; Rep Frsh Cls; Rep Soph Cls; High Hon Roll; Pres Acdmc Ftnss Awd 87.

TALTON, SONYA; Shady Side Acad; Pittsburgh, PA; (3); JA; SADD; Chorus; Church Choir; Var Bsktbl; Var Sftbl; Hon Roll; Church Yth Grp; French Clb; Acpl Chr; Chrprsn Big Bros/Bis Sis 87-88; Ofcr Oxfam Hngr Rlf Pgm 87-88; Advncd Art Awd 86-87; Law.

TALUBA, DENISE; James M Coughlin HS; Wilkes Barre, PA; (4); 24/324; FBLA; High Hon Roll; Jr NHS; NHS; Pres Schlr; PA ST Frsh Schlrshp 87-88facadc Ltr & Lamp Knwldg Pin 87; PA ST U; Bus Adm.

TALUTTO, JOE; Dunmore HS; Dunmore, PA; (3); 23/150; Varsity Clb; Ftbl; Trk; Wt Lftg; High Hon Roll; Hon Roll; PA ST; Arch Engr.

TAMBURLIN, JEFFREY; St Marys Area HS; Kersey, PA; (3); Church Yth Grp; L Bsbl; Capt Ftbl; Var Wt Lftg; Sprts Med.

TAMIN, OMAR; Cumberland Valley HS; Camp Hill, PA; (3); 40/591; Latin Clb; Model UN; Hon Roll; NHS; JV Var Bsbl; JV Bsktbl; JV Ftbl; Var Tennis; Law.

TAMMARIELLO, AMY; General Mc Lane HS; Edinboro, PA; (3); 8/220; German Clb; Capt Color Guard; Capt Drill Tm; Nwsp Rptr; Pres Jr Cls; VP Sr Cls; Capt Cheerleading; Var Sftbl; High Hon Roll; NHS; Edinboro U; Pre-Med.

TAMMARO, CYNTHIA; Fairview HS; Fairview, PA; (3); 8/165; French Clb; Varsity Clb; Pres Rep Frsh Cls; Pres Rep Soph Cls; Pres Rep Jr Cls; Rep Sr Cls; Stu Cncl; Var L Socr; Var L Swmmng; High Hon Roll; Zonta Clb Erie II Amelia Earhart Ldrshpawd 87; Schlrshp Penn ST Smmr Soccer Camp 87.

TAMMARO, DOUG; Lincoln/Ellwood City HS; Ellwood City, PA; (4); 39/170; Church Yth Grp; Latin Clb; Political Wkr; Nwsp Stf; Yrbk Stf; Pres Soph Cls; Pres Jr Cls; Pres Sr Cls; L Bsktbl; Wolves Clb Scholar 87; Spellman Schlr-Ath Awd 87; Rotary Yth Ldrshp Awd 86; Baldwin-Wallace Coll; Cmmnctns.

TAMMARO, MARIA; Lincoln HS; Ellwood City, PA; (4); 23/169; French Clb; SADD; Y-Teens; Powder Puff Ftbl; High Hon Roll; Hon Roll; Pres Schlr; IN U Of PA; Nrsng.

TAMOSAUSKAS, RONA; Avonworth JR/SR HS; Pittsbg, PA; (4); 7/99; Yrbk Stf; Lit Mag; Stat Bsbl; Var Bsktbl; CC Awd; High Hon Roll; NHS; Outstndng Bus Awd, Pres Acdmc Ftns Awd 87; Nrth Boros Yth Awd 85; U Of Pittsburgh; Phys Thrpy.

TAN, CRAIG; Gen Mc Lane HS; Edinboro, PA; (3); 3/217; VP German Clb; Ski Clb; Concert Band; Jazz Band; Symp Band; Var L Tennis; High Hon Roll; NHS; 4-H; Germn Merit Awd 86-87; Rnkd 22nd Alleghny Mtn Tnns Assn 86; Bio.

TANA, BOB; Archbishop Ryan HS For Boys; Philadelphia, PA; (2); 78/430; Ftbl; Socr; Penn ST; Comp Sci.

TANDON, ROHIT; Chartiers Valley HS; Pittsburgh, PA; (3); Intnl Clb; Model UN; Pep Clb; Red Cross Aide; Nwsp Ed-Chief; NHS; Rep Stu Cncl; Invstmnt Bankng.

TANEYHILL, DEBORAH; Altoona Area HS; Altoona, PA; (3); 8/800; Sec Computer Clb; German Clb; Q&S; Nwsp Ed-Chief; Yrbk Sprt Ed; Pres Frsh Cls; Pres Soph Cls; Capt Bsktbl; Twrlr; CC Awd; Strtr Ntl & ST Bsktbl Chmpns 86; AAU Ntl JR Olympic Bsktbl Trnmnt 86.

TANG, ANGELA; West Catholic Girls HS; Philadelphia, PA; (3); 5/250; Spanish Clb; Cheerleading; Sec Sr Cls; Sec Stu Cncl; High Hon Roll; Hon Roll; NHS; Span Awd Hghst Avg 86; Geom Hnrbl Mntn 2nd Hghst Avg 86; U Of PA; Pharmacy.

TANG, CHARLES; Gateway SR HS; Monroeville, PA; (3); Ski Clb; Orch; Yrbk Stf; Rep Sr Cls; Rep Stu Cncl; High Hon Roll; Prfct Atten Awd; Pres Schlr; Pres Clsrm Yng Amer 87; Med.

TANG, DENNY; Carrick HS; Pittsburgh, PA; (2); Math Tm; School Play; Stage Crew; Rep Stu Cncl; JV Ftbl; Im Tennis; High Hon Roll; Jr NHS; NCTE Awd; Prfct Atten Awd; Mr Zooks Attndnc Awd 85-86; CMU; Engrng.

TANG, DON; Carrick HS; Pittsburgh, PA; (3); Math Clb; School Musical; School Play; Stage Crew; Ftbl; Tennis; Cit Awd; 4-H Awd; High Hon Roll; Hon Roll; Acad Lttr 86; Most Lkly To Sccd 84; Carneige Mellon U; Elec Engrng.

TANG, NELSON; Carrick HS; Pittsburgh, PA; (1); Chess Clb; Library Aide; Math Tm; School Musical; Stage Crew; Rep Civic Clb; Trs Stu Cncl; CCAC Fst-Pcd Math 86.

TANG, RICKY P; Archbishop Ryan HS For Boys; Philadelphia, PA; (4); 28/450; Chess Clb; Cmnty Wkr; Computer Clb; Nwsp Ed-Chief; High Hon Roll; NHS; Prfct Atten Awd; Temple U; Med.

TANG, WENDY; Philadelphia H S For Girls; Philadelphia, PA; (3); Hosp Aide; Tennis; Hon Roll; Penn ST; Pre Med.

TANNENBAUM, RICHARD; George Washington HS; Philadelphia, PA; (3); 15/840; Computer Clb; VP JA; Science Clb; Pres Trs Temple Yth Grp; Yrbk Stf; Lit Mag; Gov Hon Prg Awd; Hon Roll; JETS Awd; NHS; Del PA Natl Jr Scl & Hum Symp 87; 1st DE Vly Sci Fair 86 & 87; 1st Awds PA JR Acad Sci 86 & 87; Drexel U; Physics.

TANNER, ANGELA; William Allen HS; Allentown, PA; (4); 60/559; Church Yth Grp; Drama Clb; Exploring; Hosp Aide; JA; Ski Clb; Spanish Clb; Chorus; Church Choir; Color Guard; U Of NC; Pre-Med.

TANNER, MARTHA; Shenango HS; New Castle, PA; (3); 7/123; Twrlr; Im Vllybl; High Hon Roll; Hon Roll; Jr NHS.

TANNER, PATRICK; New Castle HS; New Castle, PA; (4); 43/227; Spanish Clb; Bsbl; Bowling; Golf; Hon Roll; Pres Schlr; Acadmc All American 86-87; ICM Schl Bus; Accounting Mngmt.

TANNER, TERRY L; Warrior Run HS; Turbotville, PA; (3); 10/166; AFS; Am Leg Boys St; Church Yth Grp; Spanish Clb; Band; Concert Band; Jazz Band; Mrchg Band; Pep Band; School Musical; Flight.

TANOVAN, DAVID; Abington SR HS; Elkins Park, PA; (3); Church Yth Grp; Letterman Clb; Quiz Bowl; Spanish Clb; SADD; Varsity Clb; Chorus; Church Choir; School Musical; School Play; 1st Tm All Lg Hnrs Colonial Div Ten 86-87; Mst Insprtnl Awd Ten 85-86; Minority Adv Plcmnt Pgm 86-87; Villanova; Pre-Med.

TANTLINGER, SHAWN; Greater Latrobe SR HS; Latrobe, PA; (3); 40/379; Church Yth Grp; Letterman Clb; Office Aide; Spanish Clb; Varsity Clb; VP Frsh Cls; Pres VP Stu Cncl; Var L Bsktbl; Var L Sftbl; High Hon Roll; Hghst Scor Ag 84-85; St Vincent; Med Fld.

TAORIMINA, DEAN; Monaca JR SR HS; Monaca, PA; (3); 7/90; School Musical; Bsbl; Bsktbl; Ftbl; Vllybl; Hon Roll; NHS; Elem Ed.

TAORMINA, MARIA; St Paul Cathedral HS; Pittsburgh, PA; (3); Church Yth Grp; Civic Clb; Cmnty Wkr; Dance Clb; Exploring; German Clb; Hosp Aide; Library Aide; Natl Beta Clb; Pep Clb; Intl Affrs.

TAPIA, BRENDA; Wyoming Area SR HS; Exeter, PA; (4); 15/249; FBLA; High Hon Roll; NHS; Full Schlrhsp Mc Cann 87-88; Mc Cann Schl Bus; Accntng.

TAPPER, JACOB; Akiba Hebrew Acad; Merion, PA; (4); Art Clb; Debate Tm; Drama Clb; Political Wkr; Nwsp Stf; Pres Stu Cncl; Bsktbl; Tennis; Wt Lftg; Ntl Merit Ltr; Art Achvt 87; U Of PA Bk Awd 86; Dartmouth Coll; Crtnst.

TARABRELLA, CHRISTINA; Elizabeth Forward HS; Elizabeth, PA; (4); 60/392; 4-H; Yrbk Stf; Sec Soph Cls; Sec Jr Cls; Cheerleading; Crs Cntry; Swmmng; Trk; High Hon Roll; Hon Roll; D Klein Memrl Schlrshp 87; Smmr Dnc Fstvl 1st Pl 86; Miss Allghny Cnty Pgnt Fnls 87; U Of Pittsburgh; Phy Thrpy.

TARAN, MELISSA; Hughesville HS; Picture Rocks, PA; (4); 4/156; Art Clb; Key Clb; Letterman Clb; Ski Clb; SADD; Chorus; School Musical; Pres Soph Cls; Pres Sr Cls; Rep Stu Cncl; Green White Awawd Ldrshp Schlrshp & Prsnlty 83-86; Psychology.

TARANTO, ANTHONY; Lincoln HS; Ellwood City, PA; (3); 100/169; Church Yth Grp; Political Wkr; Spanish Clb; Rep Frsh Cls; Var Bsktbl; Coach Actv; Hon Roll; Prfct Atten Awd; Bus.

TARAS, KRISTEN; Bentworth HS; Bentleyville, PA; (4); 21/133; Ski Clb; Drm Mjr(t); School Play; Yrbk Stf; Pres Stu Cncl; High Hon Roll; NHS; Acdmc All-Amrcn Schlr 87; Penn ST U; Brdcstng.

TARASE, DAWN; Fox Chapel HS; Pittsburgh, PA; (3); 73/349; Church Yth Grp; Hosp Aide; Chorus; Variety Show; JV Powder Puff Ftbl; JV Trk; High Hon Roll; Math.

TARASIEWICZ, KAREN; St Hubert HS For Girls; Philadelphia, PA; (3); 69/421; Church Yth Grp; Cmnty Wkr; Chorus; Hon Roll; Typng Cert Merit, Shrthand Spd Cert, Cert Acdmc Merit 87; Phys Thrpy.

TARASZKI, PENNY; Villa Maria Acad; Erie, PA; (3); Science Clb; Capt Color Guard; Concert Band; Drm & Bgl; Drm Mjr(t); Capt Mrchg Band; Soph Cls; Stu Cncl; Var Trk; Hon Roll; U Of Pittsburgh; Nrsng.

TARCSON, TIM; Central Christian HS; Du Bois, PA; (4); 14/40; Pres Varsity Clb; School Play; Nwsp Ed-Chief; VP Sr Cls; Var Bsbl; Var Capt Bsktbl; Crs Cntry; Mgr(s); Var L Socr; John Klees Memrl Awd Stu Athl Yr 86-87; Gannon U Erie; Hstry.

TARDIVO, KEITH; Kiski Area SR HS; Vandergrift, PA; (3); Computer Clb; Math Clb; Ski Clb; Nwsp Rptr; Pres Stu Cncl; JV Var Bsbl; Var L Swmmng; Prfct Atten Awd; Rotary Awd; IN U PA; Acctng.

TARLE, MICHAEL J; Elizabeth Forward HS; Elizabeth, PA; (3); 14/365; Church Yth Grp; JA; Leo Clb; Crs Cntry; Capt Var Golf; Trk; Hon Roll; Arch Div W Penn Ind Arts Fair 86-87; Arch.

TARONE, DIANA; Hazleton SR HS; Hazleton, PA; (2); Drama Clb; French Clb; Pep Clb; Drill Tm; JV Bsktbl; Hon Roll; Pre-Law.

TARQUINIO, JOSEPH M; Belle Vernon Area HS; Belle Vernon, PA; (3); Chess Clb; Computer Clb; Ftbl; High Hon Roll; Hon Roll; PA ST U; Math.

TARR, GYONGYVER G; Central Bucks West HS; Doylestown, PA; (4); Intnl Clb; Library Aide; Red Cross Aide; Pres Schlr; U Of PA; Achlgy.

TARTAL, GEORGE; Southmoreland HS; Mt Pleasant, PA; (4); 7/233; French Clb; VP Math Clb; French Hon Soc; Jr NHS; NHS; Pres Schlr; PA ST U; Mech Engrng.

TARTAL, LORI A; Southmoreland SR HS; Scottdale, PA; (4); 5/230; French Clb; Trs Math Clb; Ski Clb; Yrbk Stf; Rep Stu Cncl; Sec French Hon Soc; High Hon Roll; NHS; Pres Schlr; Natl Merit Schlrshp Corp Contntl Grain 87-91; BASF Schlrshp 87; Westmnstr Coll; Acctng.

TARVIN, MIKE; Crestwood HS; Wapwallopen, PA; (3); Var L Socr; Var L Vllybl; Hon Roll.

TASSE, MICHELLE; Methacton HS; Audubon, PA; (3); 97/381; SADD; Ed Yrbk Stf; Rep Frsh Cls; Rep Soph Cls; Rep Jr Cls; Rep Sr Cls; Rep Stu Cncl; JV Var Cheerleading; Math.

TASSON, ANTOINETTE; North Star HS; Hooversville, PA; (4); 25/129; Chorus; Church Choir; Mrchg Band; Swing Chorus; VP Frsh Cls; Hon Roll; Dist Chrl Fstvls 84-86; 2nd Chr Awd, All Cnty Chrus 85-86; Hlth Prof.

TATE, JAMES; Blackhawk HS; Beaver Falls, PA; (4); Aud/Vis; Chess Clb; FFA; Chorus; School Musical; Stage Crew; High Hon Roll; Hon Roll; PIA; Air Frame Mech.

TATE, KRIS; Bradford Central Christian HS; Bradford, PA; (4); Pep Clb; SADD; Varsity Clb; Yrbk Stf; Sec Frsh Cls; Capt L Bsktbl; Stat Sftbl; Mercyhurst Coll; Sprts Med.

TATE, LISA; Altoona Area HS; Altoona, PA; (4); 29/718; Science Clb; Ski Clb; Spanish Clb; Soph Cls; Jr Cls; Stu Cncl; Bsktbl; Cheerleading; High Hon Roll; Jr NHS; NHS; Pres Physcl Ftns 84-85; U Pittsburgh; Phrmcy.

TATE, SCOTT A; South Side Area HS; Hookstown, PA; (4); 2/122; Am Leg Boys St; Boy Scts; Nwsp Rptr; VP Stu Cncl; Stat Bsktbl; Stat Ftbl; DAR Awd; Elks Awd; Pres NHS; Sal; Grnge Schlrshp 87; Air Frce Rcrtng Math & Sci Awd 87; Resdntl Acadmc Ftns Awd 87; GA Tech; Arspc Engrng.

TATE, STACIE; Penns Manor HS; Clymer, PA; (3); 23/97; Church Yth Grp; Color Guard; Mrchg Band; Var Cheerleading; Hon Roll; NHS; Chorus.

TATE, WESLEY A; Parkland HS; Allentown, PA; (4); 16/438; Sec Church Yth Grp; Drama Clb; French Clb; Church Choir; Var Mgr(s); Var Tennis; High Hon Roll; Hon Roll; NHS; Ntl Merit Schol; The U Of TX; Lbrl Arts.

TATE, YOLONDA; Bensalem HS; Bensalem, PA; (3); Dance Clb; FBLA; Key Clb; Bsktbl; Ftbl; NHS; Pep Clb; Chorus; Church Choir; Bsktbl; JR Actvty Comte 86-87; Syracuse U; Bus Admin.

TATMAN II, LESTER; St Josephs Preparatory Schl; Philadelphia, PA; (4); Pres Church Yth Grp; Math Tm; Chorus; Var L Bowling; Var L Trk; Hon Roll; Prfct Atten Awd; Hgh Hnrs Natl Greek Exam 84-86; Slvr Mdl Frnch & Math 87; FL A&M U; Phys Ther.

TATTON, DAWN; St Paul Cathedral HS; Pittsburgh, PA; (3); 8/70; Camera Clb; Church Yth Grp; Cmnty Wkr; Computer Clb; French Clb; Intnl Clb; Red Cross Aide; Science Clb; SADD; Nwsp Stf; Psych.

TATUM, JENNIFER; Wm Allen HS; Allentown, PA; (3); Letterman Clb; VP Service Clb; Varsity Clb; Yrbk Stf; Rep Soph Cls; Rep Jr Cls; JV Var Bsktbl; L Trk; Var Capt Vllybl; 1st Tm East Penn All-ST, Big A Booster Clb Trophy & East Penn Conf Hnrb Mntn For Vllybl 85-87.

TAULANE III, JOHN; St Josephs Prep; Huntingdon Vly, PA; (4); 9/225; French Clb; Pep Clb; Nwsp Rptr; Var L Bsktbl; Capt Var Socr; Var L Trk; Hon Roll; NHS; Teen Achvmnt Awd & Schlrshp 87; All Cty & All ST Sccr 86; Stu/Athlt Awd 87; Lafayette Coll; Law.

TAUSCHMAN, JODY; Northampton SR HS; Northampton, PA; (2); Chorus; Var Cheerleading; Var Trk; High Hon Roll.

TAUTKUS, CHRISTINE; Shanandoah Valley HS; Shenandoah, PA; (3); 6/79; Bsktbl; Capt Vllybl; High Hon Roll; NHS; Acad All Amer 87; Cmnctns.

TAUZIN, JEFFREY; Susquehanneck HS; Shrewsbury, PA; (2); 27/243; Off Boy Scts; Band; Mrchg Band.

TAWNEY, KRISTIAN; Ambridge Area HS; Freedom, PA; (4); Church Yth Grp; French Clb; Pep Clb; Red Cross Aide; Stage Crew; Off Jr Cls; Hon Roll; Accntng.

TAXIN, ADAM; Strath Haven HS; Wallingford, PA; (2); Debate Tm; Model UN; Political Wkr; Scholastic Bowl; Sec Spanish Clb; Jazz Band; Nwsp Sprt Ed; Rep Jr Cls; Tennis; High Hon Roll; Natl French Contest 87; Natl Spanish Contest 87; PA Govrnrs School For Intl Studies Schlrshp 87.

TAYLOR, AL; Coatesville Area SR HS; Coatesville, PA; (2); Church Yth Grp; JV Bsbl; JV Bsktbl; Prfct Atten Awd; Bst Drsd Awd 86-87; Bus.

TAYLOR, ALISON; Fairview HS; Fairview, PA; (3); Sec German Clb; Model UN; Varsity Clb; Orch; Rep Frsh Cls; Rep Jr Cls; Rep Sr Cls; Stu Cncl; Var L Socr; Trk; Pres Of Fairview Chptr Of JR Stsmn Of Am 87-88; 1st Chr Flute Dist Orch 86-87; 3rd Chr Flute Rgnl Orc; Law.

TAYLOR, BEVERLY ANN; Mahonoy Area HS; Delano, PA; (3); Hosp Aide; Spanish Clb; SADD; Teachers Aide; Chorus; Church Choir; Yrbk Stf; Bloomsburg U; Comp.

TAYLOR, BONNIE SUE; Seneca Vly HS; Mars, PA; (4); Church Yth Grp; Cmnty Wkr; Computer Clb; Drama Clb; JA; Latin Clb; Math Clb; Pep Clb; SADD; Teachers Aide; Butler.

TAYLOR, BRADLEY; Juniata HS; Mifflintown, PA; (3); 1/225; Pres Church Yth Grp; Dance Clb; Varsity Clb; Trs Frsh Cls; Var JV Bsktbl; Var JV Socr; Var Tennis; High Hon Roll; NHS; Math Tchr.

TAYLOR, CATHERINE; Kennedy Christian HS; Sharon, PA; (3); 20/97; Church Yth Grp; Hosp Aide; Concert Band; Flag Corp; Jazz Band; Mrchg Band; Stu Cncl; High Hon Roll; Hon Roll; NHS; Westminster Coll; Elem Educ.

TAYLOR, CHAMISE; Scott Intermediate HS; Coatesville, PA; (2); Nwsp Stf; Var L Bsktbl; Hon Roll; Prfct Atten Awd; Med.

TAYLOR, CHELSEA; Juniata HS; Mifflintown, PA; (4); Aud/Vis; Debate Tm; Drama Clb; SADD; School Musical; School Play; Off Stu Cncl; Cheerleading; High Hon Roll; NHS; Speech Hnr Awd 87; Juniata Coll; Dentistry.

TAYLOR, CHERYL; Northeast Bradford HS; Rome, PA; (3); Sec FHA; Chorus; Church Choir; Trs Soph Cls; High Hon Roll; NHS; Bradford Cnty Dairy Prncss 87; Diagnstc Med.

TAYLOR, CHRISTINE; Northwestern SR HS; Cranesville, PA; (2); Hon Roll.

TAYLOR, CULLEN; Faith Christian Schl; East Stroudsburg, PA; (4); 1/5; Pres Church Yth Grp; VP Soph Cls; Rep Sr Cls; Rep Stu Cncl; Var Bsktbl; Var Socr; Var Sftbl; High Hon Roll; Hon Roll; Intl Christian Hnr Soc 87; Messiah Coll.

TAYLOR, CYNTHIA; Altoona HS; Altoona, PA; (3); Library Aide; Chorus; Church Choir; High Hon Roll; Hon Roll; NHS; Ms Amer Coed Pgnt Fnlst For PA 87; IUP; Physcl Thrpy.

TAYLOR, DAVID; Schenley HS; Pittsburgh, PA; (3); 3/160; Computer Clb; German Clb; Math Clb; Math Tm; Yrbk Stf; JV L Bsbl; High Hon Roll; NHS; Engrng.

TAYLOR, DAVID; Vincentian HS; Weyford, PA; (1); Church Yth Grp; Debate Tm; NFL; Var Bsktbl; Socr; High Hon Roll.

TAYLOR, DEANN R; Connellsville Area HS; Connellsville, PA; (2); 2/525; Exploring; Hosp Aide; Pep Clb; Symp Band; Nwsp Stf; Yrbk Stf; Stu Cncl; JV Cheerleading; High Hon Roll; Pres Schlr; Mst Outstndng Stu Awd 86; Acdmc Excllnc Gold Pn Awd 86; Med.

TAYLOR, DEBRA; Big Spring HS; Newville, PA; (3); 33/258; Exploring; FHA; SADD; Hon Roll; Intrprsnl Rel Awd 86; Pol Sci.

TAYLOR, ELIZA L; Springside Schl; Glenside, PA; (3); Hosp Aide; Service Clb; SADD; Jazz Band; Orch; Lit Mag; Lcrss; Socr; Sftbl; Hon Roll; Cum Laude Soc 87; Brown U Bk Awd Engl Exprssn 87; Engl.

TAYLOR, GEOFFREY; Beaver Area SR HS; Beaver, PA; (3); Church Yth Grp; FCA; German Clb; Math Clb; Ski Clb; Ftbl; Var Ice Hcky; Var Socr; Var Swmmng; Var Tennis; Engrng.

TAYLOR III, GEORGE L; Lampeter-Strasburg HS; Strasburg, PA; (4); Church Yth Grp; German Clb; Key Clb; Spanish Clb; Varsity Clb; Chorus; Church Choir; Rep Frsh Cls; Rep Stu Cncl; Bsbl; Soccer All Stars Outstndng Offnsv Plyr 87; Cnty Lgy Top Six All Star Bsktbl 87; Adm Awd Outstndng Athl; Pittsburgh U; Sports Med.

TAYLOR, GRAHAM C; Trinity HS; Washington, PA; (3); Library Aide; W Lbrty ST Coll; Plc Ofcr.

TAYLOR, GREGORY; Hickory HS; Hermitage, PA; (3); Drama Clb; NFL; Trs Speech Tm; Jazz Band; Ed Yrbk Phtg; L Golf; NHS; Spanish NHS; Spanish Clb; Band; 8th St Forensic Trnmnt 87; Kodak, Hallmark, KS City Str Blue Rbbn Awd 84-85; Bus Admin.

TAYLOR, HEATHER; Lake Lehman HS; Shavertown, PA; (2); 4-H; Hosp Aide; Ski Clb; Temple Yth Grp; Band; Color Guard; Drill Tm; Flag Corp; Mrchg Band; Var L Twrlr; Sci.

TAYLOR, HOLLY; Knock JR SR HS; Butler, PA; (2); Church Yth Grp; SADD; Chorus; Madrigals; School Musical; Hon Roll; Ntl Merit Ltr; Slippery Rock Smmr Acad Of Perfmng Arts 87; Mst Imprvd Stu In Algebra 86; Slippery Rock; Tchr.

TAYLOR, JACKIE; Penn Manor HS; Lancaster, PA; (3); 6/300; Key Clb; Band; Concert Band; Nwsp Ed-Chief; Nwsp Rptr; High Hon Roll; Hon Roll; NHS; Spanish NHS; Am U; Cmnctns.

TAYLOR, JACQUELINE; Cambria Heights HS; Bakerton, PA; (3); Cmnty Wkr; Drama Clb; Ski Clb; Band; Concert Band; School Play; Stage Crew; Yrbk Rptr; Yrbk Stf; Penn ST; Cmmnctns.

TAYLOR, JAMES J; Northeast Catholic HS; Philadelphia, PA; (3); 30/356; Aud/Vis; Radio Clb; Nwsp Ed-Chief; Nwsp Stf; Rep Jr Cls; Hon Roll; NHS; Spnsh Ltrcy Awd 85-86; Drexel U; Bus Mgmt.

TAYLOR, JAMES LAMONTE; Westinghouse HS; Pittsburgh, PA; (3); Aud/Vis; JA; Nwsp Rptr; Nwsp Stf; Hon Roll; NY U Cazenovia; Jrnlsm.

TAYLOR, JEFF; Jamestown Area HS; Jamestown, PA; (4); 5/52; Varsity Clb; Wrstlng; Air Force; Elctrncs.

TAYLOR, JEFFREY; B Reed Henderson HS; W Chester, PA; (3); Latin Clb; JV Ftbl; Hon Roll; Ntl Merit Ltr; Econ.

TAYLOR, JENNIE; Lancaster Mennonite HS; Lancaster, PA; (3); Church Yth Grp; Band; Chorus; Church Choir; Concert Band; Mrchg Band; Orch; Swing Chorus; Hon Roll; WOLT Invlvd Intl Level 3rd & 6th Pl 85; Moody Bible Inst; Music.

TAYLOR, JENNIFER; Bellwood-Antis HS; Bellwood, PA; (3); 5/115; Varsity Clb; Chorus; Church Choir; School Musical; Yrbk Stf; Var L Cheerleading; Var L Fld Hcky; Var L Trk; High Hon Roll; NHS; Penn ST U.

TAYLOR, JENNIFER; Henderson HS; West Chester, PA; (2); 7/335; French Clb; Ski Clb; French Hon Soc; Hon Roll; 2nd Plc Law Dy Cntst 86; Vet.

TAYLOR, JENNIFER; Kennard-Dale HS; Delta, PA; (2); German Clb; Varsity Clb; Band; Concert Band; Mrchg Band; Pep Band; JV Cheerleading; JV Fld Hcky; Var Trk; Track Rcrds Long & Triple Jump 87; Dist Track 2nd Long Jump,6th Triple Jump 87; ST Track 11th Long Jp; Accntng.

TAYLOR, JODI; Lake-Lehman HS; Harveys Lake, PA; (3); Key Clb; Ski Clb; SADD; School Play; Yrbk Rptr; Yrbk Sprt Ed; Yrbk Stf; Var JV Fld Hcky; Mgr(s); Stat Trk; Accntnt.

TAYLOR, JULIE; West York Area HS; York, PA; (3); 19/189; German Clb; Hosp Aide; Trs Chorus; Church Choir; Hon Roll; F Chopin Piano Awd 86; Fnlst Ms PA Ntl Tn Pgnt 84-85; Nrsng.

TAYLOR, KELLY L; Saucon Valley SR HS; Bethlehem, PA; (4); Drm Mjr(t); Var L Swmmng; Twrlr; High Hon Roll; Hon Roll; NHS; Pres Schlr; Shippensburg U; Elem Educ.

TAYLOR, KEVIN; Neshaminy HS; Trevose, PA; (4); 63/680; Church Yth Grp; FCA; Chorus; Jazz Band; School Musical; Var JV Socr; Var Tennis; Cit Awd; Hon Roll; Ntl Hnr Soc 86-87; Rotary Intntl 87; Drexel U; Mech Engr.

TAYLOR, MARGARETTA; Boiling Springs JR HS; Boiling Spgs, PA; (3); 10/130; Band; Chorus; Church Choir; Mrchg Band; School Play; Mgr(s); Hon Roll; NHS; Dist Chrs; Rgnl Chrs; Wake Forest Coll; Bus.

TAYLOR, MARNIE; Nazareth Acad; Bensalem, PA; (3); Boy Scts; Pres Intnl Clb; Latin Clb; Model UN; Service Clb; Lit Mag; VP Jr Cls; Var Swmmng; Hon Roll; 1st Pl In Schl For The Ashme Math Tst 87; Cmnctns.

TAYLOR, MARYLYNN; Avella JR SR HS; Avella, PA; (3); French Clb; Ski Clb; Varsity Clb; Yrbk Stf; Sec Jr Cls; Score Keeper; Vllybl; Hon Roll; Slppry Rck U; Schl Tchr.

TAYLOR, MATTHEW; Central Catholic HS; Pittsburgh, PA; (3); 20/300; Dance Clb; Science Clb; JV Bsktbl; Var L Trk; High Hon Roll; Hon Roll; Trs NHS; Latin Honor Soc 87; Stu Ldrshp Awd 86; Cert Of Acad Excllnc-Latin I & III 85 & 87; Medicine.

TAYLOR, MELISSA; Montour HS; Pittsburgh, PA; (3); 10/320; Church Yth Grp; SADD; Yrbk Stf; Rep Stu Cncl; Powder Puff Ftbl; High Hon Roll; NHS; Hugh O Brian Ldrshp Awd 86; PSYCHLGY.

TAYLOR, MICHELE; Franklin Learning Ctr; Philadelphia, PA; (3); Boy Scts; Exploring; Red Cross Aide; Science Clb; Cit Awd; Prfct Atten Awd; Symposium Fox Chse Cancer Ctr; Philadelphia Wrld Affairs Cncl; Clark Coll; Oncology Dr.

TAYLOR, MICHELE; Pequea Valley HS; Gap, PA; (3); 6/141; AFS; German Clb; Girl Scts; Stage Crew; Yrbk Bus Mgr; Yrbk Ed-Chief; Yrbk Sprt Ed; Yrbk Stf; High Hon Roll; NHS; Physcs.

TAYLOR, MICHELLE; Tulpehocken HS; Bethel, PA; (2); Church Yth Grp; Drama Clb; Exploring; Girl Scts; Math Clb; Co-Capt Math Tm; Spanish Clb; SADD; VICA; Capt Band; Csmtlgst.

TAYLOR, MONICA; Taylor Allderdice HS; Verona, PA; (3); French Clb; JA; Stu Cncl; Crs Cntry; Trk; Hon Roll; Minority Schlrshp Engr 87; FL A&M; CPA.

TAYLOR, MONICA LYNN; Penn Center Acad; Philadelphia, PA; (4); VP Pres Church Yth Grp; Sec Church Choir; Pres Sr Cls; Bsktbl; Capt Lcrss; Trk; Sterling Comm Chrmn Phil Stu Ldrshp Conv 86; La Crosse Champnshp Sportsmnshp Awd 86; Track Sportsmnshp; Howard U; Pol Sci.

TAYLOR, NANCY L; Swissvale HS; Pittsburgh, PA; (4); 24/201; Church Yth Grp; Cmnty Wkr; Hosp Aide; Library Aide; Y-Teens; Acpl Chr; Yrbk Stf; Sec Bowling; Hon Roll; NHS; Medlln Ball Debutante 86; Carlow Coll; Nrsg.

TAYLOR, RACHEL; Shady Side Acad; New Kensington, PA; (4); Church Yth Grp; Girl Scts; Letterman Clb; Stage Crew; Lit Mag; Capt Cheerleading; JV Gym; Mgr Trk; Ntl Merit SF; U Of Pittsburgh; Engl.

TAYLOR, RICHARD; Ambridge Area HS; Ambridge, PA; (3); Pep Clb; Thesps; School Play; Yrbk Phtg; Yrbk Stf; Trk; Wt Lftg; Hon Roll; Jrnlsm.

TAYLOR, ROBERT; Henderson SR HS; W Chester, PA; (3); Latin Clb; JV Ftbl; French Hon Soc; High Hon Roll; Hon Roll; NHS; Osteopthc Physcn.

TAYLOR, RODNEY J; Chestnut Hill Acad; Philadelphia, PA; (4); 4/46; Church Choir; Nwsp Rptr; Pres Frsh Cls; VP Jr Cls; VP Sr Cls; Var Bsktbl; Var Ftbl; Var Capt Trk; Cit Awd; Dilworth Lees Schrlshp 83; Acad All Am 84; Cum Laude Soc 86; Harvard U.

TAYLOR, SCOTT M; Archbishop Carroll HS; Havertown, PA; (4); 14/367; Boy Scts; School Musical; Cit Awd; High Hon Roll; Hon Roll; NHS; Pres Schlr; Church Yth Grp; Cmnty Wkr; Drama Clb; John Carroll Mdl Excllnc Latin 87; St Vincnts Coll Acadmc Schlrshp 87-91; St Josephs U Schlrshp 87-91; St Josphs U; Bio.

TAYLOR, SEAN; Saegertown HS; Saegertown, PA; (3); 2/125; Yrbk Sprt Ed; JV Var Bsktbl; High Hon Roll; Hon Roll; Jr NHS; NHS; Ntl Merit Ltr; Boy Scts; Band; Concert Band; Amer Legion Schl Awd 84-85.

TAYLOR, SHANI; Burrell SR HS; Lower Burrell, PA; (4); AFS; Pres Church Yth Grp; Spanish Clb; Stage Crew; High Hon Roll; Hon Roll; Jr NHS; PA ST U; Med Tech.

TAYLOR, SHERI; Altoona Area HS; Altoona, PA; (3); 123/762; Church Yth Grp; French Clb; Intnl Clb; SADD; VICA; Church Choir; Drm & Bgl; Orch; Hon Roll; IN Inst Of Tech; Engrng.

TAYLOR, SHERI; Slippery Rock HS; Butler, PA; (4); 42/174; Art Clb; Pres 4-H; Intnl Clb; Pep Clb; Spanish Clb; Varsity Clb; Capt Cheerleading; Powder Puff Ftbl; Sftbl; Hon Roll; WV U; Bus.

TAYLOR, SHERRY; Pennsbury HS; Fairless Hills, PA; (3); Church Yth Grp; Spanish Clb; Chorus; Stage Crew; JV Crs Cntry; Var Trk; Hon Roll; Jr NHS; NHS; Pres Schlr; Stu Of Mnth 85; UCLA; Polit Sci.

TAYLOR, STARLETTE; New Brighton HS; New Brighton, PA; (4); 8/141; Teachers Aide; Band; Trs Chorus; Capt Color Guard; High Hon Roll; Hon Roll; Lion Awd; Pres Schlr; Intl Frgn Lang Awd-Spanish 86-87; All Amrcn Hall Fame Band Hnrs 87; CC Beaver County; Accntng.

TAYLOR, STEPHANIE; Coatesville Area SR HS; Coatesville, PA; (4); 37/457; Spanish Clb; Color Guard; Var Capt English Clb; Var Capt Fld Hcky; Var Capt Lcrss; Cit Awd; Hon Roll; NHS; Dr S W Ridgway Schlrshp 87; Coaches Awd In Bsktbl 86-87; Elzbthtwn Coll; Bus Adm.

TAYLOR, STEPHEN E; Bloomsburg HS; Bloomsburg, PA; (4); 8/142; NFL; Thesps; Band; Jazz Band; Yrbk Stf; Var Crs Cntry; NHS; Ntl Merit SF; Scholastic Bowl; Chorus; 1st Chr Alto Sax Colmbia Cnty, PMEA Dist & Rgn Band Fstvls 86; Div Hnrs Natl French Cont 85-86; Languages.

TAYLOR, SUZIE; Juniata HS; Mifflintown, PA; (3); Computer Clb; SADD; Varsity Clb; Stu Cncl; JV Var Bsktbl; JV Var Fld Hcky; JV Var Sftbl; High Hon Roll; Hon Roll; NHS; Schltc J Awd.

TAYLOR, THOMAS; Avon Grove HS; West Grove, PA; (3); 24/210; NFL; School Musical; School Play; Trs Soph Cls; Pres Jr Cls; Pres Stu Cncl; Var Wrstlng; French Hon Soc; NHS; Stage Crew; Wrstlng Leag All-Star 86-87; PA Free Entrprs Wk 85-86; Phys Ed Awd 84-85, 86-87; Radio/TV Comms.

TAYLOR, TIFFANY; Pen Argyl Area HS; Pen Argyl, PA; (3); Cmnty Wkr; Drama Clb; Chorus; Orch; School Play; VP Stu Cncl; Var L Cheerleading; High Hon Roll; Jr NHS; NHS; Hstry Day 1st Pl Local Comptn; Stu Rep Schl Board; Optomtry.

TAYLOR, TIWANDA; Schenley HS Teacher Center; Pittsburgh, PA; (3); Art Clb; French Clb; Rep Frsh Cls; Lawyer.

TAYLOR, TONYA; Beaver Falls SR HS; Beaver Falls, PA; (3); 60/170; Art Clb; Church Yth Grp; Cmnty Wkr; Exploring; Hon Roll; Prfct Atten Awd; 2nd Pl Yng Teen Trphy Bible Quiz Natls 83; 2nd Pl SR Teen Trphy Bible Quiz Natls 84; 1st Pl Regnls; Art.

TAYLOR, VANIDA; Chester HS; Chester, PA; (3); Church Yth Grp; Spanish Clb; Teachers Aide; Chorus; Church Choir; Drill Tm; Mrchg Band; Sftbl; Hon Roll; Prfct Atten Awd; Comp Pgmmr.

TAYLOR, VICKI; Aliquippa HS; Aliquippa, PA; (3); JA; ROTC; Band; Chorus; Concert Band; Dance Clb; JCL; Rep Stu Cncl; Cheerleading; CCAF; Aviatn.

TAYLOR, WENDY; North Penn JR SR HS; Wellsboro, PA; (3); Camera Clb; Church Yth Grp; 4-H; GAA; Girl Scts; Key Clb; Library Aide; Ski Clb; Varsity Clb; Yrbk Phtg; Outstndng In Bsktl 87; MVP In Bsktbl 86-87; Trpy In Vlybl 86-87; PA ST; Elem Ed.

TAYLOR, YONNA; Canton JR SR HS; Canton, PA; (4); 1/118; Church Yth Grp; Capt Scholastic Bowl; Capt Drill Tm; Rep Stu Cncl; Cit Awd; High Hon Roll; VP NHS; Val; Drama Clb; Deans Schlrshp Messiah Coll 86-87; Hmcmng Ct 86; Bradfd Cty Dairy Princess 86-87; Messiah Coll; Elem Ed.

TEACHOUT, DAVID; The Baptist HS; Kingsley, PA; (4); Chorus; Church Choir; Ftbl; Socr; Sftbl; Hon Roll; Baptist Bible Coll; Bible.

TEAFORD, REBECCA; Penn Wood HS; Lansdowne, PA; (3); 19/340; Girl Scts; Hosp Aide; Intnl Clb; Color Guard; Yrbk Ed-Chief; Rep Stu Cncl; Fld Hcky; Sftbl; Tennis; NHS; Bloomsburg U; Nrsng.

TEAGLE, STEPHANIE; Mercy Vocational HS; Philadelphia, PA; (3); Nwsp Stf; Bsktbl; Mgr(s); Sftbl; Katharine Gibbs Future Secy Hnrb Mntn 87; Bus Ed.

TEASDALE, HOLLY; Meadville Area SR HS; Meadville, PA; (2); Church Yth Grp; Church Choir; High Hon Roll; Hon Roll; Ntl Hstry Day 87; Sndy Schl Cls Treas/Sec 86-87.

TEASDALE, TROY; Meadville Area SR HS; Meadville, PA; (4); Church Yth Grp; Vllybl; Hon Roll; KY Chrstn Coll.

TEATS, TRACY; Du Bois Area HS; Dubois, PA; (2); 4/300; Band; Concert Band; Mrchg Band; Hon Roll; NHS; Nice Kid Awd 87; U Of Miami; Lawyr.

TEBO, LAURA; Gwynedd Mercy Acad; Spring House, PA; (2); FBLA; Pep Clb; Service Clb; Band; Chorus; School Musical; Nwsp Bus Mgr; Lcrss; Swmmng; Hugh O Brian Yth Fndnt Ldrshp Smnr 87; Child Psych.

TECK, TRACEY; St Paul Cathedral HS; N Braddock, PA; (4); Church Yth Grp; FBLA; Library Aide; Pep Clb; Teachers Aide; Cheerleading; Hon Roll; Prfct Atten Awd; Stud Secy Awd 86-87; Robert Morris Coll; Accntng.

TECONCHUK, KIMBERLY; Fairview HS; Fairview, PA; (3); French Clb; Model UN; Ski Clb; Varsity Clb; Rep Frsh Cls; Rep Soph Cls; Rep Jr Cls; L Var Swmmng; High Hon Roll; NHS.

TEDESCO, STEPHANIE; Sharpsville HS; Sharpsville, PA; (3); Science Clb; Hon Roll; Phrmcy.

TEEGARDEN, AMI; Mc Guffey HS; Washington, PA; (3); Spanish Clb; Powder Puff Ftbl; L Sftbl; Hon Roll; Sawyer Schl; Acctg.

TEEL, KRISTINA; Bangor SR HS; East Bangor, PA; (2); Concert Band; Mrchg Band; Var L Sftbl; High Hon Roll; Computer Clb; Band; Chorus; Jazz Band; Hon Roll; Presdntl Acad Ftnss Awd 85-86; Optometry.

TEEL, TONYA; Bangor Area HS; Bangor, PA; (3); 7/230; Computer Clb; Drill Tm; Stu Cncl; Var Trk; High Hon Roll; Hon Roll; Jr NHS; NHS; Nrsg.

TEES, STACY; St Basil Acad; Philadelphia, PA; (4); Cmnty Wkr; Dance Clb; French Clb; Hosp Aide; Science Clb; Yrbk Stf; Schlrshp Stu; Campus Minstry; Ukrin Club; Bio.

TEETER, GLENN; Peters Township HS; Venetia, PA; (4); Varsity Clb; Lib Sr Cls; Stu Cncl; Capt Crs Cntry; Capt Wrstlng; Prfct Atten Awd; Slippery Rock U; Bus.

TEETER, PEGGY; Elkland Area HS; Elkland, PA; (3); Girl Scts; Bsktbl; Hon Roll; Wmsprt Area CC; Sec Sci.

TEETERS, TRACY; Williamsburg HS; Williamsburg, PA; (3); 4-H; FFA; FTA; Girl Scts; Nwsp Rptr; Nwsp Stf; Yrbk Rptr; Yrbk Stf; 4-H Awd; Hon Roll; FFA Hghst Fruit Slsmn 87; S Central Co-Op 87; Clarion U; Elem Ed.

TEKAC, VICKI; Wilmington HS; Pulaski, PA; (3); Dance Clb; Drama Clb; French Clb; Capt Drm Mjr(t); Capt Twrlr; Hon Roll; Youngstown ST; Educ.

TEKLINSKI, JENNIFER; Curwensville Area HS; Grampain, PA; (3); French Clb; Stage Crew; Nwsp Stf; Stu Cncl; Hon Roll; Grampian Homcmng Qn & ST Fnlst Miss U S PA Teen Pageant; Wrestlerette Clb; Comp Mgmt.

TELEGA, SUSAN M; Hickory HS; Hermitage, PA; (2); Latin Clb; Band; Chorus; Mrchg Band; Orch; Pep Band; School Musical; Hon Roll; Speech Tm; Voice Dem Awd; Alt PA Gov Schl Arts 87.

TELENKO, MICHELLE; Elizabethtown HS; Elizabethtown, PA; (4); 69/256; Ski Clb; Mrchg Band; Twrlr; W Chester U; Bus Admin.

TELLADO, LIZA; Neshaminy HS; Langhorne, PA; (3); Bsktbl; Sftbl; High Hon Roll; Hon Roll; NHS; La Salle; Pre-Law.

TELLERS, CAROLYN; Villa Maria Acad; Erie, PA; (3); Model UN.

TELLUP, ANNE; Blue Mountain HS; Cressona, PA; (4); 15/216; SADD; Nwsp Rptr; Yrbk Stf; Var L Bsktbl; Var L Trk; Var L Vllybl; French Hon Soc; Hon Roll; Bloomsburg U; French.

TEMARANTZ, ANTOINETTE; Hanover Area JR/Sr HS; Wilkes Barre, PA; (3); Church Yth Grp; Hosp Aide; VP Key Clb; SADD; Drill Tm; Mrchg Band; Rep Stu Cncl; Twrlr; Hon Roll; Jr NHS; PA Jr Acad & Sci Excllnc Awd 87; Pharm.

TEMPEST, HEATHER; Mahanoy Area HS; Gilberton, PA; (2); VICA; High Hon Roll; Hon Roll; Comp Prgmr.

TEMPLE, JILL M; Newport JR/ SR HS; Newport, PA; (2); 30/120; FTA; German Clb; Girl Scts; Pep Clb; Varsity Clb; Chorus; School Musical; School Play; Hst Frsh Cls; Sec Soph Cls; Mdrn Music Mstrs Tri-M 86-87; Natl Chrldng Chmpnshp Fnlst 87; Spch Path.

TEMPLE, JOY; Harry S Truman HS; Levittown, PA; (4); Church Yth Grp; Library Aide; Cheerleading; Socr; Trk; Hon Roll.

TEMPLE-WEST, FRANCES; Academy Of Notre Dame; Devon, PA; (4); Debate Tm; Drama Clb; Hosp Aide; Orch; School Musical; School Play; Stage Crew; Yrbk Stf; Lit Mag; Hon Roll; Mt St Josephs Acad Music Schlrshp 83; Villa Maria Acad Schlrshp 83; Catholic U Of AM; Arch.

TEMPLETON, SUSAN; Eastern York HS; York, PA; (3); 4/180; Concert Band; Mrchg Band; Ed Nwsp Ed-Chief; Yrbk Stf; Stu Cncl; High Hon Roll; NHS; Rotary Awd; VFW Awd; Voice Dem Awd; Penn ST; Elem Ed.

TEMPLIN, BRIAN; Tunkhannock HS; Tunkhannock, PA; (4); 15/270; Computer Clb; Ski Clb; Bsktbl; Capt Socr; High Hon Roll; Ntl Ldrshp Merit Awd 86; Indiana U Of PA Physcs Tstng Awd 86; Hgh Eductn Cert Merit 86; Penn ST U; Aero Engr.

TEMPLIN, CHAD; Cedar Crest HS; Lebanon, PA; (3); 16/342; Church Yth Grp; German Clb; Pep Clb; SADD; Teachers Aide; Im Bsktbl; Im Vllybl; High Hon Roll; Hon Roll; NHS; Boostr Clb Hnrs-Brnz Mdls 85 & 87.

TEMPLIN, LAURA JEAN; Greater Latrobe HS; Greensburg, PA; (3); AFS; German Clb; Pep Clb; Ski Clb; Lit Mag; Var Swmmng; Var Trk; Bus.

TENELLY, KATHY; North Pocono HS; Moscow, PA; (4); 32/247; Church Yth Grp; Drama Clb; Ski Clb; Varsity Clb; School Play; Rep Stu Cncl; Cheerleading; High Hon Roll; NHS; Pres Schlr; Gftd Pgm 83-87; Prncpls List 87; E Stroudsburg U; Recrtn Mgmt.

TENER, ADRIAN; Northeast Prep; Philadelphia, PA; (4); 4/20; Ski Clb; JV Bsbl; JV Crs Cntry; JV Socr; Var Wrstlng.

TENNANT, KELLY M; Newport HS; Newport, PA; (3); 1/120; Cmnty Wkr; Quiz Bowl; Chorus; School Musical; Swing Chorus; Yrbk Stf; Hst Frsh Cls; Vllybl; High Hon Roll; NHS; Hugh O Brien Yth Found 86; Otstndng Acad Achiev Awds 84-87; Soph Of Yr Awd 86; Lbrl Arts.

TENNANT, RENEE; Waynesburg Central HS; Spraggs, PA; (4); Church Yth Grp; Drama Clb; French Clb; Spanish Clb; Teachers Aide; Church Choir; School Play; Stage Crew; High Hon Roll; Hon Roll; WV U; Elem Ed.

TENNANT, SARA; Waynesburg Central HS; Brave, PA; (4); Library Aide; Natl Beta Clb; Quiz Bowl; Red Cross Aide; SADD; VICA; Variety Show; High Hon Roll; Hon Roll; Outstndng Cls Stu Hlth Asst 86-87; Pres Greene Co Chptr HOSA 86-87; Prlmntrn 85-86.

TENZER, RYAN; Emmaus HS; Allentown, PA; (3); Computer Clb; Debate Tm; French Clb; Temple Yth Grp; Yrbk Bus Mgr; Yrbk Stf; High Hon Roll; Hon Roll; Jr NHS; NHS; U Of VT; Med.

TEPLEY, DEBRA; Ambridge Area HS; Baden, PA; (3); Pep Clb; Red Cross Aide; Spanish Clb; Off Soph Cls; Bradford Bus Schl; Secrtrl.

TEPLITZ, ROBERT F; Central Dauphin HS; Harrisburg, PA; (3); 7/369; Boy Scts; Exploring; Key Clb; Quiz Bowl; Temple Yth Grp; Yrbk Ed-Chief; Yrbk Rptr; Off Jr Cls; NHS; Computer Clb; 1st Pl Dauphin Cnty Juv Jstc Essy Cont, Recog Cnty Comssnrs Supprt Wrk Wth Juvs 86; Acdmc Stu Mnth 87; Attny.

TEPSIC, LISA; Western Beaver HS; Industry, PA; (3); Drama Clb; Exploring; SADD; Chorus; School Musical; Im Bowling; Var Sftbl; Var Trk; Hon Roll; NHS; Legl Asst.

TEREFENCKO JR, JOHN; Our Lady Of Lourdes HS; Paxinos, PA; (3); 12/98; Key Clb; Spanish Clb; Rep Frsh Cls; Rep Soph Cls; Rep Sr Cls; L Ftbl; Wt Lftg; Rotary Awd; Rotary Exch Stu-Brazil 85-86; Drexel; Bnkg.

TEREFENKO, KEVIN; Exeter Township SR HS; Reading, PA; (4); 2/214; Sec Key Clb; VP Pres Varsity Clb; Stu Cncl; Var L Bsbl; Var L Bsktbl; Bausch & Lomb Sci Awd; High Hon Roll; Jr NHS; NCTE Awd; Pres NHS; Latin Hnr Soc; Princeton; Pre-Med.

TERENCHIN, TAMMY; Reading SR HS; Reading, PA; (3); 60/720; Band; Concert Band; Jazz Band; Im Sftbl; Elem Ed.

TERESCHUK, CHRISTINA; Cedar Grove Christian Acad; Philadelphia, PA; (3); Church Yth Grp; Drama Clb; Band; Chorus; Nwsp Stf; Yrbk Stf; VP Jr Cls; Var Fld Hcky; Hon Roll; Kiwanis Awd; Bus Admin.

TERESKA, TODD; Liberty HS; Bethlehem, PA; (4); 77/434; Concert Band; Jazz Band; Mrchg Band; Orch; Pep Band; School Musical; School Play; Moravian Coll; Ntrl Rsrc Mgmt.

TERKAY, SYLVESTER; Canon Mc Millan SR HS; Lawrence, PA; (3); Spanish Clb; Var Crs Cntry; Var Trk; Var Wrstlng; Hon Roll; Bus.

TERNE, BRYAN R; Germantown Friends Schl; Philadelphia, PA; (4); Aud/Vis; Cmnty Wkr; Drama Clb; Hosp Aide; Political Wkr; Stage Crew; Im Bsktbl; JV Socr; Im Tennis; Im Wt Lftg; Natl Merit Scholar SF 86-87; PA Hghr Ed Asst Agency Cert Merit 86-87.

TERNOVAN, LISA; Hempfield HS; Lancaster, PA; (2); Church Yth Grp; Dance Clb; Chorus; Church Choir; Rep Jr Cls; Var Capt Cheerleading; High Hon Roll; Hon Roll; Music Awd Outstndg Achvt 85-87; Natl Honors Piano Solos 85-86; Lib Arts.

TEROSKY, JASON; Quaker Valley HS; Fair Oaks, PA; (3); 1/160; Drama Clb; German Clb; Key Clb; School Musical; School Play; Var L Bsbl; Var L Ftbl; Cit Awd; Kiwanis Awd; NHS; Best Chem & Trigmtry, Alg II Stu 86, 87; Engrng.

TERRACCINO, ANGELA; Hazleton HS; Hazelton, PA; (4); 37/388; Rep Stu Cncl; Var Capt Cheerleading; High Hon Roll; NHS; Pres Schlr; Elizabethtown Coll; Arch Engrng.

TERRELL, JUSTIN; Chambersburg Area SR HS; Chambersburg, PA; (2); Chess Clb; Computer Clb; 4-H; JCL; Latin Clb; Stage Crew; Military Intllgnc.

TERRY, BRENDA; Williamson JR SR HS; Tioga, PA; (3); 5/90; Church Yth Grp; Exploring; Hosp Aide; Church Choir; Yrbk Stf; Stat Civic Clb; Mgr(s); Stat Trk; Hon Roll; NHS; X-Ray Tech.

TERRY, COLEEN; Elizabethtown Area HS; Manheim, PA; (2); 8/280; Church Yth Grp; Teachers Aide; Yrbk Stf; Lit Mag; JV L Bsktbl; JV Sftbl; High Hon Roll; NHS; Pre Med.

TERRY, STEPHANIE; Aliquippa HS; Aliquippa, PA; (4); DECA; Mrchg Band; Hon Roll; ICM Schl Of Bus; Secy Sci.

TERSHAK, SUZANNE; State College Intermediate HS; State College, PA; (2); 29/554; Ski Clb; School Musical; Variety Show; Rep Frsh Cls; Stu Cncl; Var L Fld Hcky; Powder Puff Ftbl; Sftbl; Trk; Cit Awd; JV Fld Hcky MVP 86; Cmmnty Theatr Shenandoah Ld 86; 3rd Pl VFW Essy Cntst 86; Cmmnctns.

TERZAKEN, TARA; Pocono Mountain HS; Tobyhanna, PA; (2); Church Yth Grp; Var Bsktbl; JV Fld Hcky; Var Trk; High Hon Roll; Hon Roll; NHS; Prfct Atten Awd; Career Hnr Rl Awd 86; Prse Phys Ftns Awd 82-86; Medcl Fld.

TERZICH, MIKE; West Mifflin Area HS; West Mifflin, PA; (4); 110/335; Key Clb; Letterman Clb; Varsity Clb; Capt Var Bsbl; Capt Var Golf; Hon Roll; Hnr Rll 85-87; Slippery Rock U; Comp Sci.

TESCHE, ERIC; Dieruff HS; Allentown, PA; (2); Church Yth Grp; Nwsp Rptr; Nwsp Stf; Rep Frsh Cls; Rep Soph Cls; L Trk; Hon Roll; Jr NHS; Prfct Atten Awd.

TESTA, CYNTHIA; Valley View JR SR HS; Eynon, PA; (2); 3/190; Dance Clb; Math Tm; SADD; Stu Cncl; Capt Vllybl; French Hon Soc; High Hon Roll; Hon Roll; NHS; PJAS Excllnce Chem 87; PJAS 1st Awd Chem ST 87; PJAS Prfct Score Awd ST Chem 87; Biochem.

TESTA, DEANNA; Kiski Area HS; Apollo, PA; (3); Pep Clb; Varsity Clb; JV Var Bsktbl; Var Crs Cntry; Var Trk; High Hon Roll; Hon Roll; Prfct Atten Awd; Westmorland Cnty CC; Child Cre.

TETI, KIMBERLY; High School Of Engineering & Science; Philadelphia, PA; (3); Yrbk Stf; Rep Stu Cncl; Advrtsng.

TETLAK, TARA; Tunkhannock Area HS; Tunkhannock, PA; (2); 29/330; 4-H; French Clb; Rep Soph Cls; Gym; 4-H Awd; Hon Roll; Tunkhannock Area H S Schlrp Bnqt 86; 1st Pl Suzanne Maria Rossetti Mem Art Cntst 86; 3rd Merit Awd 4-H.

TEUFEL, GREG; Wyoming Valley West HS; Kingston, PA; (4); 11/397; Boy Scts; Chess Clb; Church Yth Grp; Cmnty Wkr; Computer Clb; Debate Tm; Exploring; Math Tm; Red Cross Aide; Ski Clb; Kngs Coll Prsdntl Fll Schlrshp 87; Prsdntl Acdmc Ftnss Awd 87; Blyth Evns Sr Mem Amrcn Hstry Awd 87; Kings Coll; Poly Sci.

TEXTES, THOMAS; Reading HS; Reading, PA; (4); 20/600; Aud/Vis; Church Yth Grp; Service Clb; Nwsp Phtg; Nwsp Rptr; Nwsp Stf; NHS; Ntl Merit Ltr; Lutztown Univ; Telecomm.

THAIK, RICHARD; Emmaus HS; Wescosville, PA; (4); #6 In Class; Chess Clb; Computer Clb; Math Tm; Scholastic Bowl; High Hon Roll; NHS; Ntl Merit SF; Pres Schlr; 1st Pl Amer Comp Sci League 86; Purdue U; Elec Engr.

THANOS, MARY; Forbes Road HS; Mc Connellsburg, PA; (4); 5/45; Trs FHA; Varsity Clb; Sec Frsh Cls; Sec Jr Cls; Capt Var Bsktbl; Cit Awd; Hon Roll; NHS; Pres Schlr; Pres 4-H; Pres Ftns Awd 82-87; L B Mc Clain Schlrshp 87; PA ST U; Athlt Trnr.

THARP, GWENDOLYN SUE; Hempfield Area SR HS; Greensburg, PA; (2); Exploring; Hosp Aide; Spanish Clb; Concert Band; Mrchg Band; Mgr(s); Spanish NHS; Psych.

THATCHER, CHRISTOPHER; Tunkhannock Area HS; Factoryville, PA; (2); 6/305; Spanish Clb; Band; Concert Band; Mrchg Band; Rep Soph Cls; Rep Stu Cncl; Crs Cntry; Trk; Co-Capt Wrstlng; Hon Roll.

THATCHER, DAWN; Mountain View HS; Susquehanna, PA; (3); Sec Church Yth Grp; Chrmn Cmnty Wkr; Sec Pep Clb; Ski Clb; Chorus; Sec Soph Cls; Rep Stu Cncl; Im Badmtn; Var L Fld Hcky; Gym; Health.

THATCHER, KATHLEEN ELEANOR; East Stroudsburg HS; East Stroudsburg, PA; (4); 9/211; Ski Clb; Teachers Aide; Var Sftbl; Var Tennis; Hon Roll; NHS; Smithfield PTO Coll Asstnc, Elks Ldg No 319 Schlrshp 87; Penn ST U; Accntng.

THEAKSTON, CANDY; Ringgold HS; Finleyville, PA; (3); Cmnty Wkr; FTA; Hosp Aide; Office Aide; Pep Clb; Ski Clb; Var Vllybl; Interact Clb 86-87; Prom Comm 86-87; SR Staff Clb 87-88; Pittsburgh U; Tchg.

THEAL, STEPHEN; Mechanicsburg HS; Shiremanstown, PA; (2); Boy Scts; Exploring; Ski Clb; Im Ftbl; IVP.

THEISS, JULIE E; Mc Donnell HS; Erie, PA; (3); 63/577; Am Leg Aux Girls St; Church Yth Grp; Model UN; Political Wkr; Ski Clb; School Play; Rep Stu Cncl; Mgr Trk; Hon Roll; NHS; Hnrs Convocation 87; Mercyhurst Coll; Hotel Mgmt.

THELMAN, JAMES; Henderson HS; W Chester, PA; (3); 29/377; French Clb; Ski Clb; Tennis; Trk; Vllybl; French Hon Soc; High Hon Roll; NHS; Penn ST; Engrng.

THEODORE, BOBBIE; Moon HS; West Palm Beach, FL; (2); DECA; French Clb; GAA; Letterman Clb; Library Aide; Chorus; Var Cheerleading; Var L Crs Cntry; JV L Sftbl; Hon Roll; Inter Desgnr.

THERIT, TRACEY; Littlestown HS; Hanover, PA; (4); 2/117; Speech Tm; School Musical; School Play; Nwsp Stf; Yrbk Stf; VP Frsh Cls; VP Soph Cls; Rep Stu Cncl; Pres NHS; Sal; Amer Bus Wmns Assn Schlrshp 87; Eagls Clb Schlrshp 87; Prsdntl Acadmc Ftns Awd Wnr 87; PA ST U Univ Park; Lbrl Arts.

THEUNE, TARA M; Academy Of Notre Dame; Devon, PA; (3); Debate Tm; FCA; Speech Tm; Chorus; Nwsp Stf; Fld Hcky; Lcrss; JV Score Keeper; Tennis; Hon Roll.

THIBAULT, JAMIE; Conestoga HS; Paoli, PA; (2); Var Lcrss; Var Socr; Hon Roll; Pres Schlr; Interact Club 86-87; All Leag Hon Ment Soccer 86-87; Vlly Forge Jr HS Schlrshp Awd 85-86; Bus.

THIEL, DENISE; Greater Latrobe HS; Latrobe, PA; (2); 54/381; Church Yth Grp; German Clb; Symp Band; Off Stu Cncl; Vllybl; High Hon Roll; Westmoreland Cnty JR High Band Festival 86.

THIEL, VICKI; Council Rock HS; Washington Crossi, PA; (4); 69/852; Church Yth Grp; Trs Jr Cls; VP Sr Cls; Var Tennis; Im Vllybl; Hon Roll; NHS; Ldrshp Schl Awds 87; Uppr Makefield Bus Assctn Schlrshp 87; Stu Mnth 86; U Vermont; Bio Chmcl Sci.

THIELE, JACKIE; Freeport SR HS; Sarver, PA; (4); Church Yth Grp; Mrchg Band; School Musical; Twrlr; Penn ST U; Radiolgy.

THINNES, SUZANNE; Mount Alvernia HS; Pittsburgh, PA; (3); Pres Church Yth Grp; Drama Clb; JA; Nwsp Stf; Yrbk Ed-Chief; Yrbk Stf; Var L Bsktbl; Hon Roll; NHS; Prfct Atten Awd; Cmmnctn.

THOMAN, JEAN; Susquehanna Township HS; Harrisburg, PA; (2); GAA; Teachers Aide; Varsity Clb; Var Fld Hcky; Var Sftbl; Penn ST; Phys Ed.

THOMAN, LAURA; Susquehanna Township HS; Harrisburg, PA; (2); Church Yth Grp; Spanish Clb; Sftbl; Vllybl; Hon Roll; Susquehanna Twp Outstndng Sftbl Plyr Awd 87; Mid-Penn Conf All Star Team Sftbl 87; Penn ST; Foreign Lang Tchr.

THOMAN, MICHAEL J; Susquehannock HS; Seven Valleys, PA; (4); 4/221; Rep Jr Cls; Rep Sr Cls; Im Tennis; High Hon Roll; Hon Roll; JETS Awd; NHS; Ntl Merit SF; Rotary Awd; Prfct Atten Awd; IN U Of PA Physcs Tstng Comptn Wnr 85-86; AHSME Schl Co-Wnr 85-86; PA ST U Schlr; PA ST U; Aerospc Engrng.

THOMAN, TERRI; Eastern York HS; Hellam, PA; (3); SADD; Yrbk Stf; Var Cheerleading; Twrlr; Hon Roll; PA Ambassadors Music 84; Pharm.

THOMAS, ANDREW; Lake-Lehman HS; Shavertown, PA; (3); 21/219; Church Yth Grp; Mrchg Band; School Play; Rep Stu Cncl; Var Golf; Hon Roll; Jr NHS; Pre Med.

THOMAS, ANGELA; Greencastle-Antrim HS; Greencastle, PA; (3); Sec French Clb; Band; Church Choir; Drm Mjr(t); Mrchg Band; JV Bsktbl; Var Trk; Hon Roll; Concert Band; Variety Show.

THOMAS, ARTHUR; Edward Bok HS; Philadelphia, PA; (3); 8/300; Boys Clb Am; Drama Clb; Exploring; FCA; JA; Math Clb; Ski Clb; SADD; Varsity Clb; VICA; Negro Schlrshp Awds; UMBC; Mech Engr.

THOMAS, BRIAN; Brownsville Area HS; Adah, PA; (3); Var Bsbl; Var Ftbl; Hnrbl Mntn Hrld Stndrd Drm Tm Ftbl 86; Engrng.

THOMAS, BRIAN; Jenkintown HS; Jenkintown, PA; (3); 10/40; Chorus; School Play; Var Bsktbl; Mgr(s); Var Capt Tennis; Cit Awd; Hon Roll.

THOMAS, BRIAN; Tunkhannock HS; Tunkhannock, PA; (3); Aud/Vis; Boy Scts; Nwsp Phtg; Yrbk Phtg; VP Stu Cncl; Var Crs Cntry; Trk; Gov Hon Prg Awd; Boy Scout Hnr,Kodak Medal Excell Schlrshp,Schltc Photo Awds 86; Sue Rossetti Memrl Art Show 87; Rochester Inst Of Tech; Photo.

THOMAS, BRIAN; Warwick HS; Lititz, PA; (2); 57/350; Church Yth Grp; Hon Roll.

THOMAS, CANDACE; West Greene HS; New Freeport, PA; (3); 1/103; French Clb; Varsity Clb; Var L Bsktbl; Var L Sftbl; Var L Vllybl; High Hon Roll; Sftbl Rookie Yr 85; Bsktbl Underclssmn 85-86; Bsktbll Hustler Awd 85-86; Schltc Achvt Awds 84-86; Sports Med.

THOMAS, CARRIE; Catasaugua HS; Catasauqua, PA; (3); 11/147; DECA; Chorus; High Hon Roll; Hon Roll; NHS; Ntl Merit Ltr; Johnson & Whales; Mktg.

THOMAS, CATHY; Oliver HS; Pittsburgh, PA; (1); Band; Mrchg Band; Orch; High Hon Roll; Prfct Atten Awd; Hghst GPA 87; Acad All Amer 87; Project Lead 87; Lwyr.

THOMAS, CHERYL; Bishop O Hara HS; Olyphant, PA; (2); 3/118; French Clb; Girl Scts; Latin Clb; High Hon Roll; U Of Pittsburgh; Acctg.

THOMAS, CHRISTIAN; Cedar Crest HS; Lebanon, PA; (2); German Clb; Concert Band; Drm & Bgl; Jazz Band; Mrchg Band; Var Swmmng; Music.

THOMAS, CHRISTINA; Shenandoah Valley HS; Shenandoah, PA; (2); Pep Clb; Band; Cheerleading; Gym; Pom Pon; Trk; Hon Roll.

THOMAS, CHRISTOPHER J; Seneca Valley SR HS; Evans Cty, PA; (3); Hon Roll; Grove City Coll; Bus.

THOMAS, CRYSTAL; Maplewood HS; Centerville, PA; (2); Debate Tm; FHA; Pep Clb; Varsity Clb; Cheerleading; Bus.

THOMAS, CYNTHIA; Central Christian HS; Du Bois, PA; (2); Math Tm; Rep Soph Cls; Rep Stu Cncl; Cheerleading; Hon Roll.

THOMAS, DAVE; Johnstown HS; Johnstown, PA; (3); JA; JV Bsktbl; US Navy; Elecs.

THOMAS, DAVID J; Hickory HS; Sharpsville, PA; (2); Drama Clb; Latin Clb; Speech Tm; Chorus; Ftbl; Wrstlng; Voice Dem Awd; Church Yth Grp; Debate Tm; Orch; Dist Regnl Orchestra, 1st Pl Drama Cmptn Wmns Club, 4th Pl Radio Announcng ST Frnscs Trnmnt 86-87; Med.

THOMAS, DEBORAH; Swenson Skill Ctr; Philadelphia, PA; (4); DECA; FBLA; Girl Scts; Office Aide; Teachers Aide; Sr Cls; Prfct Atten Awd; CCP; Bus.

THOMAS, DENISE; John Harris HS; Harrisburg, PA; (2); 25/378; Church Yth Grp; Hnrb Mntn Sci Fair 85-86; Temple U; Comp Pgmmr.

THOMAS, DONALD; Oxford HS; Nottingham, PA; (3); Yrbk Stf; Var Trk; Hon Roll; Pres Phys Ftnss Awd 85-87; Advrtsng.

THOMAS, DORIS; West Catholic Girls HS; Philadelphia, PA; (3); 11/249; JCL; Latin Clb; NFL; Rep Office Aide; Spanish Clb; Orch; School Musical; Nwsp Rptr; Var L Vllybl; High Hon Roll; White Williams Scholar 86-88; Ellis Grant 85-88; Intl Rltns.

THOMAS, ERIC; Immaculate Conception HS; Washington, PA; (3); 1/50; Math Clb; Thesps; Nwsp Rptr; Yrbk Stf; Pres Frsh Cls; Rep Stu Cncl; Var Golf; High Hon Roll; NHS; Rotary Awd; Nicholas C Tucci Chem Awd; Med.

THOMAS, FRED; Gar HS; Wilkes-Barre, PA; (3); Church Yth Grp; High Hon Roll; Hon Roll; NHS; Acctng.

THOMAS JR, FRED; Columbia Montour Avts; Catawissa, PA; (4); 2/180; Chess Clb; Computer Clb; Math Tm; Scholastic Bowl; Stu Cncl; Elks Awd; High Hon Roll; NHS; Rotary Awd; Sal; Clair C Kinney 4 Yr Schlrshp 87; Susquehanna Vly Usrs Grp Schlrshp 87; TRW Schlrshp 87; Rochester Inst Tech; Comp Engrn.

THOMAS, HOLLY ANN; Cambria Heights HS; Hastings, PA; (3); Drama Clb; FHA; Teachers Aide; Yrbk Stf; Hon Roll; Gregg Shrthnd Achvt Awd 87; Exec Secy.

THOMAS, JANEL; Faith Christian Schl; Willow Grove, PA; (2); 3/14; Church Yth Grp; Drama Clb; JV Capt Bsktbl; Coach Actv; JV Capt Socr; JV Capt Sftbl; Hon Roll; Stu Of Mth 86; Scl Wkr.

THOMAS, JEAN; Bellwood-Antis HS; Altoona, PA; (3); 12/115; VP Church Yth Grp; Chorus; Jazz Band; Mrchg Band; School Musical; Nwsp Stf; Yrbk Stf; Cheerleading; High Hon Roll; NHS; Bio.

THOMAS, JEFF; Hanover Area JR SR HS; Ashley, PA; (3); 1/195; Church Yth Grp; VP Jr Cls; Var JV Bsbl; Var L Bsktbl; Var L Trk; High Hon Roll; Jr NHS; NHS.

THOMAS, JENNIFER; Elizabeth Forward HS; Mc Keesport, PA; (3); French Clb; VP Sec JA; Pep Clb; Chorus; Rep Soph Cls; Rep Jr Cls; VP Stu Cncl; Stat Bsktbl; Trk; Hon Roll; Lbrl Arts.

THOMAS, JENNIFER; Mc Guffey HS; Washington, PA; (2); #10 In Class; Church Yth Grp; French Clb; Hosp Aide; Letterman Clb; Ski Clb; Chorus; School Musical; Var Sftbl; Var Vllybl; Bus Mgr.

THOMAS, JULIE; Aliquippa SR HS; Aliquippa, PA; (4); 10/120; Church Yth Grp; Pres French Clb; Pres Sec Concert Band; Pres Mrchg Band; Yrbk Bus Mgr; Off Jr Cls; Off Sr Cls; Hon Roll; Lion Awd; Sec NHS; U Of Pittsburgh.

THOMAS, KARA; Susquehanna HS; Harrisburg, PA; (3); Drama Clb; Cheerleading; Air Force.

THOMAS, KATHY; Lock Haven HS; Castanea, PA; (3); #1 In Class; Chorus; Pres Soph Cls; Var Cheerleading; Im Gym; L Trk; High Hon Roll; NHS; Outstndng Frnch Stu 86-87.

THOMAS, KRIS; West Greene HS; Sycamore, PA; (2); Church Yth Grp; 4-H; Science Clb; SADD; 4-H Awd; High Hon Roll; Hon Roll; Astrnmy & Englsh 86-87.

THOMAS, KRISTEL; Brownsville Area HS; Brownsville, PA; (2); Office Aide; Var L Bsktbl; Var L Sftbl; Hon Roll; Fayette Co Coachs Awd-All Star Tm Bsktbl; Rotary MVP Bsktbl; Bus.

THOMAS, LAURA; Hopewell SR HS; Aliquippa, PA; (3); Sec Art Clb; Exploring; Sec French Clb; Latin Clb; Stage Crew; Trk; Hon Roll; Socl Wrk.

THOMAS, LAWRENCE; Burgettstown HS; Bulger, PA; (4); 14/140; VP Church Yth Grp; VP SADD; VP Mrchg Band; VP Symp Band; Ed Yrbk Phtg; Rep Stu Cncl; Var L Tennis; JV Wrstlng; NHS; Pres Fit Awd 87; Diplma Merit 87; Climax Schlrshp Fnlst 87; U S Navy; Engrng.

THOMAS, LISA; Bishop Mc Cort HS; Johnstown, PA; (4); Sec VP Exploring; French Clb; Latin Clb; NFL; Pep Clb; Speech Tm; Chorus; School Musical; School Play; Nwsp Rptr; SR Actvty/Outstndg SR Awd 87; IU 8th Plc Duo-Intrprtn Spch Lg 87; Prose Intrprtn 2nd Plc 87; U Of Pittsburgh; Cmmnctns.

THOMAS, LISA; Deer Lakes HS; Cheswick, PA; (4); 35/160; Drama Clb; Varsity Clb; School Musical; School Play; Nwsp Ed-Chief; Sec Soph Cls; Sec Jr Cls; Sec Sr Cls; Pres Stu Cncl; Var L Cheerleading; SUNY Coll Fredonia; Cmnctn.

THOMAS, LISA; Harrisburg HS; Harrisburg, PA; (3); 52/265; Church Yth Grp; Sci Fair 3rd Pl 86; Temple U; Bus.

THOMAS, LISA; St Pual Cathedral HS; Pittsburgh, PA; (3); 13/53; Cmnty Wkr; VP Spanish Clb; Stage Crew; Nwsp Stf; Yrbk Stf; Rep Stu Cncl; JV Var Vllybl; High Hon Roll; Hon Roll; NHS; Ed.

THOMAS, LORI; Southmoreland HS; Connellsville, PA; (3); 3/224; Pres Church Yth Grp; French Clb; Math Clb; Band; Church Choir; Concert Band; Mrchg Band; French Hon Soc; Pres NHS; Prfct Atten Awd; Edinboro; Scndry Educ.

THOMAS, LORRIN; Central HS; Philadelphia, PA; (2); French Clb; Orch; Crs Cntry; High Hon Roll; Hon Roll; Jr NHS; 1st Pl Sci Fair At Jr High 82, 3rd Pl 83; English.

THOMAS, MATT; Garden Spot HS; New Holland, PA; (4); Boy Scts; Exploring; Band; Socr; Var High Hon Roll; Var Hon Roll; Computer Clb; VP German Clb; Library Aide; Mrchg Band; Hnrs, Chem Schlrshps Davis & Elkins Coll 87; Davis & Elkins Coll; Chem.

THOMAS, MICHAEL; Hempfield HS; Columbia, PA; (4); Boy Scts; Chorus; Concert Band; Mrchg Band; Orch; Var Trk; Eagle Sct; Widener U; Elctrcl Engrng.

THOMAS, MICHAEL DUANE; Northgate HS; Bellevue, PA; (2); Var JV Bsktbl; Var Trk; Hon Roll; U Pittsburgh.

THOMAS, MICHELE; Elizabeth Forward HS; Mc Keesport, PA; (2); Library Aide; Trs Acpl Chr; Sec Chorus; Church Choir; School Musical; Variety Show; High Hon Roll; Hon Roll; Mus Theater Shows, Dance Shows, Piano Recitals; Dist Chorus 85; Psych.

THOMAS, MICHELE; Peters Township HS; Mcmurray, PA; (3); Church Yth Grp; Exploring; FBLA; Key Clb; High Hon Roll; Hon Roll; Grove City; Elem Ed.

THOMAS, MICHELLE; Laurel Highlands SR HS; Hopwood, PA; (2); JA; JV Bsktbl; Hon Roll.

THOMAS, MICHELLE L; Waynesburg Ctl HS; Waynesburg, PA; (2); Camera Clb; Natl Beta Clb; Spanish Clb; Band; Color Guard; Concert Band; Mrchg Band; Yrbk Stf; Hon Roll; Rainbw Grls; Bus.

THOMAS, MICHELLE V; Lourdes Regional HS; Kulpmont, PA; (3); 6/92; AFS; Sec French Clb; Pep Clb; Chorus; Rep Frsh Cls; Var Cheerleading; French Hon Soc; High Hon Roll; NHS; Ntl Sec Ed Cncl Acad All Am 86.

THOMAS, OPAL; Blue Mountain Acad; Yonkers, NY; (3); Chorus; Church Choir; Bsbl; Sftbl; Swmmng; Trk; Vllybl; High Hon Roll; Hon Roll; Prfct Atten Awd; Airline Stwdrs.

THOMAS, PAMELA; Pine Grove Area HS; Tremont, PA; (4); 2/116; Varsity Clb; School Musical; Yrbk Stf; Rep Jr Cls; Rep Sr Cls; Rep Stu Cncl; Vllybl; Bausch & Lomb Sci Awd; Trs NHS; Sal; Bloomsburg U; Nrsng.

THOMAS, PATRICIA G; Southern Huntingdon County HS; Mapleton Depot, PA; (2); French Clb; SADD; Band; Chorus; Concert Band; Mrchg Band; Var Mgr(s); JV Score Keeper; Twrlr; Hon Roll; God & Chrch Awd 85; Yth Trffc Sfty Cncl 86-87.

THOMAS, REBECCA; Mc Guffey HS; Washington, PA; (3); 27/245; Spanish Clb; Stu Cncl; Var Cheerleading; Var L Sftbl; Cit Awd; Hon Roll; NHS; Outstndng Acad Achvmnt Awd 84-87; Nrsng.

THOMAS, RHONDA; East HS; West Chester, PA; (3); Church Yth Grp; 4-H; SADD; Church Choir; Bsktbl; 4-H Awd; Bradford Bus Schl; Accntng.

THOMAS, RICHARD; South Side HS; Clinton, PA; (3); 4/135; Church Yth Grp; Chorus; Church Choir; Yrbk Stf; L Socr; L Sftbl; Hon Roll; Hnrs Clb 86-87.

THOMAS, ROBERT GORDON C; Neshaminy HS; Langhorne, PA; (3); Ski Clb; Var Golf; Var Swmmng; Var Trk; Hon Roll; Cnty Courier Times Golf Scrng Avg Champ 86-87; Lndscp Arch.

THOMAS, SCOTT; Danville Area HS; Danville, PA; (2); 23/159; Ski Clb; Bsktbl; Ftbl; High Hon Roll; Prsdntl Acad Fitness Awd 85-86; Frnch Cert Of Merit 85-86.

THOMAS, SCOTT; Mechanicsburg Area HS; Mechanicsburg, PA; (2); 17/309; Ski Clb; Var Trk; High Hon Roll; Hon Roll; NHS; Engnrng.

THOMAS, SHELLEY; South Fayette HS; Oakdale, PA; (4); 5/71; Sec Pres Art Clb; Sec Pres Key Clb; Library Aide; Teachers Aide; Nwsp Stf; Ed Yrbk Stf; Rep Stu Cncl; High Hon Roll; NHS; Acad Achvr Engl 86; Duquesne U; Engl Ed.

THOMAS, SHERRY ANN; William Penn SR HS; York, PA; (4); 4/373; Pres Pep Clb; Mrchg Band; Orch; Pep Band; Off Jr Cls; Off Sr Cls; Mgr Swmmng; High Hon Roll; Jr NHS; NHS; Amer Lgn Awd 83; Early Chldhd Educ.

THOMAS, STACEY; Butler SR HS; Butler, PA; (3); Art Clb; French Clb; Pres Library Aide; VICA; Band; Rep Stu Cncl; High Hon Roll; Hon Roll; Jr NHS; Prfct Atten Awd; Pittsburgh Bty Acad; Csmtlgy.

THOMAS, STACY; West Scranton HS; Scranton, PA; (2); JA; Spanish Clb; Mrchg Band; Off Stu Cncl; Pom Pon; Hon Roll; Penn ST; Law.

THOMAS, STEVE; Conrad Weiser HS; Robesonia, PA; (2); 28/163; Church Yth Grp; Im Bsbl; Im Bsktbl; L Var Socr; High Hon Roll; Hon Roll; Mst Imprvd Off Plyr Soccr; Hnrb Mntn All Div Soccr; Engrng.

THOMAS, TAMMY; Mc Keesport Area HS; Mc Keesport, PA; (4); 2/350; FBLA; Hosp Aide; Office Aide; Q&S; Teachers Aide; School Play; Nwsp Rptr; Ed Nwsp Stf; Powder Puff Ftbl; High Hon Roll; Mc Keesport Rtry Hnr Stu 86; PA ST U; Acctg.

THOMAS, TANAKA; Philadelphia HS For Girls; Philadelphia, PA; (1); Church Yth Grp; Computer Clb; FBLA; FHA; Library Aide; Spanish Clb; Teachers Aide; Church Choir; Rep Frsh Cls; Cit Awd; Cert Awd Acadc Excel 85; Amer Lgn Cert Schl Awd 86; Temple U; Cmmnctns.

THOMAS, TARA; Mahanoy Area HS; Mahanoy City, PA; (2); FHA; Hosp Aide; Ski Clb; Teachers Aide; VICA; Drill Tm; Variety Show; Yrbk Stf; Trs Stu Cncl; Hon Roll; Drftg.

THOMAS, TRACEY; West Side Area Vo Tech; Kingston, PA; (3); Computer Clb; FBLA; Key Clb; Chorus; Yrbk Stf; Hon Roll; Accntng Clerk.

THOMAS, TRACY; Elizabeth Forward HS; Elizabeth, PA; (3); Church Yth Grp; Girl Scts; Pep Clb; Pep Band; Stage Crew; Yrbk Stf; Var Cheerleading; Var Trk; Psych.

THOMAS, TRACY; John S Fine HS; Nanticoke, PA; (3); 7/236; Ski Clb; Trs Jr Cls; L Var Fld Hcky; Mgr(s); High Hon Roll; NHS; Church Yth Grp; Hosp Aide; JV Capt Cheerleading; Pharm.

THOMAS, TRACY L; Harmony Area HS; Westover, PA; (3); 2/47; Band; Concert Band; Trs Frsh Cls; VP Soph Cls; High Hon Roll; Hon Roll; NHS; Prfct Atten Awd; Stu Mnth 85-86; Mst Imprvd Wrtng Awd 87; Cmnctns.

THOMAS, VICKI; Milton SR HS; Milton, PA; (2); Hosp Aide; Library Aide; Spanish Clb; JV Trk; Hon Roll; Pres Schlr; Penn ST.

THOMAS, WAYNE; Carver HS Of Engineering & Science; Philadelphia, PA; (3); Boys Clb Am; Rep Frsh Cls; Rep Soph Cls; Rep Jr Cls; Var Bsbl; Var Capt Socr; Hon Roll; Drexel U; Arch Engrng.

THOMAS, WILLIAM F; Msgr Bonner HS; Drexel Hill, PA; (3); 47/255; Bsbl; Ftbl; Hon Roll; Williamson Trade Schl; Elctrncs.

THOMASON, GREG; Saint James HS; Brookhaven, PA; (3); 46/176; Dance Clb; Im Bsktbl; Im Fld Hcky; Hon Roll; Bus Admn.

THOMASON, SHANNON; Spring Ford HS; Royersford, PA; (3); German Clb; Ski Clb; Yrbk Stf; Mgr Bsktbl; Var Fld Hcky; JV Lcrss; Vllybl; Wrstlng; West Chester U; Elem Ed.

THOME, DAWN; Donegal HS; Manheim, PA; (3); 40/150; Church Yth Grp; FBLA; Office Aide; Trs Pep Clb; Stage Crew; Nwsp Stf; Yrbk Stf; JV Bsktbl; JV Cheerleading; Hon Roll; Law.

THOMPKINS, CARRIE; Young SR HS; Yukon, PA; (3); French Clb; Library Aide; Pep Clb; Band; Concert Band; Mrchg Band; Symp Band; Yrbk Stf; High Hon Roll; Hon Roll; Anthrplgy.

THOMPKINS, HAZEL; West Catholic HS For Girls; Philadelphia, PA; (3); 45/246; Church Yth Grp; French Clb; FBLA; Library Aide; High Hon Roll; Hon Roll; Chrls E Ellis Schlrshp Fund 84-88; Typwrtng Awd 87; PA ST; Comp Pgrmr.

THOMPSON, ALAN D; Lock Haven SR HS; Howard, PA; (3); Boy Scts; Church Yth Grp; Varsity Clb; Ftbl; PENN ST; Pre-Law.

THOMPSON, ALISHA; Engineering And Science HS; Philadelphia, PA; (4); 9/210; Church Yth Grp; Drill Tm; Rep Frsh Cls; Rep Soph Cls; Rep Jr Cls; Trs Sr Cls; Sftbl; High Hon Roll; NHS; Prfct Atten Awd; PRIME 83-87; Outstndng Minority Stu 87; Distngshd Studies 83-87; Materials Engrng.

THOMPSON, AMY; West Middlesex HS; West Middlesex, PA; (2); Church Yth Grp; Girl Scts; Hosp Aide; Spanish Clb; Band; Concert Band; Mrchg Band; Pep Band; Trk; High Hon Roll; Stdnt Achvrs Awd 87; Crmnl Psych.

THOMPSON, AMY R; Maplewood HS; Cambridge Spgs, PA; (4); 1/125; Pres 4-H; Varsity Clb; Sec Trs VICA; Mrchg Band; Stat Bsktbl; JV Cheerleading; Bausch & Lomb Sci Awd; Elks Awd; NHS; Val; VICA ST Compu Prgmmng Cmpttn 2nd 87; PA ST 4-G Horse Show 84-86; Amer Legion Awd 84; Edinboro U; Compu Sci.

THOMPSON, ANDREA; Williams Valley JR SR HS; Tower City, PA; (1); 2/119; Art Clb; Church Yth Grp; Pep Clb; Ski Clb; Trs Spanish Clb; Chorus; Mrchg Band; Powder Puff Ftbl; Twrlr; High Hon Roll; NEDT Awd 86; Dickenson; Law.

THOMPSON, BECKY; Hopewell SR HS; Aliquippa, PA; (4); 26/245; Pres Latin Clb; Math Clb; Chorus; Stu Cncl; Bsktbl; High Hon Roll; NHS; Alderson-Broadus; Physcl Thrpy.

THOMPSON, BRENDA; Athens HS; Athens, PA; (3); German Clb; Hosp Aide; Crs Cntry; Trk; Hon Roll; Crss Cnty-Trck, Rbbns & Vrsty 86-87; Achvt Awds-Cvcs, W Cltrs, Phys Ed & Intro To Algbra 84-87; Mansfield U; X-Ray Tech.

THOMPSON, BRIAN L; Northern Lebanon HS; Annville, PA; (2); #24 In Class; Chess Clb; Church Yth Grp; Bsbl; Socr; Tennis; Vllybl; Hon Roll; Air Force Acad; Elctrcl Engr.

THOMPSON, CASSANDRA; Moshannon Valley HS; Brisbin, PA; (3); Spanish Clb; Varsity Clb; Capt Flag Corp; Yrbk Stf; VP Soph Cls; VP Sr Cls; Stu Cncl; Var Bsktbl; Var L Sftbl; High Hon Roll; Sprts Med.

THOMPSON, CHRIS; Pequea Valley HS; Gap, PA; (3); 13/137; AFS; Cmnty Wkr; FBLA; Girl Scts; Library Aide; Teachers Aide; Yrbk Stf; Cit Awd; Hon Roll; Office Aide; Outstndng Yth Vlntr 87; Penn ST; Bus.

THOMPSON, CHRISTINA; W B Saul HS; Philadelphia, PA; (2); Church Yth Grp; FFA; Girl Scts; Hosp Aide; Political Wkr; Teachers Aide; Church Choir; Bsbl; Golf; Sftbl; DE Valley Coll.

THOMPSON, CHRISTYANN; New Castle SR HS; New Castle, PA; (3); AFS; Office Aide; Pep Clb; Ski Clb; Spanish Clb; Trk; Vllybl.

THOMPSON, DANIEL M; Hollidaysburg SR HS; Hollidaysburg, PA; (3); Trs Drama Clb; VP SADD; Chorus; Rep Stu Cncl; Var Tennis; Pltcl Sci.

THOMPSON, DARLA; Fairview Christian Schl; Honey Grove, PA; (3); Church Yth Grp; Cmnty Wkr; Chorus; Bsktbl; Sftbl; Trk; Vllybl; Hon Roll; FCA; Eagle Awd Chrstn Srvc, Recrdng Artst-Gospel & Contemp Chrstn Music 1st Album Relsd Oct 87; Contemp & Gospel Singer.

THOMPSON, DAVE; Butler Area SR HS; Butler, PA; (4); 94/755; Exploring; Hon Roll; Ntl Merit Ltr; Pres Schlr; Rochester Inst Of Tech.

THOMPSON, DAVID; Kennard Dale HS; Stewartstown, PA; (3); Art Clb; Aud/Vis; Library Aide; Stage Crew; Yrbk Phtg; Yrbk Stf; Var JV Bsbl; JC Awd; Prfct Atten Awd.

THOMPSON, DIANA; Clearfield HS; Clearfield, PA; (4); 80/292; Art Clb; Sec Church Yth Grp; FCA; Library Aide; VP SADD; VICA; Chorus; Im Badmtn; JV Sftbl; JV Tennis; Spec Olymp Vol Awd 86-87.

THOMPSON, DIANE; Sayre JR/Sr HS; Sayre, PA; (3); SADD; Chorus; Church Choir; Flag Corp; Swing Chorus; High Hon Roll; Hon Roll; Bus.

THOMPSON, DONA; Bishop Mc Devitt HS; Willow Grove, PA; (3); Bsktbl; Var Fld Hcky; Var Powder Puff Ftbl; Var Vllybl; Bus.

THOMPSON, ELVA; Dauphin County Tech Schl; Harrisburg, PA; (3); ROTC; Trk; Harrisburg Area CC; Arch Tech.

THOMPSON, ERIC; Tunkhannock Area HS; Clarks Summit, PA; (4); 14/283; Am Leg Boys St; Church Yth Grp; VP French Clb; Science Clb; Crs Cntry; Trk; Wrstlng; High Hon Roll; NHS; Elec Engr.

THOMPSON, FRANCES; Gateway HS; Monroeville, PA; (3); Exploring; FBLA; Off Sr Cls; High Hon Roll; Hon Roll; Accntg.

THOMPSON II, GARY I; Linesville HS; Linesville, PA; (4); 11/90; Pres Band; Pres Concert Band; Pres Jazz Band; Pres Mrchg Band; Pres Pep Band; High Hon Roll; Hon Roll; JP Sousa Awd; NHS; Voice Dem Awd; Music Bstrs Schlrshp 87; De Vry Inst Of Tech; Elec Tech.

THOMPSON, GLENN DAVID; Moon Area HS; Coraopolis, PA; (3); CAP; Computer Clb; German Clb; Chorus; Church Choir; Color Guard; Drill Tm; Stage Crew; Ftbl; Wrstlng; Cdt Of Yr Sq 603 Cvl Air Patrol 85; Billy Mitchell Awd Cvl Air Patrol 86.

THOMPSON, J MATTHEW; Henderson HS; W Chester, PA; (3); 85/367; JCL; Ski Clb; Nwsp Sprt Ed; Rep Frsh Cls; Rep Soph Cls; Rep Jr Cls; Var Ftbl; Var Lcrss; Hon Roll.

THOMPSON, JEFFREY P; Cameron County HS; Emporium, PA; (4); 1/85; Math Clb; Mu Alpha Theta; Spanish Clb; School Musical; Yrbk Stf; Bausch & Lomb Sci Awd; High Hon Roll; Pres NHS; Val; Natl Hnr-Bausch & Lomb Sci 85-86; Mu Alpha Theta 85-86; Natl Sci Olympiad 85-86; Elizabethtown Coll; Chem.

THOMPSON, JENNIFER; Trinity HS; Washington, PA; (2); Cmnty Wkr; French Clb; Band; Mrchg Band; Yrbk Stf; Trk; Hon Roll; Syrauce; Jrnlsm.

THOMPSON, JENNIFER G; Upper Merion HS; King Of Prussia, PA; (3); Hon Roll; Bus Accntng.

THOMPSON, JILL; Chambersburg Area SR HS; Chambersburg, PA; (2); Church Yth Grp; French Clb; Band; PSYCH.

THOMPSON, JODI; Bellefonte SR HS; Bellefonte, PA; (4); 15/236; Church Yth Grp; Chorus; Concert Band; Mrchg Band; Rep Stu Cncl; Var Tennis; High Hon Roll; Hon Roll; Acad Achvt Awd 87; Lock Haven U; Elem Educ.

THOMPSON, JOYCE; Norwin SR HS; Ardara, PA; (4); 110/529; SADD; Teachers Aide; VICA; Chorus; Church Choir; Hon Roll; Vice Offcr Parlmntrn 86-87; 3rd Pl Food Svc Trades Comptn 85-86 & 86-87; Johnson & Wales Coll; Htl/Rest.

THOMPSON, JULIE; Punksutawney Area SR HS; Punxsutawney, PA; (3); FBLA; Teachers Aide; Band; Concert Band; Mrchg Band; Im Bsbl; Im Bsktbl; Im Wrstlng; High Hon Roll; Hon Roll; Dubois Bus Coll; Bus.

THOMPSON, KELLY; Coatesville Area SR HS; Coatesville, PA; (3); 26/509; Leo Clb; Spanish Clb; Trk; Hon Roll; NHS; NEDT Awd; Prfct Atten Awd; Outstndng Achvt In Spnsh II Awd 85-86; Fmly Lvng I Awd 85-86; Nrsng.

THOMPSON, KELLY; Galeton Area HS; Galeton, PA; (3); Ski Clb; Pres Spanish Clb; Sec Band; Chorus; Yrbk Ed-Chief; Yrbk Phtg; Trs Soph Cls; Sec Jr Cls; VP Stu Cncl; Capt Bsktbl; Ntl Hnr Soc 86; Art.

THOMPSON, KIM; Canon Mc Millan HS; Washington, PA; (3); Church Yth Grp; Cmnty Wkr; Sec Band; Sec Concert Band; Sec Mrchg Band; Swmmng; Trk; High Hon Roll; Hon Roll; CA U Of PA; Psychlgy.

THOMPSON, KRISTIN; Freeport SR HS; Freeport, PA; (3); Color Guard; Hon Roll; Sec Field.

THOMPSON, KRISTINA; Elizabethtown HS; Elizabeth, PA; (4); Aud/Vis; Church Yth Grp; Girl Scts; Spanish Clb; Off Jr Cls; Bsktbl; Bowling; Gym; Powder Puff Ftbl; Sftbl; Bus.

THOMPSON, LAUREL; Hatboro-Horsham SR HS; Horsham, PA; (4); 30/269; Church Yth Grp; Debate Tm; Pep Clb; Sec Soph Cls; Off Jr Cls; Sec Sr Cls; Capt Fld Hcky; Var Capt Lcrss; Powder Puff Ftbl; Schlr Athl Awd-Triangle Clb 87; Mc Donalds Chris Gabriel Awd-Ldrshp 87; Ursinus Coll; Bus Admin.

THOMPSON, LAUREN; Gwynedd Mercy Acad; Huntingdon Vly, PA; (2); Drama Clb; School Musical; JV Lcrss; JV Tennis.

THOMPSON, LISA J; Blairsville SR HS; Blairsville, PA; (4); Church Yth Grp; Concert Band; Drm Mjr(t); School Musical; Twrlr; High Hon Roll; NHS; Pres Schlr; JR Womens Clb Schlrshp 87; IN Cnty Penn ST Club Schlrshp 87; Penn ST U; Nursing.

THOMPSON, LORI; Sharpsville Area HS; Sharpsville, PA; (4); Drama Clb; Library Aide; Teachers Aide; Nwsp Rptr; Nwsp Stf; Mgr(s); Sftbl; High Hon Roll; Hon Roll; Letter & Awds Acad Achvmnt 87; Travel.

THOMPSON, MARCY; Connellsville Area SR HS; Connellsville, PA; (4); Chorus; School Musical; Rep Sr Cls; Rep Stu Cncl; Var Cheerleading; L Sftbl; Swmmng; Stat Vllybl; NHS; Spanish NHS; Frostburg ST.

THOMPSON, MARK; Holy Ghost Preparatory Schl; Philadelphia, PA; (4); Debate Tm; Library Aide; Stage Crew; Nwsp Rptr; Nwsp Stf; Lit Mag; Hon Roll; NHS; Boston U.

THOMPSON, MICHAEL; St John Neumann HS; Philadelphia, PA; (3); 29/349; Art Clb; Chorus; Madrigals; School Musical; JV Bsbl; Var L Socr; Var Trk; High Hon Roll; Hon Roll; Arch.

THOMPSON, MICHELLE; Newport HS; Newport, PA; (2); 3/116; High Hon Roll; NHS; Math.

THOMPSON, MONICA; Center HS; Monaca, PA; (3); NAACP; JV Cheerleading; Hon Roll; SC ST; Accntng.

THOMPSON, PAM; Plymouth-Whitemarsh HS; Plymouth Mtg, PA; (4); 26/330; Rep Sr Cls; Var Fld Hcky; Capt Lcrss; Hon Roll; NHS; MVP, Mst Vlbl Dfns 87; James Madison U.

THOMPSON, RICHARD; Bucktail Area HS; Renovo, PA; (2); Var Mgr(s); Lock Haven U; Naval Offcr.

THOMPSON, RICHARD; Do Bois HS; Falls Creek, PA; (3); 3/400; Hon Roll; NHS; Penn ST; Radio.

THOMPSON, RICK; Meadville SR HS; Meadville, PA; (2); Church Yth Grp; Varsity Clb; Crs Cntry; Trk; Hon Roll; NHS.

THOMPSON, SARAH; Lebanon HS; Lebanon, PA; (3); Cmnty Wkr; French Clb; Hosp Aide; Key Clb; Latin Clb; Library Aide; SADD; Chorus; School Musical; Hon Roll; Lebanon Vlly Coll; Soc Wrkr.

THOMPSON, SEAN; Northeast Catholic HS; Philadelphia, PA; (2); Church Yth Grp; Yrbk Stf; Hon Roll; NHS; Prfct Atten Awd; Mltry.

THOMPSON, SHELLEY LYNN; Oxford Area HS; Cochranville, PA; (4); 10/167; Sec Band; Sec Trs Chorus; Jazz Band; School Musical; Nwsp Stf; Yrbk Stf; NHS; Mst Vlbl Music Dept Schlrshp 87; PMEA Dist 12 Chorus 87; Rtry Intl SR Of Mth 86; Lncstr Gen Hosp Schl-Nrsg; RN.

THOMPSON, SHERI L; Central HS; Roaring Spring, PA; (3); 5/196; Church Yth Grp; Ski Clb; Band; Chorus; Concert Band; Mrchg Band; Rep Stu Cncl; Hon Roll; NHS; Pres Schlr; Phys Therapy.

THOMPSON, STEVE; Mc Keesport Area HS; White Oak, PA; (2); Exploring; Concert Band; Mrchg Band; High Hon Roll; Amer Lgn Schl Awd 85; Engrng.

THOMPSON, SUE; Vincentian HS; Pittsburgh, PA; (2); Drama Clb; GAA; VP Frsh Cls; Rep Soph Cls; JV Var Bsktbl; Im Fld Hcky; Im Ftbl; Var Socr; Im Sftbl; Im Vllybl; USMA; Psych.

THOMPSON, SUZANNE; Frankford HS; Philadelphia, PA; (2); 2/600; Church Yth Grp; Cmnty Wkr; Computer Clb; Hosp Aide; Office Aide; Teachers Aide; Var Cheerleading; JV L Vllybl; High Hon Roll; Prfct Atten Awd; Physics.

THOMPSON, TERRI; Williams Valley HS; Tower City, PA; (2); Pep Clb; Chorus; Mrchg Band; Off Frsh Cls; Twrlr; High Hon Roll; Hon Roll; Fash.

THOMPSON, TIFFANY; Sharpsville SR HS; Sharpsville, PA; (3); Church Yth Grp; FHA; Office Aide; SADD; Nwsp Stf; Yrbk Stf; Sec Soph Cls; Stu Cncl; Var Ftbl; Var Sftbl; Phys Ftns Awd 87; Wrk With Mntly Rtrd 84-87; Med Secr.

THOMPSON, TRACEY JEAN; Shaler Area HS; Pittsburgh, PA; (4); 151/509; Cmnty Wkr; Girl Scts; Office Aide; SADD; Yrbk Stf; Hon Roll; Spanish NHS; Allegheny Community; Prmry Educ.

THOMPSON, VIRGINIA M; Oil City Area SR HS; Cooperstown, PA; (4); 176/231; School Musical; Stage Crew; Variety Show; Yrbk Phtg; Im Bsktbl; Diving; Im Socr; Im Vllybl; Girl Scts; Band; Photography.

THOMSON, KAREN; Northeastern HS; Manchester, PA; (3); AFS; Art Clb; Girl Scts; VA Beach Coll; Acctng.

THOMSON, LAURA; Plum SR HS; Pittsburgh, PA; (4); AFS; Cmnty Wkr; Pres DECA; FBLA; Varsity Clb; Sftbl; Swmmng; Var L Vllybl; PA Mrktng Schlrshp 87; 2nd Pl Ntl Mrktng Cmptn 87; 3 1st Pl ST Cmptn Mrktng 86-87; Slippery Rock U; Mltry Army.

THOMSON, PAUL; Butler SR HS; Butler, PA; (3); French Clb; JA; Latin Clb; Math Tm; Red Cross Aide; Var L Bsktbl; Var L Socr; Var L Tennis; Hon Roll; Jr NHS; PA ST; Chem Engrng.

THOMSPON, DAISY; BOK Technical HS; Philadelphia, PA; (3); Church Yth Grp; Cmnty Wkr; Office Aide; Teachers Aide; Hon Roll.

THORN, JOE; East Pennsboro HS; Enola, PA; (3); Chess Clb; Pep Clb; Socr; Wrstlng; High Hon Roll; Hon Roll; Shippenburg; Militry Police.

THORN, TRACY; Ridley SR HS; Folsom, PA; (3); 22/423; JV Var Fld Hcky; High Hon Roll; Hon Roll; Pres Schlr; JV Mat Maids; Sci.

THORNBLADE, CARL; Southmoreland HS; Scottdale, PA; (2); 1/252; Church Yth Grp; French Clb; JV Golf; L Var Tennis; Im Vllybl; French Hon Soc; Ntl Knwldg Mstr Open 86 & 87.

THORNBLADE, TRACEY; Southmoreland HS; Scottdale, PA; (3); 1/230; Sec Church Yth Grp; Drama Clb; French Clb; School Musical; School Play; Nwsp Stf; Rep Stu Cncl; French Hon Soc; Sec NHS; Ntl Merit Ltr; Rep Westmoreland Cnty Stu Forum 86-87; Brdcst Jrnlsm.

THORNBURG, CHRISTINA; Rochester Area HS; Rochester, PA; (3); 7/110; Library Aide; Trs Spanish Clb; Teachers Aide; Band; Orch; Ed Nwsp Ed-Chief; Nwsp Stf; High Hon Roll; NHS; Worthy Advsr Rochester Assmbly No 51 87; Semi Fnlst Gov Schl Arts 86-87; Dance Awds 84-87; Point Park Coll; Dance.

THORNE, JAMES; Ford City JR SR HS; Ford City, PA; (4); 4/148; Boy Scts; Key Clb; Concert Band; Mrchg Band; Capt L Crs Cntry; L Var Trk; God Cntry Awd; NHS; Eagle Sct 87; Marine ROTC 4 Yr Schlrshp 87; U Of PA; Mechncl Engr.

THORNE, KAREN E; George Westinghouse HS; Pittsburgh, PA; (4); 2/190; AFS; School Play; High Hon Roll; Hon Roll; NHS; Duquesne U; Journlsm.

THORNE, TARA; Loyalsock HS; Montoursville, PA; (3); French Clb; Trs Ski Clb; SADD; Chorus; Stu Cncl; Var L Bsktbl; Score Keeper; Var L Sftbl; Var L Tennis; Law.

THORNE, TERRELL; Aliquippa HS; Aliq, PA; (2); Aud/Vis; Computer Clb; Bsbl; Hon Roll; Prfct Atten Awd; Comp Sys Anal.

THORNHILL, DAVID; Spring Ford HS; Royersford, PA; (2); 84/289; Church Yth Grp; FCA; Stage Crew; Symp Band; Variety Show; Nwsp Rptr; JV Bsbl; JV Capt Bsktbl; JV Ftbl; JV Wt Lftg; Estrn Nzrn Coll; Doctor.

THORNTON, JENNIFER; Allentown Central Catholic HS; Allentown, PA; (3); 19/241; Hosp Aide; Key Clb; Math Clb; Service Clb; Ski Clb; Y-Teens; High Hon Roll; Hon Roll; NHS; Natl Ltn Exm Cum Laude Cert 86; USA Acad Sci Natl Awd 85; Lehigh U; Bus.

THORNTON, LAURA; Carbondale Area HS; Simpson, PA; (4); 4/144; Sec French Clb; FBLA; Sec Ski Clb; Yrbk Bus Mgr; Sftbl; Tennis; High Hon Roll; Jr NHS; NHS; Wilkes Coll; Engrng.

THORNTON, LISA; Carbondale Area HS; Simpson, PA; (4); 1/144; Computer Clb; French Clb; FBLA; VP Ski Clb; Yrbk Ed-Chief; Tennis; DAR Awd; Jr NHS; NHS; Wilkes Coll; Engrng.

THORNTON, RICHARD; Penns Manor HS; Clymer, PA; (3); 12/97; Chess Clb; Sec Varsity Clb; Trs Jr Cls; Var L Bsktbl; Var L Trk; VP NHS.

THORP, SAMANTHA L; Freeport Area HS; Freeport, PA; (4); Art Clb; PAVAS; Teachers Aide; School Musical; Yrbk Ed-Chief; Yrbk Phtg; Stat Bsktbl; Var L Sftbl; High Hon Roll; Band; PA Govs Schl For The Arts 86; IN U Smmr Hppng 85; IN U Of PA; Art.

THORPE, BRENNA; Trinity HS; Washington, PA; (4); 9/350; Drama Clb; French Clb; NFL; SADD; Temple Yth Grp; Chorus; Concert Band; School Musical; School Play; Variety Show; PA Gov Schl Arts 85; Dist, Rgnl, & ST Orchstra 84; Dist, & Rgnl Chorus 87; Bennington Coll; Music.

THORPE, JENNIFER D; Upper Merion SR HS; King Of Prussia, PA; (2); 97/325; Church Yth Grp; Rep DECA; Library Aide; Nwsp Stf; Prfct Atten Awd; Am Red Crss Advncd Lifesvng & Water Sfty 86-87; Advrtsng.

THORPE, SHERRY; Pine Forge Acad; Durham, NC; (3); 5/62; Church Yth Grp; Pep Clb; Chorus; Off Soph Cls; Trs Jr Cls; Hon Roll; Little Lk Indstrys Outstndng Wrkr Awd 87; Oakwood Coll; Acct.

THORWART, JULIE; St Marys Area HS; St Marys, PA; (2); Var Trk; Hon Roll.

THUCH, SOKJETRA P; Ephrata SR HS; Ephrata, PA; (4); Boy Scts; Chess Clb; Church Yth Grp; Computer Clb; Radio Clb; Science Clb; Socr; Wrstlng; Cit Awd; Hon Roll; Hnr Grad 87; Temple Univ; Pre Med.

THURBER, ANDREW; Penncrest HS; Media, PA; (3); 58/344; Ornithology.

THURMAN, JAMES; Taylor Alderice HS; Pittsburgh, PA; (2); High Hon Roll; Hon Roll; NHS; Art.

THURMAN, JESSE; Waynesburg Central HS; Waynesburg, PA; (4); Church Yth Grp; Cmnty Wkr; Debate Tm; Drama Clb; French Clb; Spanish Clb; Speech Tm; School Play; Variety Show; Nwsp Ed-Chief; Best Actress 83-84; Waynesburg Coll; Theatre.

THYGESON JR, WILLIAM; Upper Moreland HS; Hatboro, PA; (2); 4/250; Rep Stu Cncl; Var L Bsbl; Var L Bsktbl; Var L Ftbl; Im Gym; High Hon Roll; NHS; 2nd Tm All Leag Ftbl, Hnrb Mntn All Area 86.

TIBBETTS, CHRIS; Crefeld HS; Willow Grove, PA; (1); 1/6; Art Clb; Aud/Vis; Camera Clb; Ice Hcky; Engr.

TIBEL, ALYSIA; Pittston Area HS; Dupont, PA; (4); French Clb; FBLA; Key Clb; Science Clb; Yrbk Stf; Score Keeper; Vllybl; J Hopkins U Tlnt Srch/Kngs Awd 87; 2nd Pl Miss FBLA 87; Kings Coll; Fnc.

TIBERIO, JOANNA; Western Beaver HS; Industry, PA; (4); 19/85; Symp Band; Yrbk Ed-Chief; Sec Jr Cls; Rep Stu Cncl; Stat Bsktbl; Twrlr; Cit Awd; Hon Roll; NHS; Fnlst In Beaver Cnty JR Miss Prog 86; April Stu Of Mnth Awd 87; Waynesburg Coll; Bus Adm.

TICE, DAVID; Bellefonte Area SR HS; Bellefonte, PA; (3); 60/210; Boy Scts; 4-H; Im Bsbl; JV Wrstlng; Hon Roll; Eagle Sct 85; Arch.

TIEDEKEN, ALEXANDRA; West Catholic Girls HS; Philadelphia, PA; (3); 5/248; Library Aide; Scholastic Bowl; Spanish Clb; School Play; Yrbk Stf; Capt Cheerleading; Hon Roll; NHS; Gen Excllnc Awd & Engl II Awd 86; Stanford; Bus Mgmt.

TIELLE, DAVID; Pittston Area HS; Pittston, PA; (4); 25/348; Key Clb; Ski Clb; Band; Concert Band; Jazz Band; Mrchg Band; High Hon Roll; NHS; US Natl Ldrshp Merit Awd 87; Acad All Amer 86-87; Wilkes Coll; Pre Law.

TIELSCH, BRIAN J; Penn Hills SR HS; Pittsburgh, PA; (4); 16/609; Teachers Aide; School Musical; Bsbl; Ftbl; Wrstlng; High Hon Roll; NHS; Pres Acdmc Fit Awd 86-87; St Vincent Acdmc Schlrshp Awd 87-91; Comp Mmath Asst Peer Tutr 86-87; St Vincent Coll; Pre-Med.

TIERNEY, KIMBERLY; Academy Of Notre Dame De Namur; Newtown Square, PA; (3); Art Clb; Camera Clb; Cmnty Wkr; Drama Clb; FCA; GAA; Letterman Clb; PAVAS; SADD; School Musical; Blue Rbn & Gld Key Awd Natl Photo Cont 87; Natl Hstry Day Awd 85; Denison U; Graphic Arts.

TIERNEY, LORI; West Phildlphia Girls Catholc HS; Philadelphia, PA; (3); 14/267; Church Yth Grp; Library Aide; Teachers Aide; Nwsp Bus Mgr; Nwsp Rptr; Nwsp Stf; Yrbk Stf; High Hon Roll; Hon Roll; NHS; Italian II, Religion II & Non-Western Culture Of Acdmc Awds 85-86; Villanova U; Commerce.

TIESENGA, TAMMY; Christian Schl Of York; York, PA; (4); 8/58; Church Yth Grp; Chorus; Church Choir; School Musical; Stu Cncl; Bsktbl; CC Awd; Cit Awd; Dnfth Awd; Donald R Misner Ctznshp Awd 87; ACSI Distngshd Chrstn HS Stu 87; Outstndng HS Ath Amer 87; Evangel Coll; Engl.

TIETZ, ERICA; Eisenhower HS; Chandlers Vly, PA; (3); 10/126; German Clb; Band; Mrchg Band; Nwsp Ed-Chief; Nwsp Rptr; Trs Nwsp Stf; JV Bsktbl; High Hon Roll; NHS; Chautauqua Inst Schl Art Scholar 87; Warren Art Lg H S Art Shw 1st 2nd & 3rd Pl 86; Phrmcy.

TIEU, SANH; Swarthmore Acad; Chester, PA; (3); Hosp Aide; Crs Cntry; Lcrss; Socr; Widener U; Elctrcl Engrng.

TIFFANY, SHAUN; Tunkhannock HS; Tunkhannock, PA; (3); Cmnty Wkr; Key Clb; JV Var Bsktbl; Var Tennis; Im Wt Lftg; Hon Roll; NHS; Acadmc All Amercn 85; Pltcl Sci.

TIGER, DAWNETTE; Purchase Line HS; Cherry Tree, PA; (3); Pep Clb; Score Keeper; Timer; Hon Roll; Ntl Merit Ltr; Radlgy.

TIGHE, JOHN P; Thomas Jefferson HS; Clairton, PA; (3); 22/255; Am Leg Boys St; Capt Bsktbl; L Ftbl; Hon Roll; NHS; Rotary Awd; Rtry Stu Mnth 87; PA U; Acctng.

TIGHE, STEVEN J; Spring Ford HS; Schwenksville, PA; (4); 8/239; Math Clb; Stu Cncl; Var Bsbl; JV Bsktbl; JV Socr; Hon Roll; NHS; Pres Schlr; Spring-Ford Educ Assn 87-88; Millersville ST U; Math.

TIGNOR, STEPHEN R; Williamsport Area HS; Williamsport, PA; (4); 11/518; Math Tm; Stu Cncl; Tennis; Timer; Hon Roll; Jr NHS; Ntl Merit SF; Mst Outstndng Ten Plyr Dist Champ 85-86; Lab Asst; Physcs Clb.

TIKEY, DEBRA; Connellsville Area SR HS; Connellsville, PA; (4); GAA; Band; Chorus; Church Choir; Mrchg Band; School Musical; School Play; Symp Band; Sec Soph Cls; Sec Jr Cls; Slippery Rock; Pre Dntl.

TILFORD, JEFF; Shikellamy HS; Northumberland, PA; (3); Church Yth Grp; Bsbl; Bsktbl; Bowling; Ftbl; Sftbl; Vllybl; Wt Lftg; Wrstlng; Hon Roll.

TILLERY, PAULA MONIQUE; Pine Forge Acad; Baltimore, MD; (3); Church Yth Grp; Library Aide; Office Aide; Teachers Aide; Band; Chorus; Church Choir; Drill Tm; School Musical; School Play; Crmnl Jstc.

TILLERY, STEPHANIE; Chichester SR HS; Boothwyn, PA; (3); 62/297; Church Yth Grp; Drama Clb; Model UN; SADD; Drill Tm; Lit Mag; Cheerleading; Fld Hcky; Trk; Jr NHS; Bus Manag.

TILLETT, NICOLE; Shamokin Area HS; Shamokin, PA; (2); 51/250; Art Clb; Pep Clb; Nwsp Phtg; Nwsp Rptr; Nwsp Stf; Rep Soph Cls; Cheerleading; Score Keeper; Vllybl.

TILLMAN, MARSHALL; Bok Area Vocational Technical HS; Philadelphia, PA; (4); 32/250; Varsity Clb; Im Bsktbl; Var Crs Cntry; Var Capt Ftbl; Var Capt Trk; Edward Bok AVT Alumni Awd 87; Morristown Coll; Bus Admin.

TILLMANN, DEBORAH; Saint Hubert Catholic HS; Philadelphia, PA; (3); 38/421; Church Yth Grp; Cmnty Wkr; Dance Clb; Hosp Aide; Cheerleading; Gym; Hon Roll; Med.

TILLOTSON, DENISE; Union City HS; Union City, PA; (3); 1/108; Drama Clb; SADD; Chorus; School Musical; School Play; Capt JV Cheerleading; Golf; Powder Puff Ftbl; Hon Roll; Prfct Atten Awd; Edinboro Coll; Elem Tchr.

TIMA, JANET; Hazleton SR HS; Hazleton, PA; (3); Drama Clb; Chorus; Nwsp Rptr; Cheerleading; L Trk; Vllybl; Hon Roll; Prfct Atten Awd; Psychology.

TIMBERS, NIYA; Philadelphia HS For Girls; Philadelphia, PA; (3); GAA; Office Aide; Rep Frsh Cls; Rep Jr Cls; Crs Cntry; Med.

TIMBLIN, BECKY; Bald Eagle Area H S HS; Howard, PA; (4); Sec Jr Cls; Sec Sr Cls; Rep Stu Cncl; Sec Bsktbl; Var Cheerleading; Var Mgr(s); Var Powder Puff Ftbl; Var Trk; Var Wt Lftg; Sec Wrstlng; PA ST U; Law.

TIMCHAK, ALICE ANN; North Allegheny SR HS; Sewickley, PA; (4); 170/660; Sec Church Yth Grp; School Musical; Gym; Hon Roll; KDKA-TV 2 Eywtnss Sprts Extr Effrt Awd 87; Dstngshd Achvt Awd Schl Brd 85-87; U Of Pittsburgh; Occptnl Thrpy.

TIMCHAK, ROSEMARY; Hopewell SR HS; Aliquippa, PA; (3); Cmnty Wkr; Hosp Aide; Pep Clb; Nwsp Rptr; Nwsp Stf; Powder Puff Ftbl; Hon Roll; Copy Editor Hi-Lites 86-88; Media Comm.

TIMCO, PATRICIA; Meadville Area SR HS; Meadville, PA; (3); 141/328; Church Yth Grp; Hosp Aide; Key Clb; Chorus; JV Var Cheerleading; Var Sftbl.

TIMKO, DANIEL; Ringgold HS; Monongahela, PA; (3); Church Yth Grp; Library Aide; Band; Mrchg Band; Var Bsbl; Var Bsktbl; Var Golf; Var Ice Hcky; Var Socr; Var Tennis; Air Force.

TIMKO, LISA; Our Lady Of The Sacred Heart HS; W Aliquippa, PA; (4); 4/58; Hosp Aide; Model UN; Pep Clb; School Play; Pres Jr Cls; Pres Stu Cncl; Var Capt Cheerleading; Hon Roll; NHS; Hghst Achvmnt Spnsh I II III IV 84-87; Acdmc Schlrshp Gannon U 87; Mst Vlbl Chrldr 87.

TIMKO, VALESIE; Greensburg-Salem HS; Greensburg, PA; (2); Girl Scts; Spanish Clb; Y-Teens; Hon Roll; Food Svc Industry.

TIMLIN JR, ROBERT EDWARD; Schenley HS; Pittsburgh, PA; (3); Church Yth Grp; Computer Clb; Math Tm; Rep Stu Cncl; High Hon Roll; NHS; Prfct Atten Awd; 1st Ntl Sci Olympd Chem, Amer Schlr, Ntl Ldrshp, Svc Awds 85-86; 1st Cmptr Sci Fair 86; Cranegie Mellon U; Physics.

TIMMERMANS, VANESSA; Dover Area SR HS; Dover, PA; (3); Church Yth Grp; SADD; Nwsp Phtg; Nwsp Rptr; Nwsp Sprt Ed; Nwsp Stf; Mgr(s); Mat Maids; Mgr Wrstlng; Fshn Photo.

TIMMERSON, WADE; Ft Cherry HS; Mc Donald, PA; (3); Computer Clb; Drama Clb; Letterman Clb; Math Clb; Science Clb; Ski Clb; Spanish Clb; Varsity Clb; Bsktbl; High Hon Roll; Amer Lgn Awd 84.

TIMMS, DARYL; Seneca Valley SR HS; Harmony, PA; (4); 6/352; Math Clb; Bsbl; Bsktbl; Crs Cntry; Ftbl; Tennis; High Hon Roll; Hon Roll; Garman C Murray Mem Scholar 87; Bucknell U; Mech Engr.

TIMMS, JOELLE R; Mononga Hela Valley Catholic HS; Allison, PA; (3); Band; Concert Band; Mrchg Band; Bus.

TIMNEY, JOHN; Western Beaver HS; Industry, PA; (2); Band; Jazz Band; Mrchg Band; Symp Band; Sec Soph Cls; JV Bsbl; JV Bsktbl; Mgr(s); Cit Awd; Hon Roll; PA ST; Aero.

TIMON, KATHERINE; Villa Maria Acad; Erie, PA; (4); Model UN; Yrbk Stf; Trk; Hon Roll; NHS; Pres Schlr; Amrcn Values Schlrshp, Prsdnts Hnr Awd Schlrshp, Hnr Grad 87; John Carroll U; Accntng.

TIMONY, CHERYL; Chichester HS; Boothwyn, PA; (3); Art Clb; Cmnty Wkr; French Clb; Var Lcrss; Var Swmmng; French Hon Soc; Prfct Atten Awd; Natl Art Honor Soc 85-87; Art Schlrshp At Moore Coll 87; Art Goes To Schl Prog 85-87; Therapist.

TIMS, WENDY; Middletown Area HS; Middletown, PA; (4); 92/165; Church Yth Grp; Library Aide; Band; Concert Band; Drm & Bgl; Drm Mjr(t); Jazz Band; Mrchg Band; Socr; Voice Dem Awd; Cntrl Penn Bus Schl; Admin Asst.

TINARI, CHRISTINE; B Reed Henderson HS; Westchester, PA; (3); VP Intnl Clb; JCL; Science Clb; Stage Crew; French Hon Soc; Hon Roll; Ntl Merit Ltr; Silver Maxima Cum Laude Natl Latin Exam 86-87.

TINGLE, HELENE; Tyrone Area HS; Tyrone, PA; (4); 44/185; Am Leg Aux Girls St; French Clb; Key Clb; Spanish Clb; Color Guard; Elks Awd; High Hon Roll; Hon Roll; Outstndg Japanese Awd 86-87; Juniata Coll.

TINKER, JOHN WESLEY; Forbes Road HS; Hustontown, PA; (2); Boy Scts; French Clb; FFA; Band; Concert Band; Jazz Band; Mrchg Band; Pilot.

TINKEY, WENDY; Canon-Mc Millan HS; Canonsburg, PA; (4); High Hon Roll.

TINNER, JOYCE; Dallas SR HS; Dallas, PA; (3); Girl Scts; Key Clb; Library Aide; SADD; Yrbk Stf; Sec Frsh Cls; Capt JV Bsktbl; Var L Fld Hcky; Var L Sftbl; Hon Roll; Times Ldr All-Star MVP 86; Sftbl All-Stars 85-87; Field Hcky All-Stars 86; Phys Therapy.

TINSLEY, TRACY S; Bishop Hoban HS; Mt Top, PA; (3); Computer Clb; Mu Alpha Theta; Ski Clb; L Swmmng.

TINSMAN, RICH; Brandywine Heights HS; Topton, PA; (4); 4/140; Church Yth Grp; Debate Tm; Band; Concert Band; Jazz Band; Mrchg Band; Golf; Var Tennis; Vllybl; Hon Roll; Pres Acadc Ftns Awd 85; Rtry Clb Awd 86; Penn St U; Sci.

TINTI, MICHELLE; Villa Maria Acad; Erie, PA; (3); Cmnty Wkr; Science Clb; Madrigals; School Musical; Variety Show; High Hon Roll; Hon Roll; Pharmacist.

TIPKA, ADRIENNE; Southern Columbia Area HS; Elysburg, PA; (3); Band; Concert Band; Mrchg Band; Pep Band; School Play; Nwsp Rptr; Nwsp Stf; Yrbk Stf; Var Crs Cntry; Var Trk.

TIPTON, ANDREA; Northwestern SR HS; Edinboro, PA; (3); 20/142; Sec Trs Drama Clb; Trs Thesps; Chorus; Madrigals; School Musical; School Play; Stage Crew; Yrbk Stf; Hon Roll; Modern Music Masters 86-87; Counseling.

TIPTON, KIM; Solanco HS; Oxford, PA; (3); 80/300; Art Clb; Church Yth Grp; Drama Clb; Pep Clb; Varsity Clb; Acpl Chr; Chorus; Church Choir; JV Capt Cheerleading; Trk; Art Gld Key Awd 87; Vrsty Chrldng Ltr 87; Art Hon Mntn 86-87; Intr Dsgn.

TIRACAVE, CHRISTIAN; Penn Cambria HS; Cresson, PA; (3); NFL; Speech Tm; Pres SADD; Varsity Clb; Stu Cncl; Bsbl; Ftbl; Wrstlng; Hon Roll; NHS; Pre-Law.

TIRDEL, DAVID; Valley HS; New Kensington, PA; (4); Art Clb; Drama Clb; Pep Clb; Ski Clb; Spanish Clb; SADD; Varsity Clb; Band; Chorus; Concert Band; WV U; Bus.

TIRION, ALEXANDER; Reading SR HS; Reading, PA; (4); 21/563; Sec Key Clb; Var Capt Tennis; Cit Awd; Kiwanis Awd; NHS; Rotary Awd; Mst Outstndng Stu 83-84; Bus.

TIRKO, JOSEPH; Somerset Area SR HS; Friedens, PA; (3); 12/231; Church Yth Grp; English Clb; Letterman Clb; Yrbk Stf; Bsktbl; Var Ftbl; Im Wt Lftg; High Hon Roll; Hon Roll; NHS; Acad Lttr 85-86; Bus Adm.

TIRNAUER, JUDD P; Upper Merion Area HS; Gulph Mills, PA; (4); 22/290; French Clb; Math Tm; Service Clb; Var Bsbl; Ntl Merit Ltr; Pres Schlr; Franklin & Marshall; Pre-Med.

TIRPAK JR, DAVID B; Northern Chester County Tech HS; Phoenixville, PA; (4); 15/120; Church Yth Grp; Radio Clb; Hon Roll; Elec Tech.

TIRPAK, KRISTIN; Panther Valley HS; Lehighton, PA; (1); 13/127; Drama Clb; Band; Concert Band; Jazz Band; Mrchg Band; Stage Crew; Nwsp Rptr; Nwsp Stf; Stat Bsbl; High Hon Roll; Lab Technen.

TIRUMALASETTY, PRIYA; Brookville Area HS; Brookville, PA; (3); Chess Clb; Key Clb; Pres Orch; School Musical; Nwsp Rptr; Nwsp Stf; Yrbk Ed-Chief; Lit Mag; Trk; NHS; Orthdntst.

TISCH, DENISE C; Hopewell HS; Aliquippa, PA; (4); 39/245; Church Yth Grp; Drama Clb; Hosp Aide; VP JA; Spanish Clb; Color Guard; Yrbk Stf; Rep Sr Cls; NHS; Pres Schlr; Michael Volitich Memrl Schlrshp 87; Edinboro U; Early Chldhd Ed.

TITUS, GREG; Sharpsville Area HS; Sharpsville, PA; (4); Pres Church Yth Grp; Spanish Clb; School Musical; School Play; Stage Crew; Var JV Bsktbl; Crs Cntry; Var Capt Trk; Hon Roll; NHS; Edinboro U; Educ.

TITUS, TRACY; Tamaqua Area HS; New Ringgold, PA; (3); 30/270; Drama Clb; VP French Clb; Pep Clb; Science Clb; School Musical; Var Cheerleading; Var L Swmmng; Var L Trk; French Hon Soc; Hon Roll; TASCO Grls Clb 84-88; IEP Gftd Pgm 83-88; Corp Law.

TKACH, MARKO; Fasther Judge HS; Philadelphia, PA; (4); 85/403; Art Clb; Ukrainian Schl Of Arts & Sci 87; Ukrainian Amer Yth Assoc Member; Temple U; Architecture.

TKACH, SCOTT; Ringgold HS; Finleyville, PA; (3); 78/372; Am Leg Boys St; Boy Scts; Exploring; Band; Concert Band; Mrchg Band; Var Golf; PA Bureau Of Frstry Cnsrvtn Awd 86; Wrld Cnsrvtn Awd 86; U Ptsbrgh; Jrnlsm.

TKACHUK, LORI; Bensalem HS; Oakford, PA; (2); French Clb; Key Clb; Band; Concert Band; Jazz Band; Mrchg Band; Orch; School Musical; School Play; Stage Crew.

TKACIK, KRISTIN ANN; Franklin Regional HS; Murrysville, PA; (4); Church Yth Grp; Ski Clb; Band; Church Choir; High Hon Roll; Pres Schlr; PA ST U; Lbrl Arts.

TKATCH, KIM; Crestwood HS; Mountain Top, PA; (1); Rep Stu Cncl; Cheerleading; Hon Roll; PA ST; Dtcn.

TOBACK, TRACY; Tamaqua Area HS; Tuscarora, PA; (3); Chorus; Mrchg Band; Var L Cheerleading; French Hon Soc; High Hon Roll; Schlstc Achvt Cert 85-86; Currnt Evnts Cert 84-85; Physcl Thrpst.

TOBAK, JEFF; Laurel Highlands HS; Uniontown, PA; (4); Pres Science Clb; Capt Crs Cntry; High Hon Roll; JETS Awd; Physics Awd 87; Carnegie; Physics.

TOBER, JEFF; Upper Moreland HS; Willow Grove, PA; (2); 36/242; Key Clb; SADD; Var Socr; Var Trk; Hon Roll; Physcl Ftnss Outstndng Athl 85; Comms.

TOBIA, ANNMARIE; Palmerton Area HS; Palmerton, PA; (3); Am Leg Aux Girls St; Debate Tm; Girl Scts; Church Choir; Yrbk Stf; Stu Cncl; Crs Cntry; Trk; High Hon Roll; NHS.

TOBIAS, CHRISTINA; Danville SR HS; Danville, PA; (3); Art Clb; Color Guard; High Hon Roll; Hon Roll; Smmr Reading Pgm 87; Trvl Prst Clb 85-86; Ft Lauderdale Art Inst; Art.

TOBIAS, JOY; Beaver County Christian Schl; Darlington, PA; (4); AFS; Pres VP 4-H; Chorus; Pres Concert Band; High Hon Roll; Hon Roll; Geneva Schlr Awd 87; Geneva Music Schlrshp 87; Presdntl Acadmc Ftns Awd 87; Geneva Coll; Music Educ.

TOBIAS, LISA; Shikillamy HS; Sunbury, PA; (2); Church Yth Grp; Office Aide; SADD; Color Guard; Mrchg Band; Fld Hcky; Trk; Central PA; Bus Mgmt.

TOBIN, JAMES; West Catholic HS; Philadelphia, PA; (2); 20/248; Church Yth Grp; Dance Clb; Church Choir; Rep Jr Cls; Var Ftbl; Wt Lftg; Hon Roll; Judo 86-87; Perfect Conduct Awd 85-87; Stanford; Elec Engr.

TOBIN, KIRSTI; Bishop Shanahan HS; Chadds Ford, PA; (4); Church Yth Grp; Pep Clb; Service Clb; Ski Clb; Var JV Fld Hcky; Trk; High Hon Roll; Hon Roll; NHS; Duquesne U; Law.

TOCCO, ERIC; Highlands SR HS; Natrona Heights, PA; (4); 21/288; Am Leg Boys St; Key Clb; Nwsp Stf; Yrbk Stf; Golf; Socr; Tennis; Trk; High Hon Roll; Trs NHS; WV U; Elec Engnrng.

TOCCO, JOHN B; West Catholic For Boys; Philadelphia, PA; (3); 25/248; Bsktbl; Score Keeper; High Hon Roll; Hon Roll; Outstndng Achvt Accntng 87; Conduct Awd 85-87; Hnrs 85-87; Accntng.

TOCZYDLOWSKI, JOHN E; Holy Ghost Prep; Philadelphia, PA; (3); Math Clb; Scholastic Bowl; Capt L Bsktbl; Im Ftbl; Var L Golf; Im Ice Hcky; Var L Mgr(s); JV L Trk; Hon Roll; NHS; Hvrfrd U; Law.

TOCZYDLOWSKI, JOSEPH; Acrhbishop Ryan HS; Philadelphia, PA; (4); 5/424; Nwsp Stf; Lit Mag; JV Bsbl; High Hon Roll; NHS; Prfct Atten Awd; Ldrshp Awd 85; Alg Awd 84; Spa Awd 85; U DE; Bus Admin.

TODD, GREG; Butler Intermediate HS; Butler, PA; (2); French Clb; Office Aide; Rep Stu Cncl; Var L Golf; Var L Swmmng; Hon Roll; Jr NHS.

TODD, GREG; William Allen HS; Allentown, PA; (3); 16/609; Ski Clb; Var L Bsbl; Var L Bsktbl; JV Ftbl; Hon Roll; NHS; Med.

TODD, NICOLE; Hughesville HS; Hughesville, PA; (3); 8/132; Ski Clb; Varsity Clb; Nwsp Rptr; Rep Stu Cncl; Capt Var Tennis; Var Trk; Hon Roll; NHS.

TODD, SHERBONDY; Geibel HS; Connellsville, PA; (3); Boy Scts; Church Yth Grp; Lit Mag; Var JV Bsbl; Var JV Ftbl; Hon Roll; Honor Roll Honors Banq 87; U Of Pittsburgh; Dnstry.

TOKAR, BRAD; Fort Cherry HS; Mc Donald, PA; (4); 3/120; Church Yth Grp; Drama Clb; Letterman Clb; Math Clb; Science Clb; Ski Clb; Thesps; Varsity Clb; Stage Crew; Pres Stu Cncl; MVP-OH Vly Ftbl Conf 85-86; Extra Effrt Awd-KDKA 86; Pgh Press Plyr Of Yr-Ftbl 85.

TOKAR, WILLIAM; Somerset Area SR HS; Somerset, PA; (3); 29/250; Boy Scts; Var L Ftbl; Im Wt Lftg; Hon Roll; Bus Admin.

TOKI, PAULA; Windber Area HS; Windber, PA; (3); Church Yth Grp; Math Clb; Ski Clb; Bsktbl; Coach Actv; Sftbl; Vllybl; Hon Roll; Police Acad; Phtgrphy.

TOLAN, MEREDITH; Lower Merion HS; Wynnewood, PA; (3); SADD; Thesps; School Play; Ed Nwsp Rptr; Yrbk Ed-Chief; Ed Yrbk Rptr; French Hon Soc; High Hon Roll; NHS; Off Jr Cls.

TOLAN, NOELLE; Dunmore HS; Dunmore, PA; (4); Computer Clb; French Clb; Yrbk Phtg; Sec Sr Cls; Stu Cncl; Var JV Cheerleading; Var Swmmng; Hon Roll; Jr NHS; NHS; Schlrshp Awd 87; Bloomsburg U; Psych.

TOLASSI JR, MICHAEL; North Penn SR HS; Lansdale, PA; (4) 151/651; Boy Scts; VICA; Hon Roll; NHS; Mont Co CC; Elctrnc Engr.

TOLBERT, JOEL; Upper Moreland HS; Willow Grove, PA; (4); 79/256; Band; Chorus; Concert Band; Jazz Band; Mrchg Band; Trk; High Hon Roll; Hon Roll; Music Patrons Awd 87; Bloomsburg U Of PA; Fin.

TOLER, STEVE; Cedar Crest HS; Lebanon, PA; (3); 120/360; Pres German Clb; Latin Clb; Library Aide; Pep Clb; SADD; Ftbl; Trk; Vllybl; Pre-Law.

TOLERICO, RICH; West Hazleton HS; Drums, PA; (4); 46/255; Church Yth Grp; Letterman Clb; Red Cross Aide; Ski Clb; SADD; Varsity Clb; Rep Sr Cls; Off Stu Cncl; Bsbl; Ftbl.

TOLERICO, TERRI; Hazelton SR HS; Hazleton, PA; (2); Dance Clb; Drama Clb; Pep Clb; Y-Teens; Cheerleading; High Hon Roll; Pres Schlr.

TOLIVER, WALTER; Saint Josephs Prep; Philadelphia, PA; (4); Exploring; Library Aide; Rep Stu Cncl; Mgr L Bsktbl; Mgr(s); Mgr L Trk; High Hon Roll; NHS; Prfct Atten Awd; Williams Coll Bk Awd 85-6; Phila Mayors Schrlshp 87; U Of PA; Finance.

TOLLARI, LISA; Belle Vernon Area HS; Belle Vernon, PA; (3); Pep Clb; Ski Clb; Pep Band; Sec Soph Cls; JV Cheerleading; Powder Puff Ftbl; Nrsng.

TOLOMEO, MARIA; York Catholic HS; York, PA; (3); Drama Clb; Library Aide; Stage Crew; Sec Mgr(s); High Hon Roll; Hon Roll; Arch.

TOLTESI, SUZANNE; Freedom SR HS; Bethlehem, PA; (4); 95/446; Cmnty Wkr; Library Aide; Teachers Aide; Color Guard; Drill Tm; Flag Corp; Hon Roll; Royal Dfndrs Clrgrd 83-84; Rsng Star Clrgrd 84-87; Nrthmptn Cnty Area CC; Elem Ed.

TOMA, CHUCK; Seneca Valley HS; Zelienople, PA; (3); AFS; 4-H; JA; ROTC; Ski Clb; Socr; Hon Roll.

TOMAINO, JAMES; Notre Dame HS; Easton, PA; (3); Grphc Art.

TOMAK, JACQUELINE; Lincoln HS; Ellwood City, PA; (3); 7/162; Pres Church Yth Grp; Drama Clb; French Clb; JA; Pres Chorus; Church Choir; High Hon Roll; Hon Roll; NHS; NEDT Awd; Law.

TOMAN, JULIE; Southmoreland HS; Scottdale, PA; (3); Law.

TOMANCHEK, MICHAEL; Hazleton HS; Hazleton, PA; (4); Computer Clb; Scholastic Bowl; Science Clb; Hon Roll; Penn ST U; Bus.

TOMASCIK, THOMAS; Pittston Area SR HS; Pittston, PA; (3); Art Clb; Computer Clb; Science Clb; High Hon Roll; Hon Roll; NHS; NEDT Awd.

TOMASHEFSKI, BELINDA; Southern Columbia HS; Catawissa, PA; (3); Pres Church Yth Grp; Band; Concert Band; Mrchg Band; Pep Band; Nwsp Stf; Var Bsktbl; JV Fld Hcky; JV Sftbl; Crmnl Jstc.

TOMASHEFSKI, MELINDA; Southern Columbia HS; Catawissa, PA; (3); 2/107; Pres Church Yth Grp; Varsity Clb; Nwsp Stf; Var Bsktbl; Var Mgr(s); L Sftbl; High Hon Roll; Hon Roll; NHS; Prfct Atten Awd; Bio.

TOMASIC, JOANNE ELEN; West Mifflin Area HS; W Mifflin, PA; (4); 32/328; Chess Clb; Exploring; Office Aide; Teachers Aide; Concert Band; Mrchg Band; Orch; Rep Frsh Cls; Rep Soph Cls; Rep Jr Cls; U Of Pittsburgh; Metallrgcl Sci.

TOMASKOVIC, SANDRA; Lincoln HS; Ellwood City, PA; (3); German Clb; Ski Clb; Chorus; Powder Puff Ftbl; JV Socr; High Hon Roll; Hon Roll; NHS; Acad Achvt Awd 85; Outstndng Achvt Awd In Grmn 85 & 86; Phrmcy.

TOMASO, JULIE; Bishop Mc Devitt HS; Harrisburg, PA; (4); 31/176; Art Clb; Science Clb; Service Clb; Ski Clb; Chorus; Madrigals; Yrbk Stf; Var Cheerleading; High Hon Roll; NHS; Best Of Show Awd In A Juried Art Exhbt 85; One Women Art Exhibit 86; Sci Fair 2nd Pl Hnrbl Mntn 84; Penn ST; Art.

TOMASZEWSKI, JEFF; Ambridge Area HS; Freedom, PA; (4); 4/265; Am Leg Boys St; Chess Clb; Var Crs Cntry; Var Trk; High Hon Roll; Lion Awd; NHS; Boy Scts; Church Yth Grp; Civic Clb; Army ROTC 4 Yr Schlrshp 87; AF ROTC 4 Yr Schlrshp 87; USAF Rsrvs Math Achvt Awd 87; U Miami; Elec Engrng.

TOMAZIC, KAREN; Forest City Regional HS; Forest City, PA; (3); 5/65; Dance Clb; Spanish Clb; Sec Band; Chorus; Concert Band; Jazz Band; Mrchg Band; High Hon Roll; Hon Roll; Trs NHS; Grg Typng Awd 87; Shpnsbrg U; Bus Adm.

TOMCAVAGE, MARK; Lancaster Catholic HS; Lancaster, PA; (3); 12/200; Boy Scts; Church Yth Grp; Model UN; Red Cross Aide; Band; School Musical; Nwsp Sprt Ed; JV Golf; Capt Im Swmmng; NHS; IN U PA Physcs Awd 87; Elec Engrng.

TOMCHICK, TRACEY L; Tamaqua Area SR HS; Tamaqua, PA; (3); 2/210; Am Leg Aux Girls St; French Clb; Pep Clb; Yrbk Bus Mgr; Yrbk Rptr; Yrbk Stf; Sec Frsh Cls; Pres VP Stu Cncl; JV Var Bsktbl; Mgr(s); Hugh O Brian Yth Fdntn 86 & 87; Peer Educ VP 87; PA Free Entrprs Wk 87; Psych.

TOMCHO, LORI; Coudersport JR SR HS; Coudersport, PA; (3); Church Yth Grp; Drama Clb; French Clb; Varsity Clb; Chorus; Mrchg Band; Nwsp Rptr; Yrbk Stf; Var L Cheerleading; Powder Puff Ftbl.

TOMCZAK, CHERYL; Saint Benedict Acad; Erie, PA; (3); 1/53; Am Leg Aux Girls St; Church Yth Grp; FBLA; GAA; Yrbk Bus Mgr; Yrbk Stf; Rep Stu Cncl; Var Capt Bsktbl; High Hon Roll; NHS; Business Schlrshps 85-87; Bus.

TOMCZYNSKI, MARK; Northeast Catholic HS For Boys; Philadelphia, PA; (4); 1/359; Cmnty Wkr; Science Clb; Nwsp Ed-Chief; Nwsp Stf; Yrbk Stf; High Hon Roll; NHS; Frgn Lang Lit Awd Latin & Span 83-86; JV Ltr Cmmnty Svc 85; N Cathlc Rep Gen Elecs TMOT Ldrshp Pr 85; Temple U; Pharm.

TOME, ELIZABETH; Fairview HS; Fairview, PA; (4); 87/154; Drama Clb; Library Aide; Office Aide; Chorus; Church Choir; School Musical; Nwsp Rptr; Nwsp Stf; Lit Mag; Mgr(s); Quill Or Scroll Awd Hnr 87; Edinboro U PA; Elem Ed.

TOMECSKO, MARCI; Canon Mc Millan SR HS; Canonsburg, PA; (4); Office Aide; Spanish Clb; Flag Corp; L Swmmng; Hon Roll; Sec Spanish NHS; U Of Pittsburgh; Bus.

TOMEK, LISA; Dieruff HS; Allentown, PA; (4); FFA; JA; Stat Bsktbl; Stat Crs Cntry; Mgr(s); Var Powder Puff Ftbl; Score Keeper; Timer; Stat Trk; Early Preschool Stds.

TOMERA, MICHELE; Bishop Mc Cort HS; Johnstown, PA; (2); JA; Spanish Clb; Hon Roll.

TOMETCHKO, JOSEPH; Wyoming Valley West HS; Edwardsville, PA; (3); Chess Clb; Church Yth Grp; Var Ftbl; Im Vllybl; Im Wt Lftg; Cit Awd; High Hon Roll; NHS; NEDT Awd; Prfct Atten Awd; Accntng.

TOMICH, DAVID; Beaver Area HS; Beaver, PA; (2); Chess Clb; Church Yth Grp; Exploring; German Clb; Socr; High Hon Roll; Hon Roll.

TOMINAC, THOMAS; North Hills HS; Pittsburgh, PA; (3); 1/490; Boys Clb Am; Chess Clb; Exploring; JA; Scholastic Bowl; Ski Clb; Yrbk Phtg; Rep Soph Cls; Var Ice Hcky; Var Tennis; GATE Advsry Cncl 85-87; Won YMCA Tnns Trnmnt 86; Strtd On Vrsty Hcky Team As Frshmn 84.

TOMKO, ANN MARIE; G A R HS; Wilkes-Barre, PA; (3); 35/152; FBLA; Key Clb; Library Aide; Ski Clb; Chorus; Color Guard; Off Stu Cncl; Hon Roll; Jr NHS; NHS; Empire Beauty Schl; Beautcn.

TOMKO, KERRIE; West Middlesex HS; Sharon, PA; (4); 5/100; French Clb; Band; Mrchg Band; Nwsp Rptr; Yrbk Stf; Var Cheerleading; Hon Roll.

TOMKO, MICHAEL J; Norwin SR HS; N Huntingdon, PA; (3); 317/659; Boy Scts; NFL; Off Jr Cls; Stu Cncl; Bsktbl; Mgr(s); Socr; Wt Lftg; Eagle Sct 86; Accntng.

TOMKO, MICHELLE; Bensalem HS; Bensalem, PA; (4); 126/474; Office Aide; Sec Jr Cls; Pres Sr Cls; Rep Stu Cncl; JV Var Cheerleading; Stu Of Month 86-87; Outstndng SR Awd; Sorpotimst Intl Awd; Millersville U; Med Soc Wrkng.

TOMLIANOVIC, STEPHEN; Bishop Mc Cort HS; Johnstown, PA; (1); Spanish Clb; Chorus; Pres Frsh Cls; Hon Roll; Sci Olympiad Awd 86-87.

TOMPKINS, AMY; Red Lion Area HS; Felton, PA; (3); 62/342; Yrbk Stf; Hon Roll; PA Schl Of Art; Art.

TOMPKINS, ANDREA; Bangor Area SR HS; Bangor, PA; (3); Leo Clb; Yrbk Stf; Bsktbl; U Of TN Knoxville; Educ.

TOMPKINS, TRACI; Donegal HS; Mt Joy, PA; (3); 22/177; Varsity Clb; Nwsp Rptr; Yrbk Stf; Pres Frsh Cls; Pres Soph Cls; Pres Jr Cls; Pres Sr Cls; Rep Stu Cncl; Bsktbl; Trk; Amrcn Lgn Awd 83; Dickinson; Poli Sci.

TOMS, SUSAN; Christian School Of York; Boiling Springs, PA; (2); Hosp Aide; Chorus; VP Stu Cncl; High Hon Roll; Nrsng.

TOMSAK, TOMMY; Wyoming Area HS; Pittston, PA; (3); Aud/Vis; Camera Clb; Church Yth Grp; Church Choir; Bsbl; Bowling; Ftbl; Mgr(s); Sprts Med.

TOMSHO, ROBERT; Gov Mifflin HS; Shillington, PA; (3); Church Yth Grp; Exploring; Band; Concert Band; Jazz Band; Stage Crew; Hon Roll; Unfd Achvt Awd 87; Mrn Bio.

TOMSULA, JED; Steel Valley HS; W Homestead, PA; (3); Nwsp Stf; Rep Sr Cls; JV Ftbl; JV Trk; Var Vllybl; Hon Roll; Brdcstng.

TONER, FRANCIS; Northeast Cath; Philadelphia, PA; (3); 30/350; Aud/Vis; Stage Crew; Yrbk Stf; Rep Soph Cls; Var L Trk; NHS; Law.

TONER, SUSAN; Lower Moreland HS; Huntingdon Valley, PA; (3); Cmnty Wkr; German Clb; Girl Scts; Key Clb; Office Aide; Chrmn Science Clb; Cit Awd; NHS; Grl Sct Slvr & Gld Awds 85-86; Ctatn-Hse Of Rep-PA Gld Awd 86; Cert Of Achvt Grmn Soc Of PA 86; Drexel U; Chmcl Engr.

TONER, TODD; Meadville Area SR HS; Meadville, PA; (3); JV Bsktbl; Hon Roll.

TONETTI, PAUL; Western Wayne HS; Moscow, PA; (3); 4-H; Spanish Clb; Bsktbl.

TONOFF, BARRY; Steelton-Highspire HS; Steelton, PA; (4); 2/94; FBLA; Model UN; Spanish Clb; School Musical; Lit Mag; Bausch & Lomb Sci Awd; Pres Schlr; Sal; Cmnty Wkr; Quiz Bowl; NROTC Schlrshp, Hall Fdtn Schlrshp, Engl Mdl Excllnc 87; George Washington U; Intl Rltns.

TONTY, LORI; Sharpsville HS; Sharpsville, PA; (3); Camera Clb; Chess Clb; Ski Clb; Chorus; Nwsp Stf; Var Cheerleading; Hon Roll; Sec Jr Cls; Rep Stu Cncl.

TONTY, PAMELA JANE; Mercyhurst Prep; Erie, PA; (4); 5/156; Key Clb; VP Spanish Clb; Rep Stu Cncl; Cheerleading; Sftbl; Hon Roll; VP NHS; Ntl Merit Schol; VP Spanish NHS; Acadmc All Amer 86; Cngrsnl Yth Ldrs Cncl 87; U Of Dayton; Secndry Educ.

TOOKES, MARK; Beaver HS; Midland, PA; (4); Am Leg Boys St; Church Yth Grp; Latin Clb; Chorus; Church Choir; Yrbk Stf; CC Awd; Cit Awd; Hon Roll; Pres Schlr; Prncpl Awd Excllnc 87; Amer Choral Dir Assn Awd 87; Slippry Rock.

TOOMEY, BECKY; Quigley HS; Baden, PA; (3); 18/90; Cmnty Wkr; Drama Clb; Letterman Clb; Math Tm; Chorus; Church Choir; School Musical; Var L Vllybl; Powder Puff Ftbl; High Hon Roll; Svc Awd Folk Group 86; Comm.

TOOMEY, HEATHER; Lebanon Catholic HS; Lebanon, PA; (3); Cmnty Wkr; Key Clb; Spanish Clb; Nwsp Sprt Ed; Var Stat Bsbl; Var L Bsktbl; NHS; Debate Tm; Chorus; Sftbl; 1st Pl Chem Div Sci Fair 87; Booster Club Chrstn Athl Awd 87; All Cnty Team Hon Ment 87; Intl Stds.

TOOMEY, JENNIFER; Bishop Guilfoyle HS; Altoona, PA; (3); Science Clb; Ski Clb; Speech Tm; SADD; Chorus; VP Stu Cncl; Bsktbl; Cheerleading; High Hon Roll; Hon Roll; Lock Haven; Spec Ed.

TOONDER, BRIAN; Moravian Acad; Allentown, PA; (4); Chorus; Yrbk Phtg; Golf; Tennis; High Hon Roll; Hon Roll; Rnsslr Plytch Inst; Aerosp Engr.

TOPAR, DAVID; Penns Manor HS; Alverda, PA; (4); 11/99; Trs Church Yth Grp; SADD; Chorus; Concert Band; Mrchg Band; Pep Band; School Musical; Nwsp Rptr; High Hon Roll; Hon Roll; Valley Forge Christian Coll.

TOPAR, TAMMY; Penns Manor HS; Alverda, PA; (3); 2/94; Camera Clb; Sec Church Yth Grp; Concert Band; Mrchg Band; High Hon Roll; Hon Roll; NHS; Prfct Atten Awd.

TOPP, ROGER; Plymouth-Whitemarsh SR HS; Lafayette Hill, PA; (2); Chess Clb; Math Tm; Mu Alpha Theta; Lit Mag; JV Crs Cntry; JV Swmmng; JV Trk; High Hon Roll; Prfct Atten Awd; Pres Schlr; Engnr.

TORAIN, HEATHER; Central HS; Philadelphia, PA; (3); 156/538; AFS; Church Yth Grp; Girl Scts; Orch; JV Tennis; Hon Roll; Dist 12 PMEA 84-85; Music Ed Ntl Cnfrnc 84-85; Stu Phila Yth Orch 86-87.

TORALDO, DOMINIC; Old Forge HS; Old Forge, PA; (2); Stage Crew; Acctnt Bus.

TORBET, JOHN; Exeter HS; Reading, PA; (3); 37/225; Church Yth Grp; Band; Mrchg Band; Stage Crew; Crs Cntry; Trk; Hon Roll; Air Force Acad; Pilot.

TORBJORNSEN, EINAR; Meadville Area SR HS; Meadville, PA; (2); German Clb; VP Ski Clb; Stu Cncl.

TORBJORNSEN, KAREN; Meadville Area SR HS; Meadville, PA; (3); 16/363; French Clb; NFL; Speech Tm; SADD; Chorus; Church Choir; School Play; High Hon Roll; Hon Roll; Prfct Atten Awd; Accptd Chautaugua Thtr Schl 87; Accptd Gov Schl Of Arts 87; Thtr.

TORELLI, AMY; Moon SR HS; Coraopolis, PA; (4); 20/296; Pres Church Yth Grp; Pres FBLA; Key Clb; Teachers Aide; Mgr(s); JV Vllybl; Hon Roll; NHS; 3rd Pl Regional Acctng Comptn 86; St Joseph U; Acctng.

TORELLI, MICHELE; Cardinal O Hara HS; Clifton Hgts, PA; (3); 86/710; Var Capt Crs Cntry; Var Capt Trk; Hon Roll; MVP Crs Cntry 85 & 86; MVP Indoor Track 87; Athlete Wk 87; Phys Thrpy.

TORNATORE, MELINDA; Bald Eagle-Nittany HS; Mill Hall, PA; (3); Spanish Clb; Color Guard; Mrchg Band; Yrbk Rptr; Yrbk Stf; Stat Gym; Lock Haven U.

TORO, ANGELA; Frankford HS; Philadelphia, PA; (4); 39/395; Cmnty Wkr; German Clb; Service Clb; Bsktbl; Hon Roll.

TOROCKIO, DANA; Greater Latrobe SR HS; Latrobe, PA; (4); 122/435; Letterman Clb; Pep Clb; Yrbk Stf; VP Soph Cls; Sec Sr Cls; Rep Stu Cncl; JV Var Cheerleading; High Hon Roll; Hon Roll; Hmcmng Ct, Qun; IN U Of PA; Elem Ed.

TORON, ESTHER; Yeshiva Achei Tmimmim; Cincinnati, OH; (1); Art Clb; Cmnty Wkr; Dance Clb; Drama Clb; 4-H; Science Clb; Chorus; School Musical; School Play; Frsh Cls; 1st Awd JR Acad Sci 87; Law.

TORREANCE, MELVIN; Moshannon Valley Christian Acad; Osceola Mills, PA; (1); JV Bsktbl; JV Ftbl; JV Socr; Hon Roll; Supv Awd 85; Pittsburg Inst Mortuary Sci.

TORRES, LISSETTE; Reading HS; Reading, PA; (3); 141/740; 4-H; FBLA; Cheerleading; Jr NHS; Penn ST U; Bus Adm.

TORRES, ROBERT; Central HS; Philadelphia, PA; (3); 11/538; Church Yth Grp; Spanish Clb; Church Choir; Yrbk Phtg; Bowling; Capt Vllybl; Hon Roll; Cert Rcgntn Ntl Spnsh Cntst 86; Cer Rcgntn Church Svcs 85-87; Leag Hgh Score Bwlng 86; Comp Engr.

TORRIERI, CARIN; Cardinal O Hara HS; Glenolden, PA; (3); 205/710; Church Yth Grp; JA; Service Clb; Rep Soph Cls; Prfct Atten Awd; West Chester U; Tchng.

TOSH, BRIAN; Beaver Area HS; Beaver, PA; (4); Church Yth Grp; French Clb; Band; Concert Band; Jazz Band; Mrchg Band; Pep Band; School Musical; Variety Show; Tennis; Bucknell U.

TOSLOSKY, SANDRA; Bishop Hafey HS; Hazleton, PA; (2); Am Leg Aux Girls St; Drama Clb; French Clb; Hosp Aide; Science Clb; Chorus; Orch; School Musical; School Play; French Hon Soc; Thomas Fellin Memrl Schlrshp 85; St Johns U Jamaica NY; Med.

TOSO, SUE; William Allen HS; Allentown, PA; (4); Sec Drama Clb; 4-H; VP Intnl Clb; Pres Keywanettes; Ski Clb; School Play; Ed Yrbk Stf; Rep Frsh Cls; Rep Soph Cls; Rep Jr Cls; Allentown Schl Dist Ortrcl Champ 84 & 85; Tomorrow Ortrcl Champ 86; PA ST U; Comp Sci.

TOSTI, TINA; Archbishop Carroll HS; Bala Cynwyd, PA; (3); Office Aide; Teachers Aide; Hon Roll; Pierce; Med.

TOTH, DAVE; Southern Columbia Area HS; Elysburg, PA; (3); Art Clb; Spanish Clb; SADD; Crs Cntry; Gym; Ice Hcky; Socr; Sftbl; Swmmng; Vllybl; Psych.

TOTH, DEBORAH L; Lakeland JR SR HS; Olyphant, PA; (4); Pres Church Yth Grp; Varsity Clb; Rep Stu Cncl; Var Capt Bsktbl; Var Capt Sftbl; Hon Roll; Dist II PIAA Acdmc Athltc Excllnce Awd, Schlr Athlte U S Army Rsrve Hnr Acdmc Athltc Exec 87; Penn ST Worthington; Phys Ed.

TOTH, SARA; Mercer Area JR SR HS; Mercer, PA; (1); Church Yth Grp; Trs 4-H; FFA; Concert Band; Mrchg Band; 4-H Awd; Hon Roll; Penn St; Gntcs.

TOTH, STACEY A; Upper Darby HS; Upper Darby, PA; (3); Church Yth Grp; Hosp Aide; Teachers Aide; Variety Show; Yrbk Stf; JV Lcrss; High Hon Roll; Hon Roll; Amer Legions Keystone Girls St; Nurses Aide; Teacher.

TOTSKY, TRICIA; Carbondale Area JR SR HS; Simpson, PA; (2); Ski Clb; Spanish Clb; VP Frsh Cls; VP Soph Cls; JV Bsktbl; Var Trk; High Hon Roll; 2nd Rgnl Spllng Bee 85.

TOUVELL, CHARLENE; Brookville Area HS; Brookville, PA; (4); 7/127; Pres Church Choir; Lit Mag; Pres Stu Cncl; High Hon Roll; Hon Roll; Jr NHS; Hst NHS; Natl Hstry Day Cntst Awd Wnnr 81-85; Rptr & Anchor Tv Pgm 82-87; Outstndng Sr Awd 87; U Of Pittsburgh; Commnctns.

TOVCIMAK, LUCILLE ANN; North Pocono HS; Moscow, PA; (4); 72/235; Girl Scts; Letterman Clb; Pep Clb; Ski Clb; Drill Tm; Var L Trk; Hon Roll; NHS; Marn Mdl Awd; Rfl Tm-Capt; PA ST U.

TOW, SHANI; Abington HS; Roslyn, PA; (3); FBLA; Red Cross Aide; Spanish Clb; Rep Jr Cls; Var Lcrss; High Hon Roll; NHS; Ntl Merit SF; Intnl Clb; Key Clb; HS Soc Stu Merit Awds 85-86; Mnrty Advncd Plcmnt Prog Penn ST U 87; Penn ST U; Bio Chem.

TOWER, CRAIG PHILIP; Moon Area HS; Coraopolis, PA; (4); Capt Var Bsktbl; Var Crs Cntry; Var Trk; Hon Roll; NCAA II Athltc Schlrshp Bentley Coll 87; Bentley Coll; Bus.

TOWER, KEITH RAYMOND; Moon Area HS; Coraopolis, PA; (3); Aud/Vis; German Clb; Rep Frsh Cls; Pres Soph Cls; Rep Jr Cls; Rep Sr Cls; Rep Stu Cncl; Var Bsbl; Var Capt Bsktbl; High Hon Roll; Notre Dame; Bus Comm.

TOWN, DAVID; Brockway Area HS; Brockport, PA; (3); 5/112; Exploring; Varsity Clb; VICA; Var L Socr; Bausch & Lomb Sci Awd; High Hon Roll; Hon Roll; NHS; Engrng.

TOWNSEND, DEANNA; Aliquippa HS; Aliquippa, PA; (3); French Clb; Chorus; Church Choir; Rep Jr Cls; Accntng.

TOWNSEND, JILL; Neshaminy HS; Penndel, PA; (4); 10/680; Service Clb; Cheerleading; Gym; Mgr(s); Sftbl; High Hon Roll; Hon Roll; Jr NHS; NHS; Gymnght 84-87; Villanover U; Bus.

TOWNSEND, MIKE; Calvary Baptist Christian Acad; Meadville, PA; (3); 2/14; Church Yth Grp; Chorus; School Play; Var L Bsktbl; Var L Socr; Hon Roll; Superior Rating KCEA St Spnsh II Exam & Woodwind Catagory 87; 1st-Woodwind Tlnts Christ PA St 87; Piedmont Bible; Mssnry Aviation.

TOWSEN, PAUL; Central Dauphin HS; Harrisburg, PA; (3); 26/376; Key Clb; Mgr Ice Hcky; Im Vllybl; Jr NHS; NHS; Penn ST; Bus Admin.

TOWSEY, DAWN J; Central Dauphin HS; Harrisburg, PA; (3); 3/370; Key Clb; Science Clb; Chorus; School Musical; School Play; High Hon Roll; Hon Roll; Jr NHS; Trs NHS; Ntl Merit Ltr; Natl Hnr Roll Yrbk; 3rd Pl Music Clsscs Fstvl Lat; 2 Gold 3 Slvr 2 Brnz Mdls PA ST Sci Olympd; Chin Diplmt.

TOY, BECKY; Lenape Vo-Tech; Worthington, PA; (3); Art Clb; Church Yth Grp; VICA; Var Tennis; Hon Roll; Hnr Mntn World Poetry 85; Goldn Poet Awd Poetry 85; Comp.

TOY, DEBRA; Western Wayne HS; Moscow, PA; (3); 17/192; Church Yth Grp; Spanish Clb; Band; Mrchg Band; School Play; Sec Soph Cls; Bsktbl; Trk; Hon Roll; MVP Trck 85-86; Pres Phys Ftnss Awd 82-87; U Of Scranton; Phys Thrpy.

TOZOUR, KARLA; Acad Of Notre Dame De Namur; West Chester, PA; (3); Art Clb; Camera Clb; Cmnty Wkr; Hosp Aide; Library Aide; School Musical; School Play; Yrbk Stf; Lit Mag; Boston Coll; Nrsng.

TRACEWSKI, NICOLE; Valley View JR SR HS; Eynon, PA; (2); 8/189; Church Yth Grp; French Clb; Latin Clb; SADD; Tennis; Capt Twrlr; French Hon Soc; High Hon Roll; Hon Roll; NHS; ST Twirling Champnshps 87; Acad Excllnce 86 & 87.

TRACEY, NATHAN; North Eastern HS; Mt Wolf, PA; (3); Church Yth Grp; Acpl Chr; Chorus; Church Choir; Yrbk Ed-Chief; Yrbk Phtg; Sec Yrbk Stf; Lit Mag; Hon Roll; Photo Journalist.

TRACH, TIMOTHY; Allentown Central Catholic HS; Allentown, PA; (3); 7/235; Boy Scts; Chorus; School Play; Stat Bsbl; High Hon Roll; NHS; Opt Clb Awd; Eagle Sct & 1 Palm 87; Engl.

TRACIE, DAVIES; Parkland SR HS; Coplay, PA; (3); Church Yth Grp; JCL; Latin Clb; Stu Cncl; Kutztown U; Envrnmntl Dsgn.

TRACY, MAUREEN S; Scranton Preparatory Schl; Scranton, PA; (1); 101/178; Debate Tm; Hosp Aide; Cheerleading; Comms.

TRAEGER, PAUL; Yough SR HS; W Newton, PA; (3); 20/270; Church Yth Grp; Computer Clb; Spanish Clb; High Hon Roll; Prfct Atten Awd; Co Captain Audio Visl Tm Awd 85; Penn ST; Anml Sci.

TRAIN, TIMOTHY; Delaware County Christian Schl; Newtown Sq, PA; (4); 20/78; Chorus; Church Choir; Concert Band; Madrigals; School Play; High Hon Roll; NHS; Math Tm; Speech Tm; Var Trk; Distngshd Chrstn HS Stndt Awd 86; Padewerski Medal 87; Natl Merit Cmnd 86; Johns Hopkins U; Histry.

TRAINOR, BENJAMIN; Blackhawk HS; Darlington, PA; (2); PA ST; Engr.

TRAISTER, CARA; Windber Area HS; Windber, PA; (3); French Clb; Chorus; Yrbk Stf; Rep Jr Cls; High Hon Roll; NHS; Ntl Merit Ltr; Drama Clb; Church Choir; Dist Chorus Mbr 85-86; Rengl Chorus 85-87; Pres Acadmc Ftns Awd 85.

TRALA, PATRICIA; Liberty HS; Bethlehem, PA; (3); 157/429; VP Pres Church Yth Grp; SADD; Off Band; Concert Band; Mrchg Band; Orch; School Musical; Nwsp Stf; Yrbk Ed-Chief; Yrbk Stf; PA Schl Press Assoc 1st Awd 86; Bio.

TRAMONTANO, CRAIG; Cathedral Preparatory School; Erie, PA; (3); 54/193; Church Yth Grp; JV Var Bsbl; JV Im Bsktbl; Hon Roll; Penn ST U; Engrng.

TRAN, CUONG; Central Catholic HS; Allentown, PA; (4); Chess Clb; Key Clb; Math Tm; Nwsp Stf; Rep Soph Cls; VP Jr Cls; VP Stu Cncl; Var Crs Cntry; Im Vllybl; Cit Awd; Muhlenberg Coll; Pre-Dntl.

TRAN, LE CAM; G A R Memorial HS; Wilkes-Barre, PA; (3); Hon Roll; Jr NHS; NHS; Wilkes Coll; Nrsng.

TRAN, LOC; Taylor Allderdice HS; Pittsburgh, PA; (3); Math Clb; High Hon Roll; Hon Roll; NHS; Awd 4 Pt Avg 85-87; Med.

TRAN, LY; John Harris Campus HS; Harrisburg, PA; (1); 27/468; Camera Clb; Math Clb; School Play; Nwsp Rptr; Off Frsh Cls; Socr; Vllybl; Hon Roll; Prfct Atten Awd; Math.

TRAN, MAI; W Philadelphia Catholic Girls HS; Philadelphia, PA; (3); 28/249; Art Clb; Cmnty Wkr; French Clb; Vllybl; High Hon Roll; Hon Roll; Prfct Atten Awd; Charles E Ellis Grant 85-88; White-William Schlrshp 86-88; Biomed.

TRAN, THANH; Central Buck East HS; Warrington, PA; (4); Church Yth Grp; Computer Clb; Socr; Hon Roll; NHS; PA ST U; Engrng.

TRAN, THU; Academy Of Notre Dame De Namur; Upper Darby, PA; (3); Computer Clb; Hosp Aide; Yrbk Stf; VP Jr Cls; VP Sr Cls; High Hon Roll; Hon Roll.

TRAN, THU; Franklin Lerning Ctr; Philadelphia, PA; (4); Intnl Clb; Red Cross Aide; Service Clb; Teachers Aide; Varsity Clb; Badmtn; Cheerleading; Vllybl; NHS; Prfct Atten Awd; Amer Phlsphcl Soc Schlrs Pgm 85; Schlrshp Aid Pgm Awd 87; Temple U; Pre-Med.

TRAN, THU HA; West Philadelphia Cath HS For Girls; Philadelphia, PA; (4); 9/233; French Clb; Math Tm; Variety Show; Capt Vllybl; High Hon Roll; NHS; Prfct Atten Awd; City Philadelphia Awd 87; All Catholic 1st Tm Plyr 84-87; Exmplry Stu Awd 84-87; Drexel U; Bus Adm.

TRAN, THUANH; Phila HS For Girls; Philadelphia, PA; (3); Church Yth Grp; Library Aide; Office Aide; Teachers Aide; Hon Roll; Prfct Atten Awd; Drexel; Elec Engr.

TRANGUCH, BEN A; Bishop Hafey HS; Hazleton, PA; (2); 1/108; Church Yth Grp; Math Clb; Model UN; Quiz Bowl; JV Ftbl; L Trk; Cit Awd; High Hon Roll; Acad All Amer Awd 87; Notre Dame; Nuclr Engrng.

TRANQUILL, CHRISTINA M; Avella Area JR-SR HS; Avella, PA; (3); Pres 4-H; Letterman Clb; Sec Trs Frsh Cls; Pres Soph Cls; Sec Stu Cncl; Var L Bsktbl; Var L Sftbl; Var L Vllybl; Hon Roll; NHS.

TRANSUE, CARY; Seton-La Salle HS; Bethel Park, PA; (3); 79/257; Am Leg Boys St; Ski Clb; SADD; Varsity Clb; Var Bsbl; Var Bsktbl; Var Ftbl; Var Trk; Var Wt Lftg; High Hon Roll; U Of NC; Sprts Med.

TRAPANI, ANTHONY; Penn Hills SR HS; Verona, PA; (3); Ski Clb; Spanish Clb; High Hon Roll; Hon Roll; NHS; Carnegie Mellon; Arch.

TRAPANI, CHRISTINE; Dunmore HS; Dunmore, PA; (3); 28/150; Spanish Clb; Yrbk Stf; Var Capt Cheerleading; Twrlr; Hon Roll; NHS.

TRAPOLSI, KAREN; Villa Maria Acad; Erie, PA; (3); Church Yth Grp; Dance Clb; Latin Clb; Ski Clb; Varsity Clb; Variety Show; Yrbk Stf; Sec Soph Cls; Capt JV Bsktbl; Capt Im Cheerleading; Indiana U Of PA; Physcl Thrpy.

TRAPPEN, ERIC; South Side HS; Hookstown, PA; (3); 8/155; Am Leg Boys St; Boy Scts; Letterman Clb; Ski Clb; SADD; Varsity Clb; Var L Bsktbl; Var L Ftbl; Var L Trk; High Hon Roll; Lawyer.

TRASK, TIMOTHY; Archbishop Ryan For Boys HS; Philadelphia, PA; (4); 1/421; VP Cmnty Wkr; German Clb; Nwsp Stf; Yrbk Phtg; Lit Mag; JV Crs Cntry; Hon Roll; VP NHS; Stat Bsktbl; Nabisco Schlrshp For German Exchange Trip 85; German Awd By German American Police Assn 87; U Of PA; Pre-Med.

TRATHEN, DAVID; Southern Columbia Area HS; Catawissa, PA; (3); Varsity Clb; Trs Soph Cls; Rep Stu Cncl; Var L Ftbl; Var L Trk; Var Wt Lftg; High Hon Roll; Hon Roll; Voice Dem Awd; Broomsburg U; Archaelogy.

TRAUB, GREG; William Allen HS; Allentown, PA; (3); Nwsp Stf; Lit Mag; Rep Frsh Cls; Var Swmmng; Jr NHS; NHS; Ntl Merit Ltr; PA ST U; Aerospc Engrng.

TRAUB, JEFFREY; William Allen HS; Allentown, PA; (2); #1 In Class; Nwsp Stf; Var L Swmmng; High Hon Roll; Hon Roll; Jr NHS.

TRAUGER, KIMBERLY; Spring-Ford HS; Trappe, PA; (3); 62/256; Sec French Clb; Pep Clb; Sec SADD; Pres Thesps; Chorus; School Play; Yrbk Stf; Stu Cncl; Co-Capt Cheerleading; Hon Roll.

TRAUTERMAN, JAMES; Seneca Valley SR HS; Evans City, PA; (4); U Pittsburgh; Astrnmy.

TRAUTMAN, BURK; Council Rock HS; Wash Crsng, PA; (3); 182/902; German Clb; Ftbl; Wt Lftg; Purdue U; Sprts Med.

TRAUTMAN, KIMBERLY A; Central HS; East Freedom, PA; (4); L Cheerleading; Gym; Hon Roll; Exec Secy.

TRAUTZ, F BRIAN; Lower Moreland HS; Huntingdon Valley, PA; (3); Boy Scts; Church Yth Grp; VP German Clb; Dance Clb; Var JV Ftbl; JV Swmmng; Wt Lftg; Hon Roll; Natl Hnr Rl 86-87; Aerospc Engrng.

TRAVAGLINI, DOREEN; Hamburg HS; Hamburg, PA; (3); French Clb; Library Aide; Chorus; Church Choir; School Musical; Variety Show; Church Yth Grp; Mgr(s); Trk; Fine Arts Fest Chrch 87; Phila Schl Fine Arts; Opera Sng.

TRAVERSO, JULIE; Oley Valley HS; Temple, PA; (3); 24/154; Art Clb; Key Clb; Library Aide; Teachers Aide; Chorus; Stage Crew; Nwsp Rptr; Mgr(s); Score Keeper; Hon Roll; Math.

TRAVIS, KIM; Plum SR HS; Pittsburgh, PA; (3); AFS; Church Yth Grp; French Clb; Hosp Aide; Concert Band; Mrchg Band; Symp Band; Hon Roll; Med.

TRAVITZ, ROBERT; Middletown Area HS; Middletown, PA; (3); Socr; Vllybl.

TRAXLER, LAURI; Forbes Road HS; Hustontown, PA; (2); French Clb; FHA; Teachers Aide; Varsity Clb; Nwsp Stf; Stat Bsktbl; Var L Fld Hcky; JV Var Score Keeper; Hagerstown Bus Coll; Acctg.

TRAYERS, TIMOTHY; Norwin SR HS; N Huntingdon, PA; (3); Cmnty Wkr; VICA; Chorus; Prfct Atten Awd; Pittsburgh Inst Of Aeronautics.

TRAYNOR, JENNIFER; Hempfield Area SR HS; Greensburg, PA; (3); 4/693; Church Yth Grp; Spanish Clb; Yrbk Ed-Chief; Yrbk Stf; Stu Cncl; JV Bsktbl; JV Sftbl; JV Vllybl; High Hon Roll; NHS; Sftbl All Stars 87.

TRAYNOR, JENNIFER L; Conestoga HS; Strafford, PA; (4); 142/457; Cmnty Wkr; French Clb; Hosp Aide; Model UN; Var Crs Cntry; JV Fld Hcky; Mgr(s); Var Socr; Var Trk; High Hon Roll; 1st Annual Non Prof Art Show Wnnr 86; Purchase Awd Wnnr Art Major Show 87; Excllnce French 83; PA ST U; Lang.

TREACHER, KRISTA; Connellsville SR HS; Mill Run, PA; (2); Computer Clb; Band; Concert Band; Mrchg Band; Navy; Comp Trnng.

TREESE, ETHAN; Lewisburg HS; Lewisburg, PA; (3); Spanish Clb; VP Stu Cncl; Capt Socr; Hon Roll; NHS; Vet Sci.

TREFELNER, MICHAEL; Leechburg Area HS; Leechburg, PA; (3); 35/91; Church Yth Grp; Var L Bsbl; Ftbl; IN U; Bus.

TREGO, PAMELA; Downington HS; West Chester, PA; (4); 259/555; Hosp Aide; SADD; Chorus; Pres Nwsp Rptr; Var Fld Hcky; Var Trk; Capt Vllybl; Hon Roll; Library Aide; W Chester U; Health Educ.

TREIMAN, PHILIP R; Lower Moreland HS; Huntingdon Valley, PA; (4); 7/210; Office Aide; Pres VP Science Clb; Concert Band; Jazz Band; Mrchg Band; Pep Band; Nwsp Rptr; High Hon Roll; NHS; Ntl Merit SF; Med.

TREIMAN, SAUL; Lower Moreland HS; Huntingdon Valley, PA; (3); Hosp Aide; Science Clb; Nwsp Rptr; Pres Frsh Cls; Pres Soph Cls; Pres Jr Cls; JV Bsbl; Im Bowling; JV Tennis; Hon Roll; Med.

TREMBLAY, NADINE; Notre Dame HS; Effort, PA; (3); Exploring; French Clb; Chorus; Hon Roll; Sports Med.

TREMBULAK, SHARI; Danville HS; Danville, PA; (2); 15/160; Cmnty Wkr; Key Clb; Nwsp Stf; Yrbk Stf; Rep Soph Cls; Im Mat Maids; JV Tennis; High Hon Roll; NHS; Accntnt.

TREMITIERE, CHANTEL; William Penn HS; York, PA; (4); 30/373; SADD; Varsity Clb; Stu Cncl; Var Capt Bsktbl; Var Capt Trk; Var Capt Vllybl; Hon Roll; NHS; Prfct Atten Awd; USC; Child Psych.

TREMPUS, RACHEL; Springdale HS; Springdale, PA; (3); 1/130; German Clb; GAA; Nwsp Ed-Chief; Nwsp Rptr; Nwsp Stf; Yrbk Ed-Chief; Var Capt Sftbl; High Hon Roll; VP NHS; Creative Writing Awd 87; Engrng.

TRENCH, CAROL; Nazareth Acad; Phila, PA; (3); Church Yth Grp; Girl Scts; Orch; School Musical; Yrbk Stf; Stu Cncl; JV Var Fld Hcky; Hon Roll; NHS; Grl Sct Gld & Slvr Ldrshp Awd 86; Elem Educ.

TRENKLE, MELANIE J; Bishop Mc Cort HS; Johnstown, PA; (4); German Clb; Hst Pep Clb; Ski Clb; Yrbk Stf; Trs Frsh Cls; Sec Jr Cls; Sec Sr Cls; Socr; Hon Roll; Hmcmng Queen 86-87; Prom Queen 87; Juniata Coll; Phy Thrpst.

TRENKO, LISA; West Hazleton HS; Tresckow, PA; (3); Church Yth Grp; Cmnty Wkr; FBLA; FNA; Hosp Aide; Library Aide; Nrsng.

TRENTLY, LISA; Scranton Central HS; Scranton, PA; (3); 49/300; French Clb; SADD; JV Var Cheerleading; Hon Roll; Jr NHS; Phrmcst.

TREON, ANGELA; Shikellamy HS; Northumberland, PA; (3); 38/351; Dance Clb; VP Library Aide; Office Aide; Spanish Clb; SADD; Yrbk Phtg; Trs Frsh Cls; Trs Soph Cls; Cheerleading; Hon Roll; Pre Med.

TREON, PAMELA; Shikellamy HS; Sunbury, PA; (3); 5/300; Sec Church Yth Grp; French Clb; Teachers Aide; Band; Chorus; Mrchg Band; Yrbk Phtg; Var Sftbl; French Hon Soc; SPEC Ed.

TRESCO, BRUNO; Kiski Area HS; Apollo, PA; (2); Chorus; Im JV Ftbl; CPA.

TRESKY, MARIAN; Quigley HS; Mars, PA; (4); 5/103; Math Tm; Model UN; Nwsp Rptr; High Hon Roll; Hon Roll; NHS; Ntl Merit Ltr; Toastmasters Awd 84; Typing Awd 85; Psych.

TRESSA, SHARON; James M Coughlin HS; Plains, PA; (4); Church Yth Grp; Sec French Clb; Nwsp Rptr; Yrbk Stf; Hon Roll; Jr NHS; NHS; Lock Haven Pres Scholar 87; Lynchburg Hopwood Scholar 86; Pres Acad Fit Wd 87; Lock Haven U; Jrnlsm.

TRESSLER, AMY; Turkeyfoot Valley HS; Confluence, PA; (4); Q&S; Varsity Clb; Band; Chorus; Nwsp Stf; Yrbk Stf; Rep Stu Cncl; Sftbl; High Hon Roll; Sec NHS; Dec Lionness Of The Mnth 86; Sawyer Schl Of Bus; Travel.

TRESSLER, GUY; Turkeyfoot Valley Area HS; Confluence, PA; (2); Band; Chorus; Nwsp Bus Mgr; Pres Frsh Cls; Pres Soph Cls; Stu Cncl; Capt JV Bsktbl; Capt JV Ftbl; Wt Lftg; High Hon Roll; Armed Serv.

TRESSLER, NIKKI; Connellsville SR HS; Normalville, PA; (3); Church Yth Grp; GAA; Library Aide; Office Aide; Ski Clb; Color Guard; Capt Flag Corp; Mrchg Band; High Hon Roll; NHS.

TRESSLER, PAUL; Danville HS; Riverside, PA; (2); Computer Clb; JV Bsbl; Hon Roll; NEDT Awd; Comp.

TRETER, MATT; Harborcreek HS; Erie, PA; (3); 3/215; Church Yth Grp; Computer Clb; Var Socr; High Hon Roll; Hon Roll; NHS; US Achvt Acad Ntl Art Awd 86.

TRETTEL, ROB; Freeport Area HS; Sarver, PA; (3); French Clb; Varsity Clb; Rep Soph Cls; Bsbl; Var Capt Bsktbl; JV Coach Actv; JV Ftbl; JV Score Keeper; Var Trk; JV Wt Lftg; U Of Pittsburgh; Med.

TREXLER, DENISE; William Allen High HS; Allentown, PA; (4); 85/518; GAA; JCL; Service Clb; Yrbk Stf; Rep Jr Cls; Rep Sr Cls; Rep Stu Cncl; Var L Bsktbl; Hon Roll; Jr NHS; U Of Pittsburgh; Pre-Law.

TREXLER, DONALD; Bishop Mc Cort HS; Johnstown, PA; (3); 43/155; French Clb; Letterman Clb; Ski Clb; Bsbl; Ftbl; Wt Lftg; Hon Roll.

TRIANO, MARIA; Bishop Hafey HS; Hazleton, PA; (3); Church Yth Grp; Hosp Aide; Spanish Clb; Y-Teens; Trs Jr Cls; L Trk; High Hon Roll; Hon Roll; NHS; Prfct Atten Awd; Bus.

TRIBIT, EMILY K; Penn Manor HS; Lancaster, PA; (3); Computer Clb; Drama Clb; Ski Clb; School Musical; Off Stu Cncl; JV Fld Hcky; Prfct Atten Awd; Bus.

TRIBUIANI, MELISSA; Upper Darby HS; Upper Darby, PA; (4); 10/590; Service Clb; Spanish Clb; Rep Jr Cls; Rep Stu Cncl; JV Trk; NHS; Pres Schlr; Yrbk Stf; High Hon Roll; Home & Schl Assoc Schlrshp 87; Womens Club Schlrshp 87; Engl Awd 87; Drexel U; Ped.

TRICARICO, AMI; Old Forge HS; Old Forge, PA; (3); Art Clb; Spanish Clb; Off Sec Jr Cls; JV Capt Cheerleading; High Hon Roll; Hon Roll; Dentistry.

TRICE, TRACEY; Greensburg Central Catholic HS; Mt Pleasant, PA; (4); 31/200; AFS; Church Yth Grp; Cmnty Wkr; Exploring; Hosp Aide; Lit Mag; Sftbl; Trk; High Hon Roll; Chrmn NHS; Hnr Cord 87; Seton Hill Coll.

TRICHEL III, GERVAIS WILLIAM; Seneca HS; Erie, PA; (4); 7/150; Church Yth Grp; 4-H; Yrbk Phtg; Off Stu Cncl; Ftbl; Ice Hcky; 4-H Awd; High Hon Roll; NHS; Pres Acdmc Ftnss Awd & Ted Barker Memrl Sportsmanship Awd 87; Acdmc Awd In Math 86-87; TX A&m U; Aerospc Engrng.

TRICK, DEANNA; Hughesville HS; Hughesville, PA; (3); Church Yth Grp; French Clb; Ski Clb; Chorus; School Musical; Var Bsktbl; Var Crs Cntry; Var Socr; Var Trk; Hon Roll; Psych.

TRICK, MICHELLE; Cocalico SR HS; Reinholds, PA; (4); 2/163; FTA; Quiz Bowl; Chorus; Concert Band; Rep Mrchg Band; School Play; High Hon Roll; NHS; Sal; DAR Ctznshp Awd 87; Lions Club Stu Mnth 86; Lancaster Cnty Libr Wrtng Awd Short Story 85; Juniata Coll; Socl Psych.

TRICOLLI, MARK; West Hazleton SR HS; W Hazleton, PA; (2); 1/225; L Var Bsktbl; Hon Roll; Pres Schlr; Amer Lgn 86; Schlr/Athl 86.

TRIGGS, ROBERT; Trinity Christian HS; Pittsburgh, PA; (3); Church Yth Grp; Trs JA; School Play; Stage Crew; Var Bsktbl; Var JV Ftbl; L Var Trk; Temple U; Comp Engr.

TRIMARCHI, KURT; State College Area HS; Lemont, PA; (2); Var L Golf; Cit Awd; Hon Roll; NEDT Awd; Red Crss 1st Aid/CPR 85-86; Pwr Of Paw Awd 86; Cert Of Merit-Bkkpg I 86-87; Math Awd-Alg II 86-87; Bus Law.

TRIMBATH, LINDA; Danville SR HS; Danville, PA; (4); 62/197; Art Clb; Cmnty Wkr; Drama Clb; Hst Intnl Clb; Latin Clb; Nwsp Rptr; Yrbk Stf; V W Woods Mem Schlrshp 86-87; NY U; Photo.

TRIMBER, CAROL; Walter Biddle HS; Philadelphia, PA; (3); #1 In Class; Exploring; FFA; Girl Scts; Nwsp Rptr; Jr Cls; Sr Cls; High Hon Roll; NHS; Outstndng Fresh Awd 85; PA Govr Schl For Agri 86; Outstdng Jr Awd & Supr Awd 87; Anml Sci.

TRIMBLE, JOHN; Girard HS; Girard, PA; (4); Hon Roll; Trs NHS; Penn ST Behrend; Engrng.

TRIMBLE, PAUL; Penns Manor HS; Indiana, PA; (3); Chess Clb; 4-H; 4-H Awd; Hon Roll; Gntcs.

TRIMBLE, SCOTT; Solanco HS; Peach Bottom, PA; (3); 26/273; Church Yth Grp; VP 4-H; FFA; Varsity Clb; Var L Crs Cntry; Var L Trk; High Hon Roll; NHS; Engrng.

TRIMBUR, GREG; Butler HS; Butler, PA; (3); Teachers Aide; Var Bsbl; Im Bsktbl; Var Ftbl; High Hon Roll; 1st Team All Sectnl Bsebl 87; Comm.

TRIMPEY, AMANDA C; Connellsville Area HS; Connellsville, PA; (4); Rep Model UN; Rep Political Wkr; Sec SADD; Drm Mjr(t); School Musical; Nwsp Ed-Chief; French Hon Soc; High Hon Roll; NHS; VFW Awd; 1st Pl Wnnr For PA JR Acad Of Sci; St Rep For PA To Amer JR Acad Of Sci Natl Conv 86-87; Pre Med.

TRIMPEY, TARALYN T; Connellsville Area HS; Connellsville, PA; (2); 4/600; Am Leg Aux Girls St; Church Yth Grp; Civic Clb; Cmnty Wkr; French Clb; Hosp Aide; Political Wkr; Pres Science Clb; SADD; Band; PA JR Acad Of Sci 1st Pl; Acad Excllnc Gld Pin; Med.

TRINH, HOA C; Mc Caskey HS; Lancaster, PA; (4); 16/400; AFS; Trs Church Yth Grp; Math Clb; Off Frsh Cls; Trs Soph Cls; Trs Stu Cncl; Tennis; Hon Roll; Sec NHS; Prfct Atten Awd; 1st PA Jr Acad Sci, Exch Club Stu Mnth 87; Carnegie-Mellon U; Engrng.

TRIPLETT, CHRISTINE; Laurel Highlands HS; Lemont Furnace, PA; (2); 12/355; Church Yth Grp; Exploring; Cheerleading; Trk; Engnrng.

TRIPODI, FRANK; Episcopal Acad; Drexel Hill, PA; (2); Capt Math Tm; Bsbl; Im Socr; High Hon Roll; Hon Roll.

TRIPONEY, CARRIE; Clearfield Area HS; Hyde, PA; (4); Thesps; Pres Band; Chorus; Orch; School Musical; Swing Chorus; High Hon Roll; Church Yth Grp; Drama Clb; French Clb; All ST Chrs PA Otstndng Achvmnt Chrl Music 86; All Eastern Chrs 87; Otstndng Musician Awd 87; Edinboro U PA; Music.

TRIPONEY, STEVEN; Penn View Bible Inst; Punxsutawney, PA; (3); Church Yth Grp; Band; Chorus; Church Choir; Stage Crew; Yrbk Stf; Rep Jr Cls; Hon Roll; Rlgn.

TRISCIK, JENNIFER; Ringgold HS; Donora, PA; (3); Service Clb; Hon Roll; Spanish Clb; Bus Admin.

TRITT, MARY; Riverside HS; Ellwood City, PA; (2); Church Yth Grp; NFL; PAVAS; Band; Sec Chorus; Flag Corp; School Musical; Stu Cncl; Sftbl; Trk; Pre-Dntstry.

TRITT, THERESA; Riverside HS; Ellwood City, PA; (3); Church Yth Grp; GAA; Bsktbl; Sftbl; Grphc Arts Stu Yr 85-86; Gen Spch Stu Yr 85-86; CA U Of PA; Prnt Shop Mngmt.

TRIVILINO, MAUREEN ANN; Quigley Catholic HS; Beaver, PA; (3); 40/79; Am Leg Aux Girls St; Cmnty Wkr; Chorus; Church Choir; School Musical; Powder Puff Ftbl; Trk; HOBY, & Music Mnstry Tm Svc Awd 86; Trk Tm 2 Yr Lttrmn 86-87; Elem Ed.

TROGLIONE, LESLIE; Southern Lehigh HS; Center Valley, PA; (3); 8/257; Hosp Aide; Scholastic Bowl; SADD; Varsity Clb; Coach Actv; Var L Tennis; High Hon Roll; Hon Roll; NHS; Brnz Mdl Dist XI Mxd Dbls Chmpnshp 87; Cert Schl Brd Abv Achvt 87.

TROIANI, ANNA MARIE REGINA; Quigley HS; Midland, PA; (4); Chorus; School Musical; Sec Jr Cls; Sec Sr Cls; Rep Stu Cncl; Var Powder Puff Ftbl; Var Tennis; Stat Wrstlng; Pres Girl Scts; Loyola Schlrshp-Whlng Coll 87-88; Hnrs-Dist Choir 87; Hnrs-Rgnl Choir 87; Wheeling Jesuit Coll; Psychlgy.

TROILO, LOUIS; Cardinal Ohara HS; Springfield, PA; (4); 76/780; Aud/Vis; Chess Clb; Office Aide; Yrbk Stf; Im Bsktbl; Im Ftbl; Var Tennis; Hon Roll; Lion Awd; NHS; MVP-TNNS 87; Top 10 Pct-Hnrd By Schl 86-87; St Joes U; Bus.

TROJANOWSKI, KAREN; St Pius X HS; Pottstown, PA; (1); 14/146; Latin Clb; Bsktbl; Sftbl; DAR Awd; Hon Roll; Jr NHS; Prfct Atten Awd; Outstndg Achvt Latin I 86-87; Cert Hnr Math & Sci 86; Knights Columbus Free Throw Champ 84-85; Med.

TROJANOWSKI, MICHAEL; Warren Area HS; Warren, PA; (3); Drama Clb; VP Pep Clb; SADD; Varsity Clb; Acpl Chr; Chorus; School Musical; School Play; Stage Crew; Rep Frsh Cls; Bus.

TROMBETTA, CHRISTINA; Center Area HS; Aliquippa, PA; (3); 50/187; Latin Clb; Band; Chorus; Concert Band; Mrchg Band; Pep Band; School Musical; Nwsp Stf; Hon Roll; Girl Scts; Med Tech.

TROMBETTA, CHRISTOPHER; Aliquippa HS; Aliquippa, PA; (4); Church Yth Grp; French Clb; Jr Cls; Sr Cls; Var L Wrstlng; Hon Roll; Gannon U; Med.

TROMMATTER, DAVID; Reading SR HS; Reading, PA; (3); 50/750; Sftbl; Swmmng; Wrstlng; Hon Roll; Air Force; Drftng.

TRONCONE, JANET; Villa Maria Acad; Erie, PA; (4); 45/130; Church Yth Grp; Intnl Clb; SADD; Nwsp Rptr; Nwsp Stf; Trk; High Hon Roll; Hon Roll; Jr NHS; NHS; Penn ST-BEHREND; Law.

TRONCONE, MARK; Williamson JR-SR HS; Lawrenceville, PA; (3); Church Yth Grp; Exploring; Ski Clb; Spanish Clb; Swmmng; Trk; Polc Offcr.

TRONE JR, HAROLD E; South Western HS; Hanover, PA; (3); 23/233; VP Key Clb; Ski Clb; Varsity Clb; VP L Tennis; High Hon Roll; Hon Roll; Jr NHS; Rotary Awd; Pres Phys Ftns Awd; Engrng.

TROPIANO, CHRIS; St Jon Neumann HS; Philadelphia, PA; (3); 48/349; Church Yth Grp; Im Bsktbl; JV Trk; High Hon Roll; Hon Roll; Temple U; Bus Admin.

TROPP, JESSICA; Lower Merion HS; Wynnewood, PA; (3); Service Clb; Chorus; Orch; Rep Jr Cls; Capt Bsktbl; Capt Fld Hcky; Var L Lcrss; Hon Roll; All Cntrl Lg Fld Hcky 1st Tm & All Main Line All Str Tm 86; All Main Line-Hnbl Mntn La Crosse 87; Acctg.

TROSKO, SUZANNE; Susquehanna Township HS; Harrisburg, PA; (3); 7/150; Chorus; School Musical; Rep Soph Cls; Rep Stu Cncl; JV Vllybl; High Hon Roll; Hon Roll; NEDT Awd; Art Clb; Aud/Vis; Math.

TROST, DEBORAH; Ringgold HS; Monongahela, PA; (4); Church Yth Grp; Office Aide; Band; Concert Band; Mrchg Band; Pep Band; Symp Band; Swmmng; U Of Pittsburgh; Nrsng.

TROST, KELLY; Mercyhurst Prep Schl; Erie, PA; (4); 19/155; Art Clb; Vllybl; Hon Roll; NHS; Gold Key Blue Ribbon Art Awd 87; Bio.

TROSTLE, ANNE; Boiling Springs HS; Boiling Spgs, PA; (3); Girl Scts; Ski Clb; Acpl Chr; Chorus; JV Fld Hcky; Var Sftbl; Var Swmmng; Hon Roll; Girls Swimmng-Mid-Penn Div 2 Champs 86-87; Most Imprvd Swimmer 86-87; Sports Med.

TROSTLE, DEBRA; Hempfield HS; University Park, PA; (4); 48/425; Church Yth Grp; Science Clb; Hon Roll; 3rd Pl Rbbn PA ST Frm Shw For Braided Wool Rug 84; 1st Pl Rug Brdng Manheim & Ephrata Fairs 84; PA ST U; Engrng.

TROSTLE, TERESA; Elizabethtown Area HS; Elizabethtown, PA; (3); 42/259; Bsktbl; Sftbl; Vllybl; Hon Roll; Millersville; Accntng.

TROTT, FRANK; New Castle HS; New Castle, PA; (3); Hon Roll.

TROTT, KELLY; New Castle SR HS; New Castle, PA; (3); #55 In Class; Drill Tm; JV Gym; Hon Roll; Chld Psychlgst.

TROTTA, ADRIENNE; New Castle SR HS; New Castle, PA; (4); 68/274; AFS; Dance Clb; Drama Clb; French Clb; NFL; Pep Clb; SADD; Band; Chorus; Color Guard; Js Ms 2nd Rnr-Up Awd 86; Clarion U Music Schlrshp 87; Natl Frnsc Awd 87; Slippery Rock U Of PA; Cmnctns.

TROTTER, JEFFREY K; Central HS; Philadelphia, PA; (3); Pres Church Yth Grp; Computer Clb; Im Bsktbl; Var Swmmng; Im Tennis; Im Wt Lftg; Hon Roll; Library Aide; Math Clb; Church Choir; Natl Schlr & Hons In Biol & Chem At Phillips Acad 85-87; Mngmnt.

TROUGHT, LISA; Spring-Ford SR HS; Royersford, PA; (2); 58/256; Band; Concert Band; Drm Mjr(t); Mrchg Band; Yrbk Ed-Chief; JV Capt Cheerleading; Var Lcrss; Church Yth Grp; French Clb; Pep Clb; Dist Orchrestra & Band, Rgn Band & All-ST Band 86; Dist Band Rgn Band 87; Tri-Cnty Orchestra 87; Music Thrpy.

TROUP, MELANIE; Brookville Area HS; Brookville, PA; (3); Pres Church Yth Grp; FBLA; FNA; German Clb; Med Secy.

TROUP, TAMMY; Susquehanna Community HS; Susquehanna, PA; (3); 4-H; SADD; Color Guard; Yrbk Stf; Rep Frsh Cls; Rep Soph Cls; Powder Puff Ftbl; Sftbl; Hon Roll; Chorus; Elementary Educ.

TROUT, ANDREW; N Lebanon HS; Lebanon, PA; (4); 20/166; FCA; Math Tm; Varsity Clb; Var L Ftbl; Var L Trk; Var Wt Lftg; Im Wrstlng; Hon Roll; 3rd Pl Schl Math Exm 85; 1st Pl Rgnls-Olympics Of The Mind-Decision Structr 87; Astrophyscs.

TROUT, BEVERLY; Penn-Trafford HS; Claridge, PA; (4); 56/344; VICA; Nwsp Rptr; FBLA; Library Aide; Spanish Clb; Im Vllybl; Hon Roll; Comnty Actn Pgm Awd 83; Hnr Schlrshp 87-88; Geneva Coll; Comp Sci.

TROUT, BRAD; United HS; Homer City, PA; (3); 34/147; Camera Clb; Church Yth Grp; Pres 4-H; Rep FFA; Chorus; 4-H Awd; Hon Roll; Prfct Atten Awd; FFA Public Speaking Awd 85-87; IN U Pennsylvania; Army Ofcr.

TROUT, JEREMY; Solanco SR HS; Quarryville, PA; (3); 19/273; Pres Sec Varsity Clb; Var Ftbl; Var Trk; Var Wt Lftg; JV Wrstlng; High Hon Roll; Hon Roll; Pres NHS; Schltc Art Wnnr 85-86; Engrng.

TROUT, KEN; Solanco HS; Quarryville, PA; (1); Boy Scts; FFA; Hon Roll; Fulton Grange Awd 85; Keystone Frmr Dgr 85; Red Rose Frmr Dgr 85; Henry Wenger Insurance Awd 85.

TROUT, PETER D; Boyertown Area HS; Bechtelsville, PA; (3); 40/411; Art Clb; Church Yth Grp; German Clb; Math Clb; VICA; Cit Awd; High Hon Roll; Hon Roll; NHS; Prfct Atten Awd; Auto Mech.

TROUT, TERESA; Greater Latrobe SR HS; Greensburg, PA; (4); 95/407; Teachers Aide; Concert Band; Drm Mjr(t); Nwsp Stf; Lit Mag; High Hon Roll; Turner Offc Typng Awd 86 & 87; Prffsnl Bus Wmns Clb Awd 87; Libry Typng Awd; Bradford; Secy.

TROUTMAN, CHRISTOPHER; Upper Dauphin Area HS; Lykens, PA; (2); Church Yth Grp; FFA; Dely To ST FFA Smmr Cnvntn 87; PA ST; Ag.

TROUTMAN, DIANE; Conrad Weiser HS; Myerstown, PA; (4); 75/184; JCL; Chorus; School Musical; School Play; Tennis; Hon Roll; Art Inst Pittsburg; Vis Cmmnctn.

TROUTMAN, DUSTIN; Northern Bedford County HS; Hopewell, PA; (3); Ski Clb; Varsity Clb; Rep Soph Cls; Rep Jr Cls; Var Ftbl; Var Wrstlng; Hon Roll; Elec Engr.

TROUTMAN, JULIE; Clarion-Limestone HS; New Bethlehem, PA; (3); SADD; Band; Chorus; Nwsp Stf; Cheerleading; Trk; Twrlr; Hon Roll; NHS; Accntnt.

TROUTMAN, MICHAEL T; Nativity BVM; New Philadelphia, PA; (3); 13/86; Math Tm; High Hon Roll; Hon Roll; Highest Avg In Spanish I & II 84-86; Intl Foreign Lang Awd Winner 87; PA ST U; Bus.

TROUTMAN, RYAN; Mifflinburg Area HS; Mifflinburg, PA; (1); Boy Scts; German Clb; Concert Band; Bsbl; Ftbl; Arch.

TROUTMAN, TOM; Reynolds HS; Greenville, PA; (4); 8/147; Latin Clb; Pres Band; Pres Concert Band; Pres Jazz Band; Pres Mrchg Band; Pres Pep Band; High Hon Roll; JP Sousa Awd; NHS; Math Clb; U Pttsbrgh Merit Schlrshp 86; Untd Stlwrkrs Am Schlrshp 86; U Pittsburgh; Dntstry.

TROUTMAN-ROBERTS, HEIDI; Phila Montgomery Christian Acad; Lansdowne, PA; (4); Cmnty Wkr; Hosp Aide; Library Aide; Acpl Chr; Chorus; Church Choir; School Play; High Hon Roll; NHS; Ntl Merit SF; White Williams Schlrshp & Awd 84-87; Temple U; Bus Mgmt.

TROVATO, MARGARITA; Chartiers-Houston HS; Houston, PA; (4); 27/120; Church Yth Grp; French Clb; Varsity Clb; Drill Tm; Var Sftbl; Var Trk; Var Vllybl; Hon Roll; W Liberty ST Col6; Phy Educ.

TROWER, DELLA; Sacred Heart HS; Pittsburgh, PA; (3); Church Yth Grp; JV Capt Bsktbl; Bowling; Fld Hcky; Ftbl; Im Score Keeper; Socr; Capt Im Vllybl; Hon Roll; Pre Law.

TROXEL, CHERIE; Fleetwood HS; Fleetwood, PA; (3); 23/110; Hon Roll; Kutztown U; Cmmrcl Art.

TROXEL, ELIZABETH; Hughesville HS; Hughesville, PA; (3); Drama Clb; Hosp Aide; Band; Color Guard; Mrchg Band; Nwsp Rptr; Comm.

TROXELL, DARYL; Mifflinburg Area HS; Lewisburg, PA; (1); Sec Church Yth Grp; German Clb; Band; Chorus; Concert Band; Rep Stu Cncl; Var Trk; High Hon Roll; Prfct Atten Awd; Law.

TROXELL, KELLY; Gettysburg SR HS; Gettysburg, PA; (2); 73/276; Dance Clb; Office Aide; Pep Clb; Soroptimist; Chorus; Swing Chorus; Nwsp Sprt Ed; JV Vllybl; Stat Wrstlng; Hon Roll; Acad.

TROXELL, MICHELE; Glendale HS; Glasgow, PA; (4); 8/93; Science Clb; Band; Chorus; Concert Band; Mrchg Band; Pep Band; Yrbk Phtg; Yrbk Stf; Var L Bsktbl; Stat Ftbl; Pres Acad Ftns Awd 86-87; PA ST U; Bus Admin.

TROY, DOUGLAS; Somerset Area HS; Friedens, PA; (4); 98/249; Church Yth Grp; English Clb; French Clb; JA; Varsity Clb; Band; School Play; Stage Crew; Variety Show; Rep Stu Cncl; Penn ST; Htl, Rstrnt Mgmt.

TROY, JULIE; Monessen JR SR HS; Monessen, PA; (3); JA; Chorus; High Hon Roll; Hon Roll; Nrsng.

TROYAN, JAMES; Parkland HS; Orefield, PA; (3); 25/505; JA; Math Tm; High Hon Roll; NHS; Accntng.

TROYAN, MICHAEL; Du Bois Central Christian HS; Brockway, PA; (3); Debate Tm; Varsity Clb; Yrbk Stf; Trs Frsh Cls; Trs Soph Cls; Stu Cncl; Var Bsktbl; L Var Crs Cntry; Hon Roll; VP NHS; PA ST.

TROYANO, JASON; Harry S Truman HS; Bristol, PA; (3); Bsbl; Hon Roll; Marine Bio.

TROZZOLILLO, MARIA; Bishop Hannan HS; Scranton, PA; (4); 7/123; Church Yth Grp; Hosp Aide; Math Clb; Yrbk Stf; Bowling; High Hon Roll; NHS; Pres Schlr; Natl Lat Exam Cum Laude 84; Outstndng Acvht Clscl, Mod Lang 87; U Scranton; Hlth.

TRUAX, TODD D; Southern Fulton HS; Crystal Spring, PA; (3); 5/80; Am Leg Boys St; Church Yth Grp; Science Clb; Chorus; Yrbk Stf; Var L Bsbl; Hon Roll; NHS; Shippensburg U; Mngmt Sci.

TRUBILLA, TARA; Panther Valley HS; Nesquehoning, PA; (1); 2/127; Am Leg Aux Girls St; Exploring; Hosp Aide; Library Aide; JV Vllybl; High Hon Roll; John Hopkins U; Pediatrics.

TRUEMAN, ROBERT; HS Of Enigeering & Science; Philadelphia, PA; (3); 39/250; Pres Church Yth Grp; Computer Clb; Math Tm; Science Clb; Ski Clb; Yrbk Phtg; Hon Roll; NHS; SADD; Stage Crew; PA Jr Acad Of Sci 84-87; PA Jr Acad Of Sci St Meeting 84-86; Penn ST; Aerospc Engrng.

TRUESDALE, MICHELLE L; Brockway Area HS; Brockway, PA; (3); 25/110; Art Clb; Drama Clb; Varsity Clb; Rep Stu Cncl; JV Var Cheerleading; JV Var Vllybl; Wt Lftg; Pres Ftnss Awd 86.

TRUESDALE, TODD; The Hill Schl; Cliffside Pk, NJ; (3); Pres Spanish Clb; Nwsp Rptr; Nwsp Stf; Sec Soph Cls; Sec Jr Cls; Sec Sr Cls; Rep Stu Cncl; JV Ftbl; JV Swmmng; High Hon Roll; Span 2 Awd 84-85; Econ.

TRUITT, DAVID; Elizabethtown Area HS; Elizabethtown, PA; (3); Pres Church Yth Grp; Teachers Aide; Stu Cncl; Var Socr; Var Tennis; Lancaster Lebanon All Str Sccr 86; Scl Wrkr.

TRUITT, PATRICK; Riverview HS; Oakmont, PA; (3); Boy Scts; Exploring; JA; Ski Clb; Varsity Clb; Band; Concert Band; Jazz Band; Orch; Nwsp Rptr; Physics.

TRUMAN, BELINDA; Waynesburg Central HS; Waynesburg, PA; (3); Office Aide; Spanish Clb; Teachers Aide; Sftbl; Prfct Atten Awd; Kent ST U; Psych.

TRUMAN, LORI; Sacred Heart HS; Carbondale, PA; (3); 2/50; Drama Clb; Scholastic Bowl; SADD; Chorus; Nwsp Rptr; Pres Frsh Cls; Pres Soph Cls; Pres Jr Cls; High Hon Roll; NHS; Partial HS Schlrhsp 84-85; Pennn ST; Bio.

TRUMBAUER, ERIC; Emmaus HS; Emmaus, PA; (4); 22/466; Concert Band; Lib Mrchg Band; Pep Band; High Hon Roll; Hon Roll; Jr NHS; NHS; Hnr Grad 87; Prsdntl Acdmc Ftnss Awd 87; PA ST U; Earth Sci.

TRUMBAUER, WENDY; Owen J Roberts HS; Pottstown, PA; (4); Church Yth Grp; Hosp Aide; JA; Office Aide; Band; Concert Band; Mrchg Band; Hon Roll; Lansdale Bus Schl; Sec Sci.

TRUMP, MICHAEL; Reading SR HS; Reading, PA; (3); 57/710; Boy Scts; Band; Concert Band; Jazz Band; Mrchg Band; Orch; Pep Band; School Musical; Eagle Scout Awd 86; Zeswitz Music Awd 85; Arch.

TRUMPETER, HOLLY; Monaca HS; Monaca, PA; (2); Church Yth Grp; Computer Clb; Drama Clb; Jr Civitan Int; Library Aide; Office Aide; PAVAS; SADD; Teachers Aide; Chorus; 1st Pl Snging Tlnt Shw 86; Hnr Top 10 87.

TRUNK, CHRISTINE; Middletown Area HS; Middletown, PA; (3); Cmnty Wkr; Girl Scts; Model UN; Chorus; Swmmng; Tennis; Hon Roll.

TRUSCHEL, JEANNE; Gateway SR HS; Monroeville, PA; (3); French Clb; Ski Clb; Chorus; Yrbk Stf; Off Soph Cls; Sec Jr Cls; L Capt Socr; Var L Swmmng; Var L Tennis; French Hon Soc; Speech Thrpy.

TRUSIAK, SHAWN; Springdale HS; Cheswick, PA; (3); Bsbl; Art Exhib 2nd 87.

TRUSKIE, CRAIG; Moon SR HS; Coraopolis, PA; (3); 18/353; Computer Clb; German Clb; JA; Math Tm; ROTC; Band; High Hon Roll; Hon Roll; Prfct Atten Awd; Carnegie Mellon U; Comp Engr.

TRUSSLER, SHARI; The Baptist HS; Clarks Summit, PA; (4); 1/15; Chorus; Church Choir; Yrbk Ed-Chief; Yrbk Stf; Trs Sr Cls; Var Bsktbl; Var Cheerleading; High Hon Roll; Ntl Merit Ltr; Law.

TRUSTY, ANTOINETTE; Chester HS; Brookhaven, PA; (3); 84/458; Church Yth Grp; French Clb; Sec Sr Cls; Rep Stu Cncl; French Hon Soc; Hon Roll; Soc Studs Awd 85-86; Amer Cltrs Awd 86-87; Pedtrc Nrse.

TRYNOSKY, KIMBERLY; Pine Grove Area HS; Pine Grove, PA; (4); 6/116; Am Leg Aux Girls St; Pres SADD; Varsity Clb; Nwsp Rptr; Yrbk Phtg; Rep Frsh Cls; Hst Sr Cls; Rep Stu Cncl; Stat Bsktbl; VP Capt Cheerleading; AFROTC Schlrshp; Lituanion Womans Schlrshp; WV U; Engr.

TRZECIAK, SHAWN; Highlands HS; Natrona Hts, PA; (4); 69/277; Art Clb; Pres Intnl Clb; School Play; Stu Cncl; Bsbl; Bsktbl; High Hon Roll; Hon Roll; Jr NHS; Edinboro; Graphic Art.

TSAFOS, JENNIFER; Central HS Of Phldlpha; Philadelphia, PA; (3); 19/538; Church Yth Grp; Math Tm; Nwsp Stf; Yrbk Stf; High Hon Roll; Hon Roll; Jr NHS; Editor Of SR Section Of Yrbk & Layout Editor Of Newspaper 87-88; On Editorial Bd Of Nwspr 86-87.

TSAI, DAVID; Marple Newtown HS; Broomall, PA; (3); 7/322; Church Yth Grp; Hosp Aide; Service Clb; Stu Cncl; Im Bsbl; Yth Apprctn Week Citation 86; Med.

TSAI, SHUN; Spring-Ford Sr HS; Mt Clare, PA; (3); 1/272; Off Math Clb; Math Tm; Trk; Gov Hon Prg Awd; High Hon Roll; Hon Roll; NCTE Awd; NHS; Ntl Merit SF; PA Gvrnr Schl Sci Schlrshp 87; Amer Chem Socty Awd 87; AHSME Schl Wnnr 86; MIT; Engrng.

TSANGARIS, JENNIFER; Elizabeth-Forward HS; Elizabeth, PA; (2); Pep Clb; Rep Frsh Cls; Rep Soph Cls; Var L Crs Cntry; Var L Trk; Stat Wrstlng; High Hon Roll; Med.

TSCHOPP, BARRY; Kennard-Dale HS; Stewartstown, PA; (3); Boy Scts; Ski Clb; Varsity Clb; JV Bsbl; Var Bsktbl; Var Ftbl; NHS; Most Imprvd Bsktbll Plyr 83-84; Most Ded Ftbl 83-84; Pilot.

TU, ZUNG; Neshaminy HS; Featherville, PA; (3); 21/768; Im Bsktbl; Im Gym; Var Socr; Var Trk; Im Vllybl; Hon Roll; Hnrs Soc Vp; Engrng.

TUBBS, MELISSA; Curwensville Area HS; Curwensville, PA; (4); 52/114; Drama Clb; Pres FNA; Pres Varsity Clb; Chorus; Concert Band; Mrchg Band; Var Sftbl; Var Vllybl; Natl Physcl Educ Awd 83; Art Inst Of Pittsburgh; Intr Ds.

TUBBS, PAUL; Curwensville Area HS; Curwensville, PA; (3); Church Yth Grp; FCA; Letterman Clb; Varsity Clb; Church Choir; School Play; Stage Crew; Stu Cncl; Im Ftbl; Var Wrstlng.

TUBBS, RHONDA; Central Christian HS; Du Bois, PA; (2); Art Clb; Pep Clb; Pep Band; High Hon Roll; Ntl Merit Ltr; VFW Awd; Sprts Thrpy.

TUBBS, ROBBIE; First Baptist Church Acad; Curwensville, PA; (4); Chorus; Var L Bsktbl; DAR Awd; Hon Roll; Vocalist & Athlt Of Yr 87; Pastors Awd 87; Dairy Herd Mngmnt.

TUBBS, SHERRY; Du Bois Area HS; Grampian, PA; (3); Church Yth Grp; Varsity Clb; Chorus; Yrbk Phtg; Yrbk Stf; Var Bsktbl; Var Sftbl; Var Tennis; Hon Roll; PA ST; Bus.

TUBBS, TAMMY; Elkland Area HS; Elkland, PA; (3); 4-H; Girl Scts; Hosp Aide; Nwsp Stf; High Hon Roll; Hon Roll; NHS; Nrse.

TUBO, JAMEY; Penn Cambria HS; Ashville, PA; (3); Art Clb; 4-H; French Clb; SADD; Mrchg Band; Twrlr; French Hon Soc; 4-H Awd; Hon Roll; Frnch Hnr Bk 87.

TUCCI, CHARLES; Pottsville HS; Pottsville, PA; (3); Exploring; FBLA; OEA; Ski Clb; JV Bsbl; Im Bsktbl; Im Coach Actv; Im Golf; Hon Roll; Library Aide; Yth Ldrshp Amer 87; Cabrini Coll; Accntng.

TUCCI, ESTHER; Greenwood HS; Millerstown, PA; (2); 15/68; Church Yth Grp; Chorus; Pres Frsh Cls; Rep Stu Cncl; JV Cheerleading; Trk; Hon Roll; NHS; School Play.

TUCCI, MICHELLE; Riverview HS; Oakmont, PA; (3); 26/107; Key Clb; Stu Cncl; Trk; Hon Roll; Spanish Clb; Chorus; Yrbk Stf; Bsktbl; Crs Cntry; Pom Pon; Cmmnctns.

TUCCI IV, THOMAS; Reading SR HS; Reading, PA; (4); 16/563; Hon Roll; Penn ST; Engrng.

TUCHEK, AUDRA; Geibel HS; Connellsville, PA; (3); Drama Clb; Library Aide; NFL; Spanish Clb; Yrbk Stf; Hon Roll; Spanish NHS; Psych.

TUCKER, CHRISTINE; Mon Valley Catholic HS; Charleroi, PA; (2); 6/76; Church Yth Grp; Library Aide; Ski Clb; Spanish Clb; Chorus; Yrbk Stf; Cheerleading; Score Keeper; Hon Roll; Spanish NHS; Hugh O Brian Yth Fndtn Ldrshp Awd 87; 1st In Music-Humanities Day U Of Pitt At Greensburg 87; Jrnlsm.

TUCKER, KEVIN; Scotland School For Veterans Children; Harrisburg, PA; (3); 12/46; Pres Art Clb; Boy Scts; ROTC; Varsity Clb; Yrbk Phtg; Yrbk Stf; Sec Trs Jr Cls; Sec Sr Cls; Var Bsbl; JV Var Ftbl; Vly Forge 86; MIP-WRSTLNG 87; PA ST Plc Ofcr.

TUCKER, MIKE; Penn-Trafford HS; Trafford, PA; (2); JV Ftbl; Wt Lftg; Hon Roll.

TUCKER, SCOTT; Oil City Area SR HS; Oil City, PA; (3); 37/192; Yrbk Stf; Trs Jr Cls; Trs Sr Cls; Rep Stu Cncl; Var L Ftbl; Var L Trk; VP NHS; Chess Clb; Political Wkr; Ski Clb; 4th In ST/Pwr Lftng Cmptn 87; US Air Force Acad; Spc Opers.

TUCKEY, LISA; East Pennsboro HS; Enola, PA; (3); Art Clb; Church Yth Grp; Drama Clb; Church Choir; Yrbk Stf; Hon Roll; 4th Rnnr Up & 1st Rnnr Up Miss Yth Chrst Pagnt 86 & 87; Fashn Inst Of Tech; Fashn Dsgnr.

TUDOR, TRAVIS; Sheffield Area JR SR HS; Sheffield, PA; (3); 1/85; Computer Clb; French Clb; Letterman Clb; Ski Clb; SADD; Band; Crs Cntry; High Hon Roll; Hon Roll; NHS; Bible Ed.

TUFFY, PAUL; Tunkhannock Area HS; Tunkhannock, PA; (3); 47/330; Letterman Clb; Ski Clb; Spanish Clb; Var L Ftbl; Var L Trk; Var L Wt Lftg; Hon Roll.

TUINSTRA, TIMOTHY; Seneca Valley SR HS; Mars, PA; (2); Nwsp Rptr; Nwsp Stf; Hon Roll; MVP Seneca Vlly Acad Games Tm 86-87; 1st Pl Indivdl Mr Pres Game Natl Acad Games 86-87; U Of Pittsburgh; Poltcl Sci.

TULIO, LOUISE; Bishop Kenrick HS; Collegeville, PA; (4); 50/300; Pep Clb; Drill Tm; Nwsp Stf; Mgr Ftbl; Powder Puff Ftbl; Hon Roll; Prfct Atten Awd; Cmnty Wkr; Spanish Clb; School Musical; Hmcmng Chrprsn 83-87; Prom Chrprsn 85-87; Gdnc Aid & Cnslr 85-87; Temple U; Sprts Info.

TULL, ANDREW; Plymouth-Whitemarsh HS; Lafayette Hill, PA; (3); Tennis; Hon Roll; Distngshd Hnrs 86-87; Mech Engrng.

TULL, J GREGORY; Phoenixville Area HS; Phoenixville, PA; (4); 2/202; JV Socr; Var Swmmng; CC Awd; High Hon Roll; Pres Jr NHS; NHS; Sal; 2 Time HS All Am Swmmng 50/100 Freestyle, & 2 Time YMCA All Am Swmmng 50/100 Freestyle 86-87; Harvard U; Ecnmcs.

TULLY, DENISE; Center Area HS; Monaca, PA; (2); Exploring; Spanish Clb; Varsity Clb; VP Jr Cls; Var Bsktbl; Im Bowling; Im Powder Puff Ftbl; Var L Score Keeper; Hon Roll; Penn ST; Cmmnctns.

TUMA, CHRISTINE; South Fayette JR SR HS; Mc Donald, PA; (3); Ski Clb; Band; Concert Band; Jazz Band; Mrchg Band; Nwsp Stf; JV Var Bsktbl; Mgr(s); High Hon Roll; NHS; PA ST U.

TUMAN, JOHN; Northeast Catholic H S For Boys; Philadelphia, PA; (4); 41/356; Cmnty Wkr; Band; Concert Band; Jazz Band; Mrchg Band; Yrbk Stf; Rep Frsh Cls; Rep Soph Cls; Rep Jr Cls; Rep Sr Cls; U S Natl Ldrshp Merit Awd 85-86; Hon Membr Of Natl Hnr Soc 86-87; Hon Men For Spnsh 86-87; Holy Family Coll; Psych.

TUMELTY, COLLEEN; Lansdale Catholic HS; Hatfield, PA; (4); 12/218; Hosp Aide; Math Tm; Pep Clb; Science Clb; Yrbk Stf; Powder Puff Ftbl; High Hon Roll; NHS; Pres Schlr; Anna M Vincent Memrl Schlrshp 87; Penn ST U; Bio.

TUNCHETTA, GINAMARIE A; Bishop Guilfoyle HS; Altoona, PA; (3); SADD; Chorus; DAR Awd; High Hon Roll; Hon Roll; PA ST U.

TUNG, KELLY; Council Rock HS; Churchville, PA; (3); Debate Tm; Intnl Clb; Math Tm; Chorus; Hon Roll; Spanish Clb; Teachers Aide; Stage Crew; Score Keeper; Pres Acadc Ftns Awd 84-85; Penn St Drexel; Engr.

TUNG, RAMONA; Plymouth-Whitemarsh HS; Plymouth Mtg, PA; (3); 2/350; Hosp Aide; Math Clb; Drill Tm; School Musical; Mgr(s); High Hon Roll; NHS; Ntl Merit SF; People-People Stu Ambssdr 86; Sci Olympd 87; Elec Engrng.

TUNNELL, MATTHEW; Middletown Area HS; Middletown, PA; (3); 12/187; Ski Clb; Rep Stu Cncl; Var Crs Cntry; Var Trk; Im Vllybl; Hon Roll; Lion Awd.

TUNNELL, SCOTT; Middletown Area HS; Middletown, PA; (4); 12/187; Ski Clb; Varsity Clb; Yrbk Stf; VP Jr Cls; Pres Sr Cls; Var Capt Socr; Tennis; Hon Roll; NHS; Rotary Awd; Colgate U.

TUOHY, CHRISTOPHER; Archibishop Wood For Boys HS; Hatboro, PA; (3); 4/235; Church Yth Grp; Im Vllybl; High Hon Roll; Hon Roll; NHS; Prfct Atten Awd; Chem Awd Hghst Avg; Hnrb Mntn Sci Fair; Clinical Psych.

TUOHY IV, EDWARD R; Council Rock HS; Newtown, PA; (4); 7/848; Church Yth Grp; Hosp Aide; Bsktbl; Var L Ftbl; Vllybl; Wt Lftg; High Hon Roll; NHS; Ntl Merit Schol; Bio Engr.

TURANO, LISA; Carbondale Area HS; Carbondale, PA; (4); Art Clb; Computer Clb; English Clb; French Clb; FBLA; Science Clb; Ski Clb; High Hon Roll; Hon Roll; USAF; Admin.

TURCHETTA, GINAMARIE; Bishop Guilfoyle HS; Altoona, PA; (3); 6/156; SADD; Chorus; Church Choir; High Hon Roll; Hon Roll; Ntl Sci Merit Awd 87.

TURCMANOVICH, SUSAN; Panther Valley HS; Lansford, PA; (1); 12/127; Hosp Aide; Ski Clb; Stage Crew; JV Bsktbl; Mgr(s); High Hon Roll; Hon Roll; U Of PA; Cmmnctns.

TURFLER JR, FRANK; Windber Area HS; Windber, PA; (3); Art Clb; Chess Clb; CAP; French Clb; Band; Concert Band; Mrchg Band; Stage Crew; Nwsp Stf; Acdmc Achvt Art 86-87; Parsons; Art.

TURIANO, MIRIAM; St Paul Cathedral HS; Verona, PA; (3); Dance Clb; Drama Clb; Latin Clb; Concert Band; Mrchg Band; School Musical; Stage Crew; Nwsp Stf; Crs Cntry; Gym; St Paul Cathedral Sci Fair Awd 84-85; Cougar Ambssdr 86-87; Excllnt Rtg Ntl Hstry Day 86-87.

TURIK, CARLEEN; West Branch HS; Drifting, PA; (2); 3/130; Church Yth Grp; Spanish Clb; SADD; Band; Concert Band; Mrchg Band; Hon Roll; NHS; Prfct Atten 85-86; Math.

TURIK, KRISTIE; West Branch Area HS; Drifting, PA; (4); 3/120; Church Yth Grp; Science Clb; Band; Mrchg Band; Nwsp Rptr; Bausch & Lomb Sci Awd; NHS; Bob Jones U; Vet.

TURK, BRAD; Shenango HS; New Castle, PA; (4); Varsity Clb; JV Var Bsbl; JV Var Bsktbl; Im Coach Actv; Var Capt Crs Cntry; Ftbl; Lttrd In 3 Sprts 87; Thiel.

TURK, LISA; Shenango Area JR SR HS; New Castle, PA; (4); 3/111; Capt Drill Tm; School Play; Pres Stu Cncl; Sftbl; Im Vllybl; Bausch & Lomb Sci Awd; High Hon Roll; Hon Roll; NHS; Prfct Atten Awd; Lawrence Cnty Jr Miss 87; Corning Hlth & Nutrtn Awd 87; PA ST U; Biochem Engr.

TURK, MEGAN; Central Catholic HS; Allentown, PA; (3); Church Yth Grp; Exploring; Service Clb; Spanish Clb; JV Bsktbl; Var Sftbl; Var Vllybl; Hon Roll.

TURK, RICH; Homer Center JR SR HS; Lucernemines, PA; (3); 39/112; Varsity Clb; Ftbl; Jr NHS.

TURKALY, ROBERT; Fort Cherry HS; Midway, PA; (3); Cmnty Wkr; Drama Clb; Science Clb; Ski Clb; Spanish Clb; Varsity Clb; Chorus; School Play; Bsbl; Bsktbl; IUP; Elem Ed.

TURKO, GINA M; Cambria Heights HS; Patton, PA; (4); 5/200; Art Clb; Drama Clb; NFL; Q&S; SADD; School Play; Nwsp Ed-Chief; Yrbk Ed-Chief; NHS; Pres Schlr; Full Schlrshp U MD, Outstndng Prfrmnc SAT Awd, & PTO Awd Hghst Engl GPA 87; U MD; Comp Sci.

TURKO, JASON; Ringgold SR HS; Finleyville, PA; (3); Hon Roll; Pennsylvania Insti; Arpln Mech.

TURKO, TERESSA; Mid Valley HS; Olyphant, PA; (3); 41/93; Hosp Aide; SADD; Ed Nwsp Stf; Pres Stu Cncl; Hon Roll; Frosh Hmcmng Rep 84-85; Schl Nwsp Co-Editor 86-87; Stu Cncl Pres 87-88; Scl Worker.

TURLEY, TODD; Cathdral Prepatory Schl; Erie, PA; (3); 42/193; Chess Clb; German Clb; Ftbl; Hon Roll; PA ST; Engr.

TURNER, AMY; Trinity Christian HS; Pittsburgh, PA; (3); 1/14; Church Yth Grp; Yrbk Stf; Chrmn Stu Cncl; Var Bsktbl; Var Vllybl; High Hon Roll; Jr NHS; NHS; Mst Imprvd Bsktbl Plyr Awd 85; MVP-BSKTBL Awd 86; Engrng.

TURNER, CHRISTINA; Windber Area HS; Windber, PA; (3); French Clb; FTA; Pep Clb; Ski Clb; SADD; Nwsp Stf; Yrbk Stf; Sec Frsh Cls; VP Soph Cls; VP Stu Cncl; Ldrshp Dvlpmnt Schlrshp Seton Hill Coll 86; Schl Spirit Queen 85; Poem Pblshd Amer Anthology 87.

TURNER, DAVE; Reynolds HS; Greenville, PA; (3); 15/144; Latin Clb; Spanish Clb; Varsity Clb; Bsktbl; Ftbl; Wt Lftg; Hon Roll; Penn ST; Med.

TURNER, DENISE; Tward Bok A V T HS; Philadelphia, PA; (3); Dance Clb; GAA; Hosp Aide; Office Aide; OEA; Red Cross Aide; Teachers Aide; Drill Tm; Bsktbl; Trk; Nrsng.

TURNER, KRISTIN; Eastern York HS; York, PA; (3); Ski Clb; Boy Scts; Concert Band; Mrchg Band; JV Mgr(s); High Hon Roll; Hon Roll; Fshn Merch.

TURNER, SCOTT; James M Coughlin HS; Wilkes Barre, PA; (4); 1/342; Band; Chorus; Concert Band; Jazz Band; Mrchg Band; Orch; School Play; JP Sousa Awd; Lion Awd; Val; Penn ST U; Microbio.

TURNER, SHERRY; Elizabeth Forward HS; Elizabeth, PA; (2); Church Yth Grp; Library Aide; Chorus; Church Choir; Orch; High Hon Roll; Hon Roll; Music.

TURNER, SYDNEE; Ft Cherry HS; Mc Donald, PA; (4); 45/111; Drama Clb; French Clb; Science Clb; Ski Clb; Pres Varsity Clb; Co-Capt Cheerleading; Sftbl; Hon Roll; Masonic Awd; Indiana U Of PA; Comms.

TURNER, TONIA; Claysburg-Kimmel HS; Claysburg, PA; (3); FBLA; Library Aide; Lib Band; Color Guard; Concert Band; Mrchg Band; JV Cheerleading; Hon Roll; Prfct Atten Awd; Air Force Acad.

TURNER, TONYA; Germantown HS; Philadelphia, PA; (3); Library Aide; Math Tm; Teachers Aide; Rep Soph Cls; Hon Roll; Frnch Awd 85-86; Chld Psych.

TURNER, TRENT; Lock Haven SR HS; Lock Haven, PA; (4); 7/242; Church Yth Grp; Trs Key Clb; VP Frsh Cls; Pres Soph Cls; Pres Sr Cls; Wrstlng; High Hon Roll; NHS; Rotary Awd; Outstndng Male Athlt W/ Hghst Schlstc Achvt 87; Lock Haven U; Physcl Thrpy.

TURNER, WENDY; West Perry HS; New Bloomfield, PA; (3); Drama Clb; Spanish Clb; Band; Chorus; Concert Band; School Play; Var Sftbl; Hon Roll; Harrisburg Area CC; Resp.

TURNI, LISA; St Cyrils Acad; Pine Brook, NJ; (3); 4-H; Scholastic Bowl; Chorus; Nwsp Rptr; Nwsp Stf; Im Vllybl; JV Trk; 4-H Awd; High Hon Roll; Key Clb; High Score Awd 4-H Horse Show Series 85; Most Imprvd 4-Her In Club 85; Bio Rsrch.

TURO, LYNN; Mahanoy Area HS; Mahanoy City, PA; (3); Chrmn FHA; Rep Band; Chorus; Concert Band; Drm Mjr(t); Mrchg Band; Pep Band; Variety Show; Trk; Hon Roll; Amer Lgn Essy Awd Wnnr 1st Prze County & St 86; US Air Force; Pilot.

TUROCK, STACEY; Souderton HS; Telford, PA; (3); Aud/Vis; Library Aide; Chorus; School Musical; Stu Cncl; JV Var Fld Hcky; Var Trk; Stat Wrstlng; High Hon Roll; Hon Roll; Gold Mdl Hi Jump Wisahickon Relays 87; Htl Rest Mgt.

TUROFSKI, KIMBERLY; Southern Columbia Area HS; Catawissa, PA; (3); Church Yth Grp; Pres 4-H; GAA; Math Clb; Teachers Aide; Varsity Clb; Band; Concert Band; Jazz Band; Mrchg Band; Excllnce Math 85; Math Awd 86; Voice Of Democracy Merit 87; Bloomsburg U; Math Educ.

TURONIS, CINDY; Carbondale Area HS; Carbondale, PA; (4); 27/144; Pres FBLA; Spanish Clb; Yrbk Stf; Pres Stu Cncl; Capt Bsktbl; Trk; Science Clb; Ski Clb; Chorus; Crs Cntry; Homecomng Quee 86-87; Acctng Fin.

TUROWSKI, DEE; North Catholic HS; Pittsburgh, PA; (3); Boys Clb Am; Church Yth Grp; Spanish Clb; Bsktbl; Sftbl; Hon Roll; U Of Pittsburgh; Educ.

TUROWSKI, DIANNA; North Catholic HS; Pgh, PA; (3); Church Yth Grp; Spanish Clb; Bsktbl; Hon Roll; Teaching.

TURZAK, CARA; Kennedy Christian HS; Sharpsville, PA; (4); 3/91; VP Latin Clb; Letterman Clb; Varsity Clb; Band; Stu Cncl; Bsktbl; Cheerleading; Crs Cntry; Trk; NHS; Schlrshp St Vincent Coll, St Francis Coll & Gannon U 87; St Vincent Coll; Bio.

TUSTIN, KRISTINA; West Greene HS; Waynesburg, PA; (1); Art Clb; Church Yth Grp; FHA; Church Choir; Hon Roll; Rdng, Math & Hme Eco Certs 86; Tchr.

TUSTIN, ROBERT M; Burgettstown Area JR SR HS; Slovan, PA; (2); Im Bsktbl; JV Im Ftbl; JV Wt Lftg; Hon Roll.

TUTELO, TRACY; Burrell HS; Lower Burrell, PA; (3); 12/176; Pres JA; Math Tm; Spanish Clb; SADD; Concert Band; Mrchg Band; Yrbk Phtg; NHS; Var Sftbl; Var Trk; Schlrshps-PA Free Entrprs Wk, Dale Carnegie Crs Pblc Spkng & Human Rltns 87; Acdmc Ltrs 86 & 87; Accntng.

TUTINO, LORI; North Catholic HS; Pittsburgh, PA; (3); NFL; Color Guard; School Musical; Hon Roll; PA Jr Acad Of Sci 1st Pl 87; Marine Bio.

TUTKO, LONNY; Cardinal Brennan HS; Shenandoah, PA; (3); Chess Clb; Chorus; Nwsp Phtg; Nwsp Stf; Ftbl; Hon Roll; Merit Awds 86-87; Art.

TUTTLE, CHRISTINE; St Marys Area HS; Benezett, PA; (4); Cmnty Wkr; Vllybl; High Hon Roll; Hon Roll; Kiwanis Awd; NHS; PA ST U; Htl/Rest Mgmt.

TUTTON, DARYL; Delaware County Christian Schl; Newtown Sq, PA; (4); 25/73; Drama Clb; Math Clb; School Play; Stage Crew; Var L Socr; Var Capt Trk; High Hon Roll; Distngshed Crstn HS Stu 86; Prsdntl Acdmc Ftnss Awd 87; PA Hghr Educ Cert Mrt-SAT 86; Clemson; Engnrng.

TUTTON, KIM; Elk County Christian HS; Ridgway, PA; (3); 10/72; Ski Clb; Varsity Clb; Var L Tennis; Stat Wrstlng; Hon Roll; Acctng.

TVAROK, JENNIFER; Bishop Conwell HS; Levittown, PA; (3); 28/277; Sftbl; Hon Roll; Math.

TWEED, JACQUELINE A; Bensalem HS; Bensalem, PA; (2); 4-H; Girl Scts; Letterman Clb; Varsity Clb; Rep Stu Cncl; Var L Crs Cntry; JV L Diving; Var L Swmmng; Var L Trk; Cit Awd; Law.

TWEED, JASON; Oil City Area SR HS; Oil City, PA; (4); VP FBLA; Im Coach Actv; Hon Roll; NHS; Pres Acdmc Ftnss Awd, GTE Pres Hnrs Schlrshp, & William H Locke Schlrshp 87; Edinboro U PA; Bus Admin.

TWEEDT, DAVID A; Athens HS; Sayre, PA; (3); 20/121; Concert Band; Var L Ftbl; L Trk; JV Wrstlng; Hon Roll; Outstndng Acdm Achvt Earth Sci, Algebra-Trigonometry & Chem 85 & 87; Sci.

TWELE, LORI; Mon Valley Catholic HS; Belle Vernon, PA; (3); 7/106; FBLA; JA; Ski Clb; Spanish Clb; Nwsp Stf; Yrbk Stf; High Hon Roll; Spanish NHS; Debate Tm; Library Aide; 1st Pl Spnsh Quiz Tm Spnsh Humanities Comp 86; 1st Pl Spnsh Poetry, Spnsh Humanities Comp 87; Law.

TWIGGER, LISA; Kiski Area HS; Leechburg, PA; (3); Church Yth Grp; Spanish Clb; Acpl Chr; Chorus; Color Guard; Swing Chorus; Yrbk Stf; Rep Frsh Cls; Stat L Bsktbl; Stat L Crs Cntry; Top Ten Frshmn Yr 85; Soc Wrk.

TWILLEY, KRISTIN; Central Dauphin HS; Linglestown, PA; (3); 72/369; Aud/Vis; Trs Church Yth Grp; Sec Exploring; Teachers Aide; Church Choir; Stat Bsbl; Var Fld Hcky; Im Vllybl; Band; School Musical; Sprts Mgmt.

TWINING, PETER C; Carlisle SR HS; Carlisle, PA; (3); Exploring; JV Socr; High Hon Roll; Hon Roll; 10th Rnkng US U-17 Mens Sabre 87; Schl Dist Wrtng Awd, C-3 Rtng US Pony Clb 87; Service Acad; Space.

TWIST, TODD; Milton Area SR HS; Milton, PA; (4); 54/202; Boy Scts; Church Yth Grp; Exploring; Band; Concert Band; Stu Cncl; God Cntry Awd; Zeswitz Band Awd 87; Loyal Ordr Moose Mech Drwg Awd 87; Boy Sct Of Yr Awd 87; US Army.

TWORDUSKY, LORI; Tunkhannock HS; Tunkhannock, PA; (3); 18/330; Rep Soph Cls; Rep Jr Cls; JV Fld Hcky; Var Trk; Hon Roll; Marine Bio.

TWYMAN, AMY; West Mifflin Area HS; W Mifflin, PA; (3); Sec Church Yth Grp; Dance Clb; Girl Scts; Hosp Aide; NAACP; Church Choir; Yrbk Stf; Off Stu Cncl; Co-Capt Cheerleading; Pom Pon; Acdmc Excllnc Awd Frgn Lang 86; Cert Achvt Upwrd Bnd 87; Bus.

TYCHINSKI, BRUCE; Altonna Area HS; Altoona, PA; (4); 50/714; Computer Clb; German Clb; Speech Tm; Concert Band; Drm & Bgl; Jazz Band; Mrchg Band; Orch; School Musical; Trs Frsh Cls; PA Gov Schl Arts 86; PA All ST Orchstra & Band 86-87; Charles E Mckdad/Jason Snyder Memrl Schlrshps; PA ST U; Symphnc Prfrmnc.

TYEBJEE, SHIRYN; Plymouth-Whitemarsh HS; Lafayette Hill, PA; (2); Art Clb; Church Choir; High Hon Roll; Jr NHS; Pres Schlr; Engrng.

TYGER, KEVIN; Marion Center Area HS; Creekside, PA; (3); SADD; Stage Crew; Nwsp Rptr; VP Jr Cls; Hon Roll; Jr NHS; IN U Of PA.

TYGER, MICHAEL; Jeanette HS; Jeannette, PA; (3); 32/150; French Clb.

TYLER, CYNTHIA L; Harrisburg HS; Harrisburg, PA; (4); 44/450; Library Aide; Pep Clb; Band; Chorus; Concert Band; Mrchg Band; Off Frsh Cls; Off Soph Cls; Off Jr Cls; Off Sr Cls; Empire Beauty Schl; Cosmtlgy.

TYLER, DAVID; Fairview HS; Fairview, PA; (3); 35/170; Church Yth Grp; Debate Tm; German Clb; Model UN; NFL; Quiz Bowl; Speech Tm; Teachers Aide; Varsity Clb; Var Golf; Hugh O Brian Yth Fndtn Awd 86; JR Stsmn Amer Treas 87; Econ.

TYLER, JASON B; Bishop Shanahan HS; W Chester, PA; (3); Spanish Clb; Chorus; Drill Tm; Flag Corp; JV Bsbl; JV Bsktbl; JV Ftbl; Var Trk; Hon Roll; Prfct Atten Awd; Vrsty Trck Coaches Awd 84-85; Wstchstr ST U; Art.

TYLER, TOM; Spring Grove Area SR HS; Spring Grove, PA; (3); 14/300; Church Yth Grp; Pres Computer Clb; Drama Clb; School Musical; School Play; NHS; Rurl Elec Yth Tour-Washington Pgm 87; Phscs.

TYMCZYN, MICHAEL; Wyoming Valley West HS; Larksville, PA; (4); 12/390; Band; Concert Band; Jazz Band; Nwsp Sprt Ed; Yrbk Stf; Lit Mag; Rep Stu Cncl; Var Capt Tennis; JETS Awd; NEDT Awd; U Scranton; Hmnties.

TYNAN, ROBERT T; Fairview HS; Fairview, PA; (3); 10/160; Cmnty Wkr; Model UN; ROTC; Spanish Clb; Lit Mag; High Hon Roll; Hon Roll; NHS; SAR Awd; Bronze ROTC Mdl Sons Amer Revoltn 87; Aerospc Engrng.

TYNER, MAUREEN; Penn Hills HS; Pittsburgh, PA; (3); French Clb; Hosp Aide; Stu Cncl; Bsktbl; Shadyside Schl/Nrsng; Dctr.

TYNO, SUSAN; Conemaugh Valley JR SR HS; Johnstown, PA; (3); 1/105; Drama Clb; Pep Clb; Speech Tm; Hon Roll; Jr NHS; NHS; U Pittsburgh Johnstown; Chem.

TYSINGER, MELINDA M; Waynesboro Area SR HS; Blue Ridge Smt, PA; (4); Church Yth Grp; Computer Clb; JCL; Ski Clb; Band; Chorus; Church Choir; Concert Band; Mrchg Band; Swing Chorus; Fort Fitchie Thrift Shop Schlrshp 87; Millersville U; Bus Admin.

TYSKA, JASON; Connellsville Area HS; Mount Pleasant, PA; (2); Var Stu Cncl; Var Bsbl; Var L Golf; French Hon Soc; High Hon Roll.

TYSON, ALLISON; Methacton HS; Norristown, PA; (3); 81/401; Church Yth Grp; FBLA; Fld Hcky; Lcrss; Swmmng; Trk; Hon Roll; Sports J V Ltrs.

TYSON, CANDY; Red Lion Area SR HS; Windsor, PA; (3); 29/375; Church Yth Grp; Varsity Clb; Church Choir; Vllybl; High Hon Roll; Hon Roll; Spnsh Awd 85; Elem Educ.

TYSON, DAVID C; Northeastern HS; Mt Wolf, PA; (3); 79/185; Boy Scts; Band; Concert Band; Jazz Band; Mrchg Band; Orch; Var Crs Cntry; Var Trk; God Cntry Awd; High Hon Roll.

TYSON, ELAINE; Northern Lebanon HS; Annville, PA; (4); 30/174; Drama Clb; Pep Clb; Service Clb; Teachers Aide; Acpl Chr; Sec Trs Band; Chorus; Concert Band; Mrchg Band; Pep Band; Otstndng Musicianshp 87; Stu Otstndng Musical Thtr 87; Lebanon Vly Coll Hnrs Bnd 87; Temple U; Voice Prfrmnc.

TYSON, KIMBERLY; Bermudian Springs HS; Gardners, PA; (3); 1/140; Hosp Aide; School Musical; Yrbk Stf; Pres Soph Cls; Pres Jr Cls; Pres Sr Cls; Pres Stu Cncl; Var L Bsktbl; Var L Sftbl; Var L Vllybl; Hugh O Brien Ldrshp Awd; Bnkng.

TYSON, LESLIE; Bishop Mc Devitt HS; Harrisburg, PA; (3); Ski Clb; Yrbk Sprt Ed; JV Bsktbl; Stat Var Score Keeper; Var Sftbl; Achvt Art 84; Naval Tech Schl.

TYSON, MELISSA; Newport JR SR HS; Newport, PA; (1); Hon Roll.

TYSON, SUSAN; Kutztown Area HS; Kutztown, PA; (4); Sec FHA; Teachers Aide; Variety Show; Mgr Bsktbl; Mgr Fld Hcky; High Hon Roll; NHS; SICO Fndtn Schlrshp Awd 87-91; Pres Acdmc Fit Awd 87; PA Hnrs Tst Cert 87; Kutztown U; Psych.

TYTKE, WILLIAM; Steel Valley HS; Munhall, PA; (4); 16/206; Cmnty Wkr; Ftbl; Wt Lftg; Hon Roll; NHS; Embry-Riddle; Aero Engnrng.

TZAN, CHRISTINE; Connellsville SR HS; Connellsville, PA; (2); 24/566; Church Yth Grp; Nwsp Ed-Chief; Swmmng; Tennis; Vllybl; High Hon Roll; Jr NHS; Prfct Atten Awd; Acad Excllnce Awd 85-86.

UBALDINI, TAMI; Abington Heights HS; Clarks Summit, PA; (3); Cmnty Wkr; Ski Clb; Off Stu Cncl; Gym; Hon Roll; Shrthnd Awd 87; Real Estate.

UBER, MICHELLE; Brandywine Heights HS; Alburtis, PA; (2); Varsity Clb; Trs Band; Concert Band; Mrchg Band; Var Tennis; Hon Roll; Soc Studs Awd 86-87.

UBER, MOLLY; St Marys Area HS; St Marys, PA; (4); 29/186; Church Yth Grp; Hon Roll; Jr NHS; NHS; Pres Acad Ftns Awd 87; Messiah Schlrshp 87-88; Messiah Coll; Pre-Med.

UBERTI, MICHELLE; Dubois Area SR HS; Penfield, PA; (4); 20/272; Red Cross Aide; Varsity Clb; Yrbk Phtg; Yrbk Stf; Stu Cncl; Var Capt Cheerleading; JV Var Gym; Lion Awd; NHS; Penn ST Univ; Bio.

UBRY, CHAD; New Castle SR HS; New Castle, PA; (2); Church Yth Grp; Vllybl; Hon Roll; Bus.

UDOH, MONIQUE; Upper Moreland HS; Philadelphia, PA; (4); VP Church Yth Grp; SADD; Pres Church Choir; Nwsp Sprt Ed; Nwsp Stf; Off Sr Cls; Rep Stu Cncl; Var L Bsktbl; Hon Roll; Church Fmly Of Yr 86; Frgn Lang Prgm Awd 86; PA ST U; Arch Engr.

UEBLER, JENNIFER; Garnet Valley HS; Glen Mills, PA; (4); 6/156; Model UN; Varsity Clb; Yrbk Stf; Rep Stu Cncl; Var Lcrss; Var Vllybl; Hon Roll.

UFNER, JULIE; Butler SR HS; Butler, PA; (3); Church Yth Grp; Drama Clb; French Clb; Hosp Aide; Science Clb; Thesps; Y-Teens; Chorus; Variety Show; Hon Roll; 1st & 2nd Pl Rgnl PA JR Acad Sci 85; Equestrian Stdys.

UHL, ROBERT; Hampton HS; Gibsonia, PA; (4); JV Socr; Hon Roll.

UHLER, TERRY; Bensalem SR HS; Bensalem, PA; (3); Quiz Bowl; Scholastic Bowl; Nwsp Rptr; Var Bsbl; Im Bsktbl; Im Ftbl; Im Sftbl; Im Vllybl; Hon Roll; VP Pres Chess Clb; ST Pblm Slvng Rnnr Up 87; Socl Sci.

UHLMAN, SHELLY; Conneaut Valley HS; Linesville, PA; (3); Church Yth Grp; Drama Clb; School Play; Stat Bsktbl; Stat Ftbl; Stat Vllybl.

UHRIC, REGINA; Highlands SR HS; Brackenridge, PA; (3); Church Yth Grp; Intnl Clb; Pep Clb; SADD; Hon Roll; Jr NHS; NHS; Pres Schlr; Psych.

UHRICH, KEITH; Cedar Crest HS; Lebanon, PA; (3); Boy Scts; Hon Roll; Sci.

UHRIN, AMY; Kennedy Christian HS; Greenville, PA; (3); 5/97; Church Yth Grp; Pep Clb; Science Clb; Spanish Clb; Nwsp Rptr; Var L Bsktbl; Im Vllybl; High Hon Roll; Mercer Cnty Girls Bsktbl Hnrb Mntn Tm 87; Marine Bio.

ULAN, DONNA; Northwestern SR HS; Albion, PA; (4); 3/141; VP Camera Clb; Model UN, VP Science Clb; Band; Mrchg Band; Yrbk Ed-Chief; Yrbk Phtg; Trk; High Hon Roll; NHS; Pres Hons Schlrshp 87; Serr Memrl Schlrshp 87; Floyd Mcclymonds Photo Srvc Awd 87; Edinboro U; Bio.

ULANDER, GWEN; Yough SR HS; W Newton, PA; (3); French Clb; Pep Clb; Ski Clb; Spanish Clb; SADD; Band; Chorus; Concert Band; Mrchg Band; Hon Roll; Flight Attendant.

ULERY, JOHN; Greensburg Central Catholic HS; Latrobe, PA; (3); AFS; Boy Scts; Church Yth Grp; Ski Clb; Chorus; Stage Crew; Crs Cntry; Mgr(s); Var Timer; Var Trk; Pre-Law.

ULERY, LISA; Southmoreland SR HS; Everson, PA; (3); Drama Clb; French Clb; Letterman Clb; Ski Clb; Band; Concert Band; Co-Capt Drill Tm; Mrchg Band; Nwsp Rptr; Nwsp Stf; Mst Imprvd Mjrt Awd 87; Fash Bus.

ULERY, TONYA; Connellsville SR HS; Normalville, PA; (3); #52 In Class; Pres Art Clb; Church Yth Grp; Dance Clb; Pep Clb; SADD; Band; Color Guard; Nwsp Stf; Pres Stu Cncl; NHS; Hnrs Art 86-87; Tchr.

ULIZIO, AMY; Burrell SR HS; Lower Burrell, PA; (3); Church Yth Grp; Ski Clb; Spanish Clb; SADD; Nwsp Stf; Stu Cncl; JV Cheerleading; Var L Swmmng; Hon Roll; Jr NHS; Elem Ed.

ULIZIO, THERESA; Beaver Area HS; Midland, PA; (3); Church Yth Grp; JCL; Math Clb; Chorus; Trs Soph Cls; Var JV Bsktbl; Vllybl; High Hon Roll; NHS.

ULJON, HEATHER; Elk County Christian HS; St Marys, PA; (4); Dance Clb; Drama Clb; Ski Clb; Chorus; Variety Show; Nwsp Ed-Chief; Yrbk Stf; Stat Bsktbl; High Hon Roll; Ntl Merit SF; Dance Trophy 85; Bus.

ULLERY, KATIE; Quaker Valley SR HS; Sewickley, PA; (3); 7/166; Church Yth Grp; French Clb; Q&S; Service Clb; Chorus; Yrbk Ed-Chief; Yrbk Stf; High Hon Roll; NCTE Awd; NHS; Comm.

ULLMAN, DONNA MARIE; Pottstown SR HS; Pottstown, PA; (3); 35/266; Church Yth Grp; Key Clb; Chorus; Color Guard; Capt Flag Corp; Mrchg Band; Hon Roll; NHS; Sec.

ULLOM, DENISE E; Washington HS; Washington, PA; (3); 1/150; Am Leg Aux Girls St; French Clb; Letterman Clb; Ski Clb; Band; Stu Cncl; Tennis; High Hon Roll; NHS; Rtry Clb Acadmc Achvt Hnr 87; Math.

ULLOM, TONYA; West Mifflin Area HS; Whitaker, PA; (2); Psych.

ULMAN, CHRIS; Southern Lehigh HS; Center Valley, PA; (4); 11/235; Chess Clb; Exploring; Math Tm; SADD; Yrbk Ed-Chief; High Hon Roll; NHS; Ntl Merit Ltr; Bio Med.

ULMER, BARB; Bellefonte Area HS; Bellefonte, PA; (4); 21/237; Trs Church Yth Grp; Hon Roll; Comm Awd Outstndng Abilities Schl Affairs & Comm Field 87; Sec.

ULMER, CHRIS; Mohawk Area JR SR HS; Enon Valley, PA; (4); 4-H; Latin Clb; Band; Church Choir; Mrchg Band; School Musical; School Play; Yrbk Stf; Powder Puff Ftbl; Hon Roll; Engl Stu Yr 87; Lock Haven U; Zoolgy.

ULMER, KAREN; Archbishop Ryan For Girls; Feasterville, PA; (3); 3/508; French Clb; Math Tm; Office Aide; Q&S; School Play; Nwsp Stf; French Hon Soc; Gov Hon Prg Awd; NHS; Prfct Atten Awd; Psychlgy.

ULMER, KYLE; Wallenpaupack Area HS; Greeley, PA; (3); Drama Clb; Ski Clb; Chorus; School Musical; School Play; Socr; Marine Bio.

ULMER, MICHAEL; Dubois SR HS; Dover, PA; (4); Church Yth Grp; Ski Clb; Varsity Clb; School Play; Yrbk Stf; Var Ftbl; Var Capt Socr; Var L Tennis; High Hon Roll; NHS; York Coll Deans Schlrshp, Rapid Amrcn Schlrshp 87; York Coll PA; Law.

ULMER, TAMMY; Jersey Shore SR HS; Willamsport, PA; (4); Church Yth Grp; FBLA; Sftbl; High Hon Roll; Hghst Avg Bus 87; Wllmsprt Schl Cmmrc Schlrshp 87; Cls Rnk 10 JR Yr 85-86; WACC Sympsm 1st Pl Bus 87; Williamsport Schl Cmmrc; Bus.

ULSH, CRAIG; Upper Merion Area HS; King Of Prussia, PA; (3); 9/310; Math Tm; Chorus; Crs Cntry; Socr; Trk; Hon Roll; NHS; Ntl Merit Ltr; U Of DE; Elect Engr.

ULSH, TINA; Forbes Road JR SR HS; Ft Littleton, PA; (3); Church Yth Grp; French Clb; FBLA; FHA; Teachers Aide; Band; Chorus; Color Guard; Mrchg Band; Yrbk Stf; Hagerstown JC; Bus Adm.

UMBENHAUER, SHANNON; Pine Grove Area HS; Pine Grove, PA; (3); Am Leg Aux Girls St; SADD; Trs Band; Chorus; Jazz Band; Mrchg Band; Pep Band; Yrbk Stf; Prfct Atten Awd; Arn Msc Awd 87; Cnty Dstrct & Rgnl Bnd 85-87; Amer Lgn Essy Cntst Wnr 87; Msc Prfrmnc.

UMBENHOUER, SEAN M; Hamburg Area HS; Shoemakersville, PA; (4); 51/144; FBLA; Pres German Clb; SADD; VP Band; Jazz Band; Pep Band; Stu Cncl; Bsbl; Var L Socr; JP Sousa Awd; German Natl Hnr Soc 87; Acad Awd Amer Cultures 86; York Coll; Comp Info.

UMBERGER, TRUDY; Upper Dauphin Area HS; Lykens, PA; (3); 3/115; Varsity Clb; Chorus; Stage Crew; Yrbk Ed-Chief; VP Jr Cls; Var L Bsktbl; Var L Sftbl; Hon Roll; NHS; Rotary Awd; US Achvt Acad Art Awd 85; Arch.

UMENHOFER, BONNIE; Ambridge Area HS; Baden, PA; (3); Church Yth Grp; German Clb; Office Aide; Pep Clb; SADD; Chorus; Rep Stu Cncl; Vllybl; High Hon Roll; NHS; Amer JR Miss Pagnt Fnlst 87; Bus Adm.

UMHOLTZ, HEATHER; Northern Lebanon HS; Ono, PA; (3); French Clb; Chorus; School Musical; Var JV Bsktbl; Var Sftbl; Var JV Vllybl; Hon Roll; Fashion.

UMHOLTZ, JON; Christian Schl Of York; Mechanicsburg, PA; (3); Church Yth Grp; Band; Mgr(s); Trk; Hon Roll; Puppet Ministry Awd 87; Social Studies Awd 86; Math Awd 86; Penn St; Arch.

UMSHARES, BETH; Washington HS; Washington, PA; (2); Ski Clb; Spanish Clb; High Hon Roll; Hon Roll; Penn ST; Psych.

UMSTEAD, JILL; Maplewood HS; Titusville, PA; (3); Art Clb; Aud/Vis; Church Yth Grp; 4-H; GAA; Pep Clb; Spanish Clb; SADD; Varsity Clb; Variety Show; NC U; Marine Bio.

UMSTEAD, LYN; Middleburg HS; Middleburg, PA; (4); VP Band; Pres Chorus; VP Concert Band; Stage Crew; Nwsp Stf; Ed Yrbk Stf; Stu Cncl; Capt Cheerleading; Hon Roll; NHS; Chrldg Awds 85 & 87; Susquehanna Vly Band 85-87; Shippensburg U; Elem Ed.

UNCAPHER, RICHARD; North Allegheny SR HS; Pittsburgh, PA; (3); 180/630; Yrbk Phtg; Stu Cncl; Hon Roll; Prfct Atten Awd.

UNDERBERG, THOMAS; Neshaminy HS; Levittown, PA; (3); 5/790; High Hon Roll; NHS; Med.

UNDERKOFFLER, LARA; Williams Valley JR/Sr HS; Lykens, PA; (1); Church Yth Grp; Band; Chorus; Concert Band; Jazz Band; Mrchg Band; Pep Band; Symp Band; Hon Roll.

UNDERKOFFLER, LISA; Shenandoah Valley HS; Shenandoah, PA; (4); 6/100; Ed Nwsp Stf; Yrbk Stf; Rep Frsh Cls; Hon Roll; Acadmc All Amercn Awd 85-86; Schuylkill Bus Inst; Mdcl Sec.

UNDERKOFFLER, MATT; Williams Valley HS; Tower City, PA; (3); 9/100; Concert Band; Jazz Band; Mrchg Band; Symp Band; Jr Cls; Var L Bsbl; Var L Bsktbl; High Hon Roll; Hon Roll; Sec NHS; Bsbll Unsung Hero 86; Bsbll MVP 87; Elec.

UNDERKOFFLER, TERESA; Upper Dauphin Area HS; Lykens, PA; (3); 4/115; Varsity Clb; Chorus; Stage Crew; Yrbk Stf; Var JV Bsktbl; Var L Sftbl; Hon Roll; NHS; Phys Thrpy.

UNDERWOOD, JILL; Schulkill Haven Area HS; Sch Haven, PA; (2); 6/101; Pep Clb; Science Clb; Spanish Clb; SADD; Chorus; Church Choir; Mrchg Band; School Musical; Trs Soph Cls; JV Var Cheerleading; Chem.

UNDERWOOD, MATTHEW; Montrose Area HS; Brackney, PA; (3); Art Clb; Boy Scts; Church Yth Grp; Varsity Clb; Nwsp Stf; L Var Wrstlng; Eagle Scout 87; Ricks; Art.

UNDERWOOD, SHAWN; Altoona Area HS; Altoona, PA; (3); 6/796; Pres Computer Clb; Math Tm; Ski Clb; Acpl Chr; School Musical; Yrbk Phtg; Rep Frsh Cls; High Hon Roll; NEDT Awd; Pres Schlr.

UNG, LEHSAN; Philadelphia H S For Girls; Philadelphia, PA; (3); Latin Clb; Office Aide; Teachers Aide; High Hon Roll; Hon Roll; Latin Natl Hnr Soc 87; Temple U; Phrmcy.

UNG, PADIWATH; Juniata HS; Mifflintown, PA; (3); Computer Clb; Varsity Clb; Pres Soph Cls; Hst Jr Cls; Trs Stu Cncl; Var L Socr; Var L Tennis; NHS; 1st Tm Tri-Vly League Sccr All-Stars 86; Distngshd Hnr Roll 84-86; Med.

UNGER, DIANE; Salisbury HS; Allentown, PA; (4); 68/128; Hosp Aide; Color Guard; Drm Mjr(t); Mrchg Band; Rep Jr Cls; Chapt II Tournmnt Bands Schlrshp 86; Lancaster Gnrl Hosp Schl; Nrs.

UNGERER, CHRISTOPHER; Salisbury HS; Emmaus, PA; (3); 79/170; Var Bsbl; Var Bsktbl; Var Ftbl; Wt Lftg; NHS; Shippensburg U; Crmnl Justc.

UNGOR, KELLI; Moniteau HS; Harrisville, PA; (3); Drama Clb; Exploring; Sec French Clb; Pep Clb; Chorus; Church Choir; Swing Chorus; Variety Show; Yrbk Stf; Hon Roll; Clarion U; Nrsng.

UNIK, RENEE; Springdale HS; Springdale, PA; (3); 2/128; GAA; Hosp Aide; Office Aide; Spanish Clb; Acpl Chr; Yrbk Stf; JV Capt Cheerleading; High Hon Roll; Hon Roll; NHS; Prom Committee Chrprsn 86-87; Bus.

UNRUH, BRADLEY; Fort Cherry JR SR HS; Mcdonald, PA; (2); Computer Clb; Drama Clb; Math Clb; Science Clb; Ski Clb; Spanish Clb; Varsity Clb; JV Ftbl; Var Tennis; High Hon Roll; Med.

UNRUH, PAMELA; Penn Manor HS; Pequea, PA; (3); 155/300; Church Yth Grp; FBLA; Office Aide; Band; Concert Band; Mrchg Band; Hon Roll; Sec.

UNVERDORBIN, DEBORAH; West Middle Sex HS; W Middlesex, PA; (3); 10/104; Church Yth Grp; Chorus; Flag Corp; High Hon Roll; Hon Roll; Ed.

UPDEGRAFF, DEREK; Milton Area SR HS; Montandon, PA; (3); 10/229; Boy Scts; Varsity Clb; Var Crs Cntry; Var Trk; Hon Roll; NHS; PLAA Dist Swmng & Dvng 85-87; YMCA ST Dvng Compttn 86; YMCA Dist Swmng Compttn 87.

UPHAM, ABBY; Northeast Bradford JR SR HS; Le Raysville, PA; (3); 27/101; Pres VP Church Yth Grp; Pres VP 4-H; Letterman Clb; Varsity Clb; Band; Chorus; Concert Band; Mrchg Band; VP Frsh Cls; Rep Stu Cncl; Cnty Band 84-85 & 86-87; Band Awd 83-84; Resp Thrpy.

UPLINGER, SANDRA; Steel Valley HS; Munhall, PA; (4); 19/201; Church Yth Grp; Exploring; Concert Band; Jazz Band; Mrchg Band; Off Stu Cncl; JV Bsktbl; Var Sftbl; Hon Roll; NHS; PA ST U; Engnrng.

URAM, DIANE; Lakeland HS; Mayfield, PA; (4); 15/152; Church Yth Grp; FHA; Stat Bsbl; Var L Cheerleading; Hon Roll; NHS; Prfct Atten Awd; Stu Tchng Schlrshp Marywood 87; Presdntl Acadc Ftns Awd 87; Vrsty Ltr Chrldng 87; Marywood; Nrsng.

URBAN, DAN; Panther Valley HS; Coaldale, PA; (1); Boy Scts; ROTC.

URBAN, MELISSA; Lehighton Area HS; Lehighton, PA; (2); 4/246; Am Leg Aux Girls St; 4-H; FHA; Library Aide; Concert Band; Mrchg Band; High Hon Roll; NHS; NEDT Awd; Prfct Atten Awd; Pharmacy.

URBAN, PATRICK C J; Wilson HS; Sinking Spring, PA; (3); 73/305; Boy Scts; Church Yth Grp; Spanish Clb; Var Bsbl; JV Bsktbl; JV Ftbl; Golf; God Cntry Awd; Hon Roll; Ntl Merit SF; Bloomsburg U; Accntng.

URBAN, PATRICK W; Panther Valley HS; Coaldale, PA; (4); 13/105; Am Leg Boys St; Boy Scts; Political Wkr; Radio Clb; ROTC; Church Choir; Color Guard; Yrbk Stf; God Cntry Awd; Hon Roll; Battalion Cmmndr JRTOC 86-87; Pres Acad Ftns Awd 86-87; PA ST U; Mass Comm.

URBAN, TONI; Canton Area JR-SR HS; Canton, PA; (3); 20/114; Church Yth Grp; French Clb; FBLA; Band; Acpl Chr; Jazz Band; Rep Stu Cncl; Im Sftbl; JV Vllybl; Hon Roll; Lawyer.

URBANCIC, CASEY; St Marys Area HS; Kersey, PA; (1); Hosp Aide; Cheerleading; Hon Roll; Georgetown; TV Jrnlst.

URBANI, LORI; Sto-Rox HS; Mc Kees Rocks, PA; (4); 25/144; Letterman Clb; Varsity Clb; Sec Chorus; Yrbk Stf; Rep Frsh Cls; Rep Soph Cls; Rep Jr Cls; Sec Sr Cls; Sec Stu Cncl; L Var Bsktbl; Duquesne U; Pre-Law.

URBANSKI, CHRISTOPHER; State Coll Intermediate HS; State College, PA; (1); Church Yth Grp; Computer Clb; Ski Clb; Church Choir; Nwsp Stf; Yrbk Stf; DAR Awd; Prfrmd Chrch Choir At Vatican In Rome 87; PA ST U; Rbtcs Engrng.

URBANSKI, JEN; Methacton HS; Trooper, PA; (3); 99/407; JV Var Cheerleading; JV Sftbl; Hon Roll.

URBASIK, MARIE; Cumberland Valley HS; Mechanicsburg, PA; (3); Hosp Aide; Latin Clb; SADD; Hon Roll; Outstndng Latn I Grde; Intrschlstc Latn Fstvl, Latn Drma 1st Pl; Elem Ed.

URIAN, MICHELLE; Solanco HS; Quarryville, PA; (3); 54/267; Pep Clb; Teachers Aide; Varsity Clb; Rep Frsh Cls; Rep Soph Cls; Rep Jr Cls; Rep Sr Cls; Var Capt Cheerleading; Hon Roll; Office Aide; Peer Counselor.

URICH, JODI; West Perry HS; Elliottsburg, PA; (2); 12/224; Church Yth Grp; Library Aide; Math Tm; Spanish Clb; Varsity Clb; Var Bsktbl; Var Fld Hcky; Var Sftbl; Hon Roll; NHS; Mid-Penn All Star Tm Bsktbl & Sftbl 87.

URKO, DAVE; Ringgold HS; Monongahela, PA; (3); Band; Jazz Band; Mrchg Band; Wt Lftg; Music.

URTUBEY, JASON; Stroudsburg HS; Stroudsburg, PA; (2); French Clb; Varsity Clb; Var Swmmng; Var Trk; Hon Roll; US Coast Guard Acad; Pilot.

USELMAN, STEPHANIE; Somerset Area HS; Somerset, PA; (3); 34/230; Church Yth Grp; FHA; German Clb; Girl Scts; Intnl Clb; Chorus; Mrchg Band; Yrbk Stf; Stu Cncl; Hon Roll; Grl Sct Slvr Ldrshp Awd 85; Acad Awd & Schl Ltr 87; Grove City U.

USNER, JACKQUELYN; Palisades JR SR HS; Riegelsville, PA; (4); AFS; 4-H; FBLA; Jazz Band; Mrchg Band; Pep Band; 4-H Awd; Hon Roll; NHS; Pres Schlr; Hunter Type Filley 85; Horse Bowl Tm 86; Moravian Coll; Accounting.

USNICK, MARY; West Greene HS; Rogersville, PA; (2); French Clb; Intnl Clb; Ski Clb; Variety Show; Yrbk Stf; Sftbl; Hon Roll; U Of Pittsburgh; Sprts Mngnt.

USTYNOSKI, MARIE; Bishop Hafey HS; Hazleton, PA; (2); Cmnty Wkr; Hosp Aide; Key Clb; Ski Clb; Y-Teens; Church Choir; JV Bsktbl; L Tennis; High Hon Roll; Fresh Phys Ftnss Awd 86; Acadmc All Amer 87; Space Sci.

UTCHELL, AMY; Chartiers Valley HS; Carnegie, PA; (3); Church Yth Grp; Pep Clb; Timer; Trk; Dental Hygiene.

UTLEY, SUSAN E; Moravian Acad; Bethlehem, PA; (4); Church Yth Grp; Orch; School Musical; Yrbk Ed-Chief; Lit Mag; Var Crs Cntry; JV Fld Hcky; Var Lcrss; High Hon Roll; Hon Roll; Amer U; Intl Stds.

UTZ, MICHAEL; Henderson HS; West Chester, PA; (3); 20/385; Spanish Clb; Var JV Bsbl; DAR Awd; High Hon Roll; Hon Roll; NHS; Spanish NHS; Law.

UTZ, VICTOR; Bellefonte SR HS; Bellefonte, PA; (3); Church Yth Grp; Civic Clb; Cmnty Wkr; Drama Clb; Model UN; PAVAS; Chorus; Church Choir; School Musical; School Play; Model UN Superior Delegation & Delegate Awd 87; UCLA; Poltcl Sci.

VACCARI, JOHN; Ringgold HS; Finleyville, PA; (3); 38/395; VP Church Yth Grp; Varsity Clb; Concert Band; Orch; School Musical; L Ftbl; L Trk; Hon Roll; FCA; Letterman Clb; Sci-Math Hnr Soc Chrmn; Interact Clb Pres; Wrld Affrs Smnr 87; Natl Sci Olympd 87; Bus Adm.

VACCARO, ANTOINETTE; Chambersburg Area SR HS; Chambersburg, PA; (4); 41/606; Drama Clb; Letterman Clb; Science Clb; Varsity Clb; Stage Crew; Tennis; Trk; NHS; Ntl Merit SF; Summer Hnrs Prog 87; Generl Hnrs Prog Shippensburg U 87-88; Shippensburg U; Math.

VACCARO, LISA; Hazleton SR HS; Hazleton, PA; (2); FBLA; Pep Clb; Y-Teens; Chorus; School Musical; Rep Stu Cncl; JV Cheerleading; High Hon Roll; Math Ed.

VACCONE, MICHELLE; Strath Haven HS; Wallingford, PA; (4); Aud/Vis; Church Yth Grp; Ski Clb; Spanish Clb; Chorus; School Musical; Variety Show; Hon Roll; Widener U; Psych.

VACENDAK, SHARON; Bishop O Reilly HS; Plymouth, PA; (3); Latin Clb; Ski Clb; Chorus; Mrchg Band; Stage Crew; Yrbk Stf; JV Fld Hcky; Hon Roll; Ntl Hstry Day Cert 85; Latin Cert-Lang Hnr Soc 86.

VACHINO, RENEE; Penn Hills SR HS; Pittsburgh, PA; (3); Church Yth Grp; Drama Clb; Office Aide; School Play; Vllybl; Hon Roll; RN.

VACLAVIK, STEVEN; Upper Dauphin HS; Millersburg, PA; (4); 8/111; Trs Church Yth Grp; Varsity Clb; Acpl Chr; Chorus; Church Choir; Concert Band; School Musical; School Play; Stage Crew; Swing Chorus; PA Med Soc Sci Awd 87; Rotary Stu Of Mnth 86; Rotary Ldrshp Camp 86; PA ST U; Engrng.

VAGNONI, CHRISTOPHER; Monessen JR/Sr HS; Monessen, PA; (3); French Clb; PAVAS; School Play; Variety Show; Nwsp Rptr; Yrbk Rptr; Bausch & Lomb Sci Awd; High Hon Roll; NHS; Pre-Med.

VAGO, SPENSER; Butler SR HS; Butler, PA; (3); Church Yth Grp; Latin Clb; SADD; Jazz Band; Mrchg Band; Symp Band; Variety Show; Jr NHS; James V Colonna Bnd Awd 85-86; Westminster Hnrs Bnd 86-87; Accntng.

VAHANIAN, MELISSA; Mercy Hurst Prep HS; Erie, PA; (4); Ski Clb; School Play; Yrbk Ed-Chief; Yrbk Phtg; Yrbk Rptr; Yrbk Stf; Var Capt Cheerleading; Var Powder Puff Ftbl; French Hon Soc; Berhend; Vet.

VAHEY JR, BRIAN; Kennett HS; Landenberg, PA; (4); 7/156; Boy Scts; Scholastic Bowl; Science Clb; Varsity Clb; Variety Show; Yrbk Ed-Chief; Yrbk Phtg; Rep Stu Cncl; Im Bsktbl; JV Var Crs Cntry; 3 Yr Navy & Army ROTC Schlrshps 87; U Of Notre Dame; Aerospc Engrng.

VAIA, RENEE; Greensburg Salem SR HS; Export, PA; (2); 17/294; GAA; NFL; Ski Clb; Jazz Band; Rep Stu Cncl; Sftbl; Twrlr; Vllybl; High Hon Roll; Jr NHS; Cornell; Bio Chem.

VAIL, JEFFERY W; State College Area Alternative Schl; State College, PA; (4); Cmnty Wkr; Computer Clb; Political Wkr; Chorus; School Play; Lit Mag; Cit Awd; Hon Roll; Ntl Merit SF; Scholastic Bowl; Eng Cert Merit 84; Natl Merit Schlr; Geo Washington Schlrshp; Sophie Kerr Schlrshp; Washington Coll; Jrnlsm.

VAK, STEPHEN; Kiski Area HS; New Kensington, PA; (3); Key Clb; Math Tm; Spanish Clb; Varsity Clb; Concert Band; Nwsp Stf; Ftbl; Wrstlng; High Hon Roll; NHS; NHS; Bus Mgmt.

VAK, SUSAN; Kiski Area HS; New Kensington, PA; (3); Math Tm; Spanish Clb; Color Guard; Jazz Band; Symp Band; Nwsp Stf; Yrbk Stf; Trk; High Hon Roll; NHS; Comm.

VALAHOVIC, JOSEPH; Cathedral Preparatory Schl; Erie, PA; (3); 38/193; Church Yth Grp; Rep Soph Cls; Im Bsktbl; Var Socr; Var Trk; Im Vllybl; Hon Roll.

VALCARCEL, ANN; North Allegheny SR HS; Pittsburgh, PA; (4); 114/660; Church Yth Grp; Cmnty Wkr; Off Frsh Cls; Off Jr Cls; Stat Fld Hcky; Jr NHS; NHS; Chem & Wrld Cltrs Awd 85; Engl Achvt Awd 86; Acad Fit Awd 87; Villanova U; Bus.

VALCARCEL, KATHLEEN; North Allegheny HS; Pittsburgh, PA; (2); Hon Roll; Jr NHS; Hstry Awd 86.

VALDELLON, ALLEN; Archbishop Wood HS; Richboro, PA; (2); 38/254; Rep Frsh Cls; Rep Stu Cncl; Im Bsktbl; Im Vllybl; High Hon Roll; Hon Roll; Bcks Cnty Sci Fair-2nd Pl Micro Bio 87; MD Vly Sci Fair-Hnrbl Mntn Micro Bio 87; Comp Sci.

VALDES, JOEY; Du Bois Area HS; Dubois, PA; (2); Band; Chorus; Concert Band; Mrchg Band; School Musical; Marine Bio.

VALDES, SERGIO; Garden Spot HS; New Holland, PA; (2); JV Socr; Elctrncs.

VALE, SHARI; E L Meyers HS; Wilkes-Barre, PA; (4); 8/140; SADD; Yrbk Ed-Chief; Yrbk Stf; Stu Cncl; Cheerleading; Fld Hcky; Swmmng; High Hon Roll; Hon Roll; Jr NHS; U CT Pharm; Pharm.

VALEANT, LISA; Bishop Hafey HS; Hazleton, PA; (4); 13/126; Drama Clb; 4-H; French Clb; School Play; Yrbk Stf; French Hon Soc; Hon Roll; Outstndng Achvmnt In Frnch III 86; Hmcmng Ct 86; Penn ST; Engl Prfssr.

VALENTI, ANNETTE; Burgettstown HS; Atlasburg, PA; (3); #7 In Class; Chorus; Concert Band; School Musical; Variety Show; VP Stu Cncl; High Hon Roll; Hon Roll; NHS; Spanish Clb; Band; Stu Cncl V P 86-87; Stu Cncl Pres 87-88; Lead Role In Musical 87; Bus Admn.

VALENTI, CARLA; Wyoming Area HS; West Pittston, PA; (3); 5/250; French Clb; Key Clb; Chorus; Var Trk; High Hon Roll; Jr NHS; Eurpn Hstry Awd 87; U Of Scranton; Chem.

VALENTICH JR, JOSEPH; Geibel HS; Mount Pleasant, PA; (3); 8/108; Am Leg Boys St; Church Yth Grp; Pres Frsh Cls; Pres Soph Cls; Var Bsktbl; French Hon Soc; High Hon Roll; NHS; NEDT Awd.

VALENTINE, GREGORY; Milton SR HS; Milton, PA; (3); 20/250; Computer Clb; Intnl Clb; Spanish Clb; Nwsp Stf; Rep Frsh Cls; Rep Soph Cls; Stu Cncl; Ftbl; Wt Lftg; Hon Roll; Penn ST; Law.

VALENTINE, HOPE; Pottstown SR HS; Pottstown, PA; (4); 6/181; Am Leg Aux Girls St; Church Yth Grp; French Clb; JA; Key Clb; Spanish Clb; Pres Frsh Cls; Sec Soph Cls; Trs Jr Cls; Pres Sr Cls; Miss TEEN Pgnt Fnlst, Miss Natl Teen-Ager Pgnt Fnlst 87; Rutgers U; Phrmcy.

VALENTINE, KELLIE; Northwestern HS; Albion, PA; (2); Red Cross Aide; Pres Rep Stu Cncl; JV Var Bsktbl; Rep Powder Puff Ftbl; JV Var Sftbl; Hon Roll; N W U; Cmnctns.

VALERIANO, DEENA R; Oley Valley HS; Oley, PA; (4); 44/150; Pep Clb; Mrchg Band; Pres Soph Cls; Pres Jr Cls; Sec Stu Cncl; Co-Capt Cheerleading; Var JV Sftbl; Twrlr; Vllybl; DAR Awd; Smile Cont Wnnr 83-84; Northampton Cnty Area CC; Dntl.

VALETTA, KRIS; Bucktail JR SR HS; Renovo, PA; (2); 4-H; Hosp Aide; JA; NAACP; Political Wkr; Varsity Clb; Band; Mrchg Band; Nwsp Bus Mgr; Soph Cls; Air Force; Bus.

VALKENBURG, ERIKA; Wallenpaupack Area HS HS; Lk Ariel, PA; (3); 5/160; Yrbk Stf; Gov Hon Prg Awd; High Hon Roll; Hon Roll; Jr NHS; NHS; Prfct Atten Awd; 6th Pl In Name That Organism Rgnl Sci Olympiad 87; 7th Pl In Name That Organism St Sci Olympiad 87; Vet Med.

VALKO, PATRICK; Seneca Valley HS; Mars, PA; (2); Church Yth Grp; ROTC; Teachers Aide; Hon Roll; Aero Engrng.

VALLESE, ROCHELLE R; Beaver Area HS; Beaver, PA; (4); DECA; French Clb; Pep Clb; Sec Soph Cls; JV Cheerleading; Powder Puff Ftbl; Hon Roll; Hrns Teenbrd 85-86; Sr Exec Brd 87; CC Of Beaver; Pblc Rltns.

VALLETTE, DANIEL; High Point Baptist Acad; Geigertown, PA; (3); Church Yth Grp; Varsity Clb; School Play; Off Jr Cls; Gym; Socr; Hon Roll; AACS Natl Spnsh Awd 86; Merit Char Awd 86; All Star Soccer Team 86; Missionary.

VALLEY, PAUL; Kennedy Christian HS; Hermitage, PA; (2); 24/96; Church Yth Grp; JA; Latin Clb; Band; Concert Band; Jazz Band; Mrchg Band; School Play; Stage Crew.

VALTOS, CAROLYN; Parkland HS; Schnecksville, PA; (2); Drama Clb; 4-H; SADD; Band; Chorus; School Play; Rep Stu Cncl; Tennis; Trk; 4-H Awd; Presdntl Acad Ftnss Awd 85-86; Intr Decrtr.

VALVANO, JOSEPH CHRISTOPHER; West Side Voc Tech; Hunlock Creek, PA; (4); 20/150; Var L Ftbl; Var Wt Lftg; High Hon Roll; Penn ST; Tchr.

VALVARDI, JOHN; Cardinal O Hara HS; Springfield, PA; (3); 263/727; Church Yth Grp; Cmnty Wkr; VP JA; School Musical; School Play; Stage Crew; Im Bsktbl; Prfct Atten Awd; Law Enfrcmnt.

VALVONIS, STEPHEN; Pittston Area HS; Wilkes Barre, PA; (3); 23/297; High Hon Roll; Hon Roll; Hnr Soc 86-87; ROTC; Math.

VAN ARSDALE, SUSAN; Biglerville HS; Arendtsville, PA; (3); 17/98; Varsity Clb; Sec Soph Cls; Hst Sr Cls; Off Stu Cncl; L Var Bsktbl; L Var Fld Hcky; L Var Trk; Hon Roll; Jr NHS; NHS; Fashion Merchandising.

VAN AUKEN, KEITH; Tunkhannock HS; Dalton, PA; (3); 70/350; Varsity Clb; Var L Bsbl; Var L Bsktbl; Acdmc All-Amer 86-87; US Natl Bsktbl Awd 87; Pharmacist.

VAN AULEN, JENNY; Conestoga Valley HS; Lancaster, PA; (3); Dance Clb; Yrbk Stf; Hon Roll; Stu Historians 85-86; Frgn Lang Tchr For Elem Schl French 86-87; Bus Adm.

VAN BREMEN, ALISA; Uniontown Area HS; Farmington, PA; (2); 2/310; Church Yth Grp; Drama Clb; Spanish Clb; Band; Chorus; Concert Band; Mrchg Band; School Play; High Hon Roll; Spanish NHS; Child Psych.

VAN BREMEN, ROBERT; Uniontown Area HS; Farmington, PA; (3); 49/320; Spanish Clb; Band; Chorus; Concert Band; Mrchg Band; High Hon Roll; Hon Roll; Chem Engrng.

VAN BUREN, CHRISTOPHER; Abington HS; Meadowbrook, PA; (3); 52/502; Var Bsbl; Im Bsktbl; Var Socr; JV Swmmng; Hon Roll; Jr NHS; Bus.

VAN BUSKIRK, RHONDA; Faith Christian Schl; Saylorsburg, PA; (3); 1/15; Yrbk Ed-Chief; VP Soph Cls; VP Jr Cls; Var Bsktbl; Var Cheerleading; Var Sftbl; Var Vllybl; High Hon Roll; All Conf Awd-Sftbl 86; Sportsmanship Awd 85; Busnss.

VAN CLEVE, COLEEN; Lancaster Christian HS; New Providence, PA; (3); Pep Clb; Red Cross Aide; Acpl Chr; Band; Chorus; Rep Stu Cncl; Cheerleading; High Hon Roll; Pres Jr NHS; Occu Therapy.

VAN DALE, HEATHER; Wilmington Area HS; New Wilmington, PA; (3); Church Yth Grp; Cmnty Wkr; Drama Clb; Hosp Aide; Church Choir; Concert Band; Swmmng; Trk; Vllybl; French Clb; Elem Ed.

VAN DELINDER, SCOTT; Williamson HS; Millerton, PA; (2); Ski Clb; Yrbk Stf; JV Bsktbl; Var Socr; Var Trk; High Hon Roll; Jr NHS; NHS; Record Pole Vault 86 & 87.

VAN DER LEE, FRANCES; Canon-Mc Millan HS; Canonsburg, PA; (4); 22/355; French Clb; FBLA; Nwsp Stf; High Hon Roll; Hon Roll; NHS; Prfct Atten Awd; CMEA Schlrshp 87; Bus Persn Of Yr Awd 87; Bradford Schl; Sec Sci.

VAN DER MOOREN, MARC; Archbishop Wood HS; Warminster, PA; (3); 150/280; Westchester U; Liberl Arts.

VAN DIVNER, KAREN S; Mary Fuller Frazier Memorial HS; Grindstone, PA; (2); Church Yth Grp; Pep Clb; Varsity Clb; Band; Church Choir; Concert Band; Mrchg Band; Pep Band; Cheerleading; Sftbl; Sftbl Trphy 85-86; Prfct Attndnc 85-86; Miss Co-Ed Pagnt Fnlst 85-86; Comp.

VAN DURICK, NADINE; Abington Heights HS; Waverly, PA; (3); Church Yth Grp; Ski Clb; Varsity Clb; Rep Frsh Cls; Rep Soph Cls; JV Fld Hcky; Var L Swmmng; Rookie Of Yr In Swmng 85; Mst Prmsng In Swmng 86; Fash Merch.

VAN DUSEN, BRIAN; Schenley HS Teacher Ctr; Pittsburgh, PA; (3); Pres Computer Clb; VP JA; Mgr Radio Clb; Mgr Red Cross Aide; Yrbk Phtg; Off Jr Cls; Cit Awd; High Hon Roll; NHS; SAR Awd; Stu Of Mnth 86; Schlrshp Red Crss Ldrshp Dvlmpnt Ctr 83; Natl Yth Ldrshp Cncl DC 86; CMU; Comp.

VAN DUYNE, STEVEN; Bishop Kenrick HS; Norristown, PA; (4); 100/285; PA ST U; Law.

VAN DUZER, SCOTT; Lehigh Christian Acad; Slatington, PA; (3); 1/15; Church Yth Grp; Drama Clb; School Play; Nwsp Rptr; VP Frsh Cls; Pres Soph Cls; Pres Stu Cncl; Var Bsktbl; Var Socr; Var Sftbl; Med.

VAN HORN, AMY; Meadville HS; Meadville, PA; (3); 52/275; Key Clb; Band; Concert Band; Mrchg Band; Swmmng.

VAN HORN, JENNIFER; Southmoreland SR HS; Scottdale, PA; (3); 15/230; Ski Clb; Spanish Clb; Pres Band; Concert Band; Drm Mjr(t); Jazz Band; Mrchg Band; Nwsp Stf; Yrbk Stf; Lit Mag; Spnsh Natl Hnr Sctry 86-88; Prfct Attndnce Awd In Mrchng Bnd 84-87; Wshngtn & Jffrsn; Scndry Edu.

VAN METER, JOYCE; Bishop Neumann HS; Williamsport, PA; (3); 4/45; Church Yth Grp; Cmnty Wkr; Pep Clb; SADD; Yrbk Ed-Chief; Yrbk Stf; Bsktbl; Sftbl; Tennis; High Hon Roll; Yth Alloctn Comm United Way 87; HOBY Ldrshp Ambssdr 86; Hnrb Mntn Natl Spn Tst 86-87; Chrstn Witn Awd.

VAN ORMER, RALPH; Cambria Heights HS; Patton, PA; (2); German Clb; Ski Clb; Band; Concert Band; Mrchg Band; Bsktbl; Hon Roll.

VAN PUTTEN, ZANETTA FERN C; Pine Forge Acad; Jamaica, NY; (4); Church Yth Grp; Church Choir; Flag Corp; Variety Show; Nwsp Stf; Rep Soph Cls; Hon Roll; Ntl Merit Schol; 1st Prize Wnnr Schl Oratorical Cntst 87; Southwestern Coll; Lawyer.

VAN RIET, GERALD G; The Hill Schl; Pottstown, PA; (4); 3/110; Church Yth Grp; Debate Tm; Hosp Aide; VP JA; Math Tm; Mu Alpha Theta; Radio Clb; Science Clb; Nwsp Stf; JV Bsktbl.

VAN SCOTER, ERIC WADE; Otto-Eldred JR SR HS; Eldred, PA; (3); Trk; Hon Roll; Comp.

VAN SCOYOC, VELISSA; Owen J Roberts HS; Pottstown, PA; (3); 5/331; Band; Concert Band; Mrchg Band; High Hon Roll; NHS; Amnesty Intl; Art Awds; 1st Pl Oil Anvil Studios 86; 1st Local Nwsp Create An Ad Cont; Comm Art.

VAN SCYOC, JOHN; Big Spring HS; Plainfield, PA; (4); 1/192; Quiz Bowl; Band; Concert Band; Mrchg Band; High Hon Roll; Lion Awd; NHS; Ntl Merit SF; MIT; Elec Engrng.

VAN SICKLE, JOHN; Danville HS; Riverside, PA; (3); Key Clb; High Hon Roll; NHS; Latn Hnr Soc 87; PA ST U; Cvl Engrng.

VAN TASSEL, TRACY; New Brighton Area HS; New Brighton, PA; (4); 43/144; GAA; Library Aide; VICA; Chorus; Rep Soph Cls; Rep Stu Cncl; JV Capt Cheerleading; Im Trk; Hon Roll; Pres Acadc Ftns Awd 87; Fashion Inst-Pittsburgh; Mgmt.

VAN VOORHIS, GREGG; Franklin Regional HS; Murrysville, PA; (4); Boy Scts; Pres Church Yth Grp; Band; JV Bsktbl; Var Co-Capt Crs Cntry; God Cntry Awd; High Hon Roll; NHS; JA; Ski Clb; Am U Presdntl Schlrshp 87; Eagl Sct 86; American U; Pol Sci.

VAN VORIS, TODD; Hazleton SR HS; St Johns, PA; (2); JCL; Latin Clb; Quiz Bowl; School Play; Stage Crew; Lit Mag; Mgr(s); Score Keeper; High Hon Roll; Union Coll; Law.

VAN WHY, NANCY; E L Meyers HS; Wiles Barre, PA; (4); 14/162; Hosp Aide; Sec Key Clb; Letterman Clb; Office Aide; Pep Clb; Ski Clb; SADD; Chorus; School Play; Swing Chorus; PA ST U; Advncd Scndry Ed.

VAN WINKLE, KAREN; West Allegheny HS; Oakdale, PA; (2); 30/210; Drama Clb; Band; Chorus; Color Guard; Concert Band; Jazz Band; Mrchg Band; Pep Band; Symp Band; Jr NHS; Hnr Roll Entire Schl Career.

VAN WYE, GRETCHEN; Cumberland Valley HS; Mechanicsburg, PA; (4); Church Yth Grp; Debate Tm; Key Clb; SADD; School Musical; School Play; Lit Mag; Stu Cncl; NHS; Ntl Merit Ltr; Natl Hnr Scty Schlrshp; Balfour Clthng & Textiles Awd; PTO Schlrshp; Penn ST U; Polt.

VANALMAN, JUDY; Juniata HS; Mifflintown, PA; (3); Camera Clb; Varsity Clb; Mrchg Band; Yrbk Stf; Mgr(s); Hon Roll; NHS.

VANCE, JEFFREY; Mercer Area JR SR HS; Mercer, PA; (4); 5/135; Art Clb; Ski Clb; Nwsp Rptr; Ed Nwsp Stf; Yrbk Stf; Var Golf; Var Trk; Elks Awd; High Hon Roll; NHS; Boosters Clb Cvr Dsgn Wnnr 87; Stu Of Mnth 87; Greenville Record-Stu Of Wk 87; PA ST; Advtg.

VANCE, MEREDITH; West Middlesex HS; New Wilmington, PA; (1); Church Yth Grp; French Clb; Band; Church Choir; Concert Band; Mrchg Band; High Hon Roll; Hon Roll; Outstndg Prfm Typg I 86-87.

VANDECREEK, TAMARA; Indiana Area SR HS; Indiana, PA; (3); 29/322; Church Yth Grp; Drama Clb; Acpl Chr; School Musical; Stage Crew; Vllybl; High Hon Roll; Jr NHS; Prfct Atten Awd; Engl Wrtg Awd 85.

VANDER NEUT, JENNIFER MAREE; Archbishop John Carroll HS; Malvern, PA; (4); 12/364; SADD; Nwsp Sprt Ed; Bsktbl; Var Sftbl; French Hon Soc; VP NHS; Schlr Athlete Awd 87; Syracuse U; Bioengineering.

VANDER WEELE, RICHARD; Corry Area HS; Corry, PA; (3); 17/243; Boy Scts; Church Yth Grp; German Clb; Concert Band; Jazz Band; Mrchg Band; Swmmng; Tennis; Hon Roll; Delta Epsilon Phi-Grmn Hnr Soc 86; Gannon U; Bio.

VANDERBURG, KRISTEN; Downingtown HS; Dowingtown, PA; (3); 136/614; AFS; Church Yth Grp; Drama Clb; French Clb; School Play; Rep Soph Cls; Stat Bsktbl; Hon Roll; NEDT Awd.

VANDERMARTIN, LISA; Nativity B V M HS; Pottsville, PA; (4); Aud/Vis; French Clb; VP Math Clb; Capt Drill Tm; Stat Bsktbl; Capt Bowling; Hon Roll; Penn ST; Radiological Techn.

VANDERSLOOT, ALYSSA; West York Area SR HS; York, PA; (3); 32/200; Exploring; Girl Scts; JA; Band; Mrchg Band; Symp Band; Rep Frsh Cls; Rep Soph Cls; Im Bowling; Hon Roll; PA ST U.

VANDEWATER, KEVIN; Peters Township HS; Venetia, PA; (4); 20/243; Political Wkr; Varsity Clb; Yrbk Sprt Ed; Yrbk Stf; Pres Stu Cncl; Capt Bsbl; L Bsktbl; L Ftbl; Cit Awd; DAR Awd; Pres Acdmc Fitness Awd 87; Army Rsrv Schlr/Athlete Awd 87; Rotary Sci Awd 87; US Air Force Acad; Engrng.

VANDIVER, CLAUDINE; St Hubert HS; Philadelphia, PA; (4); 70/364; Dance Clb; Drama Clb; School Musical; School Play; Soph Cls; Stu Cncl; Hon Roll; Prfct Atten Awd; Reltd Arts Awd Hgst Grd Avg 85; Dance Clb Awd, Schl Mnstry Awd 87; PA ST U Ogontz; Bus Admin.

VANDIVNER, ANTHONY; Cameron County HS; Emporium, PA; (2); Church Yth Grp; Computer Clb; Off Soph Cls; Ftbl; Wt Lftg; Wrstlng; Hon Roll; Comp Tech.

VANDYKE, MIKE; Ft Le Boeuf HS; Erie, PA; (2); Ftbl; Med Tech.

VANDZURA, MARCIA; Bishop Carroll HS; Portage, PA; (3); Ski Clb; Spanish Clb; Speech Tm; VP SADD; Rep Stu Cncl; JV Bsktbl; Stat Trk; Hon Roll; Intl Bus.

VANDZURA, REBECCA E; Lewistown SR HS; Lewistown, PA; (2); AFS; 4-H; French Clb; Key Clb; Chorus; Hst Soph Cls; Trs Stu Cncl; Stat Timer; Var Trk; 4-H Awd; Ldrshp Schl Cncl Membr 4-H Ldrshp Cngrss 87; Camp Cnslr At 4-H Camp 86 & 87; Bio.

VANEK, DENNIS; Valley HS; New Kensington, PA; (4); 14/200; Exploring; Leo Clb; Science Clb; Ski Clb; VP Spanish Clb; Varsity Clb; Var L Ftbl; Var L Trk; Jr NHS; NHS; OH U; Bus.

VANELLA, MICHELLE; HS Of Engineering & Science; Hatfield, PA; (4); Drama Clb; Intnl Clb; Model UN; School Play; Trs Jr Cls; Im Ice Hcky; Hon Roll; NHS; Science Clb; Yrbk Stf; Publshd Sci Papr 86; Pres Chinese Cmte 85-86; 1st Awd DE Vly GJ Carrer & PIAS Sci Fair 84-87; Med.

VANHORNE, MARK; Altoona Area HS; Altoona, PA; (3); Church Yth Grp; Ski Clb; Mrchg Band; Orch; Crs Cntry; Trk; Archit.

VANLEW, DEBRA E; Downington HS; Downingtown, PA; (4); 97/555; Church Yth Grp; Band; Bowling; Mgr(s); Stat Socr; High Hon Roll; Scrtrs Assc Bk Schlrshp 87; Typng Awd 87; Grgg Typng Cert 86; Katharine Gibbs Schl; Secr.

VANNUCCI, DANA; Frazier HS; Fayette City, PA; (2); Capt Cheerleading; Gym; Powder Puff Ftbl; Band; Concert Band; Pep Band; Sftbl; Hon Roll; Mss All Amrcn Chrldg Pgnt 86; U Of Pittsburgh; Med Asst.

VANNUCCI, DAVE; Frazier JR SR HS; Fayette City, PA; (4); Spanish Clb; Cheerleading; Ftbl; Golf; Gym; CA U Of PA; Bus Admin.

VANT ZELFDEN, LORI; Conestoga Valley HS; Lancaster, PA; (3); 87/219; Church Yth Grp; Dance Clb; Yrbk Stf; Var Tennis; Hon Roll; People-People Am Ambssdr Pgm 85-87; Bus Admin.

VANTIL, ETHAN S; Grove City Area HS; Grove City, PA; (4); 2/200; Key Clb; Orch; Swing Chorus; Capt Tennis; Elks Awd; High Hon Roll; NHS; Ntl Merit SF; Rotary Awd; ACE Acad & Cltrl Enrchmtn Prog Coll Couses Schl Play; Calvin Coll; Med.

VANYA, CELESTE; Mifflinburg Area HS; Mifflinburg, PA; (3); Cmnty Wkr; Drama Clb; FBLA; FHA; School Musical; School Play; Actng.

VARADY, HOLLY; Freedom HS; Bethlehem, PA; (3); 31/486; Hosp Aide; Science Clb; Spanish Clb; Im Powder Puff Ftbl; Capt Twrlr; High Hon Roll; Hon Roll; NHS; Cert Attnmnt Rcvng All A 86; Ithaca Coll; Phy Thrpy.

VARADY JR, JOSEPH J; Owen J Roberts HS; Phoenixville, PA; (4); 47/271; School Play; Stage Crew; Yrbk Phtg; JV Ftbl; Var L Trk; Vllybl; Prsdntl Acdmc Ftnss Awd 87; Gettysburg U; Lbrl Arts.

VARALLO, DEANNA; St Maria Goretti HS; Philadelphia, PA; (4); French Clb; Math Clb; Math Tm; Pep Clb; PAVAS; Chorus; School Musical; School Play; Stage Crew; Off Soph Cls; Temple U; Phys Thrpy.

VARANO, ANNA; St Huberts Catholic HS; Philadelphia, PA; (3); 97/500; Dance Clb; Drama Clb; Chorus; School Musical; School Play; JV Gym; JV Trk; Hon Roll; Prfct Atten Awd; Aud/Vis; Temple U; Elem Educ.

VARANO, CHRISTIAN; Harrisburg Christian HS; Harrisburg, PA; (3); Church Yth Grp; Drama Clb; School Play; Nwsp Rptr; JV Bsbl; Var L Bsktbl; JV Ftbl; Var L Socr; Hon Roll; Investmnt.

VARANO, NICOLE; Shikellamy HS; Sunbury, PA; (3); 1/305; Cmnty Wkr; Spanish Clb; Band; Chorus; Mrchg Band; Yrbk Stf; High Hon Roll; Hon Roll; Jr NHS; NHS; Spnsh Camp Schlrshp 87; Music Rflctns Contst Awd 1st Pl ST 84; Spanish Intrptr.

VARANO, THERESA MARIE; Mt Carmel Area JR SR HS; Kulpmont, PA; (4); 17/163; Am Leg Aux Girls St; Key Clb; Latin Clb; Band; Mrchg Band; Nwsp Rptr; Capt Trk; High Hon Roll; Jr NHS; NHS; U MD Baltimore; Phys Thrpst.

VARAVETTE, KEVIN; Western Beaver HS; Industry, PA; (4); High Hon Roll; Hon Roll; Comp Prgmng.

VARDAR, MESUT M; Chambersburgh Area S HS; Chambersburg, PA; (3); French Clb; Key Clb; Bsktbl; Diving; Socr; Swmmng; Tennis; Trk; Wt Lftg; French Hon Soc; Phys Fitness Awd 85-86; Lttrd For Hnrs 86; Shippensburg U Sprng Lang Cont 87; Hotel Mgmnt.

VARDY, LORI; Butler Area HS; Butler, PA; (2); Hon Roll; Prfct Atten Awd.

VARDY, ZOLTAN A; Central Catholic HS; Pittsburgh, PA; (3); 16/260; Boy Scts; Debate Tm; French Clb; Nwsp Ed-Chief; Nwsp Stf; Yrbk Stf; Rep Frsh Cls; Rep Stu Cncl; Var Socr; Var Tennis; History.

VARGA, RICHARD; Ringold SR HS; Monongahela, PA; (2); Computer Clb; Spanish Clb; JV Bsktbl; Bio.

VARGAS, AMY; Du Bois Area HS; Dubois, PA; (3); Band; Church Choir; Mrchg Band; Hon Roll; PA ST U; Bio Sci.

VARGAS, RANDALL T; Du Bois Area HS; Dubois, PA; (4); 91/278; Camera Clb; Lit Mag; Rep Stu Cncl; Var Capt Bsbl; Var Capt Ftbl; Tennis; Var Capt Wrstlng; Vllybl; Athltc, Ldrshp Awd 87; PA ST U; Mrktng.

VARGO, CAROLYN; Ringgold HS; Donora, PA; (3); 88/351; Hosp Aide; Chorus; Hon Roll; CA ST U; Teaching.

VARGO, DEBORAH JO; Mary Fuller Frazier HS; Star Junction, PA; (4); Drama Clb; VP FNA; Ski Clb; School Play; Yrbk Stf; Rep Stu Cncl; Stat Bsktbl; Cheerleading; Capt Powder Puff Ftbl; Capt Sftbl; Chatham Coll; Bkng.

VARGO, EDWARD; Homer Center HS; Lucerne Mines, PA; (3); 42/120; Church Yth Grp; French Clb; Library Aide; Ski Clb; Band; Chorus; Concert Band; Jazz Band; Mrchg Band; School Musical; Advrtsg.

VARGO, JENNIFER; Seneca Valley SR HS; Mars, PA; (2); Dance Clb; Library Aide; Math Clb; Capt Pom Pon; High Hon Roll; Hon Roll; Bus.

VARGO, LINDA; Liberty HS; Bethlehem, PA; (3); 138/429; Church Yth Grp; French Clb; Hosp Aide; Band; Concert Band; Mrchg Band; School Musical; School Play; Rep Soph Cls; JV Var Cheerleading; Spch Thrpy.

VARGO, TODD ALAN; Penn Trafford HS; Harrison Cty, PA; (2); Church Yth Grp; VP Drama Clb; German Clb; Chorus; School Musical; School Play; Pres Stage Crew; High Hon Roll; NHS.

VARISCHETTI, PETER; Brockway Area HS; Brockway, PA; (3); 14/115; Debate Tm; Speech Tm; Varsity Clb; Cheerleading; Ftbl; Wt Lftg; Wrstlng; High Hon Roll; Hon Roll; NHS; Lttrl 12 Lnmn Yr Ftbl, & 1st Tm Lttl 12 Offnsv Grd & Dfnsv End 86; Dist 9 Wrstlng 105 Lbs Rnnr Up 85.

VARLEY, JODI; Steel Valley HS; Munhall, PA; (4); 7/201; Band; Concert Band; Mrchg Band; Var Score Keeper; Hon Roll; NHS; Gov Schl Ag 86; 1st Pl Munhall Wmns Clb Art Shw 86; Wshngtn & Jffrsn; Pre Vet Med.

VARNER, AMY; S Hunt County HS; Saltillo, PA; (2); Trs Church Yth Grp; French Clb; GAA; Girl Scts; Varsity Clb; Band; Chorus; Stu Cncl; Var L Bsktbl; Var L Sftbl; Intl Foreign Lang Awd Winner 85-87.

VARNER, JASON D; Cambridge Springs HS; Cambridge Springs, PA; (4); 16/104; Pres Church Yth Grp; Political Wkr; Quiz Bowl; Pres SADD; School Play; Ntl Merit SF; Boy Scts; French Clb; Pres Acdmc Ftnss Awd 86-87; 2nd Pl PA Prchr Boy ST Cont 87; Bst 1st Yr Delg Modl Legsltre 84-85; Edinboro U; Theolgy.

VARNER, KEITH; Forest Hills HS; Johnstown, PA; (4); 30/148; L Bsbl; Hon Roll; Jr NHS; Lutheran Brotherhood Schlrshp Awd 87; U Of Pgh At Johnstown; Chrprctr.

VARNER, KENNY; Lewistown Area HS; Lewistown, PA; (3); Art Clb; Church Yth Grp; German Clb; Yrbk Stf; Im Bsktbl; JV Ftbl; Trk; 2 Schlstc Awds 86-87; Altrnt Gov Schl Fine Arts 86-87; Art Inst MD; Commrcl Artst.

VARNER, MARK; Columbia Montour A V T S HS; Berwick, PA; (3); 3/208; Letterman Clb; VICA; Nwsp Ed-Chief; Var Bsbl; Var Ftbl; Var Wrstlng; High Hon Roll; NHS; Most Val Dfnsv Back Ftbl Awd 86-87; Grphc Art.

VARNER, MICHAEL; South Side Beaver HS; Georgetown, PA; (3); 2/150; Am Leg Boys St; Math Tm; Teachers Aide; Nwsp Stf; Golf; High Hon Roll; NHS; Sal; Provosts Day 87; High Q Cont 87; Chem Olympics 86-87; Hnrs Club 85-87; World Affrs Council 87; Carnegie Mellon; Chem Engr.

VARNER, MICHELLE RAYNE; Seneca Valley SR HS; Harmony, PA; (4); 53/472; Pres Church Yth Grp; JA; SADD; Varsity Clb; Var Capt Cheerleading; Stat L Swmmng; Hon Roll; NHS; Yth Seminar To Japan 86; Elem Educ.

VARRATO, LYNELL; Fort Le Boeuf HS; Waterford, PA; (3); 41/207; Var JV Bsbl; Var Stat Bsktbl; High Hon Roll; Prfct Atten Awd; Penn ST Behrend; Bus Ed.

VARUGHESE, ANNIE; W Catholic Girls HS; Philadelphia, PA; (3); 44/246; Church Yth Grp; Latin Clb; Church Choir; Hon Roll; Exmplry Cert 87; Typg Cert 87; Acmc Achvmnt Alg II 87; Engnrng.

VARUOLO, LENA; Hempfield SR HS; Jeannette, PA; (3); Jazz Band; Mrchg Band; Var Socr; Var Vllybl; Cit Awd; Hon Roll; Ski Clb; Band; Concert Band; Orch; Penn ST; Engr.

VASALANI, DAN; Montour HS; Mckees Rocks, PA; (2); French Clb; Var Bsbl; Im Ftbl; Var Golf; High Hon Roll; U Of ME; Pro Bsbll.

VASARAB, JOHN; Lehighton Area HS; Palmerton, PA; (3); Chess Clb; Var L Ftbl; Wt Lftg; JV Wrstlng; Hon Roll; PA ST; Civil Engrng.

VASEL, JULIE; Central HS; Martinsburg, PA; (3); 27/187; Church Yth Grp; FCA; GAA; Ski Clb; SADD; VICA; Var Trk; Var Vllybl; High Hon Roll; Cmnty Wkr.

VASERSTEIN, GREGORY L; State College Area SR HS; State College, PA; (4); 101/568; Chess Clb; Debate Tm; French Clb; Math Tm; Orch; Socr; Ntl Merit SF; Cmmnwlth PA Cert Of Merit Outstndng Prfrmn SAT 86; USA Jnr Chss Olympcs-1st Pl Unrtd-Trphy 85; Physcs.

VASILKO, MARY; Leechburg Area HS; Leechburg, PA; (3); Trs Art Clb; Drama Clb; Chorus; Nwsp Stf; Yrbk Ed-Chief; Yrbk Sprt Ed; Trs Frsh Cls; Trs Jr Cls; Var Capt Cheerleading; Church Choir; Art Clb-Treas; Rssn Clb; Drama Clb; Chrs; Nwspr-Ftr Edtr; Yrbk-Co-Edtr & Sprts Edtr; Chrldng Var-Capt; Nrsng.

VASSELLO, DEBBIE; Beaver Area HS; Beaver, PA; (3); Church Yth Grp; FCA; Hosp Aide; Spanish Clb; SADD; Var L Cheerleading; Var L Trk; High Hon Roll; Gym; Powder Puff Ftbl; Schltc Achvt Awd 87; WPIAL Gym Awd 87; Bus.

VASSEN JR, WILLIAM D; West Middlesex HS; West Middlesex, PA; (2); Trs Aud/Vis; Boy Scts; French Clb; Presdntl Academic Fitness Awd 85-86.

VASTINE, CHRISTINA; Milton HS; W Milton, PA; (3); 24/229; Spanish Clb; Varsity Clb; Church Choir; Diving; Fld Hcky; Hon Roll; NHS; Foreign Relations.

VASTINE, POLLYANNA; Milton Area HS; West Milton, PA; (2); 2/254; Spanish Clb; Chorus; Church Choir; Color Guard; Trk; High Hon Roll; Hon Roll; Bloomsburg U; Accounting.

VATAVUK, MICHAEL J; Windber Area HS; Windber, PA; (3); Band; High Hon Roll; NHS; Pres Schlr; Concert Band; Jazz Band; Mrchg Band; Stage Crew; Jr Cls; Prfct Atten Awd; Stu Mnth-Mar 85,Dec 86,Apr 87; Var Awds & Schlrshps Music 86-87; Yth Symph Orch; Music Perf.

VATH, KRISTAL; Lakeview HS; Stoneboro, PA; (4); 1/128; Church Yth Grp; Intnl Clb; Science Clb; Band; Chorus; Church Choir; Concert Band; Jazz Band; Mrchg Band; Pep Band; Honrs Chorus Alt 86; Latin Awd 85; Schl Gftd Pgm 83-87; Cornell U; Design.

VAUGHN, ANGELA; Central York SR HS; York, PA; (2); Church Yth Grp; Ski Clb; Church Choir; Swing Chorus; Rep Frsh Cls; High Hon Roll; Hon Roll; Med.

VAUGHN, CHERYL; Wellsboro Area HS; Wellsboro, PA; (2); 28/170; Pep Clb; Chorus; Concert Band; Mrchg Band; Rep Stu Cncl; Stat Bsktbl; JV Trk; JV L Vllybl; High Hon Roll; Hon Roll; Psych.

VAUGHN, KELLY; Lewistown Area HS; Lewistown, PA; (2); French Clb; Concert Band; Mrchg Band; Yrbk Stf; High Hon Roll; Hon Roll; NHS; Ntl Merit Ltr; Young Mens Christian Assn Awd 87; Comp.

VAUGHN, LARRY; Coatesville Area SR HS; Thorndale, PA; (3); Chorus; JV Crs Cntry; JV Trk; Hon Roll; Bus Ownr.

VAUGHN, MICHAEL; Techincal Memorial HS; Erie, PA; (3); 14/311; Church Yth Grp; Letterman Clb; NAACP; Var Ftbl; Var Trk; Var Wrstlng; Hon Roll; NW Soccer Assoc Awd 87; Elec Engr.

VAUGHT, GAIL; York Catholic HS; York, PA; (4); 9/168; Spanish Clb; Chorus; Nwsp Rptr; Var Capt Bsktbl; Var L Trk; Var L Vllybl; High Hon Roll; Ntl Merit Ltr; Varsity Clb; Acpl Chr; William J Fitzpatrick Schlrshp & Pres Acdmc Ftnss Awd 87; Purdue U; Aeronautical Engrng.

VAUPEL, WAYNE G; Nativity BVM HS; Schuylkill Haven, PA; (3); 6/86; Band; Mrchg Band; Var Trk; High Hon Roll; Hon Roll; Geo, Latin & Amer Culture Awds 84-85; Magna Cum Laude Latin Awd 85-86; Var Let Track 86-87; Military Sci.

VAUX, SHERRY; Philipsburg Osceola Area HS; Philipsburg, PA; (4); 51/250; Sec Drama Clb; Sec Thesps; Sec Chorus; School Musical; School Play; Stage Crew; JV Sftbl; PA ST Altoona; Acctng.

VAVREK, KELLY; Canon Mc Millan HS; Strabane, PA; (3); 30/380; French Clb; Hosp Aide; Ski Clb; Drill Tm; Yrbk Stf; Bowling; Pom Pon; JV Tennis; Hon Roll; Cmmnty Svc Awd 83; Frnch Hnr Awd 84; Elem Ed.

VAVREK, STACEY; Carmichaels Area JR SR HS; Nemacolin, PA; (3); 7/112; 4-H; Pep Clb; Ski Clb; Spanish Clb; Pres Jr Cls; JV Bsktbl; Gov Hon Prg Awd; High Hon Roll; NHS; Pres Acdmc Ftnss Awd 84-85; WV U; Med.

VAVRICK, MICHELLE ANITA; Dunmore HS; Dunmore, PA; (4); 32/148; Drama Clb; FBLA; Ski Clb; Spanish Clb; Chorus; Nwsp Rptr; Capt Bowling; Capt Twrlr; Jr NHS; Computer Clb; Prsdntl Acdmc Ftnss Awd, Prtcpnt Dvlpmtn Of PA Hnrs Tst 87; Penn ST U; Engrng.

VAXMONSKY, LORI; Wyoming Area HS; W Pittston, PA; (3); 50/250; French Clb; Key Clb; Office Aide; Ski Clb; Off Stu Cncl; Sftbl; Trk; Hon Roll; Arch.

VAYDA, BRIAN; Hazleton HS; Hazleton, PA; (3); 105/455; Church Yth Grp; Drama Clb; FBLA; Ski Clb; Teachers Aide; JV Bsbl; Var JV Bsktbl; Var Golf; Im Vllybl; Hon Roll; Accntng.

VAZQUEZ, DAWN; Marian HS; Coaldale, PA; (3); Math Clb; Church Choir; Bsktbl; Sftbl; Hon Roll; Spanish NHS; U FL; Med.

VAZQUEZ, MAGDA; Technical Memorial HS; Erie, PA; (3); 24/330; Off SADD; Var JV Bsktbl; Var Golf; Var Sftbl; Certfd Nrses Ade 87; Awd Ldrshp Conf 86; Cmmndtn Am Math Exam 87; Apprctn Vlntr Svc United Way 87; Army; OR Nrs.

VEAHMAN, DIANE; Penn-Trafford HS; Jeannette, PA; (2); AFS; Drama Clb; FBLA; JCL; Latin Clb; JV Sftbl; High Hon Roll; Ntl Merit Ltr; Acadc All-Amer Lttr 87; Med Fld.

VEAK JR, JOHN JOLLY; East SR HS; West Chester, PA; (3); 121/446; Model UN; Ski Clb; Gldn Key Awd Schlstcs Cmptn Art 85; 2nd Chester Cnty Art Shw Jr Wmns Clb 85; Semi-Fnlst Art Cmptn 86; Arch.

VEARD, CHRISTINE; Cornell HS; Coraopolis, PA; (4); 10/76; Church Yth Grp; Key Clb; Color Guard; School Play; Nwsp Ed-Chief; Ed Yrbk Ed-Chief; Swmmng; DAR Awd; Kiwanis Awd; Trs NHS; Top 10 In Cls 87; Penn ST U; Chem Engrng.

VEAZIE, JASON; Hazleton SR HS; Drums, PA; (3); 3/445; Computer Clb; Scholastic Bowl; Concert Band; Jazz Band; Pres Mrchg Band; Stage Crew; Yrbk Stf; Hon Roll; 1ST Pl Amer Chem Scty Chem Cmptn 87; 1st Pl PA JR Acad Sci Regnl Cmptn 87; 2nd Pl PA JR Acad Sc; Astrnmy.

VECCHIO, JAMES; Penn Trafford HS; Trafford, PA; (2); Chess Clb; Letterman Clb; Spanish Clb; Varsity Clb; JV Bsktbl; JV Ftbl; Im Wt Lftg; High Hon Roll; Hon Roll; U Pittsburgh; Banking.

VECCHIO, TINA; Mapletown JR SR HS; Dilliner, PA; (4); Aud/Vis; GAA; Library Aide; Ski Clb; Varsity Clb; Chorus; Yrbk Stf; Rep Sr Cls; Rep Stu Cncl; Sftbl; Bradford Schl Bus; Exec Secr.

VECCHIOLA, ANDREA; Highlands HS; Natrona Hgts, PA; (3); Cmnty Wkr; Dance Clb; Hosp Aide; Band; Color Guard; Concert Band; Drm & Bgl; Mrchg Band; CPR Cert 87; Marching Band Awd 86; Graphcs.

VECELLIO, MARK; Bradford Central Christian HS; Bradford, PA; (2); French Clb; Letterman Clb; Stu Cncl; Bsktbl; Ftbl; Hon Roll; Jr NHS.

VEGA, CRISTINO; Mastbaum Area Vo-Tech HS; Philadelphia, PA; (3); Boy Scts; Church Yth Grp; Socr; Trk; Temple U; Accntng.

VEGELY, RAY; Churchill HS; Pittsburgh, PA; (2); 11/222; Ski Clb; Band; Concert Band; Mrchg Band; School Musical; Var L Tennis.

VEGLIA, ANN; Western Beaver JR SR HS; Industry, PA; (3); Dance Clb; Band; Chorus; Capt Co-Capt Drm Mjr(t); Mrchg Band; Nwsp Stf; Im Bowling; Capt Co-Capt Twrlr; Co Captn Majrtte Sqd 85-86, Captn 86-87; Wrld Strut Chmpn 85; Accntng.

VEIT, JENNIE; Downingtown HS; Exton, PA; (3); 214/648; Ski Clb; Spanish Clb; Chorus; Rep Stu Cncl; JV Trk; Hon Roll.

VELAZQUEZ, BONNIE; Harry S Truman HS; Levittown, PA; (3); Var Fld Hcky; Var Sftbl; Hon Roll; HS Engl Tchr.

VELLANO, JILL; Moon SR HS; Coraopolis, PA; (3); Church Yth Grp; Sec German Clb; Band; Mrchg Band; Off Stu Cncl; Mgr(s); Hon Roll; Prfct Atten Awd; Cmnctns.

VELTRI, JOSEPH; St John Neumann HS; Philadelphia, PA; (3); 88/349; Rep Frsh Cls; Rep Soph Cls; Rep Jr Cls; Off Stu Cncl; Cornell Coll; Htl Rest Mgmt.

VELTRI, PASQUALE M; Central Catholic HS; Whitaker, PA; (3); JV Wrstlng; French Hon Soc; High Hon Roll; NHS; Elect Engrng.

VENDETTI, JASON; Boyertown Area HS; Boyertown, PA; (3); Bsktbl; Hon Roll; Bio.

VENETTA, CHRISTINE; Hickory HS; Hermitage, PA; (3); Cmnty Wkr; 4-H; Hosp Aide; Spanish Clb; Band; Concert Band; Mrchg Band; Pep Band; Score Keeper; Swmmng; Band Awd-1st Yr Awd 84-85; Elem Ed.

VENGIN, MICHAEL; Minersville Area HS; Pottsville, PA; (3); 4/104; High Hon Roll; NHS; PLRA/N E Rgn Micro-Comp Prgmmng Cont 85; Penn ST; Engnrng.

VENINCASA, TERESA; Brownsville Area HS; Adah, PA; (3); Drama Clb; Girl Scts; Office Aide; Ski Clb; SADD; Band; Pep Band; Nwsp Rptr; Nwsp Stf; Hon Roll; CA U; Elem Educ.

VENKUS, AMY; Chambersburg SR HS; Chambersburg, PA; (2); French Clb; Band; Chorus; Flag Corp; Mrchg Band; Law.

VENNIE, MONICA; Harrisburg HS; Harrisburg, PA; (3); Pep Clb; Science Clb; Teachers Aide; Chorus; Trs Soph Cls; Cheerleading; High Hon Roll; Hon Roll; Natl Hnr Rl 86-87; 1st Rnnr Up Hmcmng 86; Bus Adm.

VENT, JEFF; Moon HS; Coraopolis, PA; (3); 50/306; VP JA; Band; Mrchg Band; Nwsp Sprt Ed; Rep Soph Cls; Im Bsktbl; Im Golf; Var Socr; Var L Trk; Hon Roll; Elec Engr.

VENTRESCA, FERNANDO; Lansdale Catholic HS; Hatfield, PA; (3); Drama Clb; Cmmnctns.

VENTRESCA, JOHN; Central Bucks West HS; Warrington, PA; (3); 61/481; Church Yth Grp; Political Wkr; Jazz Band; Mrchg Band; Lit Mag; Var L Bsktbl; Var L Golf; High Hon Roll; Hon Roll; NHS; Ltr Vllybl 87; Awd Hghst Avg Russian I 85-86; Awd Hghst Avg Russian II 86-87; Cmmnctns.

VENTRESCA, LOUIS; Archbishop Wood HS; Warminster, PA; (3); 130/275; Cmnty Wkr; Computer Clb; FCA; Intnl Clb; Library Aide; Office Aide; Service Clb; Spanish Clb; SADD; Yrbk Stf.

VENTURE, JIM; Du Bois Area HS; Reynoldsville, PA; (3); 39/360; Ski Clb; Varsity Clb; Var L Bsbl; Var L Ftbl; Wt Lftg; Hon Roll; Arch.

VENUS, CHRIS; Sto-Rox SR HS; Mckees Rocks, PA; (2); #3 In Class; JA; Band; Stage Crew; Nwsp Stf; Yrbk Rptr; Yrbk Stf; High Hon Roll; Hon Roll; NEDT Awd; U Of Pittsburgh; Aero Engr.

VERA, ANTHONY; Eastern York HS; York, PA; (3); SADD; Varsity Clb; Rep Sr Cls; Var L Ftbl; Hon Roll; U Of Pittsburgh; Pre Law.

VERA, DAMARID; Central HS; Philadelphia, PA; (3); Church Yth Grp; Spanish Clb; Stage Crew; Cheerleading; JV Sftbl; Bus.

VERALDI, ANGELO; Southwestern HS; Hanover, PA; (3); 56/233; Key Clb; Varsity Clb; Yrbk Phtg; Var L Ftbl; JV Golf; Var L Tennis; Var L Wrstlng; High Hon Roll; NEDT Awd.

VERBECKEN, MICHELLE; Central Dauphin East HS; Harrisburg, PA; (3); Dance Clb; Band; Chorus; School Musical; Nwsp Ed-Chief; Rep Soph Cls; Rep Stu Cncl; Var Cheerleading; Capt Twrlr; U Of CA Los Angeles; Ed.

VERBIT, SHERLYN; Central HS; Martinsburg, PA; (3); FTA; Ski Clb; Speech Tm; SADD; Chorus; Yrbk Stf; Rep Soph Cls; Rep Jr Cls; Stu Cncl; NHS; Presdntl Acadc Ftns Awd 85; Cntrl Hnr Soc 87; Penn ST Coll; Elem Educ.

VERBONITZ, KIMBERLY; Central Catholic HS; Whitehall, PA; (4); 3/210; French Clb; Intnl Clb; Math Clb; Service Clb; SADD; Nwsp Ed-Chief; Nwsp Rptr; Nwsp Stf; Rep Jr Cls; Stu Cncl; NY U Schlrs Pgm Schlrshp 87-91; AAA Schlrshp 87-91; Cngrssnl Yth Ldrshp Pgm 87; U Of PA; Cmmnctns.

VERBOYS, LORI; Carbondale Area HS; Carbondale, PA; (3); Art Clb; FBLA; Ski Clb; Spanish Clb; Twrlr; Hon Roll; Psych.

VERDAVOIR, SANDY; Cambria HS; Hastings, PA; (3); Art Clb; Computer Clb; Ski Clb; Spanish Clb; Band; Concert Band; Mrchg Band; Yrbk Stf; Var Twrlr; Hon Roll; Altoona Sch Of Nrsng; Nrsng.

VERDELLI, STEVEN; Lower Dauphin HS; Hummelstown, PA; (3); Ski Clb; Band; Chorus; School Musical; Socr; Chem.

VERDETTO, DAVID; Old Forge HS; Old Forge, PA; (4); Ski Clb; Spanish Clb; Yrbk Stf; Bsbl; Hon Roll; NHS; Frstry Engrng Schlrshp 87; Keystone JC; Frstry Engrng.

VERDUCI, CARMELA A; Bishop Shanahan HS; Westchester, PA; (4); Drama Clb; Math Tm; Office Aide; Quiz Bowl; Service Clb; Chorus; Nwsp Rptr; Hon Roll; Wstchstr U; Accntng.

VERGANO, DAVID; Du Bois Area HS; Dubois, PA; (3); 37/300; JV Socr; Var Tennis; Film Prod.

VERGARA, ANGELINA; Trinity HS; Camp Hill, PA; (2); Pep Clb; Spanish Clb; School Play; Rep Stu Cncl; JV Bsktbl; Var Crs Cntry; Hon Roll; Capital Sci Fair Hon Mntn 86; Jv Ltr Bsktbl, Cross Cntry 86-87; Notre Dame U; Fashn Merchns.

VERGASON, LORI; Montoursville HS; Trout Run, PA; (1); Dance Clb; French Clb; JV Cheerleading; Philadelphia Textile.

VERGENES, DENISE; Sto-Rox SR HS; Mc Kees Rocks, PA; (4); 18/149; Church Yth Grp; Letterman Clb; Office Aide; Color Guard; Flag Corp; Yrbk Stf; Capt Pom Pon; Vllybl; Hon Roll; NHS; Lone Star Schlrshp 87; Robert Morris Coll; Bus Admin.

VERGOTZ, CRAIG; Fort Le Boeuf HS; Erie, PA; (3); Spanish Clb; JV Var Ftbl; Im Vllybl; Wt Lftg; JV Wrstlng; Hon Roll; Bus.

VERKUILEN, ROBERT; Chambersburg Area SR HS; Chambersburg, PA; (3); Pep Clb; Variety Show; Var L Ftbl; Var L Socr; Im Vllybl; High Hon Roll; Hon Roll; Mid Penn Div I Sccr All-St Tm 1st Tm 86; Chambersburg Trojan Sccr Tm MVP 86; Bus.

VERMEULEN, TRACY; Hopewell HS; Clinton, PA; (3); 4-H; French Clb; JA; Im Sftbl; 4-H Awd; High Hon Roll; Hon Roll; Softball Trophy 85-87; Jrnlsm.

VERNA, LISA; W Philadelphia Cath Girls HS; Philadelphia, PA; (4); 14/246; Art Clb; Math Tm; Model UN; Pres Office Aide; Speech Tm; Stage Crew; VP Jr Cls; Pres Sr Cls; Hon Roll; NHS; Smmr Art Pgm, Early Accptnce Schlrshp-Moore Coll Art 86; Temple U Outstndng Achvt Italian 85; Moore Coll Art; Intr Dsgn.

VERNA, NICK; West Catholic High Schl For Boys; Philadelphia, PA; (3); 35/250; Boy Scts; Frsh Cls; Stu Cncl; Bsbl; Socr; High Hon Roll; Hon Roll; NHS; Stu Cncl Cert 85; Frgn Lang Hnr Rll 86-87; Conduct Awd 85-87; Engrng.

VERNATI, LINDA; Bishop Kenrick HS; Norristown, PA; (4); 30/295; Hosp Aide; Ski Clb; School Play; JV Crs Cntry; Hon Roll; NHS; Mont Cnty Orthpdc Schlrshp 87; Villanova Prnt Schlrshp 87; Villanova U; Nrsng.

VERNER, DAVID; Mc Guffey HS; Washington, PA; (3); Pres VP German Clb; Nwsp Stf; Pres Jr Cls; Rep Stu Cncl; Var L Bsbl; L Trk; High Hon Roll; Hon Roll; NHS; Ntl Merit Ltr; Ldrshp Awd 85-87; Boston Coll; Mech Engrng.

VERNET, MICHELE; Ringgold HS; Danora, PA; (3); PTA Rflctns Cntst Hnrbl Mntn-Lit 86; Prom Cmmtte 86; Jrnlsm.

VERNETTI, DEANA; Central Catholic HS; Reading, PA; (3); 1/120; Flag Corp; School Musical; High Hon Roll; Pres NHS; Ntl Merit Ltr; Prfct Atten Awd; Psych.

VERNUSKY, FRANK J; Cardinal Brennan HS; Frackville, PA; (3); 14/59; Bsbl; Bsktbl; Vllybl; Hon Roll; K Of C Tournament All Star Bsktbl 86; Bsbl 3 Yrs V Let 85-87; Bsktbl 2 Yrs V Let 86-87; Physcl Therapy.

VEROLI, NICOLAS J; Friends Select HS; Narberth, PA; (4); English Clb; Lit Mag; Oberlin; Author.

VERONA, MIKE; Franklin Regional HS; Murrysville, PA; (3); SADD; School Play; Var Bsktbl; JV Cheerleading; Var Capt Ftbl; Var Capt Trk; Wt Lftg; Hon Roll; NHS; Ex Comptn Awd 86-87; Sci.

VERONESI, DAVID; Belle Vernon Area HS; Belle Vernon, PA; (4); 39/270; Pres Church Yth Grp; Ski Clb; Rep Stu Cncl; Sftbl; French Hon Soc; High Hon Roll; NHS; Hmrm Pres 85-86; U Of Pittsburgh.

VEROTSKY, MARC; Cumberland Valley HS; Mechanicsburg, PA; (2); 55/604; Var L Swmmng; Hon Roll; Keystone ST Games Water Polo 87; Engrng.

VERRECCHIA, ANTHONY N; Cardinal O Hara HS; Glenolden, PA; (3); 55/770; Cmnty Wkr; Lit Mag; Hon Roll; Drexel U; Bus Adm.

VERRILL, MICHAEL D; Governor Mifflin HS; Mohnton, PA; (4); 31/257; Model UN; Varsity Clb; School Musical; Swing Chorus; Var L Crs Cntry; Var L Swmmng; Var L Trk; Hon Roll; Jr NHS; Pres Schlr; Awd Excllnc 87; Unified Achvt Awd 85-87; Sprts Perservnc Awd 87; Temple U; Biomed.

VERSHINSKI, JIM; Sun Valley HS; Media, PA; (4); 19/310; Computer Clb; Concert Band; Jazz Band; Mrchg Band; Stage Crew; Variety Show; High Hon Roll; Hon Roll; Jr NHS; NHS; Drexel U; Mchncl Engnrng.

VERTULLO, MIA; St Francis Acad; Pittsburgh, PA; (4); 3/34; Library Aide; Band; Concert Band; Jazz Band; Mrchg Band; Orch; Pep Band; Hon Roll; Pres Schlr; Natl Hnr Rl 87; Gregg Shrthd Awd 85; Bradford Schl; Legl Secy.

VERZINSKI, BECKY; Plum SR HS; Pittsburgh, PA; (3); 27/410; DECA; Pres Symp Band; Ed Nwsp Sprt Ed; Var L Mgr(s); Var L Vllybl; NHS; NEDT Awd; French Clb; FTA; Library Aide; Willow Pond Jr Olympc Vllybll Tm 87; 1st Pl In PA Cultural Arts Cont 86; Seton Hill Coll Schlrshp 86; Kent ST U; Law.

VESCO, ANGELA; Lincoln HS; Ellwood City, PA; (3); 9/150; Drama Clb; Band; Concert Band; Mrchg Band; School Musical; Stage Crew; High Hon Roll; Hon Roll; NHS; Prfct Atten Awd.

VESELENY, JILL; West Mifflin Area HS; West Mifflin, PA; (3); 11/317; Exploring; Ski Clb; Powder Puff Ftbl; Vllybl; High Hon Roll; Hon Roll; Jr NHS; Med.

VESELY, LISA; Mon Valley Catholic HS; Belle Vernon, PA; (3); French Clb; Ski Clb; Chorus; Rep Soph Cls; Rep Jr Cls; Var Cheerleading; French Hon Soc; Hon Roll; Phrmcy.

VESIANY, KATHLEEN; Meadville Area SR HS; Meadville, PA; (3); Church Yth Grp; French Clb; Sec Pep Clb; Science Clb; Ski Clb; Rep Jr Cls; Rep Stu Cncl; Hon Roll; PA Free Enterprise Schlrshp 87; Engl.

VESNESKY, DEBRA; Brownsville Area HS; Allison, PA; (3); 20/240; Drama Clb; FBLA; Intnl Clb; Ski Clb; SADD; Variety Show; Nwsp Stf; High Hon Roll; Hon Roll; Am Leg Aux Dept PA Schl Awd 84; Nrsng.

VESOTSKI, LISA; Butler Area SR HS; Washington, WV; (4); 325/699; Cmnty Wkr; Red Cross Aide; Ski Clb; Varsity Clb; Pep Band; Sec Jr Cls; Rep Stu Cncl; JV Capt Cheerleading; Stat Trk; High Hon Roll; Gd Ctzn Of Mnth; White Awd-GPA 3.0-3.5; Parkersburg CC; Bus.

VETERE, GINA; Stroudsburg HS; Stroudsburg, PA; (3); Chorus; Hon Roll; NHS; Pres Frsh Cls; Var Capt Bsktbl; JV Gym; JV Socr; Var JV Twrlr; Grammar Schl Teacher.

VETERE, SCOTT; Monessen HS; Monessen, PA; (3); 17/120; Church Yth Grp; French Clb; Stage Crew; Ftbl; Golf; Socr; High Hon Roll; Engr.

VETTESE, SHARON; Wissahickon HS; Ambler, PA; (3); 40/278; AFS; 4-H; Hosp Aide; Key Clb; SADD; JV Tennis; 4-H Awd; High Hon Roll; Hon Roll; NHS; Nrsg.

VICARIO, DENISE; Gwynedd Mercy Acad; Horsham, PA; (2); Cmnty Wkr; Intnl Clb; Model UN; Office Aide; Chorus; Im Vllybl; Intl Law.

VICCARI, GINA; Lincoln HS; New Castle, PA; (4); VP Camera Clb; Key Clb; Ski Clb; Y-Teens; Chorus; Powder Puff Ftbl; Var Capt Trk; High Hon Roll; Hon Roll; Kiwanis Awd; Slippery Rock U; Psych.

VICE, MICHAEL; Cardinal Ohara HS; Drexel Hill, PA; (2); 275/647; Band; Concert Band; Drill Tm; Jazz Band; Mrchg Band; School Musical; School Play; Comp Prgmr.

VICENT, JAIME; Cardinal Dougherty HS; Philadelphia, PA; (2); Wt Lftg; High Hon Roll; Hon Roll; Acdmc Prfcncy & Athltc Accmplshmt 87; Sci.

VICIC, ROBYN; Nativity B V M HS; Minersville, PA; (3); 3/89; Computer Clb; Chorus; Nwsp Rptr; Cheerleading; Sftbl; High Hon Roll; NHS; Intl Frgm Lang Awd 85 & 86.

VICKERMAN, LEIGH ANN; Marple Newtown SR HS; Broomall, PA; (3); 64/322; SADD; School Musical; School Play; Nwsp Stf; Yrbk Ed-Chief; Lit Mag; VP Jr Cls; Stu Cncl; Mgr Ftbl; NHS; :Phys Thrpy.

VICKERS, MARC; Ringgold HS; Eighty Four, PA; (3); 35/351; Aud/Vis; SADD; Stage Crew; Hon Roll; Outdrs Clb 86-87; Wldlf Mgmt.

VICKI, LENTZ; Millersburg Area HS; Millersburg, PA; (3); Spanish Clb; Yrbk Stf; Stu Cncl; Var Bsktbl; Var Cheerleading; Im Powder Puff Ftbl; Var Trk; High Hon Roll.

VICKROY, RAY; Greater Johnstown Area Vo-Tech Schl; Johnstown, PA; (2); VICA; Var Bsbl; Hon Roll; Voc Tech Awd 87; Vale Tech; Ins Apprsr.

VICTOR, STEPHANI; Quaker Valley SR HS; Sewickley, PA; (4); 22/168; Church Yth Grp; French Clb; JA; Chorus; Church Choir; School Musical; School Play; Nwsp Stf; VP Jr Cls; Off Stu Cncl; U Of Sthrn CA; Actng.

VICTORIA, RICHARD; Belle Vernon Area HS; Belle Vernon, PA; (3); Pres Band; Concert Band; Mrchg Band; Rep Stu Cncl; JV Var Bsktbl; Var Golf; High Hon Roll; NHS.

VIDA, MICHELLE; Peters Township HS; Bridgeville, PA; (3); Dance Clb; Intnl Clb; NFL; Yrbk Stf; High Hon Roll; Hon Roll.

VIDEON, CAREY; Marple Newtown HS; Newtown Square, PA; (3); GAA; Intnl Clb; Varsity Clb; Trs Jr Cls; Var Bsktbl; Var Fld Hcky; Var Lcrss; High Hon Roll; Hon Roll; NHS.

VIDIC, ELIZABETH; Moniteau JR SR HS; W Sunbury, PA; (4); Ski Clb; Spanish Clb; Concert Band; Mrchg Band; Stat Bsktbl; Stat Trk; NHS; Slippery Rock U; Nrsng.

VIDIC, STEPHEN; Shady Side Acad; Cheswick, PA; (3); Church Yth Grp; Cmnty Wkr; Letterman Clb; Ski Clb; SADD; Im Bsbl; L Bsktbl; Capt L Ftbl; Im Golf; Im Wt Lftg; Med.

VIDOVICH, CHRISTOPHER; Aliquippa JR SR HS; Aliquippa, PA; (3); 2/120; Church Yth Grp; French Clb; Math Tm; Band; Concert Band; Mrchg Band; Pep Band; JV Var Bsktbl; High Hon Roll; Hon Roll; Pres Of Natl Hnr Soc 87-88; Pre-Med.

VIERKORN, KRISTIN; General Mc Lane HS; Edinboro, PA; (4); 31/187; Church Yth Grp; Girl Scts; Spanish Clb; Teachers Aide; Band; Concert Band; Mrchg Band; Symp Band; Sftbl; High Hon Roll; Girls Scts Amer Silver Awd 87; Edinboro U; Elem Ed.

VIGGIANO, GREGORY; New Castle SR HS; New Castle, PA; (3); #17 In Class; Political Wkr; Spanish Clb; SADD; Concert Band; Mrchg Band; Var Trk; Var Wrstlng; God Cntry Awd; Hon Roll; Vet.

VIGILANTE, CATHERINE; West Scranton HS; Scranton, PA; (3); 30/290; Art Clb; Church Yth Grp; Cmnty Wkr; Latin Clb; Pep Clb; Red Cross Aide; Ski Clb; Speech Tm; Thesps; Sec Jr Cls; Marywood Coll; Elem Ed.

VIGILANTE, WILLIAM; West Scranton HS; Scranton, PA; (2); Latin Clb; Ski Clb; Bsktbl; Crs Cntry.

VIGLIANTI, ANTHONY; Notre Dame HS; Easton, PA; (3); 45/90; Var Bsbl; Var Bsktbl; Amer Lgn Awd 84; Millersville U; Ed.

VIGORITO, MELISSA; Villa Maria Acad; Erie, PA; (3); Cmnty Wkr; Debate Tm; Q&S; Science Clb; SADD; Teachers Aide; Temple Yth Grp; School Play; Nwsp Rptr; Hon Roll; United Way Of Erie-Vlntr Svc Awd 86; Yale Jrnlsm Wrkshp 87; 1st VP N E Lakes Temple Yth 87-88; Cornell; Pol Sci.

VILA, JENNIFER; Annville-Cleona HS; Annville, PA; (4); French Clb; VP Acpl Chr; Concert Band; Madrigals; Orch; Yrbk Sprt Ed; Var L Tennis; NHS; Voice Dem Awd; PA ST U; Bus.

VILAR, JOVELYN LANGIT; Gwynedd Mercy Acad; Horsham, PA; (2); Service Clb; Chorus; Yrbk Stf; High Hon Roll; Cum Lde-Ntl Latin Exam 86-87; Cert Awd-Acadc Excllnc-Bio, Latin II, Music & Acc Spnsh II 86-87; Med.

VILCKO, KENNETH; Hazleton HS; Drums, PA; (4); 104/376; Boy Scts; FBLA; Ftbl; SAR Awd; Wildlife Consrvtn.

VILGOS, RENEE; Lakeland HS; Mayfield, PA; (3); Rep FHA; SADD; Capt Var Cheerleading; JV Score Keeper; Hon Roll; Prfct Atten Awd; Bankng Finc.

VILLAFRANCA, JUNE; State College Intermediate Schl; State College, PA; (1); Church Yth Grp; Cmnty Wkr; Ski Clb; Band; Mrchg Band; Im Powder Puff Ftbl; Hon Roll; PA ST U; Med.

VILLALPANDO, CAMILLE; Sacred Heart HS; Pittsburgh, PA; (4); 2/138; Chorus; Jazz Band; School Musical; School Play; Elks Awd; High Hon Roll; NHS; Ntl Merit SF; Sal; Drama Clb; Prom Committee Chrprsn; Duquesne U Schlr; Storytellers Clb; Duquesne U; Music Therapy.

VILLANI, BRIDGET; Neshannock HS; Neshannock, PA; (3); 8/102; Drama Clb; Ski Clb; Teachers Aide; Chorus; School Musical; School Play; Yrbk Bus Mgr; Yrbk Stf; Sec Stu Cncl; NHS; Pres Acdmc Ftnss Awd 85; Duquesne; Comm.

VILLANI, NICKIE; Altoona Area HS; Altoona, PA; (3); Variety Show; Var Frsh Cls; Trs Stu Cncl; Cheerleading; Hon Roll; 3 Consctv K Pin Awds 85; Math Awd 85; Cls Exec Cmmtte 85; PA ST U; Pharmaceuticals.

VILLANI, SHERRI; West Scranton HS; Scranton, PA; (2); Spanish Clb; Var Cheerleading.

VILLAROSE, LENNON; Garnet Valley HS; Chaddsford, PA; (2); Church Yth Grp; Drama Clb; French Clb; Hosp Aide; Chorus; Church Choir; School Musical; Hon Roll; Penn ST U; Psych.

VILLARREAL, REBECCA; Germantown Friends Schl; Philadelphia, PA; (4); Chorus; School Musical; School Play; Nwsp Bus Mgr; Im Bsktbl; JV Fld Hcky; Var JV Lcrss; Mxcn Exchng Pgm 83-84; Smi-Fnlst-Ntl Hspnc Schlr Awds Pgm 86-87; Georgetown U; Lang.

VILLECCO, ANNA; Pequea Valley HS; Ronks, PA; (3); Sec Chrmn FFA; Chorus; Yrbk Stf; Hon Roll; NHS; Bus Mngr.

VILLEE, DEBBIE; Fort Cherry HS; Midway, PA; (4); Computer Clb; Pres Drama Clb; Math Clb; Science Clb; Ski Clb; Spanish Clb; Thesps; Varsity Clb; School Play; Var L Cheerleading.

VILLELLA, DAMON; Brookville Area HS; Summerville, PA; (3); 35/170; Chess Clb; Cmnty Wkr; Band; Concert Band; Jazz Band; Mrchg Band; Pep Band; Hon Roll; PA ST; Engrng.

VILLERS, STEVEN W; Ringgold HS; Monongahela, PA; (2); 1/350; Boy Scts; Church Yth Grp; Science Clb; Concert Band; Mrchg Band; School Musical; Swmmng; God Cntry Awd; High Hon Roll; NHS; Vet Med.

VINAY, JOHN; Steel Valley SR HS; Munhall, PA; (3); 10/273; JV Capt Ice Hcky; Pre-Med.

VINCENT, ALLYSON; New Castle SR HS; New Castle, PA; (3); 35/293; Library Aide; Sec Sr Cls; Sec Stu Cncl; Var Cheerleading; Trk; Hon Roll; Jr NHS; NHS; Natl Hon Roll 87; Italian Clb 86-88; Mercy Hurst Coll; Fashion Merch.

VINCENT, JOHN; Riverview HS; Oakmont, PA; (4); 14/126; Drama Clb; French Clb; Jazz Band; School Play; Yrbk Stf; Off Sr Cls; High Hon Roll; Hon Roll; Westchester U; Spch Comms.

VINCENT, RENEE; Duquesne HS; Duquesne, PA; (3); 6/96; French Clb; High Hon Roll; Hon Roll; NHS; Score Keeper; 4-H Awd; Rotary Awd; Mdcl Fld.

VINCENT, ROBERT; Yough SR HS; W Newton, PA; (3); 40/237; Pres Computer Clb; Spanish Clb; Golf; NHS; Westmoreland IV Microcomp Prgrmg Cntst 1st Pl 85; Elctrcl Engrng.

VINCENT, SEAN E; North Star HS; Jennerstown, PA; (2); Boy Scts; VP Church Yth Grp; Mu Alpha Theta; German Clb; Hon Roll; Embry Riddle; Aero.

VINCENT, WAYNE; Coatesville Area SR HS; Coatesville, PA; (3); Boy Scts; Nwsp Stf; Var Capt Crs Cntry; Var Capt Trk; Hon Roll; Crs Cntry MVP Awd 86; PA ST U; Bus.

VINCI, KAREN; Sto-Rox SR HS; Mc Kees Rocks, PA; (4); 35/143; Boys Clb Am; Exploring; Trs FBLA; Letterman Clb; Political Wkr; SADD; Pres Band; Ed Yrbk Stf; Pres Soph Cls; Hon Roll; Duquesne U; Law.

VINCLER, ALIZA; Leechburg Area HS; Leechburg, PA; (2); Drama Clb; GAA; JA; Spanish Clb; SADD; Chorus; Nwsp Phtg; Yrbk Phtg; Rep Stu Cncl; Hon Roll; Bus Manag.

VINEY, VINCENT S; Northeast Catholic HS; Philadelphia, PA; (2); 4/370; Boy Scts; Yrbk Rptr; JV Bsktbl; Var Ftbl; French Hon Soc; High Hon Roll; Hon Roll; NHS.

VINGELIS, KRISTINA; Penn Trafford HS; Jeannette, PA; (2); Cmnty Wkr; French Clb; Hosp Aide; Var Swmmng; High Hon Roll; Hon Roll; Med.

VINGLAS, LYNETTE; Penn Cambria HS; Ashville, PA; (3); VP DECA; GAA; Teachers Aide; Variety Show; JV Bsktbl; Var L Sftbl; Trk; JV Var Vllybl; Cit Awd; Hon Roll; Medal DECA Dist & St Conf 86-87.

VINGLAS, ORIANA; Penn Cambria HS; Portage, PA; (4); 12/196; Art Clb; Drama Clb; Pres Girl Scts; Scholastic Bowl; Ski Clb; Chorus; Yrbk Stf; JV Cheerleading; High Hon Roll; Hon Roll; U Scholar Scholarship Awd At Duquesne 87-91; Schlrshp For American U In DC 87-91; Duquesne; Law.

VINGLESS, JOHN; Moshannon Valley HS; Houtzdale, PA; (3); JV Bsbl; High Hon Roll; Hon Roll; ICM Schl Of Bus; Comp Prog.

VINKLER, LISA; Jeannette SR HS; Jeannette, PA; (3); 22/153; Hosp Aide; Band; Color Guard; Jazz Band; Off Stu Cncl; High Hon Roll; Hon Roll; French Clb; Mdcl Lab Tech.

VINSKOFSKI, KELLY; West Scranton HS; Scranton, PA; (4); 28/245; Dance Clb; French Clb; Red Cross Aide; Ski Clb; Spanish Clb; Nwsp Stf; Yrbk Stf; Off Stu Cncl; High Hon Roll; Hon Roll; Acdmc All-Amrcn Schlr, Prsdntl Acdmc Ftnss Awd 87; Hlth Careers Clb 83-87; Wilkes Coll; Med Sci.

VINSON, SHANNON; Abraham Lincoln HS; Philadelphia, PA; (3); 8/500; Rep Church Yth Grp; Pres Computer Clb; Rep French Clb; Teachers Aide; Yrbk Stf; Rep French Hon Soc; High Hon Roll; Rep Jr NHS; Rep NHS; Ntl Merit SF; Prfct Atten 86-87; Frnch Tchr.

VINZANI, KEVIN; Southmoreland HS; Scottdale, PA; (3); 14/222; Church Yth Grp; Letterman Clb; Math Clb; Spanish Clb; Rep Stu Cncl; Var L Bsktbl; Im Ftbl; Im Golf; Spanish NHS.

VIRGILI, TINAMARIE; Boyertown SR HS; Bechtelsville, PA; (3); Art Clb; 4-H; Hosp Aide; Key Clb; Pep Clb; Teachers Aide; Drill Tm; Yrbk Stf; Cheerleading; Sftbl; Art Awd 86; San Diego Mesa Coll; Fshn Dsgn.

VISCUSI, RHONDA; Nazareth Acad; Philadelphia, PA; (3); 50/125; Debate Tm; NFL; Chorus; Red Cross Aide; Ed Lit Mag; Prfct Atten Awd; JR Vrsty City Debt Champ 85; Cmmrcl Art.

VISHNISKY, WAYNE PAUL; Valley View JR SR HS; Archbald, PA; (4); 10/198; Spanish Clb; High Hon Roll; Hon Roll; Hnr Rl Awd 87; Spn Acad Awds 83-87; Acad Excllnce Awds 83-87; 18th Pl Natl Sci Lg Tsts 86-87; U Scranton; Acctng.

VISNANSKY, DORIS; Perry Traditional Acad; Pittsburgh, PA; (3); 6/190; Cmnty Wkr; JA; Library Aide; Concert Band; Nwsp Ed-Chief; Yrbk Stf; Lit Mag; Jr NHS; NHS; Prfct Atten Awd; Drftng.

VISSOTSKI, CARLA; James M Coughlin HS; Plains, PA; (4); Hosp Aide; Ski Clb; Capt Cheerleading; Var Capt Fld Hcky; Var Capt Sftbl; Mgr Wrstlng; High Hon Roll; Tom A Evans Awd 87; Dallas Kiwanis All Star MVP Sftbl 87; Miss Unico 87; Cedar Crest Coll; Pyscl Thrpst.

VISWANATHAN, AKILA; Geibel HS; Connellsville, PA; (4); 1/80; Model UN; Stage Crew; Trs Stu Cncl; Var Cheerleading; Bausch & Lomb Sci Awd; Pres French Hon Soc; Kiwanis Awd; Ntl Merit Ltr; Pres Schlr; Val; PA Govrs Schl For Intl Studies 85; PA Gvrns Sch Sci 86; Girl Of Yr Awd 87; Harvard-Radcliffe Coll; Pre-Med.

VISWANATHAN, SRI; Cedar Crest HS; Gettysburg, PA; (4); 22/306; Intnl Clb; Key Clb; Model UN; School Musical; School Play; High Hon Roll; NHS; Pres Schlr; People To People HS Ambssdr 85; Pres Acad Fit Awd 87; American U; Intl Studs.

VITALE, JOHN-PAUL; Spring-Ford HS; Pottstown, PA; (4); German Clb; SADD; Ftbl; Trk; Mansfield U; Bus.

VITALE, KAREN A; St Cyril Acad; Duryea, PA; (4); 2/14; VP Key Clb; Capt Quiz Bowl; Nwsp Ed-Chief; Nwsp Stf; Trs Sr Cls; Rep Stu Cncl; DAR Awd; High Hon Roll; NHS; Sal; Tufts U Schlrshp 87; Kings Coll Discvry Pgm Schlrshp 86; Chem Div,Best Of Show-Sci Fair 87; Tufts U; European Stds.

VITALE, RONALD; Father Judge HS; Philadelphia, PA; (3); 7/403; French Clb; Diocesan Schlrs Awd 87; Villanova U; Astrnmy.

VITALETTI, PAULA; West Scranton HS; Scranton, PA; (2); Hon Roll.

VITANZA, TIM; Hampton HS; Allison Park, PA; (4); Pres Chess Clb; Computer Clb; Math Clb; Math Tm; Scholastic Bowl; Science Clb; Var Capt Bowling; High Hon Roll; NHS; Ntl Merit Ltr; Carnegie Mellon U; Elec Engrng.

VITH, DENISE; West Allegheny HS; Cora, PA; (4); 40/201; Sec Drama Clb; Chrmn Chorus; School Play; Stat Swmmng; Hon Roll; Carnegie Mellon U; Info Systms.

VITO, KRISTA; Bishop Haley HS; Hazleton, PA; (3); Church Yth Grp; Key Clb; Ski Clb; Spanish Clb; Yrbk Stf; Off Stu Cncl; Cheerleading; Socr; Trk; Hon Roll; Ltr Wnnr Trk; Awd Outstndng Prfrmnc Phys Ed III; Penn ST; Med.

VITRO, JOSEPH; Hazleton HS; Hazleton, PA; (2); Boy Scts; Church Yth Grp; Debate Tm; Drama Clb; PAVAS; Quiz Bowl; Scholastic Bowl; Spanish Clb; Thesps; Band; Marine Bio.

VITUSZYNSKI, LAURA M; Cedar Crest HS; Lebanon, PA; (4); Church Yth Grp; Cmnty Wkr; Computer Clb; FTA; Girl Scts; Key Clb; Pep Clb; Radio Clb; Spanish Clb; SADD; Homeroom Rep 84; Comp Prgmmg.

VIVIAN, BRANDON; Moon HS; Coraopolis, PA; (2); JA; Concert Band; Mrchg Band; Bowling; Trk; Hon Roll; NHS; Outstndng Acdmc Achvt Hnr Awd 87.

VIVIAN, VALERIE; Belle Vernon Area HS; Belle Vernon, PA; (3); High Hon Roll; Hon Roll; Nrsng.

VIVINO, MELINA; Penn Hills HS; Pittsburgh, PA; (4); 45/609; French Clb; FBLA; Yrbk Phtg; Yrbk Stf; Stu Cncl; Bsktbl; High Hon Roll; Hon Roll; NHS; Penn Hebron PTA Schlrshp Awd 87; SR Cls Schlrshp 87; PA ST U; Psych.

VIVIS, LISA; Bishop Mc Cort HS; Parkhill, PA; (4); Art Clb; Church Yth Grp; Latin Clb; Pep Clb; Chorus; School Musical; Trk; U Of Pittsburgh; Psych.

VIZZA, JENNIFER; Monessen HS; Monessen, PA; (3); Church Yth Grp; French Clb; Girl Scts; JA; Band; Mrchg Band; Nwsp Stf; High Hon Roll; Prfct Atten Awd.

VIZZA, TERESA; Monessen HS; Monessen, PA; (4); 1/92; French Clb; JA; Sec Band; Yrbk Bus Mgr; Ed Yrbk Stf; Trs Frsh Cls; Stu Cncl; Bausch & Lomb Sci Awd; High Hon Roll; Pres NHS; Sons Of Italy Dist Schlrshp 87; Union Carbide Cngrssnl Smnr Schlrshp 86; Duquesnse U Schlrs Awd 87; Duquesne U; Phrmcy.

VLAICH, RANDY; Western Beaver JR-SR HS; Midland, PA; (3); Band; Chorus; Concert Band; Mrchg Band; Symp Band; Capt Bowling; JV Var Ftbl; Stat Trk; Wt Lftg; PA ST U; Comp Sci.

VLASAK, SHELLY; Daniel Boone HS; Birdsboro, PA; (3); 16/176; French Clb; German Clb; Varsity Clb; Var Cheerleading; Stat Wrstlng; High Hon Roll; Hon Roll; Engr.

VLASIC, SHERILYN; Butler Area SR HS; Butler, PA; (3); 31/709; Exploring; French Clb; VP Hosp Aide; SADD; Mrchg Band; Symp Band; Rep Stu Cncl; Jr NHS; NHS; Acad Ltr 85-86; Acad Achvt Awd 86-87; Phrmcy.

VLASNIK, JON; Meadville SR HS; Meadville, PA; (4); 16/290; Science Clb; Varsity Clb; Nwsp Bus Mgr; Var L Bsbl; Var L Ftbl; NHS; High Hon Roll; MASH Schlrshp 87; 1st Tm Def Bck, 2nd Tm Pntr NWC Ftbl 86; U Of Pittsburgh; Phrmcy.

VODA, CARIE LYNN; Steel Valley HS; Munhall, PA; (3); 22/205; SADD; Band; Concert Band; Mrchg Band; Yrbk Stf; Sftbl; Capt Var Tennis; Hon Roll; NHS; Boy Scts; Tnns MVP 86-87; Med.

VODA, LORI; Wyalusing Valley HS; Laceyville, PA; (3); Church Yth Grp; 4-H; Library Aide; Ski Clb; Spanish Clb; Concert Band; Drill Tm; Mrchg Band; Pep Band; Hon Roll; Advrtsng.

VODDI, MADHU; Downingtown SR HS; Downingtown, PA; (3); 22/648; Spanish Clb; Orch; Mgr(s); JV L Tennis; High Hon Roll; Hon Roll; NHS; NEDT Awd; Med.

VODENICHAR, JENNY; Slippery Rock Area HS; Slippery Rock, PA; (4); 14/173; 4-H; German Clb; Intnl Clb; Cheerleading; Powder Puff Ftbl; 4-H Awd; Hon Roll; NHS; Ntl Merit SF; PA ST U; Pre-Med.

VODVARKA, KAREN; East Allegheny HS; North Versailles, PA; (3); Church Yth Grp; French Clb; JA; Ski Clb; Color Guard; Mgr(s); Mgr Trk; High Hon Roll; NHS; Prfct Atten Awd; U Of Pittsburgh; Pharm.

VOELKL, DAWNA; Avonworth JR SR HS; Pittsburgh, PA; (4); 1/99; Yrbk Bus Mgr; Ed Lit Mag; Var JV Socr; High Hon Roll; NHS; Church Yth Grp; Cmnty Wkr; JCL; Stat Bsktbl; Leon Owoc Mem Schlrshp, Athenean Awd 87; MVP Offnsv Sccr 85; Bryn Mawr Coll; Pre-Med.

VOGEL, AMY; Bishop Mc Cort HS; Johnstown, PA; (2); Church Yth Grp; Hosp Aide; Service Clb; JV Co-Capt Cheerleading; Trk; High Hon Roll; Hon Roll; Pharmacist.

VOGEL, MARNIE; Leechburg Area HS; Leechburg, PA; (3); Spanish Clb; Band; Chorus; Concert Band; Mrchg Band; Pep Band; Yrbk Stf; Cheerleading; Sftbl.

VOGEL, NEIL; Lower Moreland HS; Huntingdon Valley, PA; (3); FBLA; Key Clb; Science Clb; SADD; Temple Yth Grp; Trs Soph Cls; Trs Jr Cls; Var Bsktbl; Hon Roll; NHS; Intl JR Maccabi Games Toronto Canada Bsktbl 86; Le High U Yth Ldrshp Conf Dely 86.

VOGEL, SHARON; Vincentian HS; Pittsburgh, PA; (4); Drama Clb; Nwsp Rptr; Yrbk Rptr; VP Frsh Cls; Sec Sr Cls; Capt Bsktbl; High Hon Roll; VP NHS; Prfct Atten Awd; Pres Schlr; Duquesne Unv Cmptv Schlrshp 87; HS Ldrshp Awd 87; Hghst Grd Pnt Avrg In Englsh 86; Duquesne U; Phrmcy.

VOGELIN, LORIANN; Salisbury HS; Bethlehem, PA; (3); FBLA; Girl Scts; Hon Roll; Prfct Atten Awd; Slvr Ldrshp Awd 87; Bus.

VOGELSANG, STEVE; Geibel HS; Uniontown, PA; (3); 5/100; Boy Scts; French Clb; Science Clb; Ski Clb; JV Stat Bsktbl; Var L Crs Cntry; Mgr(s); Var Trk; Trs French Hon Soc; High Hon Roll; Cross Cntry MVP 86; Comp Engrng.

VOGLER, JENNIFER; Susquehanna Community HS; Thompson, PA; (2); SADD; Rep Stu Cncl; Var Crs Cntry; Library Aide; Ski Clb; School Play; JV Cheerleading; Dr.

VOGLER, SCOTT; Susquehanna JR- SR HS; Thompson, PA; (3); Chess Clb; Ski Clb; SADD; Concert Band; Mrchg Band; Bsktbl; Cheerleading; Coach Actv; Ftbl; Mgr(s); Marines; ST Police.

VOIT, TIMOTHY; Cheltarhan HS; Cheltenham, PA; (4); 74/365; Boy Scts; Church Yth Grp; Political Wkr; Band; Im Bsktbl; JV Crs Cntry; JV Ftbl; Capt Trk; Ntl Merit Ltr; US Army Rsrv Schlr/Athl Awd 87; Trk Tm Schlr/Athl Awd 87; Natl Merit Ltr 86; Colgate U.

VOITHOFER, LORI; Fairchance-Georges SR HS; Smithfield, PA; (4); Drama Clb; Math Tm; Chorus; School Play; Nwsp Bus Mgr; Hon Roll; NHS; Pres Acdmc Ftnss Awd 86-87; Waynesburg Coll.

VOLACK, SUSAN; Little Flower HS; Philadelphia, PA; (3); 2/322; Pres Sec Church Yth Grp; Math Clb; Q&S; Orch; School Musical; School Play; Nwsp Rptr; Yrbk Stf; Lit Mag; VP NHS; Hghst Avg Wrld Cltres 87; Sci Fair Hon Mntn 85-86; Sci Fair 3rd Pl 87.

VOLK, SUSAN; Downingtown SR HS; Chester Springs, PA; (4); 12/561; French Clb; Key Clb; Ski Clb; Band; Chorus; Concert Band; Yrbk Stf; Trk; High Hon Roll; NHS; 3rd Pl Am Leg Wrtng Cont 85; Cntry Bnd 85; Vet Med.

VOLLENDORF, NICOLE; Hazleton HS; Drums, PA; (2); FBLA; Pep Clb; Service Clb; Ski Clb; Spanish Clb; Y-Teens; Rep Stu Cncl; JV Cheerleading; Gym; Achvd 4th Pl Awd In USCA Natl Grnd Chmpshp Lnsng 86; Pres Acad Ftns Awd Chrldng JV Div MI 86; Villanova U; Med.

VOLMER, STEPHANIE; Pocono Mtn HS; Pocono Pines, PA; (4); 3/328; Am Leg Aux Girls St; Scholastic Bowl; SADD; Chorus; Swing Chorus; Yrbk Bus Mgr; Yrbk Phtg; Yrbk Rptr; Yrbk Sprt Ed; Off Frsh Cls; WA Wrkshp Congrssnl Semnar 87; AM Lgn Auxilry Gilrs Ntn 86; Poltcl Sci.

VOLPE, BRADY; Saltsburg JR SR HS; Saltsburg, PA; (2); Band; Church Choir; Concert Band; Mrchg Band; Pep Band; JV Bsktbl; High Hon Roll; Hon Roll; Dist 3 Band Cncrt 86-87; Presdntl Acadc Ftnss Awd 85-86; Carnegie-Mellon U; Physcs.

VOLUCK, DAVID; Harriton HS; Penn Valley, PA; (3); FBLA; SADD; Rep Jr Cls; VP Stu Cncl; Capt Bsktbl; Capt Tennis; Hon Roll; NHS; Pres Physcl Ftns All Amer 87; Law.

VOM SAAL, DANIEL; Penn Manor HS; Holtwood, PA; (4); 1/315; Varsity Clb; Var Bsbl; Var Bsktbl; High Hon Roll; NHS; Ntl Merit SF; Rotary Awd; Spanish NHS; Voice Dem Awd; 1st Pl Atlntc-Pcfc Math Cntst; Comp Sci.

VON ARX, SUSAN; Ridgway Area HS; Ridgway, PA; (4); 15/104; Ski Clb; Yrbk Phtg; Yrbk Stf; Rep Jr Cls; Rep Sr Cls; Cheerleading; High Hon Roll; Hon Roll; IN U Of PA; Accntng.

VON BERG, KENNETH; Mastbaum HS; Philadelphia, PA; (2); Church Yth Grp; Bus Admin.

VON SCHLICHTEN, DAVID; Bangor HS; Bangor, PA; (4); 2/173; Pres Band; Chorus; Concert Band; Jazz Band; Mrchg Band; Pep Band; School Musical; School Play; Lit Mag; Bausch & Lomb Sci Awd; Most Outstndng Bnd Member For 4 Yrs; Arian Muscn Awd; Outstndng Stdnt Awd In Engl,Musc & Soc Stdies; Drew U; Engl Teacher.

VONAKIS, ANDREA L; Beaver Area JR SR HS; Beaver, PA; (3); 66/215; Sec Church Yth Grp; JCL; Latin Clb; Band; Chorus; Concert Band; Mrchg Band; School Musical; High Hon Roll; Hon Roll; Bus.

VONDELING, JOHANNA E; Academy Of Notre De Namlr HS; Valley Forge, PA; (4); Cmnty Wkr; Intnl Clb; Model UN; Service Clb; Speech Tm; School Musical; Nwsp Ed-Chief; Nwsp Rptr; Nwsp Stf; Ed Lit Mag; Brown U Bk Awd 86; Pol Sci.

VONGEIS, PEGGY; St Paul Cathedral HS; Pittsburgh, PA; (3); Church Yth Grp; CAP; GAA; Latin Clb; Pep Clb; Stage Crew; Var Bsktbl; Sftbl; U Of Pittsburgh; Law.

VOORHEES, DAWN; Pen Argyl HS; Pen Argyl, PA; (3); 3/160; Band; Orch; Trs Frsh Cls; Trs Soph Cls; Trs Jr Cls; JV Sftbl; Var Tennis; Var Trk; High Hon Roll; Jr NHS; Northampton Cnty JR Miss 87; Ldrshp Prgm Cngrssnl Yth Ldrshp Cncl 87; Ldrshp Sem Lions Clb 87; IN U PA; Math.

VORAS, RENEE; Shenango HS; New Castle, PA; (2); Office Aide; Teachers Aide; Drm Mjr(t); Nwsp Stf; Rep Soph Cls; Rep Stu Cncl; Stat Bsktbl; Stat Trk; Capt Twrlr; Hon Roll; Fash Merch.

VORE, NATHAN; Everett Area HS; Everett, PA; (3); Drama Clb; Bsbl; Art Clb; Chess Clb; Computer Clb; FFA; School Play; Stage Crew; Nwsp Stf; Golf; Archaeology.

VOSBURGH, KARA; Pennsbury HS; Yardley, PA; (3); Hosp Aide; Pep Clb; Varsity Clb; School Play; Var Cheerleading; Im Vllybl; Hon Roll; NHS; PA Free Enterprise Week 87; Bus.

VOSEFSKI, THERESA; Northampton HS; Bath, PA; (4); 14/446; AFS; Aud/Vis; Pep Clb; SADD; Off Stu Cncl; Capt Tennis; Vllybl; High Hon Roll; Hon Roll; Jr NHS; Rtry Schlrshp 87; Mst Outstndng SR Tnns 87; Qns Attndnt Jack Frost Prde 85; Bloomsburg U; Psychology.

VOSNICK, CHRISTY; Fort Cherry JR SR HS; Mcdonald, PA; (2); Math Clb; Science Clb; Ski Clb; Spanish Clb; Varsity Clb; Chorus; Tennis; High Hon Roll; Hon Roll; Hugh O Brien Awd 86-87; Educ.

VOTOVICH, JOHN A; Monongahela Valley Catholic HS; Coal Center, PA; (3); Boy Scts; Exploring; Var Capt Ftbl; Golf; Wt Lftg; Acdmc All Amer 86-87.

VOUGHT, SHERRY; Pen Argyl SR HS; Pen Argyl, PA; (4); 48/117; Drama Clb; Chorus; School Play; Nwsp Stf; Sec Frsh Cls; Sec Soph Cls; Var L Bsktbl; L JV Cheerleading; Var L Fld Hcky; Var L Trk; Golden Knight Awd 87; Air Force; Spcl Scrty Police.

VOYDIK, JANENE; Schuylkill Haven Area HS; Schuylkill Haven, PA; (3); 5/93; Church Yth Grp; FCA; German Clb; Science Clb; Bsktbl; Hon Roll; Psychtry.

VOYSZEY, SHERRI; Portage Area HS; Portage, PA; (3); 40/108; Girl Scts; Scholastic Bowl; Ski Clb; Varsity Clb; JV Bsktbl; JV Vllybl; Hon Roll; Miss Amer Coed Pgnt 85; Penn ST; Pblc Rltns.

VOYTEK, KAREN; Uniontown Area SR HS; Uniontown, PA; (4); 16/270; Sec Church Yth Grp; Spanish Clb; Yrbk Stf; High Hon Roll; NHS; Spanish NHS; Laurel Bus Inst Schlrshp 87; Laurel Bus Inst; Bnkng.

VOYTEK, KIERSTEN; Dunmore JR/Sr HS; Dunmore, PA; (3); 24/149; Trs French Clb; School Musical; Ed Yrbk Stf; Var Co-Capt Cheerleading; Var Swmmng; Var Trk; High Hon Roll; Hon Roll; Jr NHS; NHS; 1st Pl Diocese Esy Cont 86; Med.

VOYTISH, REBECCA; Monessen JR SR HS; Monessen, PA; (3); 5/115; Church Yth Grp; Drama Clb; French Clb; School Play; Cheerleading; High Hon Roll; Hon Roll; NHS; Am Leg Awd Rnnr Up 84-85; Elem Educ.

VOYTON, FRANCINE; John S Fine HS; Glen Lyon, PA; (4); Yrbk Phtg; Yrbk Stf; Luzerne Co Comm Coll; Lab Tech.

VOYTON, GENE; John S Fine HS; Nanticoke, PA; (4); Trk; Wt Lftg; High Hon Roll; Hon Roll; NHS; Penn ST; Engrng.

VRANA, LARA D; Penns Manor HS; Clymer, PA; (4); 9/97; Sec Varsity Clb; Yrbk Stf; Var Bsktbl; Var Capt Vllybl; Hon Roll; Sec NHS; Penns Manor Edctn Assn Schlrshp 87; Indiana U Of PA; Elem Educ.

VRANJES JR, DANIEL; Hickory HS; Hermitage, PA; (4); 1/170; Art Clb; Computer Clb; Latin Clb; Math Clb; NHS; Ntl Merit Ltr; Ntl Latin Hnr Soc; Cert Of Merit PA Soc Of Prfssnl Engrs; Attened PA Jr Sci & Humanties Sympsm; Engrng-Sci U; Aerospc Engr.

VRESILOVIC, JOHN; Homer Center HS; Coral, PA; (4); 6/90; Computer Clb; School Play; L Var Ftbl; Capt L Trk; Kiwanis Awd; NHS; NEDT Awd; Prfct Atten Awd; Prsdntl Acdmc Ftnss Awd 87; US Army Rsrv Ntl Schlr/Athlt Awd 87; Washington & Lee U; Engl.

VROBEL, CHAD; Punxsutawney Area HS; Punxsutawney, PA; (2); JV Bsbl; JV Ftbl; PA ST; Comp.

VROTNEY, MICHAEL; Highlands HS; Brackenridge, PA; (3); Cmnty Wkr; Office Aide; Cert Emrgncy Med Tech 86; Pioneerhse JR Fire Dept VP 86-87; Nrsng.

VU, PAMELA; Wm Allen HS; Allentown, PA; (3); 18/659; SADD; Band; Chorus; Concert Band; Flag Corp; Mrchg Band; Trk; Vllybl; Hon Roll; Sec NHS; Pol Sci.

VU, SON; Harrisburg HS; Harrisburg, PA; (3); Hnrs 84-87; Remodlng.

VU, THERESA N; Villa Maria Acad; Exton, PA; (4); 25/99; Co-Capt Math Tm; Sec Mu Alpha Theta; Science Clb; Orch; Stage Crew; Lit Mag; VP French Hon Soc; Music Hnr Soc Hist 85-87; ST Mem Of Natl Piano Plyng Aud 85-86; Finance.

VUCKOVICH, RICHARD; Greater Johnstown Vo-Tech; Johnstown, PA; (3); DECA; DECA Career Conf Dist 6th Pl Financd Credit 87; Finance.

VUGRINCIC, SUZETTE; Plum SR HS; Pittsburgh, PA; (4); 84/368; DECA; Sec French Clb; FTA; Band; Mrchg Band; Orch; School Musical; School Play; Symp Band; Hon Roll; Music Scholar Westminster Coll 87; SR All Amer Band Hall Fame Awd 87; Westminster Coll; Elem Ed.

VUKELICH, CYNTHIA; Deer Lakes JR SR HS; Russellton, PA; (4); Drama Clb; French Clb; Ski Clb; Varsity Clb; School Musical; School Play; Stat Socr; Var Twrlr; Hon Roll; Thesps; Drama Awd 87; U Pittsburgh Johnstown.

VUKICH, TRACY; Ringgold HS; Donora, PA; (4); FNA; Hosp Aide; JA; Teachers Aide; Chorus; Stu Cncl; Vllybl; Hon Roll; Nrsg.

VULLO, TAMARA ANN; Riverside HS; Taylor, PA; (4); Pres Drama Clb; Chorus; School Musical; School Play; Yrbk Stf; Rep Stu Cncl; Capt JV Cheerleading; L Capt Trk; Art Clb; 4-H; All Around High Scorer-Girls Track 86; Typing Spd Awd 87; Middle St Evaluators Stu Rep 87; Kutztown U; Spec Ed.

WACHALA, JENNIFER; Sacred Heart HS; Pittsburgh, PA; (3); 22/139; Church Yth Grp; Latin Clb; VP Library Aide; Pres NFL; Chorus; School Musical; Var Sftbl; Im Vllybl; Hon Roll; NHS; Law.

WACHHAUS, AARON; St Francis Prep HS; York Springs, PA; (3); #1 In Class; Computer Clb; Spanish Clb; Church Choir; Nwsp Rptr; NHS.

WACHINSKI, MELINDA; Panther Valley HS; Nesquehoning, PA; (2); 30/120; Sec Aud/Vis; Drama Clb; French Clb; Ski Clb; Speech Tm; Flag Corp; Mrchg Band; School Musical; Nwsp Stf; Trk; Trvl.

WACHTEL, LORI; Butler SR HS; Butler, PA; (3); Dance Clb; Sec JA; Spanish Clb; SADD; Band; Concert Band; Mrchg Band; School Play; Trk; Hon Roll; Sales Club Awd Jr Achvt 86-87; Exceptional Svc Awd SADD 87; Bus Sls.

WACHTER, AMY S; South Park HS; Finleyville, PA; (4); 8/203; Stage Crew; Yrbk Stf; High Hon Roll; NHS; Prfct Atten Awd; Math Awd; Stu Tutorial Prog; Math.

WACIK, CHRISTINE ANN; Freedom HS; Bethlehem, PA; (4); Chorus; Rep Stu Cncl; Var Powder Puff Ftbl; Capt Var Trk; Humantrn Awd, Hmcmng Ct, & Prm Ct 87; Patriot Awd 85-87; MVP Trk Relay 84-87; NCACC.

WACKLEY, RON; Pocono Mountain HS; Stroudsburg, PA; (2); Aud/Vis; Camera Clb; Church Yth Grp; Letterman Clb; Spanish Clb; Varsity Clb; Sec Frsh Cls; Ftbl; Trk; Wrstlng; Pres Physcl Ftns Awd 85-86; Aircrft Dsgn.

WACLAWIK, CHRISTINE; Cambridge Springs HS; Cambridge Spg, PA; (3); 28/93; French Clb; Pep Clb; SADD; Teachers Aide; L Mrchg Band; Nwsp Rptr; Rep Stu Cncl; JV Var Cheerleading; Stat Vllybl; Hon Roll; Presdntl Phy Ftns Awd 85-86; Stu Day 87; Grnd Crss Color Svc Awd-Intl Ordr Rainbw Grls 87; Psych.

WACLAWSKI, JOHN; John S Fine HS; Nanticoke, PA; (3); 1/230; Chorus; High Hon Roll; NHS; High Math.

WADAS, ROBIN; John S Fine SR HS; Nanticoke, PA; (2); 12/226; Library Aide; Pep Clb; Spanish Clb; Chorus; Church Choir; Variety Show; Yrbk Stf; Cheerleading; High Hon Roll; NHS; Spch Ther.

WADATZ, ASHLEY; Western Beaver HS; Industry, PA; (2); SADD; Rep Stu Cncl; Im Bowling; Var JV Cheerleading; Trk; Vllybl; Wt Lftg; Hon Roll; Cosmotologist.

WADDING, BARBARA; Penns Manor HS; Indiana, PA; (4); 17/92; Camera Clb; Spanish Clb; Band; Concert Band; Flag Corp; Mrchg Band; Twrlr; Hon Roll; Prfct Atten Awd; Awd For Perf Attndnc 84-87; Lock Haven U Of PA; Pre-Law.

WADE, AUDREY; Upper Dublin HS; Ft Washington, PA; (3); Camera Clb; Band; Civic Clb; Cmnty Wkr; Cheerleading; JV Sftbl; Hon Roll; People/People Stu Ambssdr Pgm 87; Teen Pres Jack/Jill Amer Inc 86-87; Georgetown U; Law.

WADE, CHRISTOPHER; Sacred Heart HS; Carbondale, PA; (3); Chess Clb; French Clb; Math Tm; Scholastic Bowl; Ski Clb; Nwsp Rptr; Stat L Score Keeper; High Hon Roll; NHS; Law.

WADE, ELIZABETH; Lehighton Area HS; Lehighton, PA; (4); 3/230; Pres Church Yth Grp; Chorus; Concert Band; Yrbk Ed-Chief; High Hon Roll; JP Sousa Awd; Pres NHS; JV Bsktbl; 4-H; Scholastic Bowl; Natl Hnr Soc Schlrshp 87; Mrchnt Bnk Awd Ghst Math GPA 87; Awd Outstndng Stu Comp Sci 87; Juniata Coll; Pre Vet Med.

WADE, ERIC; Elizabethtown Area HS; Elizabethtown, PA; (3); Concert Band; Mrchg Band; Hotel Mgmnt.

WADE, LYNNETTE S; Harrisburg HS; Harrisburg, PA; (3); #34 In Class; Pres Church Yth Grp; Exploring; SADD; Flag Corp; Jr Cls; Stu Cncl; Cheerleading; Twrlr; Hon Roll.

WADE, NICOLE; Carlisle HS; Mt Holly Spgs, PA; (3); JA; Concert Band; Jazz Band; Orch; Symp Band; Rep Frsh Cls; JV Bsktbl; JV Vllybl; Hon Roll; Chess Clb; Pre Coll Smr Sem Carnegie Melon U Music 87; Music.

WADE, SARETHA; G A R Memorial HS; Wilkes-Barre, PA; (3); 28/152; Key Clb; Ski Clb; Drill Tm; Fld Hcky; High Hon Roll; Hon Roll; Jr NHS; NHS; Secty.

WADSWORTH, JEFF; Connellsville Area HS; Scottdale, PA; (4); Church Yth Grp; Office Aide; Bsbl; Ftbl; High Hon Roll; Hon Roll.

WADSWORTH, JOSEPH; Lock Haven SR HS; Beech Creek, PA; (3); 2/257; Key Clb; Pres Spanish Clb; Chorus; Var Ftbl; Im Wt Lftg; High Hon Roll; NHS; NEDT Awd; Schltc All Amer 87; Physcs Awd 87; Comp Sci.

WADSWORTH, KIRA; Greater Johnstown Vo-Tech Schl; S Fork, PA; (3); Dance Clb; Hosp Aide; Sec Pep Clb; Trs Ski Clb; Chorus; Variety Show; Wt Lftg; Hon Roll; Jr NHS; NHS; U Of Pittsbgh; RN.

WADSWORTH, MICHELLE; Forest Hills SR HS; South Fork, PA; (4); 7/152; Hosp Aide; Office Aide; Scholastic Bowl; Chorus; Church Choir; School Musical; Nwsp Rptr; Yrbk Rptr; High Hon Roll; NHS; David A Glosser Schlrshp 87; U Of Pittsburgh; Occptnl Thrpy.

WAGAMAN, DAWN; Brandywine Heights HS; Mertztown, PA; (2); Girl Scts; Chorus; Color Guard; Drill Tm; Hon Roll; Pres Phys Ftnss Awd 85; Kutztown U; Comp Sci.

WAGG, LAURA; Pottstown HS; Pottstown, PA; (3); 55/155; Church Yth Grp; JA; Key Clb; Spanish Clb; Band; Chorus; Church Choir; Concert Band; Swing Chorus; Yrbk Stf; Cookng Awd 83-84; Bus.

WAGGONER, SHARON; Bellefonte Area HS; Bellefonte, PA; (3); French Clb; SADD; Color Guard; Concert Band; Mgr Jazz Band; Capt Mrchg Band; Rep Stu Cncl; Stat Bsktbl; Im Vllybl; Hon Roll; Cert Marine Sci Cnsrtm Wallops I Sland VA 87; Phys Thrpy.

WAGH, RAVI; West Greene HS; Prosperity, PA; (2); Ski Clb; Band; Concert Band; Mrchg Band; Trk; Wrstlng; U Of Pitt; Pre Med.

WAGMAN, JENNIFER; Exeter HS; Reiffton, PA; (3); 22/341; Drama Clb; Spanish Clb; Varsity Clb; Band; Concert Band; Mrchg Band; School Musical; Variety Show; Off Jr Cls; Stu Cncl; VS Achvt Acad Awd Music 84; Sci.

WAGMAN, JENNIFER; Exeter Township HS; Reading, PA; (3); 20/240; Drama Clb; Varsity Clb; Band; School Musical; Off Jr Cls; Stu Cncl; Crs Cntry; Trk; Hon Roll; Jr NHS; Sci.

WAGMAN, SHELLY M; West York Area HS; York, PA; (3); Am Leg Aux Girls St; Pres Church Yth Grp; Drama Clb; French Clb; Ski Clb; Church Choir; Concert Band; Mrchg Band; Symp Band; Vllybl; English Ed.

WAGNER, ADRIAN; Meadville Area SR HS; Meadville, PA; (3); 67/360; AFS; Church Yth Grp; SADD; Stage Crew; Hon Roll; Allegheny Coll; Fine Arts.

WAGNER, ALAN; Meadville Area SR HS; Meadville, PA; (3); 2/363; AFS; NFL; Speech Tm; Varsity Clb; Orch; Var L Crs Cntry; Var L Trk; Hon Roll; Church Yth Grp; French Clb; Qualf Spch Leag & Natl Cathlc Fornsc Champ 86-87; Hnblm Mntn Frnch Levl 4 Slppry Rock ST U 86-87; Lib Arts.

WAGNER, AMY; Linden Hall School For Girls; Lititz, PA; (3); 9/55; 4-H; Crs Cntry; Mgr(s); Trk; Hon Roll; Mayors Yth Ldrshp Sem 87; Med.

WAGNER, ANDRE; Bangor Area HS; Bangor, PA; (3); 1/200; Pres Leo Clb; Ski Clb; Nwsp Stf; VP Jr Cls; Rep Stu Cncl; NHS; Ntl Merit SF; Val; Amer Lgn Schl Awd 85; Pres Acadc Ftns Awd 86; Elec Engr.

WAGNER, CATHY; Dover Area HS; Dover, PA; (3); Nwsp Stf; JV Vllybl.

WAGNER, CATHY; Taylor Allderdice HS; Pittsburgh, PA; (3); Exploring; JA; Teachers Aide; Lit Mag; Cheerleading; High Hon Roll; Hon Roll.

WAGNER, CLEO; Danville SR HS; Danville, PA; (3); Church Yth Grp; Key Clb; Rep Stu Cncl; JV Bsktbl; JV Bsktbl; Var Fld Hcky; Var Trk; Gov Hon Prg Awd; High Hon Roll; Hon Roll; Chrch Deacon 85-87; Al-Leag Trk Mt 87.

WAGNER, COLLEEN; Vincentian HS; Pittsburgh, PA; (2); Chorus; Hon Roll.

WAGNER, CRISTINE; Ambridge Area HS; Freedom, PA; (3); Trs French Clb; GAA; JA; Pres Library Aide; Pep Clb; Teachers Aide; School Musical; Rep Soph Cls; Rep Jr Cls; Math.

WAGNER, ELLEN; Ambridge Area HS; Ambridge, PA; (3); Am Leg Aux Girls St; Sec German Clb; Red Cross Aide; Jr Cls; Sec Stu Cncl; Tennis; Gov Hon Prg Awd; High Hon Roll; NHS; Prfct Atten Awd; Sci.

WAGNER, JON; Dallas SR HS; Shavertown, PA; (3); 50/211; Off Jr Cls; Var L Bsbl; Var L Ftbl; High Hon Roll; Hon Roll.

WAGNER, JULIE; Keystone HS; Knox, PA; (3); 29/141; Sec SADD; Chorus; Concert Band; Mrchg Band; Pep Band; School Musical; Yrbk Stf; Rep Stu Cncl; Hon Roll; Bus.

WAGNER, KRIS; Solanco HS; Quarryville, PA; (3); 32/277; VP Church Yth Grp; VP Sec 4-H; Ski Clb; Sec VP Varsity Clb; Band; Church Choir; Concert Band; Mrchg Band; School Musical; Symp Band; Keystone ST Games 87; Outstndng Music Stu 86; Dist Band 86; Cnty Band 85-87; Peer Cnslng 85-87; Engl.

WAGNER, LAURA; Kennedy Christian HS; Hermitage, PA; (3); 8/97; Church Yth Grp; School Play; Nwsp Rptr; Nwsp Stf; Yrbk Stf; JV Golf; Var L Trk; High Hon Roll; Drama Clb; Hosp Aide; Kennedy Christian Schlrshp 84; Catholic Daughters Of Amer 1st Awd Poetry 85; Communications.

WAGNER, LORI; Johnstown Christian Schl; Windber, PA; (4); 5/17; Church Yth Grp; Drama Clb; Chorus; Yrbk Bus Mgr; Var Capt Cheerleading; Cit Awd; Hon Roll; Liberty U; Elem Educ.

WAGNER, MELISSA; Milton Area HS; Milton, PA; (3); Church Yth Grp; Key Clb; Pep Clb; SADD; Varsity Clb; Color Guard; Stu Cncl; Var Capt Cheerleading; Powder Puff Ftbl; Var Trk; Soc Svcs.

WAGNER, MICHELE; Conrad Weiser HS; Robesonia, PA; (3); 33/179; FBLA; Band; Chorus; Yrbk Stf; JCL; Concert Band; Mrchg Band; School Musical; JV Bsktbl; Conrad Weiser Band Indpndnc Conf Champs 85; Shippensburg; Acctnt.

WAGNER, MICHELLE; Milton SR HS; Milton, PA; (2); 4/254; Library Aide; Spanish Clb; Chorus; Hon Roll; Bloomsburg U; Engl.

WAGNER, NATHAN; William Allen HS; Allentown, PA; (3); German Clb; Political Wkr; Chorus; Church Choir; Jazz Band; Orch; Hon Roll; NHS; Schlrshp Luth Smmr Music Pgm 85; 2nd Prz Lions Clb Strs Tmrrw 86.

WAGNER, ROB; Emmaus HS; Wescosville, PA; (4); Computer Clb; Key Clb; Stage Crew; Var L Swmmng; Hon Roll; NHS; Pres Schlr; Robert A Tucker Awd 87; Mech Drwng Lion Clb Emmaus 87; Schlrshp For 4 Yrs; VA Politech Inst; Archtctr.

WAGNER, ROBERT; General Mc Lane HS; Edinboro, PA; (3); 8/223; Aud/Vis; Computer Clb; French Clb; Quiz Bowl; Nwsp Ed-Chief; Nwsp Stf; Stu Cncl; High Hon Roll; Hon Roll; NHS; HOBY Ambssdr 85-86; PA ST Edtr-YMCA Yth & Govt Prog 86-87; Olympc Trng Ctr-Rcqtbl 87; Mth.

WAGNER, ROBERT C; Old Forge-Wilkes Barre Vo Tech; Old Forge, PA; (4); 2/14; Boy Scts; Cmnty Wkr; VICA; Trk; Hon Roll; Lion Awd; Air Cond & Refrig.

WAGNER, ROBIN; Highlands HS; Tarentum, PA; (3); Intnl Clb; Jr NHS; Brwn Awd 87; QPA Schltc Achvt 87; CCAC; CPA.

WAGNER, ROBYN; Freedom HS; Bethlehem, PA; (4); 109/465; Aud/Vis; Drama Clb; Pep Clb; Chorus; School Play; Jean E Ocker Choral Awd 87; Vlntr & Svc Awd 87; Moravian Coll; Psych.

WAGNER, SCOTT; Carbondale Area HS; Carbondale, PA; (3); Aud/Vis; Ski Clb; Chorus; Stage Crew; Variety Show; Var Tennis; Pres Physcl Ftns Awd 86-87; Engrng.

WAGNER, SHARON; Marion Center Area HS; Beyer, PA; (4); 9/169; Cmnty Wkr; FBLA; FNA; Hosp Aide; Latin Clb; VICA; Twrlr; High Hon Roll; NHS; Voctnl Ind Ed.

WAGNER, SHARON; West Perry SR HS; Elliottsburg, PA; (3); 24/222; Church Yth Grp; 4-H; Math Clb; Spanish Clb; Band; Chorus; Church Choir; Concert Band; Mrchg Band; JV Var Sftbl; Vrsty Ltr Band; Rbbrs 4-H Proj; JR & SR Olympics & Tlnt Shws; Cmnty Carnvl Tlnt Shw; PA ST U; Pre-Med.

WAGNER, SHERRY; Clarion Area HS; Shippenville, PA; (3); Church Yth Grp; FHA; Library Aide; Science Clb; SADD; Yrbk Stf; Var Capt Cheerleading; Hon Roll; Clarion U; Chld Psych.

WAGNER, STACEY; Lewistown Area HS; Granville, PA; (3); 4-H; Key Clb; Ski Clb; Fld Hcky; Trk; Hon Roll.

WAGNER, STACY; Neshannock HS; New Castle, PA; (4); 4/116; Math Tm; Speech Tm; Teachers Aide; Trs Band; Capt Drill Tm; School Play; Yrbk Rptr; DAR Awd; High Hon Roll; Pres NHS; Merit Schlrshp 87; Outstndng Drl Tm 87; Westminster Coll; Educ.

WAGNER, STEPHANIE M; Mercyhurst Prep; Erie, PA; (3); Pres Church Yth Grp; Variety Show; Capt Cheerleading; Coach Actv; Hon Roll; Schlrshp Excllnc 87; Awd Excllnc Chrch Yth Grp-OLMC 85; Srvc/Vlntr Awd 86; Gannon; Educ.

WAGNER, TAMMY; Glendale JR SR HS; Irvona, PA; (3); 23/77; Nwsp Stf; Yrbk Stf; Lgl Sec.

WAGNER, WENDI; St Hubert HS; Philadelphia, PA; (3); 73/421; Cmnty Wkr; Computer Clb; Exploring; Spanish Clb; Yrbk Stf; Hon Roll; Temple U; Phrmcy.

WAGNER, WILLIAM; Lakeland HS; Jermyn, PA; (4); 12/148; Art Clb; Church Yth Grp; Drama Clb; 4-H; JA; Library Aide; Scholastic Bowl; Band; Concert Band; School Play; JA VP Prod Yr Awd 86-87; Pres Schlrshp 87; U Of Scranton; Pharm.

WAGSTAFF, BRIAN; Elizabeth Forward HS; Elizabeth, PA; (3); Office Aide; Teachers Aide; L Var Bsbl; Capt L Crs Cntry; L Var Trk; Im Wt Lftg; Pres Phys Ftnss Awds 85; CA U; Hlth.

WAHEED, KARIMAH; Sister Clara Muhammad HS; Philadelphia, PA; (3); 1/10; Computer Clb; Debate Tm; Teachers Aide; Off Stu Cncl; Cit Awd; Stu Of The Mnth 85; Superior Achvt In American Gvrnmt 85; Bus Admin.

WAHL, MARDA; Meyersdale Area HS; Meyersdale, PA; (3); Church Yth Grp; Trs Spanish Clb; Band; Chorus; Church Choir; Concert Band; School Musical; Co-Capt Cheerleading; Hon Roll; NHS; Atty.

WAID, LISA; Meadville Area SR HS; Meadville, PA; (3); 40/363; French Clb; Library Aide; Science Clb; SADD; Yrbk Stf; Bsktbl; Hon Roll.

WAIDA, SCOTT; Reynolds HS; Fredonia, PA; (4); 3/147; Latin Clb; Letterman Clb; Math Clb; Service Clb; Rep Stu Cncl; Var L Ftbl; Var L Trk; Im Wt Lftg; Cit Awd; High Hon Roll; Jarrett Engrng Schlrshp 87; Princeton U; Mech Engrng.

WAINWRIGHT, MARK; Scotland Schl For Vet Children; Phila, PA; (3); 3/42; Am Leg Boys St; Chess Clb; Computer Clb; Hosp Aide; Math Clb; Math Tm; ROTC; Drill Tm; Var Bsbl; JV Bsktbl; Chem Outstndng Stu Awd 87; Math Cert Cont Area 87; 1st Pl Indvdl Pool Trnmt 5; Villanova; Pre Med.

WAITE, CHRISTINA; Corry Area HS; Spartansburg, PA; (3); 46/223; Church Yth Grp; Spanish Clb; Chorus; Bsktbl; Comm.

WAITE, WILLIAM; Tyrone Area HS; Tyrone, PA; (3); High Hon Roll; Hon Roll; Prfct Atten Awd; Outstndng Math & Advncd Wood Stu 86-87; Williamson U; Cbnt Mkr.

WAITKUS, SUSAN; Tamaqua Area SR HS; Tamaqua, PA; (4); 25/180; Girl Scts; Q&S; Band; Chorus; Flag Corp; School Musical; Nwsp Ed-Chief; French Hon Soc; Hon Roll; ANPA Fndtn Schlstc Jrnlst Awd 87; JH Zrby Nwspr Awd 87; Shippensburg U; Comms.

WAKEFIELD, CHAD; Mount Union Area HS; Shirleysburg, PA; (3); 16/152; AFS; Art Clb; Church Yth Grp; Spanish Clb; Bsktbl; Tennis; Trk.

WAKEFIELD, HEATHER; Eastern York HS; Wrightsvlle, PA; (2); Varsity Clb; Yrbk Stf; Trs Stu Cncl; Cheerleading; Sftbl; Vllybl; Hon Roll; Prfct Atten Awd; USVBA-VLLYBL Tm 86-87.

WAKELEY, HEATHER; Bradford Area HS; Bradford, PA; (3); Church Yth Grp; Spanish Clb; Tennis; Hon Roll; Johnson-Wales Coll; Clnry Arts.

WALASKI, THERESA; Coudersport JR SR HS; Coudersport, PA; (3); Church Yth Grp; Drama Clb; French Clb; Church Choir; Flag Corp; Mrchg Band; School Play; Powder Puff Ftbl; Trk; Socl Wrk.

WALBECK, ROBERT; Homer-Center JR Sr HS; Homer City, PA; (3); 20/108; French Clb; Library Aide; Varsity Clb; Concert Band; Pres Soph Cls; Var JV Bsktbl; Hon Roll; NHS; Jr Acad Sci Regnl & States 85; Bus Mngmnt.

WALBURN, JERRY; Canton JR SR HS; Canton, PA; (3); Church Yth Grp; FFA; Bsktbl; Crs Cntry; Williamsport CC; Auto Repair.

WALBURN, KIMBERLY; Tunkhannock Area HS; Mehoopany, PA; (3); Church Yth Grp; Spanish Clb; Band; Rep Frsh Cls; Rep Soph Cls; Rep Jr Cls; Var L Trk; Var L Vllybl; Hon Roll; Dance Clb; Treas, Secr Yth Grp; US Vlybl Assn Plyr; Bus Mgmt.

WALCH, JEFFREY J; North Allegheny HS; Wexford, PA; (3); 280/649; Church Yth Grp; DECA; Radio Clb; Ski Clb; SADD; Band; Bsbl; Golf; Trk; Hon Roll; Brdcstng.

WALDMAN, MICHELE; Loyalsock HS; Williamsport, PA; (3); German Clb; Hosp Aide; Key Clb; Latin Clb; Ski Clb; SADD; Yrbk Rptr; Var Sftbl; Psych.

WALDRON III, JOHN T; Upper St Clair HS; Pittsburgh, PA; (4); 14/382; Chess Clb; Debate Tm; Nwsp Rptr; Ed Nwsp Stf; Yrbk Stf; High Hon Roll; Ntl Merit SF; Math Assoc Of Amer Cert Of Achiev 85; Upper St Clair Brd Of Dir Cert Of Recog 86; Pa Hghr Ed Ass 86; Lwyr.

WALDRON, MARY; Fort Le Boeuf HS; Waterford, PA; (3); Dance Clb; Spanish Clb; Chorus; Yrbk Stf; Stat Bsktbl; Cheerleading; Score Keeper; Timer; Hon Roll; Dist Chorus 85-87; PA Free Entrprs Wk Full Schlrshp 86-87; Cont ST Prelim Miss TEEN Pgnt 84-85; Early Chldhd Dvlpmnt.

WALDRON, WILLIAM; Blacklick Valley HS; Nanty Glo, PA; (2); 14/105; Church Yth Grp; 4-H; NFL; Ski Clb; Rep Soph Cls; Rep Stu Cncl; Ftbl; Trk; Hon Roll; Pres Acad Ftnss Awd 86; Acad All-Amer 86.

WALDROP, DANIELLE R; Friends Central Schl; Norristown, PA; (4); Hosp Aide; VP Service Clb; Yrbk Stf; Var Co-Capt Bsktbl; Var Co-Capt Fld Hcky; Main Line Nghbrs Female Ath Wk 87; 1st Tm All Main Line Fld Hcky Tm 87; MVP Bsktbl 86-87; Amherst Coll; Bio.

WALDROP, DOUGLAS; Elk Lake HS; Meshoppen, PA; (2); Cmnty Wkr; SADD; Mgr(s); Hon Roll.

WALEFF, STEVAN; Reynolds HS; Greenville, PA; (3); 8/152; Hosp Aide; Latin Clb; Varsity Clb; JV Bsktbl; JV Capt Ftbl; Wt Lftg; Hon Roll; NHS; NEDT Awd; Phys Ther.

WALIGURSKI, TINA; Governor Mifflin SR HS; Mohnton, PA; (3); 61/300; Exploring; Var Capt Bsktbl; Bloomsburg U; Acctng.

WALIZER, JOHN; Bald Eagle Nittany HS; Mill Hall, PA; (4); 7/121; Debate Tm; Key Clb; Model UN; Pep Clb; Spanish Clb; Varsity Clb; Nwsp Stf; Sec Stu Cncl; Ftbl; Wrstlng; Hugh Obrien Ldrshp 84; Math.

WALIZER, SAPRINA; Bald Eagle Ni Hany HS; Lamar, PA; (4); 57/114; Spanish Clb; Nwsp Stf; S Hills Bus; Admn Sec.

WALK, TRACY; Blacklick Valley HS; Nanty Glo, PA; (3); 10/100; Church Yth Grp; Computer Clb; German Clb; NFL; Varsity Clb; Church Choir; Trk; High Hon Roll; Acad All-Amer Awd 85; Presdntl Acad Ftnssawd 83; WV U; Med.

WALKER, AMY; Lakeland JR/Sr HS; Clarks Summit, PA; (3); 7/136; French Clb; FHA; Hon Roll; NHS; Ntl Merit Ltr; Comp Sci.

WALKER, ANDREA; Brookville Area HS; Corsica, PA; (3); 3/160; 4-H; German Clb; Band; Lit Mag; Rep Jr Cls; JV Bsktbl; NHS; Ntl Merit Ltr; Concert Band; School Musical; PA Free Enterprise Wk Schlrshp 86; PA ST Band Stu 87; Architecture.

WALKER, CARLA; Lawrence County Vo Tech; Volant, PA; (3); 4/296; VICA; Hon Roll.

WALKER, CAROL; Central HS; Quakertown, PA; (3); GAA; Office Aide; Var Sftbl; Hon Roll; Law.

WALKER, CHERYL ANNETTE; Norristown Area HS; Norristown, PA; (3); 65/451; Church Yth Grp; Intnl Clb; Pep Clb; Chorus; Church Choir; Swing Chorus; Socr; Hon Roll; Wheaton Cons; Pro Sngr.

WALKER, CHRISTINE; Salem Christian HS; Zionsville, PA; (4); 2/17; Church Yth Grp; Chorus; School Musical; Trs Sr Cls; Sec Stu Cncl; Var L Vllybl; Hon Roll; Drama Clb; Nwsp Stf; Var Bsktbl; Bible Coll; Elem Educ.

WALKER, CLINTON; Mt Union Area HS; Mt Union, PA; (3); 8/158; French Clb; Ftbl; Mat Maids; Wt Lftg; Hon Roll; Jr NHS; Engr.

WALKER, COLLEEN E; Monogahela Valley Catholic HS; Charleroi, PA; (3); 14/99; French Clb; Band; Chorus; Church Choir; French Hon Soc; High Hon Roll; NHS; Voice Dem Awd; Med Fld.

WALKER, DAWN; Upper Moreland HS; Hatboro, PA; (4); 102/253; German Clb; School Play; Lit Mag; Nrs Aide Nrnsg Home; Frankford Hosp Schl; Nrsng.

WALKER, DEBBY; Waynesburg Central HS; Waynesburg, PA; (4); Letterman Clb; Varsity Clb; Rep Stu Cncl; Capt Var Bsktbl; Var Trk; Capt Var Vllybl; Hon Roll; Hmncng Attndnt 84; Uniontown Beauty Acad Full Schlrshp 87; Schl Athlt Of Yr 87 & Mst Ahtletic 87; Uniontown Beauty Acad; Costmlgy.

WALKER, ELISE; Warren Area HS; Warren, PA; (3); Art Clb; Dance Clb; French Clb; Pep Clb; Ski Clb; Chorus; School Musical; Nwsp Stf; Off Frsh Cls; Off Soph Cls; Acad Lttr 85-86.

WALKER, G ERIC; Brookville Area School District; Brookville, PA; (4); Church Yth Grp; German Clb; School Musical; Diving; Swmmng; High Hon Roll; NHS; Boy Scts; Drama Clb; Varsity Clb; Happy Time Show Chr 85-87; PA Dist II Chrs 85-87; PA Rgn II All ST Chrs 85 & 86; Intl Bus.

WALKER, GLYNDA; Pine Forge Acad; Capitol Hgts, MD; (3); Church Choir; School Musical; School Play; Yrbk Stf; Pres Frsh Cls; Trs Stu Cncl; Cheerleading; Gym; Cit Awd; Howard U; Law.

WALKER, HEIDI; Huntingdon Area HS; Huntingdon, PA; (2); 98/200; Art Clb; Church Yth Grp; Cmnty Wkr; 4-H; Hosp Aide; Key Clb; Latin Clb; Ski Clb; SADD; Band; Smthfld Fr Qn 87; Art Awd 87; NY Police Acad; Plc Offcr.

WALKER, JAMES; Bishop Mc Cort HS; Johnstown, PA; (3); 14/178; German Clb; VP JA; Mu Alpha Theta; Ski Clb; School Musical; Yrbk Phtg; JV Ftbl; Capt L Swmmng; Trk; High Hon Roll.

WALKER, JANINE; Northern Cambria HS; Barnesboro, PA; (3); 30/180; Ski Clb; Spanish Clb; Band; Chorus; Color Guard; Concert Band; Jazz Band; Hon Roll; Fshn Inst Pittsburgh; Rtail Byr.

WALKER, JEAN; Avon Grove HS; Landenberg, PA; (4); 16/163; Drama Clb; Concert Band; Jazz Band; Mrchg Band; School Musical; School Play; JV Sftbl; High Hon Roll; Hon Roll; Svc Awds Band 85-87; U DE; Arts.

WALKER, JEFFERY; Rockwood Area HS; Rockwood, PA; (2); Pres Chess Clb; Computer Clb; NFL; Speech Tm; Band; Concert Band; Jazz Band; Mrchg Band; School Play; Bowling.

WALKER, JERRY; Hempfield Area SR HS; Ruffsdale, PA; (4); 6/693; AFS; Drama Clb; NFL; Spanish Clb; Yrbk Stf; Kiwanis Awd; NHS; Pres Schlr; Rotary Awd; Spanish NHS; Elks Fndtn Schlrshp Awd 87; PA ST U; Arch.

WALKER, JOHN; Cathedral Prep; Erie, PA; (3); 54/199; Wrstlng; Pitt; Elec Engrng.

WALKER, KAREN; Tunkhannock Area HS; Tunkhannock, PA; (3); 4/310; Key Clb; Spanish Clb; Band; Concert Band; Mrchg Band; Orch; School Musical; Stage Crew; Swmmng; Hon Roll.

WALKER, KELLI; Moniteau HS; West Sunbury, PA; (3); #8 In Class; FBLA; Spanish Clb; Band; Yrbk Bus Mgr; Var L Bsktbl; Var Trk; Var L Vllybl; High Hon Roll; NHS; Voice Dem Awd; Athl Awd 86-87; Dirctrs Awd 83-84; Acctng Awd 86-87; Slippery Rock U; Acctng.

WALKER, KENNETH; Henderson HS; West Chester, PA; (3); 30/350; Quiz Bowl; Ski Clb; Band; Chorus; School Musical; School Play; JV Tennis; Hon Roll; NHS; Church Yth Grp; Sci.

WALKER, KIRBY; Freeport Area HS; Freeport, PA; (3); 25/213; Church Yth Grp; Mrchg Band; Yrbk Stf; Rep Frsh Cls; Trs Jr Cls; Swmmng; Var L Trk; Hon Roll; Carniege Mellon U; Arch.

WALKER, KRISTEN; Archbishop Carroll HS; Narberth, PA; (3); 46/376; Church Yth Grp; Drama Clb; Service Clb; Im Bsktbl; Im Ftbl; Hon Roll; Latin Excllnc Awd 87; Teaching.

WALKER, LEE ANN; Waynesboro Area SR HS; Waynesboro, PA; (2); Church Yth Grp; Library Aide; Church Choir; Yrbk Bus Mgr; Yrbk Rptr; Yrbk Stf; Pres Frsh Cls; Rep Soph Cls; Var Bsktbl; JV Var Vllybl; X-Ray Tech.

WALKER, LISA; Susquehanna Township HS; Harrisburg, PA; (3); 18/150; Drama Clb; Key Clb; Natl Beta Clb; Band; Trs Chorus; School Musical; Rep Stu Cncl; NHS; Hon Roll; AFS; Rotary Ldrshp Cmp 87; Cnty Chorus 85-87; Comms.

WALKER, MARGUERITE; Creative & Performing Arts HS; Philadelphia, PA; (3); VP Chorus; Pres Church Choir; School Musical; School Play; Variety Show; Stat Bsktbl; JV Score Keeper; Sftbl; Hon Roll; Cmptr Pgmr.

WALKER, MATTHEW WILLIAM; Rockwood Area HS; Rockwood, PA; (4); Band; Concert Band; Mrchg Band; School Play; Stage Crew; Off Soph Cls; Off Jr Cls; Wt Lftg; Wrstlng; Hon Roll.

WALKER, MELINDA; Elizabethtown Area HS; Elizabethtown, PA; (4); 51/224; Hosp Aide; Red Cross Aide; Thesps; Pres Band; Jazz Band; Pres Mrchg Band; School Musical; School Play; Stage Crew; Church Yth Grp; East Carolina U; Phys Thrpy.

WALKER, MELISSA; Big Spring HS; Newville, PA; (4); 25/189; VP 4-H; Chorus; Nwsp Rptr; Nwsp Sprt Ed; Nwsp Stf; Powder Puff Ftbl; 4-H Awd; High Hon Roll; Lion Awd; 4-H Outstndg Awds; Grand Champ Mkrt Lamb Fair 85; Shippensburg U; Elem Ed.

WALKER, MICHAEL; Mt Union Area HS; Mount Union, PA; (4); 52/172; Church Yth Grp; Spanish Clb; JV Bsktbl; Var Capt Golf; Glf Ltr 85-87; SR Glf Awd 86-87.

WALKER, MYRON; Aliquippa HS; Aliquippa, PA; (2); Bsktbl; Ftbl; Hon Roll.

WALKER, NEAL; Bethlehem Catholic HS; Bethlehem, PA; (3); 12/210; Boys Clb Am; Ski Clb; Co-Capt Ice Hcky; Co-Capt Socr; High Hon Roll; Jr NHS; NHS.

WALKER, RAISSA; Pennsbury HS; Fairless Hls, PA; (4); 140/777; Church Yth Grp; French Clb; Quiz Bowl; Spanish Clb; SADD; Nwsp Stf; Yrbk Phtg; Lit Mag; Cit Awd; Hon Roll; ST Lang Comptn Frnch 2nd Pl 85; Pennsbrg Frgn Lang Comp Spnsh 2nd Pl 87; Acadmc Excllnc & Prtcptn; NY U; Intl Bus.

WALKER, REGINALD; Harrisburg HS; Harrisburg, PA; (2); Church Yth Grp; Cmnty Wkr; FCA; Wt Lftg; Wrstlng; Hon Roll; Mchncl Engrng.

WALKER, SHAWN O; Warren Area HS; Warren, PA; (4); 22/300; Off Art Clb; Church Yth Grp; Cmnty Wkr; French Clb; Quiz Bowl; Scholastic Bowl; Ski Clb; SADD; Off Acpl Chr; Chorus; Acad Ltr 86; Silver B Awd 84; Golden Dragon Awd 87; U Pittsburgh; Sci.

WALKER, STEPHANIE; Central HS; York, PA; (2); Drama Clb; Hosp Aide; Thesps; Band; Chorus; Mrchg Band; Orch; Rep Frsh Cls; Hon Roll; Penn ST U; Drama.

WALKER, SUZANNE; Burrell SR HS; Lower Burrell, PA; (3); Church Yth Grp; French Clb; Nwsp Rptr; Var L Bsktbl; Var L Trk; Jr NHS; NHS; HS Acdmc Letter 85-87; Rotary Schlr 86; Bio.

WALKER, WADE; South Western HS; Glen Rock, PA; (3); 59/233; Church Yth Grp; Trk; Hon Roll.

WALKER, WESLEY C; Westinghouse HS; Pittsburgh, PA; (4); 18/244; Library Aide; Nwsp Rptr; Nwsp Stf; Pres Stu Cncl; Im Bsktbl; JV Var Ftbl; Var Vllybl; PA ST; Engrng.

WALKER, WILLIAM; Bethlehem Catholic HS; Bethlehem, PA; (3); 52/200; Rep Soph Cls; L Bsktbl; L Socr; Hon Roll; Lion Awd; Pltcl Sci.

WALKER, WILLIAM K; Central Dauphin HS; Linglestown, PA; (2); 3/405; Am Leg Boys St; Boy Scts; Capt CAP; Concert Band; Jazz Band; Mrchg Band; JV Crs Cntry; High Hon Roll; Band; Chorus; Civil Air Patrol Gen Billy Mitchell & Amelia Earhart Awds 86-87; USAF Acad; Aero Engrng.

WALKLETT, KAREN; Chichester HS; Linwood, PA; (3); 78/297; SADD; Chorus; Capt Flag Corp; Mgr(s); JV Vllybl; Dental Hygienist.

WALKO, MIKE; Belle Vernon Area HS; Belle Vernon, PA; (3); Boy Scts; Wt Lftg; High Hon Roll; Hon Roll; Am Leg Awd 84; Eagle Sct 84.

WALL, BRIDGITTE; Loyalsock Township HS; Williamsport, PA; (3); French Clb; VP Key Clb; SADD; Yrbk Stf; Var Trk; Hon Roll; NHS; Mrktng.

WALL, KEVIN; Yough SR HS; Ruffsdale, PA; (4); Boy Scts; Ski Clb; Nwsp Rptr; Im Badmtn; Var L Trk; U Ptbrg/Jhnstwn; Bus.

WALLACE, ANGIE; Downingtown HS; Downington, PA; (3); 79/644; Hosp Aide; Chorus; Yrbk Ed-Chief; Trs Soph Cls; Stu Cncl; Var Capt Lcrss; High Hon Roll; NHS; NEDT Awd; Pres Schlr; Natl Choral Svc Awd 85; Penn ST U; Sci.

WALLACE, AUSTIN; Germantown HS; Philadelphia, PA; (3); Boys Clb Am; Drm & Bgl; Stage Crew; Im Bsktbl; Var Im Ftbl; Var Mgr(s); Prfct Atten Awd; Howard U; Arch.

WALLACE, CAROLYN; Harry S Truman HS; Levittown, PA; (4); 31/569; Band; Concert Band; Mrchg Band; School Musical; Rep Stu Cncl; Var Cheerleading; Var JV Socr; Hon Roll; Bucks Cnty CC; Nrsng.

WALLACE, CLAIRE; Harriton HS; Bryn Mawr, PA; (3); Hosp Aide; Science Clb; SADD; Yrbk Stf; Bsktbl; Cheerleading; JV Lcrss; Pom Pon; Var Capt Vllybl; Hon Roll; Georgetown U; Frgn Svc.

WALLACE, DAVE; Greensburg Salem SR HS; Greensburg, PA; (3); 64/288; Spanish Clb; VICA; High Hon Roll; Hon Roll; Bus Data Prcsng.

WALLACE, EILEEN; John Bartram HS; Philadelphia, PA; (3); Church Yth Grp; Hosp Aide; Teachers Aide; Var Gym; Var Sftbl; Wt Lftg; High Hon Roll; Hon Roll; NHS; Acad All Star 85-86; Air Force; Mech Engrng.

WALLACE, FRANK; Uniontown Area HS; Dunbar, PA; (3); 58/318; High Hon Roll; Hon Roll; Comp Sci.

WALLACE, GEORGINE; Waynesboro Area SR HS; Fayetteville, PA; (4); Am Leg Aux Girls St; Pres JCL; Library Aide; Rep Jr Cls; VP Sr Cls; Rep Stu Cncl; High Hon Roll; Hon Roll; NHS; Voice Dem Awd; Hood Coll; Pol Sci.

WALLACE, GREGORY; Greensburg Central Catholic HS; New Stanton, PA; (3); Church Yth Grp; French Clb; Letterman Clb; Math Clb; Ski Clb; Varsity Clb; Chorus; Yrbk Stf; Var Ftbl; L Mgr(s); U Of Pittsburgh; Sports Med.

WALLACE, LISA; Uniontown Area HS; Uniontown, PA; (3); 12/340; Church Yth Grp; Concert Band; Drm Mjr(t); School Musical; Nwsp Ed-Chief; Rep Stu Cncl; Cheerleading; High Hon Roll; NHS; Spanish NHS; PA ST U; Psych.

WALLACE, MIKE; Central Buck East; Furlong, PA; (4); 34/448; Ski Clb; Band; Capt Crs Cntry; Capt Var Socr; Capt Trk; High Hon Roll; Hon Roll; Prfct Atten Awd; Pres Schlr; Outstndg Stu Awd Citznshp Schlrshp & Athltcs 87; Army Rsrv Ntl Schlr Athltc Awd 87; Pres Acad 87; U Of DE; Mechncl Engrng.

WALLACE, QUANDRA; Center HS; Monaca, PA; (2); Trs Church Yth Grp; Dance Clb; Spanish Clb; Church Choir; Pom Pon; High Hon Roll; Hon Roll; Prfct Atten Awd; Spnsh I & II Merits 85-87.

WALLACE, ROBIN; Altoona Area HS; Duncansville, PA; (3); Key Clb; Library Aide; Band; Concert Band; Jazz Band; Mrchg Band; Pep Band; School Musical; Hon Roll; Penn ST; Child Care.

WALLACE, SHEILA S; Avon Grove HS; West Grove, PA; (4); 14/163; Pres Service Clb; Flag Corp; School Musical; Sec Frsh Cls; Sec Soph Cls; Rep Stu Cncl; Capt Cheerleading; Var Crs Cntry; Var Trk; VP NHS; PA COLL Texiles & Sci; Mrktng.

WALLACE, SUZANNE; Central Cambria HS; Colver, PA; (4); Church Yth Grp; FBLA; Library Aide; Service Clb; Chorus; Church Choir; Stat Bsktbl; Mgr(s); Hon Roll; Clarion U Of PA; Lbrary Sci.

WALLANDER, RAYMOND RUSSELL; State College Area HS; Boalsburg, PA; (4); 74/541; Faculty Schlr Awd 87; Class Of 76 Mem Schlrshp 87; Steven Zeleznick Mem Awd 87; Vo Tech Elctrncs Schlrs; Penn ST U; Elec Engr.

WALLER, MARC; Carbondale Area HS; Carbondale, PA; (3); FBLA; Spanish Clb; Bsbl; Bsktbl; Trk; Bus.

WALLEY, MATTHEW; Quigley HS; Aliquippa, PA; (4); 3/100; Capt Quiz Bowl; VP Soph Cls; Ftbl; Trk; Capt Wrstlng; High Hon Roll; NHS; Ntl Merit Schol; NROTC Schlrshp; U PA; Bus.

WALLICK, SHARON; North Pocono HS; Moscow, PA; (4); 42/240; Library Aide; High Hon Roll; Hon Roll; NHS; Hnr Grad 87; Outstndng Stu Awd Voc Tech Chldcr & Dvlpmnt 87; E Stroudsburg U; Pre-Schl Tchr.

WALLITSCH, AMY; Notre Dame HS; Easton, PA; (3); 8/95; Nwsp Sprt Ed; Nwsp Stf; VP Soph Cls; Var Bsktbl; JV Sftbl; Hon Roll; Prfct Atten Awd; Engl & Spnsh I Hghst Avg 85; Bus.

WALLS, DAVE; Lawerence Co Vo-Tech; Ellwood City, PA; (3); VICA; Band; Concert Band; Mrchg Band; Pep Band; Bsktbl; Ftbl; Mgr(s); Socr; Hon Roll; Sci.

WALLS, GARY TROY; Marion Center HS; Marion Ctr, PA; (4); French Clb; Intnl Clb; Spanish Clb; Trk; Spnsh & Frnch Awd 86-87; Pblc Rltns Awd 86.

WALLS, ORVILLE; William Penn Charter Schl; Philadelphia, PA; (4); FCA; Ski Clb; Rep Frsh Cls; Pres Soph Cls; VP Jr Cls; VP Sr Cls; Pres Stu Cncl; Var L Ftbl; Var L Trk; Var L Wrstlng; Hon Roll; U Of PA; Med.

WALLS, PEGGY; Purchase Line HS; Commodore, PA; (2); 6/147; Band; Concert Band; Mrchg Band; Nwsp Rptr; JV Sftbl; High Hon Roll; Hon Roll; NEDT Awd; Dist 3 Band 1st Chr Clrnt III 87; Rgn II Band 6th Chr Clrnt III 87; IN Gztt Ftr Stry Awd 86; Air Force Acad; Pilot.

WALLS, RHONDA; Penn Hills SR HS; Verona, PA; (3); JA; JV Sftbl; JV Trk; Hon Roll; Stu Mnth Data Procsng 87; Cert Accmplshmnt JR Achvt 84; Comp Sci.

WALLS, WAYLON; Fairchence-Georges HS; Smithfield, PA; (3); Boy Scts; Spanish Clb; High Hon Roll; Hon Roll; Jr NHS; NHS; Penn ST; Engrng.

WALMER, KAREN; Hershey HS; Hummelstown, PA; (3); 40/209; Church Yth Grp; Hosp Aide; Orch; Yrbk Phtg; Lit Mag; High Hon Roll; Stu Assoc Producer 87-88; Careers Hlth Clb Pres 87-88; Med Explrs Clb VP 87-88; Calvin Coll; Nrsng.

WALP, KIMBERLY; Emmaus HS; Macungie, PA; (4); 7/500; Key Clb; Color Guard; Sec Jazz Band; Sec Trs Mrchg Band; School Musical; Var L Trk; Im Wt Lftg; High Hon Roll; NHS; Ldrshp Awd 87; Invtn Schlrs Prg PA ST 87; PA ST U; Cvl Engr.

WALPOLE, THOMAS; Allentown Central Catholic HS; Macungie, PA; (3); Boy Scts; Chess Clb; Church Yth Grp; Cmnty Wkr; Exploring; Hosp Aide; Math Tm; Stage Crew; Hon Roll; Ntl Merit SF; Carnegie Mellon; Comp Engrng.

WALSH, BECKY; Winchester Thurston HS; Natrona Hgts, PA; (3); Office Aide; Rep Stu Cncl; Var Swmmng; Capt L Tennis; High Hon Roll; Jr NHS; NHS; Ntl Merit Ltr; Exploring; Key Clb; 2nd Pl Carnegie Awds Piano Comp At CMU 85 & 87; Pre-Law.

WALSH, BRIAN; Bishop Kenrick HS; Norristown, PA; (4); 32/295; Trk; Opt Clb Awd; Villanova; Acctng.

WALSH, BRIAN; Emmaus HS; Macungie, PA; (4); Quiz Bowl; Spanish Clb; School Musical; Im Bsbl; Off Stu Cncl; Im Socr; Jr NHS; NHS; Lafayette; Gvt.

WALSH, DAMIAN; Riverview HS; Verona, PA; (3); 12/115; JV Var Bsktbl; Var Capt Ftbl; Var Capt Trk; Carnegie Mellon U; Bus.

WALSH, DONNA; Bishop O Hara HS; Dickson City, PA; (4); 2/113; Computer Clb; French Clb; Latin Clb; High Hon Roll; Sec NHS; Ntl Merit Ltr; Law.

WALSH, JAMIE; Carbondale Area HS; Carbondale, PA; (3); Church Yth Grp; English Clb; French Clb; Math Clb; Bsktbl; Real Est.

WALSH, JERMAINE; Central High/Cheltenham HS; Laverock, PA; (2); Church Yth Grp; FCA; Teachers Aide; Church Choir; Im Bsktbl; JV Trk; Hon Roll; Villanova U; Med.

WALSH, JOANNE; Sacred Heart HS; Pittsburgh, PA; (4); 1/131; Cmnty Wkr; Debate Tm; Pres French Clb; NFL; Variety Show; Yrbk Ed-Chief; Bausch & Lomb Sci Awd; Dnfth Awd; Gov Hon Prg Awd; High Hon Roll; U Of Notre Dame; Bus Admin.

WALSH, JOHN; Trinity HS; Mechanicsburg, PA; (3); 51/160; Pep Clb; Ski Clb; Spanish Clb; Im Bsktbl; JV Ftbl; Var Golf; Im Tennis; JV Trk; Hon Roll; U Of WI-MADISON; Bus.

WALSH, JON; Penn-Trafford HS; Irwin, PA; (2) 2/329; Drama Clb; JCL; Varsity Clb; Chorus; School Musical; Lit Mag; Var Crs Cntry; Var Trk; High Hon Roll; Prfct Atten Awd; Schlrshp Geneva Coll High Q Comptn 86; PA Cncl Tchr Mthmtcs Comptn Shippensburg U 87; US Air Force Acad.

WALSH, JUSTIN; Mon Valley Catholic HS; Donora, PA; (1); Math Clb; Ski Clb; Bsktbl; Var L Ftbl; Im Socr; Im Wt Lftg; Hon Roll; Natl Sci Olympiad Awd-Bio 87; Diploma De Merito 86-87; MVEA Schrlshp Awd 87; Pre-Med.

WALSH, KEELY; Central Bucks West HS; Chalfont, PA; (3); 143/445; Cmnty Wkr; 4-H; Church Choir; Yrbk Stf; Cheerleading; Tennis; Trk; 4-H Awd; Hon Roll; Psych.

WALSH, KEIRSTEN; State College Area HS; State College, PA; (3); Church Yth Grp; Dance Clb; Hosp Aide; Sec Jr Cls; Stu Cncl; Capt Cheerleading; Gym; High Hon Roll; Hon Roll; NHS; Rgnl & Advncd To Natls-Chrldng 87; Child Psych.

WALSH, KELLIE; Carbondale Area HS; Carbondale, PA; (3); Church Yth Grp; Cmnty Wkr; Hosp Aide; Ski Clb; Spanish Clb; JV Trk; High Hon Roll; Hon Roll; Marine Bio.

WALSH, LAURENE; Center Area HS; Monaca, PA; (4); 20/188; Exploring; German Clb; Spanish Clb; Nwsp Stf; Socr; High Hon Roll; NHS; Pres Schlr; Drill Tm; Nwsp Rptr; Gifted Stu Pgm 83-87; Exchng Stu/Frndshp Cnnctn/Grmny 86; PA ST U; Psych.

WALSH, MARY; Archbishop Carroll HS; Havertown, PA; (3); Church Yth Grp; Cmnty Wkr; Hosp Aide; Service Clb; SADD; Coach Actv; Socr; Sftbl; Swmmng; Vllybl; U Of DE; Child Educ.

WALSH, MARY; Lakeland HS; Jermyn, PA; (3); 23/147; French Clb; FHA; Nwsp Stf; Stat Bsbl; Var Score Keeper; Hon Roll; NHS; Penn ST; Comp Sci.

WALSH, MAUREEN; Seneca Valley HS; Renfrew, PA; (4); 25/352; Red Cross Aide; Ski Clb; Pres Varsity Clb; Rep Jr Cls; Off Sr Cls; Var L Bsktbl; Var L Crs Cntry; Var L Swmmng; Var L Trk; NHS; Swmng Ribbons 83-84; Stu Cncl Pin 87; Sftbl Trphs & All Star 84-86; Purdue U; Bus Mgmt.

WALSH, MICHAEL; Quakertown Community HS; Pennsburg, PA; (3); Boy Scts; Camera Clb; Debate Tm; School Play; Nwsp Rptr; Yrbk Sprt Ed; Rep Stu Cncl; God Cntry Awd; Hon Roll; NHS; Law.

WALSH, MICHELE; Abington Heights HS; Clarks Summit, PA; (2); Dance Clb; Ski Clb; Var Capt Cheerleading; Hon Roll; Coaches Awd Vrsty Sccr Cheerng 86.

WALSH, PATRICIA; Villa Maria Acad; Erie, PA; (3); 18/152; Church Yth Grp; VP Sec Science Clb; Sec Frsh Cls; NHS; PA ST U; Bus Mktng.

WALSH, TRICIA; Seneca Valley SR HS; Renfrew, PA; (3); 13/450; VP JA; Pres Varsity Clb; Off Soph Cls; Pres Jr Cls; Sec Sr Cls; Stu Cncl; L Var Crs Cntry; L Var Swmmng; L Var Trk; NHS; MVP In Vrsty Swmmng 87; Mst Outstndng JR Awd In Trk 87; Rtry Yth Ldrshp Cnfrnc 87; Westminster.

WALSH, WILLIAM; Bishop Hannan HS; Scranton, PA; (4); Drama Clb; Orch; Golf; U Of Scranton; Fnc.

WALSH, WILLIAM; Mahanoy Area HS; Mahanoy City, PA; (2); Boy Scts; Var Ftbl; L Trk; Marine Biol.

WALSHESKY, TABATHA; West Mifflin Area HS; W Mifflin, PA; (3); FBLA; Hosp Aide; Office Aide; Pep Clb; Ski Clb; SADD; Chorus; Drill Tm; Stu Cncl; Mgr(s); Broadcasting Crew 84-85; Majorette Mgr 86-87; Pre-Med.

WALSKI, MICHAEL; Wyoming Valley West HS; Swoyersville, PA; (4); 3/397; Am Leg Boys St; Chess Clb; Math Clb; JV Trk; High Hon Roll; NHS; NEDT Awd; Margaret Davis Memrl Schlrshp Awd 87; Pres Acdmc Ftnss Awd 87; Lafayette Coll; Chem Engrng.

WALSTON, NATALIE; West Catholic Girls HS; Philadelphia, PA; (3); 88/246; Cmnty Wkr; Library Aide; Concert Band; Prfct Atten Awd; Johnson Wales; Culnry Art.

WALT, MICHAEL; Yough SR HS; Madison, PA; (3); 13/280; Spanish Clb; Chorus; Drm Mjr(t); Jazz Band; Mrchg Band; High Hon Roll; NHS; Hosp Aide; Ski Clb; Pre-Med.

WALTER, AMY; Penn Manor HS; Holtwood, PA; (4); 202/308; Church Yth Grp; Cmnty Wkr; Color Guard; Mrchg Band.

WALTER, BRIAN; Altoona Area HS; Altoona, PA; (3); Computer Clb; Math Clb; Math Tm; Spanish Clb; Yrbk Stf; Jr NHS; NHS.

WALTER, BRIAN; Mifflinburg Area HS; Lewisburg, PA; (1); #2 In Class; Church Yth Grp; Key Clb; Spanish Clb; Band; Concert Band; Mrchg Band; Var Bsbl; JV Bsktbl; High Hon Roll; Engrng.

WALTER, CYNTHIA; Nazareth Acad; Langhorne, PA; (3); German Clb; Pres Math Clb; Nwsp Stf; Yrbk Stf; Hon Roll; Partl Schlrshp Villa Victoria Acad 84; Dept Risk Mgmt Ins Tuit Schlrshp 87; Smmr Sci Acad 86; Engrng.

WALTER, JENNIFER; Greater Johnstown HS; Johnstown, PA; (4); Sec French Clb; Pres JA; Library Aide; Math Clb; NFL; Quiz Bowl; Ski Clb; Chorus; Concert Band; Mrchg Band; Presdntl Phys Fitness Awd 86-87; 4th Rnr Up Cambria-Somersets JR Miss 87; Miss Armed Forces 87; Carnegie Mellon U; Law.

WALTER, KATHRYN R; Norwin SR HS; N Huntingdon, PA; (4); FBLA; Letterman Clb; Office Aide; Var L Trk; FBLA-OUTSTNDNG Svc Awd 87; HS Grls Trk Mtr Run Schl Recrd 87; Yth Ftns Achvt Awd 83, 84, 86; Bradford Schl Of Bus; Exec Sec.

WALTER, KIMBERLY; Blue Mountain Acad; Quakertown, PA; (3); Chorus; School Play; Yrbk Stf; Sec Frsh Cls; Sec Stu Cncl; Vllybl; High Hon Roll; Hon Roll; Ntl Merit Schol; Columbia Union Coll; Engl.

WALTER, LISA; Shikellamy HS; Sunbury, PA; (3); 13/312; Spanish Clb; Ed Yrbk Stf; Hon Roll; NHS.

WALTER, MARK; Nazareth Area SR HS; Nazareth, PA; (4); 37/241; Boy Scts; Camera Clb; Chess Clb; Church Yth Grp; Exploring; SADD; Stage Crew; Yrbk Phtg; Yrbk Sprt Ed; Hon Roll; U Pittsburgh; Elec Engr.

WALTER, PAMELA; Meadowbrook Christian Schl; Milton, PA; (3); 1/11; Church Yth Grp; Spanish Clb; JV Socr; High Hon Roll; Prfct Atten Awd; Algebra II Awd 85; Geom Awd 86; Overall Achvmnt 86; Messiah Coll; Math.

WALTER, TARA; Nazareth Academy HS; Langhorne, PA; (4); German Clb; Math Clb; Y-Teens; Yrbk Stf; Hon Roll; Half-Tuition Schlrshp Nazareth Acad 83-87; Partial Schlrshp Villa Victoria Acad 83-87; Trinity Coll; Econ.

WALTER, VICKY; Seneca HS; Wattsburg, PA; (3); 9/160; Cmnty Wkr; Sec FBLA; Yrbk Stf; Hon Roll; NHS; 3rd Pl Trphy Acctng 86; 4th Pl Awd Steno 87; Cert Schlrshp 85-87; PA ST; Acctnt.

WALTERMIRE, JOYCE; Rockwood Area HS; Rockwood, PA; (3); Pres VP 4-H; Band; Chorus; Rep Jr Cls; Rep Stu Cncl; JV Var Bsktbl; Stat Vllybl; French Hon Soc; 4-H Awd; Hon Roll; Hoby Semnr 86; Ed.

WALTERMYER, CHRISTINE; Northern Lebanon HS; Jonestown, PA; (4); 26/163; Art Clb; Church Yth Grp; French Clb; Chorus; School Musical; School Play; Nwsp Rptr; Tennis; Hon Roll; Art.

WALTERS, AARON; Ringgold HS; Donora, PA; (3); Aud/Vis; Band; Concert Band; Mrchg Band; Stage Crew; L Ftbl; High Hon Roll; Hon Roll; Mech Engr.

WALTERS, ANDREA; Mon Valley Catholic HS; Elrama, PA; (4); 19/75; Church Yth Grp; English Clb; Girl Scts; Pep Clb; Band; Chorus; Church Choir; Concert Band; Drm Mjr(t); Mrchg Band; Gld Awd Grl Scts 87; IN U Of PA; Bus Mrktng.

WALTERS, ANNE; St Paul Cathedral HS; Verona, PA; (3); 5/53; JA; Latin Clb; Concert Band; Mrchg Band; Nwsp Stf; Yrbk Stf; Bausch & Lomb Sci Awd; High Hon Roll; NHS; NEDT Awd; Outstndng Latin Stu 85-86; Awds Buhl Sci Fair 85-86; Hist.

WALTERS, BRIAN; Monessen SR HS; Monessen, PA; (3); Cmnty Wkr; Ftbl; Monessen & Rostraver Ambulnc Svcs; Anesthesiolgst.

WALTERS, CARRIE; Tunkhannock Area HS; Tunkhannock, PA; (3); Church Yth Grp; FCA; Girl Scts; Spanish Clb; Band; Chorus; Church Choir; Concert Band; Jazz Band; Mrchg Band; Misercondia; Music Ed.

WALTERS, CHERI; Central York HS; York, PA; (3); Church Yth Grp; Chorus; Church Choir; Flag Corp; Orch; School Musical; School Play; Yrbk Stf; Hon Roll; Opt Clb Awd; Band Front Co-Capt 86; Bloomsburg; Speech Therapy.

WALTERS, DAVE; New Wilmington Area HS; Edinburg, PA; (4); 10/120; Church Yth Grp; Var Capt Crs Cntry; Var L Trk; Math Tm; Spanish Clb; Hon Roll; NHS; Ntl Merit SF; Prsdntl Acdmc Fitness Awd 87; Grove City Coll; Mech Engrng.

WALTERS, DAVID; Leechburg Area HS; Leechburg, PA; (3); 14/87; Church Yth Grp; Math Tm; Spanish Clb; Nwsp Stf; Yrbk Phtg; Im Vllybl; Hon Roll; Biol Tchr.

WALTERS, E GEORGE; Blue Mountain HS; Orwigsburg, PA; (4); 5/218; Boy Scts; ROTC; School Play; Nwsp Ed-Chief; Im Wt Lftg; NHS; Ntl Merit SF; Mu Alpha Theta; Quiz Bowl; Im Sftbl; Army ROTC Schlrshp; West Point; Elec Engrng.

WALTERS, HOLLY; Red Land HS; Lewisberry, PA; (3); 79/306; Var Trk; Wt Lftg; Hon Roll; Acad Exc Awd In Spanish II; Var Lttr In Track; Optometry.

WALTERS, JANET; Monongahela Valley Catholic HS; New Eagle, PA; (2); 13/76; Color Guard; Trs Frsh Cls; Spanish NHS; Med.

WALTERS, JENNIFER; Everett Area HS; Everett, PA; (1); Church Yth Grp; GAA; Band; Chorus; Concert Band; Mrchg Band; Pep Band; School Musical; Im L Bsktbl; Trk; IUP.

WALTERS, JUDY; Northampton SR HS; Northampton, PA; (4); 32/440; FTA; Band; Concert Band; Mrchg Band; Pres Sr Cls; High Hon Roll; Hon Roll; Hghst Avg Alg I 83-84; NCACC; Elem Ed.

WALTERS, KORI; Ephrata SR HS; Akron, PA; (3); Cmnty Wkr; German Clb; Band; Im Bsktbl; Ice Hcky; JV Tennis; Im Vllybl; Hon Roll; Pre Law.

WALTERS, LOWELL; Northern Bedford County HS; Bakers Summit, PA; (4); 3/95; VP Camera Clb; Church Yth Grp; Chorus; Church Choir; School Musical; Variety Show; Nwsp Ed-Chief; Yrbk Phtg; Hon Roll; NHS; Huntingdon Daily News-Supr Stffr Awd 87; NBC-DRAMA Awd 87; Ntl Chrl Awd 87; Liberty U; Hstry.

WALTERS, MATT; Athens Area HS; Sayre, PA; (2); 4-H; FFA; VP Of F F A 86-87; Ag Bus.

WALTERS, SHEILA; Somerset SR HS; Somerset, PA; (3); 6/230; Am Leg Aux Girls St; Model UN; Mu Alpha Theta; Pres Frsh Cls; Pres Soph Cls; Pres Jr Cls; Trs Stu Cncl; NHS; Church Yth Grp; Cmnty Wkr; Chrmn Stu Tchr Rltns 86-87; Band Cncl Rep 84-88; Capt Rifle Squad, Danceline 86-88; George Mason U.

WALTERS, STEVEN; Muncy HS; Muncy, PA; (4); 10/74; French Clb; Varsity Clb; Ftbl; Wrstlng; High Hon Roll; NHS; Chemstry Awd-Highst Ave 86; Chemstry.

WALTERSDORFF, BRIAN; Central York HS; York, PA; (3); Church Yth Grp; Computer Clb; JA; Varsity Clb; Band; Concert Band; Orch; Symp Band; Socr; Trk; Comp.

WALTERSDORFF, JENNIFER; Susquehannock HS; New Freedom, PA; (2); 47/243; Cmnty Wkr; Stat Fld Hcky; Vrsty Ltr-Statstcn-Fld Hcky 86; Law.

WALTIMYER, DUANE; Red Lion Area SR HS; Red Lion, PA; (2); 82/344; Boy Scts; Church Choir; God Cntry Awd.

WALTMAN, CRYSTAL; Blue Mountain HS; Orwigsburg, PA; (2); 15/225; Art Clb; JV Bsktbl; JV Vllybl; Hon Roll; Art Cntst 1st Pl 86; JV Let Bsktbll 86; Penn ST; Aerodynmcl Engr.

WALTMAN, JEFFREY; Karns City HS; Chicora, PA; (4); 24/116; Boy Scts; Exploring; Spanish Clb; Mrchg Band; Pep Band; Gannon U; Accntng.

WALTMAN, MELISSA; Central HS; York, PA; (4); Church Yth Grp; Drama Clb; Girl Scts; Hosp Aide; Ski Clb; Stage Crew; Sftbl; Hon Roll.

WALTMAN, MICHELLE L; Solanco SR HS; Quarryville, PA; (4); 77/241; Pres Church Yth Grp; Varsity Clb; Chorus; Flag Corp; Mrchg Band; School Musical; Rep Stu Cncl; Var Capt Fld Hcky; Var Trk; Hon Roll; Schlstc Art Awd 85-86; Miss Congeniality-Miss Solanco Pageant 87; Millersville U; Bus.

WALTMAN, STEVE; Strath Haven HS; Wallingford, PA; (3); FBLA; Ski Clb; Concert Band; Mrchg Band; Var Socr; Var Tennis; Hon Roll; Rtry Schlrshp Tmrrws Ldrs Conf 87; Bus Admin.

WALTON, AYREN; Somerset Area SR HS; Sipesville, PA; (3); 55/291; Church Yth Grp; English Clb; German Clb; Letterman Clb; Library Aide; Varsity Clb; Chorus; Church Choir; Yrbk Rptr; Yrbk Stf; Messiah; Bio.

WALTON, DANA; Kiski Area HS; Vandergrift, PA; (3); Church Yth Grp; Spanish Clb; Band; Concert Band; Var Crs Cntry; Im Sftbl; Var L Trk; High Hon Roll; Sports Medicine.

WALTON, DIANE; North Hills HS; Pittsburgh, PA; (4); 4/467; Church Yth Grp; VP Keywanettes; Chorus; Lit Mag; High Hon Roll; NHS; Gftd Tlntd Enrchmnt; Hd Ushr Commncmnt 86; Engrng Sci.

WALTON, ELIZABETH; Solanco HS; Quarryville, PA; (3); 85/273; Church Yth Grp; Teachers Aide; Chorus; Church Choir; Color Guard; Var Crs Cntry; JV Trk; Elem Ed.

WALTON, ELIZABETH G; Langley HS; Pittsburgh, PA; (3); Ski Clb; Band; Mrchg Band; School Musical; Nwsp Stf; Yrbk Ed-Chief; L Trk; Hon Roll; Prsdntl Ftnss Awd 86; Bio.

WALTON, ERIC; Lakeland HS; Jermyn, PA; (3); JV Bsbl; Var Bsktbl; L Golf; Hon Roll; NHS.

WALTON, KAREN; Spring-Ford SR HS; Mont Clare, PA; (3); 15/256; German Clb; Chorus; Stu Cncl; Fld Hcky; Lcrss; Hon Roll; NHS.

WALTON, LAUREN; Hampton HS; Allison Pk, PA; (2); VP Church Yth Grp; Band; Concert Band; Symp Band; Powder Puff Ftbl; Sftbl; High Hon Roll; Allegheny Hnrs Band 86-87; Prmsng Wmn Of Future Awd 85; Hampton Ath Assoc All Star Sftbl Plys 85-86; Med.

WALTON, NICOLE LYN; Berwick Area SR HS; Berwick, PA; (4); Drama Clb; Key Clb; Red Cross Aide; Speech Tm; Stage Crew; Ed Nwsp Rptr; Yrbk Stf; Lit Mag; Var Fld Hcky; Voice Dem Awd; 2n Pl Berwick Crspn Fld Essy 86-87; Penn ST U; Cmmnctn.

WALTON, TAMRA LYNN; Wyoming Area HS; Pittston, PA; (3); Art Clb; Aud/Vis; Church Yth Grp; FBLA; Library Aide; SADD; Band; Mrchg Band; Yrbk Stf; Hon Roll; Lic Emrgny Med Tech LCC Coll 87; RN.

WALTZ, CATHARINE; Warwick HS; Lititz, PA; (2); 58/326; Boys Clb Am; Cmnty Wkr; Computer Clb; Exploring; Model UN; Stage Crew; Off Stu Cncl; High Hon Roll; Hon Roll; Law.

WALTZ, CHRISTIN; Bucktail Area HS; Westport, PA; (2); Sec Church Yth Grp; Sec 4-H; Letterman Clb; SADD; Varsity Clb; Band; Chorus; Concert Band; Mrchg Band; Off Soph Cls; Fshn Dsgn.

WALTZ, THOMAS; Blacklick Valley HS; Nanty Glo, PA; (3); Cmnty Wkr; German Clb; Varsity Clb; Trk; High Hon Roll; Pres Fitness Awd 84-85; Acad All-Amer Awd 85-86; Engr.

WALZ, ANDREW; Williamsport Area HS; Williamsport, PA; (3); Aud/Vis; Church Yth Grp; Ski Clb; VP Soph Cls; Rep Stu Cncl; JV L Ftbl; Var L Swmmng; Psych.

WALZ JR, DAVID; Gateway HS; Monroeville, PA; (3); Church Yth Grp; Off Frsh Cls; Off Soph Cls; Off Jr Cls; Off Sr Cls; Im Ftbl; Var L Golf; Hon Roll; Prfct Atten Awd; Brdcst Jrnlsm.

WAMBOLD, SHERRY; Avon Grove HS; W Grove, PA; (4); 38/218; VP FBLA; Yrbk Stf; JV Fld Hcky; Im Wt Lftg; 4th Pl Parlmntry Procdrs FBLA ST Conf 87; Comp Info Sys.

WAMBOLDT, AMY; Mercer Area HS; Mercer, PA; (3); Church Yth Grp; Band; Concert Band; Mrchg Band; Pep Band; L Mat Maids; Trk; Stat Wrstlng; Hon Roll; Hugh O Brian Yth Ldrshp Rep 86; Math.

WANCHISN, STACY; Marion Center HS; Marion Center, PA; (4); Pres Art Clb; FBLA; Latin Clb; VP Q&S; SADD; Sec Band; Concert Band; Mrchg Band; Nwsp Ed-Chief; High Hon Roll; 1st Pl Region III Econ 87; Schlstc Jrnlsm Awd 87; Art Club Awd 87; IN U Of PA; Art.

WANDEL, KEITH; Dallas SR HS; Dallas, PA; (3); Art Clb; Aud/Vis; Library Aide; Band; Concert Band; Jazz Band; Mrchg Band; Hon Roll; Lib Aide Awd 86-87; 2nd Pl Dallas Art Show Colored Pncl 86-87; 2nd Pl Scratchbrd Dallas Art Show 86-87; Navy Acad; Math.

WANDELL, JESSICA; Laurel Highlands SR HS; Uniontown, PA; (3); 16/325; FBLA; Chorus; Nwsp Stf; High Hon Roll; Hon Roll; NHS; Law.

WANDTKE, ANN; Pen Argyl Area HS; Pen Argyl, PA; (4); 1/116; Drama Clb; Ski Clb; Band; Orch; Nwsp Rptr; High Hon Roll; Jr NHS; NHS; Ntl Merit SF; Pres Schlr; PA Gvrnor Schl Of Arts 85; PA ST Orchstr 84-85; Cngrs-Bndstg Exchng Stu 86-87; MIT-CAMBRIDGE MA; Pltcl Sci.

WANDTKE, SARAH; Pen Argyl HS; Pen Argyl, PA; (3); 21/166; Ski Clb; Orch; L Crs Cntry; Var Mgr(s); JV Sftbl; Var Trk; Hon Roll; Penn ST; Mrktng.

WANG, BRYAN; Spring-Ford HS; Oaks, PA; (1); 2/287; Computer Clb; German Clb; Math Clb; Math Tm; Band; Jazz Band; Mrchg Band; L Bsbl; Im Vllybl; L Wrstlng.

WANG, LEONARD L H; Abington Hts HS; Clarks Summit, PA; (2); Scholastic Bowl; Church Choir; Orch; Rep Stu Cncl; Hon Roll; 1st Pl Amer Chem Socty Annl Chem Exm 87; Brnz Medl Olympd Wrttn Rssn 85; Olympd Spokn Rssn 86; MA Inst Of Tech; Chem Engrng.

WANG, LISA; Kennedy Christian HS; Hermitage, PA; (3); VP French Clb; Ski Clb; Drill Tm; School Play; Nwsp Rptr; Yrbk Stf; Pres Frsh Cls; Pres Soph Cls; Sec Stu Cncl; High Hon Roll; PA JR Acad Sci 1st Pl ST Comp 85; Pre-Med.

WANGER, EDDY; Spring-Ford HS; Royersford, PA; (3); Trs German Clb; Math Clb; Ski Clb; SADD; Stu Cncl; Bsbl; Bsktbl; Ftbl; Im Sftbl; Im Vllybl.

WANNER, JOHN; Pequea Valley HS; Narvon, PA; (3); AFS; Band; Chorus; Concert Band; Jazz Band; Mrchg Band; Var JV Bsktbl; Var JV Socr; JV Tennis; Hon Roll; VFW Awd-Voice Of Dmcrcy Spch 86; Accntng.

WANNER, LYNN; Cocalico HS; Reinholds, PA; (3); Church Yth Grp; Computer Clb; Girl Scts; Band; Mrchg Band; Badmtn; Trk; Hon Roll; Prfct Atten Awd; Bus.

WANSLEY, CELESTE; Donegal HS; Marietta, PA; (3); 47/163; Church Yth Grp; Civic Clb; Drama Clb; Pep Clb; Varsity Clb; School Play; Yrbk Stf; Rep Stu Cncl; Var Trk; Hon Roll; Eastern Coll; Psych.

WANTZ, CRYSTAL; Eastern York JR/Sr HS; York, PA; (3); Church Yth Grp; SADD; Chorus; Church Choir; School Musical; High Hon Roll; Hon Roll; Jr NHS; NHS; Millersville; Spcl Educ.

WANYO, MICHAEL; Coughlin HS; Plains, PA; (3); Church Yth Grp; Var L Crs Cntry; Var L Trk; High Hon Roll; Hon Roll; Jr NHS; NHS.

WANZCO, JENNIFER; St Paul Cathedral HS; Pittsburgh, PA; (3); 12/54; Var Bsktbl; Var Vllybl; Hon Roll; NHS; Accntng.

WANZIE, MONICA; Southern Columbia Area HS; Numidia, PA; (4); 17/77; Key Clb; Ski Clb; Varsity Clb; Drm Mjr(t); Jazz Band; Nwsp Rptr; Yrbk Stf; Trs Frsh Cls; Trs Soph Cls; Trs Jr Cls; Sthrn Columbia Fne Art Awd 87; E Stroudsburg U; Sprts Med.

WARCHOL, KATHLEEN; Pennsburg HS; Yardley, PA; (4); 56/771; Church Yth Grp; French Clb; Hosp Aide; Concert Band; Mrchg Band; Nwsp Stf; Hon Roll; NHS; Pres Schlr; French Awd 84; Villanova U; Englsh.

WARCHOLIK, EILEEN; Venango Christian HS; Franklin, PA; (2); 6/39; SADD; Yrbk Stf; Sec Stu Cncl; Mgr(s); Score Keeper; Var Sftbl; JV Vllybl; High Hon Roll; Hon Roll; NHS.

WARD, ANDREA; St Huberts HS; Philadelphia, PA; (3); 263/421; Cmnty Wkr; Dance Clb; Science Clb; Hon Roll; Gwynedd-Mercy; Nrsng.

WARD, DARICA; Mifflinburg Area HS; Mifflinburg, PA; (2); German Clb; Key Clb; Pres Frsh Cls; JV Fld Hcky; JV Sftbl; High Hon Roll; JC Awd; Penn ST; Ltl Mgmt.

WARD, JAMES T W; Open Door Christian Acad; Greensburg, PA; (4); 1/7; Church Yth Grp; Capt Quiz Bowl; Church Choir; Trs Yrbk Phtg; Capt Bsktbl; High Hon Roll; Val; Schl Svc Awd 85 & 86; Natl ACE Quiz Bowl Comptn-1st Pl 86; Regnl ACE Table Tennis Comptn-1st Pl 85; Liberty U; Math/Comptr Sci.

WARD, JENNIFER; Bishop Mc Cort HS; Johnstown, PA; (3); Latin Clb; Library Aide; Mu Alpha Theta; Ski Clb; Nwsp Rptr; Sec Stu Cncl; Var L Socr; Var L Swmmng; High Hon Roll; NHS; PIAA Dist Swmmng 85-87; Red Cross Cert Lfgrd Advncd Lfsvng & Wtr Sfty 86-87; Co-Editor Schl Paper 87; Law.

WARD, JENNIFER; West Catholic Girls HS; Philadelphia, PA; (3); 20/240; NFL; Spanish Clb; Orch; Nwsp Ed-Chief; Nwsp Rptr; Rep Jr Cls; Rep Stu Cncl; Hon Roll; NHS; Prfct Atten Awd; Exemplry Stu Awd 85-87; Educ.

WARD, KATHLEEN; Panther Valley HS; Coaldale, PA; (3); 15/132; Art Clb; Drama Clb; Chorus; Flag Corp; School Musical; Nwsp Stf; Yrbk Stf; Hon Roll; Intl Bus.

WARD JR, LONIE; Trinity HS; Washington, PA; (4); Office Aide; Bsktbl; High Hon Roll; Hon Roll; Edinboro U Of PA; Nrsng.

WARD, MATT; Waynesburg Central HS; Waynesburg, PA; (3); Art Clb; Boy Scts; Chess Clb; Church Yth Grp; Cmnty Wkr; French Clb; Office Aide; Quiz Bowl; Church Choir; Yrbk Phtg; Waynesburg Coll; Bus.

WARD, SABINE; Belle Vernon Area HS; Belle Vernon, PA; (4); 65/270; Church Yth Grp; Teachers Aide; Band; Concert Band; Mrchg Band; Var JV Powder Puff Ftbl; Hon Roll; Prfct Atten Awd; Yth Ftnss Achvt Awd 84; CA U; Educ.

WARD, TRACY; Frazier HS; Grindstone, PA; (3); Med Asstnt.

WARD, TRICIA; Purchase Line HS; Commodore, PA; (3); 20/98; Church Yth Grp; FBLA; Pep Clb; Chorus; Nwsp Stf; Yrbk Stf; Cheerleading; Hon Roll; Spanish NHS; Natl Art Awd 86-87; Acdmc All-Amer 86-87; Commercial Art.

WARD, VICKI; Sharon HS; Sharon, PA; (4); 2/159; French Clb; Trs Sr Cls; Var Tennis; French Hon Soc; High Hon Roll; NHS; Sal; Amer Values Schlrshp 87; Pres Honor Awd 87; Slippery Rock U Acad Bk Awd 87; John Carroll U; Econ.

WARDER, KELLY; Chichester SR HS; Trainer, PA; (3); 2/293; Office Aide; Mrchg Band; High Hon Roll; Hon Roll; Jr NHS; Pres NHS; Spanish NHS; Cert Merit Socl Stds 85; Pres Natl Hnr Soc 87; Acctng.

WARDLE, BRIAN L; Upper Perkiomen HS; East Greenville, PA; (4); 17/250; Aud/Vis; Varsity Clb; Chorus; Var Golf; JV Socr; Var Tennis; Pres Acad Ftnss Awd 87; PA Hghr Ed Asst Agncy Cert Of Merit 86; Penn ST U.

WARDLOW, TAMMY; Carbondale Area HS; Carbondale, PA; (4); Art Clb; English Clb; French Clb; Hosp Aide; Science Clb; Yrbk Stf; Hon Roll; Marywood Ldrshp & Warner Comm Schlrshps; Marywood; Chld Psychlgy.

WARDROPPER, DEAN; Elizabeth-Forward HS; Mckeesport, PA; (2); 26/345; Chess Clb; Church Yth Grp; French Clb; VP JA; Math Clb; Golf; High Hon Roll; Fast-Pacd Math Pgm 86; Accntng.

WARE, DAWN; Sun Valley HS; Aston, PA; (3); 86/270; Church Yth Grp; Hosp Aide; Kutztown; Bus Admin.

WAREHAM, GREGORY S; Gateway SR HS; Pitcairn, PA; (4); 154/486; Am Leg Boys St; Nwsp Ed-Chief; Off Soph Cls; Off Jr Cls; Off Sr Cls; Capt Ice Hcky; Hon Roll; Masonic Awd; Drama Clb; Hosp Aide; PA Gvrnrs Schl For Arts 85; 1st Pl Anatomy Cmptn At Bio Olympics 87; Elizebethtown Coll; Occ Thrpy.

WARFEL, CYNTHIA; North Allegheny HS; Wexford, PA; (2); 59/630; Church Yth Grp; VP JA; Mrchg Band; Symp Band; Hon Roll; Jr NHS; German Awd 86-87; GOAL 85-87.

WARFEL, PAMELA; Donegal HS; Mount Joy, PA; (3); 34/177; Church Yth Grp; Sec Hst FBLA; Chorus; Church Choir; Color Guard; Nwsp Stf; Yrbk Stf; Stat Score Keeper; JV Trk; Hon Roll; Accntng.

WARGO, DANEEN; Trinity HS; New Cumberland, PA; (4); 25/138; Church Yth Grp; Pep Clb; Spanish Clb; NHS; Shippensburg U; Pblc Rltns.

WARGO, FRANCINE; Monongahela Valley Catholic HS; West Brownsville, PA; (4); 2/76; Science Clb; Spanish Clb; Concert Band; Mrchg Band; Rep Pres Stu Cncl; JV Var Bsktbl; Powder Puff Ftbl; Var L Sftbl; NHS; Sec Spanish NHS; Case Western Reserve U; Engrng.

WARGO, JOHN; Portage Area HS; Portage, PA; (3); JV VP Bsbl; Golf; French Hon Soc; High Hon Roll; Memorial Hosp; Surg Tech.

WARGO, KATHLEEN; East Allegheny HS; North Versailles, PA; (3); German Clb; Hosp Aide; Color Guard; Pres Orch; School Musical; Yrbk Bus Mgr; Yrbk Stf; Var L Sftbl; High Hon Roll; NHS; Dist Rgnl & All ST Orch 86-87; Educ.

WARGO, MICHELLE C; Monongahela Valley Catholic HS; West Brownsville, PA; (4); 3/76; Chorus; Drill Tm; Mrchg Band; School Musical; Stat Bsktbl; Sec NHS; Pres Spanish NHS; Spanish Clb; SADD; Variety Show; Century III Ldrshp Awd 86; PA JR Acad Sci ST Awds 84-86; Westinghouse Sci Tlnt Srch 86.

WARGO, ROBERT; Steel Valley HS; W Homestead, PA; (3); Exploring; Band; Concert Band; Mrchg Band; U Pittsburgh; Med.

WARGO, SCOTT; Parkland HS; Allentown, PA; (2); JV Ftbl; Var Trk; Hon Roll; Penn ST U; Elen Engnr.

WARGO, STEVE; Mt Carmel Area JR SR HS; Mt Carmel, PA; (3); 28/130; Aud/Vis; FCA; French Clb; Key Clb; Band; Concert Band; Jazz Band; Mrchg Band; School Musical; Stage Crew; Yng Amer Shwcs; Audio Prod.

WARHOLIC, LYNNE; Renns Manor HS; Clymer, PA; (3); 14/100; FBLA; Varsity Clb; Band; Chorus; Jazz Band; School Musical; Yrbk Stf; Rep Stu Cncl; L Var Vllybl; NHS; IN Evening Gazt Girls Vlybl Tm Hnr Mntn 84; IN Co Band 85-87.

WARING, CHRISTINE; Little Flower HS; Philadelphia, PA; (3); 120/312; Boys Clb Am; Varsity Clb; Var L Bsktbl; JV Socr; Var Capt Sftbl; Hon Roll; Chldhd Ed.

WARMKESSEL, MICHELLE; Palisades HS; Riegelsville, PA; (4); 11/179; Sec Pres 4-H; Teachers Aide; Chorus; Church Choir; Flag Corp; School Musical; Var Capt Cheerleading; DAR Awd; Sec NHS; Albright Coll; Math.

WARMUS, PATRICIA C; Seneca Valley SR HS; Zelie, PA; (2); Chorus; Church Choir; Variety Show; Hon Roll; Prfct Atten Awd; Full Schlrshp PPS Summrdnce Pgm 86-87; Point Pk Coll; Musicl Prfrmr.

WARNE, MATT; Newport HS; Newport, PA; (4); 5/93; Am Leg Boys St; Varsity Clb; Stu Cncl; Bsktbl; Ftbl; Wt Lftg; NHS; Quiz Bowl; School Play; Yrbk Stf; U S Military Acad; Cvl Engrng.

WARNER, BOB; Scranton Tech; Scranton, PA; (4); Boy Scts; Cmnty Wkr; Ski Clb; Boy Sct Relgn Ad Alteri Day 85; Family Htng Bus.

WARNER, CHERYL; Mechanicsburg HS; Shiremanstown, PA; (3); 43/338; JV Bsktbl; JV Tennis; Arch.

WARNER, ERIC; Loyalsock Township HS; Montoursville, PA; (3); 28/120; Church Yth Grp; German Clb; Band; Concert Band; Mrchg Band; Pep Band; Nwsp Stf; L Trk; Var L Wrstlng; Drexel U; Bus Admin.

WARNER, JIM; Juniata HS; E Waterford, PA; (3); Church Yth Grp; SADD; Varsity Clb; Band; Chorus; Church Choir; Concert Band; Jazz Band; Mrchg Band; Orch; Schltc J Awd 85 & 87; Messiah Coll; Comp Sci.

WARNER, LISA; Archbishop Prendergast HS; Glenolden, PA; (3); 52/353; Church Yth Grp; School Play; Yrbk Stf; Hon Roll; 2nd Hnrs Of Soph Hr 85-86; Penn ST U; Vet Med.

WARNER, REBECCA; Lebanon Catholic HS; Palmyra, PA; (3); Cmnty Wkr; Key Clb; Capt Color Guard; School Play; Yrbk Stf; Hon Roll; Science Clb; Spanish Clb; We The People Essay Cert 87; Artist.

WARNER, STEVE; Stroudsbrug HS; E Stroudsburg, PA; (2); Church Yth Grp; Varsity Clb; Church Choir; Var JV Bsktbl; Var L Socr; JV Trk; Hon Roll.

WARNER, TODD; South Side Area Beaver County HS; Hookstown, PA; (3); Boy Scts; Ski Clb; SADD; Band; Mrchg Band; Yrbk Rptr; Yrbk Stf; High Hon Roll; Hon Roll; Eagle Scout 87; Engrng.

WARNER, WENDY ANN; Plum SR HS; Pittsburgh, PA; (4); Cmnty Wkr; Exploring; French Clb; FTA; Chorus; School Musical; Yrbk Stf; Hon Roll; NHS; Prfct Atten Awd; Frnch Outstndng SR Awd 87; U Of Pittsburgh; Educ.

WARNICK, DAVID; Meyersdale Area HS; Meyersdale, PA; (3); 17/120; Am Leg Boys St; Church Yth Grp; Letterman Clb; Pep Clb; Quiz Bowl; Pres Spanish Clb; Band; Concert Band; Mrchg Band; Pep Band; West Point; Bus.

WARNICK, MARCIA; Butler Area SR HS; Butler, PA; (4); 127/699; Church Yth Grp; Exploring; French Clb; SADD; Band; Church Choir; Concert Band; Mrchg Band; Var Swmmng; Jr NHS; Mrchng Band Ltr 86-87; HS Aqts Ltr 86-87; W Liberty ST Coll; Dntl Hyg.

WARNKE, MARY; Tyrone Area HS; Tyrone, PA; (3); Rep Church Yth Grp; Sec Girl Scts; Spanish Clb; SADD; Teachers Aide; Band; Chorus; Church Choir; Concert Band; Jazz Band; Outstndng Musician; PA ST; Music Ed.

WARNOCK, JILL; Susquenita HS; Duncannon, PA; (3); 4/170; Church Yth Grp; Quiz Bowl; Spanish Clb; Yrbk Ed-Chief; Rep Soph Cls; Rep Jr Cls; Rep Sr Cls; Rep Stu Cncl; L Cheerleading; Patriot News Corrsp; Amer Leg Essay Awds; PA ST U; Bus Admin.

WARNTZ, LISA; Danville SR HS; Danville, PA; (1); Band; Concert Band; Mrchg Band; School Musical; Hon Roll; Penn ST.

WARNTZ, LORI; Danville SR HS; Danville, PA; (3); Key Clb; Nwsp Stf; Yrbk Stf; Psychlgy.

WARONSKY, FRANK; Kiski Area HS; Apollo, PA; (3); Key Clb; Letterman Clb; Spanish Clb; Varsity Clb; Var L Bsbl; Var L Bsktbl; Var L Ftbl; Wt Lftg; Hon Roll.

WARREN, ALLISON; Franklin SR HS; Franklin, PA; (3); Trs Church Yth Grp; Natl Beta Clb; Pep Clb; Band; Concert Band; Mrchg Band; Pep Band; School Play; Gov Hon Prg Awd; Hon Roll; Biol.

WARREN, HEATHER; Mechanicsburg SR HS; Mechanicsburg, PA; (3); 40/338; Church Yth Grp; Pres Pep Clb; Chorus; Church Choir; Rep Stu Cncl; Mgr Bsbl; JV Var Cheerleading; Radio Brdcstng.

WARREN, JEFFREY; Shamokin Area HS; Shamokin, PA; (2); 56/250; Art Clb; Aud/Vis; Camera Clb; Cmnty Wkr; Science Clb; Band; Concert Band; Mrchg Band; Pep Band; Trk.

WARREN, JODI; Canton Area HS; Canton, PA; (4); 14/175; Church Yth Grp; FBLA; Hosp Aide; Library Aide; Office Aide; Red Cross Aide; Chorus; High Hon Roll; NHS; Pres Schlr; Bst Avrg Shrthnd II Awd 87; Wlmsprt Schl Of Cmrc Schlrshp 87; Wlmsprt Schl Cmrc; Med Scrtry.

WARREN, JOHN; Seneca Valley HS; Evans City, PA; (3); ROTC; Science Clb; Rep Jr Cls; High Hon Roll; Trs NHS; Prfct Atten Awd; Supr Cadet Awd 84-86; Militry Ordr Wrld Ward Awd Merit 86-87; Aerntcl Engrng.

WARREN, KATHERINE; Kennard-Dale HS; Stewartstown, PA; (4); 1/117; Church Yth Grp; Quiz Bowl; Varsity Clb; Yrbk Ed-Chief; Var JV Cheerleading; Var Trk; High Hon Roll; NHS; Val; French Clb; PA JR SCI Hmnts Sympsm 85; Pres Acad Ftnss Awd 87; U Of PA; Math.

WARREN, KEVIN ERIC; Middletown Area HS; Middletown, PA; (4); 68/171; Boy Scts; FBLA; JCL; Pres Model UN; Political Wkr; Radio Clb; Band; Concert Band; Mrchg Band; Orch; Delta Sigma Theta Ctznshp Awd 87; Howard U; Pre Law.

WARREN, TODD; Jenkintown HS; Jenkintown, PA; (2); Chess Clb; Intnl Clb; Q&S; Nwsp Stf; Hon Roll; Jr NHS; Pres Schlr; Took Bio 101 At Penn St While In 9th Grd 85-86; Took Advncd Math Course With 30 Slct Stu 85-86; Drexel; Sci.

WARRING, JEANETTE; Forest City Regional HS; Pleasant Mount, PA; (3); 15/68; Am Leg Aux Girls St; VP Sec 4-H; German Clb; Ski Clb; Var Sftbl; 4-H Awd; Hon Roll; NHS; Vet.

WARRINGTON, KRISTA; West Chester East HS; West Chester, PA; (3); Art Clb; Drama Clb; Spanish Clb; Rep Stu Cncl; Var Gym.

WARTZENLUFT, JENNIE; Kutztown Area HS; Kutztown, PA; (3); 31/177; FBLA; VICA; Band; Chorus; Color Guard; Concert Band; Drill Tm; Mrchg Band; JV Sftbl; High Hon Roll; HOSA 2nd Pl St Conf, 1st Pl Natl Conf 85-86; HOSA 1st Pl St Conf, 2nd Pl Natl Conf 86-87; Reading Hosp; Oprtng Rm Tech.

WARUNEK, AMY; Pittston Area HS; Avoca, PA; (4); 18/348; Trs French Clb; Key Clb; Math Clb; SADD; Yrbk Stf; High Hon Roll; Hon Roll; NHS.

WARUNEK, KIMBERLY; Pittston Area SR HS; Dupont, PA; (4); 31/330; Church Yth Grp; French Clb; Key Clb; Ski Clb; SADD; Chorus; Ed Nwsp Ed-Chief; Var Swmmng; Hon Roll; PSU.

WARY, MICHELLE; Tri-Valley HS; Klingerstown, PA; (3); 11/76; DECA; FBLA; Yrbk Stf; Sftbl; Hon Roll; Bloomsburg U; Mgmt.

WARYANKA, JILL; Hempfield Area HS; Irwin, PA; (4); French Clb; NFL; Yrbk Ed-Chief; Pres Frsh Cls; Pres Stu Cncl; JV Bsktbl; French Hon Soc; Hon Roll; Jr NHS; Debate Tm; Schlrshp Wstmrlnd Med Axlry 87; Duquesne U; Phrmcy.

WARYCH, KEN; Richland HS; Gibsonia, PA; (3); AFS; Cmnty Wkr; Red Cross Aide; Mrchg Band; Yrbk Stf; Var Bsktbl; High Hon Roll; NHS; Band; Concert Band; RYF Wnnrs Club Awd 83; Slippery Rock Bsktbll Camp MIP Awd 87; Penn ST; Parks & Rec.

WASCAK, DAVID; Connellsville Area HS; Dunbar, PA; (1); Church Yth Grp; 4-H; Office Aide; Bsktbl; High Hon Roll; Jr NHS; Agri.

WASCAK, PATRICK; Connellsville Area HS; Dunbar, PA; (2); Church Yth Grp; 4-H; Chorus; School Musical; Bsktbl; 4-H Awd; Hon Roll; Am Legion Citation Of Appreciation 85; Agriculture.

WASCO, MELANIE A; Mon Valley C H S; Belle Vernon, PA; (4); 8/76; Ski Clb; Spanish Clb; SADD; Color Guard; Stage Crew; Powder Puff Ftbl; NHS; Spanish NHS; 1st Pl Humanities Day Awd 86; Sci.

WASCZCAK, MIKE; West Scranton HS; Scranton, PA; (2); 4/255; Drama Clb; Spanish Clb; Thesps; School Play; Stage Crew; High Hon Roll; Jr NHS; Prfct Atten Awd; Art Clb; Aud/Vis; PA Jr Acad Of Sci 85; Two Part-Time Jobs 86-87; PA ST U; Coll Prfssr.

WASELKO, DAVID; Kiski Area HS; Leechburg, PA; (4); Pres Church Yth Grp; JA; Jazz Band; Mrchg Band; Symp Band; Nwsp Stf; Trk; High Hon Roll; Rotary Awd; Schlrshp IBEW Union No 5 Wstrn PA Chaptr NECA Schlrshp Trst Fnd 87; Indiana U PA.

WASHBURN, HEATHER; Waynesboro HS; Waynesboro, PA; (2); Stu Cncl; Cheerleading; Trk; Hon Roll.

WASHINGTON, JERROD; Central HS; Philadelphia, PA; (2); Church Yth Grp; Church Choir; Ftbl; Trk; Engrng.

WASHINGTON, LENO; Harrisburg HS; Harrisburg, PA; (4); 33/233; Bsbl; Bsktbl; Hon Roll; Sprntndnts Awd 87; Prncpls Awd 87; Harrisburg Area CC; Elect Tech.

WASHINGTON, MARC; Roman Catholic HS; Philadelphia, PA; (3); 8/121; Church Yth Grp; Var JV Crs Cntry; Var JV Trk; NHS; Prfct Atten Awd; Hnr Acad Achvt Romans Black Culture Club 85-86; U DE; Bio.

WASHINGTON, MELODY; Philadelphia Girls HS; Philadelphia, PA; (2); Church Yth Grp; Girl Scts; Library Aide; Mu Alpha Theta; Office Aide; Teachers Aide; Church Choir; Score Keeper; Prfct Atten Awd; Fld Comp.

WASHINGTON, RODNEY; Roman Catholic HS; Philadelphia, PA; (3); 19/121; VP JA; Band; Nwsp Rptr; Yrbk Stf; Rep Soph Cls; Rep Jr Cls; Rep Stu Cncl; Hon Roll; Prfct Atten Awd; Chess Clb; Howard; Acctng.

WASHINGTON, SHELLEY; Fort Cherry JR SR HS; Westland, PA; (3); 40/147; Spanish Clb; Chorus; High Hon Roll; Hon Roll; Wshngtn-Jffrsn U; Lwyr.

WASHINGTON, SHERRY; York Catholic HS; York, PA; (3); Pres Church Yth Grp; NAACP; Speech Tm; Pres Church Choir; Rep Jr Cls; Rep Sr Cls; Rep Stu Cncl; Var Capt Trk; Hon Roll; Drama Clb; 1st Rnnr Up Intl Teen Miss Pgnt 86; York Cnty & Dist 400-Rly Tm 2nd Pl, 1st Spch Fstvl 87; Drexel U; Bus Mgmt.

WASHINGTON, YHANE; Philadelphia HS For Girls; Philadelphia, PA; (3); Dance Clb; Debate Tm; Drama Clb; 4-H; Service Clb; Varsity Clb; School Play; Rep Frsh Cls; Trs Sr Cls; Bsktbl; 2 MIP Trphs Trck & Tnns, Acdmc Recgntn 90 Pct Bttr 86; Trphy Debate 4th Pl Tm Uth Phila Co Rgnl 87; Howard U; Bus Law.

WASICKI, SHELLEY; Punxsutawney Area HS; Anita, PA; (4); Spanish Clb; Varsity Clb; Variety Show; Nwsp Phtg; Nwsp Rptr; Nwsp Sprt Ed; Nwsp Stf; Var L Bsktbl; Var L Trk; Var L Vllybl; Clairon U; Bio.

WASILCHAK, HEIDI; Valley View JR SR HS; Jessup, PA; (1); 17/204; Church Yth Grp; Chorus; Hon Roll; Orthpdc Srgry.

WASILEWSKI, BRIAN; Hanover Area JR SR HS; Wilkes Barre, PA; (3); 4/194; Ski Clb; Church Choir; Rep Stu Cncl; JV Bsktbl; Var Golf; High Hon Roll; Jr NHS; NHS; Chem.

WASILEWSKI, LISA; Hanover Area JR SR HS; Wilkes Barre, PA; (4); Key Clb; Ski Clb; Color Guard; VP Sr Cls; L Var Bsktbl; L Var Sftbl; L Var Trk; High Hon Roll; Hon Roll; Jr NHS; Kings Coll.

WASILEWSKI, MIKE; Our Lady Of Lourdes HS; Kulpmont, PA; (4); Sec Sr Cls; Bsbl; Bsktbl; Var Ftbl; Score Keeper; Stu Mnth 87; Williamsport Area CC; Bus Mgmt.

WASILITZ, RONDA; Cedar Crest HS; Lebanon, PA; (3); Church Yth Grp; Computer Clb; Dance Clb; French Clb; FTA; Hosp Aide; Ski Clb; Spanish Clb; SADD; Sec Frsh Cls; Chld Dev.

WASKIEWICZ, VANESSA; Bishop Conwell H S For Girls; Levittown, PA; (3); 40/277; Cmnty Wkr; Dance Clb; Hosp Aide; Office Aide; Science Clb; Trk; Hon Roll; Physcns Asst.

WASKO, JOSEPH; Lake Land JR-SR HS; Olyphant, PA; (3); Cmnty Wkr; SADD; JV Crs Cntry; JV Var Trk; Im Vllybl; Hon Roll; NHS; Spec Olympcs Intl Coaches Cert For Skiing 87; U OH Scrntn; Dntsty.

WASKO, LAURIE; New Wilmington HS; New Wilmington, PA; (3); Church Yth Grp; Sftbl; Cit Awd; Hon Roll; NHS; Acadc All Am Awd 87.

WASKO, SHAWN; Blairsville SR HS; Blairsville, PA; (4); 7/118; Boy Scts; Church Yth Grp; Var L Ftbl; Var L Trk; Wt Lftg; Wrstlng; High Hon Roll; NHS; Acdmc All Amer Bk 87; Pres Acdmc Fit Awd 86-87; WV U; Aerosp Engr.

WASKO, TAMMY; Meadville Area SR HS; Meadville, PA; (3); Pres Church Yth Grp; French Clb; SADD; Band; Var Trk; Hon Roll; Intr Dsgn.

WASKO, WENDY; Blairsville SR HS; Blairsville, PA; (4); 1/118; Chess Clb; Girl Scts; Band; Concert Band; Mrchg Band; Var L Bsktbl; JV L Cheerleading; Var L Trk; JV L Vllybl; Acctnt.

WASLIS, JILL; Elizabeth Forward HS; Elizabeth, PA; (3); 12/330; French Clb; JA; Yrbk Stf; Rep Soph Cls; Rep Jr Cls; L Trk; Stat Wrstlng; High Hon Roll; NHS; Pres Schlr; Penn ST U; Psych.

WASMANSKI, CHRISTINE; John Fine HS; Nanticoke, PA; (3); 26/235; Spanish Clb; Chorus; Variety Show; Cheerleading; Swmmng; High Hon Roll; Phrmcy.

WASNO, DENISE; Marian Catholic HS; Mc Adoo, PA; (3); 13/112; Church Yth Grp; GAA; Hosp Aide; Pep Clb; Service Clb; Ski Clb; SADD; Rep Soph Cls; Rep Jr Cls; Rep Stu Cncl; :Dietician.

WASS, BOYD; Mc Guffey HS; Claysville, PA; (3); Church Yth Grp; Spanish Clb; Varsity Clb; Chorus; Church Choir; Bsbl; Bsktbl; Ftbl; Wt Lftg; Hon Roll; Stu Rcgntn Awd 85-86; Pres Acdmc Ftns Awd 84; All Cnfrnc 86.

WASS, LESLIE; Central Dauphin HS; Harrisburg, PA; (3); Church Yth Grp; Exploring; Chorus; Church Choir; School Play; Rep Stu Cncl; Var Bsktbl; Var Sftbl; Im Vllybl; Hon Roll; Vet.

WASSEL, ANTOINETTE; Greensburg Central Catholic HS; Murrysville, PA; (2); 1/220; AFS; Church Yth Grp; Exploring; Var Tennis; High Hon Roll.

WASSENICH, AMY; William Allen HS; Allentown, PA; (4); 7/550; Pres Church Yth Grp; Model UN; Service Clb; Band; Nwsp Rptr; Lit Mag; Ntl Merit SF; Drama Clb; German Clb; Ski Clb; Schlrshp Untd Wrld Coll 86-88; Cngrs-Bndstg Exchng Schlrshp 86; Mt Holyoke Bk Awd 86; Natl Exm Bk Awd; Intl Stds.

WASSERMAN JR, JOHN; Bucktail Area HS; Renovo, PA; (2); JV Bsktbl; Upward Bnd 86-87; Young Athrs Awd 82-83; Comp.

WASSERMAN, LORIE; Carbondale Area HS; Carbondale, PA; (3); #3 In Class; Ski Clb; Spanish Clb; Bsktbl; Crs Cntry; Trk; High Hon Roll; Jr NHS; Hghst Awd Spanish 87; Presdntl Fitness Awd 85-86; Comp.

WASSERMAN, SCOTT; Emmaus HS; Allentown, PA; (3); 8/548; JA; Key Clb; Pres Latin Clb; Yrbk Phtg; Yrbk Stf; Chrmn Frsh Cls; Jr Cls; Var L Socr; Var L Trk; High Hon Roll; Pres Acad Ftns Awd 85; Optmst Ortrcl Cntst Rnnr-Up 85.

WASSON, STEVEN M; Central Bucks HS West; Chalfont, PA; (3); Am Leg Boys St; Ftbl; Wt Lftg; Hnrbl Ment Ftbl 86; Big Bros Amer 87.

WATERMAN, SCOTT; Wm Penn Charter HS; Philadelphia, PA; (4); Cmnty Wkr; Debate Tm; Model UN; Political Wkr; Science Clb; Nwsp Rptr; Nwsp Stf; Yrbk Bus Mgr; Sec Soph Cls; Sec Jr Cls; Tufts U.

WATERS, BRENDA; St Basil Acad; Philadelphia, PA; (3); 11/84; French Clb; Band; Concert Band; Jazz Band; Orch; Yrbk Rptr; Var Socr; Var Sftbl; Ntl Merit Ltr; Music.

WATERS, NORMAN; Scotland School Vet Children; Media, PA; (3); 2/50; Boy Scts; Capt L ROTC; Varsity Clb; L Var Bsbl; L Var Wrstlng; Hon Roll; VFW Awd; Voice Dem Awd; Color Guard; Var Ftbl; Supr Cadet Awds 86&87.

WATKINS, ERIC; Central Dauphin HS; Harrisburg, PA; (4); Church Yth Grp; School Musical; Variety Show; Hon Roll; Var L Ftbl; L Capt Trk; Var L Vllybl; Harrisburg Area CC; Bus Admin.

WATKINS, JENNIFER; Greenwood HS; Liverpool, PA; (1); Church Yth Grp; 4-H; Rep Chorus; School Musical; Hst Frsh Cls; Bsktbl; Fld Hcky; Sftbl; Hon Roll; Presdntl Acdmc Achvt Awd 86; Ntl Engl Mrt Awd 87; Penn ST.

WATKINS, LAURIE; Warren Area HS; N Warren, PA; (3); Girl Scts; Office Aide; Spanish Clb; School Play; Im Bsktbl; L Swmmng; Im Trk; High Hon Roll; Hon Roll; Jr NHS; Bus Mgmt.

WATKINS, SHAWN; Conemaugh Township HS; Holsopple, PA; (4); 34/102; Varsity Clb; Capt Var Bsbl; Var L Wrstlng; Waynesburg Coll; Acctng.

WATKINS, STACEY; G A R Memorial HS; Wilkes-Barre, PA; (4); 21/172; French Clb; Sec Key Clb; Chorus; Orch; Yrbk Ed-Chief; Vllybl; French Hon Soc; Hon Roll; Big Brothers/Big Sisters 86-87; Cmmrcl Art.

WATKINS, TAMMY; Southern Huntingdon County HS; Cassville, PA; (4); 6/102; 4-H; Trs FBLA; Sec FHA; Trs GAA; Spanish Clb; SADD; Varsity Clb; Band; Concert Band; Flag Corp; Commrcl Awd 87; Thompson Inst; Exec Sec.

WATRO, KIMBERLY; West Branch Area HS; Morrisdale, PA; (3); 14/125; Science Clb; Ski Clb; Spanish Clb; SADD; Band; Chorus; Concert Band; Rep Stu Cncl; Twrlr; Med Lab Tech.

WATSON, AARON; Washington HS; Washington, PA; (2); Boy Scts; Letterman Clb; Spanish Clb; SADD; Orch; Stat Bsktbl; Var Mgr(s); Sprts Med.

WATSON, ANGELIQUE; Harrisburg HS; Harrisburg, PA; (3); 15/265; Civic Clb; Exploring; Model UN; Temple Yth Grp; Chorus; Church Choir; Hon Roll; HOBY Smnr 86; Amer Hist Stu Yr 87; WA Wrkshps Cong Smnr 85; Corprt Law.

WATSON, CHRISTINE; Oil City SR HS; Oil City, PA; (3); AFS; FBLA; SADD; Acpl Chr; Color Guard; School Musical; Church Yth Grp; Girl Scts; Office Aide; Chorus; Point Park Coll; Photo.

WATSON, HEATHER; Bishop Guilfoyle HS; Altoona, PA; (3); Cmnty Wkr; Office Aide; SADD; Chorus; Concert Band; Flag Corp; Rep Jr Cls; Cheerleading; Hon Roll; Church Yth Grp; OH ST; Chld Psych.

WATSON, JENNIFER; Central Dauphin HS; Harrisburg, PA; (2); 8/375; Church Yth Grp; VP Frsh Cls; Co-Capt Var Bsktbl; Socr; Var L Sftbl; Vllybl; High Hon Roll; NHS; MVP Sftbl & Bsktbl 85; Mst Steals & Assists Bsktbl 2nd Scoring 87; Phrmcy.

WATSON, MARI LYNNE; Blacklick Valley JR-SR HS; Nanty Glo, PA; (3); 21/96; Library Aide; Ski Clb; Varsity Clb; Yrbk Stf; Trs Jr Cls; Sec Stu Cncl; Var Cheerleading; Hon Roll; Acad All-Amer 85-86.

WATSON, MARK; Seneca Valley SR HS; Evans Cty, PA; (2); 1/410; Boy Scts; Church Yth Grp; Math Tm; Concert Band; Jazz Band; Mrchg Band; Pep Band; Var Trk; High Hon Roll; Band; Seneca Vly 1st Yr Awd 87; PA Acad Games Leg ST Tourn 1st Pl JR Div, 1st Pl SRDIV 87; Meteorology.

WATSON, MARK W; Mapletown HS; Mapletown, PA; (4); 3/75; Pres Church Yth Grp; Drama Clb; VP Ski Clb; Varsity Clb; Nwsp Phtg; Capt L Bsbl; Im Bsktbl; Capt L Ftbl; High Hon Roll; VP NHS.

WATSON, NYCOLE; West Catholic HS For Girls; Philadelphia, PA; (3); 79/246; Church Yth Grp; Exploring; Girl Scts; Spanish Clb; Hon Roll; Prfct Atten Awd; Jrnlsm Cntst Awd 85; Villanova; Crmnl Law.

WATSON, PATRICIA; Cardinal O Hara HS; Chester, PA; (3); 16/680; Pres Church Yth Grp; Science Clb; Service Clb; Spanish Clb; School Musical; Stage Crew; Nwsp Rptr; Hon Roll; NHS; Prfct Atten Awd; Prncpls Awd-Acadmc Excllnc; Schlrshp-Temple U Smmr Colloquim Gftd Stus; Tchrs Recommndtn Schlrshp; Art.

WATSON, SHAWN; Central Dauphin HS; Harrisburg, PA; (3); Off Boy Scts; Cmnty Wkr; Math Tm; Golf; High Hon Roll; Hon Roll; Jr NHS; NHS; Pres Schlr; Arch Engrng.

WATSON, STACIE; Carbondale Area HS; Carbondale, PA; (2); Computer Clb; Ski Clb; Spanish Clb; Band; JV Trk; High Hon Roll; Marine Bio.

WATSON, THERESA; Eastern York HS; Wrightsville, PA; (4); Church Yth Grp; Chorus; Church Choir; Color Guard; Flag Corp; Powder Puff Ftbl; High Hon Roll; Jr NHS; NHS; Sal; Preston E Zeigler Awd 87; Dr & Mrs Ba Hoover Sci Awd 87; York Coll Acad Mrt Schlrshp 87; York Coll Of PA.

WATT, KATHERINE; Altoona Area HS; Altoona, PA; (4); 18/718; Girl Scts; Hosp Aide; Band; Chorus; Mgr(s); NHS; NEDT Awd; German Clb; Science Clb; Concert Band; Sea Cdt Of Yr 84; Cert Of Merit PA Hghr Ed Asstnc Agncy 86; St Francis Coll; RN.

WATT, KIMBERLY; Washington HS; Washington, PA; (2); Girl Scts; SADD; Var Trk; High Hon Roll; Hon Roll; Med.

WATT, REGINA; Altoona Area HS; Altoona, PA; (3); French Clb; School Play; Stage Crew; Crs Cntry; Trk; Ed.

WATTS, APRIL; Chester HS; Chester, PA; (3); Camera Clb; Trs Key Clb; Library Aide; Band; Off Sr Cls; Hon Roll; Outstndng Stu Itln I 85; Ms Sweethrt Wnnr 85; Vilanova U; Pltcl Sci.

WATTS, BRENTON; Reading SR HS; Reading, PA; (3); 70/790; VP Aud/Vis; Chess Clb; Sec Debate Tm; Model UN; Scholastic Bowl; Teachers Aide; Var Bsbl; Socr; Hon Roll; Prfct Atten Awd.

WATTS, CRAIG; North Catholic HS; Pittsburgh, PA; (3); Aud/Vis; Church Yth Grp; Spanish Clb; Teachers Aide; Ftbl; Hon Roll; Sci.

WATTS, JESSICA; Cocalico SR HS; Denver, PA; (4); Exploring; Pres VP 4-H; School Play; Pres Jr Cls; Pres Rep Stu Cncl; JV Var Bsktbl; 4-H Awd; Hon Roll; Lion Awd; Oustndng Teen Ldr 83-86; All Arnd SR 4-H Mbr 84-85; Best Demonstration 83-86; Shippensburg U.

WATTS, LESLEY; Taylor Allderdice HS; Pittsburgh, PA; (3); Boy Scts; VP Pres Church Yth Grp; Exploring; Church Choir; Orch; Variety Show; Sftbl; Hon Roll; Silver E Explrng 86-87; Presdnt Post Of The Year 86-87; Ceramics.

WATTS, MARK; Penn View Christian Academy; Middleburg, PA; (3); Chess Clb; Church Yth Grp; Band; VP Jr Cls; Hon Roll.

WATTS, PAMELA; Oxford Area HS; Oxford, PA; (3); High Hon Roll; Hon Roll; Dstngshd Hnr Rl 86; Flght Atten.

WATTS, TINA; Mifflinburg Area HS; Mifflinburg, PA; (2); Church Yth Grp; FHA; Trk; Barbizon Beauty Schl; Csmtlgy.

WAUGH, CINDI; Steel HS; Steelton, PA; (2); Chorus; Nwsp Phtg; Nwsp Rptr; Var Cheerleading; Hon Roll; Phy Ed.

WAUGHTEL, MICHELLE; Juniata HS; Mifflintown, PA; (3); Camera Clb; Trs 4-H; SADD; Band; Nwsp Rptr; Yrbk Rptr; 4-H Awd; Elem Educ.

WAWRZYNIAK, CHERYL; Villa Maria Acad; Erie, PA; (3); Church Yth Grp; Dance Clb; Office Aide; Spanish Clb; Bowling; Hon Roll; NHS; Accntng.

WAWRZYNSKI, ROCHELLE; Shenango JR SR HS; New Castle, PA; (4); 65/111; Library Aide; Yrbk Stf; Basic Arts Awd 86; Art Inst PA; Visual Comms.

WAY, CHARLIE; Clearfield Area HS; Clearfield, PA; (4); 65/290; Cmnty Wkr; SADD; Nwsp Stf; JV Var Ftbl; Var Trk; Im Wt Lftg; Hon Roll; Amer Lgn Essy Awd 87; Mansfield U; Ed.

WAY, TODD B; State College Area SR HS; Lemont, PA; (4); 211/541; 4-H; Ski Clb; Im Bsktbl; JV Ftbl; Im Vllybl; 4-H Awd; Hon Roll; PA ST; Engrng.

WAYMAN JR, HAROLD; Susquehanna Community HS; Susquehanna, PA; (2); Church Yth Grp; SADD; Stage Crew; Var Bsbl; Hon Roll; Mechanic.

WAYMAN, JEFFREY; Susquehanna Comm HS; Susquehanna, PA; (3); Var Bsbl; JV Bsktbl; Var Crs Cntry; Hon Roll.

WAYNE, AILEEN; Cardinal Brennan HS; Girardville, PA; (4); 9/50; Chorus; Flag Corp; Nwsp Stf; Rep Frsh Cls; Rep Soph Cls; Rep Jr Cls; Rep Sr Cls; Rep Stu Cncl; Hon Roll; Spanish NHS; Futer Teachers Awd 87; Bloomburg U; Elem Educ.

WAZENSKI, STEPHEN; Hanover Area JR/Sr HS; Wilkes Barre, PA; (4); 14/164; Cmnty Wkr; Key Clb; Red Cross Aide; Ski Clb; Wilkes Coll; Phy Thrpst.

WEACHTER, JAMES; Warwick HS; Elm, PA; (4); 118/133; Sec Varsity Clb; Var Bsbl; Var Ftbl; Im Vllybl; Alvernia Coll; Cmmnctns.

WEADER, DAVID; Danville Area HS; Danville, PA; (3); 19/198; French Clb; Band; Concert Band; Mrchg Band; Var Bsbl; Var Socr; JV Wrstlng; High Hon Roll; NHS; Amer Leg Awd 85; Engl Awd 85; Presdntl Acadmc Ftnss Awd 85; U Richmond; Hist.

WEAGRAFF, MARC; Saegertown Area HS; Saegertown, PA; (3); 1/125; Ski Clb; Chorus; Church Choir; Concert Band; Drm Mjr(t); Jazz Band; High Hon Roll; Jr NHS; NHS; Church Yth Grp; Music Voice Lesson Scholar 85-86; Music.

WEAKLAND, MICHELE; Harmony HS; Cherry Tree, PA; (4); 6/50; Band; Chorus; School Play; Yrbk Stf; Sec Jr Cls; Sec Sr Cls; High Hon Roll; NHS; Prfct Atten Awd; ICM Schl Bus; Med Asst.

WEAKLAND, TAMMY; Tyrone Area HS; Tyrone, PA; (4); Church Yth Grp; 4-H; Library Aide; Pep Clb; Chorus; Church Choir; 4-H Awd; Hon Roll; Nursing.

WEALAND, ANDREA L; Cocalico HS; Stevens, PA; (4); 1/169; Church Yth Grp; GAA; Concert Band; Jazz Band; Pres Frsh Cls; Pres Soph Cls; Co-Capt Var Cheerleading; Cit Awd; High Hon Roll; Lion Awd; Cocalico Stu Mnth 86 & 87; Lancaster New Era Teen Wk 87; Chem Awd 86; Bucknell U; Bio.

WEATHERBY, MICHELLE; New Castle SR HS; New Castle, PA; (2); 1/375; AFS; Church Yth Grp; Civic Clb; Computer Clb; French Clb; Girl Scts; Office Aide; SADD; Chorus; Church Choir; Guidance Cncl 86-87; Carnegie Mellon U; Chem Engrng.

WEATHERLY, BRAD; Fairfield Area HS; Fairfield, PA; (4); 12/40; Art Clb; Chess Clb; Computer Clb; Pep Clb; Varsity Clb; Bsktbl; Socr; Trk; Penn ST; Mech Engrng.

WEATHERS, THOMAS P; Cardinal O Hara HS; Media, PA; (4); 107/772; Var Capt Crs Cntry; JV Var Trk; Hon Roll; Ntl Merit SF; Rotary Awd; Aerospc Engrng.

WEAVER, AMY; Hollidaysburg Area SR HS; Newry, PA; (4); 102/347; Church Yth Grp; French Clb; Latin Clb; Science Clb; SADD; Teachers Aide; Chorus; Yrbk Stf; Im Vllybl; DAR Awd; Mdrn Ms Schlrshp Pgnt Cert Achvt 85; Secr Genlgy Clb 84; Editor Genlgy Clb Cookbk 84; Juniata Coll; Psych.

WEAVER, AMY; Lock Haven SR HS; Howard, PA; (3); Church Yth Grp; Drama Clb; FBLA; Spanish Clb; SADD; Band; Drm Mjr(t); Mrchg Band; Twrlr; Hon Roll; Bus.

WEAVER, ANDREA; Danville SR HS; Danville, PA; (3); 4/187; Church Yth Grp; Sec Trs Key Clb; Red Cross Aide; High Hon Roll; NHS; Prfct Atten Awd; Schlrshp Gov Schl Of Bus At U Of PA 87; Natl Latin Hnr Soc 87; Pres Acad Fitness Awd 85; Alg II Awd; Bus.

WEAVER, ANTHONY; Middleburg HS; Selinsgrove, PA; (3); 18/180; Trs Church Yth Grp; Trs Rptr FFA; German Clb; SADD; Gov Hon Prg Awd; Hon Roll; Penn St U; Vet Sci.

WEAVER, BRANDIE; Foet Le Boeuf HS; Waterford, PA; (3); Church Yth Grp; Dance Clb; Model UN; Chorus; School Musical; Sec Jr Cls; Trk; High Hon Roll; NHS; Amelia Erhart Awd 87; Edinboro U Of PA; Marine Bio.

WEAVER, CINDY; Central Dauphin HS; Harrisburg, PA; (4); 17/366; Pres Key Clb; Yrbk Sprt Ed; Off Soph Cls; Off Jr Cls; Off Sr Cls; Off Stu Cncl; Var Cheerleading; Var Vllybl; Kiwanis Awd; NHS; ABWA Colonl Pk Chptr, Winng Pblc Sfty Cmmrcl Seatble Cmpgn 87; Hmecmng Ct 83-87; Penn ST U; Commnctns.

WEAVER, COREY E; Garden Spot HS; New Holland, PA; (4); 24/201; Church Yth Grp; German Clb; Concert Band; Jazz Band; Mrchg Band; Orch; JV Socr; Hon Roll; Pres Acad Ftns Awd 87; LLMEA Estrn Div Bnd 87; PA ST Ufmech Engrng.

WEAVER, DAVID; Canton Area JR SR HS; Roaring Branch, PA; (4); 21/116; Pres Church Yth Grp; FCA; VP Band; Church Choir; Concert Band; Jazz Band; Mrchg Band; School Play; JP Sousa Awd; Stat Voice Dem Awd; Mesiah Coll.

WEAVER, DAVID; Somerset Area SR HS; Somerset, PA; (4); 40/233; Church Yth Grp; English Clb; 4-H; French Clb; JA; Math Clb; Mu Alpha Theta; Speech Tm; Band; Chorus; St Francis; Math.

WEAVER, DIANE; Cocalico HS; Stevens, PA; (4); 16/174; Trs Church Yth Grp; GAA; Var L Bsktbl; Var L Fld Hcky; High Hon Roll; Hon Roll; Lion Awd; Prfct Atten Awd; VFW Awd.

WEAVER, DIANE; Danville HS; Danville, PA; (4); 97/199; Spanish Clb; SADD; Nwsp Sprt Ed; Yrbk Sprt Ed; JV Cheerleading; Var Fld Hcky; Mat Maids; Powder Puff Ftbl; Capt Trk; Hon Roll; Slippery Rock U; Elem Educ.

WEAVER, DONNA; Garnet Valley HS; Boothwyn, PA; (4); Intnl Clb; Model UN; Ski Clb; Spanish Clb; Variety Show; Ed Nwsp Bus Mgr; Yrbk Stf; Rep Stu Cncl; Powder Puff Ftbl; Hon Roll; Peer Cnslng 84-87; Hst Cable Tv Show; Penn ST; Lawyer.

WEAVER, ELIZABETH; Abington SR HS; Meadowbrook, PA; (4); 42/486; Church Yth Grp; French Clb; Varsity Clb; Chorus; Yrbk Stf; Off Sr Cls; Capt Var Tennis; Hon Roll; Pres Schlr; Beaver Coll Awd Mst Imprvd Cls Rank 87; Vanderbilt U; Econ.

WEAVER, ELLEN; Oxford Area HS; Oxford, PA; (3); 1/216; FBLA; Chorus; Yrbk Ed-Chief; Rep Stu Cncl; Var Cheerleading; Var Fld Hcky; JV Trk; High Hon Roll; NHS.

WEAVER, ERIC; Morrisville HS; Morrisville, PA; (3); 9/98; Quiz Bowl; School Musical; School Play; Var Bsbl; JV Bsktbl; Var Bowling; High Hon Roll; Hon Roll; Acdmc All Amer Schlr Awd 87; Arch.

WEAVER III, EUGENE D; The Episcopal Acad; Philadelphia, PA; (4); Art Clb; Church Yth Grp; Cmnty Wkr; Debate Tm; NAACP; Political Wkr; Ski Clb; Spanish Clb; SADD; Var L Bsbl; Debate Team Best Spkr 86-87; Grinnell Coll; Intl Rltns.

WEAVER, GERALD; Millville HS; Bloomsburg, PA; (3); Wlmsprt CC; Drftng.

WEAVER, JAY; Lancaster Mennonite HS; Lititz, PA; (3); 63/155; Church Yth Grp; Chorus; Socr; Bus.

WEAVER, JEFF; Oxford Area HS; Oxford, PA; (3); Boy Scts; Church Yth Grp; Debate Tm; 4-H; FFA; High Hon Roll; Dairy Frmng.

WEAVER, JILL; Williams Valley HS; Tower City, PA; (1); Aud/Vis; Office Aide; Band; Chorus; Jazz Band; Mrchg Band; School Play; Symp Band; Stu Cncl; JV Bsktbl.

WEAVER, KARA R; Warren County Christian Schl; Pittsfield, PA; (3); Pres Church Yth Grp; Chorus; School Musical; Variety Show; Yrbk Rptr; VP Stu Cncl; Var Bsktbl; Crs Cntry; L Vllybl; High Hon Roll; Mst Schl Sprt Bkstbl 86-87; Chrstn Msc.

WEAVER, KELLY; Mpnorthern Lebanon HS; Lebanon, PA; (3); 4/213; NHS; German Clb; Pep Clb; Chorus; School Play; Var Cheerleading; Im Gym; JV Sftbl; High Hon Roll; Hon Roll.

WEAVER, KEVIN; Dover HS; Dover, PA; (3); High Hon Roll; Hon Roll; Hnr Roll 85 & 86; Dstngshd Hnr Roll 87.

WEAVER, KEVIN; Warwick HS; Lititz, PA; (3); 100/300; Varsity Clb; Var Ftbl; Var Trk; Im Wt Lftg; Var Wrstlng; Hon Roll; Bus.

WEAVER, KIMBERLY; Garden Spot HS; E Earl, PA; (3); 75/189; Band; Chorus; Color Guard; Concert Band; Mrchg Band; School Musical; School Play; Rep Stu Cncl; Lgl Sec.

WEAVER, KIMBERLY; Shamokin Area HS; Shamokin, PA; (2); 35/250; Church Yth Grp; SADD; Rep Frsh Cls; Stat Crs Cntry; Score Keeper; Stat Trk; Capt Twrlr; Hon Roll; Outstndng Wrtr 85; Extra Crclr Actvts Awd 86; PA ST; Chld Psychlgst.

WEAVER, LAURA; Northwestern HS; E Springfield, PA; (3); 16/162; Drama Clb; Girl Scts; Model UN; Pep Clb; Band; Concert Band; Mrchg Band; School Play; Stage Crew; Nwsp Phtg; Jrnlsm.

WEAVER, LAURIE; Penn Manor HS; Lancaster, PA; (3); 50/350; FBLA; Hon Roll; Acctg.

WEAVER, LORI; Dover Area HS; Dover, PA; (4); Varsity Clb; Color Guard; Capt Var Swmmng; Capt Var Vllybl; Hon Roll; Outstndg Fml Swmmr 87; Vlybl All-Str Tm 87; All-Amrcn Swmmg 86.

WEAVER, MARK; Garden Spot HS; New Holland, PA; (4); German Clb; Band; Jazz Band; Mrchg Band; Orch; School Musical; Bsbl; Bsktbl; Socr; NHS; John Philip Sousa Bnd Awd 87; Presdntl Acadmc Ftns Awd 87; Lancaster Wmns Symphny Awd 87; West Chester U; Music.

WEAVER, MATT; Sto-Rox SR HS; Mc Kees Rocks, PA; (3); Boys Clb Am; Letterman Clb; Stage Crew; Im Ftbl; L Trk; Hon Roll; Acctng.

WEAVER, MELISSA; Northwestern Lehigh HS; Germansville, PA; (4); 23/162; FNA; Color Guard; Sec Stu Cncl; High Hon Roll; Hon Roll; NHS; Prfct Atten Awd; Stu Of Yr 87; Outstndng Clrgrd 87; Outstndng Atten Awd 87; Lehigh County CC; Med Asst.

WEAVER, MELODIE SUE; Grace Christian HS; Myerstown, PA; (4); Church Yth Grp; FBLA; Chorus; JV Var Sftbl; High Hon Roll; Hon Roll; Outstndng Prfrmnc Awd & All Conf Tm-Sfbl 86; Dstngshd Chrstn HS Stu & Mst Imprvd Stu 86-87.

WEAVER, MICHELE; Bradford Area HS; Bradford, PA; (3); 83/302; Drama Clb; Chorus; Off Drill Tm; Rep Stu Cncl; Stat Bsktbl; Score Keeper; Hon Roll; Psych.

WEAVER, PAMELA; Northern Lebanon HS; Grantville, PA; (2); 20/210; Pres Church Yth Grp; Rep Varsity Clb; Pres Soph Cls; Pres Jr Cls; Rep Stu Cncl; Var L Fld Hcky; Hon Roll; Chorus; Church Choir; School Musical; Sno-Ball Queen Sphmr Cls 87; Med.

WEAVER, RENEE; Manheim Central HS; Manheim, PA; (4); 40/240; Church Yth Grp; Cmnty Wkr; Chorus; Yrbk Stf; JV Capt Fld Hcky; Swmmng; Hon Roll; Pep Clb; School Play; Rotary Clb Awd 87; 4-Way Tst Awd 87; Schltc Art Awd 87; Elizabethtown Coll; Nrsng.

WEAVER, SAHLEE; Du Bois Area HS; Du Bois, PA; (3); 86/350; Hosp Aide; Band; Concert Band; Mrchg Band; Pep Band; Hon Roll; Du Bois Bus Coll; Sec.

WEAVER, SHANNON; State College Intermediate HS; Port Matilda, PA; (1); Sec Band; Mgr(s); Cit Awd; Hon Roll; Achvmnt Awd Frnch 87; Achvmnt Awd In Engl 87; Penn ST U; Accntng.

WEAVER, SHARI; Chambersburg SR HS; Chambersburg, PA; (4); 75/571; Church Yth Grp; Key Clb; Library Aide; Office Aide; Pep Clb; Ski Clb; Y-Teens; Stu Cncl; Var Fld Hcky; Hon Roll; Clarion U Of PA; Fnnce.

WEAVER, SHERYL; Haverford HS; Havertown, PA; (3); Church Yth Grp; Cmnty Wkr; Service Clb; Spanish Clb; SADD; Chorus; Church Choir; Variety Show; Bsktbl; Hon Roll; Nyack Coll; Bus Adm.

WEAVER, TAMMY; North Star HS; Boswell, PA; (4); Church Yth Grp; FCA; Red Cross Aide; Band; Bsktbl; Trk; Cit Awd; U Of Pittsburg; Mech Engrng.

WEAVER, TERESA; Cocalico HS; Denver, PA; (3); 30/165; Var Bsktbl; Var Fld Hcky; Var Sftbl; Im Tennis; Im Vllybl; Cert Spcl Rcgntn Indvdl Ldrshp Socl Stds 87; Phys Thrpy.

WEAVOR, JEFFREY SCOTT; Central Dauphin HS; Harrisburg, PA; (3); 136/370; Chorus; Color Guard; Flag Corp; Mrchg Band; School Musical; School Play; Rep Jr Cls; Rep Sr Cls; VP Stu Cncl; Diving; Bus Ed.

WEBB, ALICE; Keystone HS; Knox, PA; (3); Computer Clb; Dance Clb; French Clb; Mu Alpha Theta; Drill Tm; Yrbk Stf; French Hon Soc; High Hon Roll; Hon Roll; NHS; Law.

WEBB, GREGORY; Scotland Schl For Veterans Children; Phila, PA; (3); #1 In Class; Drill Tm; Nwsp Stf; VP Soph Cls; Rep Stu Cncl; Stat Bsktbl; L Trk; High Hon Roll; NHS; VFW Awd; Voice Dem Awd; Peer Cnslng 86-87; Tutoring 86-87; JROTC 86-87; Law.

WEBB, JENNIFER; James Coughlin HS; Wlks Barr Twp, PA; (4); 1/364; Drama Clb; French Clb; School Play; Nwsp Stf; Var Trk; NHS; Philadlpha Clsscl Soc Awd Latin 86; Yth Undrstndng Certf Mert 87; Law.

WEBB, KEVIN; Greater Johnstown Area Vo Tech Schl; Johnstown, PA; (4); Church Yth Grp; VICA; Rep Stu Cncl; Var Wrstlng; Hon Roll; Vo-Tech Awd Emplyblty 84-87; Marine Ftnss Awd 86-87; Wiliamsport Area CC; Tool Dsgn.

WEBB, LAURA; Williamsburg HS; Williamsburg, PA; (4); 10/71; Speech Tm; Chorus; Church Choir; Drill Tm; Orch; Yrbk Stf; Cheerleading; Mgr(s); High Hon Roll; NHS; Wmns Civic Clb Bst Shw-Art Cntst 87; IN U Of PA; Spcl Ed Tchr.

WEBB, STACEY; Berlin Brothersvalley HS; Berlin, PA; (4); 14/81; School Play; Trs Frsh Cls; Sec Soph Cls; Sec Jr Cls; Trs Sr Cls; Sec Stu Cncl; Var L Cheerleading; Stat Ftbl; Hon Roll; Sec NHS; Shippensburg U; Elem Educ.

WEBB, SUSAN; Williamsburg HS; Williamsburg, PA; (4); 13/69; Band; Chorus; Flag Corp; Mrchg Band; Nwsp Rptr; Yrbk Stf; Bsbl; Score Keeper; Vllybl; Hon Roll; SR Cnty Band; Lockhaven Coll; Phy Thrpy.

WEBB, TOM; Ambridge Area HS; Baden, PA; (3); Am Leg Boys St; Boy Scts; Exploring; German Clb; Pep Clb; Crs Cntry; Trk; Hon Roll; Acdma All Amer 87; Law.

WEBBER, AUDREY; The Mercersburg Academy; Hickory, NC; (4); 4/125; Ed Yrbk Stf; Rep Soph Cls; Capt L Crs Cntry; L Sftbl; High Hon Roll; Pres Schlr; Erpn Hstry Awd 85; Peer Grp Ldr 87; Spnsh Awd 87; U NC Chpl Hl; Intl Law.

WEBBER, JERRY; Big Spring HS; Newville, PA; (4); 30/180; Trs Ski Clb; Rep Sr Cls; Var Bsbl; Hon Roll; SICO Fndtn Schlrshp 87; Newville Lns Clb Stu Mnth 87; West Chester U; Athltc Trng.

WEBER, AMY; Phil-Mont Christian Acad; Warrington, PA; (3); 1/48; Church Yth Grp; Chorus; JV Sftbl; High Hon Roll; NHS.

WEBER, BONNIE; Sto-Rox SR HS; Mckees Rocks, PA; (2); FBLA; JA; Yrbk Stf; Hon Roll.

WEBER, BRANDY; Hempfield HS; Columbia, PA; (2); Bsktbl; Hon Roll.

WEBER, BRUCE; Susquehanna Twp HS; Harrisburg, PA; (3); 5/150; AFS; Model UN; VP Temple Yth Grp; Varsity Clb; Rep Stu Cncl; L Crs Cntry; L Trk; High Hon Roll; NHS; Med.

WEBER, CYNTHIA JEAN; Ambridge Area SR HS; Ambridge, PA; (3); Am Leg Aux Girls St; Sec Church Yth Grp; Pep Clb; Red Cross Aide; Chorus; School Musical; School Play; Nwsp Ed-Chief; Nwsp Rptr; High Hon Roll; Bradfrd Sch Of Bus; Retail Mgmt.

WEBER, DAWN; Penn Trafford HS; Irwin, PA; (2); 15/366; Cmnty Wkr; FBLA; GAA; Varsity Clb; Rep Soph Cls; Bsbl; Var Cheerleading; Var Diving; Trk; High Hon Roll.

WEBER, GAIL; Seneca HS; Erie, PA; (3); 15/160; Drama Clb; Pep Clb; Rep Stu Cncl; Stat Ftbl; JV Sftbl; Hon Roll; Law.

WEBER, JENNIFER; Phil-Mont Christian Acad; Warrington, PA; (4); 13/35; Church Yth Grp; Cmnty Wkr; Chorus; Church Choir; High Hon Roll; Hon Roll; Eastern Coll.

WEBER, KENETTA; Garden Spot HS; Narvon, PA; (2); Church Yth Grp; Band; Chorus; Church Choir; Concert Band; Stage Crew; Gym; Mgr(s); Score Keeper; Trk; FL ST U; Photo.

WEBER, LEROY; Coatesville Area SR HS; Thorndale, PA; (3); Boy Scts; Church Yth Grp; French Clb; Leo Clb; Off ROTC; Off Jr Cls; Off Stu Cncl; Socr; Wrstlng; Hon Roll; All Cnty 1st Tm 119 Lbs Wrstlng 86-87; Outstndng Acdmcs & Ldrshp AFJROTC 84-85; USNA; Offcr.

WEBER, LISA; Ft Bentworth SR HS; Bentleyville, PA; (4); 8/138; Trs FBLA; Capt Flag Corp; School Play; VP Frsh Cls; VP Soph Cls; Stu Cncl; JV Var Bsktbl; High Hon Roll; NHS; FBLA ST Ldrshp 2nd Pl Acctng II 87; FBL Natl Ldrshp Conf 87; Grove City Coll; Elec Engrng.

WEBER, LYNDA; Cambria Heights SR HS; Carrolltown, PA; (3); 65/195; Hon Roll; Penn ST U; Corp Lawyer.

WEBER, MARILYN; Central Bucks HS East; Warrington, PA; (3); 30/488; Computer Clb; Debate Tm; Drama Clb; Band; School Play; Yrbk Ed-Chief; High Hon Roll; Hon Roll; Ntl Merit Ltr; Barnard Coll; Engl.

WEBER, MELISSA; Towanda Area HS; Towanda, PA; (4); 5/140; SADD; Rep Frsh Cls; Trs Jr Cls; Trs Sr Cls; Rep Stu Cncl; Var L Bsktbl; Capt Var Crs Cntry; Capt Var Trk; Cit Awd; DAR Awd; Franklin & Marshall.

WEBER, PAULA; Calvary Baptist Christian Acad; Meadville, PA; (4); 4-H; Mgr Yrbk Bus Mgr; Var L Vllybl; Cit Awd; DAR Awd; High Hon Roll; Sal; Church Yth Grp; Chorus; School Musical; Chrstn Ath Awd 85; Natl Hnr Soc Chrstn Schls 85 & 86; Cedarville Coll; Occ Ther.

WEBER, TAMELA; Penn Trafford HS; Irwin, PA; (4); 15/344; Cmnty Wkr; Math Clb; Mrchg Band; Stu Cncl; High Hon Roll; NHS; Natl Assn Wmn Constrctn Scholar 87; NHS Scholar 87; Pres Acad Fit Awd 87; Grove City Coll; Engrng.

WEBER, THERESA; William Allen HS; Allentown, PA; (3); 30/609; SADD; Band; Concert Band; Mrchg Band; Pep Band; High Hon Roll; Hon Roll; Jr NHS; NHS; Summo Cum Hnr Schlrshp Awd 87; Comp Sci.

WEBER, WENDY; Villa Maria Acad; Erie, PA; (3); Science Clb; Ski Clb; Spanish Clb; Yrbk Stf; Var Tennis.

WEBRECK, KEITH; Berlin Brothers Valley HS; Berlin, PA; (2); Spanish Clb; JV Var Bsktbl; Var Ftbl; Hon Roll; Pres Acadmc Ftns Awd 86.

WEBSTER, DAVE; Beaver Area HS; Beaver, PA; (2); 1/256; Church Yth Grp; FCA; JCL; Latin Clb; Trs Jr Cls; Var Bsktbl; L Crs Cntry; L Trk; High Hon Roll.

WEBSTER, DENISE; Grove City Area HS; Grove City, PA; (4); 24/167; Church Yth Grp; Girl Scts; Sec Key Clb; Library Aide; Band; Concert Band; Mrchg Band; Pep Band; Powder Puff Ftbl; Var Trk; Grove City Coll; Pre-Med.

WEBSTER, JASON; Elizabethtown Area HS; Elizabethtown, PA; (3); 10/280; Church Yth Grp; Math Tm; Varsity Clb; Variety Show; JV Var Bsbl; JV Var Wrstlng; Hon Roll; NHS; Im Wt Lftg; Natl Sci Leag-Rnr-Up 86 & 87; Wrstlng Dist Qulfr, Sctnl Rnr-Up 86; Engrng.

WEBSTER, LORI; Williamson JR SR HS; Tioga, PA; (2); Spanish Clb; Chorus; Church Choir; Yrbk Stf; Cheerleading; Hon Roll; Jr NHS; Pres Schlr.

WEBSTER, MICHAEL; Philipsburg-Osceola Area SR HS; Philipsburg, PA; (4); 3/234; Church Yth Grp; Ed Nwsp Stf; Cit Awd; High Hon Roll; NHS; Ntl Merit SF; Marie George SR Engl Awd 87; Cannon U; Med.

WEBSTER, SUSAN M; Norristown Area HS; Norristown, PA; (4); 11/413; Church Yth Grp; Debate Tm; Trs Exploring; SADD; Nwsp Stf; Yrbk Stf; High Hon Roll; NHS; Intnl Clb; Coll Crs In Wildlife Mgmt 86; Smmr Sci Smnr At Air Frc Acad 86; Engl Dept Awd 85-86; Pblc Rltns.

WECHS, HOLLY; Central HS; Martinsburg, PA; (3); 35/187; Drama Clb; GAA; Pres Library Aide; Ski Clb; Varsity Clb; Chorus; Stat Bsktbl; Var Cheerleading; L Trk; Twrlr; Vet Med.

WECHTENHISER JR, LARRY A; Shade HS; Central City, PA; (3); Boy Scts; Church Yth Grp; Pres Exploring; Ski Clb; Spanish Clb; Bsktbl; Trk; Hon Roll; Eagle Sct Awd 86; Altar Boy Awd 8 Yrs Svc 87; Crmnlgy.

WECHUCK, JENNIFER; Venango Christian HS; Franklin, PA; (3); Church Yth Grp; Hosp Aide; SADD; JV Bsktbl; Cheerleading; JV Vllybl; Hon Roll; NHS; Gld Cup-Piano-Ntl Fdrtn Music Clb 87.

WEDER, DAVE; Northern York County HS; Dillsburg, PA; (3); 71/236; JC Awd; Dist Band; Hnrs Dist Band; Tri-M Music Soc; Chorus; Nrthrn Hgh Br Sngrs; PA Lns All St Band; Drum Mjr; Mech Engr.

WEDEVEN, LIESL S; Delaware County Christian Schl; Newtown Square, PA; (4); 14/73; Trs Church Yth Grp; Concert Band; Mrchg Band; JV Bsktbl; JV Sftbl; JV Vllybl; High Hon Roll; NHS; Prfct Atten Awd; Hnrs Schlrshp Calvin Coll, Hnr Awd Exclince Fne Art 87; Awd Art Shows 85-87; Calvin Coll; Art Ed.

WEEDMAN, DIANA; State College Area HS; State College, PA; (2); 8/542; Math Clb; Spanish Clb; VP Frsh Cls; Var Gym; Var Powder Puff Ftbl; High Hon Roll; Chorus; School Musical; Wind In Willows Litry Awd 85-86; V P AIASA Chaptr 87; Penn ST U; Marine Biology.

WEEKS, BRUCE; Lake Lehman HS; Dallas, PA; (4); 33/140; High Hon Roll; Hon Roll; NHS; Worlds Mst Beloved Poems Publctn 83; World Poetry Anthology Publctn 85; PA ST U; Writing.

WEEMS III, ADOLPHUS TREY; Central Dauphin East HS; Harrisburg, PA; (4); Boy Scts; Political Wkr; Ski Clb; School Play; Stage Crew; Rep Stu Cncl; Mgr Bsktbl; Im Vllybl; Commended Stu Natl Merit 86-87; Villanova U; Cvl Engrng.

WEEMS, TREY; Central Dauphin East HS; Harrisburg, PA; (4); Boy Scts; Political Wkr; School Play; Stage Crew; Rep Stu Cncl; Im Bsktbl; Im Vllybl; Villanova U; Civil Engrng.

WEESNER, RENEE; Annville-Cleona HS; Lebanon, PA; (4); 4/115; Church Yth Grp; SADD; Chorus; JV Bsktbl; Var Trk; Bausch & Lomb Sci Awd; Hon Roll; NHS; NEDT Awd; Schltc Gold Key Wrtng Awd 87; Latin Exclince Awd 86; Presdntl Acad Fit Awd 87; West Chester U; Microbio.

WEHIBE, STEVE; Lancaster Memorial HS; Elizabethtown, PA; (3); 3/163; Pres Church Yth Grp; Rep Frsh Cls; Rep Soph Cls; Rep Jr Cls; Rep Sr Cls; Stu Cncl; Var JV Socr; Hon Roll; NHS; Frshmn Schlrshps 84; Hlth.

WEHMEYER, HEIDI; Central Bucks HS West; Doylestown, PA; (3); 183/477; Chorus; JV Bsktbl; Var Trk; Hon Roll; Engl.

WEHNER, KENNETH; Ambridge Area HS; Baden, PA; (3); Pep Clb; VICA; High Hon Roll; Hon Roll; 2nd ST Arch Dsgn, Model Mkng 87; PA Amer Lgn PA Boys ST 87; Arch Dsgn.

WEHR, LAURA; Conrad Weiser JR SR HS; Womelsdorf, PA; (3); 46/179; VICA; Chorus.

WEHR, MARCIA; Methacton HS; Audubon, PA; (3); 81/380; Church Yth Grp; Chorus; Var L Mgr(s); Var L Sftbl; Hon Roll; Lbrl Arts.

WEHRER, JILL; Avella HS; Burgettstown, PA; (4); 22/50; Pres French Clb; Letterman Clb; Ski Clb; Nwsp Rptr; Nwsp Stf; Yrbk Rptr; Yrbk Stf; VP Frsh Cls; VP Soph Cls; L Var Cheerleading; Westminster Coll; Pre Law.

WEIBLE, JOSEPH; Central Christian HS; Falls Crk, PA; (2); Boy Scts; Debate Tm; 4-H; French Clb; Math Clb; Pep Clb; Science Clb; Ski Clb; Var Socr; Engr.

WEIBLE, REBECCA; Somerset Area SR HS; Somerset, PA; (3); 4/257; Trs Art Clb; Trs 4-H; French Clb; Math Tm; Mu Alpha Theta; Scholastic Bowl; Yrbk Stf; Var L Bsktbl; Var L Socr; Var L Sftbl; Schlr-Athlt Awd 85; Outstndng Bsktbl Plyr, Al-Cnty Sftbl Tm; Neilan Engrs Math Awd; Astrnaut.

WEIBLEY, CATHY; West Perry SR HS; Shermansdale, PA; (2); Central Penn Bus Schl; Accntnt.

WEIBLEY, GREGORY H; Newport HS; Newport, PA; (3); 13/116; Varsity Clb; Stage Crew; L Var Bsbl; L Var Bsktbl; L Var Ftbl; Cit Awd; High Hon Roll; Hon Roll; Bus Admin.

WEIBLEY, JODY; West Perry HS; Ickesburg, PA; (3); 4-H; Varsity Clb; Concert Band; Jazz Band; Mrchg Band; Bsktbl; Fld Hcky; Sftbl; Hon Roll; 4-H Awd; Gentcs.

WEIBLEY, JULIE; Big Spring HS; Carlisle, PA; (2); Pres Church Yth Grp; Quiz Bowl; Band; Chorus; Church Choir; Concert Band; Mrchg Band; High Hon Roll; NHS; Jrnlsm.

WEIBLEY, ROBERT; West Perry HS; Ickesburg, PA; (3); 4-H; Varsity Clb; Band; Concert Band; Jazz Band; Mrchg Band; Pep Band; Socr; 4-H Awd.

WEICHMAN, AMY; St Marys Area HS; St Marys, PA; (3); 15/269; Yrbk Stf; High Hon Roll; NHS; Accntng.

WEICHMAN, ERICA; St Marys Area HS; St Marys, PA; (3); Office Aide; JV Var Cheerleading; NHS; Drama Clb; Erly Chldhd Ed.

WEICIKOSKY, STEVE; Nativity BVM HS; Middleport, PA; (3); Cmnty Wkr; Exploring; Math Clb; Nwsp Sprt Ed; Stat Bsktbl; Physcs.

WEIDE, KRISTEN; Canon-Mc Millan HS; Canonsburg, PA; (3); 2/378; Hosp Aide; Office Aide; Chorus; Vllybl; Hon Roll; U Of Pittsburgh; Educ.

WEIDENHEIMER, ANN; Reading SR HS; Reading, PA; (3); 40/819; Church Yth Grp; Office Aide; Hon Roll; RACC; Day Care Tchr.

WEIDERT, TERRY; Burgettstown Area HS; Burgettstown, PA; (3); Drama Clb; Library Aide; School Musical; Variety Show; Yrbk Stf; JV Bsktbl; R Morris Coll; Acctng.

WEIDLICH, KAREN; Altoona Area HS; Altoona, PA; (3); 9/400; Computer Clb; Drama Clb; German Clb; Key Clb; Speech Tm; SADD; Chorus; School Play; Variety Show; Jr NHS; Pre Med.

WEIDMAN, MARY; Garden Spot HS; Narvon, PA; (2); Church Yth Grp; Drama Clb; Exploring; Pres German Clb; Red Cross Aide; Sec Science Clb; School Musical; Rep Trs Stu Cncl; Hon Roll; Jr NHS; Congress & Bundestag Exchange Pgm 86; Languages.

WEIDMAN, SUSAN; Donegal HS; Mount Joy, PA; (2); Church Yth Grp; Band; Concert Band; Mrchg Band; Symp Band; Rep Frsh Cls; Sec Soph Cls; Stat Bsbl; Var Cheerleading; DAR Awd.

WEIDNER, GUY; Victory Christian Acad; Reading, PA; (3); Church Yth Grp; Acpl Chr; School Musical; Nwsp Ed-Chief; Yrbk Ed-Chief; Stu Cncl.

WEIDNER, MATTHEW; Cumberland Valley HS; Mechanicsburg, PA; (3); 24/578; Ski Clb; Var Socr; NHS; Ntl Merit Ltr.

WEIDNER, MIRIAM ELISABETH; Parkland SR HS; Allentown, PA; (4); 14/462; Church Yth Grp; Hosp Aide; JCL; Key Clb; VP Jr Cls; VP Sr Cls; Var Swmmng; Var L Trk; High Hon Roll; NHS; Speech Cntst Semi Fnlst IOOFUN Pilgrimage Yth 86; Lbrl Arts.

WEIDNER, PEGGY; Fleetwood HS; Fleetwood, PA; (4); 7/118; Trs Ski Clb; Capt Drill Tm; Stage Crew; Var Crs Cntry; Var Trk; High Hon Roll; NHS; US Army Resrv Schlr/Athlete Awd 86; MVP Cross Cntry 86; Lehigh Vly Bank Schlrshp 86; Ithaca NY; Engnrng.

WEIGHTMAN, AMY; Ringgold HS; Finleyville, PA; (3); 38/354; Church Yth Grp; Dance Clb; Sec Intnl Clb; Varsity Clb; Var L Bsktbl; Var Trk; Hon Roll; Slipery Rock; Elem Ed.

WEIGLE, JACQUELINE; Bermudian Springs HS; York Springs, PA; (3); 16/120; FHA; Library Aide; Band; Concert Band; Mrchg Band; Hon Roll; Psych.

WEIGLE, TAMARA; Northern HS; Dillsburg, PA; (3); 84/232; Cmnty Wkr; Color Guard; Drill Tm; Bsktbl; Fld Hcky; Powder Puff Ftbl; Trk; Hon Roll; Acctg.

WEIGLER, JILL COLLEEN; Sacred Heart HS; Pittsburgh, PA; (3); Cmnty Wkr; Dance Clb; French Clb; Hosp Aide; Pres Pep Clb; Nwsp Rptr; Nwsp Stf; Yrbk Stf; Im Bowling; Im Socr; 2nd Pl Holocst Arts & Wrtng Cont 87; Ellen Dwyer Schlrshp 84; Amer Lgn Awd 84; St Joan Arco Medl 87; Genetc Rsrch.

WEIGLEY, BRENDA; Altoona Area HS; Altoona, PA; (4); 59/718; Church Yth Grp; Cmnty Wkr; VP Key Clb; Chorus; Concert Band; Flag Corp; Jazz Band; Co-Capt Twrlr; Hon Roll; Jr NHS; Altoona Area HS Schlrshp 87; IN U Of PA; Fash Mdsg.

WEIK, LEIGH; Eastern Lebanon County HS; Myerstown, PA; (3); 67/169; Band; Chorus; Concert Band; Mrchg Band; Rep Jr Cls; Hon Roll; Trvl.

WEIKEL, TERRI; Northern Lebanon HS; Fredericksburg, PA; (2); 1/210; Varsity Clb; Band; Chorus; Pep Band; School Musical; Var Fld Hcky; Var Trk; Stat Wrstlng; High Hon Roll; NHS; Engrng.

WEIKEL, TRACY; Shamokin Area HS; Shamokin, PA; (3); 33/236; Church Yth Grp; Science Clb; Chorus; Church Choir; Color Guard; Concert Band; Mrchg Band; Orch; Nwsp Stf; Hon Roll; Comp Sci.

WEIKERT, BRIAN; Biglerville HS; Arendtsville, PA; (3); 14/100; VP Pres Varsity Clb; Var L Bsbl; JV Wrstlng; Hon Roll; Jr NHS; NHS.

WEIKERT, SUSAN; Biglerville HS; Biglerville, PA; (3); Hosp Aide; Ski Clb; Spanish Clb; SADD; Varsity Clb; Stage Crew; Yrbk Stf; Hst Stu Cncl; Var Tennis; Var L Trk; Arch.

WEILACHER, DENISE; Tidioute Area HS; Tidioute, PA; (4); 3/22; Debate Tm; SADD; Teachers Aide; Varsity Clb; Chorus; Trs Frsh Cls; Pres Soph Cls; Trs Sr Cls; Off Stu Cncl; Var L Bsktbl; Soc Dstngshd Amrcn Stu 86-87; Natl Schlr Athlt Awd, Sprts Bstrs Sprtmnshp Awd 87; Clarion U; Math Ed.

WEILAND, GEORGETTE; Bishop Carroll HS; Barnesboro, PA; (3); Church Yth Grp; NFL; Band; Chorus; Church Choir; Concert Band; Jazz Band; Mrchg Band; Pep Band; Powder Puff Ftbl.

WEILAND, KENNETH; Moniteau HS; Butler, PA; (3); Chess Clb; Church Yth Grp; CAP; Church Choir; Im Ftbl; Im Socr; High Hon Roll; Hon Roll; Pre Dentstry.

WEILAND, LORA; Penn Cambria SR HS; Loretto, PA; (3); Church Yth Grp; Spanish Clb; SADD; Hon Roll; NHS.

WEILAND, ROBERT; Cambria Heights HS; Patton, PA; (3); Church Yth Grp; Trs 4-H; ROTC; L Trk; Var Wrstlng; 4-H Awd; Hon Roll; NHS; VFW Awd; Retired Ofcrs Assn Awd 87; Penn ST; Teaching Comp Crs.

WEILER, ERICA; Gwynedd-Mercy Acad; Ambler, PA; (2); Church Yth Grp; Cmnty Wkr; Hosp Aide; Acpl Chr; Chorus; School Musical; Yrbk Stf; Bsktbl; JV Tennis; Pre-Med.

WEILMINSTER, ERIC; South Williamsport Area HS; Williamsport, PA; (3); 34/112; Key Clb; Spanish Clb; Concert Band; Jazz Band; Mrchg Band; Pep Band; Var Socr; Var JV Tennis; JV Trk; Hon Roll; Biology.

WEILMINSTER JR, RICHARD J; South Williamsport Area HS; Williamsport, PA; (4); 27/218; Key Clb; Concert Band; Jazz Band; Mrchg Band; Pep Band; Var Socr; Var Trk; Hon Roll; Penn ST U; Bio.

WEINACHT, DAWN; Beaver Area JR/Sr HS; Beaver, PA; (3); Church Yth Grp; French Clb; Ski Clb; Color Guard; Mrchg Band; Pep Band; School Musical; Powder Puff Ftbl; High Hon Roll; Hon Roll; Geneva Coll.

WEINBERG, CARIN; William Allen HS; Allentown, PA; (3); 18/659; JCL; Key Clb; Band; Off Stu Cncl; Var L Swmmng; Hon Roll; NHS; Var Trk; Jr NHS; Spanish NHS; Stu Rep Allentown Hmn Rltns Cmsn 86-88; Jewish Ctr Yth Sec & VP 86-88; Schl Dist Ortrcl Grd Chmp 86; Law.

WEINBERG, LINDA; Lower Merion HS; Bala Cynwyd, PA; (3); Temple Yth Grp; Chorus; School Musical; Hon Roll.

WEINBERGER, TERRY; The Ellis Schl; Pittsburgh, PA; (3); Church Yth Grp; Drama Clb; Library Aide; Pres Spanish Clb; School Play; Ed Yrbk Rptr; Rep Sr Cls; Hon Roll; Chorus; School Musical; 4 Yr Scholar Prep Schl 84-88; Provosts Day Semi-Fin U Pittsburgh 87; Smith Coll Bk Awd 87; Johns Hopkins U; Biol.

WEINER, GLENN A; William Penn Charter Schl; Willow Grove, PA; (4); Debate Tm; Model UN; Nwsp Rptr; Yrbk Stf; Lit Mag; JV Var Bsbl; Hon Roll; Ntl Merit SF; PA Hghr Ed Assist Agncy Cert Of Merit 86.

WEINERT, CHRISTINE; Trinity HS; Enola, PA; (4); Drama Clb; Trs Pep Clb; Spanish Clb; Nwsp Stf; Sec Stu Cncl; JV Var Cheerleading; High Hon Roll; NHS; Ntl Merit SF; Pres Schlr; Pres Schlrshp; Msgr Thomas A Leitch Peace & Justice Awd 87; Pres Acdmc Ftnss Awd 86 & 87; St Josephs U; Spnsh.

WEINGARD, AMY; North Hills HS; Pittsburgh, PA; (3); 25/488; Keywanettes; Ski Clb; Vllybl; Hon Roll; NHS.

WEINGARD, ROBYN; Maplewood HS; Townville, PA; (3); 1/146; Trs Church Yth Grp; Office Aide; Spanish Clb; Church Choir; Concert Band; Hon Roll; NHS; Prfct Atten Awd.

WEINMAN, LEIGH; South Fayette JR SR HS; Mc Donald, PA; (3); Church Yth Grp; Drama Clb; Key Clb; Ski Clb; School Play; Yrbk Stf; Stu Cncl; High Hon Roll; Hon Roll; NHS; Bethany; Elem Ed.

WEINREB, MICHAEL; State College Intermediate HS; State College, PA; (1); Temple Yth Grp.

WEINSCHEL, IRA; Mechanicsburg Area HS; Mechanicsburg, PA; (2); 9/300; Variety Show; NHS; High Hon Roll; Hon Roll; 1st Pl Intl Comp Prblm Slvng Cont 85-86; Musican.

WEINSCHENK, MATTHEW; Dunmore HS; Dunmore, PA; (3); 1/150; French Clb; Letterman Clb; Capt Var Crs Cntry; JV Var Trk; High Hon Roll; Jr NHS; NHS; Engrng.

WEINSTEIN, CHAD; Central SR HS; York, PA; (2); Im Ftbl; Im Wrstlng; Physcl Thrpst.

WEINSTOCK, RANDY; Susquehanna Twp HS; Harrisburg, PA; (3); 12/150; Model UN; Temple Yth Grp; Jazz Band; School Musical; Nwsp Sprt Ed; Yrbk Stf; Var Bsktbl; Var Trk; High Hon Roll; NHS; Penn ST; Actuary.

WEIR, CHRISTINE; Shikellamy HS; Sunbury, PA; (4); Pres Art Clb; French Clb; Chorus; Lit Mag; JV Cheerleading; Var Tennis; Schlstc Art Compttn Rgnl Fnlst 87; Packwd Hse Art Compttn Hnr Mntn 87; Intr Dsgn.

WEIR, JENNIFER; Cardinal O Hara HS; Media, PA; (3); 69/710; Sec Church Yth Grp; French Clb; Office Aide; Service Clb; SADD; School Musical; School Play; Yrbk Stf; Mgr(s); Hon Roll; Sports Med.

WEIR, JENNIFER; Washington HS; Washington, PA; (2); 4/190; Key Clb; Library Aide; Spanish Clb; Rep Stu Cncl; Cheerleading; High Hon Roll; Tennis; Med.

WEIR, LINDA L; Mount Saint Joseph Acad; Flourtown, PA; (4); Church Yth Grp; Spanish Clb; Im Bsktbl; Im Socr; Var Sftbl; Im Vllybl; Hon Roll; NHS; Ntl Merit SF; Spanish NHS; All Star Coaches Awd 84-87; Coach Vlybl Tm 84; Lafayette Coll; Civil Engr.

WEIR, MICHELE; Shikellamy HS; Northumberland, PA; (3); Library Aide; Nwsp Stf; Rep Soph Cls; Sec Stu Cncl; Var Cheerleading; Var Sftbl; Psych.

WEIR, VALERIE; Homer-Center HS; Homer City, PA; (3); Girl Scts; Varsity Clb; Var Bsktbl; Var Sftbl; Bio.

WEIRICH, DENISE L; Northeastern HS; Manchester, PA; (3); 10/195; Exploring; Lib Band; Chorus; Concert Band; Mrchg Band; Cheerleading; Vllybl; High Hon Roll; Hon Roll; NHS; York Coll; Bus.

WEIRICH, KELLY L; Conemaugh Twp Area HS; Hollsopple, PA; (3); 2/122; Drama Clb; NFL; Band; Concert Band; Mrchg Band; School Musical; Rep Stu Cncl; Dnfth Awd; NHS; Rtry Yth Ldrshp Awds Cnfrnc 87; PA ST; Psych.

WEIRICH, MATTHEW; Northeastern SR HS; Manchester, PA; (4); 1/167; Pres Varsity Clb; VP Bsbl; VP Bsktbl; VP Socr; VP Vllybl; DAR Awd; High Hon Roll; Lion Awd; NHS; Val; Coll Clb Of York Schlrshp 87; Engrng Soc Of York Schlrshp 87; York Cnty Builders Assoc Schlrshp 87; PA ST U; Arch Engrng.

WEIRICH, WENDY; Cedar Crest HS; Lebanon, PA; (4); Church Yth Grp; Pep Clb; Chorus; Hon Roll; Dntl Asst.

WEIS, LEIGH; St Marys Area HS; Saint Marys, PA; (4); Church Yth Grp; Hosp Aide; Office Aide; Pep Clb; Chorus; Stu Cncl; Mgr Ftbl; Stat Trk; Wt Lftg; PA ST U; Communications.

WEIS, MELISSA; Windber Area HS; Windber, PA; (4); 1/129; Pres Math Clb; Ski Clb; Nwsp Rptr; Yrbk Ed-Chief; Trs Stu Cncl; Bsktbl; Sftbl; High Hon Roll; NHS; Pres Schlr; Bkry, Confect, Tob Wrkrs Union Schlrshp 87; PTO Schlrshp 87; Stu Yr 84-86; Bus Wmns Clb Outstndng Girl; U Of Pitts Jhnstwn.

WEISBERGER, BRETT; Parkland SR HS; Allentown, PA; (2); Art Clb; Drama Clb; School Play; Stage Crew; Optometry.

WEISBERGER, CAROLYN; Butler HS; Butler, PA; (4); 35/755; Am Leg Aux Girls St; Hst Debate Tm; French Clb; Trs Latin Clb; Political Wkr; Temple Yth Grp; Mrchg Band; Symp Band; Nwsp Ed-Chief; Jr NHS; Regnl Wnnr Natl Hist Day Cont 84-87; U Of MA; Econ.

WEISBROD, PATTY; Steel Valley HS; West Homestead, PA; (4); 23/201; Church Yth Grp; Office Aide; Drill Tm; Yrbk Ed-Chief; Yrbk Stf; Score Keeper; Vllybl; High Hon Roll; Hon Roll; NHS; Bus Admin.

WEISE, KENNETH; Mastbaum Tech HS; Philadelphia, PA; (3); Var Crs Cntry; Mastbaum; Mach.

WEISENSTEIN, ERIC; Wilmington Area HS; Pulaski, PA; (3); 9/115; Spanish Clb; Bsktbl; Ftbl; Hon Roll.

WEISER, CONRAD; Bermudian Springs HS; York Springs, PA; (3); #20 In Class; Chess Clb; Stage Crew; Im Wt Lftg; Astronomy Club 84-86; Norfolk; Elec Engrng.

WEISER, DAVID; Cedar Crest HS; Rexmont, PA; (3); Sec German Clb; Pep Clb; Hon Roll; Forestry.

WEISER, PEGGY ANNE; Philadelphia HS For Girls; Philadelphia, PA; (3); 94/405; Girl Scts; Service Clb; Lib Band; Concert Band; Drm & Bgl; Orch; School Musical; Pres Stage Crew; Hon Roll; Jr NHS.

WEISER, TODD S; Pennsbury HS; Yardley, PA; (3); 25/800; Am Leg Boys St; Hosp Aide; Spanish Clb; Teachers Aide; Temple Yth Grp; Rep Frsh Cls; Rep Soph Cls; Rep Jr Cls; Rep Sr Cls; Rep Stu Cncl; Tufts U; Chmstry.

WEISGARBER, KRISTI; Sharon HS; Sharon, PA; (4); 12/159; Drama Clb; French Clb; Science Clb; Varsity Clb; Band; School Musical; Var Capt Cheerleading; Var Capt Gym; Var L Tennis; NHS; IN U Of PA; Phys Ed.

WEISGERBER, ROBERT; Southmoreland SR HS; Mt Pleasant, PA; (3); 5/222; Boy Scts; German Clb; Ski Clb; Nwsp Phtg; Nwsp Rptr; Yrbk Phtg; L Socr; NHS; Delta Epsilon Phi 87; Bus.

WEISHORN, LORI; Norwin SR HS; N Huntington, PA; (3); AFS; Church Yth Grp; Cmnty Wkr; Exploring; German Clb; Hosp Aide; Pep Clb; VICA; Hon Roll; Nrsng.

WEISMAN, GREGORY; Lower Moreland HS; Huntingdon Valley, PA; (2); FBLA; SADD; Bsbl; Bsktbl; JV Tennis; Hon Roll; Wrld Afrs Cncl 86-87.

WEISMAN, MICHAEL; Lower Moreland HS; Huntingdon Valley, PA; (3); French Clb; Im Bsbl; Im Bsktbl; JV Ftbl; Var Tennis; Im Vllybl; Hon Roll; Bus.

WEISMANN, ROBERT; Richland HS; Gibsonia, PA; (3); Boy Scts; French Clb; Chorus; Nwsp Rptr; Hon Roll; Egl Awd By Scts 87; Mtrlgst.

WEISMANN, TRICIA; Vincentian HS; Allison Pk, PA; (3); 7/73; Church Yth Grp; Service Clb; Var Fld Hcky; High Hon Roll; Hon Roll; Duquesne U; Early Child Educ.

WEISMANTEL, CRAIG; South Western HS; Hanover, PA; (3); 4-H; Letterman Clb; Ski Clb; SADD; Varsity Clb; Wt Lftg; Var Capt Wrstlng; Phys Thrpy.

WEISNER, JENNIFER; St Marys Area HS; St Marys, PA; (3); #48 In Class; Capt Hosp Aide; Band; Concert Band; Jazz Band; Mrchg Band; Hon Roll; NHS; Pre Med.

WEISNER, JOHN; St Marys Area HS; Saint Marys, PA; (4); Sec Mrchg Band; Trs Stu Cncl; Trk; Capt Wrstlng; NHS; MVP Wrstlng 4 Yr Lrtmn 86; Elk Co Govt Awd For Wrstlng 86; Bucknell U Schlrshp 87; Bucknell U; Mech Eng.

WEISNER, RANDY; Elk County Christian HS; St Marys, PA; (4); 13/80; Model UN; SADD; Varsity Clb; Jazz Band; Mrchg Band; Stu Cncl; JV Crs Cntry; Var L Wrstlng; Hon Roll; Elk Cty Gov Citatn Athltc Achvt 86; All Star Wrstlng 85-86; Engr.

WEISS, CHARLIE; Gateway HS; Monroeville, PA; (3); 70/455; Chorus; Rep Jr Cls; Rep Sr Cls; L Var Wrstlng; Hon Roll; Penn ST; Bus.

WEISS, DANA A; Northern Lehigh HS; Slatington, PA; (4); 41/150; Dance Clb; Drama Clb; Chorus; School Musical; Variety Show; Nwsp Phtg; Nwsp Rptr; Tennis; Hnr Awds-Engl II & III 85-87; Slatington Wmns Clb Grl Mnth 86-87; Westchester U; Cmmnctns.

WEISS, DAVID; Bensalem HS; Bensalem, PA; (3); FBLA; Intnl Clb; Model UN; SADD; Nwsp Bus Mgr; Nwsp Ed-Chief; Tennis; Wt Lftg; High Hon Roll; NHS; 1st Underclassmen Ever To Earn Stu Fo Mnth 86; Sigma Alpha Rho Chptr Vp 85-86; IMAA Chp 168 Sr Plt 87; Bus.

WEISS, JEANNE; Carlynton HS; Carnegie, PA; (4); 10/161; German Clb; Nwsp Rptr; Yrbk Stf; Lit Mag; Hon Roll; NHS; Prfct Atten Awd; Pres Schlr; Campus Exec Ofcr Schlrshp; Beaver Cmps Schlrshp; PA ST U; Scndry Engl Ed.

WEISS, JESSICA; Liberty HS; Bethlehem, PA; (3); 53/400; Debate Tm; Math Clb; Scholastic Bowl; Band; Orch; School Musical; Music.

WEISS, JESSICA; Plymouth-Whitemarsh HS; Conshohocken, PA; (3); 7/352; High Hon Roll; Ntl Merit Ltr; Church Yth Grp; Math Clb; Math Tm; Teachers Aide; Drill Tm; Hon Roll; Schlrshp Gratz Coll 86-87; Rookie Yr Band-Rfl Ln 84-85; Bet-Lvl Hnr Soc 86-87; Med.

WEISS, JOSEPH J; Archbishop Ryan HS For Boys; Philadelphia, PA; (4); 2/421; Cmnty Wkr; Political Wkr; School Musical; School Play; Nwsp Rptr; Var L Bsbl; Gov Hon Prg Awd; VP NHS; Sal; Computer Clb; Outstndg HS Stu Engrng 87; Columbia U; Biomed Engrng.

WEISS, KIMBERLY A; Full Gospel Acad; Pittston, PA; (3); 1/8; Sec Church Yth Grp; Cmnty Wkr; Math Clb; Speech Tm; Teachers Aide; Sec Soph Cls; Sec Jr Cls; Sec Stu Cncl; Capt Cheerleading; Prfct Atten Awd; Amer Lgn Oratrcl Cntst ST Semifnlst 87; Stu Yr 85-87; Ms Tnagr Pgnt Semi Fnlst 86; Bucknell U; Psych.

WEISS, LISA; Ambridge HS; Baden, PA; (2); Art Clb; Pep Clb; Spanish Clb; Hon Roll; Spanish NHS; Psychlgy.

WEISS, LISA; Purchase Line HS; Starford, PA; (3); 20/98; Church Yth Grp; French Clb; SADD; Chorus; Church Choir; School Musical; Yrbk Stf; Hon Roll; Bio-Chem.

WEISS, MARC; Council Rock HS; Richboro, PA; (3); Key Clb; Spanish Clb; SADD; Temple Yth Grp; Concert Band; Mrchg Band.

WEISS, SANDI; Council Rock HS; Churchville, PA; (3); 239/909; Elem Educ.

WEISS, SANDRA M; Altoona Area HS; Altoona, PA; (4); 31/719; English Clb; Office Aide; VP PAVAS; Spanish Clb; Speech Tm; SADD; Pres Temple Yth Grp; School Musical; School Play; Lit Mag; Child Psychology.

WEISS, STEPHANIE; St Pius X HS; Pottstown, PA; (4); 4-H; French Clb; PAVAS; Drm Mjr(t); School Play; Nwsp Rptr; Var L Crs Cntry; 4-H Awd; Hon Roll; Trstee Schlshp 87-88; Rosemont Coll; Bio.

WEISS, SUSAN; Parkland SR HS; Breinigsville, PA; (3); 77/495; FBLA; Library Aide; Office Aide; Ski Clb; Cheerleading; Mat Maids; Trk; Hon Roll; Thrpst.

WEISSER, CHRISTIAN; Hempfield HS; Columbia, PA; (3); Camera Clb; Letterman Clb; Ski Clb; Var Gym; Im Wt Lftg; Lbrl Arts.

WEISSMULLER, MICHAEL; Pennsbury HS; Yardley, PA; (3); 9/770; Scholastic Bowl; Var Crs Cntry; Var Trk; Im Vllybl; Hon Roll; VP NHS; Ntl Merit Ltr; AHMSE Ath Cmptn 87; All Leag Crs Cntry 86; Mth.

WEIST, KRISTI; Southern Fulton HS; Crystal Spg, PA; (4); 20/69; Computer Clb; French Clb; FHA; Science Clb; Nwsp Stf; Hon Roll; Shippensburg U.

WEIT, LE ANNE; Warwick HS; Lititz, PA; (3); 8/267; Church Yth Grp; Varsity Clb; Var Bsktbl; Stat Fld Hcky; Mgr(s); High Hon Roll; NHS; Schlr Grmn; Sprts Med.

WEITKAMP, CLYDE; Dover Area HS; East Berlin, PA; (3); 24/300; Boy Scts; JA; Hon Roll; Accntng.

WEITKAMP, TARA; Dover Area HS; Dover, PA; (3); 30/269; Sec Pres Church Yth Grp; Mgr Band; School Musical; Stage Crew; Yrbk Stf; Bsktbl; Cheerleading; Tennis; NHS; RN.

WEITZEL, BILL; Carrick HS; Pittsburgh, PA; (4); 14/340; Q&S; Nwsp Stf; Var L Bsbl; Var L Golf; High Hon Roll; NHS; 2nd Pl City Golf Championshp 86.

WEITZEL, JENNIE; Solanco HS; Peach Bottom, PA; (3); Varsity Clb; Cheerleading; Sftbl; Hon Roll; Med.

WEITZEL, KIM; Nazareth HS; Bethlehem, PA; (3); 4/386; Church Yth Grp; Drama Clb; German Clb; Key Clb; Math Tm; Pep Clb; Science Clb; SADD; School Play; Yrbk Rptr; Math.

WEIXEL, MARK; Bishop Carroll HS; Loretto, PA; (3); 18/128; Aud/Vis; Boy Scts; Computer Clb; Drama Clb; NFL; Madrigals; School Play; Stage Crew; Hon Roll; Yrbk Phtg; Qlfid Natl Cmptn Natl Catholic Forensics Leag 86; Commerce.

WELBER, SUSAN; Pennsbury HS; Yardley, PA; (3); 45/800; Civic Clb; Cmnty Wkr; French Clb; Crs Cntry; Trk; Hon Roll; NHS; Merit Schlsrhp Moore Coll Art Smr Prg 87; Art.

WELCH, ANDREW C; St John Neumann HS; Philadelphia, PA; (2); 56/253; Drama Clb; 4-H; Office Aide; Red Cross Aide; Ftbl; Ice Hcky; L Socr; Swmmng; Hon Roll; Hrptlgy.

WELCH, ANNA; Downingtown SR HS; Downingtown, PA; (3); Church Yth Grp; French Clb; SADD; School Musical; Vllybl; Hon Roll; Mrchg Band; Bsktbl; Mgr(s); Daisy Chain Hon Guard For Grad Ceremony 87; DEEP Acad Tlntd 11 Yrs; Jr Class Advsry Bd 86-87; Accntng.

WELCH, BRIAN W; Thomas Jefferson HS; Pittsburgh, PA; (4); 1/260; Pres AFS; Pres Church Yth Grp; French Clb; Var L Crs Cntry; Var L Tennis; Jr NHS; Pres NHS; Ntl Merit SF; U Of VA; Med.

WELCH, CHRIS; Marion Centra Area HS; Home, PA; (3); Church Yth Grp; SADD; Band; Drill Tm; Mrchg Band; Pep Band; Stage Crew; Hon Roll; Pittsbrg Prt Bsbl Hnrs Band Drmmr; Mc Donalds All Amer Bands; Food Svcs.

WELCH, JENNIFER L; Nazareth Acad; Philadelphia, PA; (4); Dance Clb; JCL; Latin Clb; School Musical; Variety Show; Hon Roll; Lit Mag; Bowling; Im Vllybl; Almnae Assn Schlrshp 86; Cty Philadelphia Schlrshp 87; Magna Cum Laudae Awd 86-87; Temple U; Bio.

WELCH, MEGAN; Nazareth Acad; Philadelphia, PA; (3); Church Yth Grp; Dance Clb; Drama Clb; NFL; Spanish Clb; Band; Church Choir; Cheerleading; Hon Roll; Variety Show; Music.

WELCH, MICHELLE; Lock Haven SR HS; Lock Haven, PA; (3); Cmnty Wkr; German Clb; SADD; Drill Tm; Yrbk Stf; Mat Maids; Lock Haven U.

WELCH, PAUL; Lock Haven SR HS; Lock Haven, PA; (3); 2/250; Computer Clb; Drama Clb; Key Clb; Spanish Clb; SADD; Nwsp Rptr; Nwsp Stf; Hon Roll; Prfct Atten Awd; Pre Law.

WELDON, JAYME; Keystone HS; Shippenville, PA; (3); Pep Clb; Spanish Clb; SADD; Chorus; Hon Roll; Prfct Atten Awd; Keystne Yth Ed Assn VP 86-87, Pres 87-88; Attnd Peer Cnslng Cnvntn 86-87; Psych.

WELESKI, TRACIE; Knoch HS; Cabot, PA; (4); 59/247; SADD; Drill Tm; Madrigals; School Musical; Trs Soph Cls; Var Capt Pom Pon; Hon Roll; Most Outstnding Knoch 86; Quartermaster 85-86; Shorthand Awds 87; Robert Morris Coll; Bus Tchr.

WELFLEY, HEIDI; Newport HS; Newport, PA; (3); 20/117; German Clb; Rep Soph Cls; Stu Cncl; Var Cheerleading; Sftbl; Hon Roll; Lngstcs.

WELKER, JIM; Shaler Area HS; Pgh, PA; (4); 16/510; Ski Clb; Jazz Band; Rep Stu Cncl; Var Capt Crs Cntry; Var Trk; High Hon Roll; NHS; Pres Schlr; Rotary Awd; Spanish NHS; OH Northern U; Bio Chem.

WELKER, RACHETTA; Conneaut Valley HS; Conneautville, PA; (3); Camera Clb; Sec Church Yth Grp; German Clb; Pep Clb; SADD; Varsity Clb; Rep Stu Cncl; Var L Bsktbl; Var L Sftbl; L Capt Vllybl; Outstndg Def Plyr Vllybl 86-87; 2nd Tm All Cnty Vllybl Select 86-87; Dntl Hyg.

WELKER, ROBERT; East Pennsboro HS; Enola, PA; (3); Chess Clb; Rep Spanish Clb; Sec VICA; Var Socr; High Hon Roll; Hon Roll; Acad Achvt Awd In Amer Hstry 85-86; USAF; Elec Engr.

WELKER, SHANNON; Williams Valley HS; Tower City, PA; (1); Church Yth Grp; Band; Chorus; Jazz Band; Mrchg Band; School Musical; Symp Band; Hon Roll; Prfct Atten Awd; Scndry Instrmntl Music.

WELLENDORF, MIKE; Center HS; Aliquippa, PA; (2); German Clb; Letterman Clb; Varsity Clb; Im Bowling; Var L Crs Cntry; Var Trk; Hon Roll.

WELLER, ANDREW; Parkland SR HS; Allentown, PA; (3); 115/503; Q&S; Ski Clb; Yrbk Ed-Chief; Yrbk Sprt Ed; Yrbk Stf; Rep Soph Cls; Var L Swmmng; Fin.

WELLER, ELIZABETH; Solanco HS; Drumore, PA; (3); 51/267; Church Yth Grp; 4-H; Band; Church Choir; Color Guard; Concert Band; Flag Corp; Mrchg Band; Orch; Pep Band; Outstndn In Orchstr; Anml Hlth Tech.

WELLER, KIM; Gaknet Valley HS; Boothwyn, PA; (4); 14/153; Art Clb; German Clb; Varsity Clb; Sec Sftbl; Var Vllybl; Hon Roll; Rotary Awd; Elizabethtown Coll; Psychlgy.

WELLER, LYNN; High School Of Engineering & Science; Philadelphia, PA; (3); Yrbk Stf; Rep Jr Cls; Hon Roll; Astrnmy.

WELLER, MELODY; Donegal HS; Mount Joy, PA; (3); Varsity Clb; Band; Sec Frsh Cls; Sec Soph Cls; Sec Jr Cls; Bsktbl; Fld Hcky; Powder Puff Ftbl; Sftbl; Hon Roll; Elem Ed.

WELLER, MONICA; Boyertown SR HS; Perkiomenville, PA; (3); 68/471; English Clb; Math Clb; SADD; Cit Awd; High Hon Roll; Hon Roll; Lebanon Vly Coll Yth Schlrs Inst 87; Pres Acad Fit Awd 84-85; Schlstc Achvts Spnsh Soc Studies & Engl; Jrnlsm.

WELLER, RHONDA; Newport JR/Sr HS; Newport, PA; (4); SADD; School Play; Yrbk Stf; Fld Hcky; Hon Roll; Cmrcl Art.

WELLER, SCOTT; Central Dauphin HS; Harrisburg, PA; (3); 24/370; Church Yth Grp; Exploring; Concert Band; Im Vllybl; High Hon Roll; Jr NHS; NHS; Pres Schlr; Band; JV Socr; Tp 10 Bibl Quzzr, Capt Chrch Quzzng Tm; 1st Pl Trphy Bsktbl Chmpns; Psych.

WELLIVER, JASON; Milton SR HS; Milton, PA; (2); JV Crs Cntry; JV Trk; Elec.

WELLIVER, MARY; Hershey SR HS; Hummelstown, PA; (4); 5/178; Church Yth Grp; Science Clb; Chorus; Nwsp Ed-Chief; Var Bsktbl; Im Vllybl; Bausch & Lomb Sci Awd; High Hon Roll; NHS; Math Tm; Treva Dise Schlrshp 87; Patriot News Journlsm Achvmnt Awd 87; Dickinson Coll.

WELLMAN, SALLY; Athens HS; Athens, PA; (3); Art Clb; SADD; Chorus; Rep Stu Cncl; Im Coach Actv; Var L Trk; PA HOBY Fndtn Rep 86; X-Ray Tech.

WELLS, DAVID; Norristown HS; Norristown, PA; (3); Hnr Rolls.

WELLS, DONNA; Philadelphia HS For Girls; Philadelphia, PA; (4); 165/365; Drill Tm; PA St U; Microbio.

WELLS, JAMES; Forest City Regional HS; Forest City, PA; (4); 3/56; Pres Letterman Clb; Spanish Clb; Band; Var L Bsktbl; Capt Var Golf; Capt Var Socr; Var L Vllybl; High Hon Roll; Hon Roll; NHS; I Dare You Awd; US Army Resrv Natl Schlr Athl Awd; Frst City Rotry Clb Stu Mnth; Penn ST; Engrng.

WELLS, JON; Harrisburg HS; Harrisburg, PA; (2); 9/352; Boys Clb Am; Boy Scts; Math Clb; ROTC; Mgr(s); Tennis; Hon Roll; Engr.

WELLS, KRIS; Dubois Area HS; Dubois, PA; (4); 43/285; Hosp Aide; Intnl Clb; Nwsp Phtg; Nwsp Rptr; Nwsp Stf; Yrbk Phtg; Yrbk Rptr; Yrbk Sprt Ed; Yrbk Stf; Stu Cncl; PENN ST; Comms.

WELLS, LISA; Saltsburg JRSR HS; Saltsburg, PA; (3); SADD; Teachers Aide; Sec Frsh Cls; VP Soph Cls; Stu Cncl; Stat Bsktbl; JV Cheerleading; Powder Puff Ftbl; High Hon Roll; Hon Roll; Miss Yng PA 85; Miss Yng Amer 85; Miss Teen PA 87; ICM; Bus.

WELLS, LISA; Tunkhannock Area HS; Dalton, PA; (3); 24/320; 4-H; Spanish Clb; Rep Soph Cls; High Hon Roll; Hon Roll.

WELLS, MARY; Seneca HS; Erie, PA; (4); 3/154; VP Church Yth Grp; Hosp Aide; VP Science Clb; Yrbk Stf; Rep Stu Cncl; Var Crs Cntry; Stat Trk; Hon Roll; NHS; Prfct Atten Awd; Daemen Coll; Phy Therapy.

WELLS, SHAWN; Bald Eagle Nittany HS; Mill Hall, PA; (2); 70/137; Church Yth Grp; Cmnty Wkr; Yrbk Stf; JV Bsktbl.

WELLS JR, THOMAS; Shamokin Area HS; Shamokin, PA; (4); 10/238; German Clb; Science Clb; Varsity Clb; Crs Cntry; Wrstlng; Hon Roll; Jr NHS; NHS; Penn ST U; Liberal Arts.

WELSH, KAREN; Garden Spot HS; New Holland, PA; (4); 30/210; Drama Clb; Chorus; Orch; School Musical; School Play; Var Fld Hcky; Var L Trk; High Hon Roll; Hon Roll; Wright Fmly Trust Music Awd 87; Best Supprtng Actress Awd 86-87; Outstndng Backstg Tech Fclty Awd; Kutztown U; Speech Pathlgy.

WELSH, KIMBERLY; Berks Christian Schl; Pottstown, PA; (3); 1/22; Church Yth Grp; Band; Chorus; School Musical; Yrbk Phtg; Yrbk Stf; Var Bsktbl; Var Cheerleading; Var Trk; High Hon Roll.

WELTON, BOBBI; Karns City JR-SR HS; Petrolia, PA; (4); Pep Clb; SADD; Teachers Aide; Yrbk Stf; Ftbl; Score Keeper; Vllybl; High Hon Roll; Hon Roll; NHS; Pres Acad Fit Awd 87; Cosmtlgst.

WELTY, JAMES; Boiling Springs HS; Boiling Spgs, PA; (4); Ski Clb; Band; Pres Chorus; Concert Band; Jazz Band; Mrchg Band; VP Stu Cncl; Var Capt Socr; Var Capt Swmmng; Hon Roll; Hugh Obrian Yth Ldrshp Fndtn 85; Cnvntn II 86; Stu Frm 87; Eckero Coll; Poly Sci.

WENDEL, STEPHEN; St Marys Area HS; Saint Marys, PA; (4); Im L Bsktbl; Im L Ftbl; Var L Trk; UPJ; Mech Engnrng.

WENDELL, JENNIFER; Bethlehem Catholic HS; Bethlehem, PA; (3); 36/210; Red Cross Aide; Ski Clb; Sftbl; High Hon Roll; Hon Roll; U Of DE; Comps.

WENDLING, MARK; Southern Lehigh HS; Coopersburg, PA; (4); 8/230; Chess Clb; Exploring; Scholastic Bowl; Band; Jazz Band; Orch; Yrbk Stf; High Hon Roll; Jr NHS; NHS; Natl Sci Merit Awd 87; Prncpls Lst 86-87; John Hopkins U; Med.

WENDT, GERHARD; Conestoga Valley HS; Leola, PA; (3); 61/256; Camera Clb; Pres Church Yth Grp; Band; Chorus; Orch; School Play; Trs Sr Cls; Var Trk; Im Wt Lftg; Voice Dem Awd; Hnr Make A Wish Fndtn Fnd Dr 87; Hnr Crop Walk & Walk For Hunger 86; Rcgnzd LARC Bike A Thon 85; Crmnl Just.

WENDTLAND, LEIGH; Meadville Area SR HS; Meadville, PA; (3); Church Yth Grp; Civic Clb; Science Clb; Spanish Clb; Varsity Clb; Church Choir; Stu Cncl; Cheerleading; Var JV Sftbl; High Hon Roll.

WENERSTROM, WENDY; Baldwin SR HS; Pittsburgh, PA; (4); 109/535; Drama Clb; Nwsp Rptr; Yrbk Ed-Chief; High Hon Roll; Hon Roll; Pres Schlr; OH U; Jrnlsm.

WENG, DAVID; Neshaminy HS; Feasterville, PA; (4); 56/700; Church Yth Grp; Band; Chorus; Jazz Band; School Musical; Yrbk Stf; Hon Roll; NHS; Rotary Awd; Patricia Mc Keaney Mem Schlrshp 87; VA Tech; Mech Engr.

WENGER, ANDREA; Lancaster Mennonite HS; Lancaster, PA; (4); VP Church Yth Grp; Chorus; Church Choir; Orch; School Play; Var Im Bsktbl; Var JV Fld Hcky; NHS; Im Vllybl; Stu Of Mo By Paradise Rotary Clb 86; Athlt Of Wk In Intelligencer Jrnl 86.

WENGER, BLAINE; Solanco HS; New Providence, PA; (3); Church Yth Grp; 4-H; Chorus; Nwsp Rptr; Yrbk Bus Mgr; JV Capt Socr; JV Trk; NHS; Chess Clb; High Hon Roll; Hgh Obrn Yth Ldrshp Smnr 86; Engrng.

WENGER, ERIC; Council Rock HS; Newtown, PA; (3); 21/908; Ftbl; Capt L Trk; Im Vllybl; High Hon Roll; NHS; Intnsv Lang Inst Schlrshp 87; U Of PA; Archlgy.

WENGER, ETHAN; Eastern Lebanon HS; Schaefferstown, PA; (3); 1/200; Rep Band; VP Chorus; Jazz Band; Mrchg Band; School Musical; Capt Crs Cntry; Var L Trk; Bausch & Lomb Sci Awd; High Hon Roll; Pres NHS; Ntl Schl Chrs Awd 86; Dstrct Chrs 86 & 87; Engrng.

WENGER, JOANNE; Hamburg Area HS; Hamburg, PA; (3); Pres VP French Clb; Library Aide; Chorus; Rep Stu Cncl; Var Trk; Hon Roll; Acadc Ltr Hstry 86; Acadc Ltr Alg II 87; Lock Haven U; Intl Rltns.

WENGER, KENT; Solanco HS; Quarryville, PA; (3); 22/240; Church Yth Grp; Thesps; Varsity Clb; Acpl Chr; Band; Jazz Band; School Musical; Var Capt Socr; Var Trk; NHS; All State Lions Band 87; Phy Sci.

WENGER, KEVIN; Mechanicsburg SR HS; Mechanicsburg, PA; (2); Ski Clb; Band; Ftbl; High Hon Roll; Hon Roll.

WENGER, LYLE; Cedar Crest HS; Lebanon, PA; (3); Pres Church Yth Grp; German Clb; Pep Clb; Stu Cncl; Var Socr; Im Vllybl; Hon Roll; NHS; Engr.

WENGER, MARSHA; Chambersburg Area SR HS; Pleasant Hall, PA; (2); Church Yth Grp; Spanish Clb; SADD; Chorus; Stage Crew; Rep Soph Cls; Hon Roll; Bus Admin.

WENGER, MICHELLE; Conestoga Valley HS; Brownstown, PA; (3); Art Clb; Dance Clb; Band; Concert Band; Mrchg Band; Hon Roll; Millersville U; Acctnt.

WENGER, PAMELA; Cocalico HS; Stevens, PA; (3); FBLA; GAA; VP Soph Cls; VP Jr Cls; JV Var Cheerleading; JV Var Fld Hcky; JV Sftbl; Wt Lftg; High Hon Roll; NHS; Marine Sci Cnsrtm Cert Of Prtcptn 86; PA ST Chptr Cert In FBLA 86; Physcl Thrpy.

WENGER, TIMOTHY; Manheim Central HS; Manheim, PA; (4); 2/224; Trs Church Yth Grp; SADD; Yrbk Stf; High Hon Roll; VP NHS; Sal; Spanish Awd, Prsdntl Acdmc Ftnss Awd 86-87; Chem Awd 85-86; Yth Evnglsm Srvc.

WENGER, TINA; Conestoga Valley HS; Leola, PA; (4); Church Yth Grp; Hosp Aide; Flag Corp; Mrchg Band; Rep Jr Cls; Capt Cheerleading; Tennis; Hon Roll; Vrsty Ltrd Med Trnr 87; Bloomsburg U; Elem Ed.

WENGERD, HEIDI; Salisbury-Elk Lick HS; Salisbury, PA; (2); 1/35; Trs Church Yth Grp; Pres 4-H; Band; Concert Band; Mrchg Band; Yrbk Stf; High Hon Roll; Pharmacy.

WENGERT, WENDY; Altoona Area HS; Altoona, PA; (3); 18/796; Pres Sec Church Yth Grp; Computer Clb; Key Clb; Flag Corp; Trs Jr Cls; Trs Sr Cls; Rep Stu Cncl; High Hon Roll; NEDT Awd; Pres Schlr; All Solid Subjects Straigh Fives 85; Bus Admin.

WENGLIK, BERNADETTE; Ambridge HS; Ambridge, PA; (2); JA; Office Aide; Pep Clb; Red Cross Aide; Band; Mrchg Band; Rep Jr Cls; Trk; Hon Roll; Prfct Atten Awd; Med.

WENGRAITIS, MATTHEW G; Archbishop Ryan HS For Boys; Philadelphia, PA; (4); 3/421; Church Yth Grp; Yrbk Stf; Var Crs Cntry; Var Trk; Elks Awd; Gov Hon Prg Awd; NHS; Ntl Merit Ltr; Lit Mag; High Hon Roll; MI Alumni Club Schlrshp 87; Penn ST U Schlr 87; Aero Engrng.

WENGRAITIS, STEPHEN; Archbishop Ryan HS For Boys; Philadelphia, PA; (4); 3/421; Yrbk Stf; Lit Mag; Var Crs Cntry; Var Trk; Gov Hon Prg Awd; High Hon Roll; NHS; Ntl Merit Ltr; Church Yth Grp; 3rd Pl Energy Ed Advsry Cncl Essay Cont 85; Physics.

WENIGER, JULIA; North Allegheny SR HS; Gibsonia, PA; (2); 42/612; Debate Tm; Concert Band; Mrchg Band; Rep Soph Cls; Stu Cncl; Cheerleading; Trk; Vllybl; Hon Roll; Jr NHS; Notre Dame.

WENNER, ANNAMARIA; Northwestern Lehigh HS; Kutztown, PA; (4); 46/160; Hosp Aide; Nwsp Stf; Yrbk Stf; Rep Stu Cncl; Mgr Bsktbl; Mgr Fld Hcky; Capt L Trk; High Hon Roll; Hon Roll; Lion Awd; Stu Mnth 84-87; U Of Pittsburgh Bedford; Psych.

WENNER, BRYAN; Benton HS; Benton, PA; (2); Am Leg Boys St; Church Yth Grp; Key Clb; Red Cross Aide; Off Stu Cncl; Var Bsbl; Socr; Wrstlng; High Hon Roll; Jr NHS; Sprts Med.

WENNER, KENNETH; Ambridge Area HS; Baden, PA; (3); Am Leg Boys St; Pep Clb; VICA; High Hon Roll; Hon Roll; 2nd ST Arch Dsgn AIASA, Qualfr ST Drwng Inter AIASA 87; Arch Drftng.

WENNER, MICHAEL G; Benton HS; Benton, PA; (3); 4/80; Am Leg Boys St; Church Yth Grp; Key Clb; Varsity Clb; Chorus; School Musical; School Play; Variety Show; Pres Frsh Cls; Pres Soph Cls; West Point; Engrng.

WENNER, TAMMY; Hazleton HS; Drums, PA; (3); 59/465; Trs Church Yth Grp; French Clb; FBLA; JV Bsktbl; French Hon Soc; High Hon Roll; Hon Roll; Elizabethtown; Corp Law.

WENRICH, ANDREW A; Governor Mifflin HS; Shillington, PA; (3); 9/360; Band; Chorus; Concert Band; Jazz Band; Mrchg Band; School Musical; Stage Crew; Socr; Gov Mifflin Hnr Soc; Harrisburg Clsscl Soc Latin Awd.

WENRICH JR, CARL; Avon Grove HS; Kemblesville, PA; (2); Computer Clb; Exploring; Concert Band; Drm & Bgl; Mrchg Band; JV Bsbl; Hon Roll; Band; JV Bsktbl; Im Ftbl; Avon Grove Yth Educ Assoc & JV Bsktbl Team Record 86-87; Accntnt.

WENRICK, SHERRI; Mifflinburg Area HS; Millmont, PA; (1); German Clb; High Hon Roll; Data Proc.

WENSEL, KYLE; Conneaut Valley HS; Conneautville, PA; (3); VP Church Yth Grp; Varsity Clb; VP Mrchg Band; Rep Sr Cls; Rep Stu Cncl; Var L Bsbl; Var L Ftbl; CC Awd; Hon Roll; Rotary Awd; PMEA Dist II Band Fstvl 87; Stu Delg Wrld Affrs Inst Rtry Intl 86; Hnry Hse Page PA Hse Reps 85; Hstry.

WENTLAND, JACOB J; North Pocono HS; Moscow, PA; (3); 34/245; Band; Chorus; Mrchg Band; Orch; School Play; Variety Show; Var L Tennis; JETS Awd; NHS; VFW Awd; PA Mus Ed Assoc State Orch & Band Fest 86&87; Gftd Pgm.

WENTLAND, REBECCA; Carbondale JR SR HS; Carbondale, PA; (3); 11/119; Church Yth Grp; German Clb; Capt Color Guard; High Hon Roll; Hon Roll; Pres Phys Fit Awd 84-85; Air Force; Fshn Merch.

WENTZ, DENISE; Northampton SR HS; Northampton, PA; (4); 10/445; AFS; Leo Clb; Nwsp Rptr; Yrbk Stf; High Hon Roll; NHS; Bloomsburg U; Psychlgy.

WENTZ III, EDWARD F; Bellefontea Area HS; Bellefonte, PA; (3); Boy Scts; Drama Clb; VP Model UN; Band; Chorus; Jazz Band; Mrchg Band; School Musical; School Play; Var Trk.

WENTZ, ERIK; Dover Area HS; Dover, PA; (4); Church Yth Grp; Church Choir; Powder Puff Ftbl; Var Capt Socr; Trk; Wt Lftg; Hon Roll; Penn ST; Hotel Mngmnt.

WENTZ, JANE; William Penn HS; York, PA; (3); 40/374; Ski Clb; Sec SADD; Capt Color Guard; Mrchg Band; Sec Orch; NHS; Stu Mnth 87; Physcl Thrpy.

WENTZ, JIL; Hanover HS; Hanover, PA; (4); Varsity Clb; Band; Concert Band; Jazz Band; Mrchg Band; School Play; Capt Cheerleading; Var L Trk; CC Awd; Hon Roll; VA Commonwealth U; Fshn Mrchnd.

WENTZ, KRISTIE; Greenwood HS; Millerstown, PA; (3); 7/70; FBLA; Office Aide; Teachers Aide; Concert Band; Mrchg Band; Pep Band; School Musical; Cheerleading; Hon Roll; NHS; Hugh O Brien Ldrshp Smnr 86; Bus.

WENTZ, T J; State College Area SR HS; Pennsylvania Furn, PA; (4); 35/580; Yrbk Rptr; Off Frsh Cls; Off Soph Cls; Var JV Bsktbl; Var Golf; Im Lcrss; Im Vllybl; Cit Awd; High Hon Roll; Ntl Merit Ltr; Northwestern U; Sci.

WENTZEL, ALICIA; Carrick HS; Pittsburgh, PA; (4); Church Yth Grp; French Clb; Q&S; Ski Clb; School Musical; Stage Crew; Nwsp Rptr; Nwsp Stf; Powder Puff Ftbl; Hon Roll; U Of Pittsburgh; Engl.

WENTZEL, ANDREA; Dover Area HS; Dover, PA; (3); Rep Stu Cncl; Var Swmmng; JV Vllybl; High Hon Roll; Hon Roll; NHS; Al-Amer Swmmng 86-87; Phy Thrpy.

WENTZEL, CHARLES; Newport HS; Newport, PA; (1); FTA; Red Cross Aide; Swmmng; Hon Roll; Teach Algebra.

WENTZEL, JEANENE; Warwick HS; Lititz, PA; (2); 49/302; Church Yth Grp; French Clb; Girl Scts; Pep Clb; Soph Cls; Cheerleading; Sftbl; Hon Roll; Psych.

WENTZEL, MICHELLE; Garden Spot HS; Denver, PA; (2); Church Yth Grp; Library Aide; Mgr(s); Hon Roll; Bus.

WENTZEL, TAMARA; Waynesburg Central HS; Waynesburg, PA; (4); 1/190; Church Yth Grp; Church Choir; Nwsp Ed-Chief; Stu Cncl; Var Trk; Im Wt Lftg; Bausch & Lomb Sci Awd; Pres NHS; Val; Voice Dem Awd; Girl Of Mnth 87; Penn ST U Schlrs Prog 87; Penn ST U.

WENTZHEIMER, LAURA; Garnet Valley HS; Glen Mills, PA; (4); 22/156; Church Yth Grp; German Clb; Model UN; Varsity Clb; Yrbk Stf; Var Cheerleading; Lcrss; Twrlr; Vllybl; Hon Roll; Wheaton; Chem.

WENZEL, AMY ELIZABETH; North Allegheny SR HS; Pittsburgh, PA; (4); 81/660; Hosp Aide; JA; Mrchg Band; School Play; Rep Stu Cncl; Diving; Hon Roll; Jr NHS; NHS; Pres Schlr; Pres Cmmtte On Emplymnt Of Hndcppd 4th Pl 86; Gftd Pgm 4 Yrs; Pres Acad Ftns Awd; PA ST U.

WENZEL, MARK WILHELM; North Allegheny HS; Pittsburgh, PA; (2); 107/630; Church Yth Grp; Computer Clb; Ski Clb; Band; Mrchg Band; Bsktbl; Trk; Hon Roll; Jr NHS.

WENZEL, ROBERT; Montoursville HS; Montoursville, PA; (4); 1/174; Pres Key Clb; VP Letterman Clb; VP Stu Cncl; Var L Ftbl; Var L Trk; Bausch & Lomb Sci Awd; Pres NHS; Ntl Merit Ltr; Val; Math Tm; Rbrt C Byrd Schlrshp 87; Deans Selct Schlrshp Vanderblt U 87; Vanderbilt U; Med.

WENZEL, SHERI; Villa Maria Acad; Erie, PA; (3); 8/168; Model UN; NFL; Quiz Bowl; Speech Tm; Rep Stu Cncl; Var Tennis; Hon Roll; NHS.

WERBOCK, SUNSHINE; Bensalem SR HS; Bensalem, PA; (2); Drama Clb; Sec FBLA; Key Clb; Model UN; Scholastic Bowl; SADD; School Play; Nwsp Rptr; Lit Mag; Hon Roll; 4th Pl Tm Future Problem Solving In St 87; Pres Wrld Affairs Clb Vp Wrld Affairs Clb 85-87; Rutgers; Pltcl Sci.

WERKHEISER, CRAIG; Pen Argyl Area HS; Nazareth, PA; (4); 18/117; Church Yth Grp; Band; Concert Band; Jazz Band; Mrchg Band; Orch; School Play; PTA Schlrshp 87; St Peters Luthern Chrch Schlrshp 87; Penn ST U; Spnsh.

WERKHEISER, KELLY; Bloomsburg SR HS; Bloomsburg, PA; (3); Church Yth Grp; Drama Clb; Pep Clb; Thesps; Varsity Clb; Band; Chorus; Concert Band; Flag Corp; School Musical; Bus Mgmt.

WERKHEISER, WENDY L; Mechanicsburg SR HS; Shiremanstown, PA; (3); 32/338; Am Leg Aux Girls St; Church Yth Grp; Speech Tm; Nwsp Ed-Chief; Yrbk Stf; Sec Bowling; High Hon Roll; Hon Roll; Abilene Christian U; English.

WERLEY, CHRISTINE; Hamburg Area JR SR HS; Lenhartsville, PA; (3); VP Church Yth Grp; Spanish Clb; Var Tennis; High Hon Roll; Hon Roll; NHS; Sec 4-H; Library Aide; Acadc Hnrs & Cert Achvt Plane Geom, Trig & Alg III 85-87; Presdntl Phys Ftns Awd 86-87.

WERLEY, DENISE; Hamburg Area HS; Hamburg, PA; (4); 41/144; High Hon Roll; Hon Roll; Stu Quarter Vo-Tech Cosmtlgy 86; Hairdresser.

WERMUTH, CHARLES; Father Judge HS; Philadelphia, PA; (3); 15/402; Cmnty Wkr; Rep Stu Cncl; L Var Bsbl; Var L Socr; Var L Swmmng; Cit Awd; Gov Hon Prg Awd; NHS; Church Yth Grp; Hosp Aide; All Cathlc 85-86 & MVP Swim Tm Awds 85-87; Cty Athl Wk Sccr 86; Cty Phldlphia Incntv Awd 85; Pre Med.

WERNER, BENJAMIN; Donegal HS; Mount Joy, PA; (3); 33/167; Concert Band; Jazz Band; Mrchg Band; School Play; Nwsp Stf; Yrbk Bus Mgr; Hon Roll; HOBY Fndtn 86; Millersville ST U; Scndry Ed.

WERNER, CATHRYN; Pine Grove Area HS; Pine Grove, PA; (3); SADD; Varsity Clb; Chorus; Mrchg Band; Yrbk Stf; Hst Frsh Cls; Hst Soph Cls; Hst Jr Cls; Rep Stu Cncl; Var L Cheerleading; Spcl Educ.

WERNER, JAMES PAUL; Ambridge Area HS; Sewickley, PA; (4); 4/260; German Clb; Pep Clb; Yrbk Bus Mgr; Yrbk Phtg; High Hon Roll; Jr NHS; NHS; Erly Admssn Stu Coll 86-87; Deans Lst 86-87; U Of Pittsburgh; Law.

WERNER, JONATHAN; Donegal HS; Mount Joy, PA; (3); 22/167; Concert Band; Drm Mjr(t); Jazz Band; Mrchg Band; School Play; JV Socr; Hon Roll; Rotary Awd; The Citadel; Hstry.

WERNER, KENNETH; William Allen HS; Allentown, PA; (2); 34/700; JV Crs Cntry; Im Ftbl; Var Trk; Hon Roll; Math.

WERNER, KIMBERLY; Red Lion Area SR HS; Windsor, PA; (3); 84/342; Church Yth Grp; Varsity Clb; Rep Stu Cncl; Powder Puff Ftbl; Var Trk; Hon Roll; PA ST U; Pedtrc Nrse Practnr.

WERNER, LISA; Quakertown Community HS; Quakertown, PA; (3); Art Clb; German Clb; Intnl Clb; SADD; Band; Yrbk Stf; Mgr(s); Church Yth Grp; Dance Clb; Girl Scts; San Francisco Art Inst; Fn Arts.

WERNER, SHAUN; Knoch HS; Cabot, PA; (4); Math Clb; Trs Science Clb; Bsbl; JV Im Bsktbl; Im Ftbl; High Hon Roll; Hon Roll; NHS; Sxnbrg Dist Wmns Clb, Cabot Athltc & Rcrtn Axlry & Geo H Adrhld Memrl Schlrshp 87; OH ST U; Arntcl Engrng.

WERNER, WENDY; Baldwin SR HS; Pittsburgh, PA; (4); 65/535; SADD; Rep Stu Cncl; Capt L Swmmng; NHS; Ath Schlrshp To Syracuse U 87; MVP Of Swim Team 86; Syracuse U; Psych.

WERNERSBACH, LORI ANN; Methacton HS; Norristown, PA; (3); 14/389; Cmnty Wkr; Trs Pres FBLA; Pres Intnl Clb; Library Aide; JV Bsktbl; Var Fld Hcky; Var Lcrss; Cit Awd; Hon Roll; NHS; Pediatrics.

WERT, ANNE; Daniel Boone HS; Birdsboro, PA; (3); 7/160; Model UN; Quiz Bowl; Science Clb; Nwsp Ed-Chief; Stu Cncl; Bausch & Lomb Sci Awd; NHS; Church Yth Grp; Hosp Aide; Acpl Chr; Choral Awds-Cnty-Dist-Rgnls; Berks Co Sci Fair Awds; Jr Miss Of Daniel Boone; Bio.

WERT, MELISSA; Solanco HS; New Providence, PA; (3); Church Yth Grp; Acpl Chr; Chorus; Church Choir; School Musical; High Hon Roll; Hon Roll; NHS; Fld Hcky; Outstndng Frshmn Choral 85; Outstndng Soph Choral 86; Acctng.

WERT, MICHAEL; Cumberland Valley HS; Mechanicsburg, PA; (2); Boy Scts; German Clb; Ski Clb; SAR Awd; Eagle Sct Awd 87; SR Ptrl Ldrs In Scts 86-87; Altar Boy 77-87.

WERT, MONICA; Juniata HS; Mifflintown, PA; (3); Pres Church Yth Grp; Sec Drama Clb; SADD; Mrchg Band; School Play; Yrbk Stf; Rep Stu Cncl; Var L Fld Hcky; High Hon Roll; NHS; :Bus.

WERT, PHILIP; Lancaster Mennonite HS; Coatesville, PA; (3); Chess Clb; Ski Clb; Chorus; Rep Frsh Cls; JV Im Bsbl; Im Bsktbl; JV Im Socr; Hon Roll.

WERT, SHELLEY; Cedar Crest HS; Lebanon, PA; (4); Church Yth Grp; Pres French Clb; Intnl Clb; Model UN; Pep Clb; Pres Band; Drm Mjr(t); Mrchg Band; Socr; Hon Roll; U Southern MS Alumni Awd 87; U Of Southern MS; Tv.

WERTHEIMER, JOSHUA; Solebury Schl; Philadelphia, PA; (3); Jazz Band; Nwsp Stf; Var Bsktbl; JV Socr; JV Trk.

WERTS, BUFFIE; Cardinal O Hara HS; Ridley Park, PA; (3); 179/719; Church Yth Grp; Office Aide; JV Bsbl; Var L Sftbl; Comm Art.

WERTZ, HOLLY; Bedford HS; Manns Choice, PA; (3); Church Yth Grp; 4-H; FBLA; Chorus; 4-H Awd; Hon Roll; 4-H Dairy Juding Awd 85; Alleghany CC; Bus.

WERTZ, MARCY; Penn Cambria SR HS; Lilly, PA; (3); Spanish Clb; SADD; Concert Band; Mrchg Band; Twrlr; Hon Roll; Elem Educ.

WERTZ, MATTHEW; Cedar Cliff HS; New Cumberland, PA; (2); 139/292; Timer; Var Trk; Gettysburg U; Hist Prof.

WERTZ, MELISSA; Butler Area SR HS; Butler, PA; (2); Church Yth Grp; French Clb; GAA; Chorus; Bsktbl; Hon Roll; Elem Ed.

WERTZ, MELISSA; Penn Cambria HS; Lilly, PA; (3); Spanish Clb; SADD; Chorus; Drm Mjr(t); Mrchg Band; Rep Stu Cncl; High Hon Roll; Hon Roll; NHS; Spanish NHS; Scndry Educ.

WERTZ, MICHAEL; Pine Grove Area HS; Pine Grove, PA; (3); Am Leg Boys St; Political Wkr; ROTC; Var Bsbl; JV Ftbl; Cit Awd; Hon Roll.

WERTZ, ROBERT; Mechanicsburg Area SR HS; Mechanicsburg, PA; (3); 23/338; Boy Scts; Church Yth Grp; Model UN; Chorus; Stage Crew; Socr; High Hon Roll.

WERTZ, VICKI; Danville Area HS; Danville, PA; (1); 70/233; Church Yth Grp; Sec 4-H; Band; Concert Band; Mrchg Band; 4-H Awd; High Hon Roll; Hon Roll; Prsdntl Acdmcs Fitness Awd & Natl Piano Playing Auditions ,M; Penn ST; Comp Sci.

WESCOE, BLAIR; South Williamsport HS; S Williamsport, PA; (3); 11/110; VP Stu Cncl; Var Bsktbl; Var Ftbl; Var Wt Lftg; Hon Roll; U Of VA; Pre Med.

WESCOE, MIKE; Parkland HS; Allentown, PA; (4); 13/459; Var Bsktbl; Var Trk; NHS; Shippensburg U; Bus Adm.

WESCOTT, CHRISSY; Unionville HS; Winter Springs, FL; (4); 106/316; Pres Exploring; Pres 4-H; FBLA; Girl Scts; Red Cross Aide; Ski Clb; Nwsp Rptr; Nwsp Stf; 4-H Awd; Hon Roll; Red Crss Bldmbl 87; Nwpr & Ecs FBLA Awd 87; Clemson U; Biochem.

WESDOCK, CHUCK; Du Bois Area HS; Reynoldsvl, PA; (2); 10/350; Boy Scts; Varsity Clb; JV Socr; DAR Awd; NHS; Pres Schlr; Order Of The Arrow 85.

WESLEY, KAREN; West York SR HS; York, PA; (3); JA; Spanish Clb; Varsity Clb; Sec Stu Cncl; Var Trk; Var Vllybl; Hon Roll; VP-PRSNNL Of Yr 87; Emplyee Of Yr-1st Rnnr Up 86; Bus.

WESLEY, RASHEED; Scotland Schl For Veterans Children; Chester, PA; (3); ROTC; Varsity Clb; Drill Tm; Nwsp Rptr; Nwsp Stf; Bsbl; L Ftbl; Mgr(s); Wt Lftg; Hon Roll; Teacher.

WESLEY, ROBIN; Mc Caskey HS; Lancaster, PA; (3); 78/617; FBLA; Bus Admin.

WESNER, ALICE; West Hazelton HS; Sugarloaf, PA; (4); 50/224; Pres VP 4-H; French Clb; FTA; Library Aide; Office Aide; SADD; 4-H Awd; Hon Roll; NHS; Penn ST U.

WESNER, AMY; Blacklick Valley HS; Ebensburg, PA; (3); 1/100; German Clb; Ski Clb; Varsity Clb; Yrbk Stf; Sec Jr Cls; Rep Stu Cncl; Bsktbl; Var Mgr(s); Hon Roll; Var Sftbl; Acad All-Amer Awd 85-86; Pres Fitness Awd 84-85.

WESSEL, STACY; Bishop Mc Cort HS; Johnstown, PA; (3); 15/178; Letterman Clb; Math Tm; Mu Alpha Theta; Yrbk Stf; Var Capt Cheerleading; Trk; High Hon Roll; NHS.

WESSELL, KIMBERLY; Abington Hts HS; Clarks Summit, PA; (3); Hosp Aide; Ski Clb; Lib Chorus; Rep Stu Cncl; JV Var Cheerleading; Hon Roll; NHS.

WESSNER, JULIE; Hamburg Area HS; Strausstown, PA; (3); Rep FBLA; German Clb; Ski Clb; SADD; Yrbk Bus Mgr; Yrbk Phtg; Var Capt Cheerleading; Gym.

WESSNER, RENEE; Annville Cleona HS; Lebanon, PA; (4); 4/215; Church Yth Grp; SADD; Chorus; Yrbk Stf; Bausch & Lomb Sci Awd; Hon Roll; NHS; NEDT Awd; Latin Excllnc Awd 85; Schlstc Gld Key Wrtng Awd 87; West Chester U; Micro Bio.

WESSNER, TAMMY; Hamburg Area HS; Hamburg, PA; (4); 16/150; Trs German Clb; Stu Cncl; Fld Hcky; Sftbl; High Hon Roll; Hon Roll; NHS; German Natl Hnr Soc-Sec/Treas; Acadmc Lttr-Algbra, Grmn, Chem, Govt/Econ; Millersville U; Bus Admin.

WEST, AMY; Villa Maria Acad; Erie, PA; (3); Computer Clb; Science Clb; SADD; Yrbk Rptr; Rep Stu Cncl; High Hon Roll; NHS; Med.

WEST, ANDRE; Big Beaver Falls SR HS; Beaver Falls, PA; (3); 58/177; Stage Crew; Var Ftbl; Var L Trk; High Hon Roll; U Of Pittsburgh; Sociology.

WEST, HEATHER; Downingtown SR HS; Chester Sprg, PA; (3); French Clb; Ski Clb; Chorus; Off Stu Cncl; JV Capt Cheerleading; Diving; Hon Roll; NHS.

WEST, JEFF; Freeport HS; Freeport, PA; (3); 21/213; JV Bsktbl; Var L Ftbl; JV Trk; Chrprctr.

WEST, LARRY; Southern Columbia HS; Catawissa, PA; (3); 34/107; Computer Clb; Band; Concert Band; Pep Band; Hon Roll; Bloomsburg U; Comp Sci.

WEST, MARK; Cumberland Valley HS; Camp Hill, PA; (3); 168/584; Nwsp Phtg; Var L Bsktbl; JV L Socr; Bus.

WEST, MASON; Pine Forge Acad; Anchorage, AK; (3); 3/68; FBLA; Spanish Clb; Church Choir; Yrbk Phtg; Pres Stu Cncl; JV Bsktbl; Im Ftbl; Var Vllybl; Cit Awd; Oakwood Coll; Acctg.

WEST, MYRON; Chester HS; Chester, PA; (3); Church Yth Grp; Church Choir; JV Wrstlng; Hon Roll; Admin Asst.

WEST, NICOLE A; Mt St Joseph Acad; Philadelphia, PA; (4); Drama Clb; Hosp Aide; JCL; Latin Clb; Office Aide; Chorus; Madrigals; School Musical; Stage Crew; Im Bsktbl; Black Incentive Schlrshp PA St U 87; Latin Hnr Society 87; Philadelphia Classicl Society Cum Laud 86; La Salle U; Psychology.

WEST, STEFANI; Lawrence County Vo Tech; New Castle, PA; (3); 4-H; FBLA; Chorus; Variety Show; Nwsp Stf; Rep Soph Cls; Rep Jr Cls; Rep Sr Cls; Bowling; Awds Excel Dntl Med Secy Shop Cls 86-87; Elem Ed.

WEST, WHITNEY; Philadelphia H S For Girls; Philadelphia, PA; (3); Chrmn Service Clb; Rep Frsh Cls; Rep Soph Cls; Rep Jr Cls; Chrmn Stu Cncl; Var Bowling; Var Vllybl; Hon Roll; NHS; Camera Clb; Latin Hnr Soc 86-87; Vet.

WESTBROOK, CYNTHIA; Elkland Area HS; Elkland, PA; (4); 8/83; Sec Trs Drama Clb; SADD; Varsity Clb; Band; Mrchg Band; Var Cheerleading; High Hon Roll; Hon Roll; Trs NHS; Pres Schlr; Prnclpls Awd 86-87; Slippery Rock U PA; Accntng.

WESTCOTT, MARTI; Neshannock HS; New Castle, PA; (3); 8/114; Church Yth Grp; Band; Concert Band; Mrchg Band; Orch; Pep Band; School Musical; Var L Tennis; NHS; Prfct Atten Awd.

WESTCOTT, STEVEN; St Josephs Prep Schl; Wyndmoor, PA; (4); 89/226; Drama Clb; French Clb; Library Aide; Ski Clb; Thesps; Chorus; School Musical; School Play; Nwsp Rptr; Lit Mag; Fordham U; Law.

WESTERGOM, KATHY; Kiski Area HS; Vandergrift, PA; (3); Church Yth Grp; Girl Scts; Pep Clb; Spanish Clb; SADD; Teachers Aide; Band; School Musical; School Play; Variety Show; Sci.

WESTERMEIER, HEIDI; Cumberland Valley HS; Mechanicsburg, PA; (3); 48/578; Band; Concert Band; Drm Mjr(t); Mrchg Band; Orch; School Musical; Symp Band; French Hon Soc; High Hon Roll; Hon Roll.

WESTFIELD, JOSEPH; Monsignor Bonner HS; Lansdowne, PA; (3); Boys Clb Am; Socr; Theolgy Awd 85.

WESTLAKE, AMY; Marple Newtown SR HS; Broomall, PA; (3); 32/322; Band; Concert Band; Drm & Bgl; Drm Mjr(t); Jazz Band; Mrchg Band; Orch; Symp Band; JV Vllybl; Hon Roll.

WESTON, AMY; Franklin Regional SR HS; Murrysville, PA; (3); AFS; Church Yth Grp; French Clb; Band; Color Guard; Yrbk Stf; High Hon Roll; Hon Roll; Bible Quiz Team Champions 86-87; Education.

WESTON, ANNE D; J P Mc Caskey HS; Lancaster, PA; (4); Drama Clb; Q&S; Orch; NHS; Pres Schlr; AFS; Church Yth Grp; Band; Chorus; Church Choir; 1st PA Stu Pub Assoc Extmprns News Wrtng Cntst 86; Franklin & Marshall Coll Bk Awd 87; Keystone Awds; Wheaton Coll; Chem.

WESTON II, JOHN LEE; Cambridge Springs HS; Waterford, PA; (2); 13/99; 4-H; SADD; Bsbl; Bsktbl; VP 4-H Clb 85-86; Res Champ Steer 83-86; PA ST; Agri-Bus.

WESTON, RICHARD; Montoursville HS; Montoursville, PA; (3); 65/185; German Clb; Concert Band; Mrchg Band; Pep Band; Penn ST Altoona; Elec Engrng.

WESTOVER, KATHY; Uniontown SR HS; Uniontown, PA; (3); High Hon Roll; WV Coll; Accntnt.

WESTPHAL, MICHELLE; Strath Halen HS; Swarthmore, PA; (3); Hosp Aide; Teachers Aide; Nwsp Sprt Ed; JV Var Fld Hcky; JV Capt Lcrss; JV Socr; Var Swmmng; JV Tennis; High Hon Roll; Wmn Engrng Awd JR Wmn Math & Sci 87; Rtry Stu Mnth 87; Stu Wrtng Cmpttn Hon Mntn 86.

WETHMAN, KATHLEEN; Downingtown HS; Exton, PA; (3); 64/648; Church Yth Grp; Drama Clb; Pres Acpl Chr; Band; Concert Band; Drm Mjr(t); Mrchg Band; School Musical; Hon Roll; NHS; Natl Educ Devel Test Awd; Ldrshp Awd.

WETMORE, LISA; Towanda Area HS; Towanda, PA; (3); 19/168; Art Clb; Church Yth Grp; Drama Clb; French Clb; Girl Scts; Hon Roll; Fete Frncs 1st Pl Rbbn 87; Math.

WETSCHLER, LEAN; Bishop Carroll HS; Westover, PA; (3); 73/128; NFL; SADD; Color Guard; Yrbk Stf; Crs Cntry; Cmnty Wkr; Duquesne Coll; Jrnlsm.

WETZEL, ANDREA; Allentown Central Catholic HS; Allentown, PA; (4); Im JV Bsktbl; Var L Vllybl; High Hon Roll; Hon Roll; S J Daday Awd In Bus Ed 87; Blmsbrg U; Accntng.

WETZEL, ANGELA; Marion Center Area HS; Marion Center, PA; (4); Church Yth Grp; VP Q&S; Science Clb; SADD; Chorus; Jazz Band; Orch; Ed Yrbk Ed-Chief; High Hon Roll; NHS; Bob Jones U; Brdcst Jrnlsm.

WETZEL, BRENDA; Reynolds HS; Fredonia, PA; (4); 12/146; Latin Clb; Political Wkr; Madrigals; Var L Crs Cntry; Var Mat Maids; Var L Trk; NHS; Church Yth Grp; 4-H; GAA; Ambsdr Awds For Sprtmnshp Crs Cntry Trk 86-87; Acad All Amercn Awd 86; Heritage Acad Schlrshp 87; Mt Union Coll; Sports Med.

WETZEL, BRYAN; Curwensville HS; Curwensville, PA; (3); Letterman Clb; Varsity Clb; School Musical; Stage Crew; Var L Ftbl; Wt Lftg; Var L Wrstlng; Hon Roll.

WETZEL, CURTIS; Garnet Valley HS; Boothwyn, PA; (4); 14/156; Church Yth Grp; Model UN; Ski Clb; Spanish Clb; Varsity Clb; Variety Show; VP Soph Cls; Var Ftbl; Wt Lftg; Var Wrstlng; Garnet Vly Ftbl Schlr/Athlt Awd & Stu Mnth Awd 86; John Hopkins Tlnt Srch 82; Med.

WETZEL, DOUGLAS; Fairfield HS; Fairfield, PA; (3); 4-H; FFA; Trk; 4-H Awd; Hon Roll; ST FFA Agrnmy 1st Pl 85; 4-H FFA Pblc Spkng 85-86; Prlmntry Procdre Tm 85; Penn ST; Prod Ag.

WETZEL, HENRY; Haverford SR HS; Havertown, PA; (3); 93/423; Band; Jazz Band; Mrchg Band; Stage Crew; Symp Band; JV Trk; Hon Roll; Agronomy.

WETZEL, MAYA CHRISTINE; Beaver Area HS; Beaver, PA; (4); 61/177; FCA; French Clb; Nwsp Stf; Ed Yrbk Phtg; Ed Yrbk Rptr; Yrbk Stf; Ed Lit Mag; Var L Bsktbl; Var L Trk; Var L Vllybl; 8 Vrsty & Athl Lttrs 83-87; Natl Athl Recruitng Guide, & Discus Record 86; PA ST U; Comm.

WETZEL, RICH; Fairfield HS; Fairfield, PA; (3); Church Yth Grp; 4-H; FFA; Socr; Trk; 4-H Awd; Hon Roll; PA FFA St Agronomy Winner 85; 4-H & FFA St Public Speaking 86; Envir Olympics 86-87; PA ST; Animal Prod.

WETZLER, DAVE; Juniata HS; Mifflintown, PA; (3); SADD; Varsity Clb; School Play; VP Jr Cls; JV L Bsbl; JV Var Bsktbl; Hon Roll; NHS; PA ST U; Arspc Engrng.

WEVODAU, EDWARD; Mechanicsburg Area SR HS; Mechanicsburg, PA; (2); 28/309; Church Yth Grp; Band; Mrchg Band; Hon Roll; Tv Film Prod.

WEYANDT, CHRISTINE; Penn Cambria HS; Lilly, PA; (3); Hon Roll; Bus.

WEYANT, JIM; Chestnut Ridge SR HS; New Paris, PA; (3); 5/141; Church Yth Grp; VP JA; Rep Stu Cncl; Var L Bsktbl; Var L Ftbl; Bausch & Lomb Sci Awd; Dnfth Awd; VP NHS; Voice Dem Awd; Cmnty Wkr; Hugh O Brien Ldrshp Awd 86; Hnrbl Mntn Al-Cnty Ftbl 86; NST Natl Hnr Soc Ldrshp Awds 87; Service Acad; Engrng.

WEYER, LAURA; Linden Hall HS; Columbia, PA; (3); FFA; Nwsp Rptr; Nwsp Stf; Trk; Hon Roll; 4-H; Red Cross Aide; Church Choir; Bst Adv Ridr 86-87; M A Gregory Mem Awd 86-87; Equine Mgmt.

WEYERS, CHERYL; Peters Township HS; Mcmurray, PA; (2); Church Yth Grp; NFL; Science Clb; Spanish Clb; High Hon Roll; Pres Schlr; Spanish NHS; 1st Pl-Lang Compttn CA :St U-Spnsh Cmprhnsn 86; Med.

WEYMAN, DALE; Seneca Valley HS; Zelienople, PA; (3); Church Yth Grp; Band; Symp Band; Var L Bsbl; Slppry Rock ST Coll; Elem Edu.

WEYMAN, HEATHER; Seneca Valley HS; Harmony, PA; (4); Ski Clb; Im Bsktbl; Sftbl; Hon Roll; Clarion U.

WEZNER, JOSEPH; Hazleton HS; Hazleton, PA; (2); German Clb; Scholastic Bowl; Ski Clb; JV Bsktbl; JV Ftbl; High Hon Roll; Am Lgn Awd 85.

WHALEN, JAMES; Monsignor Bonner HS; Drexel Hill, PA; (3); 70/280; Library Aide; Pep Clb; SADD; Nwsp Rptr; Im Bsktbl; Var Ftbl; Var Mgr(s); Im Wt Lftg; MVP Shore Bsktbl Camp 86-88; MVP Bill Mc Donough Cmp 86; Engr.

WHALEN, JOSEPH; Mahanoy Area HS; Barnesville, PA; (3); Boy Scts; Church Yth Grp; Spanish Clb; Stage Crew; Nwsp Stf; Crs Cntry; L Trk; High Hon Roll; Hon Roll; NHS.

WHALEN, KATHLEEN; Penn Hills SR HS; Pittsburgh, PA; (3); 207/707; Spanish Clb; Robert Morris Coll; Amin Spclst.

WHALEN, MATTHEW J; Northeast HS; Philadelphia, PA; (4); Boy Scts; Radio Clb; Science Clb; Gym; Drexel; Engr.

WHALEN, SHERRY; Immaculate Conception HS; Canonsburg, PA; (3); 7/40; Exploring; Letterman Clb; Nwsp Sprt Ed; Yrbk Stf; Pres Jr Cls; Pres Sr Cls; Capt Cheerleading; Mgr(s); Hon Roll; NHS; Bio.

WHAPHAM, RICHARD; Danville Area HS; Danville, PA; (3); 94/187; Church Yth Grp; Comp Sci.

WHARTENBY, TRACEY; St Hubert HS; Philadelphia, PA; (4); 2/364; Math Clb; Math Tm; Pres Spanish Clb; Nwsp Ed-Chief; Yrbk Stf; Mgr Swmmng; Hon Roll; NHS; Physcs Awd 87; Spnsh Awd 87; Pres Acdmc Fit Awd 87; Villanova U; Intl Bus.

WHARTON, TOM; Dunmore HS; Dunmore, PA; (3); Boys Clb Am; Boy Scts; VICA; Hon Roll; Elctrcn.

WHEATLEY, MEGAN ELIZABETH; Wyoming Valley West HS; Kingston, PA; (3); Key Clb; Drm Mjr(t); Jazz Band; Mrchg Band; Yrbk Phtg; Cit Awd; High Hon Roll; NHS; Sal; Band; Dstrct Hstry Day 3rd Pl 86 & 87; Music Educ.

WHEATON, RENEE; Northeast Bradford HS; Warren Center, PA; (3); Church Yth Grp; Library Aide; Band; Chorus; Mrchg Band; JV Bsktbl; L Sftbl; Bus Adm.

WHEELAND, ANDREW; Hughesville HS; Montoursville, PA; (2); Aud/Vis; French Clb; Library Aide; Hon Roll; JETS Awd; Comp Sci.

WHEELER, AMY; Knoch HS; Butler, PA; (4); German Clb; SADD; Band; Concert Band; Mrchg Band; Pep Band; School Musical; School Play; Stage Crew; Yrbk Stf; Butler Cnty Jr Miss Fnlst 87; Outstdng Stu Cncl Mbr 87; Johnson & Wales Coll; Hotel.

WHEELER, BRUCE; Penn Cambria HS; Lilly, PA; (2); Pep Clb; Ski Clb; Spanish Clb; SADD; Varsity Clb; Bsbl; Ftbl; Wt Lftg; Hon Roll; NHS; Schlstc Amrcn; US Navl Acad.

WHEELER, JAMES; Minersville HS; Minersville, PA; (3); 10/94; Boy Scts; Ski Clb; School Play; Stage Crew; VP Frsh Cls; Var Ftbl; Wt Lftg; High Hon Roll; Hon Roll; NHS.

WHEELER, JENNIFER; Washington HS; Washington, PA; (2); Sec Church Yth Grp; Dance Clb; Hosp Aide; Spanish Clb; SADD; Church Choir; Orch; Trk; Twrlr; Hon Roll; Trk Cntry Cnfrnc 1st Pl Trpl Jmp 87; Trk ST Smfnls WPIAL PIAA Dist VII 5th Pl 87; Pharm.

WHEELER, KELVIN A; Chestnut Hill Acad; Philadelphia, PA; (4); Hosp Aide; School Play; Nwsp Stf; JV Socr; Var Trk; Hon Roll; Ntl Merit Ltr; Ntl Achvt Fnlst 87.

WHEELER, LINDA; Nazareth Acad; Phila, PA; (3); GAA; Latin Clb; Chorus; School Musical; Stu Cncl; Bsktbl; Tennis; Hon Roll; Magna Cm Laud Ltn Awd 85-86; St Joseph U; Pre-Med.

WHEELER, ROBYN; West Middlesex HS; Mercer, PA; (4); 9/94; FBLA; FNA; Office Aide; Capt Flag Corp; High Hon Roll; Jr NHS; NHS; Pres Acad Ftns Awd 85-86; Bryant; Exec Sec.

WHEELER, SARA; Schuylkill Haven HS; Auburn, PA; (3); 13/82; Church Yth Grp; Hosp Aide; Science Clb; Spanish Clb; SADD; Yrbk Stf; JV Cheerleading; Hon Roll; Bio 1st Prize 85; Millersville U; Psych.

WHEELER, SHELLY; Curwensville HS; Grampian, PA; (3); Drama Clb; 4-H; French Clb; Band; Chorus; Mrchg Band; Var Capt Twrlr; 4-H Awd; Hon Roll; Acad All Amer 87; U Of PA; Elem Educ.

WHEELER, TODD; Lewistown Area HS; Lewistown, PA; (3); Pres Church Yth Grp; Computer Clb; German Clb; Chorus; Church Choir; JV Ftbl; High Hon Roll; Hon Roll; Penn ST; Engr.

WHEELING, KELLY; Maplewood HS; Titusville, PA; (3); VP Church Yth Grp; Office Aide; Pep Clb; Varsity Clb; Capt JV Cheerleading; Sftbl; Mass Comm.

WHEELING, PAULA; Venango Christian HS; Oil City, PA; (3); 16/35; Cmnty Wkr; SADD; Varsity Clb; Variety Show; Nwsp Ed-Chief; Nwsp Rptr; Nwsp Stf; Sftbl; Hon Roll; Cranberry Fstvl Queen 87; Acctnt.

WHELAND, TAMMY; Tyrone Area HS; Tyrone, PA; (3); Church Yth Grp; French Clb; SADD; French Hon Soc; Hon Roll; Postv Attd & Effrt Swng 85-86; Soc Wrk.

WHERRY, JACQUELINE; Western Beaver HS; Beaver, PA; (2); Church Yth Grp; Drama Clb; 4-H; FHA; Girl Scts; JA; Sec Office Aide; Pep Clb; Band; Concert Band; Pep Club Awd, Drama Awd CCBC 85; Beauty Pgnt Awd 86; Carnegie Weslon U; Bus Acctg.

WHERTHEY, CHRISTOPHER; Neshannock HS; New Castle, PA; (4); 8/113; Church Yth Grp; Science Clb; Band; Concert Band; Jazz Band; Mrchg Band; Pep Band; School Musical; Stage Crew; Im Bsktbl; Tri-Cnty 1st Long Jump,4th 400-M Relay 87; Art Show 3rd Pl 86,Hon Ment 87; Certachvt 83 & 85; Svc Awd; PA ST U; Bio.

WHETSEL, KENNY; Connellsville Area SR HS; Connellsville, PA; (2); Church Yth Grp; JV Bsktbl; Ftbl; Mgr(s); Elks Awd; Hon Roll; VFW Awd.

WHETSTONE, JODY; Chestnut Ridge SR HS; Manns Choice, PA; (4); 13/132; Pres SADD; Concert Band; Mrchg Band; Nwsp Rptr; Stu Cncl; Gov Hon Prg Awd; High Hon Roll; NHS; Pres Schlr; Var Bsktbl; Alleghany CC; Marine Bio.

WHETUNG, CARLA; Brandywine Heights HS; Topton, PA; (3); 3/126; Am Leg Aux Girls St; VP Church Yth Grp; Chorus; Mrchg Band; Variety Show; VP Frsh Cls; VP Soph Cls; VP Jr Cls; Pres Sec Stu Cncl; Var Cheerleading; Jr Miss 87.

WHETUNG, PAULA; Brandywine Heights HS; Topton, PA; (2); Band; Chorus; Drm Mjr(t); Pres Frsh Cls; Pres Soph Cls; Stu Cncl; Var Bsktbl; Var Fld Hcky; Hon Roll; NHS; Bus Adm.

WHIPKEY, DUANE; Rockwood Area HS; Rockwood, PA; (2); Church Yth Grp; Cmnty Wkr; Band; Mrchg Band; School Play; Socr; High Hon Roll; Hon Roll; NHS.

WHIPKEY, LACEY; Moniteau HS; Butler, PA; (3); Church Yth Grp; Cmnty Wkr; French Clb; VICA; Chorus; Church Choir; Variety Show; High Hon Roll; Hon Roll; NHS; Phys Thrpy.

WHIPPLE, BRIAN; Wyoming Area HS; Pittston, PA; (3); Church Yth Grp; German Clb; Key Clb; Ski Clb; Crs Cntry; Trk; Hon Roll; Envr Sci.

WHIPPLE, ERIC; Lake Lehman HS; Shavertown, PA; (2); Hon Roll; NHS; NEDT Awd.

WHISLER, JULIE; Elizabethtown Area HS; Elizabethtown, PA; (3); 1/259; Church Yth Grp; High Hon Roll; NHS; Ntl Merit Ltr; Lancaster Cnty Schlstc Awd Gld Key Wnnr 87; Amer Chemcl Soc Awd 87; Art.

WHITAKER, AMY; Penn Trafford HS; Trafford, PA; (3); Latin Clb; Varsity Clb; Chorus; Swmmng; Tennis; Trk; High Hon Roll; Hon Roll; Swmmg Ltr 85-87; Ten Ltr 86.

WHITAKER, B LEE; Downingtown SR HS; Exton, PA; (4); 30/523; Letterman Clb; Ski Clb; Spanish Clb; Var L Bsbl; Im Bsktbl; Var L Ftbl; Im Vllybl; High Hon Roll; NHS; Miami U; Med.

WHITAKER, KAREN; East Pennsboro HS; Enola, PA; (3); Band; School Play; Nwsp Rptr; Var Capt Cheerleading; Twrlr; Hon Roll; Big 33 Chrldr 87; Jrnlsm.

WHITCO, MICHELLE; Washington HS; Washington, PA; (4); 18/150; French Clb; Key Clb; SADD; Varsity Clb; Var Capt Bsktbl; Var Capt Tennis; High Hon Roll; Hon Roll; Pres Schlr; Elizabeth Stewart Schlrshp 87; Thiel Coll; Accntng.

WHITCOMB, CHRISTINA; Boiling Springs HS; Boiling Spgs, PA; (2); 32/150; Chess Clb; Sec Trs Girl Scts; Red Cross Aide; Stat Bsktbl; Mgr(s); JV Sftbl; Im Vllybl; Hon Roll; Voice Dem Awd; Schltc Wrtg Gold Key Essay 87; Cert De Comp Espanol III 87; CASAC Sci Fair Hnrb Mntn 86; Lang Art.

WHITCOMB, KRENA; South Middleton HS; Boiling Spgs, PA; (2); Chess Clb; Church Yth Grp; Chorus; Church Choir; JV Var Bsktbl; JV Fld Hcky; JV Sftbl.

WHITE, ANDREA; Phila HS For Girls; Philadelphia, PA; (3); 101/405; Service Clb; Spanish Clb; Teachers Aide; Nwsp Ed-Chief; Rep Frsh Cls; Sec Stu Cncl; Cit Awd; Hon Roll; JC Awd; Civic Clb; Black History Oratorical Contest Fnlst 87; Jrnlsm.

WHITE, BETH; Conestoga Valley HS; Lancaster, PA; (3); Art Clb; Church Yth Grp; Dance Clb; SADD; Yrbk Stf; Sftbl; Schlstc Art Awd 84-85, 86-87; Fshn Mrchndsng.

WHITE, BRIAN K; Valley HS; New Kensington, PA; (2); Varsity Clb; Nwsp Sprt Ed; Nwsp Stf; Yrbk Sprt Ed; Yrbk Stf; Off Soph Cls; Pres Jr Cls; Var Capt Bsktbl; L Var Ftbl; Hon Roll; Accntng.

WHITE, CAMERON; Waynesboro Area SR HS; Waynesboro, PA; (4); Pres Church Yth Grp; Band; Concert Band; Orch; Rep Soph Cls; Rep Jr Cls; Rep Sr Cls; JV Im Bsktbl; Hon Roll; Prfct Atten Awd; Instrmntlst Mgzine Musicianship Awd 87; Penn ST; Engr.

WHITE, DANNY; Uniontown Area SR HS; Vanderbilt, PA; (3); Band; Concert Band; Mrchg Band; Nwsp Rptr; VP Jr Cls; Stat Bsktbl; Golf; DAR Awd; NHS; Spanish NHS; Law.

WHITE, DAVE; Reynolds HS; Greenville, PA; (3); FFA; Ski Clb; Spanish Clb; Varsity Clb; Band; Chorus; Mrchg Band; VP Soph Cls; Stu Cncl; Trk; Pittsburgh Tech Inst; CCAD.

WHITE, DEBRA J; Fort Le Boeuf HS; Erie, PA; (3); 12/207; Var L Vllybl; High Hon Roll; NHS; Acad Achvmnt Awd 84-87; Phrmcy.

WHITE, DONNA; Carbondale Area HS; Carbondale, PA; (3); Art Clb; Hosp Aide; Spanish Clb; Color Guard; Drill Tm; Bsktbl; Sftbl; Hon Roll; Mgmt.

WHITE, DWAYNE D; Lock Haven SR HS; Lock Haven, PA; (4); 26/242; Computer Clb; VP Model UN; SADD; Kngts Of Colum Awd Exclince Comp Sci; Walter Gonz Memorl Initiative; Lock Haven U; Comp Sci.

WHITE, EDNA; Lewiston Area HS; Granville, PA; (4); 22/248; AFS; Pres 4-H; Trs Key Clb; Trs Pep Clb; Ski Clb; Hst Sr Cls; Stu Cncl; Cheerleading; High Hon Roll; NHS; Villanova U.

WHITE, GINA; Abington Heights-N Campus HS; Clarks Summit, PA; (3); 47/243; Cmnty Wkr; Rep Stu Cncl; Hon Roll; Recgntn Brkfst 87; Mrch Of Dimes Walk A Thn 85.

WHITE, GLENN; Chief Logan HS; Lewistown, PA; (4); 78/183; Art Clb; Computer Clb; Key Clb; SADD; Varsity Clb; Bsktbl; Hon Roll; Schltc Arts Awd PA ST U 86; 1st Pl Mifflin Juniata Arts Fest 86; York Coll; Mktng.

WHITE, GREG; Governor Mifflin SR HS; Shillington, PA; (4); 18/300; Q&S; VP Sr Cls; VP Stu Cncl; Cit Awd; Aud/Vis; Drama Clb; Key Clb; Model UN; Chorus; School Musical; Maxwell Ctznshp Educ Conf 87; Syracuse U; Brdcstng.

WHITE, JAMES; Sayre Area HS; S Waverly, PA; (3); JV Wrstlng; Hon Roll; Prfct Atten Awd; Art.

WHITE, JENNIFER; Sacred Heart HS; Union Dale, PA; (3); Art Clb; Cmnty Wkr; Ski Clb; SADD; Rep Jr Cls; Hon Roll; U Of Scranton; Acctg.

WHITE, JIM; Upper Merion Area HS; King Of Prussia, PA; (4); 2/300; Math Tm; Capt Bsktbl; Var Ftbl; Var Trk; NHS; Pres Schlr; Rotary Awd; Sal; Natl Exch Club Yth Mnth 86; King Prussia Park Assn Scholar 87; J Vood Platt Caddy Scholar 87; Carnegie Mellon U; Math.

WHITE, KALIMAH; West Perry HS; New Bloomfield, PA; (1); 11/235; Drama Clb; Spanish Clb; Varsity Clb; School Play; Yrbk Stf; Stu Cncl; JV Fld Hcky; JV Trk; Hon Roll; NHS; Lwyr.

WHITE, KAREN; Lake-Lehman HS; Harveys Lake, PA; (2); 1/192; Church Yth Grp; Spanish Clb; JV Bsktbl; JV Fld Hcky; JV Sftbl; High Hon Roll; Jr NHS; NHS; Med.

WHITE, KAREN; Sun Valley HS; Parkside, PA; (3); 63/270; JV Fld Hcky; JV Lcrss; Var Sftbl; Hon Roll; Htl Manag.

WHITE, KIM; Pocono Mountain HS; Canadensis, PA; (3); 17/320; SADD; Capt Mrchg Band; Stat Bsktbl; Hon Roll; NHS; Capt Color Guard; Vrsty Ltrmn Rifl Tm 85-87; Hugh O Brian Ldrshp Awd Wnnr & Outstndng Cnty Coord 86 & 87; Chem.

WHITE, KIMBERLY; Fort Cherry JR SR HS; Mcdonald, PA; (3); Exploring; FNA; Hosp Aide; Science Clb; Band; Chorus; Twrlr; High Hon Roll; Hon Roll; NHS; Hlth Admin.

WHITE, KISHA; Bok A V T Schl; Philadelphia, PA; (3); Variety Show; Off Jr Cls; Bsktbl; Mrt Awd Outstndng Geom 86; Bsktbl Cert 86-87; U VA; Comp Sci.

WHITE, LASHONDA T; John Harris Campus HS; Harrisburg, PA; (1); 4/468; Band; Jazz Band; Mrchg Band; Var Trk; High Hon Roll; Hon Roll; Opt Clb Awd; Harvard U; Marine Bio.

WHITE, LEANN; Clearfield Area HS; Olanta, PA; (4); Church Yth Grp; French Clb; Key Clb; Library Aide; Office Aide; Flag Corp; Mrchg Band; JV Bowling; Var Twrlr; Hon Roll; Dubois Bus Coll; Acctng.

WHITE, LEE-ANNE; Mifflinburg Area HS; Mifflinburg, PA; (1); Church Yth Grp; FHA; Spanish Clb; Variety Show; Bsktbl; Socr; Swmmng; Trk; High Hon Roll; Hon Roll; Pitt U; Engrng.

WHITE, LISA; Council Rock HS; Newtown, PA; (3); Drama Clb; Girl Scts; School Play; Stage Crew; Drama Club Star 87; Drama Letter 86; Drama Cert 85; Comm.

WHITE, LISA; Fort Cherry HS; Hickory, PA; (2); Math Clb; Science Clb; Ski Clb; Spanish Clb; Chorus; Drill Tm; Pom Pon; High Hon Roll; Hon Roll; Mdcl Sec.

WHITE, LORI; Fairview HS; Fairview, PA; (3); French Clb; NFL; Speech Tm; Nwsp Stf; Trk; Var Ntl Merit Ltr; Drama.

WHITE, MARCI; Punxsutawney Area HS; Punxsutawney, PA; (4); 188/256; Drama Clb; GAA; Pep Clb; Spanish Clb; Varsity Clb; Variety Show; Rep Frsh Cls; Rep Jr Cls; Bsktbl; Cheerleading; Natl Chrldng Coed Champs 87; Clarion U Of PA; Child Educ.

WHITE, MARTHA-LYNN; Haverford HS; Bryn Mawr, PA; (3); 2/395; Pres Church Yth Grp; Service Clb; Ski Clb; Orch; Var Tennis; JV Trk; High Hon Roll; NHS; Stu Of Mnth 87; Harvard Prize Book 87.

WHITE, MARY BETH; Rocky Grove JR/Sr HS; Franklin, PA; (3); Library Aide; Office Aide; Service Clb; Library Sci.

WHITE, MIKE; Fort Cherry HS; Bulger, PA; (3); Art Clb; Boy Scts; Math Clb; Science Clb; Ftbl; Physcl Ftns 84-87; Art.

WHITE, MOLLY; Lake-Lehman HS; Harveys Lake, PA; (1); 1/200; Church Yth Grp; Concert Band; Mrchg Band; Var Capt Bsktbl; Sftbl; High Hon Roll; Pres Jr NHS; NEDT Awd; Elem Educ.

WHITE, PAUL; Monsignor Bonner HS; Lansdowne, PA; (3); 19/255; Boy Scts; Letterman Clb; Library Aide; Political Wkr; SADD; VP Rep Jr Cls; JV Crs Cntry; Im Ftbl; Var L Trk; French Hon Soc; Alg I Acdmc Awd 85; Mdrn Phys Sci Acdmc Awd 85; All Cathlc Team Indoor Trk 86-87; Vet Med.

WHITE, PHILIP; Trinity HS; Washington, PA; (2); Band; Concert Band; Jazz Band; Mrchg Band; Pep Band; DAR Awd; High Hon Roll; Hon Roll.

WHITE, ROBERT; G A R Memorial HS; Wilkes-Barre, PA; (4); 14/187; Aud/Vis; German Clb; Yrbk Stf; Hon Roll; NHS.

WHITE, ROBERTA; Shenango JR SR HS; New Castle, PA; (4); 11/112; Pres Church Yth Grp; French Clb; Concert Band; Co-Capt Flag Corp; Jazz Band; Stage Crew; Var Capt Bsktbl; Ed Yrbk Stf; Stat Trk; Hon Roll.

WHITE, ROBYN L; Taylor Allderdice HS; Pittsburgh, PA; (4); 26/390; Church Yth Grp; Cmnty Wkr; Hosp Aide; JA; Office Aide; Nwsp Bus Mgr; Nwsp Stf; High Hon Roll; NHS; PA ST U; Bus.

WHITE, SHANNON; Valley HS; Arnold, PA; (3); Art Clb; Drama Clb; Pep Clb; Ski Clb; Spanish Clb; SADD; Varsity Clb; Chorus; Stu Cncl, Stat Ftbl; Elem Educ.

WHITE, SHARON D; Owen J Roberts HS; Spring City, PA; (3); Concert Band; Mrchg Band; Var Fld Hcky; NHS; Varsity Clb; Band; Symp Band; Frsh Cls; JV Sftbl.

WHITE, SHEILA; Central Dauphin HS; Harrisburg, PA; (3); Exploring; Church Choir; Trk; Vllybl; NHS; Ms Initiative 86; Runner Up In Pagent 86; Oritorical Contest 87; Morgan; Bus.

WHITE, SHERI; Ephrata SR HS; Ephrata, PA; (3); Concert Band; Rep Jr Cls; Rep Sr Cls; Rep Stu Cncl; Capt Var Cheerleading; Gov Hon Prg Awd; Hon Roll; VP JA; Pep Clb; Mrchg Band; PA Gov Schl Arts 87; Poem Pblshd Wrld Bk Anthlgy 86; U Hartford; Bus.

WHITE, SHERRY LYNN; Waynesburg Central HS; Jefferson, PA; (4); Art Clb; Pres Church Yth Grp; Computer Clb; Pres Library Aide; SADD; Chorus; Color Guard; Nwsp Stf; High Hon Roll; Hon Roll; Duquesne U; Comp Sci.

WHITE, SUSAN; Mc Guffey HS; Claysville, PA; (3); 20/230; Church Yth Grp; German Clb; Girl Scts; Chorus; School Musical; Variety Show; Var Bsktbl; Var Powder Puff Ftbl; Var Sftbl; Var Tennis; Outstndg Prfrmcne 86; Stu Recog 87; IN U PA; Med Tech.

WHITE, TAMARA; Lutheran HS; Philadelphia, PA; (2); 1/12; Church Yth Grp; Debate Tm; Temple Yth Grp; Nwsp Stf; Rep Frsh Cls; Rep Soph Cls; Stu Cncl; Cheerleading; High Hon Roll; Hon Roll; NC ST U; Fshn Dsgn.

WHITE, THERESA; Pittston Area HS; Pittston, PA; (3); 31/305; Art Clb; French Clb; FNA; Key Clb; Rep SADD; Hon Roll; Med.

WHITE, THERESA; Wallenpaupack Area HS; Hawley, PA; (3); 1/150; Church Yth Grp; Drama Clb; Band; Chorus; Concert Band; Jazz Band; Mrchg Band; School Musical; School Play; High Hon Roll; Dist & Regl Band & Chorus 85-87; Schl Centrl Treas 87-88.

WHITE, TOBI; Lutheran HS; Philadelphia, PA; (3); #1 In Class; Church Yth Grp; Debate Tm; Latin Clb; Temple Yth Grp; Score Keeper; Trk; High Hon Roll; Hon Roll; NC ST U; Comm.

WHITE, TONIA; Mercy Vocational HS; Philadelphia, PA; (4); Cmnty Wkr; Girl Scts; Church Choir; Cheerleading; Pres Schlr; The Concerned Black Men Awd 87; City Of Phil Incentive 84-85 Awd; Spec Awd Try Out Emplymnt 87; Temple U; Hosp Adm.

WHITE, VINCENT; Fort Leboeuf HS; Erie, PA; (4); 20/170; FCA; Letterman Clb; Rep Soph Cls; Bsktbl; Var L Ftbl; L Capt Trk; Wt Lftg; High Hon Roll; All Cnty Ftbll Rngng Bck 86; 3rd 300 M Intermd Hrdls Erie Cntyt Trck Meet 86; Pres Acad Ftns Awd; Lock Haven U Of PA; Sports Med.

WHITE JR, WALTER W; Roman Catholic HS; Philadelphia, PA; (3); 13/136; Church Yth Grp; Cmnty Wkr; JA; Red Cross Aide; SADD; Cit Awd; High Hon Roll; Hon Roll; JV Var Bsbl.

WHITEBREAD, DAWN; Council Rock HS; Richboro, PA; (3); 121/908; Church Yth Grp; Church Choir; Swmmng; Hon Roll; NHS; Spch Thrpy.

WHITED, KELLI; Northern Cambria HS; Barnesboro, PA; (3); 44/152; Spanish Clb; Band; Concert Band; Mrchg Band; Pep Band; Yrbk Stf; High Hon Roll; Hon Roll; Spanish NHS; Cnty Band 85-86; Typng Cert 86-87; Med Sec.

WHITEFORD, JAMES; North Catholic HS; Verona, PA; (3); 35/275; Ski Clb; Var Tennis; High Hon Roll; Hon Roll.

WHITEHEAD, CORI; Norwin SR HS; N Huntingdon, PA; (4); Letterman Clb; Pep Clb; SADD; VICA; Capt Cheerleading; Jr NHS; NHS; Ms Cngnlty-Ms Al Am Chrldr Pgnt 87; Csmtlgy.

WHITEHEAD, TAMMY; Hempfield Area SR HS; Youngwood, PA; (3); Art Clb; Hosp Aide; Red Cross Aide; Intl Order Of Jobs Daughters-Hnrd Queen 86-87; Pitts Beauty Acad; Sec.

WHITEMAN, JAMES; Faith Christian HS; Pittsburgh, PA; (2); Church Yth Grp; Nwsp Stf; Yrbk Stf; Rep Soph Cls; JV Var Bsktbl; Var Sftbl; U Of Pittsburgh; Bus Manag.

WHITEMAN, LISA; Elk County Christian HS; St Marys, PA; (4); Ski Clb; Varsity Clb; Church Choir; Rep Soph Cls; Rep Sr Cls; Rep Stu Cncl; JV Var Bsktbl; JV Var Vllybl; High Hon Roll; Daemen Coll; Physcl Thrpy.

WHITEMAN, TRACY L; Serra Catholic HS; Mc Keesport, PA; (4); 46/158; AFS; Pres Exploring; JA; Q&S; Co-Capt Color Guard; Stage Crew; Yrbk Ed-Chief; Stat Bsktbl; Var Powder Puff Ftbl; U Pittsburgh; Chem.

WHITENIGHT, CATHY; Hazleton HS; Hazleton, PA; (3); Office Aide; Pep Clb; Band; Concert Band; Mrchg Band; Pep Band; Hon Roll.

WHITENIGHT, REBECCA; Danville JR HS; Danville, PA; (1); Church Yth Grp; Teachers Aide; Color Guard; Flag Corp; Mrchg Band; High Hon Roll; Prfct Atten Awd; Physcl Thrpst.

WHITFORD, JEFFREY; Moon Area SR HS; Coraopolis, PA; (2); Exploring; Ski Clb; Socr; Trk; Wrstlng; Hon Roll; Prfct Atten Awd; Aerontcl.

WHITING, MICHONDA; Wilmington Area HS; New Wilmington, PA; (3); 30/110; Dance Clb; Drama Clb; 4-H; Office Aide; Concert Band; Drill Tm; School Play; Bsktbl; Cheerleading; Powder Puff Ftbl; Engrng.

WHITLEY, APRILAURIE; Mining & Mechanical Inst; Conyngham, PA; (3); Pep Clb; Ski Clb; L Bowling; Mgr(s); Score Keeper; Co-Capt Sftbl; Hon Roll; NEDT Awd; Trs Frsh Cls; Pres Soph Cls; Sftbl MVP 85 & 86; Psychlgy.

WHITLING, HEIDI; Keystone HS; Knox, PA; (3); 5/135; Pres Sec 4-H; Math Tm; Model UN; Office Aide; Pep Clb; School Musical; Stat School Play; Yrbk Bus Mgr; 4-H Awd; NHS; Rotary Yth Ldrshp Awd 87; Legistrtv Schl Art Show 87; Clarion Rotary Outstndg Stu Svc Awd 87; Fash Dsgn.

WHITMAN, JEFFREY; Cumberland Valley HS; Boiling Spgs, PA; (3); 94/585; Trs Church Yth Grp; Latin Clb; JV Trk; Hon Roll; Capital Area Classics Fest 2nd 85-86; Athl Trng JV & V Athl Awds 84-87; Bio-Chem.

WHITMAN, JUDI; Pennsbury HS; Yardley, PA; (4); 109/771; Intnl Clb; Flag Corp; Yrbk Phtg; Yrbk Stf; Var Trk; Brdcstng.

WHITMAN, KRISTEN; Technical Memorial HS; Erie, PA; (3); 27/331; FBLA; Girl Scts; SADD; Band; Bsktbl; Cheerleading; Hon Roll; Bradford Schl Of Bus; Legl Sec.

WHITMER, ELIZABETH; Karns City HS; Chicora, PA; (3); 3/100; FCA; VP Soph Cls; Stu Cncl; L Bsktbl; Score Keeper; L Trk; L Vllybl; Cit Awd; High Hon Roll; Hon Roll; Marines Dstngshd Athl Awd 87; Clarion Cnty Leag MVP Bsktbl 87; Mrshl 87; U Of MD; Acctng.

WHITMER, JANEL; Ft Le Boeuf HS; Waterford, PA; (3); Pres Trs Church Yth Grp; Chorus; Church Choir; School Musical; School Play; Rep Soph Cls; Pres Jr Cls; Score Keeper; High Hon Roll; Pres NHS.

WHITMIRE, AMY; Cedar Crest HS; Lebanon, PA; (3); 45/300; Church Yth Grp; Key Clb; Pep Clb; Spanish Clb; SADD; Chorus; Church Choir; School Musical; Mgr Swmmng; NHS.

WHITMORE, KATE; State College Area HS; State College, PA; (3); 31/580; German Clb; SADD; Rep Frsh Cls; Rep Soph Cls; Rep Sr Cls; Var Capt Fld Hcky; Im Socr; Cit Awd; Hon Roll; Prfct Atten Awd; U Of CA Berkeley; Law.

WHITMOYER, JEREMY R; Northern Lebanon HS; Lebanon, PA; (2); 21/208; Boy Scts; Quiz Bowl; Im JV Bsktbl; Hon Roll; Forestry.

WHITMYRE, WENDY; Milton SR HS; Milton, PA; (4); FHA; Library Aide; Red Cross Aide; Spanish Clb; Yrbk Stf; Hon Roll; EMT.

WHITNEY, JANET; Purchase Line HS; Commodore, PA; (2); FBLA; Chorus; Mrchg Band; Twrlr; High Hon Roll; Hon Roll; Bus.

WHITNEY, RANDY; Heritage Christian Acad; Erie, PA; (2); Computer Clb; Letterman Clb; Var L Bsktbl; Var L Crs Cntry; Var L Socr; Sftbl; High Hon Roll; Hon Roll; Penn ST.

WHITNEY, STEWART; Mountain View HS; Gibson, PA; (2); 17/91; Church Yth Grp; Computer Clb; FCA; Library Aide; Teachers Aide; JV Socr; Awana Clb Hnr Awd 87; Admn Mgmnt.

WHITSEL, KEVIN; Southern Huntingdon HS; Orbisonia, PA; (2); Boy Scts; Church Yth Grp; Dance Clb; 4-H; God Cntry Awd; Most Imprvd Scout Awd 86; Electro-Mechncs.

WHITSON, S LYNNE; Villa Maria Acad; Brookhaven, PA; (3); 28/98; Debate Tm; Latin Clb; Library Aide; NFL; Yrbk Stf; Rep Soph Cls; Stu Cncl; Hon Roll; NCTE Awd; Magna Cum Laude-Phila Clsscl Soc 86; Cum Laude-Phila Clsscl Soc 87; Pre-Med.

WHITTAKER, SUZANNE; Jules E Mastbaum ATVS; Philadelphia, PA; (3); Girl Scts; Trs VICA; Yrbk Stf; Off Soph Cls; Trs Jr Cls; Trs Sr Cls; Off Stu Cncl; High Hon Roll; Hon Roll; Hair Dsgn.

WHORIC, BRIAN; Southmoreland SR HS; Scottdale, PA; (4); Cmnty Wkr; Jr Cls; Sr Cls; WCCC; Paramedic.

WHORIC, TRACY; Connellsville SR HS; Vanderbilt, PA; (3); 72/493; Art Clb; Mrchg Band; Symp Band; Pres Frsh Cls; Pres Soph Cls; VP Jr Cls; High Hon Roll; Hon Roll; Jr NHS; Acad Awd Excllnce 85; Mst Personable Awd 85; Valentine Queen 85; Radlgy.

WHORL, ANGELA; Northeastern HS; Mount Wolf, PA; (3); Church Yth Grp; French Clb; German Clb; Ski Clb; SADD; Band; Chorus; Church Choir; Concert Band; Mrchg Band; Bio.

WHY II, FRANK; Beaver Falls HS; Beaver Falls, PA; (3); 5/170; Church Yth Grp; Science Clb; Pres Spanish Clb; Band; Concert Band; Jazz Band; Mrchg Band; Bsbl; High Hon Roll; NHS; Elec Engrng.

WHYBROW, ALYSON; Harry S Truman HS; Bristol, PA; (3); Pep Clb; SADD; Drill Tm; Mrchg Band; Off Stu Cncl; Cheerleading; Socr; Trk; Twrlr; Hon Roll; PSU.

WHYTE, CHRISTY; Jefferson Morgan HS; Waynesburg, PA; (3); 4/77; Church Yth Grp; Cmnty Wkr; Library Aide; Church Choir; Nwsp Rptr; Nwsp Stf; Yrbk Stf; High Hon Roll; Hosp Aide; Acad All Amer Awd 86; Interact Club Brd Of Directors 86; Secty 87; Chrmn Of Int'l Comm 87; Waynesburg Coll; Nrsg.

WIANT, DENISE; Clarion Area HS; Clarion, PA; (3); Trs FHA; Hosp Aide; Pep Clb; Chorus; Variety Show; Yrbk Stf; High Hon Roll; Hon Roll; NHS; Clarion U PA; Chld Psych.

WIATEROWSKI, TEDDY; John S Fine HS; Nanticoke, PA; (2); Computer Clb; 4-H; VICA; Nwsp Rptr; Nwsp Stf; Hon Roll; Atten Awd 86-87; Comp Pgmmr.

WIBECAN, NISSA; Solebury Schl; Brooklyn, NY; (4); 1/26; Nwsp Ed-Chief; Lit Mag; Rep Stu Cncl; High Hon Roll; Hon Roll; Quill & Scroll Soc Stu Jrnlsts 86; Bothmon Awd For Acdmcs; Bates Coll; Law.

WIBLE, BILL; Butler Area HS; Butler, PA; (3); Band; Concert Band; Jazz Band; Mrchg Band; School Musical; Symp Band; NHS; Dist, Rgnl, St Band 87; Penn ST; Elec Eng.

WICHTERMAN, ANGELINA; Nazareth Acad; Philadelphia, PA; (3); Cmnty Wkr; Service Clb; Spanish Clb; Chorus; School Musical; School Play; Nwsp Rptr; Nwsp Stf; Lit Mag; Hon Roll.

WICK, CHRIS; Seneca Valley HS; Harmony, PA; (3); 43/311; 4-H; Ski Clb; Swmmng; Hon Roll; NHS.

WICKARD, DEBRA; Big Spring HS; Newville, PA; (4); Band; Concert Band; Lit Mag; Hon Roll; Millersville U Of PA; Psych.

WICKENHEISER, SUSAN; Lancaster Catholic HS; Columbia, PA; (3); Church Yth Grp; Girl Scts; Varsity Clb; Church Choir; Nwsp Stf; Yrbk Ed-Chief; Var JV Mgr(s); Var JV Score Keeper; Var JV Sftbl; Paralegal.

WICKIZER, NANCY; Old Forge HS; Old Forge, PA; (4); 6/104; Ski Clb; Yrbk Stf; High Hon Roll; NHS; Acad Fit Awd; Wilkes Coll; Phrmcy.

WICKKISER, ELISABETH; Allentown Central Catholic HS; Allentown, PA; (3); 36/236; Pep Clb; Political Wkr; Ski Clb; Yrbk Stf; High Hon Roll; Hon Roll; NHS; PA JR Acad Sci 1st Pl Awd 85-86; Prncpls Awd 86; Law.

WICKLINE, JOSEPH; Beaver Falls SR HS; Beaver Falls, PA; (3); Army; O R Specialist.

WICKLINE, TAMMY; Moon SR HS; Coraopolis, PA; (3); Chorus; Mgr(s); High Hon Roll; Hon Roll; Bus.

WICKROWSKI, KAREN; Kennard-Dale HS; Stewartstown, PA; (2); Church Yth Grp; Chorus; Church Choir; Color Guard; Mgr(s); Stat Vllybl.

WICKS, MICKEY; Williamson HS; Tioga, PA; (2); Computer Clb; Band; Chorus; Trk; Hon Roll; Prfct Atten Awd; Comp Optr.

WICKS, ROBERTA; Abington Heights HS; Clarks Summit, PA; (3); 103/317; Cmnty Wkr; Ski Clb; Band; Chorus; Concert Band; Jazz Band; Mrchg Band; Pep Band; Swing Chorus; Hon Roll; Shooters Awd 84-87; Coaches Awd In Rifle 84-87; Let Vrsty In Rifle 84-87; Radiology.

WIDDOSS, STEVE; Stroudsburg HS; Analomink, PA; (2); 24/310; French Clb; Im Bowling; Var Trk; High Hon Roll; Hon Roll; Comp Sci.

WIDNER, MICHELE; Daniel Boone SR HS; Birdsboro, PA; (3); 34/174; German Clb; SADD; Stat Bsktbl; Var Capt Crs Cntry; Var L Trk; Sprts Med.

WIDRICK, CARYN; William Allen HS; Allentown, PA; (2); 32/634; Concert Band; Mrchg Band; Orch; Pep Band; Hon Roll; Jr NHS; Church Yth Grp; Band; Dist Band 86 & 87; Rgnl Band & Dist Orch 87; Amer Musical Fndtn Band Hnrs 86; Pre-Med.

WIEAND, ERIC; Danville HS; Milton, PA; (3); Boy Scts; Ski Clb; Rep Frsh Cls; Var Ftbl; Wt Lftg; Hon Roll; Indstrl Arts Awd 85; Math.

WIECZOREK, KEN; Father Judge HS; Philadelphia, PA; (4); #1 In Class; Boys Clb Am; Church Yth Grp; Math Clb; Nwsp Rptr; Ed Yrbk Stf; Var Crs Cntry; Var Trk; High Hon Roll; Hon Roll; Jr NHS; Phi Betta Kappa Awd 87; Outstndng Achvt Schlrshp To Temple U 87; Math Awd 87; Temple U; Phrmcy.

WIEDENHEFT, RICHARD; Tunkhannock Area HS; Falls, PA; (3); 2/330; Chess Clb; Computer Clb; German Clb; Band; Concert Band; Mrchg Band; Frsh Cls; Soph Cls; Jr Cls; Var Socr; Rotary Ldrshp 86.

WIEDL, RENEE; Highlands SR HS; Natrona Hgts, PA; (3); Church Yth Grp; Intnl Clb; Office Aide; Rep Stu Cncl; Var JV Cheerleading; JV Diving; JV Gym; Tennis; Jr NHS; NHS.

WIEGAND, BRIAN; Perry Traditional Acad; Pittsburgh, PA; (3); 10/190; Drama Clb; Math Tm; Band; Concert Band; Mrchg Band; Nwsp Rptr; Var Capt Vllybl; High Hon Roll; NHS; Debate Tm; Awd Cmpltng Toastmstrs Intl Yth Ldrshp Pgm 85; Math.

WIELUNS, DANA CARLE; Great Valley HS; Newtown Square, PA; (4); Co-Capt Debate Tm; VP Drama Clb; NFL; SADD; School Musical; School Play; Nwsp Rptr; Sec NHS; Ntl Merit Ltr; Brown U Book Awd Excllnc 86; Bucks Cnty Drama Fest-Best Acress & Excllnc Perf Play & Musical 87; Princeton U; Liberal Arts.

WIEMANN, KIMBERLY; Seneca Valley HS; Renfrew, PA; (4); 5/347; Church Yth Grp; VP JA; Math Tm; Scholastic Bowl; SADD; Mrchg Band; Lion Awd; Aud/Vis; School Musical; Gym; Amer Legn Ortrcl Cntst Cnty & Dist Wnnr 86-87; Christa Mc Auliffe Sci Ed Schlrshp For PA 87; Allegheny Coll; Sci Ed.

WIENER, JULIE; Taylor Allderdice HS; Pittsburgh, PA; (2); Drama Clb; English Clb; Political Wkr; Ski Clb; Orch; Nwsp Rptr; Nwsp Stf; High Hon Roll; NHS; Point Park Coll Awd For Bst HS News Article 87; Jrnlsm.

WIENING, JONATHAN; Henderson HS; West Chester, PA; (3); 17/354; Church Yth Grp; Debate Tm; Science Clb; Acpl Chr; Chorus; Church Choir; Jazz Band; School Musical; JV Tennis; Hon Roll; Compltn Of Savage Century-100 Mile Bike Ride 86; Alt Govrs Schl Of Arts-Clsscl Guitar 87.

WIERCINSKI, MARISSA; Scranton Prep Schl; Dickson City, PA; (3); Dance Clb; Pep Clb; Cheerleading; Crs Cntry; Hon Roll.

WIERTEL, CINDY; Red Lion SR HS; Red Lion, PA; (3); 14/342; Sec Church Yth Grp; School Musical; Rep Sec Stu Cncl; Var Im Cheerleading; Hon Roll; NHS; Nursing.

WIERZBICKI, EDWARD; Bishop Mc Devitt HS; Harrisburg, PA; (4); 4/180; Pres Church Yth Grp; Computer Clb; Drama Clb; FBLA; Service Clb; Speech Tm; School Play; L Bsbl; L Golf; NHS; Bst Supprtng Role Fresh/Soph Plys 85; Hgh Hnr Rll Awds Outstndng Achvts Acdmcs 83-87; Cert Schlst Wrtg; Dntstry.

WIESEN, NANCY; Sharpsville Area HS; Sharpsville, PA; (3); 10/103; Camera Clb; Chess Clb; Office Aide; Science Clb; Chorus; Flag Corp; Mrchg Band; Yrbk Phtg; Yrbk Stf; Bsktbl; 3-Yr Acadmc Ltrmn 84-87; Chem.

WIESNER, JENNIFER; Montour HS; Pittsburgh, PA; (3); VICA; Rep Frsh Cls; Rep Soph Cls; Rep Jr Cls; Stu Cncl; Trk; High Hon Roll; Hon Roll; Deans List At Parkway West Area Voc Tech Schl 86-87; Cosmetologst.

WIESSERT, JEFF; Highlands SR HS; Brackenridge, PA; (3); Var L Bsbl; Var L Ftbl.

WIEST, RON; Tri-Valley HS; Hegins, PA; (2); #33 In Class; Computer Clb; Letterman Clb; Ski Clb; School Musical; School Play; Bsbl; Bsktbl; Ftbl; Wt Lftg; Hon Roll.

WIEST, WILLIAM; Spring Grove Area SR HS; Porters Sideling, PA; (3); Cmnty Wkr; Letterman Clb; Varsity Clb; Var L Ftbl; Hon Roll; Telecomm.

WIEWIORA, JOY; Northern Cambria HS; Barnesboro, PA; (3); 25/152; Trs Church Yth Grp; Chorus; Church Choir; Concert Band; Drm Mjr(t); Jazz Band; Off Stu Cncl; NHS; Spanish NHS; Jr All Amer Hall Fame Band Hnrs 87; IN U Of PA; Elem Educ.

WIGGINS, BOBBY; Spring-Ford HS; Pottstown, PA; (4); 59/280; VP Frsh Cls; VP Soph Cls; VP Jr Cls; VP Sr Cls; VP Stu Cncl; Ftbl; Trk; Ursinus; Bio.

WIGGINS, GEM; Hershey HS; Hershey, PA; (3); Debate Tm; Nwsp Rptr; Nwsp Stf; Yrbk Stf; Lit Mag; High Hon Roll; Spanish NHS; Voice Dem Awd; Federated Wmns Clb Photo Awd 87; Biola; Communications.

WIGGLESWORTH, CRAIG; Dover Area HS; Dover, PA; (4); 23/237; Chorus; Variety Show; Var L Socr; Var Tennis; Var Trk; High Hon Roll; Hon Roll; NHS; German Clb; Concert Band; Top 10 Pct Grad Cls Medallion 87; Music.

WIKE, LISA M; Cedar Crest HS; Lebanon, PA; (2); German Clb; Pep Clb; Science Clb; High Hon Roll; Hon Roll; Prfct Atten Awd; Hnr Stu 87; Cert Acdmc Merit 86-87.

WIKE, SHELLEY; Lebanon Catholic HS; Lebanon, PA; (4); 7/80; FHA; Spanish Clb; School Play; Yrbk Sprt Ed; JV Var Bsktbl; Var L Sftbl; Hon Roll; Kiwanis Awd; NHS; Ntl Merit Ltr; Rotary Grl Mth 87; Duquesne U; Phrmcy.

WIKE, TINA; Penn Manor HS; Holtwood, PA; (3); 88/360; Church Yth Grp; Girl Scts; Orch; School Musical; Hon Roll.

WIKER III, JOHN SAMUEL; Belle Vernon Area SR HS; Belle Vernon, PA; (3); Church Yth Grp; Debate Tm; Socr; High Hon Roll; Hon Roll; U Of Pittsburgh.

WIKER, TOM; Solanco HS; Holtwood, PA; (3); Church Yth Grp; VP 4-H; VP FFA; Ag.

WILBER, LISA M; Bradford Area HS; Bradford, PA; (4); 14/278; AFS; Ski Clb; Concert Band; Mrchg Band; Var Tennis; High Hon Roll; NHS; Pres Schlr; Floyd C Fretz Mem Schlrshp 87; Griffith A Herold Awd 87; Slippery Rock U; Bus Admin.

WILBUR, CHERYL; Elk Lake School District HS; Springville, PA; (1); Band; Chorus; School Musical; Stage Crew; Hon Roll; Cosmetology.

WILBUR, RHODA; Williamson HS; Tioga, PA; (2); Sec Church Yth Grp; Cmnty Wkr; Office Aide; Sec OEA; Teachers Aide; Chorus; Cheerleading; High Hon Roll; Jr NHS; NHS; Hlth Awd 85-86; Nrsg.

WILBURN, TONY; Salisbury Elk Lick JR SR HS; Salisbury, PA; (4); Art Clb; FFA; Nwsp Rptr; Nwsp Stf; Hon Roll.

WILCOM, MARIE; Bishop Neumann HS; Williamsport, PA; (3); Trs Pep Clb; SADD; School Play; Yrbk Phtg; Trs Jr Cls; Rep Stu Cncl; JV Var Cheerleading; Var L Tennis; High Hon Roll; NHS; Ldrshp & Svc Awd 85; Cert Outstndng Cheerldng 85-86 & 86-87; Cert Kings Coll Spnsh Exam 86; Crmnology.

WILCOX, DAWN; Moon Area HS; Coraopolis, PA; (3); VP French Clb; GAA; Key Clb; Pep Clb; Band; Concert Band; Variety Show; Stu Cncl; Cheerleading; Sftbl; SR Orntn Cnslr 87-88; Elem Ed.

WILCOX, DAYNE; Elk Lake HS; Montrose, PA; (2); 2/100; French Clb; Band; Mrchg Band; Var Socr; Var Trk; High Hon Roll; HOBY Ambssdr 87; Archtctr.

WILCOX, MARY; Highlands HS; Tarentum, PA; (4); Exploring; Hosp Aide; SADD; Library Aide; Chorus; Var Sftbl; St Lucy Gld For Blind Mdlln 86; Schlstc Achvt Awds 87; Pres Phys Ftns Awds 84 & 87; ICM Schl Of Bus; Psychlgst.

WILCOX, SARA; Greater Johnstown HS; Johnstown, PA; (4); 17/306; Math Tm; Ski Clb; Mrchg Band; Nwsp Phtg; Yrbk Ed-Chief; Yrbk Phtg; Off Sr Cls; Stu Cncl; High Hon Roll; NHS; Tp 20 Hnr Crd 87; Jrnlsm & Photo & Freedom Shrine Awds 86 & 87; IN U; Spcl Ed.

WILCOX, TAMARA; Cambridge Springs HS; Cambridge Spgs, PA; (3); 9/98; Trs Spanish Clb; SADD; Chorus; Mrchg Band; Nwsp Stf; Yrbk Phtg; Cheerleading; Hon Roll; PA Govnrs Schl Arts 86; Allegheny Coll; Music.

WILCZYNSKI, ANNETTE; Crestwood HS; Nuangola, PA; (3); 32/177; Hosp Aide; Math Clb; Mu Alpha Theta; Office Aide; Pres Rep Stu Cncl; Mgr(s); Twrlr; High Hon Roll; PA Jr Acdmy Sci-1st Rgns & 2nd ST 85-86 & 1st Rgns & 3rd ST 86-87; Wilkes Coll; Nrsng.

WILDASIN, ELENA M; Delone Catholic HS; Hanover, PA; (3); 4/180; Nwsp Stf; Rep Soph Cls; Var Cheerleading; High Hon Roll; Sec NHS; Top 10 Pct Cls Awd; Phrmcy.

WILDAY, JENNIFER; Otto-Eldred HS; Eldred, PA; (4); 31/90; Sec Varsity Clb; Chorus; School Musical; School Play; Variety Show; Nwsp Stf; Yrbk Stf; Gym; Score Keeper; Trk; Brynt/Strttn Bus Inst; Fshn Mer.

WILDERMUTH, SCOTT; Conrad Weiser JR SR HS; Sinking Spring, PA; (3); Boy Scts; Chorus; School Musical; School Play; JV Capt Bsbl; JV Capt Socr; Daval Acad; Aero Engrng.

WILDING, DEBORAH; Penn Hills SR HS; Pittsburgh, PA; (3); French Clb; Ski Clb; Hon Roll; Elem Ed.

WILDMAN, LISA; Sharon HS; Sharon, PA; (4); 35/159; Art Clb; Drama Clb; Spanish Clb; School Musical; School Play; Var JV Cheerleading; Hon Roll; Acad Booster Clb Awd 87; Hmecmg Court SR Atten 86; U Pittsburgh; Art Ed.

WILDON, ALEISHA; Cumberland Valley HS; Mechanicsburg, PA; (3); 75/600; Latin Clb; SADD; Band; Chorus; Mrchg Band; School Musical; Hon Roll; Church Yth Grp; Ski Clb; Church Choir; Latin Hnr Roll 85-87; Hnr Carrier Awd Local Nwspr 85; Literary Arts.

WILDOW, SEAN; Penn Hills SR HS; Verona, PA; (3); Exploring; Library Aide; Spanish Clb; Hon Roll; Kent ST U; Aero.

WILDS, JEFFREY L; Norwin SR HS; N Huntingdon, PA; (4); 27/563; Computer Clb; Math Clb; Rep Stu Cncl; Var L Bsbl; Hon Roll; Jr NHS; NHS; Ntl Merit Ltr; Pres Schlr U Of Pittsburgh Johnstown 87; U Of Pittsburgh; Comp Sci.

WILEY III, JOHN A; Yough SR HS; W Newton, PA; (3); Off Church Yth Grp; Cmnty Wkr; Drama Clb; Sec French Clb; Spanish Clb; Concert Band; Jazz Band; Mrchg Band; School Play; JV Var Bsbl; Rec Bsbl ST Champ 84; Mrchg Band Amer 86; Prfct Atten Awd Sunday Schl 84 & 85; Theol.

WILEY, MARCIE J; William Allen HS; Allentown, PA; (3); 70/659; Cmnty Wkr; Dance Clb; Ski Clb; Varsity Clb; Yrbk Stf; Var JV Cheerleading; Hon Roll; Jr NHS; NHS; Mech Eng.

WILHELM, CHRIS; Central Dauphin HS; Harrisburg, PA; (3); 43/369; Drama Clb; Thesps; Band; Chorus; School Musical; School Play; Socr; Hon Roll; Jr NHS; NHS; Pre-Med.

WILHELM, LISA M; Chichester SR HS; Boothwyn, PA; (4); Teachers Aide; Band; Chorus; Concert Band; Mrchg Band; Sftbl; Pres Band 86-87; Chorus Treasr 86-87; Bst Mrchng Band Musician 87; Neumann Coll; Elem Educ.

WILHELM, MICHELLE; Mc Guffey HS; Avella, PA; (3); 15/240; Am Leg Aux Girls St; Ski Clb; Spanish Clb; Sec Stu Cncl; Cheerleading; Powder Puff Ftbl; Trk; High Hon Roll; NHS; Stu Recgntn Awd.

WILHELM, ROB; Steel Valley SR HS; Munhall, PA; (4); 23/201; Church Yth Grp; Letterman Clb; SADD; Varsity Clb; Var L Swmmng; NHS; MVP Swmmng Awd 84-86; Mrn Sci.

WILIUSZIS, VICKI; Monongahela Vly Catholic HS; New Eagle, PA; (3); French Clb; Variety Show; Powder Puff Ftbl; Sftbl; Vllybl; Wt Lftg; French Hon Soc; High Hon Roll; NHS.

WILK, JULIE; Glendale JR SR HS; Coalport, PA; (4); 5/93; Pres Church Yth Grp; Library Aide; Science Clb; Co-Capt Drm Mjr(t); Yrbk Stf; Twrlr; High Hon Roll; NHS; Pres Schlr; Thelma Hall Meml Nrsg Awd 87; Altoona Hosp Schl/Nrsg; Nrsg.

WILK, KRISTA; Owen J Roberts HS; Phoenixville, PA; (3); Letterman Clb; Band; Rep Jr Cls; Rep Stu Cncl; Lcrss; Tennis; Hon Roll.

WILK, TOM; Canon Mc Millan HS; Eighty Four, PA; (3); Boy Scts; Church Yth Grp; Exploring; Band; Concert Band; Jazz Band; Mrchg Band; Law.

WILKES, LAURA; York Catholic HS; York, PA; (4); Church Yth Grp; Sec Latin Clb; Pep Clb; Varsity Clb; Chorus; School Musical; Stage Crew; Nwsp Sprt Ed; Yrbk Stf; Var L Trk; Pres Schlrshp St Joseph U 87; PA Hghr Ed Commndtn 87; St Joseph U PA.

WILKES, MARCIA R; Reading JR Acad; Wernersville, PA; (2); 1/4; Church Yth Grp; Sec Office Aide; Teachers Aide; Pres Rep Stu Cncl; Hon Roll; Ntl Piano Plyng Adtns 86; Columbia Union Coll.

WILKES, MICHELLE; Lakeland HS; Jermyn, PA; (3); Teachers Aide; School Musical; School Play; Yrbk Stf; Rep Stu Cncl; Var Capt Cheerleading; Hon Roll; NHS; Ntl Merit Ltr; Acad All-Amer At Large Div 87; Natl Sci Merit Awd 87; Midget Chrldng Coach Awd 87; U Of Scranton; Chld Psych.

WILKINS, CHRISTOPHER I; Bethel Park SR HS; Bethel Park, PA; (4); 1/525; Boy Scts; Church Yth Grp; German Clb; Orch; School Musical; God Cntry Awd; NHS; Ntl Merit SF; Val; Eagle Scout BSA 84; Bronze Palm 84; Pittsbrgh Yth Smph 85-87; Univ Orch 86-87 Viola; Stu Ldrshp 85-86; Sarthmore Coll; Episcopal Mnstr.

WILKINS, CRAIG; Penn Trafford HS; Irwin, PA; (2); Hosp Aide; JV Bsbl; Var L Socr; High Hon Roll; Am Leg Awd 85.

WILKINS, DAVE; Hanover JR & SR HS; Wilkes Barre, PA; (3); Office Aide; Hon Roll; JV Var Bsbl; JV Var Bsktbl; Math.

WILKINS, JAMIE; Eisenhower HS; Russell, PA; (4); 13/116; Debate Tm; FCA; Political Wkr; Nwsp Sprt Ed; Yrbk Rptr; Pres Frsh Cls; Pres Jr Cls; Var Bsbl; Var Capt Bsktbl; Var Ftbl; Penn ST U; Comm.

WILKINS, JOE; Wilmington Area HS; Pulaski, PA; (4); 15/117; FBLA; Spanish Clb; Chorus; School Musical; Stage Crew; Hon Roll; Westminster Coll; Bus Admin.

WILKINS, KELLIE; Shenandoah Valley HS; Shenandoah, PA; (4); 8/102; Pep Clb; Nwsp Stf; Yrbk Sprt Ed; Yrbk Stf; Stu Cncl; Capt L Bsktbl; L Sftbl; High Hon Roll; Hon Roll; NHS; Acad All Amer 84-87; Stu Of Mnth 86; U Of RI; Bus.

WILKINS, LORI; Wilmington Area HS; Pulaski, PA; (2); Church Yth Grp; Exploring; Pres Hm Ecnmcs Clb 85-86; Med.

WILKINS, PAMELA; Middletown Area HS; Middletown, PA; (3); 3/193; Dance Clb; Hosp Aide; Model UN; Office Aide; Chorus; Capt Color Guard; Var L Gym; High Hon Roll; Capt Mrchg Band; John N Hoffman Memrl Awd 85; Loyal Order Moose Just No To Drugs 86; Biochem.

WILKINS, SHARRON; Oliver HS; Pittsburgh, PA; (3); Chorus; Color Guard; Mrchg Band; Nwsp Stf; Yrbk Stf; Tennis; High Hon Roll; Hon Roll; Atty.

WILKINSON, BRIAN; Spring Grove SR HS; Abbottstown, PA; (3); 69/301; Aud/Vis; Chess Clb; Church Yth Grp; Exploring; Church Choir; Var Ftbl; L Var Trk; JV Wrstlng.

WILKINSON, CHRISTINE; Oil City HS; Oil City, PA; (3); 22/192; AFS; French Clb; Math Tm; Varsity Clb; Chorus; Nwsp Stf; Capt L Cheerleading; High Hon Roll; NHS; Prfct Atten Awd; Stu Schl Brd Rep 86-8; US Military Acad; Elec Engrng.

WILKINSON, DANA; Penn Cambria HS; Lilly, PA; (3); Drama Clb; NFL; Spanish Clb; Speech Tm; SADD; Band; School Musical; School Play; Hon Roll; NHS; U Pittsburgh; RN.

WILKINSON, DAVID; Freeland HS; Freeland, PA; (3); 4/90; High Hon Roll; Hon Roll; Penn ST; Pre Law.

WILKINSON, DOUGLAS; Peters Twp HS; Venetia, PA; (4); 9/240; Church Yth Grp; Intnl Clb; Science Clb; Church Choir; Key Clb; Mrchg Band; Nwsp Stf; Hon Roll; NHS; Rotary Clb Awd Frgn Lang 87; Pres Acadmc Ftns Awd 87; Grove City Coll; Soclgy.

WILKINSON, LISA; West Branch HS; Munson, PA; (3); Letterman Clb; Spanish Clb; Varsity Clb; Drill Tm; Mrchg Band; Yrbk Stf; Var Sftbl; Math.

WILKINSON, RICHARD; Forest Hills HS; Mineral Pt, PA; (4); 5/152; Computer Clb; Quiz Bowl; Band; Concert Band; Jazz Band; Mrchg Band; High Hon Roll; Trs NHS; Trs Spanish NHS; Speech Tm; Natl Merit Fnlst 86; Braddock Schlrshp 87; Music Stu Yr 87; Penn ST; Sci.

WILKINSON, WILLIAM; Forest Hills SR HS; Mineral Point, PA; (4); 1/152; Drama Clb; Capt Quiz Bowl; Speech Tm; Thesps; Band; Chorus; Concert Band; Jazz Band; Mrchg Band; School Musical; Penn ST Frshmn Excllnce Awd 87; Kunkle Schlrshp 87; Forest Hls PTO Schlrshp; Penn ST Altoona; Sci Resrch.

WILKUS, JOHN; Hazleton HS; Hazleton, PA; (3).

WILL, COREY; Berlin Brothers Valley HS; Berlin, PA; (3); 4/95; VP Church Yth Grp; Pres 4-H; Sec FFA; Trs Ski Clb; Spanish Clb; Band; Yrbk Stf; Hon Roll; NHS; Highst Schltc Stu Awd 86; Engrng.

WILL, LISA; Kennedy Christian HS; Sharpsville, PA; (3); 19/97; Service Clb; Spanish Clb; Drill Tm; Flag Corp; Cheerleading; Hon Roll; Hmcmng Attndnt 85.

WILLARD, DANIEL; Upper Daupin Area HS; Gratz, PA; (3); 15/113; Boys Clb Am; Boy Scts; Varsity Clb; Ftbl; Wrstlng; NHS; Civil Engr.

WILLARD, MICHELE; South Allegheny HS; Glassport, PA; (3); 3/190; Office Aide; Science Clb; Y-Teens; Soph Cls; Stu Cncl; Bsktbl; Powder Puff Ftbl; High Hon Roll; Robert Morris Coll; Bus Adm.

WILLENBROCK, STACY; Downingtown SR HS; Downingtown, PA; (3); 86/630; French Clb; Ski Clb; SADD; Teachers Aide; Mrchg Band; Capt Twrlr; Im Vllybl; High Hon Roll; Hon Roll; NHS; Drexel; Fshn Dsgn.

WILLER, TINA; Saint Hubert HS; Philadelphia, PA; (3); Aud/Vis; Dance Clb; Drama Clb; French Clb; Office Aide; School Musical; School Play; Hon Roll.

WILLETT, DAN; Blue Mountain Acad; Hamburg, PA; (3); VP Computer Clb; Exploring; Teachers Aide; Stage Crew; Andrews U; Computer Sci.

WILLETT, MICHELE; Cambria Heights SR HS; Patton, PA; (3); 20/187; Trs Church Yth Grp; Q&S; Chorus; Church Choir; Yrbk Stf; Stat Bsktbl; Var Vllybl; Hon Roll; NHS; Natl Educ Dvlpmnt Tst Awd 86.

WILLEY, JOSEPH; Central Catholic HS; Pittsburgh, PA; (3); 18/297; Nwsp Stf; Im Bsktbl; Var L Crs Cntry; Im Ftbl; Var Ice Hcky; Var L Trk; Hon Roll; Ntl Merit SF.

WILLHEIM, DAWN; Hanover HS; Hanover, PA; (4); 73/107; Church Yth Grp; SADD; York Inter ST Fair 3rd Pl Cnnd Tomatoes 86; Du Page Hrtclturl Schl; Hrtcltr.

WILLIAMES, LEE; Dallas HS; Trucksville, PA; (3); Boy Scts; Debate Tm; Exploring; School Play; Trk; Wrstlng; Hon Roll; NHS; Ntl Merit SF; Gftd Prog 80-87; Egl Sct 84; NEDT Achvt Awd 86.

WILLIAMS, AIMEE; New Hope Solebury HS; New Hope, PA; (4); 8/78; Drama Clb; Ski Clb; Spanish Clb; Band; Stu Cncl; JV Bsktbl; L Var Cheerleading; Im Swmmng; High Hon Roll; NHS; Spnsh Awd 84; Home Econ Awd 85; Penn ST U; Spnsh.

WILLIAMS, ALLAN; Dover Area HS; Wellsville, PA; (3); Art Clb; Computer Clb; Ski Clb; Varsity Clb; Crs Cntry; Trk; Vllybl; Aud/Vis; Exploring; JA; JR Achvmt Proj Bus Awd 85; Athletic Achvmt Awd Trck,Cross Cntry 85-87; Bus Mgmt.

WILLIAMS, ANDREA; Downingtown HS; Chester Springs, PA; (3); 1/648; Model UN; Trs Spanish Clb; SADD; Stu Cncl; Var Bsktbl; High Hon Roll; NHS; NEDT Awd; Library Aide; Flag Corp; Penn St Sci Sympsm 86-87; Stu Advsry Brd 86-87.

WILLIAMS, ANGELINA; Central HS; Philadelphia, PA; (2); Hosp Aide; JV Vllybl; Temple; Med.

WILLIAMS, ANISSA; Manheim Central HS; Manheim, PA; (4); 16/217; Chorus; Orch; Powder Puff Ftbl; High Hon Roll; NHS; 4-Way Tst Awd 86; Prsdnts Physcl Ftnss Awd, MCEA Schlrshp 87; Bus Admin.

WILLIAMS, ANOTHONY TODD; Lancaster Christian Schl; Lititz, PA; (3); Church Yth Grp; Trs Jr Cls; Rep Stu Cncl; Var Bsbl; Var Bsktbl; Var Socr; Hon Roll; Physcl Thrpy.

WILLIAMS, ARDOTH; Northern Bedford County HS; Hopewell, PA; (3); Pres VP Church Yth Grp; Band; Chorus; Concert Band; Mrchg Band; School Play; Yrbk Stf; Stat Wrstlng; Hon Roll; Voice Dem Awd; Messiah Coll; Socl Wlfre.

WILLIAMS, BENJAMIN C; Bishop Mc Devitt HS; Harrisburg, PA; (4); Computer Clb; Science Clb; Timothy J Vastine Mem Awd For Achvt In Comp Sci 87; Millersville U; Comp Sci.

WILLIAMS, CAREY; Warwick HS; Lititz, PA; (3); 33/264; Fld Hcky; High Hon Roll; NHS; US Drssge Fedrtn Brnz Medl Awd 87; 4 Cert Amer Horse Shw Assn Natl Drssge Chmpnshps 85-87.

WILLIAMS, CATHERINE; Old Forge HS; Old Forge, PA; (4); Ski Clb; High Hon Roll; Hon Roll; NHS; Spanish NHS; Coll Misericordia; Occp Thrpy.

WILLIAMS, CECIL; Moniteau HS; Parker, PA; (3); 7/138; Am Leg Boys St; Boy Scts; Varsity Clb; VP Jr Cls; Off Stu Cncl; Var L Bsktbl; Var L Ftbl; High Hon Roll; Hon Roll; NHS 86-87; Engrng.

WILLIAMS, CELESTE; Harry S Truman HS; Fairless Hills, PA; (3); OEA; SADD; Rep Stu Cncl; Hon Roll; BEST.

WILLIAMS, CHARLES; J P Mc Caskey HS; Lancaster, PA; (3); Art Clb; CA Coll Of Arts; Art.

WILLIAMS, CHERYL; Crestwood HS; Mountaintop, PA; (3); 69/196; VP Exploring; Hosp Aide; Math Tm; Mu Alpha Theta; Ski Clb; Nwsp Stf; VP Stu Cncl; Mgr(s); Twrlr; Hon Roll; 1st Pl Reg & St PA Jr Acad Of Sci; Law.

WILLIAMS, CHERYL; William Allen HS; Allentown, PA; (2); German Clb; Sec JA; Office Aide; Trk; Gov Hon Prg Awd; High Hon Roll; Hon Roll; Jr NHS; Stuart Hall 2nd Annual Schltc Awds Cmptn Merit 85; M L King Jr Essay Contest 87; Temple U; Educ.

WILLIAMS, CHRISTINE; East Allegheny HS; East Mc Keesport, PA; (3); French Clb; Hon Roll; Brdfrd Schl Bus; Lgl Sctry.

WILLIAMS, CHRISTOPHER; Kennedy Christian HS; W Middlesex, PA; (2); 52/96; Boy Scts; Library Aide; Ski Clb; Ftbl; Hon Roll; Phrmcy.

WILLIAMS, CLAUDE; West Catholic HS For Boys; Philadelphia, PA; (3); 62/257; Boy Scts; Chess Clb; English Clb; Math Clb; Varsity Clb; Stage Crew; Var Bsktbl; Var Crs Cntry; Var Trk; Hon Roll.

WILLIAMS, CLAUDETTE; Danville HS; Riverside, PA; (3); Drama Clb; French Clb; Ski Clb; Band; Concert Band; Mrchg Band; School Musical; Var Fld Hcky; High Hon Roll; NHS.

WILLIAMS, CONREAU; Steel Valley HS; Homestead, PA; (3); 92/230; Church Yth Grp; JA; Concert Band; Co-Capt Drill Tm; Mrchg Band; Variety Show; Yrbk Stf; JV Var Bsktbl; Coach Actv; Crs Cntry; Head Coach Of Termite Chrldrs 84-86; Grls Vrsty Bsktbll Tm 84-85; Gnrtns Together 87; Phys Thrpy.

WILLIAMS, COREY; Churchill HS; Braddock, PA; (2); 85/222; Church Yth Grp; FCA; Church Choir; Bsbl; Var Bsktbl; Bowling; Var Ftbl; Trk; Hon Roll; Prfct Atten Awd; Law.

WILLIAMS, CRAIG; Punxsutawney SR HS; Punxsutawney, PA; (4); 81/456; Church Yth Grp; French Clb; FBLA; Math Tm; Science Clb; Variety Show; Gannon U; Phrmcy.

WILLIAMS, CRYSTAL; West Catholic H S For Girls; Philadelphia, PA; (3); 166/262; Girl Scts; Flag Corp; Orch; Hon Roll; Comp Sci.

WILLIAMS, DARNEICE; Carrick HS; Pittsburgh, PA; (3); Church Yth Grp; FCA; SADD; Chorus; Church Choir; Rep Stu Cncl; Bsktbl; Powder Puff Ftbl; Vllybl; Hon Roll; Most Successful Stu In Bus Comp Appli 87; Most Vlbl Plyr In Volleyball 86; Alumni Church Choir 87; Tuskegee Inst; Comp Pgmmr.

WILLIAMS, DAVID; Monongahela Valley Catholic HS; Monessen, PA; (3); 37/98; French Clb; Var L Golf; Var L Socr; French Hon Soc.

WILLIAMS, DAVID; West Branch Area HS; Winburne, PA; (2); Spanish Clb; Varsity Clb; Trs Soph Cls; Var JV Ftbl; Wt Lftg; Hon Roll; Prfct Atten Awd; PA ST U; Phys Ed.

WILLIAMS, DAWN; Philadelphia HS For Girls; Philadelphia, PA; (4); 166/340; GAA; Teachers Aide; Rep Jr Cls; Rep Sr Cls; Tennis; Howard U; Zoolgy.

WILLIAMS, DEANNA; Berlin-Brothers Valley HS; Glencoe, PA; (3); 5/94; Sec 4-H; Spanish Clb; Speech Tm; Concert Band; School Play; Yrbk Stf; Capt Twrlr; 4-H Awd; Hon Roll; NHS; Penn ST U; Nrsng.

WILLIAMS, DEBBIE LEE; Highlands SR HS; Natrona Heights, PA; (4); 51/281; Key Clb; Concert Band; Mrchg Band; NHS; Gld & Brwn Awds 83-87; Brd Gov Schlrshp 87; M L King JR Schlrshp 87; Slippery Rock U; Bio.

WILLIAMS, DEBORAH; Donegal HS; Mount Joy, PA; (4); 1/165; Trs Varsity Clb; Var L Bsktbl; Var L Fld Hcky; Var L Sftbl; Pres NHS; Opt Clb Awd; Val; Lut Robert Bolenius Ritchie Mem Schlrshp 87; Amer Bus Wmns Assoc Awd 87; Donegal Cochs Assoc Schlrshp; Elizabethtown Coll; Accntng.

WILLIAMS, DENISE; Indiana Area HS; Indiana, PA; (3); Key Clb; Var Trk; JV Vllybl; High Hon Roll; Hon Roll; Jr NHS; Lang.

WILLIAMS, DEREK; St Francis Prep; Dahlgren, VA; (2); 3/30; Art Clb; Boy Scts; Drama Clb; Exploring; Ski Clb; School Play; Stage Crew; Socr; Wrstlng; High Hon Roll; VA Tech; Rest Mgmt.

WILLIAMS, DESIREE; Riverside SR HS; Ellwood City, PA; (2); 66/203; AFS; Church Yth Grp; Hosp Aide; NFL; VP SADD; Band; Orch; Rep Stu Cncl; High Hon Roll; Hon Roll; Ntl Frnsc Leg Merit Awd 86; Cert Of Apprctn For Prvntn Prjct Pgm 86; Cert & Lttr R For JR Bsktbl Mgr; PA ST; Pre Law.

WILLIAMS, DIANE S; Penn-Trafford HS; Trafford, PA; (4); Drama Clb; GAA; Hosp Aide; Office Aide; Chorus; Color Guard; Swing Chorus; High Hon Roll; Hon Roll; NHS; U Of Pittsburgh.

WILLIAMS JR, DONALD R; South Fayette Township HS; Bridgeville, PA; (3); 4/96; Church Yth Grp; Letterman Clb; JV Var Bsbl; JV Var Bsktbl; Var L Socr; High Hon Roll; NHS; Stu Perfrmnc Awd 86.

WILLIAMS, DOUGLAS A; Avonworth HS; Pittsburgh, PA; (4); 8/99; Latin Clb; Varsity Clb; Nwsp Stf; Nwsp Stf; Ed Lit Mag; Var L Bsktbl; Cit Awd; High Hon Roll; NHS; Ntl Merit SF; Gazette Newspaper Carrier Yr; Acad Smmr Sem; William & Mary.

WILLIAMS, FAWN; Brandywine Heights HS; Fleetwood, PA; (3); 1/126; FBLA; Quiz Bowl; Spanish Clb; Yrbk Ed-Chief; Yrbk Stf; Golf; Vllybl; High Hon Roll; NHS; Prfct Atten Awd; U Of MI; Bus Admn.

WILLIAMS, GERALYN; Dallas SR HS; Shaverstown, PA; (3); 8/211; Key Clb; Yrbk Ed-Chief; Yrbk Stf; Rep Soph Cls; Rep Stu Cncl; Stat Fld Hcky; High Hon Roll; Hon Roll; NHS; NEDT Awd; Home Ec Awd 86.

WILLIAMS, H CLINTON; Mars Area SR HS; Mars, PA; (4); 23/141; Im Bsktbl; Im Ftbl; Im Sftbl; Im Vllybl; High Hon Roll; Hon Roll; Prfct Atten Awd; U UT; Govt Agnt.

WILLIAMS, HEATHER; Belle Vernon Area HS; Belle Vernon, PA; (4); 51/262; Drama Clb; JA; Pep Clb; Powder Puff Ftbl; NHS; Penn ST; Med.

WILLIAMS, HEATHER; Laurel Valley JR-SR HS; New Florence, PA; (2); AFS; Ski Clb; Varsity Clb; Sec Frsh Cls; Rep Soph Cls; Rep Stu Cncl; Var Cheerleading; Var Sftbl; High Hon Roll; Hon Roll.

WILLIAMS, HEATHER; Wyoming Valley West HS; Kingston, PA; (3); 41/416; Church Yth Grp; Key Clb; Red Cross Aide; Nwsp Phtg; Nwsp Stf; Yrbk Phtg; Lit Mag; Rep Jr Cls; Var Trk; NHS; Ntl Yth Ldrshp Salute.

WILLIAMS, HOLLI; Jamestown Area HS; Jamestown, PA; (2); 2/53; French Clb; Varsity Clb; Band; Chorus; School Musical; Off Frsh Cls; Stu Cncl; Mgr Bsktbl; Mgr(s); JV Capt Vllybl; Dist Band 87; Hstry Awd 86; Engrng.

WILLIAMS, JAMES; Mercer Area HS; Mercer, PA; (3); Spanish Clb; School Play; Nwsp Rptr; Nwsp Stf; Yrbk Rptr; Yrbk Stf; JV Bsktbl; Var Capt Crs Cntry; Var L Trk; Hon Roll; Biochem.

WILLIAMS III, JAMES N; Central Catholic HS; Pittsburgh, PA; (3); Cmnty Wkr; Library Aide; Sec Office Aide; Political Wkr; Teachers Aide; Drill Tm; Yrbk Stf; JV Ftbl; Prfct Atten Awd; 1st US Senate Page 87; Air Force Acad; Bus.

WILLIAMS, JASON; Williams Valley HS; Lykens, PA; (3); 5/90; Boy Scts; Chess Clb; Church Yth Grp; Var L Bsbl; High Hon Roll; Hon Roll; Scnctnd As Yaba Bowler 84-87; Lndscp Clb 86-87; Pro Bass Fld Tstrs Clb 85-86; US Cst Grd Acad; Agri.

WILLIAMS, JEAN-MICHELLE; St Basil Acad; Philadelphia, PA; (3); 2/84; Drama Clb; Trs German Clb; School Play; Symp Band; Nwsp Rptr; Yrbk Stf; Lit Mag; High Hon Roll; Cmmnctns.

WILLIAMS, JENIFER; Pen Argyl Area HS; Pen Argyl, PA; (3); 13/160; Rep Stu Cncl; Mgr(s); Tennis; Hon Roll; Pre Law.

WILLIAMS, JENNIFER; Johnsonburg Area HS; Wilcox, PA; (3); Library Aide; Yrbk Ed-Chief; Yrbk Stf; Sec Frsh Cls; VP Soph Cls; Rep Jr Cls; JV Var Cheerleading; Hon Roll; Prfct Atten Awd.

WILLIAMS, JENNIFER; Newport JR SR HS; Liverpool, PA; (3); 22/127; Aud/Vis; German Clb; Varsity Clb; School Play; Nwsp Rptr; Yrbk Stf; Var Stat Bsktbl; Var Mgr(s); Hon Roll; Broadcasting For TV.

WILLIAMS, JENNIFER A; Moon SR HS; Coraopolis, PA; (3); Drama Clb; VP JA; Office Aide; Pep Clb; School Play; Stage Crew; Variety Show; Vllybl; 1st Pl Awd DECA Dist Conf 87; Arts Spprntcshp Pgm 87-88.

WILLIAMS, JERI D; Canon Mc Millan HS; Canonsburg, PA; (4); 47/371; Church Yth Grp; French Clb; Y-Teens; Chorus; Church Choir; School Musical; Trk; High Hon Roll; NHS; Prfct Atten Awd; Shasda Awd Acdmc Excell 86; Prs Ftnss Awd 87; Washingtn & Jffrsn; Pre-Med.

WILLIAMS, JILL; Hempfield Area HS; Greensburg, PA; (2); French Clb; Pep Clb; Ski Clb; Yrbk Stf; Var Cheerleading; Medical.

WILLIAMS, JILL; York Suburban HS; York, PA; (3); 7/180; Chorus; Trk; Vllybl; High Hon Roll; NHS; Top Stu Of Cls 84-85; Top 5 Pct Of Cls 85-86; Chem.

WILLIAMS, JOHN; New Castle Vo-Tech; New Castle, PA; (3); Art Clb; Boy Scts; AFS; Spanish Clb; SADD; VICA; Chorus; Vllybl; Wt Lftg; Hon Roll; Engl.

WILLIAMS, JONATHAN; Elizabethtown Area HS; Elizabethtown, PA; (3); 36/224; Boy Scts; Stage Crew; Williamsport Area CC; Cntrctr.

WILLIAMS, JULES; Frankford HS; Philadelphia, PA; (3); 56/544; Yrbk Stf; Tennis; Wt Lftg; Prfct Atten Awd; Temple U; Business.

WILLIAMS, KAREN; Freedom HS; Bethlehem, PA; (3); 137/509; French Clb; JA; Ski Clb; SADD; Nwsp Rptr; Nwsp Stf; Var Powder Puff Ftbl; JV Var Score Keeper; JV Var Sftbl; Hon Roll; Pepperdine U; Jrnlsm.

WILLIAMS, KATHLEEN; Waynesburg Central HS; Waynesburg, PA; (3); AFS; Boys Clb Am; Church Yth Grp; Cmnty Wkr; French Clb; Girl Scts; Hosp Aide; Band; Mrchg Band; Hon Roll; Nrsng.

WILLIAMS, KEITH; Pen Argyl Area HS; Pen Argyl, PA; (4); 19/129; Chess Clb; Computer Clb; Letterman Clb; Varsity Clb; Bsktbl; Im Golf; Im Wt Lftg; Lion Awd; PA ST; Cvl Engr.

WILLIAMS, KEITH; Trinity Christian HS; Pittsburgh, PA; (4); 2/13; Boy Scts; Church Yth Grp; German Clb; Letterman Clb; Variety Show; Pres Frsh Cls; Pres Trs Stu Cncl; Var JV Bsktbl; Bowling; Var Sftbl; Black Achvt Schlrshp 87; Trinity Chrstn Schl Athl Awd 87; PA ST U; Arch.

WILLIAMS, KELLY; Brandywine Heights HS; Mertztown, PA; (4); 8/126; Hosp Aide; Var Fld Hcky; Var Capt Sftbl; High Hon Roll; NHS; Pres Schlr; Rotary Awd; All Cnty Sftbll Plyr 87; Hstrcl Soc-Brks Co Awd Soc Stds 87; Soclgy Awd 87; Kutztown U; Psychlgy.

WILLIAMS, KELLY; Corry Area HS; Corry, PA; (3); Church Yth Grp; Library Aide; Y-Teens; Variety Show; Yrbk Sprt Ed; Rep Soph Cls; VP Stu Cncl; Stat Bsktbl; JV Tennis; JV Var Vllybl; Delta Epsilon Phi 86; Stu Forum Rep; Educ.

WILLIAMS, KELLY; North Pocono HS; Lake Ariel, PA; (4); 26/240; Church Yth Grp; Capt Var Vllybl; Hon Roll; NHS; CMC; Nrsng.

WILLIAMS, KEN; Muhlenberg SR HS; Laureldale, PA; (4); 60/181; Boy Scts; Band; Concert Band; Jazz Band; Mrchg Band; Orch; Pep Band; School Musical; Zeswitz Outstndng Instrumentalist Awd & Eagle Scout 87; W Chester U; Music Educ.

WILLIAMS, KIM; Panther Valley HS; Summit Hill, PA; (1); 57/127; French Clb; GAA; Math Clb; Pep Band; Trk; Cit Awd; High Hon Roll; Hon Roll; NHS; Val.

WILLIAMS, KRISTIN; Bishop Shanahan HS; W Chester, PA; (4); 6/215; Cmnty Wkr; Chorus; Concert Band; Madrigals; School Musical; NHS; PA Govnrs Schl Art Scholar 86; ST Chrs 86 & 87; MEBC All Easter US Chrs 87; Dist XII Chrs 85-87; West Chester U; Music.

WILLIAMS, KRISTIN; Oley Valley HS; Fleetwood, PA; (3); 4/150; Trs Art Clb; Office Aide; Teachers Aide; Chorus; Jazz Band; Stage Crew; Nwsp Stf; JV Crs Cntry; Var Fld Hcky; High Hon Roll; Lock Haven U; Spec Ed.

WILLIAMS, KRISTIN; Susquehanna Community HS; Starrucca, PA; (2); 1/94; Church Yth Grp; 4-H; Girl Scts; Ski Clb; Band; Chorus; Church Choir; Mrchg Band; Lit Mag; High Hon Roll; Psych.

WILLIAMS, KRISTIN; Trinity HS; Mechanicsburg, PA; (2); 15/136; French Clb; Model UN; Scholastic Bowl; School Musical; School Play; Stat Bsktbl; Var L Crs Cntry; Var L Trk; Hon Roll; NEDT Awd.

WILLIAMS, LA VONNE; Simon Gratz HS; Philadelphia, PA; (3); 1/365; Hosp Aide; Office Aide; High Hon Roll; Hon Roll; Accntng.

WILLIAMS, LAKEDA; Thila HS For Girls; Philadelphia, PA; (3); 81/405; GAA; Orch; Rep Jr Cls; Var Crs Cntry; Var Mgr(s); Var Trk; Hon Roll; Pre-Law.

WILLIAMS, LAMAR; Scotland School For Vets Children; Philadelphia, PA; (3); Art Clb; Church Yth Grp; Letterman Clb; Capt ROTC; Pres Varsity Clb; Off Jr Cls; Pres Sr Cls; L Bsbl; Capt Ftbl; L Trk; Mst Imprvd Wrstlr 85-86; Ftbl Offnsv Plyr Yr 86-87; Lehigh U; Publc Rltns.

WILLIAMS, LASHENA BRUCE; W B Saul HS Of Agri; Philadelphia, PA; (3); Church Yth Grp; Dance Clb; FFA; Hon Roll; Prfct Atten Awd; Temple U; Gospel Singer.

WILLIAMS, LAVONNE; Simson Gratz HS; Philadelphia, PA; (3); 1/375; Computer Clb; Office Aide; Hosp Aide; Yrbk Stf; VP Jr Cls; Var Tennis; DAR Awd; High Hon Roll; NHS; VP Honor Society 87; Temple U; Attrny.

WILLIAMS, LESLIE; John S Fine SR HS; Nanticoke, PA; (2); Political Wkr; Trs Soph Cls; Var Bsbl; Im Bsktbl; Var Golf; High Hon Roll; NHS; NEDT Awd; Carrier Of Mnth, Wilkes Barre Times Ldr 86; Cert Congrssnl Rcgntn 86; Columbus Essay Cntst 86; Harvard U; Pre-Law.

WILLIAMS, LISA; Liberty HS; Bethlehem, PA; (3); 193/429; Boys Clb Am; Church Yth Grp; Library Aide; Spanish Clb; Teachers Aide; VICA; Drill Tm; Tennis; Trk; Hon Roll; Fash Indstry.

WILLIAMS, LISA; Marion Center HS; Creekside, PA; (3); 10/190; Intnl Clb; NAACP; Varsity Clb; Pres Frsh Cls; Trs Jr Cls; JV Bsktbl; Var Cheerleading; JV Var Score Keeper; Var Trk; JV Vllybl; Pitt U; Psych.

WILLIAMS, LYNNE; Waynesburg Central HS; Waynesburg, PA; (4); 2/210; Trs Sec AFS; French Clb; Pres Girl Scts; French Hon Soc; Trs NHS; Girl Scout Slvr Awd 85; Algbra Awd 85.

WILLIAMS, MARANDA; Baldwin HS; Pittsburgh, PA; (3); 75/476; Trs Girl Scts; Band; Symp Band; Hon Roll; Natl Honor Roll 87; Order Rainbow Girls 86; Nrs.

WILLIAMS, MARGARET; Old Forge HS; Old Forge, PA; (2); Ski Clb.

WILLIAMS, MARGARET S; Western Wayne HS; Lake Ariel, PA; (4); 32/140; Hosp Aide; Ski Clb; Spanish Clb; SADD; Yrbk Ed-Chief; Yrbk Stf; Trs Soph Cls; Var Cheerleading; Var JV Vllybl; Schlstc Art Gold Key Awd 87; U Of Scranton Pres V Schlrshp 87; U Of Scranton; Psychology.

WILLIAMS, MARIA; Chambersburg Area SR HS; Chambersburg, PA; (4); Sec Varsity Clb; Yrbk Stf; Capt Swmmng; Hon Roll; Widener U; Engrng.

WILLIAMS, MARQUETTE; Corry Area HS; Corry, PA; (4); 38/192; VP Drama Clb; French Clb; SADD; Band; Concert Band; Jazz Band; Mrchg Band; Pep Band; Hon Roll; Pres Acdmc Ftnss Awd, & All Erie Cnty Mc Donalds Band 86-87; Psych.

WILLIAMS, MEGAN; Lake Lehman HS; Sweet Valley, PA; (2); 48/199; Ski Clb; SADD; Rep Stu Cncl; Var Cheerleading; JV Fld Hcky; JV Sftbl; Stat Wrstlng; Hon Roll; Penn State U; Scl Wrkr.

WILLIAMS, MELANIE; Hazleton HS; Hazleton, PA; (3); 16/438; Church Yth Grp; Color Guard; Im Vllybl; Hon Roll; Kings Coll Spn Cont 2nd Pl 85, 4th Pl 86; Chem Engrng.

WILLIAMS, MELINDA; Pen Argyl Area HS; Pen Argyl, PA; (4); Computer Clb; German Clb; Math Clb; Pep Clb; Yrbk Stf; Im Bsktbl; Var Capt Cheerleading; High Hon Roll; Hon Roll; Ntl Merit Schol; Northampton County CC; Scl Wrk.

WILLIAMS, MELISSA; Yough HS; Yukon, PA; (4); Camera Clb; Dance Clb; Debate Tm; Drama Clb; Office Aide; Pep Clb; PAVAS; Band; Concert Band; Drm & Bgl; 1st Pl Photogrphr-Dist Lvl & Top Ten ST 87; 2nd Pl Grphc Artst Dist Lvl & 20th ST 87; CA U; Grphc Arts Ed.

WILLIAMS, MICHELE; Bald Eagle-Nittany HS; Beech Creek, PA; (2); 13/136; Sec Intnl Clb; Key Clb; SADD; Teachers Aide; Nwsp Rptr; Nwsp Stf; VP Stu Cncl; Var Cheerleading; Im Vllybl; Hon Roll; Physical Therapy.

WILLIAMS, MICHELE; Commodore Perry HS; Hadley, PA; (4); 6/64; Trs FNA; VP Acpl Chr; Band; Chorus; Jazz Band; Pep Band; Yrbk Stf; Var Mgr(s); Hon Roll; NHS; Gannon U; Nrsng.

WILLIAMS, MICHELE; Trinity HS; Mechanicsburg, PA; (4); French Clb; Pep Clb; Yrbk Stf; Var Trk; High Hon Roll; Spanish NHS; York Coll Of PA; Bus.

WILLIAMS, MONIQUE; Tulpehocken HS; Womelsdorf, PA; (3); Drama Clb; Chorus; Color Guard; School Play; Trk; Hon Roll; Air Force.

WILLIAMS JR, NAPOLEON; HS Creative & Performing Arts; Philadelphia, PA; (4); 19/127; Capt Debate Tm; Office Aide; Thesps; School Play; Stage Crew; VP Jr Cls; VP Sr Cls; Rep Stu Cncl; NHS; 1st Pl Blck Hstry Ortrcl Cntst; 1st Pl Thole Essay Cntst; Cobbe Fndtn Yth Awd.

WILLIAMS, NICHOLE; Edward Bok HS; Philadelphia, PA; (3); Exploring; FBLA; JA; SADD; Yrbk Stf; Trk; Gov Hon Prg Awd; Hon Roll; Prfct Atten Awd; Pres Schlr; Track Awd; Ft Lauderdale Coll; Pre-Law.

WILLIAMS, NICOLE; Penncrest HS; Media, PA; (3); Hosp Aide; Chorus; Variety Show; Yrbk Stf; JV Cheerleading; Var Trk; Hon Roll; Comms.

WILLIAMS, NOREEN; Saegertown HS; Meadville, PA; (4); 36/110; French Clb; Ski Clb; SADD; Varsity Clb; Variety Show; Sec Stu Cncl; Cheerleading; Sftbl; Hon Roll; Clarion U; Bus Ed.

WILLIAMS, NORM; Scotland Schl; Phila, PA; (3); 9/40; Art Clb; Boy Scts; Cmnty Wkr; Computer Clb; FBLA; ROTC; Varsity Clb; Nwsp Sprt Ed; Var Bsktbl; Var Trk.

WILLIAMS, PAUL; Connellsville Area HS; Mill Run, PA; (2); Church Yth Grp; JV Swmmng; High Hon Roll; Hon Roll.

WILLIAMS, PAULA; Carver HS Of Engineering & Science; Philadelphia, PA; (3); 50/248; Church Choir; Rep Frsh Cls; Rep Soph Cls; VP Stu Cncl; Var Cheerleading; Cit Awd; Hon Roll; Moore Coll Art Bsc Drwng,Txtls & Sci Bus Awds 86 & 87; PA ST U; Arch.

WILLIAMS, RAE; Clarion Area HS; Clarion, PA; (3); Church Yth Grp; Cmnty Wkr; Pep Clb; Band; Chorus; Church Choir; Concert Band; Mrchg Band; School Musical; School Play; Lgl Sec.

WILLIAMS, REBECCA; Coudersport Area JR SR HS; Coudersport, PA; (3); Church Yth Grp; Drama Clb; Band; Chorus; Church Choir; Concert Band; Jazz Band; Mrchg Band; School Play; Yrbk Stf; Culinary Arts.

WILLIAMS, REBECCA; Methacton HS; Collegeville, PA; (3); Church Yth Grp; Dance Clb; Teachers Aide; Flag Corp; Yrbk Stf; Rep Stu Cncl; Var L Socr; Var L Swmmng; High Hon Roll; Rotary Awd; Distngshd Wrtg Awd 87; Sci Fair Hnrbl Mntn 85-86; Nrsg.

WILLIAMS, RECHELLE; Cecylyan Acad; Philadelphia, PA; (3); Church Yth Grp; Cmnty Wkr; French Clb; Hosp Aide; Office Aide; Science Clb; Chorus; Church Choir; School Musical; Service Clb; Offc Aide Awd, Gospel Choir Awd & Typing Cert 86-87; Cheyney U; Hotel Mgmt.

WILLIAMS, RIAD P; Lower Merion HS; Wynnewood, PA; (4); 13/370; Pres Church Yth Grp; Scholastic Bowl; Service Clb; Nwsp Rptr; Var Sftbl; High Hon Roll; NHS; Ntl Merit Schol; Princeton U; Pol Sci.

WILLIAMS, RICHARD; Wyoming Valley West HS; Kingston, PA; (4); Church Yth Grp; Red Cross Aide; Rep Stu Cncl; Im Bsktbl; Var Ftbl; L Trk; Im Vllybl; Im Wt Lftg; Cit Awd; Hon Roll; Dist Champn 4x100 M Relay Tm 86; VA Military Inst; Ecnmcs.

WILLIAMS, ROBERT E; Wm Penn SR HS; York, PA; (3); Boys Clb Am; Church Yth Grp; Chorus; Church Choir; Var Ftbl; JV Tennis; Hon Roll; Im Bsktbl; Im Swmmng; Im Wt Lftg; Teenagr Yr 87; Penn ST; Bus Adm.

WILLIAMS II, ROY E; Nazareth Area SR HS; Nazareth, PA; (3); 16/267; Boy Scts; Chess Clb; Church Yth Grp; Cmnty Wkr; Key Clb; Var Wrstlng; God Cntry Awd; High Hon Roll; NHS; Computer Clb; Eagle Sct Awd, 8 Palms 85; Yth Ldrshp Amer Awd Boy Scts Amer 87.

WILLIAMS, RYAN; Ringgold HS; Elrama, PA; (2); Spanish Clb; JV Var Bsktbl; Wt Lftg; Hon Roll; Math.

WILLIAMS, SHANNON; Philadelphia HS For Girls; Philadelphia, PA; (4); Library Aide; Office Aide; Church Choir; Drill Tm; Variety Show; Westchester U; Nrsng.

WILLIAMS, SHANNON; West Middlesex HS; West Middlesex, PA; (2); Church Yth Grp; French Clb; Service Clb; Band; Chorus; High Hon Roll; Jr NHS; NHS; Pres Schlr; Stu Achvrs Merit Awd 87; Schlstc Achvt Awd 86; Schlstc Achvt Awd 87; Sci.

WILLIAMS, SHARON; Bishop Mc Devitt HS; Harrisburg, PA; (3); 5/230; Hosp Aide; Chorus; Madrigals; Yrbk Sprt Ed; Var Capt Cheerleading; High Hon Roll; Hon Roll; Capital Area Sci Fair 3rd Pl Awd 85; Schl Sci Fair 1st Pl Awd 85; Intr Dsgn.

WILLIAMS, SHELLEY; Nazareth SR HS; Nazareth, PA; (4); Church Yth Grp; Cmnty Wkr; Hosp Aide; Key Clb; Church Choir; Nwsp Ed-Chief; Sftbl; Northampton Co CC; TV Brdcstg.

WILLIAMS, SHERRY; Hamburg Area JR/Sr HS; Shoemakersville, PA; (3); Church Yth Grp; French Clb; Spanish Clb; SADD; Yrbk Stf; Hon Roll; Intl Frgn Lang Awd-Frnch & Spnsh 86; Acad Lttr Awd-Wrld Cultrs 86; Kutztown U; Elem Educ.

WILLIAMS, ST CLAIR; Beaver Falls SR HS; Beaver Falls, PA; (3); 95/170; Art Clb; Red Cross Aide; Chorus; Madrigals; School Musical; Bsktbl; Var L Ftbl; Var L Trk; Most Imprvd Trck 86; Most Personal Rcrds Trck 87; Hnrb Mntn Def Ftbl 86; Eastern MI; Speech.

WILLIAMS, STACEY; Upper Dauphin Area HS; Elizabethville, PA; (3); Hosp Aide; Varsity Clb; Chorus; Flag Corp; Mrchg Band; School Musical; Sec Soph Cls; Var Sftbl; Cit Awd; Nrsng.

WILLIAMS, STACEY; Valley View JR-SR HS; Archbald, PA; (3); Church Yth Grp; French Clb; Hosp Aide; JV VP Bsktbl; VP Trk; L Mgr Vllybl; French Hon Soc; Hon Roll; NHS; Prfct Atten Awd; Phys Ther.

WILLIAMS, STACY; Mid Valley HS; Olyphant, PA; (1); Dance Clb; Drama Clb; School Play; Stage Crew; Nwsp Rptr; Nwsp Stf; Rep Frsh Cls; Rep Soph Cls; Var Cheerleading; Hon Roll; Nrsng.

WILLIAMS, STEPHANIE; Hempfield HS; Landisville, PA; (3); Church Yth Grp; Dance Clb; School Play; Variety Show; Rep Soph Cls; Rep Jr Cls; Rep Sr Cls; Var Cheerleading; High Hon Roll; Hon Roll.

WILLIAMS, STEPHEN; Henderson SR HS; Westchester, PA; (3); 15/370; Debate Tm; Trs Intnl Clb; JCL; School Play; VP Frsh Cls; Stu Cncl; Var Socr; Var Capt Tennis; French Hon Soc; NHS; Stdnt Advisor To The Schl Brd 87-88; Latin Hnr Soc 87-88; JR St Men Smr Schl At Stanford U 87; Pre-Law.

WILLIAMS, STEVEN; Bradford Central Christian HS; Bradford, PA; (4); 13/26; SADD; Varsity Clb; Yrbk Stf; Stu Cncl; Bsbl; Ftbl; Score Keeper; NHS; Ntl Merit Ltr; Ltrmn-Bsbl & Ftbl 84-87; Mst Mprvd Plyr Awd 86-87; Excllnt-Accntng Awd 86-87; Mercyhurst Coll; Accntng.

WILLIAMS, SUSAN; Swissvale HS; Pittsbuirgh, PA; (4); 15/200; Church Yth Grp; French Clb; Hosp Aide; Ski Clb; SADD; Y-Teens; Yrbk Stf; High Hon Roll; NHS; Mdl Hnr Scholar Fnlst 87; Penn ST; Pre-Med.

WILLIAMS, TALASIMU; Aliquippa HS; Aliquippa, PA; (3); 42/140; Exploring; NAACP; Chorus; Church Choir; School Play; Rep Jr Cls; Rep Trk; Hon Roll; Psych.

WILLIAMS, TAMMY; Beaver Falls SR HS; Beaver Falls, PA; (3); 38/180; AFS; Aud/Vis; Chess Clb; Pres Church Yth Grp; Civic Clb; Cmnty Wkr; Computer Clb; Drama Clb; Debate Tm; Drama Clb; Prncpl Hnr Roll & Ldrshp Awd 87; Beaver Cnty Hnrs Chorus Awd 87; Meritorious Awd 87; U Of Pittsburgh; Pre-Law.

WILLIAMS, TAMMY; Elizabeth Forward HS; Monongahela, PA; (2); 17/336; Church Yth Grp; French Clb; Radio Clb; Chorus; High Hon Roll; Prfct Atten Awd.

WILLIAMS, TERRI; West Scranton HS; Scranton, PA; (2); Hosp Aide; Spanish Clb; NHS; Penn ST U; Vet.

WILLIAMS, THOMAS; Newport HS; Liverpool, PA; (1); Art Clb; German Clb; Quiz Bowl; Socr; Hon Roll; Teaching.

WILLIAMS, TINA MARIE; Sto-Rox SR HS; Mc Kees Rocks, PA; (2); Hosp Aide; JA; Teachers Aide; Y-Teens; Band; Concert Band; Jazz Band; Mrchg Band; Yrbk Rptr; Yrbk Stf; Pittsburgh Beauty Acad; Beautn.

WILLIAMS, TRACY; Blairsville HS; Blairsville, PA; (3); Bsktbl; Ftbl; Trk; 2 Ltrmn-Ftbl.

WILLIAMS, TRACY; Central SR HS; York, PA; (3); Im Badmtn; JV Bsktbl; Im Bowling; Im Golf; Im Mgr(s); Im Sftbl; Im Swmmng; Im Tennis; Im Vllybl; Hon Roll; Comm.

WILLIAMS, TRICIA; Abington SR HS; Roslyn, PA; (3); Computer Clb; Pres Exploring; Intnl Clb; NAACP; SADD; Concert Band; Orch; Rep Jr Cls; Var L Cheerleading; Hon Roll; Atlhetic Achvt Awd 87; Comp Engrng.

WILLIAMS, WALTER; North Hills HS; Pittsburgh, PA; (3); Church Yth Grp; Exploring; Ski Clb; Crs Cntry; Ftbl; Trk; High Hon Roll; NHS; Diocese Of Ptsbg Voc Prgm 84-86; Bus.

WILLIAMS, WENDELL; Tunkhannock Area HS; Tunkhannock, PA; (3); Computer Clb; Science Clb; Hon Roll; Partl Schlrshp Rensselaer Polytechnc Smmr Prog 87; Elctrcl Engr.

WILLIAMS, WENDI; Lock Haven HS; Lock Haven, PA; (3); Art Clb; Cmnty Wkr; Drama Clb; Political Wkr; Spanish Clb; SADD; Thesps; School Play; Variety Show; Cheerleading; Occptnl Thrpst.

WILLIAMS, WENDY; Belle Vernon Area HS; Fayette City, PA; (3); GAA; Band; Concert Band; Mrchg Band; Bsktbl; Powder Puff Ftbl; Trk; Hon Roll; Bus.

WILLIAMS, WENDY; Grand Army Of The Republic; Wilkes-Barre, PA; (4); Girl Scts; Key Clb; Chorus; Hon Roll; NHS; Ntl Merit Ltr; Mortician.

WILLIAMS, WENDY; West Branch Area HS; Kylertown, PA; (2); Church Yth Grp; Girl Scts; Science Clb; SADD; Band; Concert Band; Mrchg Band; Hon Roll; NHS.

WILLIAMS, WILLIAM; Altoona Area HS; Altoona, PA; (3); Computer Clb; German Clb; Key Clb; Math Tm; Hon Roll; Jr NHS; NEDT Awd; Prfct Atten Awd; German Awd, Pres Acdmc Ftns Awd, Acdmc Achvt Awd 85; Bus.

WILLIAMS, WILLIAM; Central Catholic HS; Verona, PA; (2); 19/310; Golf; NHS; SAR Awd.

WILLIAMS-MORRIS, JENNIFER; Pen Argyl Area SR HS; Pen Argyl, PA; (3); #20 In Class; VP Church Yth Grp; VP Exploring; Drama Clb; Spanish Clb; Chorus; Capt Cheerleading; Coach Actv; Tennis; Hon Roll; 1st Pl Hstry Day 85 & 86.

WILLIAMSON, BRAD; South Fayette HS; Bridgeville, PA; (3); 25/95; Ski Clb; Spanish Clb; Varsity Clb; High Hon Roll; Hon Roll; NHS; Sec Frsh Cls; Pres Jr Cls; Rep Stu Cncl; Var L Ftbl.

WILLIAMSON, CHRIS; Greenwood HS; Liverpool, PA; (4); Chorus; Yrbk Stf; Hon Roll; NHS; Shippensburg U; Crmnl Jstce.

WILLIAMSON, KARLYN; Conneaut Valley HS; Conneautville, PA; (3); Church Yth Grp; Girl Scts; SADD; Church Choir; Hon Roll; Food Svc Ownr.

WILLIAMSON, KRISTINA; Nortwestern SR HS; Albion, PA; (3); Art Clb; Drama Clb; Hon Roll; Gannon U Mrt Awd Sci & Engr 87; Physcl Thrpy.

WILLIAMSON, MATTHEW; Cornell HS; Coraopolis, PA; (3); 12/75; Key Clb; Varsity Clb; VP Frsh Cls; VP Soph Cls; VP Jr Cls; Bsbl; Bsktbl; Ftbl; Hon Roll; NHS; All Star Vly Tournmnt Bsbl; All Sctn Bsbl.

WILLIAMSON, NIEMA; Simon Gratz HS; Philadelphia, PA; (3); Office Aide; Pom Pon; Fbi Agent.

WILLIAMSON, TODD A; Taylor Auderdice HS; Pittsburgh, PA; (4); 13/390; Chess Clb; Math Tm; Science Clb; Ski Clb; SADD; Band; Color Guard; Jazz Band; Mrchg Band; Orch; Chem Olymps 3rd Pl 86; U Pittsburgh Math Scholar Provosts Day 86; Chem.

WILLIAMSON, VALECIA; Harrisburg HS; Harrisburg, PA; (3); 4/207; Band; Mrchg Band; VP Frsh Cls; Pres Soph Cls; Jr Cls; Hon Roll; NHS; Prfct Atten Awd; Acad All Amer Awd 87; Engrng.

WILLIARD, ANDREA; Mifflinburg Area HS; Mifflinburg, PA; (1); Sec Church Yth Grp; Drama Clb; French Clb; Hosp Aide; Chorus; School Play; JV Fld Hcky; Var Trk; Vrsty Ltr Track 86-87; Intr Dsgn.

WILLIARD, DOUGLAS; Upper Dauphin Area HS; Gratz, PA; (4); 52/110; Pres FFA; Williamsport Area CC; Machnst.

WILLIARD, STEPHANIE; Upper Dauphin Area HS; Lykens, PA; (3); Church Yth Grp; Exploring; Varsity Clb; Band; Chorus; Church Choir; Concert Band; Drm & Bgl; Jazz Band; Mrchg Band; Zeswitz Music Awd Outstndng Stu 87; Millersville U; Bio.

WILLING, MICHAEL; Boyertown Area HS; Barto, PA; (3); 69/461; VICA; Band; Church Choir; Hon Roll; :Elec.

WILLING, PAMELA; Boyertown Area SR HS; Boyertown, PA; (4); Office Aide; SADD; Teachers Aide; Chorus; JV Fld Hcky; Stat Trk; Cit Awd; Hon Roll; Prfct Atten Awd; Lansdale Schl Of Bus; Acctng.

WILLINGS, MICHAEL; Warren Area HS; Warren, PA; (3); Nwsp Rptr; Nwsp Stf; Var Bsktbl; Hon Roll; Chorus; Jrnlsm.

WILLIS, JAMES; Southern Huningdon County HS; Orbisonia, PA; (2); Boy Scts; Church Yth Grp; God Cntry Awd; Hon Roll; Electrncs Tech.

WILLIS, JOYCE; Creative & Performing Arts HS; Philadelphia, PA; (4); 11/127; Trs Stu Cncl; Hon Roll; NHS; Schlrshp 4 Yrs To IN U Of PA 87-88; Best Actress Awd 86; 2nd Pl Omega Psi Phi 87TLNT Hunt Fnl 87; IN U Of PA; Theater.

WILLIS, LORIE; Aliquippa SR HS; Aliquippa, PA; (3); Church Yth Grp; Rep Jr Cls; Bsktbl; Sftbl; Trk; Hon Roll; Smmr Schlrshp-Penn ST 87; Pre Med.

WILLIS, LYNN; Mechanicsburg HS; Mechanicsburg, PA; (2); 35/309; Band; Hon Roll; Doctor.

WILLIS, REBECCA; Wyoming Area HS; Falls, PA; (3); Church Yth Grp; Spanish Clb; Sftbl; Hon Roll.

WILLISON, ROBIN; Meadville Area SR HS; Meadville, PA; (2); French Clb; Hosp Aide; Concert Band; JV Trk; Corp Law.

WILLOW, TINA; Juniata HS; Mifflintown, PA; (3); SADD; Varsity Clb; Concert Band; Mrchg Band; Stage Crew; Nwsp Stf; Var JV Bsktbl; Var JV Cheerleading; Stat Trk; NHS; Central PA; Sec.

WILLS, JIM; Central York SR HS; York, PA; (4); 90/200; Boy Scts; JA; Concert Band; Mrchg Band; Orch; Symp Band; Yrbk Stf; JV Var Socr; Hon Roll; Penn ST; Aerospc.

WILLS, MELISSA; Curwensville Area HS; Curwensville, PA; (3); Church Yth Grp; Drama Clb; Girl Scts; Pep Clb; Ski Clb; Chorus; JV Var Cheerleading; Swmmng; High Hon Roll; Hon Roll; Soc Dstngshd Amer H S Stu 87; Acad All Amer 87; Penn ST; Elem Educ.

WILLS, REBECCA; Central York SR HS; York, PA; (3); Political Wkr; Flag Corp; Pol Sci.

WILLS, TED; Altoona Area HS; Altoona, PA; (4); Hon Roll; Elec Engr.

WILLSIE, LONDA; Warren Area HS; Russell, PA; (3); Art Clb; Camera Clb; Cmnty Wkr; Drama Clb; JA; Spanish Clb; School Play; Nwsp Stf; Swmmng; Hon Roll; Comm.

WILLSON, STACY; Riverside HS; Beaver Fls, PA; (3); 9/169; Church Yth Grp; Sec GAA; Y-Teens; Band; Mrchg Band; Symp Band; Nwsp Rptr; Var Sftbl; Hon Roll; NHS; Math.

WILMER, REBECCA; Central Bucks West HS; Doylestown, PA; (3); Drama Clb; Band; Concert Band; Jazz Band; Mrchg Band; School Musical; Hon Roll; Prfct Atten Awd.

WILPS, MARY; Greensburg Central Catholic HS; Herminie, PA; (3); 84/236; Church Yth Grp; GAA; Powder Puff Ftbl; Sftbl; High Hon Roll; Hon Roll; Accntng.

WILSON, ALICE; Milton Area HS; W Milton, PA; (3); Church Yth Grp; Exploring; Band; Church Choir; Concert Band; Mrchg Band; Nwsp Rptr; High Hon Roll; Hon Roll; NHS; Amer Schltc Press Assn Awd 86; 2-2nd Pl PA Schltc Press Assn Awd Feat 85; Dist VIII Band Fest 87; Jrnlsm.

WILSON, ALICIA; Bellefonte Area HS; Bellefonte, PA; (4); 6/237; SADD; Varsity Clb; Drm Mjr(t); Rep Jr Cls; Rep Sr Cls; L Capt Gym; L Trk; Elks Awd; High Hon Roll; NHS; Anthony Soo Meml Trck & Fld Awd 87; PIAA ST Intrmdt Balance Beam Chmpn 87; Dist VI Gymstc Chmpn 87; West Chester U; Scndry Educ.

WILSON, AMY E; Central HS; Scranton, PA; (4); 1/306; Pres VP Speech Tm; Thesps; School Play; Stage Crew; Rep Stu Cncl; High Hon Roll; Ntl Merit SF; Pres Church Yth Grp; French Clb; NFL; Schlrshp Ntl Inst Theatre Arts 86; Schlr Yr 86; Rnnr Up Presusv Spkng 86; Theatre Arts.

WILSON, BARBARA; Abington SR HS; North Hills, PA; (3); 72/502; Cmnty Wkr; Political Wkr; SADD; Mrchg Band; Orch; Rep Soph Cls; Rep Jr Cls; Hon Roll; Jr NHS; NHS; Pres Acad Ftns Awd 84-85; PA Hs Rep 85; Crtst Cntrbtn Orch 85; St Josephs U; Math.

WILSON, BETH; Emmaus HS; Wescosville, PA; (4); Sec Church Yth Grp; Girl Scts; Key Clb; God Cntry Awd; Hon Roll; NHS; Pres Schlr; Chorus; AAL Schlrshp 87; Grl Sct Gold Awd 86; Grl Sct Slvr Awd 84; Lincoln Tech Inst; Drftng.

WILSON, BRIAN; Altoona Area HS; Altoona, PA; (3); Boy Scts; Exploring; Band; Concert Band; Valley Forge ROTC; Med.

WILSON, BRIAN; Selinsgrove HS; Selinsgrove, PA; (4); 39/240; Art Clb; Spanish Clb; Rep Sr Cls; Rep Stu Cncl; JV Bsktbl; Mgr Crs Cntry; Var JV Ftbl; JV Trk; Hon Roll; NHS; Navy.

WILSON, BRYAN; Cedar Cliff HS; Hanover, PA; (4); 65/243; Spanish Clb; SADD; Var L Crs Cntry; Var Swmmng; Var Trk; Im Wt Lftg; High Hon Roll; Hon Roll; Ntl Merit Ltr; Ltr Cmndtn Natl Engrng Aptitd Tst 86; Presdntl Acadc Ftns Awd 87; Penn ST U.

WILSON, CARLA; Dover Area HS; Dover, PA; (3); Chorus; School Musical; School Play; Nwsp Rptr; Nwsp Stf; Rep Stu Cncl; Theatre Arts.

WILSON, CARLA; Elizabethtown Area HS; Elizabethtown, PA; (4); 57/266; Aud/Vis; Church Yth Grp; Thesps; Chorus; Church Choir; Mrchg Band; Orch; School Play; Stage Crew; JV Var Cheerleading; Wmns Symphny Assn Lancstr 87; Meredith G Germer Outstndng Musicn 87; Lebanon Vly Coll; Snd Rcrdng.

WILSON, CEDRIC; Simon Gratz HS; Philadelphia, PA; (3); #9 In Class; ROTC; JV Trk; High Hon Roll; Comp Pgmng.

WILSON, CHARLES; Southern Columbia HS; Elysburg, PA; (3); Boy Scts; Band; Chorus; Concert Band; JV Bsbl; Ftbl; Mgr(s); Hon Roll; Voice Dem Awd; Oceanogrphy.

WILSON, CHRIS; Carrick HS; Pittsburgh, PA; (3); FHA; Q&S; Church Choir; School Musical; Nwsp Stf; High Hon Roll; Hon Roll; Acad Let 85; U Of Pittsburg; Educ.

WILSON, CHRIS; Mt Pleasant Area SR HS; Mt Pleasant, PA; (4); 9/236; Gym; Math Clb; Mrchg Band; VP Sr Cls; L Ice Hcky; L Lcrss; L Tennis; L Vllybl; Capt Wrstlng; Hon Roll; Engrng Awd U Pittsburgh 87; U Pittsburgh; Engrng.

WILSON, CHRISTIAN; Kiski Area HS; Lower Burrell, PA; (3); Boy Scts; Church Yth Grp; Math Tm; Spanish Clb; Varsity Clb; Concert Band; Jazz Band; Pres Frsh Cls; Var L Bsktbl; Trk; Acadmc Ltr 87.

WILSON, CHRISTOPHER; Du Bois Area HS; Dubois, PA; (2); #13 In Class; Boys Clb Am; Boy Scts; Church Yth Grp; Letterman Clb; SADD; Varsity Clb; Stage Crew; Stu Cncl; Crs Cntry; Trk; Comp Pgmmng.

WILSON, DANIEL; Wesleyon Holiness Acad; South Fork, PA; (4); Boy Scts; Church Yth Grp; Cmnty Wkr; Math Clb; Quiz Bowl; Ski Clb; Varsity Clb; School Play; Yrbk Phtg; Yrbk Stf; Doctor.

WILSON, DAVID; Trinity HS; Washington, PA; (3); Chorus; Mbr Penn ST 86; PA ST U; Chem.

WILSON, DEAN; HS Of Engineering And Science; Philadelphia, PA; (3); #90 In Class; Law Enfrcmnt.

WILSON, DEBORAH; B Reed Henderson HS; West Chester, PA; (3); Hosp Aide; JCL; Ski Clb; Var Sftbl; Var Vllybl; Hon Roll; NHS; Spanish NHS; Lat Hnr Soc 87; Natl Lat Exam Magna Cum Laude Awd 86; Phys Ther.

WILSON, DENISE; Vincentian HS; Pittsburgh, PA; (3); Dance Clb; Science Clb; Chorus; High Hon Roll; Drama Clb; Service Clb; School Play; Natl Engl Merit Awd 86.

WILSON, DENNIS; Central Dauphin HS; Harrisburg, PA; (4); 5/868; Boy Scts; Church Yth Grp; Band; Chorus; Church Choir; Concert Band; Jazz Band; Madrigals; Mrchg Band; Orch; Penn ST U Schlr; Franklin & Marshall; Physcs.

WILSON, DESAREA; Northeast Preparatory HS; Willingboro, NJ; (4); Dance Clb; French Clb; School Play; Variety Show; Hon Roll; Hnr Roll-Wyncote Acad 85-86; Fshn Inst Of Tech; Fshn Buying.

WILSON, DOUGLAS; Kennedy Christian HS; Greenvle, PA; (3); Spanish Clb; L Bsbl; Bsktbl; Hon Roll; Law Enfrcmnt.

WILSON, ELIZABETH; Clairton HS; Clairton, PA; (3); Twrlr; High Hon Roll; NHS; Med.

WILSON, ELIZABETH; Coudersport Area JR SR HS; Coudersport, PA; (3); FHA; Pep Clb; Varsity Clb; Band; Concert Band; Drill Tm; Flag Corp; Mrchg Band; Var L Cheerleading; Hon Roll; Vrsty Ltr Chrldng 85-86; Mst Enthusstc Chrldr 84-85; Acad Awd 86-87.

WILSON IV, GABRIEL J; Devon Prep; Exton, PA; (3); Nwsp Stf; Trs Frsh Cls; Pres Soph Cls; Pres Jr Cls; JV Bsktbl; Var Crs Cntry; Var Trk; Hon Roll; NHS; Loyalty Spirit Awd 85; Hist Awd 86; Cross Cty Track 85-87; Bus.

WILSON, GREG; South Western HS; Hanover, PA; (3); 2/233; Boy Scts; High Hon Roll; NHS; Prfct Atten Awd; Eagle Scout 87; Engrng.

WILSON, GREGORY; Lampeter-Strasburg HS; Lancaster, PA; (3); 3/150; AFS; School Musical; Yrbk Stf; Var Bsbl; Var Crs Cntry; Bausch & Lomb Sci Awd; High Hon Roll; JETS Awd; NHS; PA Soc Prfsnl Engrs Awd 87; Engrng.

WILSON, HEATHER A; Mt Lebanon HS; Pittsburgh, PA; (4); 8/537; Var L Crs Cntry; Var L Trk; High Hon Roll; Ntl Merit SF; NEDT Awd.

WILSON, HOWARD; Donegal HS; Maytown, PA; (3); Pres Church Yth Grp; Drama Clb; Band; Jazz Band; Variety Show; Bsktbl; JV Socr; JV Tennis; Rotary Intl Exchng Std West Germany 86-87; Civil Engrng.

WILSON, JAMES T; Scranton Central HS; Scranton, PA; (2); Boys Clb Am; Church Yth Grp; Speech Tm; SADD; Rep Soph Cls; Var Bsktbl; High Hon Roll; Thesps; Lockawanna Cnty JR Hich Bsktbl League Sthrn Div All Star 86; Our Lady Of Fatima Ctr Yth Vlntr Awd 86.

WILSON, JEFF; Big Spring HS; Carlisle, PA; (3); 6/266; VP L Ftbl; VP L Trk; High Hon Roll; Ntl Merit SF; Dickinson Smr Schlrshp 87; Outstndng Frnch Stu 86-87; PA ST U; Aero Engr.

WILSON, JENNIFER; Bishop Mc Devitt HS; Harrisburg, PA; (3); 48/250; Art Clb; Church Yth Grp; Service Clb; SADD; Teachers Aide; Rep Jr Cls; Stu Cncl; Bsktbl; Mgr(s); Sftbl; Hon Mntn Natn Schlstc Wrtng Cont, Hon Mntn Art 86; Harrisburg Area CC; Bus Law.

WILSON, JENNIFER L; Coatesville Area SR HS; Coatesville, PA; (4); Leo Clb; Spanish Clb; Chorus; Concert Band; Mrchg Band; Hon Roll; Everett E Blevins Mem Awd 87; Kutztown U; Bus Admin.

WILSON, JENNY; Blairsville SR HS; Blairsville, PA; (1); 14/118; Church Yth Grp; Band; Concert Band; Mrchg Band; Trs Frsh Cls; Rep Stu Cncl; High Hon Roll; U Pittsburgh; Pharmacy.

WILSON, JOSEPH; West Philadelphia Catholic HS; Philadelphia, PA; (3); 9/248; Church Yth Grp; Stage Crew; Yrbk Stf; Im Bsktbl; Var L Socr; Hon Roll; Merit Awd 84; Sprtsmnshp Awd 84; Penn ST; Bus Mgmt.

WILSON, JOSETTE; Little Flower HS; Philadelphia, PA; (3); 107/386; Church Yth Grp; Dance Clb; FCA; Latin Clb; SADD; Church Choir; Bowling; Swmmng; Vllybl; Hon Roll; Miss E Frankford JR Awd 83; Bst Drss Fshn Shw 83; Miss E Frankford 84; Howard U; Educ.

WILSON, JOY; Chestnut Ridge HS; Manns Choice, PA; (3); 21/143; Church Yth Grp; Sec SADD; Band; Chorus; Church Choir; Concert Band; Mrchg Band; Nwsp Phtg; Stat Bsktbl; Var L Sftbl; IN U Of PA; Prfrmng Music.

WILSON, KATHLEEN; Harbor Creek HS; Erie, PA; (4); Spanish Clb; Chorus; Variety Show; L Var Trk; Hon Roll; Northwest Inst; Cosmtlgst.

WILSON, KELLIE; Young SR HS; W Newton, PA; (3); Spanish Clb; Band; Yrbk Stf; Var L Trk; Var Twrlr; NHS; Prfct Atten Awd; Drama Clb; Girl Scts; Office Aide; Westmoreland Cnty Chorus 85-86; PMEA Dist Chorus 87; PMEA Rgn St Chorus 87.

WILSON, KEVIN; Hempfield Area SR HS; Greensburg, PA; (3); Chess Clb; Sec Trs Church Yth Grp; Computer Clb; Ski Clb; High Hon Roll; Hon Roll; Jr NHS; NHS; Prfct Atten Awd; Science.

WILSON, KIMBERLY; Harry S Truman HS; Levittown, PA; (3); Church Yth Grp; FCA; Bsktbl; Cheerleading; Fld Hcky; Trk; Hon Roll; Bus.

WILSON, LATOSHA; Little Flower HS; Philadelphia, PA; (3); Church Yth Grp; Girl Scts; Church Choir; Prfct Atten Awd; Temple U; Phrmcy.

WILSON, MALIK; Central York SR HS; York, PA; (3); Varsity Clb; Rep Stu Cncl; Var Trk; Im Vllybl; Hon Roll; Bus.

WILSON, MICHAEL; Bishop Mc Cort HS; Johnstown, PA; (2); German Clb; JV Bsktbl; JV Ftbl; High Hon Roll; NHS.

WILSON, MICHAEL; West Catholic HS; Philadelphia, PA; (3); 74/249; Boy Scts; Debate Tm; FBLA; ROTC; Yrbk Stf; Off Sr Cls; Crs Cntry; Trk; Ntl Black Caucus Of ST Legsltr 87; Certo Of Apprctn For Job 87; Drexel; Bus Adm.

WILSON, MINDY D; Keystone HS; Emlenton, PA; (3); Church Yth Grp; FBLA; Pep Clb; SADD; Teachers Aide; Varsity Clb; Chorus; Concert Band; School Musical; Yrbk Phtg; Cty,Dist Band 82-87; Dist Track 86-87; Stu Cncl Awd 86-87; Sec.

WILSON, NATALIE; Bellevernon HS; Belle Vernon, PA; (3); FNA; JA; Nwsp Rptr; Yrbk Rptr; Hon Roll; Cntrbtd-Spnsh Lang Cmptn 87; Nrsng.

WILSON, RACHEL; Huntingdon Area HS; Huntingdon, PA; (3); 4/276; Art Clb; Science Clb; Yrbk Stf; Var Crs Cntry; Hon Roll; NHS; Ntl Merit SF; Prfct Atten Awd; PA Govrnr Schl Sci 87; Poety Publ Cricket Magzn 85; Sci Stdnt Mnth Awd May 86; Sci.

WILSON, RANDALL; Glendale JR SR HS; Blandburg, PA; (2); Drama Clb; Spanish Clb; JV Bsktbl; Wrstlng; Pres Schlr; Chrl Awd 85-87; U MD; Crimnlgy.

WILSON, RENEE; Beaver Area JR SR HS; Beaver, PA; (2); Rep Spanish Clb; Color Guard; Sftbl; Hon Roll.

WILSON, SCOTT; Oil City HS; Oil City, PA; (3); Varsity Clb; Yrbk Stf; Sec Jr Cls; Pres Stu Cncl; Var L Crs Cntry; Var L Swmmng; Var L Trk; Hon Roll; Sec NHS; Church Yth Grp; PA Free Enterprise Week 87; Bus.

WILSON, SERENA; Reynolds HS; Greenville, PA; (4); 35/149; Cmnty Wkr; Latin Clb; Library Aide; Math Tm; Q&S; Science Clb; Nwsp Stf; George Wright Fund 87; Gannon U; Engl Comm.

WILSON, SHANNON; Fairchance-Georges SR HS; Fairchance, PA; (4); Band; Concert Band; Mrchg Band; High Hon Roll; Hon Roll; Jr NHS; NHS.

WILSON, SHANNON; Mt Pleasant HS; Greensburg, PA; (3); 84/200; GAA; Latin Clb; Band; Concert Band; Mrchg Band; Swmmng; Hon Roll; Occptnl Thrpy.

WILSON, SUSANNE; Twin Valley HS; Birdsboro, PA; (3); 26/148; Church Yth Grp; Computer Clb; Hst FFA; Pep Clb; Band; Concert Band; Nwsp Ed-Chief; Nwsp Rptr; Wrtr.

WILSON, THOMAS; Bethlehem Catholic HS; Bethlehem, PA; (4); 9/200; Church Yth Grp; Key Clb; Model UN; Political Wkr; Quiz Bowl; SADD; Nwsp Ed-Chief; Nwsp Phtg; Nwsp Rptr; Nwsp Sprt Ed; Geo Wshngtn U; Poltcl Sci.

WILSON, THOMAS K R; Quakertown SR HS; Quakertown, PA; (3); 1/303; VP Church Yth Grp; Pres Soph Cls; Pres Jr Cls; Pres Sr Cls; Pres Stu Cncl; Var Capt Socr; Var Capt Wrstlng; High Hon Roll; NHS; Voice Dem Awd; Amer Legion Awd 85; Pres Ftns Awd 85.

WILSON, TODD; Dubois Area HS; Dubois, PA; (2); Hon Roll; Penn ST.

WILSON, TONYA; Jefferson-Morgan HS; Rices Landing, PA; (3); 12/69; School Play; Yrbk Stf; Hon Roll; Stu Secy 86-87; ICM Schl Of Bus; Trvl-Trsm.

WILSON, TRACI; Henderson HS; W Chester, PA; (3); Cmnty Wkr; SADD; JV Var Bsktbl; JV Var Socr; Var JV DECA; Hon Roll; GAA; Ski Clb; Varsity Clb; Soccer Awds 84-87; Athl Trngng.

WILSON, TROY; Trinity HS; Washington, PA; (3); 224/467; JV Var Bsktbl; Bus.

WILSON, ZANETTA; Jefferson-Morgan HS; Clarksville, PA; (4); 33/97; Office Aide; Sec Spanish Clb; Church Choir; School Play; Yrbk Stf; Pres Sr Cls; Stu Cncl; Hon Roll; Gregg Typing Awd 86; Girl Of Month 87; Waynesburg Coll; Criminology.

WILSONCROFT, AMY; Center Area HS; Aliquippa, PA; (2); Spanish Clb; Sec Frsh Cls; Bowling; Score Keeper; Stat Trk; Hon Roll; Merit Awds Spnsh I, II 86-87; Trvl.

WILT, CHERYL; Lower Bucks Christian Acad; Huntingdon Vly, PA; (4); 3/27; Church Yth Grp; Political Wkr; Chorus; Church Choir; Yrbk Stf; Capt Var Cheerleading; Vllybl; High Hon Roll; Acdmc Effrt Awd 87; Pres Acdmc Ftnss Awd 87; Vrsty Chrldng Coachs Awd 87; Cedarville Coll; Nrsng.

WILT, JESSICA LEIGH; State College Intermediate HS; Pa Furnace, PA; (1); 74/476; Church Yth Grp; Spanish Clb; Chorus; Cit Awd; High Hon Roll; Power Of The Paws Awd, Pres Ftnss Awd & Cntral PA Yth Ballet Smmr Pgm Schlrshp 87; Dance.

WILT, JOANN; Penn Cambria SR HS; Cresson, PA; (3); Spanish Clb; Band; Bsktbl; Vllybl; Hon Roll; IN U PA.

WILT, JOYCE K; Salisbury-Elk Lick HS; Boynton, PA; (3); Band; Chorus; School Play; Nwsp Stf; Yrbk Stf; Stat Bsktbl; Sftbl; Hon Roll; Prfct Atten Awd; Ntl Ldrshp Awd; All Cnty Band; Tri St Hnrs Band; RN.

WILT, KRIS; Salisbury-Elk Lick JR SR HS; Boynton, PA; (3); Hosp Aide; Band; School Play; Nwsp Stf; Yrbk Stf; Sftbl; Hon Roll; Prfct Atten Awd; Church Yth Grp; All Cnty Band; Tri-ST Hnrs Band; Ntl Ldrshp Awd; RN.

WILT, LORI; Altoona Area HS; Altoona, PA; (3); 2/789; Drama Clb; Key Clb; Math Clb; Spanish Clb; SADD; Band; Church Choir; School Musical; Rep Frsh Cls; High Hon Roll; Dorothy Mc Gregory Vocal Awd 85; PA ST U; Chem Engrng.

WILT, SANDY; York Suburban HS; York, PA; (3); Debate Tm; JA; Band; Chorus; Jazz Band; Mrchg Band; Orch; Pep Band; Symp Band; Pres Church Yth Grp; Shenandoah Smmr Music Camp Scholar Awds 85 & 86; Music.

WILT, STEPHANIE; Central York SR HS; York, PA; (3); Varsity Clb; Drill Tm; Mrchg Band; Nwsp Stf; Yrbk Stf; Rep Stu Cncl; Var Cheerleading; Rep Frsh Cls; Rep Jr Cls; Rep Sr Cls; Paralegal.

WILT, STEVEN; Dover Area HS; Dover, PA; (3); Art Clb; Boy Scts; Letterman Clb; Ski Clb; SADD; Varsity Clb; L Bsktbl; Crs Cntry; Ftbl; Tennis; R G Canning Outstndng Yth Awd 84; Soap Box Drby Awd Wnnr 83; 5th Pl Dist Meet Trk 3200 Rly 87; Bus Mgmnt.

WILTSCHEK, WALTER J; Christian Schl Of York; York, PA; (4); Church Yth Grp; Office Aide; School Play; Nwsp Ed-Chief; Yrbk Rptr; VP Stu Cncl; Stat Bsktbl; High Hon Roll; Ntl Merit SF; Dnfth Awd; Bryan Coll; Math Ed.

WILVER, TIM; Danville SR HS; Riverside, PA; (3); Church Yth Grp; Band; Concert Band; Jazz Band; Mrchg Band; Symp Band; Hon Roll; Prfct Atten Awd; Hstry.

WIMBERLY, ANDREA; Cedar Cliff HS; Camp Hill, PA; (3); 57/307; JCL; Latin Clb; Band; Mrchg Band; Symp Band; High Hon Roll; Latin Natl Hnr Soc; Bst Clb; SADD Clb; Accntng.

WIMBS, GEORGE; West Mifflin Area HS; W Mifflin, PA; (3); Boys Clb Am; High Hon Roll; Hon Roll; Penn ST; Math.

WIMMER, MARK; Danville SR HS; Danville, PA; (2); Band; Concert Band; Jazz Band; Mrchg Band; Var L Crs Cntry; Var L Trk; High Hon Roll; Prfct Atten Awd; Air Force Acad.

WIMMER, MAUREEN; Danville SR HS; Danville, PA; (3); 2/194; French Clb; Color Guard; Mrchg Band; High Hon Roll; NHS; NEDT Awd; Pres Schlr; Sal; Chem Engrng.

WINANS, WILLIAM; Brownsville HS; Brownsville, PA; (3); 2/200; Computer Clb; Drama Clb; Math Tm; Ski Clb; Stage Crew; Nwsp Rptr; JV Capt Ftbl; Trk; NHS; Rotary Awd; Comp Sci.

WINCHESTER, JEFFERY B; Dover Area HS; Wellsville, PA; (3); Band; Jazz Band; Mrchg Band; Orch; Hon Roll; York Coll Of PA.

WINCKO, DAVID; Central Catholic HS; W Mifflin, PA; (3); 48/260; JV Bsbl; JV Crs Cntry; Var L Trk; Hon Roll; NHS; PA ST U.

WINDISH, RICHARD; Saucon Valley HS; Hellertown, PA; (4); 20/138; Concert Band; Jazz Band; Var L Bsktbl; Var L Ftbl; Var L Trk; High Hon Roll; Hon Roll; Ftbl Schlr-Athl, Mst Outstmdng Male Athl Of Yr & Outstndng Sr Athl-Ftbl & Track 86-87; Lehigh U; Engrng.

WINDOM, ROBERT; Central Dauphin HS; Harrisburg, PA; (3); 104/370; Var Capt Ftbl; Hon Roll; Im Bsktbl; Var L Trk; Im Vllybl; JV Wrstlng; Pre-Law.

WINDSHEIMER, DANA; Burgettstown Area HS; Burgettstown, PA; (2); 18/170; Church Yth Grp; French Clb; Ski Clb; Band; Concert Band; Mrchg Band; Pep Band; Symp Band; Hon Roll; Hrvrd U; Law.

WINDSOR, ROSE; Tyrone Area HS; Tyrone, PA; (2); Drama Clb; Key Clb; Sec SADD; Chorus; Color Guard; Flag Corp; Mrchg Band; School Play; Lit Mag; Hon Roll; 1st & 2nd Mdls Flag Solo 86; U CA, Santa Cruz; Dnc.

WINEBARGER, GLENDA; Northern Lebanon HS; Jonestown, PA; (4); Pres VP Church Yth Grp; Political Wkr; Sec SADD; Band; Church Choir; School Musical; Var L Tennis; Library Aide; Pep Clb; Farm Women Grp 5 Awd Home Ec Stu Hghst Avg 87; Mansfield U; Dietetics.

WINEGARDNER, REBECCA; Blair County Christian Schl; East Freedom, PA; (2); 3/15; Church Yth Grp; Debate Tm; Yrbk Stf; Sec Frsh Cls; Trs Soph Cls; Var Capt Bsktbl; Var Cheerleading; Var Sftbl; Var Trk; High Hon Roll; Bob Jones U.

WINELAND, MELISSA A; Central HS; Roaring Spring, PA; (3); 26/187; Trs Camp Fr Inc; FBLA; FTA; Ski Clb; SADD; Chorus; Stu Cncl; Hon Roll; Hnr Mention Poem 86; Golden Poet Awd 86; Poem Pblshd Bk 87; Lock Haven; Spec Educ.

WINEY, DANIEL; Juniata HS; Mifflintown, PA; (3); Chess Clb; Church Yth Grp; Computer Clb; SADD; Varsity Clb; Var L Bsktbl; L JV Socr; Var L Tennis; Var Hon Roll; NHS; Amercn Red Crss Lfsvng Crs 85; Amercn Red Crss Bsc CPR Lfe Spprt 86; Military; Avtn.

WINEY, DENISE; Garden Spot HS; New Holland, PA; (4); 17/216; Church Yth Grp; Cmnty Wkr; Debate Tm; Drama Clb; Spanish Clb; School Musical; School Play; Rep Jr Cls; Rep Sr Cls; Var Trk; Acad Schlrshp 86-87; Varsity Letters In Theater 87; Eastern Nazarene Coll; Psychlgy.

WINFIELD, MICHAEL; Bethel Park SR HS; Bethel Park, PA; (4); 42/519; Chorus; School Musical; Swing Chorus; Variety Show; JV Ftbl; High Hon Roll; NHS; Pres Acadmc Ftns Awd 87; Grad Hi Hnrs 87; Grove City Coll; Pre Law.

WING, SUSAN; Portersville Christian Schl; Hamburg, IA; (2); Chorus; Church Choir; Nwsp Rptr; Nwsp Stf; Yrbk Phtg; Yrbk Rptr; Yrbk Stf; Rep Frsh Cls; Var Cheerleading; High Hon Roll; Geneva Coll; Plstc Srgry.

WINGARD, BARRY; Brookville Area HS; Brookville, PA; (4); Pres Art Clb; Church Yth Grp; French Clb; Library Aide; Church Choir; Stage Crew; Variety Show.

WINGARD, BOYD; Forest Hills SR HS; South Fork, PA; (4); Art Clb; Computer Clb; Ski Clb; JV Ftbl; Im Mgr Sftbl; Im Mgr Vllybl; Hon Roll; U Of Pittsburgh; Bus Mgmt.

WINGARD, BRIDGET; Keystone HS; Shippenville, PA; (3); 26/141; Church Yth Grp; Pres 4-H; ST 4-H Beef Awd 87; ST 4-H Essy Awd 83; Elem Ed.

WINGARD, JULIE; Keystone HS; Shippenville, PA; (3); 4-H; FHA; Pep Clb; Yrbk Stf; Stu Cncl; Capt Var Bsktbl; Trk; Hon Roll; Prfct Atten Awd; Psych.

WINGARD, KEVIN; W Middlesex HS; Sharon, PA; (4); 2/95; Stu Cncl; Capt Ftbl; DAR Awd; High Hon Roll; Jr NHS; NHS; Prfct Atten Awd; Sal; Spanish NHS; George Washington U; Systms Eng.

WINGARD, SHELLY; Connellsville Area HS; Dunbar, PA; (4); 38/550; Trs Camera Clb; Church Yth Grp; Hosp Aide; School Musical; School Play; Nwsp Bus Mgr; Yrbk Sprt Ed; High Hon Roll; NHS; Spanish NHS; Nurse Aide; Upward Bound; Prom Comm; CA U Of PA; Sec Math.

WINGER, ERIN; Susquenita HS; Duncannon, PA; (3); Art Clb; French Clb; Leo Clb; Ski Clb; School Play; Nwsp Stf; Rep Stu Cncl; Var L Cheerleading; Tennis; Trk; Cert Achvt Cngrssnl Art Comptn 87.

WINGERD, STEPHANIE; Chambersburg Area SR HS; Chambersburg, PA; (4); Sec Trs Church Yth Grp; JCL; Key Clb; Band; Concert Band; Mrchg Band; High Hon Roll; NHS; Shippensburg U; Acctnt.

WINGERT, CHRISTOPHER; South Western HS; Hanover, PA; (4); 60/220; Pres Key Clb; Quiz Bowl; Varsity Clb; Yrbk Stf; Pres Frsh Cls; Pres Soph Cls; Co-Capt Tennis; Elks Awd; Rep Stu Cncl; Natl Yng Ldrs Conf 86; H Obrien Yth Fndtn 85; Gettysburg Coll; Pltcl Sci.

WINGERTER, JULIE R; Mercyhurst Prep; Erie, PA; (3); 1/185; Am Leg Aux Girls St; Letterman Clb; Off Stu Cncl; Gym; High Hon Roll; NHS; Intl Bacclaureate Schlr 85-87; PA Sci Acad 86; Intl Rltns.

WINGERTER, RUTH; Belle Vernon Area HS; Belle Vernon, PA; (3); FBLA; NFL; Ski Clb; Nwsp Ed-Chief; Yrbk Ed-Chief; Stat Wrstlng; High Hon Roll; NHS; Voice Dem Awd; Stu Of Yr 85; PA ST; Lawyr.

WINGHART, CHRISTOPHER; Moniteau HS; Chicora, PA; (3); Science Clb; Spanish Clb; Teachers Aide; JV Bsktbl; JV Timer; Var Trk; JV Var Wt Lftg; Hon Roll; Butler Cnty Sprtsmn Cncl Cnsrvtn Schl Grad & PA Fsh & Game Cmmssn Awds 86; PA Jr Acad Of Sci Awd 87; Env Sci.

WINGLE, CRAIG; Sch Haven HS; Sch Haven, PA; (2); 17/101; Church Yth Grp; Cmnty Wkr; FCA; Science Clb; Spanish Clb; JV Var Bsbl; JV Bsktbl; Hon Roll; Annapolis USANA; Aviation.

WINIKOFF, CARA; Taylor Allderdice HS; Pittsburgh, PA; (3); Camera Clb; Dance Clb; Ski Clb; SADD; Temple Yth Grp; Y-Teens; Chorus; Yrbk Stf; Hon Roll.

WINK, MICHAELA; Hamburg Area JR/Sr HS; Hamburg, PA; (3); German Clb; Pres Band; Chorus; Capt Color Guard; Concert Band; Drm Mjr(t); Mrchg Band; School Musical; Hon Roll; Delta Epsilon Phi Germn Natl Hnr Soc; Ensemble; Acadc Lttr Awd German II, III; Cedar Crest; Vet.

WINKLER, ANNE; Trinity Christian HS; Monroeville, PA; (3); 2/14; Pres Church Yth Grp; German Clb; Chorus; School Play; Yrbk Stf; Cheerleading; High Hon Roll; Jr NHS; NHS; NEDT Awd; Calvin Coll; Nrsg.

WINKLER, CHRISTIAN; Trinity Christian Schl; Monroeville, PA; (2); 1/12; Church Yth Grp; Chorus; School Musical; Var Bsktbl; High Hon Roll; Jr NHS; NEDT Awd; Drama Clb; German Clb; Stage Crew; Physcs.

WINKLER, DANIEL; Kutztown Area HS; Kutztown, PA; (4); Band; Concert Band; Jazz Band; Variety Show; Rep Frsh Cls; VP Soph Cls; Rep Jr Cls; Stu Cncl; Ftbl; Socr; U Of Pittsburgh Johnstown; Engr.

WINNIES, APRIL; Spring-Ford SR HS; Royersford, PA; (3); 113/256; Spanish Clb; Chorus; Drill Tm; Flag Corp; Rep Frsh Cls; Rep Soph Cls; Rep Jr Cls; Var Fld Hcky; Var Lcrss; Advrtsng.

WINOGRODZKI, TERESA; Greater Johnstown HS; Johnstown, PA; (3); Pep Clb; Hon Roll; Sec.

WINSLEY, TORAZE; Chester HS; Chester, PA; (2); Hon Roll; Bus.

WINSLOW, HEATHER; North Hills HS; Pittsburgh, PA; (3); 43/485; Hosp Aide; JA; Keywanettes; Chorus; High Hon Roll; NHS; Grove City Coll; Bus.

WINSLOW, MELISSA; Union JR SR HS; Rimersburg, PA; (3); Church Yth Grp; Pep Clb; SADD; Var L Bsktbl; Im Trk; Var L Vllybl; Hon Roll; Psych.

WINSLOW, RANDY; Penn Trafford HS; Trafford, PA; (2); Church Yth Grp; FBLA; JCL; Latin Clb; High Hon Roll; Hon Roll; Physcl Thrpst.

WINSOCK, MARK; Wyoming Area HS; W Wyoming, PA; (2); German Clb; Jazz Band; Bowling; Comp.

WINTER, ALEXIS; William Penn SR HS; York, PA; (4); Boys Clb Am; Cmnty Wkr; Nwsp Rptr; Nwsp Stf; Var Capt Swmmng; Var Tennis; High Hon Roll; Hon Roll; Prfct Atten Awd; Bearcat For Mnth March 87; Yorktowne Bus Inst; Accntng.

WINTER, JOHN; The Episcopal Acad; Pottstown, PA; (2); JV Capt Lcrss; JV Socr; Im Wt Lftg; God Cntry Awd; Hon Roll.

WINTER, KATHRYN A; Shippensburg Area SR HS; Shippensburg, PA; (3); 17/262; Am Leg Aux Girls St; Girl Scts; Spanish Clb; Color Guard; Orch; School Musical; Mgr Trk; Hon Roll; NHS; Spanish NHS; Girl Scout Slvr Awd 87; Bio.

WINTER, SHARON; Mechanicsburg SR HS; Mechanicsburg, PA; (3); 53/343; Church Yth Grp; Dance Clb; Pep Clb; Band; Church Choir; Concert Band; High Hon Roll.

WINTERHALTER, MEGAN; Seneca Valley HS; Mars, PA; (4); 57/347; Math Clb; Ski Clb; Teachers Aide; Varsity Clb; JV Bsktbl; Capt Var Sftbl; Capt Var Tennis; JV Trk; Hon Roll; VP NHS; U Of Pittsburgh; Anestheslgst.

WINTERMANTEL, MARY; Avonworth JR-SR HS; Pittsbg, PA; (4); 5/99; AFS; Pres French Clb; High Hon Roll; VP NHS; Dstngshd Yth Awd 85-87; Engl Awd & Frnch Awd SR Cls 86-87; Pres Acad Fit Awd 86-87; Phrmcy.

WINTERS, DAWN; West Middlesex JR SR HS; West Middlesex, PA; (2); Sftbl; Swmmng; High Hon Roll; Hon Roll; Band; Concert Band; Mrchg Band; Pep Band; Stud Achvt Awd 87; Edinboro Coll; Art.

WINTERS, DEBRA; Mid-Valley HS; Olyphant, PA; (4); Pres Church Yth Grp; Drama Clb; Chorus; Nwsp Stf; Var Cheerleading; High Hon Roll; NHS; Bio.

WINTERS, JEANNE; Mt Calvary Christian Schl; Manheim, PA; (4); Church Yth Grp; Library Aide; Teachers Aide; Chorus; Orch; School Play; Yrbk Phtg; Yrbk Stf; Hon Roll; NHS; Lbrty U; Elem Educ.

WINTERS, JILL; Conrad Weiser HS; Reinholds, PA; (2); 68/163; Latin Clb; Lit Mag; JV Bsktbl; Rutgers; Chld Psych.

WINTERS, KIMBERLY; West Scranton HS; Scranton, PA; (3); Orch; Communication.

WINTERS, LISA; Warwick HS; Lititz, PA; (2); 27/300; Soph Cls; Stu Cncl; JV Fld Hcky; Vllybl; Hon Roll; Elem Ed.

WINTERS, MALISSA; Moshannon Valley HS; Madera, PA; (3); 15/120; Church Yth Grp; Letterman Clb; Spanish Clb; SADD; Varsity Clb; Chorus; Variety Show; Nwsp Stf; Yrbk Stf; Sftbl; Clarion U; Elem Educ.

WINTERS, PATRICIA; Lancaster Mennonite HS; Lancaster, PA; (3); 12/167; Pres Church Yth Grp; Chorus; Church Choir; School Play; Stat Bsktbl; Mgr(s); Vllybl; NHS; Fld Hcky; High Hon Roll; 2nd Schl Fine Arts Festvl Speech Ctgry 87; Messiah Coll; Child Psych.

WINTERS, PENNY; Red Lion SR HS; Red Lion, PA; (3); 66/342; Pres Church Yth Grp; Varsity Clb; Chorus; Church Choir; Var L Swmmng; JV Vllybl; High Hon Roll; Hon Roll; Cosmtlgy.

WINTERS, REGINA L; George Schl; Brooklyn, NY; (4); Art Clb; Cmnty Wkr; Chorus; School Musical; School Play; Variety Show; Yrbk Stf; Rep Stu Cncl; JV Crs Cntry; Ntl Merit Schol; LEAD Pgm Diploma 86; NYC Regents Scholar 87; Harvard; Advrtsng.

WINTERTON, SCOTT; Northeast Bradford RD 1 HS; Rome, PA; (3); Chess Clb; Cmnty Wkr; Ski Clb; JV Ftbl; Var Trk; Coast Guard Acad; Officer.

WINTHER, PHIL; Upland HS; West Chester, PA; (1); Church Yth Grp; School Play; Var Ice Hcky; Var Lcrss; Var Socr; High Hon Roll; Hon Roll; Benchmark Hgh Acad Awd 84.

WINWARD, DEBORAH; Kennard-Dale HS; Fawn Grove, PA; (3); Church Yth Grp; French Clb; Ski Clb; Varsity Clb; Church Choir; Stage Crew; Var Crs Cntry; Var Trk; Mdcl Asst.

WINZENRIED, TINA; Harford Christian HS; Delta, PA; (2); Chess Clb; Church Yth Grp.

WINZER, DONNA; Emmaus HS; Macungie, PA; (3); German Clb; Key Clb; Q&S; Chorus; Church Choir; School Musical; Im Bsktbl; Im Vllybl; Hon Roll; Jr NHS; Wittenberg U; Hstry.

WION, JENNIFER; Allderdice HS; Pittsburgh, PA; (4); 12/357; Ski Clb; NHS; Ntl Merit SF; Tues Music Clb Schlrshp 86-87; Keynotes Schlrshp 86-87; Ntl Fndtn Arts Awd 87; Cleveland Inst Of Music.

WIORKOWSKI, ROBIN; Riverside HS; Taylor, PA; (3); German Clb; Hosp Aide; Ski Clb; Flag Corp; Yrbk Stf; Rep Stu Cncl; Stat Bsbl; Var Trk; Gregg Typg Achvt Awd 86; Phys Ther.

WIRFEL, LINDA; Bishop Carroll HS; Ebensburg, PA; (3); 15/128; Sec Church Yth Grp; Pep Clb; Spanish Clb; Church Choir; Yrbk Stf; Trk; Vllybl; Hon Roll.

WIRFEL, TINA; Northern York County HS; Dillsburg, PA; (4); 7/200; Church Yth Grp; Science Clb; Spanish Clb; Chorus; Color Guard; Trk; High Hon Roll; Hon Roll; NHS; Pres Schlr; Ind Stds Pgm Comp 85 & Sign Lang 86-87; Math Hghst GPA 87; Bloomsburg U; Math Tchr.

WIRRICK, MICHAEL; Lewistown Area SR HS; Lewistown, PA; (2); JV Wrstlng; High Hon Roll; Hon Roll; Prfct Atten Awd; Young Mens Chrstn Assn Fit Scholar 86-87; Acad Ltr 85-86; Athletic Cert 86-87; PA ST U; Aerontcl Engrng.

WIRT, ANDREW; Christian Schl Of York; York, PA; (2); Church Yth Grp; Hosp Aide; Concert Band; Pres Frsh Cls; Chrmn Soph Cls; Var Bsbl; Var JV Bsktbl; Var Socr; Hon Roll; Med.

WIRT, LAURIE; Montoursville HS; Montoursville, PA; (3); 36/185; Church Yth Grp; Sec German Clb; Hosp Aide; Key Clb; Letterman Clb; Ski Clb; Nwsp Stf; Yrbk Rptr; Yrbk Stf; Rep Jr Cls; 2nd & 3rd Pl Artcls PSPA 85-86, 1st 86-87.

WIRTH, KRISTIE; Shikellamy HS; Sunbury, PA; (2); 21/360; Church Yth Grp; Hst Frsh Cls; Hst Soph Cls; Hst Jr Cls; Rep Stu Cncl; Cheerleading; Crs Cntry; Trk; Hon Roll.

WIRTNER, MELANIE; Bethel Park SR HS; Bethel Park, PA; (4); Capt Swmmng; Hon Roll; Schlrshp U AL 87; PIAA ST Swmmng Champ 200 & 500 Yrd 87; PIAA ST Champ Team 87; U AL; Bio.

WIRTZ, LYDIA; Hampton HS; Allison Pk, PA; (3); 11/200; Mrchg Band; Pep Band; Symp Band; Trs Frsh Cls; Trs Soph Cls; Rep Badmtn; VP L Sftbl; Tennis; High Hon Roll; VP NHS; Vrsty Sftbl Ltr 85-86; Slctd PMEA Dist I Hon Band 85-86.

WISCOUNT, BETH; Pine Grove Area HS; Tremont, PA; (4); School Play; Yrbk Stf; Trs Frsh Cls; Im Vllybl; Hon Roll; Pres Acad Ftnss Awd 87; Millersville U; Scndry Educ.

WISE, BECKY; Milton SR HS; Milton, PA; (2); 51/254; Spanish Clb; SADD; Chorus; JV Bsktbl; Pres Schlr.

WISE, BETH ANN; Red Lion SR HS; Red Lion, PA; (4); 28/337; Pres Church Yth Grp; Varsity Clb; Pres Mrchg Band; Pres Symp Band; Var Bsktbl; NHS; Pres Schlr; Mdfrn Music Mstrs & Dstrct Band 86 & 87; Hnr Stu 87; Shippensburg U; Med Tech.

WISE, CHERYL; Plum SR HS; New Kensington, PA; (3); 30/443; Dance Clb; FHA; Hosp Aide; Science Clb; Band; Concert Band; Drill Tm; Mrchg Band; Orch; School Musical; Natl Hnrs Soc 87; U Of Pittsbrgh; Nrsng.

WISE, DANA; Trinity HS; Washington, PA; (3); 235/401; French Clb; Key Clb; Pep Clb; JV Vllybl; Penn ST; Mgmt.

WISE, DENISE; Steel Valley HS; W Homestead, PA; (3); 13/206; Dance Clb; Yrbk Stf; Var Crs Cntry; Gym; Capt Twrlr; Sec Wt Lftg; High Hon Roll; Hon Roll; NHS; VFW Awd; U Of Pittsburgh; Pre-Med.

WISE, FAWN; Northwestern HS; Cranesville, PA; (4); Church Yth Grp; Drama Clb; Chorus; Church Choir; School Play; Yrbk Phtg; Yrbk Sprt Ed; Yrbk Stf; Var Cheerleading; Hon Roll; Mercyhurst Coll; Nrsng.

WISE, HEATHER; York Surburban HS; York, PA; (3); JA; Pep Clb; Varsity Clb; School Musical; Yrbk Stf; Var JV Cheerleading; High Hon Roll; Hon Roll; PA Ambassadors Music 87; York Cnty Ind Arts Exhbit 1st & 2nd Pl Awds Drftng 86; Arch Engrng.

WISE, JAMES; Shikellamy HS; Sunbury, PA; (4); 20/301; Stat Ftbl; Capt Mgr(s); Hon Roll; Auto Engr.

WISE, JENNY; Cocalico HS; Denver, PA; (1); Church Yth Grp; Varsity Clb; Cheerleading; Powder Puff Ftbl; Swmmng; Cert Awd Cheerldng 87; PA ST; Dntl Hygnst.

WISE, JOHN; Cedar Crest HS; Lebanon, PA; (3); 8/400; German Clb; Pep Clb; School Musical; Pres Frsh Cls; Pres Soph Cls; Pres Jr Cls; Pres Sr Cls; VP JV Socr; Im Vllybl; Hon Roll; Outstndng Stu Math & Sci Awd 84-87; Grmny Tour 87 Sccr Tm 87; Math.

WISE, KRISTY; Williamsport Area HS; Williamsport, PA; (4); 32/597; FBLA; Jr Civitan Int; Acpl Chr; Band; Chorus; Church Choir; Concert Band; Mrchg Band; Orch; School Musical; Floretta J Hunter Awd; Liberty Mutual Awd; Barry Campbell Awd; Williamsport Area CC; Leg Sec.

WISE, MICHELLE; Windber Area HS; Windber, PA; (3); FTA; Math Clb; Rep Stu Cncl; Var Cheerleading; L Trk; High Hon Roll; Hon Roll; NHS; Presdntl Ftnss Awds 85-87; Stu Of Mnth Awds 86-87; Chld Psych.

WISE, ONDA; Bellwood-Antis HS; Bellwood, PA; (4); 4/115; Trs Church Yth Grp; Key Clb; Ski Clb; Varsity Clb; Trs Stu Cncl; Fld Hcky; Trk; High Hon Roll; Sec NHS; US Stu Cncl Awd 86-87; Acad All Am 85-86; Mst Lkly To Sccd 86-87; St Francis Coll; Accntng.

WISE, STACEY; Valley HS; New Kensington, PA; (2); Ski Clb; Varsity Clb; Chorus; JV Var Cheerleading; Tennis; Hon Roll; Engr.

WISEMAN, ROBERT; St Josephs Prep; Philadelphia, PA; (4); 32/240; Hosp Aide; Nwsp Rptr; Lit Mag; Im Bsktbl; Im Ftbl; JV Wrstlng; High Hon Roll; Ntl Merit Ltr; Myrs Schlrshp 87; John Clark Simms Schlrshp 87; Silver Mdl In Engl 87; U Of PA; Engl.

WISEN, NATALIE; Pennsbury HS; Fairless Hls, PA; (3); Church Yth Grp; FFA; Girl Scts; Office Aide; Service Clb; Teachers Aide; Hon Roll; Masonic Awd.

WISER, KENDRA; Saltsburg JR SR HS; Saltsburg, PA; (2); 14/95; GAA; SADD; School Musical; JV Capt Bsktbl; Var Sftbl; JV Vllybl; Hon Roll; Hugh O Brien Conf 86; Penn U; Vet.

WISHNEFSKY, BRENDA; Mahanoy Area HS; Mahanoy City, PA; (3); Church Yth Grp; FHA; Spanish Clb; Drm Mjr(t); Variety Show; Nwsp Stf; JV Var Bsktbl; Var L Trk; Engr.

WISINSKI, MELANIE; Seneca HS; Erie, PA; (4); 28/138; Sec Church Yth Grp; Computer Clb; Pep Clb; Teachers Aide; Sec Soph Cls; Sec Jr Cls; Off Sr Cls; Var Cheerleading; Hon Roll; Cadettes; Mercyhurst Coll; Accntng.

WISKEMAN, TAMI; Burrell SR HS; Lower Burrell, PA; (3); AFS; Pres Church Yth Grp; SADD; Color Guard; School Play; Stu Cncl; High Hon Roll; Jr NHS; Spanish Clb; Band; H O Brian Yth Ambasdr 86; Yth Mnstrs Pres 87-88; Yth Svc Fnd Chrprsn 86; Soc Wrk.

WISMER, ALISON J; Northampton SR HS; Northampton, PA; (4); Chorus; Nwsp Phtg; Yrbk Phtg; Yrbk Stf; Stu Cncl; Cheerleading; Hon Roll; Homerm Pres 85-86; Co-Photog Edtr 86-87; Northampton Cnty CC; Photogrph.

WISNER, CAREY; Highlands HS; Tarentum, PA; (3); Office Aide; Pep Clb; Band; Color Guard; Pres Frsh Cls; Rep Stu Cncl; High Hon Roll; Jr NHS; NHS; Pres Schlr; Law.

WISNER, KEVIN; South Western HS; Glen Rock, PA; (3); 11/212; Var L Bsbl; High Hon Roll; Hon Roll; NHS; NEDT Awd; Engrng.

WISNER, STEVEN; Hanover HS; Hanover, PA; (4); Church Yth Grp; Varsity Clb; School Play; Pres Frsh Cls; Pres Soph Cls; Pres Jr Cls; Var Bsbl; Var Bsktbl; Var Ftbl; Hon Roll; Mst Imprvd Bsbl Plyr 86; Outstndng Bsktbl Plyr 87; Phy Ed.

WISNIEWSKI, CATHERINE; Lansdale Catholic HS; New Britain, PA; (3); 23/232; Church Yth Grp; Debate Tm; Drama Clb; Hosp Aide; NFL; PAVAS; SADD; Thesps; Church Choir; School Musical; Diocesan Schlrshp 87-88; Mktg.

WISNIEWSKI, MICHELLE; Mid-Valley HS; Olyphant, PA; (2); Cmnty Wkr; Y-Teens; High Hon Roll; Hon Roll; Hmcmng Queen Rep 86; Yth Ftns Achvt Awd 85-86; U Of Stroudsburg; Physcl Thrpy.

WISNIEWSKI, SUE; Fort Le Boeuf HS; Waterford, PA; (2); Concert Band; Mrchg Band; Orch; School Musical; Yrbk Stf; Bsktbl; Sftbl; Trk; High Hon Roll; Proj Enhance 85-89.

WISSER, COLIN; Fleetwood HS; Virginville, PA; (3); 7/112; Church Yth Grp; Science Clb; Band; Var Bsbl; Var Bsktbl; Hon Roll; NHS; Bsbl Sprtsmnshp Awd 86; Penn ST; Engrng.

WISSINGER, DONNA; Marion Center Area HS; Indiana, PA; (4); FBLA; Q&S; Mrchg Band; Nwsp Rptr; Pres Frsh Cls; Pres Soph Cls; Pres Jr Cls; Pres Sr Cls; Stu Cncl; Capt Twrlr; Hmcmng Queen 86-87; IUP; Elem.

WISSLER JR, WILLIAM H; Central Dauphin HS; Harrisburg, PA; (3); 12/370; Key Clb; Var L Bsbl; High Hon Roll; Hon Roll; Jr NHS; NHS; Sci Olympd 7th ST 86-87; PAC 86-87; Fin.

WITAS, PAM; Valley HS; Arnold, PA; (3); 59/255; Art Clb; Drama Clb; Spanish Clb; SADD; Mrchg Band; Yrbk Stf; Mgr Swmmng; Hon Roll; US Bus Ed Awd 86-87.

WITCRAFT, STACEY; Stroudsburg Area HS; Stroudsburg, PA; (2); 2/310; Drama Clb; Chorus; Church Choir; Concert Band; Mrchg Band; School Musical; High Hon Roll; NHS; Church Yth Grp; French Clb; Dist Chorus 87; Yng Peoples Philharmonic Orch Of The Lehigh Vly 87.

WITEK, MARK; Conestoga Valley SR HS; Lancaster, PA; (3); 101/286; Boy Scts; German Clb; Letterman Clb; Spanish Clb; Varsity Clb; Concert Band; VP Frsh Cls; Var Ftbl; Wt Lftg; Clemson U; Engl Lit.

WITEOF, KIMBERLY; Conemaugh Township Area HS; Holsopple, PA; (3); 7/122; JA; NFL; Color Guard; School Musical; Yrbk Bus Mgr; Dnfth Awd; Hon Roll; NHS; Band; Concert Band; Interact Club VP 85-88; Dist Yth Choir Sec 85-88; PA ST; Pre Med.

WITHERELL, JACOB; Central Cambria HS; Johnstown, PA; (3); 9/210; Pres 4-H; Stu Cncl; Swmmng; Hon Roll; Princpls Awd 86-87.

WITHEROW, GRACE; Curwensville Area HS; Curwensville, PA; (3); FBLA; Mat Maids; High Hon Roll; Hon Roll; Lgl Secty.

WITHERS, BRIAN; Northern Cambria HS; Barnesboro, PA; (3); 21/152; Church Yth Grp; Computer Clb; Drama Clb; Speech Tm; School Play; Nwsp Stf; Trk; High Hon Roll; Hon Roll; NHS; Elec Engrng.

WITHERS, MARGUERITE; St Maria Goretti HS; Philadelphia, PA; (3); 41/361; Art Clb; Church Yth Grp; Math Tm; Service Clb; Spanish Clb; Teachers Aide; Nwsp Stf; Hon Roll; NHS; Prfct Atten Awd; Philadelphia Cath Math Leag Div Chmps 86-87; Yth & Amrcn Pltcl Sys 87; Bus.

WITHERSPOON, ANGELA; Philadelphia HS For Girls; Philadelphia, PA; (1); Spanish Clb; Temple Yth Grp; JV Swmmng.

WITHROW, DORY; Du Bois Area HS; Dubois, PA; (2); 29/315; JV Cheerleading; Hon Roll; Penn ST.

WITIAK, ALISSA; Liberty HS; Bethlehem, PA; (4); 33/434; School Musical; Stage Crew; Lit Mag; Sec Stu Cncl; Capt L Tennis; Trk; Hon Roll; Sec VP NHS; Atten H O Brien Yth Ldrshp Smnr 85; Frank Melusky Awd 87; Grad Hnrs 87; Dickinson Coll.

WITINSKI, SANDRA; Hanover Area HS; Peely, PA; (3); 8/194; Exploring; Acpl Chr; Color Guard; Trk; Twrlr; High Hon Roll; Jr NHS; NHS; Bloomsburg; Accntng.

WITKOSKI, CHERYL; West Hazleton HS; W Hazleton, PA; (2); Church Yth Grp; Chorus; Stu Cncl; Var Capt Cheerleading; Gym; High Hon Roll.

WITKOUSKI, CHRISTINE R; Beaver Area HS; Beaver, PA; (4); French Clb; Pep Clb; VP Soph Cls; Diving; Powder Puff Ftbl; Trk; Wt Lftg; Trck Schlrshp 87; Lock Haven U.

WITKOWSKI, CHERYL; West Hazleton HS; W Hazleton, PA; (2); Church Yth Grp; Chorus; Stu Cncl; Var Capt Cheerleading; Gym; High Hon Roll.

WITKOWSKI, LYNN; Neshannock HS; Neshannock, PA; (3); 14/102; Church Yth Grp; Cmnty Wkr; Exploring; FBLA; Office Aide; School Musical; School Play; Nwsp Sprt Ed; Nwsp Stf; Yrbk Stf; Comp.

WITMAN, ANDREA; Central Catholic HS; Bally, PA; (3); German Clb; Office Aide; Hon Roll; Acdmc Excllnc German III 87; Marine Bio.

WITMAN, ELIZABETH; Spring Grove Area SR HS; Spring Grove, PA; (3); Chess Clb; Library Aide; Chorus; Stage Crew; Nwsp Stf; Var Crs Cntry; JV Fld Hcky; JV Trk; High Hon Roll; Hon Roll; Presdntl Acadc Ftns Awd 84-85.

WITMAN, PHILIP; Conestoga Valley HS; Leola, PA; (3); 45/220; Church Yth Grp; Hon Roll; Gld Ky Awd Schlstc Art Cmptn 85; Comp Sci.

WITMER, AMY; Greenwood HS; Liverpool, PA; (2); JV Fld Hcky; Trk; Hon Roll; NHS; Elem Tchr.

WITMER, ANGELA; Pine Grove Area HS; Pine Grove, PA; (3); Leo Clb; Lit Mag; Rep Frsh Cls; JV Bsktbl; Hon Roll; Antonelli Art Inst; Comm Art.

WITMER, CHRISTINE; Pine Grove HS; Tremont, PA; (4); Girl Scts; Band; Concert Band; Mrchg Band; Ed Yrbk Stf; Achvt Awd In Span, Chem 87; Pres Physcl Ftns Awd 87; Comp Sci.

WITMER, JAMES; Newport HS; Liverpool, PA; (3); 3/117; Quiz Bowl; Chorus; School Musical; School Play; Rep Stu Cncl; Trk; High Hon Roll; NHS; Ntl Merit Ltr; Rep Frsh Cls; Engr.

WITMER, JILL; Northern HS; Mechanicsburg, PA; (3); 23/232; Church Yth Grp; Model UN; Concert Band; Mrchg Band; School Musical; VP Jr Cls; VP Sr Cls; Sftbl; High Hon Roll; Pschlgy.

WITMER, LORI; Chambersburg Area SR HS; Fayetteville, PA; (4); 17/606; Letterman Clb; Pep Clb; VICA; Rep Dance Clb; Var Capt Cheerleading; High Hon Roll; Hon Roll; NHS; ST VICA Secy 85-86; ST VICA Pres & Csmtlgy Shp Pres 86-87; Penn ST U; Vo Ed Tchr.

WITMER, LYNNE; Bellefonte Area HS; Bellefonte, PA; (3); Office Aide; Spanish Clb; SADD; Nwsp Rptr; Yrbk Phtg; Yrbk Sprt Ed; Yrbk Stf; Im Powder Puff Ftbl; Score Keeper; High Hon Roll; Bnkng.

WITMER, MATTHEW R; Garden Spot HS; Terre Hill, PA; (2); Church Yth Grp; Drama Clb; French Clb; Stage Crew; Nwsp Stf; Pres Frsh Cls; Pres Soph Cls; Pres Jr Cls; JV Wrstlng; Stu Dir 86; Hstry.

WITMER II, MELVIN; Conestoga Valley HS; Ephrata, PA; (3); Chess Clb; Comp Sci.

WITOWICH, MICHAEL D; Ambridge Area HS; Ambridge, PA; (4); 90/265; French Clb; Pep Clb; Trs Chorus; School Musical; Swing Chorus; Trk; Hon Roll; Natl Choral Awd 87; PMEA Hnrs Chorus 85-86; Pmea Rgn I Chorus 85-86; IN U PA; Music Ed.

WITT, MELANIE; Connellsville HS; Connellsville, PA; (3); 38/525; Church Yth Grp; GAA; Band; Chorus; Church Choir; Concert Band; Mrchg Band; School Musical; Var Bsktbl; Jr NHS; Elem Ed.

WITT, NATALIE; Shamokin Area HS; Shamokin, PA; (3); Art Clb; Drama Clb; German Clb; Pep Clb; Science Clb; Ski Clb; Var Cheerleading; Trk; Hon Roll; Psych.

WITT, TRACY; Shamokin Area HS; Shamokin, PA; (3); Sec Art Clb; Drama Clb; German Clb; Key Clb; Pep Clb; Science Clb; Ski Clb; Nwsp Rptr; Camera Clb; Office Aide; 2nd Pl Wmns Clb Art Cntst 86; 2nd Pl Cltrl Arts Cntst 85; Graphic Dsgn.

WITTE, ERIC; Central HS; Philadelphia, PA; (3); 31/538; Camera Clb; Science Clb; Teachers Aide; Yrbk Phtg; Im Vllybl; Hon Roll; Barnwell Hnr Rll 84-87.

WITTE, KENNETH; Council Rock HS; Holland, PA; (3); Boy Scts; Church Yth Grp; Bowling; Tennis; Hon Roll; Elec.

WITTEBORT, RONALD A; Butler SR HS; Butler, PA; (2); Im Stage Crew; Im Hon Roll; Art.

WITTENBERGER, JOHN; Bethlehem Catholic HS; Bethlehem, PA; (3); 55/215; Sec Band; Concert Band; Jazz Band; Mrchg Band; Orch; School Musical; High Hon Roll; Hon Roll; Mst Imrpvd Musician & Dist Band 87; Pre-Med.

WITTENBRADER, MELANIE; Western Wayne HS; Moscow, PA; (3); Church Yth Grp; Exploring; 4-H; FHA; Girl Scts; SADD; Drill Tm; 4-H Awd; Cul Arts.

WITTENDORF, ERIC; Spring-Ford SR HS; Limerick, PA; (3); 68/256; Boy Scts; German Clb; Var Capt Crs Cntry; Var Capt Trk; Var Capt Wrstlng; Hon Roll; Psych.

WITTMAIER, KRISTEN; Conestoga Valley HS; Lancaster, PA; (3); 16/219; Art Clb; VP Pres Church Yth Grp; Dance Clb; Girl Scts; Mgr Mrchg Band; Off Jr Cls; Mgr(s); Hon Roll; NHS; Voice Dem Awd; Psych.

WITTMAN, EDWARD; Quigley HS; Sewickley, PA; (3); 2/80; Math Tm; Yrbk Bus Mgr; Yrbk Stf; High Hon Roll; Monsignor Must Awd 84; Art & Geo Awd 84-85; Compu Sci.

WITTMAN, KATY; Louis E Dieruff HS; Allentown, PA; (3); 77/489; Aud/Vis; Church Yth Grp; Dance Clb; Var L Cheerleading; Var JV Vllybl; Hon Roll; Med.

WITTMAN, PAMELA; Catasauqua HS; Catasauqua, PA; (4); 5/130; Trs Stu Cncl; Var L Fld Hcky; Hon Roll; Trs NHS; Am Leg Aux Girls St; Drama Clb; Hosp Aide; SADD; Cit Awd; Pres Schlr; Ntl Sci Merit Awds 85 & 86; Schlrshp PA Motor Truck Assn 87; Leonard Carlton Peckit Schlrshp 87; Phila Coll/Phrm/Sci; Txclgy.

WITTMANN, CAROLE; Berlin Brothers Valley HS; Berlin, PA; (3); Ski Clb; Spanish Clb; School Play; Nwsp Rptr; Nwsp Stf; Var Capt Cheerleading; Hon Roll; FBLA; SADD; JR Clss Prm Attndnt & Hmcmng Attndnt 86; Brthrs Vlly FFA Chptr Swthrt 87-88.

WIVELL, ARLENE; Sto-Rox SR HS; Mc Kees Rocks, PA; (3); Am Leg Aux Girls St; Boys Clb Am; Church Yth Grp; Library Aide; Y-Teens; Chorus; Mrchg Band; Yrbk Stf; Stu Cncl; Twrlr; Forgn Relations.

WIVELL, MARY; Ambridge Area HS; Ambridge, PA; (3); Sec Church Yth Grp; French Clb; Hosp Aide; Pep Clb; Red Cross Aide; Chorus; Nwsp Stf; Trk; High Hon Roll; Rep Frsh Cls; Rep Schlrshp PA Gov Schl Arts 87; 4th Pl Wnnr Ag Spch Cont 87; Semi Fnlst U Pittsburgh Provst Day 87.

WIVELL, NANCY; Spring Grove SR HS; Seven Valleys, PA; (4); 20/274; Trs Church Yth Grp; Nwsp Bus Mgr; JV Bsktbl; JV Trk; CC Awd; Hon Roll; NHS; Top 10% Of Class 87; Schlstc Achvmnt Awd 87; Child Study.

WODRIG, SHIRLEY; Benton Area JR SR HS; Benton, PA; (2); Library Aide; Chorus; Color Guard; Nwsp Rptr; JV Bsktbl; JV Sftbl; Lndscpng Arch.

WOELFLING, JESSICA; Lebanon Catholic HS; Lebanon, PA; (3); Cmnty Wkr; Key Clb; Spanish Clb; Chorus; Yrbk Stf; Sftbl; Hon Roll; NHS; Sci Fair 3rd Pl 87; Schl Spirit Awd 87; Sci.

WOERNER, ROBERT P; Biglerville HS; Biglerville, PA; (3); 9/99; Boy Scts; VP Trs FFA; Var Ftbl; Var Trk; Hon Roll; Jr NHS; NHS; Ag Engrng.

WOERNER, SUZANNE; Mastbaum Vocational HS; Philadelphia, PA; (3); Church Yth Grp; Med Sec.

WOGINRICH, CHERIE; Northampton SR HS; Northampton, PA; (4); 24/445; AFS; Leo Clb; Teachers Aide; Stu Cncl; Bsktbl; Capt Powder Puff Ftbl; Var Trk; High Hon Roll; Hon Roll; NHS; Rotary Club Top 30 Cls 87; Bloomsburg U; Acctng.

WOJCIECHOWSKI, JEFFREY; Shamokin Area HS; Shamokin, PA; (2); 39/221; Science Clb; JV Ftbl; Hnr Roll 86-87.

WOJCIECHOWSKI, KATHY; Northumberland Christian Schl; Shamokin, PA; (3); Spanish Clb; Chorus; Church Choir; School Musical; Bsktbl; Socr; Trk; Hon Roll; NEDT Awd; Schl Actor; Air Force.

WOJCIK, AMANDA; Ford City HS; Ford City, PA; (3); 23/160; Key Clb; Band; Concert Band; Drm Mjr(t); Mrchg Band; Pep Band; Yrbk Stf; Stu Cncl; High Hon Roll; NHS; Arch.

WOJCIK, JULIE; Western Wayne HS; Aldenville, PA; (4); 18/143; Pres Sec 4-H; Pres Sec FFA; Band; Chorus; Concert Band; Mrchg Band; School Musical; 4-H Awd; Hon Roll; NHS; Wayne Cnty Conservtn Dist Schlrshp 87; Pres Acdmc Fit Awd 87; NY ST U; Vet Tech.

WOJCIK, LYNORE; Pittston Area SR HS; Yatesville, PA; (3); 22/360; Stu Cncl; NHS; Schlstc Art Awd 85-86; Med.

WOJDYLAK, MICHAEL; Spring-Ford HS; Collegeville, PA; (3); 145/256; Camera Clb; Church Yth Grp; FBLA; Nwsp Phtg; Yrbk Phtg; Golf; Trk; Lincoln Tech; Elec Tech.

WOJNAKOWSKI, PAM; Villa Maria Acad; Erie, PA; (4); 33/128; Intnl Clb; Model UN; Ski Clb; SADD; Yrbk Phtg; Yrbk Rptr; Hon Roll; NHS; NEDT Awd; WV U; Mktg.

WOJNAR, TRACEY; St Maria Goretti HS; Philadelphia, PA; (3); 142/350; Dance Clb; Var Crs Cntry; Var Trk; Cit Awd; Labrtry.

WOJNAROWSKI, DYAN; West Greene HS; Wind Ridge, PA; (2); 11/98; Stage Crew; Hon Roll.

WOJTKOWSKI, CHRISTINE; Yough HS; West Newton, PA; (3); Pep Clb; Chorus; Nwsp Rptr; Nwsp Stf; Trvl.

WOJTON, HENRY; St Pius X HS; Trappe, PA; (2); 4/151; 4-H; Ski Clb; JV Bsbl; JV Ftbl; High Hon Roll; HS Schlrshp 85-86; Oronmental Hrtcltr.

WOLCOTT, BRIAN; Warren Area HS; Warren, PA; (3); Church Yth Grp; Chorus; High Hon Roll; Hon Roll; Sci.

WOLCZANSKI, AMY; North Catholic HS; Pgh, PA; (3); Art Clb; Camera Clb; Church Yth Grp; Cmnty Wkr; Red Cross Aide; Ski Clb; Rep Frsh Cls; Var JV Bsktbl; Var L Sftbl; Hon Roll; Pharmacy.

WOLENSKY, SUE; Bishop O Reilly HS; Luzerne, PA; (3); Spanish Clb; Hon Roll.

WOLESLAGLE, HOLLY; Altoona Area HS; Altoona, PA; (2); 1/815; Sec Church Yth Grp; Library Aide; Spanish Clb; Chorus; Orch; Rep Frsh Cls; High Hon Roll; NEDT Awd; Pres Schlr; Cmnty Wkr; PA Govrs Schl For Music Alt; Math Dpt Awd For Hghst Frshmn In Clss; Mid ST Bnk Schlrshp Awd; Sociolgy.

WOLESLAGLE, TIFFANY; South Fayette HS; Bridgeville, PA; (3); Var JV Sftbl; High Hon Roll; Hon Roll; NHS.

WOLF, AMY; Hollidaysburg Area SR HS; Duncansville, PA; (3); Lit Mag; Im Vllybl; Scndry Ed.

WOLF, BETH; Northern HS; Dillsburg, PA; (3); 3/232; Hosp Aide; Band; Concert Band; Mrchg Band; Bsktbl; Powder Puff Ftbl; French Hon Soc; High Hon Roll; Cert Merit Algebra I & II Achvmnt 84-87; French II 84-85; Nrsng.

WOLF, CHRISTINE; Spring Grove HS; York, PA; (2); Library Aide; JV Trk; Hon Roll; Sec.

WOLF, DIANA V; Oliver HS; Pittsburgh, PA; (4); Math Clb; Mu Alpha Theta; Boy Scts; Nwsp Ed-Chief; High Hon Roll; NHS; Prfct Atten Awd; Schlstc Lttr 85; PA ST U.

WOLF III, DONALD HENRY; Palmyra Area HS; Palmyra, PA; (4); 66/186; Pres Drama Clb; VP Science Clb; School Play; Stage Crew; Yrbk Phtg; Trk; Hon Roll; Eagle Scout; Order Of The Arrow; Rochester Inst Of Tech; Phys.

WOLF, JILL; Ephrata HS; Ephrata, PA; (4); 49/253; Sec Church Yth Grp; FFA; Church Choir; Rep Stu Cncl; Vllybl; Hon Roll; Rotary Awd; Towne Clb Voctnl Awd 87; Farm & Farm Schlrshp Awd 87; Garden Clb Schlrshp 87; Alfred ST Coll; Floriculture.

WOLF, JOSEPH; Dubois Area HS; Dubois, PA; (4); 26/270; Band; Concert Band; Jazz Band; Mrchg Band; Orch; Pep Band; School Musical; High Hon Roll; Hon Roll; NHS; Nice Kid Awd 87; Duquesne U.

WOLF, KIMBERLY; Beaver Area JR SR HS; Beaver, PA; (2); Art Clb; JCL; Key Clb; Co-Capt Color Guard; Yrbk Stf; Var Diving; Stat Socr; Var Sftbl; Var Trk; Hon Roll; Psych.

WOLF, MARC ROSS; George Washington HS; Philadelphia, PA; (4); 1/725; Debate Tm; Pres Spanish Clb; SADD; School Musical; Yrbk Stf; High Hon Roll; NHS; Pres Spanish NHS; Val; Math Tm; Phil Beta Kappa Awd 87; Brown U Book Awd 87; U PA; Lbrl Arts.

WOLF, MATTHEW; Big Spring HS; Carlisle, PA; (3); 28/258; Boy Scts; Band; Mrchg Band; JV Var Socr; JV Var Trk; Hon Roll; NHS; Cert Outstndng Achvt Amer Meteorological Scty 85; 1st Pl Awds Sci Proj 84-85; Assn Amer Wthr Obsrv 85; PA ST U; Meteorlgy.

WOLF, MICHELE; Langley HS; Pittsburgh, PA; (3); Pres Church Yth Grp; Cmnty Wkr; Drama Clb; Acpl Chr; Sec Chorus; School Musical; School Play; Stage Crew; Capt Co-Capt Cheerleading; High Hon Roll.

WOLF, RAY; Sto-Rox SR HS; Mckees Rocks, PA; (2); #23 In Class; Church Yth Grp; Chorus; Nwsp Rptr; Var JV Mgr(s); Var Trk; Hon Roll; Embry-Riddle Aeron U; Pilot.

WOLF, RAYMOND; Frankford HS; Philadelphia, PA; (2); Am Leg Boys St; Boys Clb Am; Chess Clb; Computer Clb; Exploring; Math Tm; Quiz Bowl; Science Clb; Spanish Clb; SADD; Penn ST; Chem Engr.

WOLF, STEPHANIE; Kennard-Dale HS; Stewartstown, PA; (3); 11/167; Exploring; Ski Clb; Sec Varsity Clb; Chorus; Yrbk Ed-Chief; Sr Cls; JV Var Bsktbl; Var Trk; JV Vllybl; High Hon Roll; Law.

WOLF, WENDY; West York Area HS; York, PA; (3); Mrchg Band; Symp Band; Hon Roll.

WOLFE, BRENDA; Eisenhower HS; Russell, PA; (3); Trs GAA; Var L Bsktbl; Var L Trk; L Capt Vllybl; High Hon Roll; NHS; Bus Mgt.

WOLFE, CHRISTINA; Bellwood-Antis HS; Altoona, PA; (4); 8/118; Capt Church Yth Grp; Sec SADD; Church Choir; School Play; Variety Show; Sec Yrbk Stf; JV Cheerleading; Hon Roll; NHS; 1st Pl Radio Prgm Awd 84-85; Hghst Acdmc Englsh Avrg 84-85; Spnsh Awd 85-86; Lbrty U VA; Elem Ed.

WOLFE, DAVID; Northern Lebanon HS; Annville, PA; (4); 20/166; Church Yth Grp; FCA; Varsity Clb; School Play; Var L Ftbl; Hon Roll; Kiwanis Awd; NHS; Spanish NHS; Var Crs Cntry; Shippensburg U.

WOLFE, DAVID E; Penns Valley Area JR SR HS; Rebersburg, PA; (4); 25/137; Church Yth Grp; Trs FFA; Varsity Clb; Stage Crew; Im Badmtn; Var Stat Bsbl; Im Vllybl; High Hon Roll; Hon Roll; US Ntnl Agri Achiev Awd 87; Williamsport; Elec Tech.

WOLFE, DAWN M; Hempfield Area HS; Irwin, PA; (4); 6/693; Trs Church Yth Grp; VP French Clb; Math Tm; NFL; Ski Clb; Powder Puff Ftbl; Swmmng; Sec French Hon Soc; NHS; Ntl Merit SF; 1st Pl Gannon U Frgn Lng 86; Acdmc Achvt Awd 84-86; ; Rotc Schlrshp 86; PA ST ; Engr.

WOLFE, DENISE; Cumberland Valley HS; Mechanicsburg, PA; (3); Key Clb; JV Var Cheerleading; Geo Washington U; Rssn.

WOLFE, DIANA; Moravian Acad; Coopersburg, PA; (3); Cmnty Wkr; Political Wkr; Yrbk Phtg; French Clb; Library Aide; Ski Clb; Nwsp Phtg; Nwsp Rptr; Nwsp Stf; Yrbk Stf; Vet Med.

WOLFE, DON; Laurel Highlands HS; Uniontown, PA; (3); 18/355; Math Clb; Math Tm; Science Clb; Stage Crew; Sec Soph Cls; Rep Stu Cncl; High Hon Roll; NHS; NEDT Awd; Stu Forum Rep 86-88; Carnegie Mellon U; Biochem Rsch.

WOLFE, HEATHER; Governor Mifflin SR HS; Reading, PA; (3); 6/340; Sec Church Yth Grp; Q&S; Church Choir; Nwsp Stf; Yrbk Stf; Jr Cls; Sec Stu Cncl; Var L Crs Cntry; Var L Trk; VP NHS; Piano High Hnrs Natl Guild Auditions 82-87; Unified Achvt Awd 86-87; Bonnie Bell X-Cntry Cir Exclnce; Cmmnctns.

WOLFE, JESSICA; Northern Lebanon HS; Jonestown, PA; (2); 1/212; Trs Spanish Clb; Teachers Aide; Chorus; School Musical; High Hon Roll; Jr NHS; NHS; Law.

WOLFE, JOY; Tulpehocken HS; Bethel, PA; (2); Art Clb; Drama Clb; German Clb; JA; Spanish Clb; Chorus; School Musical; School Play; Hon Roll; Acadc All Am 85; Ntl Ldrshp & Svc Awd 86; Lang.

WOLFE, JULIE; Berwick Area SR HS; Berwick, PA; (4); Capt Bsktbl; Capt Fld Hcky; Capt Sftbl; Hon Roll; NHS; Berwick Area Educ Assn Schrlshp 87; BHS Sr Cmmnty Svc Awd 87; Athlete Wk Sftbl, Bsktbl 85-87.

WOLFE, JULIE; Youngsville HS; Youngsville, PA; (4); Church Yth Grp; Ski Clb; Band; Yrbk Stf; Rep Soph Cls; Rep Jr Cls; Rep Sr Cls; VP Sec Stu Cncl; Trk; Wt Lftg; Thiel Coll; Nrsng.

WOLFE, KIMBERLY A; Garden Spot HS; New Holland, PA; (4); 27/201; Drama Clb; Girl Scts; Chorus; Church Choir; Stage Crew; High Hon Roll; Hon Roll; Jr NHS; NHS; Med.

WOLFE, KRISTIN; Trinity HS; Camp Hill, PA; (3); 20/150; French Clb; Hosp Aide; Pep Clb; Ski Clb; Yrbk Stf; Sec Frsh Cls; Sec Soph Cls; Sec Stu Cncl; JV L Vllybl; High Hon Roll; Pres Of FORCE 86-88; Psych.

WOLFE, MARK; Penns Manor HS; Clymer, PA; (3); 8/93; Band; Mrchg Band; Yrbk Stf; NHS; NEDT Awd; Prfct Atten Awd; Bus.

WOLFE, MATTHEW; Blair County Christian HS; Hollidaysburg, PA; (3); 2/17; Pres Church Yth Grp; Pres Soph Cls; Pres Jr Cls; Stu Cncl; Var Bsbl; Var L Bsktbl; Var Capt Socr; Var Trk; High Hon Roll; Debate Tm; Young Mans Christian Ldrshp Awd 85-86; Baseball MVP 84-85; Ed.

WOLFE, MICHELLE; Bishop Hoban HS; Mountain Top, PA; (3); Pres 4-H; FBLA; Dnfth Awd; 4-H Awd; Hon Roll; Natl Hnr Roll 87.

WOLFE, NETTIE; Spring-Ford HS; Royersford, PA; (2); 29/289; Spanish Clb; Color Guard; Mrchg Band; Nwsp Stf; Rep Stu Cncl; Im Vllybl; Hon Roll; NHS; Engl Writer Of Yr 86-87; Spanish II Stu Of Yr 86-87.

WOLFE, PAM; Carlisle SR HS; Carlisle, PA; (3); 30/480; Am Leg Aux Girls St; Drama Clb; Quiz Bowl; Ski Clb; Color Guard; Stage Crew; Rep Jr Cls; Mgr Swmmng; Hon Roll; Pres NHS; 2nd Pl Penn JR Acad Sci 87; 1st Pl Chemstry Capt Sci Engr Fair 87; Hnrbl Mentn Capt Area Sc Fr 87; Chemstry.

WOLFE, RHONDA; Turkeyfoot Valley Area HS; Addison, PA; (2); Color Guard; Mrchg Band; Nwsp Stf; Yrbk Stf; Hon Roll; Engl & Ecology Awds; Bus.

WOLFE, TAMI; Southern Columbia Area HS; Catawissa, PA; (3); Hosp Aide; Key Clb; Ski Clb; Varsity Clb; Yrbk Stf; Rep Stu Cncl; Var L Cheerleading; Var L Trk; Hon Roll; NHS.

WOLFE JR, TOM; Bishop Carroll HS; Nicktown, PA; (3); Church Yth Grp; Cmnty Wkr; Trk; Hon Roll; Bus.

WOLFE, TRACI; Marion Center Area HS; Indiana, PA; (4); SADD; Varsity Clb; Bsktbl; Sftbl; Hon Roll; IN Gzte All Gzte Land Sftbl Tm 1st Tm 85-87; Marion Ctr Sftbl MVP 85-87; Slippery Rock U; Phy Educ.

WOLFE, WENDI SUE; Conestoga Valley HS; Ephrata, PA; (4); 11/255; Church Yth Grp; Band; Chorus; Concert Band; Flag Corp; Mrchg Band; Var Capt Cheerleading; High Hon Roll; NHS; Pres Schlr; Ward Trucking Schlrshp 87; Millersville U; Elem Ed.

WOLFE, WENDY; Mechanicsburg Area SR HS; Mechanicsburg, PA; (2); Pep Clb; Speech Tm; Chorus; Flag Corp; Nwsp Rptr; Mgr(s); Hon Roll.

WOLFEL, NATALIE A; Northampton JR HS; Northampton, PA; (1); Drama Clb; FBLA; NAACP; JV Trk; Hon Roll; Jr NHS; Ntl Merit Schol; Pres Schlr; Voice Dem Awd; Pres Acdmc Ftnss Awd 86-87; Visual Comms.

WOLFENDEN, JENNIFER; Archbishop Ryan HS For Girls; Phila, PA; (3); 126/508; Exploring; Q&S; Church Choir; Color Guard; Mrchg Band; Nwsp Stf; Lit Mag; Hon Roll; Top Art Awds 86 & 87; Art Cert Prfcncy 85; Engl III Cert Prfcncy 87.

WOLFGANG, BETH; Danville HS; Danville, PA; (1); Church Yth Grp; Ski Clb; Yrbk Phtg; Hst Frsh Cls; JV Var Cheerleading; JV Gym; JV Tennis; JV Trk; High Hon Roll; Graham F Stephens Courtesy Awd & Pres Acdmc Ftnss Awd 87.

WOLFGANG, KRISTIN; Northeastern HS; Mount Wolf, PA; (3); VP Church Yth Grp; Exploring; Hosp Aide; Teachers Aide; Band; Chorus; Church Choir; School Musical; Lit Mag; Hon Roll; JR Vol 150 Hr Awd 87; Keystone Games 3rd Pl Synchrnzd Swmmng 87; Spnsh.

WOLFGANG, LISA; Shikellamy HS; Sunbury, PA; (4); 35/304; Am Leg Aux Girls St; Church Yth Grp; Spanish Clb; SADD; Yrbk Ed-Chief; Yrbk Phtg; Yrbk Rptr; Yrbk Sprt Ed; Yrbk Stf; Hon Roll; Joanne Bettley Nrsng Awd 87; Geisinger Schl Of Nrsng; Nrsng.

WOLFGANG, MICHELE; Millersburg Area HS; Millersburg, PA; (2); Library Aide; Spanish Clb; SADD; Band; Concert Band; Mrchg Band; Nwsp Rptr; Yrbk Stf; Tennis; Acdmc All Am 86-87; Outstndng Hs Stu Am 86-87; Jrnlsm.

WOLFGANG, SUSAN; Du Bois Area HS; Reynoldsville, PA; (2); 42/350; Aud/Vis; Varsity Clb; Yrbk Phtg; Yrbk Stf; Var L Swmmng; Coaches Choice Awd & Vrsty Ltr In Swmng 86-87; PA ST Clarion; Mrn Bio.

WOLFGANG, TARA; Lourdes Regional HS; Marion Hts, PA; (3); 17/96; AFS; Church Yth Grp; Pep Clb; SADD; Nwsp Stf; Yrbk Stf; JV Cheerleading; Hon Roll; NHS; Cmnty Wkr; Acad All Amer Schlr 86; Cedar Crest Coll; Clncl Psych.

WOLFGONG, KEVIN; New Brighton Area HS; New Brighton, PA; (3); Chorus; Yrbk Stf; Rep Stu Cncl; Mgr Bsktbl; Mgr(s); High Hon Roll; Wstmnstr Hnrs Chorus 86; Dist V & Rgn I Chorus 87; Engrng.

WOLFINGER, AIMEE; Avonworth JR/SR HS; Pittsbg, PA; (4); AFS; Sec Church Yth Grp; Pep Clb; Ski Clb; SADD; Varsity Clb; Nwsp Stf; Stu Cncl; Stat Bsbl; Capt Cheerleading; 97% Stnfrd Achvt Tst 86; Boston U; Brdcst Jrnlsm.

WOLFORD, CATHY; Belle Vernon Area HS; Belle Vernon, PA; (3); Sec Church Yth Grp; Pres FBLA; Hosp Aide; Sec JA; Pres SADD; Band; JV Bsktbl; Bowling; Powder Puff Ftbl; Hon Roll; Awds In JR Achiev 85-86; Cert For Hlpng In The Deaf & Blind Conv 87; Recog For Otstndng Carrier 85; Bob Jones Univ; Pre-Law.

WOLFORD, GARY; Kiskiminetas Springs Schl; Lower Burrell, PA; (3); Church Yth Grp; JA; Spanish Clb; School Play; Stage Crew; Nwsp Stf; Var Ftbl; Var Wrstlng; Elctrcl Engrng.

WOLFORD, JUDY; Beaver Area HS; Beaver, PA; (4); 12/200; Church Yth Grp; FCA; JCL; Key Clb; Library Aide; Pep Clb; Off Stu Cncl; Powder Puff Ftbl; JV Var Sftbl; Hon Roll; Top 10 Pct Cls Awd 85-87; Pres Acad Awd 87; Hnrs Grp 87; Grove City Coll; Math.

WOLGEMUTH, BURT; Eastern Lebanon County HS; Newmanstown, PA; (4); 6/159; Pres Ski Clb; Var Capt Crs Cntry; JV Socr; Var L Trk; High Hon Roll; Hon Roll; NHS; Rotary Awd; Athlt Of Wk Awd X-Cntry 85; Shippnsbrg U; Bus Adm.

WOLGEMUTH, HEIDI; Donegal HS; Mount Joy, PA; (3); 23/175; Church Yth Grp; Varsity Clb; Sec Sr Cls; Powder Puff Ftbl; Var L Trk; Hon Roll; Gold Mdl 1st Pl ST Track Meet 85; Elem Ed.

WOLGEMUTH, JENNIFER; Elizabetown Area HS; Elizabethtown, PA; (3); 4/270; Church Yth Grp; Band; Mrchg Band; Trs Soph Cls; Var L Bsktbl; Var L Tennis; Hon Roll; NHS; Ntl Merit Ltr.

WOLKO, SUZANNE; St Huberts HS; Philadelphia, PA; (4); 24/364; Camera Clb; Stage Crew; Var JV Bowling; Cit Awd; DAR Awd; High Hon Roll; Hon Roll; NHS; Hghst Gen Avrg Acctnt & Bus Ed 86-87; Pres Acadc Ftns Awd 87; Villanova U; Acctnt.

WOLLETT, DEBRA; William Allen HS; Allentown, PA; (3); Drama Clb; Hon Roll; Jr NHS; NHS; Kutztown U; Elem Ed.

WOLLMAN, JENNIFER; Villa Maria Acad; Exton, PA; (3); 11/98; Church Yth Grp; Science Clb; Lit Mag; JV Bsktbl; Var JV Fld Hcky; Var JV Tennis; DAR Awd; NHS; Ntl Merit SF; Prfct Atten Awd; Bovrnrs Schl Bus Schlrshp 87.

WOLNY, STACIE A; Baldwin HS; Pittsburgh, PA; (3); 15/477; Cmnty Wkr; Exploring; Hosp Aide; JA; Math Clb; Office Aide; Capt Color Guard; Stage Crew; Yrbk Stf; Stat Bsktbl.

WOLOSZYN, SHERRY; Lincoln HS; Wampum, PA; (4); 32/165; Art Clb; Y-Teens; Chorus; Church Choir; Powder Puff Ftbl; Var L Tennis; NEDT Awd; Pres Schlr; Duquesne Cmptv Schlrshp 87; Duquesne U; Pharm.

WOLPINK, DEBORAH; Mary Fuller Frazier Memorial HS; Newell, PA; (4); 10/130; Camp Fr Inc; Chorus; Nwsp Stf; High Hon Roll; Hon Roll; NHS; Top Ten 87; Peer Tutoring 87; CA U PA; Bus Mngmnt.

WOLSKI, BOB; Belle Vernon Area HS; Belle Vernon, PA; (3); High Hon Roll; NHS; Prfct Atten Awd; Pres Phys Fit Awd 85-86; Fin.

WOLVERTON, FAITH; West Branch HS; Hawk Run, PA; (3); Church Yth Grp; Cmnty Wkr; FCA; 4-H; FHA; Spanish Clb; SADD; Chorus; Church Choir; 4-H Awd.

WOLVERTON, JENNIFER; Bishop Conwell HS; Levittown, PA; (3); 18/277; Pres Trs Church Yth Grp; Pres Trs Girl Scts; Latin Clb; SADD; Thesps; Hon Roll; NHS; Girl Scout Silv Ldrshp Awd 84; Crimnl Psych.

WOLZ, JEFF; Center HS; Aliquippa, PA; (2); Trs German Clb; JV Bsbl; Im Mgr Bsktbl; Ftbl; High Hon Roll; Hon Roll; Prfct Atten Awd; Hnrb Mntn-Grmmr & Vrbs; Frgn Lang Cmptitn-Slppry Rck U 86 & 87; Of Pittsburgh; Bus.

WOMACK, DECHANTA; Chester HS; Chester, PA; (3); Hon Roll; Prfct Atten Awd; Nurse.

WOMELDORF, CARMEN; Montgomery Area HS; Montgomery, PA; (4); 4-H; Hosp Aide; Library Aide; Chorus; Var JV Bsktbl; Hon Roll; Bsktbl Hustle Awd 86-87; Clayton C & Rebecca H Shoemaker Awd 87; Penn ST U; Pre-Med.

WOMER, SHANE; Middleburg HS; Mt Pleasant Mills, PA; (3); Socr; Military.

WOMER, WENDY; Loyalsock Twsp HS; Montoursville, PA; (3); 12/117; Church Yth Grp; Rep French Clb; Key Clb; Ski Clb; Varsity Clb; Sec Jr Cls; Var Capt Cheerleading; Var Sftbl; Var Tennis; NHS; Elem Ed.

WONDERLING, HEATHER; Cheswick Christian Acad; Natrona Hts, PA; (3); Church Yth Grp; Chorus; School Musical; Yrbk Stf; Rep Stu Cncl; Bsktbl; Cheerleading; Sftbl; Hon Roll; Jr NHS.

WONDERS, CHRISTOPHER; Boiling Springs HS; Mt Holly Spgs, PA; (3); 3/140; Quiz Bowl; Thesps; Chorus; School Play; Yrbk Ed-Chief; Yrbk Stf; Off Stu Cncl; High Hon Roll; Hon Roll; NHS; PA Gvrnrs Schl Intl Studs 87; Wdmn Wrld Hstry Awd 87; U Of Pittsburgh; Pol Sci.

WONDERS, TAMMY; Christian Schl Of York; York, PA; (2); Sec Church Yth Grp; Chorus; Church Choir; VP Soph Cls; VP Jr Cls; Rep Stu Cncl; Var L Bsktbl; Hon Roll; Psych.

WONG, DUANE; Somerset Area SR HS; Somerset, PA; (4); 2/237; Debate Tm; Pres JA; Mu Alpha Theta; NFL; Q&S; Nwsp Phtg; Nwsp Stf; Yrbk Phtg; High Hon Roll; Sal; Merit Schlrshp U Of Pittsburgh 87; Acad Awd 87; Presdntl Acad Ftnss Awd 87; U Of Pittsburgh; Pre Med.

WONG, ERIKA CHUIMEI; William Allen HS; Allentown, PA; (4); 16/600; Exploring; Trs Intnl Clb; JCL; Model UN; Nwsp Phtg; Lit Mag; L Mgr(s); High Hon Roll; NHS; Spanish NHS; Stu Advncmnt Awd 87; PA ST U; Elec Engrng.

WONG CHONG, MICHELINE; Shaler Area SR HS; Allison Park, PA; (4); 40/493; Cmnty Wkr; Debate Tm; Drama Clb; French Clb; Girl Scts; Hosp Aide; SADD; Yrbk Stf; Stu Cncl; French Hon Soc; Natl Sci Olympd Top 10 85-87; PA Gov Schl Excllnc 86; Geneva Coll Goldn Ornado Invtnl 4th Pole Vlt 87; Pre Med.

WONG-CHONG, MICHELINE; Shaler Area SR HS; Allison Pk, PA; (3); 40/495; Debate Tm; Drama Clb; French Clb; Girl Scts; Hosp Aide; School Play; Yrbk Stf; Stu Cncl; French Hon Soc; Hon Roll; PA Gvrnrs Schl Of Excel 86; Natl Sci Olympd Top 10 85-87; Pre-Med.

WOOD, DAVID; Mid Valley Secondary Center; Dickson City, PA; (4); 1/75; Pres Drama Clb; Scholastic Bowl; Pres Band; Pres Mrchg Band; School Play; Nwsp Rptr; High Hon Roll; Pres NHS; Pres Schlr.

WOOD, DOUG; Waynesburg Central HS; Waynesburg, PA; (4); Boy Scts; Cmnty Wkr; 4-H; VICA.

WOOD, HEATHER; Carmichaels Area HS; Carmichaels, PA; (3); 15/112; French Clb; Spanish Clb; Drill Tm; Var High Hon Roll; Var Hon Roll; Natl Hnr Roll 85-86; Lang.

WOOD, JENIFER L; Lower Merion HS; Wynnewood, PA; (4); 5/370; Cmnty Wkr; Debate Tm; JCL; Political Wkr; Spanish Clb; Stu Cncl; High Hon Roll; Ntl Merit SF; English.

WOOD, KELLY; Marion Center Area HS; Indiana, PA; (4); 3/170; Church Yth Grp; FNA; Hosp Aide; Science Clb; SADD; Chorus; Church Choir; High Hon Roll; NHS; PA Free Entrprs Wk Schlrshp 86; Penn ST; Pre Med.

WOOD, KIM; Waynesburg Central HS; Waynesburg, PA; (3); Art Clb; 4-H; Letterman Clb; Spanish Clb; Sec Frsh Cls; Sec Soph Cls; JV Var Cheerleading; Coach Actv; L Trk; Hon Roll; Outstndng Chrldr Awd 86-87; JR Prom Atatndnt 86-87; U Of Pittsburgh; Bio.

WOOD, KRISTIN; Blue Ridge HS; Hallstead, PA; (3); Pep Clb; Yrbk Ed-Chief; Yrbk Phtg; VP Stu Cncl; Var Bsktbl; Var Sftbl; High Hon Roll; NHS; Hugh O Brien Cntrl PA Yth Smnr 86; Bus Admin.

WOOD, LESLIE; Pennsbury HS; Yardley, PA; (3); 93/800; French Clb; Var L Bsktbl; Var L Fld Hcky; Trk; Hon Roll; Prfct Atten Awd; Cert Of Merit 85-86; Cert Outstndng Achvt 86; Plq Of Rcgntn Exec Wmn Intl 87; Hofstra U; CPA.

WOOD, MEGAN; Montoursville HS; Montoursville, PA; (3); 50/180; Art Clb; Chorus; Mrchg Band; School Musical; Stat Bsktbl; Mgr(s); Var Sftbl; Var Twrlr; VFW Awd; Oceanogrphy.

WOOD, SHAWN; Corry Area HS; Corry, PA; (4); Aud/Vis; Library Aide; Concert Band; Pres Stage Crew; Hon Roll; Acad Achvt Awd 87.

WOOD, TAMMY; Corry Area HS; Corry, PA; (4); 68/200; Church Yth Grp; Teachers Aide; Nwsp Sprt Ed; Powder Puff Ftbl; Var L Trk; Var Capt Vllybl; Hon Roll; Prsntd Wreath To Tomb Of Unkwn Sldrs 83; 1st Tm All-Cnty For Vllybl 86; Slippery Rock U; Cmnctns.

WOOD, TERESA L; Pequea Valley HS; Strasburg, PA; (4); 15/109; Cmnty Wkr; Hosp Aide; Red Cross Aide; Varsity Clb; Band; Jazz Band; Mrchg Band; School Musical; School Play; Stage Crew; Outstndng Spnsh & Home Eco Awds 87; Odessa Coll-TX; Nrsng.

WOOD, TOM; Rocky Grove HS; Franklin, PA; (3); 15/81; Aud/Vis; Boy Scts; Church Yth Grp; Band; Var Crs Cntry; Vllybl; Mgr Wrstlng; Hon Roll.

WOODARD, LINCOLN; Avon Grove HS; West Grove, PA; (3); Boy Scts; Church Yth Grp; Var Bsbl; JV Bsktbl; JV Socr.

WOODCODK, MICHELLE; Altoona Area HS; Altoona, PA; (4); 3/718; Computer Clb; VP Trs English Clb; French Clb; Math Tm; Ski Clb; VP Speech Tm; Concert Band; Stu Cncl; Jr NHS; Sec NHS; Englsh.

WOODFORD, CAMERON; The Baptist HS; Clarks Summit, PA; (3); Church Yth Grp; Quiz Bowl; Chorus; Pres Stu Cncl; Stat Bsktbl; Var L Socr; Var Vllybl; Hon Roll; Patriots Ldrshp Awd 87; Baptist Bible Coll; Missionary.

WOODLIEF, GREGORY; Waynesboro Area SR HS; Fayetteville, PA; (4); 90/365; Boy Scts; Computer Clb; Capt Bowling; Hon Roll; Penn ST; Med.

WOODMAN, SARAH; Unionville HS; Chadds Ford, PA; (3); Church Yth Grp; Cmnty Wkr; French Clb; Yrbk Stf; Rep Jr Cls; Rep Stu Cncl; High Hon Roll; Hon Roll.

WOODRING, CRISTY S; Center Area HS; Monaca, PA; (2); Im Bowling; Hon Roll.

WOODRING, JOHN; Tamaqua Area HS; Tamaqua, PA; (3); 121/205; Var L Bsktbl; Capt L Ftbl.

WOODRING, KERI; Northampton Area SR HS; Bath, PA; (3); 39/494; AFS; VP DECA; Drama Clb; FBLA; SADD; School Musical; School Play; Stage Crew; High Hon Roll; Hon Roll; Schl Dist Schlrshp Wnr 87; ST Candidate For A DECA Pres 87; NASD Suicide Prvntn Grp 85-87; PA ST; Bus Admin.

WOODRING, PHILIP C; Bucktail Area HS; Renovo, PA; (3); 1/62; Am Leg Boys St; Church Yth Grp; Pres Computer Clb; Varsity Clb; Band; Mrchg Band; Bausch & Lomb Sci Awd; High Hon Roll; Pres NHS; Prfct Atten Awd; Comp Sci.

WOODRING, STEVE; Harbor Creek HS; Erie, PA; (4); 21/223; Computer Clb; Teachers Aide; Church Choir; Ftbl; Hon Roll; NHS; Penn ST Behrend; Nuclear Sci.

WOODRING, TAMMY; Philipsburg-Osceola HS; Osceola Mills, PA; (4); Letterman Clb; Pres Pep Clb; Band; Ed Nwsp Stf; Sec Sr Cls; Rep Stu Cncl; Var Cheerleading; Wt Lftg; Hon Roll; Stage Crew; Wmns Clb Hm Mkng Awd 84; Prsdntl Phys Ftnss Awd 84-85; Natl Hndcp Poster & Art Awd 87; Penn ST; Biochem.

WOODROW, THOMAS; Brockway Area HS; Brockway, PA; (3); 39/115; Church Yth Grp; VP Frsh Cls; JV Var Bsktbl; Var L Ftbl; Wt Lftg; Teaching.

WOODRUFF, BOB; Henderson HS; W Chester, PA; (3); Ski Clb; Var Capt Socr; All Chsmnt Soc Tm 86; Vrbl SAT Scr 87; Am Hstry Advncd Plcmnt Tst-4th 87; Econ.

WOODRUFF, CINDY; State College Area HS; State College, PA; (1); FFA; PA ST U; Ag.

WOODRUFF, DARRIN; Tunkhannock Area HS; Tunkhannock, PA; (3); Computer Clb; FCA; French Clb; Ski Clb; Spanish Clb; Bsbl; Bowling; Hon Roll; Kiwanis Awd; Most Improved Stu Of Yr; Wilkes Coll; Comp Sci.

WOODRUFF, JASON; Morrisville HS; Morrisville, PA; (4); 8/100; Am Leg Boys St; Aud/Vis; Library Aide; PAVAS; Quiz Bowl; Scholastic Bowl; Science Clb; Varsity Clb; Yrbk Phtg; Yrbk Rptr; DE Vlly Confnc Schl Athlt Awds Banquet 87; Rotary Intl Camp Neidig 86; Semi Finlst Govrns Schl Art 86; Temple U; Stockbrkr.

WOODRUFF, KARA; Danville SR HS; Danville, PA; (2); 8/150; French Clb; NFL; Ski Clb; High Hon Roll.

WOODRUFF, KAYE; Danville Area SR HS; Danville, PA; (4); French Clb; Latin Clb; SADD; Crs Cntry; Trk; High Hon Roll; NHS; Dorothy Bonawitz Awd 87; Philadelphia Coll; Phrmcy.

WOODRUFF, TIMOTHY; Meadville Area SR HS; Meadville, PA; (3); Ski Clb; Golf; Im Ice Hcky; Engrng.

WOODS, AIMEE; Ligonier Valley SR HS; Laughlintown, PA; (3); 7/128; AFS; Debate Tm; Drama Clb; French Clb; NFL; School Musical; Stage Crew; Trs Jr Cls; Rep Stu Cncl; VP NHS; Math.

WOODS, BONNIE; Seneca Valley SR HS; Mars, PA; (4).

WOODS, CINDY A; Emmaus HS; Macungie, PA; (4); 43/473; Art Clb; 4-H; Ski Clb; Yrbk Phtg; Yrbk Stf; Ed Lit Mag; Hst Jr Cls; Hst Sr Cls; Var Tennis; High Hon Roll; Hon Roll; U Of VT; Engrng.

WOODS, D SCOTT; Plum SR HS; Nw Kensington, PA; (3); Drama Clb; French Clb; Chorus; School Musical; School Play; Nwsp Ed-Chief; Rep Stu Cncl; Golf; Hon Roll; Ntl Merit SF; Music.

WOODS, DESIREE; Tyrone Area HS; Tyrone, PA; (2); Church Yth Grp; FCA; Latin Clb; Varsity Clb; Trk; High Hon Roll; Jr NHS; NHS; Ambassador Coll; Phys Ed.

WOODS, GREGORY; Downingtown HS; Downingtown, PA; (3); Boy Scts; Exploring; Ski Clb; SADD; Var Lcrss; Var Trk; Im Wt Lftg; High Hon Roll; Hon Roll.

WOODS, KATHLEEN; Mc Keesport HS; Mckeesport, PA; (3); Hst AFS; Church Yth Grp; Library Aide; Pep Clb; Acpl Chr; Church Choir; Stat Bsktbl; Var L Sftbl.

WOODS, LESLIE; Peabody HS; Pittsburgh, PA; (4); 15/292; Trs Soph Cls; Pres Jr Cls; VP Stu Cncl; Var L Bsktbl; Var L Trk; High Hon Roll; Hon Roll; Jr NHS; NHS; Acad All Amer 86; Bus Admin.

WOODS, LURETHA; Simon Gratz HS; Philadelphia, PA; (4); 2/300; Hosp Aide; Teachers Aide; High Hon Roll; Hon Roll; NHS; Prfct Atten Awd; Comm Svc Awd 85-86; Villanova U; Nrsng.

WOODS, MARY P; Lower Marion HS; Narberth, PA; (4); Var Sftbl; Hon Roll; Lwr Merion Twp Awd 87-88; Coca Cola Schlrshp 87-88; Welsh Vly Bus Prfsnl Wmns Clb Meml Awd 87-88; Penn ST U; Bus.

WOODS, MICHAEL; Cardinal O Hara HS; Havertown, PA; (4); 41/771; Aud/Vis; Latin Clb; Var Capt Crs Cntry; Var Capt Trk; Hon Roll; NHS; St Jsphs U Schlrshp 87; MVP Indr Trk 87; 2nd Tm All Cathlc Crs Cntry 87; St Josephs U; Med.

WOODS, MICHELLE; Parkland SR HS; Coplay, PA; (3); Church Yth Grp; Hosp Aide; Band; Flag Corp; Hon Roll; NHS; Oper Rm Techncn.

WOODS, NICOLE; Aliquippa JR SR HS; Aliquippa, PA; (3); Drama Clb; French Clb; Band; Church Choir; Mrchg Band; Yrbk Stf; Cheerleading; Sftbl; Hon Roll; NHS; PA ST; Pre Law.

WOODS, PAM; Seton La Salle HS; Bethel Park, PA; (3); Church Yth Grp; Cmnty Wkr; Hosp Aide; Ski Clb; SADD; Stage Crew; JV Var Cheerleading; JV Var Golf; JV Var Mgr(s); Powder Puff Ftbl; Psych.

WOODS, TAMMI; Beaver Area JR SR HS; Midland, PA; (3); French Clb; Ski Clb; Spanish Clb; Band; Chorus; Concert Band; Mrchg Band; Yrbk Stf; Var L Cheerleading; Powder Puff Ftbl.

WOODS, TERI; Brownsville Area HS; Cardale, PA; (3); FBLA; Mgr(s); Pharm.

WOODS, TRACEY; Baldwin HS; Pittsburgh, PA; (3); 57/477; French Clb; Key Clb; Mrchg Band; Yrbk Stf; Rep Stu Cncl; Hon Roll; NHS.

WOODSIDE, CHRISTOPHER; Danville SR HS; Danville, PA; (2); 107/159; Church Yth Grp; Cmnty Wkr; 4-H; SADD; Concert Band; Jazz Band; Mrchg Band; Pep Band; Symp Band; Hon Roll; Penn ST.

WOODSIDE, DONNA; Council Rock HS; Newtown, PA; (2); Pres Frsh Cls; Pres Soph Cls; Rep Stu Cncl; JV Fld Hcky; Var L Trk; Hon Roll; Presdntl Clsrm Fnlst 87; Free Entrprs Wk Schlrshp Wnnr 87; Bnkng.

WOODSIDE, WENDY; Ford City JR SR HS; Ford City, PA; (4); 8/148; FBLA; Drm Mjr(t); Yrbk Stf; Rep Stu Cncl; Var L Sftbl; Var L Vllybl; High Hon Roll; Trs NHS; AFS; Sec Church Yth Grp; Stu Activities Awd 87; IN U Of PA; Bio.

WOODWARD, BONNIE; Bensalem HS; Bensalem, PA; (3); Church Yth Grp; Yrbk Stf; Fld Hcky; Mgr(s); Score Keeper; Hon Roll; Penn ST; Nrsng.

WOODWARD, JULIE L; Troy SR HS; Alba, PA; (3); 6/184; Am Leg Aux Girls St; Drama Clb; Band; Concert Band; Jazz Band; Pep Band; Trk; NHS; Mth.

WOODWARD, KATIE; Gov Mifflin SR HS; Mohnton, PA; (3); Church Yth Grp; JA; Model UN; Political Wkr; Quiz Bowl; Scholastic Bowl; Chorus; Church Choir; Swing Chorus; Nwsp Stf; Berks Cnty Peace Essy 1st 87; Cvl Law.

WOODWARD, KIMBERLY ANNE; Tamaqua Area HS; Tamaqua, PA; (4); Am Leg Aux Girls St; Rep Drama Clb; Pres French Clb; Q&S; Rep Chorus; Capt Flag Corp; School Musical; Nwsp Rptr; Ed Yrbk Stf; Rep Frsh Cls; Fshr Mem Awd 87; Mst Prmsng & Mst Vlbl Featr Wrtr 87; Grls ST Sentr 86; PA Coll Of Textiles & Sci.

WOODWARD, LISA; Juniata HS; Honey Grove, PA; (4); Sec Church Yth Grp; Computer Clb; Band; Chorus; School Play; Yrbk Stf; Stu Cncl; Vllybl; High Hon Roll; NHS; Schlstc J 85-87; Pres Phys Fit Awd 87; 4-H Pres, Blue Rbbns 85; Dickinson Coll; Pre-Law.

WOODWARD, REGINA; Archbishop Carroll HS; Ardmore, PA; (3); Art Clb; Church Yth Grp; Cmnty Wkr; Hon Roll; Miss PA US Teen Pagaent Finalst Winner Ldrshp,Comnty Svc Awd 87; S Atlantc Regionl Champ Sil Med 87; Sports Med.

WOOLEY, JAMES J; New Brighton Area HS; New Brighton, PA; (3); 17/161; Am Leg Boys St; Varsity Clb; Yrbk Sprt Ed; Bsbl; Mgr Ftbl; Mgr(s); Hon Roll; Bowling Green U; Phys Thrpy.

WOOLGAR, ANDREW; Taylor Allderdice HS; Pittsburgh, PA; (3).

WOOLLENS, DIANE; Oxford Area HS; Oxford, PA; (3); 43/200; FTA; Stage Crew; Yrbk Sprt Ed; Sec Frsh Cls; Sec Soph Cls; Co-Capt Cheerleading; Stat Mgr(s); High Hon Roll; Home Ec Awd Sewing-Tailrng 86-87; Home Ec Awd Cookng 85-86; Messiah Coll; Home Ec Tchr.

WOOLLEY, REBECCA; Spring Grove SR HS; York, PA; (3); Church Yth Grp; Cmnty Wkr; Exploring; Acpl Chr; Orch; School Musical; Nwsp Rptr; Swmmng; 4-H Awd; Hon Roll; Lib Arts.

WOOLSLAYER, LORI; Quigley HS; Rochester, PA; (3); 10/80; Yrbk Stf; JV Bsktbl; Powder Puff Ftbl; Var Trk; High Hon Roll; NHS.

WOOLSON, CHRIS; Chichester SR HS; Ogden, PA; (3); 27/293; VP Spanish Clb; SADD; Ed Yrbk Ed-Chief; Im Vllybl; Hst NHS; VP Spanish NHS; Comp Sci 1st Awd 84-85; Olympcs Of Mnd 84-85; Enrchmnt Stds Pgm; Drexel U; Comp Pgmng.

WOOMER, CARRIE; Tyrone Area HS; Tyrone, PA; (2); Chorus; Church Choir; Color Guard; Rep Stu Cncl; Var Trk; Hon Roll; Hmcmng Princess 86-87; Guidance Cnclr.

WOOMER, SCOTT; Altoona Area HS; Altoona, PA; (4); 194/718; Boy Scts; German Clb; Key Clb; Band; Concert Band; Drm & Bgl; Mrchg Band; Pep Band; School Musical; PA ST U; Elem Ed.

WOOSTER, MELISSA; West Branch Area HS; Hawk Run, PA; (3); 32/129; Science Clb; Varsity Clb; Stu Cncl; JV Capt Cheerleading; Var Sftbl; Vllybl.

WORCESTER, CAROL; Annville-Cleona HS; Annville, PA; (4); Sec FBLA; German Clb; Office Aide; Chorus; Mrchg Band; School Musical; Cheerleading; Score Keeper; Central PA Bus Schl; Acctg.

WORDEN, BRAD; Conneaut Valley HS; Springboro, PA; (4); 2/76; Drama Clb; Spanish Clb; VP Band; Jazz Band; VP Mrchg Band; School Musical; School Play; Stage Crew; High Hon Roll; Trs NHS; Let For High Hnr Achvt 85-86; Let In Drama 83-84; Schl Sci Awd 86-87; PA ST Coll; Sci.

WORDEN, JILL; Wellsboro SR HS; Wellsboro, PA; (3); 40/112; Exploring; Pep Clb; Band; Chorus; Concert Band; Mrchg Band; Var Trk; PA Moose, Stu Cngrss-Just Say No Drgs Smnr 87; Hlth.

WORDINGER, JAMES R; Abington HS; Glenside, PA; (4); 93/491; Key Clb; Spanish Clb; Stage Crew; Yrbk Stf; Rep Jr Cls; Rep Sr Cls; Hon Roll; Jr NHS; NHS; Prfct Atten Awd; Temple U; Comm.

WOREK, MICHELE; Bishop Hafey HS; West Hazleton, PA; (3); 7/113; Church Yth Grp; Spanish Clb; Y-Teens; Sec Jr Cls; Co-Capt Cheerleading; Dnfth Awd; High Hon Roll; NHS; Ntl Merit Ltr; Spanish NHS; Villanova U; Engr.

WORGS, DONN C; Milton Hershey Schl; Brooklyn, NY; (4); 20/130; English Clb; FCA; Spanish Clb; Church Choir; Lit Mag; Hst Jr Cls; Var Sr Cls; Rep Stu Cncl; Bsktbl; Capt Ftbl; Ftbll All Cnfrnc Tm Schlrshp Lehgh U 86-87; Trck Rnnr Up Conf Dscs 86-87; Lehigh U; Engnrng.

WORK, HEATHER; Montour HS; Pittsburgh, PA; (3); Var Bsktbl; Var JV Mgr(s); Stat Score Keeper; Var Tennis; Var L Trk; U Of Pittsburgh; Elem Ed.

WORK, WALTER; Pine Grove Area HS; Tremont, PA; (3); 4-H; Latin Clb; Letterman Clb; ROTC; Varsity Clb; Drill Tm; Stage Crew; Rep Stu Cncl; Im Badmtn; JV Bsbl; Dept Of Army Supr Cadet Cmmndtn 87; Dept Of Mltry Affrs Cert Of Apprctn 87.

WORKMAN, AUDREY K; Mc Guffey HS; W Finley, PA; (3); 11/240; Sec 4-H; Trs Ski Clb; Spanish Clb; Jazz Band; Yrbk Stf; Powder Puff Ftbl; Score Keeper; High Hon Roll; Hon Roll; Trs NHS; Stu Rcgntn Awd 85-87.

WORKMAN, LEASHELL; Central York HS; York, PA; (4); 30/212; Exploring; Girl Scts; Intnl Clb; Library Aide; Band; Mrchg Band; School Musical; Nwsp Stf; Yrbk Bus Mgr; Hon Roll; Band Ltr, 1st Svc Bar 87; Schl Acadmc Excllnc Ltr 87; Millersvl U; Bio.

WORKS, J DOUGLAS; Portersville Christian Schl; New Castle, PA; (4); 6/15; Church Yth Grp; Chorus; Yrbk Phtg; Yrbk Sprt Ed; Sec VP Stu Cncl; Var L Bsktbl; Var L Socr; Elks Awd; NHS; Ntl Merit Schol; Dstngshd Chrstn HS Stu 86-87; Geneva Coll; Engrng.

WORLEY, JEFF; John Piersol Mc Caskey HS; Lancaster, PA; (3); Pres Church Yth Grp; Pres Band; Pres Chorus; Concert Band; Mrchg Band; Pep Band; Outstndng Base Plryr 8k; Penn ST.

WORLEY, JENNIFER; Southwestern HS; Hanover, PA; (2); 30/257; VP Church Yth Grp; Teachers Aide; Band; Chorus; Sec Church Choir; Concert Band; Mrchg Band; School Musical; School Play; Stage Crew; NC ST U; Phys Thrpy.

WORLINE, KRISTI; Cocalico HS; Denver, PA; (3); 12/165; Radio Clb; Rep Jr Cls; Rep Stu Cncl; Capt Bsktbl; Fld Hcky; Sftbl; Trk; High Hon Roll; NHS; Prfct Atten Awd; Socl Stds Outstdng Grp Cooprtn Intiatv Grp Ldr 85, 87; Frgn Lang.

WORLINE, LESLEY; Cocalico HS; Denver, PA; (4); Church Yth Grp; GAA; Band; Concert Band; Mrchg Band; VP Soph Cls; Stu Cncl; Var Capt Bsktbl; Var L Sftbl; Hon Roll; Denver Wmns Clb Schlrshp, Reamstown Athltc Assn Schlrshp 87; Penn ST; Hmn Dvlpmnt.

WORLING, DEVLIN; Brookville Area HS; Brookville, PA; (3); 33/190; Church Yth Grp; Pres Band; Pres Concert Band; Pres Mrchg Band; Sec Pep Band; School Musical; Symp Band; Hon Roll; Accntng.

WOROSZYLO, TRACY; Lincoln HS; Ellwood City, PA; (4); 19/169; Church Yth Grp; High Hon Roll; Hon Roll; Prfct Atten Awd; Frgn Lang Awd-Spnsh 87; Achiev Awd 84-85.

WORRALL III, ALFRED R; Mt Penn HS; Mt Penn, PA; (2); 8/52; Band; Chorus; Church Choir; Concert Band; Jazz Band; Mrchg Band; JV Bsktbl; JV Mgr(s); Hon Roll; Pres Schlr; Accntng.

WORST, BRIAN; Montour HS; Coraopolis, PA; (4); JA; Prfct Atten Awd; Dale Carnegie Schlrshp 86; Indiana U Of PA; Comp Engr.

WORTH, TRACY J; Christian School Of York; Plymouth, MN; (3); Church Yth Grp; Chorus; Church Choir; VP Frsh Cls; Hon Roll; Lawyer Mock Trial Cmpttn 87; Hist Olympiad 87; Ledrshp Conf 85; St Cloud ST U; Law.

WORTHEN, AMI; Hempfield HS; Lancaster, PA; (2); Church Yth Grp; Cmnty Wkr; English Clb; VP Keywanettes; Spanish Clb; Teachers Aide; Y-Teens; Lit Mag; Rep Frsh Cls; Sec Soph Cls; Child Devel.

WORTHINGTON, BONNIE; Downingtown SR HS; Downingtown, PA; (3); 108/648; French Clb; Hosp Aide; Ski Clb; Drm & Bgl; Flag Corp; Mrchg Band; Nwsp Stf; Lcrss; Vllybl; Hon Roll; Bloomsburgh U; Pre Med.

WORTHINGTON, RYAN; C B West HS; Doylestown, PA; (4); 4-H; JV Bsbl; 4-H Awd.

WORTHY, TRUDY; Frazier JR-SR HS; Fayette City, PA; (4); Camp Fr Inc; Band; Concert Band; Drm Mjr(t); Mrchg Band; Pep Band; Rep Soph Cls; Powder Puff Ftbl; High Hon Roll; Prom Commtte 85-86; Yth Rep; CA U Of PA; Acctnt.

WORTMAN, MISSIE; Elk County Christian HS; St Marys, PA; (3); 7/72; Intnl Clb; Church Choir; Nwsp Bus Mgr; Yrbk Stf; Sec Crs Cntry; Sec Trk; Hon Roll; Prsnl Finance.

WORTMANN, STEVE; Parkland SR HS; Orefield, PA; (3); 202/481; Rep Soph Cls; Engr.

WORTZMAN, HARRIET; Peabody HS; Pittsburgh, PA; (4); 19/292; L Swmmng; Hon Roll; NHS; Mdcl Trnscrptnst.

WOTRING, SHERRY; Parkland HS; Schnecksville, PA; (3); 124/481; Letterman Clb; Varsity Clb; Yrbk Phtg; Yrbk Stf; Rep Stu Cncl; Var Capt Fld Hcky; Sftbl; Trk; High Hon Roll; Hon Roll; Phy Therapy.

WOVCHKO II, EDWARD A; Montour HS; Coraopolis, PA; (3); VP Letterman Clb; Pres Band; Concert Band; Jazz Band; Mrchg Band; Var Capt Bsktbl; Coach Actv; Vllybl; High Hon Roll.

WOYAK, SCOTT A; Upper Dublin HS; Fort Washington, PA; (4); 21/318; JA; Math Clb; VP Math Tm; Science Clb; Ski Clb; Rep Jr Cls; Capt Im Bsktbl; Im Tennis; Im Vllybl; Im Wt Lftg; Marshall-Hahn Schlrshp 87; VA Tech; Engrng.

WOZNIAK, EDMOND; Freeport HS; Freeport, PA; (3); Var Bsbl; JV Bsktbl.

WOZNIAK, JAMES; Portage Area HS; Portage, PA; (3); #3 In Class; Var L Bsbl; Var L Bsktbl; Var L Ftbl; Im Vllybl; Im Wt Lftg; High Hon Roll; NHS; Portage Amer Legion Bsbll MVP 86.

WOZNIAK, SHELLEY; Central Cambria HS; Mineral Point, PA; (3); Church Yth Grp; Chorus; Hon Roll; Bradford Schl; Secy.

WOZNY, CHRISTINE; Windber Area HS; Windber, PA; (3); Art Clb; Hosp Aide; Library Aide; Spanish Clb; Band; Concert Band; Var L Bsktbl; Var L Sftbl; High Hon Roll; Hon Roll; Stu Of Mnth; Cert Of Hnr; Pres Acad Ftns Awd; Sci.

WRABEL, JEFF; Bishop Mc Devitt HS; Harrisburg, PA; (4); 20/251; Trs Church Yth Grp; Cmnty Wkr; Letterman Clb; Office Aide; Pep Clb; Teachers Aide; Varsity Clb; Yrbk Stf; Rep Frsh Cls; Rep Soph Cls; Amer Lgn Awd 85; Ldrshp Awd 85; Accntng.

WRAY, ELIZABETH; Trinity HS; Amity, PA; (3); Church Yth Grp; Dance Clb; Drama Clb; Stage Crew; Variety Show; Sftbl; Swmmng; Trk; Dance Instrtctr.

WRAY, YVONNE; Danville SR HS; Danville, PA; (2); 51/163; CAP; Drama Clb; Chorus; Var L Crs Cntry; Var L Trk; High Hon Roll; School Musical; School Play; High Hon Roll; Algebra Awd 85-86; Ga St Univ; Bus.

WRIEDE, CHRIS; Steel Valley HS; West Homestead, PA; (4); 14/201; Boy Scts; Pres Church Yth Grp; Church Choir; Concert Band; Mrchg Band; Var L Swmmng; High Hon Roll; NHS; Prfct Atten Awd; Champ SWPBB Yth Group 84-85; U Of NC; Psych.

WRIGHT, ALYSON; Conneaut Valley HS; Conneautville, PA; (3); Spanish Clb; SADD; Varsity Clb; Chorus; Yrbk Phtg; Yrbk Stf; Sec Jr Cls; Stat Bsktbl; Var L Cheerleading; Mgr(s); Erie Bus Ctr; Exec Sec.

WRIGHT, AMY; Corry Area HS; Spartansburg, PA; (4); 12/188; Drama Clb; French Clb; Radio Clb; Teachers Aide; Band; Concert Band; Mrchg Band; JV Vllybl; High Hon Roll; Hon Roll; Presdntl Acadc Ftns Awd 87; Clarion U Of PA; Scndry Educ.

WRIGHT, AMY; Newport JR SR HS; Newport, PA; (4); 13/92; Spanish Clb; Teachers Aide; Band; Drm Mjr(t); Pep Band; School Musical; NHS; Concert Band; Jazz Band; Mrchg Band; The Sound Of America Hnr Band & Chorus 86; PA All ST Lions Band 87; Modern Music Masters 85-87; Shippnsbrg U; Math.

WRIGHT, BRIAN; Purchaseline HS; Mahaffey, PA; (3); Boy Scts; VICA; Var JV Ftbl; Mgr(s); Im Var Trk; God Cntry Awd.

WRIGHT, DAVE; Mc Caskey HS; Lancaster, PA; (3); 125/517; FBLA; Ftbl; Hon Roll; Bus.

WRIGHT, DAWN; Scotland Schl; Philadelphia, PA; (3); Am Leg Aux Girls St; Capt Art Clb; Office Aide; ROTC; Capt Mrchg Band; Sec Soph Cls; Sec Stu Cncl; Capt Var Bsktbl; Cit Awd; Hon Roll; Outstndg Stu Cncl Rep 87; Cert Outstndg Athlt 87; Cert Trng ROTC Helicopter 84; Phila Coll Txtls-Sci; Int Dcrtr.

WRIGHT, ERIC; Gar Memorial HS; Wilkes-Barre, PA; (3); 18/152; Ski Clb; Nwsp Stf; Hon Roll; Jr NHS; NHS; NEDT Awd.

WRIGHT, ERNIE; Danville HS; Danville, PA; (1); Ski Clb; JV Bsbl; JV Var Ftbl; JV Var Wrstlng; High Hon Roll; Hon Roll; Pres Acdmc Ftns Awd 86-87; Dstngshd Wrstlng Awd 86-87.

WRIGHT, ERNIE; Glendale HS; Fallentimber, PA; (3); 9/71; Science Clb; SADD; Yrbk Stf; Var JV Bsktbl; Hon Roll; NHS.

WRIGHT, FELICITA; Philadelphia HS For Girls; Philadelphia, PA; (3); Sec Church Yth Grp; Office Aide; JV Bsktbl; Bio.

WRIGHT, FREDERICK; New Castle SR HS; New Castle, PA; (3); 12/293; Chorus; Nwsp Phtg; Nwsp Stf; Rep Stu Cncl; JV Crs Cntry; JV Trk; High Hon Roll; Hon Roll; NFL; Pep Clb; 1st Pl Jrnlsm Youngstown ST U Reading Fest 86; Marshal 86-87; Jrnlsm.

WRIGHT, JOHN; Canon-Mc Millan HS; Canonsburg, PA; (3); 59/400; Church Yth Grp; Varsity Clb; JV Bsktbl; Im Sftbl; Var L Swmmng; Var Capt Tennis; Im Vllybl; Hon Roll.

WRIGHT, KAREN; Academy HS; Erie, PA; (3); 13/226; VP Church Yth Grp; SADD; Chorus; Church Choir; Concert Band; Mrchg Band; Orch; School Musical; High Hon Roll; NHS; PA Free Entrprs Wk Schlrshp 87; Bst Flute Awd Band 86; WV U; Cmnctns.

WRIGHT, KRISTINE; West Philadelphia Catholic HS; Philadelphia, PA; (3); 50/276; Pres Church Yth Grp; French Clb; NFL; Nwsp Stf; Ntl Merit Ltr; Awd Exclnce Poetry/Forensics 84-85; Psych.

WRIGHT, LEE; West Greene Middle-SR HS; Graysville, PA; (2); Boy Scts; Cmnty Wkr; VICA; Church Choir; Hon Roll; History Honor 87; Mltry Bldg Const.

WRIGHT, LENDINA; Winchester-Thurston HS; Pittsburgh, PA; (4); AFS; Art Clb; Church Yth Grp; Dance Clb; Service Clb; Spanish Clb; SADD; Acpl Chr; Chorus; Church Choir; Radio, TV & Strwht Thtre 83-84; HS Arts Awd-Chrgrphy 83-84; Carngie-Mlln U Comp Pgm 84-85; Chatham Coll; Comm.

WRIGHT, MARCIE; Boyertown Area SR HS; Bally, PA; (4); Art Clb; French Clb; German Clb; Library Aide; Pep Clb; SADD; Flag Corp; Yrbk Stf; Cit Awd; Hon Roll; Frgn Lang.

WRIGHT, MARK; Punxsutawney Area SR HS; Summerville, PA; (4); 42/245; Math Tm; Science Clb; Variety Show; Penn ST; Engrng.

WRIGHT, MEREDITH; Hamburg Area JR-SR HS; Virginville, PA; (3); #4 In Class; Church Yth Grp; Latin Clb; Spanish Clb; Chorus; Church Choir; High Hon Roll; Hon Roll; NHS; Intl Foreign Lang Awd; Acdmc Let; Bible Clb; Marine Bio.

WRIGHT, MICHELLE; Council Rock HS; New Hope, PA; (2); Church Yth Grp; FCA; GAA; Var L Fld Hcky; Var Socr; Hon Roll; Soccer Ltr 86-87; Bucks Cnty Girls Soccer Tm Slected Golden Twelve 87; Cnty Courier Times 1st Tm Soccr; Duke U; Physcl Thrpy.

WRIGHT, MOLLY; Downington SR HS; Downingtown, PA; (3); 46/648; Church Yth Grp; French Clb; Trs Intnl Clb; SADD; Teachers Aide; Church Choir; Sec Rep Stu Cncl; Mgr(s); High Hon Roll; Hon Roll; SM Liberal Arts Schl; Ed.

WRIGHT, REBECCA; Carlisle SR HS; Newville, PA; (3); Pep Clb; Chorus; Color Guard; Cheerleading; Diving; Hon Roll; Spanish NHS; William & Mary Coll; Sci.

WRIGHT, REBECCA; Montour HS; Mckees Rocks, PA; (2); Church Yth Grp; Sftbl; Swmmng; Tennis; Hon Roll; Prfct Atten Awd; Dstngshd Amer HS Stu 87; William & Mary; Law.

WRIGHT, RICHARD; Seneca Valley HS; Mars, PA; (3); Church Yth Grp; ROTC; Ski Clb; Church Choir; Jazz Band; Mrchg Band; Symp Band; Hon Roll; NHS.

WRIGHT, RICK; Grace Christian Schl; Richland, PA; (3); Church Yth Grp; 4-H; Yrbk Stf; Var Bsbl; Var Bsktbl; 4-H Awd; Bsbl & Bsktbl Andrew Awd 86-87; CPA.

WRIGHT, RONALD; Newport HS; Newport, PA; (1); 19/124; Hon Roll; Bus.

WRIGHT, SCOTT; Henderson HS; West Chester, PA; (3); Intnl Clb; JCL; Chorus; Off Lit Mag; Rep Frsh Cls; Rep Soph Cls; Rep Jr Cls; JV Golf; VP Ice Hcky; JV Lcrss; Comm.

WRIGHT, STEFANIE; Claysburg Kimmel HS; Claysburg, PA; (3); #10 In Class; Camera Clb; Ski Clb; Speech Tm; Band; Mrchg Band; Yrbk Stf; VP Mgr Bsktbl; Var Coach Actv; Var Sftbl; High Hon Roll; Vrsty Bsktbl Tm MVP 85 & 86; Math Tchr.

WRIGHT, STEVE; Butler SR HS; Butler, PA; (3); Church Yth Grp; Spanish Clb; Im Bsktbl; Hon Roll; Accntnt.

WRIGHT, SUSAN; Ridley SR HS; Ridley Park, PA; (3); 177/423; Church Yth Grp; Hosp Aide; Pep Clb; Ski Clb; Varsity Clb; School Play; Var L Bsktbl; Var Gym; Var L Trk; Var L Twrlr; MVP Track 84-85; Acctg.

WRIGHT, SUSAN; Rockwood HS; Somerset, PA; (2); Church Yth Grp; Computer Clb; NFL; Speech Tm; Band; Chorus; VP Soph Cls; Sec Stu Cncl; Cheerleading; Var Vllybl; Phy Thrpy.

WRIGHT, TERESA; West Greene Middle-SR HS; Aleppo, PA; (4); Art Clb; Church Yth Grp; FFA; Salesmanship Of The Year 83-84; ICM Bus Schl; Acctg.

WRIGHT, TRACI; Seneca Valley HS; Harmony, PA; (3); 40/300; Art Clb; GAA; Latin Clb; Ski Clb; Rep Frsh Cls; Off Sr Cls; Stu Cncl; Cheerleading; Diving; Swmmng; 1st Pl Cortland Invitationl Roller Sktng 85; 1st & 3rd Pl Kings Invitationl Sktng 85; U Of Pittsburgh; Child Physchol.

WRIGHT, WILLIAM; Conestoga Valley HS; Leola, PA; (3); 29/400; Political Wkr; Concert Band; Jazz Band; JV Socr; Hon Roll; Prfct Atten Awd; JV Golf; JV Wrstlng; High PSAT Scores Awd 86-87; U Of PA; Biochem.

WRIGHT, WILLIAM; Seneca Valley HS; Evans City, PA; (3); 13/333; Church Yth Grp; Ski Clb; Band; Concert Band; Jazz Band; Mrchg Band; Symp Band; High Hon Roll; Hon Roll; NHS; Erie Chptr PA Engr Awd 87; Otstndng Bnd Mbr Mnth 86; Mgmt.

WRIGHTSTONE, ANDY; Mechanicsburg Area SR HS; Shiremanstown, PA; (3); 131/338; Am Leg Boys St; Exploring; Im Bsktbl; Prfct Atten Awd; Chef.

WRIGLESWORTH, CLAIR N; Curwensville Area HS; Grampian, PA; (3); VP Church Yth Grp; Pres 4-H; VP FFA; Ski Clb; Chorus; JV Ftbl; High Hon Roll; Hon Roll; Ag Engr.

WRISBY, CORNELL; Pottstown SR HS; Pottstown, PA; (4); 22/181; VP French Clb; Pres GAA; Key Clb; Spanish Clb; Nwsp Stf; Sec Sr Cls; Rep Stu Cncl; Var L Bsktbl; Var Capt Fld Hcky; Hon Roll; All Pac 8 Fld Hcky 87; Cntry Clb-HS Schlrshp-$500 87; Haywood L Butler Schlrshp-$500 87; U Of Notre Dame; Pltcl Sci.

WROBLESKI, JOSEPH GARRY; Bishop O Hara HS; Dickson City, PA; (4); 10/115; VP Latin Clb; Spanish Clb; Var Ftbl; Wt Lftg; High Hon Roll; NHS; Prfct Atten Awd; U Of Scranton; Pre-Med.

WROBLEWSKI, ERIC; North Catholic HS; Pittsburgh, PA; (3); Church Yth Grp; Drama Clb; Pres German Clb; Ski Clb; School Musical; Jr Cls; Bsbl; VFW Awd; Stu Cncl 86-87; Grmn Clb 86-87; $75-Amercn Legn Essy; Accntng.

WROBLEWSKI, FRANK; Mahonoy Area HS; Mahanoy City, PA; (4); 15/110; Var L Bsktbl; Hon Roll; Mary Comerford Memrl Schlrsp 87; Wilkes Coll; Physcs.

WROBLEWSKI, MIKE; Conrad Weiser HS; Wernersville, PA; (4); 55/184; Aud/Vis; JCL; Spanish Clb; Chorus; School Musical; Mgr Stage Crew; Var L Socr; JV Tennis; Var Wrstlng; Hon Roll; Shippensburg U; Radio.

WRONA, BILL; Wilmington Area HS; Pulaski, PA; (2); Office Aide; High Hon Roll; Hon Roll; NHS.

WRONA, JENNIFER; Ambridge Area HS; Ambridge, PA; (3); Church Yth Grp; Pep Clb; Red Cross Aide; Spanish Clb; SADD; Band; Church Choir; Concert Band; Mrchg Band; Pep Band.

WRONA, KEVIN; Mohawk JR-SR HS; Wampum, PA; (3); 34/136; French Clb; Nwsp Rptr; Nwsp Stf; Var Bsktbl; Hon Roll; Hstry.

WSZOLEK, STEVE; Valley Forge Military Acad; Philadelphia, PA; (3); 39/147; Art Clb; Aud/Vis; Church Yth Grp; Drm & Bgl; Var Crs Cntry; Hon Roll; Eisenhower Staff Schlrshp 85-87; Marine Corps Marathon Team 86-87; Kent ST; Economics.

WU, CHARLENE; Philadelphia H S For Girls; Philadelphia, PA; (4); 44/365; Cmnty Wkr; Library Aide; Math Clb; Science Clb; Temple Yth Grp; Y-Teens; JV Badmtn; JV Vllybl; High Hon Roll; VFW Awd; VIP Awd Alumnae Assn 87; Hnr Rl Awd Sci Fair 84; Drexel U; Comp Mgmt.

WU, WENDY L; Villa Maria HS; Edgerton, OH; (4); Library Aide; Ski Clb; Spanish Clb; SADD; Thesps; Chorus; School Musical; School Play; Stage Crew; Nwsp Rptr; ST Marys Coll; Bio.

WUKOVITZ, STEPHANIE W; Bloomsburg HS; Bloomsburg, PA; (4); 4/141; Chess Clb; Pres Science Clb; Orch; Symp Band; Gov Hon Prg Awd; NHS; Ntl Merit SF; Church Yth Grp; Drama Clb; Pep Clb; PA All ST Band 86; PA Gov Schl Sci 86; Regnl & ST Aikens-Cadman Awd 86; Carnegie Mellon U; Physics.

WULKOWICZ, GARY; Exeter HS; Reading, PA; (3); 5/241; Varsity Clb; Band; Jazz Band; Orch; Pep Band; Var L Crs Cntry; Var L Trk; Hon Roll; NHS.

WUNDERLY, MICHAEL; Nazareth SR HS; Nazareth, PA; (3); 18/270; Computer Clb; Band; Concert Band; Mrchg Band; Wt Lftg; Hon Roll; Arch.

WUNNER, RONALD; G A R Memorial HS; Wilkes-Barre, PA; (4); 5/172; German Clb; SADD; Chorus; Off Stu Cncl; Ftbl; Wt Lftg; Hon Roll; NHS; Ntl Merit Ltr; Mech Engr.

WURST, JENNIFER; Abraham Lincoln HS; Philadelphia, PA; (3); Church Yth Grp; Hosp Aide; Mgr(s); Score Keeper; Timer; Psych.

WUS, JOHN; Archbishop Wood HS; Warminster, PA; (3); 1/235; Math Tm; SADD; Capt Band; Jazz Band; Mrchg Band; Symp Band; Nwsp Stf; High Hon Roll; NHS; Prfct Atten Awd; Spnsh Awd 85; Physcs, Pre-Calculs Awds 87; Engrng.

WUSINICH, NICOLE; Villa Maria Acad; Downingtown, PA; (3); 7/98; Pres Church Yth Grp; Science Clb; Speech Tm; SADD; Yrbk Stf; Rep Soph Cls; Rep Jr Cls; Trs Stu Cncl; French Hon Soc; NHS; Pre-Med.

WUSTNER, JASON; Abington SR HS; Glenside, PA; (3); 160/502; Band; Concert Band; Jazz Band; Mrchg Band; Stage Crew; Symp Band; Off Stu Cncl; Audio-Visual Engrng.

WYAN, LAURA; Portersville Christina Schl; Evans City, PA; (3); 6/10; Drama Clb; Speech Tm; Variety Show; Yrbk Sprt Ed; Rep Trs Stu Cncl; Capt Bsktbl; Vllybl; Psych.

WYANDT, MARY A; Greater Johnstown HS; Johnstown, PA; (4); 3/300; Pres Exploring; Pres VP Girl Scts; Hosp Aide; Church Choir; Nwsp Ed-Chief; High Hon Roll; Lion Awd; NHS; Prfct Atten Awd; Rotary Awd; Talus Rock Grl Scout Cncl Brd Dir 86-87; Grl Scout Gld Awd 87; Sally Stewart Schlrshp 87; U Pittsburgh; Phys Ther.

WYANT, LISA; Shade Central City HS; Cairnbrook, PA; (3); 9/76; FBLA; Hosp Aide; JV Var Cheerleading; Hon Roll; Prfct Atten Awd; Olympc Natl Schltc Typng Cont 87; Accntng Awd Strght A Avrg 87; Typng Awd 60 Gwam 87; U Of Pittsburgh; Accntng.

WYANT, NICOLE; State Coll Area Intermediate HS; State College, PA; (1); Church Yth Grp; Cmnty Wkr; Band; Church Choir; Stage Crew; Variety Show; Thesps; Rep Frsh Cls; Im Bsktbl; Powder Puff Ftbl; Pre Med.

WYATT, KIMBERLY C; Villa Maria Acad; West Chester, PA; (4); 8/108; Exploring; Math Tm; Mu Alpha Theta; Quiz Bowl; Scholastic Bowl; Teachers Aide; Lit Mag; High Hon Roll; NHS; Ntl Merit SF; Latin NHS VP 86-87; Surgeon.

WYATT, SAUNDRA; Chester SR HS; Chester, PA; (3); Exploring; Letterman Clb; NFL; Chorus; Variety Show; Off Sr Cls; Golf; Socr; Sftbl; Timer; Amer Educ Assistance Cncl; Bio.

WYCKOFF, SUSAN; East Stroudsburg HS; East Stroudsburg, PA; (4); 29/215; VP Intnl Clb; Model UN; Political Wkr; Concert Band; Mrchg Band; Nwsp Rptr; Mgr(s); Sftbl; High Hon Roll; NHS; Intl Frgn Lang Awd Wnnr 86; Hnrs Banquet 84; Frnch.

WYDILA, DAVID; Mt Carmel Area JR SR HS; Mt Carmel, PA; (4); 2/172; VP Key Clb; Trs Q&S; School Musical; Nwsp Stf; Trs Soph Cls; Golf; Trk; Kiwanis Awd; NHS; Sal; Cohen Mem Awd 87; Ad Bahner Awd 87; Deppen Schlrshp 87; Bucknell U; Elec Engr.

WYLAND, ANGELA; Lewistown HS; Lewistown, PA; (2); AFS; French Clb; Ski Clb; Band; Yrbk Stf; JV Cheerleading; High Hon Roll; NHS; Achvt Awd 85-87; Penn ST; X-Ray Tech.

WYLAND, CAROLYN; Penn Cambria SR HS; Patton, PA; (3); SADD; Hon Roll; Excllnce Engl 85; Adv Art Awd 85; Aviation.

WYLAND, MICHELLE; Plum SR HS; Pittsburgh, PA; (3); 88/410; Church Yth Grp; JA; Office Aide; Service Clb; Nwsp Stf; Hon Roll; Educ.

WYLIE, LESLIE; Immaculate Conception HS; Houston, PA; (3); 14/41; Art Clb; Nwsp Stf; Yrbk Ed-Chief; Yrbk Phtg; Yrbk Stf; Stu Cncl; Bsktbl; Sftbl; Bio.

WYMAN, BENJAMIN; Schenley HS Teacher Ctr; Pittsburgh, PA; (3); Boy Scts; German Clb; Hosp Aide; Ski Clb; Yrbk Stf; Var L Crs Cntry; Var L Vllybl; High Hon Roll; Hon Roll; NHS; West Penn Hosp Vlntr Viewpoint Article 86; Law.

WYMAN, SCOTT; New Castle SR HS; New Castle, PA; (4); 27/232; Church Yth Grp; Stu Cncl; Ftbl; NHS; Prsdntl Ftnss Awd 87; U Of LA; Engnrng.

WYNN, DOUGLAS; Carmichaels Area HS; Carmichaels, PA; (4); 5/101; Drama Clb; Science Clb; Pres Spanish Clb; Pres Band; Drm Mjr(t); Mrchg Band; Rep Jr Cls; Rep Sr Cls; Lion Awd; Trs NHS; Lions Clb Oct Boy Of Mnth 86; Outstndg SR Stu 86; Gvrnrs Schl 85&86; Duquesne U; Phrmcy.

WYNN, MICHAEL; Archbishop Ryan H S For Boys; Philadelphia, PA; (2); 129/349; Rep Soph Cls; Var Swmmng; JV Trk.

WYNO, PENNY; Penns Manor Area HS; Clymer, PA; (3); 3/100; Varsity Clb; Concert Band; Jazz Band; Mrchg Band; JV Var Vllybl; High Hon Roll; Hon Roll; NHS; NEDT Awd; IN U PA; Crmnlgy.

WYPA, LYNN ANN; Lake-Lehman HS; Shavertown, PA; (4); 11/155; Hosp Aide; Key Clb; Yrbk Stf; High Hon Roll; Hon Roll; Jr NHS; NHS.

WYRICK, JANET; Fort Cherry JR-SR HS; Mcdonald, PA; (3); Sec FNA; Hosp Aide; Library Aide; Science Clb; Spanish Clb; SADD; Teachers Aide; Chorus; Drill Tm; High Hon Roll.

WYSOCHANSKI, CYNDI; Abington Heights HS; Clarks Summit, PA; (3); 26/292; Ski Clb; Band; Mrchg Band; Rep Stu Cncl; Var L Cheerleading; Hon Roll.

WYSOCHANSKI, FAITH; South Hiulls Christian HS; Bethel Park, PA; (2); 1/10; Church Yth Grp; School Play; Nwsp Stf; Capt Cheerleading; High Hon Roll; Pres Frsh Cls; Cit Awd; Liberty Bapt U; Elem Ed.

WYSOCHANSKI, MICHAEL D; South Hills Christian HS; Bethel Park, PA; (1); 1/15; Church Yth Grp; VP Frsh Cls; Var Socr.

WYSOCKI, SYLVIA; Danville Area HS; Danville, PA; (4); 30/199; Key Clb; Spanish Clb; Rep Frsh Cls; Rep Sr Cls; Capt Cheerleading; Var Fld Hcky; Var Trk; High Hon Roll; Hon Roll; NHS; WA & Jefferson Coll; Pre Law.

WYSOKINSKI, MICHELE; Pittston Area HS; Pittston, PA; (4); FNA; Key Clb; Ski Clb; Capt Drill Tm; Yrbk Stf; Sec Soph Cls; High Hon Roll; NHS; WY Vly Childrens Assn Awd 87; Coll Misercordia; Occup Therapy.

WYSZYNSKI, DENISE; Council Rock HS; Pineville, PA; (3); 202/908; 4-H; Concert Band; Sec Stu Cncl; Im Powder Puff Ftbl; Score Keeper; Trk; Hon Roll; PA ST; Advrtsng.

XAVIER, DORA; Salisbury HS; Allentown, PA; (4); Drama Clb; Sec Key Clb; Model UN; SADD; School Play; Off Stu Cncl; Stat Ftbl; High Hon Roll; Hon Roll; Prfct Atten Awd; Reuben Block Health Fund Schlrshp 87; Most Outstndng Stu In Spanish II & V 84-87; Lioness Awd 86; U Of Pittsburgh; Physical Thrpy.

XIONG, MAY; Philadelphia HS For Girls; Philadelphia, PA; (4); 173/344; Cmnty Wkr; Teachers Aide; JV Vllybl; Natl Schl Of Health Tech; Med.

YACAPSIN, GENE; Marian Catholic HS; Nesquehoning, PA; (4); Stage Crew; JV Bsktbl; Var JV Ftbl; Var Trk; Susquehanna U; Bus.

YACCINO, JEAN ANN; Hazleton SR HS; Hazleton, PA; (2); French Clb; Chorus; Yrbk Stf; French Hon Soc; High Hon Roll; Presdntl Acadmc Ftns Awd; Hnrb Mntn-Ntl Frnch Cntst; Penn ST; Pre-Med.

YACHERE, TRACY; Rockwood Area HS; Rockwood, PA; (2); 3/28; Art Clb; Cmnty Wkr; Hosp Aide; Chorus; School Musical; Nwsp Rptr; Crs Cntry; Score Keeper; Hon Roll; Pred Ftns Awd 86; Adv Lifesavng Water Safety 86; Comtlgst.

YACKULAK, SHEILA; Plum SR HS; Pittsburgh, PA; (3); Art Clb; Church Yth Grp; Drama Clb; French Clb; GAA; Pep Clb; Speech Tm; Drill Tm; School Musical; School Play; Ltrmn Sccr 86-87; Outstndng Svc Grls Ldrs Assoc 86-87; 2 Schl Svc Awds 87; Art Thrpy.

YACKULICH, JENNIFER; Conemaugh Valley JR SR HS; Park Hill, PA; (3); 14/104; Pep Clb; Concert Band; Mrchg Band; Sec Jr Cls; Stat Bsktbl; High Hon Roll; Hon Roll; NHS; Computer Clb; Chorus; Med Secr.

YACONI, GEORGE; Laurel Valley HS; New Florence, PA; (4); Boy Scts; Scholastic Bowl; Trs Science Clb; Teachers Aide; Chorus; Concert Band; Jazz Band; Mrchg Band; Cit Awd; High Hon Roll; Penn ST; Physcs.

YACOVIELLO, LORI; Moon SR HS; Corapolis, PA; (3); Office Aide; Spanish Clb; Teachers Aide; JV Trk; Hon Roll; Pre Nrsny Educ.

YACUBOSKI, STEVE; Pocono Mountain HS; Skytop, PA; (2); Art Clb; Bsbl; Hon Roll; Art Inst Of Gettsburgh; Art.

YACULAK, KIM; Pottstown HS; Pottstown, PA; (4); Office Aide; Pep Clb; Nwsp Sprt Ed; Pres Frsh Cls; Rep Soph Cls; Rep Jr Cls; Rep Sr Cls; Var Capt Bsktbl; Capt Var Fld Hcky; Church Yth Grp; Athltc Schlrshp Temple U 87; Wmn Athlte Yr Chstmnt Leag 86; All Leag 1st Tm Hcky & Bsktbl 86-87; Temple U; O C Thrpy.

YADUSH, ANN MARIE; Northampton SR HS; Walnutport, PA; (4); 18/444; AFS; Church Yth Grp; Hosp Aide; Leo Clb; SADD; Church Choir; Nwsp Stf; Ed Yrbk Stf; Var Tennis; Var Trk; Bloomsburg U.

YAGLA, BARBARA; Hempfield Area SR HS; Bovard, PA; (4); 44/695; Pep Clb; Spanish Clb; Yrbk Stf; L Vllybl; High Hon Roll; Hon Roll; VP Jr NHS; NHS; Penn ST U; Engrng.

YAHNER, ALICE; Greencastle-Antrim HS; Chambersburg, PA; (3); 108/167; Church Yth Grp; Band; Concert Band; Flag Corp; Mrchg Band; Yrbk Stf; Advrtsng.

YAKIMICK, TAUSHA; Rockwood HS; Somerset, PA; (4); 3/94; Band; Chorus; School Play; Yrbk Stf; Sec Stu Cncl; Capt Cheerleading; High Hon Roll; NHS; Penn ST U; Engrng.

YAKUPKOVIC, FRANCINE; Quigley HS; Aliquippa, PA; (4); 20/100; VP JA; Math Tm; VP SADD; Concert Band; Mrchg Band; Pres Stu Cncl; L Var Mgr(s); Powder Puff Ftbl; High Hon Roll; NHS; JR Achvt Sales Awd 87; Hon Eucharistic Mnstr 87; Tstmstrs Intl Awd 85; U Pittsburgh; Comp Engrng.

YALE, MELISSA; St Marys Area HS; Kersey, PA; (2); Church Yth Grp; Teachers Aide; Color Guard; Mrchg Band; Twrlr; Colorguard Capt 87-88; Math Tchr.

YAMALIS, GEORGE; Aliquippa HS; Aliquippa, PA; (3); 21/150; VP Church Yth Grp; French Clb; Band; Concert Band; Mrchg Band; Pep Band; Rep Jr Cls; Hon Roll; Robert Morris Coll; Acctg.

YAMAS, KIMBERLY; State College Area Intermediat HS; State College, PA; (2); Service Clb; SADD; Trs Soph Cls; Im Powder Puff Ftbl.

YAMRICK, BRAD; Indiana SR HS; Indiana, PA; (3); 97/330; Church Yth Grp; Key Clb; SADD; Yrbk Stf; JV Bsbl; Var JV Bsktbl; Golf; JV Tennis; Hon Roll; Jr NHS; Bsktbl Lttr 84-85; WVU; Comm.

YAN, SANDRA YEE-MAN; Mount Alvernia HS; Pittsburgh, PA; (4); 1/71; Computer Clb; French Clb; Hosp Aide; Yrbk Ed-Chief; Stat Bsktbl; Bausch & Lomb Sci Awd; High Hon Roll; NHS; Prfct Atten Awd; Val; Valdctrn Schlrshp 87-88; Robert C Byrd Schlrshp 87-88; John Neuman Schlrshp 86-87; U Of Pittsburgh; Engrng.

YANAK, BRENDA; St Marys Area HS; Saint Marys, PA; (4); 1/276; Debate Tm; Speech Tm; High Hon Roll; NHS; Pres Schlr; Val; Outstndng Sr Eng, Soc Stds, Chem 87; Stackpole Corp Schlrshp 87; Colgate Alumni Mem Schlr 87; Colgate U; Molecular Bio.

YANCHAK, AMY J; Charters-Houston HS; Houston, PA; (3); Drill Tm; Sec Jr Cls; Stu Cncl; Var Capt Bsktbl; Powder Puff Ftbl; Sftbl; Trk; Vllybl; Hon Roll; All Trnmnt Tm Bsktbl 86-87; Psych.

YANCHEK, MAUREEN; Sacred Heart HS; Carbondale, PA; (3); 3/42; Church Yth Grp; Computer Clb; Sec Drama Clb; Sec SADD; School Musical; Stage Crew; Nwsp Rptr; High Hon Roll; NHS; Fml Leads Schl Ply 85 & 87; Marywood Coll.

YANCHITIS, PAUL; Forest City Regional HS; Forest City, PA; (3); 4/65; German Clb; Letterman Clb; Bsbl; Golf; Dnfth Awd; High Hon Roll; NHS; Nuclear Engrng.

YANCICH, JOHN; Brownsville Area HS; Brownsville, PA; (3); 47/210; Drama Clb; Trs Math Clb; Ski Clb; SADD; Nwsp Stf; Hon Roll; Bio.

YANCIK, JOHN; Northern Chester County Tech Schl; Phoenixville, PA; (3); Hon Roll; Jr NHS; VICA Awds Electrncs 85; Comp Repair.

YANCISIN, MATTHEW; Cedar Cliff HS; Camp Hill, PA; (2); 2/294; French Clb; Stu Cncl; JV L Bsktbl; L Ftbl; Var L Socr; Var Trk; French Hon Soc; High Hon Roll; Prfct Atten Awd; Im Fld Hcky; Med.

YANDLE, KRISTA; Salisbury HS; Emmaus, PA; (3); Off Jr Cls; Off Sr Cls; Stu Cncl; JV Var Cheerleading; Im Var Coach Actv; Var L Diving; Im Powder Puff Ftbl; Var L Powder Puff Ftbl; Var L Swmmng; Hon Roll; 5th Pl Dist VI Chmpshps 87; Won Bnai Brith Essay Cntst 87fhnrbl Mntn Sftbl 87; Health Stu.

YANEK, LISA RENEE; Serra Catholic HS; N Versailles, PA; (4); 2/168; Hosp Aide; Sec Math Tm; Band; School Musical; Ed Yrbk Stf; Stat L Trk; NHS; Ntl Merit SF; Sec Spanish NHS; Drama Clb; Westnghse Sci Hnrs Inst; U Of Pittsburgh Provost Day Fnlst; Pre-Med.

YANEK, WILLIAM; Du Bois Area HS; Reynoldsville, PA; (3); 25/325; Varsity Clb; Var L Bsktbl; Var L Ftbl; Var L Trk; Im Wt Lftg; Hon Roll; NHS; Bus Mgmt.

YANG, ALVIN; Upper Dublin HS; Dresher, PA; (3); 28/295; Computer Clb; FBLA; Intnl Clb; Math Tm; Science Clb; SADD; Band; Chorus; Concert Band; Jazz Band; 2nd Pl-Mntgmry Cnty Sci Fair 86; 1st Pl-PA JR Acad Of Sci-Rgnls 86; Engrng.

YANG, BENJAMIN JAE; Harriton HS; Villanova, PA; (3); Chess Clb; JA; Math Tm; Orch; Rptr Nwsp Stf; Var Diving; JV Lcrss; Hon Roll; Jr NHS; NHS.

YANG, TINA; Upper Dublin HS; Dresher, PA; (3); 30/300; Intnl Clb; Math Tm; Science Clb; SADD; Chorus; Yrbk Stf; Lit Mag; Rep Stu Cncl; Hon Roll; NHS; US Army & USAF Awd 87; Engr.

YANGELLO, THERESE; Archbichop Prendergast HS; Drexel Hill, PA; (3); 19/327; Pres Church Yth Grp; Dance Clb; Intnl Clb; Latin Clb; Capt Bsktbl; Mgr(s); Sftbl; Vllybl; Hon Roll; Phrmcst.

YANICK, JAMES; Shamokin Area HS; Ranshaw, PA; (3); 21/236; Art Clb; Drama Clb; Science Clb; SADD; Varsity Clb; Stage Crew; Sec Stu Cncl; Capt Ftbl; Capt Trk; Jr NHS; Biochem.

YANIK, DONALYNN; West Scranton HS; Scranton, PA; (3); Thesps; Stu Cncl; Pom Pon; Hon Roll; NHS; Marywood Coll; Med.

YANKANICH, ANDREW; Parkland SR HS; Orefield, PA; (3); 4/512; Math Tm; SADD; Varsity Clb; Rep Stu Cncl; Var Model UN; High Hon Roll; NHS; Engnrng.

YANKOW, JEFFREY; Bishop O Hara HS; Olyphant, PA; (3); 5/100; Church Yth Grp; Latin Clb; Nwsp Rptr; JV Bsbl; High Hon Roll; Hon Roll; NHS; US Military Acad; Law.

YANN, KELLY; St Paul Cathedral HS; Pittsburgh, PA; (4); 1/57; Drama Clb; School Play; Nwsp Ed-Chief; Nwsp Phtg; Yrbk Ed-Chief; L Stat Vllybl; High Hon Roll; VP NHS; NEDT Awd; Prfct Atten Awd; 1st Pl JR Category Edgewood Photo Cntst 86; 3rd Pl Indivd Caregie Hist Day 86; Most Outstndng Physcs.

YANN, SOPHAL J; Mastbaum AVTS; Philadelphia, PA; (3); Math Clb; Band; Var Tennis; Var Trk; Hon Roll; NHS; Engr.

YANNACCI, MIKE; Yough SR HS; Yukon, PA; (4); Art Clb; Aud/Vis; Ski Clb; Nwsp Rptr; Rep Frsh Cls; Rep Soph Cls; Ftbl; Hon Roll.

YANNACONE, TERESA; Cardinal Ohara HS; Media, PA; (4); 90/771; Sec Church Yth Grp; Cmnty Wkr; Latin Clb; Library Aide; Pres Service Clb; Spanish Clb; SADD; Yrbk Stf; Hon Roll; NHS; Media Rotary Stu Of The Mnth 86; Acad Hnrs Cnvtn 85; 1st Pl DE Cnty Sci Fair 3rd Pl COH Sci Fair 86; Villanova Univ; Lawyer.

YANNATELL, SANDRA L; John W Hallahan Catholic Girls HS; Philadelphia, PA; (4); 29/300; Art Clb; Camp Fr Inc; Church Yth Grp; Dance Clb; Hosp Aide; JA; Office Aide; Yrbk Stf; Rep Frsh Cls; Hon Roll; PA JR Acad Sci 1st Pl Regnl 2nd Pl ST Camp 85-86; 4 Yr Scholar Employees Exch Budd Co 86-87; Philadelphia Coll Tex; Intl Dsg.

YANNEY, LUCIE; Cedar Crest HS; Lebanon, PA; (4); 34/308; Drama Clb; French Clb; Hosp Aide; JA; Latin Clb; School Musical; Hon Roll; NHS; FTA; Pep Clb; Med Steers Clb VP; Booster Clb Brnz Mdlln; Erly Chldhd Ed.

YANNI, JANELLE; Sch Haven Area HS; Sch Haven, PA; (3); 28/82; Computer Clb; Exploring; VICA; Hon Roll; Cosmtlgy.

YANNICK, CHRISTINA; Henderson HS; West Chester, PA; (2); SADD; Rep Soph Cls; Fld Hcky; JV Lcrss; Wt Lftg; Hon Roll; U Of DE; Engrng.

YANNO, EILEEN; Notre Dame HS; Easton, PA; (3); Church Yth Grp; NFL; Band; School Play; Bsktbl; Trk; Hon Roll; Opt Clb Awd; Bus.

YANNUZZI, ANDREA; St Huberts HS; Philadelphia, PA; (3); 128/421; Aud/Vis; Exploring; Hon Roll; Temple Univ; Law.

YANNUZZI, JACINE; Hazleton HS; Hazleton, PA; (3); Church Yth Grp; French Clb; FBLA; Leo Clb; Pep Clb; Political Wkr; Crs Cntry; Trk; Accntng.

YANOS JR, ROBERT D; Owen J Roberts HS; Pottstown, PA; (4); 103/264; Boy Scts; Spanish Clb; Socr; High Hon Roll; Eagle Scout Awd 87; Penn ST; Engrng.

YANOSCSIK, MICHELLE; Homer-Center HS; Homer City, PA; (4); 3/84; FBLA; Varsity Clb; Yrbk Stf; Bsktbl; Ftbl; Trk; Vllybl; High Hon Roll; NHS; Ntl Merit Ltr; Pres Acdmc Ftnss Awd, IN Counselors & Michael J Supinka Schlrshps 87; IN U Of PA; Finance.

YANOSKY, CHARLES; Bethlehem-Center HS; Fredericktown, PA; (3); 19/167; Art Clb; Aud/Vis; Spanish Clb; Hon Roll; Civil Engr.

YANOSKY, LANCE; Bethelehem-Center HS; Fredericktown, PA; (2); 17/156; Math Tm; Hon Roll; Russian Clb 85-87; PA ST; Literary.

YANOSKY, MICHAEL; Canon Mc Millan SR HS; Canonsburg, PA; (3); Trs Church Yth Grp; Spanish Clb; Varsity Clb; Ftbl; Mgr(s); Wrstlng; Hon Roll; Spanish NHS; Cmptrs.

YANTEK, JOHN; Bentworth HS; Bentleyville, PA; (4); 16/131; Ski Clb; Varsity Clb; Pres Jr Cls; Var Ftbl; Bausch & Lomb Sci Awd; Hon Roll; Jr NHS; NHS; Penn ST U; Engr.

YANTEK, SUZANNE; Charleroi JR SR HS; Charleroi, PA; (3); Pep Clb; Spanish Clb; SADD; Band; Church Choir; Nwsp Stf; Bsktbl; Bowling; Score Keeper; Twrlr; Majrtt Capt 87-88; Pre-Law.

YANUL, BRENDA; Shenango JR SR HS; New Castle, PA; (3); 14/125; Cmnty Wkr; Drill Tm; Yrbk Stf; Pom Pon; Score Keeper; Jr NHS; NHS; CPA.

YANULAITIS, MARIANNE; N Pocono HS; Moscow, PA; (3); 4/231; FBLA; Ski Clb; Chorus; Flag Corp; High Hon Roll; NHS; PTSA Libertys View Reflections Cntst 85; Bus.

YANUZZI, KRISTEN; Hazelton HS; Hazleton, PA; (2); Hon Roll; Am Leg Scl Awd Cert Hnrb Mntn 86; Presdntl Acadc Ftns Awd 86.

YAPLE, JENNIFER ANN; Moshannon Valley JR/Sr HS; Houtzdale, PA; (4); 16/120; Pres Trs 4-H; SADD; Varsity Clb; Band; Flag Corp; School Play; Var Capt Bsktbl; 4-H Awd; Ski Clb; Spanish Clb; PA ST Guernsey Qn 87-88; Cnty Dairy Prncs 86-87; Clarion U; Cmmnctns.

YARAMUS, SAMUEL; Aliguippa HS; Aliquippa, PA; (4); 5/140; Var Capt Ftbl; Lion Awd; NHS; Ftbl Schlrshp Geneva Coll 87; Geneva Coll; Acctng.

YARBORO, THERESA; Kennedy Christian HS; W Middlesex, PA; (3); 46/97; Church Yth Grp; Library Aide; NAACP; Spanish Clb; Teachers Aide; Bus Admin.

YARD, AMY; Rocky Grove HS; Franklin, PA; (4); 4-H; French Clb; Quiz Bowl; Variety Show; Yrbk Stf; JV Var Cheerleading; Im Gym; JV Vllybl; 4-H Awd; Hon Roll; Median Schl; Vtrnry Asstnt.

YARD, CYNTHIA; Rocky Grove HS; Franklin, PA; (4); 4/88; Drama Clb; School Play; Rep Jr Cls; Rep Stu Cncl; JV Var Cheerleading; Var Crs Cntry; Vllybl; High Hon Roll; NHS; Pres Schlr; IN U Of PA; Bus.

YARGAR, GRETCHEN; Central Christian HS; Dubois, PA; (3); Church Yth Grp; Girl Scts; Letterman Clb; Varsity Clb; Chorus; Variety Show; Sec Stu Cncl; Var Capt Bsktbl; Var Sftbl; Var Vllybl; MVP Bsktbl 87; MIP Vlybl 87; Grv Cty Coll; Elem Ed.

YARGER, JENNIFER; Moshannon Valley JR SR HS; Brisbin, PA; (3); 54/114; SADD; Chorus; Drill Tm; Yrbk Stf.

YARGER, JENNY; Moshannon Valley HS; Houtzdale, PA; (3); Du Bois Bus Schl; Sec.

YARGER, JOHN; Moshannon Valley HS; Brisbin, PA; (3); 8/120; School Play; Pres Rep Frsh Cls; Pres Rep Soph Cls; Pres Rep Jr Cls; Stu Cncl; Var L Ftbl; Var Socr; Var L Wrstlng; High Hon Roll; NHS; Engr.

YARGER, KEITH; Milton HS; White Deer, PA; (2); Church Yth Grp; Band; Concert Band; Mrchg Band; Rep Frsh Cls; Var Ftbl; Var L Wrstlng; MVP Wrstlng 85; Elem Tchr.

YARGER, PAULA; Moshannon Valley HS; Houtzdale, PA; (3); SADD; High Hon Roll; Hon Roll; Dubois Bus Schl; Secy.

YARGER, PENNY; Moshannon Valley JR/Sr HS; Houtzdale, PA; (4); DECA; High Hon Roll; Hon Roll; Outstndng Dstrbtv Educ Sr 87; Outstndng Vo-Tech Stu 87; Airline/Travel.

YARMOVE, TZIPPORAH; Yeshiva Achei Timim HS; Cincinnati, OH; (3); 2/15; Art Clb; Civic Clb; Cmnty Wkr; FHA; School Musical; School Play; Soph Cls; Jr Cls; Cit Awd; Poster Cont Awd 84; Arts.

YARNELL, KRISTY; State College Area Intermed HS; State College, PA; (1); 152/476; Band; Mrchg Band; Penn ST U; Corp Law.

YARNELL, STACY; Chestnut Ridge HS; Alum Bunk, PA; (4); 21/135; Dance Clb; FBLA; Office Aide; Chorus; Church Choir; Drm Mjr(t); Pres Soph Cls; Pres Jr Cls; Pres Sr Cls; Trs Stu Cncl; Bedford Cnty JR Miss-1st Rnnr Up 87; Hmcmg Qn 86; PA ST Twrlng & Modlng Awds 84 & 86; PA ST; Psych.

YARNES, MARISSA; Sacred Heart HS; Jermyn, PA; (3); Church Yth Grp; Drama Clb; Political Wkr; SADD; Church Choir; School Play; Sec Soph Cls; Sec Jr Cls; Trs Stu Cncl; Var JV Bsktbl; HOBY Ambssdr 86; Ambssdr Trip Wash DC 86; Empire Beauty Schl; Cosmetlgst.

YARNOT, AMY; Moon SR HS; Coraopolis, PA; (3); 34/306; French Clb; Var L Socr; High Hon Roll; Hon Roll; NHS; Prfct Atten Awd; Art Awd Bst Shw 85; Grphc Dsgn.

YARON, THOMAS; John S Fine HS; Nanticoke, PA; (4); 12/252; Chess Clb; Church Yth Grp; Red Cross Aide; Rep Soph Cls; Rep Jr Cls; Vllybl; NHS; Ntl Merit Ltr; Sci.

YAROSZ, JENNY; Center Area HS; Monaca, PA; (2); German Clb; Office Aide; Ski Clb; SADD; Yrbk Phtg; Yrbk Sprt Ed; Rep Stu Cncl; Bowling; Powder Puff Ftbl; Sftbl; Std Cncl Awd 86-87; Arch.

YASSEM, JEFFREY; Ford City HS; Ford City, PA; (3); Computer Clb; Hon Roll; PA JR Acad Sc Rgnl & St Meetng 1st & 2nd Awds 86; ARIN Intrmdte Unt Comp Expstn 1st Pl 86; Penn ST U.

YATES, CHRISTINE; Newport HS; Newport, PA; (3); Rptr 4-H; Band; Chorus; Concert Band; Mrchg Band; School Musical; School Play; Rep Frsh Cls; VP Jr Cls; Hon Roll; Top Enlsh Stu 86; Psychlgy.

YATES, ELIZABETH; Hampton HS; Allison Park, PA; (3); Dance Clb; French Clb; Ski Clb; Spanish Clb; Chorus; Drill Tm; Mrchg Band; Nwsp Stf; Rep Frsh Cls; Rep Soph Cls; Denison.

YATES, TAMARA; Connellsville Area SR HS; Connellsville, PA; (3); 51/535; Church Yth Grp; Drama Clb; German Clb; Girl Scts; Band; Chorus; Concert Band; Flag Corp; Jazz Band; Mrchg Band; Music.

YATSKO, CAROLYN; Lake-Lehman HS; Dallas, PA; (3); Trs Church Yth Grp; Concert Band; Mrchg Band; School Play; Rep Stu Cncl; JV Fld Hcky; Var Trk; Hon Roll; PA Rgn Aalasa Ldrshp Conf 87 & ST 84; ST & Atlantic Coast Band Champ 84-86; Chem.

YATSKO, SARAH; Tunkhannock Area HS; Harveys Lake, PA; (2); 68/; Church Yth Grp; Spanish Clb; Church Choir; Cit Awd; Hon Roll; Penn ST; Psych.

YAUDES, KELLIE; Tyrone Area HS; Tyrone, PA; (3); Key Clb; Band; Chorus; Concert Band; Mrchg Band; Powder Puff Ftbl; Sftbl; Socl Wrk.

YAUGER, MELISSA; Fairchance Georges SR HS; Uniontownd, PA; (4); 25/139; Red Cross Aide; Band; Concert Band; Mrchg Band; Trs Soph Cls; VP Jr Cls; VP Sr Cls; Stu Cncl; Cheerleading; Twrlr; Nrsg.

YAUGER, MIKE; Harry Struman HS; Levittown, PA; (3); Bsbl; Hon Roll; Engr.

YAVOROSKY, BARBARA; Carbondale Area HS; Simpson, PA; (3); 1/160; French Clb; German Clb; High Hon Roll; NHS; French Hon Soc; Prfct Atten Awd; Val; Intnsv Lang Inst Schlrshp Penn ST Russn 87; Penn ST.

YAZINSKI, DANA; Valley View HS; Archbald, PA; (2); 21/189; Church Yth Grp; Latin Clb; Ski Clb; Chorus; Trs Stu Cncl; Var Cheerleading; Var Trk; Var Vllybl; Hon Roll; Dist IX Rgnl Stu Cncl Treas 87-88; PA ST; Law.

YAZWINSKI, BECKY; Philipsburg-Osceola Area HS; Philipsburg, PA; (3); 86/243; Art Clb; Computer Clb; Ski Clb; SADD; School Play; Nwsp Stf; Hon Roll; Natl Handicapped Post Cont 2nd Pl Awd In Cnty 87; Clarion U Of PA; Comm Advert.

YEAGER, CLAY; Abington Heights HS; Waverly, PA; (2); 3/300; Leo Clb; Varsity Clb; Tennis; French Hon Soc; High Hon Roll; Hon Roll; PIAA Dist II Dbls Fnlst 86; PIAA Dist II Sngls Chmpn 87; Athlt Of Wk-Chnnl 22 87; U Of PA Wharton; Bus.

YEAGER, JENNIFER L; St Marys Area HS; St Marys, PA; (3); 70/288; Penn ST; Comp Sci.

YEAGER, KAREN; Cambria Heights HS; Hastings, PA; (3); Church Yth Grp; 4-H; Church Choir; Yrbk Stf; 4-H Awd; Church Orgnst; Centre Bus Coll; Med Sec.

YEAGER, LEAH; Cambria Hts HS; Carrolltown, PA; (3); 27/192; Cmnty Wkr; 4-H; GAA; Library Aide; PAVAS; Band; Chorus; Mrchg Band; Yrbk Sprt Ed; Yrbk Stf; Hon Roll 85-87; Natl Hon Soc 87; Physcl Thrpst.

YEAGER, MEGAN; Cardinal O Hara HS; Clifton Heights, PA; (3); 51/710; Church Yth Grp; Cmnty Wkr; Spanish Clb; Capt Flag Corp; Hon Roll; NHS; Spanish NHS; Hnrb Mntn Schls Annual Sci Fair 86-87; Newscarrier Of Yr 84-85; Spec Ed.

YEAGER, MELISSA; Mount Pleasant HS; Stahlstown, PA; (3); Church Yth Grp; Band; Concert Band; Mrchg Band; Swmmng; Psych.

YEAGER, MICHAEL P; Cardinal O Hara HS; Clifton Heights, PA; (4); 44/771; Spanish Clb; Band; Concert Band; Drm Mjr(t); Mrchg Band; JV Bsbl; Hon Roll; NHS; Opt Clb Awd; Spanish NHS; Semper Fidelis Awd Musical Excllnc 87; Pres Acdmc Ftnss Awd 87; Acdmc & Alumni Schlrshp 87-88; Cabrini Coll; Secondary Educ.

YEAGER, TAMERA; Clearfield Area HS; Woodland, PA; (1); Church Yth Grp; Ski Clb; Band; Church Choir; Mrchg Band; Cheerleading; Hon Roll; Elem Ed.

YEAGLE, DOUGLAS; York Suburban SR HS; York, PA; (1); Boy Scts; Ski Clb; Band; Mrchg Band; Soph Cls; Mgr(s); Socr; Tennis; High Hon Roll; Hon Roll; Top 10 Pct Cls 86-87; Engrng.

YEAKEL, CAROL; Bishop Hafey HS; Conyngham, PA; (3); Trs Church Yth Grp; Office Aide; Orch; Stat Bsktbl; Mgr(s); Prfct Atten Awds; Comp.

YEAKLEY, SHARON; Annville-Cleona HS; Annville, PA; (3); French Clb; Chorus; Color Guard; Mrchg Band; Stat Bsbl; JV Fld Hcky; Stat Mat Maids; Jr NHS; NHS; Mlrsvl Coll; Nrsng.

YEANEY, MERVIN; Waynesburg Central HS; Waynesburg, PA; (3); Spanish Clb; Socr; Hon Roll; Comp.

YEANEY, NATALIE K; Brookville Area HS; Mayport, PA; (3); 4/180; German Clb; Hosp Aide; Nwsp Rptr; Yrbk Stf; Trk; Jr NHS; NHS; Ntl Merit SF; Rotary Awd; Bio.

YEARICK, SABRINA; Abald Eagle-Nittany HS; Mill Hall, PA; (3); 47/130; Church Yth Grp; Hosp Aide; Library Aide; Church Choir; Color Guard; JC Awd; Nrsng.

YEASTED, KERRY; Nativity BVM; Pottsville, PA; (2); 32/77; Cmnty Wkr; Hosp Aide; Spanish Clb; Color Guard; Var Sftbl; Capt Twrlr; Prfct Atten Awd; Presdntl Phys Ftns Awd 85-87; Peer Cnslr 86-87; Syracuse; Vet.

YEBERNETSKY, MARY JO; Du Bois Area HS; Dubois, PA; (2); 25/341; Hon Roll; Poli Sci.

YECK, MICHELLE; Riverside HS; Moosic, PA; (4); Dance Clb; Girl Scts; Hosp Aide; School Play; Stu Cncl; JV Co-Capt Cheerleading; Hon Roll; Ntl Ldrshp Merit Awd 86; Acdmc All Amer Awd 86; Yth Slt Awd 86; Temple U; Phys Thrpy.

YECKLEY, CRAIG; Octorara Area HS; Coatesville, PA; (1); 48/198; Rptr FFA; Thesps; Concert Band; Mrchg Band; Capt Bowling; Trk; CO ST U; Arch.

YECKLEY, HUGH; Cambria Heights SR HS; Patton, PA; (3); Church Yth Grp; Cmnty Wkr; Exploring; Pre Med.

YECKLEY, SANDRA; Cambria Heights HS; Carrolltown, PA; (3); 27/182; FHA; Nwsp Stf; Hon Roll; Radiologic Tech.

YECKLEY, SHAWN; Cambria Heights HS; Hastings, PA; (3); Cmnty Wkr; SADD; Hon Roll.

YEDINAK, JENNIFER; Western Wayne HS; Moscow, PA; (3); 20/200; 4-H; SADD; Band; Concert Band; Mrchg Band; Mgr(s); Socr; Vllybl; 4-H Awd; Hon Roll.

YEE, MAE; Sacred Heart HS; Pittsburgh, PA; (3); #2 In Class; Cmnty Wkr; Pres French Clb; Hosp Aide; Mu Alpha Theta; Pep Clb; Yrbk Stf; Bausch & Lomb Sci Awd; High Hon Roll; Jr NHS; Biochem.

YEE, REBECCA; Blackhawk HS; Beaver Falls, PA; (4); 2/270; VP JA; Key Clb; Yrbk Stf; VP Stu Cncl; Var L Tennis; High Hon Roll; VP NHS; Ntl Merit SF; Rotary Awd; PA Gvnrs Schl Intl Stds 86; Chinese Amer Pres Clsrm Schlrshp 86; Intl Stds.

YEH, LUCINDA; B Reed Henderson HS; West Chester, PA; (2); 1/330; Hosp Aide; JCL; Ski Clb; Yrbk Stf; Lit Mag; Fld Hcky; French Hon Soc; High Hon Roll; Hugh O Brien Yth Fndtn Ambsdr; 1st Pl W Chstr Exch Clb Constitution Essay Contst; Intl Rltns.

YEH, SABRINA T; B Reed Henderson HS; West Chester, PA; (4); 3/349; Art Clb; Hosp Aide; Ski Clb; Ed Lit Mag; Var JV Fld Hcky; Trs French Hon Soc; NHS; Ntl Merit SF; Natl Cncl Of Tchrs Of Engl Wrtng Awd 86; Natl Latin Exam Gold Summa Cum Laude 86.

YEICH, JENNIFER; Exeter Township SR HS; Reading, PA; (3); 7/241; Pres Church Yth Grp; Band; Church Choir; Rep Soph Cls; Rep Jr Cls; Stu Cncl; Cheerleading; High Hon Roll; NHS; Drama Clb; Hugh O Brien Yth Fndtn Estrn PA Smnr Rep 86; Ntrtn.

YELAGOTES, MELISSA LOUISE; Warwick HS; Lititz, PA; (3); 26/270; Sec Church Yth Grp; Cmnty Wkr; Dance Clb; Drama Clb; Teachers Aide; Acpl Chr; Pres Sec Band; Trs Chorus; Church Choir; Concert Band; Bst Band Stu 86; Millersville U; Elem Ed.

YELEN, HOWARD Y; Wyoming Valley West HS; Kingston, PA; (3); Pres Science Clb; VP Y-Teens; Nwsp Stf; Yrbk Stf; Lit Mag; Im Var Bsktbl; Hon Roll; NHS; Law.

YELEN, MICHAEL; Wyoming Valley West HS; Kingston, PA; (3); 3/418; Chess Clb; Math Clb; Science Clb; Ski Clb; Im Stat Bsktbl; JV Trk; High Hon Roll; NHS; Rtry Ldrshp Cmp 86; NEDT Cert 84-86; Law.

YELLAND, MISSY; Upper Moreland HS; Hatboro, PA; (3); 62/276; Ski Clb; SADD; Frsh Cls; Soph Cls; Jr Cls; Sr Cls; Im Bsktbl; Var Socr; Gov Hon Prg Awd; High Hon Roll; Phys Thrpy.

YENCHA, MARCY; Lake Lehman HS; Shavertown, PA; (2); SADD; Band; Concert Band; Mrchg Band; Yrbk Stf; Hon Roll; Jr NHS; NHS; Phrmcy.

YENCHA, ROBERT; Freeland HS; Freeland, PA; (3); 6/90; FBLA; SADD; JV Var Ftbl; Wt Lftg; Hon Roll; Ltr Ftbl 86-87; Army; Bus.

YENCHA, STEPHEN COREY; Lake-Lehman HS; Shavertown, PA; (4); 56/155; Band; Concert Band; Jazz Band; Mrchg Band; Symp Band; JV Vllybl; Kings Coll; Accntng.

YERACE, ELIZABETH; Norwin HS; N Huntingdon, PA; (4); 18/565; French Clb; Hosp Aide; Letterman Clb; Ski Clb; SADD; Chorus; Nwsp Rptr; Rep Stu Cncl; Vllybl; High Hon Roll; MVP Vllybl 84; All Star Awds Vllybl 86; Stu Cncl Scholar 87; Penn ST U; Brdcst Jrnlsm.

YERASHUNAS, JOSEPH; Bishop Oreilly HS; Edwardsville, PA; (3); VP Church Yth Grp; Ski Clb; Spanish Clb; JV Bsktbl; Timer; Hon Roll; Trs NHS; Spanish NHS; Elec Engr.

YERGER, JESSICA; Conrad Weiser HS; Robesonia, PA; (2); 15/163; JCL; Band; Chorus; Color Guard; Concert Band; Mrchg Band; School Musical; Bowling; Cheerleading; Hon Roll; Penn ST U; Tele Comm.

YERGER, KURT; Penn Wood HS; Lansdowne, PA; (4); 24/335; Church Yth Grp; Stage Crew; Var Socr; Capt Tennis; Hon Roll; Prfct Atten Awd; Rotary Awd; Pres Acad Ftns Awd Pgm, Outstndng Achvt Awd Eng & Econ 87; Drexel U; Bus Admin.

YERICH, LYNNE; Greater Johnstown Area Vo-Tech Schl; Summerhill, PA; (3); NFL; Pep Clb; ROTC; Ski Clb; SADD; VICA; Y-Teens; Sec Trs Jr Cls; Im Bsbl; Im Bsktbl; Achvt Awds For Shop 86-87; Cmnty Srv & Cert 86-87.

YERKEY, BRETT; Belle Vernon Area HS; Belle Vernon, PA; (3); Church Yth Grp; Ski Clb; Band; Concert Band; Mrchg Band; Rep Stu Cncl; Bsbl; Golf; Hon Roll; Pre Med.

YESHO, RICH; Mt Pleasant Area HS; Hunker, PA; (3); 61/250; Chess Clb; German Clb; Latin Clb; Rep Stu Cncl; Im Bsktbl; JV Ftbl; Im Sftbl; Im Vllybl; Hon Roll; Ind Arts Awd 84-86.

YESSLER, SAMANTHA; Red Lion SR HS; York, PA; (3); 99/342; Varsity Clb; JV Bsktbl; L Var Fld Hcky; Powder Puff Ftbl; Hon Roll; Crimnl Rehab.

YESVILLE, MARY LOU; Pleasant Valley HS; Saylorsburg, PA; (4); 5/220; VP Drama Clb; 4-H; JA; Library Aide; Math Clb; Ski Clb; Capt Flag Corp; Nwsp Rptr; Yrbk Rptr; Yrbk Ed-Chief; Air Force ROTC Schlrshp; Embry-Riddle Aeronautical U.

YETTER III, CARL; Owen J Roberts HS; Spring City, PA; (3); 10/299; Boy Scts; Stage Crew; JV Socr; Var Trk; Im Vllybl; Hon Roll; NHS; Engrng.

YETTER, DAWN; Knoch HS; Marwood, PA; (4); 88/245; L Bsktbl; Trk; Bsktbl Schlrshp 87; Allegheny Vly Hosp Schl.

YETTER, RACHEL; Pen Argyl Area HS; Pen Argyl, PA; (3); 19/140; Church Yth Grp; Exploring; Chorus; Cheerleading; Crs Cntry; Trk; High Hon Roll; Northampton Area CC; Accntng.

YETTER, TAMMY; Juniata HS; Mifflin, PA; (4); Drama Clb; Speech Tm; SADD; Varsity Clb; Chorus; School Musical; Nwsp Stf; Yrbk Stf; Hon Roll; Williamsport Area CC Schlrshp, Jrnlsm Awd 87; Williamsport Area CC; Radlgy.

YETZER, JILL; Ridgway Area HS; Ridgway, PA; (4); 1/105; Church Yth Grp; Hosp Aide; Spanish Clb; Im JV Vllybl; High Hon Roll; NHS; Duquesne; Phrmcy.

YETZER, KIM; St Marys Area HS; St Marys, PA; (2); JV Bsktbl.

YI, CHUNG; Hatboro Horsham JR/Sr HS; Horsham, PA; (4); 15/258; Model UN; VP Frsh Cls; Pres Jr Cls; Rep Stu Cncl; Var Socr; Var Tennis; Hon Roll; NHS; Prfct Atten Awd; Rensselaer Polytech Inst.

YIM, DAVID; Upper Dublin SR HS; Ambler, PA; (3); 37/296; Church Yth Grp; Pres Sec FBLA; Math Tm; VP Science Clb; Chorus; Concert Band; School Musical; School Play; Yrbk Rptr; VP Stu Cncl; Gld Medl DE Vly Sci Fair Bst Proj Tri ST Area 85; 4th Pl Erth & Spc Sci Intl Sci & Engrng Fair 85; Enrgy Dsgn.

YINGLING, DORA; Red Lion Area HS; Red Lion, PA; (3); 8/342; School Musical; School Play; Stage Crew; JV L Vllybl; High Hon Roll; Hon Roll; Rcrtnl Mgmt.

YINGLING, MARK; Central HS; Roaring Spring, PA; (3); SADD; Stage Crew; Var L Bsbl; Var L Bsktbl; Var L Ftbl; Elem Ed.

YINGST, DONNA; Donegal HS; Mount Joy, PA; (4); 35/161; Varsity Clb; Yrbk Phtg; Rep Frsh Cls; Rep Soph Cls; Rep Jr Cls; Rep Sr Cls; Rep Stu Cncl; Capt Cheerleading; Powder Puff Ftbl; Millersville U Of PA; Bus Mgmt.

YINGST JR, ERIC K; Mountain View Christian School; Harrisburg, PA; (3); Political Wkr; Chorus; Yrbk Bus Mgr; VP Frsh Cls; Capt Bsktbl; Var Crs Cntry; Capt Socr; Cit Awd; Hon Roll; Prfct Atten Awd; Bob Jones U; Bus.

YINGST, JOHN; Mt Lebanon SR HS; Pittsburgh, PA; (2); SADD; Hon Roll; Robert Morris Coll; Acctg.

YOBBI, RICHARD; Central Catholic HS; Pittsburgh, PA; (3); 12/250; Im Bsktbl; Im Fld Hcky; Im Ftbl; L Golf; Im Vllybl; NHS; Dghtrs Of Amer Revltn 84; Penn ST; Acctng.

YOCCA, JENNIFER; Peters Township HS; Mc Murray, PA; (3); Church Yth Grp; Girl Scts; Sec Trs NFL; SADD; Var Capt Tennis; Spanish NHS; Vrsty Lttrmn & Capt Vrsty Tnns 84-86; Degree Of Hnr Excel & Dist Natl Frnscs 84-86; Sngls Tnns Champ 5; Sci.

YOCKLOVICH, JILL; Cedar Crest HS; Cornwall, PA; (4); Pep Clb; Spanish Clb; Bsktbl; Fld Hcky; Sftbl; Vllybl; Hon Roll; Brnz Mdl For Hnr Scty.

YOCOM, BRADLEY; Carson Long Military Inst; Vincent, OH; (4); 6/38; Chess Clb; ROTC; Color Guard; School Play; Lit Mag; Im Sftbl; Im Vllybl; Hon Roll; Rodney P Grave Bio Medl 84-85; Perry Cnty Hstrcl Scty Soc Sci Awd 86-87; Pres Acad Awd 86-87; Citadel; Pol Sci.

YOCUM, RUTH; Clearfield Area HS; Clearfield, PA; (3); 3/300; Church Yth Grp; Key Clb; Ski Clb; Spanish Clb; Concert Band; Mrchg Band; Yrbk Stf; JV Cheerleading; Var Trk; Cit Awd.

YOCUM, TOM; Huntingdon Area HS; Hesston, PA; (3); 29/221; JV Var Ftbl; Hon Roll; Envrnmntl Engr.

YODER, ANITA; Rockwood Area HS; Somerset, PA; (4); 12/96; Church Yth Grp; Computer Clb; Band; Church Choir; Yrbk Stf; Capt Bsktbl; L Sftbl; High Hon Roll; NHS; 1st Tm All Cnty Sftbl 86; Messiah Coll; Hlth Ed.

YODER, BETH; Holy Name HS; Reading, PA; (3); 28/119; Pep Clb; Spanish Clb; Sec Sr Cls; Sec Stu Cncl; Var JV Cheerleading; Sftbl; High Hon Roll; Hon Roll; NHS; Distngshd Hnrs & Varsity Ltr; Bus.

YODER, JOHN; Our Lady Of Lourdes Regional HS; Shamokin, PA; (3); Drama Clb; French Clb; Teachers Aide; School Play; Stage Crew; Rep Frsh Cls; Pres Jr Cls; Pres Stu Cncl; Im Golf; Im Tennis; Soc Sci.

YODER, KEITH; Conemaugh Township HS; Davidsville, PA; (4); 12/101; Church Yth Grp; Drama Clb; NFL; Band; Concert Band; Mrchg Band; School Musical; School Play; Cit Awd; Hon Roll; Cambria-Rowe Bus Coll Schlrshp 87; Outstndg Stu Awd 87; Drama Awd 87; Cambria-Rowe BC; Bus Mgmt.

YODER, LISA; Seneca Valley HS; Harmony, PA; (4); Pres Church Yth Grp; SADD; Stage Crew; Var L Swmmng; Hon Roll; Slippery Rock U; Bio.

YODER, REGINA; Mountain View Christian Schl; Meyersdale, PA; (3); Chorus; School Play; Sec Jr Cls; Im Bsktbl; Im Socr; Im Sftbl; Im Vllybl; Hon Roll; Bible Memory Awd 86.

YODER, SANDRA; Conemaugh Twp HS; Hollsopple, PA; (3); 12/115; Pres Sec Church Yth Grp; Spanish Clb; Hon Roll; NHS; Spnsh I Cert 84-85.

YODER, SHARON; Conemaugh Township HS; Hollsopple, PA; (4); 9/101; Spanish Clb; Nwsp Stf; Yrbk Rptr; VP Soph Cls; Pres Jr Cls; Pres Sr Cls; Var L Sftbl; DAR Awd; Lion Awd; Sec NHS; Johnstwn Bus & Prfsnl Wmn Girl Mnth Awd 87; Amer Lgn Outstndng Awd 87; Jerome Amer Lgn Ctznshp Awd 87; U Of Pittsburgh; Nrsng.

YODER, SUSAN; Mountainview Christian Schl; Salisbury, PA; (3); 1/22; Chorus; School Play; Nwsp Stf; Yrbk Stf; Im Capt Socr; Im Vllybl; Hon Roll; Val; Im Sftbl; Cert Math Achvt 86; Cert Bible Memory 85-86.

YODER, SUSAN E; Pennridge HS; Perkasie, PA; (3); 15/409; Am Leg Aux Girls St; Church Yth Grp; Trs Jr Cls; Trs Sr Cls; Var L Fld Hcky; Var L Lcrss; High Hon Roll; NHS; Acpl Chr; Church Choir; AAU JR Olympic Fld Hcky, Olympic Dvlpmntl Cmp Fld Hcky B Cmp 87; Math.

YODERS, GRETCHEN; Washington HS; Washington, PA; (3); Cmnty Wkr; Exploring; Hosp Aide; Spanish Clb; Hon Roll; 2 Awds Outstndg Achvt As Candy Striper 85 & 86; Biology.

YODIS, VINCENT; Neshaminy HS; Langhorne, PA; (4); VICA; High Hon Roll; Hon Roll; NHS; Rotary Awd; Natl Exchng Clb,Bensalem ORT & Stu Ed Ctr Awds 87; PA ST; Elec Engr.

YOGEL, MARNIE; Leechburg Area HS; Leechburg, PA; (3); Band; Chorus; Concert Band; Mrchg Band; Pep Band; Yrbk Stf; JV Cheerleading; Var Sftbl; Comms.

YOH, JAMES; Wyoming Valley West HS; Kingston, PA; (4); 34/415; Chess Clb; Science Clb; Nwsp Stf; Yrbk Stf; Lit Mag; Hon Roll; NHS; Michael Palishak Spnsh Awd 87; USWA Spnsh Awd 86; Cert Of Achvt Hghst Avg 85-87; LCCC.

YOH, WILLIAM; The Haverford Schl; Bryn Mawr, PA; (2); Letterman Clb; Rep Frsh Cls; Rep Soph Cls; Rep Jr Cls; Trs Stu Cncl; Var L Bsktbl; Var L Ftbl; High Hon Roll; Cecil B Jarvis Awd-Ldrshp 86.

YOHA, THERESA; Gateway SR HS; Monroeville, PA; (4); 55/493; Church Yth Grp; Cmnty Wkr; GAA; Science Clb; Rep Frsh Cls; Rep Soph Cls; Rep Jr Cls; Rep Sr Cls; Rep Stu Cncl; Hon Roll; Top 100 Stu Getwy Rtry 87; Ambassador Coll; Lbrl Arts.

YOHE, BRIAN; Burrell HS; Lower Burrell, PA; (3); Exploring; Spanish Clb; Hon Roll; Jr NHS; Rotary Awd; Elec.

YOHE, JOANNA; Eastern York HS; Wrightsvlle, PA; (2); 14/155; Varsity Clb; VP Frsh Cls; VP Soph Cls; Var Cheerleading; Var Sftbl; JV Vllybl; Var High Hon Roll; Stu Cncl 85-87.

YOHN, AMY; Northern Lebanon HS; Jonestown, PA; (4); 8/166; Cmnty Wkr; SADD; Chorus; Church Choir; School Musical; School Play; High Hon Roll; Hon Roll; Lion Awd; NHS; Altrst Awd 87; Cngrssnl Schlr 87; CA U Of PA; Elem Educ.

YOHN, BRENT; Southern Huntingdon County HS; Orbisonia, PA; (3); Church Yth Grp; 4-H; SADD; Varsity Clb; Rep Stu Cncl; Bsbl; 4-H Awd; Comp Sci.

YOHN, BRIAN; Palmyra Area HS; Palmyra, PA; (2); 58/233; Boy Scts; Computer Clb; Concert Band; Jazz Band; Mrchg Band; Stage Crew; Var JV Wrstlng; Hon Roll; Eagle Scout 87; Elec Engr.

YOHN JR, JACK; Greenwood HS; Millerstown, PA; (4); 6/67; Am Leg Boys St; Nwsp Ed-Chief; Nwsp Rptr; Yrbk Ed-Chief; Sec Frsh Cls; Sec Soph Cls; Rep Jr Cls; Hon Roll; NHS; Ntl Merit Ltr; Millersville ST U; Biol.

YOHO, DEANN; Shenango HS; New Castle, PA; (3); Church Yth Grp; Flag Corp; Vllybl; Draftng.

YOHO, MELISSA; New Castle SR HS; New Castle, PA; (4); 22/243; AFS; Computer Clb; Girl Scts; Ski Clb; Spanish Clb; Chorus; Mrchg Band; Var Trk; Im Vllybl; NHS; Girl Scout Gold & Silver Awd 84&86; Chem Engrng.

YOKO, MICHELLE; Center Area HS; Monaca, PA; (2); Hosp Aide; Spanish Clb; Varsity Clb; Yrbk Sprt Ed; Yrbk Stf; VP Frsh Cls; Var Capt Cheerleading; High Hon Roll; Hon Roll; Spnsh Lang Awds 85-87; Carnegie Mellon U; Bus Mgmt.

YONEK JR, JOSEPH; Kiski Area HS; Leechburg, PA; (3); Boy Scts; Chess Clb; German Clb; Varsity Clb; Swmmng; Trk; Eagle Scout 85; Invstmnt.

YONKIN, JODI; Galeton Area HS; Galeton, PA; (3); 1/43; French Clb; Sec Band; Chorus; JV Var Trk; JV Var Vllybl; NHS; Prfct Atten Awd; Pres Acad Ftnss Awd 84-85; Physcl Ftnss Awd 86; Mansfield Coll; Nrsng.

YONKOFSKI, MICHAEL; St Marys Area HS; Byrnedale, PA; (3); Bsbl; JV Ftbl; Sftbl; Vllybl; Penn ST; Comp Sci.

YONKOVITZ JR, ALBERT F; Steel Valley HS; Munhall, PA; (4); 28/201; Pres Church Yth Grp; Band; Mrchg Band; Rep Frsh Cls; Rep Soph Cls; Rep Stu Cncl; Capt Swmmng; Hon Roll; NHS; Westinghouse Sci Hnrs Inst 86-87; CC Alleghen Y Co Hnrs Math Pgm 86; Engrng.

YONKOVITZ, VICKI; Steel Valley HS; West Homestead, PA; (4); 22/201; Office Aide; Concert Band; Drm Mjr(t); Flag Corp; Yrbk Stf; Hon Roll; NHS; U Of Pittsburgh; Nrsng.

YOO, ELISA; Central Christian HS; Du Bois, PA; (4); 1/30; VP Pep Clb; Varsity Clb; Chorus; School Play; Pres Soph Cls; VP Jr Cls; Rep Stu Cncl; Var Capt Cheerleading; L Vllybl; Bausch & Lomb Sci Awd; Hmecmng Ct 86 & 87; US Army Rsrve Natl Schrl/Athlte Awd 87; Presdntl Acad Ftnss Awd; U Of PA; Med.

YORK, DENISE; Danville SR HS; Danville, PA; (4); Church Yth Grp; Ski Clb; Spanish Clb; Yrbk Stf; Pres Frsh Cls; Rep Soph Cls; Stu Cncl; Var Cheerleading; Im Gym; Var Socr; Criminal Justice.

YORK, JAMES; Lehighton Area HS; Lehighton, PA; (3); 20/253; Spanish Clb; School Play; Nwsp Rptr; Nwsp Stf; High Hon Roll; Hon Roll; Top Ten Pct Cls Awd 87; Ursinus; Med.

YORTY, MICHAEL; Archbishop Wood For Boys; Richboro, PA; (2); 64/265; German Clb; SADD; Band; Concert Band; Mrchg Band; Im Bsktbl; Music.

YOSKIN, MAURICE; Plymouth Whitemarsh SR HS; Flourtown, PA; (4); 9/336; Church Yth Grp; Math Clb; Mu Alpha Theta; Nwsp Stf; Lit Mag; Trk; High Hon Roll; Ntl Merit Ltr; Rgnl Wnnr-Spc Shuttle Stu Invlvmnt Proj 84; 3rd-Amer HS Math Exm 86; Biochem.

YOST, CAMMY; Pleasant Valley HS; Brodheadsville, PA; (4); 7/173; Varsity Clb; Sec Frsh Cls; Sec Soph Cls; Sec Jr Cls; Sec Sr Cls; Stu Cncl; Co-Capt Cheerleading; Sftbl; Hon Roll; Sec NHS; Everett-Kenkle Schlrshp 87; Bloomsburg U; Elem Ed.

YOST, CHRISTINE E; Christian School Of York; Wellsville, PA; (4); 7/59; Chorus; School Musical; Nwsp Rptr; Sec Soph Cls; Var L Fld Hcky; Var L Trk; High Hon Roll; Rotry Intl Stu Exch 85-86; Ms PA Ntl Teen-Ager Pagnt 86; Ed.

YOST, JAMIE; Mohawk HS; New Galilee, PA; (4); 10/142; French Clb; Var L Bsktbl; Var L Crs Cntry; Powder Puff Ftbl; Sftbl; Var L Trk; French Hon Soc; Hon Roll; Sec NHS; Slippery Rock U; Sec Educ.

YOST, JUDY; Shalom Christian Acad; Newville, PA; (3); Church Yth Grp; Sec 4-H; FHA; Hosp Aide; Yrbk Stf; Pres Frsh Cls; Sec Jr Cls; VP Sr Cls; Rep Stu Cncl; Prfct Atten Awd; Dstngshd Chrstn HS Stu ACSI 86-87.

YOST, KRISTA; Conestoga Valley HS; Lancaster, PA; (3); 79/240; Sec Church Yth Grp; VP Sec 4-H; Band; Church Choir; Concert Band; Mrchg Band; Yrbk Ed-Chief; Yrbk Stf; Mgr(s); Hon Roll.

YOST, TONYA; Hopewell SR HS; Aliquippa, PA; (3); Exploring; Sftbl; PA ST; Acctng.

YOTHERS, BOBBI; Mt Pleasant Area HS; Mt Pleasant, PA; (4); German Clb; Political Wkr; Ski Clb; Band; Concert Band; Mrchg Band; Rep Frsh Cls; Mat Maids; Score Keeper; Stat Wrstlng; U Of Pittsbugh; Psychlgy.

YOTHERS, JESSICA; Emmaus HS; Emmaus, PA; (3); Key Clb; Spanish Clb; Lib Band; Pres Chorus; School Musical; School Play; NHS; Dist Choir Awd 86fcnty Band 87; Vcl Ensmbl Solist 85-87; Law.

YOTTER, RICHARD E; Ridley SR HS; Woodlyn, PA; (4); 22/453; Aud/Vis; Mu Alpha Theta; Band; Concert Band; Mrchg Band; JV Var Lcrss; Var L Socr; Hon Roll; NHS; Soccer-Most Improved Player 86; Presedential Acadmc Fitness Awd 87; Penn ST; Industrial Engr.

YOUELLS, CHRISTINE; Wyoming Valley West HS; Plymouth, PA; (4); FBLA; Rep Frsh Cls; Rep Jr Cls; Hon Roll; Bus Ed Awd Outstndng Acad Achvt Bus 87; Htl/Rest Mgmt.

YOUGH, KAREN; Knoch HS; Saxonburg, PA; (4); 1/243; Church Yth Grp; SADD; School Play; Stage Crew; Nwsp Stf; Off Stu Cncl; Im Vllybl; High Hon Roll; Pres NHS; Val; Natl Presbyterian Coll Schlr 87; Grove City Coll; Frnch.

YOUGH, KELLY; Bulter Area SR HS; Butler, PA; (2); French Clb; Mrchg Band; Orch; Symp Band; Var L Socr; Var L Trk; Jr NHS; Acdmc Achvmnt Awd 86-87; Wstrn PA Coachs All-Str Tm Sccr 86; Sccr Offnsv MVP 86; Bio.

YOUNDTT, KIM; Garden Spot HS; E Earl, PA; (3); 6/196; Trs Church Yth Grp; Drama Clb; Chorus; School Musical; NHS; German Clb; School Play; Stage Crew; Var Gym; Stat Trk; Intr Dsgn.

YOUNG, AMY; Lock Haven SR HS; Lock Javen, PA; (3); 13/259; French Clb; Rep Soph Cls; Rep Jr Cls; Pres Stu Cncl; Cheerleading; Trk; Hon Roll; NEDT Awd; Church Yth Grp; Cmnty Wkr; H O Brien Yth Ldrshp Smnr; Acadc All Am; USCA Chrldng Awd.

YOUNG, ANDREA; Lock Haven SR HS; Lock Haven, PA; (3); 15/250; Service Clb; Sec Spanish Clb; SADD; Capt Mrchg Band; Capt Twrlr; Im Vllybl; Hon Roll; NHS; Hand-In-Hand Hose Co Earl Hartman Memorial Awd Outstndng Svc Majorette 87; Lock Haven U; Educ.

YOUNG, ANNE; Danville SR HS; Danville, PA; (2); Hosp Aide; NFL; Ski Clb; Hon Roll; Marine Stud.

YOUNG, BARRY; Nazareth HS; Tatamy, PA; (3); 69/270; Church Yth Grp; Computer Clb; Yrbk Phtg; Crs Cntry; Trk; Hon Roll.

YOUNG, BECKY; Lincoln HS; Portersville, PA; (3); 42/162; French Clb; Y-Teens; Chorus.

YOUNG, BOB; Beaver Area HS; Beaver, PA; (3); 23/215; Boy Scts; Spanish Clb; Var Ftbl; Hon Roll; Ordr Arrow BSA 86; Penn ST U; Aerospc Engr.

YOUNG, CATHY; Gr Johnstown AVTS HS; S Fork, PA; (3); 13/329; Cmnty Wkr; ROTC; Sec Trs VICA; Drill Tm; High Hon Roll; Trs Jr NHS; NHS; Pep Clb; Teachers Aide; Color Guard; ROTC Schlrshp Yr 85-86; ROTC Retired Offcrs Assoc 86-87; Mt Aloysious JC; Crimonology.

YOUNG, CHARI; Quakertown Comm SR HS; Quakertown, PA; (3); 4/310; SADD; Varsity Clb; Chorus; Var L Bsktbl; Var L Fld Hcky; Var L Sftbl; High Hon Roll; Hon Roll; Jr NHS; NHS; PA PIAA St Rnnr Up Fld Hcky 86; Engrng.

YOUNG, CHRISTINE; Lower Merion HS; Bala Cynwyd, PA; (3); Church Yth Grp; Thesps; Church Choir; School Play; Nwsp Bus Mgr; Ed Yrbk Stf; JV Bsktbl; Hon Roll; NHS; Drama Clb; Comm.

YOUNG, DENISE; West Branch Area HS; Morrisdale, PA; (3); 11/133; Sec Church Yth Grp; Hosp Aide; Science Clb; Sec Ski Clb; SADD; Band; Flag Corp; VP Sftbl; Hon Roll; Nrsng.

YOUNG, DONNIE; Cambridge Springs HS; Cambridge Springs, PA; (2); 8/105; Boy Scts; FBLA; SADD; Var Bsbl; Var Ftbl; Var Wt Lftg; Var Wrstlng; High Hon Roll; NHS; Accntnt.

YOUNG, DOUGLAS A; Scranton Prep; Clarks Summit, PA; (4); Letterman Clb; Ski Clb; Varsity Clb; Var L Ftbl; Var L Trk; Var L Wt Lftg; Villanova U; Elec Engr.

YOUNG, ERIN; Keystone HS; Knox, PA; (3); 17/140; Pres Church Yth Grp; Pep Clb; SADD; Varsity Clb; Chorus; Rep Stu Cncl; Var Trk; Hon Roll; Girl Scts; Letterman Clb; IUP; Elem Ed.

YOUNG, GREG M; Cedar Crest HS; Lebanon, PA; (4); 9/303; German Clb; Pep Clb; Orch; School Musical; Bsktbl; Var L Socr; Im Vllybl; High Hon Roll; NHS; Butler Fndtn Schlrshp 87; Pres Acad Ftns Awd 87; Hnr Stu Gld Mdl 87; Franklin Coll; Pre Med.

YOUNG, HEATHER; Saltsburg JR SR HS; Saltsburg, PA; (3); 5/67; Church Yth Grp; Drama Clb; Library Aide; Band; Concert Band; Mrchg Band; School Musical; Off Stu Cncl; Stat Bsktbl; Score Keeper; Gftd/Tlntd Minors Prgm 83-87; Jrnlsm.

YOUNG, HOPE; Bellwood-Antis HS; Bellwood, PA; (1); Key Clb; Ski Clb; Chorus; JV Fld Hcky; Hon Roll; Hlth.

YOUNG, JAMES; Beaver Falls HS; Beaver Falls, PA; (3); 10/170; VP AFS; JA; Spanish Clb; Varsity Clb; L Tennis; High Hon Roll; Spanish NHS; OH U; Nuclr Engrng.

YOUNG, JAMES; Central HS; Philadelphia, PA; (2); Church Yth Grp; Hosp Aide; Hon Roll; Barnwell Hnr Rl 85-86.

YOUNG, JAMES; New Wilmington Area HS; Volant, PA; (3); FBLA; Spanish Clb; Ftbl; Wt Lftg; Hon Roll; Accntng.

YOUNG, JENNIFER; Dover Area HS; Dover, PA; (3); 4/275; Varsity Clb; Chorus; Concert Band; Mrchg Band; School Musical; Nwsp Stf; Yrbk Ed-Chief; Rep Stu Cncl; High Hon Roll; NHS; Cmmnctns.

YOUNG, JENNIFER; Meadville Area SR HS; Cambridge Spri, PA; (3); Pres 4-H; Orch; Var Bsktbl; 4-H Awd; Hon Roll; Leag Bsktbl MVP 87; St Woolgrowing Cont-Tailoring 87; Math.

YOUNG, JENNIFER; Pennsbury HS; Levittown, PA; (4); 68/771; German Clb; Church Choir; School Musical; Trk; Hon Roll; NHS; Acdmc Fit Awd 87; Pennsbury Schlrshp 87; U Of DE; Acctg.

YOUNG, JESSICA; Coatesville Area SR HS; Coatesville, PA; (3); 89/512; Drama Clb; French Clb; Leo Clb; Ski Clb; Chorus; School Musical; Var L Fld Hcky; Var L Lcrss; Hon Roll; Prfct Atten Awd; Psych.

YOUNG, KATHY; Annville-Cleona HS; Cleona, PA; (3); 2/165; German Clb; Math Tm; Band; Chorus; Church Choir; Color Guard; Tennis; Bausch & Lomb Sci Awd; Hon Roll; NHS; Rensselaer Metal 87; PA Coll; Phrmcy.

YOUNG, KELLIE; Carrick HS; Pittsburgh, PA; (4); #35 In Class; Girl Scts; Hosp Aide; VP Pres Jr Cls; Rep Stu Cncl; JV Var Cheerleading; JV Var Powder Puff Ftbl; High Hon Roll; Hon Roll; Robert Morris Coll; Bus Accntg.

YOUNG, KELLY; Nazareth Area HS; Nazareth, PA; (3); #50 In Class; Art Clb; Church Yth Grp; Key Clb; Stu Cncl; Im Gym; JV Tennis; Var Trk; High Hon Roll; Hon Roll; Dsgn.

YOUNG, KIRK; Dover Area HS; Dover, PA; (3); 33/269; Boy Scts; VP Exploring; Ski Clb; JV Var Socr; Hon Roll; Bus.

YOUNG, LESLIE; Berlin Brothers Valley HS; Berlin, PA; (3); 7/98; Rptr FFA; Spanish Clb; Band; Concert Band; Mrchg Band; School Play; Hon Roll; NHS; 1st Pl Consrvtn Spch ST FFA Actvts Wk; 4th Pl ST FFA Demnstrtn Tm; Gannon U; Elec Engrng.

YOUNG, LISA; Annville-Cleona HS; Cleona, PA; (3); 4/165; Math Tm; Chorus; Church Choir; Drill Tm; Tennis; Bausch & Lomb Sci Awd; High Hon Roll; NHS; Co Winner Rensselaer Metal 87; PA Coll; Phrmcy.

YOUNG, LORI; Nativity B V M; New Philadelphia, PA; (3); Art Clb; GAA; Math Tm; Spanish Clb; Church Choir; Vllybl; Hon Roll; Penn ST Schuylkill; Prmry Ed.

YOUNG, MANDIE; Solanco HS; Drumore, PA; (4); 26/241; Art Clb; Cmnty Wkr; Pres 4-H; Girl Scts; Key Clb; Nwsp Stf; Yrbk Phtg; Yrbk Stf; Var Powder Puff Ftbl; 4-H Awd; Soroptimist Youth Ctznshp Awd 87; Amer Bus Wmns Assoc Awd 87; PA ST; Photogrphr.

YOUNG, MARGARET; Monongahela Valley Catholic HS; Monessen, PA; (3); JV Var Cheerleading; Physcl Thrpy.

YOUNG, MARGO; Kennedy Christian HS; Sharon, PA; (3); 37/109; Aud/Vis; Cmnty Wkr; French Clb; Girl Scts; Hosp Aide; JA; Library Aide; Ski Clb; Teachers Aide; Band.

YOUNG, MATTHEW; Hughesville HS; Muncy, PA; (3); Spanish Clb; Nwsp Rptr; Rep Soph Cls; Rep Jr Cls; Rep Stu Cncl; JV Bsktbl; L Trk; Im Vllybl; Hon Roll; NHS; HOBY 86; Elec Engr.

YOUNG, MELANIE; Curwensville Area HS; Mahaffey, PA; (3); 3/123; Church Yth Grp; Cmnty Wkr; Drama Clb; French Clb; Chorus; Nwsp Rptr; Stu Cncl; High Hon Roll; NHS; JR Most Likely To Succeed 87; Most Outstndg Stu In United Rural Elec Coop 87; Elem Educ.

YOUNG, MICHAEL; Danville JR HS; Danville, PA; (1); Im Bsktbl; High Hon Roll; Hon Roll; Outstndng Acad Achvt 86-87; Presdntl Acad Ftnss Awds Pgm 86-87; UCLA.

YOUNG, MICHAEL; Punxsutawney Area HS; Punxsutawney, PA; (2); Varsity Clb; JV Bsbl; Var Ftbl; Wt Lftg.

YOUNG, MICHAEL; St Marys Area HS; St Marys, PA; (3); Boy Scts; Hon Roll; Penn ST; Comp Prgmr.

YOUNG, MICHAEL W; Spring Ford SR HS; Royersford, PA; (3); 77/256; German Clb; Band; Concert Band; Jazz Band; Mrchg Band; Bsktbl; Stat Score Keeper; Med Sci.

YOUNG, MICHELE; Seneca Valley SR HS; Zelienople, PA; (2); Church Yth Grp; JA; Band; Off Stu Cncl; Hon Roll; SV 1st Yr Awd 86-87; Accntng.

YOUNG, MICHELLE ANN; J P Mc Caskey HS; Lancaster, PA; (3); 118/517; AFS; Model UN; Chorus; JV Var Fld Hcky; JV Sftbl; JV Var Trk; Hon Roll; Acad Achvt Awd 85.

YOUNG, MICHELLE O; The Philadelphia HS For Girls; Philadelphia, PA; (4); 57/365; Church Yth Grp; Drama Clb; Service Clb; Chorus; Church Choir; School Play; Sec VP Stu Cncl; High Hon Roll; Hon Roll; Kiwanis Awd; Pres Minority Schlrshp; Delta Sigma Theta Schlrshp; Stu Council Svc Awd; Villanova U; Bus Admin.

YOUNG, MINDY; Marin Center Area HS; Marion Center, PA; (3); 30/156; Q&S; SADD; Varsity Clb; Nwsp Bus Mgr; Nwsp Sprt Ed; Var Bsktbl; Var Crs Cntry; Var Trk; Hon Roll; Jr NHS; Teacher.

YOUNG, NANCY ANN; Upper Dublin HS; Willow Grove, PA; (3); 42/300; Church Yth Grp; Teachers Aide; Hon Roll; Elem Educ.

YOUNG, NICOLE; West Allegheny HS; Oakdale, PA; (3); 2/200; JA; Ed Lit Mag; High Hon Roll; NHS; Ntl Merit SF; Rotry Yth Ldrshp Awd 87.

YOUNG, PAULA; West Catholic Girls HS; Philadelphia, PA; (3); 57/289; Cmnty Wkr; FNA; School Play; Hon Roll; NHS; Ntl Merit Schol; Prfct Atten Awd; Val; Latin Clb; Annul Ltn Wk Comp-Cum Laude 85; Temple; Nrse.

YOUNG, RANDI S; Peters Twp HS; Mc Murray, PA; (4); FHA; Band; Drill Tm; Gym; Pom Pon; Hon Roll; OH U; Htl Mgmt.

YOUNG, RHONDA; Hollidaysburg HS; Hollidaysburg, PA; (3); Church Yth Grp; 4-H; Latin Clb; Y-Teens; Chorus; Mrchg Band; Twrlr; Vllybl; Penn ST; Nurse.

YOUNG, ROBERT C; St Pius X HS; Perkiomenville, PA; (4); 45/150; Office Aide; Pres Science Clb; Capt Band; Concert Band; Mrchg Band; Pep Band; School Musical; High Hon Roll; Hon Roll; Norwich U; Pol Sci.

YOUNG, ROBYN; Towanda Area HS; Towanda, PA; (3); 13/168; GAA; Letterman Clb; SADD; Varsity Clb; Yrbk Sprt Ed; Trs Stu Cncl; Capt L Bsktbl; Var L Trk; Var L Vllybl; Hon Roll; All Twin Tiers All Star Bsktbl 87; NTL All Star Bsktbl 87; MVP Grls Bsktbl 87; Hotel Mgmt.

YOUNG JR, SAMUEL; Central HS; Philadelphia, PA; (4); 9/304; Chess Clb; French Clb; Math Clb; Socr; High Hon Roll; Hon Roll; Ntl Merit Ltr; Prfct Atten Awd; Cty Of Philadelphia Schlrshp 87; OMIN Schlrshp 87; Guggenheim Schlrshp 87; Tyndale Schlrshp 87; Drexel U; Elec Engr.

YOUNG, SCOTT; Spring Grove Area SR HS; Spring Grove, PA; (3); Varsity Clb; Band; Concert Band; Jazz Band; Mrchg Band; Crs Cntry; Var Trk; Hon Roll; NHS; Bus.

YOUNG, SHEMAYAH; Franklin Learning Ctr; Philadelphia, PA; (3); Church Yth Grp; Red Cross Aide; Church Choir; School Musical; Hon Roll; Prfct Atten Awd; Creative Wrtng Awd 84; Acadc Excel Awd 86; Fox Chase Cancer Ctr Awd 87; Med.

YOUNG, SHERRI; Kutztown Area HS; Kutztown, PA; (4); Band; Chorus; Capt Flag Corp; School Play; Variety Show; Capt Cheerleading; High Hon Roll; NHS; Pres Schlr; Kutztwn JR Miss Rep & 3rd Rnnr Up Cnty Pagnt 86-87; U Of DE; Lwyr.

YOUNG, STACY; Hempfield HS; Lancaster, PA; (4); 14/420; Hosp Aide; Office Aide; Varsity Clb; Band; Chorus; Concert Band; School Play; Variety Show; Nwsp Rptr; Rep Stu Cncl; Stu Mnth Soc Stu 87; Pauline Reese Mem Schlrshp 87; Coll Of William & Mary; Govt.

YOUNG, SUSAN; State College Area HS; State College, PA; (3); Cmnty Wkr; Acpl Chr; Chorus; School Musical; Nwsp Stf; Yrbk Stf; Var Co-Capt Cheerleading; Powder Puff Ftbl; High Hon Roll; Hon Roll; Music Ed.

YOUNG, TINA; Red Lion SR HS; Windsor, PA; (2); 29/342; SADD; Hon Roll; Frnch Excel Awd 86-87.

YOUNG, TRACY; Cecilian Acad; Philadelphia, PA; (2); 1/37; Cmnty Wkr; Debate Tm; Science Clb; Rep Frsh Cls; Rep Soph Cls; Rep Stu Cncl; High Hon Roll; Phldlph Clscl Scty Certy Of Merit 87; Corp Atrny.

YOUNG, TRACY; Cocalico HS; Reinholds, PA; (3); Church Yth Grp; FTA; Hosp Aide; Teachers Aide; Capt Band; Mrchg Band; Mgr(s); Powder Puff Ftbl; Score Keeper; Twrlr; Grp Ldrshp In Scl Stds 86; Grp Cooprtn & Initiative In Scl Stds 87; Bus.

YOUNG, WENDY; Altoona Area HS; Altoona, PA; (4); 5/718; Computer Clb; Trs French Clb; VP JA; Math Clb; Rep Sr Cls; Var Bsktbl; Var Sftbl; High Hon Roll; Jr NHS; NHS; Penn ST U; Eductn.

YOUNG, WILLIAM; Northeast HS; Philadelphia, PA; (4); 13/690; Aud/Vis; Chess Clb; Computer Clb; Science Clb; Ski Clb; Stage Crew; High Hon Roll; Hon Roll; Jr NHS; NHS; 3rd Prz Dist Fnlst Natl Hstry Day 86; 2nd Prz Regnl Fnls Olympcs Mind 87; Philadelphia Fed Tchrs Awd; Drexel U; Physcs.

YOUNG, WILLIAM; York County Area Vo Tech Schl; Delta, PA; (3); Drama Clb; Band; Chorus; Concert Band; Jazz Band; Mrchg Band; Boy Scts; Chess Clb; Church Yth Grp; Computer Clb.

YOUNG, WING; S Philadelphis HS; Philadelphia, PA; (1); 4/695; Computer Clb; Math Clb; Math Tm; Var Bowling; High Hon Roll; NHS; NEDT Awd; Prfct Atten Awd; Pres Schlr; Drexel U; Elec Engrng.

YOUNG, YVETTE; Lancaster Catholic HS; Lititz, PA; (3); 9/193; Pep Clb; Rep Frsh Cls; Rep Soph Cls; L Cheerleading; Trk; NHS; Amer Clsscl League-Magna Cumlaude Natl Latin Exam 84; Hghst Avg Latin III 87; Advtsng.

YOUNGBLOOD, MELISSA; Warwick HS; Lititz, PA; (2); 4-H; JA; Color Guard; Nwsp Stf; Var Cheerleading; JV Var Fld Hcky; Var Trk; Hon Roll; Rdlgst.

YOUNGER, IAN; Oliver HS; Pittsburgh, PA; (3); Mu Alpha Theta; Jazz Band; Nwsp Rptr; Var Swmmng; Var Trk; Jr NHS; Pep Clb; Scholastic Bowl; Concert Band; Mrchg Band; CAS Hnrs Pgm 84-87; Carngie-Mlln Upwrd Bound 84-86; U Of PA; Finance.

YOUNGKIN, ROCHELLE; Lehighton Area HS; Lehighton, PA; (3); 28/154; Church Yth Grp; FHA; SADD; Church Choir; Var L Crs Cntry; Var L Trk; Centnl Leag Trk Meet 3rd Pl 100 M Hrdles 85-87; Phys Thrpy.

YOUNGMAN, KRIS; West Hazelton HS; Sugarloaf, PA; (2); 29/218; Pres 4-H; Pep Clb; Thesps; Concert Band; Drill Tm; Trk; 4-H Awd; Gov Hon Prg Awd; High Hon Roll; French Clb; PA ST Delg Natl 4-H Cong 86; Astrnt.

YOUNGS, TARRIN; Coatesville Area SR HS; Coatesville, PA; (3); 43/509; Church Yth Grp; French Clb; Leo Clb; Ski Clb; Band; Var JV Swmmng; Hon Roll; NHS; Art Clb; Concert Band; Hnr Soc 84-88; High GPA 84-88; Physcl Thrpy.

YOUNGSTROM, ERIC A; Penncrest HS; Media, PA; (4); 2/327; Church Yth Grp; SADD; School Play; Nwsp Stf; Yrbk Stf; Lit Mag; JV Capt Crs Cntry; Wt Lftg; Var Wrstlng; High Hon Roll; 3rd Pl Ovrl In Cntrl League Wrtng 83; Mst Imprvd Cross Cntry Rnr Awd 84; Rotary Stu Of Mnth 86; Psychlgy.

YOUNKIN, CHARLENE; Central Cambria HS; Johnstown, PA; (3); 32/210; Art Clb; Library Aide; Chorus; Drm Mjr(t); Yrbk Stf; Im Bsktbl; Hon Roll; Natl Hnr Roll Acad 84-85; IUP.

YOUNKIN, DREW; North Star HS; Stoystown, PA; (3); 9/136; Boy Scts; FCA; Scholastic Bowl; Chorus; Concert Band; Mrchg Band; Yrbk Stf; Rep Stu Cncl; Golf; Hon Roll; Acad Awd Amer Hstry 85; Deacon 1st Presby Church 85-88; VP Careers Clb 84-85; Bus.

YOUTZ, ANDREW; Conrad Weiser JS HS; Wernersville, PA; (3); 1/179; Computer Clb; German Clb; Quiz Bowl; Band; Concert Band; Jazz Band; Mrchg Band; School Musical; NHS; Elctrcl Engrng.

YOXTHEIMER, DAVID; Loyalsock Township HS; Williamsport, PA; (3); 12/125; French Clb; Var Bsktbl; Var Ftbl; Var Trk; Hon Roll; VP Frsh Cls; Pres Soph Cls; Rep Stu Cncl; Spcl Actvts Aka Gftd Pgm 84-87; Penn ST; Engrng.

YOZALLINAS, JAMES F; Archbishop Ryan H S For Boys; Philadelphia, PA; (3); 17/427; SADD; Rep Soph Cls; Rep Jr Cls; Var Bsbl; Bsktbl; JV Ftbl; High Hon Roll; Hon Roll; German Awd 85-86; Bus.

YOZVIAK, ANDREW; John S Fine SR HS; Nanticoke, PA; (4); 13/256; Boy Scts; Band; Chorus; Concert Band; Mrchg Band; Variety Show; Var Capt Vllybl; High Hon Roll; NHS; NEDT Awd; Dist, Rgnl Band 85-87; Sst Band 87; Dist, Rgnl Chorus 85-87; Al-ST Chorus Alt 86; Dist, Rgnl Orch 87; U Of Scranton PA; Pre-Med.

YOZVIAK, SANDRA; John S Fine HS; Nanticoke, PA; (2); 23/243; Ski Clb; Chorus; Yrbk Stf; Sec Frsh Cls; Sec Soph Cls; JV Cheerleading; JV Vllybl; High Hon Roll; NHS.

YU, KWANG; Plymouth-Whitemarsh HS; Conshohocken, PA; (3); Church Yth Grp; Math Clb; Mu Alpha Theta; Science Clb; Chorus; Church Choir; Orch; Socr; Tennis; Molecular Bio.

YU, MEGAN; Upper Dublin HS; Ambler, PA; (3); Math Tm; Science Clb; Var L Tennis; NHS; Rensselaer Math & Sci Awd 87; Amer Chem Soc Awd 87; PA ST U; Acctg.

YUCHA, JENNIFER; Shikellamy HS; Sunbury, PA; (4); 1/297; Am Leg Aux Girls St; Church Yth Grp; Sec Stu Cncl; Var Capt Bsktbl; Bausch & Lomb Sci Awd; French Hon Soc; Pres NHS; Val; French Clb; Red Cross Aide; Stu Schl Brd 85-87; Am Lgn Outstndng Girl Awd 87; Soroptmst Awd 87; Penn ST U; Math Tchr.

YUDISKI, TAMMY; Exeter SR HS; Reading, PA; (4); 33/214; Leo Clb; Library Aide; Office Aide; SADD; Varsity Clb; JV Var Bsktbl; Sftbl; High Hon Roll; Hon Roll; NHS; Kutztown; Elem Educ.

YUE, LORENE; Parkland SR HS; Allentown, PA; (3); 95/495; Drama Clb; Chorus; Flag Corp; School Musical; Stage Crew; Yrbk Stf; Lit Mag; Stat Bsktbl; L Trk; Hon Roll; Cmmnctns.

YUGOVICH, JACQUELINE C; United HS; Armagh, PA; (4); 10/164; Library Aide; Ski Clb; Teachers Aide; High Hon Roll; Hon Roll; Ntl Merit Schol; Prfct Atten Awd; IN U Of PA; Crmnlgy.

YUHAS, BONNY; Bethlehem Catholic HS; Bethlehem, PA; (3); 31/205; Church Yth Grp; French Clb; Scholastic Bowl; Yrbk Stf; Capt Var Bsktbl; Im Fld Hcky; Var Tennis; French Hon Soc; High Hon Roll; NHS; Bus.

YUHAS, DAWN; Fort Cherry HS; Hickory, PA; (3); Computer Clb; Drama Clb; French Clb; Math Clb; Science Clb; Varsity Clb; Chorus; School Play; Var Sftbl; JV Vllybl; Robert Morris Coll; Bus Inf Sys.

YUHAS, MICHELLE; Johnstown HS; Johnstown, PA; (4); 43/270; Church Yth Grp; Pres Exploring; Hosp Aide; Key Clb; Speech Tm; Chorus; Mrchg Band; School Musical; Nwsp Rptr; Nwsp Stf; Forensics Pin & Ltr 87; Hnrb Mntn Tribune Democrat Wrtng Cont 85; High Hnr Awd 87; Kings Coll; Journlsm.

YUHASZ, AMY; Rocky Grove HS; Franklin, PA; (4); 14/94; VP Drama Clb; Library Aide; Chorus; Orch; Pep Band; School Play; Yrbk Stf; L Var Sftbl; L Var Vllybl; Hon Roll; Penn ST; Pre Law.

YUHASZ, JOSEPH A; Steel Valley HS; Munhall, PA; (4); 4/201; Crs Cntry; Tennis; Trk; Wt Lftg; High Hon Roll; Hon Roll; NHS; Penn ST U; Pilot.

YUKEVICH, MICHAEL; Hampton HS; Allison Park, PA; (3); 20/210; Aud/Vis; Ski Clb; Spanish Clb; Yrbk Phtg; Yrbk Stf; VP Stu Cncl; Ftbl; Powder Puff Ftbl; High Hon Roll; NHS; Wght Lftng-300 Bnch Club 87; Bus.

YUNINGER, DAVID; Pequea Valley HS; Paradise, PA; (3); AFS; Church Yth Grp; Acpl Chr; Band; Chorus; Concert Band; Jazz Band; Mrchg Band; School Musical; Yrbk Stf.

YUNKUN, MARCIE; Ringgold HS; Finleyville, PA; (3); French Clb; Pres JA; Office Aide; Variety Show; Yrbk Phtg; Yrbk Stf; Stu Cncl; Var Mgr(s); Pom Pon; JV Tennis; JA NAJAC 87; IN U PA; Sci Tchr.

YURCHAK, THOMAS; Pennridge SR HS; Sellersville, PA; (4); Bsbl; Ftbl; Capt Wrstlng; High Hon Roll; Hon Roll; Drexel U; Chem Engr.

YURCICH, BRIAN; Hickory HS; Hermitage, PA; (3); Drama Clb; French Clb; Band; Chorus; Concert Band; Pep Band; School Musical; School Play; Stage Crew; Yrbk Phtg.

YURCONIC, MONICA A; Salisbury HS; Allentown, PA; (3); Key Clb; SADD; Nwsp Stf; Yrbk Stf; JV Var Cheerleading; Powder Puff Ftbl; Var L Tennis; Hon Roll; Pres Frsh Cls; Pres Soph Cls; Dist XI Girls Ten Rnr-Up Sngls 84 & 85; Dist XI Mxd Dbls Wnnr Ten 85 & 87; Dist XI Girls Ten Wnnr.

YURGATIS, SANDY; Wyalusing Valley JR SR HS; Laceyville, PA; (4); FBLA; Trs Library Aide; Office Aide; Spanish Clb; SADD; Yrbk Stf; Sec Stu Cncl; NHS; U Of Scranton; Acctng.

YURICH, ANDREA; Quigley HS; Midland, PA; (4); Camera Clb; Girl Scts; Hosp Aide; Chorus; Nwsp Phtg; Nwsp Stf; Yrbk Ed-Chief; Yrbk Phtg; Yrbk Stf; Vllybl; PA ST U; Bus Admin.

YURICH, LYNETTE; Beaver Falls SR HS; Beaver Falls, PA; (3); French Clb; Speech Tm; Drill Tm; Yrbk Stf; Rep Frsh Cls; Sec Soph Cls; Rep Jr Cls; Rep Stu Cncl; Bsktbl; Trk; Penn ST.

YURICK, PAMELA J; Carmichaels Area HS; Carmichaels, PA; (4); Dance Clb; Drama Clb; Sec French Clb; Library Aide; Pep Clb; Ski Clb; Yrbk Bus Mgr; Yrbk Stf; Sec Frsh Cls; Rep Soph Cls; Amer Lgn Awd 82; U Of Pittsburgh; Pre-Med.

YURICK, VICKI; St Huberts HS; Philadelphia, PA; (4); 67/364; Cmnty Wkr; French Clb; Intnl Clb; Service Clb; Orch; School Musical; School Play; Temple U; Comm.

YURISH, MARK B; Freeland HS; Freeland, PA; (4); 8/90; FBLA; School Play; Yrbk Ed-Chief; Stu Cncl; Var L Bsktbl; Var L Crs Cntry; Tennis; NHS; Boston U; Arspc Engrng.

YURISTA, MICHELE; Hazleton SR HS; Hazleton, PA; (3); FNA; Hosp Aide; Chorus; Lackawanna CC; Med Secy.

YURKANIN, ERIC; Hazleton SR HS; Hazleton, PA; (3); Chess Clb; Band; Chorus; Church Choir; Concert Band; Jazz Band; Mrchg Band; School Musical; Hon Roll; PA ST U; Music Ed.

YURKANIN, LEANNE; Valley View JR SR HS; Archbald, PA; (4); 8/200; French Clb; SADD; Drill Tm; French Hon Soc; High Hon Roll; Hon Roll; NHS; Lock Haven U; Psych.

YURT, HEATHER; Waynesburg HS; Graysville, PA; (3); Natl Beta Clb; Spanish Clb; Stu Cncl; Cheerleading; Diving; Gym; Hon Roll; Life Guard; Northeastern U; Phys Thrpy.

YURUS, BRENDA; Canon Mc Millan HS; Strabane, PA; (3); Ski Clb; Band; Concert Band; Mrchg Band; High Hon Roll; Hon Roll; WV U; Law.

YUSKO, AMY; Portage Area HS; Portage, PA; (3); 7/110; Debate Tm; Speech Tm; Band; Concert Band; Mrchg Band; Pep Band; Trs Soph Cls; Trk; High Hon Roll; Hon Roll; OH ST; Med.

YUSKOVITZ, ROBIN; Wyoming Seminary; Kingston, PA; (4); 1/98; Dance Clb; Math Clb; Red Cross Aide; School Musical; School Play; High Hon Roll; NHS; NEDT Awd; Charles Wood Math Prize 87; Wesley A Kuhn Prize Econ 87; Cum Laude Scty 86-87; Le High U; Engr.

YZKANIN, SANDY; Valley View JRSR HS; Peckville, PA; (2); 39/189; Dance Clb; FNA; Sec Spanish Clb; Chorus; Trs Jr Cls; Stu Cncl; Stat Crs Cntry; Vllybl; Spanish NHS; Yth Ftnss Achvt Awd 86-87; Acdmc Achvt Awd 85; Nrsng.

ZABIELSKI, KARINA; Old Forge HS; Old Forge, PA; (3); French Clb; Ski Clb; Var Cheerleading.

ZABINSKI, KAREN; Mastbaum AVT HS; Philadelphia, PA; (3); Math Tm; SADD; Chorus; Rep Frsh Cls; Rep Soph Cls; Rep Jr Cls; Off Sr Cls; Rep Stu Cncl; JV Sftbl; JV Swmmng; Ping Pong 85-86; Temple U; Comp Pgmmr.

ZABLOTNEY, MARSHA; Windber Area HS; Windber, PA; (4); Chess Clb; Drama Clb; Exploring; FTA; Math Clb; Chorus; Rep Jr Cls; Rep Stu Cncl; Hon Roll; Ntl Merit Schol; Smmr Yth Schlrs Pgm Lebanon Vly Coll 86; Stu Mth 85-87; Natl Merit Sci Awd 86-87; Elizabethtown Coll; Bio.

ZABOROWSKI, LIZA; Nazareth Acad; Philadelphia, PA; (3); Church Yth Grp; Math Clb; Rep Frsh Cls; Rep Soph Cls; Rep Jr Cls; Rep Sr Cls; Stu Cncl; Var Bsktbl; Var Fld Hcky; Var Sftbl; 4th Pl Amer Elec Inst Essay 85; Math.

ZACKOSKI, KIMBERLY; West Scranton HS; Scranton, PA; (3); Varsity Clb; Trs Orch; Crs Cntry; Trk; Hon Roll; Ntl Merit Ltr; Nrsng.

ZACZKIEWICZ, SUSAN; Corry Area JR SR HS; Corry, PA; (2); Church Yth Grp; Church Choir; Score Keeper; Vllybl; High Hon Roll; Delta Epsilon Phi German Hnr Soc 87.

ZADAKIS, CHARLES; Trinity HS; Washington, PA; (4); 23/322; Boy Scts; Church Yth Grp; German Clb; Band; High Hon Roll; Prfct Atten Awd; Obsrvr Rptr Paper Boy Of Yr 85-86; U Of Pittsburg; Chem Engr.

ZADINSKI, MARY; Bethel Park HS; Pittsburgh, PA; (4); Dance Clb; Chorus; Drm Mjr(t); Mrchg Band; School Musical; Variety Show; Twrlr; ICM Bus Schl; Acnctng.

ZAFFO JR, PAUL G; Plymoth Whitemarsh HS; Conshohocken, PA; (3); Aud/Vis; Boy Scts; Exploring; Library Aide; Office Aide; Chorus; High Hon Roll; Hon Roll; Prfct Atten Awd; Cmmnty Svc Ambulance Corps 85-87; Part Tme Comp Tech.

ZAFFUTO, DANA; Burrell HS; Lower Burrell, PA; (3); JV Vllybl; Nrs.

ZAGORSKI, AIMEE; Beaver Area JR/Sr HS; Beaver, PA; (2); Church Yth Grp; French Clb; School Musical; Yrbk Stf; Tennis; Hon Roll; Nrsg.

ZAGORSKI, DENISE; Nazareth Acad; Philadelphia, PA; (3); Math Clb; 2nd Pl Polish Ptry Cont 86-87.

ZAGORSKI, JACK; Holy Ghost Preparatory Schl; Bensalem, PA; (4); 1/81; Exploring; Math Clb; Math Tm; Scholastic Bowl; School Play; Im Ftbl; Var Capt Tennis; High Hon Roll; NHS; Ntl Merit SF; Rensselaer Polytech Inst; Engr.

ZAGST, KRISTEN; Highlands SR HS; Natrona Hgts, PA; (3); 1/303; Dance Clb; Key Clb; Scholastic Bowl; SADD; Jr Cls; Tennis; High Hon Roll; NHS; NEDT Awd; Pres Schlr; Pre-Med.

ZAHIRNYI, MARC; Council Rock HS; Newtown, PA; (3); 155/908; JV Var Bsbl.

ZAHN, AMY; Trinity HS; Ickesburg, PA; (2); Pres VP 4-H; Spanish Clb; Nwsp Stf; 4-H Awd; Prfct Atten Awd.

ZAHNISER, KIMBERLY; West Middlesex HS; W Middlesex, PA; (4); 32/100; Church Yth Grp; Girl Scts; Spanish Clb; Mgr Band; Mgr Concert Band; Mgr Mrchg Band; Mgr Symp Band; Vllybl; 4-H Awd; Hon Roll; Band Awds-3rd & 2nd Clss & Sr Rcgntn 86 & 87.

ZAHNISER, MELISSA; North Allegheny Intermediate HS; Gibsonia, PA; (2); 124/630; AFS; GAA; Hosp Aide; Service Clb; Ski Clb; SADD; Off Stu Cncl; JV Fld Hcky; Hon Roll; Brown U; Accntnt.

ZAHORCHAT, CHRISTINE; Cardinal Brennan HS; Shenandoah, PA; (3); 5/58; German Clb; Quiz Bowl; Science Clb; Chorus; Hon Roll; NHS; Prfct Atten Awd; Acadc All Am 86; Comp Engrng.

ZAIDAN, FREDERIC; West Middlesex HS; Pulaski, PA; (2); 2/120; Spanish Clb; Jazz Band; Mrchg Band; Orch; JV Bsktbl; High Hon Roll; NHS; Vet.

ZAJDEL, DAVID JOHN; Greater Johnstown HS; Johnstown, PA; (4); 43/306; VP French Clb; Math Clb; Capt Scholastic Bowl; Stu Cncl; Tennis; High Hon Roll; NHS; Rotary Awd; Intrct Club Div Rtry Intl Treas; Hnr Outstndg Achvmnt Sclstc Qz 86; U Of Pittsburgh; Phy Thrpy.

ZAJKOWSKI, LISA; Tech Memorial HS; Erie, PA; (2); 8/297; Hosp Aide; Library Aide; Service Clb; Hon Roll; Bus Clb, Hnr Card 86-87; Mercy Hurst Coll; Bus.

ZAKARIAN, ADAM D; Norristown Area HS; Norristown, PA; (3); 25/500; Camera Clb; Key Clb; Jazz Band; Variety Show; Var Wrstlng; Hon Roll; NHS; Amer Indstrl Arts Stdnt Assn ST Pres 85-86; Intract Clb Rotry Comm 86-87; Water Polo Tm Vrsty 86; Engrng.

ZAKOS, STEPHEN; William Allen HS; Allentown, PA; (3); 45/600; Debate Tm; Math Clb; Math Tm; Scholastic Bowl; Ski Clb; Rep Stu Cncl; Var Socr; Hon Roll; VP Pres NHS; Cmnty Wkr; Shrt Stry Pblshd Inklngs,Schl Litrary Magz 87; Fndr Chrmn Vlntrs PA Untd Way 86-88; Ec.

ZAKREWSKY, DAVID; Mahanoy Area HS; Delano, PA; (3); Drama Clb; Spanish Clb; Varsity Clb; School Play; Var Bsktbl; Var Swmmng; Var Trk; Hon Roll; Cvl Engnrng.

ZAKRZWSKI, DAVID F; Bishop Carroll HS; Cresson, PA; (4); 17/106; Pres Aud/Vis; Spanish Clb; Bsktbl; NHS; Knghts Columbus Cathlc Actn Awd 87; PA ST U; Engrng.

ZAKRZWSKI, MARY; Bishop Carroll HS; Cresson, PA; (3); Spanish Clb; L Bsktbl; Hon Roll; Var Powder Puff Ftbl; Psych.

ZALAR, PATRICIA; Shamokin Area HS; Shamokin, PA; (3); 14/223; Pres Camera Clb; Pres Key Clb; Letterman Clb; Varsity Clb; Nwsp Stf; Yrbk Sprt Ed; Var Capt Cheerleading; Capt Trk; High Hon Roll; NHS; PA Free Entrprs Wk At Lock Haven U Schlrshp 86; Pre-Law.

ZALAR, SHARON; Parkland SR HS; Fogelsville, PA; (3); 107/481; Church Yth Grp; Key Clb; SADD; Band; Chorus; Stu Cncl; Vllybl; Wt Lftg; Hon Roll.

ZALE, MICHAEL; Lancaster Catholic HS; Lititz, PA; (3); Im JV Bsktbl; Var JV Golf; Accntng.

ZALEGOWSKI, DENISE; Governor Mifflin SR HS; Reading, PA; (3); 35/326; VP Exploring; FBLA; Girl Scts; Drill Tm; Var Trk; Hon Roll; PA ST U; Acctg.

ZALETSKY, JOANNE; North Allegheny HS; Wexford, PA; (3); 175/649; AFS; School Play; Nwsp Rptr; Rep Stu Cncl; Hon Roll; Cmmnctns.

ZALEWSKI, SONDRA; Downingtown SR HS; Downington, PA; (3); 92/648; Hon Roll; Hnrb Mntn Wmn Hstry 86; Schlrshp Sat Clss Moore Coll 86-87; 1st Pl Am Educ Wk Pstr Cont 84; Cmmrcl Art.

ZAMBETTI, KAREN; Pittston Area HS; Yatesville, PA; (4); 18/365; Sec Key Clb; Math Clb; Ski Clb; SADD; Drill Tm; Stat Bsktbl; Hon Roll; NHS; Acad All Amrcn 85-86; Misericordia; Acctng.

ZAMBOLDI, RICHARD; Cathedral Prep; Erie, PA; (3); 40/200; Church Yth Grp; Cmnty Wkr; Ski Clb; Yrbk Stf; Var L Socr; Var L Swmmng; Vllybl; Hon Roll; Acad All-Amer 87.

ZAMBONI, WILLIAM; Blacklick Valley JR SR HS; Nanty-Glo, PA; (4); 1/87; Thesps; Varsity Clb; Pres Stu Cncl; Capt Bsktbl; Capt Ftbl; High Hon Roll; VP NHS; Val; US Mrns & Army Rsrv Schlr-Athlt 86-87; Stu Cncl Outstndng SR 86-87; Juniata Coll; Phrmcy.

ZAMBROSKI, MICHELLE; Shenandoah Valley JR-SR HS; Shenandoah, PA; (4); Hosp Aide; Office Aide; Pep Clb; SADD; Chorus; Color Guard; Co-Capt Drill Tm; Mrchg Band; Nwsp Stf; Yrbk Stf; Air Force.

ZAMITES, JANET; Archbishop Prendergast HS; Collingdale, PA; (3); 23/327; Math Tm; Stage Crew; Hon Roll; Psych.

ZAMPETTI, DENISE; Lake-Lehman HS; Shavertown, PA; (2); 4/199; Church Yth Grp; Hosp Aide; Library Aide; Office Aide; Ski Clb; SADD; VP Frsh Cls; Rep Soph Cls; Rep Stu Cncl; Var Bsktbl; Hugh O Brian Runnr Up 86-87; Princeton; Law.

ZAMPETTI, VICTOR; Danville HS; Danville, PA; (4); 62/198; VP Church Yth Grp; VP Frsh Cls; VP Soph Cls; Ftbl; Socr; Trk; Co-Capt Wrstlng; Hon Roll; Outstndng Wrstlr 84; Brian Stamm Awd 86 & 87; Ursinus Coll; Math.

ZAMPOGNA, MISSIE; Harbor Creek HS; Erie, PA; (3); Church Yth Grp; Band; Concert Band; Mrchg Band; School Play; Var Swmmng; Hon Roll; Lbrl Arts.

ZANDE, JILL M; Bradford Area HS; Lewis Run, PA; (4); 3/267; AFS; Cheerleading; Cit Awd; High Hon Roll; NHS; NEDT Awd; Voice Dem Awd; Ski Clb; Yrbk Stf; Trk; AFS Exch Stu Greece 86; Explore Gifted Pgm; Stu Cncl Scholar 87; William Olsen Spch Awd 87; Mem Sci Awd; PA ST U; Mar Biol.

ZANDERS, TRAVIS; Lehighton Area HS; Lehighton, PA; (3); 32/250; Church Yth Grp; 4-H; Band; Ftbl; Trk; 4-H Awd; Hon Roll; Indstrl Arts Awd-3rd Pl Mtl Shp 86; Cert Scuba Dvr UNEXSO 87; Pilot.

ZANGARI, KRISTIE; Cardinal Brennan HS; Girardville, PA; (3); 5/60; VP Band; Chorus; Concert Band; VP Mrchg Band; VP Orch; VP Pep Band; School Musical; Hon Roll; Hst NHS; Nwsp Stf; Schuykill County Chorus; Allentown Diocese Chorus; Natl Honor Soc Historian; Biology.

ZANGLA, CHRISTINE; Bethlehem Center; Fredericktown, PA; (3); 14/165; Band; Chorus; Concert Band; Mrchg Band; Hon Roll; NHS; Church Yth Grp; Spanish Clb; Seton Hill; Musician.

ZANOLI, EDWARD; Springdale HS; Cheswick, PA; (3); Pres Art Clb; FHA; German Clb; Var JV Bsktbl; High Hon Roll; NHS; Amer Lgn Awd 84; Highest GPA 84-87; Penn ST U; Engrng.

ZANONI, TRICIA; Bishop Mc Cort HS; Jerome, PA; (4); 2/130; Mu Alpha Theta; NFL; Pres Spanish Clb; Band; Pres Sr Cls; Rep Stu Cncl; Var L Socr; Sal; Spanish NHS; Civic Clb; U Of Pittsburgh Hnrs Stu 87; U Of Pittsburgh Provost Schlrshp 87; Sci Awd 87; U Of Pittsburgh; Phrmcy.

ZAPACH, SUSAN; William Allen HS; Allentown, PA; (2); Church Yth Grp; Drama Clb; Pres SADD; Nwsp Rptr; Yrbk Stf; Lit Mag; Mgr(s); Hon Roll; Jr NHS.

ZAPHIRIS, JIM; Corry Area HS; Corry, PA; (4); French Clb; Pres Jr Cls; Var L Bsktbl; Var L Crs Cntry; Var Trk; JETS Awd; Pres Schlr; Rotary Awd; U Of Dayton Presdntl Schlrshp 87; Fisher-Allen Schlrshp 87; Acadmc Awds Excllnc 87; U Of Dayton; Chem Engrng.

ZAPOLLO, LEONARD; St John Neumann HS; Philadelphia, PA; (2); 42/350.

ZAPPA, CLAUDINE; Hickory HS; Hermitage, PA; (3); 27/178; Drama Clb; Latin Clb; Varsity Clb; Chorus; Mrchg Band; School Musical; Sec Stu Cncl; Var Trk; Stat Wrstlng; NHS; Latin Hnr Soc; Stu Forum Rep; Math.

ZAPPA, JILL; Kennedy Christian HS; Farrell, PA; (3); Science Clb; Ski Clb; Trs Spanish Clb; Stu Cncl; Var L Cheerleading; Hon Roll; Psych.

ZAPPI, DEANNA; Mc Guffey HS; Claysville, PA; (4); French Clb; JA; Sec Trs Pep Clb; Spanish Clb; Varsity Clb; Rep Sr Cls; Capt Bsktbl; Mgr(s); Powder Puff Ftbl; Sftbl; St Vincent Coll; Bus.

ZAPSKY, JENNIFER; Moshannon Valley HS; Madera, PA; (3); Spanish Clb; Varsity Clb; Band; Concert Band; Drm Mjr(t); Mrchg Band; Pep Band; School Play; Pres Sr Cls; Stu Cncl; Presdntl Awd Phy Ed; Judo St Chmpn; Intl Bus Mgmt.

ZAPSKY, MARLA; Moshannon Valley HS; Houtzdale, PA; (3); Ski Clb; Spanish Clb; Band; Concert Band; Mrchg Band; Pep Band; Stage Crew; Yrbk Stf; Trs Soph Cls; Sec Jr Cls; Cmmnctns.

ZARECKY, MARC; Greenville SR HS; Greenville, PA; (4); VICA; Yrbk Rptr; Stu Of Yr Data Prcssng 86; Outstndng Comp Oprtr Awd 87; Hghst Achvr Spnsh I Awd 84; Comp Oprtr.

ZAREMBA, EDDIE; Trinity HS; Washington, PA; (3); 95/402; Band; Concert Band; Socr; Wrstlng.

ZARLENGA, MARIE; Mount Calvary Christian Schl; Annville, PA; (3); Church Yth Grp; Chorus; Nwsp Stf; Yrbk Phtg; Yrbk Stf; Cheerleading; Hon Roll; NHS.

ZARSKI, JASON; Shamokin Area HS; Shamokin, PA; (2); Chess Clb; Orch; Im Ftbl; Hon Roll; Upwrd Bnd Stu 85-87; ROTC; Sci Tech.

ZARSKI, TONIA; Shamokin Area HS; Shamokin, PA; (3); 35/217; Drama Clb; Key Clb; Pep Clb; Science Clb; Ski Clb; Chorus; Mrchg Band; Trk; Vllybl; Hon Roll; Pre-Med.

ZARY, JILL; Bethel Park HS; Bethel Park, PA; (4); 59/519; Rptr FBLA; Chorus; Drill Tm; School Musical; Yrbk Stf; Pom Pon; Powder Puff Ftbl; CC Awd; NHS; Pres Schlr; PA ST U.

ZARZYCKI JR, EDWARD; Pleasant Valley HS; Brodheadsville, PA; (3); Math Tm; Var Bsbl; Capt L Socr; Capt L Wrstlng; Hon Roll.

ZASLAVSKY, CORDELIA; Louer Merion HS; Ardmore, PA; (3); AFS; Drama Clb; JCL; PAVAS; Political Wkr; Service Clb; Thesps; School Play; Yrbk Phtg; Chld Psych.

ZATRATZ, DENISE; Holy Name HS; Mohnton, PA; (4); Sec Exploring; FBLA; Library Aide; Pep Clb; Hon Roll; SECRETARY.

ZAUCHA, AMANDA A; North Penn HS; Hatfield, PA; (2); Church Yth Grp; Drama Clb; Chorus; Church Choir; Color Guard; School Musical; School Play; Yrbk Rptr; Hon Roll.

ZAVACKY, MICHELLE; Pius X HS; Pen Argyl, PA; (3); Letterman Clb; Pep Clb; SADD; Varsity Clb; Chorus; School Play; Yrbk Stf; Stat Bsbl; Var Cheerleading; Score Keeper; Bus.

ZAVATSKI, GINA; Mc Guffey HS; Taylorstown, PA; (4); 37/203; Church Yth Grp; JA; Spanish Clb; Varsity Clb; Chorus; Var L Sftbl; Var L Vllybl; Hon Roll; NHS; Odd Fllw/Rebekhs Untd Natns Plgrmg 86; Duffs Business Inst; Med Asst.

ZAVATSKY, KELLY; Connellsville Area SR HS; Connellsville, PA; (2); School Musical; Stage Crew; Nwsp Ed-Chief; Nwsp Rptr; Nwsp Stf; Yrbk Stf; Var Diving; Var Swmmng; Var Capt Vllybl; High Hon Roll.

ZAVETSKY, WILLIAM; West Mifflin Area HS; W Mifflin, PA; (3); 57/337; Chess Clb; Church Yth Grp; CAP; Exploring; Science Clb; Coach Actv; Mgr(s); Trk; Hon Roll; Billy Mitchell, Amelia Earhart Awds Civil Air Patrol 86-87; Penn ST; Physics.

ZAVISLAK, MICHAEL R; Carbondale Area HS; Carbondale, PA; (2); 23/135; Computer Clb; Ski Clb; Spanish Clb; High Hon Roll.

ZAVITSKY, SANDY; Hazleton HS; Drums, PA; (2); FBLA; Chorus; Cheerleading; Vllybl; High Hon Roll; Hon Roll; Pres Schlr.

ZAVITSKY, SARAH; Hazleton HS; Drums, PA; (3); Drama Clb; French Clb; FBLA; Chorus; Color Guard; Yrbk Stf; Cheerleading; Vllybl; French Hon Soc; Hon Roll; Penn ST; Hotel Restrnt Mngmt.

ZAVITSKY, SUSAN; Hazleton HS; Drums, PA; (4); 28/367; Church Yth Grp; French Clb; FBLA; Leo Clb; French Hon Soc; Hon Roll; NHS; FBLA Regnl Ldrshp Conf 87; FBLA Ofc Proc 1st Pl ST Ldrshp Conf 87; Cadette Clb Scholar Awd 87; Penn ST U; Bus Adm.

ZAWADA, JOHN; Greensburg Central Catholic HS; Greensburg, PA; (4); 15/222; High Hon Roll; NHS; Natl Hnrs Soc; Grove City Coll; Intl Bus.

ZAWADZKI, CHAS; Dunmore HS; Scranton, PA; (4); 15/144; FBLA; High Hon Roll; Hon Roll; Jr NHS; Presdntl Schlrshp From U Of Scranton 87; Schlrhsp Dunmore HS 87; 1st Pl In Essay Cont 87; U Scranton; Acctng.

ZAWISTOSKI, MARYBETH; Mercyhurst Preparatory HS; Erie, PA; (4); Church Yth Grp; French Clb; Church Choir; School Musical; Nwsp Phtg; Vllybl; Exchange Stu Yth For Understanding-Netherlands 86-87; PA ST U; Photo Jrnlsm.

ZAWROTNY, LYNN; Seneca Valley HS; Mars, PA; (3); Varsity Clb; Var L Sftbl; Hon Roll; Schlstc Achvt Awd 86-87; Bst Attndnc Sftbl Tm 87; Hghst Bttng Avg Sftbl Tm 86; Bus Admin.

ZAYAC, COLEEN; Canon-Mcmillan Jhs At Cecil HS; Cecil, PA; (1); Ed Nwsp Stf; Stu Cncl; Cheerleading; Hon Roll.

ZAYKOWSKI JR, RONALD; Old Forge HS; Old Forge, PA; (3); Pres Jr Cls; Pres Sr Cls; JV Bsbl; L Ftbl; Wt Lftg; Hon Roll; NHS.

ZAZVRSKEY, LISA; Northern Cambria HS; Barnesboro, PA; (3); 41/152; Church Yth Grp; French Clb; Soroptimist; Church Choir; Hon Roll.

ZAZYCZNY, JAYDALYNN; Nazareth Acad; Philadelphia, PA; (3); Church Yth Grp; GAA; Chorus; School Musical; Variety Show; Sec Sr Cls; Rep Stu Cncl; Im Bsktbl; Var Tennis; Im Vllybl; Polish Poetry Cont 86-87; Cabrini Coll; Chld Psych.

ZBICKI, JOSEPH S; Lock Haven SR HS; Lock Haven, PA; (3); Art Clb; Church Yth Grp; Service Clb; Ski Clb; Var L Socr; Trk; Prfct Atten Awd; Frstry.

ZBIHLEY, MICHELE; Aliquippa JR SR HS; Aliquippa, PA; (2); Church Yth Grp; Trs Computer Clb; French Clb; Band; Concert Band; Pep Band; Var JV Cheerleading; High Hon Roll; Prfct Atten Awd; Med.

ZDANAVAGE, COREY; John S Fine SR HS; Nanticoke, PA; (4); 10/251; Varsity Clb; Rep Soph Cls; Var Bsbl; JV Bsktbl; Im Ftbl; Im Vllybl; VP NHS; Presdntl Ftnss Awd; Math.

ZDANAVAGE, STACEY; Crestwood HS; Mountaintop, PA; (4); Ski Clb; Stu Cncl; Bsbl; Ftbl; Hon Roll; Bloomsburg U; Bio.

ZDANCEWICZ, LISA; Bishop O Reilly HS; Swoyersville, PA; (3); Civic Clb; JV Cheerleading; Hon Roll; NEDT Awd; Catholic Dghtrs Of Amers Poetry Cont 2nd Pl 85; PA Poetry Soc Inc/Pegasus Awds 2nd 85; Jrnlsm.

ZDARKO, LAURIE; Northwestern HS; Girard, PA; (3); 10/120; Camera Clb; Drama Clb; Yrbk Phtg; Yrbk Stf; Sec Stu Cncl; Var Bsktbl; Powder Puff Ftbl; Hon Roll; Phy Thrpy.

ZDILLA, ROBYN; Belle Vernon Area HS; Belle Vernon, PA; (3); Art Clb; Nwsp Stf; Sec Sr Cls; Co-Capt Cheerleading; Powder Puff Ftbl; High Hon Roll; NHS; SR Committee & Med Interest Clb; Physcl Thrpy.

ZEAFLA, KATHLEEN; Liberty JR SR HS; Liberty, PA; (2); German Clb; Church Choir; School Musical; School Play; JV Bsktbl; Var Cheerleading; JV Var Sftbl; JV Trk; JV Vllybl; Hon Roll.

ZEARFOSS, JACKIE; Somerset SR HS; Listie, PA; (3); Cmnty Wkr; VICA; Chorus; Mst Imprvd Stu-Vo Tech 86-87; Cert Of Merit Annl All Schl Art Exhbt 85-86; Spec Olympc Brnz/Gld Mdls; Vet Asst.

ZEARLEY, JULIE; Geibel HS; Acme, PA; (3); Ski Clb; Stat Bsktbl; Stat Vllybl; Hon Roll; Foreign Lang.

ZECHMAN, NATALIE; Schuylkill Haven HS; Sch Haven, PA; (3); Am Leg Aux Girls St; Camera Clb; Science Clb; SADD; Chorus; Rep Frsh Cls; Rep Soph Cls; Rep Jr Cls; Rep Sr Cls; Rep Stu Cncl.

ZEEMAN, KIMBERLY; Northampton HS; Nazareth, PA; (4); 13/454; AFS; Drama Clb; VP Leo Clb; Library Aide; Teachers Aide; School Play; High Hon Roll; Lion Awd; NHS; Shippensburg U; Med Tech.

ZEGAR, CATHY; Swissvale HS; Swissvale, PA; (4); 5/197; Office Aide; Q&S; Spanish Clb; Y-Teens; Band; Mrchg Band; Yrbk Stf; High Hon Roll; NHS; Spnsh Comptn Hon Mntn 87; U Of Pittsburgh.

ZEGER, RONDA; Chambersburg Area SR HS; Marion, PA; (2); VP Church Yth Grp; Pep Clb; Chorus; Church Choir; Yrbk Stf; Hon Roll; Cnty Chrs Awd 86-87; Music.

ZEGLEN, ERIC; Bihsop Carroll HS; Belsano, PA; (3); 63/128; 4-H; Ski Clb; Trk; Comp Sci.

ZEHR, MARK; Rocky Grove HS; Cooperstown, PA; (3); Church Yth Grp; Hon Roll; Pastoral.

ZEIDERS, MELVIN; West Perry HS; Shermans Dale, PA; (4); 48/188; Spanish Clb; Hon Roll; Forgn Exch Stdnt To Lima Peru 86; Clarion U; Spnsh.

ZEIGLER, ANN M; Big Spring HS; Newville, PA; (3); Band; Chorus; Color Guard; Concert Band; Drill Tm; Jazz Band; Mrchg Band; School Musical; Powder Puff Ftbl; Voice Dem Awd; Choir Excel 87; Vrsty Ltr Band & Chorus 85-86; JR Mnth 87; Elem Educ.

ZEIGLER, BRIAN; Shikellamy HS; Sunbury, PA; (3); 54/319; Pres Frsh Cls; Pres Soph Cls; Pres Jr Cls; Pres Sr Cls; JV Ftbl; Hon Roll; Jr NHS; Spanish NHS; Law.

ZEIGLER, DAN; Knoch HS; Butler, PA; (2); German Clb; Letterman Clb; Rep Soph Cls; Stat Bsktbl; JV Ftbl; Hon Roll; Business.

ZEIGLER, EMILY; Hyndman Middle SR HS; Hyndman, PA; (3); 5/48; Church Yth Grp; Drama Clb; Girl Scts; Ski Clb; Spanish Clb; SADD; Band; Chorus; Church Choir; Concert Band; Lawyer.

ZEIGLER, JENNIFER; South Williamspord Area HS; S Williamsport, PA; (3); 4/111; Art Clb; Leo Clb; Sec Soph Cls; Sec Jr Cls; Trs Stu Cncl; Var L Cheerleading; Var L Trk; High Hon Roll.

ZEIGLER, RENEE; Greenwood HS; Millerstown, PA; (3); 12/72; Trs Teachers Aide; School Musical; Swing Chorus; Nwsp Ed-Chief; Rep Jr Cls; Trs Stu Cncl; Hon Roll; NCTE Awd; NHS; Acadmc All-Amer Awd 87; Psychlgy.

ZEIS, DOUG; Chambersburg Area SR HS; Chambersburg, PA; (3); Varsity Clb; Var L Bsbl; JV Bsktbl; Var L Ftbl; Im Vllybl; Hon Roll; All Str In Bsbl 87; Kystn St Games 87; Phy Ed.

ZEISE, PAUL; Penn Trafford HS; Irwin, PA; (3); Chess Clb; Church Yth Grp; Math Clb; Spanish Clb; Varsity Clb; Im Bsktbl; Var Diving; Im Ftbl; Var L Socr; Im Sftbl; 2nd Tm All Sect Sccr 86-87; Most Dedicatd Swmmr 84-85; MVP Sccr 86-87; Comp Sci.

ZEISLOFT, ERIC; Gettysburg HS; Orrtanna, PA; (2); Boy Scts; Church Yth Grp; JV Ftbl; Im Wt Lftg; Var Wrstlng; High Hon Roll; Hon Roll; Pres Acdmc Ftnss 86; Untd Brthrn Bible Qz Tm 2nd Pl Natl Compttn 85-87; Engrng.

ZEISLOFT, ERIC; Mc Dowell HS; Erie, PA; (4); 4/600; Art Clb; Cmnty Wkr; Drama Clb; German Clb; Model UN; School Musical; School Play; Cheerleading; Cit Awd; High Hon Roll; Univ Schlrs 1/2 Tuition Schlrshp Penn ST 87; PA ST U; Aerospc Engrng.

ZEITLER, JOSEPH; Venango Christian HS; Oil City, PA; (3); SADD; Hon Roll; Hahnsmann; Med.

ZEITLIN, STACEY; Episcopal Acad; Boyertown, PA; (2); Im Fld Hcky; Im Lcrss; Im Wt Lftg; Hon Roll; Law.

ZEKEK, JOE; Greensburg Salem SR HS; Greensburg, PA; (2); Boy Scts; Spanish Clb; High Hon Roll; Hon Roll; Pittsburgh U; Engrng.

ZELCZAK, JOHN; Monessen HS; Monessen, PA; (3); 15/115; Tennis; IUP; Engrng.

ZELENAK, ELAINE; Bishop Hafey HS; West Hazleton, PA; (3); Cmnty Wkr; Girl Scts; Key Clb; Service Clb; Spanish Clb; Orch; Sftbl; Hon Roll; Church Yth Grp; Teachers Aide; Northeastern PA Envrnmntl Cncl Stu Brd 86-87; Orchestra Clb Awd 87.

ZELENITZ, IVY; Allderdice HS; Pittsburgh, PA; (2); JA; SADD; Stu Cncl.

ZELINKA, DONNA; Hanover Area JR-SR HS; Ashley, PA; (3); Color Guard; Yrbk Stf; VP Sec Stu Cncl; Var Capt Cheerleading; Sec Jr NHS; NHS; WY Vly Yth Salute 87; Cmmnctns.

ZELINKA, LISA; Cowanesque Valley HS; Knoxville, PA; (4); Drama Clb; French Clb; German Clb; Ski Clb; School Musical; Hst Frsh Cls; Hst Sr Cls; Stu Cncl; JV Cheerleading; Trk; Essay Cmptn For Handicapped 87; Bus Admin.

ZELINKO, MARY; Shaler Area SR HS; Allison Pk, PA; (3); 87/486; Church Yth Grp; Band; Mrchg Band; Yrbk Stf; IN U Pennsylvania; English.

ZELINSKI, MARK; Lourdes Regional HS; Shamokin, PA; (3); 15/90; Spanish Clb; Nwsp Stf; Yrbk Stf; Im Bsktbl; Im Fld Hcky; Im Vllybl; Hon Roll; Acadc All-Amer 87; Hghst Accntng Avg 86-87; Bloomsburgh U; Accntng.

ZELINSKY, ANNA MARIE; Ringgold HS; Finleyville, PA; (3); French Clb; Office Aide; Rep Frsh Cls; Mgr(s); Hon Roll.

ZELKO, DAVIAN; Catasauqua HS; Catasauqua, PA; (4); 15/124; Drama Clb; Hosp Aide; Color Guard; School Musical; School Play; Stage Crew; High Hon Roll; Pres Acad Fit Awd 87; Lehigh Community Coll; Real Est.

ZELLEFROW, PAM; Union HS; Rimersburg, PA; (2); Pep Clb; SADD; VICA; Hon Roll; VP Frsh Cls; Culinary Arts.

ZELLER, ANDREW; Archbishop Ryan HS; Philadelphia, PA; (2); 84/349; Band; Drm & Bgl; Jazz Band; Mrchg Band; School Musical; School Play; Stage Crew; Bowling; Golf.

ZELLERS, PAMELA; Penn Trafford HS; Jeannette, PA; (4); 53/344; FBLA; Library Aide; SADD; VICA; Golf; High Hon Roll; Hon Roll; Ski Clb; Spanish Clb; Sftbl; Air Force; Hlth.

ZELLERS, TRICIA; Central Bucks East HS; Doylestown, PA; (3); Band; Concert Band; Drm Mjr(t); Jazz Band; Mrchg Band; Hon Roll; Early Childhd Educ.

ZELLMAN, HEATHER; Henderson HS; West Chester, PA; (3); 120/373; Hosp Aide; Bsktbl; Fld Hcky; Sftbl; High Hon Roll; Phys Ther.

ZELLNER, GRETCHEN E; Greensburg Central Catholic HS; Greensburg, PA; (3); Pep Clb; Ed Yrbk Stf; Var Powder Puff Ftbl; High Hon Roll; Hon Roll; Bradford Schl Of Bus; Rtl Mgmt.

ZELNICK, MICHAEL; Panther Valley HS; Lansford, PA; (1); 22/121; ROTC; Bsbl; Wt Lftg; Wrstlng; Hon Roll; MI U; Arch.

ZEMAN, DANA; North Hills HS; Pittsburgh, PA; (3); 33/493; Church Yth Grp; Drama Clb; JA; Keywanettes; School Play; Yrbk Stf; Rep Stu Cncl; Sftbl; High Hon Roll; NHS.

ZEMBA, DONNA M; Southmoreland HS; Mt Pleasant, PA; (4); Drama Clb; FFA; School Play; Powder Puff Ftbl; Sftbl; WCCC; Crt Rptng.

ZEMBA, PAM; Jefferson-Morgan HS; Rices Landing, PA; (3); 10/78; Exploring; Intnl Clb; Varsity Clb; VP Jr Cls; Var Cheerleading; High Hon Roll; Hon Roll.

ZEMBLE, DAVID; Harriton HS; Penn Valley, PA; (3); Math Tm; Concert Band; Mrchg Band; Nwsp Stf; Lit Mag; High Hon Roll; Jr NHS; Ntl Merit SF; Mtn Pctr Drctg.

ZEMBLE, MICHAEL S; Harriton HS; Narberth, PA; (4); 1/211; Pres Math Tm; Pres Jazz Band; Nwsp Sprt Ed; Rep Jr Cls; Var Crs Cntry; Var Swmmng; Var Trk; High Hon Roll; Intnl Clb; JA; Princpls Awd 84; Schlrshp Gov Schl 86; Intl Bus.

ZEMBOWER, JASON; Bedford HS; Bedford, PA; (3); Church Yth Grp; FFA; Band; Chorus; Nwsp Rptr; Nwsp Stf; Ftbl; Wt Lftg; Hon Roll; Penn State.

ZEMBRZUSKI, CAROL; Highlands SR HS; Natrona Hgts, PA; (3); 12/303; Pres Church Yth Grp; VP Exploring; Library Aide; Color Guard; Rep Jr Cls; NHS; NEDT Awd; Prfct Atten Awd; Intnl Clb; JA; PA Free Entrps Schlrshp 87; Bio.

ZEMENCIK, JEFFREY A; Schuylkill Haven Area HS; Schuylkill Haven, PA; (3); 19/103; Boy Scts; Exploring; FCA; German Clb; SADD; Bsktbl; Hon Roll; Forestry.

ZEMLIN, JENNIFER; Jenkintown HS; Jenkintown, PA; (2); Chorus; Pres Frsh Cls; Var JV Lcrss; French Hon Soc; Hon Roll; Jr NHS; NHS; Hbrw Natl Hnr Soc 85-86; Schlrshp Gratz Coll 87; Med.

ZENDT, HEIDI; Juniata HS; Mifflintown, PA; (3); Sec Church Yth Grp; 4-H; SADD; Chorus; Orch; Yrbk Ed-Chief; Stu Cncl; Var Fld Hcky; High Hon Roll; NHS; Eastern Mennonite Coll; Elem Ed.

ZEPP, STACY; South Western HS; Hanover, PA; (3); AFS; Church Yth Grp; Key Clb; Chorus; Color Guard; Mrchg Band; School Musical; Variety Show; Nwsp Stf; Rep Stu Cncl; Sundy Schl Teacher; Marine Bio.

ZERANCE, STACY; East Pennsboro Area HS; Enola, PA; (3); 34/191; Sec FBLA; Nwsp Rptr; Nwsp Stf; Rep Stu Cncl; High Hon Roll; Hon Roll; Schl Store Wrkr 86-87; Dist Rep 87; Acadmc Achvt Cert 86; Ofc Mgmt.

ZERANICK, CHRISTINE; Ambridge Area HS; Baden, PA; (2); German Clb; SADD; Band; Mrchg Band; School Musical; Off Stu Cncl; Var L Sftbl; JV Tennis; High Hon Roll; Prfct Atten Awd; Aerosp Engrng.

ZERANICK, DEBORAH; Ambridge Area HS; Baden, PA; (3); German Clb; SADD; Thesps; Band; Concert Band; Drill Tm; Mrchg Band; Orch; School Musical; Off Jr Cls; Bvr Cnty JR Miss Pgm 87; U Pittsburgh; Nrsng.

ZERANICK, DOREEN; Ambridge HS; Freedom, PA; (4); 56/250; French Clb; Pep Clb; Thesps; Chorus; Church Choir; Color Guard; Mrchg Band; School Musical; Variety Show; Pom Pon; Westminster Coll; Music.

ZERBE, DEBRA; Shikellamy HS; Sunbury, PA; (3); 16/380; Pres Church Yth Grp; Sec FBLA; Spanish Clb; Church Choir; Nwsp Ed-Chief; Hon Roll; Jr NHS; NHS; Spanish NHS; 1st Pl Clrk Typst I Cont FBLA 85; Sec Ed.

ZERBE, LAURAL; Lock Haven SR HS; Lock Haven, PA; (4); 86/242; Computer Clb; Pres FHA; Spanish Clb; SADD; Nwsp Rptr; Hon Roll; Prfct Atten Awd; Loggia Giosue Carducci 146 Sons Itly 2nd Awd 87; Wrk Merit Hm Ec Awd; Lock Haven U; Socl Wrk.

ZERBEY, SEAN; Pottstown SR HS; Pottstown, PA; (3); 44/155; French Clb; Key Clb; Ski Clb; Nwsp Stf; Yrbk Stf; Rep Jr Cls; Var Bsbl; Var L Golf; Kutztown U; Bus Mgmt.

ZERBY, JUDY; Cowanesque Valley HS; Knoxville, PA; (4); 1/77; 4-H; Letterman Clb; Band; Concert Band; Jazz Band; School Musical; Trk; Bausch & Lomb Sci Awd; DAR Awd; High Hon Roll; Stu Of Mnth 85-86 & 86-87; Mcrobio.

ZERCHER, MICHAEL; Cedar Crest HS; Mount Gretna, PA; (2); Quiz Bowl; JV Bsbl; JV Bsktbl; JV Socr; Var Trk; Hon Roll; Miltry Svc.

ZERFOSS, COLEEN; Somerset SR HS; Somerset, PA; (4); 53/242; Church Yth Grp; German Clb; Band; Concert Band; Mrchg Band; Trs Sr Cls; Stat Mgr(s); L Trk; JV Var Vllybl; Hon Roll; Pres Phys Fit Awd.

ZERNICK, SCOT; Northern Cambria HS; Barnesboro, PA; (3); #78 In Class; Church Yth Grp; Chorus; Rep Frsh Cls; Rep Soph Cls; Rep Jr Cls; Rep Stu Cncl; JV Bsktbl; Var JV Ftbl; Var JV Wt Lftg; Hon Roll; Elec Engr.

ZERO, KELLY; Gwynedd Mercy Acad; Harleysville, PA; (2); 4-H; Office Aide; Vllybl; Cit Awd; 4-H Awd; 4-H Exchange Stu; Teen Ambassadr; Toastmasters Intl; Teen Ldr; Rifle Club; Equestrienne; Villanova; Law.

ZESZUTEK, SUSAN; Canon Mc Millan HS; Cecil, PA; (4); 92/355; Sec French Clb; Office Aide; Science Clb; SADD; Varsity Clb; VP Stu Cncl; Cheerleading; Trk; High Hon Roll; U Of Pittsburgh; Nrsng.

ZETH, COREY; Nativity BVM HS; Minersville, PA; (2); 30/77; Aud/Vis; French Clb; Hon Roll; Hghst Achvt Mdrn Bio 86-87.

ZETTELMAYER, ERIK J; North Catholic HS; Pittsburgh, PA; (4); Am Leg Boys St; Pres Camera Clb; German Clb; JA; Rep Stu Cncl; L Var Ice Hcky; NHS; NEDT Awd; SAR Awd; U Of Dayton; Bus.

ZEWALK, MICHELLE E; North Allegheny SR HS; Pittsburgh, PA; (3); Church Yth Grp; DECA; JA; Teachers Aide; Stu Cncl; Vllybl; DECA-2ND Pl In Apparel & Accesories At Dist 86-87; Homecomng Queen Rep For Jr Girls 86-87; U Of Notre Dame; Bus Admn.

ZEWAN, AMY; Belle Vernon Area HS; Belle Vernon, PA; (3); Drama Clb; FBLA; Color Guard; Hon Roll; Hosp Aide; Pep Clb; Hmrm Offcr 86-87; Bus Adm.

ZIANCE, SCOTT; Altoona Area HS; Altoona, PA; (2); Church Yth Grp; Cmnty Wkr; Drama Clb; Math Tm; School Play; Off Jr Cls; JV Bsktbl; High Hon Roll; NEDT Awd; Pres Schlr; Bus.

ZIANTZ, LOUIS; Pittston Area SR HS; Dupont, PA; (4); 1/365; Computer Clb; Math Clb; Jr NHS; NHS; Ntl Merit Ltr.

ZICKAR, CAROL; Hickory HS; Hermitage, PA; (3); Sec Art Clb; Church Yth Grp; Drama Clb; Pres French Clb; Library Aide; Varsity Clb; School Play; Tennis; Vllybl; French Hon Soc; 1st Pl Mercer Cnty Water Color Art 85-86; 3rd Pl Shenango Vly Colord Pencl Drwng 86-87; Clarion; Bus.

ZIDAR, BERNIE; Seton-La Salle Regional HS; Pittsburgh, PA; (3); 18/237; Math Tm; Ski Clb; Var L Golf; High Hon Roll; NHS; Ntl Merit Ltr.

ZIDEK JR, GEORGE; Coudersport JR SR HS; Coudersport, PA; (3); School Play; Temple U; Pre-Med.

ZIEGLER, ANN; Grace Christian Schl; Myerstown, PA; (3); 5/20; Church Yth Grp; Chorus; Church Choir; School Play; Cheerleading; Fld Hcky; Sftbl; Hon Roll; Drama Clb; Band; Assn Chrstn Schls Intl Dstngshd Chrstn HS Stu 86-87; Amteur Athltc Union Of US 85-86; Bus.

ZIEGLER, GLEN; Hazleton HS; Drums, PA; (3); 14/450; Scholastic Bowl; Var Trk; French Hon Soc; Hon Roll; Engr.

ZIEGMANN, DAWN-MICHELLE; S Williamsport Area HS; Williamsport, PA; (4); 10/140; Key Clb; Band; Chorus; Jazz Band; Mrchg Band; School Musical; School Play; Nwsp Ed-Chief; High Hon Roll; NHS; Andy Brgsn Math Awd 87; WACC Schlrshp 87; Williamsport Area CC; Thrpy.

ZIELINSKI, DENINE; John S Fine SR HS; Nanticoke, PA; (2); Library Aide; Ski Clb; Yrbk Stf; JV Cheerleading; High Hon Roll; NHS; Teacher.

ZIEMBA, SHAWN; Bensalem HS; Bensalem, PA; (3); Office Aide; SADD; Varsity Clb; Var Capt Bsktbl; Fld Hcky; Sftbl; Trk; High Hon Roll; NHS; Sports Med.

ZIEVE, GLENN; Harriton HS; Gladwyne, PA; (3); 30/250; Hosp Aide; Math Tm; Science Clb; Spanish Clb; JV Socr; JV Tennis; Hon Roll; Ntl Merit Ltr; Cert For Vlntr Wrk At Bryn Mawr Hosp 87; Bio Sci.

ZIGERELLI, DONNA; Center Area HS; Monaca, PA; (3); Cmnty Wkr; Drama Clb; Library Aide; Chorus; School Musical; Nwsp Rptr; Yrbk Ed-Chief; Stu Cncl; Hon Roll; NHS; Ed.

ZIGNER, STEVEN; Shamokin Area HS; Shamokin, PA; (3); Science Clb; Ski Clb; Ftbl; Swmmng; Trk; Hon Roll.

ZIKESH, DANA L; North Allegheny HS; Allison Park, PA; (2); Hosp Aide; JA; Office Aide; Rep Frsh Cls; Im Cheerleading; Sftbl; Hon Roll; Chrldng 84-86; Hnr 84-85; MVP Sftbl Trnmnt 86; Miami U; Advrtsng.

ZIKESH, SHERRY A; North Allegheny SR HS; Allison Park, PA; (3); DECA; Rep Frsh Cls; Rep Soph Cls; Rep Jr Cls; Stu Cncl; JV Cheerleading; Awd-DECA 87; Pittsburgh U; Mrktng.

ZILKA, JENNIFER; Mon Valley Catholic HS; Monongahela, PA; (2); 7/76; JV Var Bsktbl; Var L Sftbl; JV Var Vllybl; Hon Roll; Prfct Atten Awd; Spanish NHS; Ntl Sci Olympd Awd 87; Dplma De Mrto-Spnsh Awd 86 & 87; CPA.

ZILLA, BRIAN; Bishop O Hara HS; Throop, PA; (3); 2/116; Pres Soph Cls; Off Jr Cls; Var Bsbl; Var Bsktbl; Var Ftbl; High Hon Roll; NHS; Schlrshp 83; All Star Awds Bsbl & Ftbl 85-86; MVP Awd Bsktbl Tournmnt Batting Title 85; Math.

ZILLA, RICK; Ford City HS; Ford City, PA; (3); #55 In Class; Boy Scts; Church Yth Grp; Var Ftbl; Wt Lftg; High Hon Roll; Hon Roll; Draftsman.

ZILLINSKI, JONATHAN; Upper Dauphin Area HS; Lykens, PA; (3); Concert Band; Lit Mag; Trs Stu Cncl; Var JV Bsktbl; Var JV Ftbl; Var L Trk; Hon Roll; Woodmen Wrld Amer Hstry Awd 87; Hstry.

ZIM, CHRISTOPHER; Wyoming Valley West HS; Swoyerville, PA; (4); Chess Clb; Political Wkr; Science Clb; Ski Clb; Lit Mag; JV Crs Cntry; Var Trk; Hon Roll; Technel Drftng Awd 87; Grphc Arts Awd 87; PA ST U; ; Mechncl Engrng.

ZIMMARO, DAVID; Immaculate Conception HS; Washington, PA; (3); 8/51; Stu Cncl; Var Bsktbl; Var Ftbl; Hon Roll; NHS; Ftbll Alumni Assn Schltc Achvt Awd 87; Ftbll Offnsv MVP 87; Schltc Achvt Awd Hlth 87; Norte Dame; Bus Admin.

ZIMMER, DIANA; Villa Maria Acad; Erie, PA; (3); French Clb; Model UN; PAVAS; Science Clb; Ski Clb; Stu Cncl; Tennis; Trk; Hon Roll; Schlrshp-PA Free Entrprs Wk-Lock Hvn U 87.

ZIMMER, LORI; Cumberland Valley HS; Camp Hill, PA; (3); Hosp Aide; Latin Clb; Orch; Hon Roll; Natl Lagn Arts Olympiad 1st Pl 85; Med Tech.

ZIMMERMAN, ALICIA; Villa Maria Acad; Erie, PA; (3); 4/168; Church Yth Grp; Science Clb; Service Clb; Cheerleading; Hon Roll; NHS.

ZIMMERMAN, AMIE; Lewisburg Area HS; Lewisburg, PA; (4); VP Sec Church Yth Grp; Hosp Aide; Pep Clb; Spanish Clb; Church Choir; Var Capt Bsktbl; Var Capt Sftbl; Hon Roll; Spanish NHS; Fml Athlt Yr 86-87frtry Stu Mnth 87; Lock Haven U; Bus.

ZIMMERMAN, ANDREA F; Altoona Area SR HS; Altoona, PA; (4); 1/718; VP German Clb; Key Clb; Math Clb; Math Tm; PAVAS; Pres Science Clb; Speech Tm; Mrchg Band; NHS; Val; Grmn Awd 84; Bio Chem Rsrch.

ZIMMERMAN, AUDREY; Pleasant Valley HS; Gilbert, PA; (3); Math Tm; SADD; Chorus; Nwsp Bus Mgr; Rep Stu Cncl; Var Trk; NHS; Prfct Atten Awd; Drama Clb; Office Aide; HOBY Fndntn Ldrshp Sem Rep 85-86; PA Stu Cncl Conf Rep 86-87; Ed.

ZIMMERMAN, BARBARA; Lancaster Catholic HS; Millersville, PA; (4); Church Yth Grp; Band; Concert Band; Capt Drill Tm; Mrchg Band; Bsktbl; Fld Hcky; Cit Awd; Charls W Eaby Memrl Awd Drll Tm, PA Cathlc Benefcl Leag Schlrshp 87; Mansfield U; Spcl Ed.

ZIMMERMAN, BRENDA; Punxsutawney Area HS; Punxsutawney, PA; (4); 22/245; Church Yth Grp; French Clb; Math Tm; Sec Band; Sec Concert Band; Sec Mrchg Band; Variety Show; Yrbk Stf; Hon Roll; Stu Of Mnth 84-85; PA ST U; Bus Admin.

ZIMMERMAN, CHRISTIAN; Pine Grove Area HS; Pine Grove, PA; (2); 37/175; Church Yth Grp; 4-H; German Clb; SADD; Chorus; Nwsp Rptr; Nwsp Stf; Lit Mag; Prfct Atten Awd; Awd Schyull Wrtrs Litry Magzne 87; IN U Of PA; Comp Sci.

ZIMMERMAN, CONNIE; Millersburg Area HS; Millersburg, PA; (4); 2/77; Am Leg Aux Girls St; Concert Band; Mrchg Band; Yrbk Bus Mgr; French Hon Soc; 4-H Awd; High Hon Roll; NHS; Cntry III Ldrshp Schlrshp 86.

ZIMMERMAN, DAPHNE; Cocalico HS; Stevens, PA; (4); 7/174; Church Yth Grp; Hst FBLA; FTA; Chorus; JV Tennis; High Hon Roll; Lion Awd; NHS; Prfct Atten Awd; Cocalico Educ Asscn Schlrshp; Messiah Coll; Elem Educ.

ZIMMERMAN, DAVID; Archbishop Wood HS For Boys; Hatboro, PA; (4); 25/271; Im Bsktbl; Im JV Ftbl; Wt Lftg; High Hon Roll; Hon Roll; NHS; Bus Educ Awd 87; Acctng Awd 86; Bloomsburg U; Bus.

ZIMMERMAN, DONNA; Conestoga Valley HS; Leola, PA; (4); 5/243; Sec Church Yth Grp; Pres Chorus; Capt Mrchg Band; School Play; Gym; Tennis; DAR Awd; High Hon Roll; VP NHS; Pres Schlr; Robert C Byrd Natl Hnrs Schlrshp 87; Ephrata Elks Schlrshp 87; Delta Kappa Gamma Schlrshp 87; Bloomsburg U; Elem Educ.

ZIMMERMAN, ERIC; Brookville Area HS; Brookville, PA; (3); Hon Roll; Congrsnl Yth Ldrshp Cncl 87; Aviation Engr.

ZIMMERMAN, HEIDI; Germantown Acad; Collegeville, PA; (4); Service Clb; Spanish Clb; Orch; Nwsp Rptr; Nwsp Stf; JV Cheerleading; JV Lcrss; JV Swmmng; Im Vllybl; NCTE Awd; 11th Grade Alumni Prize In Engl 86.

ZIMMERMAN, JENNIFER; Geibel HS; Scottdale, PA; (3); Church Yth Grp; French Clb; Ski Clb; Vllybl; French Hon Soc; High Hon Roll; NHS; Prfct Atten Awd; PA ST U; Bus.

ZIMMERMAN, JENNIFER; Schuylkill Haven Area HS; Sch Haven, PA; (2); FNA; German Clb; Pep Clb; Science Clb; SADD; Chorus; Bsktbl; Cheerleading; Hon Roll; Pres Schlr; Nrsng.

ZIMMERMAN, JILL; Penn Manor HS; Willow St, PA; (3); Exploring; Nwsp Stf; Rep Stu Cncl; JV Bsktbl; JV Fld Hcky; Mgr(s); Im Powder Puff Ftbl; JV Sftbl; Im Vllybl; Drg Cnslng.

ZIMMERMAN, JIM; Johnsonburg Area HS; Wilcox, PA; (4); Pres FFA; Varsity Clb; Ftbl; Marines.

ZIMMERMAN, JODI; Warren Area HS; Russell, PA; (3); Office Aide; Ski Clb; Stu Cncl; Score Keeper; Hon Roll; NHS.

ZIMMERMAN, JON; Parkland HS; Allentown, PA; (3); 20/481; Var Bsbl; Var Bsktbl; JV Ftbl; High Hon Roll; Hon Roll; NHS; Prfct Atten Awd; Lehigh Valley League All-Star Bsbll 87.

ZIMMERMAN, JUSTIN L; Big Spring HS; Shippensburg, PA; (3); 31/250; Trs Church Yth Grp; Capt Quiz Bowl; Mrchg Band; School Musical; Hst Stu Cncl; JV Trk; NHS; Rotary Awd; Boy Scts; Band; Hugh O Brian Yth Ambassador 86; Pres Awd Math & Sci 87; MA Inst Of Tech; Mech Engrng.

ZIMMERMAN, KRISTEN; Donegal HS; Mount Joy, PA; (2); Church Yth Grp; Band; Color Guard; Concert Band; Jazz Band; Mrchg Band; Bsktbl; Mgr(s); Score Keeper; Hon Roll; Bus.

ZIMMERMAN, LE ANN; Berlin Brothers Valley HS; Berlin, PA; (2); 24/72; Church Yth Grp; Library Aide; Spanish Clb; SADD; Band; Concert Band; Mrchg Band; Hon Roll; Pres Acadc Ftns Awd 85-86; Penn ST.

ZIMMERMAN, LESLIE; Everett Area HS; Everett, PA; (2); Church Yth Grp; Spanish Clb; Band; Stu Cncl; Var Cheerleading; Cit Awd; High Hon Roll; Ntl Merit Ltr.

ZIMMERMAN, LISA; Pine Grove Area HS; Pine Grove, PA; (3); Am Leg Aux Girls St; Varsity Clb; Yrbk Stf; Bsktbl; Mgr(s); Sftbl; Hon Roll; Prfct Atten Awd; Engl, French, Art Awds 87; Science.

ZIMMERMAN, MARGARET; Marion Catholic HS; Morea, PA; (3); 33/104; Civic Clb; Pep Clb; Capt Color Guard; School Play; Variety Show; Yrbk Stf; Stat Bsktbl; Stat Sftbl; Nrsng.

ZIMMERMAN, MATTHEW; Archbishop Ryan HS For Boys; Philadelphia, PA; (2); 36/352; Boy Scts; German Clb; Stage Crew; Yrbk Stf; Var Mgr(s); Hon Roll; Temple U; Comm.

ZIMMERMAN, MATTHEW; Brandywine HS; Mertztown, PA; (2); Golf; Tennis; High Hon Roll; NHS.

ZIMMERMAN, MICHELE; Pine Grove Area HS; Pine Grove, PA; (3); Trs Church Yth Grp; Concert Band; Capt Mrchg Band; Ed Yrbk Stf; Capt Twrlr; Hon Roll; NHS; Acctng.

ZIMMERMAN, MISSY; Northern Lebanon HS; Annville, PA; (2); 17/200; Trs Church Yth Grp; Hosp Aide; SADD; Band; Rep Chorus; Color Guard; Concert Band; Mrchg Band; School Musical; Hon Roll; Medcl.

ZIMMERMAN, NICOLE; Eastern Lebanon HS; Myerstown, PA; (2); 1/175; Library Aide; Chorus; Stu Cncl; Hon Roll; Ntl Sci Merit Awd 86; PA ST U; Zlgy.

ZIMMERMAN, RACHEL; Hempfield HS; Lancaster, PA; (4); 26/464; Exploring; Girl Scts; Hosp Aide; Red Cross Aide; Service Clb; Mrchg Band; Orch; School Musical; High Hon Roll; Hon Roll; All Amrcn Yth Hnr Mscn; Elizabeth Coll; Ec.

ZIMMERMAN, ROBERT E; Lewistown Area HS; Lewistown, PA; (3); French Clb; Key Clb; Ski Clb; Off Frsh Cls; Off Soph Cls; Off Jr Cls; Var Ftbl; Swmmng; Var Wt Lftg; High Hon Roll; Acad Excllnc Awd 85-86; Aviation.

ZIMMERMAN, SHARON; Ephrata SR HS; Reinholds, PA; (3); Sec Church Yth Grp; VP FFA; Library Aide; Yrbk Stf; High Hon Roll; Hon Roll; NHS, Gld Mdl-Natl FFA Dry Fds Cont 85; Ag.

ZIMMERMAN, SHAWN; Eastern Lebanon County HS; Robesonia, PA; (3); Chess Clb; Hon Roll; NHS; Arspc Engrng.

ZIMMERMAN, STEFANIE; Kennard-Dale HS; Fawn Grove, PA; (2); German Clb; Chorus; Church Choir; Sec Frsh Cls; Trs Soph Cls; Rep Stu Cncl; JV Capt Fld Hcky; High Hon Roll; Hon Roll; NEDT Awd; Phys Ther.

ZIMMERMAN, STEPHEN; Cathedral Preparatory Schl; Erie, PA; (4); 6/212; Pres Debate Tm; Speech Tm; Im Bsktbl; Im Vllybl; PA ST U; Bus.

ZIMMERMAN, SUSAN; Fleetwood HS; Fleetwood, PA; (3); Ski Clb; Color Guard; Mrchg Band; VP Frsh Cls; VP Soph Cls; Trs Stu Cncl; Var L Cheerleading; Var Fld Hcky; Hon Roll; York Coll; Nrsg.

ZIMMERMAN, TAMMY; Lewiston Area HS; Lewistown, PA; (2); AFS; German Clb; Yrbk Ed-Chief; Yrbk Rptr; Yrbk Stf; High Hon Roll; NHS; VP Church Yth Grp; Acad Lttr 85-87; Scndry Ed.

ZIMMERMAN, TERRI; Northern Bedford HS; Hopewell, PA; (3); 18/101; Church Yth Grp; SADD; Varsity Clb; Band; Chorus; Trs Jr Cls; Capt Var Bsktbl; L Var Sftbl; L Var Vllybl; Hon Roll; Socl Wrk.

ZIMMERMAN, TRAVIS L; Chambersburg Area SR HS; Fayetteville, PA; (3); 22/697; Am Leg Boys St; Computer Clb; Band; Chorus; Jazz Band; Stu Cncl; Var L Socr; High Hon Roll; SAR Awd; Boy Scts; Eagle Scouta Awd 85; Trp Sct Of Yr 85; U S Air Frc Acad; Avionics.

ZIMMERMAN, TRELL; Lehighton Area HS; Lehighton, PA; (1).

ZIMMERMAN, TRICIA; Everett Area HS; Everett, PA; (2); 19/150; Church Yth Grp; Library Aide; Spanish Clb; Jazz Band; Mrchg Band; Pep Band; Yrbk Phtg; Stu Cncl; Trk; Prfct Atten Awd; Educ.

ZINGARETTI, DAVID; Coughlin HS; Wilkes-Barre, PA; (3); 114/374; Var Bsbl; Var Bsktbl; Hon Roll; Jr NHS; Prfct Atten Awd; MVP Bsktbl 85; Mst Imprvd Bsbl 87; Bus.

ZINK, MELISSA L; William Penn SR HS; York, PA; (3); 58/450; Debate Tm; Pres Pep Clb; Thesps; Band; Chorus; Concert Band; Mrchg Band; School Musical; School Play; Sec Frsh Cls; Hstry Clb Sec 86-87.

ZINN, TERRI; Meyersdale Area HS; Meyersdale, PA; (3); Church Yth Grp; French Clb; Band; Chorus; Concert Band; Mrchg Band; Yrbk Phtg; Yrbk Stf; Stat Bsktbl; Stat Trk; Psych.

ZINNI, STEPHANIE; Interboro HS; Glenolden, PA; (3); Sec French Clb; Rep Soph Cls; Rep Jr Cls; JV Cheerleading; JV Fld Hcky; NHS; Nrsng.

ZINSKI, LYNNE RU; Fairview HS; Fairview, PA; (4); 74/154; Cmnty Wkr; Church Yth Grp; Library Aide; Office Aide; Spanish Clb; Teachers Aide; Chorus; Mgr(s); Trk; Hon Roll; Hnr Rl; St Vincent Schl/Nrsg; Nrsg.

ZINSKI, RONALD; Chartiers Valley HS; Carnegie, PA; (3); Church Yth Grp; French Clb; Ski Clb; Im JV Bsktbl; Var L Tennis; Im Vllybl; Hon Roll; NHS; Ntl Merit SF; Engrng.

ZINZ, CHRIS; Rocky Grove JR SR HS; Franklin, PA; (3); Church Yth Grp; German Clb; Hosp Aide; SADD; Pep Band; JV Bsktbl; 4-H Awd; Hon Roll; Med.

ZIOGAS, ANTONIA; Elizabethtown Area HS; Elizabethtown, PA; (4); Church Yth Grp; Model UN; Yrbk Bus Mgr; Yrbk Ed-Chief; Yrbk Stf; Im Fld Hcky; Mgr(s); JV Trk; NHS; Grl Mnth 86-87fEAEA Schlrshp 87fdist Ahepa Schlrshp 87; Millersville U; Engl.

ZIOLKOWSKI, KRISTINE; Belle Vernon Area HS; Belle Vernon, PA; (3); Sec FBLA; Ski Clb; Spanish Clb; High Hon Roll; NHS.

ZIPFEL, BRENDA; Avon Grove HS; New London, PA; (3); SADD; Coach Actv; Capt Var Fld Hcky; Var JV Sftbl; Hon Roll; All Stars Fld Hcky 86; Mst Imprvd Coll Prep Engl 87; Hghst Cls Avg AMC 86; Mitchell; Marine Sci.

ZIPPERI, DAVID; Cathedral Preparatory HS; Erie, PA; (3); 45/193; Boy Scts; Chess Clb; Hon Roll; Times Publishing Co Newscarrier Of Wk Achvmnt Awd 86; Engrng.

ZIRILLI, CHARLES; St John Neumann HS; Philadelphia, PA; (3); 46/352; Boy Scts; Exploring; Band; Concert Band; Pep Band; Penn ST; Comp Techn.

ZIRKLE, RANDY; Beth-Center SR HS; Richeyville, PA; (3); Art Clb; Church Yth Grp; Drama Clb; Ski Clb; Spanish Clb; Band; Church Choir; Concert Band; Jazz Band; Mrchg Band; WV U.

ZIRKLE, ROBERT S; Thomas Jefferson HS; Clairton, PA; (3); 25/255; Rep Am Leg Boys St; Boy Scts; Cmnty Wkr; Exploring; Cit Awd; Hon Roll; NHS; Rotary Awd; Resltn No 46 86; Alleghny Cnty Cert Achvt 86; US Cong Awd Merit 86; Chem Engrng.

ZITKUS, GEORGEANN; Shenandoah Valley HS; Shenandoah, PA; (3); 7/79; Pep Clb; Chorus; Flag Corp; Nwsp Stf; Rep Frsh Cls; Stu Cncl; Var JV Cheerleading; Gym; Sftbl; NHS; Acad All Amer 87.

ZITO, MATT; Fairview HS; Fairview, PA; (3); 32/171; Spanish Clb; VP Frsh Cls; VP Soph Cls; VP Jr Cls; VP Stu Cncl; Bsbl; Bsktbl; Ftbl; Golf; Tennis; Stud Forum NW PA Pres 87; Cngrssnl Ldrshp Yth Cncl 87; Bus.

ZITTRAIN, JONATHAN L; Shady Side Acad; Pittsburgh, PA; (4); 1/125; Cmnty Wkr; Computer Clb; Nwsp Ed-Chief; High Hon Roll; Ntl Merit SF; Aud/Vis; Debate Tm; Hosp Aide; Math Tm; Radio Clb; Gust Spkr Boston Comp Soc TI Fair, Mnthly Colmnst Comp Shppr Magz, Forum Admn 86.

ZIUS, ROBERT M; Hazleton HS; Hazleton, PA; (3); Leo Clb; Orch; High Hon Roll; Intl Frgn Lang Awd 87; Cert Merit Wrld Cltr I 85.

ZIVITZ, ANDREW; Harriton HS; Penn Valley, PA; (3); SADD; Temple Yth Grp; Var Bsbl; Hon Roll; NHS; Straight A 87.

ZIYAD, CHERELLE; Clara Muhammad HS; Philadelphia, PA; (3); Cmnty Wkr; Dance Clb; Capt Drill Tm; School Play; Nwsp Rptr; Yrbk Rptr; Capt Cheerleading; Swmmng; Trk; Cit Awd; Cert Merit 86; West Chester Coll; CPA.

ZLOCHOWER, ADENA; Yeshira Achei Tmimmim HS; Pittsburgh, PA; (3); 1/8; Art Clb; Cmnty Wkr; Dance Clb; Drama Clb; FHA; School Musical; Ed Lit Mag; Trs Jr Cls; Cit Awd; U Of Pittsburgh; Psych.

ZMICH, KURT; B Reed Henderson HS; W Chester, PA; (4); 22/350; Art Clb; Boy Scts; Lit Mag; JV Bsbl; Var Lcrss; High Hon Roll; Hon Roll; NHS; Ntl Merit SF; Spanish NHS; Cngrssnl Yth Ldrshp Cncl Washington DC 87; Awd Acadmc Excllnc W Chester Area Schl Dist 86 & 87; VA Polytechnic Inst; Engrng.

ZMITROVICH, JOE; Weatherly HS; Hazleton, PA; (3); #4 In Class; Church Yth Grp; Pep Clb; Teachers Aide; Im Bsktbl; Var L Crs Cntry; Var L Trk; Im Wt Lftg; Hon Roll; Engrng.

ZOBA, TRICIA A; Marian HS; Mc Adoo, PA; (4); 3/109; Church Yth Grp; Chorus; Color Guard; Drill Tm; School Play; French Hon Soc; High Hon Roll; Lion Awd; NHS; Allentown Coll; Bio.

ZOCK, LESLIE; Bishop Carroll HS; Portage, PA; (4); 11/107; Ski Clb; Stage Crew; Yrbk Stf; Sec Soph Cls; Sec Jr Cls; Sec Sr Cls; JV Cheerleading; JV Var Vllybl; Trs Pres NHS; German Essay Cntst Wnnr 86; Penn ST; Wildlife Bio.

ZODA, MARLO; Plymouth Whitemarsh HS; Plymouth Mtg, PA; (4); Pep Clb; Ed Nwsp Phtg; Off Frsh Cls; Off Soph Cls; Off Jr Cls; Off Sr Cls; Hon Roll; PA ST; Cmmnctns.

ZODEL, ROYCE H; Allentown Central Catholic HS; Whitehall, PA; (3); Boy Scts; Chorus; Comp Sci.

ZOGLIO, MATHEW; Archbishop Wood High Schl For Boys; Warminster, PA; (3); 35/231; Church Yth Grp; German Clb; VP Stu Cncl; Capt Ftbl; L Trk; Hon Roll; NHS; 2nd Pl Cnty Sci Fair 87; Hon Ment Vly Sci Fair 87; Civil Engr.

ZOHNER, SHELLY; Hamburg Area HS; Shoemakersvl, PA; (3); VP FBLA; Rep German Clb; Library Aide; Ski Clb; Yrbk Phtg; Sec Sr Cls; Cheerleading; Trk; Hon Roll; NHS; German II Academic Awd 85-86; German III Academic Awd 86-87.

ZOKA, KRISTA J; Bishop Hoban HS; Kingston, PA; (3); 23/203; Computer Clb; Mu Alpha Theta; Chorus; Rep Frsh Cls; Rep Soph Cls; Rep Jr Cls; VP Sr Cls; JV Var Bsktbl; Hon Roll; NHS; Phys Thrpy.

ZOLA, JAMES; Hazleton HS; Hazleton, PA; (3); 48/450; Church Yth Grp; Leo Clb; Scholastic Bowl; High Hon Roll; PA ST U; Sci.

ZOLKOWSKI, MARK J; Hampton HS; Gibsonia, PA; (3); French Clb; School Musical; Stage Crew; Nwsp Stf; Yrbk Stf; Rep Jr Cls; Rep Sr Cls; Bowling; Hon Roll; Hnr Rl 85-87; Stu Bdy Rep 87-88; Frnch Clb 86-88; Jrnlsm.

ZOLL, KATHLEEN; Gwynedd Mercy Acad; Oreland, PA; (2); Hon Roll; Schlrshp Gwynedd Mercy & MT ST Joseph Acads 85; Art.

ZOLL, SUSAN; Plymouth Whitemarsh HS; Plymouth Mtg, PA; (3); Swmmng; Vllybl; High Hon Roll; Hon Roll; Jr NHS.

ZOMAK, DEBORA A; Canon-Mc Millan HS; Cecil, PA; (4); 31/371; Varsity Clb; Band; Drill Tm; Var Bsktbl; Var Sftbl; High Hon Roll; NHS; Natl Physcl Edu Awd 87; Grove City Coll; Math.

ZONA, GERALD; New Castle SR HS; New Castle, PA; (4); 24/230; Church Yth Grp; Hon Roll; Prsdntl Awd 87; PA League Of Ctys Essy Cntst 87; Outdrs & Italn Club; Ntl Hnr Soc; Penn ST U; Bio.

ZONA, JOSHUA; New Castle HS; New Castle, PA; (3); 19/320; SADD; Jazz Band; Mrchg Band; Pep Band; Symp Band; High Hon Roll; Hon Roll; U Of MI; Music.

ZONIES, MELISSA; Northeast HS; Philadelphia, PA; (4); 80/600; Red Cross Aide; Hon Roll; NHS; SR Awd Srvc Schl 86-87; Drexel U; Bus Adm.

ZONTS, JOSEPH; Purchase Line HS; Marion Ctr, PA; (2); Church Yth Grp; French Clb; Spanish Clb; JV Ftbl; Wt Lftg; US Air Force; Air Trfc Cntrl.

ZOOK, JOEL; Elizabethtown Area HS; Elizabethtown, PA; (3); Boys Clb Am; Church Yth Grp; Varsity Clb; Bsbl; Bsktbl; Ftbl; Wt Lftg; Pres Physcl Ftns & Cntry 21 Acctng Awds 87; Acctng.

ZOOK, JUDY CHRISTINE; Oxford HS; Oxford, PA; (4); 28/167; Church Yth Grp; Chorus; Nwsp Stf; Trs Yrbk Stf; Stu Cncl; Var Crs Cntry; JV Fld Hcky; Var Trk; Vllybl; Hon Roll; Ministerium Schlrshp 87; Mc Mullen Schlrshp 87; Taylor U; Scl Wrk.

ZOOK, LINDA; Easter Lebanon County HS; Myerstown, PA; (3); Pres FFA; Quiz Bowl; JV Score Keeper; JV Sftbl; Hon Roll; Kiwanis Awd; NHS; Band; Concert Band; Mrchg Band; De Kalb Awd Vocatnl Ag 86-87; Top Stu FFA 86-87; DE Vly Coll; Food Indus.

ZOOK, STEVE; Pequed Valley HS; Gap, PA; (3); Chorus; Cmmnctns.

ZOOLALIAN, CATHARINE M; H S For Creative & Performing Arts; Philadelphia, PA; (4); 15/121; Nwsp Stf; Hon Roll; Hnr Roll Merit 86-87; Teamsters Scholar 87; Trenton ST Coll; Clin Psych.

ZORE, CATHY; St Marys Area HS; Saint Marys, PA; (4); Church Yth Grp; Cmnty Wkr; Girl Scts; Hosp Aide; Spanish Clb; Hon Roll; Grl Sct Gld Awd 85; St Vincent Coll; Chld Psych.

ZORETICH, MARIA; Chester HS; Chester, PA; (4); FBLA; Hon Roll; FBLA Mst Outstndng Typst, & Acdmc Excllnc Lttr 86-87; Math Awd 4.0 Av 85-86; Lgl Sec.

ZORGER, ROBERT J; Neshaminy HS; Oakford, PA; (3); Aud/Vis; Band; Chorus; Concert Band; Mrchg Band; Orch; Symp Band; Hon Roll; Pernco Tech Inst; Elec.

ZOSH, WENDY; Lake-Lehman HS; Dallas, PA; (2); Rep Soph Cls; Off Stu Cncl; L Cheerleading; JV Fld Hcky; Hon Roll; NEDT Awd; MD Coll; Marine Bio.

ZOTOS, JASON; Bensalen HS; Bensalem, PA; (2); Yrbk Stf; JV Var Tennis; Finance.

ZOTOS, PETER; Bensalem HS; Bensalem, PA; (4); 47/475; Var JV Tennis; High Hon Roll; Hon Roll; Ntl Merit SF; Pres Schlr; Courtesy Awd; George Washington U; Intl Bus.

ZROWKA, KENNETH; Carbondale Area JR SR HS; Simpson, PA; (4); FBLA; Scholastic Bowl; Ski Clb; Spanish Clb; Chorus; Yrbk Phtg; Bsktbl; Crs Cntry; Trk; NHS; PA Free Enterprise Week 85; Penn ST; Bus.

ZUBRIS, GARY; Marian HS; Tamaqua, PA; (3); 26/104; Church Yth Grp; Ski Clb; Stage Crew; Rep Frsh Cls; Pres Sr Cls; Pres Stu Cncl; JV Var Bsbl; JV Ftbl; Tennis; Hon Roll; Penn ST; Engr.

ZUBRITSKI, TORI; John S Fine HS; Wanamie, PA; (4); 18/256; Varsity Clb; Var Capt Bsktbl; Var Sftbl; Var Tennis; High Hon Roll; NHS; Church Yth Grp; Yrbk Stf; Physcl Thrpy.

ZUCCARO, MICHELLE; Aliquippa JR-SR HS; Aliquippa, PA; (3); French Clb; Math Tm; Band; Mrchg Band; Pep Band; Yrbk Stf; Stat Wrstlng; Hon Roll.

ZUCHELLI, MARY; North Star HS; Boswell, PA; (2); #19 In Class; Pres Church Yth Grp; FCA; SADD; Yrbk Stf; Sec Frsh Cls; Trs Soph Cls; Bsktbl; Mat Maids; Score Keeper; Hon Roll; U Pittsburgh; Dnstry.

ZUCOSKY, HELEN ANNE; Cardinal Brennan HS; Girardville, PA; (3); Library Aide; Band; Chorus; Church Choir; Concert Band; Mrchg Band; School Musical; Yrbk Stf; Engl, Chem & Theo Awds; Hotel/Rest Mgt.

ZUCZEK, KAREN; Bishop O Hara HS; Dickson City, PA; (3); 2/102; French Clb; Latin Clb; Nwsp Ed-Chief; Rep Stu Cncl; High Hon Roll; NHS; Journlsm.

ZUDER, JOSHUA; Pocono Mountain HS; Swiftwater, PA; (2); Camera Clb; Chess Clb; Var Golf; Hon Roll; Prfct Atten Awd; Golf Pro.

ZUG, IRENE; Solanco SR HS; Peach Bottom, PA; (3); 8/273; Pres 4-H; Concert Band; Mrchg Band; School Musical; L Mgr(s); Cit Awd; High Hon Roll; NHS; Prfct Atten Awd; Solance Schlr Music 87; Math Educ.

ZUKAS, JOHN; Marian Catholic HS; Barnesville, PA; (3); 10/104; Aud/Vis; Math Clb; Ski Clb; Var JV Ftbl; L Trk; Hon Roll; Algebra II Awd 86; Hnrbl Mntn Kings Coll Spnsh Cntst 86.

ZUKOSKY, AMY; Wyoming Valley West HS; Kinston, PA; (3); Cmnty Wkr; Hosp Aide; Key Clb; Stu Cncl; Hon Roll; NHS; Sclstc Arts Awd Gold Key Fnlst 85-86; Pre-Law.

ZUKOWSKI, CHRISTINE; Harbor Creek HS; Erie, PA; (4); 3/224; SADD; Teachers Aide; Var Capt Bsktbl; Sftbl; High Hon Roll; NHS; Church Yth Grp; Model UN; Office Aide; Political Wkr; Full Tuition Acad Scholar 87; Bsktbl Athltc Scholar 87; Gannon U; Chem.

ZUKOWSKI, CYNDI; Cardinal Brennan HS; Shenandoah, PA; (3); 20/58; Library Aide; NFL; Chorus; Concert Band; Nwsp Stf; Yrbk Stf; Off Stu Cncl; Hon Roll; NHS; Cls Princess-Homcmng 85; Bloomsburg U; Child Educ.

ZUKOWSKI, WAYNE; Mercyhurst Prep Schl; Erie, PA; (2); 71/202; Band; Chorus; Concert Band; School Musical; School Play; Bowling; Creatve Arts Schrlhsp Music 85-86.

ZULICK, CYNDI; Butler SR HS; Butler, PA; (4); 47/755; Trs Church Yth Grp; Spanish Clb; SADD; Chorus; L Nwsp Rptr; Hon Roll; L Jr NHS; NHS; Aqttes-Lttrd-Chrgrphr 85-87; Ushrs Clb-Lttrd 86-87; Rnbws-Wrthy Advsr 85-86; Butler CC; Physcl Thrpy.

ZULICK, TRENT; Sch Haven HS; Sch Haven, PA; (2); 20/101; Boy Scts; Band; Mrchg Band; Stage Crew; Var Wrstlng; Hon Roll; Army.

ZUMBRUM, LORI; Spring Grove SR HS; York, PA; (3); 21/305; Pres 4-H; Chorus; Orch; School Musical; Stu Cncl; Var Bsktbl; L Tennis; 4-H Awd; Hon Roll; NHS; Tnns Ltrs 85-87; Natl Hnr Soc Hnr Rl.

ZUNDEL, EVON; William Allen HS; Allentown, PA; (3); Church Yth Grp; Spanish Clb; Chorus; Church Choir; Concert Band; Mrchg Band; High Hon Roll; Hon Roll; Jr NHS; NHS; Kutztown U; Spn.

ZUPAN, KATHY; Kennedy Christian HS; Hermitage, PA; (2); 22/96; Dance Clb; Latin Clb; Hon Roll; X-Ray Tech.

ZUPAN, MATTHEW; Duquesne HS; Duquesne, PA; (3); French Clb; Scholastic Bowl; Band; Mrchg Band; Nwsp Sprt Ed; Stu Cncl; High Hon Roll; Hon Roll; NHS; Crmnl Jstc.

ZUPKO, BRIAN; Bishop O Reilly HS; Kingston, PA; (2); Boy Scts; Computer Clb; Ski Clb; SADD; Stage Crew; JV Bsktbl; Var Ftbl; Var Socr; Im Wt Lftg; Cit Awd; BMX Rcr Yr 86; Villanova; Bio.

ZUPON, DIANE; Penn Cambria HS; Dysart, PA; (3); 36/209; Spanish Clb; SADD; Concert Band; Mrchg Band; Hon Roll; NHS.

ZUPSIC, CHRIS; Center SR HS; Aliquippa, PA; (2); Computer Clb; Latin Clb; Varsity Clb; Capt Bowling; L Trk; High Hon Roll; Hon Roll; Latin Cert 86-87; Bwlng Champs 85-87; MAC Bwlng Tourn 86-87.

ZUPSIC, DAVID; Center HS; Monaca, PA; (2); Spanish Clb; Concert Band; JV Bsbl; Im Bsktbl; Im Bowling; Var Ftbl; Wt Lftg; Hon Roll.

ZUPSIC, JANICE; Center Area HS; Monaca, PA; (3); Spanish Clb; Concert Band; Drill Tm; Mrchg Band; School Musical; Stage Crew; Rep Stu Cncl; Powder Puff Ftbl; Sftbl; Clarion U; Elem Ed.

ZURASKY, JULIA; Wilmington Area HS; Pulaski, PA; (3); 25/114; Drama Clb; Spanish Clb; Teachers Aide; Bsktbl; Sftbl; Trk; Vllybl; Bradford Schl Of Bus; Accntng.

ZURAT, KELLY; Bradford Area HS; Bradford, PA; (4); 21/273; Pep Clb; Ski Clb; Chorus; Stu Cncl; Var L Tennis; Im Vllybl; High Hon Roll; Hon Roll; NHS; Edinboro Coll.

ZURICK, DELLA; York Catholic HS; Manchester, PA; (2); 9/135; JA; Color Guard; Im JV Bsktbl; High Hon Roll; Hon Roll; Spch Festvl Semifnlst 87; Law.

ZURINSKY, CHRISTOPHER L; Northwestern HS; E Springfield, PA; (3); 33/144; Science Clb; Band; Concert Band; Jazz Band; Mrchg Band; Pep Band; School Play; Var L Trk; Tri-M 85-88; Dist & Rgnl Band 85-88; Cnty & Dist Trck 87-88.

ZUZELSKI JR, LOUIS A; James M Coughlin HS; Wilkes Barre, PA; (3); Drama Clb; French Clb; Key Clb; School Musical; School Play; Hon Roll; Jr NHS; NEDT Awd; Pres Acad Ftns Awd 85; Cnmtgrphy.

ZVOCH, KEITH; Steel Valley HS; Munhall, PA; (3); 32/205; Nwsp Stf; Var Ice Hcky; JV Vllybl; Hon Roll; W PA Acad All Star Team Ice Hockey 87.

ZVONAR, KRISTIN; Center HS; Monaca, PA; (3); Church Yth Grp; Spanish Clb; Varsity Clb; Chorus; School Musical; Sec Stu Cncl; Var Capt Trk; High Hon Roll; NHS; Beaver Co Times Athlt Wk 87.

ZWEIG, KELLY; Greater Nanticoke Area HS; Hunlock Creek, PA; (4); Art Clb; Church Yth Grp; Chorus; Yrbk Stf; Hon Roll; Lion Awd; Schlstc Art Awd 86-87; Hallmark Awd Francis Larkin Mc Common 87; Savanah Coll Of Art Schlrshp 87; Kutztown U; Art.

ZYLA, RHONDA; Our Lady Of Lourdes HS; Shamokin, PA; (3); 15/89; Pep Clb; Spanish Clb; SADD; Rep Stu Cncl; Bsktbl; Sftbl; Hon Roll; NHS; Phys Ed Awd 86 & 87; Sp Ed.

ZYRA, KELLY; Canevin HS; Carnegie, PA; (3); Ski Clb; Consecutive Hnr Roll Achvt 86-87.

NEW JERSEY

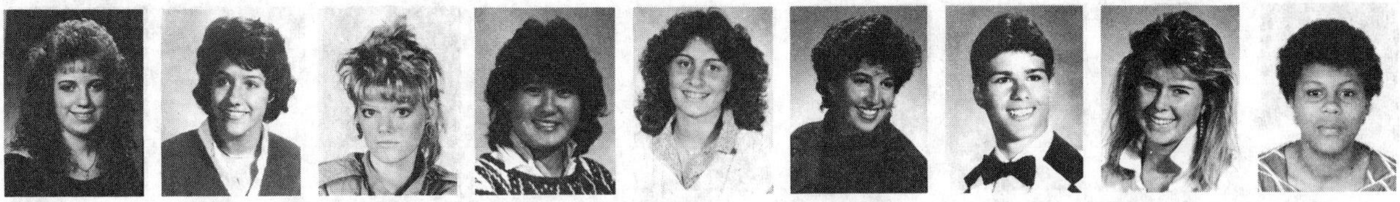

Abaray, Cheryl
John F Kennedy Memorial HS
Avenel, NJ

Abate, Holly
Holmdel HS
Holmdel, NJ

Abbott, Cindy
Millville SR HS
Millville, NJ

Abiko, Megumi
Hillsborough HS
Belle Mead, NJ

Aboulhosn, Nada
Lenape Valley Regional HS
Netcong, NJ

Abraham, Julie M
Pascack Hills HS
Woodcliff Lake, NJ

Abramo, Teddy
Hudson Catholic HS
Hoboken, NJ

Abrutyn, Elise
Montville Twp HS
Pine Brook, NJ

Accilien, Olga
Vailsburg HS
Newark, NJ

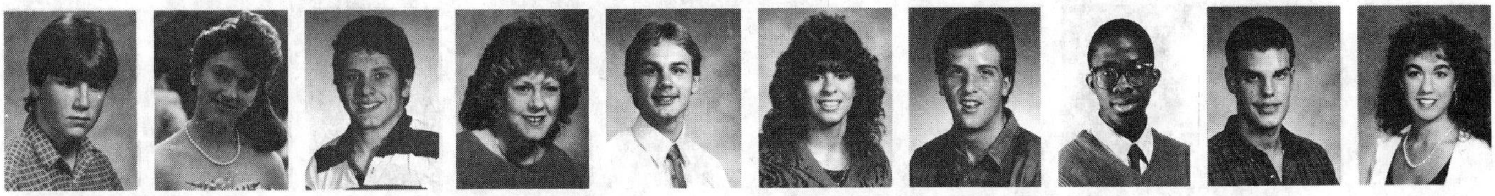

Ackers, Jared
Southern Regional
N Beach, NJ

Acosta, Iris
Vineland HS
Vineland, NJ

Adam, Raymond
Wood-Ridge HS
Wood Ridge, NJ

Adamczyk, Diane
Lyndhurst HS
Lyndhurst, NJ

Adamec, James
St John Vianney HS
Aberdeen, NJ

Adams, Debbie
Rancocas Valley HS
Mt Holly, NJ

Adams, Tom
Toms River HS
Beachwood, NJ

Adjoga-Otu, Nii-Abladey
Arts HS
Newark, NJ

Adler, Scott
Westwood Regional
Washington Twp, NJ

Adriance, Laura A
Westfield HS
Westfield, NJ

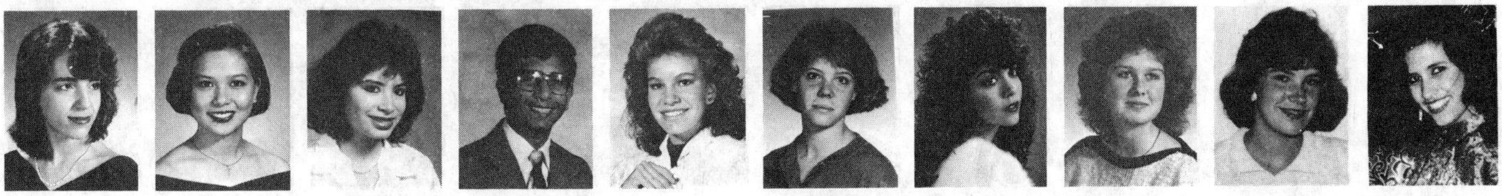

Affsa, Jennifer
Hillside HS
Hillside, NJ

Aguilar, Anita
Immaculate Heart
Paramus, NJ

Aguilar, Silvia A
Our Lady Of Good Counsel HS
Newark, NJ

Ahmed, Khurram
Ridgefield Park HS
Ridgefield Pk, NJ

Aidala, Jennifer
Sparta HS
Sparta, NJ

Alban, Therese M
Somerville HS
Somerville, NJ

Albanese, Tracy
Nutley HS
Nutley, NJ

Alber, Julie
Middletown HS
Middletown, NJ

Albers, Jennifer
Parsippany Hills HS
Morris Plains, NJ

Alberto, Norah
Holy Rosary Acad
Jacksonerg, NJ

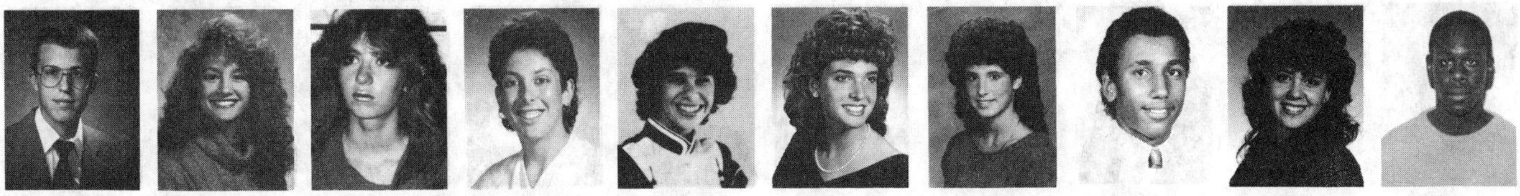

Albertson, Christopher E
Millville HS
Mauricetown, NJ

Alesandro, Stacy
Bridgewater Raritan HS East
Bridgewater, NJ

Alessandrini, Patricia
Paramus Catholic Girls HS
Wallington, NJ

Alessi, Kelly
Hamilton High West
Trenton, NJ

Alexander, Amy
Hawthorne HS
Hawthorne, NJ

Alexander, Mary Jo
Red Bank Catholic
Rumson, NJ

Alizieri, Lori Ann
Memorial HS
Cedar Grove, NJ

Allaway, Richard D
West Orange HS
West Orange, NJ

Allen, Cheryl
Watchung Hills Regional HS
Gillette, NJ

Allen, Earnest Chris
Marist HS
Bayonne, NJ

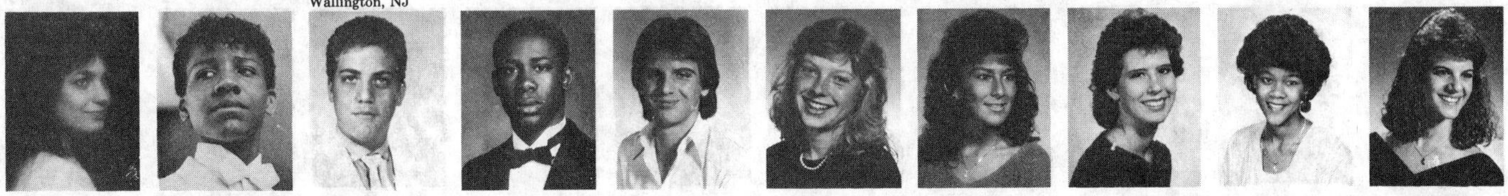

Allen, Lisa
Hamilton HS East
Trenton, NJ

Allen, III Payton Edward
Linden HS
Linden, NJ

Alliegro, III Joseph A
Pennsville Memorial
Salem, NJ

Allrich, Jr Jacques
Irvington HS
Irvington, NJ

Allshouse, David
Phillipsburg HS
Bloomsbury, NJ

Allspach, Erika
Watchung Hills Regional HS
Warren, NJ

Almeida, Janice P
Union Catholic Regional HS
Union, NJ

Alpaugh, Becky
Delaware Valley Reg
Bloomsbury, NJ

Alston, Monique
Plainfield HS
Plainfield, NJ

Altenau, Lisa
St Pius X Reginal
S Plainfield, NJ

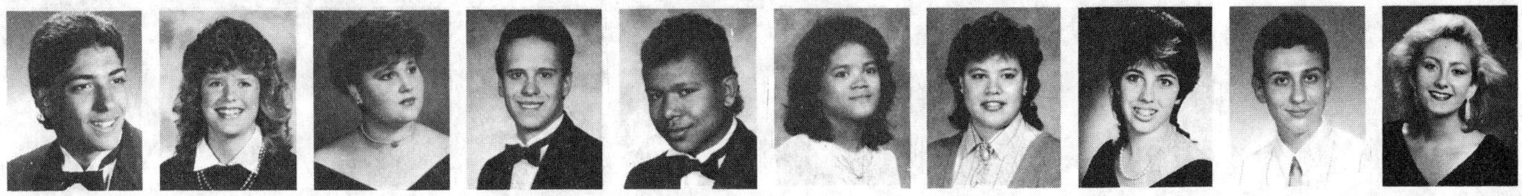

Altilio, Michael
Secaucus HS
Secaucus, NJ

Altman, Heather
Deptford HS
Deptford, NJ

Altman, Meredith
Manalapan HS
Manalapan, NJ

Altobello, Ken
Paramus HS
Paramus, NJ

Alvarez, Juan
Memorial HS
West New York, NJ

Alvear, Antoinette
Southern Regional
Barnegat, NJ

Alvez, Debbie
Dwight Morrow HS
Englewood, NJ

Amatelli, Sally
Neptune HS
Neptune, NJ

Amatucci, Glenn
Immaculata HS
Raritan, NJ

Ambrico, Sherry
Kingsway Regional
Mullica Hl, NJ

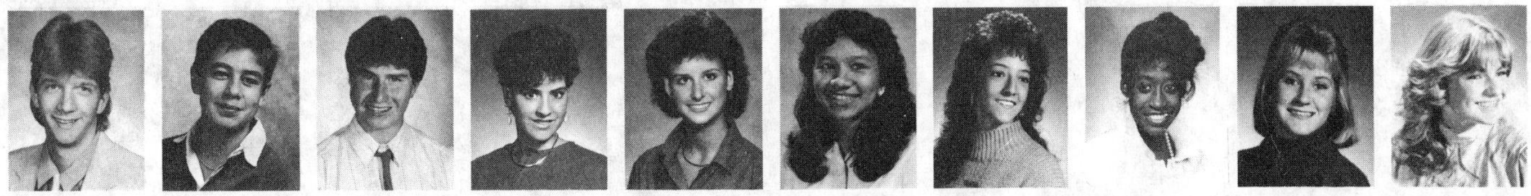

Ambruster, Mark
Union Catholic Regional HS
Union, NJ

Amet, Chris D
Collingwood HS
Collingswood, NJ

Amman, Timothy R
Holy Cross HS
Mt Laurel, NJ

Ammerman, Keri A
Secaucus HS
Secaucus, NJ

Ammerman, Shari
Wayne Hills HS
Wayne, NJ

Ampuero, Manuela
St Aloysius HS
Jersey City, NJ

Anastasio, Christine
Madison Central HS
Old Bridge, NJ

Anatol, Giselle
Scotch Plains Fanwood HS
Fanwood, NJ

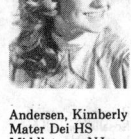

Andersen, Elaine
Hightstown HS
East Windsor, NJ

Andersen, Kimberly
Mater Dei HS
Middletown, NJ

Anderson, Adrienne
Mount Saint Mary
S River, NJ

Anderson, Angel
Clifford J Scott HS
East Orange, NJ

Anderson, Barbara
Green Brook HS
Green Brook, NJ

Anderson, Elizabeth
Hunterdon Central
Flemington, NJ

Anderson, Jacquita
K
Morris Knolls HS
Denville, NJ

Andl, Evelyn
New Milford HS
New Milford, NJ

Andreeko, Andrew A
Warren Hills
Regional HS
Hackettstown, NJ

Andrews, Debbie
Orange HS
Orange, NJ

Angello, Philip
Monmouth Regional
Eatontown, NJ

Angster, Scott
Wall HS
Manasquan, NJ

Annasenz, Marie
Mc Corristin
Catholic HS
Trenton, NJ

Anouna, Larry
Columbia HS
South Orange, NJ

Antico, Kimberly
Red Bank Catholic
Freehold, NJ

Antonelle, Gregory
Watchung Hills HS
Watchung, NJ

Antonova, Pavlina
Lawrence HS
Lawrenceville, NJ

Antonucci, Steven F
Keyport HS
Keyport, NJ

Apparicio, Sean R
Piscataway HS
Piscataway, NJ

Appel, Courtney
Vernon Twsp HS
Sussex, NJ

Appio, Rocco
Don Bosco
Technical HS
W Paterson, NJ

Aquino, Alan
Union Hill HS
Union City, NJ

Arahill, Jacqueline
Ramapa HS
Wyckoff, NJ

Arangio, Luanne
St James HS
Mullica Hill, NJ

Arasin, Jo Anne
St James HS
Carneys Point, NJ

Arasz, Jamie
Brick Township HS
Brick, NJ

Archer, David E
Bordentown
Regional HS
Bordentown, NJ

Archie, Desiree
Denise
Immaculate
Conception HS
Irvington, NJ

Aria, Lalena
Long Branch HS
Long Br, NJ

Armstrong,
Marcelline
Pemberton
Township HS
Browns Mills, NJ

Arndt, John P
Raritan HS
Hazlet, NJ

Arnella, Jr Benedict
Christian Brothers
Colts Neck, NJ

Arnold, Mark
De Paul Diocesan
Lincoln Pk, NJ

Arnold, Sonia
Colonia HS
Colonia, NJ

Arocho, Brenda
Mary Help Of
Christians Acad
Paterson, NJ

Aronson, Tracy
Wayne Hills HS
Wayne, NJ

Arroyo, Christofer
Bergen Catholic HS
Hasbrouck Hts, NJ

Ashton, Stacey
Parsippany Hills HS
Parsippany, NJ

Astor, Tara
Rancocas Valley
Regional HS
Mt Holly, NJ

Atwell, Deborah
Cumberland
Regional HS
Bridgeton, NJ

Auer, Jeff
Monsignor Donovan
Island Heights, NJ

Auletto, Lisa Marie
Secaucus HS
Secaucus, NJ

Autenrieth, Danielle
Pt Pleasant Beach
Pt Plsnt Bch, NJ

Aversa, Frances
Highland Regional
Erial, NJ

Ayayo, Chris
Emerson HS
Emerson, NJ

Aziz, Abid
West Windsor
Plainsboro HS
Princeton Jct, NJ

Azzarano, Anthony
Washington
Township HS
Sewell, NJ

Baber, Sharon
South River HS
South River, NJ

Babinski, Carl
Kearny HS
Kearny, NJ

Babola, Kim
Notre Dame HS
Mercerville, NJ

Babuschak,
Gretchen
Monsignor Donovan
Toms River, NJ

Babyak, Karleen
Linden HS
Linden, NJ

Baccarella, Michele
Holy Family Acad
Bayonne, NJ

Bachmura, Debra
Morristown-Beard
Randolph, NJ

Bacho, Brett
Phillipsburg HS
Phillipsburg, NJ

Backer, Samantha
Vernon Township
Highland Lks, NJ

Bacon, Bruce H
Salem HS
Salem, NJ

Baduklu, Arzu
Mary Help Of
Christians Acad
Paterson, NJ

Bagatelle, Adrien
Wayne Hills HS
Wayne, NJ

Bahtiarian, Donna V
Northern Valley
Regional HS
Closter, NJ

Bailey, Lisa D
Vineland HS
Vineland, NJ

Baine, Julie
Brick Memorial HS
Point Pleasant, NJ

Bajger, Jacqueline
Roselle Catholic HS
Linden, NJ

Baker, Andrew S
Spotswood HS
Milltown, NJ

Baker, Donyale
Cherry Hill High
Schl West
Cherry Hill, NJ

Bakia, Marianne
Manalapan HS
Englishtown, NJ

Bakos, Gwen
Red Bank Catholic
Atlantic Highland,
NJ

Bakos, Jennifer
Linden HS
Linden, NJ

Balf, Deborah A
Toms River HS
Beachwood, NJ

Balica, Ana
Kearny HS
Belleville, NJ

Balista, Toni
Manchester Twp HS
Lakehurst, NJ

Ballas, Angela
Camden Catholic
Pennsauken, NJ

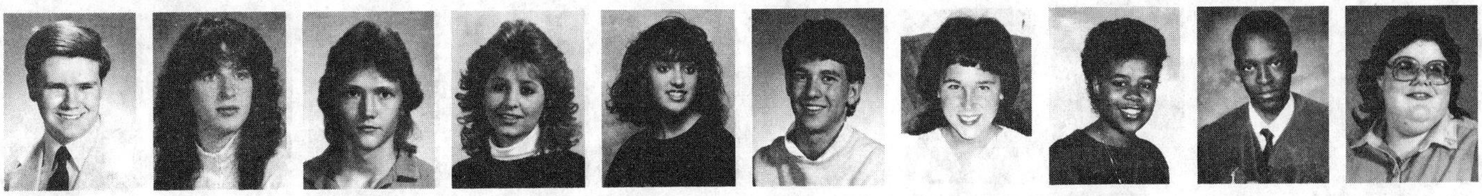

Ballasty, Robert M
Mater Dei HS
Middletown, NJ

Balsley, Elizabeth
North Hunterdon
Lebanon, NJ

Banas, Robert
Jackson Memorial
Jackson, NJ

Bandola, Lizabeth
De Paul HS
Pompton Lakes, NJ

Bangash, Hilary
Saddle River Day
Ridgewood, NJ

Banko, Matthew
Freehold Township
Freehold, NJ

Bankowski, Brenda
Manchester
Regional HS
Haledon, NJ

Banks, Melissa Ann
Paulsboro HS
Paulsboro, NJ

Banks, Noel
Marist HS
Jersey City, NJ

Bannon, Denise
Monongahela HS
Sewell, NJ

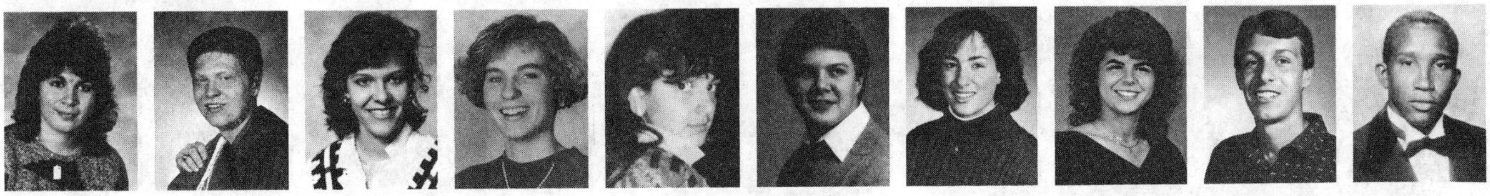

Baran, Caysel
North Bergen HS
Guttenberg, NJ

Baratta, David
Passiac County Tech
Paterson, NJ

Barber, Linda
Vineland HS
Millville, NJ

Barber, Sherry
Red Bank Regional
Red Bank, NJ

Barbosa, Marie
East Side HS
Newark, NJ

Barckley, Michael
Florence Twp Mem
Florence, NJ

Barger, Michelle
Red Bank Regional
Shrewsbury, NJ

Barile, Nicole
Ocean City HS
Marmora, NJ

Barker, Chris
Mount Olive HS
Flanders, NJ

Barlatier, Henry
Franklin Morrel HS
Irvington, NJ

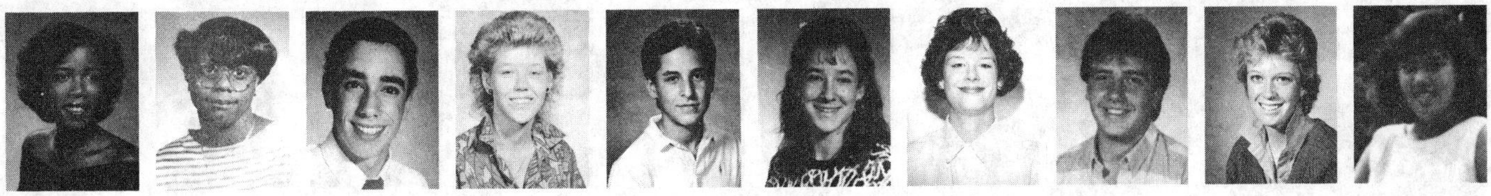

Barnes, April
Union Catholic
Regional HS
Plainfield, NJ

Barnes, Joy
West Side HS
Newark, NJ

Barnock, Brian
Notre Dame HS
Hamilton Sq, NJ

Barr, Debbie
Gloucester City
JR-SR HS
Gloucester, NJ

Barr, Jon-Henry
Arthur L Johnson
Regional HS
Clark, NJ

Barr, Penni
West Windsor
Plainsboro HS
Princeton Junct, NJ

Barrett, Tracy
Scotch
Plains-Fanwood HS
Fanwood, NJ

Barry, Steven
Lenape Valley HS
Andover, NJ

Barry, Suzanne
Newton HS
Andover, NJ

Barsczewski, Lisa
Notre Dame HS
Hamilton Sq, NJ

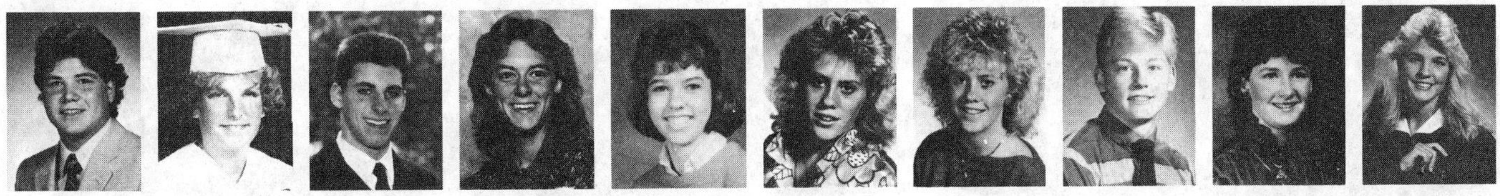

Bartolomei, Marc J
Hamilton HS West
Trenton, NJ

Basich, Michele
Delsea Regional HS
Vineland, NJ

Bastardi, III
Anthony V
Delbarton Schl
Boonton, NJ

Batchelor, Karen
Vernon Township
Sussex, NJ

Bates, Liisa
Northwest Christian
Sussex, NJ

Batiato, Maureen
Ann
Brick Town HS
Brick Town, NJ

Batiato, Michelle
Brick Town HS
Brick Town, NJ

Bator, Richard
St Joseph Regional
Norwood, NJ

Bauer, Kimberly
Paul VI HS
Waterford, NJ

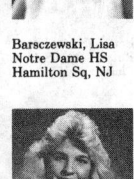

Bautz, Jennifer
Bloomfield HS
Bloomfield, NJ

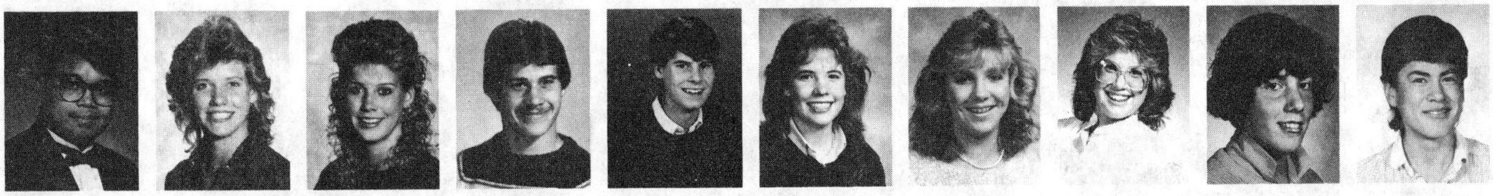

Bauzon, Benjamin
Passaic HS
Passaic, NJ

Baykowski, Lori
Beth
Linden HS
Linden, NJ

Baykowski, Susan
Linden HS
Linden, NJ

Beamer, Curtis
Pinelands Regional
Tuckerton, NJ

Beaney, James
Cherry Hill High
School East
Cherry Hill, NJ

Beard, Elissa-Lynn
St John Vianney HS
Colts Neck, NJ

Becker, Mary
Delaware Valley Reg
Bloomsbury, NJ

Becker, Stacey
Secaucus HS
Secaucus, NJ

Beckert, Amy
Cinnaminson HS
Cinnaminson, NJ

Beckett, Robert A
West Morris Central
Long Valley, NJ

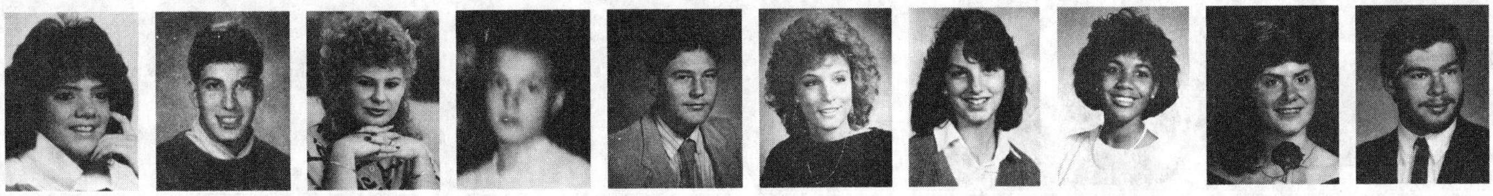

Beckman, Jennifer
Clearview HS
Sewell, NJ

Bedell, Barry
West Essex Regional
Fairfield, NJ

Bednarz, Irena
Wallington HS
Wallington, NJ

Beer, Amy
Trenton HS
Trenton, NJ

Belcea, Dan
Notre Dame HS
Princeton, NJ

Belcher, Sue
Hunterdon Central
White House Stati,
NJ

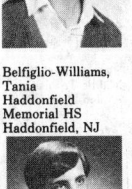

Belfiglio-Williams,
Tania
Haddonfield
Memorial HS
Haddonfield, NJ

Bell, Carole V
Newark Acad
Livingston, NJ

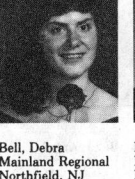

Bell, Debra
Mainland Regional
Northfield, NJ

Bell, Jason
Edison HS
Edison, NJ

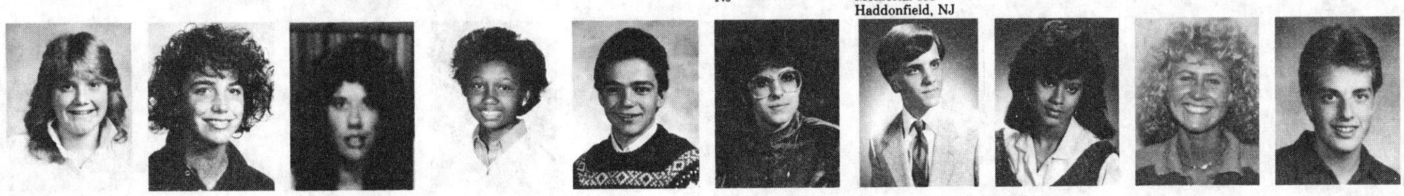

Bell, Kathleen
Mainland Regional
Northfield, NJ

Bell, Ronni
Palmyra HS
Palmyra, NJ

Belluscio, Kim
John P Stevens HS
Edison, NJ

Belton,
Monica-Andrea
Newton HS
Andover, NJ

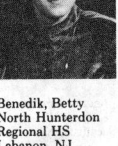

Benedict, William F
Wayne Hills HS
Wayne, NJ

Benedik, Betty
North Hunterdon
Regional HS
Lebanon, NJ

Benigno, John
Jonathan Dayton
Regional HS
Springfield, NJ

Benjamin, Michelle
A
Jonathan Dayton
Regional HS
Springfield, NJ

Bennett, Jessica
Vineland HS
Vineland, NJ

Bennington, Todd
North Hunterdon
Asbury, NJ

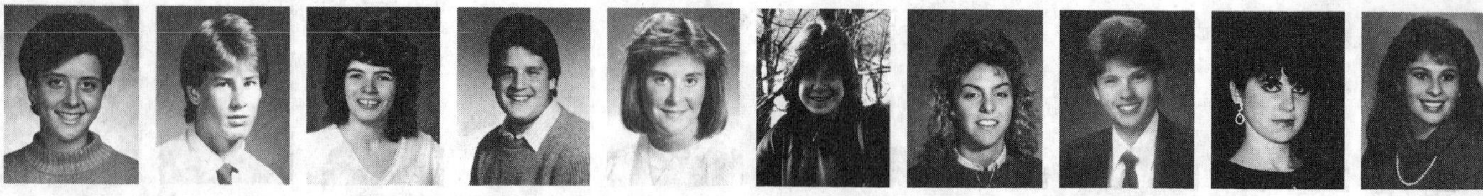

Bennis, Eileen
Hunterdon Central
Flemington, NJ

Benoit, Artie
St Joseph Regional
New City, NY

Benshoff, Kim A
Spotswood HS
Spotswood, NJ

Bentrovato, Giorgio
Boonton HS
Boonton, NJ

Berg, Debra
Highstown HS
East Windsor, NJ

Berger, Michelle
Barnstable Acad
Orangeburg, NY

Berish, Lori
Notre Dame HS
Trenton, NJ

Berk, Scott
Ocean Township HS
Oakhurst, NJ

Berlin, Rita
Fair Lawn HS
Fair Lawn, NJ

Berliner, Roberta
W Morris Mendham
Brookside, NJ

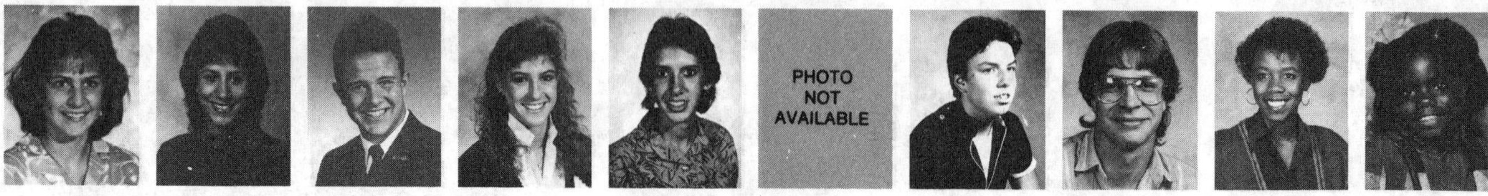

Berlingeri, Linda
Washington Twp
Sewell, NJ

Bernardi, Patricia
Vineland HS
Vineland, NJ

Bernath, Brian
Marine Acad Of
Science & Technlgy
Matawan, NJ

Bernstein, Bonnie
Howell HS
Howell, NJ

Berrington, Kimberly
Highland Regional
Erial, NJ

Berry, Stephanie
Michele
Holy Cross HS
Mount Laurel, NJ

Bersani, Dean
Highland Regional
Laurel Springs, NJ

Bertoldo, Jonathan
Delaware Valley
Regional HS
Milford, NJ

Best, Tanya E
Dwight Morrow HS
Englewood, NJ

Bethea, Keisha
St Anthony HS
Jersey Cty, NJ

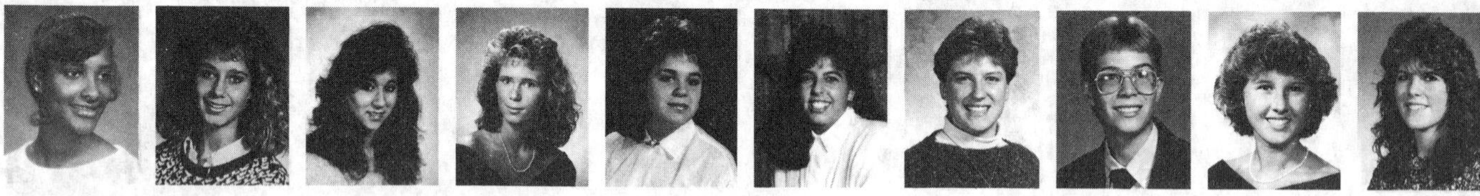

Bethel, Kama Lynn
Rutgers Prep Schl
Plainfield, NJ

Betz, Colleen
De Paul HS
Wayne, NJ

Bevilaqua, Gina
Highland Regional
Blackwood, NJ

Biagi, Susan
Our Lady Of Mercy
Vineland, NJ

Bianchini, Mirella
Columbia HS
South Orange, NJ

Biazzo, Dawn
Collegiate Schl
Garfield, NJ

Bielski, Therese
Hackettstown HS
Hackettstown, NJ

Bihlmier, Joseph M
Southern Regional
Ship Bottom, NJ

Bill, Jennifer
Woodstown HS
Monroeville, NJ

Bilow, Kathy
Mount Olive HS
Budd Lake, NJ

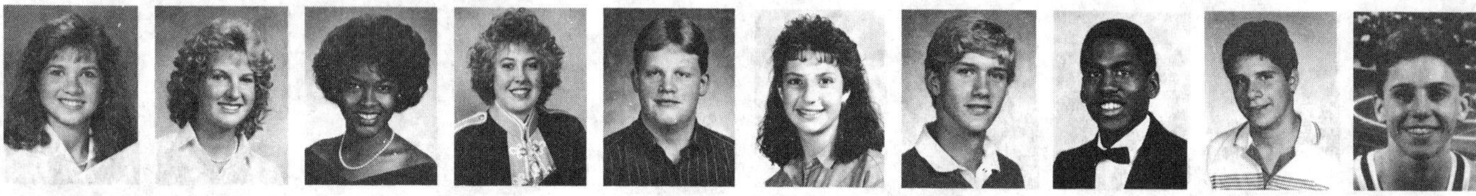

Bindas, Pamela
Manalapan HS
Manalapan, NJ

Bingler, Aimee
St John Vianney HS
Colts Neck, NJ

Birch, Cindy M
St Pius X HS
Piscataway, NJ

Bird, Christine
Phillipsburg HS
Phillipsburg, NJ

Bird, Patrick
Hunterdon Central
Stockton, NJ

Birkner, Sharon
Wayne Hills HS
Wayne, NJ

Bischoff, Doug
Hunterdon Central
Flemington, NJ

Bivans, Lorenzo A
Cherokee HS
Marlton, NJ

Biviano, Angelo
Wood-Ridge HS
Wood Ridge, NJ

Black, Drew S
Mahwah HS
Mahwah, NJ

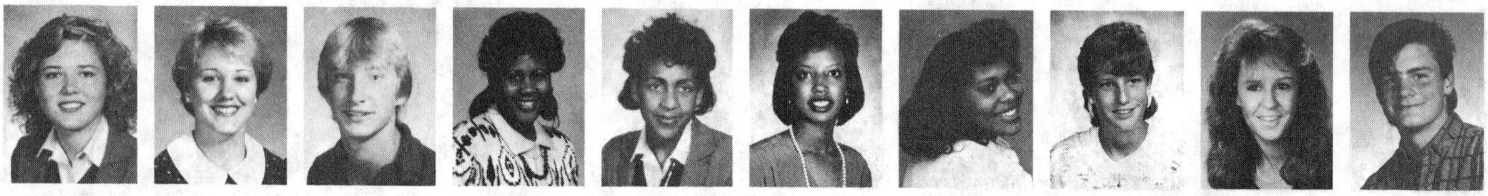

Black, Regina Marie
Mt St Dominic Acad
Boonton, NJ

Blair, Dawn Louise
Hillsborough HS
Hillsborough, NJ

Blair, William
Madison HS
Madison, NJ

Blake, Dahlia
St Vincent Acad
Newark, NJ

Blakely, Candice
Mt St Dominic Acad
E Orange, NJ

Blakely, Dawn
John F Kennedy HS
Paterson, NJ

Blanton, Lisa
Vineland SR HS
Vineland, NJ

Blecker, Kathy
Hunterdon Central
Ringoes, NJ

Blejwas, Amy
Bridgewater Raritan
HS East
Bridgewater, NJ

Blessing, Thomas W
Watchung Hills
Regional HS
Warren, NJ

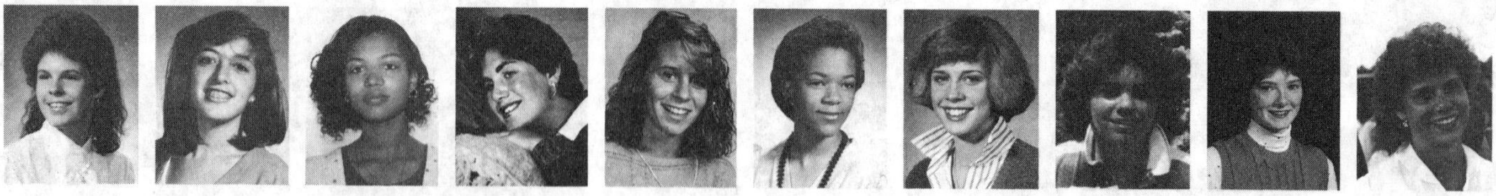

Blich, Jacqueline
Morris Catholic HS
Mine Hill Dover, NJ

Block, Amy
Hightstown HS
Roosevelt, NJ

Blocker, Lori
Westfield HS
Westfield, NJ

Blood, Cheryl Lyn
Middle Township
Avalon Manor, NJ

Bloom, Karen
Haddonfield
Memorial HS
Haddonfield, NJ

Blow, Deneen K
Piscataway HS
Piscataway, NJ

Bloxham, Heather
Newton HS
Andover, NJ

Boccio, Dawn E
John F Kennedy HS
Willingboro, NJ

Boden, Elizabeth
Cumberland
Christian HS
Bridgeton, NJ

Bodine, Jane
Gateway Regional
Westville, NJ

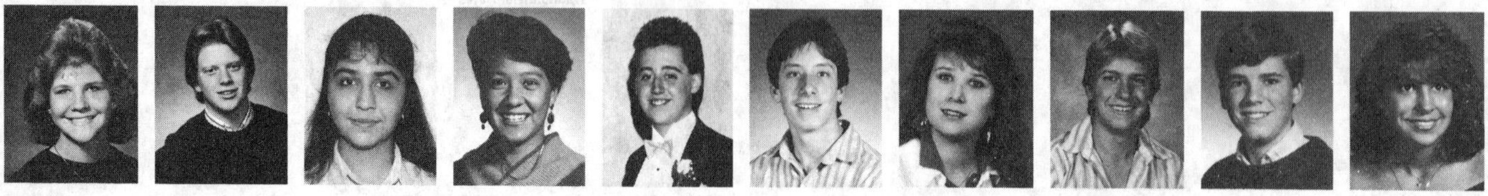

Bodnar, Debra
South River HS
S River, NJ

Bohringer, Joe
Millville SR HS
Millville, NJ

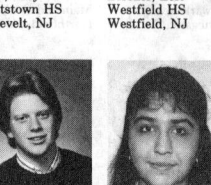

Bolat, Minat
Paterson Catholic
Regional HS
Paterson, NJ

Bonado, Marideth L
Shore Regional HS
W Long Br, NJ

Bonanni, Anthony
Secaucus HS
Secaucus, NJ

Bonczek, Joseph V
Neptune SR HS
Neptune, NJ

Boner, Mary
Bridgeton HS
Bridgton, NJ

Bonifacio, Mark
Dwight-Englewood
Leonia, NJ

Bonwell, III
Raymond E
HS East
Toms River, NJ

Booker, Lora
Moorestown SR HS
Moorestown, NJ

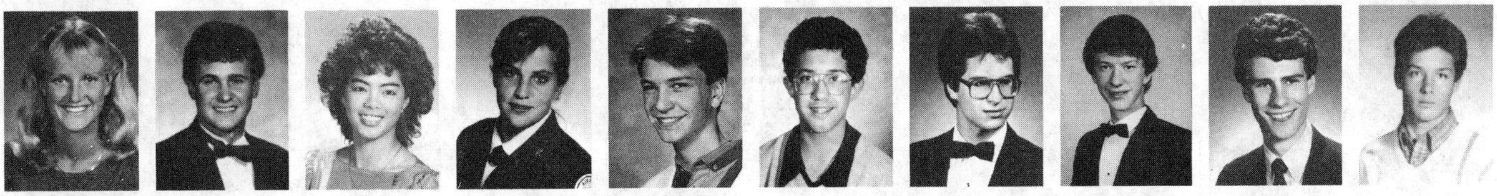

Boos, Karen
Scotch Plains
Fanwood HS
Fanwood, NJ

Bopp, James
Paramus HS
Paramus, NJ

Bordamonte, Mae
Hope
Paul VI Regional
Passaic, NJ

Borges, Cheri
Brick Township HS
Brick, NJ

Borgstrom, Henrik
West Essex SR HS
N Caldwell, NJ

Borino, Jr Anthony
Sussex County Vo
Vernon, NJ

Borino, Mark
St Peters Prep Schl
Bayonne, NJ

Borota, Nicolae
Andrew
Fidrence Memorial
Roebling, NJ

Borowski, Brett
Clifton HS
Clifton, NJ

Borys, Michael
North Arlington HS
N Arlington, NJ

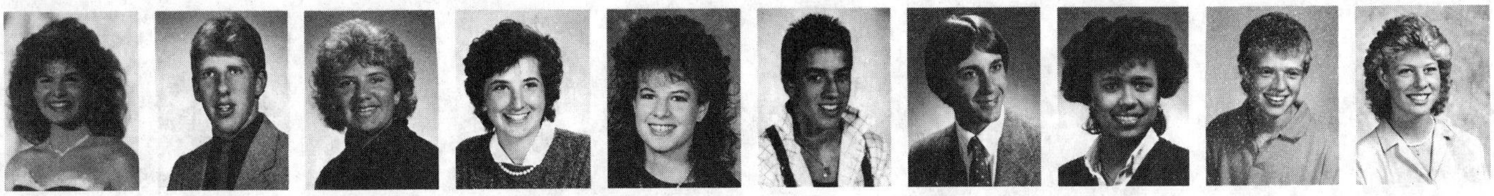

Bostrom, Melanie
Rahway HS
Rahway, NJ

Boszak, David
Hamilton High West
Yardville, NJ

Boszak, Dawn
Hamilton High West
Yardville, NJ

Bott, Michelle
Long Branch HS
Long Branch, NJ

Botti, Dawn Marie
West Morris Central
Long Valley, NJ

Bove, Matthew
Highland Regional
Blackwood, NJ

Bowers, Steven
Bound Brook HS
S Bound Brook, NJ

Bowser, Kisha
Camden Catholic
Glassboro, NJ

Boxer, Ari
Lakewood HS
Lakewood, NJ

Boyce, Cheryl L
Lenape HS
Vincentown, NJ

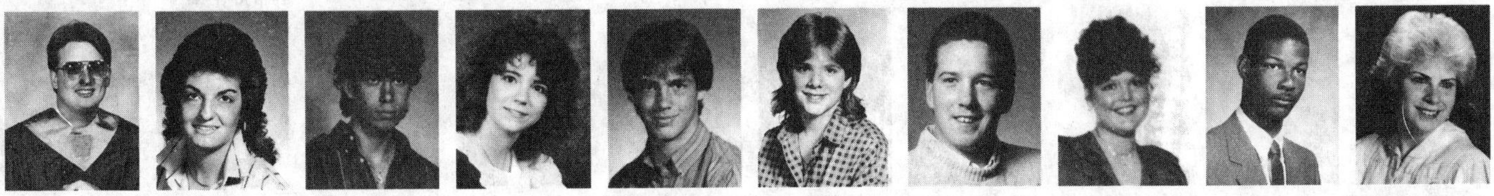

Boyce, Jr H Charles
Raritan HS
W Keansburg, NJ

Boydell, Tammie
Hawthorne HS
Paterson, NJ

Boyer, Robert L
Dunellen HS
Duneller, NJ

Boyle, Georgeanne
Lakewood HS
Lakewood, NJ

Boyle, Joseph
Toms River HS
Pine Beach, NJ

Boyler, Tricia
South River HS
South River, NJ

Bradley, Steven P
Florence Twp
Memorial HS
Florence, NJ

Brady, Erin
Gloucester Catholic
Wenonah, NJ

Braithwaite, Darren
Burlington City HS
Edgewater Pk, NJ

Brand, Diana Lynn
Brick Township HS
Brick Town, NJ

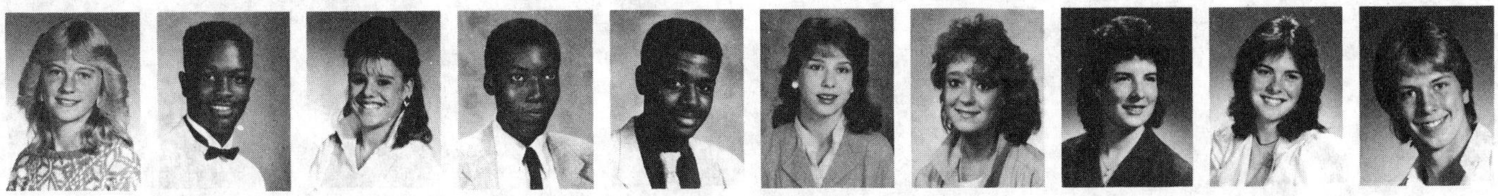

Brandt, Sharon
Toms River HS East
Toms River, NJ

Brangman, Ronald
Essex Catholic Boys
Orange, NJ

Branic, Lisa
Brick Memorial HS
Lakewood, NJ

Branker, Henry
Essex Catholic Boys
Bloomfield, NJ

Brantley-Butler,
Eric O
Buena Regional HS
Buena, NJ

Braszko, Natalie
Calvary Lighthouse
Ft Monmouth, NJ

Breault, Denise
Neumann Prep
Loomingdale, NJ

Bredder, Charlene C
Randolph HS
Randolph, NJ

Bredehoft, Mary
Alice
Toms River H S
Toms River, NJ

Breidt, Keith
High Point Regional
Branchville, NJ

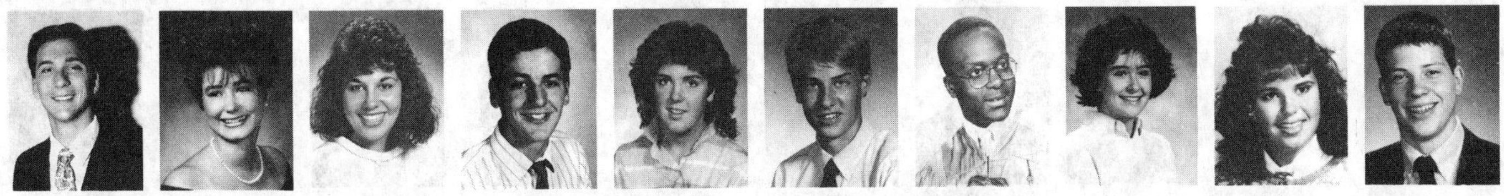

Breitenbach, Paul T
Shore Regional HS
Oceanport, NJ

Brennan, Maryanne
Academy Of The
Holy Angels
Bergenfield, NJ

Brescia, Michelle
Toms River HS East
Toms River, NJ

Breslin, Daniel P
Holy Cross HS
Moorestown, NJ

Breslin, Shannon
Hanover Park
Regional HS
Florham Park, NJ

Brewer, Richard
West Windsor
Plainsboro HS
Princeton, NJ

Brewster, Matthew J
Bloomfield SR HS
Bloomfield, NJ

Brey, Lauren
Glen Ridge HS
Glen Ridge, NJ

Brill, Kellie
Lacey Township HS
Forked River, NJ

Brinkerhoff,
Stephen G
Midland Park HS
Midland Park, NJ

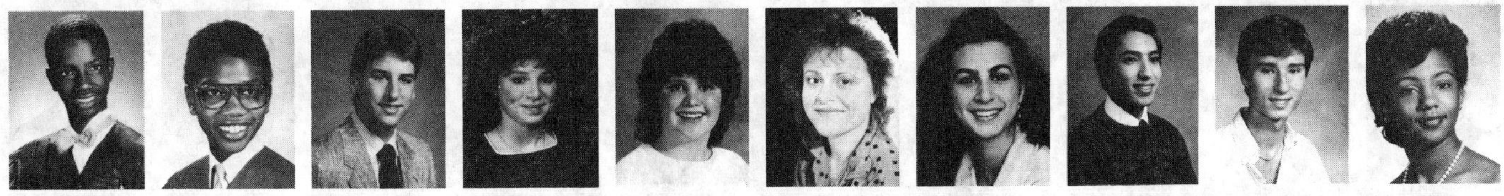

Brinkley, De Nard
Hillside HS
Hillside, NJ

Brinson, Reginald
Essex Catholic Boys
East Orange, NJ

Bristow, Al C
Haddon Township
Westmont, NJ

Brittin, Beth
Gloucester County
Christian HS
Williamstown, NJ

Broberg, Noelle
Howell HS
Howell, NJ

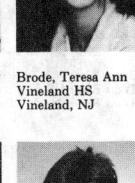

Brocklehurst,
Jeannine M
Sterling HS
Somerdale, NJ

Brode, Teresa Ann
Vineland HS
Vineland, NJ

Brollesy, Hany
Sayed
Cedar Ridge HS
Matawan, NJ

Bromley, Steven M
Haddonfield
Memorial HS
Haddonfield, NJ

Brooks, April L
Ewing HS
West Trenton, NJ

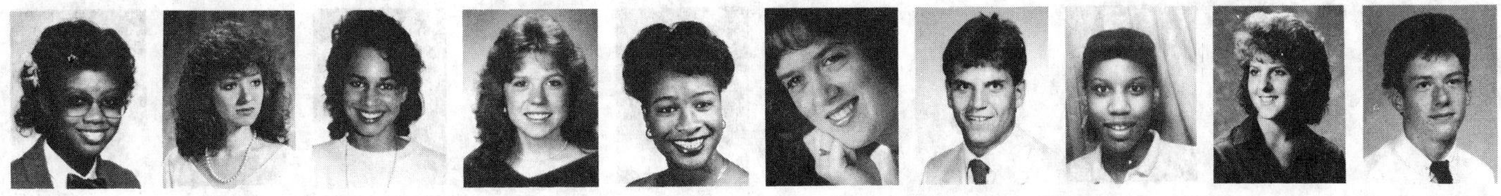

Brooks, Shirnett
Dwight Morrow HS
Englewood, NJ

Brosonski, Dawn
Pompton Lakes HS
Pompton Lakes, NJ

Brossoie, Nicole
Villa Victoria Acad
Trenton, NJ

Brower, Pam
Midland Park HS
Midland Park, NJ

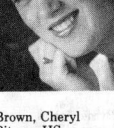

Brown, Alia
Edgewood SR HS
Sicklerville, NJ

Brown, Cheryl
Pitman HS
Pitman, NJ

Brown, David W
Bayonne HS
Bayonne, NJ

Brown, Jene M
Eastside HS
Paterson, NJ

Brown, Jill P
Vineland HS
Vineland, NJ

Brown, John J
Burlington County
Vo Tech HS
Edgewater Pk, NJ

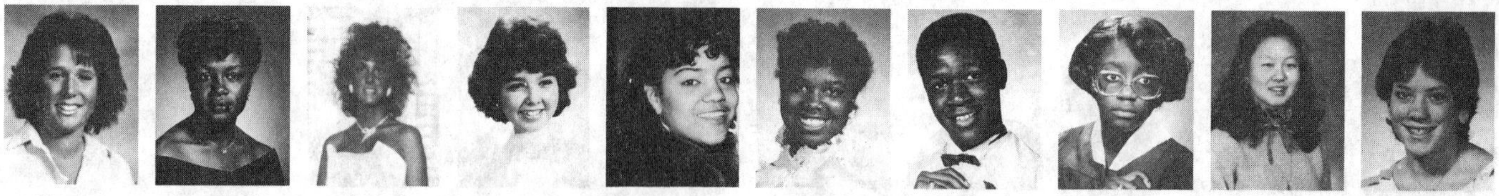

Brown, Kathryn
St John Vianney HS
Colts Neck, NJ

Brown, Katrina
James J Ferris HS
Jersey City, NJ

Brown, Kimberly
Gloucester Catholic
Woodbury, NJ

Brown, Loretta
Roselle Catholic HS
Roselle, NJ

Brown, Marlo
St Mary HS
Jersey City, NJ

Brown, Renata
Weequahic HS
Irvington, NJ

Brown, Robert
Essex Catholic Boys
Newark, NJ

Brown, Sandra
Clifford J Scott HS
E Orange, NJ

Brown, Sara
Holy Spirit HS
Atlantic City, NJ

Brown, Sherri
High Point Regional
Sussex, NJ

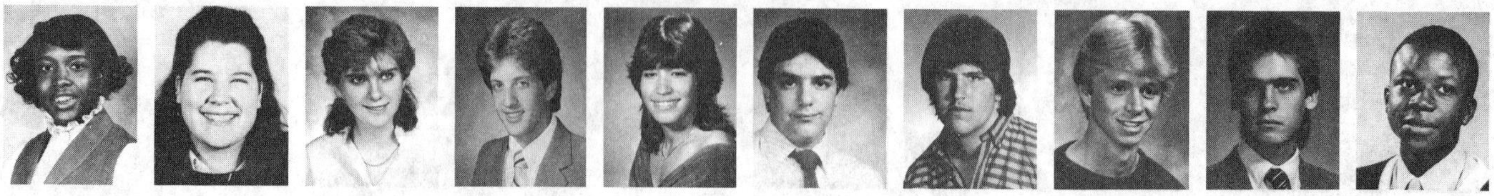

Brown, Tyese
Essex Catholic Girls
S Orange, NJ

Browning, Kathleen E
Academy Of The Holy Angels
New Milford, NJ

Brozoski, Brenda
Hunterdon Central
White House Sta, NJ

Bruen, Charles J
Paramus Catholic Boys HS
Lodi, NJ

Brugal, Maggin
Emerson HS
Union City, NJ

Brunozzi, Dominick
Buena Regional HS
Vineland, NJ

Bruseo, Pete
Dover HS
Mine Hill, NJ

Bruther, Chris
Manasquan HS
Brielle, NJ

Bruzaitis, Eric Mason
Manchester Township HS
Toms River, NJ

Bryant, Gus
Essex Catholic Boys
Newark, NJ

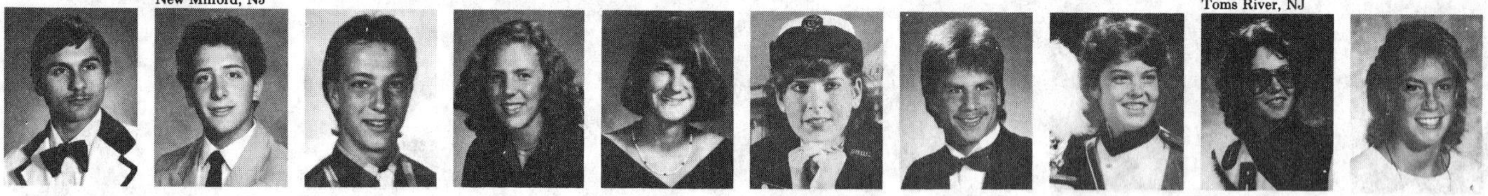

Brzosko, Jan R
Hudson Catholic HS
Jersey City, NJ

Buccino, Gary M
Memorial HS
Cedar Grove, NJ

Buchner, Brian
Pennsville HS
Pennsville, NJ

Buckholz, Geri-Lynn
Lakewood HS
Lakewood, NJ

Buckley, Ellen
St Rose HS
Sea Girt, NJ

Budach, Tammi
Marine Acad Of Science & Technlgy
Spring Lake, NJ

Budinick, John
Bayonne HS
Bayonne, NJ

Buehler, Marjorie
Overbrook Regional
Berlin, NJ

Buehler, Robin
Overbrook Regional SR HS
Berlin, NJ

Buff, Tammy
Washington Township HS
Sewell, NJ

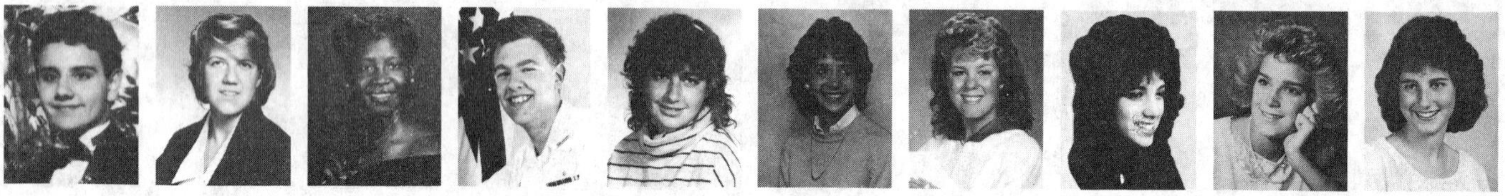

Bufort, Anthony
Paramus HS
Paramus, NJ

Bukata, Susan V
New Milford HS
New Milford, NJ

Bullock, Calandra
Holy Spirit HS
Pleasantville, NJ

Bullock, Geoffrey
Marine Acad Of Science & Tech
East Keandburg, NJ

Bulwin, Lori Ann
Union HS
Union, NJ

Bumgarner, Laura
Timothy Christian
Somerset, NJ

Buob, Maureen
Scotch Plains-Fanwood HS
Fanwood, NJ

Buono, Lisa Joan
St Marys HS
Garfield, NJ

Burch, Nancy
Gateway Regional
Woodbury Hts, NJ

Burch, Sherri
Notre Dame HS
Trenton, NJ

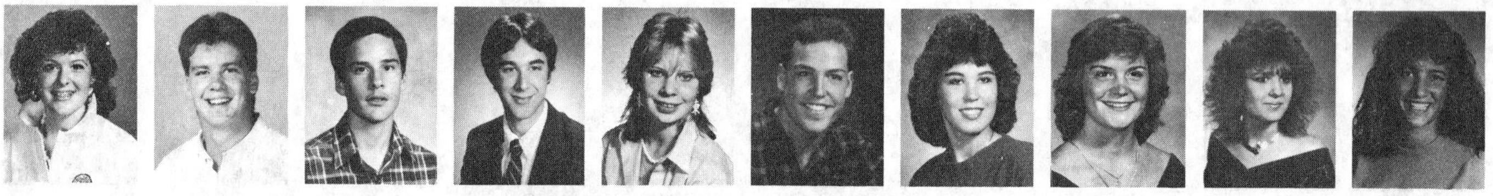

Burke, Christine
St Rose HS
Neptune, NJ

Burke, Craig
Wildwood HS
Wildwood Crest, NJ

Burke, Dennis
A P Schlaick HS
Elmer, NJ

Burke, Jonas
Freehold Township
Freehold Twp, NJ

Burke, Victoria M
St Josephs Of The
W New York, NJ

Burklow, Timothy M
Pequannock Twnshp
Pompton Plains, NJ

Burlew, Heidi
Arthur P Schalick
Elmer, NJ

Burrows, Loree
Matawan Regional
Matawan, NJ

Burrows, Lorrin
St Mary HS
Spotswood, NJ

Burski, Heather
West Windsor-Plainsbor
Robbinsville, NJ

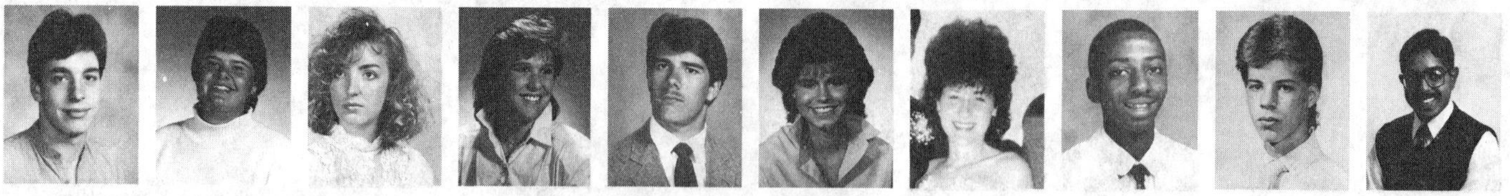

Burton, James
Mainland Regional
Linwood, NJ

Burzynski, Deborah
Toms River HS East
Toms River, NJ

Busch, Jennifer L
Notre Dame HS
Lawrenceville, NJ

Bush, Kim
Toms River HS
Toms River, NJ

Bushell, Jr John T
Central Regional HS
Seaside Park, NJ

Butcher, Ann
Newton HS
Greendell, NJ

Butler, Danielle
Southern Regional
Barnegat, NJ

Butler, Derrick
Essex Catholic Boys
East Orange, NJ

Butler, Gregory E
Monmouth Regional
Tinton Falls, NJ

Butte, Atul
Cherry Hill HS East
Cherry Hill, NJ

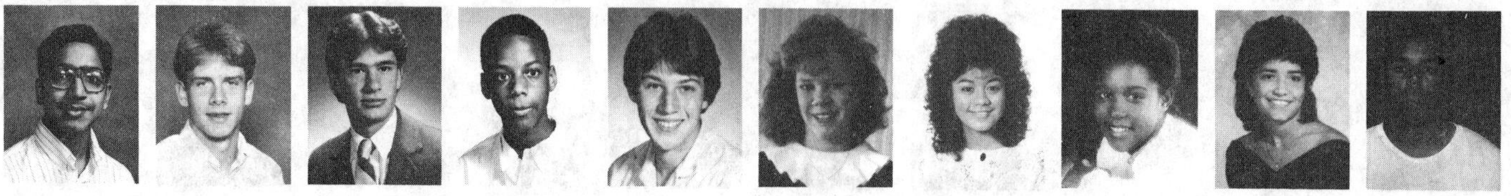

Butte, Manish
Cherry Hill HS East
Cherry Hill, NJ

Buytkins, Jr Paul
Delaware Valley Regional HS
Milford, NJ

Byelick, Christopher J
Bound Brook HS
South Bound Brk, NJ

Byers, Jr Eugene B
Hillside HS
Hillside, NJ

Byrne, James
Union HS
Union, NJ

Byron, Erin
West Morris Mendham HS
Mendham, NJ

Cabaccang, Michelle
Moutn St Dominic
West Orange, NJ

Cabba-Gestalk, Shaunice
Linden HS
Linden, NJ

Cachola, Yvette
Washington Twp
Sewell, NJ

Caesar, Mark
West Side HS
Newark, NJ

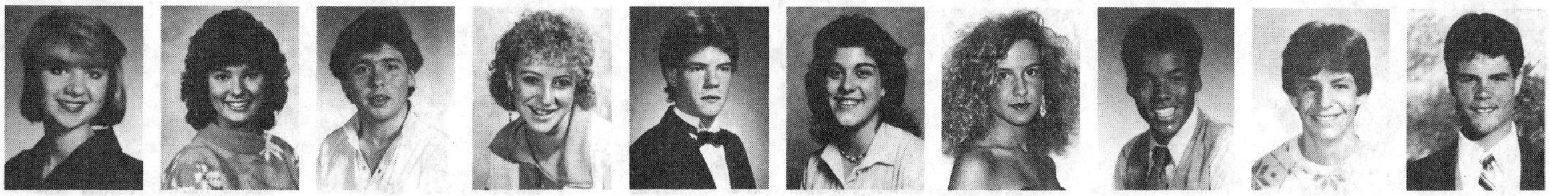

Cahill, Arla Dawn
Randolph HS
Randolph, NJ

Cahill, Elizabeth
Pennsville Memorial
Pennsville, NJ

Cahill, Shawn
Phillipsburg HS
Phillipsburg, NJ

Cain, Brenda
Cherokee HS
Marlton, NJ

Cain, Mark
Don Bosco Prep
Westwood, NJ

Calabro, Kristine
Mahwah HS
Mahwah, NJ

Calautti, Linda
St Josephs HS
Ridgefield, NJ

Caldwell, Michael
West
Windsor-Plainsbor
Princeton Junct, NJ

Calhoun, Sean
Jackson Memorial
Jackson, NJ

Caliendo, Paul
Manaipan HS
Englishtown, NJ

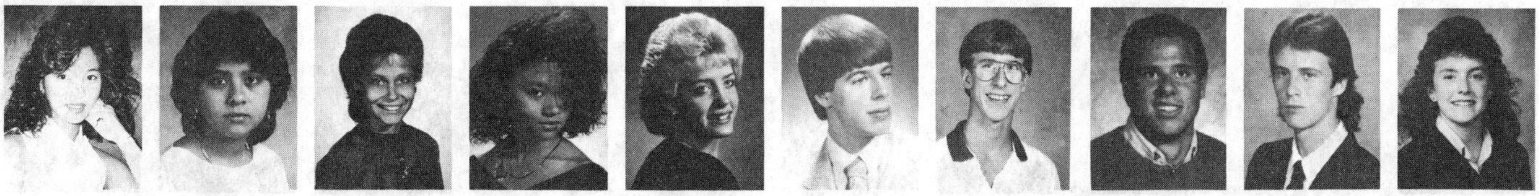

Calilap, Charmane B
St Aloysius HS
Jersey City, NJ

Calizaya, Ivonne
Mary Help Of
Christians Acad
Cedar Grove, NJ

Callahan, Katherine
Highland Regional
Blackwood, NJ

Camado, Maria
Rona
Belleville HS
Belleville, NJ

Cameron, Karen
Jeanne
Mountain Lakes HS
Mountain Lakes, NJ

Cameron, Robert
Ramapo Regional
Wyckoff, NJ

Campanella, Craig
Park Ridge HS
Park Ridge, NJ

Campanella, Pete
Washington
Township HS
Sewell, NJ

Campbell, Edward
West Orange HS
W Orange, NJ

Campbell, Karen
Queen Of Peace HS
Kearny, NJ

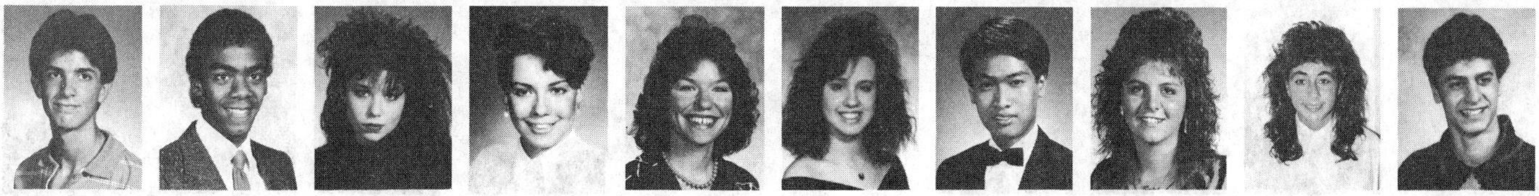

Campbell, Scott
Shore Regional HS
Oceanport, NJ

Canady, Steven L
Roselle Catholic HS
Roselle, NJ

Canavan, Kristie
Middletown HS
Red Bank, NJ

Candon, Christa
Union Catholic
Regional HS
Clark, NJ

Cangelosi, Joann
Washington
Township HS
Sewell, NJ

Canizares, Lourdes
Memorial HS
West New York, NJ

Canseco, Eduardo
St Peters Prep
Bloomfield, NJ

Canzano, Claudine
Madison Central HS
Old Bridge, NJ

Capelli, Lisa
Hoboken HS
Hoboken, NJ

Capoli, Anthony
Eastern HS
West Berlin, NJ

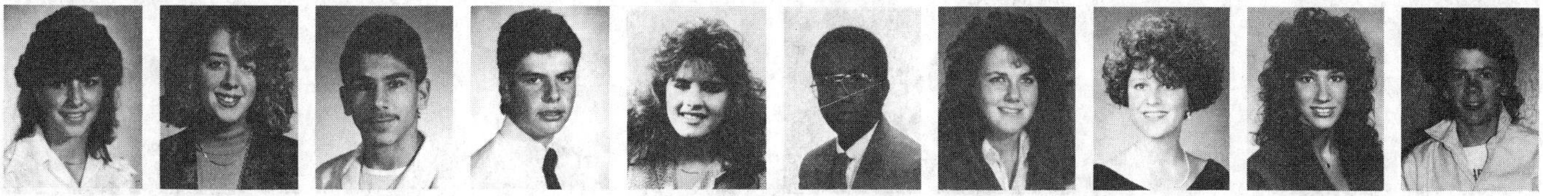

Caporaletti,
Michelle
Holy Cross HS
Willingboro, NJ

Capozzi, Danielle
Indian Hills HS
Franklin Lks, NJ

Capriglione, Ronnie
Belleville HS
Belleville, NJ

Caracci, Douglas
Holy Cross HS
Burlington, NJ

Caravetta, Denise
Ann
Nutley HS
Nutley, NJ

Cardona, Alfredo
Javier
Vineland SR HS
Vineland, NJ

Carey, Lynne
Notre Dame HS
Kendall Pk, NJ

Carini, Laurie
Millville SR HS
Millville, NJ

Carino, Theresa
West Morris
Mendham HS
Chester, NJ

Carlson, Timothy
North Warren
Regional HS
Blairstown, NJ

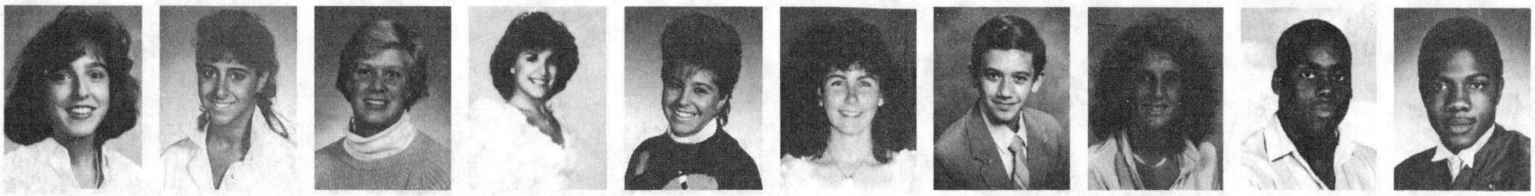

Carnevale, Lynn
St John Vianney HS
Colts Neck, NJ

Caro, Ellen
Columbia HS
Maplewood, NJ

Caroe, Christina
Westfield HS
Westfield, NJ

Carozza, Debra
Academy Of Holy
Angels HS
Upper Saddle Rive,
NJ

Carpenter, Kim
Toms River East HS
Toms River, NJ

Carr, Colleen
Pinelands Regional
Tuckerton, NJ

Carrelle, Raymond
Don Bosco HS
Paramus, NJ

Carrozza, Vicki
Monsignor Donovan
Seaside Heights, NJ

Carruth, Kevin
Haddon Heights HS
Lawnside, NJ

Carswell, III Jasper
Lee
St Pius X HS
Plainfield, NJ

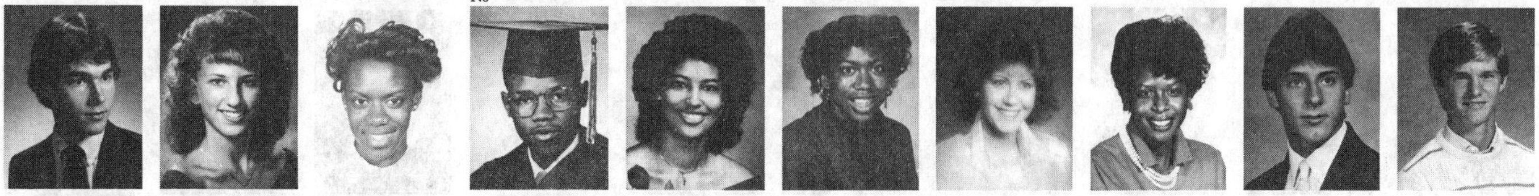

Carter, Allen G
Carteret HS
Carteret, NJ

Carter, Colleen K
St Joseph HS
Franklinville, NJ

Carter, Dawn
Eastside HS
Paterson, NJ

Carter, Jr Donald P
Seton Hall Prep
Newark, NJ

Carter, Elizabeth J
Edgewood Regional
Sicklerville, NJ

Carter, Javette
Sharee
Eastern Christian
Paterson, NJ

Carter, Michelle M
Baptist HS
Haddon Heights, NJ

Carter, Tresa
Washington Twp
Turnersville, NJ

Caruso, Dante V
Triton Regional HS
Somerdale, NJ

Caruso, Michael P
Hamilton HS North
Trenton, NJ

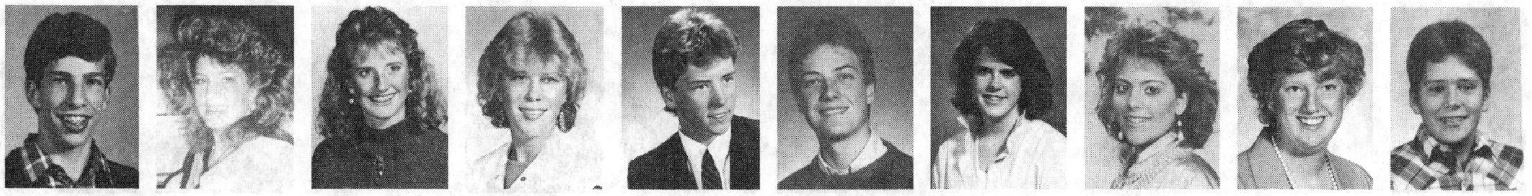

Carver, Kevin
Baptist HS
Marlton, NJ

Cary, Christine
Gateway Regional
Woodbury Hts, NJ

Case, Michele
Henry Hudson
Regional HS
Highlands, NJ

Casey, Janet
Livingston HS
Livingston, NJ

Casey, William
Madison Central HS
Old Bridge, NJ

Cashion, Brannon
Hightstown HS
E Windsor, NJ

Cashion, Kimberly
Ridge HS
Basking Ridge, NJ

Casola, Christina
Red Bank Catholic
Marlboro, NJ

Casper, Conni
Salem HS
Salem, NJ

Cass, Brian
Boonton HS
Denville, NJ

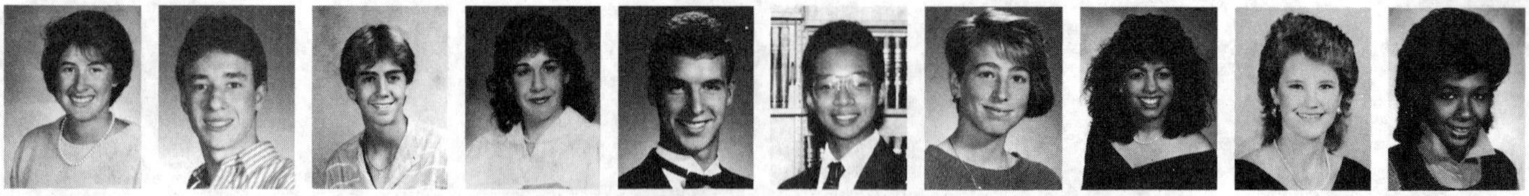

Cassidy, Lynne
Westfield HS
Westfield, NJ

Castaldo, Andrew P
River Dell HS
River Edge, NJ

Castellani, Joseph
Maple Shade HS
Maple Shade, NJ

Castellucci, Christina
Saint Dominic
Jersey City, NJ

Castrillon, Daniel M
Don Bosco Prep
Montvale, NJ

Castro, Noriel
Leonia HS
Leonia, NJ

Castronvovo, Lynne
Cliffside Park HS
Fairview, NJ

Catallo, Gina
St Mary HS
Sayreville, NJ

Cathcart, Lauren
Delran HS
Delran, NJ

Catlett, Crystal
Cinnaminson HS
Cinnaminson, NJ

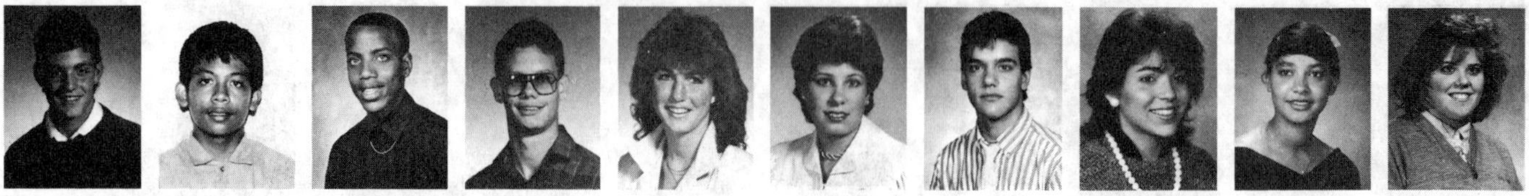

Catozzo, Christian
Montville HS
Pinebrook, NJ

Catral, John
Cliffside Park HS
Cliffside Park, NJ

Cauthen, Kraven
Passaic County Tech & Voc HS
Paterson, NJ

Cavallaro, Paul
Toms River HS East
Toms River, NJ

Cavanaugh, Nancy
Toms River HS
Toms River, NJ

Cecil, Sherri
Union HS
Union, NJ

Celano, Chris
Union Catholic Regional HS
Scotch Plains, NJ

Celeste, Catherine
Wayne Valley HS
Wayne, NJ

Centeno, Maria
Millville SR HS
Millville, NJ

Ceres, Jennifer L
Holy Spirit HS
Mays Landing, NJ

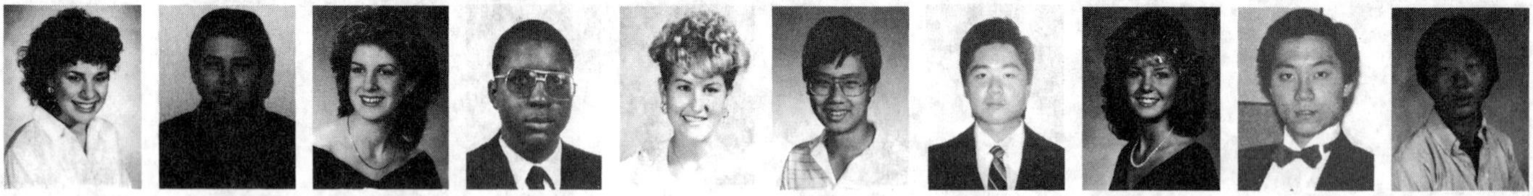

Cerrone, Cynthia
Holy Cross HS
Florence, NJ

Cervenak, George
Toms River H S
Toms River, NJ

Chaillet, Nicole
Rahway HS
Rahway, NJ

Chambers, Marquis
Angelo St V Manchester Township HS
Toms River, NJ

Chambers, Nicole
Eastern Regional
West Berlin, NJ

Chan, Geoffrey
Montville Township
Montville, NJ

Chan, Kin H
Belleville HS
Belleville, NJ

Chandler, Natalie
Triton Regional HS
Runnemede, NJ

Chang, Attica
Paramus HS
Paramus, NJ

Chang, Haejin
Holmdel HS
Holmdel, NJ

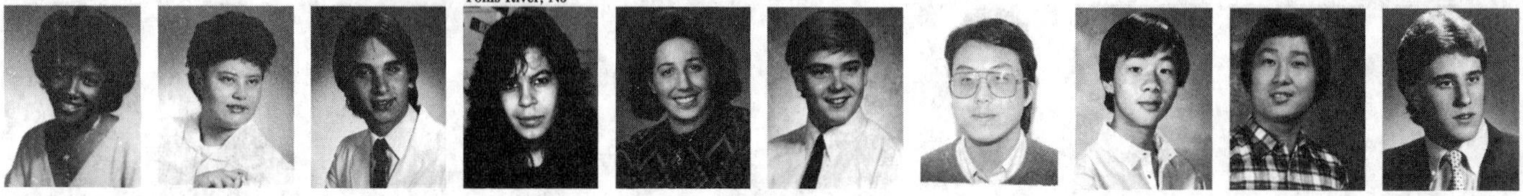

Chapman, Ericka
Atlantic City HS
Atlantic City, NJ

Chargualaf, Tricia
Monmouth Regional
Eatontown, NJ

Charnick, Barry
Monmouth Regional
Eatontown, NJ

Chavarria, Evelyn
St Joseph Of The Palisades HS
Guttenberg, NJ

Cheddar, Christina
Woodbridge HS
Port Reading, NJ

Cheney, Michael
Pennington Prepratory HS
Robbinsville, NJ

Cheng, Edward
Parsippany Hills HS
Morris Plains, NJ

Cheng, Jenfu
West Essex HS
No Caldwell, NJ

Cheng, Weiyu
Clifton HS
Clifton, NJ

Cherry, Bradley
Phillipsburg HS
Phillipsburg, NJ

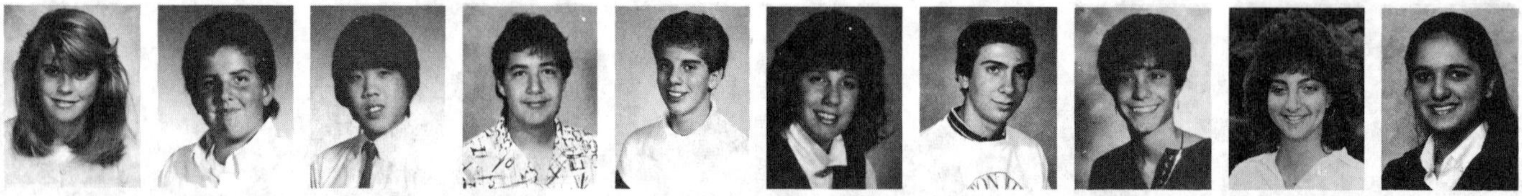

Cherry, Paige
Hunterdon Central
Stockton, NJ

Chestnut, Keith
Morristown HS
Morris Plains, NJ

Cheung, Frederick
Franklin HS
Somerset, NJ

Cheung, Octavio
Matawan Regional
Aberdeen, NJ

Chiafullo, Chris
Long Branch HS
Long Br, NJ

Chianese, Kimberly
Notre Dame HS
Yardville, NJ

Chiappetta, Jason
West Essex HS
N Caldwell, NJ

Chiavetta, Cathy
Northern Valley Regional HS
Harrington Pk, NJ

Chiliberti, Danielle
Paul VI HS
Laurel Sp, NJ

Chima, Kuljit
Mother Seton Regional HS
Carteret, NJ

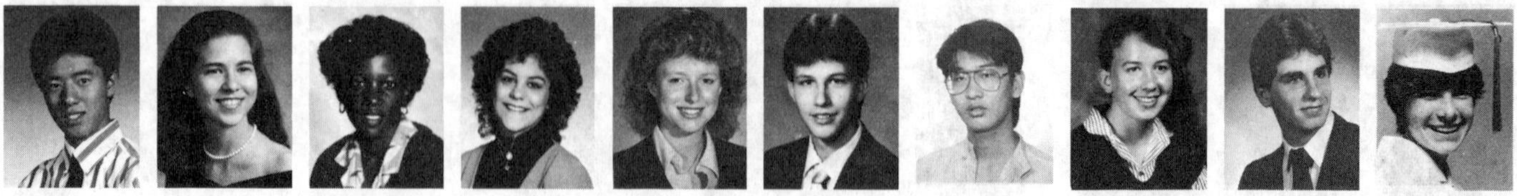

Chin, David H
Franklin HS
Somerset, NJ

Chinappi, Marissa
Moorestown HS
Moorestown, NJ

Chisholm, Cheryl
Linden HS
Linden, NJ

Chmara, Regina
Brick Memorial HS
Brick, NJ

Chmiel, Elizabeth
Notre Dame HS
Hamilton Square, NJ

Chominsky, John P
Wayne Hills HS
Wayne, NJ

Chow, Kenneth
The Pennington
New York, NY

Christensen, Carman
Ocean Township HS
Ocean, NJ

Christiana, Russell
Wood-Ridge HS
Wood Ridge, NJ

Christine, Coyle
Paul VI HS
Laurel Springs, NJ

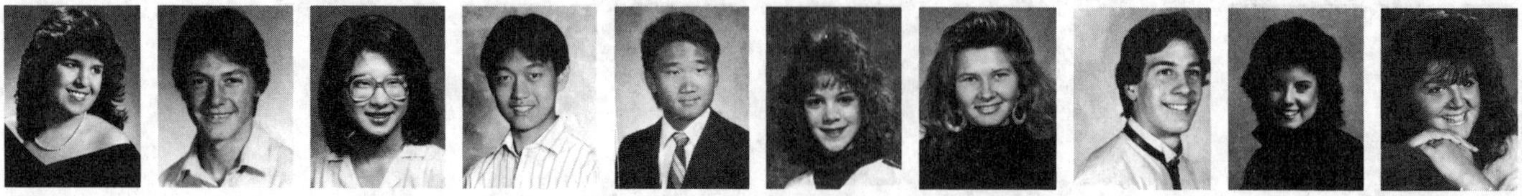

Christofilis, Carol
De Paul HS
Pompton Lakes, NJ

Christopher, Dave
Brick Township HS
Brick, NJ

Chu, Alice
Westfield SR HS
Westfield, NJ

Chun, Dal
Waldwick HS
Waldwick, NJ

Chun, Sam H
Moorestown SR HS
Moorestown, NJ

Chupak, Carol Anne
Immaculate Conception HS
Lodi, NJ

Chwatko, Shirley
Rutgers Prep Schl
Old Bridge, NJ

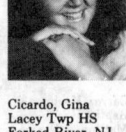

Ciampi, Marc
Holy Cross HS
Marlton, NJ

Ciarco, Shauna
Lyndhurst HS
Lyndhurst, NJ

Cicardo, Gina
Lacey Twp HS
Forked River, NJ

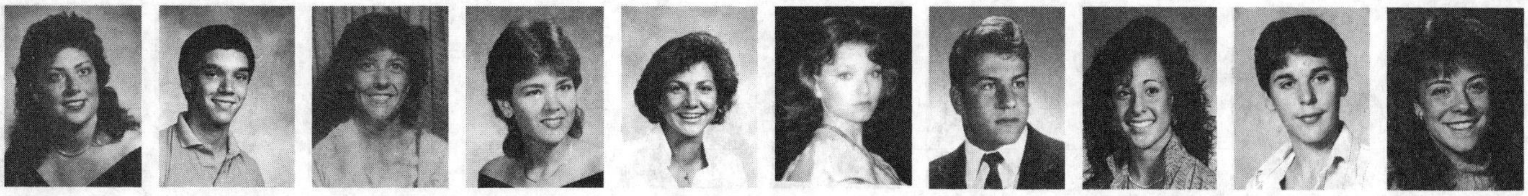

Cicarelli, Jill
Holy Spirit HS
Brigantine, NJ

Ciccarelli, Robert
Haddonfield
Memorial HS
Haddonfield, NJ

Cicchino, Susan E
Monsignor Donovan
Jackson, NJ

Ciemnolonski, Laura
Burlington City HS
Burlington, NJ

Cioffi, Michele
Saint John Vianney
Freehold, NJ

Cipolla, Kelly
Pennsville Memorial
Pennsville, NJ

Cirello, Vincent
Anthony
Fair Lawn HS
Fair Lawn, NJ

Cirianni, Sarina
Bridgewater-Raritan
Raritan, NJ

Cirigliano, III Joe
Oakcrest HS
Mays Lndg, NJ

Cirillo, Tara
West Essex SR HS
Fairfield, NJ

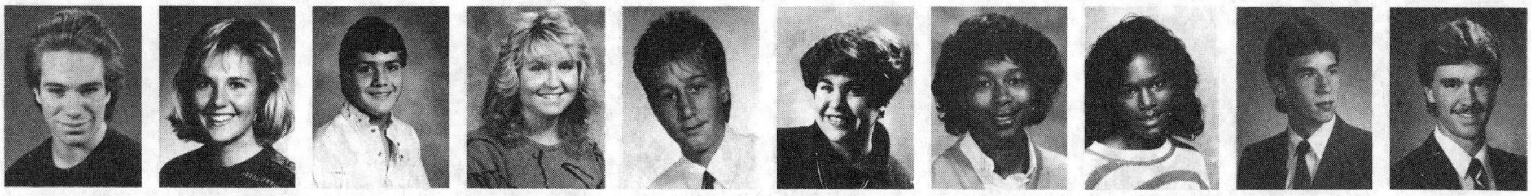

Ciulla, Jr Peter
Nutley HS
Nutley, NJ

Cividanes, Ame
Toms River HS
Toms River, NJ

Clarizio, Joseph
Lyndhurst HS
Lyndhurst, NJ

Clark, Cheryl A
Spotwood HS
Milltown, NJ

Clark, Gordon
Brick Town HS
Brick Town, NJ

Clark, Jennifer
Ridge HS
Basking Ridge, NJ

Clark, Loretta
Mc Corristin
Catholic HS
Yardville, NJ

Clark, Tiffani
Evangeline
Garden State Acad
New Rochelle, NY

Clark-Christie,
Jason
John P Stevens HS
Edison, NJ

Clarke, Donald
Millville SR HS
Millville, NJ

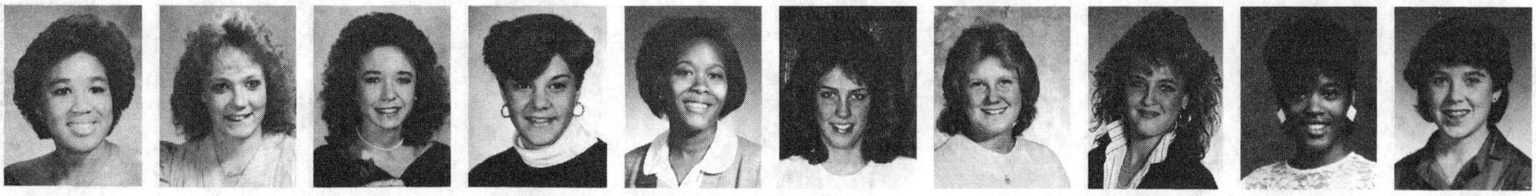

Clarke, Kim
Jackson Memorial
Jackson, NJ

Clarkson, Shannin
Jackson Memorial

Clauser, Vera
Delran HS
Delran, NJ

Clayman, Amy Jill
Westfield HS
Westfield, NJ

Clayton, Tammie
Paterson Catholic
Regional HS
Paterson, NJ

Cleary, Cheryl
Clifton HS
Clifton, NJ

Clemens, Lisa
Bordentown
Regional HS
Bordentown, NJ

Clemente, Donna
Wood Ridge HS
Woodridge, NJ

Clemons, Lisa
Monmouth Regional
Neptune, NJ

Clifford, Anne
Morristown HS
Morris Plains, NJ

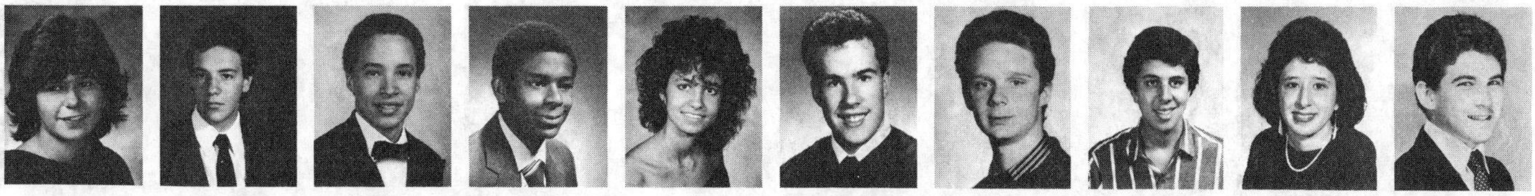

Clinton, Barbara
Paramus Catholic
Girls Regional
Leonia, NJ

Coceano, Thomas
St Marys
Hall-Doane Acad
Willingboro, NJ

Cochrane, Craig A
Lenape HS
Mt Laurel, NJ

Cody, Daniel A
Ramapo HS
Wyckoff, NJ

Coelho, Carla A
Kearny HS
Kearny, NJ

Cogan, William E
Paul VI Regional
Clifton, NJ

Coglianese,
Christopher
Linden HS
Linden, NJ

Cohen, Marc
Eastern HS
Voorhees, NJ

Cohen, Marcy
Middlesex HS
Middlesex, NJ

Cohen, Mark
John P Stevens HS
Edison, NJ

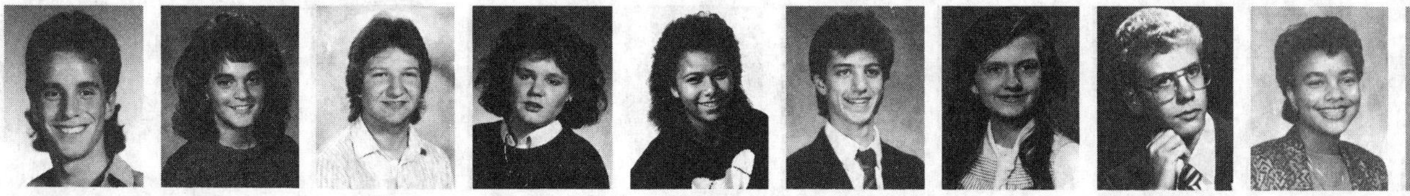

Cohen, Seth D
Cedar Ridge HS
Matawan, NJ

Colavita, Leslie
West Essex SR HS
Fairfield, NJ

Cole, Douglas
Washington
Township HS
Sewell, NJ

Coleman, Beth Ann
De Paul Diocesan
Wayne, NJ

Coleman, Penny
Barnstable Acad
Upper Saddle Rive,
NJ

Coleman, Shawn
Holy Spirit HS
Absecon, NJ

Coles, Sheri
Cumberland
Regional HS
Brigeton, NJ

Collins, Edmond A
The Pinry Schl
Short Hills, NJ

Collins, Natalie
Burlington Twp HS
Burlington, NJ

PHOTO NOT AVAILABLE

Collins, Thomas
Morristown HS
Convent Station, NJ

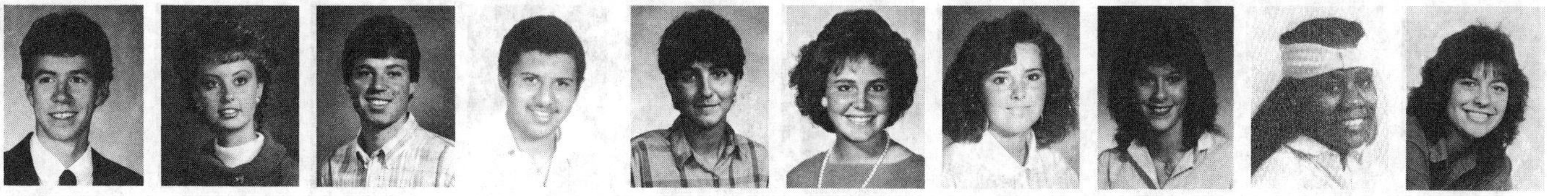

Collins, Timothy
Verona HS
Verona, NJ

Colomy, Heidi
Sacred Heart HS
Newfield, NJ

Colonna, Todd
Ridge HS
Basking Ridge, NJ

Colpas, Oscar
Eastside HS
Paterson, NJ

Comparri, Melissa
Buena Regional HS
Richland, NJ

Conboy, Kim
Sparta HS
Sparta, NJ

Conboy, Patricia
Notre Dame HS
Lawrenceville, NJ

Condon, Joy
Randolph HS
Randolph, NJ

Coney, Sophia
Trenton Central HS
Trenton, NJ

Conklin, Christie
Toms River HS East
Toms River, NJ

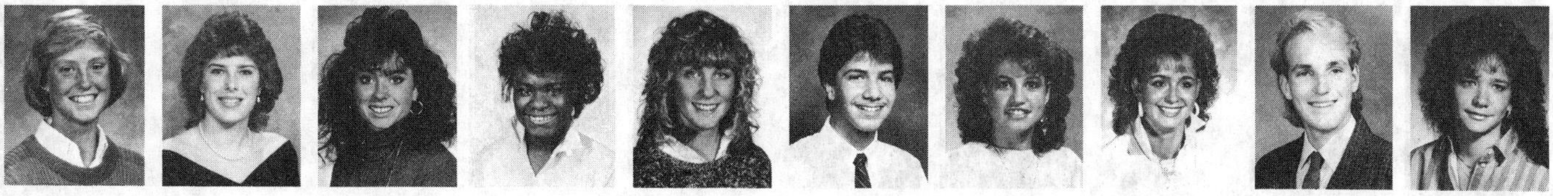

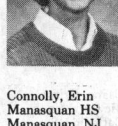

Connolly, Erin
Manasquan HS
Manasquan, NJ

Connor, Wendy
Salem HS
Salem, NJ

Connors, Debbie
Ann
Sparta HS
Sparta, NJ

Constable,
Riches-Ann
Lacordaire Acad
East Orange, NJ

Constant, Alicia
Cinnaminson HS
Cinnaminson, NJ

Conte, Gary
St John Vianney HS
Freehold, NJ

Conte, Luann
Lawrence HS
Lawrenceville, NJ

Conville, Susan
Washington
Township HS
Blackwood, NJ

Conway, David S
Ocean City HS
Ocean City, NJ

Conway, Lauren
Highstown HS
E Windsor, NJ

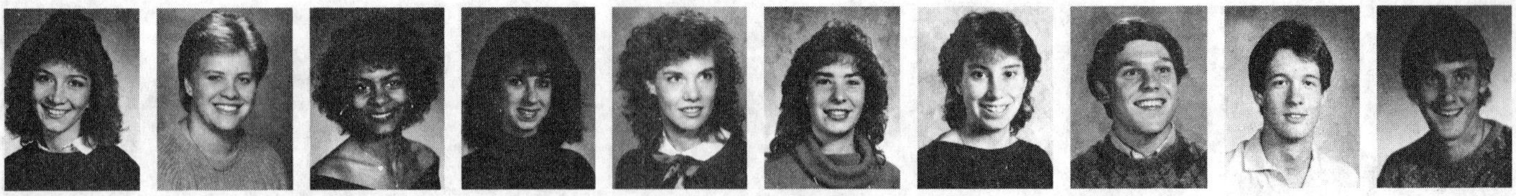

Cook, Andria
Morris Hills HS
Dover, NJ

Cook, Betsy
Eastern Christian
Mahwah, NJ

Cook, Chanel
Mount Saint Mary
Plainfield, NJ

Cook, Karen
Park Ridge HS
Park Ridge, NJ

Cook, Lauren
Eastern Christian
Hawthorne, NJ

Cook, Laurie
Hackettstown HS
Hackettstown, NJ

Cook, Tricia E
Ewing HS
Trenton, NJ

Cooke, David A
Midland Park HS
Midland Park, NJ

Coon, Rodney L
Palmyra HS
Riverton, NJ

Cooper, Christopher
Brick HS
Brick, NJ

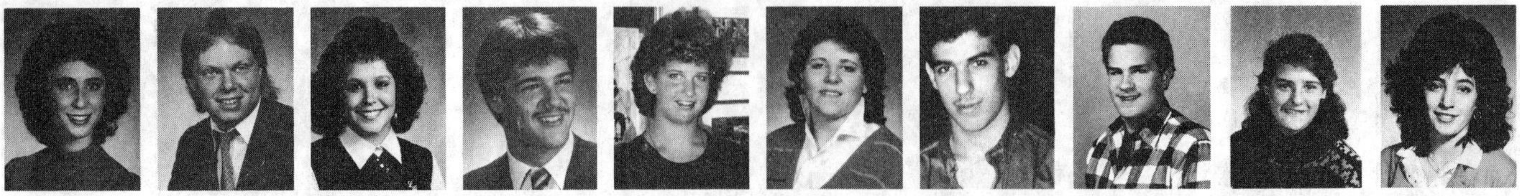

Cooperman, Joelle
Cherry Hill East HS
Cherry Hill, NJ

Cooperman, Marc S
Newark Acad
Short Hills, NJ

Copper, Jacqueline
Life Center Acad
Burlington, NJ

Corallo, David
Passaic Valley HS
Little Falls, NJ

Corallo, Stacey
Summit HS
Summit, NJ

Cordeiro, Brenda
St Mary HS
Spotswood, NJ

Cores, Alvaro J
Union Hill HS
Union City, NJ

Corlett, Michael
Lower Cape May
Regional HS
Erma, NJ

Cornejo, Jenny
Dover HS
Dover, NJ

Cornett, Kimberly
Hawthorne HS
Hawthorne, NJ

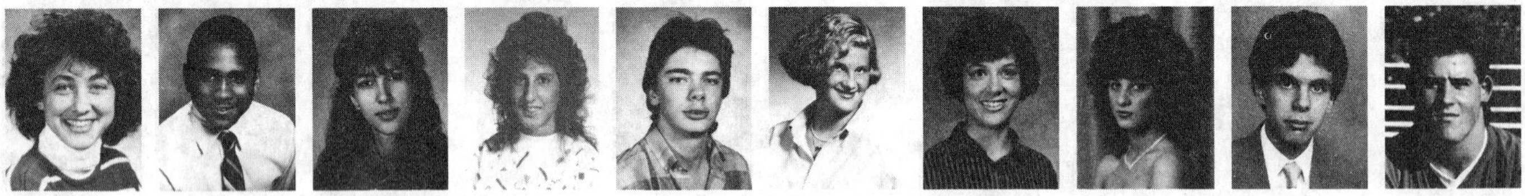

Cornish, Megan
Phillipsburg
Catholic HS
Stewartsville, NJ

Cornish, Rodney J
Eastside HS
Paterson, NJ

Corona, Rosa
Perth Amboy HS
Perth Amboy, NJ

Corrao, Denise
North Arlington HS
N Arlington, NJ

Corry, Daniel
Cumberland
Regional HS
Bridgeton, NJ

Corton, Jannette
St Josephs Of The
W New York, NJ

Costa, Lisa
Pitman HS
Pitman, NJ

Costa, Victoria
Holy Family Acad
Bayonne, NJ

Costalas, Michael
Marlboro HS
Englishtown, NJ

Costantino, Brian
Paul VI HS
Laurel Springs, NJ

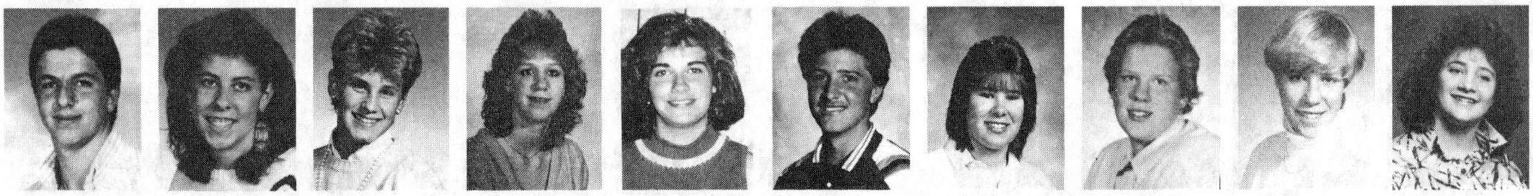

Costantino, Robert
Ocean City HS
Sea Isle City, NJ

Costanza, Juslaine
West
Windsor-Plainsbor
W Windsor, NJ

Coster, Cindy
Chatham Township
Chatham Twp, NJ

Cotton, Jennifer
Riverside HS
Riverside, NJ

Couchman, Claire E
New Providence HS
New Providence, NJ

Coughlin, Jeff
Linden HS
Linden, NJ

Counterman, Jodie
Belvidere HS
Phillipsburg, NJ

Courtright, Cheryl
Sussex County
Vo-Tech HS
Franklin, NJ

Covert, Hannah
Middletown High
School South
Middletown, NJ

Cowgill, Dawn
Paulsboro HS
Paulsboro, NJ

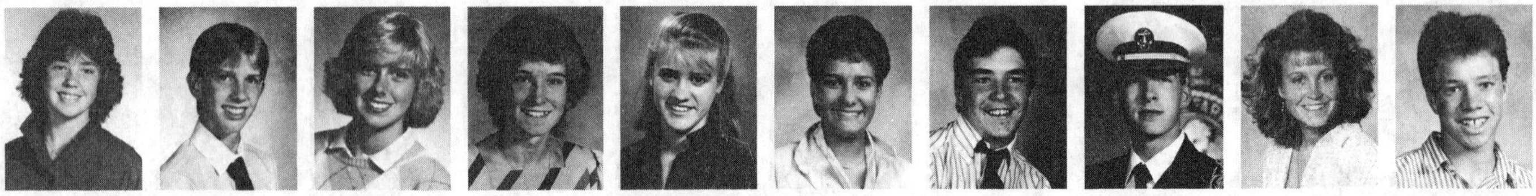

Cox, Christine
Morristown HS
Morristown, NJ

Cox, Joseph
Holy Cross HS
Mount Laurel, NJ

Cox, Mary Jude
Red Bank Regional
Little Silver, NJ

Coyle, Cynthia
Pope Paul VI HS
Laurel Springs, NJ

Cramer, Abby
Ridge HS
Basking Ridge, NJ

Cramer, Christine
Delaware Valley
Regional HS
Milford, NJ

Cramer, Michael
Holy Cross HS
Beverly, NJ

Crane, Brian E
Admiral Farragut
Colts Neck, NJ

Crane, Marybeth
Oakcrest HS
Egg Harbor, NJ

Crawford, Jeffrey
Mainland Regional
Somers Point, NJ

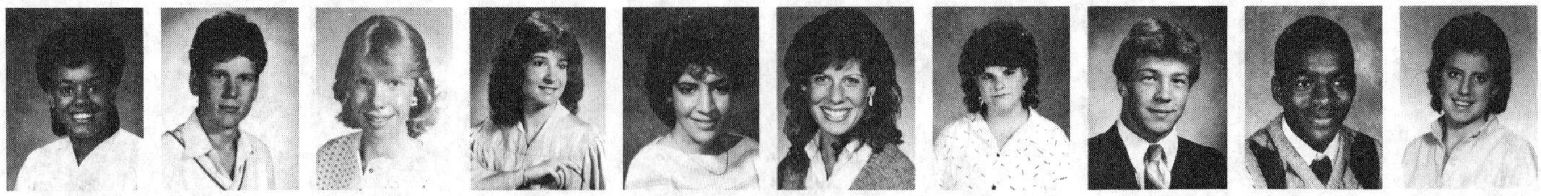

Crawford, Vista
Millville SR HS
Millville, NJ

Creagh, Kevin
Cinnaminson HS
Cinnaminson, NJ

Cregan, Christina
Morristown HS
Morristown, NJ

Cressen, Lynn Marie
Toms River East HS
Toms River, NJ

Crincoli, Kristin
S River HS
S River, NJ

Cristell, Marla
Scotch Plains
Fanwood HS
Scotch Plains, NJ

Cristinzio, Toni
Monongahela HS
Deptford, NJ

Crocco, Todd
Hunterdon Central
Ringoes, NJ

Cropper, Jonathan
Williamstown HS
Williamstown, NJ

Crosby, Kathleen
St Pius X Regional
Parlin, NJ

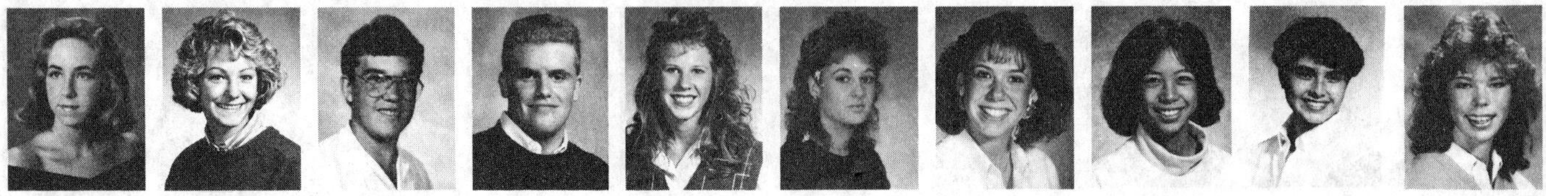

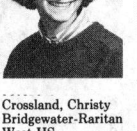

Crossland, Bonnie
Atlantic City HS
Ventnor, NJ

Crossland, Christy
Bridgewater-Raritan
West HS
Bridgewater, NJ

Crouch, Kevin
Woodstown HS
Woodstown, NJ

Crowley, Carl C
Mainland Reg HS
Somers Point, NJ

Crowley, Jocelyn
Watchung Hills
Regional HS
Warren, NJ

Crowley, Mary
Park Ridge HS
Park Ridge, NJ

Crucili, Stacie
Notre Dame HS
Trenton, NJ

Cruz, Anne Marie
Ridgewood HS
Ridgewood, NJ

Cruz, Magdala
St Joseph Of The
Palisades HS
West New York, NJ

Csapo, Krista
Mc Corristin
Catholic HS
Trenton, NJ

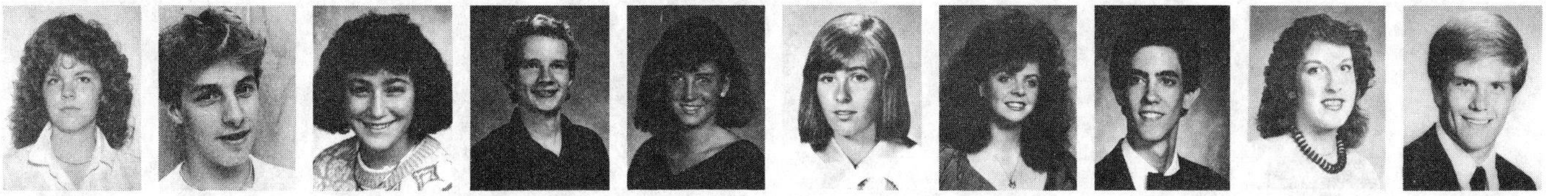

Csercsevits, Mary E
Holy Cross HS
Mt Holly, NJ

Cuccarese, Jon
Brick Township HS
Brick Town, NJ

Culcasi, Rosemary
Hunterdon Central
Flemington, NJ

Cumberland, Joseph
Burlington County
Fort Dix, NJ

Cummings, Elizabeth
Westfield HS
Westfield, NJ

Cummings, Pamela
Holy Family Acad
Bayonne, NJ

Cuneo, Donna L
Paul VI HS
Somerdale, NJ

Cunningham, Jr Dennis J
Mc Corristin HS
Trenton, NJ

Cunningham, Kira
Rancocas Valley Regional HS
Mt Holly, NJ

Cunningham, Matthew E
Red Bank Catholic
W Allenhurst, NJ

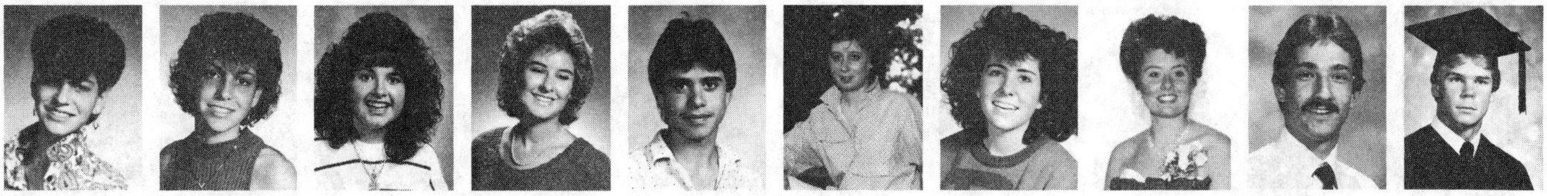

Cuozzo, Jeanne
West Windsor-Plainsbor
Princeton Junct, NJ

Cuozzo, Theresa
West Windsor-Plainsbor
Princeton Junct, NJ

Cupaiuolo, Danielle
Gateway R HS
Westville, NJ

Cupon, Leanne N
Phillipsburg HS
Alpha, NJ

Curcio, Joseph
Buena Regional HS
Newfield, NJ

Cure, Joan Ann
Oak Knoll HS
Oldwick, NJ

Curran, Bridget
De Paul HS
Ringwood, NJ

Curry, Laura Lyn
Lyndhurst HS
Lyndhurst, NJ

Curry, Stephen
Monsignor Donovan
Toms River, NJ

Curtis, Glenn
Deptford HS
Deptford, NJ

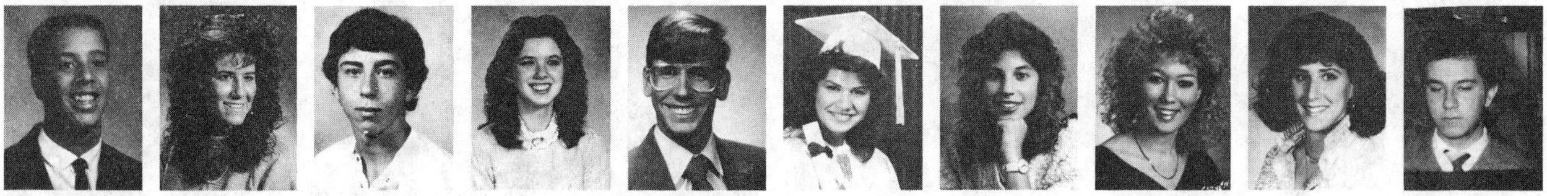

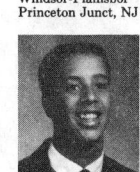

Curtis, Jr Kenneth
Essex Catholic Boys
East Orange, NJ

Cutler, Lisa
Cherry Hill East HS
Cherry Hill, NJ

Cutti, Eric M
St John Vianney HS
Morganville, NJ

Czachur, Christine
Middlesex HS
Middlesex, NJ

Czebieniak, Daniel J
Spotswood HS
Millton, NJ

Czechowski, Sarah
Delran HS
Delran, NJ

Czerniecki, Jeanna
Paul Vi Regional HS
Clifton, NJ

D Addario, Gina
Rahway HS
Rahway, NJ

D Addio, Diane
Cranford HS
Cranford, NJ

D Agostino, Leonard
Holy Spirit HS
Atlantic City, NJ

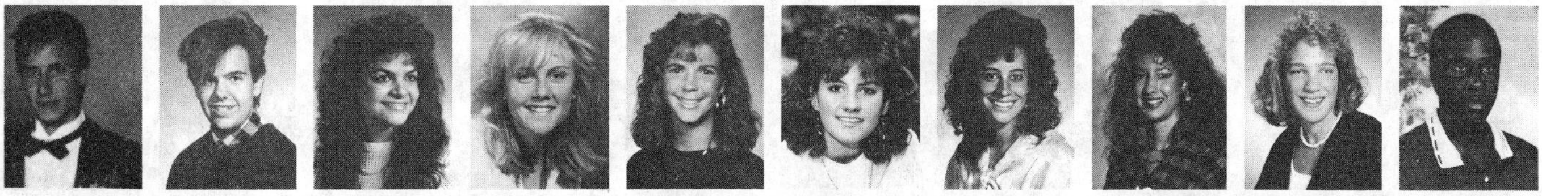

D Amore, Paul
St Augustine Prep
Richland, NJ

D Angelo, Robert
Lodi HS
Lodi, NJ

D Aniello, Susan
Immaculata HS
Somerville, NJ

D Anna, Rita Kristine
The Morristown Beard Schl
Oldwick, NJ

D Antuono, Christine G Scotch
Plains-Fanwood HS
Fanwood, NJ

D Zio, Dena S
Lakewood HS
Lakewood, NJ

Da Salla, Suzanne
High Point Reg HS
Sussex, NJ

Da Silva, Michelle
Linden HS
Linden, NJ

Dabagian, Gaye M
Ramapo Regional
Franklin Lks, NJ

Daily, III Albert
Perth Amboy HS
Perth Amboy, NJ

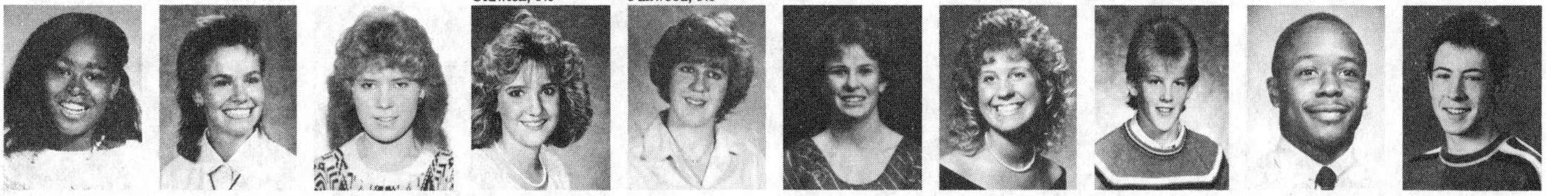

Dale, Tara
Orange HS
Orange, NJ

Dalton, Jill
Manasquan HS
Manasquan, NJ

Dalton, Melissa
Pope Paul VI HS
Williamstown, NJ

Daly, Cathy
Roselle Park HS
Roselle Park, NJ

Daly, Kim
Holy Rosary Acad
N Bergen, NJ

Dalziel, Jan
Neptune HS
Neptune, NJ

Danese, Michele
Shawnee HS
Medford, NJ

Daniels, Bradley
Pennington Prep
Hamilton Square, NJ

Daniels, Jr James R
John F Kennedy HS
Willingboro, NJ

Daniels, Jeffrey
John P Stevens HS
Edison, NJ

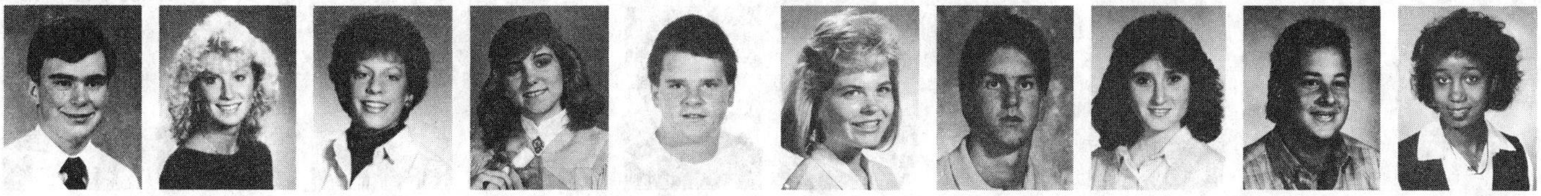

Daniels, Keith
Holy Spirit HS
Absecon, NJ

Daniels, Kimberly
Passaic Valley HS
Little Falls, NJ

Danko, Noelle
Brick Memorial HS
Brick, NJ

Darchi, Debbi
Central Regional HS
Bayville, NJ

Darcy, Kevin
Brick Township HS
Brick Town, NJ

Daren, Heather
Hamilton H S West
Trenton, NJ

Darminio, Jr Joseph T
Delsea Regional HS
Newfield, NJ

Darroch, Shannon
Sayreville War Memorial HS
Parlin, NJ

Dash, Ben
Cinnaminson HS
Cinnaminson, NJ

Davenport, Michelle
Mary Help Of Christians Acad
Paterson, NJ

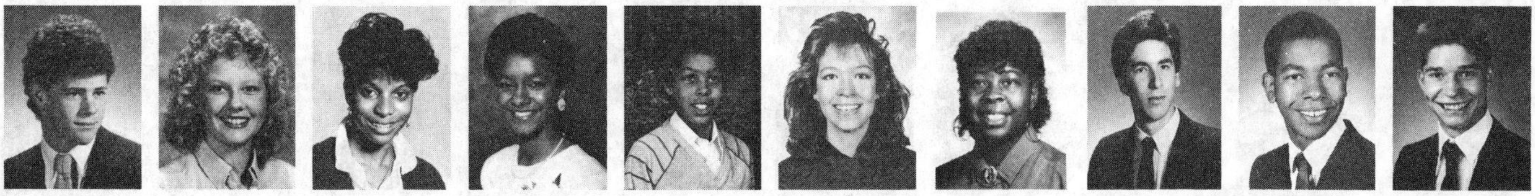

Davenport, Ted
Mt Olive Township
Flanders, NJ

Davidson, Christina Theresa
Monsignor Donovan
Toms River, NJ

Davis, Deanne
Saint James HS
Paulsboro, NJ

Davis, Elisa
Kingsway Regional
Swedesboro, NJ

Davis, Gregory
Burlington County
Willingboro, NJ

Davis, Heather
Sparta HS
Sparta, NJ

Davis, Louise Janine
Hamilton HS West
Trenton, NJ

Davis, Marc
Bridgewater-Raritan West HS
Bridgewater, NJ

Davis, Mark G
Highland Park HS
Highland Park, NJ

Davis, Matthew D
Ocean Twp HS
Ocean, NJ

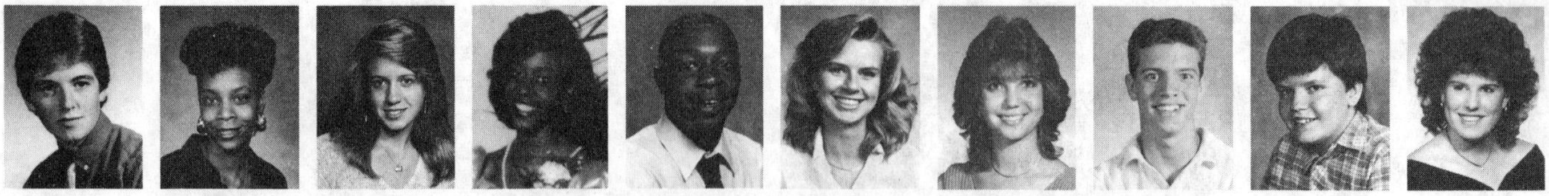

Davis, Randy
Dover HS
Mine Hill, NJ

Davis, Regina
Bridgeton HS
Bridgeton, NJ

Davis, Tammy
Westwood HS
Westwood, NJ

Davis, Vanessa
Eastside HS
Paterson, NJ

Davis, Vincent
St Anthony HS
Jersey Cty, NJ

Day, Pamela
St John Vianney HS
Colts Neck, NJ

De Bari, Marta M
South Brunswick
Kendall Pk, NJ

De Blasi, Frank
Manalapan HS
Manalapan, NJ

De Carlo, Anthony
Brick Memorial HS
Brick, NJ

De Carlo, Tammy
Paramus HS
Paramus, NJ

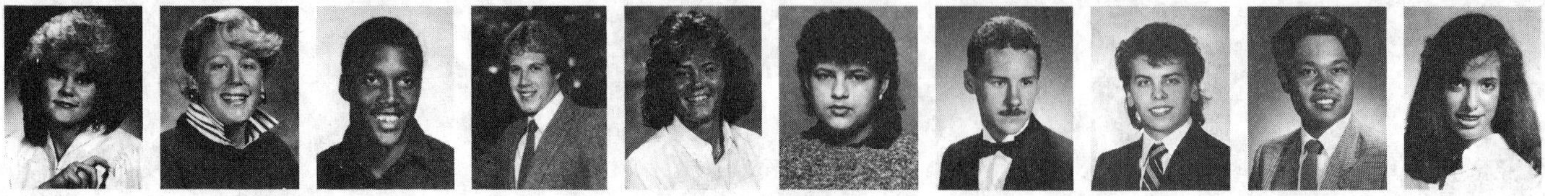

De Carlo, Yvonne
Wood-Ridge HS
Wood Ridge, NJ

De Castro, Jennifer
Manasquan HS
Sea Girt, NJ

De Causey, Lafayette
Lakewood HS
Lakewood, NJ

De Cesare, R
Blair Acad
Portland, PA

De Filippis, Jilene
Monsignor Donovan
Bayville, NJ

De Freese, Christine
Mahwah HS
Mahwah, NJ

De Gennaro, Joseph
St Josephs Of The Palisades HS
N Bergen, NJ

De La Cruz, Enrique M
Kearny HS
Kearny, NJ

De La Cruz, Michael S
Perth Amboy HS
Perth Amboy, NJ

De Latorre, Michelle
St Josephs Of The
Guttenberg, NJ

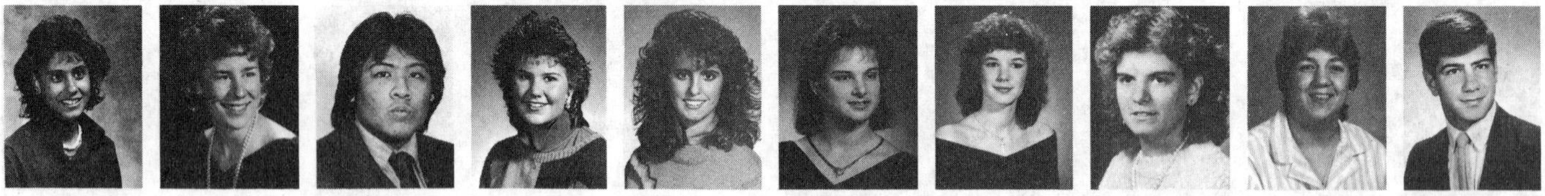

De Leon, Sandee
Spotswood HS
Spotswood, NJ

De Long, Lara
Kittatinny Regional
Newton, NJ

De Los Reyes, Marc
Marist HS
Jersey City, NJ

De Manss, Toni
West Milford HS
West Milford, NJ

De Marco, Toni Ann
Lakeland Regional
Wanaque, NJ

De Miglio, Dawn
St Peters HS
New Brunswick, NJ

De Puy, Carol
Immaculate Heart
Allendale, NJ

De Rienzo, Denise
Paramus Catholic
Garfield, NJ

De Sousa, Sharon
Southern Regional
Barnegat, NJ

De Vivo, Paul J
Randolph HS
Columbia, MD

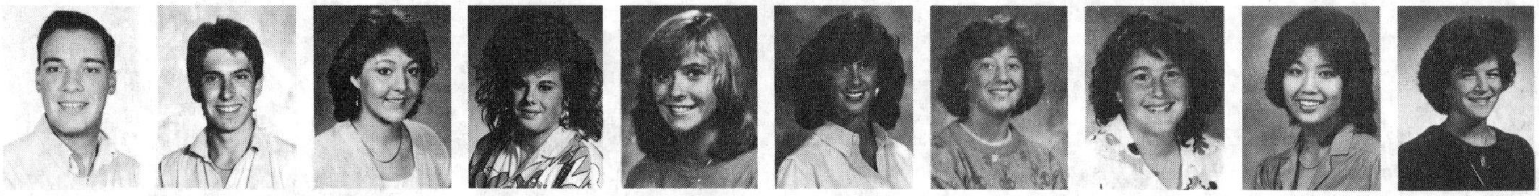

Deas, Geoffrey S
Rumson Fair Haven Regional HS
Rumson, NJ

Debonis, Frank
Northern Valley Regional HS
Harrington Pk, NJ

Decker, Sharon
Eastern Christian
Franklin Lakes, NJ

Decker, Tasha
High Point Regional
Branchville, NJ

Deegan, Dale
Manasquan HS
Brielle, NJ

Degruccio, Sally Ann
Monsignor Donovan
Lavallette, NJ

Deicke, Marion
Manasquan HS
Belmar, NJ

Deitch, Dany
Manalapan HS
Englishtown, NJ

Dela Pena, Lorraine Cheryl
Sayreville War Memorial HS
Sayreville, NJ

Delaney, Dena
Ewing HS
Trenton, NJ

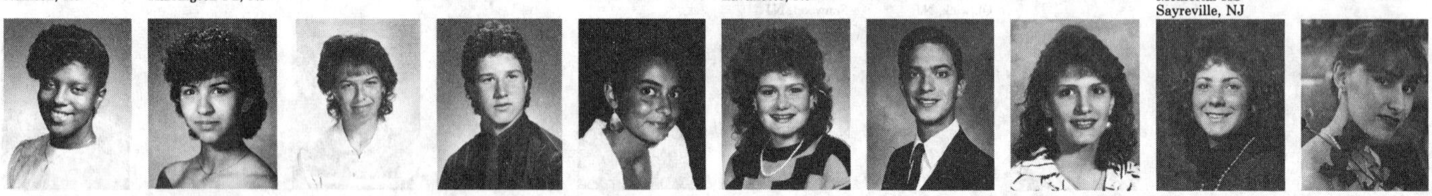

Delee, Adrienne
University HS
Newark, NJ

Delgado, Elaine
Emerson HS
Union City, NJ

Delgardio, Bridgid
Jackson Memorial
Jackson, NJ

Dellanno, Anthony
North Warren Regional HS
Blairstown, NJ

Delli Santi, Ondrea
Immaculate Conception HS
Newark, NJ

Delnero, Tara
Union Catholic Regional HS
Roselle Park, NJ

Delosso, Thomas Nicholas
Triton Regional HS
Runnemede, NJ

Demarco, Melodie
Ambassador Christian Acad
Toms River, NJ

Demarest, Annette
West Milford HS
Hewitt, NJ

Demarest, Jacqueline M
Scotch Plains-Fanwood HS
Scotch Plains, NJ

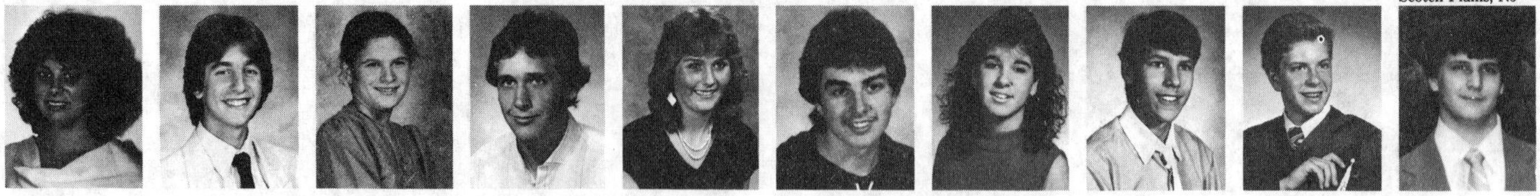

Demartini, Jennifer
Bayonne HS
Bayonne, NJ

Demartino, Jason
Essex Catholic Boys
Montclair, NJ

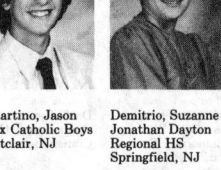

Demitrio, Suzanne L
Jonathan Dayton Regional HS
Springfield, NJ

Demm, Matthew
Morris Catholic HS
Morris Plns, NJ

Dempsey, Ann
Spotswood HS
Milltown, NJ

Dempsey, Michael
Matawan Regional
Matawan, NJ

Denice, Sharon
West Milford Township HS
West Milford, NJ

Denkowycz, Nicholas
Cinnaminson HS
Cinnaminson, NJ

Dennis, Shawn
De Paul Dioceram
Pompton Plains, NJ

Denton, Eric
Edgewood SR HS
Atco, NJ

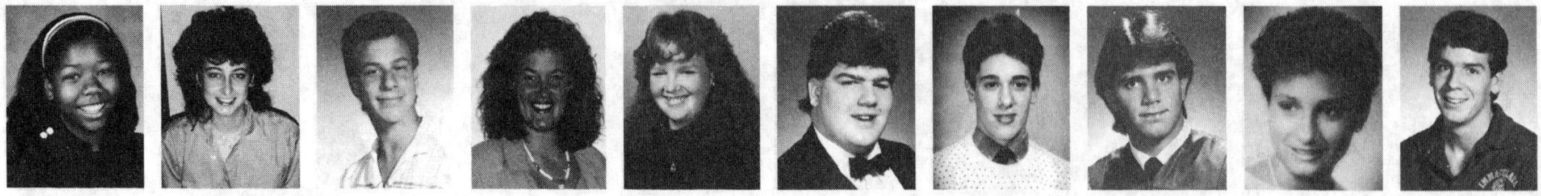

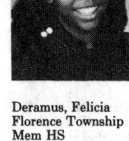

Deramus, Felicia
Florence Township Mem HS
Florence, NJ

Derienzo, Laura
Paramus Catholic Girls HS
Rochelle Pk, NJ

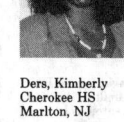

Derringer, Adam
Franklin HS
Somerset, NJ

Ders, Kimberly
Cherokee HS
Marlton, NJ

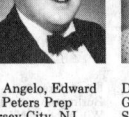

Devine, Shannan
Lower Cape May Regional HS
Villas, NJ

Di Angelo, Edward
St Peters Prep
Jersey City, NJ

Di Bella, Alfred
Gloucester County
Swedesboro, NJ

Di Bella, Craig
Toms River HS
Beachwood, NJ

Di Enna, Michelle
Haddonfield Memorial HS
Haddonfield, NJ

Di Giovanni, Peter
Immaculata HS
Belle Mead, NJ

Di Nardo, Michael
Lyndhurst HS
Lyndhurst, NJ

Di Pasquale, Frank
Manalapan HS
Englishtown, NJ

Di Pietro, Anthony
Vineland HS
Vineland, NJ

Diaz, Mario
Memorial HS
West New York, NJ

Dibease, James
Edgewood Regional SR HS
Sicklerville, NJ

Dickerson, Karen L
Highland Regional
Clementon, NJ

Dickey, Christine
Pennsville HS
Pennsville, NJ

Dickinson, Christopher
Trenton Central HS
Trenton, NJ

Dieker, Maryann
Sayreville Mar Memorial HS
S Amboy, NJ

Diem, Jr Arthur N
South River HS
South River, NJ

Dieterich, III Henry
Highland Regional
Blenheim, NJ

Digan, Marjorie L
Southern Regional
Manahawkin, NJ

Digneo, Cosmo
Chery Hill HS West
Cherry Hill, NJ

Dilauro, Michelle
Westfield HS
Westfield, NJ

Dileo, Russell
Palmyra HS
Palmyra, NJ

Dill, Keri
West Milford Twp
West Milford, NJ

Dillon, Cheryl
Morris Knolls HS
Rockaway Twp, NJ

Dillon, Tara
St John Vianney HS
Hazlet, NJ

Dionisio, Francis
St Josephs Prep
Hazlet, NJ

Dionisio, Rommel T
Morristown-Beard
Parsippany, NJ

Dipoto, Marc
Toms River HS
Leawood, KS

Dipoto, Nicole
Secaucus HS
Secaucus, NJ

Direnzo, Beth
Cherry Hill West
Cherry Hill, NJ

Direnzo, Jennifer
Cherry Hill West
Cherry Hill, NJ

Dispenza, Philip
Memorial HS
West New York, NJ

Dituri, Frank L
Morris Catholic HS
Morris Plains, NJ

Divers, Georgianna
Perth Amboy HS
Perth Amboy, NJ

Dix, Janet M
Montclair Kimberley
Wayne, NJ

Djurasovic, George
Union HS
Union, NJ

Dobie, Robert Dennis
Haddonfield Memorial HS
Haddonfield, NJ

Dobies, Justine
Paulsboro HS
Gibbstown, NJ

Dobovich, Scott
Jackson Memorial
Jackson, NJ

Dodge, William Hees
Montgomery HS
Princeton, NJ

Doe, Renee
Bayonne HS
Bayonne, NJ

Dohanick, Michele
Pinelands Regional
Tuckerton, NJ

Doherty, Debbie
John P Stevens HS
Edison, NJ

Doherty, Sheila
Elizabeth HS
Elizabeth, NJ

Dolan, Jr Robert M
Msgr Donovan HS
Toms River, NJ

Doll, Lilya A
Columbia HS
Maplewood, NJ

Dolson, Anita
Buena Reg HS
Vineland, NJ

Domzalski, Jr Joseph L
Morris Hills HS
Rockaway, NJ

Don, Richard E
Delran HS
Delran, NJ

Donahue, Sean
Pinelands Regional
New Gretna, NJ

Dondero, Tom
West Essex HS
No Caldwell, NJ

Donio, Adrienne
St Joseph HS
Hammonton, NJ

Donnelly, John
Bridgewater-Raritan HS West
Bridgewater, NJ

Donohue, Jr James F
Clearview Regional
Mantua, NJ

Donohue, Robert
Clearview Regional
Mantua, NJ

Donovan, Jean D
Parsippany Hills HS
Parsippany, NJ

Donus, David C
West Milford HS
Hewitt, NJ

Dooley, Christine
Mt St Mary Acad
Bernardsville, NJ

Dorio, Christine
Notre Dame HS
Trenton, NJ

Dorizas, Denise
Belleville SR HS
Belleville, NJ

Dorr, Gene
Notre Dame HS
Hamilton Sq, NJ

Dorsey, Joy A
Acad Of Saint
Jersey City, NJ

Dos Santos, Jennifer
Parkridge HS
Park Ridge, NJ

Doscher, Kerrie
Monsignor Donovan
Bayville, NJ

Dotter, Katherine
Bergenfield HS
Bergenfield, NJ

Douenias, Mickey
Morris Hills HS
Rockaway, NJ

Douglas, Catherine
Buena Regional HS
Vineland, NJ

Douglas, David
Lincoln HS
Jersey City, NJ

Doyle, Thomas
Bishop Goerge Ahr
Plainfield, NJ

Doyle, Thomas M
Bishop George AHR
Old Bridge, NJ

Doyle, Timothy
Atlantic City HS
Ventnor, NJ

Doyle, Tracey
Belleville HS
Belleville, NJ

Draegert, Ellen M
Madison HS
Madison, NJ

Dragish, Blythe
Collingswood SR HS
Woodlynne, NJ

Drake, James
Ewing HS
Trenton, NJ

Drayton, Gwendolyn S
Academy Of The Sacred Heart
Hoboken, NJ

Drellock, Karen
Toms River H S
Toms River, NJ

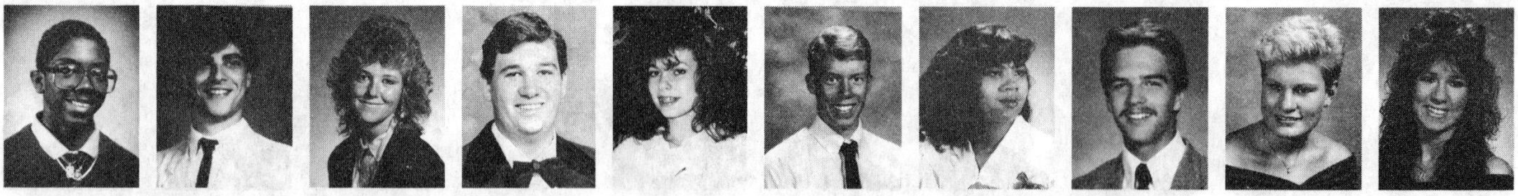

Drew, Devlin
John F Kennedy HS
Willingboro, NJ

Drexler, Harry John
Lacey Township HS
Forked River, NJ

Driscoll, Maureen
St Mary Of The
Assumption HS
Hillside, NJ

Drummond, Jr
Robert G
Salem HS
Hancocks Bridge,
NJ

Du Bois, Holly
Marie
Paul VI HS
Voorhees, NJ

Ducey, John
Monsignor Donovan
Toms River, NJ

Dudley, Tanayo
West Side HS
Newark, NJ

Dudling, Michael G
Edison HS
Edison, NJ

Duespohl, Kris
Overbrook Regional
SR HS
Pine Hill, NJ

Duff, Dawn Marie
Clifton HS
Clifton, NJ

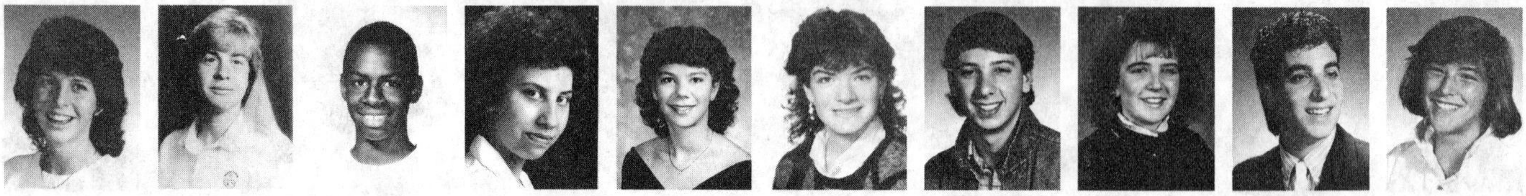

Duffy, Elizabeth
Morristown HS
Morris Plains, NJ

Duffy, Lois
Immaculata HS
Flemington, NJ

Duffy, Obun
St John Nianney HS
Marlboro, NJ

Dukiet, Linda
John P Stevens HS
Edison, NJ

Duman, Cheryl
Williamstown HS
Williamstown, NJ

Dunican, Annmarie
L
Paramus Catholic
Teaneck, NJ

Dunleavy, Timothy
Ramapo Regional
Wyckoff, NJ

Dunn, Dawn
Notre Dame HS
Trenton, NJ

Dunoff, Glenn A
Cherry Hill HS East
Cherry Hill, NJ

Dupignac, Emily
Toms River HS
Toms River, NJ

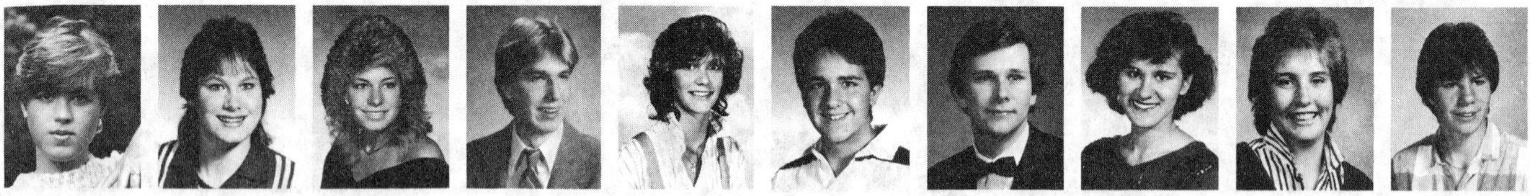

Dupuis, Elizabeth A
Govewrnor
Livingston Regiona
Berkeley Heights,
NJ

Durbin, Kim
Toms River HS
Beachwood, NJ

Durrenberger, Sheri
Paramus HS
Paramus, NJ

Duve, Mark F
Warren Hills
Regional HS
Washington, NJ

Duyck, Kimberly
Lynn
Ocean City HS
Woodbine, NJ

Dybice, Mike
Parsippany HS
Parsippany, NJ

Dychtwald, Dana
Cherokee HS
Marlton, NJ

Dzingala, Christina
Morris Knolls HS
Denville, NJ

Dzury, Robyn
Delaware Valley
Regional HS
Milford, NJ

Ebert, Christopher
Lakewood HS
Lakewood, NJ

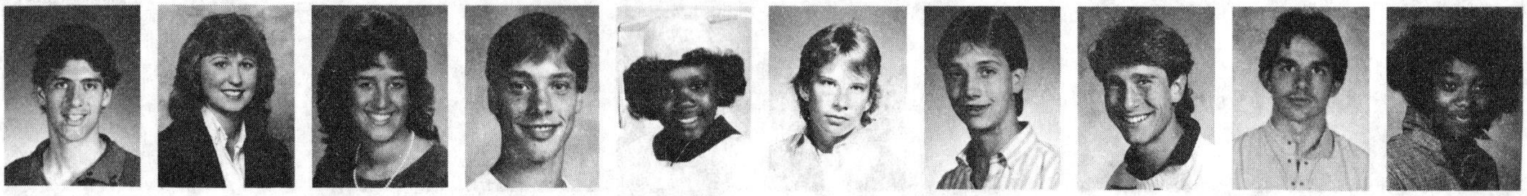

Echandy, Milton A
Neptune SR HS
Neptune, NJ

Eckert, Marta
Mother Seton
Regional HS
Mountainside, NJ

Edelstein, Andrea B
Scotch
Plains-Fanwood HS
Scotch Plns, NJ

Edge, Brian
Burlington City HS
Edgewater Pk, NJ

Edmond, Calandra
Essex Catholic Girls
Newark, NJ

Edward, Jennifer
Columbia HS
Maplewood, NJ

Edwards, Brian L
Kingsway Regional
Mickleton, NJ

Edwards, Charles
Madison HS
Morristown, NJ

Edwards, Donald
Lenape Valley
Regional HS
Stanhope, NJ

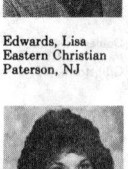

Edwards, Lisa
Eastern Christian
Paterson, NJ

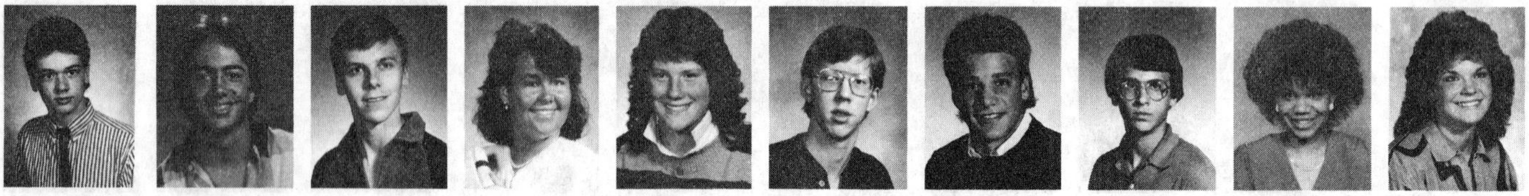

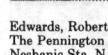

Edwards, Robert
The Pennington
Neshanic Sta, NJ

Egan, Andrew J
Palisades Park
JR-SR HS
Palisades Pk, NJ

Egan, William J
Kittatinny Regional
Newton, NJ

Eger, Deana
Mainland Regional
Somers Pt, NJ

Eible, Jen
Mendham HS
Chester, NJ

Eichlin, Scott
Delaware Valley
Regional HS
Frenchtown, NJ

Eike, Jason C
Phillipsburg HS
Alpha, NJ

Eisner, Edward C
New Providence HS
New Providence, NJ

El, Lisa
Our Lady Of Mercy
Vineland, NJ

Elk, Monica
Salem HS
Salem, NJ

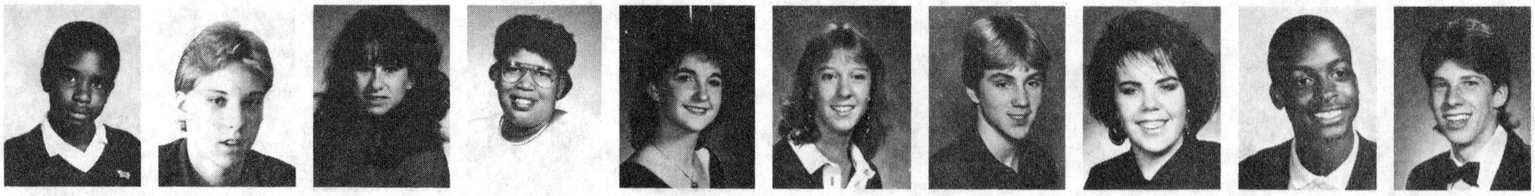

Ellen, Martin
Wallington HS
Wallington, NJ

Elliott, Clifford
Alexander
Edgewood Regional
Sicklerville, NJ

Elliott, Jamie
Freehold Township
Freehold, NJ

Ellis, April
Weequahic HS
Newark, NJ

Ellis, Cheryl
Pleasantville HS
Pleasantville, NJ

Ellis, Kristin
Ocean Township HS
Asbury Park, NJ

Ellis, Steve Roger
Rancocas Valley
Regional HS
Lumberton, NJ

Elmiger, Joann
Union Catholic
Regional HS
Cranford, NJ

Elmore, Dwight
Lakewood SR HS
Lakewood, NJ

Embleton, Michael
Vernon Township
Vernon, NJ

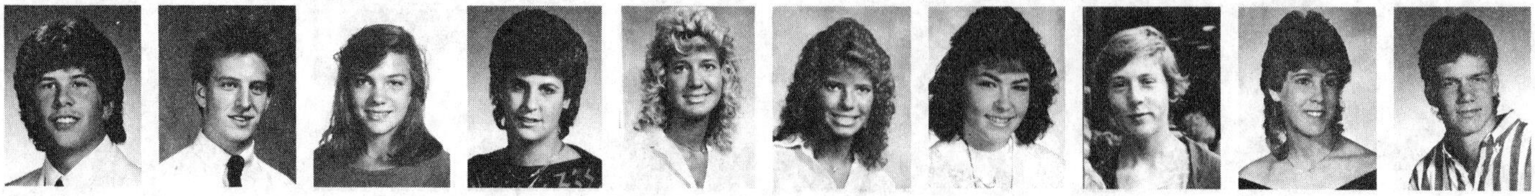

Embley, Gary
Hamilton HS West
Trenton, NJ

Emenheiser, Rick
Willingboro HS
Willingboro, NJ

Emery, Jennifer L
Scotch Plains
Fanwood HS
Scotch Plains, NJ

Emmerling, Lorin E
West Milford HS
West Milford, NJ

Emmons, Debra
St John Vianney HS
Keyport, NJ

Emmons, Lisa
St John Vianney HS
Keyport, NJ

Engeke, Shelly
Hunterdon Central
Lebanon, NJ

Engel, Andrew
Dwight Engelwood
Norwood, NJ

English, Valerie
Kearny HS
Kearny, NJ

Enser, Jon
Ramapo HS
Wyckoff, NJ

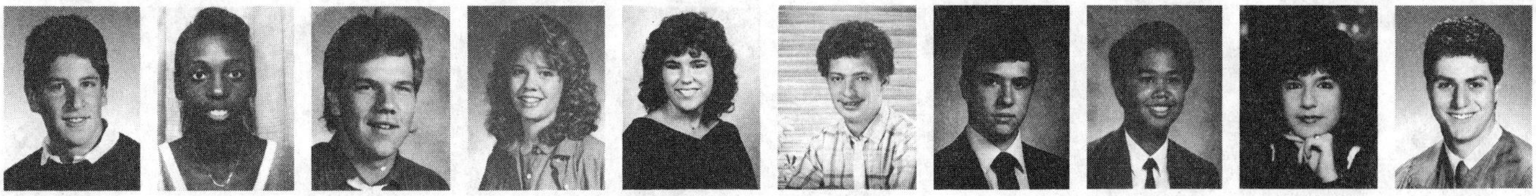

Entis, Ira S
Morristown HS
Morristown, NJ

Epps, Andrea
Pennsauken HS
Delair, NJ

Erdman, Ronnie J
Haddon Township
Westmont, NJ

Erdo, Kristiane
Toms River HS
Beachwood, NJ

Erianne, Joan
Cumberland
Regional HS
Bridgeton, NJ

Errickson, Jr David
Middle Township
Del Haven, NJ

Errico, Marcus R
Hunterdon Central
Sergeantsville, NJ

Escobinas, Ariel A J
Essex Catholic Boys
Bloomfield, NJ

Esmurdoc, Carolina
Frances
Oak Knoll Schl
Elizabeth, NJ

Esposito, Glen
Hawthorne HS
Hawthorne, NJ

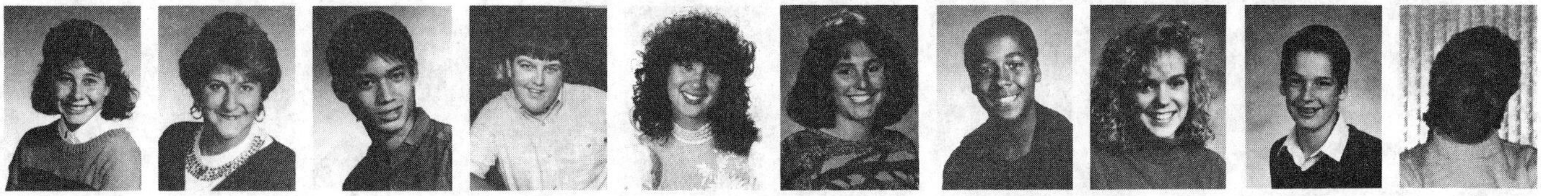

Esposito, Jennifer
Randolph HS
Ironia, NJ

Esposito, Sharon
Dover HS
Dover, NJ

Esquieres, Ronald
Indian Hills HS
Oakland, NJ

Estelle, Eddie
Lakewood HS
Lakewood, NJ

Estevez, Marisol
Memorial HS
W New York, NJ

Estis, Michelle
Manalapan HS
Manalapan, NJ

Eubanks, III John
Scott
Clifford J Scott HS
East Orange, NJ

Eugster, Laura
Woodbury HS
Woodbury, NJ

Evans, Thomas
Concord HS
Concord, NH

Everett, Mark
St Anthony HS
Jersey Cty, NJ

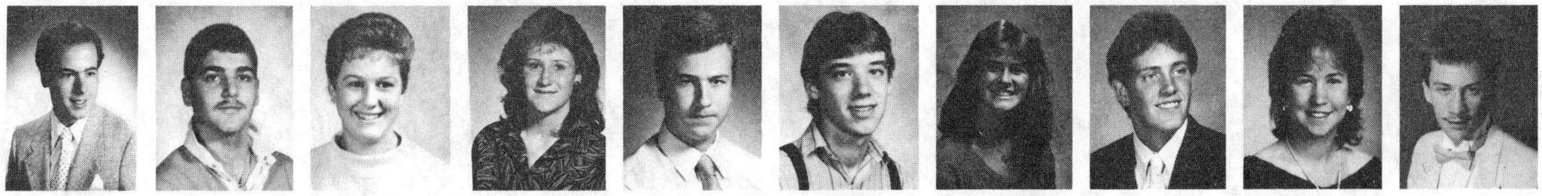

Everitt, Christopher
Brick Township
Memorial HS
Brick, NJ

Evola, Maurice
Delran HS
Delran, NJ

Ewan, Jill
Edgewood Regional
Cedar Brook, NJ

Faasse, Jean
West Milford
Township HS
West Milford, NJ

Fabiszewski, Walter
St Joseph Regional
Valley Cottage, NY

Faherty, Sean
South Hunterdon
Regional HS
Lambertville, NJ

Fahey, Rosalind
Ann
Bernards HS
Bernardsville, NJ

Fahey, Sean
Point Pleasant Boro
Point Pleasant, NJ

Fahner, Rosemary
Rahway HS
Rahway, NJ

Fahs, Frank
Paulsboro HS
Gibbstown, NJ

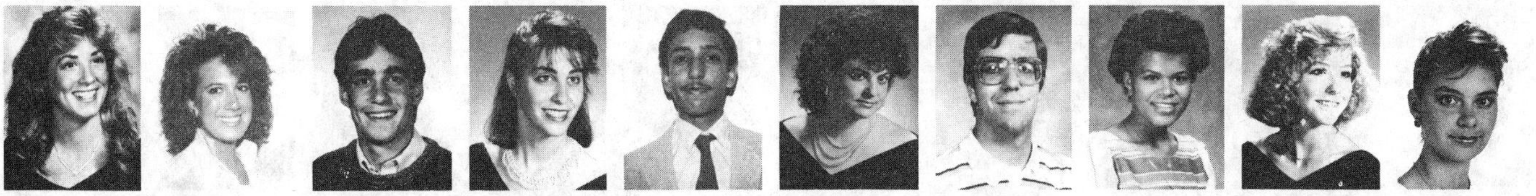

Failla, Cindy
Jackson Memorial
Jackson, NJ

Faktor, Stacy
Freehold Township
Freehold, NJ

Falcone, Tom
Verona HS
Verona, NJ

Faliveno, Karleen
Belleville HS
Belleville, NJ

Fallah, Mazyar
West Windsor HS
Robbinsville, NJ

Falvo, Gina
Watching Hills
Regional HS
Stirling, NJ

Falvo, James
South Hunterdon
Regional HS
Lambertville, NJ

Fancis, Stephanie
Willingboro HS
Willingboro, NJ

Farella, Angelina
Brick Township HS
Brick, NJ

Farias, Tamara
John P Stevens HS
Edison, NJ

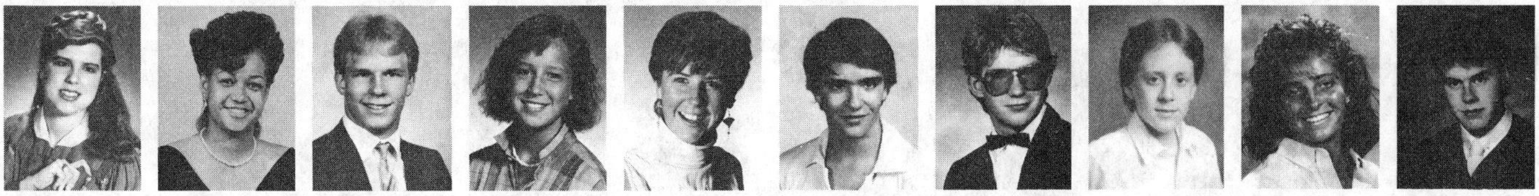

Farinas, Lissette
St Joseph Of The
Palisades HS
W New York, NJ

Farmer, Shannon
Holy Spirit HS
Pleasantville, NJ

Farmer, William
Cumberland
Regional HS
Bridgeton, NJ

Farnam, Meredith
Columbia HS
Maplewood, NJ

Farnan, Missy
Ramapo HS
Wyckoff, NJ

Farrell, David
Collingswood HS
Oaklyn, NJ

Farrell, Frank H
Sussex County
Andover, NJ

Farrell, II James
Pope John XXIII
Andover, NJ

Farrell, Meghan
Monsignor Donovan
Toms River, NJ

Fatouros, Tony
Marist HS
Bayonne, NJ

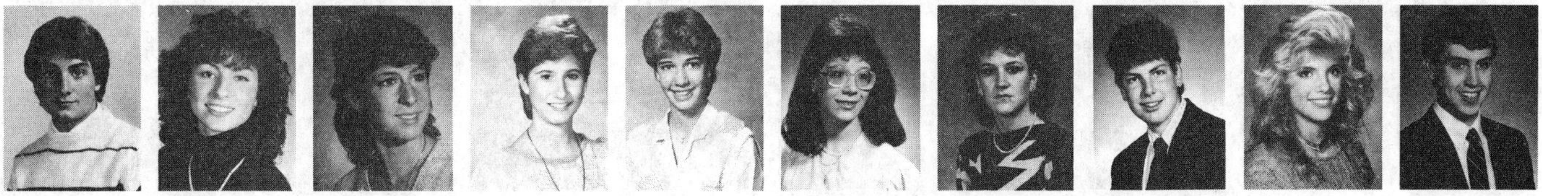

Faulseit, Ronald K
Kinnelon HS
Riverdale, NJ

Faustini, Ann-Marie
Barbara
River Dell SR HS
Oradell, NJ

Fava, Jennifer
Notre Dame HS
Trenton, NJ

Favor, Denise
Arthur L Johnson
Regional HS
Clark, NJ

Favretto, Sandi
Vineland HS
Vineland, NJ

Febres, Gloria I
Morris Knolls HS
Denville, NJ

Federici, Tracey
John F Kennedy HS
Willingboro, NJ

Feeney, Thomas F
X
Glen Rock HS
Glen Rock, NJ

Feith, Amy
Roselle Park HS
Roselle Park, NJ

Feivelson, Neal K
Westfield HS
Westfield, NJ

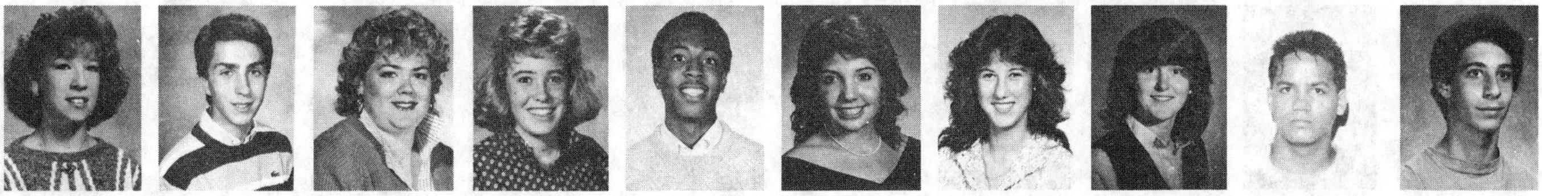

Feld, Jennifer
Pequannock
Township HS
Pequannock, NJ

Feldt, Eric
West Essex HS
Fairfield, NJ

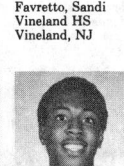

Fell, Dee Ann
Paulsboro HS
Bridgeport, NJ

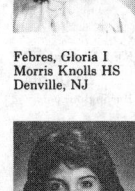

Felsman, Kim
Wayne Valley HS
Wayne, NJ

Fennell, Patrick L
Lenape Valley
Regional HS
Stanhope, NJ

Feola, Angela
North Plainfield HS
North Plainfield, NJ

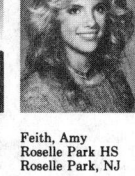

Ferdinando, Andrea
Kingsway Regional
Mullica Hl, NJ

Ferencz, Jennifer
Notre Dame HS
Hamilton Sq, NJ

Fermaglich, Michael
Ocean Township HS
Ocean Tsp, NJ

Fernandez,
Fernando
Weehawken HS
Weehawken, NJ

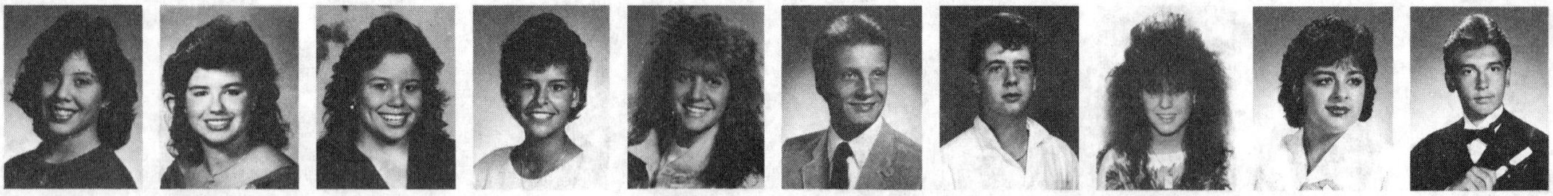

Fernandez, Karina
Red Bank Regional
Hazlet, NJ

Fernandez, Rosa
St Aloysius HS
Jersey City, NJ

Fernandez, Veronica
Raritan HS
Hazlet, NJ

Ferrara, Laura
Bridgewater Raritan
HS West
Bridgewater, NJ

Ferrara, Lori
Brick Town HS
Brick Town, NJ

Ferrari, Michael R
Brick Township
Memorial HS
Brick, NJ

Ferraris, Eric
Woodbridge HS
Sewaren, NJ

Ferraro, Susan
Bayonne HS
Bayonne, NJ

Ferreira, Isabel
St Patricks HS
New York, NY

Ferreira, Nelson
Alexander
East Side HS
Newark, NJ

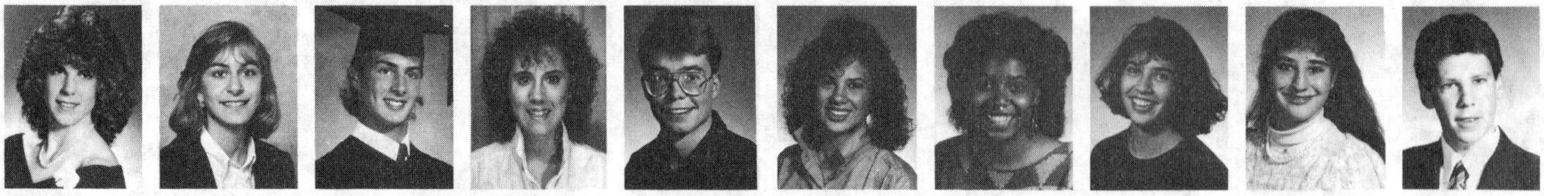

Ferry, Sheryl
Kingsway Regional
Clarksboro, NJ

Fichner, Lisa Jean
Mother Seton
Regional HS
Linden, NJ

Fiedler, Jr Paul
Holy Spirit HS
Pleasantville, NJ

Finaldi, Melissa
Mother Seton
Regional HS
Pt Reading, NJ

Finan, Tom
Red Bank Regional
Little Silver, NJ

Findlay, Christine
Middletown South
Middletown, NJ

Findley, Sharon
Morristown HS
Morristown, NJ

Fine, Jocelyn
Leonia HS
Leonia, NJ

Finkelstein, Ariana
Hightstown HS
East Windsor, NJ

Finken, Jeffrey
Union HS
Union, NJ

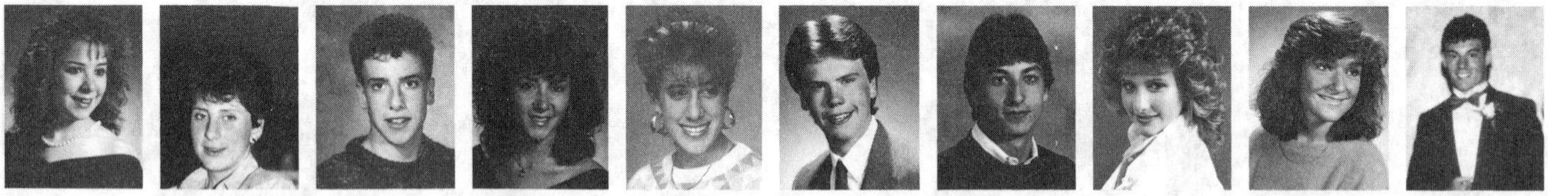

Finn, Renee
St Pius X Regional
New Brunswick, NJ

Finneran, Sharon
Vineland HS
Vineland, NJ

Fiore, Kevin
West Essex HS
Roseland, NJ

Fiorello, Kathleen
De Paul Diocesan
Wayne, NJ

Fioresi, Jackie
Vineland HS
Vineland, NJ

Fippinger, Jeffrey D
West Milford
Township HS
West Milford, NJ

Firriolo, Christopher
Howell HS
Howell, NJ

Fiscella, Keri
Paramus Catholic
Maywood, NJ

Fischer, Christine
Passaic Valley HS
Little Falls, NJ

Fischer, Harry
Toms River HS
Toms River, NJ

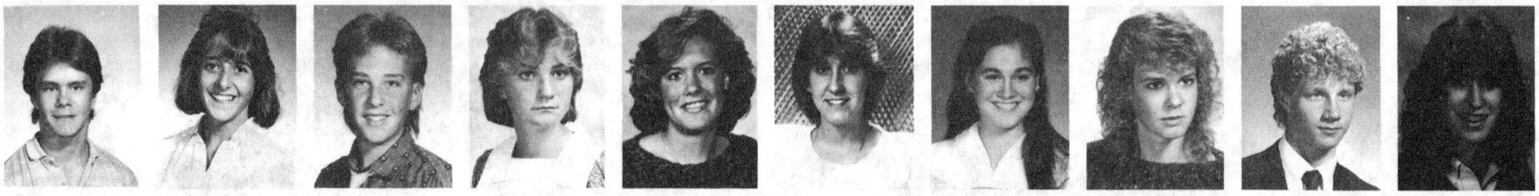

Fischer, Jr Martin
Clifton HS
Clifton, NJ

Fishburn, Debbie
Kingsway Regional
Swedesboro, NJ

Fishelberg, Jason T
South Brunswick
Kendall Park, NJ

Fisher, Marlo
Wildwood Catholic
Cape May, NJ

Fisher, Nicole
Woodstown HS
Alloway, NJ

Fitzgerald, Carolyn
Millville SR HS
Port Elizabeth, NJ

Fitzhenry, Stephanie
Erin
Mt Saint Dominic
N Caldwell, NJ

Flannery, Patricia
Jackson Memorial
Jackson, NJ

Flecke, Thomas
Ramapo Indian Hills
Regional HS
Wyckoff, NJ

Fleischmann, Tobi
Monsignor Donovan
Howell, NJ

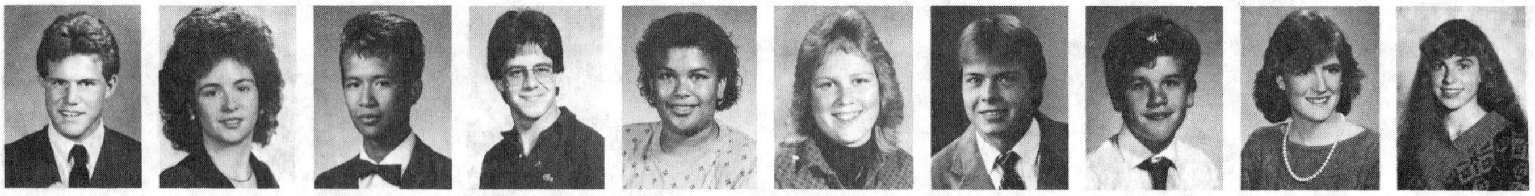

Flicker, Michael T
Ocean City HS
Ocean City, NJ

Flood, Stephanie
Gloucester City HS
Brooklawn, NJ

Florento, Veroni C
St Marys HS
Jersey City, NJ

Flowers, Jonathan D
Livingston HS
Livingston, NJ

Floyd, Amy
Ridgefield Park HS
Ridgefield Pk, NJ

Fluhr, Melissa
Howell HS
Howell, NJ

Flynn, Keith
Ridge HS
Basking Ridge, NJ

Flynn, Timothy
St Joseph Regional
Dumont, NJ

Fogarty, Allison
Mount St Mary
Berkeley Hts, NJ

Foldessy, Heather
Northern Highlands
Regional HS
Allendale, NJ

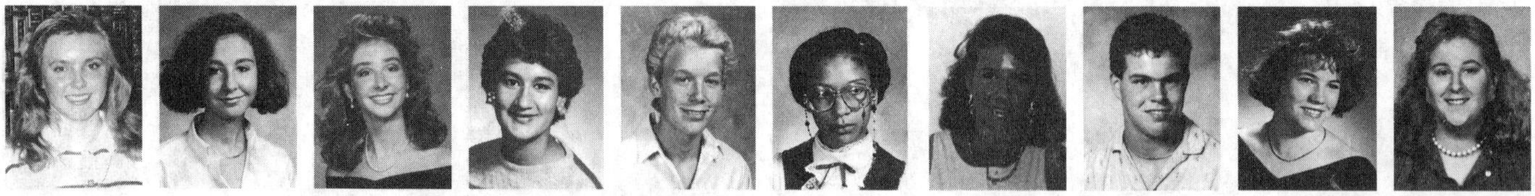

Folescu, Simona
James Caldwell HS
W Caldwell, NJ

Folio, Amy
St John Vianney HS
Colts Neck, NJ

Folio, Kim
St John Vianney HS
Colts Neck, NJ

Fontanez, Cynthia
Freehold Township
Freehold, NJ

Ford, Richard
Burlington
Township HS
Burlington, NJ

Fore, Christina A
Dickinson HS
Jersey City, NJ

Forrar, Jayne
Red Bank Regional
Shrewsbury, NJ

Forrest, Brian
Vineland HS North
Vineland, NJ

Forsyth, Nora
Red Bank Catholic
Red Bank, NJ

Forsythe, Joanne
Millville SR HS
Millville, NJ

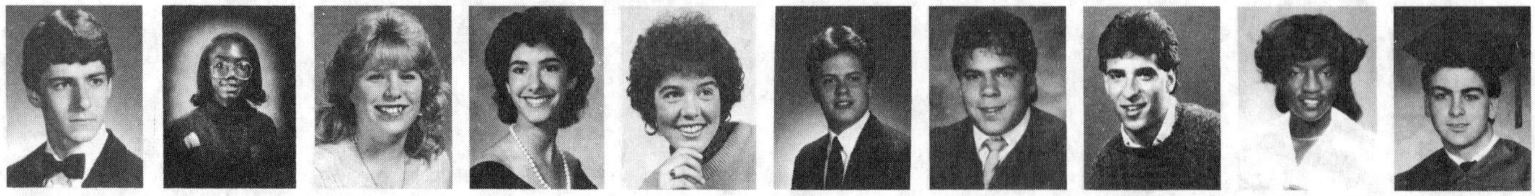

Fortna, Carl Hunter
Elizabeth HS
Elizabeth, NJ

Fortune, Annetta
John F Kennedy HS
Willingboro, NJ

Foster, Deanna
Hamilton HS
Trenton, NJ

Fox, Erica L
Anorthern Valley
Regional HS
Haworth, NJ

Foxson, Jennifer
Wallkill Valley
Regional HS
Hamburg, NJ

Foytlin, Daniel C
Toms River North
Toms River, NJ

Fracasso, Joseph
Marist HS
Bayonne, NJ

Fragola, Dean
Newton HS
Newton, NJ

Francis, Louise
Emily
St Dominic Acad
Jersey City, NJ

Franco, Ronnie
Memorial HS
West New York, NJ

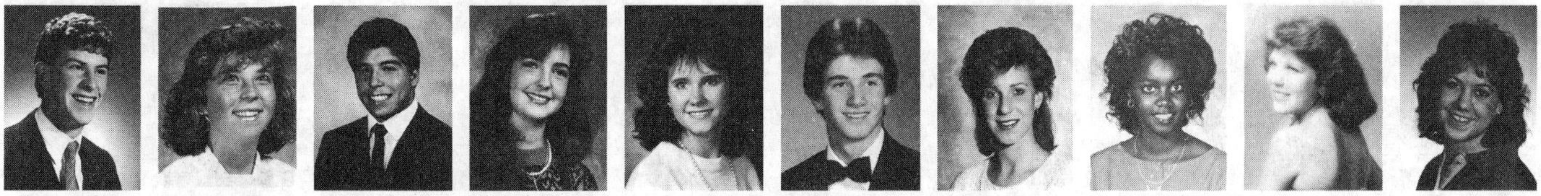

Frankenberg, Brett
Toms River HS
Toms River, NJ

Franklin, Dawn
Manasquan HS
Belmar, NJ

Franks, Ralph
Robert
Highland Regional
Blackwood, NJ

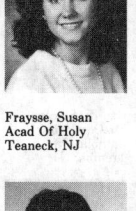

Fratkin, Amy
Manasquan HS
Manasquan, NJ

Fraysse, Susan
Acad Of Holy
Teaneck, NJ

Frazee, Stephen
St Mary HS
Keansburg, NJ

Frazier, Allison
Linden HS
Linden, NJ

Frazier, Kimberli
Immaculate
Conception HS
Verona, NJ

Freas, Tara
Elizabeth
Glenvar HS
Tuckertown, NJ

Freda, Dawn-Marie
Wood-Ridge HS
Wood Ridge, NJ

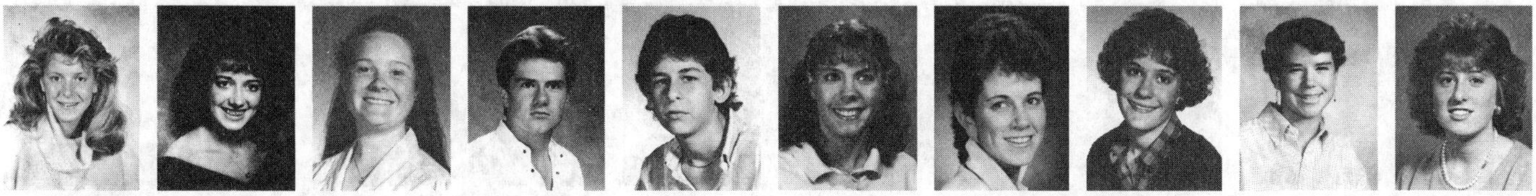

Freeman, Jacquline
Sparta HS
Sparta, NJ

Frey, Julie
St Joseph HS
Waterford, NJ

Fricks, Kathryn
Toms River HS
Toms River, NJ

Friddell, Rance
Burlington Cty
Vo-Tech Schl
Edgewater, NJ

Friedman, Mark
Parsippany HS
Parsippany, NJ

Fritschie, Renee
Southern Regional
Barnegat, NJ

Fritzscha, Sandra
Highland Regional
Erial, NJ

Fuchs, Heather
Indian Hills HS
Oakland, NJ

Fuges, Christin
Hopewell Valley
Central HS
Titusville, NJ

Fullagar, Melanie
Ridge HS
Basking Ridge, NJ

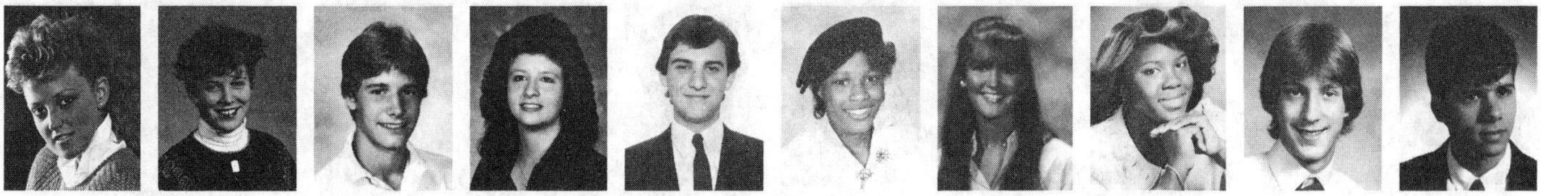

Fulmer, Linda
Toms River Norm
Toms River, NJ

Fulton, Melissa
Baptist HS
Voorhees, NJ

Furfari, Frank
Woodstown HS
Newfield, NJ

Furgiuele, Catherine
Lenape Valley
Regional HS
Andover, NJ

Furman, Steven
Shore Regional HS
W Long Branch, NJ

Gaddis, Cherie
Raritan HS
Hazlet, NJ

Gaffney, Jennifer
Monsignor Donovan
Forked River, NJ

Gainey, Kera Lashy
Dwight Morrow HS
Englewood, NJ

Gajewski, II Stephen
J
St John Vianney HS
Laurence Hrbr, NJ

Galano, Scott
Watchung Hills
Regional HS
Watchung, NJ

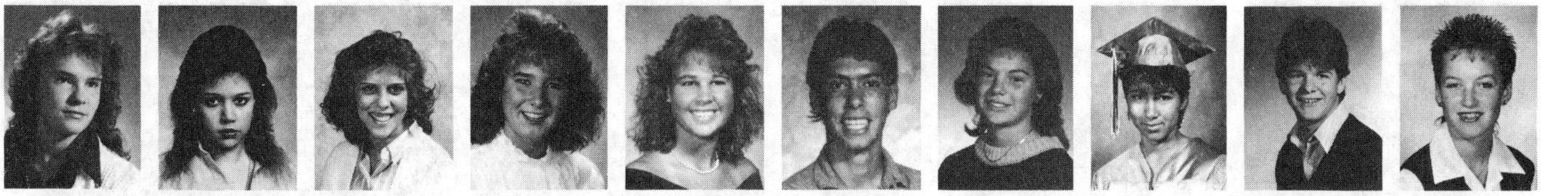

Galbraith, Renee
East Brunswick HS
E Brunswick, NJ

Galetta, Angela
Pemberton
Township HS No 1
Browns Mills, NJ

Gallaccio, Anne
Wildwood Catholic
N Cape May, NJ

Gallagher, Kathryn
M
Roselle Catholic HS
Port Reading, NJ

Gallagher, Michele
Holy Spirit HS
Linwood, NJ

Gallicchio, Diego J
Washington
Township HS
Sewell, NJ

Gallipoli, Kerri
Toms River HS
Toms River, NJ

Gallo, Aura
Eastside HS
Paterson, NJ

Galofaro, David A
Boonton HS
Lincoln Park, NJ

Gambert, Nancy
Mary Help Of
Christians Acad
Elmwood Park, NJ

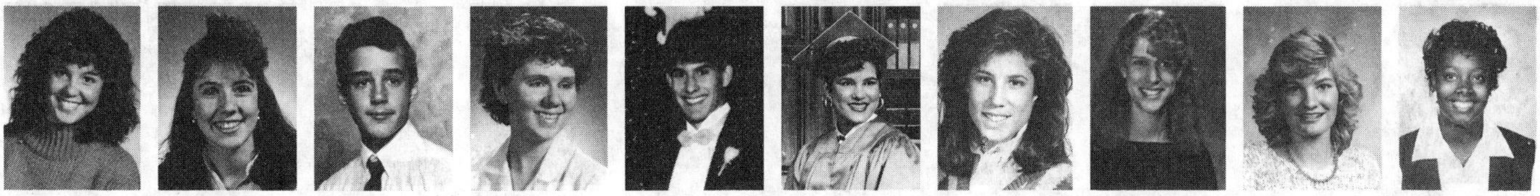

Gamble, Jessica
Brick Township HS
Brick Town, NJ

Gannon, Gia
Camden Catholic
Tansboro, NJ

Gannon, James
Vernon Township
Hewitt, NJ

Garber, Melissa
Clifton HS
Clifton, NJ

Garcia, Sean
Michael
Ridgefield Park HS
Little Ferry, NJ

Garcia, Sonia
Vineland SR HS
Millville, NJ

Gargano, Nicole
De Paul Diocesan
Lincoln Pk, NJ

Garrabrant, Karen
Pitman HS
Pitman, NJ

Garrahan, Jennifer
Arthur P Schalick
Elmer, NJ

Garris, Yvette
Mary Help Of
Christians Acad
Paterson, NJ

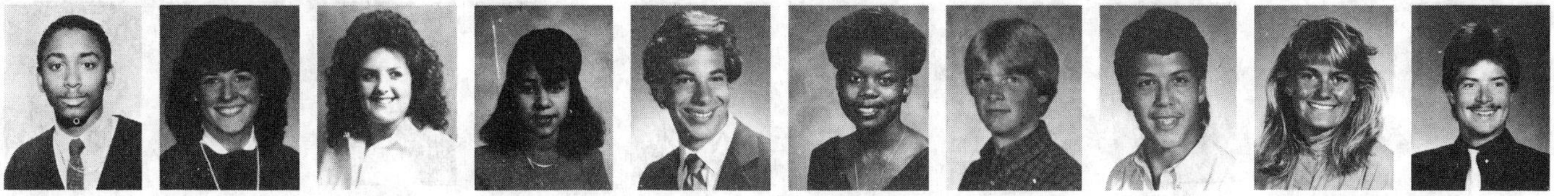

Garrison, III George
C
Plainfield HS
Plainfield, NJ

Garubo, Christa
Noel
West Morris
Mendham HS
Mendham, NJ

Garwood, Kathleen
M
Holy Cross HS
Willingboro, NJ

Gates, Tara
Pemberton TWP
HS No II
Fort Dix, NJ

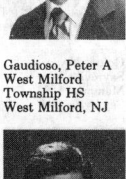

Gaudioso, Peter A
West Milford
Township HS
West Milford, NJ

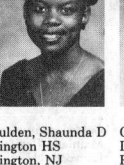

Gaulden, Shaunda D
Irvington HS
Irvington, NJ

Gausepohl, Steven
Lenape Valley
Regional HS
Andover, NJ

Gavrilovic, Igor
Wood-Ridge HS
Wood Ridge, NJ

Gearing, Maureen
Toms River HS
Pine Bch, NJ

Geddes, Robert
Edison HS
Edison, NJ

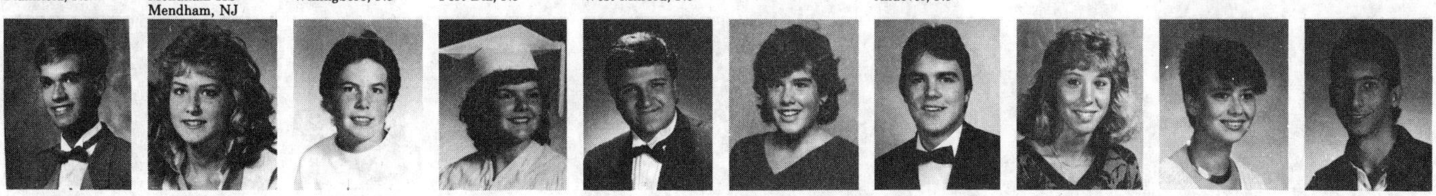

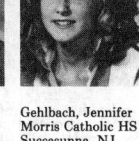

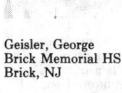

Gehbauer, John C
Roxbury HS
Succasunna, NJ

Gehlbach, Jennifer
Morris Catholic HS
Succasunna, NJ

Geisler, George
Brick Memorial HS
Brick, NJ

Gels, Michelle
Hamilton High West
Trenton, NJ

Genovese, Carmen
Red Bank Catholic
Neptune, NJ

Gensone, Gina
Tenafly HS
Tenafly, NJ

Genus, Michael
Holy Cross HS
Burlington, NJ

George, Janet
Burlington Twp HS
Burlington Twnshp,
NJ

Georgiu, Andreea
Glen Ridge HS
Glen Ridge, NJ

Geraci, Nicholas
Freehold Township
Freehold, NJ

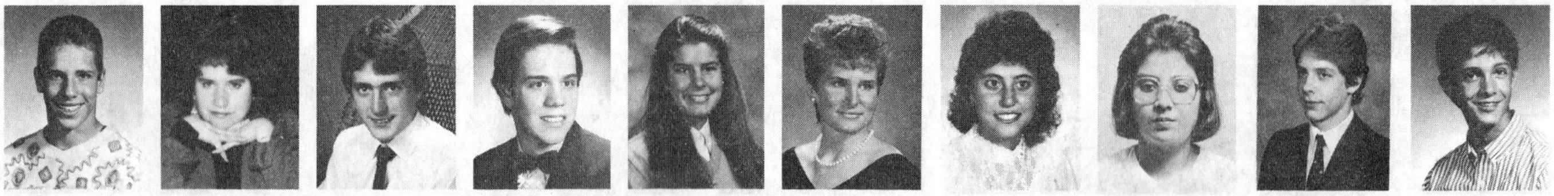

Gerber, Bart
Lodi HS
Lodi, NJ

Gerber, Natalie
Fair Lawn HS
Fair Lawn, NJ

Gerbereux, Kirk
Millville SR HS
Mauricetown, NJ

Gerling, William
Brick HS
Brick Town, NJ

Gerofsky, Tracey
Mc Corristin
Catholic HS
Trenton, NJ

Geurds, Stacey
Mc Corrisitin
Catholic HS
Trenton, NJ

Ghanim, Cathy
Middlesex HS
Middlesex, NJ

Ghia, Pauravi D
Holy Rosary Acad
Jersey City, NJ

Ghio, Christopher
Memorial HS
Cedar Grove, NJ

Giallourakis, Cosmas
Chris
Red Bank Regional
Shrewsbury, NJ

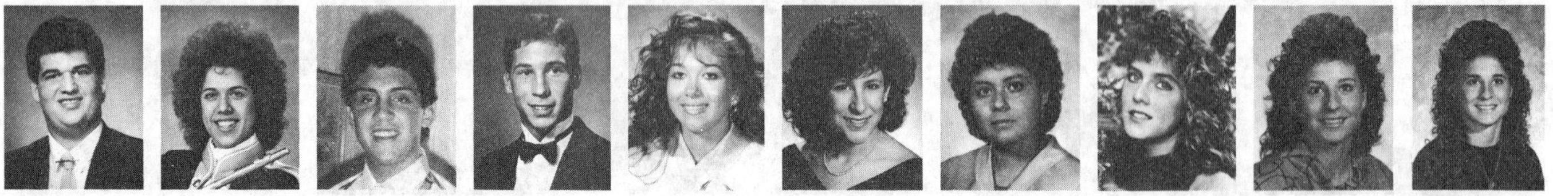

Giampetro, Andrew
Eastern Regional
Voorhees, NJ

Giancamilli, Paula
Phillipsburg HS
Alpha, NJ

Giancaspro, John A
Becton Regional HS
Carlstadt, NJ

Giangiordano,
Richard
Shawnee HS
Medford, NJ

Giannobile, Joan
Holy Family Acad
Bayonne, NJ

Giardina, Lora
De Paul HS
Ringwood, NJ

Gibson, Elizabeth
Anne
Jefferson Township
Milton, NJ

Giddings, Tara
Lakewood HS
Lakewood, NJ

Gigliotti, Deana
Washington
Township HS
Sewell, NJ

Gigliotti, Frances
Washington
Township HS
Sewell, NJ

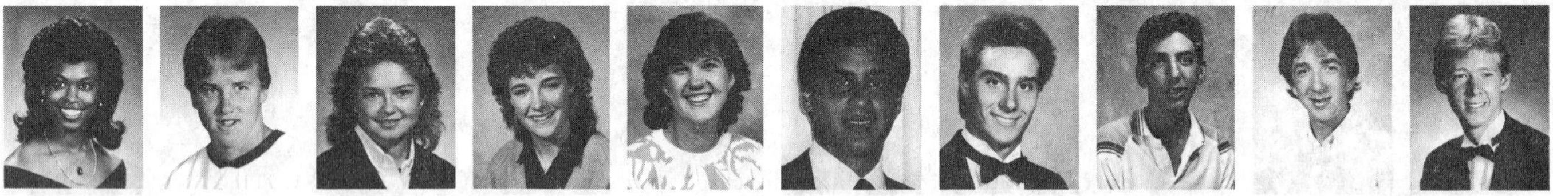

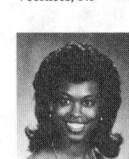

Gilbert, Taraka
Plainfield HS
Plainfield, NJ

Gilbert, Timothy
Dover HS
Mine Hill, NJ

Gilleece, Jennifer
Immaculate Heart
Spring Valley, NY

Gilmore, Heather
Newton HS
Andover, NJ

Gilster, Jeana A
Cherokee HS
Marlton, NJ

Ginsberg, Andrew R
Moorestown HS
Moorestown, NJ

Giorgianni, Nick
St James HS
Gibbstown, NJ

Girardy, Matthew J
Bernards HS
Gladstone, NJ

Girouard, James
Newton HS
Andover, NJ

Gisler, Scott
Kitlatinny Regional
Newton, NJ

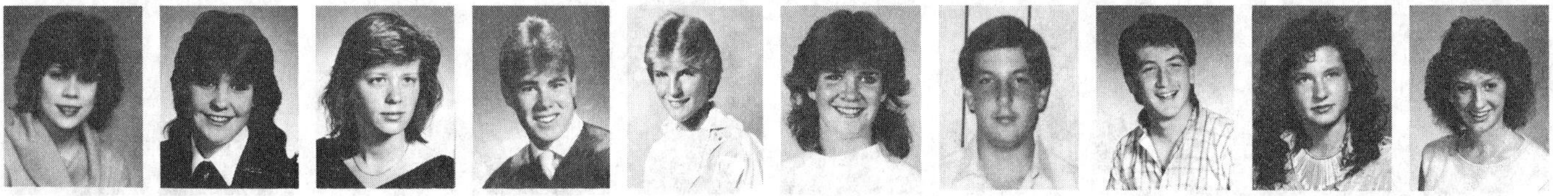

Giuliano, Angela
Our Lady Of Mercy
Sewell, NJ

Giuriceo, Nancy
Marine Acad Of Sci
And Tech
Belford, NJ

Glamkowski, Cathy
Watchung Hills
Regional HS
Warren, NJ

Glaser, John
De Paul HS
Kinnelon, NJ

Glass, Amy Sue
Point Pleasant
Beach HS
Pt Pleasant Beach,
NJ

Glass, Colleena
Central Regional HS
Bayville, NJ

Glazer, Mark
New Milford HS
New Milford, NJ

Glenn, Robert
Brick Memorial HS
Brick, NJ

Glenn, Tokar
Elizabeth
Southern Regional
Beach Haven, NJ

Gletow, Donna
Jackson Memorial
Jackson, NJ

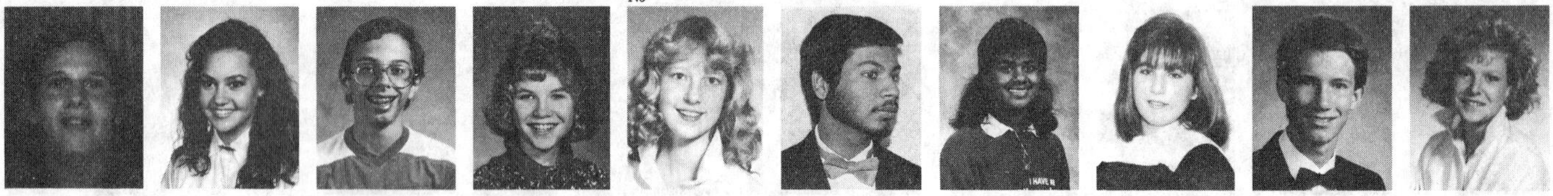

Glik, Robert A
North Bergen HS
North Bergen, NJ

Glucksman, Sharon
West Morris
Mendham HS
Bernardsville, NJ

Glynn, David
Park Ridge HS
Park Ridge, NJ

Gmach, Pamela
Edison HS
Edison, NJ

Gnirrep, Jocelyn
Mt Olive HS
Budd Lake, NJ

Gobin, Andre
Memorial HS
West New York, NJ

Gobin, Denise
Spotswood HS
Spotswood, NJ

Gobo, Michele
Cliffside Park HS
Fairview, NJ

Goessel, Chuck A
Cherokee HS
Marlton, NJ

Goff, Teresa
Boonton HS
Canada

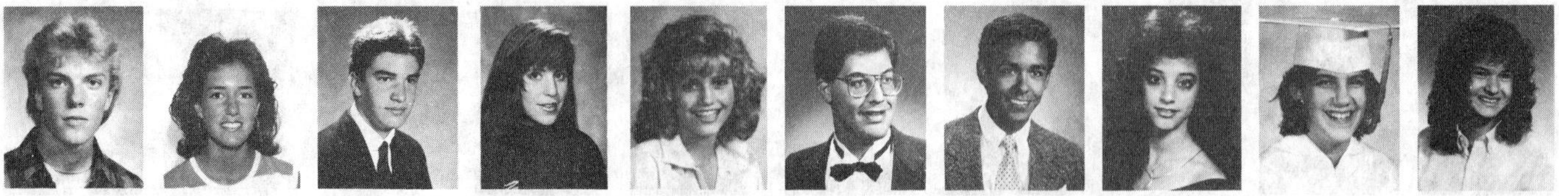

Goldberg, Douglas
Westwood HS
Wash Twp, NJ

Goldberg, Kimberly
Ann
James Caldwell HS
W Caldwell, NJ

Goldberg, Scott M
James Caldwell HS
W Caldwell, NJ

Goldstein, Joanna
Bruriah HS
Teaneck, NJ

Goldsworthy, Amy
Mainland Regional
Linwood, NJ

Golub, Neal
Sayreville War
Memorial HS
Sayreville, NJ

Gomez, Richard
Madison HS
Madison, NJ

Gomory, Pamela
Abraham Clark HS
Roselle, NJ

Gonzalez, Annie
Paramus Catholic
Girls HS
Teaneck, NJ

Gonzalez, Isaura
St Joseph Of The
Palisades HS
Guttenburg, NJ

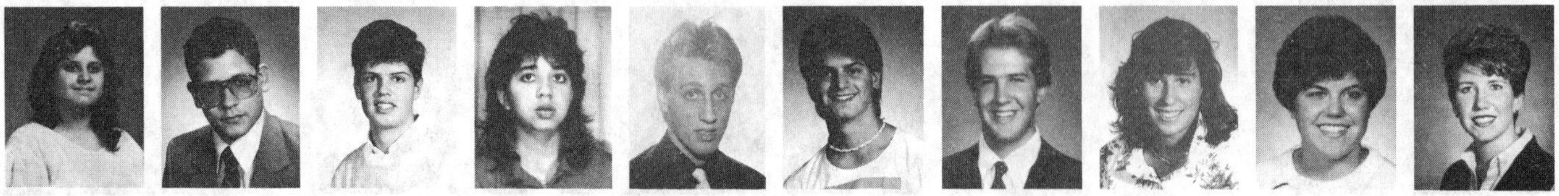

Gonzalez, Jennifer
Burlington County
Mount Holly, NJ

Gonzalez, Kenneth
Perth Amboy HS
Perth Amboy, NJ

Gonzalez, Manuel
Elizabeth HS
Elizabeth, NJ

Gonzalez, Maria E
Barringer HS
Newark, NJ

Goodman, Bruce
Arthur L Johnson
Regional HS
Clark, NJ

Goodrich, Jay
Montville HS
Pinebrook, NJ

Gordon, Eric
Scotch
Plains-Fanwood HS
Scotch Plains, NJ

Gordon, Jamie
West Windsor
Plainsboro HS
Princeton Jct, NJ

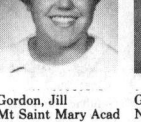

Gordon, Jill
Mt Saint Mary Acad
Somerset, NJ

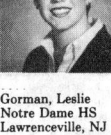

Gorman, Leslie
Notre Dame HS
Lawrenceville, NJ

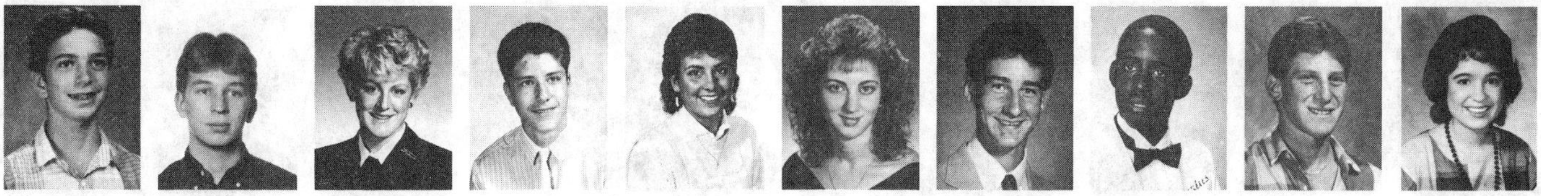

Gormbogi, Daniel
Pitman HS
Pitman, NJ

Gorzelany, Robert J
Clifton HS
Clifton, NJ

Goss, Abigail
Marine Acad Of Sci & Tech
Little Silver, NJ

Gostovich, Steven V
Overbrook Regional SR HS
Pine Hill, NJ

Gott, Karen
Pennsville Memorial
Pennsville, NJ

Gottschalk, Lisa
Ridgefield Park HS
Little Ferry, NJ

Goubeaud, Paul
Notre Dame HS
East Windsor, NJ

Gourdine, Darrius
Essex Catholic Boys
East Orange, NJ

Grabelle, Dean
Ocean Township HS
Wayside, NJ

Graber, Amy
Timothy Christian
Scotch Plains, NJ

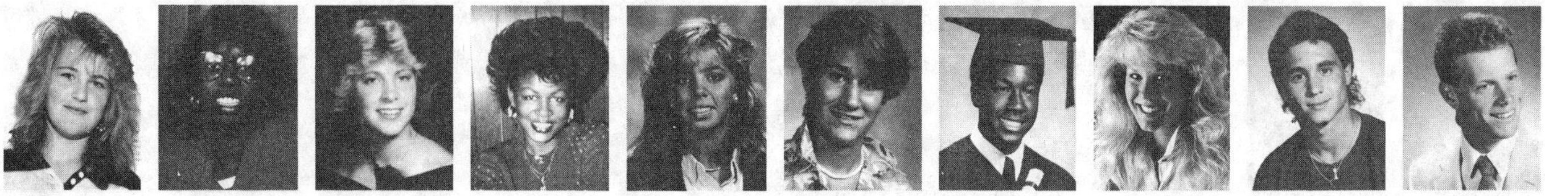

Grace, Lisa
Neptune SR HS
Neptune, NJ

Graham, Coretta
Hackensack HS
Hackensack, NJ

Graham, Dori Laine
Northern Burlington Regional HS
Allentown, NJ

Graham, Marsha Denise
Camden HS
Camden, NJ

Graichen, Suzanne
Monsignor Donovan
Seaside Heights, NJ

Gramkowski, Laurie
Haddenfield Memorial HS
Haddonfield, NJ

Gramling, Timothy S
John F Kennedy HS
Willingboro, NJ

Gramm, Kelly
Lenape Regional HS
Mt Laurel, NJ

Grande, Paul
Belleville SR HS
Belleville, NJ

Grant, Daniel R
Montville HS
Towaco, NJ

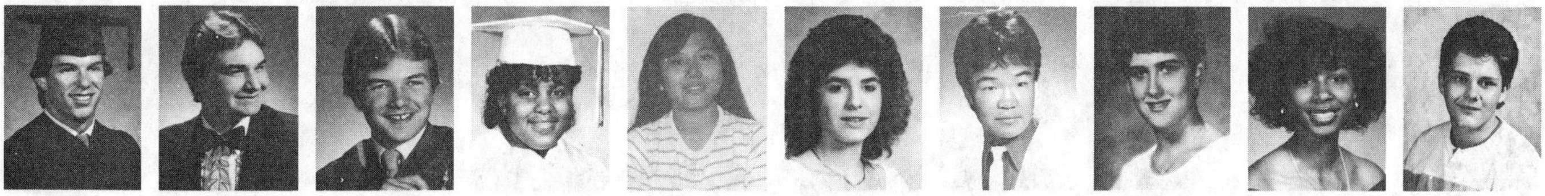

Grasmick, III Louis F
Haddon Township
Westmont, NJ

Gratale, Dominick
Secaucus HS
Secaucus, NJ

Gravatt, Wayne
Freehold Twp HS
Adelphia, NJ

Graves, Rene
Morristown HS
Morristown, NJ

Gray, Maribel
Notre Dame HS
Princeton, NJ

Gray, Tammy
Buena Regional HS
Collings Lks, NJ

Graybush, Marc
Randolph HS
Randolph, NJ

Graziano, Lisa
Rutherford HS
Rutherford, NJ

Green, Candace
Plainfield HS
Plainfield, NJ

Green, Paul
Sacred Heart HS
Vineland, NJ

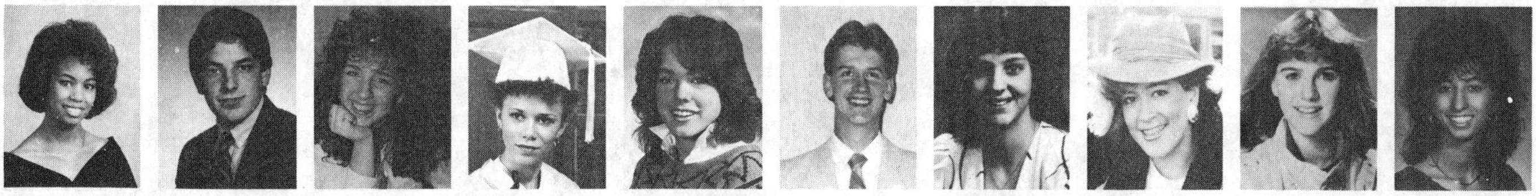

Greene, Kim
Franklin HS
Somerset, NJ

Greenspun, Robert
Atlantic City HS
Margate, NJ

Greenstein, Karen
Glen Rock HS
Glen Rock, NJ

Greer, Lisa
Pleasantville HS
Pleasantville, NJ

Greff, Michelle
Wayne Hills HS
Wayne, NJ

Gregorec, Glenn
Lyndhurst HS
Lyndhurst, NJ

Gregory, Michele
East Brunswick HS
E Brunswick, NJ

Grenti, Stephanie Marie
Hopatcong HS
Hopatcong, NJ

Gretchen, Lippert
Life Center Acad
Willingboro, NJ

Grieco, Annamaria
Mount Saint Dominic Acad
Bloomfield, NJ

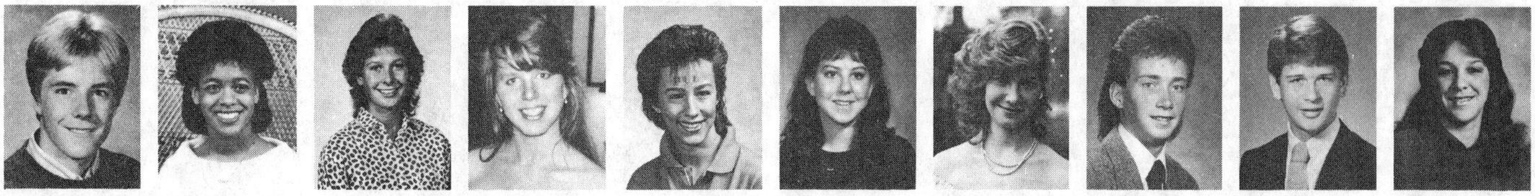

Griffin, Eric F
Teaneck HS
Teaneck, NJ

Griffin, Karen
Pennsauken HS
Pennsauken, NJ

Griffin, Kimberly Ann
Pennsville Memorial
Pennsville, NJ

Griffis, Kate
Morristown-Beard
Montclair, NJ

Griffith, Jennifer
Edgewood SR HS
Waterford, NJ

Grim, Katherine
Delaware Valley Regional HS
Milford, NJ

Grodman, Jacquelyn
Manalapan HS
Manalapan, NJ

Groff, Robert
Buena Regional HS
Collings Lake, NJ

Grogan, James E
St Peters Prep
Wayne, NJ

Gronsky, Tanya
North Hunterdon
Hampton, NJ

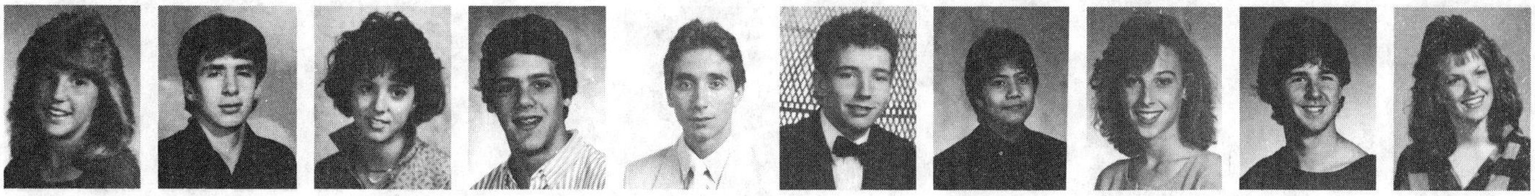

Gross, Melanie
Morris Knolls HS
Denville, NJ

Groves, Lee
Victory Christian
Blue Anchor, NJ

Gruccio, Maria
Sacred Heart HS
Vineland, NJ

Gruchacz, Todd M
Hunterdon Central
Stockton, NJ

Grungo, Joe
Holy Cross HS
Mount Holly, NJ

Grunwald, Jason P
Cherokee HS
Marlton, NJ

Guanzon, James Paul
Essex Catholic Boys
East Orange, NJ

Guarino, Donna
Watchung Hills Regional HS
Warren, NJ

Guarnaccia, Darren
Toms River East HS
Toms River, NJ

Guerrieri, Katrina Ann
Manchester Twp HS
Toms River, NJ

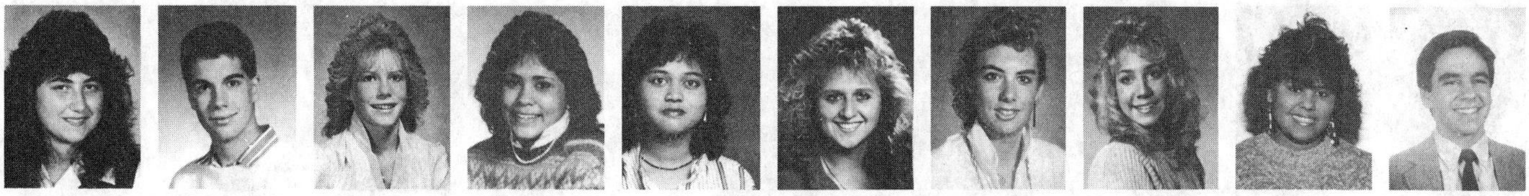

Guerriero, Jenine
Mary Help Of Christians Acad
Totowa, NJ

Guglielmo, Louis
East Brunswick HS
E Brunswick, NJ

Guiles, Stacey
Belvidere HS
Belvidere, NJ

Gupta, Anita
Franklin Twsp HS
Somerset, NJ

Gupta, Kavita
Paul VI HS
Lindenwold, NJ

Gurevich, Tanya
Cherry Hill HS East
Cherry Hill, NJ

Gursky, Melissa
Notre Dame HS
Robbinsville, NJ

Gustis, Jennifer
West Milford HS
W Milford, NJ

Guzman, Ana
Pennsauken HS
Pennsauken, NJ

Guzman, Carlos M
St Joseph Of The Palisades HS
Secaucus, NJ

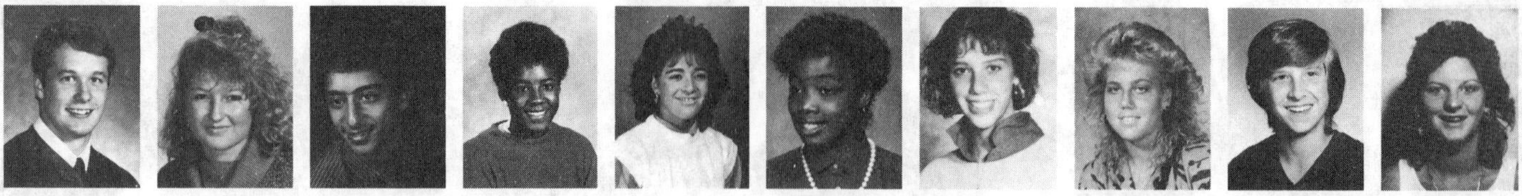

Haas, Edward
Absegami HS
Egg Harbor, NJ

Haase, Alyssa
Long Branch HS
Long Br, NJ

Habib, Alfred
St Josephs HS
Old Bridge, NJ

Hackney, Janel
Howell HS
Howell, NJ

Hadden, Susan
Pitman HS
Pitman, NJ

Hadnott, Danielle B
Teaneck HS
Teaneck, NJ

Hagen, Tara
Waldwick HS
Waldwick, NJ

Hagopian, Debra Ann
Timothy Christian
East Brunswick, NJ

Hague, Erik
St Pius X Regional
E Brunswick, NJ

Haines, Cheri
A P Schalick HS
Bridgeton, NJ

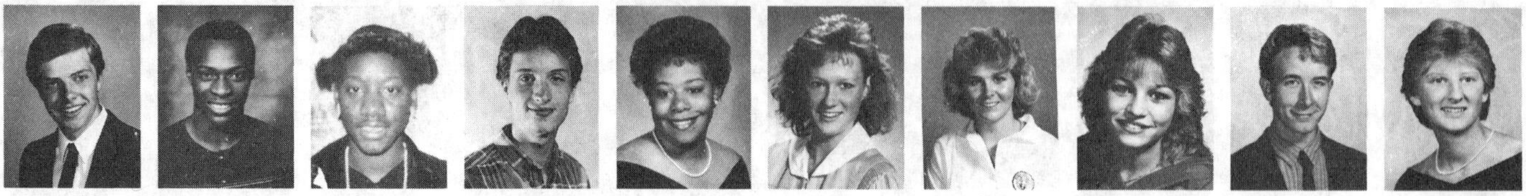

Hale, Warner
St Rose HS
Sea Girt, NJ

Hall, David
Bridgeton HS
Cedarville, NJ

Hall, Gloria
Vailsburg HS
Newark, NJ

Hall, Kevin
The Kings Christian
Marlton, NJ

Hall, Sherry
Plainfield HS
Plainfield, NJ

Halliday, Wendy
Brick Memorial HS
Brick, NJ

Halm, Eileen Michele
Saint Rose HS
Jackson, NJ

Halosz, Doreen
Carteret HS
Carteret, NJ

Halpin, John
Christian Brothers
Middletown, NJ

Hamilton, Carrie
Cumberland Regional HS
Bridgeton, NJ

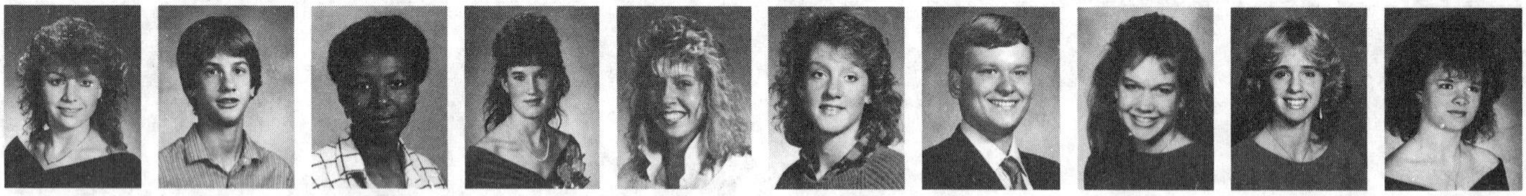

Hamma, Amy
Sayreville War Memorial HS
Parlin, NJ

Hammell, Christopher
Rancocas Valley Regional HS
Mt Holly, NJ

Hammond, Missy
Baptist HS
Camden, NJ

Hampton, Kelly
Holy Family Acad
Bayonne, NJ

Hanham, Jean Mari
Lakeland Regional
Ringwood, NJ

Hanley, Rebecca
Glen Rock HS
Glen Rock, NJ

Hannah, III David Charles
Rancocas Valley Regional HS
Medford, NJ

Hansen, Chrissie
Scotch Plains Fanwood HS
Scotch Plains, NJ

Hansen, Heather
Delaware Valley Reg
Bloomsbury, NJ

Hansen, Maryann
Holy Rosary Acad
Jersey City, NJ

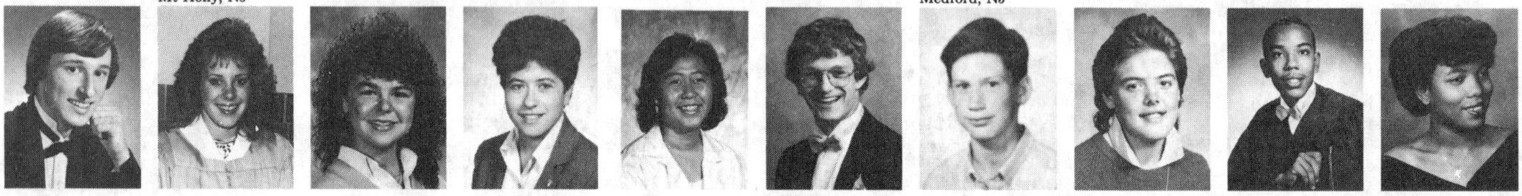

Hansen, Michael
Kittatinny Regional
Stillwater, NJ

Hanson, Danielle
Kearny HS
Kearny, NJ

Hanusi, Christine
Mc Corristin Catholic HS
Trenton, NJ

Hapij, Lada
Mt St Dominic Acad
Livingston, NJ

Harada, Ayako
Washington Township HS
Turnersville, NJ

Hardenburg, Alan William
Jefferson Township
Wharton, NJ

Hardy, Edmond
Morris Catholic HS
Denville, NJ

Hare, Terri
Roncocas Valley Regional HS
Mt Holly, NJ

Hargrove, Scott R
Hillside HS
Hillside, NJ

Hargrove, Tamica
Frank H Morrell HS
Irvington, NJ

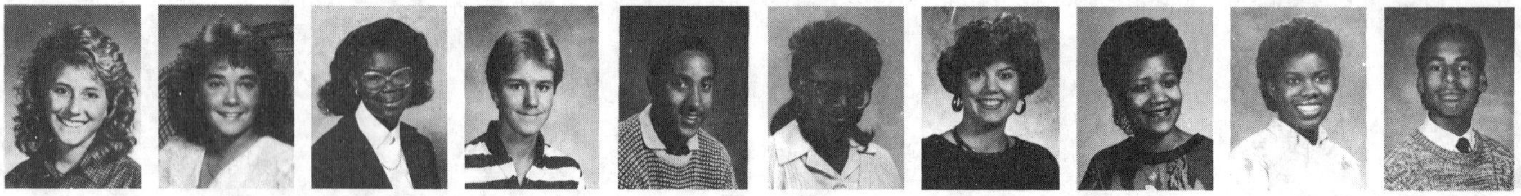

Hark, Jill
Whippany Park HS
Cedar Knolls, NJ

Harker, Kimberly
Baptist HS
Pennsauken, NJ

Harmon, Yvonne D
Mother Seton Regional HS
Rahway, NJ

Harris, Chad
Rancocas Valley Regional HS
Mt Holly, NJ

Harris, Jonathan
Summit HS
Summit, NJ

Harris, Margo L
Our Lady Of Mercy
Sicklerville, NJ

Harris, Michelle
Hackettstown HS
Hackettstown, NJ

Harris, Paulette
Manchester Township HS
Toms River, NJ

Harris, Robyn
John F Kennedy HS
Willingboro, NJ

Harrison, Benjamin A
Dwight-Englewood
Englewood, NJ

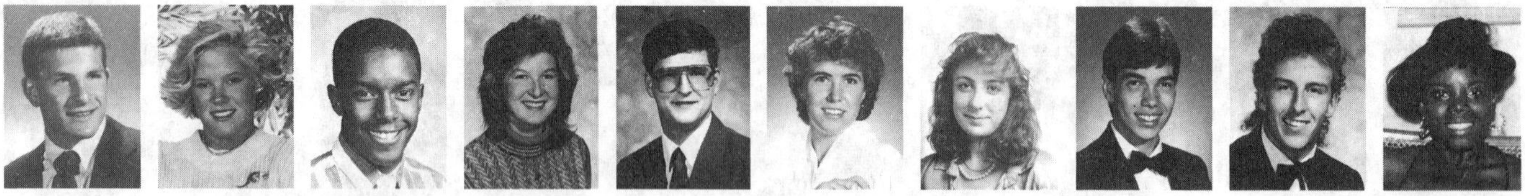

Harrison, Dean
Atlantic City HS
Margate, NJ

Harrison, Laura Lea
Middle Township
Stone Harbor, NJ

Harrison, Marc
Woodburg HS
Woodbury, NJ

Hartley, Katherine
Bordentown Regional HS
Bordentown, NJ

Hartley, Scott
Bordentown Regional HS
Bordentown, NJ

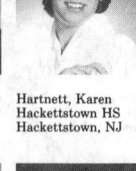

Hartnett, Karen
Hackettstown HS
Hackettstown, NJ

Hartranft, Lisha
Vineland HS
Vineland, NJ

Hartwich, Jeff
Vernon Twp HS
Sussex, NJ

Hartz, Chris
Washington Township HS
Turnersville, NJ

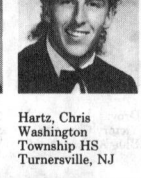

Harvey, Mary K
Bishop Eustace Prep
Somerdale, NJ

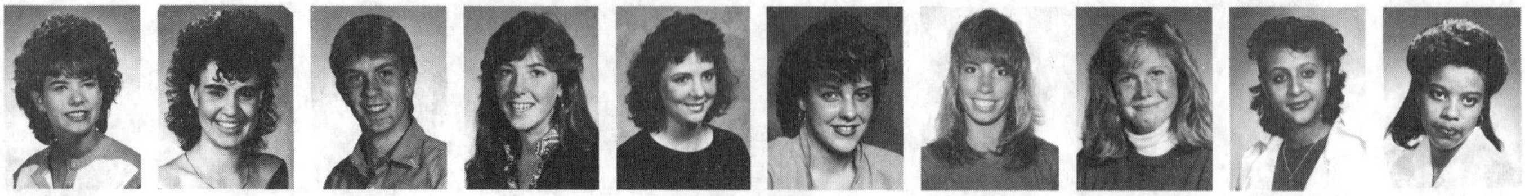

Hassan, Donna
Hamilton High West
Trenton, NJ

Hasse, Susan
Saint Alousius HS
Jersey City, NJ

Hastings, John
Wood-Ridge HS
Wood Ridge, NJ

Hatton, Darryl
Mt Olive HS
Flanders, NJ

Haughian, Maria
Southern Regional
Barnegat, NJ

Havers, Sharon
Palmyra HS
Palmyra, NJ

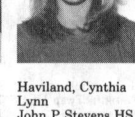

Haviland, Cynthia Lynn
John P Stevens HS
Edison, NJ

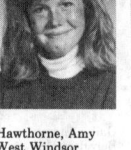

Hawthorne, Amy
West Windsor Plainsboro HS
Robbinsville, NJ

Hayden, Andrea
Union Catholic Regional HS
Newark, NJ

Hayes, Angelique R
Abraham Clark HS
Roselle, NJ

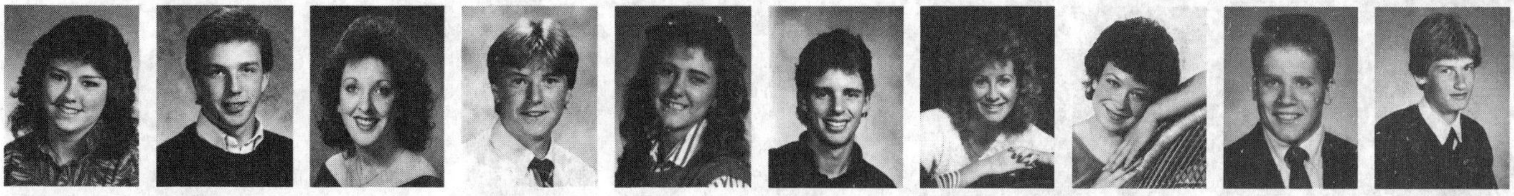

Hayner, Michelle
Brick Township
Memorial HS
Brick, NJ

Hazy, Michael
Bridgewater-Raritan
HS East
Bridgewater, NJ

Healey, Patti
Buena Regional HS
Williamstown, NJ

Heaney, James
Monsignor Donovan
Manchester, NJ

Heater, Jodie
High Point Regional
Branchville, NJ

Hebble, Christopher R
Highland Park HS
Highland Park, NJ

Heckel, Winnie
Paul VI Regional
Newark, NJ

Hefter, Lisa
Newton HS
Newton, NJ

Heindrichs, Kurt M
Green Brook HS
Green Brook, NJ

Heinemann, John
Don Bosco Prep HS
Wyckoff, NJ

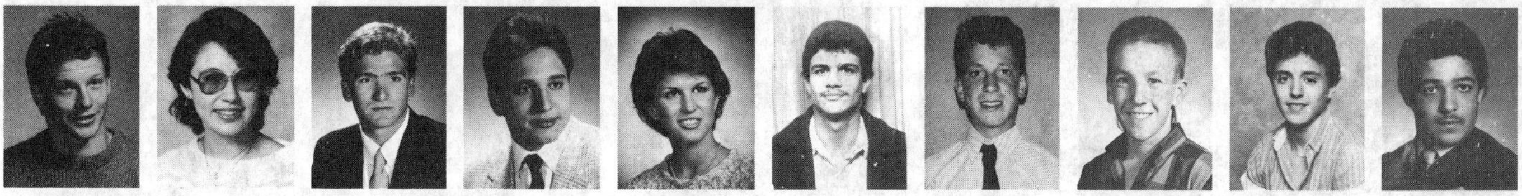

Heinrichs, Dale
Pinelands Regional
Tuckerton, NJ

Heleman, Beth
Vineland HS
Vineland, NJ

Hellmers, Cliff
Shore Regional HS
West Long Branch, NJ

Helmstetter, Tom
Immaculata HS
Pisataway, NJ

Helriegel, Valerie
Hunterdon Central
Whitehouse St, NJ

Helwani, Ghassan
Manchester
Regional HS
P Dark, NJ

Hemberger, Michael M
North Bergen HS
North Bergen, NJ

Henderson, Frank J
West Milford
Township HS
West Milford, NJ

Henderson, Joe
Lyndhurst HS
Lyndhurst, NJ

Henderson, Joseph
Morristown HS
Morristown, NJ

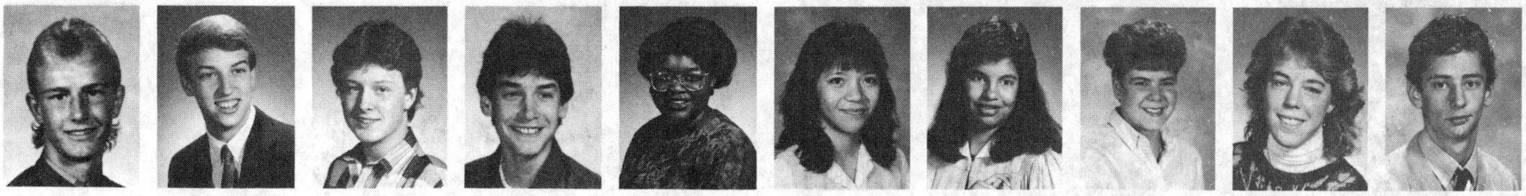

Hendricks, David
Pennsille HS
Pennsville, NJ

Hendrix, Michael
Lakeland Regional
Ringwood, NJ

Henkel, Richie
Secaucus HS
Secaucus, NJ

Henry, Paul
Pinelands Regional
Tuckerton, NJ

Henson, Sharon
University HS
Newark, NJ

Hermanus, Marvela
Marylawn Of The
East Orange, NJ

Hernandez, Ileana
Brick Memorial HS
Brick, NJ

Hernandez, Sonia M
Holy Rosary
Union City, NJ

Herne, Kelli
Hightstown HS
E Windsor, NJ

Herrera, Jr Daniel F
Mc Corristin HS
Trenton, NJ

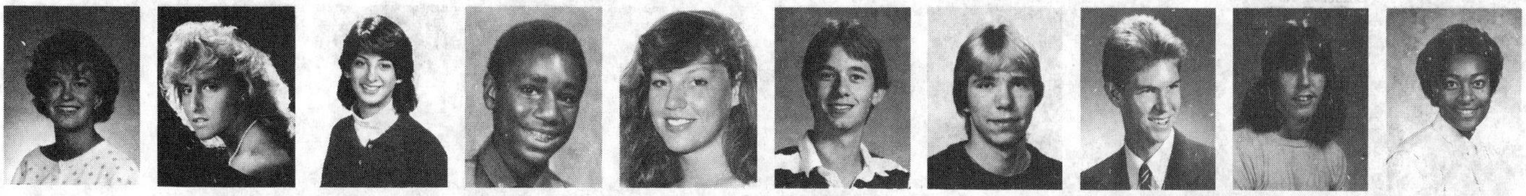

Hertell, Kerry
Westfield SR HS
Westfield, NJ

Hertlein, Helena
Gateway Reg HS
Wenonah, NJ

Hertzberg, Lori A
The Pingry Schl
Watchung, NJ

Hester, Daniel
Manasquan HS
Brielle, NJ

Hetzel, Mollie
West
Windsor-Plainsbor
Princeton Jct, NJ

Heuschkel, Glen A
Montgomery HS
Skillman, NJ

Hewitt, Jr Jeffrey
Pennsville Memorial
Pennsville, NJ

Heyt, Gregory J
Cherry Hill East HS
Cherry Hill, NJ

Hickman, Robert
Burl Co Voc & Tech
Mt Holly, NJ

Hickman, Sherri D
Hackettstown HS
Great Meadows, NJ

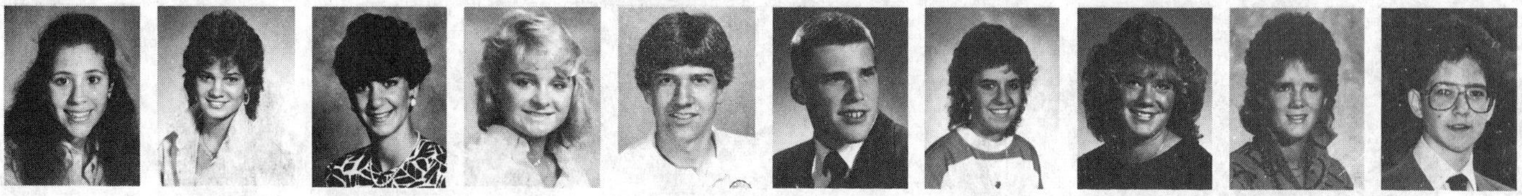

Hicks, Jodi
Notre Dame HS
Kendall Pk, NJ

Hicks, Michelle
Ridgefield Park HS
Ridgefield Pk, NJ

Hidalgo, Patricia E
Villa Walsh Acad
Basking Ridge, NJ

Hierspiel, Stacy
St John Vianney HS
Matawan, NJ

Higgins, Christopher
Saint Rose HS
Neptune, NJ

Hildick, Mike
Toms River HS
Toms River, NJ

Hill, Donna
Cinnaminson HS
Cinnaminson, NJ

Hill, Heather
High Point Regional
Branchville, NJ

Hill, Lisa
Salem HS
Salem, NJ

Hillman, Ira
Wayne Hills HS
Wayne, NJ

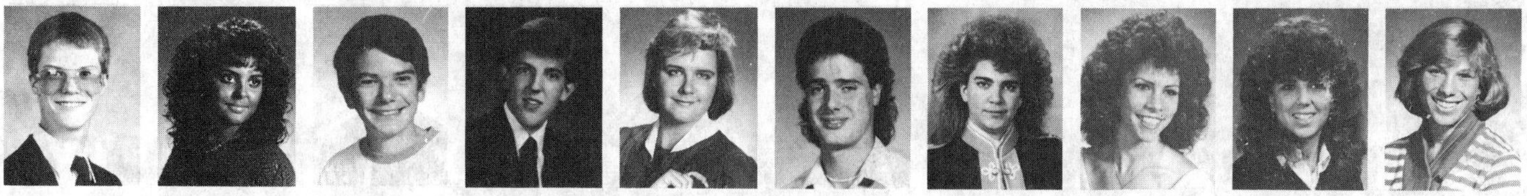

Hillman, Richard
St Augustine Prep
Newfield, NJ

Hilway, Vikki
Passaic Valley
Regional HS
Totowa, NJ

Hines, Kevin
Parsippany HS
Parsippany, NJ

Hinrichsen, David
Ocean Twp HS
Oakhurst, NJ

Hinrichsen, Maria
Lakeland Regional
Ringwood, NJ

Hippe, Daniel
Brick Twsp
Memorial HS
Brick, NJ

Hirko, Kim
Phillipsburg HS
Phillipsburg, NJ

Hirsch, Korinna
South Plainfield HS
S Plainfield, NJ

Hitchner, Le Ann
Holy Spirit HS
Ventnor, NJ

Hiza, Larua
West
Windsor-Plainsbor
Princeton Junct, NJ

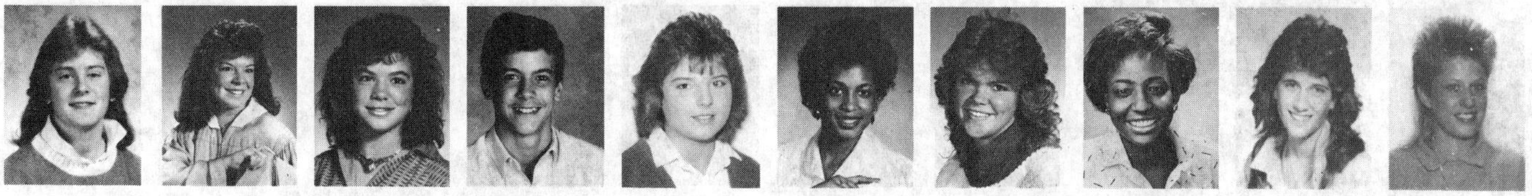

Hmirak, Kristin
Hackettstown HS
Great Meadows, NJ

Hoar, Lisa
West Milford
Township HS
West Milford, NJ

Hoar, Tracy A
West Milford HS
West Milford, NJ

Hobbie, Edward
Westfield HS
Westfield, NJ

Hobby, Gail
Bayonne HS
Bayonne, NJ

Hobson, Renee P
North Plainfield HS
N Plainfield, NJ

Hodde, Sharon
Morris Hills HS
Dover, NJ

Hodge, Juvonda
Manalapan HS
Manalapan, NJ

Hodge, Nicole
Union HS
Union, NJ

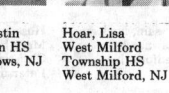

Hodi, Lisa
E Brunswick
Vo-Tech HS
Spotswood, NJ

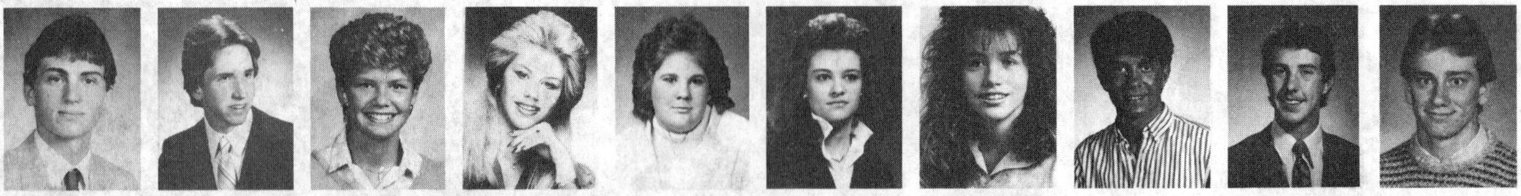

Hodson, Darryl
Arthur P Schalick
Elmer, NJ

Hoehler, David C
S Plainfield HS
S Plainfield, NJ

Hoelbinger, Jennifer
Gateway Regional
Woodbury Hts, NJ

Hoersch, Tracy L
Hasbrouck Hts HS
Hasbrouck Heights, NJ

Hoffman, Diane
Millville SR HS
Dorchester, NJ

Holahan, Karen
John F Kennedy HS
Willingboro, NJ

Holldand, Shannon
Paul VI Regional
Cedar Grove, NJ

Hollenbeck, Jr Robert C
Middletown HS
Red Bank, NJ

Holliday, Eric
Hamilton High Schl
Trenton, NJ

Holliday, Michael M
Westfield HS
Westfield, NJ

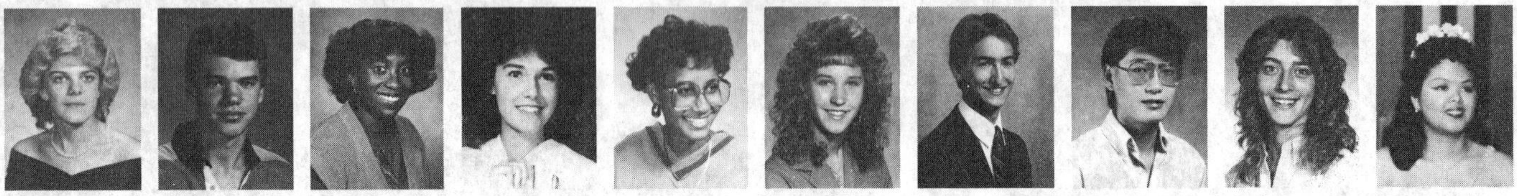

Hollister, Bridget
Vineland HS
Vineland, NJ

Holm, David
Montgomery HS
Raleigh, NC

Holmes, La Coyya Jaton
Eastern Christian
Irvington, NJ

Holmes, Patricia
Lenape Valley Regional HS
Netcong, NJ

Holmes, Stacy
Lakewood HS
Lakewood, NJ

Holowachuk, Stacie
Wayne Hills HS
Wayne, NJ

Holub, David C
Monmouth Regional
Eatontown, NJ

Holub, Frederick N
Ocean Township HS
Wayside, NJ

Holub, Laura
Middlesex HS
Middlesex, NJ

Hom, Elaine
John P Stevens HS
Edison, NJ

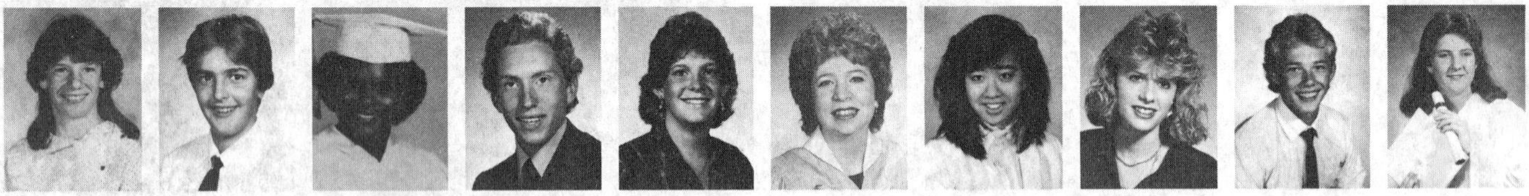

Homan, Karen
Rancocas Valley Regional HS
Mt Holly, NJ

Honeymar, Jr Michael G
Union Catholic Regional HS
Elizabeth, NJ

Honis, Monica
Paramus Catholic Girls HS
Teaneck, NJ

Hooker, Thomas F
Steinert HS
Hamilton, NJ

Hope, Patricia
Pennsville Memorial
Pennsville, NJ

Hopler, Tracy
Morris Knolls HS
Rockaway, NJ

Hor, Trina
Matawan Regional
Matawan, NJ

Horan, Leanne S
West Milford Twp
West Milford, NJ

Hornberger, Mark
Holy Cross
Cinnaminson, NJ

Horner, Sherie
Burlington City HS
Edgewater Pk, NJ

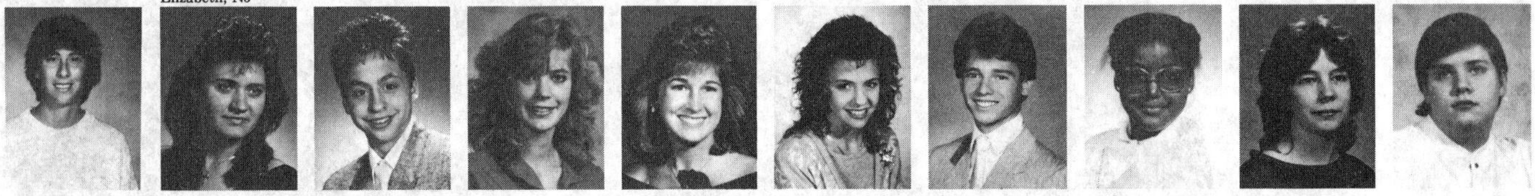

Horowitz, Deborah
Bloomfield HS
Bloomfield, NJ

Horvath, Angela
Franklin HS
Somerset, NJ

Horvath, Nick
Toms River North
Toms River, NJ

Horvath, Stephanie
North Hunterdon
Clinton, NJ

Houlihan, Patrice
St John Vianney HS
Hazlet, NJ

House, Christine
Highland Regional
Erial, NJ

Houston, Ed
Edison HS
Edison, NJ

Houston, Laura
Toms River HS
S Toms River, NJ

Howe, Christine
Burlington County
Bordentown, NJ

Howe, Jeffrey
Vineland SR HS
Vineland, NJ

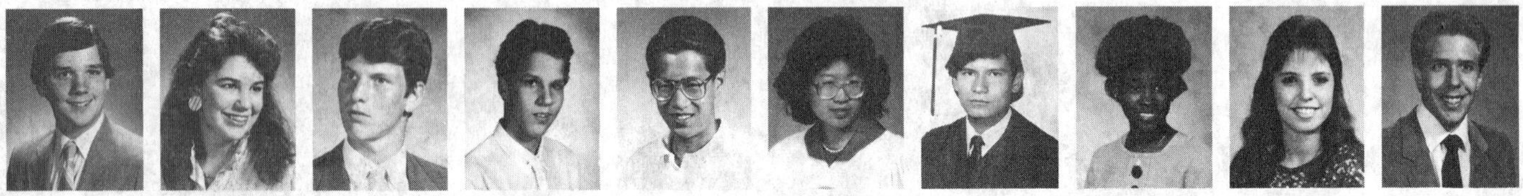

Howe, Theodore S
Cherry Hill High Schl East
Cherry Hill, NJ

Howlett, Donna
Paul VI Regional
W Orange, NJ

Hratko, Thomas
Jackson Memorial
Jackson, NJ

Hrobak, Jr James P
Holy Cross HS
Mt Laurel, NJ

Hsia, Philip H
Morris Knolls HS
Denville, NJ

Hsu, Lillian
Scotch Plains-Fanwood HS
Scotch Plains, NJ

Huaman, Rafael
Kearny HS
Kearny, NJ

Hubbard, Paula
Vineland HS
Vineland, NJ

Hudson, Janet
Cherokee HS
Tabernacle, NJ

Huebner, Matthew
Southern Regional
Manahawkin, NJ

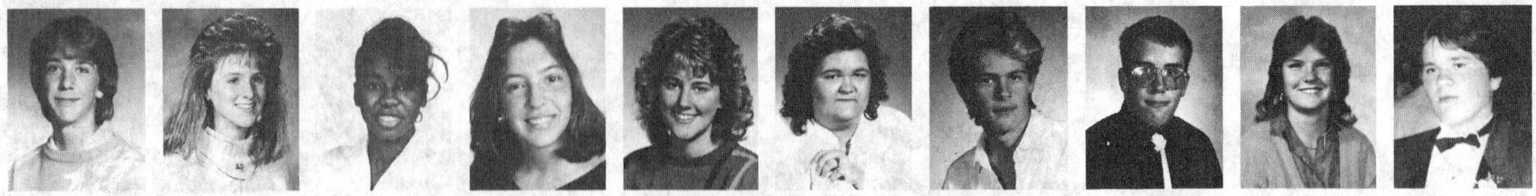

Huebsch, Michele
Boonton HS
Boonton, NJ

Hughes, Kelly
Wayne Valley HS
Wayne, NJ

Hughes, Sandra
Benedictine Acad
Newark, NJ

Hughes, Theresa
John P Stevens HS
Edison, NJ

Huhn, Jennifer
Randolph HS
Ironia, NJ

Hull, Donna
Burlington County Vo-Tech Schl
Vincetown, NJ

Hulst, Burk
Kingsway Regional
Mickleton, NJ

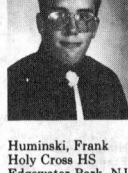

Huminski, Frank
Holy Cross HS
Edgewater Park, NJ

Humphreys, Michelle
Woodstown HS
Monroeville, NJ

Hunecke, Edward
Dickinson HS
Jersey City, NJ

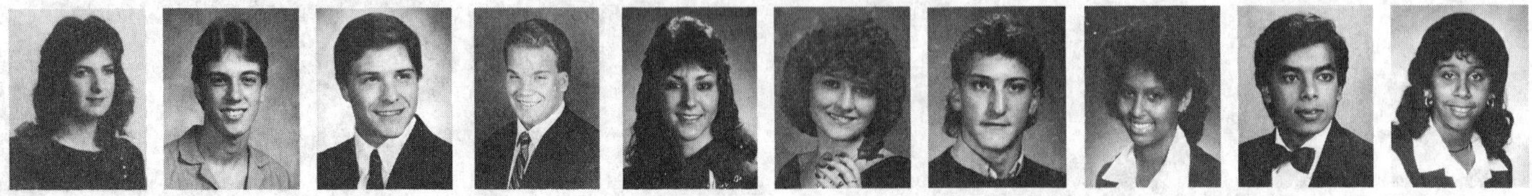

Hunnewell, Wendy L
Morris Knolls HS
Denville, NJ

Hunsinger, David
Gateway Regional
Wenonah, NJ

Hunt, Thomas
Hunterdon Central
Readington, NJ

Hunter, III George K
Triton HS
Glendora, NJ

Hunter, Theresa A
John F Kennedy Memorial HS
Avenel, NJ

Hurff, Sandra
Paulsboro HS
Gibbstown, NJ

Hurley, Brett
Southern Regional
Ship Bottom, NJ

Hussain, Jahanara
Mary Help Of Christians Acad
Paterson, NJ

Hussain, Nadeem
Shawnee HS
Medford, NJ

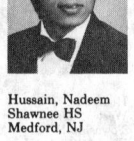

Hussain, Rhukea
Mary Help Of Christians Acad
Paterson, NJ

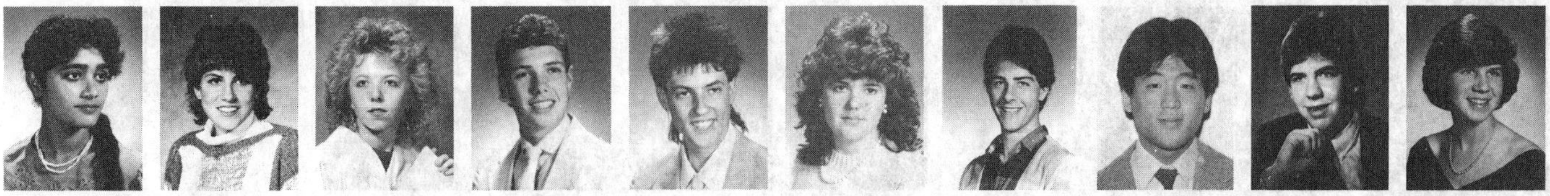

Hussain, Sabeena
West Windsor
Plainsboro HS
Robbinsville, NJ

Hutchinson, Deanna
Vineland HS
Vineland, NJ

Hutchinson, Lisa
Lyndhurst HS
Lyndhurst, NJ

Hutchison, David
Bloomfield HS
Bloomfield, NJ

Hutchison, Jr
Donald
Bloomfield HS
Bloomfield, NJ

Hutchison, Monica
Bloomfield HS
Bloomfield, NJ

Hutmaker, Michael
South Brunswick
Monmouth
Junction, NJ

Hwang, Son C
H P Becton Reg HS
East Rutherford, NJ

Hyde, Christopher
Atlantic Friends
Linwood, NJ

Hyland, Susan
North Plainfield HS
N Plainfield, NJ

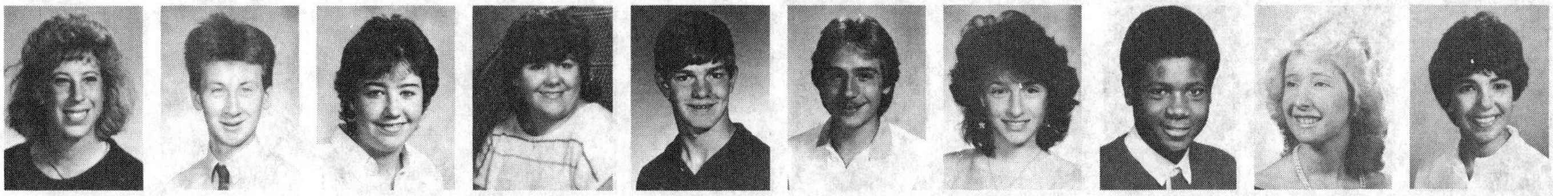

Hynds, Victoria
Jackson Memorial
Jackson, NJ

Hynes, Joseph M
Edison HS
Edison, NJ

Hynes, Linda
St John Vianney HS
Hazlet, NJ

Hyson, Suzanne
Lower Cape May
Regional HS
Erma, NJ

Iacono, Joseph
Middlesex HS
Middlesex, NJ

Iadanza, Raymond
Jackson Memorial
Jackson, NJ

Iazzetta, Diane
Union Catholic
Regional HS
Cranford, NJ

Ibitoye, David
Dwight Morrow HS
Englewood, NJ

Incarvito, Dorothy
Bishop Eustace Prep
Delran, NJ

Incolla, Josephine
St Rose HS
Brielle, NJ

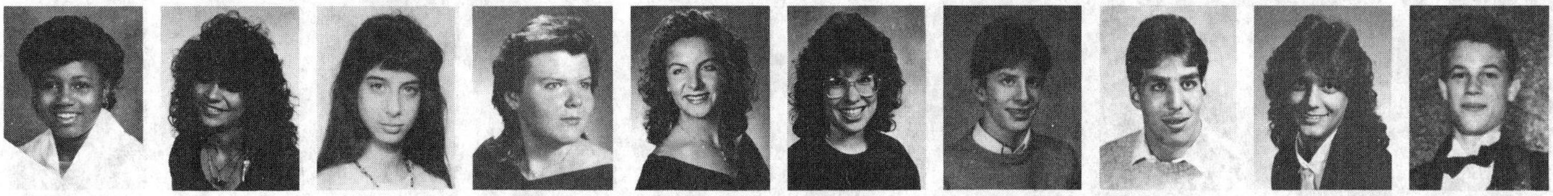

Ingram, Keeshia
Monette
West Orange HS
W Orange, NJ

Insana, Phyllis
Wood-Ridge HS
Wood-Ridge, NJ

Inslicht, Sabra
Cherry Hill H S
Cherry Hill, NJ

Ippolito, Cynthia
St Josephs HS
N Bergen, NJ

Iredell, Lee Ann
Kittatinny Regional
Newton, NJ

Irick, Corinn
Buena Regional HS
Vineland, NJ

Italiano, Frank
Edgewood HS
Elm, NJ

Italiano, Joe
Edgewood SR HS
Hammonton, NJ

Iuliano, Tina Marie
St Marys Of The
Assumption HS
Elizabeth, NJ

Ivahnenko, Greg
Florence Twp Mem
Roebling, NJ

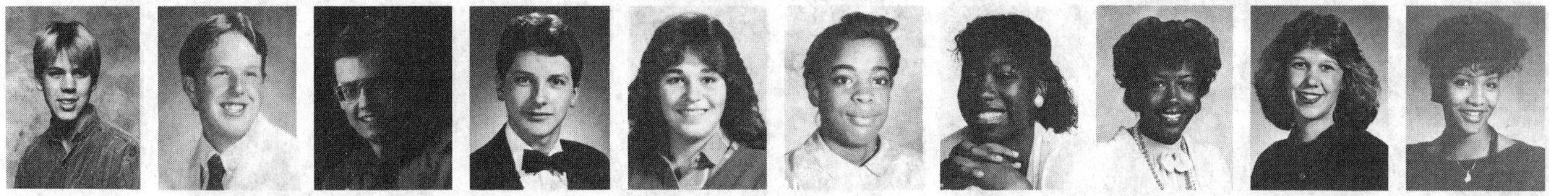

Iverson, Bradford
Cresskill HS
Cresskill, NJ

Iveson, David
Arthur P Schalick
Elmer, NJ

Jablonski, Jeffrey R
St Peters Prep
Kearny, NJ

Jablow, Leon
St Peters
Preparatory Schl
Jersey City, NJ

Jacco, Jeanine
Fair Lawn HS
Fair Lawn, NJ

Jackson, Adriane
Vailsburg HS
Newark, NJ

Jackson, Cheryl
John F Kennedy HS
Willingboro, NJ

Jackson, Ginina
Burlington City HS
Burlington, NJ

Jackson, Jennifer
Whippany Park HS
Whippany, NJ

Jackson, Latonya
Monmouth Regional
Eatontown, NJ

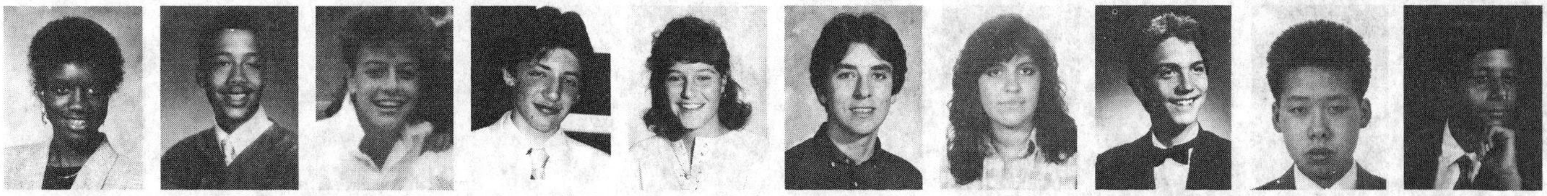

Jackson, Marcia
Vineland HS
Vineland, NJ

Jackson, Scott
Scotch
Plain-Fanwood HS
Scotch Pl, NJ

Jacob, Kellylyn
Paramus Catholic
Saddle Brk, NJ

Jacobs, Paul
Brick Memorial HS
Lakewood, NJ

Jacobs, Valerie
Northern Valley HS
Old Tappan, NJ

Jacobus, Robert D
Bordentown
Regional HS
Bordentown, NJ

Jacome, Sonia
Emerson HS
Union City, NJ

Jadwinski, Michael
Sayreville War
Memorial HS
Parlin, NJ

Jae, Jo
South Brunswick
Kendall Pk, NJ

Jain, Sanjay
John Paul Stevens
Edison, NJ

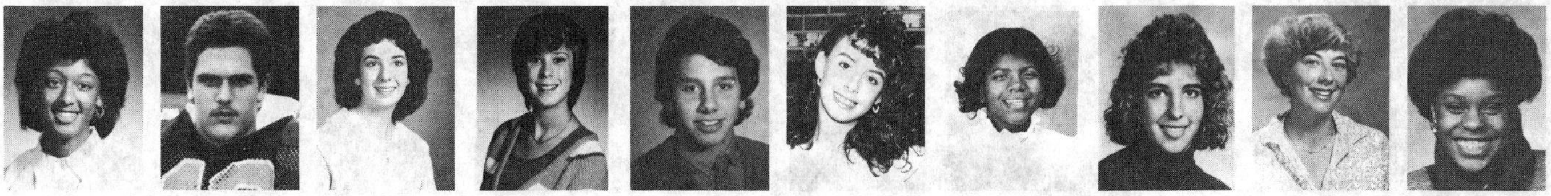

James, Charisse
Paterson Catholic
Paterson, NJ

Jandoli, Douglas
West Orange HS
W Orange, NJ

Janowsky, Karen
North Hunterdon
Boca Raton, FL

Janulin, Christine
High Point Regional
Sussex, NJ

Januzzi, George
Notre Dame HS
Monmouth Jct, NJ

Jaskiewicz, Francine
Bishop Eustace Prep
Medford, NJ

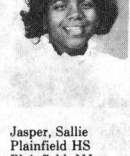

Jasper, Sallie
Plainfield HS
Plainfield, NJ

Jefferis, Thyra
South Hunterdon
Regional HS
Lambertville, NJ

Jeffery, Joanne
Pequamock
Township HS
Pompton Plains, NJ

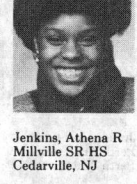

Jenkins, Athena R
Millville SR HS
Cedarville, NJ

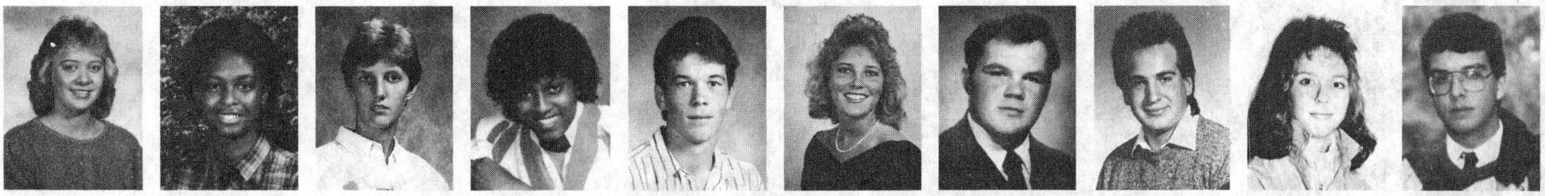

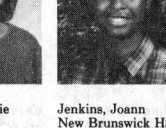

Jenkins, Jackie
Riverside HS
Delanco, NJ

Jenkins, Joann
New Brunswick HS
New Brunswick, NJ

Jenkins, Kimberley
B
Spotswood HS
Spotswood, NJ

Jenkins, La Shawn
Antoinette
Red Bank Regional
Red Bank, NJ

Jenkins, Michael L
Northern Burlington
Cnty Rgnl HS
Mc Guire Afb, NJ

Jenkins, Tina
Cherokee HS
Marlton, NJ

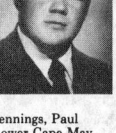

Jennings, Paul
Lower Cape May
Regional HS
N Cape May, NJ

Jenssen, James
Indian Hills HS
Oakland, NJ

Jent, Angela
Absegami HS
Mays Landing, NJ

Jerris, Randon
Matthew
Delbarton Schl
Brookside, NJ

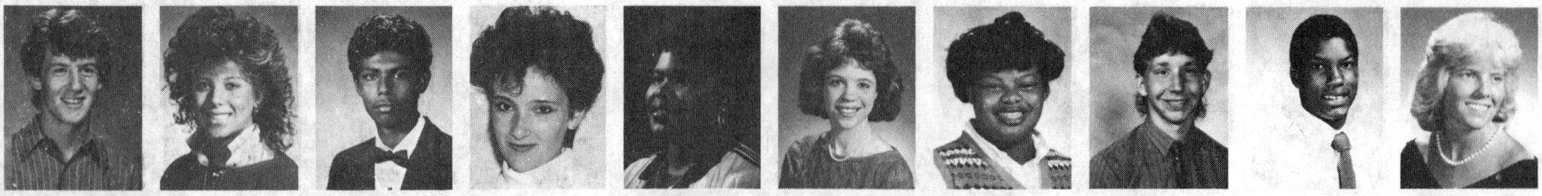

Jetter, Jr Christian
Pitman HS
Pitman, NJ

Joehnk, Tracy
Secaucus HS
Secaucus, NJ

John, Varghese P
St Mary HS
Jersey City, NJ

Johnson, Barbara
Annette
Moorestown Friends
Riverside, NJ

Johnson, Crystal
Camden Catholic
Camden, NJ

Johnson, Cynthia D
Ramapo HS
Franklin Lakes, NJ

Johnson, Deborah
Benedictine Acad
Newark, NJ

Johnson, Hans
Woodstown HS
Hixson, TN

Johnson, Jay M
Cherokee HS
Marlton, NJ

Johnson, Joanna Lee
Neptune SR HS
Neptune, NJ

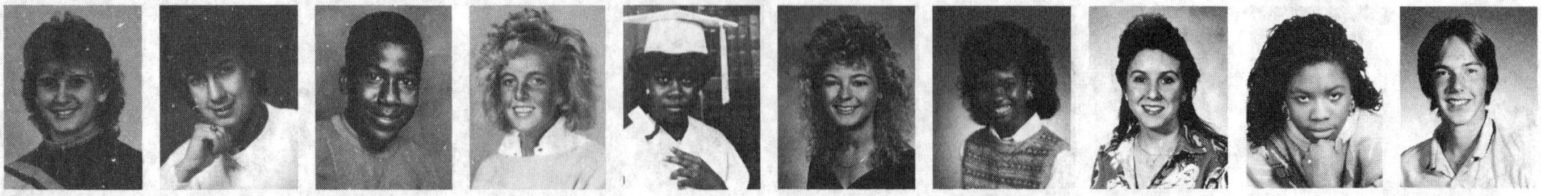

Johnson, Justine
Lower Cape May
Regional HS
Cape May, NJ

Johnson, Kenny
Rahway HS
Rahway, NJ

Johnson, Kyle O
Burlington City HS
Burlingon, NJ

Johnson, Megan
Wildwood HS
Wildwood Crest, NJ

Johnson, Stephanie
Pleasantville HS
Pleasantville, NJ

Johnson, Tammy
Triton Regional HS
Somerdale, NJ

Johnson, Tiffiny
West Deptford HS
Mantua, NJ

Johnson, Tracy
Newton HS
Newton, NJ

Johnson, Yvette
Acad Of The Holy
Westwood, NJ

Johnston, Kevin
Wall HS
Wall, NJ

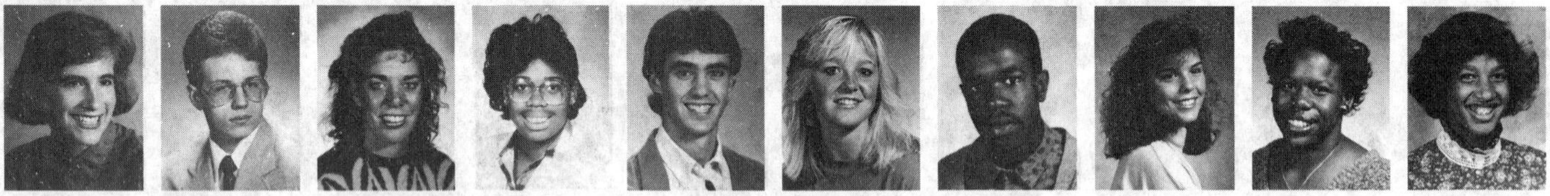

Johnston, Lynne M
Mahwah HS
Worthington, OH

Johnston, Robert B
Hackensack HS
Maywood, NJ

Johnstone, Christine
Highland HS
Blackwood, NJ

Jones, Charlene
Plainfield HS
Plainfield, NJ

Jones, Cordell
Tomasson
Pequannock
Township HS
Pompton Plains, NJ

Jones, Dana
Morristown HS
Morristown, NJ

Jones, Herbert
Montclair HS
Montclair, NJ

Jones, Jennifer
Haddon Township
Westmont, NJ

Jones, Juanita
Hillside HS
Hillside, NJ

Jones, Keri
Burlington
Township HS
Burlington, NJ

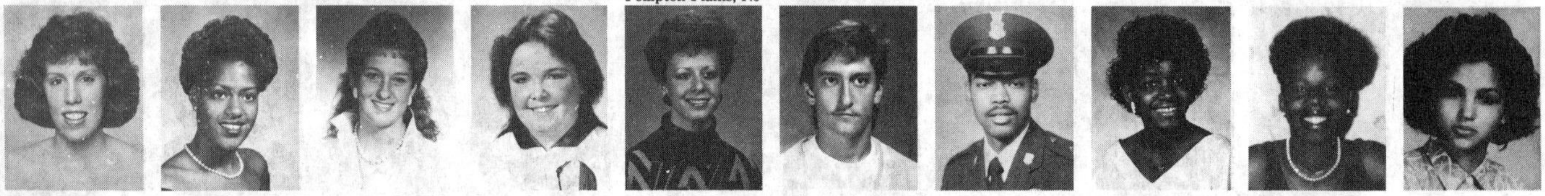

Jones, Kristyn
Marie
Garden State Acad
Pennsauken, NJ

Jones, L Tanya
Oakcrest HS
Mizpah, NJ

Jones, Lori
Phillipsburg HS
Phillipsburg, NJ

Jones, Margaret
Linden HS
Linden, NJ

Jones, Maria
Southern Regional
Manahawkin, NJ

Jones, Michael
Pitman HS
Pitman, NJ

Jones, Randy L
Piscataway HS
Piscataway, NJ

Jones, Sheril
Vineland HS North
Vineland, NJ

Jones, Sonya
James J Ferris HS
Jersey, NJ

Jones, Tiffany
Notre Dame HS
Trenton, NJ

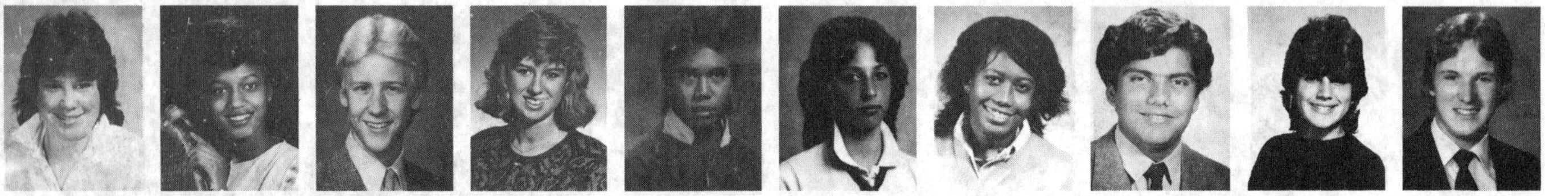

Jones, Tina
Central Regional HS
Bayville, NJ

Jones, Tonya
Science HS
Orange, NJ

Jonker, Todd
Wayne Hills HS
Wayne, NJ

Jordan, Susan A
West
Windsor-Plainsbor
Plainsboro, NJ

Jose, Jr Renato
Palisades Park JR
SR HS
Palisades Pk, NJ

Joseph, Rebecca
Delaware Valley
Regional HS
Frenchtown, NJ

Joseph, Simone
St Pius X Regional
Somerset, NJ

Joshi, Parag
Clifton HS
Clifton, NJ

Jost, Michele
Middle Township
Avalon, NJ

Judson, Stan
South River HS
South River, NJ

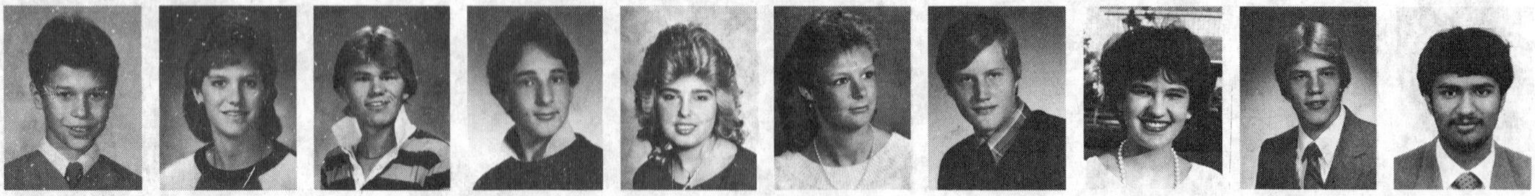

Jurado, Jose
Perth Amboy HS
Perth Amboy, NJ

Kaeppler, Suzanne
Cumberland
Christian HS
Millville, NJ

Kafer, Donald
Burlington County
Bordentown, NJ

Kahn, Russell
Brick Memorial HS
Bricktown, NJ

Kalapos, Connie
Linden HS
Linden, NJ

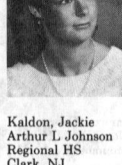

Kaldon, Jackie
Arthur L Johnson
Regional HS
Clark, NJ

Kaleda, David C
North Warren
Regional HS
Blairstown, NJ

Kalfrin, Valerie
Burlington
Township HS
Burlington, NJ

Kalnins, Andis
Wood-Ridge HS
Wood Ridge, NJ

Kamath, Gautham
D
Marlboro HS
Marlboro, NJ

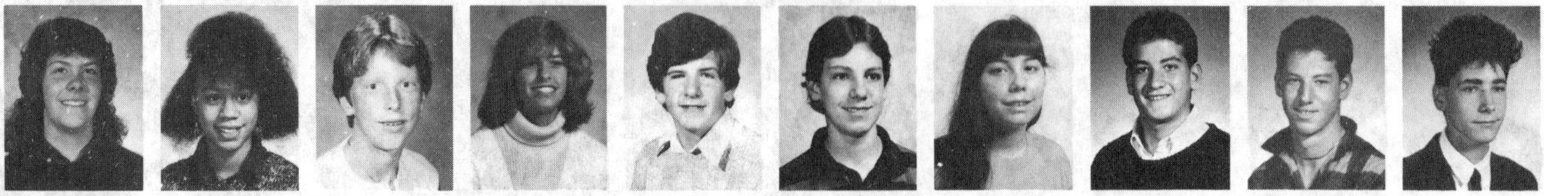

Kambach, Melissa
Lenape Valley
Regional HS
Andover, NJ

Kane, Neisha
Manchester
Township HS
Lakehurst, NJ

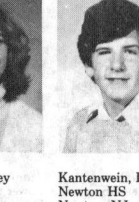

Kane, Jr Richard
Manalapan HS
Englishtown, NJ

Kane, Whitney
Madison HS
Madison, NJ

Kantenwein, Dave
Newton HS
Newton, NJ

Kantner, Michael J
Shawnee HS
Medford Lakes, NJ

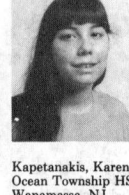

Kapetanakis, Karen
Ocean Township HS
Wanamassa, NJ

Kaplan, Douglas
Middletown HS
Middletown, NJ

Kaplan, Lawrence
Middletown HS
Red Bank, NJ

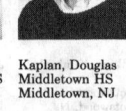

Kapuscinski, Gregg
Montville Township
Montville, NJ

Karagias, Kally
Manasquan HS
Brielle, NJ

Karas, Jr Richard
Huntedon Central
Flemington, NJ

Karim, Ahmad
Ocean Township HS
Wayside, NJ

Kartatos, Mariggela
Timothy Christian
Piscataway, NJ

Kartikis, Jill
Toms River HS
Toms River, NJ

Kashper, Eugene M
The Lawrenceville
Wayside, NJ

Kasilag, Maria
Zenaida
Saint Mary HS
Jersey City, NJ

Kasparian, Yervant
Ridgefield Park HS
Little Ferry, NJ

Katsoulis, Dimitrios
Edison HS
Edison, NJ

Kauffman, Donna
Howell HS
Farmingdale, NJ

Kawut, Steven M
The Pingry Schl
Clark, NJ

Kay, Troy
West Windsor
Plainsboro HS
Princeton Junct, NJ

Kayser, Leigh Ann
Pequannock
Township HS
Pequannock, NJ

Kazelis, Karen
Haddon Heights HS
Haddon Hts, NJ

Keeffe, Nicole
Depaul HS
Pompton Plains, NJ

Keegan, Patricia
Anne
Westfield HS
Westfield, NJ

Keeley, Stan
R V R H S HS
Mt Holly, NJ

Kehoe, Patrick
Bishop Ahr HS
Perth Amboy, NJ

Kekesi, Kristine
Bordentown
Regional HS
Bordentown, NJ

Keldsen, David P
Notre Dame HS
Clarksburg, NJ

Kelleher, Patricia
Haddonfield
Memorial HS
Haddonfield, NJ

Keller, Gayle
Manasquan HS
Belmar, NJ

Keller, J Michael
Woodstown HS
Woodstown, NJ

Keller, Laura
Manasquan HS
Belmar, NJ

Keller, Una
Bordentown
Regional HS
Yardville, NJ

Kelley, Brian
Millville SR HS
Millville, NJ

Kelley, John A
Jackson Memorial
Jackson, NJ

Kelley, Peter
Jackson Memorial
Jackson, NJ

Kellmyer, Jeff E
St James HS
Carneys Point, NJ

Kelly, Greg
Ocean City HS
Marmora, NJ

Kelly, John J
St Joseph Regional
Garnerville, NY

Kelly, Terence P
Roselle Catholic HS
Union, NJ

Kelmer, Kenneth J
Watchung Hills
Regional HS
Millington, NJ

Kelusak, Stephanie
Lakewood HS
Lakewood, NJ

Kennard, Yolanda
Bordentown
Regional HS
Wrightstown, NJ

Kennedy, Brian
Manalapan HS
Englishtown, NJ

Kennedy, Shannon
Our Lady Of Mercy
Glassboro, NJ

Kenney, Nancy Joan
Anne
Riverside HS
Riverside, NJ

Kent, Sheila
Vineland HS
Vineland, NJ

Kent, Tara Anne
Pope John XXIII
Vernon, NJ

Kephart, William
Pitman HS
Pitman, NJ

Kepner, Terrence J
Holy Spirit HS
Ventnor, NJ

Kern, Edward
Bridgewater-Raritan
HS West
Bridgewater, NJ

Kerr, Donna
Gloucester County
Christian Schl
Sewell, NJ

Kerrigan, Kathleen
A
Wayne Valley HS
Wayne, NJ

Kerstner, Christine
Newton HS
Andover, NJ

Kerzic, Catherine
Kearny HS
Kearny, NJ

Kesler, Charles E
St Augustine Prep
Millville, NJ

Kessler, Aimee
Livingston HS
Livingston, NJ

Ketcik, Shannon
Moorestown HS
Moorestown, NJ

Kharod, Amit
Saint Rose HS
Asbury Pk, NJ

Khlyavich,
Alexandra
Randolph HS
Randolph, NJ

Kidd, Joe
Paulsboro HS
Paulsboro, NJ

Kiefer, Dori
Brick Memorial HS
Brick, NJ

Kiely, Daniele
St Dominic Acad
Hoboken, NJ

Kiernan, Robert
Monsignor Donovan
Howell, NJ

Kiesznowski, Sheri
Anne
St John Vianney HS
Freehold, NJ

Kilduff, Patrick J
Don Bosco Prep
Tomkins Cove, NY

Kilgore, Alison
Bridgewater-Rantan
HS East
Bridgewater, NJ

Killeen, Nancy
Westfield HS
Westfield, NJ

Kilpatrick, Andrea
Cherry Hills HS
Cherry Hill, NJ

Kilpatrick, Christian
Manasquan HS
S Belmar, NJ

Kim, Cecilia
Tenafly HS
Columbia, MO

Kim, Suhyon
Ocean Twsp HS
Asbury Park, NJ

Kimes, Damon
Vineland HS
Vineland, NJ

Kinder, Constance
Benedictine Acad
Newark, NJ

King, Christine
Eastern HS
Berlin, NJ

King, Danny
Cranford HS
Cranford, NJ

King, Rachel Edna
Luise
Cumberland
Regional HS
Bridgeton, NJ

King, Richard
Pinelands Regional
Tuckerton, NJ

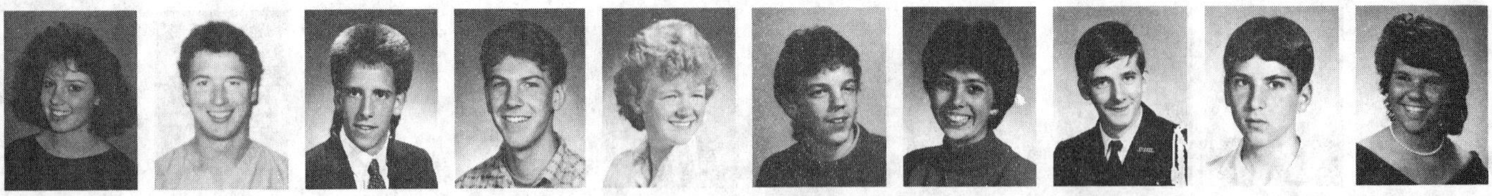

King, Treva
Shawnee HS
Vincetown, NJ

Kinney, John
Ramapo HS
Franklin Lakes, NJ

Kinney, Todd A
Cherry Hill HS East
Cherry Hill, NJ

Kirchofer, Maurice
Green Brook HS
Green Brook, NJ

Kirk, Bonnie
Union HS
Union, NJ

Kirk, John
Pinelands Regional
Tuckerton, NJ

Kirkendall, Tara
Phillipsburg HS
Phillipsburg, NJ

Kirkpatrick, Jr
Claude R
Marine Academy Of
Science & Tech
Keansburg, NJ

Kisala, Douglas
Mt Olive HS
Budd Lake, NJ

Kistler, Donna
Butler HS
Butler, NJ

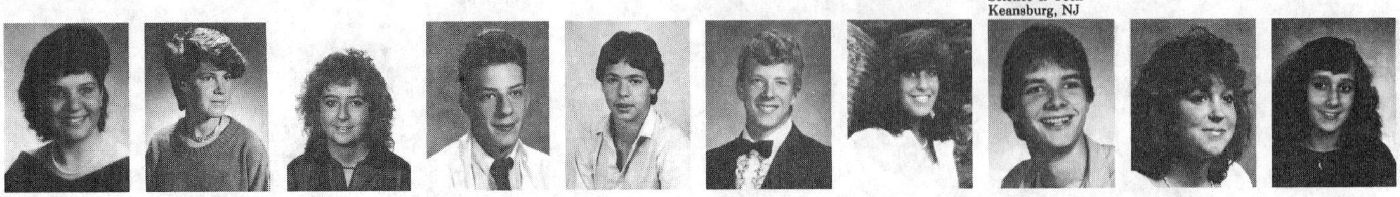

Kistler, Dyan
Butler HS
Butler, NJ

Klaiman, Jean M
The Pingry Schl
Summit, NJ

Klak, Barbara
Immaculate
Conception HS
Wallington, NJ

Klehm, Robert
Essex Catholic Boys
Newark, NJ

Kleidermacher,
David N
Cherokee HS
Marlton, NJ

Klein, Timothy E
Upper Freehold
Regional HS
New Egypt, NJ

Kleinberg, Elizabeth
A
Mountain Lakes HS
Mountain Lakes, NJ

Klinsky, Steven J
Toms River High
Schl North
Toms River, NJ

Klotz, Tammy A
Bordentown
Regional HS
Cookstown, NJ

Klucsarits, Lori
Hunterdon Central
Flemington, NJ

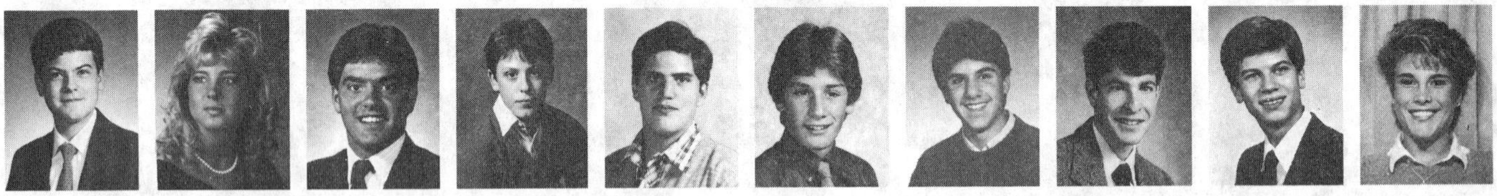

Knehr, Helmut T
Union HS
Union, NJ

Knipfelberg, Debora
John P Stevens HS
Edison, NJ

Knutelsky, Thomas
Wallkill Valley
Regional HS
Franklin, NJ

Koch, Joseph F
Sussex County
Vo-Tech HS
Montague, NJ

Koch, Kenneth
Kinnelon HS
Kinnelon, NJ

Koch, Stephen J
Collingswood HS
Collingswood, NJ

Kochberg, Joseph
Hightstown HS
East Windsor, NJ

Koenig, Andrew S
Moorestown HS
Moorestown, NJ

Koenig, Robert H
Livingston HS
Livingston, NJ

Koerner, Darlene
Pennsauken HS
Pennsauken, NJ

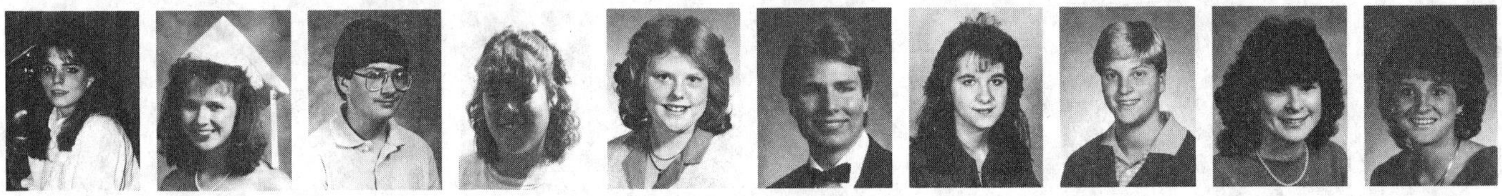

Koerner, Dorothy
Immaculate
Conception HS
Ridgefield Prk, NJ

Koetting, Jacquelyn
Paramus HS
Paramus, NJ

Kokoska, Stephen
M
Spotswood HS
Spotswood, NJ

Kolodij, Christine
St Aloysius HS
Jersey City, NJ

Kolodziej, Stacey
Ann
Elizabeth HS
Elizabeth, NJ

Komeshak, Patrick
Cherokee HS
Marlton, NJ

Kondek, Karen
Matawan Regional
Matawan, NJ

Kornmueller, Jason
West
Morris-Mendha
Chester, NJ

Kosydar, Christie
Jean
Bancocas Valley
Regional HS
Mount Holly, NJ

Kotyuk, Kim
Manville HS
Manville, NJ

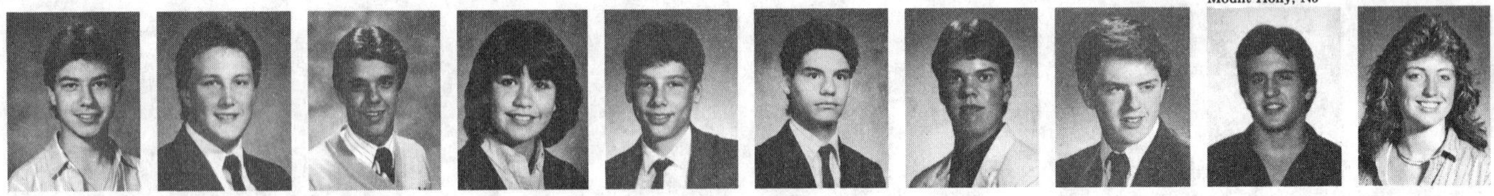

Koukourdelis, Tom
South River HS
S River, NJ

Kovach, Mark
Northern Burlington
Allentown, NJ

Kovacs, Albert
Mc Corristin
Catholic HS
Trenton, NJ

Kovacs, Michelle
Notre Dame HS
Crosswicks, NJ

Kovaly, Michael
St Mary Of The
Linden, NJ

Kozachenko,
Michael J
John F Kennedy HS
Willingboro, NJ

Kozak, Michael J
Hamilton High West
Trenton, NJ

Kramer, Jeffrey
Mount Olive HS
Budd Lake, NJ

Krankel, Daniel
Fair Lawn HS
Fair Lawn, NJ

Krause, Brenda
Alisha
West Milford HS
W Milford, NJ

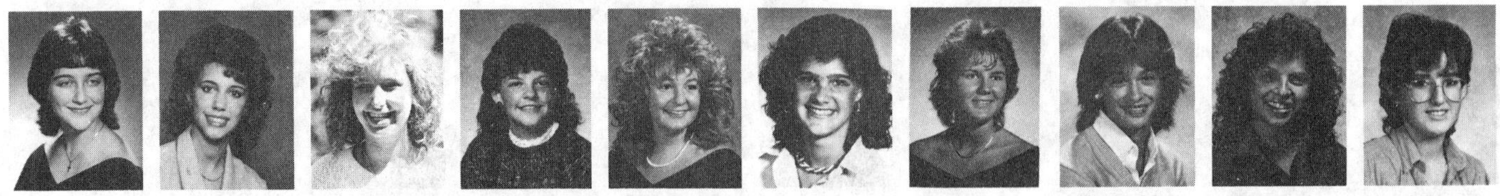

Krause, Joanne
Sayreville War
Memorial HS
Sayreville, NJ

Krieger, Kimberly
Delaware Valley
Regional HS
Frenchtown, NJ

Krinsky, Tamara
Manalapan HS
Englishtown, NJ

Krohn, Jill
Oakcrest HS
Mays Landing, NJ

Krueger, Tricia
Lynn
Mc Corristin HS
Trenton, NJ

Kruge, Karissa
Ramapo HS
Wyckoff, NJ

Kruitwagen,
Antoinette
Bridgeton SR HS
Bridgeton, NJ

Krulikowski, Lisa
Ann
Mc Corristin
Catholic HS
Hamilton Sq, NJ

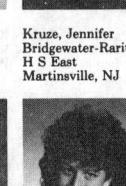

Kruze, Jennifer
Bridgewater-Raritan
H S East
Martinsville, NJ

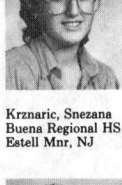

Krznaric, Snezana
Buena Regional HS
Estell Mnr, NJ

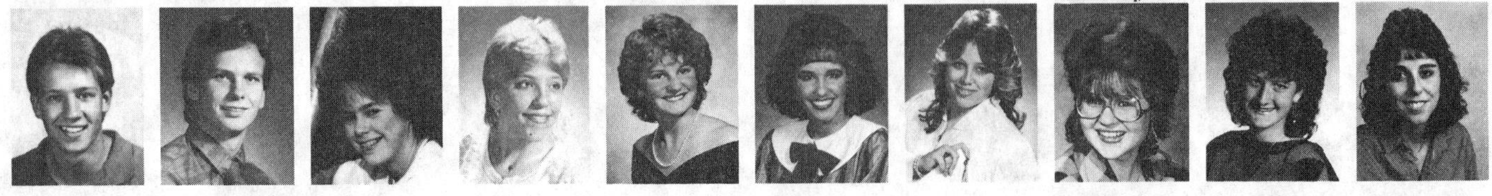

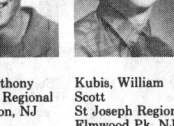

Kubat, Anthony
Edgewood Regional
Hammonton, NJ

Kubis, William
Scott
St Joseph Regional
Elmwood Pk, NJ

Kuczkuda, Marianne
Sussex Vo Tech
Andover, NJ

Kugit, Kelly
Freehold Township
Freehold, NJ

Kuhn, Alyssa G
Moorestown HS
Moorestown, NJ

Kukan, Patricia
Union Catholic
Regional HS
Mountainside, NJ

Kukla, Josephine
Mary
Indian Hills HS
Oakland, NJ

Kulberda, Carolyn
Linden HS
Linden, NJ

Kurland, Meredith
Parsippany HS
Parsippany, NJ

Kurtz, Kimberly
Buena Regional HS
Newfield, NJ

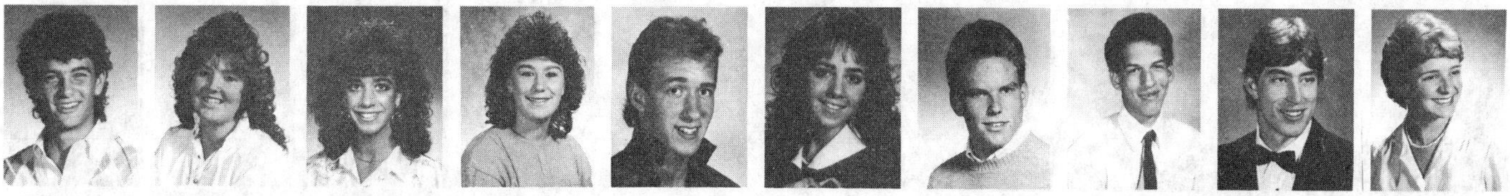

Kurzweil, Jordan
Montville Township
Montville, NJ

Kwitkoski, Dawn
Sayreville War
Memorial HS
Sayreville, NJ

La Badia, Jill
Indian Hills HS
Oakland, NJ

La Barre,
Laurie-Ann
Hackettstown HS
Belvidere, NJ

La Chance, Norman
Riverside HS
Riverside, NJ

La Greca, Susan
Lakeland Regional
Ringwood, NJ

La Gullo,
Christopher S
Phillipsburg HS
Bloomsbury, NJ

La Monaca, Vincent
St Joseph HS
Hammonton, NJ

La Rocca, Joseph
Mc Corristin
Catholic HS
New Egypt, NJ

La Rosa, Kathleen
Dumont HS
Dumont, NJ

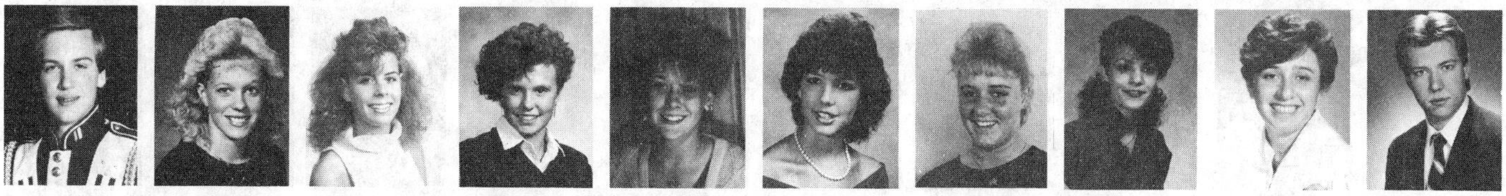

Labay, Robert
Union HS
Union, NJ

Labowicz, Joanne
South River HS
South River, NJ

Lacher, Britt
Franklin HS
Somerset, NJ

Laczko, Ildiko
St John Vianney HS
Hazlet, NJ

Lafferty, Cindi
Overbrook SR HS
Lindenwald, NJ

Lafferty, Dawn
Overbrook Regional
Pine Hill, NJ

Laffey, Michele
Wildwood Catholic
N Wildwood, NJ

Lagambina, Susan
Burlington Co
Mt Holly, NJ

Lager, Irena
New Milford HS
New Milford, NJ

Lair, James
Belleville HS
Belleville, NJ

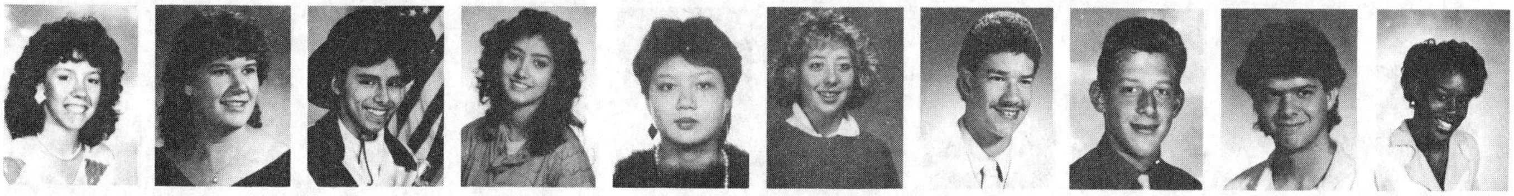

Lake, Kelley Ann
Paulsboro HS
Paulsboro, NJ

Lake, Leeann
Egg Harbor
Township HS
Farmington, NJ

Lalama, John
Hoboken HS
Hoboken, NJ

Lalwani, Leena
Dwight Englewood
Englewood, NJ

Lam, Helen
Edison HS
Edison, NJ

Lamey, Michele
Pitman HS
Pitman, NJ

Lamicella, Peter
Toms River HS
Beachwood, NJ

Lamson, Marc L
Paulsboro HS
Gibbstown, NJ

Land, David
Phillipsburg HS
Phillipsburg, NJ

Land, Margaret
Highland HS
Blackwood, NJ

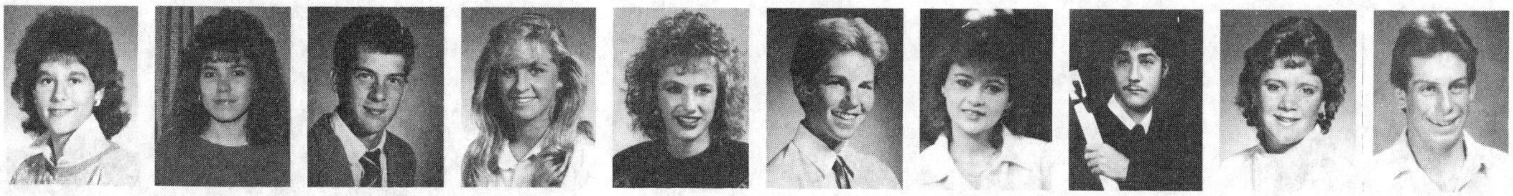

Landau, Deborah
Middletown High
Schl South
Leonardo, NJ

Landrud, Lisa
Vernon Twp HS
Sussex, NJ

Lane, Gregory
Joseph
Notre Dame HS
Hamilton Sq, NJ

Langbert, Marni
East Brunswick HS
East Brunswick, NJ

Lange, Carol
Edgewood HS
Atco, NJ

Langer, Thomas
St Joseph Regional
Congers, NY

Langley, Denise
Arthur S Uchalick
Elmer, NJ

Langley, George
Charles
Cumberland
Regional HS
Rosenhayn, NJ

Langon, Gina
Middle Twp HS
Goshen, NJ

Laning, Christopher
Clearview Regional
Mullica Hill, NJ

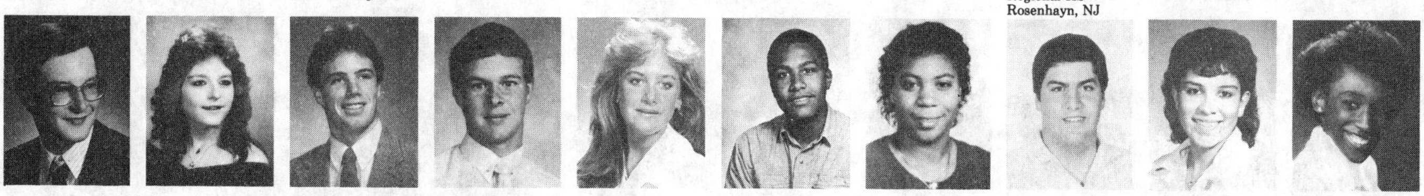

Lantry, Matthew F
Morris Knolls HS
Denville, NJ

Lanute, Michelle
Edgewood HS
Sicklerville, NJ

Laracy, Rich
Point Pleasant Boro
Point Pleasant, NJ

Laraway, II John
Stone
Rancocas Valley
Regional HS
Mt Holly, NJ

Largey, Lori
Middletown HS
Middletown, NJ

Larkins, Alvin
Dwight Morrow HS
Englewood, NJ

Larmore, Gerri Y
Burlington City HS
Edgewater Park, NJ

Larosa, Adam
Middletown HS
Middletown, NJ

Larraz, Lina M
Paterson Catholic R
Paterson, NJ

Larue, Yolette
Roselle Catholic HS
Roselle, NJ

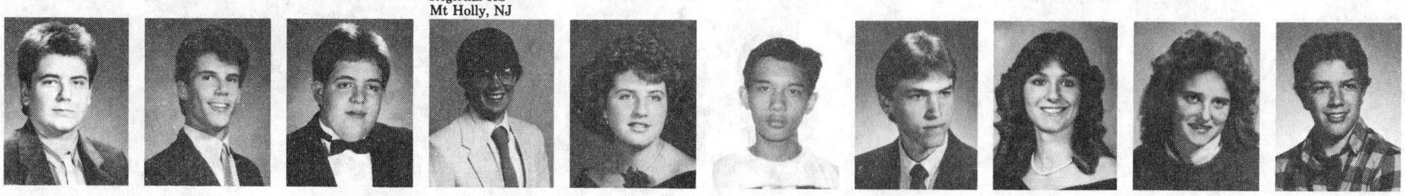

Lasser, Robert
Don Bosco Prep HS
Wallington, NJ

Lassiter, Michael J
Northern Burlington
Mc Guire Afb, NJ

Latour, Richard
North Bergen HS
North Bergen, NJ

Latronica, Joseph E
West Milford
Township HS
West Milford, NJ

Lavan, Michele
St John Vianney HS
Hazlet, NJ

Lavarro, Jr Rolando
St Peters Prep
Jersey City, NJ

Lavender, Joshua
North Brunswick
Top HS
N Brunswick, NJ

Law, Kathleen
Middle Township
Avalon, NJ

Lawless, Denise
Pinelands Regional
West Creek, NJ

Lawlor, Jason
Morristown HS
Morris Plains, NJ

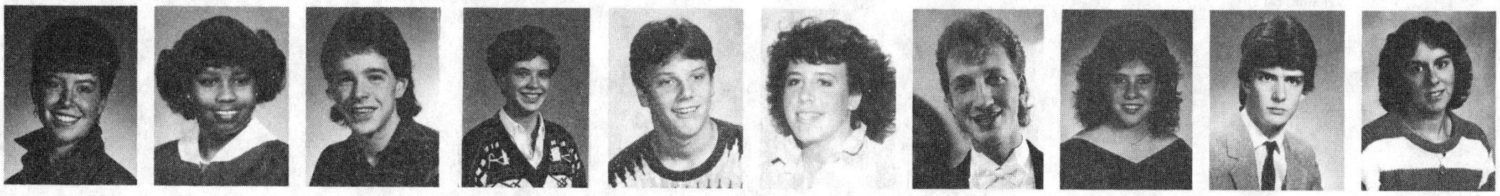

Lawson, Christie
High Point Regional
Branchville, NJ

Lawson, Lauren
Plainfield HS
Plainfield, NJ

Lawwill, Brad
Randolph HS
Randolph, NJ

Layhew, Denise
Baptist HS
Haddon Hts, NJ

Layton, Sean
Lakewood HS
Lakewood, NJ

Lazarus, Nicole
Freehold Township
Freehold, NJ

Le Page, Mark
Paramus HS
Paramus, NJ

Le Schack, Sharon
A
St Pius X HS
Somerset, NJ

Leach, Joseph J
Hackettstown HS
Hackettstown, NJ

Leap, Heather
Delaware Valley
Regional HS
Frenchtown, NJ

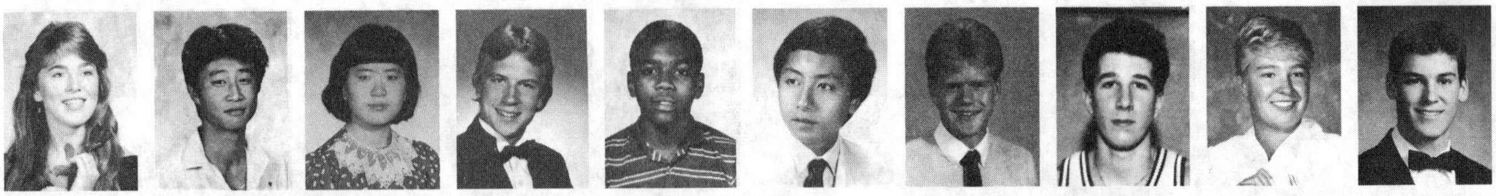

Leash, Dainna
Colleen
West Deptford HS
Mantua, NJ

Lee, Jae
Bordentown
Regional HS
Cookstown, NJ

Lee, Jeanny
Ft Lee HS
Fort Lee, NJ

Lee, Mark T
Whippany Park HS
Whippany, NJ

Lee, Oswald
John F Kennedy HS
Paterson, NJ

Lee, Steven
Kennelon HS
Smoke Rise, NJ

Leeds, Douglas
Baptist HS
Lindenwold, NJ

Leestma, James L
Elmwood Park
Memorial HS
Elmwood Park, NJ

Leggin, Julianne S
Lenape Valley
Regional HS
Stanhope, NJ

Lehner, Richard A
Cherokee HS
Marlton, NJ

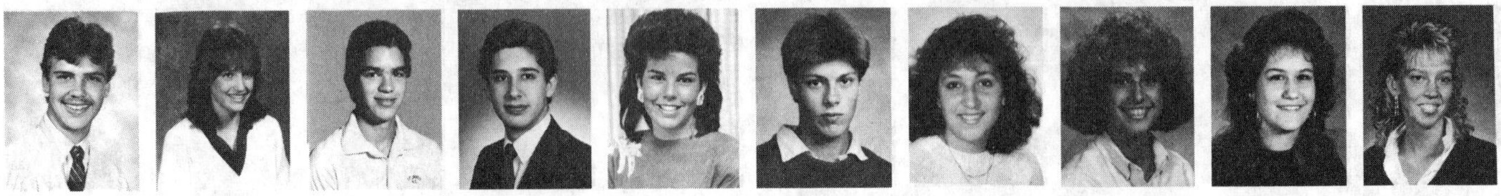

Lehr, Rodger B
Pennsville Memorial
Pennsville, NJ

Leiser, Gail
Spotswood HS
Spotswood, NJ

Leisner, III Thomas
St James HS
Pennsville, NJ

Leit, David
Livingston HS
Livingston, NJ

Leitman, Jennifer
Wayne Hills HS
Wayne, NJ

Leitner, Marty
Rancocas Valley
Regional HS
Mt Holly, NJ

Lekatis, Kiki
Mother Seton
Regional HS
Irvington, NJ

Lemaldi, Maria
Monsignor Donovan
Toms River, NJ

Lemise, Michele
De Paul Butler HS
Bloomingdale, NJ

Lennon, Colleen
Union Catholic
Regional HS
Elizabeth, NJ

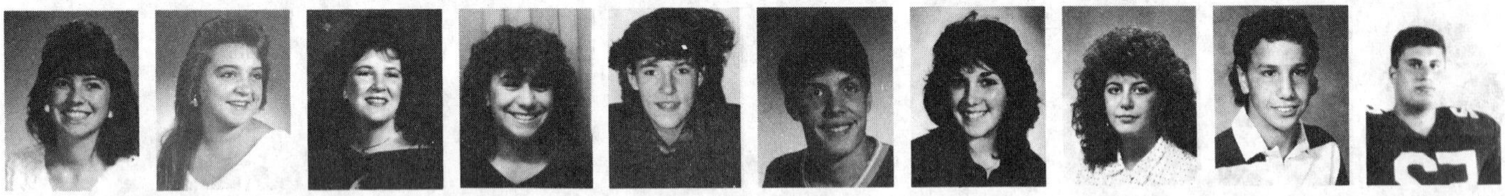

Lennon, Shareen
Pinelands Regional
Tuckerton, NJ

Lenz, Cheryl
Morris Knolls HS
Denville, NJ

Leonard, Antoinette
St John Vianney HS
Hazlet, NJ

Leonardis, Joanne
Kearny HS
Kearny, NJ

Lesko, Jo Ann
Madison Central HS
Old Bridge, NJ

Lessig, Scott
Phillipsburg HS
Phillipsburg, NJ

Letterie, Barbara
Cinaminson HS
Cinnaminson, NJ

Levi, Jeanine
Morris Catholic HS
Parsippany, NJ

Levine, Stephen
West Essex Regional
No Caldwell, NJ

Levine, Todd
Manalapan HS
Englishtown, NJ

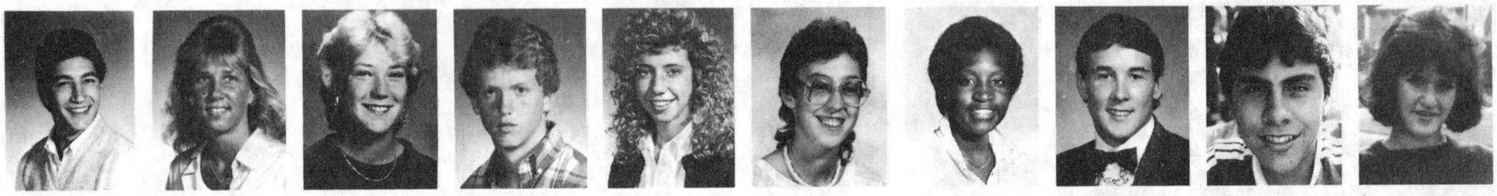

Leviss, Jonathan A
Mountain Lakes HS
Mountain Lakes, NJ

Levonaitis, Barbara
Bridgewater-Raritan
HS West
Bridgewater, NJ

Lewis, Allison K
Pequannock
Township HS
Pompton Plains, NJ

Lewis, Jeff
Toms River HS
Pine Beach, NJ

Lewis, Monica
Red Bank Catholic
Brielle, NJ

Lewis, Vicki
Riverside HS
Riverside, NJ

Lewis, Yuenge
St James HS
Salem, NJ

Ley, Gregory S
Gateway Regional
Woodbury Hts, NJ

Leyva, Edward
Paramus Catholic
Teaneck, NJ

Lifshey, Joanna
Cherry Hill High
School West
Cherry Hill, NJ

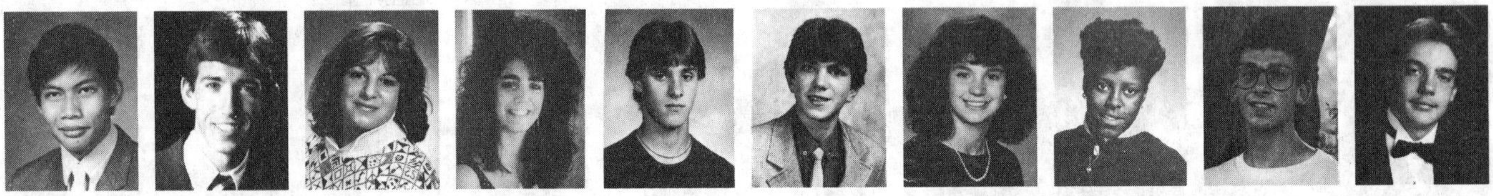

Ligeralde, Davidson
Glen Ridge HS
Glen Ridge, NJ

Ligon, Greg
Ridge HS
Basking Ridge, NJ

Ligorner, Karyn
Lesli
Newark Acad
Springfield, NJ

Limbardo, Michelle
Paramus Catholic
Fort Lee, NJ

Limouze, Robert
Westwood HS
Westwood, NJ

Lindaberry, Jeffrey
S
Faith Christian HS
Willingboro, NJ

Linden, Stacey Ann
Teaneck HS
Teaneck, NJ

Linder, Juzetta
Paterson Catholic
Regional HS
Paterson, NJ

Lindner, Steven J
Lenape Valley
Regional HS
Netcong, NJ

Lippai, Stephen P
Woodbridge HS
Fords, NJ

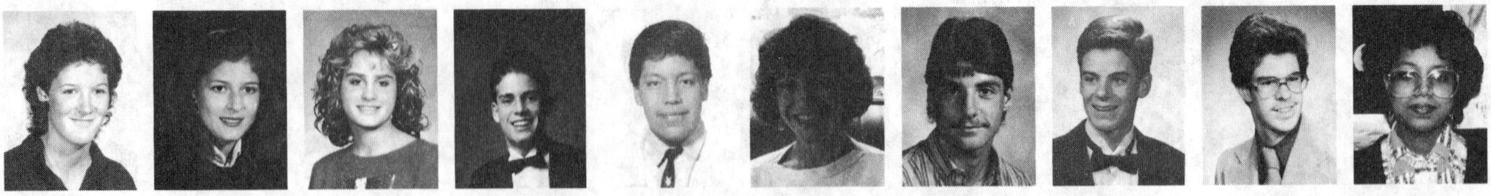

Lippincott, Jennifer
Riverside HS
Delanco, NJ

Lisehora, Kathleen
E
St Marys
Hall-Doane Acad
Trenton, NJ

Liss, Louisa
Edison HS
Edison, NJ

Litten, Jordan
Cinnaminson HS
Riverton, NJ

Live, Henry P
Emerson HS
Union City, NJ

Lo Bello, Rose
St Mary HS
Rutherford, NJ

Lobb, Dusty
Buena Regional HS
Newfield, NJ

Lobb, William
James
Bishop Eustace Prep
Medford, NJ

Lock, Walter G
Red Bank Regional
Pt Monmouth, NJ

Lomax, Mitzi
Plainfield HS
Plainfield, NJ

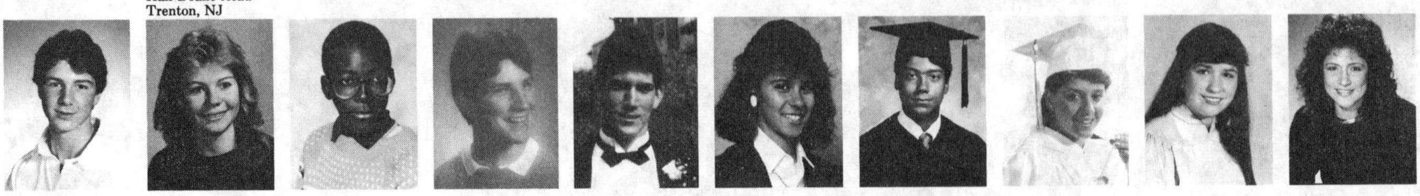

Lombardi, Owen
Dwight-Englewood
Prep Schl
Leonia, NJ

Lombardi, Regina
Pinelands Regional
Mystic Island, NJ

London, David
Oakcrest HS
Mays Landing, NJ

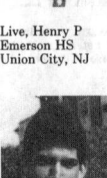

Long, Michael
Paul VI HS
Sicklerville, NJ

Longo, Brian
Mt Olive HS
Budd Lake, NJ

Lopez, Adriana
Mother Seton
Regional HS
Hillside, NJ

Lopez, Anthony
Bordentown
Regional HS
Bordentown, NJ

Lopez, Ardith M
Perth Amboy HS
Perth Amboy, NJ

Lopez, Diana M
St Joseph Of The
Palisades HS
Union City, NJ

Lopez, Laura E
Oakcrest HS
Hammonton, NJ

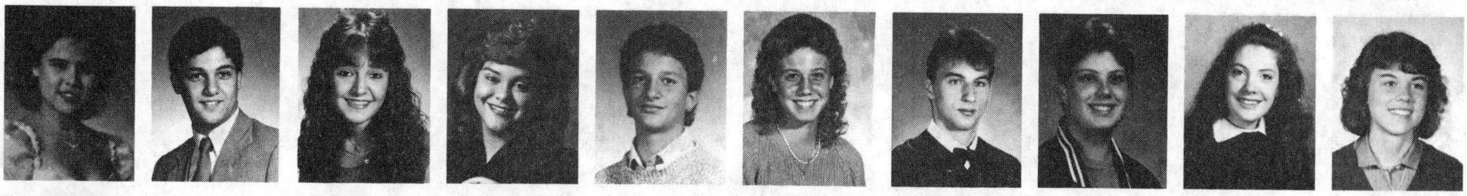

Lopez, Lydia
Millville SR HS
Millville, NJ

Lopez, Michael
Union HS
Union, NJ

Lopez, Michele
Hightstown HS
East Windsor, NJ

Lopez, Nancy
Mother Seton
Regional HS
Elizabeth, NJ

Lorenzo, Peter
Morristown HS
Morristown, NJ

Loretangeli, Kathryn
Bordentown
Regional HS
Bordentown, NJ

Lorfink, Robert
Hudson Catholic HS
Jersey City, NJ

Losito, Albert
Burlington Co
Riverside, NJ

Lotito, Elizabeth Anne L
St Rose HS
Spring Lk, NJ

Loughner, Diana
West Morris Central
Long Valley, NJ

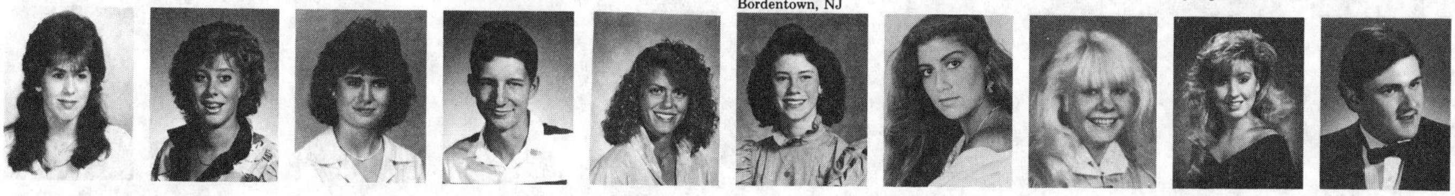

Loughran, Kimberly
Henry Hudson
Regional HS
Atlntic Hglds, NJ

Loveland, Jana
Lakeland Regional
Ringwood, NJ

Lovell, Eileen
Our Lady Of Mercy
Franklinville, NJ

Lowe, Joseph
Kingsway Regional
Clarksboro, NJ

Lowe, Karin
Cumberland
Regional HS
Bridgeton, NJ

Lubrano, Treasa
Villa Walsh Acad
Mendham, NJ

Lucarelli, Rosanne C
Ocean Twp HS
West Deal, NJ

Lucas, Danielle
Bayonne HS
Bayonne, NJ

Lucca, Tracy
St Joseph HS
Hammonton, NJ

Lucchesi, Eric
Rigefield Park HS
Cliffside Park, NJ

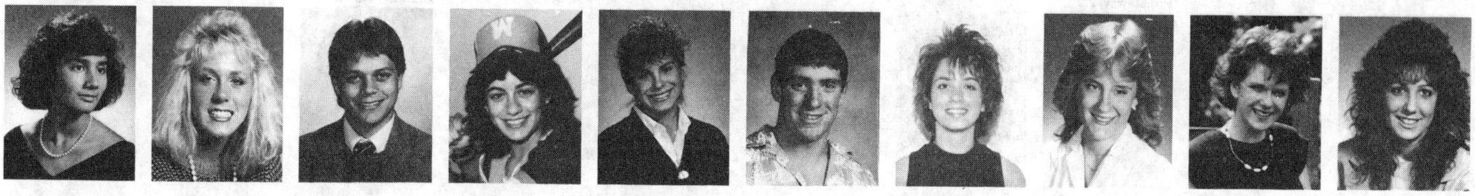

Luciano, Kim-Thu
Neptune SR HS
Wall Township, NJ

Luckenbill, Holly
Hillbrough HS
Somerville, NJ

Ludden, Robert
Chrisian Brothers
Middletown, NJ

Ludovich, Joel
Edgewood Regional
SR HS
Waterford, NJ

Luisi, Stephanie
Immaculate Heart
Moonachie, NJ

Lukis, Richard
Burlington City HS
Beverly, NJ

Lullo, Tina
William L Dickinson
Jersey City, NJ

Lum, Linda
Hackensack HS
Maywood, NJ

Lumer, Mary A
Governor Livingston
Reg HS
Murray Hill, NJ

Luna, Sheri
Lodi HS
Lodi, NJ

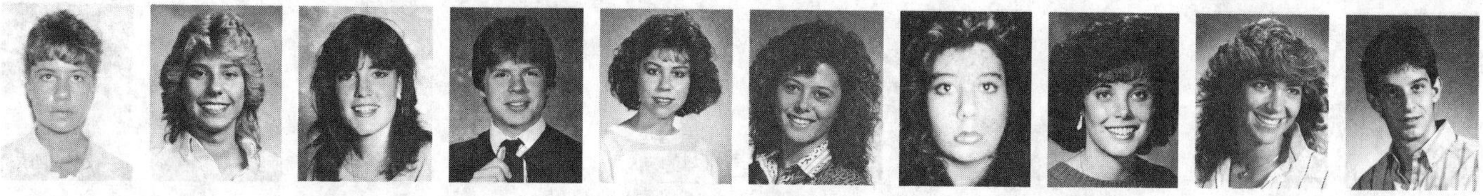

Luppino, Cathy
Bayonne HS
Bayonne, NJ

Luszik, Ann Marie
St John Vianney HS
Englishtown, NJ

Lutz, Kristen
Waldwick HS
Waldwick, NJ

Lutz, Nicholas
Verona HS
Verona, NJ

Luvera, Maria Del Carmen
Cliffside Park HS
Fairview, NJ

Luy, Tiffany
Watchung Hills Reg
Ellicott City, MD

Luzzi, Roseann
Lyndhurst HS
Lyndhurst, NJ

Lynch, Erinn Jane
West Essex Regional
Fairfield, NJ

Lynch, Jennifer
Toms River H S
Toms River, NJ

Lynch, Thomas
Bridgewater Raritan
West HS
Bridgewater, NJ

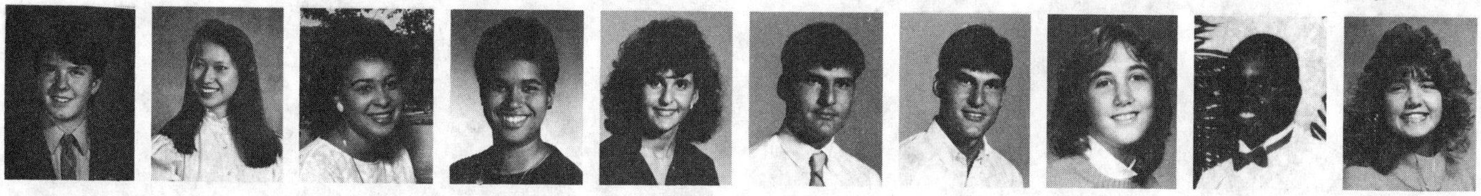

Lynes, David
St Marys Hall
Doane Acad
Cherry Hill, NJ

Ma, Jui Sun
Holy Spirit HS
Somers Pt, NJ

Macaulay, Alice
Phillipsburg HS
Phillipsburg, NJ

Macaulay, Helen
Phillipsburg HS
Phillipsburg, NJ

Maccarone, Donna
St James HS
Swedesboro, NJ

Maccarone, Joseph
St James HS
Swedesboro, NJ

Maccarone, Samuel
St James HS
Swedesboro, NJ

Macdonald, Michelle
Delaware Valley
Regional HS
Milford, NJ

Maceia, Antonio
Oakcrest HS
Elwood, NJ

Machak, Jill Allison
Pequannock
Township HS
Pompton Plains, NJ

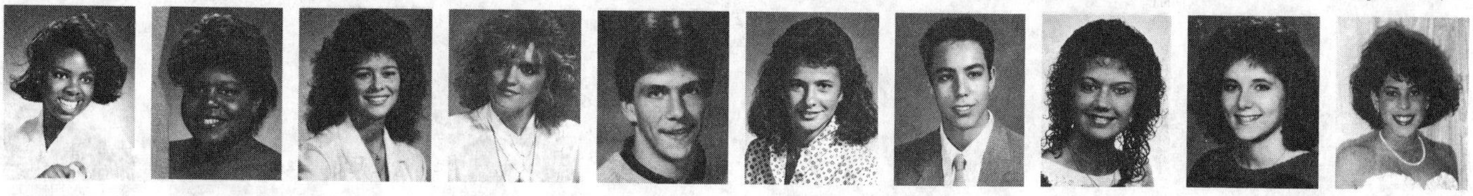

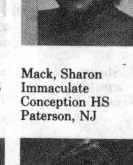

Mack, Myria
Whippany Park HS
Whippany, NJ

Mack, Sharon
Immaculate
Conception HS
Paterson, NJ

Mackey, Cheryl
St Joseph Schl
Berlin, NJ

Mackey, Laura
Manchester
Township HS
Lakehurst, NJ

Mackiewicz, James
South River HS
South River, NJ

Macur, Juliet
Bridgewater-Raritan
West HS
Bridgewater, NJ

Madamba, Aaron
Pinelands Regional
Mystic Island, NJ

Madara, Belinda
Holy Cross HS
Mount Holly, NJ

Madden, Suzanne E
Teaneck HS
Teaneck, NJ

Maestrale, Michelle
Paul Vi HS
Laurel Springs, NJ

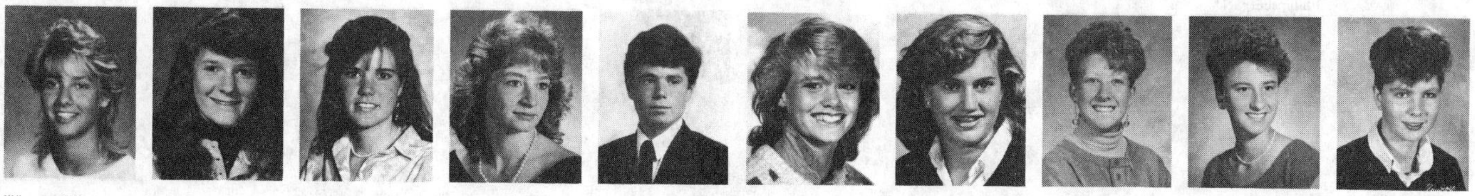

Magaletta, Lynn
Mt St Dominic Acad
W Caldwell, NJ

Magaw, Beth
South River HS
South River, NJ

Magee, Jennifer
Linden HS
Linden, NJ

Magnotti, Lauri
Clifton HS
Clifton, NJ

Maguire, Brendan
Haddon Township
Westmont, NJ

Maguire, Marianne
Ocean City HS
Ocean City, NJ

Maguire, Meghan
Villa Victoria Acad
Jacobstown, NJ

Maher, Heather
Pequannock
Township HS
Pequannock, NJ

Mahon, Debra Anne
Notre Dame HS
Trenton, NJ

Mahoney, Lynn
Holy Rosary Acad
Jersey City, NJ

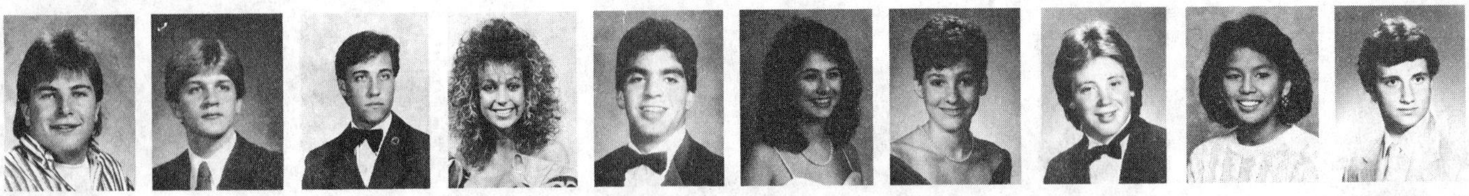

Mahony, John J
Phillipsburg
Catholic HS
Stewartsville, NJ

Mahr, Christopher
Belvidere HS
Arnold, CA

Maier, Christopher
Paul VI HS
Voorhees, NJ

Maillaro, Kathleen
Holy Spirit HS
Brigantine, NJ

Mairone, Richard
Holy Spirit HS
Northfield, NJ

Makarewicz, Monica
Edison HS
Hampstead, NH

Makowski, Kim
Weehawken HS
Weehawken, NJ

Makransky, Jim
Sayreville War
Memorial HS
Parlin, NJ

Malantic, Grace
Saddle River Day
Oradell, NJ

Malatesta, Ralph
Watchung Hills
Regional HS
Warren, NJ

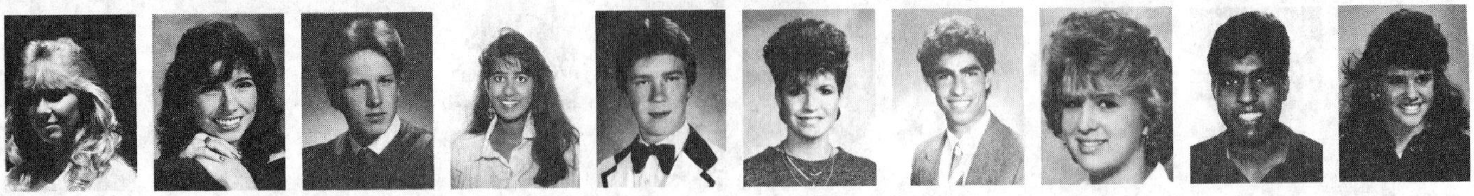

Malia, Bobbi O
Malley
Immaculate Heart
Emerson, NJ

Malinowski,
Michelle
Jackson Memorial
Jackson, NJ

Malinowski, Robert
A
Piscataway Voctnl &
Technl HS
Piscataway, NJ

Mallik, Kamala
Pequannock
Township HS
Pequannock, NJ

Maloney, Robert
Hudson Catholic HS
Hoboken, NJ

Maltese, Lisa
Buena Regional HS
Vineland, NJ

Mamalian, Paul
New Milford HS
New Milford, NJ

Mamczak, Natalie
Denise
Mother Seton
Regional HS
Rahway, NJ

Manchand, Shaun
Montclair HS
Montclair, NJ

Mandell, Beverly
Lakewood HS
Lakewood, NJ

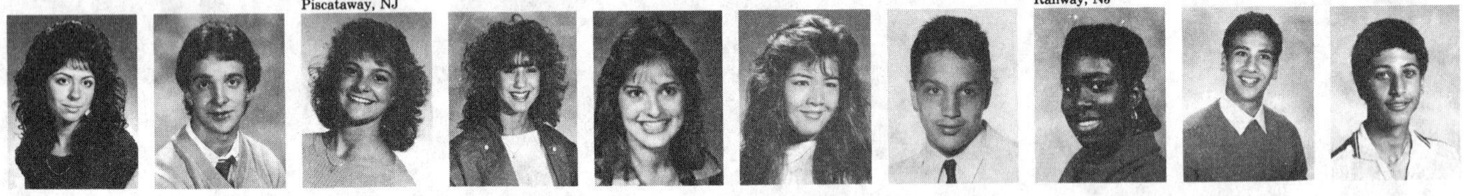

Manekas, Kay
Madison Central HS
Old Bridge, NJ

Mangione, Jim
Mc Corristin HS
Mercerville, NJ

Manheimer, Krista
Morristown HS
Morris Plains, NJ

Manion, Kimberly
Rutherford HS
Rutherford, NJ

Mannion, Debbie
Manalapan HS
Manalapan, NJ

Maqsudi, Mahnaz
Parsippany Hills HS
Parsippany, NJ

Marandino, Jared
Buena Regional HS
Newfield, NJ

Marant, Donna
Eastside HS
Paterson, NJ

Marascio, Frank
Rutherford HS
Rutherford, NJ

Marashlian,
Alexander
Parsippany Hills HS
Morris Plains, NJ

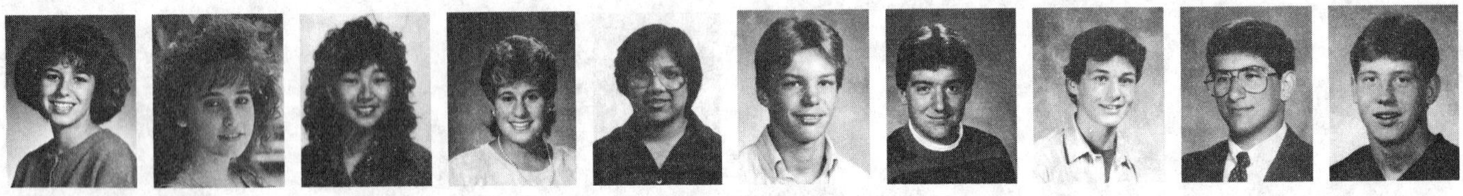

Marcel, Danielle
Kittatinny Regional
Newton, NJ

Marchitto, Christa
Bayonne HS
Bayonne, NJ

Marciante, Missy
Central Regional HS
Bayville, NJ

Mariano, Gia
Arthur L Johnson
Regional HS
Clark, NJ

Mariano, Marjorie
May
River Dell SR HS
Oradell, NJ

Marinari,
Christopher
Allentown HS
New Egypt, NJ

Marino, Andrew
West Essex Regional
Fairfield, NJ

Marino, John
Manasquan HS
Belmar, NJ

Marino, Michael
West Essex Regional
Fairfield, NJ

Marion, III James
W
Wallkill Valley Reg
Franklin, NJ

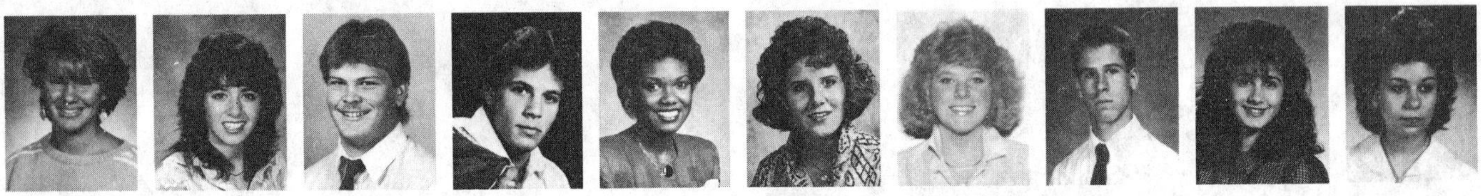

Marione, Tricia
Westfield HS
Westfield, NJ

Mark, Nancy
Manalapan HS
Englishtown, NJ

Markley, Craig
Lower Cape May
Regional HS
North Cape May,
NJ

Markovich, Michael
Toms River North
Toms River, NJ

Marks, Erica L
Burlington City HS
Burlington, NJ

Marks, Janet
Collings HS
Collingswood, NJ

Marler, Rebecca
Watchung Hills
Regional HS
Warren, NJ

Marlin, Jason
Pitman HS
Pitman, NJ

Marousis, Despina
Brick Memorial HS
Brick, NJ

Marques, Anabela
Alves
East Side SR HS
Newark, NJ

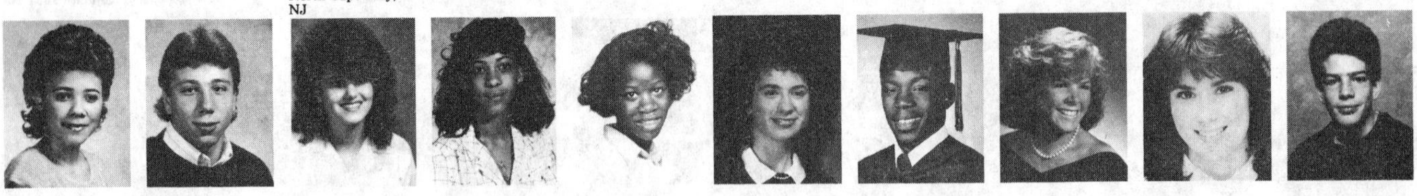

Marquez, Eileen
Sacred Heart HS
Vineland, NJ

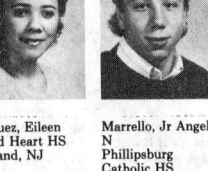

Marrello, Jr Angelo
N
Phillipsburg
Catholic HS
Phillipsburg, NJ

Marrero, Julieta
Our Lady Of Good
Counsel HS
Newark, NJ

Marriott, Lauri
Washington
Township HS
Sewell, NJ

Marsan, Ena
Dwight Morrow HS
Englewood, NJ

Marsden, Monica R
Pitmna HS
Pitman, NJ

Marseille, Philippe
Linden HS
Linden, NJ

Marsh, Amy
Neptune SR HS
Neptune City, NJ

Marshello, Meta
Oakcrest HS
Mays Landing, NJ

Marsiglio, Peter
Mahwah HS
Mahwah, NJ

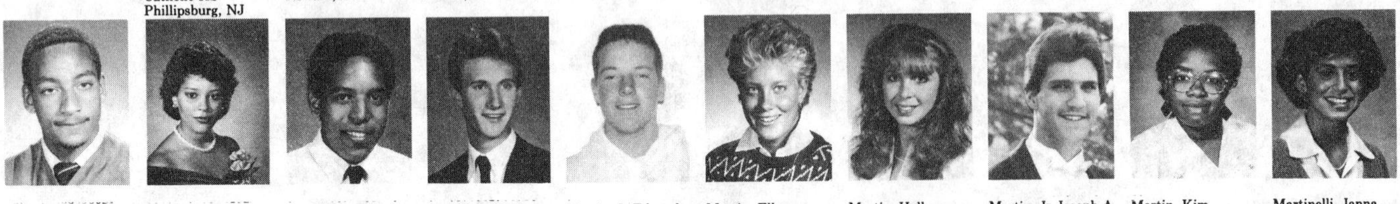

Martin, Alec
Saint Peter HS
Somerset, NJ

Martin, Carla
Emerson HS
Union City, NJ

Martin, David R
Willingboro HS
Willingboro, NJ

Martin, Edward
Westfield HS
Westfield, NJ

Martin, Jr Edward
R
St Peters Prep Schl
White House Sta,
NJ

Martin, Ellen
Bridgewater Raritan
HS West
Bridgewater, NJ

Martin, Holly
Morris Knolls HS
Green Pond, NJ

Martin, Jr Joseph A
Southern Regional
Manahawkin, NJ

Martin, Kim
Marylawn Of The
Newark, NJ

Martinelli, Janna
Our Lady Of Mercy
Vineland, NJ

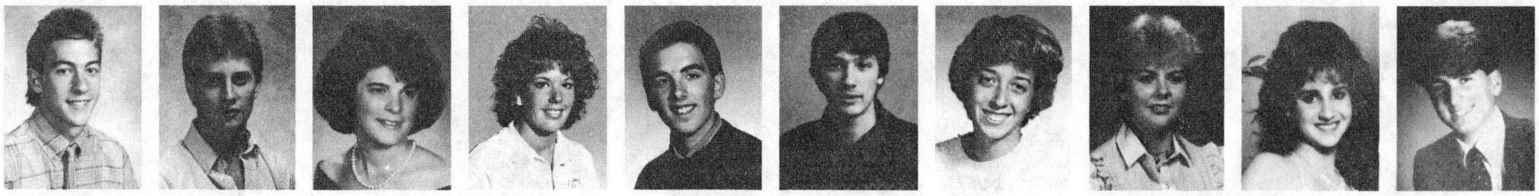

Martino, Jr Thomas J
Palmyra HS
Palmyra, NJ

Marton, Kevin
Bridgewater-Raritan HS East
Martinsville, NJ

Martorana, Tara
Mt Saint Mary Acad
Colts Neck, NJ

Marts, Jonel
St James HS
Salem, NJ

Marucci, Jr Anthony C
Mount Olive HS
Flanders, NJ

Marx, Jr Ronald
Sussex Vo Tech
Hopatcong, NJ

Mascaro, Julie Ann
Kingsway Regional
Mickleton, NJ

Mascenik, Nanette
Woodbridge SR HS
Woodbridge, NJ

Masciantonio, Stellamarie
Cherry Hill West
Cherry Hill, NJ

Mascola, John
John P Stevens HS
Edison, NJ

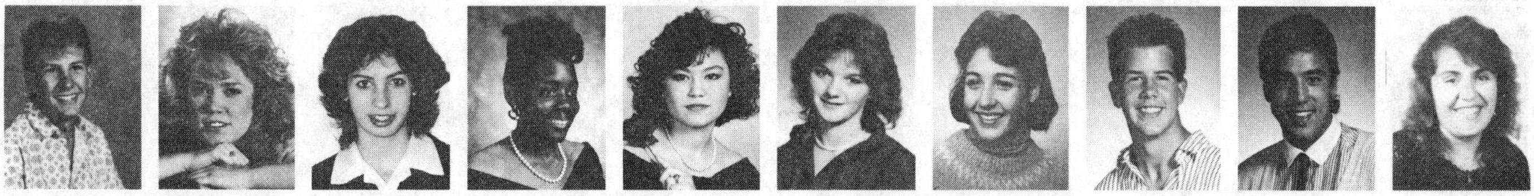

Mason, David
Egg Harbor Twp HS
Linwood, NJ

Mason, Melissa
Paul VI HS
Audubon, NJ

Massa, Linda
Immaculate Conception HS
Kearny, NJ

Massenat, Vertulie
Mc Corristain Catholic HS
Trenton, NJ

Mastin, Janet
Florence Township Memorial HS
Florence, NJ

Mastorio, Tracie
Cedar Ridge HS
Cliffwood Bch, NJ

Mastro, Elena Michele
West Windsor-Plainsbor
Lawrenceville, NJ

Mato, Shawn
West Milford Township HS
W Milford, NJ

Matonti, John
Montville Twsp HS
Montville, NJ

Matos, Lidia
East Side HS
Newark, NJ

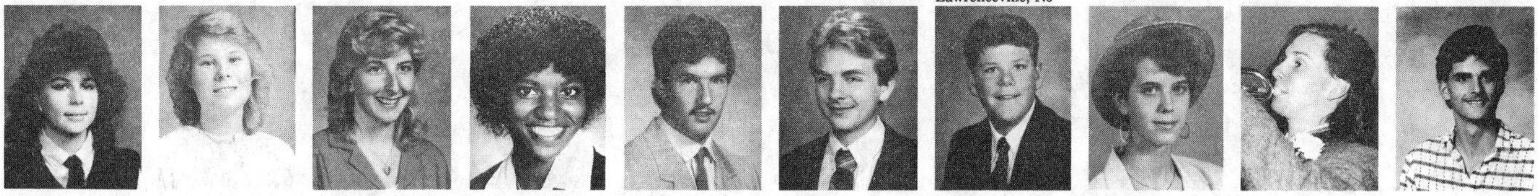

Matrisciano, Teresa
Rancocas Valley Regional HS
Mt Holly, NJ

Mattera, Deanna
Oakcrest HS
Mays Landing, NJ

Matteson, Susann
Southern Regional
Surf City, NJ

Matthews, Calandra
Mary Help Of Christians Acad
Paterson, NJ

Matthews, Donald
Northern Burlington Cnty Regnl HS
Jobstown, NJ

Matthews, Jr James J
Memorial HS
Cedar Grove, NJ

Matthews, Roger C
West Morris Mendham HS
Mendham, NJ

Matus, Valerie
Baptist HS
Gloucester City, NJ

Mauger, Christopher M
Haddonfield Memorial HS
Haddonfield, NJ

Maurer, Darrin
Vineland H S North
Vineland, NJ

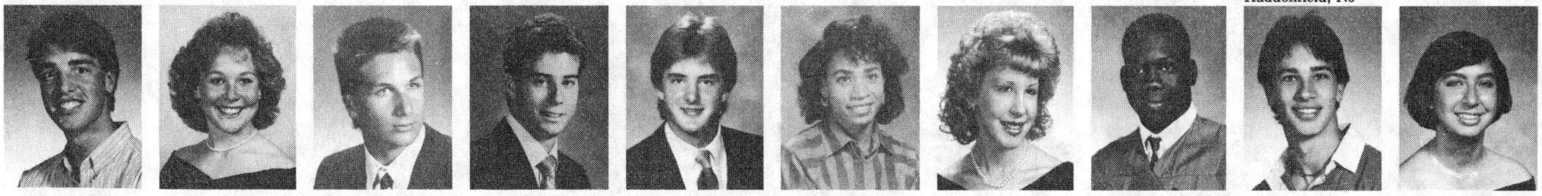

Maurer, Geoffrey M
West Windsor Plainsboro HS
Plainsboro, NJ

Mauroff, Kimberly
Lenape Regional HS
Vincentown, NJ

Maxwell, Michael
Immaculata HS
Piscataway, NJ

May, John D
Absegami HS
Cologne, NJ

May, Joseph C
South River HS
S River, NJ

May, Paula
Rahway HS
Rahway, NJ

Mayer, Laurie Gail
J P Stevens HS
Edison, NJ

Mayo, Erike
St Mary HS
Teaneck, NJ

Mayo, Shawn
Glen Rock HS
Glen Rock, NJ

Mayr, Annabelle
Vineland SR HS
Vineland, NJ

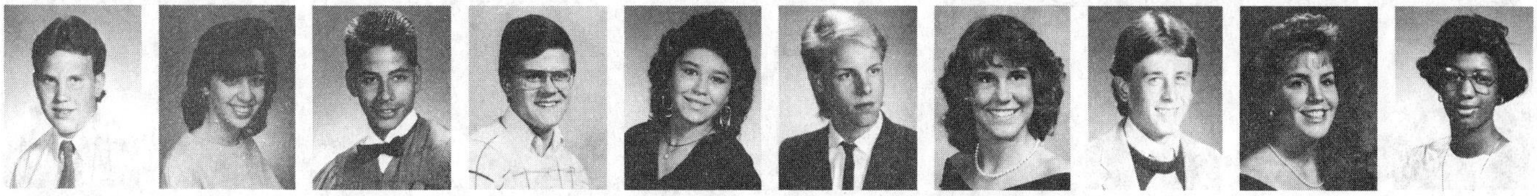

Mayrides, Mark
Immaculata HS
Belle Mead, NJ

Mays, Jennifer
Vineland HS
Vineland, NJ

Maze, Adam K
Sayreville War Memorial HS
Sayreville, NJ

Mazel, Joseph W
Fair Lawn HS
Fair Lawn, NJ

Mazur, Joann
Dover HS
Dover, NJ

Mazurek, Richard Michael
Midland Park HS
Midland Park, NJ

Mc Aleer, Susan
Shawnee HS
Medford, NJ

Mc Andrew, Kevin
Don Bosco Prep
Pearl River, NY

Mc Bride, Ellen
Wildwood Catholic
Cape May, NJ

Mc Burrows, Shanta
Hillside HS
Hillside, NJ

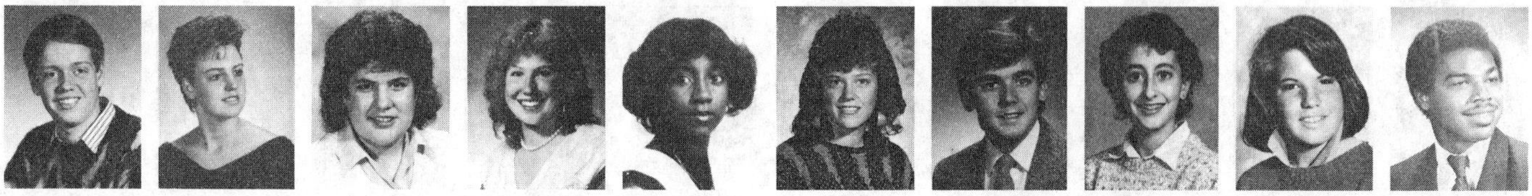

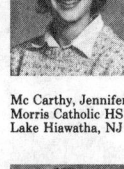

Mc Cabe, Eugene
Brick Memorial HS
Brick, NJ

Mc Cabe, Jennifer
Kinnelon HS
Kinnelon, NJ

Mc Cabe, Rosemary
Monsignor Donovan
Howell, NJ

Mc Caffrey, Eileen
Morris Catholic HS
Denville, NJ

Mc Call, Angela
Hillside HS
Hillside, NJ

Mc Cart, Keri
Washington Township HS
Turnersville, NJ

Mc Carthy, Hugh
Mt Olive HS
Flanders, NJ

Mc Carthy, Jennifer
Morris Catholic HS
Lake Hiawatha, NJ

Mc Carthy, Kara
Waldwick HS
Wladwick, NJ

Mc Clammy, James I
West Windsor-Plainsbor
Princeton, NJ

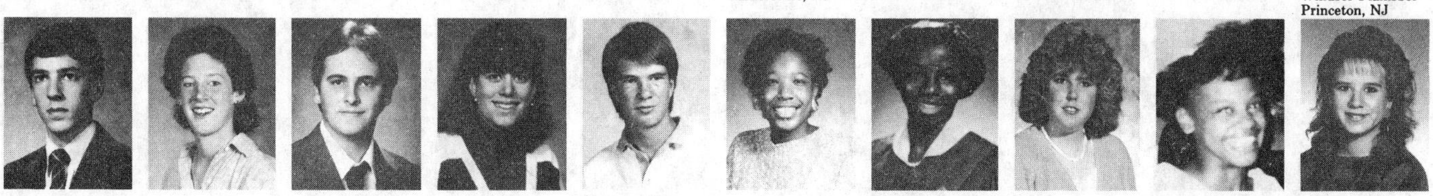

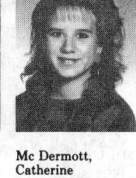

Mc Clane, James
Park Ridge HS
Park Ridge, NJ

Mc Clane, Sharon
Park Ridge HS
Park Ridge, NJ

Mc Connell, Jason
Millville SR HS
Pt Norris, NJ

Mc Cormick, Meghan
Bridgeton HS
Bridgeton, NJ

Mc Coy, James
Collingswood SR HS
Collingswood, NJ

Mc Coy, Monique
Neptune SR HS
Neptune, NJ

Mc Crae, Wanda L
E Orange HS
E Orange, NJ

Mc Cutcheon, Gwen Lea
Washington Twp
Turnersville, NJ

Mc Daniel, Maria Antoinette
Edgewood SR HS
Sicklerville, NJ

Mc Dermott, Catherine
Sayreville War Memorial HS
Sayreville, NJ

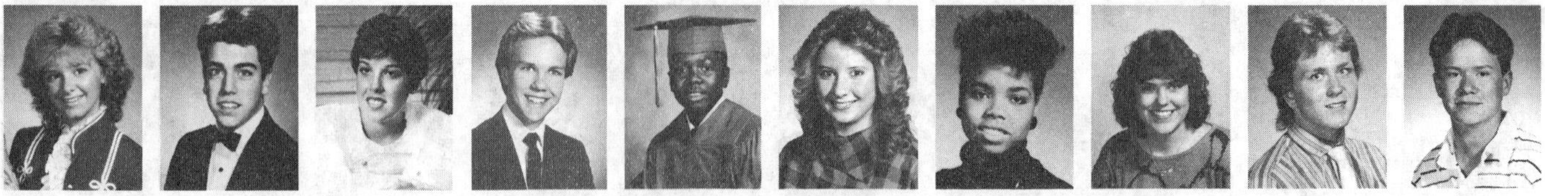

Mc Dermott, Maryann
Sayreville War Memorial HS
Sayreville, NJ

Mc Donald, John
St Joseph Regional
Demarest, NJ

Mc Donald, Keeley
Roxbury HS
Landing, NJ

Mc Donnell, Kevin G
Piscataway HS
Piscataway, NJ

Mc Duffie, Ivan
Eastside HS
Paterson, NJ

Mc Elroy, Melissa
North Warren Regional HS
Columbia, NJ

Mc Fall, Kathleen
Glen Rock SR HS
Glen Rock, NJ

Mc Fall, Patricia
Lacey Township HS
Forked River, NJ

Mc Farland, Thomas F
St Joseph Regional
Spring Valley, NY

Mc Gahn, Daniel
Atlantic City HS
Brigantine, NJ

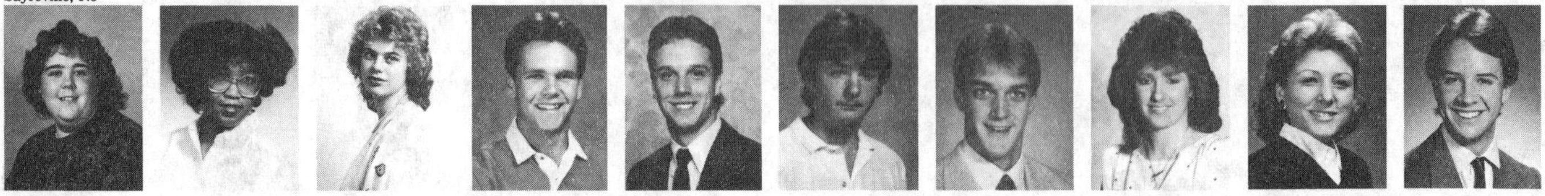

Mc Gay, Kelly
Lower Cape May Regional HS
Townbank, NJ

Mc Gee, Volante
Mt St Dominic Acad
East Orange, NJ

Mc Gill, Gretchen Ann
Bloomfield HS
Bloomfld, NJ

Mc Govern, Christopher
Clearview Regional
Sewell, NJ

Mc Govern, Michael
Vernon Township
Sussex, NJ

Mc Grath, Edward
Southern Regional
Barnegat, NJ

Mc Guigan, Michael
Notre Dome HS
Trenton, NJ

Mc Guire, Maureen
Linden HS
Linden, NJ

Mc Hose, Jamie
Holy Spirit HS
Brigantine, NJ

Mc Hugh, Edward
Lakeland Reg HS
Ringwood, NJ

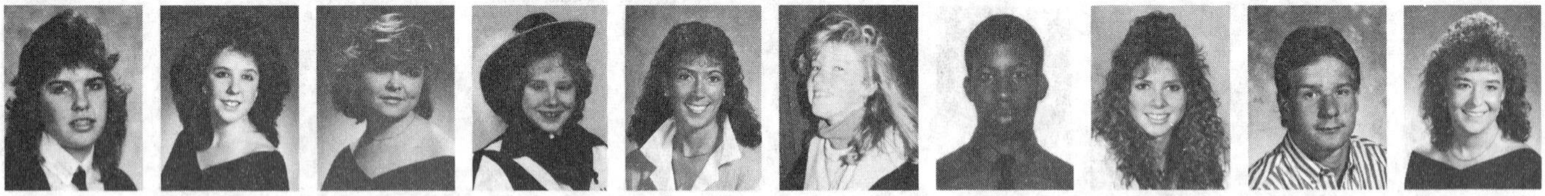

Mc Intyre, Deidre
Gloucester City JE SR HS
Brooklawn, NJ

Mc Ivor, Maureen
Sayreville War Memorial HS
Sayreville, NJ

Mc Kean, Julie
Red Bank Catholic
Middletown, NJ

Mc Kee, Julie Ellen
Holy Cross HS
Maple Shade, NJ

Mc Kenna, Kathleen Ann Marie
Belvidere HS
Hope, NJ

Mc Kenna, Pamela
Immaculate Heart
Oakland, NJ

Mc Kenzie, Kurt
Essex Catholic Boys
Irvington, NJ

Mc Keown, Ellen
Matawan Regional
Aberdeen, NJ

Mc Kinney, Dallas
Gloucester City HS
Brooklawn, NJ

Mc Laughlin, Colette
Bayonne HS
Bayonne, NJ

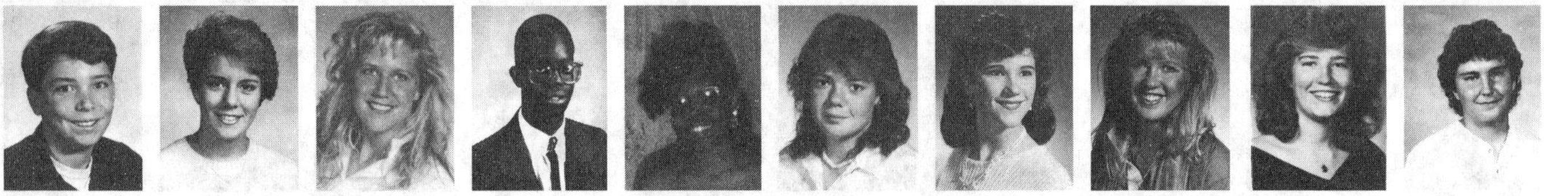

Mc Mahon, Michael
Morristown HS
Morristown, NJ

Mc Manus, Jennifer
Rancocas Valley Regional HS
Hainesport, NJ

Mc Mullen, Carrie
Columbia HS
Bayville, NJ

Mc Nair, Kevin
Highland Regional
Clementon, NJ

Mc Nair, Shantesia
Our Lady Of Good Counsel HS
Newark, NJ

Mc Nicholas, Cori
Bricktown HS
Brick Town, NJ

Mc Pherson, Cynthia S
Randolph HS
Mendham, NJ

Mc Pherson, Pam
Montville Township
Montville, NJ

Mc Shane, Sarah Anne
Mahwah HS
Mahwah, NJ

Mc Vey, Scott
Pennsville Memorial
Pennsville, NJ

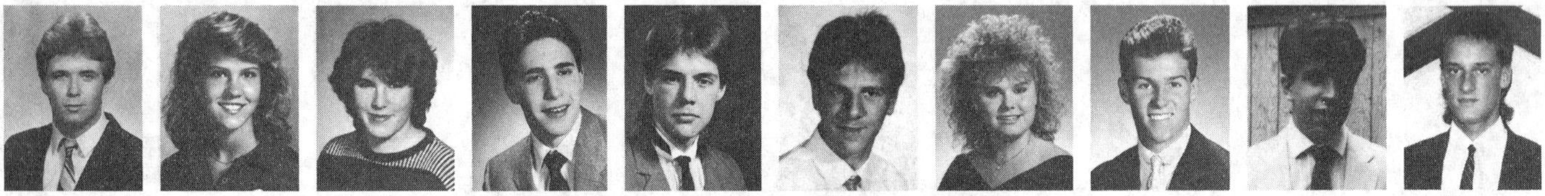

Mcalary, David Lee
Marist HS
Bayonne, NJ

Meade, Jennifer
Saint Rose HS
Bricktown, NJ

Meade, Michelle
Cranford HS
Cranford, NJ

Meade, Steven M
Bergenfield HS
Bergenfield, NJ

Meegan, John
MSGR Donovan HS
Jackson, NJ

Meglis, Edward
Holy Cross HS
Mt Laurel, NJ

Meicke, Lisa
Secaucus HS
Secaucus, NJ

Meisenbacher, Mark A
Immaculata HS
Middlesex, NJ

Meissner, Robert
Mt Olive HS
Budd Lake, NJ

Mejzak, Ronald
Paul VI HS
Williamstown, NJ

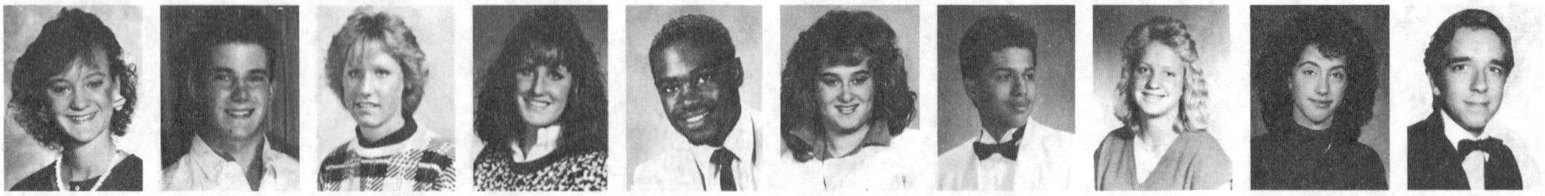

Melchionne, Sandi
Waldwick HS
Waldwick, NJ

Melko, Glenn J
Paul VI HS
Blackwood, NJ

Melly, Mary Beth
De Paul Diocesan
Riverdale, NJ

Melly, Michele
De Paul Diocesan
Riverdale, NJ

Melton, Gary P
Absegami HS
Egg Harbor City, NJ

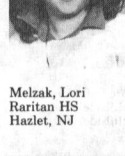

Melzak, Lori
Raritan HS
Hazlet, NJ

Mendez, James
E Exxex Catholic
E Orange, NJ

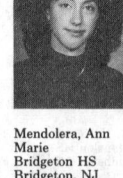

Mendoker, Lynn
South River HS
South River, NJ

Mendolera, Ann Marie
Bridgeton HS
Bridgeton, NJ

Mendonca, Francisco M
East Side HS
Newark, NJ

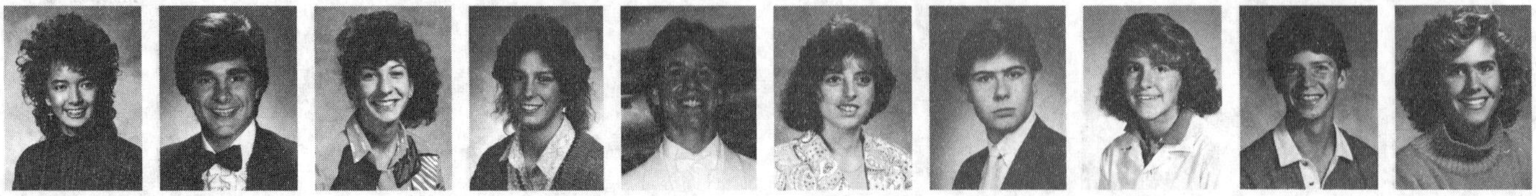

Mendoza, Jewel
Vineland HS
Vineland, NJ

Menendez, Alex
Secaucus HS
Secaucus, NJ

Menichelli, Sandi
Hamilton High
Mercerville, NJ

Menzak, Sandy
Hunterdon Central
White House Sta, NJ

Merkle, Robert
Oratory Prep
New Providence, NJ

Merlino, Sherriann
Burlington Co
Mt Holly, NJ

Merola, Stephen
Parsippany Hills HS
Morris Plains, NJ

Merone, Jennifer
Mount Olive HS
Budd Lake, NJ

Merrick, Geoffrey W
Madison HS
Madison, NJ

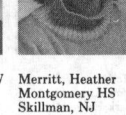

Merritt, Heather
Montgomery HS
Skillman, NJ

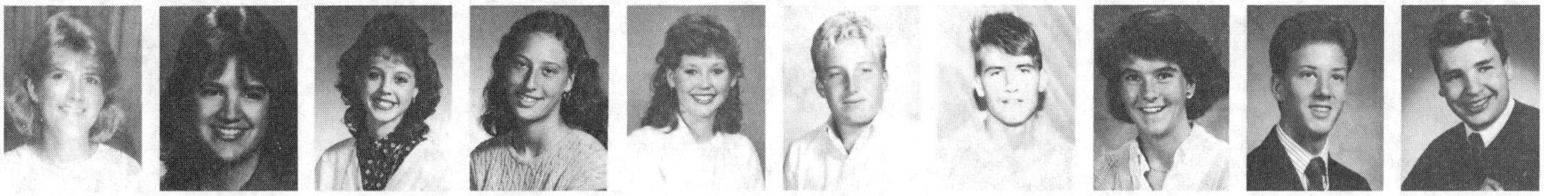

Merritt, Joan
Bridgewater HS
Bound Brook, NJ

Merritt, Tina
Montville Township
Towaco, NJ

Messenger, Kim
Toms River East HS
Toms River, NJ

Metzger, Nicole
Mount Olive HS
Flanders, NJ

Meyer, Karen
Paramus Catholic
Girls Reg HS
Oradell, NJ

Meyer, R Wesley
Pt Plsnt Bch HS
Pt Plsnt Bch, NJ

Meyers, Andrew
Saint Josephs
Regional HS
Ramsey, NJ

Michallis, Kelly
Manasquan HS
Brielle, NJ

Michel, Christian C
Bishop Eustace Prep
Cherry Hill, NJ

Michel, Erich
Bogota HS
Bogota, NJ

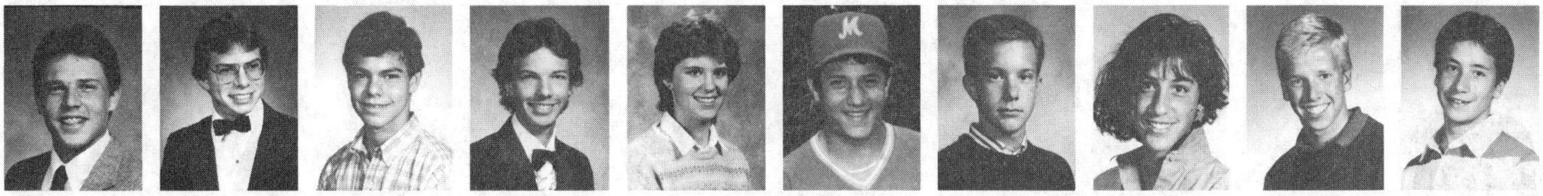

Michel, Mark E
Ewing HS
Trenton, NJ

Michitsch, Edward
F
Bergen Catholic HS
Hackensack, NJ

Midelton, Gary
Atlantic City HS
Ventnor, NJ

Mielechowsky, III
Alex
Gateway Regional
National Park, NJ

Miglin, Patricia E
Spotswood HS
Spotswood, NJ

Mignone,
Christopher
Brick Memorial HS
Brick, NJ

Mihalecz, Michael
Arthur P Schalick
Elmer, NJ

Mikaelian, Vicki
Toms River HS
Toms River, NJ

Mikesell, Andrew
Parsippany HS
Parsippany, NJ

Mikucki, Paul
Toms River HS
Toms River, NJ

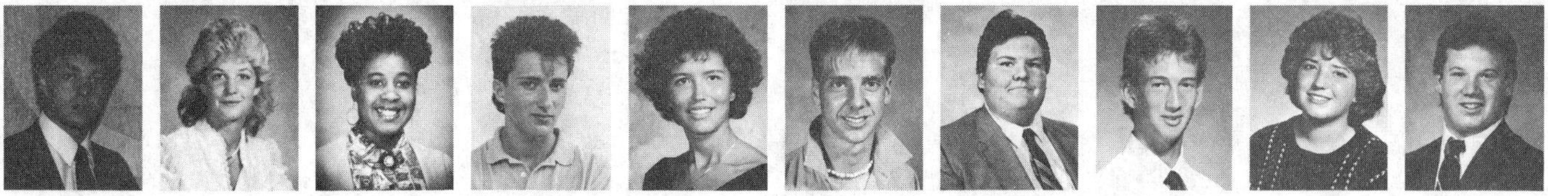

Milano, Marc
Union HS
Union, NJ

Miles, Rene
Saint Joseph HS
Williamstown, NJ

Miles, Tamieqkya
John F Kennedy HS
Willingboro, NJ

Mill, Alexander
Vineland HS
Vineland, NJ

Miller, Andrea
Pitman HS
Pitman, NJ

Miller, Erik
South Plainfield HS
S Plainfield, NJ

Miller, Glenn E
Pennsville Memorial
Pennsville, NJ

Miller, Jeffery Hart
St Joseph Regional
Ramsey, NJ

Miller, Jennifer
West Milford
Township HS
Hewitt, NJ

Miller, Korey B
Saddle Brook HS
Saddle Brook, NJ

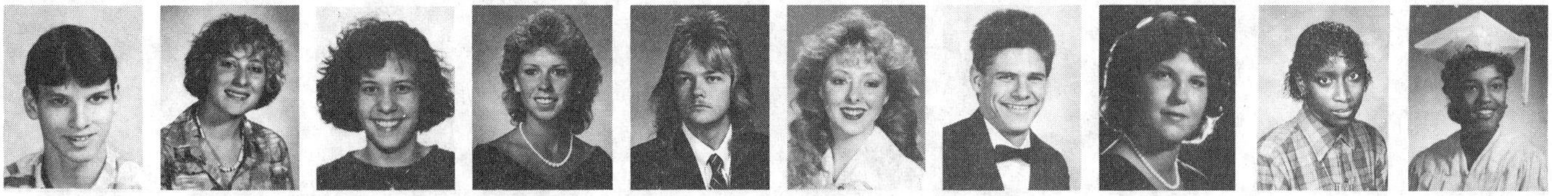

Miller, Lawrence J
Lenape HS
Vincentown, NJ

Miller, Melissa
Florence Twp Mem
Roebling, NJ

Miller, Naomi
Millville SR HS
Millville, NJ

Miller, Patricia Ann
Eastern Regional
Berlin, NJ

Miller, Jr Ronald K
Pinelands Regional
Tuckertown, NJ

Miller, Sandee
Middletown HS
Leonardo, NJ

Miller, Scott
Delran HS
Delran, NJ

Miller, Stephanie L
Lower Cape Max
Regional HS
Cape May, NJ

Miller, Tonya
Irvington HS
Irvington, NJ

Mills, Charlene
Willingbor HS
Willingboro, NJ

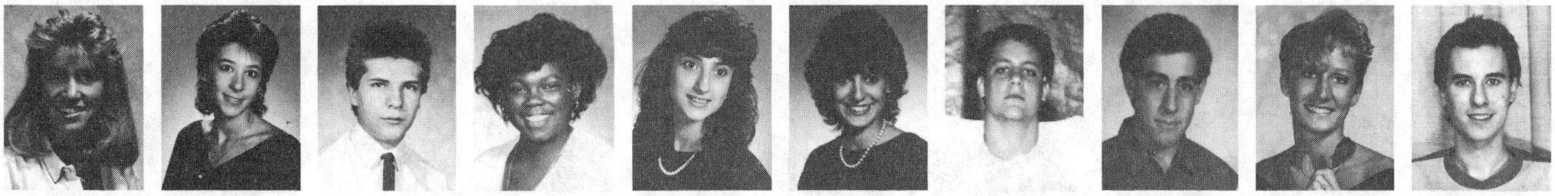

Mills, Kathy
Bridgewater Raritan
East HS
Bridgewater, NJ

Milone, Kristin
Kittatinny Regional
Newton, NJ

Milosevic, Vladimir
Passaic County
Vo-Tech HS
Paterson, NJ

Mingo, Nicole
Plainfield HS
Plainfield, NJ

Minhas, Kirnjit
Kour
Parsippany Hills HS
Parsippany, NJ

Minichino, Mary
Beth
Glen Rock HS
Glen Rock, NJ

Minnick, David F
Hamilton High
School East
Trenton, NJ

Minniti, Anthony
Cinnaminson HS
Cinnaminson, NJ

Minore, Dominica
Washington
Township HS
Turnersville, NJ

Minutella, Anthony
Passaic County Tech
& Voc HS
Passaic, NJ

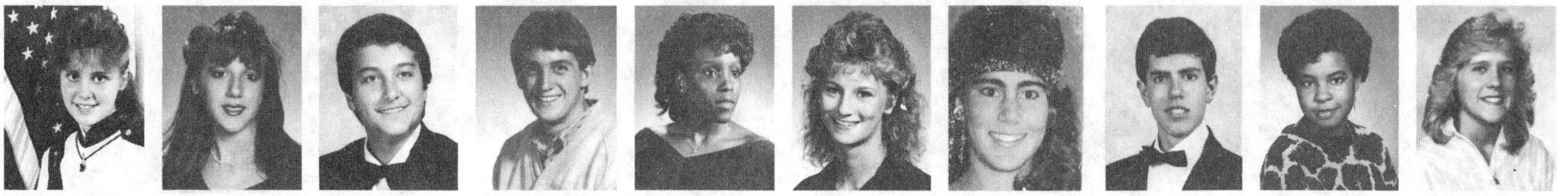

Miolovic, Mirijana
Elmwood Park
Memorial JR SR HS
Elmwood Pk, NJ

Miragliotta, Tina
Kittatinny Regional
Newton, NJ

Mirzai, Hossein
Washington
Township HS
Sewell, NJ

Misasi, Anthony
Lakeland Regional
Wanaque, NJ

Mishoe, Shalinni
Anique
St Pius X Regional
Plainfield, NJ

Missaggia, Lisa
Mt Olive HS
Flanders, NJ

Mitchell, Audra I
Southern Regional
Manahawkin, NJ

Mitchell, Martin
Cherokee HS
Marlton, NJ

Mitchell, Samantha
L
Morristown HS
Morristown, NJ

Mitchell, Suzanne
Woodstown HS
Woodstown, NJ

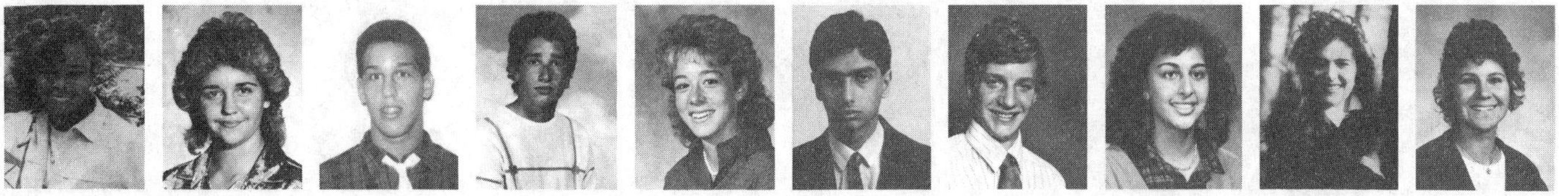

Mitchell, Tanya
Cherie
Dwight Morrow HS
Englewood, NJ

Mitrik, Kathryn
Marie
Linden HS
Linden, NJ

Modernel, Eric
St Marys Of The
Elizabeth, NJ

Moffitt, Kevin
Ocean City HS
Ocean View, NJ

Mog, Meredith
Timothy Christian
North Plainfield, NJ

Mohamed-Taki,
Assif
Lakeland Regional
Ringwood, NJ

Mohn, Robert
St John Vianney HS
Matawan, NJ

Mohsen, Nancy
Ocean Township HS
Wayside, NJ

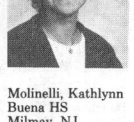

Molinaro, Melissa
Bishop Eustace Prep
Cherry Hill, NJ

Molinelli, Kathlynn
Buena HS
Milmay, NJ

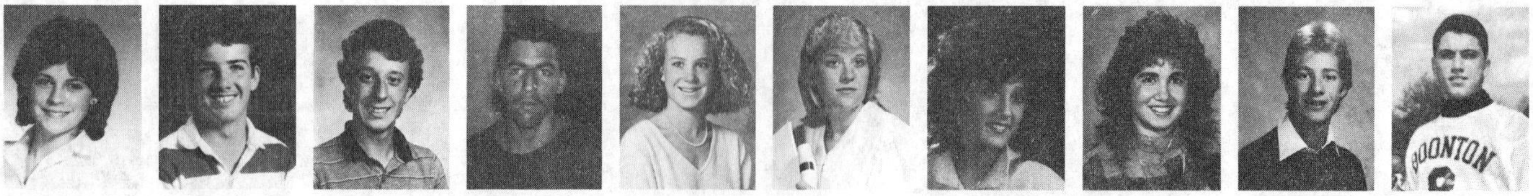

Mollach, Laura
Union HS
Union, NJ

Mollenkopf, Richard
Friends Schl
Glassboro, NJ

Monfardini, Michael
Buena Regional HS
Landisville, NJ

Monfort, Oscar
Memorial HS
West New York, NJ

Mongey, Mary
Denice
Villa Walsh Acad
Morristown, NJ

Moninghoff, Lara
Belvidere HS
Belvidere, NJ

Monsorno, Cheryl
Roselle Catholic HS
Linden, NJ

Montalbano, Rosa
West Essex Regional
Fairfield, NJ

Montano, Marc
Bridgewater-Raritan
H S East
Bridgewater, NJ

Monteleone, Vincent
Boonton HS
Lincoln Pk, NJ

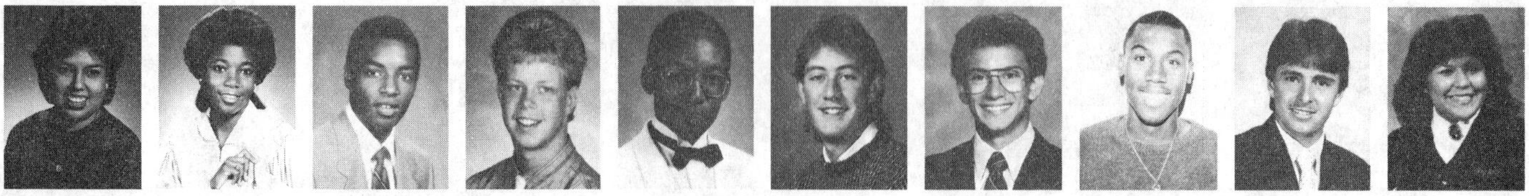

Montesinos, Diana
Parsippany Hills HS
Parsippany, NJ

Moody, Vanessa
Camden HS
Camden, NJ

Moody, Vincent G
Scotch
Plains-Fanwood HS
Scotch Plains, NJ

Mooney, Thomas
Cranford HS
Cranford, NJ

Moore, Arthur
Essex Catholic Boys
East Orange, NJ

Moore, James
Middle Township
Cape May Court, NJ

Moore, Kevin
West Orange HS
West Orange, NJ

Moore, Marc L
Piscataway HS
Piscataway, NJ

Moore, Ronald
Cumberland
Regional HS
Bridgeton, NJ

Morales, Yasminnie
Holy Spirit HS
Pleasantville, NJ

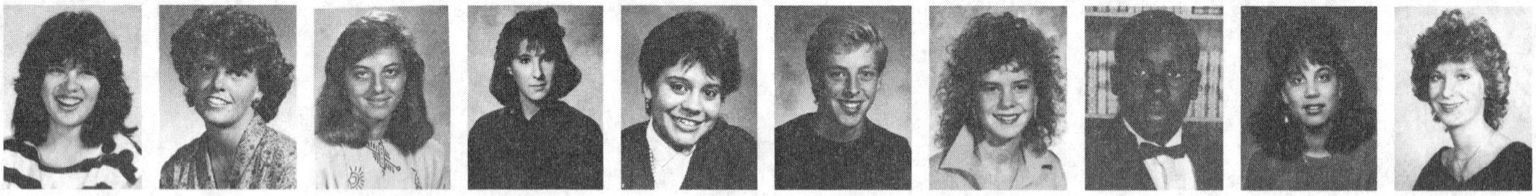

Moran, Donna
Pinelands Regional
Tuckerton, NJ

Moran, Katie
Morristown HS
Convent Sta, NJ

Moreira, Maria
Pequannock
Township HS
Pompton Plains, NJ

Morello, Jennifer A
Vineland HS
Vineland, NJ

Moreno, Maria
Columbia HS
Maplewood, NJ

Morgan, Adam
Madison HS
Madison, NJ

Morgan, Becky
Washington
Township HS
Sewell, NJ

Morgan, Dorion
Burlington TWP HS
Burlington, NJ

Morita, Katherine
Bridgeton HS
Bridgeton, NJ

Morrell, Sherri
Delsea Regional HS
Williamstown, NJ

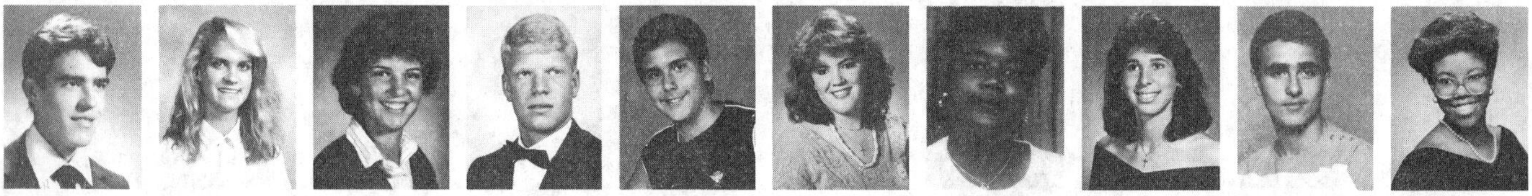

Morriello, Gregori
Belleville HS
Belleville, NJ

Morris, Leslee
Mainland Regional
Linwood, NJ

Morris, Linda L
Florence Twp Mem
Roebling, NJ

Morrissey, Sean
Holy Cross HS
Willingboro, NJ

Morrone, Thomas
Paul Vi HS
Sicklerville, NJ

Mortensen, Tammy
L
Dumont HS
Dumont, NJ

Morton, Alicia S
Woodrow Wilson HS
Camden, NJ

Moschetti, Angela
Immaculate Heart
Nanuet, NY

Mosery, Nizan Bud
Cresskill HS
Cresskill, NJ

Moses, Denise
Essex Catholic Girls
Newark, NJ

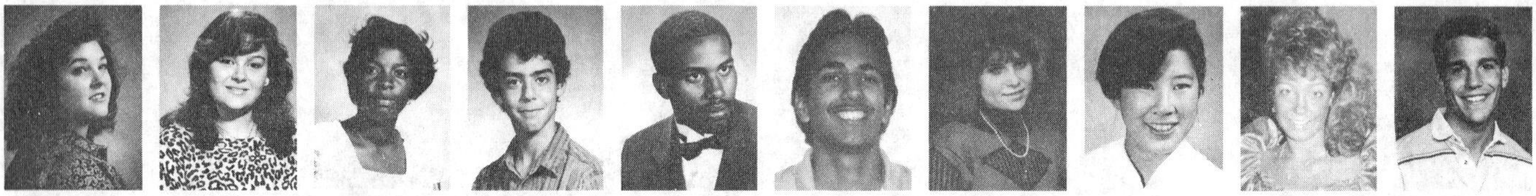

Mosiello, Laura
Hunterdon Central
Flemington, NJ

Moskowitz, Liz
Cliffside Park HS
Cliffside Park, NJ

Mosley, Maria
Pemberton
Township HS
Fort Dix, NJ

Mostafavi, Ramin
Secaucus HS
Secaucus, NJ

Motley, Byron
Lincoln HS
Jersey City, NJ

Motwani, Bobby
Raritan HS
Hazlet, NJ

Mount, Megan
Immaculata HS
Somerset, NJ

Moy, Catherine
Freehold HS
Englishtown, NJ

Moy, Tracy
Delran HS
Delran, NJ

Moyer, Michael G
Haddonfield
Memorial HS
Haddonfield, NJ

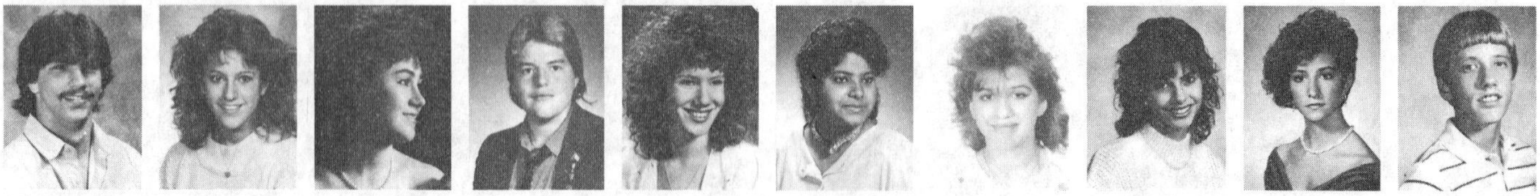

Mrotek, Douglas M
Spotswood HS
Spotswood, NJ

Muccia, Maggie
Edison HS
Edison, NJ

Mueller, Kris Ann
Woodbridge HS
Fords, NJ

Mueller, Siegfried
Kittatinny Reg HS
Newton, NJ

Muenz, Heather
Leigh
Hawthorne HS
Hawthorne, NJ

Mukherjee, Moon
Parsippany Hills HS
Parsippany, NJ

Mulbauer, Victoria
Fair Lawn HS
Fair Lawn, NJ

Mulder, Pamela T
Buena Regional HS
Newfield, NJ

Mullane, Lisa M
Holy Family Acad
Bayonne, NJ

Mullen, Kevin
Florence Township
Roebling, NJ

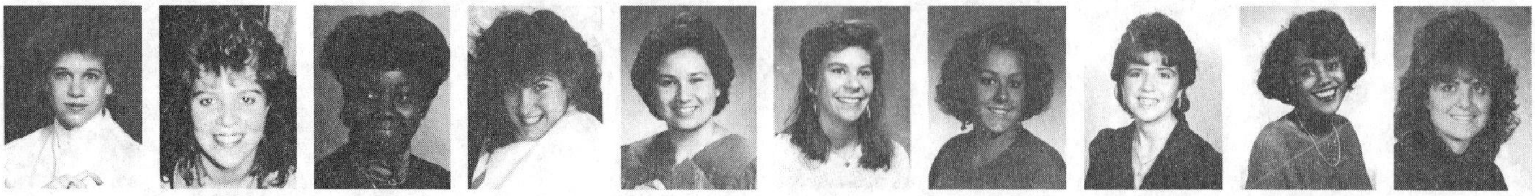

Mullin, Kathleen
Hawthorne HS
Hawthorne, NJ

Mulvihill, Bridget
Immaculate
Conception HS
Orange, NJ

Murchison, Tara
Asbury Park HS
Asbury Pk, NJ

Murdoch, Jennifer
St Rose HS
Manasquan, NJ

Murdoch, Karen
Spotswood HS
Spotswood, NJ

Murphy, Colleen
Oceantownship HS
Wanamassa, NJ

Murphy, Elizabeth
West Windsor
Plainsboro HS
Princeton Junct, NJ

Murphy, Judith Ann
North Bergen HS
Guttenberg, NJ

Murphy, Kathy Jo
Ewing HS
Trenton, NJ

Murphy, Tara
Lenape Valley
Regional HS
Andover, NJ

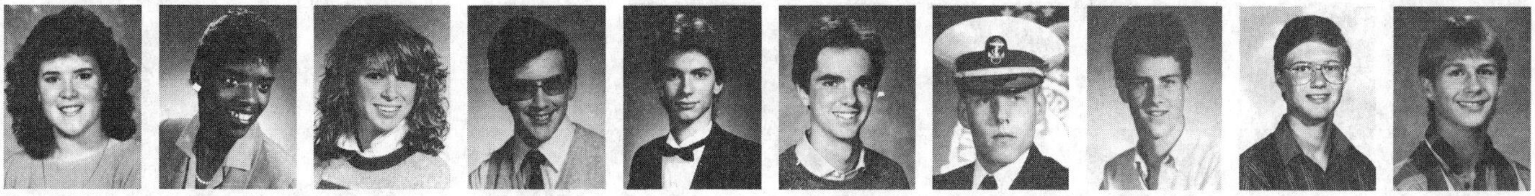

Murray, Christine
West Morris Central
Regional HS
Long Valley, NJ

Murray, Deatrix L
Toms River South
Beachwood, NJ

Murray, Michele K
Millburn HS
Short Hills, NJ

Murray, Robert
Middle Township
Cape May Court, NJ

Murray, Russel
Don Bosco Prep HS
Hawthorne, NJ

Murray, Sean P
West Essex Regional
Roseland, NJ

Murray, Theodore
Admiral Farragut
Manasquan, NJ

Murrray, Brad
West
Windsor-Plainsbor
Princeton Junct, NJ

Murschell, Jason
Paulsboro HS
Gibbstown, NJ

Murschell, II Wayne
M
Pitman HS
Pitman, NJ

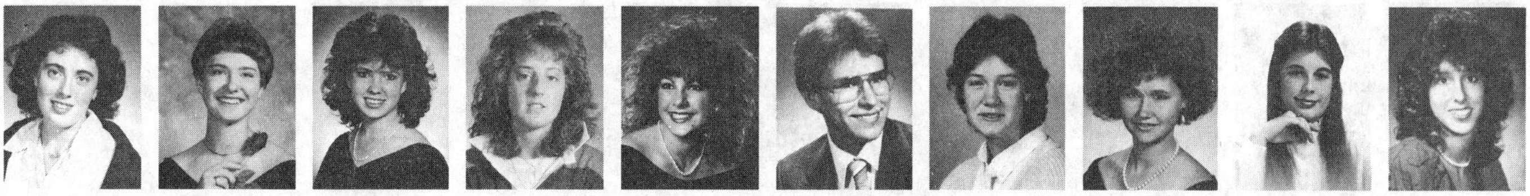

Musillo, Teresa
Paterson Catholic
Paterson, NJ

Musser, Erica Lynn
Williamston HS
Williamstown, NJ

Muster, Marlo
Middletown H S
Lincroft, NJ

Musto, Michele
Manalapan HS
Manalapan, NJ

Musumeci, Gina
St James HS
Swedesboro, NJ

Muth, Robert
Mount Olive HS
Hackettstown, NJ

Myers, Amy
Lower Cape May
Regional HS
Erma, NJ

Myers, Elizabeth C
Somerville HS
Somerville, NJ

Nagler, Anastasia
Ambassoador
Christian Acad
Gibbstown, NJ

Nagy, Donna
Paramus Catholic
Fairlawn, NJ

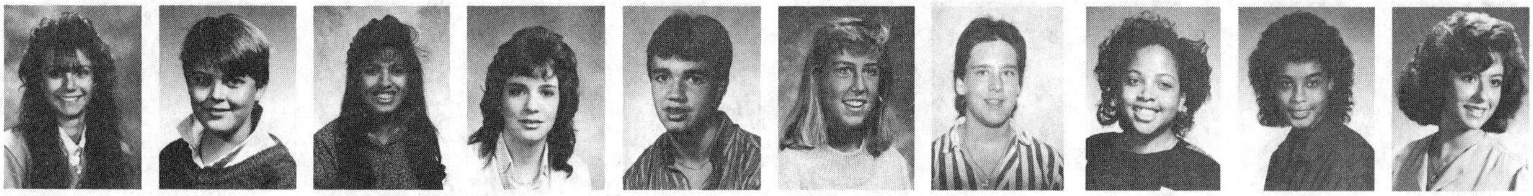

Nagy, Jeanette
Mc Corristin HS
Wrightstown, NJ

Nahas, Sara
Chatham Township
Chatham, NJ

Naik, Arpana
Hackettstown HS
Hackettstown, NJ

Nanfeldt, Christine
St John Vianney HS
Holmdel, NJ

Napoliello, Dennis
Morris Catholic HS
Ironia, NJ

Nappi, Stephanie
Manosquan HS
Manasquan, NJ

Naseef, III George S
Parsippany Hills HS
Parsippany, NJ

Nash, Christine
University HS
Newark, NJ

Nash, Sibylla
Neptune SR HS
Neptune, NJ

Natale, Filomena
Bridgewater Raritan
HS West
Raritan, NJ

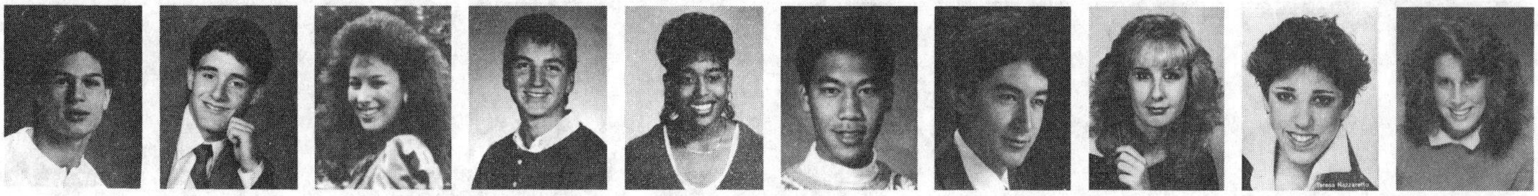

Natale, Patrick
Summit HS
Summit, NJ

Nathan, Edward
Manalapan HS
Englishtown, NJ

Nathanson, Cortney
John P Stevens HS
Edison, NJ

Nathanson, Eric
Atlantic City HS
Ventnor, NJ

Navarro, Chrystal A
Lakewood HS
Lakewood, NJ

Navarro, Joel
West Essex HS
Fairfield, NJ

Navas, Julio C
Ocean Township HS
Ocean, NJ

Naylor, Bonnie
Riverside HS
Riverside, NJ

Nazzaretto, Teresa
Bergen County
Vo-Tech HS
Fairlawn, NJ

Neall, Leslie
Ocean City HS
Ocean City, NJ

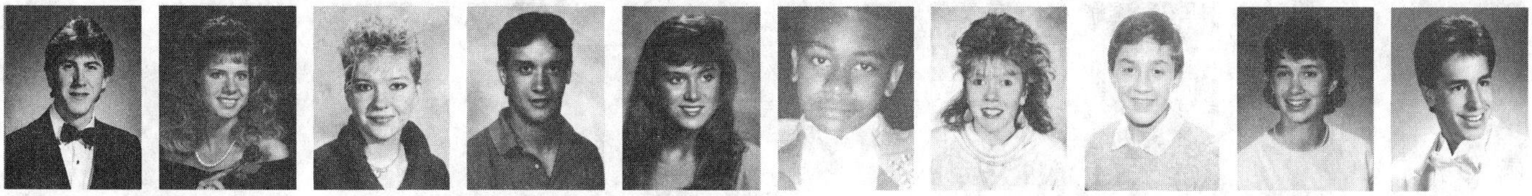

Nealon, Joseph
St Joseph Regional
Spring Valley, NY

Negrin, Joanne
John F Kennedy HS
Willingboro, NJ

Nehila, Nancy
Howell HS
Howell, NJ

Nelson, David S
Woodstown HS
Woodstown, NJ

Nelson, Simone
West Essex Regional
North Caldwell, NJ

Nelson, Tim D
John F Kennedy HS
Willingboro, NJ

Nelson, Tina Marie
Sussex Vo Tech
Stanhope, NJ

Neubig, Jeffrey P
Blair Acad
Stockholm, NJ

Neumaier, Andrea L
Rutgers Preparatory
Edison, NJ

Nevarez, Ivan M
Hillside HS
Hillside, NJ

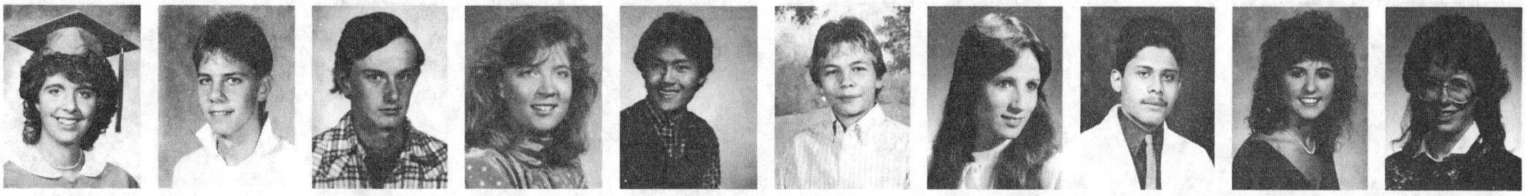

Newhard, Stefanie
St James HS
Pennsville, NJ

Newkirk, Chris
Timothy Christian
Cranford, NJ

Newkirk, Kenneth
Dale
Cumberland
Regional HS
Bridgeton, NJ

Newton, Lisa Marie
Haddon Township
JR SR HS
Westmont, NJ

Nguyen, Thang
Burlington County
Willingboro, NJ

Nicolich, Anthony
St Joseph Of
Palisades HS
Weehaven, NJ

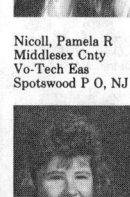

Nicoll, Pamela R
Middlesex Cnty
Vo-Tech Eas
Spotswood P O, NJ

Nieto, Hernan
Dickinson HS
Jersey City, NJ

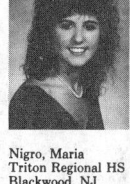

Nigro, Maria
Triton Regional HS
Blackwood, NJ

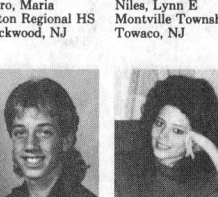

Niles, Lynn E
Montville Township
Towaco, NJ

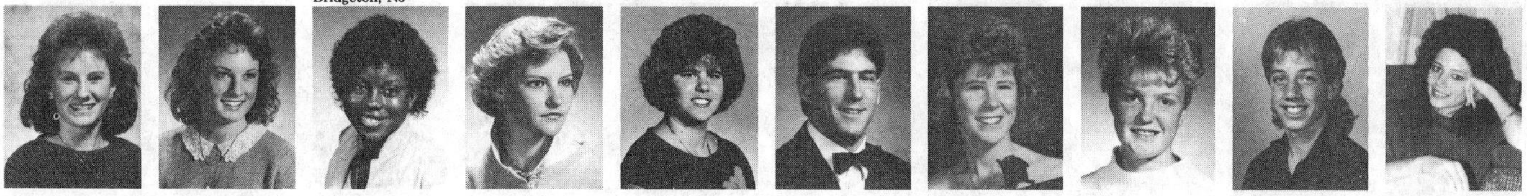

Nipps, Susan Ray
Manville HS
Manville, NJ

Nisbet, Kimberly
Immaculata HS
Bridgeswater, NJ

Nix, Tulin L
Abraham Clark HS
Roselle, NJ

Niznik, Jennifer
Hawthorne HS
Hawthorne, NJ

Noakes, Laura
St James HS
Carneys Point, NJ

Nocella, Richard J
Cherokee HS
Marlton, NJ

Nollar, Linda
Allentown HS
Cream Ridge, NJ

Nolte, Vera
Kingsway Regional
Clarksboro, NJ

Nordone, Tony
Lower Cape May
Regional HS
Erma, NJ

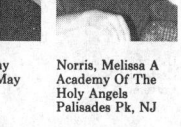

Norris, Melissa A
Academy Of The
Holy Angels
Palisades Pk, NJ

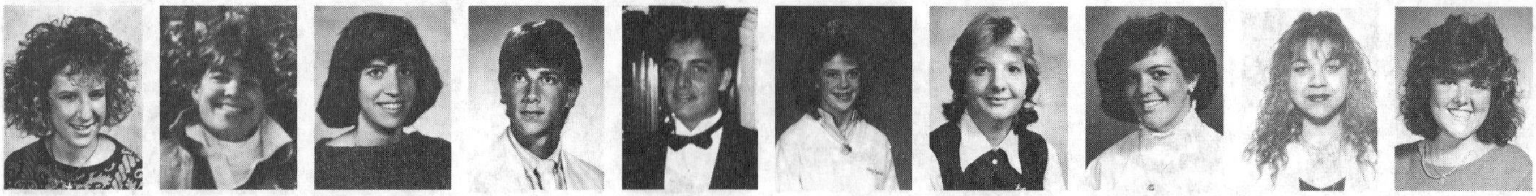

Notaro, Noelle
Eastern HS
Berlin, NJ

Novak, Karen
Millburn HS
Millburn, NJ

Novakowski, Joelle
Woodstown HS
Alloway, NJ

Novembre, Mark
Hamilton HS West
Trenton, NJ

Noviello, Jr Nicholas R
Bridgewater-Raritan H S West
Bridgewater, NJ

Nowicki, Nicole
Holy Spirit HS
Pomona, NJ

Nowicki, Tammy
Life Center Acad
Willingboro, NJ

Noyes, Jennifer
Ridge HS
Basking Ridge, NJ

Nshaiwat, Florida Ferial
Dickinson HS
Jersey City, NJ

Nucci, Robynne
Toms River North
Toms River, NJ

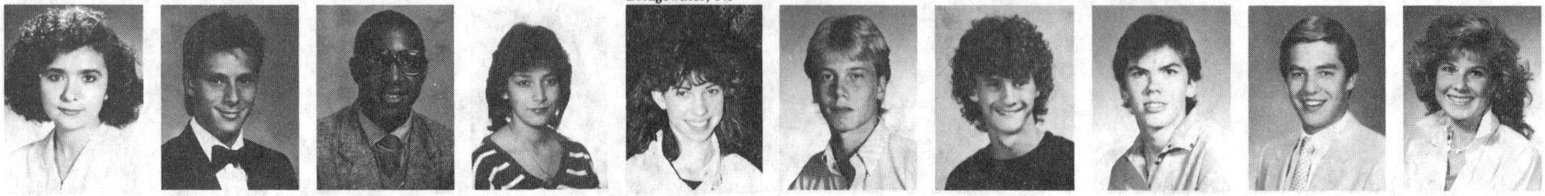

Nunes, Emilia
East Side HS
Newark, NJ

Nunes, Kenneth J
Raritan HS
Keyport, NJ

Nunes, Richard
Essex Catholic HS For Boys
East Orange, NJ

Nunez, Lisette
Immaculate Conception HS
Wallington, NJ

Nunnenkamp, Heidi
Edgewood Regional SR HS
Berlin, NJ

O Boyle, Thomas J
Dover HS
Dover, NJ

O Brien, David
Edgewood Regional
Hammonton, NJ

O Brien, Kevin
Mount Olive HS
Flanders, NJ

O Brien, Kevin
Westfield SR HS
Westfield, NJ

O Brien, Patricia
Morris Catholic HS
Morris Plains, NJ

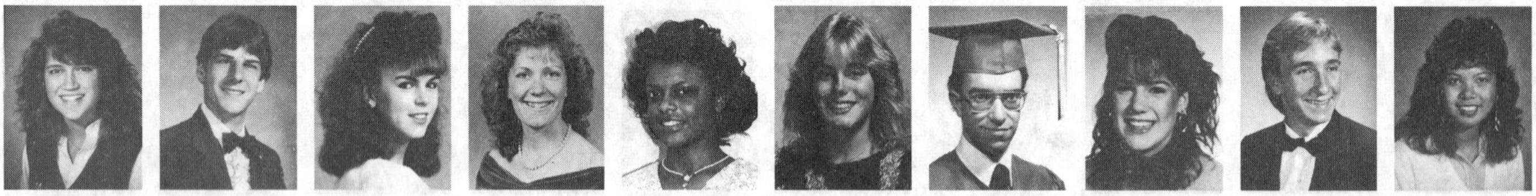

O Connor, Jennifer
Notre Dame HS
E Windsor, NJ

O Hara, Daniel P
Pemberton Township HS
Browns Mills, NJ

O Keefe, Karen
Notre Dame HS
Mercerville, NJ

O Leary, Kellie
Timothy Christian
South Plainfield, NJ

O Neal, Kimberly
Paterson Catholic Regional HS
Paterson, NJ

O Neill, Kelly
Bridgewater Raritan H S East
Basking Ridge, NJ

O Neill, Michael
St Josephs Prep
Philadelphia, PA

O Rourke, Heather
Indian Hills HS
Franklin Lks, NJ

O Such, Jr Robert
Sayreville War Memorial HS
Parlin, NJ

Obed, Leonora
Notre Dame HS
West Trenton, NJ

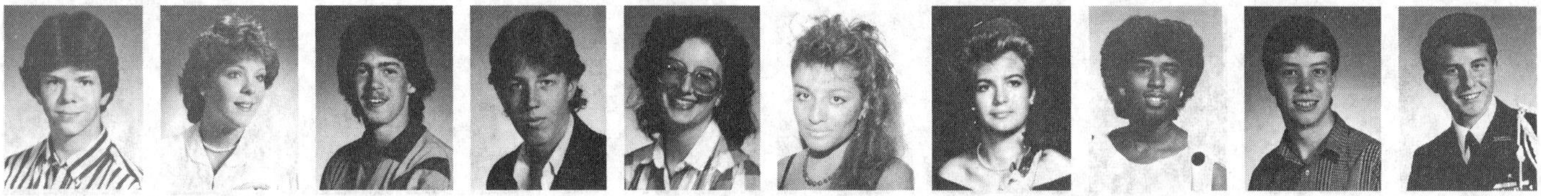

Obertubbesing, Edwin
Middletown HS
Leonardo, NJ

Obertubbesing, Mary Ann
Middletown H S
Leonardo, NJ

Obiso, Rick
High Point Regional
Sussex, NJ

Obrien, Geoffrey
Columbia HS
Maplewood, NJ

Ocallaghan, Kathleen
Lakeland Regional
Bethlehem, PA

Occhipinti, Daniela M
Marylawn Of The Oranges HS
Orange, NJ

Occhiuzzo, Marrianna
Pemberton Twp HS
Browns Mills, NJ

Odio, Veronica
Hillside HS
Hillside, NJ

Oestreicher, Kurt
Freehold Township
Freehold, NJ

Offerdahl, Thomas
Marine Acad Of Science & Tech
Little Silver, NJ

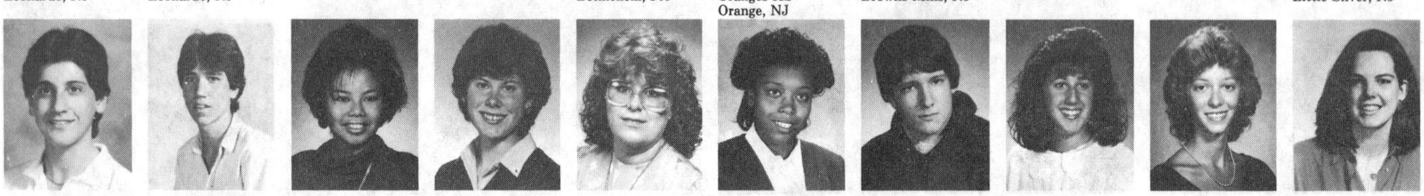

Okun, Scott
Wayne Hills HS
Wayne, NJ

Olear, Conrad
Fair Lawn HS
Fair Lawn, NJ

Olegario, Lisa
Mount Saint Marys
Edison, NJ

Olekna, Michelle
St Pius X Regional
Highland Park, NJ

Olesnicki, Annette
Union HS
Union, NJ

Oliver, Christy M
Academy Of St
Jersy City, NJ

Oliveri, Charles
Middlesex County Vo-Tech Schl
New Brunswick, NJ

Oliveri, Marijo
Mt St Mary Acad
Hillside, NJ

Oliveri, Mary E
Saint James HS
Gibbstown, NJ

Olsen, Kristina
Central Regional HS
Bayville, NJ

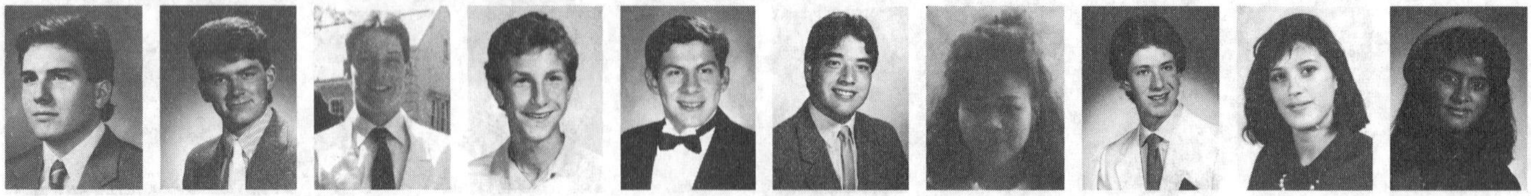

Onorevole, Kevin
Nutley HS
Nutley, NJ

Opalski, Mark
West Windsor-Plainsbor
Plainsboro, NJ

Orban, Timothy
Wayne Hills HS
Wayne, NJ

Ordino, Keith
Lakewood HS
Lakewood, NJ

Ordonez, Ivan
North Bergen HS
North Bergen, NJ

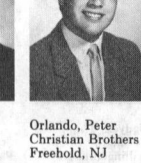

Orlando, Peter
Christian Brothers
Freehold, NJ

Orlina, Clarinda
Saint Marys HS
Jersey City, NJ

Orr, Alexander
Wood-Ridge HS
Wood Ridge, NJ

Ortiz, Priscilla
Edgewood Regional Sr HS
Sicklerville, NJ

Ortiz, Yvonne
Hightstown HS
Hightstown, NJ

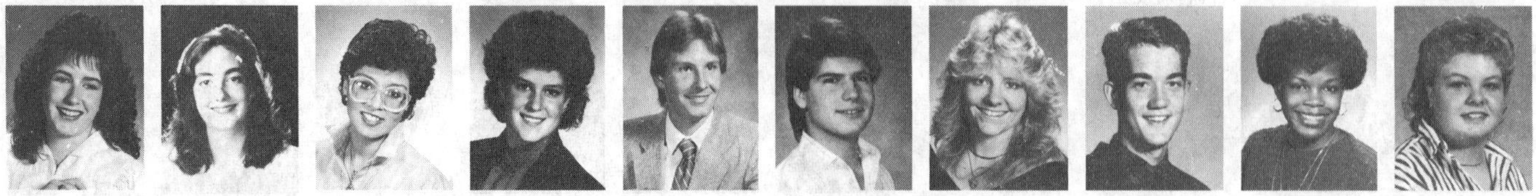

Osborne, Patricia A
Carteret HS
Carteret, NJ

Oser, Corey J
Rumson-Fair Haven
Fair Haven, NJ

Osman, Gihan
Madison Central HS
Old Bridge, NJ

Osmun, Maureen
Phillpsburg HS
Phillipsburg, NJ

Ossowski, David
Jackson Memorial
Jackson, NJ

Ostrega, Marc
Manalapan HS
Englishtown, NJ

Otten, Joy
De Paul HS
Pompton Lakes, NJ

Otten, Theodore
St James HS
Paulsboro, NJ

Owens, Monique N
Monmouth Regional
Eatontown, NJ

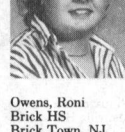

Owens, Roni
Brick HS
Brick Town, NJ

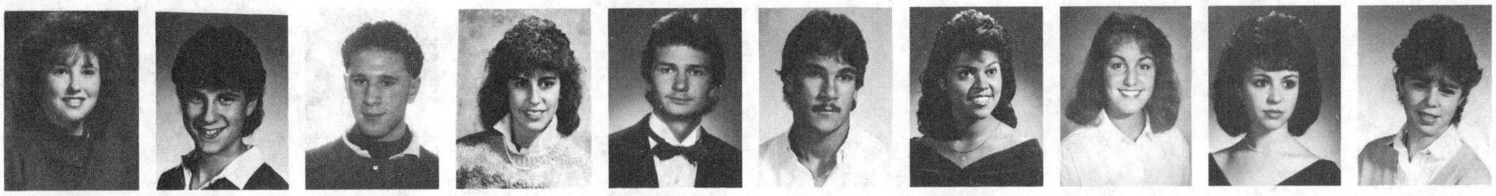

Oxton, Lori
Palisades Park JR SR HS
Palisades Pk, NJ

Paccione, Joe
Toms River HS
Toms River, NJ

Paci, Jr Robert J
The Lawrenceville
Trenton, NJ

Pacichelli, Angela
Sacred Heart HS
Bridgeton, NJ

Paciorkowski, Patrick James
Bayonne HS
Bayonne, NJ

Padron, Doug
Jackson Memorial
Jackson, NJ

Paez, Vivian
William Dickinson
Jersey City, NJ

Paglione, Cheryl
Notre Dame HS
Robbinsville, NJ

Pajak, Karen Annette
Sayreville War Memorial HS
Sayreville, NJ

Pajak, Susan Ellen
Sayreville War Memorial HS
Sayreville, NJ

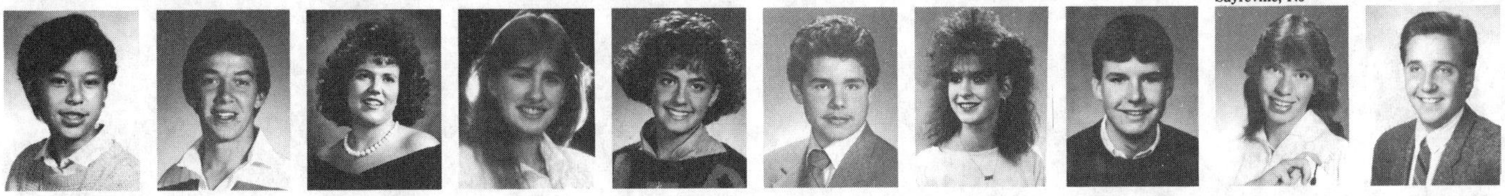

Pajarillo, Karen
Union HS
Union, NJ

Pallis, Mark P
High Point Regional
Branchville, NJ

Palmer, Kelly
Clayton HS
Clayton, NJ

Palmucci, Susan
Rahway HS
Rahway, NJ

Palomo, Kimberly A
Atlantic City HS
Atlantic City, NJ

Palumbo, Lenny
Belleville HS
Belleville, NJ

Pampanin, Tina
Paul VI Regional
Clifton, NJ

Panas, Richard
Millville SR HS
Millville, NJ

Pansera, Angela
Kingsway Regional
Swedesboro, NJ

Panster, Mike
J P Stevens HS
Edison, NJ

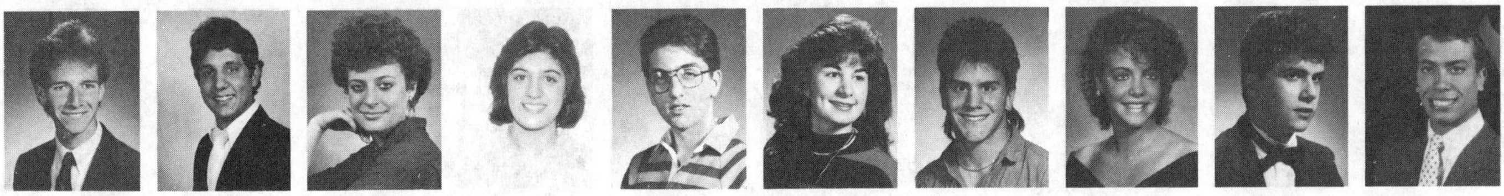

Pantos, David M
Madison Central HS
Old Bridge, NJ

Panzitta, Thomas
Notre Dame HS
Trenton, NJ

Paola, Maryann Di
Hamilton HS
Trenton, NJ

Paolini, Gloria
Hillsborough HS
S Somerville, NJ

Papadatos, Louis
West Milford HS
W Milford, NJ

Papagelopoulos, Maria
Dover HS
Dover, NJ

Pappalardo, Marc
Toms River East HS
Toms River, NJ

Pappas, Eleni
St Dominic Acad
Bayonne, NJ

Parinello, Daniel
Sayreville War Memorial HS
Parlin, NJ

Paris, Peter B
Princeton HS
Princeton, NJ

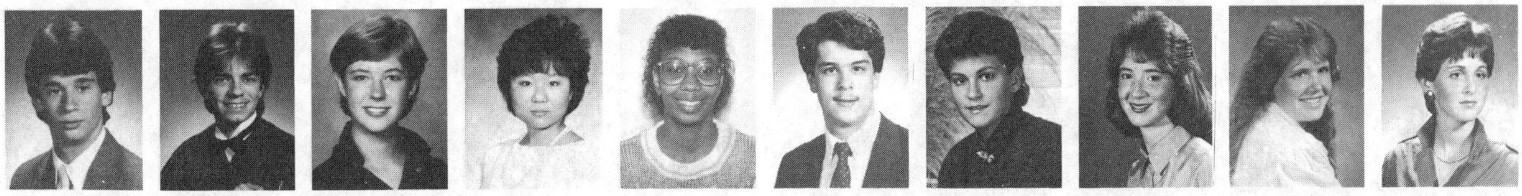

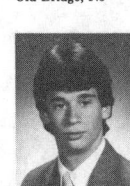

Paris, Peter F
Glen Rock SR HS
Glen Rock, NJ

Parisi, David Edward
Ridgefield Park HS
Little Ferry, NJ

Park, Christina
Eastern Christian
Wyckoff, NJ

Park, Mary
Fort Lee HS
Ft Lee, NJ

Parker, Katrina
Franklin HS
Somerset, NJ

Parker, W Larry
Eatontown HS
Eatontown, NJ

Parkhurst, Pamela R
Middle Township
Cape May C H, NJ

Parks, Amy C
Vineland HS
Vineland, NJ

Parks, Judith A
Buena Regional HS
Dorothy, NJ

Parlin, Allison
Atlantic City HS
Margate, NJ

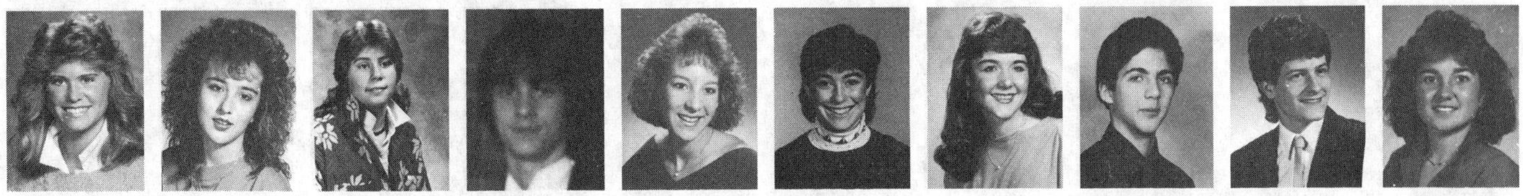

Parrillo, Christine
Wayne Valley HS
Wayne, NJ

Parrillo, Rickie Ann
Belleville HS
Belleville, NJ

Parrinello, Lori A
Spotswood HS
Spotswood, NJ

Parrish, Michael
Burlington County Vo Tech HS
Bordentown, NJ

Parry, Debra
Bishop George AHR
Colonia, NJ

Parson, Kim
Baptist HS
Mt Laurel, NJ

Partlow, Sandra
North Hunterdon
Annandale, NJ

Pascale, Anthony L
Triron Regional HS
Bellmawr, NJ

Pashman, Robert
Clifton HS
Clifton, NJ

Passaro, Gina Marie
Pequannock Township HS
Pompton Plains, NJ

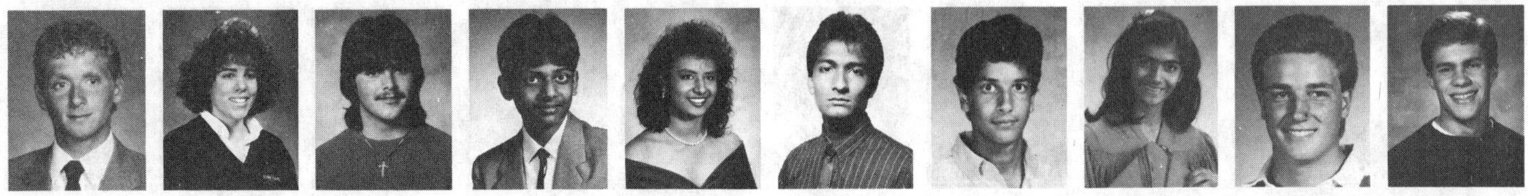

Paster, Thomas M
Cranford HS
Cranford, NJ

Patane, Theresa
Holy Spirit HS
Ocean City, NJ

Patch, Jr Thomas J
Vineland HS
Vineland, NJ

Patel, Ashish
Union HS
Union, NJ

Patel, Bella
Acad Of St Aloysius
Jersey City, NJ

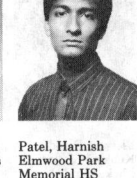

Patel, Harnish
Elmwood Park Memorial HS
Elmwood Pk, NJ

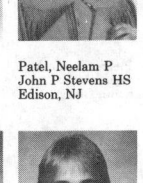

Patel, Manish
Memorial HS
Cedar Grove, NJ

Patel, Neelam P
John P Stevens HS
Edison, NJ

Patrick, Charles
Whippany Park HS
Whippany, NJ

Patrick, Scott
West Essex Regional
No Caldwell, NJ

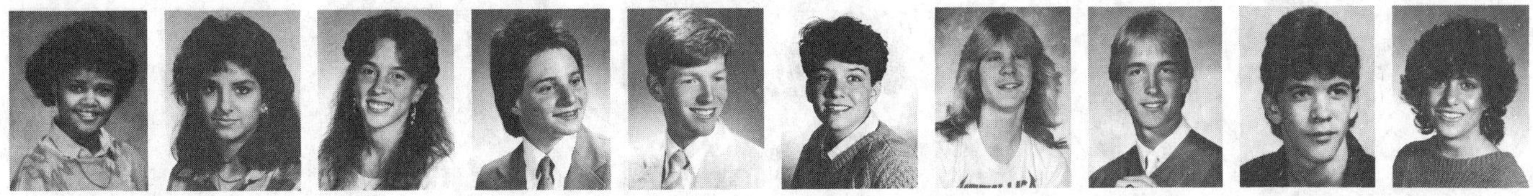

Patterson, Danette
Ocean Township HS
Ocean Tsp, NJ

Paul, Monik
South Brunswick
Kendall Pk, NJ

Pauwels, Susan
Wood-Ridge HS
Wood Ridge, NJ

Pauzner, Jeffrey J
Clifton HS
Clifton, NJ

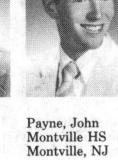

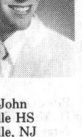

Payne, John
Montville HS
Montville, NJ

Payne, Nancy
Paul VI HS
Audubon, NJ

Pearce, Donald
Sussex Cnty Vctnl Tech Schl
Sparta, NJ

Pearce, Mike
Jefferson Township
Oak Ridge, NJ

Pearson, Robert
Collingswood HS
Collingswood, NJ

Pecker, Michelle
Parsippany HS
Parsippany, NJ

Pedersen, Jacqueline
Holy Family Acad
Bayonne, NJ

Pedersen, Karin
Newton HS
Newton, NJ

Peer, Christopher
Dover HS
Dover, NJ

Peet, Faith V
Woodstown HS
Woodstown, NJ

Pelkey, Mike
Brick Memorial HS
Brick, NJ

Pellegrini, Jeffrey
Buena Regional HS
Buena, NJ

Pellegrino, Vicky
Mother Seton
Regional HS
Perth Amboy, NJ

Pelouze, Mark P
Cherry Hill HS
Cherry Hill, NJ

Peluso, Mike
Piscataway HS
Piscataway, NJ

Pena, Anna
St Josephs Of The
Palisades HS
W New York, NJ

Pena, Jeanette
Emerson HS
Union City, NJ

Penick, Josh
Columbia HS
South Orange, NJ

Penn, Stephanie
Freehold Township
Freehold, NJ

Penswater, John J
Holy Cross HS
Delran, NJ

Pereira, Feliciano H
East Side HS
Newark, NJ

Peric, Elizabeth
Immaculate
Conception HS
Guttenberg, NJ

Peris, Marshal
Scotch
Plains-Fanwood HS
Scotch Plains, NJ

Perry, Gretchen
Riverside HS
Delanco, NJ

Perry, Kevin
Jefferson Township
Oak Ridge, NJ

Perry, Philip
Barnstable Acad
Garnerville, NY

Persak, Allison
Glen Ridge HS
Glen Ridge, NJ

Peters, Bonnie Lynn
Riverside HS
Delanco, NJ

Peters, Melanie
The Friends Schl
Brooklawn, NJ

Petersen, Ken
North Warren
Regional HS
Blairstown, NJ

Petersen, Lou Anne
South River HS
South River, NJ

Petersen, Robert N
Arthur L Johnson
Reg HS
Westfield, NJ

Peterson, Daniel
Hunterdon Central
Whitehouse, NJ

Peterson, Pam
Shawnee HS
Medford, NJ

Peterson, Pamela
Monsignor Donovan
Brick, NJ

Peterson, Taralee
De Paul HS
Butler, NJ

Petillo, Alyssa
St John Vianney HS
Colts Neck, NJ

Petrizzi, Suzanne
Manalapan HS
Manalapan, NJ

Petronella, Michele
L
Hamilton HS West
Trenton, NJ

Pettinelli, Dino
Phillipsburg HS
Alpha, NJ

Petway, Randy E
Vindland HS
Vineland, NJ

Peypoch, III Ramon
J
Christian Brothers
Middletown, NJ

Pezza, Kelly Ann
Westwood HS
Westwood, NJ

Pezzano, Renee
Lyndhurst HS
Lyndhurst, NJ

Pfeffer, Michelle
Penns Grove HS
Penns Grove, NJ

Pfeiffer, Monica
Florence Twp
Memorial HS
Roebling, NJ

Pflaum, Wendy
Oak Knoll Schl
Scotch Plns, NJ

Phair, Regina Marie
Madison Central HS
Old Bridge, NJ

Phelan, Cathy
Matawan Regional
Matawan, NJ

Phelps, Denise
Highland HS
Erial, NJ

Philipp, Denise
Pualsboro HS
Gibbstown, NJ

Phillips, Rikki
Fair Lawn HS
Fair Lawn, NJ

Picone, Donna
Marie
Brick Memorial HS
Brick, NJ

Picone, Rachael
Hunterdon Central
Whitehouse Sta, NJ

Piddington, Joseph
Jackson HS
Jackson, NJ

Piell, Fred
Delaware Valley
Regional HS
Pittstown, NJ

Pierce, Edward D
West Morris
Mendham HS
Cliffside Park, NJ

Pierce, Lazette
St Vincent Acad
Newark, NJ

Pierce, Valerie A
Columbia HS
South Orange, NJ

Pierre, Ginia
Abraham Clark HS
Roselle, NJ

Pierson, David
Kingsway Regional
Mickleton, NJ

Pierson, Gina
Lenape Valley
Regional HS
Andover, NJ

Pietrangelo, Gina
Toms River HS East
Toms River, NJ

Pietro, Laura Ann
Central Regional HS
Bayville, NJ

Pietsch, Chryssa
Steinert HS
Crosswicks, NJ

Pike, Leanne
Cherry Hill HS East
Cherry Hill, NJ

Pilch, Lance
Hunterdon Central
Stockton, NJ

Pinckney, Lisa
Delaware Valley
Regional HS
Frenchtown, NJ

Pinder, Louvenia
Edgewood Regional
Chesilhurst, NJ

Pineiro, Judy
Newton HS
Newton, NJ

Pinnix, Charlette
Mt St Dominic Acad
East Orange, NJ

Pino, Gerardo
Dickinson HS
Jersey City, NJ

Pippitt, Nancy
Riverside HS
Riverside, NJ

Piret, Brian
Wood-Ridge HS
Wood Ridge, NJ

Pisapia, Jessica
Timothy Chrstn
North Plainfield, NJ

Piscitelli, Karen
South River HS
South River, NJ

Pitcher, Brian S
Pemberton Twp H S
Fayetteville, NC

Pittman, Gregory
Dickinson HS
Jersey City, NJ

Pizarro, Maximiliano F
Christian Brothers
Holmdel, NJ

Placek, Danianne
Brick Township HS
Brick Town, NJ

Platt, Corry T
Pequannock Township HS
Pompton Pl, NJ

Ploetz, Janine
Neumann Prep Schl
Ringwood, NJ

Plummer, Patricia
Dwight Morrow HS
Englewood, NJ

Plummer, Thomas
Cherry Hill HS
Cherry Hill, NJ

Podurgiel, Jane C
Princeton Day Schl
Princeton, NJ

Poedubicky, Jeffrey S
Northern Burlington Regional HS
Columbus, NJ

Poirier, Jennifer
Holy Cross HS
Delran, NJ

Polak, Alicia
Cinnaminson HS
Cinnaminson, NJ

Polaszek, Christopher
Lenape Valley Regional HS
Stanhope, NJ

Polera, Michelle
Holy Family Acad
Bayonne, NJ

Polizzotto, Michelle
Belvidere HS
Belvidere, NJ

Pollock, Lisa
Highland Regional
Blackwood, NJ

Pollock, Mindy
Vineland HS
Vineland, NJ

Polster, Elizabeth
Mc Corristin Catholic HS
Mercerville, NJ

Pomatto, Michael M
Egg Harbor Twp HS
Scullville, NJ

Pometti, Frank
Howell HS
Howell, NJ

Pomilio, Angela
Cherokee HS
Marlton, NJ

Poreda, Stanley
Burlington Cnty
Riverside, NJ

Poretta, Trina
Phillipsburg HS
Phillipsburg, NJ

Porpora, Gina
Holy Spirit HS
Brigantine, NJ

Porreca, Christopher G
Montville Township
Pine Brook, NJ

Porredon, Isabel
Holy Rosary Acad
Union City, NJ

Porter, John
Deptford Township
Deptford, NJ

Portik, Jeffrey M
Dunellen HS
Dunellen, NJ

Portnoy, Jessica
John P Stevens HS
Edison, NJ

Porzio, Ray
St John Vianney HS
Morganville, NJ

Post, Megan Anne
Our Lady Of Mercy
Marmora, NJ

Posten, III Samuel
Middletown HS
Navesink, NJ

Postma, Lauren
Eastern Christian
Towaco, NJ

Potter, Kathryn M
Toms River North
Toms River, NJ

Potter, Michaela
Morristown HS
Morristown, NJ

Powell, James
Mt Olive HS
Flanders, NJ

Powell, Jennifer
Rahway HS
Rahway, NJ

Powell, Steven
Glassboro HS
Glassboro, NJ

Power, Barbara
Burlington City HS
Edgewater Park, NJ

Praml, Heather
Wayne Hills SR HS
Wayne, NJ

Prego, Maria
De Paul HS
Wayne, NJ

Prelich, Karen Ann
Paramus Catholic Girls HS
Lodi, NJ

Prelog, Stefan
Pompton Lakes HS
Pompton Lakes, NJ

Preolo, Susan
Ridgefield Park HS
Ridgefield Pk, NJ

Presley, Sonya
Franklin HS
Somerset, NJ

Price, Carla
St James HS
Gibbstown, NJ

Price, Tracy
Bunea Regional HS
Vineland, NJ

Prickett, Deanna West
Windsor-Plainsbor
Plainsboro, NJ

Priestley, Vanjia
Lower Cape May Regional HS
Cape May, NJ

Primus, Sybilree
Paterson Catholic Regional HS
Paterson, NJ

Prisco, Robert R
Riverside HS
Riverside, NJ

Pritzlaff, Ode
Middletown HS
Lincroft, NJ

Prohowich, Theodore
Millville SR HS
Millville, NJ

Pronti, Joseph
Brick Memorial HS
Brick, NJ

Proudman, Sara
Gill St Bernards HS
Watchung, NJ

Pryduluk, Deana
St Pius Regional HS
Piscataway, NJ

Psaras, Barbara
Monsignor Donovan
Toms River, NJ

Ptasnik, Michele
Monroe Twp HS
Jamesburg, NJ

Pucci, Michael
Belleville HS
Belleville, NJ

Puente, Aristides
St Joseph HS
Union City, NJ

Purcell, Denise
Cliffside Park HS
Fairview, NJ

Puryar, Marc
Long Branch HS
Long Branch, NJ

Putlock, Doug
Pequannolk Township HS
Pequannock, NJ

Puzio, Raymond
Collegiate Schl
Passaic, NJ

Puzo, Emilio
West Essex SR HS
Fairfield, NJ

Pyne, Bradley
Holy Cross HS
Medford, NJ

Quan, Eric
Don Bosco Prep
Waldwick, NJ

Quick, David
North Warren Regional HS
Columbia, NJ

Quinlan, Michael
Lenape Valley Regional HS
Stanhope, NJ

Quinn, Colleen
Lakewood HS
Lakewood, NJ

Quinn, Jason M
Hackensack HS
Rochelle Park, NJ

Quinn, Karen Anne
Lakewood HS
Lakewood, NJ

Quinonez, Anthony
Edgewood Regional
SR HS
Blue Anchor, NJ

Quintavalle, Alisa
Jackson Memorial
Jackson, NJ

Rabbito, Janet
St John Vianney HS
Freehold, NJ

Rabel, Susan E
Hopewell Valley
Central HS
Trenton, NJ

Rabey, Suzanne
Mainland Regional
Somers Point, NJ

Racioppi, Gerard
Essex Catholic Boys
Verona, NJ

Raditz, Nancy L
Cherokee HS
Marlton, NJ

Radzik, Mark
De Paul HS
Wayne, NJ

Ragland, Maurice
Parsippany HS
Parsippany, NJ

Ragone, Joe
Victory Christian
Elmer, NJ

Ragonese, Gregory
Alan
Paulsboro HS
Gibbstown, NJ

Rainier, Christine
Bordentown
Regional HS
Bordentown, NJ

Raissis, Irene
Woodbridge HS
Colonia, NJ

Rajhansa, Dipak
Washington
Township HS
Turnersville, NJ

Ramos, Maria
Belleville HS
Belleville, NJ

Ramos, II Oscar
Paul VI HS
Passaic, NJ

Rana, Manoj
Passaic HS
Passaic, NJ

Randow, Patrick
Mc Corristin
Catholic HS
Trenton, NJ

Rankin, Kiesha
Pawsboro HS
Paulsboro, NJ

Rao, Sumana D
East Brunswick HS
East Brunswick, NJ

Raps, Robert J
Spotswood HS
Spotswood, NJ

Rascio, Lauren L
Saddle River Day
N Haledon, NJ

Rashduni, David
Glen Rock JR SR
Glen Rock, NJ

Raskind, Craig H
The Frisch Schl
West Orange, NJ

Rasmussen, Micah
Vineland HS
Vineland, NJ

Rasmussen, Michael
Monsignor Donovan
Toms River, NJ

Raven, Sharon
Bruriah High School
For Girls
Old Bridge, NJ

Ravo, Tina
Kittatinny Regional
Branchville, NJ

Ray, Teresa
Monongahela JR HS
Wenonah, NJ

Reade, John A
Ocean City HS
Beesleys Pt, NJ

Reagan, Michelle
Toms River East HS
Toms River, NJ

Reahm, Jeffrey
Holy Spirit HS
Mays Landing, NJ

Reams, Shikieta J
John F Kennedy HS
Paterson, NJ

Reaves, Ja Meda A
St Vincent Acad
Newark, NJ

Rebels, Stephanie
Morris Knolls HS
Dover, NJ

Reber, Hope
Mount Olive HS
Flanders, NJ

Redish, Stephanie
Monsignor Donovan
Jackson, NJ

Reed, Glen
Mount Olvie HS
Flanders, NJ

Reed, Susan
Woodstown HS
Monroeville, NJ

Reeves, Katherine
Kent Place Schl
Summit, NJ

Reger, Christina
Notre Dame HS
Robbinsville, NJ

Rehberg, Kriston J
Don Bosco Prep HS
Monroe, NY

Rehborn, Diana C
Edgewood Regional
SR HS
Berlin, NJ

Reho, James
St Josephs Prep
Princeton, NJ

Reid, Amee Suzanne
Kingsway Regional
Mullica Hill, NJ

Reif, Carl J
Bishop Eustace Prep
Bellmawr, NJ

Reilly, Christopher
Haddonfield
Memorial HS
Haddonfield, NJ

Reim, Deanne
Buena Regional HS
Newfield, NJ

Reingold, Caren
Wayne Hills HS
Wayne, NJ

Reinhold, Robyn
Pinelands Regionall
Tuckerton, NJ

Reinknecht, Janet
High Point Regional
Sussex, NJ

Reisdorf, Christina
Chatham HS
Chatham, NJ

Reitz, Kathleen
Toms River HS
S Toms River, NJ

Rekker, Robert
Collegiate HS
Passaic, NJ

Rembert, Diane
Mount St Dominic
East Orange, NJ

Remig, Edward W
Millburn HS
Short Hills, NJ

Renart, Krystal
Mainland Regional
Northfield, NJ

Renner, Crystal
Lyndhurst HS
Lyndhurst, NJ

Rensky, Gabrielle
Holy Cross HS
Burlington, NJ

Renwick, Ian
Wayne Hills HS
Wayne, NJ

Renz, Patricia
Holy Cross HS
Cinnaminson, NJ

Rettew, James H
Moorestown HS
Moorestown, NJ

Reu, Raymond
Watchung Hills
Regional HS
Warren, NJ

Reuben, Edward
Wecquakie HS
Newark, NJ

Reuben, Larissa
Mt St Dominic Acad
Newark, NJ

Reuter, Ronald
Mc Corriston
Catholic HS
Allentown, NJ

Reuther, Dana
Manalapan HS
Manalapan, NJ

Rever, Scott
Union HS
Union, NJ

Rey, Cristian
Memorial HS
West New York, NJ

Reynolds, Frederick
Secaucus HS
Secaucus, NJ

Reynolds, Melissa
West Morns
Mendham HS
Mendham, NJ

Ribavaro, Ruthann
John F Kennedy HS
Willingboro, NJ

Ribeiro, Fernando
Essex Catholic Boys
Newark, NJ

Ribeiro, Nancy J
Kearny HS
Kearny, NJ

Ribon, Nelson
Keansburg HS
Keansburg, NJ

Ricci, Karen
Columbia HS
Maplewood, NJ

Ricci, Kristine
Bridgeton HS
Port Norris, NJ

Ricco, Tricia
Wildwood Catholic
Wildwood Crest, NJ

Rice, Shelly
Bridgeton HS
Bridgeton, NJ

Richard, Jr John W
Shawnee HS
Vincentown, NJ

Richards, Michelle
Bishop George
AHR/ST Thoma
Plainfield, NJ

Richards, Rosann E
Benedictine Acad
Newark, NJ

Richardson, Dori
Jackson Memorial
Jackson, NJ

Richardson, Nikki
Cinnaminson HS
Cinnaminson, NJ

Richardson, Pamela
S
Camden HS
Camden, NJ

Richardson, Tracy
Toms River High
School North
Toms River, NJ

Richmond, Eric C
Woodstown HS
Elmer, NJ

Richmond, Fredrick
Teaneck HS
Teaneck, NJ

Richmond, Keith
Lakeland Regional
Wanaque, NJ

Rickwalder, Daniel
Whippany Park HS
Whippany, NJ

Ridgeway, Nicole
Penns Grove
Carneys Point HS
Carneys Point, NJ

Riess, Patricia
Ridge HS
Basking Ridge, NJ

Rifkind, Adam
West
Windsoro-Plainsbor
Trenton, NJ

Riggert, Jennifer
North Hunterdon
Annandale, NJ

Riggio, Kerry
Kerstin
Morris Knolls HS
Denville, NJ

Rikeman, Marykay
Southern Regional
Barnegat, NJ

Riley, Chrissy
Eastern Regional
West Berlin, NJ

Riley, John
North Warren
Regional HS
Columbia, NJ

Riley, Susan
Cumberland
Regional HS
Bridgeton, NJ

Rinaldi, Gisele
Mother Seton
Regional HS
Hillside, NJ

Rincavage, Lori A
Monroe Twp HS
Spotswood, NJ

Ring, Margot
Summitt HS
Summit, NJ

Rippey, Ronald
De Paul Diocesan
Kinnelon, NJ

Ritchey, Jr Daniel E
Lakewood HS
Lakewood, NJ

Ritter, Amy
Academy Of St
Morristown, NJ

Ritter, Bentley
Paul VI HS
Somerdale, NJ

Ritter, Jacqueline
Notre Dame HS
Lawrenceville, NJ

Ritter, Terry A
Bridgewater Raritan
HS East
Basking Ridge, NJ

Rizzo, Frank
St James HS
Gibbstown, NJ

Roa, Carolina
Dickinson HS
Jersey City, NJ

Roach, Gary R
Middle Township
Rio Grande, NJ

Robart, Forrest
Linden HS
Linden, NJ

Robb, Ashleigh
Notre Dame HS
Hamilton Sq, NJ

Robbins, April
Hunterdon Central
Ringoes, NJ

Robbins, Tavette
Cumberland
Regional HS
Bridgeton, NJ

Roberson, Brian W
Ewing HS
Trenton, NJ

Roberts, Lisa
Elmwood Park
Memorial HS
Elmwood Pk, NJ

Roberts, Nathaniel
Arts HS
Newark, NJ

Robertson, Bryan S
Mount Olive HS
Budd Lake, NJ

Robertson, Pamela
Matawan Regional
Cliffwood Bch, NJ

Robertson, Tammi
South River HS
South River, NJ

Robichaud, Michael
Verona HS
Verona, NJ

Robinson, Carol
Woodstown HS
Elmer, NJ

Robinson, Demetrius
Edgewood SR HS
Sicklerville, NJ

Robinson, Doug
Boonton HS
Lincoln Park, NJ

Robinson, Francine
Morris Catholic HS
Wharton, NJ

Robinson, Gina
Paterson Catholic
Regional HS
Paterson, NJ

Robinson, Howard A
Millville SR HS
Millville, NJ

Robinson, Nichole
Trenton Central HS
Trenton, NJ

Rocke, Robert
Bloomfield HS
Bloomfield, NJ

Rocky, Ruth
Carteret HS
Carteret, NJ

Roden, Frederick
The Oratory Schl
Springfield, NJ

Rodriguez, Edward
L
Randolph HS
Randolph, NJ

Rodriguez, Elvin
Passaic County
Vo-Tech HS
Paterson, NJ

Rodriguez, Gabriela
Perth Amboy HS
Perth Amboy, NJ

Rodriguez, Laura
Holy Rosary Acad
W New York, NJ

Rodriguez, Lillian
Bloomfield HS
Bloomfield, NJ

Rodriguez, Steve R
Hasbrouck Heights
Hasbrouck Heights,
NJ

Roesel, Steven P
Scotch
Plains-Fanwood HS
Fanwood, NJ

Roever, Kathleen A
Hunterdan Central
Flemington, NJ

Rogers, Dana
Brick Twp Memorial
Brick, NJ

Rogers, Janice
Toms River North
Toms River, NJ

Rogers, Linda
Bishop George Ahr/
St Thomas HS
Perth Amboy, NJ

Rogers, Ted
Vernon Township
Sussex, NJ

Rohaty, Deborah
Mt St Mary Acad
Flemington, NJ

Roig, Melinda
St John Vianney HS
Marlboro, NJ

Rokuskie, Kevin
Kingsway Regional
Swedesboro, NJ

Rolland, Timothy M
The Pennington
Trenton, NJ

Roller, Rhonda C
Lenape Valley
Regional HS
Netcong, NJ

Roman, Orlando
Passaic County Tech
& Voc HS
Paterson, NJ

Romanelli, Philip F
Lawrenceville School
Havertown, PA

Roost, Tina
Waldwick HS
Waldwick, NJ

Rooth, Michele
Holy Family Acad
Bayonne, NJ

Rosander, David
Timothy Christian
Piscataway, NJ

Rosati, Elaine
Washington
Township HS
Blackwood, NJ

Roscher, Brian
Hunterdon Central
Flemington, NJ

Rosciszewski, Karen
Bayonne HS
Bayonne, NJ

Rose, Gwendolyn
Belvidere HS
Oxford, NJ

Roseberry, James
Gloucester County
Christian HS
Monroeville, NJ

Rosen, Melissa
Manacapan HS
Englishtown, NJ

Rosen, Pam
Parsippany HS
Parsippany, NJ

Rosenberg, Adam C
East Brunswick HS
E Brunswick, NJ

Rosenblatt, Todd
Ocean Township HS
Ocean, NJ

Rosenfarb, Jason
Randolph HS
Randolph, NJ

Rosenfeld, Marissa
Beth
The Pilgrim Acad
Egg Harbor City, NJ

Ross, Debra
Hightstown HS
East Windsor, NJ

Ross, Rosemarie
St James HS
Alloway, NJ

Rossetti, Carolyn
Saint Mary HS
Keansburg, NJ

Rossi, Michael
Bishop Eustace
Preparatory Schl
Sewell, NJ

Rossiter, Russell
Gloucester Catholic
National Pk, NJ

Roswech, Marc
Toms River High
School South
Beachwood, NJ

Rothery, Richard
Wall HS
Wall, NJ

Rothstein, Michele
Denise
West Milford
Township HS
West Milford, NJ

Rotondo, Danielle
Notre Dame HS
Trenton, NJ

Routon, Carol Ann
Haddon Heights HS
Haddonfield, NJ

Rovee, Chris K
Hunterdon Central
Stockton, NJ

Rovelli, Joseph D
Bergen Catholic HS
Dumont, NJ

Rowe, Jeanne Anne
Teaneck HS
Teaneck, NJ

Roy, Pryia
Rahway SR HS
Rahway, NJ

Royds, Robert K
John F Kennedy HS
Willingboro, NJ

Royster, Jason
Immaculata HS
Piscataway, NJ

Ruderfer, Stuart B
Livingston HS
Livingston, NJ

Ruding, Jennifer
Neptune SR HS
Ocean Grove, NJ

Rue, Chris
Rancocas Valley
Regional HS
Mount Holly, NJ

Rueck, Christine
Middletown North
Middletown, NJ

Ruff, Dawn Marie
Maple Shade HS
Maple Shade, NJ

Ruffin, Damon J
Passaic County HS
Paterson, NJ

Ruger, IV A Nelson
Atlantic Friends
Mays Landing, NJ

Ruiz, Raoul
Edison HS
Edison, NJ

Ruiz, Rex B
Bergen Catholic HS
Oradell, NJ

Ruiz, Tanya
Wayne Hills HS
Wayne, NJ

Runko, Aaron
Howell HS
Howell, NJ

Runnells-Green,
Crystal M
Jackson Memorial
Lakewood, NJ

Rupp, Kristin
North Brunswick
Twp HS
N Brunswick, NJ

Ruppert, Susanne
Watchung Regional
Gillette, NJ

Rusek, Christopher
Ridge HS
Basking Ridge, NJ

Rush, Rebecca
Kearny HS
Kearny, NJ

Rush, Scott
Indian Hills HS
Oakland, NJ

Russell, Linda
Union HS
Union, NJ

Russell, Mary Lynn
Randolph HS
Randolph, NJ

Russell, Melissa
Woodstown HS
Woodstown, NJ

Russo, Amy Kristine
Shawnee HS
Medford, NJ

Russo, Christopher
A
Bridgewater Raritan
HS West
Bridgewater, NJ

Russo, Joann
Phillipsburg HS
Phillipsburg, NJ

Russo, Stephanie
Morris Hills HS
Rockaway, NJ

Russoniello, Janine
Saint Rose HS
Pt Pleasant, NJ

Rvan, Thomas
St John Vianney HS
Hazlet, NJ

Ryan, Catherine
Keansburg HS
Keansburg, NJ

Ryan, Daniel
Patrick
Monroe Township
Spotswood, NJ

Ryan, Erin
West Windsor
Plainsboro HS
Princeton Junct, NJ

Ryan, III John T
Seton Hall Prep
New Providence, NJ

Ryan, Kellie
Woodstown HS
Alloway, NJ

Ryan, Tom
Morristown HS
Morris Plains, NJ

Saam, Bill
Voorhees HS
Hampton, NJ

Saavedra, Alicia M
Mount St Mary
Hillside, NJ

Saba, Roy M
Moorestown SR HS
Moorestown, NJ

Sabatino, Anthony
Metuchen HS
Metuchen, NJ

Sable, Carl
Fair Lawn HS
Fair Lawn, NJ

Sabo, Greg P
Lawrence HS
Lawrenceville, NJ

Sacco, III Anthony
Michael
Buena Regional HS
Minotola, NJ

Safont, Jacqueline
Mary Help Of
Christian Acad
Paterson, NJ

Sagrestano, Brian M
Bridgewater-Raritan
HS East
Bridgewater, NJ

Sahli, Jennifer E
Spotswood HS
Spotswood, NJ

Saini, Tina
West
Windsor-Plainsbor
Princeton Junct, NJ

Saini, Vanita
Montville HS
Montville, NJ

Sakamoto, Hiroko
Dwight-Englewood
Cliffside Pk, NJ

Saks, William
Dover HS
Mine Hill, NJ

Salcedo, Mariefel
William L Dickinson
Jersey City, NJ

Salem, Susan
John P Stevens HS
Edison, NJ

Salerno, Karen A
Spotswood HS
Spotswood, NJ

Sales, Michele
Mary Help Of
Christians HS
Wayne, NJ

Salfelder, Mark
Sussex County Vo
Sparta, NJ

Salgado, Marilyn
Perth Amboy HS
Perth Amboy, NJ

Salim, Jennifer
Dwight Morrow HS
Englewood, NJ

Sallata, Suzanne
Atlantic City HS
Ventnor, NJ

Salley, Dolly
Immaculate
Conception HS
East Orange, NJ

Salvatore, Allison
Clayton HS
Clayton, NJ

Salvatore, Dave
Paulsboro HS
Paulsboro, NJ

Salvatore, Kenneth
J
Bound Brook HS
Bound Brook, NJ

Samora, David
Middletown South
Middletown, NJ

Samson, Elizabeth
Toms River North
Toms River, NJ

Samuels, Robin L
West Morris Central
Hackettstown, NJ

Sanchez, Lilibeth
Watchung Hills R
Watchung, NJ

Sanders, Raquel
Dover HS
Dover, NJ

Sanderson, Kristen
St John Vianney HS
Colts Neck, NJ

Sandman, Lisa M
Shawnne HS
Tabernacle, NJ

Sankar, Nandhini
Montville Township
Montville, NJ

Santangelo, Donald
Bridgewater Raritan
HS East
Bridgewater, NJ

Santangini, Paul
Washington
Township HS
Sewell, NJ

Santiago, Marc
Pasamus Catholic
Boys HS
Fort Lee, NJ

Santini, Laurie
Saint John Vianney
Colts Neck, NJ

Santorini, Vicki
Hillsborough HS
Belle Mead, NJ

Santoro, Chuck
Paramus HS
Paramus, NJ

Santucci, Lisa
St James HS
Penns Grove, NJ

Saperstein, Dawn L
Roxbury HS
Succasunna, NJ

Saraceni, Frank
North Bergen HS
North Bergen, NJ

Saracevic, Alan
Hillsborough HS
Hillsborough, NJ

Sarambo, Christine
M
Neptune SR HS
Neptune City, NJ

Sarchio, Chad T
Wayne Hills HS
Wayne, NJ

Sarcone, Anthony
Saint Mary HS
Holmdel, NJ

Sargenti, Joseph
Essex Catholic HS
For Boys
Clifton, NJ

Sarkisian, David
Kinnelon HS
Kinnelon, NJ

Sarn, Susan
Red Bank Catholic
Little Silver, NJ

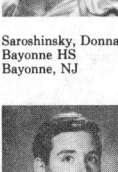

Saroshinsky, Donna
Bayonne HS
Bayonne, NJ

Sasse, Christopher
Edgewood Regional
SR HS
Sicklerville, NJ

Satorski, Andrea
South River HS
S River, NJ

Sauer, James
Union Catholic HS
Cranford, NJ

Saunders, Dionicia
K
Egg Harbor
Township HS
W Atlantic City, NJ

Saunders, Emily
Hunterdon Central
Flemington, NJ

Savatore, Allison
Clayton HS
Clayton, NJ

Saverino, Denise
Monsignor Donovan
Brick Town, NJ

Savola, Stacie L
Spotswood HS
Milltown, NJ

Sawhney, Roger Anu
Wardlaw-Hartridge
Edison, NJ

Sawyer, Kevin
West Essex HS
Essex Falls, NJ

Saxon, Jerilyn
Rutherford HS
Rutherford, NJ

Saxton, Erin Eileen
Whippany Park HS
Whippany, NJ

Scaglione, Kristin
St Pius X Regional
Dunellen, NJ

Scaler, Kathleen
Somerville HS
Somerville, NJ

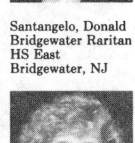

Scales, Tara
Marylawn Of The
East Orange, NJ

Scanlon, Jr Robert
A
Don Bosco Prep HS
Fairlawn, NJ

Scarpa, Salvatore
Kearny Christian
Comm Ed Ctr
Kearny, NJ

Scavuzzo, Paul
Toms River HS
Toms River, NJ

Scerbo, Carolyn
De Paul Diocesan
Lincoln Park, NJ

Schad, Donald
Washington Twp
Turnersville, NJ

Schaefer, Cynthia
Ocean Township HS
Ocean, NJ

Schaefer, Stuart
Don Bosco Prep
Wayne, NJ

Schafer, Gene
Paramus Catholic
Rochelle Pk, NJ

Schafle, Michelle
Rancocas Valley
Regional HS
Mt Holly, NJ

Schatz, Stephen M
Morris Hills
Regional HS
Rockaway, NJ

Scheible, Robert
Belleville HS
Belleville, NJ

Scherff, Susan
Sparta HS
Sparta, NJ

Schiller, Jean
Marlboro HS
Colts Neck, NJ

Schindel, Rachel
Sharon
Kingsway Regional
Swedesboro, NJ

Schlenker, Sally K
Academy Of The
Holy Angels
Old Tappan, NJ

Schlissel, Jennifer
Mt Olive HS
Flanders, NJ

Schmauder, Valerie
M
Bernards HS
Bernardsville, NJ

Schmidheiser, Brad
Clearview Regional
Mullica Hill, NJ

Schmidling, Donna
Brick Twp Memorial
Brick, NJ

Schmidt, Connie
Howell HS
Howell, NJ

Schmidt, Jon
Hunterdon Central
Whitehouse Sta, NJ

Schmidt, Kristin
Union HS
Union, NJ

Schmidt, Ryan
Randolph HS
Randolph, NJ

Schneeman, Laurie
Victory Christian
Monroeville, NJ

Schneider, Beth
Southern Regional
Manahawkin, NJ

Schnettler, Marcelo
Academic HS
Jersey City, NJ

Schnitzer, Lori
Linden HS
Linden, NJ

Schnock, Christina
Marie
Manalapan HS
Manalapan, NJ

Schoenberg,
Amanda
Dwight Englewood
Tenafly, NJ

Schor, Justin
Waldwick SR HS
Waldwick, NJ

Schott, Darlene
Mahwah HS
Mahwah, NJ

Schuetzler, Brian
Sparta HS
Sparta, NJ

Schujko, Jo Anne
Bordentown
Regional HS
Yardville, NJ

Schuldes, Felicia
Notre Dame HS
Trenton, NJ

Schultze, Wendy
Toms River High
School East
Toms Rvr, NJ

Schulz, James
Hamilton High West
Yardville, NJ

Schuster, Ron
John P Stevens HS
Edison, NJ

Schutzer, Romi
Secaucus HS
Secaucus, NJ

Schwaeble, Diana
West Morris
Mendham HS
Mendham, NJ

Schwager, David
Steinert HS
North Crosswicks,
NJ

Schwartz, Matthew
Lenape Valley
Regional HS
Andover, NJ

Schwarz, Kenneth
Somerset County Vo
Tech HS
Princeton, NJ

Schwier, Catherine
Manasquan HS
Spring Lake, NJ

Schwingel, Colleen
Parsippany Hills HS
Dover, NJ

Sciarrillo, Tina
Hanover Park HS
E Hanover, NJ

Scibek, Tamara
Sayreville War
Memorial HS
Sayreville, NJ

Sciglitano,
Christopher D
Paramus Catholic
Boys HS
Ridgefield, NJ

Scillieri, Christopher
Memorial HS
Elmwood Pk, NJ

Scimeme, Doriann
Bishop George AHR
Milltown, NJ

Scimene, Doriann
Bishop George Ahr
Milltown, NJ

Scott, Christopher
High Point Regional
Branchville, NJ

Scott, Dexter L
Florence Twp
Memorial HS
Edgewater Park, NJ

Scott, Jr Evan Paul
Pennsville Memorial
Pennsville, NJ

Scott, Johnetta
Plainfield HS
Plainfield, NJ

Scott, Karl
Gateway Regional
Westville, NJ

Scott, Saburnia
Belvidere HS
Belvidere, NJ

Scott, Tammy
Camden HS
Camden, NJ

Scott, Vicki
Toms River HS
Pine Beach, NJ

Scotti, Regina
Glen Rock SR HS
Glen Rock, NJ

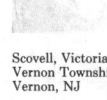

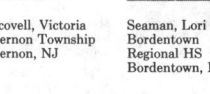

Scovell, Victoria
Vernon Township
Vernon, NJ

Seaman, Lori
Bordentown
Regional HS
Bordentown, NJ

Sebben, Trish
Belleville HS
Belleville, NJ

Sebesta, Michael
Admiral Farragut
Solvay, NY

Secco, Michele Anne
Dover HS
Dover, NJ

Segar, Valerie
Paulsboro HS
Paulsboro, NJ

Seidel, Robert
Brick Memorial HS
Brick, NJ

Seidelmann, Chris
Toms River HS
Toms River, NJ

Seidle, Jr John
Burl Co Vo Tech
Burlington, NJ

Sekula, Jeffrey J
De Paul Diocesan
Wayne, NJ

Selby, Aleshia
Weequahic HS
Newark, NJ

Semiraro, Rich
Hunterdon Central
Flemington, NJ

Sengupta, Shampa
St Anthonys HS
Jersey Cty, NJ

Sennett, Brad
Woodbury JR/SR
Woodbury, NJ

Sepp, James
Bogota HS
Bogota, NJ

Serin, Amy C
Wallkill Valley
Regional HS
Franklin, NJ

Serrano, Johnny
Bayonne HS
Bayonne, NJ

Sexton, Matt
Madison Avenue
Baptist Acad
Paterson, NJ

Shableski, Lynn
Monsignor Donovan
Lavallette, NJ

Shack, Stephanie
Mt Olive HS
Flanders, NJ

Shade, Dawn
Marine Acad
Union Beach, NJ

Shah, Anju
Holy Rosary Acad
Jersey City, NJ

Shah, Nilesh A
Bound Brook HS
S Bound Brook, NJ

Shah, Nrupa
Bishop George Ahr
Edison, NJ

Shah, Shishir
North Bergen HS
North Bergen, NJ

Shannon, Jr Donald R
Neumann Prep
Hawthorne, NJ

Sharkey, Patti
Our Lady Of Mercy
Cape May Ct Hse, NJ

Sharp, Ardan
Edgewood Regional
SR HS
Tansboro, NJ

Sharp, Ken
Ocean City HS
Ocean City, NJ

Sharpless, Anne Marie
Bridgeton HS
Bridgeton, NJ

Shaw, Jennifer
Maple Shade HS
Maple Shade, NJ

Shaw, Robye
Morris Hills HS
Rockaway, NJ

Shea, Catherine
H G Hoffman HS
South Amboy, NJ

Sheehan, Garrett
Brick Township HS
Brick, NJ

Sheldon, Steve
Bridgeton HS
Bridgeton, NJ

Shell, Kevin
Paul VI HS
Haddonfield, NJ

Shellhammer, Joe
St Peters HS
Somerset, NJ

Sheppard, Sherri
Lower Cape May
Regional HS
Cape May, NJ

Sheridan, John
Seton Hall
Preparatory Schl
Whippany, NJ

Sheridan, Michael
Egg Harbor
Township HS
Mayslanding, NJ

Sherlock, Allison
Victory Christian
Sicklerville, NJ

Sherman, John
Bridgeton HS
Cedarville, NJ

Sherron, James A
Hammonton HS
Hammonton, NJ

Shetty, Smitha
Immaculata HS
Bridgewater, NJ

Shibata, Lisa
Scotch-Plains
Fanwood HS
Fanwood, NJ

Shields, Leslie
Hunterdon Central
Neshanic Sta, NJ

Shiels, Catherine
Hillsborough HS
Neshanic, NJ

Shin, Gina
Glen Rock SR HS
Glen Rock, NJ

Shone, Jennifer B
Pitman HS
Pitman, NJ

Short, Kristine
Manalapan HS
Manalapan, NJ

Shotwell, Michelle
New Milford HS
New Milford, NJ

Shrem, Andrea J
Red Bank Regional
Bradley Beach, NJ

Shum, Charlotte
Livingston HS
Livingston, NJ

Shupp, Theresa
Mother Seton
Regional HS
Rahway, NJ

Shute, Donna
Cherokee HS
Marlton, NJ

Siano, Anna
Essex Catholic Girls
Irvington, NJ

Siano, Salvatore R
Passaic Valley HS
W Paterson, NJ

Siebert, Susan
Pitman HS
Pitman, NJ

Sigel, Kirk
Ocean City HS
Ocean City, NJ

Siggins, Lisa
High Point Regional
Branchville, NJ

Signorella, Maria
Rosell Park HS
Roselle Park, NJ

Silkowski, Margaret D
Ocean Township HS
Ocean, NJ

Sills, Taunya Lynnette
East Orange HS
East Orange, NJ

Silvani, Valerie
Secaucus HS
Secaucus, NJ

Silverman, Jennifer
Mount Olive HS
Budd Lake, NJ

Silvers, Colleen
Kearny HS
Kearny, NJ

Simmerman, Lorna
Pitman HS
Pitman, NJ

Simone, Leah
Watching Hills
Regional HS
Gillette, NJ

Simpson, Henry L
J P Stevens HS
Rahway, NJ

Simpson, Sandra
Paul VI HS
Turnersville, NJ

Simrany, Cheryl Ann
Mt Olive HS
Hackettstown, NJ

Sinanian, Lisa
North Bergen HS
N Bergen, NJ

Sinfield, Joseph Victor
Vernon Township
Glenwood, NJ

Singer, Sara
Ocean Township HS
Ocean Tsp, NJ

Sinnott, Adrienne
Academic HS
Jersey City, NJ

Sisto, Jessica
Dover HS
Dover, NJ

Sitarik, Tina A
South Brunswick
Kendall Park, NJ

Sivadas, Rekha
Immaculate Heart
Hillsdale, NJ

Skanes, Debra A
Cherokee HS
Marlton Lakes, NJ

Skeenes, Amy
Florence Township
Memorial HS
Florence, NJ

Skewes, William A
Ridgewood HS
Ridgewood, NJ

Slattery, Stephen
Morris Catholic HS
Succasunna, NJ

Slavin, Eric
Central Regional HS
Seaside Pk, NJ

Sloan, Scott J
Christian Brothers
Colts Neck, NJ

Slocum, Jr Daniel A
St John Vianney HS
Keyport, NJ

Small, Pamela A
Shawnee HS
Tabernacle, NJ

Smalley, Leslie
Wall HS
Manasquan, NJ

Smith, Anna Lynn
Our Lady Of Mercy
Vineland, NJ

Smith, Christina
Millville SR HS
Millville, NJ

Smith, Christine
Ewing HS
Trenton, NJ

Smith, Craig
Montville HS
Boonton, NJ

Smith, Dawn
Phillipsburg HS
Phillipsburg, NJ

Smith, Deborah
Holy Cross HS
Cinnaminson, NJ

Smith, Donald
Holy Cross HS
Delran, NJ

Smith, Donna
Pennsville Memorial
Pennsville, NJ

Smith, Earlyne
Weequahie HS
Newark, NJ

Smith, Eric K
Lawrence HS
Cranbury, NJ

Smith, Gail
Paramus Catholic
Girls HS
Teaneck, NJ

Smith, Heather
Marie
Freehold Borough
Colts Neck, NJ

Smith, Jeannette
Kittatinny Regional
Newton, NJ

Smith, Jennifer
John F Kennedy HS
Willingboro, NJ

Smith, Kimberly
Hackettstown HS
Great Meadows, NJ

Smith, Leslie Lynn
Haddonfield
Memorial HS
Haddonfield, NJ

Smith, Linda
St James HS
Wenonah, NJ

Smith, Margaret E
Union Catholic
Regional HS
Fanwood, NJ

Smith, Mark
Burlington City HS
Burlington, NJ

Smith, Michael
Toms River HS
Pine Beach, NJ

Smith, Monica Y
Metuchen HS
Metuchen, NJ

Smith, Raymond
Scott
Burlington County
Riverside, NJ

Smith, Jr Robert W
Atlantic Christian
Ocean City, NJ

Smith, Sharon
St Rose HS
Brick, NJ

Smith, Jr Sheldon V
Summit HS
Summit, NJ

Smith, Tina
Glen Rock SR HS
Glen Rock, NJ

Smith, Vincent J
Millburn SR HS
Millburn, NJ

Smith, Wayne
Riverside HS
Riverside, NJ

Smolen, Heather L
Bishop Ahr HS
Edison, NJ

Snead, Kimberly
Our Lady Of Good
Newark, NJ

Snodgrass, Matthew
R
Woodbury HS
Woodbury, NJ

Snyder, Jason
Wallington HS
Wallington, NJ

Sobelman, Joshua
Pennsville Memorial
Pennsville, NJ

Sobieski, Allison
Ocean Township HS
Wayside, NJ

Soderman, Elsa
Howell HS
Farmingdale, NJ

Solanko, Karin
Manasquan HS
Brielle, NJ

Solda, Susan
Immaculate
Conception HS
Woodridge, NJ

Soler, William
Essex Catholic Boys
East Orange, NJ

Solomon, James
Newton HS
Newton, NJ

Solomon, Sharon
Morristown-Beard
Budd Lake, NJ

Soltesz, Susan
Woodbridge HS
Woodbridge, NJ

Somma, Gretchen
Middlesex HS
Middlesex, NJ

Sommer, Julie
Parsippany Hills HS
Denville, NJ

Song, Tae
Cliffside Park HS
Cliffside Pk, NJ

Soni, Rajesh N
Mount Olive HS
Flanders, NJ

Sontakay, Arati
Summit HS
Summit, NJ

Sookram, Arnold
Paramus HS
Paramus, NJ

Sooy, Christina
Holy Spirit HS
Absecon, NJ

Sorrell, Terrence M
Salem HS
Salem, NJ

Soto, Migdalia
Phillipsburg HS
Phillipsburg, NJ

Southard, James T
Florence Twp Mem
Roebling, NJ

Sowers, Teresa
Penns Grove HS
Carneys Point, NJ

Spaihts, Jonathan S
Ewing HS
Ewing, NJ

Spall, Lynley
Vineland HS
Vineland, NJ

Sparks, Sharron
Manalapan HS
Englishtown, NJ

Spatola, Jeffrey
Middletown HS
Leonardo, NJ

Spears, James
Pennsville HS
Pennsville, NJ

Spector, Jennifer
Manalapan HS
Manalapan, NJ

Speed, La-Shanna D
Laine
Vailsburg HS
Newark, NJ

Speeney, John
Madison Central HS
Old Bridge, NJ

Spencer, John C
Pequannock
Township HS
Pompton Plains, NJ

Spigner, Charlene
Hillside HS
Hillside, NJ

Spillman, Sandra A
David Brearley
Regional HS
Kenilworth, NJ

Spilsbury, Jeff
Belleville HS
Belleville, NJ

Spinks, Justine
Paulsboro HS
Paulsboro, NJ

Spizzuco, Jr Daniel
Toms River HS East
Toms River, NJ

Spoelstra, Charles G
Indian Hills HS
Oakland, NJ

Sprague, Scott
Brick Memorial HS
Bricktown, NJ

Spring, Dawn
Clifton HS
Clifton, NJ

Springer, Douglas W
Hillside HS
Hillside, NJ

Spuler, Albert
Washington Twp
Sewell, NJ

Spurr, David
Parsippany Hills HS
Morris Plns, NJ

Spychalski, Stacie
Bridgewater-Raritan
West HS
Bridgewater, NJ

Squadrito, Josephine
Glassboro HS
Glassboro, NJ

Squiccimarra, Lynn
Spotswood HS
Spotswood, NJ

Squier, Stephanie
Pennsville Memorial
Pennsville, NJ

St John, Christopher
Union Cathlic
Regional HS
Roselle, NJ

Stach, Melinda
Mahwah HS
Mahwah, NJ

Stafford, Andrea
Lynn
Paterson Catholic
Regional HS
Passaic, NJ

Stafford, Bob
Gloucester JRSR
Gloucester, NJ

Stancati, Carolyn
Mc Corristin
Catholic HS
Trenton, NJ

Stanford, Christine
Huntendon HS
Stockton, NJ

Stanton, John J
Maple Shade HS
Maple Shade, NJ

Starace, Kimberly
Paramus HS
Paramus, NJ

Starke, Todd
Vernon Township
Sussex, NJ

Starrett, Cynthia
Brick Memorial HS
Brick, NJ

Stassou, Andrea
Dwight Morrow HS
Englewood Cliffs,
NJ

Staton, Randy
Eastside HS
Paterson, NJ

Staton, Tiffany
John F Kennedy HS
Willingboro, NJ

Steele, Sondra
Paul VI HS
Haddon Hts, NJ

Steger, Christopher
D
Christian Brothers
Manasquan, NJ

Steil, Laura
Watching Hills
Regional HS
Warren, NJ

Steinmacher,
Kimberly
Rahway HS
Rahway, NJ

Steinmetz, Thomas
Camden Catholic
Pennsauken, NJ

Steinmeyer, Debra
Passaic Valley HS
Little Falls, NJ

Steinwehr, Jr
George
Toms River HS East
Toms River, NJ

Steiskal, Susan
Pennsville HS
Pennsville, NJ

Stellman, Jaime
Morris Knolls HS
Rockaway, NJ

Stephen, Sharon
John P Stevens HS
Edison, NJ

Stephens, Brian
Columbia HS
Maplewood, NJ

Stephenson, Erica L
Montclair HS
Upper Montclair,
NJ

Stevens, Mary Ann
Wall Township HS
Manasquan Park,
NJ

Stevens, Scott
Hamilton High
School North Nvm
Mercerville, NJ

Stevens, Tracey
Lynn
Boonton HS
Lincoln Park, NJ

Steward, James
Paterson Catholic
Regional HS
Paterson, NJ

Stewart, Colin G
Piscataway HS
Piscataway, NJ

Stewart, Erica
Orange HS
Orange, NJ

Stewart, Jeffrey T
Butler HS
Bloomingdale, NJ

Stewart, Mark
Dwight Morrow HS
Englewood, NJ

Stewart, Reed
Glen Rock HS
Glen Rock, NJ

Stift, Kristin
Watchung Hills
Regional HS
Watchung, NJ

Stipes, Doug
Cumberland
Regional HS
Bridgeton, NJ

Stitt, Wayne
Pitman HS
Pitman, NJ

Stokes, Jon L
St James HS
Carneys Point, NJ

Stokes, Theresa
Edgewood Regional
Chesilhurst, NJ

Stone, Treniese
Parsippany Hills HS
Morris Plains, NJ

Stoots, Teresa
Medford Technical
Browns Mills, NJ

Stoppiello, Colleen
Immaculate Heart
Hawthorne, NJ

Stout, Victoria
Phillipsburg HS
Phillipsburg, NJ

Stowell, Bruce
Edgewood Regional
Cedarbrook, NJ

Strada, Dina
Wall HS
Wall, NJ

Street, Lawrence E
South Plainfield HS
S Plainfield, NJ

Strillacci, Jill
Mt Olive HS
Flanders, NJ

Strippoli, Marisa
Clifton HS
Clifton, NJ

Strubbe, Jr Walter
Waldwick HS
Waldwick, NJ

Strunk, Scott
Life Center Acad
Burlington, NJ

Struthers, Meredith
Delaware Valley
Regional HS
Frenchtown, NJ

Stubbmann, Allison
Raritan HS
Hazlet, NJ

Studer, Deirdre
De Paul HS
Ringwood, NJ

Sturgis, Merisha
John F Kennedy HS
Willingboro, NJ

Stutzmann, Konrad
Bridgeton HS
Bridgeton, NJ

Su, Tina
Manchester
Township HS
Lakehurst, NJ

Suarez, Joyceann
Lodi HS
Lodi, NJ

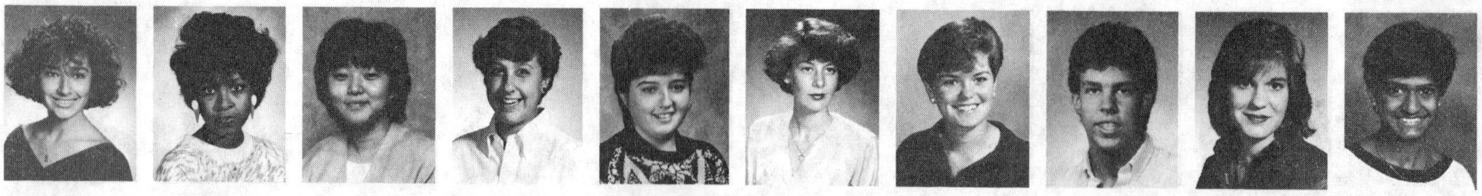

Suarez, Rosa
Ridgefield Park HS
Ridgefield Pk, NJ

Sugg, Angela
Highland Regional
Somerdale, NJ

Suh, Youn Joo
Dwight-Englewood
Tenafly, NJ

Sukinik, Amy
Shore Regional HS
Oceanport, NJ

Sulkowski, Colleen M
Spotswood HS
Helmetta, NJ

Sullivan, Mary Elizabeth
Mount Saint Mary
Elizabeth, NJ

Sullivan, Meghan
Saint Rose HS
Belmar, NJ

Sullivan, Robert
Morris Catholic HS
Dover, NJ

Sullivan, Stacie Ann
Dover HS
Dover, NJ

Sunder, Madhavi
Mainland Regional
Northfield, NJ

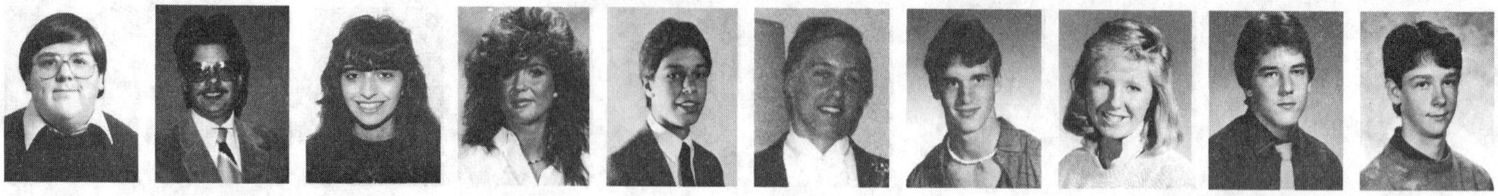

Sungenis, Paul
Sacred Heart HS
Vineland, NJ

Susko, Andrew
Woodbridge HS
Sewaren, NJ

Sutera, Maryanne
Fort Lee HS
Fort Lee, NJ

Suwak, Jennifer
Monsignor Donovan
Toms River, NJ

Swartley, Brandon
The Kings Christian
Haddonfield, NJ

Swartz, Andrew
Hunterdon Central
Flemington, NJ

Swayze, Daniel
Dover HS
Dover, NJ

Sweeney, Kelly A
West Milford Township HS
West Milford, NJ

Sweeney, Shawn
St Joseph Regional
Upr Saddle Rvr, NJ

Sweeney, William
Bordentown Regional HS
Bordentown, NJ

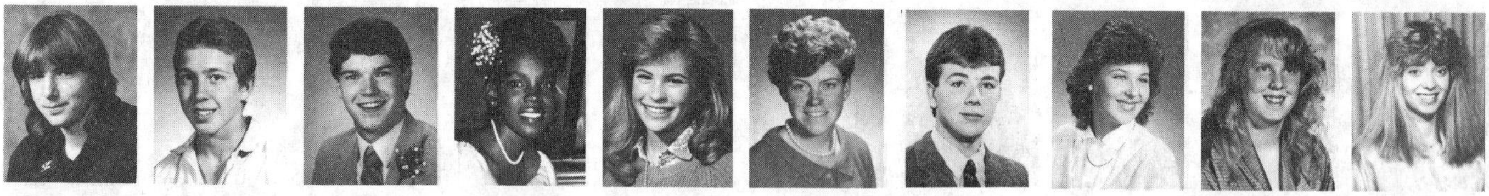

Sweet, Jared
Lakewood Prep
Freehold, NJ

Sweeten, Edwin
Kingway Regional
Mt Royal, NJ

Swezey, Wayne W
Midland Park HS
Midland Park, NJ

Swindle, Robyn
Matawan Regional
Cliffwood, NJ

Swon, Kimberly A
West Morris Mendham HS
Brookside, NJ

Sykes, Katherine J
Lakeland Regional
Ringwood, NJ

Syme, Geoffrey
James Caldwell HS
Caldwell, NJ

Szabo, Gabriella
North Warren Regional HS
Delaware, NJ

Szalma, Samantha
W/T HS
Sewell, NJ

Szcykalski, Lisa
Maple Shade HS
Maple Shade, NJ

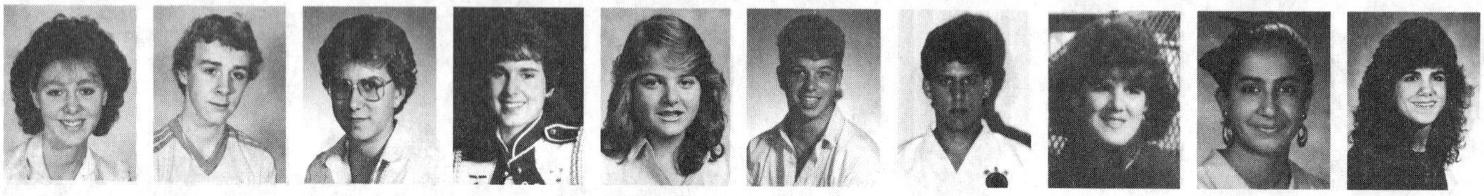

Szczepaniak, Nancy
Matawan Regional
Matawan, NJ

Szczepaniak, Richard J
Matawan Regional
Matawan, NJ

Szobota, Jennifer
Morristown HS
Morristown, NJ

Szotak, Susann
Union HS
Union, NJ

Tabert, Kristen
Saint John Vianney Regional HS
Old Bridge, NJ

Taccone, Gerard A
Montville HS
Montville, NJ

Tahan, David G
Wayne Hills HS
Wayne, NJ

Tahaney, Kristen
Bishop Eustace Prep
Atco, NJ

Taheripour, Morvarid
Dwight Englewood
Wash Township, NJ

Tahmoosh, Susan
John F Kennedy HS
Paterson, NJ

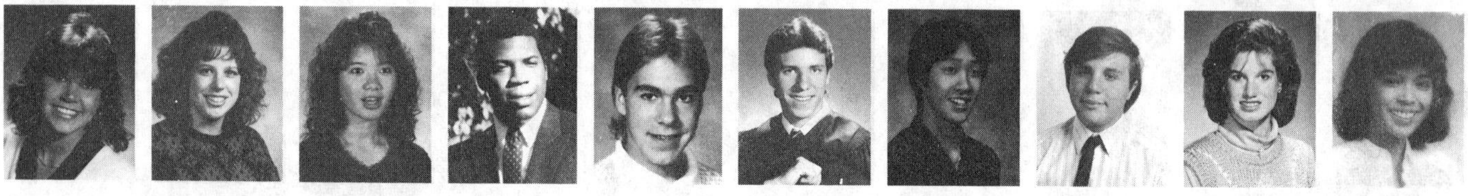

Takacs, Doreen
Clifton HS
Clifton, NJ

Talbot, Joanne
Haddon Township
Westmont, NJ

Taldelore, Vivian
Rutherford HS
Rutherford, NJ

Taliaferro, Jeffrey W
Wardlaw-Hartridge
Plainfield, NJ

Talish, Chris
West Essex SR HS
Fairfield, NJ

Talpas, Chris
Phillipsburg HS
Phillipsburg, NJ

Tang, Neil
Monroe Township
Spotswood, NJ

Tanier, Michael
Gloucester Catholic
Mt Ephraim, NJ

Tanner, Delisa R
Ramsey HS
Saddle River, NJ

Tanudtanud, Lynlee
St John Vianney HS
Freehold, NJ

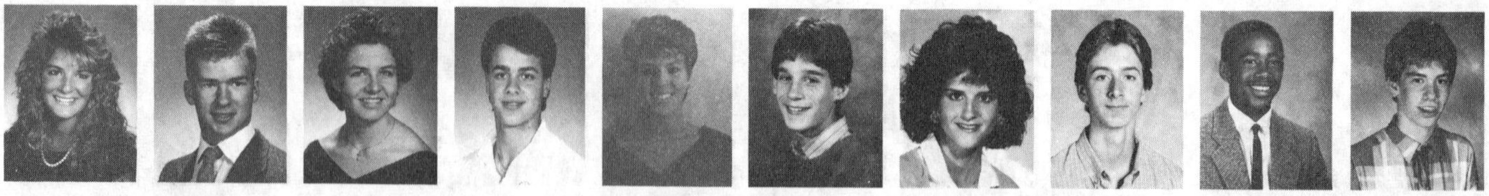

Tarantolo, Patricia Ann
Monmouth Regional
Eatontown, NJ

Tarbox, Eric Alexander
Morristown HS
Morristown, NJ

Tarnowski, Ann Marie
Bridgewater Raritan West HS
Raritan, NJ

Tartaglione, Kevin
Immaculata HS
Belle Mead, NJ

Tarves, Lori Ann V
Paul VI HS
Somerdale, NJ

Taskowitz, Gregg
South River HS
S River, NJ

Tassone, Judi L
Hammonton HS
Hammonton, NJ

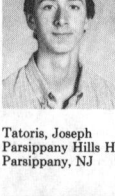

Tatoris, Joseph
Parsippany Hills HS
Parsippany, NJ

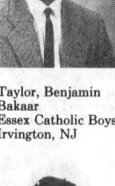

Taylor, Benjamin Bakaar
Essex Catholic Boys
Irvington, NJ

Taylor, Darryl
Williamstown HS
Williamstown, NJ

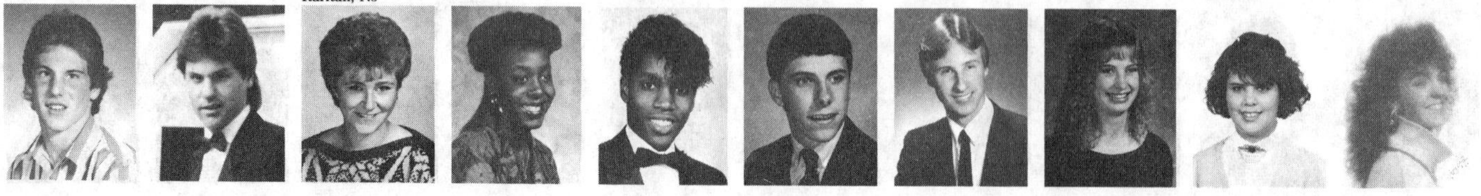

Taylor, Jeffrey P
West Milford Township HS
W Milford, NJ

Taylor, Jerry Mark
Manchester HS
Toms River, NJ

Taylor, Michele
Manchester Twp HS
Toms River, NJ

Taylor, Toschia
Burlington Township HS
Burlington, NJ

Taylor, Tyrone
Montclair HS
Montclair, NJ

Teevan, Martin
Christian Brothers
Holmdel, NJ

Telesh, John
Hopatcong HS
Hopatcong, NJ

Tellefsen, Cora
Spotswood HS
Spotswood, NJ

Telleria, Olga M
St Josephs Of The Palisades HS
Union City, NJ

Temple, Amy
Hamilton H S West
Trenton, NJ

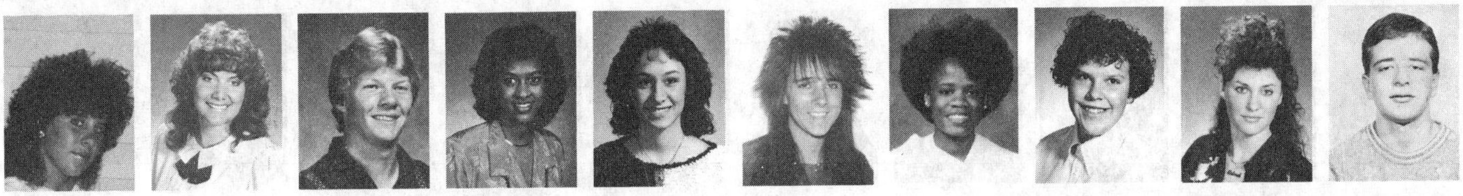

Tendler, Jodi
Paramus HS
Paramus, NJ

Tercek, Kristin L
Dumont HS
Dumont, NJ

Terhune, Kevin
Ocean Township HS
Ocean, NJ

Terry, Norna
Life Center Acad
Mt Holly, NJ

Tesoriero, Vikki
Jackson Memorial
Jackson, NJ

Tettamanti, Rosemarie
Bayonne HS
Bayonne, NJ

Thaxton, Cheryl
Orange HS
East Orange, NJ

Theobald, Stacey
St Joseph Of The Palisade HS
W New York, NJ

Thier, Deborah
Madison Central HS
Old Bridge, NJ

Thomas, Alex
Brick Memorial HS
Brick, NJ

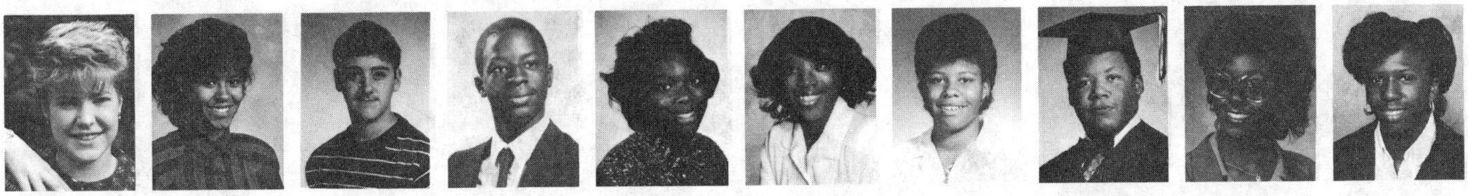

Thomas, Karen E
Governor Livingston Reg HS
Berkeley Height, NJ

Thomas, Lisa
Pemberton Township HS
Pemberton, NJ

Thomas, Russell
Hightstown HS
E Windsor, NJ

Thomas, Shawn Eugene
Essex Catholic Boys
Orange, NJ

Thomas, Tiffanie C
Cumberland Regional HS
Bridgeton, NJ

Thomas, Tuesday
Kent Place Schl
Irvington, NJ

Thomas, Velissa
Paterson Catholic
Paterson, NJ

Thompson, Arthur
Bridgeton SR HS
Bridgeton, NJ

Thompson, Melissa
Eastern Christian
Paterson, NJ

Thompson, Nykita
Mother Seton Regional HS
Irvington, NJ

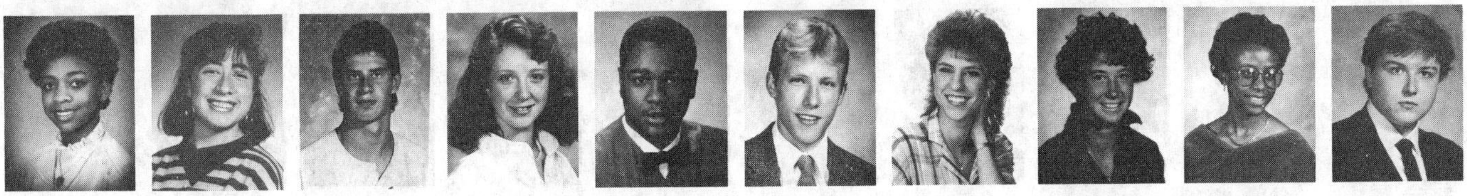

Thompson, Rotanda
John F Kennedy HS
Willingboro, NJ

Thompson, Sandra Ann
Toms River HS
Beachwood, NJ

Thomson, Kevin
Gloucester City HS
Gloucester, NJ

Thornton, Christine
Monsignor Donovan
Jackson, NJ

Thornton, Marc
Essex Catholic HS
E Orange, NJ

Thorpe, Tom
Hunterdon Central
Flemington, NJ

Timko, Donna
Spotswood HS
Milltown, NJ

Timmons, Susan
Cinnaminson HS
Cinnaminson, NJ

Tindell, Shannan
Benedictine Acad
Newark, NJ

Tirenin, Michael
Hopewell Valley Central HS
Trenton, NJ

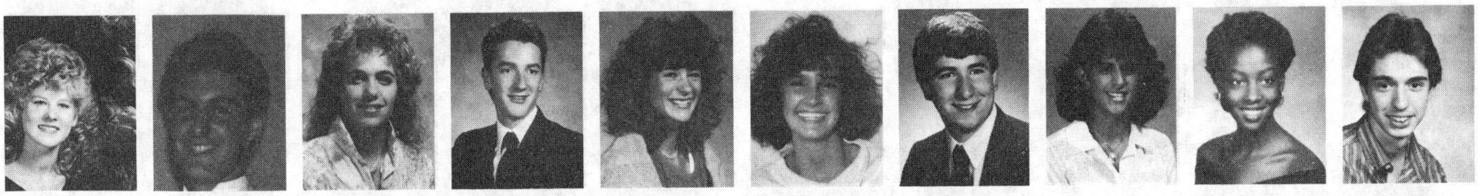

Tkatschenko, Tamara
Williamstown HS
Williamstown, NJ

Tobia, Christopher
Paul VI HS
Laurel Spr, NJ

Todd, Jill M
Warren Hills Regional SR HS
Washington, NJ

Tolmayer, Robert J
Rancocas Valley Regional HS
Mt Holly, NJ

Tolocka, Allison
Southern Regional
Shipbottom, NJ

Tomasello, Claudia
Morristown-Beard
Morris Plains, NJ

Tomasi, III Peter
Hawthorne HS
Hawthorne, NJ

Torchia, Maria
Our Lady Of Mercy
Turnersville, NJ

Torchon, Marjorie
Saint Dominic Acad
Jersey City, NJ

Toriello, Peter J
Westwood HS
Westwood, NJ

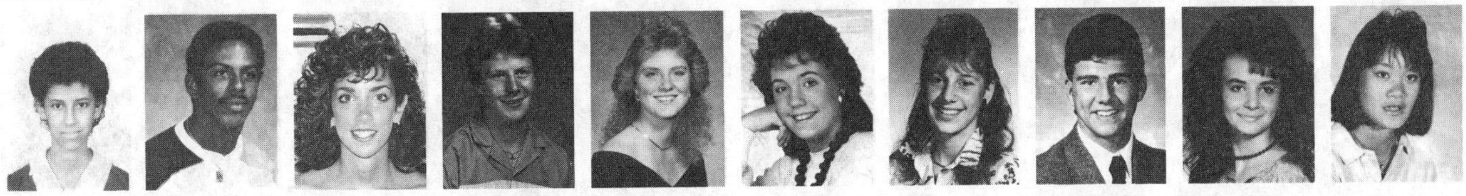

Torregroza, Ingrid
Mary Help Of Christians Acad
Haledon, NJ

Torres, Manuel
Burlington Township HS
Burlington, NJ

Torrisi, Jennifer L
Cherry Hill E HS
Cherry Hill, NJ

Toth, David
Woodbridge HS
Woodbridge, NJ

Toth, Jacqueline
St John Vianney HS
Union Beach, NJ

Tozer, Renee Lynn
Middle Township
Cape May C H, NJ

Tracy, Danielle
Boonton HS
Lincoln Pk, NJ

Traeger, Geoffrey
Lenape Valley Regional HS
Andover, NJ

Trajkovska, Violet
Garfield HS
Garfield, NJ

Tran, Mai-Anh
Rutherford HS
Rutherford, NJ

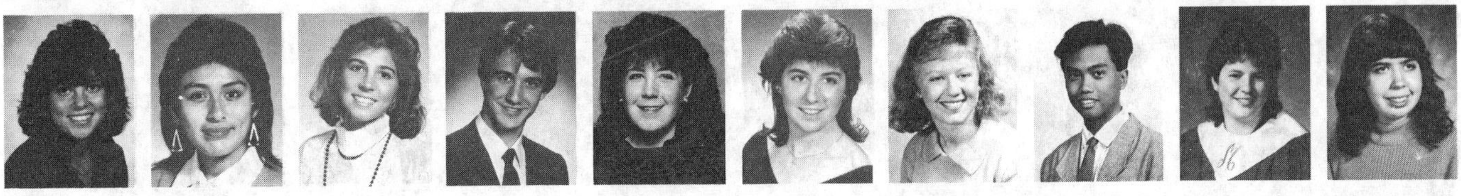

Travaline, Stefanie
Cumberland Regional HS
Bridgeton, NJ

Travezano, Angela
Paterson Catholic Regional HS
Paterson, NJ

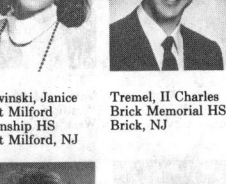

Trawinski, Janice
West Milford Township HS
West Milford, NJ

Tremel, II Charles
Brick Memorial HS
Brick, NJ

Triant, Jennifer K
Cresskill HS
Cresskill, NJ

Trilone, Donna
Manville HS
Manville, NJ

Trimble, Kelly
Lenape Regional HS
Vincentown, NJ

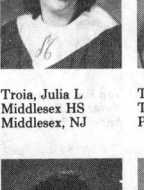

Trinidad, Victor Joel
Municipal Schl Of Williamson, WV

Troia, Julia L
Middlesex HS
Middlesex, NJ

Troidl, Lisa E
The Hun School Of Pennington, NJ

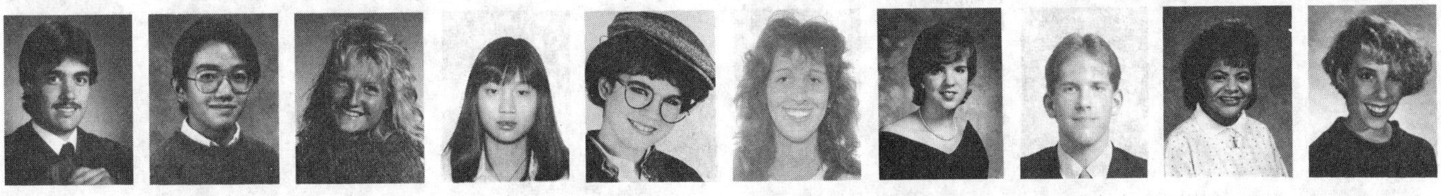

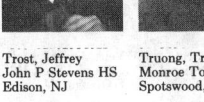

Trost, Jeffrey
John P Stevens HS
Edison, NJ

Truong, Tri M
Monroe Township
Spotswood, NJ

Truppo, Cindy
Randolph HS
Randolph, NJ

Tseng, Yi Ping
Passaic County Tech & Voc HS
Passaic, NJ

Tubbs, Laura
Montville Twp HS
Pinebrook, NJ

Tuber, Michelle
Livingston HS
Livingston, NJ

Tuccillo, Anna M
Bordentown Regional HS
Bordentown, NJ

Tucker, II Charles B
Lenape HS
Vincentown, NJ

Tucker, Kathryn
Burlington County
Beverly, NJ

Tuella, Kethley Ann
Rutherford HS
Rutherford, NJ

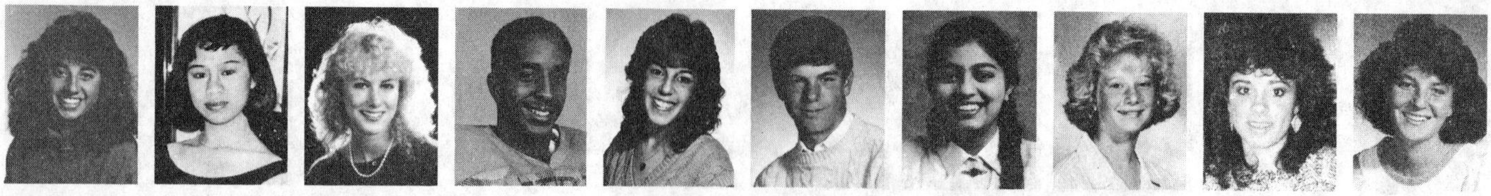

Tufaro, Christina
Bishop George Ahr
S Plainfield, NJ

Tumang, Michele
Academic HS
Jersey City, NJ

Tunison, Audra
Hunterdon Central
Whitehouse Sta, NJ

Tunstall, Vaughn S
Woodbury JR SR
Woodbury, NJ

Tupler, Teri
Franklin HS
Somerset, NJ

Turanchik, Stephen
Glen Rock HS
Glen Rock, NJ

Turna, Chainchal
Elwood Park
Memorial HS
Elmwood Pk, NJ

Turner, Heather
Atlantic Christian
Mays Landing, NJ

Turner, Terri L
Audubon HS
Mt Ephraim, NJ

Tursky, Dawn
Morristown HS
Morristown, NJ

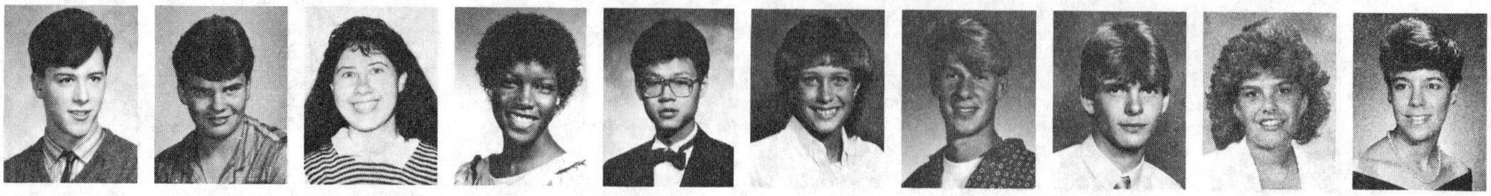

Twombly, Jonathan
D
Dwight Morrow HS
Englewood, NJ

Twomey, John
Lakewood HS
Lakewood, NJ

Tykotskaya, Ilona
Academic HS
Jersey City, NJ

Tyndall, Esther
Hillside HS
Hillside, NJ

Tzeng, Jausheng
Paramus HS
Paramus, NJ

Udvarhely, Denise
St John Vianney HS
Freehold, NJ

Ulasewich, Timothy
Toms River HS
Toms River, NJ

Ulashkevich, Paul
Saint John Vianney
Marlboro, NJ

Ulissi, Kim L
Pennsville Memorial
Pennsville, NJ

Ulloa, Jean Marie
Vernon Township
Sussex, NJ

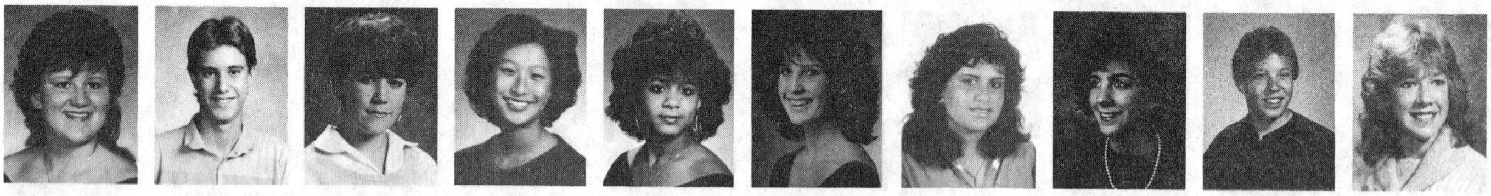

Umland, Dawn
Renee
Cliffside Park HS
Cliffside Pk, NJ

Umstead, Stephen
Burlington City HS
Burlington, NJ

Underwald, Suzanne
Summit HS
Summit, NJ

Ung, Alice
Whippany Park HS
Whippany, NJ

Ungar, Tracey
Lodi HS
Lodi, NJ

Unice, Bridget R
Watchung Hills
Regional HS
Warren, NJ

Uribe, Gladys
Memorial HS
West New York, NJ

Uricher, Amy
Kingsway Regional
Mickleton, NJ

Usatine, Warren
Lakewood HS
Lakewood, NJ

Utz, Annemarie
Ridge HS
Basking Ridge, NJ

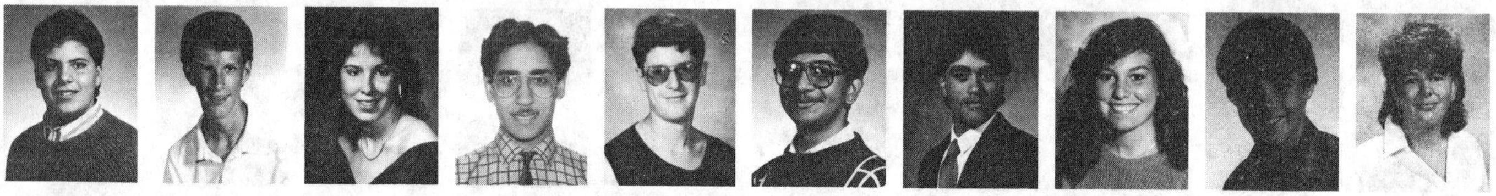

Vacca, Thomas
Lakeland Regional
Wanaque, NJ

Vacha, Jeffrey
Phillipsburg HS
Phillipsburg, NJ

Vaclavicek, Renee
Immaculate
Conception HS
Little Falls, NJ

Vadehra, Vivek
Hudson Catholic HS
Jersey City, NJ

Vaidman, Gregory
Arthur L Johnson
Regional HS
Clark, NJ

Vaidyanathan,
Rajeev
Kingsway Regional
Mantua, NJ

Valdes, Jorge
Tenafly HS
Tenafly, NJ

Valensi, Lisa
N Valley Reg HS
Harrington Pk, NJ

Valenta, Jay K
West Milford HS
West Milford, NJ

Valentini, Kimberly
Monsignor Donovan
Seaside Hts, NJ

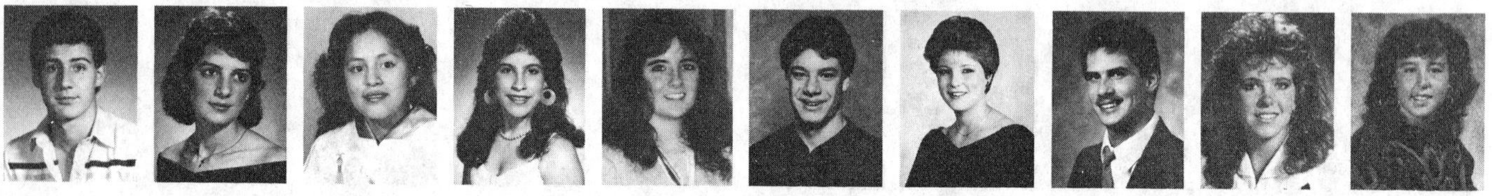

Valenza, Joseph
Lodi HS
Lodi, NJ

Vallancourt, Nancy
Immaculate Heart
Park Ridge, NJ

Valle, Roxana
Mary Help Of
Christians Acad
Paterson, NJ

Valle, Socorro
Dover HS
Dover, NJ

Vallier, Erin
John P Stevens HS
Edison, NJ

Van Dyk, Victor S
Saddle Brook HS
Saddle Brook, NJ

Van Horn, Denise
Delsea Regional HS
Franklinville, NJ

Van Kouteren, Mark
A
Roxbury Public HS
Flanders, NJ

Van Meir, Vickie
Secaucus HS
Secaucus, NJ

Van Nest, Megan
Manasquan HS
Manasquan, NJ

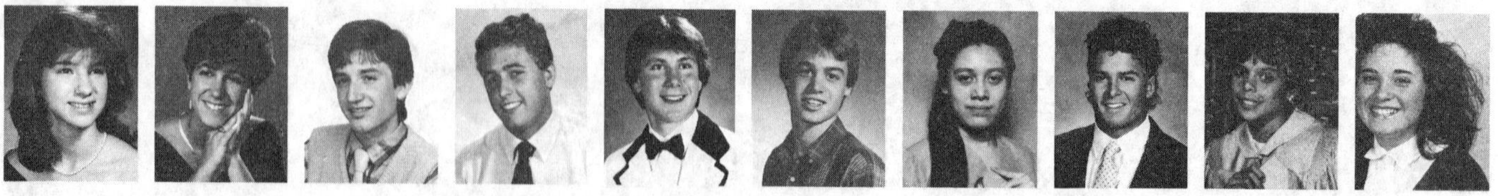

Van Orden, Amy
Northern Highlands
Regional HS
Allendale, NJ

Van Riper, Lisa
Newton HS
Andover, NJ

Van Sant, Bradley
Vineland North HS
Vineland, NJ

Van Sciver,
Chancellor
St Marys
Hall-Doane Acad
Beverly, NJ

Van Winkle, James
Hudson Catholic HS
Secaucus, NJ

Vander Meer, David
Toms River HS
Toms River, NJ

Vanegas, Veronica
Ferris HS
Jersey City, NJ

Varano, Michael
Westfield HS
Westfield, NJ

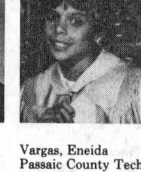

Vargas, Eneida
Passaic County Tech
& Voc HS
Paterson, NJ

Varisco, Eleanor
Notre Dame HS
Kendall Park, NJ

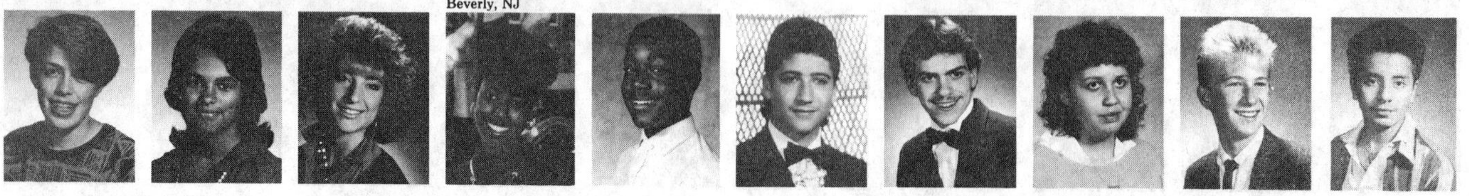

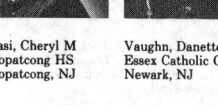

Varona, Lydia
North Arlington HS
N Arlington, NJ

Vasan, Sandhya
West
Windsor-Plainsbor
Princeton Junct, NJ

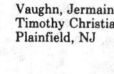

Vasi, Cheryl M
Hopatcong HS
Hopatcong, NJ

Vaughn, Danette
Essex Catholic Girls
Newark, NJ

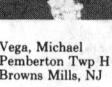

Vaughn, Jermaine
Timothy Christian
Plainfield, NJ

Vega, Michael
Pemberton Twp H S
Browns Mills, NJ

Velasco, Julian
Bishop George AHR
Perth Amboy, NJ

Velasquez, Dawn
St Mary HS
S Amboy, NJ

Velechko, Scott
Paul VI Regional
Clifton, NJ

Veliz, Javier
Clifford J Scott HS
E Orange, NJ

Veliz, Paulina
Morris Catholic HS
Dover, NJ

Venanzi, John Paul
Bordentown
Regional HS
Trenton, NJ

Vera, Marianela
Emerson HS
Union City, NJ

Vercelli, Thomas C
Ridgefield Park HS
Ridgefield, NJ

Verrone, Roseanne
Immaculate Heart
N Haledon, NJ

Viani, Craig
Christian Brothers
Middletown, NJ

Viau, Florence
Emerson HS
Union City, NJ

Viau, Mireille
Emerson HS
Union City, NJ

Vickers, Richard A
Pennsauken HS
Pennsauken, NJ

Vieira, Kristie
Arthur L Johnso
Reg HS
Clark, NJ

Vieira, Sonya
De Paul Diocesan
Pompton Lakes, NJ

Viereck, Michelle
Gloucester City JR
SR HS
Gloucester, NJ

Vilacha, Bobbi Jo
Union HS
Union, NJ

Villa, Ramon
Shore Regional HS
West Long Branc,
NJ

Villabon, Luis
Boonton HS
Wayne, NJ

Villani, Katrina
Toms River High
School South
Beachwood, NJ

Villasenor,
Bishop Eustace Prep
Seaford, DE

Vincent, Margaret
Camden Catholic
Camden, NJ

Vining, Patrick J T
St Peters Prep
Essex Fells, NJ

Visconti, George J
Arthur L Johnson
Regional HS
Clark, NJ

Viscuso, Marc
Livingston HS
Livingston, NJ

Vogel, Christopher
Manasquan HS
Brielle, NJ

Vogel, Jeffrey
Manasquan HS
Brielle, NJ

Vogel, Jr Robert A
Randolph HS
Randolph, NJ

Von Fabrice,
Brianne
Bridgewater-Raritan
East HS
Bridgewater, NJ

Von Glahn, John
Cresskill HS
Cresskill, NJ

Voorhees, Bill
Phillipsburg HS
Maroa, IL

Voorman, Marinus
Eastern Christian
Allendale, NJ

Vosinakis, Vasilios
Madison Central HS
Old Bridge, NJ

Voss, Heather
Hamilton HS East
Yardville, NJ

Vowell, Amy
Toms River South
Beachwood, NJ

Vreeland, Sherry
Brick Mem HS
Brick, NJ

Wagner, Anisia
Cheryl
Westwood HS
Westwood, NJ

Wagner, Wendy
The Hun School Of
Lawrenceville, NJ

Wahlgren, Patricia
Mainsquan HS
Manasquan, NJ

Wahner, Kristin
Cinnaminson HS
Cinnaminson, NJ

Wain, Katie
Newton HS
Newton, NJ

Wain, Tommy
Bridgewater-Raritan
East HS
Bridgewater, NJ

Walder, Kathleen
Riverside HS
Delanco, NJ

Walder, Traci E
Bordentown
Regional HS
Bordentown, NJ

Walker, Erika
John F Kennedy HS
Willingboro, NJ

Walker, Harvey
Marist HS
Bayonne, NJ

Walker, James
Northrn Burlngtn
County Regnl HS
Juliustown, NJ

Walker, Jenny
Secaucus HS
Secaucus, NJ

Walker, Kenneth
Essex Catholic Boys
East Orange, NJ

Walker, Robin
Passaic County Tech
Paterson, NJ

Walker, Russell J
Memorial HS
Cedar Grove, NJ

Walker, Shannon B
West Milford HS
West Milford, NJ

Walker, Tracy
Edison Vo Tech HS
Elizabeth, NJ

Walkes, Wendi
Cherry Hill HS
Cherry Hill, NJ

Wall, Mary Beth
Manchester
Regional HS
Prospect Park, NJ

Wallace, Clinton
Morristown HS
Morristown, NJ

Wallace, Marie B
Lower Cape May
Regional HS
North Cape May,
NJ

Wallaco, Walter
Bernard
Weequahic HS
Newark, NJ

Walsh, Andrew
Red Bank Regional
Little Silver, NJ

Walsh, Karen
St John Vianney HS
Manalapan, NJ

Walsh, Kerry
Morris Catholic HS
Denville, NJ

Walsh, Liz
Secaucus HS
Secaucus, NJ

Walter, Christopher
D
North Bergen HS
Guttenberg, NJ

Walter, Eric
Millville HS
Millville, NJ

Walter, Randy S
Princeton Day Schl
Belle Mead, NJ

Walters, Roberta
Manville HS
Manville, NJ

Waltman, Sheila
Paulsboro HS
Bridgeport, NJ

Wan, Genevieve
East Brunswick HS
E Brunswick, NJ

Wanamaker,
Patricia
Eastern Christian
North Haledon, NJ

Wanamaker, Sheri
Hoboken HS
Hoboken, NJ

Wang, Yi-Ren
Ocean Township HS
Oakhurst, NJ

Waples, Joy
Teaneck HS
Teaneck, NJ

Ward, Brewster
Kingsway Regional
Swedesboro, NJ

Wardell, Ed
Vernon Twp HS
Highland Lks, NJ

Warfle, Renee
Nikos Acad
Port Norris, NJ

Warnken, Chad
Christian Brothers
Pt Pleasant, NJ

Warr, Stacey M
Southern Regional
Manahawkin, NJ

Warrington, Melissa
Buena Regional HS
Newtonvlle, NJ

Wasko, William
Toms River H S
Toms River, NJ

Wassily, Mary Rose
G
John F Kennedy HS
Willingboro, NJ

Wastell, Charlotta
Bridgeton HS
Bridgeton, NJ

Waszak, Jeannine M
St John Vianney HS
Hazlet, NJ

Watkins, Bryan
Gerard
Christian Brothers
Howell, NJ

Watkins, Mark
Millville SR HS
Millville, NJ

Watkins, Willie
River Dell SR HS
River Edge, NJ

Watson, Matthew
Don Bosco Prep
Pearl River, NY

Watts, Joseph
Manchester
Regional HS
N Haledon, NJ

Weachock, Jackie
Linden HS
Linden, NJ

Weber, Carl D
New Milford HS
New Milford, NJ

Weber, Erika
West Essex HS
No Caldwell, NJ

Weber, Susan
New Milford HS
New Milford, NJ

Webster, Lawrence
Montville Township
Pine Brook, NJ

Weedon, Jr David E
Asbury Park HS
Asbury Park, NJ

Wegrzyn, Celeste
Roselle Park HS
Roselle Park, NJ

Weigand, Kevin
Queen Of Peace HS
Rutherford, NJ

Weigand, Sandra
Toms River H S
South Toms River,
NJ

Weiler, Molly
Bound Brook HS
Bound Brook, NJ

Weiner, Jill
Lakeland Reg HS
Wanaque, NJ

Weingartner, Laura
Notre Dame HS
Hightstown, NJ

Weinstein, Kiersten
Delaware Valley
Regional HS
Milford, NJ

Weischadle, David E
Mc Corristin HS
Trenton, NJ

Weischadle, Douglas
E
Mc Corristin HS
Trenton, NJ

Weiss, Heidi Lynn
Millville SR HS
Millville, NJ

Weissbein, Daniel A
Bridgewater-Raritan
HS East
Bridgewater, NJ

Weller, Jill
Villa Victoria Acad
Churchville, PA

Weller, Jr Ronald
St Pius X Regional
Piscataway, NJ

Wen, Kaiti
Sayreville War
Memorial HS
Parlin, NJ

Weremijenko,
Chrissy
Notre Dame HS
Trenton, NJ

Werth, Kathleen
Monsignor Donovan
Toms River, NJ

Wertz, Kevin
Baptist HS
Williamstown, NJ

West, Holly J
West Milford HS
West Milford, NJ

Wetmore, Allison
Marine Acad Of
Science & Tech
Leonard, NJ

Wetmore, James
Ridgewood HS
Ridgewood, NJ

Whaley, Jr James C
Camden HS
Camden, NJ

Whalley, Diana
Lynn
Watchung Hills
Regional HS
Gillette, NJ

Wheaton, Cheryl
Bridgeton HS
Cedarville, NJ

Whisten, Scott
Secaucus HS
Secaucus, NJ

Whitacre, Kim
Notre Dame HS
Lawrenceville, NJ

Whitaker, Katrina
Shirese
Franklin HS
Somerset, NJ

Whitaker, Lossie
Arts HS
Newark, NJ

White, Elaine
Franklin HS
Somerset, NJ

White, Janine
Henry Hudson
Regional HS
Highlands, NJ

White, La Nissir
Hillside HS
Hillside, NJ

White, Lori Ann
Paulsboro HS
Paulsboro, NJ

White, Michael
Essex Catholic Boys
Orange, NJ

White, Paul
Hunterdon Central
Sergeantsville, NJ

White, Suzanne L
Academy Of The
Holy Angels
Oradell, NJ

Whitefleet, Kevin
Bergen Tech
Elmwood Park, NJ

Whiting, Terri
Clayton HS
Clayton, NJ

Whitley, Dionne
Abraham Clark HS
Roselle, NJ

Whitney, Alexander
D
Jackson Memorial
Jackson, NJ

Whitsitt, Deanna
Union Catholic
Regional HS
Scotch Plains, NJ

Whorley, April
West Morris
Mendham HS
Chester, NJ

Wiener, Andrew
Craig
Ocean Township HS
Wayside, NJ

PHOTO
NOT
AVAILABLE

Wilbert, Charity
North West
Christian HS
Newton, NJ

Wilgus, Jim
Biernarus HS
Gladstone, NJ

Wilhelm, Scott
Phillipsburg HS
Phillipsburg, NJ

Wilhelms, Mark
Toms River HS
Pine Bch, NJ

Wilkey, Heather
Marie
St Marys HS
Rutherford, NJ

Willbus, Michelle
Plainfield HS
Plainfield, NJ

Williams, Amy
Newton HS
Newton, NJ

Williams, Beverly
Matawan Regional
Cliffwood, NJ

Williams, Dale L
Montclair HS
Montclair, NJ

Williams, Deborah E
Middle Township
Ocean View, NJ

Williams, Dennis P
Mc Corristin HS
Hamilton Square, NJ

Williams, Jo Anne
Piscataway HS
Piscataway, NJ

Williams, Joe
Vineland HS
Newfield, NJ

Williams, Kevin
West Windsor
Plainsboro HS
Princeton Junct, NJ

Williams, Kimberly
Jackson Memorial
Jackson, NJ

Williams, Lori
Suxxex County Voc
Tech HS
Franklin, NJ

Williams, Nakesha
Woodrow Wilson HS
Camden, NJ

Williams, Ronald
Bloomfield HS
Bloomfield, NJ

Williams, Tara
Our Lady Of Good
Counsel HS
Newark, NJ

Williams, Veronica
Immaculate
Conception HS
Englewood, NJ

Williamson, Patricia D
Franklin HS
Somerset, NJ

Wilson, Dennis
Absegami HS
Absecon, NJ

Wilson, Janet
Edgewood Regional
SR HS
Atco, NJ

Wilson, II John C
Pemberton HS II
Browns Mills, NJ

Wilson, Maureen P
Haddontownship HS
Oaklyn, NJ

Wilson, Natalie
Middletown South
Lincroft, NJ

Wilson, Pamela
Eastern HS
Berlin, NJ

Wilson, Robert
Essex Catholic Boys
Irvington, NJ

Wingert, Christopher
De Paul HS
W Milford, NJ

Winicky, Eric
North Hunterdon
Hampton, NJ

Winterbottom, Heather
Absegami HS
Egg Harbor City, NJ

Wisbeski, Henry C
Bound Brook HS
South Bound Brook, NJ

Wise, Lily
Princeton Day Schl
Belle Mead, NJ

Wlazlowski, Judith
Notre Dame HS
Englishtown, NJ

Wojcik, Craig
Bordentown
Regional HS
Fieldsboro, NJ

Wolert, Judith
Madison Central HS
Old Bridge, NJ

Wolfersberger, III Joseph
Pt Pleasant Beach
Pt Pleasant Bch, NJ

Wondrack, Jennifer
Paramus Catholic
Girls Rgnl HS
Teaneck, NJ

Wong, Christine P
Cherokee HS
Mariton, NJ

Wood, Scott
Deptford HS
Deptford, NJ

Wood, Stacie
Florence Township
Memorial HS
Burlington, NJ

Woodruff, Edward
Pinelands Regional
Tuckertown, NJ

Woods, Nancy
Bridgewater-Raritan
West HS
Bridgewater, NJ

Woody, Elizabeth
Notre Dame HS
Lawrenceville, NJ

Woody, Mary
Notre Dame HS
Lawrenceville, NJ

Woolfolk, Staci
Mary Help Of
Christians Acad
Paterson, NJ

Woroch, Chrystia
Mount Saint
Dominic Acad
West Orange, NJ

Wottawa, Larraine
Mt St Dominic Acad
Roseland, NJ

Wozney, Aaron
Waldwick HS
Waldwick, NJ

Wright, Davarn
Eastside HS
Paterson, NJ

Wright, Julie
Kingsway Reg HS
Swedesboro, NJ

Wright, Lori Ann
Allentown HS
Allentown, NJ

Wright, Theodore S
Albury Park HS
Asbury Park, NJ

Wright, Theresa
Millville SR HS
Millville, NJ

Wright, Theresa A
Perth Amboy HS
Perth Amboy, NJ

Wrobel, Danielle
Ewing HS
Trenton, NJ

Wrobel, Tricia
Mt St Dominic Acad
West Orange, NJ

Wroblewski, Patrick
Summit HS
Summit, NJ

Wurst, Karen M
Toms Rivers HS
Toms River, NJ

Wylie, Latrell
Mt St Dominic Acad
Irvington, NJ

Wysocki, Carolyn
Edgewood Regional
SR HS
Sicklerville, NJ

Xanthacos, Athena
Lakewood HS
Lakewood, NJ

Yakow, Kelly
Vineland HS
Vineland, NJ

Yalong, Frances
Bayonne HS
New Brunswick, NJ

Yanik, Lee M
West Milford HS
Hewitt, NJ

Yao, Joyce
Morris Knolls HS
Denville, NJ

Yarborough, Daniel
Plainfield HS
Plainfield, NJ

Yasunas, Frank J
Hunterdon Central
Sergeantsville, NJ

Yates, Timothy
Sparta HS
Sparta, NJ

Yavor, Theresa
Sayreville War
Memorial HS
S Amboy, NJ

Yearicks, Valerie
Lower Cape May
Regional HS
Green Creek, NJ

Yeh, Mimi
Ridgewood HS
Ridgewood, NJ

Yerovi, Katherine
North Arlington HS
N Arlington, NJ

Ynaya, Donna
Toms River H S
Toms River, NJ

Yoelson, Mara
Marlboro HS
Morganville, NJ

Yoka, John
Kearny HS
Kearny, NJ

Yonker, II Donald
Woodstown HS
Pedricktown, NJ

Yoon, Anna
Cumberland
Regional HS
Bridgeton, NJ

Young, Caroline
The Dwight
Englewood Schl
Alpine, NJ

Young, Chris
Madison HS
New Vernon, NJ

Young, Gang
Elizabeth HS
Elizabeth, NJ

Young, Kelli
Randolph HS
Randolph, NJ

Young, Kisha
Marylawn Of The Oranges HS
Newark, NJ

Younglove, Catherine
Holy Cross HS
Willingboro, NJ

Younus, Zainab N
Washington Township HS
Sewell, NJ

Youssef, Susan
Franklin HS
Somerset, NJ

Ytkin, Andrea
Notre Dame HS
Trenton, NJ

Yuhas, Jennifer A
Wayne Valley HS
Wayne, NJ

Yun, Kyongsop
Cherry Hill West
Cherry Hill, NJ

Zagra, Christine
Phillipsburg HS
Phillipsburg, NJ

Zain, Michael
Don Bosco Tech HS
Paterson, NJ

Zakhary, Randa
Ocean Township HS
Ocean, NJ

Zakrzewski, Wendy
Sayreville War Memorial HS
S Amboy, NJ

Zaleski, Erika
Union HS
Union, NJ

Zamkotowicz, Christine
Hillsborough Twp
Somerville, NJ

Zanes, Susan
Egg Harbor Township HS
Scullville, NJ

Zangari, Antonia
Belleville HS
Belleville, NJ

Zapico, Anthony
Kearny HS
Kearny, NJ

Zappala, David
St James HS
Woodstown, NJ

Zarbatany, Matthew
Phillipsburg HS
Phillipsburg, NJ

Zaretski, Patrick
Dwight-Englewood
Haledon, NJ

Zasadzinski, Regina
Whippany Park HS
Whippamy, NJ

Zavada, Karin
Pequannock Township HS
Pequannock, NJ

Zavada, Michele
West Milford Township HS
West Milford, NJ

Zdanowicz, Richard
St Joseph Regional
Dumont, NJ

Zdorovyak, Igor
Passaic HS
Passaic, NJ

Zeigler, Penny
Cumberland Christian HS
Williamstown, NJ

Zemaitaitis, Diane
Woodstown HS
Elmer, NJ

Zettler, Daniel
Paramus HS
Paramus, NJ

Ziegler, Eric
Gloucester County Christian Schl
Sicklerville, NJ

Ziegler, William
Friends Schl
Turnersville, NJ

Zielinski, Doreen
Woodbridge HS
Woodbridge, NJ

Zilai, Mark
St Rose HS
Brielle, NJ

Zilles, Michelle
Emerson JR SR HS
Emerson, NJ

Zimarowski, Paul
John F Kennedy HS
Willingboro, NJ

Zimmerman, Brian M
Middletown South
Middletown, NJ

Zimmerman, Sarah
Kent Place HS
Warren, NJ

Zimmermann, Craig
Morris HS
Hackettstown, NJ

Zito, Lisa Ann
Cranford HS
Cranford, NJ

Zizwarek, Michelle
Jackson Memorial
Jackson, NJ

Zorowitz, Stacey
Hightstown HS
East Windsor, NJ

Zozzaro, John
Fair Lawn HS
Toms River, NJ

Zsorey, Michael D
Sayreville War Memorial HS
Parlin, NJ

Zuidema, David
Eastern Christian
N Haledon, NJ

Zuniga, Alexander
A L Johnson Reg
Clark, NJ

Zupko, Roger
Perth Amboy HS
Perth Amboy, NJ

PENNSYLVANIA

Abrams, Judy
Northern Cambria
Spangler, PA

Abuk, Roy
Valley Forge Military Acad
Kinnelon, NJ

Achenne, Nicole
Burrell HS
Lower Burrell, PA

Ackard, Diann M
State College Area SR HS
State College, PA

Acker, Brett
Council Rock HS
Churchville, PA

Acker, Kelli
Central Cambria HS
Ebensburg, PA

Ackerman, Cheryl
S Williamsport Area SR HS
S Williamsport, PA

Ackerman, Christine
Abington Heights
Clarks Summit, PA

Ackerman, Peter
Danville Area HS
Danville, PA

Ackerman, R Christian
Danville Area HS
Danville, PA

Acklin, II Timothy Patrick
Central Catholic HS
Pittsburgh, PA

Adair, John
Valley Forge Military Acad
Baltimore, MD

Adam, Jamie
Hamburg Area HS
Hamburg, PA

Adamchik, Tracy
Hempfield SR HS
Greensburg, PA

Adametz, Karen Jean
Richland HS
Wexford, PA

Adams, Ashley
Fairview HS
Fairview, PA

Adams, Bradford
Altoona Area HS
Altoona, PA

Adams, Brian
Connellsville SR HS
Connellsville, PA

Adams, Dan
Trinity Area HS
Washington, PA

Adams, Holly
Central SR HS
York, PA

Adams, Marsha
Northwestern SR
Albion, PA

Adams, Monica
Northwestern HS
Albion, PA

Adams, Stacy
Elizabeth Forward SR HS
Elizabeth, PA

Adomaitis, Michelle
Cedar Crest HS
Lebanon, PA

Adzentoivich, Ernest J
Mahanoy Area HS
New Boston, PA

Affleck, John R
North Allegheny SR
Bradford Woods, PA

Agamedi, Mary Kathryn
Belle Vernon Area
Smithton, PA

Agle, Grant
Upland Country Day Schl
West Chester, PA

Ahearn, Matthew
Daniel Bonne Area
Birdsboro, PA

Ahola, Kristen
Coatesville Area HS
Thorndale, PA

Aicher, Jed
Wilson Area HS
Easton, PA

Aiello, James
West Hazleton HS
W Hazleton, PA

Aiello, Ronald C
Monessen JR SR
Monessen, PA

Ainsley, Marcia
Connellsville SR HS
Normalville, PA

Aker, Heather
Harry S Truman HS
Bristol, PA

Alan, Wagner
Blairsville SR HS
Blairsville, PA

Alba, Michael
Father Judge HS
Philadelphia, PA

Alba, Jr Robert
Reading HS
Reading, PA

Albano, Marybeth
Kennard Dale HS
Felton, PA

Albert, Bridget
Johnstown HS
Johnstown, PA

Albert, Jan
E Stroudsburg HS
Marshalls Creek, PA

Alberta, Robert
Valley HS
New Kensington, PA

Albrecht, Lori
James M Coughlin
Wilkes-Barre, PA

Albright, Ingrid
West Perry SR HS
Landisburg, PA

Albright, Lisa
Connellsville SR HS
White, PA

Albright, Shane R
Cumberland Valley
Mechanicsburg, PA

Albright, Theresa
Mechanicsburg Area SR HS
Mechanicsburg, PA

Alcaraz, Lori
Shenandoah Valley
Shenandoah, PA

Aldinger, Drew
W B Saul HS
Philadelphia, PA

Aldous, Jr Thomas
Hershey HS
Palmyra, PA

Aldrich, Kimberly
Monessen SR HS
Monessen, PA

Alexander, Dawn
Halifax Area HS
Halifax, PA

Alexander, Jennifer
Tunkhannock Area
Tunkhannock, PA

Alexander, Pete
West Branch HS
Karthaus, PA

Alexander, S Shane
Butler Area SR HS
Butler, PA

Alexander, Timothy
Cumberland Valley
Carlisle, PA

Alfera, Rachelle
Kennedy Christian
Sharpsville, PA

Alfery, Peter
Greensburg Central Catholic HS
Youngwood, PA

Alindogan, Daffodel
Blue Mountain Acad
Philadelphia, PA

Allebach, Kathy
Souderton Area HS
Souderton, PA

Allen, Daren T
Seneca HS
Union City, PA

Allen, Molly
Boiling Springs HS
Carlisle, PA

Allen, Yvette
Pennridge HS
Telford, PA

Allesch, Cynthia
Panther Valley HS
Coaldale, PA

Allis, Jr Andrew P B
York Suburban HS
York, PA

Allison, Andrea
Chambersburg Area SR HS
Chambersburg, PA

Allison, Caryn
Central Dauphin HS
Harrisburg, PA

Allison, Jeannine
Lansdale Catholic
Lansdale, PA

Allison, Mike
Mt Pleasant Area
Mt Pleasant, PA

Allott, George T
Chartiers Valley HS
Carnegie, PA

Alspach, Alex D
Wilmington Area
New Wilmington, PA

Alston, Tracey
Bishop Mc Davitt
Philadelphia, PA

Altemare, Jr Clifford D
Mon Valley Catholic
Monongahela, PA

Altemose, Rodney
Nazareth SR HS
Nazareth, PA

Altier, Marci
Greensburg Salem SR HS
Greensburg, PA

Altieri, Kimberly
Canon Mc Millan SR HS
Cecil, PA

Altland, Sally
Susquehannock HS
Glen Rock, PA

Altman, David
Shenango HS
New Castle, PA

Altman, Matthew T
Cowanesque Valley
Westfield, PA

Alton, James
Harrisburg HS
Harrisburg, PA

Alu, Nicole
Wyoming Area SR
Exeter, PA

Alvarez, Laurie
Mon Valley Catholic
Donora, PA

Amati, Lee
Ringgold HS
Monongahela, PA

Amato, Dennis M
Archbishop Ryan H S For Boys
Philadelphia, PA

Amick, Wade
Elizabethtown Area
Elizabethtown, PA

Ammon, Wendy
Pequea Valley HS
Gap, PA

Amoroso, Karla
Mon Valley Catholic
Monongahela, PA

Amow, Mike
Pleasant Valley HS
Saylorsburg, PA

Amrhein, Jennifer
Bishop Conwell HS
Levittown, PA

Ananea, Norhala
Villa Maria Acad
Erie, PA

Anchors, Janet
Mt Lebanon SR HS
Pittsburgh, PA

Anderson, Beth
Dover Area HS
Dover, PA

Anderson, Dawn
Central Dauphin East HS
Harrisburg, PA

Anderson, Heather
Lakeview HS
Mercer, PA

Anderson, Holly
St Paul Cathedral
Pittsburgh, PA

Anderson, Janet
Mercer Area HS
Sharpsville, PA

Anderson, Julie
Columbia Montour
Area Vo Tech
Bloomsburg, PA

Anderson, Kelly
Kristin
Nazareth Acad
Holland, PA

Anderson, Kristen
Warren Area HS
Warren, PA

Anderson, Lenni
California Area SR
California, PA

Anderson, Lisa M
Gwynedd Mercy
Ft Washington, PA

Anderson, Melinda
L
Crestwood HS
Mountaintop, PA

Anderson, Nicole
Lynn
Palmyra Area SR
Palmyra, PA

Anderson, Renee
Ringgold HS
Donora, PA

Anderson, Rhonda
Northwestern HS
Girard, PA

Anderson, Stacy
Connellsville SR HS
Connellsville, PA

Anderson, Tiffany
Connellsville Area
Connellsville, PA

Anderson, Todd
Michael
Milton Area SR HS
Milton, PA

Anderson, Vicki
Western Beaver HS
Midland, PA

Andersson, J Kris
North Allegheny HS
Wexford, PA

Andes, Jennifer
Donville SR HS
Danville, PA

Andrews, Jr John F
St Pius X HS
Phoenixville, PA

Andrews, Karen
Jim Thorpe SR HS
Jim Thorpe, PA

Andrews, Melissa
South Allegheny
JR-SR HS
Glassport, PA

Andrews, Michelle
Fleetwood Area HS
Fleetwood, PA

Andrezze, Marina
Berwick Area SR
Berwick, PA

Angelelli, Joseph J
Bethel Park SR HS
Bethel Park, PA

Angello, Jr Michael
J
Ford City HS
Ford City, PA

Angello, Toni M
Northampton SR
Northampton, PA

Angelo, Kimberly
Bishop Hafey HS
Hazleton, PA

Angelo, Philip
Downingtown SR
Downingtown, PA

Ansari, Bushra
Lincoln HS
Zelienople, PA

Ansell, Patti
Connellsville SR HS
Vanderbilt, PA

Anspach, Scott
Nothern Lebanon
JR SR HS
Palmyra, PA

Anthony, Garnett
Germantown HS
Philadelphia, PA

Anthony, Ray
Northampton SR
Northampton, PA

Anthony, Jr William
H
Altoona Area HS
Altoona, PA

Anton, Yvonne
Ringgold HS
Donora, PA

Antonini, Michelle
Hopewell HS
Aliquippa, PA

Antoun, Vanessa
Chambersburg Area
SR HS
Chambersburg, PA

Anzur, Suzanne
Yough HS
Herminie, PA

Apicella,
Anne-Marie
W Philadelphia
Catholic Girls HS
Philadelphia, PA

Archer, Brett
Mc Guffey HS
Claysville, PA

Archer, Denelle T
Living Word Acad
Lancaster, PA

Archer, Michael
Moshannon Valley
Houtzdale, PA

Archer, Oliver B J
Blue Mountain Acad
Brooklyn, NY

Archie, Keita
Springside Schl
Philadelphia, PA

Ardito, Alec
Burrell HS
Lower Burrell, PA

Ardizzi, Joseph
Cardinal O Hara HS
Havertown, PA

Ardrey, Jacqueline
Bensalem HS
Bensalem, PA

Arena, Cary A
Pittston Area HS
Pittston, PA

Armagost, Stacy
Clarion-Limestone
Corsica, PA

Armbrust, Michelle
Penn Trafford HS
Irwin, PA

Arminas, Lara
Geibel HS
Uniontown, PA

Armitage, Vicki
Wyalusing Valley
Wyalusing, PA

Armon, Lori Ellen
Bensalem HS
Bensalem, PA

Armour, Timothy
Trinity HS
Washington, PA

Armstrong, Judith
Lower Dauphin HS
Hershey, PA

Armstrong, Ricky
Pocono Mt SR HS
Stroudsburg, PA

Arnold, Bruce C
Central Bucks HS
Buckingham, PA

Arnold, Dawn
Tunkhannock Area
Tunkhannock, PA

Arnold, Kevin
Salisbury HS
Allentown, PA

Arnold, Laurie Lynn
Lower Merion HS
Narberth, PA

Arnold, Steve
Meadville Area SR
Meadville, PA

Arost, Sylvia
Council Rock HS
Richboro, PA

Arrowsmith, Helen
Solanco HS
Peach Bottom, PA

Arthur, Amy
Kennard-Dale HS
Fawn Grove, PA

Artigiani, Tabetha
Lancaster Catholic
Lancaster, PA

Artz, Sandra
Tri-Valley HS
Spring Glen, PA

Asbury, Anson
Warren Area HS
Pittsfield, PA

Asche, Jim
Butler Intermediate
Butler, PA

Ashari, Aslinda
Schenley HS
Pittsburgh, PA

Ashburn, Doyle
Carlisle SR HS
Carlisle, PA

Ashcraft, Jr Terry
Charleroi Area JR/
SR HS
Charleroi, PA

Ashton, Kirk
Meadville SR HS
Meadville, PA

Asiello, Douglas
Carlisle SR HS
APO, NY

Askey, Melissa
Mechanicsburg SR
Mechanicsburg, PA

Atcheson, Deborah
Bethlehem Ctr
Fredericktown, PA

Atchison, Jennifer
Plum SR HS
Pittsburgh, PA

Athanasion,
Constance
St Francis Acad
Bethelehem, PA

Atiyeh, Shannon
William Allen HS
Allentown, PA

Atkinson, Sonya
Center HS
Aliquippa, PA

Atticks, Bill
Central Dauphin HS
Harrisburg, PA

Atwater, Jason D
Reading SR HS
Reading, PA

Augustine, Rita M
Mount Saint Joseph
Huntingdon Val, PA

Augustine, Shauna
Greenville SR HS
Greenville, PA

Aukburg, Brett
Lower Marion HS
Cynwyd, PA

Ault, Patricia
Trinity HS
Washington, PA

Auman, Alan
Conrad Welser HS
Womelsdorf, PA

Aunkst, Karen
Montgomery Area
JR SR HS
Montgomery, PA

Austin, Patti
Wyoming Valley
West HS
Kingston, PA

Austin, Ronald
Western Beaver JR
SR HS
Industry, PA

Austra, Tammy
Wyoming Valley
West HS
Larksville, PA

Averbukh, Irina
High School Of
Engineering
Philladelphia, PA

Averett, Tanya
Oxford Area HS
Lincoln Univers, PA

Avey, Lori
Waynesboro SR HS
Waynesboro, PA

Axe, Brian
Ridley SR HS
Secane, PA

Ayers, Denise
Lancaster Christian
Lancaster, PA

Ayers, Mary
Oswayo Valley JR
SR HS
Shinglehouse, PA

Ayers, Michele
Franklin Learning
Philadelphia, PA

Aylesowrth, Scott
Lackawanna Trail
Nicholson, PA

Azar, Rodman
Tunkhannock Area
Tunkhannock, PA

Babb, Angela
Fannett-Metal HS
Willow Hill, PA

Babic, Nicholas
Council Rock HS
Newtown, PA

Babinsack, Stefanie
Highlands SR HS
Natrona, PA

Babst, Michael
Stephen
Archbishop Wood
HS For Boys
Holland, PA

Bachstein, Shanin
Lehigh Christian
Stewartsville, NJ

Bacon, Joel
Conrad Weiser HS
Robesonia, PA

Bacon, Kimberly
Farrell HS
Farrell, PA

Baden, Candice
W Scranton SR HS
Scranton, PA

Badinger, Jill Marie
Schuylkill Valley HS
Reading, PA

Baer, Cindy Lee
Mechanicsburg SR
Mechanicsburg, PA

Bagay, Lisa
Ringgold HS
Monongahela, PA

Bailey, Amanda
Meadville Area SR
Meadville, PA

Bailey, Gregory M
Meadville Area SR
Meadville, PA

Bailey, Jodi
Peters Township HS
Venetia, PA

Bailey, Michelle
South Side Area HS
Georgetown, PA

Bailey, Sharon A
Tyrone Area HS
Tyrone, PA

Bailey, Wendy
West Scranton HS
Scranton, PA

Baine, Kristin
Archbishop Carroll
Audubon, PA

Bair, Brian
West Mifflin Area
W Mifflin, PA

Bair, Laurie
Northeastern SR HS
Manchester, PA

Baker, Gena
Peters Township HS
Mcmurray, PA

Baker, Jeffrey S
Mifflinburg Area HS
Lewisburg, PA

Baker, Lisa
Tussey Mountain
Saxton, PA

Baker, Lorna
Nazareth Area SR
Nazareth, PA

Baker, Natalie
Monogahela Valley
Catholic HS
Charleroi, PA

Baker, Paul
Butler SR HS
Butler, PA

Baker, Regina
Cambria Heights SR
Carrolltown, PA

Baker, Susanne
Huntingdon Area
Allensville, PA

Balas, Wendy A
Central Bucks East
Buckingham, PA

Balbach, Angie
Hampton HS
Wildwood, PA

Balcerek, Kimberly
Southmoreland SR
Mt Pleasant, PA

Balcita, Judith
Joyce Guevara
Burrell HS
Lower Burrell, PA

Baldauf, E Michael
Ringgold HS
Finleyville, PA

Baldonieri, Ken
Gr Latrobe SR HS
Latrobe, PA

Baldwin, James
Linesville HS
Linesville, PA

Balenovich, Renea
Yough SR HS
W Newton, PA

Ballarino, Alissa
Council Rock HS
Richboro, PA

Balliet, Antoinette
Northampton Area
SR HS
Walnutport, PA

Balliet, Jamie
Palmerton Area HS
Palmerton, PA

Balmer, Kim
Ephrata HS
Stevens, PA

Balog, James
Conemaugh Valley
Johnstown, PA

Balouris, Maria
Northgate JR SR
Pittsburgh, PA

Balsam, Ilyse
Bensalem HS
Bensalem, PA

Balter, Kim
Saint Benedict Acad
Erie, PA

Baltosser, Michael
Susquenita HS
Marysville, PA

Bamberger, Todd
West York Area HS
York, PA

Bamford, Susan
Ringgold HS
Donora, PA

Bamford, Tracey
Shamokin Area HS
Shamokin, PA

Bandholz, Bill
Nativity B V M HS
Orwigsburg, PA

Banes, Brenda
Central Bucks West
Doylestown, PA

Baney, Renee
Juniata HS
Pt Royal, PA

Baney, Todd
Bellwood-Antis HS
Tyrone, PA

Banicky, Lisa
Middletown Area
Middletown, PA

Barach, Jenny
Gettysburg HS
New Oxford, PA

Barackman, Christopher
Greater Latrobe HS
Latrobe, PA

Barakat, Labiba
L E Dieruff HS
Allentown, PA

Barber, Jean
Lake Lehman SR
Hunlock Creek, PA

Barber, Kathy
Mifflinburg Area HS
Mifflinburg, PA

Barbin, Tracey
Canon Mc Millan
Cecil, PA

Barclay, Janice E
Creative & Performing Arts HS
Philadelphia, PA

Barclay, Robert
Moniteau HS
Parker, PA

Bardash, Linda
Shenango Area HS
New Castle, PA

Barger, Patricia
Karns City HS
Fenelton, PA

Barker, Carl
Coatesville HS
Coatesville, PA

Barker, Thomas
Solanco HS
Kirkwood, PA

Barkman, Christie
Everett Area HS
Everett, PA

Barkovic, Lea
Center HS
Aliquippa, PA

Barkovic, Lori
Center Area HS
Aliquippa, PA

Barkus, Joseph
Hazleton HS
Hazleton, PA

Barlow, Danielle
Northern Lehigh HS
Slatington, PA

Barndt, Tracy
Windber Area HS
Windber, PA

Barner, Jody
Sheffield Area JR-SR HS
Sheffield, PA

Barnes, Jr Paul Z
Carlisle SR HS
Burke, VA

Barnett, Jr John
Spring-Ford HS
Schwenksville, PA

Barnett, Judy
Reading SR HS
Reading, PA

Barnhart, Beth
Chapel Christian HS
New Stanton, PA

Baroni, Michael
Homer Ctr HS
Indiana, PA

Barr, Michael
Central SR HS
York, PA

Barr, Michael
Hopewell Area HS
Aliquippa, PA

Barrett, Matthew
Ringgold HS
Finleyville, PA

Barrett, Raymond
West Catholic Boys
Philadelphia, PA

Barron, Amy
Mon Valley Catholic
Belle Vernon, PA

Barron, Jerome
Moh Valley Catholic
Belle Vernon, PA

Barron, Lisa
Somerset Area HS
Somerset, PA

Barry, Gayle
Northgate JR/SR
Pittsburgh, PA

Barry, Michael
Lehighton Area HS
Lehighton, PA

Bartelmo, Debbie
Bishop Shanahan
West Chester, PA

Barthlow, Thomas E
Northern Lehigh HS
Neffs, PA

Bartlett, Jason E
Cumberland Valley
Boiling Springs, PA

Bartley, Paul E
Wyoming Seminary
Tunkhannock, PA

Bartolacci, Paulette
Notre Dame HS
Easton, PA

Bartoletti, Amy
James M Coughlin
Wilkes Barre, PA

Bartow, Susan Marie
Boyertown Area SR
Boyertown, PA

Barwick, Mary
Norte Dame HS
Stroudsburg, PA

Basinger, Dawn
Jefferson-Morgan
Waynesburg, PA

Bass, Michael
Penn-Trafford HS
Levelgreen, PA

Basso, Christine
Wm Allen HS
Allentown, PA

Basso, Rebecca
Pen Argyl Area HS
Nazareth, PA

Basso, Steven
Carlisle SR HS
Harker Heights, TX

Basta, Angela
Pittston Area HS
Pittston, PA

Bateman, Mike
Chichester HS
Boothwyn, PA

Batovich, Tamara
Bishop Mc Cort HS
Johnstown, PA

Batross, Jonathan
Riverview HS
Oakmont, PA

Batte, Erica
Churchill HS
Braddock, PA

Bauer, Amy
Seneca Valley SR
Mars, PA

Bauer, Kelly
St Marys Area HS
St Marys, PA

Bauersfeld, Jennifer
The Ellis Schl
Pittsburgh, PA

Baum, Katrina
Eastern York HS
York, PA

Baum, Sherry
Cumberland Valley
Camp Hill, PA

Bauman, Andrea
Pittston Area HS
Duryea, PA

Bauman, Bevin
Hampton HS
Allison Park, PA

Bautz, Amy
Monongahela Valley
Catholic HS
New Eagle, PA

Baxter, Daniel V
Valley Forge
Military Acad
Gretna, LA

Baxter, John
Brockway Area HS
Brockport, PA

Baxter, Michelle
Warren Area HS
Warren, PA

Bayles, Autumn
Bethlehem Catholic
Nazareth, PA

Be Hanna,
Christopher G
Norwin SR HS
N Huntingdon, PA

Beach, Jeffrey
Oil City SR HS
Oil City, PA

Beaghan, Robert
Kennard-Dale HS
Stewartstown, PA

Beale, Jacqueline
Freeport Area SR
Freeport, PA

Bear, Shonda
Parkland SR HS
Allentown, PA

Beasley, Candice
Westinghouse HS
Pittsburgh, PA

Beasley, Mona
William Penn SR
York, PA

Beaston, Robin
Fannett-Metal HS
Concord, PA

Beatty, Tara J
Norristown Area HS
Norristown, PA

Beauchamp, Jon
Paul
St Pius X HS
Gilbertsville, PA

Beauford, Angel
Big Beaver Falls
Area HS
Beaver Falls, PA

Beaumont, Gregg
West Allegheny SR
Oakdale, PA

Beaver, Daniel
Bermudian Springs
E Berlin, PA

Beaver, Karen
Elisabeth
East Pennsboro HS
Enola, PA

Beaver, Lee Ann
Marie
Meadowbrook
Christian HS
Milton, PA

Beaverson, Brenda
Spring Grove SR HS
Thomas Ville, PA

Beblo, Dan
Butler Entermediate
Butler, PA

Beccari, Beth
West Phila Catholic
Girls HS
Philadelphia, PA

Beck, Karyn
Penncrest HS
Chester, PA

Beck, Katherine
Palmerton Area HS
Bowmanstown, PA

Beck, Lance
Monessen SR HS
Monessen, PA

Beck, Laura
Belle Vernon Area
Belle Vernon, PA

Beck, Michelle
York County
York, PA

Beck, Nichole
Moshannon Valley
Houtzdale, PA

Beck, Robert
Nazareth Area SR
Wind Gap, PA

Becker, Brent
Lampeter Strasburg
Strasburg, PA

Becker, Joshua B
Harriton HS
Villanova, PA

Beckinger, Craig
Ringgold HS
Monongahela, PA

Beckman, Jodi
South Williamsport
SR HS
S Williamsport, PA

Beckman, Ronald
Bishop Neumann
Williamsport, PA

Beckwith, Amy
Corry Area HS
Corry, PA

Beckwith, Kimberly
Freeport SR HS
Sarver, PA

Bedford, Richard
Du Bois Area HS
Reynoldsville, PA

Bednar, Chris
Marian HS
Tamaqua, PA

Bednarczyk, John
Carbondale Area HS
Simpson, PA

Bednarovsky, Craig
E
Mc Keesport SR HS
White Oak, PA

Bedner, Kimberly
Mohessen JR SR
Monessen, PA

Bedwick, Jennifer
E L Meyers HS
Wilkes-Barre, PA

Bee, Matthew
Greenville HS
Greenville, PA

Beedle, Ari
Meadville SR HS
Meadville, PA

Beegle, Jodie
Northern Bedford
County HS
New Enterprise, PA

Beers, Dawn
Clarion Area HS
Clarion, PA

Beers, Trevor
Du Bois Area HS
Reynoldsvl, PA

Beery, Rhonda
Bellwood-Antis HS
Tyrone, PA

Begley, Carol
St Huberts Catholic
Philadelphia, PA

Beglin, Robert
Jefferson Morgan
JR-SR HS
Clarksville, PA

Behling, Karen
Ringgold HS
Monongahela, PA

Behrens, Dayna
Bishop Guilfoyle HS
Altoona, PA

Behun, Bill
Council Rock HS
Washington Crssng,
PA

Beigi, Richard
Fox Chapel SR HS
Pittsburgh, PA

Beil, Cynthia M
Saucon Valley SR
Hellertown, PA

Beiler, Joel
Pequea Valley HS
New Holland, PA

Belak, Brett
Norwin HS
N Huntingdon, PA

Bell, Ashley
Hempfield HS
Lancaster, PA

Bell, Jennifer
Elk Lake HS
Springville, PA

Bell, John
Elizabeth Forword
Elizabeth, PA

Bell, Julia
West Branch HS
Grassflat, PA

Bell, Michele
Blue Mountain HS
Pottsville, PA

Bell, Robin
Carlisle SR HS
Carlisle, PA

Bell, Thomas J
Mercersburg Acad
Boyce, VA

Belles, Thomas
James M Coughlin
Wilkes Barre, PA

Belleteri,
Christopher
Upper Merion Area
King Of Prussia, PA

Belli, Richard
Aliquippa HS
Aliquippa, PA

Bellomo, Alan J
Central Cambria HS
Ebensburg, PA

Belotti, Rob
Deleware Valley HS
Dingmans Ferry, PA

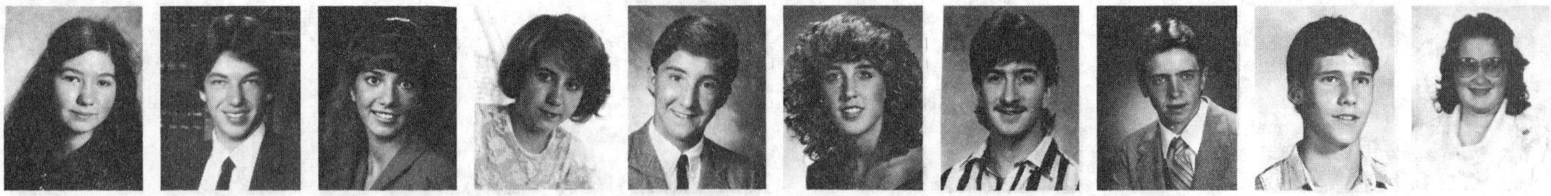

Bender, Elizabeth
Mt Alvernia HS
Pittsburgh, PA

Bender, Greg
Riverside HS
Beaver Falls, PA

Bender, Jeanette
Ephrata SR HS
Ephrata, PA

Bender, Tammy
Williamsport Area
Williamsport, PA

Benedick, Rodney N
James Buchanan HS
Fort Loudon, PA

Benedix, Brooke
Downingtown Joint
SR HS
Exton, PA

Benes, Thomas B
Plum SR HS
Pittsburgh, PA

Benford, Sheldon
Rockwood Area HS
Rockwood, PA

Benini, Anthony
Somerset SR HS
Sipesville, PA

Benner, Cynthia
Steelton-Highspire
Highspire, PA

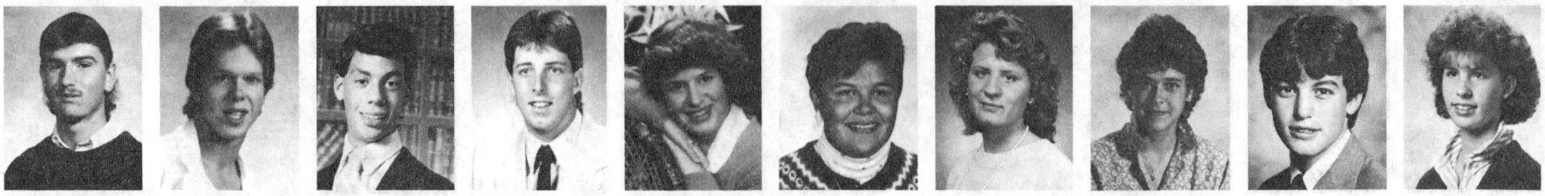

Bennett, Dennis
Belle Vernon Area
Belle Vernon, PA

Bennett, Edward J
Meadville Area SR
Meadville, PA

Bennett, Matthew
Mac George
The Haverford Schl
Paoli, PA

Bennett, Michael
Greater Johnstown
Johnstown, PA

Bennett, Shelley
Fort Le Boeuf HS
Waterford, PA

Bense, Victoria
Windber Area HS
Windber, PA

Benson, Sue
Palmyra Area HS
Palmyra, PA

Benton, Becky
Blairsville SR HS
Blairsville, PA

Benton, James
Hollidaysburg SR
Duncansville, PA

Berardinelli, Bridget
Trinity HS
Washington, PA

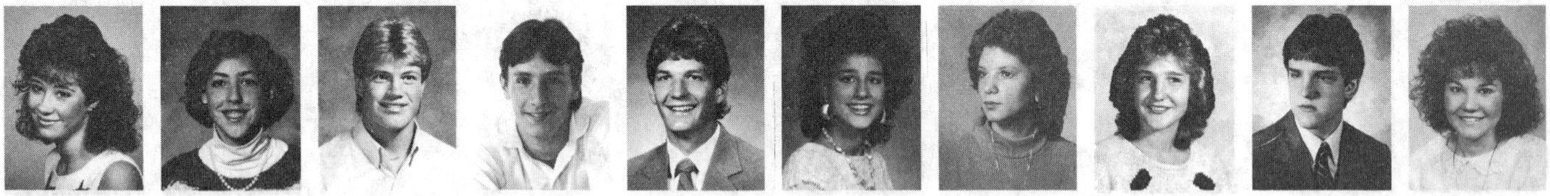

Berdar, Michaeleen
West Mifflin Area
W Mifflin, PA

Berg, Karla
Hampton HS
Allison Park, PA

Berger, Matthew
Hempfield HS
Landisville, PA

Bergerstock, Steve
Milton Area SR HS
Milton, PA

Berkebile, Wallace
North Star HS
Stoystown, PA

Bernard, Elisa
Nazareth Acad
Philadelphia, PA

Bernardini, Patricia
South Park HS
Pittsburgh, PA

Bernot, Kathleen
Blacklick Valley HS
Nanty-Glo, PA

Bernot, Lawrence
Blacklick Valley HS
Nanty-Glo, PA

Bernstein, Elizabeth
Bishop Hafey HS
Conyngham, PA

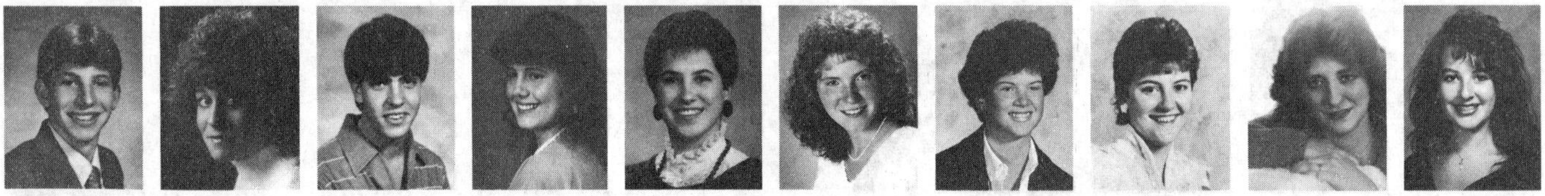

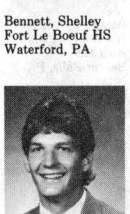

Berret, Thomas
Central Catholic HS
Pittsburgh, PA

Berrettini, Susan
Wyoming Valley
West HS
Forty Fort, PA

Bertelli, Anthony
Sharon HS
Sharon, PA

Berube, Heather
Suzanne
St College Area
Intermediate HS
State College, PA

Berzinsky, Clarissa
Greater Johnstown
Johnstown, PA

Best, Barbara
Chartiers Valley HS
Presto, PA

Best, Marguerite A
Lancaster Catholic
Lancaster, PA

Betker, Faitha
Turkey Foot Valley
Area HS
Confluence, PA

Betta, Santina
Somerset Area HS
Somerset, PA

Bettole, Gina
Cardinal Ohara HS
Morton, PA

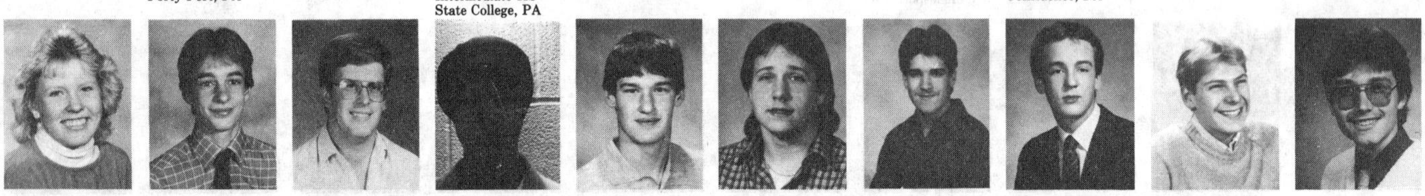

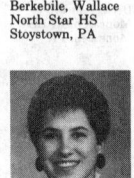

Betz, Dawn
Crestwood HS
Mountaintop, PA

Beveridge, Greg
Meadville HS
Meadville, PA

Bewley, John
Avon Grove HS
West Grove, PA

Bey, Amber Arnold
Schenley HS
Teachers Ctr
Pittsburgh, PA

Beyrent, John
Abington Heights
Clarks Summit, PA

Bialon, Aaron
Mon Valley Catholic
Belle Vernon, PA

Biancuzzo, Steven P
Moshannon Valley
Houtzdale, PA

Bibus, Chris
Hamburg Area HS
Hamburg, PA

Bickert, Todd
Pen Argyl Area HS
Nazareth, PA

Bickford, Rod
Albert Gallatin HS
Masontown, PA

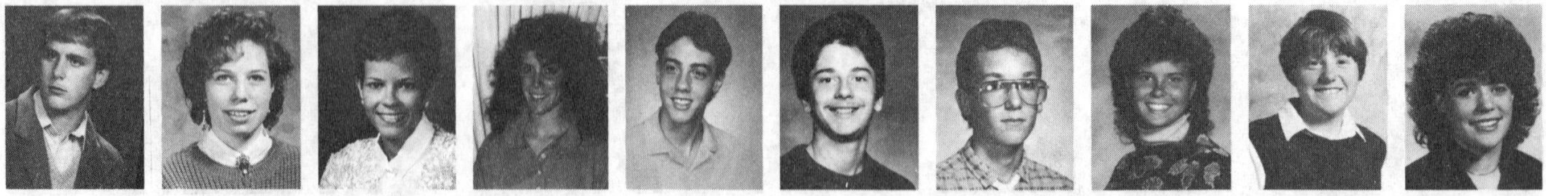

Bicksler, Gary
Tulpehocken HS
Richland, PA

Biddle, Tracy
Red Land HS
New Cumberland,
PA

Bieber, Becky
Burgettstown Area
JR-SR HS
Pittsburgh, PA

Bieda, Kelly
Red Lion SR HS
Felton, PA

Biega, Doug
Center Area HS
Monaca, PA

Bielski, Gary
Ringgold HS
New Eagle, PA

Bienko, Chris
Central Catholic HS
Oakmont, PA

Biernesser, Darlene
Fox Chapel Area HS
Pittsburgh, PA

Bievenour, Patricia
York Catholic HS
York, PA

Bilger, Kim
Westmont Hilltop
SR HS
Johnstown, PA

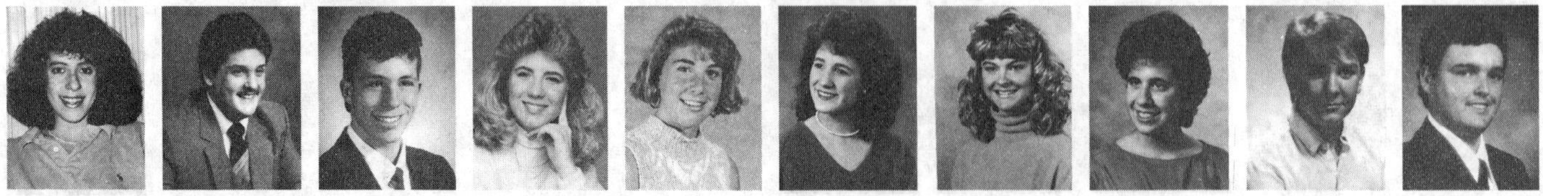

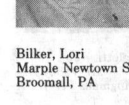

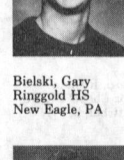

Bilker, Lori
Marple Newtown SR
Broomall, PA

Bill, Darric
South Allegheny HS
Mckeesport, PA

Billard, John
Wallenpaupack Area
Hawley, PA

Biller, Allison
Mt Pleasant Area
SR JR HS
Mt Pleasant, PA

Billet, Melissa
Conestoga SR HS
Devon, PA

Billey, Elisa E
Hempfield SR HS
New Stanton, PA

Bingham, Susanne
North Allegheny HS
Wexford, PA

Birch, Christine
Trinity HS
Washington, PA

Birckbichler,
Edward
Wilmington Area
Volant, PA

Bird, Brian
Danville HS
Danville, PA

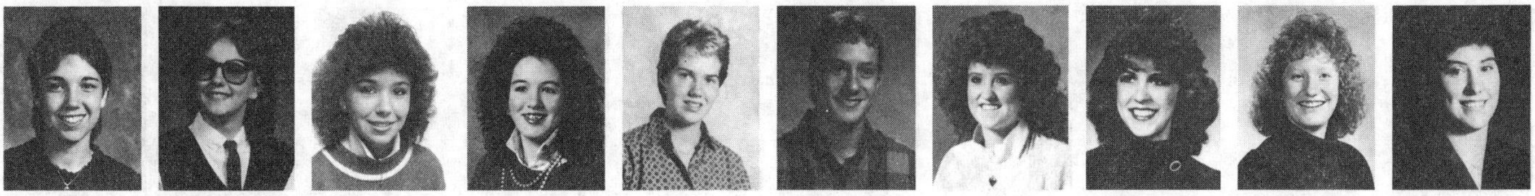

Bird, Deborah Mercer JR SR HS Mercer, PA	Biringer, Michele Fort Cherry HS Hickory, PA	Biscontini, Laura J M Coughlin HS Wilkes Barre, PA	Biskup, Kathleen Center Area HS Monaca, PA	Bittner, Gina Northwestern Lehigh HS Germansville, PA	Bitzel, Gerald Northeastern SR HS Mt Wolf, PA	Bixler, Darlene Center HS Aliquippa, PA	Bjes, Tiffany North Star HS Boswell, PA	Blac, Klynanne Bishop Mc Cort HS Johnstown, PA	Black, Deborah Coudersport Area JR SR HS Coudersport, PA

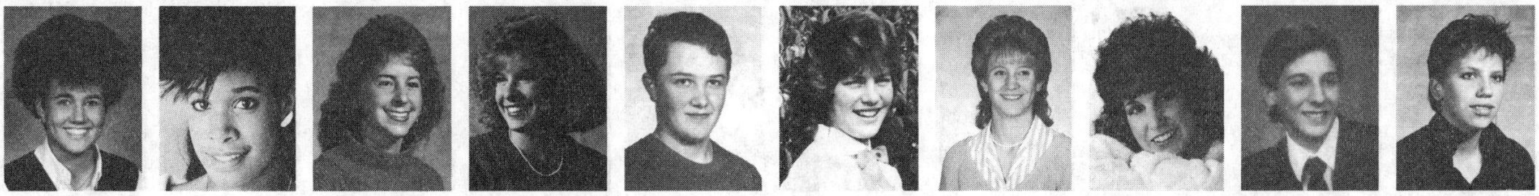

Black, Jennifer Nazareth Acad Philadelphia, PA	Blackwell, Genevieve Chichester HS Aston, PA	Blair, Amy Weatherly Area HS Weatherly, PA	Blair, Kristy Warren Area HS Warren, PA	Blair, Paul Knoch JR SR HS Butler, PA	Blair, Rebecca Mt Union Area HS Mt Union, PA	Blanarik, Caryn Ambridge HS Baden, PA	Blanchard, Gabrielle Meadville SR HS Meadville, PA	Blanchette, John Notre Dame HS E Stroudsburg, PA	Blanco, Christina Central Bucks East Mechanicsville, PA

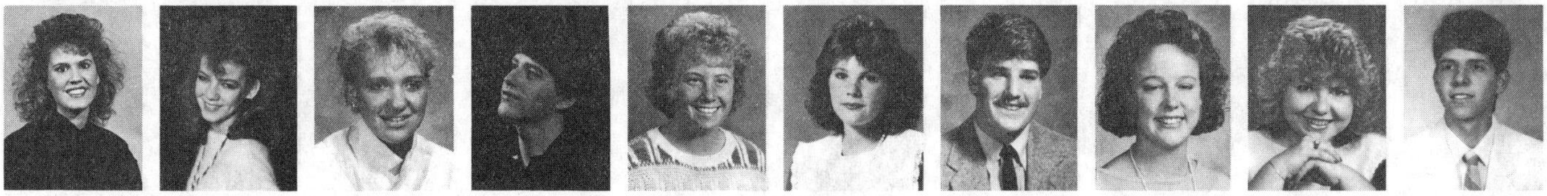

Blanco, Karen Canon Mc Millan SR HS Cecil, PA	Blaney, Dianne St Hubert HS Philadelphia, PA	Blase, Mary Bishop Neumann Williamsport, PA	Blass, Timothy Danville SR HS Danville, PA	Blather, Gretta Central York HS York, PA	Blatt, Caryn South Park HS Tampa, FL	Blemler, Mark Boiling Springs HS Boiling Spgs, PA	Blessman, Jennifer Neshaminy HS Langhorne, PA	Blevins, Lesa Twin Valley HS Morgantown, PA	Blicha, John M Canon Mc Millan SR HS Eighty Four, PA

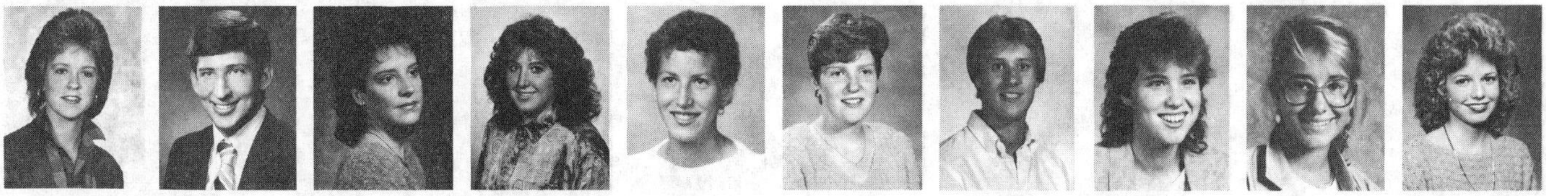

Blithe, Tracy Interboro HS Glenolden, PA	Bloch, Jonathan Parkland HS Allentown, PA	Blodgett, Diane Everett Area HS Severna Park, MD	Blodgett, Stacey Canon Mc-Millian SR HS Canonsburg, PA	Bloom, Shari Curwensville Area Curwensville, PA	Blosser, Elizabeth Harbor Creek HS Erie, PA	Blouch, Timothy Northern Lebanan Jonestown, PA	Blue, Kathy Danville SR HS Danville, PA	Bluemle, Amy The Agnes Irwin Rosemont, PA	Boal, Kimberly Ringgold HS Finleyville, PA

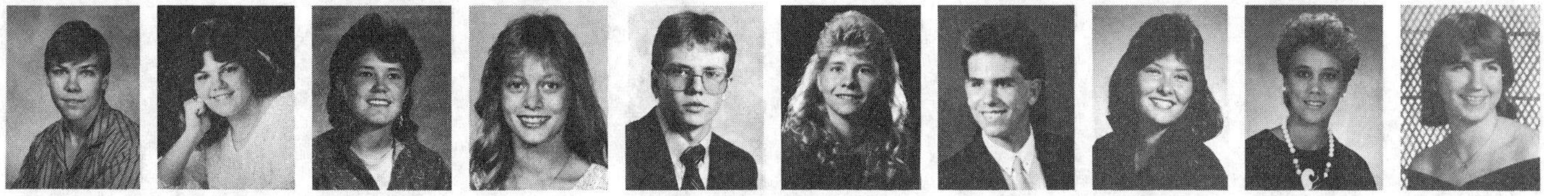

Bobak, Justin Northern Cambria Barnesboro, PA	Boban, Allyson Conneaut Valley HS Conneautville, PA	Bobon, Shanan Oxford Area HS Cochranville, PA	Bobro, Darlene Sto Rox SR HS Mckees Rocks, PA	Bobrowsky, Bryan Cardinal Brennan Shenandoah, PA	Bock, Jodie Fleetwood Area HS Kutztown, PA	Bodani, Frank C Susquehannock HS Glen Rock, PA	Bode, Anne-Marie Western Wayne HS Hamlin, PA	Boden, Jennifer S Elizabeth Forward Monongahela, PA	Bodine, Heather Unionville HS Kennett Square, PA

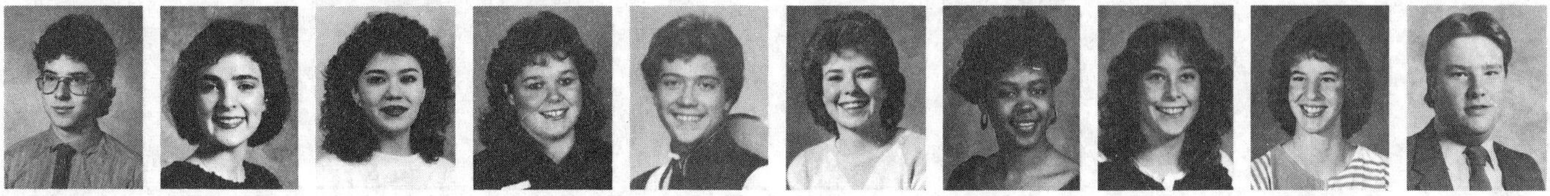

Bodura, Paul Steel Valley HS Munhall, PA	Boehne, Lisa F The Baldwin Schl Devon, PA	Bogan, Nicole Freeport Area SR Freeport, PA	Bogats, Jennifer Carlynton HS Carnegie, PA	Bogdon, Michael Wyoming Valley West HS Plymouth, PA	Boggess, Teresa South Side HS Hookstown, PA	Boggs, Leah St Maria Goretti HS Philadelphia, PA	Bohn, Christine Avon Grove HS Chatham, PA	Bolam, Janel Waynesburg Central Brave, PA	Bolich, Edward Nativity BVM HS Pottsville, PA

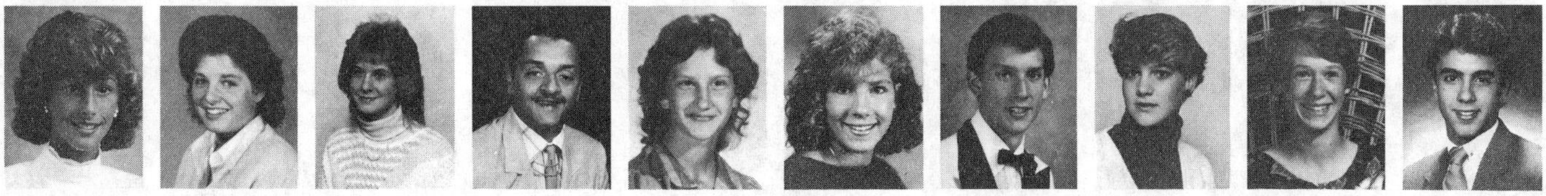

Bollinger, Becky J Mechanicsburg SR Mechanicsburg, PA	Bollinger, Denise Huntingdon Area Mill Creek, PA	Bolton, Kris Greenwood HS Millerstown, PA	Bomar, Shawn A East Allegheny HS North Versailles, PA	Bomgardner, Kynel Denise Northern Lebanon Ono, PA	Bonacci, Beth Bishop Hafey HS Oneida, PA	Bonenberger, Jr Kenneth J Bishop Egan HS Levittown, PA	Bonetti, Ann Marie Danville Area SR Danville, PA	Boney, Michelle Mifflinburg Area HS Mifflinburg, PA	Boni, Eric N Peters Township HS Mc Murray, PA

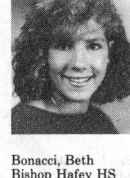

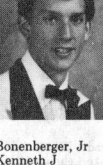

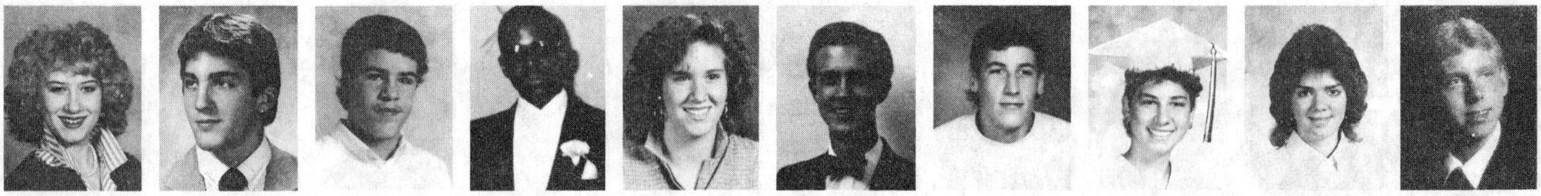

Boniger, Julie
Villa Maria Acad
Erie, PA

Bonita, John A
James M Coughlin
Plains, PA

Bonner, Sam
Jim Thorpe Area
Jim Thorpe, PA

Bonner, Shawn
Carver H S
Engineering
Philadelphia, PA

Book, Bonnie
Neshannock HS
New Castle, PA

Book, Doug Parker
Palisades HS
Pipersville, PA

Book, Garth
West Hazleton HS
Sugarloaf, PA

Boornazian, Michele
Penn Wood HS
Lansdowne, PA

Booth, Angela
Southern Fulton HS
Warfordsburg, PA

Booth, Jeffrey
Hershey HS
Hershey, PA

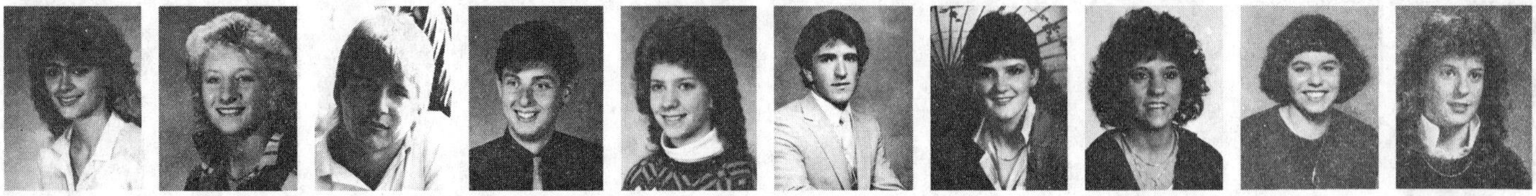

Booth, Mary
Saltsburg JR/SR HS
Saltsburg, PA

Boozer, Nycole
Shanksville-Stony
Creek HS
Shanksville, PA

Borden, Sheldon T
S R U HS
Gillett, PA

Borek, Jr Thomas
Connellsville Area
SR HS
Connellsville, PA

Boring, Donna
Penns Manor HS
Strongstown, PA

Borodaty, Gregory
Ringgold HS
Charleroi, PA

Borosky, Patricia
Carbondale Area HS
Simpson, PA

Borrelli, Melinda
New Castle SR HS
New Castle, PA

Bortz, Lisa
Hickory HS
Hermitage, PA

Bortz, Michelle
Hempfield HS
Columbia, PA

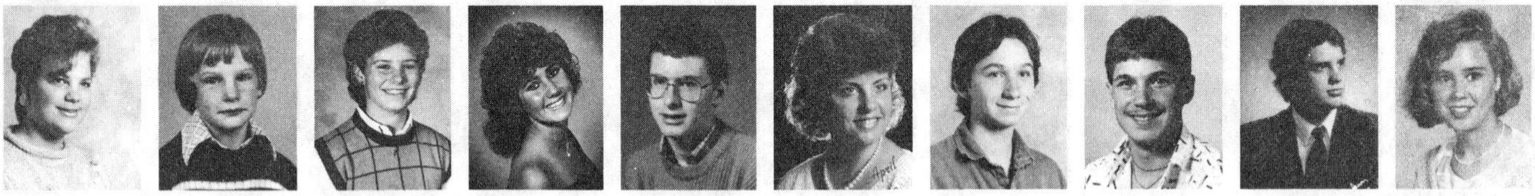

Borum, Sandy
Coughlin HS
Wilkes Barre, PA

Borys, Sean
Lake-Lehman SR
Hunlock Crk, PA

Bosnjak, Michelle
Steelton Highspire
Highspire, PA

Boss, Susan
Penn Hills HS
Pittsburgh, PA

Bosserman, Brian
Michael
Peters Township HS
Bridgeville, PA

Bostian, April
Danville Ssr HS
Danville, PA

Bott, Charles
Jim Thorpe SR HS
Jim Thorpe, PA

Botte, Michael
Western Beaver HS
Industry, PA

Bottiger, Jason
Shi Kellamy HS
Sunbury, PA

Bouch, Katherine
Lower Pauphin HS
Hummelstown, PA

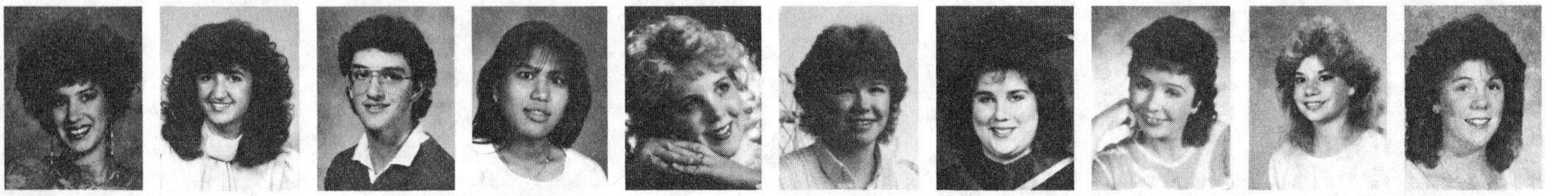

Bouikidis, Eugenia
Upper Darby HS
Upper Darby, PA

Bourg, Michelle
Canon Mc Millan
Muse, PA

Boutiller, George
Bellwood Antis HS
Tyrone, PA

Bouvier, Maria
Henderson HS
Thornton, PA

Bowen, Lynn
Beaver Area HS
Beaver, PA

Bowers, Carol
Butler SR HS
Butler, PA

Bowers, Geralyn
Cardinal Dougherty
Philadelphia, PA

Bowers, Julie A
Academy HS
Erie, PA

Bowers, Kristi Lynn
Saltsburg JR SR HS
Clarksburg, PA

Bowersox, Julianne
Chichester HS
Linwood, PA

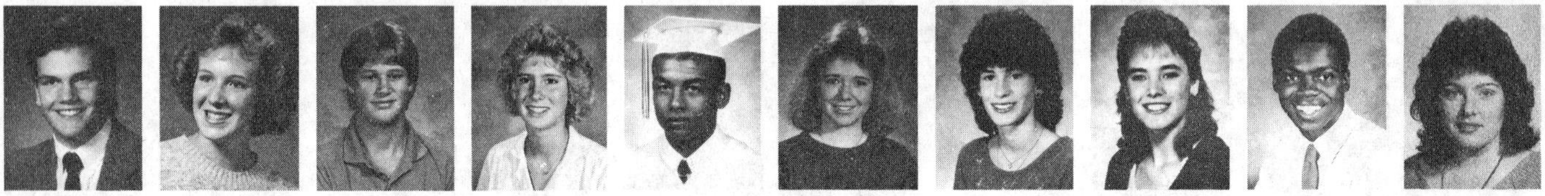

Bowman, Erik
Lehighton Area HS
Lehighton, PA

Bowman, Laura C
Central HS
York, PA

Bowman, Matthew
Cedar Crest HS
Lebanon, PA

Bowman, Tyann
Venango Christian
Reno, PA

Bowmer, Derek
Scotland Schl
Philadelphia, PA

Bowser, Jennifer
Butler Intermediate
Butler, PA

Bowser, Kristen
Kittaning SR HS
Worthington, PA

Bowser, Lisa
Ford City HS
Ford City, PA

Boyd, Albert
Reading HS
Reading, PA

Boyd, Laurie Jo
Belle Vernon Area
Belle Vernon, PA

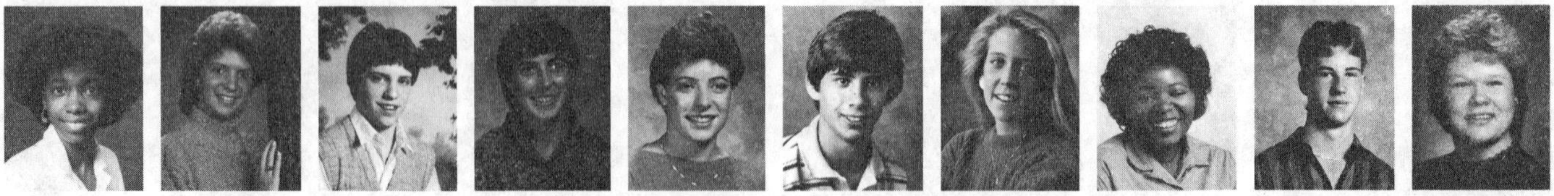

Boyd, Rhonda
Philadelphia Girls
Philadelphia, PA

Boyer, Kelly
Rhonda
Pine Grove Area HS
Pine Grove, PA

Boyer, Leroy
Schuylkill Haven
Schuylkill Haven,
PA

Boyer, Michelle
Elizabethtown Area
Elizabethtown, PA

Boyer, Natalie
West Perry HS
New Bloomfield, PA

Boyer, Stephen
Lewistown Area HS
Lewistown, PA

Boyer, Wendy
Bermudian Springs
York Spgs, PA

Bracey, Niccole
Frankford HS
Philadelphia, PA

Bradley, Lewis
Blue Mountain HS
Orwigsburg, PA

Bradley, Renee
Blue Mountain HS
Pottsville, PA

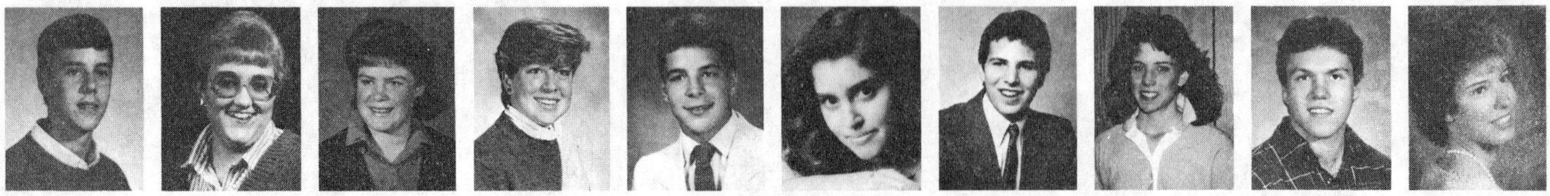

Bradley, Robert
Stroudsburg HS
Stroudsburg, PA

Bradnick, Melissa
Forbes Road JR-SR
Hustontown, PA

Brady, Diana
Connellsville SR HS
Connellsville, PA

Brady, Erin Garey
Lake-Lehman HS
Lehman, PA

Braido, III Joseph
Easton Area HS
Easton, PA

Brand, Melissa
Chambersburg Area
SR HS
Fayetteville, PA

Brand, Stuart
Lowr Moreland HS
Huntingdon Valley,
PA

Brandau, Lorri
Wilson Area HS
Easten, PA

Brandon, Sean
Butler SR HS
Butler, PA

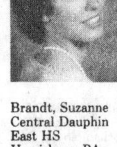

Brandt, Suzanne
Central Dauphin
East HS
Harrisburg, PA

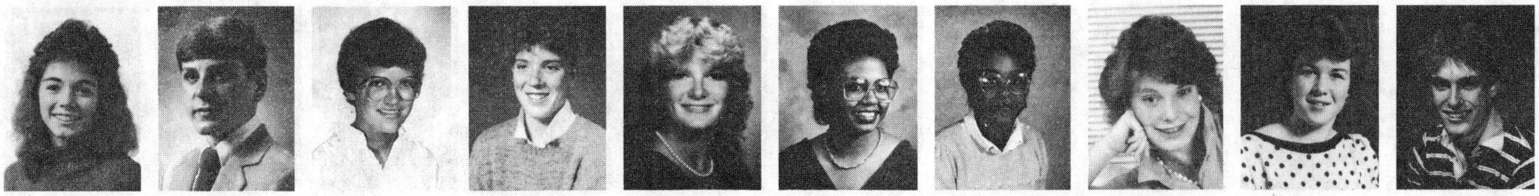

Brannan, Terri
Lewistown HS
Lewistown, PA

Branstetter, Terry
Tyrone Area HS
Tyrone, PA

Brant, Gretchen
Shippensburg Area SR HS
York, PA

Brantner, Kelly
Rochester Area HS
Rochester, PA

Brantner, Michele
Oxford Area HS
Oxford, PA

Bratcher, Beverly
Cardinal O Hara HS
Media, PA

Bratcher, Yvonne
Cardinal O Hara HS
Media, PA

Bratt, Kelly
Iroquois HS
Erie, PA

Braun, Donna
Cardinal Dougherty
Philadelphia, PA

Braund, Jay
Troy SR HS
Troy, PA

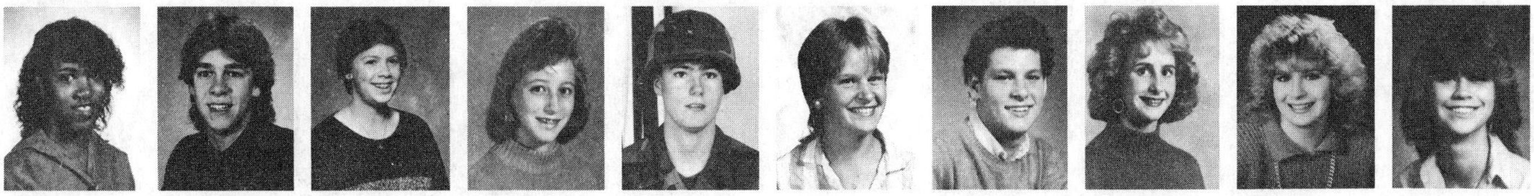

Bray, Jeannine D
Creative And Performing Arts
Philadelphia, PA

Breindel, Glenn
Ford City HS
Ford City, PA

Breiner, Marsha L
Tamaqua Area SR
Andreas, PA

Breitenbach, Kristine
Methacton SR HS
Collegeville, PA

Breitenstein, Brett
Moon SR HS
Coraopolis, PA

Breitfeld, Michele
Louis E Dieruff HS
Allentown, PA

Brennan, Gary
Tunkhannock HS
Tunkhannock, PA

Brennan, Melissa
Nativity BVM HS
Pottsville, PA

Brenneman, Danielle
Red Lion Area SR
Red Lion, PA

Brenneman, Dawn
Frankford HS
Philadelphi, PA

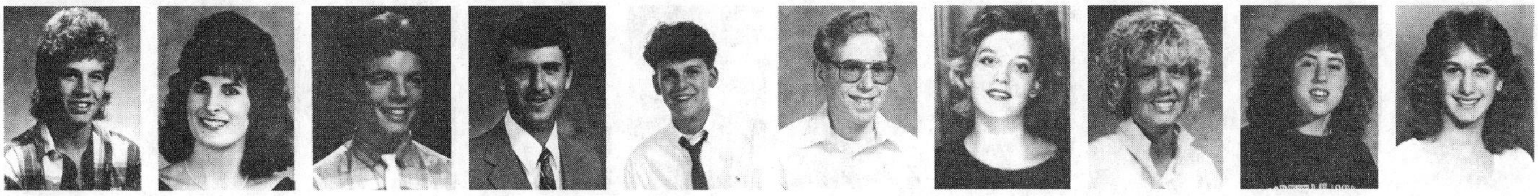

Brenner, Dale
Wilmington Area
New Castle, PA

Breslin, Mary
Cardinal O Hara HS
Havertown, PA

Bressi, Joseph
Shamokin Area HS
Shamokin, PA

Bressler, Scott
Johnsonburg Area
Johnsonburg, PA

Brewer, James
Cedar Crest HS
Lebanon, PA

Brewer, James
Manheim Central
Manheim, PA

Brewer, Margie
Penn Center Acad
Philadelphia, PA

Bricker, Anne
Fairview HS
Erie, PA

Bricklin, Alisa
Upper Merion Area
Wayne, PA

Bridge, Danielle
Cranberry Area HS
Oil City, PA

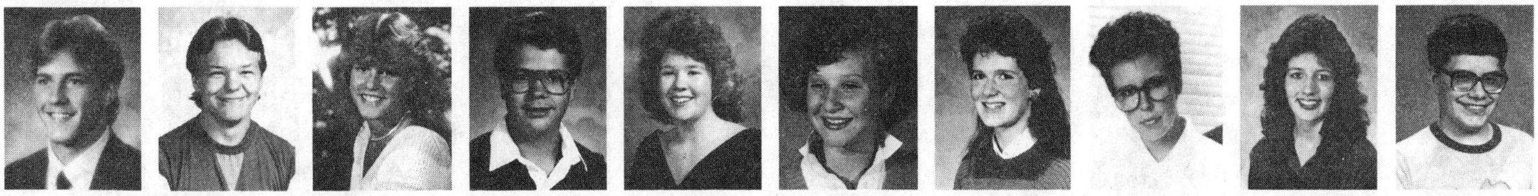

Briel, II James L
Mahanoy Area HS
Mahanoy City, PA

Briggs, Glenn
Southern Fulton HS
Needmore, PA

Briggs, Gwen
John Pierson Mc Caskey HS
Lancaster, PA

Bright, Scott
Shaler Area School
Glenshaw, PA

Brighter, Virginia
St Hubert HS
Philadelphia, PA

Brighton, Kelly
Connellsville SR HS
Indian Head, PA

Brink, Luann
Saltsburg JRSR HS
Saltsburg, PA

Brink, Melinda
Dunmore HS
Dunmore, PA

Brion, Janelle
Liberty JR/SR HS
Liberty, PA

Briskey, Shawn
Meyersdale Area HS
Meyersdale, PA

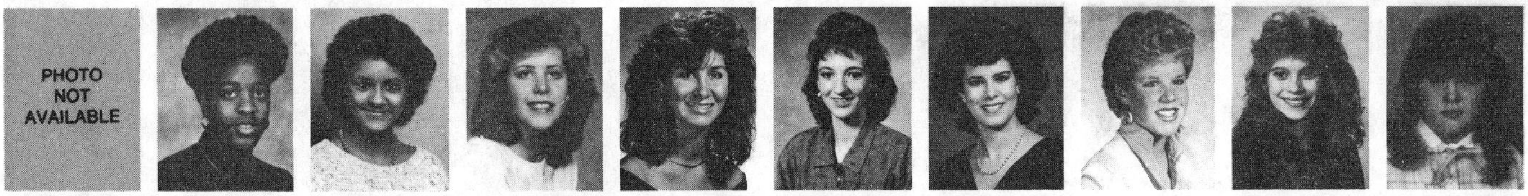

Bristow, Sharmaine
West Mifflin Area
W Mifflin, PA

Britten, Gloria
Bensalem HS
Trevose, PA

Britton, Ursela
Berks Christian Schl
W Reading, PA

Britz, Christine
Central Bucks West
New Britain, PA

Brodsky, Aileen F
George Washington
Philadelphia, PA

Brodsky, Geeia
South Fayette HS
Bridgeville, PA

Brogan, Beth
Cardinal O Hara HS
Swarthmore, PA

Brogley, Kimberly
Haverford HS
Drexel Hill, PA

Brojack, Lori
Lakeland HS
Olyphant, PA

Broker, Marsha
Penn Trafford HS
Harrison City, PA

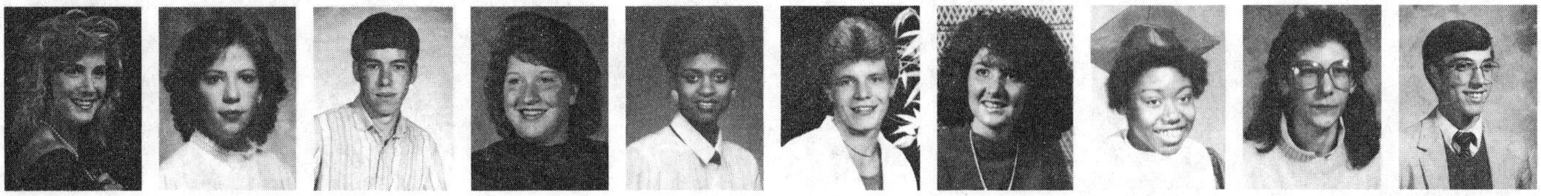

Brooke, Jennifer
Bishop Conwell HS
Yardley, PA

Brooks, Debra L
Shaler SR HS
Pittsburgh, PA

Brooks, Gregory A
Kaoch JR SR HS
Saxanburg, PA

Brooks, Rana
Connellsville Area SR HS
Connellsville, PA

Brooks, Tina
Canon Mc Millan
Canonsburg, PA

Brooks, Troy
Corry Area HS
Corry, PA

Brookshire, Amy
Central York SR HS
York, PA

Broomes, Genevieve
Lutheran HS
Philadelphia, PA

Brosius, Christie
Mifflinburg Area HS
Mifflinburg, PA

Brosius, Steve
Calvary Baptist Christian Schl
Lancaster, PA

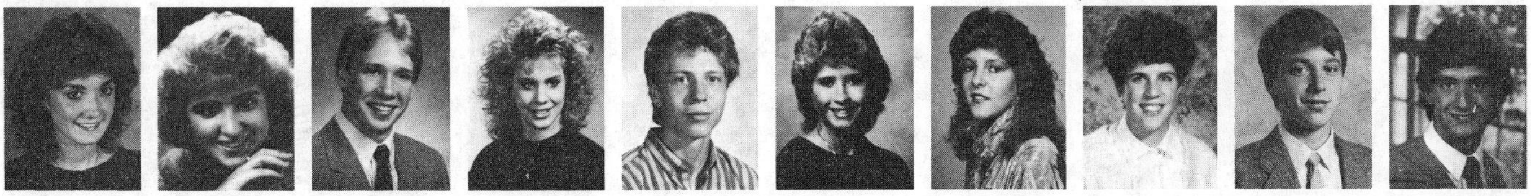

Brougher, Christine
Penn-Trafford HS
Irwin, PA

Browder, Karyn
Meadville Area SR
Meadville, PA

Brower, Shane
Bald Eagle Area HS
Howard, PA

Brown, Belinda
Valley View JR SR
Peckville, PA

Brown, Chad
Coatesville Area SR
Coatesville, PA

Brown, Debbie
Du Bois Area HS
Dubois, PA

Brown, Deborah
West Mifflin Area
West Mifflin, PA

Brown, Dreama
Shalom Christian
Chambersburg, PA

Brown, Harry J
Nativity BVM HS
Schuylkill Haven, PA

Brown, J Todd
Pequea Valley HS
Gap, PA

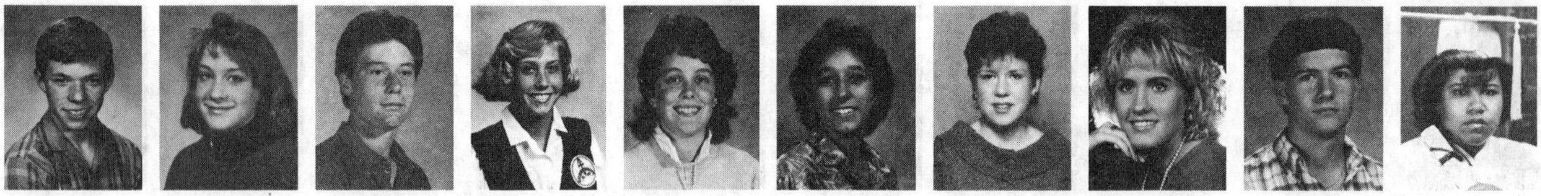

Brown, Jr James
Abington Heights
Clarks Summit, PA

Brown, Janet
Parkland HS
Orefield, PA

Brown, Jason
Downingtown HS
Exton, PA

Brown, Jodi
Trinity HS
Mechanicsburg, PA

Brown, Karen
Avon Grove HS
Landenberg, PA

Brown, Karin
Spring-Ford SR HS
Phoenixville, PA

Brown, Kathryn
Cranberry HS
Seneca, PA

Brown, Kelli
Greater Works Acad
North Versailles, PA

Brown, Kenneth
Annville Cleona HS
Annville, PA

Brown, Kimberly D
Harrisburg HS
Harrisburg, PA

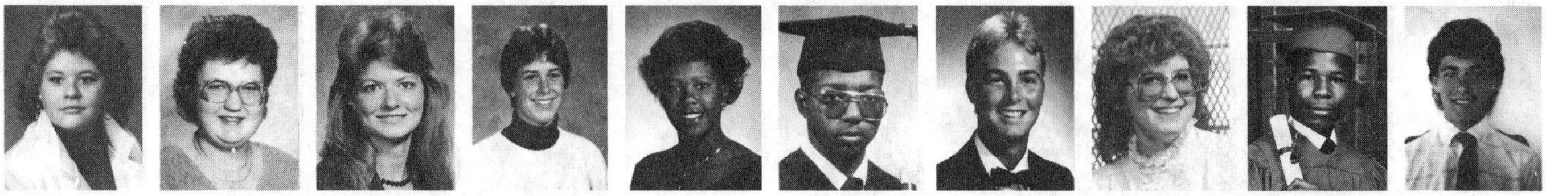

Brown, Kristy Lee
Riverside JR SR HS
Moosic, PA

Brown, Marcelle
Blairsville SR HS
Blairsville, PA

Brown, Melissa
Connellsville SR HS
Acme, PA

Brown, Melissa S
Governor Mifflin HS
Shillington, PA

Brown, Nicole D
Penncrest HS
Media, PA

Brown, II Niles K
HS Engineering &
Philadelphia, PA

Brown, Owen
Downingtown HS
Downingtown, PA

Brown, Rachel
Warrior Run HS
Turbotville, PA

Brown, Richard
Olney HS
Philadelphia, PA

Brown, Jr Richard S
Moon HS
Coraopolis, PA

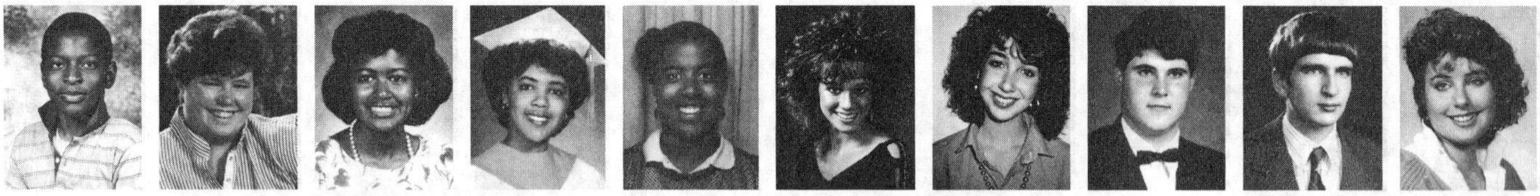

Brown, Rohan
Martin L King HS
Philadelphia, PA

Brown, Shelley
Northeast Bradford
Rome, PA

Brown, Stacey
Pottstown SR HS
Pottstown, PA

Brown, Stephanie
W B Saul HS
Philadelphia, PA

Brown, Tamara
Solebury Prep Schl
Trenton, NJ

Brown, Tina
Plymouth
Whitemarsh HS
Lafayette Hill, PA

Brown, Tricia
Faith Community
Christian Schl
Pittsburgh, PA

Browning, Scott
Saint Pius X HS
Pottstown, PA

Brubacker, David
Grace Christian HS
Bethel, PA

Brubaker, Lauren
Monongahela Valley
Catholic HS
Monongahelan, PA

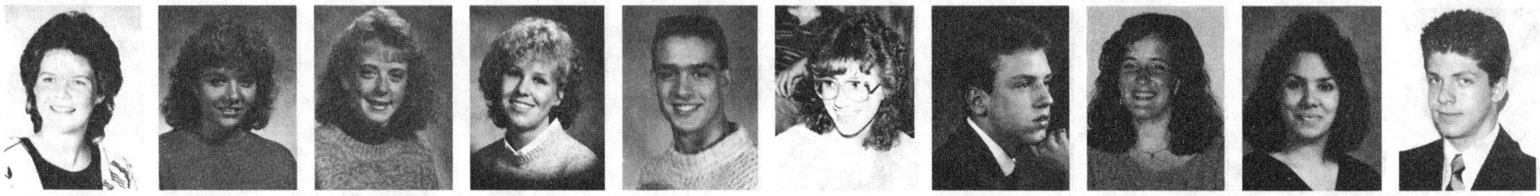

Bruck, Beth
Hyndman Middle
SR HS
Hyndman, PA

Brucker, Jennifer
Valley HS
New Kensington,
PA

Brucker, Michele
Shaler Area SR HS
Pittsburgh, PA

Brudnicki, Brenda
Southern Columbia
Area HS
Elysburg, PA

Brumbaugh, Joseph
Altoona Area HS
Altoona, PA

Brunner, Bonita
Southern
Huntingdon HS
Mapleton Depot, PA

Bruno, Brad
Norwin HS
N Huntingdon, PA

Bruno, Jenifir
Wyoming Area HS
West Pittston, PA

Bruno, Margaret
Archbishop
Prendergast HS
Upper Darby, PA

Bruno, Robert John
Crestwood HS
Mountaintop, PA

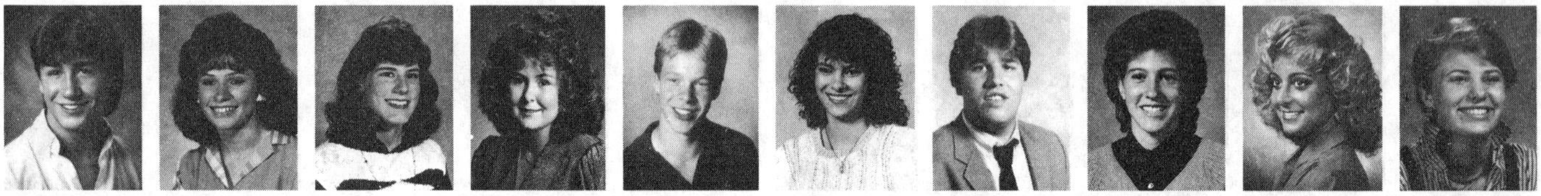

Bruno, Stephen
Trinity HS
Washington, PA

Bruzda, Mary
Saltsburg JR SR HS
Saltsburg, PA

Bryan, Kathy
Great Valley HS
Malvern, PA

Bryant, Richann
Bethel Park HS
Bethel Pk, PA

Bryant, William T
Fairview HS
Fairview, PA

Brychik, Melissa
Quigley HS
Beaver, PA

Bubnis, John
Cardinal Brennan
Ashland, PA

Bubonic, Eileen
Hopewell SR HS
Aliquippa, PA

Buccitelli, Diane E
Freedom Area HS
Conway, PA

Buchanan, Deanna
Susquehannock HS
Glen Rock, PA

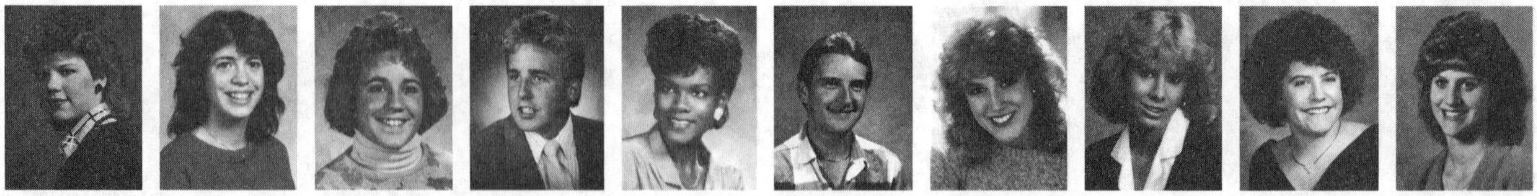

Buck, Angela
Clearfield Area HS
Woodlands, PA

Buck, Genevra
Lower Dauphin HS
Elizabethtown, PA

Buck, Janelle
Cocalico SR HS
Adamstown, PA

Buckley, Doyle
Adam
Red Lion SR HS
Felton, PA

Buckner, Adrienne
Wilkinsburg JR/SR
Pittsburgh, PA

Buckwalter, Jr
Terry E
Wilmington Area
New Wilmington,
PA

Buday, Gretchen
Villa Maria HS
Poland, OH

Buehler, Christine
M
Cedar Crest HS
Lebanon, PA

Buehner, Patricia
Little Flower HS
Philadelphia, PA

Bufalini, Carol
Ambridge HS
Ambridge, PA

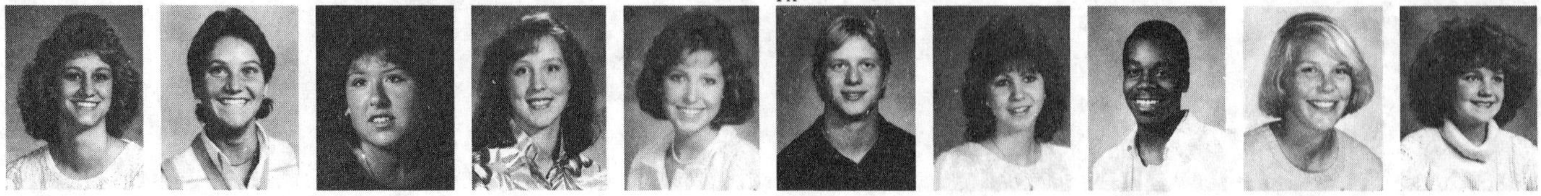

Bufalini, Rebecca
Ambridge Area HS
Ambridge, PA

Buffington, Patricia
Upper Dauphin
Areea HS
Elizabethville, PA

Bugash, Andrea
Red Lion Area SR
Red Lion, PA

Buka, Stephanie
Richland HS
Wexford, PA

Bula, Jacquelyn
Villa Maria Acad
Erie, PA

Bullock, Edward
Northern HS
Wellsville, PA

Bumbarger, Sherri
Westbranch JR SR
Morrisdale, PA

Bundrige, Darryl
Gateway SR HS
Monroeville, PA

Bundy, Carolyn A
Chambersburg Area
SR HS
Chambersburg, PA

Bunevicius, Susan
Scranton Central
Scranton, PA

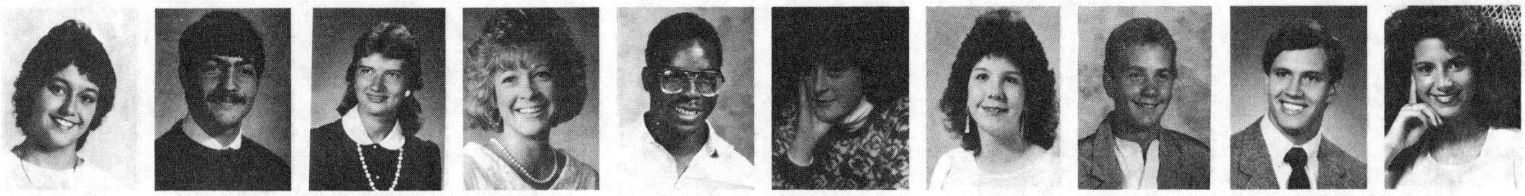

Bunso, Samantha
Jim Thorpe Area
Jim Thorpe, PA

Buonanno, Anthony J
Great Valley HS
Malvern, PA

Burba, Christine
Purchase Line JR SR HS
Arcadia, PA

Burch, Dawn E
Plumstead Christian
Perkasie, PA

Burden, Terence A
West York Area SR
York, PA

Burdette, Tricia
Dallas SR HS
Trucksville, PA

Burek, Kim
Springdale HS
Cheswick, PA

Burgard, Brent
Solonco HS
Quarryville, PA

Burgbacher, David
Westmont Hilltop
Johnstown, PA

Burge, Jodi
Carmichaels Area
Carmichaels, PA

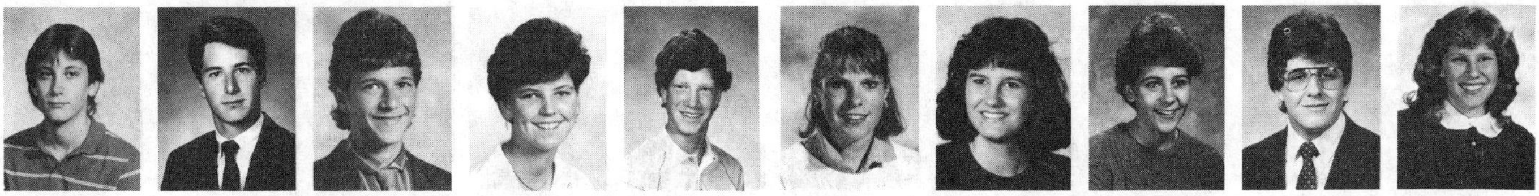

Burger, Richard
Belle Vernon Area
Belle Vernon, PA

Burgess, Christopher J
Bethel Park SR HS
Bethel Pk, PA

Burgess, Jason L
Navity Bvm HS
Pottsville, PA

Burgoyne, Amy
Gwynedd Mercy
Warrington, PA

Burke, Dennis
Abington Heights
Clarks Summit, PA

Burke, Lisa
Westmont Hilltop
Johnstown, PA

Burke, Shannon
Upper St Clair HS
Pittsburgh, PA

Burke, Wendy
Eastern York HS
Hellam, PA

Burkett, Scott
Greensburg-Salem SR HS
Greensburg, PA

Burkey, Kirsten
Bishop Carroll HS
Loretto, PA

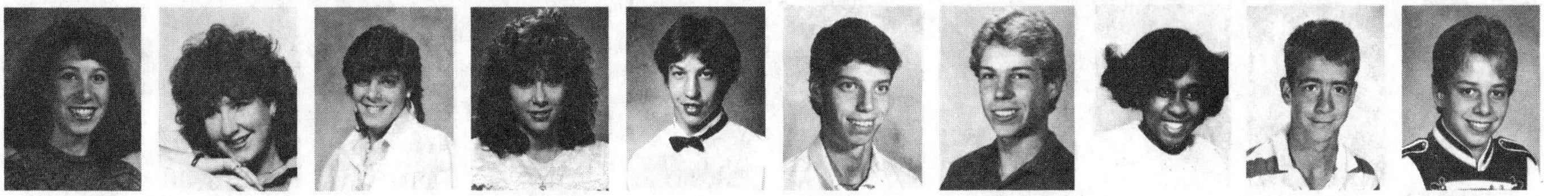

Burkey, Rebecca
Governor Mifflin SR
Mohnton, PA

Burkhardt, Kim M
Bethlehem Catholic
Bethlehem, PA

Burkhart, Annette
Cambria Heights HS
Carrolltown, PA

Burkhoder, Kelly
Lockhaven SR HS
Lock Haven, PA

Burkholder, Don
Ringgold HS
Finleyville, PA

Burkholder, Eric S
Chambersburg Area SR HS
Chambersburg, PA

Burkley, Richard Craig
Penns Manor HS
Penn Run, PA

Burley, Alicia
Franklin HS
Franklin, PA

Burn, Jonathan
Gettysburg SR HS
York, PA

Burnard, Jr Warren W
Northern Lehigh HS
Walnutport, PA

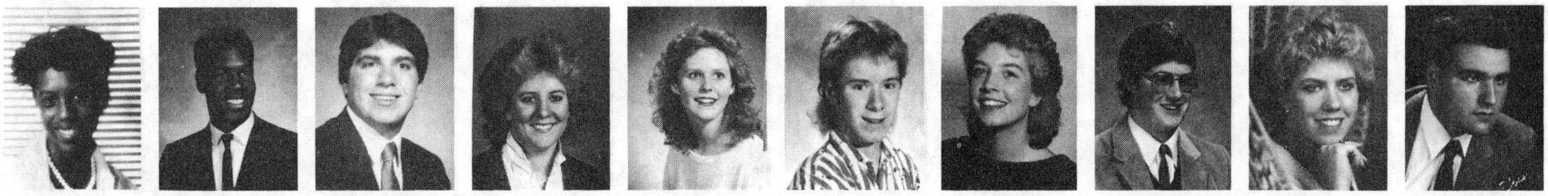

Burnett, Lachelle
Coatesville Area SR
Coastesville, PA

Burnett, Steve
Central Catholic HS
Pittsburgh, PA

Burnley, Jeffrey L
Upper Moreland HS
Hatboro, PA

Burns, Karen
Neshannock HS
New Castle, PA

Burns, Kathy A
Central HS
Scranton, PA

Burns, Kevin
Meadville Area SR
Meadville, PA

Burns, Lisa
Mc Keesport Area
Mc Keesport, PA

Burns, Sean
West Snyder HS
Beavertown, PA

Burns, Susan
Penn Trafford HS
Irwin, PA

Burns, Tom
Pennsbury HS
Fairless Hills, PA

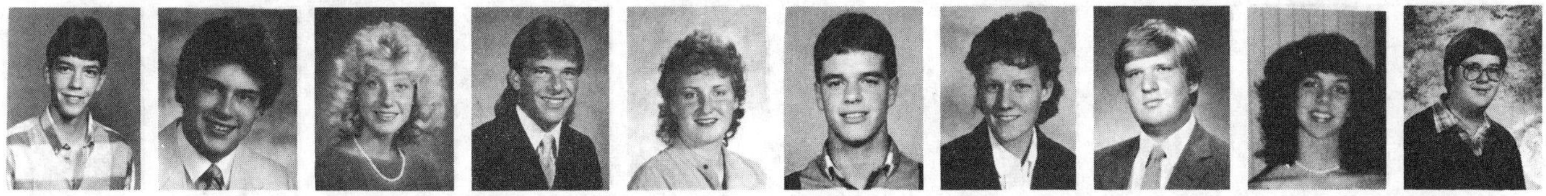

Burprich, Thomas
Hickory HS
Hermitage, PA

Burr, R William
Keystone Oaks HS
Castle Shannon, PA

Burrell, Beth
Hempfield SR HS
Irwin, PA

Burstein, Andrew
Lower Moreland HS
Huntingdon Valley, PA

Bury, Teresa
Oley Valley HS
Fleetwood, PA

Busch, David
West Mifflin Area
W Mifflin, PA

Bush, Darlene
St Benedict Acad
Erie, PA

Bush, Gary
Windber Area HS
Windber, PA

Bush, Michelle L
Sewickley Acad
Pittsburgh, PA

Bush, Robert
Stroudsburg HS
East Stroudsburg, PA

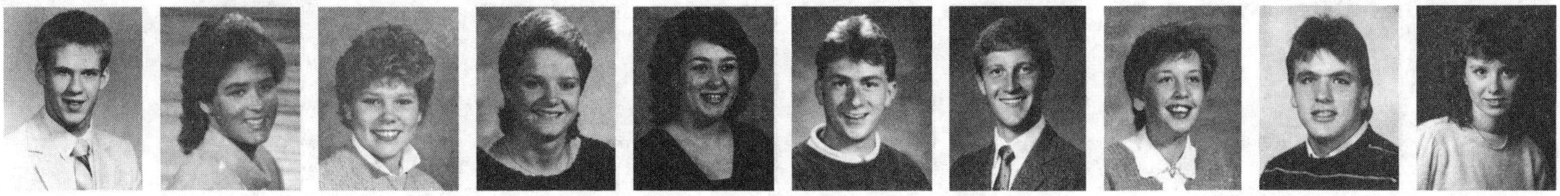

Bushner, Joseph A
William Allen HS
Allentown, PA

Bushong, Judy
Solanco SR HS
Quarryville, PA

Bushwack, Jennifer
Greater Latrobe HS
Greensburg, PA

Butensky, Lee Ann
Minersville Area HS
Branch Dale, PA

Buterbaugh, Lianne
Fannett-Metal HS
Ft Loudon, PA

Buterbaugh, Scott
Seneca Valley HS
Mars, PA

Butler, Bradley
Bethal Park SR HS
Bethel Park, PA

Butler, Evelyn Dorinda
Oxford HS
Oxford, PA

Butson, Randy J
Warwick HS
Lititz, PA

Buttery, Tamara
Punxsutawney Area SR HS
Punxsutawney, PA

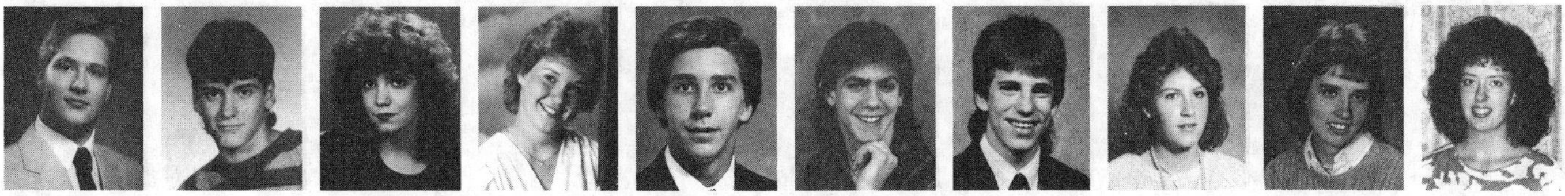

Butts, Darron
Mcconnellsburg HS
Mcconnellsburg, PA

Butz, Chris
William Allen HS
Allentown, PA

Buynak, Sonya
Philipsburg-Osceola SR HS
Osceola Mills, PA

Buzard, Brenda
Fort Le Boeuf HS
Waterford, PA

Buzzard, Scott
Pen Argyl HS
Windgap, PA

Byers, James
Belle Vernon Area
Belle Vernon, PA

Byers, Jeff
Gateway SR HS
Monroeville, PA

Byers, Kellie
South Allegheny HS
Mckeesport, PA

Byler, Nadine L
Lower Dauphin HS
Hershey, PA

Byler, Suann
Shenango HS
New Castle, PA

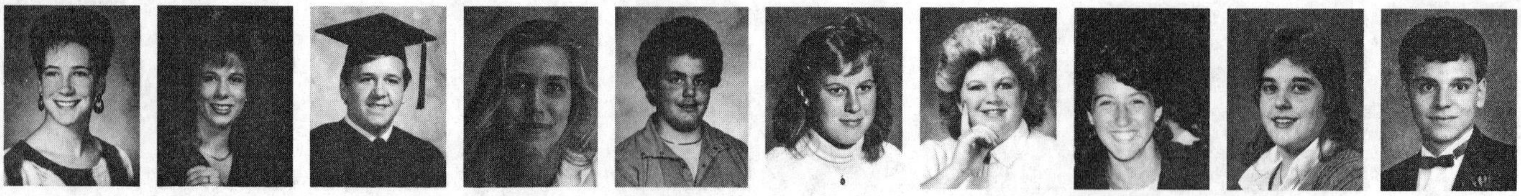

Byrne, Julia S
Mt Lebanon HS
Pittsburgh, PA

Byrne, Stephanie
Cardinal O Hara HS
Springfield, PA

Cade, Michael
Interboro HS
Glenolden, PA

Cadwell, Kajsa
Springside Schl
Glenside, PA

Cafeo, David S
Penn Cambria HS
Cassandra, PA

Caffrey, Trisha
Pen Argyl HS
Pen Argyl, PA

Cagni, Bertha Anne
Peters Township HS
Mc Murray, PA

Cahill, Christine
Nativity Bvm HS
Orwigsburg, PA

Cain, Leslie
South Side Beaver
Georgetown, PA

Calabretta, Mario
Bishop Kenrick HS
Norristown, PA

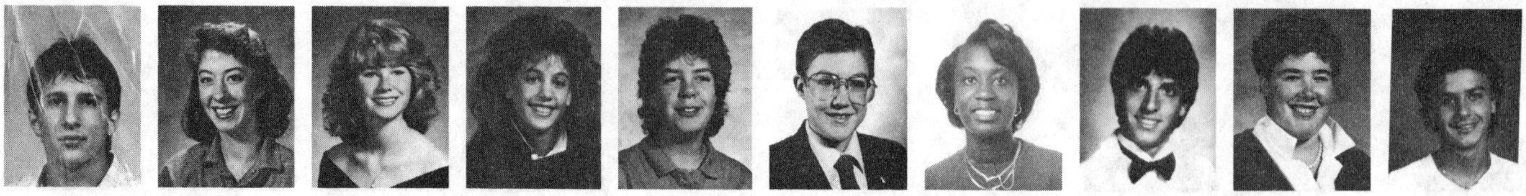

Calabro, David
Canon-Mc Millan
Canonsburg, PA

Calarie, Natalie
Indiana SR HS
Indiana, PA

Caldwell, Debbie
Upper Moreland HS
Hatboro, PA

Caldwell, Melissa
Donegal HS
Maytown, PA

Caldwell, Melissa
Newport JRSR HS
Newport, PA

Caldwell, Russell
Waynesburg Central
Waynesburg, PA

Callwood, Joycelyn
Monice
Harrisburg HS
St John, PR

Cally, Steven J
Sun Valley HS
Brookhaven, PA

Calnan, Danielle
Donegal HS
Mount Joy, PA

Calve, Robert
Mohawk JR-SR HS
Hillsville, PA

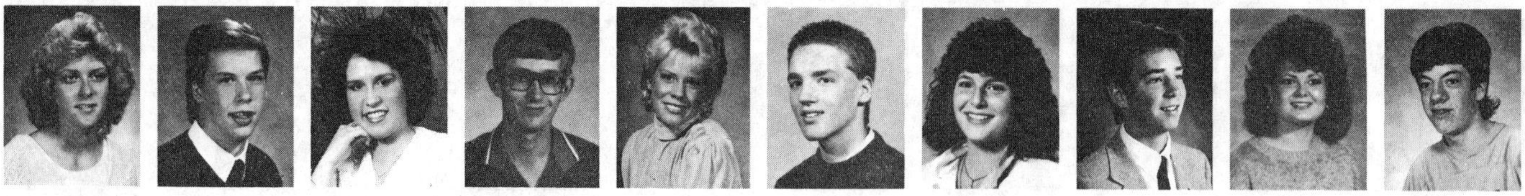

Calvert, Kandice
Conneaut Lake Area
Hartstown, PA

Camp, James
Cathedral Prep
Erie, PA

Camp, Lisa
St Benedict Acad
Erie, PA

Campbell, Brian
Ft Cherry HS
Bulger, PA

Campbell, Christine
Bellwood-Antis JR
SR HS
Tyrone, PA

Campbell, Jeff
Canon-Mc Millan
SR HS
Canonsburg, PA

Campbell, Jennifer
Riverside HS
Beaver Falls, PA

Campbell, Mark
Exeter Twp SR HS
Reading, PA

Campbell, Monica
Oxford Area HS
Nottingham, PA

Campbell, Jr
Richard Lee
Saltsburg SR HS
Saltsburg, PA

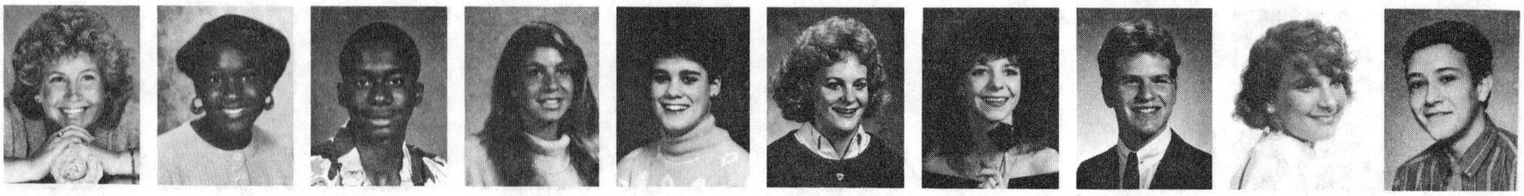

Campbell, Sheri
Lynn
West Mifflin Area
West Mifflin, PA

Campbell, Yolanda
M
Harry S Truman HS
Levittown, PA

Camper, Thomas
Chester HS
Chester, PA

Campion, Elizabeth
S
Harriton HS
Villanova, PA

Canavan, Jennifer
Methacton HS
Lansdale, PA

Cane, Cathy Jo
Rockwood Area HS
Somerset, PA

Canjar, Jennifer
Morrisville HS
Morrisville, PA

Cannella, Jeremy C
Downingtown SR
West Chester, PA

Cannon, Amy
Trinity HS
Camp Hill, PA

Canosa, Hans
Blue Mountain Acad
Hamburg, PA

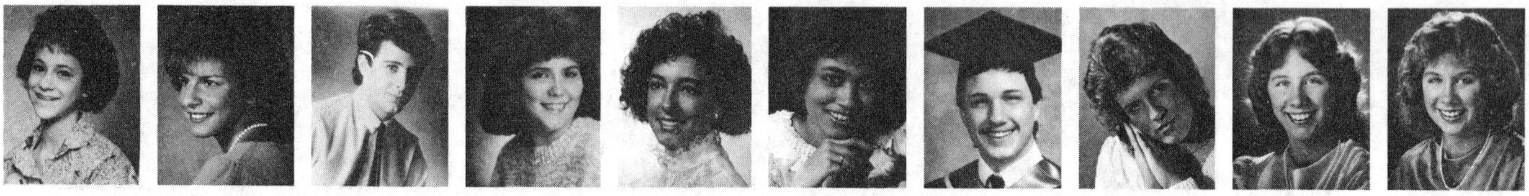

Canosa, Heidi
Blue Mountain Acad
Hamburg, PA

Capasso, Cinda
Hempfield Area SR
Greensburg, PA

Capecci, Michael E
Mt Lebanon HS
Pittsburgh, PA

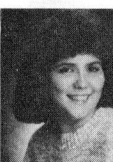

Caplinger, Jill
Center Area HS
Monaca, PA

Capobianco, Dena
Norte Dame HS
Martins Creek, PA

Capobres, Kimberly
Immaculate
Conception HS
Washington, PA

Capocci, Christopher
Saint John
Neumann HS
Philadelphia, PA

Capone, Christine
Marie
Mahanoy Area HS
Mahanoy City, PA

Capp, Cynthia
Bethel Park SR HS
Bethel Park, PA

Capp, Sandra
Bethel Park SR HS
Bethel Park, PA

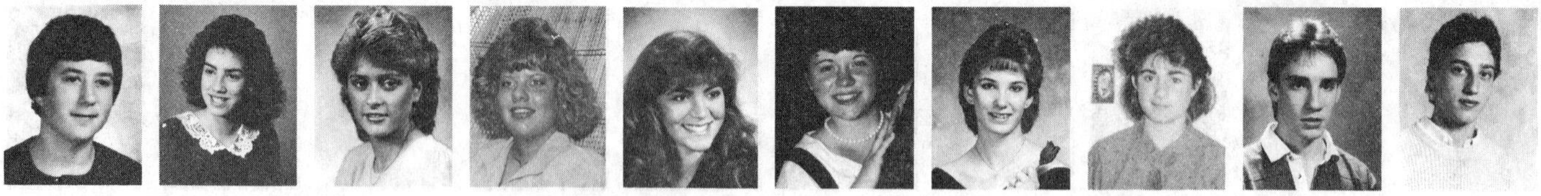

Capparell, Scott
Parkland HS
Allentown, PA

Caputo, Jennifer
Bethlehem Center
Brownsville, PA

Caravella, Lisa M
Freeland HS
White Haven, PA

Carbaugh, Marianne
E
James Buchanan HS
Mercersburg, PA

Carbo, Natalie
Fairview HS
Fairview, PA

Card, Shawna
Northwestern SR
Albion, PA

Cardell, Diane
Interboro HS
Glenolden, PA

Cardello, Chris
Pleasant Valley HS
Tannersville, PA

Cardiff, Bill
Penn Trafford HS
Level Green, PA

Cardoni, Jeff
Coughlin HS
Plains, PA

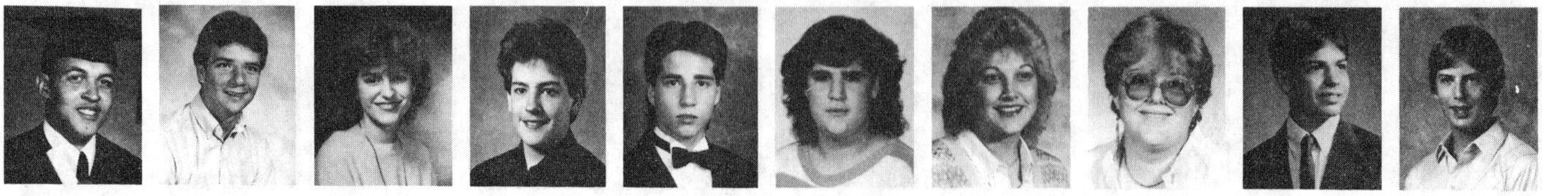

Cardwell, Jeffrey
Walter Biddle Saul
Philadelphia, PA

Carey, Kevin
Lake Lehman HS
Harveys Lake, PA

Carey, Kristin
Washington HS
Washington, PA

Carifo, Nicholas
Center Area HS
Aliquippa, PA

Caristo, Anthony M
St John Neumann
Philadelphia, PA

Caristo, Gina
STO-ROX HS
Mckees Rocks, PA

Carl, Beth
Tri Valley HS
Hegina, PA

Carl, Cindy L
William Allen HS
Allentown, PA

Carlier, Curt
Salisbury HS
Allentown, PA

Carlson, John A
Eisenhower HS
Sugar Grove, PA

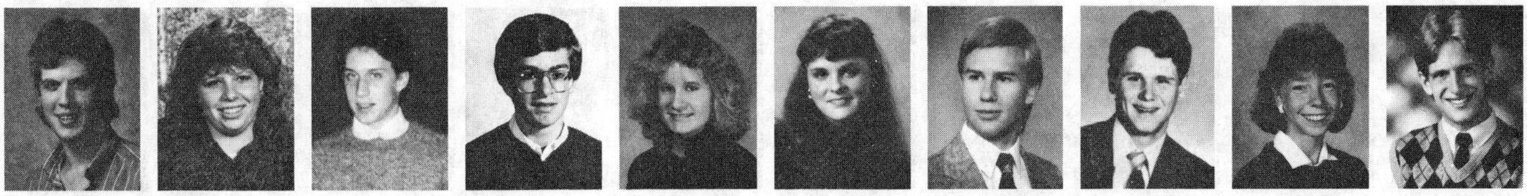

Carlson, Matthew
Warren Area HS
Warren, PA

Carman, Stacey
Richelle
Athens HS
Sayre, PA

Carnathan, John
Jeannette SR HS
Jeannette, PA

Carney, Daniel
Penn Cambria SR
Gallitzin, PA

Carney, Kathryn M
Altoona Area HS
Altoona, PA

Carniello, Sean
Waynesboro SR HS
Waynesboro, PA

Carpenter, Charles
Wyoming Valley
West HS
Forty Fort, PA

Carpenter, Chris
Hyndman HS
Buffalo Mls, PA

Carpenter, Kendra
Everett Area HS
Breezewood, PA

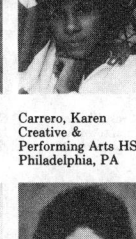

Carpenter, Mark J
Slippery Rock Area
Slippery Rock, PA

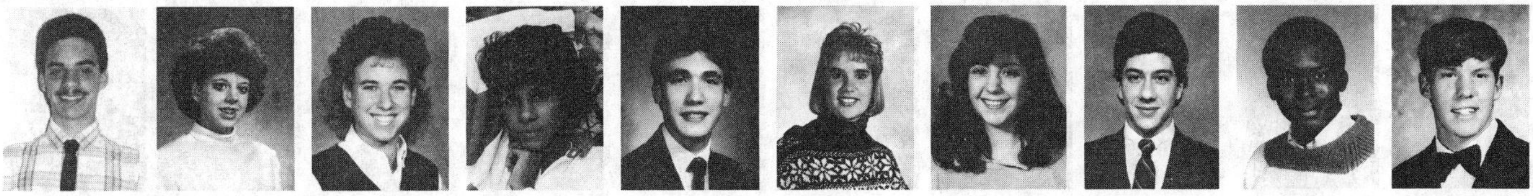

Carpinella, Michael
St John Neumann
Philadelphia, PA

Carr, Diana
West Branch Area
Morrisdale, PA

Carr, Lisa Ann
Nazareth Academy
Phila, PA

Carrero, Karen
Creative &
Performing Arts HS
Philadelphia, PA

Carriglitto, Jim
Blue Mountain HS
Rew Ringgold, PA

Carroll, Susan
East HS
Thornton, PA

Carroto, Christin
Mon Valley Catholic
Monessen, PA

Carruthers, Brad
Homer Center JR
SR HS
Homer City, PA

Carson, Jr William
M
William Allen HS
Allentown, PA

Carter, Chris
St Josephs Prep
Moorestown, NJ

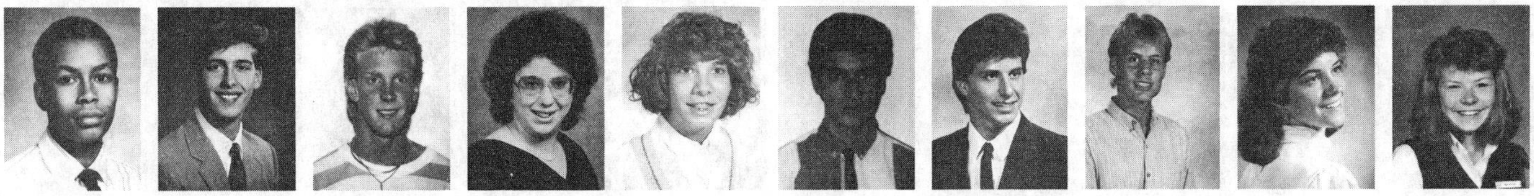

Carter, George
Central Catholic HS
Pittsburgh, PA

Carter, Jack
Wyomissing Area
Wyomissing, PA

Caruso, Andy
Archbishop Wood
HS For Boys
Willow Grove, PA

Caruso, Rochelle
Upper Darby HS
Upr Darby, PA

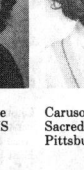

Caruso, Tonia
Sacred Heart HS
Pittsburgh, PA

Carvalho, Jose
G W C Career HS
Engineering
Philadelphia, PA

Casciani, Marc
Belle Vernon Area
Belle Vernon, PA

Case, Bradley L
Northern Lebanon
Myerstown, PA

Case, Chris
Millville HS
Millville, PA

Casey, Mary Beth
Nazareth Acad
Philadelphia, PA

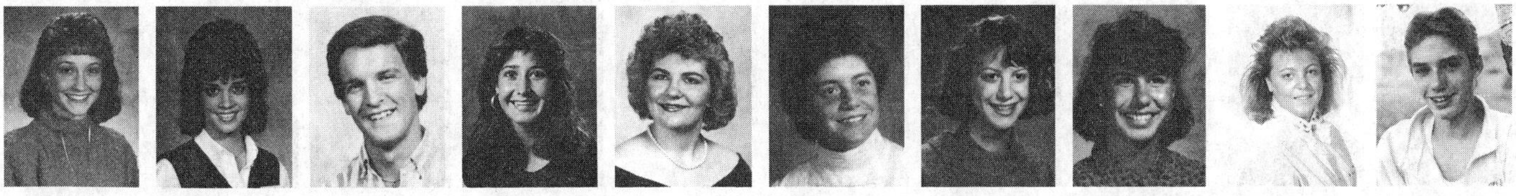

Casey, Michele Lyn
Knoch HS
Saxonburg, PA

Casey, Theresa
Nazareth Acad
Philadelphia, PA

Cashdollar, Charles
Carrick HS
Pittsburgh, PA

Cason, Dawn L
Philadelphia HS For
Philadelphia, PA

Casper, Theresa
HS For The
Creative & Perf Arts
Philadelphia, PA

Cassel, Jacqueline
Maryon
Lower Dauphin HS
Hummelstown, PA

Cassel, Jennifer
Emmaus HS
Macungie, PA

Castagna, Carla
Garden Spot HS
New Holland, PA

Castellano, Nadine
Scranton Central
Scranton, PA

Casto, Steven
New Covenant Acad
Mansfield, PA

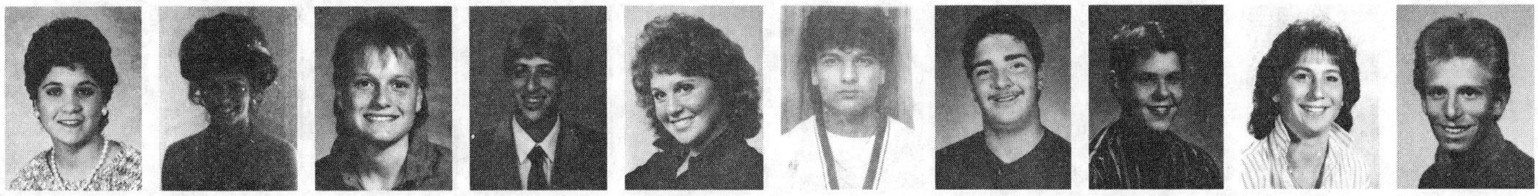

Catalone, Gwenn
St Marys Area HS
St Marys, PA

Caterino, Lynn
West Mifflin Area
W Mifflin, PA

Caul, Ashlee
Ambridge Area HS
Ambridge, PA

Cavalier, Joe
Central Cambria HS
Ebensburg, PA

Cavalier, Robin
Connellsville HS
Connellsville, PA

Cavallo, Fernando F
Archbishop Ryan
For Boys
Philadelphia, PA

Caviris, Mike
Monessen HS
Monessen, PA

Cawley, Tom
Indiana Area SR HS
Indiana, PA

Cazzille, Charyl
Scott/Cashs HS
Coatesville, PA

Cecere, Jr Ralph J
Swissvale HS
Swissvale, PA

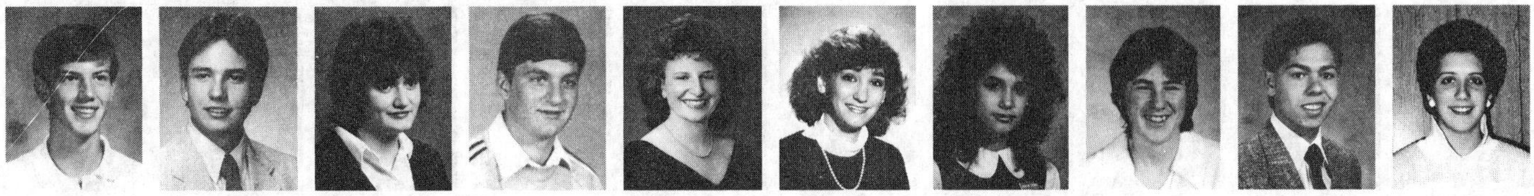

Cecil, Christopher
Boiling Springs JR
SR HS
Boiling Spgs, PA

Ceklosky, Jr Joseph
F
Wyoming Valley
West HS
Kingston, PA

Cekola, Amy
Mc Guffey HS
Washington, PA

Cell, Paul
Council Rock HS
Richboro, PA

Cellini, Deena
Strath Haven HS
Wallingford, PA

Censurato, Laura
Acad Of Notre
Dame De Namur
King Of Prussia, PA

Cepparulo,
Jacqueline
West Catholic Girls
Philadelphia, PA

Cerezo, Shawn
Fort Cherry JR-SR
Bulger, PA

Cernuto, Jr Terence
F
Greensburg Central
Catholic HS
Mt Pleasant, PA

Cerra, Kim
Carbondale Area JR
SR HS
Carbondale, PA

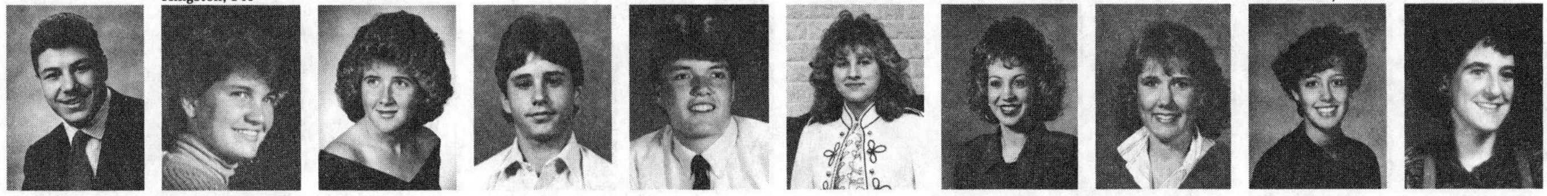

Cervone, Robert S
Meadville Area SR
Meadville, PA

Cesarini, Carrie
Bishop O Hara HS
Peckville, PA

Cessna, Julie
Meyersdale Area HS
Wellersburg, PA

Cessna, Robert
Connellsville HS
Connellsville, PA

Cessna, Todd A
Bedford HS
Bedford, PA

Chamberlain,
Katrina
Everett Area HS
Everett, PA

Chambliss, Eden
Center HS
Monaca, PA

Champion, Christie
Leechburg Erea HS
Leechburg, PA

Champness, Jennifer
Central York SR HS
York, PA

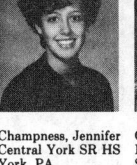

Chandler, Jodi
Northern Lehigh HS
Slatington, PA

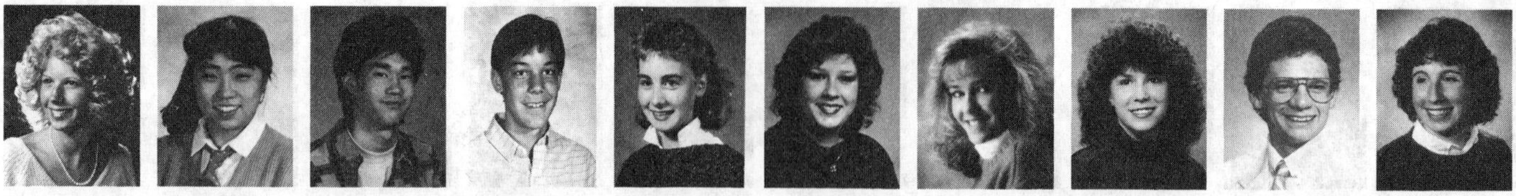

Chandler, Michelle C
Wilson HS
Sinking Spring, PA

Chaney, Yoshimi
Philadelphia HS For
Philadelphia, PA

Chang, Eric
Methacton HS
Audubon, PA

Chapman, Craig
Elizabethtown Area
Elizabethtown, PA

Chapman, Jenny
Moon SR HS
Coraopolis, PA

Chapman, Kimberly
Frankford HS
Philadelphia, PA

Chappell, Cynthia
Richland HS
Gibsonia, PA

Chappie, Leanna
Greater Johnstown
Johnstown, PA

Chapple, David
Coughlin HS
Wilkes Barre, PA

Chariton, Debbie
E L Meyers HS
Wilkes-Barre, PA

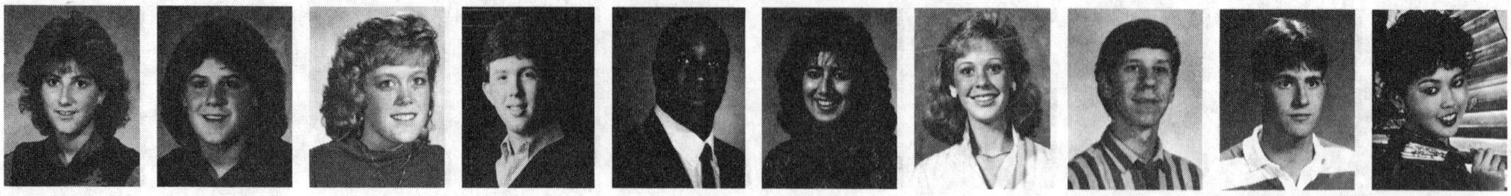

Charlier, Jodi
Burgettstown Area
JR SR HS
Bulger, PA

Charlier, Rebecca A
Burgettstown Area
JR SR HS
Bulger, PA

Charnock, Julie
West Chester East
West Chester, PA

Chart, Dave
General Mclane HS
Edinboro, PA

Chatman, Shaun
Norristown HS
Norristown, PA

Chaudry, Rabia
Gateway SR HS
Monroeville, PA

Check, Shannon
Uniontown Area HS
Uniontown, PA

Checket, William J
Northern Lebanon
Jonestown, PA

Chelen, Daniel
Greensburg-Salem
New Alexandria, PA

Chen, Julia
Altoona Area HS
Altoona, PA

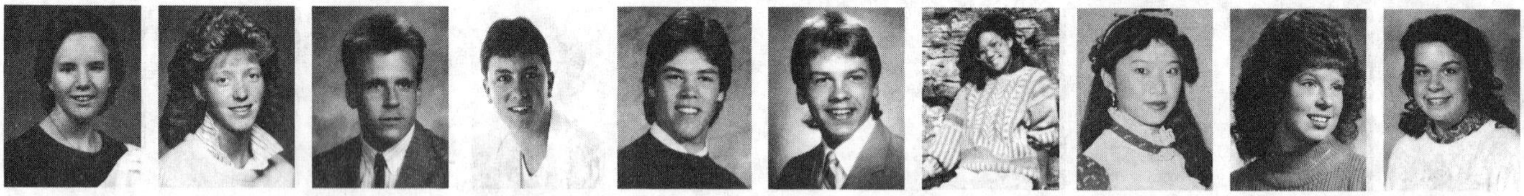

Cheney, Tracy
Pocono Christian
Stroudsburg, PA

Cheplic, Lori
Ringgold HS
Finleyville, PA

Cheplick, Dennis R
Marian HS
Nesquehoning, PA

Cherry, Ken
Bellwood-Antis HS
Tyrone, PA

Chesla, Matthew
Lawsdale Catholic
North Wales, PA

Chesonis, Derrick
Shenandoah Valley
Shenandoah, PA

Cheu, Jennifer B K
East Stroudsburg
Area HS
East Stroudsburg, PA

Chhour, Lorng
Olney HS
Philadelphia, PA

Childs, Denise
Connellsville Area
Connellsville, PA

Chille, Maria
Bellwood-Antis HS
Bellwood, PA

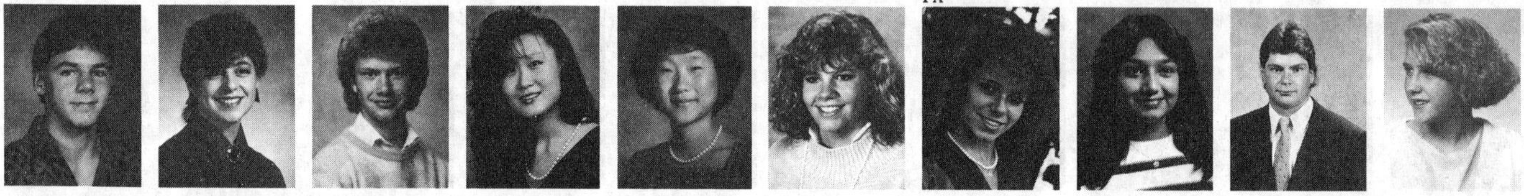

Chipeleski, Daryl
West Hazleton HS
Drums, PA

Chipoletti, Kara
Valley HS
Arnold, PA

Chisek, Joe
Forest City Regional
Browndale, PA

Choi, Mindy
Cardinal O Hara HS
Newtown Square, PA

Choi, Un Jung
Plymouth
Whitemarsh HS
Conshohocken, PA

Chopp, Danielle
Yough SR HS
West Newton, PA

Chopp, Kimberly
Yough HS
Smithton, PA

Chopra, Gitanjali
Ridley SR HS
Ridley Pk, PA

Choroszewski, Jeff
Ambridge Area HS
Ambridge, PA

Chrismer, Lisa
York Catholic HS
York, PA

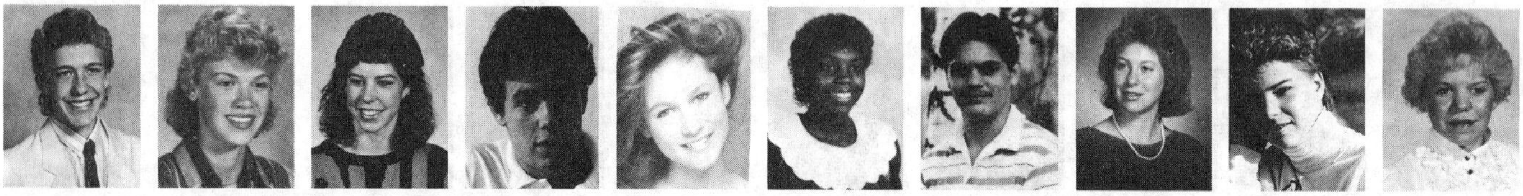

Christensen, P Niels
Devon Preparatory
Broomall, PA

Christian, Laura
Upper Marion Area
King Of Prussia, PA

Christie, Andrea
North Allegheny
SDR HS
Pittsburgh, PA

Christie, Craig
Central Bucks West
Chalfont, PA

Christie, Heather
Oley Valley HS
Oley, PA

Christmas, Katina Simone
Coatesville HS
Coatesville, PA

Chronister, M Shane
Tyrone Area HS
Tyrone, PA

Chuba, Kellie
Valley HS
Arnold, PA

Chupp, Kristin J
Garden Spot HS
New Holland, PA

Chura, Cheryl
Purchase Line HS
Burnside, PA

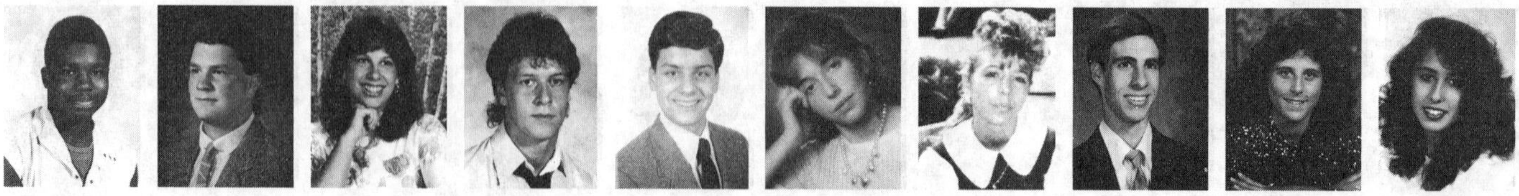

Churchman, James A
Reading HS
Reading, PA

Ciabattoni, David
Exeter Twp HS
Reading, PA

Ciardi, Lori
Sayre Area HS
Sayre, PA

Cicchino, Steve
Canevin HS
Pittsburgh, PA

Cicerini, Gary
Scranton Prep
Dunmore, PA

Cicero, Kathleen
Pleasant Valley HS
Kresgeville, PA

Cina, Elena
West Philadelphia
Cthlc Girls HS
Philadelphia, PA

Cinfici, William
Reading HS
Reading, PA

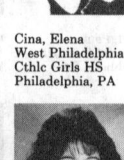

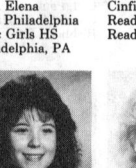

Cioppa, Rosemary
New Castle HS
New Castle, PA

Civiletti, Pia
Wyoming Area HS
Pittston, PA

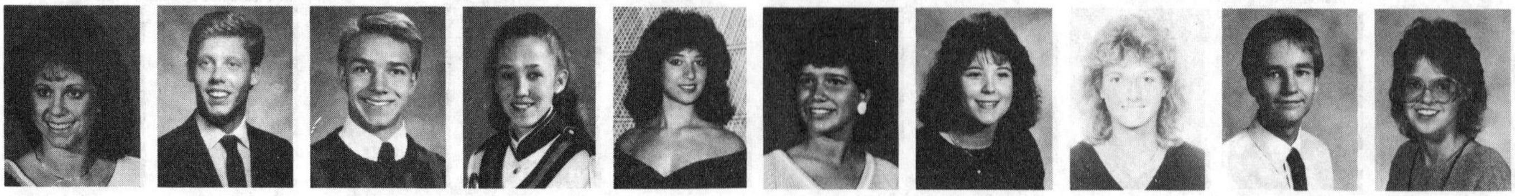

Clabaugh, Denise
Connellsville SR HS
Connellsville, PA

Clark, Brett A
North Allegheny HS
Allison Pk, PA

Clark, Chris
Butler Area HS
Butler, PA

Clark, Claudia
Upper Darby SR HS
Drexel Hill, PA

Clark, Cynthia
High School Of
Engineering
Philadelphia, PA

Clark, Cynthia
Waynesburg HS
Waynesburg, PA

Clark, Hollie
Meadville HS
Meadville, PA

Clark, Kimberly
Upper Darby HS
Drexel Hill, PA

Clark, Matthew B
Redland HS
Zionsville, PA

Clark, Melinda J
Everett Area HS
Everett, PA

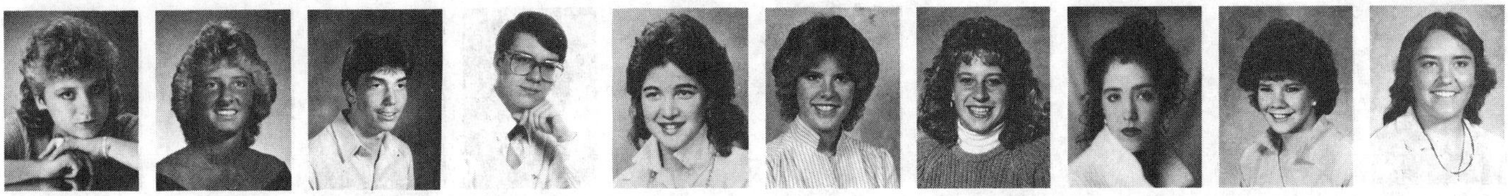

Clark, Melissa
Northern Bedford County HS
Everett, PA

Clark, Rebecca L
Downingtown Area
West Chester, PA

Clark, Richard
Brockway Area HS
Brockway, PA

Clark, Todd R
Shikellamy HS
Sunbury, PA

Clark, Tracy
Curwensville Area
Curwensville, PA

Clark, Tracy M
Harbor Creek HS
Erie, PA

Claus, Linda A
Hampton HS
Allison Park, PA

Claypole, Heidi
Aliquippa JR SR
Aliquippa, PA

Claypool, Jennifer
Kittaning HS
Worthington, PA

Claypoole, Martha
Oxford Area HS
Oxford, PA

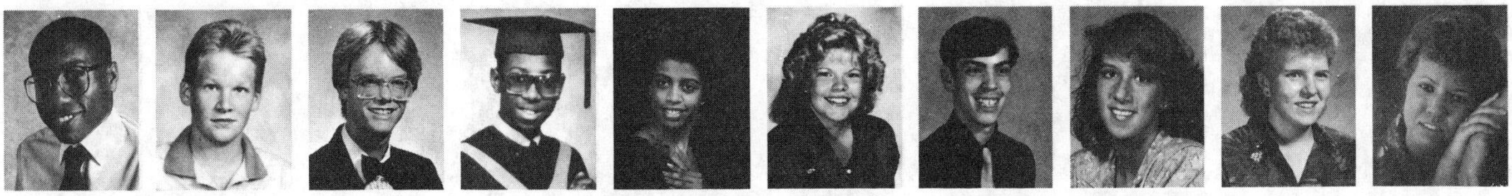

Clayton, Jr James
The Christian Acad
Chester, PA

Cleet, Chris
Quakertown Comm SR HS
Quakertown, PA

Clemans, Corey
Downingtown HS
Downingtown, PA

Clements, David
Chester HS
Brookhaven, PA

Clements, Kia La Dawn
Cardinal O Hara HS
Chester, PA

Cline, Amy
Northern HS
Dillsburg, PA

Cline, Austin Reed
Downingtown SR
Coatesville, PA

Cline, Jeannine
Central York SR HS
York, PA

Cline, Jennifer L
Forbes Road HS
Waterfall, PA

Cline, Nicole
Biglerville HS
Gardners, PA

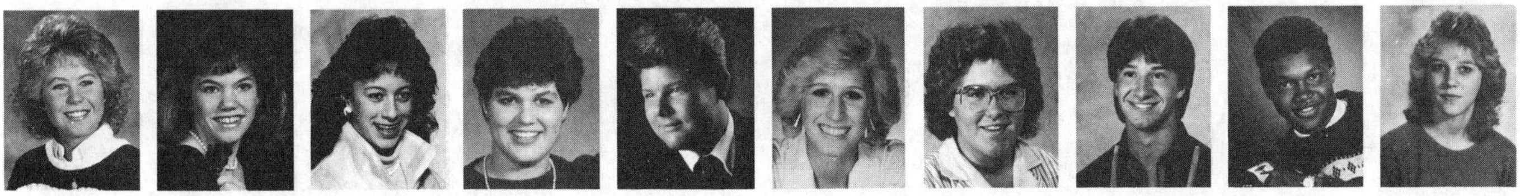

Clinger, Dawn
Keystone JR SR HS
Knox, PA

Cloran, Karen
Cardinal O Hara HS
Secane, PA

Close, Nicole
Claysburg-Kimmel
Claysburg, PA

Clouse, Amy L
Butler Area SR HS
Butler, PA

Clouser, Jeffrey
Boyertown SR HS
Bechtelsville, PA

Clouser, Megan
Newport HS
Newport, PA

Clutter, Jennifer
Mc Guffey HS
West Finley, PA

Clutter, Lawrence
Mc Guffey HS
Claysville, PA

Cobb, Eugene
Ambridge Area HS
Ambridge, PA

Coble, Mandy Kay
Purchase Line HS
Clymer, PA

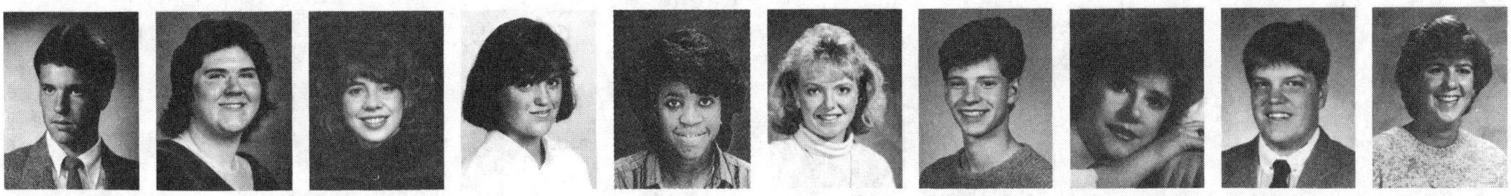

Coble, Scott
Elizabethtown Area
Elizabethtown, PA

Coccagna, Carol
West Phila Catholic Girls HS
Philadelphia, PA

Cochran, Beth
Beaver Area SR HS
Beaver, PA

Cody, Colleen
Gwynedd-Mercy
Warrington, PA

Cody, Janine R
Coatesville Area HS
Coatesville, PA

Cody, Susan
Seneca Valley SR
Evans Cty, PA

Coeyman, Chad
Red Lion SR HS
Red Lion, PA

Coffin, Dawn Renee
Northern Lehigh HS
Slatington, PA

Coffman, John
Beth Center
Fredericktown, PA

Coffman, Megan
Carlisle HS
Carlisle, PA

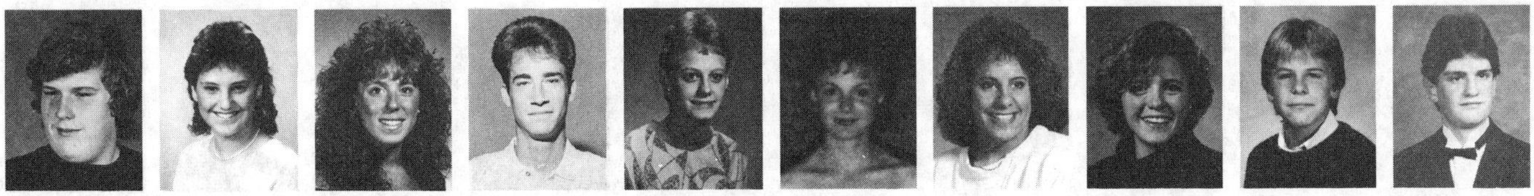

Coffman, Tom
Connellsville Area
Connellsville, PA

Coggins, Donna
Lakeland HS
Carbondale, PA

Cohen, Beth
Abington SR HS
Abington, PA

Cohen, Brett-Evan
Plymouth Whitemarsh HS
Flourtown, PA

Cohick, Stephanie
Shamokin Area HS
Shamokin, PA

Colacicco, Lynda
North Pocano HS
Moscow, PA

Colaizzi, Maureen
Beaver Falls HS
Beaver Falls, PA

Colaizzi, Merritt
Ellis School
Glenshaw, PA

Colangelo, IV Augustus B
State College Area Intermediat HS
State College, PA

Colden, Richard
Cardinal O Hara HS
Clifton Hgts, PA

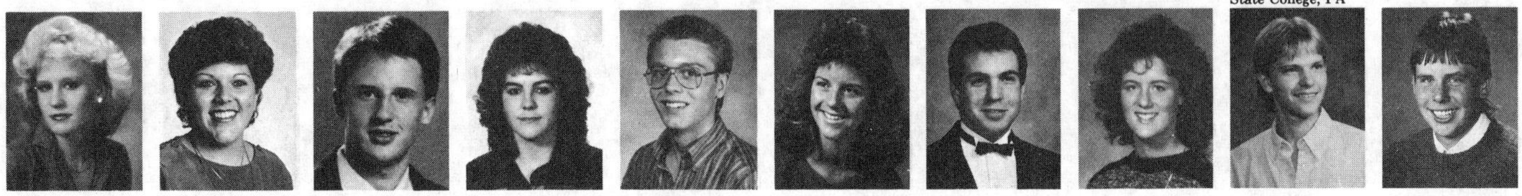

Cole, Christine
Meadville Area SR
Conneaut Lake, PA

Colella, Candace
New Castle SR HS
New Castle, PA

Coleman, April
Mercy Vocational
Philadelphia, PA

Coleman, Brenda
Oil City SR HS
Oil City, PA

Coleman, Dale
Brookville Area HS
Summerville, PA

Coleman, Joann M
Central York SR HS
York, PA

Coleman, Kevin
Cardinal O Hara HS
Newtown Sq, PA

Coleman, Tracy
Central York SR HS
York, PA

Coleson, Brian
Ephrata SR HS
Ephrata, PA

Colgan, Scott
Burrell SR HS
Lower Burrell, PA

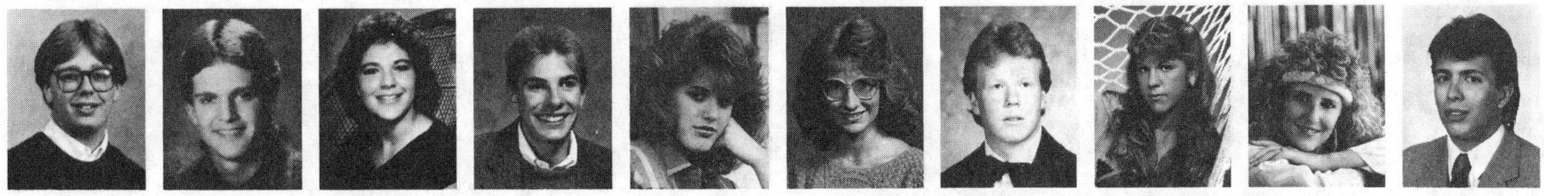

Collar, Todd
Freeport Area HS
Freeport, PA

Collette, David C
Lincoln HS
Portersville, PA

Collins, Anita
Neshaminy HS
Parkland, PA

Collins, Dwight
Cedar Crest HS
Lebanon, PA

Collins, Kris
Acad Of The New
Charlotte, NC

Collins, Lenora
Belle Vernon Area
West Newton, PA

Collins, Sean
St Josephs Preparatory Schl
Philadelphia, PA

Collins, Stephanie
Everett Area HS
Clearville, PA

Collins, Susan
Hopewell HS
Aliquippa, PA

Collura, Joseph
Palmyra HS
Palmyra, PA

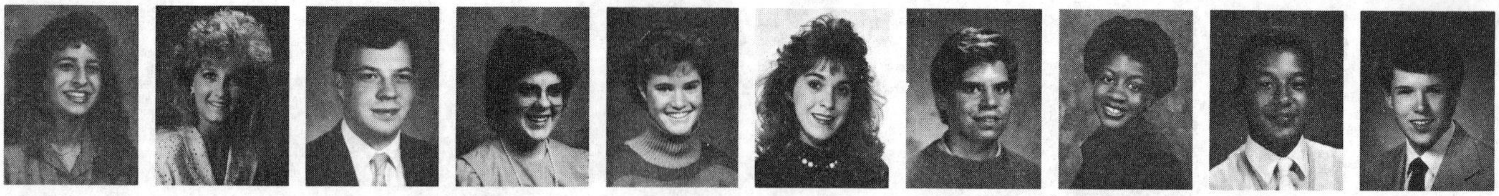

Colmenares, Yvonne M
Governor Mifflin HS
Reading, PA

Colombo, Stacylee
Altoona Area HS
Altoona, PA

Colonna, Matthew
Greensburg Centra
Catholic HS
Greensburg, PA

Colvin, Tricia
Punxsutawney Area
Punxsutawney, PA

Conahan, Ann
Notre Dame HS
Stroudsburg, PA

Condella, Tammy
Mid Valley
Secondary Ctr
Olyphant, PA

Confer, Sean
Lock Haven SR HS
Howard, PA

Conix, Lucinda
West Catholic Girls
Philadelphia, PA

Conjura, Ed
Our Lady Of
Lourdes Regiona
Shamokin, PA

Conklin, Timothy Allen
Salisbury HS
Allentown, PA

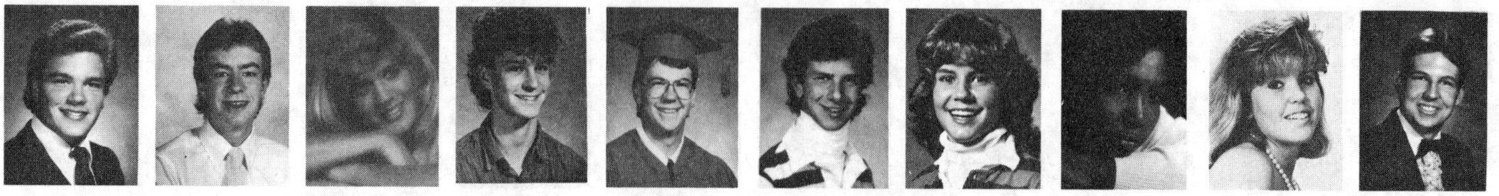

Conlen, Jr John J
Norristown Area HS
E Norriton, PA

Conley, Scott
Phil-Mont Christian
Glenside, PA

Conner, Kirsten
Fairview HS
Fairview, PA

Conner, Kyle
Henderson HS
West Chester, PA

Conner, Patrick W
Quakertown HS
Quakertown, PA

Connolly, Joseph
Abington Heights
Clarks Summit, PA

Connolly, Meghan
The Ellis Schl
Allison Park, PA

Connor, Carol Ann
Susquehanna
Township HS
Harrisburg, PA

Connor, Casey
Scranton Prep Schl
Scranton, PA

Connor, Timothy
John Bartram HS
Philadelphia, PA

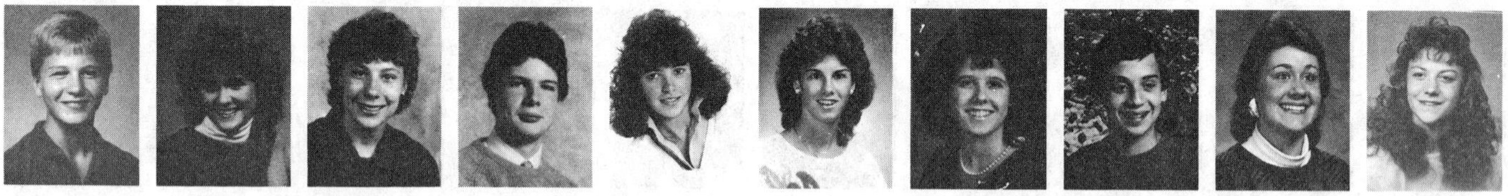

Conrad, IV John B
West Perry HS
Shermans Dale, PA

Conrad, Melissa L
Conrad Weiser HS
Wernersville, PA

Conroy, Melissa
Greater Latrobe HS
Latrobe, PA

Conroy, Paul W P
Pocono Central
Catholic HS
Canadensis, PA

Consiglio, Jackie
Bishop Guilfoyle HS
Altoona, PA

Consiglio, Kellie L
Hollidaysburg Area
Hollidaysburg, PA

Conte, Maria
Bishop Kenrick HS
Norristown, PA

Conti, Eric
Mercer Area HS
Sharpsville, PA

Cook, Amanda
Pequea Valley HS
Gap, PA

Cook, Heather
Northern Lehigh HS
Slatington, PA

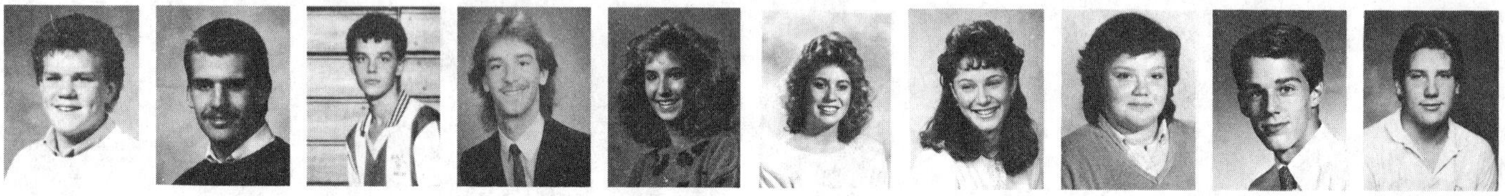

Cook, John
Churchill HS
Pittsburgh, PA

Cook, Kenneth
Du Bois Area HS
Dubois, PA

Cooke, Derek
Blair Co Christian
Hollidaysburg, PA

Coolbaugh, Eugene E
Schuylkill Haven
Schuylkill Haven, PA

Coon, Lesley
Warren Area HS
Warren, PA

Coon, Stacie
Marion Center Area
Home, PA

Cooney, Colleen
West Scranton HS
Scranton, PA

Cooper, Amelia
Villa Maria Acad
Erie, PA

Cooper, Carl
Notre Dame HS
Easton, PA

Cooper, Doug
Ringgold HS
Monongahela, PA

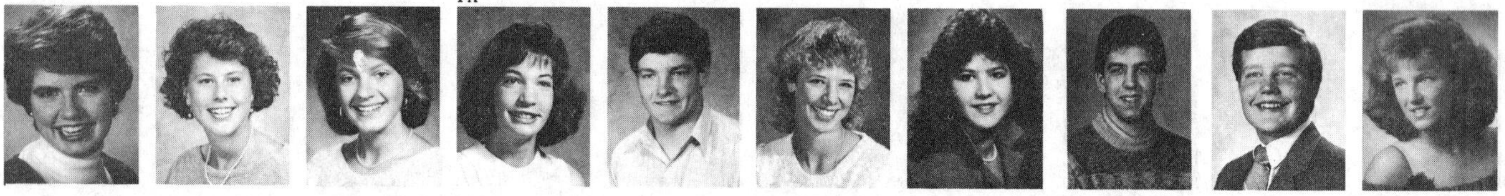

Cooper, Jane
Tunkhannock Area
Mehoopany, PA

Cooper, Meaghen E
Gwynedd Mercy
Doylestown, PA

Cooper, Nicole
Huntingdon HS
Huntingdon, PA

Cooperman, Cindy
Lancaster Country
Day Schl
Reading, PA

Corbett, David
Jefferson-Morgan
Mather, PA

Corbin, Stephanie
Brockway Area HS
Reynoldsville, PA

Cordero, Brenda
Freedom HS
Bethlehem, PA

Cordisio, Gino
Monongahelo Valley
Catholic HS
Brownsville, PA

Cordwell, Curtis
Blue Mt S D A
Orwigsburg, PA

Corey, Tasha
Linesville HS
Linesville, PA

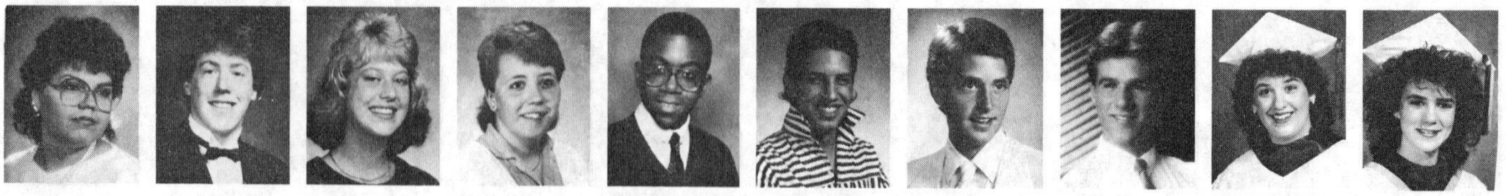

Corkell, Theresa
John S Fine SR HS
W Nanticoke, PA

Corkery, William
Monsignor Bonner
Folcroft, PA

Corle, Nicole
Claysburg-Kimmel
Imler, PA

Cornell, Kim
Saltsburg JR-SR HS
Saltsburg, PA

Corprew, Warren
Blue Mountain Acad
Willow Grove, PA

Corradene, Albert
Valley HS
New Kensington, PA

Corradino, Michael C
Penn Manor HS
Conestoga, PA

Corradino, Randy
Old Forge HS
Old Forge, PA

Corsi, Diane
Cardinal O Hara HS
Broomall, PA

Cosenza, Margaret
Saint Huberts HS
For Girls
Philadelphia, PA

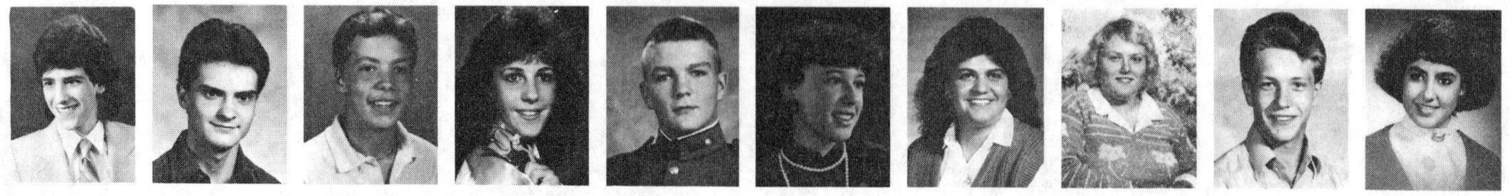

Costabile, Richard
Dover Area HS
Dover, PA

Costella, Sean
Danville Area HS
Danville, PA

Costellic, Robert P
Penn-Trafford HS
Irwin, PA

Costello, Carole
Sun Valley HS
Aston, PA

Costello, Keith
Valley Forge
Military Acad
Norristown, PA

Costello, Kelly
Northwestern
Lehigh HS
Schnecksvile, PA

Costentine, Colette
Ambridge Area HS
Freedom, PA

Courtney, Vanessa
Cambridge Springs
Cambridge Spg, PA

Courtot, Robert
Penn Cambria HS
Lilly, PA

Coviello, Alisa
Bishop O Hara HS
Jessup, PA

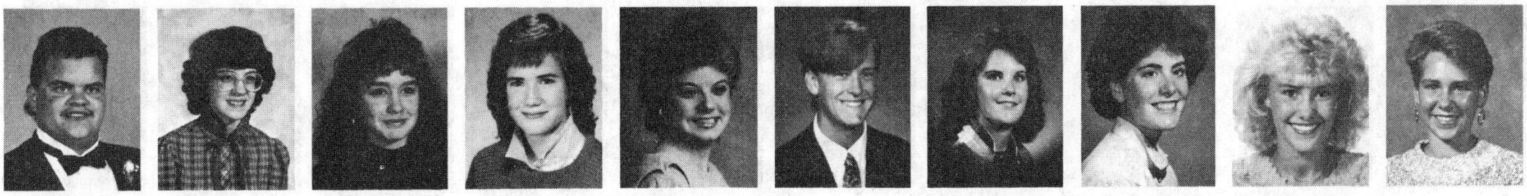

Cowan, Christopher
Fort Le Boeuf HS
Waterford, PA

Cowan, Kristina Caroline
Mifflinburg Area HS
Mufflinburg, PA

Cox, Heather
Meadville Area SR
Meadville, PA

Cox, Kathryn S
Wellsboro Area HS
Wellsboro, PA

Cox, Melissa A
South Side Beaver
Clinton, PA

Cox, Michael S
Lancaster Catholic
Lititz, PA

Coxon, Amy
Central Dauphin HS
Harrisburg, PA

Coyle, Donna
Nazareth SR HS
Nazareth, PA

Crable, Jennifer
Uniontown Area HS
Uniontown, PA

Crable, Sara
Uniontown Area HS
Uniontown, PA

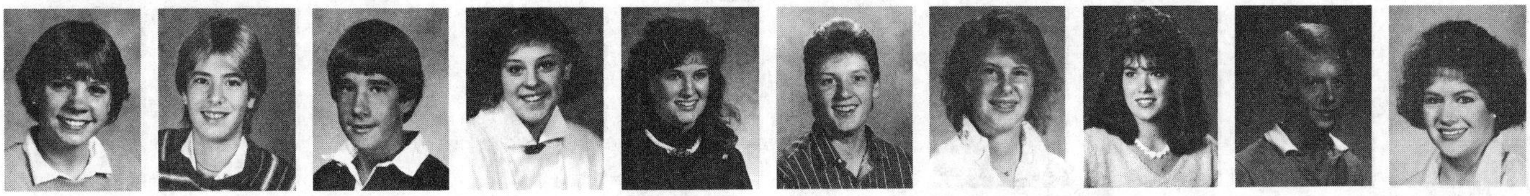

Craig, Jennifer
Danville HS
Danville, PA

Craig, Michael
Carlynton JR/SR
Carnegie, PA

Craighead, Benjamin
State Coll Area Intermediate HS
State College, PA

Cramer, Becky
Mon Valley Catholic
Monongahela, PA

Cramer, Jennifer
Stroudsburg HS
Stroudsburg, PA

Cramer, Robert
Blacklick Valley JR SR HS
Twin Rocks, PA

Craven, Dorothy
Upper Dublin HS
Oreland, PA

Cravener, Peggysue
Highlands SR HS
Tarentum, PA

Cravotta, Samuel
Tri Valley SR HS
Fairchance, PA

Crawford, Kelly
Tyrone Area HS
Tyrone, PA

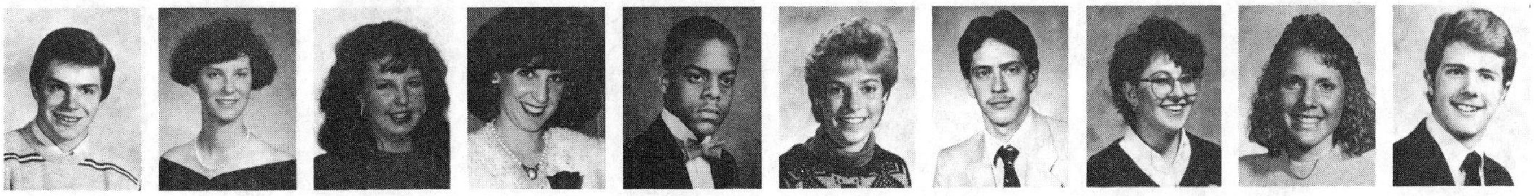

Crawford, Robert
Blacklic Valley HS
Ebensburg, PA

Creighton, Christine S
Methacton HS
Audubon, PA

Cremeans, Stacy
Cedarcrest HS
Lebanon, PA

Creswell, Laura
Daniel Boone HS
Douglassville, PA

Crews, Jason B
Roman Catholic HS
Philadelphia, PA

Cribbs, Heather
Blairsville SR HS
Blairsville, PA

Crilley, Joseph Peter
Northwestern SR
E Springfield, PA

Crinti, Lisa
Lancaster Catholic
Lancaster, PA

Crise, Tricia
Belle Vernon Area
West Newton, PA

Crist, Brian
Williams Valley HS
Mechanicsville, MD

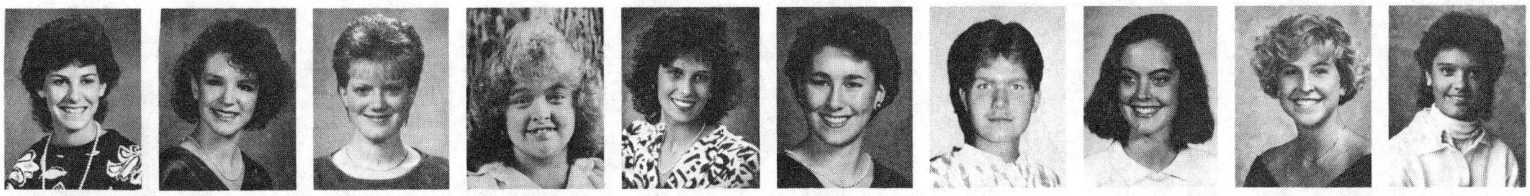

Crist, Michelle Denise
Eastern York HS
York, PA

Crist, Nicolle
Archbishop Prendergast HS
Collingdale, PA

Crocker, Kimberly
West Scranton HS
Scranton, PA

Cromis, Rebecca
Danville SR HS
Washingtonville, PA

Crompton, Melissa
Trinity HS
Washington, PA

Cronin, Megan
Bishop Mc Devitt
Oreland, PA

Crosby, James
Northeast Catholic
Philadelphia, PA

Crosby, Kristen
North Allegheny SR
Pittsburgh, PA

Croskey, Yvette M
Mount Saint Joseph
Sumter, SC

Crosson, Lori
Lewistown HS
Lewistown, PA

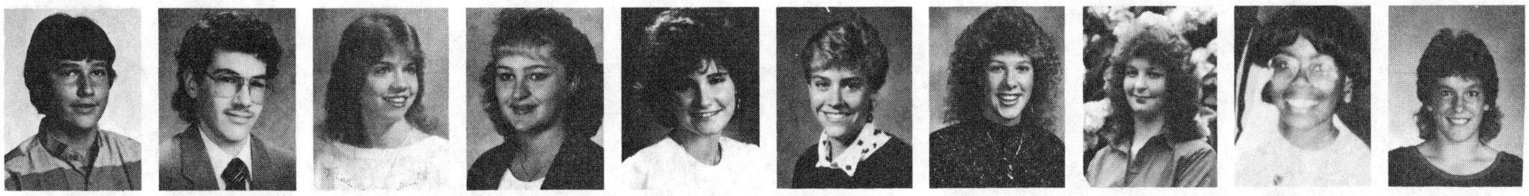

Crosten, Jeffrey
New Castle HS
New Castle, PA

Croteau, Craig
Wyoming Area SR
W Pittston, PA

Croushore, Deanna Elaine
Belle Vernon Area
Belle Vernon, PA

Croyle, Linda
Penns Manor HS
Alverda, PA

Croyle, Maria
Somerset Area SR
Somerset, PA

Croyle, Toddy
Moon SR HS
Coraopolis, PA

Crozier, Patricia
Neshaminy SR HS
Langhorne, PA

Cruley, Stacy
Blacklick Valley HS
Nanty Glo, PA

Crummy, Tammi A
William Penn HS
Philadelphia, PA

Csuhta, Christine
Canon-Mc Millan
Canonsburg, PA

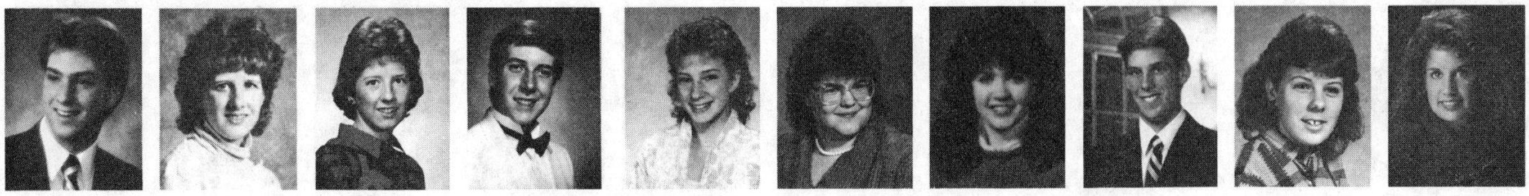

Cuff, Tom
Cardinal Brennan
Frackville, PA

Culp, Cathy
Dallas SR HS
Dallas, PA

Culp, Kimberly
Dallas SR HS
Dallas, PA

Cummings, Craig
Sun Valley HS
Brookhaven, PA

Cummins, Erin
Bradford Central Christian HS
Bradford, PA

Cunningham, Amy Beth
Wyalusing Valley
Laceyville, PA

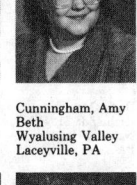

Cunningham, April
Steel Valley SR HS
Homestead, PA

Cunningham, Gregory Graham
Mercer HS
Mercer, PA

Cunningham, Tanya
Oxford Area HS
W Nottingham, PA

Cupp, Michelle
Center HS
Monaca, PA

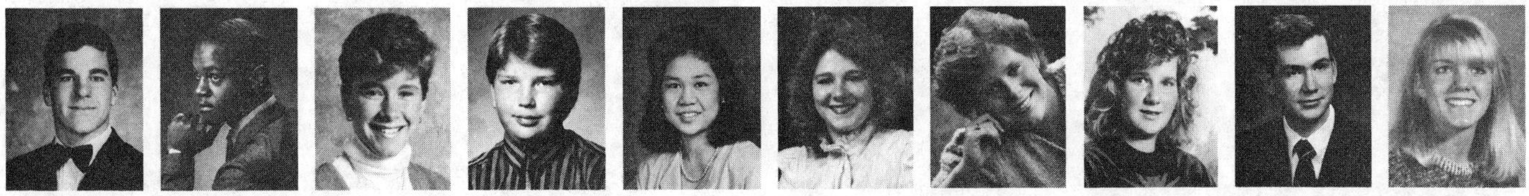

Curran, Vincent
St Josephs Prep
Villanova, PA

Curry, Juan
Uniontown Area HS
New Salem, PA

Curtis, Courtney
Academy Of Notre
West Chester, PA

Cushey, Erich
Ringgold SR HS
Finleyville, PA

Custodio, Maribel A
Bethlehem Catholic
Bethlehem, PA

Cuthbertson, Jill
Bradford Area HS
Bradford, PA

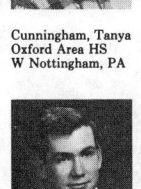

Cyphert, Amy
Wilmington Area
New Wilmington, PA

Cywinski, Tara
Bishop O Reilly HS
Swoyersville, PA

Czarnecki, John
Bishop Mc Devitt
Harrisburg, PA

Czop, Keely
Henderson HS
West Chester, PA

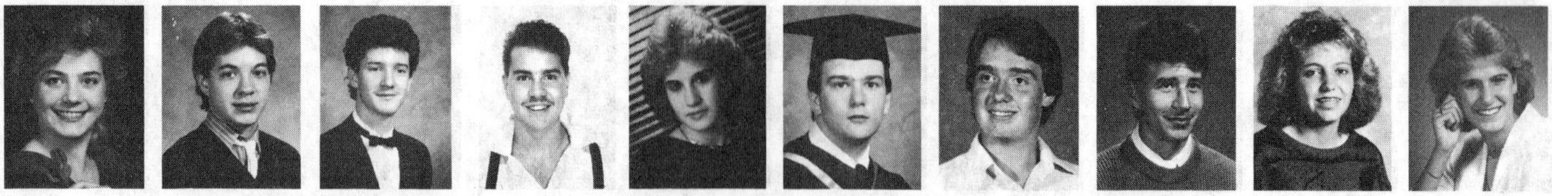

Czuchan, Andrea
Cardinal O Hara HS
Media, PA

Czulewicz, Roger A
Cathedral
Preparatory HS
Fairview, PA

D Ambrosio, Ralph
V
St John Neumann
Philadelphia, PA

D Amico, Jack A
East Allegheny HS
North Versailles, PA

D Amico, Melanie
Central HS
Scranton, PA

D Arcy, Jr William
F
Archbishop Wood
For Boys
Holland, PA

D Auria, Richard W
Connellsville Area
Connellsville, PA

D Avanti, Anthony
Our Lady Of
Lourdes Regiona
Kulpmont, PA

Dacey, Tresa
Panther Valley HS
Nesquehoning, PA

Dadio, Terri
Freedom HS
Easton, PA

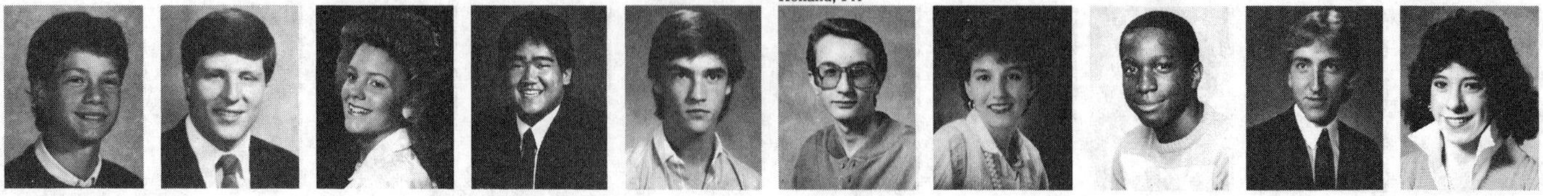

Dager, Eric
Central Bucks West
Chalfont, PA

Dainty, Daniel
Belle Vernon Area
Belle Vernon, PA

Daisley, Dawn
Reynolds HS
Greenville, PA

Dait, Pierre
Perkiomen Schl
Lehighton, PA

Dale, Jon
West Branch Area
Morrisdale, PA

Dalessandri, James
Aliquippa HS
Aliquippa, PA

Dalessandri, Susan
Aliquippa HS
Aliquippa, PA

Daley, Edsel
Blue Mountain Acad
Queens, NY

Dalmagro, William
Butler Area SR HS
Butler, PA

Daman, Tonya
Rochester HS
New Brighton, PA

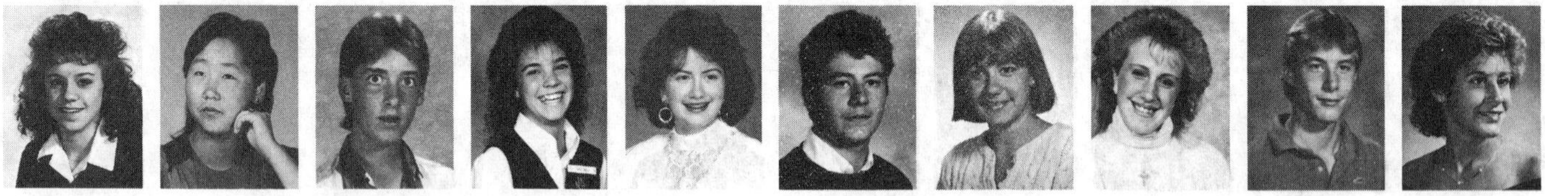

Dambeck, Jolene
Bishop Guilpoyle
Altoona, PA

Dambrosia,
Christine
Serra Catholic HS
Monroeville, PA

Danese, Rich
Central Bucks West
Warrington, PA

Dangelo, Nicole
Nazareth Acad
Philadelphia, PA

Daniel, Maria
Cristina
Center Area HS
Monaca, PA

Daniello, Dennis
Reynolds HS
Greenville, PA

Daniels, Deana
Springfield HS
Oreland, PA

Daniels, Erica
Fort Le Boeuf HS
Erie, PA

Daniels, Michael
Corry Area HS
Corry, PA

Danowski, Rebecca
Hatboro-Horsham
Hatboro, PA

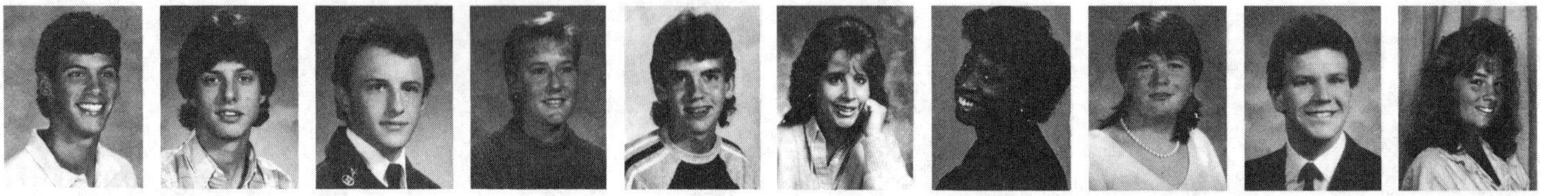

Danzis, Loren
Central Bucks HS
Doylestown, PA

Daquelente, Tony
Richland HS
Wexford, PA

Dashem, Howard
Penns Valley Area
Centre Hall, PA

Daugherty, Amy
Annville-Cleona HS
Annville, PA

Daveler, Phillip J
Ridley SR HS
Ridley Park, PA

Davenport, Julie A
Jamestown HS
Greenville, PA

Davenport, Sonya
Susquehanna HS
Harrisburg, PA

Davey, Patricia
Bishop Mc Devitt
Philadelphia, PA

Davidick, Timothy
Hazleton SR HS
Hazleton, PA

Davidow, Michelle
Norwin HS
N Huntingdon, PA

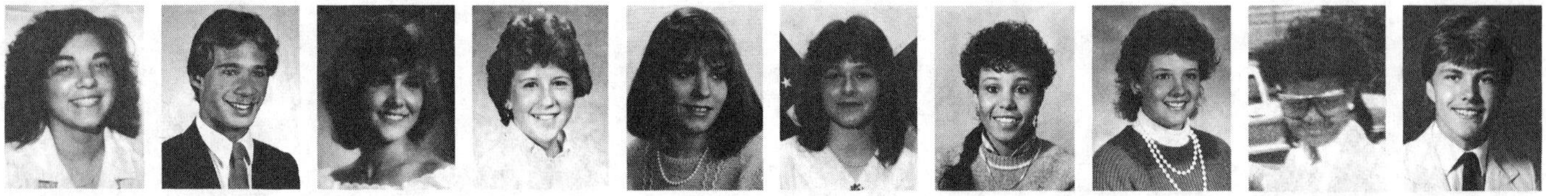

Davidson, Rachel
Conestoga SR HS
Berwyn, PA

Davie, William
Blacklick Valley HS
Vintondale, PA

Davies, Jenefer M
Bishop Neumann
Montoursville, PA

Davis, Barbara Lynn
Pennsbury HS
Morrisville, PA

Davis, Beth
Wyoming Valley
West HS
Kingston, PA

Davis, Christina M
Ontario Street
Baptist Schl
Philadelphia, PA

Davis, Crystal
Moon SR HS
Coraopolis, PA

Davis, Denise
Lake-Lehman HS
Sweet Valley, PA

Davis, Iesha
Martin Luther King
Philadelphia, PA

Davis, Jeff
William Penn HS
York, PA

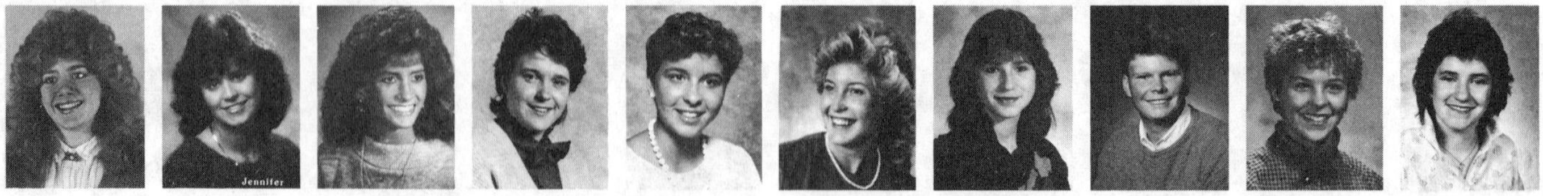

Davis, Jennifer
Beaver Valley
Christian Acad
New Brighton, PA

Davis, Jennifer
Bishop Hafey HS
Hazleton, PA

Davis, Kathy
Plum Borough SR
Pittsburgh, PA

Davis, Kathy Jo
Pocono Central
Catholic HS
Tobyhanna, PA

Davis, Mary
Highlands SR HS
Natrona Heights,
PA

Davis, Meagan
Gateway SR HS
Monroeville, PA

Davis, Melissa
Chambersburg Area
SR HS
Chambersburg, PA

Davis, Michael
Clarioni-Limestone
Strattanville, PA

Davis, Michelle
Indiana JR HS
Indiana, PA

Davis, Myra E
Slippery Rock Area
Prospect, PA

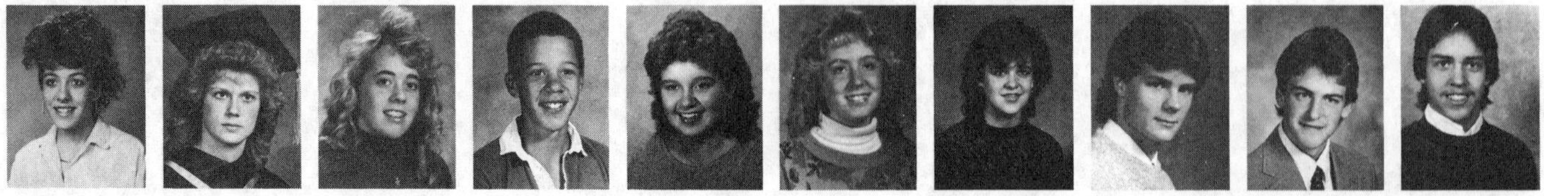

Davis, Nancy
Mid-Valley
Secondary Ctr
Throop, PA

Davis, Regina
Cardinal Dougherty
Philadelphia, PA

Davis, Regina
Lansadle Catholic
Kulpsville, PA

Davis, Robert
Oxford Area HS
Cochranville, PA

Davis, Stacey
Jefferson-Morgan
JR SR HS
Mather, PA

Davis, Tamara
Kennard-Dale HS
Stewartstown, PA

Davis, Vickie
Central Dauphin HS
Harrisburg, PA

Davis, W Bradley
Clearfield Area HS
Clearfield, PA

Davis, W Steven
Central Cambria HS
Ebensburg, PA

Davison, William R
Northwestern HS
Albion, PA

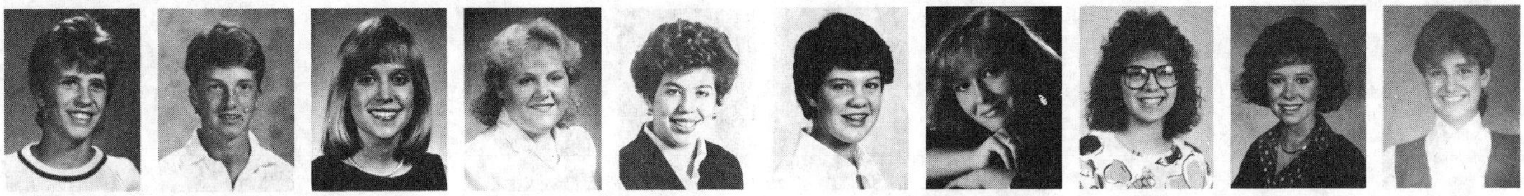

Dawson, Chris
Louis E Dieruff HS
Allentown, PA

Dawson, III John T
Mifflinburg Area HS
Mifflinburg, PA

Dawson, Kimberly J
North Hills HS
Pittsburgh, PA

Dawson, Marie Elaine
Carmichaels Area SR HS
Carmichaels, PA

Day, Colleen
York Catholic HS
York, PA

Day, Maureen
Gwynedd-Mercy
Hatfield, PA

Day, Sandi
Abington Heights
Clarks Summit, PA

Daytner, Sandi
New Castle SR HS
New Castle, PA

De Agostino, Sherry
Altoona Area HS
Altoona, PA

De Angelis, Gina
Lebanon Catholic
Hershey, PA

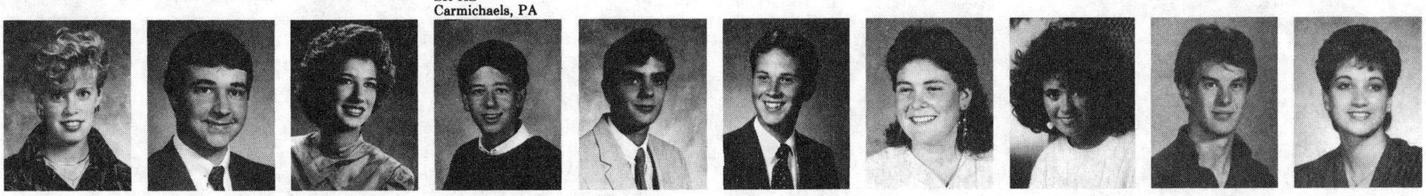

De Angelis, Melissa
Kennedy Christian
Hermitage, PA

De Angelis, Michael
Upper Moreland HS
Hatboro, PA

De Angelo, Debra
Parkland HS
Allentown, PA

De Balli, III Peter
Central Cambria HS
Ebensburg, PA

De Berardinis, Ralph
Salesianum HS
Aston, PA

De Bolt, Richard
Pennsbury HS
Fallsington, PA

De Bord, Rissie Lynn
Brownsville Area HS
East Millsboro, PA

De Capua, Camille
Sharon HS
Sharon, PA

De Cray, James
Haverford SR HS
Ardmore, PA

De Heck, Beth Anne
Central Bucks East
Jamison, PA

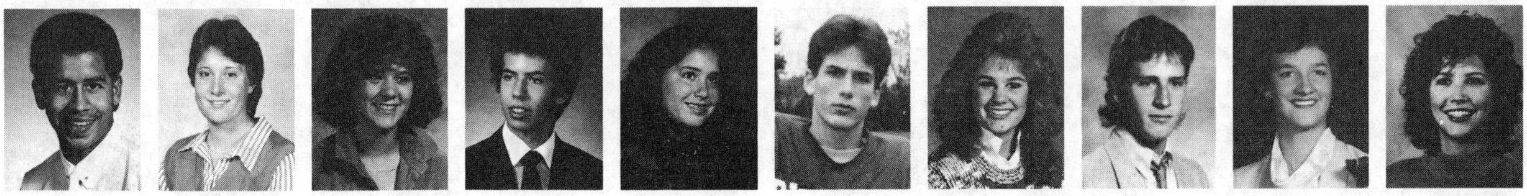

De Jesus, Jose
William Allen HS
Allentown, PA

De Laney, Bobbie Jo
Brookville Area HS
Brookville, PA

De Lattre, Lara
Kennard-Dale HS
Fawn Grove, PA

De Luca, Aaron
Charlerio Area HS
Charleroi, PA

De Lucca, Danielle
West Hazleton HS
West Hazleton, PA

De Marzo, Dave
Riverside JR SR HS
Taylor, PA

De Meester, Heather
Bensalem HS
Bensalem, PA

De Milio, III Philip
Pius X HS
Roseto, PA

De Moreland, Donna
Central Bucks East
Warrington, PA

De Nero, Kristen
Gateway SR HS
Monroeville, PA

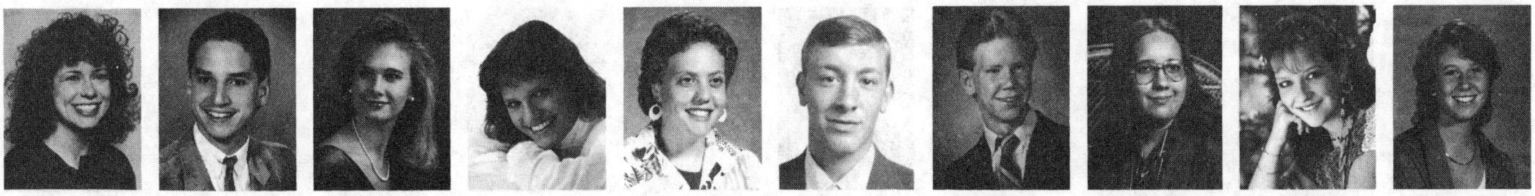

De Priest, Heather
Oil City SR HS
Oil City, PA

De Sarno, Michael Fiore
Penn Hills HS
Penn Hills, PA

De Sipio, Susan
Lansdale Catholic
Souderton, PA

Deater, Larisa
Meadville SR HS
Meadville, PA

Deaver, Claudine
Henderson SR HS
West Chester, PA

Deaver, David
Big Spring HS
Newville, PA

Debenedict, Raymond
Marian Catholic HS
Tamaqua, PA

Dec, Theresa A
Sacred Heart HS
Mc Kees Rocks, PA

Decker, Natalie Tonwen
Abington Hgts HS
Clarks Summit, PA

Deckert, Diana
Mount St Joseph
Warminster, PA

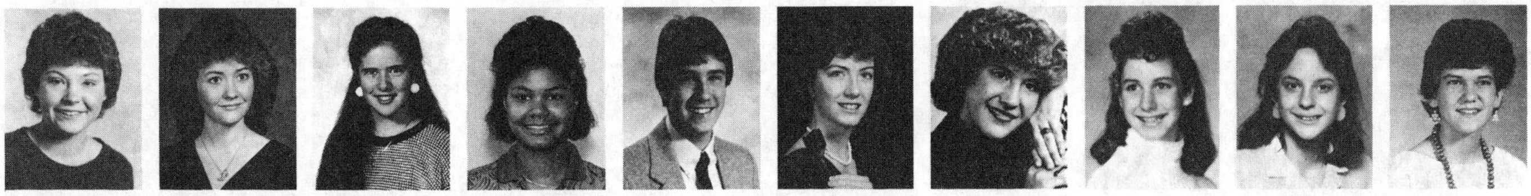

Deebel, Kathy
Cardinal Brennan
Frackville, PA

Deery, Anessa
Upper Darby HS
Primos, PA

Deets, Christine
Oil City SR HS
Titusville, PA

Defrantz, Waltrina
G A R Memorial HS
Wilkes-Barre, PA

Degol, Anthony
Bishop Guilfoyle HS
Altoona, PA

Dehner, Stacy
Bishop Kenrick HS
Norristown, PA

Deibert, Julie
Tri-Valley HS
Sacramento, PA

Deily, Kris
Abington Heights
Scranton, PA

Deily, Lisa
North Catholic HS
Pittsburgh, PA

Deischer, Kristen
Henderson SR HS
West Chester, PA

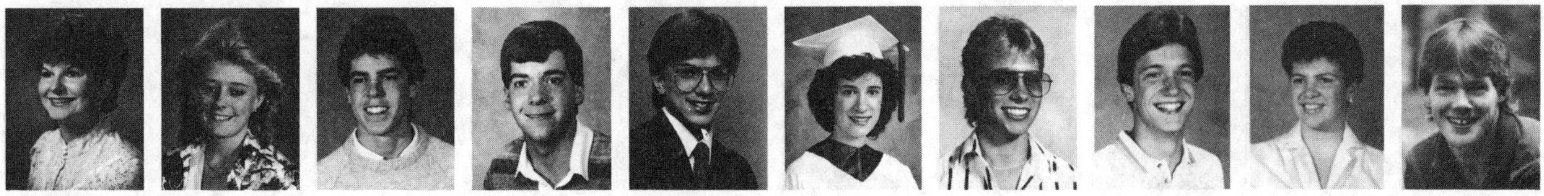

Deist, Donna
Schuylkill Valley HS
Reading, PA

Deitz, Stacy
Union HS
Rimersburg, PA

Delara, Greg
Connellsville HS
Connellsville, PA

Delauter, Ronald
Greencastle-Antrim
Greencastle, PA

Delcamp, Marc
Fleetwood Area HS
Fleetwood, PA

Delconte, Lisa
Cardinal O Hara HS
Broomall, PA

Dell, Jason
Somerset Area HS
Somerset, PA

Dellafiora, James M
Homer-Center HS
Homer City, PA

Dellarose, Laurie
Brownsville Area HS
La Belle, PA

Dellinger, Mark
New Oxford SR HS
New Oxford, PA

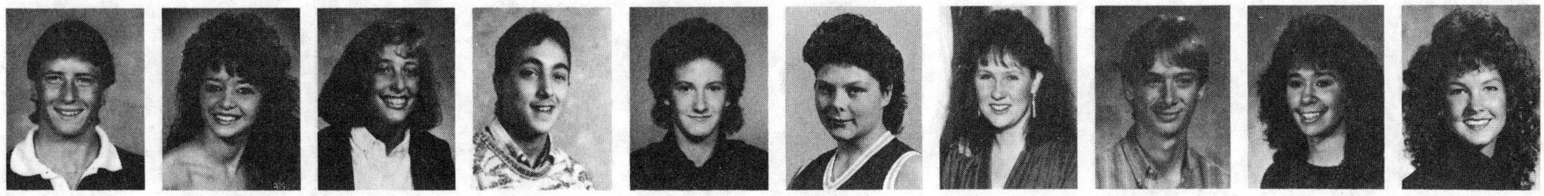

Delnero, Jeffrey
Central Columbia
Bloomsburg, PA

Demaglio, Michelle
Penn Hills SR HS
Verona, PA

Demarco, Kimberly
Lancaster Catholic
Lancaster, PA

Dematteo, John
Pocono Central Catholic HS
Mt Pocono, PA

Demis, Tara
Mc Keesport Area
Mckeesport, PA

Demkosky, Cheryil
Mid-Valley HS
Throop, PA

Dempsey, Suzanne
Bishop Conwell HS
Levittown, PA

Dengler, Charles
Steelton-Highspire
High Spire, PA

Denitti, Laura
Yough HS
Smithton, PA

Denney, Mindi
Connellsville SR HS
Connellsville, PA

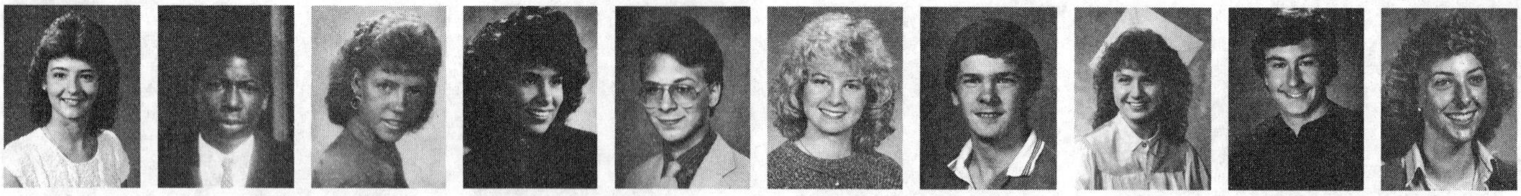

Denney, Monica
Brownsville Area HS
Isabella, PA

Dennis, Dietrich C
Blue Mountain Acad
Philadelphia, PA

Dennis, Lorena
Valley View JR SR
Peckville, PA

Dennler, Dena M
North Catholic HS
Pittsburgh, PA

Dent, Jeff
El Meyers HS
Wiles Barre, PA

Dent, Kimberly
Hempfield HS
Greensburg, PA

Dentzel, Edward
Leechburg Area HS
Leechburg, PA

Depp, Julie Anne
North Catholic HS
Pittsburgh, PA

Derosky, Jr Frank W
West Allegheny SR
Imperial, PA

Derr, Vicki
Donegal HS
Maytown, PA

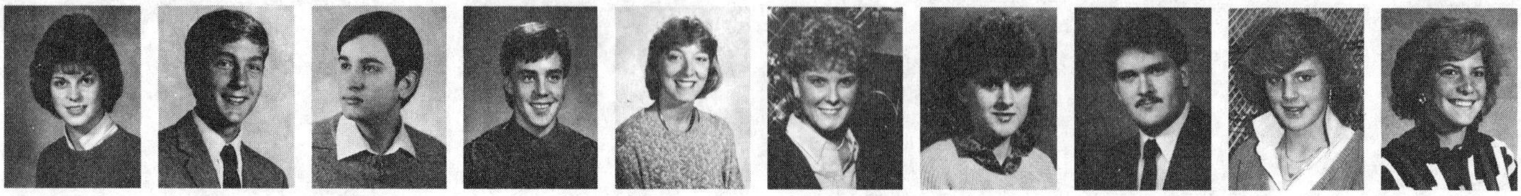

Descavish, Barbara
Moshannon Valley JR-SR HS
Houtzdale, PA

Desciak, Edward
Bishop Hoban HS
Mountaintop, PA

Deskevich, Andrew
Blacklick HS
Nanty Glo, PA

Detar, Corey
Greensburg Salem
Greensburg, PA

Detournay, Chantal
Coatesville Area SR
Coatesville, PA

Deturk, Lisa
Oley Valley HS
Temple, PA

Detweiler, Cindi
Pen Argyl Area HS
Pen Argyl, PA

Devenney, Preston
Avella JR-SR HS
Washington, PA

Devine, Michelle
Lower Dauphin SR
Hershey, PA

Devlin, Holly
Phoenixville Area
Phoenixville, PA

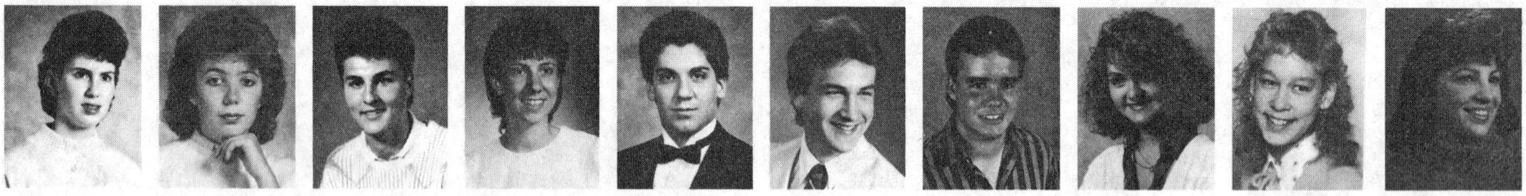

Dewald, Dawn
Schuykill Haven Area HS
Auburn, PA

Deweese, Dana
Kennedy Christian
Jamestown, PA

Dewit, Richard
Moon SR HS
Coraopolis, PA

Dey, Lynne
Brandywine Heights
Fleetwood, PA

Dezii, Randolph
St John Neumann
Philadelphia, PA

Dherit, Gregory
Northeastern HS
Manchester, PA

Di Bernardo, Jerome
Penn-Trafford HS
Irwin, PA

Di Cicco, Aimee
Cornell HS
Coraopolis, PA

Di Cicco, Jennifer
Northern Chester County Tech HS
Berwyn, PA

Di Clemente, Diane
Hershey HS
Hershey, PA

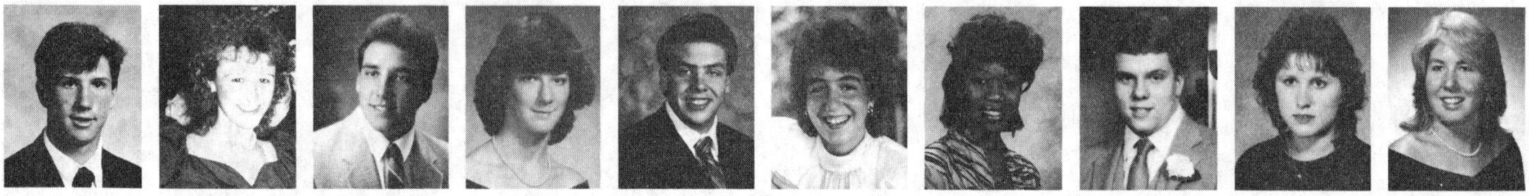

Di Mascio, Michael
Trinity HS
Camp Hill, PA

Di Minico, Mindy
Neshaminy SR HS
Penndel, PA

Di Nardo, Michael Anthony
Hopewell HS
Aliquippa, PA

Di Piano, Jennifer
Perkiomen Valley
Collegeville, PA

Di Sipio, Anthony
Benton Area HS
Benton, PA

Di Vecchio, Lori
Sto-Rox SR HS
Mc Kees Rocks, PA

Dia, Diye E
West Phila Catholic HS For Girls
Philadelphia, PA

Diamond, Eric
Beaver Area JR SR
Beaver, PA

Diamond, Melanie
Burgettstown Area JR-SR HS
Midway, PA

Diamond, Tracy
Abington SR HS
Jenkintown, PA

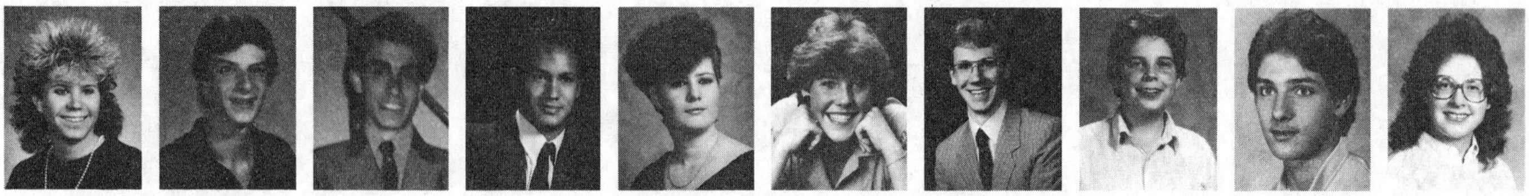

Dianna, Alexandra
Northern Lehigh HS
Walnutport, PA

Diaz, John
Sun Valley HS
Aston, PA

Diaz, Nelson
Father Judge HS
Philadelphia, PA

Diaz-Sandi, Eduardo Licurgo
Reading SR HS
Wyomissing Hills, PA

Dibeler, Sonya
Saint Maria Goretti
Philadelphia, PA

Dice, Tina
Waynesboro Area SR HS
Chambersburg, PA

Dick, Brian
Commadore Perry
Hadley, PA

Dick, Christopher
Danville Area HS
Riverside, PA

Dick, Kevin
Penns Manor HS
Penn Run, PA

Dick, Michele
Danville Area HS
Riverside, PA

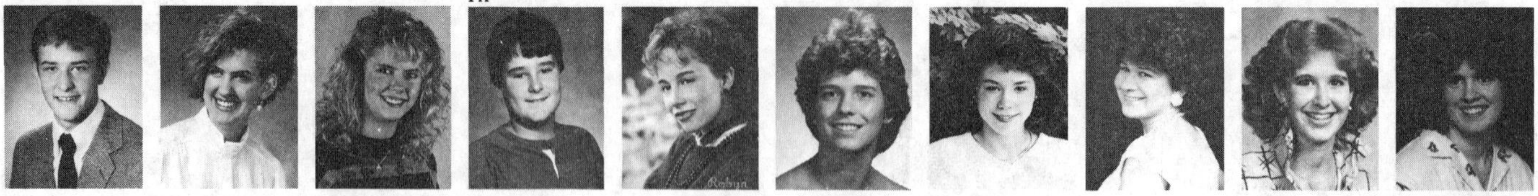

Dickensheets, Scott K
Southwestern HS
Hanover, PA

Dickensheets, Tricia
S Western HS
Hanover, PA

Dickey, Dina
Beaver Valley Christian Acad
S Hts, PA

Dickey, Kevin
Ringold HS
New Eagle, PA

Dickinson, Robyn
Tunkhannock Area
Lake Winola, PA

Dickson, Melissa J
George Washington
Philadelphia, PA

Dicton, Donna
Wyoming Valley West HS
Forty Fort, PA

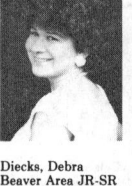

Diecks, Debra
Beaver Area JR-SR
Beaver, PA

Diehl, Joanne
Quakertown Communtiy HS
Quakertown, PA

Diehl, Kathy
Columbia Montour
Bloomsburg, PA

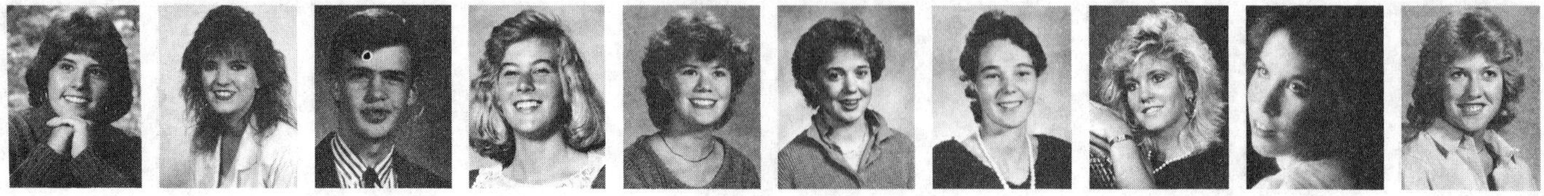

Dieringer, Noelle
Du Bois Area HS
Rockton, PA

Dietel, Sandy
Bermudian Springs
East Berlin, PA

Dieteman, David
Cathedral Prep Schl
Erie, PA

Dieter, Becky
Hampton HS
Allison Park, PA

Dietrich, Pamela
Downingtown SR
Downingtown, PA

Dietterich, Susan
Pleasant Valley HS
Brodheadsville, PA

Dietz, Erin L
Northampton Area SR HS
Walnutport, PA

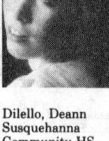

Dietz, Michelle Y
York Vo-Tech
York, PA

Dilello, Deann
Susquehanna Community HS
Lanesboro, PA

Dilks, Jennifer
Upper Merion Area
King Of Prussia, PA

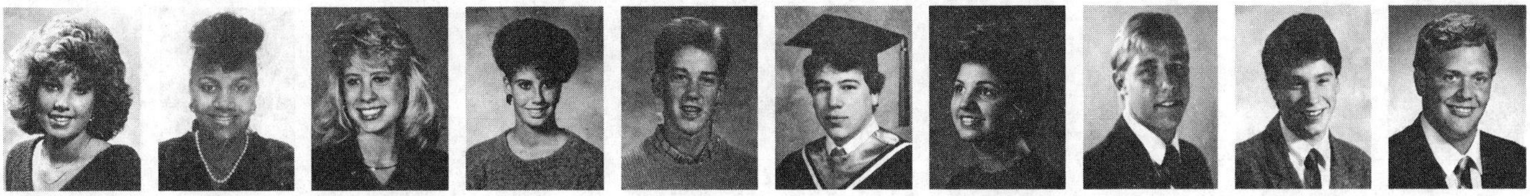

Dill, Julie Ann
Peters Township HS
Erie, PA

Dillard, Camelia
St Paul Cathedral
Pittsburgh, PA

Dillig, Paula
Laurel Highlands
SR HS
Hopwood, PA

Dillon, Laura
Downingtown HS
Exton, PA

Dillow, Steve
Donegal HS
Mt Joy, PA

Dilossi, Joe
St John Neumann
Philadelphia, PA

Dimitriou, Eleni
Holy Name HS
Wyomissing, PA

Dimmick, Jack
Mahanoy Area HS
Mahanoy City, PA

Dinardo, John
Bishop Guilfoyle HS
Altoona, PA

Dinnocenti, Brian
Spring-Ford HS
Royersford, PA

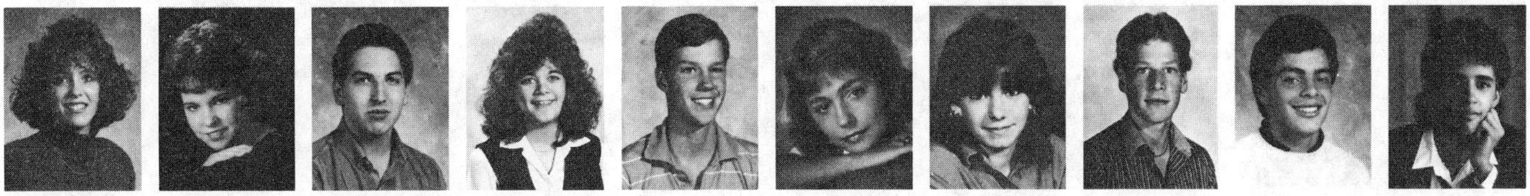

Dinunzio, Andrea
Neshaminy HS
Langhorne, PA

Dionne, Theresa
Northampton SR
Walnutport, PA

Direnzo, Stephen
Kennedy Christian
Sharon, PA

Disabato, Charlyn
Bishop Guilfoyle HS
Altoona, PA

Dissinger, Paul
Cedar Crest HS
Lebanon, PA

Ditrich, Laura
Villa Maria
Academy HS
Erie, PA

Dittman, Heather
Pocono Mt HS
Bartonsville, PA

Dittmar, Clint J
Norristown Area HS
Norristown, PA

Divens, William
Kennedy Christian
Sharpsville, PA

Dixon, Anthony
Pittston Area HS
Pittston, PA

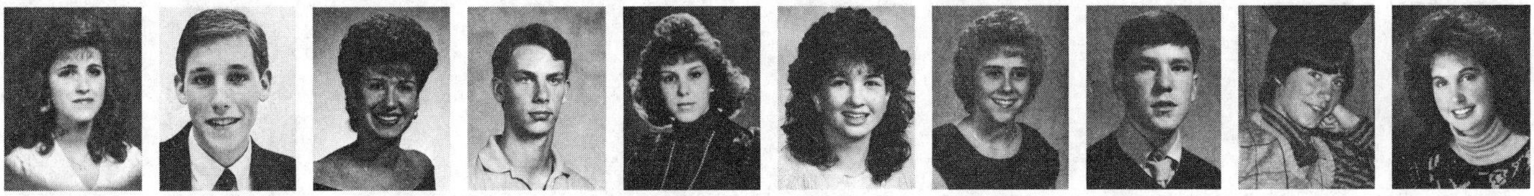

Dixon, Shellene
Tunkhannock HS
Tunkhannock, PA

Dixson, Thomas
Homer Center JR
SR HS
Lucernemines, PA

Dmytryszyn, Lana
Central HS
Philadelphia, PA

Dobb, Marc
Lower Dauphin HS
Hummelstown, PA

Dobbie, Krista
Bellwood-Antis HS
Altoona, PA

Dobson, Danielle
Neshaminy HS
Levittown, PA

Dobson, Susan
Sun Valley HS
Aston, PA

Dobzynski, Mark
Cathedral Prep
Erie, PA

Dodson, Jr Carl
Central HS
Martinsburg, PA

Dodson, Gayle
Claysburg-Kimmel
Claysburg, PA

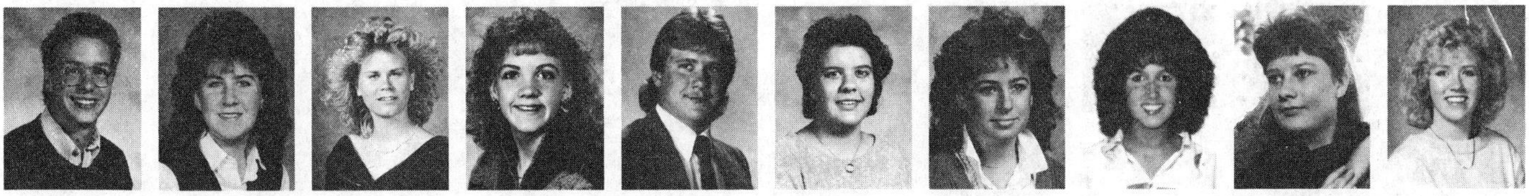

Doerfler, J Douglas
Lake-Lehman HS
Harveys Lake, PA

Doherty, Jeanmarie
Nazareth Acad
Philadelphia, PA

Dolack, Joanne
Archbishop Ryan
HS For Girls
Philadelphia, PA

Dolan, Lori
St Marys Area HS
St Marys, PA

Dolmajer, Jeffrey
Highlands SR HS
Brackenridge, PA

Domanski, Brenda
Danville SR HS
Riverside, PA

Domin, Justine
Emmaus HS
Wescosville, PA

Dominick, Jodi
Wyoming Area SR
Wyoming, PA

Domitrovich, Laura
Our Lady Of The
Sacred Heart HS
Aliquippa, PA

Domrzalski, Kathy
Parkland HS
Coplay, PA

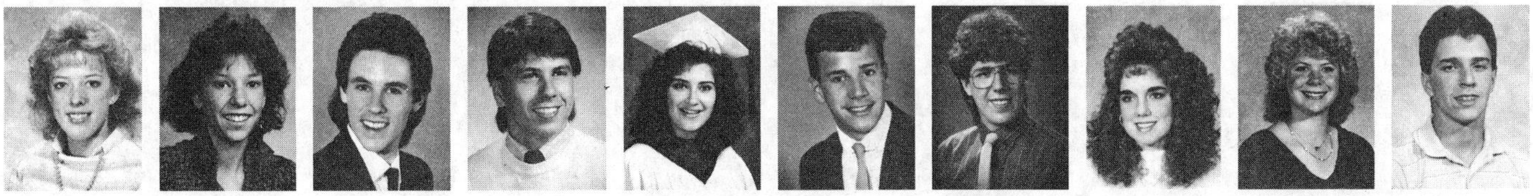

Donachy, Colette
St Marys Area HS
St Marys, PA

Donahue, Stacey A
Mountain View JR/
SR HS
Nicholson, PA

Donald, James
Penn Hills SR HS
Pittsburgh, PA

Donati, David W
Fort Cherry HS
Hickory, PA

Donato, Lisa
Little Flower
Catholic HS
Philadelphia, PA

Donato, Mark L
Penn Hills HS
Pittsburgh, PA

Donel, Tim
Trinity HS
Washington, PA

Donelli, Jennifer L
North Allegheny SR
Allison Pk, PA

Donges, Ingrid
Great Valley HS
Phoenixville, PA

Donini, Sam
Charleroi Area HS
Charleroi, PA

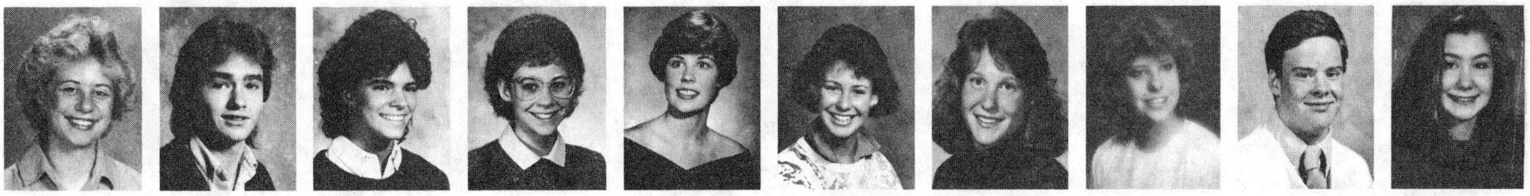

Donley, Paula
Meyersdale Area HS
Meyersdale, PA

Donlin, Jr Paul
Dallas SR HS
Dallas, PA

Donmoyer, Nicole
Annville-Cleona HS
Lebanon, PA

Donner, Monica
Greenville JR SR
Greenville, PA

Donohue, Christine
M
Villa Maria Acad
Drexel Hill, PA

Donovan, Kimberly
Riverside JR SR HS
Moosic, PA

Dopera, Kristine
Parkland HS
Schnecksville, PA

Dopp, Jane
Shaler Area SR HS
Glenshaw, PA

Doran, Christopher
Monsignor Bonner
Yeadon, PA

Dorfield, Jennifer
Butler SR HS
Butler, PA

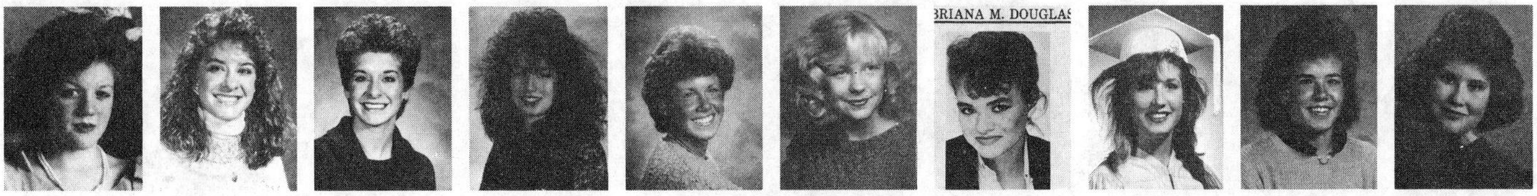

Dotson, Leslie A
Lower Merion HS
Boulder, CO

Dotter, Jennifer
Seneca Valley HS
Evans Cty, PA

Dotter, Tracy
Seneca Valley HS
Evans Cty, PA

Dougherty, Andrea
The Philadelphia
HS For Girls
Philadelphia, PA

Dougherty, Colleen
Bishop Hafey HS
Hazleton, PA

Doughty, Shannon
Montour HS
Coraopolis, PA

Douglas, Briana
Michelle
Villa Maria Acad
Phoenixville, PA

Douglas, Stephanie
Northeast HS
Philadelphia, PA

Doutrich, Noel
Donegal HS
Maytown, PA

Doutt, Jennifer
Lynn
Sharpsville HS
Clark, PA

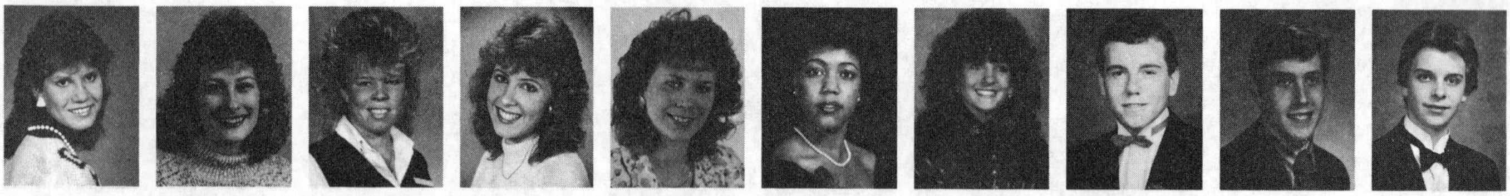

Douty, Kami
Juniata HS
Mifflintown, PA

Downes, Christine
Kiski Area HS
Export, PA

Downey, Michelle
Nazareth Acad
Philadelphia, PA

Downey, Michelle
Penn Hills SR HS
Pittsburgh, PA

Downie, Rachel L
Beaver County
Christian HS
Beaver Falls, PA

Downing, Lynn
West Phila Catholic
Girls HS
Philadelphia, PA

Downs, Lisa
Sun Valley HS
Aston, PA

Doyle, John
West Catholic Boys
Darby, PA

Doyle, Thomas
Cathedral Prep
Erie, PA

Doyle, Jr William F
Bishop Mc Devitt
Roslyn, PA

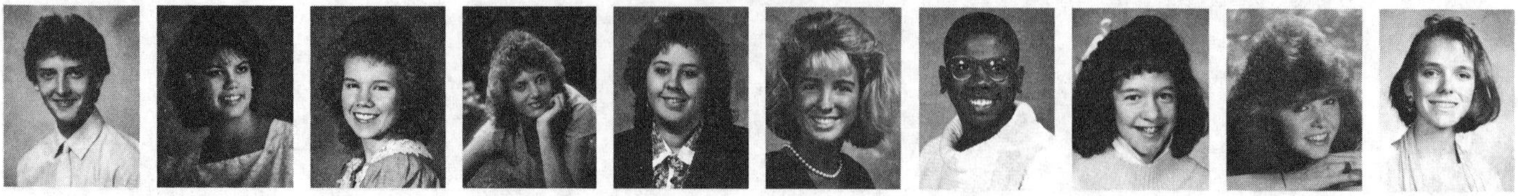

Dragwa, Richard
Forest City Regional
Forest City, PA

Drakulic, Milana
Norwin HS
Ardara, PA

Dran, Shari
Bethlehem Center
SR HS
Amity, PA

Drass, Renee Marie
Altoona Area HS
Altoona, PA

Dravk, Stephanie
Eastern York HS
Wrightsville, PA

Dreger, Christine M
Archbishop
Prendergast HS
Drexel Hill, PA

Dreher, Christian
Beaver Falls SR HS
Beaver Falls, PA

Dretar, Nicole
Abington Heights
Clarks Summit, PA

Driscoll, Tracy
Hazleton HS
Hazleton, PA

Driver, Kerry
Quakertown HS
Quakertown, PA

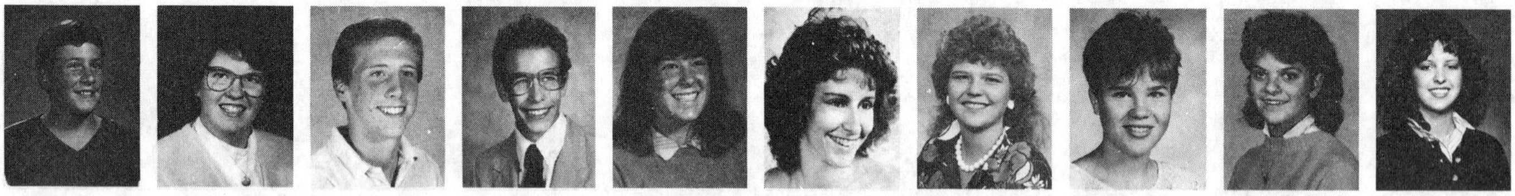

Druckenmiller, Paul
E
Catasauqua HS
Catasauqua, PA

Drury, Deborah J
Lampeter-Strasburg
Lancaster, PA

Drury, John
Wissahickon HS
Blue Bell, PA

Dryzal, John
Central Cambria HS
Johnstown, PA

Dubbs, Nicole
Lower Merion HS
Bala Cynwyd, PA

Dubbs, Scheri
Dianna
Williams Valley JR
SR HS
Reinerton, PA

Dubnansky, Rachel
Charleroi Area HS
Charleroi, PA

Ducellier, Michelle
Quakertown SR HS
Quakertown, PA

Duck, Kimberly
Southwestern HS
Hanover, PA

Dudash, Jonna
Ringgold HS
Eighty Four, PA

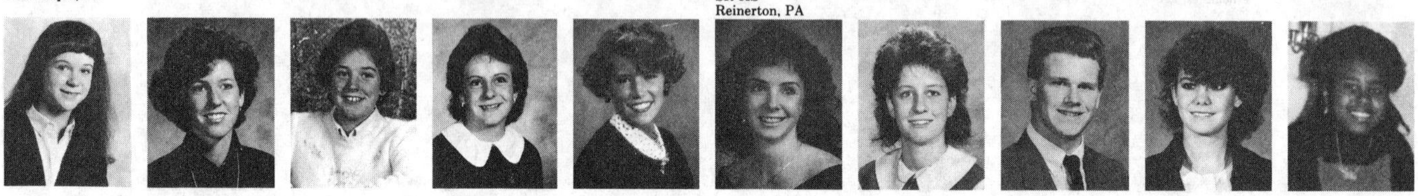

Dudding, Suzette
Central Catholic HS
Allentown, PA

Duffalo, Deidra Lee
Mechancisburg SR
Mechanicsburg, PA

Duffield, Bonnie
Wyalusing Valley
Wyalusing, PA

Duffner, Theresa
Archbishop Ryan
For Girls HS
Philadelphia, PA

Duffy, Michele
Danville HS
Danville, PA

Duffy, Nancy M
Archbishop Wood
For Girls
Holland, PA

Duffy, Theresa A
St Hubert Catholic
HS For Girls
Philadelphia, PA

Dufner, Dan
Archbishop Wood H
S Boys
Southampton, PA

Dulany, Kelly
Waynesburg Central
Spraggs, PA

Duley, Angela
Cecilian Acad
Philadelphia, PA

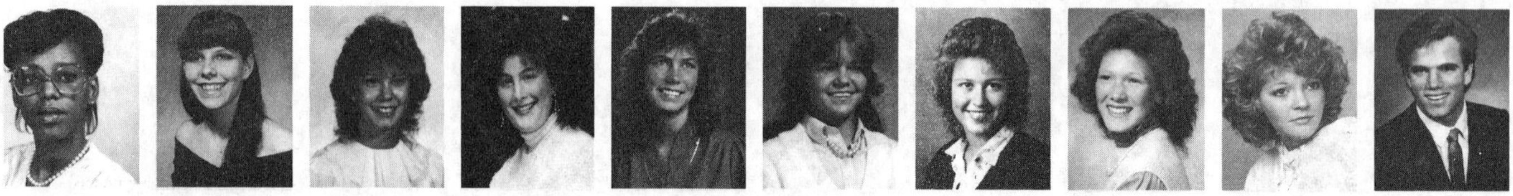

Dunbar, Chavock
Harrisburg HS
Harrisburg, PA

Duncan, Jennifer L
Methacton SR HS
Audubon, PA

Dunchak, Lara
Central Cambria HS
Ebensburg, PA

Dunham, Patricia
Cedar Crest HS
Lebanon, PA

Dunkle, Jennifer
Northern HS
Dillsburg, PA

Dunkle, Rebecca
Ann
Mifflinburg Area HS
Mifflinburg, PA

Dunmire, Lisa
Lewistown Area HS
Mc Veytown, PA

Dunmyer, Nancy J
Richland SR HS
Johnstown, PA

Dunn, Georgie
Cumberland Valley
Mechanicsburg, PA

Dunn, Keary
Lampeter-Strasburg
Strasburg, PA

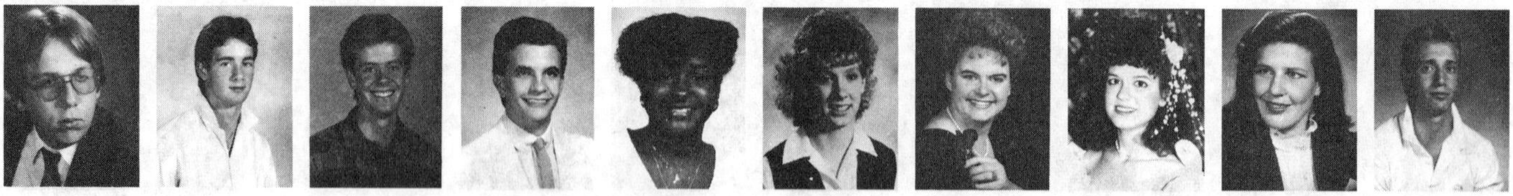

Dunn, Kevin M
Henderson HS
Downingtown, PA

Dunn, Michael P
East Stroudsburg
East Stroudsburg,
PA

Dunne, Raymond
Penncrest HS
Media, PA

Dunski, Jonathan F
Whitehall HS
Whitehall, PA

Dupree, Marlo
Scotland School For
Vet Children
Phila, PA

Durbin, Laura
Bishop Guilfoyle HS
Altoona, PA

Duross, Jeannette
West Phila Catholic
Girls HS
Philadelphia, PA

Durrant, Julia
Nazareth Acad
Philadelphia, PA

Dutchko, Donna
Mon Valley Catholic
Elizabeth, PA

Dutchko, Stan
Southmoreland HS
Ruffsdale, PA

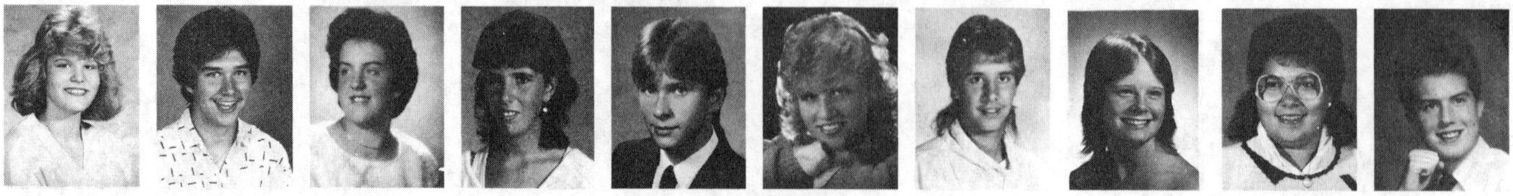

Dutkiewicz, Barbara
Archbishop Ryan
HS For Girls
Philadelphia, PA

Duzyk, John
Mohawk HS
New Castle, PA

Dydynski, Lori
Wyoming Valley
West HS
Plymouth, PA

Dyer, Lorri
Octorara HS
Christiana, PA

Dziak, Jason
Bentworth HS
Bentleyville, PA

Dzuricsko, Tawnya
Mercer HS
Mercer, PA

Dzurkovich,
Donovan
Reading HS
Reading, PA

Early, Elizabeth
Ann
Upper Merion HS
King Of Prussia, PA

Earnesty, Ann
Connellsville SR HS
Connellsville, PA

Eastwood, Craig B
Perkiomen Valley
Schwenksville, PA

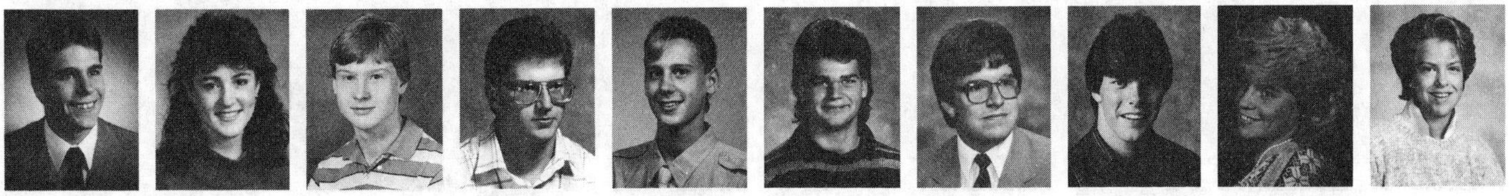

Eaton, Jr John
Red Lion Area SR
Windsor, PA

Eberhardt, Eadie
Jouderton Area HS
Philadelphia, PA

Eberhart, II Loye
Mt Pleasant Area
Mt Pleasant, PA

Ebersole, Joe
Hempfield HS
Manheim, PA

Ebert, Brian
Greater Works Acad
Pittsburgh, PA

Ebling, William
Hamburg Area HS
Hamburg, PA

Eby, David
Ephrata HS
Ephrata, PA

Echard, James
Laewistown Area
Mc Veytown, PA

Eck, Jodie
Lancaster Catholic
Columbia, PA

Eckard, Phyllis
Perkiomen Valley
Collegeville, PA

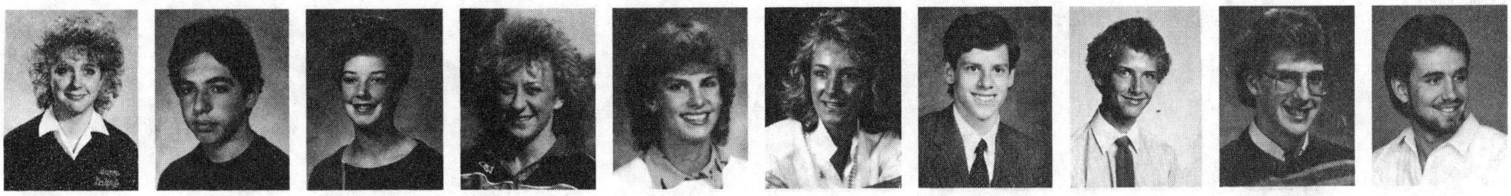

Eckenrode, Lisa
Bishop Guilfoyle HS
Altoona, PA

Eckenrode, Robert
Saltsburg JR SR HS
Saltsburg, PA

Eckerd, Karen
Cumberland Valley
Mechanicsburg, PA

Eckert, Michelle
Northeastern SR HS
York, PA

Eckley, Linda
Claysburg Kimmel
Claysburg, PA

Eder, Lori
Jefferson-Morgan
JR SR HS
Waynesburg, PA

Eder, Paul
Bethlehem Catholic
Bethlehem, PA

Edgerton, Joseph
New Castle SR HS
New Castle, PA

Edmunds, Sean
West Branch Area
Karthaus, PA

Edris, Gregory
Blue Mountain Acad
Leesport, PA

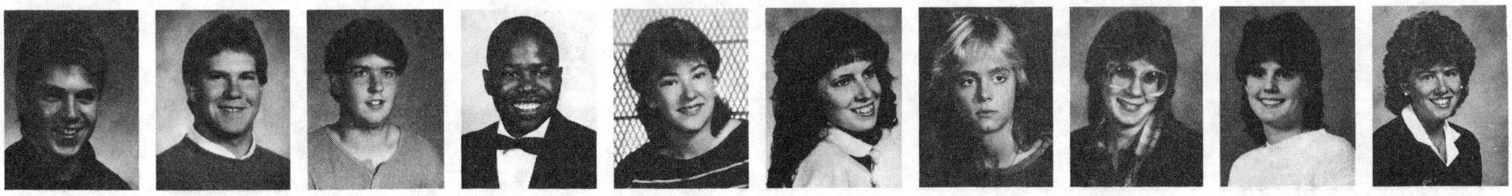

Edwards, Anthony
John
Punxsutawaney Area
Punxsutawney, PA

Edwards, Carl A
Wyoming Valley
West HS
Kingston, PA

Edwards, Eddie
Octorara HS
Cochranville, PA

Edwards, Michael
William Penn HS
Philadelphia, PA

Edwards, Shelley
Garden Spot HS
Terre Hill, PA

Effting, Valerie A
Freedom HS
Bethlehem, PA

Efird, Heather
Benton Area JR SR
Benton, PA

Eggers, Tina Sue
Rocky Grove HS
Franklin, PA

Ehlinger, Michele
Center HS
Monaca, PA

Ehrensberger, Kelly
Elk County
Christian HS
St Marys, PA

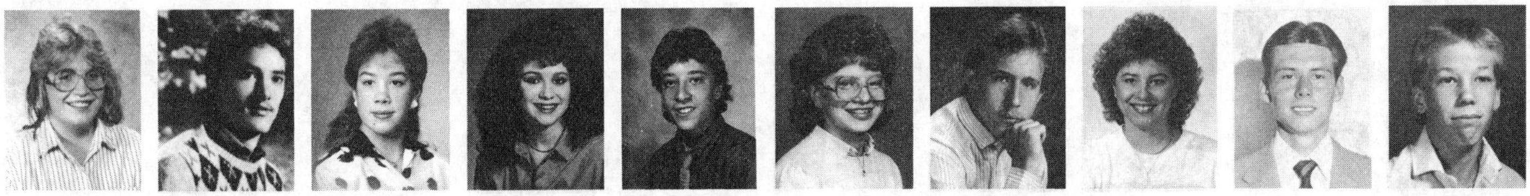

Ehrensberger,
Rebecka
St Marys Area HS
St Marys, PA

Ehrgott, Daniel
Meadville Area SR
Meadville, PA

Ehrhardt, Beth
N Pocono HS
Moscow, PA

Ehrhardt, Kathy
Beaver Falls HS
Beaver Falls, PA

Eichelberger, Ron
Northern Bedford
County HS
Hopewell, PA

Eicher, Beth
Fairchance Georges
JR SR HS
Fairchance, PA

Eicher, Jr Richard
W
Claysburg-Kimmel
East Freedom, PA

Eicher, Tracy
Fairchance Georges
JR/SR HS
Fairchance, PA

Eiler, David
Valley HS
New Kensington,
PA

Eisenacher, Ronald
C
Sun Valley HS
Aston, PA

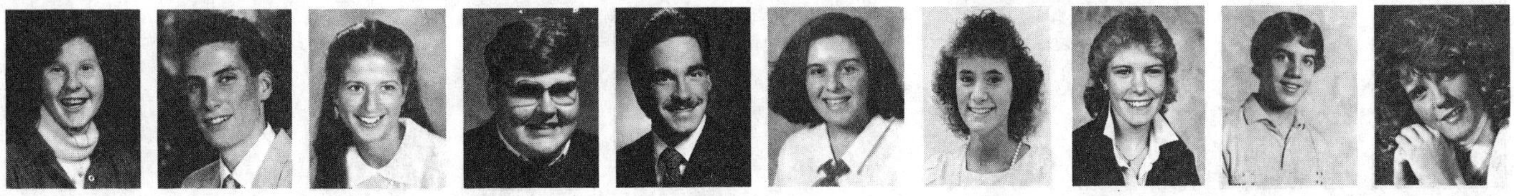

Eisenberg, Judith
Carver HS For
Science & Engr
Phillladelphia, PA

Eisenberg, Steven
Upper Dublin HS
Ambler, PA

Eisenman, Bonnie
North Clarion JR
SR HS
Marble, PA

Eiserman, Amy
Cedar Crest HS
Cornwall, PA

Eklund, Keith L
Baldwin HS
Pittsburgh, PA

El Bassuni, Nabila
Stroudsburg HS
Stroudsburg, PA

Elby, Shannon
Connellsville SR HS
Connellsville, PA

Eliason, Lynn
Fort Le Boeuf HS
Erie, PA

Elick, Thomas
Coughlin HS
Wilkes Barre, PA

Elicker, Karen
South Western HS
Hanover, PA

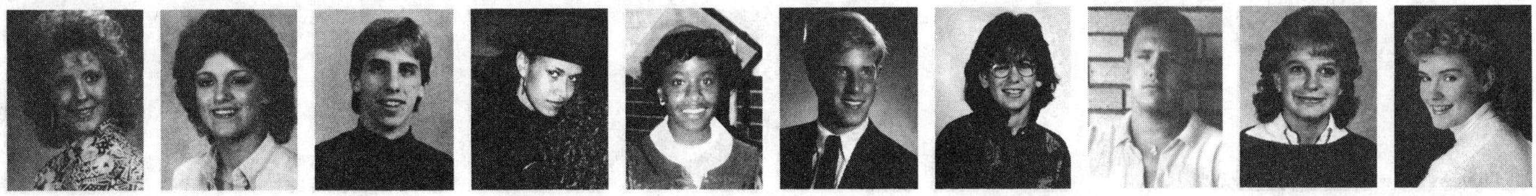

Ellenberger, Julie
Punxsutawney SR
Stump Creek, PA

Elliott, Sheila
Penns Manor HS
Alverda, PA

Elliott, Steven J
Kiski Area HS
Apollo, PA

Ellis, Tiffany Anne
Schenley HS
Pittsburgh, PA

Ellison, Angela
Central HS
Philadelphia, PA

Ellison, James P
Hanover HS
Hanover, PA

Ellman, Susan
Lower Moreland HS
Huntingdon Valley,
PA

Ely, David
Seton La Salle
Regional HS
Pittsburgh, PA

Ely, Jennifer
Downingtown SR
Downingtown, PA

Ely, Kathleen
Hikellamy HS
Sunbury, PA

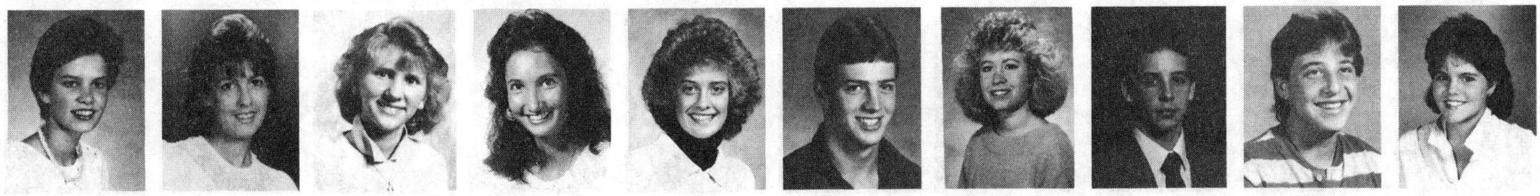

Emanuel, Diana
Saltsburg HS
New Alexandria, PA

Emerich, Shelly
Lynn
Tulpehocken HS
Bethel, PA

Emerick, Jennifer
Berlin
Brothersvalley HS
Fairhope, PA

Emerson, Jaa
Northern HS
Dillsburg, PA

Emery, Denise
Spring-Ford SR HS
Royersford, PA

Emigh, James
West Branch Area
Morrisdale, PA

Emmonds, Heather
Ford City HS
Ford City, PA

Ems, Jr Frank W
East Stroudsburg
Area HS
Marshalls Creek, PA

Enders, Howie
Council Rock HS
Richboro, PA

Engel, Kathy
Carlynton HS
Pittsburgh, PA

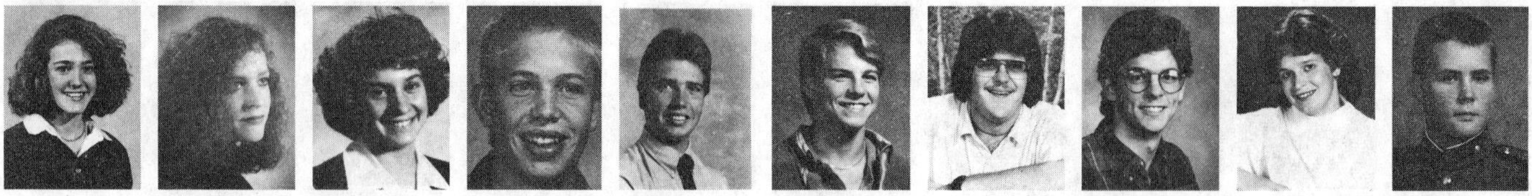

Engelhardt, Allison A
Canon-Mc Millan SR HS
Canonsburg, PA

Engelman, Marla
Millville Area HS
Millville, PA

Engelman, Mary
Bishop Guilfoyle HS
Altoona, PA

Engle, Timothy
Elizabethtown Area
Elizabethtown, PA

Engleman, Jr Carl
Central Catholic HS
Oley, PA

Englert, Jr Michael W
Hempfield HS
Columbia, PA

Enlow, Robert
Sayre HS
Sayre, PA

Enoch, Christopher L
Palisades SR HS
Ottsville, PA

Ensminger, Rynell
Grace Christian Schl
Lebanon, PA

Entenman, Douglas
Valley Forge Military Acad
Norristown, PA

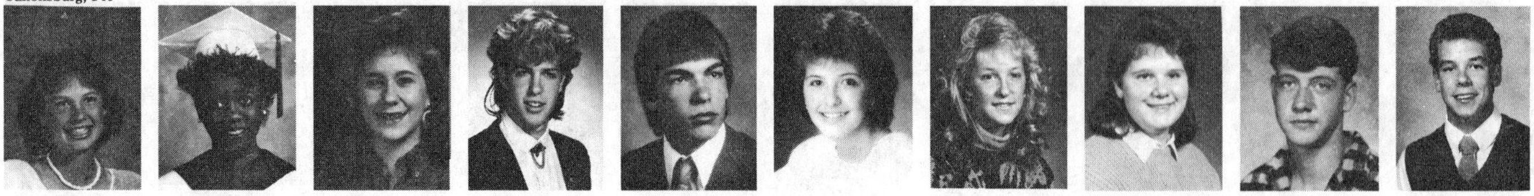

Eppinger, Christy
Kennard Dale HS
Stewartstown, PA

Epps, Lisa
St Maria Goretti HS
Philadelphia, PA

Erb, Heidi
Danville HS
Danville, PA

Erb, Jeffrey D
Great Valley HS
Malvern, PA

Erb, Lester
Milton Area SR HS
Milton, PA

Erb, Michelle
Mifflinburg Area HS
Mifflinburg, PA

Erdman, Kristin L
Shikellamy HS
Sunbury, PA

Erdman, Lori
Upper Dauphin Area HS
Gratz, PA

Ergott, Blu
Jersey Shore SR HS
Avis, PA

Erich, Martin
Elk County Christian HS
St Marys, PA

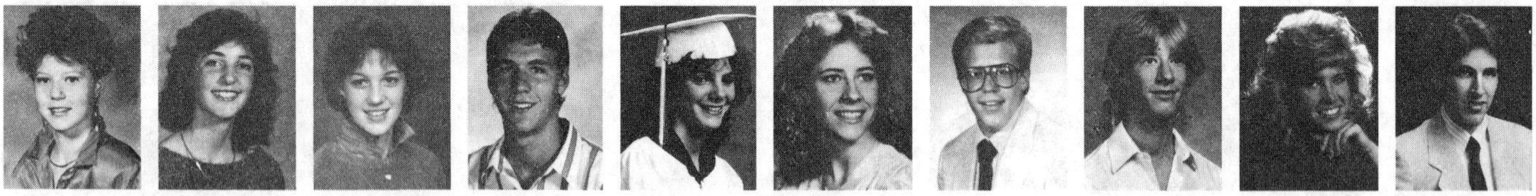

Erin, Vocke
Huntingdon Area
Huntingdon, PA

Ermilio, Jennifer
Conestoga SR HS
Paoli, PA

Ernst, Jennifer
William Allen HS
Allentown, PA

Ernst, Michael
Fleetwood Area HS
Fleetwood, PA

Erwin, Pam
Frankford HS
Philadelphia, PA

Eshbach, Debbie
Freedom HS
Bethlehem, PA

Eshbach, Gregory
Bethlehem Catholic
Bethlehem, PA

Eshelman, Scott
Elizabethtown Area
Elizabethtown, PA

Eshenower, Kristin
Central Dauphin HS
Harrisburg, PA

Esper, William John
Butler SR HS
Butler, PA

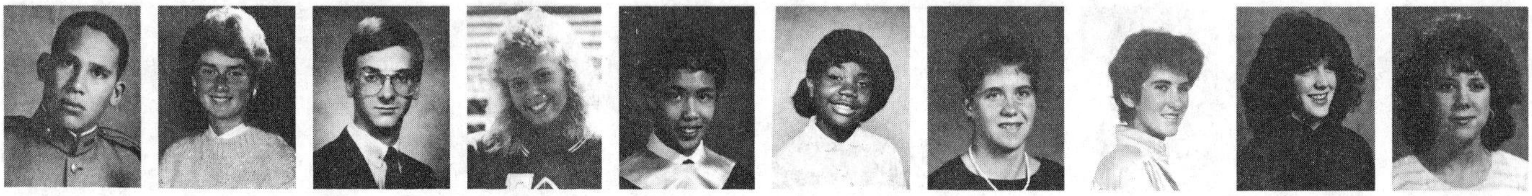

Essex, David P C
Valley Forge Military Acad
Upper Marlboro, MD

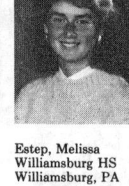

Estep, Melissa
Williamsburg HS
Williamsburg, PA

Esther, Jr Charles R
Freedom HS
Bethlehem, PA

Estkowski, Jacqueline
Lincoln HS
Ellwood City, PA

Estrada, Cromwell
Bethlehem Catholic
Bethlehem, PA

Etheridge, Wendy
Methacton SR HS
Eagleville, PA

Etzweiler, Cindy
Upper Dauphin Area HS
Halifax, PA

Eustice, Amy
Great Valley SR HS
Frazer, PA

Eutsey, April S
Connellsville Area
Mt Pleasant, PA

Evans, Audra
West Perry SR HS
Loysville, PA

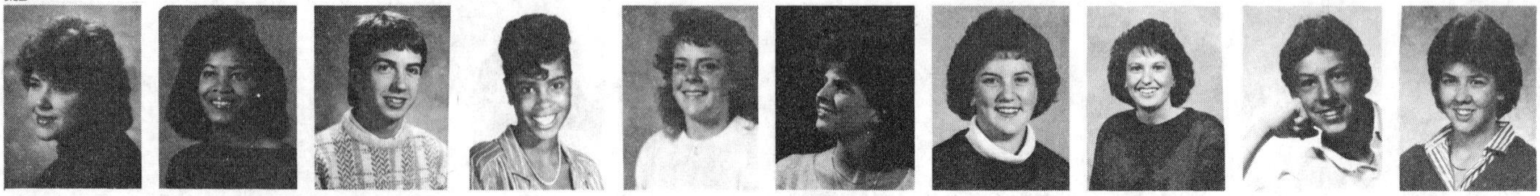

Evans, Barbara
Crestwood HS
White Haven, PA

Evans, Claudia
Center HS
Monaca, PA

Evans, Doug
Indiana Area SR HS
Indiana, PA

Evans, Lakey
Reading HS
Reading, PA

Evans, Lauren
North Allegheny HS
Wexford, PA

Evans, Mindy
Wyoming Valley West HS
Luzerne, PA

Evans, Tammy
The Baptist HS
Clarks Summit, PA

Evelsizer, Suzanne
Canon Mc Millan SR HS
Eighty Four, PA

Evens, Jamie
Port Allegany HS
Port Allegany, PA

Evens, Julie
Port Allegany HS
Port Allegany, PA

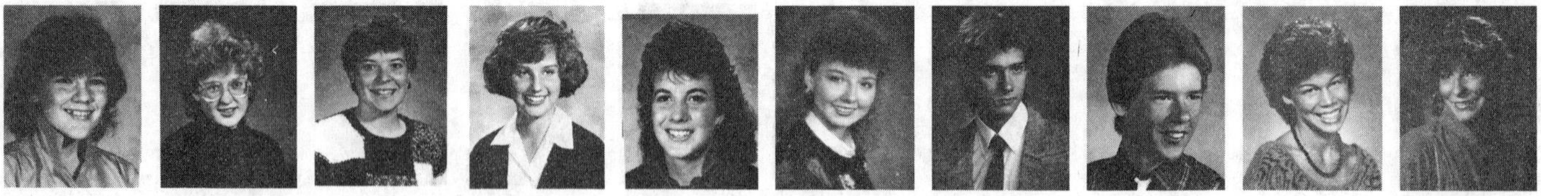

Everett, Missy
Mechanicsburg Area SR HS
Mechanicsburg, PA

Everitt, Denise
Tunkhannock HS
Tunkhannock, PA

Everly, Jodie
Moniteau HS
Slippery Rock, PA

Evey, Eileen
Bishop Guilfoyle HS
Hollidaysburg, PA

Ewart, Bevin
Plum SR HS
Pittsburgh, PA

Ewing, Robin
Hempfield Area SR
Greensburg, PA

Eye, Kurt S
Penn Manor HS
Lancaster, PA

Eytcheson, Eric
York County Area Vo Tech HS
York, PA

Fabbri, Leslie
Penn Cambria SR
Gallitzin, PA

Fabian, Lisa R
Lancaster Christian
Reinholds, PA

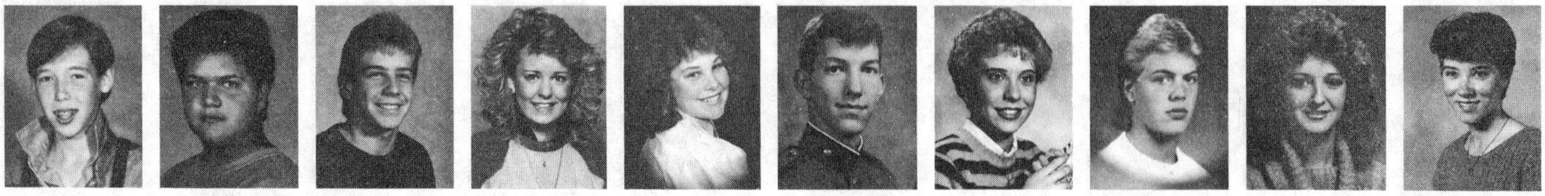

Fabio, James
Faith Community Christian Schl
Bethel Park, PA

Fahnestock, William
South Western HS
Hanover, PA

Fair, Craig D
Twin Valley HS
Elverson, PA

Fair, Jennifer
West Middlesex HS
West Middlesex, PA

Fairley, Shannon
Panther Valley HS
Lansford, PA

Fairnak, David M
Valley Forge Military Acad
Piscataway, NJ

Falcone, Joni
Pius X HS
Roseto, PA

Faley, Jim
Central Dauphin HS
Harrisburg, PA

Falton, Pauline
Our Lady Of Lourdes Regiona
Kulpmont, PA

Falvo, Nicole
North Allegheny Intermediate HS
Powell, OH

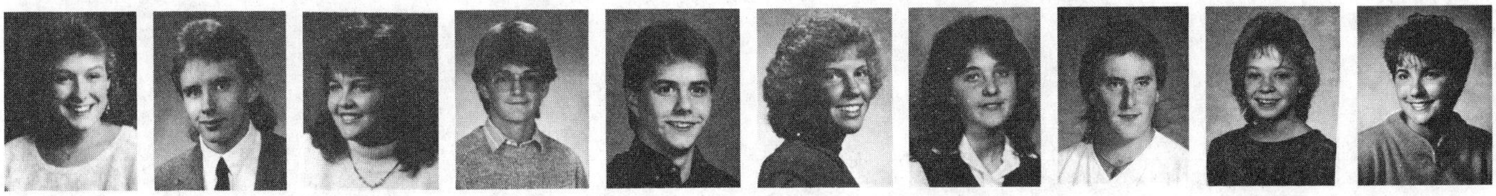

Fannin, Cathy
St Marys Area HS
Weedville, PA

Fargo, Michael
Meadville Area SR
Meadville, PA

Farmer, Andrea
Northern Lebanon
Fredericksburg, PA

Farmer, III William S
Elizabeth Forward SR HS
Elizabeth, PA

Farr, Robert
Exeter Township SR
Reading, PA

Farrell, Kathleen
Dallas SR HS
Dallas, PA

Farrell, Kelly Anne
Nazareth Acad
Philadelphia, PA

Farrow, Ray
Ambridge Area HS
Freedom, PA

Fartini, Angela
North Star HS
Stoystown, PA

Fasano, Carol
Mifflinburg Area HS
Mifflinburg, PA

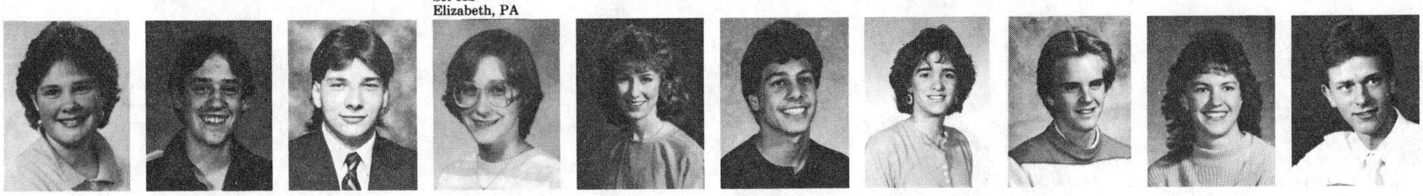

Fashouer, Jacqueline
West Scranton HS
Scranton, PA

Fasnacht, Daryle
Annville-Cleona HS
Palmya, PA

Fasnacht, Larry
Cocalico HS
Denver, PA

Fasold, Melissa
State College Intermediate HS
State College, PA

Fassl, Krista
Bethlehem Catholic
Bethlehem, PA

Fatiga, Anthony
Archbishop Wood
Willow Grove, PA

Faunce, Samantha
Bensalem HS
Bensalem, PA

Faurl, Randy
Emmaus HS
Macungie, PA

Fawcett, Sylvia
Ambridge Area HS
Baden, PA

Faybik, Jason P
Burrell SR HS
Arnold, PA

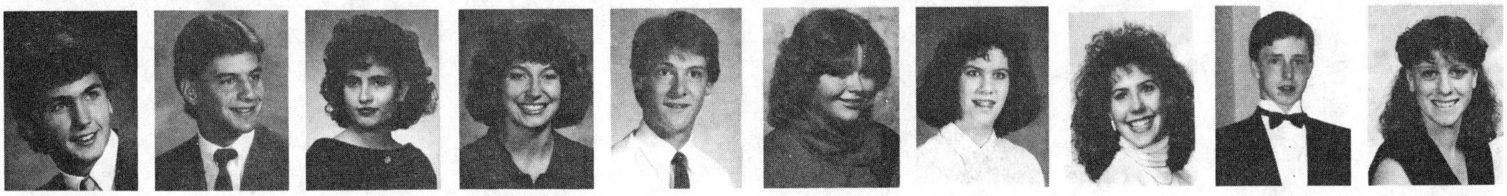

Fayocavitz, David
Abington Heights
Clarks Summit, PA

Fazio, Frank
Hampton HS
Allison Park, PA

Fazzi, Heather L
Dallas SR HS
Wyoming, PA

Feaser, Michelle
Cedar Crest HS
Lebanon, PA

Feather, Allan J
Hatboro-Horsham
Hatboro, PA

Feathers, Vicki
Claysburg-Kimmel
Imler, PA

Feczko, Janine
Greensburg Central Catholic HS
So Greensburg, PA

Fedorchak, Sandra K
Mid-Valley Secondary Ctr
Olyphant, PA

Fee, J Kevin
Plymouth-Whitemarsh HS
Lafayette Hill, PA

Feeley, Jennifer
Cheltenham HS
Cheltenham, PA

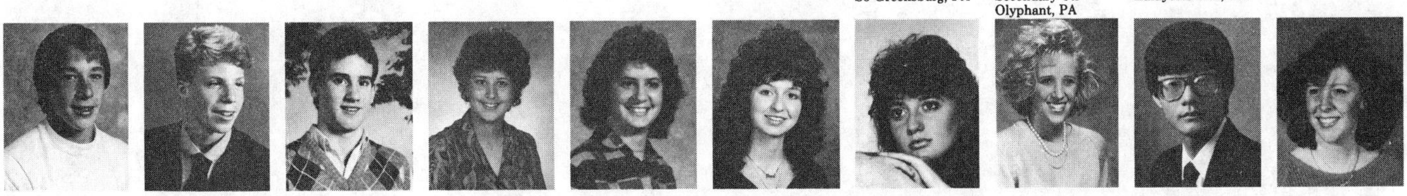

Feese, Eric
Southern Columbia Area HS
Catawissa, PA

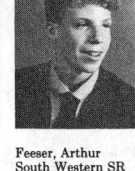

Feeser, Arthur
South Western SR
Brodbecks, PA

Feger, Kyle E
Schuylkill Haven Area HS
Schuylkill Haven, PA

Feick, Marie
Elizabeth Forward
Monongahela, PA

Feinberg, Fern
Hatboro-Horsham SR HS
Hatboro, PA

Feindt, Frances
Cardinal O Hara HS
Brookhaven, PA

Felegy, Tania
William Allen HS
Allentown, PA

Feller, Alexa Gram
Conrad Weiser HS
Reinholds, PA

Feng, Wu-Che
State College Area SR HS
State College, PA

Feniello, Stacey
Cornellsville Area
Connellsvl, PA

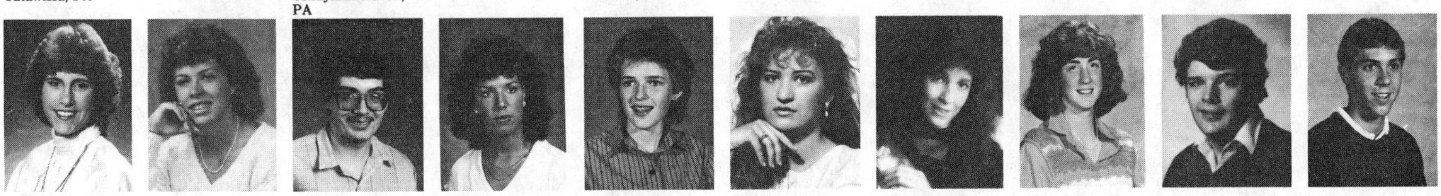

Fennessey, Julia
Peters Township HS
Mcmurray, PA

Fenton, Carol
Said Eagle Nittany
Mill Hall, PA

Fenwick, James
Tunkhannock Area
Mehoopany, PA

Ference, Mary Jean
Greensburg Central Catholic HS
Greensburg, PA

Ferencuha, Lisa A
Connellsville Area SR HS
S Connellsville, PA

Ferguson, Beth
Brownsville Area HS
Brownsville, PA

Ferguson, Cassandra
Pocono Mountain
E Stroudsburg, PA

Ferguson, Rebecca
Abington SR HS
Abington, PA

Ferguson, Ron
Du Bois Area HS
Dubois, PA

Ferko, Ed
Phoenixville Area
Phoenixville, PA

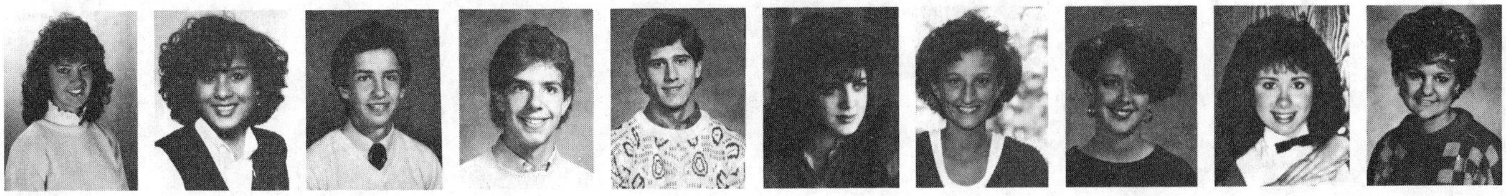

Fernandez, Gina
Mahanoy Area HS
Mahanoy City, PA

Fernandez, Selena
Nazareth Acad
Philadelphia, PA

Fernandez, Todd R
Methacton HS
Audubon, PA

Fernsler, Matthew
Lancaster Country Day Schl
Quentin, PA

Ferrara, Brad
Ringgold HS
Donora, PA

Ferraro, Kim
Pittston Area SR
Hughestown, PA

Ferree, Jessica
Spring Grove SR HS
Spring Grove, PA

Ferrence, Krista
West York Area SR
York, PA

Ferretti, Michelle
Leechburg Area HS
Leechburg, PA

Ferringer, Elizabeth
Keystone HS
Knox, PA

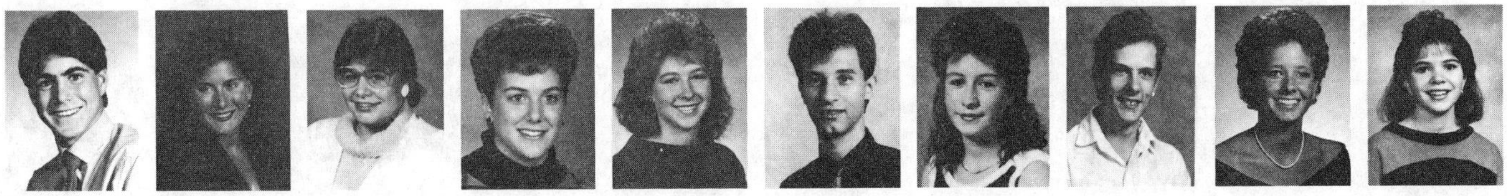

Ferris, Louis
Notre Dame HS
Easton, PA

Ferro, Danielle
Berwick HS
Berwick, PA

Fetcenko, Susan Michelle
West Branch Area
Hawk Run, PA

Fetch, Kristin
Penn Trafford HS
Trafford, PA

Fetchen, Kimberly
Elizabeth Forward
Elizabeth, PA

Fetchko, Matthew
Bishop Hafey HS
Hazleton, PA

Fetsick, Lisa
Churchill HS
Pittsburgh, PA

Fetter, Colby
Biglerville HS
Gettysburg, PA

Fetters, Jill
Downingtown SR
Downingtown, PA

Ficarotta, Tracy
Morrisville HS
Morrisville, PA

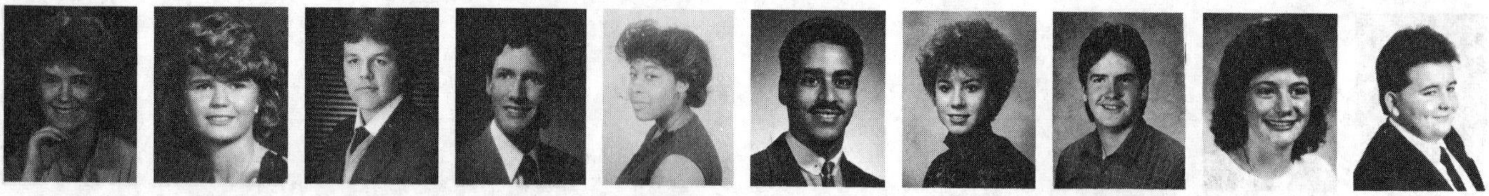

Fichtner, Michele
Solaneo HS
Quarryville, PA

Ficke, Alana
Lower Moreland HS
Huntingdon Valley, PA

Fidler, Steven
Center Twp HS
Aliquippa, PA

Fields, Rex
Mc Connellsburg HS
Mcconnellsburg, PA

Fields, Sharon Denise
Frankford HS
Philadelphia, PA

Figueroa, Nelson
Northeast HS
Philadelphia, PA

Fike, Michelle
Du Bois Area HS
Sykesville, PA

Filbern, Matthew
Yough SR HS
Ruffs Dale, PA

Filby, Donna Jean
Chartiers-Houston
Houston, PA

Filer, Alan
Pennsbury HS
Tullytown, PA

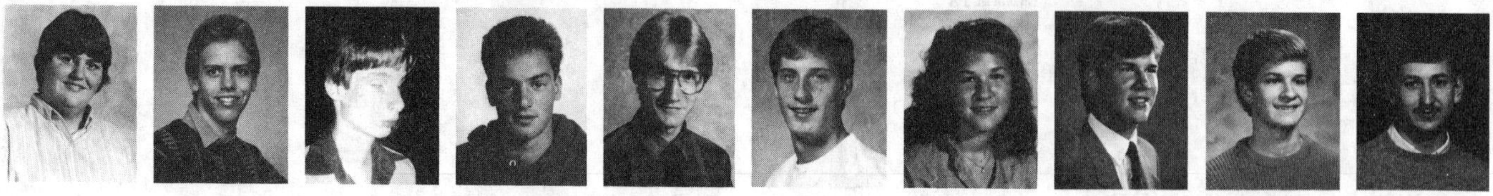

Filippini, Susan
James M Coughlin
Wilkes-Barre, PA

Finarelli, III Al
Bishop O Reilly HS
Dallas, PA

Finch, Brian
Overbrook School For The Blind
Philadelphia, PA

Fine, Matthew
Lower Merion HS
Philadelphia, PA

Fink, James
The Christian Acad
Brookhaven, PA

Fink, Jason
Montgomery Area
Montgomery, PA

Fink, Melanie
Fleetwood Area HS
Fleetwood, PA

Fink, Mitch
Fleetwood HS
Fleetwood, PA

Fink, Vance
Lampeter-Strasburg
Lancaster, PA

Finklestine, Scott
Penn Cambria SR
Gallitzin, PA

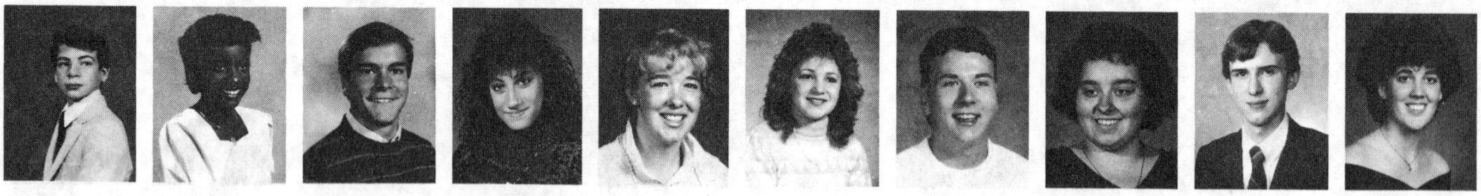

Finlan, Martin
Cardinal Brennan
Ashland, PA

Finley, Stacey D
Cedar Grove Christian Acad
Philadelphia, PA

Finton, Chris
Meadville SR HS
Meadville, PA

Fiorentini, Heidi
Chartiers Valley SR
Bridgevi Le, PA

Fiori, Dawn
Shikellamy HS
Northumberland, PA

Firely, Amy
Norristown Area HS
Norristown, PA

Firestine, Shawn
Cocalico SR HS
Stevens, PA

Firestone, Denise
Laurel Highlands
Lemont Furnace, PA

Fischer, Danny
Franklin JR SR HS
Franklin, PA

Fischer, Lisa M
Upper Moreland SR
Willow Grove, PA

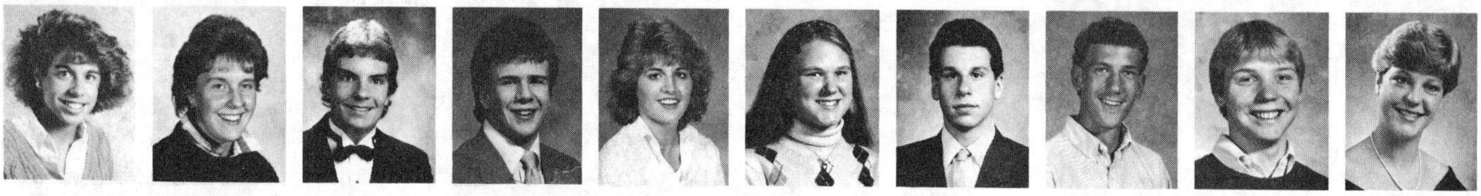

Fischer, Monnette
York Catholic HS
Shawsbury, PA

Fischl, Beth
Northampton SR
Bath, PA

Fish, Brian
Cathedral Prep Schl
Erie, PA

Fish, Jeremy B
Coudersport JR/SR
Coudersport, PA

Fish, Kathy
Elkland Area HS
Elkland, PA

Fisher, Cindy
Calvary Baptist Chirstian Sch
Lancaster, PA

Fisher, Clark
Milton Hershey HS
Windber, PA

Fisher, Conrad
Boyertown Area SR
Green Lane, PA

Fisher, Dan
Garden Spot HS
Narvan, PA

Fisher, Debbie
Cumberland Valley
Mechanicsburg, PA

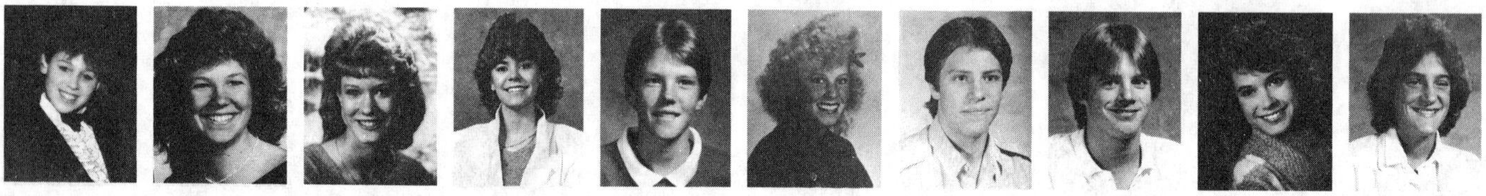

Fisher, Denise
Blairsville SR HS
Blairsville, PA

Fisher, Denise M
Abraham Lincoln
Philadelphia, PA

Fisher, Georgina C
Lampeter-Strasburg
Strasburg, PA

Fisher, Jamie
Uniontown Area SR
Markleysburg, PA

Fisher, John
Cedar Crest HS
Lebanon, PA

Fisher, Kristina
Reading SR HS
Reading, PA

Fisher, Matthew
Sharon HS
Sharon, PA

Fisher, Michael E
Solanco HS
Drumore, PA

Fisher, Uneva
Mc Guffey HS
Washington, PA

Fitz, Tana
Northeastern HS
Manchester, PA

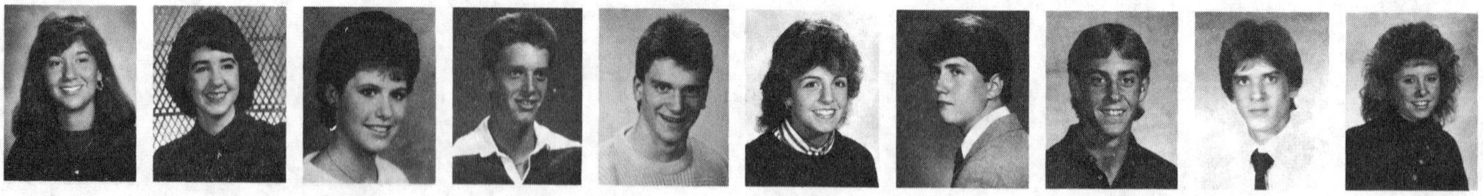

Fitzbiggons, Jill C
Mount Lebanon HS
Pittsburgh, PA

Fitzpatrick, Sheila M
Central Bucks West
Doylestown, PA

Fix, Carla
Penn Trafford HS
Trafford, PA

Fix, Joseph
Salisbury HS
Allentown, PA

Flannery, David
West Scranton HS
Scranton, PA

Fleck, Jennifer
Oley Valley HS
Douglassville, PA

Fleck, Jon
Altoona Area HS
Altoona, PA

Flecker, Tim
Shaler Area SR HS
Glenshaw, PA

Flecksteiner, John W
Bethlehem Catholic
Bethlehem, PA

Fleming, Jennifer
Phil-Mont Christian
Huntingdon Valley, PA

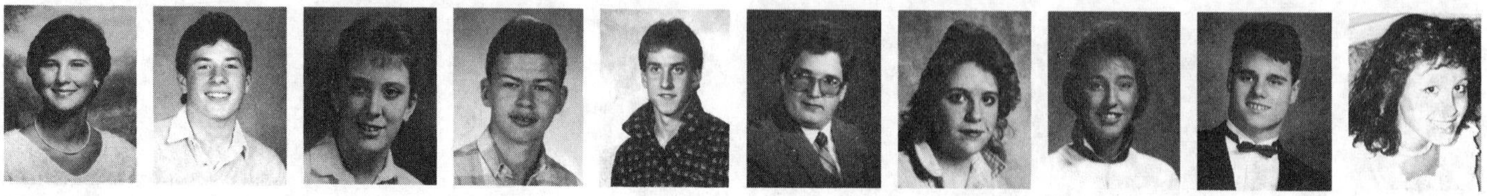

Fleming, Lisa
Knoch JR SR HS
Butler, PA

Flenner, Michael
Carlynton JR-SR
Coraopolis, PA

Fletcher, Marlene
Valley View JR/SR
Blakely, PA

Fletcher, Todd
Elizabeth Forward
Elizabeth, PA

Flick, John
Oil City HS
Oil City, PA

Flick, Samuel
Somerset Area HS
Somerset, PA

Flickinger, Debra
Lehighton Area HS
Lehighton, PA

Flickinger, Jeneen
Newport HS
Newport, PA

Florence, Raymond
West Catholic HS
Philadelphia, PA

Flot, Heidi Wilson
Trinity HS
New Cumberland, PA

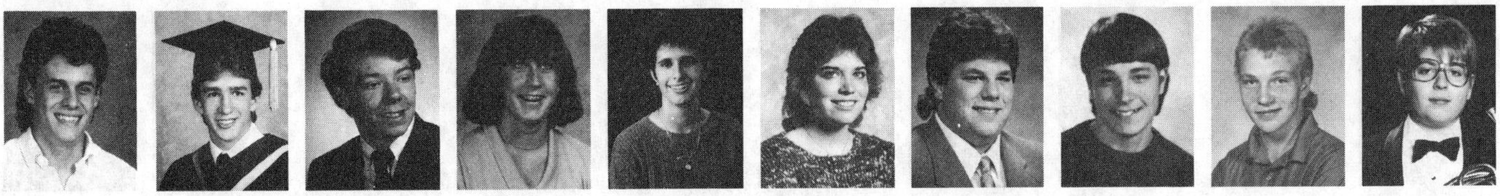

Flout, Kevin
Neshannock HS
New Castle, PA

Flynn, Bill
Father Judge HS
Philadelphia, PA

Focht, Jr Richard L
Huntingdon Area
Huntingdon, PA

Fogal, Ann Marie
Fannett,metal HS
Doylesburg, PA

Foglia, Tracey
Ringgold HS
Monongahela, PA

Foley, Sharon
Pine Grove Area HS
Tremont, PA

Fontanazza, Mario
Mt Pleasant Area
Mt Pleasant, PA

Foor, Damien
North Penn HS
Lansdale, PA

Foor, Ronald
Everett Area HS
Breezewood, PA

Foote, Brian
Quaker Valley HS
Sewickley Hls, PA

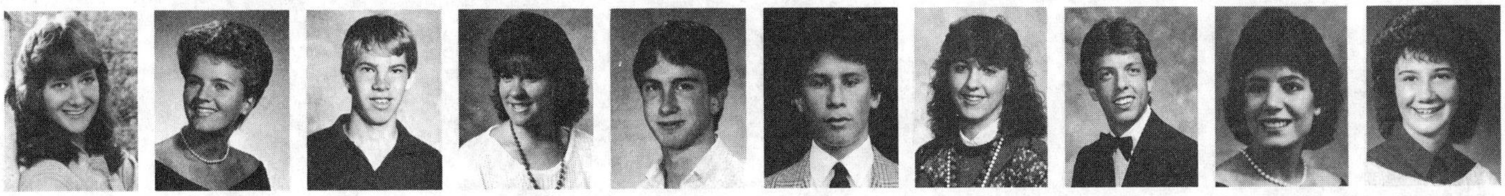

Forbes, Stacey Rene
Tawanda Area HS
Towanda, PA

Ford, Bethany A
Downingtown HS
Downingtown, PA

Ford, Robert
Hampton HS
Allison Park, PA

Fordyce, Karry
Trinity HS
Amity, PA

Foreman, Jr John
Waynesboro Area
SR HS
Waynesboro, PA

Foremny, Steve
Kennard-Dale HS
New Park, PA

Forgas, Krista
Belle Vernon Area
Belle Vernon, PA

Forney, Geoff
Interboro HS
Prospect Park, PA

Fornwalt, Danielle
Middletown Area
Middletown, PA

Forry, Tammie
Eastern HS
Hallam, PA

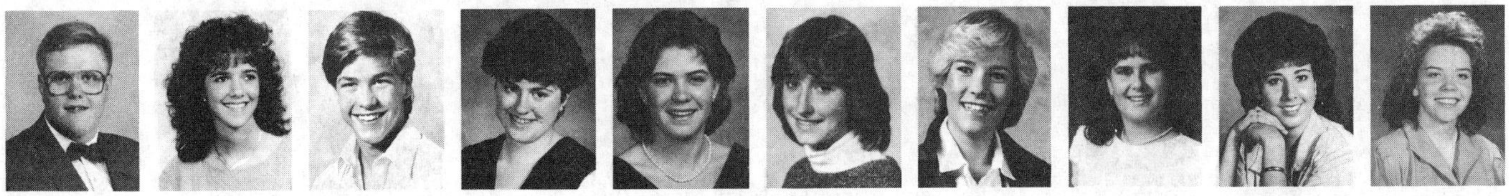

Fortunato, Jr James
Shannock Valley HS
Rural Valley, PA

Fosco, Denise
Mc Dowell HS
Erie, PA

Foster, Christopher
Shady Side Acad
Pittsburgh, PA

Foster, Dawn
Corry Area HS
Corry, PA

Foster, Jill
Cardinal O Hara HS
Media, PA

Foster, Leslie
Montrose Area JR/
SR HS
Montrose, PA

Foster, Pamela
Warren Area HS
Warren, PA

Fotopoulos, Afroditi
William Allen HS
Allentown, PA

Fotopoulos, Antonia
Reading SR HS
Reading, PA

Fowler, Holly
Bishop Conwell HS
Yardley, PA

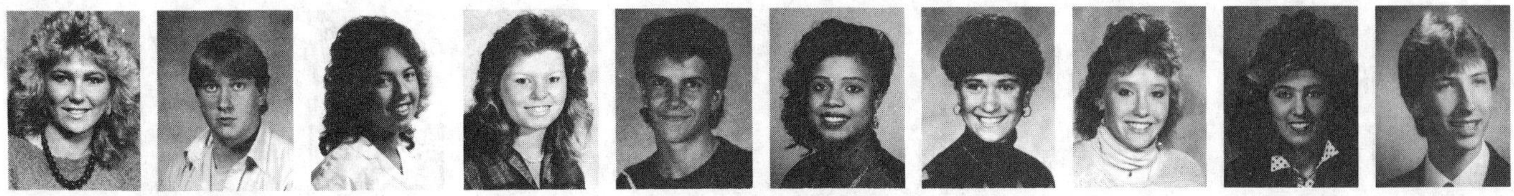

Fowler, Irene
Sharpsville HS
Sharpsville, PA

Fowles, Mark
State Coll Area
Intermediate HS
Pine Grove Mills,
PA

Fox, Holly
Gettysburg SR HS
Gettysburg, PA

Fox, Shannon
Reading SR HS
Reading, PA

Foy, Sean
Downington SR HS
Coatsville, PA

Foy, Tammy
West Mifflin Area
W Mifflin, PA

Fragin, Jodi
Abington Hgts HS
Clarks Green, PA

Frail, Charlene
E L Meyers HS
Wilkes-Barre, PA

Franceschi, Elsa
Mon Valley Catholic
Belle Vernon, PA

Franceschina, Gene
North Hills HS
Pittsburgh, PA

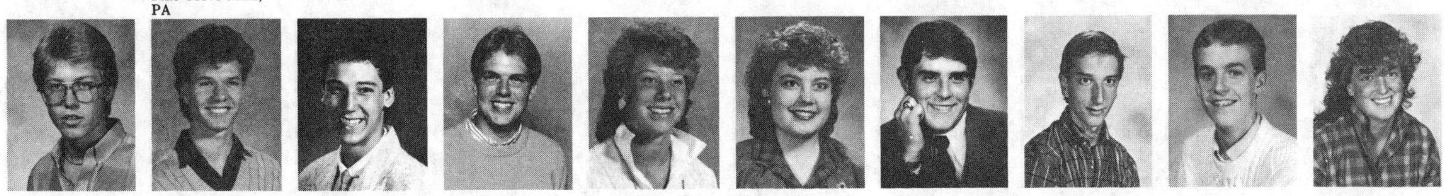

Franchock, Neal
Moshannon Valley
Glen Hope, PA

Francis, Greg
Conestoga HS
Strafford, PA

Francis, Jr Joseph
M
Bishop Guilfoyle HS
Altoona, PA

Frangakis, John
Robert
West Middlesex
JR-SR HS
West Middlesex, PA

Frank, Heather
Downingtown SR
Exton, PA

Frank, Jodi
Shenango HS
New Castle, PA

Frank, Kevin
Sugar Valley HS
Loganton, PA

Frank, Jr Robert E
Norristown Area HS
Norristown, PA

Frank, Tim
Altoona Area HS
Altoona, PA

Frank, Tisha
Chambersburg Area
SR HS
Chambersburg, PA

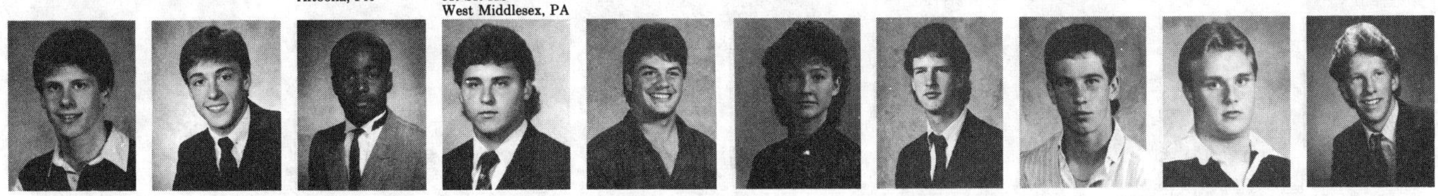

Frank, II Vincent P
Altoona Area HS
Altoona, PA

Frankenberry,
Robert N
North East HS
North East, PA

Franklin, Jr Barrett
M
Bishop Boyle HS
Homestead, PA

Franklin, Ben
Northern Cambria
Barnesboro, PA

Franklin,
Christopher
Hatboro-Horsham
Horsham, PA

Franks, Melinda
Kiski Area SR HS
New Kensington,
PA

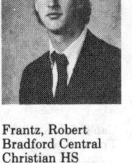

Frantz, Robert
Bradford Central
Christian HS
Bradford, PA

Fraser, Jack
United HS
Seward, PA

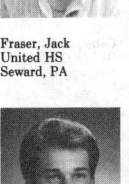

Fravel, Bradley
Neshaminy HS
Levittown, PA

Frazier, David
Eastern Lebanon
County HS
Lebanon, PA

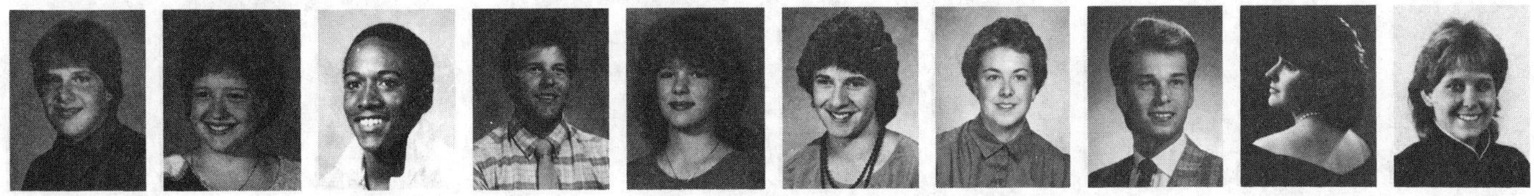

Frazier, David
Hollidaysburg Area
SR HS
Duncansville, PA

Frazier, Jodi
Connellsville Area
SR HS
Connellsville, PA

Frazier, Scott
Gateway HS
Monroeville, PA

Frazier, Scott
Lock Haven SR HS
Lock Haven, PA

Frechione, Tina
Trinity Christian
Pittsburgh, PA

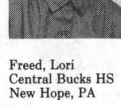

Frederick, Amy
North Star HS
Boswell, PA

Freed, Lori
Central Bucks HS
New Hope, PA

Freedman, Jeffrey
Mark
George Washington
Philadelphia, PA

Freeland, Theresa
Susquenita HS
Duncannon, PA

Freeman, Carol Lee
Jim Thorpe Area SR
Albrightsville, PA

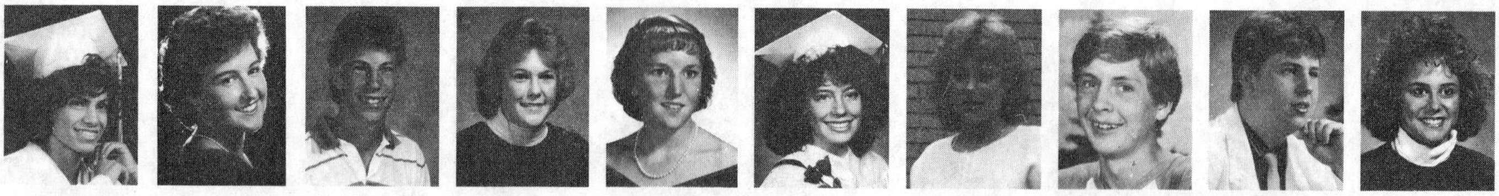

Freeman, Erica K
Julia R Masterman
Philadelphia, PA

Freeman, Kelly
Garnet Valley HS
Chester Heights, PA

Freese, Gregory
Kennard-Dale HS
Stewartstown, PA

Freese, Kerry
Solanco SR HS
Nottingham, PA

Freilich, Margaret
Upper Merion Area
Wayne, PA

Freiling, Patricia
Nazareth Acad
Philadelphia, PA

Frelick, Amibeth
Hempfield Area HS
Greensburg, PA

French, Lloyd
Northeast Bradford
Athens, PA

Frew, Michael
Minersville Area HS
Newtown, PA

Frey, Christy
Eastern York HS
Hellam, PA

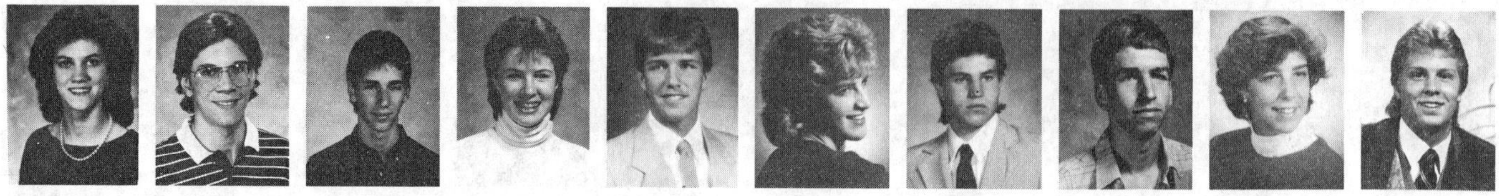

Frey, Crystal
Liberty JR SR HS
Liberty, PA

Frey, II William R
Liberty JR-SR HS
Liberty, PA

Friday, Joseph
Fort Cherry HS
Hickory, PA

Friedhofer, Corinne A
Hempfield HS
Lancaster, PA

Friend, Eric
Chambersburg Area
Chambersburg, PA

Fries, Jean
Allentown Central Catholic HS
Allentown, PA

Frisch, John J
Northwestern Lehigh HS
Germansville, PA

Fritz, Bradley
Cocalico HS
Adamstown, PA

Fritz, Kelly Evans
North Hills HS
Pittsburgh, PA

Froggatt, Rory
Montiteau HS
W Sunbury, PA

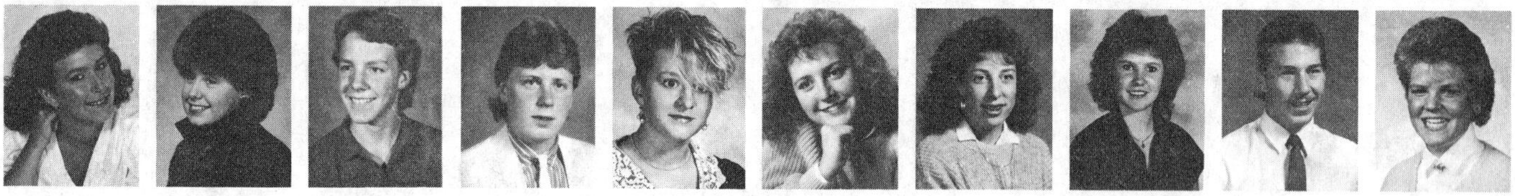

Frollo, Cathy
Penn Hills HS
Verona, PA

Frontino, Amy
Williamson JR SR
Lawrenceville, PA

Frost, Douglas
Laurel Highlands
Uniontown, PA

Frost, Shawn
Shikellamy HS
Sunbury, PA

Frucella, Heidi
Linden Hall HS
Frederick, MD

Fry, Bridget
Butler Area HS
Butler, PA

Fry, Joyce
Donegal HS
Mount Joy, PA

Fry, Kimberly
Marion Center HS
Home, PA

Fry, Larry
West Perry HS
New Bloomfield, PA

Frye, Beatrice
Susquehanna Community HS
Thompson, PA

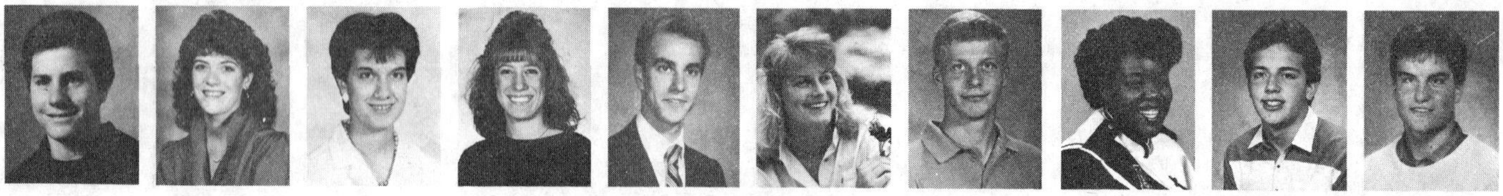

Frye, Gary
Center HS
Monaca, PA

Frye, Michelle
Altoona Area HS
Altoona, PA

Fryer, Barbara A
Norristown Area HS
Norristown, PA

Frynkewicz, Pamela
Ambridge HS
Freedom, PA

Fuerman, Richard
The Hill Schl
Pottstown, PA

Fuhrman, Jennifer
Hanover SR HS
Hanover, PA

Fuller, Craig
Calvary Baptist Christian Acad
Conneautville, PA

Fuller, Debbie
Aliquippa HS
Aliquippa, PA

Fuller, Jason
Ford City HS
Ford City, PA

Fuller, II Roy G
Geibel HS
Vanderbilt, PA

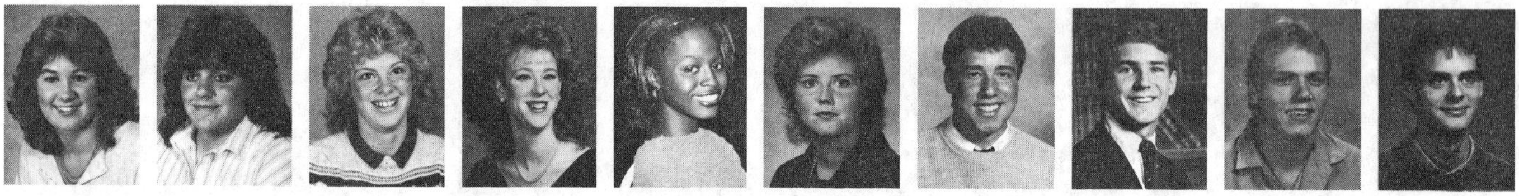

Fulmer, Janet
Yough SR HS
West Newton, PA

Fulmer, Lu Anne
Yough SR HS
Yukon, PA

Fulmer, Missy
Ft Cherry HS
Mc Donald, PA

Fulmer, Victoria
Little Flower Catholic HS Fo
Philadelphia, PA

Fulton, Wendy
Taylor Allderdice
Pittsburgh, PA

Fuoss, Margie
Montgomery JR SR
Montgomery, PA

Furfari, Eric
Bishop Carroll HS
Lilly, PA

Furia, Fred
The Haverford Schl
Haverford, PA

Furlong, Christopher
Cedar Cliff HS
Camp Hill, PA

Furst, Todd
Salisbury HS
Allentown, PA

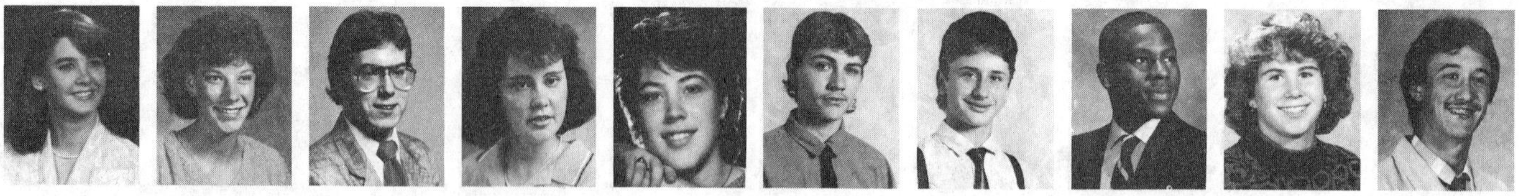

Fuss, Michele
Lampeter Strasburg
Lancaster, PA

Fusting, Heather M
James Buchanan HS
St Thomas, PA

Gabel, Martin
Bishop O Reilly HS
Swoyersville, PA

Gable, Sarah Jane
Trinity HS
Camp Hill, PA

Gable, Tara L
Blue Mountain HS
Pottsville, PA

Gabriel, Michael
Bishop Hafey HS
Hazleton, PA

Gadola, Jr Angelo M
Bishop Hafey HS
Hazleton, PA

Gadsden, James L
Coatesville Area SR
Coatesville, PA

Gaffney, Mary Kathryn
Lansdale Catholic
Ambler, PA

Gagliardi, Blake
MMI Prep Schl
Hazleton, PA

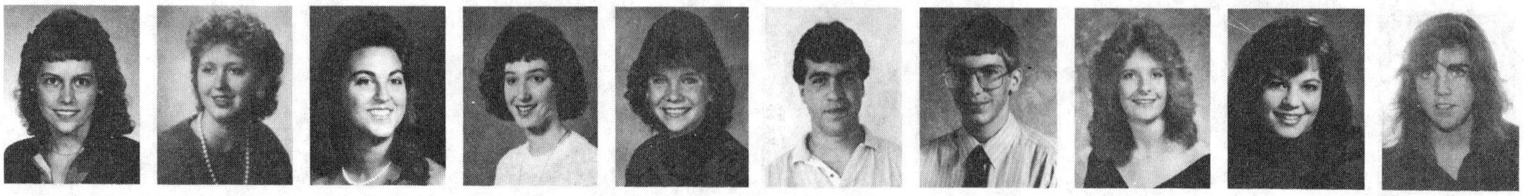

Gagnon, Andrea
Bethlehem Center
Brownsville, PA

Gajdowski, Anastasia M
Saegertown HS
Saegertown, PA

Galante, Elaine
Bensalem HS
Bensalem, PA

Galas, Amy
Center Area HS
Monaca, PA

Galford, Daphne
Cameron County HS
Emporium, PA

Galiatsatos, Nicholas J
Marple Newtown SR
Springfield, PA

Galitsky, Leon
Allentown Central Catholic HS
Whitehall, PA

Gallagher, Carolyn
Interboro HS
Essington, PA

Gallagher, Colleen
Allentown Central
Allentown, PA

Gallagher, Donna
St Basil Acad
Philadelphia, PA

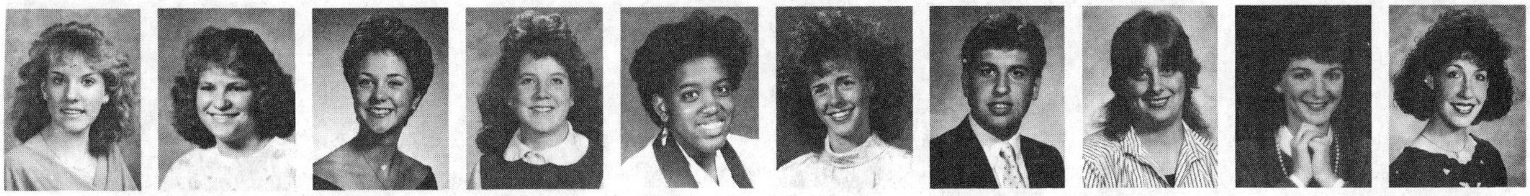

Gallagher, Jean
Cardinal O Hara HS
Ridley Park, PA

Gallagher, Jennifer
Riverside HS
Ellwood City, PA

Gallagher, Laurie Ann
Downingtown SR
Exton, PA

Gallagher, Maureen
St Hubert HS For
Philadelphia, PA

Gallimore, Tamika L
Henderson SR HS
West Chester, PA

Gallis, Heidi
Geibel HS
Uniontown, PA

Gallo, Robert
Central Catholic HS
Pittsburgh, PA

Galonski, Jennie
Belle Vernon Area
Belle Vernon, PA

Galt, Danielle
Harbor Creek HS
Erie, PA

Galvin, Luanne
New Castle SR HS
New Castle, PA

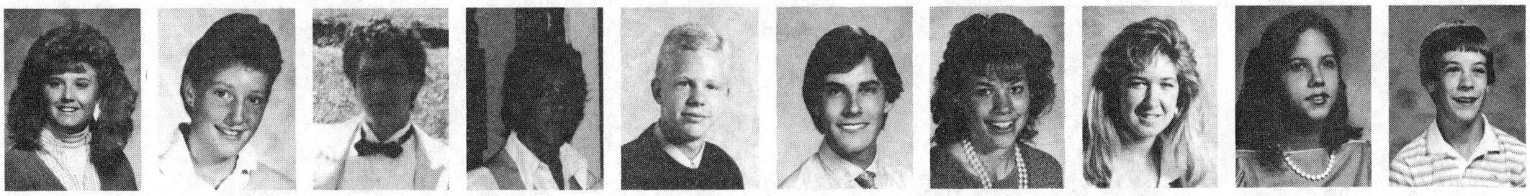

Gambill, Susan M
North Allegheny HS
Wexford, PA

Gammell, Chanin
Schuylkill Valley HS
Reading, PA

Gampo, Brett
West Greene HS
New Freeport, PA

Gampo, Talby
West Greene HS
New Freeport, PA

Gangloff, Benjamin
York Catholic HS
York, PA

Gannon, Shawn
Bishop Mc Devitt
Harrisburg, PA

Gano, Jayne
Reading HS
Reading, PA

Gans, Stephanie
Acad Of Notre
Havertown, PA

Gansley-Ortiz, Deidre
Harrisburg HS
Harrisburg, PA

Gantt, Matthew
Greenwood HS
Millerstown, PA

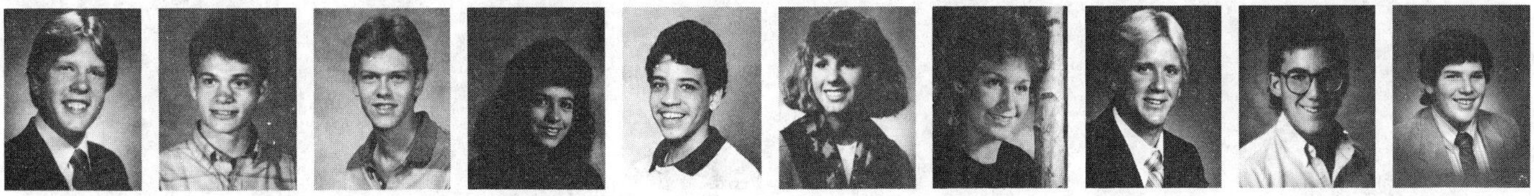

Gantz, John
Shenandoah Valley
Shenandoah, PA

Garber, Charles J
Waynesboro Central
Waynesburg, PA

Garber, Todd
Parkland SR HS
Allentown, PA

Garcia, Diana
Carbondale Area HS
Carbondale, PA

Garcia-Zayas, Ricardo M
Blue Mountain Acad
Mayaguez, PR

Gardner, Heidi
Warwick HS
Lititz, PA

Gardner, Lesley
Elkland Area HS
Elkland, PA

Gargasz, Joe
Lakeview HS
Mercer, PA

Gargon, Frank
Trinity HS
Washington, PA

Gariepy, Jack
West Scranton HS
Scranton, PA

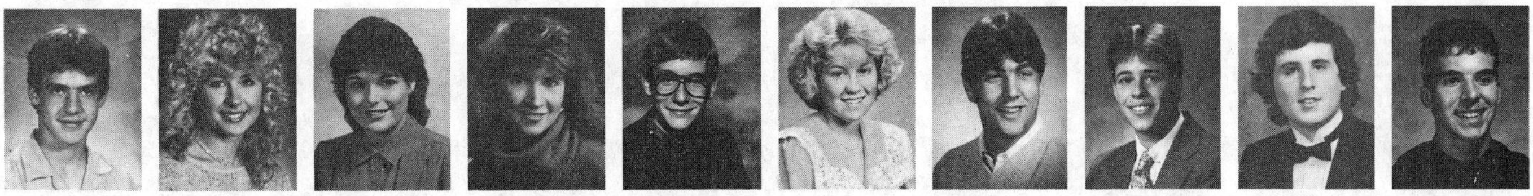

Garing, John
Karns City HS
Chicora, PA

Garner, Deirdre Rae Anna
St Marys Area HS
Saint Marys, PA

Garrick, Teri
Belle Vernon Area
Belle Vernon, PA

Garrison, Gail
Mt Lebanon SR HS
Pittsburgh, PA

Garrison, John
Tunkhannock Area
Falls, PA

Garry, Kristin
Homer Center HS
Homer City, PA

Gartley, Bill
Hopewell HS
Aliquippa, PA

Garver, Timothy
Altoona Area HS
Altoona, PA

Garvin, Gregory
Upper Darby HS
Drexel Hill, PA

Gary, Brian
Bishop Neumann
Williamsport, PA

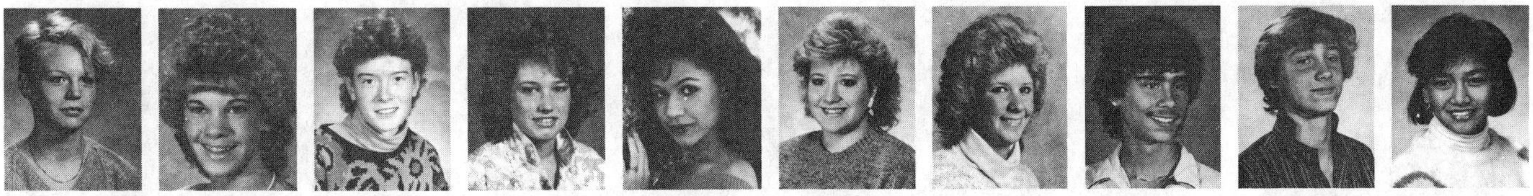

Gasser, Kristin
Carlisle HS
Carlisle, PA

Gaston, Kelli
Harmony HS
Westover, PA

Gates, Gretchen
Seneca Valley HS
Evans City, PA

Gatzke, Kelly
Tunkhannock Area
Mehoopany, PA

Gaudio, Alyson C
Villa Maria HS
Youngstown, OH

Gavazzi, Marsha
Burgettstown Area JR SR HS
Burgettstown, PA

Gawrylik, Traci
Shenandoah Valley
Shenandoah, PA

Gaydos, Phil
Laurel Highlands
Hopwood, PA

Gazewood, Jason
Fairview HS
Fairview, PA

Gazmen, Nina
Abington Heights
Waverly, PA

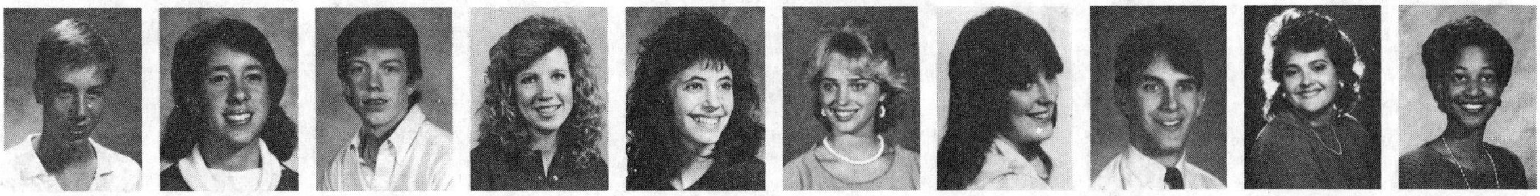

Gazze, Ronald
Greensburg-Salem
Greensburg, PA

Gearhart, Barbara
Hershey SR HS
Hershey, PA

Gearhart, Gary
Altoona Area HS
Altoona, PA

Geary, Coleen
Kiski Area HS
Apollo, PA

Geary, Kimberley
Connellsville HS
Champion, PA

Geary, Lou
Connellsville SR HS
Normalville, PA

Geary, Michelle Lee
Belle Vernon Area
Belle Vernon, PA

Gebicki, Michael
Greensburg Central Catholic HS
Greensburg, PA

Gedney, Tonya A
Norristown Area HS
Norristown, PA

Gee, Cheryl
West Catholic Girls
Philadelphia, PA

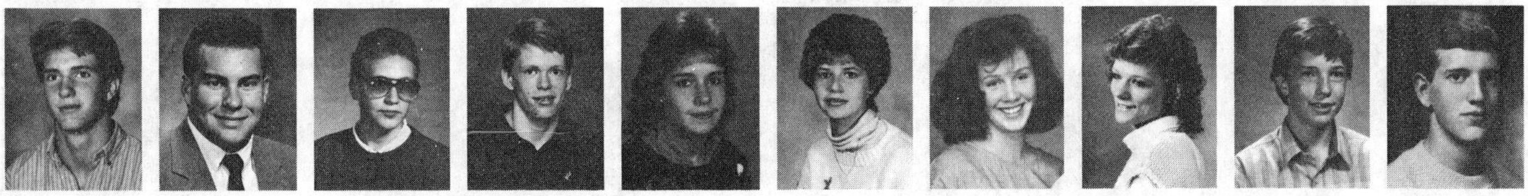

Gefrides, Chris
Montoursville Area
Montoursville, PA

Gehman, Timothy
Ephrata SR HS
Ephrata, PA

Geho, Patrick
Ambridge Area HS
Baden, PA

Gehris, Brian
Reading HS
Reading, PA

Geiger, Jo Ellen
Penn Trafford HS
Irwin, PA

Geiner, Susan
Altoona Area HS
Altoona, PA

Geisel, Elizabeth
St Pius X HS
Douglasville, PA

Geiselman, Chris
Dover Area HS
Dover, PA

Geiser, Thom
Wilmington Area JR/SR HS
West Middlesex, PA

Geisler, David
Washington HS
Washington, PA

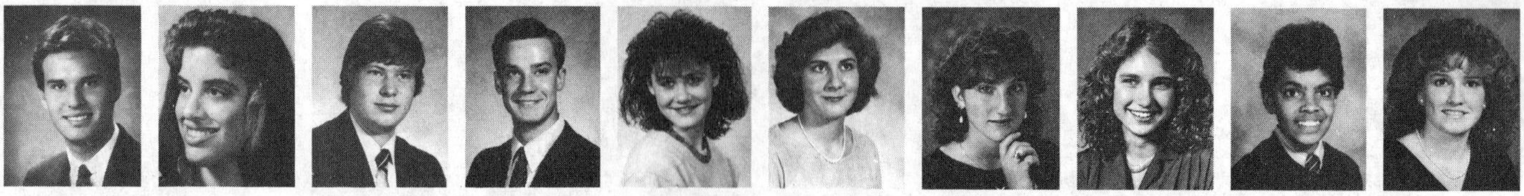

Geisler, Ronald J
Washington HS
Washington, PA

Gelli, Jennifer
James M Goughlin
Plains, PA

Genetti, Jim
Mining And
Mechanical Inst
Weatherly, PA

Genicola, Lance S
Whitehall HS
Whitehall, PA

Genovese, Lynne
West Scranton HS
Scranton, PA

Gensel, Cindy
Lake-Lehman HS
Sweet Vly, PA

Gentile, Deanna
Mt Alvernia HS
Pittsburgh, PA

Gentile, Michele
Gateway SR HS
Monroeville, PA

Gentles, Peter
Upper Darby HS
Upper Darby, PA

Gentry, Lori
Bishop Mc Devitt
Huntingdon Vall,
PA

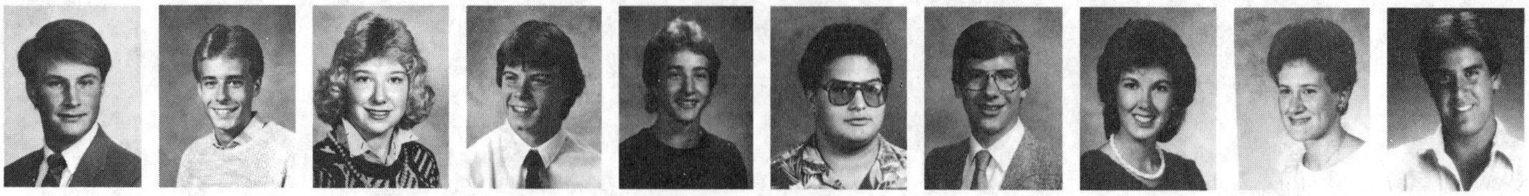

Georg, Jeffrey
Dover Area HS
Dover, PA

George, II James
Moon SR HS
Coraopolis, PA

George, Kelli
Meadville Area SR
Meadville, PA

George, Larry
Trinity HS
Washington, PA

George, Ronald
Shenango HS
New Castle, PA

Geramita, Jr
Anthony J
Neshannock HS
New Castle, PA

Gerard, Jason
Charlerdi Area HS
Charleroi, PA

Gerber, Ronna
Penns Manor HS
Clymer, PA

Gerber, Wendy
Penns Manor Area
Clymer, PA

Geregach, George
Montour HS
Coraopolis, PA

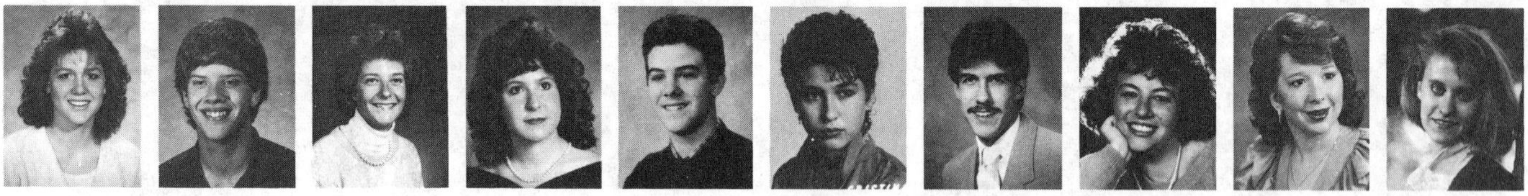

Gerhardt, Christine
Bishop Conwell HS
Levittown, PA

German, Frank
Yough District HS
Herminie, PA

Gessner, Angela
Shikellamy HS
Paxinos, PA

Getman, Laura
Central Dauphin HS
Harrisburg, PA

Getty, Corey
Columbia Montour
Catawissa, PA

Gheorghiu, Cristina
Kennedy Christian
Greenville, PA

Gibbel, Dean
Tulpehocken HS
Bethel, PA

Gibbons, Molly
Hopewell HS
Hookstown, PA

Gibbs, Michaela
Yough SR HS
Irwin, PA

Gibel, Jeannine M
The
Winchester-Thursto
Pittsburgh, PA

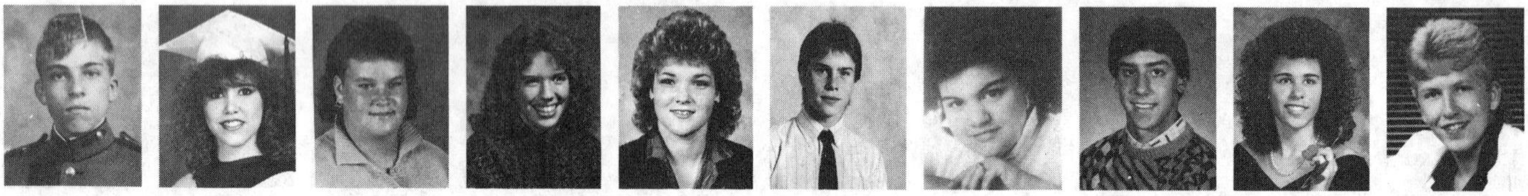

Cibson, Alex
Valley Forge
Military Acad
Poolesville, MD

Gibson, Dawn
Little Flower H S
For Girls
Philadelphia, PA

Gibson, Deborah
Penn-Trafford HS
Trafford, PA

Gibson, Jennifer
Cedar Crest HS
Lebanon, PA

Gibson, Melissa
Nortahwestern SR
Albion, PA

Gifford, Jason
Allentown Central
Catholic HS
Kutztown, PA

Gigantino, Adrienne
Dunmore HS
Canadensis, PA

Gigliotti, A Jason
Monessen JR SR
Monessen, PA

Gildein, Barbara
Jean
Abraham Lincoln
Philadelphia, PA

Giles, Arthur
Monaca JR SR HS
Monaca, PA

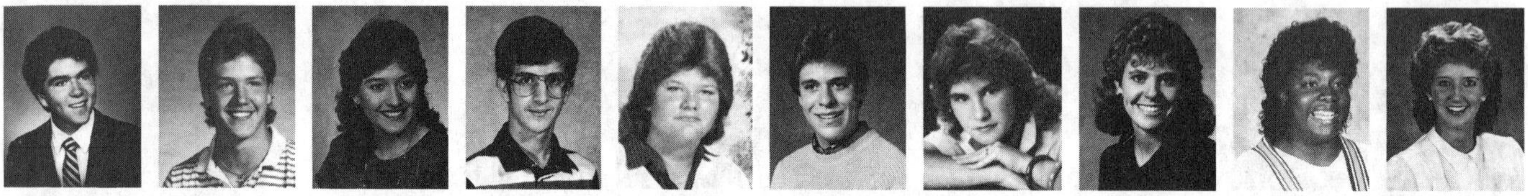

Giles, Eric J
Blackhawk HS
Beaver Falls, PA

Giles, Mark
Ambridge HS
Ambridge, PA

Gilkey, Michelle
Highlands HS
Natrona Hts, PA

Gill, John
Owen J Roberts HS
Pottstown, PA

Gill, Tove Marie
Northern York Co
Dillsburg, PA

Gillespie, Kevin
Springdale HS
Cheswick, PA

Gillette, Margo
Dunmore HS
Dunmore, PA

Gilleylen, Aimee
Gateway SR HS
Monroeville, PA

Gillis, Paulette
Steelton-Highspire
Steelton, PA

Gilmore, Kristina
Bishop Mc Devitt
Dauphin, PA

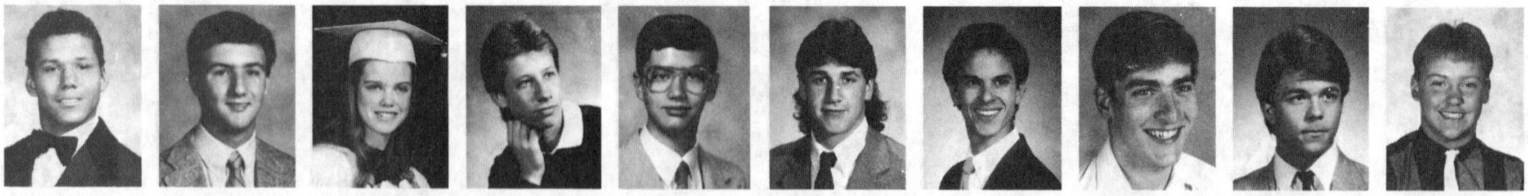

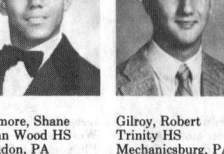

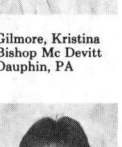

Gilmore, Shane
Penn Wood HS
Yeadon, PA

Gilroy, Robert
Trinity HS
Mechanicsburg, PA

Gimbel, Rita Mary
Saint Hubert HS
Philadelphia, PA

Ginder, John
Donegal HS
Mt Joy, PA

Gindlesperger,
Ronald
Conemaugh Twp
Area HS
Johnstown, PA

Ginn, Mark
Corry HS
Corry, PA

Ginsberg, Neil A
Scranton Central
Scranton, PA

Ginter, D Barry
Homer-Center HS
Homer City, PA

Gioffre, Edward
Northeast HS
Philadelphia, PA

Gipe, Jarrod
Chambersburg Area
SR HS
Chambersburg, PA

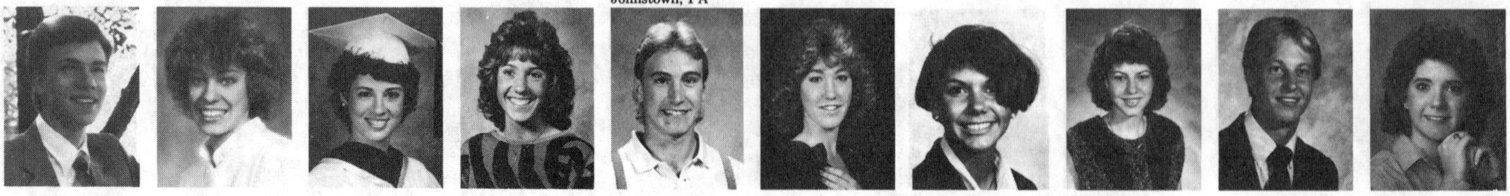

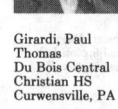

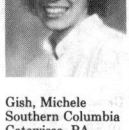

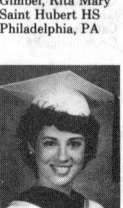

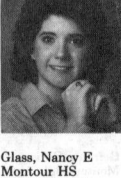

Girardi, Paul
Thomas
Du Bois Central
Christian HS
Curwensville, PA

Gish, Michele
Southern Columbia
Catawissa, PA

Giunta, Carolyn
Bishop Shanahan
West Chester, PA

Giunta, Marnie
Gateway SR HS
Monroeville, PA

Gizdic, John
Wilmington Area
West Middlesex, PA

Glacken, Jennifer L
Archbishop
Prendergast HS
Upper Darby, PA

Gladu, Julie
Gwynedd Mercy
Horsham, PA

Gladys, Tracy
Karns City HS
Chicora, PA

Glas, William
Salesianum HS
West Chester, PA

Glass, Nancy E
Montour HS
Pittsburgh, PA

Glass, Paul
Bishop Shanahan
Westchester, PA

Glassman, Matt
Emmaus HS
Allentown, PA

Glazenski, Joseph
Pittston Area HS
Pittston, PA

Glenn, Chena
Juniata HS
Pt Royal, PA

Glenn, Mary Ann
Waynesboro Area
SR HS
Waynesboro, PA

Glick, James
Northeast Catholic
HS For Boys
Philadelphia, PA

Glick, Julie Helene
Lower Moreland HS
Huntingdon Valley,
PA

Glisan, Carla
Uniontown HS
Markleysburg, PA

Glowaski, Joseph
Danville Area HS
Danville, PA

Gloystein, John
Cathedral Prep
Erie, PA

Gnall, Kevin
Salisbury HS
Bethlehem, PA

Gochin, Alan
HS Of Engineering
& Sci
Philadelphia, PA

Godfrey, Keith
Bishop O Reilly HS
Kingston, PA

Godfrey, Rachel
Ringgold HS
Donora, PA

Godish, Donna
Penn Cambria SR
Lilly, PA

Godish, Virginia
Penn Cambria SR
Lilly, PA

Godwin, Douglas P
South Fayette HS
Bridgeville, PA

Goehring, Jr Robert
New Brighton Area
New Brighton, PA

Goetter, Scott
Bensalem HS
Bensalem, PA

Goheen, Tracey
York Catholic HS
York, PA

Goldberg, Dawn
Pennsbury HS
Yardley, PA

Goldschmidt,
Andrew
Parkland HS
Allentown, PA

Goldsmith, Colleen
Nazareth Acad
Phila, PA

Goldstein, Martin
Upper Dublin HS
Ambler, PA

Goldstein, Rachel
Taylor Allderdice
Pittsburgh, PA

Golingan, Carol
Abington SR HS
Ardsley, PA

Gomola, Joe
Sheffield Area HS
Sheffield, PA

Gonasun, Glenn
Bishop Mc Devitt
Jenkintown, PA

Gontarski, Ann M
Central Bucks West
Doylestown, PA

Gonzalez, Dawn
Villa Maria Acad
Erie, PA

Gonzalez, Jr Jack
Northampton Area
Joint HS
Northampton, PA

Good, Kristen
Aliquippa JR SR
Aliquippa, PA

Goodelle, Jason
Cathedral Prep
Erie, PA

Goodling, Keith
Middleburg HS
Middleburg, PA

Goodman, Leon
Central HS
Philadelphia, PA

Goodman, Mark
Cranberry HS
Oil City, PA

Goodman, William
D
Tunkhannock Area
Tunkhannock, PA

Goodwin, Brian T
Reading SR HS
Reading, PA

Goodwin, George
Milton SR HS
New Columbia, PA

Goon, Christopher
Altoona Area HS
Altoona, PA

Gopez, Noreen
Mechanicsburg HS
Chadds Ford, PA

Gordanier,
Mike-Judd
Carson Long
Military HS
Linden, NJ

Gordner, Donna
Lynne
Millville Area HS
Millville, PA

Gordon, Brenda
Uniontown Area HS
Smock, PA

Gordon, Elizabeth
Central HS
Martinsburg, PA

Gordon, Jeffrey
Pennsbury HS
Morrisville, PA

Gordon, Jr R Craig
Abington SR HS
Hunt Valley, PA

Gordon, Robin
Exeter HS
Reading, PA

Gore, Sachin
Council Rock HS
Holland, PA

Gorgas, Stephanie
Lincoln HS
Wampum, PA

Gorman, Kimberly
Elk Lake Schl
Owego, NY

Gorman, Jr Peter C
Montour HS
Pittsburgh, PA

Gorwall, Emily
Peters Township HS
Mcmurray, PA

Gosnell, Tim
Cumberland Valley
Mechanicsburg, PA

Gotshall, Donna
Hillside Christian
Lewisburg, PA

Gottlieb, Terri
George Washington
Philadelphia, PA

Gottron, Mark
Vincentian HS
Gibsonia, PA

Gotwols, Danielle
Eastern York HS
Wrightsville, PA

Gould, Kara D
N Allegheny SR HS
Pittsburgh, PA

Gould, Todd E
Lower Dauphin SR
Middletown, PA

Goulding, Richard
Mt Pleasant JR HS
Mt Pleasant, PA

Gourley, Ann Marie
Villa Maria Acad
Norristown, PA

Govan, Cindy
Lakeland HS
Olyphant, PA

Govanucci, Renee
Serra Catholic HS
Mc Keesport, PA

Gowatski, Kelly
Connellsville Area
Mt Pleasant, PA

Gowaty, Margaret
Mc Keesport Area
Mc Keesport, PA

Grabarits, Richard
Northampton Area
Northampton, PA

Grabiak, Beverly L
Mt Pleasant A HS
Calumet, PA

Grabowski, Sherry
Mid-Valley HS
Throop, PA

Grace, Christopher
Norristown Area HS
Norristown, PA

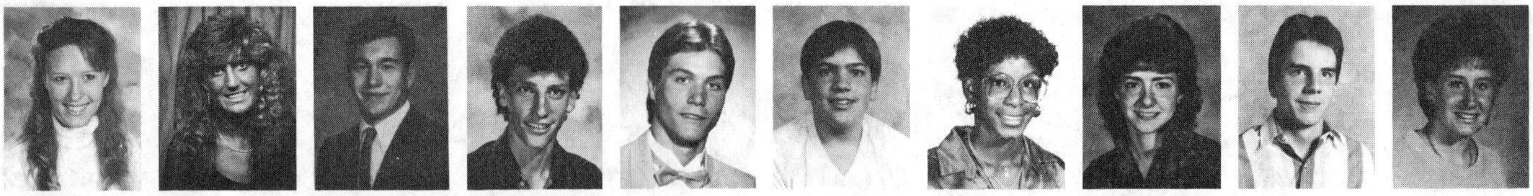

Grace, Lorie
Northern York
County HS
Dillsburg, PA

Graczyk, Heather
William Tennent
Warminster, PA

Grados, Robert
Fox Chapel Area HS
Monessen, PA

Graf, Jr Kenneth W
Northern HS
Dillsburg, PA

Graf, Robert
Ridley SR HS
Holmes, PA

Grafton, Ryan
Freeport SR HS
Freeport, PA

Graham, Sonya L
Norristown Area HS
Norristown, PA

Graham, Wanda
West Forest JR-SR
Tionesta, PA

Grajewski, Mark
Shenandoah Valley
Shenandoah, PA

Grammes, Jill
Saucon Valley SR
Hellertown, PA

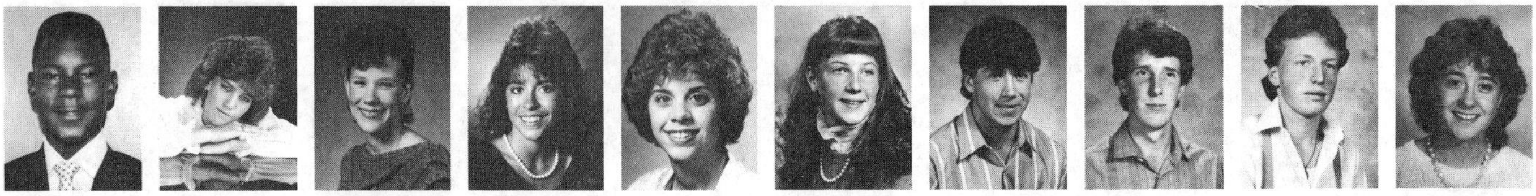

Granderson, Kenneth
Central HS
Philadelphia, PA

Grannas, Christine
Bellwood-Antis HS
Bellwood, PA

Grant, Dana
East Allegheny HS
North Versailles, PA

Grant, Jennifer
Ambridge Area HS
Sewickley, PA

Grant, Jody
Riverside HS
Ellwood City, PA

Grassell, Julie
Greater Latrobe SR
Latrobe, PA

Gratzinger, Greg
Southmoreland SR
Mtpleasant, PA

Graver, Patrick
Solanco HS
Oxford, PA

Graves, Brian
Northwestern HS
Albion, PA

Graves, Kimberly Moore
Northwestern HS
Lake City, PA

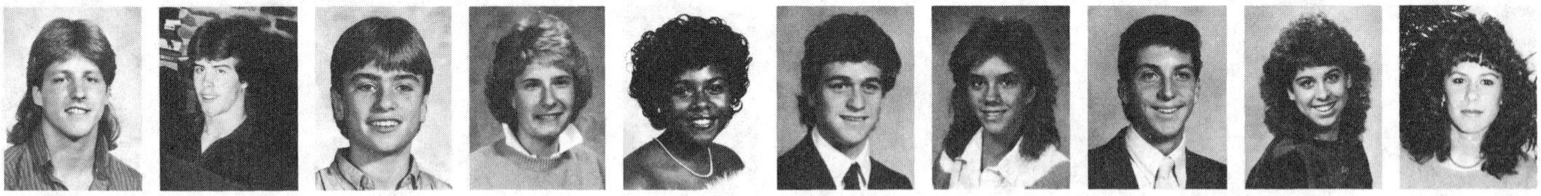

Gray, Dave
Charleroi Area JR SR HS
Charleroi, PA

Gray, Jeff
Northern Lebanon JR SR HS
Jonestown, PA

Gray, Josh
Danville SR HS
Danville, PA

Gray, Laura
Governor Mifflin HS
Shillington, PA

Gray, Marla L
Susquehanna HS
Harrisburg, PA

Gray, Michael
Devon Prep Schl
Newtown Sq, PA

Gray, Stacy
South Western HS
Hanover, PA

Graziano, Leonard
Devon Prep Schl
Buckingham, PA

Graziano, Mari Jo
Old Forge HS
Old Forge, PA

Graziano, Nicole
Cardinal Brenna HS
Frackville, PA

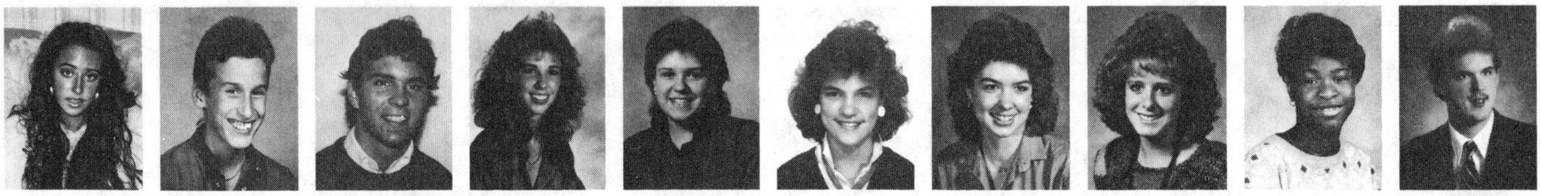

Grealy, Stephanie M
Council Rock HS
Newtown, PA

Greaser, Shawn
Hollidaysburg Area SR HS
Hollidaysburg, PA

Green, Brian
Sharon HS
Sharon, PA

Green, Caroline
Northampton SR
Northampton, PA

Green, Cathy
Springdale HS
Springdale, PA

Green, Elizabeth
Carlisle SR HS
Carlisle, PA

Green, Johanna
Rocky Grove HS
Franklin, PA

Green, Judy
Gateway SR HS
Monroeville, PA

Green, Valerie Renee
Bensalem HS
Bensalem, PA

Greenawalt, Dale W
Sharon HS
Sharon, PA

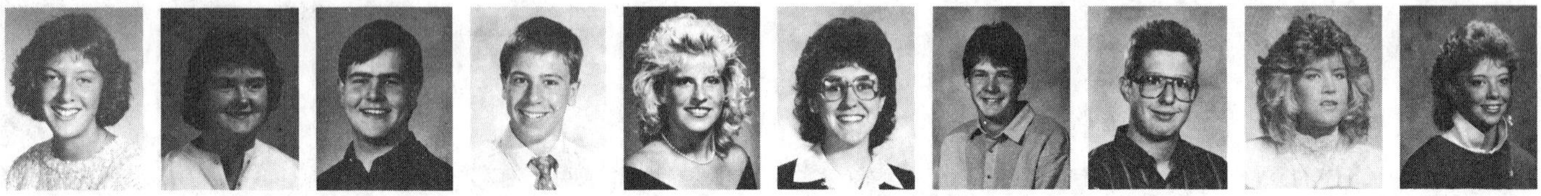

Greenberg, Dana
Allen HS
Allentown, PA

Greendoner, Debbi
Lock Haven SR HS
Blanchard, PA

Greenlee, John
Monongahela Valley Catholic HS
Fredericktown, PA

Gregorchik, Eddie
Bishop Mc Cort HS
Johnstown, PA

Greim, April Jean
Palisades HS
Kintnersville, PA

Greiner, Theresa
Bishop Guilfoyle HS
Altoona, PA

Gresco, Brian
Cambria Heights HS
Carrolltown, PA

Grevera, Robert
John S Fine HS
Nanticoke, PA

Grew, Tammie
Shaler Area SR HS
Glenshaw, PA

Gribble, Tonja
Rockwood Area HS
Somerset, PA

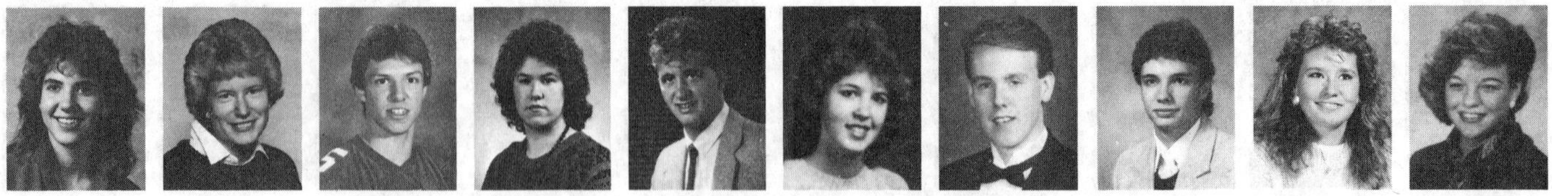

Grieb, Elizabeth
Williamsport Area
Cogan Station, PA

Grieb, Vicki
Lock Haven SR HS
Flemington, PA

Griebel, Steve
Clarion-Limestone
Clarion, PA

Griffin, Brenda
Carbondale Area JR SR HS
Carbondale, PA

Griffin, Todd
Trinity HS
Washington, PA

Griffis, Stephanie
Tunkhannock Area
Tunkhannock, PA

Griffith, George
St John Neumann
Philadelphia, PA

Griffith, John
United HS
Indiana, PA

Griffith, Karen
Garnet Valley HS
Boothwyn, PA

Griffiths, Dana
Geigel HS
S Connellsville, PA

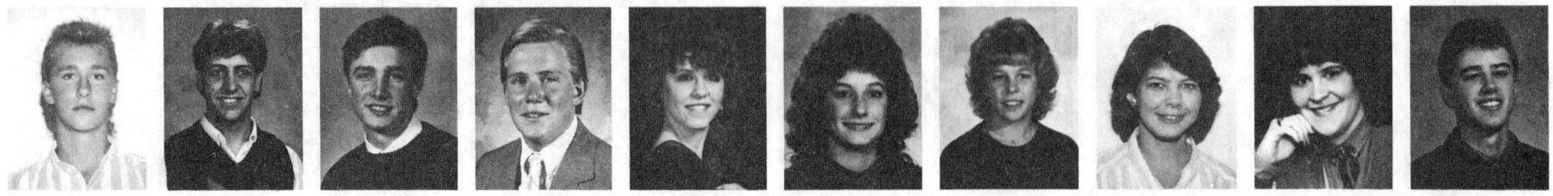

Griffiths, Lonnie P
Montrose Area HS
Montrose, PA

Grim, Bradley K
Christian School Of
Thomasville, PA

Grimes, Francis
Mon Valley Catholic
Donora, PA

Grimme, Timothy
Conemough Twp Area HS
Holsapple, PA

Grisillo, Christina
Archbishop Prendergast HS
Yeadon, PA

Grobinski, Angela
John S Fine HS
Nanticoke, PA

Grodack, Cindy
Western Wayne HS
Lake Ariel, PA

Groff, Kristin
Cumberland Vly HS
Mechanicsburg, PA

Groff, Marcey
Grace Christian Schl
Ephrata, PA

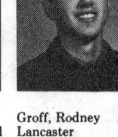

Groff, Rodney
Lancaster Mennonite HS
Kinzer, PA

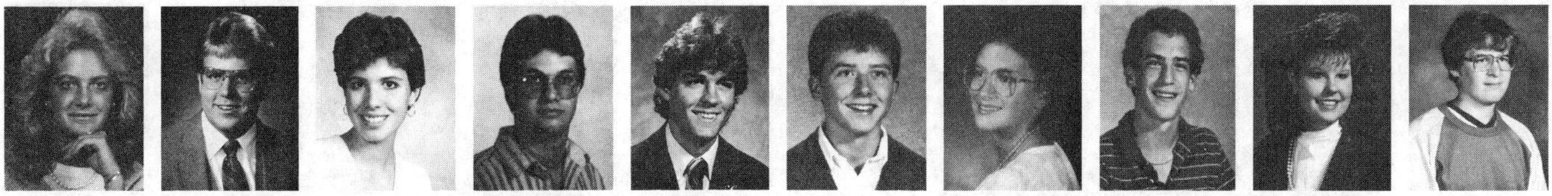

Groff, Tina
J D Mccaskey HS
Lancaster, PA

Groff, Wayne
Faith Mennonite HS
Gap, PA

Grohowski, Rebecca
Quakertown
Community SR HS
Quakertown, PA

Groller, Matthew S
Northampton Area
SR HS
Bath, PA

Gronauer, Robert
G A R Memorial HS
Wilkes-Barre, PA

Groschopp, Kenneth
Central Bucks West
Perkasie, PA

Gross, Barbara
Exeter Township
Douglassville, PA

Gross, Kenneth
Marple Newtown SR
Broomall, PA

Gross, Linda
Bethlehem Catholic
Bethlehem, PA

Gross, William
Ernest
Pocono Mountain
Mt Pocono, PA

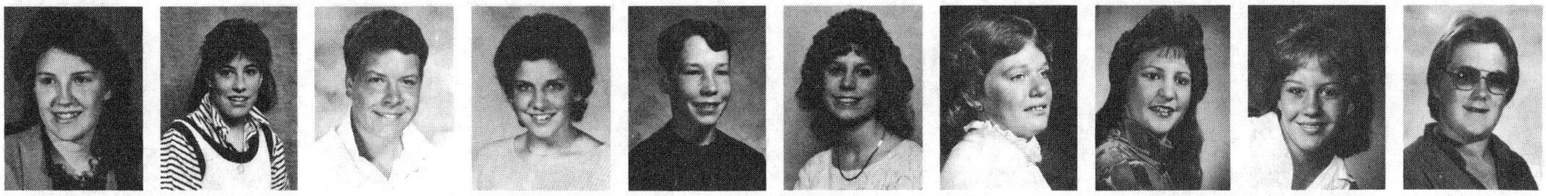

Grosser, Rae Ann
Connellsville Area
SR HS
Connellsville, PA

Grossi, Patricia A
Villa Maria Acad
King Of Prussia, PA

Grottola, Shawn
Northern SR HS
Dillsburg, PA

Grove, Carol
Central Cambria HS
Ebensburg, PA

Grove, Jason
Mifflinburg Area HS
Mifflinburg, PA

Grove, Tammy
Lincoln HS
Wampum, PA

Grubb, Linda
Everett Area HS
Clearville, PA

Grubbs, Gretchen
Albert Gallatin HS
Smithfield, PA

Grubbs, Kate
Avonworth JR/SR
Pittsbg, PA

Grube, Wiliam
Nazareth HS
Nazareth, PA

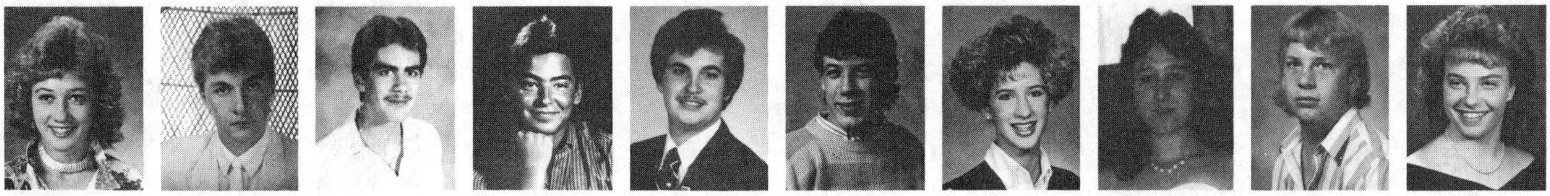

Gruber, Heidi
East Pennsboro
Area HS
Enola, PA

Gruber, Mark
East Pennsboro
Area HS
Enola, PA

Gruesu, Paul
Johnsonburg Area
Johnsonburg, PA

Grum, Alexander
Pocono Central
Catholic HS
E Stroudsburg, PA

Grunewald, Jeffrey
Emmaus HS
Emmaus, PA

Grushecky, Shawn
Warren Area HS
Warren, PA

Gruszka, Lisa
Nazareth Acad
Philadelphia, PA

Gruver, Kathy
Penn Hills HS
Pittsburgh, PA

Gruver, Perry
Montgomery Area
Montgomery, PA

Gryczko, Margaret
Scranton Prep Schl
Clarks Green, PA

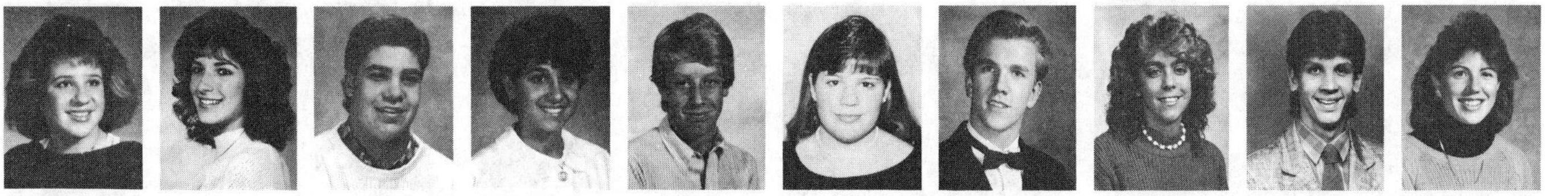

Grzegorek, Denise
Ambridge Area HS
Ambridge, PA

Grzywinski, Patricia
Southmoreland SR
Scottdale, PA

Guarino, Joseph
Hempfield HS
Lancaster, PA

Guarlotti, Michele L
Greensburg Central
Catholic HS
Jeannette, PA

Guckert, Jeffrey
Fairview HS
Fairview, PA

Guerra, Cheryl
Phil-Mont Christian
Maple Glen, PA

Guicheteau, Michael
Bishop Mc Devitt
Fort Washington,
PA

Guille, Sheri
Spring Ford HS
Royersford, PA

Gula, III Joseph F
Ringgold HS
Donora, PA

Gumbiner, Heather
L
Owen J Roberts HS
Pottstown, PA

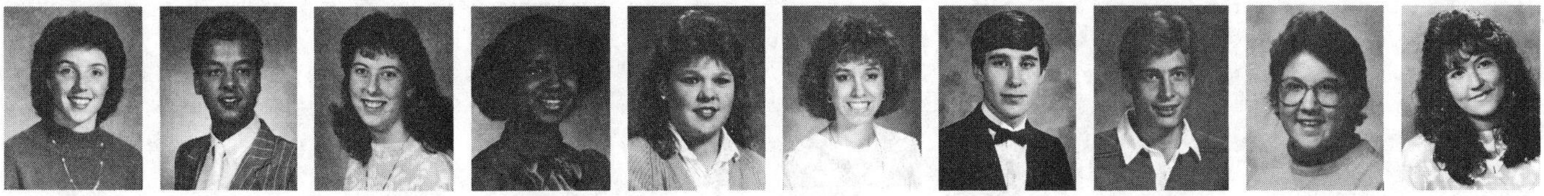

Gumbiner, Laura M
Owen J Roberts HS
Pottstown, PA

Gumina, Scott J
Elizabeth Forward
Elizabeth, PA

Gummo, Renea
Bellwood Antis Jr Sr
Altoona, PA

Gundy, Denise
Philadelphia High
School For Girls
Philadelphia, PA

Gunter, Laura
West Branch Area
Morrisdale, PA

Guskiewicz, Laura
Greensburg Central
Catholic HS
Greensburg, PA

Gustitis, Randal D
Cardinal O Hara HS
Broomall, PA

Guthridge, Scott
Living Wood Acad
Manheim, PA

Gutowski, Jennifer
Du Bois Area HS
Dubois, PA

Guy, Rachel
Lincoln HS
Wampum, PA

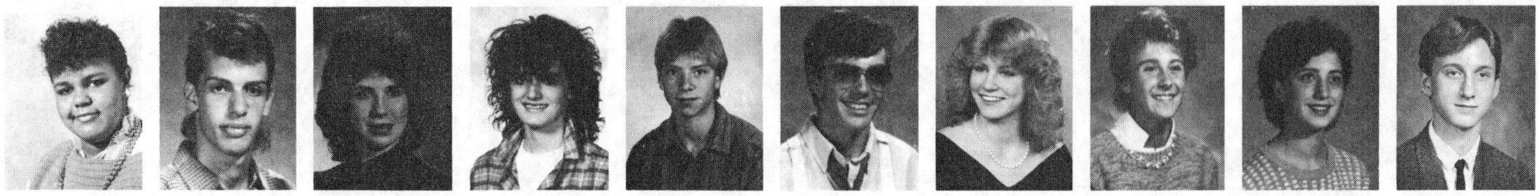

Guy, Tina
Valley HS
Arnold, PA

Guzzardo, Gary
Fairview HS
Fairview, PA

Gwynn, Dayna
Carmichaels Area
JR SR HS
Carmichaels, PA

Haag, Michelle
Oil City SR HS
Oil City, PA

Haas, Jeff
Brandywine Hts HS
Mertztown, PA

Haas, Keith
Northeastern SR HS
Manchester, PA

Haba, Darlene
Kennard-Dale HS
Oxford, PA

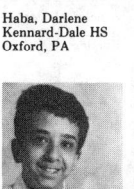

Habalar, Carey
Garden Spot HS
New Holland, PA

Haber, Brett
Hamton HS
Gladwyne, PA

Haber, James
Northeast Catholic
Philadelphia, PA

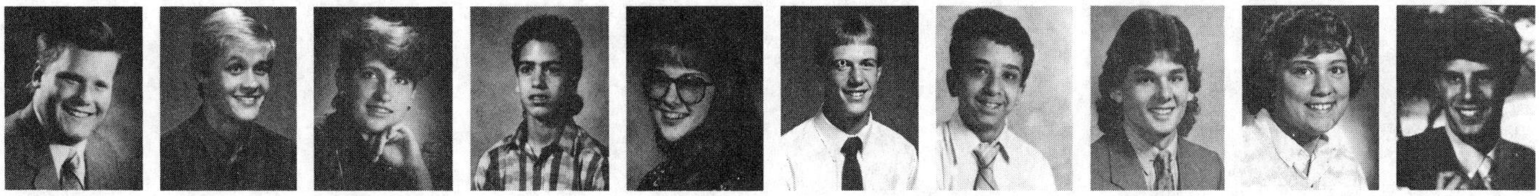

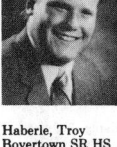

Haberle, Troy
Boyertown SR HS
Boyertown, PA

Haberstumpf, Craig
Emmaus HS
Emmaus, PA

Hable, Kim
Garden Spot HS
New Holland, PA

Haboush, Michael
Hopewell SR HS
Aliquippa, PA

Hack, Lydia
Juniata HS
Mifflintown, PA

Hackenberg, Erick
Marian Catholic HS
Nesquehoning, PA

Haddad, John
Central Catholic HS
Allentown, PA

Haddock, Craig
Belle Vernon Area
W Newton, PA

Haehn, Lisa
Youngsville JR Sr
Grand Valley, PA

Haertter, Timothy
Catholic HS Of
Lancaster, PA

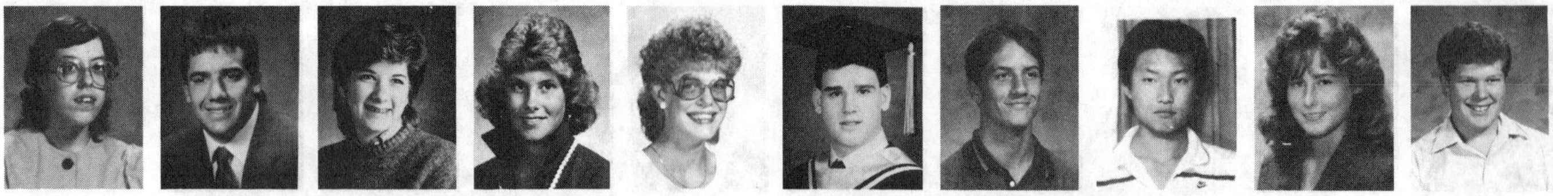

Haffly, Elizabeth
Middletown Area
Middletown, PA

Hagadus, Paul
Central Catholic HS
Allentown, PA

Hagel, Kathryn
Salem Christian
Allentown, PA

Hager, Tawnia
Conneaut Lake HS
Conneaut Lake, PA

Hagge, Cynthia
Oley Valley HS
Boyertown, PA

Haggerty, Tim
St John Neumann
Philadelphia, PA

Hahn, Corey
Hanover HS
Hanover, PA

Hahn, John
Plymouth-Whitemar sh HS
Lafayette Hill, PA

Haid, Lisa Rene
Altoona Area HS
Altoona, PA

Haines, Allen
Littlestown SR HS
Littlestown, PA

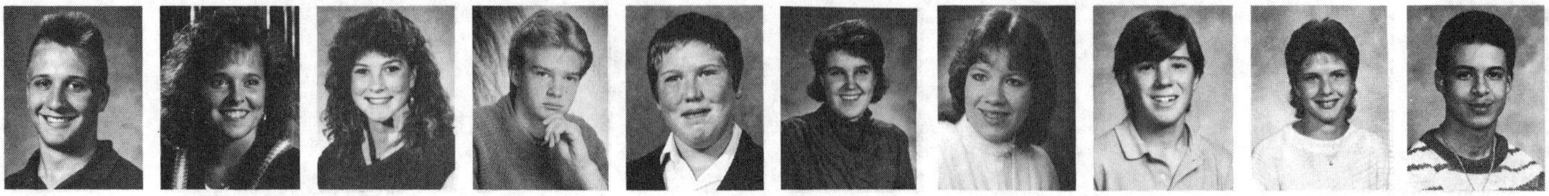

Hajdukiewicz, Andrew J
Gateway HS
Monroeville, PA

Hake, Christine
Red Lion Area SR
Red Lion, PA

Haldaman, Ann
Bethlehem Catholic
Bath, PA

Haley, James
Center HS
Monaca, PA

Hall, Bill
Connellsville HS
Connellsville, PA

Hall, Connie
Moniteau HS
West Sunbury, PA

Hall, Cynthia
Freedom HS
Bethlehem, PA

Hall, Darren
Upper Moreland HS
Willow Gr, PA

Hall, Deena
Mary Fuller Frazier JR-SR HS
Dawson, PA

Hall, Floyd
Bensalem SR HS
Bensalem, PA

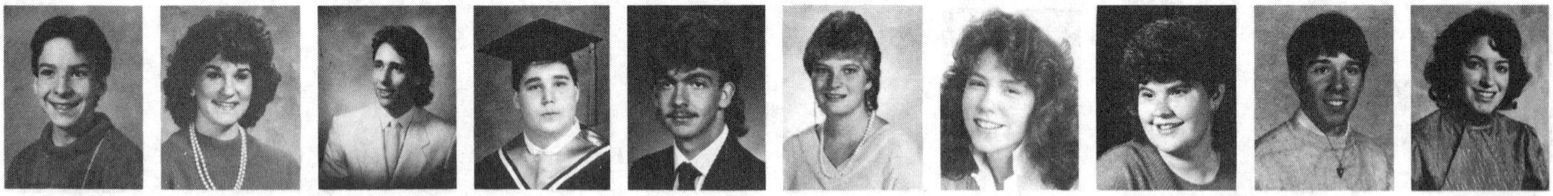

Hall, Gary
Center HS
Aliquippa, PA

Hall, Heather
Cedar Crest HS
Lebanon, PA

Hall, Howard
Schuylkill Haven
Sch Haven, PA

Hall, James
St John Newmann
Philadelphia, PA

Hall, III John T
Solanco HS
Christiana, PA

Hall, Kim
Western Wayne HS
Newfoundland, PA

Hall, Melissa
Hazleton SR HS
Drums, PA

Hall, Rebecca
Jefferson-Morgan
Waynesburg, PA

Hallinger, Mark R
Council Rock HS
Newtown, PA

Hallock, Michele
Coughlin HS
Wilkes Barre, PA

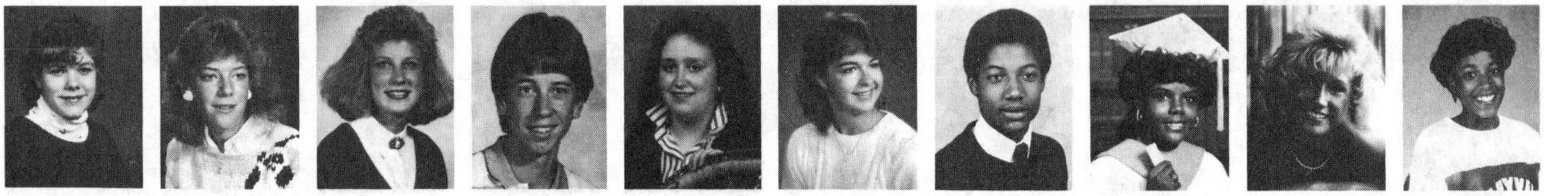

Hallock, Sandy
Tunkhannock HS
Tunkhannock, PA

Halm, Kerry
Benton JR/SR HS
Benton, PA

Halper, Jodi
Cedar Grove Christian Acad
Philadelphia, PA

Halterman, Tim
Danville SR HS
Danville, PA

Hamer, Wendie
Johnstown SR HS
Johnstown, PA

Hamilton, Anita
Yough SR HS
W Newton, PA

Hamilton, Damon
John S Fine HS
Nanticoke, PA

Hamilton, Karen
H S For Girls
Philadelphia, PA

Hamilton, Tracy
Ambridge SR HS
Baden, PA

Hamlet, Tania
Bristol JR-SR HS
Bristol, PA

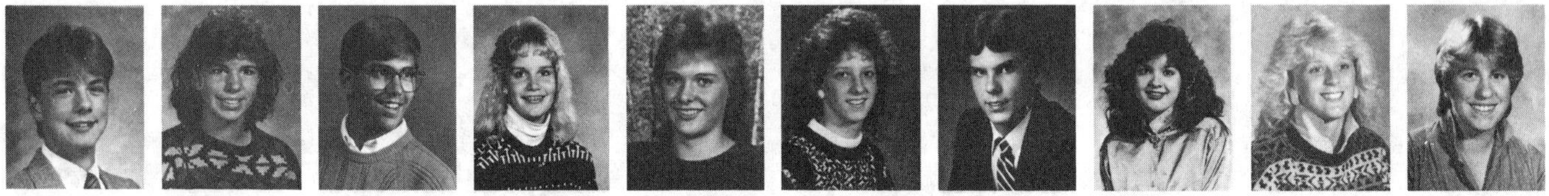

Hammaker, Jr Kenneth L
Cumberland Valley
Mechanicsburg, PA

Hamman, Karen
W Perry HS
Landisburg, PA

Hamme, Jr Jeffrey E
Wm Penn SR HS
York, PA

Hammerbacher, Noelle
E L Meyers HS
Wilkes-Barre, PA

Hammerly, Amy
Northeast Bradford JR SR HS
Leraysville, PA

Hammond, Diane
Bishop Conwell HS
Penndel, PA

Hammond, Michael W
Meadville Area SR
Meadville, PA

Hamrock, Bridget
United HS
Homer City, PA

Hamson, Connie
Octorara HS
Cochranville, PA

Hancock, Jennifer
Mercyhurst Prep
Erie, PA

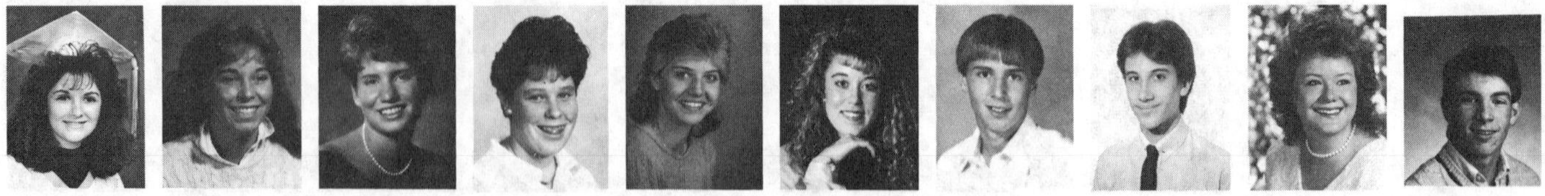

Hancock, Lisa L
St Hubert HS
Philadelphia, PA

Hancock, Shannon
Susquenita HS
Duncannon, PA

Hand, Jacqueline E
Saucon Valley SR
Bethlehem, PA

Handler, Melissa
Gwynedd Mercy
Huntingdon Vly, PA

Haney, Michele A
Northern Lebanon
Jonestown, PA

Hanford, Holli
Highlands SR HS
Natrona Hgts, PA

Hanks, Brian
Huntingdon Area
Huntingdon, PA

Hanley, II Michael E
David B Oliver HS
Pittsburgh, PA

Hanlon, Lisa
Penn Cambria HS
Cresson, PA

Hann, Lawrence
Swarthmore Acad
Media, PA

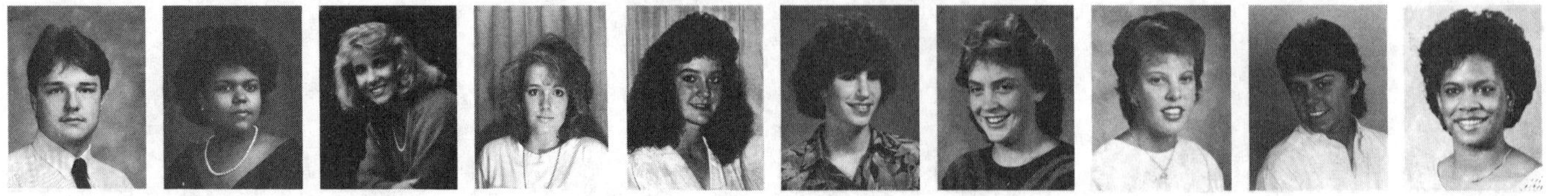

Hannah, David W
Pennsbury HS
Levittown, PA

Hannah, Dawn Dichele
Merion Mercy Acad
Philadelphia, PA

Hannan, Karen L
North Allegheny HS
Pittsburgh, PA

Hansen, Christina
Franklin Regional SR HS
Murrysville, PA

Hansotte, Sandra
Ford City HS
Ford City, PA

Hanych, Jean
Louis G Dieruff HS
Allentown, PA

Harbaugh, Wendy
Hempfield Area HS
Greensburg, PA

Harbold, Tanya
Bermudian Springs
York Spgs, PA

Harclerode, Sonja
Chestnut Ridge HS
New Paris, PA

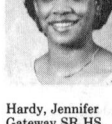

Hardy, Jennifer
Gateway SR HS
Monroeville, PA

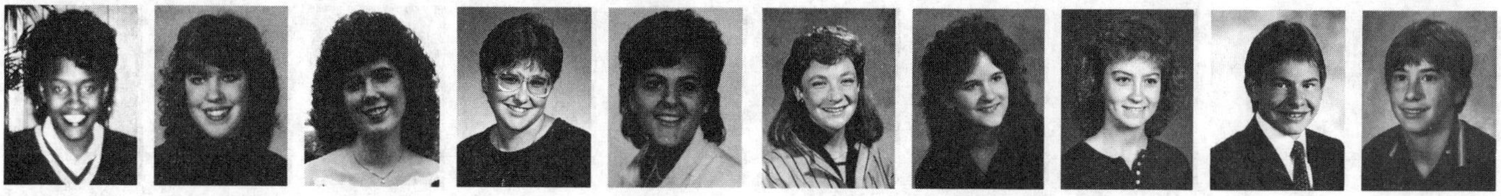

Hardy, Mia
Scott Intermediate
Coatesville, PA

Harger, Patricia
Monongabela Valley
Catholic HS
Monessen, PA

Haring, Tracy
Pottstown SR HS
Pottstown, PA

Harkins, Tammy
William Allen HS
Allentown, PA

Harkness, Shannon
Delaware Valley HS
Milford, PA

Harman, Amy
Fairview HS
Fairview, PA

Harman, Jodi
York County Area
Voctnl Tech Schl
York, PA

Harman, Michele
Upper Dauphin
Area HS
Millersburg, PA

Harman, Jr Ronald
R
Freeland HS
Freeland, PA

Harmon, Eddie
West Greene HS
New Freeport, PA

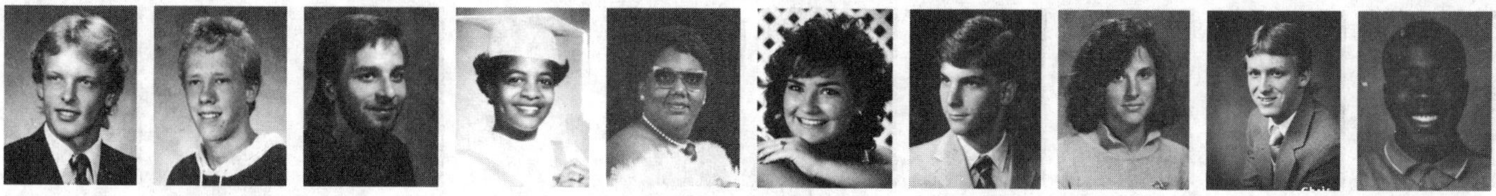

Harmon, Michael
Shanksville
Stonycreek HS
Berlin, PA

Harmon, Mike
Mc Guffey HS
Washington, PA

Harnish, Brett
Hempfield HS
Lancaster, PA

Harper, Adrienne
Chester HS
Chester, PA

Harper, Carol
Bishop Mc Devitt
Philadelphia, PA

Harper, Cyndi
Mc Guffey HS
Amity, PA

Harper, Jr Richard
Biddle
Conrad Weiser JR
SR HS
Robesonia, PA

Harper, Shelley
Conrad Weiser HS
Robesonia, PA

Harpst, Christopher
Commodore Perry
Hadley, PA

Harrell, Stephen
G Westinghse/
Taylor Allderdice
HS
Pittsburgh, PA

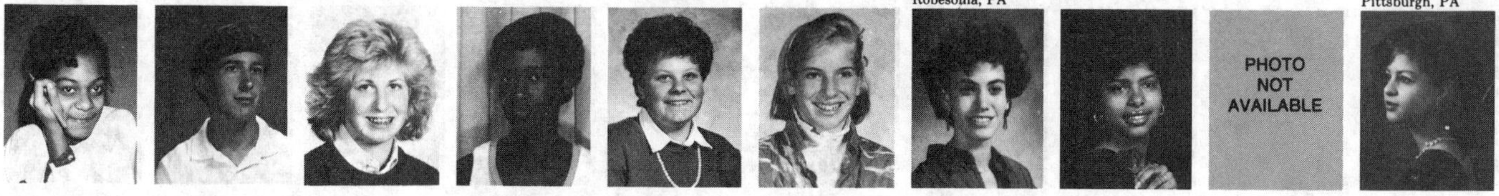
PHOTO
NOT
AVAILABLE

Harrigan, Okifa
Phila HS For Girls
Philadelphia, PA

Harrigle, Jr Dale
Catasauqua HS
Catasauqua, PA

Harrington, Sue
Ellen
Gwynedd-Mercy
Blue Bell, PA

Harris, Desiree
Chester HS
Chester, PA

Harris, Jill
Millersburg Area HS
Millersburg, PA

Harris, Marijane
Mifflinburg Area HS
Mifflinburg, PA

Harris, Meagan
Taylor Allderdice
Pittsburgh, PA

Harris, Tasha
West Catholic Girls
Philadelphia, PA

Harris, Todd
Mercrer JR & SR
Mercer, PA

Harris, Tonya L
Penn Manor HS
Millersville, PA

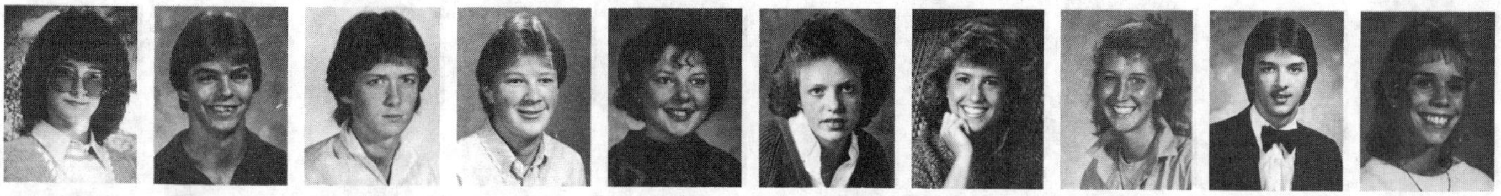

Harrison, Karen
Columbia Montour
Area Vo-Tech Schl
Stillwater, PA

Harrison, Matthew
Eastern York HS
York, PA

Harry, Jeff
Scott Intermediate
Coatesville, PA

Harry, Lance
Council Rock HS
Holland, PA

Harsh, Cheryl
Garden Spot SR HS
New Holland, PA

Harshbarger, Betsy
Lewistown Area HS
Mc Veytown, PA

Hart, Kristena
Trinity SR HS
Amity, PA

Hart, Kristi
Boyertown Area HS
Boyertown, PA

Hart, Tony
Interboro HS
Prospect Park, PA

Hartkopf, Tamara
Upper Merion Area
King Of Prussia, PA

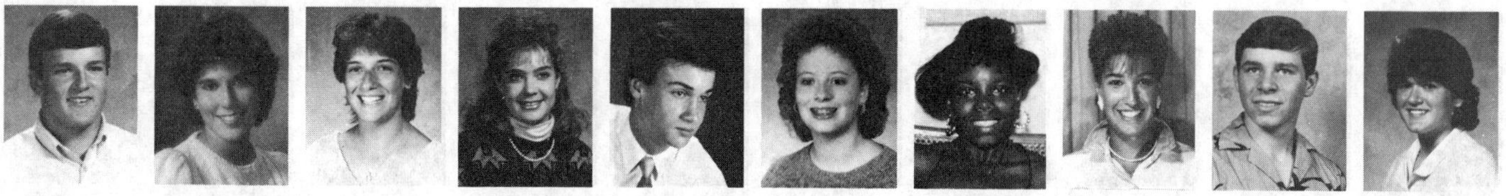

Hartle, Michael
Lock Haven SR HS
Flemington, PA

Hartley, Melissa L
South Williamsport
Area HS
S Williamsport, PA

Hartman, Catherine
A
Plum HS
New Kensington,
PA

Hartman, Jennifer
Palmyra Area SR
Annville, PA

Hartman, Raymond
Pennsbury HS
Morrisville, PA

Hartzell, Michelle
Mc Guffey HS
Washington, PA

Harvey, Chennita
Cecilian Acad
Willingboro, NJ

Harvey, Deborah
Pennsbury HS
Yardley, PA

Harvey, John
Harborcreek HS
Harborcreek, PA

Harvey, Sue Ann
Central Cambria HS
Ebensburg, PA

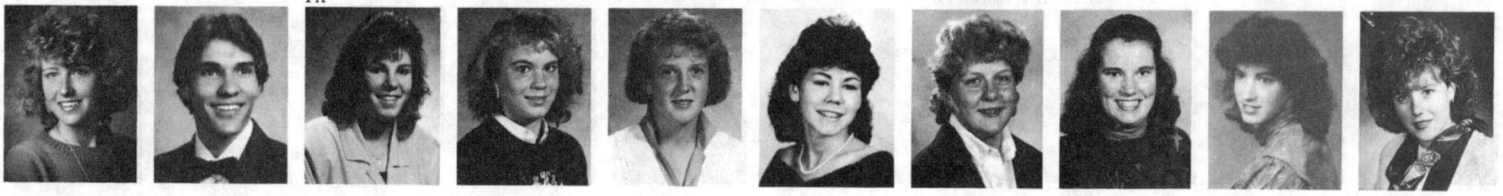

Harvey, Tammy
Trinity HS
Washington, PA

Haseltine, Todd
The Christian Acad
Brookhaven, PA

Haskins, Lisa
New Wilmington HS
Volant, PA

Hassler, Marybeth
Twin Valley HS
Morgantown, PA

Hassler, Stephanie
Cocalico HS
Denver, PA

Hasson, Traci
Bristol JR SR HS
Bristol, PA

Hastings, Elizabeth
St Benedict Acad
Erie, PA

Hathaway, Kristen
Villa Maria Acad
Erie, PA

Hatton, Jennifer
Mechanicsburg Area
SR HS
Mechanicsburg, PA

Haueisen, Lainie
Conrad Weiser HS
Robesonia, PA

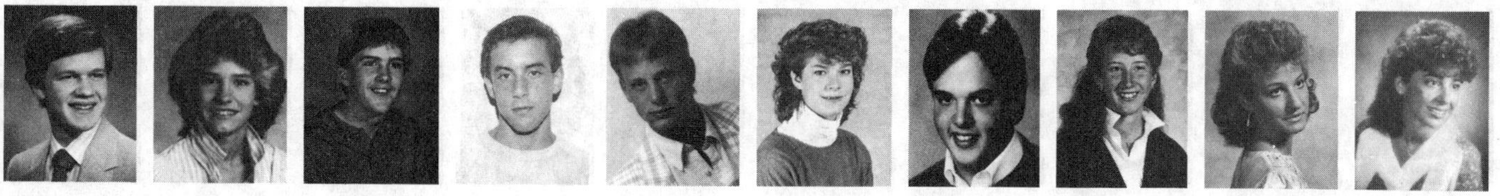

Hauger, Keith
Mt Pleasant Area
Stahlstown, PA

Haus, Shannon
Milton HS
West Milton, PA

Hauser, Daniel
Clarion Area HS
Clarion, PA

Hauserman, David
Pennsbury HS
Yardley, PA

Haushalter, Kurt
State College Area
State College, PA

Havert, Pamela
Conestoga HS
Berwyn, PA

Hawk, Joseph W
Pittston Area SR
Hughestown, PA

Hawkins, Leslie
Donegal HS
Mount Joy, PA

Hawranko, Alyssa
Mary Fuller Frazier
Perryopolis, PA

Hay, Kelly
Northampton SR
Bath, PA

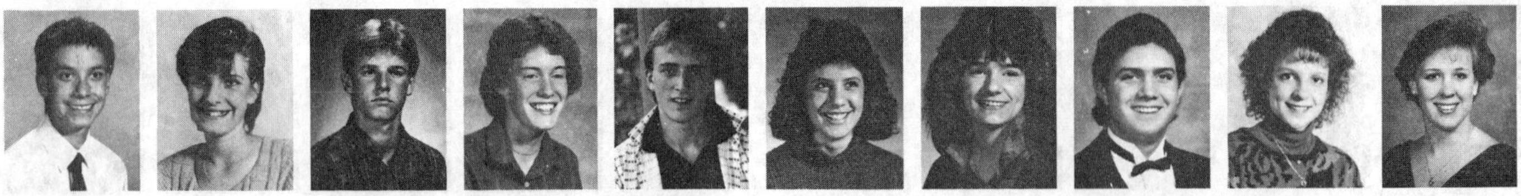

Hayes, Doug
Greater Johnstown
Cntrl SR HS
Johnstown, PA

Hayes, Melissa
Jim Thorpe Area
Jim Thorpe, PA

Haylett, Kevin
Conneaut Lake HS
Conn Lake, PA

Hazel, Mary
Boyertown Area HS
Boyertown, PA

Hazlett, Darin
Lakeview HS
Stoneboro, PA

Heacock, Kimberly
Lake-Lehmon HS
Sweet Valley, PA

Healey, Angie
Ambridge Area HS
Ambridge, PA

Healey, Jr Bob
Cardival O Hara HS
Glenolden, PA

Healey, Marilyn
Coughlin HS
Laflin, PA

Heaney, Susan
Cardinal O Hara HS
Havertown, PA

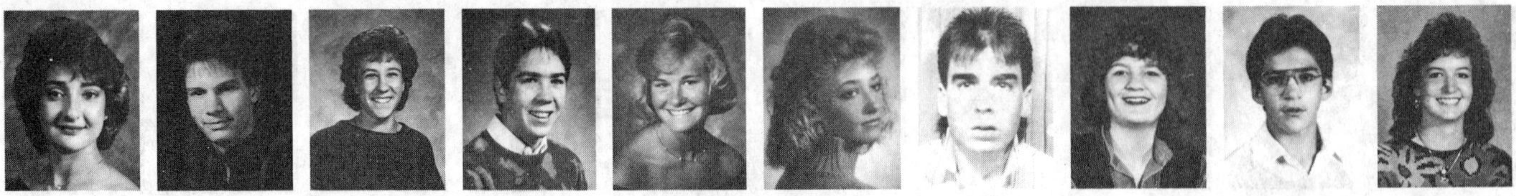

Heasley, Christina
Belle Vernon Area
Belle Vernon, PA

Heath, Dennis
Elizabeth Forward
Greenock, PA

Heath, Jennifer
Middletown Area
Middletown, PA

Heberle, Douglas M
Bethel Park HS
Bethel Park, PA

Heck, Melissa G
Spring-Ford HS
Royersford, PA

Heck, Renee
E L Meyers HS
Wilkes Bare, PA

Hecker, Tom
Archbishop Wood
For Boys
Oakford, PA

Heckman, Jody
East Pennsboro
Area HS
Enola, PA

Heddings, Jeffrey
Milton SR HS
Potts Grove, PA

Hedrich, Kathleen
M
Interboro HS
Prospect Park, PA

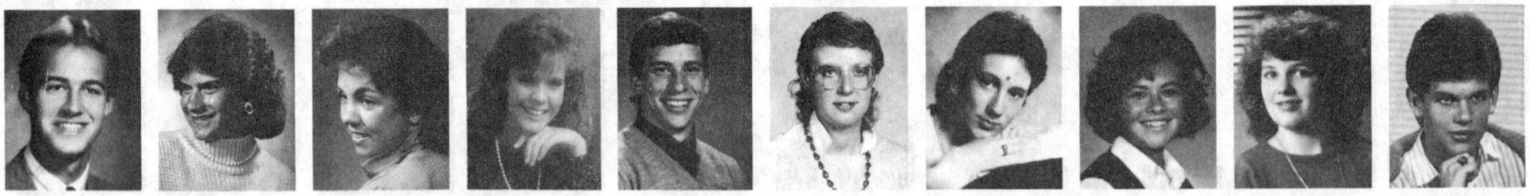

Heffelfinger, Ronald
Neshaminy HS
Penndel, PA

Heffner, Lora
Elizabethtown HS
Elizabethtotwn, PA

Hegarty, Maureen E
Central Catholic HS
Whitehall, PA

Heh, Kelly
Cumberland Valley
Camp Hill, PA

Heidt, Dean
Cathedral Prep
Erie, PA

Heikes, Susan
Juniata HS
Mifflintown, PA

Heim, Heather
Line Mountain HS
Dalmatia, PA

Heim, Jill
Nazareth Acad
Phila, PA

Heim, Lisa
Scranton Central
Scranton, PA

Heiney, Jeffrey
Lampeter Strasburg
Lancaster, PA

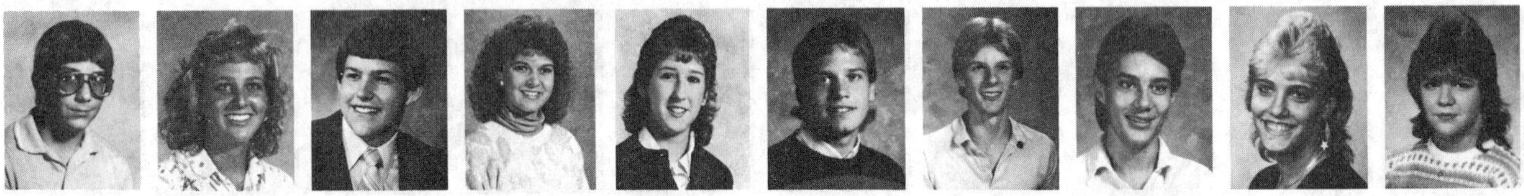

Heinrich, Jeff
Windber Area HS
Windber, PA

Heiser, Lori
Central Bucks East
Doylestown, PA

Heisey, Leon
Manheim Central
Manheim, PA

Heisey, Teri
Daniel Boone HS
Douglassville, PA

Heisner, Kelly
Nativity BVM HS
Middleport, PA

Heist, Roert
Dallas SR HS
Wyoming, PA

Helfrich, Michael
West York Area HS
York, PA

Heller, Christopher
Eastern York HS
York, PA

Heller, Heidi
Delaware Valley HS
Milford, PA

Heller, Lesley
Bald Eagle Nittany
Mill Hall, PA

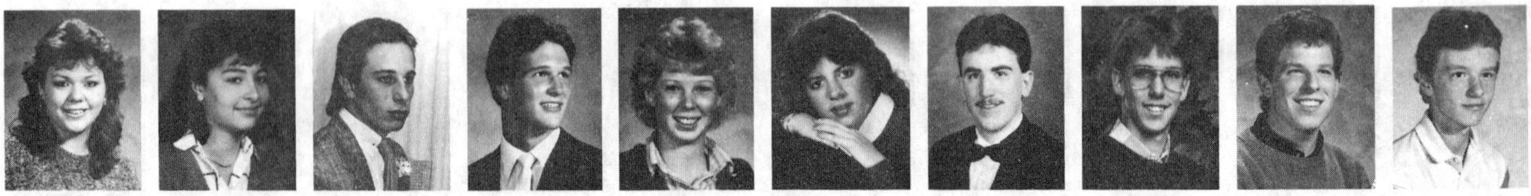

Helman, Valerie
Seneca Valley SR
Zelienople, PA

Helock, Andrea R
West Halzeton
JR-SR HS
Sheppton, PA

Helon, David
North Hills HS
Pittsburgh, PA

Hemingway, Jr
David C
Coatesville Area
Schl District
Downingtown, PA

Hemma, Christi
Shaler Area SR HS
Glenshaw, PA

Hemmings, Nicole
Mon Vly Catholic
Monongahela, PA

Henderson, Dan
St John Neumann
Philadelphia, PA

Henderson, Erin
Meadville Area HS
Meadville, PA

Henderson, Mark P
Middletown Area
Middletown, PA

Henderson, Michael
Bangor Area SR HS
Bangor, PA

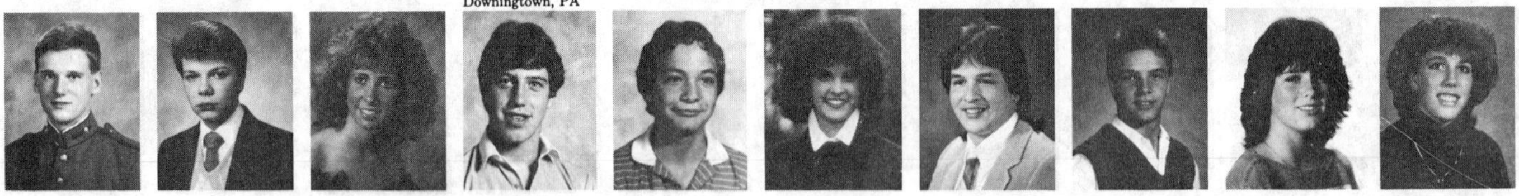

Henderson, Richard
Valley Forge
Military Acad
Roswell, GA

Henderson, Scott
Indiana Wesleyen
Aultman, PA

Henderson, Tina
Western Beaver HS
Industry, PA

Hendricks, Shawn D
Pine Grove HS
Pine Grove, PA

Hendrickson, Barry
Danville SR HS
Danville, PA

Hengst, Tina
Greenwood HS
Millerstown, PA

Henkel, David W
Mt Pleasant Area
Mt Pleasant, PA

Henne, Terrance
Shaler Area HS
Pittsburgh, PA

Hennegan,
Bernadette A
Cheltenham HS
Cheltenham, PA

Hennessey, Megan
Conestoga SR HS
Malvern, PA

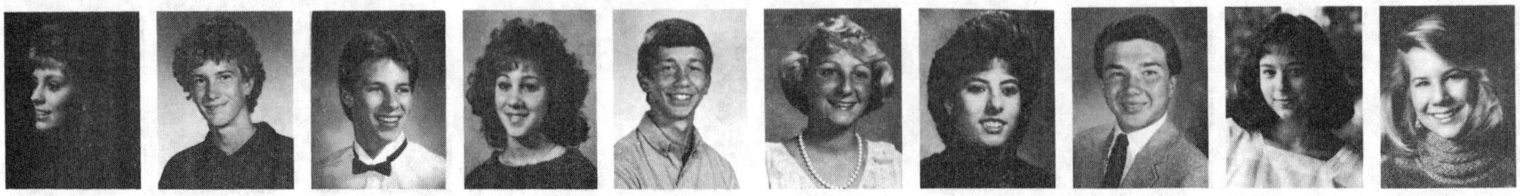

Hennigan, Patricia
Wyoming Area HS
Exeter, PA

Henninger, Dion
William Allen HS
Allentown, PA

Henninger, Thad E
Huntingdon Area
Petersburg, PA

Hennon, Melinda
West Allegheny HS
Oakdale, PA

Henry, Eric
Fleetwood Area HS
Fleetwood, PA

Henry, Glory
Garden Spot HS
New Holland, PA

Henry, Janet Lynn
Lampeter-Strasburg
Willow Street, PA

Henry, John S
Mt Penn HS
Mt Penn, PA

Heovik, Darcey E
Radnor HS
Wayne, PA

Herb, Nicole S
Shady Side Acad
Pittsburgh, PA

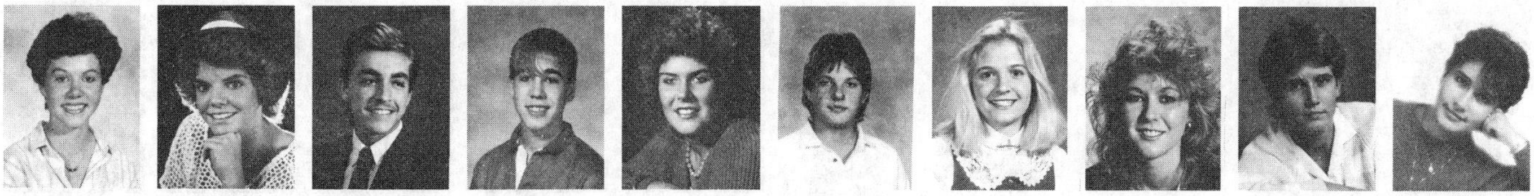

Herley, Colleen
East HS
West Cheseter, PA

Herman, Amy
Dover Area HS
Dover, PA

Herman, Brad
Northeastern HS
Manchester, PA

Herman, David
Southwestern HS
Hanover, PA

Herman, Teresa
Canton Area HS
Roaring Branch, PA

Hermanofski, Robert
John S Fine HS
Nanticoke, PA

Herold, Danielle
Butler Area SR HS
Butler, PA

Herr, Linda
Mt Alvernia HS
Pittsburgh, PA

Herr, Sandy
Northern Lebanon
Jonestown, PA

Herrera, Monique
St Cyril Acad
Sun Valley, CA

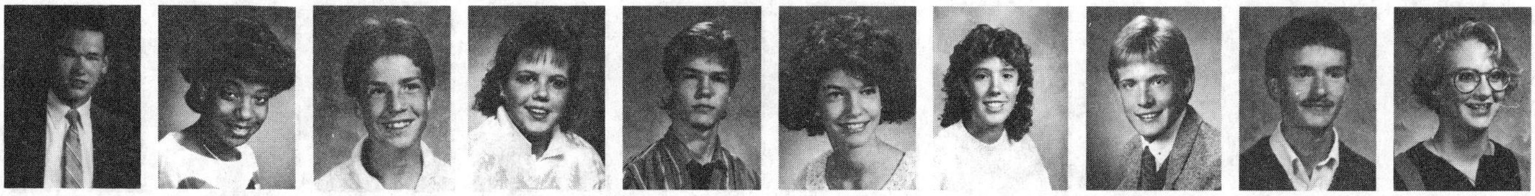

Herrick, Todd
Mercer Area HS
Mercer, PA

Herring, Dara M
Central HS Of Phila
Philadelphia, PA

Herrington, Matthew
Garden Spot HS
New Holland, PA

Herron, Jennifer
Carrick HS
Pittsburgh, PA

Hersch, Jr Daryl
Cathedral Prep HS
Erie, PA

Herschman, Cathy
Northampton SR
Northampton, PA

Hershberger, Marcia
Perkiomen Valley
Perkiomenville, PA

Hershbine, Todd
State College Area SR HS
State College, PA

Hershey, Kevin F D B
Pequea Valley HS
Gap, PA

Hershman, Alison
Garden Spot HS
New Holland, PA

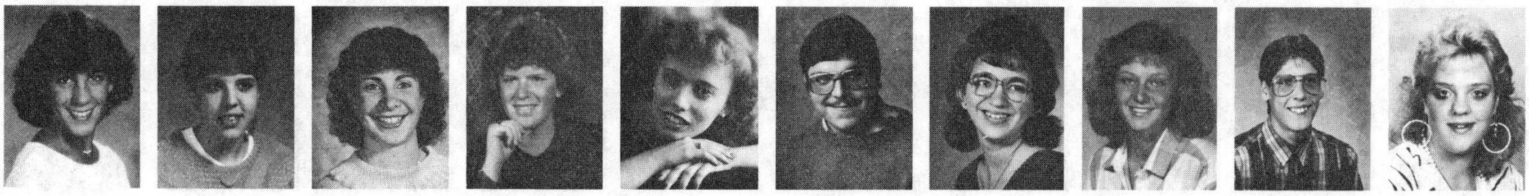

Hervey, Bethann D
Hampton HS
Allison Pk, PA

Hess, Chrissy
Hempfield HS
Lancaster, PA

Hess, Jennifer
William Penn SR
York, PA

Hess, Lisa D
Solanco HS
Quarryville, PA

Hess, Sherry L
Monaca Jr-Sr HS
Monaca, PA

Hesser, Jr Richard
Lewistown Area HS
Lewistown, PA

Hesson, Karen
Southmoreland SR
Scottdale, PA

Hester, Jennifer
Central York SR HS
York, PA

Hetrick, II Wilbur
Jefferson Morgan JR SR HS
Clarksville, PA

Heuston, Kristina
Harry S Truman HS
Levittown, PA

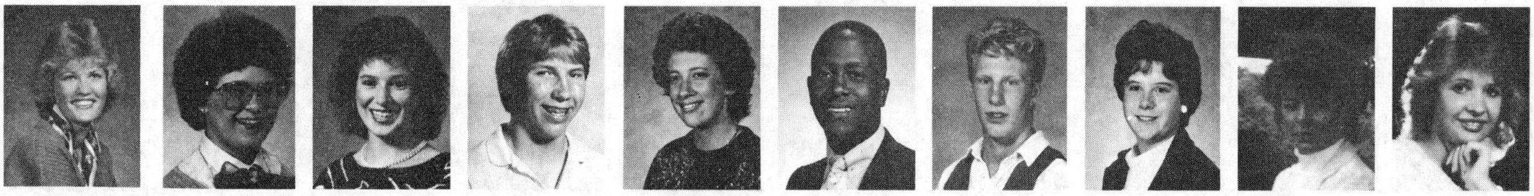

Heverly, Beth
Jersey Shore SR HS
Jersey Shore, PA

Hickman, Amy
Mc Guffey HS
Prosperity, PA

Hickman, Lisa
Hopewell SR HS
Aliquippa, PA

Hicks, Jay
Windber Area HS
Windber, PA

Hicks, Teressa R
Saltsburg HS
Saltsburg, PA

High, Eric Donovan
Central HS
Philadelphia, PA

Hildebrand, Craig
Central York SR HS
York, PA

Hileman, Carol
Saltsburg JR SR HS
Clarksburg, PA

Hiles, Lisa
Wilmington Area
New Bedford, PA

Hilkert, Melany
Danville SR HS
Danville, PA

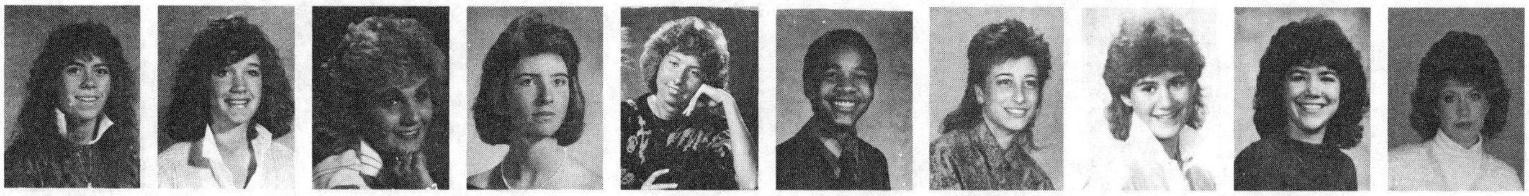

Hill, Amanda
Conestoga HS
Malvern, PA

Hill, Carrie
Great Valley SR HS
Frazer, PA

Hill, Christina
Elkland Area HS
Nelson, PA

Hill, Judith A
Souderton Area HS
Souderton, PA

Hill, Karen
Brownsville Area HS
Labelle, PA

Hill, Milon E
West Philadelphia Catholic HS
Philadelphia, PA

Hillenbrand, Debra
Council Rock HS
Holland, PA

Hilson, Nicole
West Scranton HS
Scranton, PA

Hiltebeitel, Jessica
Springford SR HS
Royersford, PA

Himes, Cathy
West Perry SR HS
New Bloomfield, PA

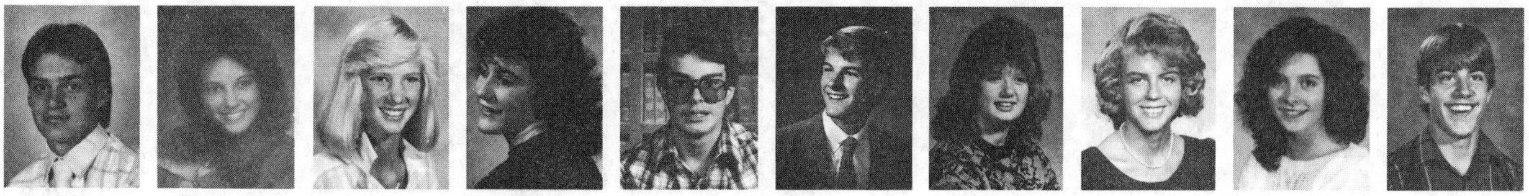

Hincher, Timothy
West Perry HS
New Germantown, PA

Hincy, Valerie
Ringgold HS
Eighty Four, PA

Hindson, Kamron
Fairview HS
Fairview, PA

Hine, Lori
Coughlin HS
Wilkes Barre, PA

Hines, William
Hazelton SR HS
Beaver Mdws, PA

Hinkle, Randy
Fleetwood Area HS
Fleetwood, PA

Hinkle, Theresa
Weatherly Area HS
Weatherly, PA

Hinko, Valerie
Wyoming Seminary Prep Schl
Hudson, PA

Hinman, Regina
Cowanesque Valley
Westfield, PA

Hinton, Brian
Ridgway Area HS
Ridgway, PA

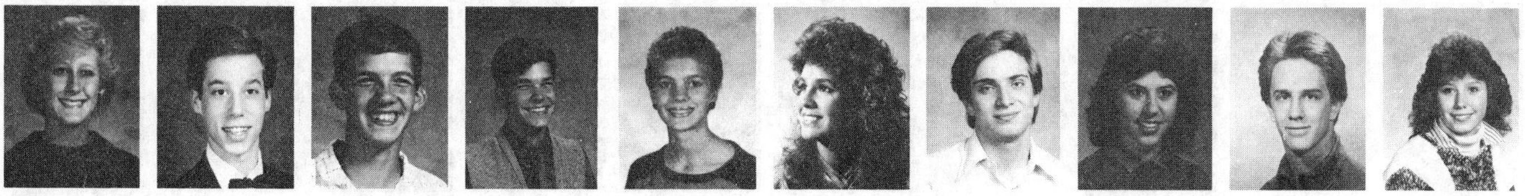

Hinton, Kimberly
Kennard Dale HS
Stewartstown, PA

Hiriak, Nicholas F
St Pius X HS
Pottstown, PA

Hissong, Brian
James Buchanan HS
Lemasters, PA

Hissong, Craig
James Buchanan HS
Lemasters, PA

Hittinger, Jaime
Freedom HS
Bethlehem, PA

Hixenbaugh, Sharon
Canan-Mc Millan SR HS
Mcdonald, PA

Hladczuk, Thomas
HS Of Engr & Sci
Pliladelphia, PA

Hnaras, Anna Stacie
Fairchance-Georges
Uniontown, PA

Hoch, Eric
Nazareth Area HS
Nazareth, PA

Hockenberry, Shendelle
Juniata HS
Honey Grove, PA

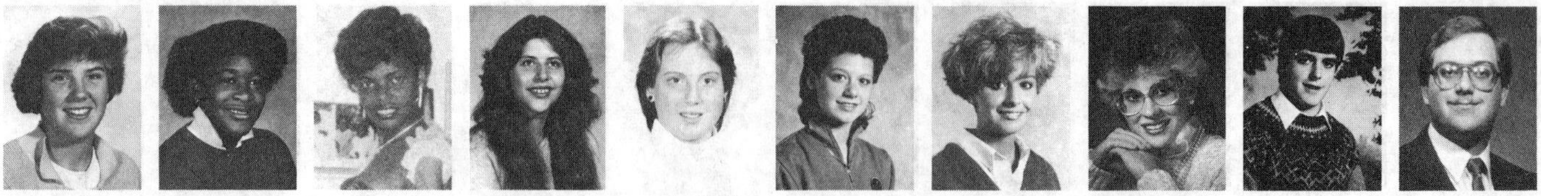

Hocker, Amy
Ridley SR HS
Milmont Park, PA

Hodge, Sabrina
Exeter SR HS
Reading, PA

Hodge, Selena
Little Flower
Catholic HS Fo
Philadelphia, PA

Hoepfl, Suzanne
Upper Darby HS
Upr Darby, PA

Hoffer, Denise
Abraham Lincoln
Philadelphia, PA

Hoffman, Angel
SR HS
Schuylkill Havn, PA

Hoffman, Bridgett
York Catholic HS
York, PA

Hoffman, Cindy
Salem Christian
Whitehall, PA

Hoffman, Craig
Sch Haven Area HS
Schuylkill Haven, PA

Hoffman, Eric
Pleasant Valley HS
Brodheadsville, PA

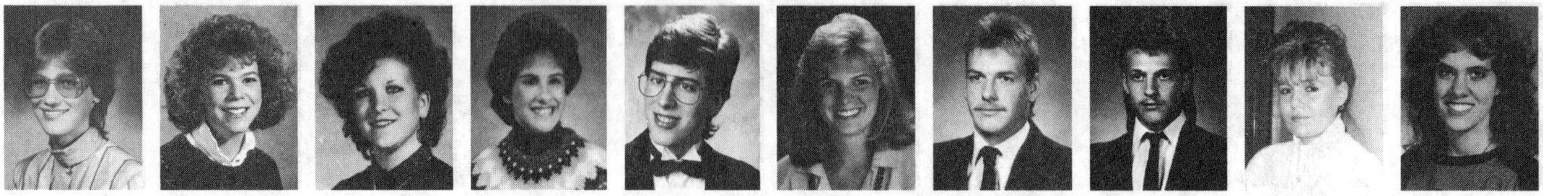

Hoffman, Jennifer
Central SR HS
York, PA

Hoffman, Karen
Owen J Roberts HS
Chester Springs, PA

Hoffman, Kelly
Pottstown SR HS
Pottstown, PA

Hoffman, Michelle
Chambersburg Area SR HS
Fayetteville, PA

Hoffman, Richard
Cathedral
Preparatory Schl
Erie, PA

Hoffman, Sharon
Montour HS
Coraopolis, PA

Hoffmeyer, Dean
North Star HS
Boswell, PA

Hoffmeyer, Jon
North Star HS
Boswell, PA

Hofmann, Johanna
Linden Hall HS
Richland, PA

Hofmann, Tammy
William Allen HS
Allentown, PA

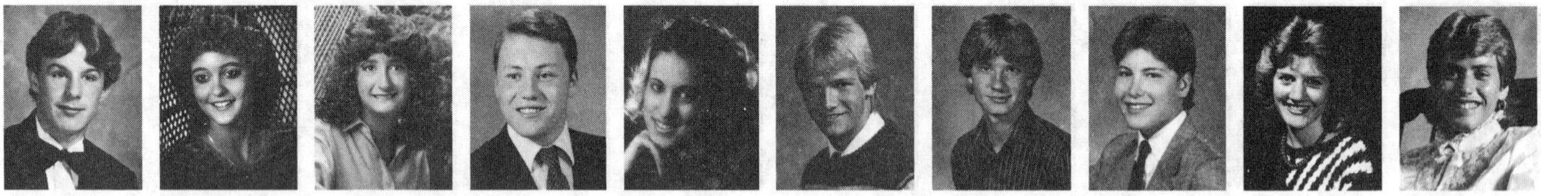

Hogan, Jr Edward James
Father Judge HS
Philadelphia, PA

Hoge, Amy
Mcguffey HS
Washington, PA

Hohl, Vicki L
Emmaus HS
Wescosville, PA

Hoke, Mark
Dover Area HS
E Berlin, PA

Holcombe, Stephanie
Susquehanna
Township HS
Harrisburg, PA

Holden, Scott
Philipsburg-Osceola Area HS
Philipsburg, PA

Holes, Todd
Bellwood-Antis HS
Bellwood, PA

Hollen, Gareth Eric
Greater Johnstown SR HS
Johnstown, PA

Hollenback, Michele
Troy Area HS
Towanda, PA

Holley, Roxanne
North Penn HS
Morris Run, PA

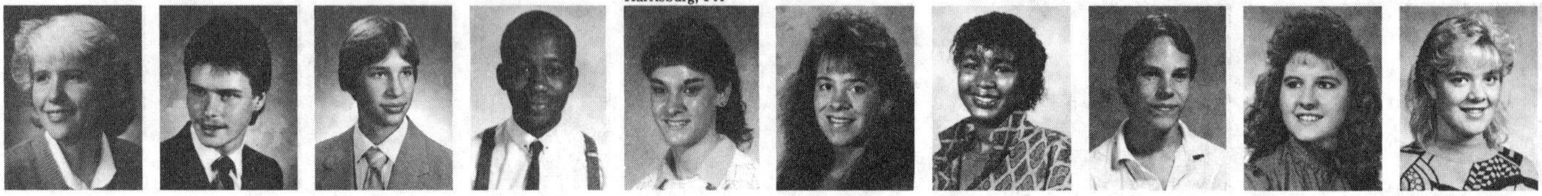

Hollinger, Kathleen E
Lebanon SR HS
Lebanon, PA

Hollingsworth, G Scott
Blacklick Valley HS
Ebensburg, PA

Hollis, Mark
Bentworth HS
Bentleyville, PA

Hollis, Robert
Yrichland HS
Johnstown, PA

Holloman, Carla
Geibel HS
Uniontown, PA

Holloway, Amy E
Mcguffey HS
Washington, PA

Holly, Michele
Perry Traditional
Pittsburgh, PA

Holman, Randy
Susquenita HS
Duncannon, PA

Holmes, Diane
Kiski Area HS
Vandergrift, PA

Holmes, Elizabeth
Neshaminy SR HS
Langhorne, PA

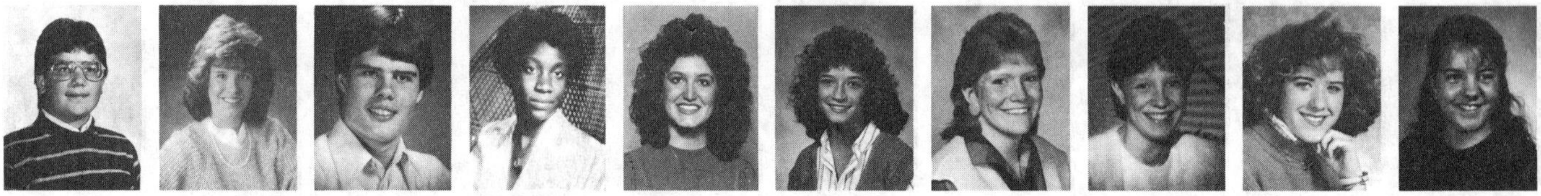

Holmes, Keith
Northampton Area SR HS
Northampton, PA

Holmes, Lee
Saucon Valley HS
Bethlehem, PA

Holmes, Lee C
Hopewell HS
Aliquippa, PA

Holmes, Stacey
Southwark
Motivation HS
Philadelphia, PA

Holsapfel, Brook
West Middlesex HS
Sharon, PA

Holsopple, Colleen
Central Cambria HS
Johnstown, PA

Holt, Kimberly
West Branch HS
Philipsburg, PA

Holt, Melissa
York Catholic HS
York, PA

Holt, Tina
Kennedy Christian
Sharon, PA

Holtzhauser, Heidi
Conneaut Lake HS
Conneaut Lake, PA

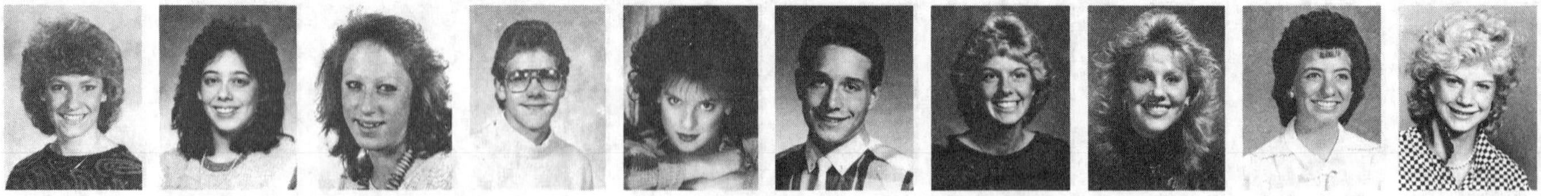

Holtzman, Judith
Bishop Mc Cort HS
Johnstown, PA

Holupka, Heidi
Kiski Area HS
Leechburg, PA

Holzapfel, Faith A
Hickory HS
Hermitage, PA

Honard, III Harry W
Academy HS
Erie, PA

Honey, Christine
Strong Vincent HS
Erie, PA

Honsel, Jason
Notre Dame HS
Nazareth, PA

Hoober, Alissa
Garden Spot HS
New Holland, PA

Hood, Amy
Ephrata SR HS
Ephrata, PA

Hood, Katrina
Avon Grove HS
West Grove, PA

Hooper, Jennifer
Hickory HS
Hermitage, PA

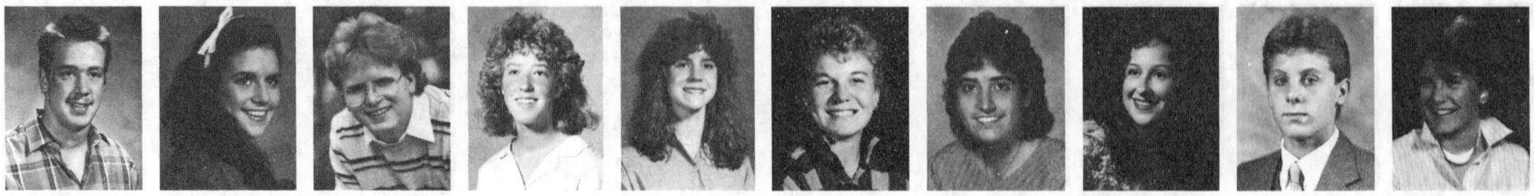

Hoover, Dan
Shenango JR SR HS
New Castle, PA

Hoover, Gina
Grace Christian Schl
Myerstown, PA

Hoovler, Mark
General Mc Lane
Mckean, PA

Hopf, Christina
Peters Twp HS
Mcmurray, PA

Hopf, Jennifer
Council Rock HS
Churchville, PA

Hopkins, Gail
Penn Cambria HS
Cresson, PA

Hopkins, Krista
Brookville Area HS
Brookville, PA

Hopkins, Sherry
State College Area SR HS
State College, PA

Hoppy, Jason
Hazleton HS
Hazleton, PA

Horan, Dianne
Abington Heights
Clarks Green, PA

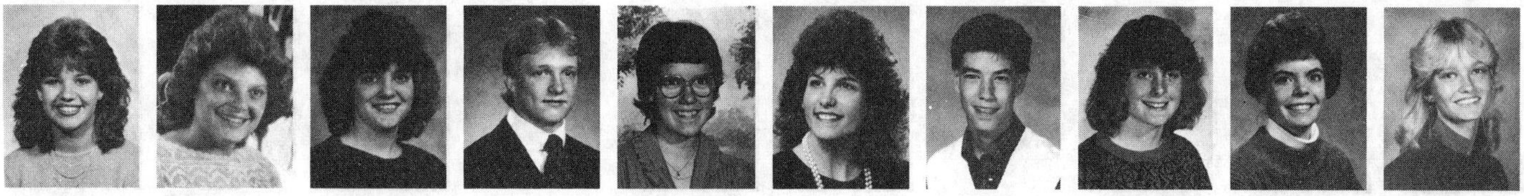

Horan, Kerie
Belle Vernon Area
Belle Vernon, PA

Hornak, Gena
Nicole
Boyertown HS
Perkiomenville, PA

Hornberger, Wendy
Bensalem HS
Bensalem, PA

Horne, Gregory
Columbia-Mobtour
AVTS HS
Berwick, PA

Horner, Jane
Beaver County
Christian Schl
New Brighton, PA

Horner, Melissa
Berlin Brothers
Valley HS
Berlin, PA

Horst, John
Central York HS
York, PA

Horst, Wendy S
Chambersburg Area
SR HS
Chambersburg, PA

Horting, Elisabeth
Newport JR SR HS
Newport, PA

Hott, Christine
Everett Area HS
Everett, PA

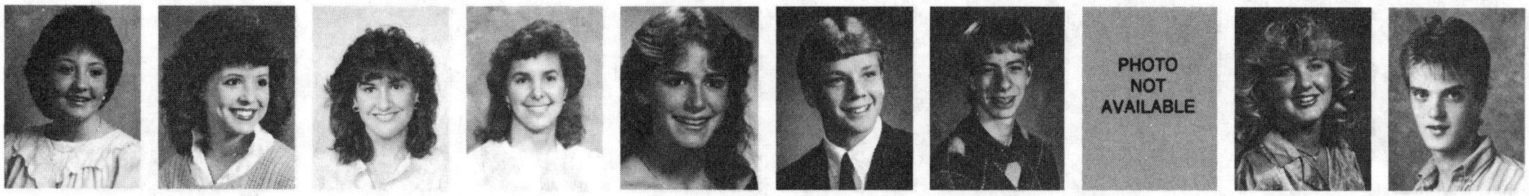

Houp, Glenda
Calvary Christian
James Creek, PA

Houser, Gretchen
Eastern York JR/SR
E Prospect, PA

Houser, Melanie
Upper Moreland HS
Hatboro, PA

Houston, Claire
Abraham Lincoln
Philadelphia, PA

Howald, Maryann
Abington SR HS
Elkins Park, PA

Howard, Dean
Ridgway HS
Ridgway, PA

Howard, III Edward
H
Union HS
Rimersburg, PA

Howard, Theresa
Creative &
Performing Arts HS
Philadelphia, PA

Howe, Monika
Salisbury HS
Bethlehem, PA

Howe, Shawn
Lewistown HS
Mc Veytown, PA

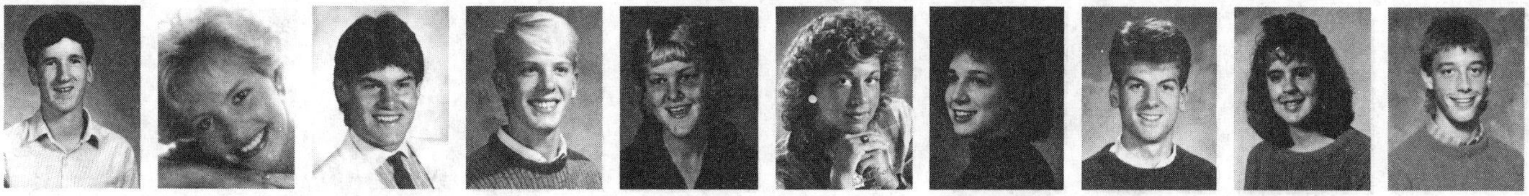

Howe, Tim
West Branch Area
Hawk Run, PA

Howsare, Angela
Bedford HS
Bedford, PA

Hoy, Robert Todd
Waynesburg Central
Waynesburg, PA

Hoyes, Brock
Danville SR HS
Danville, PA

Hoyman, Jacqueline
M
Connelsville Area
SR HS
Connellsville, PA

Hrach, Jennifer S
Mt Alvernia HS
Pittsburgh, PA

Hrezik, Kim
Schuylkill Valley HS
Leesport, PA

Hrivnak, Michael
Seneca Valley HS
Zelienople, PA

Hrivnak, Patti
Gateway SR HS
Monroeville, PA

Hromyak, Michael
Tamaqua Area HS
Tamaqua, PA

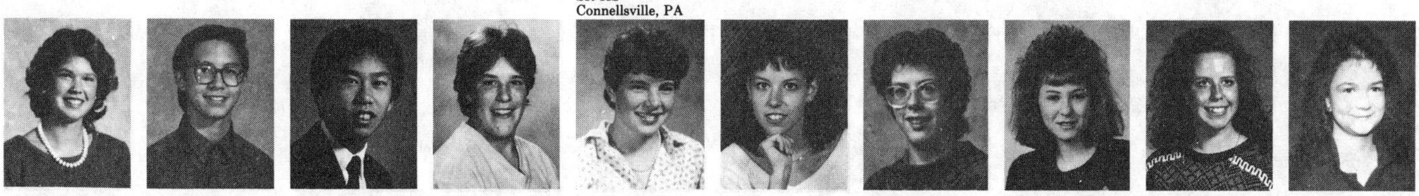

Hrzic, Jennifer
Montoursville HS
Montoursville, PA

Hsieh, Michael
Conestoga SR HS
Wayne, PA

Hu, James Y
State College Area
SR HS
Kensington, CA

Huber, Brian
Harry S Truman HS
Levittown, PA

Huber, Jenni
Indiana Area HS
Indiana, PA

Huber, Tammie
Solanco SR HS
New Providence, PA

Huckabone, Mary Jo
Warren Area HS
Warren, PA

Hudachek, Barbara
West Scranton HS
Scranton, PA

Hudacsek, Christine
Ambridge Area HS
Ambridge, PA

Hudgeons, Alesha
Lansdale Catholic
Lansdale, PA

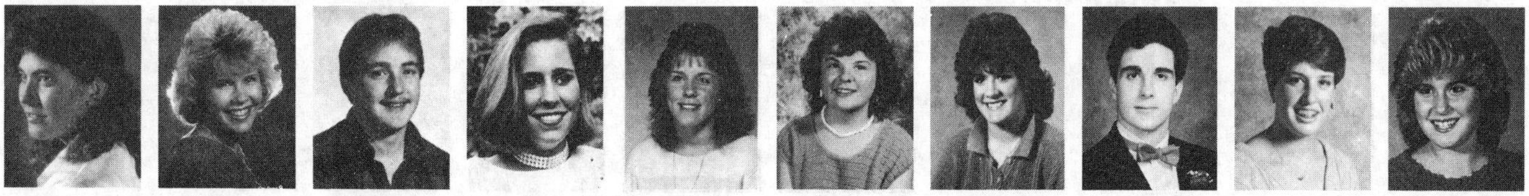

Huey, Vickie
Hamburg Area HS
Hamburg, PA

Huff, Susan
West Hazleton HS
Conyngham, PA

Huffman, Brent A
Blairsville SR HS
Blacklick, PA

Huffnagle, Heather
Lancaster Country
Day Schl
Lancaster, PA

Hufnagel, Christine
Plum SR HS
Pittsburgh, PA

Huge, Lisa
Stroudsburg HS
Sciota, PA

Hughes, Cathy
West Allegheny SR
Imperial, PA

Hughes, Christopher
Roman Catholic HS
Philadelphia, PA

Hughes, Jennifer
Academy Of Notre
Dame De Namur
West Chester, PA

Hughes, Kristie
Connellsville Area
Vanderbilt, PA

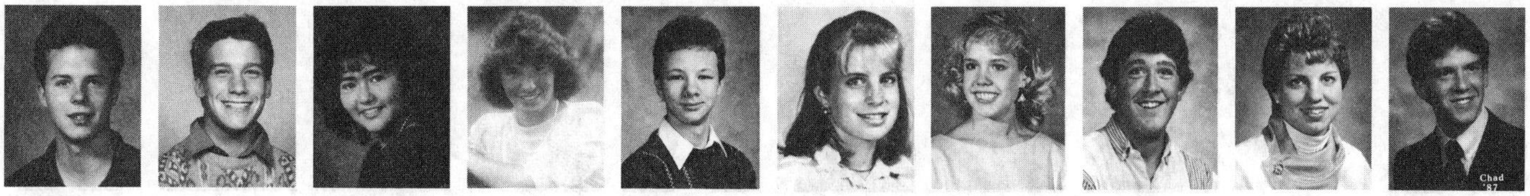

Hughes, Shawn
Leechburg HS
Leechburg, PA

Hughes, Thomas
Serra Catholic HS
W Mifflin, PA

Humberger, Doris
Lee
Hempfield Area SR
Grapeville, PA

Hummel, Camille I
Mifflinburg HS
New Berlin, PA

Hummel, Thomas
Bensalem HS
Bensalem, PA

Hunger, Jill
Pennsbury HS
Yardley, PA

Hunnell, Sherry
Lynn
Waynesburg Central
Waynesburg, PA

Hunsberger, Eric
Spring-Ford HS
Collegeville, PA

Hunsicker, Lisa
Cedar Crest HS
Lebanon, PA

Hunt, Chad
West Hazleton HS
Weston, PA

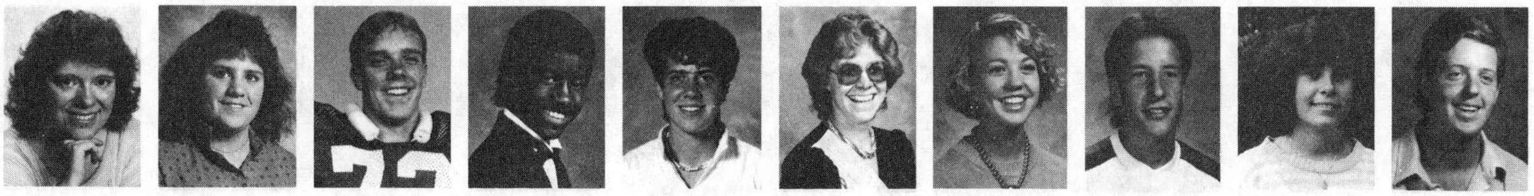

Hunt, Elisa
Corry Area HS
Corry, PA

Hunter, Melissa
Carbondale Area
JR-SR HS
Carbondale, PA

Huntley, Steve
Bensalem HS
Bensalem, PA

Hurd, William
Clearfield Area HS
Clearfield, PA

Hurley, Kathryn M
Fox Chapel Area HS
Pittsburgh, PA

Hurlock, Patricia
Pennsbury HS
Fairless Hls, PA

Hurst, Aimee
Garden Spot HS
New Holland, PA

Hurst, Doug
Garden Spot HS
Bowmansville, PA

Huss, Becci D
Chambersburg Area
Fayetteville, PA

Husted, Thomas
Hempfield HS
Mountville, PA

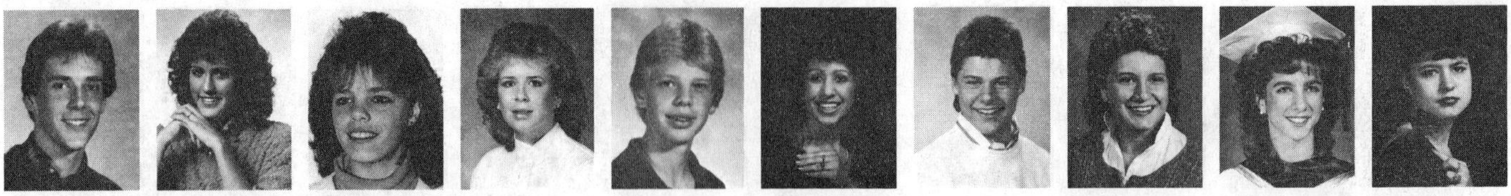

Hutzel, Greg J
Exeter HS
Reading, PA

Hvizda, Sherry
Jefferson-Morgan
Waynesburg, PA

Hydrusko, Laura
Pleasant Valley HS
Saylorsburg, PA

Hynd, Lisa
West Branch Area
Lanse, PA

Hynick, Richard
Lake Lehman HS
Hunlock Crk, PA

I Goe, Tina
St Huberts HS
Philadelphia, PA

Iacavazzi, Peter
West Scranton SR
Scranton, PA

Iacono, Michelle
Dover HS
Dover, PA

Iacovella, Fosca L
Archbishop
Prendergast HS
Havertown, PA

Iacullo, Barbara
St Huberts HS
Philadelphia, PA

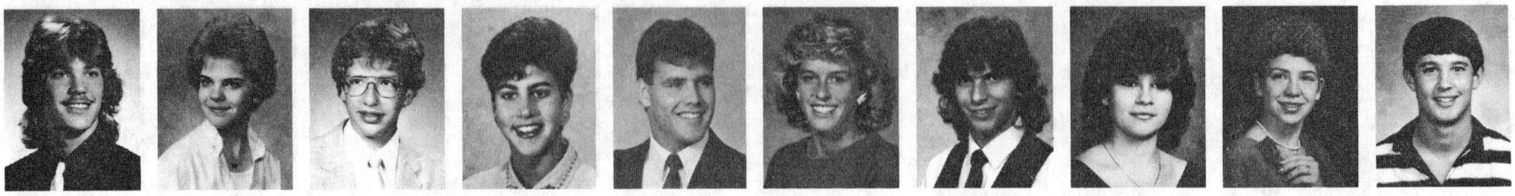

Iannucci, Mike
Penncrest HS
Media, PA

Ibinson, Linda
North Catholic HS
Pittsburgh, PA

Ickes, Chris
North Star HS
Boswell, PA

Ieni, Lisa
Franklin Regional
Export, PA

Ignozzi, Jeffery S
Burrell SR HS
Lower Burrell, PA

Ilgen, Amy
Central York SR HS
York, PA

Imbarlina, Sergio
Plum SR HS
New Kensington, PA

Imbrogno, Lisa
Cardinal O Hara HS
Brookhaven, PA

Imburgia, Deborah
Cardinal O Hara HS
Boothwyn, PA

Imler, James L
Claysburg Kimmel
Imler, PA

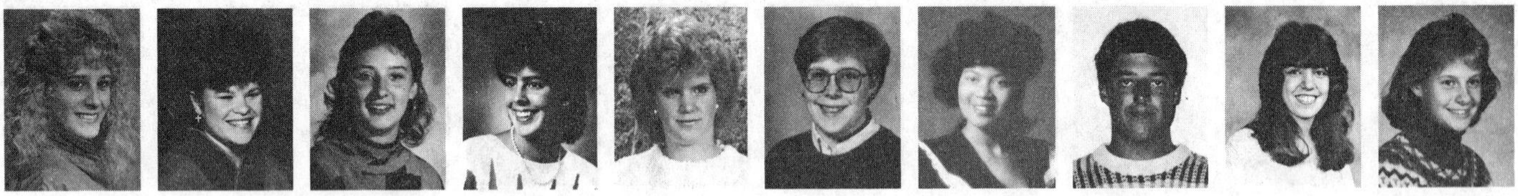

Indof, Marianne
Belle Vernon Area
Belle Vernon, PA

Insalaca, Sarina
Notre Dame HS
Easton, PA

Irvin, Heather
Glendale JR SR HS
Irvona, PA

Isaac, Kristin
Wilson Area HS
Easton, PA

Isaacs, Sarah
Towanda HS
Towanda, PA

Isenberg, Julie
Huntingdon Area
Huntingdon, PA

Isom, Janai E
Harrisburg HS
Harrisburg, PA

Israel, James
Butler HS
Lyndora, PA

Ivins, Lisa
Bensalem HS
Bensalem, PA

Iwanciw, Natalie
Phoenixville Area
Phoenixville, PA

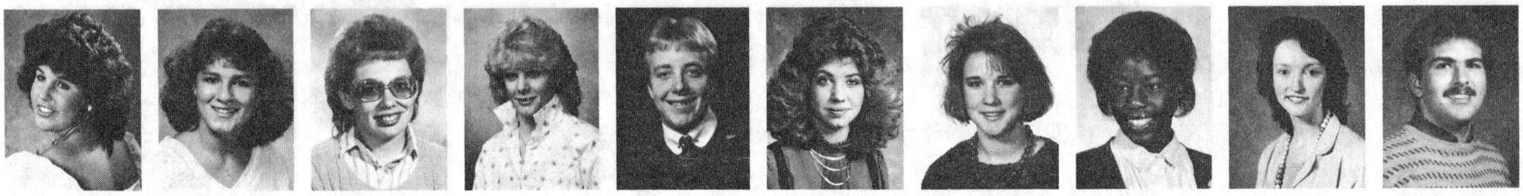

Izzo, Celeste
Connellsville HS
Dunbar, PA

Jabara, Robbi
Greensburg-Salem
Greensburg, PA

Jabco, Lisa
Bellefonte Area HS
Pleasant Gap, PA

Jablonski, Christina
Du Bois Area HS
Dubois, PA

Jack, Todd
Allegheny-Clarion
Valley HS
Lamartine, PA

Jackal, Yvonne
Sharpsville HS
Sharpsville, PA

Jackson, Candi
Oil City Area Senior
Oil City, PA

Jackson, Jennifer
Claire
North Allegheny SR
Pittsburgh, PA

Jackson, Jill
Moon SR HS
Coraopolis, PA

Jackson, John
Bethlehem Center
Brownsville, PA

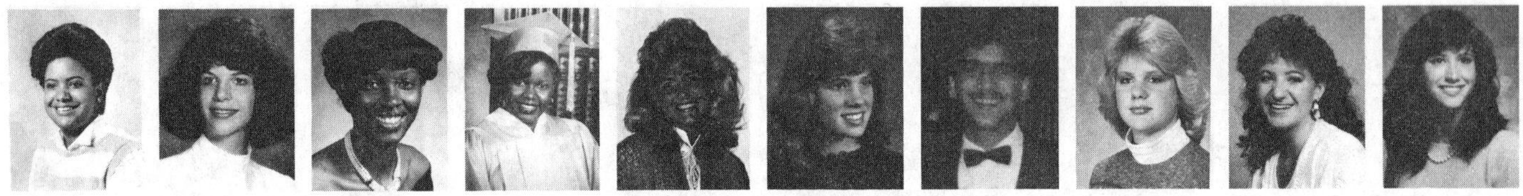

Jackson, Kimberly
Quaker Valley SR
Sewickley, PA

Jackson, Kimberly
G
Hampton HS
Allison Park, PA

Jackson, Meredith L
HS Of Engineering
& Science
Philadelphia, PA

Jackson, Mia P
Westinghouse HS
Pittsburgh, PA

Jackson, Tricia
Kiski Area HS
Apollo, PA

Jacob, Elizabeth
Ann
Somerset Area SR
Somerset, PA

Jacob, Matthew
Butler HS
Butler, PA

Jacobs, Donna
Yough HS
Irwin, PA

Jacobs, Holly Lynn
South Allegheny HS
Port Vue, PA

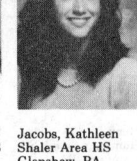

Jacobs, Kathleen
Shaler Area HS
Glenshaw, PA

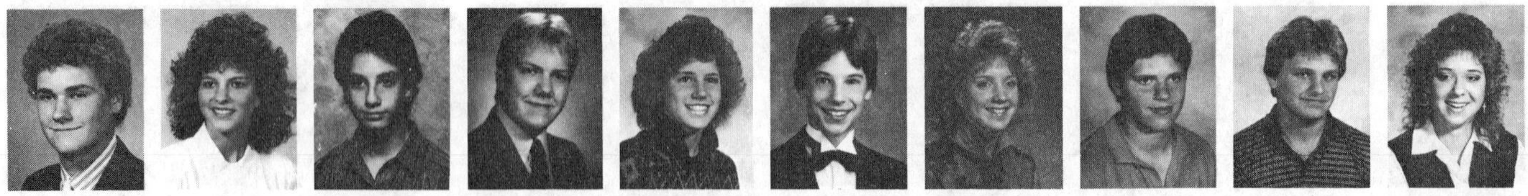

Jacobs, Stephen
West Mifflin Area
W Mifflin, PA

Jakubetz, Jo Anne
Canon Mc Millan
Canonsburg, PA

Jaman, Andrew
Solebury HS
Monroe, NY

Jamann, Frederick
Liberty HS
Bethlehem, PA

James, Carolyn
Lake-Lehman HS
Dallas, PA

Janikowski, Jan
Cathedral Prep Schl
Erie, PA

Janis, Crystal
Wilmington Area
Volant, PA

Jankovich, Jeff
Mercer Area JR SR
Mercer, PA

Janotka, Jeffrey
Northampton SR
Bath, PA

Jaronieski, Paula
Bishop Guilfoyle HS
Altoona, PA

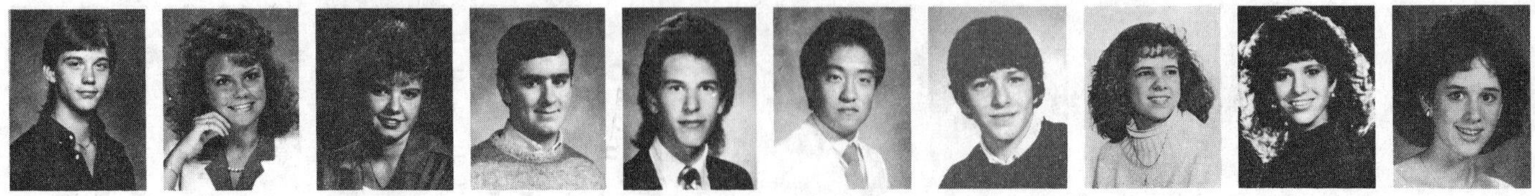

Jasko, Mark D
Ringgold HS
Finleyville, PA

Jaskulski, Jodi
West Mifflin Area
West Mifflin, PA

Jasniewicz, Ann
Benton JR SR HS
Benton, PA

Jasper, Todd E
Neshaminy HS
Penndel, PA

Javorka, Michael
John
Liberty HS
Bethlehem, PA

Jekarl, Edward Kap
Plymouth-Whitemar
sh HS
Lafayette Hill, PA

Jenkins, Jason
Allen HS
Allentown, PA

Jenkins, Karen
Central HS
Scranton, PA

Jenkins, Kathryn
Neshaminy HS
Langhorne, PA

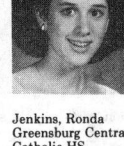

Jenkins, Ronda
Greensburg Central
Catholic HS
Trafford, PA

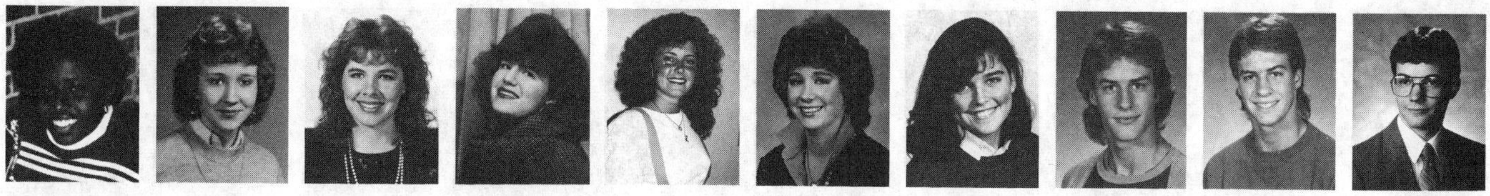

Jenkins, Yalanda
Overbrook School
For The Blind
Philadelphia, PA

Jennes, Renee
Bishop O Hara HS
Throop, PA

Jennings, Beth
Laurel Highlands
Hopwood, PA

Jennings, Nikole D
Delaware Valley HS
Milford, PA

Jennings, Rhoda
Chartiers Valley HS
Bridgeville, PA

Jeschonek, Tonya
Greater Johnstown
Johnstown, PA

Jesko, Jennifer
Gwynedd Mercy
Huntingdon Vally,
PA

Jewell, Aaron
Monessen SR HS
Monessen, PA

Jewell, Justin
Monessen HS
Monessen, PA

Jewell, William
Mark
Commodore Perry
Fredonia, PA

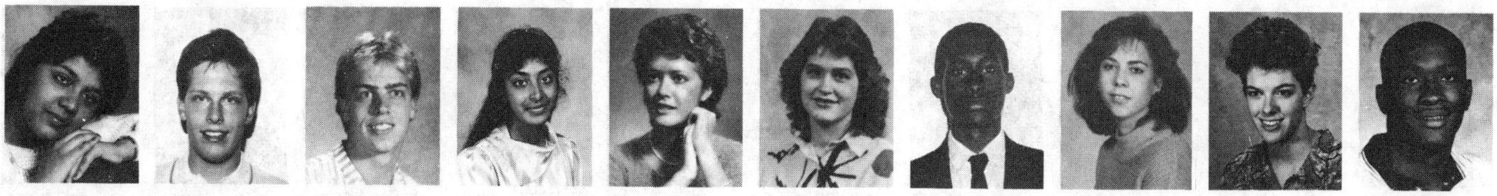

Jindal, Shivani
Central Dahphin
East HS
Harrisburg, PA

John, Eric
Archbishop Wood
Hatboro, PA

John, Jeffrey
Henderson SR HS
W Chester, PA

Johns, Bindhu
Hollidaysburg Area
SR HS
Duncansville, PA

Johns, Kerry
Lakeview HS
Fredonia, PA

Johns, Tracey
Kiski Area HS
Sahsburg, PA

Johnson, Anthony
Roman Catholic HS
Philadelphia, PA

Johnson, Astrid
Altoona Area HS
Altoona, PA

Johnson, Carla
Jefferson-Morgan
Jefferson, PA

Johnson, Clarence
Rosco
Chichester HS
Twin Oaks, PA

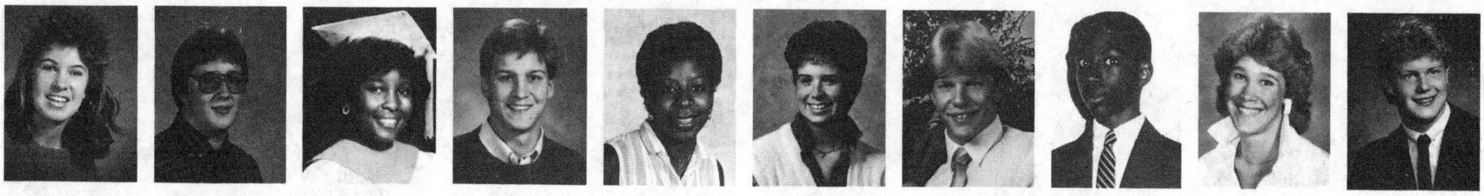

Johnson, Darlene
Andrea
Wallenpaupack Area
Hawley, PA

Johnson, David S
Twin Valley HS
Elverson, PA

Johnson, Denise L
Philadelphia High
Schl For Girls
Philadelphia, PA

Johnson, Dirk
Butler SR HS
Butler, PA

Johnson, Faith M
Philadelphia
Montgomery Chrst
Philadelphia, PA

Johnson, Genine
Warren Area HS
Warren, PA

Johnson, Gerald R
Warren Area HS
Warren, PA

Johnson, Marc
Roman Catholic HS
Philadelphia, PA

Johnson, Mary
Venango Christian
Cooperstown, PA

Johnson, Michael
North Pocono HS
Moscow, PA

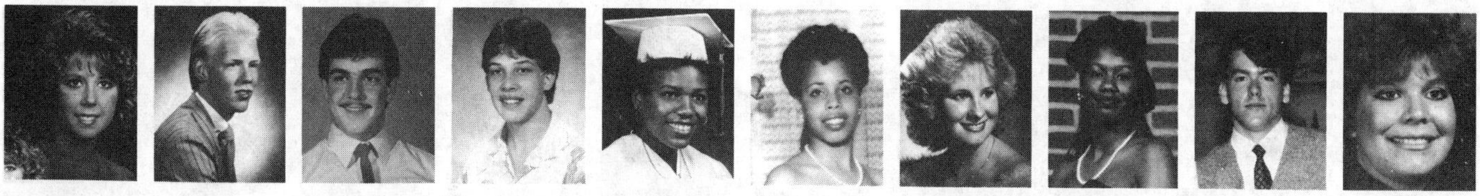

Johnson, Michelle
Upper Moreland HS
Hatboro, PA

Johnson, Scott
Manesen HS
Monessen, PA

Johnson, Sean
Brownsville HS
Brier-Hill, PA

Johnson, Sean
Geibel HS
Connelsville, PA

Johnson, Shannon
M
J R Masterson HS
Philadelphia, PA

Johnson, Tiffany
Chester HS
Chester, PA

Johnson, Tinna
Towanda Area HS
Towanda, PA

Johnson, Tomika
Creative &
Performing Arts HS
Philadelphia, PA

Johnson, Wesley D
York Suburban HS
York, PA

Johnston, Damian
Governor Mifflin HS
Shillington, PA

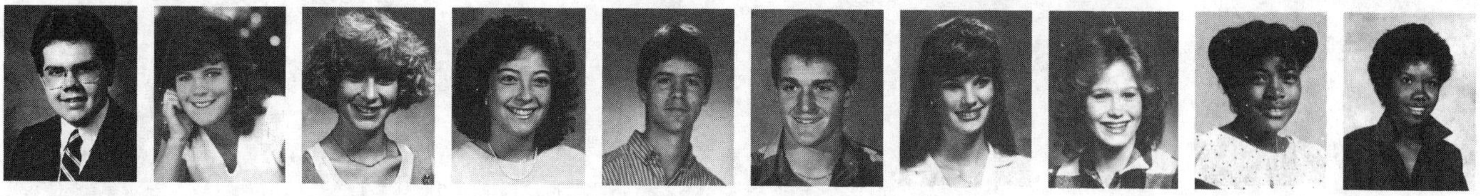

Johnston, Daren
Marion Center Area
Creekside, PA

Johnston, Melanie
North East HS
North East, PA

Johnston, Tracey
Punxsutawney Area
Big Run, PA

Johrend, Ursula
Governor Mifflin HS
Reading, PA

Joll, Scott
Elizabeth Forward
SR HS
Monongahela, PA

Jones, Adam
Laurel Highlands
Uniontown, PA

Jones, Beth
Mechanicsburg SR
Mechanicsburg, PA

Jones, Beth Ann
Charleroi Area HS
Charleroi, PA

Jones, Cherritta
Craig
Chester HS
Chester, PA

Jones, Christine
Central HS
Philadelphia, PA

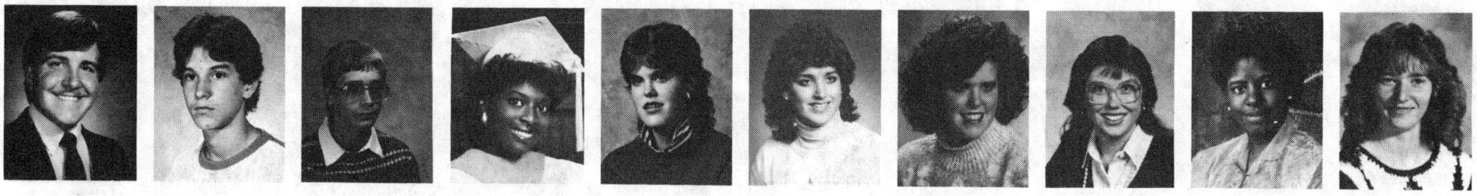

Jones, Evan
Blue Mountain HS
Orwigsburg, PA

Jones, Jason H
Saltsburg JR SR HS
Slickville, PA

Jones, John
Middleburg HS
Middleburg, PA

Jones, Kadijah
Philadelphia HS For
Philadelphia, PA

Jones, Katherine
Warren Area HS
Warren, PA

Jones, Kristin
West Mifflin Area
W Mifflin, PA

Jones, Lara
Pittston Area HS
Pittston, PA

Jones, Leigh
Juniata HS
Thompsontown, PA

Jones, Lori A
Sacred Heart HS
Pittsburgh, PA

Jones, Michelle
Purchase Line HS
Commodore, PA

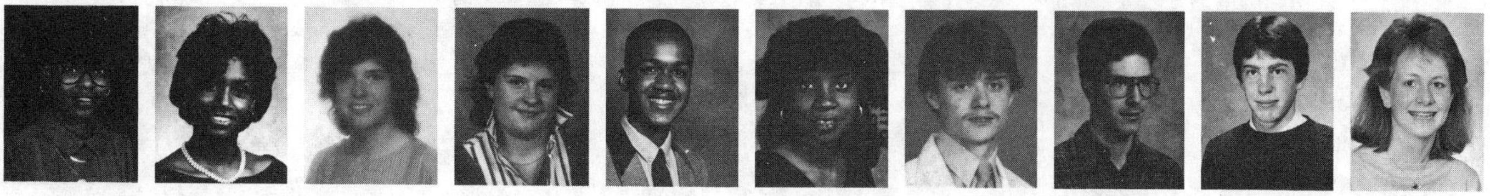

Jones, Michelle J
Philadelphia HS For
Philadelphia, PA

Jones, Nicole Maria
Carlisle SR HS
Carlisle, PA

Jones, Paula M
Villa Maria Acad
Malvern, PA

Jones, Rebecca
Penn-Trafford HS
Harrison City, PA

Jones, Richard
Carver HS Of
Engineering
Philadelphia, PA

Jones, Sharon
John W Hallahan
Philadelphia, PA

Jones, Steve
James Buchanan HS
St Thomas, PA

Jones, Thomas
West Perry HS
Shermansdale, PA

Jones, Todd M
Burgettstown Area
Paris, PA

Jones, Valerie
Wyoming Area
Senior HS
West Pittston, PA

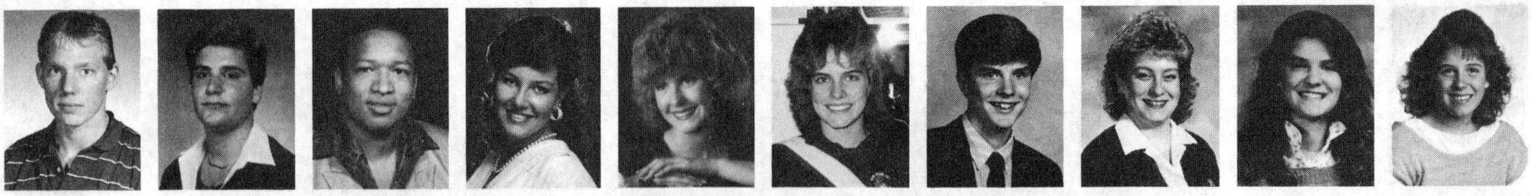

JonesII, David W
Allen HS
Allentown, PA

Jordan, Jeffrey
Geibel HS
Uniontown, PA

Jordan, Joe
Mc Keesport Area
Mckeesport, PA

Jordan, Karen
St Marys Area HS
Kersey, PA

Jordan, Kelly Lynn
North Schuykill HS
Frackville, PA

Jordan, Kristie
North Schuylkill HS
Trackville, PA

Jordan, Michael
Devon Prep
Broomall, PA

Jorden, Amy
Bishop Guilfoyle HS
Altoona, PA

Jorgensen, Karin L
Pennsbury HS
Yardley, PA

Joseph, Diana
New Castle SR HS
New Castle, PA

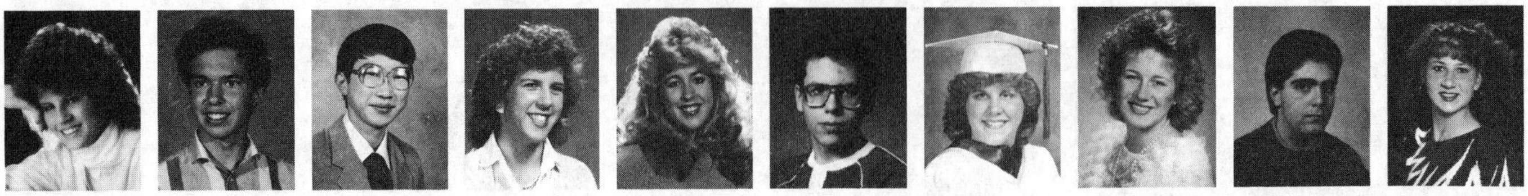

Jover, Doreen
Valleyview HS
Peckville, PA

Joy, Jason
Laurel Highlands
Uniontown, PA

Juang, Oliver
Mc Dowell HS
Erie, PA

Jucknik, Stacy
Louis E Dieruff HS
Allentown, PA

Jurasko, Diane
Hopewell HS
Aliquippa, PA

Kacinko, John
Churchill HS
Pittsburgh, PA

Kaczmarski, Debbie
Bishop Shanahan
W Chester, PA

Kaczynski, Kris
North Hills HS
Pittsburgh, PA

Kaffenes, Harry
Aliquippa JR SR
Aliquippa, PA

Kahkonen, Sonja
Trinity HS
Washington, PA

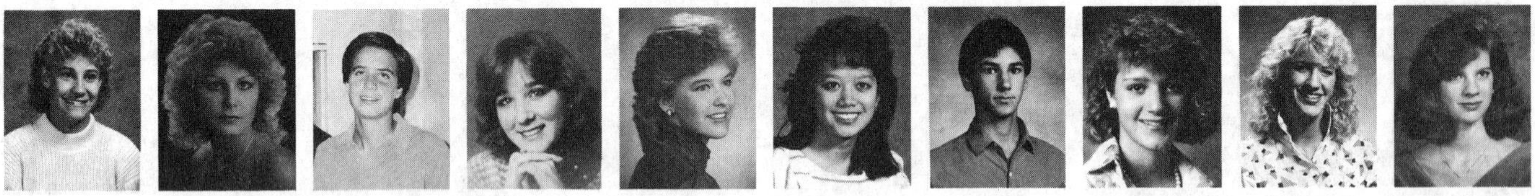

Kain, Stacy
Newport HS
Newport, PA

Kalamasz, Ann
Center HS
Aliquippa, PA

Kaliner, Daniel J
Haverford SR HS
Philadelphia, PA

Kalinik, Christine
Belle Vernon Area
Belle Vernon, PA

Kalochie, Jennifer
Minersville Area HS
Minersville, PA

Kalugdan, Irene
Bensalem HS
Bensalem, PA

Kaminski, Steve
Neshaminy HS
Feasterville, PA

Kane, Carol
Trinity HS
Amity, PA

Kane, Megan
Wilmington Area
New Wilmington, PA

Kane, Michelle
Cardinal O Hara HS
Swarthmore, PA

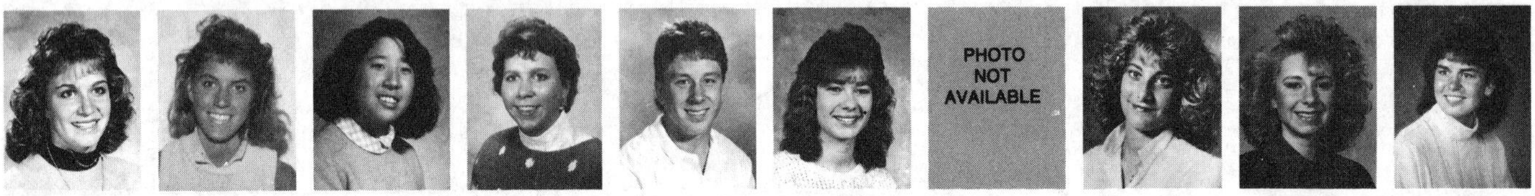
PHOTO
NOT
AVAILABLE

Kane, Robin Lynne
Canevin Catholic
Carnegie, PA

Kane, Tabatha
Academy Of Notre
Wayne, PA

Kang, Shulamith
Deborah
Upper Merion Area
Gulph Mills, PA

Kania, Michele
Geibel HS
Uniontown, PA

Kanich, William
Blacklick Valley HS
Nanty-Glo, PA

Kapala, Sherri
Northwestern HS
Albion, PA

Kapanyko, Wendi
Hopewell SR HS
Aliquippa, PA

Kappel, Maria
Center HS
Monaca, PA

Karaba, Monica
Monongahela Valley
Catholic HS
Scenery Hl, PA

Kargle, Michele
Yough SR HS
West Newton, PA

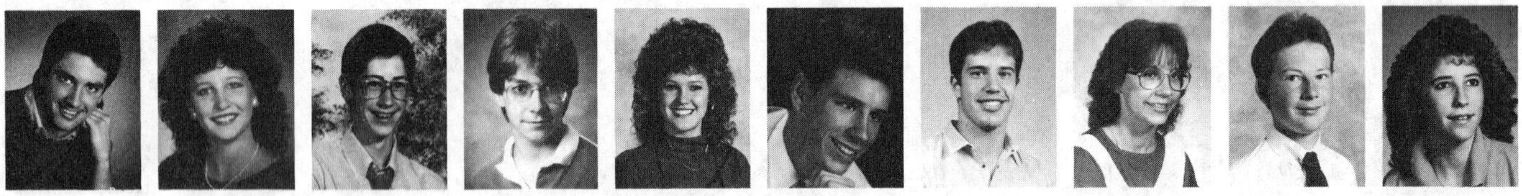

Kargo, Ray
Portage Area HS
Portage, PA

Karkalla, Amy
Bethel Park HS
Bethel Park, PA

Karns, David
Meadville Area HS
Meadville, PA

Karoleski, Michael
Trinity HS
Washington, PA

Kasecky, Tonya
Blacklick Valley JR
SR HS
Ebensburg, PA

Kash, Brian
Henderson HS
W Chester, PA

Kashubara, Pete
New Castle HS
New Castle, PA

Kasko, Mary Ann
Lake-Lehman HS
Shavertown, PA

Kasper, William
Nativity BVM HS
Pottsville, PA

Kastriba, Linda
Ambridge Area HS
Ambridge, PA

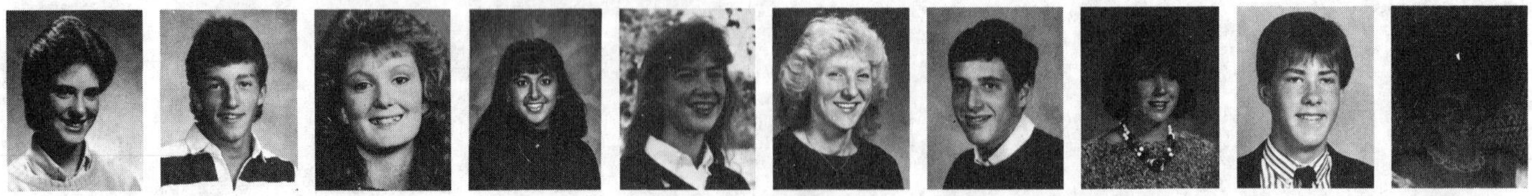

Kaszowski, Tammy
Wilmington Area
New Wilmington, PA

Kaszupski, Jim
Neshaminy HS
Feasterville, PA

Kates, Heather
Mt St Joseph Acad
Philadelphia, PA

Katyal, Shalini
Shaler Area SR HS
Allison Park, PA

Katzmar, Denise
Harry S Truman HS
Levittown, PA

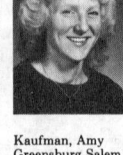

Kaufman, Amy
Greensburg Salem
SR HS
New Alexandria, PA

Kaufman, David
Alan
Altoona Area HS
Altoona, PA

Kaufold, Heather
Cumberland Valley
Mechanicsburg, PA

Kaune, Douglas
Devon Prep Schl
Wayne, PA

Kazimerski, Cheryl
Frankford HS
Philadelphia, PA

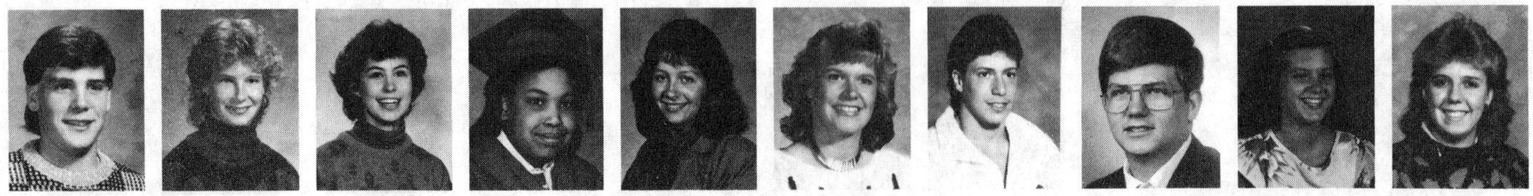

Keach, III Elmer R
Red Land HS
Etters, PA

Kearney, Barbara
Annville-Cleona HS
Annville, PA

Kearney, Erin
John S Fine SR HS
Nanticoke, PA

Kearney, Hope
University City HS
Philadelphia, PA

Kearney, Shelly
Hollidaysburg Area
SR HS
Hollidaysburg, PA

Kearns, Kimberly
Methacton HS
Trooper, PA

Keat, Kevin
Pen Argyl Area HS
Pen Argyl, PA

Keating, James Alan
Penn Trafford HS
Level Green, PA

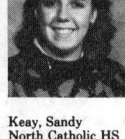

Keating, Rebecca Jo
Penn Trafford HS
Level Green, PA

Keay, Sandy
North Catholic HS
Pittsburgh, PA

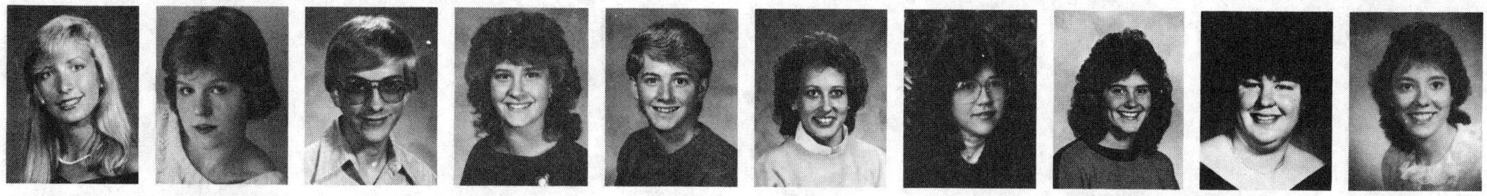

Kebuz, Lana
Lower Moreland HS
Huntingdon Valley, PA

Keck, Aries Claire
Upper Dauphin Area HS
Pillow, PA

Keck, Gordon J
Knoch HS
Sarver, PA

Keech, Susan
Hollidaysburg SR
Hollidaysburg, PA

Keefer, Eric
Central HS
York, PA

Keefer, Kelly
Big Spring HS
Shippensburg, PA

Keefer, Leona
Dover Area HS
Dover, PA

Keefer, Michelle
Medaville Area SR
Meadville, PA

Keen, Cynthia
W B Saul HS
Philadelphia, PA

Keen, Vanessa
Lock Haven HS
Lock Haven, PA

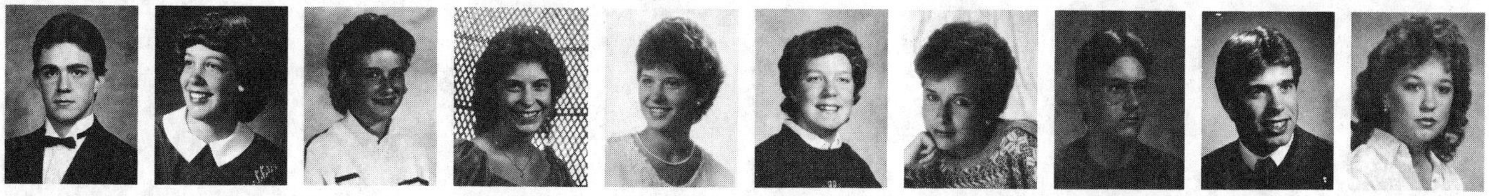

Keena, Joseph
Monsignor Bonner
Glenolden, PA

Keene, Deborah A
Indiana Area SR HS
Indiana, PA

Keener, Marcie
Reading SR HS
Reading, PA

Keeney, Yvonne
Central SR HS
York, PA

Keeport, Kendra
Penn Manor HS
Millersville, PA

Keeter, Paige
Pottsville Area HS
Pottsville, PA

Keeton, Kimberly
Seneca Valley SR
Harmony, PA

Keifer, II Charles E
Lewisburg Area HS
West Milton, PA

Keim, David
North Hills HS
Pittsburgh, PA

Keim, Kathy
Phoenixville Area
Phoenixville, PA

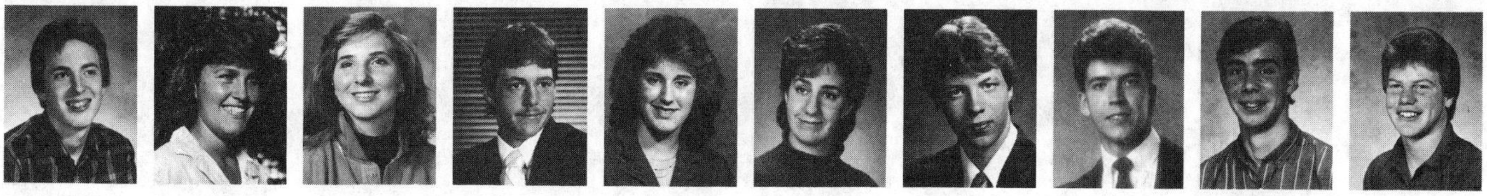

Keiper, Michael
Elk Lake HS
Springville, PA

Keiser, Amy
Milton SR HS
Milton, PA

Keister, Loretta
East Pennsboro HS
Harrisburg, PA

Keith, La Mar R
Northern Bedford County HS
Roaring Sprgs, PA

Keith, Shannon
Franklin HS
Franklin, PA

Kelberg, Sharon
Pennsbury HS
Fairless Hls, PA

Kell, David
West Perry HS
New Bloomfield, PA

Keller, David
Chambersburg Area SR HS
Chambersburg, PA

Kellerman, William
Bald Eagle-Nittany
Beech Creek, PA

Kelley, Joe
Saltsburgh JR SR
New Alexandria, PA

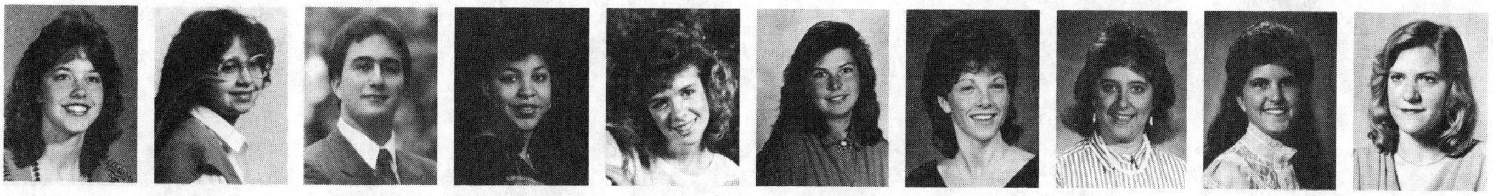

Kelley, Raquel
Methacton HS
Norristown, PA

Kelley, Sharon E
Connellsville Area
Connellsville, PA

Kellman, Andrew
Wyoming Seminary
Shavertown, PA

Kelly, Charla
Bishop Mc De Vitt
Philadelphia, PA

Kelly, Deborah Ann
Conrad Weiser HS
Sinking Spring, PA

Kelly, Joan M
Norristown Area HS
Norristown, PA

Kelly, Michelle
Archbishop Wood For Girls
Holland, PA

Kelly, Monica
Butler Intermediate
Evans City, PA

Kelly, Tammy
Altoona Area HS
Altoona, PA

Kelmereit, Laura C
Moon SR HS
Coraopolis, PA

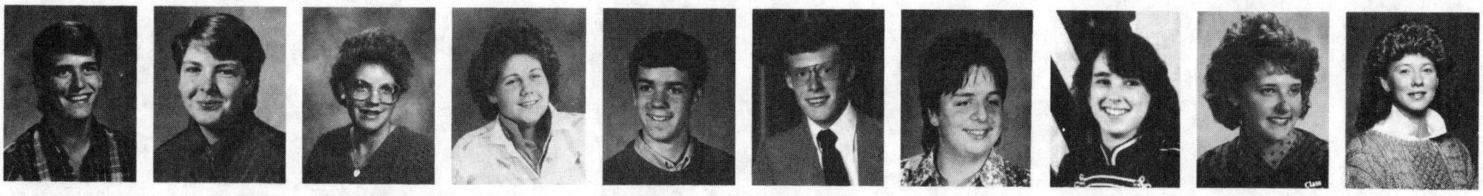

Kelsey, Michael
Living Word Acad
Ephrata, PA

Kelshaw, Rachel
Quaker Valley HS
Sewickely, PA

Kemmerer, Kathy
Brockway Area HS
Brockway, PA

Kemp, Amy
Hopewell Area HS
Aliquippa, PA

Kemp, Mark
Connellsville Area SR HS
Normalville, PA

Kempf, III Edward J
Northwestern HS
Cranesville, PA

Kendall, Joe
Laurel Highlands
Uniontown, PA

Kenderdine, Charlene
Pocono Mountain
Henryville, PA

Kendzor, Bonnie
Pittston Area HS
Pittston, PA

Kennedy, Deanna
Ringgold HS
Monongahela, PA

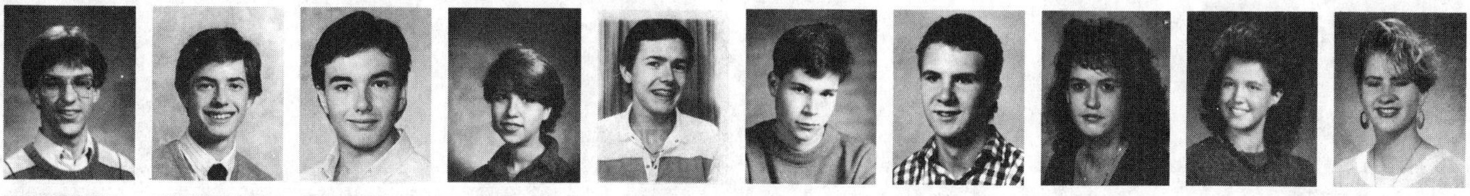

Kennedy, James
Seneca Valley HS
Evans Cty, PA

Kennedy, Jeffrey
York Catholic HS
York, PA

Kennedy, John O
Wyoming Valley West HS
Plymouth, PA

Kennedy, Rachel
St Cyril Acad
Stillwater, PA

Kennedy, Sean
Archbishop Wood HS For Boys
Ambler, PA

Kennedy, Sean
Loyalsock Township
Williamsport, PA

Kennelly, Robert
Hopewell HS
Aliquippa, PA

Kennemuth, Jennifer
Brookville Area HS
Brookville, PA

Kenneweg, Dawn
Fort Cherry JR/SR
Mcdonald, PA

Kenney, Tara
Geibel HS
Scottdale, PA

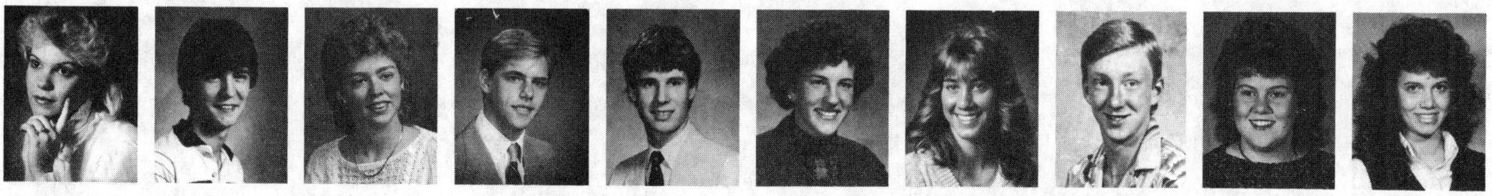

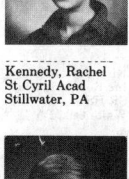

Kensinger, Anissa
Juniata Valley HS
Petersburg, PA

Kent, Michael
Columbia Montour
Nescopeck, PA

Kephart, Amy
Moshannon Valley
Houtzdale, PA

Kepple, Ken
Franklin Regional
Delmont, PA

Kercsmar, Michael
Central Bucks HS
Chalfont, PA

Keriazes, Ellena P
Hanover SR HS
Hanover, PA

Kern, Kristi
Trinity HS
Washington, PA

Kern, Sean
Dover Area HS
York, PA

Kern, Tammy
Connellsville Area SR HS
Connellsville, PA

Kernan, Deborah
Nazareth Acad
Philadelphia, PA

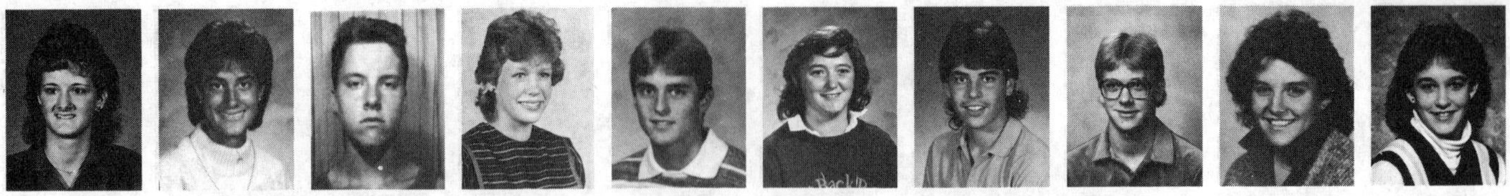

Kerr, Gwen
Waynesburg Central
Waynesburg, PA

Kerr, Trisha
Shaler Area HS
Allison Park, PA

Kerrigan, Sean P
Bensalem HS
Bensalem, PA

Kershner, Tiffany
West Haqzleton HS
Hazleton, PA

Kerstetter, Brian
Warwick HS
Lititz, PA

Kerwin, Angela
Millersburg Area HS
Millersburg, PA

Kessler, G Brian
Monessen JR SR
Monessen, PA

Kessler, Joseph
Du Bois Area SR
Du Bois, PA

Kessler, Lisa
Central York SR HS
York, PA

Kessler, Stacy
Central Columbia
Bloomsburg, PA

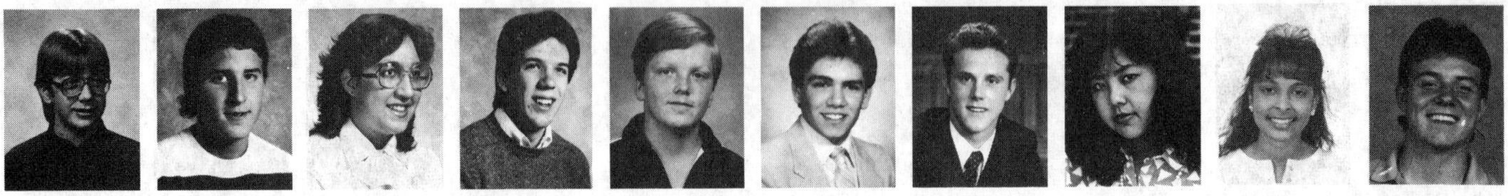

Kessler, Wally
Du Bois Area SR
Du Bois, PA

Kester, Michael
Dallas SR HS
Shavertown, PA

Kester, Susan M
Sun Valley SR HS
Aston, PA

Ketch, Mark
Sch Hoven HS
Sch Haven, PA

Key, Mark
Claysburg Kimmel
Claysburgh, PA

Keyes, IV William R
Norristown Area HS
Norristown, PA

Keys, Richard D
Beth-Center HS
Brownsville, PA

Kha, Ko
Pequea Valley HS
Gordonville, PA

Khandhar, Alpa
Neshaminy HS
Feasterville, PA

Kidwell, John
Archbishop Ryan
HS For Boys
Philadelphia, PA

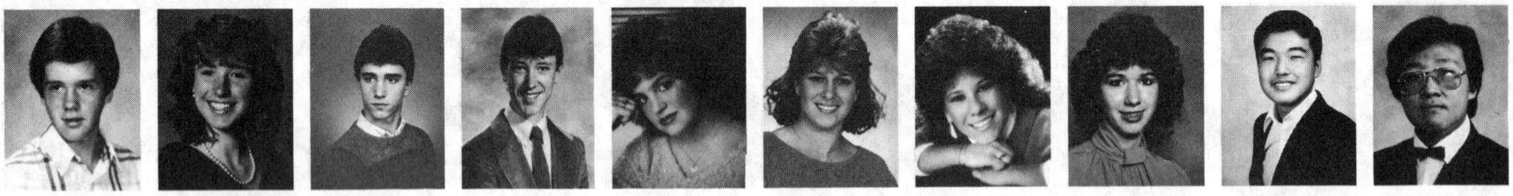

Kiefer, Joseph
Abington Heights
Clarks Summit, PA

Kiely, Kitty
Archbishop Carroll
Havertown, PA

Kieninger, Thad
Latrobe HS
Greensburg, PA

Kiesewetter, Kent
Bishop Guilfoyle HS
Altoona, PA

Kilker, Tara
Bishop O Hara HS
Blakely, PA

Killar, Claudine
Elizabeth Forward
Springboro, OH

Killino, Michelle
Old Forge HS
Old Forge, PA

Kilmer, Victoria
Blue Mt Acad
Hop Bottom, PA

Kim, Chae
Olney HS
Philadelphia, PA

Kim, Heerak
Phil-Mont Christian
Philadelphia, PA

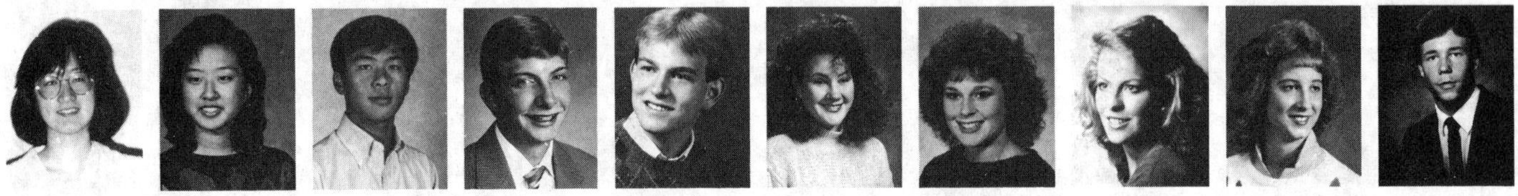

Kim, Jiyoung
Schenley HS
Pittsburgh, PA

Kim, Julie
Laurel Highlands
Uniontown, PA

Kim, Sung
Downingtown SR
Downingtown, PA

Kimmel, Jeffrey
Berlin-Brothervalley
Berlin, PA

Kinard, Brian
Central York SR HS
York, PA

Kindle, Kathleen
Lincoln HS
Ellwood City, PA

Kindred, Tricia
Yough HS
Lowber, PA

King, Amy
Waynesburg Central
Waynesburg, PA

King, Deborah
Dover Area HS
Dover, PA

King, James
Saucon Valley HS
Bethleham, PA

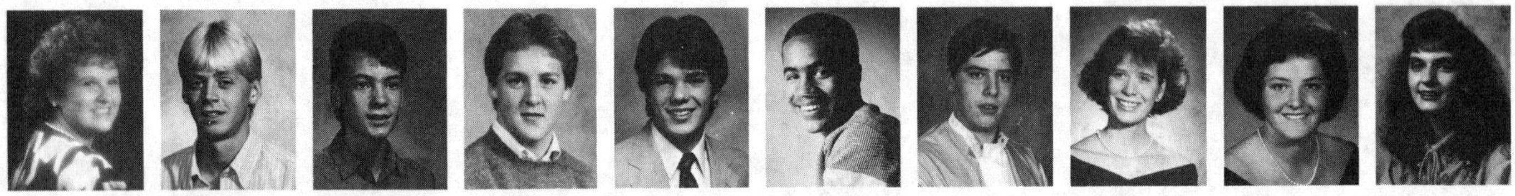

King, Jane
Riverview HS
Oakmont, PA

King, Jason
Belle Vernon Area
Fayette City, PA

King, John
Living Word Acad
Leola, PA

King, Keith
Freeport Area SR
Freeport, PA

King, Richard A
Ringgold HS
Eighty Four, PA

King, Terry
Schenley HS
Pittsburgh, PA

King, Tim
Union HS
Rimersburg, PA

Kingsley, Cynthia
Villa Maria
Jeffersonville, PA

Kinsey, Pamela Lee
Solanco HS
Paradise, PA

Kioumourtzis, Sandra
Warren Area HS
Warren, PA

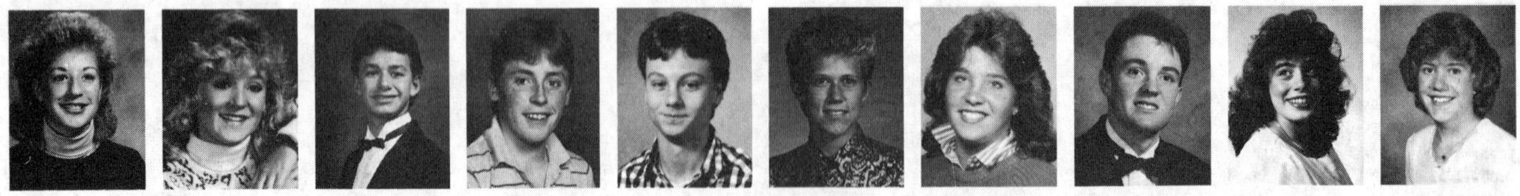

Kipp, Diane
Newport HS
Newport, PA

Kirby, Bernice
Charleroi Area JR/SR HS
Charleroi, PA

Kirby, Joseph J
Archibishop Ryan HS For Boys
Philadelphia, PA

Kirchhofer, Sean
Nazareth Area SR
Nazareth, PA

Kirchner, Jeffrey
Keystone Oaks HS
Pittsburgh, PA

Kirish, Anastasia
Ambridge Area HS
Ambridge, PA

Kirk, Juliann
Mc Keesport Area SR HS
White Oak, PA

Kirk, Thomas
Msgr Bonner HS
Drexel Hill, PA

Kirkpatrick, Amy Beth
Bell Vernon Area
Belle Vernon, PA

Kirsch, Donna
Northern Cambria
Spangler, PA

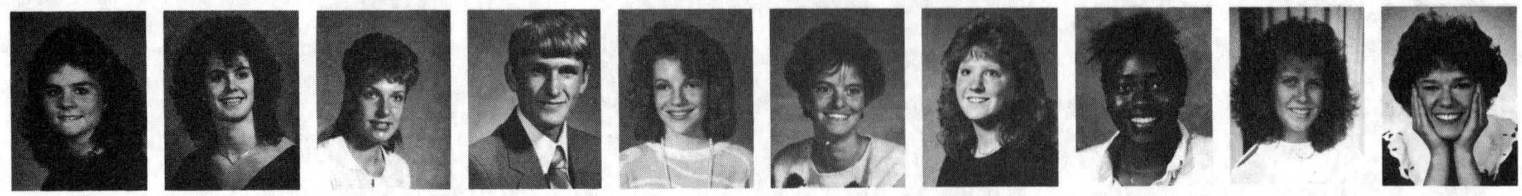

Kirsch, Paula
Northern Cambria
Nicktown, PA

Kirwin, Colleen
St Huberts HS
Philadelphia, PA

Kis Halas, Krisztina
Upper Merion Area SR HS
King Of Prussia, PA

Kishbaugh, Wayne
Wyalusing Valley
Laceyville, PA

Kishel, Kimberly
Brownsville Area HS
Allison, PA

Kisiday, Paulette
Ambridge HS
Freedom, PA

Kiss, Suzanne
W Allegheny HS
Oakdale, PA

Kitchen, Ivy
Uniontown Area HS
Uniontown, PA

Kitchen, Michele
Council Rock HS
Wash Cross, PA

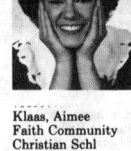

Klaas, Aimee
Faith Community Christian Schl
Clairton, PA

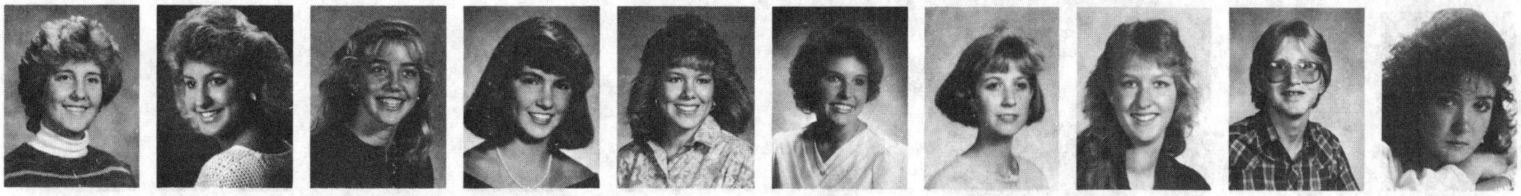

Klaczak, Carolyn
Archbishop
Wood-Girls HS

Klapkowski, Kristin
Mc Guffy HS
Claysville, PA

Kleckner, Jacqueline
B Reed Henderson
W Chester, PA

Kleckner, Zoe
Delaware County
Christian Schl
Haverton, PA

Kleigleng, Marie
Amridge Area SR
Baden, PA

Klein, Karen
Peters Twp HS
Mc Murray, PA

Kleinsak, Michelle
Bishop Mc Devitt
Harrisburg, PA

Kleinstuber, Ellen L
Lampeter-Strasburg
Lancaster, PA

Kleintop, Jeff
Pleasant Valley HS
Saylorsburg, PA

Kleist, Stacey
Meadville Area HS
Meadville, PA

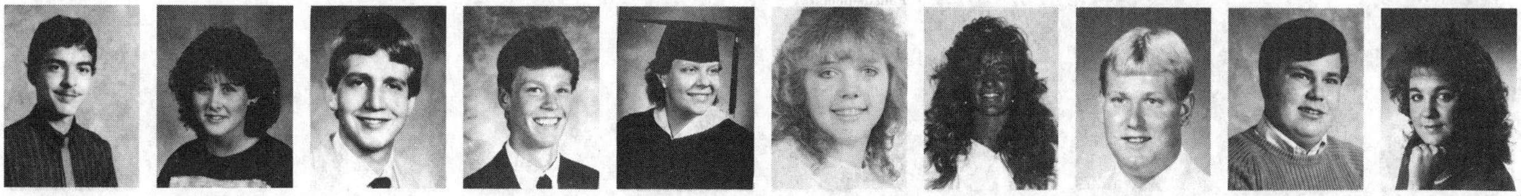

Klemer, John
Shenandoah Valley
JR SR HS
Shenandoah, PA

Klepfer, Zandra
Brookville Area HS
Sigel, PA

Klimek, John
Crestwood HS
Mountaintop, PA

Kline, Jr Craig
Holy Name HS
Shillington, PA

Kline, Francesca
Lock Haven SR HS
Lock Haven, PA

Kline, Heidi
Eisenhower HS
Russell, PA

Kline, Kimberly
Upper Darby HS
Drexel Hill, PA

Kline, Patrick
Greater Johnstown
Area Vo-Tech Schl
Summerhill, PA

Kline, Scott
Schuylkill Haven
Area HS
Sch Haven, PA

Kline, Tina
Easton Area HS
Easton, PA

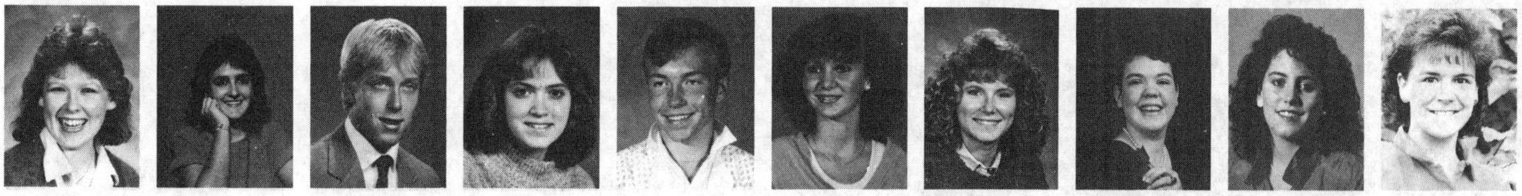

Klinefelter, Michelle
Seneca Valley SR
Zelienople, PA

Klinehans, Stacy
Blacklick Valley JR
SR HS
Nanty-Glo, PA

Klingaman, Randy
Parkland HS
Trexlertown, PA

Klingel, Roree
Tunkhannock Area
Tunkhannock, PA

Klink, III Harry
William
Connellsville Area
Dunbar, PA

Klippi, Marci
Connellsville Area
SR HS
S Connellsville, PA

Klir, Amy
Shaler Area HS
Pittsburgh, PA

Klotz, Marigrace B
Archbishop
Prendergast HS
Yeadon, PA

Klotz, Maureen Ann
Shaler Area SR HS
Pittsburgh, PA

Kluck, Carolyn
Carbondale Area JR
SR HS
Simpson, PA

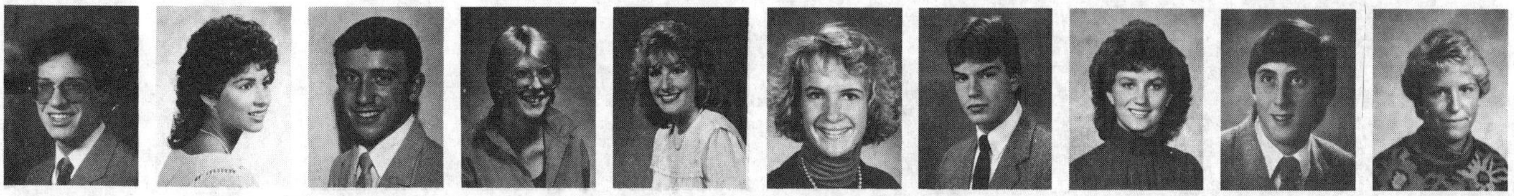

Kluck, John
Venango Christian
Rouseville, PA

Knapich, Mary G
Bishop Hoban HS
Shickshinny, PA

Knee, Ron
Moshannon Vly JR
& Sr HS
Smith Mill, PA

Knepp, Cathy
Middleburg HS
Middleburg, PA

Knight, Elizabeth
Frazier HS
Perryopolis, PA

Knight, Kathleen
Seneca Valley SR
Mars, PA

Knipple, Douglas
Geibel HS
Scottdale, PA

Knisel, Lynne
Forest Hills HS
Summerhill, PA

Knizner, Keith
Immaculate
Conception HS
Washington, PA

Knoebel, Kris
Perkiomen Valley
Trappe, PA

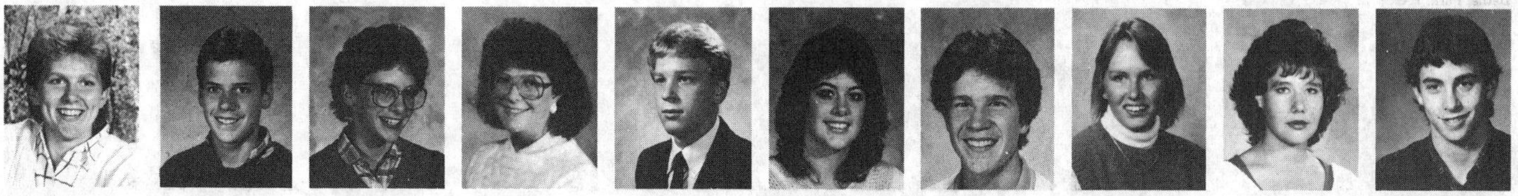

Knolles, Bette A
Wyalusing Valley JR
Sr HS
Wyalusing, PA

Knopfel, Drew
Plum SR HS
Pittsburgh, PA

Knopp, Brenda
Watsontown
Christian Acad
Muncy, PA

Knorr, Dana
Altoona Area HS
Altoona, PA

Knorr, Eric
James M Coughlin
Wilkes Barre, PA

Knowles, Donna
Alinda
Chichester SR HS
Twin Oaks, PA

Knowlton, David
Caudersport JR SR
Coudersport, PA

Knox, Hillary
Delaware Valley HS
Milford, PA

Knych, Stacey
Hanover Area JR
SR HS
Marion Terr, PA

Kober, Christopher
William Allen HS
Allentown, PA

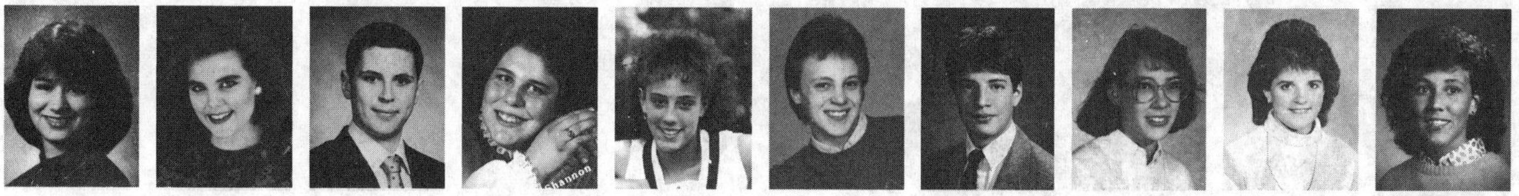

Kobuck, Lori
Tyrone Area HS
Warriors Mk, PA

Koch, Carol
Notre Dame Acad
Ridley Park, PA

Koch, Lee
Methacton HS
Audubon, PA

Koch, Shannon
Oil City Area HS
Oil City, PA

Koch, Stephanie
Altoona Area HS
Altoona, PA

Kochanowski,
Robert
Pittston Area SR
Duryea, PA

Kochenash, Frank
Bethlehem Catholic
Bethlehem, PA

Kocher, Cynthia
Pen Argyl HS
Pen Argyl, PA

Kocher, Kristen
Hanover Area JR
SR HS
Wilkes Barre, PA

Kocher, Lisa
Upper Dauphin
Area HS
Elizabethville, PA

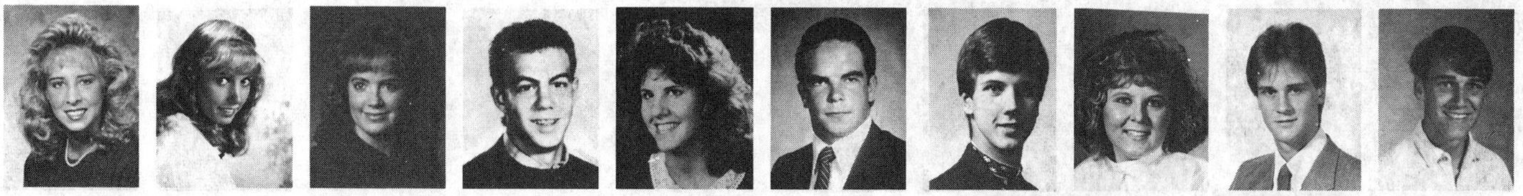

Kocis, Christine
Connellsville Area
SR HS
Cnlvle, PA

Koehler, Karen
Wilson HS
Sinking Spring, PA

Koepfer, Michelle
Moon SR HS
Coraopolis, PA

Kohl, Thomas
Reading HS
Reading, PA

Kohlbus, Theresa
Red Lion Area SR
Red Lion, PA

Kohler, Lance
Muncy HS
Muncy, PA

Kohut, Mark
Central HS
Philadelphia, PA

Kokoska, Denise
Monagahela
Catholic HS
Monessen, PA

Kolander, Jeff
Riverside JR/SR HS
Moosic, PA

Kolb, E Anders
Central Bucks East
Doylestown, PA

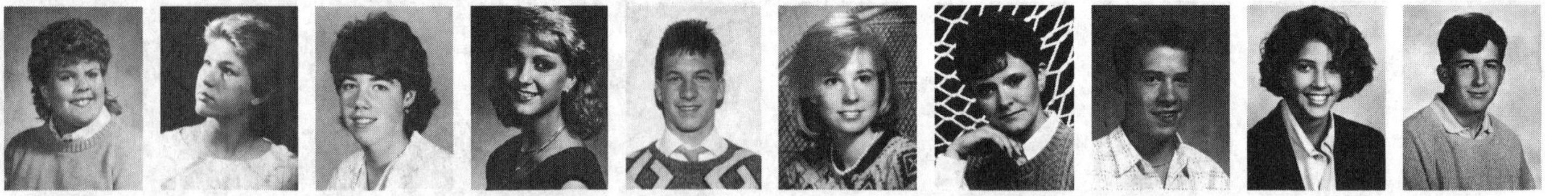

Kolessar, Melissa
Pottsgrove HS
Pottstown, PA

Kolling, Carrie
Jeannette SR HS
Jeannette, PA

Koncle, Kathryn
Warwick HS
Lititz, PA

Konieczny, Vickie
Louis E Dieruff HS
Allentown, PA

Konstance, II Richard P
Archbishop Ryan For Boys HS
Philadelphia, PA

Kool, Lisa
Harriton HS
Pen Vly, PA

Koontz, Tina Ann
Everett Area HS
Everett, PA

Kopas, James
Fairchance Georges SR HS
Fairchance, PA

Kopensky, Susan
Gwynedd Mercy
Blue Bell, PA

Kopicz, Charles
Fleetwood Area HS
Fleetwood, PA

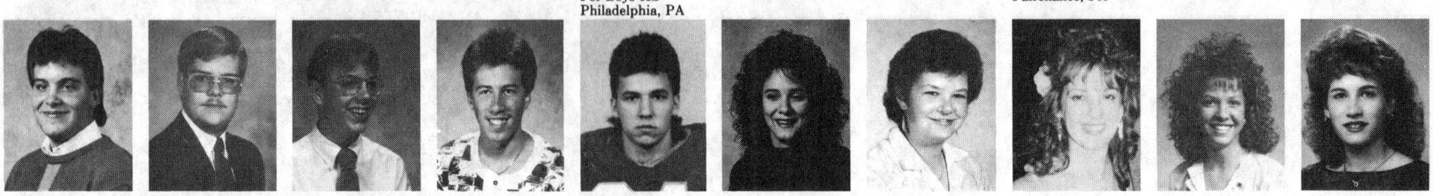

Kopko, Larry
Warren Area HS
Warren, PA

Kopp, Michael J
Fox Chapel Area HS
Sharpsburg, PA

Koppenhaver, Brian
Cedar Crest HS
Lebanon, PA

Koratich, Chad
Jefferson-Morgan JR SR HS
Rices Landing, PA

Kordish, Randy
Valley View HS
Jessup, PA

Koren, Martina
Hopewell Area HS
Aliquippa, PA

Korenkiewicz, Paula
Garnet Valley HS
Boothwyn, PA

Kormas, Lisa
Villa Maria Acad
Erie, PA

Korowicki, Rachel
Mc Guffey HS
Washington, PA

Korty, Janet K
Richland HS
Johnstown, PA

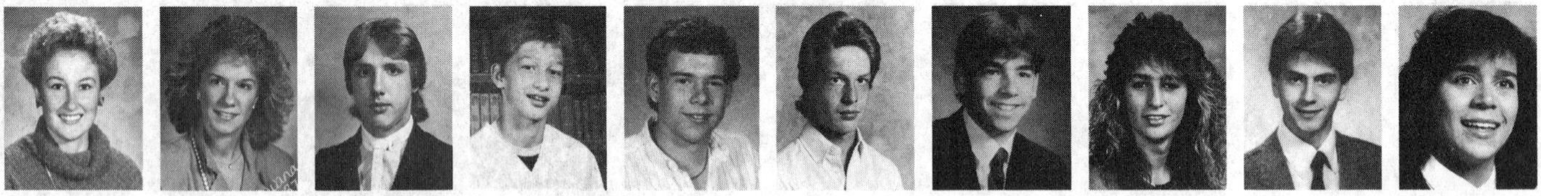

Kosht, Malorie
Seneca Valley HS
Zelienople, PA

Koss, Diana
Central Cambria HS
Revloc, PA

Kossar, Todd
Belle Vernon Area
Belle Vernon, PA

Kossmann, Bill
Hazleton HS
Hazleton, PA

Kostial, Craig
Hempfield SR HS
Greensburg, PA

Kostowskie, John
Shenandoah Valley
Shenandoah, PA

Kostura, III James
Notre Dame HS
Easton, PA

Koszowski, Victoria
Bensalem HS
Bensalem, PA

Kotarski, Anthony
James M Coughlin
Laflin, PA

Kothari, Lisa
Trinity HS
Westlake, OH

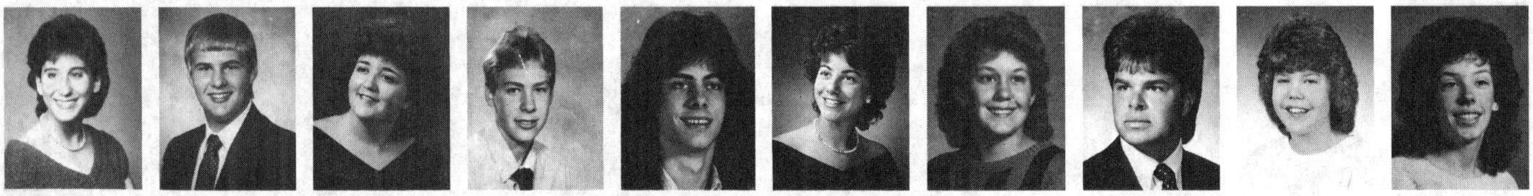

Kotsagrelos, Michelle Marie
Bethel Park SENIOR HS
Bethel Park, PA

Kotsko, John
John S Fine HS
Nanticoke, PA

Kottacmp, Billie
Northeastern HS
Manchester, PA

Kotz, John
John S Fine HS
Nanticoke, PA

Kotzen, Jr Rich
Daniel Boone HS
Birdsboro, PA

Koutoulakis, Diane
Quigley HS
Conway, PA

Kouvolo, Lisa
Ambridge Area HS
Freedom, PA

Kovac, Craig
Freeport HS
Sarver, PA

Kovacic, Shelley
Greater Johnstown SR HS
Johnstown, PA

Koval, Dawna
Center HS
Monaca, PA

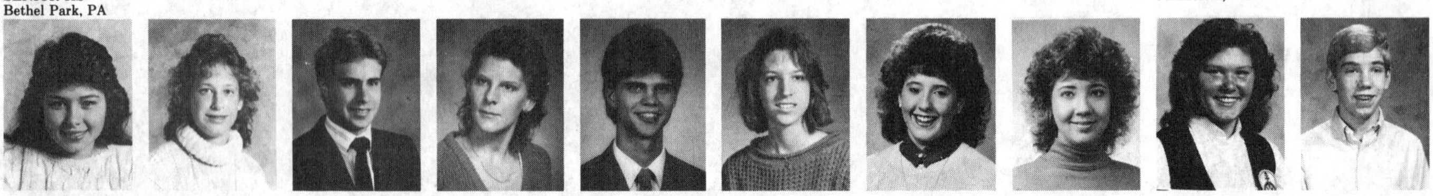

Kovalovich, Karol
Our Lady Of Lourdes Regiona
Strong, PA

Kovatch, Kathy
Panther Valley HS
Nesquehoning, PA

Kovitch, John D
Central Columbia
Bloomsburg, PA

Kowalewski, Caroline
Carmichaels Area
Crucible, PA

Kowalo, Frederick E
Canon Mc Millan
Mcdonald, PA

Kowalski, Sandra
Ambridge Area HS
Baden, PA

Kowalski, Tracey
Mid-Valley HS
Olyphant, PA

Kowell, Paula
Mon Valley Catholic
Monessen, PA

Kowker, Kimberly
Trinity HS
Camp Hill, PA

Kownacki, Paul
Boiling Springs HS
Boiling Spgs, PA

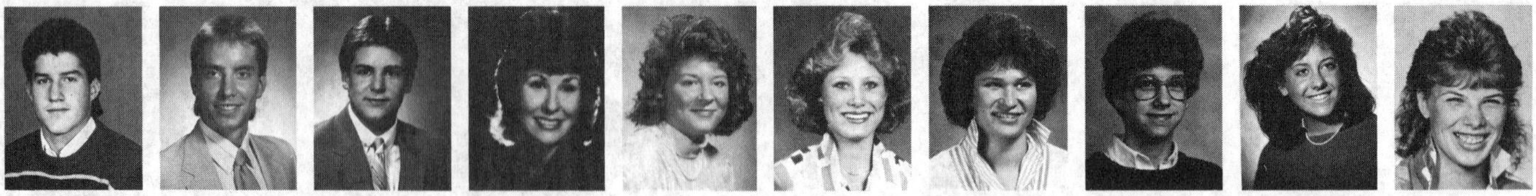

Kozar, Scott
Cornell HS
Coraopolis, PA

Kozden, Michael
Southern Lehigh HS
Center Valley, PA

Kraemer, Eric
Carrick HS
Pittsburgh, PA

Kraft, Melissa
Freedom SR HS
Bethlehem, PA

Krajci, Tracey
Central Bucks HS
New Britain, PA

Kramer, Lisa
Central Dauphin HS
Harrisburg, PA

Krammes, Mary
Tri-Valley HS
Hegins, PA

Krankowski, Kimberly
Lebanon Catholic
Fredericksburg, PA

Krasas, Jennifer L
Academy Of Notre Dame De Namur
Newtown Square, PA

Kraski, Amy
Carrick HS
Pittsburgh, PA

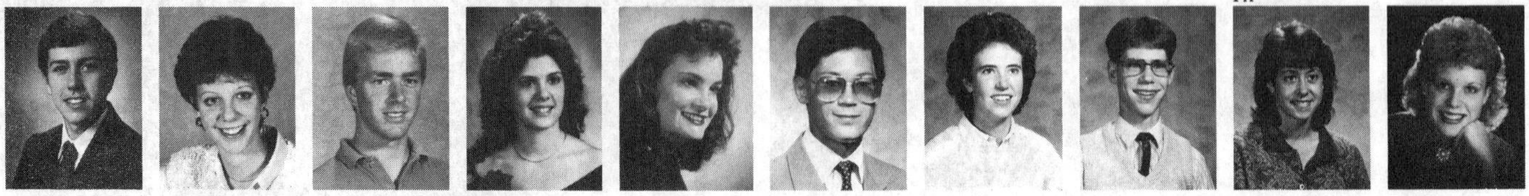

Krater, Bradley
Blair County Christian HS
Altoona, PA

Kratzer, Kimberly Lyn
Emmaus HS
Emmaus, PA

Krause, Christopher J
Conestoga SR HS
Paoli, PA

Krause, Kimberly Ann
Pine Grove Area HS
Pine Grove, PA

Krause, Maura Frances
Franklin Regional
Murrysville, PA

Kraynak, James S
Connellsville Area
Connellsville, PA

Krebs, Michelle L
Christian School Of York, PA

Krebs, Ryan
Christian School Of York, PA

Kreider, Cindy
Lancaster Mennonite HS
Oxford, PA

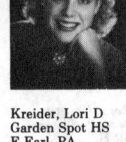

Kreider, Lori D
Garden Spot HS
E Earl, PA

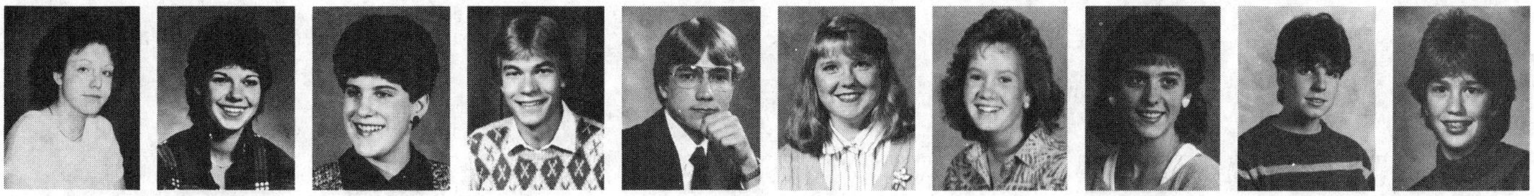

Kreig, Erica
Central Scranton
Scranton, PA

Kreiger, Deanna
West Branch HS
Kylertown, PA

Kreinbrook, Stacy
Connellsville Area
SR HS
Mount Pleasant, PA

Kreiser, Todd M
Eastern Lebanon
County HS
Newmanstown, PA

Kreitzer, Jr Eugene
Northern Lebanon
Fredericksburg, PA

Kremer, Beth
Uniontown Area SR
Uniontown, PA

Krentz, Tammy
Warwick HS
Lititz, PA

Krespan, Stacey
Eisenhower HS
Sugargrove, PA

Kress, Brian
Coughlin HS
Hudson, PA

Kretchmar, Jennifer
State College Area
SR HS
State College, PA

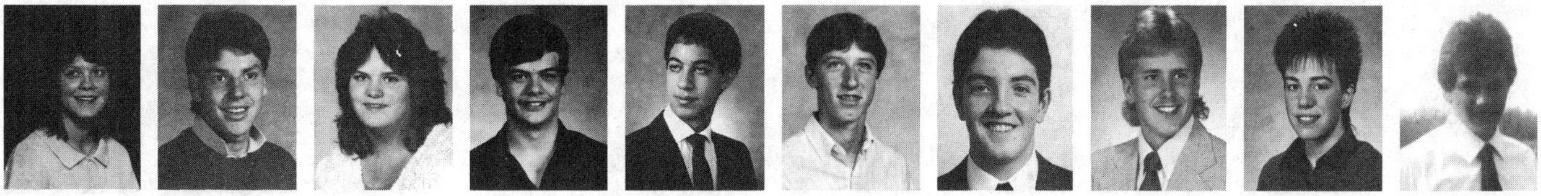

Kreuter, Christine
Belle Vernon Area
Belle Vernon, PA

Krezanosky, Tom
Pottstown SR HS
Pottstown, PA

Krider, Glenda
Tyrone Area HS
Tyrone, PA

Krieger, William
Fort Cherry HS
Mc Donald, PA

Krifcher, Ronald
Shady Side Acad
Uniontown, PA

Kriner, Michael
Lower Dauphin HS
Grantville, PA

Krise, Benjamin
Seneca Valley HS
Mars, PA

Kristen, Scot
Elizabeth Forward
Mckeesport, PA

Kristoff, Jan
Burgettstown Area
JR SR HS
Burgettstown, PA

Kroesen, Rick
Wilmington Area
Pulaski, PA

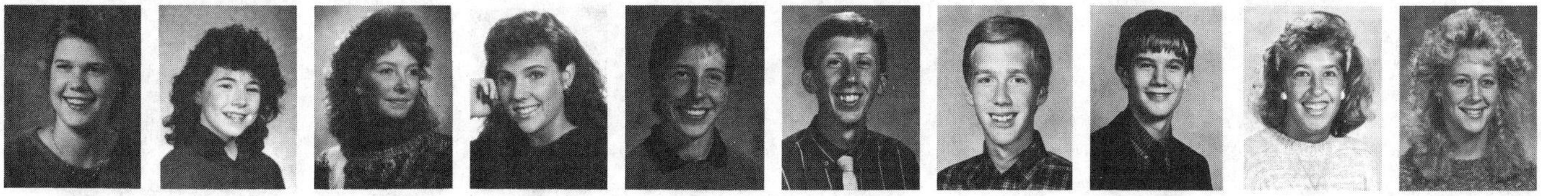

Kroh, Krista
Bradford Area HS
Bradford, PA

Krolick, Amy Jo
Garnet Valley JR
SR HS
Boothwyn, PA

Kropp, Caroline
Lake-Lehman HS
Shavertown, PA

Krous, Krista
Hempfield HS
Lancaster, PA

Krout, Derek
West York HS
York, PA

Krow, Bradley
Steelton-Highspire
Steelton, PA

Krug, Stephen
South Western HS
Hanover, PA

Krull, James
Devon Prep
Strafford, PA

Krum, Leslie
Coatesville Area SR
Coatesville, PA

Kruse, Karla
Penn Manor HS
Millersville, PA

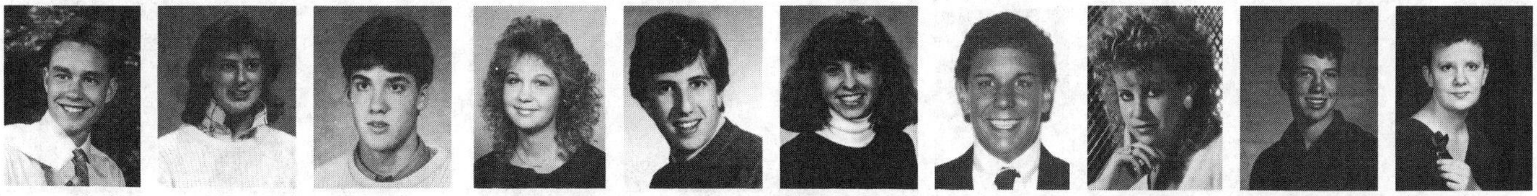

Kruszewski, Joseph
Serra Catholic HS
W Mifflin, PA

Krywokulski, Beth
Newport HS
Newport, PA

Krzeczowski, Kevin
Burgettstown JR/SR
Langeloth, PA

Kubancsek, Wendy
West Mifflin Area
W Mifflin, PA

Kubel, John
Notre Dame HS
Easton, PA

Kubick, Patti
Abington Heights
Falls, PA

Kuczinski, Brian
Chartiers Valley HS
Pittsburgh, PA

Kudlik, Cheryl
Monessen JR-SR
Monessen, PA

Kudrna, John D
Ambridge Area HS
Freedom, PA

Kugler, Michele
Saint Huberts H S
For Girls
Philadelphia, PA

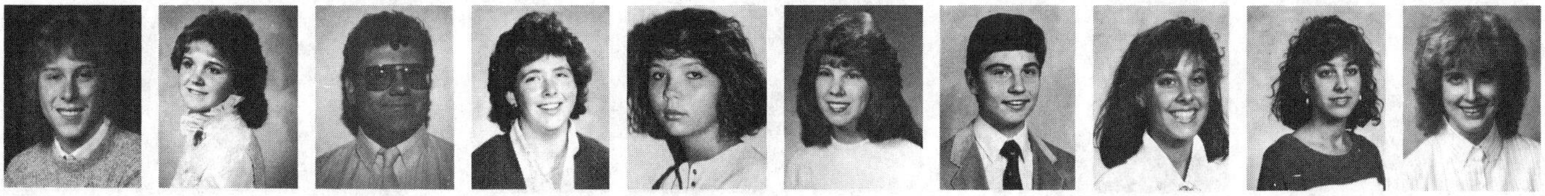

Kuharcik, Frank
Wyoming Valley
West HS
Larksville, PA

Kuhns, Tricia
United HS
Armagh, PA

Kukles, Michael
Pen Argyl Area HS
Pen Argyl, PA

Kuklewicz, Dawn
Hanover JR-SR HS
Sugar Notch, PA

Kulakowski, J
Bianka
State College Area
Lemont, PA

Kulback, Krysteen
Greater Johnstown
Area Vo-Tech Schl
Windber, PA

Kulchar, Andrew C
Devon Prep Schl
Rosemont, PA

Kulick, Dawn Marie
Bishop Mc Devitt
Harrisburg, PA

Kulick, Lisa
Bishop Mc Devitt
Harrisburg, PA

Kulinski, Maria
Forest City Regional
Forest City, PA

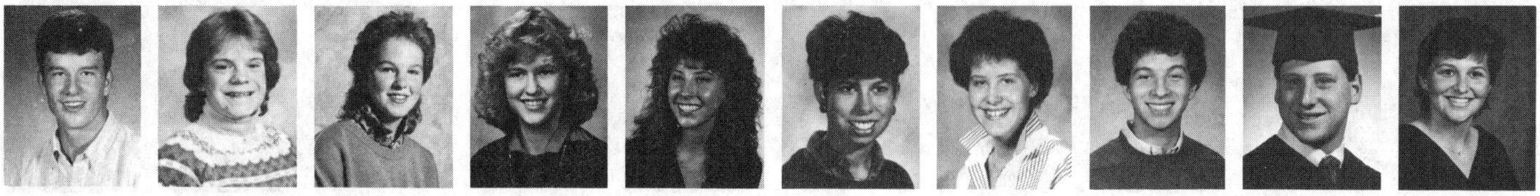

Kunder, Aaron
Monessen HS
Monessen, PA

Kunkely, Tracey
Upper Morehand
Willow Grove, PA

Kunkle, Michelle
Blue Mountain HS
New Ringgold, PA

Kuntz, Debra
Du Bois Area HS
Dubois, PA

Kupchella, Karen
Blacklick Valley HS
Nanty Glo, PA

Kupfer, Jennifer E
Meadville Area SR
Meadville, PA

Kuppelweiser, Toni
Cameron County HS
Driftwood, PA

Kurman, Jeff
Hempfield Area SR
Greensburg, PA

Kurtz, Daniel
Central HS
Philadelphia, PA

Kurtz, Melissa
St Pius X HS
East Greenville, PA

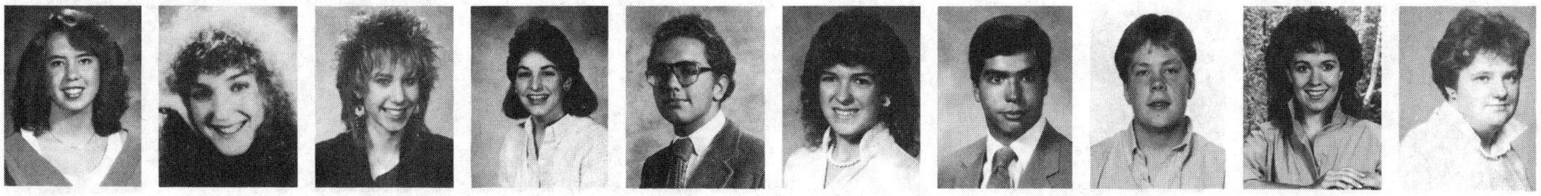

Kurtzrock, Sheila
Shaler Area HS
Glenshaw, PA

Kurzweil, Dena
West Scranton HS
Scranton, PA

Kurzweil, Robyn
West Scranton HS
Scranton, PA

Kustaborder, Laura
Altoona Area HS
Altoona, PA

Kutch, Michael J
Nativity Blessed
Virgin Mary HS
Pottsville, PA

Kutruff, Tammy
Cambria Heights HS
Patton, PA

Kutsick, Gregory
Northern Cambria
Barnesboro, PA

Kutzler, David
Liberty HS
Bethlehem, PA

Kuykendall, Christy
L
Athens HS
Sayre, PA

Kuzio, Nicole
South Allegheny HS
Port Vue, PA

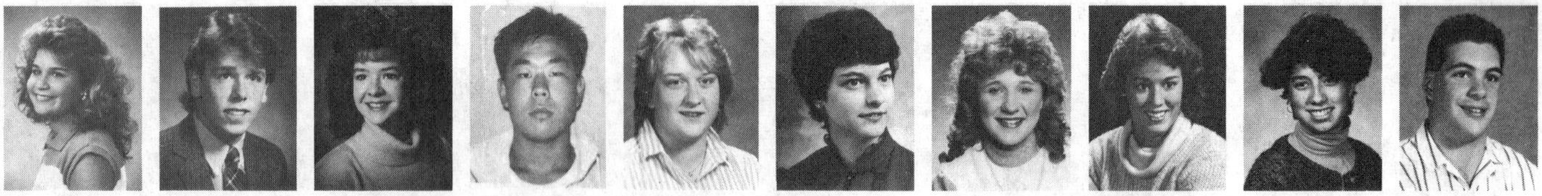

Kuzmiak, Tina Marie
Bishop Mc Cort HS
Johnstown, PA

Kweller, Jon
William Allen HS
Allentown, PA

Kwiatkowski, Ann
West Scranton HS
Scranton, PA

Kwon, Danny
Marple Newtown
Newtown Square, PA

Kyler, Darla
West Branch Area
Kylertown, PA

Kyper, Aleisa E
Mechanicsburg Area SR HS
Grantham, PA

Kytic, Evelyn
Montour HS
Mc Kees Rocks, PA

La Barre, Laurie
Northeast Bradford
Rome, PA

La Luna, Christina
Abington Heights N
Clarks Summit, PA

Labella, Lou
Methalton HS
Eagleville, PA

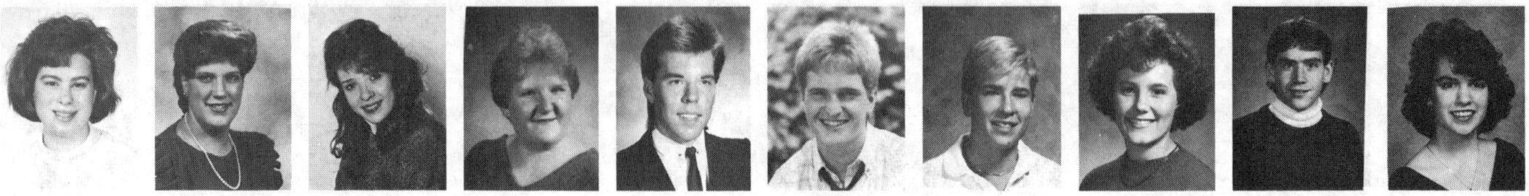

Labella, Reniea
Sto-Rox SR HS
Mckees Rocks, PA

Labenberg, Lynn
W Hazleton HS
Zion Grove, PA

Lacey, Nancy Jo
Bishop Boyle HS
North Braddock, PA

Lachat, Lisa
Lock Haven SR HS
Castanea, PA

Lacount, Rob
Waynesburg Central
Waynesburg, PA

Ladlee, Kenneth
E Stroudsburg HS
E Strdbg, PA

Lagyak, Jeffrey
Steelton-Highspire
Steelton, PA

Lahr, Melissa
Shamokin Area HS
Shamokin, PA

Laidlaw, Patrick
Butler HS
Butler, PA

Lailone, Laura
Cardinal O Hara HS
Broomall, PA

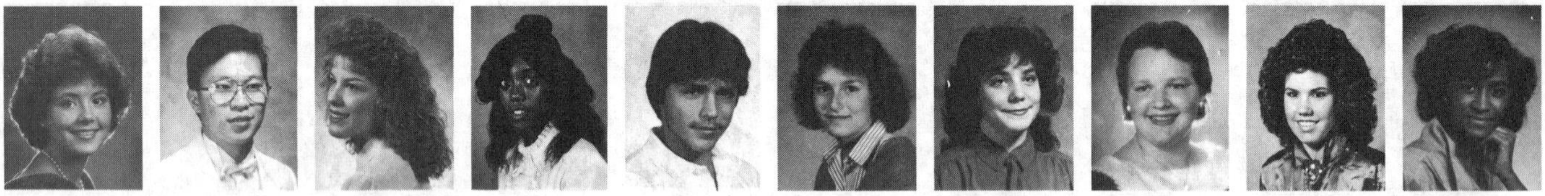

Lakitsky, Michelle
Tamaqua Area HS
Andreas, PA

Lam, Phat
William Penn HS
York, PA

Lambert, Aimee
Ringgold SR HS
Monongahela, PA

Lambert, Vicky
H S Of Performing
Philadelphia, PA

Lambiase, Mario
Liberty HS
Bethlehem, PA

Lamont, Linda
Northern Cambria
Barnesboro, PA

Lamonte, Pamela
Williams Valley HS
Williamstown, PA

Lamoreaux, Paula Mae
Lake Lehman SR
Hunlock Creek, PA

Lampe, Sherri
Southside HS
Shippingport, PA

Lampkins-Fielder, Raina
Quaker Valley SR
Sewickley, PA

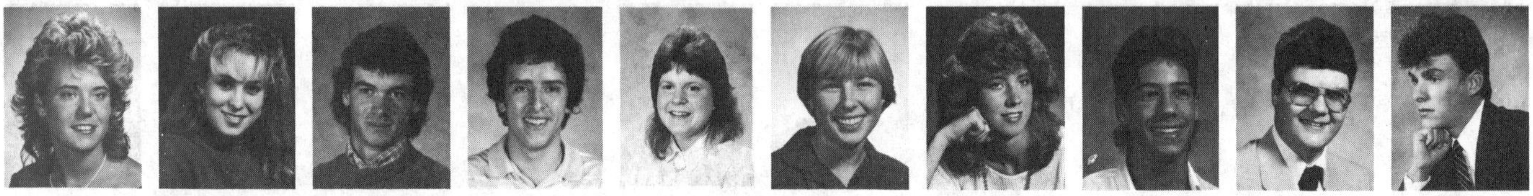

Lance, Barbara
Roxborough HS
Philadelphia, PA

Lance, Hope
Tunkhannock Area
Dalton, PA

Lander, George
Yough SR HS
Rillton, PA

Lander, Martin
Fort Cherry HS
Midway, PA

Lander, Michelle
Burgettstown HS
Joffre, PA

Landerkin, Kelly
Central HS
Makakilo, HI

Landis, Kim
Canton Area JR-SR
Troy, PA

Landis, Paul
Cedar Cliff HS
Mechanicsburg, PA

Landis, Raymond
Souderton Area HS
Hatfield, PA

Landmesser, Chris
Lake-Lehman HS
Shavertown, PA

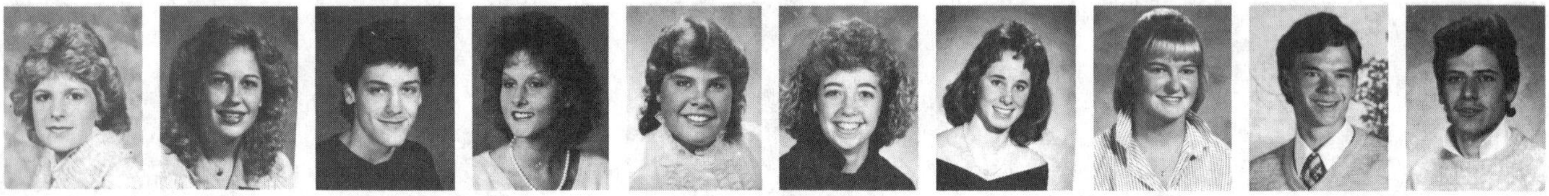

Landmesser, Patricia
Bishop O Reilly HS
Larksville, PA

Landvater, Tricia
Donegal HS
Maytown, PA

Lane, Jr James A
Bethlehem Center
Millsboro, PA

Lang, Colleen
Burrell HS
New Kensington, PA

Lang, Deborah Ann
Cochranton JR SR
Cochranton, PA

Lang, Shelly
Seneca Valley HS
Renfrew, PA

Langan, Karen
Villa Maria Acad
Exton, PA

Langley, Cheryl
Carlisle SR HS
Carlisle, PA

Langstaff, David
West Greene HS
Chagrin Falls, OH

Lannan, Curt
Jersey Shore HS
Jersey Shore, PA

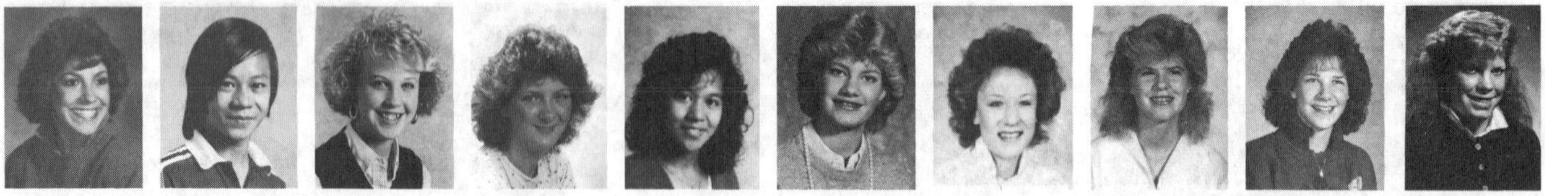

Lanzoni, Sandra Mary
Brockway HS
Brockway, PA

Laov, Pert
H S For Creative & Performing Arts
Philadelphia, PA

Lapp, Candice
York Catholic HS
York, PA

Larouere, Kelly
Norwin SR HS
N Huntingdon, PA

Larrazabal, Emilie
Academy Of Notre Dame De Namur
Glen Mills, PA

Larsen, Andrea
Dallastown Area HS
York, PA

Larsen, Heather
Northwestern HS
Albion, PA

Larsen, Michelle
Steelton-Highspire
Highspire, PA

Larson, April
Methacton SR HS
Worcester, PA

Larson, Kim
Wilmington Area
New Castle, PA

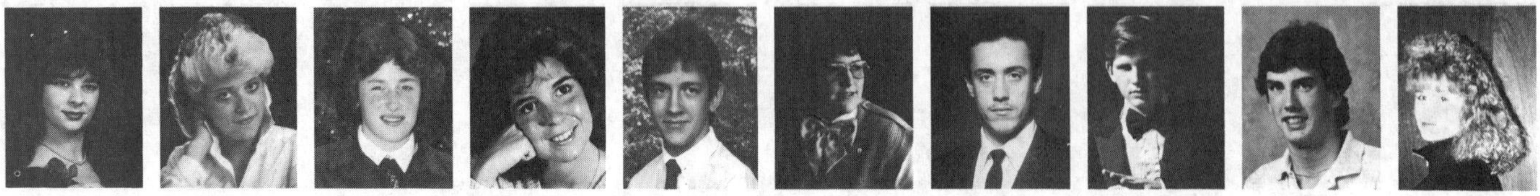

Lasanta, Lisa
West Catholic Girls
Philadelphia, PA

Lasher, Candy
Mercer Area JR SR
Mercer, PA

Lasher, Tammy
Annville-Cleona HS
Lebanon, PA

Lashley, Tracie
Bedford HS
Bedford, PA

Lassak, Randy
Central Dauphin HS
Harrisburg, PA

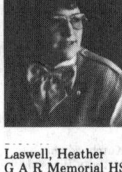

Laswell, Heather
G A R Memorial HS
Wilkes-Barre, PA

Latchem, Brian
Mon Valley HS
Monessen, PA

Laterza, Sam
Downington SR HS
Downington, PA

Latimer, Patrick
Warren Area HS
Sheffield, PA

Latina, Raena
Henderson HS
West Chester, PA

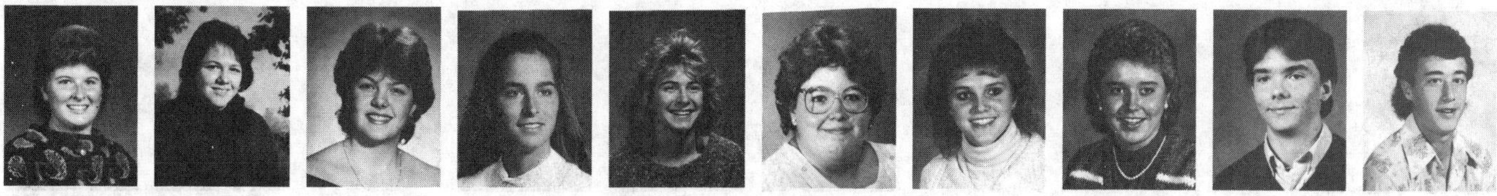

Latsha, Lucinda
Upper Dauphin Area HS
Pillow, PA

Laubenstein, Kathy
Schuylkill Haven Area HS
Schuylkill Haven, PA

Lauber, Ellen
Villa Maria Acad
West Chester, PA

Lauchlan, Christina
Cumberland Valley
Mechanicsburg, PA

Lauchnor, Debbi
Emmaus HS
Allentown, PA

Lauer, Lisa
Shanksville Stonycreek HS
Friedens, PA

Laughlin, Amy
Union HS
Sligo, PA

Laughlin, Mary
Union HS
Rimersburg, PA

Laughlin, Rick
South Side HS
Hookstown, PA

Laurento, David
Coatesville Area SR
Coatesville, PA

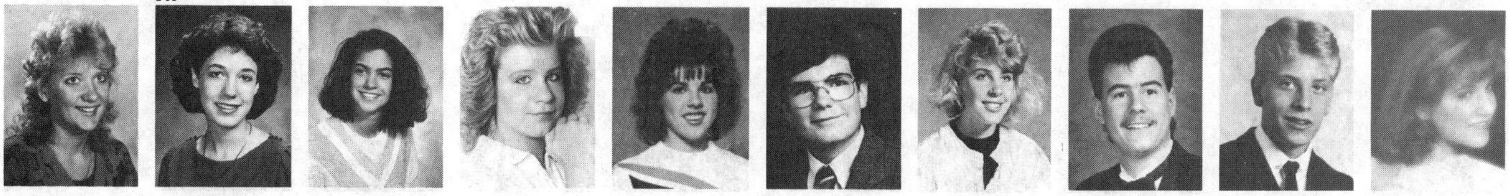

Laurnoff, Amy
Mercyhurst Prep
Erie, PA

Lawler, Jane
Bishop Mc Devitt
Harrisburg, PA

Lawley, Heather
Dallas SR HS
Shaverstown, PA

Lawniczak, Lori
Moniteau HS
West Sunbury, PA

Lawrence, Christina
Panther Valley HS
Summit Hill, PA

Lawrence, Dwayne N
Northern York HS
Dillsburg, PA

Lawrence, Kristin
Owen J Roberts HS
Coventryville, PA

Lawson, Jerry
St John Neumann
Philadelphia, PA

Lazar, Gregory
Bishop Hafey HS
Beaver Mdws, PA

Lazorchick, Susan
Emmaus HS
Allentown, PA

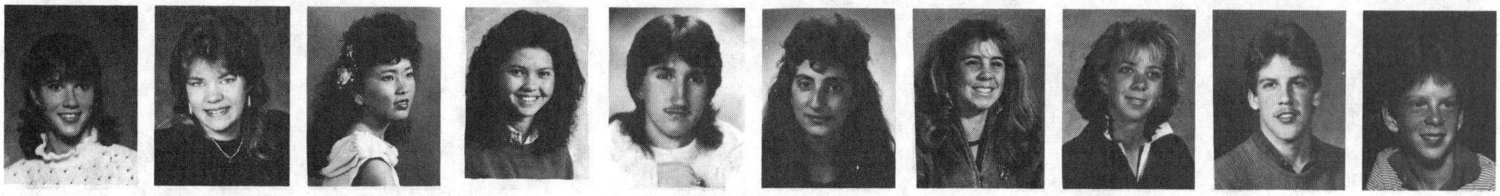

Lazur, Ranee
Tamaqua Area HS
Tamaqua, PA

Lazzaretti, Judy
Our Lady Of The Sacred Heart HS
Ambridge, PA

Le, Nga Kim
William Penn HS
York, PA

Le, Nguyet
York Catholic HS
York, PA

Le Febvre, Jerome
Western Beaver HS
Industry, PA

Le Par, Felice
Abington SR HS
Rydal, PA

Le Pera, Keely Marie
Mt Saint Joseph
Upper Southampton, PA

Le Pera, Krista
Mt Saint Joseph
Upper Southampton, PA

Leach, Daniel
Mon Valley Catholic
Monongahela, PA

Leach, Patrick
Mon Valley Catholic
Monongahela, PA

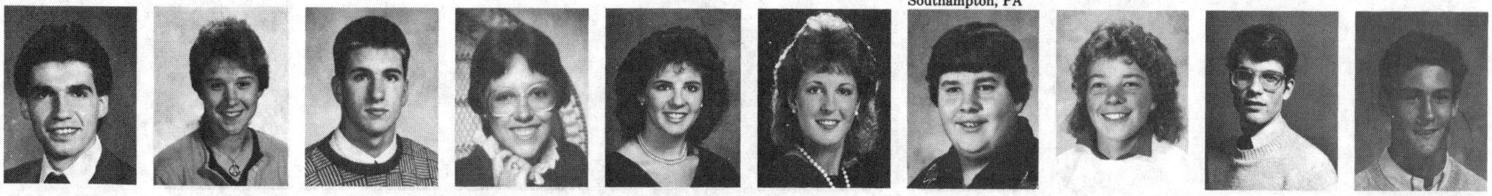

Leandro, Paulo
Cambridge Springs
Cambridge Spgs, PA

Leap, Karen
Greater Johnstown
Johnstown, PA

Lear, Christian
Upper Moreland HS
Willow Grove, PA

Lear, Heather
Crestwood JR/SR
Mountaintop, PA

Leardi, Mary
Cardinal Ohara HS
Springfield, PA

Leasgang, Lisa
St Marys Area HS
Kersey, PA

Leasure, Tom
Hempfield SR HS
Hunker, PA

Leatherman, Michelle
Wellsboro SR HS
Wellsboro, PA

Leatherman, Neal B
Hope Christian
Tamaqua, PA

Lebda, Douglas R
Lewisburg HS
Lewisburg, PA

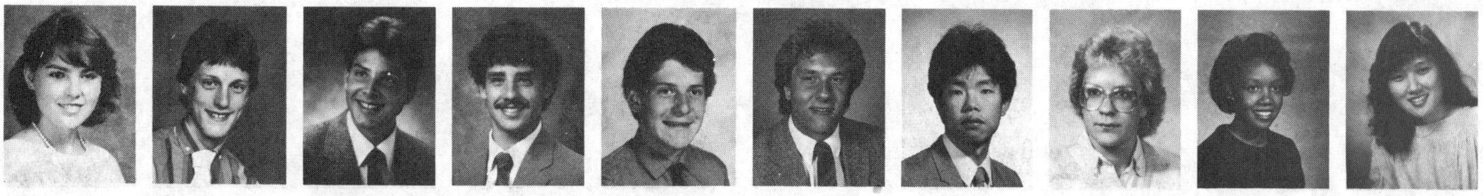

Lebiedzinski, Karen M
Mount Saint Joseph
Warminster, PA

Lecher, Mark Christopher
Blue Ridge HS
Great Bend, PA

Lechman, Eric R
Center HS
Aliquippa, PA

Lechner, Brian
Bradford SR HS
Bradford, PA

Lecrone, K Mark
Spring Grove Area
Spring Grove, PA

Lee, Bill
Palmyra HS
Palmyra, PA

Lee, Chi
Central HS
Philadelphia, PA

Lee, Diane
Portage Area HS
Portage, PA

Lee, Gina
Mathaeton SR HS
Eagleville, PA

Lee, Hee Sun
Meadville Area SR
Meadville, PA

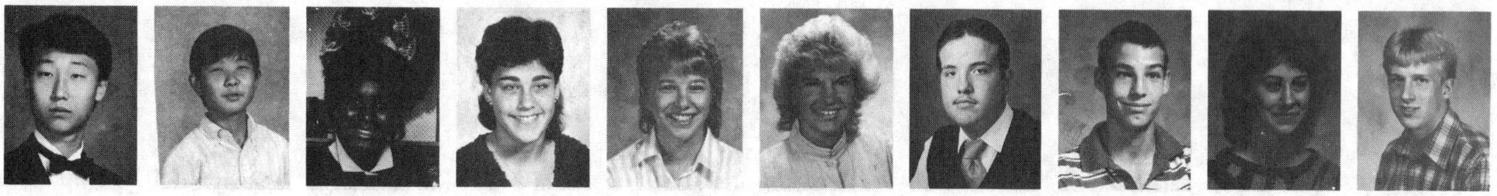

Lee, Peter
Cardinal O Hara HS
Broomall, PA

Lee, Roger
Conestoga SR HS
Berwyn, PA

Lee, Teresa
Coatesville HS
Coatesville, PA

Leech, Sandra
Gettysburg HS
Gettysburg, PA

Leeds, Stephanie
West Snyder HS
Middleburg, PA

Leedy, Kristina
Lower Dauphin HS
Palmyra, PA

Leeper, Jr Frank
Northern Lebanon
Jonestown, PA

Leese, Bryan
Boiling Springs HS
Dillsburg, PA

Lefever, Kimberly
Elizabethtown Area
Mt Joy, PA

Lefevre, Douglas
Brookville Area HS
Brookville, PA

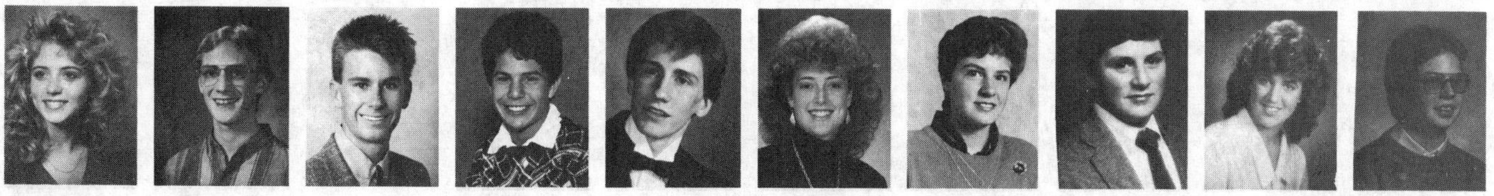

Legge, Jennifer A
Greater Latrobe SR
Latrobe, PA

Legler, Jeffrey
Washington HS
Washington, PA

Lehman, David
Cheltenham HS
Cheltenham, PA

Lehmann, Christopher
Pennsbury HS
Yardley, PA

Lehmann, Richard
Northeast Catholic
Philadelphia, PA

Lehner, Amy
Elizabeth Forward
Mckeesport, PA

Lehnert, Jennifer L
Bishop Hoban HS
Mt Top, PA

Lehnert, Richard
M M I Prepatory
Mountaintop, PA

Lehr, Debra
Northampton Area SR HS
Treichlers, PA

Leib, Mike
Boiling Springs HS
Mt Holly Spgs, PA

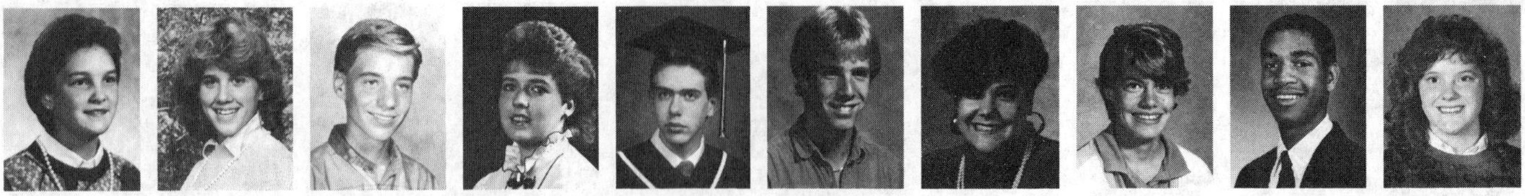

Leibman, Karen
James M Coughlin
Wilkes Barre, PA

Leidich, Dawn
Wilson Area HS
Easton, PA

Leidig, Jeffrey
Chambersburg Area SR HS
Chambersburg, PA

Leidy, Pamela
Mount Union Area
Shirleysburg, PA

Leighthardt, Joseph
Archbishop Ryan HS For Boys
Philadelphia, PA

Leinbach, Jeffrey
Biglerville HS
Biglerville, PA

Leister, Monica
Avonworth JR/SR
Sewickley, PA

Leister, Pamela L
Boyertown JR High East Center
Gilbertsville, PA

Leisure, London
Pottstown SR HS
Pottstown, PA

Lemley, Sandra
Waynesburg Central
Waynesburg, PA

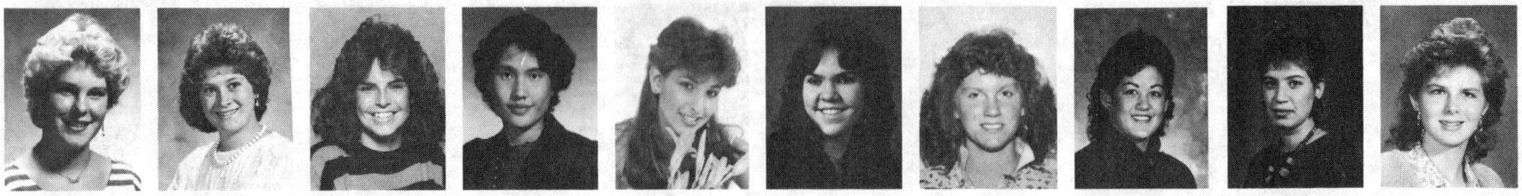

Lenn, Marie
Union Area HS
New Castle, PA

Lenz, Mary
Indiana SR HS
Indiana, PA

Leo, Darcy
Hickory HS
Hermitage, PA

Leon, Jeanette
Notre Dame HS
Nazareth, PA

Leon, Sandra
Northern HS
Dillsburg, PA

Leonard, Lucinda
Tidioute HS
Warren, PA

Leonard, Marsha
Penncrest HS
Media, PA

Leonard, Susan
Chichester SR HS
Boothwyn, PA

Leone, Tina
Tunkhannock HS
Mehoopany, PA

Leonowicz, Beverly
Bishop Conwell HS
Bensalem, PA

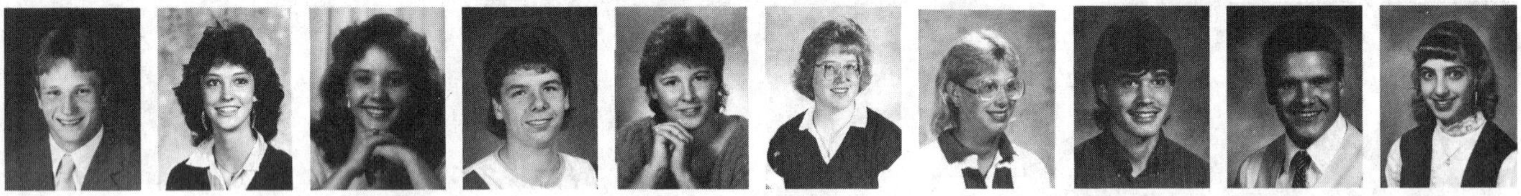

Lepley, Michael A
West Snyder HS
Beaver Spgs, PA

Lerch, Christina Elizabeth
Interboro HS
Glenolden, PA

Lerch, Jennifer
Pen Argyl HS
Nazareth, PA

Lesako, Mark
Bethlehem Center
Brownsville, PA

Lese, Vickie
Bentworth HS
Bentleyville, PA

Lesher, Beth
Reading SR HS
Reading, PA

Lesher, Cynthia
Cocalico HS
Denver, PA

Lesher, Donald
Cocalico HS
Reinholds, PA

Lesher, Jr James M
Upper Dauphin Area HS
Gratz, PA

Lesher, Juliana
Gateway Christian
Kutztown, PA

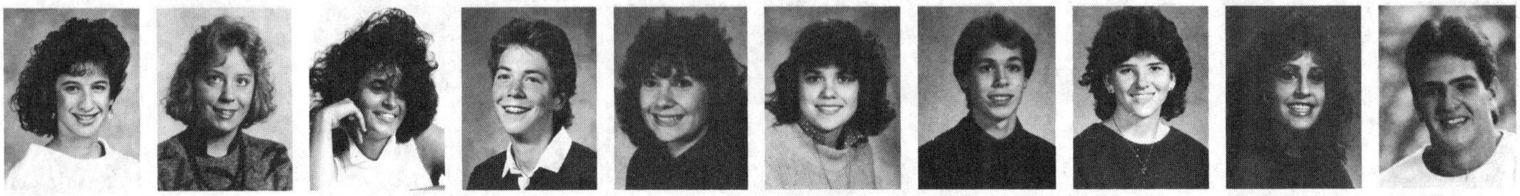

Leshner, Sharon
Bensalem SR HS
Bensalem, PA

Lesko, Maureen
Cardinal Brennan
Shenandoah, PA

Lesko, Rachel
Serra Central HS
Duquesne, PA

Leslie, Jonathan
Gateway HS
Monroeville, PA

Lesnak, Danielle
Young SR HS
West Newton, PA

Lesney, Melissa
Butler Area HS
Butler, PA

Lessig, Kurt
Exeter SR HS
Reading, PA

Lester, Karen L
Boyertown JR High
Perkiomenville, PA

Lester, Melissa
Punxsutawney Area
Punxsutawney, PA

Lettieri, Michael
Old Forge HS
Old Forge, PA

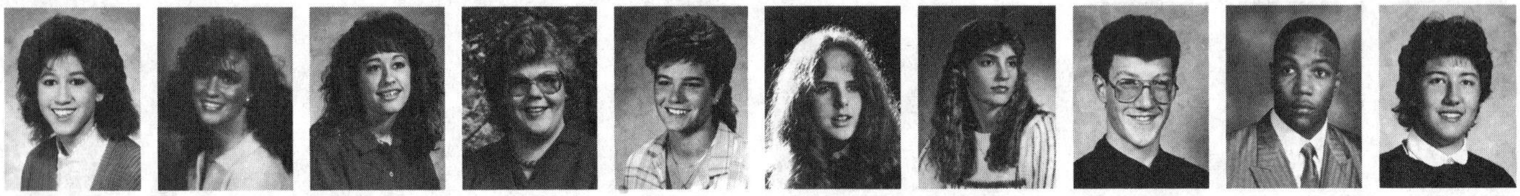

Levenduski, Ann
Saint Marys Area
Weedville, PA

Levin, Jennifer
Hempfield HS
Lancaster, PA

Levin, Jodi
Council Rock HS
Newtown, PA

Levin, Wendy
Clearfield Area HS
Clearfield, PA

Levine, Amy
West Greene HS
Holbrook, PA

Levitas, Allyson S
Lower Merion HS
Ardmore, PA

Lewgood, Leslie
Monessen JR-SR
Monessen, PA

Lewinger, Alex
Academy HS
Erie, PA

Lewis, Aaron
Susquehanna Township HS
Harrisburg, PA

Lewis, Bethany
West Perry HS
New Bloomfield, PA

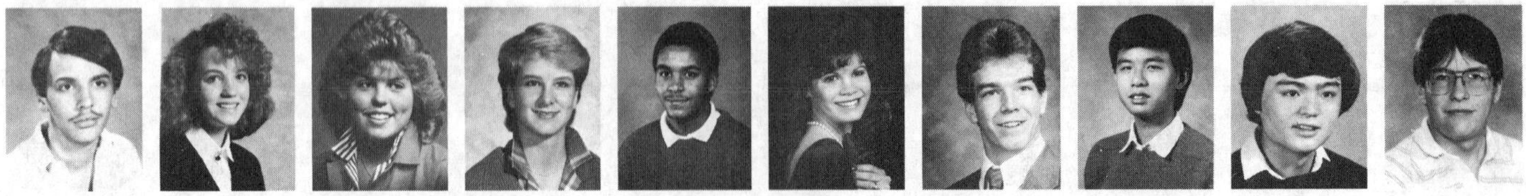

Lewis, Jr Dana
Harbor Creek JRSR
Erie, PA

Lewis, Dana C
Nativity BVM HS
Pottsville, PA

Lewis, Debra
Harry S Truman HS
Levittown, PA

Lewis, Dionee
Northumberland Christian Schl
Northumberland, PA

Lewis, Edward
Cornell HS
Coraopolis, PA

Lex, Michele
Cardinal O Hara HS
Aston, PA

Lezynski, Michael D
Archbishop Wood Boys HS
Holland, PA

Liang, Michael
Gateway SR HS
Monroeville, PA

Liaw, Danny
Plymouth-Whitemarsh HS
Lafayette Hill, PA

Libus, Christopher
John S Fine SR HS
Nanticoke, PA

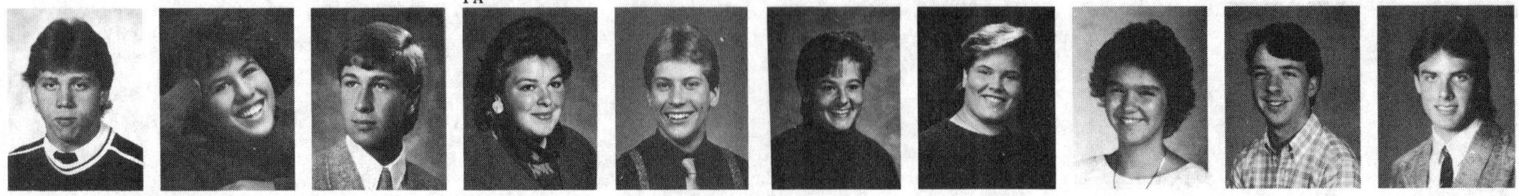

Lichtenberger, Paul
Oil City SR HS
Oil City, PA

Licker, Lorane
Lebanon HS
Lebanon, PA

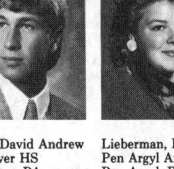

Lieb, David Andrew
Hanover HS
Hanover, PA

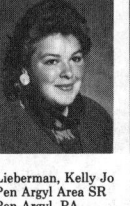

Lieberman, Kelly Jo
Pen Argyl Area SR
Pen Argyl, PA

Lieberum, Michael
West Mifflin Area
W Mifflin, PA

Lied, Jodi
Cocalico HS
Reinholds, PA

Lied, Tracy
Ephrata SR HS
Ephrata, PA

Lienard, Sherilyn
Canon Mc Millan
Mc Donald, PA

Lightner, Mike
Hollidaysburg Area SR HS
Duncansville, PA

Lilly, Jr Gary James
Highlands SR HS
Natrona Hgts, PA

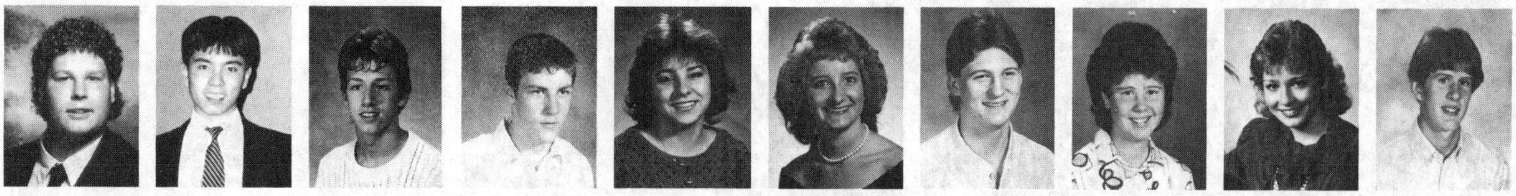

Limbacher, John E
Knoch JR SR HS
Saxonburg, PA

Lin, Dave
Emmaus HS
Allentown, PA

Lindauer, David
Yough SR HS
W Newton, PA

Lindemuth, Stan
Brockway Area HS
Reynoldsville, PA

Linder, Ilona A
Shaler SR HS
Glenshaw, PA

Lindner, Alyse M
North Penn HS
North Wales, PA

Lindner, Jeffrey
Lincoln HS
Ellwood City, PA

Lindsey, Lori
Mohawk JR/SR HS
New Castle, PA

Lindsey, Sherry
Northampton Area
SR HS
Northampton, PA

Lingle, Don
Grove City HS
Grove City, PA

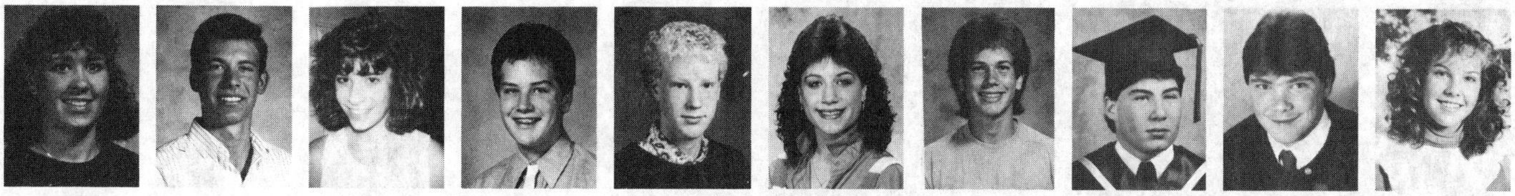

Link, Carey
Susquenita HS
New Buffalo, PA

Link, John
West York SR HS
York, PA

Link, Kristin
Gwynedd Mercy
Bluebell, PA

Link, Matthew
Cambria Heights SR
Dysart, PA

Linn, Andy
Central Dauphin HS
Harrisburg, PA

Linn, Jennifer
Bald Eagle-Nittany
Mill Hall, PA

Linn, Ken
Greenwood HS
Liverpool, PA

Linus, Joseph
Bishop Egau HS
Yardley, PA

Lipinski, Jospeh
Scranton Central
Scranton, PA

Lipinski, Leane
Bishop O Reilly HS
Swoyersville, PA

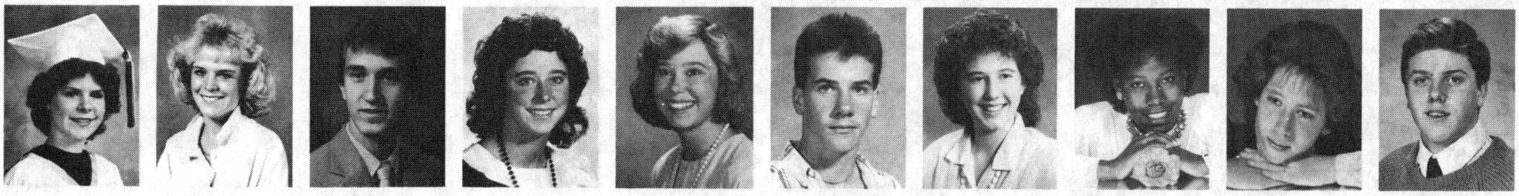

Lipp, Theresa
St Hubert Catholic
HS For Girls
Philadelphia, PA

Lippencott, Erin
Peters Township HS
Mc Murray, PA

Lishinsky, David
Punxsutawney Area
Punxsutawney, PA

Lishman, Amy
Brandywine Heights
Topton, PA

Lishman, Jennifer
Brandywine Heights
Area HS
Topton, PA

List, Kevin
Oxford Area HS
Oxford, PA

Liszcz, Lydia I
Garden Spot HS
Terre Hill, PA

Little, Crystal
Lynne
Mc Keesport SR HS
Mckeesport, PA

Little, Sandy
Mary Fuller Frazier
Perryopolis, PA

Litzelman, Brian
Liberty JR SR HS
Liberty, PA

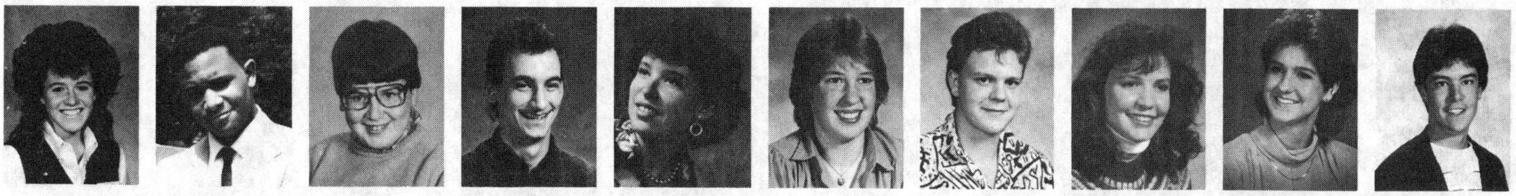

Livermore, Patrice
Nazareth Acad
Phila, PA

Livingston, Edward
G Washington
Carver HS Engrn
Philadelphia, PA

Livolsi, Jeffrey
Canon-Mc Millan
JR HS
Cecil, PA

Lo Faso, Randall
Lincoln HS
Ellwood City, PA

Lobaugh, Tamara
Biglerville HS
Aspers, PA

Loch, Amy
Elk Lake HS
Springville, PA

Loch, James
Mountain View JR/
SR HS
Nicholson, PA

Lockard, Jennifer
Immaculate
Conception HS
Washington, PA

Lockerman, Laurie
Vincentian HS
Pittsburgh, PA

Loeb, Richard
Ridley HS
Woodlyn, PA

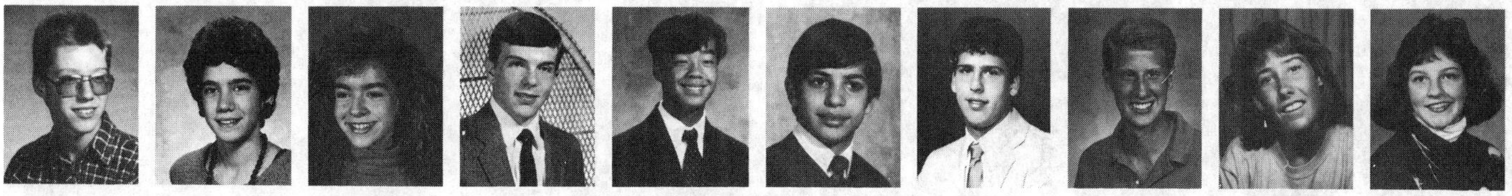

Loedding, Mark
Ambridge Area HS
Sewickley, PA

Loeffler, Julia
St Marys Area HS
St Marys, PA

Logan, Lara
Connellsville Area
Connellsville, PA

Loghing, David L
Lower Moreland HS
Huntingdon Vly, PA

Loh, Lawrence
Carlisle SR HS
Carlisle, PA

Loielo, Daniel
Central HS
Philadelphia, PA

Lomago, Dean
Ringgold HS
Monongahela, PA

Lomax, Andrew
York Suburban HS
York, PA

Lombard, Barbara
Gwynedd-Mercy
Centre Sq, PA

Lombardi, Becky
Mon Valley Catholic
Charleroi, PA

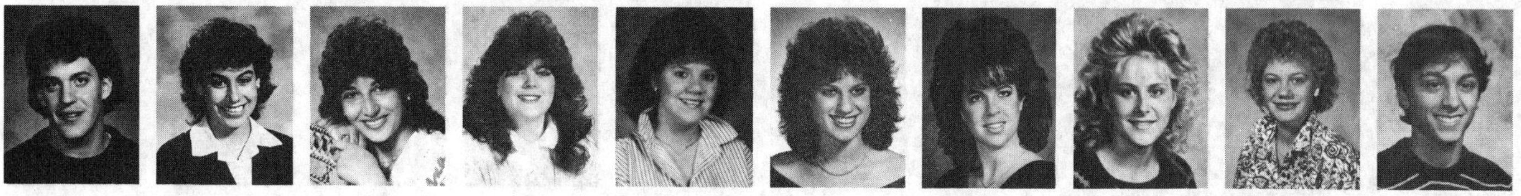

Lombardi,
Christopher
Ringgold HS
Finleyville, PA

Lombardo, Alicia
Bishop Guilfoyle HS
Altoona, PA

Lombardo, Diana
Mohawk JR SR HS
New Castle, PA

Lombardo, Donna
Exeter Township SR
Birdsboro, PA

Lonczynski, Jeanine
West Hazleton HS
W Hazleton, PA

London, Susan
Upper Merion Area
King Of Prussa, PA

Lonergan, Lauren
Cardinal O Hara HS
Broomall, PA

Long, Andrea
Quakertown SR HS
Quakertown, PA

Long, Carleen M
Cambria Heights SR
Carrolltown, PA

Long, Gordon
Shamokin Area HS
Shamokin, PA

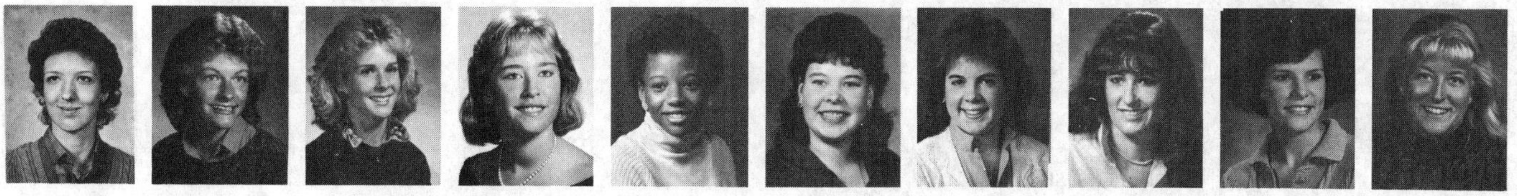

Long, Julie
Northwestern HS
W Springfield, PA

Long, Kelli
Lehighton Area HS
Lehighton, PA

Long, Kristine
Valley HS
New Kensington,
PA

Long, Sandy
Downingtown HS
Downingtown, PA

Long, Sheree
Washington HS
Washington, PA

Long, Stacey
Monongahela Valley
Cath HS
Beallsville, PA

Longacre, Tammy
East Juniata HS
Richfield, PA

Longenbach, Lynn
Allentown Central
Catholic HS
Allentown, PA

Longenberger, Lori
Bloomsburg HS
Bloomsburg, PA

Longenecker, Amy
Lebanon SR HS
Lebanon, PA

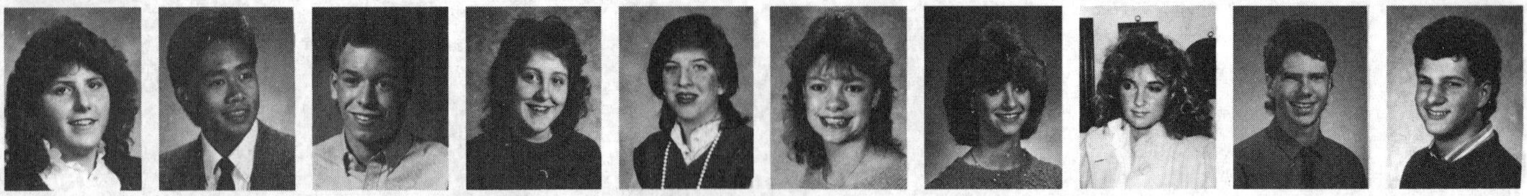

Longley, Jennifer Jo
Nazareth Area SR
Easton, PA

Lopez, Donato
Pennsbury HS
Fairless Hills, PA

Lopus, Allen
Peters Township HS
Venetia, PA

Lorah, Tammy
Lehighton Area HS
Lehighton, PA

Lord, Cynthia
Altoona Area HS
Altoona, PA

Lord, Laura
Yough HS
Irwin, PA

Lorelli, Lisa
Punxsutawney Area
Punxsutawney, PA

Lorence, Colleen
Peters Township HS
Mc Murray, PA

Lorigan, Brian
Bishop O Reilly HS
Edwardsville, PA

Loriso, Anthony
Burgettstown JR-SR
Coraopolis, PA

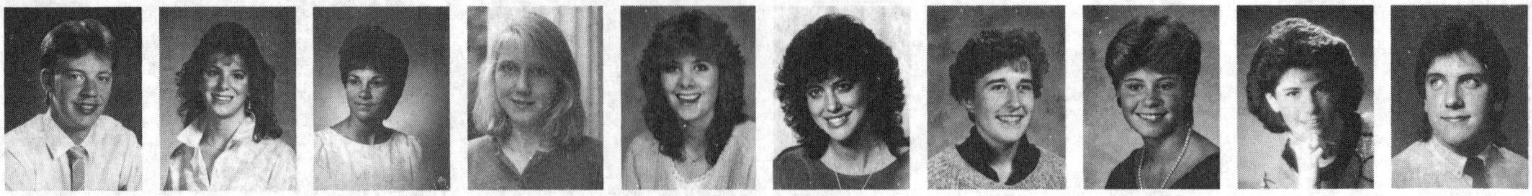

Lorkovich, Paul
Aliquippa HS
Aliquippa, PA

Losca, Tina
Ambridge HS
Sewickley, PA

Losten, Diane E
Jeannette SR HS
Jeannette, PA

Lottick, Karen
Wyoming Seminary
Kingston, PA

Loudenslager, Susan R
Elkland Area HS
Elkland, PA

Louder, Dana
Clarion Area HS
Clarion, PA

Loughman, Kathleen
Governor Mifflin HS
Shillington, PA

Loughman, Marci
West Greene HS
Sycamore, PA

Loving, Debbie
Bethlehem Catholic
Hellertown, PA

Loving, George
Upper Darby HS
Drexel Hill, PA

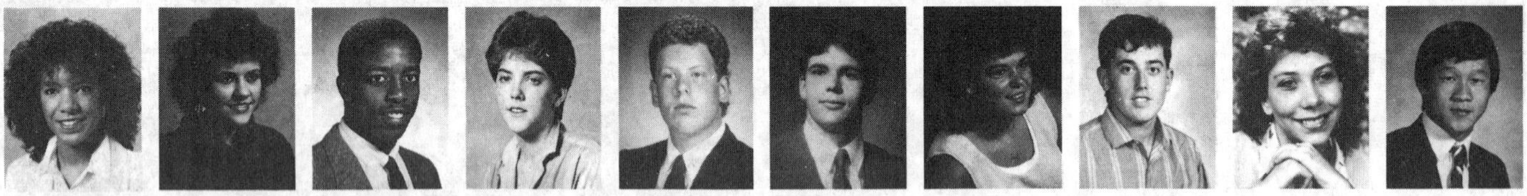

Loving, Lela
East Allegheny HS
East Mc Keesport, PA

Lovis, Michele
Frazier Mem JR SR
Vanderbilt, PA

Lowe, Rod
Great Valley SR HS
Malvern, PA

Lowry, Sharon
Riverside HS
Beaver Falls, PA

Lowry, Tim
Fort Cherry HS
Washington, PA

Lowson, Alan
Waynesboro Area SR HS
Mont Alto, PA

Lowther, Amy
Connellsville Area SR HS
Vanderbilt, PA

Loy, Richard J
Quakertown SR HS
Pennsburg, PA

Lozinak, Lisa
Forest City Regional
Forest City, PA

Lu, That
Unionville HS
Embreeville, PA

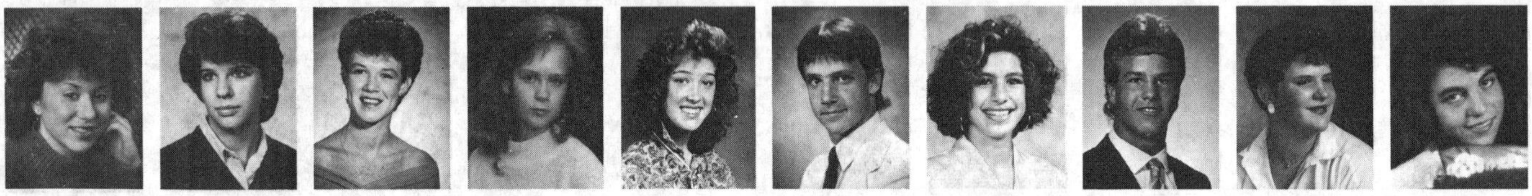

Lubert, Michelle
Monaca JR SR HS
Monaca, PA

Lucas, Jennifer
Emmaus HS
Emmaus, PA

Lucas, Kimberly
Ridley HS
Morton, PA

Lucas, Lisa
Cashs HS
Chambersburg, PA

Lucas, Shane
Shikellamy HS
Sunbury, PA

Lucas, Tim
Mt Pleasant Area SR HS
Mt Pleasant, PA

Lucci, Stephanie
Pennsbury HS
Yardley, PA

Lucerne, David
Downington SR HS
Downingtown, PA

Luckenbaugh, Kimberly S
Newoxford SR HS
Hanover, PA

Ludt, Shari L
Big Spring HS
Carlisle, PA

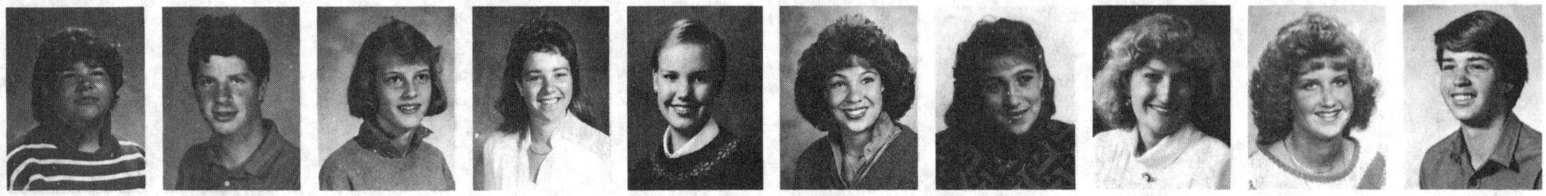

Ludwig, Tammy
Cocalico HS
Denver, PA

Lugg, Robert
Elkland Area HS
Nelson, PA

Lukasavage, Allyson
Lake Lehman HS
Dallas, PA

Lundberg, Marcie
Brockway Area HS
Brockway, PA

Lundvall, Christine
Lewistown Area HS
Lewistown, PA

Lupinetti, Andrea
Penn Cambria SR
Gallitzin, PA

Lure, Rebecca
State College Area SR HS
State College, PA

Lurowist, Kristin
Central Columbia
Bloomsburg, PA

Lusckay, Dori
West Mifflin Area
W Mifflin, PA

Lusk, Steve
Chapel Christian
Bentleyville, PA

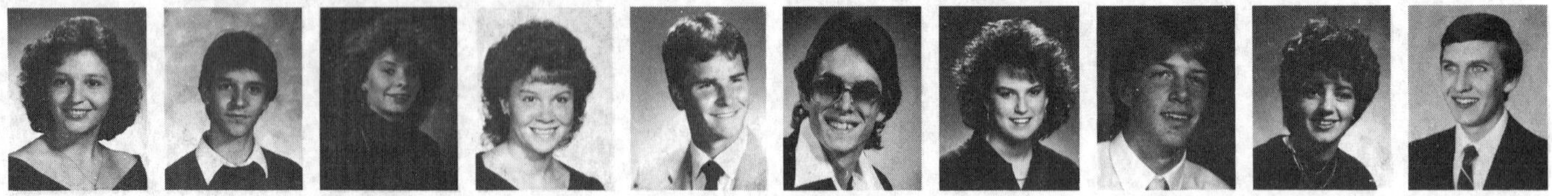

Lutcavage, Catherine
Spring-Ford SR HS
Royersford, PA

Lutcavage, Christopher
Danville HS
Danville, PA

Lutes, Andrea
Washington HS
Washington, PA

Lutes, Judy
Carrick HS
Pittsburgh, PA

Lutterschmidt, Timothy
William Allen HS
Allentown, PA

Lutz, George
Columbia Montour
Danville, PA

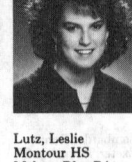

Lutz, Leslie
Montour HS
Mckees Rks, PA

Lutz, Matthew
Immaculate Conception HS
Washington, PA

Lutz, Susan
Wilmington Area
Volant, PA

Luyk, Derek A
Burrell SR HS
Lower Burrell, PA

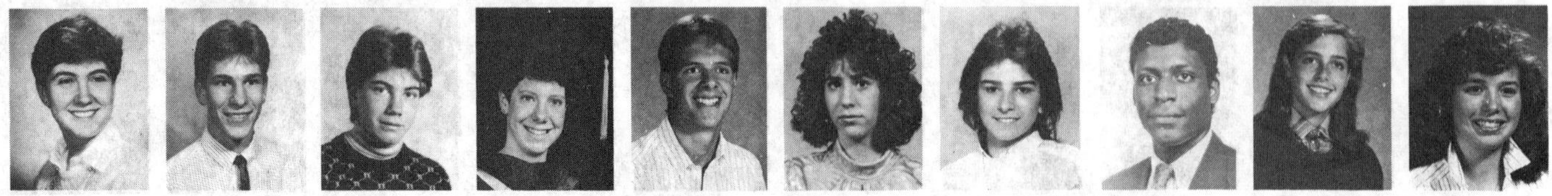

Lynch, Beth A
Blue Mountain HS
Orwigsburg, PA

Lynch, Brian
Meadville Area SR
Meadville, PA

Lynch, Christopher
Coughlin HS
Wilkes-Barre, PA

Lynch, Kathleen V
Cardinal Dougherty
Cheltenham, PA

Lynn, Donald
Downingtown HS
Downingtown, PA

Lyon, Melissa
Caron Mc Millan
Eighty Four, PA

Ma Coy, Denise J
Big Spring HS
Shippensburg, PA

Ma Lone, Christopher
Moon SR HS
Coraopolis, PA

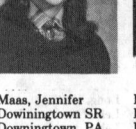

Maas, Jennifer
Dowiningtown SR
Downingtown, PA

Maas, Michele
Fairview HS
Fairview, PA

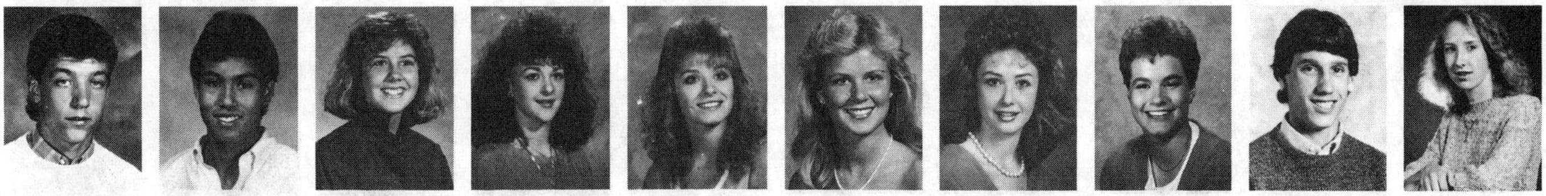

Mac Arthur,
Douglas
Strong Vincent HS
Erie, PA

Mac Donald, Mark
State Coll Area
Intermediate HS
State College, PA

Mac Kinney,
Katherine
Downingtown SR
Exton, PA

Mac Lure, Anne
Marie
Archbishop
Prendergast HS
Havertown, PA

Mac Murray,
Patricia
Cedar Cliff HS
Camp Hill, PA

Macaulay, Catherine
Lower Moreland HS
Huntingdon Valley,
PA

Machamer, Jodi
Cardinal O Hara HS
Parkside, PA

Machinak, Darla
Jefferson-Morgan
Clarksville, PA

Machulsky, Michael
Coughlin HS
Plains, PA

Macijowsky, Carrie
Tunkhannock Area
Dalton, PA

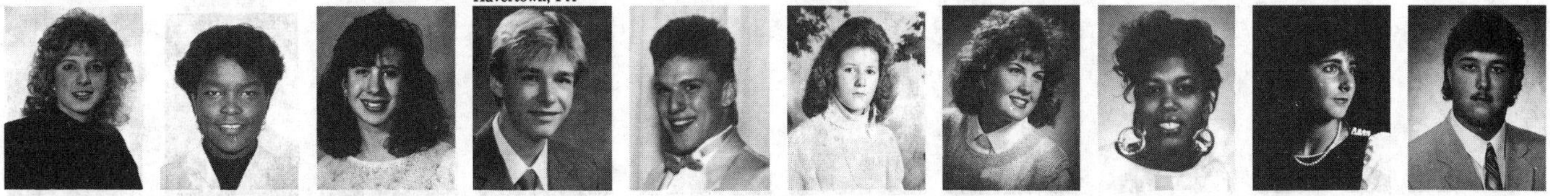

Mackie, Maury
Scranton Central
Scranton, PA

Macklin, Ella
Schenley HS
Teacher Center
Pittsburgh, PA

Macko, Renee
Monongahela Valley
Catholic HS
Charleroi, PA

Macler, Mark L
Hickory HS
Hermitage, PA

Maconaghy, Jeffrey
D
Abraham Lincoln
Philadelphia, PA

Madden, Lisa-Ann
Bishop O Reilly HS
Forty Fort, PA

Madden, Paula
North Hills HS
Pittsburgh, PA

Madyun, Rashida
Westinghouse HS
Pittsburgh, PA

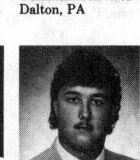

Magaro, Stephanie
Northern HS
Wellsville, PA

Magera, George
Bentworth SR HS
Cokeburg, PA

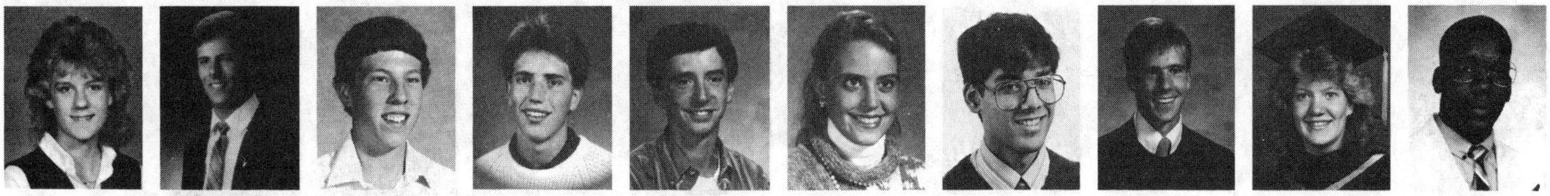

Magilton, Monica
Nazareth Acad
Langhorne, PA

Magnotta, Joe H
Center HS
Monaca, PA

Magnuson, Pete
Phoenixville Area
Phoenixville, PA

Mahan, Eric
Central Dauphin HS
Harrisburg, PA

Mahar, Andrew
Cumberland Valley
Mechanicsburg, PA

Mahers, Christine
Henderson SR HS
W Chester, PA

Mahidhara, Raja S
Shady Side Acad
Pittsburgh, PA

Mahoney, Gregory
Carlisle SR HS
Carlisle, PA

Mahoney, Jennifer
Cardinal Dougherty
Huntingdon Valley,
PA

Mahoney, Nathaniel
Scotland Schl Vets
Philadelphia, PA

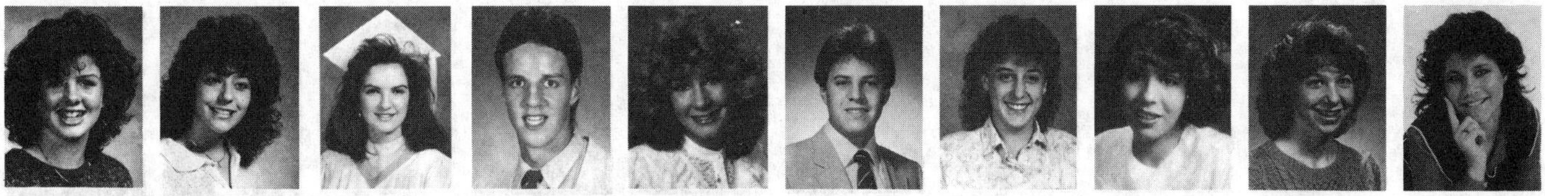

Main, Becca
Pennsbury HS
Yardley, PA

Mainello, Julie
Daniel Boone JR SR
Douglassville, PA

Malfara, Kristin
West Catholic Girls
Philadelphia, PA

Malinchak, James
Monessen HS
Monessen, PA

Malingowski, Chris
Bethel Park HS
Bethel Pk, PA

Malinoff, Josh
George Washington
Philadelphia, PA

Malinosky, Carol
German Township
Mc Clellandtown,
PA

Malizia, Cheryl
Bishop Mc Devitt
Harrisburg, PA

Mallin, Stacy
West Branch HS
Lanse, PA

Malloy, Bernadette
M
Christian School Of
York, PA

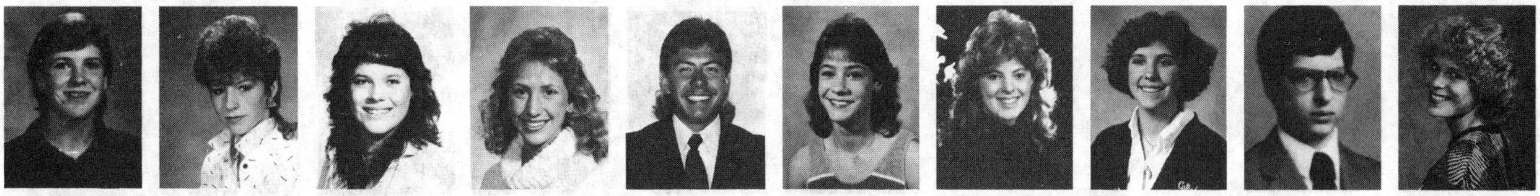

Malone, Jan
Conrad Weiser JR
SR HS
Womelsdorf, PA

Maloney, Tracey
Upper Darby HS
Drexel Hill, PA

Malush, Tammie Jo
Belle Vernon Area
Belle Vernon, PA

Manack, Kelly
Belle Vernon Area
Belle Vernon, PA

Manack, Randolph
E
Belle Vernon Area
Belle Vernon, PA

Mancini, Sheri A
West Allegheny HS
Oakdale, PA

Mancino, Barb
Corry Area HS
Corry, PA

Manes, Monica
St Paul Cathedral
Pittsburgh, PA

Manko, Gerard
Our Lady Of The
Sacred Heart HS
Ambridge, PA

Mann, Dana
West Branch Area
Kylertown, PA

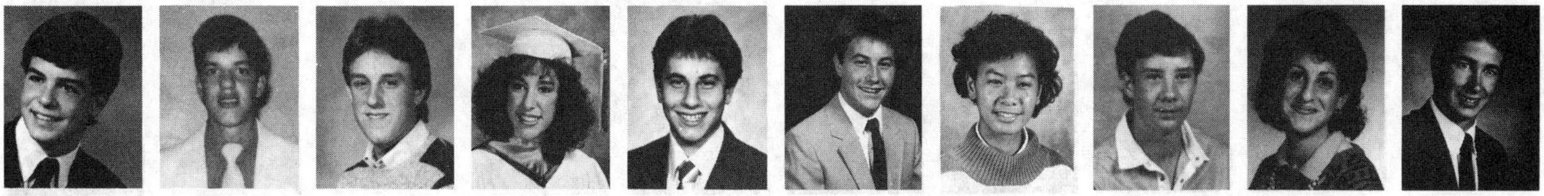

Mann, James S
York Suburban SR
York, PA

Mann, Rudolph
Monongahela Valley
Catholic HS
Monongahela, PA

Manning, Scott
S Williamsport Area
JR/SR HS
S Williamsport, PA

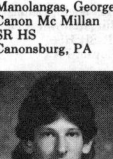

Mannino, Jennifer
Bishop Conwell HS
Bensalem, PA

Manolangas, George
Canon Mc Millan
SR HS
Canonsburg, PA

Mansberger, James
Mount Union Area
Calvin, PA

Manubany, Jeanne
Reading HS
Reading, PA

Manzoni, Alfred
Lake-Lehman HS
Dallas, PA

Maragulia, Kelly
Notre Dame HS
Easton, PA

Marakovits, Thomas
Northampton Area
SR HS
Northampton, PA

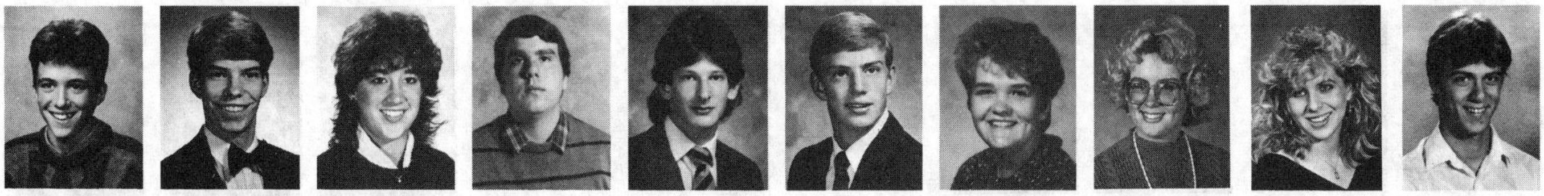

Marasco, Matthew
Dubois Area HS
Dubois, PA

Marburger, Keith A
Upper Merion Area
Wayne, PA

March, Cheryl
C A S HS
Glenmoore, PA

Marcin, James
Panther Valley HS
Lansford, PA

Marder, Jeffrey I
Council Rock HS
Richboro, PA

Marengo, Brian G
Conestoga HS
Berwyn, PA

Marhefka, Ronna
Central Cambria HS
Mineral Pt, PA

Marietta, Cheryl
Connellsville Area
Acme, PA

Marinaccio,
Kathleen P
Delaware Valley HS
Milford, PA

Marines, Aaron
Blacklick Valley JR
SR HS
Vintondale, PA

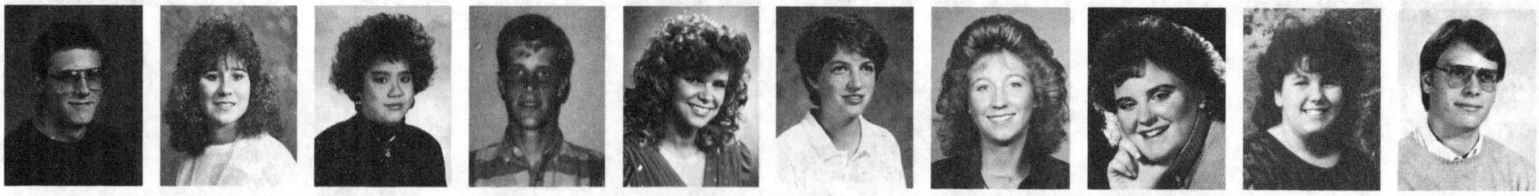

Marino, Mark J
Penn Trafford HS
Irwin, PA

Marinos, Robin
Monessen HS
Monessen, PA

Mark, Judy
Philadelphia HS For
Philadelphia, PA

Markarian, Elizabeth
Pennsburg HS
Yardley, PA

Marker, Stacy
Dallastown Area HS
Dallastown, PA

Markey, Monique
Wyomissing Area
West Lawn, PA

Markiewicz, Missy
West Mifflin Area
W Mifflin, PA

Markle, Christine
South Western HS
Hanover, PA

Markle, Michelle
Trinity HS
Washington, PA

Marko, Carl
Readinga Rea HS
Reading, PA

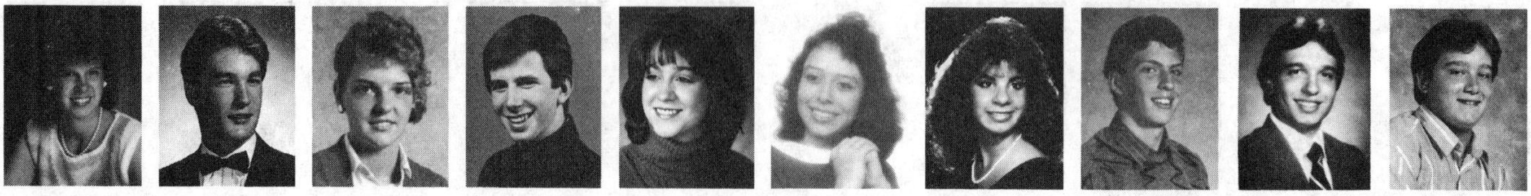

Markowski, Annette
Conrad Weisser HS
St Johns, PA

Marks, Eric
Downingtown SR
Exton, PA

Marks, Kristin
Allentown Central Catholic HS
Northampton, PA

Marmol, Eric J
Fairchance Georges
Uniontown, PA

Marnell, Mary
Greensburg Central Catholic HS
Greensburg, PA

Marone, Tina
Windber Area HS
Windber, PA

Maroney, Amy
Sun Valley HS
Brookhaven, PA

Marosek, John
Phoenixville Area
Phoenixville, PA

Marouchoc, Jim
Freedom HS
Allentown, PA

Marrangoni, Nicholas
Kennedy Christian
New Castle, PA

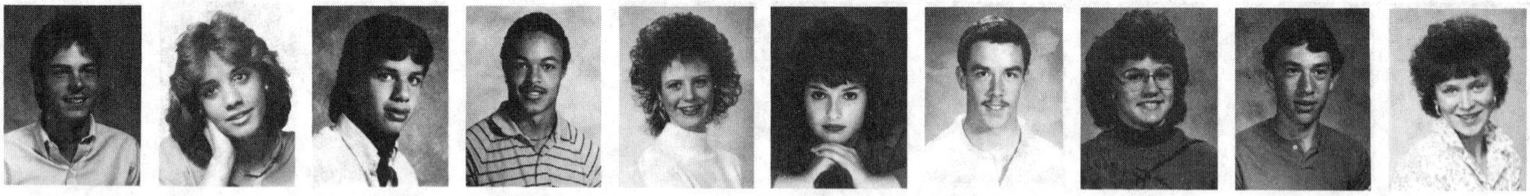

Marsh, Dave
Elizabethtown Area
Elizabethtown, PA

Marsh, Megan
East Pennsboro Area HS
Enola, PA

Marshall, Eric A
Dallas Area HS
Shaverstown, PA

Marshall, Mike
Bedford HS
Bedford, PA

Marta, Monica L
West Scranton HS
Scranton, PA

Martin, Aliza
Greater Works Acad
Pittsburgh, PA

Martin, Brian
Seneca Valley HS
Mars, PA

Martin, Cherie
Living Word Acad
Ephrata, PA

Martin, Christopher L
Cocalico HS
Reinholds, PA

Martin, Cynthia
West Scranton HS
Scranton, PA

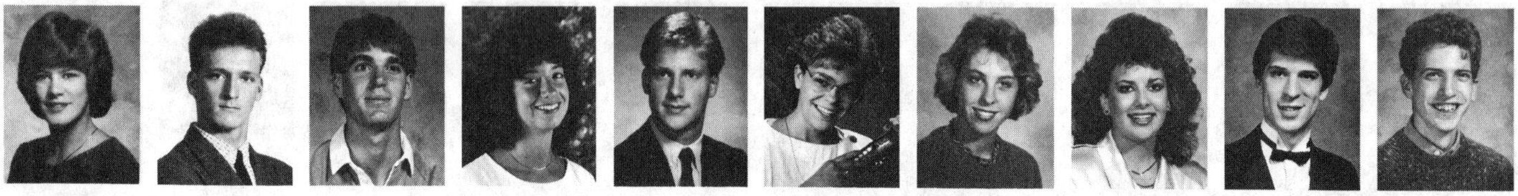

Martin, Deborah
North Allegheny HS
Pittsburgh, PA

Martin, Eldred Chad
Charleroi Area HS
Stockdale, PA

Martin, Greg
Cocalico HS
Steven, PA

Martin, Lisa
St Hubert HS
Philadelphia, PA

Martin, Stephen
Riverview HS
Oakmont, PA

Martin, Tammy L
Garden Spot HS
New Holland, PA

Martin, Tracy
Meadville Area SR
Meadville, PA

Martinak, Trina Louise
Frazier HS
Perryopolis, PA

Martini, Jr Charles C
Monsignour Bonneir
Havertown, PA

Martorana, Charles R
William Penn SR
York, PA

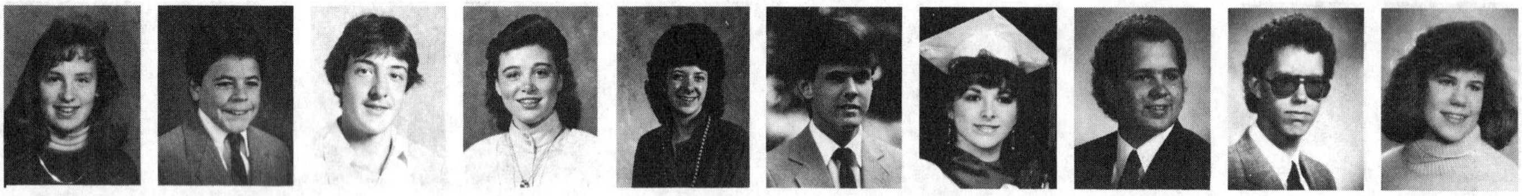

Martuccio, Michelle
Hickory HS
Hermitage, PA

Martz, Bob
Mt Pleasant Area SR HS
Mt Pleasant, PA

Martz, Jr Philip Berlin
Brothersvalley HS
Berlin, PA

Marvin, Deana
Uniontown Area SR
Waltersburg, PA

Maschak, Jeannine
United HS
Seward, PA

Mascherino, Joseph A
Coatesville Area SR
Coatesville, PA

Masci, Valerie
St Maria Goretti HS
Philadelphia, PA

Mascilli, Brian
Valley HS
Arnold, PA

Mascilli, Scott
Valley HS
Arnold, PA

Mascioli, Dana
Wyoming Valley West HS
Swoyersville, PA

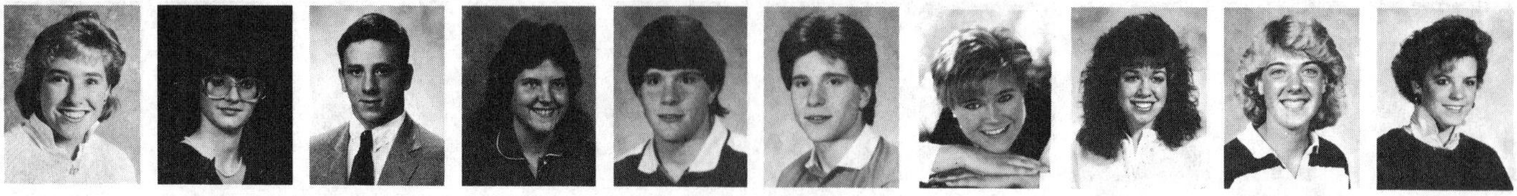

Mascioli, Jenifer
Notre Dame Acad
West Chester, PA

Mason, Pamela
Cardinal O Hara HS
Glenolden, PA

Mason, Jr Perry G
Purchase Line HS
Commodore, PA

Massa, Brenda Lee
Hazleton SR HS
Hazleton, PA

Massengill, Daniel
Burgettstown Area JR-SR HS
Slovan, PA

Massengill, Dennis
Burgettstown Area JR-SR HS
Slovan, PA

Massey, Elizabeth
Villa Maria HS
New Castle, PA

Massicci, Julia
Canevin HS
Pittsburgh, PA

Massing, Cindy
Mc Dowell Intermediate HS
Erie, PA

Masteller, Tracie L
Brandywine Heights
Fleetwood, PA

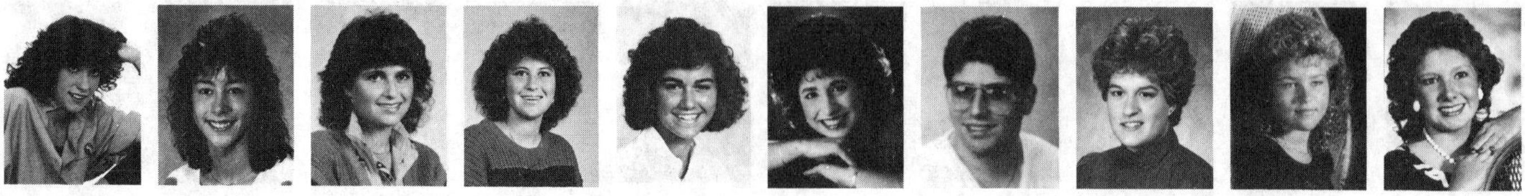

Masterson, Krissy
Fort Cherry HS
Mc Donald, PA

Mastillo, Candace
North Star HS
Holsopple, PA

Mastrangelo, Debbie
New Castle SR HS
New Castle, PA

Mastrangelo, Luann
New Castle SR HS
New Castle, PA

Mastrangelo, Maria
Gwynedd Mercy
Plymouth, PA

Mastroianni, Angela
Bishop Hannan HS
Scranton, PA

Mastroianni, Mario
West Scranton SR
Scranton, PA

Matalik, Michelle L
Burgettstown Area JR Sr HS
Burgettstown, PA

Matchicka, Nicole
Reading SR HS
Reading, PA

Mather, Melissa
Strong Vincent HS
Erie, PA

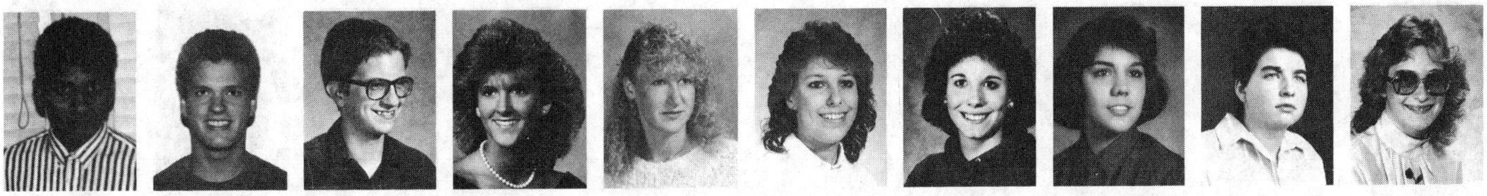

Mathew, Abraham
Central HS
Philadelphia, PA

Mathews, Jeff
J P Mc Caskey HS
Lancaster, PA

Mathias, Christopher
Boyertown HS
Gilbertsville, PA

Mathias, Denise
Spring Grove SR HS
Spring Grove, PA

Matianski, Jackie
Charleroi Area HS
Monongahela, PA

Matrician, Christine
Palmerton Area HS
Palmerton, PA

Matscherz, Kathryn
West Greene Middle SR HS
Prosperity, PA

Matteo, Mary Anne
Hershey HS
Hershey, PA

Matter, Sandra
East Juniata HS
Millerstown, PA

Matthews, Michele
Greenville SR HS
Greenville, PA

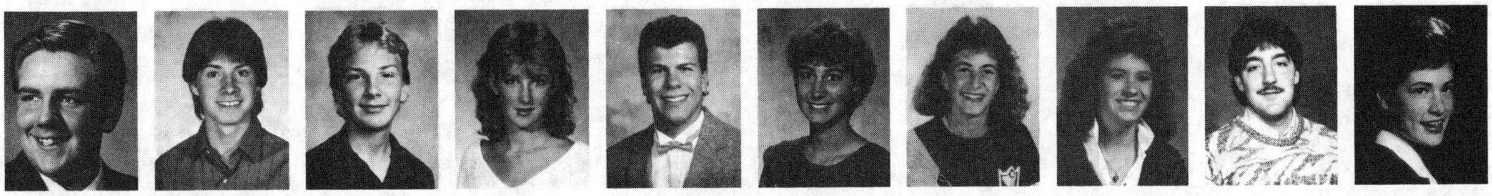

Mattson, John A
Cash HS
Coatesville, PA

Mattuch, Brian
Ambridge Area HS
Baden, PA

Mattus, David
Upper Morel.and
Willow Grove, PA

Matty, Stacy
Monessen JR-SR
Monessen, PA

Matulevich, Jonathan
West Hazleton HS
Harwood Mines, PA

Matusz, Karen
Plum SR HS
Pittsburgh, PA

Maula, Rosemary
East Stroudsburg
E Stroudsburg, PA

Maurer, Jody
Susquenita HS
Marysville, PA

Mauro, Anthony F
Kinggold HS
Donora, PA

Maus, Shelley
Central Dauphin HS
Harrisburg, PA

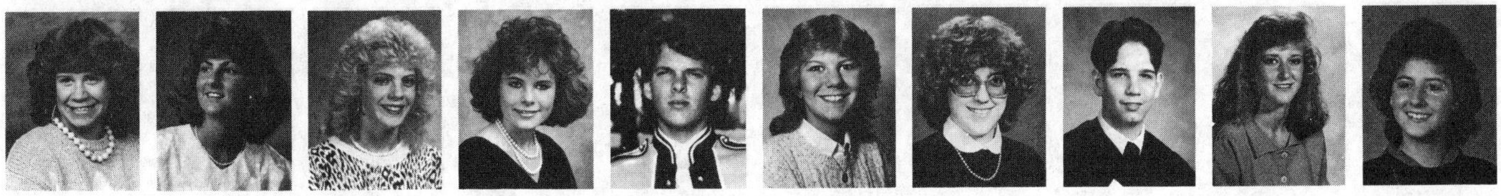

Maxwell, Connie
Peters Township HS
Mcmurray, PA

Maxwell, Dina
Exeter SR HS
Reading, PA

Maxwell, Magdalene
Donegal HS
Mount Joy, PA

Maxwell, Margaret
Bishop Mc Devitt
Glenside, PA

Maxwell, Robert
Penn Manor HS
Millersville, PA

Maxwell, Shannon
West Mifflin Area
W Mifflin, PA

May, Renee M
Palmyra Area HS
Palmyra, PA

Mayer, Gary
Morrisville HS
Morrisville, PA

Mayer, Marci
Fleetwood Area HS
Fleetwood, PA

Mayers, Carrie
Brownsville Area HS
Grindstone, PA

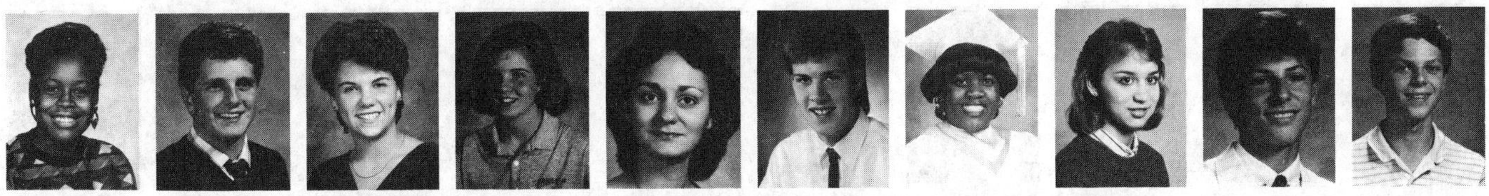

Maynard, Crystal
Cornell HS
Coraopolis, PA

Maynard, Nathaniel
Cathedral Preparatory Schl
Edinboro, PA

Maynes, Shannon
Cardinal Dougherty
Philadelphia, PA

Mayo, Jane-Margaret
Parkland HS
Allentown, PA

Mayor, Alisa G
Council Rock HS
Holland, PA

Mays, Christopher L
Chartiers Valley HS
Carnegie, PA

Mays, Tabitha Love
West Catholic Girls
Philadelphia, PA

Mazeitis, Jamie
Bishop O Reilly HS
Courtdale, PA

Mazias, John
Carlisle HS
Carlisle, PA

Mazich, Edward
Danville Area HS
Danville, PA

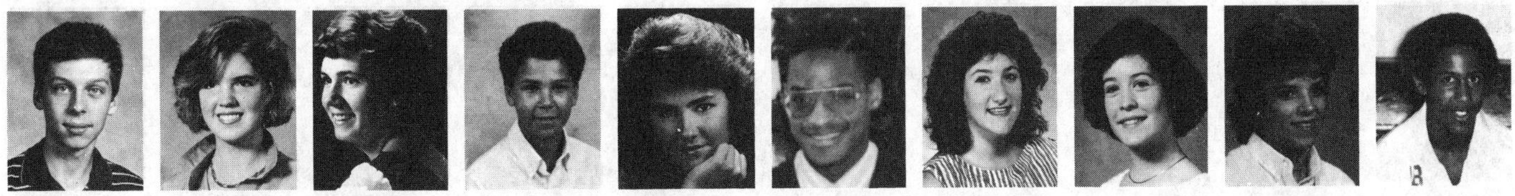

Mazich, James
Danville Area SR
Danville, PA

Mazon, Mary Beth
Gateway SR HS
Monroeville, PA

Mazur, Michelle
Ambridge HS
Baden, PA

Mazyck, David
Lake-Lehman HS
Harveys Lake, PA

Mazzatesta, Jennifer
Susquehanna Township HS
Harrisburg, PA

Mbonu, Dozie
Church Farm Schl
Philadelphia, PA

Mc Adams, Amy
Saltsburg JR SR HS
New Alexandria, PA

Mc Allister, Donna
Steel Valley HS
W Homestead, PA

Mc Allister, Kristie
Fairchance-Georges
Fairchance, PA

Mc Allister, Lenny
Central Catholic HS
Verona, PA

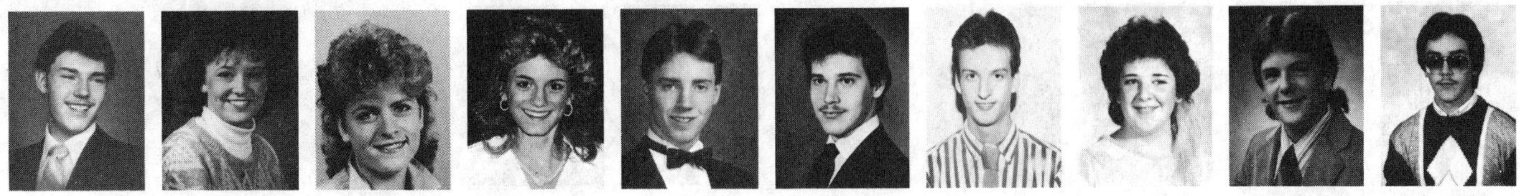

Mc Anallen, Eric
Lincoln HS
New Castle, PA

Mc Anallen, Laura
Washington HS
Washington, PA

Mc Aninch, Kelli
Freeport Area SR
Sarver, PA

Mc Atee, Jennifer
Neshaminy HS
Langhorne, PA

Mc Blain, Joseph
Monsignor Bonner
Aldan, PA

Mc Briar, Mark
Penn Hills SR HS
Penn Hills, PA

Mc Cabe, James P
Archbishop Ryan For Boys
Philadelphia, PA

Mc Cabe, Linda
Portage Area HS
Portage, PA

Mc Cain, James
Meadville Area SR
Meadville, PA

Mc Cain, Thomas
Oil City SR HS
Rouseville, PA

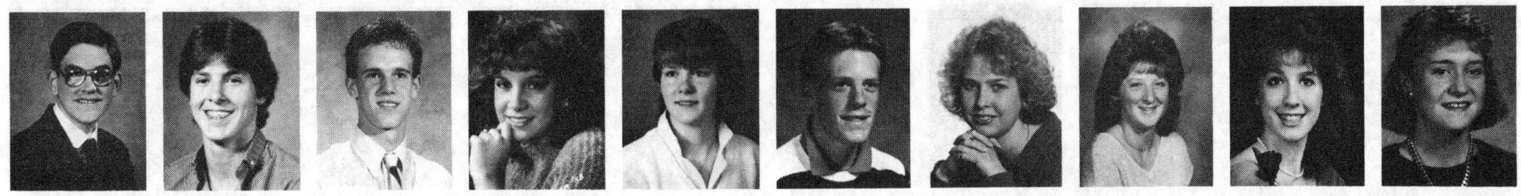

Mc Call, Brian
Monsignor Bonner
Lansdowne, PA

Mc Call, Flynn
Keystone Oaks HS
Pittsburgh, PA

Mc Cann, Anthony
Lansdale Catholic
Chalfont, PA

Mc Cann, Joan
Seneca Valley HS
Zelienople, PA

Mc Cardle, Jennifer
Chief Logan HS
Yeagertown, PA

Mc Carthy, Brian
Susquehannock HS
Glen Rock, PA

Mc Caslin, Kelly
Lincoln HS
Ellwood City, PA

Mc Cauley, Dianna
North Clarion HS
Fryburg, PA

Mc Cauley, Leeann
Saint Huberts HS
Philadelphia, PA

Mc Cauley, Mary
Solanco HS
Drumore, PA

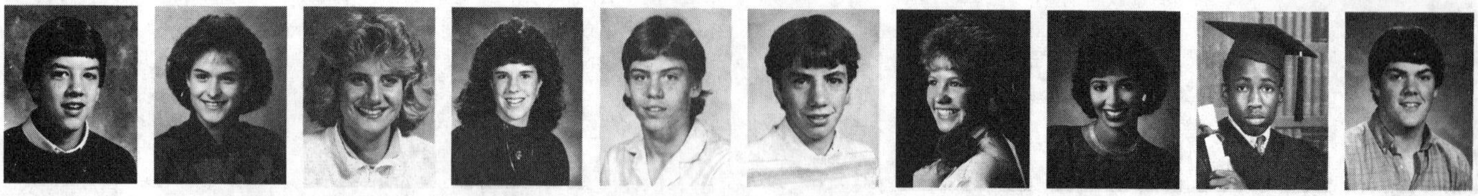

Mc Clay, Scott
Mercer Area HS
Mercer, PA

Mc Cleary, Bridgot
Du Bois Area SR
Rockton, PA

Mc Cleary, Brynn
Biglerville HS
Biglerville, PA

Mc Cleary, Carrie
Seneca Valley HS
Evans Cty, PA

Mc Cleary, Michael
Brookville Area HS
Mayport, PA

Mc Cleland, Dave
Quakertown SR HS
Green Lane, PA

Mc Clellan, Cindy
West Greene HS
Sycamore, PA

Mc Clelland, Laura J
Mercer Area JR SR
Mercer, PA

Mc Clendon, Marvin
Harrisburg HS
Harrisburg, PA

Mc Climans, Scott
Moniteau JR-SR HS
West Sunbury, PA

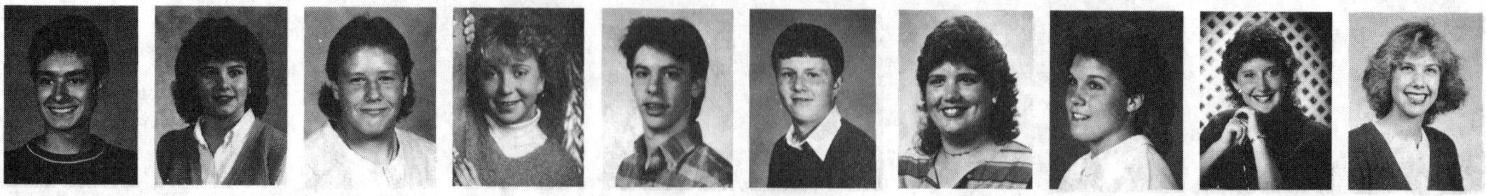

Mc Clintock, Kevin Lee
Laurel Highlands SR HS
Uniontown, PA

Mc Closkey, Beth Ann
United HS
Homer City, PA

Mc Clure, Vincent
Homer Center HS
Indiana, PA

Mc Clymonds, Ann
Grove City SR HS
Grove City, PA

Mc Coll, Ron
Susquehanna Community HS
Union Dale, PA

Mc Combie, Blaze
Northern Cambria
Nicktown, PA

Mc Connell, Kristin
Trinity HS
Washington, PA

Mc Conville, Melissa
Freeport SR HS
Sarver, PA

Mc Cormick, Diana
Mc Guffey HS
Washington, PA

Mc Cormick, Julie
New Castle SR HS
New Castle, PA

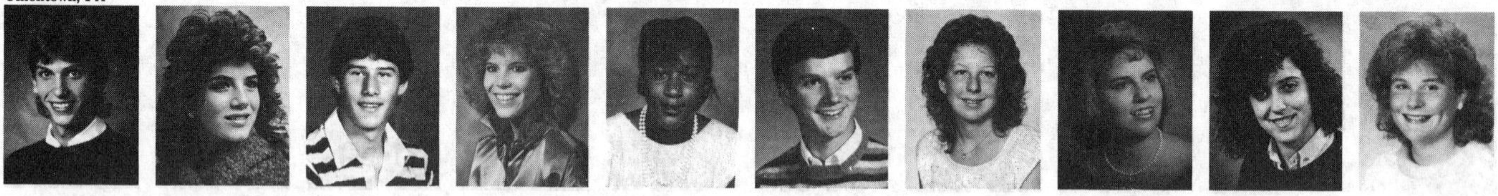

Mc Cormick, Kevin
Trinity HS
Washington, PA

Mc Cormick, Maureen
Cumberland Valley
Mechanicsburg, PA

Mc Coy, John
Pocono Mountain
Bartonsville, PA

Mc Coy, Margo
Oil City SR HS
Franklin, PA

Mc Cray, Felicia
Vo-Tech HS
Mc Keesport, PA

Mc Cready, David O
Beaver Falls HS
Beaver Falls, PA

Mc Cue, Deneen
Carrick HS
Pittsburgh, PA

Mc Culla, Amy
Youngsville HS
Pittsfield, PA

Mc Culligan, Jennifer
Saint Basil Acad
Philadelphia, PA

Mc Cullough, Holly
Burgettstown JR SR
Burgettstown, PA

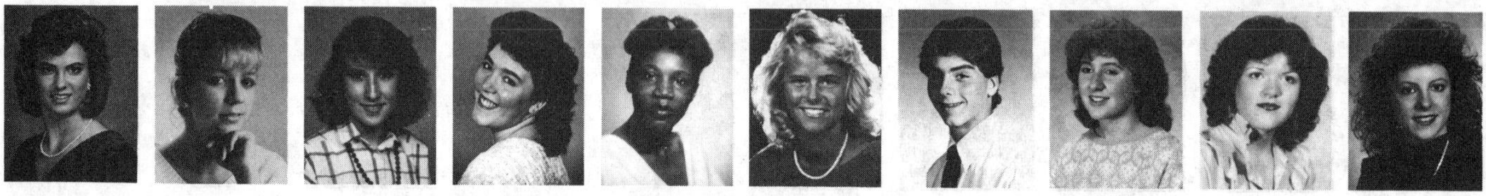

Mc Cullough, Kelly
Bishop Shanahan
West Chester, PA

Mc Cullough, Mary E
Pennsboro HS
Camp Hill, PA

Mc Cusker, Mary
Mc Keesport Area
Mckeesport, PA

Mc Dade, Karen
Penn Hills SR HS
Verona, PA

Mc Daniel, Julie
Germantown HS
Philadelphia, PA

Mc Donald, Colleen
Lancaster Catholic
Lancaster, PA

Mc Donald, James
Notre Dame G P HS
Easton, PA

Mc Donald, Kelly
Jamestown Area HS
Jamestown, PA

Mc Donald, Mary R
Southern Lehigh HS
Coopersburg, PA

Mc Donald, Tammy
Belle Vernon Area
Belle Vernon, PA

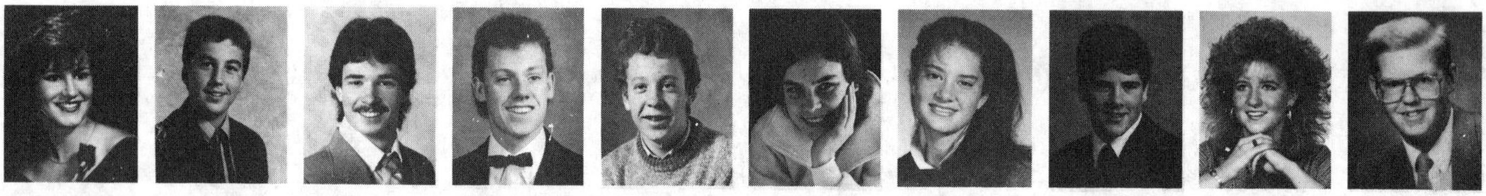

Mc Donnell, Kelly
St Basil Acad
Philadelphia, PA

Mc Donnell, Sean
Pocono Central Catholic HS
Pocono Lake, PA

Mc Donnell, Stephen
Eastern Montgomery Count
Cheltenham, PA

Mc Dowell, Thomas
Cardinal Dougherty
Philadelphia, PA

Mc Elhaney, Bruce
Center HS
Monaca, PA

Mc Elhattan, Tammy
Quigley HS
Lacey, WA

Mc Elroy, Helen
William Allen HS
Allentown, PA

Mc Elwain, Kevin Patrick
Parkland HS
Allentown, PA

Mc Ewen, Heidi
Canon Mc Millan
Eighty Four, PA

Mc Fadden, Kevin
Central Cathloic Of
Allentown, PA

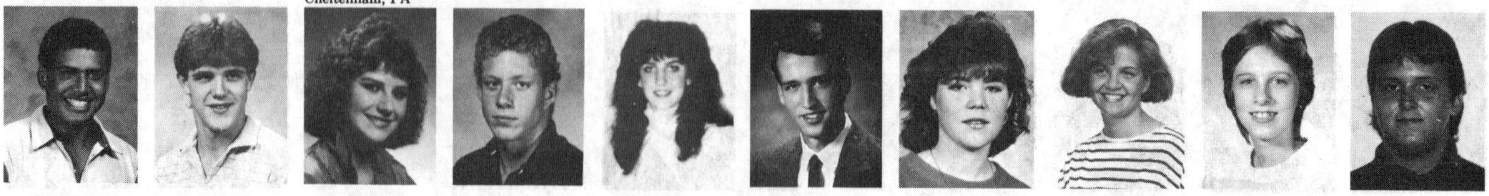

Mc Fadden, Tony
Garden Spot HS
New Holland, PA

Mc Garry, Chris
Curwensville HS
Curwensville, PA

Mc Gary, Michelle
Wilmington Area
Volant, PA

Mc George, Jr David S B
State College Area Intermediat HS
Penna Furnace, PA

Mc Gill, Danielle
Acad Of Notre Dame De Namur
Springfield, PA

Mc Gill, Matt
North Pocono HS
Moscow, PA

Mc Gill, Tammie
Fort Le Boeuf HS
Waterford, PA

Mc Glone, Jennifer
Scranton Prep
Scranton, PA

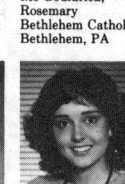

Mc Gouldrick, Rosemary
Bethlehem Catholic
Bethlehem, PA

Mc Govern, Edward C
Pine Grove Area HS
Pine Grove, PA

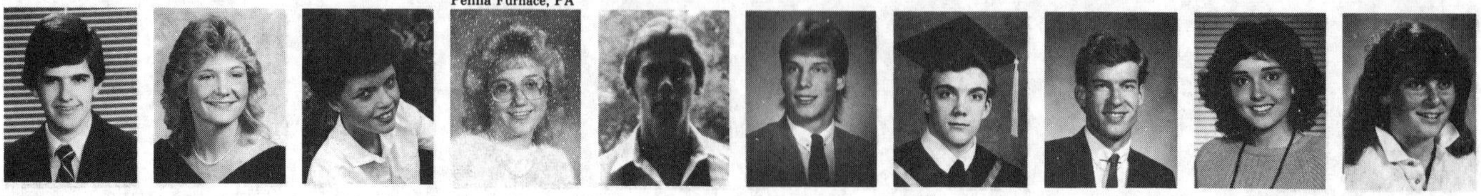

Mc Gowan, John
Coughlin HS
Wilkes Barre, PA

Mc Gowan, Kellie
Chichester SR HS
Boothwyn, PA

Mc Gowan, Tammy
Cocalico HS
Stevens, PA

Mc Grath, Crystal
St Marys Area HS
St Marys, PA

Mc Grath, James
West Catholic HS
Philadelphia, PA

Mc Grosky, Mark
Bethel Pk HS
Bethel Pk, PA

Mc Grother, Shawn
Cardinal Dougherty
Philadelphia, PA

Mc Grotty, Kyle A
Upper Moreland HS
Huntingdon Vly, PA

Mc Guire, Margaret
Moon SR HS
Coraopolis, PA

Mc Guire, Nicole
Linesville HS
Linesville, PA

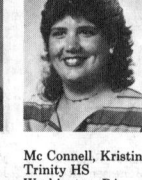

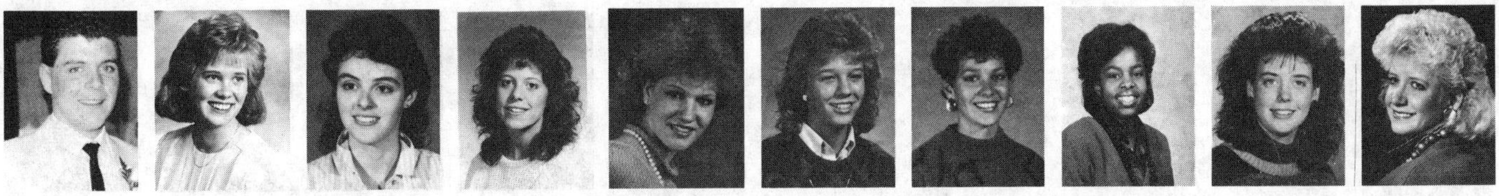

Mc Hale, Timothy
W Seranton HS
Scranton, PA

Mc Henry, Jennifer A
Greater Latrobe SR
Latrobe, PA

Mc Henry, Samantha
Waynesburg Central
Waynesburg, PA

Mc Hugh, Kelly
Notre Dame HS
Easton, PA

Mc Ilnay, Jodi
Mt Pleasant HS
Stahlstown, PA

Mc Kain, Sheila
Donegal HS
Marietta, PA

Mc Kean, Amanda
Hatboro Horsham SR HS
Hatboro, PA

Mc Kee, Lynn
Sharon HS
Sharon, PA

Mc Keever, Tina Marie
St Huberts Catholic
Philadelphia, PA

Mc Kenzie, Cori
New Castle SR HS
New Castle, PA

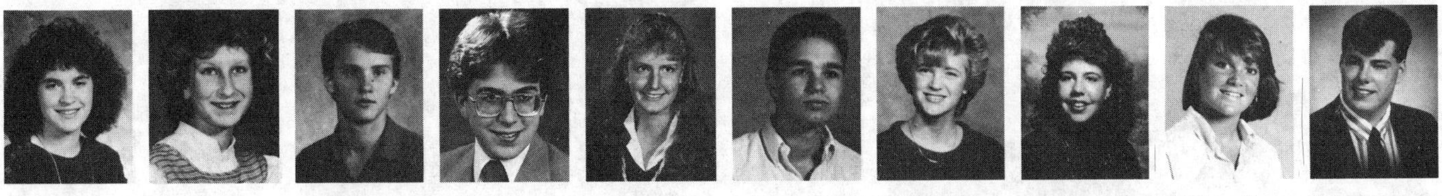

Mc Kernan, Lisa
Kennedy Christian
Sharon, PA

Mc Kiernan, Amanda M
Cardinal Dougherty
Philadelphia, PA

Mc Killip, Ronald
United HS
New Florence, PA

Mc Kim, Kevin
De Lone Catholic
Hanover, PA

Mc Kinley, Charlotte S
Clarion Area HS
Clarion, PA

Mc Kinley, Matthew G
Upper Merion Area
King Of Prussia, PA

Mc Kinley, Yvonne
Franklin HS
Clintonville, PA

Mc Kinney, Terriann
Knoch JR SR HS
Cabot, PA

Mc Kinsey, Shayne
Springside Schl
Oreland, PA

Mc Laughlin, Grant Reed
North Hills HS
Pittsburgh, PA

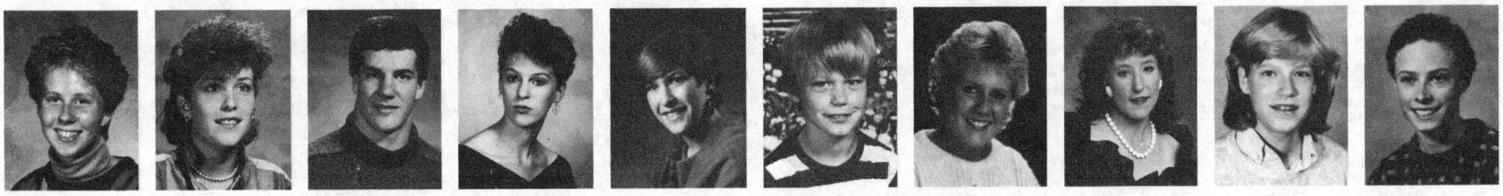

Mc Lean, Denise
Bald Eagle Nittany
Mill Hall, PA

Mc Lean, Kristen
Schuylkill Valley HS
Leesport, PA

Mc Lister, Dennis
Butler HS
Butler, PA

Mc Loughlin, Heather L
Creative & Performing Arts HS
Philadelphia, PA

Mc Mahon, Patricia
Boyertown SR HS
Green Lane, PA

Mc Mahon, Sean
Mohawk JR/SR HS
Enon Valley, PA

Mc Manama, Maureen
Montour HS
Mckees Rocks, PA

Mc Martin, Leianne
Northern Lebanon JR/SR HS
Jonestown, PA

Mc Menamin, Deirdre
W B Saul HS
Philadelphia, PA

Mc Millan, Danny
Center Area HS
Aliquippa, PA

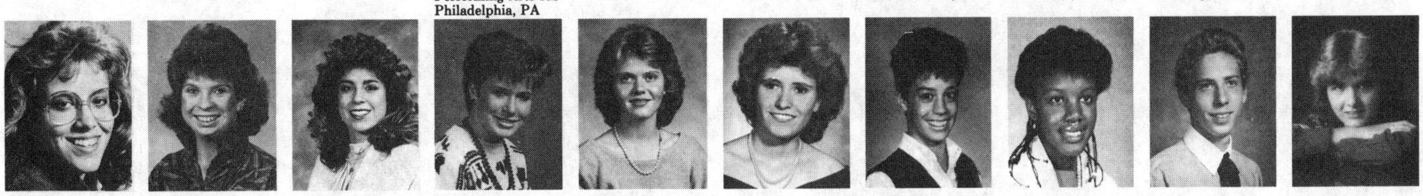

Mc Millen, Diane
Marion Center Area
Creekside, PA

Mc Millen, Janet
Mapletown JR SR
Greensboro, PA

Mc Mullen, Sherrie
Bensalem SR HS
Bensalem, PA

Mc Murray, Wendy
Clearfield HS
Clearfield, PA

Mc Murry, Susan
Shikellamy HS
Sunbury, PA

Mc Nabb, Barbara
Villa Maria Acad
Malvern, PA

Mc Namee, Marlene
Nazareth Acad
Phila, PA

Mc Neil, Tashia E
Easton Area HS
Easton, PA

Mc Owen, David
Archbishop Wood High Schl For Boys
Warminster, PA

Mc Queen, Julie
C A S HS
Fayetteville, PA

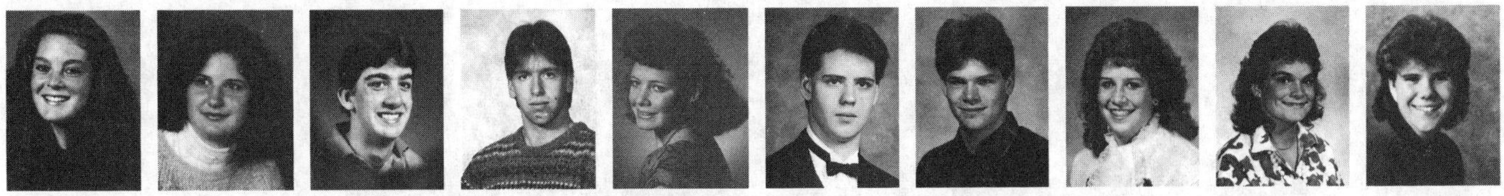

Mc Quillen, Clare Ann
Peters Township HS
Mc Murray, PA

Mc Quillin, Patricia
Dwynedd Mercy
Chalfont, PA

Mc Redmond, Michael T
Central Dauphin HS
Harrisburg, PA

Mc Sparren, Bobby
Oil City SR HS
Rouseville, PA

Mc Tighe, Mary Anne
Greensburg Central Catholic HS
Jeannette, PA

Mc Veigh, Kevin
Cardinal O Hara HS
Clifton Heights, PA

Mc Vey, David
Blair County Christian HS
Duncansville, PA

Mc Vey, Susan
Blair County Christian Schl
Duncansville, PA

Mc Vicker, Kimberly
Faith Christian Schl
Saylorsburg, PA

Mc Watters, Traci
Lewistown Area HS
Lewistown, PA

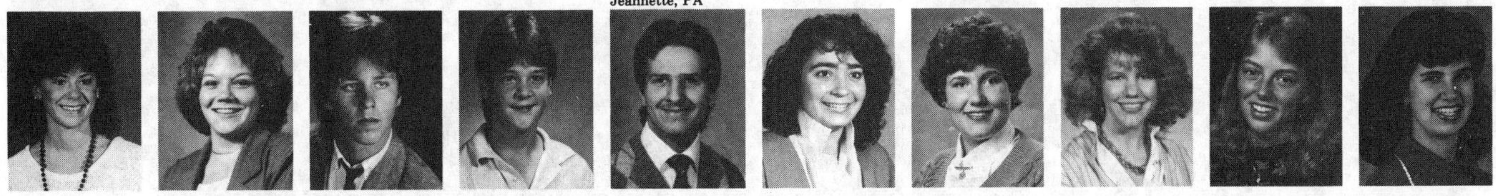

Mc Williams, Betsy
Waynesburg Central
Fremont, CA

Mc Williams, Sherry
Hopewell SR HS
Aliquippa, PA

Meacham, III Roger H
Henderson SR HS
Exton, PA

Means, Robert
Punxsutawney Area
Punxsutawney, PA

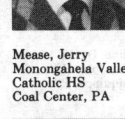

Mease, Jerry
Monongahela Valley Catholic HS
Coal Center, PA

Meccariello, Lorenza
Phoenixville Area
Phoenixville, PA

Meckley, Ann Margaret
Chambersburg Area SR HS
Chambersburg, PA

Meckley, Erin
Hempfield HS
Greensburg, PA

Meckley, Suzanne
Cocalico HS
Stevens, PA

Medici, Amy V
North Pocono HS
Lake Ariel, PA

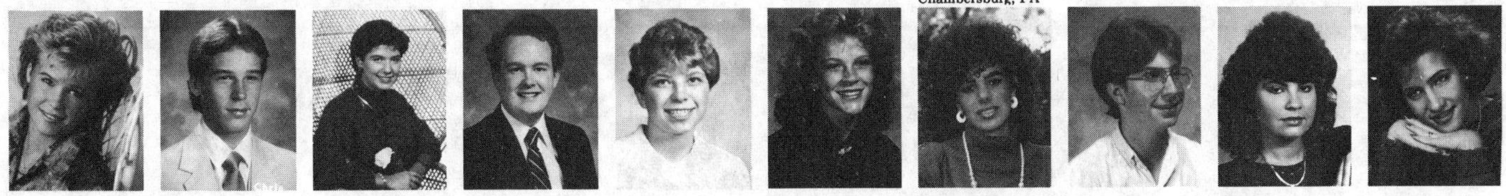

Meeker, Stacie
Fairview HS
Fairview, PA

Mehallo, Chris
West Hazelton HS
Hazleton, PA

Mehegan, Kelly
Villa Maria Acad
Erie, PA

Meier, Alfred G
Council Rock HS
Richboro, PA

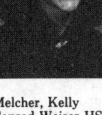

Meixsell, Stephanie
Nazareth Area SR
Nazareth, PA

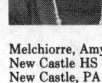

Melcher, Kelly
Conrad Weiser HS
Robesonia, PA

Melchiorre, Amy
New Castle HS
New Castle, PA

Mellinger, J Michael
Solanco SR HS
Peach Bottom, PA

Melnick, Jennifer
Belle Vernon Area
Belle Vernon, PA

Melovich, Suzanne
Pennsbury HS
Levittown, PA

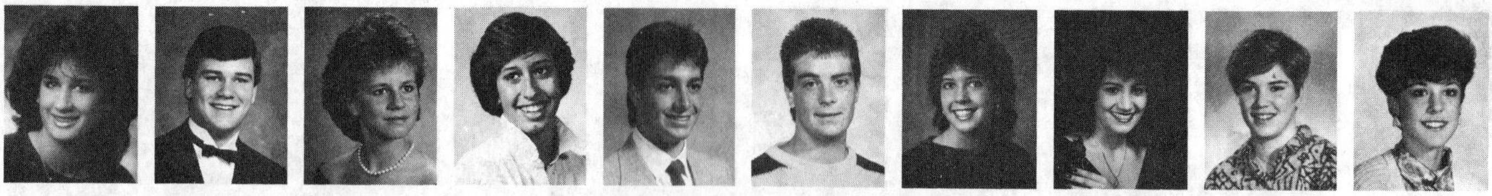

Melucci, Michele
St Francis Acad
Pittsburgh, PA

Meluskey, Michael
Cardinal O Hara HS
Media, PA

Melwsky, Sherry
Minersville Area HS
Minersville, PA

Memolo, Missy
Abington Heights
South Campus
Clarks Green, PA

Mendola, Edward
Charleroi Area HS
Charleroi, PA

Mendola, Eric
Charleroi HS
Charleroi, PA

Menzel, Karin
Mercyhurst
Preparatory Schl
Erie, PA

Mercante, Debra
Archbishop
Prendergast HS
Collingdale, PA

Mercatoris, Adele
Meadville Area SR
Meadville, PA

Merget, Amy S
Reading HS
Reading, PA

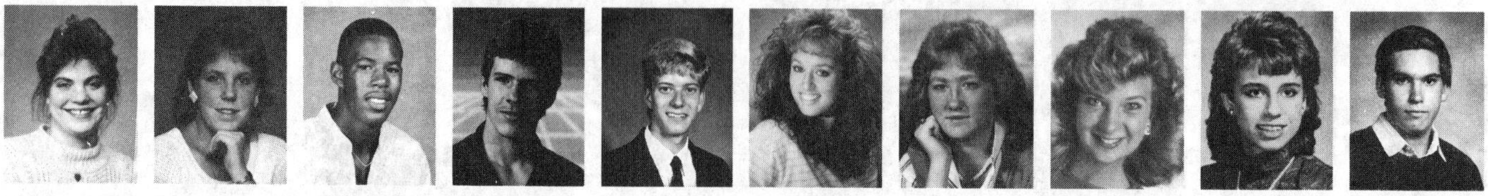

Mericle, Jennifer
Wyoming Valley
West HS
Kingston, PA

Merkel, Malissa
Kutztown Area HS
Lenhartsville, PA

Merrill, N Gai
The Haverford Schl
Ardmore, PA

Merrill, Randy
Berlin Brothers
Valley HS
Berlin, PA

Merryman, Grey
Central Dauphin HS
Harrisburg, PA

Merulli, Wendy
Center HS
Monaca, PA

Meshey, Tammy
Conestoga Valley
Ronks, PA

Mesnar, Ginger
Highlands SR HS
Tarentum, PA

Messenlehner, Mary
Louise
Nazareth Area SR
Nazareth, PA

Messer, Jeff
Upper Moreland HS
Hatboro, PA

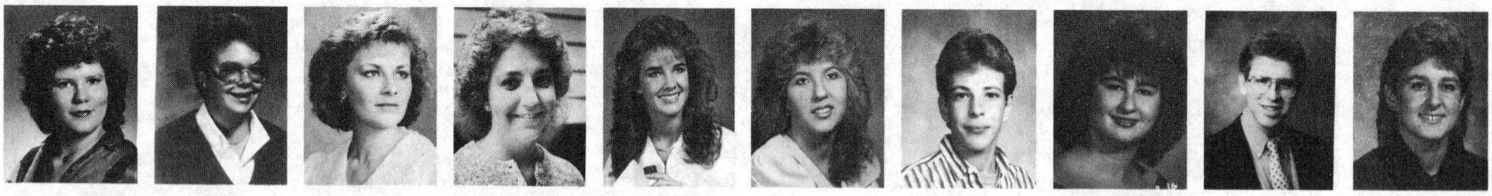

Messinger, Charlene
J
William Allen HS
Allentown, PA

Messner, Tracey
Tri-Valley HS
Valley View, PA

Mestishen, Loretta
A
Pottsville Area HS
Pottsville, PA

Metrocavage, Maria
Our Lady Of
Lourdes Regiona
Shamokin, PA

Metz, Kathy
Bensalem HS
Bensalem, PA

Metz, Lisa
Hamburg Area HS
Hamburg, PA

Metzger, Matthew
Nazareth Area HS
Bethlehem, PA

Meyer, Christine
Saint Basil Acad
Philadelphia, PA

Meyer, David J
The Baptist HS
Clarks Summit, PA

Meyer, Dawn
Cumberland Valley
Carlisle, PA

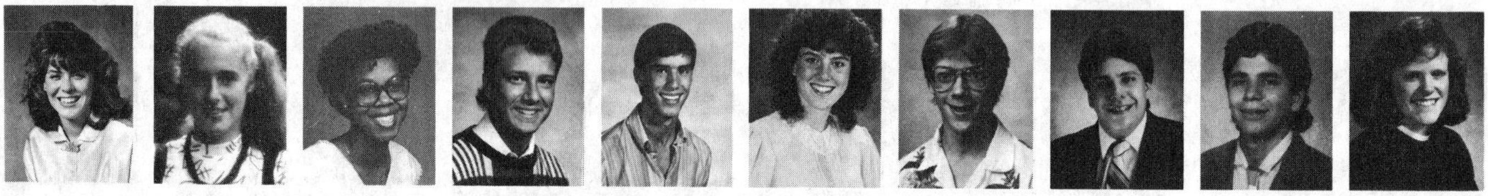

Meyer, Donna
Gateway SR HS
Monroeville, PA

Meyer, Heidi
North East HS
North East, PA

Meyers, Desiree
John Harris HS
Harrisburg, PA

Meyers, Kenneth
Souderton Area HS
Souderton, PA

Meyers, Kent
Chambersburg Area
SR HS
Chambersburg, PA

Miceli, Christine
Bishop Mc Devitt
Dauphin, PA

Michael, Bierly
Du Bois Area SR
Reynoldsville, PA

Michael, Mark
Center Area HS
Aliquippa, PA

Michael, Thomas
Tri-Valley HS
Mc Clellandtown,
PA

Michaels, Karen
Taylor Allderdice
Pittsburgh, PA

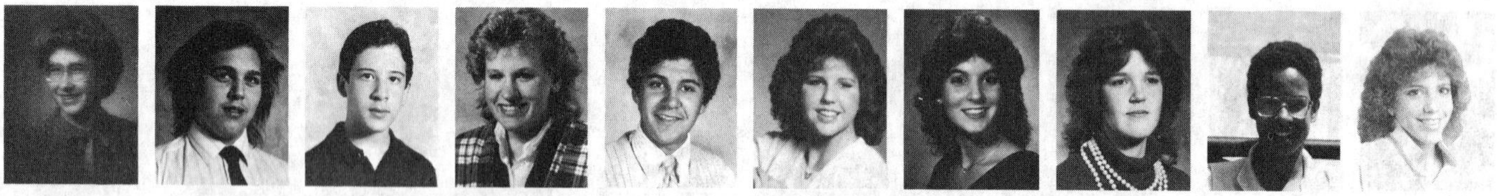

Michajluk, Susan M
Greencastle Antrim
Greencastle, PA

Michalek, Richard
Carbondale Area HS
Carbondale, PA

Michalski, Anthony
Coughlin HS
Wilkes Barre, PA

Michel, Jennifer
Our Lady Of The
Sacred Heart HS
Aliquippa, PA

Michele, Joseph
Marion Ctr
Rochester Mills, PA

Michels, Tricia K
Laurel HS
New Castle, PA

Middleton, Linda
Anne
Sun Valley HS
Brookhaven, PA

Miers, Susan
Dallas SR HS
Dallas, PA

Mieth, Alfred J
Northgate JRSR HS
Pittsburgh, PA

Mihalak, Jane M
Seton Catholic HS
Moosic, PA

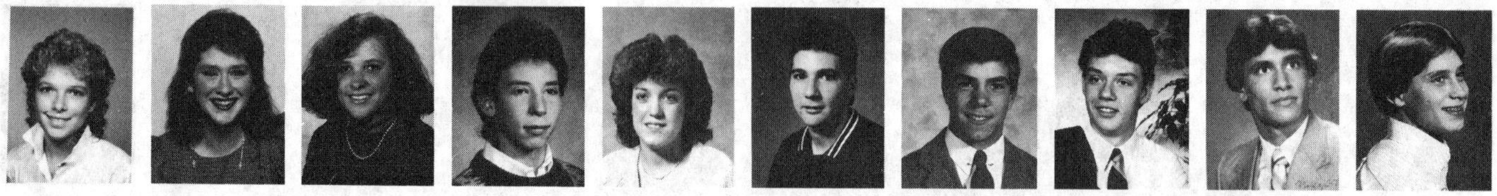

Mihalic, Melissa
Mc Keesport Area
SR HS
Mc Keesport, PA

Mihalko, Anna
Marie
Uniontown Area SR
Uniontown, PA

Mihalko, Kristen
Yough HS
Lowber, PA

Mihalko, Taras
Wyoming Valley
West HS
Larksville, PA

Mihelic, Michelene
Aliquippa HS
West Aliquippa, PA

Mike, David
Aliquippa HS
Aliquippa, PA

Miklos, Peter
Lancaster Catholic
Bainbridge, PA

Mikovch, Eric
Northwestern HS
Cranesville, PA

Mikula, Eric
Altoona Area HS
Altoona, PA

Mikula, Keith
Altoona Area HS
Altoona, PA

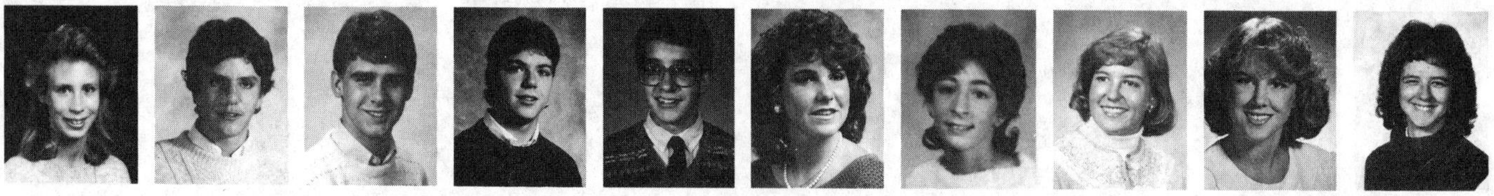

Mikulka, Milissa
Tunkhannock Area
Tunkhannock, PA

Milazzo, II Joseph S
Blairsville SR HS
Blairsville, PA

Miles, Christian
West Scranton HS
Scranton, PA

Miley, Jeff
Carbondale Area HS
Carbondale, PA

Milinovich, Jim
Waynesburg Central
Waynesburg, PA

Milke, Dana
Cumberland Valley
Mechanicsburg, PA

Milko, Gina
Northern Cambria
Barnesboro, PA

Milkovich, Amy
Westmont Hilltop
Johnstown, PA

Miller, Abigail
Southern Lehigh HS
Emmaus, PA

Miller, Ally-Karen D
Oil City Area SR
Cooperstown, PA

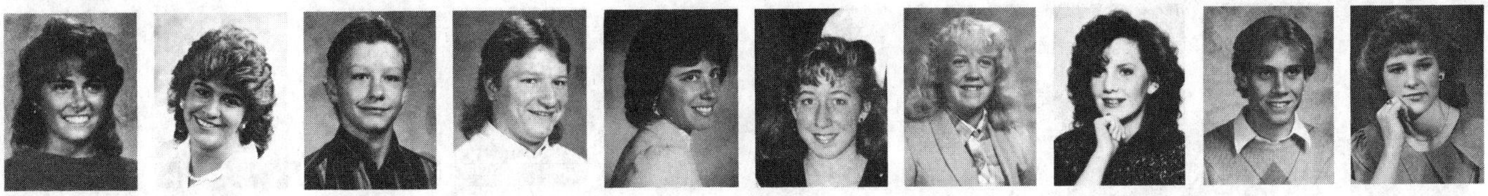

Miller, Andrea
Pequea Valley HS
Paradise, PA

Miller, Ann Marie
Williams Vly HS
Lykens, PA

Miller, Brandon
Halifax Area HS
Halifax, PA

Miller, Brian
Lincoln HS
Ellwood City, PA

Miller, Camela
Central Dauphin
East HS
Dauphin, PA

Miller, Caroline
Upper Moreland HS
Willow Grove, PA

Miller, Carrie
Christian Schl Of
Thomasville, PA

Miller, Christine E
North Pocono HS
Moscow, PA

Miller, Christopher
Emmaus HS
Allentown, PA

Miller, Cindy
Calvary Baptist
Christian Schl
Reinholds, PA

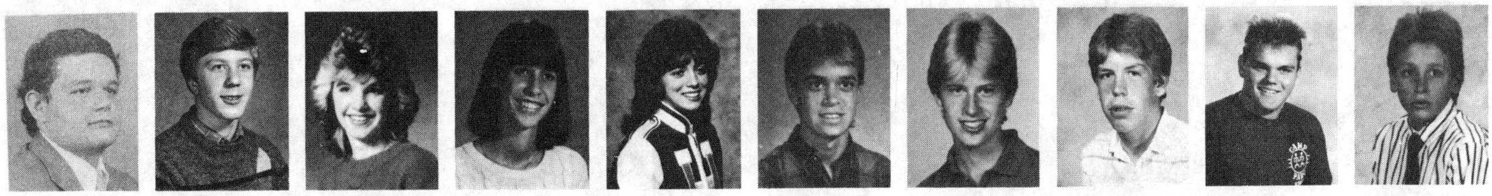

Miller, Cory
Lehighton Area SR
Lehighton, PA

Miller, Curtis
Exeter HS
Reading, PA

Miller, Debbie
Springdale HS
Cheswick, PA

Miller, Elisabeth
Harriton HS
Villanova, PA

Miller, Elizabeth
Hollidaysburg Area
SR HS
Duncansville, PA

Miller, Eric
Avon Grove HS
Lincoln Univ, PA

Miller, Frank
Patrick
Sto-Rox SR HS
Mckees Rocks, PA

Miller, Fred
Tyrone Area HS
Tyrone, PA

Miller, Gerald
Conemaugh
Township Area HS
Hollsopple, PA

Miller, H Eric
St Pius X HS
Pottstown, PA

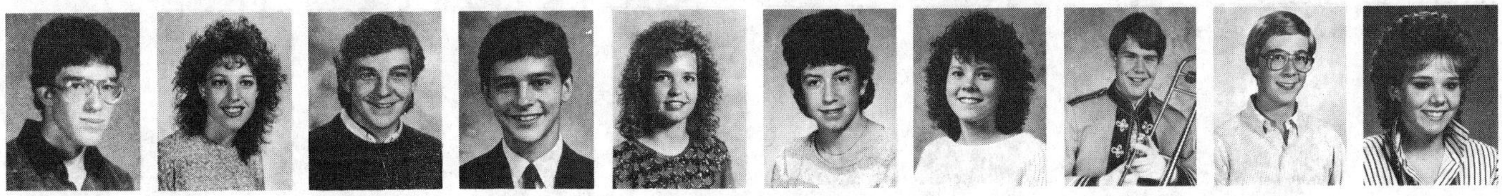

Miller, H Jerrold
Methacton HS
Trooper, PA

Miller, Heather A
Whitehall-Coplay
Coplay, PA

Miller, J Douglas
York County Area
Felton, PA

Miller, James
Cumberland Valley
Mechanicsburg, PA

Miller, Jennifer
Nativity B V M HS
Branchdale, PA

Miller, Jill Marie
Kennedy Christian
Grenville, PA

Miller, Jody
Eisenhower HS
Russell, PA

Miller, Jonathan
Williams Valley JR
SR HS
Williamstown, PA

Miller, Joshua
Andrew
Reading SR HS
Reading, PA

Miller, Karen
Emmaus HS
Allentown, PA

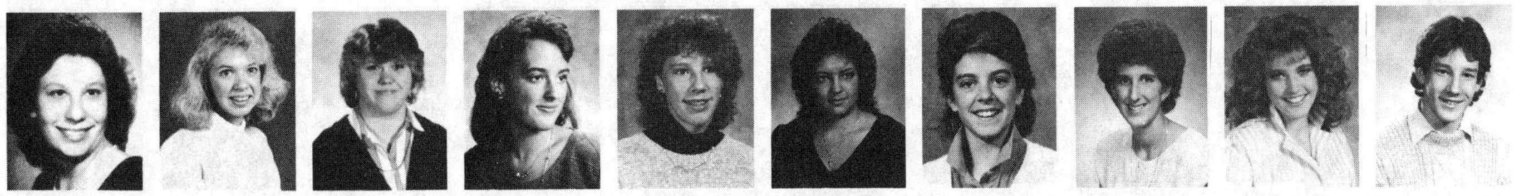

Miller, Karen
Neshaminy HS
Penndel, PA

Miller, Kim
Barmudian Springs
Idaville, PA

Miller, Kim
Marion Ctr
Shelocta, PA

Miller, Kimberly
Sacred Heart HS
Pittsburgh, PA

Miller, Kimm
Governor Mifflin HS
Mohnton, PA

Miller, Kris
Belle Vernon Area
Belle Vernon, PA

Miller, Kristi
Connellsville Area
SR HS
Connellsville, PA

Miller, Kristine
Bellwood-Antis HS
Bellwood, PA

Miller, Lainie
Kennedy Christian
Wheatland, PA

Miller, Larry
Greater Johnstown
Johnstown, PA

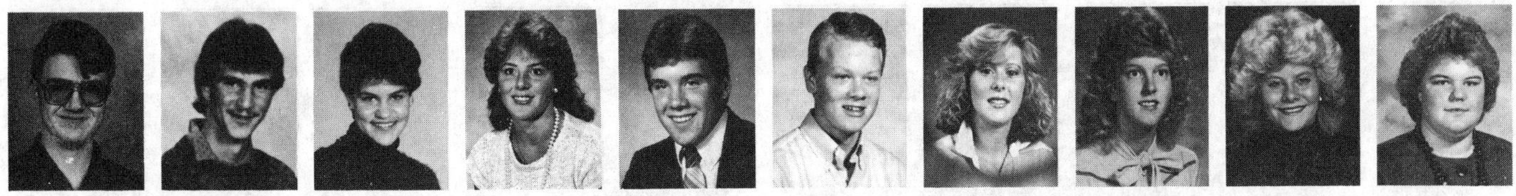

Miller, Lee
Tri-Valley SR HS
Fairchance, PA

Miller, Lenny
Harry S Truman HS
Levittown, PA

Miller, Marci
Berlin
Brothersvalley HS
Berlin, PA

Miller, Melinda
North Star HS
Stoystown, PA

Miller, Michael
Lehighton Area HS
Lehighton, PA

Miller, Michael T
Chambersburg Area
SR HS
Chambersburg, PA

Miller, Michelle
Central Dauphin HS
Harrisburg, PA

Miller, Michelle
Conrad Weiser HS
Sinking Spring, PA

Miller, Michelle
Fort Cherry HS
Midway, PA

Miller, Michelle M
York Area Vo-Tech
Airville, PA

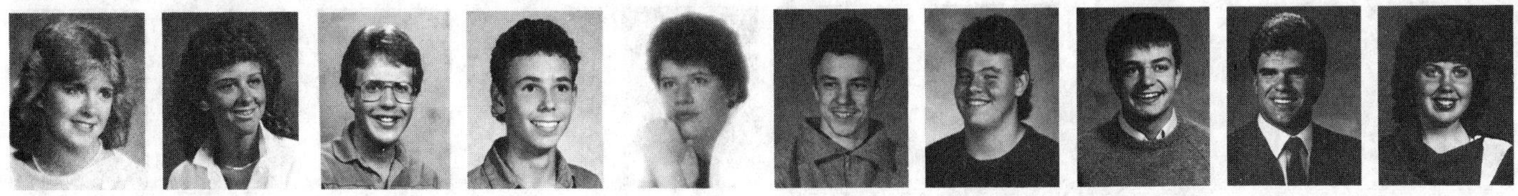

Miller, Penny
Avonworth SR HS
Pittsburgh, PA

Miller, Rebecca
Spring Grove Area
Spring Grove, PA

Miller, Jr Robert
Penn-Trafford HS
Level Green, PA

Miller, Rollin
Pleasant Valley HS
Effort, PA

Miller, Roxanne
Lock Haven SR HS
Castanea, PA

Miller, Russell
Connellsville Area
SR HS
Connellsville, PA

Miller, Ryan
Fort Cherry HS
Midway, PA

Miller, Stephen
Boiling Springs HS
Carlisle, PA

Miller, Stephen D
Spring Grove Area
SR HS
Codorus, PA

Miller, Tanya
Southmoreland HS
Scottdale, PA

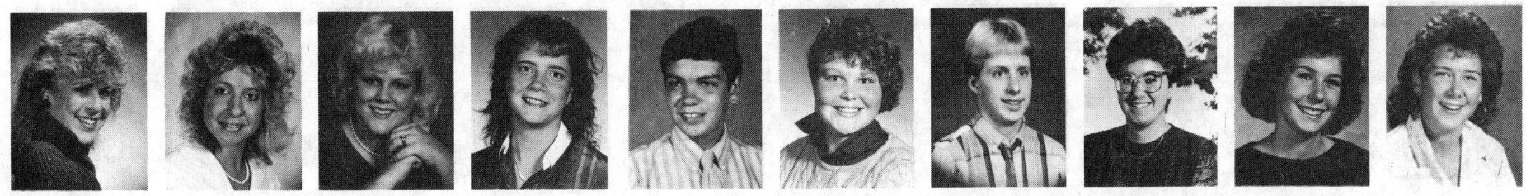

Miller, Theresa
Saltsburg JR-SR HS
Saltsburg, PA

Miller, Tina
Brandywine Heights
Alburtis, PA

Miller, Tracy
Rocky Grove JR SR
Franklin, PA

Miller, Trisha
William Allen HS
Allentown, PA

Miller, Wade T
Connellsville Area
SR HS
Connellsville, PA

Miller, Wendy Sue
Wm Allen HS
Allentown, PA

Miller, William
Tunkhannock Area
Factoryville, PA

Millham, Mary P
Bishop Oreilly HS
Shavertown, PA

Mills, Carrie
Northeastern SR HS
Manchester, PA

Mills, Kim
Garnet Valley JRSR
Glen Mills, PA

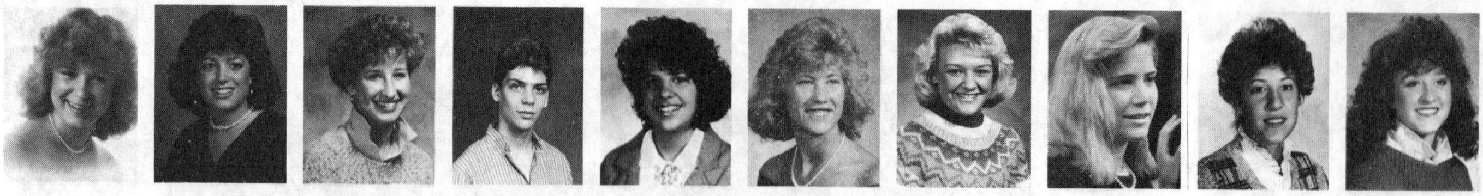

Mills, Marcie Jo
Punxsutawney Area
Punxsutawney, PA

Mills, Michele
Bishop Shanahan
W Chester, PA

Mills, Tamara
Solanco HS
Quarryville, PA

Milner, Michael
Tunkhannock Area
Tunkhannock, PA

Milshaw, Suzanne
Reading HS
Reading, PA

Mingle, Michelle
Bensalem HS
Bensalem, PA

Minich, Lori
Butler SR HS
Butler, PA

Minissale, Angela
Country Day Schl
Of The Sacre
Gladwyne, PA

Minnich, Amy
Northampton HS
Bath, PA

Minnich, Andrea
Bangor Area SR HS
Bangor, PA

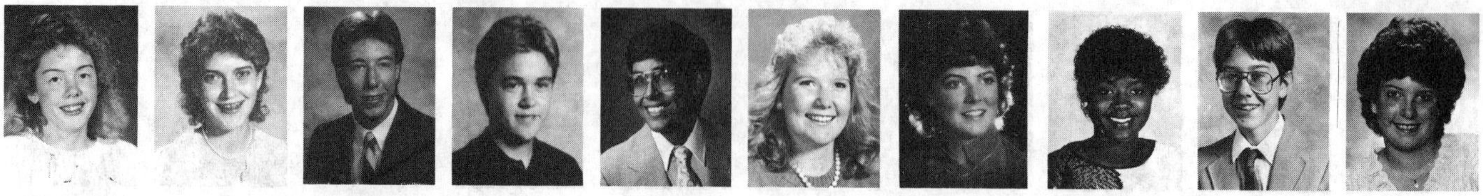

Minskey, Renee
Beth-Center SR HS
Fredericktown, PA

Minto, Janet
Purchase Line HS
Cherry Tree, PA

Miorelli, Paul
West Hazleton HS
Conyngham, PA

Miscannon, Jr
Joseph S
Shenandoah Valley
JR- SR HS
Shenandoah, PA

Mishra, Vijoy
Waynesburg Central
Waynesburg, PA

Mistretta, Shannon
Homer Center JR
SR HS
Homer City, PA

Mitchell, Andrea
Central Dauphin HS
Harrisburg, PA

Mitchell, Anissa
Norristown Area HS
Norristown, PA

Mitchell,
Christopher J
Nativity BVM HS
Port Carbon, PA

Mitchell, Cynthia
Jean
Peters Twp HS
Mc Murray, PA

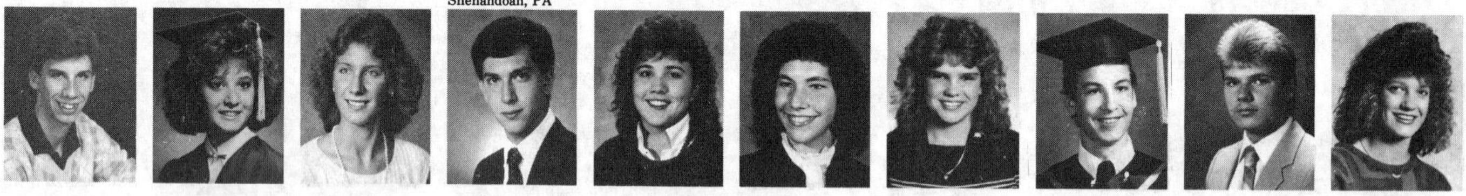

Mitchell, David W
Mercyhurst Prep
Erie, PA

Mitchell, Kimberly
William Allen HS
Allentown, PA

Mitchell, Laurie R
Burrell HS
Lower Burrell, PA

Mitre, Edward E S
Shady Side Acad
Pittsburgh, PA

Mitstifer, Samantha
A
Liberty JR/SR HS
Troutrun, PA

Mitts, Darla
Connellsville Area
SR HS
Connellsville, PA

Mitzel, Theresa
Red Lion HS
Red Lion, PA

Mlodzinski, Paul
Cardinal Dougherty
Philadelphia, PA

Modesitt, Keith
Center HS
Aliquippa, PA

Modresky,
Michalene
James M Coughlin
Wilkes Barre, PA

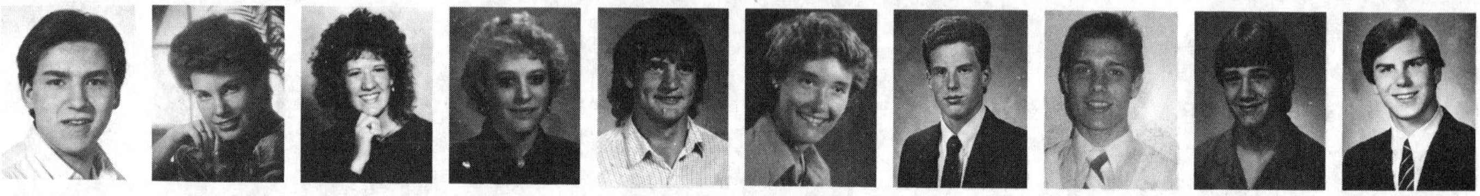

Moeckel, Mark
Dunmore HS
Dunmore, PA

Moffatt, Elizabeth
West Perry SR HS
Millerstown, PA

Moffett, Lisa
Bangor Area SR HS
Bangor, PA

Mohler, Lizabeth M
William Penn SR
York, PA

Mohler, Robert
Penn Manor HS
Pequea, PA

Mohr, Rhonda
Boyertown Area SR
New Berlinvl, PA

Molchen, Gregory
Carl
Ambridge Area HS
Ambridge, PA

Molishus, Jeffrey F
Archbishop Ryan
HS For Boys
Philadelphia, PA

Molitierno, Joseph
Punxsutawney Area
Punxsutawney, PA

Monaco, Steven
Peters Township HS
Mc Murray, PA

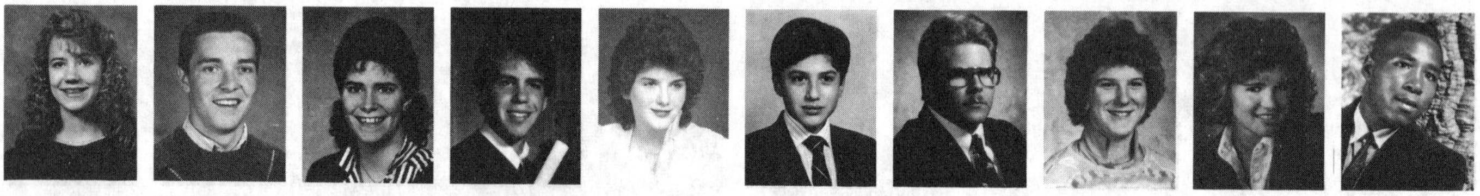

Monahan, Tawnya
Connellsville Area Jr
High West
Connellsville, PA

Monley, Robert
Greensburg Central
Catholic HS
Murrysville, PA

Monroe, Bethany
Galeton JR SR HS
Galeton, PA

Monroe, Jason S
Plymouth HS
Plymouth Meeting,
PA

Monstrola, Deanna
Jeannette SR HS
Jeannette, PA

Montecinos,
Guillermo P
Devon Prep Schl
Audubon, PA

Moody, John
Shamokin Area HS
Paxinos, PA

Moody, Lisa
Shamokin HS
Paxinos, PA

Moody, Melissa
Farrell Area HS
Farrell, PA

Mooney, Keith
Reading SR HS
Reading, PA

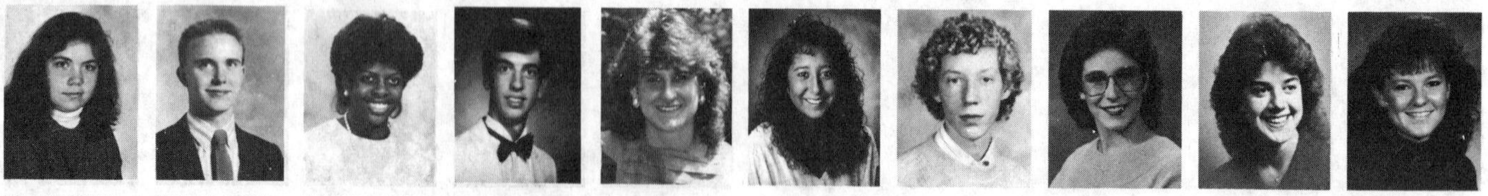

Mooney, Lisa
Chambersburg Area
SR HS
Chambersburg, PA

Mooney, Marty
Nativity BVM HS
St Clair, PA

Mooney, Stephanie
Villa Maria Acad
Erie, PA

Moore, Bill
Sun Valley HS
Aston, PA

Moore, Gayle
York County
Vo-Tech HS
Lancaster, PA

Moore, Gloria
Meadville Area SR
Meadville, PA

Moore, Jeffrey
Bensalem HS
Bensalem, PA

Moore, Lisa
Yough SR HS
Herminite, PA

Moore, Lori
Bethlehem-Center
Clarksville, PA

Moore, Margie
Shaler Area HS
Glenshaw, PA

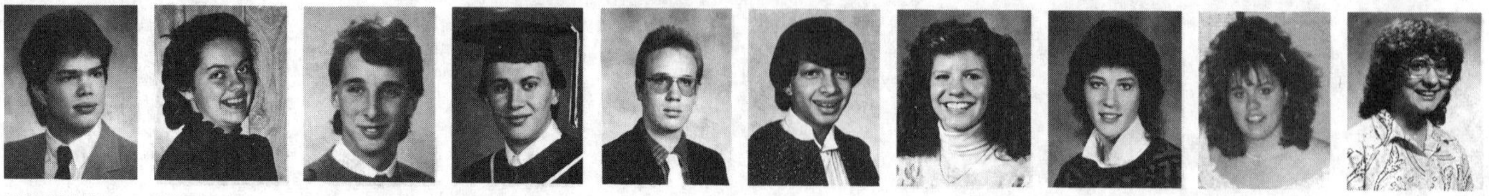

Moore, Mike
E L Meyers HS
Wilkes Barre, PA

Moore, Tracy
Brownsville Area HS
E Millsboro, PA

Moran, Jr Michael F
West Scranton HS
Scranton, PA

Moreira, Carlos F
Archbishop Ryan
HS For Boys
Philadelphia, PA

Morgan, Caz
Danville SR HS
Danville, PA

Morgan, Debbie
Oxford Area HS
Oxford, PA

Morgan, Heather
Peters Township HS
Mcmurray, PA

Morgan, Holly
Southern
Huntingdon Count
Saltillo, PA

Morgan, Kathleen
Harry S Truman HS
Levittown, PA

Morgan, Michele
Wilmington Area
Grove City, PA

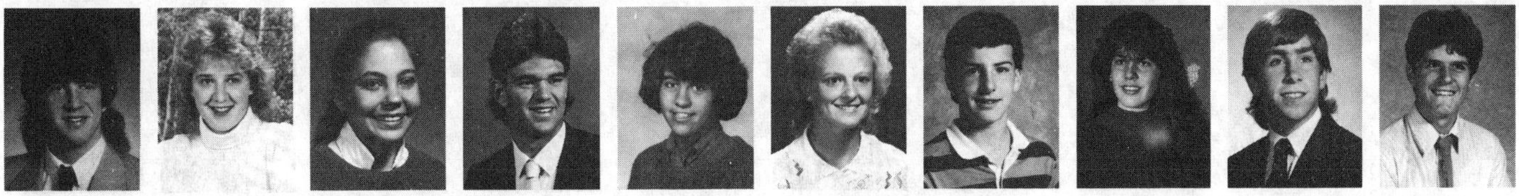

Morgan, Scott
Jamestown Area HS
Jamestown, PA

Morgan, Tammey
Sayre HS
Waverly, NY

Morganosky, Janice
Fairchance-Georges
SR HS
Mcclellandtown, PA

Morley, John
Dover Area HS
Dover, PA

Morningstar, Amber
South Western HS
Brodbecks, PA

Moroskie, Larissa
Shamokin Area HS
Shamokin, PA

Morris, David
Dallas SR HS
Trucksville, PA

Morris, Emily S
Waynesburg Central
Waynesburg, PA

Morris, III Harris L
Penncrest HS
Media, PA

Morris, Jeffrey S
Pennridge HS
Dublin, PA

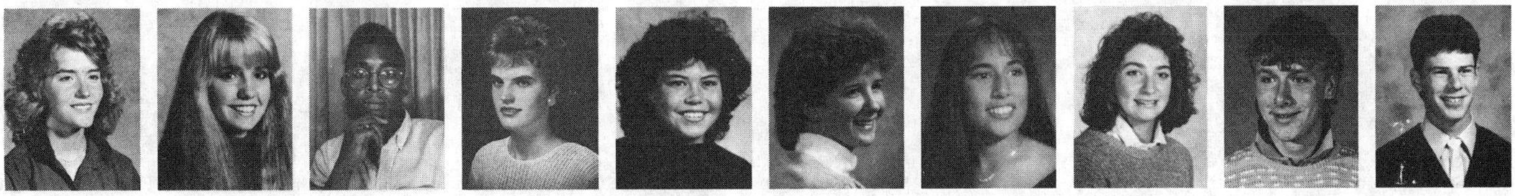

Morris, Kymberly
Phoenixville HS
Phoenixville, PA

Morris, Nicole
Shenandoah Valley
JR SR HS
Shenandoah, PA

Morris, Richard
Malik
Westinghouse HS
Pittsburgh, PA

Morris, Sharon
Pittston Area SR
Pittston, PA

Morris, Suzanne
Danville SR HS
Danville, PA

Morrison, Amy
Central Columbia
Bloomsburg, PA

Morrison, Colette
Warren Area HS
Warren, PA

Morrison, Danielle
Northampton SR
Nazareth, PA

Morrison, David
Connellsville Area
Dunbar, PA

Morrison, Matthew
Boiling Springs HS
Carlisle, PA

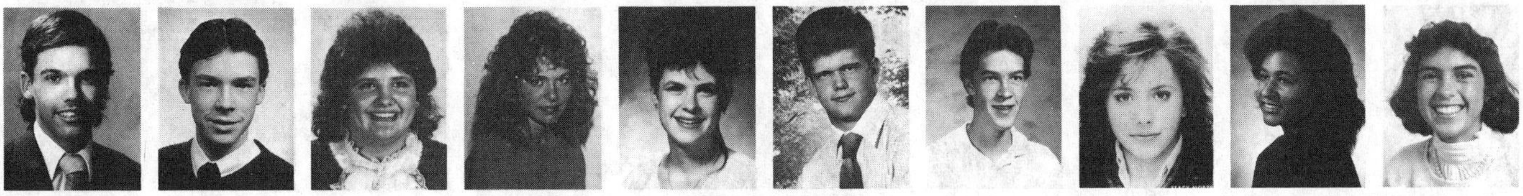

Morrison, Jr
Raymond G
Eisenhower HS
Pittsfield, PA

Morrison, Robert
Frankford HS
Philadelphia, PA

Morrone, Kim
Marion Ctr
Clymer, PA

Morroni, Kathleen
Moshannon Valley
Smithmill, PA

Morrow, Megan
Freeport Area SR
Freeport, PA

Mortimer, III Leo F
Ambridge HS
Freedom, PA

Morton, John
Biglerville HS
Biglerville, PA

Morze, Stacy
Nazareth Acad
Phila, PA

Mosely, Maria
Monessen JR & SR
Monessen, PA

Moser, Cristie
Knoch HS
Cabot, PA

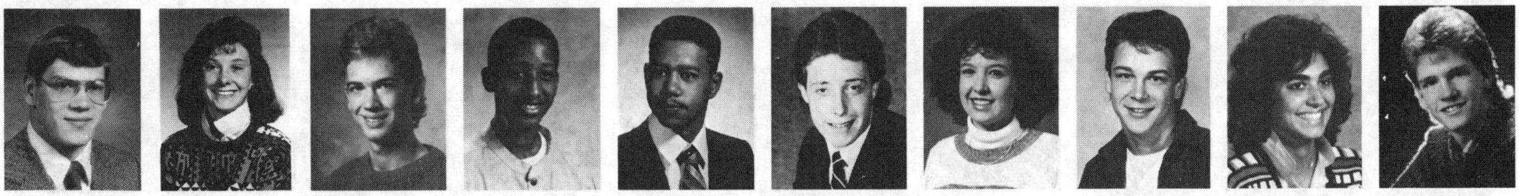

Moser, Daniel
Milton HS
New Columbia, PA

Moser, Melissa
Notre Dame HS
Easton, PA

Mosier, Randy
Trinity HS
Washington, PA

Mosley, Nicholas
Scotland Schl For
Vetrans Children
Philadelphia, PA

Moss, Eric
Central HS
Philadelphia, PA

Mott, Michael
Penn Manor HS
Elizabethtown, PA

Motta, Kristina
Steel Valley HS
Munhall, PA

Motter, Travis
South Western HS
Hanover, PA

Moukoulis, Joann
Phoenixville Area
SR HS
Phoenixville, PA

Mould, Daniel W
Lackawanna Trail
Factoryville, PA

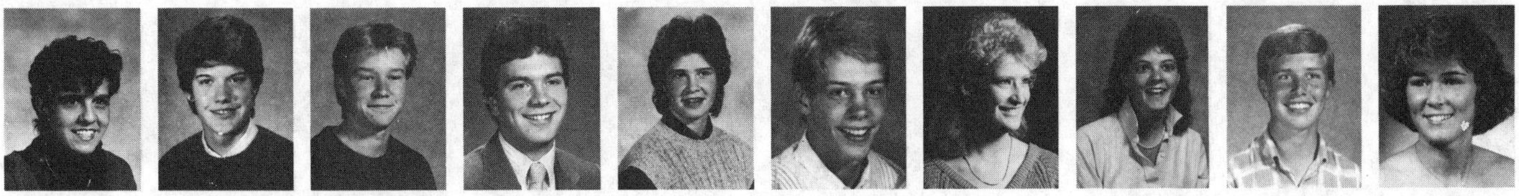

Mowad, Nicole
Danville SR HS
Danville, PA

Mower, Beth
Waynesboro Area
Waynesboro, PA

Mowery, Chris
Pottstown SR HS
Pottstown, PA

Mowrey, Brian
First Baptist Church
Sykesville, PA

Mowris, Jennifer
Meadville HS
Meadville, PA

Mowry, Bradley
Clarion Area HS
Shippenville, PA

Moyar, Gina
Canon Mc Millan
SR HS
Canonsburg, PA

Moyer, Janet
Susquenita HS
Duncannon, PA

Moyers, Jason
Henderson SR HS
Exton, PA

Mozingo, Rebecca J
Shippensburg SR
Newsburg, PA

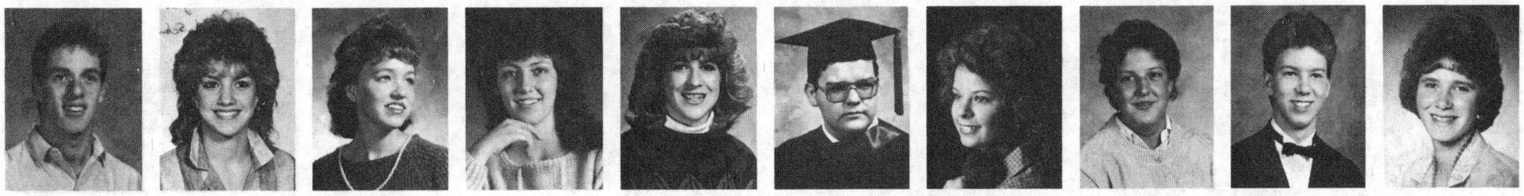

Muckey, Wesley
Conrad Weiser HS
Wernersville, PA

Mueller, Erin
Carrick HS
Pittsburgh, PA

Muir, Nancy
Connellsville Area
S Connellsville, PA

Muir, Rita
United JR SR HS
Blairsville, PA

Mulaney, Luann
Millville HS
Benton, PA

Mulholland, Joseph
Holy Ghost Prep
Philadelphia, PA

Mulholland,
Kathleen
Waynesburg Central
Waynesburg, PA

Mull, Ronda
Milton SR HS
Milton, PA

Mullen, Daniel
Cardinal O Hara HS
Broomall, PA

Mullen, Jodie
Rocky Grove JR/SR
Franklin, PA

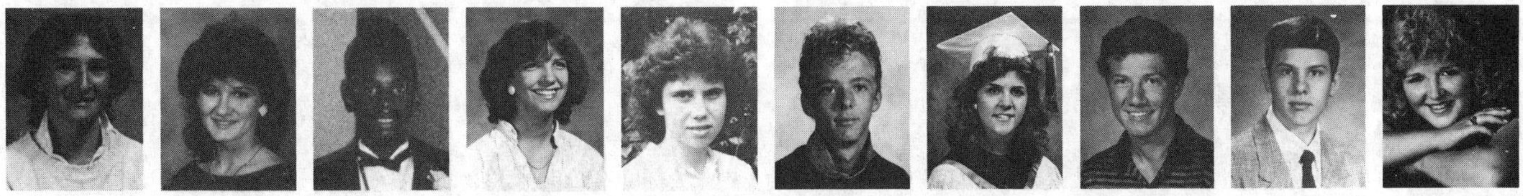

Mullen, Susan
Lock Haven SR HS
Lock Haven, PA

Mulraney, Renae
Cambria Heights SR
Elmora, PA

Mumford, Frank
Chester HS
Chester, PA

Mummert, Angela
Hanover SR HS
Hanover, PA

Mummert, Brenda
Spring Grove SR HS
Thomasville, PA

Mummert, George
Coatesville Area SR
Thorndale, PA

Munnelly, Alice
Archbishop Ryan
HS For Girls
Philadelphia, PA

Murawski, Richard
Moshannon Valley
Houtzdale, PA

Murdick, William
Butler HS
Butler, PA

Murdock, Tami
Conneaut Lake Area
Conneaut Lake, PA

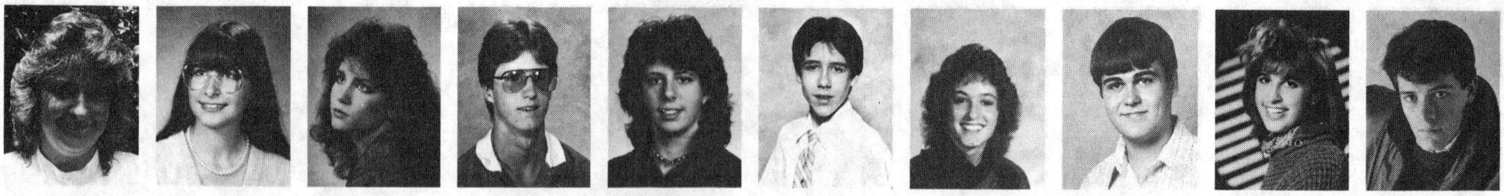

Murlo, Lorie
Panther Valley HS
Lansford, PA

Murphey, Melissa
North Star HS
Boswell, PA

Murphy, Donna
Johnstown Vo-Tech
South Fork, PA

Murphy, Jess A
Jefferson-Morgan
JR SR HS
Waynesburg, PA

Murphy, Johanna
Bishop Mc Devitt
Harrisburg, PA

Murphy, Paul
Red Lion Area SR
Red Lion, PA

Murphy, Theresa
Shade-Central City
Cairnbrk, PA

Murphy, William
High Point Baptist
Elverson, PA

Murray, April
Mohawk HS
Pulaski, PA

Murray, II Austin P
The Haverford Schl
Narberth, PA

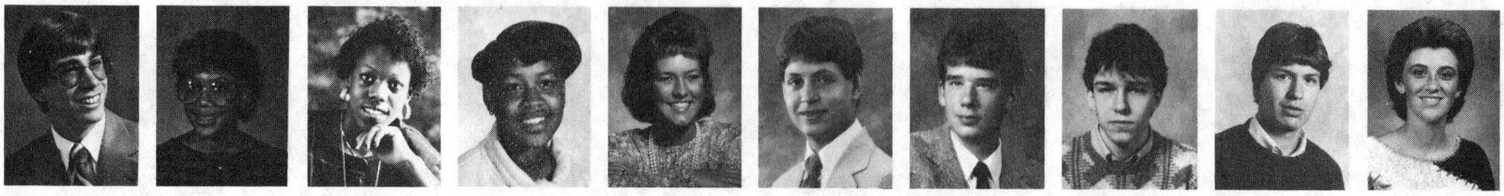

Murray, Michael W
Spring Grove Area
York, PA

Murray, Rawnette
Laurel Highlands JR
Uniontown, PA

Murray, Regina
Ambridge HS
Ambridge, PA

Murray, Reshemma
Ridley SR HS
Woodlyn, PA

Murray, Traci
North Allegheny SR
Bradfordwoods, PA

Murray, William
Vann
Shalom Christian
Hagerstown, MD

Musch, Scott
Bradford SR HS
Bradford, PA

Mushinsky, Bob
Vincentian HS
Pittsburgh, PA

Mushinsky, Russell
James M Coughlin
Wilkes Barre, PA

Musselman, Cathy
Claysburg-Kimmel
Claysburg, PA

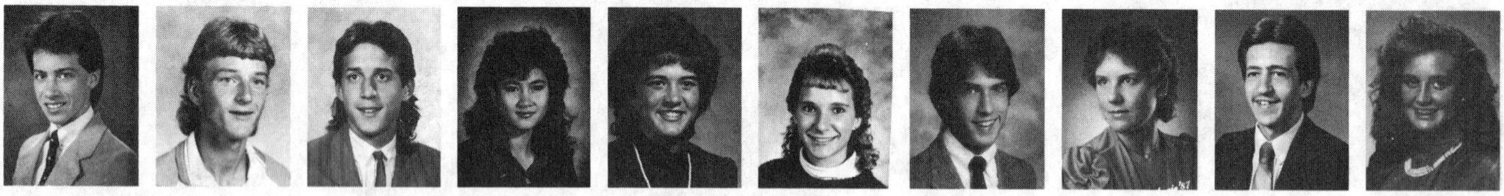

Musser, John Evans
Mt Pleasant Area
Somerset, PA

Musser, Lance
East Juniata HS
Mc Alisterville, PA

Mutch, Michael
West Mifflin Area
W Mifflin, PA

Muy, Sophong
William Penn SR
York, PA

Myer, Gwendolyn R
Lancaster Christian
Lititz, PA

Myer, Jenna
Wilson HS
Sinking Spring, PA

Myers, Andrew
MMI Prep Schl
Mountaintop, PA

Myers, Angela K
South Western HS
Hanover, PA

Myers, Barry E
Northeastern HS
York Haven, PA

Myers, Christy
Hempfield HS
Lancaster, PA

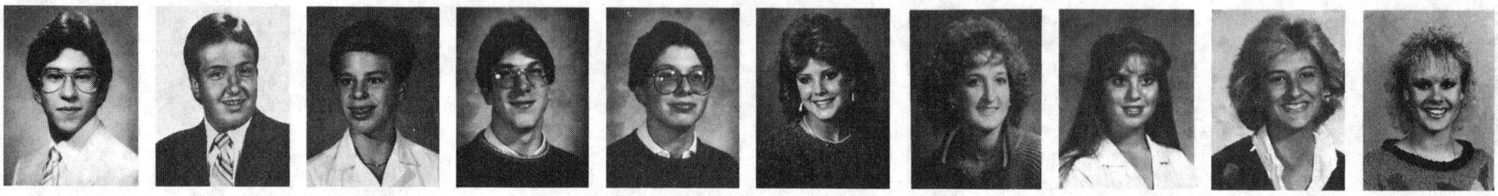

Myers, Dave
Blue Mountain HS
Schuylkill Haven,
PA

Myers, Jason
Uniontown Area HS
Markleysburg, PA

Myers, Jeff
Laurel Highlands
Lemont Furnace, PA

Myers, Jeffrey
Wm Penn SR HS
York, PA

Myers, Lisa
Wm Penn SR HS
York, PA

Myers, Nicole
Newport HS
Newport, PA

Myers, Pamela
Central Catholic HS
Coplay, PA

Myers, Stephanie M
Red Land HS
Lewisberry, PA

Myers, Tina
Carlisle SR HS
Carlisle, PA

Myford, Megan
Freeport Area HS
Sarver, PA

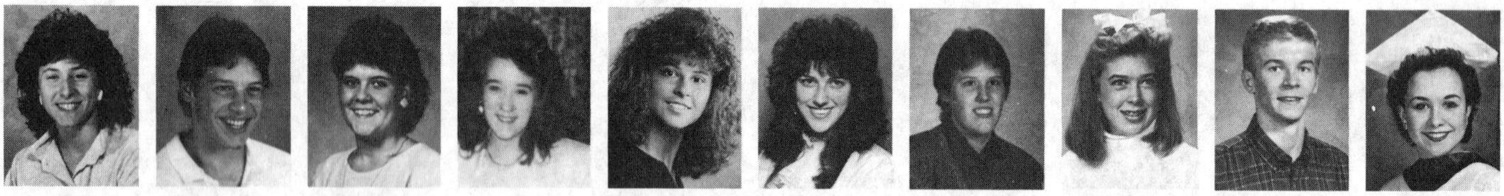

Mylan, Lori
Jefferson-Morgan
Clarksville, PA

Nadzady, Joseph
Homer Center HS
Coral, PA

Nagle, Donna
Cambria Heights HS
Patton, PA

Nagy, Donna J
Freeport Area SR
Freeport, PA

Nagy, Michelle
Blairsville SR HS
Blairsville, PA

Nale, Deanna
E Juniata HS
Mcalisterville, PA

Nalesnik, Cathy
Palmerton Area HS
Palmerton, PA

Nalevanko, Kathryn
Abington Heights
Dalton, PA

Namesnik, Eric
Butler SR HS
Butler, PA

Napoli, Maria
Cardinal O Hara HS
Springfield, PA

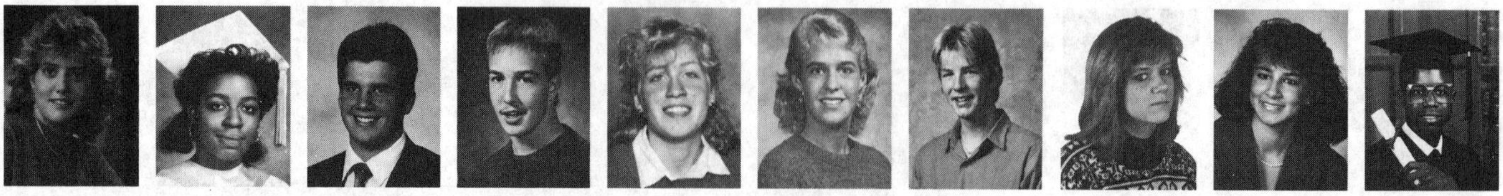

Napovanic, Noelle A
Mononhahela Valley
Catholic HS
Donora, PA

Napson, Theresa
West Catholic Girls
Philadelphia, PA

Nardone, James
Albert
Pittston Area SR
Pittston, PA

Naser, Howard
Washington HS
Washington, PA

Nash, Marilyn
Lebanon Catholic
Lebanon, PA

Naski, Kimberly
Strath Haven HS
Wallingford, PA

Nasman, Shaun
Warren Area HS
Russell, PA

Nass, Christine M
St Basil Acad
Philadelphia, PA

Nath, Ritika
Mt Lebanon HS
Pittsburgh, PA

Nathan, Horace
Simon Gratz HS
Philadelphia, PA

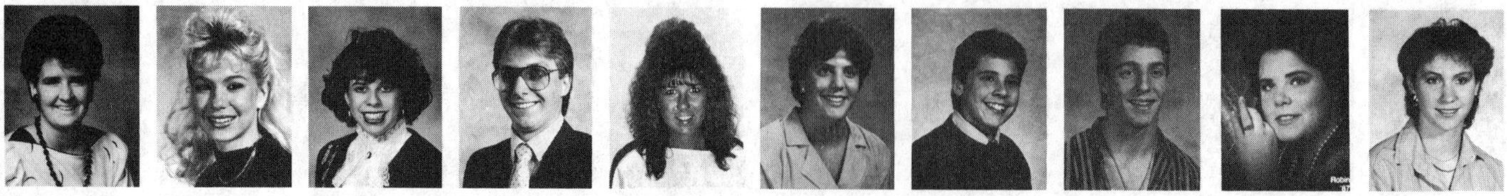

Naumann, Lisa M
Oley Valley HS
Oley, PA

Navas, Laurie
Canevin Catholic
Pittsburgh, PA

Naveh, Sharon
Parkland HS
Allentown, PA

Nawrocki,
Christopher
Nativity BVM HS
New Philadelphi,
PA

Nawrocki, Eldena
Pocono Central
Catholic HS
Gouldsboro, PA

Naylor, Debra
Northeastern HS
Manchester, PA

Neal, Matthew
St Plus X HS
Douglassville, PA

Neal, Michael
Donegal HS
Marietta, PA

Neal, Robin Lynn
Franklin JR/SR HS
Polk, PA

Nealman, Stephanie
Norristown Area HS
Norristown, PA

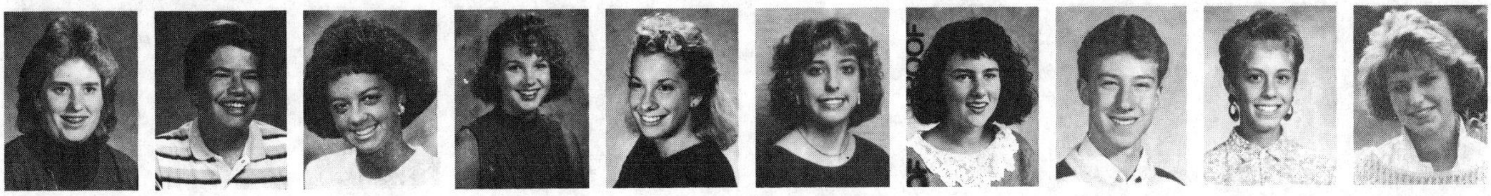

Nearhood, Krista
West Branch Area
Kylertown, PA

Nederostek, Douglas
Catasauqua HS
Catasauqua, PA

Neff, Tonya
Garden Spot HS
New Holland, PA

Negler, Jennifer
Cedar Cliff HS
Camp Hill, PA

Negley, Becky
Saltsburg JR/SR HS
Clarksburg, PA

Negvesky, Maria E
Central Columbia
Bloomsburg, PA

Neibert, Jill
Mechanisburg SR
Mechanicsburg, PA

Neigh, Matthew
Butler HS
Butler, PA

Neiman, Shelbi A
Quakertown
Community SR HS
Quakertown, PA

Neipert, Renee L
Pocono Mountain
Tobyhanna, PA

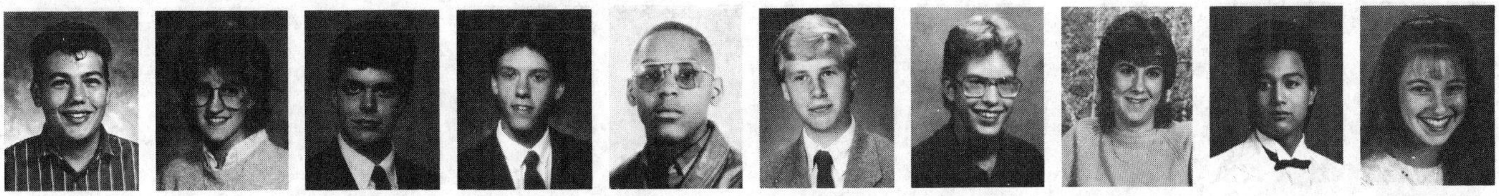

Neiswonger, Kevin
Mercer JR SR HS
Mercer, PA

Nelson, Bridget
Corry Area HS
Corry, PA

Nelson, Don
Central Dauphin HS
Harrisburg, PA

Nelson, Edward
Warren Area HS
Warren, PA

Nelson, Haikeem
Sister Clara
Muhammad HS
Philadelphia, PA

Nelson, Michael G
B Reed Henderson
SR HS
West Chester, PA

Nelson, Todd
Penn Trafford HS
Irwin, PA

Nemeth, Phylann
Towanda HS
Wysox, PA

Nepomuceno, Randy
Ray
Saint Josephs Prep
Jenkintown, PA

Neral, Melissa
Penn Trafford HS
Irwin, PA

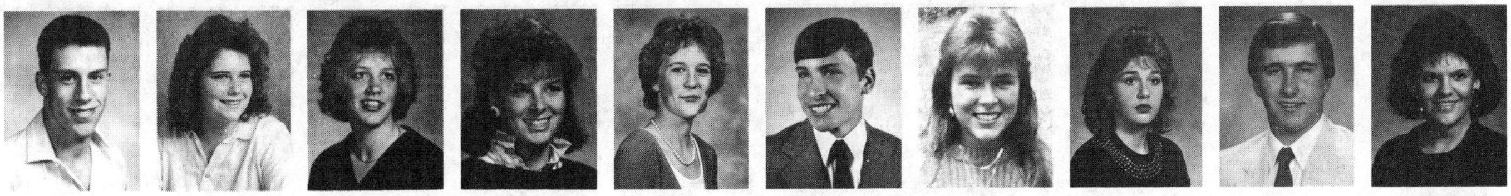

Neri, John
Neshaminy
Longhorne HS
Feasterville, PA

Nesbitt, Jill
Archbishop Carroll
King Of Prussia, PA

Nesbitt, Susan
Ambridge Area HS
Ambridge, PA

Ness, Anissa
Christian Schl Of
Dallastown, PA

Nester, Christine
Spring-Ford SR HS
Royersford, PA

Nestor, Adam
Blacklick Valley
JR-SR HS
Nanty Glo, PA

Nestor, Julie
Richland HS
Mars, PA

Netterblade,
Jeannine
West Branch Area
JR-SR HS
Lanse, PA

Nettles, Jr James A
Minersville Area HS
Pottsville, PA

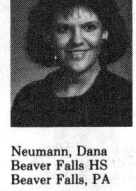

Neumann, Dana
Beaver Falls HS
Beaver Falls, PA

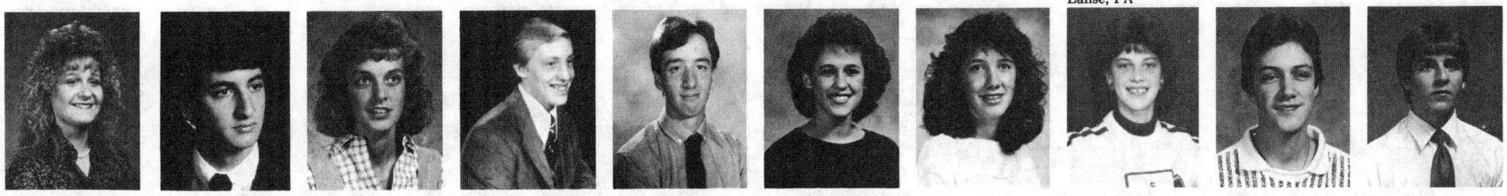

Neumann, Serina
Northern Lehigh HS
Slatington, PA

Neumyer, Todd M
Central Dauphin E
Harrisburg, PA

Neustadter, Amy
Hempfield HS
Lancaster, PA

Nevel, Michael
Berwick Area SR
Berwick, PA

Newcamp, James
Mercy Hurst Prep
Erie, PA

Newcomb, Kris
Bethel Christian HS
Erie, PA

Newcomer, Emily
Pennsbury HS
Yardley, PA

Newell, Shelley
John S Fine HS
Nanticoke, PA

Newhart, Brian
Millville HS
Bloomsburg, PA

Newton, Scott
Marian HS
Nesquehoning, PA

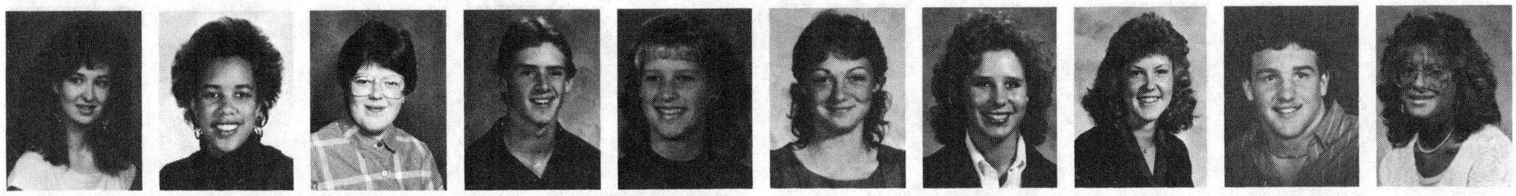

Nicholls, Heather
Solanco HS
Quarryville, PA

Nichols, Jill
Philadelphia HS For
Philadelphia, PA

Nichols, Sharon L
Calvary Baptist
Hatfield, PA

Nicholson, Jr P
Geoffrey
Kennard Dale HS
Delta, PA

Nickelson, Erin
Connellsville Area
SR HS
Connellsville, PA

Nickey, Lisa
Donegal HS
Marietta, PA

Nicklaus, Karen
Lancaster Catholic
Lancaster, PA

Nicodemus, Kelly
Bedford HS
Manns Choice, PA

Nicol, David
Beaver Area SR HS
Beaver, PA

Nicolo, Lisa
Cameron County HS
Emporium, PA

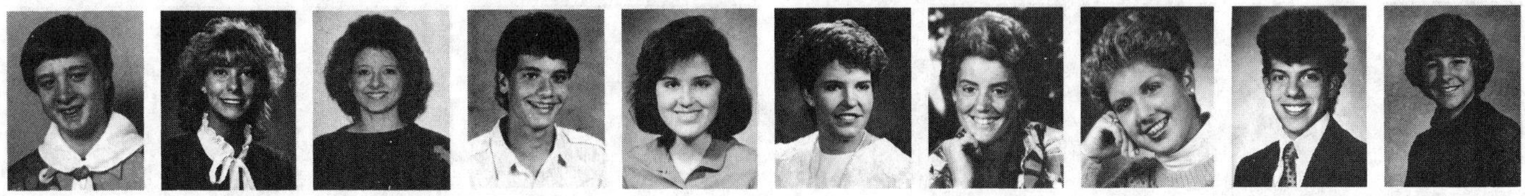

Niedzwiecki, John
Nativity B V M HS
Orwigsburg, PA

Niehaus, Amy
Wyomissing Area
Wyomissing, PA

Nieroda, Christine
Norht Pocono HS
Moscow, PA

Nigut, Bryan
Penn Trafford HS
Irwin, PA

Nikolopoulos, Peggy
St Basil Acad
Philadelphia, PA

Nissley, Kristin
Bishop Mcdevitt HS
Harrisburg, PA

Nissly, Sharon L
Donegal HS
Mt Joy, PA

Nitterhouse, Jodi
Chambersburg Area
SR HS
Chambersburg, PA

Nix, James
Mt Lebanon HS
Pittsburgh, PA

Noble, Tricia M
Owen J Roberts HS
Pottstown, PA

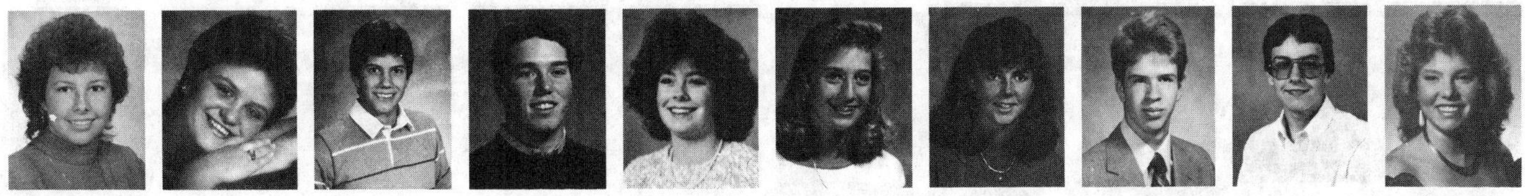

Nocek, Cathy
Wyoming Area HS
West Wyoming, PA

Noel, Kelley
Danville SR HS
Danville, PA

Noel, Michael
Outler Area SR HS
Butler, PA

Noll, Christopher
Newport HS
Newport, PA

Noll, Melissa
Center Area HS
Monaca, PA

Nolt, Kristin
Hempfeild HS
Lancaster, PA

Noonan, Kathy
Cumberland Valley
Mechanicsburg, PA

Norman, Thomas
Northern Chester
County Tech Schl
Phoenixville, PA

Noullet, Scott
Peters Twp HS
Venetia, PA

Nouse, Stacie
Dover Area HS
Dover, PA

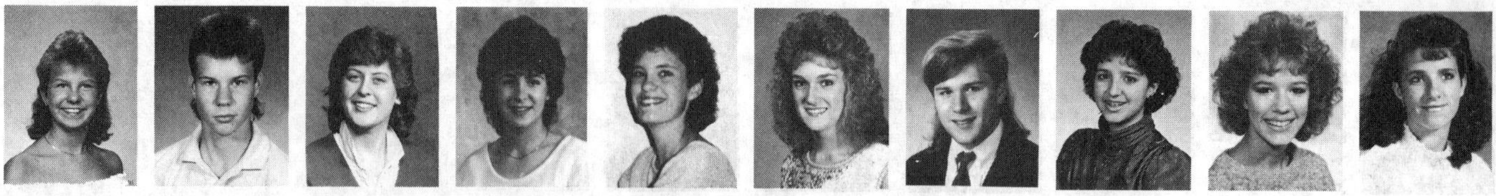

Nouse, Susan
Middletown Area
Middletown, PA

Novak, Don
Monessen JR SR
Monessen, PA

Novak, Janette
North Catholic HS
Allison Park, PA

Novak, Shelly
United JR SR HS
Blairsville, PA

Novakoski, Sharon
Valley SR HS
New Kensington, PA

Novella, Dianne
Northern Cambria
Spangler, PA

Novello, Jay C
Henderson HS
W Chester, PA

Novobilski, Patricia
Carbondale Area HS
Simpson, PA

Nucci, Terri
Charleroi Area HS
Stockdale, PA

Nugent, Mary
Council Rock HS
Wash Corss, PA

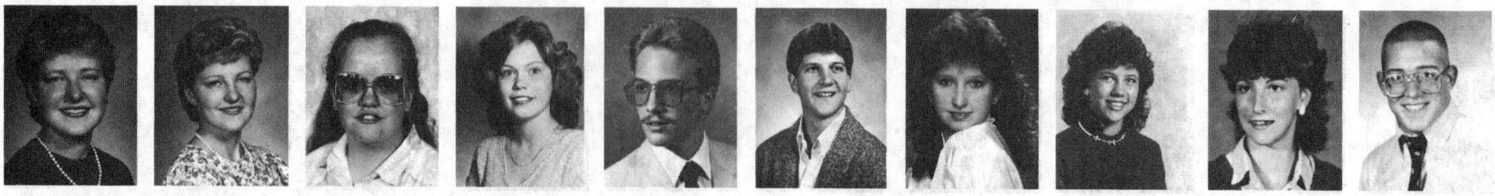

Nulty, Amy
Nazareth Acad
Philadelphia, PA

Nulty, Leslie
Nazareth Acad
Philadelphia, PA

Nunamaker, June
Dayton JR/SR HS
Templeton, PA

Nurss, Leanne
Wilson Christian
Mckeesport, PA

Nutter, Scott
Christian School Of
Wrightsville, PA

Nuzzo, Michael M
Bethel Park SR HS
Bethel Park, PA

Nypaver, Patty
Springdale HS
Harwick, PA

O Boyle, Laura Beth
Pocono Central Catholic HS
Pocono Summit, PA

O Brien, Debra
Connellsville SR HS
S Connellsville, PA

O Brien, Kevin E
Bethlehem Catholic
Allentown, PA

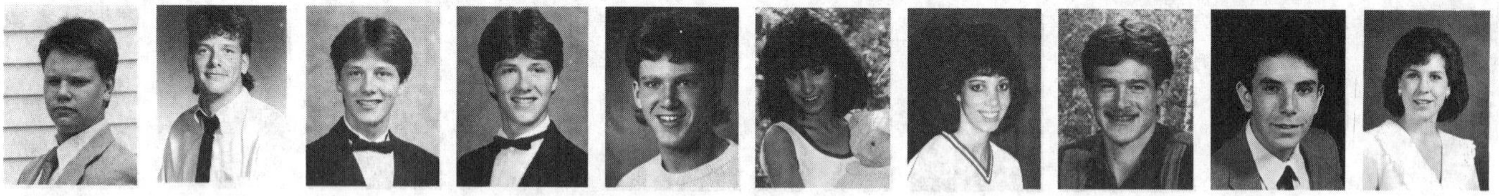

O Brien, Philip
Pittston Area HS
Inkerman, PA

O Connell, Shaun
Notre Dame HS
Easton, PA

O Connor, Chris
St James H S For
Brookhaven, PA

O Connor, Kevin Francis
St James Catholic
Brookhaven, PA

O Connor, Michael B
Trinity HS
Washington, PA

O Donnell, Heather
Mid-Valley Secondary HS
Dickson City, PA

O Donnell, Jeniffer
Lincoln HS
Ellwood City, PA

O Donnell, Robert
Towanda Area HS
Towanda, PA

O Malley, David
Cardinal O Hara HS
Springfield, PA

O Meara, Amy K
Mount St Joseph
Huntingdon Valley, PA

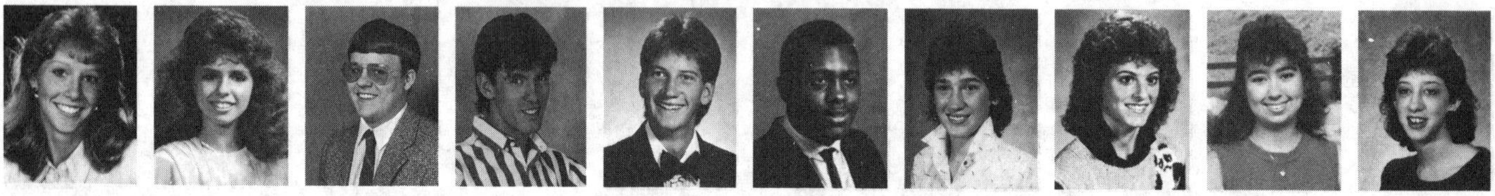

O Neal, Kelley E
Henderson HS
West Chester, PA

O Neil, Shannon
Cedar Crest HS
Lebanon, PA

O Neill, Patrick
Bishop Hafey HS
White Haven, PA

O Shea, Patrick
Beaver Area JR SR
Beaver, PA

Oakes, Duane M
Downingtown SR
Exton, PA

Oakley, Bryan
Chartiers-Houston
Houston, PA

Oaks, Cindy
Harmony HS
Westover, PA

Oates, Michelle
Linesville HS
Linesville, PA

Ober, Geraldine
Hopewell HS
Aliquippa, PA

Ober, Tracy
Yough SR HS
Irwin, PA

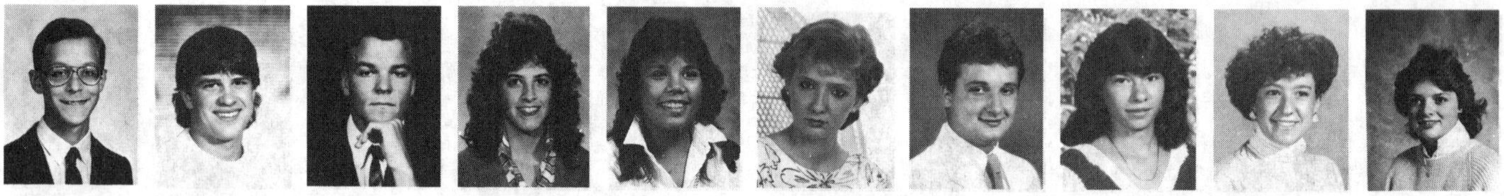

Oberhardt, Matthew
Trinity HS
Camp Hill, PA

Oberlander, Mike
Fort Le Boeuf HS
Waterford, PA

Oberman, James
Liberty HS
Bethlehem, PA

Obes, Nicole
John S Fine HS
Nanticoke, PA

Ocampo, Beth
Hempfield HS
Mountville, PA

Oconnell, Jayne
Williamsport Area
Williamsport, PA

Odelli, Terry
Yough HS
Smithton, PA

Oesterling, Dianne
Butler Area SR HS
Butler, PA

Offshack, Kristine
Plymouth-Whitemarsh HS
Norristown, PA

Ogozaly, Laura
Carbondale Area JR SR HS
Carbondale, PA

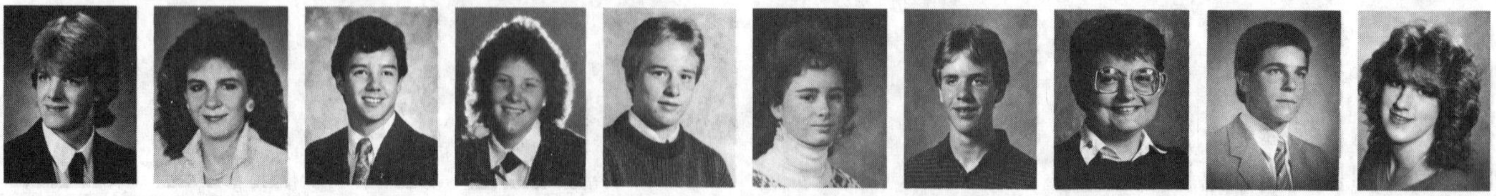

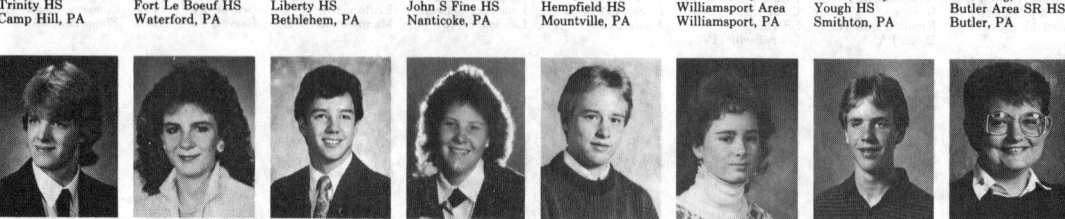

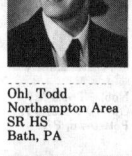

Ohl, Todd
Northampton Area SR HS
Bath, PA

Ohlrich, Christina
Technical Memorial
Erie, PA

Okamoto, Neil E
Council Rock HS
Holland, PA

Olczak, Laura
Mc Guffey HS
Prosperity, PA

Oley, Richard
James M Coughlin
Plainsville, PA

Oliver, April
Washington HS
Washington, PA

Oliver, Mark
North Allegheny HS
Pittsburgh, PA

Olosky, Christi
Du Bois Area SR
Du Bois, PA

Omlor, Stephen
Millville HS
Millville, PA

Oncay, Rebecca Katherine
Wyoming Valley West HS
Swoyersville, PA

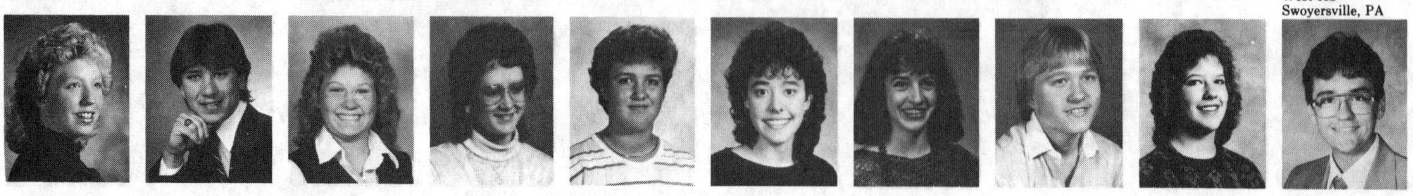

Onder, Sharon
Portage JR SR HS
Portage, PA

Ondish, Mike
Norwin SR HS
N Huntingdon, PA

Onimus, Melissa
Nazareth Acad
Philadelphia, PA

Opel, Kathy
Brownsville Area HS
W Brownsville, PA

Opperman, Sharon B
Brandywine Heights
Fleetwood, PA

Orem, Lynn
Nazareth Area SR
Tatamy, PA

Organ, Jodi
Punxsutawney SR
Punxsutawney, PA

Orlick, Christoher
Neshaminy HS
Langhorne, PA

Orloff, Erica A
Nativity BVM HS
Cumbola, PA

Orlowski, James
Ambridge Area HS
Ambridge, PA

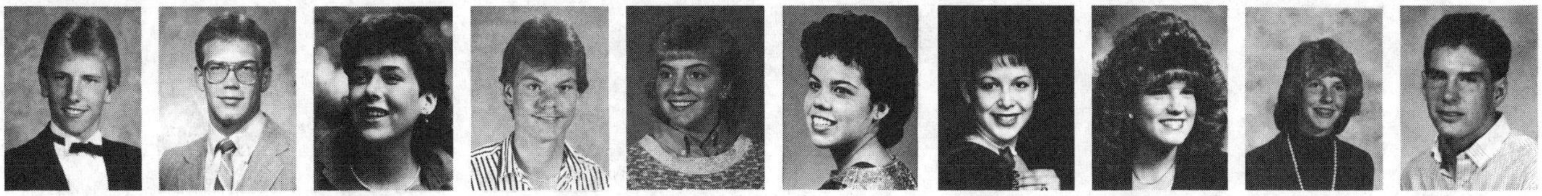

Ormond, Valdamir
Father Judge HS
Philadelphia, PA

Orndorff, Robbie
Connellsville Area
Mill Run, PA

Orner, Melissa K
Oxford Area HS
Oxford, PA

Orobono, Michael
Downingtown SR
West Chester, PA

Orr, Jamie
Connelsville Area
SR HS
Dawson, PA

Ortigoza, Brenda
Gateway HS
Monroeville, PA

Ortiz, Myra
Little Flower HS
Philadelphia, PA

Orvosh, La Rayne
Kiski Area HS
Saltsburg, PA

Osborne, Jennifer
Solanco HS
Quarryville, PA

Oshea, Eric
Moshannon Valley
Houtzdale, PA

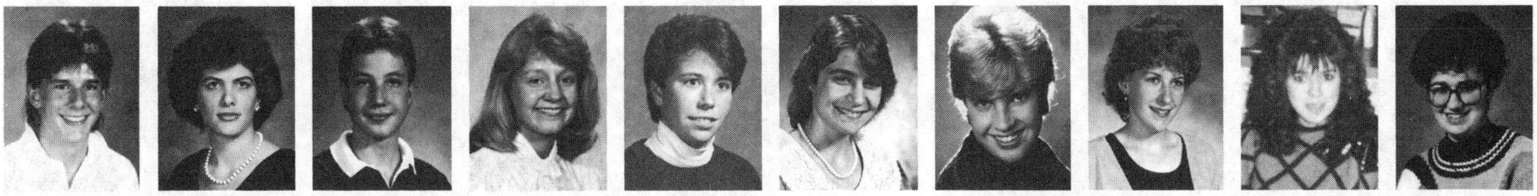

Oskin, Jeff
Penn-Trafford HS
Irwin, PA

Ososki, Melissa
Cardinal O Hara HS
Milmont Park, PA

Osterrieder, Scott E
Richland HS
Gibsonia, PA

Ostovic, Sarah
Washington HS
Washington, PA

Ostoyich, Jennifer
Council Rock HS
Holland, PA

Ostroski, Lori Ann
Reading SR HS
Reading, PA

Ostrowski, Lori
Pittston Area HS
Pittston, PA

Osullivan, Maureen
Elk Lake HS
Laceyville, PA

Oteri, Corinne
Northeast Prep HS
Philadelphia, PA

Otoole, Maureen
Steel Valley HS
Homestead, PA

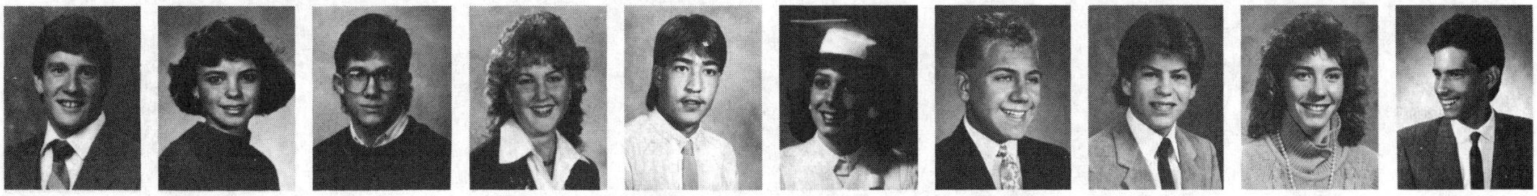

Ott, Dan
Punxsutawney Area
SR HS
Big Run, PA

Ott, Dana
Abington Heights
Chinchilla, PA

Ott, Gary
Du Bois Area HS
Du Bois, PA

Ott, Kathy
Saint Benedict Acad
Erie, PA

Ott, Ron
Meadville Area SR
Meadville, PA

Otto, Roseanne
Scotland Schl For
Veterans Children
Aldan, PA

Ovitsky, Eric
Hempfield Area HS
Greensburg, PA

Owens, Brian
Clearfield HS
Clearfield, PA

Owings, Heidi
Biglerville HS
Biglerville, PA

Pacak, Robert S
Monessen HS
Monessen, PA

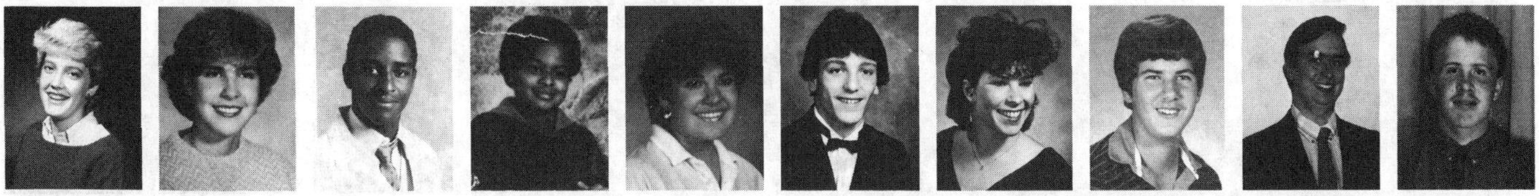

Packard, Terri
Troy HS
Troy, PA

Pacoe, Elizabeth
Sacred Heart HS
Pittsburgh, PA

Padgett,
Aleksondrick D
York Catholic HS
York, PA

Padgett, Malik
Chevez
York Catholic HS
York, PA

Pagano, Sandra
Greensburg Central
Catholic HS
New Stanton, PA

Paglia, Anthony M
Cardinal O Hara HS
Aston, PA

Pagliaro, Susanna F
Strath Haven HS
Swartmore, PA

Pagotto, Christopher
Northampton Area
JR HS
Northampton, PA

Paida, Douglas
Bishop Shanahan
W Chester, PA

Painter, Jr Russ
Highlands HS
Tarentum, PA

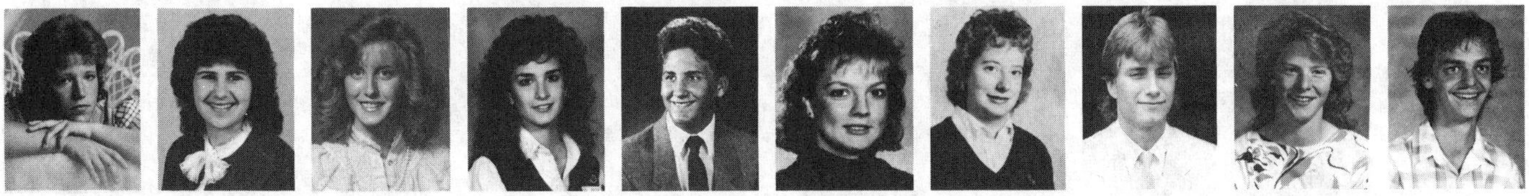

Painter, Tiffany
Seneca Valley SR
Evans City, PA

Paisley, Janet L
Tamaqua Area HS
Tamaqua, PA

Pajak, Jo Ellen
Hopewell HS
Aliquippa, PA

Palaia, Laurie
Nazareth Acad
Philadelphia, PA

Palastro, Gregg
Chartiers Valley HS
Carnegie, PA

Palczewski, Roxanne
John S Fine HS
Nanticoke, PA

Paletski, Marla Ann
Bishop Hafey HS
Hazleton, PA

Palm, Michael
Charleroi Area HS
Charleroi, PA

Palmer, Ellen
Donegal HS
Maytown, PA

Palmer, Ricky
Oxford Area HS
Oxford, PA

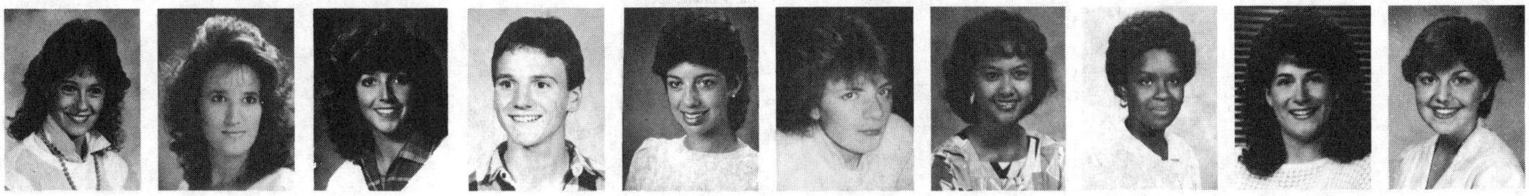

Palmiero, Allison
Meadville HS
Meadville, PA

Palombi, Sue
Carlynton HS
Carnegie, PA

Palumbo, Kelly
Neshannock HS
New Castle, PA

Paluselli, Andy
North Allegheny HS
Pittsburgh, PA

Paluso, Cynthia L
Mc Guffey HS
Washington, PA

Panczak, Christina
Northern Cambria
Ebensburg, PA

Panganiban,
Zsandra
Bishop Neumann
Montoursville, PA

Pankey, Michaele
W Catholic HS For
Philadelphia, PA

Pantaleo, Kim
Hopewell HS
Aliquippa, PA

Papoutsis, Diane
South Western HS
Hanover, PA

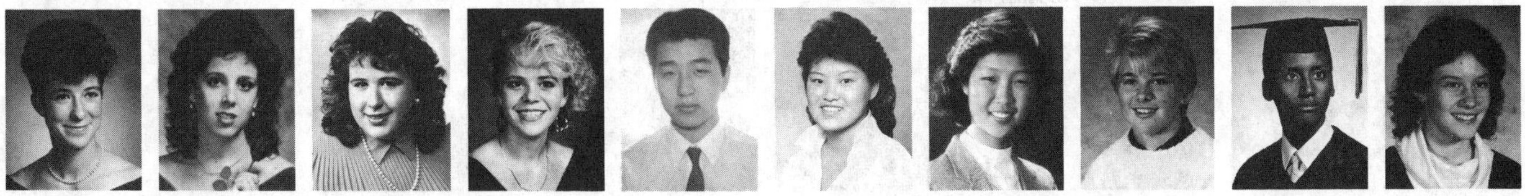

Papp, Susan
Spring-Ford SR HS
Limerick, PA

Paquet, Karen
Interboro HS
Prospect Park, PA

Pardi, Carolyn M
Greater Latrobe HS
Latrobe, PA

Parent, Dawn
St Plus X HS
Pottstown, PA

Park, Jae
Engineering &
Science HS
Philadelphia, PA

Park, Joanne
Blue Mountain Acad
Pottsville, PA

Park, Lisa
Radnor HS
Newtown Square,
PA

Park, Sherri
Greencastle-Antrim
Waynesboro, PA

Parker, Dean W
Central HS
Philadelphia, PA

Parker, Jodi
Danville Area JR
Washingtonville, PA

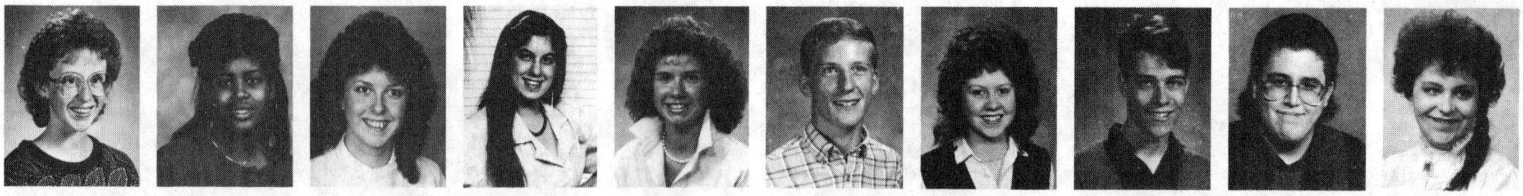

Parker, Kristi
Linesville Conneaut Summit HS
Conneaut Lk, PA

Parker, Leslie Rene
Bensalem HS
Trevose, PA

Parkhurst, Donanne
Hempfield Area SR
Manor, PA

Parks, Jo L
New Brighton Area SR HS
New Brighton, PA

Parks, Michelle
Conemaugh Township HS
Jerome, PA

Parlett, Michael
Kennard Dale HS
Stewartstown, PA

Parlier, Rebecca
Christian Life Acad
West Pittston, PA

Parr, David
Richland HS
Valencia, PA

Parrotto, Joseph
North Catholic HS
Allison Park, PA

Parry, Amy
Du Bois Area HS
Du Bois, PA

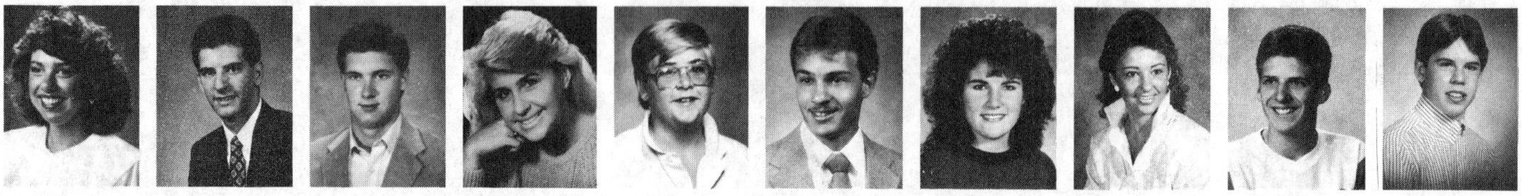

Parry, Kimberly
Nazareth Area SR
Nazareth, PA

Parsch, Jr John C
Hollidaysburg Area
Hollidaysburg, PA

Parson, Tim
West Greene HS
Windridge, PA

Parsons, Brenda
Wellsboro SR HS
Wellsboro, PA

Parsons, James
Ringgold HS
Monongahela, PA

Parsons, Troy S
Frobes Road HS
Hustontown, PA

Partington, Megan
Seneca Valley HS
Zelienople, PA

Paruso, Leslie A
Brockway Area HS
Falls Creek, PA

Pash, John
Lakeland HS
Jermyn, PA

Pashel, Jr Robert
Peabody HS
Pittsburgh, PA

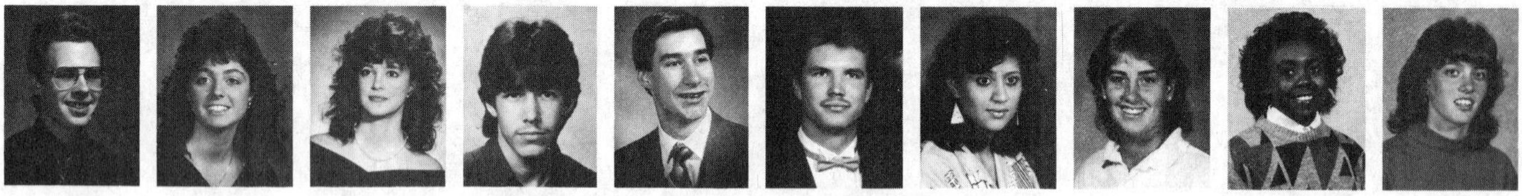

Pasich, Stephen
Marian HS
Haddock, PA

Pasqualini, Christina
Archbishop Kennedy HS
Conshohocken, PA

Pasquarello, Lisa
Villa Maria Acad
Glenmoore, PA

Passmore, Matthew
Curwensville Area
Curwensville, PA

Pastor, Jr Frank
North Hills HS
Pittsburgh, PA

Pastor, Samuel
Duquesne HS
Duquesne, PA

Patel, Manisha
Pocono Mountain
Canadensis, PA

Patete, Dana
Hollidaysburg Area
Duncansville, PA

Patmon, Daughn La Rae
Canon Mc Millan
Canonsburg, PA

Patrick, Julia
Harverford SR HS
Havertown, PA

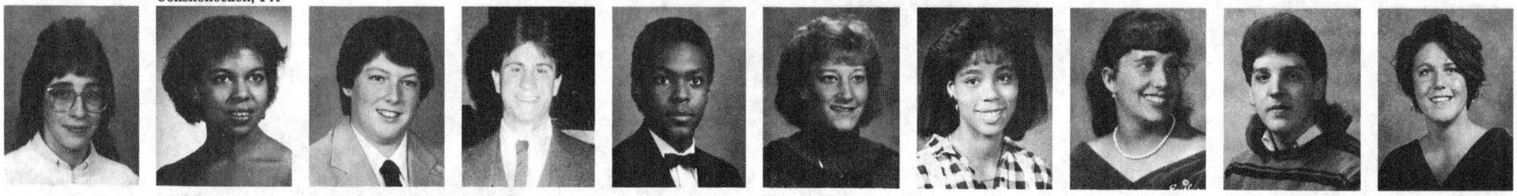

Patrick, Paula S
Greensburg Central Catholic HS
Greensburg, PA

Patrinos, Nya
Central HS
Philadelphia, PA

Patterson, Brandon
Mt Pleasant Area
Mt Pleasant, PA

Patterson, Christopher
Father Judge HS
Philadelphia, PA

Patterson, Eric V
Cardinal Dougherty
Philadelphia, PA

Patterson, Lori
Hanover SR HS
Hanover, PA

Patterson, Stephanie
Washington HS
Washington, PA

Patterson, Valerie
Coatesville Area SR
Coatesville, PA

Patton, Bradley
Wyoming Valley West HS
Luzerne, PA

Paul, Christine M
Mount St Joseph
Dresher, PA

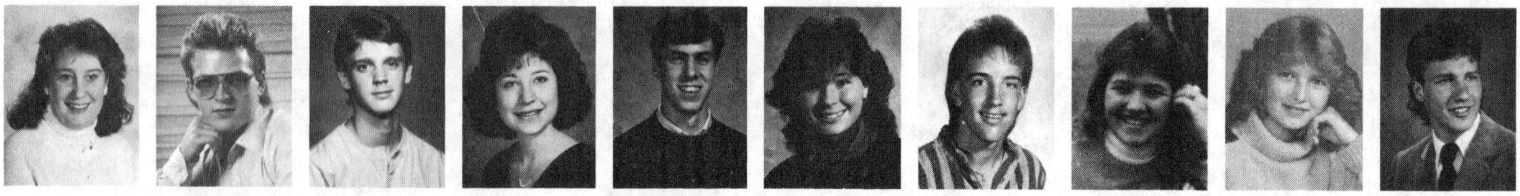

Paul, Melissa
Bishop Mc Cort HS
Johnstown, PA

Paul, Mike
Bethlehem Center SR HS
Marianna, PA

Pauley, Garry
Ringgold HS
Monongahela, PA

Paulina, Maria
Cardinal O Hara HS
Havertown, PA

Pauling, William
Watsontow Christian Acad
Montgomery, PA

Pavalone, Pamela Sue
Carbondale Area JR/SR HS
Carbondale, PA

Pavelik, Eric
Scott Intermediate
Coatesville, PA

Pavlick, Dawn
Lake-Lehman SR
Hunlock Crk, PA

Pavlick, Robyn
Lake Lehman HS
Hunlock Creek, PA

Pavlocak, Jeff
Mt Pleasant HS
Mt Pleasant, PA

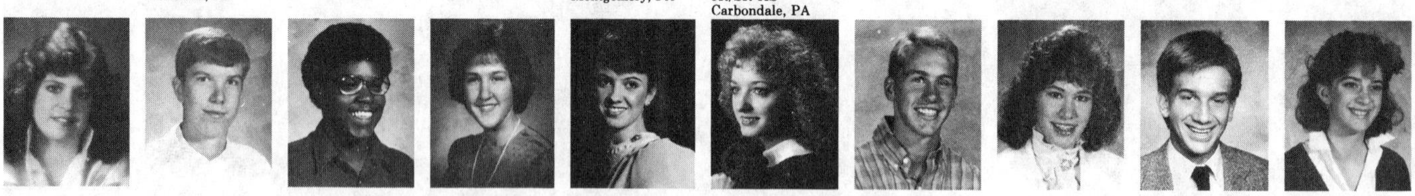

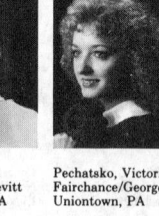

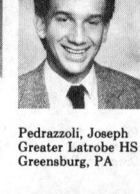

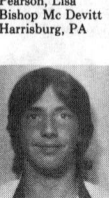

Pavtis, Laurie
Belle Vernon Area
Belle Vernon, PA

Pawlowicz, Jerry T
Knoch HS
Butler, PA

Payne, Adrienne
Garden Spot HS
Bowmansville, PA

Peachey, Gwendolyn K
Kishacoquillas JR/SR HS
Belleville, PA

Pearson, Lisa
Bishop Mc Devitt
Harrisburg, PA

Pechatsko, Victoria
Fairchance/Georges
Uniontown, PA

Pechin, G Keith
Oxford Area HS
Oxford, PA

Peciulis, Lori
Knoch JR SR HS
Sarver, PA

Pedrazzoli, Joseph
Greater Latrobe HS
Greensburg, PA

Peffley, Andrea
Governor Mifflin SR
Shillington, PA

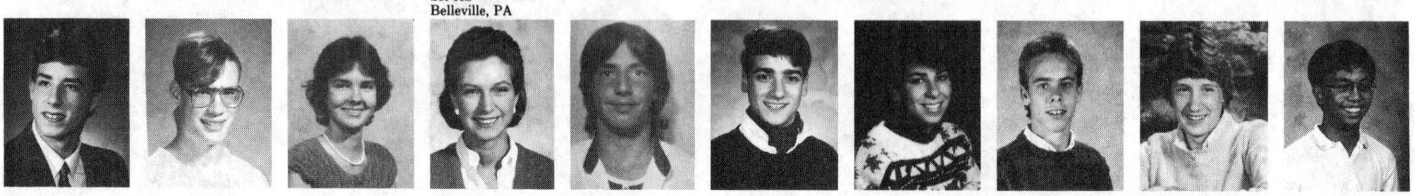

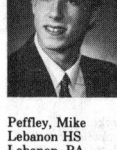

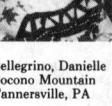

Peffley, Mike
Lebanon HS
Lebanon, PA

Peich, Brent
Henderson HS
West Chester, PA

Peifer, Laurel
Milton Area SR HS
Milton, PA

Peiffer, Anissa
Cedar Crest HS
Lebanon, PA

Peirce, Francis R
Bishop Egan HS
Philadelphia, PA

Pellegrino, Brian
Butler SR HS
Butler, PA

Pellegrino, Danielle
Pocono Mountain
Tannersville, PA

Pelotte, Michael
Downingtown SR
Chester Springs, PA

Pelton, Michele
Northeast Bradford JR SR HS
Rome, PA

Pena, Ernest
Cedar Cliff HS
Mechanicsburg, PA

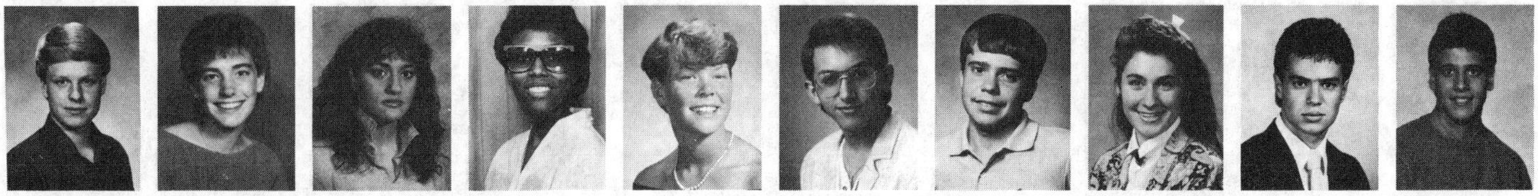

Pencek, Mark
Abington Heights
Clarks Summit, PA

Penecale, Gina
Upper Moreland HS
Hatboro, PA

Penland, Michele
Archbishop Carroll
Wayne, PA

Pennick, Kelly
Penn Center Acad
Philadelphia, PA

Peoples, Brenda
Perkiomen Valley
SR HS
Harleysville, PA

Pepe, Joseph C
State College Area
Boalsburg, PA

Pepke, Alexander
Ringgold HS
Elrama, PA

Peranich, Melissa
West Scranton HS
Scranton, PA

Pereira, Leonardo
Lower Merion HS
Merion, PA

Peretin, Jeffrey
Baldwin HS
Pittsburgh, PA

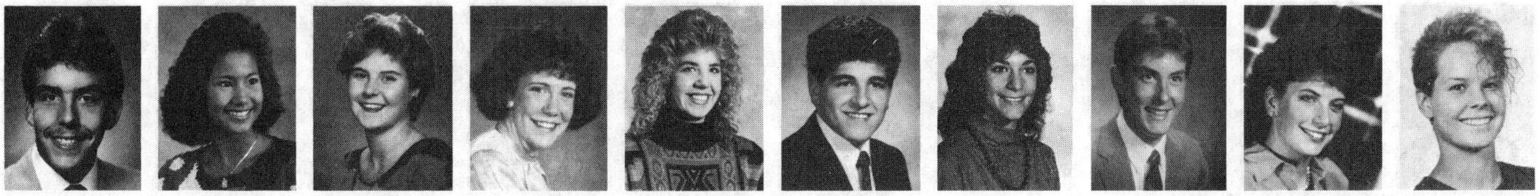

Peretin, Joe
Baldwin HS
Pittsburgh, PA

Perez, Gemma
Geibel HS
Connellsville, PA

Perini, Kendra Sue
Lebanon Catholic
Lebanon, PA

Perkins, Melissa
Hempfield Area HS
Greensburg, PA

Perkins, Pamela M
Bishop Hoban HS
Mountaintop, PA

Perla, Anthony
Central Catholic HS
Pittsburgh, PA

Pero, Kelly
Meadville SR HS
Meadville, PA

Perose, Robert
William Allen HS
Allentown, PA

Perricone, Carrie
Brandywine Heights
Area HS
Alburtis, PA

Perrine, Jennifer
Moon SR HS
Coraopolis, PA

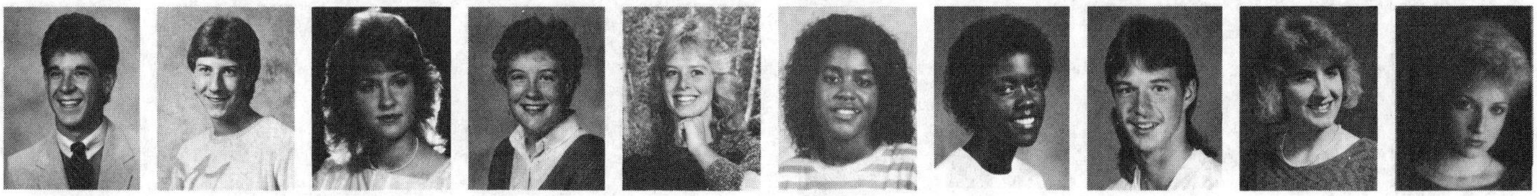

Perrins, Gerald
Pittston Area HS
Pittston, PA

Perrotti, Michael
Warren Area HS
Warren, PA

Perry, Abby
Freedom HS
Bethlehem, PA

Perry, Amy
Everett Area HS
Everett, PA

Perry, Clara
Sayre Area HS
Sayre, PA

Perry, Julie
Coatesville Area SR
Coatesville, PA

Perry, Sonya Raine
Coastesville Area SR
Coatesville, PA

Pershing, John
Northern Cambria
Barnesboro, PA

Persuda, Janet
Charleroi Area HS
Charleroi, PA

Peters, Jennifer
Monessen HS
Monessen, PA

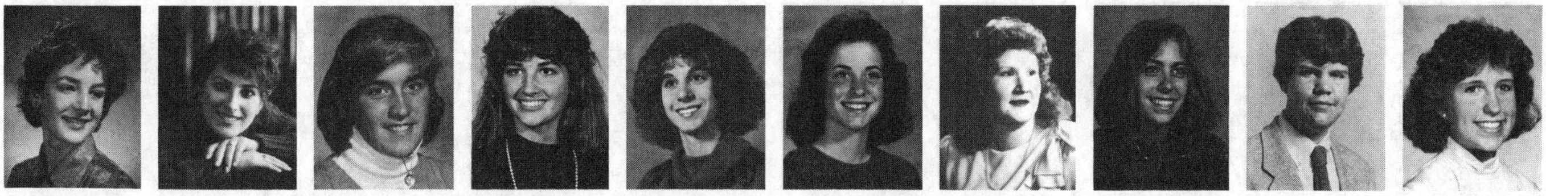

Peters, Kimberly S
Mon Valley Catholic
Brownsville, PA

Peters, Stephanie
Caroline
Quigley Catholic HS
Freedom, PA

Petersen, Margaret
Grosse Pointe South
Newtown Square,
PA

Peterson, Stacy
North Allegheny SR
Wexford, PA

Petey, Sheryl
Center Area HS
Monaca, PA

Peticca, Leanne
Oxford Area HS
Oxford, PA

Petitjean, Beth
Governor Mifflin HS
Shillington, PA

Petito, Anita
Saucon Valley HS
Bethlehem, PA

Petonak, Paul
Bishop O Reilly HS
Exeter, PA

Petrasic, Kathy
Bishop Mc Devitt
Harrisburg, PA

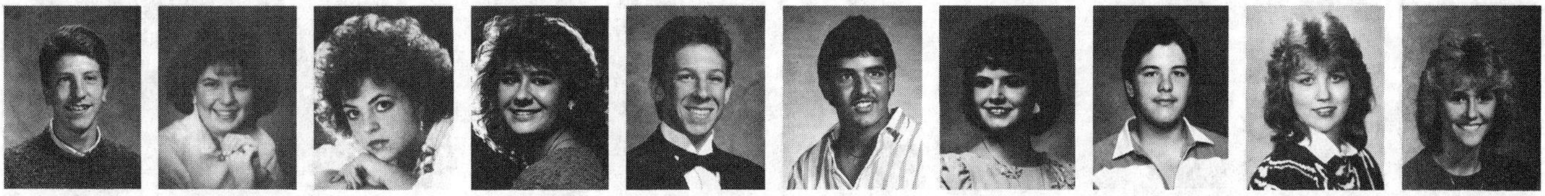

Petrick, Robert A
West Perry HS
Loysville, PA

Petricko, Jennifer
West Alllegheny SR
Oakdale, PA

Petritus, Rosemarie
E
Bishop Hannan HS
Scranton, PA

Petro, Christine
Ringgold HS
Donora, PA

Petrocelli, Domenic
Monsignor Bonner
Aldan, PA

Petroff, Ron
Ambridge Area HS
Ambridge, PA

Petroske, Jennifer
Ringgold HS
Donora, PA

Petroskey, Nick
Ringgold HS
Monongahela, PA

Petrosky, Pamela
Old Forge HS
Old Forge, PA

Petrovich, Laurie
Saucon Valley HS
Hellertown, PA

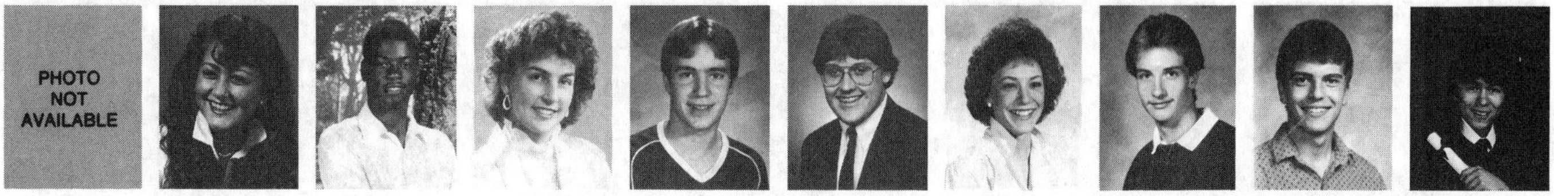
PHOTO
NOT
AVAILABLE

Petrucelli, Jason
Coughlin HS
Wilkes Barre, PA

Petruzzello, Andrea
South Western HS
Hanover, PA

Petty, Kelly
Reading SR HS
Reading, PA

Peyton, Shelley
West Allegheny SR
Mcdonald, PA

Pfeifer, Marc
Butler HS
Butler, PA

Pfeiffer, Jr John B
Emmaus HS
Wescosville, PA

Pfeil, Jamie
Bishop Mc Cart HS
Johnstown, PA

Pfirman, David
South Williamsport
Williamsport, PA

Pfleiger, Dennis
Quakertown
Community HS
Quakertown, PA

Phan, Nini
HS For Creative
Performing Arts
Philadelphia, PA

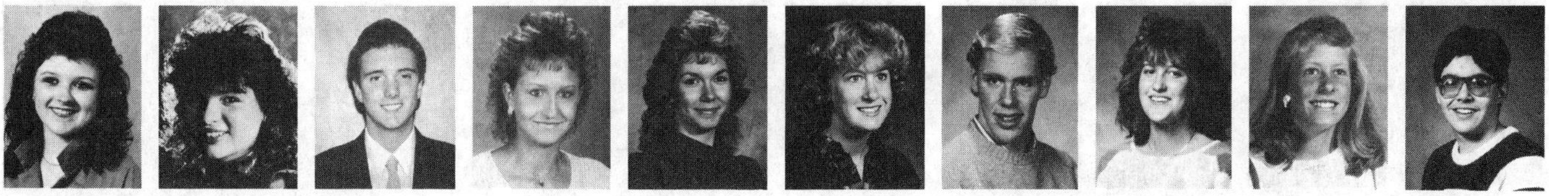

Phillippi, Le Anne
Hopewell SR HS
Aliquippa, PA

Phillips, Anneleze
Bethlehem Center
SR HS
Vestaburg, PA

Phillips, David
Pennsbury HS
Levittown, PA

Phillips, Erin
Penn Ftrafford HS
Irwin, PA

Phillips, Gloriann M
West Catholic HS
Philadelphia, PA

Phillips, Harmony
Kay
Shikellamy HS
Danville, PA

Phillips, III John
Scott
Abington Heights
Clarks Summit, PA

Phillips, Karlene
Ringgold HS
Eighty Four, PA

Phillips, Katrina
Oxford Area HS
Oxford, PA

Phillips, Larry
Western Beaver JR
SR HS
Midland, PA

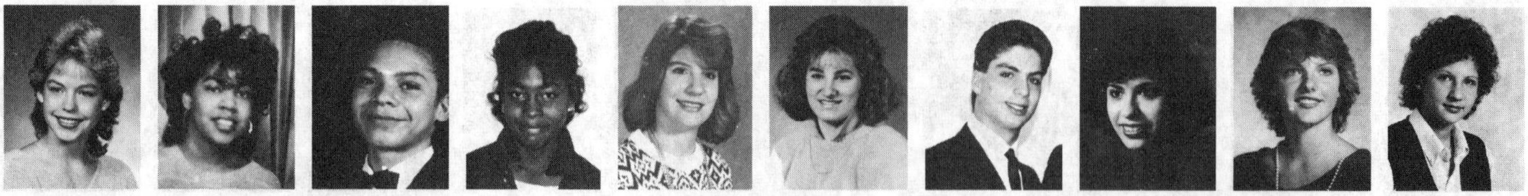

Phillips, Lynn
Windber Area HS
Windber, PA

Phillips, Rachel
Franklin Learning
Philadelphia, PA

Phoenix, Harvey
West Catholic HS
Philadelphia, PA

Phoenix, Tara
Central Dauphin HS
Harrisburg, PA

Picciano, Valerie
Marple Newtown SR
Broomall, PA

Piccirilli, Rosanna
Our Lady Of The
Sacred Heart HS
Coraopolis, PA

Piccoli, Albert
HS Of Engineering
& Science
Phila, PA

Piccolomini, Marla
Laurel Highlands
Uniontown, PA

Pickens, Jennifer
Northampton SR
Nazareth, PA

Piehota, Tanya
Bishop Hafey HS
Hazleton, PA

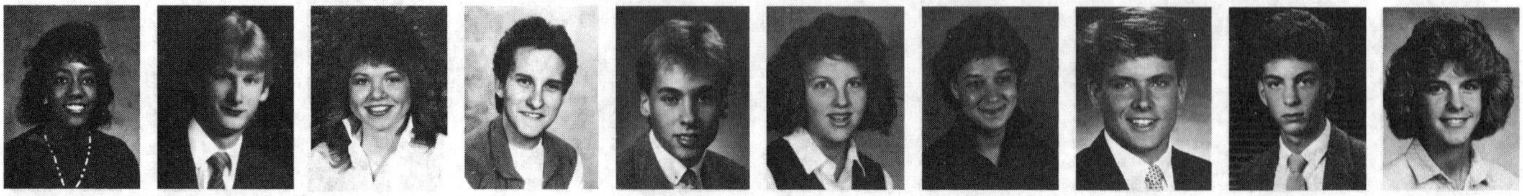

Pierce, Karla
Cumberland Valley
Mechanicsburg, PA

Pierce, Richard
Mercer HS
Hermitage, PA

Pierlott, Maryann
Billig
South Side HS
Clinton, PA

Pierosh, Robert
Harry S Truman HS
Levittown, PA

Pierson, Duane
Wilson Area HS
West Easton, PA

Pierson, Theresa
Nazareth Acad
Phila, PA

Pieseski, Kristin
Penn Trafford HS
Levelgreen, PA

Pigman, Matthew
Mackie
Peterstwp HS
Bridgeville, PA

Pike, Bradley A
Altoona Area HS
Altoona, PA

Pileggi, Denise
Upper Moreland HS
Willow Grove, PA

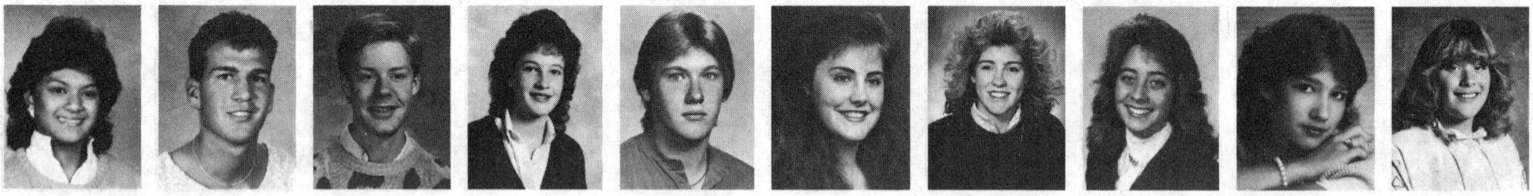

Pillay, Kamala
Wilmington Area
New Castle, PA

Pines, Noah
Haverford HS
Havertown, PA

Pinkerton, Owen J
Cumberland Valley
Camp Hill, PA

Piotrowski,
Cari-Lynn
Allentown Central
Catholic HS
Allentown, PA

Piper, Thomas
Juniata HS
Pt Royal, PA

Pipher, Kristy
Cumberland Valley
Mecahnicsburg, PA

Pirrotta, Kathryn
Ann Colette
Peters Township HS
Mc Murray, PA

Pisano, Karen
Warwick HS
Lititz, PA

Pisarchick, Tammy
Lynesville HS
Linesville, PA

Pitcavage, Holly
Dallas SR HS
Shavertown, PA

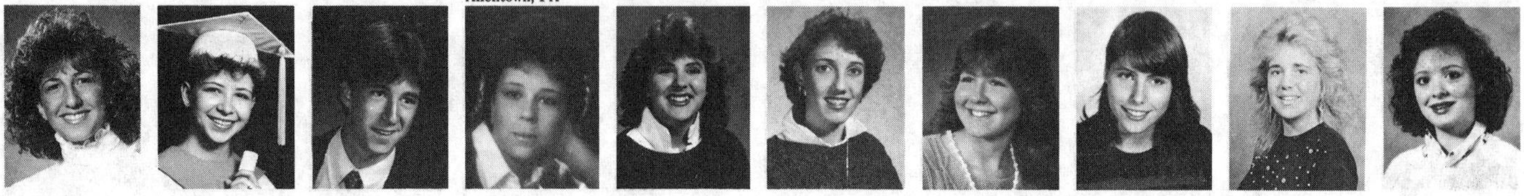

Pitzer, Michele
Wilmington Area
New Wilmington,
PA

Pizarro, Shelly
Philadelphia HS For
Philadelphia, PA

Pizii, Geoff
Henderson HS
W Chester, PA

Placek, Tracy
Our Lady Of The
Sacred Heart HS
Coraopolis, PA

Plank, Sonja
Newport JR SR HS
Newport, PA

Plasha, Barbara A
Garnet Valley SR
Glen Mills, PA

Plassio, Shelly
Yough SR HS
Irwin, PA

Platt, Kathleen
Gettysburg SR HS
Gettysburg, PA

Plauschinat, Suzette
Plymouth
Whitemarsh HS
Norristown, PA

Pletcher, Amy
West Allegheny SR
Oakdale, PA

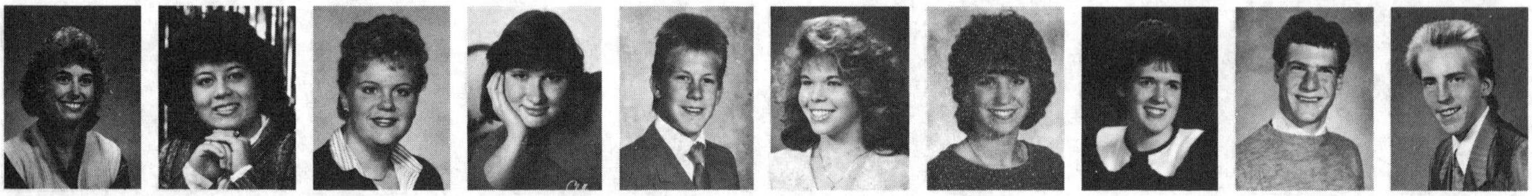

Pletcher, Patti
Rockwood Area HS
Rockwood, PA

Plocinik, Lynda
Rochester Area HS
Rochester, PA

Plummer, Helen
Barbara
Faith Community
Christian Schl
Pittsburgh, PA

Plummer, Jean M
Conrad Weiser HS
Robesonia, PA

Plunkett, Patrick
Arch Bisoph Ryan
For Boys HS
Philadelphia, PA

Pochinsky, Ann
Mt Pleasant Area
Latrobe, PA

Podolsky, Micha
Freedom HS
Bethlehem, PA

Pogozelec, Teresa
Lincoln HS
Wampum, PA

Pohl, Robert
Pius X HS
Columbia, NJ

Poindexter, James
Bethlehem-Center
SR HS
Denbo, PA

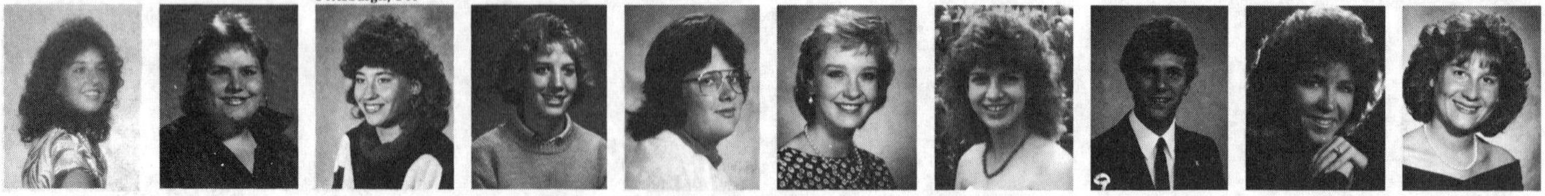

Pokrifka, Annette
Steel Valley HS
Munhall, PA

Poley, Kristina
Middletown Area
Middletown, PA

Policz, Michelle
Jefferson-Morgan
Rices Landing, PA

Polites, Ann
Lourdes Regional
Mt Carmel, PA

Pollack, Anne
Bishop Hafey HS
Freeland, PA

Pollard, Tracy C
East HS
West Chester, PA

Pologruto, Patricia
M
Mt Pleasant SR HS
Mt Pleasant, PA

Poloyac, Sam
Conemaugh Valley
Johnstown, PA

Polsenberg, Lisarose
Lebanon Catholic
Palmyra, PA

Polsky, Candice
Haverford HS
Havertown, PA

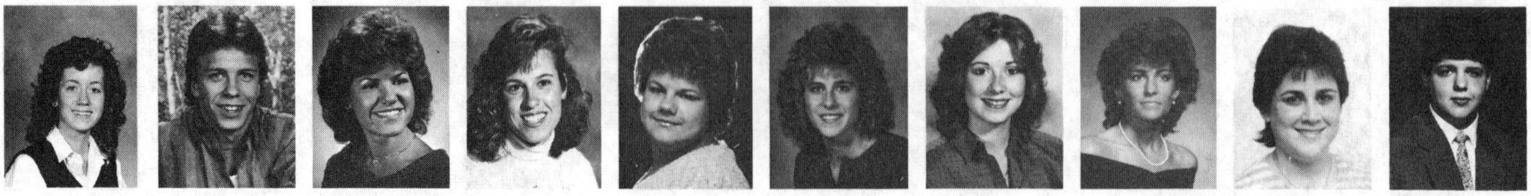

Pomroy, Theresa
Nazareth Acad
Phila, PA

Pond, Donald
Athens HS
Athens, PA

Poness, Michele
Chartiers-Houston
Houston, PA

Ponist, Sherry
Pen Argyl Area HS
Easton, PA

Pontzer, Melissa
St Marys Area HS
Kersey, PA

Poore, Victoria
Huntingdon Area
Huntingdon, PA

Popadak, Stefanie J
Villa Maria HS
Erie, PA

Pope, Kimberly Dee
Methaeton HS
Audubon, PA

Popky, Judith
Wyoming Valley
West HS
Kingston, PA

Poroda, Jay
Ringgold HS
Monongahela, PA

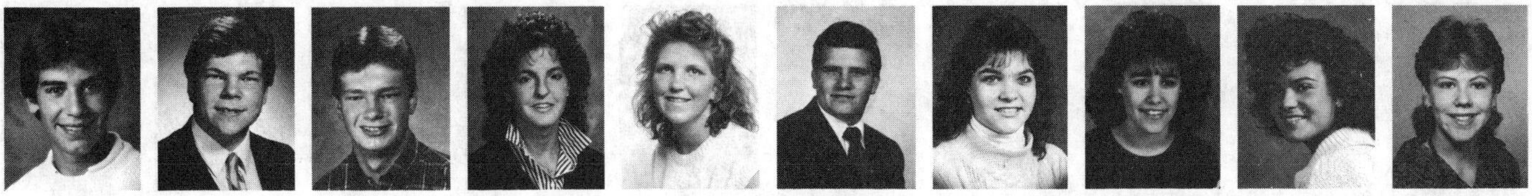

Porter, Brian Nelson
Trinity HS
Washington, PA

Porter, David
Spring-Ford HS
Royersford, PA

Posey, Brian
Waynesboro Area SR HS
Waynesboro, PA

Postlethwait, Teresa
Central Christian
Rockton, PA

Potak, Lynn
Wyoming Valley West HS
Edwardsville, PA

Poteat, David
Cedar Grove Christian Acad
Philadelphia, PA

Potteiger, Michelle
Central Dauphin HS
Harrisburg, PA

Pottinger, Darlene J
Penn Trafford HS
Jeannette, PA

Potts, Rebecca
Clearfield Area HS
Clearfield, PA

Potts, Wendy
Mc Keesport Area
Mc Keesport, PA

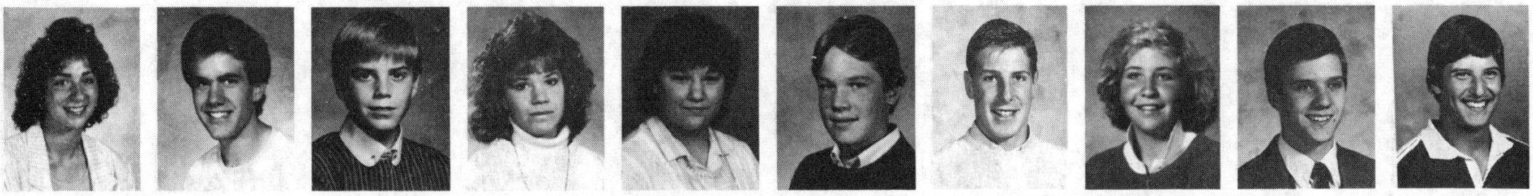

Pouch, Andrea Shondell
Northern Lebanon
Fredericksburg, PA

Poulos, James
Plum HS
Pittsburgh, PA

Povich, Jaison
Ringgold HS
New Eagle, PA

Powell, Michelle
Northwest Area HS
Huntington Mills, PA

Powell, Yvonne
Fairchance-Georges
Smithfield, PA

Power, Michael
State College HS
State College, PA

Powers, Brandon C
Camp Hill HS
Camp Hill, PA

Prasko, Elena
Hopewell HS
Aliquippa, PA

Prater, Nathan C
Calvary Christian
Kirkwood, PA

Pratt, Christopher
Wilmington Area
Pulaski, PA

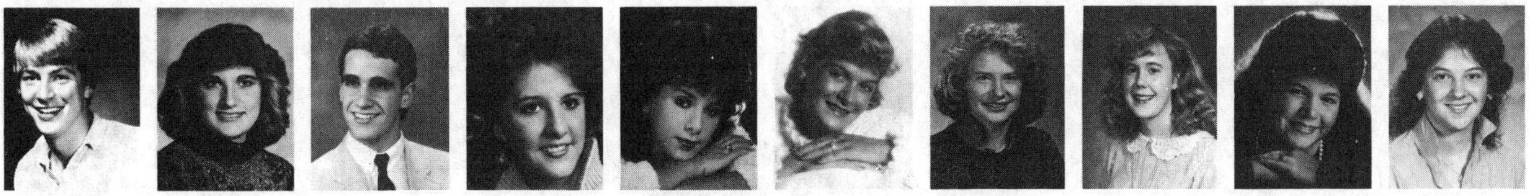

Pratt, Mark
Troy HS
Granville Summit, PA

Pratt, Sara
Conemaugh Township Area HS
Hollsopple, PA

Pratt, Thomas
Gerbel HS
Connellsville, PA

Prescott, Michelle L
North Catholic HS
Pittsburgh, PA

Presogna, Christine
Villa Maria Acad
Erie, PA

Pressler, Melissa A
State College Area SR HS
Port Matilda, PA

Preston, Heather
Kennard Dale HS
Fawn Grove, PA

Prevenslik, Lisa A
Greenburg Central Catholic HS
Youngwood, PA

Price, Becky
Slippery Rock Areia
Portersville, PA

Price, Carrie
Butler SR HS
Herman, PA

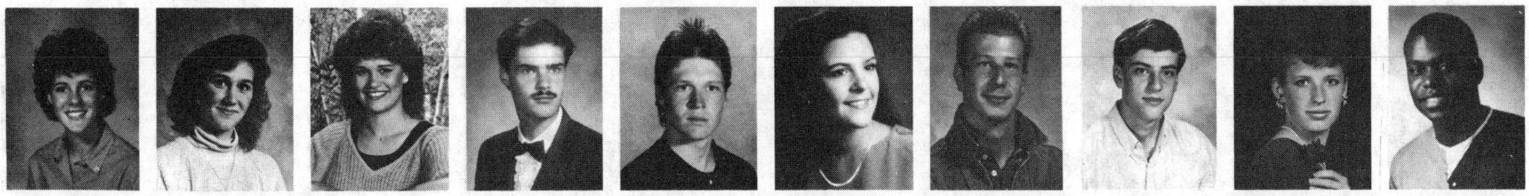

Price, Jennifer
Everett Area HS
Everett, PA

Price, Marie
Carbondale Area HS
Carbondale, PA

Price, Rebecca
Wyalusing Valley
Dushore, PA

Price, Robert H
Perkiomen Valley
Collegeville, PA

Price, Samuel
Blacklick Valley HS
Nanty-Glo, PA

Prichard, Jill
Harbor Creek HS
Erie, PA

Prickett, John
Steelton-Highspire
Highspire, PA

Pride, Jr Alan R
East Stroudsburg
East Stroudsburg, PA

Priebe, Kristen
Upper Darby HS
Drexel Hill, PA

Primeaux, Andre
City Center Acad
Philadelphia, PA

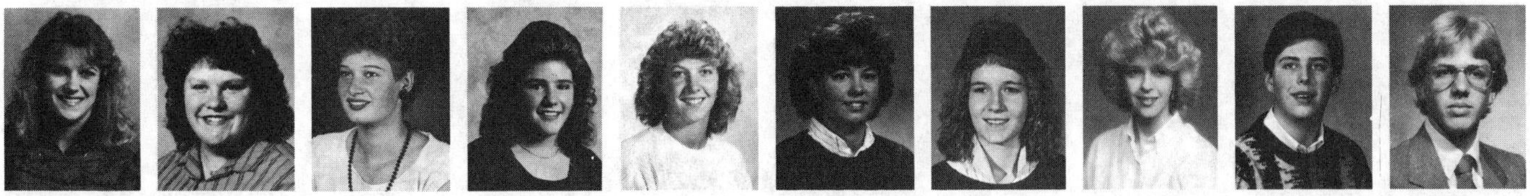

Prince, Lynne Marie
Mt Pleasant Area
Mt Pleasant, PA

Prince, Phoebe
Hopewell HS
Aliquippa, PA

Prinkey, Georgia
Southmoreland HS
Scottdale, PA

Printy, Lori
Cardinal Brennan
Shenandoah, PA

Priori, Jeanna
Coatesville Area SR
Coatesville, PA

Pristash, Michelle
West Branch Area
Philipsburg, PA

Pritts, Kandi
Connesville Area SR
Indian Head, PA

Prizniak, Jennifer
John S Fine HS
Nanticoke, PA

Procko, Scott
Monongahela Valley Catholic HS
Charleroi, PA

Procopio, Michael
Northwestern Lehigh HS
Kempton, PA

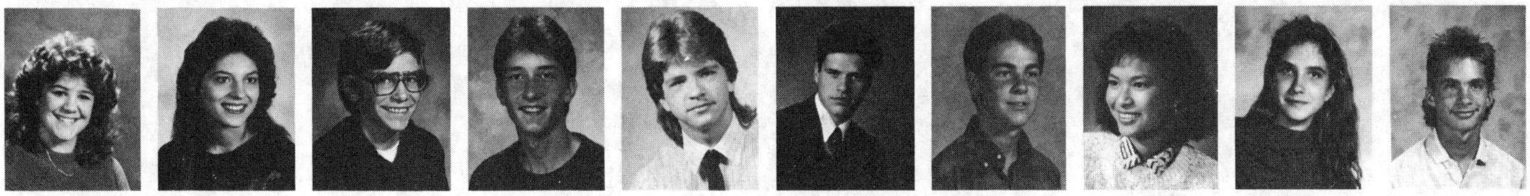

Proctor, Kellee
Penn-Trafford HS
Levelgreen, PA

Proietto, Denise
Pittston Area HS
Dupont, PA

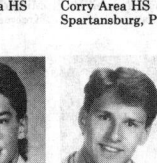

Proper, Allen
Corry Area HS
Spartansburg, PA

Proper, Erik S
Titusville HS
Titusville, PA

Prough, Jason
Elizabethtown Area
Elizabehtown, PA

Prozzoly, Dean
Keystone Oaks HS
Carnegie, PA

Pruitt, Matthew Shane
Downingtown HS
Exton, PA

Prum, Piset Ang
Lebanon SR HS
Lebanon, PA

Pruss, Mary
Shade HS
Cenral City, PA

Prutzman, Shannon
Mifflinburg HS
Mifflinburg, PA

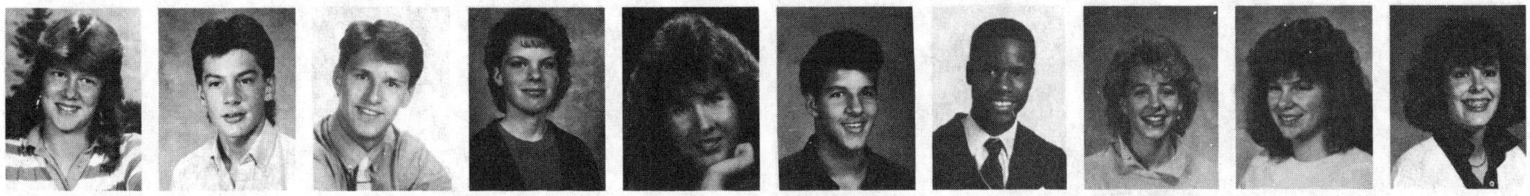

Pruyne, Patricia
Northeast Bradford JR-SR HS
Towanda, PA

Pryal, Shane
North Star HS
Stoystown, PA

Pryor, William
Henderson SR HS
W Chester, PA

Przybycien, Pamela
Fort Le Boeuf HS
Waterford, PA

Pudlowski, Heather Anne
Lower Dauphin HS
Grantville, PA

Pugh, Alan
Neshannock HS
Neshannock, PA

Pugh, Bernard
Cardinal Dougherty
Philadelphia, PA

Pugliese, Michelle
Williams Valley JR/SR HS
Tower City, PA

Pulaski, Leanne M
Bentworth SR HS
Bentleyville, PA

Pulvino, Dennise
Harbor Creek SR
Erie, PA

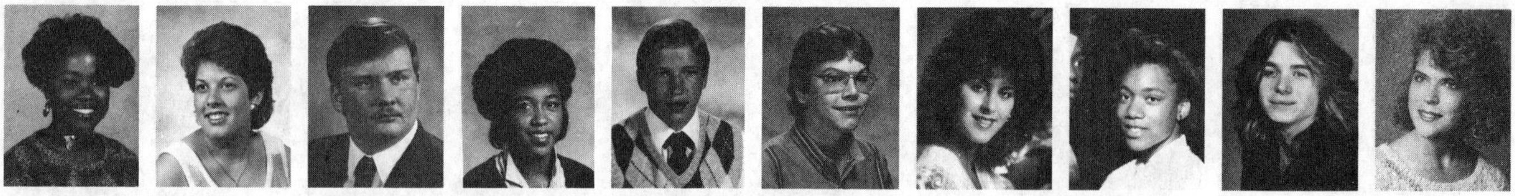

Pumphrey, Patricia
Chester HS
Brookhaven, PA

Pupa, Lisa
Pittston Area SR
Pittston, PA

Purcell, Joseph
Minersville Area HS
Minersville, PA

Purdy, Carol L
Harrisburg HS
Harrisburg, PA

Puschnigg, Greg
Ligonier Valley SR
Latrobe, PA

Pysher, Todd
Conrad Weiser HS
Wernersville, PA

Quaglieri, Lisa
Gateway SR HS
Monroeville, PA

Quarles, Atasha
The Cecilian Acad
Philadelphia, PA

Quay, Scott
Altoona Area HS
Altoona, PA

Querio, Andrea M
Highlands SR HS
Brackenridge, PA

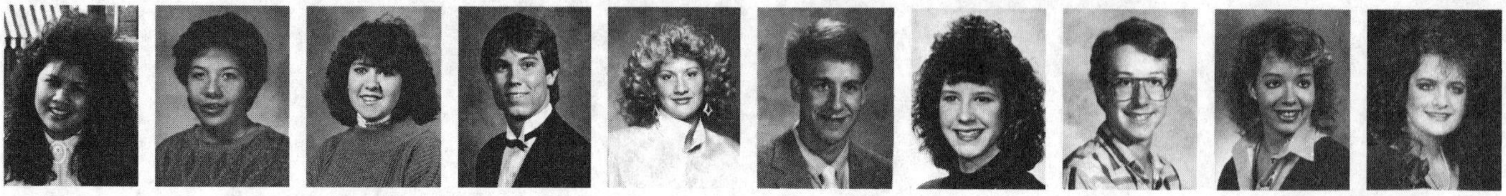

Quiachon, Divine
S Philadelphia HS
Philadelphia, PA

Quigg, Colleen
Parkland HS
Allentown, PA

Quigley, Heather
Quigley HS
Sewickley, PA

Quinlan, Gerard
Monsignor Bonner
Havertown, PA

Quinlivan, Krista
Ringgold HS
Monongahela, PA

Raab, Gregg E
Carlisle SR HS
Carlisle, PA

Rabel, Kelly
Mid-Valley HS
Olyphant, PA

Rabish, Jeffrey M
Penn Cambria HS
Gallitzin, PA

Rabits, Jennifer
Bishop Guilfoyle HS
Altoona, PA

Rabutino, Dawn
St Maria Goretti HS
Philadelphia, PA

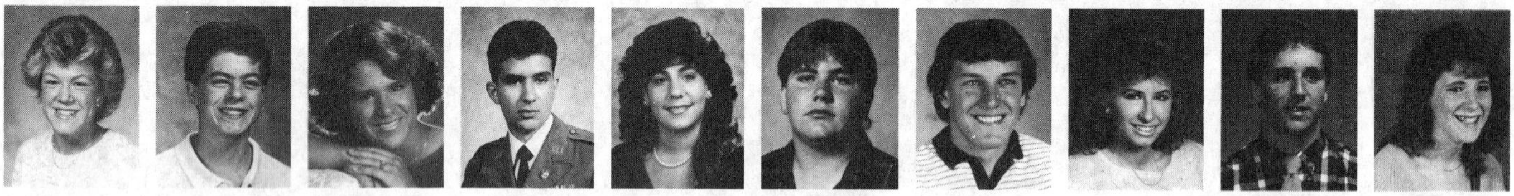

Rachael, Melinda
So Williamsport
Area HS
Williamsport, PA

Rachford, Tobin
Cumberland Valley
Mechanicsburg, PA

Racho, Maria
West Hazleton HS
Conyngham, PA

Racicot, Arthur
Carson Long
Military Inst
Drayton Plains, MI

Raciti, Linda
Bishop Kenrick HS
Norristown, PA

Rader, Christopher
Riverside Of Beaver
County HS
Beaver Falls, PA

Rado, Mark
Homer Center JR
SR HS
Homer City, PA

Rady, Noelle
Our Lady Of The
Sacred Heart HS
Aliquippa, PA

Rafferty, Robert D
Marian Catholic HS
Nesquehoning, PA

Rager, Dawn
Penn-Trafford HS
Irwin, PA

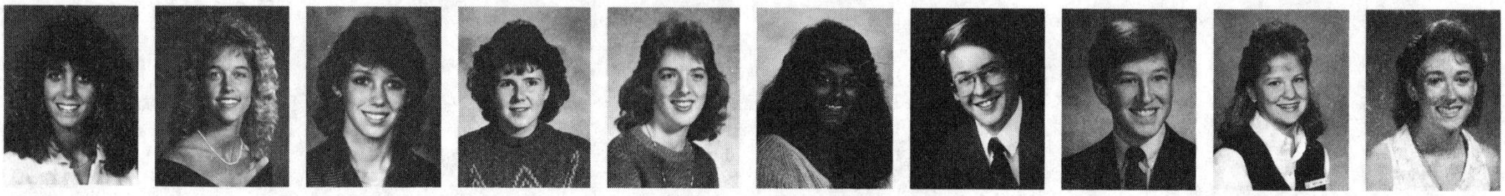

Ragnelli, Dina
Northwestern
Lehigh HS
Germansvile, PA

Rahn, Debra L
Muhlenberg HS
Reading, PA

Rain, Kimberly
Penn-Trafford HS
Irwin, PA

Rairigh, Judy
Purchase Line JR
SR HS
Hillsdale, PA

Raisner, Melissa
Bangor Area SR HS
E Bangor, PA

Rajaratnam, Emilie
Phil-Mont Christian
Philadelphia, PA

Raker, Robert
South Park HS
Library, PA

Rakowski, Paul
Central Catholic HS
Allison Pk, PA

Rambo, Meredith L
Nazareth Acad
Feasterville, PA

Ramey, Kristin
Fairview HS
Erie, PA

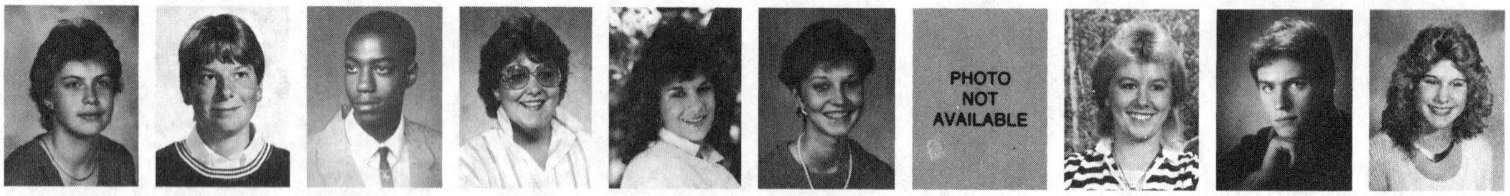

Ramey, Tina
Brookville Area HS
Brookville, PA

Ramsden, Brandon
Blairsville SR HS
Blairsville, PA

Ramseur, Michael
Clairton HS
Clairton, PA

Ramsey, Kelly
Coudersport Jr Sr
Coudersport, PA

Ramsey, Kimberly
Allegheny Clarion
Valley HS
Emlenton, PA

Ramsey, Stacey
Everett Area HS
Breezewood, PA

Ranck, Sharon
Pennsbury-Medial
Bair HS
Fairless Hls, PA

Randall, Connie
Northeast Bradford
Wysox, PA

Randall, Jeffrey
Todd
Garden Spot HS
Narvon, PA

Randall, Kelli
Meadville Area SR
Meadville, PA

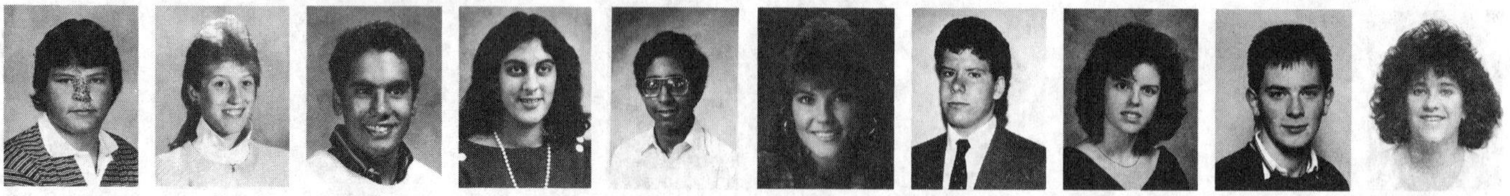

Randolph, Thomas
Northern Cambria
Marsteller, PA

Rankin, Tammy
Blacklick Valley
JR-SR HS
Ebensburg, PA

Rao, Anand
Fairview HS
Fairview, PA

Rao, Vani
Mechanicsburg Area
SR HS
Mechanicsburg, PA

Rao, Vivek
Gateway SR HS
Monroeville, PA

Rape, Lisa A
Seneca Valley HS
Zelienople, PA

Rapone, William J
Arch Ryan HS For
Philadelphia, PA

Rapp, Karen
Bishop Conwell HS
Morrisville, PA

Rapp, Martin
Middleburg HS
Kreamer, PA

Rappaport, Sharyn
Wyoming Valley
West HS
Kingston, PA

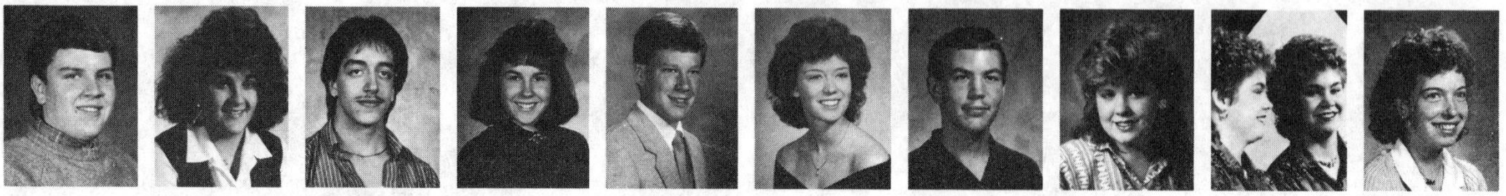

Rasel, Jarett
Bethlehem Center
SR HS
Amity, PA

Ratchford, Danyiel
Bishop Guilfoyle HS
Altoona, PA

Rathburn, Chris
Fort Le Boeuf HS
Erie, PA

Rathfon, Stephanie
Butler SR HS
Butler, PA

Rathke, Jeffrey D
Hampton HS
Gibsonia, PA

Raub, Devlyn
Souderton Area HS
Tylersport, PA

Raudabaugh,
Michael
Big Spring HS
Newville, PA

Ravoira, Heather
The University Schl
Washington, PA

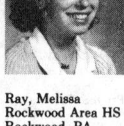

Ray, Holly
Sharpsville HS
Greenville, PA

Ray, Melissa
Rockwood Area HS
Rockwood, PA

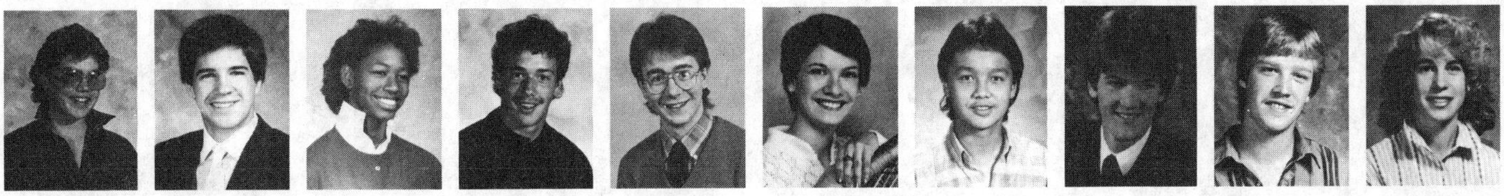

Ray, Michele
Solanco HS
Quarryville, PA

Rayer, Thomas J
Marple-Newtown
Broomall, PA

Rayford, Lisa
Methacton HS
Eagleville, PA

Raymond, John
Bellefonte HS
Bellefonte, PA

Raymond, Ken
Northwestern SR
Albion, PA

Raymont, Doreen
Lenape Vo Tech
Ford City, PA

Raymundo, Jose
Seneca Valley HS
Harmony, PA

Rea, Tim
Upper Perkiomen
Pennsburg, PA

Reagle, Scott
Mercert Jt
Consolidated HS
Mercer, PA

Ream, Desiree
Mechanicsburg HS
Mechanicsburg, PA

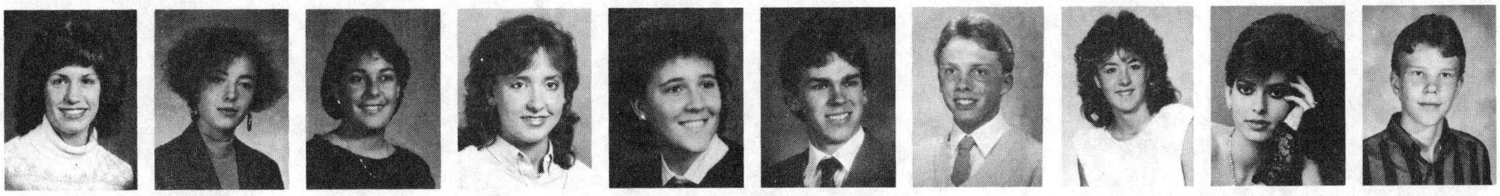

Ream, Kimberly
Central Douphin HS
Harrisburg, PA

Rearden, Jennifer
Mt Penn HS
Reading, PA

Reardon, Marianne
Downingtown SR
Exton, PA

Rebert, Beth
Wilson HS
Reading, PA

Rebert, Laura
Littlestown SR HS
Hanover, PA

Rebuck, Craig
Line Mountain HS
Klingerstown, PA

Rechenberg, Richard
Geibel HS
Dunbar, PA

Rechtorik, Tanya
Carrick HS
Pittsburgh, PA

Rector, Ingrid S
Lawrence County
Vo-Tech HS
New Castle, PA

Reddig, Scott
Cocalico HS
Reamstown, PA

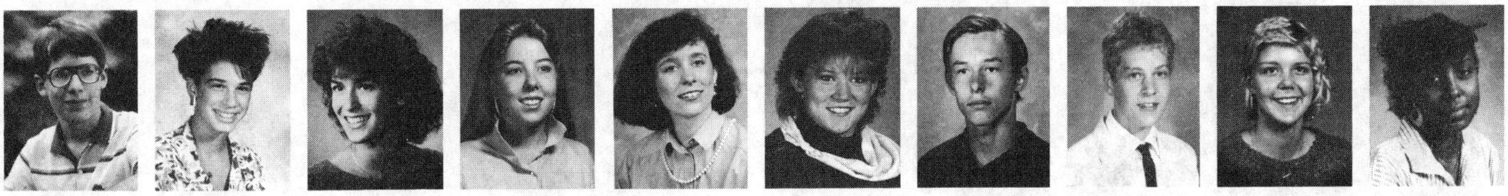

Redding, Mark
Anthony
Hanover SR HS
Hanover, PA

Redlich, Allison D
Norristown Area HS
Norristown, PA

Reduzzi, Tracy
Peb Argyl Area HS
Pen Argyl, PA

Reed, Anjela
Elizabethtown Area
Elizabethtown, PA

Reed, Jennifer L
Gwynedd Mercy
North Wales, PA

Reed, Jennifer L
Upper Perkiomen
Red Hill, PA

Reed, John
Greencastle-Antrim
Greencastle, PA

Reed, Kurt E
Allegheny-Clarion
Valley HS
Volant, PA

Reed, Lori
Central Dauphin HS
Harrisburg, PA

Reed, Shelley
Taylor Allderdice
Pittsburgh, PA

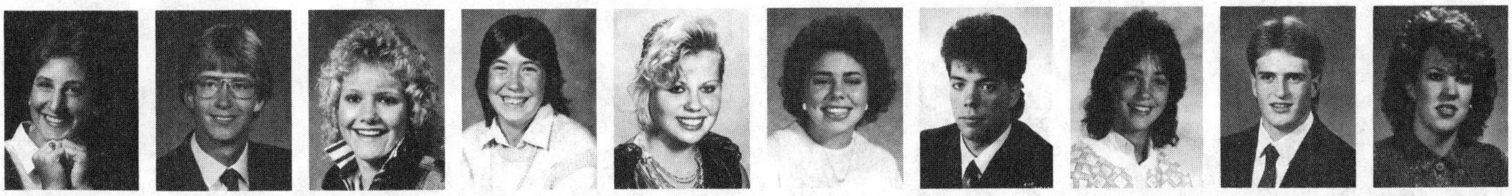

Reed, Stephanie
Allegheny-Clarion
Valley HS
Volant, PA

Reeder, Mike
Lampeter-Strasburg
Strasburg, PA

Reeher, Jonna
New Brighton Area
New Brighton, PA

Reese, Colleen
Hollidaysbury Area
SR HS
Hollidaysburg, PA

Reeves, Jennifer
Harry S Truman HS
Levittown, PA

Refford, Michelle
Downingtown SR
Downingtown, PA

Regal, Shane
Northern HS
Lewisberry, PA

Regel, Sharon
Belelfonte Area HS
Pleasant Gap, PA

Reiber, Richard
West York Area HS
York, PA

Reiber, Tricia
Wilmington Area
Volant, PA

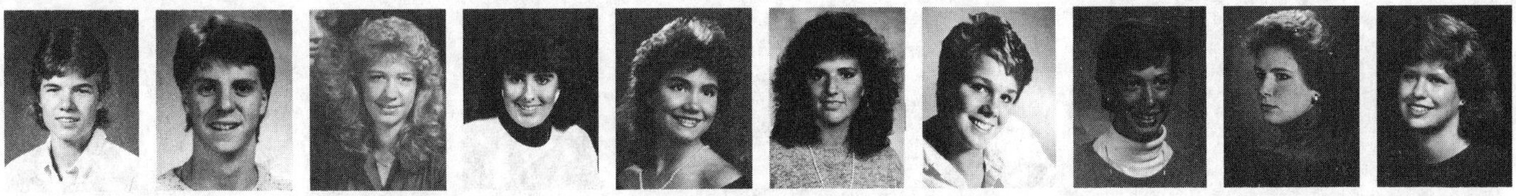

Reibold, Marc
Peters Township HS
Mcmurray, PA

Reibold, Robert L
Bethel Park SR HS
Bethel Park, PA

Reibsane, Dawn
Williams Valley JR
SR HS
Tower City, PA

Reich, Celina
Tunkhannock Area
Tunkhannock, PA

Reichenbach, Tandi
East Juniata HS
Mc Alisterville, PA

Reichley, Tami
Quakertown SR HS
Quakertown, PA

Reichman, Lynne
Marie
Wallenpaupack Area
Greentown, PA

Reider, Tami
Garden Spot HS
Terre Hill, PA

Reigh, Pamela
Algoona Area HS
Altoona, PA

Reihart, Michelle
Juniata Valley HS
Huntingdon, PA

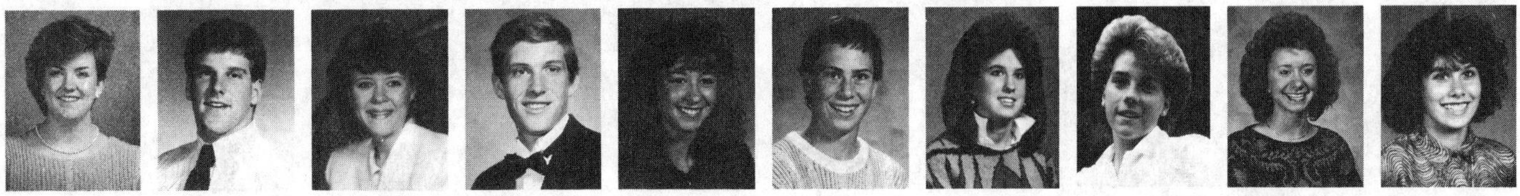

Reilly, Heather A
Gwynedd Mercy
Colmar, PA

Reilly, John
Notre Dame HS
Hellertown, PA

Reilly, Kerri
Freedom SR HS
Bethlehem, PA

Reilly, Patrick J
Malvem Prep Schl
Exton, PA

Reilly, Susan
Greensburg Central
Catholic HS
Ruffs Dale, PA

Reinard, Brian
Cumberland Valley
Carlisle, PA

Reinboth, Wendy
Council Rock HS
Richboro, PA

Reiner, Denise
Line Mountain HS
Leck Kill, PA

Reiner, Renee
Williams Valley HS
Muir, PA

Reinhart, Nicole
Central Dauphin HS
Harrisburg, PA

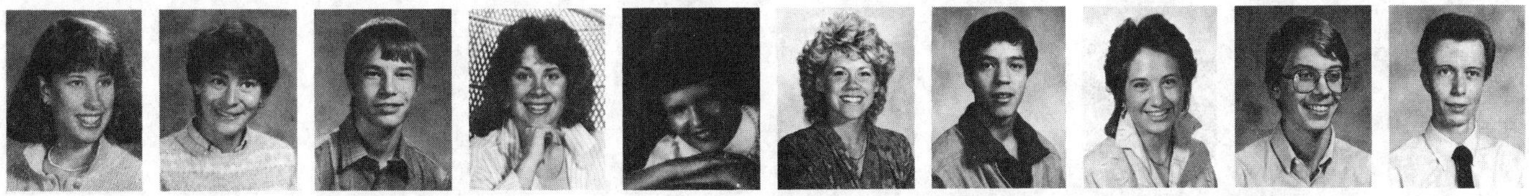

Reinsel, Kristi
Hampton HS
Allison Pk, PA

Reisinger, Laura
Kennard Dale HS
Stewartstown, PA

Reisinger, Samuel
West Perry SR HS
Elliottsburg, PA

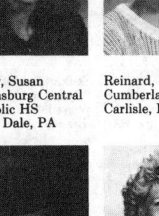

Reisinger, Susan R
Lakeview HS
Jackson Center, PA

Reiss, Robin
Northampton SR
Northampton, PA

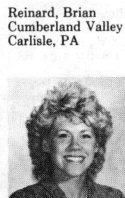

Remaly, Kimberly
Northampton Area
SR HS
Bath, PA

Rementer, Richard
Neshaminy HS
Penndel, PA

Remick, Vicki
Valley View JR SR
Peckville, PA

Renn, Christopher
Danville HS
Danville, PA

Renn, Jr William
Danville HS
Danville, PA

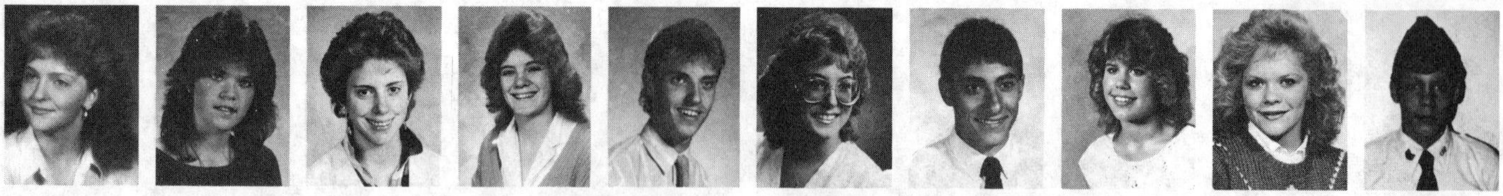

Renshaw, Linda
Pequea Valley HS
Gap, PA

Rentner, Amy
Montrose JR SR HS
Montrose, PA

Rentschler, Rhonda
Norther Chester
County Vo-Tech
Spg City, PA

Renwick, Terri
St Marys Area HS
Kersey, PA

Repko, Robert
Bangor Area SR HS
Bangor, PA

Reppert, Angela
Allentown Central
Catholic HS
Northampton, PA

Resick, Chris
Bishop Carroll HS
South Fork, PA

Reskovac, Renee
Riverside HS
New Brighton, PA

Ress, Tricia
Frazier Memorial JR
SR HS
Fayette City, PA

Reveron, Daniel A
Mc Caskey HS
Lancaster, PA

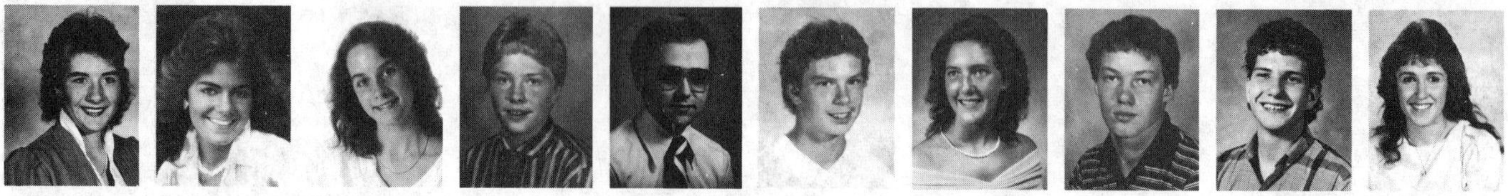

Reynolds, Alexa
Lakeview HS
Sandy Lake, PA

Reynolds, Michelle
Maplewood HS
Guys Mills, PA

Rheasant, Janelle M
Juniata Valley HS
Alexandria, PA

Rhoades, Andrew
Tyrone Area HS
Tyrone, PA

Rhoades, Scott
Wesleyan Holiness
Nanty-Glo, PA

Rhoads, Edward
Northern Lebanon
JR SR HS
Lebanon, PA

Rhodes, Rhonda
Shippensburg Area
SR HS
Shippensburg, PA

Rhymestine, George
D
Moshannon Valley
Madera, PA

Ribar, Edward
Gateway SR HS
Monroeville, PA

Ribortella, Evelyn
Ann
Western Wayne HS
Moscow, PA

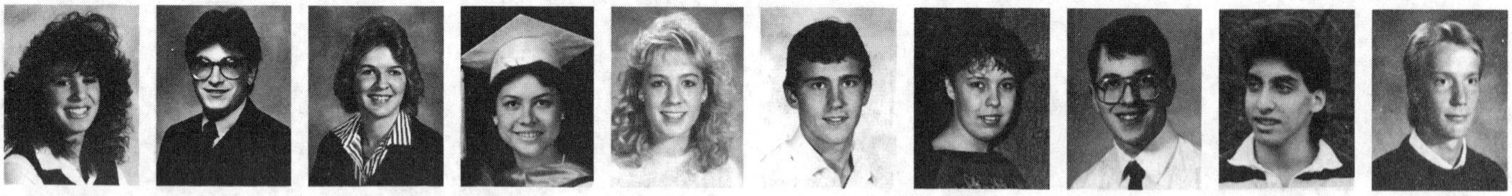

Ricche, Kerry
Bishop Guilfoyle HS
Altoona, PA

Ricci, Mark
Ringgold HS
New Eagle, PA

Rice, Jennifer
Rocky Grove HS
Cooperstown, PA

Rice, Karla
Bishop Conwell HS
Penndel, PA

Rice, Lara
Seneca Valley HS
Harmony, PA

Rice, Michael Z
Ferndale HS
Johnstown, PA

Rice, Nance
Pocono Mountain
SR HS
Tobyhanna, PA

Rice, Stanley G
Mon Valley Catholic
Monongahela, PA

Rich, David S
Akiba Hebrew Acad
Philadelphia, PA

Richards, Daniel
Brockway Area HS
Brockport, PA

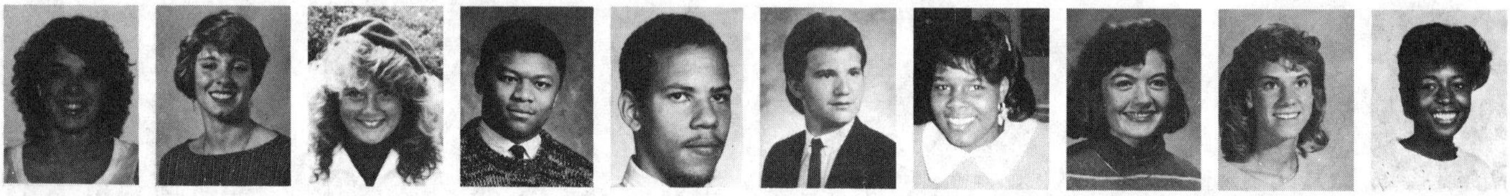

Richards, Jennifer
Wyoming Valley
West HS
Kingston, PA

Richards, Jodi
South Park HS
Library, PA

Richards, Karen F
Peters Township HS
Venetia, PA

Richards, Kirk
Kennedy Christian
Farrell, PA

Richards, Michael H
Bishop Mc Devitt
Harrisburg, PA

Richards, Rahn
Tri-Valley JR-SR
Hegins, PA

Richardson, Crystal
Cardinal Ohara HS
Chester, PA

Richardson, Jennifer
L
Christian School Of
Manchester, MD

Richardson, Lisa
Henderson HS
West Chester, PA

Richardson, Yvette
Bishop Mc Devitt
Harrisburg, PA

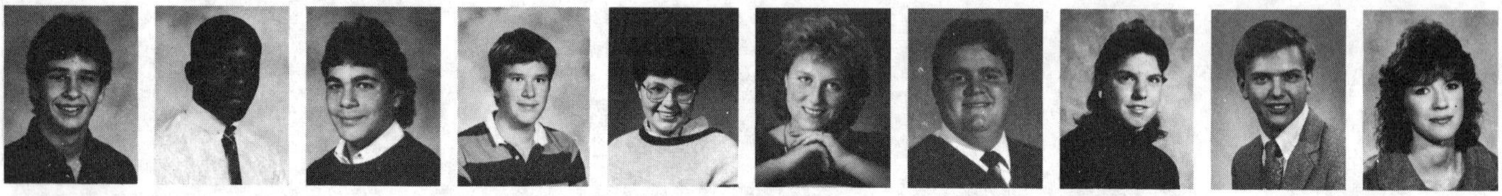

Richart, Michael
Milton SR HS
Milton, PA

Richet, Jr Curtis L
Norristown Area HS
Norristown, PA

Richie, Rami
Parkland HS
Easton, PA

Richter, Mark
Meadville Area SR
Meadville, PA

Rickard, Nancy
Churchill HS
Braddock, PA

Rickert, Jill Marie
Meadville Area SR
Meadville, PA

Rickert, Scott
Daniel Boone HS
Douglassville, PA

Ridderhoff, Amy
Sch Haven Area HS
Sch Haven, PA

Rider, William
Bishop Neumann
Williamsport, PA

Ridzon, Rochelle
Crestwood HS
Wapwallopen, PA

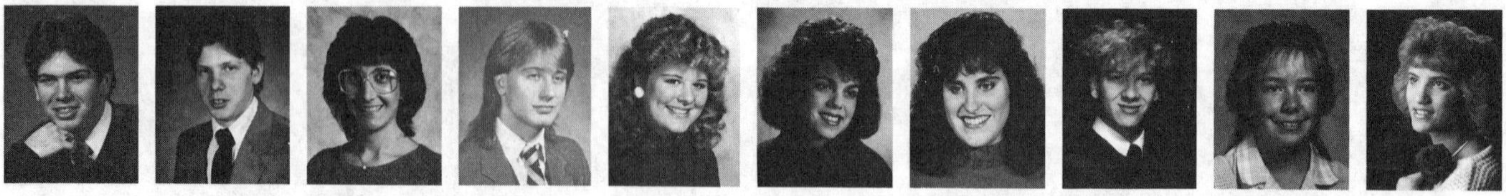

Riecks, Shannon
Bethlehem Center
SR HS
Clarksville, PA

Riedel, Richard
W B Saul HS
Philadelphia, PA

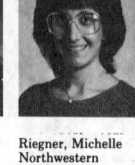

Riegner, Michelle
Northwestern
Lehigh HS
Germansville, PA

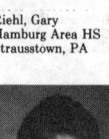

Riehl, Gary
Hamburg Area HS
Strausstown, PA

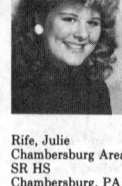

Rife, Julie
Chambersburg Area
SR HS
Chambersburg, PA

Rifkin, Stacey
Wyoming Valley
West HS
Kingston, PA

Riggs, Linda Rae
North Allegheny HS
Bradford Woods, PA

Riley, III James
South Philadelphia
Philadelphia, PA

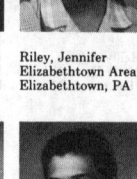

Riley, Jennifer
Elizabethtown Area
Elizabethtown, PA

Riley, Kim
Waynesburg Central
Waynesburg, PA

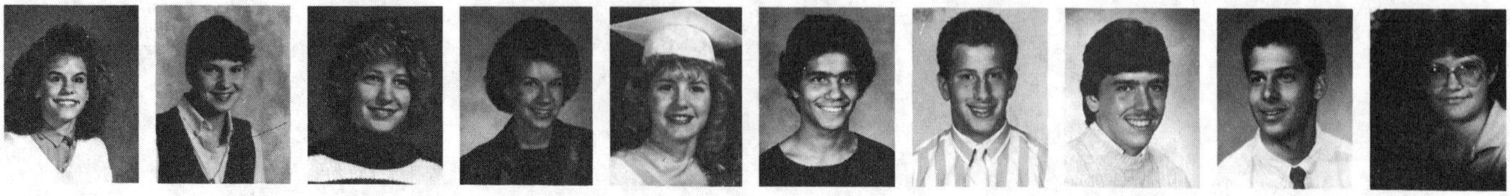

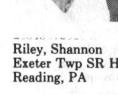

Riley, Shannon
Exeter Twp SR HS
Reading, PA

Rindock, Pamela
Allentown Central
Catholic HS
Allentown, PA

Rinehart, Tammy
Susquehannock HS
Shrewsbury, PA

Ringer, Lisa
Fort Cherry HS
Mcdonald, PA

Riordan, Rita
West Philadelphia
Catholic Girls
Philadelphia, PA

Rios, Richard Lee
J P Mc Caskey HS
Lancaster, PA

Rippole, Craig
Sto-Rox SR HS
Mckees Rocks, PA

Risch, Frederick
John
Wyoming Area SR
Harding, PA

Rishel, Adam
Central York HS
York, PA

Rishel, Dawn
Mifflinburg Area HS
Mifflinburg, PA

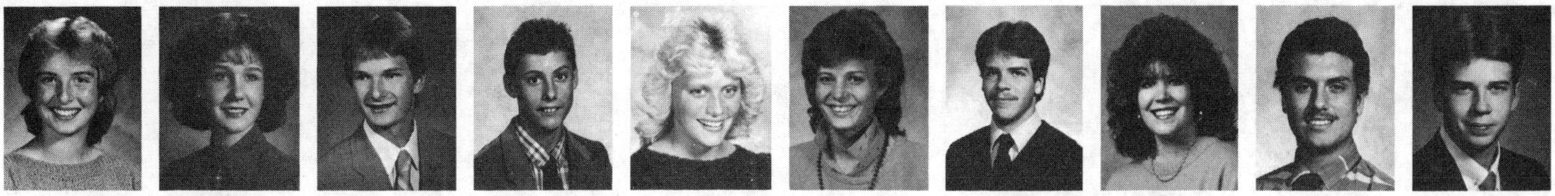

Rishel, Kimberly K
Shaler Area SR HS
Glenshaw, PA

Rishko, Tara
Allentown Central Catholic HS
Allentown, PA

Risser, Randy
Solanco HS
Holtwood, PA

Rist, Eddy
Trinity HS
New Cumberland, PA

Ritchey, Tammy S
Dover Area HS
Dover, PA

Ritchey, Tera
Blair County Christian Schl
Duncansville, PA

Ritchie, Jr Barry W
Belle Vernon Area
Belle Vernon, PA

Ritchie, Lisa D
Eisenhower HS
Warren, PA

Ritenour, Scott
Belle Vernon Area
Belle Vernon, PA

Ritter, Brian
Salisbury HS
Allentown, PA

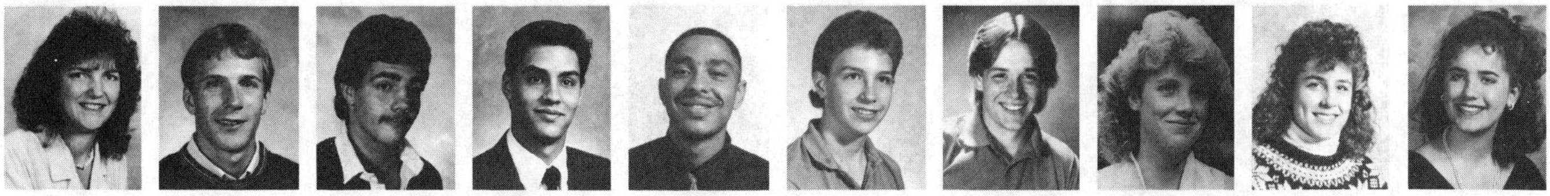

Ritter, Melody
Harry S Truman HS
Bristol, PA

Ritz, Rodney
Southmoreland SR
Mt Pleasant, PA

Rivenbark, III Harry L
Maplewood HS
Norristown, PA

Rivera, Ramon
Carlisle SR HS
Carlisle, PA

Rivera, Ruben
Olney HS
Philadelphia, PA

Rixman, Todd
Bangor Area SR HS
E Bangor, PA

Rizor, Bill
West Allegheny HS
Imperial, PA

Rizor, Melissa
West Greene HS
New Freeport, PA

Rizzo, Ramona
James M Coughlin
Wilkes Barre, PA

Roach, Christina
Saint Hubert HS For Girls
Philadelphia, PA

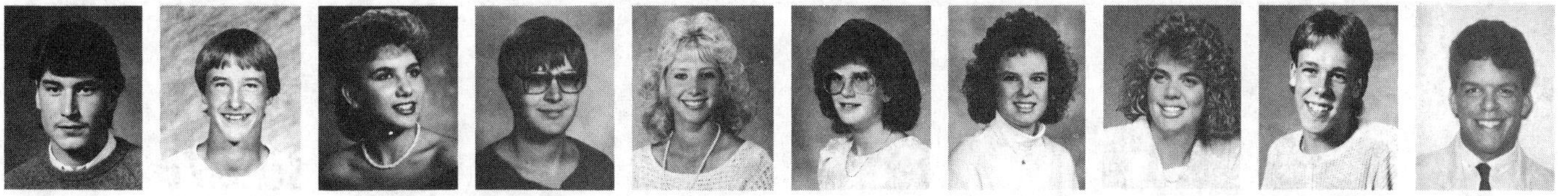

Roach, Patrick
Western Beaver JR-SR HS
Industry, PA

Roadman, Sam
Avella Area JR SR
Avella, PA

Robbins, Elizabeth
Youngsville HS
Bear Lake, PA

Robbins, Paul
Cambridge Springs Joint HS
Cambridge Springs, PA

Roberts, Amy
Jefferson-Morgan
Rices Landing, PA

Roberts, Brenda
Everett Area HS
Everett, PA

Roberts, Karen
Bensalem HS
Bensalem, PA

Roberts, Melissa S
Beaver Area JR/SR
Beaver, PA

Roberts, Michael
Gateway SR HS
Monroeville, PA

Roberts, Michael L
Twin Valley HS
Birdsboro, PA

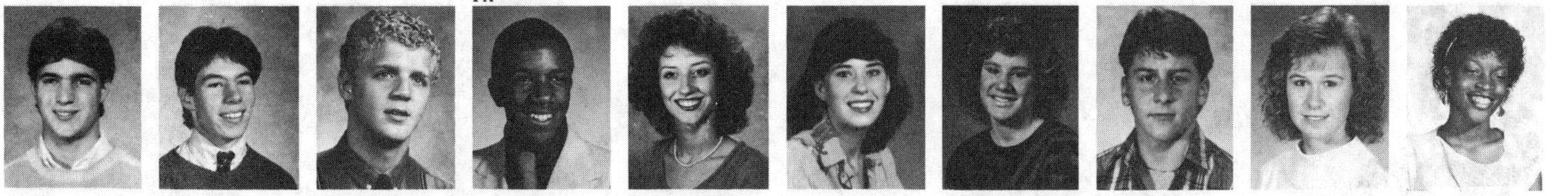

Robertson, Bryan
Burgettstown Area JR SR HS
Burgettstown, PA

Robertson, Christopher
Owen J Roberts HS
Chester Springs, PA

Robidoux, Raymond A
Milton Hershey Schl
Manchester, NH

Robinson, Keino
John Bartram HS
Philadelphia, PA

Robinson, Kelly
Jefferson Morgan
Waynesburg, PA

Robinson, Maryann
Shikellamy HS
Northumberland, PA

Robl, Sheila
East Allegheny HS
North Versailles, PA

Rocco, Mike
Bald Eagle Nittany
Mill Hall, PA

Rocereta, Lee Ann
Monessen HS
Monessen, PA

Rochelle, Jinada
Cedar Crest HS
Lebanon, PA

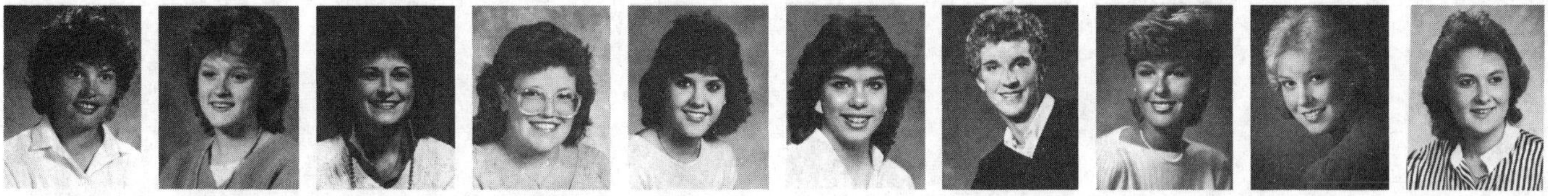

Rock, Cathy
Lock Haven SR HS
Lock Haven, PA

Rockey, Crystal
Penns Valley Area JR/SR HS
Millheim, PA

Rocuskie, Kim
Marian HS
Tamaqua, PA

Rodenbaugh, Patricia
Kennedy Christian
Hermitage, PA

Rodenhaver, Tammy
Danville Area HS
Danville, PA

Rodgers, Brenda
Cranberry HS
Cranberry, PA

Rodgers, Bruce
Wilmington Area
New Wilmington, PA

Rodgers, Keirsten
Parkland HS
Allentown, PA

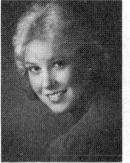

Rodgers, Susan
Grove City HS
Grove City, PA

Rodgers, Tammi K
Rocky Grove HS
Reno, PA

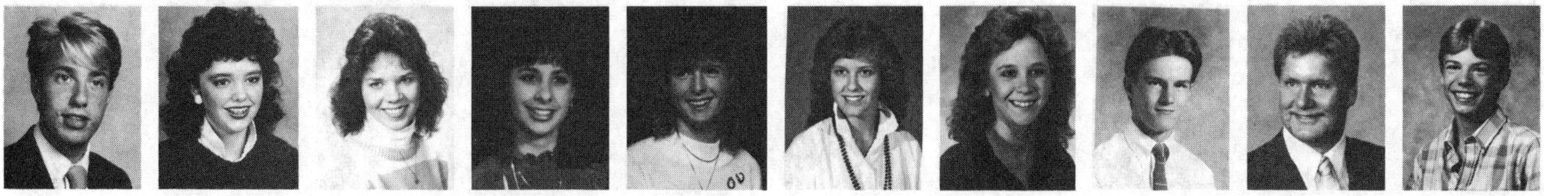

Rodriguez, Gregory
Devon Preparatory
Philadelphia, PA

Roe, Rhonda
Penn-Trafford HS
Trafford, PA

Rogalewicz, Judith
West Scranton SR
Scranton, PA

Rogalski, Lynne
Old Forge HS
Old Forge, PA

Rogel, Rena
Northern Cambria
Barnesboro, PA

Rogers, Heather L
Waynesburg Central
Blacksville, WV

Rogers, Linda
Jefferson-Morgan
Jefferson, PA

Rogozinski, Ronald
Allentown Central Catholic HS
Coopersburg, PA

Rohland, Jr Jack Wade
Freeport Area HS
Sarver, PA

Rohlin, Richard J
Eisenhower HS
Russell, PA

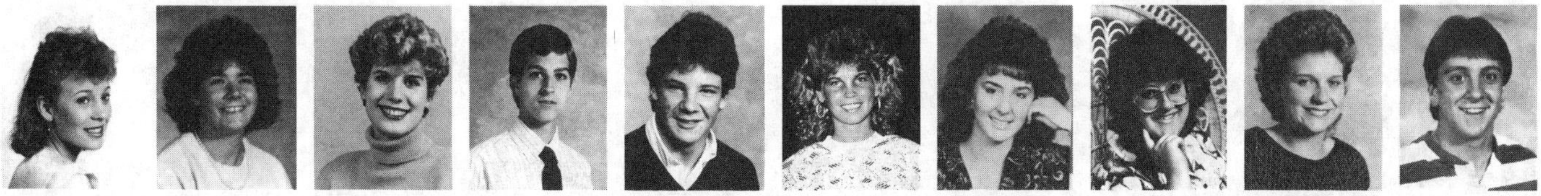

Rohrbach, Jennifer Debra
Brandywine Heights
Fleetwood, PA

Rohrer, Tiffany
Oxford Area HS
Nottingham, PA

Rolf, Ann
Kiski Area HS
New Kensington, PA

Rolleston, Howard
The Chrisitan Acad
Glen Mills, PA

Rollinson, Thomas
Hermitage School
Hermitage, PA

Rolls, Heather
Lower Moreland HS
Huntingdon Valley, PA

Romanic, Mary Lynne
St Marys Area HS
Byrnedale, PA

Romano, Amelia
Pocono Mountain
Tobyhanna, PA

Romanuski, Connie
Shenandoah Valley JR/SR HS
Shenandoah, PA

Rombold, John
Sharon HS
Sharon, PA

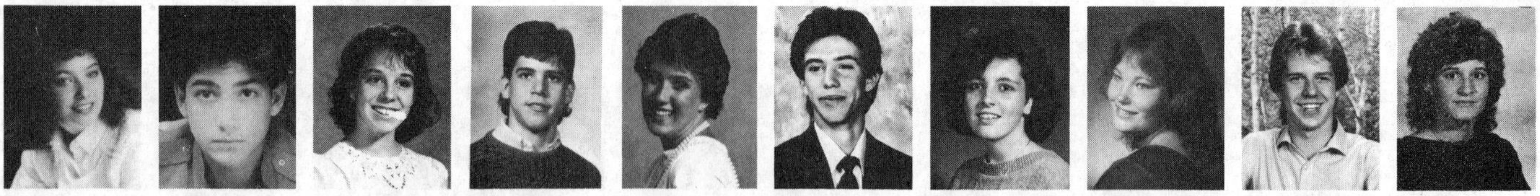

Romeo, Anita
Center HS
Monaca, PA

Romeo, Michael
St John Neumann
Philadelphia, PA

Romig, Cynthia
Owen J Roberts HS
Pottstown, PA

Rongaus, Lee
Mon Valley Catholic
Donora, PA

Ronghi, Anne Marie
Hopewell HS
Aliquippa, PA

Roofner, Franklin
Leechburg Area HS
Vandergrift, PA

Rooney, Becky
Chriss
Central Dauphin
East HS
Dauphin, PA

Roose, Tracy
Yough SR HS
Hutchinson, PA

Root, James
Athens HS
Athens, PA

Rose, Jennifer
Seneca HS
Erie, PA

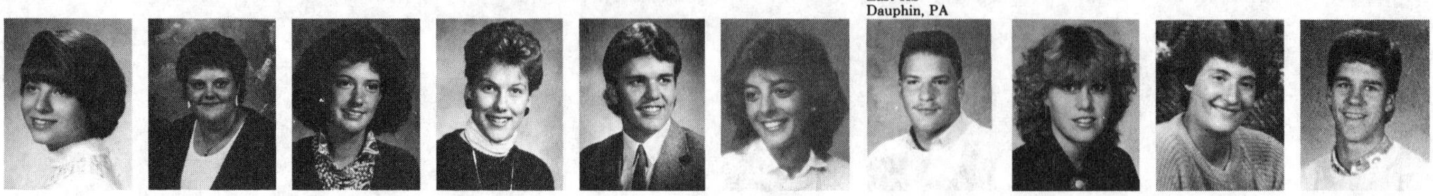

Rose, Susan E
Greensburg Salem
Greensburg, PA

Rose, Veda
Athens HS
Athens, PA

Roseboro, Melissa
Cocalico HS
Denver, PA

Roselli, Pamela
Pleasant Valley HS
Saylorsburg, PA

Rosemeier, Randal
G
Monongahela Valley
Catholic HS
Cokeburg, PA

Rosenberger,
Heather
Northern York
County HS
Dillsburg, PA

Rosenberry, Linn
Greencastle-Antrim
Greencastle, PA

Rosensteel, Monica
Warwick HS
Lititz, PA

Rosh, Sharon
Sayre Area HS
Sayre, PA

Roskos, Raymond
Monessen HS
Monessen, PA

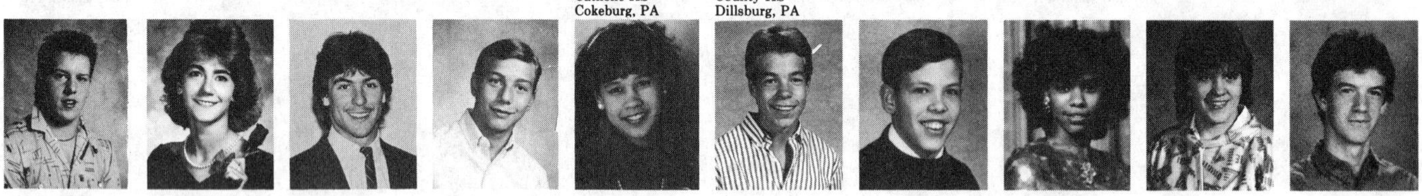

Rosler, Sean
Carbondale Area HS
Carbondale, PA

Ross, Debby
Marple Newtown
Broomall, PA

Ross, Erik
West Hazleton HS
Drums, PA

Ross, James
Mountain View HS
Nicholson, PA

Ross, Jennifer
West Scranton HS
Clarks Summit, PA

Ross, Matthew
Downingtown SR
Downingtown, PA

Ross, Michael
Marple-Newtown
SR HS
Broomall, PA

Ross, Monica
Philadelphia HS For
Philadelphia, PA

Ross, Pam
Rocky Grove HS
Franklin, PA

Ross, Victor
Neshannock HS
New Castle, PA

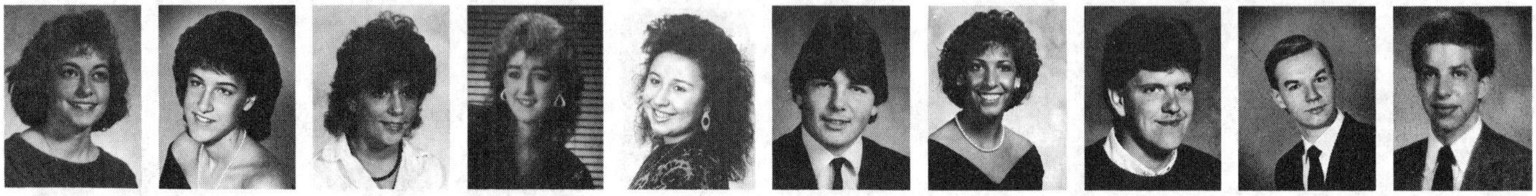

Rossell, Shelley M
Saucon Valley SR
Bethlehem, PA

Rossetti, Tracy L
Pann Hills SR HS
Verona, PA

Rossi, Eileen
Villa Maria Acad
Erie, PA

Rossi, Teresa
Hopewell SR HS
Aliquippa, PA

Rossini, Melanie
Geibel HS
Masontown, PA

Rosso, Anthony
Morrisville HS
Morrisville, PA

Roth, Ferne
Council Rock HS
Newtown, PA

Roth, Michael Q
Pen Argyl HS
Nazareth, PA

Roth, Mike
Penn Hills HS
Pittsburgh, PA

Rothermel, Jeff
Danville HS
Danville, PA

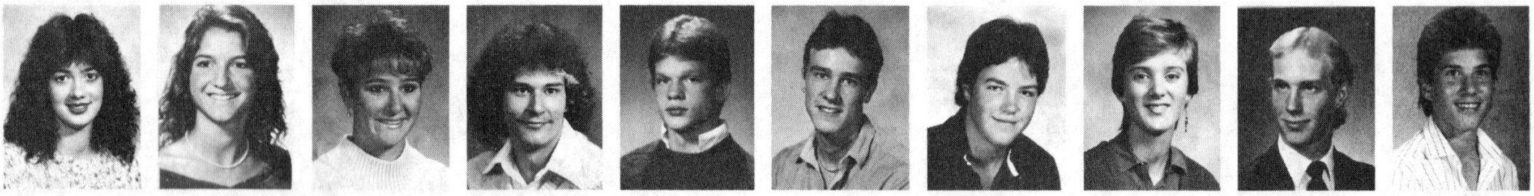

Rotolo, Carissa
Belle Vernon Area
Belle Vernon, PA

Rotondo, Nadine
Upper Merion HS
Bridgeport, PA

Rotundo, Gabbie
Cocalico HS
Denver, PA

Rouscher, Aaron
Dover Area HS
Dover, PA

Route, Denny
Canton HS
Ralston, PA

Rowan, David
Parkland HS
Allentown, PA

Rowe, Brian
Dover Area HS
Dover, PA

Rowe, Nancy
Perkiomen Valley
Perkiomenville, PA

Rowles, Ray
Brockway Area HS
Brockport, PA

Roy, Stephane A
Boyertown JR High
Perkiomenville, PA

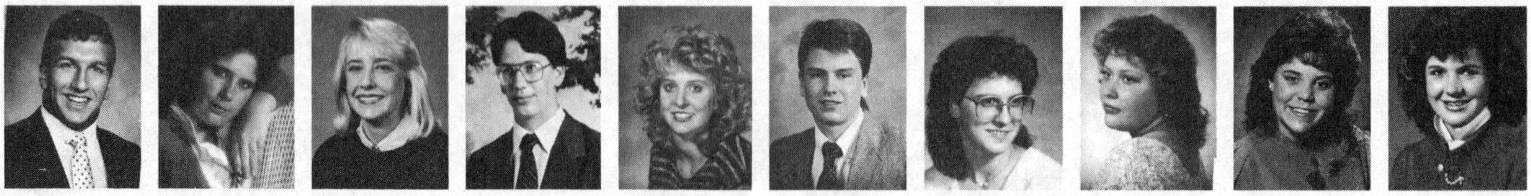

Royal, James John
E L Meyers HS
Wilkes-Barre, PA

Rubincan, Dawn
Coatesville Area SR
Coatesville, PA

Ruby, Eden
Faith Christian HS
Turtle Crk, PA

Ruchak, Joseph
Bishop O Hara HS
Dunmore, PA

Ruck, Kelly
Central SR HS
York, PA

Ruck, Kenneth
Archbishop Wood
HS For Boys
Hatboro, PA

Ruck, Lori
Ambridge Area SR
Baden, PA

Ruda, Mary
Lake-Lehman HS
Hunlock Creek, PA

Rudar, Heather
Peters Township HS
Venetia, PA

Rudiger, Christine
Peters Twp HS
West Chester, PA

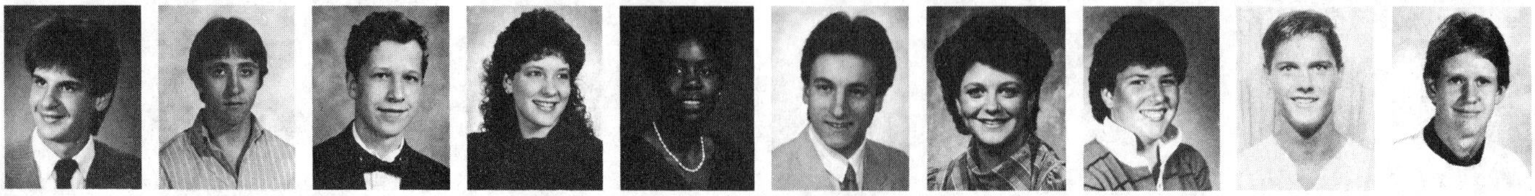

Rudnik, Michael
Hempfield Area HS
Jeannette, PA

Rudock, Chris
Solanco HS
Nottingham, PA

Rudolph, Theodore
Cardinal O Hara HS
Springfield, PA

Ruev, Cassandra
Ringgold HS
Donora, PA

Ruffin, Janene
ABP Carroll HS
Wayne, PA

Ruggeri, David M
Norwin HS
N Huntingdon, PA

Ruggles, Diane
Central HS
East Freedom, PA

Ruhl, Jennifer A
Spring-Ford HS
Royersford, PA

Rundle, Brian
Lancaster Country
Day HS
Reading, PA

Runk, David
Coatesville HS
Coatesville, PA

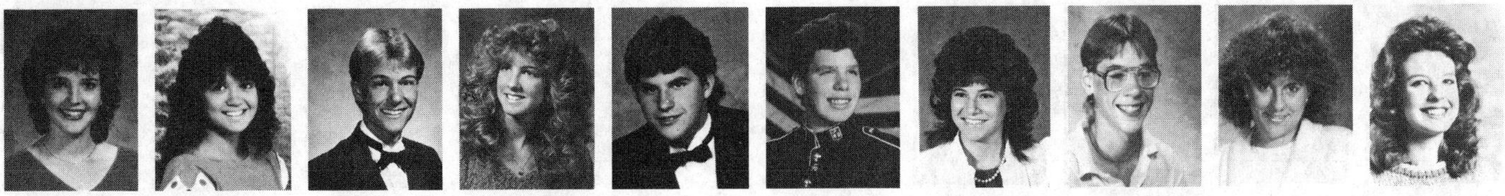

Runkle, Rebecca
Kennard Dale HS
Felton, PA

Rupert, Theresa
Fred City JR SR HS
Ford City, PA

Rupp, III Louis
Palisades HS
Kintnersville, PA

Ruppert, Kimberly
Dover Area HS
Dover, PA

Ruscitto, Jason
Mon Valley Catholic
Scenery Hill, PA

Rush, Christopher
Liberty HS
Bethlehem, PA

Rush, Kristie
Connellsville Area SR HS
Connellsville, PA

Rush, Matthew
Mc Guffey HS
Claysville, PA

Rush, Robin L
Keystone HS
Woodbridge, VA

Rushanan, Marie Therese
Nativity B V M HS
Minersville, PA

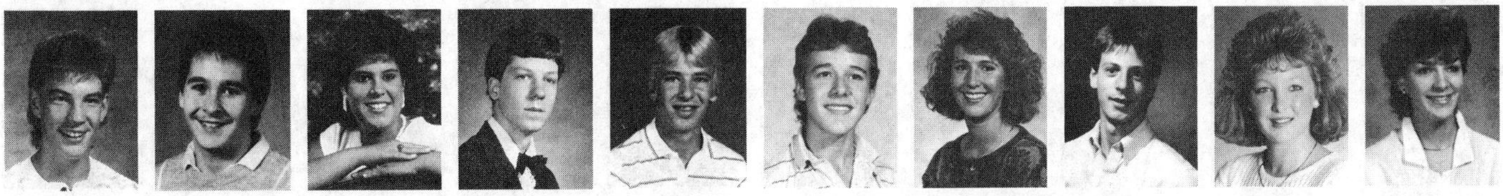

Rushton, John
West Perry SR HS
Duncannon, PA

Rusinko, Joseph Vincent
East Allegheny HS
North Versailles, PA

Russ, Amy
Mc Keesport Area
Mc Keesport, PA

Russell, Alexander
George Washington Ctr H S Engr Sci
Philadelphia, PA

Russell, Chris
Shikellamy HS
Sunbury, PA

Russell, Harrison Scott
Neshaminy HS
Langhorne, PA

Russell, Jennifer
Charleroi Area JR SR HS
Charleroi, PA

Russell, Jon D
Troy SR HS
Towanda, PA

Russell, Kristin
Highlands SR HS
Pittsburgh, PA

Russell, Michele
Solanco HS
Quarryville, PA

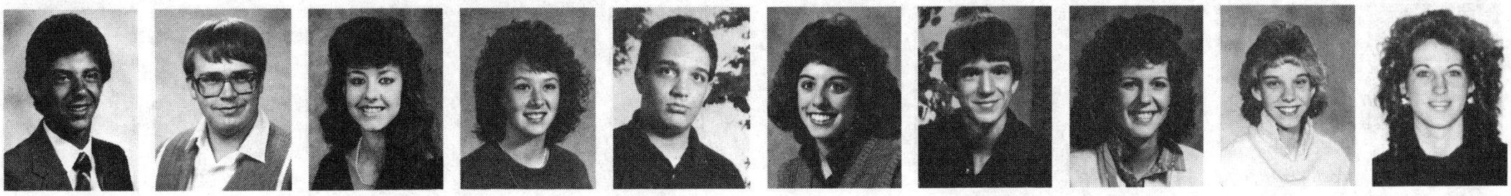

Russell, Nicholas
West Hazleton HS
West Hazleton, PA

Russell, Robert L
Curwensville HS
Grampian, PA

Russo, Barbara
St Maria Goretti HS
Philadelphia, PA

Russo, Lynn
Methacton HS
Audubon, PA

Russo, Nick
Bishop O Reilly HS
Swoyersville, PA

Russo, Nicole
Peters Township HS
Venetia, PA

Russo, Shawn
Karns City JR SR
Parker, PA

Ruth, Laurie
Donegal HS
Mt Joy, PA

Rutkowski, Tracy
John S Fine SR HS
Nanticoke, PA

Rutkowsky, Susan
Saint Basil Acad
Philadelphia, PA

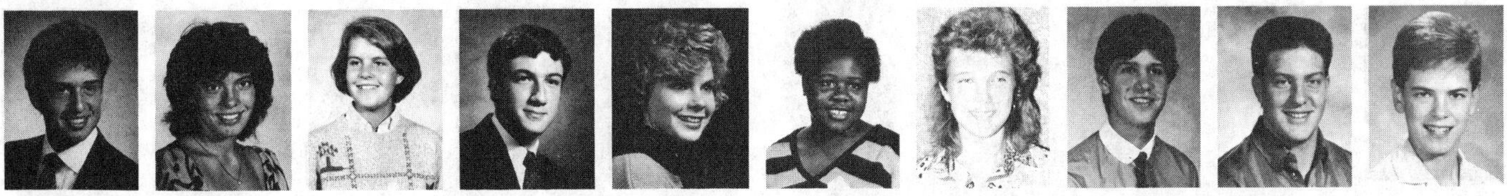

Rutt, Jamie
Mt Calvary Christian Schl
Hummelstown, PA

Rutzmoser, Christina
Phil Mont Christian
Huntingdon Valley, PA

Ruzanic, Marhea
North Allegheny HS
Allison Pk, PA

Ruzzi, Vincent J
Strath Haven HS
Princeton Jct, NJ

Ryan, Anne Marie
Clearfield Area HS
Clearfield, PA

Ryan, Celeste
Blue Mountain Acad
E Branch, NY

Ryan, Connie
Norwin HS
N Huntingdon, PA

Ryan, Kevin
Perkiomen Valley
Collegeville, PA

Ryan, Thomas
Somerset Area SR
Somerset, PA

Ryder, Sean
Knoch JR/SR HS
Butler, PA

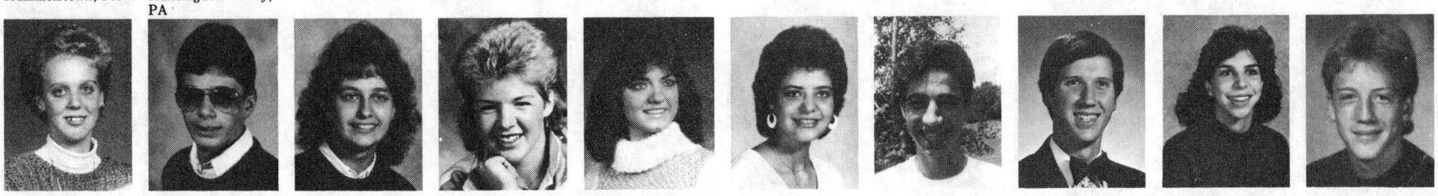

Rydzeski, Cindy
Shikellamy HS
Northumberland, PA

Ryen, Jr William L
West Branch Area
Morrisdale, PA

Rylke, Patrice
Bishop Carroll HS
Portage, PA

Rynd, Annie
Mercer JR SR HS
Mercer, PA

Rzeszotarski, Tracey M
Sullivan County HS
Dushore, PA

Saba, Caroline A
Penncrest HS
Lima, PA

Sabatini, Carlo
Wyoming Seminary
Dallas, PA

Sabotta, Christian
Downingtown SR
Downingtown, PA

Saddic, Kimberly
Henderson SR HS
West Chester, PA

Sadler, Glenn
South Western HS
Hanover, PA

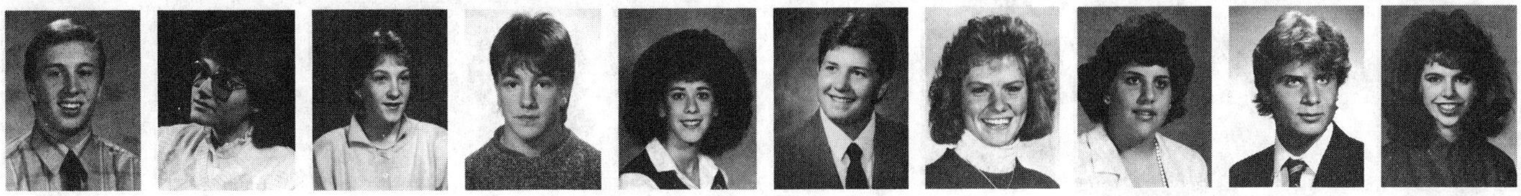

Sadler, Mark
Donegal HS
Marietta, PA

Sadvari, Laurie
Windber Area HS
Windber, PA

Saeger, Jennifer
Emmaus HS
Allentown, PA

Safford, Shawn
Annville-Cleona HS
Annville, PA

Saggiomo, Marybeth
Nazareth Acad
Phila, PA

Sahm, Shannon
Cocalico HS
Denver, PA

Saidt, Susan
North Penn HS
Lansdale, PA

Saienni, Mary
Avon Grove HS
W Grove, PA

Saks, Scott
Southern Lehigh HS
Coopersburg, PA

Saladna, Antoinette
Monon Gahela Valley Catholic HS
Belle Vernon, PA

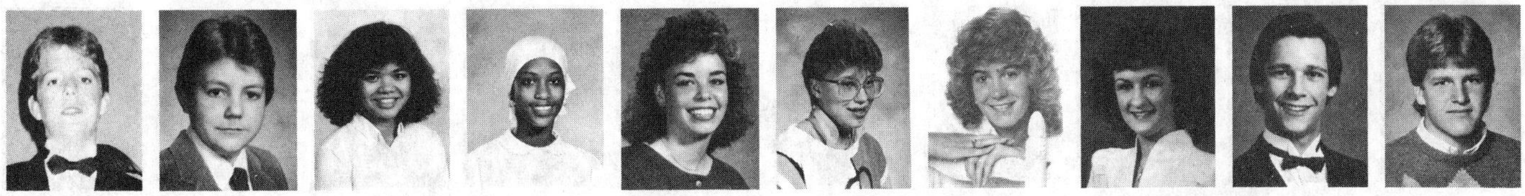

Salak, Gary
Western Wayne HS
Waymart, PA

Salak, Mike
Western Wayne HS
Waymart, PA

Saldivar, Madelaine
Gwynedd-Mercy
Hatfield, PA

Saleem-Ugdah, Najla
Sis Clara Muhammad HS
Philadelphia, PA

Salinger, Christine
Methacton HS
Audubon, PA

Salko, Heather
Lake-Lehman HS
Shavertown, PA

Salmon, Rebecca
Mc Dowell HS
Erie, PA

Saloom, Charlene R
Mt Pleasant Area SR HS
Mount Pleasant, PA

Salotto, Steven P
Monsignor Bonner
Upper Darby, PA

Salus, Dave
Wyoming Valley West HS
Swoyersville, PA

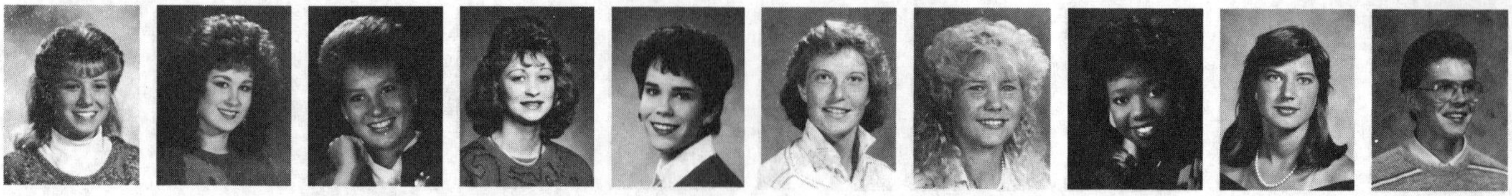

Salvanish, Melissa
Bellefonte Area SR
Howard, PA

Salvato, Claudine
Bishop Conwell HS
Hulmeville, PA

Salvia, Jacqueline
Pennsbury HS
Yardley, PA

Salzman, Kellie
Ringgold SR HS
Monongahela, PA

Sam, Michelle
Windber Area HS
Windber, PA

Sample, Kirstin
Fairview HS
Fairview, PA

Sanders, Jennifer L
Penn Trafford HS
Export, PA

Sanders, Sandra
Renee
Kennedy Christian
Wheatland, PA

Sandin, Ann
Margaret
Lower Moreland HS
Huntingdon Valley,
PA

Sandoe, Sean
Pequea Valley HS
New Holland, PA

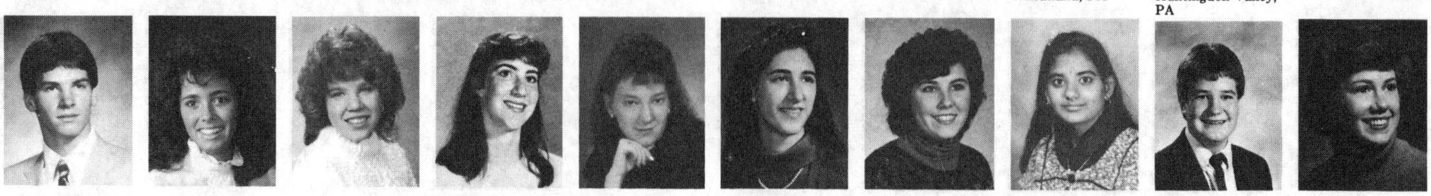

Sands, IV William
Upper Perklomen
Pennsburg, PA

Sandy, Laura
Red Lion HS
Red Lion, PA

Sandy, Mary Grace
West Scranton HS
Scranton, PA

Sanford, Kristen
Downingtown SR
Downingtown, PA

Sanford, Sheila
Heritage Christian
Erie, PA

Sanger, Sharon
Lebanon HS
Lebanon, PA

Sanguinito, Michele
Pen Argy Area HS
Pen Argyl, PA

Sankaran, Vedavalli
Altoona Area HS
Altoona, PA

Sankey, Shawn
Bishop Gbuilfoyle
Altoona, PA

Sanner, Kristin
Noelle
Penns Valley HS
Spring Mills, PA

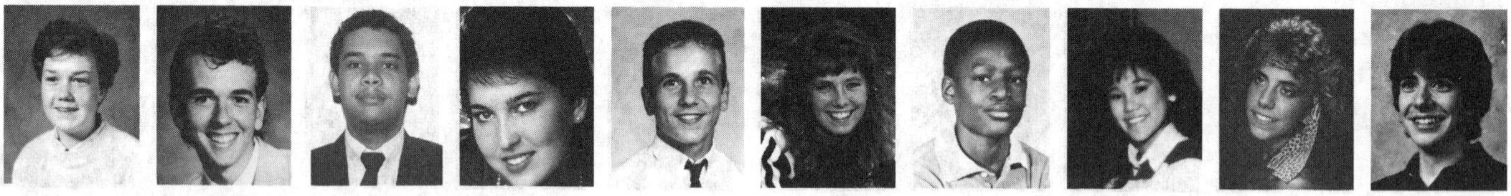

Sanner, Shelley
Penns Valley Area
Spring Mills, PA

Santarsiero, Robert
Dunmore HS
Dunmore, PA

Santiago, Daniel
Lutheran HS
Philadelphia, PA

Santone, Pam
Grove City HS
Grove City, PA

Santoni, Thomas
Bishop Mc Devitt
Harrisburg, PA

Santora, Gina
Meadville Area SR
Meadville, PA

Santos, Gerson
Saul Agricultural
Philadelphia, PA

Santos, Shilla
Dover HS
Dover, PA

Sapolio, Tracey
Peters Township HS
Bridgeville, PA

Saporito, James
Warren Area HS
Warren, PA

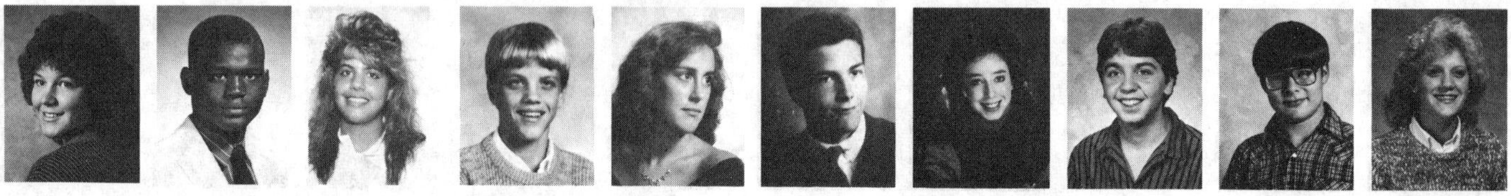

Sapp, Debbie
Marion Center HS
Marion Center, PA

Sapp, Theodore
Maurice
Northeast/Swenson
Skills Center
Philadelphia, PA

Sarikianos, Pamela
Upper Merion Area
Wayne, PA

Sassaman, Peter
Danville SR HS
Danville, PA

Sassani, Carla
Our Lady Of
Lourdes HS
Mount Carmel, PA

Sastokas, Bryan
Kennedy Christian
Sharpsville, PA

Satter, Stephanie
Conrad Weiser HS
Wernersville, PA

Satterly, Brent
Wellsboro Area HS
Wellsboro, PA

Sauer, David
G A R Memorial HS
Wilkes-Barre, PA

Sauer, Stacy
Conrad Weiser HS
Womelsdorf, PA

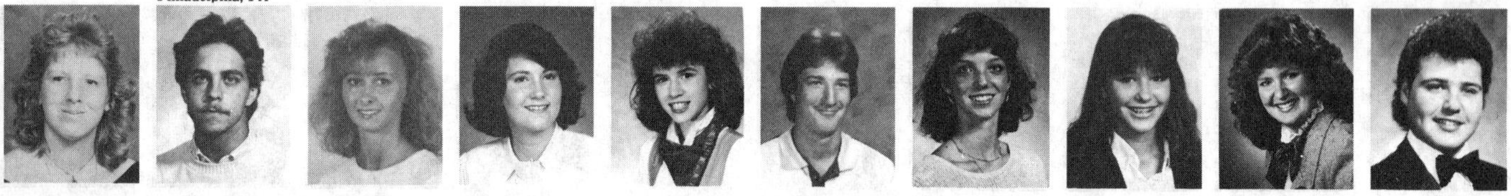

Saur, Dawn
Council Rock HS
Newtown, PA

Sauritch, Patrick
Belle Vernon Area
Belle Vernon, PA

Savage, Jennifer
Nazareth Acad
Phila, PA

Savage, Rebecca L
Highlands SR HS
Brackenridge, PA

Savakes, Wendy M
Plum SR HS
Pittsburgh, PA

Savant, James
Tulpehocken HS
Bethel, PA

Sawhill, Kendell
North Hills HS
Pittsburgh, PA

Sawicky, Christina
Irene
Gwynedd Mercy
Ambler, PA

Sawyer, Stacey
Ringgold HS
Finleyville, PA

Sawyer, Jr William
Inverboro HS
Prospect Park, PA

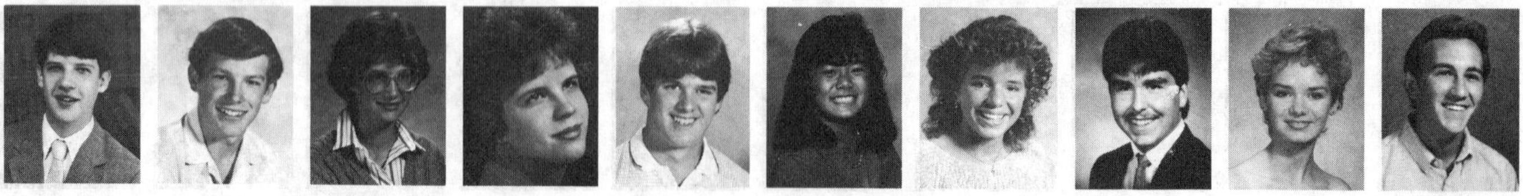

Say, Brad
Ford City JR SR
Ford City, PA

Saylor, James
Bellefonte HS
Bellefonte, PA

Saylor, Kathy
Donegal HS
Mount Joy, PA

Saylor, Michele
Gateway SR HS
Monroeville, PA

Saylor, Richie
Blacklick Valley HS
Vintondale, PA

Sayson, Clarissa
Lebanon Catholic
Lebanon, PA

Scafaria, Aimee
Academy Of Notre
West Chester, PA

Scaff, David W
Lock Haven HS
Loganton, PA

Scampone, Melissa
L
Perkiomen Valley
Schwenksville, PA

Scancella, Joseph J
Council Rock HS
Newtown, PA

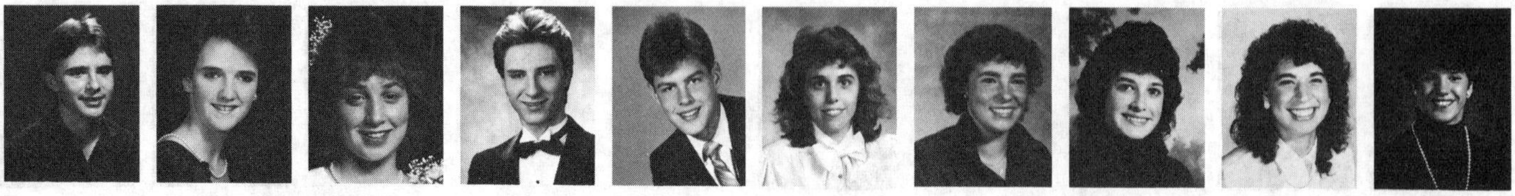

Scandle, Michael
Shamokin Area HS
Sunbury, PA

Scanlan, Jennifer
Cardinal O Hara HS
Clifton Hgts, PA

Scarfaro, Erin
Faith Christian HS
Roseto, PA

Schaaf, Jr Joseph R
Catherdral
Preparatory Schl
Erie, PA

Schaaf, Paul
Penn Hills SR HS
Penn Hills, PA

Schaeffer, Crystal
Souderton Area HS
Telford, PA

Schaeffer, Cynthia
Boyertown Area SR
Boyertown, PA

Schaeffer, Jennifer
Schuylkill Haven
Sch Haven, PA

Schafer, Tricia
Reading HS
Reading, PA

Schaffer, Carol Ann
Bishop Guilfoyle HS
Duncansville, PA

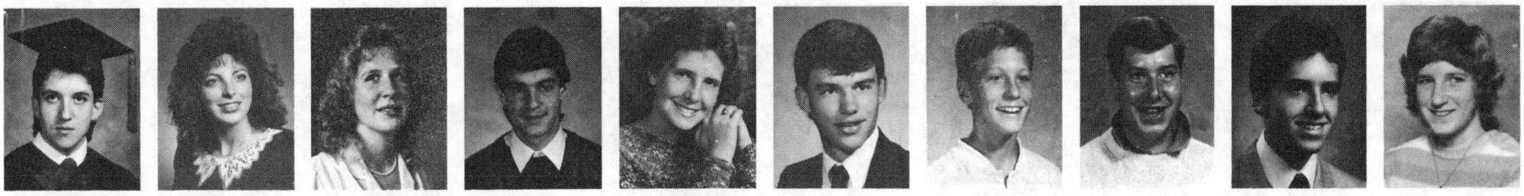

Schaffer, Jason
Cardinal O Hara HS
Media, PA

Schantz, Melissa
Emmaus HS
Wescosville, PA

Schappell, Lisa
Hamburg Area HS
Hamburg, PA

Schaub, Ron
Fort Cherry HS
Washington, PA

Schell, Elizabeth
Clearfield Area HS
Clearfield, PA

Schellhamer, Chris D
Northwestern Lehigh HS
Slatington, PA

Schenck, Gregory
Henderson HS
W Chester, PA

Schenke, Todd
Pequa Valley HS
Paradise, PA

Schiavi, Michael
Chartiers Valley HS
Pittsburgh, PA

Schields, Colleen
Red Lion Area SR
Red Lion, PA

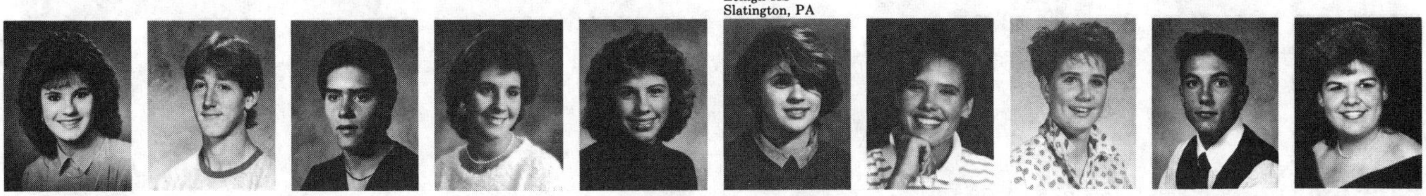

Schill, Valerie
Clarion-Limestone Area HS
Clarion, PA

Schiller, Eric
Plum SR HS
Pittsburgh, PA

Schinosi, Kirk
South Park HS
Library, PA

Schlack, Bobbi Marie
Shenandoah Valley JR-SR HS
Shenandoah, PA

Schlake, Heidi
Nazareth Area SR
Nazareth, PA

Schlegel, Jennifer
Pen Argyl Area SR
Nazareth, PA

Schleig, Lisa Ann
Council Rock HS
Churchville, PA

Schleppy, Liz
Stroudsburg HS
Sciota, PA

Schlimm, II John
Elk County Christian HS
St Marys, PA

Schloss, Judeanne
Cardinal O Hara HS
Eddystone, PA

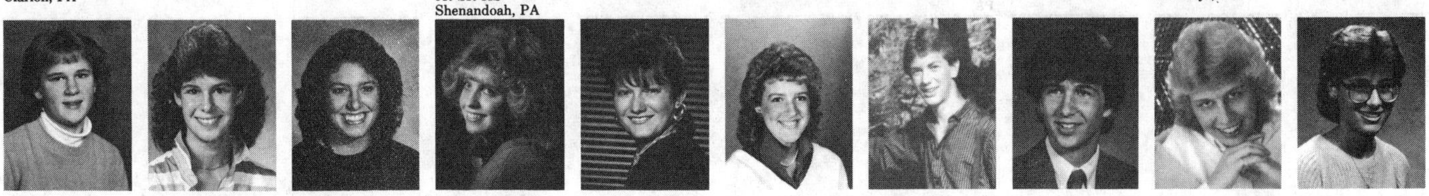

Schlosser, Dawn
Souderton Area HS
Telford, PA

Schlosser, Donia
East Pennsboro HS
Mechanicsburg, PA

Schlosser, Tina
Cambridge Springs
Cambridge Spgs, PA

Schmader, Debbie
North Clarion HS
Lucinda, PA

Schmader, Gretta
Clarion Area HS
Shippenville, PA

Schmidt, Debbie
Fort Cherry HS
Mc Donald, PA

Schmidt, Douglas
Garnet Valley HS
Glen Mills, PA

Schmidt, Eric William
Hempfield HS
Manheim, PA

Schmidt, Jeannine Anne
Cambridge Springs
Conneautville, PA

Schmidt, Kristine
Greesburg Salem HS
Greensburg, PA

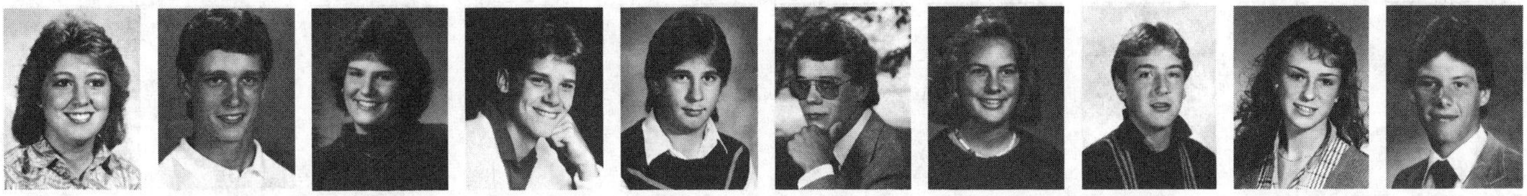

Schmidt, Lory
Freedom HS
Bethlehem, PA

Schmidt, Mark
Homer-Center HS
Coral, PA

Schmidt, Rebecca Anne
Cambridge Springs
Saegertown, PA

Schmidt, Robert
Cambridge Springs
Saegertown, PA

Schmitt, Jr Edward
Corry Area HS
Corry, PA

Schmitt, Eugene V
Lancaster Catholic
Columbia, PA

Schmoyer, Julie
Emmaus HS
Emmaus, PA

Schneck, Brad
Northampton SR
Northampton, PA

Schneck, Wendy
William Allen HS
Allentown, PA

Schneider, Greg
St Marys Area HS
St Marys, PA

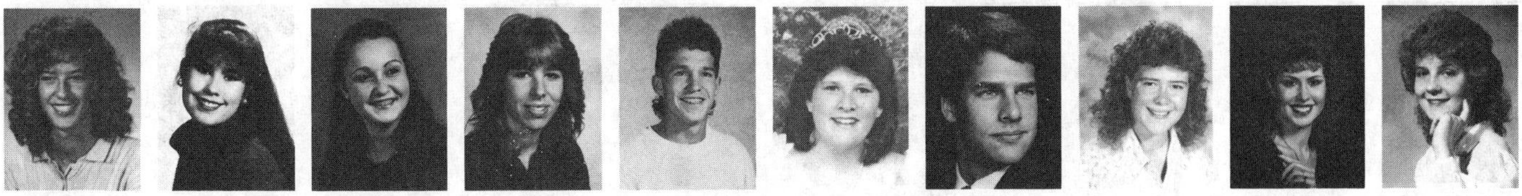

Schnorr, Amy
York Catholic HS
York, PA

Schock, Marcine Ann
Charleroi Area JR SR HS
N Charlaroi, PA

Schoen, Erika
Eastern York JR-SR
Wrightsville, PA

Schoenberger, Christine
Upper Moreland HS
Horsham, PA

Schoenebeck, Scott
Council Rock HS
Newtown, PA

Schofield, Lori
Hopewell Area HS
Aliquippa, PA

Scholl, Greg J
Avonworth HS
Pittsburgh, PA

Scholl, Patricia
Northern York HS
Dillsburg, PA

Schooley, Kimberli
St Huberts Catholic HS For Girls
Philadelphia, PA

Schoonover, Paula J
Bucktail Area HS
Renovo, PA

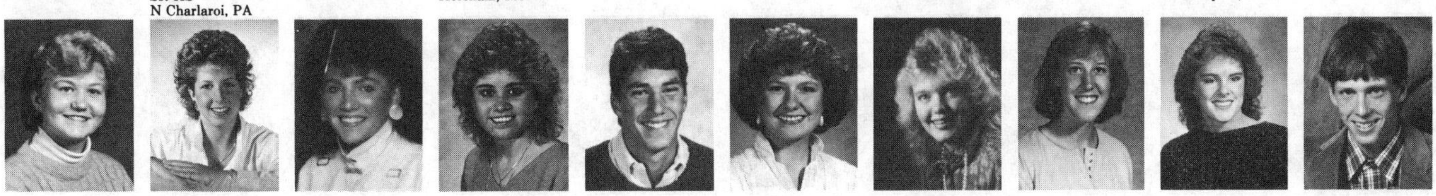

Schoonover, Stacey
Tunkhannock Area
Tunkhannock, PA

Schorn, Colleen
Reading SR HS
Reading, PA

Schrecongost, Tina
Freeport Area Joint
Freeport, PA

Schreiber, Kelly
St Marys Area HS
Kersey, PA

Schrufer, Matthew
Ole Valley HS
Oley, PA

Schubert, Amy
Shaler Area HS
Glenshaw, PA

Schubert, Heidi
Boyertown SR HS
Boyertown, PA

Schubert, Margaret
B Reed Henderson
West Chester, PA

Schucker, Kathy
Kutztown HS
Kempton, PA

Schueller, John C
Tulpehocken Area
Bernville, PA

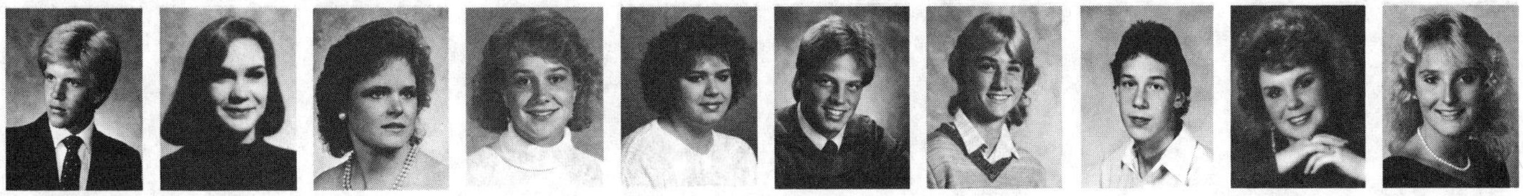

Schuerer, Douglas J
Gateway SR HS
Monroeville, PA

Schuld, Michelle
Downingtown SR
Downingtown, PA

Schull, Cynthia
Milton Hershey Schl
San Diego, CA

Schull, Julia
Central Bucks HS
Doylestown, PA

Schulte, Paula
Clairton HS
Clairton, PA

Schultz, Christian
General Mclane HS
Mc Kean, PA

Schultz, Karen
Montoorsville Area
Muncy, PA

Schultz, Scott
Parkland HS
Breinigsville, PA

Schultz, Sherri
Seton-La-Salle HS
Pittsburgh, PA

Schulz, Linda F
Cheltenham HS
Glenside, PA

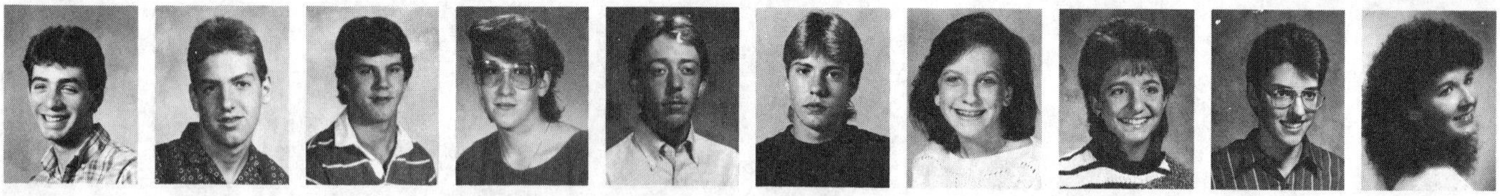

Schurer, Joseph
Perry Traditional
Pittsburgh, PA

Schuster, Kevin M
Quakertown
Community HS
E Greenville, PA

Schutt, Burt
Northampton Area
SR HS
Northampton, PA

Schwab, Rochelle
Monessen HS
Monessen, PA

Schwalm, Michael
Tri-Valley HS
Hegins, PA

Schwartz, Jeff
Hampton HS
Allison Park, PA

Schwartz, Jennifer
State Coll Area
Intermediate HS
State College, PA

Schwartz, Kimberly
Tri-Valley HS
Hegins, PA

Schwartz, Steven
Hempfield HS
Lancaster, PA

Schwartz, Susan A
Nativity BVM HS
New Philadelphia,
PA

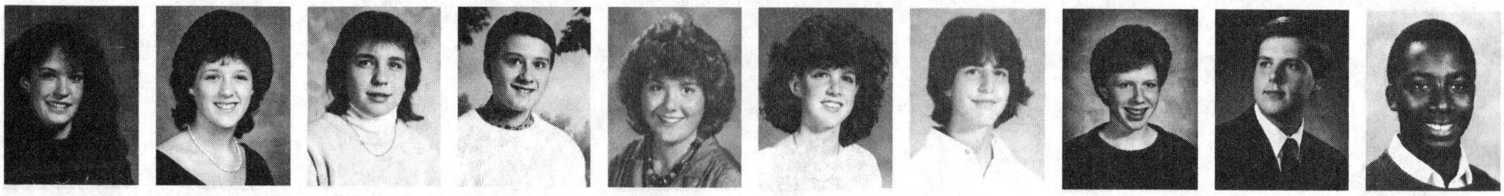

Schwartz, Tamara
Cumberland Valley
Mechanicsburg, PA

Schwegel, Theresa
Archbishop Ryan
Philadelphia, PA

Schweigert, Lori
Schuylkill Haven
Area HS
Sch Haven, PA

Schweigert, Scott
Schuylkill Haven
Area HS
Schuylkill Haven,
PA

Schweitzer, Lori
Correy Area HS
Spartansburg, PA

Schweizer, Chris
St Huberts HS
Philadelphia, PA

Sciarra, Gina
Wissahickon HS
Gwynedd, PA

Sciortino, Angela
Renee
William Penn SR
York, PA

Scollick, Keith
Wyomissing Area
Shillington, PA

Scott, John
Harry S Truman HS
Bristol, PA

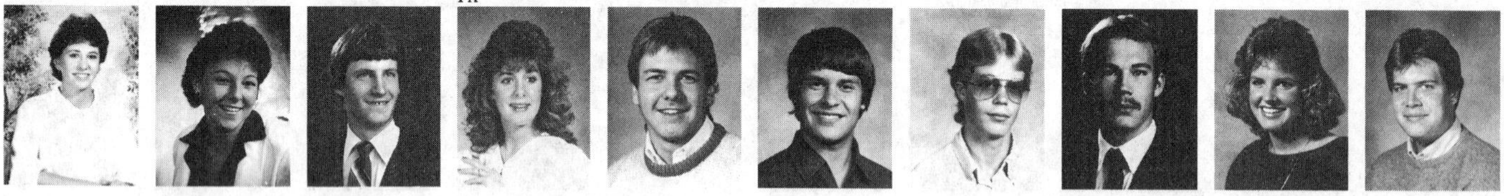

Scott, Kimberly
Shippensburg Area
SR HS
Shippensburg, PA

Scott, Peggy
Lakeview HS
Stoneboro, PA

Scott, William
Juniata HS
Mifflintohn, PA

Scotti, Stacey
Bensalem HS
Bensalem, PA

Scrip, Joe
Mon Valley Catholic
Monessen, PA

Seals, Peter
Quakertown
Community HS
Quakertown, PA

Seaman, Dale
East Juniata HS
Richfield, PA

Seaman, Daniel
East Juniata HS
Richfield, PA

Seaman, Sheryl
Peters Twp HS
Mcmurray, PA

Searfass, Michael
Parkland HS
Schnecksville, PA

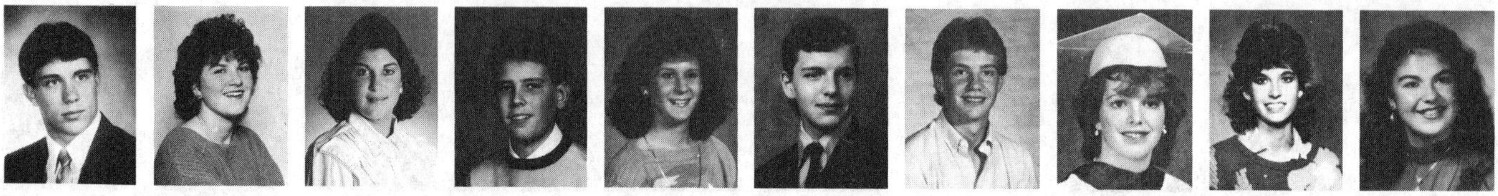

Searfoss, John S
Jim Thorpe Area
Jim Thorpe, PA

Seaver, Maureen
Panther Valley HS
Lansford, PA

Sebastian, Beth A
Open Door Christian
Saltsburg, PA

Seburn, III Jess
West Hazleton HS
Sugarloaf, PA

Secko, Elana
Greensburg Central
Catholic HS
Irwin, PA

Sederburg, Jr Loren
Neil
Sheffield JR SR HS
Tiona, PA

Sedwick, Raymond
Karns City JR/SR
Chicora, PA

Seeds, Megan
Cardinal O Hara HS
Broomall, PA

Seery, Jennifer
Ringgold HS
Finleyville, PA

Seesholtz, Kimberly
Bishop Mc Cort HS
Johnstown, PA

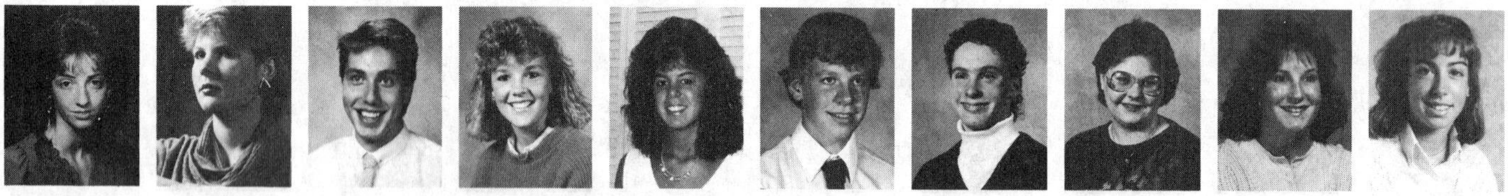

Segebart, Chris
Millersburg Area HS
Millersburg, PA

Seger, Tammy
Curwensville Area
Grampian, PA

Sehulster, Donald
Delaware Valley HS
Shohola, PA

Seibert, Dianne
Stephanie
Peters Township HS
Library, PA

Seiden, Jennifer
Upper Dublin HS
Dresher, PA

Seiger, Gregory
Red Land HS
Lewisberry, PA

Seiss, Jeffrey
Steel Valley HS
Munhall, PA

Seitz, Amy
Perry Traditional
Pittsburgh, PA

Seitz, Melissa
Elizabethtown Area
Elizabethtown, PA

Seitzinger, Kathy
Allentown Central
Macungie, PA

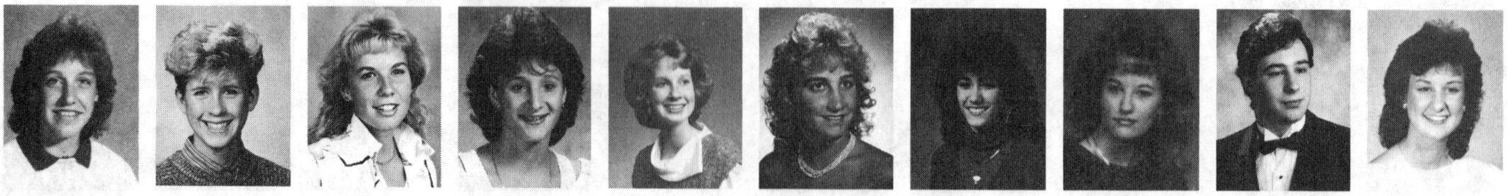

Sekellick, Kristin M
Boyertown Jr HS
Frederick, PA

Sekol, Allison
Delaware Valley HS
Matamoras, PA

Seler, Jennifer
West Snyder HS
Mc Clure, PA

Selfe, Amy
Lock Haven SR HS
Lock Haven, PA

Sell, Anita
Holy Name HS
Leesport, PA

Sellman, Patricia M
Upper Merion Area
King Of Prussia, PA

Seltz, Joset
Aliquippa HS
Aliquippa, PA

Semans, Kristi
Frazier HS
Perryopolis, PA

Sementelli, Arthur
Cathedral Prep
Erie, PA

Semic, Beth
Central Dauphin
East HS
Harrisburg, PA

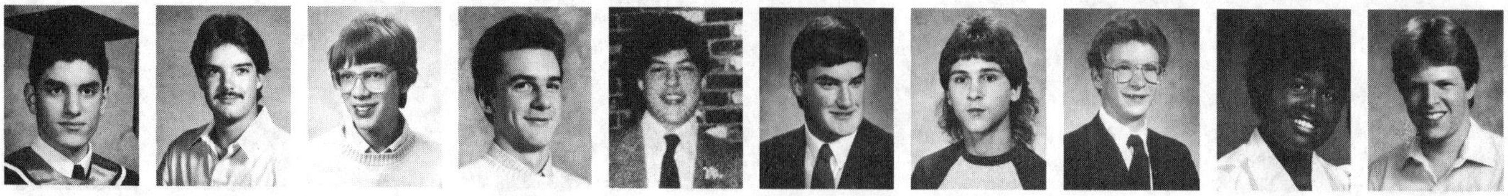

Seminara, Carmelo
St John Neumann
Philadelphia, PA

Sephakis, Jr
Thomas
Ambridge Area HS
Sewickley, PA

Serbak, Michael
Trinity HS
Washington, PA

Serniak, Alan
Sacred Heart HS
Jermyn, PA

Serotta, Andrew H
North Penn HS
Lansdale, PA

Sestock, Douglas
Mt Pleasant Area
Mt Pleasant, PA

Seth, Joe
Kittanning SR HS
Worthington, PA

Settlemyer,
Jonathan
Jersey Shore SR HS
Jersey Shore, PA

Sewell, Carla
Westinghouse HS
Pittsburgh, PA

Seybert, Craig A
Columbia-Montour
AVTS HS
Berwick, PA

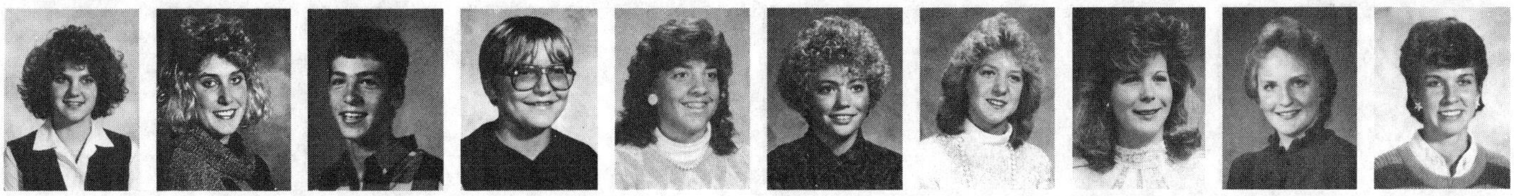

Seymore, Pamela J
Bishop Guilfoyle HS
Altoona, PA

Seymour, Elizabeth
Bishop Guifoyle HS
Altoona, PA

Seymour, James
Quaker Valley HS
Sewickley, PA

Shade, Thomas A
Lock Haven HS
Lock Haven, PA

Shadle, Kelly
Littlestown SR HS
Littlestown, PA

Shadle, Kristi
Williams Valley HS
Tower City, PA

Shadle, Pamela
Watsontown
Christian Acad
Winfield, PA

Shafer, Deborah
Cumberland Valley
Mechanicsburg, PA

Shaffer, Brenda
Somerset Area HS
Somerset, PA

Shaffer, Carla
Ligonier Valley SR
Ligonier, PA

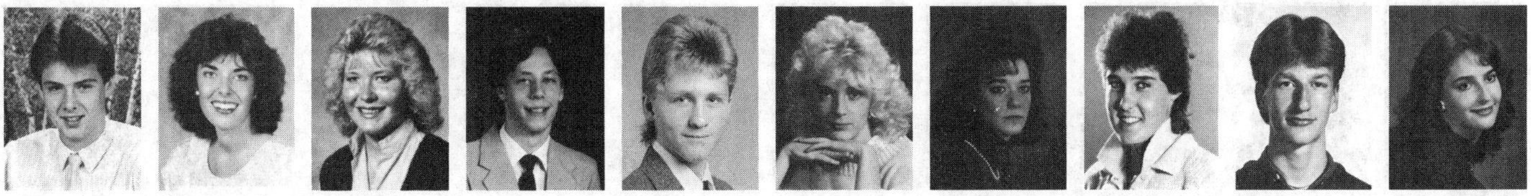

Shaffer, Christopher
Sayre Area HS
S Waverly, PA

Shaffer, Heather
Conemaugn Twp
Area HS
Boswell, PA

Shaffer, Holli
Riverside SR HS
Ellwood City, PA

Shaffer, Jr James M
Montgomery Area
Montgomery, PA

Shaffer, John
St Marys Area HS
St Marys, PA

Shaffer, Kathy
Central SR HS
York, PA

Shaffer, Keri
East Pennsboro HS
Enola, PA

Shaffer, Lisa
Marion Center HS
Marion Center, PA

Shaffer, Mark
Blairsville SR HS
Blairsville, PA

Shaffer, Melissa
Garden Spot HS
Morgantown, PA

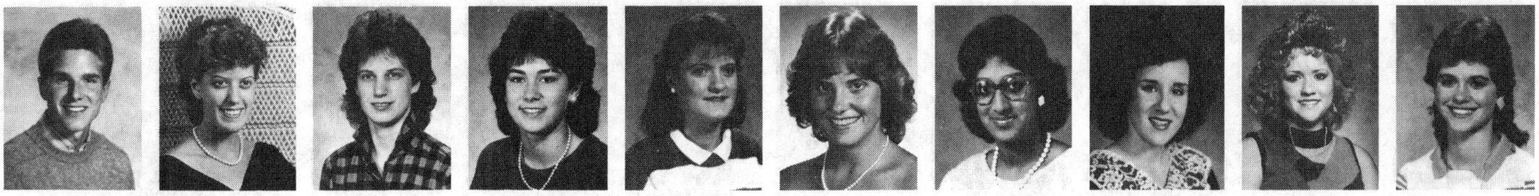

Shaffer, Michael
Alan
Shade-Central City
Stoystown, PA

Shaffer, Michelle
York Catholic HS
York, PA

Shaffer, Nicole
Bald Eagle Nittany
Mill Hall, PA

Shaffer, Penny
North Star HS
Hooversville, PA

Shaffer, Sharon
Harrisburg Christian
Harrisburg, PA

Shaffert, Jennifer
Abington SR HS
Doylestown, PA

Shah, Anita
Moon SR HS
Coraopolis, PA

Shamitis, Renee
Central Catholic HS
Herminie, PA

Shandor, Pamela
Rae
Ringgold SR HS
Finleyville, PA

Shaner, Joy
Galeton Area HS
Galeton, PA

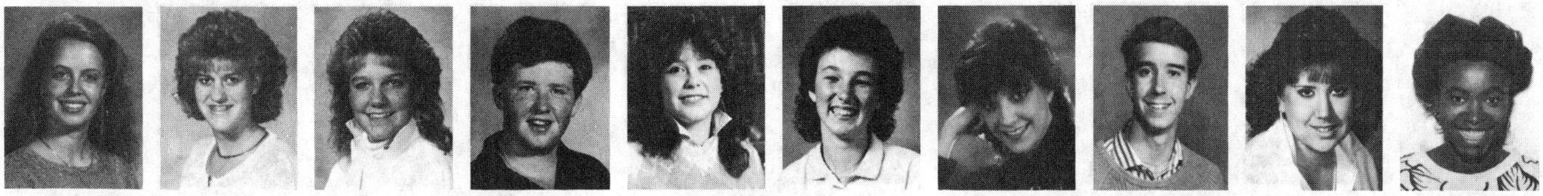

Shank, Diana
Germantown Acad
Harleysville, PA

Shankweiler, Ann
Parkland HS
Schnecksville, PA

Shankweiler,
Paulette
Wallenpaupack Area
Greentown, PA

Shanley, Edward
Saegertown HS
Meadville, PA

Share, Shirley
West Scranton HS
Scranton, PA

Sharek, Diane
Hopewell SR HS
Aliquippa, PA

Sharkey, Cheryl Ann
West Scranton SR
Scranton, PA

Sharpe, John
North Catholic HS
Pittsburgh, PA

Sharpe, Kimberley
Clarion Area HS
Shippenville, PA

Shatteen, Tamika
Coatesville Area SR
Coatesville Hts, PA

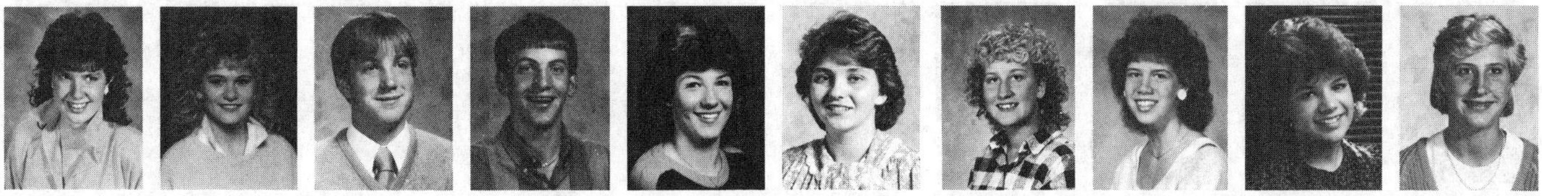

Shattenberg, Cara
Venango Christian
Shippenville, PA

Shatzer, Stephanie
C
James Buchanan HS
St Thomas, PA

Shaub, Michael
Lampeter-Strasburg
Lampeter, PA

Shaubach, Robert A
Pequea Valley HS
Paradise, PA

Shaughnessy, Amy
Tunkhannock HS
Tunkhannock, PA

Shaulis, Angela
Berlin Brothers
Valley HS
Berlin, PA

Shaulis, Kristie
Saltsburg JR SR HS
Saltsburg, PA

Shaw, Christine
Cambria Heights HS
Patton, PA

Shaw, Kelli
Central HS
E Freedom, PA

Shay, Heather
Cedar Crest HS
Lebanon, PA

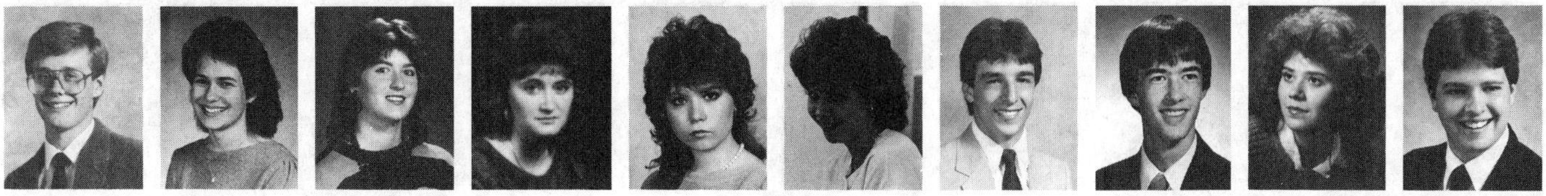

Shay, Michael
Nativity BVM
Pottsville, PA

Shea, Keri
Canon Mc Millan
Mc Donald, PA

Shea, Lia
Cambersburg Area
SR HS
Chambersburg, PA

Shea, Tammy
Tunkhannock HS
Tunkhannock, PA

Sheaffer, Annmarie
Owen J Roberts HS
Elverson, PA

Shearer, Christine
Hazleton SR HS
Hazleton, PA

Shearer, Peter W
Belle Vernon Area
Belle Vernon, PA

Sheckler, Craig D
Southern Lehigh HS
Coopersburg, PA

Sheehan, Amy
Kennedy Christian
Brookfield, OH

Sheetz, Randy S
Cumberland Valley
Mechanicsburg, PA

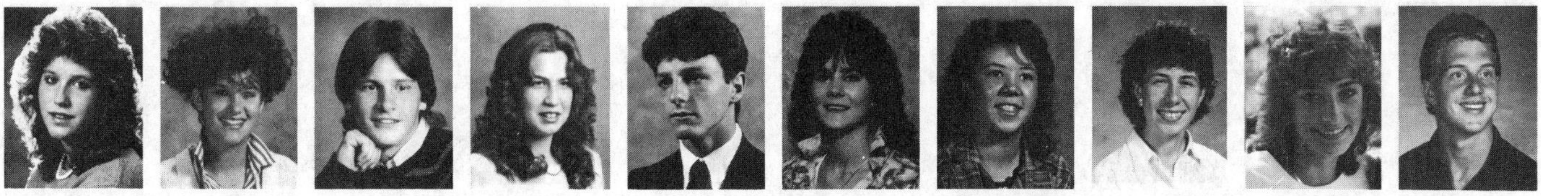

Shelby, Michele
Marie
West Hazleton HS
Hazleton, PA

Shellenberger, Diane
West York Area HS
York, PA

Shellenberger,
Parrish
Juniata Joint HS
Port Royal, PA

Shelton, Cynthia
B Reed Henderson
Exton, PA

Shelton, Scott M
William Penn SR
York, PA

Shenk, Pam
Hempfield HS
Lancaster, PA

Shepherd, Ronda
Oxford Area HS
Lincoln Univ, PA

Shepley, Nicole
Millersburg Area HS
Millersburg, PA

Sheppard, Cheryl
Penn-Trafford HS
Jeannette, PA

Sheppela, John
Ambridge Area HS
Baden, PA

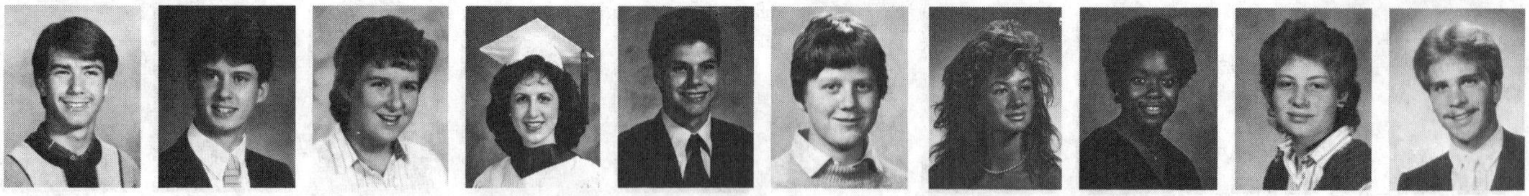

Sherbine, Robert
Portage Area HS
Portage, PA

Sheridan, John
Hershey HS
Hummelstown, PA

Sheriff, Cheryl
Great Hope Baptist
Carlisle, PA

Sherlock, Denise
Lynn
Cardinal O Hara HS
Clifton Heights, PA

Sherman, Brett A
Carlisle SR HS
Carlisle, PA

Sherman, Jr C
Richard
West Scranton HS
Scranton, PA

Sherman, Vivi
George Washington
Philadelphia, PA

Sherrod, Robin M
John W Hallahan
Philadelphia, PA

Sherry, Tara
Northern Cambria
Barnesboro, PA

Shertzer, Jere
Lancaster Christian
Lancaster, PA

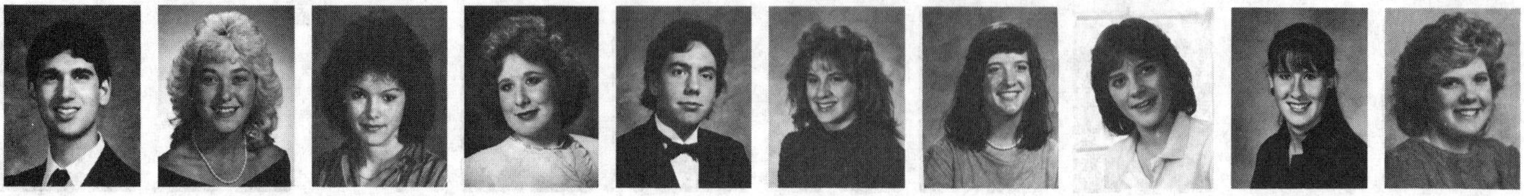

Sherwin, Joe
Council Rock HS
Churchville, PA

Shetzline, Jessica
Harry S Truman HS
Bristol, PA

Shick, Shanin
Union HS
Rimersburg, PA

Shields, Lorianne
Pittston Area SR
Hughestown, PA

Shillingford, Frank
Monsignor Bonner
Drexel Hill, PA

Shimon, Shelley
Burgettstown JR SR
Bulger, PA

Shimp, Lora
Carlisle SR HS
Carlisle, PA

Shindler, Alana L
Garden Spot HS
New Holland, PA

Shinham, Lisa
State College
State College, PA

Shinnamon, Heather
Beaver Area HS
Beaver, PA

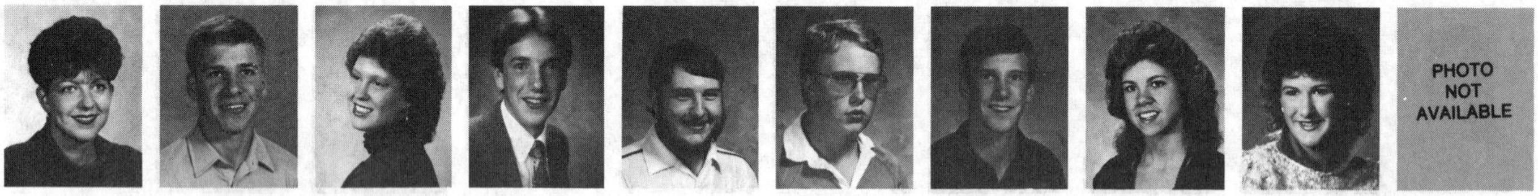

Shinsky, Coleen
Canon Mcmillan SR
Canonsburg, PA

Shirey, Andrew M
Daniel Boon Area
School District
Douglassville, PA

Shirey, Anita
United JR-SR HS
Robinson, PA

Shiring, Steve
Western Beaver HS
Beaver, PA

Shirk, James
Garden Spot-Elanco
School Dist
E Earl, PA

Shirk, John
Garden Spot HS
E Earl, PA

Shirk, Michael
Cocalico HS
Reinholds, PA

Shirley, Brenda
Saltsburg JR SR HS
Saltsburg, PA

Shively, Nicole
Milton Area HS
Milton, PA

PHOTO NOT AVAILABLE

Shoaff, Kevin
Hatboro-Horsham
Hatboro, PA

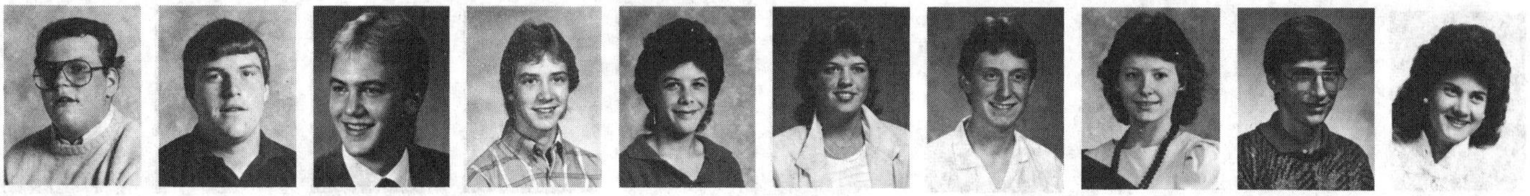

Shober, J
Panther Valley HS
Nesquehoning, PA

Shober, Theodore
Panther Valley HS
Nesquehoning, PA

Shoemaker, Barry
Ray
Dover Area HS
Dover, PA

Shoemaker, Robert
Chambersburg Area
SR HS
Orrstown, PA

Shoener, Holly
Pine Grove Area HS
Pine Grove, PA

Shofran, Sarah
Marian Catholic HS
Weatherly, PA

Sholley, Aaron
Watsontown
Christian Acad
Hartleton, PA

Shomo, Peggy
United HS
Robinson, PA

Shondeck, Jr
Michael
Valley HS
New Kensington,
PA

Shook, Kimberly
West Mifflin Area
W Mifflin, PA

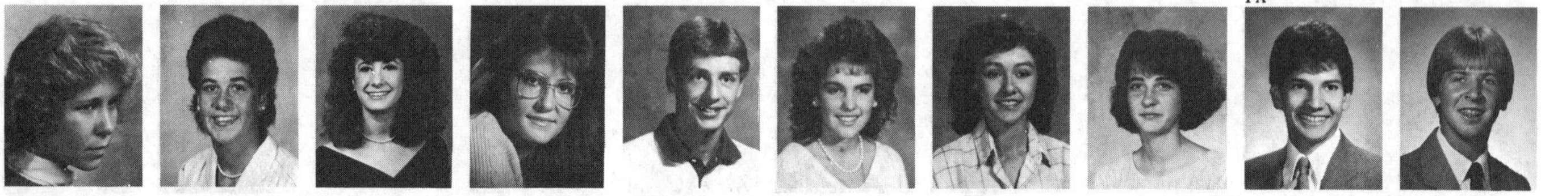

Shoop, Tricia
Halifax HS
Halifax, PA

Shortencarrier, Lea
Northern Cambria
Barnesboro, PA

Shouldis, Theresa C
Wiliam Tennent SR
Warminster, PA

Shoup, Caroline
Millville Area HS
Orangeville, PA

Showaker, Ronald
Biglerville HS
Biglerville, PA

Showers, Hope
St Marys Area HS
Benezett, PA

Showers, Lena
Biglerville HS
Gardners, PA

Showers, Tracey
Bald Eagle Nittany
Mill Hall, PA

Shreiber, David
Central Bucks HS
Warrington, PA

Shreiner, Jr Harry I
Downingtown SR
Exton, PA

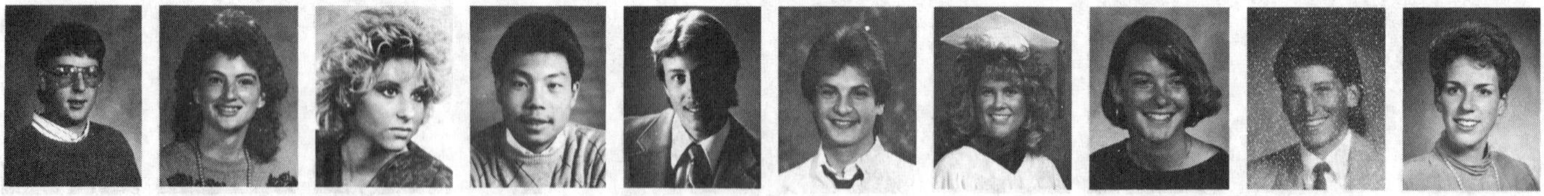

Shreve, Lauren
Corry Area HS
Corry, PA

Shreve, Patricia A
Conneaut Valley HS
Springboro, PA

Shriver, Michelle A
Trinity HS
Mechanicsburg, PA

Shu, John W
Loyalsock Township
Montoursville, PA

Shuber, Michael
Norwin HS
N Huntingdon, PA

Shuck, Steven
Lehigh Christian
Bethlehem, PA

Shuda, Kelly
Cardinal O Hara HS
Drexel Hill, PA

Shue, Amy L
York Suburban HS
York, PA

Shuey, Bill
Central Dauphin
East HS
Harrisburg, PA

Shuey, Jennifer
Bellefonte Area HS
Pleasant Gap, PA

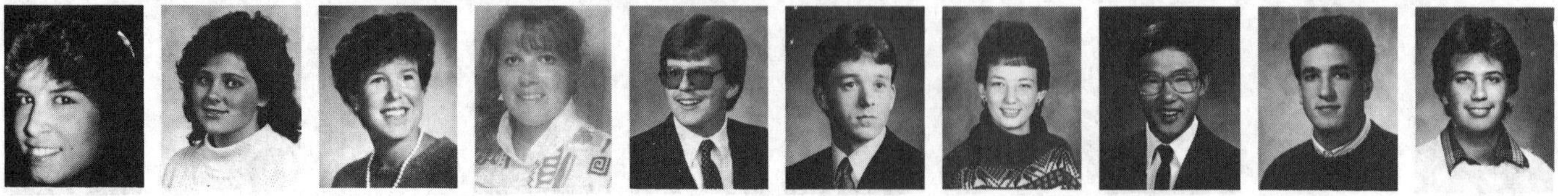

Shukwit, Kimberly
Pennsbury HS
Levittown, PA

Shuler, Christine
Danville SR HS
Danville, PA

Shuler, Hallie
Muncy HS
Muncy, PA

Shultz, Linda
Hazelton SR HS
Drums, PA

Shultz, Mike
York County
York Haven, PA

Shultz, Robert J
Upper Moreland HS
Willow Grove, PA

Shumaker,
Jacqueline
North Clarion HS
Leeper, PA

Shuman, Joel Lee
Lower Dauphin HS
Hershey, PA

Shuman, Larry
Wyoming Valley
West HS
Kingston, PA

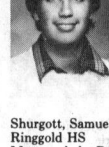

Shurgott, Samuel
Ringgold HS
Monongahela, PA

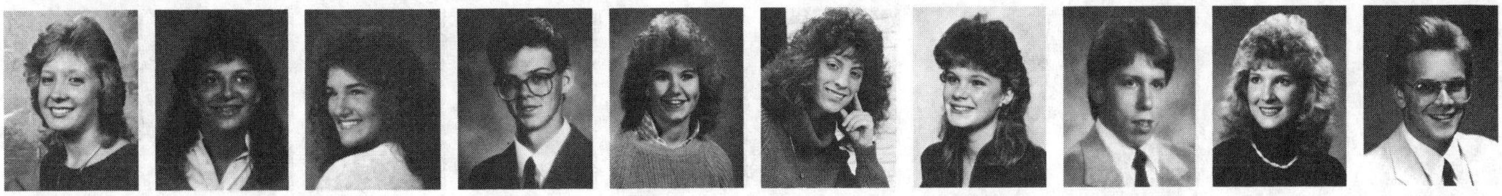

Shutt, Andrea
Pine Grove HS
Pine Grove, PA

Shutt, Kelley Ann
Elizabethtown Area
Elizabethtown, PA

Shutt, Kerri
Hempfield SR HS
Bovard, PA

Shyk, Todd
Central Dauphin
East HS
Harrisburg, PA

Siar, Kim
Shaler Area HS
Glenshaw, PA

Sibeto, Jacqueline
New Castle SR HS
New Castle, PA

Sidney, Dael
Towanda Area HS
Towanda, PA

Sieck, Frank
Mahanoy Area HS
Mahanoy City, PA

Siecko, Lori Ann
Berwick Area SR
Berwick, PA

Siefring, Leo
Valley View JR SR
Peckville, PA

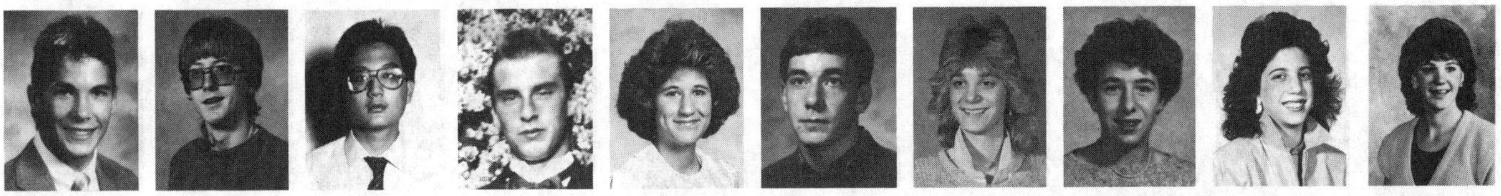

Siegfried, Chris
West Hazleton HS
Drums, PA

Siegworth, Dave
Steel Valley SR HS
Munhall, PA

Sieh, Hubert
Central HS
Philadelphia, PA

Sierzenski, Paul
Father Judge HS
Philadelphia, PA

Sigler, Susan
Bishop Mc Devitt
Dauphin, PA

Signor, Stephen R
Mechanicsburg SR
Mechanicsburg, PA

Sikina, Kim
Brownsville HS
Cardale, PA

Sikora, Tracy
Owen J Roberts HS
Pottstown, PA

Sikowitz, Jackie
Bensalem HS
Bensalem, PA

Silbaugh, Sheila
United HS
Homer City, PA

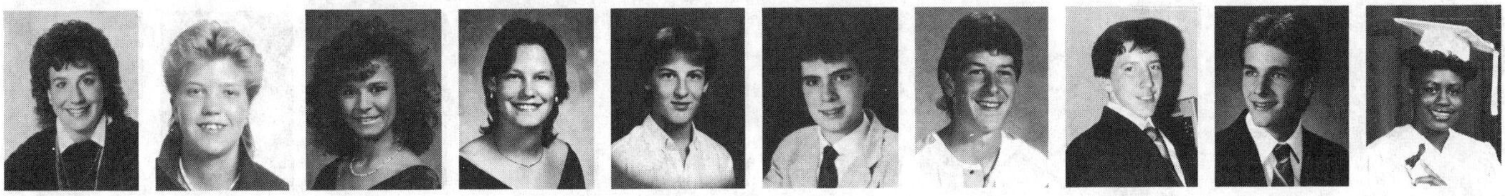

Sildra, Danielle
Aliquippa SR HS
Aliquippa, PA

Silva, Katrina
Strath Haven HS
Wallingford, PA

Silva, Melissa
Archbishop
Ryan-Girls HS
Philadelphia, PA

Silver, Lynda
Penn Wood HS
Darby, PA

Silverstrim, Thomas
Tunkhannock Area
Tunkhannock, PA

Silvester, David
Richland HS
Gibsonia, PA

Silvestri, Chris
Downington SR HS
Downingtown, PA

Silvis, Brian
Mc Dowell HS
Erie, PA

Simkovic, Jerry
Jefferson-Morgan
Clarksville, PA

Simmons, April
HS For Creative &
Performing Arts
Philadelphia, PA

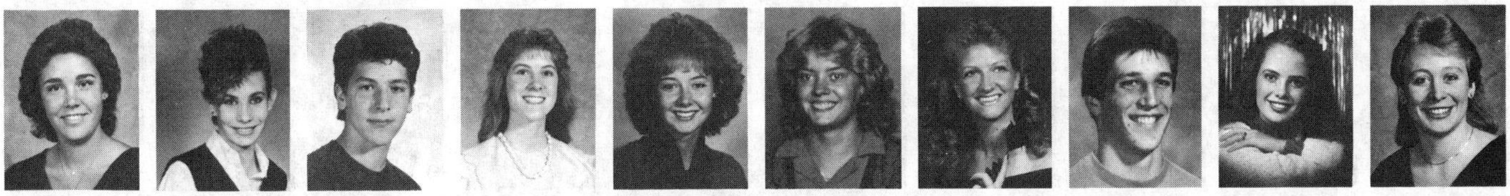

Simms, Susan
Upper Darby HS
Drexel Hl, PA

Simon, Adrienne
Nazareth Acad
Phila, PA

Simon, Jeffrey
Lower Moreland HS
Meadowbrook, PA

Simon, Jerusha
Ruth
Avon Grove HS
Lincoln Univ, PA

Simpkins, Nanci
Reynolds HS
Transfer, PA

Simpson, Amy
Lebanon Catholic
Lebanon, PA

Simpson, Amy
Methacton SR HS
Norristown, PA

Simpson, Greg
Brockway Area HS
Brockport, PA

Simpson, Heather
Monaca JR SR HS
Monaca, PA

Simpson, Rosemarie
St Maria Goretti HS
Philadelphia, PA

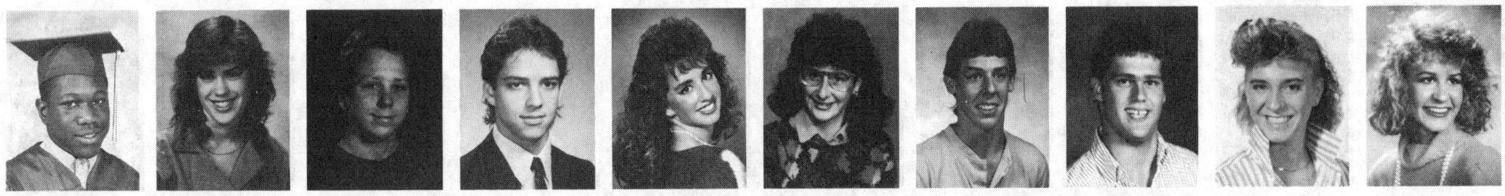

Simpson, Samuel
Pine Forge Acad
Brooklyn, NY

Simpson, Tricia
Wallenpaupack Area
Hawley, PA

Sims, David
York Co Vo Tech
Red Lion, PA

Sindaco, Mario
G A R Memorial HS
Wilkes-Barre, PA

Singleton, Kirsten
Leigh
Penn Hills HS
Pittsburgh, PA

Sinopoli, Tracy
Hickory HS
Sharpsville, PA

Siple, Duane
Punxsutawney Area
Punxsutawney, PA

Sipowicz, Phillip
Pocono Mountain
Stroudsburg, PA

Sisco, Maria
North Pocono HS
Moscow, PA

Sisk, Doreen
Wyoming Area HS
Pittston, PA

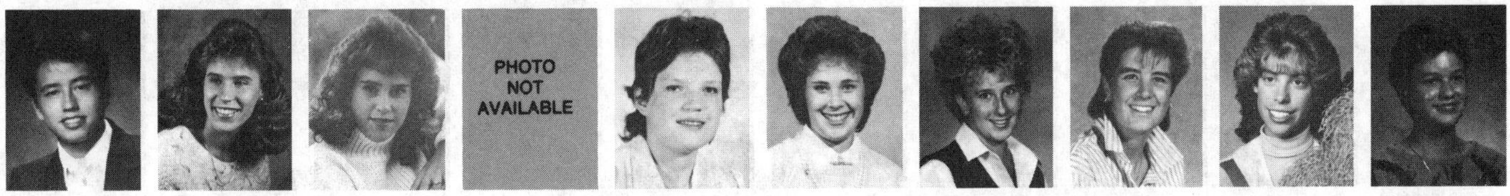
PHOTO
NOT
AVAILABLE

Sitar, Shawn
Abington Heights
Clarks Green, PA

Siuniak, Stephanie
Blacklick Valley JR
& SR HS
Nanty Glo, PA

Skane, Debbie
East SR HS
West Chester, PA

Skelley, II Patrick J
Westmont Hilltop
Johnstown, PA

Skinner, Nanci
Philadelphia HS For
Philadelphia, PA

Skirpan, Tonya
Cannon-Mc Millan
Eighty Four, PA

Skladzien, Vanessa
Nazareth Acad
Phila, PA

Skoropowski, Julie
Upper Dublin SR
Maple Glen, PA

Skriba, Jennifer
Plum SR HS
Pittsburgh, PA

Skutlin, Wendy
Elizabethtown Area
Elizabethtown, PA

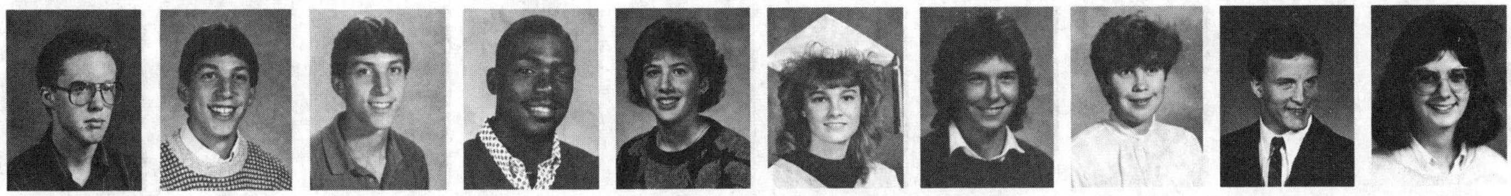

Slack, Edward D
Penn-Trafford HS
Trafford, PA

Slack, Greg
Henderson HS
West Chester, PA

Slack, Jeff
Henderson HS
West Chester, PA

Slade, Willie
Steelton-Highspire
Steelton, PA

Slagle, Susan
Blair County
Christian Schl
Altoona, PA

Slater, Jennifer
Saint Huberts HS
For Girls
Philadelphia, PA

Slaugenhaupt, Janet
Big Spring HS
Newville, PA

Slavik, Stephanie
Bishop Carroll HS
Barnesboro, PA

Slaymaker, Michael
Lampeter Strasburg
Strasburg, PA

Slazinski, Kelly
Mercer Area HS
Mercer, PA

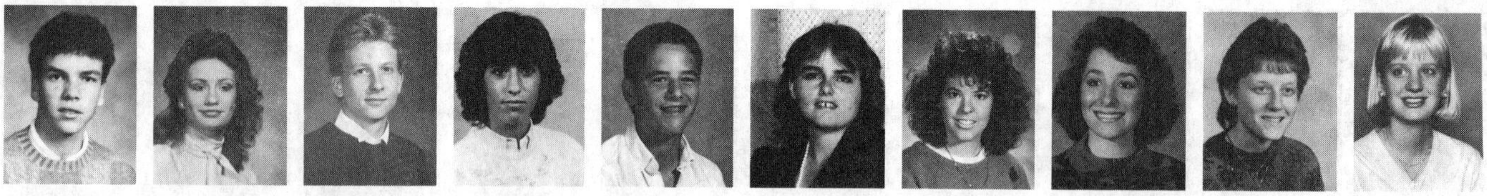

Sleutaris, Rick
Upper Moreland HS
Hatboro, PA

Slichter, Chanda
Hamburg Area HS
Shoemakersville, PA

Sloan, Scott
Bethlehem Center
Fredericktown, PA

Slocum, Susie
Lake-Lehman HS
Dallas, PA

Slogoff, Frederick
Lower Merion HS
Bala Cynwyd, PA

Slonaker, Jean
Elizabeth
Phila HS Gor Girls
Philadelphia, PA

Slupe, Kelly
Butler SR HS
Lyndora, PA

Slusarick, Amy
Brownsville Area HS
Brownsville, PA

Sluzele, Jennifer
Pittston Area HS
Inkerman, PA

Smagiel, Jennifer
Lebanon Catholic
Cleona, PA

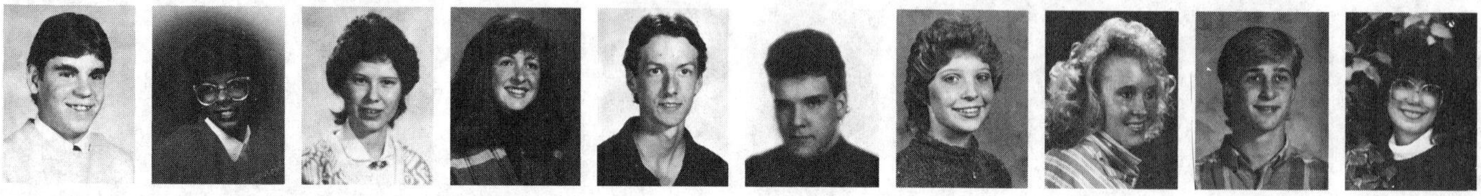

Small, Michael T
Cashs HS
Chambersburg, PA

Smallwood, Solita
William Penn SR
York, PA

Smarsh, Rebecca
Greater Johnston
Johnstown, PA

Smarto, Carrie
Council Rock HS
Wrightstown, PA

Smeltz, Adam
Oley Valley HS
Fleetwood, PA

Smeltz, Kane
Line Mountain HS
Dornsife, PA

Smerekar, Michele
Penn Trafford HS
Trafford, PA

Smith, Amy
Brownsville Area HS
Brownsville, PA

Smith, Andrew
Lampeter Strasburg
Lancaster, PA

Smith, Annette
Annville-Cleona HS
Cleona, PA

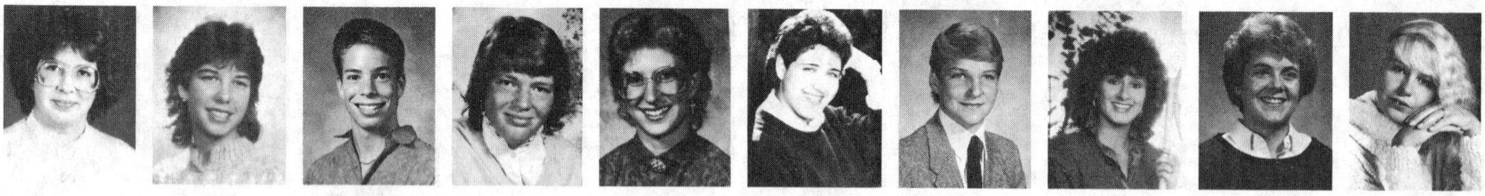

Smith, Beth
Fairfield Area HS
Fairfield, PA

Smith, Betsy
E L Meyers HS
Wilkes-Barre, PA

Smith, Jr Charles G
Gateway Senior HS
Monroeville, PA

Smith, Cheryl
Red Lion Area SR
Red Lion, PA

Smith, Christine
Leechburg Area HS
Leechburg, PA

Smith, Colleen
Pocono Mountain
Freeland, PA

Smith, David T
Phoenixville Area
Phoenixville, PA

Smith, Dawn
Lake Lenman HS
Wilkes-Barre, PA

Smith, Deborah
Wilmington Area
New Wilmington,
PA

Smith, Diane
Wilson HS
Reading, PA

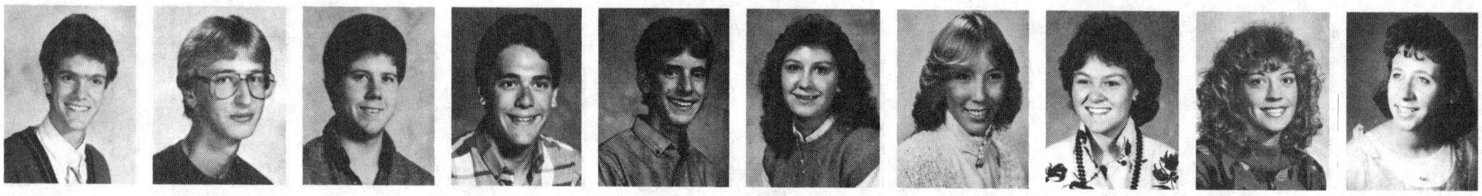

Smith, Donald
Marion Center Area
Indiana, PA

Smith, Doug
Northampton Area
SR HS
Bath, PA

Smith, Douglas J
Bloomsburg SR HS
Bloomsburg, PA

Smith, Eric J
Pen Argyl Area HS
Wind Gap, PA

Smith, Gregory
New Church Acad
Freeport, PA

Smith, Heather
Blair County
Christian Schl
Newry, PA

Smith, Heather
Du Bois SR HS
Du Bois, PA

Smith, Heather
Waynesburg Central
Waynesburg, PA

Smith, Holly
Belle Vernon Area
Belle Vernon, PA

Smith, J Bonnie
Peters Township HS
Mc Murray, PA

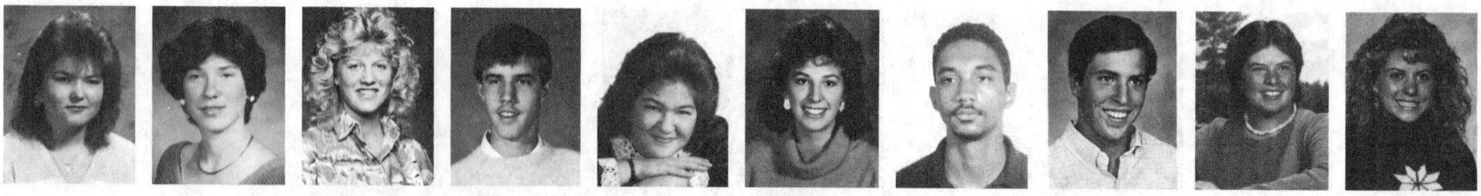

Smith, Jennifer
Donegal HS
Mt Joy, PA

Smith, Jennifer
Plum SR HS
Pittsburgh, PA

Smith, Jennifer
Ringgold HS
Monongahela, PA

Smith, Jim
Connellsville Area
Dunbar, PA

Smith, Jodeen
Blair County
Christian HS
Duncansville, PA

Smith, Jodi
Clarion Area HS
Shippenville, PA

Smith, John
HS For Engineering
& Science
Philadelphia, PA

Smith, Jonathan
York Suburban HS
York, PA

Smith, Karen
Athens Area HS
Athens, PA

Smith, Kathy
Baldwin HS
Pittsburgh, PA

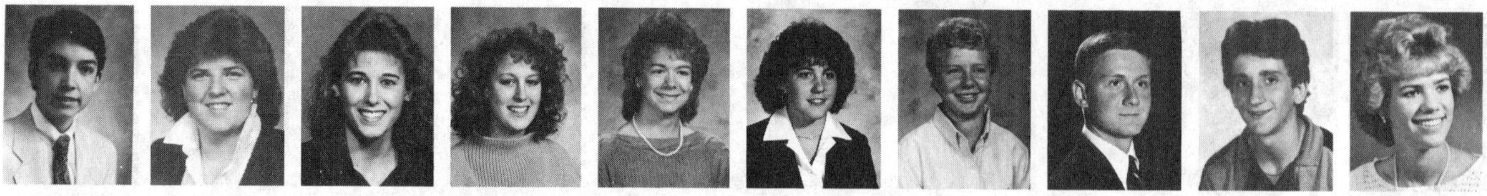

Smith, Kel
Cumberland Valley
Mechanicsburg, PA

Smith, Kelly
Center SR HS
Monaca, PA

Smith, Kimberly
Hickory HS
Hermitage, PA

Smith, Kristin
Upper Moreland HS
Willow Grove, PA

Smith, Kristine
Donegal HS
Mount Joy, PA

Smith, Krystal
Lancaster Catholic
Columbia, PA

Smith, Leslie
Fannett-Metal HS
East Waterford, PA

Smith, Jr Leslie V
Brockway Area HS
Brockport, PA

Smith, Lewis
Western Wayne HS
Waymart, PA

Smith, Maria
Eastern York HS
York, PA

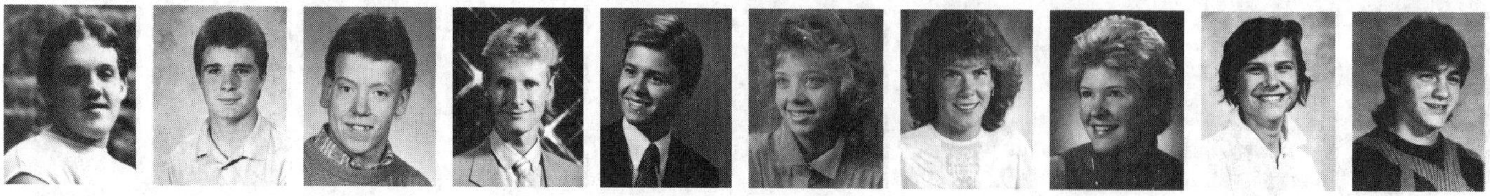

Smith, Mark
Southern
Huntingdon Count
Rockhill Furnace,
PA

Smith, Michael
Bald Eagle-Nittany
Mill Hall, PA

Smith, Michael
Hempfield Area SR
Irwin, PA

Smith, Michael
Middleburg HS
Middleburg, PA

Smith, Michael D
York Suburban SR
York, PA

Smith, Michelle
Annville-Cleona HS
Annville, PA

Smith, Michelle
Jean
Chartiers Valley HS
Bridgeville, PA

Smith, Mindy
Red Lion Area SR
Brogue, PA

Smith, Missie
Spring-Ford SR HS
Royersford, PA

Smith, Randall
Pottstown HS
Pottstown, PA

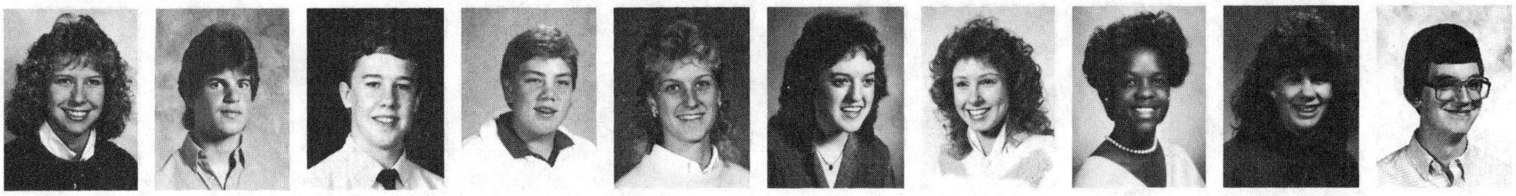

Smith, Renee
Meadville Area SR
Meadville, PA

Smith, Richard
Northwestern
Lehigh HS
Germansville, PA

Smith, Jr Robert J
Lower Dauphin HS
Hummelstown, PA

Smith, Ryan D
Exeter Township
Reading, PA

Smith, Shani
Beth-Center SR HS
Marianna, PA

Smith, Sharon
Columbia-Montour
Drums, PA

Smith, Shawna M
Chapel Christian
West Newton, PA

Smith, Sherry Y
Chester HS
Chester, PA

Smith, Tammy
Shenango HS
New Castle, PA

Smith, Timothy
Louis E Dieruff HS
Allentown, PA

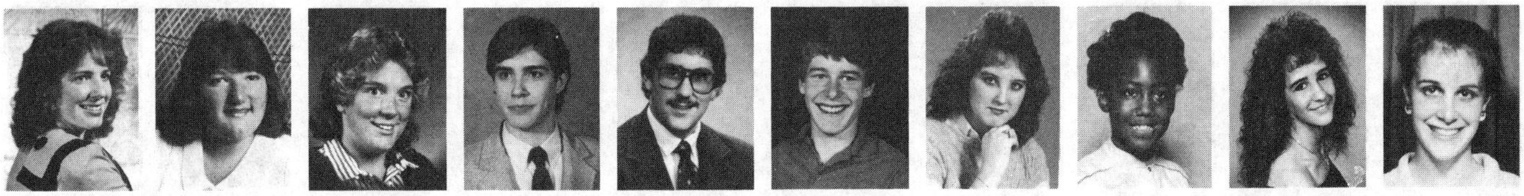

Smith, Tina M
Brandywine Heights
Mertztown, PA

Smith, Tracey
Punxsutawney Area
Punxsutawney, PA

Smith, Tracy
Central Dauphin HS
Harrisburg, PA

Smith, III Warren
Brownsville Area HS
East Millsboro, PA

Smith, William
Greater Johnstown
Johnstown, PA

Smith, William
Jeannette HS
Jeannette, PA

Smith, Yvonne
The Baptist HS
Dalton, PA

Smith, Zanetta
Philadelphia HS For
Philadelphia, PA

Smola, Tara
Penn Hills SR HS
Pittsburgh, PA

Smoyer, Diane
Cumberland Valley
Camp Hill, PA

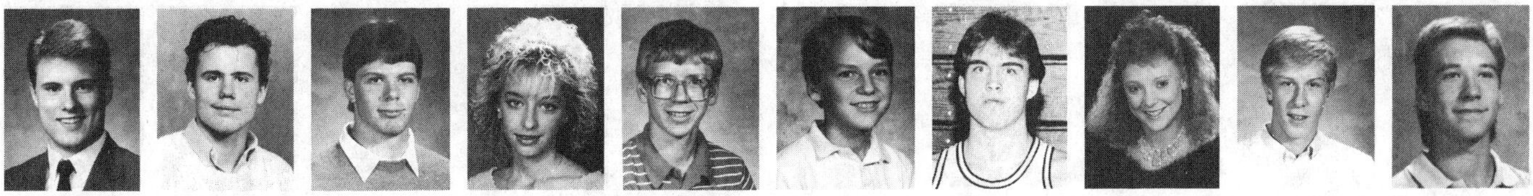

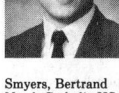

Smyers, Bertrand
North Catholic HS
Glenshaw, PA

Smyers, Gregory
North Catholic HS
Glenshaw, PA

Smyth, Mitch
Moniteau HS
Harrisville, PA

Snavely, Richanda
Williamsburg HS
Williamsburg, PA

Snell, Dan
Southern Fulton HS
Needmore, PA

Snell, Paul
Southern Fulton HS
Needmore, PA

Snisky, Gene
Panther Valley HS
Nesquehoning, PA

Snock, Cindy
South Philadelphia
Philadelphia, PA

Snow, Jamie
Butler SR HS
Butler, PA

Snyder, Bobby
Lancaster
Mennonite HS
Ephrata, PA

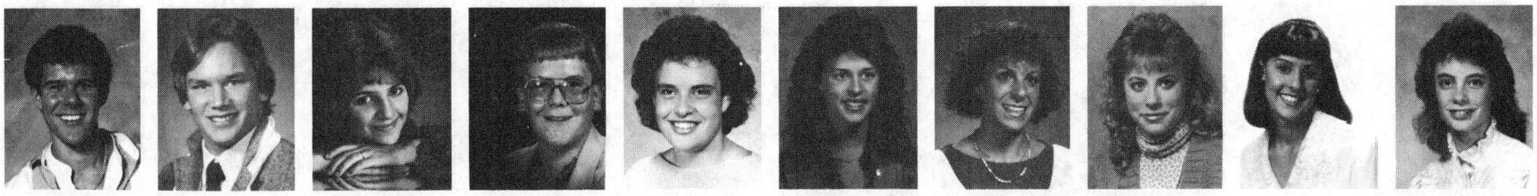

Snyder, Brad
Hampton HS
Allison Park, PA

Snyder, Bryan
Salisbury HS
Bethlehem, PA

Snyder, Cheryl A
Northern Lehigh HS
Slatedale, PA

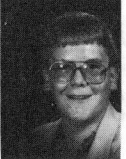

Snyder, Christoph
Mifflinburg Area HS
Lewisburg, PA

Snyder, Dawn
Bald Eagle-Nittany
Mill Hall, PA

Snyder, Deborah J
Elizabethtown Area
Elizabethtown, PA

Snyder, Elena
Emmaus HS
Emmaus, PA

Snyder, Elizabeth
High Point Baptist
Phoenixvl, PA

Snyder, Jennifer
Meadville Area SR
Meadville, PA

Snyder, Joanna
Blair County
Christian Schl
Duncansville, PA

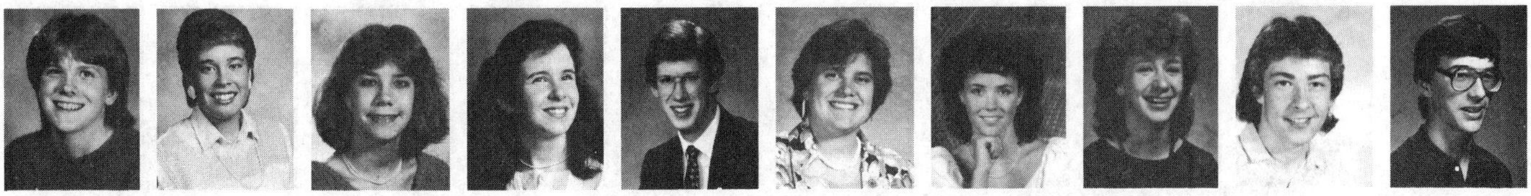

Snyder, Leslie
Brookville Area HS
Brookville, PA

Snyder, Lisa
Nazareth Area HS
Tatamy, PA

Snyder, Melissa
Windber Area HS
Windber, PA

Snyder, Monica
Lebanon Catholic
Lebanon, PA

Snyder, III Nelson B
Bishop Oreilly HS
Harvey Lake, PA

Snyder, Pamela
Avon Grove HS
West Grove, PA

Snyder, Patricia
Solanco HS
Quarryville, PA

Snyder, Paula
Cedar Crest HS
Lebanon, PA

Snyder, Richard
Northern Lebaron
Jonestown, PA

Snyder, Ronald
Louis E Dieruff HS
Allentown, PA

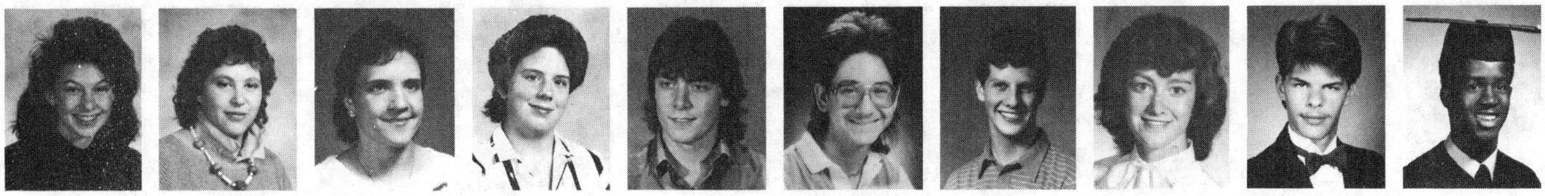

Snyder, Rosemarie
Philadelphia HS For
Philadelphia, PA

Snyder, Samantha
Pleasant Valley HS
Brodheadsville, PA

Snyder, Susan Lee
Salisbury SR HS
Bethlehem, PA

Snyder, Tracy
East Juniata HS
Richfield, PA

Soika, John
Connellsville Area
Connellsville, PA

Sokac, Daniel
Montour HS
Mckees Rocks, PA

Sokol, Frank
Burrell HS
Lower Burrell, PA

Sokolowski, Dnese
William Allen HS
Allentown, PA

Solomon, Aaron
Clarion Area HS
Clarion, PA

Solomon, Jr Robert
L
Central HS
Philadelphia, PA

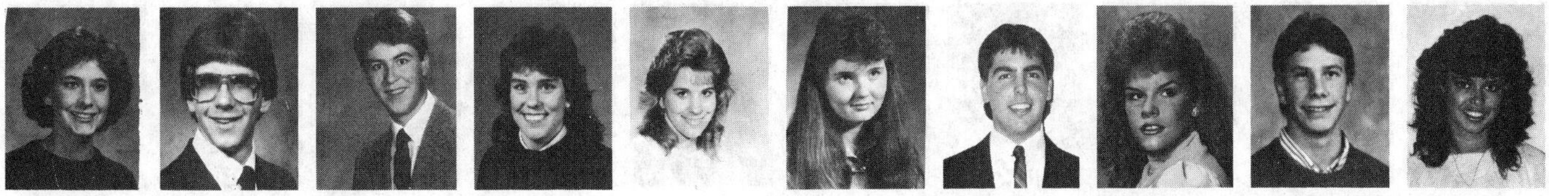

Sonnen, Becky
Conrad Weiser HS
Richland, PA

Sonnen, David
Conrad Weiser HS
Richland, PA

Sonnett, John
Hampton HS
Gibsonia, PA

Sopata, Janine
South Park HS
Library, PA

Sopko, Kimberly
John S Fine HS
Nanticoke, PA

Sorber, Lisa A
Lake Lehman HS
Hunlock Creek, PA

Sotack, Scott
West Hazleton HS
Hazleton, PA

Sotak, Amy L
Bethlehem Ctr
Brownsville, PA

Sottung, Robert L
Bensalem HS
Bensalem, PA

Souchak, Joann
Mahanoy Area HS
Mahanoy City, PA

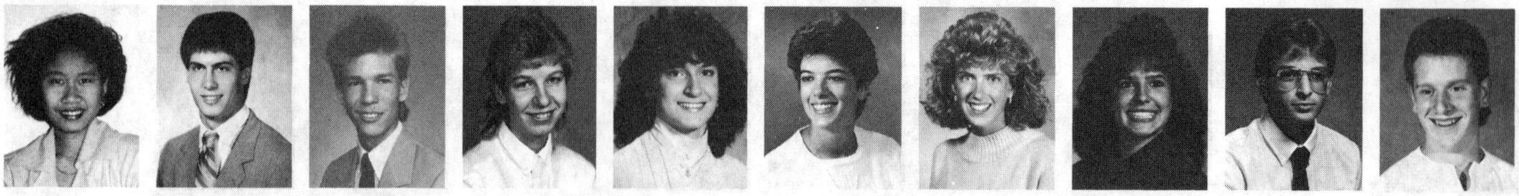

Soun, Saveth
William Allen HS
Allentown, PA

Sowalla, Jason
Northern Cambria
Cherry Tree, PA

Sowers, Matthew
Pequea Valley HS
Paradise, PA

Spade, Angela
Fairchange-Georges
SR HS
Uniontown, PA

Spade, Cynthia
Bishop Conwell HS
Fairless Hls, PA

Spangler, Kathleen
William Penn SR
York, PA

Spangler, Tiffany
Central SR HS
York, PA

Spanik, Kristen
Ambridge Area HS
Ambridge, PA

Sparich, Salvatore
Marian Catholic HS
Weatherly, PA

Spaugy, Jr Harold
Connellsville Area
Connellsville, PA

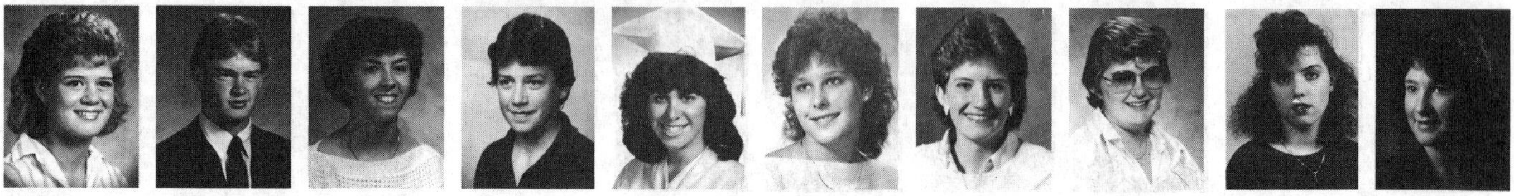

Spease, Christy
Saint Cyril Acad
Bloomsburg, PA

Speck, Andrew
Carlisle HS
Burke, VA

Speck, Karen L
Carlisle HS
Carlisle, PA

Speck, Robert
Dubois Area HS
Dubois, PA

Spector, Jill
Springfield
Township HS
Wyndmoor, PA

Speelman, Veronica
Connellsville Area
Connellsville, PA

Speerhas, Tracy
Western Beaver HS
Midland, PA

Spees, Gina
Oswayo Valley JR
SR HS
Shinglehouse, PA

Speicher, Nicole
Kiski HS
Apollo, PA

Spelgatti, Cheryl
Elizabethtown Area
Elizabethtown, PA

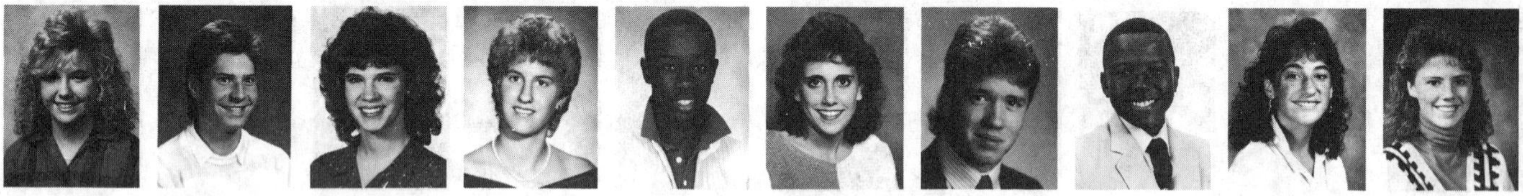

Spenard, Joyce
Forest City Regional
Forest City, PA

Spence, Bradley
Wilmington Area
Pulaski, PA

Spence, Melanie
Oil City HS
Oil City, PA

Spencer, Ann
Haverford HS
Havertown, PA

Spencer, Henry
Elizabeth Forward
SR HS
Mckeepsort, PA

Spencer, Melissa
Blue Mountain Acad
Glenmoore, PA

Spencer, Jr Robert
Rand
Wyoming Area HS
Falls, PA

Spencer, Sean D
Harrisburg HS John
Harris Campus
Harrisburg, PA

Sperling, Jill
Jenkintown HS
Jenkintown, PA

Spiegel, Sunny
Washington HS
Washington, PA

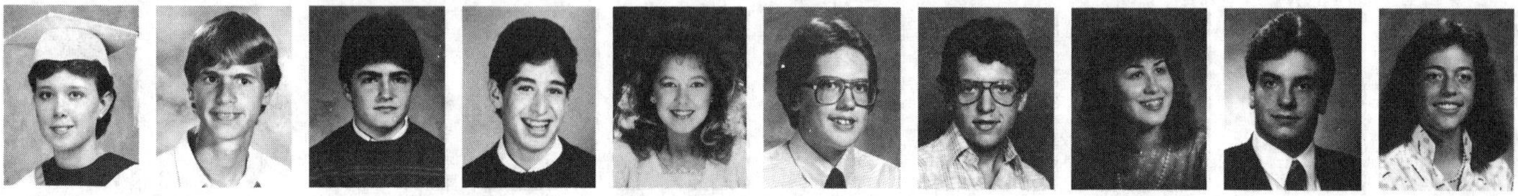

Spiegle, Karen
St Hubert HS For
Philadelphia, PA

Spila, Timothy P
Shippensburg Area
SR HS
Shippensburg, PA

Spilsbury, Theodore
Danville HS
Danville, PA

Spivak, Robert
Carlynton HS
Carnegie, PA

Spivey, Shanna
Seneca HS
Erie, PA

Spohn, Kenneth
Robert
West Perry SR HS
Shermans Dale, PA

Spoor, James
Blue Ridge HS
Susquehanna, PA

Spore, Rachel Alicia
Youngsville HS
Youngsville, PA

Sposato, Brian
Thomas Jefferson
Finleyville, PA

Spotts, Mary
West Perry SR HS
New Bloomfield, PA

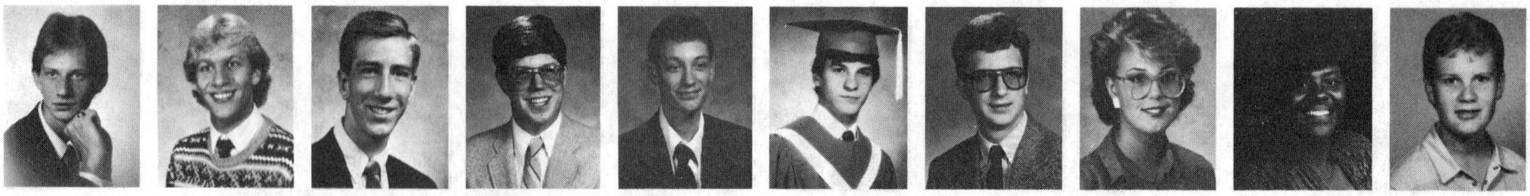

Spotts, Vincent J
Seneca Valley HS
Renfrew, PA

Sprando, Chris
Burgettstown HS
Langeloth, PA

Sprengel, Scott
Carlisle SR HS
Carlisle, PA

Sprenkle, Lloyd
Spring Grove Area
SR HS
York, PA

Springer,
Christopher
Lancaster Catholic
Ephrata, PA

Springer, Clayton
Norristown Area HS
Jeffersonville, PA

Springer, Kenneth
Spring Grove SR HS
Seven Valleys, PA

Sprowls, Paula L
Mc Guffey HS
Washington, PA

Spruill, Dionne
Steelton Highspire
Steelton, PA

Spurgeon, David L
Mc Keesport SR HS
Mc Keesport, PA

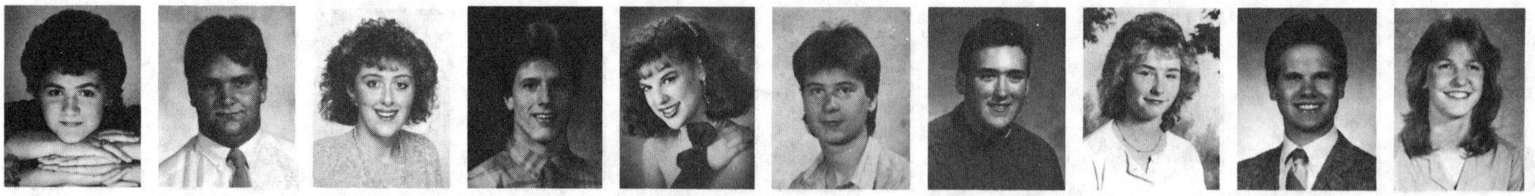

St Amant, Kelly
Rocky Grove HS
Franklin, PA

St Pierre, Jon
Bishop Carroll HS
Ebensburg, PA

Stachel, Wendy Lee
Scranton Central
Scranton, PA

Stack, John
Washington HS
Washington, PA

Stacy, Heather
Beaver Area HS
Beaver, PA

Stadler, Nicholas
Scranton Central
Scranton, PA

Stagi, Patrick
West Branch Area
JR SR HS
Philipsburg, PA

Stahler, Holly
Bishop O Reilly HS
Wyoming, PA

Stahurski, Neil E
Elizabeth-Forward
Mc Keesport, PA

Staikides, Meg
Avon Grove HS
West Grove, PA

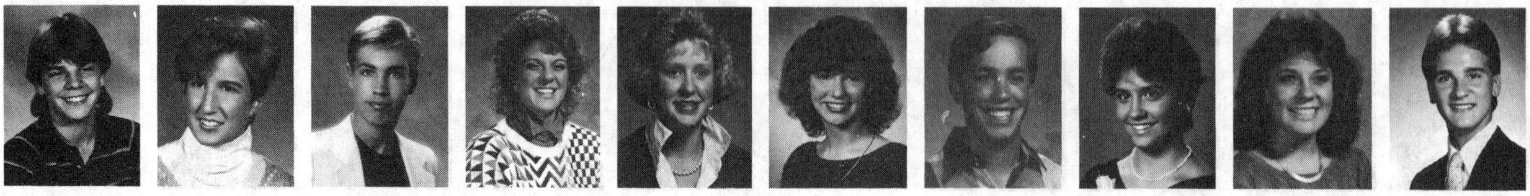

Stainbrook, Tim
Mercer Area SR JR
Mercer, PA

Stairs, Ann
Hempfield HS
Monheim, PA

Stake, Brad
Chambersburg Area
SR HS
Chambersburg, PA

Staker, Elizabeth
Middletown HS
Middletown, PA

Stalgaitis, Karen
Marian Catholic HS
Mcadoo, PA

Stallone, Karen Ann
E L Meyers HS
Wilkes-Barre, PA

Staman, Matthew W
Warrior Run HS
Turbotville, PA

Stambaugh, Denise
Hatboro-Horsham
Hatboro, PA

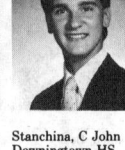

Stamboolian, Kristin
Henderson SR HS
West Chester, PA

Stanchina, C John
Downingtown HS
Downingtown, PA

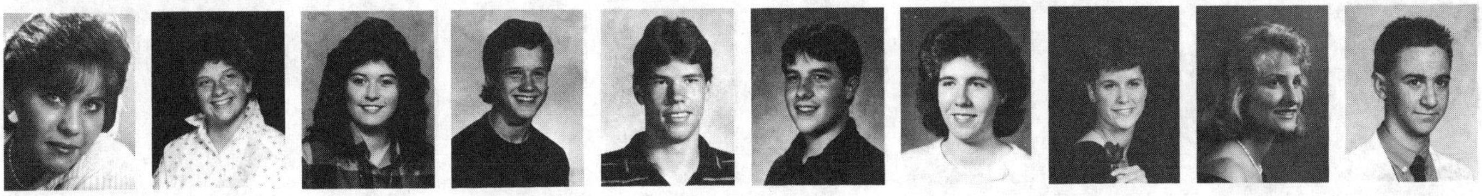

Stanczak, Kimberly
Pittston Area SR
Inkerman, PA

Stanczyk, Louise
Valley View JR SR
Jessup, PA

Stanford, Heather
West Middlesex
JR-SR HS
West Middlesex, PA

Stanford, Keith
Meadville Area SR
Meadville, PA

Stankan, Albert
Conemaugh
Township Area HS
Boswell, PA

Stanko, Brian
Kittanning SR HS
Adrian, PA

Stanley, Kim
Riverside HS
Fombell, PA

Stanley, Sheila
St Pius X HS
Royersford, PA

Stape, Sandra N
North Penn HS
Lansdale, PA

Starasinic, Garrett
Bishop Mc Devitt
Oberlin, PA

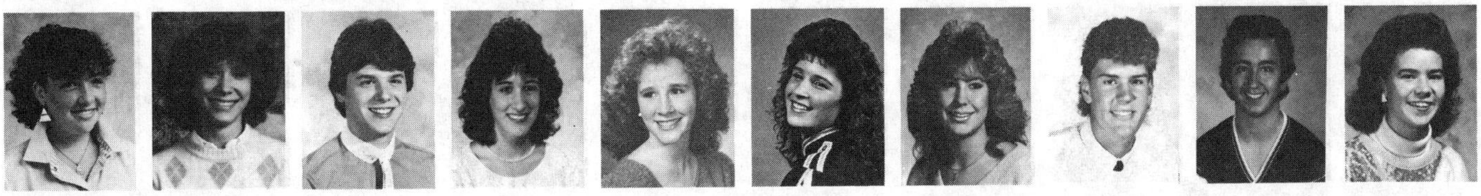

Starobin, Jennifer
East Pennsboro
Area HS
Camp Hill, PA

Starolis, Sue
Dallas SR HS
Wyoming, PA

Staroschuck, Scott
Canevin HS
Mckees Rocks, PA

Starr, Brenda
Port Allegany HS
Port Allegany, PA

Starr, Chrissy
Brockway Area HS
Brockway, PA

Starry, Amy
United HS
New Florence, PA

States, Alyson
Ambridge Area HS
Baden, PA

Statler, Chad
Chambersburg Area
Chambersburg, PA

Staub, John
Fort Cherry HS
Imperial, PA

Stauffer, Kris
Solanco SR HS
Quarryville, PA

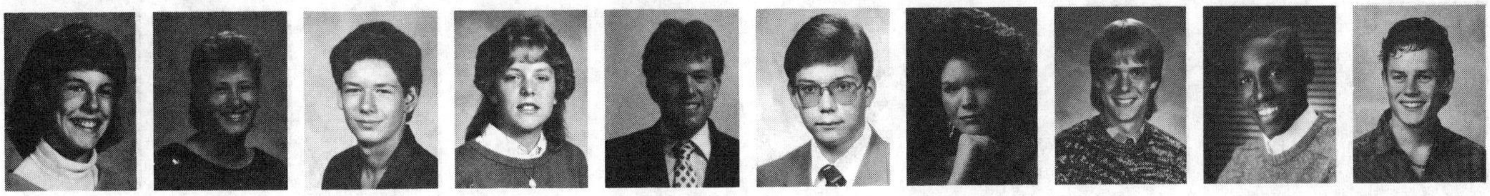

Stauffer, Marcy L
Boyertown Area JR
High East
Gilbertsville, PA

Stauffer, Michele
Garden Spot HS
Terre Hill, PA

Stauffer, Scott
Northern Cambria
Spangler, PA

Stauffer, Sharon
Upper Moreland HS
Hatboro, PA

Staunton, Peter J
Archbishop Ryan
For Boys
Philadelphia, PA

Stavas, Myles
Bishop Mc Cort HS
Johnstown, PA

Steadle, Robinn
Lake Lehman HS
Wilkes-Barre, PA

Steadman, Mel
Butler SR HS
Butler, PA

Steals, Tyrone T
Aliquippa JR SR
Aliquippa, PA

Stear, Roger
Wallenpaupack Area
Hawley, PA

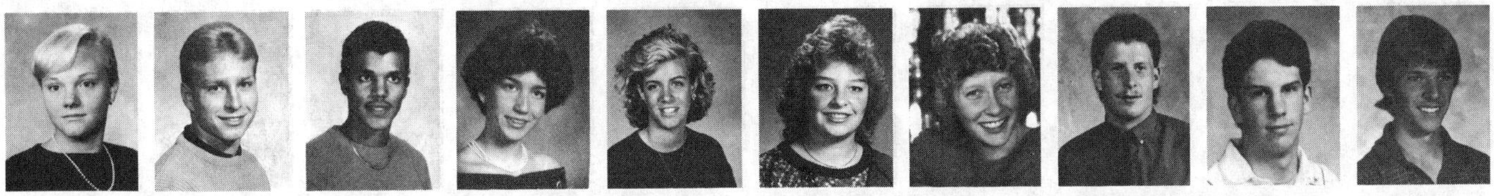

Steck, Stacy
Wyoming Valley
West HS
Swoyersville, PA

Steeber, Greg
Belle Vernon Area
Belle Vernon, PA

Steele, Corey
Reading HS
Reading, PA

Steele, Lu Ann
Central Dauphin HS
Harrisburg, PA

Steele, Martha Jane
Central SR HS
York, PA

Steele, Stacy
Shamokin Area HS
Shamokin, PA

Steele, Teresa
Punxsutawney Area
Punxsutawney, PA

Steele, Timothy
United JR SR HS
Seward, PA

Steele, Tom
Souderton Area HS
Souderton, PA

Stees, David
Greenwood HS
Millerstown, PA

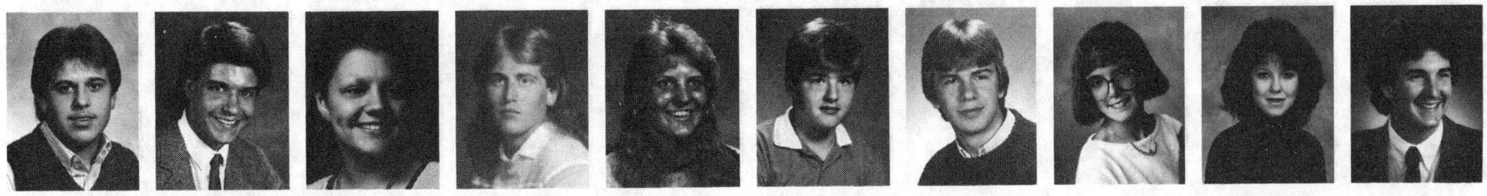

Stefanick, Jon
Belle Vernon Area
Belle Vernon, PA

Steffen, Roderick D
Oley Valley HS
Boyertown, PA

Steffy, Dana
Punxsutawney Area
Punxsutawney, PA

Stegenga, II David I
Charters-Houston
Houston, PA

Stehr, Angela K
Tri-Valley HS
Pitman, PA

Stehr, John
Shamokin Area HS
Shamokin, PA

Steidel, Jason
Louis E Dieruff HS
Allentown, PA

Steiger, Kimberly
Mt Penn HS
Reading, PA

Stein, Randee
Bensalem HS
Bensalem, PA

Stein, Wade
Red Lion Area SR
Red Lion, PA

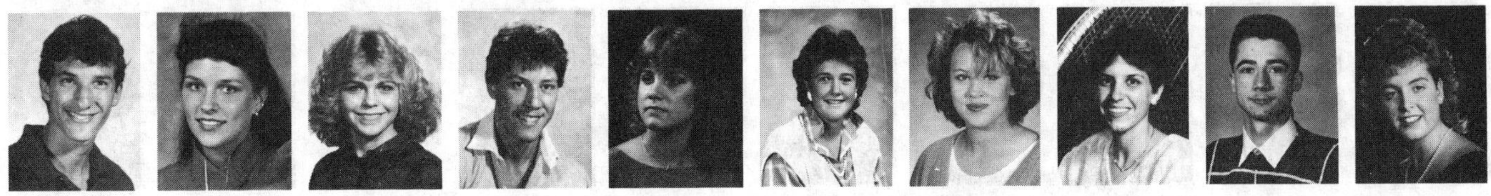

Steinberg, Jeffrey H
Germantown Acad
Meadowbrook, PA

Steinbring, Michele
Lea
Greater Johnstown
Johnstown, PA

Steiner, Laurie
Belle Vernon Area
Belle Vernon, PA

Steiner, Stephen
Coatesville Area SR
Coatesville, PA

Steiner, Val
Belle Vernon Area
Fayette City, PA

Steinman, Michele
Lee
Spring-Ford SR HS
Royersford, PA

Steinmetz, Dawn
Monessen JR SR
Monessen, PA

Steinruck, Lara
Benton Area HS
Benton, PA

Stelma, Walter
Mon Valley Catholic
Charleroi, PA

Stem, Barbara
East Stroudsburg
Area HS
East Stroudsburg,
PA

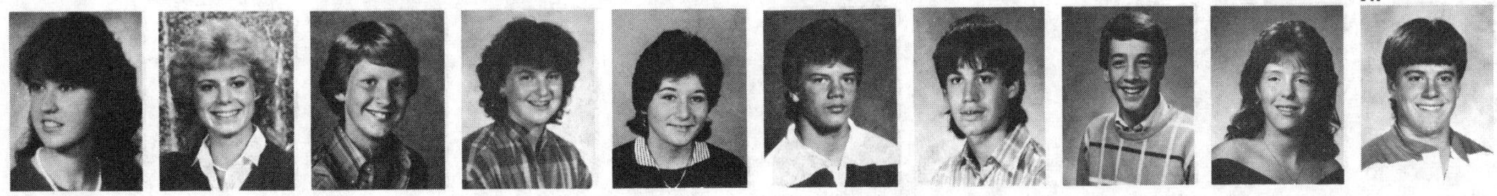

Stempleski, Pamela
E L Meyers HS
Wilkes-Barre, PA

Stepanski, Catherine
Northeast Bradford
Rome, PA

Stephens, Bradey
Lewistown Area HS
Lewistown, PA

Sterner, Linda
Brandywine Hgts
Fleetwood, PA

Sterner, Michele
Rockwood Area HS
Rockwood, PA

Sterner, Richard
Pen Argyle Area HS
Wind Gap, PA

Stevanns, Samuel
Salisbury Elk-Lick
Salisbury, PA

Steve, T Matthew
Indiana Area SR HS
Indiana, PA

Stevens, Danielle P
Octorara HS
Coatesville, PA

Stevens, Mark
Meadville Area SR
Meadville, PA

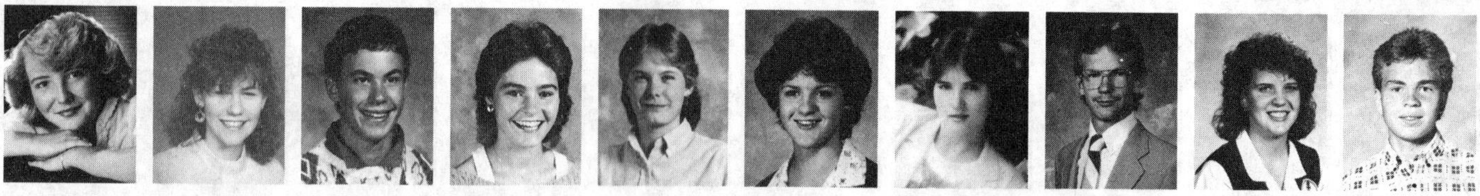

Stevens, Michele
North Pocono SR
Lake Ariel, PA

Stevenson, Amanda
Lincoln HS
Ellwood City, PA

Stevenson, John
Cocalico HS
Denver, PA

Steverson, Elizabeth
Taylor Allderdice
Pittsburgh, PA

Steves, Patricia M
Millville HS
Millville, PA

Stewart, Crystal
West Greene SR HS
Holbrook, PA

Stewart, Diana
West Greene Mid
SR HS
New Freeport, PA

Stewart, Eric J
Fort Le Boeuf HS
Erie, PA

Stewart, Frances
Trinity HS
Carlisle, PA

Stewart, Jeff
Hampton HS
Allison Park, PA

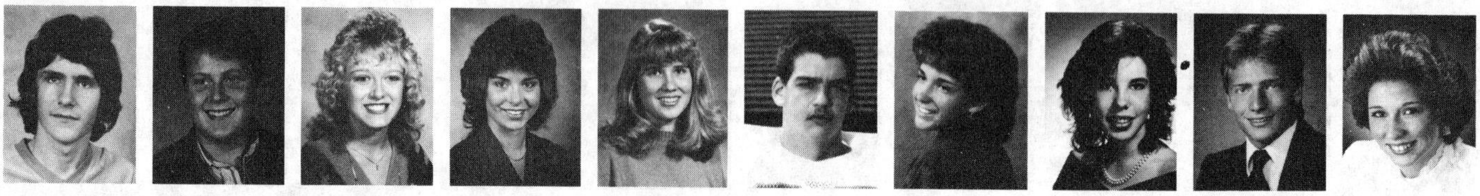

Stewart, Joseph
East HS
Erie, PA

Stewart, Jr Kenneth
F
Connellsville SR HS
Connellsville, PA

Stewart, Sheri
Meadville Area SR
Meadville, PA

Stewart, Stacy
Marion Center Area
Marion Ctr, PA

Stickles, Dusty
Butler Intermediate
Butler, PA

Stickles, Steven A
Hopewell HS
Aliquippa, PA

Sticklin, Danielle
Danville Area HS
Danville, PA

Stieffenhofer, Heidi
Abington SR HS
Glenside, PA

Stiffey, Brian
Hempfield Area HS
Greensburg, PA

Stiffler, Karolyn
Central HS
Martinsburg, PA

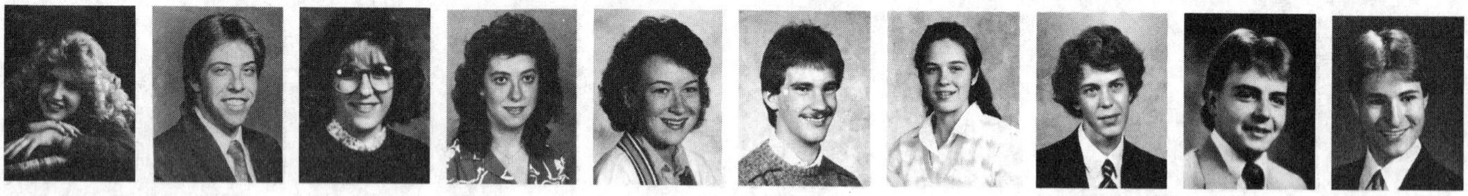

Stiffler, Kristine
Quigley HS
Aliquippa, PA

Stiffler, Mark
Southern
Huntingdon Count
Orbisonia, PA

Stigliano, Melissa
Sharpsville Area SR
Transfer, PA

Stiles, Jodi
Homer Ctr
Homer City, PA

Stimpson, Stephanie
Meadville Area SR
Meadville, PA

Stinson, Jeff
Northwestern SR
Albion, PA

Stinson, Nellie
United HS
Seward, PA

Stirling, Thomas
David
MMI Prep Schl
Sugarloaf, PA

Stitley, Robert
Dover Area HS
Dover, PA

Stoback, James
Athens HS
Sayre, PA

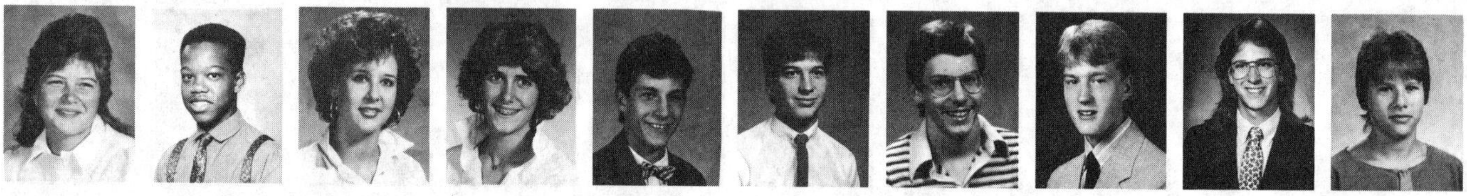

Stoddard, Amy
Corry Area HS
Corry, PA

Stoddart, John
Blue Mountain Acad
Philadelphia, PA

Stoddart, Stephanie
Carlisle SR HS
Selfridge Ang, MI

Stoeckel, Holly
William Allen HS
Allentown, PA

Stoffa, Charles
MMI Prep Schl
White Haven, PA

Stoffey, Scott
Marian HS
Tamaqua, PA

Stokes, Brian
Greensburg Salem
SR HS
Delmont, PA

Stokes, Brian J
Carlynton HS
Crafton, PA

Stone, Stephen C
Mt Lebanon SR HS
Pittsburgh, PA

Stone, Jr Thomas
Shalom Christian
Sharpsburg, MD

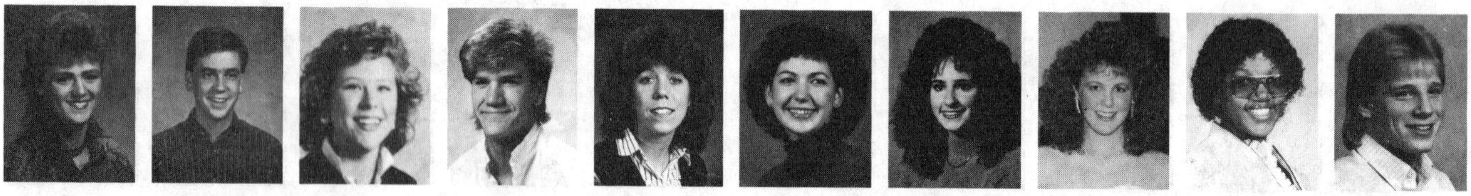

Stoneking, Kelly
Fairchance Georges
Fairchance, PA

Stoner, Daniel P
Hershey SR HS
Hershey, PA

Stoner, Dawn
York Catholic HS
York, PA

Stoner, John
Trinity HS
Washington, PA

Stoner, Kelli
Central Dauphin
East HS
Dauphin, PA

Stonesifer, Luann
Chambersburg Area
SR HS
Chambersburg, PA

Stotka, Andrea
Center HS
Aliquippa, PA

Stotsenburgh, Lori
Bishop Conwell HS
Levittown, PA

Stoudmire, Renata
The Philadelphia
HS For Girls
Philadelphia, PA

Stoudnour, Eric
Altoona HS
Altoona, PA

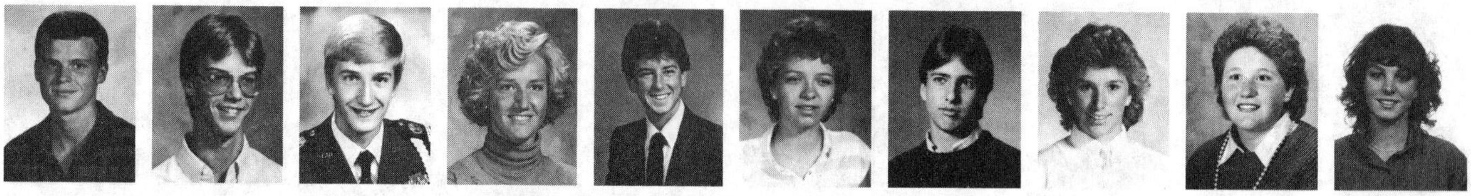

Stoudt, Joseph N
Fleetwood HS
Fleetwood, PA

Stoudt, Lance
Garden Spot HS
Narvon, PA

Stouffer, Lawrence
Greater Latrobe SR
Latrobe, PA

Stouffer, Phoebe
West Perry SR HS
New Bloomfield, PA

Stough, Scott
West York Area HS
York, PA

Stover, Lisa
West York Area SR
York, PA

Stover, Robert
Hopewell Area HS
Monaca, PA

Stowers, Yvette
Conemaugh
Township HS
Hollsopple, PA

Straley, Sue
Greencastle Antrim
Greencastle, PA

Strally, Tammy
Richland HS
Gibsonia, PA

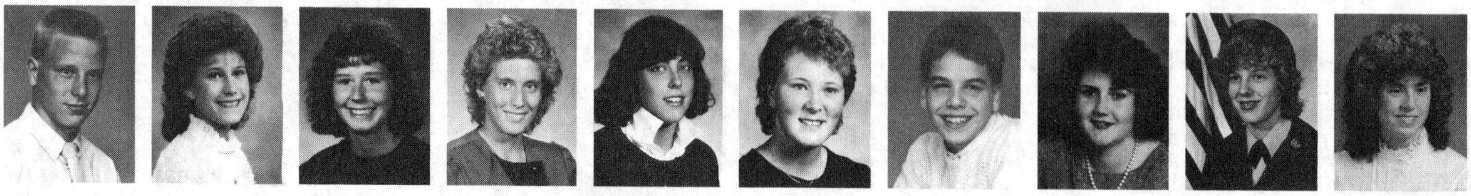

Strange, Jon
Dallas SR HS
Dallas, PA

Strank, Paula
Conemaugh Valley
JR SR HS
Johnstown, PA

Strasiser, Stacy
North Star HS
Hooversville, PA

Strasser, Debra
Hempfield SR HS
Greensburg, PA

Stratford, Carolyn
Lake-Lehman HS
Harveys Lake, PA

Straub, Cynthia
Danville SR HS
Danville, PA

Strauch, Richard
West Scranton HS
Scranton, PA

Strauss, Leslie
Northern Lebanon
Jonestown, PA

Strausser, Daffney
K
Millville HS
Bloomsburg, PA

Straw, Lisa
West York SR HS
York, PA

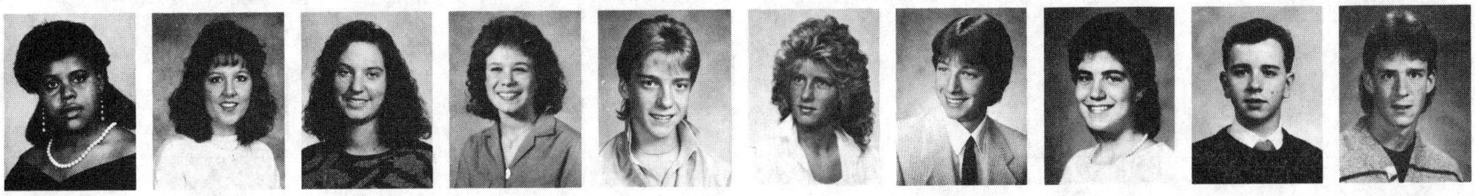

Strawberry, II
Dorethea M
Creative And
Performing Arts
Philadelphia, PA

Stremic, Darlene
Bensalem HS
Bensalem, PA

Strenske, Susan
Belle Vernon Area
Belle Vernon, PA

Streppa, Mary Jo
West Allegheny HS
Coraopolis, PA

Streznetcky, Jeffrey
Blue Ridge HS
New Milford, PA

Stright, Lisa
Academy HS
Erie, PA

Stringert, Michael
Commodore Perry
Clarks Mills, PA

Strittmatter, Leslie
Cambria Heights HS
Patton, PA

Strizzi, Jon
Bishop Mc Devitt
Harrisburg, PA

Strobel, Patrick
Damian
Butler SR HS
East Butler, PA

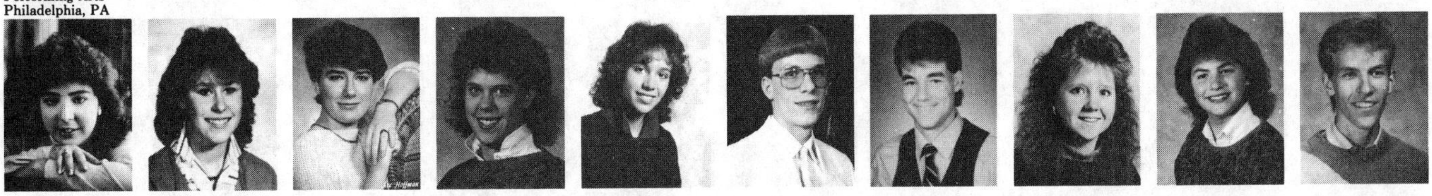

Strojek, Leslie
Ambridge Area HS
Ambridge, PA

Strong, Kim
Punxsutawney HS
Mahaffey, PA

Strope, Rebecca
E L Meyers HS
Wiles Barre, PA

Strosnider, Charlene
Mapletown JR SR
Dilliner, PA

Stuck, Beth
Carmichaels Area
Carmichaels, PA

Stuck, III William
Chief Logan HS
Yeagertown, PA

Stuckey, Jr Tom
Newport HS
Newport, PA

Studders, Colleen
James M Coughlin
Wilkes Barre, PA

Stufft, Laura
North Star HS
Boswell, PA

Stump, Bart
Dallastown Area HS
Dallastown, PA

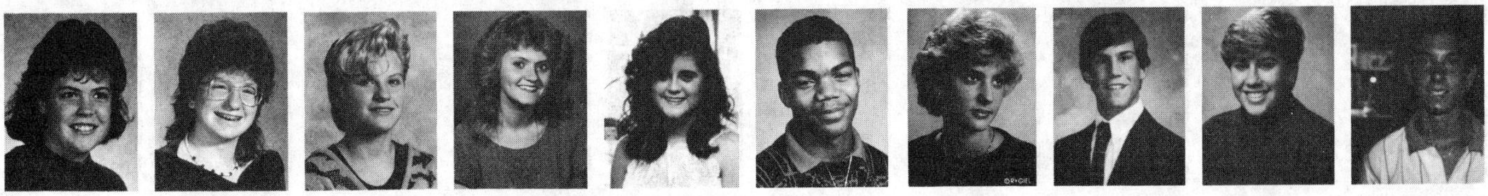

Stump, Denine
Bangor Area HS
Bangor, PA

Stump, Sharon
Octorara Area HS
Atglen, PA

Stumpp, Kelly A
Nativity B V M HS
Pottsville, PA

Stutts, Catherine
Canon Mc Millan
Canonsburg, PA

Suchodolski, Susan
Nazareth Acad
Phila, PA

Sudler, III Samuel G
HS Of Engineering
& Science
Philadelphia, PA

Sudol, Patricia D
Dallas Senior HS
Wyoming, PA

Sugar, Thomas
Conestock HS
Berwyn, PA

Suhosky, Lisa
Forest City Regional
Forest City, PA

Sukitch, William
North Catholic HS
Pittsburgh, PA

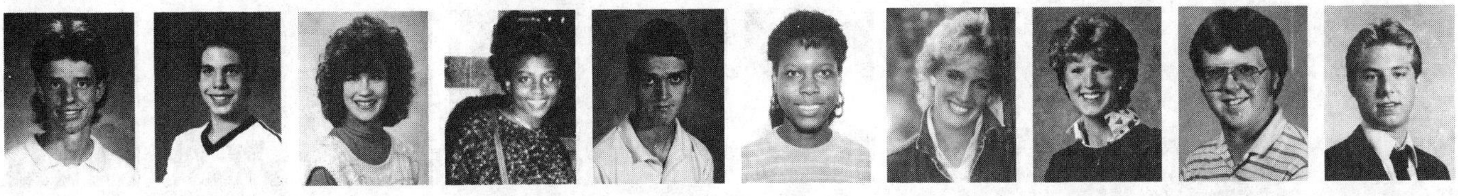

Sullivan, Brian
Shaler Area SR HS
Pittsburgh, PA

Sullivan, III John B
Rochester Area HS
Rochester, PA

Sullivan, Lisa
West Scranton HS
Scranton, PA

Suluki, Sahar
Sister Clara
Muhammad HS
Philadelphia, PA

Summerville, Bruce
Union HS
Sligo, PA

Sumner, Makeba
Cecilian Academy
Philadelphia, PA

Sumner, Theresa
Northwestern HS
Albion, PA

Sundahl, Lisa
Bradford Central
Christian HS
Bradford, PA

Sunderland, Michael
Huntingdon Area
Huntingdon, PA

Supernavage,
William
Cardinal Brennan
Shenandoah Hgts,
PA

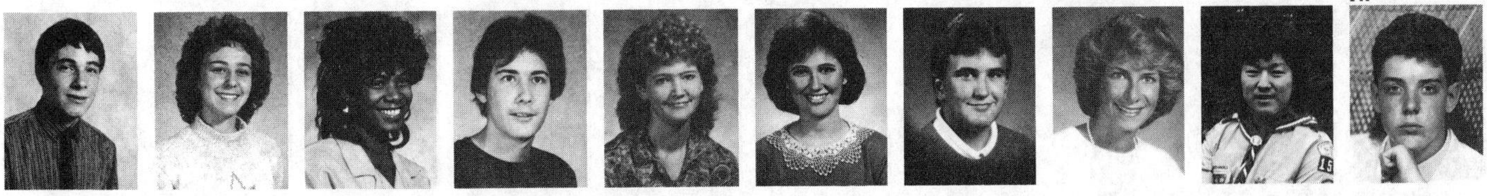

Suranofsky, Michael
Central Catholic HS
Whitehall, PA

Surgeoner, Nadine
Exeter SR HS
Reading, PA

Surginer, Doniele
Lutheran HS
Philadelphia, PA

Sutcavage, Albert
Dallas HS
Trucksville, PA

Suter, Melissa
Southmoreland HS
Ruffsdale, PA

Sutherland, Nancy
North Hills HS
Pittsburgh, PA

Sutovich, Kevin
Central Dauphin HS
Harrisburg, PA

Sutton, Laura
Central Bucks East
New Hope, PA

Sutton, Mike
Belle Vernon Area
Belle Vernon, PA

Sutton, Shawn
Canon Mc Millon
SR HS
Canonsburg, PA

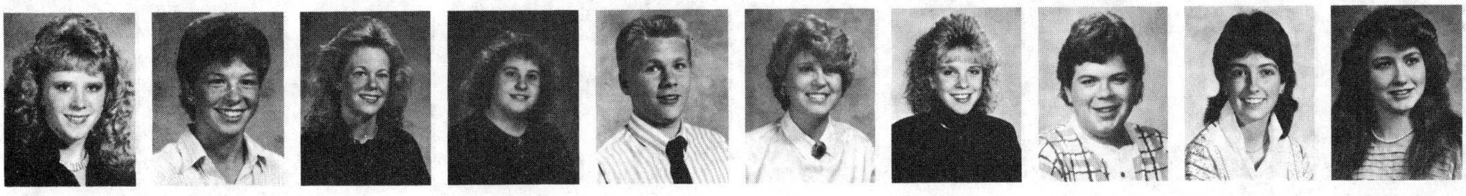

Sutton, Tammy
Saegertown HS
Saegertown, PA

Suydam, Kristine
Donegal HS
Mount Joy, PA

Suydam, Michele
Donegal HS
Mount Joy, PA

Svidron, Dena
Greensburg Central
Catholic HS
Latrobe, PA

Svrcek, Jr Andrew
Nativity BVM HS
New Phila, PA

Swails, Tracie
Grace Christian
High Spire, PA

Swan, Allison
Hanover Area JR
SR HS
Ashley, PA

Swan, Brian
Du Bois Senior HS
Dubois, PA

Swanhart, Melissa
Blacklick Valley HS
Nanty-Glo, PA

Swank, Denise
Cumberland Valley
Mechanicsburg, PA

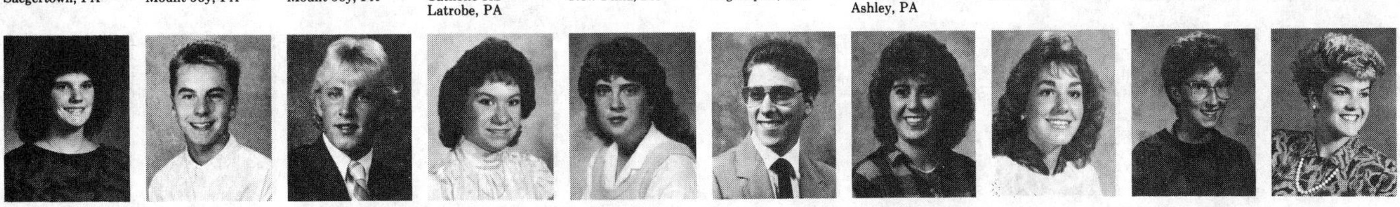

Swank, Jamie
Shamokin Area HS
Shamokin, PA

Swanson, Jim
Franklin Regional
Murrysville, PA

Swanson, Jim
Warren Area HS
Warren, PA

Swarner, Cindy
Great Hope Baptist
Carlisle, PA

Swartz, Carla
Montgomery Area
Montgomery, PA

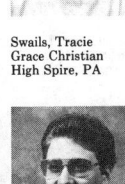

Swartz, Todd
Sheffield Area HS
Sheffield, PA

Swartz, Tricia
Sheffield Area HS
Sheffield, PA

Swede, Lisa
Plymouth-Whitemar
sh HS
Norristown, PA

Sweger, Angela
Cumberland Valley
Carlisle, PA

Sweigard, Holly Ann
William Penn SR
York, PA

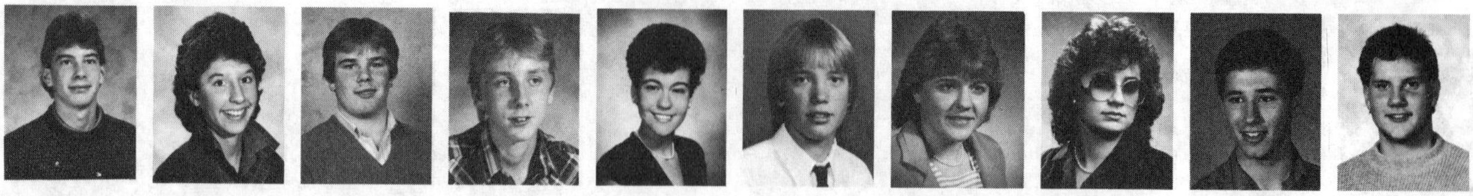

Sweigart, Dennis
Hershey HS
Hershey, PA

Swenn, Kris
Meadville Area SR
Meadville, PA

Swenson, Jr John
Mc Dowell HS
Erie, PA

Swetland, Jamie
Elk Lake HS
Montrose, PA

Swier, Terri L
Norristown Area HS
Norristown, PA

Swift, Robert Todd
Blue Mountain Acad
Lancaster, PA

Swindell, Teresa
Huntingdon Area
James Creek, PA

Swinehart, Lisa
Northern York HS
Dillsburg, PA

Swink, Michael
Connellsville SR HS
Dawson, PA

Switzer, Scott
Oil City Area HS
Oil City, PA

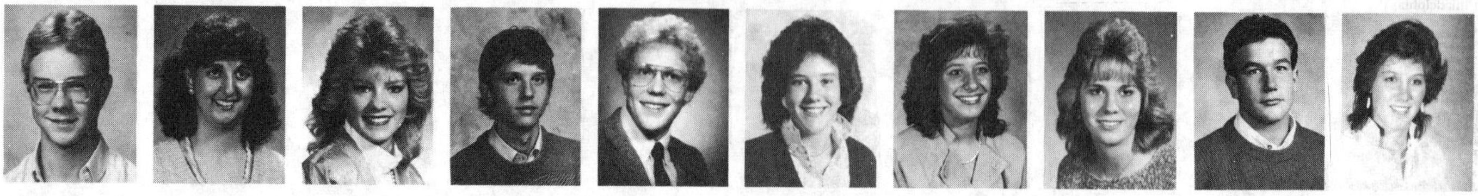

Swope, Todd
Du Bois Area HS
Luthersburg, PA

Syphard, Tracy
Wilmington Area
Pulaski, PA

Sypolt, Cynthia
Liski Area HS
Apollo, PA

Szabo, James
Louis E Dieruff HS
Allentown, PA

Szanyi, Neil A
Liberty HS
Bethlehem, PA

Szczerbowicz, Kathleen
Shenandoah Valley
Shenandoah, PA

Szlavik, Tania
Upper Merion Area
King Of Prussia, PA

Szolis, Leigh A
Richland HS
Wexford, PA

Szulborski, Jason
Pleasant Valley HS
Effort, PA

Szymala, Michelle
Spring-Ford HS
Royersford, PA

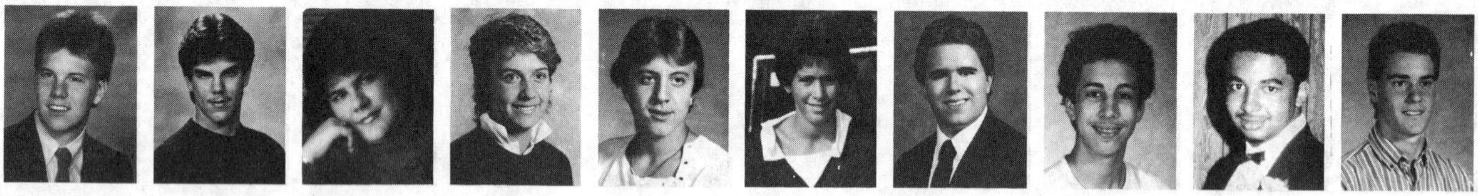

Szymkowiak, Aaron
Hampton HS
Gibsonia, PA

Tabarrini, Richard
Old Forge HS
Old Forge, PA

Tabarrini, Tara
Old Forge HS
Old Forge, PA

Tacelosky, Robin
Shenandoah Valley
Shenandoah, PA

Taddeo, Joe
Ambridgea Area HS
Baden, PA

Tagert, Steve
Upper Darby HS
Aldan, PA

Tagliente, Don
Clearfield Area HS
Clearfield, PA

Tahar, Michael
Downingtown SR
Downingtown, PA

Talbert, Bruce
Chester HS
Chester, PA

Talbot, Richard
Penncrest HS
Media, PA

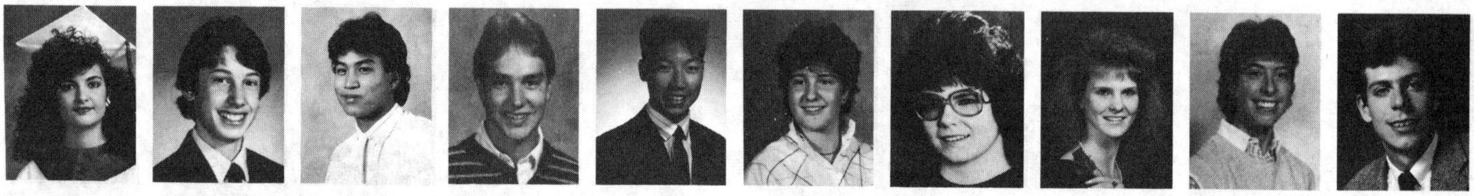

Talotta, Angel
St Maria Goretti HS
Philadelphia, PA

Tana, Bob
Archbishop Ryan HS For Boys
Philadelphia, PA

Tang, Charles
Gateway SR HS
Monroeville, PA

Tanner, Terry L
Warrior Run HS
Turbotville, PA

Tanovan, David
Abington SR HS
Elkins Park, PA

Tantlinger, Shawn
Greater Latrobe SR
Latrobe, PA

Tapia, Brenda
Wyoming Area SR
Exeter, PA

Tarasiewicz, Karen
St Hubert HS For
Philadelphia, PA

Taraszki, Penny
Villa Maria Acad
Erie, PA

Tarcson, Tim
Central Christian
Du Bois, PA

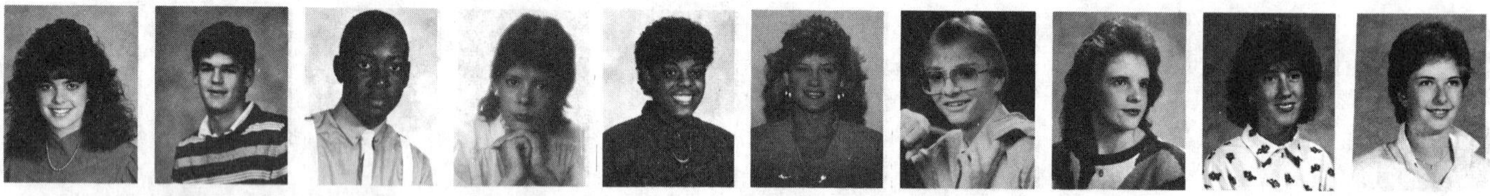

Tate, Lisa
Altoona Area HS
Altoona, PA

Taxin, Adam
Strath Haven HS
Wallingford, PA

Taylor, Al
Coatesville Area SR
Coatesville, PA

Taylor, Bonnie Sue
Seneca Vly HS
Mars, PA

Taylor, Chamise
Scott Intermediate
Coatesville, PA

Taylor, Cynthia
Altoona HS
Altoona, PA

Taylor, Graham C
Trinity HS
Washington, PA

Taylor, Heather
Lake Lehman HS
Shavertown, PA

Taylor, Jackie
Penn Manor HS
Lancaster, PA

Taylor, Jennifer
Henderson HS
West Chester, PA

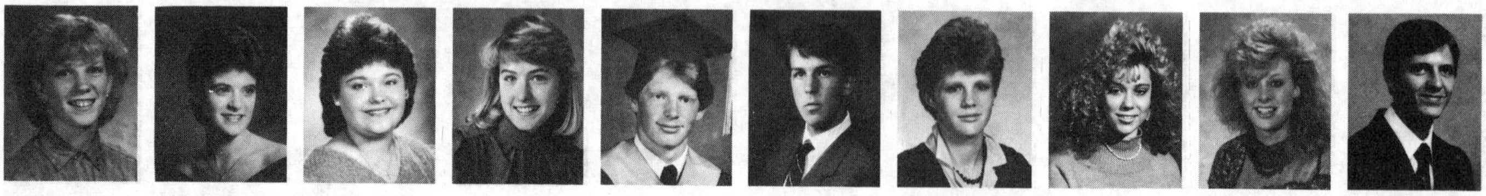

Taylor, Jennifer
Kennard-Dale HS
Delta, PA

Taylor, Kelly L
Saucon Valley SR
Bethlehem, PA

Taylor, Nancy L
Swissvale HS
Pittsburgh, PA

Taylor, Rachel
Shady Side Acad
New Kensington, PA

Taylor, Scott M
Archbishop Carrroll
Havertown, PA

Taylor, Stephen E
Bloomsburg HS
Bloomsburg, PA

Taylor, Suzie
Juniata HS
Mifflintown, PA

Taylor, Tiffany
Pen Argyl Area HS
Pen Argyl, PA

Taylor, Wendy
North Penn JR SR
Wellsboro, PA

Teachout, David
The Baptist HS
Kingsley, PA

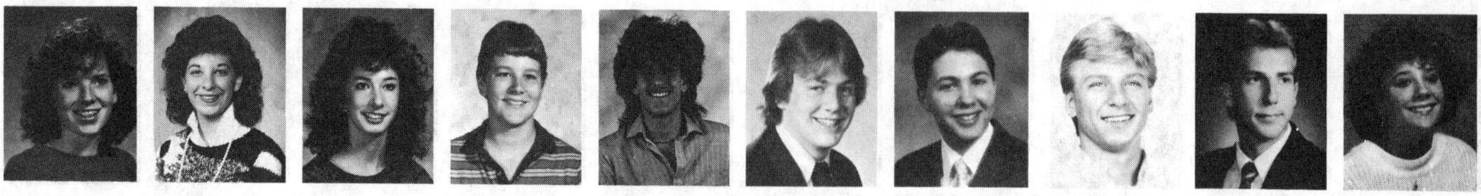

Teconchuk, Kimberly
Fairview HS
Fairview, PA

Temarantz, Antoinette
Hanover Area JR/SR HS
Wilkes Barre, PA

Templeton, Susan
Eastern York HS
York, PA

Templin, Chad
Cedar Crest HS
Lebanon, PA

Tener, Adrian
Northeast Prep
Philadelphia, PA

Tenzer, Ryan
Emmaus HS
Allentown, PA

Teplitz, Robert F
Central Dauphin HS
Harrisburg, PA

Terefencko, Jr John
Our Lady Of Lourdes HS
Paxinos, PA

Terefenko, Kevin
Exeter Township SR
Reading, PA

Terry, Coleen
Elizabethtown Area
Manheim, PA

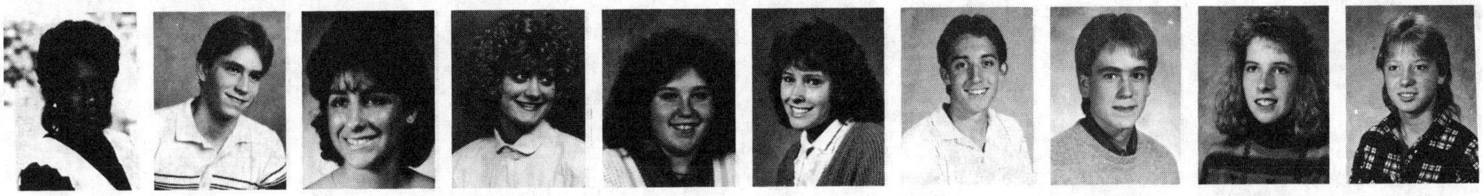

Terry, Stephanie
Aliquippa HS
Aliquippa, PA

Tesche, Eric
Dieruff HS
Allentown, PA

Thanos, Mary
Forbes Road HS
Mc Connellsburg, PA

Theakston, Candy
Ringgold HS
Finleyville, PA

Theiss, Julie E
Mc Donnell HS
Erie, PA

Theodore, Bobbie
Moon HS
West Palm Beach, FL

Thibault, Jamie
Conestoga HS
Paoli, PA

Thomas, Andrew
Lake-Lehman HS
Shavertown, PA

Thomas, Angela
Greencastle-Antrim
Greencastle, PA

Thomas, Candace
West Greene HS
New Freeport, PA

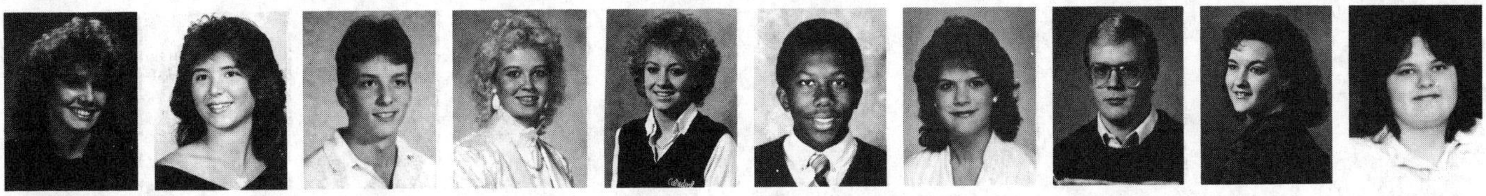

Thomas, Carrie
Catasaugua HS
Catasauqua, PA

Thomas, Deborah
Swenson Skill Ctr
Philadelphia, PA

Thomas, Donald
Oxford HS
Nottingham, PA

Thomas, Holly Ann
Cambria Heights HS
Hastings, PA

Thomas, Lisa
St Pual Cathedral
Pittsburgh, PA

Thomas, Michael Duane
Northgate HS
Bellevue, PA

Thomas, Michele Elizabeth Forward
Mc Keesport, PA

Thomas, Richard
South Side HS
Clinton, PA

Thomas, Sherry Ann
William Penn SR
York, PA

Thomas, Tracey
West Side Area
Kingston, PA

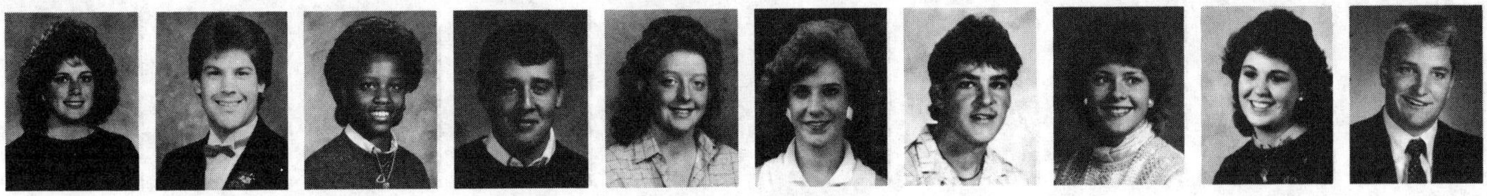

Thomas, Tracy
John S Fine HS
Nanticoke, PA

Thomason, Greg
Saint James HS
Brookhaven, PA

Thompkins, Hazel
West Catholic HS For Girls
Philadelphia, PA

Thompson, Alan D
Lock Haven SR HS
Howard, PA

Thompson, Amy
West Middlesex HS
West Middlesex, PA

Thompson, Andrea
Williams Valley JR SR HS
Tower City, PA

Thompson, Brian L
Northern Lebanon
Annville, PA

Thompson, Darla
Fairview Christian
Honey Grove, PA

Thompson, Frances
Gateway HS
Monroeville, PA

Thompson, J Matthew
Henderson HS
W Chester, PA

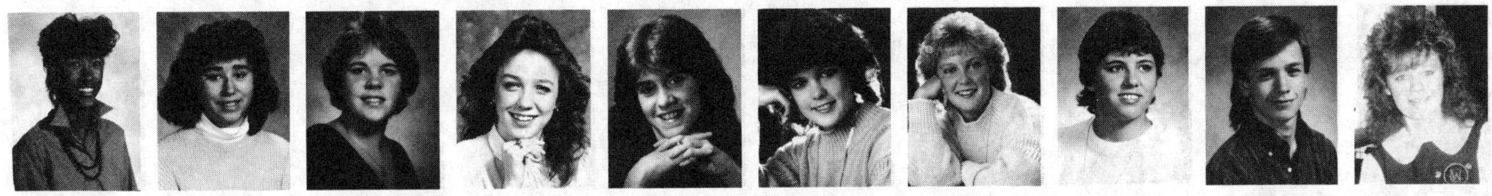

Thompson, Kelly
Coastesville Area SR
Coatesville, PA

Thompson, Sarah
Lebanon HS
Lebanon, PA

Thompson, Shelley Lynn
Oxford Area HS
Cochranville, PA

Thompson, Tiffany
Sharpsville SR HS
Sharpsville, PA

Thompson, Virginia M
Oil City Area SR
Cooperstown, PA

Thornton, Laura
Carbondale Area HS
Simpson, PA

Thornton, Lisa
Carbondale Area HS
Simpson, PA

Thorp, Samantha L
Freeport Area HS
Freeport, PA

Thurman, James
Taylor Alderice HS
Pittsburgh, PA

Tiedeken, Alexandra
West Catholic Girls
Philadelphia, PA

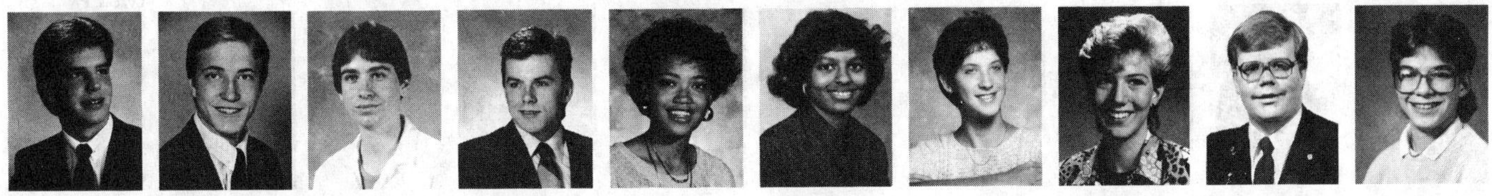

Tielle, David
Pittston Area HS
Pittston, PA

Tielsch, Brian J
Penn Hills SR HS
Pittsburgh, PA

Tiffany, Shaun
Tunkhannock HS
Tunkhannock, PA

Tighe, John P
Thomas Jefferson
Clairton, PA

Tillery, Stephanie
Chichester SR HS
Boothwyn, PA

Timbers, Niya
Philadelphia HS For
Philadelphia, PA

Timchak, Alice Ann
North Allegheny SR
Sewickley, PA

Timko, Valesie
Greensburg-Salem
Greensburg, PA

Timlin, Jr Robert Edward
Schenley HS
Pittsburgh, PA

Timney, John
Western Beaver HS
Industry, PA

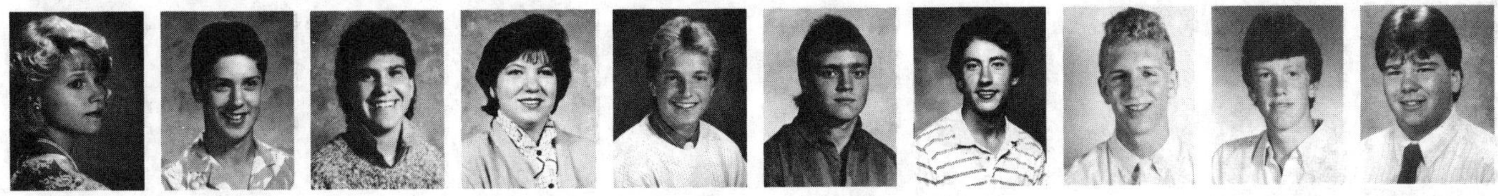

Tingle, Helene
Tyrone Area HS
Tyrone, PA

Tinker, John Wesley
Forbes Road HS
Hustontown, PA

Tinner, Joyce
Dallas SR HS
Dallas, PA

Tipton, Andrea
Northwestern SR
Edinboro, PA

Tirion, Alexander
Reading SR HS
Reading, PA

Tirko, Joseph
Somerset Area SR
Friedens, PA

Tkach, Scott
Ringgold HS
Finleyville, PA

Toczydlowski, John E
Holy Ghost Prep
Philadelphia, PA

Todd, Greg
William Allen HS
Allentown, PA

Todd, Sherbondy
Geibel HS
Connellsville, PA

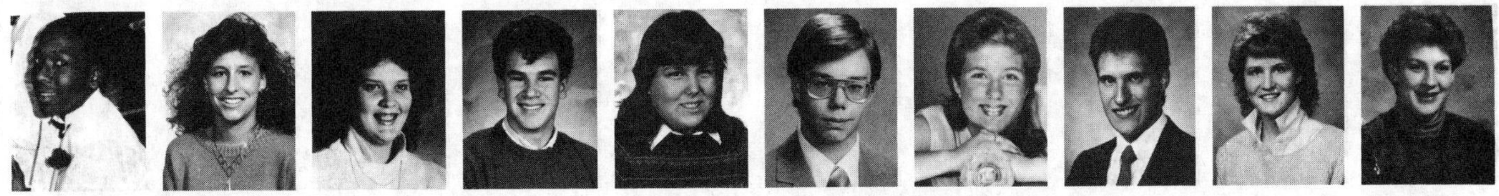

Toliver, Walter
Saint Josephs Prep
Philadelphia, PA

Tollari, Lisa
Belle Vernon Area
Belle Vernon, PA

Toltesi, Suzanne
Freedom SR HS
Bethlehem, PA

Toma, Chuck
Seneca Valley HS
Zelienople, PA

Toman, Julie
Southmoreland HS
Scottdale, PA

Tomascik, Thomas
Pittston Area SR
Pittston, PA

Tomasic, Joanne Elen
West Mifflin Area
W Mifflin, PA

Tomaszewski, Jeff
Ambridge Area HS
Freedom, PA

Tomazic, Karen
Forest City Regional
Forest City, PA

Tompkins, Traci
Donegal HS
Mt Joy, PA

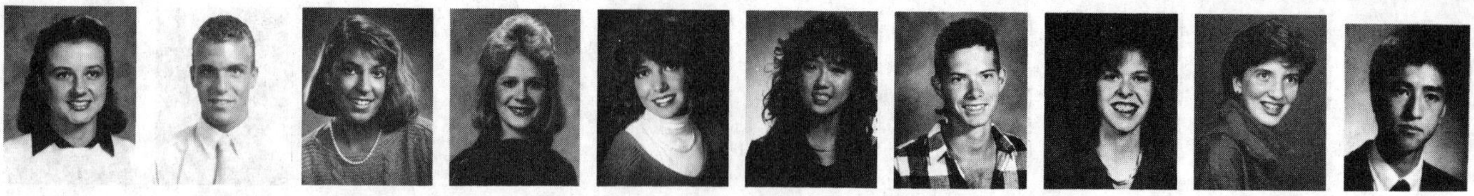

Toms, Susan
Christian School Of
Boiling Springs, PA

Tomsula, Jed
Steel Valley HS
W Homestead, PA

Toso, Sue
William Allen HS
Allentown, PA

Touvell, Charlene
Brookville Area HS
Brookville, PA

Tovcimak, Lucille
Ann
North Pocono HS
Moscow, PA

Tow, Shani
Abington HS
Roslyn, PA

Town, David
Brockway Area HS
Brockport, PA

Towsey, Dawn J
Central Dauphin HS
Harrisburg, PA

Tracewski, Nicole
Valley View JR SR
Eynon, PA

Tran, Cuong
Central Catholic HS
Allentown, PA

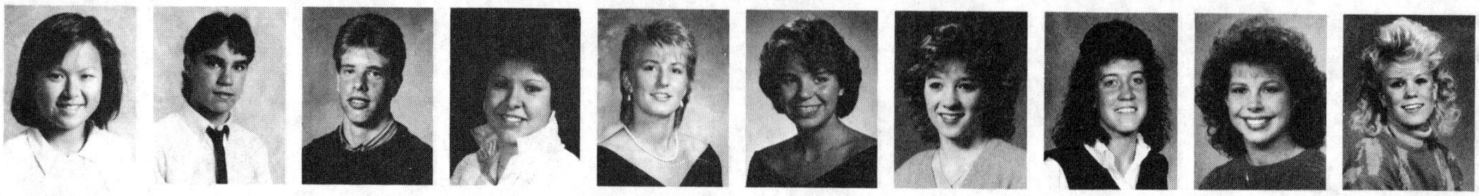

Tran, Thu
Academy Of Notre
Dame De Namur
Upper Darby, PA

Tranguch, Ben A
Bishop Hafey HS
Hazleton, PA

Trappen, Eric
South Side HS
Hookstown, PA

Traxler, Lauri
Forbes Road HS
Hustontown, PA

Traynor, Jennifer L
Conestoga HS
Strafford, PA

Trego, Pamela
Downington HS
West Chester, PA

Trempus, Rachel
Springdale HS
Springdale, PA

Trench, Carol
Nazareth Acad
Phila, PA

Trenkle, Melanie J
Bishop Mc Cort HS
Johnstown, PA

Treon, Angela
Shikellamy HS
Northumberland,
PA

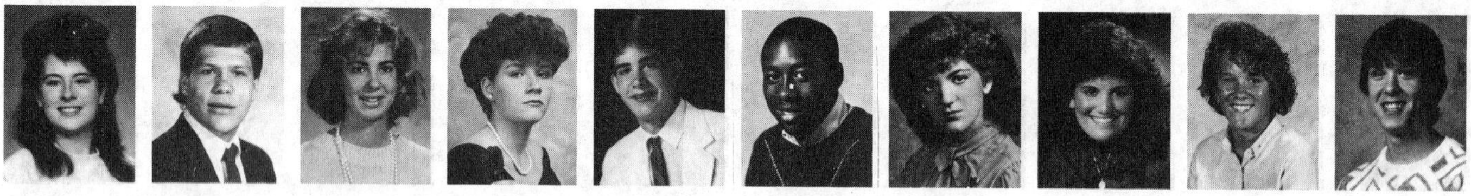

Tressa, Sharon
James M Coughlin
Plains, PA

Trexler, Donald
Bishop Mc Cort HS
Johnstown, PA

Tribit, Emily K
Penn Manor HS
Lancaster, PA

Tribuiani, Melissa
Upper Darby HS
Upper Darby, PA

Trichel, III Gervais
William
Seneca HS
Erie, PA

Triggs, Robert
Trinity Christian
Pittsburgh, PA

Triponey, Carrie
Clearfield Area HS
Hyde, PA

Troiani, Anna Marie
Regina
Quigley HS
Midland, PA

Trojanowski, Karen
St Pius X HS
Pottstown, PA

Trojanowski,
Michael
Warren Area HS
Warren, PA

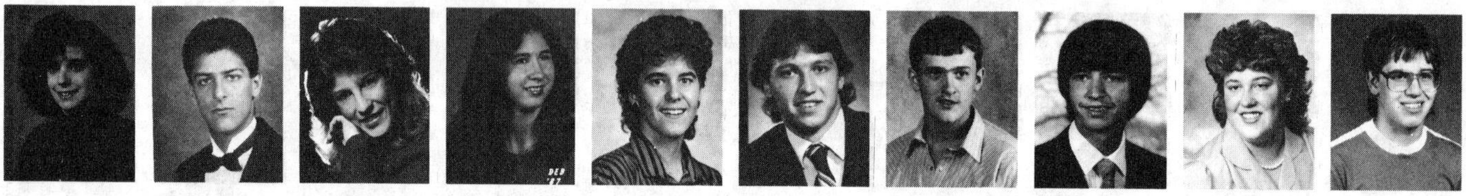

Trombetta,
Christina
Center Area HS
Aliquippa, PA

Tropiano, Chris
St Jon Neumann HS
Philadelphia, PA

Trost, Deborah
Ringgold HS
Monongahela, PA

Trostle, Debra
Hempfield HS
University Park, PA

Trought, Lisa
Spring-Ford SR HS
Royersford, PA

Trout, Andrew
N Lebanon HS
Lebanon, PA

Trout, Brad
United HS
Homer City, PA

Trout, Ken
Solanco HS
Quarryville, PA

Trout, Teresa
Greater Latrobe SR
Greensburg, PA

Troutman,
Christopher
Upper Dauphin
Area HS
Lykens, PA

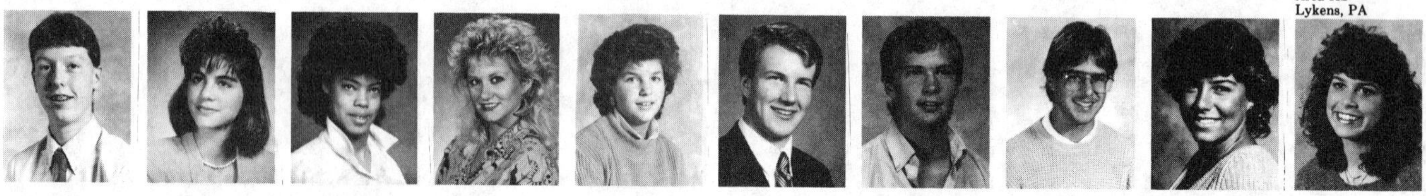

Troutman, Michael
T
Nativity BVM
New Philadelphia,
PA

Trovato, Margarita
Chartiers-Houston
Houston, PA

Trower, Della
Sacred Heart HS
Pittsburgh, PA

Troy, Julie
Monessen JR SR
Monessen, PA

Trubilla, Tara
Panther Valley HS
Nesquehoning, PA

Truesdale, Todd
The Hill Schl
Cliffside Pk, NJ

Truitt, David
Elizabethtown Area
Elizabethtown, PA

Trump, Michael
Reading SR HS
Reading, PA

Trunk, Christine
Middletown Area
Middletown, PA

Truschel, Jeanne
Gateway SR HS
Monroeville, PA

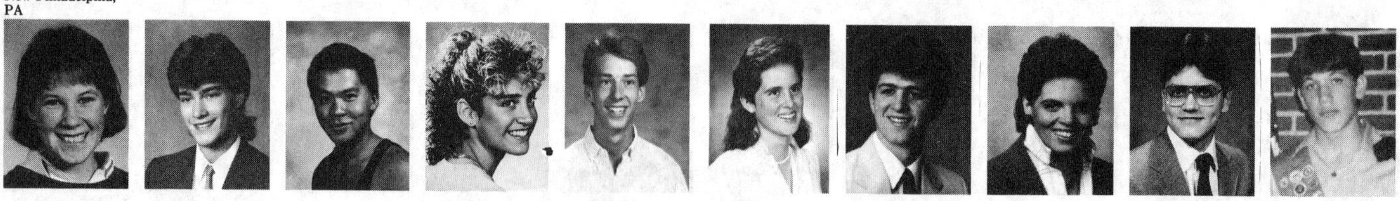

Trussler, Shari
The Baptist HS
Clarks Summit, PA

Trzeciak, Shawn
Highlands HS
Natrona Hts, PA

Tsai, Shun
Spring-Ford Sr HS
Mt Clare, PA

Tsangaris, Jennifer
Elizabeth-Forward
Elizabeth, PA

Tschopp, Barry
Kennard-Dale HS
Stewartstown, PA

Tubbs, Melissa
Curwensville Area
Curwensville, PA

Tubbs, Robbie
First Baptist Church
Curwensville, PA

Tubbs, Sherry
Du Bois Area HS
Grampian, PA

Tucci, IV Thomas
Reading SR HS
Reading, PA

Tucker, Kevin
Scotland School For
Veterans Children
Harrisburg, PA

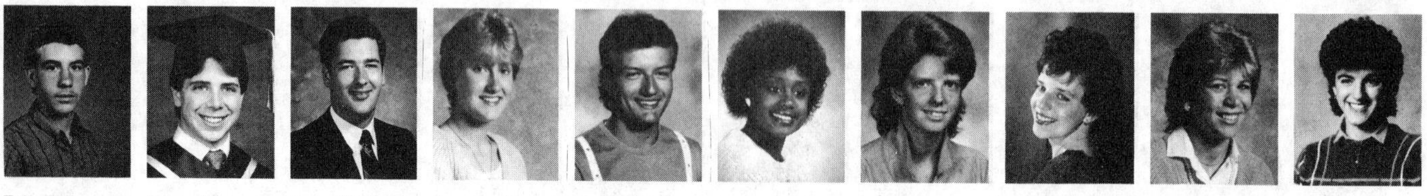

Tuffy, Paul
Tunkhannock Area
Tunkhannock, PA

Tuman, John
Northeast Catholic
H S For Boys
Philadelphia, PA

Tuohy, IV Edward
R
Council Rock HS
Newtown, PA

Turcmanovich,
Susan
Panther Valley HS
Lansford, PA

Turner, Dave
Reynolds HS
Greenville, PA

Turner, Sydnee
Ft Cherry HS
Mc Donald, PA

Turner, Tonia
Claysburg-Kimmel
Claysburg, PA

Turo, Lynn
Mahanoy Area HS
Mahanoy City, PA

Turofski, Kimberly
Southern Columbia
Area HS
Catawissa, PA

Tutelo, Tracy
Burrell HS
Lower Burrell, PA

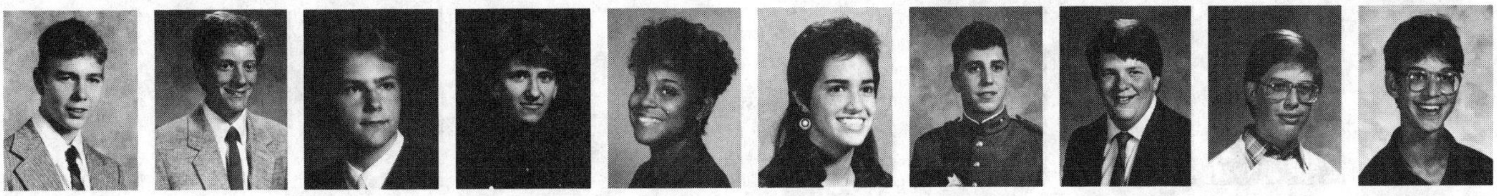

Tutko, Lonny
Cardinal Brennan
Shenandoah, PA

Twining, Peter C
Carlisle SR HS
Carlisle, PA

Twist, Todd
Milton Area SR HS
Milton, PA

Twordusky, Lori
Tunkhannock HS
Tunkhannock, PA

Twyman, Amy
West Mifflin Area
W Mifflin, PA

Tyebjee, Shiryn
Plymouth-Whitemar
sh HS
Lafayette Hill, PA

Tyler, Jason B
Bishop Shanahan
W Chester, PA

Tyler, Tom
Spring Grove Area
SR HS
Spring Grove, PA

Tynan, Robert T
Fairview HS
Fairview, PA

Tyson, David C
Northeastern HS
Mt Wolf, PA

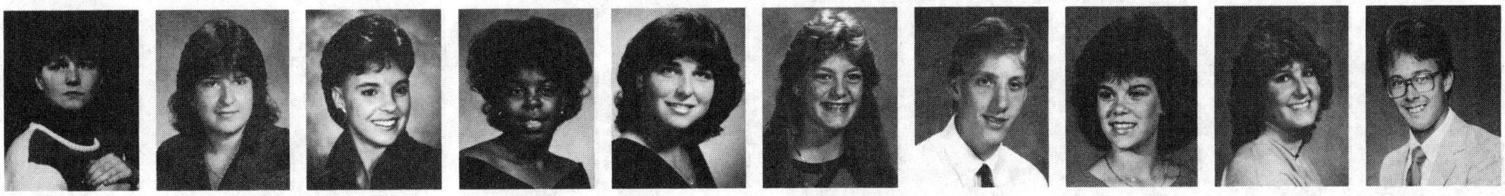

Tyson, Leslie
Bishop Mc Devitt
Harrisburg, PA

Tyson, Susan
Kutztown Area HS
Kutztown, PA

Ubaldini, Tami
Abington Heights
Clarks Summit, PA

Udoh, Monique
Upper Moreland HS
Philadelphia, PA

Uebler, Jennifer
Garnet Valley HS
Glen Mills, PA

Uhlman, Shelly
Conneaut Valley HS
Linesville, PA

Ulery, John
Greensburg Central
Catholic HS
Latrobe, PA

Ulery, Tonya
Connellsville SR HS
Normalville, PA

Ulmer, Tammy
Jersey Shore SR HS
Willamsport, PA

Umbenhouer, Sean
M
Hamburg Area HS
Shoemakersville, PA

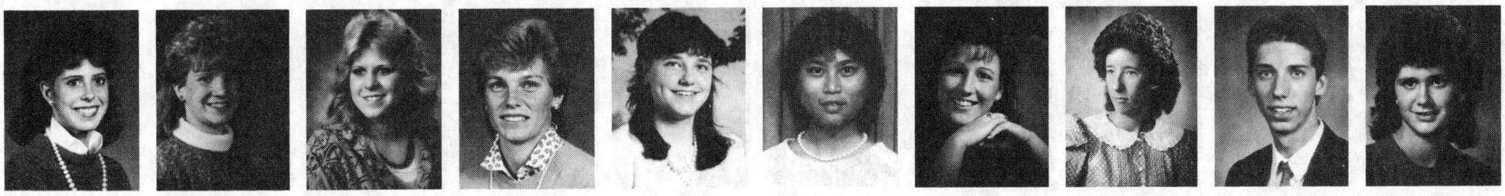

Umberger, Trudy
Upper Dauphin
Area HS
Lykens, PA

Umshares, Beth
Washington HS
Washington, PA

Underkoffler, Lisa
Shenandoah Valley
Shenandoah, PA

Underkoffler, Teresa
Upper Dauphin
Area HS
Lykens, PA

Underwood, Jill
Schulkill Haven
Area HS
Sch Haven, PA

Ung, Lehsan
Philadelphia H S
For Girls
Philadelphia, PA

Unger, Diane
Salisbury HS
Allentown, PA

Unruh, Pamela
Penn Manor HS
Pequea, PA

Updegraff, Derek
Milton Area SR HS
Montandon, PA

Urban, Melissa
Lehighton Area HS
Lehighton, PA

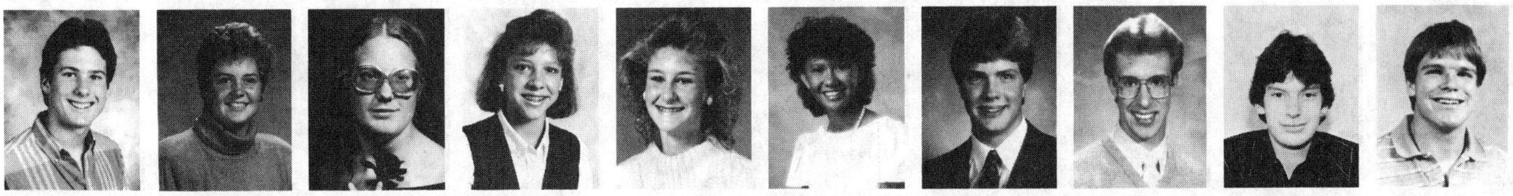

Urban, Patrick C J
Wilson HS
Sinking Spring, PA

Urich, Jodi
West Perry HS
Elliottsburg, PA

Usner, Jackquelyn
Palisades JR SR HS
Riegelsville, PA

Ustynoski, Marie
Bishop Hafey HS
Hazleton, PA

Utchell, Amy
Chartiers Valley HS
Carnegie, PA

Vaccaro, Antoinette
Chambersburg Area
SR HS
Chambersburg, PA

Vaclavik, Steven
Upper Dauphin HS
Millersburg, PA

Vago, Spenser
Butler SR HS
Butler, PA

Vail, Jeffery W
State College Area
Alternative Schl
State College, PA

Vak, Stephen
Kiski Area HS
New Kensington,
PA

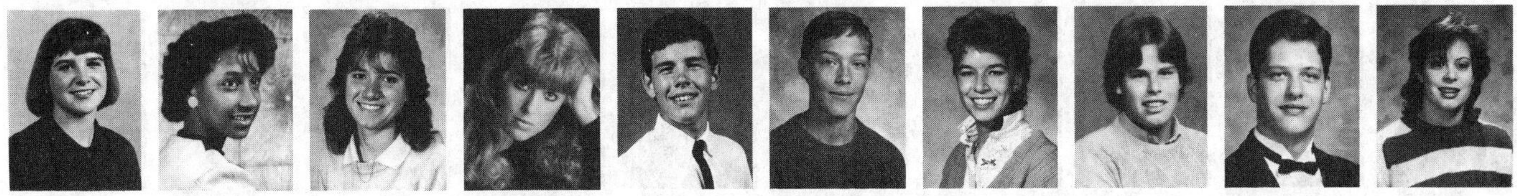

Vak, Susan
Kiski Area HS
New Kensington,
PA

Valentine, Hope
Pottstown SR HS
Pottstown, PA

Valetta, Kris
Bucktail JR SR HS
Renovo, PA

Vallese, Rochelle R
Beaver Area HS
Beaver, PA

Vallette, Daniel
High Point Baptist
Geigertown, PA

Valley, Paul
Kennedy Christian
Hermitage, PA

Valtos, Carolyn
Parkland HS
Schnecksville, PA

Valvano, Joseph
Christopher
West Side Voc Tech
Hunlock Creek, PA

Valvardi, John
Cardinal O Hara HS
Springfield, PA

Van Aulen, Jenny
Conestoga Valley
Lancaster, PA

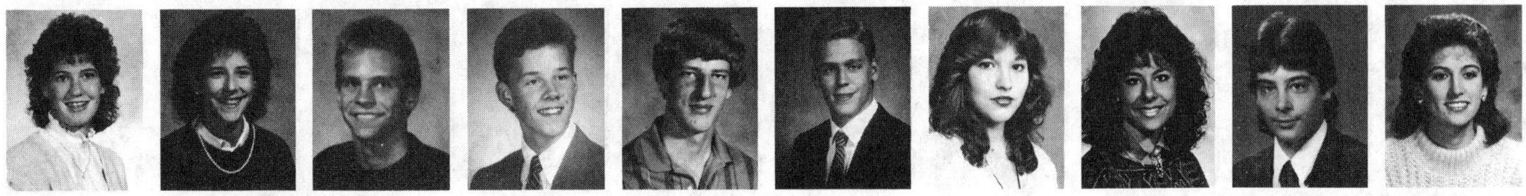

Van Buskirk,
Rhonda
Faith Christian Schl
Saylorsburg, PA

Van Cleve, Coleen
Lancaster Christian
New Providence, PA

Van Delinder, Scott
Williamson HS
Millerton, PA

Van Voorhis, Gregg
Franklin Regional
Murrysville, PA

Vander Weele,
Richard
Corry Area HS
Corry, PA

Vanek, Dennis
Valley HS
New Kensington,
PA

Vanella, Michelle
HS Of Engineering
& Science
Hatfield, PA

Vannucci, Dana
Frazier HS
Fayette City, PA

Vannucci, Dave
Frazier JR SR HS
Fayette City, PA

Vant Zelfden, Lori
Conestoga Valley
Lancaster, PA

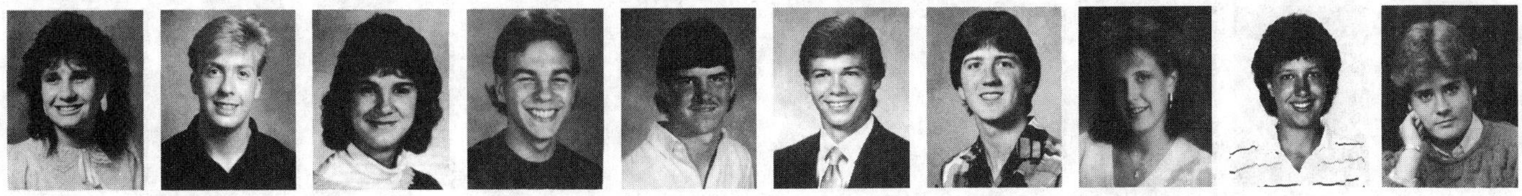

Vargo, Carolyn
Ringgold HS
Donora, PA

Vargo, Edward
Homer Center HS
Lucerne Mines, PA

Vargo, Linda
Liberty HS
Bethlehem, PA

Vargo, Todd Alan
Penn Trafford HS
Harrison Cty, PA

Varischetti, Peter
Brockway Area HS
Brockway, PA

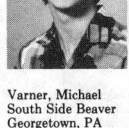

Varner, Keith
Forest Hills HS
Johnstown, PA

Varner, Michael
South Side Beaver
Georgetown, PA

Varner, Michelle
Rayne
Seneca Valley SR
Harmony, PA

Varuolo, Lena
Hempfield SR HS
Jeannette, PA

Vasel, Julie
Central HS
Martinsburg, PA

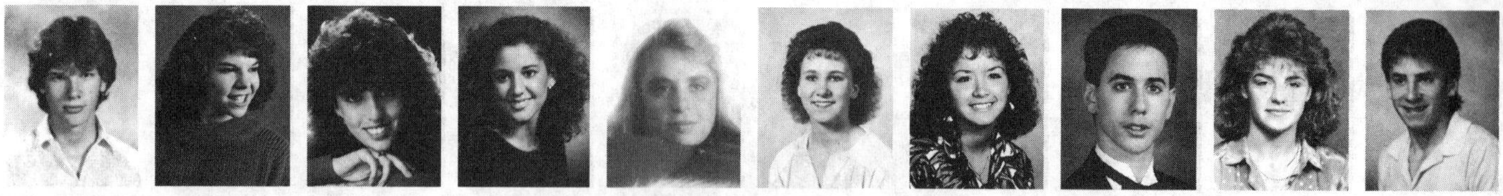

Vatavuk, Michael J
Windber Area HS
Windber, PA

Vaught, Gail
York Catholic HS
York, PA

Vavrick, Michelle Anita
Dunmore HS
Dunmore, PA

Vecchio, Tina
Mapletown JR SR
Dilliner, PA

Vecchiola, Andrea
Highlands HS
Natrona Hgts, PA

Veglia, Ann
Western Beaver JR SR HS
Industry, PA

Velazquez, Bonnie
Harry S Truman HS
Levittown, PA

Veltri, Joseph
St John Neumann
Philadelphia, PA

Venetta, Christine
Hickory HS
Hermitage, PA

Venture, Jim
Du Bois Area HS
Reynoldsville, PA

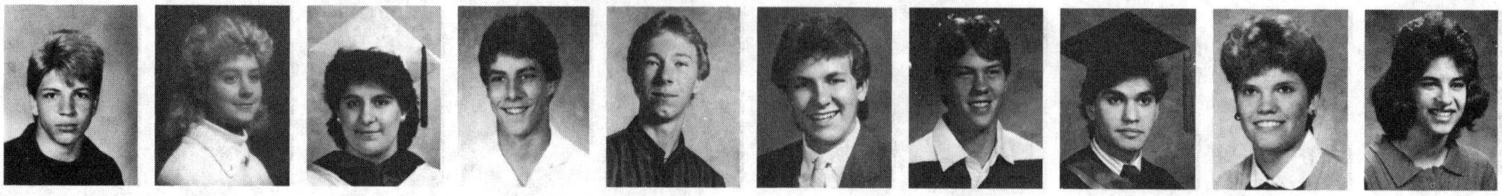

Veraldi, Angelo
Southwestern HS
Hanover, PA

Verbecken, Michelle
Central Dauphin East HS
Harrisburg, PA

Verduci, Carmela A
Bishop Shanahan
Westchester, PA

Verner, David
Mc Guffey HS
Washington, PA

Vernusky, Frank J
Cardinal Brennan
Frackville, PA

Veronesi, David
Belle Vernon Area
Belle Vernon, PA

Verotsky, Marc
Cumberland Valley
Mechanicsburg, PA

Verrecchia, Anthony N
Cardinal O Hara HS
Glenolden, PA

Verzinski, Becky
Plum SR HS
Pittsburgh, PA

Vesco, Angela
Lincoln HS
Ellwood City, PA

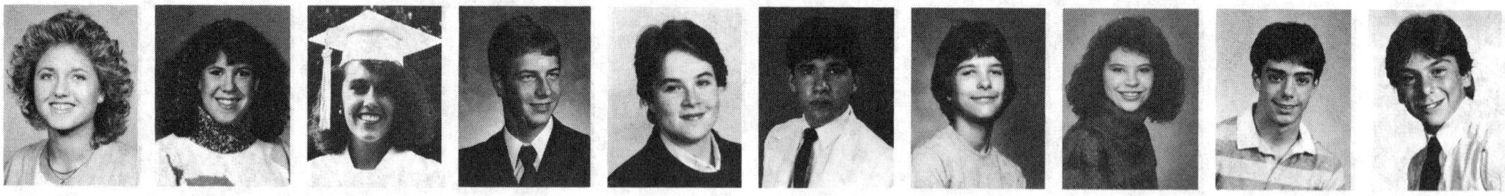

Veseleny, Jill
West Mifflin Area
West Mifflin, PA

Vesely, Lisa
Mon Valley Catholic
Belle Vernon, PA

Vesotski, Lisa
Butler Area SR HS
Washington, WV

Vetere, Scott
Monessen HS
Monessen, PA

Vicario, Denise
Gwynedd Mercy
Horsham, PA

Vicent, Jaime
Cardinal Dougherty
Philadelphia, PA

Vickers, Marc
Ringgold HS
Eighty Four, PA

Vida, Michelle
Peters Township HS
Bridgeville, PA

Viggiano, Gregory
New Castle SR HS
New Castle, PA

Viglianti, Anthony
Notre Dame HS
Easton, PA

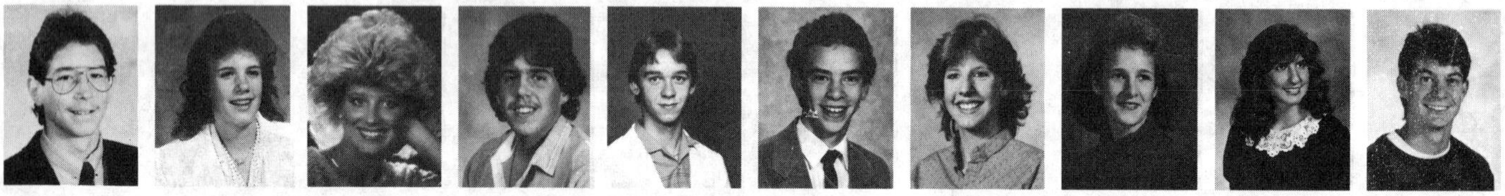

Vilcko, Kenneth
Hazleton HS
Drums, PA

Villecco, Anna
Pequea Valley HS
Ronks, PA

Villee, Debbie
Fort Cherry HS
Midway, PA

Villella, Damon
Brookville Area HS
Summerville, PA

Villers, Steven W
Ringgold HS
Monongahela, PA

Viney, Vincent S
Northeast Catholic
Philadelphia, PA

Visnansky, Doris
Perry Traditional
Pittsburgh, PA

Vituszynski, Laura M
Cedar Crest HS
Lebanon, PA

Vivian, Valerie
Belle Vernon Area
Belle Vernon, PA

Vogel, Neil
Lower Moreland HS
Huntingdon Valley, PA

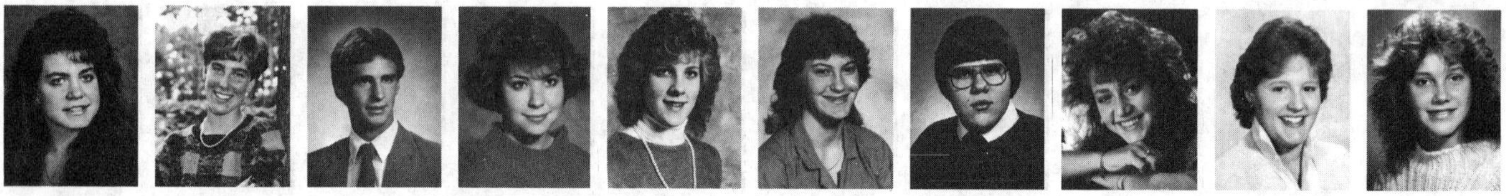

Volack, Susan
Little Flower HS
Philadelphia, PA

Volmer, Stephanie
Pocono Mtn HS
Pocono Pines, PA

Vom Saal, Daniel
Penn Manor HS
Holtwood, PA

Voorhees, Dawn
Pen Argyl HS
Pen Argyl, PA

Voydik, Janene
Schuylkill Haven Area HS
Schuylkill Haven, PA

Voyszey, Sherri
Portage Area HS
Portage, PA

Vranjes, Jr Daniel
Hickory HS
Hermitage, PA

Vullo, Tamara Ann
Riverside HS
Taylor, PA

Wachala, Jennifer
Sacred Heart HS
Pittsburgh, PA

Wacik, Christine Ann
Freedom HS
Bethlehem, PA

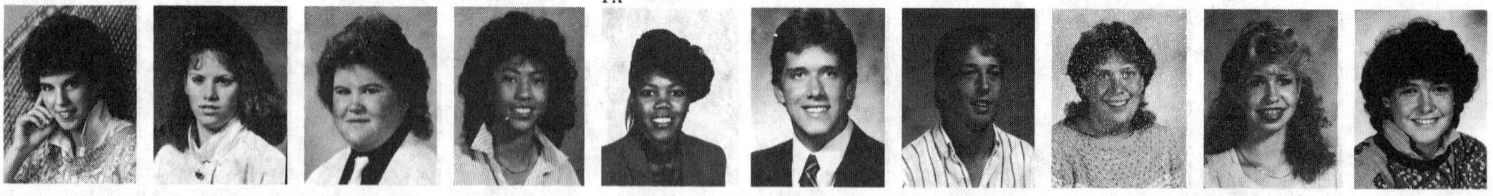

Waclawik, Christine
Cambridge Springs
Cambridge Spg, PA

Wadatz, Ashley
Western Beaver HS
Industry, PA

Wadding, Barbara
Penns Manor HS
Indiana, PA

Wade, Audrey
Upper Dublin HS
Ft Washington, PA

Wade, Lynnette S
Harrisburg HS
Harrisburg, PA

Wadsworth, Jeff
Connellsville Area
Scottdale, PA

Wadsworth, Joseph
Lock Haven SR HS
Beech Creek, PA

Wagaman, Dawn
Brandywine Heights
Mertztown, PA

Wagman, Shelly M
West York Area HS
York, PA

Wagner, Cathy
Dover Area HS
Dover, PA

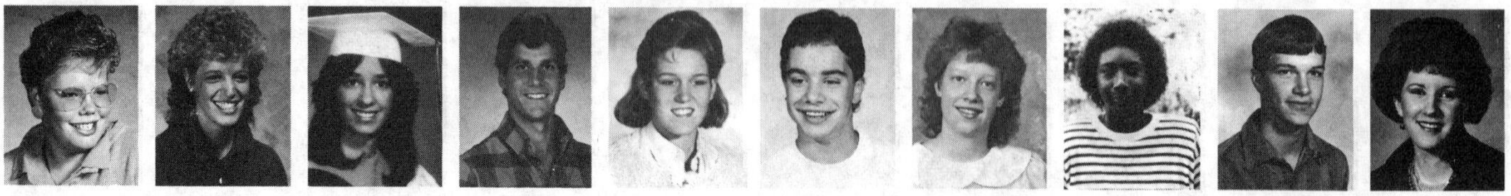

Wagner, Cristine
Ambridge Area HS
Freedom, PA

Wagner, Kris
Solanco HS
Quarryville, PA

Wagner, Robyn
Freedom HS
Bethlehem, PA

Wagstaff, Brian
Elizabeth Forward
Elizabeth, PA

Waid, Lisa
Meadville Area SR
Meadville, PA

Walch, Jeffrey J
North Allegheny HS
Wexford, PA

Waldron, Mary
Fort Le Boeuf HS
Waterford, PA

Waldrop, Danielle R
Friends Central Schl
Norristown, PA

Waleff, Stevan
Reynolds HS
Greenville, PA

Walker, Colleen E
Monogahela Valley Catholic HS
Charleroi, PA

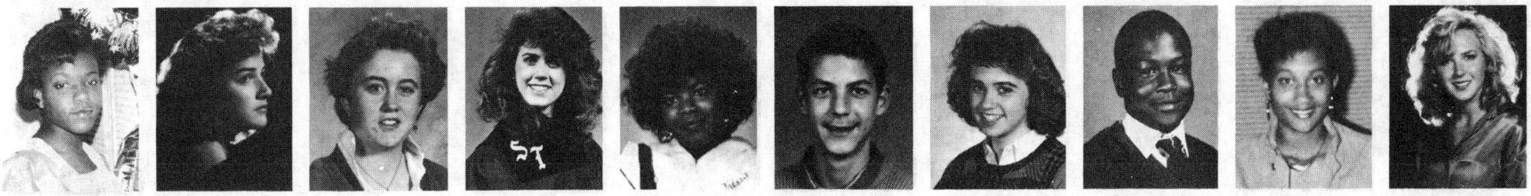

Walker, Glynda
Pine Forge Acad
Capitol Hgts, MD

Walker, Jean
Avon Grove HS
Landenberg, PA

Walker, Kristen
Archbishop Carroll
Narberth, PA

Walker, Lisa
Susquehanna
Township HS
Harrisburg, PA

Walker, Raissa
Pennsbury HS
Fairless Hls, PA

Walker, William K
Central Dauphin HS
Linglestown, PA

Wallace, Angie
Downingtown HS
Downington, PA

Wallace, Austin
Germantown HS
Philadelphia, PA

Wallace, Claire
Harriton HS
Bryn Mawr, PA

Wallace, Sheila S
Avon Grove HS
West Grove, PA

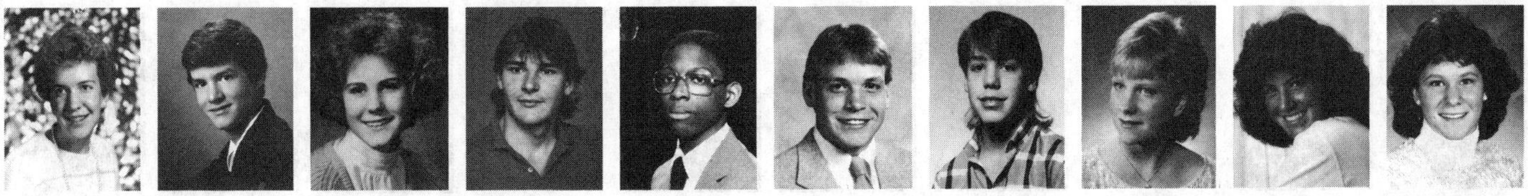

Wallace, Suzanne
Central Cambria HS
Colver, PA

Wallander,
Raymond Russell
State College Area
Boalsburg, PA

Wallitsch, Amy
Notre Dame HS
Easton, PA

Walls, Dave
Lawerence Co
Ellwood City, PA

Walsh, Jermaine
Central High/
Cheltenham HS
Laverock, PA

Walsh, John
Trinity HS
Mechanicsburg, PA

Walsh, Justin
Mon Valley Catholic
Donora, PA

Walsh, Laurene
Center Area HS
Monaca, PA

Walsh, Maureen
Seneca Valley HS
Renfrew, PA

Walsh, Tricia
Seneca Valley SR
Renfrew, PA

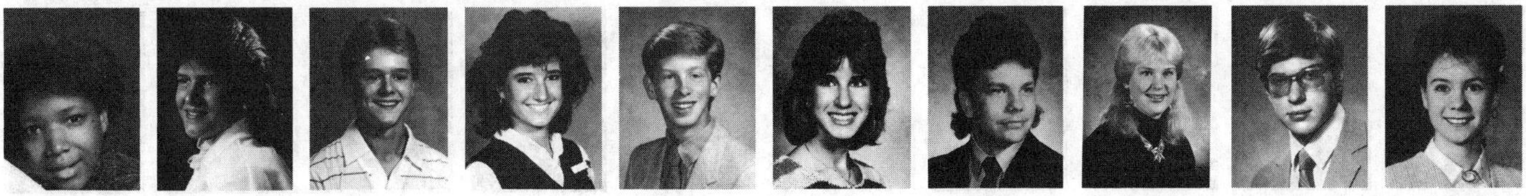

Walston, Natalie
West Catholic Girls
Philadelphia, PA

Walter, Amy
Penn Manor HS
Holtwood, PA

Walter, Brian
Mifflinburg Area HS
Lewisburg, PA

Walter, Cynthia
Nazareth Acad
Langhorne, PA

Walter, Mark
Nazareth Area SR
Nazareth, PA

Walter, Tara
Nazareth Academy
Langhorne, PA

Walters, Brian
Monessen SR HS
Monessen, PA

Walters, Carrie
Tunkhannock Area
Tunkhannock, PA

Walters, Dave
New Wilmington
Area HS
Edinburg, PA

Walters, Janet
Monongahela Valley
Catholic HS
New Eagle, PA

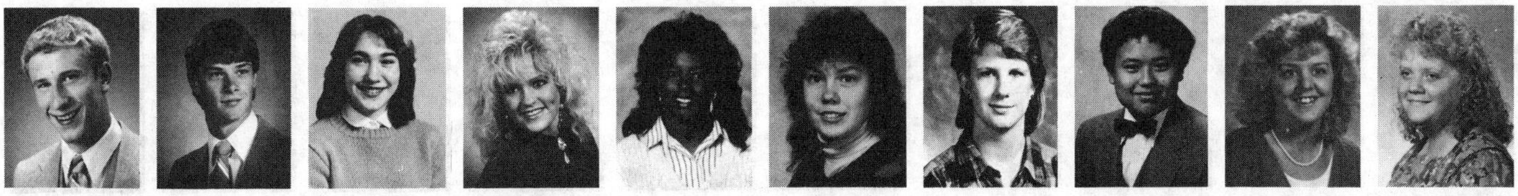

Walters, Lowell
Northern Bedford
County HS
Bakers Summit, PA

Walters, Steven
Muncy HS
Muncy, PA

Waltman, Crystal
Blue Mountain HS
Orwigsburg, PA

Walton, Diane
North Hills HS
Pittsburgh, PA

Walton, Lauren
Hampton HS
Allison Pk, PA

Waltz, Catharine
Warwick HS
Lititz, PA

Wamboldt, Amy
Mercer Area HS
Mercer, PA

Wang, Leonard L H
Abington Hts HS
Clarks Summit, PA

Wanner, Lynn
Cocalico HS
Reinholds, PA

Warcholik, Eileen
Venango Christian
Franklin, PA

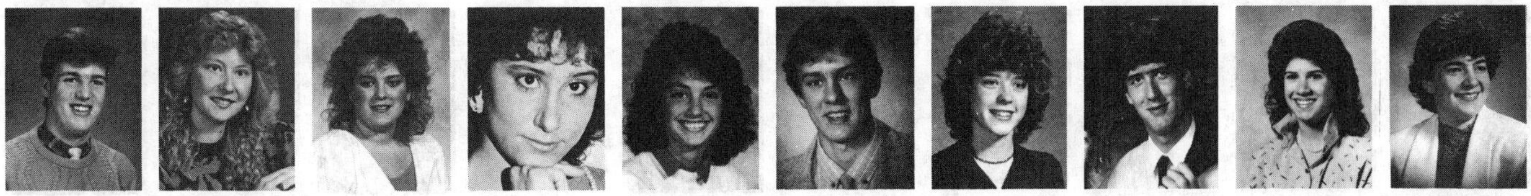

Ward, James T W
Open Door Christian
Greensburg, PA

Ward, Sabine
Belle Vernon Area
Belle Vernon, PA

Ward, Tracy
Frazier HS
Grindstone, PA

Ward, Tricia
Purchase Line HS
Commodore, PA

Warder, Kelly
Chichester SR HS
Trainer, PA

Wardle, Brian L
Upper Perkiomen
East Greenville, PA

Ware, Dawn
Sun Valley HS
Aston, PA

Wareham, Gregory S
Gateway SR HS
Pitcairn, PA

Warfel, Cynthia
North Allegheny HS
Wexford, PA

Wargo, Francine
Monongahela Valley
Catholic HS
West Brownsville,
PA

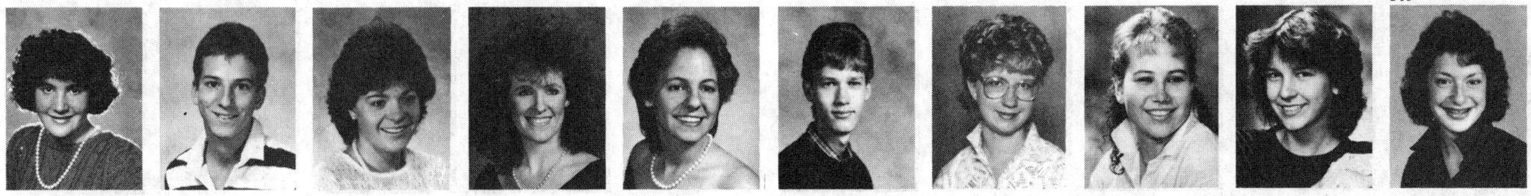

Wargo, Michelle C
Monongahela Valley
Catholic HS
West Brownsville,
PA

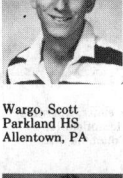

Wargo, Scott
Parkland HS
Allentown, PA

Warholic, Lynne
Renns Manor HS
Clymer, PA

Waring, Christine
Little Flower HS
Philadelphia, PA

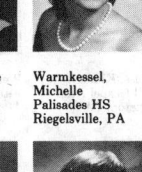

Warmkessel,
Michelle
Palisades HS
Riegelsville, PA

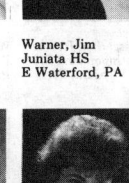

Warner, Jim
Juniata HS
E Waterford, PA

Warner, Rebecca
Lebanon Catholic
Palmyra, PA

Warntz, Lisa
Danville SR HS
Danville, PA

Warntz, Lori
Danville SR HS
Danville, PA

Warren, Allison
Franklin SR HS
Franklin, PA

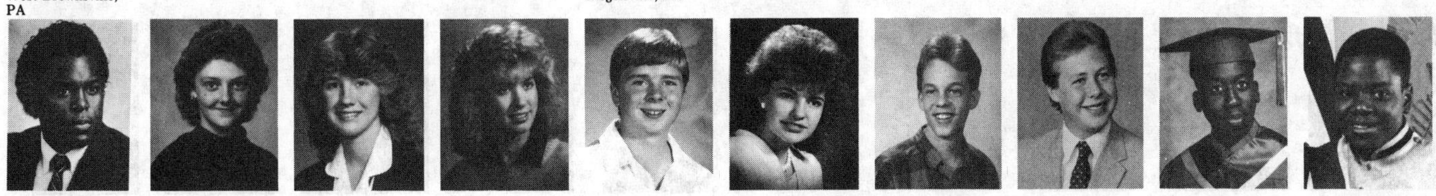

Warren, Kevin Eric
Middletown Area
Middletown, PA

Warring, Jeanette
Forest City Regional
Pleasant Mount, PA

Wartzenluft, Jennie
Kutztown Area HS
Kutztown, PA

Warunek, Kimberly
Pittston Area SR
Dupont, PA

Warych, Ken
Richland HS
Gibsonia, PA

Wasco, Melanie A
Mon Valley C H S
Belle Vernon, PA

Wasczcak, Mike
West Scranton HS
Scranton, PA

Waselko, David
Kiski Area HS
Leechburg, PA

Washington, Marc
Roman Catholic HS
Philadelphia, PA

Washington, Rodney
Roman Catholic HS
Philadelphia, PA

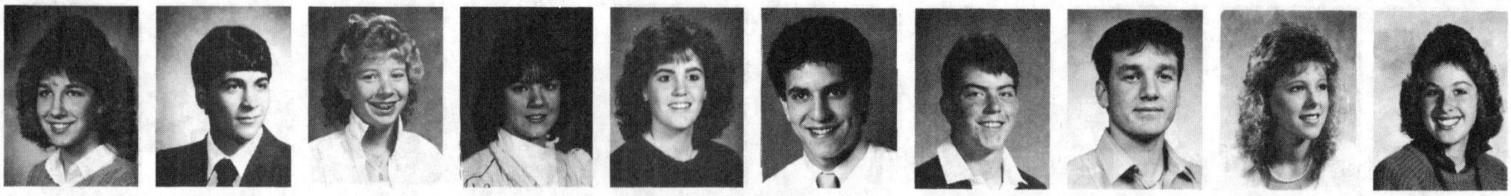

Wasilewski, Lisa
Hanover Area JR
SR HS
Wilkes Barre, PA

Wasilewski, Mike
Our Lady Of
Lourdes HS
Kulpmont, PA

Wasilitz, Ronda
Cedar Crest HS
Lebanon, PA

Waskiewicz, Vanessa
Bishop Conwell H S
For Girls
Levittown, PA

Wassel, Antoinette
Greensburg Central
Catholic HS
Murrysville, PA

Wasserman, Scott
Emmaus HS
Allentown, PA

Wasson, Steven M
Central Bucks HS
Chalfont, PA

Waters, Norman
Scotland School Vet
Media, PA

Watkins, Stacey
G A R Memorial HS
Wilkes-Barre, PA

Watson, Mari Lynne
Blacklick Valley
JR-SR HS
Nanty Glo, PA

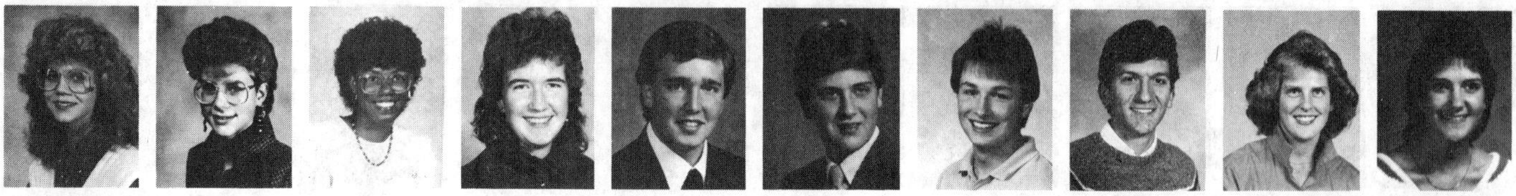

Watt, Katherine
Altoona Area HS
Altoona, PA

Watt, Regina
Altoona Area HS
Altoona, PA

Watts, Pamela
Oxford Area HS
Oxford, PA

Wawrzyniak, Cheryl
Villa Maria Acad
Erie, PA

Way, Charlie
Clearfield Area HS
Clearfield, PA

Way, Todd B
State College Area
SR HS
Lemont, PA

Wayman, Jeffrey
Susquehanna Comm
Susquehanna, PA

Weagraff, Marc
Saegertown Area HS
Saegertown, PA

Weatherby, Michelle
New Castle SR HS
New Castle, PA

Weaver, Amy
Lock Haven SR HS
Howard, PA

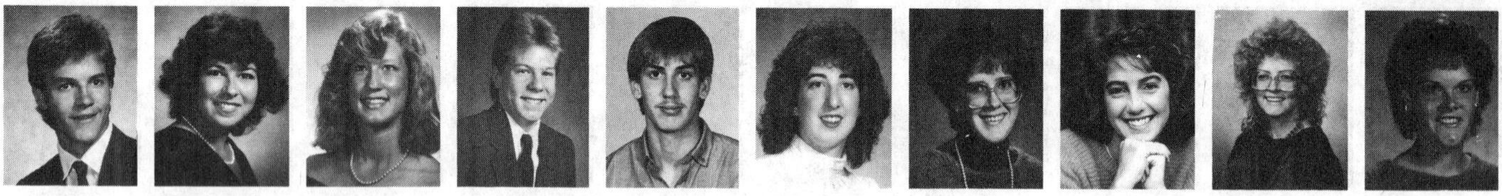

Weaver, Corey E
Garden Spot HS
New Holland, PA

Weaver, Donna
Garnet Valley HS
Boothwyn, PA

Weaver, Elizabeth
Abington SR HS
Meadowbrook, PA

Weaver, Eric
Morrisville HS
Morrisville, PA

Weaver, Matt
Sto-Rox SR HS
Mc Kees Rocks, PA

Weaver, Melissa
Northwestern
Lehigh HS
Germansville, PA

Weaver, Melodie
Sue
Grace Christian HS
Myerstown, PA

Weaver, Renee
Manheim Central
Manheim, PA

Weaver, Sahlee
Du Bois Area HS
Du Bois, PA

Weaver, Teresa
Cocalico HS
Denver, PA

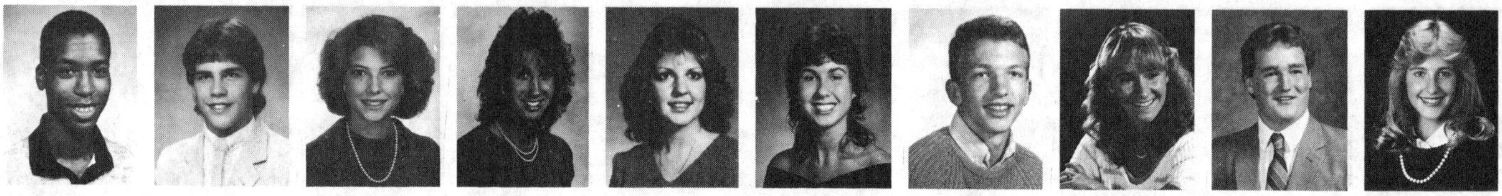

Webb, Gregory
Scotland Schl For
Veterans Children
Phila, PA

Webb, Kevin
Greater Johnstown
Area Vo Tech Schl
Johnstown, PA

Webber, Audrey
The Mercersburg
Hickory, NC

Weber, Amy
Phil-Mont Christian
Warrington, PA

Weber, Cynthia
Jean
Ambridge Area SR
Ambridge, PA

Weber, Jennifer
Phil-Mont Christian
Warrington, PA

Weber, Leroy
Coatesville Area SR
Thorndale, PA

Weber, Melissa
Towanda Area HS
Towanda, PA

Webster, Michael
Philipsburg-Osceola
Area SR HS
Philipsburg, PA

Wechs, Holly
Central HS
Martinsburg, PA

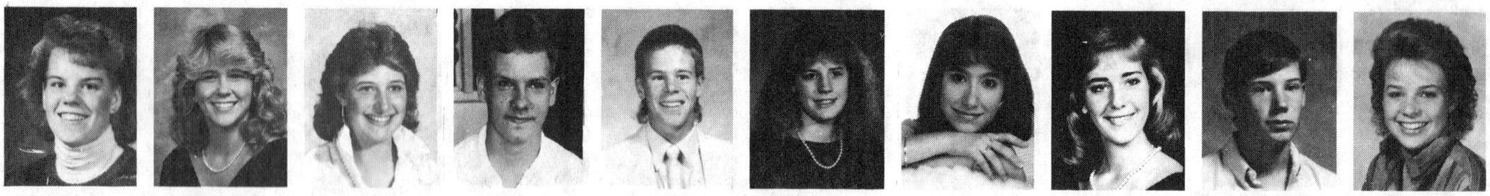

Weder, Dave
Northern York
County HS
Dillsburg, PA

Weedman, Diana
State College Area
State College, PA

Weibley, Jody
West Perry HS
Ickesburg, PA

Weibley, Robert
West Perry HS
Ickesburg, PA

Weidner, Matthew
Cumberland Valley
Mechanicsburg, PA

Weidner, Peggy
Fleetwood HS
Fleetwood, PA

Weigle, Tamara
Northern HS
Dillsburg, PA

Weigler, Jill Colleen
Sacred Heart HS
Pittsburgh, PA

Weikert, Brian
Biglerville HS
Arendtsville, PA

Weinberg, Carin
William Allen HS
Allentown, PA

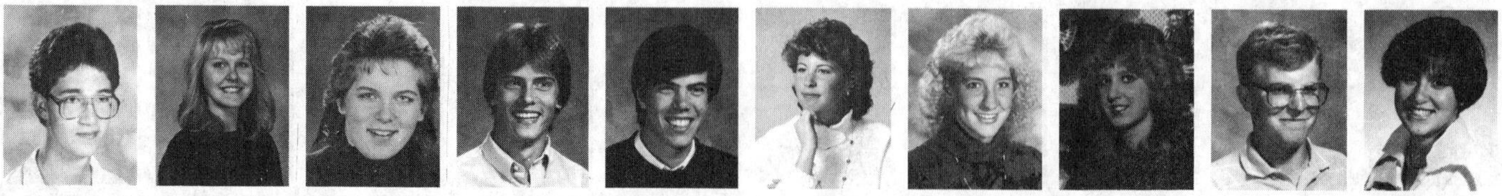

Weir, Jennifer
Washington HS
Washington, PA

Weir, Linda L
Mount Saint Joseph
Flourtown, PA

Weirich, Denise L
Northeastern HS
Manchester, PA

Weise, Kenneth
Mastbaum Tech HS
Philadelphia, PA

Weisgerber, Robert
Southmoreland SR
Mt Pleasant, PA

Weiss, Kimberly A
Full Gospel Acad
Pittston, PA

Weiss, Sandra M
Altoona Area HS
Altoona, PA

Weiss, Stephanie
St Pius X HS
Pottstown, PA

Weisser, Christian
Hempfield HS
Columbia, PA

Weit, Le Anne
Warwick HS
Lititz, PA

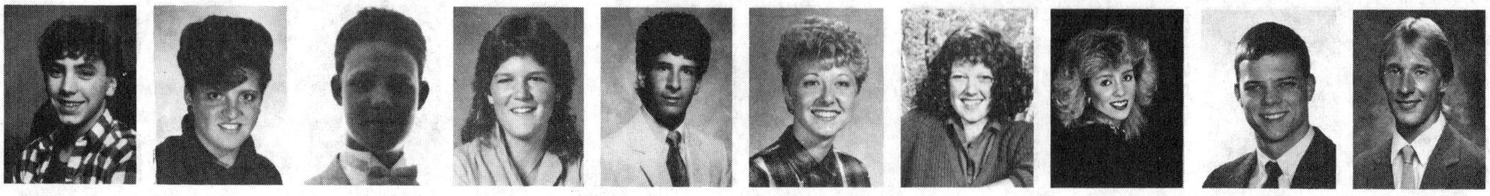

Weitkamp, Clyde
Dover Area HS
East Berlin, PA

Weitkamp, Tara
Dover Area HS
Dover, PA

Welch, Andrew C
St John Neumann
Philadelphia, PA

Welch, Anna
Downingtown SR
Downingtown, PA

Welker, Jim
Shaler Area HS
Pgh, PA

Weller, Monica
Boyertown SR HS
Perkiomenville, PA

Wellman, Sally
Athens HS
Athens, PA

Wells, Lisa
Saltsburg JRSR HS
Saltsburg, PA

Welty, James
Boiling Springs HS
Boiling Spgs, PA

Wendel, Stephen
St Marys Area HS
Saint Marys, PA

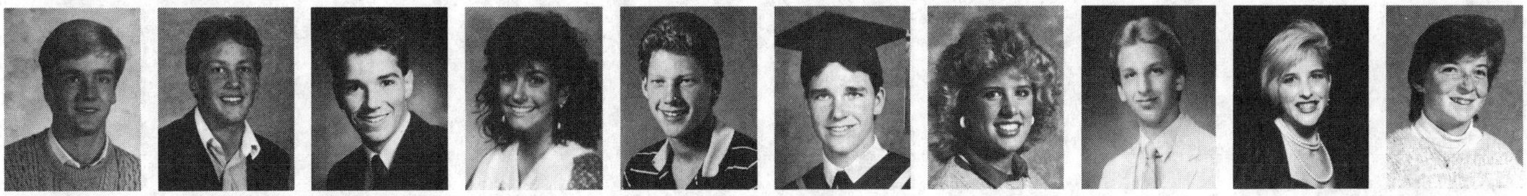

Wenger, Kent
Solanco HS
Quarryville, PA

Wenrich, Jr Carl
Avon Grove HS
Kemblesville, PA

Wentland, Jacob J
North Pocono HS
Moscow, PA

Wentzel, Jeanene
Warwick HS
Lititz, PA

Wenzel, Mark
Wilhelm
North Allegheny HS
Pittsburgh, PA

Wermuth, Charles
Father Judge HS
Philadelphia, PA

Werner, Cathryn
Pine Grove Area HS
Pine Grove, PA

Werner, James Paul
Ambridge Area HS
Sewickley, PA

Werner, Lisa
Quakertown
Community HS
Quakertown, PA

Wernersbach, Lori
Ann
Methacton HS
Norristown, PA

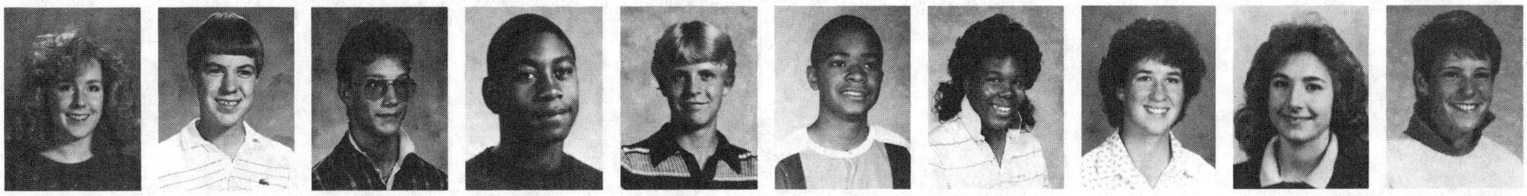

Wert, Anne
Daniel Boone HS
Birdsboro, PA

Wert, Michael
Cumberland Valley
Mechanicsburg, PA

Wertz, Matthew
Cedar Cliff HS
New Cumberland,
PA

Wesley, Rasheed
Scotland Schl For
Veterans Children
Chester, PA

West, Larry
Southern Columbia
Catawissa, PA

West, Myron
Chester HS
Chester, PA

West, Nicole A
Mt St Joseph Acad
Philadelphia, PA

Westcott, Marti
Neshannock HS
New Castle, PA

Westergom, Kathy
Kiski Area HS
Vandergrift, PA

Wethman, Kathleen
Downingtown HS
Exton, PA

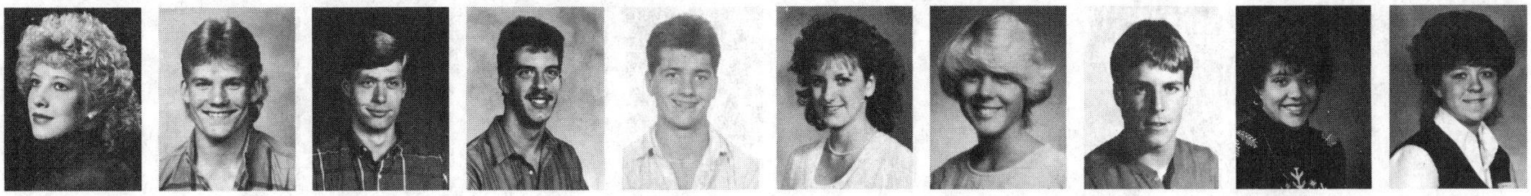

Wetzel, Brenda
Reynolds HS
Fredonia, PA

Wetzel, Bryan
Curwensville HS
Curwensville, PA

Wetzel, Rich
Fairfield HS
Fairfield, PA

Wetzler, Dave
Juniata HS
Mifflintown, PA

Whalen, James
Monsignor Bonner
Drexel Hill, PA

Whalen, Sherry
Immaculate
Conception HS
Canonsburg, PA

Wheatley, Megan
Elizabeth
Wyoming Valley
West HS
Kingston, PA

Wheeler, Bruce
Penn Cambria HS
Lilly, PA

Wheeler, Jennifer
Washington HS
Washington, PA

Wheeler, Linda
Nazareth Acad
Phila, PA

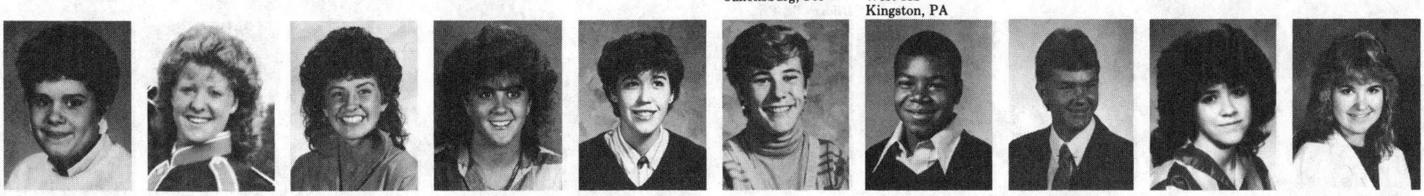

Wheland, Tammy
Tyrone Area HS
Tyrone, PA

Wherry, Jacqueline
Western Beaver HS
Beaver, PA

Whetung, Carla
Brandywine Heights
Topton, PA

Whitaker, Amy
Penn Trafford HS
Trafford, PA

Whitcomb, Christina
Boiling Springs HS
Boiling Spgs, PA

Whitcomb, Krena
South Middleton HS
Boiling Spgs, PA

White, Brian K
Valley HS
New Kensington,
PA

White, Danny
Uniontown Area SR
Vanderbilt, PA

White, Gina
Abington Heights-N
Campus HS
Clarks Summit, PA

White, Kim
Pocono Mountain
Canadensis, PA

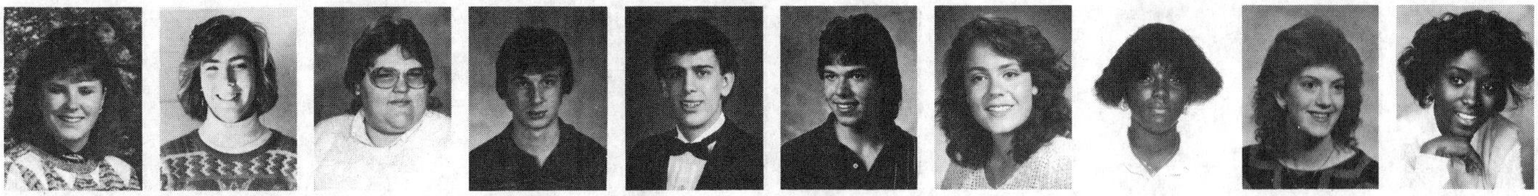

White, Leann
Clearfield Area HS
Olanta, PA

White, Martha-Lynn
Haverford HS
Bryn Mawr, PA

White, Mary Beth
Rocky Grove JR/SR
Franklin, PA

White, Mike
Fort Cherry HS
Bulger, PA

White, Paul
Monsignor Bonner
Lansdowne, PA

White, Philip
Trinity HS
Washington, PA

White, Robyn L
Taylor Allderdice
Pittsburgh, PA

White, Tamara
Lutheran HS
Philadelphia, PA

White, Theresa
Pittston Area HS
Pittston, PA

White, Tobi
Lutheran HS
Philadelphia, PA

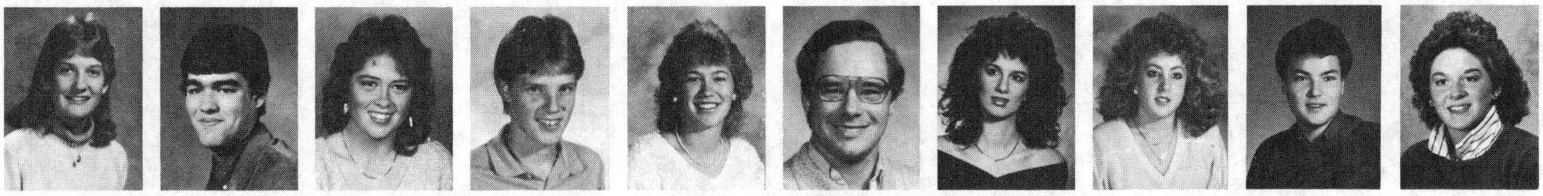

Whitenight, Rebecca
Danville JR HS
Danville, PA

Whitford, Jeffrey
Moon Area SR HS
Coraopolis, PA

Whiting, Michonda
Wilmington Area
New Wilmington,
PA

Whitmoyer, Jeremy
R
Northern Lebanon
Lebanon, PA

Whitney, Janet
Purchase Line HS
Commodore, PA

Whitney, Stewart
Mountain View HS
Gibson, PA

Whitson, S Lynne
Villa Maria Acad
Brookhaven, PA

Whittaker, Suzanne
Jules E Mastbaum
Philadelphia, PA

Why, II Frank
Beaver Falls HS
Beaver Falls, PA

Whyte, Christy
Jefferson Morgan
Waynesburg, PA

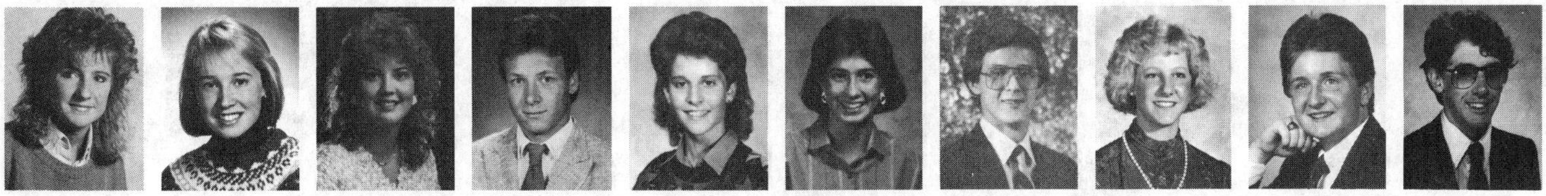

Wickkiser, Elisabeth
Allentown Central
Catholic HS
Allentown, PA

Wieluns, Dana Carle
Great Valley HS
Newtown Square,
PA

Wiemann, Kimberly
Seneca Valley HS
Renfrew, PA

Wiest, William
Spring Grove Area
SR HS
Porters Sideling, PA

Wiewiora, Joy
Northern Cambria
Barnesboro, PA

Wike, Lisa M
Cedar Crest HS
Lebanon, PA

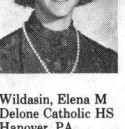

Wilburn, Tony
Salisbury Elk Lick
JR SR HS
Salisbury, PA

Wildasin, Elena M
Delone Catholic HS
Hanover, PA

Wilds, Jeffrey L
Norwin SR HS
N Huntingdon, PA

Wiley, III John A
Yough SR HS
W Newton, PA

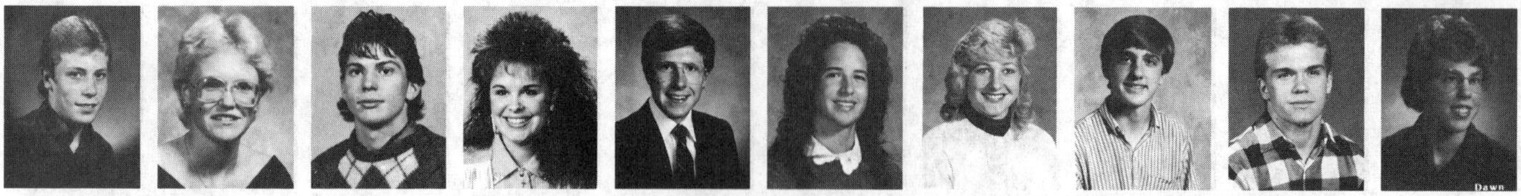

Wilhelm, Chris
Central Dauphin HS
Harrisburg, PA

Wilhelm, Lisa M
Chichester SR HS
Boothwyn, PA

Wilk, Tom
Canon Mc Millan
Eighty Four, PA

Wilkes, Michelle
Lakeland HS
Jermyn, PA

Wilkins, Christopher I
Bethel Park SR HS
Bethel Park, PA

Wilkins, Pamela
Middletown Area
Middletown, PA

Wilkinson, Lisa
West Branch HS
Munson, PA

Will, Corey
Berlin Brothers Valley HS
Berlin, PA

Willard, Daniel
Upper Daupin Area
Gratz, PA

Willheim, Dawn
Hanover HS
Hanover, PA

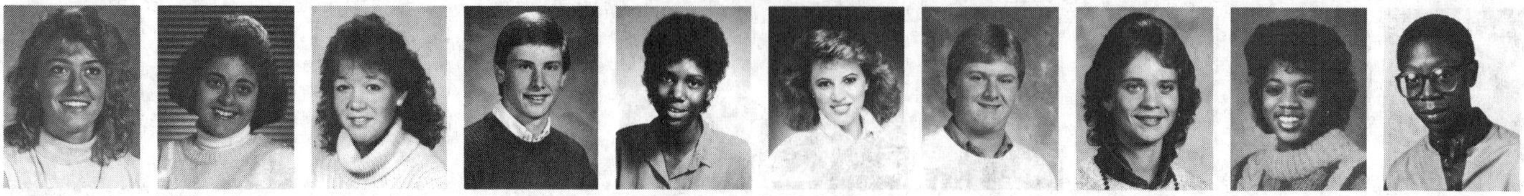

Williams, Andrea
Downingtown HS
Chester Springs, PA

Williams, Ardoth
Northern Bedford County HS
Hopewell, PA

Williams, Carey
Warwick HS
Lititz, PA

Williams, Cecil
Moniteau HS
Parker, PA

Williams, Cheryl
William Allen HS
Allentown, PA

Williams, Christine
East Allegheny HS
East Mc Keesport, PA

Williams, Christopher
Kennedy Christian
W Middlesex, PA

Williams, Claudette
Danville HS
Riverside, PA

Williams, Conreau
Steel Valley HS
Homestead, PA

Williams, Corey
Churchill HS
Braddock, PA

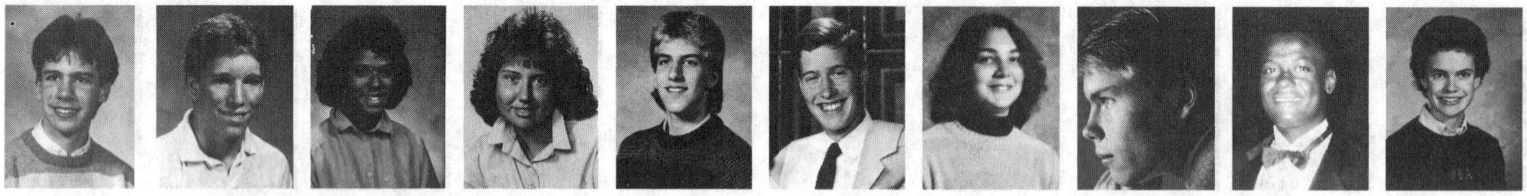

Williams, David
Monongahela Valley Catholic HS
Monessen, PA

Williams, David
West Branch Area
Winburne, PA

Williams, Denise
Indiana Area HS
Indiana, PA

Williams, Desiree
Riverside SR HS
Ellwood City, PA

Williams, Jr Donald R
South Fayette Township HS
Bridgeville, PA

Williams, Douglas A
Avonworth HS
Pittsburgh, PA

Williams, Geralyn
Dallas SR HS
Shaverstown, PA

Williams, H Clinton
Mars Area SR HS
Mars, PA

Williams, III James N
Central Catholic HS
Pittsburgh, PA

Williams, Jean-Michelle
St Basil Acad
Philadelphia, PA

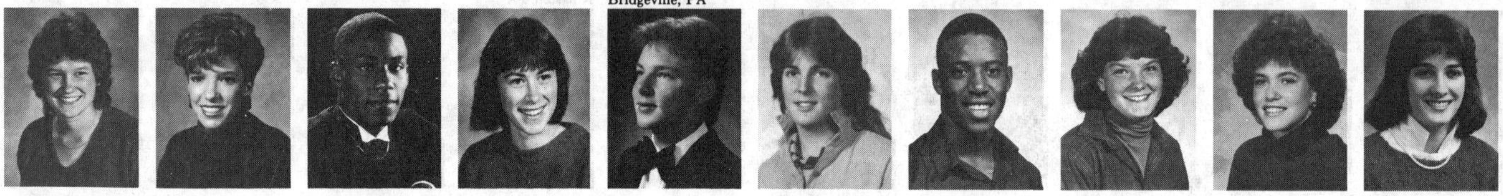

Williams, Jennifer
Johnsonburg Area
Wilcox, PA

Williams, Jennifer A
Moon SR HS
Coraopolis, PA

Williams, Keith
Trinity Christian
Pittsburgh, PA

Williams, Kelly
Corry Area HS
Corry, PA

Williams, Ken
Muhlenberg SR HS
Laureldale, PA

Williams, Kristin
Susquehanna Community HS
Starrucca, PA

Williams, Lamar
Scotland School For Vets Children
Philadelphia, PA

Williams, Megan
Lake Lehman HS
Sweet Valley, PA

Williams, Michele
Bald Eagle-Nittany
Beech Creek, PA

Williams, Michele
Trinity HS
Mechanicsburg, PA

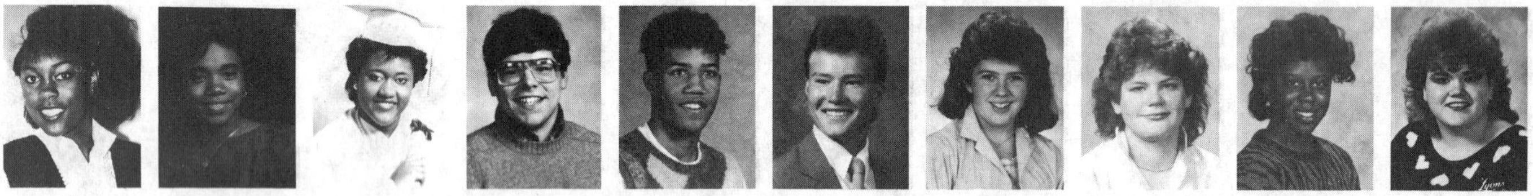

Williams, Nicole
Penncrest HS
Media, PA

Williams, Paula
Carver HS Of Engineering
Philadelphia, PA

Williams, Riad P
Lower Merion HS
Wynnewood, PA

Williams, II Roy E
Nazareth Area SR
Nazareth, PA

Williams, Stephen
Henderson SR HS
Westchester, PA

Williams, Steven
Bradford Central Christian HS
Bradford, PA

Williams, Tammy
Elizabeth Forward
Monongahela, PA

Williams, Terri
West Scranton HS
Scranton, PA

Williams, Tricia
Abington SR HS
Roslyn, PA

Williams, Wendy
Grand Army Of The
Wilkes-Barre, PA

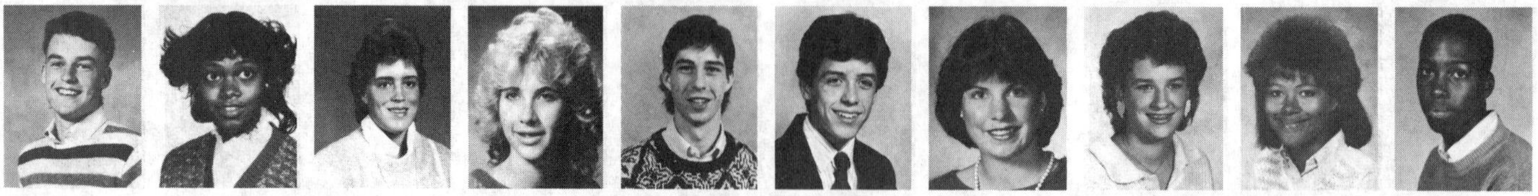

Williamson, Brad
South Fayette HS
Bridgeville, PA

Williamson, Valecia
Harrisburg HS
Harrisburg, PA

Williard, Stephanie
Upper Dauphin Area HS
Lykens, PA

Wilson, Beth
Emmaus HS
Wescosville, PA

Wilson, Christian
Kiski Area HS
Lower Burrell, PA

Wilson, IV Gabriel J
Devon Prep
Exton, PA

Wilson, Heather A
Mt Lebanon HS
Pittsburgh, PA

Wilson, Jenny
Blairsville SR HS
Blairsville, PA

Wilson, Kellie
Young SR HS
W Newton, PA

Wilson, Malik
Central York SR HS
York, PA

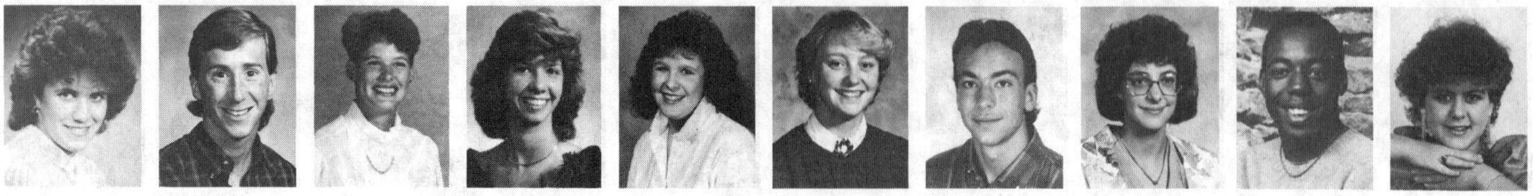

Wilson, Shannon
Mt Pleasant HS
Greensburg, PA

Wilson, Thomas K R
Quakertown SR HS
Quakertown, PA

Wilson, Traci
Henderson HS
W Chester, PA

Wilt, Cheryl
Lower Bucks Christian Acad
Huntingdon Vly, PA

Wilt, Lori
Altoona Area HS
Altoona, PA

Wilt, Sandy
York Suburban HS
York, PA

Wilt, Steven
Dover Area HS
Dover, PA

Wimmer, Maureen
Danville SR HS
Danville, PA

Windom, Robert
Central Dauphin HS
Harrisburg, PA

Winebarger, Glenda
Northern Lebanon
Jonestown, PA

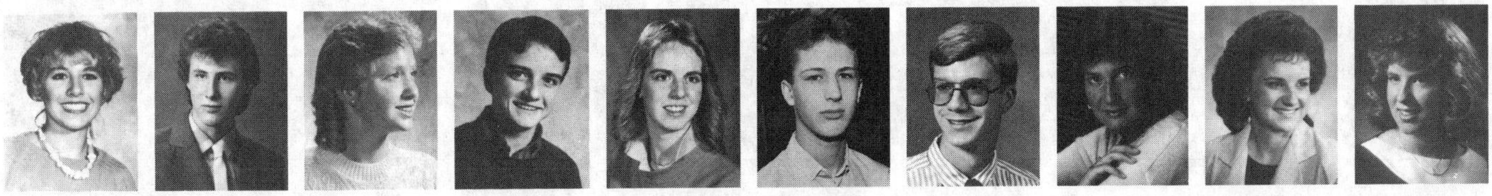

Wing, Susan
Portersville
Christian Schl
Hamburg, IA

Wingard, Barry
Brookville Area HS
Brookville, PA

Wingard, Shelly
Connellsville Area
Dunbar, PA

Wingle, Craig
Sch Haven HS
Sch Haven, PA

Winslow, Melissa
Union JR SR HS
Rimersburg, PA

Winsock, Mark
Wyoming Area HS
W Wyoming, PA

Winter, Alexis
William Penn SR
York, PA

Winterhalter, Megan
Seneca Valley HS
Mars, PA

Wintermantel, Mary
Avonworth JR-SR
Pittsbg, PA

Winters, Jeanne
Mt Calvary
Christian Schl
Manheim, PA

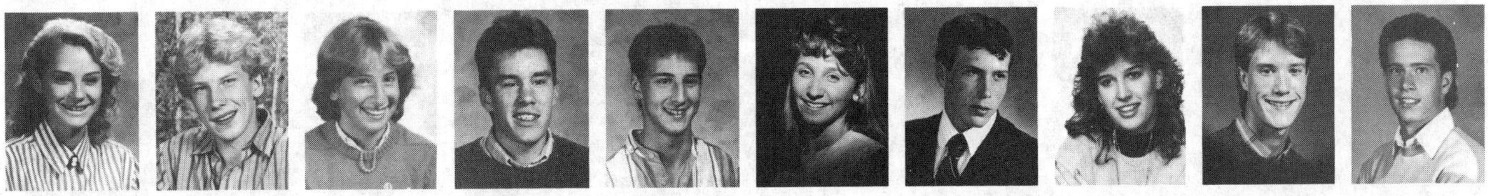

Winters, Patricia
Lancaster
Mennonite HS
Lancaster, PA

Winterton, Scott
Northeast Bradford
RD 1 HS
Rome, PA

Winzer, Donna
Emmaus HS
Macungie, PA

Wirt, Andrew
Christian Schl Of
York, PA

Wise, John
Cedar Crest HS
Lebanon, PA

Wise, Stacey
Valley HS
New Kensington,
PA

Wisner, Kevin
South Western HS
Glen Rock, PA

Wisniewski,
Michelle
Mid-Valley HS
Olyphant, PA

Wissler, Jr William
H
Central Dauphin HS
Harrisburg, PA

Withers, Brian
Northern Cambria
Barnesboro, PA

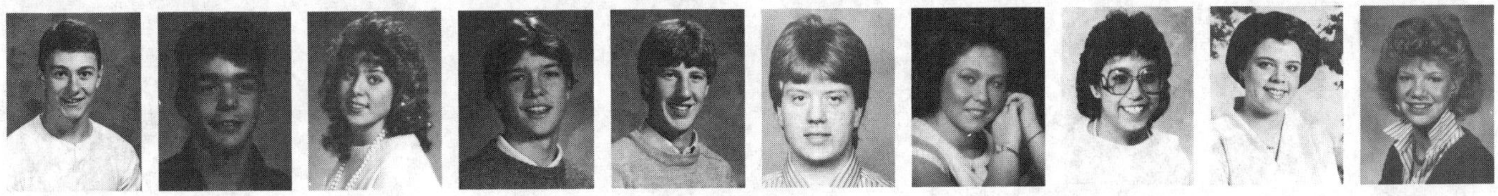

Witmer, James
Newport HS
Liverpool, PA

Witmer, Matthew R
Garden Spot HS
Terre Hill, PA

Witt, Natalie
Shamokin Area HS
Shamokin, PA

Wittebort, Ronald A
Butler SR HS
Butler, PA

Woerner, Robert P
Biglerville HS
Biglerville, PA

Wojciechowski,
Jeffrey
Shamokin Area HS
Shamokin, PA

Wojnakowski, Pam
Villa Maria Acad
Erie, PA

Wojnarowski, Dyan
West Greene HS
Wind Ridge, PA

Wolensky, Sue
Bishop O Reilly HS
Luzerne, PA

Woleslagle, Holly
Altoona Area HS
Altoona, PA

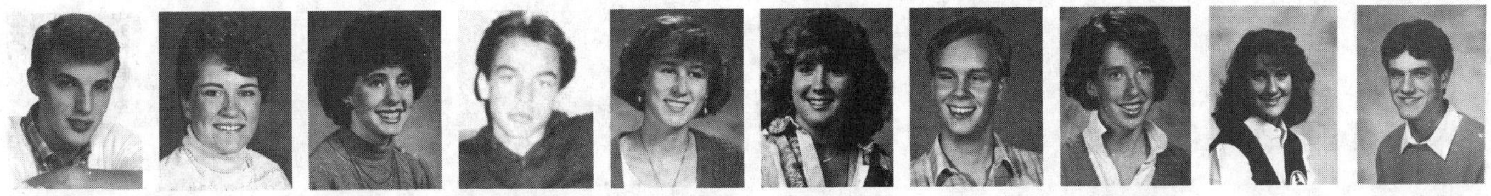

Wolf, III Donald
Henry
Palmyra Area HS
Palmyra, PA

Wolf, Jill
Ephrata HS
Ephrata, PA

Wolf, Michele
Langley HS
Pittsburgh, PA

Wolf, Raymond
Frankford HS
Philadelphia, PA

Wolf, Stephanie
Kennard-Dale HS
Stewartstown, PA

Wolfe, Brenda
Eisenhower HS
Russell, PA

Wolfe, Don
Laurel Highlands
Uniontown, PA

Wolfe, Heather
Governor Mifflin SR
Reading, PA

Wolfe, Kristin
Trinity HS
Camp Hill, PA

Wolfe, Matthew
Blair County
Christian HS
Hollidaysburg, PA

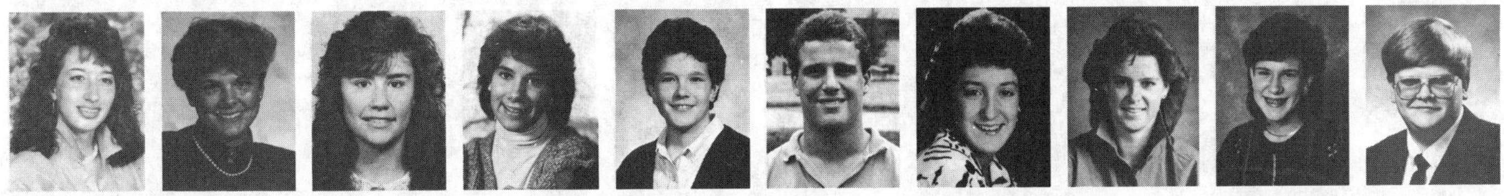

Wolfe, Michelle
Bishop Hoban HS
Mountain Top, PA

Wolfe, Pam
Carlisle SR HS
Carlisle, PA

Wolfe, Tami
Southern Columbia
Area HS
Catawissa, PA

Wolfe, Wendi Sue
Conestoga Valley
Ephrata, PA

Wolford, Cathy
Belle Vernon Area
Belle Vernon, PA

Wolford, Gary
Kiskiminetas
Springs Schl
Lower Burrell, PA

Womeldorf, Carmen
Montgomery Area
Montgomery, PA

Womer, Wendy
Loyalsock Twsp HS
Montoursville, PA

Wonderling,
Heather
Cheswick Christian
Natrona Hts, PA

Wood, Shawn
Corry Area HS
Corry, PA

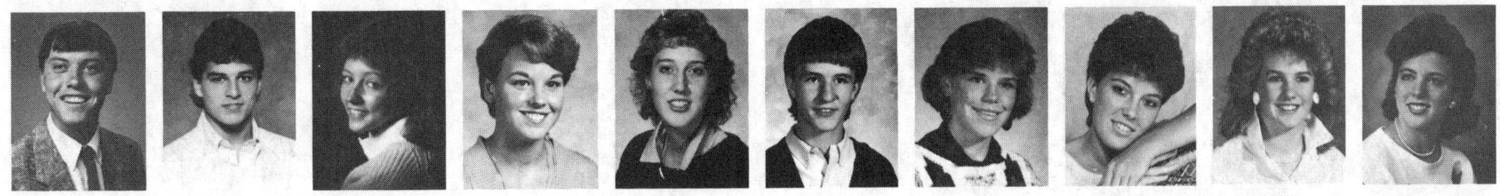

Woodlief, Gregory
Waynesboro Area
SR HS
Fayetteville, PA

Woodring, John
Tamaqua Area HS
Tamaqua, PA

Woodring, Tammy
Philipsburg-Osceola
Osceola Mills, PA

Woodruff, Kara
Danville SR HS
Danville, PA

Woods, Michelle
Parkland SR HS
Coplay, PA

Woodside,
Christopher
Danville SR HS
Danville, PA

Woodside, Donna
Council Rock HS
Newtown, PA

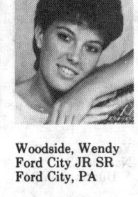

Woodside, Wendy
Ford City JR SR
Ford City, PA

Woodward, Bonnie
Bensalem HS
Bensalem, PA

Woodward,
Kimberly Anne
Tamaqua Area HS
Tamaqua, PA

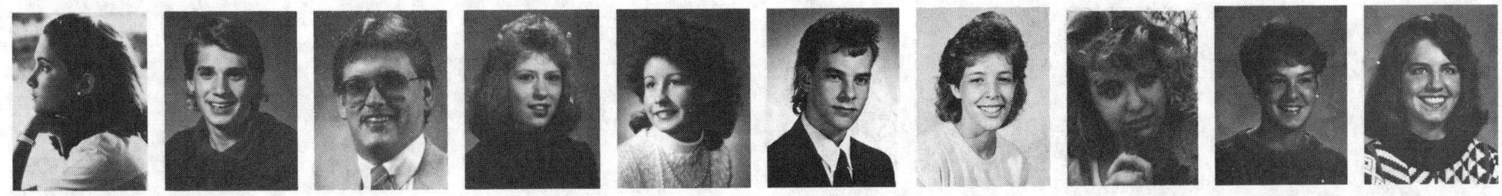

Woodward, Regina
Archbishop Carroll
Ardmore, PA

Wooley, James J
New Brighton Area
New Brighton, PA

Woomer, Scott
Altoona Area HS
Altoona, PA

Wooster, Melissa
West Branch Area
Hawk Run, PA

Worcester, Carol
Annville-Cleona HS
Annville, PA

Wordinger, James R
Abington HS
Glenside, PA

Workman, Audrey K
Mc Guffey HS
W Finley, PA

Worley, Jennifer
Southwestern HS
Hanover, PA

Worline, Kristi
Cocalico HS
Denver, PA

Worth, Tracy J
Christian School Of
Plymouth, MN

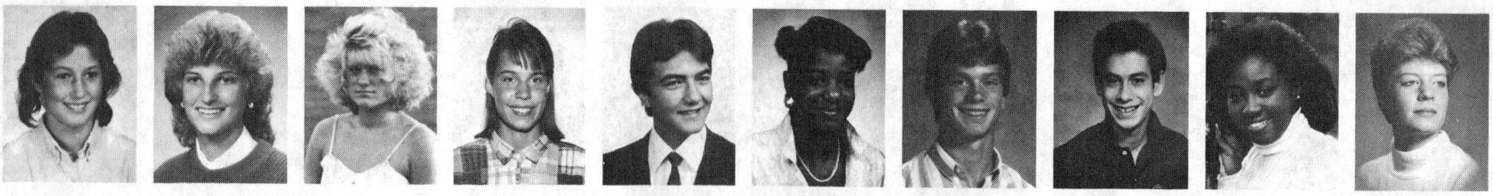

Wotring, Sherry
Parkland HS
Schnecksville, PA

Wozny, Christine
Windber Area HS
Windber, PA

Wray, Elizabeth
Trinity HS
Amity, PA

Wray, Yvonne
Danville SR HS
Danville, PA

Wriede, Chris
Steel Valley HS
West Homestead, PA

Wright, Dawn
Scotland Schl
Philadelphia, PA

Wright, Ernie
Danville HS
Danville, PA

Wright, Frederick
New Castle SR HS
New Castle, PA

Wright, Lendina
Winchester-Thurston HS
Pittsburgh, PA

Wright, Michelle
Council Rock HS
New Hope, PA

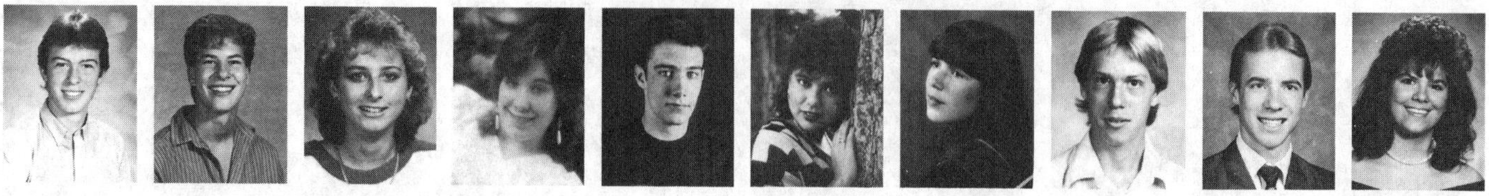

Wright, Richard
Seneca Valley HS
Mars, PA

Wright, Scott
Henderson HS
West Chester, PA

Wright, Stefanie
Claysburg Kimmel
Claysburg, PA

Wright, Teresa
West Greene
Middle-SR HS
Aleppo, PA

Wszolek, Steve
Valley Forge
Military Acad
Philadelphia, PA

Wu, Wendy L
Villa Maria HS
Edgerton, OH

Wukovitz, Stephanie W
Bloomsburg HS
Bloomsburg, PA

Wunderly, Michael
Nazareth SR HS
Nazareth, PA

Wus, John
Archbishop Wood
Warminster, PA

Wusinich, Nicole
Villa Maria Acad
Downingtown, PA

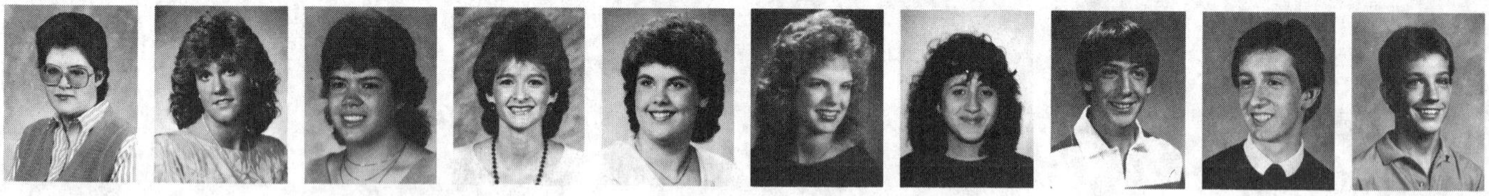

Wyandt, Mary A
Greater Johnstown
Johnstown, PA

Wyckoff, Susan
East Stroudsburg
East Stroudsburg, PA

Wyno, Penny
Penns Manor Area
Clymer, PA

Wysochanski, Faith
South Hiulls
Christian HS
Bethel Park, PA

Yackulich, Jennifer
Conemaugh Valley
JR SR HS
Park Hill, PA

Yadush, Ann Marie
Northampton SR
Walnutport, PA

Yamas, Kimberly
State College Area
Intermediat HS
State College, PA

Yamrick, Brad
Indiana SR HS
Indiana, PA

Yancich, John
Brownsville Area HS
Brownsville, PA

Yancisin, Matthew
Cedar Cliff HS
Camp Hill, PA

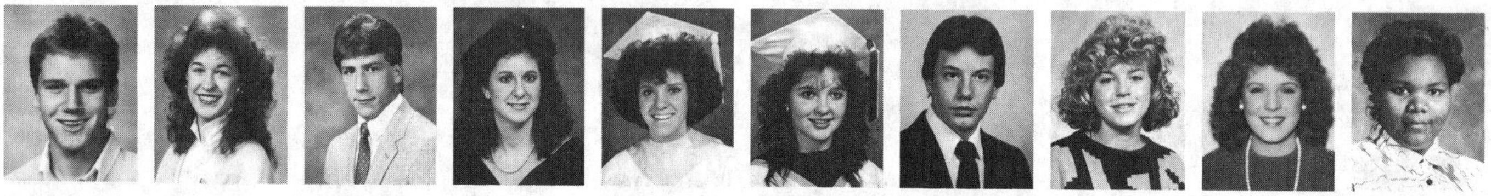

Yanek, William
Du Bois Area HS
Reynoldsville, PA

Yanik, Donalynn
West Scranton HS
Scranton, PA

Yannacci, Mike
Yough SR HS
Yukon, PA

Yannacone, Teresa
Cardinal Ohara HS
Media, PA

Yannatell, Sandra L
John W Hallahan
Catholic Girls HS
Philadelphia, PA

Yannuzzi, Andrea
St Huberts HS
Philadelphia, PA

Yanos, Jr Robert D
Owen J Roberts HS
Pottstown, PA

Yantek, Suzanne
Charleroi JR SR HS
Charleroi, PA

Yanulaitis, Marianne
N Pocono HS
Moscow, PA

Yarboro, Theresa
Kennedy Christian
W Middlesex, PA

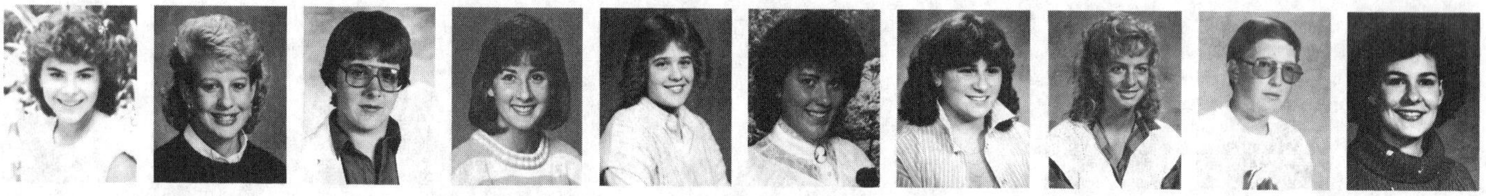

Yard, Amy
Rocky Grove HS
Franklin, PA

Yargar, Gretchen
Central Christian
Dubois, PA

Yarger, Keith
Milton HS
White Deer, PA

Yarnot, Amy
Moon SR HS
Coraopolis, PA

Yatsko, Sarah
Tunkhannock Area
Harveys Lake, PA

Yeager, Karen
Cambria Heights HS
Hastings, PA

Yeager, Melissa
Mount Pleasant HS
Stahlstown, PA

Yeakley, Sharon
Annville-Cleona HS
Annville, PA

Yeckley, Craig
Octorara Area HS
Coatesville, PA

Yeich, Jennifer
Exeter Township SR
Reading, PA

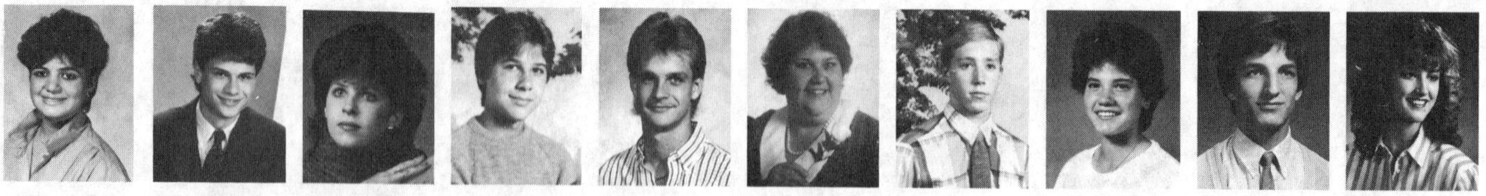

Yelagotes, Melissa Louise
Warwick HS
Lititz, PA

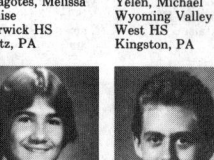

Yelen, Michael
Wyoming Valley
West HS
Kingston, PA

Yerace, Elizabeth
Norwin HS
N Huntingdon, PA

Yerashunas, Joseph
Bishop Oreilly HS
Edwardsville, PA

Yerkey, Brett
Belle Vernon Area
Belle Vernon, PA

Yetter, Tammy
Juniata HS
Mifflin, PA

Yingst, Jr Eric K
Mountain View
Christian School
Harrisburg, PA

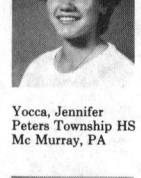

Yocca, Jennifer
Peters Township HS
Mc Murray, PA

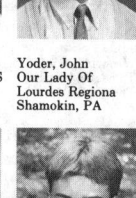

Yoder, John
Our Lady Of
Lourdes Regiona
Shamokin, PA

Yoders, Gretchen
Washington HS
Washington, PA

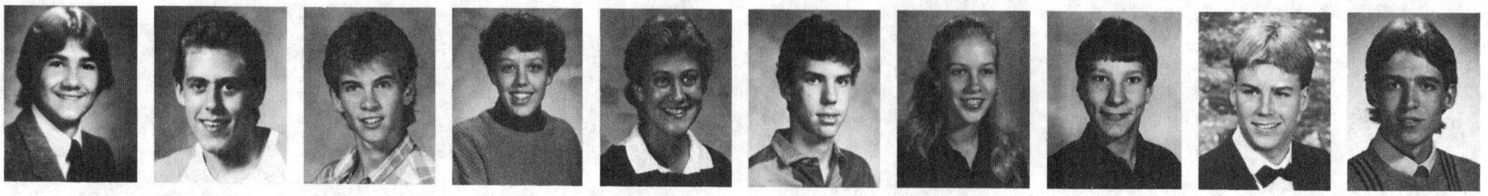

Yodis, Vincent
Neshaminy HS
Langhorne, PA

Yohe, Brian
Burrell HS
Lower Burrell, PA

Yohn, Brent
Southern
Huntingdon Count
Orbisonia, PA

Yough, Kelly
Bulter Area SR HS
Butler, PA

Young, Andrea
Lock Haven SR HS
Lock Haven, PA

Young, Barry
Nazareth HS
Tatamy, PA

Young, Christine
Lower Merion HS
Bala Cynwyd, PA

Young, Donnie
Cambridge Springs
Cambridge Springs, PA

Young, Douglas A
Scranton Prep
Clarks Summit, PA

Young, Greg M
Cedar Crest HS
Lebanon, PA

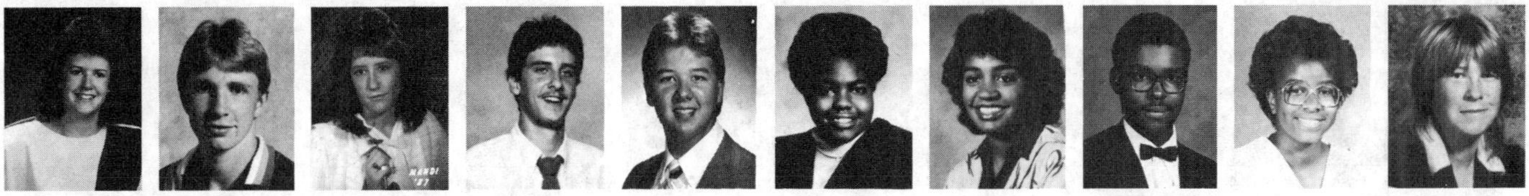

Young, Jennifer
Pennsbury HS
Levittown, PA

Young, Leslie
Berlin Brothers
Valley HS
Berlin, PA

Young, Mandie
Solanco HS
Drumore, PA

Young, Matthew
Hughesville HS
Muncy, PA

Young, Michael W
Spring Ford SR HS
Royersford, PA

Young, Michelle O
The Philadelphia
HS For Girls
Philadelphia, PA

Young, Nicole
West Allegheny HS
Oakdale, PA

Young, Robert C
St Pius X HS
Perkiomenville, PA

Young, Tracy
Cecilian Acad
Philadelphia, PA

Young, William
York County Area
Vo Tech Schl
Delta, PA

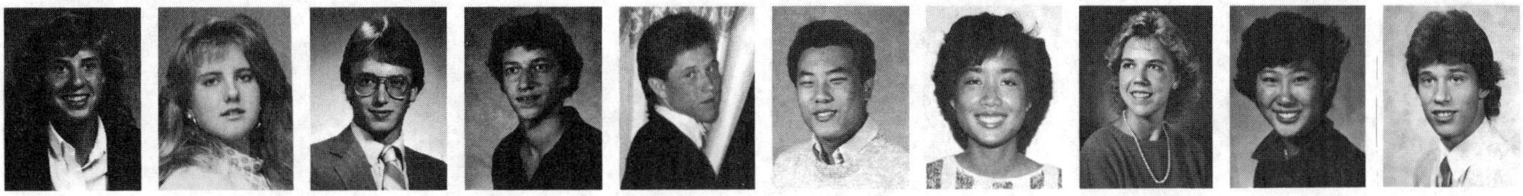

Young, Yvette
Lancaster Catholic
Lititz, PA

Youngman, Kris
West Hazelton HS
Sugarloaf, PA

Youngstrom, Eric A
Penncrest HS
Media, PA

Younkin, Drew
North Star HS
Stoystown, PA

Yozallinas, James F
Archbishop Ryan H
S For Boys
Philadelphia, PA

Yu, Kwang
Plymouth-Whitemar
sh HS
Conshohocken, PA

Yu, Megan
Upper Dublin HS
Ambler, PA

Yudiski, Tammy
Exeter SR HS
Reading, PA

Yue, Lorene
Parkland SR HS
Allentown, PA

Yuhasz, Joseph A
Steel Valley HS
Munhall, PA

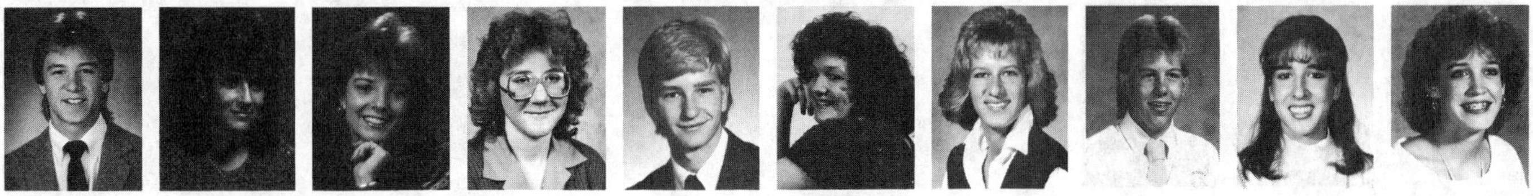

Yurchak, Thomas
Pennridge SR HS
Sellersville, PA

Yurconic, Monica A
Salisbury HS
Allentown, PA

Yuskovitz, Robin
Wyoming Seminary
Kingston, PA

Zajkowski, Lisa
Tech Memorial HS
Erie, PA

Zakos, Stephen
William Allen HS
Allentown, PA

Zalar, Patricia
Shamokin Area HS
Shamokin, PA

Zalar, Sharon
Parkland SR HS
Fogelsville, PA

Zale, Michael
Lancaster Catholic
Lititz, PA

Zaletsky, Joanne
North Allegheny HS
Wexford, PA

Zalewski, Sondra
Downingtown SR
Downington, PA

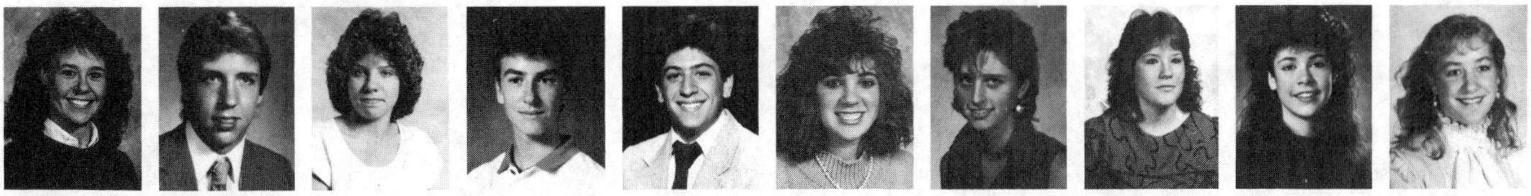

Zamites, Janet
Archbishop
Prendergast HS
Collingdale, PA

Zanders, Travis
Lehighton Area HS
Lehighton, PA

Zangari, Kristie
Cardinal Brennan
Girardville, PA

Zanoli, Edward
Springdale HS
Cheswick, PA

Zapollo, Leonard
St John Neumann
Philadelphia, PA

Zappa, Jill
Kennedy Christian
Farrell, PA

Zapsky, Jennifer
Moshannon Valley
Madera, PA

Zarski, Tonia
Shamokin Area HS
Shamokin, PA

Zatratz, Denise
Holy Name HS
Mohnton, PA

Zaucha, Amanda A
North Penn HS
Hatfield, PA

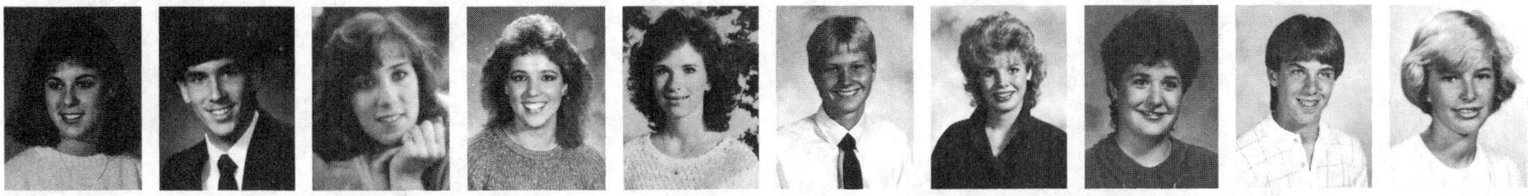

Zavatsky, Kelly
Connellsville Area
SR HS
Connellsville, PA

Zawadzki, Chas
Dunmore HS
Scranton, PA

Zawistoski,
Marybeth
Mercyhurst
Preparatory HS
Erie, PA

Zawrotny, Lynn
Seneca Valley HS
Mars, PA

Zdancewicz, Lisa
Bishop O Reilly HS
Swoyersville, PA

Zeglen, Eric
Bihsop Carroll HS
Belsano, PA

Zeigler, Emily
Hyndman Middle
SR HS
Hyndman, PA

Zeigler, Renee
Greenwood HS
Millerstown, PA

Zeisloft, Eric
Gettysburg HS
Orrtanna, PA

Zeitlin, Stacey
Episcopal Acad
Boyertown, PA

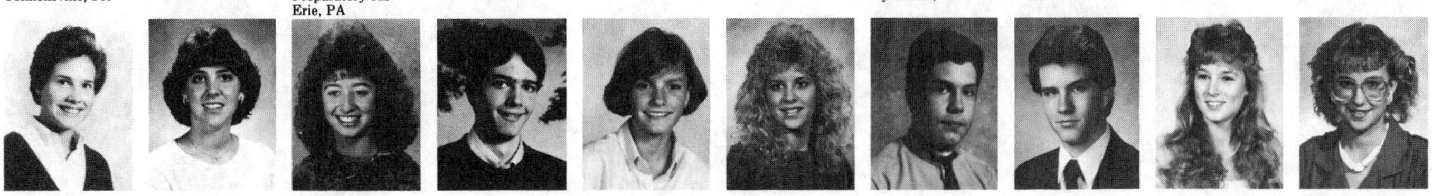

Zelenak, Elaine
Bishop Hafey HS
West Hazleton, PA

Zeman, Dana
North Hills HS
Pittsburgh, PA

Zemba, Pam
Jefferson-Morgan
Rices Landing, PA

Zemencik, Jeffrey A
Schuylkill Haven
Area HS
Schuylkill Haven,
PA

Zero, Kelly
Gwynedd Mercy
Harleysville, PA

Zeszutek, Susan
Canon Mc Millan
Cecil, PA

Zeth, Corey
Nativity BVM HS
Minersville, PA

Zettelmayer, Erik J
North Catholic HS
Pittsburgh, PA

Zewalk, Michelle E
North Allegheny SR
Pittsburgh, PA

Zewan, Amy
Belle Vernon Area
Belle Vernon, PA

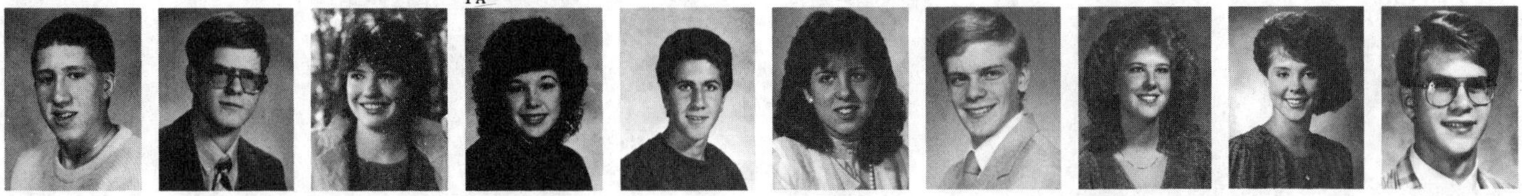

Ziance, Scott
Altoona Area HS
Altoona, PA

Ziantz, Louis
Pittston Area SR
Dupont, PA

Ziegmann,
Dawn-Michelle
S Williamsport Area
Williamsport, PA

Zielinski, Denine
John S Fine SR HS
Nanticoke, PA

Zieve, Glenn
Harriton HS
Gladwyne, PA

Zilka, Jennifer
Mon Valley Catholic
Monongahela, PA

Zim, Christopher
Wyoming Valley
West HS
Swoyerville, PA

Zimmer, Lori
Cumberland Valley
Camp Hill, PA

Zimmerman, Andrea
F
Altoona Area SR HS
Altoona, PA

Zimmerman, Justin
L
Big Spring HS
Shippensburg, PA

Zimmerman,
Margaret
Marion Catholic HS
Morea, PA

Zimmerman,
Matthew
Archbishop Ryan
HS For Boys
Philadelphia, PA

Zimmerman,
Michele
Pine Grove Area HS
Pine Grove, PA

Zimmerman, Travis
L
Chambersburg Area
SR HS
Fayetteville, PA

Ziolkowski, Kristine
Belle Vernon Area
Belle Vernon, PA

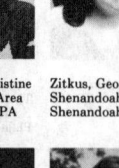

Zitkus, Georgeann
Shenandoah Valley
Shenandoah, PA

Zittrain, Jonathan L
Shady Side Acad
Pittsburgh, PA

Zivitz, Andrew
Harriton HS
Penn Valley, PA

Zola, James
Hazleton HS
Hazleton, PA

Zomak, Debora A
Canon-Mc Millan
Cecil, PA

Zonies, Melissa
Northeast HS
Philadelphia, PA

Zook, Judy Christine
Oxford HS
Oxford, PA

Zoolalian, Catharine
M
H S For Creative &
Performing Arts
Philadelphia, PA

Zrowka, Kenneth
Carbondale Area JR
SR HS
Simpson, PA

Zukas, John
Marian Catholic HS
Barnesville, PA

Zupko, Brian
Bishop O Reilly HS
Kingston, PA

Zupsic, Chris
Center SR HS
Aliquippa, PA

Zupsic, David
Center HS
Monaca, PA

Zupsic, Janice
Center Area HS
Monaca, PA

Zurat, Kelly
Bradford Area HS
Bradford, PA

Zurinsky,
Christopher L
Northwestern HS
E Springfield, PA

Zuzelski, Jr Louis A
James M Coughlin
Wilkes Barre, PA

Zweig, Kelly
Greater Nanticoke
Area HS
Hunlock Creek, PA